SUBJECT GUIDE TO

BOOKS IN PRINT®

2012 - 2013

This edition of

SUBJECT GUIDE TO BOOKS IN PRINT® 2012 - 2013
was prepared by R.R. Bowker's Database Publishing Group
in collaboration with the Information Technology Department.

Michael Gersch, Senior Vice President & General Manager
Sharon Lubrano, Vice President & General Manager
Philip Evans, Chief Financial Officer
Angela D'Agostino, Vice President Business Development
Paul Brennan, Senior Director Content Operations

International Standard Book Number/Standard Address Number Agency
Beat Barblan, Director Identifier Services
John Purcell, Manager, ISBN Agency
Richard Smith, Product Manager, Identifier Services
John D'Agostino and Cheryl Russo, Publisher Relations Representatives
Patrick David, User Interface Designer

Data Services
Lisa Heft, Senior Manager Content Operations
Adrene Allen, Kathleen Cunningham, Manager Content Operations
Ron Butkiewicz, Latonia Hall, Marissa Hubbard, Ila Joseph,
John Litzenberger, Rhonda McKendrick, Jesse Ricablanca, Tom Lucas,
Beverly Palacio, Cheryl Patrick and Misty Poush, Mervaine Ricks Data Analyst QA Sr.
Jenny Marie DeJesus, Supervisor Data Quality
Terry Campesi, Suzanne Franks, E-Content Editor II
Lynda Keller, Mark Ahmad, Rosemary Walker, Profiler

Publisher Relations
Patricia Payton, Senior Director
Rebecca Albani, Jack Tipping, Ralph Coviello, Publisher Relations Managers
Erica Ferris, Publisher Liaison
Claire Edwards, Publisher Relations Administrator
Joanne Firca, Assistant Publisher Relations Analyst

Data Services Production
Doreen Gravesande, Senior Manager Content Operations
Stephanie Halpern, Manager Customer Care
Myriam Nunez, Business Systems Analyst
Brittany Hartman, Project Manager

Editorial Systems Group
Mark Heinzelman, Chief Data Architect

Computer Operations Group
John Nesselt, UNIX Administrator
Ed Albright, UNIX Administrator

Bowker®

SUBJECT GUIDE TO BOOKS IN PRINT®

2012 - 2013

VOLUME 1

A – Ch

GREY HOUSE PUBLISHING

R.R. Bowker LLC
630 Central Avenue
New Providence, NJ 07974
Phone: 908-286-1090
Toll-free: 1-888-BOWKER2 (1-888-269-5372)
Fax: 908-219-0098
E-mail: info@bowker.com
URL: http://www.bowker.com

Grey House Publishing, Inc.
4919 Route 22
Amenia, NY 12501
Phone: 518-789-8700
Toll-free: 1-800-562-2139
Fax: 518-789-0545
E-mail: books@greyhouse.com
URL: http://www.greyhouse.com

Michael Gersch, Senior Vice President & General Manager

Subject Guide to Books In Print® 2012-2013 is published by Grey House Publishing, Inc. under exclusive license from R.R. Bowker LLC.

Readers may send any corrections and/or updates to the information in this work to R.R. Bowker through the "Send Corrections" option on the Bowker web site at http://www.bowker.com. Publishers may update or add to their listings by accessing the **BowkerLink Publisher Access System** at http://www.bowkerlink.com.

No payment is either solicited or accepted for the inclusion of entries in this publication.

R.R. Bowker has used its best efforts in collecting and preparing material for inclusion in **Subject Guide to Books In Print® 2012-2013**, but does not warrant that the information herein is complete or accurate, and does not assume, and hereby disclaims any liability to any person for the loss or damage caused by errors or omissions in **Subject Guide to Books In Print® 2012-2013**, whether such errors or omissions result from negligence, accident or any other cause.

International Standard Book Numbers

ISBN 13: 978-1-59237-966-8 (Set)
ISBN 13: 978-1-59237-967-5 (Vol.1)
ISBN 13: 978-1-59237-968-2 (Vol. 2)
ISBN 13: 978-1-59237-969-9 (Vol. 3)
ISBN 13: 978-1-59237-970-5 (Vol. 4)
ISBN 13: 978-1-59237-971-2 (Vol. 5)
ISBN 13: 978-1-59237-972-9 (Vol. 6)

International Standard Serial Number
0000-0159

Library of Congress Control Number
74-643573

Printed and bound in Canada
Subject Guide to Books In Print® is a registered trademark of R.R. Bowker LLC, used under license.

CONTENTS

HOW TO USE SUBJECT GUIDE TO BOOKS IN PRINT®

This 56th annual edition of **Subject Guide to Books In Print®** was produced from the Books In Print database. This edition includes the Publisher Name Index as well as full ordering information for Wholesalers and Distributors section at the end of Volume 6.

CLASSIFICATION

Subject Guide follows the headings assigned by the Library of Congress. Entries listed by author and title in **Books In Print® 2012-2013** were searched in the catalogs and database of the Library of Congress to determine the headings assigned. To some books LC assigned a single heading, to others it assigned two, three, or more headings. Therefore, books can appear two, three, or more times in the following pages. Approximately 1,806,670 books appear under 79,212 populated headings and cross references.

Headings and cross-references were selected based on LC subject and name authority information found at http://catalog.loc.gov. Subdivisions were consolidated when they seemed too cumbersome for the needs of **Subject Guide to Books In Print®** and a few headings were changed when the needs of this book diverged from LC practice.

There are several types of works not included in **Subject Guide.**

- Books published prior to 2006.
- Bibles are omitted, although commentaries, histories, and versions other than Standard English are covered.
- Imported books must have a U.S. distributor or wholesaler.
- Poetry and drama by a single author (whether collections or individual works) are generally omitted. However, multiple author collections, as well as critical works, are included.
- Single-author fiction is not represented. Criticism and multiple author collections are included.
- Juvenile fiction or nonfiction is not included, except for those annotated titles mentioned above. All Juvenile titles can be found in the Author, Title, and Illustrator indexes of **Children's Books In Print®** and in the LC subject categories of **Subject Guide to Children's Books In Print®.**

Current information was solicited from all publishers contained in the Books In Print database. These publishers include participants in Bowker's Electronic Data Interchange (EDI) program as well as publishers who regularly submit Advance Book Information forms and their current book catalogs. Less active publishers are asked to review their active titles on checklists or online at http://www.bowkerlink.com. Every effort was made to get up-to-date, complete information on the in-print titles published and distributed in the United States for inclusion in this edition of **Subject Guide to Books In Print®.**

GENERAL EDITORIAL POLICIES

Every effort is made by most publishers to submit their material with consideration for its accuracy throughout the life of the edition of **Subject Guide to Books In Print®.** Most publishers anticipate price changes when they revise their catalogs, list forthcoming books even if publication dates and prices are not set, and for the most part try not to list books that may shortly become unavailable. In spite of these efforts, a number of changes in price will occur and a number of titles in this edition will become unavailable before the new edition of **Subject Guide to Books In Print®** is published. The **Books In Print Supplement® 2012-2013** will be published in February 2013 and will reflect any changes that have occurred in the interim. All publishers' prices are subject to change without notice.

ARRANGEMENT AND USAGE OF SUBJECTS

Subject Guide's to Books In Print® first principle is to list books where the user will be most likely to look for them, with as many references as seem necessary.

Although a constant effort is made to maintain consistency and to avoid splitting entries on a given subject among several headings, a certain amount of inconsistency is inevitable. The Library of Congress updates its subject headings constantly but cannot make such updating retroactive to cards and catalogs previously issued. For example, LC is now classifying materials on EVOLUTION based on what is evolving, e.g., HUMAN EVOLUTION; PLANTS-EVOLUTION. If old entries, which may belong in more precise subdivisions, did not indicate by their titles where they should be listed, they were left under the main entry. The basic presentation of subject headings is alphabetical; however, in accordance with the Library of Congress, the following sequencing rules are followed:

- Given equivalent spellings of a heading, people come before places and places come before things.
- Headings beginning with "Da [space]" and "De [space]" are treated as if there were no space.
- Headings beginning with "Mc" and "Mac" are treated as if they all began with "Mac" and spacing is ignored.
- People with the same name are arranged with the earlier birth date first.
- "Heading" precedes "Heading-Subdivision," which precedes "Heading, Phrase Following a Comma," which proceeds "Heading (Parenthetical Text)," which precedes "Heading as Start of Phrase."
- Under a given heading, standard subdivisions precede chronological subdivisions, which precede geographical subdivisions. For example (please note that there are headings that may appear between the examples given):

ARTS
ARTS—BLIOGRAPHY
ARTS—AUSTRALIA
ARTS AND CRAFTS MOVEMENT
CLAY, HENRY, 1777-1852
CLAY
CLEVELAND, JOHN, 1613-1658
CLEVELAND (OHIO)
CLEVELAND BROWNS (FOOTBALL TEAM)
COOKERY
COOKERY—PICTORIAL WORKS
COOKERY (PASTA)
COOKERY, MEXICAN
COOKERY FOR ONE
DENIAL OF JUSTICE
DE NIRO, ROBERT, 1945
DENMARK
MACINTOSH (COMPUTER)
MCIVER, CHARLES DUNCAN, 1860-1906
MC JUNKIN, GEORGE
MACKAIL, JOHN WILLIAM, 1859-1945
UNITED STATES
UNITED STATES—FOREIGN RELATIONS
UNITED STATES—FOREIGN RELATIONS—1993-2001
UNITED STATES—FOREIGN RELATIONS—JAPAN
UNITED STATES-HISTORY
UNITED STATES—HISTORY—SOURCES
UNITED STATES—HISTORY—COLONIAL PERIOD, 1600-1775
UNITED STATES-HISTORY—REVOLUTION, 1775-1783
UNITED STATES—HISTORY—1783-1809
UNITED STATES—HISTORY—1783-1865
UNITED STATES—HISTORY—19TH CENTURY
UNITED STATES—HISTORY—1809-1817
UNITED STATES—HISTORY—WAR OF 1812
UNITED STATES—HISTORY—1815-1861
UNITED STATES—HISTORY—CIVIL WAR, 1861-1865
UNITED STATES—HISTORY—1865-
UNITED STATES—HISTORY—1865-1898
UNITED STATES-HISTORY—20TH CENTURY
UNITED STATES—HISTORY—1945-
UNITED STATES EXPLORING EXPEDITION, 1838-1842
WEBER, MAX, 1864-1920
WEBER, MAX, 1881-1961

As seen from the above examples, it is always useful to look past the main heading to the various subdivisions.

Headings are explicit rather than general. Thus books about Cost Accounting are listed under COST ACCOUNTING as opposed to ACCOUNTING. "See also" and "See" cross-references are provided in order to help users locate more specific or related headings under which books may be found. Subjects with "see also" references may have books listed under them. For example:

ANTIQUITIES
see also Antiques; Archaeology; Christian Antiquities; Classical Antiquities; Forgery of Antiquities; Oriental Antiquities; also subdivision Antiquities under names of countries, cities, etc.

"See" references are provided in order to lead users from the heading they are looking at to the heading(s) under which books are actually listed. Subjects with a "see" reference do not have books listed under them. For example:

ATM (DATA TRANSFER)
see Asynchronous Transfer Mode

DISPUTE SETTLEMENT
see Conflict Management; Dispute Resolution (Law)

Scope notes are provided to define a heading and help differentiate the use of that heading from others similar to it. For example:

DIVING
Here are entered works on diving from a board, platform, or springboard into a swimming pool or other body of water. Works on underwater diving using equipment are entered under Deep Diving.

ALPHABETICAL ARRANGEMENT OF ENTRIES WITHIN SUBJECT

Entries are arranged alphabetically by author within subject. If no author is given, the entry is filed by title within the author arrangement.

Author names in Subject Guide to Books In Print have been alphabetized using the following rules:

- Proper names beginning with "Mc" and "Mac" are filed in strict alphabetical order. For example, entries for contributors' names such as Mac Adam, MacAvory, and MacCarthy are located prior to the pages with entries for names such as McAdam, McCoy, and McDermott.
- Compound names are listed under their first

component. For example, Van Holland is listed under Van.

- When author names are represented with initials, they are alphabetized before author first names. For example, Smith, H.C appears before Smith, Harold A.
- If more than two authors or editors are responsible for a certain publication, only the name of the first is given, followed by et al.

INFORMATION INCLUDED IN ENTRIES

Entries include the following bibliographic information, when available: author, co-author, editor, co-editor, translator, co-translator, title, number of volumes, edition, series information, language other than English, whether or not illustrated, grade range, year of publication, type of binding if other than cloth over boards, price, ISBN--13 (ISBN-10 prefix), publisher's order number, imprint and publisher. ISBNs new to this year's edition appear in bold type. Information on the International Standard Book Numbering System used in the United States is available from R.R. Bowker by calling 877-310-7333, faxing 908-219-0188, or through the ISBN/SAN Web site at http://www.isbn.org.

PUBLISHER NAME INDEX

An index to the publisher names (e.g., "Mid Atlantic"), with more than 64,125 publishers used in the bibliographic entries of **Subject Guide to Books In Print®**, is found at the end of Volume 6. Entries in this index contain each publisher's abbreviated name, followed by its ISBN prefix(es), business affiliation, when available (e.g., Div. of International Publishing), ordering address(es), SAN (Standard Address Number), telephone number(s), fax, and toll-free numbers. Editorial address(es) (and associated contact numbers) follow.

Publishers' imprint names are followed by their symbols within parentheses. E-mail and Web site addresses are then supplied. A listing of distributors associated with the publisher concludes each entry; each distributor's abbreviated name is in bold type. Full information for these distributors, as well as some 974 book wholesalers, is found in the Wholesaler & Distributor Name Index. Note that those publishers who also serve as distributors may be listed both here and in the Publisher Name Index. A dagger(†) preceding a publisher's name and the note "CIP" at the end of an entry both indicate the publisher participates in the Cataloging in Publication Program of the Library of Congress.

Cross-reference lines indicate company name changes that have occurred since the last edition of **Subject Guide to Books In Print®**.

The first example on the following page is a typical publisher name entry.

Foreign publishers with U.S. distributors are listed, followed by their three-character ISO (International Standards Organization) country code ("GBR," "CAN," etc.), ISBN prefix(es), if available, and a cross-reference to their U.S. distributor, as shown below:

Atrium (GBR) (0-9535353) Dist by **DuFour**.

Publishers with like or similar names are referenced by a "Do not confuse with... " notation at the end of the entry. In addition, cross-references are provided from imprints and former company names to the new names.

WHOLESALER & DISTRIBUTOR NAME INDEX

The Wholesaler & Distributor Name Index is arranged alphabetically by company name and contains business affiliation as well as ISBN prefix(es), when available; full address and ordering information; SAN(s); and telephone, fax, and toll-free numbers, E-mail, and Web site addresses. See the sample entry on the following page.

ISBN AGENCY

Each title included in **Subject Guide to Books In Print®** has been assigned an International Standard Book Number (ISBN) by the publisher. All ISBNs listed in this directory have been validated by using the check digit control, ensuring accuracy. ISBNs allow order transmission and bibliographic information updating using publishing industry supported EDI formats (e.g., ONIX). Publishers not currently participating in the ISBN system may request the assignment of an ISBN Publisher Prefix from the ISBN Agency by calling 877-310-7333, faxing 908-219-0188, or through the ISBN Agency's web site at **http://www.myidentifiers.com**. Please note: The ISBN prefix 0-615 is for decentralized use by the U.S. ISBN Agency and has been assigned to many publishers. It is not unique to one publisher

SAN AGENCY

Another listing feature in **Subject Guide to Books In Print®** is the Standard Address Number (SAN), a unique identification number assigned to each address of an organization in or served by the publishing industry; it facilitates communications and transactions with other members of the industry.

The SAN identifies either a bill to or ship to address for purchasing, billing, shipping, receiving, paying, crediting, and refunding, and can be used for any other communication or transaction between participating companies and organizations in the publishing supply chain.

To obtain an application or further information on the SAN system, please email the SAN Agency at **SAN@bowker.com**, or visit **www.myidentifiers.com**

ADDITIONAL RESOURCES

A wealth of current bibliographic data (more than 5 million records, including OP titles, audiobooks, and videos) can also be searched by customers on Bowker's Web site http://www.booksinprint.com. The Books In Print database is also available on CD-ROM. For further information about subscribing to these services, contact Bowker at 1-888-269-5372.

SAMPLE ENTRY – SUBJECT

1 **BEACH EROSION**

2 **see also Coast Changes; Shore Protection**

3 Akyeampong, Emmanuel. **4** Between the Sea & the Lagoon:

5 An Eco-Social History of the Anlo of Southeastern Ghana: c. 1850 to Recent Times

6 2008 **7** (Western African Studies). **8** (Illus.). **9** **256p.** **10** pap. **11** 24.95.

12 978-0-8214-1409-5(7). **13** Ohio Univ. Pr.

14 — **15** Between the Sea & the Lagoon:

16 An Eco-Social History of the Anlo of Southeastern Ghana: C. 1850 to Recent Times

17 2008 **18** Tchr's Ed. **19** (Western African Studies). **20** (Illus.). 95 **21** 256p.

22 34.99 **23** 978-0-8214-1408-8(9). **24** Ohio Univ. Pr.

BEACH EROSION

see also Coast Changes; Shore Protection

Akyeampong, Emmanuel Kwaku. Between the Sea & the Lagoon : An Eco-Social History of the Anlo of South-eastern Ghana: c. 1850 to Recent Times. 2002. (Western African Studies). (Illus.). 256p. pap. 24.95 978-0-8214-1409-5(7) . Ohio Univ. Pr.

—Between the Sea & the Lagoon : An Eco-Social History of the Anlo of Southeastern Ghana: C. 1850 to Recent Times. 2002. (Western African Studies). (Illus.). 256p. 44.95 978-0-8214-1408-8(9) . Ohio Univ. Pr.

Footnote:
This sample entry does not include all elements that can be found in an entry

KEY

1 Subject Heading
2 Subject x-reference information
3 Main Contributor's last name, first M. I.
4 Title of the book
5 Subtitle
6 Publication year
7 Title of the Series
8 Illustration Indicator
9 Total pages
10 Binding - format
11 Price
12 International Standard Book Number - ISBN13 (ISBN10 check digit)
13 Publisher
14 New title under same contributor indicator
15 Title of book
16 Subtitle
17 Publication year
18 Edition Information
19 Title of Series
20 Illustration Indicator
21 Total pages
22 Price
23 International Standard Book Number ISBN13 (ISBN10 check digit)
24 Publisher

SAMPLE ENTRY PUBLISHER NAME INDEX

1 † 2 Mosby, Inc. 3 (0-323; 0-7234; 0-8151; 0-88416; 0-941158; 1-55664; 1-56375, 1-56815), 4 Div. of Harcourt, Inc., A Harcourt Health Sciences Co., 5 Orders Addr.: 6227 Sea Harbor Dr., Orlando FL 32887 6 Toll Free Fax: 800-235-0256 7 Toll Free: 800-543-1918 63146 8 Edit Addr.: 11830 Westline Industrial Dr., Saint Louis, MO 9 (SAN 200-2280) 10 Toll Free: 800-325-4177 11 Web Site: http://www.mosby.com/ 12 Dist(s): PenWell Corp (*PennWell Corp.*) 13 CIP.

This law entry does not exist, but was compiled from contrived data in order to demonstrate all feasible points of information.

KEY

1. CIP Identifier
2. Publisher Name
3. ISBN Prefixes
4. Division of
5. Orders Address
6. Orders Fax
7. Orders Telephone
8. Editorial Address
9. SAN
10. Toll-Free
11. Web site
12. Distributors
13. Cataloguing in Publication

SAMPLE ENTRY WHOLESALER & DISTRIBUTOR NAME INDEX

1 **New Life Distributing Co., Inc.,** 2 Div. of Al-Wali Corp., 3 (0-962709), 4 401 Thomton Rd., Lithia Springs, GA 30122-1557 5 (SAN 169-1449) 6 Tel: 770-948-7845; 7 Fax: 770-944-2313; 8 Toll Free: 800-326-2665 9 Toll Free: 800-326-2665 10 Email: NewLeaf@NewLeaf-dist.com 11 Web Site: http://www.NewLeaf-dist.com/

This law entry does not exist, but was compiled from contrived data in order to demonstrate all feasible points of information.

KEY

1. Distributor Name
2. Division of
3. ISBN Prefix
4. Editorial Address
5. SAN
6. Telephone
7. Fax
8. Toll Free
9. Toll Free
10. E-mail
11. Web site

PUBLISHER COUNTRY CODES

Foreign Publishers are listed with the three letter International Standards Organization (ISO) code for their country of domicile. This is the complete list of ISO codes though not all countries may be represented. The codes are mnemonic in most cases. The country names here may be shortened to a more common usage form.

Code	Country
AFG	AFGHANISTAN
AGO	ANGOLA
ALB	ALBANIA
AND	ANDORRA
ANT	NETHERLANDS ANTILLES
ARE	UNITED ARAB EMIRATES
ARG	ARGENTINA
ARM	ARMENIA
ASM	AMERICAN SAMOA
ATA	ANTARCTICA
ATG	ANTIGUA & BARBUDA
AUS	AUSTRALIA
AUT	AUSTRIA
AZE	AZERBAIJAN
BDI	BURUNDI
BEL	BELGIUM
BEN	BENIN
BFA	BURKINA FASO
BGD	BANGLADESH
BGR	BULGARIA
BHR	BAHRAIN
BHS	BAHAMAS
BIH	BOSNIA & HERZEGOVINA
BLR	BELARUS
BLZ	BELIZE
BMU	BERMUDA
BOL	BOLIVIA
BRA	BRAZIL
BRB	BARBADOS
BRN	BRUNEI DARUSSALAM
BTN	BHUTAN
BWA	BOTSWANA
BWI	BRITISH WEST INDIES
CAF	CENTRAL AFRICAN REP
CAN	CANADA
CH2	CHINA
CHE	SWITZERLAND
CHL	CHILE
CHN	CHINA
CIV	IVORY COAST
CMR	CAMEROON
COD	ZAIRE
COG	CONGO (BRAZZAVILLE)
COL	COLOMBIA
COM	COMOROS
CPV	CAPE VERDE
CRI	COSTA RICA
CS	CZECHOSLOVAKIA
CUB	CUBA
CYM	CAYMAN ISLANDS
CYP	CYPRUS
CZE	CZECH REPUBLIC
DEU	GERMANY
DJI	DJIBOUTI
DMA	DOMINICA
DNK	DENMARK
DOM	DOMINICAN REPUBLIC
DZA	ALGERIA
ECU	ECUADOR
EG	East Germany
EGY	EGYPT
EI	EUROPEAN UNION
EN	England
ESP	SPAIN
EST	ESTONIA
ETH	ETHIOPIA
FIN	FINLAND
FJI	FIJI
FLK	FALKLAND ISLANDS
FRA	FRANCE
FRO	FAEROE ISLANDS
FSM	MICRONESIA
GAB	GABON
GBR	UNITED KINGDOM
GEO	GEORGIA
GHA	GHANA
GIB	GIBRALTAR
GIN	GUINEA
GLP	GUADELOUPE
GMB	GAMBIA
GNB	GUINEA-BISSAU
GNQ	EQUATORIAL GUINEA
GRC	GREECE
GRD	GRENADA
GRL	GREENLAND
GTM	GUATEMALA
GUF	FRENCH GUIANA
GUM	GUAM
GUY	GUYANA
HKG	HONG KONG
HND	HONDURAS
HRV	Croatia
HTI	HAITI
HUN	HUNGARY
IDN	INDONESIA
IND	INDIA
IRL	IRELAND
IRN	IRAN
IRQ	IRAQ
ISL	ICELAND
ISR	ISRAEL
ITA	ITALY
JAM	JAMAICA
JOR	JORDAN
JPN	JAPAN
KAZ	KAZAKSTAN
KEN	KENYA
KGZ	KYRGYZSTAN
KHM	CAMBODIA
KNA	ST. KITTS-NEVIS
KO	Korea
KOR	SOUTH KOREA
KOS	KOSOVA
KWT	KUWAIT
LAO	LAOS
LBN	LEBANON
LBR	LIBERIA
LBY	LIBYA
LCA	ST. LUCIA
LIE	LIECHTENSTEIN
LKA	SRI LANKA
LSO	LESOTHO
LTU	LITHUANIA
LUX	LUXEMBOURG
LVA	LATVIA
MAC	MACAO
MAR	MOROCCO
MCO	MONACO
MDA	MOLDOVA
MDG	MALAGASY REPUBLIC
MDV	MALDIVE ISLANDS
MEX	MEXICO
MHL	MARSHALL ISLANDS
MKD	MACEDONIA
MLI	MALI
MLT	MALTA
MMR	UNION OF MYANMAR
MNE	MONTENEGRO
MNG	MONGOLIA
MOZ	MOZAMBIQUE
MRT	MAURITANIA
MSR	MONTESERRAT
MTQ	MARTINIQUE
MUS	MAURITIUS
MWI	MALAWI
MYS	MALAYSIA
NAM	NAMIBIA
NCL	NEW CALEDONIA
NER	NIGER
NGA	NIGERIA
NIC	NICARAGUA
NLD	THE NETHERLANDS
NOR	NORWAY
NPL	NEPAL
NRU	NAURU
NZL	NEW ZEALAND
OMN	SULTANATE OF OMAN
PAK	PAKISTAN
PAN	PANAMA
PER	PERU
PHL	PHILIPPINES
PNG	PAPUA NEW GUINEA
POL	POLAND
PRI	Puerto Rico
PRK	NORTH KOREA
PRT	PORTUGAL
PRY	PARAGUAY
PYF	FRENCH POLYNESIA
REU	REUNION
ROM	RUMANIA
RUS	RUSSIA
RWA	RWANDA
SAU	SAUDI ARABIA
SC	Scotland
SCG	SERBIA & MONTENEGRO
SDN	SUDAN
SEN	SENEGAL
SGP	SINGAPORE
SLB	SOLOMON ISLANDS
SLE	SIERRA LEONE
SLV	EL SALVADOR
SMR	SAN MARINO
SOM	SOMALIA
STP	SAO TOME E PRINCIPE
SU	Soviet Union
SUR	SURINAM

Code	Country
SVK	Slovakia
SVN	SLOVENIA
SWE	SWEDEN
SWZ	SWAZILAND
SYC	SEYCHELLES
SYN	SYNDETICS
SYR	SYRIA
TCA	TURKS NDS
TCD	CHAD
TGO	TOGO
THA	THAILAND
TKM	TURKMENISTAN
TON	TONGA
TTO	TRINIDAD AND TOBAGO
TUN	TUNISIA
TUR	TURKEY
TWN	TAIWAN
TZA	TANZANIA
UGA	UGANDA
UI	UNITED KINGDOM
UKR	UKRAINE
UN	UNITED NATIONS
URY	URUGUAY
USA	UNITED STATES
UZB	UZBEKISTAN
VAT	VATICAN CITY
VCT	ST. VINCENT
VEN	VENEZUELA
VGB	BRITISH VIRGIN ISLANDS
VIR	U.S. VIRGIN ISLANDS
VNM	VIETNAM
VUT	VANUATU
WA	Wales
WSM	WESTERN SAMOA
YEM	REPUBLIC OF YEMEN
YUG	YUGOSLAVIA
ZAF	SOUTH AFRICA
ZMB	ZAMBIA
ZWE	ZIMBABWE

COUNTRY SEQUENCE

Country	Code
AFGHANISTAN	AFG
ALBANIA	ALB
ALGERIA	DZA
AMERICAN SAMOA	ASM
ANDORRA	AND
ANGOLA	AGO
ANGUILLA	AIA
ANTARCTICA	ATA
ANTIGUA & BARBUDA	ATG
ARGENTINA	ARG
ARMENIA	ARM
ARUBA	ABW
AUSTRALIA	AUS
AUSTRIA	AUT
AZERBAIJAN	AZE
BAHAMAS	BHS
BAHRAIN	BHR
BANGLADESH	BGD
BARBADOS	BRB
BELARUS	BLR
BELGIUM	BEL
BELIZE	BLZ
BENIN	BEN
BERMUDA	BMU
BHUTAN	BTN
BOLIVIA	BOL
BOSNIA & HERZEGOVINA	BIH
BOTSWANA	BWA
BOUVET ISLAND	BVT
BRAZIL	BRA
BRITISH INDIAN OCEAN TERRITORY	IOT
BRITISH WEST INDIES	BWI
BRUNEI DARUSSALAM	BRN
BULGARIA	BGR
BURKINA FASO	BFA
BURUNDI	BDI
CAMBODIA	KHM
CAMEROON	CMR
CANADA	CAN
CAPE VERDE	CPV
CAYMAN ISLANDS	CYM
CENTRAL AFRICAN REPUBLIC	CAF
CHAD	TCD
CHILE	CHL
CHINA	CHN
CHRISTMAS ISLAND	CXR
COCOS (KEELING) ISLANDS	CCK
COLOMBIA	COL
COMOROS	COM
CONGO	COG
CONGO, THE DEMOCRATIC REPUBLIC OF THE CONGO	COD
COOK ISLANDS	COK
COSTA RICA	CRI
COTE' D' IVOIRE	CIV
CROATIA	HRV
CUBA	CUB
CYPRUS	CYP
CZECH REPUBLIC	CZE
CZECHOSLOVAKIA	CSK
DENMARK	DNK
DJIBOUTI	DJI
DOMINICA	DMA
DOMINICAN REPUBLIC	DOM
EAST TIMOR	TMP
ECUADOR	ECU
EGYPT (ARAB REPUBLIC OF EGYPT)	EGY
EL SALVADOR	SLV
EQUATORIAL GUINEA	GNQ
ERITREA	ERI
ESTONIA	EST
ETHIOPIA	ETH
EAST GERMANY	DDR
FALKLAND ISLANDS	FLK
FAROE ISLANDS	FRO
FEDERATED STATES OF MICRONESIA	FSM
FIJI	FJI
FINLAND	FIN
FRANCE	FRA
FRENCH GUIANA	GUF
FRENCH POLYNESIA	PYF
FRENCH SOUTHERN TERRITORIES	ATF
GABON	GAB
GAMBIA	GMB
GEORGIA	GEO
GERMANY	DEU
GHANA	GHA
GIBRALTAR	GIB
GREECE	GRC
GREENLAND	GRL
GRENADA	GRD
GUADELOUPE	GLP
GUAM	GUM
GUATEMALA	GTM
GUINEA	GIN
GUINEA-BISSAU	GNB
GUYANA	GUY
HAITI	HTI
HEARD ISLAND & MCDONALD ISLANDS	HMD
HONDURAS	HND
HONG KONG	HKG
HUNGARY	HUN
ICELAND	ISL
INDIA	IND
INDONESIA	IDN
IRAN, ISLAMIC REPUBLIC OF	IRN
IRAQ	IRQ
IRELAND	IRL
ISRAEL	ISR
ITALY	ITA
JAMAICA	JAM
JAPAN	JPN
JORDAN	JOR
KAZAKSTAN	KAZ
KENYA	KEN
KIRIBATI	KIR
KOREA, DEMOCRATIC PEOPLE'S REPUBLIC OF	PRK
KOREA, REPUBLIC OF	KOR
KUWAIT	KWT
KYRGYZSTAN	KGZ
KOSOVA	KOS
LAO PEOPLE'S DEMOCRATIC REPUBLIC	LAO
LATVIA	LVA
LEBANON	LBN
LESOTHO	LSO
LIBERIA	LBR
LIBYAN ARAB JAMAHIRIYA	LBY
LIECHTENSTEIN	LIE
LITHUANIA	LTU
LUXEMBOURG	LUX
MACAU	MAC
MACEDONIA, THE FORMER YUGOSLAV REPUBLIC OF	MKD
MADAGASCAR	MDG
MALAWI	MWI
MALAYSIA	MYS
MALDIVE ISLANDS	MDV
MALI	MLI
MALTA	MLT
MARSHALL ISLANDS	MHL
MARTINIQUE	MTQ
MAURITANIA	MRT
MAURITIUS	MUS
MAYOTTE	MYT
MEXICO	MEX
MOLDOVA, REPUBLIC OF	MDA
MONACO	MCO

Country	Code
MONGOLIA	MNG
MONTENEGRO	MNE
MONTSERRAT	MSR
MOROCCO	MAR
MOZAMBIQUE	MOZ
MYANMAR	MMR
NAMIBIA	NAM
NAURU	NRU
NEPAL	NPL
NETHERLANDS	NLD
NETHERLANDS ANTILLES	ANT
NEW CALEDONIA	NCL
NEW ZEALAND	NZL
NICARAGUA	NIC
NIGER	NER
NIGERIA	NGA
NIUE	NIU
NORFOLK ISLAND	NFK
NORTHERN MARIANA ISLANDS	MNP
NORWAY	NOR
OMAN	OMN
OCCUPIED PALESTINIAN TERRITORY	PSE
PAKISTAN	PAK
PALAU	PLW
PANAMA	PAN
PAPUA NEW GUINEA	PNG
PARAGUAY	PRY
PERU	PER
PHILIPPINES	PHL
PITCAIRN	PCN
POLAND	POL
PORTUGAL	PRT
PUERTO RICO	PRI
QATAR	QAT
REUNION	REU
ROMANIA	ROM
RUSSIAN FEDERATION	RUS

Country	Code
RWANDA	RWA
SAINT HELENA	SHN
SAINT KITTS & NEVIS	KNA
SAINT PIERRE & MIQUELON	SPM
SAINT VINCENT & THE GRENADINES	VCT
SAMOA	WSM
SAN MARINO	SMR
SAO TOME E PRINCIPE	STP
SAUDI ARABIA	SAU
SENEGAL	SEN
SERBIA	SRB
SERBIA & MONTENEGRO	SCG
SEYCHELLES	SYC
SIERRA LEONE	SLE
SINGAPORE	SGP
SLOVAKIA	SVK
SLOVENIA	SVN
SOLOMON ISLANDS	SLB
SOMALIA	SOM
SOUTH AFRICA	ZAF
SOUTH GEORGIA & THE SANDWICH ISLANDS	SGS
SPAIN	ESP
SRI LANKA	LKA
ST. LUCIA	LCA
SUDAN	SDN
SURINAME	SUR
SVALBARD & JAN MAYEN	SJM
SWAZILAND	SWZ
SWEDEN	SWE
SWITZERLAND	CHE
SYRIAN ARAB REPUBLIC	SYR
TAIWAN, REPUBLIC OF CHINA	TWN
TAJIKISTAN	TJK

Country	Code
TANZANIA, UNITED REPUBLIC OF	TZA
THAILAND	THA
TOGO	TGO
TOKELAU	TKL
TONGA	TON
TRINIDAD & TOBAGO	TTO
TUNISIA	TUN
TURKEY	TUR
TURKMENISTAN	TKM
TURKS & CAICOS ISLANDS	TCA
TUVALU	TUV
U.S.S.R.	SUN
UGANDA	UGA
UKRAINE	UKR
UNITED ARAB EMIRATES	UAE
UNITED KINGDOM	GBR
UNITED STATES	USA
UNITED STATES MINOR OUTLYING ISLANDS	UMI
URUGUAY	URY
UZBEKISTAN	UZB
VANUATU	VUT
VATICAN CITY STATE (HOLY SEE)	VAT
VENEZUELA	VEN
VIET NAM	VNM
VIRGIN ISLANDS, BRITISH	VGB
VIRGIN ISLANDS, U. S.	VIR
WALLIS & FUTUNA	WLF
WESTERN SAHARA	ESH
West Germany	BRD
YEMEN	YEM
YUGOSLAVIA	YUG
ZAMBIA	ZMB
ZIMBABWE	ZWE
ZAIRE	ZAR

LANGUAGE CODES

ACE Achioli
AFA Afro-Asiatic
AFR Afrikaans
AKK Akkadian
ALB Albanian
ALE Aleut
ALG Algonquin
AMH Amharic
ANG Anglo-Saxon
APA Apache
ARA Arabic
ARC Aramaic
ARM Armenian
ARN Araucanian
ARP Arapaho
ARW Arawak
ASM Assamese
AVA Avar
AVE Avesta
AYM Aymara
AZE Azerbaijani
BAK Bashkir
BAL Baluchi
BAM Bambara
BAQ Basque
BAT Baltic
BEJ Beja
BEL Belorussian
BEM Bemba
BEN Bengali
BER Berber Group
BIH Bihari
BLA Blackfoot
BRE Breton
BUL Bulgarian
BUR Burmese
CAD Caddo
CAI Central American
CAM Cambodian
CAR Carib
CAT Catalan
CAU Caucasian
CEL Celtic Group
CHB Chibcha
CHE Chechen
CHI Chinese
CHN Chinook
CHO Choctaw
CHR Cherokee
CHU Church Slavic
CHV Chuvash
CHY Cheyenne
COP Coptic
COR Cornish
CRE Cree
CRO Croatian
CRP Creoles and Pidgins
CUS Cushitic
CZE Czech
DAK Dakota
DAN Danish
DEL Delaware
DIN Dinka
DOI Dogri
DRA Dravidian
DUA Duala

DUT Dutch
EFI Efik
EGY Egyptian
ELX Elamite
ENG English
ENM English, Middle
ESK Eskimo
RUM Romanian
RUN Rundi
RUS Russian
SAD Sandawe
SAG Sango
SAI South American
SAM Samaritan
SAN Sanskrit
SAO Sampan
SBC Serbo-Croatian
SCO Scots
SEL Selkup
SEM Semitic
SER Serbian
SHN Shan
SHO Shona
SID Sidamo
SIO Siouan Languages
SIT Sino-Tibetan
SLA Slavic
SLO Slovak
SLV Slovenian
SMO Samoan
SND Sindhi
SNH Singhalese
SOG Sogdian
SOM Somali
SON Songhai
ESP Esperanto
EST Estonian
ETH Ethiopic
EWE Ewe
FAN Fang
FAR Faroese
FEM French, Middle
FIJ Fijian
FIN Finnish
FIU Finno-Ugrian
FLE Flemish
FON Fon
FRE French
FRI Frisian
FRO French, Old
GAA Ga
GAE Gaelic
GAG Gallegan
GAL Galla
GEC Greek, Classical
GEH German, Middle h
GEM Germanic
GEO Georgian
GER German
GLG Galician
GOH German, Old High
GON Gondi
GOT Gothic
GRE Greek
GUA Guarani
GUJ Gujarati

HAU Hausa
HAW Hawaiian
HEB Hebrew
HER Herero
HIL Hiligaynon
HIN Hindi
HUN Hungarian
HUP Hupa
IBA Iban
IBO Igbo
ICE Icelandic
IKU Inuktitut
ILO Ilocano
INC Indic
IND Indonesian
INE Indo-European
INT Interlingua
IRA Iranian
IRI Irish
IRO Iroquois
ITA Italian
JAV Javanese
JPN Japanese
KAA Karakalpak
KAC Kachin
KAM Kamba
KAN Kannada
KAR Karen
KAS Kashmiri
KAU Kanuri
KAZ Kazakh
KHA Khasi
KHM Khmer, Central
KIK Kikuyu
KIN Kinyarwanda
KIR Kirghiz
KOK Konkani
KON Kongo
KOR Korean
KPE Kpelle
KRO Kru
KRU Kurukh
SOT Sotho, Southern
SPA Spanish
SRD Sardinian
SRR Serer
SSA Sub-Saharan
SUK Sukuma
SUN Sundanese
SUS Susu
SUX Sumerian
SWA Swahili
SWE Swedish
SYR Syriac
TAG Tagalog
TAJ Tajik
TAM Tamil
TAR Tatar
TEL Telugu
TEM Temne
TER Tereno
THA Thai
TIB Tibetan
TIG Tigre
TIR Tigrinya
TOG Tonga, Nyasa

TON	Tonga, Tonga
TSI	Tsimshian
TSO	Tsonga
TSW	Tswana
KUA	Kwanyama
KUR	Kurdish
LAD	Ladino
LAH	Lahnda
LAM	Lamba
LAO	Laotian
LAP	Lapp
LAT	Latin
LAV	Latvian
LIN	Lingala
LIT	Lithuanian
LOL	Lolo
LUB	Luba
LUG	Luganda
LUI	Luiseno
MAC	Macedonian
MAI	Maithili
MAL	Malayalam
MAN	Mandingo
MAO	Maori
MAP	Malayo-Polynesian
MAR	Marathi
MAS	Masai
MAY	Malay
MEN	Mende
MIC	Micmac
MIS	Miscellaneous
MLA	Malagasy
MLT	Malteses
MNO	Manobo
MOL	Moldavian
MON	Mongol
MOS	Mossi
MUL	Multiple Languages
MUS	Muskogee
MYN	Mayan
NAI	North American
NAV	Navaho
NBL	Ndebele, Southern
NDE	Ndebele, Northern
NEP	Nepali
NEW	Newari
NIC	Niger-Congo
NNO	Norwegian
NOB	Norwegian Bokmal
NOR	Norwegian
NSO	Sotho, Northern
NUB	Nubian
NYA	Nyanja
NYM	Nyamwezi
NYO	Nyoro Group
OES	Ossetic
OJI	Ojibwa
ORI	Oriya
OSA	Osage
OTO	Otomi
PAA	Papuan-Australian
PAH	Pahari
PAL	Pahlavi
PAN	Panjabi
PEO	Persian, Old
PER	Persian, Modern
PLI	Pali
POL	Polish
POR	Portuguese
PRA	Prakrit
PRO	Provencal
PUS	Pushto
QUE	Quechua
RAJ	Rajasthani
ROA	Romance
ROH	Romanish
ROM	Romany
TUK	Turkmen
TUR	Turkish
TUT	Turko-Tataric
TWI	Twi
UGA	Ugaritic
UIG	Uigur
UKR	Ukrainian
UMB	Umbundu
UND	Undetermined
URD	Urdu
UZB	Uzbek
VIE	Vietnamese
VOT	Votic
WAL	Walamo
WAS	Washo
WEL	Welsh
WEN	Wendic
WOL	Wolof
XHO	Xhosa
YAO	Yao
YID	Yiddish
YOR	Yoruba
ZAP	Zapotec
ZEN	Zenaga
ZUL	Zulu
ZUN	Zuni

LIST OF ABBREVIATIONS

Abr.	abridged
act. bk.	activity book
adapt.	adapted
aft.	afterword
alt.	alternate
Amer.	American
anniv.	anniversary
anno.	annotated by
annot.	annotation(s)
ans.	answer(s)
app.	appendix
Apple II	Apple II disk
approx.	approximately
assn.	association
audio	analog audio cassette
auth.	author
bd.	bound
bdg.	binding
bds.	boards
bibl(s).	bibliography(ies)
bk(s).	book(s)
bklet(s).	booklet(s)
boxed	boxed set, slipcase or caseboard
Bro.	Brother
C	college audience level
co.	company
comm.	commission, committee
comment.	commentaries
comp.	complied
cond.	condensed
contrib.	contributed
corp.	corporation
dept.	department
des	designed
diag(s).	diagram(s)
digital audio	digital audio cassette
dir.	director
disk	software disk or diskette
dist.	distributed
Div.	Division
doz.	dozen
ea.	each
ed.	edited, edition, editor
eds.	editions, editors
educ.	education
elem.	elementary
ency.	encyclopedia
ENG	English
enl.	enlarged
epil.	epilogue
exp.	expanded
expr.	experiments
expurg.	expurgated
fac.	facsimile
fasc.	fascicule
fict.	fiction
fig(s).	figure(s)
flmstrp.	filmstrip
footn.	
for.	foreign
frwd.	foreword
gen.	general
gr.	grade(s)
hndbk.	handbook
illus.	Illustrated, illustration(s), Illustrator(s)
in prep.	in preparation
incl.	includes, including
info.	information
inst.	institute
intro.	introduction
ISBN	International Standard Book Number
ISO	International Standards Organization
ITA	Italian
i.t.a.	initial teaching alphabet
J.	juvenile audience level
JPN	Japanese
Jr.	Junior
jt. auth.	joint author
jt. ed.	joint editor
k	kindergarten audience level
lab	laboratory
lang(s).	language(s)
LC	Library of Congress
lea.	leather
lib.	library
lib. bdg.	library binding
lit.	literature, literary
lp	record, album, long playing
l.t.	large type
ltd.	limited
ltd. ed.	limited edition
mac hd	144M, Mac
mac ld	800K, Mac
mass mkt.	mass market paperbound
math.	mathematics
mic. film	microfilm
mic form	microform
mod.	modern
MS(S)	manuscript(s)
natl.	national
net	net price
no(s).	number(s)
o.p.	out of print
orig.	original text, not a reprint (paperback)
o.s.i.	out of stock indefinitely
p.	pages
pap.	paper
per.	perfect binding
photos	photographer, photographs
pop. ed.	Popular edition
prep.	preparation
probs.	problems
prog. bk.	programmed books
ps.	preschool audience level
pseud.	pseudonym
pt(s).	part(s)
pub.	published, publisher publishing
pubn.	publication
ref(s).	reference(s)
rep.	reprint
reprod(s).	reproduction(s)
ret.	retold by
rev.	revised
rpm.	revolution per minute (phono records)
SAN	Standard Address Number
S&L	signed and limited
sec.	section
sel.	selected
ser.	series
Soc.	society
sols.	solutions
s.p.	school price
Sr. (after given name)	Senior
Sr. (before given name	Sister
St.	Saint
stu.	student manual, study guide, etc.
subs.	subsidiary
subsc.	subscription
suppl.	supplement
tech.	technical
text ed.	text edition
tr.	translated, translation translator
trans.	transparencies
unabr.	unabridged
unexpurg.	unexpurgated
univ.	university
var.	variorum
vdisk	videodisk
VHS	video, VHS format
vol(s).	volume(s)
wkbk.	workbook
YA	Young adult audience level
yrbk.	yearbook
3.5 hd	1.44M, 3.5 disk, DOS
3.5 ld	720, 3.5 Disk, DOS
5.25 hd	1.2M, 5.25 Disk, DOS
5.25 ld	360K, 5.25 Disk, DOS

SUBJECT GUIDE TO BOOKS IN PRINT®
2012-2013

Volume 1

A – Ch

A

A. & P.
see Great Atlantic & Pacific Tea Company

A. E.
see Russell, George William, 1867-1935

A FOUR D BOMBER
see Skyhawk Bomber

A PRIORI

Boghossian, Paul A. Content & Justification: Philosophical Papers. 2008. (ENG.). 360p. 110.00 *(978-0-19-929210-3(8))*; 376p. pap. 45.00 *(978-0-19-929216-5(7))* Oxford Univ. Pr., Inc.

Casullo, Albert. Essays on a Priori Knowledge & Justification. 2012. (ENG.). 384p. 74.00 ***(978-0-19-977786-0(1))*** Oxford Univ. Pr., Inc.

Greenberg, Robert. Kant's Theory of a Priori Knowledge. 2008. (ENG.). 292p. per. 25.95 *(978-0-271-02817-0(3))* Pennsylvania State Univ. Pr.

Harari, Orna. Knowledge & Demonstration: Aristotle's Posterior Analytics. 2010. (New Synthese Historical Library). ix, 161p. pap. 159.00 *(978-90-481-6722-7(1)*, 9048167221) Springer.

Kompa, Nikola, et al. The a Priori & Its Role in Philosophy. 2009. 269p. *(978-3-89785-662-2(X))* Mentis Verlag GmbH.

Piazza, Tommaso. A Priori Knowledge: Toward a Phenomenological Explanation. 2007. (ENG.). 193p. (gr. 11). 84.00 *(978-3-937202-92-1(7))* Ontos Verlag DEU. Dist: Transaction Pubs.

A. T-6 (TRAINING PLANES)
see T-Six (Training Planes)

A-THIRTY-SIX (FIGHTER-BOMBER PLANES)
see Mustang (Fighter Planes)

AALTO, ALVAR, 1898-1976

Aalto, Alvar & Fixler, David. Aalto & America. Anderson, Stanford & Fenske, Gail, eds. 2012. (ENG., Illus.). 320p. 75.00 *(978-0-300-17600-1(7))* Yale Univ. Pr.

Aalto Museum, The Alvar, compiled by. Alvar Aalto: Architecture to Read. 2011. 144p. pap. 25.95 *(978-88-492-0376-9(4))* Gangemi ITA. Dist: International Publishers Marketing.

Alvar & Aalto, Aino. Design: Collection Bischofberger. Kellein, Thomas, ed. 2006. (Illus.). 224p. 40.00 *(978-3-7757-1598-0(3))* Hatje Cantz Verlag GmbH & Co KG DEU. Dist: D.A.P./Distributed Art Pubs.

Charrington, Harry & Nava, Vezio, eds. Alvar Aalto: The Mark of the Hand. 2012. (ENG., Illus.). 400p. pap. 58.95 ***(978-951-682-995-4(3))*** Rakennustieto oy FIN. Dist: Independent Pubs. Group.

Dominguez, Luis Angel & Domínguez, Lluís Àngel. Alvar Aalto, Una Arquitectura Dialogica. 2010. (SPA.). 154p. *(978-84-8301-679-4(6))* UPC, S.L., Edicions.

Finnish Committee for the Restoration of Viipuri Library Staff & Karjalainen, Markku. Alvar Aalto Library in Vyborg: Saving a Modern Masterpiece. 2010. (ENG., Illus.). 144p. pap. 69.00 *(978-951-682-938-1(4)*, Art Stock Bks. Ltd/Csi) Continental Sales, Inc.

Gutheim, Frederick & Aalto, Alvar. Alvar Aalto. 2011. 128p. (Orig.). 40.95 ***(978-1-258-01180-2(8))*** Literary Licensing, LLC.

Helamaa, E. & Jetsonen, J. Alvar Aalto Summer Homes. 2008. 120p. pap. 67.00 *(978-951-682-857-5(4))* Rakennustieto oy FIN. Dist: Independent Pubs. Group.

Holma, M. Alvar Aalto, A Gentler Structure for Life. 2008. 176p. *(978-951-682-457-7(9))* Art Stock.

Jetsonen, Jari & Jetsonen, Sirkkaliisa. Alvar Aalto Houses. 2011. (ENG., Illus.). 224p. 50.00 *(978-1-56898-982-2(2))* Princeton Architectural Pr.

—Sacral Space: Modern Finnish Churches. 2008. (ENG.). 144p. pap. 69.00 *(978-951-682-731-8(4))* Rakennustieto oy FIN. Dist: Independent Pubs. Group.

Lahti, Louna. Alvar Aalto. Gossel, Peter, ed. 25th ed. 2009. (25 Ser.). (ENG.). 96p. 14.99 *(978-3-8365-1294-7(7))* TASCHEN DEU. Dist: Ingram Pub. Services.

Lahtti, Marku & Rakennustieto Publishing Staff. Alvar Aalto: A Gentler Structure for Life. 2009. (ENG, GER, ITA & FIN., Illus.). 176p. 99.00 *(978-951-682-475-1(7))* Rakennustieto oy FIN. Dist: Independent Pubs. Group.

Louna, Lahti. Alvar Aalto-Ex Intimo. 2008. 192p. pap. 26.00 *(978-951-682-619-9(9))* Rakennustieto oy FIN. Dist: Independent Pubs. Group.

Pelkonen, Eeva-Liisa. Alvar Aalto: Architecture, Modernity, & Geopolitics. 2009. (ENG., Illus.). 228p. 45.00 *(978-0-300-11428-7(1))* Yale Univ. Pr.

Roger, Connah & Connah, Roger. Aaltomania. 2008. 144p. pap. 26.00 *(978-951-682-613-7(X))* Rakennustieto oy FIN. Dist: Independent Pubs. Group.

Sato, Tomoko, et al. Alvar Aalto: Through the Eyes of Shigeru Ban. Sato, Tomoko, ed. 2007. (ENG., Illus.). 271p. 45.00 *(978-1-904772-64-4(1))* Black Dog Publishing Ltd. GBR. Dist: Perseus Distribution.

AARON (BIBLICAL PRIEST)

McNally SJ, Dennis. The Priest & the Pendulum: Reconciling the Orders of Melchizedek & Aaron. 2010. pap. 12.95 *(978-0-7414-6143-8(9))* Infinity Publishing.

AARON, HANK, 1934-

Aaron, Hank. I Had a Hammer: The Hank Aaron Story. 2007. (ENG., Illus.). 496p. per. 14.95 *(978-0-06-137360-2(5)*, HarperPerennial) HarperCollins Pubs.

Bryant, Howard. The Last Hero: A Life of Henry Aaron. (ENG.). 2011. 640p. pap. 16.95 *(978-0-307-27992-7(8)*, Anchor) 2010. (Illus.). 624p. 29.95 *(978-0-375-42485-4(7)*, Pantheon) Knopf Doubleday Publishing Group.

Poolos, J. Hank Aaron. 2008. (Baseball Superstars Ser.). (Illus.). 128p. (gr. 6-12). pap. 11.95 *(978-0-7910-9844-8(3)*, Checkmark Bks.) Facts On File, Inc.

AARON WARD (SHIP)

Lott, Arnold S. Brave Ship, Brave Men. (Bluejacket Paperback Ser.). 288p. pap. 19.95 *(978-1-55750-523-1(3))* Naval Institute Pr.

AARONSOHN, SARAH, 1891-1917

Katz, Shmuel. Aaronsohn Saga. 2007. 370p. 29.95 *(978-965-229-416-6(0))* Gefen Publishing Hse., Ltd ISR. Dist: Gefen Bks.

ABACUS

Goldman, Thomas F. AbacusLaw: Hands-On Tutorial & Guide. 2010. (ENG.). 336p. (C). pap. 43.40 *(978-0-13-139172-7(0)*, Prentice Hall) Prentice Hall PTR.

GREEN, P. A. U. L. HOW to USE A CHINESE ABACUS: A step-by-step guide to addition, subtraction, multiplication, division, roots & More. 2007. 156p. pap. 27.95 *(978-1-84799-864-4(X))* Lulu Enterprises Inc.

Shibusawa, Eiichi, et al. Lun Yu Yu Suan Pan. 2010. (CHI.). 325p. *(978-986-6274-10-7(1))* Asian Culture Co., Ltd.

ABAILARD, PIERRE, 1079-1142
see Abelard, Peter, 1079-1142

ABALONES

Field, Les W. Abalone Tales: Collaborative Explorations of Sovereignty & Identity in Native California. 2008. (Narrating Native Histories Ser.). (ENG., Illus.). 208p. pap. 22.95 *(978-0-8223-4233-5(2))*; 79.95 *(978-0-8223-4216-8(2))* Duke Univ. Pr.

ABALUYIA (AFRICAN PEOPLE)
see Luyia (African People)

ABAMBO (AFRICAN PEOPLE)
see Fingo (African People)

ABANDONED CHILDREN

Adie, Kate. Nobody's Child. 2006. (ENG., Illus.). 336p. pap. 15.95 *(978-0-340-83801-3(9))* Hodder General Publishing Div. GBR. Dist: Independent Pubs. Group.

Bentley, Lisa Misraje. Saving Levi: Left to Die ... Destined to Live. 2006. (ENG., Illus.). 176p. per. 13.99 *(978-1-58997-449-4(2))* Tyndale Hse. Pubs.

Berejena, Esther Judith. Learning & the Orphaned Children. 2011. 112p. pap. ***(978-3-8443-2616-1(2))*** Lambert Academic Publishing.

Chan, Yeeshan. Abandoned Japanese in Postwar Manchuria. 2011. (Japan Anthropology Workshop Ser.). (ENG., Illus.). 208p. (C). 140.00 *(978-0-415-59181-2(3))* Routledge.

Clark, Paul. Southern Cross: Lost & Found on the Streets & in the Jungles of Peru. 2008. 180p. per. *(978-0-9809231-0-0(7))* BPS Bks.

Crane, Maxine Weaver. Ask for Nothing: A True Story 1846-1925. 2007. (Illus.). 228p. per. 18.95 *(978-0-944019-53-5(6))* Empire Publishing, Inc.

Droeger, Linda. Bound by Love: The Journey of Lily Nie & Thousands of China's Forsaken Children. 2010. *(978-0-615-34737-0(1))* Meriwether Publishing, Ltd.

Eriksen, Olof A. Memoirs of an Immigrant. 2008. 560p. 29.95 *(978-1-4327-1014-9(1))* Outskirts Pr., Inc.

Escobari de Querejazu, Laura. Mentalidad Social y Niñez Abandonada: La Paz, 1900-1948. 2009. (SPA., Illus.). 281p. *(978-99954-1-241-8(1))* Instituto Francés de Estudios Andinos, IFEA.

Evans, Karin. The Lost Daughters of China: Adopted Girls, Their Journey to America, & the Search for a Missing Past. 2008. (ENG.). 400p. (gr. 12-18). 14.95 *(978-1-58542-676-8(8)*, Tarcher) Penguin Group (USA) Inc.

Grafton, Gordon J., compiled by. Lost Children of the Ohio Valley. 2008. (Illus.). vii, 175p. pap. *(978-1-55856-492-3(6))* Closson Pr.

Hart, Christine Joanna. Searching for Daddy. 2010. (ENG.). 320p. pap. *(978-0-340-91924-8(8))* Hodder & Stoughton Canada CAN. Dist: Hachette Bk. Group.

Haskett, Mary. Reverend Mother's Daughter: A Real Life Story. 2007. (ENG., Illus.). 216p. 14.99 *(978-0-9787428-1-2(8))* Believe Bks., LLC.

Holman, William Roger. The Orphans' Nine Commandments. 2009. (ENG., Illus.). 246p. pap. 19.95 *(978-0-87565-403-4(7))* Texas Christian Univ. Pr.

Itoh, Mayumi. Japanese War Orphans in Manchuria: Forgotten Victims of World War II. 2010. (ENG.). 288p. 89.00 *(978-0-230-62281-4(X))* Palgrave Macmillan.

Lauck, Jennifer. Found: A Memoir. (ENG.). 2012. 280p. pap. 17.00 ***(978-1-58005-395-2(5))*** 2011. 272p. 24.95 *(978-1-58005-367-9(X))* Seal Pr.

Miller, Julie. Abandoned: Foundlings in Nineteenth-Century New York City. 2008. (ENG., Illus.). 336p. 75.00 *(978-0-8147-5725-3(1))*; pap. 24.00 *(978-0-8147-5726-0(X))* New York Univ. Pr.

Nieuwenhuizen, Patricia. Street Children in Bangalore (India) Their Dreams & Their Future. 2008. (ENG.). 160p. pap. 29.95 *(978-90-5589-269-3(6))* Het Spinhuis NLD. Dist: Transaction Pubs.

Robinson, John. Somebody's Child: The Story of a Man Who Found Hope — and Took It Back to the Streets, 1 vol. 2007. (Illus.). 176p. pap. 11.99 *(978-0-8254-6149-1(9)*, Monarch Bks.) Lion Hudson PLC GBR. Dist: Kregel Pubns.

Salter, Shane. When a Child Becomes the Four-Year-Old Parent,,, Trouble Don't Last Always. 2006. 217p. pap. 13.95 *(978-0-7414-3695-5(7))* Infinity Publishing.

Seale, Shelley. The Weight of Silence: Invisible Children of India. 2009. (ENG.). 334p. pap. 16.95 *(978-0-9802323-7-0(6))* Dog's Eye View Media.

Star, Matthew. Android: Book One in the Star Family Series. 2006. (ENG.). 129p. pap. 19.95 *(978-1-4241-4191-3(5))* PublishAmerica, Inc.

Tuor-Kurth, Christina. Kindesaussetzung und Moral in der Antike: Jüdische und christliche Kritik am Nichtaufziehen und Töten neugeborener Kinder. 2010. (Forschungen Zur Kirchen- und Dogmengeschichte Ser.). (GER.). 404p. (C). 117.00 *(978-3-525-56398-4(1))* Vandenhoeck & Ruprecht GmbH & Co. KG DEU. Dist: ISD.

Yarborough, Trin. Surviving Twice: Amerasian Children of the Vietnam War. 2006. (Illus.). 336p. per. 16.95 *(978-1-57488-865-2(X))* Potomac Bks., Inc.

ABANDONED CITIES
see Extinct Cities

ABATEMENT OF TAXES
see Tax Remission

ABATTOIRS
see Slaughtering and Slaughter-Houses

ABBAYE DE SAINT-DENIS (SAINT-DENIS, FRANCE)

Jordan, W. C., et al. A Tale of Two Monasteries: Westminster & Saint-Denis in the Thirteenth Century. 2009. (ENG., Illus.). 296p. (C). 45.00 *(978-0-691-13901-2(6))* Princeton Univ. Pr.

ABBEY, EDWARD, 1927-1989

Abbey, Edward. Postcards from Ed: Dispatches & Salvos from an American Iconoclast. Petersen, David, ed. (ENG.). 2007. 336p. pap. 16.00 *(978-1-57131-285-3(4))* 2006. (Illus.). 304p. 24.95 *(978-1-57131-284-6(6))* Milkweed Editions.

Pozza, David M. Paradox: The Literary Landscape of Edward Abbey. 2006. 108p. (C). 52.95 *(978-0-8204-6330-8(2))* Lang, Peter Publishing, Inc.

ABBEY OF BURY ST. EDMUNDS

Gransden, Antonia. A History of the Abbey of Bury St Edmunds, 1182-1256: Samson of Tottington to Edmund of Walpole. 2007. (Studies in the History of Medieval Religion Ser.: Volume 31). (Illus.). 398p. 99.00 *(978-1-84383-324-6(7)*, Boydell Press) Boydell & Brewer, Ltd. GBR. Dist: Boydell & Brewer, Inc.

Jocelin of Brakelond. Chronica Jocelini De Brakelonda. (Camden Society, London, Publications, First Ser.: No. 13). reprint ed. 45.00 *(978-0-404-50113-6(3))* AMS Pr., Inc.

—Chronicle of the Abbey of Bury St. Edmunds. 2009. (Oxford World's Classics Ser.). (ENG., Illus.). 192p. pap. 13.95 *(978-0-19-955493-5(5))* Oxford Univ. Pr., Inc.

ABBEY OF SAINT-DENIS (SAINT-DENIS, FRANCE)
see Abbaye de Saint-Denis (Saint-Denis, France)

ABBEY THEATRE

Barnes, Ben. Plays & Controversies: Abbey Theatre Diaries 2000-2005. 2009. (ENG., Illus.). 475p. pap. 67.95 *(978-1-904505-38-9(4))* Carysfort Pr. IRL. Dist: Dufour Editions, Inc.

Gerard, Fay. The Abbey Theatre, Cradle of Genius. reprint ed. 24.50 *(978-0-404-20097-8(4))* AMS Pr., Inc.

Holloway, Joseph. Joseph Holloway's Abbey Theatre: A Selection from His Unpublished Journal Impressions of a Dublin Playgoer. Hogan, Robert & O'Neill, Michael J., eds. 2009. (Crosscurrents/Modern Critiques Ser.). (ENG.). 316p. pap. 35.00 *(978-0-8093-2937-3(9))* Southern Illinois Univ. Pr.

Joyce, James. Two Essays: A Forgotten Aspect of the University Question & the Day of the Rabblement. reprint ed. lib. bdg. 98.00 *(978-0-7426-3129-8(X))* Classic Bks.

Maples, Holly. Culture War: Conflict, Commemoration & the Contemporary Abbey Theatre. 2011. (Reimagining Ireland Ser.). 282p. pap. 63.95 (978-3-0343-0137-4(5)) Lang, Peter AG GBR. Dist: Lang, Peter.

ABBEYS

see also Priories

also names of specific abbeys, e.g. Lindisfarne Abbey

Alex, Erdmute & Spindler, Barbara. Time to Travel-Travel in Time to Germany's Finest Stately Homes, Gardens, Castles, Abbeys & Roman Remains: Official Joint Guide of the Heritage Administrations Baden-Wurttemberg, Bavaria, Berlin-Brandenburg, Dessau-Worlitz, Hesse, Rhineland-Palatinate, Saxony, Saxony-Anhalt, Thuringia. 2nd ed. 2007. (Illus.). 256p. pap. 29.95 (978-3-7954-1411-5(3)) Schnell und Steiner GmbH, Verlag DEU. Dist: Independent Pubs. Group.

Billings, Robert William. Baronial & Ecclesiastical Antiquities of Scotland , The - 2008. (Illus.). 792p. pap. (978-1-84530-058-6(0)) Grimsay Pr.

Colvin, Howard. Calke Abbey. 2006. (National Trust Guidebooks Ser.). (ENG., Illus.). 56p. pap. 13.95 (978-1-84359-036-1(0)) History Pr. Ltd.,The GBR. Dist: Independent Pubs. Group.

Coulton, G. G. Scottish Abbeys & Social Life. 2010. (Cambridge Library Collection - History Ser.). (ENG., Illus.). 322p. pap. 24.99 (978-1-108-01062-7(8)) Cambridge Univ. Pr.

Crossley, Frederick. The English Abbey. 2007. (Illus.). 232p. per. (978-1-905217-87-8(0)) Mills, Jeremy Publishing.

Engs, Ruth Clifford, ed. Conversations in the Abbey: Senior monks of Saint Meinrad reflect on their Lives. 2007. 384p. per. 18.95 (978-0-87029-411-2(3)) Booklocker.com, Inc.

Gaud, Henri, photos by. Cistercian Abbeys: History & Architecture. 2008. (Art & Architecture Ser.). (Illus.). 399p. 49.95 (978-0-8416-0061-4(9)) American Map Corp.

Harkins, Franklin T. Reading & the Work of Restoration: History & Scripture in the Theology of Hugh of St. Victor. 2009. (Studies & Texts). (LAT & ENG.). xii, 336p. 80.00 (978-0-88844-167-6(3)) Pontifical Institute of Mediaeval Studies, Dept. of Pubns. CAN. Dist: Univ. of Toronto Pr.

Hockey, S. F. Account Book of Beaulieu Abbey. (Camden Fourth Ser.). (LAT & ENG.). vi, 348p. 27.00 (978-0-901050-27-4(X)) Brown, David Bk. Co., The.

Jack And Marcia Kelly. Sanctuaries, the Complete United States: A Guide to Lodgings in Monasteries, Abbeys, & Retreats. 2010. 332p. pap. 21.95 (978-1-4401-8160-3(8)) iUniverse, Inc.

Keith, Robert & Spottiswoode, John. An Historical Catalogue of the Scottish Bishops down to the Year 1688. 2011. pap. 101.56 (978-1-61143-896-3(9)) Gorgias Pr., LLC.

King, Peter. Peterborough Abbey 1086-1310. 2008. (Cambridge Studies in Economic History Ser.). (ENG., Illus.). 228p. pap. 32.99 (978-0-521-07947-1(0)) Cambridge Univ. Pr.

Knoll, J. T. Where the Pavement Ends: Retreats at Assumption Abbey & other Contemplative Journeys. 2009. 388p. pap. 24.95 (978-1-4401-7511-4(X)) iUniverse, Inc.

Konemann Staff. Spanish Abbeys. Date not set. (Illus.). 250p. 19.95 (978-3-8290-4076-1(8), 521510) Konemann.

Mauchline, Mary & Greeves, Lydia. Fountains Abbey & Studley Royal. 2006. (National Trust Guidebooks Ser.). (ENG., Illus.). 64p. pap. 12.95 (978-1-84359-123-8(5)) History Pr. Ltd.,The GBR. Dist: Independent Pubs. Group.

Maude, Thomas. Guided by a Stone-Mason: Exploring the Cathedrals, Abbeys & Churches of Britain. 2011. (ENG., Illus.). 176p. pap. 17.00 (978-1-84885-547-2(8), Tauris Parke Paperbacks) I. B. Tauris & Co., Ltd. GBR. Dist: Macmillan.

Moore, Cathal, et al. Mottisfont Abbey: Garden, House & Estate. 2006. (National Trust Guidebooks Ser.). (ENG., Illus.). 32p. pap. 9.95 (978-1-84359-178-8(2)) History Pr. Ltd.,The GBR. Dist: Independent Pubs. Group.

Mortimer, Richard & Rodwell, Warwick, eds. Westminster Abbey Chapter House: The History, Art & Architecture of 'A Chapter House Beyond Compare' 2010. (ENG., Illus.). 317p. (C). 99.95 (978-0-85431-295-5(1)) Society of Antiquaries of London GBR. Dist: Brown, David Bk. Co., The.

Spence, H.D.M. Cloister Life in the Days of Coeur de Lion. 2007. (ENG.). 214p. 39.95 (978-0-548-04762-0(6)) Kessinger Publishing, LLC.

Tatton-Brown, Tim & Crook, John. The Abbeys & Priories of England. 2007. (ENG., Illus.). 160p. 39.95 (978-1-84537-116-6(X)) New Holland Pubs., Ltd. GBR. Dist: National Bk. Network.

Wilkinson, Philip. England's Abbeys: Monastic Buildings & Culture. 2006. (ENG., Illus.). 192p. (C). 40.00 (978-1-85074-944-8(2)) English Heritage GBR. Dist: Brown, David Bk. Co., The.

ABBOTS

Dufrasne, Dieudonné. Dom Anselme le Bail, 1913-1956, Abbot of Scourmont: A Monk, an Abbot, a Community. 2010. (978-0-87907-023-6(4)) Cistercian Pubns., Inc.

Ioann. May God Give You Wisdom! The Letters of Fr. John Krestiankin. 2007. (Illus.). 519p. (978-1-887904-39-1(5), St. Xenia Skete Pr.) St. Herman Pr.

Kagaris, Dimitri, tr. The Garden of the Holy Spirit: Elder Iakovos of Evia. 2007. Orig. Title: Blessed Iakovos Tsalikis. (978-0-9778970-0-1(1)) Orthodox Witness.

McGinley, Gerard. A Trappist Writes Home: Letters of Abbot Gerard Mcginley, to His Family. 2011. 192p. 42.95 (978-1-258-01232-8(4)) Literary Licensing, LLC.

Talbot, C. H. Letters from the English Abbots to the Chapter at Citeaux, 1442-1521. (Camden Fourth Ser.: No. 4). 200p. 27.00 (978-0-901050-64-9(4)) Brown, David Bk. Co., The.

ABBOTT, BERENICE, 1898-1991

Morel, Gaëlle. Berenice Abbott. 2012. (ENG., Illus.). 240p. pap. 50.00 (978-0-300-18200-2(7)) Yale Univ. Pr.

O'Neal, Hank. Berenice Abbott, 1 vol. 2008. (ENG., Illus.). 548p. 145.00 (978-3-86521-592-5(0)) Steidl, Gerhard Druckerei und Verlag DEU. Dist: Innovative Logistics.

O'Neal, Hank, intro. Berenice Abbott. 2010. (Photofile Ser.). (ENG., Illus.). 144p. pap. 15.95 (978-0-500-41100-1(X), 541100) Thames & Hudson.

Weissman, Terri. The Realisms of Berenice Abbott: Documentary Photography & Political Action. 2011. (Phillips Book Prize Ser.). (Illus.). 240p. 60.00 (978-0-520-26675-9(7)) Univ. of California Pr.

Weissman, Terri, et al. American Modern: Documentary Photography. 2010. (Illus.). 213p. 39.95 (978-0-520-26562-2(9)) Univ. of California Pr.

ABBOTT, LYMAN, 1835-1922

Abbott, Lyman. Reminiscences. 2009. 354p. pap. (978-0-217-98393-8(6)) Books LLC.

—Reminiscences. 2007. 556p. 57.95 (978-0-548-11186-4(3)) Kessinger Publishing, LLC.

ABBREVIATIONS

see also Acronyms; Ciphers; Periodicals—Abbreviations of Titles; Shorthand; Signs and Symbols

also subdivision Abbreviations under subjects, e.g. Law—Abbreviations

Acronyms, Initialisms & Abbreviations Dictionary, 4.0. 45th ed. 2011. 1404.00 (978-1-4144-6817-4(2)) Cengage Gale.

Acronyms, Initialisms & Abbreviations Dictionary, 4 vols., Set 4 vols. 43rd rev. ed. 2010. (ENG.). 1404.00 (978-1-4144-4537-3(7)) Cengage Gale.

American Heritage Dictionaries Editors, ed. The American Heritage Abbreviations Dictionary: A Compilation of Today's Acronyms & Abbreviations Including Cyberspeak. 3rd ed. 2007. (American Heritage Bks.). (ENG.). 304p. 6.95 (978-0-618-85747-0(8)) Houghton Mifflin Harcourt Trade & Reference Pubs.

The Codo: Basics for Texting & Instant Messaging. 2009. (ENG., Illus.). 192p. pap. 12.95 (978-0-615-27198-9(7)) Handy Tabs, Inc.

Espasa Staff. Diccionario Enciclopedico Abreviado. (SPA.). lib. bdg. 1295.00 (978-0-8288-2726-3(5)) French & European Pubns., Inc.

Kirchner, Hildebert. Abkürzungsverzeichnis der Rechtssprache. 2nd ed. (GER.). XII, 499p. 285.00 (978-3-11-218367-0(3)) De Gruyter, Walter Inc.

—Abkürzungsverzeichnis der Rechtssprache. 2nd ed. (GER.). XII, 499p. 192.00 (978-3-11-116617-9(1)) De Gruyter, Walter Inc.

Kirchner, Hildebert & Kastner, Fritz. Abkürzungsverzeichnis der Rechtssprache. 3rd ed. (GER.). XV, 412p. 240.00 (978-3-11-217515-6(8)); 160.00 (978-3-11-113356-0(7)) De Gruyter, Walter Inc.

Kirchner, Hildebert & Pannier, Dietrich. Abkurzungsverzeichnis der Rechtssprache. 6th ed. 2008. (GER.). XI, 771p. 77.00 (978-3-89949-336-8(2)) De Gruyter, Walter Inc.

Kobler-Trill, Dorothea. Das Kurzwort im Deutschen: Eine Untersuchung zu Definition, Typologie und Entwicklung. (Reihe Germanistische Linguistik Ser.). (GER.). XI, 238p. 150.00 (978-3-11-186684-0(X)) De Gruyter, Walter Inc.

Leistner, Georg. Abbreviations' guide to French forms in justice & Administration. 2nd ed. (GER.). 191p. 210.00 (978-3-11-202155-2(X)) De Gruyter, Walter Inc.

Periodical Title & Abbreviation by Title, 2 Vol, Vol. 217. 2006. 313.00 (978-1-4144-0116-4(7)) Cengage Gale.

Reverse Acronyms Initialisms & Abbreviations Dictionary, 4.0. 45th ed. 2011. 926.00 (978-1-4144-6908-9(X)) Cengage Gale.

The Association of Desk & Derrick Clubs, compiled by. D&D Standard Oil & Gas Abbreviator. 6th ed. 2007. 384p. pap. 49.00 incl. cd-rom (978-1-59370-108-6(X)) PennWell Corp.

Thomson Gale Staff. Periodical Title & Abbreviation by Abbreviation V1 17th Ed. 17th rev. ed. 2006. 313.00 (978-1-4144-0114-0(0)) Cengage Gale.

Unterman, Alan. Historical Dictionary of the Jews. 2010. (Historical Dictionaries of Peoples & Cultures Ser.: 9). (ENG.). 276p. 70.00 (978-0-8108-5525-0(9)) Scarecrow Pr., Inc.

Van Hoesen, Henry Bartlett. Roman Cursive Writing. 2008. 320p. pap. 30.95 (978-1-4371-1592-5(6)) Kessinger Publishing, LLC.

Walter, Frank Keller. Abbreviations & Technical Terms Used in Book Catalogs & in Bibliographies. 2009. 182p. 22.99 (978-1-116-46275-3(3)); pap. 21.75 (978-1-116-46277-7(X)) BiblioBazaar.

Wilson, John. A Treatise on English Punctuation with an Appendix, Containing Rules on the Use of Capitals, a List of Abbreviations, Hints on the Preparation Of. 2006. 348p. per. 26.99 (978-1-4255-3642-8(5)) MPublishing.

ABBREVIATIONS, MEDICAL

see Medicine—Abbreviations

ABD AL-RAHMAN III, CALIPH OF CORDOVA, 891-961

Fierro, Maria Isabel. Abderraman III y el califato Omeya de Cordoba. 2011. (SPA.). 250p. pap. 45.95 (978-84-96431-85-0(1)) Nerea Editorial ESP. Dist: Independent Pubs. Group.

ABD AL-RAZIQ, ALI, 1888-1966

Ali, Souad Tagelsir. A Religion, Not a State: Ali Abd Al-Raziq's Islamic Justification of Political Secularism. 2009. (Utah Series in Turkish & Islamic Stud Ser.). (ENG.). 180p. (gr. 13). pap. 25.00 (978-0-87480-951-0(7)) Univ. of Utah Pr.

ABDOMEN

see also Intestines; Kidneys; Liver; Peritoneum; Stomach

Arellano, Ronald S. Non-Vascular Interventional Radiology of the Abdomen. 2011. (ENG., Illus.). xiv, 107p. pap. 49.95 (978-1-4419-7731-1(7), 1441977317) Springer.

Barr, Frances J. & O'Brien, Robert, eds. BSAVA Manual of Canine & Feline Abdominal Imaging. 2009. (BSAVA British Small Animal Veterinary Association Ser.). (ENG., Illus.). 250p. pap. 157.99 (978-1-905319-10-7(X)) British Small Animal Veterinary Assn. (BSAVA) GBR. Dist: Wiley, John & Sons, Inc.

Block, Berthold. Abdominal Ultrasound - Step by Step. 2nd ed. 2011. (ENG., Illus.). 304p. 79.99 (978-3-13-138362-4(3)) Thieme Medical Pubs., Inc.

Calais-Germain, Blandine. No-Risk Abs. 2011. (ENG., Illus.). 1p. pap. 19.95 (978-1-59477-389-1(0)) Inner Traditions International, Ltd.

Coakley, Fergus. Pearls & Pitfalls in Abdominal Imaging: Pseudotumors, Variants & Other Difficult Diagnoses. 2010. (ENG., Illus.). 376p. 99.00 (978-0-521-51377-7(4)) Cambridge Univ. Pr.

Collins, Paul. Awesome Abs: Build Your Leanest Midsection Ever with Australia's Body Coach. 2008. (Body Coach: Ser.). (Illus.). 133p. pap. 14.95 (978-1-84126-232-1(3)) Meyer & Meyer Sport, Ltd. GBR. Dist: Cardinal Pubs. Group.

Dalrymple, Neal C., et al. Problem Solving in Abdominal Imaging with CD-ROM. 2009. (ENG., Illus.). 686p. 170.00 (978-0-323-04353-3(4), Mosby) Elsevier - Health Sciences Div.

Delavier, Frederic & Gundill, Michael. Delavier's Core Training Anatomy. 2011. (Illus.). 144p. pap. 21.95 (978-1-4504-1399-2(4)) Human Kinetics Pubs.

Eades, Michael R. & Eades, Mary Dan. The 6-Week Cure for the Middle-Aged Middle: The Simple Plan to Flatten Your Belly Fast! 2011. 320p. pap. 15.00 (978-0-307-45072-2(4), Three Rivers Pr.) Crown Publishing Group.

Federle, Michael P., et al. Chest, Abdomen, Pelvis. 2006. (Diagnostic & Surgical Imaging Anatomy Ser.). (ENG., Illus.). 1250p. 249.00 (978-1-931884-33-4(1)) Lippincott Williams & Wilkins.

Flizanes, J. J. Knack Absolute Abs: Routines for a Fit & Firm Core. 2011. (Knack: Make It Easy Ser.). (ENG., Illus.). 256p. pap. 19.95 (978-1-59921-947-9(6), Knack) Globe Pequot Pr., The.

Freytag, Chris. Prevention 2008 Shortcuts to Big Weight Loss: Slim Your Belly, Butt, & Thighs — And Get Fit Twice As Fast. 2007. (Illus.). x, 373p. (978-1-59486-875-7(1)) Rodale Pr., Inc.

Geiger, Bill, ed. The Big Book of ABS. 2007. (ENG., Illus.). 192p. pap. 22.95 (978-1-60078-031-8(8)) Triumph Bks.

Hagen-Ansert, Sandra L. Textbook of Diagnostic Sonography: 2-Volume Set, 2 vols. 7th ed. 2011. (ENG., Illus.). 1552p. (C). 310.00 (978-0-323-07301-1(8), Mosby) Elsevier - Health Sciences Div.

—Workbook for Textbook of Diagnostic Sonography. 7th ed. 2011. (ENG.). 656p. (C). pap. 61.95 (978-0-323-07300-4(X), Mosby) Elsevier - Health Sciences Div.

Harisinghani, Mukesh G., et al. Teaching Atlas of Abdominal Imaging. 2008. (ENG., Illus.). 544p. 139.99 (978-1-58890-656-4(6)) Thieme Medical Pubs., Inc.

Human Kinetics. Core Assessment & Training. 2010. (ENG., Illus.). 160p. 44.00 (978-0-7360-7384-4(1)) Human Kinetics Pubs.

Infectious Diseases Society of America and Surgical Infection Society, Infecti. Complicated Intra-Abdominal Infection GUIDELINES Pocketcard (2010) 2010. 10p. 9.95 (978-0-9845053-2-6(6)) International Guidelines Ctr., Inc.

Kawamura, Diane & Lunsford, Bridgette. Diagnostic Medical Sonography: A Guide to Clinical Practice Abdomen & Superficial Structures. 3rd rev. ed. 2012. (Diagnostic Medical Sonography Ser.). (ENG.). 864p. 179.95 (978-1-60547-995-8(0)) Lippincott Williams & Wilkins.

—Workbook for Diagnostic Medical Sonography: A Guide to Clinical Practice, Abdomen & Superficial Structures. 3rd rev. ed. 2012. (ENG.). 240p. pap. 34.95 (978-1-60547-996-5(9)) Lippincott Williams & Wilkins.

Lluch, Alex A. Sexy Abs Diet. 2011. (ENG.). 368p. pap. 17.95 (978-1-936061-37-2(6)) WS Publishing.

Multislice-CT of the Abdomen. 2011. (Medical Radiology / Diagnostic Imaging Ser.). 329.00 (978-3-540-43821-2(1), 3540438211) Springer.

Penny, Steven M. Examination Review for Ultrasound: Abdomen & Obstetrics & Gynecology. 2010. (ENG., Illus.). 392p. pap. 74.95 (978-0-7817-7978-4(2)) Lippincott Williams & Wilkins.

Ribes, Ramón & Luna, Antonio. Learning Abdominal Imaging. 2011. (Learning Imaging Ser.). (ENG., Illus.). 250p. pap. 59.95 (978-3-540-88002-8(X), 354088002X) Springer.

Sahani, Dushyant V. & Samir, Anthony E. Abdominal Imaging, 2 vols., Set. 2010. (Expert Radiology Ser.). (ENG., Illus.). 1600p. (C). 329.00 (978-1-4160-5449-8(9), Saunders) Elsevier - Health Sciences Div.

Semelka, Richard C. Abdominal-Pelvic MRI, 2 vols., Set. 3rd ed. 2010. (ENG., Illus.). 1912p. 320.95 (978-0-470-48775-4(5), Wiley-Blackwell) Wiley, John & Sons, Inc.

Smith, Scott G. The Absolutely Abominable Abdominal Encyclopedia. 2009. 84p. pap. 12.99 (978-0-557-04334-7(4)) Lulu Enterprises Inc.

Stork, Travis & Moore, Peter. The Lean Belly Prescription: The Fast & Foolproof Diet & Weight-Loss Plan from America's Favorite E.R. Doctor. 2011. (978-1-60961-797-4(5)) Rodale Pr., Inc.

Stork, Travis & Moore, Peter. The Lean Belly Prescription: The Fast & Foolproof Diet & Weight-Loss Plan from America's Top Urgent-Care Doctor. (ENG., Illus.). 288p. 2012. pap. 15.99 (978-1-60961-377-8(5)) 2010. 24.99 (978-1-60961-023-4(7)) Rodale Pr., Inc.

Vaccariello, Liz. El Plan Panza Plana! Un Abdomen Plano Es Cuestion de Actitud y Nutricion. Punto. (Por Cierto, No Requiere ni un Solo Abdominal) 2009. (SPA.). pap. 13.99 (978-1-60529-504-6(3)) Rodale Pr., Inc.

Vaccariello, Liz & Arathuzik, Gillian. Flat Belly Diet! Diabetes: Lose Weight, Target Belly Fat, & Lower Blood Sugar with This Tested Plan from the Editors of Prevention. 2010. (Illus.). vii, 390p. (978-1-60529-685-2(6)) Rodale Pr., Inc.

Vaccariello, Liz & Sass, Cynthia. El Plan Panza Plana! Un Abdomen Plano Es Cuestion de Actitud y Nutricion. Punto. (Por Cierto, No Requiere ni un Solo Abdominal) 2008. (SPA.). (978-1-60529-936-5(7)) Rodale Pr., Inc.

—El Plan Panza Plana! Un Abdomen Plano es Cuestion de Actitud y Nutricion. Punto. (Por Cierto, No Requiere ni un Solo Abdominal) 2009. (ENG., Illus.). 400p. pap. 19.99 (978-1-60529-937-2(5)) Rodale Pr., Inc.

Vaccariello, Liz & Stokes, D. Milton. Flat Belly Diet! for Men: Real Food, Real Men, Real Flat Abs. 2010. (ENG., Illus.). 304p. pap. 15.99 (978-1-60529-166-6(8)) Rodale Pr., Inc.

VanEs, Howard/Allan. Abs! 50 of the best exercises to strengthen, tone & slenderize your Mid-section. 2008. 112p. pap. 15.95 (978-0-9722094-3-4(3)) Letsdoyoga.

ABDOMEN—DISEASES

Begg, James D. Abdominal X-Rays Made Easy. 2nd rev. ed. 2006. (Made Easy Ser.). (ENG., Illus.). 228p. (C). pap. 34.95 (978-0-443-10257-8(0), Churchill Livingstone) Elsevier - Health Sciences Div.

Cope, Zachary. Cope's Early Diagnosis of the Acute Abdomen, 1 vol. 2nd ed. 2010. (ENG., Illus.). 320p. pap. 39.95 (978-0-19-973045-2(8)) Oxford Univ. Pr., Inc.

Federle, Michael P. Abdomen. 2008. (EXPERTddx™ Ser.). (ENG., Illus.). 600p. 299.00 (978-1-931884-09-9(9)) Lippincott Williams & Wilkins.

Leyendecker, John R., et al. Practical Guide to Abdominal & Pelvic MRI. 2nd rev. ed. 2010. (ENG.). 416p. 157.99 (978-1-60547-144-0(5)) Lippincott Williams & Wilkins.

Meyers, Morton A., et al. Meyers' Dynamic Radiology of the Abdomen: Normal & Pathologic Anatomy. 6th ed. 2010. (Illus.). xviii, 800p. 269.00 (978-1-4419-5938-6(6), 1441959386) Springer.

Morton, Darren. The 'stitch' Story. 2010. 236p. pap. (978-3-639-26129-5(1)) VDM Verlag Dr. Mueller e.K.

Pasricha, Pankaj Jay, et al, eds. Chronic Abdominal & Visceral Pain: Theory & Practice. 2006. (ENG., Illus.). 552p. 300.00 (978-0-8493-2897-8(7)) Taylor & Francis Group.

Shibata, Yoshiharu & Wu, Jean. Kampo Treatment for Climacteric Disorders. (Illus.). 274p. (Orig.). (C). 29.95 (978-0-912111-51-3(8)) Paradigm Pubns.

Yang, Grace Chia-yu Hsu & Tao, Liang-Che. Transabdominal Fine-Needle Aspiration Biopsy: A Color Atlas & Monograph. 2nd ed. 2007. (Illus.). 461p. 235.00 incl. cd-rom (978-981-256-882-3(4)) World Scientific Publishing Co., Inc.

Yaqoob, Nausheen, et al, eds. Desmoplastic Small Round Cell Tumor. 2012. (Cancer Etiology, Diagnosis & Treatments Ser.). 93p. pap. 47.00 (978-1-61470-452-2(X)) Nova Science Pubs., Inc.

ABDOMEN—RADIOGRAPHY

Bates, Jane A. & Smith, Jane A., eds. Abdominal Ultrasound. 3rd ed. 2010. (How, Why & When Ser.). (ENG., Illus.). 368p. (C). 81.95 (978-0-443-06919-2(0), Churchill Livingstone) Elsevier - Health Sciences Div.

Begg, James D. Abdominal X-Rays Made Easy. 2nd rev. ed. 2006. (Made Easy Ser.). (ENG., Illus.). 228p. (C). pap. 34.95 (978-0-443-10257-8(0), Churchill Livingstone) Elsevier - Health Sciences Div.

Federle, Michael P., et al. Abdomen. 2nd rev. ed. 2009. (ENG., Illus.). 1288p. 339.00 (978-1-931884-71-6(4)) Lippincott Williams & Wilkins.

Gourtsoyiannis, Nicholas, ed. Clinical MRI of the Abdomen: Why,How,When. 2009. (Illus.). 600p. 339.00 (978-3-540-85688-7(9)) Springer.

Hamm, Bernd, et al. MR Imaging of the Abdomen & Pelvis. 2009. (ENG., Illus.). 392p. 199.99 (978-3-13-145591-8(8)) Thieme Medical Pubs., Inc.

Meyers, Morton A., et al. Meyers' Dynamic Radiology of the Abdomen: Normal & Pathologic Anatomy. 6th ed. 2010. (Illus.). xviii, 800p. 269.00 (978-1-4419-5938-6(6), 1441959386) Springer.

Misra, Rakesh. A-Z of Abdominal Radiology. 2009. (ENG., Illus.). 366p. (C). pap. 75.00 (978-0-521-70014-6(0)) Cambridge Univ. Pr.

Ros, Pablo R. & Mortele, Koenraad J., eds. CT & MRI of the Abdomen & Pelvis: A Teaching File. 2nd rev. ed. 2006. (LWW Teaching File Ser.). (ENG., Illus.). 528p. 149.99 (978-0-7817-7237-2(0)) Lippincott Williams & Wilkins.

Taourel, Patrice, ed. CT of the Acute Abdomen. 2011. (Medical Radiology / Diagnostic Imaging Ser.). (ENG., Illus.). ix, 473p. 319.00 (978-3-540-89231-1(1), 3540892311) Springer.

Zech, Christoph Johannes, et al, eds. Multislice-CT of the Abdomen. 2012. (Medical Radiology / Diagnostic Imaging Ser.). (ENG., Illus.). xiv, 367p. 239.00 (978-3-642-17862-7(6), 3642178626) Springer.

ABDOMEN—SURGERY

see also Appendicitis; Intestines—Surgery

Aly, Al S. Abdominoplasty, an Issue of Clinics in Plastic Surgery. 2010. (Clinics: Surgery Ser.: 37-3). (ENG., Illus.). viii, 408p. 105.00 (978-1-4377-2485-1(X), Saunders) Elsevier - Health Sciences Div.

Baranski, Andrzej. Surgical Technique of the Abdominal Organ Procurement: Step by Step. 2008. (Illus.). 148p. 129.00 (978-1-84800-250-0(5)) Springer.

Clavien, Pierre-Alain, et al, eds. Atlas of Upper Gastrointestinal & Hepato-Pancreato-Biliary Surgery. 2008. (Illus.). 990p. 529.00 (978-3-540-20004-8(5), 3540200045) Springer.

Farinon, Attilio Maria, ed. Advances in Abdominal Surgery 2002. 2010. 434p. pap. 219.00 (978-90-481-6135-5(5), 9048161355) Springer.

Hunstad, Joseph P. & Repta, Remus. Atlas of Abdominoplasty. 2008. (ENG., Illus.). 242p. 164.00 (978-1-4160-4080-4(3), Saunders) Elsevier - Health Sciences Div.

MacFadyen, Bruce V., Jr., et al, eds. Laparoscopic Surgery of the Abdomen. 2012. (ENG., Illus.). xix, 535p. pap. 229.00 *(978-1-4419-3126-9(0),* 1441931260) Springer.

Niles, Jacqui D. & Williams, John M., eds. BSAVA Manual of Canine & Feline Abdominal Surgery. 2007. (BSAVA British Small Animal Veterinary Association Ser.). (ENG., Illus.). 200p. pap. 146.99 *(978-0-905214-81-8(1))* British Small Animal Veterinary Assn. (BSAVA) GBR. Dist: Wiley, John & Sons, Inc.

Reichl, Tobias. Tracking of Laparoscopic Ultrasound - Online Error Correction for Electromagnetic Tracking. 2008. 80p. per. *(978-3-8364-7350-7(X))* VDM Verlag Dr. Mueller e.K.

Rogers, Paul & Assalla, Ahmad. Schein's Common Sense Emergency Abdominal Surgery: An Unconventional Book for Trainees & Thinking Surgeons. Schein, Moshe, ed. 3rd ed. 2010. (ENG., Illus.). xxiii, 650p. pap. 89.95 *(978-3-540-74820-5(2),* 3540748202) Springer.

Schier, Felix. Laparoscopy in Children. 2010. (ENG., Illus.). v, 147p. pap. 115.00 *(978-3-642-07694-7(7),* 3642076947) Springer.

Shiffman, Melvin A. & Mirrafati, Sid, eds. Aesthetic Surgery of the Abdominal Wall. 2010. (Illus.). xii, 236p. pap. 289.00 *(978-3-642-05943-8(0),* 3642059430) Springer.

Zinner, Michael. Maingot's Abdominal Operations. Ashley, Stanley W., ed. 11th rev. ed. 2007. (ENG., Illus.). 1488p. 307.00 *(978-0-07-144176-6(X),* 007144176X) McGraw-Hill Professional Publishing.

ABDOMEN—WOUNDS AND INJURIES

Stead, Latha G. & Cline, David. Abdominal Emergencies. Stead, Latha G., ed. 2007. (ENG., Illus.). 296p. 105.00 *(978-0-07-146861-9(7),* 0071468617) McGraw-Hill Professional Publishing.

Tilson Iii Staff. Abdominal Aortic Aneurysm: Genetics, Pathophysiology, & Molecular Biology. Kuivaniemi, Helena et al, eds. 2nd ed. 2006. (Annals of the New York Academy of Sciences Ser.: Vol. 1088). (ENG., Illus.). 352p. pap. 139.95 *(978-1-57331-657-6(1),* Wiley-Blackwell) Wiley, John & Sons, Inc.

ABDOMINAL DELIVERY

see Cesarean Section

ABDUCTION

see also Alien Abduction

Bronson, Charles. Bronson. (Illus.). xiv, 352p. 24.95 *(978-1-85782-393-6(1));* 352p. pap. 17.99 *(978-1-85782-500-8(4))* Blake, John Publishing, Ltd. GBR. Dist: Trafalgar Square Publishing.

—Bronson. 2009. (ENG., Illus.). 368p. pap. 12.95 *(978-1-84454-655-8(1))* Blake, John Publishing, Ltd. GBR. Dist: Independent Pubs. Group.

Connelly, Ken. Throwing Stones: Parental child abduction through the eyes of a Child. 2009. 288p. pap. 20.95 *(978-1-4401-0441-1(7))* iUniverse, Inc.

Council of Europe Staff, compiled by. CIA above the Law? Secret detentions & unlawful inter-state transfers of detainees in Europe. 2008. (Illus.). 300p. pap. *(978-92-871-6419-3(3))* Council of Europe FRA. Dist: Manhattan Publishing Co.

Fisher, Lawrence & Kach, Tanya Nicole. Memoir of A Milk Carton Kid: The Tanya Nicole Kach Story. 2011. pap. 17.99 ***(978-1-61346-759-6(1))*** Tate Publishing & Enterprises, LLC.

Hall, Allan & Leidig, Michael. Girl in the Cellar: The Natascha Kampusch Story. 288p. 2010. mass mkt. 7.99 *(978-0-06-194529-8(3))* 2007. (Illus.). 24.95 *(978-0-06-134510-4(5))* HarperCollins Pubs.

Jasper, Margaret C. Missing & Exploited Children: How to Protect Your Child. 2006. (Legal Almanac Ser.). 232p. 47.00 *(978-0-19-532157-9(X))* Oxford Univ. Pr., Inc.

Kampusch, Natascha. 3,096 Days in Captivity: The True Story of My Abduction, Eight Years of Enslavement, & Escape. 2011. (ENG.). 320p. (gr. 12). 9.99 *(978-0-425-24428-9(8),* Berkley) Penguin Group (USA) Inc.

Maltzahn, Kathleen. Trafficked. 2008. (ENG.). 128p. pap. 17.95 *(978-0-86840-913-9(8),* UNSW Press) NewSouth Publishing AUS. Dist: Independent Pubs. Group.

Marsh, Stefanie & Pancevski, Bojan. I'm No Monster: The Horrifying True Story of Josef Fritzl. 2011. (ENG.). 336p. (gr. 12). 9.99 *(978-0-425-24452-4(0),* Berkley) Penguin Group (USA) Inc.

McDonald, Stephen & McDonald, Po Chu. The Mind of a Child: Thoughts of a Predator, Prevention for a Parent. 2008. 106p. pap. 14.95 *(978-0-7414-4749-4(5))* Infinity Publishing.

Muhsen, Zana. A Promise to Nadia: A True Story of a British Slave in the Yemen. 2010. (ENG.). 288p. pap. 14.95 *(978-0-7515-4369-8(1))* Little, Brown Bk. Group Ltd. GBR. Dist: Independent Pubs. Group.

Rodenborg, Benjamin H. The History of Child Abduction in the United States & an Analysis of Today's AMBER Alert System. 2010. 46p. pap. 6.75 *(978-0-557-45107-4(8))* Lulu Enterprises Inc.

Shattuck, Randy & Lundblad, Kristina. Frequently Asked Questions about Kidnapping & Abduction. 2011. (FAQ: Teen Life Ser.). (ENG.). 64p. (YA). (gr. 7-12). lib. bdg. 30.60 ***(978-1-4488-5563-6(2))*** Rosen Publishing Group, Inc., The.

Snow, Robert L. Child Abduction: Prevention, Investigation, & Recovery, 1 vol. 2008. 192p. 44.95 *(978-0-313-34786-3(7),* C34786, Praeger Pubs.) Greenwood Publishing Group, Inc.

Sommers, Michael. The Dangers of Online Predators. 2009. (Cyber Citizenship & Cyber Safety Ser.). 48p. (gr. 5-5). 53.00 *(978-1-61512-106-9(4),* Rosen Central) Rosen Publishing Group, Inc., The.

Sommers, Michael A. The Dangers of Online Predators. 2008. (Cyber Citizenship & Cyber Safety Ser.). (Illus.). 48p. (YA). (gr. 8-12). lib. bdg. 26.50 *(978-1-4042-1350-0(3))* Rosen Publishing Group, Inc., The.

Wilson, Melanie H., ed. Child Abduction Resources. 2010. (Children's Issues, Laws & Programs Ser.). 195.00 *(978-1-61668-247-7(7))* Nova Science Pubs., Inc.

ABDUCTION (LOGIC)

Aliseda, Atocha. Abductive Reasoning: Logical Investigations into Discovery & Explanation. 2010. (Synthese Library). xvi, 225p. pap. 189.00 *(978-90-481-6993-1(3),* 9048169933) Springer.

Flach, P. A. & Kakas, Antonis C., eds. Abduction & Induction: Essays on their Relation & Integration. 2010. (Applied Logic Ser.). 336p. pap. 249.00 *(978-90-481-5433-3(2),* 9048154332) Springer.

Gabbay, Dov M. & Smets, Philippe, eds. Handbook of Defeasible Reasoning & Uncertainty Management Systems: Volume 4: Abductive Reasoning & Learning. 2010. (Handbook of Defeasible Reasoning & Uncertainty Management Systems Ser.). 448p. pap. 329.00 *(978-90-481-5560-6(6),* 9048155606) Springer.

Walton, Douglas. Character Evidence: An Abductive Theory. (Argumentation Library). xv, 239p. 2010. pap. 159.00 *(978-90-481-7235-1(7),* 9048172357) 2006. (Illus.). (C). 159.00 *(978-1-4020-4942-2(0),* 1402049420) Springer.

ABDUCTION OF HUMANS BY ALIENS

see Alien Abduction

ABDUL-HAMID II, 1842-1918

Dodd, Anna Bowman. In the Palaces of the Sultan. 2007. (ENG.). 504p. 53.95 *(978-0-548-16823-3(7));* 508p. per. 38.95 *(978-1-4304-6548-5(4))* Kessinger Publishing, LLC.

Pears, Edwin. Life of Abdul Hamid. 2009. 382p. 38.99 *(978-1-116-14708-7(4));* 33.99 *(978-1-116-14709-4(2));* pap. 33.75 *(978-1-116-14710-0(6));* pap. 32.75 *(978-1-116-14711-7(4))* BiblioBazaar.

—Life of Abdul Hamid. 2009. 262p. pap. *(978-0-217-01206-5(X))* Books LLC.

—Life of Abdul Hamid. 2009. 384p. 48.95 *(978-1-120-83237-5(3));* pap. 33.95 *(978-1-120-63747-5(3))* Kessinger Publishing, LLC.

ABDUL-JABBAR, KAREEM, 1947-

Abdul-Jabbar, Kareem. On the Shoulders of Giants: My Journey Through the Harlem Renaissance. 2010. (ENG.). 288p. pap. 18.99 *(978-1-4165-3489-1(X))* Simon & Schuster.

ABEL, NIELS HENRIK, 1802-1829

Ore, Oystein. Niels Henrik Abel: Mathematician Extraordinary. 2008. (AMS Chelsea Publishing Ser.). (Illus.). 277p. 51.00 *(978-0-8218-4644-5(2),* Chelsea Publishing Co., Inc.) American Mathematical Society.

—Niels Henrik Abel: Mathematician Extraordinary. 2009. (ENG.). 292p. pap. 50.00 *(978-0-8166-6024-7(7))* Univ. of Minnesota Pr.

Stubhaug, Arild. NIELS HENRIK ABEL & his Times: Called Too Soon by Flames Afar. Daly, R. H., tr. 2010. (ENG., Illus.). x, 580p. pap. 69.95 *(978-3-642-08610-6(1),* 3642086101) Springer.

ABELARD, PETER, 1079-1142

Abelard, Peter. Letters of Peter Abelard, Beyond the Personal. 2007. (Medieval Texts in Translation). (Illus.). 232p. per. 29.95 *(978-0-8132-1505-1(6))* Catholic Univ. of America Pr.

Abelard, Peter & Heloise. The Letters & Other Writings: Selected Songs & Poems Translated by Stanley Lombardo & by Barbara Thorburn. Levitan, William, tr. from LAT. & intro. by. 2007. (Illus.). 352p. 41.95 *(978-0-87220-876-6(1));* pap. 14.95 *(978-0-87220-875-9(3))* Hackett Publishing Co., Inc.

Bell, Thomas J. Peter Abelard after Marriage: The Spiritual Direction of Heloise & Her Nuns Through Liturgical Song. 2008. (Cistercian Studies). 346p. per. 39.95 *(978-0-87907-311-4(X),* CS211P) Cistercian Pubns., Inc.

Godman, Peter. Paradoxes of Conscience in the High Middle Ages: Abelard, Heloise & the Archpoet. 2009. (Cambridge Studies in Medieval Literature Ser.). (ENG.). 242p. (C). 98.00 *(978-0-521-51911-3(X))* Cambridge Univ. Pr.

Luscombe, D. E. The School of Peter Abelard: The Influence of Abelard's Thought in the Early Scholastic Period. 2008. (Cambridge Studies in Medieval Life & Thought: New Ser.). (ENG.). 376p. pap. 48.00 *(978-0-521-08882-4(8))* Cambridge Univ. Pr.

Mews, Constant J. Lost Love Letters of Heloise & Abelard: Perceptions of Dialogue in Twelfth-Century France. Chiavaroli, Neville & Mew, Constant, trs. from LAT. 2nd rev. ed. 2008. (New Middle Ages Ser.). (ENG.). 432p. pap. 33.00 *(978-0-230-60813-9(2))* Palgrave Macmillan.

Moore, George. Héloïse & Abélard. 2008. (ENG.). 236p. pap. 14.95 *(978-1-60597-265-7(7))* 2007. 240p. per. 16.45 *(978-1-59462-799-6(1))* Standard Pubns., Inc. (Book Jungle).

Pinzani, R. The Logical Grammar of Abelard. 2010. (New Synthese Historical Library). 242p. pap. 139.00 *(978-90-481-6275-8(0),* 9048162750) Springer.

Ruys, Juanita Feros, et al. The Repentant Abelard. rev. ed. 2013. (New Middle Ages Ser.). (ENG.). 256p. 74.95 *(978-0-312-24002-8(3))* Palgrave Macmillan.

Waddell, Helen. Peter Abelard. 2007. (ENG.). 284p. per. *(978-1-4067-4453-8(0))* Read Bks.

ABELARD, PETER, 1079-1142—DRAMA

Brenton, Howard. In Extremis: The Story of Abelard & Heloise. 2007. (Nick Hern Book Ser.). (ENG.). 96p. per. 18.95 *(978-1-85459-940-7(2))* Theatre Communications Group, Inc.

ABELIAN GROUPS

see also Homology Theory

Accola, R. D. M. Riemann Surfaces, Theta Functions, & Abelian Automorphisms Groups. 2008. (Lecture Notes in Mathematics Ser.). 116p. pap. 39.95 *(978-3-540-07398-7(1))* Springer.

Adleman, L. M. Primality Testing & Abelian Varieties Over Finite Fields. 2008. (Lecture Notes in Mathematics Ser.). pap. 26.00 *(978-3-540-55308-3(8))* Springer.

Alekseev, V. B. Abel's Theorem in Problems & Solutions: Based on the lectures of Professor V. I. Arnold. Aicardi, Francesca, tr. 2010. 269p. pap. 149.00 *(978-90-481-6609-1(8),* 9048166098) Springer.

Alexeev, Valery, et al, eds. Curves & Abelian Varieties. 2008. (Contemporary Mathematics Ser.). 274p. pap. 81.00 *(978-0-8218-4334-5(6))* American Mathematical Society.

Arnold, D. M. Finite Rank Torsion Free Abelian Groups & Rings. 2008. (Lecture Notes in Mathematics Ser.). pap. 39.95 *(978-3-540-11557-1(9))* Springer.

Bernstein, J. & Lunts, V. Equivariant Sheaves & Functors. 2008. (Lecture Notes in Mathematics Ser.). 144p. pap. 39.95 *(978-3-540-58071-3(9))* Springer.

Bosch, Siegfried. Neron Models. 2008. (Ergebnisse der Mathematik und ihrer Grenzgebiete. 3. Folge A Series of Modern Surveys in Mathematics Ser.). (Illus.). 335p. 189.00 *(978-3-540-50587-7(3))* Springer DEU. Dist: Springer.

Casals-Ruiz, Montserrat & Kazachkov, Ilya. On Systems of Equations over Free Partially Commutative Groups. 2011. (Memoirs of the American Mathematical Society Ser.). (Illus.). 153p. pap. 77.00 *(978-0-8218-5258-3(2))* American Mathematical Society.

Coates, John, et al, eds. Non-abelian Fundamental Groups & Iwasawa Theory. 2011. (London Mathematical Society Lecture Note Ser.). (ENG., Illus.). 320p. pap. 90.00 ***(978-1-107-64885-2(8))*** Cambridge Univ. Pr.

Faticoni, Theodore G. Direct Sum Decompositions of Torsion-Free Finite Rank Groups. 2007. (Pure & Applied Mathematics Ser.). (ENG., Illus.). 344p. 113.95 *(978-1-58488-726-3(5),* Chapman & Hall/CRC) CRC Pr. LLC.

Geck, Meinolf & Jacon, Nicolas. Representations of Hecke Algebras at Roots of Unity. 2011. (Algebra & Applications Ser.). (Illus.). xii, 401p. 129.00 *(978-0-85729-715-0(5),* 0857297155) Springer.

Gobel, R., ed. Abelian Group Theory: Proceedings of the Conference held at the University of Hawaii, Honolulu, USA, December 28, 1982 - January 4, 1983. 2008. (Lecture Notes in Mathematics Ser.). pap. 59.00 *(978-3-540-12335-4(0))* Springer.

Goodearl, Kenneth R. Partially Ordered Abelian Groups with Interpolation. 2010. (Mathematical Surveys & Monographs). 336p. pap. 103.00 *(978-0-8218-4980-4(8))* American Mathematical Society.

Göbel, R. & Walker, E., eds. Abelian Group Theory: Proceedings of the Oberwolfach Conference, January 12-17, 1981. 2008. (Lecture Notes in Mathematics Ser.). 472p. pap. 69.95 *(978-3-540-10855-9(6))* Springer.

Heyer, Herbert. Structural Aspects in the Theory of Probability, Vol. 8. 2nd ed. 2009. 424p. 111.00 *(978-981-4282-48-2(0))* World Scientific Publishing Co., Inc.

Jancarik, Antonin. Products of Abelian Groups. 2011. 124p. pap. ***(978-3-8433-9230-3(7))*** Lambert Academic Publishing.

Katok, Anatole & Nitica, Viorel. Rigidity in Higher Rank Abelian Group Actions: Volume 1, Introduction & Cocycle Problem. 2011. (Cambridge Tracts in Mathematics Ser.). (ENG., Illus.). 320p. 85.00 *(978-0-521-87909-5(4))* Cambridge Univ. Pr.

Krylov, P. A., et al. Endomorphism Rings of Abelian Groups. 2010. (Algebra & Applications Ser.). 442p. pap. 129.00 *(978-90-481-6349-6(8),* 9048163498) Springer.

Luong, Bao. Fourier Analysis on Finite Abelian Groups. 2009. (Illus.). xvi, 156p. E-Book ***(978-0-8176-4916-6(6))*** Birkhauser Verlag AG.

—Fourier Analysis on Finite Abelian Groups. 2009. (Applied & Numerical Harmonic Analysis Ser.). (Illus.). xvi, 160p. 59.95 *(978-0-8176-4915-9(8),* 0817649158) Birkhauser Verlag AG CHE. Dist: Springer.

Metaplectic Groups & Segal Algebras. 2008. (Lecture Notes in Mathematics Ser.). pap. 39.95 *(978-3-540 51417-6(1))* Springer.

Norman, Christopher. Finitely Generated Abelian Groups & Similarity of Matrices over a Field. 2012. (Springer Undergraduate Mathematics Ser.). (ENG., Illus.). xii, 381p. pap. 49.95 ***(978-1-4471-2729-1(3),*** 1447127293) Springer.

Passman, Donald S. Groups, Rings & Algebras. Chin, William et al, eds. 2006. (Contemporary Mathematics Ser.). (Illus.). 301p. pap. 92.00 *(978-0-8218-3904-1(7))* American Mathematical Society.

Schmidt, Klaus. Dynamical Systems of Algebraic Origin. 2012. (Modern Birkhäuser Classics Ser.). (ENG., Illus.). xviii, 310p. pap. 74.95 ***(978-3-0348-0276-5(5),*** 3034802765) Birkhauser Verlag AG CHE. Dist: Springer.

Székelyhidi, László. Discrete Spectral Synthesis & Its Applications. 2006. (Springer Monographs in Mathematics Ser.). (Illus.). xvi, 120p. 129.00 *(978-1-4020-4636-0(7),* 1402046367) Springer.

Valcan, D., et al. Exercises in Abelian Group Theory. 2010. (Texts in the Mathematical Sciences Ser.). 362p. pap. 109.00 *(978-90-481-6249-9(1),* 9048162491) Springer.

Wolf, Joseph Albert. Harmonic Analysis on Commutative Spaces. 2007. (Mathematical Surveys & Monographs). 387p. (C). 102.00 *(978-0-8218-4289-8(7))* American Mathematical Society.

ABENAKI INDIANS

see Indians of North America—Canada

ABERDEEN, GEORGE HAMILTON GORDON, EARL OF, 1784-1860

Conacher, J. B. The Aberdeen Coalition 1852-1855. 2008. (ENG.). 628p. (C). pap. 79.00 *(978-0-521-07161-1(5))* Cambridge Univ. Pr.

ABERDEEN (SCOTLAND)

Aberdeen: Dyce, Peterculter, Portlethen. (Illus.). iv, 61p. pap. 7.99 *(978-0-7495-2821-8(4))* Automobile Assn. GBR. Dist: Trafalgar Square Publishing.

Blew, William, ed. Breviarium Aberdonense, 2 vols. (Bannatyne Club, Edinburgh Publications: No. 96). reprint ed. 335.00 *(978-0-404-52844-7(9))* AMS Pr., Inc.

Boece, Hector. Hectoris Boetii Murthlacensium Et Aberdonensium Episcoporum Vitae, Iterum in Lucem Editae. (Bannatyne Club, Edinburgh Publications: No. 11). reprint ed. 44.50 *(978-0-404-52711-2(6))* AMS Pr., Inc.

Collins UK Staff. Aberdeen Streetfinder Atlas. 5th ed. 2007. (ENG., Illus.). 72p. pap. 6.95 *(978-0-00-722987-1(9))* HarperCollins Pubs. Ltd. GBR. Dist: Independent Pubs. Group.

Hoffman, Aaron. The Temperance Movement in Aberdeen, Scotland, 1830-1845: Distilled Death & Liquid Damnation. 2012. (ENG.). 604p. 159.95 ***(978-0-7734-2582-8(9))*** Mellen, Edwin Pr., The.

Holder, Geoff. Haunted Aberdeen & District. 2010. (Haunted Ser.). (ENG., Illus.). 96p. pap. 18.95 *(978-0-7524-5533-4(8))* History Pr. Ltd.,The GBR. Dist: Independent Pubs. Group.

Smith, Paul. Aberdeen Who?'s Who. 2012. (ENG.). 288p. 39.95 ***(978-1-908051-11-0(6))*** Pitch Publishing (Brighton) Ltd. GBR. Dist: Independent Pubs. Group.

ABERDEEN-ANGUS CATTLE

Pala, Akin. Crossbreeding in Beef Cattle Using Terminal Sires. 2010. 112p. pap. *(978-3-639-23524-1(X))* VDM Verlag Dr. Mueller e.K.

ABERDEEN UNIVERSITY

see University of Aberdeen

ABERFAN (WALES)

Attie, Shimon. The Attraction of Onlookers: Aberfan - An Anatomy of a Welsh Village. 2008. (ENG., Illus.). 108p. 80.00 *(978-1-905762-40-8(2))* Parthian Bks. GBR. Dist: D.A.P./Distributed Art Pubs.

ABERNATHY, RALPH, 1926-1990

Abernathy, Ralph David. And the Walls Came Tumbling Down: An Autobiography. 2010. (ENG., Illus.). 672p. pap. 19.95 *(978-1-56976-279-0(1),* Hill, Lawrence Bks.) Chicago Review Pr., Inc.

ABERRATION, CHROMATIC AND SPHERICAL

see Lenses; Mirrors; Optical Instruments

ABHIDHARMA

Mahathera, Nyanatiloka. Guide Through the Abhidhamma Pitaka. Date not set. *(978-955-24-0133-6(X))* Buddhist Publication Society LKA. Dist: Pariyatti Publishing.

ABILENE (TEX.)

Fink, Rob & Fink, Tiffany M. Love Unbounded: The Influence of First Baptist Church on Abilene, Texas. 2009. (ENG., Illus.). 120p. 24.95 *(978-1-933337-32-6(X))* State Hse. Pr.

Frazier, Donald S. & Pace, Robert F. Abilene Landmarks: An Illustrated Tour. 2009. (Illus.). xi, 248p. 49.95 *(978-1-933337-30-2(3))* State Hse. Pr.

Sledge, Robert W. A People, A Place: The Story of Abilene Volume 2: the Modern City, 1940-2010. 2011. (ENG., Illus.). 344p. pap. 29.99 ***(978-1-933337-45-6(1))*** State Hse. Pr.

Sledge, Robert W. A People, a Place - The Story of Abilene Vol. 1: The Future Great City, 1881-1940. 2009. (ENG., Illus.). 316p. pap. 24.95 *(978-1-933337-31-9(1))* State Hse. Pr.

ABILITIES, INC.

Viscardi Jr., Henry. Give Us the Tools: The Inspiring Story of America's Most Incredible People. 2011. 288p. 48.95 ***(978-1-258-02260-0(5))*** Literary Licensing, LLC.

ABILITY

see also Athletic Ability; Creative Ability; Executive Ability; Leadership; Learning Ability; Mathematical Ability; Motor Ability; Musical Ability; Psychic Ability

Al Abduwani, Taki Abdul Redha. The Value & Development of Soft Skills. 2010. (Illus.). 240p. pap. *(978-3-8383-8622-5(1))* Lambert Academic Publishing.

Amer, Beverly. New Perspective: Portfolio Projects for Soft Skills. 2011. (New Perspectives Ser.). (ENG., Illus.). 125p. pap. 81.95 *(978-1-111-58155-8(X))* Course Technology.

Anders, George. The Rare Find: Spotting Exceptional Talent Before Everyone Else. 2011. (ENG.). 288p. (gr. 12). 26.95 *(978-1-59184-425-9(8),* Portfolio (Hardcover)) Penguin Group (USA) Inc.

Bagley, William C. Determinism in Education. 2011. 194p. 42.95 ***(978-1-258-02171-9(4))*** Literary Licensing, LLC.

Belding, Shaun. Win at Work: Navigate the Nasties, Get Things Done, & Get Ahead. 2010. (ENG.). 192p. pap. 19.95 *(978-0-7494-5711-2(2))* Kogan Page, Ltd. GBR. Dist: Ingram Pub. Services.

Binder, Jeffrey L. Key Competencies in Brief Dynamic Psychotherapy: Clinical Practice Beyond the Manual. 2010. (ENG.). 292p. pap. 27.00 *(978-1-60918-168-0(9))* Guilford Pubns., Inc.

Bisseret, Noelle. Education, Class Language & Ideology (RLE Edu L) 2011. (Routledge Library Editions: Education Ser.). (ENG.). 160p. 100.00 ***(978-0-415-50414-0(7))*** Routledge.

Bixby, Jennifer & McVeigh, Joe. Q - Skills for Success - Reading & Writing 2. 2011. (ENG.). 128p. pap., tchr. ed. 47.44 *(978-0-19-475628-0(9))* Oxford Univ. Pr., Inc.

Blass, Eddie, ed. Talent Management: Cases & Commentary. 2009. (ENG., Illus.). 326p. 110.00 *(978-0-230-22419-3(9))* Palgrave Macmillan.

Brauner, Marygail K., et al. Improving Development & Utilization of U. S. Air Force Intelligence Officers. 2009. 84p. pap. 23.50 *(978-0-8330-4716-8(7),* tr-628) RAND Corp., The.

Brooks, Margaret. Q Skills for Success: Listening & Speaking, No. 2. 2011. (ENG.). 128p. pap., tchr. ed. 47.44 *(978-0-19-475616-7(5))* Oxford Univ. Pr., Inc.

Bryson, Jane, ed. Beyond Skill: Institutions, Organisations & Human Capability. 2010. (ENG., Illus.). 190p. 100.00 *(978-0-230-23057-6(1))* Palgrave Macmillan.

Buckingham, Marcus. Go Put Your Strengths to Work: 6 Powerful Steps to Achieve Outstanding Performance. 2010. (ENG.). 320p. pap. 16.00 *(978-0-7432-6168-5(2),* Free Pr.) Free Pr.

Carson, John. The Measure of Merit: Talents, Intelligence, & Inequality in the French & American Republics, 1750-1940. 2006. (ENG., Illus.). 422p. (C). 49.95 *(978-0-691-01715-0(8))* Princeton Univ. Pr.

Casey, Tom, et al. Talent Readiness: The Future Is Now. 2010. (ENG.). 119p. pap. 14.99 *(978-1-59932-221-6(8))* Advantage Media Group.

Cerny, Rosanne, et al. Outstanding Library Service to Children: Putting the Core Competencies to Work. 2006. (Illus.). 94p. per. 30.00 *(978-0-8389-0922-5(1))* American Library Assn.

Coyle, Daniel. The Little Book of Talent: 52 Tips for Improving Skills. 2012. (ENG., Illus.). 144p. 18.00 ***(978-0-345-53025-7(X))*** Random House Publishing Group.

Coyle, Daniel. The Talent Code: Greatness Isn't Born. It's Grown. Here's How. (ENG., 256p. 2013. Illus.). pap. 15.00 *(978-0-553-38533-5(X))* 2009. 25.00 *(978-0-553-80684-7(X))* Random House Publishing Group.

Craven, Miles, et al. Q Skills for Success - Listening & Speaking, Bk. 3. 2011. (ENG.). 128p. pap., tchr. ed. 47.44 *(978-0-19-475617-4(3))* Oxford Univ. Pr., Inc.

Davis, Tony, et al, eds. Talent Assessment: A New Strategy for Talent Management. 2007. (Illus.). 256p. 124.95 *(978-0-566-08731-8(6),* Gower Publishing Co., Ltd.) Ashgate Publishing, Ltd. GBR. Dist: Ashgate Publishing Co.

Edenborough, Robert & Edenborough, Marion. The Psychology of Talent: Exploring & Exploding the Myths. 2011. (Illus.). 152p. 34.80 *(978-0-88937-396-9(5))* Hogrefe Publishing.

Edwards, Anne. Being an Expert Professional Practitioner: The Relational Turn. 2010. (Professional & Practice-based Learning Ser.). (ENG., Illus.). xi, 160p. 159.00 *(978-90-481-3968-2(6),* 9048139686) Springer.

Fairburn, William Armstrong. Mentality & Freedom: Essays. 2007. pap. 27.95 *(978-1-4304-8098-3(X))* Kessinger Publishing, LLC.

Flowers, Sarah. Young Adults Deserve the Best: YALSA's Competencies in Action. 2010. 125p. 45.00 *(978-0-8389-3587-3(7))* American Library Assn.

Fox, Brent I., et al. Building Core Competencies in Pharmacy Informatics. 2010. 400p. pap. 44.95 *(978-1-58212-144-4(3))* American Pharmacists Assn.

Freire, Robert & Jones, Tamara. Q - Skills for Success - Listening & Speaking, No. 4. 2011. (ENG.). stu. ed. 59.95 *(978-0-19-475613-6(0))* Oxford Univ. Pr., Inc.

—Q Skills for Success Bk. 4: Listening & Speaking. 2011. (ENG.). 128p. pap., tchr. ed. 47.44 *(978-0-19-475618-1(1))* Oxford Univ. Pr., Inc.

Galton, Francis. Inquiries into Human Faculty & Its Development. 2009. 312p. 29.99 *(978-0-559-07327-4(5));* 28.99 *(978-0-559-07340-3(2));* pap. 29.75 *(978-0-559-07330-4(5));* pap. 28.75 *(978-0-559-07338-0(0))* BiblioBazaar.

—Inquiries into Human Faculty & Its Development. 2009. 274p. pap. *(978-0-217-49038-2(7))* Books LLC.

—Inquiries into Human Faculty & Its Development. Wozniak, Robert H., ed. (Classics in Psychology Ser.). (Illus.). 405p. *(978-1-85506-671-7(8),* Burns & Oates) Continuum International Publishing Group, Ltd.

—Inquiries into Human Faculty & Its Development. 2007. (Illus.). 348p. per. *(978-1-4065-1745-3(3))* Dodo Pr.

Gonon, Philipp & Kraus, Katrin, eds. Work, Education & Employability. 2008. (Studien zur Berufs- und Weiterbildung - Studies in Vocational & Continuing Education Ser.). (Illus.). 324p. pap. *(978-3-03911-294-4(5))* Lang, Peter.

Gordon, Edward E. Winning the Global Talent Showdown: How Businesses & Communities Can Partner to Rebuild the Jobs Pipeline. 2009. (Illus.). xiii, 249p. pap. *(978-1-60509-303-1(3))* Berrett-Koehler Pubs., Inc.

Heene, Aime & Sanchez, Ron, eds. Managing Firm Growth & Diversification. 2010. (Advances in Applied Business Strategy Ser.). (Illus.). 275p. 124.95 *(978-1-84855-876-2(7))* Emerald Group Publishing Ltd. GBR. Dist: Turpin Distribution Services Ltd.

Hirsch, Marissa Alexandra. The Word Pyramid: The Key to Success in School & Life. 2011. (ENG., Illus.). 88p. pap. 12.95 *(978-0-9841447-5-4(7))* Hilton Publishing Co.

Holt, Jon & Perry, Simon A. A Pragmatic Guide to Competency: Tools, Frameworks & Assessment. 2011. (ENG., Illus.). 192p. pap. 49.99 ***(978-1-906124-70-0(1))*** British Computer Society, The GBR. Dist: Turpin Distribution Services Ltd.

Humphries Merritt, Pamela. You Can Do It! 2009. 20p. pap. 12.49 *(978-1-4389-8860-3(5))* AuthorHouse.

Hunter, Celestine. Dramas of the End Time. 2010. 102p. pap. 15.99 *(978-1-4500-5319-8(X))* Xlibris Corp.

Idoko, Ode A. Putting Your Talent to Work: Rediscovering the Real you in You. 2011. 172p. pap. 14.69 *(978-1-4520-9518-9(3))* AuthorHouse.

Kotsko, Adam. Awkwardness. 2010. (ENG.). pap. 12.95 *(978-1-84694-391-1(4))* O Bks.,John Hunt.

Kraak, Andre, ed. Sectors & Skills: The Need for Policy Alignment. 2010. (ENG., Illus.). 380p. pap. 34.95 *(978-0-7969-2265-6(9))* Human Sciences Research Council ZAF. Dist: Independent Pubs. Group.

Lehr, Michael. Poker: Four Lessons Emphasizing Talent Identification & Development: an Intuitive Business Model. 2007. spiral bd. 14.95 *(978-0-9786613-3-5(8))* Dragon Slayer, LLC.

Levin, Ginger & Ward, J. LeRoy. Program Management Complexity: A Competency Model. 2011. (ESI International Project Management Ser.). (ENG., Illus.). 222p. 69.95 *(978-1-4398-5111-1(5))* Auerbach Pubs., Inc.

Matias, Linda. 201 Knockout Answers to Tough Interview Questions: The Ultimate Guide to Handling the New Competency-Based Interview Style, 1 vol. 2009. (ENG.). 208p. pap. 13.95 *(978-0-8144-1500-9(8))* Amacom.

Maxwell, John C. Talent Is Never Enough, 0 vols. 2007. 256p. pap., wbk. ed. 17.99 *(978-1-4185-2773-0(4))* Nelson, Thomas Inc.

Michalewicz, Zbigniew & Michalewicz, Matthew. Puzzle-Based Learning. 2008. 348p. pap. *(978-1-876462-63-5(9))* Hybrid Pubs.

Miller, Dan. No More Dreaded Mondays: Ignite Your Passion - And Other Revolutionary Ways to Discover Your True Calling at Work. 2009. (ENG.). 272p. pap. 14.99 *(978-0-307-58877-7(7),* Broadway Business) Knopf Doubleday Publishing Group.

Moore, S. Craig, et al. Targeting the Occupational Skill Pairings Needed in New Air Force Colonels. 2010. 178p. pap. 26.00 *(978-0-8330-4931-5(3))* RAND Corp., The.

National Research Council (U.S.), Committee on Core Competencies for Federal Facilities Asset Management, 2005-2020 Staff, et al, contrib. by. Core Competencies for Federal Facilities Asset Management Through 2020: Transformational Strategies. 2008. (ENG., Illus.). 136p. pap. 29.00 *(978-0-309-11400-4(4))* National Academies Pr.

Nichols, Quienton. Connecting Core Competencies: A Workbook for Social Work Students. rev. ed. 2010. (MySocialWorkLab Ser.). (ENG.). 168p. (C). pap. 44.80 *(978-0-205-01246-6(9),* Prentice Hall) Prentice Hall PTR.

Nichols, Quienton P. Advancing Core Competencies: Emphasizing Practice Behaviors & Outcomes. 2011. (Advancing Core Competencies Ser.). (ENG.). 192p. (C). pap. 45.40 ***(978-0-205-20228-7(4),*** Prentice Hall) Prentice Hall PTR.

Norloff, Charl, et al. Q - Skills for Success - Reading & Writing, No. 4. 2011. (ENG.). stu. ed. 59.95 *(978-0-19-475625-9(4))* Oxford Univ. Pr., Inc.

—Q Skills for Success: Reading & Writing. 2011. (ENG.). 128p. pap. 47.44 *(978-0-19-475030-3(0))* Oxford Univ. Pr., Inc.

Phillipson, Shane N. & McCann, Maria. Conceptions of Giftedness: Sociocultural Perspectives. 2007. (ENG., Illus.). 544p. (C). 175.00 *(978-0-8058-5750-4(8));* per. 64.95 *(978-0-8058-5751-1(6))* Routledge.

Rao, M. S. Soft Skills - Enhancing Employability: Connecting Campus with Corporate. 2010. 256p. (C). pap. *(978-93-80578-38-5(5))* I.K. International Publishing House Pvt. Ltd.

Rath, Tom. StrengthsFinder 2.0. 2007. (ENG., Illus.). 192p. 24.95 *(978-1-59562-015-6(X))* Gallup Pr.

Rathaur, Manish Kumar. Puzzles for Brain Exercise. 2011. 172p. pap. ***(978-3-8443-3084-7(4))*** Lambert Academic Publishing.

Sanchez, Ron & Heene, Aime. A Focused Issue on Identifying, Building & Linking Competences. 2010. (Research in Competence-Based Management Ser.). (Illus.). 272p. 124.95 *(978-1-84950-990-9(5))* Emerald Group Publishing Ltd. GBR. Dist: Turpin Distribution Services Ltd.

Scanlon, Jaime. Q - Skills for Success - Listening & Speaking 1. 2011. (ENG.). 128p. pap., tchr. ed. 47.44 *(978-0-19-475615-0(7))* Oxford Univ. Pr., Inc.

Schiemann, Bill & Schiemann, William A. Reinventing Talent Management: How to Maximize Performance in the New Marketplace. 2009. (ENG., Illus.). 288p. 29.95 *(978-0-470-45226-4(9),* Wiley) Wiley, John & Sons, Inc.

Schiemann, William. The ACE Advantage: How Smart Companies Unleash Talent for Optimal Performance. 2012. (ENG.). 240p. pap. 28.95 ***(978-1-58644-270-5(8))*** Society for Human Resource Management.

Schiller, Pam. Start Smart! Building Brain Power in the Early Years. 2nd rev. ed. 2012. (ENG., Illus.). 160p. pap. 19.95 ***(978-0-87659-393-6(7))*** Gryphon Hse., Inc.

Shenk, David. The Genius in All of Us: New Insights into Genetics, Talent, & IQ. 2010. (ENG., Illus.). 320p. 26.95 *(978-0-385-52365-3(3),* Doubleday) Knopf Doubleday Publishing Group.

Silberg, Jackie. 125 Brain Games for Babies. 2nd rev. ed. 2012. (ENG., Illus.). 144p. pap. 16.95 ***(978-0-87659-391-2(0))*** Gryphon Hse., Inc.

Smith, Roland & Campbell, Michael. Talent Conversations: What They Are, Why They're Crucial, & How to Do Them Right. 2011. 32p. pap. 11.95 ***(978-1-60491-093-3(3),*** CCL Pr.) Ctr. for Creative Leadership.

Solimano, Andrés, ed. The International Mobility of Talent: Types, Causes, & Development Impact. 2008. (WIDER Studies in Development Economics Ser.). (ENG., Illus.). 352p. 125.00 *(978-0-19-953260-5(5))* Oxford Univ. Pr., Inc.

Spearman, C. Abilities of Man Their Nature & Measu. 2007. 464p. per. *(978-1-4067-8998-0(4),* Pierides Pr.) Read Bks.

Stehr, Nico & Grundmann, Reiner. Experts: The Knowledge & Power of Expertise. 2011. (Key Ideas Ser.). (ENG., Illus.). 160p. (C). 110.00 *(978-0-415-60803-9(1))* Routledge.

StrengthsQuest. 2006. (C). per. 35.00 *(978-1-59562-011-8(7))* Gallup Pr.

StrengthsQuest - Spanish Language Edition. 2006. (C). per. *(978-1-59562-013-2(3))* Gallup Pr.

Syed, Matthew. Bounce: Mozart, Federer, Picasso, Beckham, & the Science of Success. 2011. (P. S. Ser.). (ENG.). 320p. pap. 14.99 *(978-0-06-172376-6(2),* HarperPerennial) HarperCollins Pubs.

Ward, Colin S. & Gramer, Margot F. Q Skills for Success - Reading & Writing, Bk. 3. 2011. (ENG.). 128p. pap., tchr. ed. 47.44 *(978-0-19-475629-7(7))* Oxford Univ. Pr., Inc.

Warner, Jon. Rapid Skill-Builder Series Library. 2011. (ENG.). ring bd. 199.95 ***(978-1-59996-218-4(7))*** Human Resource Development Pr.

Watson, Donna S. How to Get & Keep A Job. 2011. pap. 24.99 ***(978-1-61777-405-8(7))*** Tate Publishing & Enterprises, LLC.

Winterton, Jonathan & Magnusson, Lars, eds. Trade Union Strategies for Competence Development. 2011. (Routledge Studies in Human Resource Development Ser.). (ENG.). 288p. (C). 125.00 *(978-0-415-55428-2(4))* Routledge.

Younger, Sandra Millers. Understanding Core Competencies. 2007. (ENG.). 16p. pap. 24.95 *(978-1-56286-196-4(4))* American Society for Training & Development.

ABILITY—TESTING

see also Differential Aptitude Tests; Mathematical Ability—Testing; Mechanical Ability—Testing; Musical Ability—Testing; Occupational Aptitude Tests; Physical Fitness—Testing; Preliminary Scholastic Assessment Test

also subdivision Ability Testing under topical headings, and subdivision Testing under phrase headings for types of ability for discussions of tests of native aptitude or acquired proficiency in a particular field

Alexander-Travis, Pauline. TestBuster for the GRE General Test. 4th ed. 2010. (Illus.). xii, 466p. ***(978-0-7386-0861-7(0))*** Research & Education Assn.

Asera, Rose, et al. Student Success in Community Colleges: A Practical Guide to Developmental Education. 2010. (ENG., Illus.). 272p. pap. 40.00 *(978-0-470-45555-5(1),* Jossey-Bass) Wiley, John & Sons, Inc.

Barrett, Jim. The Aptitude Test Workbook: Discover Your Potential & Improve Your Career Options with Practice Psychometric Tests. 2nd rev. ed. 2011. (ENG., Illus.). 208p. pap. 19.95 *(978-0-7494-6190-4(X))* Kogan Page, Ltd. GBR. Dist: Ingram Pub. Services.

—How to Pass Advanced Aptitude Tests: Assess Your Potential & Analyse Your Career Options with Graduate & Managerial Level Psychometric Tests. 2nd rev. ed. 2010. (ENG., Illus.). 192p. pap. 17.95 *(978-0-7494-6142-3(X))* Kogan Page, Ltd. GBR. Dist: Ingram Pub. Services.

Block, Martin E., et al. Developmental & Adapted Physical Activity Assessment. 2006. (ENG., Illus.). 256p. (C). (gr. 13-16). 49.00 *(978-0-7360-5107-1(4))* Human Kinetics Pubs.

Bobrow Test Preparation Servic, ed. Barron's Civil Service Clerical Exam. 6th rev. ed. 2010. (ENG.). 480p. pap. 18.99 *(978-0-7641-4302-1(6))* Barron's Educational Series, Inc.

Bowers, Linda, et al. TOPS 2 Adolescent Test Form. 2007. (YA). 41.95 *(978-0-7606-9999-7(2))* LinguiSystems, Inc.

Bracken, Bruce A. & Nagle, Richard J., eds. Psychoeducational Assessment of Preschool Children. 4th rev. ed. 2006. (ENG., Illus.). 504p. 100.00 *(978-0-8058-5263-9(8))* Routledge.

Charyton, Christine. Creativity & Risk Tolerance. 2008. 176p. pap. *(978-3-639-08751-2(8))* VDM Verlag Dr. Mueller e.K.

Clark, Timothy R. The Leadership Test: Will You Pass? 2009. 104p. pap. 12.95 *(978-0-578-04210-7(X))* Oxonian Pr.

COMPASS Exam Secrets Test Prep Staff, ed. COMPASS Exam Practice Questions: COMPASS Practice Tests & Review for the Computer Adaptive Placement Assessment & Support System. 2011. 34.99 *(978-1-61403-511-4(3))* Mometrix Media LLC.

CPAt Exam Secrets Test Prep Staff, ed. CPAt Practice Questions: CPAt Practice Tests & Exam Review for the Career Programs Assessment Test. 2011. 34.99 *(978-1-61403-512-1(1))* Mometrix Media LLC.

Cram101 Textbook Reviews Staff. Outlines & Highlights for Tests & Assessment by Bruce Isbn: 0130959472. 2008. 68p. pap. 10.95 *(978-1-4288-6010-0(X))* Cram101 Inc.

DeVries, Beverly A. Literacy Assessment & Intervention for K-6 Classrooms. 2nd ed. 2008. *(978-1-890871-82-6(6))* Holcomb Hathaway, Inc.

Escalona, Sibylle Korsch. Application of the Level of Aspiration E. 2006. pap. 20.95 *(978-1-4286-6126-4(3))* Kessinger Publishing, LLC.

Farmer, Lesley S. J. & Henri, James. Information Literacy Assessment in K-12 Settings. 2007. (ENG., Illus.). 224p. per. 45.00 *(978-0-8108-5695-0(0))* Scarecrow Pr., Inc.

General Aptitude Test Battery, Bk. 2, Form A (Controlled Item) 21p. pap. 3.50 *(978-0-16-003932-4(0),* Labor Dept.) United States Government Printing Office.

Gilbert, Dr.Grant O. & Madsen, Terry L., MS. Lakeland Village Adaptive Behavior Grid Manual. 2008. 138p. pap. 13.50 *(978-0-615-21184-8(4))* Gilbert, Tristan.

Hart, Anne & Sheldon, George. Employment Personality Tests Decoded: Includes Sample & Practice Tests for Self-Assessment. 2007. (ENG., Illus.). 1p. per. 16.99 *(978-1-56414-946-6(3))* Career Pr., Inc.

IAFC. Exam Prep: Fire Officer I & Ii 2E. 2nd rev. ed. 2010. 206p. pap. 45.95 *(978-0-7637-8597-0(0))* Jones & Bartlett Learning, LLC.

Irvine, S. H. & Berry, J. W., eds. Human Abilities in Cultural Context. 2011. (ENG., Illus.). 636p. pap. 60.00 *(978-0-521-14211-3(3))* Cambridge Univ. Pr.

Kelly, Luke, et al. Everyone Can! Skill Development & Assessment in Elementary Physical Education with Web Resources. 2010. (ENG., Illus.). 160p. (gr. k-6). pap. 62.00 *(978-0-7360-6212-1(2))* Human Kinetics Pubs.

Kilgour, Peter. What Are Classrooms Like When Children Are Sorted by Ability. 2009. 208p. pap. *(978-3-639-08661-4(9))* VDM Verlag Dr. Mueller e.K.

Kloo, Daniela. Theory of Mind & Executive Functions. 2008. 200p. pap. *(978-3-639-01139-5(2))* VDM Verlag Dr. Mueller e.K.

Lassonde, Cynthia A. Barron's New York State Grade 6 English Language Arts Test. 2008. (ENG., Illus.). 240p. pap. 12.99 *(978-0-7641-4030-3(2))* Barron's Educational Series, Inc.

LearningExpress Staff. Math & Vocabulary for Civil Service Exams. 4th ed. 2008. (ENG., Illus.). 400p. per. 19.95 *(978-1-57685-606-2(2))* LearningExpress, LLC.

—THEA: Texas Higher Education Assessment. 2nd rev. ed. 2010. (Complete Preparation Guides). (ENG.). 288p. pap. 19.95 *(978-1-57685-756-4(5))* LearningExpress, LLC.

LearningExpress Staff, contrib. by. CBEST: California Basic Educational Skills Test. 4th ed. 2008. *(978-1-156-85608-6(6))* LearningExpress, LLC.

Lehman, Richard, et al. DAT: Dental Admissions Test. 2nd rev. ed. 2009. (ENG.). 512p. 34.99 *(978-0-7641-9384-2(8))* Barron's Educational Series, Inc.

Lichtenberger, Elizabeth O., et al. Essentials of WIAT-III & KTEA-II Assessment. 2010. (Essentials of Psychological Assessment Ser.: 78). (ENG., Illus.). 368p. pap. 48.95 *(978-0-470-55169-1(0),* Wiley) Wiley, John & Sons, Inc.

Linden, Wim J. van der & Glas, Cees A. W. Elements of Adaptive Testing. 2010. (Illus.). xiii, 437p. E-Book *(978-0-387-85461-8(4))* Springer.

Linden, Wim J. van der & Glas, Cees A. W., eds. Computerized Adaptive Testing: Theory & Practice: Theory & Practice. 2010. 336p. pap. 209.00 *(978-90-481-5511-8(8),* 9048155118) Springer.

Ma, William, et al. ACT Cram Plan. 2009. (ENG., Illus.). 336p. pap. 14.99 *(978-0-470-47173-9(5),* Cliff Notes) Wiley, John & Sons, Inc.

Malthouse, Richard & Roffey-Barentsen, Jodi. Verbal & Numerical Reasoning Exercises for the Police Recruit Assessment Process. 2010. (ENG., Illus.). 168p. pap. *(978-1-84445-462-4(2))* Learning Matters Ltd.

Maxwell, John C. Le Talent Ne Suffit Jamais: French Version of Talent Is Never Enough. 2008. (ENG.). 299p. pap. 24.95 *(978-2-922969-19-1(3))* Editions le mieux-etre CAN. Dist: AtlasBooks Distribution.

McCune, Sandra J., et al. THEA: Texas Higher Education Assessment. 5th rev. ed. 2010. (ENG.). 624p. pap. 18.99 *(978-0-7641-4198-0(8))* Barron's Educational Series, Inc.

McLoughlin, James A. & Lewis, Rena B. Assessing Students with Special Needs. 7th ed. 2007. (ENG.). 648p. (C). 143.60 *(978-0-13-196191-3(8),* Prentice Hall) Prentice Hall PTR.

Name & Number Checking. (General Aptitude & Abilities Ser.: CS-43). pap. 19.95 *(978-0-8373-6743-9(3),* CS-43) National Learning Corp.

Neukrug, Edward S. & Fawcett, R. Charles. Essentials of Testing & Assessment: A Practical Guide for Counselors, Social Workers, & Psychologists. 2nd ed. 2009. (PSY 660 Clinical Assessment & Decision Making Ser.). (ENG.). 336p. (C). pap. 124.95 *(978-0-495-60458-7(5))* Brooks/Cole.

Nonreading Aptitude Test Battery 1982 Edition: Sample Demonstration (Controlled Item) 5p. ring bd. 4.00 *(978-0-16-003961-4(4),* Labor Dept.) United States Government Printing Office.

O'Connor, Johnson. The Unique Individual. 2007. (ENG.). 258p. 42.95 *(978-0-548-07187-8(X))* Kessinger Publishing, LLC.

Papatheodorou, Theodora, et al. Child Observation for Learning & Research. rev. ed. 2012. (ENG., Illus.). 200p. pap. 55.00 ***(978-1-4058-2467-5(0))*** Longman Publishing Group.

Phelps, Richard P. Standardized Testing Primer. 2007. (Peter Lang Primer Ser.). 168p. (C). pap. 18.95 *(978-0-8204-9741-9(X))* Lang, Peter Publishing, Inc.

Professional Aptitude Council. Pac Review: The PAC Examination. Benson, Kristina, ed. 2008. 68p. pap. 24.95 *(978-1-60332-054-2(7))* Equity Pr.

Rudman, Jack. Scholastic Communications & Aptitude Test. (General Aptitude & Abilities Ser.: CS-52). pap. 29.95 *(978-0-8373-6752-1(2))* National Learning Corp.

—Social Services Specialist. (Career Examination Ser.: No. C-3747). pap. 29.95 *(978-0-8373-3747-0(X))* National Learning Corp.

Schmitt, Neal, ed. The Oxford Handbook of Personnel Assessment & Selection, 1 vol. 2012. (Oxford Library of Psychology Ser.). (ENG.). 944p. 175.00 ***(978-0-19-973257-9(4))*** Oxford Univ. Pr., Inc.

Spies, Robert A., et al, eds. Mental Measurements Yearbook. 17th ed. 2007. (Buros Mental Measurements Yearbooks Ser.). (ENG., Illus.). 1100p. 195.00 *(978-0-910674-60-7(4))* Buros Institute of Mental Measurements.

Teaford, Patricia, et al. HELP 3-6: Curriculum Guide. 2nd ed. 2010. xvi, 234p. ***(978-0-89718-207-2(3))*** VORT Corp.

van der Linden, Wim J. & Glas, Cees A. W., eds. Elements of Adaptive Testing. 2010. (Statistics for Social & Behavioral Sciences Ser.). (ENG., Illus.). xiv, 462p. 89.95 *(978-0-387-85459-5(2),* 0387854592) Springer.

Winseman, Albert L., et al. Living Your Strengths: Discover Your God-Given Talents, & Inspire Your Community. 2nd ed. 2008. xviii, 249p. *(978-1-59562-022-4(2))* Gallup Pr.

Wynne, Sharon. CBEST California Basic Educational Skills Test. 2008. (Xam Cset Ser.). (ENG., Illus.). 222p. pap., pupil's gde. ed. 21.95 *(978-1-58197-596-3(1))* XAMonline, Inc.

ABILITY, EXECUTIVE

see Executive Ability

ABILITY, INFLUENCE OF AGE ON

see also Age and Employment

Galenson, David W. Old Masters & Young Geniuses: The Two Life Cycles of Artistic Creativity. 2007. (ENG., Illus.). 256p. (C). per. 22.95 *(978-0-691-13380-5(8))* Princeton Univ. Pr.

Painter, Karen & Crow, Thomas, eds. Late Thoughts: Reflections on Artists & Composers at Work. 2006. (Issues & Debates Ser.: Vol. 14). (Illus.). 264p. pap. 40.00 *(978-0-89236-813-6(6))* Oxford Univ. Pr., Inc.

Winningham, Robert G. Train Your Brain: How to Maximize Memory Ability in Older Adulthood. 2009. 58.95 *(978-0-89503-349-9(6))* Baywood Publishing Co., Inc.

ABILITY, MUSICAL
see Musical Ability

ABILITY, SOCIAL
see Social Skills

ABILITY GROUPING IN EDUCATION
see also School Grade Placement

Ban, Balazs. Grouping Students in the Secondary English Language Classroom. 2008. 64p. pap. *(978-3-8364-9419-9(1))* VDM Verlag Dr. Mueller e.K.

Burns, M. Susan, et al. Preschool Education in Today's World: Teaching Children with Diverse Backgrounds & Abilities. 2011. 240p. 59.95 *(978-1-59857-195-0(8))* Brookes, Paul H. Publishing Co.

Burris, Carol Corbett & Garrity, Delia T. Detracking for Excellence & Equity. 2008. (Illus.). ix, 180p. pap. 26.95 *(978-1-4166-0708-3(0))* Assn. for Supervision & Curriculum Development.

Chapman, Carolyn. Differentiated Instructional Strategies: One Size Doesn't Fit All. Gregory, Gayle H., ed. 2nd rev. ed. 2006. (Illus.). 208p. (gr. 17). pap. 36.95 *(978-1-4129-3640-8(3),* B3639XP) Corwin Pr.

Collins, Kathleen M., ed. Ability Profiling & School Failure: One Child's Struggle to Be Seen As Competent. 2nd rev. ed. 2012. (ENG.). 272p. 150.00 *(978-0-415-89822-5(6))*; pap. 37.95 *(978-0-415-89823-2(4))* Routledge.

Cooper, Damian. Redefining Fair: How to Plan, Assess, & Grade for Excellence in Mixed-Ability Classrooms. 2011. (Illus.). 200p. pap. 29.95 ***(978-1-935542-14-8(1))***; (ENG., lib. bdg. 54.95 ***(978-1-935542-15-5(X))*** Solution Tree Pr.

Cram101 Textbook Reviews & Cram101 Textbook Reviews. Outlines & Highlights for Differentiated Instructional Management: Work Smarter, Not Harder by Rita King, ISBN. 2011. 80p. pap. 27.95 ***(978-1-4288-6482-5(2))*** Cram101 Inc.

Crawford, Glenda Beamon, ed. Differentiation for the Adolescent Learner: Accommodating Brain Development, Language, Literacy, & Special Needs. 2008. (Illus.). 184p. pap. 36.95 *(978-1-4129-4054-2(0),* B40532P) Corwin Pr.

Creekside Middle School, Team Explorers. Diary of a Team Explorers Kid. 2010. 176p. pap. 7.95 *(978-1-60844-633-9(6))* Dog Ear Publishing, LLC.

Jackson, Brian. Streaming (RLE Edu L Sociology of Education) An Education System in Miniature. 2011. (Routledge Library Editions: Education Ser.). (ENG.). 170p. 100.00 ***(978-0-415-50435-5(X))*** Routledge.

Lundy, Kathleen Gould. Teaching Fairly in an Unfair World. 2008. (ENG.). 144p. (C). (gr. 4-12). pap. 21.00 *(978-1-55138-231-9(8))* Stenhouse Pubs.

Middendorf, Cindy. Differentiating Instruction in Kindergarten: Planning Tips, Assessment Tools, Management Strategies, Multi-Leveled Centers, & Activities That Reach & Nurture Every Learner. 2007. (ENG., Illus.). 128p. (gr. k-k). pap. 18.99 *(978-0-439-87029-0(1),* Teaching Resources) Scholastic, Inc.

O'Meara, Jodi. Beyond Differentiated Instruction. 2010. (Illus.). 160p. pap. 31.95 *(978-1-4129-8203-0(0),* B82030P) Corwin Pr.

Roberts, Julia L. & Inman, Tracy F. Strategies for Differentiating Instruction: Best Practices for the Classroom. 2nd rev. ed. 2008. (ENG.). 200p. pap. 29.95 *(978-1-59363-357-8(2))* Prufrock Pr.

Westphal, Laurie. Ready-to-Use Differentiation Strategies. 2011. (ENG.). 125p. (gr. 3-5). pap. 19.95 *(978-1-59363-705-7(5))* Prufrock Pr.

Westphal, Laurie E. Ready-to-Use Differentiation Strategies: Grades 6-8. 2011. (ENG.). 137p. (gr. 6-8). pap. 19.95 *(978-1-59363-838-2(8))* Prufrock Pr.

ABILITY TESTS
see Ability—Testing

ABINGTON, FRANCES BARTON, 1737-1815

Anonymous. The Life of Mrs Abington: With Full Accounts of Her Various Performances in the Theaters of London & Dublin (1888) 2009. 130p. 35.95 *(978-1-104-93383-8(7))*; pap. 20.95 *(978-1-104-91647-3(9))* Kessinger Publishing, LLC.

The Life of Mrs. Abington. 2009. 128p. pap. *(978-0-217-54749-9(4))* Books LLC.

ABIOGENESIS
see Life—Origin; Spontaneous Generation

ABM (ANTIBALLISTIC MISSILES)
see Antimissile Missiles

ABNORMAL CHILDREN
see Exceptional Children

ABNORMAL E (IONOSPHERE)
see Sporadic E (Ionosphere)

ABNORMAL HEMOGLOBIN
see Hemoglobinopathy

ABNORMAL PSYCHOLOGY
see Psychology, Pathological

ABNORMALITIES
see Abnormalities, Human; Animals—Abnormalities

ABNORMALITIES, HUMAN
see also Birth Injuries; Conjoined Twins; Dislocations; Dwarfs; Fetal Alcohol Syndrome; Fetus—Abnormalities; Giants; Medical Genetics; Prader-Willi Syndrome
also subdivision Abnormalities under individual organs and regions of the body, e.g. Heart—Abnormalities

Ali, Nagi Ibrahim. A Novel Role of Nuclear Medicine in Vitro Technology in Pregnancy. 2011. 112p. pap. ***(978-3-8454-1749-3(8))*** Lambert Academic Publishing.

Bartone, John Charles. Birth Defects Caused by ALCOHOL: Index, Reference & Medical Analysis of New Research Information for All Nations. 2008. (Illus.). 160p. ring bd. 69.95 *(978-0-7883-3830-4(7))* ABBE Pubs. Assn. of Washington, D.C.

Blumberg, Mark. Freaks of Nature: What Anomalies Tell Us about Development & Evolution. 2010. (ENG.). 336p. pap. 17.95 *(978-0-19-973618-8(9))* Oxford Univ. Pr., Inc.

Brannan, Dan. Boy Giant. 2006. 158p. 19.95 *(978-0-9650228-5-9(4))* Brannan, Dan Pubns.

Burton, Barbara & Kumar, Praveen. Congenital Malformations: Evidence-Based Evaluation & Management. Burton, Barbara K., ed. 2007. (ENG., Illus.). 408p. 103.00 *(978-0-07-147189-3(8),* 0071471898) McGraw-Hill Professional Publishing.

Cappa, M., et al, eds. Endocrine Involvement in Developmental Syndromes. 2009. (Endocrine Development Ser.). (ENG., Illus.). 188p. *(978-3-8055-9041-9(5))* Karger, S. AG.

Cassidy, Suzanne B. & Allanson, Judith E. Management of Genetic Syndromes. 3rd ed. 2010. (ENG., Illus.). 984p. 215.95 *(978-0-470-19141-5(4),* Wiley-Blackwell) Wiley, John & Sons, Inc.

Chemers, Michael M. Staging Stigma: A Critical Examination of the American Freak Show. 2008. (Palgrave Studies in Theatre & Performance History Ser.). (ENG., Illus.). 192p. 89.00 *(978-0-230-61066-8(8))* Palgrave Macmillan.

Cram101 Textbook Reviews & Cram101 Textbook Reviews. Outlines & Highlights for Before We Are Born: Essentials of Embryology & Birth Defects 7th by Keith L. Moore; T. V. N. Persaud, ISBN. 2011. 372p. pap. 34.95 ***(978-1-61461-515-6(2))*** Cram101 Inc.

—Outlines & Highlights for Congenital Malformations: Evidence-Based Evaluation & Management by Praveen Kumar, ISBN. 2011. 120p. pap. 28.95 ***(978-1-61461-441-8(5))*** Cram101 Inc.

—Outlines & Highlights for Langmans Medical Embryology by Thomas W Sadler, Isbn: 9780781790697 0781790697. 2011. 494p. pap. 31.95 ***(978-1-61490-047-4(7))*** Cram101 Inc.

—Outlines & Highlights for the Developing Human by Keith L Moore, Isbn: 9781416037064 1416037063. 2011. 380p. pap. 34.95 ***(978-1-61490-307-9(7))*** Cram101 Inc.

Crawford, Julie. Marvelous Protestantism: Monstrous Births in Post-Reformation England. 2011. (ENG., Illus.). 282p. (gr. 17). pap. 35.00 ***(978-1-4214-0586-5(5))*** Johns Hopkins Univ. Pr.

Deardorff, Daniel. The Other Within: The Genius of Deformity in Myth, Culture, & Psyche. 2008. (ENG.). 264p. pap. 16.95 *(978-1-55643-760-1(9))* North Atlantic Bks.

Durbach, Nadja. The Spectacle of Deformity: Freak Shows & Modern British Culture. 2009. (ENG., Illus.). 256p. 45.00 *(978-0-520-25768-9(5))* Univ. of California Pr.

Elden, Lisa M. & Zur, Karen B., eds. Congenital Malformations of the Head & Neck. 2011. (ENG., Illus.). 200p. 189.00 *(978-1-4419-1713-3(6),* 1441917136) Springer.

Floyd, Calla. Meagan Will Fly... Clipped Wings or Not. 2008. 73p. pap. 16.95 *(978-1-60703-276-2(7))* PublishAmerica, Inc.

Ford, Peter & Howell, Michael. The True History of the Elephant Man: The Definitive Account of the Tragic & Extraordinary Life of Joseph Carey Merrick. 2010. (ENG., Illus.). 224p. pap. 12.95 *(978-1-60239-736-1(8),* 239736) Skyhorse Publishing Co., Inc.

Fries, Kenny. The History of My Shoes & the Evolution of Darwin's Theory. 2007. (ENG., Illus.). 224p. per. 14.95 *(978-0-7867-2007-1(7))* Da Capo Pr., Inc.

Garland, Robert. The Eye of the Beholder: Deformity & Disability in the Graeco-Roman Worlds. 2nd ed. 2011. (Illus.). 280p. pap. 34.95 *(978-1-85399-737-2(4))* Duckworth Publishers GBR. Dist: International Publishers Marketing.

Gaslem, Nelson A. New Developments in Birth Defects Research. 2006. (Illus.). 241p. (C). 225.00 *(978-1-60021-400-4(2))* Nova Science Pubs., Inc.

Gibson, Gregory. Hubert's Freaks: The Rare-Book Dealer, the Times Square Talker, & the Lost Photos of Diane Arbus. (ENG.). 288p. 2009. pap. 14.95 *(978-0-15-603308-4(9),* Mariner Bks.) 2008. (Illus.). 24.00 *(978-0-15-101233-6(4))* Houghton Mifflin Harcourt Trade & Reference Pubs.

Glover, Jonathan. Choosing Children: Genes, Disability, & Design. 2008. (Uehiro Series in Practical Ethics Ser.). (ENG.). 128p. per. 19.95 *(978-0-19-923849-1(9))* Oxford Univ. Pr., Inc.

Gupta, Shalabh. Complex Systems in Engineering: A Symbolic Dynamics Approach for Anomaly Detection. 2008. 152p. pap. *(978-3-639-10105-8(7))* VDM Verlag Dr. Mueller e.K.

Holden, Lynn A. Forms of Deformity. 2009. (Library of Hebrew Bible/Old Testament Studies, the Ser.). (ENG.). 370p. 60.00 *(978-1-4411-2079-3(3),* T&T Clark) Continuum International Publishing Group, Ltd. GBR. Dist: National Bk. Network.

Holmes, Lewis B. Common Malformations, 1 vol. 2011. (ENG., Illus.). 400p. 125.00 *(978-0-19-513602-9(0))* Oxford Univ. Pr., Inc.

Jay, Ricky. Celebrations of Curious Characters. 2011. (ENG., Illus.). 112p. 26.00 *(978-1-936365-03-6(0))* McSweeney's Publishing.

Kalter, Harold. Mortality & Maldevelopment: The Saga of Neural Tube Defects. 2009. (ENG.). xii, 268p. 169.00 *(978-1-4020-9605-1(4),* 1402096054) Springer.

—Mortality & Maldevelopment Part I: Congenital Cardiovascular Malformations. 2007. (Illus.). 222p. 139.00 *(978-1-4020-5917-9(5))* Springer.

—Teratology in the Twentieth Century Plus Ten. 2010. (ENG.). xv, 266p. 179.00 *(978-90-481-8819-2(9),* 9048188199) Springer.

Klausen, Pia R. Trends in Birth Defects Research. 2006. (Illus.). 163p. 225.00 *(978-1-60021-398-4(7))* Nova Science Pubs., Inc.

Levin, Alex V. & Wilson, Thomas W., eds. The Hospital for Sick Children's Atlas of Pediatric Ophthalmology & Strabismus. 2006. (Illus.). 320p. 198.99 *(978-0-7817-4309-9(5))* Lippincott Williams & Wilkins.

Lewis, Michael & Kestler, Lisa, eds. Gender Differences in Prenatal Substance Exposure. 2011. 69.95 ***(978-1-4338-1033-6(6))*** American Psychological Assn.

Massaro, Edward J. & Rogers, John M., eds. Folate & Human Development. 2010. (Illus.). 376p. pap. 124.00 *(978-1-61737-262-9(5),* 1617372625) Humana Pr.

McCredie, Janet. Beyond Thalidomide: Birth Defects Explained. 2007. (Illus.). 418p. *(978-1-85315-741-7(4),* Royal Society of Medicine) Hodder Education.

Merz, Eberhard. Ultrasound in Obstetrics & Gynecology, Vol. 2. 2nd ed. 2006. (ENG., Illus.). 319p. 199.99 *(978-1-58890-146-0(7))* Thieme Medical Pubs., Inc.

Metzler, Irina. Disability in Medieval Europe. 2010. (ENG., Illus.). 364p. (C). pap. 39.95 *(978-0-415-58204-9(0))* Routledge.

Mix, Terence. The Price of Ovulation: The Truth about Fertility Drugs & Birth Defects - & a Solution to the Problem. 2009. 566p. pap. *(978-0-9802190-0-5(0))* Tendril Pr., LLC.

Moore, Gudrun, et al, eds. Embryos, Genes & Birth Defects. 2nd rev. ed. 2006. (ENG., Illus.). 562p. 199.95 *(978-0-470-09010-7(3),* Wiley) Wiley, John & Sons, Inc.

Moore, Keith L., et al. Before We Are Born: Essentials of Embryology & Birth Defects. (Illus.). 7th ed. 2008. x, 353p. *(978-0-8089-2398-5(6))* 8th ed. 2011. (ENG., 368p. (C). pap. 59.95 ***(978-1-4377-2001-3(3))*** Elsevier - Health Sciences Div. (Saunders).

Moore, Keith L., et al. The Developing Human: Clinically Oriented Embryology. 9th ed. 2011. (ENG., Illus.). 560p. (C). pap. 74.95 ***(978-1-4377-2002-0(1),*** Saunders) Elsevier - Health Sciences Div.

Opitz, John M., et al. Human Development & Malformations: Evolutionary, Genetic & Morphogenetic Perspectives. 2008. 576p. 179.00 *(978-0-471-23597-2(0),* Wiley-Liss) Wiley, John & Sons, Inc.

Parens, Erik, ed. Surgically Shaping Children: Technology, Ethics, & the Pursuit of Normality. 2008. (ENG., Illus.). 304p. (gr. 17). pap. 25.00 *(978-0-8018-9090-1(X))* Johns Hopkins Univ. Pr.

Radinger, Anna Maria. Interleukin-6 (-174) G/C polymorphism & its correlation with cPVL. 2008. 84p. pap. *(978-3-8364-9304-8(7))* VDM Verlag Dr. Mueller e.K.

Reagan, Leslie J. Dangerous Pregnancies: Mothers, Disabilities, & Abortion in Modern America. 2010. (ENG., Illus.). 396p. 29.95 *(978-0-520-25903-4(3))* Univ. of California Pr.

Reardon, William. The Bedside Dysmorphologist. 2007. (ENG., Illus.). 304p. pap. 65.00 *(978-0-19-530045-1(9))* Oxford Univ. Pr., Inc.

Rough, Bonnie J. Carrier: Untangling the Danger in My DNA. 2010. (ENG.). 324p. pap. 15.95 *(978-1-58243-578-7(2),* Counterpoint Pr.) Basic Bks. GBR. Dist: Perseus-PGW.

Sadler. Langman Medical Embryology Us Ed Pb. 12th rev. ed. 2011. (ENG.). 400p. pap. 71.99 ***(978-1-4511-1342-6(0))*** Lippincott Williams & Wilkins.

Sadler, Thomas W. Langman's Medical Embryology. 11th rev. ed. 2009. (Illus.). 414p. pap. 62.95 *(978-0-7817-9069-7(1))* Lippincott Williams & Wilkins.

Sahin, Nevin Hotun & Gungor, Ilkay. Birth Defects: Issues on Prevention & Promotion. 2010. (Health Care Issues, Costs & Access Ser.). viii, 131p. pap. 49.00 *(978-1-61668-967-4(6),* Nova Novinka) Nova Science Pubs., Inc.

Sharpe, Andrew N. Foucault's Monsters: The Challenge of Law. 2010. (ENG.). 200p. 120.00 *(978-0-415-43031-9(3),* Routledge Cavendish) Taylor & Francis Group GBR. Dist: Taylor & Francis Group.

Shepard, Thomas H. Catalog of Teratogenic Agents. 13th ed. 2010. (ENG., Illus.). 608p. (gr. 17). 270.00 *(978-0-8018-9784-9(X))* Johns Hopkins Univ. Pr.

Stagg, Kevin & Turner, David M., eds. Social Histories of Disability & Deformity. 2006. (Routledge Studies in the Social History of Medicine: Vol. 25). (ENG., Illus.). 224p. (C). 153.00 *(978-0-415-36098-2(6))* Routledge.

Tibber, Marc. Developmental Abnormalities Associated with the Hypopigmented Retin. 2011. 256p. pap. ***(978-3-8443-1034-4(7))*** Lambert Academic Publishing.

Tromp, Marlene, ed. Victorian Freaks: The Social Context of Freakery in Britain. 2008. (ENG.). cd-rom 14.95 *(978-0-8142-9166-5(X))*; (Illus.). 368p. 64.95 *(978-0-8142-1086-4(4))* Ohio State Univ. Pr.

Upledger, D.O., O.M.M, John E. A Brain Is Born: Exploring the Birth & Development of the Central Nervous System. 2010. (ENG., Illus.). 400p. pap. 49.95 *(978-1-58394-301-4(3))* North Atlantic Bks.

Usman, Saad. Spatio Temporal Anomaly Detector. 2011. 84p. pap. ***(978-3-8443-2139-5(X))*** Lambert Academic Publishing.

Vallee Hiter, Shirley. Big Things in Little Packages - My Growing up with Turner Syndrome. 2008. 107p. pap. 9.95 *(978-1-4357-5318-1(6))* Lulu Enterprises Inc.

Velásquez, Lizzie, et al. Lizzie Beautiful, the Lizzie Velásquez Story. 2010. 84p. pap. 19.95 *(978-0-9825190-0-4(1),* Epigraph Bks.) Monkfish Bk. Publishing Co.

Weaver, Nan. Little Arms, Big Heart. 2010. 152p. 30.95 *(978-1-4497-0524-4(3))*; pap. 13.95 *(978-1-4497-0523-7(5))* Author Solutions, Inc. (WestBow Pr.).

Wiesner-Hanks, Merry E. The Marvelous Hairy Girls: The Gonzales Sisters & Their Worlds. 2009. (ENG., Illus.). 250p. 30.00 *(978-0-300-12733-1(2))* Yale Univ. Pr.

Wilcox, M. V. & Wilcox, Michael V. The Pueblo Revolt & the Mythology of Conquest: An Indigenous Archaeology of Contact. 2009. (ENG., Illus.). 336p. 45.00 *(978-0-520-25205-9(5))* Univ. of California Pr.

Wilson, James G. & Fraser, F. Clark, eds. Handbook of Teratology: General Principles & Etiology. 488p. 69.50 *(978-0-306-36241-5(4))* Springer.

Wynshaw-Boris, Anthony. Inborn Errors of Development: The Molecular Basis of Clinical Disorders of Morphogenesis. Epstein, Charles J. & Erickson, Robert P., eds. 2nd ed. 2008. (Oxford Monographs on Medical Genetics Ser.: No. 54). (ENG., Illus.). 1808p. 299.99 *(978-0-19-530691-0(0))* Oxford Univ. Pr., Inc.

ABNORMALITIES (ANIMALS)
see Animals—Abnormalities

ABNORMALITIES IN ANIMALS
see Animals—Abnormalities

ABOLITION OF SLAVERY
see Slavery

ABOLITIONISTS

Abruzzo, Margaret Nicola. Polemical Pain: Slavery, Cruelty, & the Rise of Humanitarianism. 2011. (New Studies in American Intellectual & Cultural History Ser.). (ENG., Illus.). 344p. (gr. 17). 55.00 *(978-0-8018-9852-5(8))* Johns Hopkins Univ. Pr.

Aitken, Jonathan. John Newton: From Disgrace to Amazing Grace. 2007. 400p. 21.99 *(978-1-58134-848-4(7))* Crossway.

Anonymous. The Life of William Wilberforce. 2010. 432p. pap. 35.75 *(978-1-142-39800-2(5))* BiblioBazaar.

Bacon, Margaret Hope. But One Race: The Life of Robert Purvis. (Excelsior Editions Ser.). (Illus.). 2010. 293p. pap. 24.95 *(978-0-7914-7008-4(3),* Suny Pr.) 2007. 279p. 36.00 *(978-0-7914-7007-7(5))* State Univ. of New York Pr.

Bacon, Margaret Hope & Lapsansky-Werner, Emma, eds. Back to Africa: Benjamin Coates & the Colonization Movement in America, 1848-1880. 2007. (ENG.). 368p. pap. 27.00 *(978-0-271-02763-0(0))* Pennsylvania State Univ. Pr.

Baehr, Ted, et al. The Amazing Grace of Freedom: The Inspiring Faith of William Wilberforce, the Slaves' Champion. 2d ed. 2007. (Illus.). 143p. 19.99 *(978-0-89221-673-4(5))* New Leaf Pr., Inc.

Barnes, L. Diane. Frederick Douglass: In Bondage & Freedom. 2012. (Routledge Historical Americans Ser.). (ENG., Illus.). 224p. (C). 150.00 *(978-0-415-89111-0(6))*; pap. 26.95 *(978-0-415-89112-7(4))* Routledge.

Belmonte, Kevin. William Wilberforce: A Hero for Humanity, 1 vol. 2007. (ENG., Illus.). 352p. pap. 12.99 *(978-0-310-27488-9(5))* Zondervan.

Benezet, Anthony, et al. Early American Abolitionists: A Collection of Anti-Slavery Writings, 1760-1820. Basker, James G. & Ahlstrom, Justine, eds. 2007. (Illus.). 372p. pap. 0.00 *(978-1-932821-06-2(6))* Gilder Lehrman Institute of American History, The.

Biographiq. Harriet Tubman - African American Abolitionist. 2008. 76p. pap. 9.99 *(978-1-59986-369-6(3),* Biographiq) Filiquarian Publishing, LLC.

—John Brown - American Abolitionist (Biography) 2008. 76p. pap. 9.99 *(978-1-59986-064-0(3),* Biographiq) Filiquarian Publishing, LLC.

—William Wilberforce - British Politician & Philanthropist (Biography) 2008. 72p. pap. 9.99 *(978-1-59986-388-7(X),* Biographiq) Filiquarian Publishing, LLC.

Birney, Catherine H. The Grimke Sisters. 2008. 280p. 28.99 *(978-0-554-24107-4(2))*; 25.99 *(978-0-554-33410-3(0))* BiblioBazaar.

—The Grimke Sisters. 2010. 214p. 39.95 *(978-1-161-46527-3(8))* Kessinger Publishing, LLC.

—The Grimké Sisters. 2010. (Illus.). 158p. pap. 24.49 *(978-1-4432-2950-0(4))* General Bks. LLC.

—The Grimke Sisters. 319p. reprint ed. 98.00 *(978-0-7222-9843-5(9))* Library Reprints, Inc.

—The Grimké Sisters: Sarah & Angelina Grimké: the First American Women Advocates of Abolition & Woman's Rights. 2007. 248p. pap. 20.99 *(978-1-4264-5774-6(X))*; 276p. pap. 23.99 *(978-1-4264-5834-7(7))* BiblioBazaar.

Blue, Frederick J. No Taint of Compromise: Crusaders in Antislavery Politics. 2006. (Antislavery, Abolition, & the Atlantic World Ser.). (Illus.). 301p. per. 22.95 *(978-0-8071-3205-0(5))* Louisiana State Univ. Pr.

Books. The Life of William Wilberforce. 2009. 404p. pap. 15.89 *(978-1-150-31334-9(X))* General Bks. LLC.

Brandt, Nat. In the Shadow of the Civil War: Passmore Williamson & the Rescue of Jane Johnson. 2007. (Illus.). 216p. 29.95 *(978-1-57003-687-3(X))* Univ. of South Carolina Pr.

Brendlinger, Irv A. To Be Silent... Would Be Criminal: The Antislavery Influence & Writings of Anthony Benezet. 2006. (Revitalization: Explorations in World Christian Movements Ser.: No. 20). (ENG., Illus.). 246p. per. 45.00 *(978-0-8108-5765-0(0))* Scarecrow Pr., Inc.

Brown, Henry Box. Narrative of the Life of Henry Box Brown. 2008. 84p. pap. 18.75 *(978-0-559-33903-5(8))* BiblioBazaar.

—Narrative of the Life of Henry Box Brown. 2009. 84p. pap. 17.95 *(978-1-104-29915-6(1))* Kessinger Publishing, LLC.

Calarco, Tom. People of the Underground Railroad: A Biographical Dictionary, 1 vol. 2008. (Illus.). 408p. 75.00 *(978-0-313-33924-0(4),* GR3924) Greenwood Publishing Group, Inc.

Calarco, Tom, et al. Places of the Underground Railroad: A Geographical Guide, 1 vol. 2010. (Illus.). 422p. 85.00 *(978-0-313-38146-1(1),* A2583C) Greenwood Publishing Group, Inc.

Campbell, Tom. Fighting Slavery in Chicago: Abolitionists, the Law of Slavery, & Lincoln. 2009. (ENG., Illus.). 206p. 38.95 *(978-0-9818126-2-5(7),* Ampersand) Ampersand, Inc.

Carton, Evan. Patriotic Treason: John Brown & the Soul of America. 2009. (ENG., Illus.). 400p. pap. 19.95 *(978-0-8032-1946-5(6))*, Bison Bks.) Univ. of Nebraska Pr.

Chaney, Michael A. Fugitive Vision: Slave Image & Black Identity in Antebellum Narrative. 2009. (Blacks in the Diaspora Ser.). (ENG., Illus.). 272p. pap. 19.95 *(978-0-253-22108-7(0)*, 0253221080) Indiana Univ. Pr.

Chesnutt, Charles Waddell. Frederick Douglass. (Beacon Biographies of Eminent Americans Ser.). 141p. reprint ed. 88.00 *(978-0-7222-9064-4(0))* Library Reprints, Inc.

—Frederick Douglass. 141p. reprint ed. 48.00 *(978-0-7950-1413-0(9))* New Library Press LLC.

Child, Lydia Maria. Letters of Lydia Maria Child, with a Biographical Introduction by John G Whittier & an Appendix by Wendell Phillips. 2006. 328p. per. 23.99 *(978-1-4255-3287-1(X))* MPublishing.

Chittick, Andrew. Patronage & Community in Medieval China: The Xiangyang Garrison, 400-600 Ce. 2010. (Illus.). 208p. pap. 23.95 *(978-1-4384-2898-7(7)*, Suny Pr.) State Univ. of New York Pr.

Clapp, Elizabeth J. & Jeffrey, Julie Roy. Women, Dissent & Anti-Slavery in Britain & America, 1790-1865. 2011. (ENG.). 272p. 110.00 *(978-0-19-958548-9(2))* Oxford Univ. Pr., Inc.

Coffin, Levi. Reminiscences of Levi Coffin: The Reputed President of the Underground Railroad. 712p. reprint ed. lib. bdg. 148.00 *(978-0-7222-0794-9(8))* Library Reprints, Inc.

Colton, Calvin. Abolition a Sedition. 2009. 94p. pap. *(978-1-151-55992-0(X))* Books LLC.

Cooper, Valerie C. Word, Like Fire: Maria Stewart, the Bible, & the Rights of African Americans. (Carter G. Woodson Institute Ser.). 2012. (ENG., Illus.). 224p. (gr. 17). 39.50 *(978-0-8139-3188-3(6))* 2011. E-Book ***(978-0-8139-3207-1(6))*** Univ. Pr. of Virginia.

Crowell, Cheryl. New Richmond. 2012. (Images of America Ser.). (ENG., Illus.). 128p. pap. 21.99 ***(978-0-7385-8868-1(7))*** Arcadia Publishing.

Crump, Ralph & Crump, Marjorie. Augusta's Journal: Volume III. 2009. 344p. 28.49 *(978-1-4490-2697-4(4))*; pap. 19.99 *(978-1-4490-2698-1(2))* AuthorHouse.

DeCaro, Louis A., Jr. John Brown: The Cost of Freedom. 2007. (Illus.). 192p. pap. 14.00 *(978-0-7178-0742-0(8))* International Publishers Co., Inc.

Delbanco, Andrew. The Abolitionist Imagination. 2012. (Alexis de Tocqueville Lectures on American Politics Ser.). (ENG.). 224p. 24.95 ***(978-0-674-06444-7(5))*** Harvard Univ. Pr.

Deters, Ruth. The Underground Railroad Ran Through My House! 2010. 343p. pap. 24.95 *(978-0-578-00213-2(2))* Eleven Oaks Publishing.

Dicey, Edward. Six Months in the Federal States, Vol. 1. 2008. (Civil War Ser.). (ENG.). 340p. pap. 21.95 *(978-1-4290-1548-6(9))*; 348p. pap. 21.95 *(978-1-4290-1622-3(1))* Applewood Bks.

—Six Months in the Federal States. 2010. 344p. pap. 31.75 *(978-1-146-61465-8(9))*; 342p. pap. 31.75 *(978-1-146-19256-9(8))*; 342p. pap. 31.75 *(978-1-142-13616-1(7))* BiblioBazaar.

—Six Months in the Federal States. 2009. 184p. pap. *(978-0-217-87745-9(1))* Books LLC.

—Six Months in the Federal States. 2010. (Illus.). 134p. pap. 19.99 *(978-1-154-39848-9(X))* 2010. (Illus.). 136p. pap. 13.81 *(978-1-154-32769-4(8))* 2010. 132p. pap. 22.16 *(978-1-152-60728-6(6))* 2010. 150p. pap. 13.83 *(978-1-152-60726-2(X))* 2010. 254p. pap. 33.40 *(978-1-152-60732-3(4))* 2009. 172p. pap. 19.99 *(978-1-150-97193-8(2))* General Bks. LLC.

Donna Patten Goldsmith-Day. The Banditti & the Regulators: Passion & Terrorism in Lincoln's Wild Midwest. 2009. 304p. 33.40 *(978-1-4269-1610-6(8))*; pap. 23.40 *(978-1-4269-1611-3(6))* Trafford Publishing.

Douglass, Frederick. My Bondage & My Freedom. 2008. 388p. 29.99 *(978-0-554-33779-1(7))* 2008. 388p. 31.99 *(978-0-554-24476-1(4))* 2007. (ENG.). 352p. pap. 25.99 *(978-1-4264-6569-7(6))* BiblioBazaar.

—My Bondage & My Freedom. 2009. 268p. pap. *(978-1-150-57694-2(4))* Books LLC.

—My Bondage & My Freedom. 2008. 204p. pap. 7.99 *(978-1-4209-3060-3(5))* Digireads.com.

—My Bondage & My Freedom. 2007. 468p. 52.95 *(978-0-548-21690-3(8))*; 472p. per. 37.95 *(978-1-4325-3712-8(1))* Kessinger Publishing, LLC.

—My Bondage & My Freedom - Frederick Douglass. 2007. 316p. pap. 14.95 *(978-1-60424-492-2(5)*, Book Jungle) Standard Pubns., Inc.

—My Bondage & My Freedom (an African American Heritage Book) 2008. 272p. 24.95 *(978-1-60459-229-0(X))*; (ENG.). per. 8.99 *(978-1-60459-228-3(1))* Wilder Pubns., Ltd.

—My Bondage & My Freedom by Frederick Douglass with an Introduction by Dr James M'Cune Smith. 2006. 468p. per. 29.99 *(978-1-4255-5165-0(3))* MPublishing.

—Narrative of the Life of Frederick Douglass. 2010. (Illus.). 70p. pap. 6.40 *(978-1-4432-0125-4(1))* General Bks. LLC.

—Narrative of the Life of Frederick Douglass. 2010. 112p. pap. 12.95 *(978-1-60444-238-0(7))* IndoEuropeanPublishing.com.

—Narrative of the Life of Frederick Douglass. 2006. (YA). 1.25 ***(978-1-4193-8516-2(X))*** Recorded Bks., LLC.

—Narrative of the Life of Frederick Douglass. 100p. 2011. pap. 6.99 ***(978-1-61382-062-9(3))*** 2010. pap. 6.75 ***(978-1-936041-50-3(2))*** 2010. pap. 4.94 *(978-1-936041-20-6(0))* Simon & Brown.

—Narrative of the Life of Frederick Douglass. 2011. (ENG.). 114p. pap. 7.77 *(978-1-936594-18-4(8))* Tribeca Bks.

—The Narrative of the Life of Frederick Douglass. 2008. (ENG.). 112p. pap. 10.45 *(978-1-60597-228-2(2)*, Book Jungle) Standard Pubns., Inc.

—Narrative of the Life of Frederick Douglass. 2009. 7.62 *(978-0-7848-0700-2(0))*; 9.12 *(978-0-7848-2758-1(3))* Marco Bk. Co. (Everbind).

—Narrative of the Life of Frederick Douglass: An American Slave. 2009. 102p. pap. 18.75 *(978-1-110-36675-0(2))* BiblioBazaar.

—Narrative of the Life of Frederick Douglass: An American Slave, Written by Himself. 2007. (ENG.). 128p. 19.99 *(978-1-59986-703-8(6))* Filiquarian Publishing, LLC.

—Narrative of the Life of Frederick Douglass: An American Slave, Written by Himself. 2009. (John Harvard Library). (Illus.). 176p. pap. 8.50 *(978-0-674-03401-3(5)*, Belknap Pr.) Harvard Univ. Pr.

—Narrative of the Life of Frederick Douglass, an American Slave. McDowell, Deborah E., ed. 2009. (Oxford World's Classics Ser.). (ENG.). 176p. pap. 9.95 *(978-0-19-953907-9(3))* Oxford Univ. Pr., Inc.

—Narrative of the Life of Frederick Douglass, an American Slave. 2008. 144p. pap. *(978-1-4086-6779-8(7))* Read Bks.

Douglass, Frederick & Davis, Angela Y. Narrative of the Life of Frederick Douglass, an American Slave, Written by Himself: A New Critical Edition by Angela Y. Davis. 2009. (City Lights Open Media Ser.). (ENG., Illus.). 220p. pap. 12.95 *(978-0-87286-527-3(4))* City Lights Bks.

Douglass, Frederick & Smith, James McCune. My Bondage & My Freedom. 2009. (ENG.). 469p. pap. 36.75 *(978-1-117-61826-5(9))* BiblioBazaar.

Du Bois, W. E. B. John Brown. (American Crisis Biographies Ser.). 406p. reprint ed. 98.00 *(978-0-7222-8437-7(3))*; 98.00 *(978-0-7222-9835-0(8))* Library Reprints, Inc.

—John Brown. 2007. *(978-0-19-532574-4(5))* Oxford Univ. Pr., Inc.

Dugan, Frank H. An Illinois Martyrdom. 2011. 52p. 36.95 ***(978-1-258-01598-5(6))*** Literary Licensing, LLC.

Dunphy, John J. Abolitionism & the Civil War in Southwestern Illinois. 2011. ***(978-1-60949-328-8(1))*** History Pr., The.

Elliott, Mark & Elliot, Mark. Color Blind Justice: Albion Tourgee & the Quest for Racial Equality from the Civil War to Plessy V. Ferguson. 2008. (ENG., Illus.). 400p. pap. 17.95 *(978-0-19-537021-8(X))* Oxford Univ. Pr., Inc.

Elliott, Mark & Smith, John David, eds. Undaunted Radical: The Selected Writings & Speeches of Albion W. Tourgée. 2010. (Conflicting Worlds: New Dimensions of the American Civil War Ser.). 448p. pap. 24.95 *(978-0-8071-3593-8(3))* Louisiana State Univ. Pr.

Elliott, Mark Emory. Color-Blind Justice: Albion Tourgee & the Quest for Racial Equality - From the Civil War to Plessy V. Ferguson. 2006. (ENG., Illus.). 400p. 30.00 *(978-0-19-518139-5(5))* Oxford Univ. Pr., Inc.

Everett, Betty Steele. William Wilberforce: Freedom Fighter. 2007. (Faith's Adventurers Ser.). (ENG.). 106p. mass mkt. 6.99 *(978-0-87508-976-8(3))* CLC Pubns.

Faulkner, Carol. Lucretia Mott's Heresy: Abolition & Women's Rights in Nineteenth-Century America. 2011. (Illus.). 312p. (C). 45.00 *(978-0-8122-4321-5(8))* Univ. of Pennsylvania Pr.

Finkelman, Paul, ed. Abolitionists in Northern Courts: The Pamphlet Literature. 2007. 25.00 *(978-1-58477-739-7(7))* Lawbook Exchange, Ltd., The.

Finkelman, Paul, ed. & intro. Slave Rebels, Abolitionists, & Southern Courts: The Pamphlet Literature, 2 vols. 2007. 250.00 *(978-1-58477-744-1(3))* Lawbook Exchange, Ltd., The.

Frederick Douglass. My Bondage & My Freedom. l.t. ed. 2007. (ENG.). 384p. pap. 26.99 *(978-1-4264-6628-1(5))* BiblioBazaar.

Fulton, Justin D. (Justin Dewey). Memoir of Timothy Gilbert, by Justin D Fulton. 2006. 260p. per. 23.99 *(978-1-4255-2299-5(8))* MPublishing.

Gallman, J. Matthew. America's Joan of Arc: The Life of Anna Elizabeth Dickinson. 2008. (ENG., Illus.). 272p. pap. 18.95 *(978-0-19-533926-0(6))* Oxford Univ. Pr., Inc.

Gellman, David. Emancipating New York. 2008. 312p. pap. 22.95 *(978-0-8071-3368-2(X))* Louisiana State Univ. Pr.

Gellman, David N. Emancipating New York: The Politics of Slavery & Freedom, 1777-1827. 2006. (Antislavery, Abolition, & the Atlantic World Ser.). (Illus.). 297p. 50.00 *(978-0-8071-3174-9(1))* Louisiana State Univ. Pr.

Gerteis, Louis S. Morality & Utility in American Antislavery Reform. 2011. (ENG.). 280p. pap. 40.00 ***(978-0-8078-5732-8(7))*** Univ. of North Carolina Pr.

Gilbert, Olive. Narrative of Sojourner Truth. 2009. 90p. pap. *(978-1-151-69604-5(8))* Books LLC.

—Narrative of Sojourner Truth. 2011. 122p. pap. 9.99 ***(978-1-61203-035-7(1))*** Bottom of the Hill Publishing.

Gilpin, Robert B. & Gilpin, R. Blakeslee. John Brown Still Lives! America's Long Reckoning with Violence, Equality, & Change. 2011. (ENG., Illus.). 304p. 30.00 *(978-0-8078-3501-2(3))* Univ. of North Carolina Pr.

Gougeon, Len. Virtue's Hero: Emerson, Antislavery, & Reform. 2010. (ENG.). 424p. pap. 29.95 *(978-0-8203-3469-1(3))* Univ. of Georgia Pr.

Groth, Bobbie. The Incredible Story of Ephraim Nute: Scandal, Bloodshed, & Unitarianism on the American Frontier. 2011. pap. 16.00 *(978-1-55896-609-3(9))*; E-Book 9.99 *(978-1-55896-611-6(0))* Unitarian Universalist Assn. (Skinner Hse. Bks.).

Grow, Matthew J. Liberty to the Downtrodden: Thomas L. Kane, Romantic Reformer. 2009. (Lamar Series in Western History Ser.). (ENG., Illus.). 368p. 40.00 *(978-0-300-13610-4(2))* Yale Univ. Pr.

Guiducci, James V. Natural Religion against Slavery: William Ellery Channing on Slavery. 2007. pap. 10.00 *(978-0-8059-7185-9(8))* Dorrance Publishing Co., Inc.

Hawkins, Walter. Old John Brown: The Man whose Soul Is Marching on. 2007. 48p. per. *(978-1-4065-4371-1(3))* Dodo Pr.

Hinton, Richard J. John Brown & His Men; with Some Account of the Roads They Traveled to Reach Harper's Ferry, by Richard J Hinton. 2011. 756p. pap. 40.99 ***(978-1-4181-8929-7(4))*** MPublishing.

Hinton, Richard Josiah. John Brown & his Men. 2011. (ENG.). 756p. pap. 41.95 ***(978-1-4585-0106-6(X))*** Univ. of Michigan Library.

Hinton, Richard Josiah. John Brown & His Men: Accounts of the Roads They Traveled to Reach Harper's Ferry. (American Reformers Ser.). 752p. reprint ed. 148.00 *(978-0-7222-8998-3(7))* Library Reprints, Inc.

Hints on Colonization & Abolition. 2010. pap. 19.00 *(978-1-61143-184-1(0))* Gorgias Pr., LLC.

Hodges, Graham Russell. David Ruggles: A Radical Black Abolitionist & the Underground Railroad in New York City. 2010. (John Hope Franklin Series in African American History & Culture Ser.). (ENG., Illus.). 264p. 30.00 *(978-0-8078-3326-1(6))* Univ. of North Carolina Pr.

Honeck, Mischa. We Are the Revolutionists: German-Speaking Immigrants & American Abolitionists after 1848. 2011. (Race in the Atlantic World, 1700-1900 Ser.). (ENG & ACE., Illus.). 256p. 59.95 *(978-0-8203-3800-2(1))*; pap. 24.95 *(978-0-8203-3823-1(0))* Univ. of Georgia Pr.

Horwitz, Tony. Midnight Rising: John Brown & Raid That Sparked the Civil War. 2011. ***(978-1-4104-4186-7(5))*** Thorndike Pr.

Horwitz, Tony. Midnight Rising: John Brown & the Raid That Sparked the Civil Wa. 2011. (ENG., Illus.). 384p. 29.00 *(978-0-8050-9153-3(X))* Holt, Henry & Co.

Hume, John F. The Abolitionists: Together with Personal Memories of the Struggle Fo. 2006. (ENG.). 162p. pap. 19.99 *(978-1-4264-6788-2(5))*; 178p. pap. 21.99 *(978-1-4264-6851-3(2))* BiblioBazaar.

—The Abolitionists, with Personal Memories, 1830-64. 224p. reprint ed. 98.00 *(978-0-7222-9833-6(1))* Library Reprints, Inc.

Husband, Julie. Antislavery Discourse & Nineteenth-Century American Literature: Incendiary Pictures. 2010. (ENG., Illus.). 192p. 84.00 *(978-0-230-62148-0(1))* Palgrave Macmillan.

Isaac Wilberforce, Samuel Wilberforce. The Life of William Wilberforce. 2008. 340p. 29.99 *(978-0-554-51881-7(3))*; 28.99 *(978-0-554-51888-6(0))*; pap. 30.75 *(978-0-554-51886-2(4))*; pap. 31.75 *(978-0-554-51883-1(X))* BiblioBazaar.

Jackson, Maurice. Let This Voice Be Heard: Anthony Benezet, Father of Atlantic Abolitionism. 2010. (Illus.). 400p. (C). pap. 24.95 *(978-0-8122-2126-8(5))* Univ. of Pennsylvania Pr.

James, Henry Field. Abolitionism Unveiled; or, Its Origin, Progress, & Pernicious Tendency Fully Developed by Henry Field James. 2006. 256p. per. 23.99 *(978-1-4255-2167-7(3))* MPublishing.

Jeffrey, Julie Roy. Abolitionists Remember: Antislavery Autobiographies & the Unfinished Work of Emancipation. 2008. (ENG., Illus.). 352p. 66.50 *(978-0-8078-3208-0(1))*; pap. 27.95 *(978-0-8078-5885-1(4))* Univ. of North Carolina Pr.

Jordan, Ryan P. Slavery & the Meetinghouse: The Quakers & the Abolitionist Dilemma, 1820-1865. 2007. (ENG., Illus.). 200p. 29.95 *(978-0-253-34860-9(9)*, 0253348609) Indiana Univ. Pr.

Joseph, Sturge. A Visit to the United States In 1841. 2008. 328p. 29.99 *(978-0-554-23578-3(1))* 2008. 328p. 28.99 *(978-0-554-32881-2(X))* 2007. (ENG.). 292p. pap. 21.99 *(978-1-4264-4695-5(0))* 2007. (ENG.). 324p. pap. 24.99 *(978-1-4264-4726-6(4))* BiblioBazaar.

Kenny, Gale L. Contentious Liberties: American Abolitionists in Post-Emancipation Jamaica, 1834-1866. (Race in the Atlantic World, 1700-1900 Ser.). (ENG.). 212p. 2011. pap. 24.95 ***(978-0-8203-4045-6(6))*** 2010. 44.95 *(978-0-8203-3399-1(9))* Univ. of Georgia Pr.

Kinealy, Christine. Daniel O'Connell & the Anti-Slavery Movement: The Saddest People the Sun Sees, 1 vol. 2010. (ENG.). 240p. 99.00 *(978-1-85196-633-2(1))* Pickering & Chatto Pubs., Ltd. GBR. Dist: Ashgate Publishing Co.

Knepp, Gary L. Freedom's Struggle: A Response to Slavery from the Ohio Borderlands. (Illus.). 2009. (ENG.). 260p. pap. 22.50 *(978-1-932250-71-8(9))* 2008. 272p. 32.50 *(978-1-932250-60-2(3))* Little Miami Publishing Co.

Lee, Maurice S., ed. The Cambridge Companion to Frederick Douglass. 2009. (Cambridge Companions to Literature Ser.). (ENG.). 212p. (C). 88.00 *(978-0-521-88923-0(5))*; pap. 27.99 *(978-0-521-71787-8(6))* Cambridge Univ. Pr.

Marks, Carole C. Moses & the Monster & Miss Anne. 2009. (ENG., Illus.). 256p. 37.00 *(978-0-252-03394-0(9))* Univ. of Illinois Pr.

Martin, Zachary. Martyr to Freedom: The Life & Death of CA. 2nd ed. 2011. (ENG.). 130p. pap. 21.99 ***(978-0-7618-5422-7(3))*** Hamilton Bks.

Matthews, Nicky & Pollock, John. Abolition! Newton, the Ex-Slave Trader, & Wilberforce, the Little Liberator. 2007. (Illus.). 107p. per. 11.00 *(978-1-903087-99-2(6))* DayOne Pubns. GBR. Dist: STL Distribution North America.

McCall, G. J. H. The Pilkington Gene. 2011. (Illus.). 168p. pap. ***(978-0-7552-1331-3(9))*** Authors OnLine, Ltd.

McGinty, Brian. John Brown's Trial. 2009. (Illus.). 384p. 27.95 *(978-0-674-03517-1(8))* Harvard Univ. Pr.

McGlone, Robert E. John Brown's War Against Slavery. 2009. (ENG., Illus.). 462p. 35.00 *(978-0-521-51443-9(6))* Cambridge Univ. Pr.

McGowan, James A. Station Master on the Underground Railroad: The Life & Letters of Thomas Garrett. alt. rev. ed. 2009. (ENG., Illus.). 232p. pap. 45.00 *(978-0-7864-4240-9(9))* McFarland & Co., Inc. Pubs.

McKivigan, John R. Forgotten Firebrand: James Redpath & the Making of Nineteenth-Century America. 2008. (Illus.). 280p. 47.50 *(978-0-8014-4673-3(2))* Cornell Univ. Pr.

—The War Against Proslavery Religion: Abolitionism & the Northern Churches, 1830-1865. 2009. (Illus.). 328p. pap. 31.50 *(978-0-8014-7576-4(7))* Cornell Univ. Pr.

Metaxas, Eric. Amazing Grace: William Wilberforce & the Heroic Campaign to End Slavery. 2007. (ENG., Illus.). 320p. pap. 13.99 *(978-0-06-117388-2(6)*, HarperOne) HarperCollins Pubs.

Mitchell, Thomas G. Antislavery Politics in Antebellum & Civil War America, 1 vol. 2007. 296p. 49.95 *(978-0-275-99168-5(7)*, C9168, Praeger Pubs.) Greenwood Publishing Group, Inc.

Morgans, James Patrick. John Todd & the Underground Railroad: Biography of an Iowa Abolitionist. 2006. (ENG., Illus.). 224p. per. 35.00 *(978-0-7864-2783-3(3))* McFarland & Co., Inc. Pubs.

Mueller, Owen W. Theodore Dwight Weld & the American Anti-Slavery Society. 2011. (ENG.). 236p. pap. 45.00 ***(978-0-7864-6396-1(1))*** McFarland & Co., Inc. Pubs.

Mueller, Owen W. The Underground Railroad in Western Illinois. 2007. (ENG., Illus.). 199p. 45.00 *(978-0-7864-3141-0(5))* McFarland & Co., Inc. Pubs.

Mull, Carol E. The Underground Railroad in Michigan. 2010. (ENG., Illus.). 223p. 55.00 *(978-0-7864-4638-4(2))* McFarland & Co., Inc. Pubs.

Murphy, Larry G. Sojourner Truth: A Biography, 1 vol. 2011. (Greenwood Biographies Ser.). (Illus.). 176p. 35.00 *(978-0-313-35728-2(5)*, GR5728); E-Book *(978-0-313-35729-9(3)*, Greenwood Pr.) Greenwood Publishing Group, Inc.

Myers, John L. Senator Henry Wilson & the Civil War. 2007. (ENG.). 244p. 68.50 *(978-0-7618-3876-0(7))*; per. 40.99 *(978-0-7618-3877-7(5))* Univ. Pr. of America, Inc.

Nelson, Truman. The Old Man: John Brown at Harper's Ferry. 2009. (ENG., Illus.). 324p. pap. 17.00 *(978-1-931859-64-6(7))* Haymarket Bks.

Newman, Richard & Mueller, James, eds. Antislavery & Abolition in Philadelphia: Emancipation & the Long Struggle for Racial Justice in the City of Brotherly Love. 2011. (Antislavery, Abolition, & the Atlantic World Ser.). 264p. 39.95 ***(978-0-8071-3991-2(2))*** Louisiana State Univ. Pr.

Noraian, Monica & Noraian, Monica Cousins. Women's Rights, Racial Integration, & Education From, 1850-1920: The Case of Sarah Raymond, the First Female Superintendent. 2009. (ENG.). 200p. 89.00 *(978-0-230-61322-5(5))* Palgrave Macmillan.

Oakes, James. The Radical & the Republican: Frederick Douglass, Abraham Lincoln, & the Triumph of Antislavery Politics. 2008. (ENG.). 352p. per. 17.95 *(978-0-393-33065-6(6)*, 33065) Norton, W. W. & Co., Inc.

Oickle, Alvin & Walker, Jonathan. The Man with Branded Hand. 2011. (ENG., Illus.). 384p. 28.00 *(978-1-59416-136-0(4))* Westholme Publishing.

Pelster, Mae. Abolitionists, Copperheads & Colonizers in Hudson & the Western Reserve. 2011. 128p. pap. 21.99 ***(978-1-60949-253-3(6))*** History Pr., The.

Pickard, Samuel T. Life & Letters of John Greenleaf Whitt. 2006. (ENG.). pap. 36.95 *(978-1-4286-4203-4(X))* Kessinger Publishing, LLC.

Piper, John. Amazing Grace in the Life of William Wilberforce. 2007. 80p. pap. 7.99 *(978-1-58134-875-0(4))* Crossway.

—The Roots of Endurance: Invincible Perseverance in the Lives of John Newton, Charles Simeon, & William Wilberforce. 2nd ed. 2006. (Swans Are Not Silent Ser.: Vol. 3). 176p. pap. 14.99 *(978-1-58134-814-9(2))* Crossway.

Plank, Geoffrey Gilbert. John Woolman's Path to the Peaceable Kingdom: A Quaker in the British Empire. 2012. (Early American Studies). (Illus.). 320p. (C). 39.95 ***(978-0-8122-4405-2(2))*** Univ. of Pennsylvania Pr.

Ralph Marjorie Crump Staff. Augusta's Journal. 2009. 336p. 36.49 *(978-1-4389-3572-0(2))*; pap. 22.99 *(978-1-4389-3571-3(4))* AuthorHouse.

Reynolds, David S. John Brown, Abolitionist: The Man Who Killed Slavery, Sparked the Civil War, & Seeded Civil Rights. 2006. (Vintage Ser.). (ENG., Illus.). 592p. per. 18.00 *(978-0-375-72615-6(2)*, Vintage) Knopf Doubleday Publishing Group.

Risley, Ford. Abolition & the Press: The Moral Struggle Against Slavery. 2008. (Medill Visions of the American Press Ser.). (ENG.). 248p. pap. 24.95 *(978-0-8101-2507-0(2))* Northwestern Univ. Pr.

Roberts, Benson T. Holiness Teachings: The Life & Work of B. T. Roberts. 2011. 168p. pap. ***(978-1-84902-502-7(9))*** Benediction Classics.

Robertson, Stacey M. Hearts Beating for Liberty: Women Abolitionists in the Old Northwest. 2010. (ENG., Illus.). 336p. 39.95 *(978-0-8078-3408-4(4))* Univ. of North Carolina Pr.

Rogers, D. Laurence. Apostles of Equality: The Birneys, the Republicans, & the Civil War. 2011. (ENG., Illus.). 250p. 39.95 *(978-1-61186-015-3(6))* Michigan State Univ. Pr.

Ronda, Bruce A. Reading the Old Man: John Brown in American Culture. 2008. (ENG., Illus.). 218p. 39.95 *(978-1-57233-620-9(X))* Univ. of Tennessee Pr.

Ross, D. Reid. Lincoln's Veteran Volunteers Win the War: The Hudson Valley's Ross Brothers & the Union's Fight for Emancipation. (Illus.). 470p. 2011. pap. 29.95 ***(978-0-7914-7642-0(1)***, Suny Pr.) 2008. 40.00 *(978-0-7914-7641-3(3))* State Univ. of New York Pr.

Sadlier, Rosemary. Harriet Tubman: Freedom Seeker, Freedom Leader. 2012. (Quest Biography Ser.). (ENG., Illus.). 192p. pap. 19.99 *(978-1-4597-0150-2(X))* Dundurn CAN. Dist: Ingram Pub. Services.

Sanders, Nancy. Black Abolitionists. 2011. (Perspectives on History Ser.). (ENG.). 120p. (gr. 9-14). pap. 7.95 *(978-1-932663-26-6(6))* History Compass, LLC.

Shone, Steve J. Lysander Spooner: American Anarchist. 2010. (ENG.). 138p. 57.99 *(978-0-7391-4450-3(2))* Lexington Bks.

Simmons, George F. Public Spirit & Mobs: Two sermons delivered at Springfield, Mass. , on Sunday, February 23, 1851, after the Thompson Riot. 2011. 34p. pap. 11.99 ***(978-1-4181-9387-4(9))*** MPublishing.

Slaughter, Thomas P. The Beautiful Soul of John Woolman, Apostle of Abolition. 2009. (ENG., Illus.). 464p. pap. 22.00 *(978-0-8090-2848-1(4)*, Hill & Wang) Farrar, Straus & Giroux.

Slavery & Abolition. Vol. 29, Pt. 1. *(978-0-404-60929-0(5))* Vol. 30, Pt. 2. *(978-0-404-60930-6(9))* AMS Pr., Inc.

Smith, David G. On the Edge of Freedom: The Fugitive Slave Issue in South Central Pennsylvania, 1820-1870. 2012. (ENG.). 260p. 45.00 ***(978-0-8232-4032-6(0))*** Fordham Univ. Pr.

Smith, K. Carl & Smith, Kamie C. Frederick Douglass Republicans: The Movement to Re-Ignite America's Passion for Liberty. 2011. 120p. 23.99 ***(978-1-4567-5815-8(2))*** AuthorHouse.

Smith, Kamie C. & Smith, K. Carl. Frederick Douglass Republicans: The Movement to Re-Ignite America's Passion for Liberty. 2011. 102p. pap. 14.99 ***(978-1-4567-5816-5(0))*** AuthorHouse.

Snodgrass, Mary Ellen. The Underground Railroad: An Encyclopedia of People, Places, & Operations, 2 vols., Set. 2007. (ENG., Illus.). 872p. 199.00 *(978-0-7656-8093-8(9)*, Sharpe Reference) Sharpe, M.E. Inc.

Stauffer, John. Giants: The Parallel Lives of Frederick Douglass & Abraham Lincoln. 2009. (ENG.). 448p. pap. 14.99 *(978-0-446-69898-6(9)*, Twelve) Grand Central Publishing.

Stewart, James Brewer. Abolitionist Politics & the Coming of the Civil War. 2008. 256p. pap. 24.95 net. *(978-1-55849-634-7(3))*; 236p. per. 80.00 net. *(978-1-55849-635-4(1))* Univ. of Massachusetts Pr.

Stewart, James Brewer, ed. William Lloyd Garrison at Two Hundred. 2008. (David Brion Davis (Gilder Lehrman) Ser.). (ENG.). 160p. pap. 35.00 *(978-0-300-13658-6(7))* Yale Univ. Pr.

Still, William. The Underground Railroad: Authentic Narratives & First-Hand Accounts. Finseth, Ian Frederick, ed. 2007. (African American Ser.). (ENG., Illus.). 304p. per. 14.95 *(978-0-486-45553-2(X))* Dover Pubns., Inc.

Stoneham, Michae. John Brown & the Era of Literary Confrontation. 2009. (Studies in American Popular History & Culture Ser.). (ENG.). 240p. 125.00 *(978-0-415-99682-2(1))* Routledge.

Stowe, Harriet Beecher. Stowe in Her Own Time: A Biographical Chronicle of Her Life, Drawn from Recollections, Interviews, & Memoirs by Family, Friends, & Associates. Belasco, Susan, ed. 2009. (Writers in Their Own Time Ser.). (ENG., Illus.). 332p. pap. 27.95 *(978-1-58729-782-3(5))* Univ. of Iowa Pr.

Sweets, Judy & DeCaro, Louis A., contrib. by. John Brown Photo Chronology: Catalog of the exhibition at Harpers Ferry 2009. 2009. (Illus.). 96p. pap. 45.00 *(978-0-9773638-7-2(2))* Allies for Freedom Pubs.

Swisshelm, Jane Grey Cannon. Half a Century. 2007. (ENG.). 308p. pap. 23.99 *(978-1-4264-5780-7(4))*; 332p. pap. 24.99 *(978-1-4264-5840-8(1))* BiblioBazaar.

—Half a Century. 2007. (ENG.). 300p. per. *(978-1-4065-6464-8(8))* Dodo Pr.

—Half a Century. 2009. 252p. pap. 16.95 *(978-1-4385-1574-8(X)*, Book Jungle) Standard Pubns., Inc.

Tomkins, Stephen. William Wilberforce: A Biography. 2007. (Illus.). 238p. per. 18.00 *(978-0-8028-2593-3(1))* Eerdmans, William B. Publishing Co.

Trotman, C. James. Frederick Douglass: A Biography. 1 vol. 2011. (Greenwood Biographies Ser.). (Illus.). 158p. 35.00 *(978-0-313-35036-8(1)*, GR5036); E-Book *(978-0-313-35037-5(X)*, Greenwood Pr.) Greenwood Publishing Group, Inc.

Truth, Sojourner. The Narrative of Sojourner Truth. 2007. 110p. pap. 18.99 *(978-1-4346-1053-9(5))*; (ENG.). 122p. pap. 19.99 *(978-1-4346-1152-9(3))* BiblioBazaar.

Truth, Sojourner & Gilbert, Olive. The Narrative of Sojourner Truth. 2008. 124p. 24.99 *(978-0-554-26440-0(4))*; 21.99 *(978-0-554-35743-0(7))* BiblioBazaar.

—Narrative of Sojourner Truth: Literary Touchstone Classic. 2007. 144p. pap. 3.99 *(978-1-58049-733-6(0))* Prestwick Hse., Inc.

Truth, Sojourner, et al. Three Narratives of Slavery. 2008. (African American Ser.). (ENG.). 320p. pap. 8.95 *(978-0-486-46834-1(8))* Dover Pubns., Inc.

Upchurch, T. Adams. Abolition Movement. 1 vol. 2011. (Landmarks of the American Mosaic Ser.). 195p. 35.00 *(978-0-313-30600-0(4)*, A3045C) Greenwood Publishing Group, Inc.

Upchurch, Thomas Adams. Abolition Movement. 2011. E-Book *(978-0-313-38607-7(2)*, Greenwood Pr.) Greenwood Publishing Group, Inc.

VanHorne-Lane, Janice. Safe Houses & the Underground Railroad in East Central Ohio. 2010. (ENG., Illus.). 128p. pap. 19.99 *(978-1-59629-246-8(6))* History Pr., The.

Walters, Kerry. The Underground Railroad: A Reference Guide. 1 vol. 2012. (Guides to Historic Events in America Ser.). (Illus.). 226p. 58.00 ***(978-1-59884-647-8(7)***, A3206C) ABC-CLIO, LLC.

Walters, Kerry S. The Underground Railroad: A Reference Guide. 2012. (Illus.). x, 223p. E-Book ***(978-1-59884-648-5(5))*** ABC-CLIO, LLC.

Webber, Christopher. American to the Backbone: The Life of James W. C. Pennington, the Fugitive Slave Who Became One of the First Black Abolitionists. 2011. (ENG.). 432p. 29.95 *(978-1-60598-175-8(3)*, 605175) Pegasus Bks.

Wells, Helen. Escape by Night: A Story of the Underground Railway. Matschat, Cecile & Carmer, Carl, eds. 2011. 194p. 42.95 ***(978-1-258-02279-2(6))*** Literary Licensing, LLC.

Wheeler, Henry. The Slaves' Champion: The Life, Deeds, & Historical Days of William Wilberforce. 3rd ed. 2007. 230p. per. *(978-0-89221-670-3(0))* New Leaf Pr., Inc.

White, Barbara. Visits with Lincoln: Abolitionists Meet the President at the White House. 2011. (ENG.). 180p. 65.00 ***(978-0-7391-6416-7(3))***; pap. 27.95 ***(978-0-7391-6417-4(1))*** Lexington Bks.

White, Barbara A. Visits with Lincoln: Abolitionists Meet the President at the White House. 2011. E-Book ***(978-0-7391-6418-1(X))*** Lexington Bks.

Wilberforce, Robert I. Life of William Wilberforce, 5 Vols. reprint ed. 625.00 *(978-0-7222-9849-7(8))* Library Reprints, Inc.

Wilberforce, Robert Isaac. The Life of William Wilberforce. 2009. 240p. pap. *(978-1-4588-8707-8(3))*; 338p. pap. *(978-0-217-80095-2(5))*; 706p. pap. *(978-0-217-55906-5(9))* Books LLC.

—The Life of William Wilberforce. 2009. 408p. pap. 22.81 *(978-1-150-51677-1(1))*; 292p. pap. 19.99 *(978-1-150-18665-3(8))* General Bks. LLC.

—The Life of William Wilberforce by His Sons, 2; & Samuel Wilberforce In. 2009. 292p. pap. 19.99 *(978-1-150-72924-9(4))* General Bks. LLC.

Wilberforce, Robert Isaac & Wilberforce, Samuel. The Life of William Wilberforce. 2010. (ENG.). 410p. pap. 34.75 *(978-1-177-58330-5(5))*; 418p. pap. 34.75 *(978-1-177-53491-8(6))*; 576p. pap. 43.75 *(978-1-177-58329-9(1))*; 438p. pap. 35.75 *(978-1-177-61406-1(5))*; 474p. pap. 37.75 *(978-1-177-33822-6(X))* BiblioBazaar.

—The Life of William Wilberforce V3. 572p. 2010. 47.16 ***(978-1-165-73992-9(5))*** 2010. pap. 35.16 ***(978-1-165-69931-5(1))*** 2009. 58.95 *(978-1-104-45531-6(5))* 2009. pap. 43.95 *(978-1-104-37596-6(6))* Kessinger Publishing, LLC.

Wilberforce, Robert Isaac & Wilberforce, Samuel. The Life of William Wilberforce V4. 2010. 404p. pap. 27.96 *(978-1-164-10242-7(7))* 2010. 404p. 39.96 ***(978-1-164-40131-5(9))*** 2008. 402p. 49.95 *(978-1-4365-9200-0(3))* 2007. (ENG.). 404p. per. 34.95 *(978-0-548-79173-8(2))* Kessinger Publishing, LLC.

Wilberforce, Robert Isaac, et al. The Life of William Wilberforce. 2010. 352p. pap. 32.75 *(978-1-177-94989-7(X))*; (ENG.). 554p. pap. 42.75 *(978-1-176-79136-7(2))* BiblioBazaar.

Wilberforce, Samuel. The Life of William Wilberforce. 2010. 406p. pap. 34.75 *(978-1-146-92693-5(6))*; 582p. pap. 43.75 *(978-1-146-97677-0(1))*; 428p. pap. 35.75 *(978-1-144-50417-3(1))*; 564p. pap. 43.75 *(978-1-142-21351-0(X))* BiblioBazaar.

—Life of William Wilberforce. 2010. 466p. 42.99 *(978-1-140-10282-3(6))*; pap. 37.75 *(978-1-140-10283-0(4))* BiblioBazaar.

—Life of William Wilberforce. 2010. (Illus.). 290p. pap. 15.89 *(978-1-154-76962-3(3))* General Bks. LLC.

Wilberforce, Samuel & Wilberforce, Robert Isaac. The Life of William Wilberforce. 2010. 472p. pap. 37.75 *(978-1-146-46212-9(3))*; 416p. pap. 34.75 *(978-1-146-60812-1(8))*; 422p. pap. 34.75 *(978-1-147-69779-7(5))*; 576p. pap. 43.75 *(978-1-146-74222-1(3))*; 424p. pap. 35.75 *(978-1-145-15098-0(5))*; 422p. pap. 34.75 *(978-1-146-10903-1(2))*; 480p. pap. 37.75 *(978-1 145 13090-6(9))*; 410p. pap. 34.75 *(978-1-142-71989-0(8))*; 418p. pap. 34.75 *(978-1-142-76588-0(1))*; 480p. pap. 37.75 *(978-1-142-45475-3(4))*; 582p. pap. 43.75 *(978-1-142-74400-7(0))*; 420p. pap. 34.75 *(978-1-142-00616-7(6))*; 420p. pap. 34.75 *(978-1-142-47598-7(0))*; 550p. pap. 41.75 *(978-1-142-02515-1(2))*; 422p. pap. 34.75 *(978-1-142-13398-6(2))* BiblioBazaar.

Wilberforce, Samuel, et al. The Life of William Wilberforce. 2010. 336p. pap. 31.75 *(978-1-146-86940-9(1))*; 776p. pap. 53.75 *(978-1-146-81339-6(2))*; 550p. pap. 41.75 *(978-1-143-05011-4(8))* BiblioBazaar.

Wilberforce, William. The Correspondence of William Wilberforce. Wilberforce, Robert Isaac & Wilberforce, Samuel, eds. 2011. (Cambridge Library Collection - Slavery & Abolition Ser.). (ENG.). 552p. pap. 39.99 *(978-1-108-02512-6(9))*; 442p. pap. 32.99 *(978-1-108-02511-9(0))* Cambridge Univ. Pr.

—The Life of William Wilberforce. Wilberforce, Robert Isaac & Wilberforce, Samuel, eds. 2011. (Cambridge Library Collection - Slavery & Abolition Ser.). (ENG.). 428p. pap. 31.99 *(978-1-108-02509-6(9))*; 416p. pap. 31.99 *(978-1-108-02505-8(6))*; 468p. pap. 34.99 *(978-1-108-02506-5(4))*; 412p. pap. 31.99 *(978-1-108-02508-9(0))*; 578p. pap. 43.00 *(978-1-108-02507-2(2))* Cambridge Univ. Pr.

—William Wilberforce Greatest Works. 2007. (Pure Gold Classics). (ENG., Illus.). 288p. pap. 13.99 incl. audio compact disk *(978-0-88270-370-1(6))* Bridge-Logos Foundation.

Wood, Edward J. A Fierce, Wild Joy: The Civil War Letters of Colonel Edward J. Wood, 48th Indiana Volunteer Infantry Regiment. Towne, Stephen E., ed. 2007. (Voices of the Civil War Ser.). (ENG., Illus.). 320p. 38.00 *(978-1-57233-599-8(8))* Univ. of Tennessee Pr.

Young, Neely. Ripe for Emancipation. 2011. 236p. pap. 19.95 ***(978-0-9841128-9-0(8))*** Mariner Media, Inc.

ABOMINABLE SNOWMAN
see Yeti

ABORIGINAL AUSTRALIAN ART
see Art, Aboriginal Australian

ABORIGINAL AUSTRALIAN MYTHOLOGY
see Mythology, Aboriginal Australian

ABORIGINAL AUSTRALIAN PAINTING
see Painting, Aboriginal Australian

ABORIGINAL AUSTRALIAN PHILOSOPHY
see Philosophy, Aboriginal Australian

ABORIGINAL AUSTRALIAN SONGS
see Songs, Aboriginal Australian

ABORIGINAL AUSTRALIANS
see also Aranda (Australian People); Kumai (Australian People); Pitjantjatjara (Australian People); Tiwi (Australian People); Torres Strait Islanders; Walbiri (Australian People); Wik-Mungkan (Australian People)

Allen, Lindy & Lakic, Mira. Women's Work: Aboriginal Women's Artefacts in the Museum of Victoria. 2007. (ENG., Illus.). 72p. pap. 19.95 *(978-0-7306-8711-5(2))* Museum Victoria Publishing AUS. Dist: National Bk. Network.

Allerding, Amanda. Signing off on the State. 2010. 120p. pap. *(978-3-639-24158-7(4))* VDM Verlag Dr. Mueller e.K.

Altman, Jon & Nieuwenhuysen, John P. Economic Status of Australian Aborigines. 2006. (ENG.). 256p. pap. 53.00 *(978-0-521-29490-4(8))* Cambridge Univ. Pr.

ATF Press, creator. Rainbow Spirit Theology: Toward an Australian Aboriginal Theology. 2011. (ENG., Illus.). 97p. (C). per. 5.00 *(978-1-920691-80-6(4))* ATF Pr. AUS. Dist: Brown, David Bk. Co., The.

Atkinson, Caroline. The Violence Continuum. 2010. 336p. pap. *(978-3-8383-2172-1(3))* Lambert Academic Publishing.

Attenbrow, Val. Sydney's Aboriginal Past: Investigating the Archaeological & Historical Records. 2nd ed. 2010. (ENG., Illus.). 240p. pap. 49.95 *(978-1-74223-116-7(0)*, UNSW Press) NewSouth Publishing AUS. Dist: Independent Pubs. Group.

Barkley-Jack, Jan. Hawkesbury Settlement Revealed: A New Look at Australia's Third Mainland Settlement, 1793-1802. 2009. (Illus.). 488p. 59.95 *(978-1-877058-88-2(2))* Rosenberg Publishing Pty, Ltd. AUS. Dist: International Specialized Bk. Services.

Bell, Diane, ed. Listen to Ngarrindjeri Women Speaking. 2009.Tr. of Kungun Ngarrindjeri Miminar Yunnan. (ENG., Illus.). xiii, 146p. pap. 24.95 *(978-1-876756-69-7(1))* Spinifex Pr. AUS. Dist: Independent Pubs. Group.

Blackmore, Ernie. Speakin' Out Blak - an Examination of Finding an Urban Indigenous Voice Through Contemporary Australian Theatre. 2008. 188p. pap. *(978-3-639-06884-9(X))* VDM Verlag Dr. Mueller e.K.

Bonwick, James. The Daily Life & Origin of the Tasmanians. 2011. (Cambridge Library Collection - History Ser.). (ENG., Illus.). 342p. pap. 28.99 ***(978-1-108-03895-9(6))*** Cambridge Univ. Pr.

Brady, Veronica. The God-Shaped Hole. 2008. 124p. pap. 10.00 *(978-1-920691-87-5(1))* ATF Pr. AUS. Dist: International Publishers Marketing.

Brockwell, Sally. Archaeological Settlement Patterns & Mobility Strategies: Lower Adelaide River, Northern Australia. 2009. (Bar S Ser.). (ENG., Illus.). 141p. (C). pap. 95.00 *(978-1-4073-0461-8(5))* British Archaeological Reports Ltd. GBR. Dist: Brown, David Bk. Co., The.

Brooks, David. A Town Like Mparntwe: A Guide to the Dreaming Tracks & Sites of Alice Springs. 2007. (ENG., Illus.). 32p. pap. 11.95 *(978-1-86465-045-7(1))* IAD Pr. AUS. Dist: Independent Pubs. Group.

Budden, Chris. Following Jesus in Invaded Space. 2011. (ENG.). 256p. pap. 37.50 *(978-0-227-17358-9(9))* Clarke, James Co., Ltd. GBR. Dist: Brown, David Bk. Co., The.

—Following Jesus in Invaded Space: Doing Theology on Aboriginal Land. 2009. (Princeton Theological Monographs). 190p. pap. 22.00 *(978-1-60608-608-7(1)*, Pickwick Pubns.) Wipf & Stock Pubs.

Calder, J. E. Some Accounts of the Wars Extirpation Ha. 2006. pap. 20.95 *(978-1-4286-3611-8(0))* Kessinger Publishing, LLC.

Calvert, Albert F. The Aborigines of Western Australia. 2009. 60p. pap. *(978-1-4099-3558-2(2))* Dodo Pr.

Chatwin, Bruce. The Songlines. rev. ed. 2012. (ENG.). 320p. (gr. 12). pap. 16.00 ***(978-0-14-242257-1(6)***, Penguin Classics) Penguin Group (USA) Inc.

Chowdhury, Khairul. Empowering & Disempowering Indigenes. 2010. 328p. pap. *(978-3-8383-4953-4(9))* Lambert Academic Publishing.

Clark, Jennifer. Aborigines & Activism: Race, Aborigines & the Coming of the Sixties to Australia. 2008. 308p. (C). pap. 35.95 *(978-0-9802965-7-0(9))* UWA Publishing AUS. Dist: International Specialized Bk. Services.

Clarke, Banjo & Chance, Camilla. Wisdom Man: Biography of Banjo Clarke. 2012. (ENG., Illus.). 304p. pap. 15.95 *(978-0-14-300345-8(3)*, Penguin Global) Penguin Group (USA) Inc.

Clarke, Philip. Aboriginal People & Their Plants. 2007. (Illus.). 192p. 39.95 *(978-1-877058-51-6(3))* Rosenberg Publishing Pty, Ltd. AUS. Dist: International Specialized Bk. Services.

Clelland-Stokes, Sacha. Representing Aboriginality: A Post-Colonial Analysis of the Key Trends of Representing Aboriginality in South African, Australian & Aotearoa/New Zealand Film. 2009. (Intervention Press Ser.). (ENG.). 231p. pap. 34.95 *(978-87-89825-15-1(2))* Left Coast Pr., Inc.

Corrigan, Florence. Miles of Post & Wire. 2010. (ENG., Illus.). 150p. pap. 20.95 *(978-1-921248-15-3(7))* Magabala Bks. AUS. Dist: Independent Pubs. Group.

Costa, Ravi De. A Higher Authority: Indigenous Transnationalism & Australia. annot. ed. 2006. (ENG.). 254p. per. 40.95 *(978-0-86840-954-2(5)*, UNSW Press) NewSouth Publishing AUS. Dist: Independent Pubs. Group.

Cowlishaw, Gillian. The City's Outback. 2009. (ENG.). 272p. pap. 25.99 *(978-1-921410-87-1(6)*, UNSW Press) NewSouth Publishing AUS. Dist: Independent Pubs. Group.

Croft, Brenda L. Michael Riley Sights Unseen. 2007. (ENG., Illus.). 176p. 60.00 *(978-0-642-54162-8(0))* National Gallery of Australia AUS. Dist: Univ. of Washington Pr.

Darian-Smith, Kate, et al, eds. Seize the Day: Exhibitions, Australia & the World. 2008. (ENG.). 372p. pap. 54.95 *(978-0-9804648-0-1(3))* Monash Univ. Publishing AUS. Dist: International Specialized Bk. Services.

Deger, Jennifer. Shimmering Screens: Making Media in an Aboriginal Community. 2006. (Illus.). 256p. pap. 22.50 *(978-0-8166-4922-8(7))*; (Visible Evidence Ser.: Vol. 19). 67.50 *(978-0-8166-4921-1(9))* Univ. of Minnesota Pr.

Eckersley, Richard, et al. Australia: A Work in Progress - the Natural & Built Environment. Poiner, Gretchen, ed. 2008. 128p. pap. *(978-0-9775076-3-4(7))* Independent Scholars Assn. of Australia.

Edmonds, Penelope. Urbanizing Frontiers: Indigenous Peoples & Settlers in 19th-Century Pacific Rim Cities. 2010. (ENG., Illus.). 328p. (C). pap. 39.95 *(978-0-7748-1622-9(8))* UBC Pr. CAN. Dist: Univ. of Washington Pr.

Eickelkamp, Ute, ed. Growing up in Central Australia: New Anthropological Studies of Aboriginal Childhood & Adolescence. 2011. (Illus.). 310p. 95.00 *(978-0-85745-082-1(4))* Berghahn Bks., Inc.

Elder, Catriona. Dreams & Nightmares of White Australia: Representing Aboriginal Assimilation in the Mid-Twentieth Century. 2009. (Illus.). 257p. pap. *(978-3-03911-722-2(X))* Lang, Peter.

Ellinghaus, Katherine. Taking Assimilation to Heart: Marriages of White Women & Indigenous Men in the United States & Australia, 1887-1937. 2009. (ENG.). 312p. pap. 24.95 *(978-0-8032-2487-2(7))* Univ. of Nebraska Pr.

Esosa, Osaghae. Mythic Reconstruction - the Study of Australian Aboriginal & South African Literature. 2008. 128p. pap. *(978-3-639-03706-7(5))* VDM Verlag Dr. Mueller e.K.

Eyre, Edward John. Journals of Expeditions of Discovery into Central Australia & Overland from Adelaide to King George's Sound in the Years 1840-1, Vol. 1. 2007. (Illus.). 360p. per. *(978-1-4065-3397-2(1))* Dodo Pr.

—Journals of Expeditions of Discovery into Central Australia, & Overland from Adelaide to King George's Sound, in the Years 1840-1, Vol. 1. 2011. (Cambridge Library Collection - Travel & Exploration Ser.). (ENG., Illus.). 492p. pap. 35.99 ***(978-1-108-03897-3(2))*** Cambridge Univ. Pr.

—Journals of Expeditions of Discovery into Central Australia & Overland from Adelaide to King George's Sound in the Years 1840-1, Vol. 2. 2007. (Illus.). 392p. per. *(978-1-4065-3398-9(X))* Dodo Pr.

Eyre, Edward John. Journals of Expeditions of Discovery into Central Australia, & Overland from Adelaide to King George's Sound, in the Years 1840-1, Vol. 2. 2011. (Cambridge Library Collection - Travel & Exploration Ser.). (ENG., Illus.). 546p. pap. 39.99 ***(978-1-108-03898-0(0))*** Cambridge Univ. Pr.

Ford, Lisa. Settler Sovereignty: Jurisdiction & Indigenous People in America & Australia, 1788-1836. (Harvard Historical Studies: 166). (Illus.). 328p. 2011. (ENG.). pap. 24.95 *(978-0-674-06188-0(8))* 2010. 52.50 *(978-0-674-03565-2(8))* Harvard Univ. Pr.

Franzke, Leonora. Aboriginal Australi. 2008. 72p. pap. *(978-3-639-05125-4(4))* VDM Verlag Dr. Mueller e.K.

Gabbrielli, Emilio. Polenta & Goann. McGilvray, Barbara, tr. 2008. 240p. pap. *(978-88-95145-23-5(2))* Italian Paths of Culture.

Gale, Fay, et al. Aboriginal Youth & the Criminal Justice System: The Injustice of Justice? 2010. (ENG.). 172p. pap. 27.99 *(978-0-521-12598-7(7))* Cambridge Univ. Pr.

Genat, Bill, et al. Aboriginal Healthworkers: Primary Health Care at the Margins. 2006. (Contemporary Issues Ser.). (Illus.). 240p. (C). pap. 35.95 *(978-1-920694-76-0(5))* UWA Publishing AUS. Dist: International Specialized Bk. Services.

Genever, Geof. Failure of Justice: The Story of the Irvinebank Massacre. 2006. (Illus.). 26p. pap. *(978-0-9803177-0-1(3))* Eacham Historical Society Incorporated.

Gerritsen, Rupert. Australia & the Origins of Agriculture. 2008. (Bar S Ser.). (Illus.). 205p. (C). 92.50 *(978-1-4073-0354-3(6))* British Archaeological Reports Ltd. GBR. Dist: Brown, David Bk. Co., The.

Gilligan, Ian. Another Tasmanian Paradox. Clothing & Thermal Adaptations in Aboriginal Australia. 2007. (Bar S Ser.). (Illus.). 124p. (C). 65.00 *(978-1-4073-0154-9(3))* British Archaeological Reports Ltd. GBR. Dist: Brown, David Bk. Co., The.

Harrison, Neil. Teaching & Learning in Aboriginal Education. 2nd rev. ed. 2012. (Illus.). x, 213p. pap. 65.00 ***(978-0-19-557459-3(1))*** Oxford Univ. Pr., Inc.

Hettiarachchi, Dhanushka. Antibacterial Compounds of Conkerberry. 2010. 88p. pap. *(978-3-8383-8079-7(7))* Lambert Academic Publishing.

Hinton, Martin, et al. Indigenous Australians & the Law: Indigenous Australians & the Law 2/e. 2nd rev. ed. 2007. (Illus.). 224p. 140.00 *(978-1-876905-39-2(5)*, Routledge Cavendish) Taylor & Francis Group GBR. Dist: Taylor & Francis Group.

Hokari, Minoru. Gurindji Journey: A Japanese Historian in the Outback. 2011. pap. 29.00 *(978-0-8248-3614-6(6))* Univ. of Hawaii Pr.

Hooley, Neil. Liberating Experience: Narrative Knowledge for Critical Communities. 2010. *(978-1-4331-0944-7(1))*; *(978-1-4331-0945-4(X))* Lang, Peter Publishing, Inc.

Hooper, Chloe. Tall Man: The Death of Doomadgee. 2009. (ENG., Illus.). 272p. 24.00 *(978-1-4165-6159-0(5)*, Scribner) Scribner.

—Tall Man: The Death of Doomadgee. 2009. pap. *(978-1-4165-6161-3(7)*, Scribner) Simon & Schuster.

Howitt, Alfred William. The Native Tribes of South-East Australia, 2 vols. 2010. (Cambridge Library Collection - Linguistics Ser.). (ENG.). 878p. pap. 65.00 *(978-1-108-00632-3(9))* Cambridge Univ. Pr.

Jacobs, Margaret D. White Mother to a Dark Race: Settler Colonialism, Maternalism, & the Removal of Indigenous Children in the American West & Australia, 1880-1940. 2011. (ENG., Illus.). 592p. pap. 30.00 *(978-0-8032-3516-8(X))* Univ. of Nebraska Pr.

Jensz, Felicity. German Moravian Missionaries in the British Colony of Victoria, Australia, 1848-1908: Influential Strangers. 2010. (Studies in Christian Mission Ser.). 264p. *(978-90-04-17921-9(6))* BRILL.

Jones, Roy & Shaw, Brian, eds. Geographies of Australian Heritages: Loving a Sunburnt Country. 2007. (Heritage, Culture & Identity Ser.). (Illus.). 248p. 114.95 *(978-0-7546-4858-1(3))* Ashgate Publishing Co.

Jose, Nicholas. Anthology of Australian Aboriginal Literature. Heiss, Anita & Minter, Peter, eds. 2008. (ENG.). 288p. (C). *(978 0 7735 3450 0(8))* McGill-Queen's Univ. Pr.

Kerwin, Dale. Aboriginal Dreaming Paths & Trading Routes: The Colonisation of the Australian Economic Landscape. (Illus.). 230p. 2012. pap. 37.95 ***(978-1-84519-529-8(9))*** 2010. (ENG., 89.95 *(978-1-84519-338-6(5))* Sussex Academic Pr. GBR. Dist: International Specialized Bk. Services.

Kidd, Rosalind. Trustees on Trial: Recovering the Stolen Wages. 2006. (ENG., Illus.). 224p. pap. 31.45 *(978-0-85575-546-1(6))* Aboriginal Studies Pr. AUS. Dist: Independent Pubs. Group.

Konishi, Shino. The Aboriginal Male in the Enlightenment World, 1 vol. 2012. (Body, Gender & Culture Ser.). (ENG., Illus.). 256p. 99.00 ***(978-1-84893-216-6(2))*** Pickering & Chatto Pubs., Ltd. GBR. Dist: Ashgate Publishing Co.

Kruger, Alec & Waterford, Gerard. Alone on the Soaks: The Life & Times of Alec Kruger. 2007. (ENG.). 350p. pap. 27.00 *(978-1-86465-078-5(8))* IAD Pr. AUS. Dist: Independent Pubs. Group.

Lally, Janice. The Australian Aboriginal Collection in the Museum Fnr Völkerkunde, Berlin. 2008. 488p. pap. *(978-3-639-03491-2(0))* VDM Verlag Dr. Mueller e.K.

Landon, Carolyn. Jackson's Track Revisited: History, Remembrance & Reconciliation. 2006. (Illus.). 136p. pap. 22.95 ***(978-0-9757475-7-5(6))***; (ENG., pap. 22.95 *(978-0-9757475-6-8(8))* Monash Univ. Publishing AUS. Dist: International Specialized Bk. Services.

Law, Wallace Boone. Measured on Stone: Stone Artefact Reduction, Residential Mobility, & Aboriginal Land Use in Arid Central Australia. 2009. (Illus.). 154p. (C). pap. 92.50 *(978-1-4073-0445-8(3))* British Archaeological Reports Ltd. GBR. Dist: Brown, David Bk. Co., The.

Lea, Tess. Bureaucrats & Bleeding Hearts: Indigenous Health in Northern Australia. 2008. (ENG.). 304p. pap. 44.95 *(978-1-921410-18-5(3)*, UNSW Press) NewSouth Publishing AUS. Dist: Independent Pubs. Group.

Leitner, Gerhard & Malcolm, Ian G. The Habitat of Australia's Aboriginal Languages: Past, Present, & Future. 2007. (Trends in Linguistics Ser.: Vol. 179). (ENG.). VIII, 389p. 154.00 *(978-3-11-019079-3(6))* De Gruyter, Mouton DEU. Dist: de Gruyter, Walter GmbH & Co. KG.

Leitner, Gerhard & Malcolm, Ian G., eds. The Habitat of Australia's Aboriginal Languages: Past, Present & Future. 2007. (Trends in Linguistics. Studies & Monographs [TiLSM] Ser.). (ENG.). VIII, 389p. 238.00 ***(978-3-11-916632-4(4))*** De Gruyter, Mouton DEU. Dist: de Gruyter, Walter GmbH & Co. KG.

Lester, Yami. Learning from the Land. 2007. (ENG.). 32p. pap. 9.95 *(978-1-86465-955-9(6))* IAD Pr. AUS. Dist: Independent Pubs. Group.

Lewis, Megan. Conversations with the Mob. 2008. 240p. 45.00 *(978-1-921401-03-9(6))* UWA Publishing AUS. Dist: International Specialized Bk. Services.

Lickers, Michael. Urban Aboriginal Leadership. 2008. 92p. pap. *(978-3-639-03499-8(6))* VDM Verlag Dr. Mueller e.K.

Lowe, Pat & Pike, Jimmy. You Call It Desert: We Used to Live There. 2010. Orig. Title: Jilji - Life in the Great Sandy Desert. (ENG & AUS., Illus.). 168p. pap. 29.95 *(978-1-921248-11-5(4))* Magabala Bks. AUS. Dist: Independent Pubs. Group.

Lydon, Jane. Fantastic Dreaming: The Archaeology of an Aboriginal Mission. 2009. (Worlds of Archaeology Ser.). (ENG.). 330p. pap. 35.00 *(978-0-7591-1105-9(7))*; (Illus.). 85.00 *(978-0-7591-1104-2(9))* AltaMira Pr.

Mackinlay, Elizabeth. Disturbances & Dislocations: Understanding Teaching & Learning Experiences in Indigenous Australian Women's Music & Dance. 2007. (European University Studies: Vol. 932). (Illus.). 294p. pap. 59.95 *(978-0-8204-8031-2(2))* Lang, Peter Publishing, Inc.

Marchetti, Elena. Missing Subjects. 2009. 324p. pap. *(978-3-639-01692-5(0))* VDM Verlag Dr. Mueller e.K.

Marett, Allan. Songs, Dreamings, & Ghosts: The Wangga of North Australia. 2nd ed. 2009. (Music Culture Ser.). (ENG., Illus.). 320p. pap. 34.95 *(978-0-8195-6934-9(8))* Wesleyan Univ. Pr.

Marsden, J.B. Memoirs of the Life & Labours of the Rev. Samuel Marsden of Paramatta, Senior Chaplain of New South Wales: And of his Early Connexion with the Missions to New Zealand & Tahiti. 2011. (Cambridge Library Collection - Religion Ser.). (ENG., Illus.). 342p. pap. 28.99 ***(978-1-108-03891-1(3))*** Cambridge Univ. Pr.

May, Sally K. Collecting Cultures: Myth, Politics, & Collaboration in the 1948 Arnhem Land Expedition. 2009. (Indigenous Archaeologies Ser.). (ENG.). 250p. 75.00 *(978-0-7591-0598-0(7))* AltaMira Pr.

Maynard, John. Fight for Liberty & Freedom: The Origins of Australian Aboriginal Activism. 2007. (ENG.). 208p. pap. 35.95 *(978-0-85575-550-8(4))* Aboriginal Studies Pr. AUS. Dist: Independent Pubs. Group.

McAllister, P.A. National Days & the Politics of Indigenous & Local Identities in Australia & New Zealand. 2012. ***(978-1-59460-814-8(8))*** Carolina Academic Pr.

McCoy, Brian F. Holding Men: Kanyirninpa & the Health of Aboriginal Men. 2009. (ENG.). 296p. pap. 31.95 *(978-0-85575-658-1(6))* Aboriginal Studies Pr. AUS. Dist: Independent Pubs. Group.

McLean, Ian. White Aborigines: Identity Politics in Australian Art. 2009. (ENG., Illus.). 216p. (C). pap. 33.99 *(978-0-521-12067-8(5))* Cambridge Univ. Pr.

Memmott, Paul. Gunyah, Goondie & Wurley: The Aboriginal Architecture of Australia. 2008. (ENG., Illus.). 432p. pap. 70.00 *(978-0-7022-3245-9(9))* Univ. of Queensland Pr. AUS. Dist: Independent Pubs. Group.

Moreton-Robinson, Aileen, ed. Sovereign Subjects: Indigenous Sovereignty Matters. 2008. (Cultural Studies Ser.). (ENG.). xvi, 240p. pap., pap., mass mkt. 29.95 *(978-1-74114-724-7(1))* Allen & Unwin AUS. Dist: Independent Pubs. Group.

Morgan, Sally. My Place. 2008. (ENG.). 496p. 25.00 *(978-1-921361-22-7(0))* Fremantle Pr. AUS. Dist: Independent Pubs. Group.

National Museum of Australia. A Different Time: The Expedition Photopgraphs of Herbert Basedow 1903-1928. 2008. (ENG.). 224p. 44.95 *(978-1-876944-65-0(X))* National Museum of Australia AUS. Dist: Independent Pubs. Group.

Nazvanov, Greg. The australian aboriginal art investment Handbook. 2010. 374p. pap. 40.47 *(978-1-4457-7607-1(3))* Lulu Enterprises Inc.

Parker, Anne Z. Stories from the Origin. 2007. 186p. pap. 15.50 *(978-0-615-16538-7(9))* Parker, Anne Z.

Parker, Katie Langloh. The Euahlayi Tribe-A Study of Aboriginal Life in Australia. 2006. pap. *(978-1-84702-597-5(8))* Echo Library.

Paterson, Alistair. The Lost Legions: Culture Contact in Colonial Australia. 2008. (Indigenous Archaeologies Ser.). (ENG., Illus.). 288p. 90.00 *(978-0-7591-0683-3(5))*; per. 37.95 *(978-0-7591-0684-0(3))* AltaMira Pr.

Prentis, Malcolm & Prentis, Malcolm D. A Concise Companion to Aboriginal History. 2008. (Illus.). 264p. (C). 29.95 *(978-1-877058-62-2(9))* Rosenberg Publishing Pty, Ltd. AUS. Dist: International Specialized Bk. Services.

Pritchard, Sarah, ed. Indigenous Peoples, the United Nations & Human Rights. (Illus.). 256p. pap. *(978-1-86287-259-2(7))* Federation Pr. AUS. Dist: Gaunt, Inc.

Reinfjord, Kristine. Marginalisation of Australian Aborigines. 2009. 116p. pap. *(978-3-639-15035-3(X))* VDM Verlag Dr. Mueller e.K.

Ritter, David. Native Title Market. 2009. 90p. pap. 18.00 *(978-1-921401-16-9(8))* UWA Publishing AUS. Dist: International Specialized Bk. Services.

Robinson, Deborah. Daisy Bates: In Her Own Words. Peyton, Dianne, ed. 2007. 240p. per. 50.00 *(978-0-9709263-2-6(4))* Robinson Omnimedia Publishing & Studios.

Robinson, Gary, et al, eds. Contexts of Child Development: Culture, policy & Intervention. 2008. (Illus.). 290p. pap. *(978-0-9803846-8-0(5))* Darwin, Charles Univ. Pr.

Roe, Paddy. Gularabulu. 120p. 16.10 *(978-0-909144-65-4(6))* Fremantle Pr. AUS. Dist: Independent Pubs. Group.

Rolls, Mitchell & Johnson, Murray. Historical Dictionary of Australian Aborigines. 2011. E-Book *(978-0-8108-7475-6(X))* Scarecrow Pr., Inc.

Rolls, Mitchell, et al. Historical Dictionary of Australian Aborigines. 2010. (Historical Dictionaries of Peoples & Cultures Ser.). (ENG.). 244p. 75.00 *(978-0-8108-5997-5(1))* Scarecrow Pr., Inc.

Roth, Henry Ling, et al. Aborigines of Tasmania. 2009. (Cambridge Library Collection - Linguistics Ser.). (ENG.). 398p. pap. 31.99 *(978-1-108-00664-4(7))* Cambridge Univ. Pr.

Rowse, Tim. After Mabo: Interpreting Indigenous Traditions. 2011. 172p. 25.00 ***(978-1-59740-811-0(5))*** ACLS Humanities E-Book.

Ruppe-Senn, Sigrid. Aboriginal Autobiographical Writings. 2008. 92p. pap. *(978-3-639-05626-6(4))* VDM Verlag Dr. Mueller e.K.

Russell, Lynette. Roving Mariners: Australian Aboriginal Whalers & Sealers in the Southern Oceans, 1790-1870. 2012. (Tribal Worlds: Critical Studies in American Indian Nation Building Ser.). (ENG.). 256p. 80.00 ***(978-1-4384-4423-9(0))*** State Univ. of New York Pr.

Sarra, Chris. Strong & Smart - Towards a Pedagogy for Emancipation: Education for First Peoples. 2011. (New Studies in Critical Realism & Education Ser.). (ENG., Illus.). 224p. 130.00 *(978-0-415-61560-0(7))* Routledge.

Scheffler, Harold W. Australian Kin Classification. 2007. (Cambridge Studies in Social & Cultural Anthropology Ser.). (ENG.). 592p. pap. 105.00 *(978-0-521-04052-5(3))* Cambridge Univ. Pr.

Schmalegger, Doris. Aboriginal Tourism Development in Central Australia: How to reach the four-wheel-drive market. 2008. 160p. pap. *(978-3-639-10658-9(X))* VDM Verlag Dr. Mueller e.K.

Shellam, Tiffany. Shaking Hands on the Fringe: Negotiating the Aboriginal World at King George's Sound. 2009. 267p. pap. 27.95 *(978-1-921401-26-8(5))* UWA Publishing AUS. Dist: International Specialized Bk. Services.

Simon, Bill, et al. Back on the Block: Bill Simon's Story. 2009. (ENG., Illus.). 224p. pap. 31.95 *(978-0-85575-677-2(2))* Aboriginal Studies Pr. AUS. Dist: Independent Pubs. Group.

Smith, Keith Vincent. Mari Nawi: Aboriginal Odysseys. 2010. (Illus.). 216p. pap. 35.00 *(978-1-921719-00-4(1))* Rosenberg Publishing Pty, Ltd. AUS. Dist: International Specialized Bk. Services.

South West Aboriginal Land and Sea Council Staff, et al. It's Still in My Heart, This Is My Country: The Single Noongar Claim History. 2009. 327p. pap. 39.95 *(978-1-921401-42-8(7))* UWA Publishing AUS. Dist: International Specialized Bk. Services.

Spencer, Baldwin & Gillen, F. J. Native Tribes of Central Australia. 2010. (Cambridge Library Collection - Linguistics Ser.). (ENG., Illus.). 740p. pap. 48.00 *(978-1-108-02044-2(5))* Cambridge Univ. Pr.

Strelein, Lisa. Compromised Jurisprudence: Native Title Cases since Mabo. 2nd ed. 2010. (ENG.). 240p. pap. 40.95 *(978-0-85575-663-5(2))* Aboriginal Studies Pr. AUS. Dist: Independent Pubs. Group.

Summers, Ronnie & Gee, Helen. Ronnie: Tasmanian Songman. 2010. (ENG., Illus.). 164p. pap. 21.95 *(978-1-921248-10-8(6))* Magabala Bks. AUS. Dist: Independent Pubs. Group.

Tacey, David. Edge of the Sacred: Jung, Psyche, Earth. 2009. 207p. pap. 25.00 *(978-3-85630-729-5(X))* Daimon Verlag CHE. Dist: AtlasBooks Distribution.

Tatz, Colin. Aboriginal Suicide Is Different: A Portrait of Life & Self-Destruction. 2nd rev. ed. 2007. (ENG., Illus.). 212p. pap. 31.45 *(978-0-85575-498-3(2))* Aboriginal Studies Pr. AUS. Dist: Independent Pubs. Group.

Terszak, Mary. Orphaned by the Colour of my Skin: A survival story from the stolen Generation. 2007. (ENG., Illus.). 156p. por. *(978-1-921348-08-2(9)*, Verdant Hse.) eContent Management Pty Ltd.

Thomas, Northcote W. Kinship Organisations & Group Marriage in Australia, 163. reprint ed. 88.00 *(978-0-7222-1990-4(3))* Library Reprints, Inc.

Thomas, Northcote Whitridge. Kinship Organisations & Group Marriage in Australia. 2010. (Cambridge Library Collection - Travel & Exploration Ser.). (ENG., Illus.). 188p. pap. 19.99 *(978-1-108-01051-1(2))* Cambridge Univ. Pr.

Tonkinson, Myrna, et al. Mortality, Mourning & Mortuary Practices in Indigenous Australia. 2009. (Anthropology & Cultural History in Asia & the Indo-Pacific Ser.). (Illus.). 260p. 114.95 *(978-0-7546-7449-8(5))* Ashgate Publishing Co.

Tuckey, James Hingston. An Account of a Voyage to Establish a Colony at Port Philip in Bass's Strait, on the South Coast of New South Wales: In His Majesty's Ship Calcutta, in the Years 1802-3-4. 2011. (Cambridge Library Collection - History Ser.). (ENG.). 260p. pap. 23.99 ***(978-1-108-03903-1(0))*** Cambridge Univ. Pr.

Vanderwal, Ron, ed. John Bulmer's Recollections of Victorian Aboriginal Life, 1855-1980. 2006. (ENG., Illus.). 106p. (J). pap. 19.95 *(978-0-9577471-2-8(8))* Museum Victoria Publishing AUS. Dist: National Bk. Network.

Veth, Peter, et al, eds. Strangers on the Shore: Early Coastal Contact in Australia. 2008. (ENG.). 248p. pap. 29.95 *(978-1-876944-63-6(3))* National Museum of Australia AUS. Dist: Independent Pubs. Group.

Veth, Peter Marius. The Archaeology of Montebello Islands, North-West Australia: Late Quaternary Foragers on an Arid Coastline. 2007. (Bar S Ser.). (ENG., Illus.). 84p. (C). pap. 62.50 *(978-1-4073-0103-7(9))* British Archaeological Reports Ltd. GBR. Dist: Brown, David Bk. Co., The.

Webb, Stephen. Palaeopathology of Aboriginal Australians: Health & Disease across a Hunter-Gatherer Continent. 2009. (ENG., Illus.). 340p. pap. 42.00 *(978-0-521-11049-5(1))* Cambridge Univ. Pr.

Weir, Jessica K. Murray River Country: An Ecological Dialogue with Traditional Owners. 2009. (ENG., Illus.). 256p. pap. 31.95 *(978-0-85575-678-9(0))* Aboriginal Studies Pr. AUS. Dist: Independent Pubs. Group.

Westphalen, Linda. An Anthropological & Literary Study of Two Australian Aboriginal Women's Life Histories: The Impacts of Enforced Child Removal & Policies of Assimilation. 2012. 480p. 159.95 ***(978-0-7734-1593-5(9))*** Mellen, Edwin Pr., The.

Wiseman, Judith Proctor. Thomson Time: Arnhem Land in the 1930s: a Photographic Essay. 2006. (Illus.). 212p. 24.95 *(978-0-7306-2509-4(5))* Museum Victoria Publishing AUS. Dist: Antique Collectors' Club.

Wright, Alexis. Grog War: Shifting the Blame - One Town's Fight Against Alcohol. 2010. (ENG.). 224p. pap. 21.95 *(978-1-921248-12-2(2))* Magabala Bks. AUS. Dist: Independent Pubs. Group.

Young, Cynthia Y. Australian Aborigines. Date not set. (Illus.). 60p. pap. 59.50 *(978-0-582-87041-3(0))* Addison-Wesley Longman, Ltd. GBR. Dist: Trans-Atlantic Pubns., Inc.

ABORIGINAL AUSTRALIANS—GOVERNMENT RELATIONS

Attwood, Bain & Markus, Andrew. The 1967 Referendum: Race, Power & the Australian Constitution. 2nd ed. 2007. 196p. pap. 31.45 *(978-0-85575-555-3(5))* Aboriginal Studies Pr. AUS. Dist: Independent Pubs. Group.

Babidge, Sally. Aboriginal Family & the State: The Conditions of History. 2010. (Anthropology & Cultural History in Asia & the Indo-Pacific Ser.). (Illus.). 292p. 114.95 *(978-0-7546-7935-6(7))* Ashgate Publishing Co.

Banfield, E. J. Tropic Days. 2008. 264p. 25.99 *(978-0-554-31728-1(1))* 2008. 264p. 28.99 *(978-0-554-22425-1(9))* 2007. (ENG.). 250p. pap. 20.99 *(978-1-4264-2288-1(1))* 2007. (ENG.). 262p. pap. 23.99 *(978-1-4264-2323-9(3))* BiblioBazaar.

Basedow, H. Erotic Rituals of Australian Aboriginals. 2011. 46p. 35.95 ***(978-1-258-01504-6(8))*** Literary Licensing, LLC.

Basedow, H. & Roth, W. E. Venus Oceanic: The Sexual Life of South Sea Natives. Schidloff, B., ed. 2011. 412p. 54.95 ***(978-1-258-01502-2(1))*** Literary Licensing, LLC.

Bates, Daisy. The Passing of the Aborigines: A Lifetime Spent among the Natives of Australia. 2010. 228p. pap. 45.95 *(978-1-4092-2468-6(6))* Lulu Enterprises Inc.

Behrendt, Larissa, et al. Indigenous Legal Relations in Australia. 2009. (ENG., Illus.). 352p. pap. 115.00 *(978-0-19-556201-9(1))* Oxford Univ. Pr., Inc.

Coopes, Rhonda. Australian Aboriginal Marginalisation in Policy Making & Education. 2010. 256p. pap. *(978-3-8383-0148-8(X))* Lambert Academic Publishing.

Cornell, Stephen. JOPNA 2006-02 Indigenous Peoples, Poverty & Self-Determination in Australia, Canada & the United States. 2006. 5.00 *(978-1-931143-33-2(1))* Univ. of Arizona, Udall Ctr. for Studies in Public Policy.

Flanagan, Roderick J. The Aborigines of Australia. 2009. 178p. 37.95 *(978-1-104-54749-3(X))*; 180p. pap. 22.95 *(978-1-104-47641-0(X))* Kessinger Publishing, LLC.

Hendrix, Burke A. & Hendrix, Burke. Ownership, Authority, & Self-Determination: Moral Principles & Indigenous Rights Claim. 2008. (ENG.). 232p. (C). 55.00 *(978-0-271-03398-3(3))* Pennsylvania State Univ. Pr.

Lindqvist, Sven. Terra Nullius: A Journey Through No One's Land. Death, Sarah, tr. from SWE. 2007. Orig. Title: Terra Nullius: en Resa Genom Ingens Land. (ENG., Illus.). 248p. 24.95 *(978-1-59558-051-1(4))* New Pr., The.

McGregor, Russell. Imagined Destinies: Aboriginal Australians & the Doomed Race Theory, 1880-1939. 2011. 342p. 51.00 ***(978-1-59740-810-3(7))*** ACLS Humanities E-Book.

McIntyre-Mills, Janet J. User-Centric Policy Design to Address Complex Needs. McIntyre-Mills, Janet, ed. 2008. (Illus.). xix, 450p. 79.00 *(978-1-60456-683-3(3))* Nova Science Pubs., Inc.

Prentis, Malcolm. A Study in Black & White: The Aborigines in Australian History. 3rd rev. ed. 2009. (Illus.). 192p. pap. 29.95 *(978-1-877058-78-3(5))* Rosenberg Publishing Pty, Ltd. AUS. Dist: International Specialized Bk. Services.

Rowse, Tim & Goot, Murray. Divided Nation: Indigenous Australians in Australian Political Culture. 2007. (ENG., Illus.). 192p. per. 18.95 *(978-0-522-85342-1(0))* Melbourne Univ. Publishing AUS. Dist: Independent Pubs. Group.

Stephenson, Peta. The Outsiders Within: Telling Australia's Indigenous-Asian Story. 2007. (ENG., Illus.). 256p. per. 35.95 *(978-0-86840-836-1(0)*, UNSW Press) NewSouth Publishing AUS. Dist: Independent Pubs. Group.

Trigger, David Samuel. Whitefella Comin' Aboriginal Responses to Colonialism in Northern Australia. 2010. (ENG.). 276p. pap. 27.99 *(978-0-521-13178-0(2))* Cambridge Univ. Pr.

ABORIGINAL AUSTRALIANS—JUVENILE LITERATURE

Colson, Mary. Indigenous Australian Cultures. 2012. (Global Cultures Ser.). (ENG.). 48p. (gr. 4-6). pap. 8.99 ***(978-1-4329-6791-8(6)***, NA-h) Heinemann-Raintree.

ABORIGINAL AUSTRALIANS—LANGUAGES

see also Australian Languages

Baker, Brett J. Word Structure in Ngalakgan. 2008. (Illus.). 332p. pap. 45.00 *(978-1-57586-562-1(9))* CSLI Pubns.

Dawson, James. Australian Aborigines: The Languages & Customs of Several Tribes of Aborigines in the Western District of Victoria, Australia. 2007. (Illus.). 232p. per. 26.95 *(978-0-548-31827-0(1))* Kessinger Publishing, LLC.

Dixon, R. M. W. Searching for Aboriginal Languages: Memoirs of a Field Worker. 2011. (Cambridge Library Collection - Linguistics Ser.). (ENG.). 350p. pap. 28.99 *(978-1-108-02504-1(8))* Cambridge Univ. Pr.

Icon Group International, Inc. Staff, compiled by. Webster's Awabakal - English Thesaurus Dictionary. 2008. 100p. ring bd. 28.95 incl. audio compact disk *(978-0-497-83429-6(4))* Icon Group International, Inc.

—Webster's Ayapathu - English Thesaurus Dictionary. 2008. 33p. ring bd. 28.95 incl. audio compact disk *(978-0-497-83430-2(8))* Icon Group International, Inc.

—Webster's Kamilaroi - English Thesaurus Dictionary. 2008. 73p. ring bd. 28.95 incl. audio compact disk *(978-0-497-83539-2(8))* Icon Group International, Inc.

—Webster's Kauma - English Thesaurus Dictionary. 2008. 100p. ring bd. 28.95 incl. audio compact disk *(978-0-497-83542-2(8))* Icon Group International, Inc.

—Webster's Pitta Pitta - English Thesaurus Dictionary. 2008. 94p. ring bd. 28.95 incl. audio compact disk *(978-0-497-83669-6(6))* Icon Group International, Inc.

Moore, Bruce, et al. Australian Aboriginal Words in English: Their Origin & Meaning. 2nd rev. ed. 2006. (ENG., Illus.). 276p. (Orig.). pap. 45.00 *(978-0-19-554073-4(5))* Oxford Univ. Pr., Inc.

Tsunoda, Tasaku. A Grammar of Warrongo. (Mouton Grammar Library [MGL] Ser.: 53). (ENG., Illus.). 2012. (gr. 17-17). E-Book 321.00 ***(978-3-11-026182-0(0))*** 2011. XXX, 751p. 210.00 ***(978-3-11-023876-1(4))*** De Gruyter, Mouton DEU. Dist: de Gruyter, Walter GmbH & Co. KG.

ABORIGINAL PEOPLES' FIRST CONTACT WITH OCCIDENTAL CIVILIZATION

see First Contact of Aboriginal Peoples with Westerners

ABORIGINES

see Indigenous Peoples

ABORIGINES, AMERICAN

see Indians

ABORIGINES, AUSTRALIAN

see Aboriginal Australians

ABORTION

Abortion. 2010. (Information Plus Reference Ser.). (ENG.). 160p. 58.00 *(978-1-4144-4112-2(6))* Cengage Gale.

Baumgardner, Jennifer. Abortion & Life. 2008. (ENG.). 250p. pap. 16.95 *(978-1-933354-59-0(3))* Akashic Bks.

Bishop, Susan. Taboo Work: Caring for Women Having Pregnancy Terminations. 2010. 132p. pap. *(978-3-639-22510-5(4))* VDM Verlag Dr. Mueller e.K.

Brooks, Christie. Our Heartbreaking Choices. 2008. 420p. pap. 26.95 *(978-0-595-53047-2(8))* iUniverse, Inc.

Clyne, Elizabeth. Abortion: the Truth about the Lie; One woman's Choice. 2008. 103p. pap. 17.95 *(978-0-557-00335-8(0))* Lulu Enterprises Inc.

Collective, Sage-Femme. Natural Liberty: Rediscovering Self-Induced Abortion Methods. 2008. (Illus.). x, 454p. *(978-0-9645920-0-1(2))* Sage-femme.

Coope, Christopher Miles & Coope, Christopher. Worth & Welfare in the Controversy over Abortion. 2006. (ENG.). 360p. 106.00 *(978-0-333-76018-5(2))* Palgrave Macmillan.

Cram101 Textbook Reviews & Cram101 Textbook Reviews. Outlines & Highlights for Management of Unintended & Abnormal Pregnancy: Comprehensive Abortion Care by Maureen Paul, ISBN. 2011. 78p. pap. 27.95 ***(978-1-61744-991-8(1))*** Cram101 Inc.

Devereux, George. A Study of Abortion in Primitive Societies. 2011. 406p. 54.95 (978-1-258-01802-3(0)) Literary Licensing, LLC.

Faundes, Anibal & Barzelatto, Jose S. The Human Drama of Abortion: A Global Search for Consensus. 2006. (Illus.). 216p. (ENG.). 59.95 (978 0 8265 1525 4(8)); (POR, SPA & ENG.). per. 24.95 (978-0-8265-1526-1(6)) Vanderbilt Univ. Pr.

Flavius, Susanna Magdalene. The World will Fight to stop Abortion until it sees Abortion. 2010. 75p. pap. 12.50 (978-1-4452-3682-7(6)) Lulu Enterprises Inc.

Fredenburg, Michaelene, et al, contrib. by. Grief & Abortion: Creating A Safe Place to Heal. 2011. 160p. pap. 12.95 (978-0-9800633-1-8(0)) Perspectives.

Goldberg, Michelle. The Means of Reproduction: Sex, Power, & the Future of the World. 2010. (ENG.). 272p. (gr. 12-18). 16.00 (978-0-14-311688-2(6), Penguin (Non-Classics)) Penguin Group (USA) Inc.

Goretzlehner, Gunther & Romer, Thomas. Langzyklus und Langzeiteinnahme mit OC. 2010. (FrauenÄrztliche Taschenbacher Ser.). (GER., Illus.). XI, 141p. pap. 49.00 (978-3-11-022102-2(0)) De Gruyter, Walter Inc.

Hagen, Lisa Hall. Examining the Use of Safety, Confrontation, & Ambivalence in Six Depictions of Reproductive Women on the American Stage, 1997-2007: Staging 'the Place' of Abortion. 2010. 424p. 129.95 (978-0-7734-1466-2(5)) Mellen, Edwin Pr., The.

Hale, E. M. (Edwin Moses). A Systematic Treatise on Abortion: By Edwin M. Hale, M. D. 2006. 356p. per. 26.99 (978-1-4255-3682-4(4)) MPublishing.

Hall, David. Taking Sides: Clashing Views in Family & Personal Relationships. 9th ed. 2012. (Taking Sides Ser.). (ENG.). 416p. (C). pap. 48.00 (978-0-07-805038-1(3), 0078050383, McGraw-Hill/Dushkin) McGraw-Hill Higher Education.

Haugen, David M. Abortion. 2010. (Opposing Viewpoints Ser.). (Illus.). 240p. (J). 38.50 (978-0-7377-4747-8(1)); pap. 26.75 (978-0-7377-4748-5(X)) Cengage Gale. (Greenhaven Pr., Inc.).

Johnsen, Jennifer. Choosing Abortion. 2007. pap. (978-1-930996-93-9(4)) Planned Parenthood Federation of America, Inc.

Kaiser, László. Midtrimester Foetal Loss - Pathological Correlations. 2011. 64p. pap. (978-3-8433-9366-9(4)) Lambert Academic Publishing.

Knowles, Jon. Abortion Procedures: Questions & Answers. 2007. (978-1-930996-96-0(9)) Planned Parenthood Federation of America, Inc.

Lee, Rosalind J. Brantley Goes Home. 2010. 40p. pap. 8.50 (978-1-4457-7951-5(X)) Lulu Enterprises Inc.

MacKay, Jennifer. Teen Pregnancy. 2011. (Hot Topics Ser.). 128p. lib. bdg. 33.45 (978-1-4205-0479-8(7), Lucent Bks.) Cengage Gale.

Macleod, Catriona I. Adolescence Pregnancy & Abortion: Constructing a Threat of Degeneration. 2010. (Women & Psychology Ser.). (ENG., Illus.). 184p. 80.00 (978-0-415-55339-1(3), Routledge) Taylor & Francis Group GBR. Dist: Taylor & Francis Group.

Macleod, Catriona Ida. Adolescence, Pregnancy & Abortion: Constructing a Threat of Degeneration. 2010. (Women & Psychology Ser.). (ENG., Illus.). 184p. pap. 27.50 (978-0-415-55338-4(5), Routledge) Taylor & Francis Group GBR. Dist: Taylor & Francis Group.

Miguel, Mark San. Wannababies: Birth Pangs. 2011. 148p. pap. 14.95 (978-1-4502-7648-1(2)) iUniverse, Inc.

Moore, Shirley. This Change Is Crucial: We Change or Suffer Loss, 1 vol. 2009. 91p. pap. 16.95 (978-1-60836-565-4(4)) PublishAmerica, Inc.

Moulding, Karen. Abortion, New Editon. 2nd rev. ed. 2011. (Library in a Bk Ser.). 45.00 (978-0-8160-8177-6(8)) Facts On File, Inc.

Mullins, Jackie. Convergence in the Midst of Divergence. 2009. 84p. pap. (978-3-639-12993-9(8)) VDM Verlag Dr. Mueller e.K.

Pan, Yi, et al. Young Women with Unplanned Pregnancies in Bangkok, Thailand: Wireless Sensor Networks Security. 2008. (Illus.). viii, 101p. pap. 50.00 (978-1-60456-458-7(X)) Nova Science Pubs., Inc.

Paul, Maureen, et al, eds. Management of Unintended & Abnormal Pregnancy: Comprehensive Abortion Care. 2009. (ENG., Illus.). 392p. 157.95 (978-1-4051-7696-5(2), Wiley-Blackwell) Wiley, John & Sons, Inc.

Perrucci, Alissa C. Decision Assessment & Counseling in Abortion Care: Philosophy & Practice. 2012. (ENG.). 208p. (gr. 17). 59.95 (978-1-4422-1456-9(2)) Rowman & Littlefield Publishers, Inc.

Reed, John M. Crusading Against Athens. 2011. 166p. 29.99 (978-1-4653-3639-2(7)) Xlibris Corp.

Regushevskaya, Elena. Abortions & sexually transmitted infections among women in St. Petersburg in the Early 2000's: Comparison by population - based surveys in Estonia & Finland. 2009. (Acta Universitatis Tamperensis Ser.). 70p. pap. 82.50 (978-951-44-7825-3(8)) Tampere Univ. Pr. FIN. Dist: Coronet Bks.

Reid, Katie. When the Bough Breaks. 2010. 245p. pap. 22.94 (978-0-557-20517-2(4)) Lulu Enterprises Inc.

Rubiano, Mauricio. Aborto U Homicidio? (SPA.). 64p. 2.95 (978-958-607-791-0(8)) Sociedad de San Pablo ESP. Dist: St Pauls/Alba Hse. Pubs.

Schwarz, Stephen D. Understanding Abortion: From Mixed Feelings to Rational Thought. 2011. (ENG.). 228p. 70.00 (978-0-7391-6770-0(7)); pap. 29.95 (978-0-7391-6771-7(5)) Lexington Bks.

Solinger, Rickie. Pregnancy & Power: A Short History of Reproductive Politics in America. 2007. (ENG., Illus.). 312p. pap. 23.00 (978-0-8147-9828-7(4)) New York Univ. Pr.

Soske, Becky. I Am Not Ashamed. 2008. 80p. pap. 16.95 (978-1-60610-091-2(2)) PublishAmerica, Inc.

Storer, Horatio Robinson & Heard, Franklin Fiske. Criminal Abortion: Its Nature, Its Evidence, & Its Law. 2007. 223p. 35.00 (978-1-58477-767-0(2)) Lawbook Exchange, Ltd., The.

Stormer, John. Betrayed by the Bench: Betrayed by the Bench: How Judge-made Law Has Transformed America's Constitution, Courts & Culture. 2007. 192p. pap. 14.50 (978-0-914053-18-7(3)) Liberty Bell Pr.

Tunc, Tanfer. Technologies of Choice - a History of Abortion Techniques in the United States, 1850 - 1980. 2008. 188p. pap. (978-3-639-06002-7(4)) VDM Verlag Dr. Mueller e.K.

Vilar, Irene. Impossible Motherhood: Testimony of an Abortion Addict. 2009. (ENG.). 240p. pap. 15.95 (978-1-59051-320-0(7)) Other Pr., LLC.

World Health Organization. Frequently Asked Clinical Questions about Medical Abortion: Conclusions of an International Consensus Conference on Medical Abortion in Early First Trimester, Bellagio, Italy. 2006. (Nonserial Publication). (ENG.). 35p. pap. 12.00 (978-92-4-159484-4(5)) World Health Organization.

Zimmerman, William D. Dearest Angel ... A Father's Post-Abortion Journal of Hurt & Healing. 2010. (ENG.). 200p. pap. 16.95 (978-1-4502-3140-4(3)) iUniverse, Inc.

—Dearest Angel... A Father's Post-Abortion Journal of Hurt & Healing. 2010. 200p. 26.95 (978-1-4502-3142-8(X)) iUniverse, Inc.

ABORTION—BIOGRAPHY

Harper, Sheila. Survivor: A Journey Through Abortion & Back. 2009. (ENG.). pap. 9.95 (978-1-60037-540-8(5)) Morgan James Publishing.

ABORTION—GOVERNMENT POLICY

Hendershott, Anne. The Politics of Abortion. 2006. (ENG.). 190p. 25.95 (978-1-59403-148-9(7)) Encounter Bks.

Levine, Phillip B. Sex & Consequences: Abortion, Public Policy, & the Economics of Fertility. 2007. (ENG., Illus.). 240p. (C). per. 23.95 (978-0-691-13045-3(0)) Princeton Univ. Pr.

Visaria, Leela & Ramachandran, Vimala, eds. Abortion in India: Ground Realities. 2007. (Illus.). 352p. 110.00 (978-0-415-42412-7(7)) Routledge.

Whittaker, Andrea, ed. Abortion in Asia: Local Dilemmas, Global Politics. 2010. (FRS Ser.). (Illus.). 270p. 90.00 (978-1-84545-734-1(X)) Berghahn Bks., Inc.

ABORTION—GOVERNMENT POLICY—UNITED STATES

Ainsworth, Scott H. & Hall, Thad E. Abortion Politics in Congress: Strategic Incrementalism & Policy Change. 2010. (ENG., Illus.). 240p. 80.00 (978-0-521-51581-8(5)); pap. 24.99 (978-0-521-74004-3(5)) Cambridge Univ. Pr.

Caron, Simone M. Who Chooses? American Reproductive History Since 1830. (ENG.). 2010. 384p. pap. 29.95 (978-0-8130-3504-8(X)) 2008. (Illus.). 416p. 69.95 (978-0-8130-3199-6(0)) Univ. Pr. of Florida.

The Mexico City Policy/Global Gag Rule: Its Impact on Family Planning & Reproductive Health: Hearing Before the Committee on Foreign Affairs, House of Representatives, One Hundred Tenth Congress, First Session, October 31, 2007. 2008. (Illus.). iii, 132p. (978-0-16-080141-9(9), 552-070-36881-7) United States Government Printing Office.

O'Brien, George Dennis. The Church & Abortion: A Catholic Dissent. 2010. (ENG.). 192p. 34.95 (978-1-4422-0577-2(6)) Rowman & Littlefield Publishers, Inc.

ABORTION—LAW AND LEGISLATION

A.M. McLean, Sheila & Elliston, Sarah, eds. Regulating Pre-Implantation Genetic Diagnosis: A Comparative & Theoretical Analysis. 2012. (Biomedical Law & Ethics Library). (ENG.). 280p. (C). 135.00 (978-0-415-68644-0(X)) Routledge.

Carlson, Carolyn S. Who Is Confused on Abortion? 2008. 124p. pap. (978-3-8364-3863-6(1)) VDM Verlag Dr. Mueller e.K.

Ehrenreich, Nancy, ed. The Reproductive Rights Reader: Law, Medicine, & the Construction of Motherhood. 2008. (ENG.). 448p. 85.00 (978-0-8147-2230-5(X)) New York Univ. Pr.

Haigh, Gideon. The Racket: How Abortion Became Legal in Australia. 2009. (ENG.). 288p. pap. 22.95 (978-0-522-85578-4(4)) Melbourne Univ. Publishing AUS. Dist: Independent Pubs. Group.

Hanafin, Patrick. Conceiving Life: Reproductive Politics & the Law in Contemporary Italy. 2007. (Law, Justice & Power Ser.). 124p. 114.95 (978-0-7546-4635-8(1)) Ashgate Publishing Co.

Jacob, Krista, ed. Abortion under Attack: Women on the Challenges Facing Choice. 2006. (ENG.). 250p. per. 15.95 (978-1-58005-185-9(5)) Seal Pr.

Joseph, Rita. Human Rights & the Unborn Child. 2009. 367p. (978-90-04-17560-0(1)) BRILL.

Kaczor, Christopher. The Ethics of Abortion: Women's Rights, Human Life, & the Question of Justice. 2010. (Routledge Annals of Bioethics Ser.). (ENG.). 256p. 115.00 (978-0-415-88468-6(3)); pap. 39.95 (978-0-415-88469-3(1)) Routledge.

Kato, Masae. Women's Rights? The Handicapped Foetus & Abortion in Japan. 2009. (IIAS Publications Ser.). 245p. pap. (978-90-5356-793-7(3), Leiden Univ. Pr.) Amsterdam Univ. Pr.

Levine, Phillip B. Sex & Consequences: Abortion, Public Policy, & the Economics of Fertility. 2007. (ENG., Illus.). 240p. (C). per. 23.95 (978-0-691-13045-3(0)) Princeton Univ. Pr.

Mason, J.K. The Troubled Pregnancy: Legal Wrongs & Rights in Reproduction. 2007. (Cambridge Law, Medicine & Ethics Ser.). (ENG.). 346p. 149.00 (978-0-521-85075-9(4)); per. 60.00 (978-0-521-61624-9(7)) Cambridge Univ. Pr.

Merino, No'l, ed. Abortion. 2012. (Introducing Issues with Opposing Viewpoints Ser.). (ENG., Illus.). 144p. (gr. 7-10). lib. bdg. 36.80 (978-0-7377-5670-8(5), Greenhaven Pr., Inc.) Cengage Gale.

Opara, Victor. Abortion Dilemmas. 2010. 68p. pap. (978-3-639-23867-9(2)) VDM Verlag Dr. Mueller e.K.

Schweppe, Jennifer, ed. The Unborn Child, Article 40. 3. 3 & Abortion in Ireland: Twenty-Five Years of Protection. 2009. (ENG.). 424p. pap. 69.95 (978-1-905785-51-3(8)) Liffey Pr., The IRL. Dist: Dufour Editions, Inc.

Scott, Charles C. Bridging the Abortion Divide. 2008. 224p. per. 10.95 (978-1-4327-0888-7(0)) Outskirts Pr., Inc.

Shroyer, Stephen John. Abortion: the Legal, Medical, & Bioethical Perspectives. 2010. 59p. pap. 27.81 (978-0-557-58276-1(8)) Lulu Enterprises Inc.

Steinbock, Bonnie. Life Before Birth: The Moral & Legal Status of Embryos & Fetuses. 2nd ed. 2011. (ENG.). 328p. (C). pap. 39.95 (978-0-19-534162-1(7)) Oxford Univ. Pr., Inc.

ABORTION—LAW AND LEGISLATION—CANADA

Fainman, Jack & Penner, Roland. They Shoot Doctors Don't They: A Memoir. 2011. (ENG.). 176p. pap. 24.95 (978-1-926531-17-5(5)) Great Plains Pubns. CAN. Dist: Univ. of Toronto Pr.

Halfmann, Drew. Doctors & Demonstrators: How Political Institutions Shape Abortion Law in the United States, Britain, & Canada. 2011. (ENG., Illus.). 336p. 105.00 (978-0-226-31342-9(5)); pap. 35.00 (978-0-226-31343-6(3)) Univ. of Chicago Pr.

ABORTION—LAW AND LEGISLATION—GREAT BRITAIN

Halfmann, Drew. Doctors & Demonstrators: How Political Institutions Shape Abortion Law in the United States, Britain, & Canada. 2011. (ENG., Illus.). 336p. 105.00 (978-0-226-31342-9(5)); 105.00 (978-0-226-31342-9(5)); pap. 35.00 (978-0-226-31343-6(3)) Univ. of Chicago Pr.

ABORTION—LAW AND LEGISLATION—UNITED STATES

Ainsworth, Scott H. & Hall, Thad E. Abortion Politics in Congress: Strategic Incrementalism & Policy Change. 2010. (ENG., Illus.). 240p. 80.00 (978-0-521-51581-8(5)); pap. 24.99 (978-0-521-74004-3(5)) Cambridge Univ. Pr.

Balkin, Jack M., ed. What Roe V. Wade Should Have Said: The Nation's Top Legal Experts Rewrite America's Most Controversial Decision. 2007. (ENG., Illus.). 304p. pap. 23.00 (978-0-8147-9986-4(8)) New York Univ. Pr.

Bose, Feler. Evolutionary Impulses in Law. 2008. 148p. pap. (978-3-639-09063-5(2)) VDM Verlag Dr. Mueller e.K.

The Consequences of Roe V. Wade & Doe V. Bolton: Hearing Before the Subcommittee on the Constitution, Civil Rights, & Property Rights of the Committee on the Judiciary, United States Senate, One Hundred Ninth Congress, First Session, June 23, 2005. 2009. iii, 165p. (978-0-16-082944-4(5), 552-070-38856-7) United States Government Printing Office.

Dworkin, Ronald. The Supreme Court Phalanx: The Court's New Right-Wing Bloc. 2008. (ENG.). 96p. pap. 12.95 (978-1-59017-293-3(0)) New York Review of Bks., Inc., The.

Ehrenreich, Nancy, ed. The Reproductive Rights Reader: Law, Medicine, & the Construction of Motherhood. 2008. (ENG.). 448p. per. 28.00 (978-0-8147-2231-2(8)) New York Univ. Pr.

Ekland-Olson, Sheldon & Aseltine, Elyshia. How Ethical Systems Change: Abortion & Neonatal Care. 2011. (Framing 21st Century Social Issues Ser.). (ENG.). 88p. pap. 9.95 (978-0-415-50449-2(X)) Routledge.

Freedman, Lori R. Willing & Unable: Doctors' Constraints in Abortion Care. 2010. (ENG.). 200p. pap. 24.95 (978-0-8265-1715-9(3)); lib. bdg. 59.95 (978-0-8265-1714-2(5)) Vanderbilt Univ. Pr.

Hillstrom, Laurie Collier. Roe v. Wade. 2008. (Defining Moments Ser.). (Illus.). 260p. 49.00 (978-0-7808-1026-6(0)) Omnigraphics, Inc.

Hoffer, Peter & Hull, Neh. Roe V Wade. 2nd ed. 2010. 384p. 39.95 (978-0-7006-1753-1(1)) Univ. of Kansas Pubns.

Hull, Neh & Hoffer, Peter. Roe V Wade. 2nd ed. 2010. 384p. pap. 19.95 (978-0-7006-1754-8(X)) Univ. of Kansas Pubns.

Johnson, Donald William. Black but Not My Brother: Why I cannot vote for Barack Huessin Obama. 2008. 96p. pap. 15.00 (978-1-4389-2878-4(5)) AuthorHouse.

Judges, Donald P. Hard Choices, Lost Voices: How the Abortion Conflict Has Divided America, Distorted Constitutional Rights, & Damaged the Courts. 2007. (ENG., Illus.). 352p. per. 19.95 (978-1-56663-680-3(9)) Dee, Ivan R. Pub.

Klimek, Daniel P. Secrets of the High Court: On Political Culture, U. S. Constitutionalism, & the Foundations of the Abortion Industry. 2007. 224p. per. 12.95 (978-1-4327-1425-3(2)) Outskirts Pr., Inc.

Landmark Abortion Cases: Planned Parenthood vs. Casey. 1400p. 195.00 (978-0-89093-819-5(9)) ProQuest LLC.

Linton, Paul Benjamin. Abortion under State Constitutions: A State-by-State Analysis. 2nd ed. 2012. 730p. 85.00 (978-1-61163-069-5(X)) Carolina Academic Pr.

—Abortion under State Constitutions: A State-by-State Analysis. 2008. 75.00 (978-1-59460-604-5(8)) Custom Academic Publishing Co. (CAPCO).

McBride, Dorothy E. Abortion in the United States: A Reference Handbook, 1 vol. 2007. (Contemporary World Issues Ser.). 303p. 55.00 (978-1-59884-098-8(3), ABORT1C) ABC-CLIO, LLC.

Merino, Noël. Birth Control. 2010. (Issues on Trial Ser.). (ENG.). 240p. 39.70 (978-0-7377-4947-2(4), Greenhaven Pr., Inc.) Cengage Gale.

No Taxpayer Funding for Abortion ACT: Hearing Before the Subcommittee on the Constitution of the Committee on the Judiciary, House of Representatives, One Hundred Twelfth Congress, First Session, on H.R. 3, February 8, 2011. 2011. iv, 154p. (978-0-16-088623-2(6), 552-070-42792-9) United States Government Printing Office.

Nolan, Kevin G., ed. Abortion: Legislative & Legal Issues. 2010. (Laws & Legislation Ser.). 69.00 (978-1-60741-522-0(4)) Nova Science Pubs., Inc.

Perry, Michael J. Constitutional Rights, Moral Controversy, & the Supreme Court. 2008. (ENG.). 264p. 79.00 (978-0-521-75595-5(6)) Cambridge Univ. Pr.

Rafferty, Philip A. What's Really Going on with Pro-Roe V. Wade Catholic Politicians. 2011. pap. 17.99 (978-1-61663-693-7(9)) Tate Publishing & Enterprises, LLC.

Scope & Myths of Roe V. Wade: Hearing Before the Subcommittee on the Constitution of the Committee on the Judiciary, House of Representatives, One Hundred Ninth Congress, Second Session, March 2, 2006, 2 vols. 2007. (978-1-57588-945-0(5)) Hein, William S. & Co., Inc.

Shapiro, I. Abortion: The Supreme Court Decisions, 1965-2007. 3rd rev. ed. 2008. 296p. (C). lib. bdg. 39.95 (978-0-87220-904-6(0)) Hackett Publishing Co., Inc.

Shapiro, I., ed. Abortion: The Supreme Court Decisions, 1965-2007. 3rd rev. ed. 2008. 296p. (C). pap. 14.95 (978-0-87220-903-9(2)) Hackett Publishing Co., Inc.

Silverstein, Helena. Girls on the Stand: How Courts Fail Pregnant Minors. 2009. (ENG.). 256p. pap. 23.00 (978-0-8147-4073-6(1)) New York Univ. Pr.

ABORTION—MORAL AND ETHICAL ASPECTS

see also Pro-Choice Movement; Pro-Life Movement

Anderson, Carl. Beyond a House Divided: The Moral Consensus Ignored by Washington, Wall Street, & the Media. 2010. (ENG.). 160p. pap. 12.00 (978-0-307-88774-0(X), Image) Doubleday Religious Publishing Group, The.

Bailey, Jacqui. Abortion. 2011. (Ethical Debates Ser.). (ENG.). 48p. (YA). (gr. 5-8). pap. 11.75 (978-1-4488-7005-9(4)); (Illus.). 27.95 (978-1-4488-6017-3(2)) Rosen Publishing Group, Inc., The. (Rosen Central).

Beckwith, Francis J. Defending Life: A Moral & Legal Case Against Abortion Choice. 2007. (ENG.). 312p. 89.00 (978-0-521-87084-9(4)); (Illus.). (C). per. 25.00 (978-0-521-69135-2(4)) Cambridge Univ. Pr.

Berne, Emma Carlson, ed. Abortion. 2007. (Introducing Issues with Opposing Viewpoints Ser.). (ENG., Illus.). 120p. (YA). (gr. 7-12). pap. 34.70 (978-0-7377-3563-5(5)) Cengage Gale.

Bindig, Todd S. Identity, Potential & Design - How They Impact the Debate over the Morality of Abortion. 2008. 180p. pap. (978-3-8364-5331-8(2)) VDM Verlag Dr. Mueller e.K.

Chew, Cheryl. Make Me Your Choice: Compelling Personal Stories of Struggle & Healing from Those Who Have Had or Dealt with Abortion. 2006. 197p. per. 15.99 (978 0 7684-2372-3(4)) Destiny Image Pubs.

Dennehy, Raymond. Anti-Abortionist at Large: How to Argue Abortion Intelligently & Live. 2007. (ENG.). 212p. 29.95 (978-1-4251-6706-6(3)) Trafford Publishing.

Di Mauro, Dennis. A Love for Life: Christianity's Consistent Protection of the Unborn. 2008. 178p. pap. 20.00 (978-1-55635-828-9(8), Wipf and Stock) Wipf & Stock Pubs.

Ekland-Olson, Sheldon & Aseltine, Elyshia. How Ethical Systems Change: Abortion & Neonatal Care. 2011. (Framing 21st Century Social Issues Ser.). (ENG.). 88p. pap. 9.95 (978-0-415-50449-2(X)) Routledge.

Farrell, Courtney. The Abortion Debate. 2008. (Essential Viewpoints Set 2 Ser.). (Illus.). 112p. (YA). (gr. 7-12). 34.22 (978-1-60453-053-7(7)) ABDO Publishing Co.

Garcia, Lisa. The Least of These: Calling on America's Youth to Defend the Unborn. 2010. pap. 12.99 (978-1-61663-399-8(9)) Tate Publishing & Enterprises, LLC.

Hillstrom, Laurie Collier. Roe v. Wade. 2008. (Defining Moments Ser.). (Illus.). 260p. 49.00 (978-0-7808-1026-6(0)) Omnigraphics, Inc.

Hunter, James Davidson. Before the Shooting Begins. 2007. (ENG.). 272p. pap. 21.95 (978-1-4165-7324-1(0), Free Pr.) Free Pr.

Judges, Donald P. Hard Choices, Lost Voices: How the Abortion Conflict Has Divided America, Distorted Constitutional Rights, & Damaged the Courts. 2007. (ENG., Illus.). 352p. per. 19.95 (978-1-56663-680-3(9)) Dee, Ivan R. Pub.

Kaczor, Christopher. The Ethics of Abortion: Women's Rights, Human Life, & the Question of Justice. 2010. (Routledge Annals of Bioethics Ser.). (ENG.). 256p. 115.00 (978-0-415-88468-6(3)); pap. 39.95 (978-0-415-88469-3(1)) Routledge.

Lee, Patrick. Abortion & Unborn Human Life, Second Edition. 2nd ed. 2010. (C). pap. 24.95 (978-0-8132-1730-7(X)) Catholic Univ. of America Pr.

MacNair. Achieving Peace in the Abortion War. 2008. 180p. pap. 16.95 (978-1-4401-1325-3(4)) iUniverse, Inc.

Martinelli-Fernandez, Susan A., et al. Interdisciplinary Views on Abortion: Essays from Philosophical, Sociological, Anthropological, Political, Health & Other Perspectives. Martinelli-Fernandez, Susan A. et al, eds. 2009. (ENG., Illus.). 223p. pap. 39.95 (978-0-7864-3494-7(5)) McFarland & Co., Inc. Pubs.

McGeoch, Ms. Mary & Rivka Witenberg. The Influence of Age, Gender & Context on Moral Reasoning. 2011. 172p. pap. (978-3-8383-9183-0(7)) Lambert Academic Publishing.

McMahan, Jeff. The Ethics of Killing: Self-Defense, War, & Punishment. 2010. 544p. 49.95 (978-0-19-518721-2(0)) Oxford Univ. Pr., Inc.

Meyers, Chris. The Fetal Position: A Rational Approach to the Abortion Issue. 2010. 260p. pap. 19.00 (978-1-59102-768-3(3)) Prometheus Bks., Pubs.

Napier, Stephen, ed. Persons, Moral Worth, & Embryos: A Critical Analysis of Pro-Choice Arguments. 2011. (Philosophy & Medicine / Catholic Studies in Bioethics Ser.). (Illus.). xiv, 283p. 139.00 (978-94-007-1601-8(X), 940071601X) Springer.

O'Brien, George Dennis. The Church & Abortion: A Catholic Dissent. 2010. (ENG.). 192p. 34.95 (978-1-4422-0577-2(6)) Rowman & Littlefield Publishers, Inc.

Oehlschlaeger, Fritz. Procreative Ethics. 2009. 380p. pap. 42.00 *(978-1-60608-230-0(2)*, Cascade Bks.) Wipf & Stock Pubs.

Page, Christina. How the Pro-Choice Movement Saved America: Freedom, Politics, & the War on Sex. 2006. (ENG.). 256p. per. 15.00 *(970-0-465-05400-0(0))* Basic Bks.

Paris, Ginette. The Psychology of Abortion. 2nd ed. 2007. (ENG.). 72p. pap. 18.00 *(978-0-88214-560-0(6))* Spring Pubns., Inc.

Renshaw, Jessica Shaver. Gianna: Aborted ... & Lived to Tell about It. 2010. (ENG.). 272p. pap. 12.99 *(978-1-58997-600-9(2))* Tyndale Hse. Pubs.

Renshaw, Jessica Shaver & Jessen, Gianna. Gianna: Aborted, & Lived to Tell about It. rev. ed. 2011. (ENG.). 224p. pap. 14.99 *(978-1-58997-639-9(8))* Tyndale Hse. Pubs.

Richardson, C. G. No One to Hear Their Cries. 2008. 230p. pap. 19.95 *(978-1-4357-4050-1(5))* Lulu Enterprises Inc.

Roberts, Melinda A. Abortion & the Moral Significance of Mere Possible Persons: Finding Middle Ground in Hard Cases. 2010. (Philosophy & Medicine Ser.). (ENG., Illus.). x, 225p. 159.00 *(978-90-481-3791-6(8)*, 9048137918) Springer.

Satris, Stephen. Taking Sides: Clashing Views on Moral Issues. 13th ed. 2011. (Taking Sides Ser.). (ENG.). 352p. (C). pap. 48.00 *(978-0-07-805009-1(X)*, 007805009X, McGraw-Hill/Dushkin) McGraw-Hill Higher Education.

Satris, Stephen. Taking Sides: Clashing Views on Moral Issues, Expanded. 13th ed. 2012. (Taking Sides Ser.). (ENG.). 400p. (C). pap. 48.00 ***(978-0-07-805013-8(8)***, 0078050138, McGraw-Hill/Dushkin) McGraw-Hill Higher Education.

Schwarz, Stephen D. & Latimer, Kiki. Understanding Abortion: From Mixed Feelings to Rational Thought. 2012. ***(978-0-7391-6772-4(3))*** Lexington Bks.

Singular, Stephen. The Wichita Divide: The Murder of Dr. George Tiller, the Battle over Abortion, & the New American Civil War. 2011. (ENG., Illus.). 368p. 26.99 *(978-0-312-62505-4(7))* St. Martin's Pr.

Sproul, R. C. Abortion: A Rational Look at an Emotional Issue. 20th ed. 2010. xxii, 225p. (Orig.). *(978-1-56769-209-9(5))* Reformation Pubs.

Steinbock, Bonnie. Life Before Birth: The Moral & Legal Status of Embryos & Fetuses. 2nd ed. 2011. (ENG.). 328p. (C). pap. 39.95 ***(978-0-19-534162-1(7))*** Oxford Univ. Pr., Inc.

Tooley, Michael, et al. Abortion: Three Perspectives. 2009. (Point/Counterpoint Ser.). (ENG.). 272p. (C). 54.95 *(978-0-19-538027-9(4))* Oxford Univ. Pr., Inc.

Weber, Linda. Life Choices: The Teachings of Abortion. 2011. (ENG.). 192p. pap. 16.95 *(978-1-59181-174-9(0))* Sentient Pubns.

Whittaker, Andrea. Abortion, Sin & the State in Thailand. 2009. pap. 39.95 *(978-0-415-54603-4(6))* Routledge.

ABORTION—PSYCHOLOGICAL ASPECTS

Harper, Sheila. Saveone: A Guide to Emotional Healing after Abortion. 2008. pap. 12.95 *(978-1-60037-437-1(9))* Morgan James Publishing.

—Saveone (Spanish) A Guide to Emotional Healing after Abortion. 2009. (ENG & SPA.). pap. 12.95 *(978-1-60037-630-6(4))* Morgan James Publishing.

—Survivor: A Journey Through Abortion & Back. 2009. (ENG.). pap. 9.95 *(978-1-60037-540-8(5))* Morgan James Publishing.

Johnson, Trudy. C. P. R. Choice Processing & Resolution. 2009. 124p. pap. 15.95 *(978-1-4327-4329-1(5))* Outskirts Pr., Inc.

MacGibbon, Heather. Screening Choice. 2009. 272p. pap. *(978-3-639-16120-5(3))* VDM Verlag Dr. Mueller e.K.

Masse, Sydna. Her Choice to Heal: Finding Spiritual & Emotional Peace after Abortion. 2009. (ENG.). 192p. pap. 12.99 *(978-1-4347-6872-8(4))* Cook, David C.

Powlison, David. Healing after Abortion: God's Mercy Is for You. 2008. (ENG.). 24p. 3.99 *(978-1-934885-51-2(7))* New Growth Pr.

Richardson, C. G. No One to Hear Their Cries. 2008. 230p. pap. 19.95 *(978-1-4357-4050-1(5))* Lulu Enterprises Inc.

Scope & Myths of Roe V. Wade: Hearing Before the Subcommittee on the Constitution of the Committee on the Judiciary, House of Representatives, One Hundred Ninth Congress, Second Session, March 2, 2006, 2 vols. 2007. *(978-1-57588-945-0(5))* Hein, William S. & Co., Inc.

Shroyer, Stephen John. Abortion: the Legal, Medical, & Bioethical Perspectives. 2010. 59p. pap. 27.81 *(978-0-557-58276-1(8))* Lulu Enterprises Inc.

Weber, Linda. Life Choices: The Teachings of Abortion. 2011. (ENG.). 192p. pap. 16.95 *(978-1-59181-174-9(0))* Sentient Pubns.

ABORTION—PUBLIC OPINION

Scope & Myths of Roe V. Wade: Hearing Before the Subcommittee on the Constitution of the Committee on the Judiciary, House of Representatives, One Hundred Ninth Congress, Second Session, March 2, 2006, 2 vols. 2007. *(978-1-57588-945-0(5))* Hein, William S. & Co., Inc.

ABORTION—RELIGIOUS ASPECTS

see also Pro-Choice Movement; Pro-Life Movement

Al-Kawthari, Muhammad ibn Adam. Birth Control & Abortion in Islam, 1. 2nd enl. ed. 2006. 88p. per. 9.95 *(978-1-933764-00-9(7))* White Thread Pr.

Bolden, Teresa. So What's in Your Box? 2006. 32p. per. 9.95 *(978-1-56167-939-3(9))* American Literary Pr.

Conrad, Myrna. Discarded Lives. 2007. 196p. per. 13.99 *(978-1-60266-488-3(9))* Xulon Pr., Inc.

Disney, Jennifer L. Up from the Ashes: A Handbook for Healing. 2010. 100p. pap. 11.95 *(978-1-4502-5274-4(5))* iUniverse, Inc.

Durand, Josephine. The Abortion: Before I formed you, I knew You. 2009. 112p. 21.49 *(978-1-4389-3865-3(9))*; pap. 10.99 *(978-1-4389-3866-0(7))* AuthorHouse.

Evans, John H. Contested Reproduction: Genetic Technologies, Religion, & Public Debate. 2010. (ENG., Illus.). 280p. 45.00 *(978-0-226-22265-3(9))* Univ. of Chicago Pr.

The Four Steps to Healing (Catholic) 2007. pap. 12.99 *(978-0-9728769-2-6(8))* Tabor Garden Pr.

The Four Steps to Healing (Non-denominational) 2007. (Illus.). pap. 12.99 *(978-0-9728769-4-0(4))* Tabor Garden Pr.

Harper, Sheila. Saveone (Spanish) A Guide to Emotional Healing after Abortion. 2009. (ENG & SPA.). pap. 12.95 *(978-1-60037-630-6(4))* Morgan James Publishing.

Hovey, Angel Renee. Life Interrupted, 1 vol. 2009. 146p. pap. 24.95 *(978-1-60749-184-2(2))* PublishAmerica, Inc.

Irshai, Ronit. Fertility & Jewish Law: Feminist Perspectives on Orthodox Responsa Literature. 2012. (Brandeis Series on Gender, Culture, Religion, & Law & HBI Series on Jewish Women Ser.). (ENG.). 328p. (C). 85.00 ***(978-1-61168-239-7(8))***; pap. 39.95 ***(978-1-61168-240-3(1))*** Univ. Pr. of New England. (Brandeis University Press).

Maguire, Daniel C., ed. Sacred Rights: The Case for Contraception & Abortion in World Religions. 2007. 295p. reprint ed. pap. 25.00 *(978-1-4223-6831-2(9))* DIANE Publishing Co.

Martinelli-Fernandez, Susan A., et al. Interdisciplinary Views on Abortion: Essays from Philosophical, Sociological, Anthropological, Political, Health & Other Perspectives. Martinelli-Fernandez, Susan A. et al, eds. 2009. (ENG., Illus.). 223p. pap. 39.95 *(978-0-7864-3494-7(5))* McFarland & Co., Inc. Pubs.

Muthumbi, Jane W. Participation, Representation & the Global Civil Society: Christian & Islamic Fundamentalist, Anti-Abortion Networks, & United Nations Conferences. 2010. (ENG.). 62.99 *(978-0-7391-4461-9(8))* Lexington Bks.

O'Brien, George Dennis. The Church & Abortion: A Catholic Dissent. 2010. (ENG.). 192p. 34.95 *(978-1-4422-0577-2(6))* Rowman & Littlefield Publishers, Inc.

Paris, Ginette. The Psychology of Abortion. 2nd ed. 2007. (ENG.). 72p. pap. 18.00 *(978-0-88214-560-0(6))* Spring Pubns., Inc.

Waterhouse, Steven. Life's Tough Questions. 2007. 212p. 9.95 *(978-0-9702418-6-3(0))* Westcliff Pr.

Weber, Linda. Life Choices: The Teachings of Abortion. 2011. (ENG.). 192p. pap. 16.95 *(978-1-59181-174-9(0))* Sentient Pubns.

Wilkins, Infant "James". Survivor: A Story of Truth & Hope. 2011. 112p. 29.99 ***(978-1-4628-6286-3(1))***; pap. 19.99 ***(978-1-4628-6285-6(3))*** Xlibris Corp.

Wilson, Jeff. Mourning the Unborn Dead: A Buddhist Ritual Comes to America. 2009. (ENG., Illus.). 304p. 35.00 *(978-0-19-537193-2(3))* Oxford Univ. Pr., Inc.

ABORTION—RELIGIOUS ASPECTS—CATHOLIC CHURCH

Connor, Charles P. John Cardinal & the Culture of Life. 2011. *(978-0-8189-1332-7(0)*, St. Pauls) St Pauls/Alba Hse. Pubs.

Dombrowski, Daniel A. & Deltete, Robert. A Brief, Liberal, Catholic Defense of Abortion. 2006. (Illus.). 168p. per. 20.95 *(978-0-252-07397-7(5))* Univ. of Illinois Pr.

Len Belter. Is Being Pro-Choice a Sin? Some Questions for America's Catholic Bishops from a Pro-Choice Catholic. 2009. 164p. 25.95 *(978-1-4401-5756-1(1))*; pap. 15.95 *(978-1-4401-5754-7(5))* iUniverse, Inc.

Madigan, Janet Holl & Madigan, Janet. Truth, Politics, & Universal Human Rights. 2007. (ENG.). 256p. 89.00 *(978-1-4039-7623-9(6))* Palgrave Macmillan.

Medina, Jose Antonio. Temas Calientes para Los Jovenes Cristianos/Controversial Topics for Young Christians: El Aborto, la Eutanasia, la Pena de Muerte, en Defensa de la Vida/ Abortion, Euthanasia, Death Penalty, in Defense of Life. 2007. (Illus.). 63p. pap. 3.95 *(978-0-7648-1527-0(X)*, Libros Liguori) Liguori Pubns.

Melina, Livio & Anderson, Carl A. Oil on the Wounds: A Response to the Aftermath of Divorce & Abortion. 2010. *(978-0-7570-0360-8(5))* Square One Pubs.

Napier, Stephen, ed. Persons, Moral Worth, & Embryos: A Critical Analysis of Pro-Choice Arguments. 2011. (Philosophy & Medicine / Catholic Studies in Bioethics Ser.). (Illus.). xiv, 283p. 139.00 *(978-94-007-1601-8(X)*, 940071601X) Springer.

Rhonheimer, Martin. Ethics of Procreation & the Defense of Human Life: Contraception, Artificial Fertilization, & Abortion. 2010. 309p. pap. 39.95 *(978-0-8132-1722-2(9))* Catholic Univ. of America Pr.

—Vital Conflicts in Medical Ethics: A Virtue Approach to Craniotomy & Tubal Pregnancies. 2009. 192p. pap. 24.95 *(978-0-8132-1718-5(0))* Catholic Univ. of America Pr.

Sinclair, Mary B. It's So Easy to Be Smart with Someone Else's Heart: The Sound of Your Own Wheels. 2011. 58p. pap. 16.95 ***(978-1-4560-8549-0(2))*** PublishAmerica, Inc.

ABORTION—RELIGIOUS ASPECTS—CHRISTIANITY

Arand, Charles P. & Lamb, James. In the Beginning: A Collection of Essays & Bible Studies on the Sanctity of Early Human Life. 2007. 80p. pap. 7.99 *(978-0-7586-1502-2(7))* Concordia Publishing Hse.

Arner, Rob. Consistently Pro-Life: The Ethics of Bloodshed in Ancient Christianity. 2010. 152p. pap. 17.00 *(978-1-60608-612-4(X)*, Pickwick Pubns.) Wipf & Stock Pubs.

Burchett, Author Walter, BA. Heavenly angel lay lay explains why aborted babies do not go to Heaven. 2007. 48p. pap. 14.95 *(978-0-615-17470-9(1))* Crossover Ministries.

Chew, Cheryl. Make Me Your Choice: Compelling Personal Stories of Struggle & Healing from Those Who Have Had or Dealt with Abortion. 2006. 197p. per. 15.99 *(978-0-7684-2372-3(4))* Destiny Image Pubs.

Comm, Mary. Building Bridges: Paving the Way for Partnering with the Churches in Your Area. 2008. (ENG.). pap. 12.95 *(978-1-60037-410-4(7))* Morgan James Publishing.

—Secret Sin: When God's Children Choose Abortion. 2006. (ENG.). 108p. per. 12.95 *(978-1-60037-148-6(5))* Morgan James Publishing.

—Secret Sin: When God's People Choose Abortion: Unmasking the Secret Shame & Silent Suffering of Post-Abortive Christians. 2007. (ENG.). 22.95 *(978-1-60037-149-3(3))* Morgan James Publishing.

Cromwell-Hillenburg, Mary. Close to Mommy's Heart: A Gift of Life. 2008. 96p. pap. 9.99 *(978-1-60477-672-0(2))* Xulon Pr., Inc.

Di Mauro, Dennis. A Love for Life: Christianity's Consistent Protection of the Unborn. 2008. 178p. pap. 20.00 *(978-1-55635-828-9(8)*, Wipf and Stock) Wipf & Stock Pubs.

Dixon, Patricia. A Question of Choice. 2007. 144p. per. 13.99 *(978-1-60266-392-3(0))* Xulon Pr., Inc.

Donelan, Thomas. What the Bible Says. 2009. 40p. pap. 10.00 *(978-0-557-22030-4(0))* Lulu Enterprises Inc.

Driscoll, Margaret & Faugno, Emily. Saving Women & Infants from Abortion: A Dance in the Rain. 2006. 83p. per. 9.95 *(978-0-8091-4393-1(3)*, 4393-3) Paulist Pr.

Edwards, Kyle. From Pieces to Peace. 2007. 64p. per. 9.99 *(978-1-60477-219-7(0))* Xulon Pr., Inc.

Everhard, Matthew. Abortion: The Evangelical Perspective. 2007. pap. *(978-1-930566-61-3(1)*, BIBAL Pr.) Scott, D.& F. Publishing, Inc.

Gentry, Kenneth L., Jr. Christian Case Against Abortion. 80p. pap. 5.95 *(978-1-877818-05-9(4))* Footstool Pubns.

Hanks, Sarah. Drifting in & Out of Sleep. 2008. 356p. pap. 20.99 *(978-1-60647-704-5(8))* Xulon Pr., Inc.

Harrison, Jim. What Makes God Cry the Most. 2008. 72p. pap. 10.99 *(978-1-60647-924-7(5))* Xulon Pr., Inc.

Hartshorn, Margaret H. Foot Soldiers Armed with Love: Heartbeat International's First Forty Years. 2011. ***(978-1-57864-721-7(5))*** Donning Co. Pubs.

Horak, Barbara C., ed. Real Abortion Stories: The Hurting & the Healing. 2006. 120p. per. 7.95 *(978-0-9787551-3-3(8))* Strive For the Best Publishing.

Horton, Joneen M. Journey to Restoration Healing for the Post-Abortive Woman. 2009. 44p. pap. 12.95 *(978-0-557-04149-7(X))* Lulu Enterprises Inc.

Howard, Sonya. Almost Wasn't - a Memoir of My Abortion & How God Used Me. 2011. 128p. 29.99 ***(978-1-4653-4830-2(1))***; pap. 19.99 ***(978-1-4653-4829-6(8))*** Xlibris Corp.

Klusendorf, Scott, et al. The Case for Life: Equipping Christians to Engage the Culture. 2009. 256p. pap. 15.99 *(978-1-4335-0320-7(4))* Crossway.

Long, Maureen. Birthright. 4.00 *(978-0-687-85091-4(6))* Abingdon Pr.

Masse, Sydna. Her Choice to Heal: Finding Spiritual & Emotional Peace after Abortion. 2009. (ENG.). 192p. pap. 12.99 *(978-1-4347-6872-8(4))* Cook, David C.

Oehlschlaeger, Fritz. Procreative Ethics. 2009. 380p. pap. 42.00 *(978-1-60608-230-0(2)*, Cascade Bks.) Wipf & Stock Pubs.

Powlison, David. Healing after Abortion: God's Mercy Is for You. 2008. (ENG.). 24p. 3.99 *(978-1-934885-51-2(7))* New Growth Pr.

Roberson, Donna. Can't Turn Back: Abortion Decision to Help Teens. 2009. (Illus.). 83p. pap. 14.95 *(978-1-4327-4672-8(3))* Outskirts Pr., Inc.

Schultea, Bonnie Jb. Muddy Waters. 2008. 124p. pap. 11.99 *(978-1-60647-682-6(3))* Xulon Pr., Inc.

Sproul, R. C. Abortion: A Rational Look at an Emotional Issue. 20th ed. 2010. xxii, 225p. (Orig.). *(978-1-56769-209-9(5))* Reformation Pubs.

Tu, Stephen. Pro-Life Pulpit: Preaching & the Challenge of Abortion. 2011. 170p. pap. 20.00 ***(978-1-61097-357-1(7)***, Wipf and Stock) Wipf & Stock Pubs.

Williams, Sarah C. The Shaming of the Strong: The Challenge of an Unborn Life. 2007. (ENG.). 180p. per. *(978-1-57383-407-0(6))*, Regent College Publishing) Regent College Publishing.

ABORTION—AFRICA

Save, The. Willing Fathers, Reluctant Parents: Young Men's Perspectives on Unwanted Pregnancies & Abortion in Kenya. 2008. 70p. pap. 19.95 *(978-99944-55-29-4(X))* African Bks. Collective, Ltd. GBR. Dist: Lightning Source, Inc.

ABORTION—ASIA

Purewal, Navtej. Son Preference: Sex Selection, Gender & Culture in South Asia. 2010. (ENG.). 192p. 99.95 *(978-1-84520-467-9(0))*; pap. 29.95 *(978-1-84520-468-6(9))* Berg Pubs. GBR. Dist: Macmillan.

Whittaker, Andrea. Abortion, Sin & the State in Thailand. 2009. pap. 39.95 *(978-0-415-54603-4(6))* Routledge.

Whittaker, Andrea, ed. Abortion in Asia: Local Dilemmas, Global Politics. 2010. (FRS Ser.). (Illus.). 270p. 90.00 *(978-1-84545-734-1(X))* Berghahn Bks., Inc.

ABORTION—EUROPE

Usborne, Cornelie. Cultures of Abortion in Weimar Germany. 2007. (Monographs in German History). (Illus.). 296p. (C). 90.00 *(978-1-84545-389-3(1))* Berghahn Bks., Inc.

—Cultures of Abortion in Weimar Germany. 2011. (MGH Ser.). (Illus.). 296p. 29.95 *(978-0-85745-166-8(9))* Berghahn Bks., Inc.

ABORTION—GREAT BRITAIN

Brookes, Barbara. Abortion in England 1900-1967, Volume 7. 2012. (Routledge Library Editions). (ENG.). 208p. (C). 115.00 ***(978-0-415-62299-8(9))*** Routledge.

Horobin, Gordon. Experience with Abortion: A Case Study of North-East Scotland. 2009. (ENG.). 396p. pap. 53.00 *(978-0-521-11277-2(X))* Cambridge Univ. Pr.

ABORTION—INDIA

Patel, Tulsi, ed. Sex-Selective Abortion in India: Gender, Society & New Reproductive Technologies. 2006. (Illus.). 432p. (C). per. 37.00 *(978-0-7619-3539-1(8)*, B35398P) SAGE Pubns., Inc.

Shepherd, Mary E. Sex-Selective Abortion in India: The Impact on Child Mortality. 2007. (C). 109.95 *(978-1-934043-69-1(9))* Cambria Pr.

Visaria, Leela & Ramachandran, Vimala, eds. Abortion in India: Ground Realities. 2007. (Illus.). 352p. 110.00 *(978-0-415-42412-7(7))* Routledge.

ABORTION—JAPAN

Kato, Masae. Women's Rights? The Handicapped Foetus & Abortion in Japan. 2009. (IIAS Publications Ser.). 245p. pap. *(978-90-5356-793-7(3)*, Leiden Univ. Pr.) Amsterdam Univ. Pr.

ABORTION—UNITED STATES

Becker, David A., ed. Problems with Death. 2006. (Opposing Viewpoints Ser.). (ENG., Illus.). 247p. (gr. 10-12). (J). pap. 39.70 *(978-0-7377-2953-5(8))*; 27.50 *(978-0-7377-2954-2(6))* Cengage Gale. (Greenhaven Pr., Inc.).

Berne, Emma Carlson, ed. Abortion. 2007. (Introducing Issues with Opposing Viewpoints Ser.). (ENG., Illus.). 120p. (YA). (gr. 7-12). pap. 34.70 *(978-0-7377-3563-5(5))* Cengage Gale.

—Teen Pregnancy. 2006. (Introducing Issues with Opposing Viewpoints Ser.). (ENG., Illus.). 128p. (YA). (gr. 8-12). lib. bdg. 35.75 *(978-0-7377-3625-0(9)*, Greenhaven Pr., Inc.) Cengage Gale.

Camasso, Michael. Family Caps, Abortion, & Women of Color: Research Connection & Political Rejection. 2007. (ENG., Illus.). 288p. (C). 39.95 *(978-0-19-517905-7(6))* Oxford Univ. Pr., Inc.

Caron, Simone M. Who Chooses? American Reproductive History Since 1830. (ENG.). 2010. 384p. pap. 29.95 *(978-0-8130-3504-8(X))* 2008. (Illus.). 416p. 69.95 *(978-0-8130-3199-6(0))* Univ. Pr. of Florida.

Colb, Sherry F. When Sex Counts: Making Babies & Making Law. annot. ed. 2007. (ENG.). 248p. 26.95 *(978-0-7425-5150-3(4))* Rowman & Littlefield Publishers, Inc.

Connor, Charles P. John Cardinal & the Culture of Life. 2011. *(978-0-8189-1332-7(0)*, St. Pauls) St Pauls/Alba Hse. Pubs.

Doan, Alesha. Opposition & Intimidation: The Abortion Wars & Strategies of Political Harassment. 2007. (ENG.). 232p. 75.00 *(978-0-472-09975-7(2))*; (Illus.). (C). pap. 24.95 *(978-0-472-06975-0(6))* Univ. of Michigan Pr.

Edelin, Kenneth C. Broken Justice: A True Story of Race, Sex & Revenge in a Boston Courtroom. 2007. (Illus.). 362p. per. 17.95 *(978-0-9792060-0-9(6))* PondView Pr.

Everhard, Matthew. Abortion: The Evangelical Perspective. 2007. pap. *(978-1-930566-61-3(1)*, BIBAL Pr.) Scott, D.& F. Publishing, Inc.

Farrell, Courtney. The Abortion Debate. 2008. (Essential Viewpoints Set 2 Ser.). (Illus.). 112p. (YA). (gr. 7-12). 34.22 *(978-1-60453-053-7(7))* ABDO Publishing Co.

Freedman, Lori R. Willing & Unable: Doctors' Constraints in Abortion Care. 2010. (ENG.). 200p. pap. 24.95 *(978-0-8265-1715-9(3))*; lib. bdg. 59.95 *(978-0-8265-1714-2(5))* Vanderbilt Univ. Pr.

Garcia, Lisa. The Least of These: Calling on America's Youth to Defend the Unborn. 2010. pap. 12.99 *(978-1-61663-399-8(9))* Tate Publishing & Enterprises, LLC.

Guy, Mallard E. Bloodshed Before Birth: America's Choice. 2011. pap. 19.99 ***(978-1-61346-074-0(0))*** Tate Publishing & Enterprises, LLC.

Hoffman, Merle. Intimate Wars: The Life & Times of the Woman Who Brought Abortion from the Back Alley to the Board Room. 2012. (ENG., Illus.). 336p. pap. 18.95 *(978-1-55861-751-3(5))* Feminist Pr. at The City Univ. of New York.

Hunter, James Davidson. Before the Shooting Begins. 2007. (ENG.). 272p. pap. 21.95 *(978-1-4165-7324-1(0)*, Free Pr.) Free Pr.

Jefferis, Jennifer & Jefferis, Jennifer L. Armed for Life: The Army of God & Anti-Abortion Terror in the United States, 1 vol. 2011. (PSI Guides to Terrorists, Insurgents, & Armed Groups Ser.). (Illus.). 176p. 49.95 ***(978-0-313-38753-1(2)***, A3180C) Greenwood Publishing Group, Inc.

Joffe, Carole. Dispatches from the Abortion Wars: The Costs of Fanaticism to Doctors, Patients, & the Rest of Us. (ENG.). 208p. 2011. pap. 16.00 *(978-0-8070-0128-8(7))* 2010. 27.95 *(978-0-8070-3502-3(5))* Beacon Pr.

MacNair. Achieving Peace in the Abortion War. 2008. 180p. pap. 16.95 *(978-1-4401-1325-3(4))* iUniverse, Inc.

McBride, Dorothy E. Abortion in the United States: A Reference Handbook, 1 vol. 2007. (Contemporary World Issues Ser.). 303p. 55.00 *(978-1-59884-098-8(3)*, ABORT1C) ABC-CLIO, LLC.

Palmer, Louis J. & Palmer, Xueyan Z. Encyclopedia of Abortion in the United States. 2nd rev. ed. 2008. (ENG., Illus.). 632p. 150.00 *(978-0-7864-3838-9(X))* McFarland & Co., Inc. Pubs.

Powlison, David. Healing after Abortion: God's Mercy Is for You. 2008. (ENG.). 24p. 3.99 *(978-1-934885-51-2(7))* New Growth Pr.

Press, Eyal. Absolute Convictions: My Father, a City, & the Conflict That Divided America. 2007. (ENG., Illus.). 304p. pap. 15.00 *(978-0-312-42657-6(7))* Picador.

Reagan, Leslie J. Dangerous Pregnancies: Mothers, Disabilities, & Abortion in Modern America. 2010. (ENG., Illus.). 396p. 29.95 *(978-0-520-25903-4(3))* Univ. of California Pr.

Renshaw, Jessica Shaver. Gianna: Aborted ... & Lived to Tell about It. 2010. (ENG.). 272p. pap. 12.99 *(978-1-58997-600-9(2))* Tyndale Hse. Pubs.

Renshaw, Jessica Shaver & Jessen, Gianna. Gianna: Aborted, & Lived to Tell about It. rev. ed. 2011. (ENG.). 224p. pap. 14.99 *(978-1-58997-639-9(8))* Tyndale Hse. Pubs.

Rose, Melody. Abortion: A Documentary & Reference Guide, 1 vol. 2008. (Documentary & Reference Guides). (Illus.). 272p. 85.00 (978-0-313-34032-1(3), GR4032, Greenwood Pr.) Greenwood Publishing Group, Inc.

Scope & Myths of Roe V. Wade: Hearing Before the Subcommittee on the Constitution of the Committee on the Judiciary, House of Representatives, One Hundred Ninth Congress, Second Session, March 2, 2006, 2 vols. 2007. (978-1-57588-945-0(5)) Hein, William S. & Co., Inc.

Singular, Stephen. The Wichita Divide: The Murder of Dr. George Tiller, the Battle over Abortion, & the New American Civil War. 2011. (ENG., Illus.). 368p. 26.99 (978-0-312-62505-4(7)) St. Martin's Pr.

Slack, James D. Abortion, Execution, & the Consequences of Taking Life. 2011. (ENG., Illus.). 228p. pap. 24.95 (978-1-4128-4222-8(0)) Transaction Pubs.

Solinger, Rickie. Reproductive Politics, 1 vol. 2013. (What Everyone Needs to Know Ser.). (ENG.). 192p. pap. 16.95 **(978-0-19-981141-0(5))** Oxford Univ. Pr., Inc.

Tallman, Jamie Q. The Notorious Dr. Flippin: Abortion & Consequence in the Early Twentieth Century. 2011. (Plains Histories Ser.). (ENG., Illus.). 228p. 34.95 (978-0-89672-675-8(4)) Texas Tech Univ. Pr.

Wells, Jon. Sniper: The True Story of Anti-Abortion Killer James Kopp. 2008. (ENG., Illus.). 312p. pap. 17.95 (978-0-470-15546-2(9), Wiley) Wiley, John & Sons, Inc.

Wicklund, Susan & Kesselheim, Alan S. This Common Secret: My Journey as an Abortion Doctor. 2008. (ENG.). 288p. pap. 15.99 (978-1-58648-647-1(0)) Perseus Bks. Group.

ABORTION CLINICS
see Abortion Services

ABORTION COUNSELING
see also Pregnancy, Unwanted

Collective, Sage-Femme. Natural Liberty: Rediscovering Self-Induced Abortion Methods. 2008. (Illus.). x, 454p. (978-0-9645920-0-1(2)) Sage-femme.

Harper, Sheila. Saveone (Spanish) A Guide to Emotional Healing after Abortion. 2009. (ENG & SPA.). pap. 12.95 (978-1-60037-630-6(4)) Morgan James Publishing.

Needle, Rachel B. & Walker, Lenore E. A. Abortion Counseling: A Clinician's Guide to Psychology, Legislation, Politics, & Competency. 2007. 251p. per. 40.00 (978-0-8261-0257-7(3)) Springer Publishing Co., Inc.

Powlison, David. Healing after Abortion: God's Mercy Is for You. 2008. (ENG.). 24p. 3.99 (978-1-934885-51-2(7)) New Growth Pr.

ABORTION FACILITIES
see Abortion Services

ABORTION IN ANIMALS
see also Brucellosis in Cattle

Njaa, Bradley L., ed. Kirkbride's Diagnosis of Abortion & Neonatal Loss in Animals. 4th ed. 2012. (ENG., Illus.). 256p. 124.99 **(978-0-470-95852-0(9)**, Wiley-Blackwell) Wiley, John & Sons, Inc.

Ortega-Mora, Luis M., et al, eds. Protozoal Abortion in Farm Ruminants: Guidelines for Diagnosis & Control. 2007. (Illus.). 320p. 145.00 (978-1-84593-211-4(0)) CABI GBR. Dist: Stylus Publishing, LLC.

ABORTION SERVICES
see also Abortion Counseling

Joffe, Carole. Dispatches from the Abortion Wars: The Costs of Fanaticism to Doctors, Patients, & the Rest of Us. (ENG.). 208p. 2011. pap. 16.00 (978-0-8070-0128-8(7)) 2010. 27.95 (978-0-8070-3502-3(5)) Beacon Pr.

Press, Eyal. Absolute Convictions: My Father, a City, & the Conflict That Divided America. 2007. (ENG., Illus.). 304p. pap. 15.00 (978-0-312-42657-6(7)) Picador.

ABOTH
see Mishnah—Avot

ABOUKIR, BATTLE OF, EGYPT, 1798
see Nile, Battle of the, Egypt, 1798

ABRAHAM (BIBLICAL PATRIARCH)

Baker Publishing Group Staff. A Walk Thru the Life of Abraham: Faith in God's Promises, 1 vol. 2010. (Walk Thru the Bible Discussion Guides). (ENG.). 96p. pap. 7.99 (978-0-8010-7178-2(X)) Baker Bks.

Binz, Stephen J. Abraham: Father of All Believers. 2011. (Ancient-Future Bible Study: Experience Scripture Through Lectio Divina Ser.). 192p. pap. 11.99 (978-1-58743-277-4(3)) Brazos Pr.

Biographiq. Abraham - the Patriarch of Many Faiths. 2008. 64p. pap. 9.99 (978-1-59986-047-3(3), Biographiq) Filiquarian Publishing, LLC.

Boehm, Omri. The Binding of Isaac: A Religious Model of Disobedience. 2007. (Library of Hebrew Bible/Old Testament Studies). (ENG.). 164p. 125.00 (978-0-567-02613-2(2), T&T Clark Int'l) Continuum International Publishing Group, Ltd. GBR. Dist: National Bk. Network.

Boesel, Chris. Risking Proclamation, Respecting Difference: Christian Faith, Imperialistic Discourse & Abraham. 2010. (ENG.). 305p. (C). pap. 43.00 (978-0-227-17314-5(7)) Clarke, James Co., Ltd. GBR. Dist: Brown, David Bk. Co., The.

Caldwell, Michael. Abraham's Blessing: Ancient Promise & New Hope. 2009. 60p. pap. 12.00 (978-1-4490-0391-3(5)) AuthorHouse.

Canan, Ibrahim. The Message of Abraham: His Life, Virtues, & Mission. 2008. (ENG.). 220p. pap. 16.95 (978-1-59784-075-0(0)) Tughra Bks.

Carstens, Pernille & Lemche, Niels Peter, eds. The Reception & Remembrance of Abraham. 2011. 100.00 **(978-1-4632-0054-1(4))** Gorgias Pr., LLC.

Coates, Jessie. Being Abraham: Growing Old with God. 2007. 132p. per. 11.95 (978-1-4327-1699-8(9)) Outskirts Pr., Inc.

Cohen, Abe M. The Monotheistic Religions: Islam, Christianity & Judaism. 2009. (YA). pap. 9.95 (978-1-4222-0803-8(6)) Mason Crest Pubs.

De Roo, Jacqueline C. R. 'Works of the Law' at Qumran & in Paul. 2007. (ENG.). 296p. (978-1-905048-30-4(C)) Sheffield Phoenix Pr.

Deane, William J. Abraham-Su Vida y Sus Tiempos: The Life & Times of Abraham. (SPA.). (978-84-7645-167-0(9), 223209) Clie, Editorial.

Ego, Beate & Bottrich, Christfried. Abraham in Judentum, Christentum und Islam: Judentum, Christentum und Islam, Hierarchie Ltd. Nr. 001. 2009. (GER.). 188p. (C). 27.00 (978-3-525-63398-4(X)) Vandenhoeck & Ruprecht GmbH & Co. KG DEU. Dist: ISD.

Fretheim, Terence E. Abraham: Trials of Family & Faith. 2007. (Studies on Personalities of the Old Testament Ser.). (Illus.). 262p. 44.95 (978-1-57003-694-1(2)) Univ. of South Carolina Pr.

Goodman, Martin & Van Kooten, George, eds. Abraham, the Nations, & the Hagarites: Jewish, Christian, & Islamic Perspectives on Kinship with Abraham. 2010. (Themes in Biblical Narrative Ser.). xxxv, 577p. (978-90-04-18843-3(6)) BRILL.

Gossai, Hemchand. Barrenness & Blessing: Abraham, Sarah & the Journey of Faith. 2010. (ENG.). 136p. pap. 33.00 (978-0-7188-9216-6(X)) Lutterworth Pr., The GBR. Dist: Brown, David Bk. Co., The.

—Power & Marginality in the Abraham Narrative - Second Edition. 2nd ed. 2009. (Princeton Theological Monographs). 168p. pap. 19.00 (978-1-55635-874-6(1), Pickwick Pubns.) Wipf & Stock Pubs.

Granerod, Gard. Abraham & Melchizedek: Scribal Activity of Second Temple Times in Genesis 14 & Psalm 110. 2010. (Beihefte Zur Zeitschrift Für Die Alttestamentliche Wissenschaft Ser.). (ENG.). XIV, 317p. 112.00 (978-3-11-022345-3(7)) De Gruyter, Walter Inc.

Grant Bishop Williams, Jr. Abraham's Other Sons. 2009. 124p. pap. 15.95 (978-1-4389-9709-4(4)) AuthorHouse.

Hicks, Esther & Hicks, Jerry. La Ley de Atracción: Conceptos Basicos de las Enseñanzas de Abraham. 2007. (SPA & ENG.). 256p. pap. 14.95 (978-1-4019-1752-4(6)) Hay Hse., Inc.

Hunt, Steven A. & Wilson, Marvin R. Perspectives on Our Father Abraham: Essays in Honor of Marvin R. Wilson. 2010. 26.00 (978-0-8028-6252-5(7)) Eerdmans, William B. Publishing Co.

Johnson, Joey. God Is Greater Than Family Mess. 2009. (ENG.). 214p. 24.99 (978-0-9825303-5-1(8)) St. Paul Pr.

Kamudzandu, Israel. Abraham as Spiritual Ancestor: A Postcolonial Zimbabwean Reading of Romans 4. 280p. (978-90-04-18164-9(4)) BRILL.

Kellogg, Alfred H. Abraham, Joseph & Moses in Egypt. 2007. (ENG.). 180p. 37.95 (978-0-548-03752-2(3)) Kessinger Publishing, LLC.

King, Sandra. Abraham: The Traveling Man of Faith. 2011. 306p. pap. 23.95 (978-1-4327-6798-3(4)) Outskirts Pr., Inc.

Levenson, Jon Douglas. Abraham Between Torah & Gospel. 2011. (978-0-87462-592-9(0)) Marquette Univ. Pr.

Lodahl, Michael. Claiming Abraham: Reading the Bible & the Qur'an Side by Side, 1 vol. 2010. (ENG.). 240p. pap. 23.00 (978-1-58743-239-2(0)) Brazos Pr.

Lowin, Shari L. The Making of a Forefather: Abraham in Islamic & Jewish Exegetical Narratives. 2006. (Islamic History & Civilization Ser.). 308p. (978-90-04-15226-7(1)) BRILL.

Mashni, Steve. Trees of Abraham. 2008. per. 8.00 (978-0-9798207-2-4(3)) LoJo Publishing.

Meyer, F. B. Abraham. (SPA.). 208p. (978-84-7228-678-8(9), 220001) Clie, Editorial.

Meyer, F. b. & Meyer, F. B. Abraham, or the Obedience of Faith. 2011. 156p. pap. 12.99 **(978-1-61203-262-7(1))** Bottom of the Hill Publishing.

Moe, John. They Testify of Me. 2007. (Insight Ser.). 48p. pap. 5.99 (978-0-7586-1466-7(7)) Concordia Publishing Hse.

Murphy, Dick. Covenant Promises. 2008. 216p. pap. 15.00 (978-1-59755-108-3(2), Advantage Inspirational) Advantage Bks.

Nee, Watchman. Changed into His Likeness. 2007. (ENG.). 161p. pap. 9.99 (978-0-87508-859-4(7)) CLC Pubns.

—Changed into His Likeness. 2007. per. 8.00 (978-1-4245-0786-3(3)) Treasures Media Inc.

Nibley, Hugh. The COLL Works of Hugh Nibley,8. 2009. 512p. 45.95 (978-1-60641-054-7(7)) Deseret Bk. Co.

Nibley, Hugh, et al. One Eternal Round. 2010. (978-1-60641-237-4(X)) Deseret Bk. Co.

Ochs, Peter & Johnson, William Stacy, eds. Crisis, Call, & Leadership in the Abrahamic Traditions. 2009. (ENG.). 288p. 95.00 (978-0-230-61825-1(1)) Palgrave Macmillan.

Polish, Daniel F. Talking about God: Exploring the Meaning of Religious Life with Kierkegaard, Buber, Tillich & Heschel. 2010. (ENG.). 160p. pap. 16.99 (978-1-59473-272-0(8)) SkyLight Paths Publishing.

Schliesser, Benjamin. Abraham's Faith in Romans 4: Paul's Concept of Faith in Light of the History of Reception of Genesis 15:6. 2007. (Wissenschaftliche Untersuchungen zum Neuen Testament 2 Ser.). 548p. (C). pap. 145.00 (978-3-16-149197-9(1)) Mohr Siebeck GmbH & Co. KG DEU. Dist: Coronet Bks.

Soloveitchik, Joseph B., et al. Abraham's Journey: Reflections on the Life of the Founding Patriarch. 2008. 252p. 25.00 (978-1-60280-004-5(9)) Ktav Publishing Hse., Inc.

Thompson, Debra. Get off the Fence: But Be Prepared to Leave A Lot Behind. 2010. 104p. pap. 15.99 (978-1-4500-4223-9(6)) Xlibris Corp.

Tomkins, Henry George. Abraham & His Age. 2007. (ENG.). 304p. 43.95 (978-0-548-03657-0(8)) Kessinger Publishing, LLC.

Waskow, Arthur, et al. The Tent of Abraham: Stories of Hope & Peace for Jews, Christians, & Muslims. 2007. (ENG.). 240p. per. 17.00 (978-0-8070-7729-0(1)) Beacon Pr.

Whidden, Theodore L. The Bible Plumb Line: Life of the Prophet Abraham, Sarah, & Noah's Flood. 2006. per. (978-0-9786684-4-0(8)) Heritage Ink Christian Publishing Co., LLC.

Wolf, Robert & Lefkowitz, Zvi. Forgotten Children of the Bible: Conflict & Consequences. 2009. 87p. 18.95 (978-1-934440-71-1(X), Devora Publishing) Simcha Media Group.

Worschech, Udo. «Ich will Ismael segnen»: Gemeinsame Wurzeln in Christentum und Islam. 2011. (Friedensauer Schriftenreihe. Reihe A: Theologie Ser.). 154p. 47.95 (978-3-631-60644-5(3)) Lang, Peter GmbH, Europaischer Verlag der Wissenschaften DEU. Dist: Lang, Peter.

Worthington, Frances. Abraham: One God, Three Wives, Five Religions. 2011. xiii, 242p. 17.00 **(978-1-931847-89-6(4))** Baha'i Publishing.

ABRAHAM, PLAINS OF (QUEBEC), BATTLE OF THE, 1759
see Plains of Abraham, Battle of the, Quebec, 1759

ABRAHAM A SANCTA CLARA, FATHER, 1644-1709

Eybl, Franz M. Abraham a Sancta Clara: Vom Prediger zum Schriftsteller. (Frahe Neuzeit Ser.). (GER.). X, 553p. 270.00 **(978-3-11-183624-9(X))** De Gruyter, Walter Inc.

ABRASIVES

Guo, Dongming, et al, eds. Advances in Abrasive Technology IX. 2007. (Key Engineering Materials Ser.: Vol. 329). (Illus.). 820p. (978-0-87849-416-3(2)) Trans Tech Pubns., Ltd.

Huang, Han, et al, eds. Advances in Abrasive Technology XII. 2009. (Advanced Materials Research Ser.: Vol. 76-78). (Illus.). 752p. pap. (978-0-87849-314-2(X)) Trans Tech Pubns., Ltd.

Kuriyagawa, Tsunemoto & Zhou, Libo, eds. Advances in Abrasive Technology XI. 2009. (Key Engineering Materials Ser.:). 544p. pap. (978-0-87849-364-7(6)) Trans Tech Pubns., Ltd.

Momber, A. Blast Cleaning Technology. 2010. (ENG., Illus.). xii, 540p. pap. 159.00 (978-3-642-09280-0(2), 3642092802) Springer.

Momber, Andreas. Blast Cleaning Technology. 2008. (ENG., Illus.). xii, 540p. 159.00 (978-3-540-73644-8(1), 3540736441) Springer.

Practicas de Seguridad Para el Chorreado con Abrasivo. Date not set. (SPA.). (978-0-9675287-2-4(0)) Clemco Industries Corp.

Technology Research Editors, ed. Abrasive Wear: Theoretical & Practical Considerations, 2007 Ed. 2007. pap. 128.50 (978-1-60030-460-6(5), Search-In-Print) CSA Journal Division.

Xu, Jiuhua & Etal. Advances in Grinding & Abrasive Technology XIV: Selected Papers from the 14th Conference of Abrasive Technology in China 26th-28th October, 2007, Nanjing, China. 2008. (Illus.). 586p. pap. 273.00 (978-0-87849-459-0(6)) Trans Tech Pubns., Ltd. CHE. Dist: Enfield Publishing & Distribution Co., Inc.

Xu, Xipeng, ed. Progress in Abrasive & Grinding Technology. 2009. 206p. pap. (978-0-87849-342-5(5)) Trans Tech Pubns., Ltd.

Zhao, Bo, et al, eds. Advances in Grinding & Abrasive Technology XV. 2009. (Key Engineering Materials Ser.: Vol. 416). (Illus.). 648p. pap. (978-0-87849-313-5(1)) Trans Tech Pubns., Ltd.

ABRAVANEL, DON ISAAC, 1437-1508

Abravanel, Isaac. Isaac Abravanel: Letters. Skalli, Cedric Cohen, ed. 2007. (Studia Judaica Ser.). (ENG.). XV, 193p. 119.00 (978-3-11-019492-0(9)) De Gruyter, Walter Inc.

Feldman, Seymour. Philosophy in A Time of Crisis. 2010. 220p. pap. 39.95 (978-0-415-59304-5(2)) Routledge.

ABSALOM, SON OF DAVID

Blackburn, William M. The Rebel Prince: Lessons from the Tragic Life & Death of Absalom. 2011. 268p. pap. 20.00 **(978-1-59925-253-7(8))** Solid Ground Christian Bks.

ABSAROKA RANGE (MONT. AND WYO.)
see also Beartooth Mountains (Mont. and Wyo.)

Marcuson, Pat. Fishing the Beartooths: An Angler's Guide to More Than 400 Prime Fishing Spots. 2nd ed. 2008. (Fishing Ser.). (ENG., Illus.). 272p. pap. 18.95 (978-0-7627-4227-1(5), Lyons Pr.) Globe Pequot Pr., The.

ABSENCE FROM SCHOOL
see School Attendance

ABSENT TREATMENT
see Mental Healing

ABSENTEE VOTING
see Voting

ABSENTEEISM (LABOR)
see also Sick Leave

Badura, B., et al, eds. Fehlzeiten-Report: Arbeit, Geschlecht und Gesundheit. 2007. (Fehlzeiten-Report). (Illus.). 521p. pap. 49.95 (978-3-540-72543-5(1)) Springer.

Badura, Bernhard, et al, eds. Fehlzeiten-Report 2006: Chronische Krankheiten. 2006. (Fehlzeiten-Report). (Illus.). XVI, 456p. pap. 48.95 (978-3-540-34367-7(9), 3540343679) Springer.

Eggert, Max. Absence Management Pocketbook. 2009. (Illus.). 128p. pap. (978-1-906610-02-9(9)) Management Pocketbooks GBR. Dist: Ware-Pak, Inc.

European Foundation for the Improvement of Living and Working Conditions Staff, contrib. by. Preventing Absenteeism at the Workplace. 39p. (978-92-828-0339-4(2)) European Commission BEL. Dist: Balogh International, Inc.

Findlay, James V. & Morrison, Richard G. Supervisory Control of Absenteeism. (Illus.). 62p. ring bd. 69.50 (978-0-88061-018-6(2)) International Loss Control Institute, Inc.

Hamann, Petra. Die Kündigung wegen häufiger Kurzerkrankungen. 2009. (Schriften zum deutschen und europäischen Arbeitsrecht Ser.). (GER.). 208p. 64.95 (978-3-631-59201-4(9)) Lang, Peter GmbH, Europaischer Verlag der Wissenschaften DEU. Dist: Lang, Peter.

Kunst, M. J. J., et al. Aggression & Violence, Posttraumatic Stress, & Absenteeism among Employees in Penitentiaries. 2008. 60p. (C). pap. 32.50 (978-90-5454-980-2(7)) Eleven International Publishing NLD. Dist: International Specialized Bk. Services.

Lehr, Michael. Attendance Problems ¿ Case Studies: Maximizing Effectiveness with Intrinsic Approaches. 2007. spiral bd. 14.96 (978-0-9786613-4-2(6)) Dragon Slayer, LLC.

Murray, John E. Origins of American Health Insurance: A History of Industrial Sickness Funds. 2007. (Yale Series in Economic History). (ENG., Illus.). 336p. 40.00 (978-0-300-12091-2(5)) Yale Univ. Pr.

Reinke, Tanja. Der Krankenstand Bei Lehrkräften: Ausmass, Ursachen und Erklärungsansätze. 2007. (GER., Illus.). 239p. (978-3-631-56443-1(0)) Lang, Peter GmbH, Europaischer Verlag der Wissenschaften.

Stinson, Angela. Anxiety & Stress: How Poor Performance & Absenteeism Affect the Workplace. 2010. 98p. pap. 25.95 (978-1-59942-302-9(2), Dissertation.com) Universal Pubs.

ABSOLUTE, THE

Callaway, Webster R. The Absolute Subject (A Pathological Excess of Synonyms) 2008. pap. 35.00 (978-1-60456-966-7(2)) Nova Science Pubs., Inc.

Conterno, Chiara. Metamorfosi Della Fuga: La Ricerca Dell'assoluto Nella Lirica Di Nelly Sachs. 2010. (ITA.). 351p. (978-88-8098-282-1(6)) Unipress.

Crocenzi, Gina. Literature & the Science of the Unknowable. 2010. 212p. pap. (978-3-8383-0757-2(7)) Lambert Academic Publishing.

De Waters, Lillian. The Finished Kingdom: A Study of the Absolute. 2007. (ENG.). 244p. 41.95 (978-0-548-28152-9(1)) Kessinger Publishing, LLC.

DeWaters, Lillian. The Christ Within: A Study of the Absolute. 2007. 252p. per. 19.95 (978-1-60206-193-4(9)) Cosimo, Inc.

Goris, Wouter. Absolute Beginners: Der mittelalterliche Beitrag zu einem Ausgang vom Unbedingten. 2007. (Studien und Texte Zur Geistesgeschichte des Mittelalters Ser.). 328p. (978-90-04-16215-0(1)) BRILL.

Krausz, Michael. Dialogues on Relativism, Absolutism, & Beyond: Four Days in India. (New Dialogues in Philosophy Ser.). 2011. (ENG.). 140p. 80.00 (978-0-7425-6032-1(5)) 2011. (ENG.). 140p. pap. 22.95 (978-0-7425-6033-8(3)) 2010. vii, 131p. (978-1-4422-0930-5(5)) Rowman & Littlefield Publishers, Inc.

Meijer, Hans. Initiation into Reality. 2011. (ENG.). 143p. pap. 16.95 **(978-1-84694-523-6(2))** Hunt, John Publishing Ltd. GBR. Dist: National Bk. Network.

Mullen, Matt. The Ultimate Distinction: Resolving Our Biggest Philosophical, Spiritual, & Practical Problem. 2011. (ENG., Illus.). 56p. pap. 9.95 (978-1-59181-169-5(4)) Sentient Pubns.

Plato & Hermann, Arnold. Plato's Parmenides: Text, Translation & Introductory Essay. 2010. (ENG.). 272p. (C). (gr. 13). 65.00 (978-1-930972-71-1(7)) Parmenides Publishing.

Rothschild, Richard. Three Gods Give an Evening to Politics: Jefferson, Lenin, Socrates. 2011. 216p. 44.95 **(978-1-258-05837-1(5))** Literary Licensing, LLC.

ABSOLUTE DIFFERENTIAL CALCULUS
see Calculus of Tensors

ABSOLUTE LIABILITY
see Strict Liability

ABSOLUTE RIGHTS
see Natural Law

ABSOLUTION
see also Confession; Forgiveness of Sin; Indulgences; Penance

Capel, Thomas John. Confession & Absolution. 2009. 48p. pap. (978-0-217-91897-8(2)) Books LLC.

—Confession & Absolution. 2007. pap. (978-1-4065-1262-5(1)) Dodo Pr.

—Confession & Absolution. 2007. (ENG.). 48p. per. 15.95 (978-0-548-79565-1(7)) Kessinger Publishing, LLC.

Costa, Anne. Lord, I Hurt! The Grace of Forgiveness & the Road to Healing. 2012. 11.95 **(978-1-59325-200-7(5))** Word Among Us Pr.

Lloyd, Trevor & Tovey, Phillip. Celebrating Forgiveness. 2009. 88.00 (978-1-60724-348-9(2)) Gorgias Pr., LLC.

ABSOLUTISM
see Despotism

ABSORPTION
see also Gases—Absorption and Adsorption

Aristov, Yuriy. Nanocomposite Sorbents for Multiple Applications. 2011. 350p. 149.00 (978-981-4267-50-2(3)) Pan Stanford Publishing SGP. Dist: Independent Pubs. Group.

Delville, Jean-Pierre. Optical Deformability of Fluid Interfaces. 2009. pap. 37.00 (978-1-60692-431-0(1)) Nova Science Pubs., Inc.

Garcia-Jares, Carmen, et al. The Role of Sorbents in Sampling & Analysis of Emerging Pollutants in Indoor Environments. 2010. (Pollution Science, Technology & Abatement Ser.). (Illus.). 108p. pap. 43.00 *(978-1-61761-004-2(6)*, Nova Novinka) Nova Science Pubs., Inc.

Loureiro, José Miguel & Kartel, Mykola T., eds. Combined & Hybrid Adsorbents: Fundamentals & Applications. 2006. (NATO Science for Peace & Security Series / NATO Science for Peace & Security Series C: Environmental Security Ser.). (Illus.). xii, 370p. 249.00 *(978-1-4020-5170-8(0)*, 1402051700); IX, 361p. pap. 109.00 *(978-1-4020-5171-5(9)*, 1402051719) Springer.

Mechel, Fridolin. Room Acoustical Fields. 2012. (ENG., Illus.). xiii, 595p. 229.00 ***(978-3-642-22355-6(9)***, 3642223559) Springer.

Willis, Thomas P. Sorbents: Properties, Materials & Applications. 2009. (Environmental Research Advances Ser.). 135.00 *(978-1-60741-851-1(7))* Nova Science Pubs., Inc.

Wozniak, Bogdian & Dera, Jerzy. Light Absorption in Sea Water. 2010. (Atmospheric & Oceanographic Sciences Library). (Illus.). viii, 456p. pap. 229.00 *(978-1-4419-2149-9(4)*, 1441921494) Springer.

ABSORPTION (HEAT)
see Heat—Radiation and Absorption

ABSORPTION (PHYSIOLOGY)
see also Osmosis

Dowler, Brynn C. Endocytosis: Structural Components, Functions & Pathways. 2010. (Cell Biology Research Progress Ser.). (Illus.). 259p. 129.00 *(978-1-61668-189-0(6))* Nova Science Pubs., Inc.

Ivanov, Andrei I., ed. Exocytosis & Endocytosis. 2007. (Methods in Molecular Biology Ser.). (Illus.). 412p. 129.00 *(978-1-58829-865-2(5)*, 1588298655) Humana Pr.

Lazaridis, Mihalis & Colbeck, Ian, eds. Human Exposure to Pollutants via Dermal Absorption & Inhalation. 2010. (Environmental Pollution Ser.). (ENG., Illus.). x, 308p. 199.00 *(978-90-481-8662-4(5)*, 9048186625) Springer.

Li, Xiaoling. Oral Bioavailability: Basic Principles, Advanced Concepts, & Applications. Hu, Ming, ed. 2011. (Wiley Series in Drug Discovery & Development Ser.: 16). (ENG., Illus.). 568p. 149.95 *(978-0-470-26099-9(8)*, Wiley) Wiley, John & Sons, Inc.

Metelsky, Sergey T. Transport Phenomena & Membrane Digestion in Small Intestinal Mucosa: An Electrophysiological Approach. 2011. (Illus.). 298p. pap. 149.50 ***(978-954-642-592-8(3))*** Pensoft Pubs. BGR. Dist: Coronet Bks.

Schulz, Megan A., ed. CACO-2 Cells & their Uses. 2011. (Cell Biology Research Progress Ser.). (Illus.). 218p. 89.00 *(978-1-61209-917-0(3))* Nova Science Pubs., Inc.

Surber, C., et al, eds. Topical Applications & the Mucosa. 2011. (Current Problems in Dermatology Ser.). (ENG., Illus.). 166p. *(978-3-8055-9615-2(4))* Karger, S. AG.

Touitou, Elka & Barry, Brian W., eds. Enhancement in Drug Delivery. 2006. (ENG., Illus.). 656p. 226.95 *(978-0-8493-3203-6(6)*, CRC Press) Taylor & Francis Group GBR. Dist: Taylor & Francis Group.

ABSORPTION, ATMOSPHERIC
see Solar Radiation

ABSORPTION IN SOILS
see Soil Absorption and Adsorption

ABSORPTION OF GASES
see Gases—Absorption and Adsorption

ABSORPTION OF SOUND
see also Architectural Acoustics; Soundproofing

Agostini, Luigi. Creating Soundscapes. 2008. 144p. 35.95 *(978-1-4092-0036-9(1))* Lulu Enterprises Inc.

Bucur, Voichita. Urban Forest Acoustics. 2010. (ENG., Illus.). x, 181p. pap. 159.00 *(978-3-642-06804-1(9)*, 3642068049) Springer.

Cox, Trevor & D'Antonio, Peter. Acoustic Absorbers & Diffusers: Theory, Design & Application. 2nd rev. ed. 2009. (ENG., Illus.). 496p. 160.00 *(978-0-415-47174-9(5)*, CRC Press) Taylor & Francis Group GBR. Dist: Taylor & Francis Group.

Oechsner, Andreas & Augustin, Christian, eds. Multifunctional Metallic Hollow Sphere Structures: Manufacturing, Properties & Application. 2009. (Engineering Materials Ser.). (ENG., Illus.). vi, 258p. 209.00 *(978-3-642-00490-2(3)*, 3642004903) Springer.

Trusler, M. Physical Acoustics & Metrology of Fluids. 2nd ed. 2009. (Illus.). 300p. 119.95 *(978-0-7503-0940-0(7))* Taylor & Francis Group.

ABSORPTION SPECTRA
see also Astronomical Spectroscopy; Heat—Radiation and Absorption; Internal Reflection Spectroscopy; Molecular Spectra; Spectrum Analysis

also subdivision Spectra under subjects, e.g. Stars—Spectra

Anderson, Basil & Payne, James. The Spectroscope & Gemmology. Mitchell, R. Keith, ed. 2006. (Illus.). 269p. per. 49.95 *(978-0-943763-52-1(5))* GemStone Pr.

Bunker, Grant. Introduction to XAFS: A Practical Guide to X-ray Absorption Fine Structure Spectroscopy. 2010. (ENG., Illus.). 268p. 70.00 *(978-0-521-76775-0(X))* Cambridge Univ. Pr.

Hedman, Britt & Pianetta, Piero, eds. X-Ray Absorption Fine Structure — XAFS13: 13th International Conference. 2007. (AIP Conference Proceedings Ser.). xxii, 937p. 346.00 *(978-0-7354-0384-0(8))* American Institute of Physics.

Milosevic, Milan. Internal Reflection & ATR Spectroscopy. 2012. (Chemical Analysis: a Series of Monographs on Analytical Chemistry & Its Applications Ser.: 176). (ENG.). 264p. 89.95 ***(978-0-470-27832-1(3)***, Wiley) Wiley, John & Sons, Inc.

Pajot, Bernard & Clerjaud, Bernard. Optical Absorption of Impurities & Defects in Semiconducting Crystals: Electronic Absorption of Deep Centres & Vibrational Spectra. 2011. (Springer Series in Solid-State Sciences Ser.). (Illus.). x, 415p. 169.00 ***(978-3-642-18017-0(5)***, 3642180175) Springer.

Pajot, Bernard & Clerjaud, Bernard. Semiconducting & Insulating Crystals: Optical Absorption of Impurities & Defects. 2010. (Springer Series in Solid-State Sciences Ser.). (ENG., Illus.). xix, 474p. 229.00 *(978-3-540-95955-7(6)*, 3540959556) Springer.

Platt, Ulrich & Stutz, Jochen. Differential Optical Absorption Spectroscopy: Principles & Applications. 2008. (Physics of Earth & Space Environments Ser.). (Illus.). 500p. 179.00 *(978-3-540-21193-8(4))* Springer.

—Differential Optical Absorption Spectroscopy: Principles & Applications. 2010. (Physics of Earth & Space Environments Ser.). (Illus.). xvi, 597p. pap. 179.00 *(978-3-642-05946-9(5)*, 3642059465) Springer.

Stöhr, Joachim. NEXAFS Spectroscopy. 2010. (Springer Series in Surface Sciences Ser.). (Illus.). xv, 403p. pap. 209.00 *(978-3-642-08113-2(4)*, 3642081134) Springer.

Zhang, Ru. Spectroscopic Studies of Carbon Nanotubes. 2009. 108p. pap. *(978-3-639-17374-1(0))* VDM Verlag Dr. Mueller e.K.

ABSTINENCE
see Fasting; Temperance

ABSTINENCE, SEXUAL
see Sexual Abstinence

ABSTRACT ALGEBRA
see Algebra, Abstract

ABSTRACT ART
see Art, Abstract

ABSTRACT AUTOMATA
see Machine Theory

ABSTRACT DATA TYPES (COMPUTER SCIENCE)
see also Data Structures (Computer Science)

Carrano, Frank M. Data Abstraction & Problem Solving with C++ 5th rev. ed. 2006. (ENG., Illus.). 992p. (C). per. 131.00 *(978-0-321-43332-9(7))* Addison Wesley.

Corradini, Andrea & Montanari, Ugo. Recent Trends in Algebraic Development Techniques: 19th International Workshop, WADT 2008, Pisa, Italy, June 13-16, 2008, Revised Selected Papers. 2009. (Lecture Notes in Computer Science / Theoretical Computer Science & General Issues Ser.). (ENG.). viii, 343p. pap. 83.00 *(978-3-642-03428-2(4)*, 3642034284) Springer.

Fiadeiro, Jose Luiz, ed. Recent Trends in Algebraic Development Techniques: 18th International Workshop, WADT 2006 la Roche en Ardenne, Belgium, June 1-3, 2006 Revised Selected Papers. 2007. (Lecture Notes in Computer Science Ser.). (Illus.). 170p. pap. 69.95 *(978-3-540-71997-7(0))* Springer.

Johnson, Michael & Pavlovic, Dusko, eds. Algebraic Methodology & Software Technology: 13th International Conference, AMAST 2010, Lac-Beauport, QC, Canada, June 23-25, 2010, Proceedings. 2011. (Lecture Notes in Computer Science / Programming & Software Engineering Ser.). x, 238p. pap. 72.00 *(978-3-642-17795-8(6)*, 3642177956) Springer.

Johnson, Michael & Vene, Varmo. Algebraic Methodology & Software Technology: 11th International Conference, AMAST 2006, Kuressaare, Estonia, July 5-8, 2006, Proceedings. 2006. (Lecture Notes in Computer Science Ser.: Vol. 4019). (Illus.). XI, 389p. pap. 79.95 *(978-3-540-35633-2(9)*, 3540356339) Springer.

Orejas, F. & Ehrig, H., eds. Recent Trends in Data Type Specification: 9th Workshop on Specification of Abstract Data Types Joint with the 4th COMPASS Workshop, Caldes de Malavella, Spain, October 26 - 30, 1992. Selected Papers. 2007. (Lecture Notes in Computer Science Ser.). 364p. per. 69.95 *(978-3-540-57867-3(6))* Springer.

Weichselberger, K. & Pohlmann, S. A Methodology for Uncertainty in Knowledge-Based Systems. 2007. (Lecture Notes in Computer Science Ser.). 320p. per. 29.95 *(978-3-540-52336-9(7))* Springer.

ABSTRACT EXPRESSIONISM

Albers, Patricia. Joan Mitchell: Lady Painter. 2011. (ENG., Illus.). 544p. 40.00 *(978-0-375-41437-4(1)*, Knopf) Knopf Doubleday Publishing Group.

Anfam, David. Conrad Marca-Relli. 2008. (ENG., Illus.). 336p. *(978-88-902804-2-9(5)*, Museum Srl,Bruno Alfieri Edt (Acc)) Antique Collectors' Club.

Anfam, David, text. Abstract Expressionism. 2010. (ENG., Illus.). 150p. 75.00 *(978-1-905620-28-9(4))* Haunch of Venison GBR. Dist: D.A.P./Distributed Art Pubs.

Burgard, Timothy Anglin. Matter & Spirit: Stephen de Staebler. 2012. (ENG., Illus.). 224p. 65.00 ***(978-0-520-27230-9(7))*** Univ. of California Pr.

—Matter & Spirit - Stephen de Staebler. 2012. (ENG., Illus.). 224p. pap. 34.95 ***(978-0-520-27231-6(5))*** Univ. of California Pr.

Craft, Catherine. An Audience of Artists: Dada, Neo-Dada, & the Emergence of Abstract Expressionism. 2012. (ENG., Illus.). 336p. 55.00 ***(978-0-226-11680-8(8))*** Univ. of Chicago Pr.

Dickey, Tina. Color Creates Light: Studies with Hans Hofmann. 2011. (Illus.). 424p. *(978-0-9866511-0-6(9))* Trillistar Bks.

Ducthing, Hajo. Wassily Kandinsky. 2008. (Illus.). 128p. pap. 14.95 *(978-3-7913-3958-0(3))* Prestel Publishing.

Engelmann, Ines Janet. Jackson Pollock & Lee Krasner. 2007. (Pegasus Library). (Illus.). 95p. pap. 14.95 *(978-3-7913-3882-8(X))* Prestel Publishing.

Hainley, Bruce, intro. Jay Defeo: Works from the Estate of Jay Defeo. 2007. (Illus.). 48p. per. 20.00 *(978-0-9713548-3-8(9))* Nielsen Gallery.

Halasz, Piri. A Memoir of Creativity: Abstract Painting, Politics & the Media, 1956-2008. 2009. 524p. pap. 30.95 *(978-1-4401-2323-8(3))*; (Illus.). 40.95 *(978-1-4401-2322-1(5))* iUniverse, Inc.

Hans Hofmann: Exuberant Eye. 2007. per. *(978-0-9795323-0-6(2))* KN Gallery.

Hess, Barbara. Abstract Expressionism. 2009. (25 Ser.). (ENG., Illus.). 96p. 14.99 *(978-3-8365-1385-2(4))* TASCHEN DEU. Dist: Ingram Pub. Services.

Jachec, Nancy. Politics & Painting at the Venice Biennale, 1948-1964: Italy & the Idea of Europe. 2008. (Critical Perspectives in Art History Ser.). (ENG., Illus.). 224p. 84.00 *(978-0-7190-6896-6(7))* Manchester Univ. Pr. GBR. Dist: Macmillan.

Kim, Hee-Young. The Vestige of Resistance. 2009. 196p. pap. *(978-3-639-19544-6(2))* VDM Verlag Dr. Mueller e.K.

Kingsley, April, et al. Suitcase Paintings: Small Scale Abstract Expressionism. 2007. 25.00 *(978-0-9671013-6-1(0))* Art Enterprises, Ltd.

Kleeblatt, Norman L. Action/Abstraction: Pollock, de Kooning, & American Art, 1940-1976. Kleeblatt, Norman L., ed. 2009. (ENG., Illus.). 344p. pap. 50.00 *(978-0-300-13920-4(9))* Yale Univ. Pr.

Kuspit, Donald, frwd. Grillo: Abstract Expressionism - Beyond the Fifties. 2011. (ENG., Illus.). 134p. 50.00 *(978-0-9823196-8-0(1))* Fields Publishing.

Kwint, Marius & Sandler, Irving. Natvar Bhavsar: Poetics of Color. 2009. (ENG., Illus.). 192p. 80.00 *(978-88-6130-795-7(7))* Skira Editore ITA. Dist: Random Hse., Inc.

Lanchner, Carolyn, text. Jackson Pollock. 2009. (ENG., Illus.). 48p. pap. 9.95 *(978-0-87070-769-8(8))* Museum of Modern Art.

Landauer, Susan, frwd. Grillo: Abstract Expressionism: the Formative Years 1946-1948. 2010. (ENG.). 134p. 50.00 *(978-0-9823196-6-6(5))* Fields Publishing.

Mareyna-Fallo, Rafael. The Book-the Game. 2009. 56p. pap. 23.99 *(978-1-4389-8275-5(5))* AuthorHouse.

Marter, Joan, ed. Abstract Expressionism: The International Context. 2007. (Na Ser.). (ENG., Illus.). 320p. pap. 29.95 *(978-0-8135-3975-1(7))* Rutgers Univ. Pr.

Matter, Mercedes. Mercedes Matter. 2010. (ENG., Illus.). 276p. 55.00 *(978-0-615-30990-3(9))* Borghi, Mark Fine Art.

McKinnon, E. Luanne. Michael Von Helms: Painted Dialogue. 2006. (ENG., Illus.). 96p. pap. 40.00 *(978-0-9762523-8-2(4))* Fresco Fine Art Pubns., LLC.

Morris, Stuart. Colourfield Painting: Minimal, Cool, Hard Edge, Serial & Post-Painterly Abstract Art of the Sixties to the Present. 2007. (Illus.). 228p. per. *(978-1-86171-026-0(7))* Crescent Moon Publishing.

Motherwell, Robert. The Writings of Robert Motherwell. Ashton, Dore, ed. 2007. (Documents of Twentieth-Century Art Ser.). (Illus.). 387p. 70.00 *(978-0-520-25047-5(8))*; per. 34.95 *(978-0-520-25048-2(6))* Univ. of California Pr.

Pace, Stephen. Stephen Pace: Abstract Expressionist. 2011. (Illus.). 32p. ***(978-1-935617-11-2(7)***, Orbit Books) Spanierman Gallery.

Parcerisas, Pila, ed. Viennese Actionism. 2008. 440p. pap. *(978-84-96954-44-1(7))* Actar Birkhauser Distribution.

Price, Marshall. The Abstract Impulse: Fifty Years of Abstraction at the National Academy, 1956-2006. 2007. (ENG., Illus.). 88p. pap. 29.50 *(978-1-887149-17-4(1))* Hudson Hills Pr. LLC.

Reid, Sheila. A Place Between Thoughts: The Art of Sheila Reid. ltd. ed. 2010. 173p. pap. *(978-0-9646268-2-9(9))* Rush Editions.

Rosand, David. The Invention of Painting in America. 2007. (Leonard Hastings Schoff Lectures). (ENG., Illus.). 246p. (gr. 17). pap. 27.00 *(978-0-231-13297-8(2))* Columbia Univ. Pr.

Sandler, Irving. Abstract Expressionism & the American Experience: A Re-Evaluation. Rubenstein, Raphael, ed. 2009. (ENG., Illus.). 240p. 45.00 *(978-1-55595-311-9(5))* Hudson Hills Pr. LLC.

Siegel, Katy, et al. Abstract Expressionism. 2011. (ENG., Illus.). 304p. 75.00 *(978-0-7148-4415-2(2))* Phaidon Pr., Inc.

Sylvester, Julie. Willem de Kooning: Late Paintings. 2006. (Illus.). 83p. 65.00 *(978-3-8296-0226-6(X))* Schirmer/Mosel Verlag GmbH DEU. Dist: Prestel Publishing.

Tinterow, Gary, et al. Abstract Expressionism & Other Modern Works: The Muriel Kallis Steinberg Newman Collection in the Metropolitan Museum of Art. 2007. (Illus.). x, 214p. 29.95 *(978-1-58839-274-9(0))* Metropolitan Museum of Art, The.

Wechsler, Jeffrey, text. Pathways & Parallels: Roads to Abstract Expressionism. 2007. pap. *(978-0-9759954-9-5(9))* Taggart, Hollis Galleries.

Whyte, Robert A., frwd. Grillo - Expressionism: Figurative Works. 2011. (ENG.). 134p. 50.00 *(978-0-9846186-5-1(1))* Fields Publishing.

ABSTRACT MACHINES
see Machine Theory

ABSTRACT METRICS
see Distance Geometry

ABSTRACT PAINTING
see Painting, Abstract

ABSTRACT PHOTOGRAPHY
see Photography, Abstract

ABSTRACT WRITING
see Abstracting

ABSTRACTING
see also Indexing

Kerr, Gordon. Precies Writing. 2006. 356p. per. *(978-1-4067-3412-6(8)*, Hesperides Pr.) Read Bks.

Koltay, Tibor. Abstracts & Abstractions: A Genre & Skills for the 21st Century. 2010. (Illus.). 200p. 80.00 *(978-1-84334-517-6(X)*, Chandos Publishing) Woodhead Publishing Ltd. GBR. Dist: Neal-Schuman Pubs., Inc.

Meyers, Larry. 2011 Pennsylvania Abstract: A Statistical Fact Book: 2011. Meyers, Larry & Shultz, Jennifer, eds. 2011. (Illus.). 360p. pap. 65.00 ***(978-1-58036-842-1(5))*** Pennsylvania State Data Ctr.

Nenkova, Ani & McKeown, Kathleen. Automatic Summarization. 2011. 146p. pap. 99.00 ***(978-1-60198-470-8(7))*** Now Pubs.

O'Connor, Brian C., et al. Doing Things with Information: Beyond Indexing & Abstracting, 1 vol. 2008. (Illus.). 264p. pap. 50.00 *(978-1-59158-577-0(5)*, LU8577) Libraries Unlimited, Inc.

Smith, Michael A. & Kanade, Takeo. Multimodal Video Characterization & Summarization. 2010. (International Series in Video Computing Ser.). (Illus.). xii, 204p. pap. 179.00 *(978-1-4419-5351-3(5)*, 1441953515) Springer.

ABSTRACTING AND INDEXING SERVICES
see also Information Storage and Retrieval Systems

Hedden, Heather. Indexing Specialties: Web Sites. Zafran, Enid, ed. & anno. by. 2007. pap. 40.00 *(978-1-57387-302-4(0))* Information Today, Inc.

Swales, John M. & Feak, Christine B. Abstracts & the Writing of Abstracts. 2009. (Michigan Series in English for Academic & Professional Purposes Ser.). (ENG., Illus.). 104p. (C). pap. 16.00 *(978-0-472-03335-5(2))* Univ. of Michigan Pr.

ABSTRACTION
see also Concepts; Mental Representation

Association for Computing Machinery (ACM) Staff, compiled by. International Workshop on the Role of Abstraction in Software Engineering (ROA'06) 2007. 28p. pap. 50.00 *(978-1-60423-111-3(4))* Curran Assocs., Inc.

Cook, Roy T., ed. The Arché Papers on the Mathematics of Abstraction. 2010. (Western Ontario Series in Philosophy of Science Ser.). xxxviii, 454p. pap. 219.00 *(978-90-481-7090-6(7)*, 9048170907) Springer.

Crisp, Richard J., ed. The Psychology of Social & Cultural Diversity. 2010. (Social Issues & Interventions Ser.: 4). (ENG., Illus.). 384p. pap. 49.95 *(978-1-4051-9561-4(4))*; 110.95 *(978-1-4051-9562-1(2))* Wiley, John & Sons, Inc. (Wiley-Blackwell).

Damerow, Peter. Abstraction & Representation: Essays on the Cultural Evolution of Thinking. 2010. (Boston Studies in the Philosophy of Science Ser.). 436p. pap. 259.00 *(978-90-481-4644-4(5)*, 9048146445) Springer.

Edling, Agnes. Abstraction & Authority in Textbooks: The Textual Paths Towards Specialized Language. 2006. (Studia Linguistica Upsaliensia Ser.: No. 2). 206p. pap. 53.50 *(978-91-554-6600-8(1))* Uppsala Universitet/Acta Universitatis Uppsaliensis SWE. Dist: Coronet Bks.

Elson, Linda G. & Ponikvar, Alan. Paradox Lost: A Cross-Contextual Definition of Levels of Abstraction. 2009. *(978-1-57273-946-8(0))*; *(978-1-57273-945-1(2))* Hampton Pr., Inc.

Fine, Kit. The Limits of Abstraction. 2008. (ENG.). 214p. pap. 35.00 *(978-0-19-953363-3(6))* Oxford Univ. Pr., Inc.

Hill, Richard. Modular Methods in the Supervisory Control of Discrete Event Systems. 2010. 200p. pap. *(978-3-639-21031-6(X))* VDM Verlag Dr. Mueller e.K.

Kang, Dae-Ki. Abstraction, Aggregation & Recursion for Accurate & Simple Classifiers. 2008. 140p. pap. *(978-3-639-06976-1(5))* VDM Verlag Dr. Mueller e.K.

Märtsin, Mariann. Dialogicality in Focus: Challenges to Theory, Method & Application. 2011. (Illus.). xxi, 269p. pap. *(978-1-61209-593-6(3))* Nova Science Pubs., Inc.

Märtsin, Mariann, et al. Dialogicality in Focus: Challenges to Theory, Method & Application. 2011. (Psychology Research Progress Ser.). (Illus.). 291p. 145.00 *(978-1-61122-817-5(4))* Nova Science Pubs., Inc.

Schwartzman, Lisa H. Challenging Liberalism: Feminism as Political Critique. 2007. (ENG.). 224p. pap. 24.00 *(978-0-271-02854-5(8))* Pennsylvania State Univ. Pr.

ABU BAKR, CALIPH, D. 634

Sherwani, Muhammad Habibur Rahman Khan. Hadrat Abu Bakr: The First Caliph of Islam. Haq, Syed Moinul, tr. 2011. 218p. 44.95 ***(978-1-258-02993-7(6))*** Literary Licensing, LLC.

ABU DHABI (UNITED ARAB EMIRATES)
see Abu Zaby (United Arab Emirates)

ABU GHRAIB PRISON

Bower, Janine. All in a Day's Work. 2007. 164p. per. *(978-3-8364-2868-2(7))* VDM Verlag Dr. Mueller e.K.

CACITeam Staff & London, J. Phillip. Our Good Name: A Company's Fight to Defend Its Honor & Get the Truth Told about Abu Ghraib. 2008. (ENG., Illus.). 780p. 29.95 *(978-1-59698-539-1(9))* Regnery Publishing, Inc., An Eagle Publishing Co.

Caldwell, Ryan Ashley. Fallgirls: Gender & the Framing of Torture at Abu Ghraib. 2012. (Classical & Contemporary Social Theory Ser.). (Illus.). 240p. 99.95 ***(978-1-4094-2969-2(5))*** Ashgate Publishing Co.

Casteel, Joshua Eric. Letters from Abu Ghraib. 2008. 118p. pap. 12.95 *(978-0-9791189-3-7(X))* Essay Pr.

Danner, Mark. Torture & Truth: America, Abu Ghraib, & the War on Terror. 2008. (ENG.). 573p. pap. 30.00 *(978-1-4379-6436-3(2))* DIANE Publishing Co.

Delgado, Aidan. The Sutras of Abu Ghraib: Notes from a Conscientious Objector in Iraq. 2008. (ENG.). 224p. pap. 15.00 *(978-0-8070-7271-4(0))* Beacon Pr.

Eisenman, Stephen F. The Abu Ghraib Effect. (ENG., Illus.). 128p. 2010. pap. 14.95 *(978-1-86189-646-9(8))* 2007. 19.95 *(978-1-86189-309-3(4))* Reaktion Bks., Ltd. GBR. Dist: Chicago Distribution Ctr.

Germain, Deanna. Reaching Past the Wire: A Nurse at Abu Ghraib. 2007. (ENG., Illus.). 224p. 24.95 *(978-0-87351-606-8(0),* Borealis Bk.) Minnesota Historical Society Pr.

Gourevitch, Philip & Morris, Errol. The Ballad of Abu Ghraib. 2009. (ENG.). 304p. (gr. 12-18). 16.00 *(978-0-14-311539-7(1),* Penguin (Non-Classics)) Penguin Group (USA) Inc.

Graveline, Christopher & Clemens, Michael. The Secrets of Abu Ghraib Revealed: American Soldiers on Trial. 2010. (Illus.). 334p. 29.95 *(978-1-59797-441-7(2))* Potomac Bks., Inc.

Jaffer, Jameel & Singh, Amrit. Administration of Torture: A Documentary Record from Washington to Abu Ghraib & Beyond. 2007. (ENG., Illus.). 456p. (gr. 17). 50.00 *(978-0-231-14052-2(5))* Columbia Univ. Pr.

Keller, Michael. Torture Central: E-mails from Abu Ghraib. 2008. 188p. pap. 16.95 *(978-1-935278-06-1(1),* iUniverse Star) iUniverse, Inc.

Lagouranis, Tony & Mikaelian, Allen. Fear up Harsh: An Army Interrogator's Dark Journey Through Iraq. 2008. (ENG.). 272p. (gr. 12-18). 16.00 *(978-0-451-22315-9(2),* N A L Trade) Penguin Group (USA) Inc.

Lazreg, Marnia. Torture & the Twilight of Empire: From Algiers to Baghdad. 2007. (Human Rights & Crimes Against Humanity Ser.). (ENG., Illus.). 354p. (C). 42.00 *(978-0-691-13135-1(X))* Princeton Univ. Pr.

McKelvey, Tara. Monstering: Inside America's Policy of Secret Interrogations & Torture in the Terror War. 2008. (ENG.). 320p. pap. 16.95 *(978-0-465-00546-8(2))* Basic Bks.

Miles, Steven H. Oath Betrayed: America's Torture Doctors. 2nd ed. 2009. (ENG., Illus.). 250p. pap. 21.95 *(978-0-520-25968-3(8))* Univ. of California Pr.

Mokhtari, Shadi. After Abu Ghraib: Exploring Human Rights in America & the Middle East. (Cambridge Studies in Law & Society Ser.). 2011. 270p. pap. 32.99 *(978-1-107-40148-8(8))* 2009. (ENG.). 264p. 88.00 *(978-0-521-76753-8(9))* Cambridge Univ. Pr.

Oliver, Kelly. Women as Weapons of War: Iraq, Sex, & the Media. (ENG.). 224p. (gr. 17). 2010. pap. 19.50 *(978-0-231-14191-8(2))* 2007. (Illus.). 29.50 *(978-0-231-14190-1(4))* Columbia Univ. Pr.

Sands, Philippe. Torture Team: Rumsfeld's Memo & the Betrayal of American Values. (ENG., 2009. Illus.). 288p. pap. 16.95 *(978-0-230-61443-7(4))* 2008. 272p. 26.95 *(978-0-230-60390-5(4))* Palgrave Macmillan.

Sharbonne, Riley & Rezac, Matthew, texts. Monica Haller: Riley & His Story. 2009. (ENG., Illus.). 480p. 55.00 *(978-2-915359-38-1(5))* Onestar Pr. FRA. Dist: D.A.P./Distributed Art Pubs.

Sharrock, Justine. Tortured: When Good Soldiers Do Bad Things. 2010. (ENG.). 272p. 25.95 *(978-0-470-45403-9(2),* Wiley) Wiley, John & Sons, Inc.

Skowera, Dianna. Of Those So Close Beside Me. Strozier, M. Stefan & Torke, Kyle, eds. 2010. 374p. 22.99 *(978-1-935444-15-2(8))* World Audience Pubs.

Winkler, Gary S. Tortured: Lynndie england, abu Ghraib & the Photographs that shocked the World. 2009. 27.95 *(978-0-578-02370-0(9))* Bad Apple Bks.

ABU-JAMAL, MUMIA

Abu-Jamal, Mumia. We Want Freedom: A Life in the Black Panther Party. 2008. (ENG., Illus.). 176p. pap. 20.00 *(978-0-89608-718-7(2))* South End Pr.

Faulkner, Maureen & Smerconish, Michael A. Murdered by Mumia: A Life Sentence of Loss, Pain, & Injustice. 2009. (ENG., Illus.). 368p. pap. 16.95 *(978-1-59921-558-7(6),* Lyons Pr.) Globe Pequot Pr., The.

Gardner, Thomas N. The Media Rhetoric of Law & Order: How ABC Framed the Mumia Abu-Jamal Story. 2009. (Illus.). viii, 462p. *(978-0-7734-4683-0(4))* Mellen, Edwin Pr., The.

O'Connor, J. Patrick. The Framing of Mumia Abu-Jamal. 2008. (ENG.). 256p. pap. 16.95 *(978-1-55652-744-9(6),* Hill, Lawrence Bks.) Chicago Review Pr., Inc.

ABU ZABY (UNITED ARAB EMIRATES)

Davidson, Christopher. Abu Dhabi: Oil & Beyond. 2011. (Columbia/Hurst Ser.). (ENG.). 256p. (gr. 17). pap. 22.50 ***(978-0-231-70107-5(1))*** Columbia Univ. Pr.

Davidson, Christopher M. Abu Dhabi: Oil & Beyond. 2009. (Columbia/Hurst Ser.). (ENG.). 256p. (gr. 17). 35.00 *(978-0-231-70106-8(3))* Columbia Univ. Pr.

Explorer Publishing. Abu Dhabi Mini Explorer. 2nd ed. 2008. (Explorer - Mini Visitor's Guides). (ENG.). 350p. pap. 11.95 *(978-9948-8584-0-9(9))* Explorer Publishing UAE. Dist: Globe Pequot Pr., The.

Suleiman, Atef, et al. The Petroleum Experience of Abu Dhabi: The Emirates Center for Strategic Studies & Research. 2008. (ENG., Illus.). 224p. pap. 46.00 *(978-9948-00-911-5(8),* Emirates Center for Strategic Studies) I. B. Tauris & Co., Ltd. GBR. Dist: Macmillan.

Tatchell, Jo. A Diamond in the Desert: Behind the Scenes in Abu Dhabi, the World's Richest City. 2010. (ENG.). 304p. pap. 14.95 *(978-0-8021-7079-8(X),* Black Cat) Grove/Atlantic, Inc.

Thomas, Gavin. Frommer's Dubai & Abu Dhabi Day by Day. 2010. (Frommer's Day by Day - Pocket Ser.: 80). (ENG., Illus.). 184p. pap. 12.99 *(978-0-470-72112-4(X),* Frommers) Wiley, John & Sons, Inc.

ABU ZABY (UNITED ARAB EMIRATES)—DESCRIPTION AND TRAVEL

Explorer Publishing. Abu Dhabi. 8th rev. ed. 2011. (Explorer - Residents' Guides). (ENG., Illus.). 430p. pap. 24.95 ***(978-9948-442-67-7(9))*** Explorer Publishing UAE. Dist: Globe Pequot Pr., The.

—Abu Dhabi Atlas: A Comprehensive A to Z of Abu Dhabi's Ever-Growing Road Network. 2011. 350p. spiral bd. 24.95 *(978-9948-441-19-9(2))* Explorer Publishing UAE. Dist: Globe Pequot Pr., The.

Explorer Publishing. Abu Dhabi Mini Map: Auh_mmp_3. 3rd rev. ed. 2011. (Explorer - Mini Maps Ser.). (ENG.). 2p. pap. 5.95 ***(978-9948-441-91-5(5))*** Explorer Publishing UAE. Dist: Globe Pequot Pr., The.

Explorer Publishing, creator. Hong Kong Explorer Residents' Guide. 2007. (Explorer (Explorer Publishing) Ser.). (ENG., Illus.). 430p. per. 24.95 *(978-976-8192-79-1(2))* Explorer Publishing UAE. Dist: Globe Pequot Pr., The.

Explorer Publishing Staff. Abu Dhabi. 3rd rev. ed. 2011. (Explorer - Mini Visitor's Guides). (ENG., Illus.). 240p. pap. 11.95 *(978-9948-442-99-8(7))* Explorer Publishing UAE. Dist: Globe Pequot Pr., The.

—Abu Dhabi Jumbo Atlas: A Comprehensive A to Z of Abu Dhabi's Ever-Growing Road Network. 2010. 250p. spiral bd. 58.95 *(978-9948-441-20-5(6))* Explorer Publishing UAE. Dist: Globe Pequot Pr., The.

Gems, Sören. Socio-Cultural Impacts of Tourism in Abu Dhabi: Analyzing Attitudes, Beliefs, & Behavior of Localstowards Tourism. 2008. 156p. pap. *(978-3-639-10691-6(1))* VDM Verlag Dr. Mueller e.K.

ABUSE, EMOTIONAL
see Psychological Abuse

ABUSE, PSYCHOLOGICAL
see Psychological Abuse

ABUSE, RITUAL
see Ritual Abuse

ABUSE, SEXUAL
see Sex Crimes

ABUSE, VERBAL
see Invective

ABUSE OF ANIMALS
see Animal Welfare

ABUSE OF CHILDREN
see Child Abuse

ABUSE OF MEDICATION
see Medication Abuse

ABUSE OF MEDICINES
see Medication Abuse

ABUSE OF PERSONS
see Offenses Against the Person

ABUSE OF POWER
see Despotism

ABUSE OF PROCESS
see False Imprisonment

ABUSE OF SUBSTANCES
see Substance Abuse

ABUSE OF THE AGED
see Older People—Abuse Of

ABUSE OF WIVES
see Wife Abuse

ABUSED CHILDREN

Here are entered works on children who are victims of child abuse. Works on adults who were abused as children are entered under Adult Child Abuse Victims.

see also Adult Child Abuse Victims; Child Abuse; Sexually Abused Children

Abrahamse, Andrina D. Through the Eyes of a South African Woman & Other Children. 2010. 218p. pap. 13.95 *(978-1-60911-219-6(9),* Eloquent Bks.) AEG Literary Publishing Services, Inc.

Albert, Isabel. Innerfamiliäre Gewalt gegen Kinder: Eine kriminologische und rechtliche Betrachtung der Erscheinungsformen, Ursachen und Möglichkeiten der Bekämpfung. 2008. (Würzburger Schriften zur Kriminalwissenschaft Ser.). 292p. pap. 74.95 *(978-3-631-57862-9(8))* Lang, Peter GmbH, Europaischer Verlag der Wissenschaften DEU. Dist: Lang, Peter.

Alexander, Randell. Child Fatality Review Guide/Atlas Set: An Interdisciplinary Guide & Photographic Reference. 2007. (ENG., Illus.). 832p. 175.00 *(978-1-878060-58-7(9))* STM Learning, Inc.

Alexander, Randell & Case, Mary E. Child Fatality Review Quick-Reference: For Health Care, Social Service, & Law Enforcement Professionals. 2011. (ENG., Illus.). 400p. spiral bd. 55.00 *(978-1-878060-59-4(7))* STM Learning, Inc.

Allen, Noel Linton. From the Ghettos to the White House Hotel. 2007. 18.00 *(978-0-8059-8832-1(7))* Dorrance Publishing Co., Inc.

Ammerman, Robert T. & Hersen, Michel, eds. Children at Risk. 2010. (ENG.). 332p. pap. 89.95 *(978-1-4419-3214-3(3),* 1441932143) Springer.

Annette Morris. Happily Ever After: A Compassionate Guide for Releasing Blocks to Love. 2009. 144p. pap. 14.95 *(978-1-4401-7714-9(7))* iUniverse, Inc.

Anthony, Robert. Ending the Epidemic of Child Abuse. 2009. 285p. pap. 24.95 *(978-0-557-02691-3(1))* Lulu Enterprises Inc.

Arlether, Wilson/Ann. Rewriting the Script. 2007. 399p. pap. 15.95 *(978-0-9797627-0-3(7))* Jerant Publishing.

Avant, Brenda. A Mother's Nightmare: The Building of a Case. 2011. 148p. pap. 15.95 ***(978-1-4327-7063-1(2))*** Outskirts Pr., Inc.

Awoke, Tadesse. Psychological Problems of Physically Abused Children. 2011. 88p. pap. ***(978-3-639-32341-2(6))*** VDM Verlag Dr. Mueller e.K.

Bamba, Sachiko & Haight, Wendy. Child Welfare & Development: A Japanese Case Study. 2011. (ENG., Illus.). 224p. 80.00 ***(978-1-107-00284-5(2))*** Cambridge Univ. Pr.

Banks, LuWanda. Fragments. 2006. per. 13.95 *(978-0-9788000-0-0(1))* Bronze Goose Pr.

Barker, Judy & Hodes, Deborah. The Child in Mind. 3rd rev. ed. 2007. (Illus.). 128p. 31.95 *(978-0-415-42602-2(2))* Routledge.

—The Child in Mind: A Child Protection Handbook. 4th rev. ed. 2012. (ENG.). 136p. 115.00 *(978-0-415-60995-1(X))*; pap. 31.95 *(978-0-415-60996-8(8))* Routledge.

Barlow, Susanna. What Peace There May Be: A Memoir. 2007. 252p. (ENG.). 29.95 *(978-0-595-67832-7(7))*; per. 19.95 *(978-0-595-40777-4(3))* iUniverse, Inc.

Barrett, Janice L. Choosing to Survive: Seeds of Hope for Abused Children of All Ages. 2007. per. 9.95 *(978-0-9759116-2-4(7))* R. E. Farrellbooks, LLC.

Batmanghelidjh, Camila. Shattered Lives: Children Who Live with Courage & Dignity. 2007. (ENG., Illus.). 176p. per. *(978-1-84310-603-6(5))* Kingsley, Jessica Ltd.

B'Dunn, G. W. Dora's Child, 1 vol. 2009. 48p. pap. 16.95 *(978-1-60563-393-0(3))* PublishAmerica, Inc.

Benson, Edmund F. & Benson, Susan. Life Skills Curriculum: ARISE Work in Progress, Book 3. 2011. (Work in Progress Ser.). (Illus.). 102p. (YA). pap., wbk. ed. 14.95 *(978-1-58614-019-9(1))* Arise Foundation.

Bernard, Judy. Wanted — LOVE, 1 vol. 2010. 118p. pap. 19.95 *(978-1-4512-0000-3(5))* PublishAmerica, Inc.

Bibb, Wanda "Rose". Rose's Story. rev. ed. 2010. 86p. (C). pap. 18.95 *(978-1-57766-662-2(3))* Waveland Pr., Inc.

Bilo, Rob A. C., et al. Forensic Aspects of Pediatric Fractures: Differentiating Accidental Trauma from Child Abuse. 2010. (ENG., Illus.). xiv, 210p. 139.00 *(978-3-540-78715-0(1),* 3540787151) Springer.

Biniek, Lynese. Wearing Jeans to the Ball. 2007. pap. 19.95 *(978-0-9799156-0-4(0))* Parlo Bks.

Bisson, David & de Schonen, Evangéline. L' Enfant Derriere la Porte, Level B. (FRE.). 9.99 *(978-0-8219-1459-5(6),* 40335) EMC/Paradigm Publishing.

Borgstedt, John. I Love You Mom: Please Don't Break My Heart. 2009. 108p. 24.99 *(978-1-4490-4443-5(3))* AuthorHouse.

Brian Shawn. Downhill from the Projects. 2009. 528p. pap. 19.86 *(978-1-4269-2130-8(6))* Trafford Publishing.

Briggs, Kay. The Magic Seashells, from a Sea of Darkness to an Ocean of Love: Healing Depression & Childhood Abuse. Allen, Beth, ed. 2007. (ENG.). 158p. pap. 17.50 *(978-0-615-15762-7(9))* Briggs Benchmarks.

Brockliss, Laurence & Montgomery, Heather. Childhood & Violence in the Western Tradition. 2010. (Children in Archaeology Ser.). (ENG., Illus.). 352p. (C). 80.00 *(978-1-84217-978-9(0))* Oxbow Bks., Ltd. GBR. Dist: Brown, David Bk. Co., The.

Brown, Catherine. Laughter Calls Me: A Young Woman's Search for Truth Leads to a Courageous Battle to Save Her Children. 2nd ed. 2007. (ENG., Illus.). 160p. pap. 12.95 *(978-0-9721512-6-9(5))* Lighthouse Trails Publishing Co.

Brown, Petie. The Orphan & the King. 2007. 230p. per. *(978-0-615-16064-1(6))* Coqui Pr.

Burch, Cynthia. You'll See Jesus on My Face. 2011. 144p. pap. 12.95 ***(978-1-60920-014-5(4))*** Ajoyin Publishing, Inc.

Burke, Suzie. Wholeness: My Healing Journey from Ritual Abuse. 2010. 204p. 24.99 *(978-1-4490-5720-6(9))* AuthorHouse.

Campbell, Bobbie. Through it All, God Kept Me: A Candid Story of Feeling Unloved. 2007. 280p. per. 20.95 *(978-0-595-43457-2(6))* iUniverse, Inc.

Casey. Child of Stone. 2011. 68p. pap. 10.99 ***(978-1-4670-4418-9(0))*** AuthorHouse.

Castro, Joy. Island of Bones: Essays. 2012. (American Lives Ser.). (ENG.). 144p. pap. 16.95 ***(978-0-8032-7142-5(5),*** Bison Bks.) Univ. of Nebraska Pr.

Cattanach, Ann. Play Therapy with Abused Children: Second Edition. 2nd ed. 2008. (ENG., Illus.). 192p. pap. *(978-1-84310-587-9(X))* Kingsley, Jessica Ltd.

Chadwick, David L. The Child Abuse Doctors. 2010. (Illus.). 192p. lib. bdg. 35.00 *(978-1-878060-69-3(4))* STM Learning, Inc.

Chibaya Mbuya, John. Women & Child Abuse. 2010. 240p. pap. *(978-3-8383-7083-5(X))* Lambert Academic Publishing.

Childress, Nicole. Divine Providence: Finding Purpose in the in Between. 2009. pap. 14.99 *(978-1-60696-266-4(3))* Tate Publishing & Enterprises, LLC.

Clements, Paul T. & Seedat, Soraya. Mental Health Issues of Child Abuse, Guide/Atlas with CD. 2012. (ENG., Illus.). 650p. 275.00 *(978-1-878060-18-1(X))* STM Learning, Inc.

—Mental Health Issues of Child Maltreatment Quick Reference: For Healthcare, Social Service, & Law Enforcement Professionals. 2012. (ENG., Illus.). spiral bd. 52.00 *(978-1-878060-19-8(8))* STM Learning, Inc.

Cole, Trena. Splintered Emotions: Aftermath of Child Abuse. 2006. 208p. per. 14.95 *(978-0-9723535-9-5(3),* OPI) Oberpark Publishing, Inc.

Cram101 Textbook Reviews & Cram101 Textbook Reviews. Outlines & Highlights for Tell Me What Happened: Structured Investigative Interviews of Child Victims & Witnesses by Michael E. Lamb (University Of. 2011. 220p. pap. 30.95 ***(978-1-4288-4717-0(0))*** Cram101 Inc.

—Outlines & Highlights for Understanding Child Abuse & Neglect by Cynthia Crosson-Tower, Isbn: 9780205769155 0205769152. 2011. 170p. pap. 29.95 ***(978-1-4288-9068-8(8))*** Cram101 Inc.

Crawford, K. Renee. Christ Brings Out the Child in Me, 1 vol. 2009. 73p. pap. 16.95 *(978-1-60474-634-1(3))* PublishAmerica, Inc.

Crosson-Tower & Cram101 Textbook Reviews Staff. Understanding Child Abuse & Neglect. 2007. 136p. per. 11.95 *(978-1-4288-1984-9(3))* Cram101 Inc.

Crosson-Tower, Cynthia. Understanding Child Abuse & Neglect. 8th ed. 2009. (ENG.). 448p. (C). pap. 101.80 *(978-0-205-76915-5(2),* Prentice Hall) Prentice Hall PTR.

Curtis, Patricia. Legends of the Plastic Chairs. 2007. 204p. per. 19.95 *(978-1-59858-463-9(4))* Dog Ear Publishing, LLC.

Dance, Vivian L. & Vontress, Linda E. They Called me Slow, but the Light was Hidden in Me. 2011. 56p. pap. 11.49 *(978-1-4520-9184-6(6))* AuthorHouse.

Daniel, Brigid, et al. Recognizing & Helping the Neglected Child: Evidence-Based Practice for Assessment & Intervention. 2011. (ENG., Illus.). 176p. pap. ***(978-1-84905-093-7(7))*** Kingsley, Jessica Ltd.

D'Argan, Tanua LaSon. A Shelter in the Midst of a Storm: A True Life's Testimony, 1 vol. 2010. 395p. pap. 29.95 *(978-1-60703-302-8(X))* PublishAmerica, Inc.

Daro, Deborah. Confronting Child Abuse. 2007. (ENG.). 368p. pap. 23.95 *(978-1-4165-7334-0(8),* Free Pr.) Free Pr.

Daugherty, Lynn B. Why Me? Help for Victims of Child Sexual Abuse (Even if they are adults now), Fourth Edition. 4th rev. ed. 2007. 128p. per. 12.95 *(978-0-9771614-3-0(9))* Cleanan Pr., Inc.

Davidson, Julia & Hamerton, Christopher. International Perspectives on Child Victimisation. 2012. (ENG.). 208p. 125.00 *(978-0-415-57957-5(0))* Routledge.

Davies, Liz. Protecting Children: A resource Book. 2nd ed. 2010. (ENG., Illus.). 136p. pap. *(978-1-905179-07-7(3),* Lonely Scribe) Armadillo Design Ltd.

Davis, Diane. Groupwork with Adolescents: Ending the Intergeneration Cycle of Domestic Violence. ring bd. 49.95 *(978-0-9706637-4-0(9),* 04) Domestic Abuse Project.

Dawson, Revel & Dawson, Revel, III. Managing the Madness: From Addictions to Devotions. 2007. 354p. per. 19.99 *(978-1-60247-095-8(2))* Tate Publishing & Enterprises, LLC.

Dietrich, Anne. When the Hurting Continues. 2008. 120p. pap. *(978-3-639-02345-9(5))* VDM Verlag Dr. Mueller e.K.

Dodge, Kenneth A. Preventing Child Maltreatment: Community Approaches. Dodge, Kenneth A. & Coleman, Doriane Lambelet, eds. 2009. (Duke Series in Child Develpment & Public Policy Ser.). (ENG., Illus.). 203p. 45.00 *(978-1-59385-973-2(2))* Guilford Pubns., Inc.

Douglas, Kim. High Desert: A Journey of Survival & Hope. 2009. vii, 270p. *(978-1-931847-59-9(2))* Baha'i Publishing Trust, U.S.

Doyle, Celia. Working with Abused Children: Focus on Child. 4th rev. ed. 2012. (Practical Social Work Ser.). (ENG., Illus.). 304p. (C). pap. 31.00 ***(978-0-230-29794-4(3))*** Palgrave Macmillan.

Du Val, Talia & Du Val, Evelyn. After Maths: Cutting Silence. 2006. 254p. pap. 21.25 *(978-1-4120-9400-9(3))* Trafford Publishing.

Dubowitz, Howard & Merrick, Joav. International Aspects of Child Abuse & Neglect. 2011. (Series: Health & Human Development Ser.). xxii, 286p. pap. 69.00 *(978-1-61122-049-0(1))* Nova Science Pubs., Inc.

Dubowitz, Howard & Merrick, Joav, eds. International Aspects of Child Abuse & Neglect. 2010. (Health & Human Development (Joav Merrick - Series Editor - National Institute of Child Health & Human Development, Ministry of Social Affairs, Jerusalem Ser.). (Illus.). xxii, 286p. 125.00 *(978-1-60876-703-8(5))* Nova Science Pubs., Inc.

Finkelhor, David. Childhood Victimization: Violence, Crime & Abuse in the Lives of Young People. 2008. (Interpersonal Violence Ser.). (ENG., Illus.). 256p. 39.99 *(978-0-19-534285-7(2))* Oxford Univ. Pr., Inc.

Fleeman, Michael. Love You Madly: The True Story of a Small-town Girl, the Young Men She Seduced, & the Murder of her Mother. 2011. (ENG., Illus.). 256p. mass mkt. 7.99 ***(978-0-312-53089-1(7),*** St. Martin's True Crime) St. Martin's Pr.

Flegel, Monica. Creating Cruelty to Children in Nineteenth-Century England: Literature, Representation, & the NSPCC. 2009. (Ashgate Studies in Childhood, 1700 to the Present Ser.). 214p. 99.95 *(978-0-7546-6456-7(2))* Ashgate Publishing Co.

Fletcher, Tiffany. Mother Had a Secret: Learning to Love My Mother & Her Multiple Personalities: A True Story. 2010. 188p. ***(978-1-60861-058-7(6))*** Covenant Communications.

Fogle, Steve. Waiting for Dried Blood: Verbal Rain. 2009. 132p. 21.95 *(978-1-4401-8716-2(9))* iUniverse, Inc.

Foster, Chrissie. Hell on the Way to Heaven: An Australian Mother's Love - The Power of the Catholic Church, & a Fight for Justice over Child Sexual Abuse. 2010. (ENG., Illus.). 391p. 27.95 *(978-1-74166-952-7(9))* Random Hse. Australia AUS. Dist: Independent Pubs. Group.

Frasier, Lori D., et al. Abusive Head Trauma in Infants & Children; Supplementary CD-ROM: A Medical, Legal, & Forensic Reference Supplementary CD-ROM, 1 disc. 2007. (ENG., Illus.). cd-rom 215.00 *(978-1-878060-64-8(3))* STM Learning, Inc.

Garner, The Greatest Painful Blessings Scott. The Greatest PAINFUL Blessings. 2010. 71p. pap. 10.60 *(978-0-557-10981-4(7))* Lulu Enterprises Inc.

Gatling, Karen J. Behind the Bricks. 2009. 112p. pap. 14.99 *(978-1-4389-2085-6(7))* AuthorHouse.

Gayle, Petula. Unburried Secret. 2010. 96p. pap. 12.95 *(978-1-4389-9280-8(7))* AuthorHouse.

Gaynel, D. J. Child Abuse, Alcohol & Cancer: I Survived It All. 2008. 108p. 21.49 *(978-1-4389-1692-7(2))*; pap. 10.99 *(978-1-4389-1691-0(4))* AuthorHouse.

Gentles, Nicole K. Abby's Secret Abyss: 3D Child Abuse. 2011. 142p. 29.99 ***(978-1-4628-9400-0(3))***; pap. 19.99 ***(978-1-4628-9399-7(6))*** Xlibris Corp.

Gerali, Steven. What Do I Do When Teenagers Are Victims of Abuse?, 1 vol. 2009. (What Do I Do When Ser.). (ENG.). 128p. pap. 6.99 *(978-0-310-29195-4(X))* Zondervan.

Giardino, Angelo P., et al, eds. A Practical Guide to the Evaluation of Child Physical Abuse & Neglect. 2nd ed. 2010. (ENG., Illus.). xxxii, 400p. 159.00 *(978-1-4419-0701-1(7)*, 1441907017) Springer.

Gil, Eliana. Helping Abused & Traumatized Children: Integrating Directive & Nondirective Approaches. 2011. (ENG., Illus.). 254p. pap. 26.00 *(978-1-60918-474-2(2))* Guilford Pubns., Inc.

Gil, Eliana, ed. Working with Children to Heal Interpersonal Trauma: The Power of Play. 2010. (ENG., Illus.). 336p. 40.00 *(978-1-60623-892-9(2))* Guilford Pubns., Inc.

Gillard, Linda. The Broken Boy. 2008. 132p. pap. 11.95 *(978-1-4327-2678-2(1))* Outskirts Pr., Inc.

Glass, Cathy. Cut: The True Story of an Abandoned, Abused Little Girl Who Was Desperate to Be Part of a Family. 2009. (ENG.). 352p. pap. 12.95 *(978-0-00-728099-5(8))* HarperCollins Pubs. Ltd. GBR. Dist: Independent Pubs. Group.

—Damaged: The Heartbreaking True Story of a Forgotten Child. 2007. (ENG.). 352p. pap. 12.95 *(978-0-00-723636-7(0))* HarperCollins Pubs. Ltd. GBR. Dist: Independent Pubs. Group.

—Mummy Told Me Not to Tell: The True Story of a Troubled Boy with a Dark Secret. 2010. (ENG.). 352p. 11.95 *(978-0-00-736296-7(X))* HarperCollins Pubs. Ltd. GBR. Dist: Independent Pubs. Group.

—The Saddest Girl in the World. 2009. (ENG.). 320p. 13.95 *(978-0-00-728104-6(8))* HarperCollins Pubs. Ltd. GBR. Dist: Independent Pubs. Group.

Godley, Janey. Handstands in the Dark: A True Story of Growing up & Survival. 2006. (ENG.). 416p. per. 14.95 *(978-0-09-190877-5(9))* Random Hse. GBR. Dist: Independent Pubs. Group.

Grafton, Gordon J., compiled by. Lost Children of the Ohio Valley. 2008. (Illus.). vii, 175p. pap. *(978-1-55856-492-3(6))* Closson Pr.

Grande, Reyna. The Distance Between Us: A Memoir. 2012. pap. ***(978-1-4516-6178-1(9))***; (ENG., Illus.). 336p. 25.00 ***(978-1-4516-6177-4(0))*** Atria Bks. (Beyond Words/Atria Bks.).

Gunner, Rachel & Gabriele, Hanna. Beyond These Walls: The True Story of a Lost Child's Journey to a Whole Life. 2006. (Illus.). 244p. per. 16.95 *(978-0-9777691-0-0(0))* Argun Bks.

Hague, Gill, et al. The Experiences of Adult Survivors of Domestic Violence in Childhood: Strategies for Recovery for Children & Adults. 2012. (ENG.). 160p. pap. ***(978-1-84905-096-8(1))*** Kingsley, Jessica Ltd.

Hall, Tammie. Journey of Courage: A healing workbook for those who've experienced or are experiencing Abuse. 2010. pap. 14.99 *(978-1-61566-956-1(6))* Tate Publishing & Enterprises, LLC.

Harrell, Erika. Adolescent Victimization & Delinquent Behavior. 2010. 180p. pap. 32.95 *(978-1-59332-435-3(9))* LFB Scholarly Publishing LLC.

Harris, John. Still I Cry. 2007. 136p. per. *(978-1-84748-070-5(5))* Athena Pr.

Hattery, Angela & Smith, Earl. The Social Dynamics of Family Violence. 2012. (ENG.). 432p. (C). pap. 55.00 ***(978-0-8133-4463-8(8))***; E-Book ***(978-0-8133-4562-8(6))*** Westview Pr.

Heathman, Patricia Diann. Abused but Not Shaken, II: Child Neglect & Abuse. 2009. 77p. pap. 12.96 *(978-0-615-19498-1(2))* Voice of the Spirit.

Heimlich, Janet. Breaking Their Will: Shedding Light on Religious Child Maltreatment. 2011. (ENG.). 360p. pap. 20.00 *(978-1-61614-405-0(X))* Prometheus Bks., Pubs.

Henderson, Crystal. When My Father Preys. 2010. 256p. pap. 13.99 *(978-1-60844-477-9(5))* Dog Ear Publishing, LLC.

Heras, Ruth. My Pastures of Many Colors: A Diverse Journey to Godly Healing. 2010. 208p. 25.99 *(978-1-61579-538-3(3))*; pap. 15.99 *(978-1-61579-537-6(5))* Xulon Pr., Inc.

Hobart, Christine & Frankel, Jill. Good Practice in Safeguarding Children 3rd Edition. Walker, Miranda, ed. 3rd rev. ed. 2009. (ENG., Illus.). 224p. pap. 57.50 ***(978-1-4085-0491-8(X))*** Nelson Thornes Ltd. GBR. Dist: Trans-Atlantic Pubns., Inc.

Holland, Jimmy. Lost in Care: The True Story of a Forgotten Child. 2007. (Illus.). 288p. per. 14.95 *(978-1-84454-361-8(7))* Blake, John Publishing, Ltd. GBR. Dist: Independent Pubs. Group.

Howe, Mark L., et al, eds. Stress, Trauma, & Children's Memory Development: Neurobiological, Cognitive, Clinical, & Legal Perspectives. 2008. (ENG., Illus.). 352p. 55.00 *(978-0-19-530845-7(X))* Oxford Univ. Pr., Inc.

Humphreys, Cathy, et al. Talking about Domestic Abuse: A Photo Activity Workbook to Develop Communication Between Mothers & Young People. 2006. (ENG., Illus.). 112p. per. *(978-1-84310-423-0(7))* Kingsley, Jessica Ltd.

—Talking to My Mum: A Picture Workbook for Workers, Mothers & Children Affected by Domestic Abuse. 2006. (ENG., Illus.). 112p. per. *(978-1-84310-422-3(9))* Kingsley, Jessica Ltd.

Humphreys, Margaret. Oranges & Sunshine: Empty Cradles. 2011. (ENG., Illus.). 382p. pap. 12.95 ***(978-0-552-16335-4(X))*** Transworld Publishers Ltd. GBR. Dist: Independent Pubs. Group.

Hunter, William. Through Our Eyes: A Foster Family Shares Their Secret World. 2010. (ENG.). 274p. pap. 38.99 *(978-0-7618-5067-0(8))* Hamilton Bks.

Infancia y violencia en los Medios: Monitoreo de medios de Difusión. 2007. (SPA.). 64p. *(978-92-806-4159-2(X))* United Nations Children's Fund, The (UNICEF).

Itzin, Catherine, et al. Domestic & Sexual Violence & Abuse. 2010. (ENG., Illus.). 240p. (C). pap. 42.95 *(978-0-415-55532-6(9))* Routledge.

—Domestic & Sexual Violence & Abuse: Tackling the Health & Mental Health Effects. 2010. (ENG., Illus.). 240p. (C). 125.00 *(978-0-415-55531-9(0))* Routledge.

Iuculano, Margaret & Iuculano, Margaret. My God Box: Parable of the Incorrigible Child. 2007. pap. 14.95 *(978-0-9801415-0-4(8))* Penance Publishing.

Jaffe, Peter G., et al. Growing up with Domestic Violence. 2011. (Illus.). 78p. pap. 29.80 *(978-0-88937-336-5(1))* Hogrefe Publishing.

Jameel, Issam. Iraq Through a Bullet Hole: A Civilian Returns Home. 2008. 212p. pap. 19.95 *(978-1-932690-70-5(0)*, Modern History Pr.) Loving Healing Pr., Inc.

Jarrett, Billy D. Pretty Much Dead. 2007. per. 16.95 *(978-0-9797616-3-8(8))* Lionhead Pr., The.

Jenny, Carole. Child Abuse & Neglect: Diagnosis, Treatment & Evidence. 2010. (ENG., Illus.). 688p. 99.95 *(978-1-4160-6393-3(5)*, Saunders) Elsevier - Health Sciences Div.

Julsen, Sue. Bitter Memories: A Memoir of Heartache & Survival. 2010. 317p. pap. 18.95 *(978-1-4327-5048-0(8))* Outskirts Pr., Inc.

Kagan, Richard. Real Life Heroes: A Life Storybook for Children. 2nd rev. ed. 2007. (ENG., Illus.). 144p. per. 38.95 *(978-0-7890-2951-5(0))* Routledge.

—Real Life Heroes: Practitioner's Manual. 2007. (ENG., Illus.). 220p. per. 44.95 *(978-0-7890-2952-2(9))* Routledge.

Katherine, Nola. I Can Begin Again. 2011. 310p. 29.99 ***(978-1-4535-1162-6(8))***; pap. 19.99 ***(978-1-4535-1161-9(X))*** Xlibris Corp.

Keen, Shellie, et al. Why Me? A Programme for Children & Young People Who Have Experienced Victimization. 2010. (ENG., Illus.). 128p. pap. *(978-1-84905-097-5(X))* Kingsley, Jessica Ltd.

Keitt, Charlene Neal. A Journey into Wholeness: Walk into Your Journey of Wholeness. 2008. 164p. 22.49 *(978-1-4389-2311-6(2))*; pap. 11.99 *(978-1-4389-2310-9(4))* AuthorHouse.

Kemp, Suzi. The Shadows Within. 2010. pap. 10.99 *(978-1-61566-106-0(9))* Tate Publishing & Enterprises, LLC.

Key, Craig. A Deadly Game of Tug of War: The Kelsey Smith-Briggs Story. 2007. (ENG., Illus.). 145p. 26.95 *(978-1-60037-312-1(7))* Morgan James Publishing.

Kidd, Sharon W. Bloodpies: PAIN, TERROR, BLOOD... as experienced by an abused child who survived the trauma by floating Away. 2010. 100p. pap. 13.00 *(978-1-60844-452-6(X))* Dog Ear Publishing, LLC.

Kiser, Roger Dean. A Better Yesterday: Living Life after Abuse. 2010. (ENG.). 240p. pap. 12.95 *(978-0-7573-1360-8(4))* Health Communications, Inc.

Knight, Adam. Inside the Hurricane: Memories of Alcoholism & Child Abuse. 2010. 260p. pap. 19.95 *(978-1-4502-5613-1(9))* iUniverse, Inc.

Krill, William E. Gentling: A Practical Guide to Treating PTSD in Abused Children. 2009. *(978-1-61599-003-0(8))* 2nd ed. 2011. 274p. ***(978-1-61599-107-5(7))*** 2nd ed. 2011. 284p. pap. ***(978-1-61599-106-8(9))*** Loving Healing Pr., Inc.

Lamb, Michael E., et al. Tell Me What Happened: Structured Investigative Interviews of Child Victims & Witnesses. 2008. (Wiley Series in Psychology of Crime, Policing & Law Ser.). (ENG.). 386p. pap. 71.95 *(978-0-470-51866-3(9))*; 172.95 *(978-0-470-51865-6(0))* Wiley, John & Sons, Inc. (Wiley).

Lewis, James, III & Griffin, Dawn. Children Exposed to Violence: Current Issues, Interventions & Research. Zellner, Jennifer, ed. 2009. 266p. pap. 45.95 *(978-0-7890-3828-9(5))* Routledge.

—Children Exposed to Violence: Current Issues, Interventions & Research. Geffner, Bob & Zellner, Jennifer, eds. 2009. 266p. 130.00 *(978-0-7890-3827-2(7))* Routledge.

Linch, Jenna Kandyce. Heart & Soul of a Survivor. 2008. 288p. pap. 19.95 *(978-0-557-01354-8(2))* Lulu Enterprises Inc.

Lloyd, David. And God Was Watching. 2010. 150p. pap. 12.99 *(978-0-557-33793-4(3))* Lulu Enterprises Inc.

Lorier, April. God's Battered Child. 2007. 159p. pap. 15.95 *(978-0-7414-3896-6(8))* Infinity Publishing.

Louis, David. Scars That Can Heal: Does every life have Value? 2006. 420p. pap. 24.95 *(978-1-60145-053-1(2))* Booklocker.com, Inc.

Love, Jennifer C., et al. Skeletal Atlas of Child Abuse. 2011. (Springerâ€(tm)s Forensic Laboratory Science Ser.). (ENG., Illus.). xiii, 122p. 189.00 *(978-1-61779-215-1(2)*, 1617792152) Humana Pr.

Lund, Marynell. The Normal Side of Insanity. 2010. pap. 18.95 *(978-0-7414-5896-4(9))* Infinity Publishing.

Lutzker, John R., ed. Handbook of Child Abuse Research & Treatment. 2012. (Issues in Clinical Child Psychology Ser.). (ENG.). 596p. pap. 199.00 *(978-1-4419-3278-5(X)*, 144193278X) Springer.

M., Christy. A Life of Abuse. 2011. 76p. pap. 12.00 *(978-1-4269-4988-3(X))* Trafford Publishing.

MacLean, Gary E. I Didn't Know I Wasn't Black, 1 vol. 2009. 378p. pap. 29.95 *(978-1-60563-829-4(3))* PublishAmerica, Inc.

Madden, Amy. Stolen Beauty: Healing the Scars of Child Abuse: One Woman's Journey. 2007. 196p. per. 14.95 *(978-0-929636-74-0(0))* Syren Bk. Co.

Maloney, James. The Wounded Cry: A Testimony of Acceptance in Jesus Christ. 2011. 52p. pap. 9.95 ***(978-1-4497-2392-7(6)***, WestBow Pr.) Author Solutions, Inc.

Martin, W. C. Small Town, Big Miracle: How Love Came to the Least of These. 2007. (ENG., Illus.). 168p. pap. 13.99 *(978-1-58997-443-2(3))* Tyndale Hse. Pubs.

McGovern, Sharon. Afraid. (ENG.). 2010. 224p. pap. 14.95 *(978-0-7528-8412-7(3))* 2008. 244p. pap. 27.95 *(978-1-4091-0120-8(7))* Orion Publishing Group, Ltd. GBR. Dist: Independent Pubs. Group.

McKenzie, R. Strength from Within. 2008. 140p. per. *(978-1-84747-433-9(0))* Chipmunkapublishing.

Medina, Sarah. Abuse & Neglect. 2008. (Emotional Health Issues Ser.). (Illus.). 48p. (YA). (gr. 7-12). lib. bdg. 31.00 *(978-0-8368-9198-0(8))* Stevens, Gareth Publishing LLLP.

Mehrban, Shaida. Blossom & I: Tears Behind Closed Doors. 2010. 174p. pap. *(978-1-84748-702-5(5))* Athena Pr.

Mellvum, Sarah Jane. Life What's the Point. 2009. 332p. pap. 17.99 *(978-1-4389-2881-4(5))* AuthorHouse.

Merrick. Social Work & Child Abuse: Still Walking the Tightrope? 2nd rev. ed. 2006. 256p. 49.95 *(978-0-415-35415-8(3))* Routledge.

Merrick, Dave. Social Work & Child Abuse: Still Walking the Tightrope? 2nd rev. ed. 2006. 239p. 160.00 *(978-0-415-35414-1(5))* Routledge.

Merrikin, Elaine. God's Lent Child. 2006. 12.00 *(978-0-8059-9193-2(X))* Dorrance Publishing Co., Inc.

Milano, Rachel Elizabeth. The Mosaic: Shattered Pieces. Milano, Rachel Elizabeth, ed. ltd. ed. 2007. *(978-0-9794344-0-2(8))* Kekoon Publishing.

Miller, Alice. The Body Never Lies: The Lingering Effects of Hurtful Parenting. Jenkins, Andrew, tr. from GER. 2006. (ENG.). 224p. per. 15.95 *(978-0-393-32863-9(5)*, 32863) Norton, W. W. & Co., Inc.

Molho, George. Scarred: A Memoir. 2010. 408p. 32.95 *(978-1-4401-9514-3(5))*; pap. 22.95 *(978-1-4401-9513-6(7))* iUniverse, Inc.

Morellen, Gail. No Broken Bones. 2008. 272p. pap. 15.95 *(978-0-7414-4995-5(1))* Infinity Publishing.

Myers, Elizabeth. Shackled by Deceit, 1 vol. 2009. 267p. pap. 27.95 *(978-1-60813-749-7(X))* PublishAmerica, Inc.

Myers, John E. B. & American Professional Society on the Abuse of Children Staff. The APSAC Handbook on Child Maltreatment. Greenbaum, Jordan, ed. 3rd ed. 2010. 464p. (C). pap. 86.00 *(978-1-4129-6681-8(7)*, B66818P) SAGE Pubns., Inc.

Nash, Bryan. A Phoenix Rising: Defining the Moments. 2007. 286p. pap. 25.00 *(978-0-9797604-0-2(2))* Bryan Nash Pubns., LLC.

Nason-Clark, Nancy, et al, eds. Responding to Abuse in Christian Homes: A Challenge to Churches & their Leaders. 2011. (House of Prisca & Aquila Ser.). 262p. pap. 29.00 *(978-1-61097-178-2(7)*, Wipf and Stock) Wipf & Stock Pubs.

Neal, Gerald W. Quiet Desperation: The Effects of Competition in School on Abused & Neglected Children. 2008. (ENG.). 136p. pap. 29.50 *(978-0-7618-3993-4(3))* Hamilton Bks.

Neustein, Amy, ed. Tempest in the Temple: Jewish Communities & Child Sex Scandals. 2009. (Brandeis Series in American Jewish History, Culture & Life Ser.). (ENG.). 308p. 35.00 *(978-1-58465-671-5(9)*, Brandeis University Press) Univ. Pr. of New England.

NYSPCC Staff. The NYSPCC Professional's Handbook — Supervised Visitation for High-Risk Families. 2008. pap. 24.95 *(978-0-9628247-2-2(0))* New York Society for the Prevention of Cruelty to Children, The.

O'Malley, Kathleen. Childhood Interrupted: Growing up Unaer the Cruel Regime of the Sisters of Mercy. 2006. 244p. reprint ed. pap. 22.00 *(978-1-4223-5723-1(6))* DIANE Publishing Co.

Osinski, Jackie. Breaking the Back of Depression. 2010. 168p. pap. 14.95 *(978-1-60844-400-7(7))* Dog Ear Publishing, LLC.

Owen, Sue. Sue's Story: How I Survived a Lost Childhood. 2007. (ENG., Illus.). 288p. per. 15.95 *(978-1-84358-166-6(3))* Blake, John Publishing, Ltd. GBR. Dist: Independent Pubs. Group.

Palusci, Vincent J. & Fischer, Howard. Child Abuse & Neglect: A Diagnostic Guide for Physicians, Surgeons, Pathologists, Dentists, Nurses & Social Workers. 2010. (ENG., Illus.). 272p. 120.00 *(978-1-84076-123-8(7))* Manson Publishing, Ltd. GBR. Dist: Thieme Medical Pubs., Inc.

Past, Stormy. Caution: Surviving Your Childhood. 2010. 92p. pap. 13.99 *(978-1-4520-1286-5(5))* AuthorHouse.

Pearce, John W. & Pezzot-Pearce, Terry Dianne. Psychotherapy of Abused & Neglected Children. 2nd rev. ed. 2006. (ENG., Illus.). 411p. 50.00 *(978-1-59385-213-9(4))* Guilford Pubns., Inc.

Pelzer, Richard B. A Teenager's Journey: Overcoming a Childhood of Abuse. 2007. (ENG.). 240p. per. 13.99 *(978-0-446-69835-1(0))* Grand Central Publishing.

Penglase, Joanna. Orphans of the Living. 2007. (ENG.). 384p. pap. 18.00 *(978-1-920731-66-3(0))* Fremantle Pr. AUS. Dist: Independent Pubs. Group.

Pernicano, Pat. Family-Focused Trauma Intervention: Using Metaphor & Play with Victims of Abuse & Neglect. 2010. (ENG., Illus.). 212p. 52.50 *(978-0-7657-0772-7(1)*, Aronson, Jason) Rowman & Littlefield Publishers, Inc.

Peters, Martin. Wind Is Only a Spirit. 2009. 412p. 34.99 *(978-1-4363-8204-5(1))*; pap. 23.99 *(978-1-4363-8203-8(3))* Xlibris Corp.

Preventing Child Abuse & Improving Responses to Families in Crisis: Hearing Before the Subcommittee on Healthy Families & Communities, Committee on Education & Labor, U.S. House of Representatives, One Hundred Eleventh Congress, First Session, Hearing Held in Washington, DC, November 5, 2009. 2010. (Illus.). iii, 123p. *(978-0-16-086315-8(5)*, 552-070-41402-9) United States Government Printing Office.

Protecting Children, Strengthening Families: Reauthorizing CAPTA: Hearing Before the Subcommittee on Children & Families of the Committee on Health, Education, Labor, & Pensions, United States Senate, One Hundred Tenth Congress, Second Session, on Examining Reauthorization of the Child Abuse Prevention & Treatment ACT (CAPTA) (Public Law 93-247), Focusing on Protecting Children & Strengthening Families, June 26, 2008. 2009. iii, 83p. *(978-0-16-084909-1(8)*, 552-070-40305-1) United States Government Printing Office.

Ramsay, Mara. Abused Child Survivor: Could There Be Love at the End of the Tunnel? 2008. 48p. pap. 16.95 *(978-1-60672-304-3(9))* PublishAmerica, Inc.

Registrato, Joseph J. A Death in the Family. 2007. pap. 15.00 *(978-0-8059-8483-5(6))* Dorrance Publishing Co., Inc.

Reilly, Frances. Suffer the Little Children: The Harrowing True Story of a Girl's Brutal Convent Upbringing. 2010. (ENG.). 272p. pap. 12.95 *(978-0-7528-8080-8(2))* Orion Publishing Group, Ltd. GBR. Dist: Independent Pubs. Group.

—Suffer the Little Children: The True Story of an Abused Convent Up. 2010. (ENG.). 272p. pap. 19.95 *(978-0-7528-7533-0(7))* Orion Publishing Group, Ltd. GBR. Dist: Independent Pubs. Group.

Richards, Jo Lynn. The Ejected Child, 1 vol. 2009. 50p. pap. 16.95 *(978-1-61546-088-5(8))* PublishAmerica, Inc.

Richards, Nancy. Heal & Forgive II: The Journey from Abuse & Estrangement to Reconciliation. 2008. 172p. pap. 16.00 *(978-1-57733-220-6(2))* Blue Dolphin Publishing, Inc.

Richie, Douglas. My Annie: The True to Life Story of A Liberated Woman Written by Her Husband. 2011. (ENG.). 343p. pap. 15.95 ***(978-1-4327-7964-1(8))*** Outskirts Pr., Inc.

Robson, Julie. Can't Wait to Grow Older. 2009. 80p. pap. 9.95 *(978-1-60693-218-6(7)*, Eloquent Bks.) AEG Literary Publishing Services, Inc.

Ross, Timothy. Child Welfare: The Challenges of Collaboration. 2009. *(978-0-87766-756-8(X))* Urban Institute Pr.

Ross, Tracy. The Source of All Things: A Memoir. (ENG.). 2012. 320p. pap. 15.00 ***(978-1-4391-7298-8(6))*** 2011. 304p. 26.00 *(978-1-4391-7297-1(8))* Free Pr. (Free Pr.).

Rubio, John Agustin. Wounded Dogs & Werewolves: Out of a Life of Wreckage. 2011. 264p. 35.95 ***(978-1-4497-1851-0(5))***; pap. 19.95 ***(978-1-4497-1852-7(3))*** Author Solutions, Inc. (WestBow Pr.).

Sabbagh, Karl. Remembering our Childhood: How Memory Betrays Us. 2011. (ENG., Illus.). 240p. pap. 19.95 *(978-0-19-921841-7(2))* Oxford Univ. Pr., Inc.

Sabrina. Only the Strong Survive: O. T. S. s. 2009. 168p. pap. 13.99 *(978-1-4389-4827-0(1))* AuthorHouse.

Sahari, Nadia. Breakaway: How I Survived Abuse. 2008. 272p. pap. 19.95 *(978-0-9820413-0-7(6))* Pink Butterfly Pr.

Salmon, Doreen. One of a Kind. 2011. *(978-1-58982-786-8(4))* American Bk. Publishing Group.

Schuster, Mary Lay & Propen, Amy D. Victim Advocacy in the Courtroom: Persuasive Practices in Domestic Violence & Child Protection Cases. 2011. (Northeastern Series on Gender, Crime, & Law Ser.). (Illus.). 256p. (ENG.). (C). 85.00 *(978-1-55553-750-0(2))*; pap. 32.95 *(978-1-55553-749-4(9))* Univ. Pr. of New England. (Northeastern University Pr.).

Scott, Robert. Driven to Murder. 2008. (ENG., Illus.). 304p. 6.99 *(978-0-7860-1819-2(4)*, Pinnacle Bks.) Kensington Publishing Corp.

Seed, Michael & Botham, Noel. Nobody?'s Child. 2008. (ENG.). 288p. pap. 15.95 *(978-1-84454-588-9(1))* Blake, John Publishing, Ltd. GBR. Dist: Independent Pubs. Group.

—Nobody's Child. 2007. (ENG., Illus.). 288p. 27.95 *(978-1-84454-343-4(9))* Blake, John Publishing, Ltd. GBR. Dist: Independent Pubs. Group.

Shannon, Joyce, ed. Child Abuse Sourcebook. 2nd rev. ed. 2009. (Health Reference Ser.). 632p. lib. bdg. 93.00 *(978-0-7808-1037-2(6))* Omnigraphics, Inc.

Sirotnak, Andrew. Child Abuse & Neglect - Advancements & Challenges in the 21st Century: Pediatric Clinics of North America. 2009. (Clinics: Internal Medicine Ser.: 56-2). (ENG., Illus.). 240p. 78.00 *(978-1-4377-0519-5(7)*, Saunders) Elsevier - Health Sciences Div.

Smith, Misty. Why the Abuse. 2008. 72p. pap. 12.69 *(978-1-4389-2228-7(0))* AuthorHouse.

Smith, Nancy S. Ode to the Wicker Man: Book II (Bum Baby Bum!) 2007. 724p. per. 38.95 *(978-0-595-47457-8(8))* iUniverse, Inc.

Soares, Stacy. State of Sadness. 2008. 127p. pap. 11.95 *(978-0-7414-4669-5(3))* Infinity Publishing.

Sontag, Rachel. House Rules: A Memoir. 2009. (P. S. Ser.). 288p. pap. 13.99 *(978-0-06-134123-6(1)*, HarperPerennial) HarperCollins Pubs.

Spencer, Madeline A. A Shattered Life an Amazing God: When Fear Collides with Love. 2009. 364p. pap. 20.99 *(978-1-61579-259-7(7))* Xulon Pr., Inc.

Spiteri, Ylenia & Galea, Elizabeth M. Psychology of Neglect. 2012. (Psychology Research Progress Psychology of Emotions, Motivations & Actions Ser.). 212p. 95.00 ***(978-1-62100-180-5(6))*** Nova Science Pubs., Inc.

Stark, Sharon. Victims of Abuse, an Issue of Nursing Clinics. 2011. (Clinics: Nursing Ser.: 46-4). (ENG., Illus.). viii, 386p. 99.00 ***(978-1-4557-7986-4(5)***, Saunders) Elsevier - Health Sciences Div.

Sterne. Domestic Violence & Children: A Handbook for Schools & Early Years Settings. 2009. (ENG., Illus.). 160p. (C). 37.95 *(978-0-415-46551-9(6))* Routledge.

Sterne, Abigail & Poole, Liz. Domestic Violence & Children: A Handbook for Schools & Early Years Settings. 2009. (ENG., Illus.). 160p. (C). 130.00 *(978-0-415-55632-3(5))* Routledge.

Steve Fogle. Waiting for Dried Blood: Verbal Rain. 2009. 132p. pap. 11.95 *(978-1-4401-8715-5(0))* iUniverse, Inc.

Storm, Mystic. To Speak Out & Heal: The Good the Bad & the Ugly. 2009. 164p. pap. 15.00 *(978-1-4251-3992-6(2))* Trafford Publishing.

Sullivan, Irene. Raised by the Courts: One Judge's Insight into Juvenile Justice. 2010. (ENG.). 304p. 24.99 *(978-1-60714-638-4(X))* Kaplan Publishing.

Supernatural Soldier. Another-Way: Living to Live Again. 2011. 280p. 37.48 *(978-1-4269-5980-6(X))*; pap. 27.48 *(978-1-4269-5981-3(8))* Trafford Publishing.

Taiwo, Lydia Ola. A Broken Childhood: A True Story of Abuse. 2011. 94p. 22.50 ***(978-1-84624-590-9(7))*** Book Guild, Ltd. GBR. Dist: Trans-Atlantic Pubns., Inc.

Taylor, Kennesaw. Informally Educated: A True Tale of Child Abuse, Survival, & Murder. 2010. 256p. pap. 14.99 *(978-0-9844183-4-3(2))* Lemon Pr. LLC.

Theodore, Robert & Theodore, Shelly. Broken Child; Broken World, 1 vol. 2010. 192p. pap. 24.95 *(978-1-4489-4305-0(1))* PublishAmerica, Inc.

Thomas, Angela. Holding On. 2009. 60p. pap. 9.95 *(978-0-595-53305-3(1))* iUniverse, Inc.

Thomas, Sheale. I Walked A Mile with Sorrow. 2007. 336p. 29.95 *(978-1-4241-1987-5(1))* PublishAmerica, Inc.

Tracy, Steven R. Mending the Soul: Understanding & Healing Abuse. 2008. (ENG., Illus.). 272p. pap. 16.99 *(978-0-310-28529-8(1))* Zondervan.

Valerie Ann Hobbs. Learn to Love Not Hate: Now You Have a Place in the World Not Just in My Heart. 2009. (Illus.). 132p. pap. 10.99 *(978-1-4389-2884-5(X))* AuthorHouse.

Wade, Janelle. Out of Darkness. 2009. 244p. pap. 15.99 *(978-1-60791-517-1(0))* Xulon Pr., Inc.

Wade, Jim, et al. Caring for Abused & Neglected Children: Making the Right Decisions for Reunification or Long-Term Care. 2011. (ENG., Illus.). 240p. pap. *(978-1-84905-207-8(7))* Kingsley, Jessica Ltd.

Watson, Casey. The Boy No One Loved: A Heartbreaking True Story of Abuse Abandonment & Betrayal. 2011. (ENG.). 304p. 12.95 ***(978-0-00-743656-9(4))*** HarperCollins Pubs. Ltd. GBR. Dist: Independent Pubs. Group.

—Crying for Help: The Shocking True Story of a Damaged Girl with a Dark Past. 2012. (ENG.). 304p. 12.95 ***(978-0-00-743658-3(0))*** HarperCollins Pubs. Ltd. GBR. Dist: Independent Pubs. Group.

Watson, Irene. The Sitting Swing: Finding Wisdom to Know the Difference. 2009. 248p. pap. *(978-1-932690-67-5(0))* Loving Healing Pr., Inc.

Watt, Kelly. The Fourteenth Year. 2007. 124p. pap. 12.95 *(978-1-934248-25-6(8))* Mill City Pr., Inc.

Wattey, Linda D. Something about an Angel. 2007. 240p. per. 15.99 *(978-0-9798084-8-7(0))* Leading Lady Pubns.

Weinberg, Lois A. The Systematic Mistreatment of Children in the Foster Care System: Through the Cracks. 2007. (ENG.). 358p. (C). 125.00 *(978-0-7890-2392-6(X))*; 354p. per. 60.50 *(978-0-7890-2393-3(8))* Routledge.

Welles, Caryn. Hollyhocks on the Fence: Hope blooms among the Weeds. 2009. pap. 16.99 *(978-1-61566-072-8(0))* Tate Publishing & Enterprises, LLC.

Wells, Mary Ann. Damaged & Broken: Memoirs of an Abused Child, 1 vol. 2009. 91p. pap. 14.95 *(978-1-61582-928-6(8))* PublishAmerica, Inc.

Westfall, L. A. Mother II. 2007. 212p. per. *(978-1-84747-439-1(X))* Chipmunkapublishing.

White, Earnestine. Plucked Flower We Made It! 2009. 172p. pap. 11.99 *(978-1-4490-1686-9(3))* AuthorHouse.

Wilde, James. Three Shattered Souls. 2009. 380p. pap. 28.49 *(978-1-4490-3354-5(7))* AuthorHouse.

Wilson, Betty Lee. One Link at a Time: Chains Can Be Broken. 2007. 140p. per. 13.95 *(978-0-595-44806-7(2))* iUniverse, Inc.

Winner, Karen. Placing Children at Risk: Questionable Psychologists & Therapists in the Sacramento Family Court... pap. 25.00 *(978-0-9669126-1-6(6))* Justice Seekers, Inc., The.

Wright, Danny E. Road to Redemption. 2007. 91p. pap. 9.95 *(978-0-7414-4200-0(0))* Infinity Publishing.

ABUSED HUSBANDS

Cook, Philip W., ed. Abused Men: The Hidden Side of Domestic Violence, 1 vol. 2nd ed. 2009. (Illus.). 260p. 49.95 *(978-0-313-35618-6(1))*, C35618, Praeger Pubs.) Greenwood Publishing Group, Inc.

ABUSED MEN

see also Husband Abuse

Blotner, Edward S. No Family Album: Chronicles of a Foster Care Survivor. 2010. 204p. 27.95 *(978-1-4502-1254-0(9))*; pap. 17.95 *(978-1-4502-1252-6(2))* iUniverse, Inc.

Burchett, Author Walter, BA. An abused man's battles, trying to protect his Boys. 2007. 65p. pap. 14.95 *(978-0-615-15191-5(4))* Crossover Ministries.

Cook, Philip W., ed. Abused Men: The Hidden Side of Domestic Violence, 1 vol. 2nd ed. 2009. (Illus.). 260p. 49.95 *(978-0-313-35618-6(1))*, C35618, Praeger Pubs.) Greenwood Publishing Group, Inc.

León, Karlonda. Beautiful Black Bastard. 2009. 56p. pap. 15.99 *(978-1-4415-3784-3(8))* Xlibris Corp.

Mantell, Andy & Scragg, Terry, eds. Safeguarding Adults in Social Work. 2nd rev. ed. 2011. (ENG., Illus.). 224p. pap. *(978-0-85725-401-6(4))* Learning Matters Ltd.

McGuire, Stephen Ezra. My History of Drug Abuse, 1 vol. 2009. 48p. pap. 16.95 *(978-1-61546-529-1(X))* PublishAmerica, Inc.

Oakes, Samuel Lee. Spring in Black & White: A Partner's Journey Through Abuse. 2012. pap. 12.95 ***(978-0-7414-6970-0(7))*** Infinity Publishing.

Owen Esquire, Sally A. How to Destroy a Man in One Easy Step: MEN; Guilty until Proven Innocent! 2008. 88p. pap. 11.95 *(978-1-4401-0790-0(4))* iUniverse, Inc.

Penhale, Bridget & Parker, Jonathan. Working with Vulnerable Adults. (Social Work Skills Ser.). (Illus.). 189p. 2008. 150.00 *(978-0-415-30190-9(4))* 2007. per. 39.95 *(978-0-415-30191-6(2))* Routledge.

Pritchard, Jacki. Working with Adult Abuse: A Training Manual for People Working with Vulnerable Adults. 2007. (Jkp Resource Materials Ser.). (ENG., Illus.). 416p. per. *(978-1-84310-509-1(8))* Kingsley, Jessica Ltd.

Pritchard, Jacki & Pritchard, Jackie Lee. Recording Skills in Safeguarding Adults: Best Practice & Evidential Requirements. 2010. (ENG., Illus.). 192p. pap. *(978-1-84905-112-5(7))* Kingsley, Jessica Ltd.

Vargas Sánchez, Juan. El Hombre Que Ejerce la Violencia Intrafamiliar: Hacia una Psicoterapia Psicoanalítica Desde Ciudad Juárez. 2010. (SPA., Illus.). 131p. *(978-607-7519-78-2(2))*; *(978-607-477-331-6(3))* Universidad Autonoma Metropolitana.

Wedlake, Nick. Eat the Pretty Ones: A Testament. 2009. 236p. 24.99 *(978-1-4490-1714-9(2))* AuthorHouse.

Wexler, David B. Stop Domestic Violence: Innovative Skills, Techniques, Options, & Plans for Better Relationships. 2nd ed. 2006. (ENG., Illus.). 288p. pap. 32.00 incl. cd-rom *(978-0-393-70514-0(5))*, 70514) Norton, W. W. & Co., Inc.

ABUSED PARENTS

Lutzker, John R., ed. Handbook of Child Abuse Research & Treatment. 2012. (Issues in Clinical Child Psychology Ser.). (ENG.). 596p. pap. 199.00 *(978-1-4419-3278-5(X))*, 144193278X) Springer.

ABUSED WIVES

see also Children of Abused Wives

Abrahams, Hilary. Rebuilding Lives after Domestic Violence: Understanding Long-Term Outcomes. 2010. (Illus.). 176p. pap. *(978-1-84310-961-7(1))* Kingsley, Jessica Ltd.

Al-Banz, Rania. Disfigured: A Saudi Woman's Story of Triumph over Violence. Spencer, Catherine, tr. from FRE. 2008. (ENG.). 176p. pap. 15.00 *(978-1-56656-735-0(1))* Interlink Publishing Group, Inc.

Armstrong, Taylor. Hiding from Reality: My Story of Love, Loss, & Finding the Courage Within. 2012. (ENG., Illus.). 272p. 25.00 ***(978-1-4516-7771-3(5))*** Gallery Pr., The IRL. Dist: Simon & Schuster, Inc.

Attaud, Ivette. My Life, My Soul - Surviving, Healing & Thriving after an Abusive Relationship: Part 1: Surviving. 2011. 232p. mass mkt. 15.95 *(978-0-615-44061-3(4))* MLMS Publishing.

B., Annie. The Life I Was Dealt: Right When You Think You Can't Handle Anything Else. 2009. 244p. 29.95 *(978-1-4401-2508-9(2))*; pap. 19.95 *(978-1-4401-2506-5(6))* iUniverse, Inc.

Benson, Edmund F. & Benson, Susan. Life Skills Curriculum: ARISE Work in Progress, Book 3. 2011. (Work in Progress Ser.). (Illus.). 102p. (YA). pap., wbk. ed. 14.95 *(978-1-58614-019-9(1))* Arise Foundation.

Brown, Emma. The Abuser's Shadow. 2009. 144p. pap. *(978-1-84923-872-4(3))* YouWriteOn.

Brownridge, Douglas A. & Brownridge, Douglas A. Violence Against Women: Vulnerable Populations. 2009. (Contemporary Sociological Perspectives Ser.). (ENG., Illus.). 320p. 41.95 *(978-0-415-99608-2(2))*; 144.00 *(978-0-415-99607-5(4))* Routledge.

Chapman, Geraldine. Dressed Like Your Father: A Battered Wife's Story of Survival. 2007. 192p. per. *(978-1-55452-220-0(X))*, Guardian Bks.) Essence Publishing.

Conrad, Becky. A Better Day Dawning. 2006. 734p. pap. 29.95 *(978-0-7414-3363-3(X))* Infinity Publishing.

Cordwell, Sheila. Before Lynn. 2010. (Illus.). 92p. pap. *(978-1-84748-730-8(0))* Athena Pr.

Cory, Jill & McAndless-Davis, Karen. When Love Hurts: A Woman's Guide to Understanding Abuse in Relationships. 2nd ed. 2008. 106p. (Orig.). pap. 19.95 *(978-0-9686016-1-7(8))* WomanKind Pr. CAN. Dist: AtlasBooks Distribution.

Dalpiaz, Christina M. Breaking Free, Starting Over: Parenting in the Aftermath of Family Violence, 1 vol. 2008. 248p. pap. 19.95 *(978-0-313-36315-3(3))*, B36315, Praeger Trade) Greenwood Publishing Group, Inc.

Dolan, Frances E. Marriage & Violence: The Early Modern Legacy. 2009. (Illus.). 248p. (C). pap. 22.50 *(978-0-8122-2082-7(X))* Univ. of Pennsylvania Pr.

Ellis. Surviving Domestic Abuse. 2011. 332p. pap. 18.99 ***(978-1-61379-023-6(6))*** Xulon Pr., Inc.

Giles, Janice. Growing Through Adversity - Personal Growth & Recovery from Intimate Partner Abuse. 2008. 292p. pap. *(978-3-639-04274-0(3))* VDM Verlag Dr. Mueller e.K.

James, Nikola T. The Price of Love. 2007. (ENG.). 224p. per. 20.95 *(978-0-283-07056-3(0))* Macmillan Pubs., Ltd. GBR. Dist: Independent Pubs. Group.

Kinman, Diane, ed. Traveling in Time from the Philippines to Alaska: A Memoir. 2007. per. *(978-0-9763929-1-0(7))* Wimer Publishing Co.

Landon, Maria. Escaping Daddy. 2009. (ENG.). 352p. 12.95 *(978-0-00-726883-2(1))* HarperCollins Pubs. Ltd. GBR. Dist: Independent Pubs. Group.

Leonarde, Marie B. Domestic Violence. My Story. 2006. pap. 14.95 *(978-0-9786296-5-6(5))* Hudson Bks.

Mitchell, Connie. Intimate Partner Violence: A Health-Based Perspective. Mitchell, Connie, ed. 2009. (ENG., Illus.). 336p. 98.50 *(978-0-19-517932-3(3))* Oxford Univ. Pr., Inc.

Muhammad, Mildred. Scared Silent. 2010. (ENG.). 304p. pap. 19.99 *(978-1-59309-242-9(3))*, Strebor Bks.) Strebor Bks.

Oriola, Bukola. Imprisoned: The Travails of a Trafficked Victim. rev. ed. 2009. 155p. pap. 19.50 *(978-0-615-32880-5(6))* Bukola Braiding & Beauty Supply.

Plesset, Sonja. Sheltering Women: Negotiating Gender & Violence in Northern Italy. 2006. (ENG.). 264p. 50.00 *(978-0-8047-5301-2(6))* Stanford Univ. Pr.

Roth, Marika. All the Pretty Shoes. 2011. 254p. pap. 15.00 ***(978-1-936214-27-3(X))*** Wyatt-MacKenzie Publishing.

Salamone, Nancy. Victory over Violence: Nancy's Story & the Business of Me. 2010. 108p. (ENG.). 22.50 *(978-1-4520-2508-7(8))*; pap. 10.99 *(978-1-4520-2507-0(X))* AuthorHouse.

Steiner, Leslie Morgan. Crazy Love. 2010. (ENG.). 352p. pap. 14.99 *(978-0-312-37746-5(0))*, St. Martin's Griffin) St. Martin's Pr.

Van Buskirk, Penelope. For Worse Never Better: Diary of an Abused Wife & Escape to Freedom. 2010. 244p. 24.99 *(978-1-4520-3863-6(5))*; pap. 10.99 *(978-1-4520-3864-3(3))* AuthorHouse.

Wall, Elissa & Pulitzer, Lisa. Stolen Innocence: My Story of Growing Up in a Polygamous Sect, Becoming a Teenage Bride, & Breaking Free of Warren Jeffs. 2009. (ENG.). 464p. mass mkt. 7.99 *(978-0-06-173496-0(9))* HarperCollins Pubs.

Wooldridge, Sue. Miracles upon Miracles. 2006. 120p. per. 15.95 *(978-1-59858-182-9(1))* Dog Ear Publishing, LLC.

Wyatt, Caryl. Look Me in the Eye: Caryl's Story. 2008. 248p. pap. 18.95 *(978-1-920143-06-0(8))* 30° South Pubs. ZAF. Dist: International Publishers Marketing.

ABUSED WIVES—LEGAL STATUS, LAWS, ETC.

Freeman, Michael A. Domestic Violence. 2008. (Family, Law & Society Ser.). 638p. 350.00 *(978-0-7546-2644-2(X))* Ashgate Publishing Co.

Meyersfeld, Bonita. Domestic Violence & International Law. 2010. (ENG.). 370p. 90.00 *(978-1-84113-911-1(4))* Hart Publishing Ltd. GBR. Dist: International Specialized Bk. Services.

Radford, Lorraine & Hester, Marianne. Mothering Through Domestic Violence. 2006. (ENG., Illus.). 176p. per. *(978-1-84310-473-5(3))* Kingsley, Jessica Ltd.

ABUSED WIVES—SERVICES FOR

Strom, Kay Marshall. In the Name of Submission: A Painful Look at Wife Battering. 2008. 140p. pap. 17.00 *(978-1-55635-770-1(2))* Wipf & Stock Pubs.

ABUSED WIVES' CHILDREN

see Children of Abused Wives

ABUSED WOMEN

see also Abused Wives

Adams-Evans, Gwendolyn D. Jobleen: A Woman of Strength. 2011. 88p. pap. 11.99 ***(978-1-4670-3596-5(3))*** AuthorHouse.

Adams, Rebekkah. Glass Houses: Saving Feminist Anti-Violence Agencies from Self-Destruction. 2008. (ENG.). 128p. pap. 17.95 *(978-1-55266-265-6(9))* Fernwood Publishing Co., Ltd. CAN. Dist: Independent Pubs. Group.

Akseer, Riaz & Arai, Susan. Accessing Community Supports among Women Who Have Experienced Traum. 2010. 188p. pap. *(978-3-8383-7883-1(0))* Lambert Academic Publishing.

Allen Garland, Emily. Baby Heart. 2009. 324p. pap. 17.99 *(978-1-4389-4835-5(2))* AuthorHouse.

Allen, Mary. Narrative Therapy for Women Experiencing Domestic Violence: Supporting Women's Transitions from Abuse to Safety. 2011. (ENG.). 144p. pap. ***(978-1-84905-190-3(9))*** Kingsley, Jessica Ltd.

AmHealthResInst. Assault of Females in the U. S. with Index & Medical Analysis of New Research Information for All Nations, 5 vols. 2006. (Reference & Research Ser.: 2). 160p. Vol. 2. 59.95 *(978-0-7883-4626-2(1))*, 07883-46261) Vol. 3. 3rd ed. 59.95 *(978-0-7883-4627-9(X))*, 07883-4627X) ABBE Pubs. Assn. of Washington, D.C.

AmResInst. Assault of Females in the U. S. with Index & Medical Analyis of New Research Information for All Nations, 5 vols, Vol. 1. 2006. (Reference & Research Ser.: 1). 160p. 59.95 *(978-0-7883-4625-5(3))*, 07883-46253) ABBE Pubs. Assn. of Washington, D.C.

Anding, Rose Maria McCarthy. High Heels, Honey Lips, & White Powder: The Tales & Salvation of a Proverbs 5 Woman. 2010. pap. 14.99 *(978-1-61663-360-8(3))* Tate Publishing & Enterprises, LLC.

Andrews, Sophie. Scarred: One Girl's Triumph over Shocking Abuse & Self-Harm. 2008. (ENG.). 326p. pap. 25.95 *(978-0-340-93748-8(3))*, Hodder & Stoughton) Hodder General Publishing Div. GBR. Dist: Independent Pubs. Group.

Arlether, Wilson/Ann. Rewriting the Script. 2007. 399p. pap. 15.95 *(978-0-9797627-0-3(7))* Jerant Publishing.

Armstrong, Alice. Culture & Choice: Lessons from Survivors of Gender Violence in Zimbabwe. (Illus.). 149p. 12.00 *(978-0-7974-1835-6(0))*, WE429) Southern African Research & Documentation Centre ZWE. Dist: Women Ink.

Bancroft, Mel. The Melody of My BitterSweet Blues. 2009. 238p. 22.99 *(978-1-4415-8924-8(4))*; pap. 15.99 *(978-1-4415-8923-1(6))* Xlibris Corp.

Banks, Evangelist Rosie L. Abused & Suffered for You. 2011. 48p. pap. 12.95 *(978-1-4502-8037-2(4))* iUniverse, Inc.

Banks, T. He Won't Hit Me, He Won't Hit Me Again, We Thought That Too. 2007. 56p. per. 16.95 *(978-1-4241-7782-0(0))* PublishAmerica, Inc.

Bannon, S. S. Thriving the 8th Step. 2010. pap. 10.95 *(978-0-7414-6085-1(8))* Infinity Publishing.

Bedford, Terri-Jean. Dominatrix on Trial: Bedford vs. Canada. 2011. 276p. 28.95 ***(978-1-4620-2677-7(X))***; pap. 18.95 ***(978-1-4620-2676-0(1))*** iUniverse, Inc.

Belle, Anna. Broken Image. 2011. 332p. pap. 29.95 ***(978-1-4626-0683-2(0))*** PublishAmerica, Inc.

Bergen, Raquel Kennedy, et al, eds. Companion Reader on Violence Against Women. 2011. (Illus.). 424p. (C). pap. 36.00 *(978-1-4129-9649-5(X))*, B96495P) SAGE Pubns., Inc.

Bergen, Raquel Kennedy, et al. Sourcebook on Violence Against Women. Edleson, Jeff, ed. 2nd ed. 2010. (Illus.). 424p. (C). pap. 86.00 *(978-1-4129-7166-9(7))*, B71669P) SAGE Pubns., Inc.

Bernard, Judy. Wanted — LOVE, 1 vol. 2010. 118p. pap. 19.95 *(978-1-4512-0000-3(5))* PublishAmerica, Inc.

Black, Mona Lisa. You Can't Fall off the Floor. 2011. 140p. pap. 11.95 *(978-1-4620-0811-7(9))* iUniverse, Inc.

Blankenship, Richard. Sarah. 2007. pap. 13.99 *(978-1-60034-972-0(2))* Xulon Pr., Inc.

Blea-Torres, Antonia. On the Wings of Hope: Devotions on Life Transformation. 2011. pap. 10.99 *(978-1-61739-718-9(0))* Tate Publishing & Enterprises, LLC.

Blitz, Lisa. Sanctuary from Oppression. 2009. 364p. pap. *(978-3-639-11222-1(9))* VDM Verlag Dr. Mueller e.K.

Boucher, Jane. Escaping Domestic Abuse: How Women Get Out & Stay Out. 2009. pap. 12.99 *(978-1-60374-091-3(0))* Whitaker Hse.

Brake, Jacqueline. The Victim of Abuse. 2008. 132p. per. 12.95 *(978-1-4327-1507-6(0))* Outskirts Pr., Inc.

Brennan, Kate & None. In His Sights: One Woman's Stalking Nightmare. 2009. (P. S. Ser.). (ENG.). 304p. pap. 13.99 *(978-0-06-145162-1(2))*, HarperPerennial) HarperCollins Pubs.

Brown, Tiffany D. My Heart Wonders: My Hurt & Pain. 2011. 80p. pap. 13.99 ***(978-1-4567-5939-1(6))*** AuthorHouse.

Brownridge, Douglas A. & Brownridge, Douglas A. Violence Against Women: Vulnerable Populations. 2009. (Contemporary Sociological Perspectives Ser.). (ENG., Illus.). 320p. 41.95 *(978-0-415-99608-2(2))*; 144.00 *(978-0-415-99607-5(4))* Routledge.

Brush, Lisa D. Poverty, Battered Women, & Work in U. S. Public Policy, 1 vol. 2011. (Interpersonal Violence Ser.). (ENG., Illus.). 208p. 35.00 ***(978-0-19-539850-2(5))*** Oxford Univ. Pr., Inc.

Burrell, Yvonne D. The Positive Effects of Psycho-Educational Treatment on Female Victims of Sexual Trauma. 2007. 264p. (ENG.). 69.95 *(978-1-4327-0713-2(2))*; per. 59.95 *(978-1-4327-0040-9(5))* Outskirts Pr., Inc.

Byrns, Jeanne. The Eyes Have It. 2011. 208p. 25.05 ***(978-1-4269-8168-5(6))***; pap. 15.05 ***(978-1-4269-8167-8(8))*** Trafford Publishing.

Cairns, Kathleen A. The Enigma Woman: The Death Sentence of Nellie May Madison. 2009. (Women in the West Ser.). (ENG., Illus.). 328p. pap. 16.95 *(978-0-8032-2450-6(8))*, Bison Bks.) Univ. of Nebraska Pr.

Capozzi, Ruth Joy. With Tender Hand: Abuse Is Not Love / Love Is Not Abuse. 2011. 108p. 28.95 ***(978-1-4497-1818-3(3))***; pap. 9.95 ***(978-1-4497-1815-9(7))*** Author Solutions, Inc. (WestBow Pr.).

Carr, Latunya E. A Psalm to Dance To. 2011. 200p. pap. 15.99 ***(978-1-61379-021-2(X))*** Xulon Pr., Inc.

Carroll, Elishiva. Corrupted. 2010. 171p. pap. 14.63 *(978-0-557-52228-6(5))* Lulu Enterprises Inc.

Carver, M. Heather & Lawless, Elaine J. Troubling Violence: A Performance Project. (ENG.). 160p. 2010. pap. 25.00 *(978-1-60473-869-8(3))* 2009. 50.00 *(978-1-60473-208-5(3))* Univ. Pr. of Mississippi.

Champe, E. Diane. Conquering Incest: My Life as a Trauma Survivor. 2011. 300p. pap. 24.95 ***(978-1-4575-0117-3(1))*** Dog Ear Publishing, LLC.

Chesney-Lind, Meda & Morash, Merry. Feminist Theories of Crime. 2011. (Library of Essays in Theoretical Criminology Ser.). 592p. 325.00 ***(978-0-7546-2971-9(6))*** Ashgate Publishing Co.

Chibaya Mbuya, John. Women & Child Abuse. 2010. 240p. pap. *(978-3-8383-7083-5(X))* Lambert Academic Publishing.

Chubb, Eileen. Beyond the Facade. 2008. 356p. pap. *(978-1-84747-633-3(3))* Chipmunkapublishing.

Clark, Ron. Freeing the Oppressed: A Call to Christians concerning Domestic Abuse. 2009. 172p. pap. 20.00 *(978-1-60608-484-7(4))*, Cascade Bks.) Wipf & Stock Pubs.

Clark, Sharon L. The Wife Who Walked Away: A Journey Through Abuse. 2009. 220p. pap. 17.95 *(978-1-4401-6605-1(6))* iUniverse, Inc.

Cook, Daphiny. Bourbon Street Stripper to New Orleans Lady! The Life of My Dreams; the Dreams of A Life. 2011. 144p. pap. 24.95 ***(978-1-4560-5460-1(0))*** PublishAmerica, Inc.

Cook, Lupita -Luna. Deliverance Out of Egypt: Time to Break the Chains from Physical Abuse, Mental Abuse & Suicidal Abuse! Time to do it Gods Way! 2011. 64p. pap. 10.43 ***(978-1-4269-7658-2(5))*** Trafford Publishing.

Cook, Philip W., ed. Abused Men: The Hidden Side of Domestic Violence, 1 vol. 2nd ed. 2009. (Illus.). 260p. 49.95 *(978-0-313-35618-6(1))*, C35618, Praeger Pubs.) Greenwood Publishing Group, Inc.

Cory, Jill & McAndless-Davis, Karen. When Love Hurts: A Woman's Guide to Understanding Abuse in Relationships. 2nd ed. 2008. 106p. (Orig.). pap. 19.95 *(978-0-9686016-1-7(8))* WomanKind Pr. CAN. Dist: AtlasBooks Distribution.

Costello, Angel. I Died a Little Every Night. 2011. 220p. 24.59 ***(978-1-4567-6184-4(6))***; pap. 14.03 ***(978-1-4567-6186-8(2))*** AuthorHouse.

Cota, Dee. A Monster in Disguise/Is He Jekel or Is He Hyde: 12 Signs You May Be in an Abusive/Dangerous/Relationship. 2010. 96p. pap. 11.95 *(978-1-4502-2986-9(7))* iUniverse, Inc.

Cox, M. J. Sour Face: A domestic abusive Relationship. 2008. 264p. pap. *(978-1-84747-760-6(7))* Chipmunkapublishing.

Dauplaise, Mike. Torture at the Back Forty: The Gang Rape & Slaying of Margaret Anderson. 2009. pap. 12.95 *(978-0-9820009-3-9(6))* Titletown Publishing LLC.

Davidson, Melody. Ain't Nothing Like Being Married to an Old, Elderly Man. 2011. 132p. 24.99 ***(978-1-4634-0913-5(3))***; pap. 16.00 ***(978-1-4634-0914-2(1))*** AuthorHouse.

Davis, Dana-Ain. Battered Black Women & Welfare Reform: Between a Rock & a Hard Place. 2006. (SUNY Series in African American Studies). 215p. per. 29.95 *(978-0-7914-6844-9(5))* State Univ. of New York Pr.

Denney, Sue. Garden of Life. 2011. 20p. pap. 13.95 ***(978-1-61507-901-8(7))*** Cross Bks. Publishing.

DeOrio, Randy A. Jaded: A True Story. 2011. 292p. 29.95 *(978-1-4567-1287-7(X))*; pap. 19.95 *(978-1-4567-1289-1(6))* AuthorHouse.

Deverick, Helen. Thought's of Mind. 2010. 68p. pap. 10.49 *(978-1-4490-8220-8(3))* AuthorHouse.

Dillner, Eva. Secrets of Transformation. 2008. 256p. *(978-91-976309-8-6(5))* Divine Design.

Doe, Jane. My Name Is Jane Doe: Book Two. 2011. 208p. pap. 17.95 *(978-1-4620-0641-0(8))* iUniverse, Inc.

Donaldson MA, Charlie. Restorative Treatment: The Newest Specialty in Counseling. 2007. 160p. pap. 30.00 *(978-0-9801390-0-6(7))* Therapist Outfitters Pubns.

Donaldson MA LLP LPC CAC1, Charlie. Interventions for Men Who Abuse Women: Manual & Activities for Facilitating Domestic Abuse Groups. 2007. 67p. pap. 20.00 *(978-0-9801390-1-3(5))* Therapist Outfitters Pubns.

Dragiewicz, Molly. Equality with a Vengeance: Men's Rights Groups, Battered Women, & Antifeminist Backlash. 2011. (Northeastern Series on Gender, Crime, & Law Ser.). (Illus.). 168p. (C). 85.00 *(978-1-55553-738-8(3))*; (ENG., pap. 26.00 *(978-1-55553-739-5(1))* Univ. Pr. of New England. (Northeastern University Pr.).

Dunaway, Martha. A Clock Without Hands: A Story of Abuse, Neglect, Escape & Survival in Eastern Kentucky. 2007. 212p. per. 24.95 *(978-1-4241-3634-6(2))* PublishAmerica, Inc.

Durham, Stella. Lord Help Me!A I Still Love Him. 2008. 81p. pap. 16.95 *(978-1-60672-108-7(9))* PublishAmerica, Inc.

Ebbe, Obi N. I. & Das, Dilip K., eds. Criminal Abuse of Women & Children: An International Perspective. 2009. (ENG., Illus.). 396p. 124.95 *(978-1-4200-8803-8(3)*, CRC Press) Taylor & Francis Group GBR. Dist: Taylor & Francis Group.

Einstein, Jessica Victoria. Family Is an 'F' Word: Perceptions of Love. 2010. 132p. 28.89 *(978-1-4490-0246-6(3))*; pap. 17.39 *(978-1-4490-0245-9(5))* AuthorHouse.

Elizabeth, Alexandra. When Love Hurts: A Pathway to Healing. 2010. pap. 12.99 *(978-1-61566-834-2(9))* Tate Publishing & Enterprises, LLC.

Elmer, Emma. If You're Going Through Hell, Keep Going. 2007. 143p. pap. 13.95 *(978-0-7414-4322-9(8))* Infinity Publishing.

Ensler, Eve & Doyle, Mollie, eds. A Memory, a Monologue, a Rant, & a Prayer. 2007. (ENG.). 240p. per. 13.95 *(978-0-345-49791-8(0)*, Villard Bks.) Random House Publishing Group.

Errion, Kathleen. Go Bark at the Moon! 2007. 168p. per. 24.95 *(978-1-4241-3695-7(4))* PublishAmerica, Inc.

Evans, Leah. Easy Prey: Don't Be Conned, Too. 2009. 108p. 21.99 *(978-1-4490-5250-8(9))*; pap. 12.99 *(978-1-4490-5251-5(7))* AuthorHouse.

Evers, Kelly Ann. Hurt No More! A Journey of Healing from Abuse: Finding Peace, Healing, Hope, & Comfort through Prayer & the Word of God. 2011. 244p. pap. 14.95 *(978-0-9832928-0-7(9))* El Roi Publishing.

Fairweather, Lynn. Stop Signs: Recognizing, Avoiding, & Escaping Abusive Relationships. 2012. (ENG.). 352p. pap. 18.00 ***(978-1-58005-387-7(4))*** Seal Pr.

Fernandez, Marilyn. Restorative Justice for Domestic Violence Victims: An Integrated Approach to Their Hunger for Healing. (ENG.). 206p. 2011. pap. 29.95 ***(978-0-7391-1554-1(5))*** 2010. 68.50 *(978-0-7391-1553-4(7))* Lexington Bks.

Ferraro, Kathleen. Neither Angels nor Demons: Women, Crime, & Victimization. 2006. (Northeastern Series on Gender, Crime, & Law Ser.). (ENG.). 344p. pap. 29.95 *(978-1-55553-663-3(8)*, Northeastern University Pr.) Univ. Pr. of New England.

Fife. Family Violence: What Health Care Providers Need to Know. rev. ed. 2011. (Illus.). 248p. pap. 62.95 *(978-0-7637-8034-0(0))* Jones & Bartlett Learning, LLC.

Floyd, Brenda E. Free at Last: How chains are broken to be set Free. 2009. pap. 8.99 *(978-1-60799-962-1(5))* Tate Publishing & Enterprises, LLC.

Foley, Paul. Black Cassock: Memoir of a Spoiled Priest. 2008. 124p. pap. 11.95 *(978-1-4327-2277-7(8))* Outskirts Pr., Inc.

Foroozandeh, Lori. Lori's Song: The true story of an American woman held captive in Iran. 2009. (Illus.). 243p. 30.95 *(978-1-4327-1182-5(2))*; (ENG., pap. 17.95 *(978-1-4327-3829-7(1))* Outskirts Pr., Inc.

Frank, Donna L. The Shame Vault: Unlocking the Pain. 2010. pap. 11.99 *(978-1-61739-084-5(4))* Tate Publishing & Enterprises, LLC.

Frawley, Julie. Thirty Minutes: Changed Forever. 2008. (ENG.). 208p. pap. 12.95 *(978-1-933916-11-8(7))* Nelson Publishing & Marketing.

Freeman, Michael A. Domestic Violence. 2008. (Family, Law & Society Ser.). 638p. 350.00 *(978-0-7546-2644-2(X))* Ashgate Publishing Co.

Fromont, Isabelle. Moi, Femme Battue. 2010. (FRE.). 189p. *(978-2-7538-0634-4(9))* Alphee, Editions.

Galvani, Sarah. Women's Perspectives. 2010. 396p. pap. *(978-3-8383-3959-7(2))* Lambert Academic Publishing.

Garfoot, Jill. Inside Child Welfare: A Caseworker's Story, 1 vol. 2010. 196p. pap. 24.95 *(978-1-4489-3982-4(8))* PublishAmerica, Inc.

Garlock, Alice & Garlock, Rick. Spirit Unbroken: The Two Sides of Love. 2008. 252p. per. 19.95 *(978-1-59299-331-4(1))* Inkwater Pr.

Giglio, Diana R. What to Look Out For: A Dynamic Story of How to Survive an Abusive Spouse, 1 vol. 2010. 71p. pap. 16.95 *(978-1-4489-5647-0(1))* PublishAmerica, Inc.

Goodson, Narda. Will the Real Me, Please Stand Up! 2007. 224p. per. 18.95 *(978-0-9791566-5-6(3))* To His Glory Publishing Co., Inc.

Grady, Mel. The Pain Within. 2009. 226p. pap. 27.50 *(978-1-4092-4437-0(7))* Lulu Enterprises Inc.

Graves, Lori. Chasing the Light: ... a Journey Through the Healing. 2010. 128p. 24.50 *(978-1-4269-3873-3(X))*; pap. 14.50 *(978-1-4269-3872-6(1))* Trafford Publishing.

Greentower, Maya. Homeward Bound, a Journey from Darkness to Light. 2009. 128p. pap. 12.50 *(978-0-557-00552-006-3(3))* Lulu Enterprises Inc.

Griffith, Marilynn, compiled by. SistahFaith: Real Stories of Pain, Truth, & Triumph. 2010. (ENG.). 240p. pap. 14.99 *(978-1-4391-5277-5(2)*, Howard Bks.) Howard Books.

Hamilton, Melissa. Expert Testimony on Domestic Violence: A Discourse Analysis. 2009. (Law & Society Ser.). 214p. *(978-1-59332-323-3(9))* LFB Scholarly Publishing LLC.

Hanna, Cheryl & Dalton, Clare. Domestic Violence & the Law: Theory & Practice. 2nd ed. 2008. (Illus.). xlv, 997p. pap. *(978-1-58778-417-0(3)*, Foundation Pr.) West.

Harrington, Gwyndelon L. Damaged but Not Destroyed. 2011. 126p. pap. 19.99 ***(978-1-4628-7039-4(2))*** Xlibris Corp.

Harris, Latoya. Life Beyond a Miserable Child. 2010. 198p. pap. 14.95 *(978-0-9840660-4-9(7))* Second Time Media & Communications.

Hattery, Angela & Smith, Earl. The Social Dynamics of Family Violence. 2012. (ENG.). 432p. (C). pap. 55.00 ***(978-0-8133-4463-8(8))***; E-Book ***(978-0-8133-4562-8(6))*** Westview Pr.

Hellegers, Desiree. No Room of Her Own: Women's Stories of Homelessness, Life, Death, & Resistance. 2011. (Palgrave Studies in Oral History Ser.). (ENG., Illus.). 240p. pap. 28.00 *(978-0-230-11658-0(2))* Palgrave Macmillan.

Hero, Rhonda Kay. She Has Awaken: Darkness to Light. 2008. 140p. (ENG.). 25.49 *(978-1-4520-5238-0(7))*; pap. 15.49 *(978-1-4520-5237-3(9))* AuthorHouse.

Hippen, Karyn Gall. Make Me New: One woman's fight to mend a broken Past. 2009. pap. 14.99 *(978-1-60799-782-5(7))* Tate Publishing & Enterprises, LLC.

Hogenes, Patricia B. I Wasn't Going to Take It Anymore! True Stories by Survivors of Domestic Violence Who Got Out & Stayed Out ~Forever~. 2008. 260p. pap. 15.99 *(978-1-60647-595-9(9))* Xulon Pr., Inc.

Hunter, Jane. Psychological Abuse of Married Women. 2010. 104p. pap. *(978-3-639-24850-0(3))* VDM Verlag Dr. Mueller e.K.

Hunter, Joanna. But He'll Change: End the Thinking That Keeps You in an Abusive Relationship. 2010. (ENG.). 248p. pap. 14.95 *(978-1-59285-818-7(X))* Hazelden Publishing & Educational Services.

Imoru, Austin. The Woman & Her Sexuality. 2008. viii, 167p. pap. *(978-0-9555562-9-6(5))* Esteemworld Pubns.

Jacobson, Neil & Gottman, John. When Men Batter Women. 2007. (ENG.). 304p. pap. 20.95 *(978-1-4165-5133-1(6))* Simon & Schuster.

James, Kim Yancey. Breaking the Silence: The Voiceless Victims of Physical & Emotional Violence. 2010. 260p. 29.99 *(978-1-4500-4855-2(2))*; pap. 19.99 *(978-1-4500-4854-5(4))* Xlibris Corp.

James M Stone. The Murder of Mingo Jack: New Jersey's only nineteenth century Lynching. 2010. 104p. pap. 11.95 *(978-1-4502-1320-2(0))* iUniverse, Inc.

Jasper, Margaret C. The Law of Violence Against Women. 2nd ed. 2007. (Legal Almanac Ser.). (ENG.). 262p. 45.00 *(978-0-19-533904-8(5))* Oxford Univ. Pr., Inc.

Jenkins, Susan Elaine. Scandalon: Running from Shame & Finding God's Scandalous Love. 2009. 288p. pap. 13.99 *(978-0-9818929-0-0(6))* CLADACH Publishing.

Jessica Martin Flannery. There Is No Edge. 2010. 232p. 28.95 *(978-1-4502-0215-2(2))*; pap. 18.95 *(978-1-4502-0213-8(6))* iUniverse, Inc.

Johnson Davis, Anne A. Over It & on with It! Power Through Adversity. 2007. 110p. per. 7.95 *(978-0-9788348-1-4(X))* Davis, Anne A Johnson.

Johnson, Eloise Susan. Dancing Around the Cracks: Before During & after Divorce Court. 2011. 245p. pap. 18.95 ***(978-1-4327-7455-4(7))*** Outskirts Pr., Inc.

Johnson, Geraldine. Irreconcilable Bondage, 1 vol. 2009. 59p. pap. 16.95 *(978-1-61546-476-0(X))* PublishAmerica, Inc.

Johnson, Holly & Dawson, Myrna. Violence Against Women in Canada: Research & Policy Perspectives. 2010. (ENG., Illus.). 234p. 24.95 *(978-0-19-542981-7(8))* Oxford Univ. Pr., Inc.

Johnson, Kayla D. Why Must I Cry? 2011. 132p. 23.95 ***(978-1-4620-5028-4(X))***; pap. 13.95 ***(978-1-4620-5026-0(3))*** iUniverse, Inc.

Jones, Mark. From Victims to Victors: Overcoming Abuse by the Power of Jesus Christ. 2011. 176p. 25.95 ***(978-1-4620-3704-9(6))***; pap. 15.95 ***(978-1-4502-8383-0(7))*** iUniverse, Inc.

Jones, Shelley G. Healing of a Violated Spirit. 2008. 452p. pap. 26.99 *(978-1-60477-667-6(6))* Xulon Pr., Inc.

Josée Perrine. The Saber-Toothed Tiger: The One Reason Women Stay with Abusive Men. 2010. 176p. 25.95 *(978-1-4502-0079-0(6))*; pap. 15.95 *(978-1-4502-0077-6(X))* iUniverse, Inc.

Kahn, Rosalie B. My Healing Heart: A Life Journey to Find Love. 2011. 256p. 26.95 ***(978-1-4620-3104-7(8))***; pap. 16.95 ***(978-1-4620-3102-3(1))*** iUniverse, Inc.

Katy. The Girl Behind the Pink. 2010. 84p. pap. 10.49 *(978-1-4490-3418-4(7))* AuthorHouse.

Kendall-Tackett, Kathleen A. & Giacomoni, Sarah M. Intimate Partner Violence. 2007. ***(978-1-887554-60-2(2))*** Civic Research Institute, Inc.

Key, Carolyn. From Darkness into the Light: Based on the True Story of Alexis Ann Caswell. 2010. pap. 10.99 *(978-1-61663-766-8(8))* Tate Publishing & Enterprises, LLC.

Knights, Everard. A Look Through My Eyes. 2011. 270p. pap. 16.99 ***(978-1-61215-785-6(8))*** Xulon Pr., Inc.

Lakey, Vallery. Domestic Violence Remember Me. 2011. 24p. pap. 11.32 ***(978-1-4634-0491-8(3))*** AuthorHouse.

Latus, Janine. If I Am Missing or Dead: A Sister's Story of Love, Murder, & Liberation. 2008. (ENG., Illus.). 336p. pap. 15.00 *(978-0-7432-9654-0(0))* Simon & Schuster.

—If I Am Missing or Dead: A Sister's Story of Love, Murder, & Liberation. l.t. ed. 2007. (Thorndike Basic Ser.). (Illus.). 501p. 30.95 *(978-0-7862-9660-6(7))* Thorndike Pr.

Levenkron, Steven. Stolen Tomorrows: Understanding & Treating Women's Childhood Sexual Abuse. 2007. (ENG.). 224p. 25.95 *(978-0-393-06086-7(1)*, 6086) Norton, W. W. & Co., Inc.

Levenkron, Steven & Levenkron, Abby. Stolen Tomorrows: Understanding & Treating Women's Childhood Sexual Abuse. 2008. (ENG.). 288p. pap. 15.95 *(978-0-393-33201-8(2)*, 33201) Norton, W. W. & Co., Inc.

Lindorfer, Simone & Lindorfer. Sharing the Pain of the Bitter Hearts: Liberation Psychology & Gender-Related Violence in Eastern Africa. 2008. (ENG.). 528p. pap. 69.95 *(978-3-8258-9038-4(4))* Lit Verlag DEU. Dist: Transaction Pubs.

Lopez, Ernestine. Silent No More. 2008. 60p. pap. 8.95 *(978-0-595-46329-9(0))* iUniverse, Inc.

Lund, Marynell. The Normal Side of Insanity. 2010. pap. 18.95 *(978-0-7414-5896-4(9))* Infinity Publishing.

MLana. Huh? One Woman's Struggle to Survive Her Abuse, 1 vol. 2009. 202p. pap. 24.95 *(978-1-61582-161-7(9))* PublishAmerica, Inc.

Maddigan, Debbie. A Little Girl Called Squeaks: A Story of Hope. 2011. 344p. 35.00 ***(978-1-4567-5406-8(8))***; pap. 26.58 ***(978-1-4567-5405-1(X))*** AuthorHouse.

Mahill, Wendy. Growing a Passionate Heart. 2007. 212p. per. 16.99 *(978-1-60266-461-6(7))* Xulon Pr., Inc.

Maricle, Francoise. Hold on to Your Dreams: Regardless of Your Past. 2008. 244p. pap. 14.95 *(978-1-59858-655-8(6))* Dog Ear Publishing, LLC.

Masih, Viera. Mahima: A Memoir. 2010. 248p. pap. 19.95 *(978-1-4502-6949-0(4))* iUniverse, Inc.

Mason, Gillian E. The Search for Help. 2010. 124p. pap. *(978-3-639-25763-2(4))* VDM Verlag Dr. Mueller e.K.

May, Shirley. Abused Not Destroyed. 2011. 52p. pap. 12.00 ***(978-1-4269-4655-4(4))*** Trafford Publishing.

Mayer, Lisa Brassard. Silent Victim Running Free. 2008. 356p. pap. 14.95 *(978-1-4327-2115-2(1))* Outskirts Pr., Inc.

McCloskey, Kathy A. & Sitaker, Marilyn. Backs Against the Wall: Battered Women's Resistance Strategies. 2008. (Illus.). ix, 213p. 150.00 *(978-0-7890-3583-7(9))*; 49.95 *(978-0-7890-3584-4(7))* Routledge.

McKinney, Leslie Ann. Accepted in the Beloved: A Devotional Bible Study for Women on Finding Healing & Wholeness in God's Love. 2008. (House of Prisca & Aquila Ser.). 56p. pap. 10.00 *(978-1-55635-936-1(5))* Wipf & Stock Pubs.

Melton, Rita. Alpine Rose: I am a Victor. 2007. 44.00 *(978-0-8059-7307-5(9))* Dorrance Publishing Co., Inc.

Michelle, Jen. Beautiful Nightmare. 2009. 56p. pap. 17.74 *(978-0-557-20018-4(0))* Lulu Enterprises Inc.

Miller, Emma Sue. Silent for Too Long. 2009. 124p. pap. 24.95 *(978-1-61582-891-3(5))* PublishAmerica, Inc.

Mills, Lucinda. Let Yesterday Go: Finding Grace in the Midst of the Storm. 2011. pap. 19.99 *(978-1-61739-722-6(9))* Tate Publishing & Enterprises, LLC.

Mims, Elaine. The Hidden Face of Laur. 2009. 136p. 21.75 *(978-1-4490-3307-1(5))*; pap. 11.65 *(978-1-4490-3306-4(7))* AuthorHouse.

Mitchell, Lori. Lighting Mary's House. 2011. 88p. pap. 9.95 ***(978-1-61507-788-5(X))*** Cross Bks. Publishing.

Moise, Leslie. Love Is the Thread: A Knitting Friendship. 2011. 186p. pap. ***(978-1-59719-048-0(9))***; E-Book ***(978-1-59719-049-7(7))*** Pearlsong Pr.

Morgan, Delilah. Out of the Darkness. 2011. 108p. 21.23 *(978-1-4567-2141-1(0))*; pap. 12.95 *(978-1-4567-2139-8(9))* AuthorHouse.

Mueller, Deborah M. Sadistic Love: My Twenty-Two Year Marriage to A Sexual Sadist. 2009. 228p. 28.95 *(978-1-4490-1020-1(2))*; pap. 18.95 *(978-1-4490-1019-5(9))* AuthorHouse.

Murdin, Doreen & Vella, Nicci. DaiNa - Domestic Abuse Is Never Acceptable: A Manual for Working with Women Who Have Experienced, or Are Experiencing, Domestic Abuse. 2009. 82p. spiral bd. 49.95 *(978-1-905541-51-5(1))* Russell Hse. Publishing Ltd. GBR. Dist: International Specialized Bk. Services.

Murphy, Annamae. My Life of Abuse, Heart Break & Depression. 2011. 52p. 24.99 ***(978-1-4568-8573-1(1))***; pap. 15.99 ***(978-1-4568-8572-4(3))*** Xlibris Corp.

Nelson, Eular. Tishunda' Diary of an Empty Heart: And the Search to Fill It. 2010. 48p. pap. 9.98 *(978-1-4269-4298-3(2))* Trafford Publishing.

Nelson, Thorana S. & Bowen, Ellen L. Domestic Violence Treatment for Abusive Women: A Treatment Manual. 2008. (Illus.). (ENG.). 214p. 152.95 *(978-0-7890-3810-4(2))*; 158p. pap. 47.50 *(978-0-7890-3811-1(0))* Routledge.

Norman, Sonya B. Drinking among Female Victims of Intimate Partner Violence: Mechanisms & Intervention. 2010. 52p. pap. 49.00 *(978-1-61761-332-6(0))* Nova Science Pubs., Inc.

Norman, Sonya B., et al. Drinking among Female Victims of Intimate Partner Violence: Mechanisms & Intervention. 2011. (Women's Issues Ser.). pap. 43.00 *(978-1-61761-830-7(6))* Nova Science Pubs., Inc.

Oakley, Barbara. Cold-Blooded Kindness: Neuroquirks of a Codependent Killer, or Just Give Me a Shot at Loving You, Dear, & Other Reflections on Helping that Hurts. 2011. (ENG., Illus.). 275p. 26.00 *(978-1-61614-419-7(X))* Prometheus Bks., Pubs.

O'Brien, Astrid M. A Mysticism of Kindness: The Lucie Christine Story. 2011. (ENG., Illus.). 270p. pap. 25.00 *(978-1-58966-206-3(7))* Univ. of Scranton Pr.

Orenstein, Peggy. Flux. pap. *(978-0-385-72897-3(2))*; *(978-0-385-72894-2(8))* Knopf Doubleday Publishing Group.

Otti, Oluchi. Why Doesn't She Just Leave? Understanding Why Women Stay in Abusive Relationships. 2011. 72p. pap. 14.95 ***(978-1-4327-6055-7(6))*** Outskirts Pr., Inc.

Paludi, Michele A. Feminism & Women's Rights Worldwide, 3 vols. 2009. (Women's Psychology Ser.). (Illus.). 806p. 154.95 *(978-0-313-37596-5(8)*, C37596, Praeger Pubs.) Greenwood Publishing Group, Inc.

Parker, Rose. Beat up, Beat down & Still Standing: The Rose Parker Story. 2007. 308p. per. 24.95 *(978-0-9787317-1-7(9))* Cole Publishing.

Parks, Laura M. Under the Broken Halo. 2011. 264p. pap. 27.95 ***(978-1-4560-0498-9(0))*** PublishAmerica, Inc.

Parmenter, Wanita. Journeys Begin, 1 vol. 2010. 56p. pap. 16.95 *(978-1-4489-5032-4(5))* PublishAmerica, Inc.

Pastmak, Theresa. I Love You, Rachel Lynn. 2011. 78p. pap. 8.95 ***(978-1-60594-671-9(0))***, Llumina Pr.) Aeon Publishing Inc.

Penhale, Bridget & Parker, Jonathan. Working with Vulnerable Adults. (Social Work Skills Ser.). (Illus.). 189p. 2008. 150.00 *(978-0-415-30190-9(4))* 2007. per. 39.95 *(978-0-415-30191-6(2))* Routledge.

Penrose-Garcia, Sonya. From Pain to Glory: A Young Woman's Journey of God's Ability to Take Our Pain & Turn It into Glory, 1 vol. 2010. 68p. pap. 16.95 *(978-1-4489-4951-9(3))* PublishAmerica, Inc.

Perry, Becky. Living Hell: True Story of a Single Abused Mother, 1 vol. 2009. 90p. pap. 16.95 *(978-1-60672-889-5(X))* PublishAmerica, Inc.

Petersen, Trina. Good Morning Great Day. 2007. 204p. per. 16.95 *(978-0-9791566-0-1(2))* To His Glory Publishing Co., Inc.

Polk-Palmer, Caroline. Dead Girl Walking: My Story of Molesting Abuse, Addiction, Prostitution, Incarceration, Struggle & Survival. 2007. 48p. pap. 10.95 *(978-1-4327-0269-4(6))* Outskirts Pr., Inc.

Posa, Charlotte. To Women with Love: Walking Away from the Abuse. Lowe, Fran D., ed. 2011. 168p. lib. bdg. 15.00 ***(978-1-886068-52-0(6))*** Fruitbearer Publishing, LLC.

Potter, Hillary. Battle Cries: Black Women & Intimate Partner Abuse. 2008. (ENG.). 295p. (C). pap. 24.00 *(978-0-8147-6730-6(3))* New York Univ. Pr.

Powlison, David. Sexual Assault: Healing Steps for Victims. 2010. 30p. 3.99 *(978-1-935273-78-3(7))* New Growth Pr.

Pritchard, Jacki & Pritchard, Jackie Lee. Recording Skills in Safeguarding Adults: Best Practice & Evidential Requirements. 2010. (ENG., Illus.). 192p. pap. *(978-1-84905-112-5(7))* Kingsley, Jessica Ltd.

Ptacek, James, ed. Restorative Justice & Violence Against Women, 1 vol. 2009. (Interpersonal violence Ser.). (ENG.). 312p. 39.95 *(978-0-19-533548-4(1))* Oxford Univ. Pr., Inc.

Putit, Zabidah. Domestic Violence: Towards a better Exit. 2010. 256p. pap. *(978-3-8383-6781-1(2))* Lambert Academic Publishing.

Quackenbos, Radica. In My Fathers Hands: God's Grace. My Testimony. 2011. 152p. pap. 13.95 ***(978-1-61507-845-5(2))*** Cross Bks. Publishing.

—In My Father's Hands: God's Grace. My Testimony. 2011. 152p. 30.95 ***(978-1-61507-846-2(0))*** Cross Bks. Publishing.

Rain, Felica. Tears Pave the Way to Triumph. 2011. 168p. pap. 14.50 *(978-1-4269-6030-7(1))* Trafford Publishing.

Rambo, Kirsten S. Trivial Complaints: The Role of Privacy in Domestic Violence Law & Activism in the U. S. 2008. (ENG.). 264p. (gr. 17). 60.00 *(978-0-231-13557-3(2))* Columbia Univ. Pr.

Raphael, Jody. Freeing Tammy: Women, Drugs, & Incarceration. 2007. (Northeastern Series on Gender, Crime, & Law Ser.). (ENG.). 232p. pap. 24.95 *(978-1-55553-673-2(5)*, Northeastern University Pr.) Univ. Pr. of New England.

Ratliff, Willie Bell. 'Women', Get Out of the Domestic Violence Relationship. 2009. 94p. pap. 15.99 *(978-1-4363-8447-6(8))* Xlibris Corp.

Raunea, Auna. The Innocent & the Merciless. 2011. 176p. 24.23 ***(978-1-4269-6276-9(2))***; pap. 14.23 ***(978-1-4269-6275-2(4))*** Trafford Publishing.

Reid-Scott, Virginia. Silent Victims Innocent Tears: Unspoken Hurts. 2010. 56p. pap. 10.16 *(978-1-4269-3480-3(7))* Trafford Publishing.

Researcher, C. Q., ed. Issues for Debate in Family Violence: Selections from CQ Researcher. 2010. (Illus.). 200p. (C). pap. 37.00 *(978-1-4129-9032-5(7)*, B90325P) SAGE Pubns., Inc.

Resko, Stella M. Intimate Partner Violence & Women's Economic Insecurity. 2010. (Criminal Justice). 250p. 70.00 *(978-1-59332-368-4(9))* LFB Scholarly Publishing LLC.

Reynolds, Suzanne & Delgado, Alvaro. Born with A Veil: Tragedy to Triumph. 2010. pap. 15.99 *(978-1-61579-776-9(9))* Xulon Pr., Inc.

Richie, Beth. Arrested Justice: Black Women, Violence, & America's Prison Nation. 2012. E-Book ***(978-0-8147-0822-4(6))***; E-Book ***(978-0-8147-2391-3(8))*** New York Univ. Pr.

Richmond, Helen. Living Past the Pain: Reflections of the Past. 2008. 119p. pap. 21.95 (978-1-4357-4226-0(5)) Lulu Enterprises Inc.

Riley, Liliana. Rising from the Ashes: A Journey of Self-Discovery. 2011. 56p. pap. 8.95 (978-1-4620-1099-8(7)) iUniverse, Inc.

Robinson, Cynthia P. No Longer the Victim. 2007. per. (978-0-9793095-0-2(6)) VisionWorks.

Russel, Brenda L. Battered Woman Syndrome as a Legal Defense: History, Effectiveness & Implications. 2010. (ENG., Illus.). 256p. pap. 45.00 (978-0-7864-5883-7(6)) McFarland & Co., Inc. Pubs.

—Battered Woman Syndrome As a Legal Defense: History, Effectiveness & Implications. 2010. viii, 248p. E-Book (978-0-7864-6004-5(0)) McFarland & Co., Inc. Pubs.

Sahari, Nadia. Breakaway: How I Survived Abuse. 2008. 272p. pap. 19.95 (978-0-9820413-0-7(6)) Pink Butterfly Pr.

Salbi, Zainab & Becklund, Laurie. Between Two Worlds: Escape from Tyranny - Growing up in the Shadow of Saddam. 2006. (ENG.). 304p. (gr. 12-18). 16.00 (978-1-59240-244-1(5), Gotham) Penguin Group (USA) Inc.

Sapia-Ruffin, Genna. Delivered from Temptation: From Temptation to Salvation. 2010. 476p. pap. 25.95 (978-1-4490-6955-1(X)) AuthorHouse.

Sargent, Angela D. Rituals of Season. 2009. 88p. pap. 11.00 (978-1-4389-8824-5(9)) AuthorHouse.

Savage, Shawna. Psycho Girl: Overcoming Abuse Through Positive Spirituality. 2011. pap. 11.99 (978-1-61739-358-7(4)) Tate Publishing & Enterprises, LLC.

Schiller, Dawn. The Road Through Wonderland: Surviving John Holmes. 2010. (ENG., Illus.). 300p. pap. 19.95 (978-1-60542-083-7(2), Gold Medallion) Medallion Pr., Inc.

Schneider, Eric C. Smack: Heroin & the American City. 2011. (Politics & Culture in Modern America Ser.). (Illus.). 280p. (C). pap. 24.95 (978-0-8122-2180-0(X)) Univ. of Pennsylvania Pr.

Schweik, Susan. Arrested Justice: Black Women, Violence, & America's Prison Nation. 2012. (ENG.). 240p. 74.00 (978-0-8147-7622-3(1)) New York Univ. Pr.

Shahbazz, Setaareh. Tortured in the Name of Islam. 2008. 132p. pap. 11.95 (978-1-4343-6669-4(4)) AuthorHouse.

Shaw, Bertha L. Midnight Ballerina. 2011. 56p. pap. 12.84 (978-1-4343-0251-9(2)) AuthorHouse.

Shearer-Cremean, Christine & Winkelmann, Carol L., eds. Survivor Rhetoric: Negotiations & Narrativity in Abused Women's Language. 2007. (ENG.). 240p. pap. (978-0-8020-9491-9(0)) Univ. of Toronto Pr.

Sherree. A Living TestimonyWho Will Cry for Me? 2011. 142p. pap. 15.95 (978-1-4327-7177-5(9)) Outskirts Pr., Inc.

Sherrie Watkins. Touching Temptation. 2010. 468p. 38.95 (978-1-4502-0223-7(3)) iUniverse, Inc.

Shooter, Susan. How Survivors of Abuse Relate to God the Authentic Spirituality of the Annihilated Soul. 2012. (Explorations in Practical, Pastoral & Empirical Theology Ser.). 196p. 99.95 (978-1-4094-4126-7(1)) Ashgate Publishing Co.

Siegel, Racquel Vera. Intimate partner violence: a closer look In. 2009. 115p. pap. 20.10 (978-0-557-25750-8(6)) Lulu Enterprises Inc.

Simms, Hazel. My Life's Journey. 2011. 92p. pap. 13.95 (978-1-4670-3578-1(5)) AuthorHouse.

Sjoberg, Laura & Gentry, Caron E., eds. Women, Gender, & Terrorism. 2011. (Studies in Security & International Affairs Ser.). (ENG., Illus.). 224p. 59.95 (978-0-8203-3583-4(5)); pap. 24.95 (978-0-8203-4038-8(3)) Univ. of Georgia Pr.

Small, Kertina. The Long Road Back: 37 Years in the Wilderness. 2011. 56p. pap. 14.99 (978-1-4567-4182-2(9)) AuthorHouse.

Smith-Scott, Glennese. Surviving a Thousand Deaths: The Glennese Smith-Scott Story. 2011. 54p. pap. 16.95 (978-1-4560-3511-2(8)) PublishAmerica, Inc.

Smith, Tammie Walker. Prey for the Predator in the Pulpit. 2010. pap. 10.99 (978-1-61663-746-0(3)) Tate Publishing & Enterprises, LLC.

Sommerfeld, Lelia Rae. Beyond Our Control: Restructuring Your Life after Sexual Assault, 1 vol. 2009. 232p. pap. 13.99 (978-0-8254-3682-6(6)) Kregel Pubns.

Sotelo, Nicole. Women Healing from Abuse: Meditations for Finding Peace. 2006. 98p. per. 10.95 (978-0-8091-4424-2(7), 4424-7) Paulist Pr.

Spore, Jaquita. Past & Tense. 2008. 212p. pap. 12.95 (978-1-4327-2171-8(2)) Outskirts Pr., Inc.

Stark, Evan. Coercive Control: How Men Entrap Women in Personal Life. 2009. (Interpersonal Violence Ser.). (ENG.). 464p. pap. 24.95 (978-0-19-538404-8(0)) Oxford Univ. Pr., Inc.

Stark, Evan & Buzawa, Eva Schlesinger, eds. Violence Against Women in Families & Relationships, 4 vols. 2009. 888p. 400.00 (978-0-275-99846-2(0), C9846, Praeger Pubs.) Greenwood Publishing Group, Inc.

Stark, Heather & Wetturs, Emilee. Why Doesn't She Just Leave? 2008. 100p. 24.99 (978-0-9746967-6-8(5)) LegacyONE.

Stark, Sharon. Victims of Abuse, an Issue of Nursing Clinics. 2011. (Clinics: Nursing Ser.: 46-4). (ENG., Illus.). viii, 386p. 99.00 (978-1-4557-7986-4(5), Saunders) Elsevier - Health Sciences Div.

Starr. Indigo the Journey. 2011. 412p. pap. 29.95 (978-1-60749-952-7(5)) PublishAmerica, Inc.

Steiner, Leslie Morgan. Crazy Love. 2010. (ENG.). 352p. pap. 14.99 (978-0-312-37746-5(0), St. Martin's Griffin) St. Martin's Pr.

Stephens, Lori L. TRAPpED: Memoirs of an EX-METH addict & her RECOVERY out of the insanity of it All. 2011. 228p. pap. 18.99 (978-1-4567-3646-0(9)) AuthorHouse.

—Trapped: Memoirs of an Ex-Meth Addict & heR RECOVERY out of the Insanity of it All. 2011. 228p. 26.59 (978-1-4567-3645-3(0)) AuthorHouse.

Stewart, Olynthia. One Sista's Pain & Glory. 2007. pap. 12.00 (978-0-8059-8970-0(6)) Dorrance Publishing Co., Inc.

Suk, Jeannie. At Home in the Law: How the Domestic Violence Revolution Is Transforming Privacy. 2011. 218p. pap. 24.00 (978-0-300-17262-1(1)) Yale Univ. Pr.

Survivor, Ima. The Tormenting Factor: Generation to Generation. 2011. 512p. 32.00 (978-1-4567-2965-3(9)); pap. 28.00 (978-1-4567-2967-7(5)) AuthorHouse.

Tate, Sarah. Web of Lies: My Life with a Narcissist. 2011. 278p. pap. 21.50 (978-1-4476-8999-7(2)) Lulu Enterprises Inc.

Thomas, Susan A. A Family Changed Forever. 2009. 104p. pap. 7.95 (978-1-60594-194-3(8), Llumina Pr.) Aeon Publishing Inc.

Thompson, Brenda J. Was It You, Lord?, 1 vol. 2009. 79p. pap. 16.95 (978-1-60836-777-1(0)) PublishAmerica, Inc.

Thompson, C.L. If Only Regrets Were A Good Thing. 2011. 192p. 24.59 (978-1-4567-6160-8(9)); pap. 14.03 (978-1-4567-6161-5(7)) AuthorHouse.

Truman, Kelly A. A Beautiful Mess: Confessions from the Second Closet. 2011. 298p. pap. 15.95 (978-1-257-38157-9(1)) Lulu Enterprises Inc.

Tsutsumi, Mieko. Life's a Pair of Chopsticks: An Autobiography of Hope & Overcoming. 2011. 72p. pap. 19.95 (978-1-4560-9574-1(9)) PublishAmerica, Inc.

Turner, P. Ann. Such Is Life. 2010. 102p. pap. 17.43 (978-0-557-06596-7(8)) Lulu Enterprises Inc.

V. The Infamous Schlemiel, 1 vol. 2009. 135p. pap. 24.95 (978-1-60836-885-3(8)) PublishAmerica, Inc.

Vann, Hed. Taking Back Hedy. 2010. 408p. 29.95 (978-1-4520-8711-5(3)) AuthorHouse.

Vann, Hedy. Taking Back Hedy. 2010. 408p. pap. 19.95 (978-1-4520-8710-8(5)) AuthorHouse.

VBU Ministries. The Mentality of the Abused Woman. 2007. (ENG.). 125p. per. 9.99 net. (978-0-9766774-1-3(5)) VBU Ministries.

Vranceanu, Ana-Maria & Robert Johnson / Stevan Hobfoll, /. Sequelae of Child Abuse. 2010. 76p. pap. (978-3-8383-0227-0(3)) Lambert Academic Publishing.

Ware, Flossie. A Costly Pearl, 1 vol. 2010. 74p. pap. 19.95 (978-1-4489-6012-5(6)) PublishAmerica, Inc.

Wassmer, Karen Anne. Crack the Case: Are You Married to a Crack Addict. 2007. pap. 10.00 (978-0-8059-8500-9(X)) Dorrance Publishing Co., Inc.

Waywardson, Kelly. The Descent into Grace. 2011. 156p. pap. 13.95 (978-1-4627-0555-9(3)) Cross Bks. Publishing.

Welch, Edward T. Living with an Angry Spouse: Help for Victims of Abuse. 2008. (ENG.). 24p. 3.99 (978-1-934885-35-2(5)) New Growth Pr.

Wells, Kamisha. No More Pain: One Girl's Courage to Survive. 2009. 48p. pap. 14.95 (978-1-4327-3006-2(1)) Outskirts Pr., Inc.

WHO Regional Office for the Western Pacific. Gender-based Violence in the Western Pacific Region: A Hidden Epidemic? 2006. (WPRO Nonserial Publication). (ENG.). 144p. pap. 24.00 (978-92-9061-226-1(6)) World Health Organization.

Wies, Jennifer R. & Haldane, Hillary J., eds. Anthropology at the Front Lines of Gender-Based Violence. 2011. (ENG., Illus.). 256p. 69.95 (978-0-8265-1780-7(3)); pap. 27.95 (978-0-8265-1781-4(1)) Vanderbilt Univ. Pr.

Wilcox, Paula. Surviving Domestic Violence: Gender, Poverty & Agency. 2006. (ENG.). 240p. 100.00 (978-1-4039-4113-8(0)) Palgrave Macmillan.

Wilkins, Ebony Joy & Lewis, Dorene. Someone to Hear Me. 2009. 76p. pap. 14.95 (978-0-557-00091-3(2)) Lulu Enterprises Inc.

Willis, Deatrix. A Little Lost Soul Found a Friend. 2011. 52p. pap. 10.03 (978-1-4269-5672-0(X)) Trafford Publishing.

Woman Submit! Christians & Domestic Violence. 2007. per. 19.99 (978-0-9794293-0-9(7)) One Way Cafe Pr. LLC.

Wright, Kathleen. At Full Bloom. 2011. 120p. pap. 12.95 (978-1-4620-2057-7(7)) iUniverse, Inc.

ABUSED WOMEN—SERVICES FOR

Abrahams, Hilary. Supporting Women after Domestic Violence: Loss, Trauma & Recovery. 2007. (ENG., Illus.). 16p. per. (978-1-84310-431-5(8)) Kingsley, Jessica Ltd.

Betancourt, Marian. What to Do When Love Turns Violent: A Practical Resource for Women in Abusive Relationships. 2009. 288p. pap. 19.95 (978-1-4401-3754-9(4)) iUniverse, Inc.

Cleghorn, Andrea. Rosie's Place: Offering Women Shelter & Hope. Date not set. (Illus.). 184p. pap. (978-1-889242-00-2(4)) VanderWyk & Burnham.

Fernández Santiago, Pedro & Santiago, Pedro Fernández. Violencia Familiar: La Visión de la Mujer en Casas de Acogida. 2007. (SPA., Illus.). 277p. (978-84-8456-966-4(7)) Tirant lo Blanch.

Gondolf, Edward W. The Future of Batterer Programs: Reassessing Evidence-Based Practice. 2012. (Northeastern Series on Gender, Crime, & Law Ser.). (ENG.). 336p. (C). 85.00 (978-1-55553-769-2(3)); pap. 35.00 (978-1-55553-770-8(7)) Univ. Pr. of New England. (Northeastern University Pr.).

Goodman, Lisa A. & Epstein, Deborah. Listening to Battered Women: A Survivor-Centered Approach to Advocacy, Mental Health, & Justice. 2007. (Psychology of Women Book Ser.). 208p. 49.95 (978-1-4338-0239-3(2)) American Psychological Assn.

Haaken, Janice. Hard Knocks: Domestic Violence & the Psychology of Storytelling. 2010. (Women & Psychology Ser.). (ENG., Illus.). 208p. 80.00 (978-0-415-56338-3(0)); pap. 26.95 (978-0-415-56342-0(9)) Routledge.

Mantell, Andy & Scragg, Terry, eds. Safeguarding Adults in Social Work. 2nd rev. ed. 2011. (ENG., Illus.). 224p. pap. (978-0-85725-401-6(4)) Learning Matters Ltd.

Morgan, Angela. Surviving Domestic Abuse Empowerment Through Education. 2008. 72p. pap. (978-3-639-09499-2(9)) VDM Verlag Dr. Mueller e.K.

Pritchard, Jacki. Working with Adult Abuse: A Training Manual for People Working with Vulnerable Adults. 2007. (Jkp Resource Materials Ser.). (ENG., Illus.). 416p. per. (978-1-84310-509-1(8)) Kingsley, Jessica Ltd.

Suiter, Sarah VanHooser. Magdalene House: A Place about Mercy. 2012. (ENG.). 200p. 45.00 (978-0-8265-1837-8(0)); pap. 22.50 (978-0-8265-1838-5(9)) Vanderbilt Univ. Pr.

The Violence Against Woman [sic] ACT: Building on 17 Years of Accomplishments: Hearing Before the Committee on the Judiciary, United States Senate, One Hundred Twelfth Congress, First Session, July 13, 2011. 2011. (Illus.). iv, 333p. (978-0-16-090152-2(9), 552-070-43855-6) United States Government Printing Office.

White, Barbara W., frwd. Battered Women & Their Families. 3rd ed. 2007. (Springer Series on Family Violence Ser.). (Illus.). 626p. 65.00 (978-0-8261-4592-5(2)) Springer Publishing Co., Inc.

White, Kelly. A Safe Place for Women: How to Survive Domestic Abuse & Create a Successful Future. 2011. (ENG.). 288p. pap. 17.95 (978-0-89793-527-2(6)) Hunter Hse., Inc.

ABUSIVE FAMILIES

see Abusive Parents

ABUSIVE MEN

Bowen, Erica. The Rehabilitation of Partner-Violent Men. 2011. (ENG., Illus.). 278p. 104.95 (978-0-470-99771-0(0)); pap. 56.95 (978-0-470-99772-7(9)) Wiley, John & Sons, Inc. (Wiley-Blackwell).

Clark, Ron. Freeing the Oppressed: A Call to Christians concerning Domestic Abuse. 2009. 172p. pap. 20.00 (978-1-60608-484-7(4), Cascade Bks.) Wipf & Stock Pubs.

Cosimo, S. Deborah. Domestic Violence: Legal Sanctions & Recidivism Rates among Male Perpetrators. 2011. 65.00 (978-1-59332-488-9(X)) LFB Scholarly Publishing LLC.

Cota, Dee. A Monster in Disguise/Is He Jekel or Is He Hyde: 12 Signs You May Be in an Abusive/Dangerous/Relationship. 2010. 96p. pap. 11.95 (978-1-4502-2985-9(7)) iUniverse, Inc.

Cram101 Textbook Reviews & Cram101 Textbook Reviews. Outlines & Highlights for Family Violence & Men of Color: Healing the Wounded Male Spirit by Carrillo, ISBN. 2011. 58p. pap. 26.95 (978-1-61461-625-2(6)) Cram101 Inc.

Donaldson MA, Charlie. Restorative Treatment: The Newest Specialty in Counseling. 2007. 160p. pap. 30.00 (978-0-9801390-0-6(7)) Therapist Outfitters Pubns.

Donaldson MA LLP LPC CAC1, Charlie. Interventions for Men Who Abuse Women: Manual & Activities for Facilitating Domestic Abuse Groups. 2007. 67p. pap. 20.00 (978-0-9801390-1-3(5)) Therapist Outfitters Pubns.

Dutton, Donald G. The Abusive Personality: Violence & Control in Intimate Relationships. 2nd rev. ed. 2006. (ENG., Illus.). 262p. 55.00 (978-1-59385-371-6(8)) Guilford Pubns., Inc.

Edleson, Jeffrey L. & Williams, Oliver J. Parenting by Men Who Batter: New Directions for Assessment & Intervention. Edleson, Jeffrey L. & Williams, Oliver J., eds. 2006. (Interpersonal Violence Ser.). (ENG., Illus.). 176p. 32.95 (978-0-19-530934-4(0)) Oxford Univ. Pr., Inc.

Fall, Kevin A. & Howard, Shareen. Alternatives to Domestic Violence: A Homework Manual for Battering Intervention Groups, Third Edition. 3rd rev. ed. 2011. (ENG., Illus.). 260p. pap. 32.95 (978-0-415-88901-8(4)) Routledge.

Giglio, Diana R. What to Look Out For: A Dynamic Story of How to Survive an Abusive Spouse, 1 vol. 2010. 71p. pap. 16.95 (978-1-4489-5647-0(1)) PublishAmerica, Inc.

Gondolf, Edward W. The Future of Batterer Programs: Reassessing Evidence-Based Practice. 2012. (Northeastern Series on Gender, Crime, & Law Ser.). (ENG.). 336p. (C). 85.00 (978-1-55553-769-2(3)); pap. 35.00 (978-1-55553-770-8(7)) Univ. Pr. of New England. (Northeastern University Pr.).

Harne, Lynne. Violent Fathering & the Risks to Children: The Need for Change. 2011. (Illus.). 216p. 85.00 (978-1-84742-917-9(3)) Policy Pr. GBR. Dist: Chicago Distribution Ctr.

Hilton, N. Zoe, et al. Risk Assessment for Domestically Violent Men: Tools for Criminal Justice, Offender Intervention, & Victim Services. 2009. (Law & Public Policy: Psychology & the Social Sciences Ser.). (Illus.). 240p. 59.95 (978-1-4338-0466-3(2)) American Psychological Assn.

Hunter, Joanna. But He'll Change: End the Thinking That Keeps You in an Abusive Relationship. 2010. (ENG.). 248p. pap. 14.95 (978-1-59285-818-7(X)) Hazelden Publishing & Educational Services.

Jacobson, Neil & Gottman, John. When Men Batter Women. 2007. (ENG.). 304p. pap. 20.95 (978-1-4165-5133-1(6)) Simon & Schuster.

Jenkins, Alan. Becoming Ethical: A Parallel, Political Journey with Men Who Have Abused. 2009. (Illus.). 208p. pap. 34.50 (978-1-905541-40-9(6)) Russell Hse. Publishing Ltd. GBR. Dist: International Specialized Bk. Services.

Jepsen, Susan. Guarded: Surviving as A Female Prison Officer A Memoir. 2011. 188p. pap. 10.95 (978-1-4327-6931-4(6)) Outskirts Pr., Inc.

Laming, Chris. Challenging Men's Violence Against Women - a Constructivist Approach. 2008. 384p. pap. (978-3-639-03705-0(7)) VDM Verlag Dr. Mueller e.K.

Mills, Linda G. Insult to Injury: Rethinking Our Responses to Intimate Abuse. 2006. (ENG.). 192p. (C). pap. 23.95 (978-0-691-12772-9(7)) Princeton Univ. Pr.

Pandya, Varsha. Men Share Stories of Violence at Home. 2009. 176p. pap. (978-3-639-15172-5(0)) VDM Verlag Dr. Mueller e.K.

Presser, Lois. Been a Heavy Life: Stories of Violent Men. 2008. (Critical Perspectives in Criminology Ser.). (ENG., Illus.). 200p. 67.00 (978-0-252-03358-2(2)); pap. 26.00 (978-0-252-07558-2(7)) Univ. of Illinois Pr.

Ritchie, Daniel, et al. The Batterer as Parent: Addressing the Impact of Domestic Violence on Family Dynamics. 2nd ed. 2011. (SAGE Series on Violence Against Women Ser.). 352p. pap. 50.00 (978-1-4129-7205-5(1), B72055P) SAGE Pubns., Inc.

Welch, Edward T. Living with an Angry Spouse: Help for Victims of Abuse. 2008. (ENG.). 24p. 3.99 (978-1-934885-35-2(5)) New Growth Pr.

Welland, Christauria & Ribner, Neil. Healing from Violence: Latino Men's Journey to a New Masculinity. 2007. 294p. 50.00 (978-0-8261-2477-7(1)) Springer Publishing Co., Inc.

Wexler, David B. The Stop Program Handouts & Homework: Innovative Skills, Techniques, Options, & Plans for Better Relationships. 2nd ed. 2006. (ENG.). 128p. pap. 12.00 (978-0-393-70515-7(3), 70515) Norton, W. W. & Co., Inc.

Zilney, Lisa Anne. Linking Animal Cruelty & Family Violence. 2007. (ENG.). 248p. (C). 99.95 (978-1-934043-67-7(2)) Cambria Pr.

ABUSIVE PARENTS

Albert, Isabel. Innerfamiliäre Gewalt gegen Kinder: Eine kriminologische und rechtliche Betrachtung der Erscheinungsformen, Ursachen und Möglichkeiten der Bekämpfung. 2008. (Würzburger Schriften zur Kriminalwissenschaft Ser.). 292p. pap. 74.95 (978-3-631-57862-9(8)) Lang, Peter GmbH, Europaischer Verlag der Wissenschaften DEU. Dist: Lang, Peter.

Armstrong, Valerie Diane. Family Tides. 2008. 68p. pap. 10.49 (978-1-4343-7238-3(3)) AuthorHouse.

Bank, Steven A. & Stark, Kirk J. Selected Sections: Corporate & Partnership Income Tax Code & Regulations, 2011-2012. 2011. 836p. pap. 32.00 (978-1-59941-949-7(1), Foundation Pr.) West.

Bunn, J. K. Stand up & let Go 2010. 2010. 27p. 27.65 (978-0-578-05272-4(5)) Bunn, J. K.

Cornelious-Gresham, Valerie Diana. My Eyes No Longer Closed. 2011. 260p. pap. 27.95 (978-1-4560-9900-8(0)) PublishAmerica, Inc.

Harrison, Kathryn. While They Slept: An Inquiry into the Murder of a Family. 2009. (ENG.). 288p. mass mkt. 7.99 (978-0-345-51660-2(5), Ballantine Bks.) Random House Publishing Group.

Quijada, Neftali. The Father & the Son. 2009. 104p. pap. 15.99 (978-1-4415-9745-8(X)) Xlibris Corp.

Rebecca Diamond. Saving the Kids a Grandmother's Story. 2010. 128p. 23.95 (978-1-4502-0050-9(8)); pap. 13.95 (978-1-4502-0049-3(4)) iUniverse, Inc.

Schwartz, Lita Linzer & Isser, Natalie K. Endangered Children. 2nd rev. ed. 2011. (ENG., Illus.). 287p. 79.95 (978-1-4398-7626-8(6), CRC Press) Taylor & Francis Group GBR. Dist: Taylor & Francis Group.

St. Clair, Chip. The Butterfly Garden: Surviving Childhood on the Run with One of America's Most Wanted. 2008. (ENG.). 304p. pap. 15.95 (978-0-7573-0695-2(0)) Health Communications, Inc.

ABYDOS (EGYPT: EXTINCT CITY)

Caulfeild, Algernon Saint George & Christie, H. Lawrence. The Temple of the Kings. 2010. 85.88 (978-1-61719-486-3(7)) Gorgias Pr., LLC.

Mariette, Auguste E. Abydos (Egyptienne), 3 vols. in 1. vii, 749p. reprint ed. (978-3-487-06719-3(6)) Olms, Georg Verlag AG.

Murray, Margaret Alice & Milne, J. Grafton. The Osireion. 2010. 90.08 (978-1-61719-482-5(4)) Gorgias Pr., LLC.

O'Connor, David. Abydos: Egypt's First Pharaohs & the Cult of Osiris. 2011. (ENG., Illus.). 216p. pap. 29.95 (978-0-500-28900-6(X), 528900) Thames & Hudson.

ABYSSAL ZONE

Dorschel, Boris, et al. Atlas of the Deep-Water Seabed: Ireland. 2010. (ENG., Illus.). xv, 164p. 129.00 (978-90-481-9375-2(3), 9048193753) Springer.

Favali, Paolo, et al. Sea Floor Observatories: A New Vision of the Earth from the Abyss. 2011. (Springer Praxis Books / Geophysical Sciences Ser.). (ENG.). 500p. 209.00 (978-3-642-11373-4(7), 3642113737) Springer.

Morozov, Eugene G., et al. Abyssal Channels in the Atlantic Ocean: Water Structure & Flows. 2010. (ENG., Illus.). xxii, 266p. 129.00 (978-90-481-9357-8(5), 9048193575) Springer.

ABYSSINIA

see Ethiopia

ABYSSINIAN LANGUAGE

see Amharic Language

ABYSSINO-ITALIAN WAR, 1895-1896

see Italo-Ethiopian War, 1895-1896

ABZUG, BELLA S., 1920-1998

Levine, Sb M. Bella Abzug: How One Tough Broad from the Bronx Fought Jim Crow & Joe McCarthy, Pissed off Jimmy Carter, Battled for the Rights of Women & Workers, Rallied Against War & for the Planet, & Shook up Politics along the Way. Levine, Suzanne Braun & Thom, Mary, eds. 2008. (ENG., Illus.). 352p. pap. 23.00 (978-0-374-53149-2(8)) Farrar, Straus & Giroux.

ACADEMIA NACIONAL DE SAN CARLOS (MEXICO)

Cárdenas de la Peña, Enrique. Historia de la Academia Mexicana de la Lengua, 1946-2000. 2007. (Vida y Pensamiento de México Ser.). (SPA., Illus.). 365p. 29.99 (978-968-16-7993-4(8)) Fondo de Cultura Economica USA.

A

Charlot, Jean. Mexican Art & the Academy of San Carlos, 1785-1915. 2011. 176p. 42.95 ***(978-1-258-08509-4(7))*** Literary Licensing, LLC.

ACADEMIC ACHIEVEMENT

see also Achievement Tests; Prediction of Scholastic Success

AAUW Educational Foundation, et al. Where the Girls Are: The Facts about Gender Equity in Education. 2008. 100p. pap. 10.00 *(978-1-879922-38-9(X))* American Assn. of Univ. Women Educational Foundation.

Abode, Philip. Strategy & Performance among California's Largest School Districts. 2010. 112p. pap. *(978-3-8383-1841-7(2))* Lambert Academic Publishing.

Abrams, Fran. Learning to Fail. 2009. (ENG., Illus.). 184p. 35.95 *(978-0-415-48396-4(4))* Routledge.

Academic Advising for Student Success & Retention. Date not set. tchr. ed., stu. ed., ring bd. incl. VHS *(978-1-887842-10-5(1))* USA Group Noel-Levitz.

Aglobitse, Peter Borkly. Parental Decision & Schooling of Children in Ghan. 2011. 212p. pap. ***(978-3-8443-2532-4(8))*** Lambert Academic Publishing.

Agudelo, Fresia. The Relationship Between Parents' Level of Education. 2011. 80p. pap. ***(978-3-8433-7220-6(9))*** Lambert Academic Publishing.

Airasian, Peter & Russell, Michael. Classroom Assessment. 7th ed. 2011. (ENG., Illus.). 448p. (C). pap. 100.00 *(978-0-07-811021-4(1)*, 0078110211) McGraw-Hill Cos., The.

Alderman, M. Kay. Motivation for Achievement: Possibilities for Teaching & Learning. 3rd rev. ed. 2007. (ENG., Illus.). 360p. pap. 50.95 *(978-0-8058-6048-1(7))* Routledge.

Allen, Jeanie K. & Bracken, Susan J., eds. Most College Students Are Wom. 2008. (Women in Academe Ser.). 210p. pap. 29.95 *(978-1-57922-191-1(2))*; (C). 75.00 *(978-1-57922-190-4(4))* Stylus Publishing, LLC.

Allison, Elle. A Leader's Guide to People, Practices, & Processes. 2011. (ENG.). 240p. pap. 29.95 ***(978-1-935588-11-5(7))*** Lead+Learn Pr.

Almeida, Lisa & Ainsworth, Larry. Standards & Assessment: The Core of Quality Instruction. 2011. (ENG.). 256p. pap. 27.95 *(978-1-935588-03-0(6))* Lead+Learn Pr.

Anderson, Kristin R. Real-Time Decisions: Educators Using Formative Assessment to Change Lives Now! 2012. (ENG., Illus.). 144p. pap. 24.95 ***(978-1-935588-13-9(3))*** Lead+Learn Pr.

Antill, Sara. 10 Ways I Can Be a Better Student. 2012. (I Can Make a Difference Ser.). (ENG.). 24p. (J). (gr. 2-5). pap. 8.25 ***(978-1-4488-6369-3(4))***; lib. bdg. 21.25 ***(978-1-4488-6205-4(1))*** Rosen Publishing Group, Inc., The. (PowerKids Pr.).

Archer, Louise & Francis, Becky. Understanding Minority Ethnic Achievement: Race, Gender, Class & Success. 2006. (Illus.). 205p. 160.00 *(978-0-415-37281-7(X))* Routledge.

—Understanding Minority Ethnic Achievement: Race, Gender, Class And 'Success' 2006. (Illus.). 205p. per. 46.95 *(978-0-415-37282-4(8))* Routledge.

Arroyo, Evelyn. A+RISE Instructional Strategy Card Set 6-12. 2011. (ENG.). 80p. (C). ring bd. 89.99 *(978-0-13-270022-1(0))* Allyn & Bacon, Inc.

—A+RISE Instructional Strategy Card Set K-5. 2011. (ENG.). 80p. (C). ring bd. 89.99 *(978-0-13-273037-2(5))* Allyn & Bacon, Inc.

Artis, Shamnia. Moving from Ordinary to Extraordinary: Strategies for Preparing for College & Scholarships. 2010. 160p. pap. 12.95 *(978-1-936236-10-7(9))* iUniverse, Inc.

Arum, Richard & Velez, Melissa, eds. Improving Learning Environments: School Discipline & Student Achievement in Comparative Perspective. 2012. (Studies in Social Inequality Ser.). (ENG.). 360p. 60.00 ***(978-0-8047-7803-9(5))*** Stanford Univ. Pr.

Assaye, Legesse. Early Adolescents' Perceived School Environment: Patterns of Cognitions, Affects & Behavior of Adolescents in Upper Primary Schools: A Path Analysis. 2011. 108p. pap. ***(978-3-639-33795-2(6))*** VDM Verlag Dr. Mueller e.K.

Badgett, John L. & Christmann, Edwin P., eds. Designing Elementary Instruction & Assessment: Using the Cognitive Domain. 2009. (Illus.). 152p. 68.95 *(978-1-4129-7120-1(9)*, B71218C); pap. 28.95 *(978-1-4129-7121-8(7)*, B71218P) Corwin Pr.

—Designing Middle & High School Instruction & Assessment: Using the Cognitive Domain. 2009. 152p. 68.95 *(978-1-4129-7117-1(9)*, B71171C); pap. 28.95 *(978-1-4129-7118-8(7)*, B71171P) Corwin Pr.

Baldwin, Amy, et al. NSSI Engaging Activities for Academic Success. 2009. (Engaging Activities For Ser.). (ENG.). 50p. (C). pap. 21.20 *(978-0-13-705028-4(3)*, Prentice Hall) Prentice Hall PTR.

Bardige, Art. New Physical Ideas Are Here Needed: Revolutionizing Education. 2007. 364p. pap. 27.96 *(978-1-4303-1257-4(2))* Lulu Enterprises Inc.

Barkley, Stephen G. & Bianco, Terri. Instructional Coaching with the End in Mind: Using Backward Planning to Increase Student Achievement. 2012. pap. ***(978-1-892334-27-5(5))*** Performance Learning Systems, Inc.

Barkley, Stephen G. & Bianco, Terri. Tapping Student Effort, Increasing Student Achievement. 2007. pap. *(978-1-892334-23-7(2))* Performance Learning Systems, Inc.

Barratt, Will. Social Class on Campus: Theories & Manifestations. 2011. (Illus.). 256p. pap. 24.95 *(978-1-57922-572-8(1))*; 75.00 *(978-1-57922-571-1(3))* Stylus Publishing, LLC.

Basilo, Eric. Closing the Reading Gap: Case Studies of Reading Performance of Male Students & the Single-Sex Classroom. 2008. 112p. pap. *(978-3-639-10292-5(4))* VDM Verlag Dr. Mueller e.K.

Bazan, Laura & Johnson, Elvira, compiled by. ACA 118 Planner 2011. 2011. (C). spiral bd. 10.00 ***(978-1-59494-049-1(5))*** CPCC Pr.

Beam, Andrea. Inclusion Versus Pullout. 2008. 100p. pap. *(978-3-639-08164-0(1))* VDM Verlag Dr. Mueller e.K.

Bean, Rita M. & Swan Dagen, Allison, eds. Best Practices of Literacy Leaders: Keys to School Improvement. 2011. (ENG., Illus.). 392p. (gr. k-12). 55.00 *(978-1-60918-942-6(6))*; pap. 35.00 *(978-1-60918-941-9(8))* Guilford Pubns., Inc.

Becker, Karen A., et al. Understanding & Engaging under-Resourced College Students: A fresh look at the influence of economic class on teaching & learning in higher Education. 2009. 314p. pap. 39.95 *(978-1-934583-33-3(2))* aha! Process, Inc.

Bedore Jr. Online Student Success & Completion Rates. 2010. 176p. pap. *(978-3-8383-0126-6(9))* Lambert Academic Publishing.

Bell, Paul D. Self Regulated Learning & Epistemological Beliefs- a Predictive Model for Undergraduate Asynchronous Web-Based Learning. 2007. 208p. per. *(978-3-8364-2981-8(0))* VDM Verlag Dr. Mueller e.K.

Bembenutty, Héfer, ed. Self-Regulated Learning, No. 126. 2011. (J-B TL Single Issue Teaching & Learning Ser.: 126). (ENG.). 128p. pap. 29.00 *(978-1-118-09163-0(9)*, Jossey-Bass) Wiley, John & Sons, Inc.

Bembenutty, Héfer. Academic Delay of Gratification. 2009. 72p. pap. *(978-3-639-19706-8(2))* VDM Verlag Dr. Mueller e.K.

—Homework Completion & Academic Achievement. 2009. 92p. pap. *(978-3-639-19328-2(8))* VDM Verlag Dr. Mueller e.K.

Bendt, John G. A Roadmap to Career Success: 25 Tips for College Bound Students. 2007. 80p. (YA). per. 10.95 *(978-0-9790707-0-9(8))* Career Mentor Pr., LLC.

Bennett, Neville, et al. Quality of Pupil Learning Experiences (Rle Edu O) 2011. (Routledge Library Editions: Education Ser.). (ENG.). 280p. 115.00 ***(978-0-415-50873-5(8))*** Routledge.

Berger, Beth. Correlating Character Education, Achievement, Behavior, & Attendance. 2009. 160p. pap. *(978-3-639-12745-4(5))* VDM Verlag Dr. Mueller e.K.

Berry, Vivien. Personality Differences & Oral Test Performance. 2007. 246p. pap. 54.95 *(978-0-8204-8785-4(6))* Lang, Peter Publishing, Inc.

Bessoondyal, Hemant. Factors Affecting Mathematics Achievement. 2008. 276p. pap. *(978-3-639-06840-5(8))* VDM Verlag Dr. Mueller e.K.

Best, Brin. Accelerated Learning. 2nd rev. ed. 2011. (Illus.). 128p. pap. *(978-1-906610-34-0(7)*, Teachers' Pocketbooks) Management Pocketbooks GBR. Dist: Ware-Pak, Inc.

Betts, Julian R. Does School Choice Work? Effects on Student Integration & Achievement. 2006. *(978-1-58213-114-6(7))* Public Policy Institute of California.

Betts, Julian R., et al. Lessons in Reading Reform: Finding What Works. 2010. *(978-1-58213-140-5(6))* Public Policy Institute of California.

Betty'S Children'S Academy. Ready! Set! Go! Preparing Preschoolers for Kindergarten. 2009. 64p. pap. 25.49 *(978-1-4389-4785-3(2))* AuthorHouse.

Billingsley, Joanne M. Aim to Grow Your Brain. 2009. 152p. pap. 24.00 *(978-1-60844-114-3(8))* Dog Ear Publishing, LLC.

Black-Hawkins, Kristine. Achievement & Inclusion in Schools. 2007. (Illus.). X, 166p. 190.00 *(978-0-415-39197-9(0))* Routledge.

Black-Hawkins, Kristine, et al. Achievement & Inclusion in Schools. 2007. (ENG., Illus.). 176p. per. 42.50 *(978-0-415-39198-6(9))* Routledge.

Blackburn, Barbara R. Rigor Made Easy: Getting Started. 2012. ***(978-1-59667-215-4(3))*** Eye On Education, Inc.

Blackburn, Barbara R. Study Guide: Classroom Motivation from A to Z. 2006. (ENG.). 96p. pap. 16.95 *(978-1-59667-033-4(9))* Eye On Education, Inc.

Blackburn, Desmond. Socio-Cultural Leadership: The art of restructuring schools through research-based principal Leadership. 2009. 88p. pap. 10.95 *(978-0-595-52826-4(0))* iUniverse, Inc.

Blackett, Karine. Career Achievement: Growing Your Goals. 2010. (ENG., Illus.). 336p. (C). pap. 72.00 *(978-0-07-337700-1(7)*, 0073377007) McGraw-Hill Higher Education.

Blankenship, Jane. Coming to Terms: The Collected Works of Jane Blankenship. Muir, Janette Kenner, ed. 2011. (Lexington Studies in Political Communication Ser.). (ENG., Illus.). 440p. (gr. 17). 85.00 ***(978-0-7391-4568-5(1))*** Lexington Bks.

Blankstein, Alan M. Facilitator's Guide to Failure Is Not an Option: Six Principles for Making Student Success the Only Option. 2nd ed. 2009. 88p. pap. 17.95 *(978-1-4129-8174-3(3)*, B79238F) Corwin Pr.

—Failure Is Not an Option: 6 Principles for Making Student Success the Only Option. 2nd ed. 2009. (Illus.). 288p. pap. 36.95 *(978-1-4129-7923-8(4)*, B79238P) Corwin Pr.

Blankstein, Alan M., et al. Engaging Every Learner. 2007. (Soul of Educational Leadership Ser.: 1). (Illus.). 224p. 76.95 *(978-1-4129-3853-2(8)*, B38538C); per. 33.95 *(978-1-4129-3854-9(6)*, B38538P) Corwin Pr.

—Sustaining Professional Learning Communities. 2008. (Soul of Educational Leadership Ser.: 3). (Illus.). 224p. 76.95 *(978-1-4129-4937-8(8)*, B49378C); per. 33.95 *(978-1-4129-4938-5(6)*, B49378P) Corwin Pr.

Blink, Rebecca J. & Blink, Rebecca. Data-Driven Instructional Leadership. 2007. (ENG., Illus.). 150p. pap. 29.95 *(978-1-59667-037-2(1))* Eye On Education, Inc.

Blythe, Sally Goddard, et al. Attention, Balance, & Coordination: The A. B. C. of Learning Success. 2009. (ENG., Illus.). 442p. pap. 74.95 *(978-0-470-51623-2(2)*, Wiley) Wiley, John & Sons, Inc.

Bohrnstedt, George W., et al, eds. No Child Left Behind & the Reduction of the Achievement Gap: Sociological Perspectives on Federal Educational Policy. 2007. (Illus.). 406p. per. 39.95 *(978-0-415-95531-7(9))* Routledge.

Bok, Derek. Our Underachieving Colleges: A Candid Look at How Much Students Learn & Why They Should Be Learning More. 2007. (ENG.). 434p. (C). pap. 27.95 *(978-0-691-13618-9(1))* Princeton Univ. Pr.

Borrero, Noah & Bird, Shawn. Closing the Achievement Gap: How to Pinpoint Student Strengths to Differentiate Instruction & Help Your Striving Readers Succeed. 2009. (ENG.). 144p. (gr. 6-12). pap. 19.99 *(978-0-545-04876-7(1)*, Teaching Resources) Scholastic, Inc.

Boudett, Kathryn Parker & Steele, Jennifer L., eds. Data Wise in Action: Stories of Schools Using Data to Improve Teaching & Learning. 2007. 192p. pap. 29.95 *(978-1-891792-80-9(6)*, Harvard Education Pr.) Harvard Education Publishing Group (HEPG).

Bouquett, Kimberly Ewing & Lindsey, Stephanie. Systematic Sight Word Instruction for Reading Success: A 35-Week Program. 2008. (ENG.). 478p. pap. 89.99 *(978-0-545-03688-7(7)*, Teaching Resources) Scholastic, Inc.

Boyle, Jerry. It's All about People Skills: Surviving Challenges in the Classroom. 2011. (ENG.). 116p. 35.00 ***(978-1-61048-609-5(9))***; pap. 17.95 ***(978-1-61048-610-1(2))*** Rowman & Littlefield Education.

Brackett, Marc A. & Kremenitzer, Janet P. Creating Emotionally Literate Classrooms. 2011. per. 24.50 *(978-1-934032-18-3(2)*, Dude Publishing) National Professional Resources, Inc.

Brayman, Jacqueline & Grey, Maureen. Taking Flight to Literacy & Leadership: Soaring to New Heights in Learning. 2010. (ENG.). 262p. 80.00 *(978-1-60709-858-4(X))*; pap. 32.95 *(978-1-60709-859-1(8))* Rowman & Littlefield Education.

Brayman, Jacqueline J. & Grey, Maureen A. Taking Flight to Literacy & Leadership! Soaring to New Heights in Learning. 2010. *(978-1-60709-860-7(1))* Rowman & Littlefield Education.

Brier, Norman. Self-Regulated Learning: Practical Interventions for Struggling Teens. 2010. 186p. pap. 29.95 *(978-0-87822-631-3(1))* Research Pr.

Britner, Shari, ed. Self-Efficacy in School & Community Settings. 2012. 260p. ***(978-1-61470-828-5(2))*** Nova Science Pubs., Inc.

Broadbent, Peggy. Early Childhood Programs: Opportunities for Academic, Cognitive & Personal Success. 2010. (Illus.). 160p. pap. 49.95 *(978-1-4520-0458-7(7))* AuthorHouse.

Brookhart, Susan M. Grading & Learning: Practices That Support Student Achievement. 2011. 168p. pap. 24.95 ***(978-1-935542-84-1(2))***; lib. bdg. 44.95 ***(978-1-935542-85-8(0))*** Solution Tree Pr.

Brown, D. S. An Educational Primer for the Majority Student. 2011. 160p. pap. 14.99 ***(978-1-4567-5769-4(5))*** AuthorHouse.

Brown, Dave F. Why America's Public Schools Are the Best Place for Your Kids: Reality vs. Negative Perceptions. 2011. ***(978-1-61048-359-9(6))*** Rowman & Littlefield Education.

Brown, M. Christopher. Broken Cisterns: African American Education Fifty Years after Brown. 2008. *(978-1-59311-043-7(X))*; pap. *(978-1-59311-042-0(1))* Information Age Publishing, Inc.

Brown, Phillip, et al. The Global Auction: The Broken Promises of Education, Jobs, & Incomes. 2012. (ENG.). 208p. pap. 19.95 ***(978-0-19-992644-2(1))*** Oxford Univ. Pr., Inc.

Building on What Works at Charter Schools: Hearing Before the Committee on Education & Labor, U.S. House of Representatives, One Hundred Eleventh Congress, First Session, Hearing Held in Washington, DC, June 4, 2009. 2009. (Illus.). iii, 57p. *(978-0-16-084447-8(9)*, 552-070-39974-7) United States Government Printing Office.

Bulach, Cletus R. Creating a Culture for High-Performing Schools: A Comprehensive Approach to School Reform & Dropout Prevention. 2008. (ENG., Illus.). 340p. 110.00 *(978-1-57886-796-7(7))*; pap. 49.95 *(978-1-57886-797-4(5))* Rowman & Littlefield Education.

Bulach, Cletus R., et al. Creating a Culture for High-Performing Schools: A Comprehensive Approach to School Reform, Dropout Prevention, & Bullying Behavior. 2nd ed. 2011. (ENG.). 188p. 55.00 ***(978-1-61048-321-6(9))***; (ENG.). 188p. pap. 26.95 ***(978-1-61048-322-3(7))***; ***(978-1-61048-323-0(5))*** Rowman & Littlefield Education.

Burris, Carol Corbett & Garrity, Delia T. Detracking for Excellence & Equity. 2008. (Illus.). ix, 180p. pap. 26.95 *(978-1-4166-0708-3(0))* Assn. for Supervision & Curriculum Development.

Butler-Derge, Shirley R. Rites of Passage: A Program for High School African American Males. 2009. (ENG., Illus.). 70p. pap. 15.99 *(978-0-7618-4320-7(5))* Univ. Pr. of America, Inc.

Caldwell, Brian & Harris, Jessica. Why Not the Best Schools? Case Studies: Australia. 2008. 52p. pap. 29.95 *(978-0-86431-979-1(7))* ACER Pr. AUS. Dist: International Specialized Bk. Services.

—Why Not the Best Schools? Case Studies: China. 2008. 34p. pap. 29.95 *(978-0-86431-987-6(8))* ACER Pr. AUS. Dist: International Specialized Bk. Services.

—Why Not the Best Schools? Case Studies: England. 2008. 46p. pap. 29.95 *(978-0-86431-812-1(X))* ACER Pr. AUS. Dist: International Specialized Bk. Services.

—Why Not the Best Schools? Case Studies: Finland. 2008. 44p. pap. 29.95 *(978-0-86431-804-6(9))* ACER Pr. AUS. Dist: International Specialized Bk. Services.

—Why Not the Best Schools? Case Studies: USA. 2008. 33p. pap. 29.95 *(978-0-86431-995-1(9))* ACER Pr. AUS. Dist: International Specialized Bk. Services.

—Why Not the Best Schools? Case Studies: Wales. 2008. 39p. pap. 29.95 *(978-0-86431-971-5(1))* ACER Pr. AUS. Dist: International Specialized Bk. Services.

Caldwell, Brian J. & Harris, Jessica. Why Not the Best Schools? 2008. 200p. pap. 39.95 *(978-0-86431-955-5(X))* ACER Pr. AUS. Dist: International Specialized Bk. Services.

Cantwell, Robert H. & Scevak, Jill J. An Academic Life: A Handbook for New Academics. 2010. 205p. pap. 34.95 *(978-0-86431-908-1(8))* ACER Pr. AUS. Dist: International Specialized Bk. Services.

Carman, Tim J. The Forces Behind School Change: Defining & Understanding the Call for Perfection. Carman, Tim J., ed. 2008. (ENG.). 132p. pap. 24.95 *(978-1-57886-585-7(9))*; 65.00 *(978-1-57886-584-0(0))* Rowman & Littlefield Education.

Carol Judd. Principal Practices: Addressing Human Needs for Successful School Administration. 2009. 332p. 32.95 *(978-1-4401-4756-2(6))*; pap. 22.95 *(978-1-4401-4754-8(X))* iUniverse, Inc.

Carpenter, Makenzie. TECHNOLOGY-BASED LEARNING ON AT-RISK HIGH SCHOOL STUDENTS: AN EVALUATION OF THE MARTIN LUTHER KING JR. COMMUNITY TECHNOLOGY CENTER AFTER-SCHOOL PROGRAM. 2008. 140p. pap. *(978-3-639-02399-2(4))* VDM Verlag Dr. Mueller e.K.

Carrasquillo, Angela. Easy Steps for Implementing & Evaluating a Dual Language Programs. 2007. (ENG.). 50p. (C). per. 20.00 *(978-0-9777197-5-4(8))* Linus Pubns., Inc.

Carter, Carol. Sophomore Guide to College & Career: Preparing for Life after High School. 2007. (Illus.). 163p. per. 16.95 *(978-0-9742044-6-8(3))* LifeBound.

Carter, Prudence L. Keepin' It Real: School Success Beyond Black & White. 2007. (Transgressing Boundaries: Studies in Black Politics & Black Communities Ser.). (ENG., Illus.). 240p. per. 19.95 *(978-0-19-532523-2(0))* Oxford Univ. Pr., Inc.

Carter, Samuel Casey. On Purpose: How Great School Cultures Form Strong Character. 2010. (Illus.). 208p. pap. 31.95 *(978-1-4129-8672-4(9)*, B86724P) Corwin Pr.

Casiano, Rosario. The Impact of a Hispanic/Latino Advocacy Program in a High School. 2008. 100p. pap. *(978-3-8364-9782-4(4))* VDM Verlag Dr. Mueller e.K.

Challenges Facing Bureau of Indian Education Schools in Improving Student Achievement: Hearing Before the Subcommittee on Early Childhood, Elementary, & Secondary Education, Committee on Education & Labor, U.S. House of Representatives, One Hundred Tenth Congress, Second Session, Hearing Held in Washington, DC, September 29, 2008. 2008. iii, 48p. *(978-0-16-082331-2(5)*, 552-070-38388-3) United States Government Printing Office.

Chantel, Zwiefelhofer. The Summer Slide to Underachievement: An Analysis of Summer School Programs. 2011. 64p. pap. ***(978-3-639-33502-6(3))*** VDM Verlag Dr. Mueller e.K.

Chase, Erica M., ed. Comparing U. S. Students to Their International Peers. 2010. (Illus.). viii, 344p. 235.00 *(978-1-61761-287-9(1))* Nova Science Pubs., Inc.

Chase, Rebecca Tarver, et al. Pathways: Listening, Speaking, & Critical Thinking 2 Student Book. 2011. (Pathways Ser.). (ENG.). 240p. (C). pap. 40.95 ***(978-1-111-39863-7(1))*** Cengage Heinle.

—Pathways: Listening, Speaking, & Critical Thinking 3 Student Book. 2011. (Pathways Ser.). (ENG.). (C). pap. 40.95 ***(978-1-111-39865-1(8))*** Cengage Heinle.

Chen, Hsin-Tzu (Tommy). Research on Taiwanese Adolescent's Learning Styles. 2010. 196p. pap. *(978-3-8383-2103-5(0))* Lambert Academic Publishing.

Chen, Jennifer Jun-Li. How the Academic Support of Parents, Teachers, & Peers Contributes to a Student's Achievement: The Case of Hong Kong. 2007. (Illus.). 196p. *(978-0-7734-5507-8(8))* Mellen, Edwin Pr., The.

Chenoweth, Karin. It's Being Done: Academic Success in Unexpected Schools. 2007. 250p. pap. 26.95 *(978-1-891792-39-7(3))*; lib. bdg. 54.95 *(978-1-891792-40-3(7))* Harvard Education Publishing Group (HEPG). (Harvard Education Pr.).

Childress, Stacey M., et al. Leading for Equity: The Pursuit of Excellence in the Montgomery County Public Schools. 2009. 192p. pap. 26.95 *(978-1-934742-22-8(8))*; (ENG.). lib. bdg. 49.95 *(978-1-934742-23-5(6))* Harvard Education Publishing Group (HEPG). (Harvard Education Pr.).

Chilver, Tamara Larraine. Tutoring Your Elementary Child with TLC. 2007. per. 11.95 *(978-0-9796313-1-3(9))* TLC Editions.

Christmann, Edwin P. & Badgett, John L. Interpreting Assessment Data: Statistical Techniques You Can Use. 2009. (ENG.). 194p. pap. 24.95 *(978-1-933531-36-6(3))* National Science Teachers Assn.

Cizek, Gregory J. Handbook of Formative Assessment. Andrade, Heidi L., ed. 2009. (ENG., Illus.). 380p. 104.95 *(978-0-415-99320-3(2))* Routledge.

Cizek, Gregory J., ed. Handbook of Formative Assessment. 2009. (Illus.). 396p. 220.00 *(978-0-415-99319-7(9))* Routledge.

Cleveland, Kathleen Palme. Teaching Boys Who Struggle in School: Strategies That Turn Underachievers into Successful Learners. 2011. 233p. pap. 27.95 *(978-1-4166-1150-9(9))* Assn. for Supervision & Curriculum Development.

Cole, Robert W., ed. Educating Everybody's Children: Diverse Teaching Strategies for Diverse Learners, Revised & Expanded 2nd Edition. 2nd ed. 2008. 295p. pap. 29.95 *(978-1-4166-0674-1(2))* Assn. for Supervision & Curriculum Development.

Coleman, Arthur L., et al. Achieving Educational Excellence for All: A guide to diversity-related policy strategies for school Districts. 2011. 50p. pap. ***(978-0-88364-316-7(2))*** National Schl. Boards Assn.

Coleman, Rhoda P. & Goldenberg, Claude. Promoting Academic Achievement among English Learners: A Guide to the Research. 2010. (Illus.). 192p. pap. 34.95 *(978-1-4129-5549-2(1)*, B55483P) Corwin Pr.

Colón, Diego L. Puerto Ricans: Value Orientations & Achievement Potential. 2010. 120p. (ENG.). 22.95 *(978-1-4502-0433-0(3))*; pap. 12.95 *(978-1-4502-0435-4(X))* iUniverse, Inc.

Condition of Education (1995) 518p. pap. 50.00 *(978-0-7881-2903-2(1))* DIANE Publishing Co.

Connolly, Faith & Protheroe, Nancy. Principals & Counselors Partnering for Student Success. 2009. *(978-1-931762-87-8(2))* Educational Research Service.

Conway, Joan. Collective Intelligence in Schools. 2009. 280p. pap. *(978-3-639-16319-3(2))* VDM Verlag Dr. Mueller e.K.

Cooper, Bridget. Empathy in Education: Engagement, values & Achievement 2011. (ENG., Illus.). 296p. 140.00 *(978-1-4411-0144-0(6))* Continuum International Publishing Group, Ltd. GBR. Dist: National Bk. Network.

Cooper, Paul W., et al. From Inclusion to Engagement: Helping Students Engage with Schooling Through Policy & Practice. 2011. (ENG., Illus.). 258p. pap. 45.00 *(978-0-470-01946-7(8)*, Wiley) Wiley, John & Sons, Inc.

Cornelius-White, Jeffrey H. D. & Harbaugh, Adam P. Learner-Centered Instruction: Building Relationships for Student Success. 2009. (Illus.). 240p. (C). pap. 55.00 *(978-1-4129-5498-3(3)*, B54975P) SAGE Pubns., Inc.

Corporal Punishment in Schools & Its Effect on Academic Success: Hearing Before the Subcommittee on Healthy Families & Communities, Committee on Education & Labor, U.S. House of Representatives, One Hundred Eleventh Congress, Second Session, Hearing Held in Washington, D.C., April 15, 2010. 2010. iii, 65p. ***(978-0-16-087673-8(7)***, 552-070-42225-1) United States Government Printing Office.

Cotton, H. F. A + a = F. 2009. 124p. 29.99 *(978-1-4415-4741-5(X))* Xlibris Corp.

Craig, Debra. Welcome to My Nightmare, Classroom! A Teacher in the Trenches Shatters the Myths, Lies, & Half-truths about Public Education. 2007. per. 15.95 *(978-0-9740534-3-1(0))* AT Publishing.

Craig, Pamela S. Literacy Leadership Teams: Collaborative Leadership for Improving & Sustaining Student Achievement. 2009. 29.95 *(978-1-59667-125-6(4))* Eye On Education, Inc.

Cram101 Textbook Reviews Staff. Outlines & Highlights for Focus on College Success by Constance C Staley, Isbn: 9780534638658. 2009. 122p. pap. 28.95 *(978-1-4288-7719-1(3))* Cram101 Inc.

Creasey, Gary & Jarvis, Patricia A., eds. Adolescent Development & School Achievement in Urban Communities: Resilience in the Neighborhood. 2012. (ENG.). 264p. 135.00 *(978-0-415-89415-9(8))*; pap. 44.95 *(978-0-415-89416-6(6))* Routledge.

Creason, Linda & Garavalia, Linda. Can They Succeed? 2008. 108p. pap. *(978-3-639-04714-1(1))* VDM Verlag Dr. Mueller e.K.

Creemers. A Dynamic Model of Educational Effectiveness: A Contribution to Policy, Practice & Theory in Contemporary Schools. 2007. (Contexts of Learning Ser.). (ENG., Illus.). 320p. (C). 47.95 *(978-0-415-39953-1(X))* Routledge.

Creemers, Bert P. M. & Kyriakides, Leonidas. A Dynamic Model of Educational Effectiveness: A Contribution to Policy, Practice & Theory in Contemporary Schools. 2007. (Contexts of Learning Ser.). (Illus.). 320p. 170.00 *(978-0-415-38951-8(8))* Routledge.

Croft, Lee B., et al. Getting Through: Achieving Success in College. 2011. 152p. pap. 24.50 ***(978-1-257-05856-3(8))*** Lulu Enterprises Inc.

Cuban, Larry. As Good As It Gets: What School Reform Brought to Austin. 2010. (Illus.). 304p. 25.95 *(978-0-674-03554-6(2))* Harvard Univ. Pr.

Cunningham, Kimberly R. & Chance Fox, Ashley. Success Strategies for College & Life. 3rd rev. ed. 2011. 154p. pap. 54.95 ***(978-0-7575-9031-3(4))*** Kendall Hunt Publishing Co.

Curry, Sandra. Emotional Intelligence in Educational Leadership. 2008. 144p. pap. *(978-3-639-09470-1(0))* VDM Verlag Dr. Mueller e.K.

Cuseo. Thriving in College & Beyond: Research-Based Strategies for Academic Success & Personal Development - Custom Ch 2. rev. ed. 2011. 28p. ring bd. 10.00 ***(978-0-7575-9494-6(8))*** Kendall Hunt Publishing Co.

Cuseo, Joe, et al. Thriving in College & Beyond. rev. ed. 2009. (ENG.). pap. 54.95 *(978-0-7575-6708-7(8))* Kendall Hunt Publishing Co.

—Thriving in College & Beyond: Concise Version. rev. ed. 2010. (ENG.). 448p. pap. 49.20 *(978-0-7575-6709-4(6))* Kendall Hunt Publishing Co.

Cusworth, Linda. The Impact of Parental Employment: Young People Well-Being & Educational Achievement. 2009. (Studies in Cash & Care Ser.). (Illus.). 260p. 114.95 *(978-0-7546-7559-4(9))* Ashgate Publishing Co.

Dancy, Deborah D. Yes! We Can: Strategies to Close the Achievement Gap. 2007. 112p. per. 24.95 *(978-1-4327-1587-8(9))* Outskirts Pr., Inc.

Danville Community Staff. Bridges to Success in College & Beyond 8233. 2nd rev. ed. 2010. (MSSTKT Ser.). (ENG.). pap. 48.53 *(978-0-7575-4582-5(3))* Kendall Hunt Publishing Co.

Davis, Jeff. The First-Generation Student Experience: Implications for Campus Practice, & Strategies for Improving Persistence & Success. 2010. (ACPA Publication). 214p. 75.00 *(978-1-57922-369-4(9))*; pap. 29.95 *(978-1-57922-370-0(2))* Stylus Publishing, LLC.

Dean, Ceri B., et al. Classroom Instruction That Works: Research-Based Strategies for Increasing Student Achievement, 2nd Edition. 2nd ed. 2012. 188p. pap. 28.95 ***(978-1-4166-1362-6(5))*** Assn. for Supervision & Curriculum Development.

Dei, George J. Sefa, ed. Learning to Succeed: The Challenges & Possibilities of Educational Achievement for All. 2010. 442p. pap. 59.99 *(978-1-934844-13-7(6))* Teneo Pr.

Demerath, Peter. Producing Success: The Culture of Personal Advancement in an American High School. 2009. (ENG., Illus.). 224p. 55.00 *(978-0-226-14239-5(6))*; pap. 22.00 *(978-0-226-14241-8(8))* Univ. of Chicago Pr.

Denby, Neil, et al. Masters Level Study in Education. 2008. (ENG.). 240p. (C). 117.00 *(978-0-335-23413-4(5)*, 0335234135); pap. 40.00 *(978-0-335-23414-1(3)*, 0335234143) McGraw-Hill Education GBR. Dist: McGraw-Hill Cos., The.

Deneen, Christopher. Assessing Student Achievement: A Guide for Teachers & Administrators. 2008. (ENG.). 222p. 95.00 *(978-1-57886-809-4(2))*; pap. 32.95 *(978-1-57886-810-0(6))* Rowman & Littlefield Education.

Deneen, James R. Schools That Succeed, Students Who Achieve: Profiles of Programs Helping All Students to Learn. 2010. (ENG.). 110p. 60.00 *(978-1-60709-340-4(5))*; pap. 27.95 *(978-1-60709-341-1(3))* Rowman & Littlefield Education.

The Department of Education Inspector General's Review of Standards for Program Length in Higher Education: Hearing Before the Committee on Education & Labor, U.S. House of Representatives, One Hundred Eleventh Congress, Second Session, Hearing Held in Washington, DC, June 17, 2010. 2010. iii, 48p. *(978-0-16-087064-4(X)*, 552-070-41921-7) United States Government Printing Office.

DeShano da Silva, Carol, et al, eds. The Opportunity Gap: Achievement & Inequality in Education. 2007. (Harvard Educational Review Ser.: 43). 340p. pap. 32.95 *(978-0-916690-47-2(4)*, Harvard Educational Review Reprint Series) Harvard Education Publishing Group (HEPG).

Dinah, Dovona-Ope. Academic Achievment in Secondary Schools in Papua New Guinea: Female Students' Attributions for Academic Achievement in Secondary Schools in Papua New Guinea. 2011. 412p. pap. ***(978-3-639-32197-5(9))*** VDM Verlag Dr. Mueller e.K.

Dinan, Andrea. The Academic Impact of Service-Learning New Jersey High Schools. 2010. 160p. pap. *(978-3-8383-8430-6(X))* Lambert Academic Publishing.

Diniz, Felipe. Estimating a Technology of Cognitive Skill Formation in Brazil. 2009. 72p. pap. *(978-3-639-14574-8(7))* VDM Verlag Dr. Mueller e.K.

Dix, Paul. Classroom Assessment. 2010. (ENG., Illus.). 148p. pap. 45.00 *(978-1-4082-3025-1(9)*, Longman) Pearson Education, Ltd. GBR. Dist: Trans-Atlantic Pubns., Inc.

Doepker, Gina. Should Standardized Reading Tests Be Untimed? 2010. 72p. pap. *(978-3-8383-8121-3(1))* Lambert Academic Publishing.

Doll, Carol A. & Doll, Beth. The Resilient School Library. 2010. (Illus.). 123p. pap. 40.00 *(978-1-59158-639-5(9)*, LU8639) Libraries Unlimited, Inc.

Doty, Gwen. Focused Instruction: An Innovative Teaching Model for All Learners. (Teaching in Focus Ser.). (Illus.). 158p. 2009. pap. 27.95 *(978-1-935249-65-8(7))* 2008. pap. 27.95 *(978-1-934009-28-4(8))* Solution Tree.

Downey, Carolyn J., et al. 50 Ways to Close the Achievement Gap. 3rd ed. 2008. (Illus.). 336p. 90.95 *(978-1-4129-5897-4(0)*, B58974C); pap. 41.95 *(978-1-4129-5898-1(9)*, B58974P) Corwin Pr.

Doyle, Dan. When Kids Know Why, They Try: Motivation Through Purpose & Leadership. 2007. (Illus.). 208p. pap. *(978-0-9796612-0-4(X))* Leading Children Pr.

Dubose, Darlene. College Survival Skills: Topics in Academic Advancement. rev. ed. 2009. (ENG.). 288p. pap. 60.30 *(978-0-7575-7045-2(3))* Kendall Hunt Publishing Co.

DuFour, Richard & Marzano, Robert J. Leaders of Learning: How District, School, & Classroom Leaders Improve Student Achievement. 2011. 248p. pap. 24.95 ***(978-1-935542-66-7(4))***; (ENG.). lib. bdg. 44.95 ***(978-1-935542-67-4(2))*** Solution Tree Pr.

Dunsworth, Marcale & Billings, Dawn L. The High-Performing School: Benchmarking the 10 Indicators of Effectiveness. 2009. xxii, 361p. pap. 34.95 *(978-1-934009-47-5(4))* Solution Tree.

—The High-Performing School: Benchmarking the 10 Indicators of Effectiveness. 2009. xxii, 361p. *(978-1-935249-14-6(2))* Solution Tree Pr.

DuVivier, Roxanne L. Your Online Learning Success Plan. 2007. (ENG.). (C). 15.95 *(978-1-4180-5151-8(9))* Delmar Cengage Learning.

Dye, Angela. Empowerment Starts Here. 2011. (ENG.). 182p. 60.00 ***(978-1-61048-581-4(5))***; pap. 29.95 ***(978-1-61048-582-1(3))*** Rowman & Littlefield Education.

—Empowerment Starts Here: The Seven Principles to Empowering Urban Youth. 2011. xxxiv, 147p. ***(978-1-61048-583-8(1))*** Rowman & Littlefield Education.

Ebang Toung Mve, Franck Tucker. Standing for My Dream: A true story on the power of determination for a foreign student to succeed in America. 2011. 248p. pap. 24.95 ***(978-1-4560-3891-5(5))*** PublishAmerica, Inc.

Eccles, Lynette. Gender & Teacher-Student Interactions in Middle School Science. 2009. 140p. pap. *(978-3-639-14263-1(2))* VDM Verlag Dr. Mueller e.K.

Education in the Nation: Examining the Challenges & Opportunities Facing America's Classrooms: Hearing Before the Committee on Education & the Workforce, U.S. House of Representatives, One Hundred Twelfth Congress, First Session, Hearing Held in Washington, DC, February 10, 2011. 2011. (Illus.). iii, 62p. ***(978-0-16-088588-4(4)***, 552-070-42764-3) United States Government Printing Office.

Edwards, Jacqueline M. Now That's a N. I. C. E. Zone! 2008. 160p. 37.90 *(978-1-4357-1169-3(6))* Lulu Enterprises Inc.

Edwards, Patricia A., et al. Change Is Gonna Come: Transforming Literacy Education for African American Students. 2010. (Language & Literacy Ser.). (ENG., Illus.). 224p. pap. 24.95 *(978-0-8077-5084-1(0))*; 59.00 *(978-0-8077-5085-8(9))* Teachers College Pr., Teachers College, Columbia Univ.

Egel, Andrew, et al. School Success for Kids with Autism. 2011. (ENG.). 250p. pap. 16.95 *(978-1-59363-746-0(2))* Prufrock Pr.

Elahi Shirvan, Majid. The Relationship Between Locus of Control. 2011. 128p. pap. ***(978-3-8443-2066-4(0))*** Lambert Academic Publishing.

Ephgrave, Anna. The Reception Year in Action: A Month-by-Month Guide to Success in the Classroom. 2011. (ENG., Illus.). 160p. pap. 37.95 *(978-0-415-61850-2(9))* Routledge.

Esbrandt, Philip & Hayes, Bruce. Curing Student Underachievement: Clinical Practice for School Leaders. 2011. (ENG.). 206p. 75.00 ***(978-1-61048-536-4(X))*** Rowman & Littlefield Education.

ESEA Reauthorization: Options for Improving NCLB's Measures of Progress: Hearing Before the Committee on Education & Labor, U.S. House of Representatives, One Hundred Tenth Congress, First Session, Hearing Held in Washington, DC, March 21, 2007. 2007. (Illus.). iii, 76p. *(978-0-16-079569-5(9)*, 552-070-36536-2) United States Government Printing Office.

Etim, James S., ed. Essays in Helping Diverse Students Attain Educational Success: When the Classroom Isn't White & Middle Class. 2011. 252p. 109.95 ***(978-0-7734-3936-8(6))*** Mellen, Edwin Pr., The.

Ets compiled by. Student Assessment in College Courses: Enhancing & Verifying Student Learning. 2008. lib. bdg. 36.00 *(978-0-88685-389-1(3))* Educational Testing Service.

Ewing, Christopher J. Does Causality Orientation Moderate the Relationship Between Assignment Choice & Academic Achievement in Air Force Officers Performing the Nuclear M. 2011. 70p. pap. 25.95 ***(978-1-59942-386-9(3)***, Dissertation.com) Universal Pubs.

Examining Innovative Practices to Improve Child Nutrition: Hearing Before the Subcommittee on Healthy Families & Communities, Committee on Education & Labor, U.S. House of Representatives, One Hundred Eleventh Congress, First Session, Hearing Held in Washington, DC, October 8, 2009. 2010. iii, 50p. *(978-0-16-085109-4(2)*, 552-070-40465-1) United States Government Printing Office.

Farenga, Stephen J. The Importance of Average: Playing the Game of School to Increase Success & Achievement. 2010. (ENG., Illus.). 224p. (gr. k-2). 94.95 *(978-0-7425-7012-2(6))* Rowman & Littlefield Publishers, Inc.

Farnette, Cherrie & Jones, Jonathan. Strategies for Practicing Postive Choices: A Quick-Reference Resource for Helping Students with Self-Awareness, Proactivity, Perseverance, Goal Setting, Use of Support Systems, & Emotional Coping. 2007. (Greatest & Latest Teaching Tips Ser.). pap. 6.99 *(978-0-86530-706-3(7))* Incentive Pubns., Inc.

Fattig, Melinda L. & Taylor, Maureen Tormey. Co-Teaching in the Differentiated Classroom: Successful Collaboration, Lesson Design, & Classroom Management, Grades 5-12. 2007. (ENG., Illus.). 144p. per. 29.95 *(978-0-7879-8744-2(1)*, Jossey-Bass) Wiley, John & Sons, Inc.

Fay, Charles. From Bad Grades to a Great Life! Unlocking the Mystery of Achievement for Your Child. 2011. xiv, 146p. pap. 17.95 ***(978-1-935326-08-3(2))*** Love & Logic Institute, Inc.

Ferlazzo, Larry & Hammond, Lorie A. Building Parent Engagement in Schools, 1 vol. 2009. 87p. pap. 35.00 *(978-1-58683-342-8(1)*, A2652P) Linworth Publishing, Inc.

Fernandez, Paula B. Academic Orientations of African-American Adolescents. 2008. 120p. pap. *(978-3-639-08195-4(1))* VDM Verlag Dr. Mueller e.K.

Ferrett, Sharon. Peak Performance: Success in College & Beyond. 6th rev. ed. 2006. 552p. (C). pap. 61.00 *(978-0-07-312549-7(0)*, 9780073125497, McGraw-Hill Humanities, Social Sciences & World Languages) McGraw-Hill Higher Education.

Ferrett, Sharon & Ferrett, Sharon K. Peak Performance: Success in College & Beyond. 7th ed. 2009. (ENG., Illus.). 568p. (C). pap. 80.00 *(978-0-07-337512-0(8)*, 0073375128) McGraw-Hill Higher Education.

Ferrett, Sharon K. Peak Performance: Success in College & Beyond. (Illus.). 5th ed. 2009. (ENG.). pap., pap. 86.50 *(978-0-07-329386-8(5))* 7th ed. 2010. xxxvii, 530p. pap. *(978-0-07-722771-5(9))* 8th ed. 2012. xxxii, 493p. *(978-0-07-747154-5(7))* McGraw-Hill Cos., The.

—Peak Performance: Success in College & Beyond. 8th ed. 2011. (ENG., Illus.). 528p. (C). pap. 80.00 *(978-0-07-337519-9(5)*, 0073375195) McGraw-Hill Higher Education.

Fielding, Lynn, et al. Annual Growth, Catch-up Growth: Annual Growth for All Students, Catch-up Growth for Those Who Are Behind. 2007. 254p. pap. 17.95 *(978-0-9666875-2-1(3))* New Foundation Pr., The.

Finnan, Christine R. Upper Elementary Years: Ensuring Success in Grades 3-6. 2008. (Illus.). 232p. pap. 36.95 *(978-1-4129-4099-3(0)*, B40982P) Corwin Pr.

—The Upper Elementary Years: Ensuring Success in Grades 3-6. 2008. (Illus.). 232p. 82.95 *(978-1-4129-4098-6(2)*, B40982C) Corwin Pr.

Fisher, Douglas, et al. How to Create a Culture of Achievement in Your School & Classroom. 2012. 223p. pap. 27.95 ***(978-1-4166-1408-1(7))*** Assn. for Supervision & Curriculum Development.

Fletcher, Stephen. Burned In: Fueling the Fire to Teach. Friedman, Audrey A. & Reynolds, Luke, eds. 2011. (ENG.). 168p. pap. 21.95 *(978-0-8077-5196-1(0))* Teachers College Pr., Teachers College, Columbia Univ.

Fletcher, Stephen & Brooks, Jacqueline Grennon. Partnerships for New Teacher Learning: A Guide for Universities & School Districts. 2011. (Early Childhood Education Ser.). (ENG.). 192p. pap. 26.95 *(978-0-8077-5195-4(2))* Teachers College Pr., Teachers College, Columbia Univ.

Fletcher, Stephen, et al. Partnerships for New Teacher Learning: A Guide for Universities & School Districts. 2011. (ENG., Illus.). 112p. pap. 25.95 *(978-0-8077-5183-1(9))* Teachers College Pr., Teachers College, Columbia Univ.

Flores-Mejorado, Dina. Students Perception of Services at a Mitc or a Main Campus. 2009. 120p. pap. *(978-3-639-15521-1(1))* VDM Verlag Dr. Mueller e.K.

Foley, David. Transforming School Culture. 2008. 144p. pap. *(978-3-639-06708-8(8))* VDM Verlag Dr. Mueller e.K.

Francis, Becky, et al. The Identities & Practices of High Achieving Pupils: Negotiating Achievement & Peer Cultures. 2012. (ENG., Illus.). 216p. 140.00 *(978-1-4411-5719-5(0))*; pap. 44.95 *(978-1-4411-2156-1(0))* Continuum International Publishing Group, Ltd. GBR. Dist: National Bk. Network.

Francis, Becky, et al. The Identities & Practices of High-Achieving Pupils: Negotiating Achievement & Peer Cultures. 2012. 256p. E-Book ***(978-0-8264-2177-7(6))***; E-Book ***(978-1-4411-9923-2(3))*** Continuum International Publishing Group, Ltd.

Frank, Marjorie. Study Skills Planner: A Quick-Reference Resource to Prepare Students for Study & Test-Taking Success. 2007. (Greatest & Latest Teaching Tips Ser.). pap. 6.99 *(978-0-86530-701-8(6))* Incentive Pubns., Inc.

French, Dan, et al. Creating Small Schools: A Handbook for Raising Equity & Achievement. 2007. 248p. per. 36.95 *(978-1-4129-4178-5(4)*, B41776P); (Illus.). 72.95 *(978-1-4129-4177-8(6)*, B41776C) Corwin Pr.

Frossard, John. How to Raise Student Achievement - 101 Simple Strategies for Teachers. 2008. 136p. pap. 17.95 *(978-0-9817507-1-2(0))* HowToAchieve, LLC.

The Future of Learning: How Technology Is Transforming Public Schools: Hearing Before the Committee on Education & Labor, U.S. House of Representatives, One Hundred Eleventh Congress, First Session, Hearing Held in Washington, DC, June 16, 2009. 2009. (Illus.). iii, 71p. *(978-0-16-084500-0(9)*, 552-070-40023-1) United States Government Printing Office.

Gabelko, Nina Hersch & Sosniak, Lauren A. Every Child's Right: Academic Talent Development by Choice, Not Chance. 2008. (ENG.). 176p. pap. 27.95 *(978-0-8077-4870-1(6))* Teachers College Pr., Teachers College, Columbia Univ.

Gamoran, Adam. Standards-Based Reform & the Poverty Gap: Lessons for No Child Left Behind. 2007. (ENG., Illus.). 340p. 64.95 *(978-0-8157-3032-3(2))*; per. 29.95 *(978-0-8157-3033-0(0))* Brookings Institution Pr.

Geramian, Maryam & RAHMANDOUST, Mohsen. Social Behavior Recognition & Higher Academic Achievement. 2011. 92p. pap. ***(978-3-8443-1947-7(6))*** Lambert Academic Publishing.

Gibbs, Jeanne. Guiding Your School Community to Live a Culture of Caring & Learning: The Process Is Called Tribes. 2007. pap. *(978-0-932762-12-2(3))* CenterSource Systems, LLC.

—Reaching All by Creating Tribes Learning Communities. 2006. Orig. Title: Tribes, A New Way of Learning & Being Together. 431p. pap. 32.95 *(978-0-932762-41-2(7)*, 100) CenterSource Systems, LLC.

Gilbert, Robert. How to Have Fun Without Failing Out: 430 Tips from a College Professor. 2007. (ENG., Illus.). 128p. pap. 12.95 *(978-0-7573-0577-1(6))* Health Communications, Inc.

Gimpel Peacock, Gretchen & Collett, Brent R. Collaborative Home/School Interventions: Evidence-Based Solutions for Emotional, Behavioral, & Academic Problems. 2009. (Guilford Practical Intervention in Schools Ser.). (ENG., Illus.). 207p. (gr. -1-12). pap. 35.00 *(978-1-60623-345-0(9))* Guilford Pubns., Inc.

Glaude, Catherine. Protocols for Professional Learning Conversations: Cultivating the Art & Discipline. 2011. (ENG.). 96p. pap. 19.95 ***(978-1-935543-82-4(2))***; lib. bdg. 39.95 ***(978-1-935543-83-1(0))*** Solution Tree Pr.

Goastellec, Gaële, ed. Understanding Inequalities in, Through & by Higher Education. 2010. 158p. *(978-94-6091-307-5(5))*; pap. *(978-94-6091-306-8(7))* Sense Pubs.

Goldhaber, Dan & Hannaway, Jane, eds. Creating a New Teaching Profession. 2009. (Illus.). 348p. pap. 29.50 *(978-0-87766-762-9(4))* Urban Institute Pr.

Golga, Dawit Negassa. Care, Communication, & Support Relationships in the Classroom: The Case of Pupils with Emotional & Behavioral Difficulties. 2008. 120p. pap. *(978-3-639-06911-2(0))* VDM Verlag Dr. Mueller e.K.

Good, Rebecca. Understanding the Data Analysis Process Using a Collaborative Model. 2010. 144p. pap. *(978-3-8383-1428-0(X))* Lambert Academic Publishing.

Gordon, Edmund W. & Bridglall, Beatrice L. Affirmative Development: Cultivating Academic Ability. 2006. (Critical Issues in Contemporary American Education Ser.). (ENG., Illus.). 310p. 97.00 *(978-0-7425-1658-8(X))* Rowman & Littlefield Publishers, Inc.

Gordon, Edmund W. & Bridglall, Beatrice L., eds. Affirmative Development: Cultivating Academic Ability. 2006. (Critical Issues in Contemporary American Education Ser.). (ENG., Illus.). 310p. per. 31.95 *(978-0-7425-1659-5(8))* Rowman & Littlefield Publishers, Inc.

Graham, Joyce M. & Nessel, Denise D. Thinking Strategies for Student Achievement: Improving Learning Across the Curriculum, K-12. 2nd rev. ed. 2006. (Illus.). 248p. per. 36.95 *(978-1-4129-3881-5(3)*, B38805P) Corwin Pr.

Graham, Stephanie M., et al, eds. Culturally Proficient Inquiry: A Lens for Identifying & Examining Educational Gaps. 2008. (Illus.). 256p. pap. 36.95 *(978-1-4129-2602-7(5)*, B26017P) Corwin Pr.

Green, Gordon W. Making Your Education Work for You: A Proven System for Success in School & for Getting the Job of Your Dreams. 2010. (ENG.). 304p. 26.99 *(978-0-7653-1952-4(7)*, Forge Bks.) Doherty, Tom Assocs., LLC.

Green, Gordon W., Jr. Making Your Education Work for You: A Proven System for Success in School & for Getting the Job of Your Dreams. 2010. (ENG.). 304p. pap. 12.99 *(978-0-7653-1953-1(5)*, Forge Bks.) Doherty, Tom Assocs., LLC.

Gregory, Kathleen, et al. Self-Assessment & Goal Setting. 2nd ed. 2011. (ENG.). 80p. pap. 17.95 ***(978-1-935543-76-3(8))***; lib. bdg. 35.95 ***(978-1-935543-77-0(6))*** Solution Tree Pr.

Gregory, Sheila T. Voices of Native American Educators: Integrating History, Culture, & Language to Improve Learning Outcomes for Native American Students. 2011. xv, 248p. ***(978-0-7391-7193-6(3))*** Lexington Bks.

Griffiths-Prince, Dr. Marcia. Cultivating Parental Involvement in Middle Schools: A Case Study. 2009. 214p. pap. 21.56 *(978-0-557-15414-2(6))* Lulu Enterprises Inc.

Grove Deniz, Bethany, et al. Strategies for Success. 2011. 108p. pap. ***(978-3-8443-0159-5(3))*** Lambert Academic Publishing.

Guarino, Cassandra M., et al. Teacher Qualifications & Kindergartners' Achievements. 2009. 43.00 *(978-1-60741-180-2(6))* Nova Science Pubs., Inc.

Gurian, Michael. The Minds of Boys: Saving Our Sons from Falling Behind in School & Life. 2007. (ENG., Illus.). 368p. per. 15.95 *(978-0-7879-9528-7(2)*, Jossey-Bass) Wiley, John & Sons, Inc.

Guskey, Thomas R. The Teacher As Assessment Leader. 2009. pap. *(978-1-934009-49-9(0))* Solution Tree Pr.

Guskey, Thomas R., ed. The Teacher as Assessment Leader. 2009. *(978-1-935249-11-5(8))* Solution Tree Pr.

Habeeb, Scott. The Ninth Grade Opportunity: Transforming Schools from the Bottom Up. 2008. 116p. pap. 12.95 *(978-0-595-48472-0(7))* iUniverse, Inc.

Habeeb, Scott, et al. The Ninth Grade Opportunity: Transforming Schools from the Bottom Up. 2008. 116p. 22.95 *(978-0-595-71990-7(2))* iUniverse, Inc.

Haig, Brian R. & Haig, Jeffrey D. Unlock Your Eduational Potential: What Every Student Needs to Know to Succeed. 2009. (Illus.). 259p. pap. 16.95 *(978-0-9815659-2-7(1))* THF Publishing.

Haimerl, Charlotte. Self-Fulfilling Prophecy in Self-Regulated Learning. 2008. 276p. pap. *(978-3-639-02215-5(7))* VDM Verlag Dr. Mueller e.K.

Halberstam, Joshua & Gonsher, Debra. Community College Guide: The Essential Reference from Application to Graduation. 2009. (ENG.). 244p. pap. 14.95 *(978-1-933771-73-1(9))* BenBella Bks.

Hansen, Sally. Gender Differences & Writing. 2010. 100p. pap. *(978-3-8383-1858-5(7))* Lambert Academic Publishing.

Hanushek, Eric A. & Lindseth, Alfred. Schoolhouses, Courthouses, & Statehouses: Solving the Funding-Achievement Puzzle in America's Public Schools. 2009. (ENG., Illus.). 432p. (C). 30.95 *(978-0-691-13000-2(0))* Princeton Univ. Pr.

Hanushek, Eric Alan, ed. Courting Failure: How School Finance Lawsuits Exploit Judges' Good Intentions & Harm Our Children. 2006. (Hoover Inst Press Publication). (Illus.). 366p. 25.00 *(978-0-8179-4781-1(7))* Hoover Institution Pr.

Hardesty, Larry L. The Role of the Library in the First College Year. 2007. *(978-1-889271-54-5(3))* National Resource Ctr. for The First Year Experience & Students in Transition.

Hargrove, Jesse J. Closing the Achievement Gap in America: A National Imperative for A Super Man, A Super Woman, & A Superintendent. 2011. 196p. pap. 31.00 ***(978-1-4634-0952-4(4))*** AuthorHouse.

Harmon, Hugh J. Bridging the Achievement Gap. 2010. 118p. pap. 14.99 *(978-0-557-05822-8(8))* Lulu Enterprises Inc.

Harris, Alma & Hargreaves, Andy. Schools Performing Beyond Expectations. 2012. (ENG.). 176p. (C). pap. 35.95 ***(978-0-415-69231-1(8))*** Routledge.

Harris, Angel L. Kids Don't Want to Fail: Oppositional Culture & the Black-White Achievement Gap. 2011. (ENG., Illus.). 336p. 35.00 *(978-0-674-05772-2(4))* Harvard Univ. Pr.

Harris, Bryan. Battling Boredom: 99 Strategies to Spark Student Engagement. 2010. 29.95 *(978-1-59667-166-9(1))* Eye On Education, Inc.

Harris, Theresa & Taylor, George. Raising African American Males: Strategies & Interventions for Successful Outcomes. 2012. ***(978-1-60709-300-8(6))*** Rowman & Littlefield Education.

Harris, Theresa & Taylor, George, eds. Raising African-American Males: Strategies & Interventions for Successful Outcomes. 2012. (ENG.). 116p. 40.00 ***(978-1-60709-298-8(0))*** Rowman & Littlefield Education.

Harris/Taylor, ed. Raising African-American Males: Strategies & Interventions for Successful Outcomes. 2012. (ENG.). 116p. pap. 18.95 ***(978-1-60709-299-5(9))*** Rowman & Littlefield Education.

Hartman, Kathleen & Stewart, Thomas. 35 Ways to Discover a Major. 2nd ed. 2009. (ENG.). 160p. (C). pap. 23.95 *(978-0-547-19990-0(2))* Wadsworth.

Harvard, et al. Spotlight on Student Engagement, Motivation, & Achievement. 2009. xiv, 153p. pap. *(978-1-934742-26-6(0)*, Debolsillo) Harvard Education Publishing Group (HEPG).

Hattie, John & Anderman, Eric M., eds. International Guide to Student Achievement. 2012. (ENG.). 750p. 295.00 ***(978-0-415-87898-2(5))***; pap. 114.95 ***(978-0-415-87901-9(9))*** Routledge.

Hayes/Esbrandt. Curing Student Underachievement: Clinical Practice for School Leaders. 2011. (ENG.). 206p. pap. 36.95 ***(978-1-61048-537-1(8))*** Rowman & Littlefield Education.

Hazard, Laurie L. & Nadeau, Jean-Paul. Foundations for Learning: Claiming Your Education. 3rd ed. 2011. (ENG., Illus.). 208p. (C). pap. 42.20 *(978-0-13-231806-8(7)*, Prentice Hall) Prentice Hall PTR.

Hebert, Terri & Durham, Sherry. High-Stakes Teaching: Practices That Improve Student Learning. 2008. (ENG.). 132p. 65.00 *(978-1-57886-880-3(7))* Rowman & Littlefield Education.

—High Stakes Teaching: Practices That Improve Student Learning. 2008. (ENG.). 132p. pap. 21.95 *(978-1-57886-881-0(5))* Rowman & Littlefield Education.

Henneberg, Susan. Top 10 Tips for Enjoying Success in School. 2012. (Tips for Success Ser.). (ENG., Illus.). 64p. (YA). (gr. 7-12). lib. bdg. 31.95 ***(978-1-4488-6860-5(2))*** Rosen Publishing Group, Inc., The.

Henning, Marcus. Students' Motivation to Learn, Academic Achievement, & Academic Advising. 2008. 256p. pap. *(978-3-639-00357-4(8))* VDM Verlag Dr. Mueller e.K.

Hickman, Richard. Art & Craft of Pedagogy: Portraits of Effective Teachers. 2011. (Continuum Studies in Educational Research Ser.). (ENG.). 192p. 140.00 *(978-1-84706-290-1(3))* Continuum International Publishing Group, Ltd. GBR. Dist: National Bk. Network.

Hill, Paul Thomas, ed. Charter Schools Against the Odds. 2006. (Hoover Inst Press Publication). (Illus.). 219p. 25.00 *(978-0-8179-4761-3(2))* Hoover Institution Pr.

Hill, S. / Laurie. How Do High School Students Make the Transition to University? Factors Contributing to Success or Failure. 2010. (Illus.). vii, 414p. *(978-0-7734-1318-4(9))* Mellen, Edwin Pr., The.

Hill, Teresa. Every Closed Eye Ain't Sleep: African American Perspectives on the Achievement Gap. 2011. (ENG., Illus.). 126p. 40.00 *(978-1-61048-104-5(6))*; pap. 19.95 *(978-1-61048-105-2(4))* Rowman & Littlefield Education.

Hill, Teresa D. Every Closed Eye Ain't Sleep: African American Perspectives on the Achievement Gap. 2011. E-Book ***(978-1-61048-106-9(2))*** Rowman & Littlefield Publishers, Inc.

Hodgins, Daniel J. Boys: Changing the Classroom, Not the Child. 2009. *(978-89-23-56894-4(5))* Wilderness Adventure Bks.

Hoell, Melanie. College Students' Experience of Academic Turnaround. 2010. 344p. pap. *(978-3-8383-1976-6(1))* Lambert Academic Publishing.

Hogges, Ralph. The Love of Books & Academic Excellence: A Memoir, 1 vol. 2010. 74p. pap. 19.95 *(978-1-4512-0082-9(X))* PublishAmerica, Inc.

Holcomb-McCoy, Cheryl. School Counseling to Close the Achievement Gap: A Social Justice Framework for Success. 2007. 176p. 72.95 *(978-1-4129-4183-9(0)*, B41830C) Corwin Pr.

Holcomb-McCoy, Cheryl C., ed. School Counseling to Close the Achievement Gap: A Social Justice Framework for Success. 2007. (Illus.). 176p. per. 31.95 *(978-1-4129-4184-6(9)*, B41830P) Corwin Pr.

Holly, Rich & Watson, Lemuel W. Majoring in Education: All the Stuff You Need to Know. 2011. (ENG.). 89p. pap. 14.95 *(978-1-57463-164-7(0)*, 1574631640) Meredith Music Pubns.

Hong, Eunsook & Milgram, Roberta M. Preventing Talent Loss. 2007. (ENG., Illus.). 256p. 140.00 *(978-0-8058-5712-2(5))* Routledge.

Hossler, Don, ed. Enhancing Institutional & State Initiatives to Increase Student Success: Studies of the Indiana Project on Academic Success. 2009. (Illus.). 210p. 137.50 *(978-0-404-10124-4(0))* AMS Pr., Inc.

Howard, Tyrone C. Why Race & Culture Matter in Schools: Closing the Achievement Gap in America's Classrooms. 2010. (Multicultural Education Ser.). (ENG., Illus.). 208p. pap. 27.95 *(978-0-8077-5071-1(9))*; 27.95 *(978-0-8077-5072-8(7))* Teachers College Pr., Teachers College, Columbia Univ.

H.R. 4330: The All Students Achieving Through Reform ACT of 2009: Hearing Before the Committee on Education & Labor, U.S. House of Representatives, One Hundred Eleventh Congress, Second Session, Hearing Held in Washington, DC, February 24, 2010. 2010. (Illus.). iii, 71p. *(978-0-16-086857-3(2)*, 552-070-41769-9) United States Government Printing Office.

Hung Leung, Chi. Modeling of Parenting Style, Achievement Variables & Learning Approaches: Hong Kong Chinese & Anglo-Australian Perspectives. 2012. 230p. ***(978-1-61942-308-4(1))*** Nova Science Pubs., Inc.

Hurst, Allison. Burden of Academic Success: Managing Working-Class Identities in College. 2010. (ENG., Illus.). 320p. 83.99 *(978-0-7391-4059-8(0))* Lexington Bks.

Ilodi D.P.M. F.A.A.F.S., George H. Sure Way to Higher Grade Scores. 2007. 56p. per. 16.95 *(978-1-4241-8903-8(9))* PublishAmerica, Inc.

Institutional Research Staff. Conducting Research on Asian Americans in Higher Education: New Directions for Institutional Research, No. 142. Museus, Samuel D., ed. 2009. (J-B IR Single Issue Institutional Research Ser.: 98). (ENG., Illus.). 112p. pap. 29.00 *(978-0-470-52961-4(X)*, Jossey-Bass) Wiley, John & Sons, Inc.

—Using Nsse in Institutional Research: New Directions for Institutional Research. Kuh, George D. & Gonyea, Robert M., eds. 2009. (J-B IR Single Issue Institutional Research Ser.: 97). (ENG., Illus.). 112p. pap. 29.00 *(978-0-470-49928-3(1)*, Jossey-Bass) Wiley, John & Sons, Inc.

Iwunze, Cajetan. The Factors Responsible for Low Educational Achievement among African-Caribbean Youths. 2009. (Illus.). 196p. pap. 16.99 *(978-1-4490-2710-0(5))* AuthorHouse.

Jackson, Gaines Bradford. An Academic Plan for Success Known As the Pentagram Spectrum of Success. 2009. 164p. 29.99 *(978-1-4415-0914-7(3))*; pap. 19.99 *(978-1-4415-0913-0(5))* Xlibris Corp.

James, Abigail Norfleet, ed. Teaching the Male Brain: How Boys Think, Feel, & Learn in School. 2007. (Illus.). 304p. 90.95 *(978-1-4129-3662-0(4)*, B36624C); per. 39.95 *(978-1-4129-3663-7(2)*, B36624P) Corwin Pr.

Janovy, John. Outwitting College Professors: A practical Guide to Secrets of the System. 2008. (ENG.). (C). pap. 21.60 *(978-0-536-41850-0(0))* Pearson Learning Solutions.

Jason, Martin H., ed. Evaluating Programs to Increase Student Achievement. 2nd ed. 2008. (Illus.). 208p. 72.95 *(978-1-4129-5124-1(0)*, B51240C); pap. 36.95 *(978-1-4129-5125-8(9)*, B51240P) Corwin Pr.

Jerome, Bonnie. The Relationship of Parent Involvement & Student Achievement. 2008. 228p. per. *(978-3-8364-3648-9(5))* VDM Verlag Dr. Mueller e.K.

Jeynes. Parental Involvement & Academic Success. 2009. pap. 44.95 *(978-0-415-99054-7(8))* Routledge.

Johns Hopkins University Press Staff. Student's Quest Guide: Aristotle Leads the Way. 2007. (Story of Science Ser.). (ENG.). 112p. (YA). pap. 12.95 *(978-1-58834-254-6(9))* Smithsonian Institution Pr.

Johnson, C. & Ronald, E. Teaching Eagles to Soar: Guidance & counseling for a fatherless Generation. 2009. pap. 15.99 *(978-1-60799-256-1(6))* Tate Publishing & Enterprises, LLC.

Johnson, Sarah C. A Journey to Academic Excellence. rev. ed. 2011. (ENG.). 182p. pap. 50.00 ***(978-0-7575-9089-4(6))*** Kendall Hunt Publishing Co.

Jones, Jami Biles & Zambone, Alana M. The Power of Media Specialists to Raise Academic Achievement & Strengthen At-Risk Youth. 2007. 108p. pap. 44.95 *(978-1-58683-229-2(8))* Linworth Publishing, Inc.

Jones, Richard. The Educational Pyramid of Success. 2007. 96p. per. 16.95 *(978-1-4241-7209-2(8))* PublishAmerica, Inc.

Jones-Smith, Elsie. Spotlighting the Strengths of Every Single Student: Why U. S. Schools Need a New, Strengths-Based Approach, 1 vol. 2011. 285p. 44.95 *(978-0-313-39153-8(X)*, A3198C) Greenwood Publishing Group, Inc.

Kafele, Baruti. Motivating Black Males to Achieve in School & in Life. 2009. pap. 16.95 *(978-1-4166-0857-8(5))* Assn. for Supervision & Curriculum Development.

Karim, Atai. High Achieving Schools of Aga Khan University-Examination Board. 2010. 124p. pap. *(978-3-8383-8198-5(X))* Lambert Academic Publishing.

Karoly, Lynn A. Preschool Adequacy & Efficiency in California: Issues, Policy Options & Recommendations. 2009. 194p. pap. 37.00 *(978-0-8330-4743-4(4)*, mg-889) RAND Corp., The.

Kasomo, Daniel W. Career & Aids Counselling for University Students. 2010. 60p. pap. *(978-3-8383-8681-2(7))* Lambert Academic Publishing.

Kawazoe, A. Stories from Schools - Case Studies of California Academic Partnership Program. 2009. (Illus.). 214p. pap. 22.95 *(978-0-615-27731-8(4))* Univ. of California Pr.

Kerckhoff, Alan C. Diverging Pathways: Social Structure & Career Deflections. 2007. (ENG.). 280p. pap. 58.00 *(978-0-521-03320-6(9))* Cambridge Univ. Pr.

Kettlewell, Janet S. & Henry, Ronald J. Increasing the Competitive Edge in Math & Science. Kettlewell/Henry, ed. 2009. (ENG.). 226p. pap. 36.95 *(978-1-60709-014-4(7))* Rowman & Littlefield Education.

Kettley. Educational Attainment & Society. 2007. (Continuum Studies in Education). (ENG., Illus.). 246p. 130.00 *(978-0-8264-8856-5(0))* Continuum International Publishing Group, Ltd. GBR. Dist: National Bk. Network.

Kiewra, Kenneth A. Teaching How to Learn: The Teacher's Guide to Student Success. 2008. (Illus.). 208p. pap., instr.'s training gde. ed. 36.95 *(978-1-4129-6534-7(9)*, B65330P) Corwin Pr.

King, David. International Handbook of Academic Research & Teaching: Ihart, Volume 1. 2007. 346p. per. 45.00 *(978-0-9800418-9-7(9))* Intellectbase International Consortium.

Kizer, Gene H., Jr. The Elements of Academic Success: How to Graduate Magna Cum Laude from College (or How to Just Graduate ... PERIOD!) Kizer, Gene H., Jr., ed. 2012. (ENG., Illus.). 220p. pap. 17.95 *(978-0-9818980-1-8(7))* Charleston Athenaeum Pr.

Kopp, Wendy. A Chance to Make History: What Works & What Doesn't in Providing an Excellent Education for All. 2011. (ENG.). 240p. 25.99 *(978-1-58648-740-9(X))* PublicAffairs.

Kramer, Gary L., ed. Fostering Student Success in the Campus Community. 2007. (Wiley Desktop Editions Ser.: 108). (ENG., Illus.). 512p. 50.00 *(978-1-933371-24-5(2)*, Jossey-Bass) Wiley, John & Sons, Inc.

Kronin, Judith. Creating Smart Schools: The Education Instructional Coaching Model. 2011. 118p. 29.99 ***(978-1-4628-9165-8(9))***; pap. 19.99 ***(978-1-4628-9166-5(7))*** Xlibris Corp.

Kuczala, Michael S. & Lengel, Traci. The Kinesthetic Classroom: Teaching & Learning Through Movement. 2010. (Illus.). 176p. pap. 31.95 *(978-1-4129-7954-2(4)*, B79542P) Corwin Pr.

Kuh, George D., et al. Piecing Together the Student Success Puzzle: Research, Propositions, & Recommendations: ASHE Higher Education Report. 2007. (J-B ASHE Higher Education Report Series (AEHE) Ser.: 116). (ENG.). 200p. pap. 29.00 *(978-0-7879-9776-2(5)*, Jossey-Bass) Wiley, John & Sons, Inc.

Kunjufu, Jawanza. Reducing the Black Male Dropout Rate. 2010. (ENG., Illus.). 192p. pap. 15.95 *(978-1-934155-22-6(5))* African American Images.

Kunjufu, Jawanza. There Is Nothing Wrong with Black Students. 2012. (ENG., Illus.). 128p. pap. 15.95 ***(978-1-934155-60-8(8))*** African American Images.

Lamb, Jerry D. Fifty Ways to Achieve Excellence in Education: Building Student Relationships & Creating Success. 2009. 116p. pap. 12.95 *(978-1-4401-2735-9(2))* iUniverse, Inc.

Lambert, Wendy Ecklund. Servant Leader Principals. 2011. 112p. pap. ***(978-3-8443-1970-5(0))*** Lambert Academic Publishing.

Lassiter, Wright L. Commencement Messages: Education Starts, Not Ends, with the Diploma. 2011. 220p. 27.00 ***(978-1-4269-9579-8(2))***; pap. 17.00 ***(978-1-4269-9578-1(4))*** Trafford Publishing.

Lauder, Hugh & Nash, Roy, eds. Explaining Inequalities in School Achievement: A Realist Analysis. 2010. (Illus.). 282p. 114.95 *(978-0-7546-7904-2(7))* Ashgate Publishing Co.

Le, Vi-Nhuan, et al. Improving Mathematics & Science Education: A Longitudinal Investigation of the Relationship between Reform-Oriented Instruction & Student Achievement. 2006. 280p. pap. 30.00 *(978-0-8330-3964-4(4))* RAND Corp., The.

Leana, Frank C. & Clark, Carole S. Pathfinder: an Action Plan: Making the Most of High School. 2010. 104p. pap. 11.95 *(978-1-4502-7015-1(8))* iUniverse, Inc.

Lehman, Christopher, et al. Pathways to the Common Core: Accelerating Achievement. 2012. 224p. pap. 33.13 ***(978-0-325-04355-5(8)***, E04355) Heinemann.

Lemov, Doug. Teach Like a Champion: 49 Techniques That Put Students on the Path to College. 2010. (ENG., Illus.). 352p. pap. 27.95 *(978-0-470-55047-2(3)*, Jossey-Bass) Wiley, John & Sons, Inc.

Leting. Socio-Economic Factors Influencing Academic Performance. 2011. 104p. pap. ***(978-3-8443-1813-5(5))*** Lambert Academic Publishing.

Levenstein, Phyllis & Levenstein, Susan. Messages from Home: The Parent-Child Home Program for Overcoming Educational Disadvantage. 2nd ed. 2008. (ENG., Illus.). 288p. (C). 83.50 *(978-1-59213-676-6(1))*; pap. 30.95 *(978-1-59213-677-3(X))* Temple Univ. Pr.

Levin, Benjamin. More High School Graduates: How Schools Can Save Students from Dropping Out. 2011. (Illus.). 208p. pap. 33.95 ***(978-1-4129-9224-4(9)***, B92244P) Corwin Pr.

Lewis, Harry R. Excellence Without a Soul: Does Liberal Education Have a Future? 2007. (ENG.). 336p. per. 15.95 *(978-1-58648-501-6(6))* PublicAffairs.

Lin, Jun. Parental Expectations of Chinese Immigrants for Children's School Achievement: Sociocultural Context, Psychological Adjustment, & Educational Consequences. 2009. 232p. 109.95 *(978-0-7734-4837-7(3))* Mellen, Edwin Pr., The.

Lindner, Heike. Bildung, Erziehung und Religion in Europa: Politische, rechtshermeneutische und pädagogische Untersuchungen zum europäischen Bildungsauftrag in evangelischer Perspektive. 2009. (Praktische Theologie im Wissenschaftsdiskurs Ser.).Tr. of Formation, Education & Religion in Europe. (GER.). XX, 522p. 140.00 *(978-3-11-020921-1(7))* De Gruyter, Walter Inc.

Lindsey, Randall B. & Robins, Kikanza Nuri, eds. Cultural Proficiency: A Manual for School Leaders. 3rd ed. 2009. (Illus.). 344p. 90.95 *(978-1-4129-6362-6(1)*, B63626C) Corwin Pr.

—Cultural Proficiency: A Manual for School Leaders. 3rd ed. 2009. (Illus.). 344p. pap. 41.95 *(978-1-4129-6363-3(X)*, B63626P) Corwin Pr.

Liu, Cungang. Adjustment to a New Education System. 2010. 128p. pap. *(978-3-8383-6787-3(1))* Lambert Academic Publishing.

Lluch, Alex. Simple Principles to Excel at School. 2008. (Simple Principles Ser.). (ENG.). 290p. pap. 9.95 *(978-1-934386-22-4(7))* WS Publishing.

Locke, Terry. Resisting Qualifications Reforms in New Zealand: The English Study Design as Constructive Dissent. 2007. 184p. per. *(978-90-8790-215-5(8))* Sense Pubs.

Lopez, Nancy. Unequal Educations. 2015. (ENG.). 224p. 135.00 *(978-0-415-87506-6(4))* Routledge.

Lord, Thomas R., et al, eds. College Science Teachers Guide to Assessment. 2009. (ENG.). 159p. pap. 25.95 *(978-1-933531-11-3(8))* National Science Teachers Assn.

Love, Nancy. Using Data to Improve Learning for All: A Collaborative Inquiry Approach. Love, Nancy, ed. 2008. (Illus.). 192p. 78.95 *(978-1-4129-6084-7(3)*, B60847C) Corwin Pr.

Love, Nancy, ed. Using Data to Improve Learning for All: A Collaborative Inquiry Approach. 2008. (Illus.). 192p. pap. 34.95 *(978-1-4129-6085-4(1)*, B60847P) Corwin Pr.

Loveless, Tom. The Brown Center Report on American Education: How Well Are American Students Learning? 2008. (ENG., Illus.). 100p. per. 12.95 *(978-0-8157-5328-5(4))* Brookings Institution Pr.

—Brown Center Report on American Education: How Well Are American Students Learning. 2012. (ENG.). 36p. pap. 12.95 *(978-0-8157-0493-5(3))* Brookings Institution Pr.

—The 2008 Brown Center Report on American Education: How Well Are American Students Learning? 2009. (ENG.). 100p. pap. 12.95 *(978-0-8157-0279-5(5))* Brookings Institution Pr.

Loveless, Tom. The 2010 Brown Center Report on American Education: How Well Are American Students Learning? With Sections on International Tests, Who's Winning the Real Race to the Top, & Naep & the Common Core State Standards. 2011. (ENG.). 32p. pap. 12.95 ***(978-0-8157-2232-8(X))*** Brookings Institution Pr.

Lovett, C. Academics & Career Change. Date not set. *(978-0-275-90016-8(9)*, C0016, Praeger Pubs.) Greenwood Publishing Group, Inc.

Maccabe, James. Excellent & Poor School Performance & Risk for Severe Mental Disorders: The Extremes of the Bell Curve. 2010. (Maudsley Ser.). (ENG., Illus.). 200p. (C). 44.95 *(978-1-84872-045-9(9)*, Psychology Press) Taylor & Francis Group GBR. Dist: Taylor & Francis Group.

MacInnes, Gordon. In Plain Sight: Simple, Difficult Lessons from New Jersey's Expensive Effort to Close the Achievement Gap. 2009. (ENG., Illus.). 138p. pap. 14.95 *(978-0-87078-513-9(3))* Century Foundation, The.

Mack, Darlene, et al. Building A High Achieving School: 3 Cs to Success. 2007. (Illus.). 64p. pap. 20.00 net. *(978-0-9801315-1-2(0))* Warwick Hse. Publishing.

Malik, Aftab, et al. Decision Support System for Students Performance Analysis. 2011. 96p. pap. ***(978-3-8443-1943-9(3))*** Lambert Academic Publishing.

Mandarino, Desa Marie. What Students Need, Want, & Love! 2007. 110p. pap. 12.95 *(978-0-7414-3891-1(7))* Infinity Publishing.

Mandel, Scott. The Parent-Teacher Partnership: How to Work Together for Student Achievement. 2008. (ENG., Illus.). 144p. (gr. k-12). pap. 19.95 *(978-1-56976-217-2(1)*, Zephyr Pr.) Chicago Review Pr., Inc.

Manson, Tony J. Ways Teachers Cope with the Physical, Psychological, & Social Disabilities of Their Students: Diabetes, Autism, ADHD, Hunger, Anger, &

Other Infirmities. Manson, Tony J., ed. 220p. 109.95 *(978-0-7734-4976-3(0))* Mellen, Edwin Pr., The.

Marat, Deepa. Self-Efficacy & Achievement. 2008. 256p. pap. *(978-3-8364-8347-6(5))* VDM Verlag Dr. Mueller e.K.

Marjoribanks, K. Family & School Capital: Towards a Context Theory of Students' School Outcomes: Towards a Context Theory of Students' School Outcomes. 2011. (Illus.). 214p. pap. 110.00 *(978-90-481-6003-7(0)*, 9048160030) Springer.

Marriner, Nigel. Predicting the Academic Success of Gifted Postsecondary Students - What High School Grades, Sats, Creativity, & Self-Efficacy Tells Us. 2008. 156p. per. *(978-3-8364-6402-4(0))* VDM Verlag Dr. Mueller e.K.

Marsh, Julie A. & Springer, Matthew G. A Big Apple for Educators: New York City's Experiment with Schoolwide Performance Bonuses:Final Evaluation Report. 2011. (ENG.). 312p. pap. 34.50 ***(978-0-8330-5251-3(9))*** RAND Corp., The.

Marshall, Jeff C. Overcoming Student Apathy: Motivating Students for Academic Success. 2008. (ENG.). 142p. 80.00 *(978-1-57886-852-0(1))*; pap. 27.95 *(978-1-57886-853-7(X))* Rowman & Littlefield Education.

Martin, Andrew. Building Classroom Success: Eliminating Academic Fear & Failure. 2010. (ENG., Illus.). 240p. 29.95 *(978-1-84706-560-5(0))* Continuum International Publishing Group, Ltd. GBR. Dist: National Bk. Network.

Massey, Douglas S., et al. Taming the River: Negotiating the Academic, Financial, & Social Currents in Selective Colleges & Universities. 2009. (ENG., Illus.). 320p. (C). 39.95 *(978-0-691-13964-7(4))* Princeton Univ. Pr.

Massy, William F., et al. Academic Quality Work: A Handbook for Improvement. 2007. (JB - Anker Ser.: 107). (ENG.). 304p. 42.00 *(978-1-933371-23-8(4)*, Jossey-Bass) Wiley, John & Sons, Inc.

Maton, Karl & Moore, Rob, eds. Social Realism, Knowledge & the Sociology of Education: Coalitions of the Mind. 2010. (ENG.). 208p. 140.00 *(978-1-84706-505-6(8))* Continuum International Publishing Group, Ltd. GBR. Dist: National Bk. Network.

Mattison, Gary. Does Venue Selection Affect the Gp. 2008. 124p. pap. *(978-3-639-05200-8(5))* VDM Verlag Dr. Mueller e.K.

Mawoyo, Tatenda. Grade 7 Learners' Perception of Their Transition to High School. 2011. 92p. pap. ***(978-3-8443-2879-0(3))*** Lambert Academic Publishing.

McCormick, et al. College Talk: Conversations for Central Success. 2nd rev. ed. 2010. (ENG.). 178p. pap. 43.34 *(978-0-7575-8145-8(5))* Kendall Hunt Publishing Co.

McDonald, Betty. Self Assessment in Action. 2009. 136p. pap. 30.00 *(978-1-86335-513-8(4))* Common Ground Publishing Pty, Ltd.

McEwan, Elaine K. 10 Traits of Highly Effective Schools: Raising the Achievement Bar for All Students. 2008. (Illus.). 248p. 82.95 *(978-1-4129-0527-5(3)*, B05273C); pap. 36.95 *(978-1-4129-0528-2(1)*, B05273P) Corwin Pr.

McGuire, C. Kent & Ikpa, Vivian W. Policy, Leadership, & Student Achievement: Implications for Urban Communities. 2008. (Achievement Gap, Research, Practice, & Policy Ser.). 292p. *(978-1-59311-974-4(7))*; pap. *(978-1-59311-973-7(9))* Information Age Publishing, Inc.

McKay, Joanne. Intertextual Connections in Classroom Reading Experiences. 2008. 112p. pap. *(978-3-639-08551-8(5))* VDM Verlag Dr. Mueller e.K.

McKinley, Johnnie. Raising Black Students' Achievement Through Culturally Responsive Teaching. 2010. 214p. pap. 28.95 *(978-1-4166-1059-5(6))* Assn. for Supervision & Curriculum Development.

McMillan, James H., ed. Formative Classroom Assessment. 2007. (ENG., Illus.). 168p. pap. 26.95 *(978-0-8077-4799-5(8))* Teachers College Pr., Teachers College, Columbia Univ.

—Formative Classroom Assessment: Theory into Practice. 2007. (ENG., Illus.). 168p. 56.00 *(978-0-8077-4800-8(5))* Teachers College Pr., Teachers College, Columbia Univ.

Mcnerney, Norma. College Forum: A Connection to Success. rev. ed. 2009. (ENG.). 214p. pap. 42.91 *(978-0-7575-5721-7(X))* Kendall Hunt Publishing Co.

McPherson, Michael S. & Schapiro, Morton Owen, eds. Succeeding in College: What It Means & How to Make It Happen. 2008. (ENG., Illus.). 200p. 18.95 *(978-0-87447-830-3(8))* College Board, The.

Meetze, Tracy. Dr First-Generation. 2008. 56p. pap. *(978-3-639-01183-8(X))* VDM Verlag Dr. Mueller e.K.

Melissa V. Tamblyn. Higher Education Recruitment & Finance. 2011. (Series: Education in a Competitive & Globalizing World Ser.). 115.00 *(978-1-61122-544-0(2))* Nova Science Pubs., Inc.

Melius, Janelle. Student Engagement as a Factor in Academic Achievement: The Case Study of Undergraduates at Norfolk State University, Virginia. 2010. (Illus.). v, 189p. *(978-0-7734-1347-4(2))* Mellen, Edwin Pr., The.

Metcalf, Deborah, ed. Succeeding in the Inclusive Classroom: K-12 Lesson Plans Using Universal Design for Learning. 2010. (Illus.). 72p. (C). pap. 23.00 *(978-1-4129-8971-3(X)*, B89718P) SAGE Pubns., Inc.

Meyer, Jared. Strategies for Synthesis: Putting Information Together for Classroom Homework, & Test Success. (Library of Higher Order Thinking Skills Ser.). (ENG.). 48p. (gr. 5-8). 2009. 50.50 *(978-1-60853-678-8(5))*, Rosen Central) 2006. (Illus.). per. 11.75 *(978-1-4042-0658-8(2))* Rosen Publishing Group, Inc., The.

Milgram, Roberta M. Preventing Talent Loss. Hong, Eunsook, ed. 2007. (ENG., Illus.). 256p. 54.95 *(978-0-8058-5713-9(3))* Routledge.

Mislevy, Robert, et al. Design, Analysis, & Reporting in Large-Scale Assessment. 2006. (Statistics for Social Science & Public Policy Ser.). 200p. 64.95 *(978-0-387-40085-3(0))* Springer.

Mogollón, Oscar & Solano, Marina. Active Schools: Our Convictions for Improving the Quality of Education. Flórez, Ana, ed. 2011. pap. ***(978-0-89492-173-5(8))*** FHI Development 360.

—Escuelas Activas: Apuestas para Mejorar la Calidad de la Educación. Flórez, Ana, ed. 2011. pap. ***(978-0-89492-174-2(6))*** FHI Development 360.

Mohammed, Linda & Rollocks, Steve. Examination of the Factors Associated with Poor Academic Achievement. 2010. 264p. pap. *(978-3-8383-4602-1(5))* Lambert Academic Publishing.

Molina, Eva S. From D's & F's to A's & B's: Easy steps for making good grades in school & College. 2007. (ENG., Illus.). 58p. ring bd. 29.95 *(978-0-9799748-0-9(1))* Mariposa Pubns.

Montgomery, D. Bruce. Able, Gifted & Talented Underachievers. Montgomery, Diane L., ed. 2nd ed. 2009. (ENG., Illus.). 370p. pap. 65.00 *(978-0-470-77940-8(3*, Wiley) Wiley, John & Sons, Inc.

Montgomery, Diane L., et al. Able, Gifted & Talented Underachievers. Montgomery, Diane, ed. 2nd ed. 2009. (ENG., Illus.). 370p. 105.00 *(978-0-470-74097-2(3)*, Wiley) Wiley, John & Sons, Inc.

Montgomery, Soncerey L. The Heart of a Student: Success Principles for College Students. 2011. 144p. pap. 12.95 ***(978-1-936513-27-7(7))*** FearlStone Publishing, Inc.

Moody, Michael S. & Stricker, Jason M. Strategic Design for Student Achievement. 2008. (ENG., Illus.). 144p. pap. 24.95 *(978-0-8077-4925-8(7))* Teachers College Pr., Teachers College, Columbia Univ.

Mooney, Nancy J. & Mausbach, Ann T. Align the Design: A Blueprint for School Improvement. 2008. (Illus.). 202p. per. 0.00 *(978-1-4166-0625-3(4))* Assn. for Supervision & Curriculum Development.

Moore, Jenifer. Adequate Yearly Progress: Leaving Explanation Behind. 2010. 116p. pap. *(978-3-8383-4066-1(3))* Lambert Academic Publishing.

Moore, Michele. Variations in Test Anxiety & Locus of Control Orientation - in Achieving & Underachieving Gifted Middle School Students. 2008. 92p. pap. *(978-3-639-05777-5(5))* VDM Verlag Dr. Mueller e.K.

Morales, Erik E., ed. How Protective Factors Mitigate Risk & Facilitate Academic Resilience among Poor Minority College Students. 2009. (Social Issues, Justice & Status Ser.). pap. 43.00 *(978-1-61728-285-0(5)*, Nova Novinka) Nova Science Pubs., Inc.

Mork, Gretchen. Nurturing a Willing Student: A Better Approach to Achievement & Teaching Reading. 2007. 176p. per. 15.95 *(978-0-595-43435-0(5))* iUniverse, Inc.

Mueller, Michael P., et al, eds. Assessing Schools for Generation R (Responsibility) A Guide to Legislation & School Policy in Science Education. 2012. (Contemporary Trends & Issues in Science Education Ser.). (ENG., Illus.). 250p. 139.00 ***(978-94-007-2747-2(X)***, 940072747X) Springer.

Mullen, Kimberly. Higher Education Resiliency for at-Risk Students. 2009. 216p. pap. *(978-3-639-17161-7(6))* VDM Verlag Dr. Mueller e.K.

Mullins, Victor. African American Students in College. 2009. 144p. pap. *(978-3-639-17694-0(4))* VDM Verlag Dr. Mueller e.K.

Murphy, Carlene U. & Lick, Dale W., eds. The Whole-Faculty Study Groups Fieldbook: Lessons Learned & Best Practices from Classrooms, Districts, & Schools. 2006. (Illus.). 328p. 80.95 *(978-1-4129-1324-9(1)*, B13241C); per. 41.95 *(978-1-4129-1325-6(X)*, B13241P) Corwin Pr.

Murray, Kim. Humanity: Academia: The 100 Most Significant Universities. 2011. (Humanity Ser.). (ENG.). 260p. pap. 19.95 *(978-1-926654-10-2(2))* Patrick Bonneville Society CAN. Dist: Independent Pubs. Group.

Murray, Sarah. Effects of Peer Coaching on Collaborative Interactions & Student Achievement. 2008. 200p. pap. *(978-3-639-06328-8(7))* VDM Verlag Dr. Mueller e.K.

Murrell, Peter, Jr. Race, Culture, & Schooling. 2007. (Illus.). 224p. 130.00 *(978-0-8058-5537-1(8))* Erlbaum, Lawrence Assocs., Inc.

Murrell, Peter C., Jr. Race, Culture, & Schooling: Identities of Achievement in Multicultural Urban Schools. 2007. (Illus.). 208p. per. 28.95 *(978-0-8058-5538-8(6))* Erlbaum, Lawrence Assocs., Inc.

Muse, Charles. The Prentice Hall Planner for Student Success. 7th ed. 2007. (ENG., Illus.). 144p. (C). per. 4.00 *(978-0-13-219947-6(5)*, Prentice Hall) Prentice Hall PTR.

Mwenji, Benedict. Effect of Intestinal Parasites on Cognition & Educational Achievement. 2011. 256p. pap. ***(978-3-8443-8060-6(4))*** Lambert Academic Publishing.

Nadler, Paula. Creating Foundations. 2008. 236p. pap. *(978-3-639-07063-7(1))* VDM Verlag Dr. Mueller e.K.

Nagel, Michael & Lidstone, John. Green Doesn't Always Mean Go! 2008. 260p. pap. *(978-3-639-04830-8(X))* VDM Verlag Dr. Mueller e.K.

Naglieri, Jack & Pickering, Eric B. Helping Children Learn: Intervention Handouts for Use in School & at Home, Second Edition. Otero, Tulio & Moreno, Mary, trs. 2nd ed. 2010. (Illus.). 176p. pap. 39.95 *(978-1-55766-998-8(8))* Brookes, Paul H. Publishing Co.

Nahmijas, Sara. Implementation of Bologna on Croatian Colleges. 2010. 80p. pap. *(978-3-8383-5572-6(5))* Lambert Academic Publishing.

Nancy, Levenson. Intervention to Facilitate Narrative Development. 2010. 124p. pap. *(978-3-8383-3688-6(7))* Lambert Academic Publishing.

Naparstek, Nathan & Greenwood. Successful Educators. 2009. 204p. pap. 45.99 *(978-1-60752-072-6(9))* Information Age Publishing, Inc.

Nash, Roy. Classrooms Observed: The Teacher's Perception & the Pupil's Peformance. 2011. (Routledge Library Editions: Education Ser.). (ENG.). 152p. 100.00 ***(978-0-415-50443-0(0))*** Routledge.

Nasir, Na'ilah Suad. Racialized Identities: Race & Achievement among African American Youth. 2011. (ENG.). 216p. 70.00 *(978-0-8047-6018-8(7))*; pap. 22.95 *(978-0-8047-6019-5(5))* Stanford Univ. Pr.

Nderu-Boddington, Eulalee Maria. Academic Achievement, Perceptions & the Arts. 2008. 148p. pap. *(978-3-639-03711-1(1))* VDM Verlag Dr. Mueller e.K.

Nell, Marcia. Promoting Positive Parental Perceptions. 2007. 160p. per. *(978-3-8364-3432-4(6))* VDM Verlag Dr. Mueller e.K.

Ness/Johnson/Farença. Importance of Average: Playing the Game of School to Increase Success & Achievement. 2011. (ENG.). 224p. (gr. k-2). pap. 26.95 *(978-0-7425-7013-9(4))* Rowman & Littlefield Publishers, Inc.

Nessel, Denise & Graham, Joyce M. Thinking Strategies for Student Achievement: Improving Learning Across the Curriculum, K-12. 2nd rev. ed. 2006. (Illus.). 248p. 82.95 *(978-1-4129-3880-8(5)*, B38805C) Corwin Pr.

Neuman, Susan B. Changing the Odds for Children at Risk: Seven Essential Principles of Educational Programs that Break the Cycle of Poverty, 1 vol. 2008. (Illus.). 240p. 44.95 *(978-0-313-36222-4(X)*, C36222, Praeger Pubs.) Greenwood Publishing Group, Inc.

Newman, Michael & Greenwood. The Designs of Academic Literacy. 2009. 200p. pap. 45.99 *(978-1-60752-065-8(6))* Information Age Publishing, Inc.

Newton, Willie J. An Evaluation of Findings from Cleveland's State-Funded Voucher Program. 2011. 52p. pap. 25.95 ***(978-1-59942-389-0(8)***, Dissertation.com) Universal Pubs.

Nicholas-Omoregbe, Olanike Sharon. Parental Socio-Economic Background: Implication for students' Outcome. 2011. 68p. pap. ***(978-3-8433-9096-5(7))*** Lambert Academic Publishing.

Nichols, Beverly. Improving Student Achievement: 50 Research-Based Strategies. 2008. pap. *(978-1-58683-293-3(X))* Linworth Publishing, Inc.

—Improving Student Achievement: 50 Research-Based Strategies for Educators, 1 vol. 2008. 120p. 44.95 *(978-1-58683-290-2(5)*, A2457P) Linworth Publishing, Inc.

Nigatie Enideg, Workneh. Teacher Support for Student Success. 2010. 104p. pap. *(978-3-639-28325-9(2))* VDM Verlag Dr. Mueller e.K.

Nist-Olejnik, Sherrie L. & Holschuh, Jodi. College Success Strategies. 3rd ed. 2008. (Pearson English Value Textbook Ser.). (ENG., Illus.). 304p. (C). pap. 40.00 *(978-0-205-64634-0(4))* Longman Publishing.

Nist-Olejnik, Sherrie L. & Holschuh, Jodi. College Success Strategies. 4th rev. ed. 2012. (ENG.). 304p. (C). pap. 40.00 ***(978-0-205-19091-1(X))*** Longman Publishing Group.

Noguera, Pedro A. & Noguera. The Trouble with Black Boys: And Other Reflections on Race, Equity, & the Future of Public Education. 2009. (ENG.). 368p. pap. 17.95 *(978-0-470-45208-0(0)*, Jossey-Bass) Wiley, John & Sons, Inc.

Noguera, Pedro A. & Noguera, Pedro. The Trouble with Black Boys: ...And Other Reflections on Race, Equity, & the Future of Public Education. 2008. (ENG.). 352p. 24.95 *(978-0-7879-8874-6(X)*, Jossey-Bass) Wiley, John & Sons, Inc.

Noguera, Pedro A. & Wing, Jean Yonemura, eds. Unfinished Business: Closing the Racial Achievement Gap in Our Schools. 2008. (ENG.). 352p. pap. 18.95 *(978-0-470-38444-2(1)*, Jossey-Bass) Wiley, John & Sons, Inc.

Northern Michigan University. Freshman Seminar: Achieving Success. 3rd rev. ed. 2007. 380p. pap. 49.76 *(978-0-7575-4391-3(X))* Kendall Hunt Publishing Co.

Notari-Syverson, Angela, et al. Ladders to Literacy: A Preschool Activity Book. 2nd ed. 2007. 368p. spiral bd. 49.95 *(978-1-55766-913-1(9))* Brookes, Paul H. Publishing Co.

Nyman, Terri R. Key Characteristics of Effective Middle Schools. 2008. 84p. pap. *(978-3-639-07828-2(4))* VDM Verlag Dr. Mueller e.K.

O. Otti, Leonard, et al. Creativity Within the University Environment. 2011. 240p. pap. ***(978-3-8443-1870-8(4))*** Lambert Academic Publishing.

O'Conner, John. Turning Average Instruction into Great Instruction: School Leadership's Role in Student Achievement. 2009. (ENG., Illus.). 136p. 65.00 *(978-1-57886-948-0(X))*; pap. 28.95 *(978-1-57886-949-7(8))* Lexington Bks.

Odden, Allan & Archibald, Sarah. Doubling Student Performance: ... & Finding the Resources to Do It. Odden, Allan R. & Archibald, Sarah J., eds. 2009. (Illus.). 184p. pap. 34.95 *(978-1-4129-6963-5(8)*, B69628P) Corwin Pr.

Odden, Allan R., ed. 10 Strategies for Doubling Student Performance. 2009. 192p. 78.95 *(978-1-4129-7147-8(0)*, B71478C); pap. 34.95 *(978-1-4129-7148-5(9)*, B71478P) Corwin Pr.

Odden, Allan R. & Archibald, Sarah J., eds. Doubling Student Performance: ... & Finding the Resources to Do It. 2009. (Illus.). 184p. 78.95 *(978-1-4129-6962-8(X)*, B69628C) Corwin Pr.

Ogbu, John U. Minority Status, Oppositional Culture & Schooling. 2008. (Sociocultural, Political, & Historical Studies in Education). (ENG., Illus.). 688p. 56.95 *(978-0-8058-5104-5(6))* Routledge.

Ogbu, John U., ed. Minority Status, Oppositional Culture & Schooling. 2008. (Sociocultural, Political, & Historical Studies in Education). (ENG., Illus.). 688p. 170.00 *(978-0-8058-5103-8(8))* Routledge.

Ogunsunlade, Olutunde A. Surviving the Freshman Year & Beyond. 2011. 54p. 24.99 ***(978-1-4568-2633-8(6))***; pap. 15.99 ***(978-1-4568-2632-1(8))*** Xlibris Corp.

Okeke, Chinedu. Gender & Schooling. 2010. 296p. pap. *(978-3-639-26871-3(7))* VDM Verlag Dr. Mueller e.K.

Ong Mcbride, Josephine. Achieving Your Dream for College Success. 2009. (ENG.). 224p. pap. 65.39 *(978-0-7575-7049-0(6))* Kendall Hunt Publishing Co.

Ongeri, Joseph. Teaching Economics from a Learner-Centered Perspective. 2009. 116p. pap. *(978-3-639-17910-1(2))* VDM Verlag Dr. Mueller e.K.

Orelus, P. W. Academic Achievers: Whose Definition? 2010. 226p. *(978-94-6091-236-8(2))*; (Illus.). pap. *(978-94-6091-235-1(4))* Sense Pubs.

Organisation for Economic Co-operation and Development. Against the Odds: Disadvantaged Students who Succeed in School. 2011. (Illus.). 200p. pap. 54.00 ***(978-92-64-08995-2(0))*** Organization for Economic Cooperation & Development.

Organisation for Economic Co-Operation and Development. Pisa 2009 Results Vol. 1: What students know & can do: student performance in reading, mathematics & Science. 2010. (Illus.). 272p. pap. 33.00 ***(978-92-64-09144-3(0))*** Organization for Economic Cooperation & Development.

—Pisa 2009 Results Vol. 3: Learning to learn: student engagement, strategies & Practices. 2010. (Illus.). 266p. pap. 56.00 ***(978-92-64-09147-4(5))*** Organization for Economic Cooperation & Development.

Organisation for Economic Co-operation and Development Staff. Pisa 2006: Volume 2: Annex-Pisa 2006: Volume 2: Annexe. 2008. (ENG.). 350p. pap. 52.00 *(978-92-64-04014-4(5))* Organization for Economic Cooperation & Development.

—Pisa 2006: Initial Report: Volume 1. 2008. (ENG.). 350p. pap. 52.00 *(978-92-64-04000-7(5))* Organization for Economic Cooperation & Development.

—Pisa Set: Pisa 2006: Volumes 1 & 2, 2 vols. 2008. (ENG.). 700p. pap. 98.00 *(978-92-64-04016-8(1))* Organization for Economic Cooperation & Development.

—Pisa Top of the Class: High Performers in Science in Pisa 2006. 2009. (Illus.). 163p. pap. 63.00 *(978-92-64-06068-5(5))* Organization for Economic Cooperation & Development.

Osguthorpe, Russell T. & Osguthorpe, Lolly. Choose to Learn: Teaching for Success Every Day. 2008. (Illus.). 136p. 60.95 *(978-1-4129-6138-7(6)*, B61387C) Corwin Pr.

Osguthorpe, Russell T. & Osguthorpe, Lolly S. Choose to Learn: Teaching for Success Every Day. 2008. (Illus.). 136p. pap. 24.95 *(978-1-4129-6139-4(4)*, B61387P) Corwin Pr.

Otsuka, Setsuo. Culture & Achievement: Cultural Influences on Academic Performance in Fiji. 2008. 300p. pap. *(978-3-8364-7684-3(3))* VDM Verlag Dr. Mueller e.K.

Oyanoafoh, Michael Osezua. Teachers' Perception of the Influence of Students' Indiscipline. 2011. 88p. pap. ***(978-3-8443-0371-1(5))*** Lambert Academic Publishing.

Page, Daniel. The Definitive Community College Guide: A Concise Roadmap to Academic Success. 2008. 73p. pap. 16.95 *(978-1-60474-896-3(6))* PublishAmerica, Inc.

Pagliaro, Marie Menna. Research-Based Unit & Lesson Planning: Maximizing Student Achievement. 2012. (ENG.). 236p. 70.00 ***(978-1-61048-453-4(3))*** 2012. (ENG.). 236p. pap. 34.95 ***(978-1-61048-454-1(1))*** 2011. E-Book ***(978-1-61048-455-8(X))*** Rowman & Littlefield Education.

Paige, Rod & Witty, Elaine. The Black-White Achievement Gap: Why Closing It Is the Greatest Civil Rights Issue of Our Time, 1 vol. 2010. (ENG.). 240p. 22.00 *(978-0-8144-1519-1(9))* Amacom.

Palmer, Richard. Passing Your Weak Subjects: You are much better than you Think! 2008. (Illus.). XIV, 146p. 130.00 *(978-0-415-40470-9(3))* Routledge.

—Passing Your Weak Subjects: You Are Much Better Than You Think! 2008. (Illus.). XIV, 146p. 31.95 *(978-0-415-40471-6(1))* Routledge.

Palomares, Susanna. Anger Control & Conflict Management for Kids. 2011. 134p. pap. 25.95 ***(978-1-56499-078-5(8))*** Innerchoice Publishing.

Palos-Tuley, Belen. An Examination of Fine Arts Experiences of Hispanic Students Examination of the Relationship Between Fine Arts Experiences & Creative Thinking, Ac. 2009. 240p. pap. *(978-3-639-12961-8(X))* VDM Verlag Dr. Mueller e.K.

Pamela, Dath. Psychosocial Effects of Humor. 2010. 100p. pap. *(978-3-8383-3974-0(6))* Lambert Academic Publishing.

Pang, Katherine & Mehler, Tricia. Strategies for Academic Success & Retention. 2011. 200p. pap. ***(978-3-8443-9451-1(6))*** Lambert Academic Publishing.

Parcels, Ed. D. Cognitive Style & Achievement in Distance Education. 2009. 140p. pap. *(978-3-639-03613-8(1))* VDM Verlag Dr. Mueller e.K.

Parrett, William H. & Budge, Kathleen M. Turning High-Poverty Schools into High-Performing Schools. 2012. 221p. pap. 30.95 ***(978-1-4166-1313-8(7))*** Assn. for Supervision & Curriculum Development.

Payne, Ruby K. Research-Based Strategies: Narrowing the Achievement Gap for under-Resourced Students. 2009. 290p. pap. 25.00 *(978-1-934583-34-0(0))* aha! Process, Inc.

—Under-Resourced Learners: 8 Strategies to Improve Student Achievement. 2008. 208p. pap. 25.00 *(978-1-934583-00-5(6))* aha! Process, Inc.

Payne, Ruby K. & Magee, Donna S. School Improvement: Creating Sustainable Excellence. 2010. pap. 15.00 *(978-1-934583-44-9(8))* aha! Process, Inc.

Pearlstein, Mitch. Female Political Leadership & Athletics: The Educational, Economic, & Social Costs of Family Fragmentation. 2011. (New Frontiers in Education Ser.). (ENG.). 165p. pap. 24.95 *(978-1-60709-362-6(6))* Rowman & Littlefield Education.

—From Family Collapse to America's Decline: The Educational, Economic, & Social Costs of Family Fragmentation. 2011. (New Frontiers in Education Ser.). (ENG.). 165p. 50.00 *(978-1-60709-361-9(8))* Rowman & Littlefield Education.

Pearlstein, Mitchell B. Shortchanging Student Achievement: The Educational, Economic, & Social Costs of Family Fragmentation. 2011. xxv, 165p. ***(978-1-60709-363-3(4))*** Rowman & Littlefield Education.

A

Pearson Education Staff & Pearson, Bruce M. Success Tips. rev. ed. 2011. (ENG.). 6p. (C). pap. 13.33 *(978-0-13-278807-6(1),* Prentice Hall) Prentice Hall PTR.

Pearson Education Staff & Pearson, Craig. MyStudentSuccessLab NEW Student Access Code Card (Standalone) 2010. (ENG.). (C). 36.00 *(978-0-13-706108-2(0),* Prentice Hall) Prentice Hall PTR.

Peggram, Rosemary. Personality Traits. 2008. 128p. pap. *(978-3-639-06756-9(8))* VDM Verlag Dr. Mueller e.K.

Pei, Z. J. Tips on Getting an Academic Position. 2009. 96p. pap. 8.80 *(978-0-557-05363-6(3))* Lulu Enterprises Inc.

Pelaia, Bill. Parents & the Schools: How to Insure Your Child's Academic Success... & Much More. 2011. 128p. pap. 16.95 ***(978-1-4670-6290-9(1))*** AuthorHouse.

Pendergast, Joan. Factors That Contribute to Middle School Academic Achievement. 2008. 128p. pap. *(978-3-8364-9859-3(6))* VDM Verlag Dr. Mueller e.K.

Perna, Laura W. & Thomas, Scott L. Theoretical Perspectives on Student Success: Understanding the Contributions of the Disciplines. Ward, Kelly & Wolf, Lisa E., eds. 2008. (J-B ASHE Higher Education Report Series (AEHE) Ser.: 124). (ENG.). 112p. pap. 29.00 *(978-0-470-41078-3(7),* Jossey-Bass) Wiley, John & Sons, Inc.

Perozzi, Brett, ed. Enhancing Student Learning Through College Employment. 2009. 288p. 75.00 *(978-1-60844-124-2(5))* Dog Ear Publishing, LLC.

Phillips, Ronnie. Survival Kit for High School Students: Practical Approaches to High School Success. 2010. 77p. pap. 11.95 *(978-1-4327-5620-8(6))* Outskirts Pr., Inc.

Phillipson, Sivanes. Parent & Children Voices. 2010. 72p. pap. *(978-3-8383-0482-3(9))* Lambert Academic Publishing.

—Role of Parents in Children's Academic Achievement. 2010. 300p. pap. *(978-3-8383-0149-5(8))* Lambert Academic Publishing.

Piercy, Thomasina Depinto. Compelling Conversations: Connecting Leadership to Achievement. Curtis, Sarah, ed. 2007. (ENG., Illus.). 208p. per. 24.95 *(978-1-933196-25-1(4))* Lead+Learn Pr.

Pollock, Jane E. Improving Student Learning One Teacher at a Time. 2007. 143p. per. 23.95 *(978-1-4166-0520-1(7))* Assn. for Supervision & Curriculum Development.

Pollock, Jane E. & Ford, Sharon M. Improving Student Learning One Principal at a Time. 2009. (Illus.). 149p. pap. 25.95 *(978-1-4166-0768-7(4))* Assn. for Supervision & Curriculum Development.

Pollock, Jane E., et al. Minding the Achievement Gap One Classroom at a Time. 2012. pap. 23.95 ***(978-1-4166-1384-8(6))*** Assn. for Supervision & Curriculum Development.

Popham, W. James. Appropriate & Inappropriate Tests for Evaluating Schools, Mastering Assessment: A Self-Service System for Educators, Pamphlet 1. 2nd rev. ed. 2011. (Mastering Assessment Ser.). (ENG.). 32p. (C). pap. 10.99 *(978-0-13-273487-5(7))* Allyn & Bacon, Inc.

—Assessing Student Affect, Mastering Assessment: A Self-Service System for Educators, Pamphlet 2. 2nd rev. ed. 2011. (Mastering Assessment Ser.). (ENG.). 32p. (C). pap. 10.99 *(978-0-13-273488-2(5))* Allyn & Bacon, Inc.

—Assessing Students with Disabilities, Mastering Assessment: A Self-Service System for Educators, Pamphlet 3. 2nd rev. ed. 2011. (Mastering Assessment Ser.). (ENG.). 32p. (C). pap. 10.99 *(978-0-13-273489-9(3))* Allyn & Bacon, Inc.

—Assessment Bias: How to Banish It, Mastering Assessment: A Self-Service System for Educators, Pamphlet 4. 2nd rev. ed. 2011. (Mastering Assessment Ser.). (ENG.). 32p. (C). pap. 10.99 *(978-0-13-273490-5(7))* Allyn & Bacon, Inc.

—Constructed-Response Tests: Building & Bettering, Mastering Assessment: A Self-Service System for Educators, Pamphlet 7. 2nd rev. ed. 2011. (Mastering Assessment Ser.). (ENG.). 32p. (C). pap. 10.99 *(978-0-13-273499-8(0))* Allyn & Bacon, Inc.

—How Testing Can Help Teaching, Mastering Assessment: A Self-Service System for Educators, Pamphlet 8. 2nd rev. ed. 2011. (Mastering Assessment Ser.). (ENG.). 32p. (C). pap. 10.99 *(978-0-13-273498-1(2))* Allyn & Bacon, Inc.

—Interpreting the Results of Large-Scale Assessments, Mastering Assessment: A Self-Service System for Educators, Pamphlet 9. 2nd rev. ed. 2011. (Mastering Assessment Ser.). (ENG.). 32p. (C). pap. 10.99 *(978-0-13-273497-4(4))* Allyn & Bacon, Inc.

—Mastering Assessment: A Self-Service System for Educators. 2nd rev. ed. 2011. (Mastering Assessment Ser.). (ENG.). 480p. (C). pap., pap., pap. 150.00 *(978-0-13-273291-8(2))* Allyn & Bacon, Inc.

—Portfolio Assessment & Performance Testing, Pamphlet 10. 2nd rev. ed. 2011. (Mastering Assessment Ser.). (ENG.). 32p. (C). pap. 10.99 *(978-0-13-273486-8(9))* Allyn & Bacon, Inc.

—Reliability: What Is It & Is It Necessary, Mastering Assessment: A Self-Service System for Educators, Pamphlet 11. 2nd rev. ed. 2011. (Mastering Assessment Ser.). (ENG.). 32p. (C). pap. 10.99 *(978-0-13-273496-7(6))* Allyn & Bacon, Inc.

—The Role of Rubrics in Testing & Teaching: Mastering Assessment - A Self-Service System for Educators. 2nd rev. ed. 2011. (Mastering Assessment Ser.). (ENG.). 32p. (C). pap. 10.99 *(978-0-13-273494-3(X))* Allyn & Bacon, Inc.

—Selected-Response Tests: Building & Bettering, Mastering Assessment: A Self-Service System for Educators, Pamphlet 12. 2nd rev. ed. 2011. (Mastering Assessment Ser.). (ENG.). 32p. (C). pap. 10.99 *(978-0-13-273495-0(8))* Allyn & Bacon, Inc.

—Test Preparation: Sensible or Sordid?, Mastering Assessment: A Self-Service System for Educators, Pamphlet 14. 2nd rev. ed. 2011. (Mastering Assessment Ser.). (ENG.). 32p. (C). pap. 10.99 *(978-0-13-273493-6(1))* Allyn & Bacon, Inc.

—Validity: Assessment's Cornerstone, Mastering Assessment: A Self-Service System for Educators, Pamphlet 15. 2nd rev. ed. 2011. (Mastering Assessment Ser.). (ENG.). 32p. (C). pap. 10.99 *(978-0-13-273492-9(3))* Allyn & Bacon, Inc.

Popovic, Celia & Green, David A. Understanding Undergraduates: Challenging Our Preconceptions of Student Performance. 2012. (SEDA Ser.). (ENG., Illus.). 280p. 125.00 *(978-0-415-66754-8(2));* pap. 44.95 *(978-0-415-66755-5(0))* Routledge.

Portes & Sheets. Handbook of Research on Ethnic Identity & School Achievement. 2010. (ENG.). pap. 89.95 *(978-0-8058-6262-1(5))* Erlbaum, Lawrence Assocs., Inc.

Poston, William K., Jr., et al. 50 Ways to Close the Achievement Gap (Multimedia Kit) A Multimedia Kit for Professional Development. 2010. 248p. 327.00 *(978-1-4129-7746-3(0),* B77463K) Corwin Pr.

Potter, Charles Anthony. 12 Steps to College Success: A parental empowerment Program. 2009. pap. 49.95 *(978-1-61623-242-9(0))* Independent Pub.

Powell, Marilyn. Predicting Performance. 2011. 216p. pap. ***(978-3-8433-8722-4(2))*** Lambert Academic Publishing.

Pradere, Steven. Effective Staff Development Connected to Increased Student Achievement - Building a Measureable Connection Between Effective. 2008. 132p. pap. *(978-3-639-02689-4(6))* VDM Verlag Dr. Mueller e.K.

Pratt, Robert. The Academic Warrior: Becoming a Purposeful Learner. 2011. (Illus.). 105p. spiral bd. 18.95 ***(978-0-9833842-0-5(7))*** Cook County Higher Education.

Price, Hugh B. Mobilizing the Community to Help Students Succeed. 2008. vii, 141p. pap. 21.95 *(978-1-4166-0696-3(3))* Assn. for Supervision & Curriculum Development.

Price, Paul H. Childhood Dying: The Repercussions of Pushing Our Kids Too Fast & Too Hard in School. 2008. 192p. pap. 19.95 *(978-1-58982-466-9(0),* American Univ. & College Pr.) American Bk. Publishing Group.

Provinchain, Adam. The Student's Secret to Success. 2007. (J). per. *(978-1-60458-041-9(0))* Instant Pub.

—The Student's Secret to Success. 2007. (ENG., Illus.). 50p. (J). per. *(978-1-59916-370-3(5),* 48HrBks.com) Printing Systems.

Pruitt, Mark. Making the Grade: How to Study at the College Level. 2010. 252p. pap. 19.95 *(978-1-4520-7332-3(5))* AuthorHouse.

Quinn, Gary W. Improving Test Scores in Five Easy Steps: The Silver Bullet. 2010. (ENG.). 128p. 95.00 *(978-1-60709-503-3(3));* 174p. pap. 29.95 *(978-1-60709-504-0(1))* Rowman & Littlefield Education.

Race, Phil & Race, Philip. How to Get a Good Degree: Making the Most of Your Time at University. 2nd rev. ed. 2007. (Illus.). 288p. (C). (ENG.). 146.00 *(978-0-335-22266-7(8),* 0335222668); pap. 48.00 *(978-0-335-22265-0(X),* 033522265X) McGraw-Hill Education GBR. (Open University Pr.). Dist: McGraw-Hill Cos., The.

Rafcliffe, Martin J. A. & Harts, Melissa L. Schools that Make the Grade: What Successful Schools Do to Improve Student Achievement. 2011. (Illus.). 208p. pap. 29.95 *(978-1-59857-090-8(0))* Brookes, Paul H. Publishing Co.

Ramsey, Robert D. Don't Teach the Canaries Not to Sing: Creating a School Culture That Boosts Achievement. 2007. 176p. 72.95 *(978-1-4129-4893-7(2),* B48932C); per. 31.95 *(978-1-4129-4894-4(0),* B48932P) Corwin Pr.

Rawlinson, Regenia Mitchum. My Teacher Told Me I Could. 2007. 120p. (ENG.). 22.95 *(978-0-595-68447-2(5));* per. 12.95 *(978-0-595-42777-2(4))* iUniverse, Inc.

Rebell, Michael A. & Wolff, Jessica R. Moving Every Child Ahead: From NCLB Hype to Meaningful Educational Opportunity. 2008. (ENG.). 192p. 24.95 *(978-0-8077-4850-3(1));* pap. *(978-0-8077-4851-0(X))* Teachers College Pr., Teachers College, Columbia Univ.

—NCLB at the Crossroads: Reexamining the Federal Effort to Close the Achievement Gap. Rebell, Michael A. & Wolff, Jessica R., eds. Wolff, Jessica, ed. rev. ed. 2009. (ENG., Illus.). 312p. 36.00 *(978-0-8077-4944-9(3))* Teachers College Pr., Teachers College, Columbia Univ.

Reddy, Vijay. Mathematics & Science Achievement at South African Schools in TIMSS 2003. 2007. (Human Sciences Research Council Publication Ser.). (ENG., Illus.). 148p. per. 25.95 *(978-0-7969-2158-1(X))* Human Sciences Research Council ZAF. Dist: Independent Pubs. Group.

Reeves & Reeves, Angela. College: What You Need to Know & How to Succeed. 2nd rev. ed. 2011. (ENG.). ring bd. 51.95 *(978-0-7575-8354-4(7))* Kendall Hunt Publishing Co.

Reeves, Douglas B. Finding Your Leadership Focus: What Matters Most for Student Results. 2010. (ENG., Illus.). 176p. pap. 52.00 *(978-0-8077-5171-8(5));* 23.95 *(978-0-8077-5170-1(7))* Teachers College Pr., Teachers College, Columbia Univ.

Reinhart, Susan M., et al. Academic Interactions: Communicating on Campus. 2009. (Michigan Series in English for Academic & Professional Purposes Ser.). (ENG., Illus.). 216p. (C). 29.50 *(978-0-472-03332-4(8))* Univ. of Michigan Pr.

Reklaw, Jesse, ed. Applicant. 2nd ed. 2006. (Illus.). 48p. per. 4.00 *(978-0-9770557-6-0(0))* Microcosm Publishing.

A Review & Assessment of the Use, Impact, & Accomplishments of Federal Appropriations Provided to Improve the Education of Children in the District of Columbia: Hearings Before a Subcommittee of the Committee on Appropriations, United States Senate, One Hundred Eleventh Congress, First Session: Special Hearings, September 16, 2009, Washington, DC: September 29, 2009, Washington, DC. 2010. (Illus.). iv, 167p. ***(978-0-16-085918-2(2),*** 552-070-41114-3) United States Government Printing Office.

Reynolds, Laureen. Catch Your Kids Before They Fall: 140+ Skill-Builders to Boost Academic Success. 2010. *(978-1-934026-83-0(2))* CSB Enterprises.

Rhamie, Jasmine. Eagles Who Soar: How Black Learners Find the Path to Success. 2008. (Illus.). 140p. per. 31.95 *(978-1-85856-394-7(1))* Trentham Bks. Ltd. GBR. Dist: Stylus Publishing, LLC.

Rhodes, Len, et al. Life Skills for Student Success: Achieving Financial Literacy. rev. ed. 2011. 270p. pap. 62.50 ***(978-0-7575-8911-9(1))*** Kendall Hunt Publishing Co.

Richardson, Amy, et al. Effects of Soldiers Deployment on Children. 2011. (Illus.). 176p. pap. 28.00 *(978-0-8330-5181-3(4))* Royal Pavilion, Art Gallery & Museums GBR. Dist: National Bk. Network.

Richardson, Marti. Succeeding with Struggling Students: A Planning Resource for Raising Achievement. 2006. (Illus.). 248p. 85.95 *(978-1-4129-4462-5(7),* B44627C); per. 38.95 *(978-1-4129-4463-2(5),* B44627P) Corwin Pr.

Richardson, Temeca L. Can the Black Church Save Young Black America? Closing the Educational Achievement Gap. 2007. pap. 19.95 *(978-0-9789560-0-4(1))* Much Lov 2 Give, LLC.

Richburg, Cynthia McCormick & Smiley, Donna Fisher. School-Based Audiology. 2011. (Illus.). 300p. pap. 59.95 *(978-1-59756-385-7(4))* Plural Publishing, Inc.

Ricoha, Oliver T., ed. Educational Assessment: Measuring Progress in Schools. 2010. (Education in a Competitive & Globalizing World Ser.). 115.00 *(978-1-60876-818-9(X))* Nova Science Pubs., Inc.

Rieg, Sue A. & Paquette, Kelli R. Striving for the 'Perfect' Classroom — Part II: Teachers' Responsibilities Beyond Instruction & Assessment. 2011. (Education in a Competitive & Globalizing World Ser.). 220p. 69.00 *(978-1-61122-030-8(0))* Nova Science Pubs., Inc.

Riley, Keith. The Case for Student Athletes Who Achieve - Time Use Patterns Influence on Academic Achievement among African American & Hispanic Male High School S. 2008. 124p. pap. *(978-3-639-11071-5(4))* VDM Verlag Dr. Mueller e.K.

Rimm, Sylvia B. Why Bright Kids Get Poor Grades & What You Can Do about It: A Six-Step Program for Parents & Teachers. 3rd ed. 2008. 388p. pap. 24.95 *(978-0-910707-87-9(1))* Great Potential Pr., Inc.

Ringrose, Jessica. Postfeminist Education? 2012. (Foundations & Futures of Education Ser.). (ENG.). 200p. (C). pap. 44.95 ***(978-0-415-55749-8(6));*** 135.00 ***(978-0-415-55748-1(8))*** Routledge.

Riordan, Cornelius H. Equality & Achievement: An Introduction to the Sociology of Education. 2nd ed. 2006. pap. 8.95 *(978-1-4288-1666-4(6))* Cram101 Inc.

Riverside County Staff. Steps to Success: A Blueprint for the Achievement of All Students. 2009. spiral bd. 476.40 *(978-1-59746-082-8(6))* Lakeshore Learning Materials.

Roberts, Julia L. & Inman, Tracy F. Assessing Differentiated Student Products: A Protocol for Development & Evaluation. 2008. (ENG.). 200p. pap. 24.95 *(978-1-59363-355-4(6))* Prufrock Pr.

Robustelli, Stacy. There Is More Than One Yellow Brick Road to Achievement. 2008. 116p. pap. *(978-3-639-00513-4(9))* VDM Verlag Dr. Mueller e.K.

Romberg, Thomas & Shafer, Mary C. The Impact of Reform Instruction on Student Mathematics Achievement: An Example of a Summative Evaluation of a Standards-Based Curriculum. 2008. (Studies in Mathematical Thinking & Learning Ser.). (Illus.). XII, 188p. 145.00 *(978-0-415-99009-7(2))* Routledge.

Roney, Kathleen, et al. Creating Organizationally Healthy & Effective Middle Schools: Research That Supports the Middle School Concept & Student Achievement. 2008. (Illus.). xv, 220p. *(978-1-56090-223-2(X))* National Middle Schl. Assn.

Rooks-Dotson, Karen P. An Educational Applied Dissertation Model: Effectively Identifying Students at Risk Using School-Based Problem-Solving. 2009. 87p. pap. 24.95 *(978-1-4327-4156-3(X))* Outskirts Pr., Inc.

Ross, Marilyn J. & Greenwood. Success Factors of Young African American Women at a Historically Black College. 2009. 152p. pap. 45.99 *(978-1-60752-074-0(5))* Information Age Publishing, Inc.

Ross, Shelley. Motivation Correlates of Academic Achievement. 2010. 224p. pap. *(978-3-639-25040-4(0))* VDM Verlag Dr. Mueller e.K.

Rovai, Alfred P., et al, eds. Closing the African American Achievement Gap in Higher Education. 2007. (ENG., Illus.). 224p. 49.00 *(978-0-8077-4778-0(5))* Teachers College Pr., Teachers College, Columbia Univ.

Rubie-Davies, Christine. Expecting Success. 2008. 288p. pap. *(978-3-8364-9679-7(8))* VDM Verlag Dr. Mueller e.K.

Rueda, Robert. The 3 Dimensions of Improving Student Performance: Finding the Right Solutions to the Right Problems. 2011. (Illus.). 144p. pap. 23.95 *(978-0-8077-5240-1(1))* Teachers College Pr., Teachers College, Columbia Univ.

Rury, John L. & Hill, Shirley A. The African American Struggle for Secondary Schooling, 1940-1980: Closing the Graduation Gap. 2011. (ENG., Illus.). 264p. 78.00 ***(978-0-8077-5278-4(9));*** pap. 36.95 ***(978-0-8077-5277-7(0))*** Teachers College Pr., Teachers College, Columbia Univ.

Sadovnik, A. &. No Child Left Behind & the Reduction of the Achievement Gap. 2007. (Illus.). 424p. 147.00 *(978-0-415-95530-0(0))* Routledge.

Saifer, Steffen, et al. Culturally Responsive Standards-Based Teaching: Classroom to Community & Back. 2nd ed. 2010. (Illus.). 248p. pap. 38.95 *(978-1-4129-8702-8(4),* B87028P) Corwin Pr.

Salazar, Pam & Salazar, Pamela. High-Impact Leadership for High-Impact Schools: The Actions That Matter Most. 2008. (ENG.). 128p. pap. 29.95 *(978-1-59667-076-1(2))* Eye On Education, Inc.

Salend, Spencer & Salend, Spencer J. Classroom Testing & Assessment for ALL Students: Beyond Standardization. 2009. (Illus.). 176p. 76.95 *(978-1-4129-6642-9(6),* B66429C); pap. 33.95 *(978-1-4129-6643-6(4),* B66429P) Corwin Pr.

Sam, Trodd. The Approach to & Goals of the Study. 2010. 312p. pap. *(978-3-8383-3977-1(0))* Lambert Academic Publishing.

Samimi, Sia. Qualities of Outstanding Teachers That Contribute to Student Success: Personal, Technical, & Professional Attributes of Outstanding Teachers in Post-secondary Education. 2008. 112p. pap. *(978-3-8364-9339-0(X))* VDM Verlag Dr. Mueller e.K.

Sampson, Shellie. The Motivated Life: A Study on Goal-Setting, Well-Being & Achievement. 2010. 224p. (ENG.). 28.95 *(978-1-4502-2896-1(8));* pap. 18.95 *(978-1-4502-2248-8(X))* iUniverse, Inc.

Santibanez, Lucrecia. Haciendo Camino: Análisis del sistema de evaluación y del impacto del programa de estímulos docentes Carrera Magisterial en México. 2006. 198p. pap. 25.00 *(978-0-8330-3918-7(0),* MG471/1) RAND Corp., The.

Saroyan, Alenoush & Frenay, Mariane, eds. Building Teaching Capacities in Higher Education: A Comprehensive International Model. 2010. (Illus.). 240p. 35.00 *(978-1-57922-410-3(5))* Stylus Publishing, LLC.

Schargel, Franklin P., et al. From At-Risk to Academic Excellence: Instructional Leaders Speak Out. 2007. (ENG.). 176p. pap. 34.95 *(978-1-59667-046-4(0))* Eye On Education, Inc.

Schlechty, Phillip C. Engaging Students: The Next Level of Working on the Work. 2nd ed. 2011. (ENG., Illus.). 224p. pap. 30.00 *(978-0-470-64008-1(1),* Jossey-Bass) Wiley, John & Sons, Inc.

Schoem, David. College Knowledge for the Jewish Student: 101 Tips. 2010. (ENG., Illus.). 248p. (C). pap. 20.95 *(978-0-472-03430-7(8))* Univ. of Michigan Pr.

Schroth, Stephen, et al. Planning Differentiated Instruction & Assessing Results: Teaching to Assure Each Student's Success. rev. ed. 2011. (ENG.). 126p. pap. 57.00 *(978-0-7575-8852-5(2))* Kendall Hunt Publishing Co.

Schuermann, Patrick & Guthrie, James W. Leading Schools to Success: Constructing & Sustaining High-Performing Learning Cultures. 2010. (Illus.). 304p. (C). pap. 44.00 *(978-1-4129-7901-6(3),* B79016P) SAGE Pubns., Inc.

Schunk, Dale H. & Zimmerman, Barry J., eds. Motivation & Self-Regulated Learning: Theory, Research, & Applications. 2007. (Illus.). 416p. 150.00 *(978-0-8058-5897-6(0))* Erlbaum, Lawrence Assocs., Inc.

—Motivation & Self-Regulated Learning: Theory, Research, & Applications. 2007. (ENG., Illus.). 432p. (C). per. 51.95 *(978-0-8058-5898-3(9))* Routledge.

Schwartz, Daylle Deanna. Nice Girls Can Finish First: Getting the Results You Want & the Respect You Deserve... While Still Being Liked. 2009. (ENG.). 256p. pap. 16.95 *(978-0-07-160907-4(5),* 0071609075) McGraw-Hill Cos., The.

Scott, Lawrence L. African American Male Academic Success. 2011. 128p. pap. 25.95 ***(978-1-61233-762-3(7),*** Dissertation.com) Universal Pubs.

Sedrak, Mona. Understanding the Role of Achievement Motivation in Medical Education. 2008. 100p. pap. *(978-3-8364-8252-3(5))* VDM Verlag Dr. Mueller e.K.

Seebaran, Ben. The 7 Keys to Success at High School & Beyond: Unlocking Your Full Potential. 2010. 116p. pap. 15.70 *(978-1-4520-8960-7(4))* AuthorHouse.

Seidman, Alan. College Student Retention: Formula for Student Success. 2nd ed. 2012. ***(978-1-4422-1253-4(5))*** Rowman & Littlefield Publishers, Inc.

Seidman, Alan, ed. College Student Retention: Formula for Student Success. 2nd rev. ed. 2012. (ENG.). 312p. (C). (gr. 13-17). pap. 44.00 ***(978-1-4422-1252-7(7))*** Rowman & Littlefield Publishers, Inc.

Seldin, Scott. Mentoring Human Potential: Student Peer Mentors as Catalysts for Academic Success. 2011. 176p. pap. 15.95 ***(978-1-4620-4019-3(5))*** iUniverse, Inc.

Sellars, Maura. Using Students' Strengths to Support Learning Outcomes. 2008. 104p. pap. *(978-3-639-04847-6(4))* VDM Verlag Dr. Mueller e.K.

Shabangu, Bheki. 7 Master Secrets to Becoming a Distinguished University or College Student: Vision. focus. passion. Confidence. 2009. 112p. pap. 16.49 *(978-1-4389-3644-4(3))* AuthorHouse.

Shavers-Sublett, Shawn. Special Eduation Students Academic Performance on Tests: The Performance of Special Education Students in Inclusive & Non-Inclusive Settings on Norm- Referenced Tests. 2008. 68p. pap. *(978-3-639-09027-7(6))* VDM Verlag Dr. Mueller e.K.

Sheets & Portes. Handbook of Research on Ethnic Identity & School Achievement. 2010. (ENG.). 195.00 *(978-0-8058-6261-4(7))* Erlbaum, Lawrence Assocs., Inc.

Shell Education Staff, et al. Vocabulary Instruction for Academic Success. 2008. (Professional Bks.). (ENG.). 216p. (gr. k-12). pap. 29.99 *(978-1-4258-0266-0(4))* Shell Educational Publishing.

Sherfield, Robert M., et al. Cornerstone: Building on Your Best. 4th ed. 2006. pap. incl. cd-rom *(978-0-13-612728-4(2))* Pearson Education Canada.

Shernoff, David J. The Experience of Student Engagement in High School Classrooms. 2010. 240p. pap. *(978-3-8383-2219-3(3))* Lambert Academic Publishing.

Shindler, John. Transformative Classroom Management: Positive Strategies to Engage All Students & Promote a Psychology of Success. 2009. (ENG., Illus.). 384p. pap. 29.95 *(978-0-470-44843-4(1),* Jossey-Bass) Wiley, John & Sons, Inc.

Shores, Cara F., ed. The Best of Corwin: Response to Intervention: Response to Intervention. 2011. (Best of Corwin Ser.). 208p. pap. 27.95 (978-1-4522-1741-3(6), B17413P) Corwin Pr.

Shorrocks-Taylor, Diane & Jenkins, Edgar W., eds. Learning from Others: International Comparisons in Education. 2010. (Contemporary Trends & Issues in Science Education Ser.). 324p. pap. 189.00 (978-90-481-5471-5(5), 9048154715) Springer.

Silverman, Stephan M. & Weinfeld, Rich. School Success for Children with Asperger's Syndrome. 2007. (ENG.). 229p. pap. 16.95 (978-1-59363-215-1(0)) Prufrock Pr.

Sindelar, Nancy. Using Test Data for Student Achievement: Answers to No Child Left Behind. 2nd ed. 2011. (ENG.). 184p. 50.00 (978-1-60709-960-4(8)); pap. 24.95 (978-1-60709-961-1(6)) Rowman & Littlefield Education.

Sindelar, Nancy W. Using Test Data for Student Achievement: Answers to "No Child Left Behind" 2nd ed. 2011. (978-1-60709-952-8(4)) Rowman & Littlefield Education.

Singleton, Glenn E. & Linton, Curtis. Facilitator's Guide to Courageous Conversations about Race: A Field Guide for Achieving Equity in Schools. 2006. (Illus.). 58p. per. 16.95 (978-1-4129-4156-3(3)) Corwin Pr.

Sinha, Manisha. Underachievers: Parents' Perception, Participation & Academic Progress. 2011. 212p. pap. (978-3-8443-0381-0(2)) Lambert Academic Publishing.

Sisler, Harvey. Grades, an Advanced Guide to Better Grades. Smith, Tim, ed. pap. 7.95 (978-1-880398-15-9(X)) S.J.T. Enterprises, Inc.

Skoglund, Frederic & Ness, Judy. Student Success: How to Make It Happen. 2011. (978-1-61048-356-8(1)) Rowman & Littlefield Education.

Skoglund/Ness. Student Success: How to Make It Happen. 2011. 156p. pap. 26.95 (978-1-61048-355-1(3)) Rowman & Littlefield Education.

—Student Success: Tools to Make. 2011. (ENG.). 156p. 55.00 (978-1-61048-354-4(5)) Rowman & Littlefield Education.

Slavin, Robert E., et al. 2 Million Children: Success for All. 2nd ed. 2008. (Illus.). 408p. 95.95 (978-1-4129-5307-8(3), B53073C); pap. 44.95 (978-1-4129-5308-5(1), B53073P) Corwin Pr.

Smith-Collins, Searetha. An Agenda for Equity: Responding to the Needs of Diverse Learners. 2011. (ENG.). 156p. (gr. 17). 70.00 (978-1-61048-723-8(0)); pap. 25.95 (978-1-61048-724-5(9)) Rowman & Littlefield Education.

—An Agenda for Equity: Responding to the Needs of Diverse Learners. 2012. (978-1-61048-725-2(7)) Rowman & Littlefield Publishers, Inc.

Smith, Douglas W. Using What We Know: A Practical Guide to Increasing Student Achievement. 2009. 108p. pap. 27.95 (978-1-4327-4172-3(1)) Outskirts Pr., Inc.

Smith, Peter. Harnessing America's Wasted Talent: A New Ecology of Learning. 2010. (ENG.). 208p. 40.00 (978-0-470-53807-4(4), Jossey-Bass) Wiley, John & Sons, Inc.

Smith, Robert G. Gaining on the Gap: Changing Hearts, Minds, & Practice. 2011. (Illus.). (ENG.). 204p. pap. 28.95 (978-1-61048-289-9(1)); xii, 192p. (978-1-61048-290-5(5)) Rowman & Littlefield Education.

Smith, Robert G., et al. Gaining on the Gap: Changing Hearts, Minds, & Practice. 2011. (ENG., Illus.). 204p. 65.00 (978-1-61048-288-2(3)) Rowman & Littlefield Education.

Snodgrass, Dawn M. & Bevevino, Mary M. The ABCs of College Success-Information, Inspiration, & Just Plain Fun: Information Inspiration & Just Plain Fun. 2007. (ENG.). 72p. pap. 19.95 (978-0-9788140-1-4(0)) MDJ Dickens, Ltd.

Snow, Catherine E., et al. Is Literacy Enough? Pathways to Academic Success for Adolescents. 2007. (Illus.). 153p. per. 29.95 (978-1-55766-914-8(7)) Brookes, Paul H. Publishing Co.

Sosniak, Lauren A. & Hersh Gabelko, Nina. Every Child's Right: Academic Talent Development by Choice, Not Chance. 2008. (ENG.). 176p. (C). (978-0-8077-4871-8(4)) Teachers College Pr., Teachers College, Columbia Univ.

Soto-Hinman, Ivannia & Hetzel, June, eds. The Literacy Gaps: Bridge-Building Strategies for English Language Learners & Standard English Learners. 2009. (Illus.). 272p. 90.95 (978-1-4129-7520-9(4), B75209C); pap. 39.95 (978-1-4129-7521-6(2), B75209P) Corwin Pr.

St. John, Edward, et al. Breaking Through the Access Barrier: How Academic Capital Formation Can Improve Policy in Higher Education. 2010. (ENG., Illus.). 296p. pap. 44.95 (978-0-415-80033-4(1)) Routledge

St. John, Edward P. & Droogsma Musoba, Glenda. Pathways to Academic Success in Higher Education: Expanding Opportunity for Underrepresented Students. (ENG., Illus.) 316p. 2012. pap. 44.95 (978-0-415-53868-8(8)) 2010. 135.00 (978-0-415-87525-7(0)) Routledge.

Starkman, Neal, et al. Great Places to Learn: Creating Asset-Building Schools That Help Students Succeed. 2nd ed. 2006. (ENG., Illus.). 216p. pap. 34.95 (978-1-57482-245-8(4)) Search Institute.

Steele, Jennifer L., et al. Incorporating Student Performance Measures into Teacher Evaluation Systems. 2011. 55p. pap. 21.50 (978-0-8330-5250-6(0)) RAND Corp., The.

Steineke, Nancy. Assessment Live! 10 Real-Time Ways for Kids to Show What They Know — & Meet the Standards. 2009. 256p. pap. 30.63 (978-0-325-02177-5(5), E02177) Heinemann.

Steingass, Jon & Sykes, Seth. Soaring to New Heights: Modifying Your MINDSET to Leave Academic Difficulty Behind. 2007. (ENG.). 189p. (C). pap. 51.40 (978-0-536-51265-6(3)) Pearson Learning Solutions.

Strike, Kimberly T. Mentoring the Educational Leader: A Practical Framework for Success. 2011. E-Book (978-1-61048-287-5(5)); (ENG.). 160p. pap. 24.95 (978-1-61048-286-8(7)) Rowman & Littlefield Education.

Strong, Michael. The Highly Qualified Teacher: What Is Teacher Quality & How Do We Measure it? 2011. (Illus.). 168p. 27.95 (978-0-8077-5226-5(6)); pap. 27.95 (978-0-8077-5225-8(8)) Teachers College Pr., Teachers College, Columbia Univ.

Stronge, James H. Effective Teachers = Student Achievement: What the Research Says. 2010. 29.95 (978-1-59667-154-6(8)) Eye On Education, Inc.

Stronge, James H., et al. Student Achievement Goal Setting: Using Data to Improve Teaching & Learning. 2009. (ENG.). 160p. pap. 34.95 (978-1-59667-114-0(9)) Eye On Education, Inc.

Suárez-Orozco, Carola, et al. Learning a New Land: Immigrant Students in American Society. 2010. (Illus.). 440p. pap. 19.95 (978-0-674-04580-4(7), Belknap Pr.) Harvard Univ. Pr.

Swanson Ed.D, Charles H. F Means Floundering: A Guide to Becoming an Efficient & Effective Student. 2007. 144p. (ENG.). 23.95 (978-0-595-69636-9(8)); per. 13.95 (978-0-595-45548-5(4)) iUniverse, Inc.

Sweeney, Diane. Student-Centered Coaching: Coaches & Principals. 2010. (Illus.). 232p. pap. 36.95 (978-1-4129-8043-2(7), B80432P) Corwin Pr.

Systemic Research. AIHEC AIMS Fact Book 2005: Tribal Colleges & Universities Report, 1 vol. 2006. (Illus.). 215p. per. (978-0-9761402-3-8(3)) Systemic Research, Inc.

Szarlan, John, et al. Striving for Excellence: A Manual for Goal Achievement. 2010. (ENG.). 288p. (C). pap. 39.40 (978-0-13-700519-2(9), Prentice Hall) Prentice Hall PTR.

Tankersley, Karen. Tests That Teach: Using Standardized Tests to Improve Instruction. 2007. 176p. per. 23.95 (978-1-4166-0579-9(7)) Assn. for Supervision & Curriculum Development.

Taylor, Catherine S. . & Nolen, Susan Bobbitt. Classroom Assessment: Supporting Teaching & Learning in Real Classrooms. 2nd ed. 2007. (ENG., Illus.). 552p. (C). per. 96.40 (978-0-13-233554-6(9), Prentice Hall) Prentice Hall PTR.

Taylor, Cyril, et al. A Good School for Every Child. 2009. (Illus.). 212p. pap. 37.95 (978-0-415-48253-0(4)) Taylor & Francis Group.

Taylor, Rosemarye T., ed. Leading Learning: Change Student Achievement Today! 2009. (Illus.). 152p. pap. 28.95 (978-1-4129-7870-5(X), B78705P) Corwin Pr.

Teach for America Staff & Farr, Steven. Teaching As Leadership: The Highly Effective Teacher's Guide to Closing the Achievement Gap. 2010. (ENG., Illus.). 352p. pap. 22.95 (978-0-470-43286-0(1), Jossey-Bass) Wiley, John & Sons, Inc.

Teaching & Counseling Youths: Ways to Succeed in Life. 2006. (YA). pap. 5.95 (978-0-9661598-8-2(8)) Ekwike Bks. & Publishing.

Templeton, Beth Lind. Understanding Poverty in the Classroom: Changing Perceptions for Student Success. 2011. (ENG.). 114p. 40.00 (978-1-61048-363-6(4)); pap. 19.95 (978-1-61048-364-3(2)) Rowman & Littlefield Education.

Tennant, Noah. Black Students, White Schools- Caught Between Two Worlds. 2007. 152p. per. (978-3-8364-2867-5(9)) VDM Verlag Dr. Mueller e.K.

Teranishi, Robert T. Asians in the Ivory Tower: Dilemmas of Racial Inequality in American Higher Education. 2010. (Multicultural Education Ser.). (ENG., Illus.). 216p. 68.00 (978-0-8077-5131-2(6)); pap. 31.95 (978-0-8077-5130-5(8)) Teachers College Pr., Teachers College, Columbia Univ.

Thanh, Duong Van. Family,Community-Based Social Capital & Education in Viet Nam. 2010. 276p. pap. (978-3-8383-0308-6(3)) Lambert Academic Publishing.

Thayer, Scott. Where You from? - the Impact of a Trio Upward Bound Program on the Academic Achievement of African-American Male Students. 2008. 184p. pap. (978-3-639-02625-2(X)) VDM Verlag Dr. Mueller e.K.

Thiam, Pascal. I Play in the School Band therefore, I am Smart: Effects of School Band Experience on the Motivation of High School Students. 2008. 140p. pap. (978-3-639-09898-3(6)) VDM Verlag Dr. Mueller e.K.

Ting, Siu-Man. Structured Groups for Non-Traditional College Students: Noncognitive Assessment & Strategies. 2008. (ENG.). 120p. pap. 26.50 (978-0-7618-3975-0(5)) Univ. Pr. of America, Inc.

Tovani, Cris. So What Do They Really Know? Assessment That Informs Teaching & Learning. 2011. (ENG.). 184p. (C). (gr. 6-12). pap. 22.50 (978-1-57110-730-5(4)); E-Book (978-1-57110-918-7(8)) Stenhouse Pubs.

Tree of Knowledge Press: We Educate Children One Child at a Time. Learn English for Japanese Students: The Language of Global Communication. 2012. (ENG.). 180p. per. 21.99 (978-1-885872-56-2(9)) Tree of Knowledge Pr.

Troy, Terry. The Effects of after-School Programs on Student Achievement: A Research Study. 2011. 116p. pap. (978-3-639-32727-4(6)) VDM Verlag Dr. Mueller e.K.

Turner, Philip M., et al. Next Generation Course Redesign. 2010. (Illus.). 152p. (C). pap. 29.95 (978-1-4331-0681-1(7)) Lang, Peter Publishing, Inc.

Tuttle, Harry Grover. Formative Assessment in Your Classroom: Responding to Your Students. 2008. (ENG.). 160p. pap. 34.95 (978-1-59667-096-9(7)) Eye On Education, Inc.

Tyre, Peg. The Trouble with Boys: A Surprising Report Card on Our Sons, Their Problems at School, & What Parents & Educators Must Do. 2009. (ENG.). 320p. pap. 15.00 (978-0-307-38129-3(3), Three Rivers Pr.) Crown Publishing Group.

Tyson, Karolyn, ed. Integration Interrupted: Tracking, Black Students, & Acting White after Brown. 2011. (ENG., Illus.). 256p. pap. 24.95 (978-0-19-973645-4(6)) Oxford Univ. Pr., Inc.

United States, Congress Senate Committee on Health, Education, Labor, and Pensions Subcommittee on Education and Early Childhood Development Staff, contrib. by. A Fresh Start for New Orleans' Children: Improving Education after Katrina: Hearing Before the Subcommittee on Education & Early Childhood Development of the Committee on Health, Education, Labor, & Pensions, United States Senate, One Hundred Ninth Congress, Second Session, on Examining the Education System of New Orleans, July 14, 2006 (New Orleans, LA) 2007. (Illus.). iii, 72p. (978-0-16-078208-4(2), 552-070-35592-8) United States Government Printing Office.

Uppal, Preena, et al. Cause & Effect of School Absenteeism in Children. 2011. 80p. pap. (978-3-8443-3348-0(7)) Lambert Academic Publishing.

Valeem, Irfan Elahi, et al. The Effect of Socioeconomic Status on Academic Achievements in Science: Special Reference to Students Studying in Intermediate Part-I. 2011. 144p. pap. (978-3-639-33304-6(7)) VDM Verlag Dr. Mueller e.K.

Valverde, Carlos. Engaging Latino Communities for Education: Closing the Achievement Gap. 2008. (Illus.). 11p. (978-1-58024-497-8(1)) National Conference of State Legislatures.

Van Blerkom, Dianna L. Taking Charge of Your Learning: A Guide to College Success. 2007. (ENG., Illus.). 312p. (C). per. 69.95 (978-0-534-53949-8(1)) Wadsworth.

van der Graaf, Vanessa Khankeo & Van Der Graaf, Vanessa Khankeo. Extended & Conventional Year School: Effects on Academic Achievement. 2010. 108p. pap. (978-3-8383-4259-7(3)) Lambert Academic Publishing.

Varnava-Marouchou, Despina. Can Conceptions of Teaching Influence Conceptions of Learning? 2010. 300p. pap. (978-3-639-23445-9(6)) VDM Verlag Dr. Mueller e.K.

Vegas, Emiliana & Petrow, Jenny. Raising Student Learning in Latin America: The Challenge for the 21st Century. 2007. (Latin American Development Forum Ser.). (ENG., Illus.). 262p. per. 30.00 (978-0-8213-7082-7(0), 9780821370827) World Bank Pubns.

Vequist, David G., et al. Capstone & Experiential Class Workbook. rev. ed. 2009. (ENG.). 86p. spiral bd. 66.00 (978-0-7575-6264-8(7)) Kendall Hunt Publishing Co.

Vinella, Michael. Student Achievement - the Relationship Between Student Achievement & the Scores on the Learning Organization Survey. 2008. 184p. pap. (978-3-639-01914-8(8)) VDM Verlag Dr. Mueller e.K.

Waggoner, et al. Strategies for Academic Success. 4th rev. ed. 2011. (ENG.). 438p. spiral bd. 55.50 (978-0-7575-8980-5(4)) Kendall Hunt Publishing Co.

Waggoner, Reneau & Galyon, Maria. Stratgies for Academic Success. 3rd rev. ed. 2009. (ENG.). 428p. pap. 60.50 (978-0-7575-6333-1(3)) Kendall Hunt Publishing Co.

Walberg, Herbert J. Advancing Youth Accomplishments & Learning. 2010. (Hoover inst press Publication). (ENG.). 117p. 25.00 (978-0-8179-4951-8(8)); pap. 15.00 (978-0-8179-4952-5(6)) Hoover Institution Pr.

Wallace, Belle, et al. Practical Strategies for Raising the Achievement of Able Pupils: Inclusive Schools Sharing Best Practice. 2009. (ENG., Illus.). 212p. pap. 35.95 (978-0-415-54949-3(3)) Routledge.

—Raising the Achievement of All Pupils Within an Inclusive Setting: Practical Strategies for Developing Best Practice. 2009. (ENG., Illus.). 212p. 120.00 (978-0-415-54948-6(5)) Routledge.

Walters, Sue. Ethnicity, Race & Education: An Introduction. 2012. (ENG.). 192p. 130.00 (978-1-4411-7673-8(X)); pap. 39.95 (978-1-84706-232-1(6)) Continuum International Publishing Group, Ltd. GBR. Dist: National Bk. Network.

Wamba, Nathalis. Exit Narratives: Reflections of Four Retired Teachers. 2010. (ENG.). 160p. pap. 26.50 (978-0-7618-5115-8(1)) Univ. Pr. of America, Inc.

Wankel, Charles & DeFillippi, Bob. University & Corporate Innovations in Lifelong Learning. 2008. (Research in Management Education & Development Ser.). (Illus.). 288p. (C). (978-1-59311-810-5(4)); per. (978-1-59311-809-9(0)) Information Age Publishing, Inc.

Ward, Peter. Strategies to Improve Student Achievement. 2009. 212p. pap. (978-3-639-14153-5(9)) VDM Verlag Dr. Mueller e.K.

Warikoo, Natasha Kumar. Balancing Acts: Youth Culture in the Global City. 2011. (ENG.) 296p. 55.00 (978-0-520-26210-2(7)); pap. 21.95 (978-0-520-26211-9(5)) Univ. of California Pr.

Warner, Donald D. ABC's: A Booty Call: Naked Educational Truth. 2011. 294p. pap. 21.95 (978-1-4327-7028-0(4)) Outskirts Pr., Inc.

Warner-Prokos, LuAnn, et al. Study Skills Tool Kit. 2008. (ENG., Illus.). 80p. (gr. 4-10). pap. 15.95 (978-0-9777760-2-3(6)) Palm Tree Educational Pr.

Warring, William H., Jr. Leaving No Child Behind: A Teacher's Model for Meeting the Challenges of the No Child Left Behind. 2008. 196p. pap. 27.95 (978-0-9815414-0-2(2)) Warring & Assocs. Pubs.

Watanabe, Maika, ed. Heterogenius Classrooms: Detracking Math & Science — A Look at Groupwork in Action. 2012. (ENG.). 100p. 36.95 (978-0-8077-5246-3(0)) Teachers College Pr., Teachers College, Columbia Univ.

Weems, Denise. Raising Student Achievement. 2010. 160p. pap. (978-3-8383-0009-2(2)) Lambert Academic Publishing.

Weert, Egbert de. The Changing Face of Academic Life: Analytical & Comparative Perspectives. Enders, Jürgen et al, eds. 2009. (Issues in Higher Education Ser.). (ENG., Illus.). 272p. 100.00 (978-0-230-52103-2(7)) Palgrave Macmillan.

Were, Charles M. The Relationship Between Self-Concept & Achievement in Maths. 2010. 76p. pap. (978-3-639-27496-7(2)) VDM Verlag Dr. Mueller e.K.

Western Michigan University Staff. Western Michigan University: First Year Experience: A Customized Version of Thriving in College & Beyond: Research-Based Strategies for Academic Success & Personal Development by Joseph B. Cuseo. rev. ed. 2011. (ENG.). 248p. spiral bd. 48.95 (978-0-7575-9411-3(5)) Kendall Hunt Publishing Co.

Westphal, R. Chris, et al. Culturally Proficient Inquiry: A Lens for Identifying & Examining Educational Gaps. Graham, Stephanie M. et al, eds. 2008. (Illus.). 256p. 80.95 (978-1-4129-2601-0(7), B26017C) Corwin Pr.

White, Stephen H. Leadership Maps. 2010. 248p. pap. 24.95 (978-1-933196-93-0(9)) Lead+Learn Pr.

Whitinui, Paul. The Indigenous Factor. 2008. 220p. pap. (978-3-639-10797-5(7)) VDM Verlag Dr. Mueller e.K.

Whitley, Renee Y. Mcgee. Mr & Mrs Sunflower & the World Around Them. 2009. (J). (978-1-61623-479-9(2)) Independent Pub.

Whittle, Thomas. Accreditation: A Hands-on Approach for Principals. 2007. 60p. per. 16.95 (978-1-4241-7664-9(6)) PublishAmerica, Inc.

Wiggan, Greg, ed. Power, Privilege & Education: Pedagogy, Curriculum & Student Outcomes. 2013. (Illus.). xvii, 189p. 75.00 (978-1-61209-627-8(1)) Nova Science Pubs., Inc.

Wilcox, Kristen C. & Angelis, Janet I. Best Practices from High-Performing High Schools: How Successful Schools Help Students Stay in School & Thrive. 2011. (Illus.). 144p. (ENG.). 58.00 (978-0-8077-5169-5(3)); pap. 26.95 (978-0-8077-5168-8(5)) Teachers College Pr., Teachers College, Columbia Univ.

Wiliam, Dylan. Embedded Formative Assessment. 2011. 200p. pap. 29.95 (978-1-934009-30-7(X)); lib. bdg. 54.95 (978-1-935249-33-7(9)) Solution Tree Pr.

Wilkins, Rhonda. Swimming Upstream. 2008. 248p. pap. (978-3-8364-7843-4(9)) VDM Verlag Dr. Mueller e.K.

Williams, Angela. Christian Spirituality Manifested in African American Students: Christian Spirituality Impacts the Academic Attitudes & Behaviors of African American Students. 2008. 108p. pap. (978-3-639-09078-9(0)) VDM Verlag Dr. Mueller e.K.

Williams, Tony G. Reaching Algebra Readiness: Preparing Middle School Students to Succeed in Algebra - the Gateway to Career Success. 2011. 182p. (978-94-6091-508-6(6)); pap. (978-94-6091-507-9(8)) Sense Pubs.

Wilson, Gary & Wilson, Gary B. Breaking Through Barriers to Boys' Achievement: Developing a Caring Masculinity. 2007. (ENG., Illus.). 152p. per. 49.95 (978-1-85539-211-3(9), Network Continuum Education) Continuum International Publishing Group, Ltd. GBR. Dist: National Bk. Network.

Wilson, Leslie Walker. Improving Your Elementary School: Ten Aligned Steps for Administrators, Teams, Teachers, Families, & Students. 2006. (ENG., Illus.). 150p. pap. 29.95 (978-1-59667-036-5(3)) Eye On Education, Inc.

Winebrenner, Susan & Brulles, Dina. The Cluster Grouping Handbook: How to Challenge Gifted Students & Improve Achievement for All. 2008. (ENG., Illus.). 224p. (gr. k-8). 39.99 (978-1-57542-279-4(4)) Free Spirit Publishing, Inc.

Witter, Raymond W. Classroom Assessment for Teachers. 2011. (ENG., Illus.). 448p. (C). pap. 98.33 (978-0-07-337870-1(4), 0073378704) McGraw-Hill Cos., The.

Woessmann, Ludger, et al. School Accountability, Autonomy & Choice Around the World. 2009. (IFO Economic Policy Ser.). (Illus.). 160p. 119.00 (978-1-84844-529-1(6)) Elgar, Edward Publishing, Inc.

Wong, Ovid K. High Poverty, High Performing Schools. 2011. (ENG.). 116p. 55.00 (978-1-60709-789-1(3)) Rowman & Littlefield Education.

—High Poverty High Performing Schools. 2011. (ENG.). 116p. pap. 22.95 (978-1-60709-790-7(7)) Rowman & Littlefield Education.

—High-Poverty, High-Performing Schools: Foundations for Real Student Success. 2011. (978-1-60709-791-4(5)) Rowman & Littlefield Education.

Woodrow, George. The Instructional Leadership Pyramid. rev. ed. 2010. (ENG.). 240p. pap. 65.55 (978-0-7575-7645-4(1)) Kendall Hunt Publishing Co.

Wylie, Elizabeth Caroline, et al. Improving Formative Assessment Practice to Empower Student Learning. 2012. 160p. pap. 31.95 (978-1-4129-9701-0(1), B97010P) Corwin Pr.

Wynn, Mychal. Increasing Achievement & Inspiring Family Involvement. Bascome, Glenn, ed. 2011. (Illus.). 160p. pap. (978-1-880463-20-8(2)) Rising Sun Publishing, Inc.

Yayan, Betül. A Cross-Cultural Comparison of Mathematics Achievement. 2010. 132p. pap. (978-3-8383-4173-6(2)) Lambert Academic Publishing.

Yeh, Stuart S. The Cost-Effectiveness of 22 Approaches for Raising Student Achievement. 2011. 85.99 (978-1-61735-403-8(1)); pap. (978-1-61735-402-1(3)); E-Book (978-1-61735-404-5(X)) Information Age Publishing, Inc.

Yeh, Stuart S. Raising Student Achievement Through Rapid Assessment & Test Reform. 2006. (ENG., Illus.). 208p. pap. 26.95 (978-0-8077-4723-0(8)); 53.00 (978-0-8077-4724-7(6)) Teachers College Pr., Teachers College, Columbia Univ.

Yossi, Shavit & Richard, Arum, eds. Stratification in Higher Education: A Comparative Study. 2010. (Studies in Social Inequality Ser.). (ENG., Illus.). 504p. pap. 29.95 (978-0-8047-7152-8(9)) Stanford Univ. Pr.

Yuan, Kun, et al. Strengthening Mental Muscles: Impact of Computerized Cognitive Training on Working Memory, Fluid Intelligence, & Science Achievement. 2008. 124p. pap. (978-3-639-10072-3(7)) VDM Verlag Dr. Mueller e.K.

Yusuf, Muhammed. A Study of Integrated Motivational Models. 2011. 184p. pap. **(978-3-8443-1562-2(4))** Lambert Academic Publishing.

Zamani-Gallaher, Eboni M. & Polite, Vernon C. The State of the African American Male. Campbell, Alec, ed. 2010. (CourageousConversations series Ser.). (ENG.). 303p. pap. 29.95 *(978-0-87013-870-6(7))* Michigan State Univ. Pr.

Zimmerman, Barry J. & Schunk, Dale H., eds. Handbook of Self-Regulation of Learning & Performance. 2011. (Educational Psychology Handbook Ser.). (ENG., Illus.). 504p. 295.00 *(978-0-415-87111-2(5))*; pap. 114.95 *(978-0-415-87112-9(3))* Routledge.

Zmuda, Allison. Breaking Free from Myths about Teaching & Learning: Innovation as an Engine for Student Success. 2010. 196p. pap. 26.95 *(978-1-4166-1091-5(X))* Assn. for Supervision & Curriculum Development.

Zyngier, David. Engaging Pedagogies & Pedagogues. 2010. 308p. pap. *(978-3-8383-5676-1(4))* Lambert Academic Publishing.

ACADEMIC ADJUSTMENT

see Student Adjustment

ACADEMIC ADVISING

see Counseling in Higher Education

ACADEMIC COSTUME

Boria, Arianna, ed. Mila e la Notte: Abiti da Sera di Mila Schon 1966-1993. 2010. (ITA.). 160p. pap. 54.00 *(978-88-370-7486-9(7))* Electa ITA. Dist: Trans-Atlantic Pubns., Inc.

MacDonald, Cecily Glowik & LaBarre, Melissa. Weekend Hats: 25 Knitted Caps, Berets, Cloches, & More. 2011. (ENG., Illus.). 128p. pap. 22.95 *(978-1-59668-438-6(0))* Interweave Pr., LLC.

Schiller, Robert. Schirmmützen: Imperial German Cavalry Field Service Caps. 2010. (Illus.). 192p. 59.99 *(978-0-7643-3528-0(6))* Schiffer Publishing, Ltd.

ACADEMIC DEGREES

see Degrees, Academic

ACADEMIC DISSERTATIONS

see Dissertations, Academic

ACADEMIC ETIQUETTE

Twale, Darla J. & De Luca, Barbara M. Faculty Incivility: The Rise of the Academic Bully Culture & What to Do about It. 2008. (JB - Anker Ser.: 128). (ENG.). 240p. 42.00 *(978-0-470-19766-0(8))*, Jossey-Bass) Wiley, John & Sons, Inc.

ACADEMIC FAILURE

see School Failure

ACADEMIC FREEDOM

Here are entered comprehensive works on the freedom of the members of the academic community to carry on their functions, including the right to teach, learn, communicate, publish, conduct research, etc.

see also Loyalty Oaths; Students—Legal Status, Laws, etc.; Teaching, Freedom of

Abraham, Matthew. Out of Bounds: Academic Freedom & the Question of Palestine. 2012. (ENG.). 256p. 80.00 *(978-0-7453-2767-9(2))*; pap. 29.95 *(978-0-7453-2766-2(4))* Pluto Pr. GBR. Dist: Macmillan.

Aby, Stephen H., ed. The Academic Bill of Rights Debate: A Handbook, 1 vol. 2007. 248p. 39.95 *(978-0-275-99244-6(6)*, C9244, Praeger Pubs.) Greenwood Publishing Group, Inc.

American Association of University Professors Staff. AAUP Policy Documents & Reports. 10th rev. ed. 2006. (ENG.). 342p. (gr. 17). per. 30.00 *(978-0-9649548-3-0(4))* American Assn. of Univ. Professors.

Angus, Ian. Love the Questions: University Education & Enlightenment. 2009. (ENG., Illus.). 176p. pap. 14.95 *(978-1-894037-40-2(5))* Arbeiter Ring Publishing CAN. Dist: AK Pr. Distribution.

Asgedom, Amare. Academic Freedom in Higher Education of Ethiopi. 2011. 232p. pap. **(978-3-8454-2212-1(2))** Lambert Academic Publishing.

Bidwell, Paul T. & Findlay, L. M., eds. Pursuing Academic Freedom: Free & Fearless ? 2006. 248p. *(978-1-895830-18-7(4))* Purich Publishing.

Carvalho, Edward J. & Downing, David B., eds. Academic Freedom in the Post-9/11 Era. (Education, Politics & Public Life Ser.). (ENG., Illus.). 310p. 2011. pap. 28.00 *(978-0-230-11700-6(7))* 2010. 95.00 *(978-0-230-10834-9(2))* Palgrave Macmillan.

Castagnera, James. Al-Qaeda Goes to College: Impact of the War on Terror on American Higher Education, 1 vol. 2009. (Illus.). 204p. 49.95 *(978-0-313-36428-0(1)*, C36428, Praeger Pubs.) Greenwood Publishing Group, Inc.

Chachage, Chachage Seithy L., ed. Academic Freedom & the Social Responsibilities of Academics in Tanzani. 2008. 104p. pap. *(978-2-86978-243-3(8))* Council for the Development of Social Science Research in Africa SEN. Dist: Michigan State Univ. Pr.

Comstock, Michelle, et al. Composing Public Space: Teaching Writing in the Face of Private Interests. 2010. 160p. pap. 26.25 *(978-0-86709-598-2(9)*, 0598) Heinemann.

Currie, Jan, et al. Academic Freedom in Hong Kong. 2006. (ENG., Illus.). 204p. 73.50 *(978-0-7391-1081-2(0))* Lexington Bks.

Downs, Donald Alexander. Restoring Free Speech & Liberty on Campus. 2006. (ENG., Illus.). 318p. per. 24.99 *(978-0-521-68971-7(6))* Cambridge Univ. Pr.

Finkin, Matthew W. & Post, Robert C. For the Common Good: Principles of American Academic Freedom. 2011. (ENG.). 272p. pap. 20.00 *(978-0-300-17752-7(6))* Yale Univ. Pr.

Gerstmann, Evan & Streb, Matthew, eds. Academic Freedom at the Dawn of a New Century: How Terrorism, Governments, & Culture Wars Impact Free Speech. 2006. (ENG.). 260p. per. 24.95 *(978-0-8047-5980-9(4))* Stanford Univ. Pr.

Gregg, Judd, ed. Is Intellectual Diversity an Endangered Species on America's College Campuses? Congressional Hearing. 2006. (Illus.). 57p. (C). reprint ed. pap. 20.00 *(978-1-4223-0623-9(2))* DIANE Publishing Co.

Hamdan, Marwan. Drittmittelforschung in der Medizin: Eine Gratwanderung zwischen strafbarer Vorteilsannahme und verfassungsgarantierter Forschungsfreiheit. 2009. (Schriften zum Strafrecht und Strafprozeßrecht Ser.). (GER.). 152p. pap. 49.95 *(978-3-631-58092-9(4))* Lang, Peter GmbH, Europaischer Verlag der Wissenschaften DEU. Dist: Lang, Peter.

Hilwig, Stuart J. Italy And 1968: Youthful Unrest & Democratic Culture. 2009. (ENG., Illus.). 248p. 89.00 *(978-0-230-57568-4(4))* Palgrave Macmillan.

Holliday, H. E. Boys Transitioning fro Athletic Aggression to Academinc Affirmation. 2010. pap. 24.95 *(978-1-61623-862-9(3))* Independent Pub.

—Boys Transitioning from Athletic Aggression to Academic Affirmation. 2010. pap. 19.95 *(978-1-61623-559-8(4))* Independent Pub.

Horowitz, David. Indoctrination U: The Left's War Against Academic Freedom. 2007. (ENG.). 175p. 21.95 *(978-1-59403-190-8(8))* Encounter Bks.

—Indoctrination U. The Left's War Against Academic Freedom. 2009. (ENG.). 170p. pap. 17.95 *(978-1-59403-237-0(8))* Encounter Bks.

Jones, Barbara M. Protecting Intellectual Freedom in Your Academic Library: Scenarios from the Front Lines. 2009. 256p. 55.00 *(978-0-8389-3580-4(X))* American Library Assn.

Kingsbury, Henry. The Secret Trial of Brown University: April 26-May 5, 2004. 2008. (Illus.). 135p. pap. **(978-0-9769269-1-7(1)**, Full Quart Pr.) Holly Hall Pubns., Inc.

Klaw, Elena. Mentoring & Making It in Academe. 2008. (ENG.). 86p. pap. 24.50 *(978-0-7618-4437-2(6))* Univ. Pr. of America, Inc.

LaRue, James. The New Inquisition: Understanding & Managing Intellectual Freedom Challenges, 1 vol. 2007. (Illus.). 172p. per. 40.00 *(978-1-59158-285-4(7)*, LU2857) Libraries Unlimited, Inc.

Laughlin, Robert B. The Crime of Reason: And the Closing of the Scientific Mind. 2010. (ENG.). 192p. (gr. 9). pap. 15.95 *(978-0-465-02028-7(3))* Basic Bks.

Lea, John. Political Correctness & Higher Education: British & American Perspectives. 2008. (Illus.). XII, 284p. 48.95 *(978-0-415-96259-9(5))*; 155.00 *(978-0-415-96258-2(7))* Routledge.

Lefkowitz, Mary. History Lesson: A Race Odyssey. 2009. (ENG.). 208p. pap. 17.50 *(978-0-300-15126-8(8))* Yale Univ. Pr.

Moshman, David. Liberty & Learning: Academic Freedom for Teachers & Students. 2009. 176p. pap. 24.38 *(978-0-325-02121-8(X)*, E02121) Heinemann.

Nelson, Cary. No University Is an Island: Saving Academic Freedom. (ENG.). 2011. 304p. pap. 24.00 **(978-0-8147-2533-7(3))** 2010. 288p. 65.00 *(978-0-8147-5859-5(2))* New York Univ. Pr.

Nocella, Anthony J., II, et al, eds. Academic Repression: Reflections from the Academic Industrial Complex. 2010. (ENG.). 600p. pap. 24.95 *(978-1-904859-98-7(4))* AK Pr. GBR. Dist: Consortium Bk. Sales & Distribution.

Office for Intellectual Freedom. Intellectual Freedom Manual. 8th ed. 2010. 512p. 65.00 *(978-0-8389-3590-3(7))* American Library Assn.

O'Neil, Robert M. Academic Freedom in the Wired World: Political Extremism, Corporate Power, & the University. 2008. 320p. 40.50 *(978-0-674-02660-5(8))* Harvard Univ. Pr.

Pan, Su Yan. University Autonomy, the State, & Social Change in China. 2009. (Education in China: Reform & Diversity Ser.). (ENG.). 276p. (gr. 17). 50.00 *(978-962-209-936-4(X))* Hong Kong Univ. Pr. HKG. Dist: Columbia Univ. Pr.

Pappé, Ilan. Out of the Frame: The Struggle for Academic Freedom in Israel, 1 vol. 2010. (ENG.). 224p. pap. 22.00 *(978-0-7453-2725-9(7))* Pluto Pr. GBR. Dist: Macmillan.

Paradeise, Catherine. University Governance: Western European Comparative Perspectives. 2009. (Higher Education Dynamics Ser.). (Illus.). 332p. 149.00 *(978-1-4020-8637-3(7))* Springer.

Philipsen, Maike Ingrid & Bostic, Timothy B. Helping Faculty Find Work-Life Balance: The Path Toward Family-Friendly Institutions. 2010. (ENG.). 240p. 42.00 *(978-0-470-54095-4(8)*, Jossey-Bass) Wiley, John & Sons, Inc.

Post, Robert C. Democracy, Expertise, & Academic Freedom: A First Amendment Jurisprudence for the Modern State. 2012. (ENG.). 192p. 30.00 *(978-0-300-14863-3(1))* Yale Univ. Pr.

Rice, Charles E. What Happened to Notre Dame? 2009. (ENG.). 224p. pap. 15.00 *(978-1-58731-920-4(9))* St. Augustine's Pr., Inc.

Scatamburlo-D'Annibale, Valerie. Cold Breezes & Idiot Winds: Patriotic Correctness & the Post-9/11 Assault on Academe. 2011. 276p. **(978-94-6091-408-9(X))**; pap. **(978-94-6091-407-2(1))** Sense Pubs.

Schrecker, Ellen. The Lost Soul of Higher Education: Corporatization, the Assault on Academic Freedom, & the End of the American University. 2010. (ENG.). 304p. 27.95 *(978-1-59558-400-7(5))* New Pr., The.

Selverstone, Harriet S. Encouraging & Supporting Student Inquiry: Researching Controversial Issues, 1 vol. 2007. (Libraries Unlimited Professional Guides for Young Adult Librarians Ser.). (Illus.). 288p. per. 40.00 *(978-1-59158-496-4(5)*, LU4965) Libraries Unlimited, Inc.

Streb, Matthew J., ed. Academic Freedom at the Dawn of a New Century: How Terrorism, Governments, & Culture Wars Impact Free Speech. 2006. (ENG.). 260p. 55.00 *(978-0-8047-5444-6(6))* Stanford Univ. Pr.

Tight, Malcolm, ed. Autonomy in Social Science Research: The View from United Kingdom & Australian Universities. 2007. (International Perspectives on Higher Education Research Ser.). 244p. 111.95 *(978-0-7623-1405-8(2))* Emerald Group Publishing Ltd. GBR. Dist: Turpin Distribution Services Ltd.

Turk, James, ed. Universities at Risk: How Politics, Special Interests & Corporatization Threaten Academic Integrity. 2008. (ENG.). 416p. pap. 24.95 *(978-1-55277-040-5(0))* Lorimer, James & Co., Ltd., Pubs. CAN. Dist: Casemate Pubs. & Bk. Distributors, LLC.

Turk, James & Manson, Allan, eds. Free Speech in Fearful Times: After 9/11 in Canada, the U. S., Australia & Europe. 2007. (CAUT Ser.). 344p. pap. 24.95 *(978-1-55028-986-2(1))* Lorimer, James & Co., Ltd., Pubs. CAN. Dist: Casemate Pubs. & Bk. Distributors, LLC.

Weber, Max. Max Weber's Complete Writings on Academic & Political Vocations. 2008. 40.00 *(978-0-87586-549-2(6))*; 221p. pap. 24.95 *(978-0-87586-548-5(8))* Algora Publishing.

Wiarda, Howard. Military Brass vs. Civilian Academics at the National War College: A Clash of Cultures. 2011. (ENG.). 176p. 60.00 *(978-0-7391-5085-6(5))* Lexington Bks.

Wiarda, Howard J. Military Brass vs. Civilian Academics at the National War College: A Clash of Cultures. 2011. *(978-0-7391-5087-0(1))* Lexington Bks.

Wilson, John K. Patriotic Correctness: Academic Freedom & its Enemies. 2007. (Cultural Politics & the Promise of Democracy Ser.). (ENG.). 280p. 125.00 *(978-1-59451-193-6(4))* Paradigm Pubs.

Wilson, John K. & Starbuck, Gene H. Families in Context Study Guide. 2006. (ENG.). 160p. pap. 29.95 *(978-1-59451-199-8(3))* Paradigm Pubs.

Wilson, Todd & Wilson, John K. Patriotic Correctness: Academic Freedom & its Enemies. 2008. (Cultural Politics & the Promise of Democracy Ser.). (ENG.). 280p. pap. 38.95 *(978-1-59451-194-3(2))* Paradigm Pubs.

Wirth, Rex, et al, eds. What Is Wrong with Academia Today? Essays on the Politicization of American Education. 2008. xxxix, 300p. *(978-0-7734-4974-9(4))* Mellen, Edwin Pr., The.

Woodhouse, Howard Robert. Selling Out: Academic Freedom & the Corporate Market. 2009. (ENG.). 350p. (C). *(978-0-7735-3580-0(2))* McGill-Queen's Univ. Pr.

Zwerling, Philip, ed. The CIA on Campus: Essays on Academic Freedom & the National Security State. 2011. (ENG.). 254p. pap. 45.00 **(978-0-7864-6346-6(5))** McFarland & Co., Inc. Pubs.

ACADEMIC LIBRARIES

Works on academic libraries in special fields, such as law school libraries, are entered under headings for special libraries, e.g. Law Libraries; Business Libraries.

see also Junior College Libraries

also names of individual academic libraries and subdivision Libraries under names of individual educational institutions

Academic Librarianship in the 21st Century. 2009. 69.00 *(978-1-60456-865-3(8))* Nova Science Pubs., Inc.

The Academic Library Budget & Expenditures Report. Date not set. 125p. pap. 125.00 *(978-1-57440-002-1(9))* Primary Research Group.

Almquist, Sharon G. Distributed Learning & Virtual Librarianship, 1 vol. 300p. pap. 55.00 *(978-1-59158-906-8(1)*, A2246P); 2011. E-Book **(978-1-59158-907-5(X))** Libraries Unlimited, Inc.

Alvite, Luisa & Barrionuevo, Leticia. Libraries for Users: Services in academic Libraries. 2010. (Illus.). 200p. pap. 75.00 *(978-1-84334-595-4(1)*, Chandos Publishing) Woodhead Publishing Ltd. GBR. Dist: Neal-Schuman Pubs., Inc.

Applegate, Rachel. Managing the Small College Library, 1 vol. 2010. (Libraries Unlimited Library Management Collection). (Illus.). 349p. pap. 55.00 *(978-1-59158-917-4(7)*, A2252P) Libraries Unlimited, Inc.

—Managing the Small School Library. 2010. vii, 349p. E-Book *(978-1-59158-918-1(5))* Libraries Unlimited, Inc.

Arif, Muhammad. The Role of Libraries in Distance Education. 2010. 116p. pap. *(978-3-639-23000-0(0))* VDM Verlag Dr. Mueller e.K.

Aspatore Books Staff, compiled by. The Changing Role of Academic Law Librarianship: Leading Librarians on Teaching Legal Research Skills, Responding to Emerging Technologies, & Adapting to Changing Trends (Inside the Minds) 2008. (Inside the Minds Ser.). 220p. pap. 40.00 *(978-0-314-19410-7(X))* Aspatore Bks.

—How to Manage a Law School Library: Leading Librarians on Updating Resources, Managing Budgets, & Meeting Expectations (Inside the Minds) 2008. 180p. pap. 40.00 *(978-0-314-19411-4(8))* Aspatore Bks.

Association of College and Research Libraries, contrib. by. Sailing into the Future: Charting Our Destiny: Proceedings of the Thirteenth National Conference of the Association of College & Research Libraries, March 29-April 1, 2007, Baltimore, Maryland. 2007. (ENG., Illus.). 344p. per. *(978-0-8389-8419-2(3))* Assn. of College & Research Libraries.

Baldwin, David A., et al. Complete Guide for Supervisors of Student Employees in Today's Academic Libraries, 1 vol. 2007. 304p. pap. 50.00 *(978-1-59158-335-6(7)*, LU3357) Libraries Unlimited, Inc.

Bell, Steven J. & Shank, John D. Academic Librarianship by Design: A Blended Librarian's Guide to the Tools & Techniques. 2007. (Illus.). 181p. per. 50.00 *(978-0-8389-0939-3(6))* American Library Assn.

Bernstein, Alan. The Nether World of Academic Librarians. 2010. 96p. pap. *(978-3-8383-6988-4(2))* Lambert Academic Publishing.

Bivens-Tatum, Wayne. Libraries & the Enlightenment. 2012. (ENG.). pap. 25.00 *(978-1-936117-42-0(8)*, Library Juice Pr.) Litwin Bks., LLC.

Booth, Char. Informing Innovation: Tracking Student Interest in Emerging Library Technologies at Ohio University. 2009. (Illus.). iii, 136p. pap. *(978-0-8389-8526-7(2))* American Library Assn.

Brumley, Rebecca. The Academic Library Manager's Forms, Policies, & Procedures Handbook with CD-ROM. 2007. 11.50 *(978-1-55570-597-8(9))* Neal-Schuman Pubs., Inc.

Budd, John. Framing Library Instruction. 2009. pap. *(978-0-8389-8513-7(0))* Assn. of College & Research Libraries.

Building Area Studies Collections. 2007. (Beiträge Zum Buch- und Bibliothekswesen Ser.: Vol. 52). viii, 163p. *(978-3-447-05512-3(X))* Harrassowitz, Otto Verlag.

Cambridge Library Collection, 475 vols., Set. 2009. (ENG.). pap. 14250.00 *(978-1-108-00902-7(6))* Cambridge Univ. Pr.

Carr, Reg. The Academic Research Library in a Decade of Change. 2007. 200p. *(978-1-84334-246-5(4))*; (ENG.). pap. *(978-1-84334-245-8(6))* Woodhead Publishing Ltd. (Chandos Publishing).

Cheung, Ophelia, et al. New Approaches to E-Reserve: Linking Sharing & Streaming. 2010. (Illus.). 200p. pap. 75.00 *(978-1-84334-509-1(9)*, Chandos Publishing) Woodhead Publishing Ltd. GBR. Dist: Neal-Schuman Pubs., Inc.

Chowdhury, Salma. The Management of Academic Libraries. 2010. 352p. pap. *(978-3-8383-0481-6(0))* Lambert Academic Publishing.

Cohen, Laura B., ed. Library 2.0 Initiatives in Academic Libraries. 2007. 179p. pap. 35.00 *(978-0-8389-8452-9(5))* Assn. of College & Research Libraries.

Collection Development Issues in the Online Enviroment. 2006. (ENG., Illus.). 190p. per. 31.95 *(978-0-7890-3087-0(X))* Routledge.

Collection Development Issues in the Online Environment. 2006. (ENG., Illus.). 190p. 50.95 *(978-0-7890-3086-3(1))* Routledge.

Collins, Maria D. D. & Carr, Patrick L. Managing the Transition from Print to Electronic Journals & Resources: A Guide for Library & Information Professionals. 2008. (Routledge Studies in Library & Information Science). (ENG., Illus.). 392p. 143.00 *(978-0-7890-3336-9(4))* Routledge.

Collins, Maria D. D. & Carr, Patrick L., eds. Managing the Transition from Print to Electronic Journals & Resources: A Guide for Library & Information Professionals. 2008. (Routledge Studies in Library & Information Science). (Illus.). XVIII, 374p. *(978-0-7890-3337-6(2)*, Haworth Information Pr., The) Haworth Pr., Inc., The.

Connor, Elizabeth. An Introduction to Staff Development in Academic Libraries. 2009. (ENG., Illus.). 248p. 132.00 *(978-0-7890-3844-9(7))*; pap. 41.95 *(978-0-7890-3845-6(5))* Routledge.

Connor, Elizabeth, ed. An Introduction to Instructional Services in Academic Libraries. 2008. (ENG., Illus.). 320p. 132.00 *(978-0-7890-3707-7(6))*; pap. 45.95 *(978-0-7890-3708-4(4))* Routledge.

—An Introduction to Reference Services in Academic Libraries. 2006. (ENG., Illus.). 222p. (C). pap. 39.95 *(978-0-7890-2958-4(8))* Routledge.

—Introduction to Reference Services in Academic Libraries. 2006. (ENG., Illus.). 222p. 60.95 *(978-0-7890-2957-7(X))* Routledge.

Cook, Douglas & Cooper, Natasha, eds. Teaching Information Literacy Skills to Social Sciences Students & Practitioners: A Casebook of Applications. 2006. (Illus.). xvii, 289p. *(978-0-8389-8389-8(8))* Assn. of College & Research Libraries.

Cook, Douglas & Farmer, Lesley S. J. Using Qualitative Methods in Action Research: How Librarians Can Get to the Why of Data. 2011. pap. *(978-0-8389-8576-2(9))* Assn. of College & Research Libraries.

Courtney, Nancy. Academic Library Outreach: Beyond the Campus Walls, 1 vol. Courtney, Nancy, ed. 2008. 276p. pap. 45.00 *(978-1-59158-725-5(5)*, LU8725) Libraries Unlimited, Inc.

Dabas, K. C. Quality Management in Libraries. 2008. 272p. (C). 43.00 *(978-81-7000-548-3(5))* Ess Ess Pubns. IND. Dist: International Specialized Bk. Services.

Dale, Penny, et al, eds. University Libraries & Environments. 2011. (Illus.). 304p. 114.95 *(978-0-7546-7957-8(8))* Ashgate Publishing Co.

Dalston, Teresa R. & Pullin, Michael, eds. Virtual Reference on a Budget: Case Studies, 1 vol. 2007. (Illus.). 192p. pap. 39.95 *(978-1-58683-287-2(5)*, A2460P) Linworth Publishing, Inc.

Day, Joan & Hanson, Terry. Managing the Electronic Library: A Practical Guide for Information Professionals. (ENG.). 300p. **(978-3-11-182008-6(4))** Saur, K. G. Verlag GmbH & Co.

Deuink, Amy & Seiler, Marianne. The Library Student Advisory Board: Why Your Academic Library Needs It & How to Make It Work. 2009. (ENG., Illus.). 207p. pap. 49.95 *(978-0-7864-3560-9(7))* McFarland & Co., Inc. Pubs.

Diamond, Tom. Middle Management in Academic & Public Libraries. 2011. (Illus.). xi, 233p. E-Book *(978-1-59884-690-4(6))* Libraries Unlimited, Inc.

Diamond, Tom & Sanders, Mark, eds. Reference Assessment & Evaluation. 2006. (ENG., Illus.). 218p. pap. 27.95 *(978-0-7890-3194-5(9))* Routledge.

Diaron, Rina. Current Awareness Program of Saint Louis University Library. 2009. 112p. pap. *(978-3-639-19152-3(8))* VDM Verlag Dr. Mueller e.K.

Dinesh, K. S. & Khaiser, Nikam. Strategic Management: Of Engineering College Libraries in Karnataka. 2011. 428p. pap. **(978-3-639-28902-2(1))** VDM Verlag Dr. Mueller e.K.

Drabinski, Emily, et al, eds. Critical Library Instruction: Theories & Methods. 2010. pap. 35.00 *(978-1-936117-01-7(0)*, Library Juice Pr.) Litwin Bks., LLC.

Driscoll, Lori & Mitchell, W. Bede. Best Practices in Access Services. 2008. (Illus.). viii, 381p. 160.00 *(978-0-7890-3852-4(8))* Routledge.

Dubicki, Eleonora. Marketing & Promoting Electronic Resources: Creating the E-Buzz! 2008. (Illus.). 232p. 150.00 *(978-0-7890-3585-1(5))*; pap. 45.95 *(978-0-7890-3586-8(3))* Routledge.

Dubicki, Eleonora, compiled by. Strategic Planning in College Libraries. 2011. pap. **(978-0-8389-8588-5(2))** Assn. of College & Research Libraries.

Dugan, Robert E., et al. Viewing Library Metrics from Different Perspectives: Inputs, Outputs, & Outcomes, 1 vol. 2009. (Illus.). 346p. pap. 45.00 (978-1-59158-665-4(8), LU8665) Libraries Unlimited, Inc.

Duke, Lynda M. & Asher, Andrew D. College Libraries & Student Culture: What We Now Know. 2012. **(978-0-8389-1116-7(1))** American Library Assn.

Easun, Susan. Library Data: Empowering Practice & Persuasion, 1 vol. Orcutt, Darby, ed. 2009. (Illus.). 302p. pap. 50.00 (978-1-59158-826-9(X), LU8826) Libraries Unlimited, Inc.

Eden, Bradford Lee. The Associate University Librarian Handbook: A Resource Guide. 2012. (ENG.). 208p. (gr. 17). 80.00 **(978-0-8108-8381-9(3))** Scarecrow Pr., Inc.

Evans, G. Edward & Alire, Camila A. Academic Librarianship. 2010. 350p. 65.00 (978-1-55570-702-6(5)) Neal-Schuman Pubs., Inc.

Falk, Patricia K. & Hunker, Stefanie. Cataloguing Outside the Box: A Practical Guide to Cataloguing Special Collections Materials. 2010. 200p. pap. 75.00 (978-1-84334-553-4(6), Chandos Publishing) Woodhead Publishing Ltd. GBR. Dist: Neal-Schuman Pubs., Inc.

Farber, Evan Ira. College Libraries & the Teaching/Learning Process: Selections from the Writings of Evan Ira Farber. Gansz, David, ed. 2007. 213p. 23.00 (978-1-879117-18-1(5)) Earlham Pr.

Farmer, Lesley S. J. The Human Side of Reference & Information Services in Academic Libraries: Adding Value in the Digital World. 2007. 200p. (978-1-84334-258-8(8)); pap. (978-1-84334-257-1(X)) Woodhead Publishing Ltd. (Chandos Publishing).

Fields, Anne M. & Diaz, Karen R. Fostering Community Through Digital Storytelling: A Guide for Academic Libraries. 2008. (Illus.). 128p. pap. 42.00 (978-1-59158-552-7(X), LU8552) Libraries Unlimited, Inc.

Fischer, Christine, contrib. by. Middle Management in Academic & Public Libraries, 1 vol. 2011. (Illus.). 233p. pap. 45.00 (978-1-59884-689-8(2), A3269P) Pearson Education GBR. Dist: ABC-CLIO, LLC.

Fitzpatrick, Jane Brodsky. Mrs. Magavero: A History Based on the Career of an Academic Librarian. 2007. (Illus.). 104p. per. 15.00 (978-0-9778617-5-0(9), Library Juice Pr.) Litwin Bks., LLC.

Foster, Nancy Fried. Scholarly Practice, Participatory Design, & the EXtensible Catalog. 2011. pap. **(978-0-8389-8574-8(2))** Assn. of College & Research Libraries.

Foster, Nancy Fried & Gibbons, Susan. Studying Students: The Undergraduate Research Project at the University of Rochester. 2007. (C). pap. (978-0-8389-8437-6(1)) Assn. of College & Research Libraries.

Fritts, Jack. Mistakes in Academic Library Management: Grievous Errors & How to Avoid Them. 2009. (ENG.). 140p. (gr. 17). pap. 55.00 (978-0-8108-6744-4(3)) Scarecrow Pr., Inc.

Fulkerson, Diane M., ed. Remote Access Technologies for Library Collections: Tools for Library Users & Managers. 2012. 487p. 175.00 **(978-1-4666-0234-2(1)**, Information Science Reference) IGI Global.

Gaskell, Philip. Trinity College Library, the First 150 Years: The Sanders Lectures 1978-9. 2010. (Cambridge Library Collection - Cambridge Ser.). (Illus.). 300p. pap. 23.99 (978-1-108-01593-6(X)) Cambridge Univ. Pr.

Gibbons, Susan. The Academic Library & the Net Gen Student: Making the Connections. 2007. (Illus.). 119p. per. 50.00 (978-0-8389-0946-1(9)) American Library Assn.

Gordon, Rachel Singer, ed. Information Tomorrow: Reflections on Technology & the Future of Public & Academic Libraries. 2007. 280p. pap. 35.00 (978-1-57387-303-1(9)) Information Today, Inc.

Hanna, Kathleen A., et al. Diversity Programming & Outreach for Academic Libraries. 2011. (Illus.). 200p. pap. 75.00 (978-1-84334-635-7(4), Chandos Publishing) Woodhead Publishing Ltd. GBR. Dist: Neal-Schuman Pubs., Inc.

Hardesty, Larry L. The Role of the Library in the First College Year. 2007. (978-1-889271-54-5(3)) National Resource Ctr. for The First Year Experience & Students in Transition.

Harris, Amy & Rice, Scott E. Gaming in Academic Libraries: Collections, Marketing, & Information Literacy. 2008. pap. (978-0-8389-8461-9(9)) Assn. of College & Research Libraries.

Hernon, Peter & Powell, Ronald R. Convergence & Collaboration of Campus Information Services. 2008. (Illus.). 252p. pap. 50.00 (978-1-59158-603-6(8), LU8603) Libraries Unlimited, Inc.

Hernon, Peter & Rossiter, Nancy. Making a Difference: Leadership & Academic Libraries, 1 vol. 2006. (Illus.). 316p. per. 45.00 (978-1-59158-291-5(1), LU2911) Libraries Unlimited, Inc.

Hernon, Peter, et al. Academic Librarians as Emotionally Intelligent Leaders, 1 vol. 2007. (Illus.). 172p. per. 50.00 (978-1-59158-513-8(9), LU5139) Libraries Unlimited, Inc.

Hesperides. College & University Libraries & Librarianship: An Examination of Their Present Status & Some Proposals for Their Future Development (1945) 2007. 176p. per. (978-1-4067-5930-3(9), Hesperides Pr.) Read Bks.

Holder, Sara, comment. The Survey of American College Students: Student Library Research Practices & Skills. 2009. pap. 80.00 (978-1-57440-126-4(2)) Primary Research Group.

Hurlbert, Janet McNeil, ed. Defining Relevancy: Managing the New Academic Library. 2007. (Libraries Unlimited Library Management Collection). (Illus.). 274p. per. 45.00 (978-1-59158-419-3(1), LU4191) Libraries Unlimited, Inc.

Jackson, Pamela A. & Sullivan, Patrick. International Students & Academic Libraries: Initiatives for Success. 2011. **(978-0-8389-9377-4(X))**; pap. **(978-0-8389-8593-9(9))**; E-Book **(978-0-8389-9378-1(8))** Assn. of College & Research Libraries.

Jacobson, Trudi & Mackey, Thomas P. Information Literacy Collaborations That Work. 2007. (Illus.). xxii, 264p. 85.00 (978-1-55570-579-4(0)) Neal-Schuman Pubs., Inc.

James, M. R. A Descriptive Catalogue of the Manuscripts in the Library of Gonville & Caius College. 2009. (Cambridge Library Collection - Cambridge Ser.). (ENG.). 444p. pap. 32.99 (978-1-108-00246-2(3)); 448p. pap. 32.99 (978-1-108-00247-9(1)) Cambridge Univ. Pr.

Jenkins, David & Klem, Karl. Free University of Berlin: The Philological Library. 2011. (Illus.). 96p. 29.95 (978-3-7913-4544-4(3)) Prestel Publishing.

Jennings, Karlene N. & Thompson, Kimberly A. More Than a Thank You Note: Academic Library Fund-Raising for the Dean or Director. 2009. 200p. pap. 75.00 **(978-1-84334-443-8(2)**, Neal-Schuman Pubs., Inc.

Johnson, Katherine, ed. The Sherman Fairchild Library: A Celebration of Ten Years. 2nd rev. ed. 2007. (Illus.). 110p. lib. bdg. 37.95 (978-1-60049-002-6(6)) California Institute of Technology.

Johnston, Edward. Catalogue of the Library of the South Carolina College. 2010. (AccessAble Bks.). (ENG.). 140p. pap. 14.95 (978-1-57003-928-7(3)) Univ. of South Carolina Pr.

Jones, Barbara M. Protecting Intellectual Freedom in Your Academic Library: Scenarios from the Front Lines. 2009. 256p. 55.00 (978-0-8389-3580-4(X)) American Library Assn.

Jones, Wayne, ed. E-Journals Access & Management. 2008. (Routledge Studies in Library & Information Science). (Illus.). XXII, 338p. (978-0-7890-3386-4(0), Haworth Information Pr., The) Haworth Pr., Inc., The.

Kallendorf, Craig. A Catalogue of the Junius Spencer Morgan Collection of Virgil in the Princeton University Library. 2009. 95.00 (978-1-58456-263-4(3)) Oak Knoll Pr.

Kebbell, Christian, ed. Directory of University Libraries in Europe. 3rd rev. ed. 2006. (Directory of University Libraries in Europe Ser.). 478p. 500.00 (978-1-85743-401-9(3)) Routledge.

Kennedy, James R., et al. Our New Public, a Changing Clientele: Bewildering Issues or New Challenges for Managing Libraries?, 1 vol. Kennedy, James R. et al, eds. 2007. (Libraries Unlimited Library Management Collection). (Illus.). 324p. 45.00 (978-1-59158-407-0(8), LU4078) Libraries Unlimited, Inc.

Keogh, Patricia & Crowley, Rachel, compiled by. Copyright Policies. 2008. pap. (978-0-8389-8459-8(2)) Assn. of College & Research Libraries.

Kopycinski, Doreen & Sando, Kimberley, compiled by. User Surveys in College Libraries. 2007. (ENG.). per. (978-0-8389-8433-8(9)) Assn. of College & Research Libraries.

Kvenild, Cassandra & Calkins, Kaijsa. Embedded Librarians: Moving Beyond One-Shot Instruction. 2011. pap. **(978-0-8389-8587-8(4))** Assn. of College & Research Libraries.

Langley, Anne. A Practical Writing Guide for Academic Librarians: Keeping It Short & Sweet. Wallace, Jon, ed. 2010. (Illus.). 172p. pap. 75.00 (978-1-84334-532-9(3), Chandos Publishing) Woodhead Publishing Ltd. GBR. Dist: Neal-Schuman Pubs., Inc.

Lankes, R. David. New Concepts in Digital Reference. 2009. (Synthesis Lectures on Information Concepts, Retrieval, & Services Ser.). 64p. (C). pap. 25.00 (978-1-59829-744-7(9)) Morgan & Claypool Pubs.

Lee Eden, Bradford, ed. Twenty-First Century Metadata Operations. 2011. (ENG., Illus.). 160p. (C). 145.00 **(978-0-415-68969-4(4))** Routledge.

Lee, Leslie A. & Wu, Michelle M. Beyond the Books: People, Politics, & Librarianship. 2007. ix, 401p. (978-0-8377-3413-2(4)) Hein, William S. & Co., Inc.

Lee, Sul H. Digital Information & Knowledge Management: New Opportunities for Research Libraries. 2007. (ENG., Illus.). 140p. 125.00 (978-0-7890-3565-3(0)); per. 62.00 (978-0-7890-3566-0(9)) Routledge.

—Print vs. Digital: The Future of Coexistence. 2007. (Illus.). 138p. 68.00 (978-0-7890-3575-2(8)) Routledge.

Lee, Sul H., ed. Climbing Out of the Box. 2011. (ENG., Illus.). 168p. (C). 125.00 **(978-0-415-69743-9(3))** Routledge.

Li, LiLi. Emerging Technologies for Academic Libraries in the Digital Age. 2008. (Illus.). 300p. (978-1-84334-323-3(1)); pap. (978-1-84334-320-2(7)) Woodhead Publishing Ltd. (Chandos Publishing).

Liebers, Gerhard. Funktion und Gestalt der Bibliothek: 2., Korrigierte Auflage. (Arbeiten und Bibliographien zum Buch und Bibliothekswesen Ser.: Bd. 14). (GER.). 52.95 (978-3-631-37521-1(2)) Lang, Peter Publishing, Inc.

Little, Geoffrey, ed. Library Architecture at Yale, Vol. 1. 2010. (ENG., Illus.). 152p. pap. 50.00 (978-0-300-16477-0(7)) Yale Univ. Pr.

Lorenzen, Michael. Academic Library Development Officers in Fund Raising. 2009. 200p. pap. (978-3-639-19373-2(3)) VDM Verlag Dr. Mueller e.K.

Mackey, Thomas P. & Jacobson, Trudi. Collaborative Information Literacy Assessments: Strategies for Evaluating Teaching & Learning. 2009. (Illus.). xxi, 242p. 90.00 (978-1-55570-693-7(2)) Neal-Schuman Pubs., Inc.

—Using Technology to Teach Information Literacy. 2008. (Information Literacy Sourcebooks). 175p. 75.00 (978-1-55570-637-1(1)) Neal-Schuman Pubs., Inc.

Mackey, Thomas P. & Jacobson, Trudi E. Teaching Information Literacy Online. 2010. (Illus.). 200p. 75.00 (978-1-55570-735-4(1)) Neal-Schuman Pubs., Inc.

Marketing & Managing Electronic Reserves. 2006. (ENG., Illus.). 172p. 60.95 (978-0-7890-3403-8(4)); pap. 36.95 (978-0-7890-3404-5(2)) Routledge.

Mash, S. David. Decision-Making in the Absence of Certainty: A Study in the Context of Technology & the Construction of 21st Century Academic Libraries. 2010. pap. (978-0-8389-8571-7(8)) Assn. of College & Research Libraries.

Mathews, Brian. Marketing Today's Academic Library: A Bold New Approach to Communicating with Students. 2009. (Illus.). 136p. 48.00 (978-0-8389-0984-3(1)) American Library Assn.

Matthews, Joseph R. Library Assessment in Higher Education. 2007. (Illus.). 148p. per. 45.00 (978-1-59158-531-2(7), LU8531) Libraries Unlimited, Inc.

McAdoo, Monty L. Building Bridges: Connecting Faculty, Students, & the College Library. 2009. 192p. (978-0-8389-1019-1(X)) American Library Assn.

McGuinness, Claire. Becoming Confident Teachers: A Guide for Academic Librarians. 2011. 246p. pap. 75.00 (978-1-84334-629-6(X), Chandos Publishing) Woodhead Publishing Ltd. GBR. Dist: Neal-Schuman Pubs., Inc.

McKitterick, David. Cambridge University Library, 2 vols., Set. 2009. (ENG.). 826p. pap. 105.00 (978-0-521-14253-3(9)) Cambridge Univ. Pr.

Mcknight, Sue. Envisioning Future Library Services: Initiatives Ideas & Challenges. 2010. (Illus.). xxii, 247p. pap. 105.00 **(978-1-85604-691-6(5))** Neal-Schuman Pubs., Inc.

Minčic-Obradovic, Ksenija. E-books in Academic Libraries. 2010. (Illus.). 200p. 80.00 (978-1-84334-586-2(2), Chandos Publishing) Woodhead Publishing Ltd. GBR. Dist: Neal-Schuman Pubs., Inc.

Mitchell, Marilyn, et al. Library Workflow Redesign: Six Case Studies. Mitchell, Marilyn, ed. 2007. vii, 81p. per. 20.00 net. (978-1-932326-27-7(8)) Council on Library & Info. Resources.

Moses, James, et al, contrib. by. Training College Students in Information Literacy: 2006-07 Edition. 2006. 73p. per. 69.50 (978-1-57440-081-6(9)) Primary Research Group.

Mothukuri, Anjaiah. Library Support Services to Distance Learners in Indi. 2010. 304p. pap. (978-3-639-27085-3(1)) VDM Verlag Dr. Mueller e.K.

Mueller, Dawn M. Declaration of Interdependence: The Proceedings of the ACRL 2011 Conference, March 30-April 2, 2011, Philadelphia, PA. Mueller, Dawn M., ed. 2011. 528p. pap. 98.00 **(978-0-8389-8579-3(3))** Assn. of College & Research Libraries.

Mueller, Dawn M. Pushing the Edge: Explore, Extend, Engage: Proceedings of the Fourteenth National Conference of the Association of College & Research Libraries, March 12-15, 2009, Seattle, Washington. 2009. pap. (978-0-8389-8514-4(9)) Assn. of College & Research Libraries.

Muhammed Rabiu, Aliyu. Application of Ict to Information Resources Sharing. 2011. 92p. pap. **(978-3-8443-2662-8(6))** Lambert Academic Publishing.

Mullen, Laura Bowering. Open Access & Its Practical Impact on the Work of Academic Librarians: Collection Development, Public Services, & the Library & Information Science Literature. 2009. 254p. pap. 75.00 (978-1-84334-593-0(5), Chandos Publishing) Woodhead Publishing Ltd. GBR. Dist: Neal-Schuman Pubs., Inc.

Munde, Gail & Marks, Kenneth. Surviving the Future: Academic Libraries, Quality & Assessment. 2009. (Illus.). 200p. pap. 80.00 **(978-1-84334-477-3(7))** Neal-Schuman Pubs., Inc.

Neely, Teresa Y., ed. How to Stay Afloat in the Academic Library Job Pool. 2010. 152p. pap. (978-0-8389-1080-1(7)) American Library Assn.

Northwestern University Staff. Deering Lib: An Illustrated History. Barrett, Nina, ed. 2008. (ENG., Illus.). 160p. pap. 40.00 (978-0-8101-2502-5(1)) Northwestern Univ. Pr.

Oates, J. C. T. Cambridge University Library: A History: From the Beginnings to the Copyright Act of Queen Anne. 2009. (ENG.). 532p. pap. 69.00 (978-0-521-11833-0(6)) Cambridge Univ. Pr.

Pankl, Elizabeth, et al. Recruitment, Development & Retention of Information Professionals: Trends in Human Resources & Knowledge Management. 2010. 350p. 180.00 (978-1-61520-601-8(9)) IGI Global.

Parker, David C. Codex Bezae: An Early Christian Manuscript & its Text. 2008. (LAT, GEC & ENG., Illus.). 376p. pap. 48.00 (978-0-521-07236-6(0)) Cambridge Univ. Pr.

Phillips, Loreen S. Cruise to Success: How to Steer Your Way Through the Murky Waters of Marketing Your Library. 2008. (Illus.). 136p. pap. (978-1-84334-482-7(3), Chandos Publishing) Woodhead Publishing Ltd.

Poll, Roswitha & Boekhorst, Peter te. Measuring Quality: Performance Measurement in Libraries. 2nd ed. 2007. (IFLA Publications). (ENG., Illus.). 269p. (978-3-598-22033-3(2)) Saur, K. G. Verlag GmbH & Co.

Priestner, Andy & Tilley, Elizabeth. Personalised Library Services in Higher Education: The Boutique Approach. 2012. (Illus.). 224p. 99.95 **(978-1-4094-3180-0(0))** Ashgate Publishing Co.

Primary Research Group staff. Academic Library Websites Benchmarks. 2008. per. 85.00 (978-1-57440-094-6(0)) Primary Research Group.

—The Survey of Library Cafes. 2007th ed. 2007. 59p. per. 75.00 (978-1-57440-089-2(4)) Primary Research Group.

Primary Research Group Staff, contrib. by. Academic Library Cataloging Practices Benchmarks. 2008. 253p. pap. 89.50 (978-1-57440-106-6(8)) Primary Research Group.

Radcliff, Carolyn J., et al. A Practical Guide to Information Literacy Assessment for Academic Librarians, 1 vol. 2007. (Illus.). 196p. per. 45.00 (978-1-59158-340-0(3), LU3403) Libraries Unlimited, Inc.

Radford, Marie L. & Snelson, Pamela. Academic Library Research: Perspectives & Current Trends. 2008. 332p. pap. (978-0-8389-0983-6(3)) Assn. of College & Research Libraries.

Ragains, Patrick. Information Literacy Instruction That Works: A Guide to Teaching by Discipline & Student Population. 2006. (Information Literacy Sourcebooks: No. 3). (Illus.). 329p. 89.95 (978-1-55570-573-2(1)) Neal-Schuman Pubs., Inc.

Reference Assessment & Evaluation. 2006. (ENG., Illus.). 218p. 55.95 (978-0-7890-3193-8(0)) Routledge.

Richards, Graham. 50 Years at Oxford. 2011. 96p. pap. 12.10 **(978-1-4567-7861-3(7))** AuthorHouse.

Rutherford, Henry William, ed. Catalogue of the Library of Charles Darwin now in the Botany School, Cambridge: Compiled by H. W. Rutherford, of the University Library; with an Introduction by Francis Darwin. 2009. (Cambridge Library Collection - Life Sciences Ser.). (ENG.). 112p. pap. 12.99 (978-1-108-00236-3(6)) Cambridge Univ. Pr.

Sahai, Shri. Academic Library System: Second Edition. 2009. 344p. 50.00 (978-81-7000-583-4(3)); pap. 21.00 (978-81-7000-584-1(1)) Ess Ess Pubns IND. Dist: International Specialized Bk. Services.

Sanchez, Elaine. Emerging Issues in Academic Library Cataloging & Technical Services. 2007. per. 72.95 (978-1-57440-086-1(X)) Primary Research Group.

Saunders, Laura. Information Literacy as a Student Learning Outcome: The Perspective of Institutional Accreditation, 1 vol. 2011. (Illus.). 294p. pap. 45.00 (978-1-59884-852-6(6), A3479P) Pearson Education GBR. Dist: ABC-CLIO, LLC.

Schader, Barbara, ed. Learning Commons: Evolution & Collaborative Essentials. 2008. (Illus.). 200p. (978-1-84334-313-4(4)); pap. (978-1-84334-312-7(6)) Woodhead Publishing Ltd. (Chandos Publishing).

Siegel, Gretta E. Libraries & Graduate Students: Building Connections. 2008. (Illus.). 226p. 150.00 (978-0-7890-3054-2(3)); pap. 45.95 (978-0-7890-3443-4(3)) Routledge.

Sobel, Karen. Information Basics for College Students, 1 vol. 2012. 132p. pap. 40.00 **(978-1-59884-958-5(1)**, A3633P) Pearson Education GBR. Dist: ABC-CLIO, LLC.

Somerville, Mary M. Working Together: Collaborative Information Practices for Organizational Learning. 2009. pap. (978-0-8389-8531-1(9)) Assn. of College & Research Libraries.

Spencer, John. Critical Thinking Within the Library Program. Millson-Martula, Christopher, ed. 2009. (ENG., Illus.). 264p. 125.00 (978-0-415-99838-3(7)) Routledge.

Srivastava, Pushp Lata. Copyright in Academic Libraries in Digital Environment. 2008. 159p. 25.00 (978-81-7000-546-9(9)) Ess Ess Pubns. IND. Dist: International Specialized Bk. Services.

State Historical Society of Wisconsin. L. Catalogue of the Library of the State Historical Society of Wisconsin Prepared by Daniel S Durrie, Librarian, & Isabel Durrie, Assistant. 2006. 644p. per. 34.99 (978-1-4255-6656-2(1)) MPublishing.

Steiner, Sarah K. & Madden, M. Leslie. The Desk & Beyond: Next Generation Reference Services. 2008. pap. (978-0-8389-0964-5(7)) Assn. of College & Research Libraries.

Stemmer, John. Merged Information Services Organizations at Liberal Arts Colleges. 2008. 112p. pap. (978-3-639-02680-1(2)) VDM Verlag Dr. Mueller e.K.

Stepchyshyn, Vera & Nelson, Robert S., compiled by. Library Plagiarism Policies. 2007. (ENG., Illus.). 128p. per. (978-0-8389-8416-1(9)) Assn. of College & Research Libraries.

Stewart, Christopher. The Academic Library: Building in the Digital Age. Association of Library Services to Children, ed. 2010. pap. (978-0-8389-8552-6(1)) American Library Assn.

Sweetman, Kimberly Burke. Managing Student Assistants: A How-To-Do-It Manual for Librarians. 2006. (Illus.). 187p. 59.95 (978-1-55570-581-7(2)) Neal-Schuman Pubs., Inc.

Swords, David A., ed. Patron-Driven Acquisitions: History & Best Practices. 2011. (Current Topics in Library & Information Practice Ser.). (ENG.). X, 205p. **(978-3-11-219095-1(5)); (978-3-11-025301-6(1))** Saur, K. G. Verlag GmbH & Co.

The Teaching Library: Approaches to Assessing Information Literacy Instruction. 2008. (ENG., Illus.). 282p. 58.00 (978-0-7890-3149-5(3)) Routledge.

Thomas, Marcia L. & Voss, Anke, compiled by. Emergency Response Planning in College Libraries. 2009. pap. (978-0-8389-8524-3(6)) Assn. of College & Research Libraries.

Todaro, Julie. Emergency Preparedness for Libraries. 2009. (ENG.). 206p. 85.00 (978-0-86587-166-3(3)) Government Institutes.

Tornberg, C. J. Oriental Codices of Lund University Library. 2008. (LAT.). 89.00 (978-1-59333-893-0(7)) Gorgias Pr., LLC.

The Twelfth Off-Campus Library Services Conference Proceedings. 2007. (ENG., Illus.). 628p. 161.00 (978-0-7890-3476-2(X)); pap. 102.00 (978-0-7890-3477-9(8)) Routledge.

University of Delaware Library. Building the Future, Remembering the Past: Fifty Years of the University of Delaware Library Associates. 2008. (Illus.). 69p. pap. 21.50 (978-0-9712360-3-5(8)) Univ. of Delaware Library.

University of Vermont. Library. Alphabetical & Analytical Catalogue of the Library of the University of Vermont, Burlington. 2006. 172p. per. 18.99 (978-1-4255-1292-7(5)) MPublishing.

Van Impe, Jan. University Library of Leuven: The Story of a Phoenix. 2006. (Illus.). 90p. (Orig.). pap. 16.30 (978-90-5867-557-6(2)) Leuven Univ. Pr. BEL. Dist: Cornell Univ. Pr.

Varvel, Virgil E., Jr., compiled by. Academic Library Trends & Statistics for Carnegie Classification: Associate's Colleges. 2009. (Academic Library Trends & Statistics for Carnegie Classification Ser.). (Illus.). 147p. pap. 140.00 (978-0-8389-8492-5(4)) American Library Assn.

—Academic Library Trends & Statistics for Carnegie Classification: Baccalaureate Colleges, Master's Colleges & Institutions. 2009. (Academic Library Trends & Statistics for Carnegie Classification Ser.). (Illus.). 288p. pap. 160.00 (978-0-8389-8494-9(0)) American Library Assn.

—Academic Library Trends & Statistics for Carnegie Classification: Doctorate-Granting Institutions. 2009. (Academic Library Trends & Statistics for Carnegie Classification Ser.). (Illus.). 166p. pap. 140.00 *(978-0-8389-8493-2(2))* American Library Assn.

Walter, Scott & Williams, Karen. The Expert Library: Staffing, Sustaining, & Advancing the Academic Library in the 21st Century. Association for Library Service to Children (ALSC), ed. 2011. (Illus.). xvi, 373p. pap. 48.00 *(978-0-8389-8551-9(3))* American Library Assn.

Warner, Dorothy Anne. A Disciplinary Blueprint for the Assessment of Information Literacy, 1 vol. 2008. 136p. pap. 35.00 *(978-1-59158-593-0(7)*, LU8593) Libraries Unlimited, Inc.

Weaver, Margaret. Transformative Learning Support Models in Higher Education: Educating the Whole Student. 2008. (Illus.). 192p. 125.00 ***(978-1-85604-644-2(3))*** Neal-Schuman Pubs., Inc.

Welburn, William C., et al. Advocacy, Outreach, & the Nation's Academic Libraries: A Call for Action. 2010. pap. *(978-0-8389-8549-6(1))* Assn. of College & Research Libraries.

Wikoff, Karin. Electronics Resources Management in the Academic Library: A Professional Guide. 2011. E-Book ***(978-1-61069-006-5(0))*** Libraries Unlimited, Inc.

—Electronics Resources Management in the Academic Library: A Professional Guide, 1 vol. 137p. pap. 40.00 ***(978-1-61069-005-8(2)***, A3687P) Pearson Education GBR. Dist: ABC-CLIO, LLC.

Wilkinson, Frances C., et al. Comprehensive Guide to Emergency Preparedness & Disaster Recovery. 2010. pap. *(978-0-8389-8548-9(3))* Assn. of College & Research Libraries.

Williams, Joe M. & Goodwin, Susan P. Teaching with Technology: An Academic Librarian's Guide. 2007. (Illus.). 176p. *(978-1-84334-173-4(5))*; per. *(978-1-84334-172-7(7))* Woodhead Publishing Ltd. (Chandos Publishing).

Wood, Elizabeth J., et al. Beyond Survival: Managing Academic Libraries in Transition, 1 vol. 2006. (Illus.). 224p. per. 45.00 *(978-1-59158-337-0(3)*, LU3373) Libraries Unlimited, Inc.

Woodward, Jeannette A. Creating the Customer-Driven Academic Library. 2008. 208p. 58.00 *(978-0-8389-0976-8(0))* American Library Assn.

Wright, Matthew. Survey on Law Library Liaison Services. 2007. pap. *(978-0-8377-1404-2(4))* Hein, William S. & Co., Inc.

Yale University. Linonian society. Libra. Catalogue of the Library of the Linonian Society, Yale College, June 1860. 2006. 312p. per. 23.99 *(978-1-4255-3007-5(9))* MPublishing.

Yeap, Chun Keat. A Citation Analysis of Mlis Dissertations. 2011. 148p. pap. ***(978-3-8443-9278-4(5))*** Lambert Academic Publishing.

Zdravkovska, Nevenka. Academic Branch Libraries in Changing Times. 2011. (Illus.). 230p. 80.00 *(978-1-84334-630-2(3)*, Chandos Publishing) Woodhead Publishing Ltd. GBR. Dist: Neal-Schuman Pubs., Inc.

ACADEMIC PROBATION

see College Attendance

ACADEMIC WRITING

Aaron, Jane E. Little, Brown Compact Handbook. 7th ed. 2009. (English MLA Updated Books Ser.). (ENG., Illus.). 584p. (C). spiral bd. 75.00 *(978-0-205-65163-4(1))* Longman Publishing Group.

—The Little, Brown Compact Handbook with Exercises. 7th ed. 2009. (English MLA Updated Books Ser.). (ENG., Illus.). 648p. (C). pap. 75.00 *(978-0-205-65170-2(4))* Longman Publishing Group.

Ackley, Katherine Anne. Perspectives on Contemporary Issues. 3rd ed. pap. 64.95 *(978-0-8384-8039-7(X))*; pap. 43.95 *(978-0-8384-7082-4(3))* Cengage Heinle.

—Perspectives on Contemporary Issues. 6th ed. 2011. (ENG.). 592p. (C). pap. 91.95 *(978-0-495-91292-7(1))* Wadsworth.

Alexander, Olwyn. New Approaches to Materials Development for Language Learning: Proceedings of the 2005 Joint BALEAP/SATEFL Conference. 2007. (Illus.). 364p. pap. 83.95 *(978-3-03910-909-8(X))* Lang, Peter Publishing, Inc.

Alvarez, Marino C. & Gowin, D. B. Conceptual Elements of Research. 2010. (ENG.). 76p. pap. 18.95 *(978-1-60709-293-3(X))* Rowman & Littlefield Education.

Amato, Carol J. The World's Easiest Guide to Using the APA: A User-Friendly Manual for Formatting Research Papers According to the American Psychological Association Style Guide. 4th ed. 2009. (World's Easiest Guides). (ENG., 384p. (C). Illus.). 23.95 *(978-1-933277-07-3(6))*; spiral bd. 23.95 *(978-1-933277-04-2(1))* Stargazer Publishing Co.

American Historical Association, Committee for Graduate Students Staff, contrib. by. From Concept to Completion: A Dissertation-Writing Guide for History Students. 2008. *(978-0-87229-162-1(6))* American Historical Assn.

Anderson, Daniel. Writing about Literature in the Media Age. 1008p. tchr. ed., per. 18.97 *(978-0-321-20944-3(3))* Longman Publishing.

Anderson, Judith H. & Farris, Christine R., eds. Integrating Literature & Writing Instruction: First-Year English, Humanities Core Courses, Seminars. 2007. (ENG.). 336p. per. 25.00 *(978-0-87352-949-5(9))* Modern Language Assn. of America.

Anker, Susan. Real Essays with Readings with 2009 MLA Update: Writing Projects for College, Work, & Everyday Life. 3rd ed. 2009. (ENG.). 944p. (C). pap. 77.95 *(978-0-312-60755-5(5))* Bedford/Saint Martin's.

Anker, Susan & Gallagher, Eddye S. Supplemental Exercises for Real Writing with Readings. 5th ed. 2009. (ENG.). 160p. (C). pap. 9.95 *(978-0-312-56708-8(1))* Bedford/Saint Martin's.

Arnold, Danny R. 147 Publishing Tips for Professors. 2008. *(978-1-891859-72-4(2))* Atwood Publishing.

Axelrod, Rise B. & Cooper, Charles R. St. Martin's Guide to Writing. 9th ed. 2010. (ENG.). 1088p. (C). 84.95 *(978-0-312-53612-1(7))* Bedford/Saint Martin's.

—The St. Martin's Guide to Writing Short Edition. 9th ed. 2010. (ENG.). 944p. (C). pap. 79.95 *(978-0-312-53613-8(5))* Bedford/Saint Martin's.

Axelrod, Rise B., et al. Reading Critically, Writing Well: A Reader & Guide. 9th ed. 2011. (ENG.). 736p. (C). pap. 60.95 *(978-0-312-60761-6(X))* Bedford/Saint Martin's.

Bailey, Stephen. Academic Writing. 3rd rev. ed. 2011. (ENG., Illus.). 320p. 135.00 *(978-0-415-59580-3(0))* Routledge.

—Academic Writing: A Handbook for International Students. 3rd rev. ed. 2011. (ENG., Illus.). 320p. pap. 37.95 *(978-0-415-59581-0(9))* Routledge.

—Academic Writing for International Students of Business. 2010. (ENG., Illus.). 336p. (C). pap. 39.95 *(978-0-415-56471-7(9))*; 130.00 *(978-0-415-56470-0(0))* Routledge.

Ballanger & Ballenger, Bruce. Curious Writer, the, Brief Edition, Books a la Carte Edition. 3rd ed. 2011. (ENG.). 704p. (C). ring bd. 61.33 ***(978-0-205-11556-3(X))*** Longman Publishing Group.

Ballenger, Bruce. Curious Writer. 3rd ed. 2010. (ENG.). 448p. (C). 49.33 *(978-0-205-71742-2(X))* Longman Publishing Group.

—The Curious Writer: Concise Edition. 3rd ed. 2010. (ENG., Illus.). 448p. (C). pap. 64.20 *(978-0-205-78019-8(9))* Longman Publishing Group.

Ballenger, Bruce. The Curious Writer, Books a la Carte Edition. 3rd ed. 2011. (ENG.). 784p. (C). ring bd. 64.67 ***(978-0-205-11574-7(8))*** Longman Publishing Group.

Ballenger, Bruce P. The Curious Writer. 3rd ed. 2010. (ENG., Illus.). (C). 704p. pap. 94.33 *(978-0-205-70765-2(3))*; 784p. 99.33 *(978-0-205-70764-5(5))* Longman Publishing Group.

Baratta, Alex. Visual Writing. 2010. (Illus.). 290p. *(978-1-4438-2327-2(9))* Cambridge Scholors Pub.

Barbara Smith-Palinkas & Croghan-Ford, Kelly. Key Concepts 2: Reading & Writing Across the Disciplines. 2009. (Key Concepts Ser.). (ENG.). 320p. (C). pap. 38.95 *(978-0-618-47462-2(5)*, 339101) CENGAGE Learning.

Barry, Marian. Steps to Academic Writing. 2011. (Georgian Press Ser.). (ENG., Illus.). 160p. pap. 21.00 *(978-0-521-18497-7(5))* Cambridge Univ. Pr.

Barton, Matthew & Cummings, Robert, eds. Wiki Writing: Collaborative Learning in the College Classroom. 2008. (ENG., Illus.). 280p. pap. 25.95 *(978-0-472-11671-3(1))* Univ. of Michigan Pr.

Baruch, Yehuda. Opening the Black Box of Editorship. Baruch, Yehuda et al, eds. 2008. (ENG., Illus.). 328p. 100.00 *(978-0-230-01360-5(0))* Palgrave Macmillan.

Becker, Howard Saul. Writing for Social Scientists: How to Start & Finish Your Thesis, Book, or Article. 2nd ed. 2007. (Chicago Guides to Writing, Editing, & Publishing Ser.). (Illus.). 208p. 32.50 *(978-0-226-04130-8(1))*; per. 12.00 *(978-0-226-04132-2(8))* Univ. of Chicago Pr.

Behrens, Laurence & Rosen, Leonard J. A Sequence for Academic Writing. 5th rev. ed. 2011. (ENG.). 384p. (C). pap. 60.40 *(978-0-205-17288-7(1))* Longman Publishing Group.

—Writing & Reading Across the Curriculum, Books a la Carte Edition. 11th ed. 2011. (ENG.). 816p. (C). ring bd. 54.67 ***(978-0-205-23850-7(5))*** Longman Publishing Group.

Behrens, Laurence & Rosen, Leonard J. Writing & Reading Across the Curriculum, Brief Edition. 4th ed. 2010. (ENG., Illus.). 464p. (C). pap. 58.40 *(978-0-205-00069-2(X))* Longman Publishing Group.

Behrens, Laurence M. & Rosen, Leonard J. Sequence for Academic Writing, Writing Research Papers: A Complete Guide, & MyCompLab with Pearson eText Valuepack Access Card Package. 5th ed. 2011. (ENG.). (C). pap., pap. 100.00 ***(978-0-205-79677-9(X))*** Longman Publishing Group.

Behrens, Laurence M. & Rosen, Leonard J. Writing & Reading Across the Curriculum. 11th ed. 2010. (ENG.). 816p. (C). pap. 83.20 *(978-0-205-72765-0(4))* Longman Publishing Group.

Belletti, Adrian. Structures & Strategies. 2008. (Routledge Leading Linguists Ser.). (Illus.). 304p. 141.00 *(978-0-415-96201-8(3))* Routledge.

Biggam, John. Succeeding with you Master's Dissertation. 2008. (ENG., Illus.). 208p. (C). 117.00 *(978-0-335-22720-4(1)*, 0335227201) McGraw-Hill Education GBR. Dist: McGraw-Hill Cos., The.

—Succeeding with Your Master's Dissertation. 2008. (Illus.). 208p. (C). pap., instr.'s hndbk. ed. 45.00 *(978-0-335-22719-8(8)*, 0335227198, Open University Pr.) McGraw-Hill Education GBR. Dist: McGraw-Hill Cos., The.

Birkenstein, Cathy, et al. They Say/I Say: The Moves That Matter in Academic Writing. 2nd ed. 2009. (ENG., Illus.). 245p. (C). pap. 22.69 *(978-0-393-93361-1(X)*, 93361) Norton, W. W. & Co., Inc.

Bitchener, John. Writing an Applied Linguistics Thesis or Dissertation: A Guide to Presenting Empirical Research. 2010. (ENG.). 176p. 74.95 *(978-0-230-22453-7(9))*; (Illus.). pap. 26.95 *(978-0-230-22454-4(7))* Palgrave Macmillan.

Blackwell, John & Martin, Jan. A Scientific Approach to Scientific Writing. 2011. (ENG., Illus.). x, 114p. pap. 49.95 *(978-1-4419-9787-6(3)*, 1441997873) Springer.

Blue, George, ed. Developing Academic Literacy. 2010. 246p. pap. 56.95 *(978-3-03911-545-7(6))* Lang, Peter AG GBR. Dist: Lang, Peter.

Boardman, Cynthia A. Writing to Communicate: Paragraphs. 2007. (Illus.). 14p. *(978-0-13-614192-1(7))* Pearson Education.

—Writing to Communicate: Paragraphs, 1. 2007. (ENG.). (C). pap. 45.00 *(978-0-13-614191-4(9))* Prentice Hall, ESL Dept.

Boardman, Cynthia A. & Frydenberg, Jia. Writing to Communicate: Paragraphs & Essays. 3rd ed. 2007. 19p. *(978-0-13-235115-7(3))* Pearson Education.

—Writing to Communicate: Paragraphs & Essays. 3rd ed. 2008. (ENG.). (C). pap. 45.00 *(978-0-13-235116-4(1))* Prentice Hall, ESL Dept.

Borkowski, David. The Emergence of a New Rhetoric since the 1960s: A History of the Linguistic Reformation of American Culture. 2008. 400p. 119.95 *(978-0-7734-5130-8(7))* Mellen, Edwin Pr., The.

Botta, J. J. A Writing Safety Net: the Survival Kit for Those Who Have Forgotten - & Those Who Never Learned. 2007. 136p. pap. 9.95 *(978-1-4303-1170-6(3))* Lulu Enterprises Inc.

Brace-Govan, Jan. Write Now! How to Get Started & Keep Going. 2011. 100p. pap. 29.95 *(978-0-7346-1127-7(7))* Tilde Publishing AUS. Dist: International Publishers Marketing.

Brewer, Robert. Your PhD Thesis: How to Plan, Draft, Revise & Edit Your Thesis. 2007. (Illus.). 219p. pap. 29.50 *(978-1-84285-070-1(9))* GLMP Ltd. GBR. Dist: Chicago Distribution Ctr.

Bromley, Karen D'Angelo. Writing for Educators: Personal Essays & Practical Advice (HC) Bromley, Karen, ed. 2009. 256p. *(978-1-60752-104-4(0))* Information Age Publishing, Inc.

—Writing for Educators: Personal Essays & Practical Advice (PB) Bromley, Karen, ed. 2009. 256p. pap. *(978-1-60752-103-7(2))* Information Age Publishing, Inc.

Brown, Stephen. Writing Across the Curriculum: A Prentice Hall Pocket. 7th ed. 2006. (ENG.). (C). pap. 32.60 *(978-0-13-156581-4(8))* Longman Publishing Group.

Bruce, Ian. Academic Writing & Genre: A Systematic Analysis. 2010. (ENG., Illus.). 202p. 44.95 *(978-1-4411-0308-6(2))* Continuum International Publishing Group, Ltd. GBR. Dist: National Bk. Network.

—Theory & Concepts of English for Academic Purposes. 2011. (ENG., Illus.). 256p. 85.00 *(978-0-230-24974-5(4))* Palgrave Macmillan.

Bruce, Susan, et al. Academic Writing & Genre: A Systematic Analysis. 2008. (ENG.). 202p. 150.00 *(978-0-8264-9844-1(2))* Continuum International Publishing Group, Ltd. GBR. Dist: National Bk. Network.

Burnett, Judith. Doing Your Social Science Dissertation. 2009. (SAGE Study Skills Ser.). 280p. (C). 108.00 *(978-1-4129-3112-0(6)*, B31126C); pap. 41.00 *(978-1-4129-3113-7(4)*, B31126P) SAGE Pubns., Ltd. GBR. Dist: SAGE Pubns., Inc.

Butin, Dan W., ed. The Education Dissertation: A Guide for Practitioner Scholars. 2009. (Illus.). 184p. pap. 36.95 *(978-1-4129-6044-1(4)*, B60434P) Corwin Pr.

Butler, Linda. Fundamentals of Academic Writing. 2006. (Illus.). xi, 227p. *(978-0-13-613390-2(8))* Pearson Education.

—Fundamentals of Academic Writing. 2006. (ENG., Illus.). xi, 227p. (C). pap. 46.80 *(978-0-13-199557-4(X))* Prentice Hall, ESL Dept.

Cadle, Lanette & Feyh, Lori. Composing Ourselves: Writing from the Composition Program at Missouri State University. 2007. (C). pap. *(978-0-913785-08-9(3)*, Moon City Pr.) Department of English.

Calabrese, Raymond L. Dissertation Desk Reference: The Doctoral Student's Manual to Writing the Dissertation. 2009. (ENG.). 196p. 85.00 *(978-1-60709-473-9(8))* Rowman & Littlefield Education.

Canseco, Grace. Inside Academic Writing: Understanding Audience & Becoming Part of an Academic Community. 2010. (ENG., Illus.). 200p. (C). pap. 25.95 *(978-0-472-03389-8(1))* Univ. of Michigan Pr.

Carnell, Eileen, et al. Passion & Politics: Academics Reflect on Writing for Publication. 2008. (ENG., Illus.). 232p. pap. 38.95 *(978-0-85473-802-1(9))* Institute of Education GBR. Dist: Stylus Publishing, LLC.

Caro, Sarah. How to Publish Your PhD. 2009. 144p. (C). 112.00 *(978-1-4129-0790-3(X)*, B0790XC); pap. 41.00 *(978-1-4129-0791-0(8)*, B0790XP) SAGE Pubns., Ltd. GBR. Dist: SAGE Pubns., Inc.

Castello, Montserrat & Donahue, Christiane, eds. University Writing: Selves & Texts in Academic Societies. 2012. (Studies in Writing Ser.). (Illus.). 250p. ***(978-1-78052-386-6(6))*** Emerald Group Publishing Ltd.

Century College English Department Staff. Composition Guide. rev. ed. 2010. 118p. pap. 23.90 *(978-0-7575-8142-7(0))* Kendall Hunt Publishing Co.

Chapnick, Adam & Stone, Craig. Academic Writing for Military Personnel. 2009. (ENG.). 148p. pap. *(978-0-7766-0734-4(0))* Univ. of Ottawa Pr./Presses de l'Universite d'Ottawa.

Charles, Maggie. Academic Writing: At the Interface of Corpus & Discourse. Hunston, Susan & Pecorari, Diane, eds. 2010. (ENG.). 316p. 150.00 *(978-1-84706-436-3(1))* Continuum International Publishing Group, Ltd. GBR. Dist: National Bk. Network.

Charles, Maggie, et al, eds. Academic Writing: At the Interface of Corpus & Discourse. 2011. (ENG.). 316p. pap. 49.95 ***(978-1-4411-1236-1(7))*** Continuum International Publishing Group, Ltd. GBR. Dist: National Bk. Network.

Chodorow, Stanley. Writing a Successful Research Paper: A Simple Approach. 2011. 115p. (C). pap. 8.95 ***(978-1-60384-440-6(6))***; (ENG.). lib. bdg. 27.95 ***(978-1-60384-441-3(4))*** Hackett Publishing Co., Inc.

Clark, Jessica L. & Murray, Kristen E. Scholarly Writing: Ideas, Examples, & Execution. 2010. 218p. pap. 25.00 *(978-1-59460-663-2(3))* Carolina Academic Pr.

Clarke, Dawne, pref. A Sociological Study of Scholarly Writing & Publishing: How Academics Produce & Share Their Research. 2010. 148p. 99.95 *(978-0-7734-3717-3(7))* Mellen, Edwin Pr., The.

Cochran, Susan Miller & Hagopian, Katherine. Academic Discourse an Anthology of Student Writing. rev. ed. 2009. (ENG.). 196p. pap. 19.85 *(978-0-7575-6701-8(0))* Kendall Hunt Publishing Co.

Colombo, Gary, et al. Rereading America: Cultural Contexts for Critical Thinking & Writing. 8th ed. 2010. (ENG.). 832p. (C). pap. 62.95 *(978-0-312-54854-4(0))* Bedford/Saint Martin's.

Comley, Nancy R. Fields of Reading: Motives for Writing. 9th ed. 2010. xxiiii, 839p. ***(978-0-312-59019-2(9))*** Bedford/Saint Martin's.

Comley, Nancy R., et al. Fields of Reading: Motives for Writing. 9th ed. 2009. (ENG.). 864p. (C). pap. 62.95 *(978-0-312-55374-6(9))* Bedford/Saint Martin's.

Cooper, Sheila & Patton, Rosemary. Writing Logically, Thinking Critically. 6th ed. 2009. (Illus.). xvi, 240p. tchr. ed. *(978-0-205-66858-8(5))* 6th ed. 2009. (ENG., Illus.). 256p. (C). pap. 60.00 *(978-0-205-66856-4(9))* 7th rev. ed. 2011. (ENG.). 256p. (C). pap. 60.00 ***(978-0-205-11912-7(3))*** Longman Publishing Group.

Copus, Julia. Brilliant Writing Tips for Students. 2010. (ENG., Illus.). 112p. pap. 10.00 *(978-0-230-22002-7(9))* Palgrave Macmillan.

Costanzo, William V. The Writer's Eye: Composition in the Multimedia Age. 2007. (ENG., Illus.). 528p. (C). pap. 89.33 *(978-0-07-237260-1(5)*, 0072372605) McGraw-Hill Cos., The.

Cram101 Textbook Reviews. Outlines & Highlights for the Modern Researcher by Barzun & Graff, Isbn: 0155055291. 2011. 304p. pap. 32.95 ***(978-1-61812-997-0(X))*** Cram101 Inc.

Creme, Phyllis & Lea, Mary R. Writing at University. 3rd rev. ed. 2008. (ENG.). 208p. (C). pap. 34.00 *(978-0-335-22116-5(5)*, 0335221165) McGraw-Hill Education GBR. Dist: McGraw-Hill Cos., The.

Cullen, Jim. Essaying the Past: How to Read, Write, & Think about History. 2009. (ENG.). 208p. 73.95 *(978-1-4051-8278-2(4))*; pap. 23.95 *(978-1-4051-8279-9(2))* Wiley, John & Sons, Inc. (Wiley-Blackwell).

Cullen, Jim. Essaying the Past: How to Read, Write & Think about History. 2nd ed. 2012. (ENG.). 224p. pap. 21.95 ***(978-1-4443-5140-8(0)***, Wiley-Blackwell) Wiley, John & Sons, Inc.

Cumming, Alister. Goals for Academic Writing. (Illus.). xii,202p. pap. *(978-90-272-1971-8(0))* Benjamins, John Publishing Co.

Cummings, Robert E. Lazy Virtues: Teaching Writing in the Age of Wikipedia. 2009. (ENG.). 216p. (C). pap. 29.95 *(978-0-8265-1616-9(5))*; 69.95 *(978-0-8265-1615-2(7))* Vanderbilt Univ. Pr.

de Gruchy, John W. & Holness, Lyn. The Emerging Researcher: Nurturing Passion, Developing Skills, Producing Output. 2008. (ENG.). 208p. spiral bd. 31.00 *(978-1-919895-01-7(9))* Juta Academic ZAF. Dist: Independent Pubs. Group.

Deane, Mary & O'Neill, Peter. Writing in the Disciplines. 2011. (Universities into the 21st Century Ser.). (ENG., Illus.). 304p. pap. 35.00 *(978-0-230-23708-7(8))* Palgrave Macmillan.

Dew, Debra & Horning, Alice, eds. Untenured Faculty As Writing Program Administrators: Institutional Practices & Politics. 2007. 316p. per. 30.00 *(978-1-60235-016-8(7))* Parlor Pr.

Dew, Debra Frank & Horning, Alice S. Untenured Faculty As Writing Program Administrators: Institutional Practices & Politics. 2007. *(978-1-60235-017-5(5))* Parlor Pr.

DiYanni, Robert. Writing about the Humanities. 3rd ed. 2007. (ENG., Illus.). 208p. (C). per. 43.00 *(978-0-13-615141-8(8)*, Prentice Hall) Prentice Hall PTR.

Doleschal, Ursula & Gruber, Helmut, eds. Wissenschftliches Schreiben abseits des Englischen Mainstreams Academic Writing in Languages Other than English. pap. 57.95 *(978-3-631-54232-3(1))* Lang, Peter Publishing, Inc.

Donahue, Thomas. A Style & Usage Guide to Writing about Music. 2010. (ENG.). 114p. (gr. 17). pap. 27.00 *(978-0-8108-7431-2(8))* Scarecrow Pr., Inc.

Donehower, Kim, et al, eds. Reclaiming the Rural: Essays on Literacy, Rhetoric, & Pedagogy. 2011. (Illus.). 304p. pap. 35.00 ***(978-0-8093-3065-2(2))*** Southern Illinois Univ. Pr.

Donehower, Kim, et al. Reclaiming the Rural: Essays on Literacy, Rhetoric, & Pedagogy. 2012. E-Book ***(978-0-8093-3066-9(0))*** Southern Illinois Univ. Pr.

Donehower, Kim, et al. Rural Literacies. Brooke, Robert, ed. 2007. (Studies in Writing & Rhetoric). (ENG.). 256p. per. 32.00 *(978-0-8093-2749-2(X))* Southern Illinois Univ. Pr.

Dowhan, Chris, et al. Essays That Will Get You into College. 3rd rev. ed. 2009. (Essays That Will Get You into... Ser.). (ENG.). 192p. pap. 13.99 *(978-0-7641-4210-9(0))* Barron's Educational Series, Inc.

Drew, Chris, et al. Dispatches from the Classroom: Graduate Students on Creative Writing Pedagogy. 2011. (ENG.). 240p. pap. 32.95 ***(978-1-4411-5680-8(1))***; 110.00 ***(978-1-4411-2740-2(2))*** Continuum International Publishing Group, Ltd. GBR. Dist: National Bk. Network.

Edgerton, Larry G. The Less-Is-More Handbook: A Guide to College Writing. rev. ed. 2012. (ENG.). 576p. spiral bd. 44.95 ***(978-0-7575-9287-4(2))*** Kendall Hunt Publishing Co.

Ehrenhaft, George. Writing a Successful College Application Essay. 4th rev. ed. 2008. (ENG.). 176p. pap. 13.99 *(978-0-7641-3637-5(2))* Barron's Educational Series, Inc.

Emerson, Robert M., et al. Writing Ethnographic Fieldnotes. 2nd ed. 2011. ***(978-0-226-20682-0(3))*** Univ. of Chicago Pr.

Emerson, Robert M., et al. Writing Ethnographic Fieldnotes, Second Edition. 2nd ed. 2011. (Chicago Guides to Writing, Editing, & Publishing Ser.). (Illus.). 320p. pap. 19.00 *(978-0-226-20683-7(1))* Univ. of Chicago Pr.

English, Fiona. Student Writing & Genre: Reconfiguring Academic Knowledge. 2011. (ENG.). 240p. 140.00 *(978-1-4411-7161-0(4))* Continuum International Publishing Group, Ltd. GBR. Dist: National Bk. Network.

Ezhova-Heer, Irina. Schreiben an russischen und deutschen Schulen: Unter besonderer Berücksichtigung der Textproduktion russischsprachiger Aussiedler und Spätaussiedler. 2008. (Europäische Hochschulschriften. Reihe 21: Linguistik Ser.). 324p. pap. 74.95 *(978-3-631-58844-4(5))* Lang, Peter GmbH, Europaischer Verlag der Wissenschaften DEU. Dist: Lang Peter.

Faigley & Faigley, Lester. Writing: A Guide for College & Beyond, Books a la Carte Plus MyCompLab. 2nd ed. 2011. (ENG.). (C). ring bd. 71.33 *(978-0-205-13114-3(X))* Longman Publishing Group.

Faigley, Lester. Backpack Writing. 3rd ed. 2011. (ENG.). 464p. (C). pap. 64.20 ***(978-0-205-84639-9(4))*** Longman Publishing Group.

—Backpack Writing, Books a la Carte Edition. 3rd ed. 2011. (ENG.). 464p. (C). ring bd. 42.30 ***(978-0-205-85076-1(6))*** Longman Publishing Group.

—Writing: A Guide for College & Beyond. 2006. (ENG.). pap. 84.00 *(978-0-205-54282-6(4))* Dorling Kindersley Publishing, Inc.

—Writing: A Guide for College & Beyond. 2nd ed. 2009. (Faigley Ser.). (ENG., Illus.). 784p. (C). 99.33 *(978-0-205-64870-2(3))* Longman Publishing Group.

—Writing: A Guide for College & Beyond, Books a la Carte Edition. 3rd ed. 2011. (ENG.). 736p. (C). ring bd. 64.67 ***(978-0-205-85502-5(4))*** Longman Publishing Group.

—Writing: A Guide for College & Beyond, Brief Edition, Books a la Carte Edition. 3rd ed. 2011. (ENG.). 704p. (C). ring bd. 61.33 ***(978-0-205-85137-9(1))*** Longman Publishing Group.

—Writing: A Guide for College & Beyond, Brief Edition Spiral. 2nd ed. 2009. (ENG., Illus.). 736p. (C). spiral bd. 91.60 *(978-0-205-69620-8(1))* Longman Publishing Group.

Faigley, Lester. Writing, A Guide for College & Beyond, Brief Edition, Books a la Carte Plus MyCompLab. 2nd ed. 2011. (ENG.). (C). ring bd. 68.00 ***(978-0-205-13131-0(X))*** Longman Publishing Group.

Faigley, Lester B. Writing: A Guide for College & Beyond. 3rd rev. ed. 2011. (ENG., Illus.). 736p. (C). 99.33 ***(978-0-205-22331-2(1))*** Longman Publishing Group.

—Writing: A Guide for College & Beyond, Books a la Carte Plus MyCompLab. 3rd ed. 2011. (ENG.). (C). ring bd. 71.33 ***(978-0-205-85510-0(5))*** Longman Publishing Group.

—Writing: A Guide for College & Beyond, Brief Edition. 3rd rev. ed. 2011. (ENG., Illus.). 704p. (C). pap. 94.33 ***(978-0-205-22329-9(X))*** Longman Publishing Group.

Fairbairn, Gavin & Winch, Christopher. Reading, Writing & Reasoning: A guide for Students. 3rd ed. 2011. (ENG.). 304p. (C). pap. 39.00 ***(978-0-335-23887-3(4)***, 0335238874) McGraw-Hill Education GBR. Dist: McGraw-Hill Cos., The.

Fajans, Elizabeth & Falk, Mary R. Scholarly Writing for Law Students, Seminar Papers, Law Review Notes & Law Review Competition Papers, 4th. 4th rev. ed. 2011. (American Casebook Ser.). 256p. 44.00 *(978-0-314-20720-3(1)*, West Legalworks) West.

Fanning, Paul. Grammar Practice for Professional Writing. 2009. 288p. pap. *(978-1-84748-573-6(2))* Athena Pr.

Feak, Christine & Swales, John M. Creating Contexts: Writing Introductions across Genres. 2011. (Michigan Series in English for Academic & Professional Purposes Ser.). (ENG., Illus.). 136p. (C). pap. 16.00 ***(978-0-472-03456-7(1))*** Univ. of Michigan Pr.

Feng-Checkett, Gayle & Checkett, Lawrence. The Write Start: Paragraphs to Essays with Student & Professional Readings. 4th ed. 2010. (Basic Writing Ser.). (ENG., Illus.). 528p. (C). pap. 110.95 *(978-0-495-80258-7(1))* Wadsworth.

Flateby, Terri L. Writing assessment Hb. 2007. pap. *(978-1-57922-183-6(1))* Stylus Publishing, LLC.

Fontaine, Sheryl I. & Smith, Cherryl. Writing Your Way Through College: A Student's Guide. 2008. 176p. pap., stu. ed. 26.25 *(978-0-86709-591-3(1)*, 0591, Boynton/Cook) Heinemann.

Foss, Sonja K. & Waters, William. Destination Dissertation: A Traveler's Guide to a Done Dissertation. Foss, Sonja K. & Waters, William, eds. 2007. (ENG.). 380p. 83.00 *(978-0-7425-5439-9(2))*; pap. 29.95 *(978-0-7425-5440-5(6))* Rowman & Littlefield Publishers, Inc.

Franke, David, et al. Design Discourse: Composing & Revising Programs in Professional & Technical Writing. 2010. *(978-1-60235-165-0(X))*; pap. *(978-1-60235-165-3(1))* Parlor Pr.

Friedman, Lauri S., ed. The War in Afghanistan. 2012. (Writing the Critical Essay: an Opposing Viewpoints Guide Ser.). (ENG., Illus.). 128p. (gr. 6-10). lib. bdg. 32.75 ***(978-0-7377-5911-2(9)***, Greenhaven Pr., Inc.) Cengage Gale.

Furman, Rich. Practical Tips for Publishing Scholarly Articles: Writing & Publishing in the Helping Professions. 2007. (ENG.). 128p. (C). 19.95 *(978-1-933478-07-4(1))* Lyceum Bks., Inc.

Furman, Rich & Kinn, Julie. Practical Tips for Publishing Scholarly Articles: Writing & Publishing in the Helping Professions. 2nd ed. 2012. (ENG.). xix, 127p. pap. 23.95 ***(978-1-935871-10-1(2))*** Lyceum Bks., Inc.

Gage, John T., ed. The Promise of Reason: Studies in the New Rhetoric. 2011. (Illus.). 272p. 60.00 *(978-0-8093-3025-6(3))* Southern Illinois Univ. Pr.

Ganobcsik-Williams, Lisa. Academic Writing: Theories & Practices. 2006. (Universities into the 21st Century Ser.). (ENG., Illus.). 256p. pap. 31.95 *(978-1-4039-4535-8(7))* Palgrave Macmillan.

Gaughan, Frank & Khost, Peter H. Collaborating(,) Literature(,) & Composition: Essays for Teachers & Writers of English. 2007. (C). *(978-1-57273-709-9(3))*; pap. *(978-1-57273-710-5(7))* Hampton Pr., Inc.

George, Diana & Trimbur, John. Reading Culture. 8th rev. ed. 2011. (ENG., Illus.). 576p. (C). pap. 76.40 ***(978-0-205-21125-8(9))*** Longman Publishing Group.

George, Diana & Trimbur, John. Reading Culture: Contexts for Critical Reading & Writing. 7th ed. 2009. (ENG.). 592p. (C). pap. 76.40 *(978-0-205-68807-4(1))* Longman Publishing Group.

Gibaldi, Joseph. MLA Handbook for Writers of Research Papers. 6th lit. ed. 2006. (Illus.). 361p. pap. 20.00 *(978-0-87352-987-7(1)*, S178L) Modern Language Assn. of America.

Gibaldi, Joseph & Modern Language Association of America Staff. MLA Handbook for Writers of Research Papers. 7th ed. 2009. (ENG., Illus.). xxi, 292p. pap. 22.00 *(978-1-60329-024-1(9))*; pap. 30.00 *(978-1-60329-025-8(7))* Modern Language Assn. of America.

Glau, Greg R. & De Duttagupta, ChitraLekha. Everyday Writing (with MyWritingLab Pearson eText Student Access Code Card) 2011. (ENG.). (C). pap. 89.20 ***(978-0-205-25441-5(1))*** Longman Publishing Group.

Glenn, Cheryl. Making Sense: A Real-World Rhetorical Reader. 3rd ed. 2010. (ENG.). 816p. (C). pap. 60.95 *(978-0-312-46383-0(9))* Bedford/Saint Martin's.

Godfrey, Jeanne. Writing for University. 2011. (Palgrave Pocket Guides). (ENG., Illus.). 96p. pap. 9.99 *(978-0-230-29120-1(1))* Palgrave Macmillan.

Goodall, H. L., Jr. Writing Qualitative Inquiry: Self, Stories, & Academic Life. 2008. (Writing Lives Ser.). (ENG., Illus.). 256p. (C). 94.00 *(978-1-59874-323-4(6))* Left Coast Pr., Inc.

Goodall, H. L., Jr., et al. Writing Qualitative Inquiry: Self, Stories, & Academic Life. 2009. (Writing Lives Ser.). (ENG.). 256p. (C). pap. 29.95 *(978-1-59874-324-1(4))* Left Coast Pr., Inc.

Goodson, Patricia. The Academic Writer's Workbook: 50 Exercises for Paced, Productive, & Powerful Writing. 2012. 248p. (C). pap. 35.00 ***(978-1-4522-0336-7(5)***, B03867P) SAGE Pubns., Inc.

Gordon, Avi. MBA Admissions Strategy: From profile building to essay Writing. 2nd ed. 2010. (ENG., Illus.). 240p. (C). pap. 30.00 *(978-0-335-24117-0(4)*, 0335241174) McGraw-Hill Education GBR. Dist: McGraw-Hill Cos., The.

Goshert, John. Entering the Academic Conversation: Strategies for Research Writing. 2010. (ENG.). 512p. (C). pap. 51.60 *(978-0-13-243597-0(7)*, Prentice Hall) Prentice Hall PTR.

Gotti, Maurizio. Commonality & Individuality in Academic Discourse. Gotti, Maurizio, ed. 2009. (Linguistic Insights. Studies in Language & Communication Ser.). 398p. pap. *(978-3-0343-0023-0(9))* Lang, Peter.

Graff, Gerald, et al. They Say / I Say: The Moves That Matter in Academic Writing with Readings. 2nd ed. 2011. (ENG.). 736p. (C). pap. 39.00 net. ***(978-0-393-91275-3(2)***, 91275) Norton, W. W. & Co., Inc.

Greasley, Pete. Doing Essays & Assignments: Essential Tips for Students. 2011. (Illus.). 192p. (C). 94.00 *(978-1-84920-202-2(8)*, B02022C); pap. 24.00 *(978-1-84920-203-9(6)*, B02022P) SAGE Pubns., Ltd. GBR. Dist: SAGE Pubns., Inc.

Green Lister, Pam. Integrating Social Work Theory & Practice. 2012. (Student Social Work Ser.). (ENG., Illus.). 144p. (C). 125.00 *(978-0-415-48112-0(0))* Routledge.

Greene, et al. From Inquiry to Academic Writing: A Practical Guide. 2nd ed. 2011. (ENG.). 368p. (C). pap. 40.95 *(978-0-312-60140-9(9))* Bedford/Saint Martin's.

Greene, Stuart & Lidinsky, April. From Inquiry to Academic Writing: A Practical Guide. 2nd ed. 2011. (Illus.). xx, 334p. ***(978-0-312-69233-9(1))*** Bedford/Saint Martin's.

—From Inquiry to Academic Writing: A Text & Reader. 2nd ed. 2012. (Illus.). xxxiii, 908p. ***(978-0-312-69232-2(3))*** Bedford/Saint Martin's.

Greene, Stuart & Lidinsky, April. From Inquiry to Academic Writing: A Text & Reader. 2nd ed. 2011. (ENG.). 944p. (C). pap. 72.95 ***(978-0-312-60141-6(7))*** Bedford/Saint Martin's.

Greer, Michael. What Every Student Should Know about Citing Sources with MLA Documentation, Update Edition. 2009. (What Every Student Should Know about... (WESSKA Series) Ser.). (ENG.). (C). pap. 9.80 *(978-0-205-71511-4(7))* Longman Publishing Group.

Greetham, Bryan. How to Write Better Essays. 2nd rev. ed. 2008. (Palgrave Study Skills Ser.). (ENG., Illus.). 320p. pap. 25.00 *(978-0-230-22480-3(6))* Palgrave Macmillan.

—How to Write Your Undergraduate Dissertation. 2009. (Palgrave Study Guides). (ENG., Illus.). 416p. pap. 25.00 *(978-0-230-21875-8(X))* Palgrave Macmillan.

Hacker, Diana. Writing in the Disciplines: A Hacker Handbooks Supplement. 7th ed. 2011. (ENG.). 144p. (C). pap. 9.95 *(978-0-312-65683-6(1))* Bedford/Saint Martin's.

Hacker, Diana & Sommers, Nancy. A Writer's Reference with Writing in the Disciplines. 7th ed. 2011. (ENG.). 736p. (C). spiral bd. 64.95 *(978-0-312-60144-7(1))* Bedford/Saint Martin's.

Hacker, Diana & Sommers, Nancy I. A Writer's Reference: [Instructor's Ed.]. 7th ed. 2011. (Illus.). xxvi, 31p. pap. 60.95 *(978-0-312-60146-1(8))* Bedford/Saint Martin's.

Hamilton, Carole L. Anthem Guide to Essay Writing. 2011. (ENG., Illus.). 216p. pap. 19.95 *(978-0-85728-975-9(6))* Anthem Pr. GBR. Dist: Books International, Inc.

Hamp-Lyons, Liz & Heasley, Ben. Study Writing: A Course in Written English for Academic Purposes. 2nd rev. ed. 2006. (ENG., Illus.). 214p. per. 27.04 *(978-0-521-53496-3(8))* Cambridge Univ. Pr.

Harris, Joseph. Rewriting: How to Do Things with Texts. 2006. (ENG.). 150p. (C). (gr. 10). per. 19.95 *(978-0-87421-642-4(7)*, Utah State Univ. Pr.) Univ. Pr. of Colorado.

Harris-Leonard, Barbara. Discoveries in Academic Writing. tchr. ed. *(978-0-15-507256-5(0))* Harcourt College Pubs.

Harris, Muriel G. Prentice Hall Reference Guide (with MyWritingLab Student Access Code Card) 7th ed. 2008. (ENG.). 624p. (C). pap. 75.00 *(978-0-205-70876-5(5)*, Prentice Hall) Prentice Hall PTR.

Harrison, Steven. How to write a PhD in less than 3 Years: A practical Guide. 2010. 120p. pap. 13.99 *(978-1-4520-8995-9(7))* AuthorHouse.

Hartley, James. Academic Writing & Publishing: A Practical Handbook. 2008. (Illus.). X, 198p. 150.00 *(978-0-415-45321-9(6))*; (ENG., 208p. 37.95 *(978-0-415-45322-6(4))* Routledge.

Hauptman, Robert. Authorial Ethics: How Writers Abuse Their Calling. 2011. (ENG.). 214p. 60.00 *(978-0-7391-3444-3(2))* Lexington Bks.

Haynes, Anthony. Writing Successful Academic Books. 2010. (ENG., Illus.). 192p. 60.00 *(978-0-521-51498-9(3))*; pap. 24.00 *(978-0-521-73074-7(0))* Cambridge Univ. Pr.

Henderson, Eric. The Active Reader: Strategies for Academic Reading & Writing. 2nd ed. 2012. (ENG., Illus.). 544p. 69.95 ***(978-0-19-543974-8(0))*** Oxford Univ. Pr., Inc.

Henderson, Eric. Writing by Choice. 2nd ed. 2011. (ENG.). 504p. pap. 62.95 *(978-0-19-543186-5(3))* Oxford Univ. Pr., Inc.

Hennessy, Brendan. How to Write Coursework & Exam Essays: An Accessible Guide to Developing the Skills Needed to Excel in Written Work & Exams. 6th rev. ed. 2011. (ENG., Illus.). 213p. pap. 20.00 *(978-1-84528-440-4(2)*, How To Books GBR. Dist: Parkwest Pubns., Inc.

—Writing an Essay: Simple Techniques to Transform Your Coursework & Examinations. 5th ed. 2008. (Illus.). 254p. pap. *(978-1-84528-249-3(3))* How To Books.

Herbert, Trevor. Music in Words: A Guide to Researching & Writing about Music. 2009. (ENG., Illus.). 256p. 99.00 *(978-0-19-537372-1(3))*; pap. 19.95 *(978-0-19-537373-8(1))* Oxford Univ. Pr., Inc.

Hewings. Academic Writing in Context: Implications & Applications. 2006. (ENG., Illus.). 256p. 70.00 *(978-0-8264-8131-3(0))* Continuum International Publishing Group, Ltd. GBR. Dist: National Bk. Network.

Hidi, Suzanne & Boscolo, Pietro, eds. Writing & Motivation. 2006. (Studies in Writing Ser.). (Illus.). 334p. 140.95 *(978-0-08-045325-5(2))* Emerald Group Publishing Ltd. GBR. Dist: Turpin Distribution Services Ltd.

Hirsh, David. Academic Vocabulary in Context. 2010. (Linguistic Insights. Studies in Language & Communication Ser.). (Illus.). 217p. pap. *(978-3-0343-0426-9(9))* Lang, Peter.

Hoffman, Gary & Hoffman, Glynis. Adios, Strunk & White, 4th Edition: A Handbook for the New Academic Essay. 2007. (ENG., Illus.). 256p. per. 18.95 *(978-0-937363-40-9(5))* Verve Pr.

Hoffman, Gary & Hoffman, Glynis. Adios, Strunk & White, 5th Edition: A Handbook for the New Academic Essay. 2011. (Illus.). 254p. pap. 20.95 ***(978-0-937363-41-6(3))*** Verve Pr.

Hogue, Ann. First Steps in Academic Writing. 2nd ed. 2007. (Illus.). 32p. *(978-0-13-241490-6(2))* Pearson Education.

—First Steps in Academic Writing. 2nd ed. 2007. (ENG., Illus.). x, 218p. (C). pap., stu. ed. 46.80 *(978-0-13-241488-3(0))* Prentice Hall, ESL Dept.

Hogue, Ann & Oshima, Alice. Introduction to Academic Writing. 3rd ed. 2006. (Illus.). xii, 221p. tchr. ed. *(978-0-13-241028-1(1))* Longman Publishing Group.

—Introduction to Academic Writing. 3rd ed. 2006. (ENG., Illus.). 221p. (C). pap 46.80 *(978-0-13-193395-8(7))* Prentice Hall, ESL Dept.

Hood, Susan. Appraising Research: Evaluation in Academic Writing. 2010. (ENG., Illus.). 240p. 89.00 *(978-0-230-55349-1(4))* Palgrave Macmillan.

How to Write an Exceptional Thesis or Dissertation: A Step-by-Step Guide from Proposal to Successful Defense. 2012. (ENG.). 288p. pap. 24.95 *(978-1-60138-603-8(6))* Atlantic Publishing Co.

Howard & Howard, Rebecca Moore. Research Matters. 2nd ed. 2012. (ENG., Illus.). 448p. (C). pap. 51.67 *(978-0-07-340594-0(9)*, 0073405949) McGraw-Hill Cos., The.

Howard & Taggart, Amy Rupiper. Research Matters. 2010. (ENG., Illus.). 480p. (C). pap. 51.67 *(978-0-07-338374-3(0)*, 0073383740) McGraw-Hill Cos., The.

Howard, Rebecca. Writing Matters. 2009. (ENG., Illus.). 992p. (C). 75.63 *(978-0-07-241875-0(3)*, 0072418753) McGraw-Hill Higher Education.

Howarth, Peter Andrew. Phraseology in English Academic Writing: Some Implications for language learning & dictionary Making. (Lexicographica. Series Maior Ser.). (ENG.). XIV, 230p. 165.00 ***(978-3-11-183704-8(1))*** De Gruyter, Walter Inc.

Huber, Sonya. The Backwards Research Guide for Writers: Using Your Life for Reflection, Connection & Inspiration. 2011. (Frameworks for Writing Ser.). (ENG., Illus.). 342p. (C). 115.00 *(978-1-84553-441-7(7))*; pap. 39.95 *(978-1-84553-442-4(5))* Equinox Publishing Ltd. GBR. Dist: ISD.

Hume, Stephen Eaton. Economics Writing. 2010. (ENG.). (C). pap. 46.67 *(978-0-555-00326-8(4))* Pearson Learning Solutions.

Hutchinson, Hazel. Write Winning Essays & Dissertations. 2011. (Teach Yourself Ser.). (ENG.). 252p. pap. 15.95 *(978-1-4441-0508-7(6)*, Hodder & Stoughton) Hodder General Publishing Div. GBR. Dist: Independent Pubs. Group.

Huttner, Julia Isabel. Academic Writing in a Foreign Language: An Extended Genre Analysis of Student Texts. (Illus.). 337p. pap. 68.95 *(978-3-631-55522-4(9))* Lang, Peter GmbH, Europaischer Verlag der Wissenschaften DEU. Dist: Lang, Peter Publishing, Inc.

—Academic Writing in a Foreign Language: An Extended Genre Analysis of Student Texts. 2007. (Sprache im Kontext Ser.: Vol. 28). 337p. pap. 68.95 *(978-0-8204-8702-1(3))* Lang, Peter Publishing, Inc.

Hyland, Ken. Writing in the Academy: Reputation, Education & Knowledge. 2007. (Professorial Lectures). (ENG., Illus.). 28p. per. 9.95 *(978-0-85473-771-0(5))* Institute of Education GBR. Dist: Stylus Publishing, LLC.

Hyland, Ken & Bondi, Marina. Academic Discourse Across Disciplines. 2006. (Illus.). 328p. pap. 82.95 *(978-3-03911-183-1(3))*; Vol. 42. 320p. pap. 59.95 *(978-0-8204-8396-2(6))* Lang, Peter Publishing, Inc.

Hyland, Ken & Diani, Giuliana, eds. Academic Evaluation: Review Genres in University Settings. 2009. (ENG., Illus.). 256p. 95.00 *(978-0-230-22433-9(4))* Palgrave Macmillan.

Irby, Beverly J., et al. Writing a Successful Thesis or Dissertation: Tips & Strategies for Students in the Social & Behavioral Sciences. 2007. (Illus.). 352p. 90.95 *(978-1-4129-4224-9(1)*, B42249C) Corwin Pr.

Isbell, Mary. Writing Through Literature: An Anthology of Literary Texts for Academic Inquiry. rev. ed. 2011. (ENG.). 370p. pap. 59.99 ***(978-0-7575-9068-9(3))*** Kendall Hunt Publishing Co.

Johnson, W. Brad, et al. Write to the Top! How to Become a Prolific Academic. 2007. (ENG.). 224p. 84.00 *(978-1-4039-7742-7(9))*; pap. 19.00 *(978-1-4039-7743-4(7))* Palgrave Macmillan.

Kane, Loretta. Conceptualizing Academic Essay Writing. 2008. 336p. pap. *(978-3-8364-9065-8(X))* VDM Verlag Dr. Mueller e.K.

Kaplan Publishing Staff, ed. Sharp Writing: Building Better Writing Skills. 4th ed. 2008. (Smart Ser.). (ENG.). 304p. pap. 9.95 *(978-1-4195-5037-9(3))* Kaplan Publishing.

Kas, Kinga. Teaching Theory & Academic Writing: A Guide to Undergraduate Lecturing in Political Science. Brosig, Malte & Kas, Brosig, eds. 2008. 160p. pap. 29.95 *(978-3-940755-01-8(X))* Budrich-Esser, Barbara DEU. Dist: International Specialized Bk. Services.

Kendall-Tackett, Kathleen A. How to Write for a General Audience: A Guide for Academics Who Want to Share Their Knowledge with the World & Have Fun Doing It. 2007. 286p. per. 19.95 *(978-0-9792125-3-6(7))* American Psychological Assn.

Kennedy, Mary Lynch & Kennedy, William J. Writing in the Disciplines: A Reader & Rhetoric for Academic Writers. 7th rev. ed. 2011. (ENG.). 640p. (C). pap. 90.67 *(978-0-205-72662-2(3))* Longman Publishing Group.

—Writing in the Disciplines: A Reader for Writers. 6th ed. 2007. (ENG., Illus.). 704p. (C). per. 87.00 *(978-0-13-231999-7(3)*, Prentice Hall) Prentice Hall PTR.

Kennedy, Mary Lynch & Smith, Hadley M. Reading & Writing in the Academic Community. 4th ed. 2009. (ENG.). 552p. (C). pap. 89.60 *(978-0-205-68946-0(9)*, Prentice Hall) Prentice Hall PTR.

Kirszner, Laurie G. Literature: Reading, Reacting, Writing. pap. 55.95 *(978-0-8384-7489-1(6))*; pap. 47.95 *(978-0-8384-7294-1(X))*; pap. 47.95 *(978-0-8384-7280-4(X))*; pap. 47.95 *(978-0-8384-7277-4(X))*; pap. 74.95 *(978-0-8384-8038-0(1))*; pap. 47.95 *(978-0-8384-7300-9(8))*; pap. 47.95 *(978-0-8384-7299-6(0))*; pap. 47.95 *(978-0-8384-7298-9(2))*; pap. 47.95 *(978-0-8384-7295-8(8))*; pap. 47.95 *(978-0-8384-7291-0(5))*; pap. 47.95 *(978-0-8384-7290-3(7))*; pap. 47.95 *(978-0-8384-7281-1(8))*; 4th ed. pap. 65.95 *(978-0-8384-7250-7(8))*; 4th ed. pap. 65.95 *(978-0-8384-7236-1(2))*; 4th ed. pap. 65.95 *(978-0-8384-7237-8(0))*; 4th ed. pap. 65.95 *(978-0-8384-7245-3(1))*; 4th ed. pap. 65.95 *(978-0-8384-7235-4(4))*; 4th ed. pap. 65.95 *(978-0-8384-7248-4(6))*; 4th ed. pap. 65.95 *(978-0-8384-7253-8(2))*; 4th ed. pap. 65.95 *(978-0-8384-7246-0(X))*; 4th ed. pap. 65.95 *(978-0-8384-7244-6(3))*; 4th ed. pap. 65.95 *(978-0-8384-7241-5(9))*; 4th ed. pap. 77.95 *(978-0-8384-7239-2(7))* Cengage Heinle.

Kirszner, Laurie G. & Mandell, Stephen R. Patterns for College Writing with 2009 MLA Update: A Rhetorical Reader & Guide. 11th ed. 2009. (ENG.). 864p. (C). pap. 60.95 *(978-0-312-60152-2(2))* Bedford/Saint Martin's.

—Portable Literature: Reading, Reacting, Writing. 7th ed. 2009. (ENG.). 1280p. (C). pap. 67.95 *(978-1-4282-6296-6(2))* Wadsworth.

Kitchens, Marshall & DeVoss, Danielle. Writing Culture. 2009. (ENG.). 576p. (C). pap. 53.33 *(978-0-321-46845-1(7))* Longman Publishing.

Koppl, Heidi I. Establishing Appearances as Divine: Rongzom Chozang on Reasoning, Madhyamaka, & Purity. 2008. (TIB & ENG.). 152p. 29.95 *(978-1-55939-288-4(5))* Snow Lion Pubns., Inc.

Kroeker, Dean. Undergraduate Writing Guide: Writing tools for the Adult Student (APA 5th Edition) 2007. 60p. per. 14.95 *(978-1-4327-0519-0(9))* Outskirts Pr., Inc.

Lague, Victoria. Formulas for Composition. 3rd rev. ed. 2011. (ENG.). 128p. pap. 54.26 *(978-0-7575-6637-0(5))* Kendall Hunt Publishing Co.

Levin. Excellent Dissertations! 2nd ed. 2011. (ENG.). 152p. (C). pap. 20.00 ***(978-0-335-23861-3(0)***, 0335238610) McGraw-Hill Education GBR. Dist: McGraw-Hill Cos., The.

Levin, Peter. Write Great Essays! 2nd ed. 2009. (ENG., Illus.). 200p. (C). pap. 20.00 *(978-0-335-23727-2(4)*, 0335237274) McGraw-Hill Education GBR. Dist: McGraw-Hill Cos., The.

Levy, Stacia. Lexical Bundles. 2010. 184p. pap. *(978-3-8383-1809-7(9))* Lambert Academic Publishing.

—Lexical Bundles in Professional & Student Writing. 2008. 148p. pap. *(978-3-639-05697-6(3))* VDM Verlag Dr. Mueller e.K.

Lewis, Jill. Academic Literacy: Readings & Strategies. 4th ed. 2006. (ENG., Illus.). 656p. (C). pap. 108.95 *(978-0-618-63946-5(2)*, 332991) CENGAGE Learning.

—Academic Literacy: Readings & Strategies. 4th ed. 2007. (Illus.). xxii, 632p. *(978-0-618-73204-3(7))* Houghton Mifflin Harcourt Publishing Co.

Lillis, Theresa & Curry, Mary Jane. Academic Writing. 2010. (ENG., Illus.). 224p. 44.95 *(978-0-415-46883-1(3))*; 140.00 *(978-0-415-46881-7(7))* Routledge.

Lockwood, Robyn Brinks & Folse, Keith S. Four Point Listening & Speaking Intro: English for Academic Purposes, 13 vols. Folse, Keith S., ed. 2011. (Four Point Ser.). (ENG.). 208p. (C). 25.50 ***(978-0-472-03472-7(3))*** Univ. of Michigan Pr.

Lopez, Nancy. Unequal Educations: Dismantling the Achievement Gaps. 2015. (ENG.). 224p. pap. 31.95 *(978-0-415-87507-3(2))* Routledge.

Luey, Beth. Revising Your Dissertation: Advice from Leading Editors. Luey, Beth, ed. 2nd rev. ed. 2007. (Illus.). 263p. per. 21.95 *(978-0-520-25401-5(5))* Univ. of California Pr.

Lunsford, Andrea A. EasyWriter, Canadian Edition: A Pocket Reference. 4th ed. 2010. (ENG.). 368p. (C). pap. 26.95 *(978-0-312-61442-3(X))* Bedford/Saint Martin's.

—Exercises for EasyWriter. 4th ed. 2009. (ENG.). 144p. (C). pap. 9.95 *(978-0-312-58387-3(7))* Bedford/Saint Martin's.

—The St. Martin's Handbook. 7th ed. 2011. (ENG.). 992p. (C). 77.95 *(978-0-312-60292-5(8))*; pap. 73.95 *(978-0-312-60293-2(6))* Bedford/Saint Martin's.

Lussier, Robert N. Publish Don't Perish: 100 Tips That Improve Your Ability to Get Published. 2010. *(978-1-61735-114-3(8))*; pap. *(978-1-61735-113-6(X))*; E-Book *(978-1-61735-115-0(6))* Information Age Publishing, Inc.

Lykke, Nina, ed. Writing Academic Texts Differently: Intersectional Feminist Methodologies & the Playful Art of Writing. 2012. (Routledge Advances in Feminist Studies & Intersectionality Ser.). (ENG.). 256p. (C). 125.00 ***(978-0-415-50225-2(X))*** Routledge.

Lynn, Steven J. Texts & Contexts: Writing about Literature with Critical Theory. 6th ed. 2010. (ENG.). 288p. (C). pap. 64.00 *(978-0-205-71674-6(1)*, Prentice Hall) Prentice Hall PTR.

Mabbett, I. W. Writing History Essays. 2006. (ENG.). 192p. stu. ed. 95.00 *(978-1-4039-9769-2(1))* Palgrave Macmillan.

—Writing History Essays. 2006. (ENG.). 184p. pap., stu. ed. 24.00 *(978-1-4039-9770-8(5))* Palgrave Macmillan.

MacDonald, Susan Peck. Professional Academic Writing in the Humanities & Social Sciences. 2010. (ENG.). 250p. pap. 35.00 *(978-0-8093-3007-2(5))* Southern Illinois Univ. Pr.

Macgowan-Gilhooly, Adele. Achieving Clarity in English: A Whole-Language Book. 5th rev. ed. 2010. (ENG.). 210p. pap. 32.33 *(978-0-7575-5690-6(6))* Kendall Hunt Publishing Co.

Mailloux, Steven. Disciplinary Identities: Rhetorical Paths of English, Speech, & Composition. 2006. 165p. per. 19.75 *(978-0-87352-974-7(X))*; (Illus.). 37.50 *(978-0-87352-973-0(1))* Modern Language Assn. of America.

Maimon, Elaine & Peritz, Janice. Writing Intensive. 2nd ed. 2008. (Illus.). 464p. (C). pap., spiral bd. 26.25 *(978-0-07-729367-3(3)*, 0077293673, McGraw-Hill Humanities, Social Sciences & World Languages) McGraw-Hill Higher Education.

—Writing Intensive, MLA / APA / CSE Update. 2nd ed. 2008. 464p. (C). pap. 26.25 *(978-0-07-332768-6(9)*, 9780073327686, McGraw-Hill Humanities, Social Sciences & World Languages) McGraw-Hill Higher Education.

Maimon, Elaine, et al. The Brief McGraw-Hill Handbook. 2010. (ENG.). (C). spiral bd. 49.67 *(978-0-07-739622-0(7)*, 0077396227) McGraw-Hill Cos., The.

—Catalyst. 2008. (C). 79.69 *(978-0-07-729540-0(4)*, 9780077295400, McGraw-Hill Humanities, Social Sciences & World Languages) McGraw-Hill Higher Education.

—The McGraw-Hill Handbook. 2nd ed. 2009. (ENG.). (C). 110.67 *(978-0-07-735569-2(5)*, 0077355695) McGraw-Hill Cos., The.

—The McGraw-Hill Handbook. 3rd ed. 2011. (ENG., Illus.). 1024p. (C). 103.00 ***(978-0-07-338404-7(6)***, 0073384046) McGraw-Hill Cos., The.

—The McGraw-Hill Handbook. 3rd ed. 2011. (ENG., Illus.). 1024p. (C). pap. 103.00 ***(978-0-07-739730-2(4)***, 0077397304) McGraw-Hill Cos., The.

—The McGraw-Hill Handbook Includes 2009 MLA & APA Updates. 2nd ed. 2009. (ENG.). (C). 101.67 *(978-0-07-739577-3(8)*, 0077395778) McGraw-Hill Cos., The.

—New Mcgraw-Hill Handbook. 2008. (ENG., Illus.). 1120p. (C). pap., pap. 82.19 *(978-0-07-729539-4(0)*, 0077295390, McGraw-Hill Humanities, Social Sciences & World Languages) McGraw-Hill Higher Education.

—New Mcgraw-Hill Handbook (hardcover) MLA / APA / CSE Update. 2008. 1120p. (C). 73.13 *(978-0-07-338368-2(6)*, 9780073383682, McGraw-Hill Humanities, Social Sciences & World Languages) McGraw-Hill Higher Education.

Maimon, Elaine P. & Peritz, Janice. Writing Intensive. (Illus.). 2007. 398p. *(978-0-07-313093-4(1))* 2nd ed. 2012. (ENG., 480p. (C). spiral bd. 33.67 ***(978-0-07-338405-4(4)***, 0073384054) McGraw-Hill Cos., The.

Maimon, Elaine P., et al. The Brief McGraw-Hill Handbook. 2nd ed. 2011. (ENG., Illus.). 704p. (C). pap. 49.67 ***(978-0-07-338398-9(8)***, 0073383988) McGraw-Hill Cos., The.

Mallette, Leo & Berger, Clare. Writing for Conferences: A Handbook for Graduate Students & Faculty. 2011. E-Book *(978-0-313-39407-2(5)*, Greenwood Pr.) Greenwood Publishing Group, Inc.

Mallette, Leo A. & Berger, Clare. Writing for Conferences: A Handbook for Graduate Students & Faculty, 1 vol. (Illus.). 229p. 2011. 55.00 *(978-0-313-39406-5(7)*, A3418C) pap. 29.95 *(978-0-313-39408-9(3)*, A3419P) ABC-CLIO, LLC.

Maples, Wendy & Redman, Peter. Good Essay Writing: A Social Sciences Guide. 3rd ed. 2011. (SAGE Study Skills Ser.). (Illus.). 184p. (C). 104.00 *(978-0-85702-370-4(5)*, B23704C); pap. 21.00 *(978-0-85702-371-1(3)*, B23704P) SAGE Pubns., Ltd. GBR. Dist: SAGE Pubns., Inc.

Marius, Richard & Page, Melvin E. A Short Guide to Writing about History. 8th ed. 2012. (Illus.). xiv, 219p. pap. ***(978-0-205-11905-9(0))*** Pearson Bks.

Marius, Richard A. & Page, Mel. A Short Guide to Writing about History. 7th ed. 2009. (Short Guides Ser.). (ENG.). 240p. (C). pap. 42.00 *(978-0-205-67370-4(8))* Longman Publishing.

Marius, Richard A. & Page, Melvin E. A Short Guide to Writing about History. 8th rev. ed. 2011. (ENG., Illus.). 240p. (C). pap. 43.80 ***(978-0-205-11860-1(7))*** Longman Publishing Group.

Markman, Peter T., et al. 10 Steps in Writing the Research Paper. 7th rev. ed. 2011. (ENG., Illus.). 176p. pap. 12.99 *(978-0-7641-4598-8(3))* Barron's Educational Series, Inc.

Mayfield, Marlys. Thinking for Yourself. 5th ed. pap. 80.95 *(978-0-8384-8956-7(7))* Cengage Heinle.

—Thinking for Yourself. 8th ed. 2009. (Available Titles CengageNOW Ser.). (ENG.). 416p. (C). pap. 110.95 *(978-1-4282-3144-3(7))* Wadsworth.

McShane, Marilyn D. & Williams, Frank P., III. A Thesis Resource Guide for Criminology & Criminal Justice. 2006. (ENG., Illus.). 240p. (C). per. 63.60 *(978-0-13-236895-7(1)*, Prentice Hall) Prentice Hall PTR.

Melzer, Dan. Exploring College Writing: Reading, Writing & Researching across the Curriculum. 2012. (Frameworks for Writing Ser.). (ENG., Illus.). 448p. (C). 130.00 *(978-1-84553-780-7(7))* Equinox Publishing Ltd. GBR. Dist: ISD.

Miller, Alison B. Finish Your Dissertation Once & for All! How to Overcome Psychological Barriers, Get Results, & Move on with Your Life. 2008. 264p. (C). pap. 29.95 *(978-1-4338-0415-1(8))* American Psychological Assn.

Miller, Robert Keith. The Informed Argument: Brief Edition. pap. 39.95 *(978-0-8384-5273-8(6))* Cengage Heinle.

Miller, Toby, et al. Connections: Literature for Composition. 2007. (ENG.). 1504p. (C). pap. 116.95 *(978-0-618-48114-9(1)*, 337790) Cengage Heinle.

Modern Language Association of America Staff, creator. MLA Style Manual & Guide to Scholarly Publishing. 3rd ed. 2008. (ENG., Illus.). 336p. 32.50 *(978-0-87352-297-7(4))* Modern Language Assn. of America.

Modern Language Association of America Staff, ed. MLA Style Manual & Guide to Scholarly Publishing. 3rd l.t. ed. 2008. (ENG.). 400p. pap. 37.50 *(978-0-87352-298-4(2))* Modern Language Assn. of America.

Monroe, Jonathan, ed. Local Knowledges, Local Practices: Writing in the Disciplines at Cornell. 2006. (Pitt Comp Literacy Culture Ser.). (Illus.). 320p. (C). per. 25.95 *(978-0-8229-5961-8(5))* Univ. of Pittsburgh Pr.

Moran, Kathleen & Henderson, Eric. The Empowered Writer: Writing, Reading, & Research. 2010. (ENG., Illus.). 520p. 59.95 *(978-0-19-543161-2(8))* Oxford Univ. Pr., Inc.

Moreno, Michael P. & Brunnemer, Kristin C. Term Paper Resource Guide to Latino History, 1 vol. 2010. (Term Paper Resource Guides). 345p. 65.00 *(978-0-313-37932-1(7)*, GR7932) Greenwood Publishing Group, Inc.

Muller, Gilbert. The McGraw-Hill Reader: Issues Across the Disciplines. 11th ed. 2010. (ENG., Illus.). 912p. (C). pap. 88.67 *(978-0-07-338394-1(5)*, 0073383945) McGraw-Hill Cos., The.

Muller, Gilbert H. The Brief McGraw-Hill Reader: Issues Across the Disciplines. 2011. (ENG., Illus.). 528p. (C). pap. 62.33 *(978-0-07-340599-5(X)*, 007340599X) McGraw-Hill Cos., The.

Murray, Donald. Write to Learn. 7th ed. pap. 56.95 *(978-0-8384-9240-6(1))*; pap. 44.95 *(978-0-8384-9173-7(1))*; pap. 37.95 *(978-0-8384-9170-6(7))* Cengage Heinle.

Murray, Neil & Hughes, Geraldine. Writing up your university assignments & research Projects. 2008. (ENG., Illus.). 256p. (C). 107.00 *(978-0-335-22718-1(X)*, 033522718X) McGraw-Hill Education GBR. Dist: McGraw-Hill Cos., The.

—Writing up Your University Assignments & Research Projects: A Practical Handbook. 2008. (ENG., Illus.). 256p. (C). pap. 30.00 *(978-0-335-22717-4(1)*, 0335227171) McGraw-Hill Education GBR. Dist: McGraw-Hill Cos., The.

Murray, Rowena. How to Write a Thesis. 3rd ed. 2011. (ENG.). 384p. (C). pap. 39.00 *(978-0-335-24428-7(9)*, 0335244289) McGraw-Hill Education GBR. Dist: McGraw-Hill Cos., The.

—Writing for Academic Journals. 2nd ed. 2009. (ENG.). 288p. (C). pap. 40.00 *(978-0-335-23458-5(5)*, 0335234585) McGraw-Hill Education GBR. Dist: McGraw-Hill Cos., The.

Murray, Rowena & Moore, Sarah. The Handbook of Academic Writing. 2006. (Illus.). 216p. (C). 136.95 *(978-0-335-21934-6(9)*, 9780335219346, Open University Pr.) McGraw-Hill Education GBR. Dist: McGraw-Hill Cos., The.

—The Handbook of Academic Writing: A Fresh Approach. 2006. (Illus.). 216p. (C). pap. 57.00 *(978-0-335-21933-9(0)*, 0335219330, Open University Pr.) McGraw-Hill Education GBR. Dist: McGraw-Hill Cos., The.

Nash, Robert J. Me-Search & Re-Search: A Guide for Writing Scholarly Personal Narrative Manuscripts. 2011. ***(978-1-61735-394-9(9))***; pap. ***(978-1-61735-393-2(0))***; E-Book ***(978-1-61735-395-6(7))*** Information Age Publishing, Inc.

National Writing Project Staff. Writing for a Change: Boosting Literacy & Learning Through Social Action. Boulton, Ian et al, eds. 2006. (ENG., Illus.). 192p. per. 22.95 *(978-0-7879-8657-5(7)*, Jossey-Bass) Wiley, John & Sons, Inc.

Neville, Colin. How to Improve Your Assignment Results. (ENG., Illus.). 184p. (C). 2009. 98.00 *(978-0-335-23436-3(4)*, 0335234364) 2008. pap. 26.00 *(978-0-335-23437-0(2)*, 0335234372) McGraw-Hill Education GBR. Dist: McGraw-Hill Cos., The.

Noguchi, Judy. The Science Review Article: An Opportune Genre in the Construction of Science. 2006. 274p. pap. 73.95 *(978-3-03910-426-0(8))* Lang, Peter Publishing, Inc.

Obrecht, Fred. Barron's California State University Writing Proficiency Exams. 4th rev. ed. 2011. (ENG., Illus.). 360p. pap. 16.99 *(978-0-7641-4574-2(6))* Barron's Educational Series, Inc.

O'Hara, Mark, et al. Successful Dissertations: The Complete Guide for Education, Childhood & Early Childhood Studies. 2011. (ENG., Illus.). 288p. 29.95 *(978-1-4411-1275-0(8))*; 100.00 *(978-0-8264-2728-1(6))* Continuum International Publishing Group, Ltd. GBR. Dist: National Bk. Network.

Oliver, Paul. Writing Your Thesis. 2nd ed. 2008. (SAGE Study Skills Ser.). (Illus.). 184p. (C). 121.00 *(978-1-4129-4688-9(3)*, B46889C); pap. 49.00 *(978-1-4129-4689-6(1)*, B46889P) SAGE Pubns., Ltd. GBR. Dist: SAGE Pubns., Inc.

Olsen, Amy E. Reading Across the Disciplines & Academic Vocabulary: Academic Words, MyReadingLab — Valuepack Access Card (12-month access), Thinking Through the Test: A Study Guide for the Florida College Basic Skill Exit Test, Reading & Writing - w/o Answers. 4th ed. 2011. (ENG.). (C). pap., pap., pap. 111.40 ***(978-0-205-24878-0(0))*** Longman Publishing Group.

O'Neill, Peggy & Smith, William L. Blurring Boundaries: Developing Writers, Researchers & Teachers: A Tribute to William L. Smith. 2006. (Research & Teaching in Rhetoric & Composition Ser.). (Illus.). (C). viii, 379p. *(978-1-57273-708-2(5))*; *(978-1-57273-707-5(7))* Hampton Pr., Inc.

Owtram, Nicola T. The Pragmatics of Academic Writing: A Relevance Approach to the Analysis of Research Article Introductions. 2010. (ENG., Illus.). 311p. pap. *(978-3-0343-0060-5(3))* Lang, Peter.

Page, Mary & Winstanley, Carrie. Writing Essays for Dummies. 2009. (ENG., Illus.). 332p. pap. 21.99 ***(978-0-470-74290-7(9)***, For Dummies) Wiley, John & Sons, Inc.

Palmquist, Mike. The Bedford Researcher. 4th ed. 2011. (ENG., Illus.). 496p. (C). spiral bd. 44.95 *(978-0-312-67512-7(7))* Bedford/Saint Martin's.

PALTRIDGE. Thesis & Diss Writing in a SEC La. 2007. (Illus.). VIII, 192p. 41.95 *(978-0-415-37173-5(2))*; 170.00 *(978-0-415-37170-4(8))* Routledge.

Paltridge, Brian Richard, et al. Teaching Academic Writing: An Introduction for Teachers of Second Language Writers. 2009. (Michigan Teacher Training Ser.). (ENG., Illus.). 200p. pap. 28.50 *(978-0-472-03334-8(4))* Univ. of Michigan Pr.

Paquot, Magali. Academic Vocabulary in Learner Writing: From Extraction to Analysis. 2010. (Corpus & Discourse Ser.). (ENG., Illus.). 256p. 140.00 *(978-1-4411-3036-5(5))* Continuum International Publishing Group, Ltd. GBR. Dist: National Bk. Network.

Patton, Martha Davis. Writing in the Research University: A Darwinian Study of WID with Cases from Civil Engineering. 2010. (Illus.). 336p. *(978-1-57273-900-0(2))*; pap. *(978-1-57273-901-7(0))* Hampton Pr., Inc.

Pawar, Badrinarayan Shankar & Monippally, Mathukutty M. Academic Writing: A Guide for Management Students & Researchers. 2010. (Response Bks.). (Illus.). 264p. (C). pap. 33.00 *(978-81-321-0441-4(2)*, B04414P) SAGE Pubns., Inc.

Payne, Darin & Desser, Daphne. Teaching Writing in Globalization: Remapping Disciplinary Work. 2011. E-Book ***(978-0-7391-7244-5(1))*** Lexington Bks.

Pecorari, Diane. Academic Writing & Plagiarism: A Linguistic Analysis. 2010. (ENG.). 224p. pap. 44.95 *(978-1-4411-3953-5(2))* Continuum International Publishing Group, Ltd. GBR. Dist: National Bk. Network.

—Academic Writing & Plagiarism: A Linguistic Anaylsis. 2008. (ENG.). 224p. 150.00 *(978-0-8264-9166-4(9))* Continuum International Publishing Group, Ltd. GBR. Dist: National Bk. Network.

Perelman, Chaïm & Gage, John T. The Promise of Reason: Studies in the New Rhetoric. 2011. E-Book 60.00 ***(978-0-8093-8628-4(3))*** Southern Illinois Univ. Pr.

Peters, Michael A., ed. Academic Writing, Philosophy & Genre. 2009. (Educational Philosophy & Theory Special Issues Ser.: 5). (ENG.). 128p. pap. 39.95 *(978-1-4051-9400-6(6)*, Wiley-Blackwell) Wiley, John & Sons, Inc.

Pharr, Donald & Buscemi, Santi V. Writing Today. 2nd ed. 2008. (ENG., Illus.). 880p. (C). pap. 98.00 *(978-0-07-353322-3(X)*, 007353322X) McGraw-Hill Cos., The.

Pike, David L. & Acosta, Ana. Literature: A World of Writing Stories, Poems, Plays, & Essays, Books a la Carte Edition. 2011. (ENG.). 736p. (C). ring bd. 39.33 *(978-0-205-22171-4(8))* Longman Publishing Group.

—Literature: A World of Writing Stories, Poems, Plays, & Essays, Books a la Carte plus MyLiteratureLab. 2011. (ENG.). (C). ring bd. 46.00 *(978-0-205-22197-4(1))* Longman Publishing Group.

Piltch, Charles & Terry, Karen J. A Short Guide to Writing about Criminal Justice. 2010. (ENG.). 160p. (C). pap. 43.40 *(978-0-13-802902-9(4)*, Prentice Hall) Prentice Hall PTR.

Poore, Megan & Craswell, Gail. Writing for Academic Success. 2nd ed. 2012. (SAGE Study Skills Ser.). (Illus.). 264p. (C). 100.00 ***(978-0-85702-927-0(4)***, B29270C); pap. 43.00 ***(978-0-85702-928-7(2)***, B29270P) SAGE Pubns., Ltd. GBR. Dist: SAGE Pubns., Inc.

Pryal, Katie Rose Guest. Short Guide to Writing about Law. 2010. (ENG.). 240p. (C). pap. 41.60 *(978-0-205-75201-0(2))* Longman Publishing Group.

Rabinowitz, Harold & Vogel, Suzanne. The Manual of Scientific Style: A Guide for Authors, Editors, & Researchers. Rabinowitz, Harold & Vogel, Suzanne, eds. 2009. (ENG., Illus.). 984p. 56.95 *(978-0-12-373980-3(2)*, Academic Pr.) Elsevier Science & Technology Bks.

Rankin, Jamie & Wells, Larry. Student Activity Manual for Rankin/Wells' Handbuch zur deutschen Grammatik. 5th ed. 2010. (ENG.). 208p. (C). 86.95 *(978-0-495-90594-3(1))* Cengage Heinle.

Ridge, Noel. A Teachers' Guide to Genre Grades 3-8: Improving reading & writing by knowing how texts Work. 2008. (Professional Bks.). pap. 35.00 *(978-1-60457-150-9(0))* Pacific Learning, Inc.

Ridley, Diana. The Literature Review: A Step-by-Step Guide for Students. 2008. (SAGE Study Skills Ser.). (Illus.). 184p. (C). pap. 41.00 *(978-1-4129-3426-8(5)*, B34257P) SAGE Pubns., Ltd. GBR. Dist: SAGE Pubns., Inc.

Ritter, Kelly. Before Shaughnessy: Basic Writing at Yale & Harvard, 1920-1960. 2nd ed. 2009. (Studies in Writing & Rhetoric Ser.). (ENG.). 192p. pap. 32.00 *(978-0-8093-2924-3(7))* Southern Illinois Univ. Pr.

Ritter, Kelly. To Know Her Own History: Writing at the Woman's College, 1943-1963. 2012. (Pitt Comp Literacy Culture Ser.). (ENG.). 264p. pap. 27.95 ***(978-0-8229-6186-4(5))*** Univ. of Pittsburgh Pr.

Roberts, Edgar V. Writing about Literature. 11th ed. 2006. pap. *(978-0-13-615615-4(0))* Pearson Education Canada.

—Writing about Literature. (ENG.). (C). 12th ed. 2009. 432p. pap. 60.00 *(978-0-13-601456-0(9))* 13th rev. ed. 2011. (Illus.). 400p. pap. 60.00 ***(978-0-205-23031-0(8))*** Prentice Hall PTR. (Prentice Hall).

Rocco, Tonette S. & Hatcher, Timothy G. The Handbook of Scholarly Writing & Publishing. 2011. (ENG., Illus.). 368p. pap. 35.00 *(978-0-470-39335-2(1)*, Jossey-Bass) Wiley, John & Sons, Inc.

Rose, Jean. The Mature Student's Guide to Writing. 2nd rev. ed. 2007. (Palgrave Study Guides). (ENG., Illus.). 344p. pap. 25.00 *(978-1-4039-8995-6(8))* Palgrave Macmillan.

Rosen, Leonard J. Academic Writer's Handbook. (ENG., (C). 2nd ed. 2008. Illus.). 592p. spiral bd. 72.80 *(978-0-205-66178-7(5))* 3rd ed. 2010. 576p. pap. 75.00 *(978-0-205-71761-3(6))* Longman Publishing Group.

Rosen, Leonard J. & Behrens, Laurence. Writing & Reading Across the Curriculum, Books a la Carte Plus MyCompLab. 11th ed. 2011. (ENG.). (C). ring bd. 61.33 ***(978-0-205-23855-2(6))*** Longman Publishing Group.

Rosenwasser, David. Writing Analytically. 3rd ed. pap. 33.95 *(978-0-8384-7098-5(X))* Cengage Heinle.

Rosenwasser, David & Stephen, Jill. Writing Analytically. 6th ed. 2011. (ENG.). 496p. (C). pap. 77.95 *(978-0-495-91008-4(2))* Wadsworth.

—Writing Analytically with Readings. 2nd ed. 2011. (ENG.). 864p. (C). pap. 90.95 *(978-0-495-91007-7(4))* Wadsworth.

Rossen-Knill, Deborah F. & Bakhmetyeva, Tatyana. Including Students in Academic Conversations: Principles & Strategies for Teaching Theme-Based Writing Courses Across the Disciplines. 2011. (Illus.). 258p. *(978-1-61289-015-9(6))*; *(978-1-61289-014-2(8))* Hampton Pr., Inc.

Ruetten, Mary K., et al. Refining Composition Skills. 6th ed. 2011. (Developing / Refining Composition Skills Ser.). (ENG.). 432p. (C). pap., stu. ed. 50.95 *(978-1-111-22119-5(7))* Cengage Heinle.

Ruszkiewicz, John J. How to Write Anything: A Guide & Reference. 2nd ed. 2012. (ENG.). 704p. (C). pap. 49.95 ***(978-0-312-67490-8(2))*** Bedford/Saint Martin's.

Ruszkiewicz, John J. How to Write Anything with 2009 MLA & 2010 APA Updates. 2010. (ENG.). 608p. (C). pap. 49.95 *(978-0-312-66831-0(7))* Bedford/Saint Martin's.

Ruszkiewicz, John J. & Dolmage, Jay T. How to Write Anything: A Guide & Reference with Readings with 2009 MLA & 2010 APA Updates. rev. ed. 2010. (ENG.). 910p. (C). pap. 65.95 *(978-0-312-66830-3(9))* Bedford/Saint Martin's.

Ruszkiewicz, John J. & Dolmage, Jay T. How to Write Anything: A Guide & Reference with Readings. 2nd ed. 2012. (ENG.). 1072p. (C). pap. 65.95 ***(978-0-312-67489-2(9))*** Bedford/Saint Martin's.

Sabrio, David & Burchfield, Mitchel. Insightful Writing: A Process Rhetoric with Readings. 2008. (ENG., Illus.). 336p. (C). pap. 83.95 *(978-0-618-87026-4(1)*, 351085) CENGAGE Learning.

Sabrio, David & Burchfield, Mitchell. Insightful Writing: A Process Rhetoric with Readings. 2009. (Illus.). xvii, 302p. *(978-0-618-95840-5(1))* Houghton Mifflin Harcourt Publishing Co.

Salager-Meyer, Françoise & Lewin, Beverly A. Crossed Words: Criticism in Scholarly Writing. 2011. (Linguistic Insights. Studies in Language & Communication Ser.). (Illus.). 371p. pap. ***(978-3-0343-0049-0(2))*** Lang, Peter.

Savage, Alice, et al. Effective Academic Writing: Answer Key 1: Answer Key 1. 2007. (ENG.). 14p. pap. *(978-0-19-430882-3(0))* Oxford Univ. Pr., Inc.

Schilb, John & Clifford, John. Making Literature Matter: An Anthology for Readers & Writers. 5th ed. 2011. (ENG.). 1712p. (C). pap. 82.95 *(978-0-312-65354-5(9))* Bedford/Saint Martin's.

—Making Literature Matter with 2009 MLA Update: An Anthology for Readers & Writers. 4th ed. 2010. (ENG.). 1600p. (C). pap. 82.95 *(978-0-312-67730-5(8))* Bedford/Saint Martin's.

Schmidt, Diane E. Writing in Political Science: A Practical Guide. 4th ed. 2009. (ENG.). 400p. (C). pap. 61.20 *(978-0-205-61736-4(0))* Longman Publishing Group.

Scott, Gregory M. & Garrison, Stephen M. The Political Science Student Writer's Manual. 7th ed. 2011. (ENG.). 216p. (C). spiral bd. 43.00 *(978-0-205-83012-1(9))* Longman Publishing Group.

—The Political Science Student Writer's Manual. 6th ed. 2007. (ENG.). 312p. (C). per. 58.80 *(978-0-13-602945-8(0))* Prentice Hall Higher Education.

Scott, Tony. Dangerous Writing: Understanding the Political Economy of Composition. 2009. (ENG.). 216p. (gr. 13). pap. 24.95 *(978-0-87421-734-6(2)*, Utah State Univ. Pr.) Univ. Pr. of Colorado.

Sebranek, Patrick, et al. Write, No. 1. 2011. (ENG.). 496p. (C). pap. 68.95 *(978-0-618-64219-9(6))* Wadsworth.

—Write 2. 2011. (Basic Writing Ser.). (ENG.). 528p. (C). pap. 67.95 *(978-0-618-64286-1(2))* Wadsworth.

See, Patti & Taylor, Bruce. Higher Learning: Reading & Writing about College. 3rd ed. 2011. (ENG., Illus.). 304p. (C). pap. 27.00 *(978-0-13-231801-3(6)*, Prentice Hall) Prentice Hall PTR.

Seech, Zachary. Writing Philosophy Papers. 5th ed. 2008. (ENG.). 176p. (C). per. 52.95 *(978-0-495-50684-3(2))* Wadsworth.

Shiach, Don. How to Write Essays. 2nd ed. 2009. (Illus.). 240p. pap. 20.00 *(978-1-84528-341-4(4))* How To Books GBR. Dist: Parkwest Pubns., Inc.

—How to Write Essays: A Step-by-Step Guide for All Levels, with Sample Essays. 2006. (Illus.). 163p. per. 20.00 *(978-1-84528-164-9(0))* How To Books GBR. Dist: Parkwest Pubns., Inc.

Shields, MunLing. Essay Writing. 2010. (SAGE Study Skills Ser.). (Illus.). 240p. (C). stu. ed. 102.00 *(978-1-84787-089-6(9)*, B70896C) SAGE Pubns., Ltd. GBR. Dist: SAGE Pubns., Inc.

—Essay Writing: A Student's Guide. 2010. (SAGE Study Skills Ser.). (Illus.). 240p. (C). pap. 26.00 *(978-1-84787-090-2(2)*, B70896P) SAGE Pubns., Ltd. GBR. Dist: SAGE Pubns., Inc.

Shipka, Jody. Toward a Composition Made Whole. 2011. (Pitt Comp Literacy Culture Ser.). (ENG., Illus.). 176p. pap. 24.95 *(978-0-8229-6150-5(4))* Univ. of Pittsburgh Pr.

Silvia, Paul J. How to Write a Lot: A Practical Guide to Productive Academic Writing. 2007. (Illus.). 149p. per. 14.95 *(978-1-59147-743-3(3))* American Psychological Assn.

Sims, Marcie. Sims: Write Stuff The. 2011. (ENG.). (C). pap. 103.60 ***(978-0-205-18907-6(5))*** Longman Publishing Group.

—The Write Stuff: Paragraphs. 2011. (ENG.). 672p. (C). pap. 103.60 ***(978-0-13-224306-3(7))*** Longman Publishing Group.

—The Write Stuff: Paragraphs, Books a la Carte Edition. 2011. (ENG.). 672p. (C). ring bd. 66.00 ***(978-0-205-11394-1(X))*** Longman Publishing Group.

—The Write Stuff: Paragraphs, Books a la Carte Plus MyWritingLab. 2011. (ENG.). (C). ring bd. 72.67 ***(978-0-205-11403-0(2))*** Longman Publishing Group.

—The Write Stuff: Thinking Through Essays. 2nd ed. 2011. (ENG.). (C). 752p. pap. 103.60 *(978-0-205-02952-5(3))*; 768p. pap. 103.60 *(978-0-205-10182-5(8))*; ring bd. 74.67 *(978-0-205-11415-3(6))* Longman Publishing Group.

—The Write Stuff: Thinking Through Essays, Books a la Carte Edition. 2nd ed. 2011. (ENG.). 752p. (C). ring bd. 68.00 *(978-0-205-11413-9(X))* Longman Publishing Group.

—The Write Stuff: Thinking Through Essays (with MyWritingLab Student Access Code Card) 2008. 720p. (C). pap. 76.67 *(978-0-205-63368-5(4))* Prentice Hall Higher Education.

—The Write Stuff: Thinking Through Essays (with MyWritingLab Student Access Code Card) 2008. (ENG.). 768p. (C). 86.60 *(978-0-205-70873-4(0)*, Prentice Hall) Prentice Hall PTR.

Single, Peg Boyle. Demystifying Dissertation Writing: A Streamlined Process from Choice of Topic to Final Text. 2009. 192p. 70.00 *(978-1-57922-312-0(5))*; pap. 19.95 *(978-1-57922-313-7(3))* Stylus Publishing, LLC.

Smith, Pauline. How to Write an Assignment. 7th ed. 2009. (Illus.). 128p. 18.00 *(978-1-84528-352-0(X))* How To Books GBR. Dist: Parkwest Pubns., Inc.

—How to Write an Assignment: Proven Techniques for Producing Essays, Reports & Dissertations That Succeed. 8th rev. ed. 2011. (ENG., Illus.). 102p. pap. 18.00 *(978-1-84528-441-1(0))* How To Books GBR. Dist: Parkwest Pubns., Inc.

Soles, Derek. The Essentials of Academic Writing. 2nd ed. 2009. (ENG.). 456p. (C). pap. 57.95 *(978-0-547-18133-2(7))* Wadsworth.

Starke-Meyerring, Doreen. Writing in Knowledge Societies. 2011. 452p. ***(978-1-60235-269-8(0))***; ***(978-1-60235-271-1(2))***; 452p. pap. ***(978-1-60235-268-1(2))*** Parlor Pr.

Storey, William Kelleher. Writing History: A Guide for Students. 4th ed. 2012. 144p. (Orig.). (C). pap. 19.95 ***(978-0-19-983004-6(5))*** Oxford Univ. Pr., Inc.

Strahan, Linda, et al. Write It Review: A Process Approach to College Essays with Readings. 3rd rev. ed. 2012. (ENG.). 462p. pap. 64.01 *(978-0-7575-6719-3(2))* Kendall Hunt Publishing Co.

Stubbs, Andrew James. Rhetoric, Uncertainty, & the University As Text: How Students Construct the Academic Experience. 2008. (Canadian Plains Studies(CPS) Ser.). (ENG.). 250p. pap. 29.95 *(978-0-88977-203-8(7))* Canadian Plains Research Ctr. CAN. Dist: Univ. of Toronto Pr.

Sunstein, Bonnie Stone & Chiseri-Strater, Elizabeth. FieldWorking: Reading & Writing Research. 4th ed. 2011. (ENG.). 432p. (C). pap. 46.95 *(978-0-312-62275-6(9))* Bedford/Saint Martin's.

Swales, John M. & Feak, Christine. Navigating Academia: Writing Supporting Genres. 2011. (Michigan Series in English for Academic & Professional Purposes Ser.). (ENG., Illus.). 120p. (C). pap. 16.00 *(978-0-472-03453-6(7))* Univ. of Michigan Pr.

Sword, Helen. Stylish Academic Writing. 2012. (ENG., Illus.). 240p. 21.95 ***(978-0-674-06448-5(8))*** Harvard Univ. Pr.

Takayoshi, Pamela & Sullivan, Patricia. Labor, Writing Technologies, & the Shaping of Composition in the Academy. 2006. (New Dimensions in Computers & Composition Ser.). (Illus.). (C). *(978-1-57273-666-5(6))*; ix, 349p. *(978-1-57273-667-2(4))* Hampton Pr., Inc.

Tang, Ramona. Academic Writing in a Second or Foreign Language: Issues & challenges facing ESL/EFL academic Writers. 2012. (ENG., Illus.). 272p. 140.00 *(978-1-4411-1216-3(2)*, Continuum International Publishing Group, Ltd. GBR. Dist: National Bk. Network.

Tardy, Christine M. Building Genre Knowledge. 2009. 332p. *(978-1-60235-113-4(9))*; 332p. pap. *(978-1-60235-112-7(0))*; E-Book *(978-1-60235-114-1(7))* Parlor Pr.

Thomson, William. A Guide for the Young Economist. 2nd ed. 2011. (ENG., Illus.). 184p. (gr. 17). 44.00 *(978-0-262-01616-2(3))*; pap. 22.00 *(978-0-262-51589-4(X))* MIT Pr.

Thonney, Teresa. Writing Across & Within the Disciplines. 2007. 528p. (C). pap. 58.67 *(978-0-321-48047-7(3))* Longman Publishing.

Topping, Donna & McManus, Roberta. Stuck in the Middle: Helping Adolescents Read & Write in the Content Areas. 2010. 168p. pap. 23.75 *(978-0-325-02146-1(5)*, E02146) Heinemann.

Tovares, Raul Damacio & Tovares, Alia V. How to Write about the Media Today. 1 vol. 2010. (Writing Today Ser.). 183p. 35.00 *(978-0-313-37519-4(4)*, GR7519) Greenwood Publishing Group, Inc.

Troiano, Edna M. & Draus, Julia A. Write to Know: A Cross-Disciplinary Approach to Composition. (C). *(978-0-15-503133-3(3))* Harcourt College Pubs.

Turabian, Kate L. A Manual for Writers of Research Papers, Theses, & Dissertations: Chicago Style for Students & Researchers. 7th ed. 2007. (Chicago Guides to Writing, Editing, & Publishing Ser.). (ENG., Illus.). 482p. 40.00 *(978-0-226-82336-2(9))* Univ. of Chicago Pr.

—Student's Guide to Writing College Papers. Colomb, Gregory G. et al, eds. 4th ed. 2010. (Chicago Guides to Writing, Editing, & Publishing Ser.). (Illus.). (C). 304p. stu. ed. 39.00 *(978-0-226-81630-2(3))*; (ENG., 288p. pap., stu. ed. 15.00 *(978-0-226-81631-9(1))* Univ. of Chicago Pr.

Turabian, Kate L., et al. A Manual for Writers of Research Papers, Theses, & Dissertations: Chicago Style for Students & Researchers. 7th rev. ed. 2007. (Chicago Guides to Writing, Editing, & Publishing Ser.). (Illus.). 436p. per. 17.00 *(978-0-226-82337-9(7))* Univ. of Chicago Pr.

Veit, Richard & Gould, Christopher. Writing, Reading, & Research. 8th ed. 2009. (ENG., Illus.). 640p. (C). pap. 112.95 *(978-0-547-19104-1(9))* Wadsworth.

Vernon, Laura. What Every Student Should Know About... Writing Across the Curriculum. 2007. (What Every Student Should Know About... (WESSKA Series) Ser.). (ENG.). 112p. (C). pap. 9.80 *(978-0-205-58913-5(8))* Longman Publishing Group.

Vopat, Jim. Micro Lessons in Writing, 3 vols. 2007. (Illus.). 96p. pap. 27.50 *(978-0-325-01077-9(3)*, E01077) Heinemann.

Wallace, Mike & Wray, Alison. Critical Reading & Writing for Postgraduates. 2nd ed. 2011. (SAGE Study Skills Ser.). (Illus.). 264p. (C). 104.00 *(978-1-84920-561-0(2)*, B05610C); pap. 45.00 *(978-1-84920-562-7(0)*, B05610P) SAGE Pubns., Ltd. GBR. Dist: SAGE Pubns., Inc.

Walliman, Nicholas, et al. Your Dissertation in Education. 2008. (SAGE Study Skills Ser.). (Illus.). 328p. (C). 105.00 *(978-1-4129-4622-3(0)*, B46220C); pap. 49.00 *(978-1-4129-4623-0(9)*, B46220P) SAGE Pubns., Ltd. GBR. Dist: SAGE Pubns., Inc.

Wang, Fei. Problems in Learning to Present Qualitative Research in Written Form: Four Case Studies. 2011. 240p. 119.95 *(978-0-7734-1540-9(8))* Mellen, Edwin Pr., The.

Waye, Laurie. Managing Your Thesis or Dissertation: A Workbook for Graduate Students. rev. ed. 2011. (ENG.). 106p. spiral bd. 34.00 *(978-0-7575-8764-1(X))* Kendall Hunt Publishing Co.

Weideman, Albert. Academic Literacy: Prepare to Learn. 2nd ed. 2007. (Illus.). xii, 237p. *(978-0-627-02690-4(7))* Van Schaik Uitgewers.

Wilhoit, Stephen. Wilhoit: Brief Guide Writin Readin_6. 6th rev. ed. 2011. (ENG.). 336p. (C). pap. 65.33 ***(978-0-205-24574-1(9))*** Longman Publishing Group.

Wilhoit, Stephen W. A Brief Guide to Writing Academic Arguments. 2008. (Pearson English Value Textbook Ser.). (ENG.). 352p. (C). pap. 46.60 *(978-0-205-56861-1(0))* Longman Publishing Group.

Williams, Kate, et al. Reflective Writing. 2012. (Pocket Study Skills Ser.). (ENG., Illus.). 128p. (C). pap. 10.00 ***(978-0-230-37725-7(4))*** Palgrave Macmillan.

Willis, Jerry & Valenti, Ron. Completing a Professional Practice Dissertation: A Guide for Doctoral Students & Faculty. 2010. (Illus.). 418p. *(978-1-60752-440-3(6))*; pap. *(978-1-60752-439-7(2))* Information Age Publishing, Inc.

Wilson, Douglas & Wilson, Nathan D. The Rhetoric Companion Answer Key. 2011. 8.00 ***(978-1-59128-103-0(2))*** Canon Pr.

Windell, James. The Student's Guide to Writing a Criminal Justice Research Paper. rev. ed. 2010. (ENG.). 74p. spiral bd. 35.87 *(978-0-7575-7643-0(5))* Kendall Hunt Publishing Co.

Wolffensperger, Yochie. What's in Academic Literacy Mentoring. 2011. 284p. pap. ***(978-3-8443-8348-5(4))*** Lambert Academic Publishing.

Yagelski, Robert P. Reading Our World. 2nd ed. 2009. (ENG.). 768p. (C). pap. 97.95 *(978-1-4282-3125-2(0))* Wadsworth.

Yong, Fung Lan. Academic Writing. 2010. 176p. pap. *(978-3-8383-8894-6(1))* Lambert Academic Publishing.

Zwier, Lawrence J. Mastering Academic Reading. 2010. (ENG., Illus.). 248p. (C). pap. 28.95 *(978-0-472-03223-5(2))* Univ. of Michigan Pr.

Zwier, Lawrence J. & Bennett, Gena R. Teaching a Lexis-Based Academic Writing Course: A Guide to Building Academic Vocabulary. 2006. (ENG., Illus.). 264p. (C). per. 28.00 *(978-0-472-03101-6(5))* Univ. of Michigan Pr.

ACADEMIE DE FRANCE A ROME

see Accademia di Francia (Rome, Italy)

ACADEMIE DES JEUX FLORAUX (FRANCE)

Dawson, John Charles. Toulouse in the Renaissance: The Floral Games; University & Student Life; Etienne Dolet 1532-1534. 216p. 2008. 39.95 *(978-1-4366-7303-7(8))* 2007. per. 24.95 *(978-1-4304-8659-6(7))* Kessinger Publishing, LLC.

ACADEMIES (LEARNED SOCIETIES)

see Learned Institutions and Societies; Societies

ACADEMY AWARDS (MOTION PICTURES)

Beale, Charles. Frankly Speaking. 2007. (Faber Edition: Choral Basics Ser.). (ENG.). pap. 5.50 *(978-0-571-52630-7(6))* Faber & Faber, Ltd. GBR. Dist: Alfred Publishing Co., Inc.

Clark, Henry. Academy Award Diary, 1928-1955. 2011. 192p. 42.95 ***(978-1-258-06159-3(7))*** Literary Licensing, LLC.

Cosgrave, Bronwyn. Made for Each Other: Fashion & the Academy Awards. 2006. (ENG., Illus.). 320p. 29.95 *(978-1-59691-087-4(9))* Bloomsbury Publishing.

Granozio, Gerald. So You Think You Know Oscar: Test Your Academy Award I. Q. 2007. 62p. pap. 9.00 *(978-0-8059-7516-1(0))* Dorrance Publishing Co., Inc.

Kinn, Gail & Piazza, Jim. The Academy Awards: The Complete Unofficial History. rev. ed. 2011. (ENG., Illus.). 368p. pap. 22.95 *(978-1-57912-878-4(5)*, 1579128785) Black Dog & Leventhal Pubs., Inc.

Levy, Emanuel. All about Oscar: The History & Politics of the Academy Awards. 2007. (Illus.). 400p. 30.00 *(978-1-4223-6631-8(6))* DIANE Publishing Co.

Mapp, Edward. African Americans & the Oscar: Decades of Struggle & Achievement. 2nd ed. 2008. (ENG., Illus.). 218p. 50.00 *(978-0-8108-6105-3(4))*; per. 25.00 *(978-0-8108-6106-0(2))* Scarecrow Pr., Inc.

Osborne, Robert & Osborne, Robert A. 80 Years of the Oscar: The Official History of the Academy Awards. 2008. (ENG., Illus.). 439p. 75.00 *(978-0-7892-0992-4(6))* Abbeville Pr., Inc.

Pawlak, Debra Ann. Bringing up Oscar: The Story of the Men & Women Who Founded the Academy. 2011. (ENG., Illus.). 336p. 27.95 *(978-1-60598-137-6(0)*, 605137) Pegasus Bks.

Perry, Joel. The Q Guide to Oscar Parties & Other Award Shows. 2007. (Q Guides: Lifestyle Out There Ser.). (ENG.). 180p. per. 12.95 *(978-1-55583-988-8(6))* Alyson Pubns.

Robert. 80 Years of the Oscars: The Official History of the Academy Awards. 2008. (Illus.). 432p. 75.00 *(978-0-7895-0992-5(X))* Abbeville Pr., Inc.

Vogel, Frederick G. Hollywood Musicals Nominated for Best Picture. alt. ed. 2009. (ENG.). 384p. pap. 45.00 *(978-0-7864-4342-0(1))* McFarland & Co., Inc. Pubs.

ACADEMY OF MOTION PICTURE ARTS AND SCIENCES

Pawlak, Debra Ann. Bringing up Oscar: The Story of the Men & Women Who Founded the Academy. 2011. (ENG., Illus.). 336p. 27.95 *(978-1-60598-137-6(0)*, 605137) Pegasus Bks.

ACADIA

Here are entered works about the area of French territorial possessions on the Atlantic seaboard between New England and the Gulf of Saint Lawrence during the 17th and early part of the 18th centuries.

Cozzens, Frederic Swartwout. Acadia, or, a Month with the Blue Noses. 2006. 340p. per. 23.99 *(978-1-4255-3407-3(4))* MPublishing.

Denys, Nicolas. The Description & Natural History of the Coasts of North America (Acadia) 625p. reprint ed. 128.00 *(978-0-7222-6726-4(6))* Library Reprints, Inc.

Doughty, Arthur George. The Acadian Exiles: A Chronicle of the Land of Evangeline. 178p. reprint ed. 88.00 *(978-0-7222-6767-7(3))* Library Reprints, Inc.

—The Acadian Exiles: A Chronicle of the Land of Evangeline Chronicles of Canada series: Volume 09. 2007. 100p. pap. 16.99 *(978-1-4346-4545-6(2))* BiblioBazaar.

—The Acadian Exiles: A Chronicle of the Land of Evangeline Chronicles of Canada series: Volume 10. l.t. ed. 2007. (ENG.). 112p. pap. 19.99 *(978-1-4346-4546-3(0))* BiblioBazaar.

Ganong, William F. Champlain's Island: An Expanded Edition of Ste. Croix (Dochet) Island. exp. ed. (Illus.). 172p. pap. 15.95 *(978-0-919326-57-6(9))* New Brunswick Museum CAN. Dist: Goose Lane Editions.

Lescarbot, Marc. History of New France, 3 vol., set. (Publications of the Champlain Society). reprint ed. 375.00 *(978-0-7222-6738-7(X))* Library Reprints, Inc.

Perrin, Warren A. Une Saga Acadienne, 1755-2003: De Beausoleil Broussard à la Proclamation Royale. 2009. (Illus.). 242p. pap. 22.75 *(978-0-9768927-1-7(5))* Andrepont Publishing.

Slafter, Edmund F., ed. Sir William Alexander & American Colonization: Including Three Royal Charters. 2007. (ENG.). 290p. 43.95 *(978-0-548-21515-9(4))*; 292p. per. 28.95 *(978-1-4325-3488-2(2))* Kessinger Publishing, LLC.

Slafter, Edmund Farwell. Sir William Alexander & American Colonization. 2009. 300p. 24.99 *(978-1-103-52040-4(7))*; pap. 18.99 *(978-1-103-52036-7(9))* BiblioBazaar.

—Sir William Alexander & American Colonization. 2009. 182p. pap. 19.99 *(978-0-217-79134-2(4))* General Bks. LLC.

Slafter, Edmund Farwell, et al. Sir William Alexander & American Colonization: Including Three Royal Charters; a Tract on Colonization; a Patent of the County of Canada & of Lo. 2010. 314p. pap. 29.75 *(978-1-146-57596-6(3))* BiblioBazaar.

Swandick, Eric. The Acadiensis Index, 1971-1991. 177p. pap. 15.95 *(978-0-919107-35-9(4))* Acadiensis Pr. CAN. Dist: Goose Lane Editions.

ACADIA NATIONAL PARK (ME.)

Abrell, Diane. Carriage Roads of Acadia National Park. 3rd ed. 2011. (ENG.). 64p. pap. 7.95 *(978-0-89272-924-1(4))* Down East Bks.

Camuto, Christopher. Time & Tide in Acadia: Seasons on Mount Desert Island. 2010. (ENG.). 216p. pap. 16.95 *(978-0-88150-912-0(4)*, 150912) Countryman Pr.

Kavanagh, James. Acadia National Park Wildlife: An Introduction to Familiar Species. 2006. (Pocket Naturalist - Waterford Press Ser.). (ENG., Illus.). 1p. 5.95 *(978-1-58355-355-8(X))* Waterford Pr., Inc.

Kong, Dolores & Ring, Dan. Acadia National Park. 2nd ed. 2011. (Best Easy Day Hikes Ser.). (ENG., Illus.). 112p. pap. 9.95 *(978-0-7627-6132-6(6)*, Falcon Guides) Globe Pequot Pr., The.

—Best Easy Day Hiking Guide & Trail Map Bundle: Acadia National Park. 2nd ed. 2011. (Best Easy Day Hikes Ser.). (ENG.). pap. 19.95 *(978-0-7627-7159-2(3)*, Falcon Guides) Globe Pequot Pr., The.

LiBrizzi, Marcus. Ghosts of Acadia. 2011. (ENG.). 144p. pap. 12.95 *(978-0-89272-921-0(X))* Down East Bks.

Malitz, Jerome & Malitz, Susan. Acadia National Park: Dayhiker's Guide: Maine's Coastal Gem. 2007. (Illus.). 144p. pap. 17.00 *(978-1-55566-337-7(0))* Johnson Bks.

Manning, Robert E., ed. Parks & People: Managing Outdoor Recreation at Acadia National Park. 2009. (ENG., Illus.). 352p. pap. 49.95 *(978-1-58465-791-0(X)*, University of Vermont Press) Univ. Pr. of New England.

Minetor, Randi S. Acadia National Park Pocket Guide. 2008. (Falcon Guide Ser.). (ENG., Illus.). 96p. 9.95 *(978-0-7627-4802-0(8)*, Falcon Guides) Globe Pequot Pr., The.

Monkman, Jerry & Monkman, Marcy. Discover Acadia National Park: The Best Hiking, Biking, & Paddling. 3rd ed. 2010. (AMC Discover Ser.). (ENG., Illus.). 288p. pap. 21.95 *(978-1-934028-29-2(0))* Appalachian Mountain Club Bks.

—The Photographer's Guide to Acadia National Park. 2010. (Photographer's Guide Ser.). (ENG., Illus.). 96p. pap. 14.95 *(978-0-88150-886-4(1)*, 150886) Countryman Pr.

—Wild Acadia: A Photographic Journey to New England's Oldest National Park. 2007. (ENG., Illus.). 122p. 19.95 *(978-1-58465-524-4(0))* Univ. Pr. of New England.

Nangle, Hilary. Acadia National Park. 3rd ed. 2009. (Moon Handbooks Ser.). (ENG.). 312p. pap. 17.95 *(978-1-56691-985-2(1))* Westview Pr.

—Moon Coastal Maine: Including Acadia National Park. 2010. (Moon Handbooks). (ENG., Illus.). 480p. pap. 19.95 *(978-1-59880-363-1(8))* Avalon Travel Publishing.

Nyiri, Alan. Acadia Panorama: Images of Maine's National Park. 2008. (ENG., Illus.). 82p. pap. 18.95 *(978-0-89272-740-7(3))* Down East Bks.

Taylor, Marie C. Doggy Walks & Destinations Acadia National Park & Vicinity. 2007. per. 8.95 *(978-0-9797334-0-6(5))* 2nd ed. 2008. (ENG., Illus.). 102p. pap. 8.95 *(978-0-9797334-1-3(3))* On Point, Inc.

ACADIANS

Bleakney, J. Sherman. Sods, Soil, & Spades: The Acadians at Grand Pré & Their Dykeland Legacy. 2009. (ENG., Illus.). 320p. (C). pap. *(978-0-7735-3550-3(0))* McGill-Queen's Univ. Pr.

Chetro-Szivos, John. Talking Acadian: Communication, Work, & Culture. 2006. per. 27.95 *(978-0-9764359-6-9(9))* YBK Pubs., Inc.

Griffiths, Naomi E. S. The Golden Age of Liberalism: A Portrait of Roméo Leblanc. 2011. (ENG., Illus.). 376p. 35.00 ***(978-1-55277-896-8(7))*** Lorimer, James & Co., Ltd., Pubs. CAN. Dist: Casemate Pubs. & Bk. Distributors, LLC.

Hodson, Christopher. The Acadian Diaspora: An Eighteenth-Century History. 2012. (ENG., Illus.). 272p. 34.95 ***(978-0-19-973977-6(3))*** Oxford Univ. Pr., Inc.

Lanteigne, Florent. The Fisherman's Wife. 2012. (ENG.). 125p. pap. 14.95 ***(978-0-9865278-9-0(0))*** DreamCatcher Publishing CAN. Dist: Univ. of Toronto Pr.

Loya, Alex. History of the Cajuns (from Ancient France to Nova Scotia to Louisiana to Colonial Texas) Including the Participation of Louisiana & Texas in the American Revolution. 2007. per. 30.00 *(978-1-60458-144-7(1))* Instant Pub.

Lundy, Kathleen Gould. Broken Dreams. 2007. (Timeline Ser.). (Illus.). 48p. pap. 8.99 *(978-1-4190-4403-8(6))* Houghton Mifflin Harcourt Supplemental Pubs.

Madore, Nelson & Rodrigue, Barry, eds. Voyages: A Maine Franco-American & Acadian Reader. 2010. (Illus.). 480p. pap. 30.00 *(978-0-88448-294-9(4))* Tilbury Hse. Pubs.

Magord, André. The Quest for Autonomy in Acadia. 2009. (Études Canadiennes - Canadian Studies). 183p. pap. 40.95 *(978-90-5201-476-0(0))* PIE - Peter Lang BEL. Dist: Lang, Peter.

Marshall, Dianne. Heroes of the Acadian Resistance: The Story of Joseph Beausoleil Broussard & Pierre II Surette, 1702-1765. 2011. (ENG., Illus.). 208p. pap. 22.95 ***(978-0-88780-978-1(2))*** Formac Publishing Co., Ltd. CAN. Dist: Casemate Pubs. & Bk. Distributors, LLC.

Perrin, Warren A. Une Saga Acadienne, 1755-2003: De Beausoleil Broussard à la Proclamation Royale. 2009. (Illus.). 242p. pap. 22.75 *(978-0-9768927-1-7(5))* Andrepont Publishing.

Reed, William B. The Acadian Exiles, or French Neutrals, in Pennsylvania to Which Is Appended a Relation of Their Misfortunes, by John Baptiste Galerm. 2011. 34p. pap. 11.99 ***(978-1-4181-9445-1(X))*** MPublishing.

Richard, Edouard. Acadia, 2 vol., reprint ed. 250.00 *(978-0-7222-6824-7(6))* Library Reprints, Inc.

Robichaud, Stella & Robichaud, Hélène. La Corneille et le Goéland. 2009. (FRE., Illus.). 162p. *(978-2-89627-177-1(5))* Editions de la Francophonie.

Rudin, Ronald. Remembering & Forgetting in Acadie: A Historian's Journey Through Public Memory. 2009. (ENG.). 384p. *(978-0-8020-9950-1(5))*; pap. *(978-0-8020-9657-9(3))* Univ. of Toronto Pr.

Runte, Hans R., et al. Entre Textes et Images: Constructions Identitaires en Acadie et Au Québec. 2010. (FRE., Illus.). 392p. *(978-0-9810041-5-0(6))* Institut d'études acadiennes.

Savoie, Donald J. I'm from Bouctouche, Me: Roots Matter. 2009. (Footprints Ser.). (ENG., Illus.). 288p. *(978-0-7735-3575-6(6))* McGill-Queen's Univ. Pr.

—Moi, Je Suis de Bouctouche: Les Racines Bien Ancrées. 2009. (FRE & ENG., Illus.). 224p. (C). *(978-0-7735-3576-3(4))* McGill-Queen's Univ. Pr.

ACANTHACEAE

Beentje, Henk J. & Ghazanfar, S. A., eds. Flora of Tropical East Africa: Acanthaceae II, 2 vols. 2010. (Royal Botanic Gardens, Kew-Flora of Tropical East Africa Ser.). (Illus.). 350p. pap. 136.00 *(978-1-84246-386-4(1))* Kew Publishing GBR. Dist: Chicago Distribution Ctr.

Kulyal, Poonam. Chemical Constituents Isolated from Andrographis Paniculat. 2011. 80p. pap. *(978-3-8433-7600-6(X))* Lambert Academic Publishing.

ACANTHOCEPHALA

Crompton, D. W. T. An Ecological Approach to Acanthocephalan Physiology. 2009. (Cambridge Monographs in Experimental Biology Ser.). (ENG.). 136p. pap. 31.99 *(978-0-521-10470-8(X))* Cambridge Univ. Pr.

Crompton, D. W. T. & Nickol, Brent B., eds. Biology of the Acanthocephala. 2009. (ENG.). 532p. pap. 63.00 *(978-0-521-10511-8(0))* Cambridge Univ. Pr.

Kennedy, C. R. Ecology of the Acanthocephala. 2006. (ENG., Illus.). 260p. 148.00 *(978-0-521-85008-7(8))* Cambridge Univ. Pr.

Nasira, Khatoon & Bilqees, F. M. Acanthocephala of Vertebrates a World Record. 2011. 576p. pap. *(978-3-639-32875-2(2))* VDM Verlag Dr. Mueller e.K.

ACAPULCO (MEXICO)—GUIDEBOOKS

Whipperman, Bruce. Acapulco, Ixtapa & Zihuatanejo. 3rd ed. 2009. (Moon Handbooks Ser.). (ENG.). 400p. pap. 19.95 *(978-1-59880-087-6(6))* Westview Pr.

ACARI

see Mites

ACARINA

see Ticks

ACAROLOGY

see also Mites; Ticks

Bernini, Fabio, et al, eds. Acarid Phylogeny & Evolution: Adaptation in Mites & Ticks. 2012. (ENG.). 472p. pap. 299.00 *(978-90-481-5950-5(4), 9048159504)* Springer.

Hoy, Marjorie. Agricultural Acarology: Introduction to Integrated Mite Management. 2011. (ENG., Illus.). 430p. 99.95 *(978-1-4398-1751-3(0),* CRC Press) Taylor & Francis Group GBR. Dist: Taylor & Francis Group.

Sabelis, Maurice. Trends in Acarology: Proceedings of the 12th International Congress. Sabelis, Maurice W. & Bruin, Jan, eds. 2010. (Illus.). xx, 650p. 279.00 *(978-90-481-9836-8(4), 9048198364)* Springer.

ACCADEMIA DI FRANCIA (ROME, ITALY)

Franchi-Verney. L' Académie de France À Rome, 1666-1903. 2009. 184p. 26.99 *(978-1-110-76954-4(7))*; pap. 21.75 *(978-1-110-76952-0(0))* BiblioBazaar.

ACCADIAN LANGUAGE

see Akkadian Language

ACCADIANS (SUMERIANS)

see Sumerians

ACCELERATED READING

see Developmental Reading; Speed Reading

ACCELERATION (MECHANICS)

see also Inertia (Mechanics)

Berman, Marcelo Samuel. General Relativity & the Pioneers Anomaly. 2011. (Physics Research & Technology Ser.). 75.00 *(978-1-62100-003-7(6))* Nova Science Pubs., Inc.

Li, Gang. Particle Acceleration & Transport in the Heliosphere & Beyond: 7th Annual International Astrophysics Conference. Li, Gang et al, eds. 2008. (AIP Conference Proceedings / Astronomy & Astrophysics Ser.). 454p. 209.00 *(978-0-7354-0566-0(2))* American Institute of Physics.

Toledo, Tomer. Integrated Model of Driving Behavior. 2008. 200p. per. *(978-3-8364-3556-7(X))* VDM Verlag Dr. Mueller e.K.

ACCELERATORS, ELECTRON

see Particle Accelerators

ACCELERATORS, LINEAR

see Linear Accelerators

ACCEPTANCE (CONTRACTS)

see Offer and Acceptance

ACCEPTANCE, SOCIAL

see Social Acceptance

ACCEPTANCE AND COMMITMENT THERAPY

see also Commitment (Psychology); Self-Acceptance

Acceptance & Mindfulness at Work: Applying Acceptance & Commitment Therapy & Relational Frame Theory to Organizational Behavior Management. 2006. (ENG., Illus.). 194p. 57.95 *(978-0-7890-3478-6(6))*; per. 41.95 *(978-0-7890-3479-3(4))* Routledge.

Bach, Patricia A. & Moran, Daniel J. ACT in Practice: Case Conceptualization in Acceptance & Commitment Therapy. 2008. (Professional Ser.). (ENG., Illus.). 352p. 59.95 *(978-1-57224-478-8(X))* New Harbinger Pubns.

Batten, Sonja. Essentials of Acceptance & Commitment Therapy. 2011. 136p. (C). 104.00 *(978-1-84920-167-4(6),* B01674C); pap. 39.00 *(978-1-84920-168-1(4),* B01674P) SAGE Pubns., Ltd. GBR. Dist: SAGE Pubns., Inc.

Blackledge, J. T., et al, eds. Acceptance & Commitment Therapy: Contemporary Theory, Research & Practice. 2009. (ENG.). 348p. pap. 59.95 *(978-1-921513-14-5(4))* Australian Academic Pr. AUS. Dist: Ingram Pub. Services.

Blonna, Richard. Maximize Your Coaching Effectiveness with Acceptance & Commitment Therapy. 2011. (Professional Ser.). (ENG.). 184p. pap. 39.95 *(978-1-57224-931-8(5))* New Harbinger Pubns.

—Stress Less, Live More: How Acceptance & Commitment Therapy Can Help You Live a Busy yet Balanced Life. 2010. (ENG.). 184p. pap. 16.95 *(978-1-57224-709-3(6))* New Harbinger Pubns.

Bond, Frank & Flaxman, Paul. Acceptance & Commitment Therapy: Distinctive Features. 2010. (CBT Distinctive Features Ser.). (ENG., Illus.). 184p. (C). 17.95 *(978-0-415-45066-9(7))*; 90.00 *(978-0-415-45065-2(9))* Routledge.

Ciarrochi, Joseph V. & Bailey, Ann. A CBT Practitioner's Guide to ACT: How to Bridge the Gap Between Cognitive Behavioral Therapy & Acceptance & Commitment Therapy. 2008. (Professional Ser.). (ENG., Illus.). 224p. pap. 39.95 *(978-1-57224-551-8(4))* New Harbinger Pubns.

Coyne, Lisa W. & Murrell, Amy R. The Joy of Parenting: An Acceptance & Commitment Therapy Guide to Effective Parenting in the Early Years. 2009. (ENG.). 216p. pap. 17.95 *(978-1-57224-593-8(X))* New Harbinger Pubns.

Cram101 Textbook Reviews & Cram101 Textbook Reviews. Outlines & Highlights for Acceptance & Mindfulness in Cognitive Behavior Therapy: Understanding & Applying the New Therapies by James Herbert, IS. 2011. 140p. pap. 28.95 *(978-1-61461-029-8(0))* Cram101 Inc.

Dahl, JoAnne C. & Plumb, Jennifer. The Art & Science of Valuing in Psychotherapy: Helping Clients Discover, Explore, & Commit to Valued Action Using Acceptance & Commitment Therapy. 2009. (Professional Ser.). (ENG.). 256p. 49.95 *(978-1-57224-626-3(X))* New Harbinger Pubns.

Forsyth, John P., et al. The Mindfulness & Acceptance Workbook for Anxiety: A Guide to Breaking Free from Anxiety, Phobias, & Worry Using Acceptance & Commitment Therapy. 2008. (Workbook Ser.). (ENG., Illus.). 288p. pap. 24.95 *(978-1-57224-499-3(2))* New Harbinger Pubns.

Greco, Laurie A. Acceptance & Mindfulness Treatments for Children & Adolescents. Hayes, Steven C., ed. 2008. (Context / NHP Ser.). (ENG., Illus.). 312p. 59.95 *(978-1-57224-541-9(7))* New Harbinger Pubns.

Harris, Russ. ACT Made Simple: An Easy-to-Read Primer on Acceptance & Commitment Therapy. 2009. (Professional Ser.). (ENG.). 280p. pap. 39.95 *(978-1-57224-705-5(3))* New Harbinger Pubns.

—ACT with Love: Stop Struggling, Reconcile Differences, & Strengthen Your Relationship with Acceptance & Commitment Therapy. 2009. (Professional Ser.). (ENG., Illus.). 240p. pap. 17.95 *(978-1-57224-622-5(7))* New Harbinger Pubns.

—The Reality Slap. 2012. *(978-1-60882-282-9(6))* New Harbinger Pubns.

—The Reality Slap: Finding Peace & Fulfillment When Life Hurts. 2012. (ENG.). 208p. pap. 16.95 *(978-1-60882-280-5(X))* New Harbinger Pubns.

Hayes, Steven C., et al, eds. Mindfulness & Acceptance: Expanding the Cognitive-Behavioral Tradition. 2011. (ENG.). 319p. pap. 25.00 *(978-1-60918-989-1(2))* Guilford Pubns., Inc.

Hayes, Steven C. & Lillis, Jason. Acceptance & Commitment Therapy. 2012. pap. 24.95 *(978-1-4338-1153-1(7))* American Psychological Assn.

Hayes, Steven C. & Strosahl, Kirk D., eds. A Practical Guide to Acceptance & Commitment Therapy. 2010. xvii, 395p. pap. 84.95 *(978-1-4419-3617-2(3), 1441936173)* Springer.

Hayes, Steven C., et al. Acceptance & Commitment Therapy, Second Edition: The Process & Practice of Mindful Change. 2nd rev. ed. 2011. (ENG., Illus.). 402p. 45.00 *(978-1-60918-962-4(0))* Guilford Pubns., Inc.

Herbert, James D. & Forman, Evan M., eds. Acceptance & Mindfulness in Cognitive Behavior Therapy: Understanding & Applying the New Therapies. 2010. (ENG., Illus.). 368p. pap. 68.00 *(978-0-470-47441-9(6),* Wiley) Wiley, John & Sons, Inc.

Lejeune, Chad. The Worry Trap: How to Free Yourself from Worry & Anxiety Using Acceptance & Commitment Therapy. 2007. (ENG.). 208p. per. 16.95 *(978-1-57224-480-1(1))* New Harbinger Pubns.

McCracken, Lance M. Mindfulness & Acceptance in Behavioral Medicine: Current Theory & Practice. 2011. (Context Press Mindfulness & Acceptance Practica Ser.). (ENG., Illus.). 400p. pap. 49.95 *(978-1-57224-731-4(2))* New Harbinger Pubns.

McCurry, Christopher. Parenting Your Anxious Child with Mindfulness & Acceptance: A Powerful New Approach to Overcoming Fear, Panic, & Worry Using Acceptance & Commitment Therapy. 2009. (ENG.). 248p. pap. 17.95 *(978-1-57224-579-2(4))* New Harbinger Pubns.

Pearson, Adria & Heffner, Michelle. Acceptance & Commitment Therapy for Body Image Dissatisfaction: A Practitioner's Guide to Using Mindfulness, Acceptance, & Values-Based Behavior Change Strategies. 2010. (Professional Ser.). (ENG.). 216p. 49.95 *(978-1-57224-775-8(4))* New Harbinger Pubns.

Pistorello, Jacqueline & Follette, Victoria M. Finding Life Beyond Trauma: Using Acceptance & Commitment Therapy to Heal from Post-Traumatic Stress & Trauma-Related Problems. 2007. (ENG., Illus.). 280p. per. 21.95 *(978-1-57224-497-9(6))* New Harbinger Pubns.

Robinson, Patricia J. & Gould, Debra. Real Behavior Change in Primary Care: Improving Patient Outcomes & Increasing Job Satisfaction. 2011. (Professional Ser.). (ENG.). 264p. 59.95 *(978-1-57224-832-8(7))* New Harbinger Pubns.

Robinson, Patricia J. & Strosahl, Kirk D. The Mindfulness & Acceptance Workbook for Depression: Using Acceptance & Commitment Therapy to Move Through Depression & Create a Life Worth Living. 2008. (New Harbinger Self-Help Workbook Ser.). (ENG., Illus.). 320p. pap. 24.95 *(978-1-57224-548-8(4))* New Harbinger Pubns.

Roemer, Lizabeth & Orsillo, Susan M. Mindfulness- & Acceptance-Based Behavioral Therapies in Practice. (Guides to Individualized Evidence-Based Treatment Ser.). (ENG.). 244p. 2010. pap. 28.00 *(978-1-60623-999-5(2))* 2008. 55.00 *(978-1-59385-997-8(X))* Guilford Pubns., Inc.

Sandoz, Emily, et al. The Mindfulness & Acceptance Workbook for Bulimia: A Guide to Breaking Free from Bulimia Using Acceptance & Commitment Therapy. 2011. (ENG., Illus.). 152p. pap. 21.95 *(978-1-57224-735-2(5))* New Harbinger Pubns.

Shannon, Jennifer. The Shyness & Social Anxiety Workbook for Teens: CBT & ACT Skills to Help You Build Social Confidence. 2012. (ENG.). 136p. (J). pap. 16.95 *(978-1-60882-187-7(0))* Play2Grow.

Shapiro, Shauna, et al. Art & Science of Mindfulness: Integrating Mindfulness into Psychology & the Helping Professions. 2009. (Illus.). 232p. 59.95 *(978-1-4338-0465-6(4))* American Psychological Assn.

Wilson, Kelly & DuFrene, Troy. Things Might Go Terribly, Horribly Wrong: A Guide to Life Liberated from Anxiety. 2010. (10 Simple Solutions Ser.). (ENG.). 184p. pap. 16.95 *(978-1-57224-711-6(8))* New Harbinger Pubns.

Wilson, Kelly G., et al. Acceptance & Commitment Therapy for Eating Disorders: A Process-Focused Guide to Treating Anorexia & Bulimia. 2011. (Professional Ser.). (ENG., Illus.). 312p. 59.95 *(978-1-57224-733-8(9))* New Harbinger Pubns.

Woods, Douglas W. & Twohig, Michael P. Trichotillomania: An ACT-Enhanced Behavior Therapy Approach. 2008. (Treatments That Work Ser.). (ENG.). 144p. pap., instr.'s gde. ed. 37.95 *(978-0-19-533603-0(8))* Oxford Univ. Pr., Inc.

—Trichotillomania: An ACT-enhanced Behavior Therapy Approach Workbook. 2008. (Treatments That Work Ser.). (ENG., Illus.). 96p. pap. 24.95 *(978-0-19-533605-4(4))* Oxford Univ. Pr., Inc.

ACCEPTANCE SAMPLING

Kang, Chang Wok & Kvam, Paul H. Basic Statistical Tools for Improving Quality. 2011. (ENG., Illus.). 244p. pap. 54.95 *(978-0-470-88949-7(7),* Wiley) Wiley, John & Sons, Inc.

Schilling, Edward G. & Neubauer, Dean V. Acceptance Sampling in Quality Control. 2nd rev. ed. 2009. (Statistics: A Series of Textbooks & Monographs). (ENG., Illus.). 700p. 119.95 *(978-1-58488-952-6(7),* Chapman & Hall/CRC) CRC Pr. LLC.

Squeglia, Nicholas L. Zero Acceptance Number Sampling Plans. 5th ed. 2008. 44.00 *(978-0-87389-739-6(0))* ASQ Quality Pr.

ACCEPTANCES

Here are entered works on drafts or bills of exchange for which a bank or other drawee has accepted the obligation to honor at maturity.

see also Bills of Exchange; Discount

Amiet, Don. Never Cross the Everglades with an Angry Howler Monkey: A Rather Strange Memoir, 1 vol. 2009. 256p. pap. 21.95 *(978-1-61582-591-2(6))* PublishAmerica, Inc.

Hamadeh, Ahmed. The Impact. 2010. 104p. pap. *(978-3-8383-8130-5(0))* Lambert Academic Publishing.

Merton, Jacob. Bank Acceptances. 2009. 24p. pap. 14.75 *(978-1-113-13501-8(8))* BiblioBazaar.

Stuart Bell, James. Living the Serenity Prayer: True Stories of Acceptance, Courage, & Wisdom. Littleton, Jeanette Gardner, ed. 2007. (ENG.). 192p. per. 9.95 *(978-1-59869-116-0(3))* Adams Media Corp.

The American Exchange National Bank New. Acceptances: Their Importance As A Means of Increasing & Simplifying Domestic & Foreign Trade (1921) 2008. 120p. 34.95 *(978-1-4368-8993-3(6))*; pap. 19.95 *(978-1-4367-5956-4(0))* Kessinger Publishing, LLC.

Trust Company Of New York, Guaranty. Acceptances. 2008. 80p. pap. 17.75 *(978-0-559-79166-6(6))* BiblioBazaar.

ACCESS (COMPUTER PROGRAM)

see Microsoft Access (Computer Program)

ACCESS TO BUILDINGS FOR PEOPLE WITH DISABILITIES

see Barrier-Free Design

ACCESS TO HEALTH CARE

see Health Services Accessibility

ACCESSIBILITY FOR PEOPLE WITH DISABILITIES

see Barrier-Free Design

ACCESSIBILITY OF HEALTH SERVICES

see Health Services Accessibility

ACCESSORIES (DRESS)

see Dress Accessories

ACCESSORY SINUSES OF THE NOSE

see Paranasal Sinuses

ACCIDENT INSURANCE

see also Disability Evaluation; Life Insurance—Disability Benefits

Bush, Allen. How to Evaluate & Settle Personal Injury Cases. 2011. 160p. 41.95 *(978-1-258-08149-2(0))* Literary Licensing, LLC.

Cole, Jeff & Brendtro, Daniel. 7 Deadly Sins That Can Wreck Your Injury Claim. 2011. pap. 16.95 *(978-1-59571-668-2(8))* Word Association Pubs.

Matthews, Joseph. How to Win Your Personal Injury Claim. (ENG.). 304p. 7th rev. ed. 2009. pap. 34.99 *(978-1-4133-1016-0(8))* 8th rev. ed. 2012. pap. 34.99 *(978-1-4133-1716-9(2))* NOLO.

Workers Compensation & Employers Liability. 2007. iv, 220p. pap. *(978-1-56461-297-7(X))* Rough Notes Co., Inc., The.

ACCIDENT LAW

see also Assistance in Emergencies; Damages; Employers' Liability; Industrial Safety—Law and Legislation; Liability for Building Accidents; Liability for Marine Accidents; Liability for Nuclear Damages; Liability for School Accidents; Liability for Traffic Accidents; Negligence; Personal Injuries; Torts; Traffic Violations

Adams, Brenton. North Carolina's Essential Guide to Accident Cases. 2007. pap. 12.95 *(978-1-59571-177-9(5))* Word Association Pubs.

Boyk, Charles E. The Ohio Accident Book: Don't Get Caught in Insurance Company Traps. 2007. pap. 12.95 *(978-1-59571-174-8(0))* Word Association Pubs.

Butterworth Staff, compiled by. Butterworths Legislation Service: Motor Vehicle Accidents Act 84 of 1986. Date not set. *(978-0-409-01433-4(8),* MICHIE) LEXIS Publishing.

—Butterworths Legislation Service: Multilateral Motor Vehicle Accidents Fund Act 93 of 1989. Date not set. *(978-0-409-01434-1(6),* MICHIE) LEXIS Publishing.

Cane, Peter. Atiyah's Accidents, Compensation & the Law. 7th rev. ed. 2006. (Law in Context Ser.). 514p. per. 59.00 *(978-0-521-68931-1(7))* Cambridge Univ. Pr.

Exall, Gordon & Chambers, Zenith. APIL Guide to Fatal Accidents. 2nd rev. ed. 2009. (ENG.). 368p. pap. *(978-1-84661-115-5(6))* Jordan Publishing, Ltd.

Feldman, Joel, et al. The Pennsylvania Library of Personal Injury Forms. Shotsberger, Amanda, ed. 2009. (ENG.). 500p. pap. 179.00 *(978-1-57786-337-3(2))* Incisive Media.

Hähle, Lutz. Die strafrechtliche Relevanz von Sportverletzungen: Zur Problematik des Schutzes der körperlichen Unversehrtheit, insbesondere im Fußballsport. 2008. (Strafrecht und Rechtsphilosophie in Geschichte und Gegenwart Ser.). 268p. pap. 65.95 *(978-3-631-57499-7(1))* Lang, Peter GmbH, Europaischer Verlag der Wissenschaften DEU. Dist: Lang, Peter.

Johnson, Fred M. Slips & Falls: A New Approach to Friction Measurements. 2008. pap. *(978-1-933264-51-6(9))* Lawyers & Judges Publishing Co., Inc.

Massachusetts Personal Injury Sourcebook: 2001 Edition. *(978-1-57589-207-8(3))* Massachusetts Continuing Legal Education, Inc.

Nelson-Jones, Rodney & Burton, Frank. Personal Injury Limitation Law. 2nd ed. 2007. 629p. pap. 136.00 *(978-1-84592-297-9(2),* Bloomsbury Professional) Bloomsbury Publishing Plc GBR. Dist: International Specialized Bk. Services.

Ritchie, Andrew. APIL Guide to RTA Liability. 2nd rev. ed. 2012. 300p. pap. 120.00 *(978-1-84661-323-4(X))* Jordan Publishing, Ltd. GBR. Dist: International Specialized Bk. Services.

Shaffer, Jerry & Leland, Leslie H. Left to Die: Chappaquiddick Grand Jury Foreman Reveals Explosive, Never-told Before Information. 2010. 168p. 26.95 *(978-1-60911-139-7(7),* Strategic Bk. Publishing) AEG Literary Publishing Services, Inc.

Shavell, Steven. Economic Analysis of Accident Law. 2007. (Illus.). 320p. per. 34.50 *(978-0-674-02417-5(6))* Harvard Univ. Pr.

Witt, John Fabian. The Accidental Republic: Crippled Workingmen, Destitute Widows, & the Remaking of American Law. 2006. 322p. per. 25.50 *(978-0-674-02261-4(0))* Harvard Univ. Pr.

ACCIDENT MEDICINE

see Traumatology

ACCIDENTS

see also Ambulances; Asphyxia; Assistance in Emergencies; Burns and Scalds; Children's Accidents; Crash Injuries; Disasters; Drowning; Employers' Liability; Explosions; Falls (Accidents); Fires; First Aid in Illness and Injury; Industrial Accidents; Lifesaving; Medical Emergencies; Mountaineering Accidents; Railroad Accidents; Shipwrecks; Shock; Sports Accidents; Traffic Accidents; Traumatism

also subdivision Wounds and Injuries under names of regions and organs of the body

AAOS Staff. Emtb 9E(R9): Emerg Care Trans Sick Inj (Pb) W/Dvd/2010 Gdlns. 9th ed. 2011. 1195p. pap. 97.95 *(978-1-4496-2972-4(5))* Jones & Bartlett Learning, LLC.

The Accident Survival Kit. 2007. per. *(978-1-59930-003-0(6))* LifeSuccess Publishing.

Adams, James, et al. Emergency Medicine - Concepts & Clinical Practice, 2 vols., Set. Marx, John et al, eds. 7th ed. 2009. (ENG., Illus.). 2894p. 389.00 *(978-0-323-05472-0(2),* Mosby) Elsevier - Health Sciences Div.

Adams, James G. Emergency Medicine. Barton, Erik D. et al, eds. 2008. (ENG., Illus.). 2312p. 199.00 *(978-1-4160-2872-7(2),* Saunders) Elsevier - Health Sciences Div.

Advanced Life Support Group. Advanced Paediatric Life Support: The Practical Approach. 5th ed. 2011. (ENG., Illus.). 404p. pap. 73.95 *(978-1-4443-3059-5(4))* Wiley, John & Sons, Inc.

Aehlert, Barbara. Emergency Medical Responder: First Responder in Action. 2nd ed. 2010. (ENG., Illus.). 832p. (C). pap. 94.33 *(978-0-07-351980-7(4)* 0073519804) McGraw-Hill Higher Education.

Allman, Keith, et al. Emergencies in Anaesthesia. Allman, Keith et al, eds. 2nd ed. 2009. (Emergencies in Ser.). (ENG., Illus.). 560p. pap. 42.50 *(978-0-19-956082-0(X))* Oxford Univ. Pr., Inc.

American Academy of Orthopaedic Surgeons (AAOS). Emergency Medical Responder. 5th ed. 2011. 514p. pap. 95.95 *(978-1-4496-5022-3(8))* Jones & Bartlett Learning, LLC.

American Academy of Pediatrics (AAP). PEPP for the BLS Provider. 2008. 332p. pap. 49.95 *(978-0-7637-5587-4(7))* Jones & Bartlett Learning, LLC.

American Red Cross Staff, contrib. by. American Red Cross Emergency Medical Response Participant's Manual. 2011. *(978-1-58480-327-0(4))* StayWell Co., The.

Anaesthesia, Pain, Intensive Care & Emergency A. P. I. C. E. 2007. (Illus.). 423p. pap. 99.00 *(978-88-470-0772-7(0))* Springer.

Bailitz, John, et al. Emergent Management of Trauma, Third Edition. 3rd ed. 2010. (ENG., Illus.). 640p. pap. 63.00 *(978-0-07-162434-3(1),* 007162434I) McGraw-Hill Professional Publishing.

Beard, Steve. Voodoo Science Park. Rushdy, Hatem, ed. 2011. (ENG., Illus.). 115p. pap. 14.95 *(978-1-84694-527-4(5))* O Bks.,John Hunt.

Becker, Chris. Death in the West: Fatal Stories from America's Last Frontiers. 2007. (ENG., Illus.). 224p. per. 16.95 *(978-0-87358-893-5(2))* Cooper Square Publishing Llc.

Beebe, Richard, et al. Workbook for Beebe/Scadden/Funk's Fundamentals of Basic Emergency Care, 3rd. 3rd ed. 2009. (ENG.). 320p. (C). pap. 70.95 *(978-1-4354-4218-4(0))* Delmar Cengage Learning.

Benedetto, George P., Jr. & DiPrima, Peter A., Jr. McGraw-Hill's EMT-Basic, Second Edition. 2nd ed. 2011. (ENG., Illus.). 438p. (C). pap. 31.00 *(978-0-07-175127-8(0)*, 0071751270) McGraw-Hill Medical Publishing Div.

—McGraw-Hill's EMT-Paramedic, Second Edition. 2nd ed. 2011. (ENG., Illus.). 936p. (C). pap. 37.00 *(978-0-07-175201-5(3)*, 0071752013) McGraw-Hill Medical Publishing Div.

Bentley, Peter J. Why Sh*t Happens: The Science of a Really Bad Day. 2009. (ENG.). 320p. 16.95 *(978-1-59486-956-3(1))* Rodale Pr., Inc.

Bledsoe, Bryan E., et al. Paramedic Care: Principles & amp; Practice, Volume 1. 4th rev. ed. 2012. (ENG.). 240p. (C). 41.33 ***(978-0-13-211208-6(6)***, Prentice Hall) Prentice Hall PTR.

Borden Institute, Walter Reed Army Medical Center, et al, eds. Pediatric Surgery & Medicine for Hostile Environments. 2011. (ENG., Illus.). 588p. 67.00 *(978-0-16-086980-8(3)*, Dept. of the Army) United States Government Printing Office.

Breen, Lauren. Silenced Voices. 2008. 228p. pap. *(978-3-639-06596-1(4))* VDM Verlag Dr. Mueller e.K.

Bruni, Joseph. Occupational Health & Safety for the Fire Service. rev. ed. 2011. (ENG.). 320p. (C). 70.67 ***(978-0-13-513808-3(6)***, Prentice Hall) Prentice Hall PTR

Buettner, Jennifer R. Fast Facts for the ER Nurse: Emergency Room Orientation in a Nutshell. 2009. 260p. pap. *(978-0-8261-0521-9(1))* Springer.

Burnett, Jim. Hey Ranger 2: More True Tales of Humor & Misadventure from the Great Outdoors. 2007. (ENG., Illus.). 270p. per. 16.95 *(978-1-58979-329-3(3))* Taylor Trade Publishing.

Burnham, John C. Accident Prone: A History of Technology, Psychology, & Misfits of the Machine Age. 2009. (ENG., Illus.). 336p. 40.00 *(978-0-226-08117-5(6))* Univ. of Chicago Pr.

Carroll, William. Death Only Needs to Win Once: The Trials & Tribulations of One Liverpool Lad. 2008. (ENG.). 104p. pap. 11.95 *(978-0-595-49844-4(2))* iUniverse, Inc.

Chen, Li Hui. Injury Episodes & Circumstances: National Health Interview Survey, 1997-2007. 2009. *(978-0-8406-0632-7(X))* National Ctr. for Health Statistics.

Christine Scharmer. Raising Mario Twice: How Love Can Transform a Life after a Tragic Event. 2009. 200p. pap. 16.95 *(978-1-4401-7178-9(5))* iUniverse, Inc.

Computer Assisted Loss Management System (CALMS) Accident/Incident Investigation. Date not set. *(978-0-88061-103-9(0))* International Loss Control Institute, Inc.

Cram101 Textbook Reviews. Outlines & Highlights for Emergency Care in Athletic Training by Keith M Gorse, Isbn: 9780803614963 0803614969. 2011. 208p. pap. 30.95 ***(978-1-61490-314-7(X))*** Cram101 Inc.

—Outlines & Highlights for Emt: Prehospital Care by Mark C. Henry, ISBN. 2011. 332p. pap. 33.95 ***(978-1-61490-315-4(8))*** Cram101 Inc.

—Outlines & Highlights for Hazardous Materials Incidents by Christopher David Hawley. 2011. 114p. pap. 28.95 ***(978-1-61490-884-5(2))*** Cram101 Inc.

Cram101 Textbook Reviews & Cram101 Textbook Reviews. Outlines & Highlights for Emergent Management of Trauma by John Bailitz, Isbn: 9780071624343. 2011. 66p. pap. 27.95 ***(978-1-61744-945-1(8))*** Cram101 Inc.

Cram101 Textbook Reviews Staff. Outlines & Highlights for Emergency Care by Limmer, Isbn: 0131593625. 2008. 132p. pap. 11.95 *(978-1-4288-5845-9(8))* Cram101 Inc.

Death, Despair, & Second Chances in Rocky Mountain National Park. 2010. 304p. pap. 18.50 *(978-1-55566-440-4(7))* Johnson Bks.

Delmarlearning's the Practiceof Paramedic Care Wb. 2009. (C). pap. 32.95 *(978-1-4018-8035-4(5))* Delmar Cengage Learning.

Dickens, Charles. Dickens' Dreadful Almanac. 2011. (ENG., Illus.). 224p. pap. 17.95 *(978-0-7524-5828-1(0))* History Pr. Ltd.,The GBR. Dist: Independent Pubs. Group.

Dumas, Lloyd. The Technology Trap: Where Human Error & Malevolence Meet Powerful Technologies, 1 vol. 2010. 394p. 54.95 *(978-0-313-37888-1(6)*, C37888, Praeger Pubs.) Greenwood Publishing Group, Inc.

Edwards, Frances L. & Steinhausler, Friedrich, eds. NATO & Terrorism: On Scene: New Challenges for First Responders & Civil Protection. 2007. (NATO Science for Peace & Security Series / NATO Science for Peace & Security Series B: Physics & Biophysics Ser.). (Illus.). 262p. 219.00 *(978-1-4020-6275-9(3))* Springer.

—NATO & Terrorism on Scene: New Challenges for First Responders & Civil Protection. 2007. (NATO Science for Peace & Security Series B: Physics & Biophysics Ser.). (ENG., Illus.). 262p. per. 119.00 *(978-1-4020-6276-6(1))* Springer.

Fernandez, Rick. An Uncharted Desert Isle. 2009. 260p. 24.99 *(978-1-4343-6032-8(6))*; pap. 19.95 *(978-1-4343-3738-2(3))* AuthorHouse.

Fish, Raymond M. & Geddes, L. A. Electrical Injuries: Medical & Bioengineering Aspects. 2nd ed. 2008. pap. *(978-1-933264-63-9(2))* Lawyers & Judges Publishing Co., Inc.

Flynn, Estelle. Head Injury - A Family Nightmare. 2011. 68p. pap. 11.24 ***(978-1-4567-5180-7(8))*** AuthorHouse.

Ford, Richard B. & Mazzaferro, Elisa. Kirk & Bistner's Handbook of Veterinary Procedures & Emergency Treatment. 9th ed. 2011. (ENG., Illus.). 784p. pap. 87.95 *(978-1-4377-0798-4(X)*, Saunders) Elsevier - Health Sciences Div.

Forum on Medical and Public Health Preparedness for Catastrophic Events Staff & Institute of Medicine. Dispensing Medical Countermeasures for Public Health Emergencies: Workshop Summary. 2008. (ENG.). 126p. pap. 32.75 *(978-0-309-12096-8(9))* National Academies Pr.

Funk, Mary Margaret. Into the Depths: A Journey of Loss & Vocation. 2011. 178p. 15.00 *(978-1-59056-235-2(6))* Lantern Bks.

Garmel, Gus M. & Levis, Joel T. Clinical Emergency Medicine Casebook. 2009. (ENG., Illus.). 506p. pap. 85.00 *(978-0-521-71964-3(X))* Cambridge Univ. Pr.

Gebbie, Kristine M., et al. What to Do Before, During, & after an Emergency or Disaster: A Preparedness Toolkit for Office-Based Health Care Practices. 2009. (Illus.). 112p. 35.00 *(978-1-60359-202-4(4))* American Medical Assn.

Gerstein, Marc. Flirting with Disaster: Why Accidents Are Rarely Accidental. 2008. (ENG., Illus.). 352p. 24.95 *(978-1-4027-5303-9(9))* Union Square Pr.

Gilchrist, M. D., ed. IUTAM Symposium on Impact Biomechanics: from Fundamental Insights to Applications: From Fundamental Insights to Applications. 2010. (Solid Mechanics & Its Applications Ser.). xv, 489p. pap. 239.00 *(978-90-481-6968-9(2)*, 9048169682) Springer.

Gorse, Keith M., et al. Emergency Care in Athletic Training. 2009. (Illus.). 352p. 64.95 *(978-0-8036-1496-3(9))* Davis, F. A. Co.

Griffiths, Pauline. Emergency Nursing. 2011. (Illus.). 528p. pap. ***(978-1-901831-12-2(4))*** Lippincott Williams & Wilkins.

Hamilton, Ross. Accident: A Philosophical & Literary History. 2008. (Illus.). 320p. 37.50 *(978-0-226-31484-6(7))* Univ. of Chicago Pr.

Henry, Mark C. & Stapleton, Edward R. EMT Prehospital Care - Text (Softcover) & Virtual Patient Encounters Revised Reprint Package. 4th ed. 2011. (ENG.). (C). pap. 98.95 ***(978-0-323-09777-2(4)***, Mosby) Elsevier - Health Sciences Div.

Institute of Medicine Staff, creator. PEPFAR Implementation: Progress & Promise. 2007. (ENG., Illus.). 400p. 42.00 *(978-0-309-10982-6(5))* National Academies Pr.

Iserson, Kenneth. Improvised Medicine. 2011. (ENG., Illus.). 578p. pap. 54.00 ***(978-0-07-175497-2(0)***, 0071754970) McGraw-Hill Professional Publishing.

Jeanmonod, Rebecca, et al, eds. Case Studies in Emergency Medicine. 2010. (ENG., Illus.). 426p. pap. 65.00 *(978-0-521-73649-0(X))* Cambridge Univ. Pr.

Jeffrey, R. Brooke. Diagnostic Imaging: Emergency. 2007. *(978-0-8089-2397-8(8))* Harcourt Health Sciences Group.

Kaplan, Marcelle. Understanding & Managing Oncologic Emergencies: A Resource for Nurses. 2nd ed. 2012. ***(978-1-935864-20-2(3))*** Oncology Nursing Society.

Katsilambros, Nicholas, et al. Diabetic Emergencies: Diagnosis & Clinical Management. 2nd ed. 2011. (ENG.). 220p. pap. 69.95 ***(978-0-470-65591-7(7)***, Wiley-Blackwell) Wiley, John & Sons, Inc.

Keen, David. Complex Emergencies. 2008. (ENG.). 296p. 74.95 *(978-0-7456-4019-8(2))* Polity Pr. GBR. Dist: Wiley, John & Sons, Inc.

Keen, David J. Complex Emergencies. 2008. (ENG., Illus.). 296p. pap. 24.95 *(978-0-7456-4020-4(6))* Polity Pr. GBR. Dist: Wiley, John & Sons, Inc.

King, Leonard J. & Wherry, David C., eds. ABC of Imaging in Trauma. 2010. (ABC Ser.: 89). (ENG., Illus.). 144p. pap. 50.95 *(978-1-4051-8332-1(2))* Wiley, John & Sons, Inc.

Knoop, Kevin, et al. The Atlas of Emergency Medicine 3rd ed. 2009. (ENG., Illus.). 932p. 239.00 *(978-0-07-149618-6(1)*, 0071496181) McGraw-Hill Professional Publishing.

Kuhlman, Raymond L. Professional Accident Investigation: Investigator's Field Workbook. Date not set. ring bd., wbk. ed. *(978-0-88061-013-1(1))* International Loss Control Institute, Inc.

—Professional Accident Investigation: Supervisory Training. Date not set. ring bd. *(978-0-88061-015-5(8))* International Loss Control Institute, Inc.

Kulczyk, David. Death in California: The Bizarre, Freakish, & Just Curious Ways People Die in the Golden State. 2009. (ENG., Illus.). 169p. pap. 15.95 *(978-1-884995-57-6(8))* Linden Publishing Co., Inc

Le Baudour, Chris, et al. Emergency Medical Responder: First on Scene & Resource Central EMS Student Access Code Card Package. 9th rev. ed. 2011. (ENG.). (C). pap. 92.00 ***(978-0-13-283335-6(2)***, Prentice Hall) Prentice Hall PTR.

LearningExpress Staff, contrib. by. EMT-Basic Exam. 5th ed. 2011. (ENG.). 208p. pap. 19.95 *(978-1-57685-790-8(5))* LearningExpress, LLC.

Lee, Andrew G. Emergencies in Neuro-Ophthalmology: A Case Based Approach. 2010. 300p. 66.00 *(978-981-4295-01-7(9))* World Scientific Publishing Co., Inc.

Lennox, Doug. Now You Know Disasters: The Little Book of Answers. 2008. (Now You Know Ser.). (ENG., Illus.). 96p. pap. 9.99 *(978-1-55002-807-2(3)*, Dundurn Pr.) Dundurn CAN. Dist: Ingram Pub. Services.

Limmer, Daniel. BLS Vital Signs. 2008. (ENG.). 244p. (C). cd-rom 22.00 *(978-0-13-174877-4(7)*, Prentice Hall) Prentice Hall PTR.

Lowe, Robert C. & Farraye, Francis A. GI Emergencies: A Quick Reference Guide. 2011. (ENG.). 296p. pap. 42.95 *(978-1-55642-990-3(8))* SLACK, Inc.

Ma, O. John, et al. Emergency Ultrasound. 2nd ed. 2007. (ENG., Illus.). 576p. 155.00 *(978-0-07-147904-2(X)*, 007147904X) McGraw-Hill Professional Publishing.

Marchenko, Nataliya. Russian Arctic Seas: Navigational conditions & Accidents. 2012. (RUS & ENG., Illus.). xxii, 274p. 129.00 ***(978-3-642-22124-8(6)***, 3642221246) Springer.

Marchetta, Mark. EMT-Paramedic Exam. 2nd ed. 2008. *(978-0-7641-3939-0(8))* Barron's Educational Series, Inc.

Marini, John J. & Wheeler, Arthur P. Critical Care Medicine: The Essentials. 4th rev. ed. 2009. (ENG., Illus.). 720p. pap. 81.99 *(978-0-7817-9839-6(5))* Lippincott Williams & Wilkins.

Martindale, Jennifer L. & Brown, David F. M. Rapid Interpretation of Ecgs in Emergency Medicine: A Visual Guide. 2012. (ENG., Illus.). 488p. pap. 64.95 ***(978-1-4511-2837-6(1))*** Lippincott Williams & Wilkins.

Marx, John, et al. Rosen's Emergency Medicine: Expert Consult Premium Edition: Enhanced Online Features & Print. 7th ed. 2009. (Illus.). 2720p. 399.00 *(978-0-323-06682-2(8)*, Mosby) Elsevier - Health Sciences Div.

Mishler, William. A Measure of Endurance: The Unlikely Triumph of Steven Sharp. 2008. 320p. pap. 25.00 *(978-1-58420-066-6(9)*, Lindisfarne Bks.) SteinerBooks, Inc.

Moore, Forrest O., et al, eds. Surgical Critical Care & Emergency Surgery: Clinical Questions & Answers. 8th ed. 2012. (ENG.). 476p. pap. 85.00 ***(978-0-470-65461-3(9)***, Wiley-Blackwell) Wiley, John & Sons, Inc.

NAEMT. Advanced Medical Life Support: An Assessment-Based Approach. 2011. (ENG., Illus.). 576p. (C). pap. 64.95 *(978-0-323-07160-4(0)*, Mosby/JEMS) Elsevier - Health Sciences Div.

Nelson, Bret, et al. Manual of Emergency & Critical Care Ultrasound. 2007. (ENG., Illus.). 254p. 72.00 *(978-0-521-68869-7(8))* Cambridge Univ. Pr.

Nelson, Lewis & Goldfrank, Lewis R. Goldfrank's Toxicologic Emergencies. 9th ed. 2011. (Illus.). xxvii, 1940p. E-Book *(978-0-07-160594-6(0))* McGraw-Hill Medical Publishing Div.

Nelson, Lewis, et al. Goldfrank's Toxicologic Emergencies, Ninth Edition. 9th ed. 2010. (ENG., Illus.). 1968p. 270.00 *(978-0-07-160593-9(2)*, 0071605932) McGraw-Hill Professional Publishing.

Noble, Vicki & Nelson, Bret. Manual of Emergency & Critical Care Ultrasound. 2nd rev. ed. 2011. (ENG., Illus.). 360p. pap. 75.00 *(978-0-521-17091-8(5))* Cambridge Univ. Pr.

Nouwen, Henri J. M. Here & Now: Living in the Spirit. 2006. (ENG.). 232p. pap. 16.95 *(978-0-8245-1967-4(1)*, Crossroad 8 Avenue) Crossroad Publishing Co., The.

Palanque, Philippe, et al. Human Error, Safety & Systems Development: 7th IFIP WG 13. 5 Working Conference, HESSD 2009, Brussels, Belgium, September 23-25, 2009, Revised Selected Papers. 2010. (Lecture Notes in Computer Science / Information Systems & Applications, incl. Internet/Web, & HCI Ser.). (Illus.). 102p. pap. 99.00 *(978-3-642-11749-7(X)*, 364211749X) Springer.

Perkins, Jack, et al. Inpatient Medicine. 2007. (In a Page Ser.). (ENG.). 239p. per. 41.99 *(978-0-7817-6499-5(8))* Lippincott Williams & Wilkins.

Plantz, Scott H. & Wipfler, E. John, eds. NMS Emergency Medicine. 2nd rev. ed. 2006. (National Medical Series for Independent Study Ser.). (ENG., Illus.). 736p. per. 51.99 *(978-0-7817-8884-7(6))* Lippincott Williams & Wilkins.

Porter, Robert S. Paramedic Care Vol. 4: Principles & Practice. 3rd ed. 2008. (ENG.). 224p. (C). pap. 40.00 *(978-0-13-515075-7(2)*, Prentice Hall) Prentice Hall PTR.

—Student Workbook for Paramedic Care Vol. 2: Principles & Practice, Vol. 2. 3rd ed. 2008. (ENG., Illus.). 128p. (C). pap. 40.00 *(978-0-13-515071-9(X)*, Prentice Hall) Prentice Hall PTR.

Porter, Robert S., et al. Paramedic Care: Principles & Practice - Introduction to Advanced Prehospital Care, 5 vols. 3rd ed. 2008. (ENG., Illus.). 750p. (C). 81.33 *(978-0-13-513704-8(7)*, Prentice Hall) Prentice Hall PTR.

—Student Workbook for Essentials of Paramedic Care Update. 2nd ed. 2010. (ENG.). 744p. (C). pap. 96.00 *(978-0-13-138442-2(2)*, Prentice Hall) Prentice Hall PTR.

Ragaini. International Seminar on Nuclear War . . 2008. 175.00 *(978-981-283-463-8(X))*; 202.00 *(978-981-283-464-5(8))* World Scientific Publishing Co., Inc.

Reauthorization of the National Transportation Safety Board: Hearing Before the Subcommittee on Aviation of the Committee on Transportation & Infrastructure, House of Representatives, One Hundred Tenth Congress, Second Session, April 23, 2008. 2008. (Illus.). xvii, 100p. *(978-0-16-083711-1(1)*, 552-070-39418-4) United States Government Printing Office.

Roberts, James R. & Hedges, Jerris R. Clinical Procedures in Emergency Medicine: Expert Consult - Online & Print. Roberts, James R., ed. 5th ed. 2009. (ENG., Illus.). 1416p. 219.00 *(978-1-4160-3623-4(7)*, Saunders) Elsevier - Health Sciences Div.

Roux, Océane M. Brain Hypoxia-Ischemia Research Progress. 2008. (C). 129.00 *(978-1-60456-139-5(4))* Nova Science Pubs., Inc.

Rozelle, Ron. My Boys & Girls Are in There: The 1937 New London School Explosion. 2012. 184p. 24.95 ***(978-1-60344-761-4(X))*** Texas A&M Univ. Pr.

Salmon, Paul M., et al. Human Factors Methods & Accident Analysis: Practical Guidance & Case Study Applications. 2011. (Illus.). 216p. 99.95 ***(978-1-4094-0519-1(2))*** Ashgate Publishing Co.

Sanders, Mick J. Mosby's Paramedic Textbook - Text, Workbook, & RAPID Paramedic Package. 4th ed. 2012. (ENG.). (C). 235.00 *(978-0-323-07273-1(9)*, Mosby/JEMS) Elsevier - Health Sciences Div.

Sanders, Mick J. & McKenna, Kim D. Mosby's Paramedic Textbook. 4th ed. 2011. (ENG., Illus.). 1792p. (C). 160.00 ***(978-0-323-07275-5(5)***, Mosby/JEMS) Elsevier - Health Sciences Div.

Sanders, Mick J. & McKenna, Kim D. RAPID Paramedic. 2nd ed. 2012. (ENG., Illus.). 240p. (C). pap. 25.95 *(978-0-323-07267-0(4)*, Mosby/JEMS) Elsevier - Health Sciences Div.

Schwester, Richard Wilmot. Handbook of Critical Incident Analysis. 2012. (ENG., Illus.). 408p. 99.95 ***(978-0-7656-2724-7(8))*** Sharpe, M.E. Inc.

Selbst, Steven M. & Cronan, Kate. Pediatric Emergency Medicine Secrets. 2nd ed. 2008. (Secrets Ser.). (ENG., Illus.). 635p. (C). pap. 54.95 *(978-1-4160-2990-8(7)*, Mosby) Elsevier - Health Sciences Div.

Shah, Kaushal, et al, eds. Essential Emergency Trauma. 2011. (ENG., Illus.). 432p. pap. 77.99 *(978-1-60831-894-0(X))* Lippincott Williams & Wilkins.

Shah, Kaushal H., et al. Essential Emergency Imaging. 2011. (ENG., Illus.). 688p. pap. 92.99 *(978-1-60831-893-3(1))* Lippincott Williams & Wilkins.

Sherwood, Ben. The Survivors Club: The Secrets & Science That Could Save Your Life. 2010. (ENG.). 400p. pap. 14.99 *(978-0-446-69885-6(7))* Grand Central Publishing.

Smith, Keri. Mess: The Manual of Accidents & Mistakes. 2010. (ENG.). 224p. (gr. 12). pap. 13.95 *(978-0-399-53600-7(0)*, Perigee Trade) Penguin Group (USA) Inc.

Smith, Kim. Truckers. 2008. v, 230p. pap. *(978-0-87218-743-6(8))* National Underwriter Co.

Strange, Gary, et al. Pediatric Emergency Medicine: Just the Facts. 2nd ed. 2011. (Just the Facts Ser.). (ENG., Illus.). 868p. pap. 90.00 ***(978-0-07-174434-8(7)***, 0071744347) McGraw-Hill Professional Publishing.

Thomas, Marcia L. & Voss, Anke, compiled by. Emergency Response Planning in College Libraries. 2009. pap. *(978-0-8389-8524-3(6))* Assn. of College & Research Libraries.

Tintinalli, Judith E. & Stapczynski, J. Stephan. Tintinalli's Emergency Medicine: A Comprehensive Study Guide. 7th ed. 2011. (Illus.). xl, 2120p. *(978-0-07-174467-6(3))*; *(978-0-07-174466-9(5))* McGraw-Hill Cos., The.

Todd Andrew Rohrer. The Quick & the Demotic. 2009. 160p. pap. 21.95 *(978-1-4401-7838-2(0))* iUniverse, Inc.

Toy, Eugene C., et al. Case Files Emergency Medicine. 2nd ed. 2009. (LANGE Case Files Ser.). (ENG., Illus.). 542p. pap. 36.00 *(978-0-07-159899-6(5)*, 0071598995) McGraw-Hill Medical Publishing Div.

Trott, Alexander T. Wounds & Lacerations: Emergency Care & Closure (Expert Consult - Online & Print) 4th ed. 2012. (ENG., Illus.). 336p. 85.00 ***(978-0-323-07418-6(9)***, Saunders) Elsevier - Health Sciences Div.

Wardrope, Jim, et al. Community Emergency Medicine. 2008. (ENG., Illus.). 256p. pap. 55.95 *(978-0-443-10325-4(9)*, Churchill Livingstone) Elsevier - Health Sciences Div.

West, Jerry L. 50 Ways to Die: Homicides, Accidents, Suicides, Infanticides & Acts of Mother Nature. 2011. 232p. pap. 14.99 ***(978-1-4567-4677-3(4))*** AuthorHouse.

Wilkinson, Freddie. One Mountain Thousand Summits: The Untold Story Tragedy & True Heroism on K2. 2010. (ENG.). 352p. (gr. 12). 24.95 *(978-0-451-23119-2(8)*, N A L Hardcover) Penguin Group (USA) Inc.

Wingfield, Wayne E., et al. Veterinary Disaster Medicine: Working Animals. 2009. (ENG., Illus.). 344p. 82.99 *(978-0-8138-1017-1(5)*, Wiley-Blackwell) Wiley John & Sons, Inc.

Wolf, Ronni, et al, eds. Emergency Dermatology. 2011. (ENG., Illus.). 400p. 130.00 *(978-0-521-71733-5(7))* Cambridge Univ. Pr.

Wolfson, Allan B. Clinical Practice of Emergency Medicine. 5th rev. ed. 2009. (ENG.). 1792p. 245.99 *(978-0-7817-8943-1(5))* Lippincott Williams & Wilkins.

Woolcock, Mark & Thygerson, Alton L. Emergency First Aid. 2008. 160p. pap. 8.95 *(978-0-7637-6461-6(2))* Jones & Bartlett Learning, LLC.

Wycliffe, Beena & Rosen, Peter. Bullets in Emergency Medicine: Review & Reminders in Pursuit of Evidence-Based Decisions. 2008. (ENG.) 372p. pap. 51.95 *(978-0-7637-5416-7(1))* Jones & Bartlett Learning, LLC.

Zane, Richard D. & Kosowsky, Joshua M., eds. Pocket Emergency Medicine. 2nd rev. ed. 2010. (Pocket Notebook Ser.). (ENG., Illus.). 288p. ring bd 54.99 *(978-1-60547-731-2(1))* Lippincott Williams & Wilkins.

ACCIDENTS—LAW AND LEGISLATION

see Accident Law

ACCIDENTS—PREVENTION

see also Industrial Safety; Safety Education

also subdivisions Safety Appliances or Safety Measures under subjects, e.g. Railroads—Safety Appliances, Automobiles—Safety Measures

Ale, Ben J. M., et al, eds. Reliability Risk & Safety - Back to the Future. 2010. (ENG.). 2448p. cd-rom 490.00 *(978-0-415-60427-7(3)*, CRC Press) Taylor & Francis Group GBR. Dist: Taylor & Francis Group.

American Academy of Orthopaedic Surgeons (AAOS), et al. Wilderness First Aid Field Guide. 2011. 131p. spiral bd. 26.50 ***(978-1-4496-4123-8(7))*** Jones & Bartlett Learning, LLC.

American Academy of Orthopaedic Surgeons Staff, et al. Wilderness First Aid Field Guide. 2010. 131p. spiral bd. 25.50 *(978-0-7637-9456-9(2))* Jones & Bartlett Learning, LLC.

American Society of Mechanical Engineers Staff, ed. Nail Puller Bars: Safety Requirements. 16p. 28.00 *(978-0-7918-2493-1(4))* ASME Pr.

Avery, J.Gordon & Jackson, R.Hugh. Children & Their Accidents. (Illus.). 192p. pap. *(978-0-340-37001-8(7)*, Hodder Arnold) Hodder Education.

Barsky, Steven M. Diving in High-Risk Environments, 4th Edition. 2007. (Illus.). 256p. per. 36.95 *(978-0-9674305-7-7(7))* Hammerhead Pr.

Bartlow, Jean. Live to Ride. 2011. 108p. 24.99 ***(978-1-4568-3402-9(9))***; pap. 15.99 ***(978-1-4568-3401-2(0))*** Xlibris Corp.

Bever, David L. Safety: A Personal Focus. 4th ed. 2006. pap. 9.95 *(978-1-4288-1841-5(3))* Cram101 Inc.

Bogner, Marilyn Sue. Human Error in Medicine. 2nd ed. 2009. (Human Error & Safety Ser.). 368p. pap. 49.95 *(978-0-8058-4522-8(4))* Erlbaum, Lawrence Assocs., Inc.

Branche, C., et al. World Report on Child Injury Prevention. 2009. (Nonserial Publication Ser.). 228p. pap. 48.00 (978-92-4-156357-4(5)) World Health Organization.

Brown, Diane L. Accident Prevention & Resident Supervision: Preparing Your SNF for F-Tag #323. 2008. (Survey Solved! Ser.). 139p. pap. 99.00 incl. cd-rom (978-1-60146-066-0(X)) Opus Communications.

Brown, F. & Seitz, R., eds. Advances in Transfusion Safety 2001: International Symposium, Langen, June 2001, Vol. 108. (Developments in Biologicals Ser.: Vol. 108). (Illus.). (978-3-8055-7426-6(6)) Karger, S. AG.

Clutter, Don. Moto Medic. 2009. 116p. pap. 17.50 (978-1-4251-9019-4(7)) Trafford Publishing.

Committee on Promoting Safe and Secure Chemical Management in Developing Countries & National Research Council. Promoting Chemical Laboratory Safety & Security in Developing Countries. 2010. (ENG.). 136p. pap. 33.75 (978-0-309-15041-5(8)) National Academies Pr.

The Complete OSHA Guide to Fall Protection: From Selected Title 29 Code of Federal Regulations ... 2008. (Illus.). ii, 142p. (978-1-59959-136-0(7)) Mangan Communications, Inc.

Crabtree, Jack. Better Safe Than Sued, 1 vol. 2008. (ENG.). 208p. pap. 16.99 (978-0-310-28261-7(6)) Zondervan.

Cram101 Textbook Reviews & Cram101 Textbook Reviews. Outlines & Highlights for Injury Prevention & Public Health: Practical Knowledge, Skills & Strategies by Tom Christoffel, ISBN. 2011. 274p. pap. 32.95 **(978-1-61461-523-1(3))** Cram101 Inc.

David, Albert. Keeping our Children Safe & Healthy from Pre-K through High School: An A to Z Emergency Guide for Educators & Parents. 2007. (Illus.). 100p. per. 19.95 (978-0-9794652-0-8(6)) Abey World Pr.

Davis, James R. Motorcycle Safety & Dynamics: Vol 1 - BandW. 2011. 178p. pap. 35.50 **(978-1-257-44016-0(0))** Lulu Enterprises Inc.

—Motorcycle Safety & Dynamics: Vol 1 - Color. 2011. 178p. pap. 74.99 **(978-1-257-64588-6(9))** Lulu Enterprises Inc.

De Paolo, Tom, et al. Fear of Falling: Self-Help for Seniors to Protect Your Precious Bones & Enjoy a Longer Life. 2008. 28p. 15.99 (978-1-4389-3401-3(7)) AuthorHouse.

Di Pilla, Steven. Slip, Trip, & Fall Prevention: A Practical Handbook. 2nd ed. 2009. (ENG., Illus.). 480p. instr.'s hndbk. ed. 107.95 (978-1-4200-8234-0(5), CRC Press) Taylor & Francis Group GBR. Dist: Taylor & Francis Group.

Doll, Lynda S., et al, eds. Handbook of Injury & Violence Prevention. 2006. (ENG., Illus.). xviii, 598p. 109.00 (978-0-387-25924-6(4), 0387259244) Springer.

Fasulo, David. Self-Rescue. 2nd ed. 2011. (How to Climb Ser.). (ENG., Illus.). 256p. pap. 16.95 (978-0-7627-5533-2(4), Falcon Guides) Globe Pequot Pr., The.

Fisher, Len. Crashes, Crises, & Calamities: How We Can Use Science to Read the Early-Warning Signs. 2011. (ENG.). 256p. (gr. 9). 23.99 (978-0-465-02102-4(6)) Basic Bks.

Flin, Rhona & Mitchell, Lucy. Safer Surgery: Analysing Behaviour in the Operating Theatre. 2009. (Illus.). 482p. 144.95 (978-0-7546-7536-5(X)) Ashgate Publishing Co.

The Future of the Coast Guard Dive Program: Hearing Before the Subcommittee on Oceans, Atmosphere, Fisheries, & Coast Guard of the Committee on Commerce, Science, & Transportation, United States Senate, One Hundred Tenth Congress, First Session, March 28, 2007. 2010. iii, 49p. (978-0-16-086755-2(X), 552-070-41676-5) United States Government Printing Office.

Gile, Terry Jo. Complete Guide to Lab Safety. 2007. 364p. 279.00 (978-1-57839-994-9(7)) Opus Communications.

—Lab Safety Training Made Simple. 2006. (Illus.). 152p. spiral bd. incl. cd-rom (978-1-57839-854-6(1)) Opus Communications.

Goetsch, David L. Basics of Occupational Safety. 2009. (ENG.). 528p. (C). 116.40 (978-0-13-502613-7(X), Prentice Hall) Prentice Hall PTR.

Gottlieb, Marc S. Car Accidents, the Best Treatments & Worst Pitfalls to Avoid. 2009. pap. 9.95 (978-1-61623-063-0(0)) Independent Pub.

Greco, Paolo S. & Conti, Francesco M. Accidental Falls: Causes, Preventions & Interventions. 2008. (Illus.). 366p. (C). 129.00 (978-1-60456-766-3(X)) Nova Science Pubs., Inc.

Hagan and Montg, Reilly. Accident Prevention Manual. 2006. pap. 12.95 (978-1-4288-1014-3(5)) Cram101 Inc.

Hagan, Philip, et al. Accident Prevention Manual for Business & Industry: Administration & Programs. 13th ed. 2009. (978-0-87912-280-5(3)) National Safety Council.

—Accident Prevention Manual for Business & Industry: Engineering & Technology. 13th ed. 2008. (978-0-87912-281-2(1)) National Safety Council.

Hahn, Pat. Maximum Control: Mastering Your Heavyweight Bike. 2010. (ENG., Illus.). 160p. pap. 24.99 (978-0-7603-3674-8(1), 0760336741, Motorbooks) MBI Publishing Co. LLC.

Hemenway, David. While We Were Sleeping: Success Stories in Injury & Violence Prevention. 2009. (ENG.). 240p. 60.00 (978-0-520-25845-7(2)); pap. 26.95 (978-0-520-25846-4(0)) Univ. of California Pr.

Hollnagel, Erik. FRAM: The Functional Resonance Analysis Method - Modelling Complex Socio-Technical Systems. 2012. (Illus.). 165p. 119.95 **(978-1-4094-4552-4(6))** Ashgate Publishing Co.

—Fram the Frequency Resonance Analysis Me. 2012. (Illus.). 165p. pap. 39.95 **(978-1-4094-4551-7(8))** Ashgate Publishing Co.

H.R. 5663: Miner Safety & Health ACT of 2010: Hearing Before the Committee on Education & Labor, U.S. House of Representatives, One Hundred Eleventh Congress, Second Session, Hearing Held in Washington, D.C., July 13, 2010. 2010. iv, 148p. **(978-0-16-087955-5(8)**, 552-070-42387-7) United States Government Printing Office.

Institute of Electrical and Electronics Engineers Staff & Klotz Associates Staff, contrib. by. IEEE 1512 Implementation Guide: Deliverable 5. 2007. (978-0-7381-5674-3(4)) IEEE Computer Society Pr.

Jackson, Scott. Architecting Resilient Systems: Accident Avoidance & Survival & Recovery from Disruptions. 2009. (Wiley Series in Systems Engineering & Management Ser.: 66). (ENG., Illus.). 297p. pap. 88.95 (978-0-470-40503-1(1), Wiley) Wiley, John & Sons, Inc.

Jones, Julie Scott. Risks Identities & the Everyday. Raisborough, Jayne, ed. 2007. 148p. 99.95 (978-0-7546-4861-1(3)) Ashgate Publishing Co.

Kalra, Jay. Medical Errors & Patient Safety: Strategies to reduce & disclose medical errors & improve patient Safety. 2011. (Patient Safety Ser.). (ENG., Illus.). VIII, 113p. 112.00 **(978-3-11-218787-6(3))** De Gruyter, Walter Inc.

Kapoor, Tanya. Child Occupant Protection in Vehicles. 2009. 364p. pap. (978-3-639-14776-6(6)) VDM Verlag Dr. Mueller e.K.

Kendzior, Russell. Falls Aren't Funny: America's Multi-Billion Dollar Slip-and-Fall Crisis. 2010. (ENG., Illus.). 224p. 79.95 (978-0-86587-016-1(0)) Government Institutes.

—Falls Arent Funny: America's Multi-Billion Dollar Slip-and-Fall Crisis. 2010. (ENG., Illus.). 256p. pap. 29.95 (978-1-60590-696-6(4)) Government Institutes.

Krause, Thomas R. & Hidley, John. Taking the Lead in Patient Safety: How Healthcare Leaders Influence Behavior & Create Culture. 2008. (ENG., Illus.). 304p. 73.95 (978-0-470-22539-4(4), Wiley) Wiley, John & Sons, Inc.

Krueger, Edward J. Accident Prevention Manual for Business & Industry: Security Management. 2nd ed. 2010. (978-0-87912-260-7(9)) National Safety Council.

Lancaster, J. F. Fatal Accidents & Catastrophic Losses: How Prosperity & Safety Are Linked. 2009. 144p. (978-1-84569-530-9(5)) Woodhead Publishing Ltd.

Lancaster, J. F., ed. Fatal Accidents & Catastrophic Losses: How Prosperity & Safety Are Linked. 2009. 192p. 189.95 (978-1-4200-9483-1(1)) CRC Pr. LLC.

LaTourrette, Tom & Mendeloff, John. Workplace Safety & Health Programs: Implementation, Effectiveness, & Benefit-Cost Trade-Offs. 2008. 48p. pap. 22.00 (978-0-8330-4557-7(1), tr-604) RAND Corp., The.

Legislation to Improve Consumer Product Safety for Children: Hearing Before the Subcommittee on Commerce, Trade, & Consumer Protection of the Committee on Energy & Commerce, House of Representatives, One Hundred Tenth Congress, First Session, on H.R. 2474, H.R. 1699, H.R. 814, H.R. 1721, June 6, 2007. 2008. (Illus.). v, 110p. (978-0-16-082549-1(0), 552-070-38578-9) United States Government Printing Office.

Liu, Jian. Aging Effect on Successful Reactive-Recovery from Unexpected Slips. 2009. 108p. pap. (978-3-639-15890-8(3)) VDM Verlag Dr. Mueller e.K.

McConnell, Thomas S. Balloon Safety Seminars. 2009. pap. 20.00 (978-1-890689-45-2(9), Rio Grande Bks.) LPD Pr.

Michaelides-Mateou, Sofia & Mateou, Andreas. Flying in the Face of Criminalization: The Safety Implications of Prosecuting Aviation Professionals for Accidents. 2010. (Illus.). 234p. 99.95 (978-1-4094-0767-6(5)) Ashgate Publishing Co.

Miller, Jonathan T. & Gurton, Lisa M. Pipeline Safety & Security. 2011. (Energy Science, Engineering & Technology Ser.). 156p. 115.00 (978-1-61209-147-1(4)) Nova Science Pubs., Inc.

Morice, Amandine & Hervé, Nicolas d'. Justice de Sûreté et Gestion des Risques: Approche Pratique et Réflexive. 2010. (FRE.). 214p. (978-2-296-12559-9(X)) Editions L'Harmattan.

Morse, Janice M. Preventing Patient Falls: Establishing a Fall Intervention Program. 2nd ed. 2008. 192p. 50.00 (978-0-8261-0389-5(8)) Springer Publishing Co., Inc.

Musingafi, Tsitsi & Nomusa Musingafi, Rutendo. Causes & the Impact of Road Traffic Accidents in the Civil Service. 2011. 64p. pap. **(978-3-8443-0630-9(7))** Lambert Academic Publishing.

The National Transportation Safety Board's Most Wanted Aviation Safety Improvements: Hearing Before the Subcommittee on Aviation of the Committee on Transportation & Infrastructure, House of Representatives, One Hundred Tenth Congress, First Session, June 6, 2007. 2007. xvi, 166p. (978-0-16-079953-2(8), 552-070-36780-2) United States Government Printing Office.

Newsom, Emery. College Student Safety Tips: The 2nd Edition. 2008. 95p. (C). pap. (978-0-9820003-5-9(9)) Carrington Bks.

Newsom, Tony. College Student Safety Tips. 2007. (Illus.). 95p. (C). pap. 8.99 (978-0-9787143-3-8(4)) Carrington Bks.

Omale, James. Basic Concepts in Laboratory Safety for Researchers & Students. 2011. 128p. pap. **(978-3-8454-0327-4(6))** Lambert Academic Publishing.

Payson, Carol A. Patient Falls Assessment & Prevention. 2007. 136p. pap. 129.00 (978-1-60146-078-3(3)) Opus Communications.

Pecheux, Kelley Klaver. Guidebook for Mitigating Fixed-Route Bus-And-Pedestrian Collisions. 2008. (Illus.). 65p. 38.00 (978-0-309-09915-8(3)) Transportation Research Board.

Petersen, Carol. AORN Guidance Statement: Safe Patient Handling & Movement in the Perioperative Setting. 2007. (Illus.). 36p. (978-1-888460-59-9(8)) AORN, Inc.

Public Safety, Binder 6, TITLE 13. (978-0-327-06377-3(7)) LEXIS Publishing.

Rabom, Craig. Guidance for Implementation of the AASHTO Strategic Highway Safety Plan. 2008. (Illus.). (978-0-309-09922-6(6)) Transportation Research Board.

Reviews of Research Programs of the National Institute for Occupational Safety and Health, et al. The Personal Protective Technology Program at NIOSH. 2008. (ENG.). 214p. pap. 44.50 (978-0-309-12018-0(7)) National Academies Pr.

Rhodes, Alison. Honey, I Lost the Baby in the Produce Aisle! Safety Mom's Guide to Childproofing Your Life. 2011. (ENG.). 240p. pap. 16.99 (978-1-4354-5970-0(9)) Course Technology.

Rivara, Frederick P., et al, eds. Injury Control: A Guide to Research & Program Evaluation. 2009. (ENG., Illus.). 320p. pap. 58.00 (978-0-521-10024-3(0)) Cambridge Univ. Pr.

Rudman, Jack. Certified Safety Professional Examination (CSP) (Admission Test Ser.: Vol. 72). 69.95 (978-0-8373-5172-8(3)) National Learning Corp.

Runway Safety: An Update: Hearing Before the Subcommittee on Aviation of the Committee on Transportation & Infrastructure, House of Representatives, One Hundred Tenth Congress, Second Session, September 25, 2008. 2008. (Illus.). xiii, 217p. (978-0-16-083849-1(5), 552-070-39546-6) United States Government Printing Office.

Schuster, Pamela & Nykolyn, Linda. Communication for Nurses: How to Prevent Harmful Events & Promote Patient Safety. 2010. (Illus.). 336p. pap. 42.95 (978-0-8036-2080-3(2)) Davis, F. A. Co.

Sethi, Dinesh & World Health Organization: Regional Office for Europe. European Report on Child Injury Prevention. 2009. (EURO Nonserial Publication Ser.). (ENG., Illus.). 113p. pap. 24.00 (978-92-890-4295-6(8)) World Health Organization.

Shaheen, Amira. Child Injury. 2010. 260p. pap. (978-3-639-22833-5(2)) VDM Verlag Dr. Mueller e.K.

Shayler, David J. & Shayler, David. Space Rescue: Ensuring the Safety of Manned Spacecraft. 2008. (Springer Praxis Books / Space Exploration Ser.). (Illus.). 500p. pap. 39.95 (978-0-387-69905-9(8), 0387699058, Springer-Praxis) Springer.

Simpson, Geoff, et al. Understanding Human Error in Mine Safety. 2009. (Illus.). 174p. 124.95 (978-0-7546-7869-4(5)) Ashgate Publishing Co.

Spellman, Frank R. & Whiting, Nancy E. The Handbook of Safety Engineering: Principles & Applications. 2009. (ENG.). 378p. instr.'s hndbk. ed. 99.00 (978-1-60590-671-3(9)) Government Institutes.

Spyra, Wolfgang & Katzsch, Michael. Environmental Security & Public Safety: Problems & Needs in Conversion Policy & Research after 15 Years of Conversion in Central & Eastern Europe. 2007. (NATO Science for Peace & Security Series / NATO Science for Peace & Security Series C: Environmental Security Ser.). (ENG., Illus.). xvi, 207p. 189.00 (978-1-4020-5642-0(7), 1402056427) Springer London, Ltd. GBR. Dist: Springer.

Spyra, Wolfgang & Katzsch, Michael, eds. Environmental Security & Public Safety: Problems & Needs in Conversion Policy & Research after 15 Years of Conversion in Central & Eastern Europe. 2007. (NATO Science for Peace & Security Series / NATO Science for Peace & Security Series C: Environmental Security Ser.). (ENG., Illus.). xvi, 207p. pap. 79.95 (978-1-4020-5643-7(5), 1402056435) Springer London, Ltd. GBR. Dist: Springer.

Subcommittee on Investigations & Oversight Hearing on the Consumer Product Safety Improvement ACT & Small Business: Hearing Before the Committee on Small Business, United States House of Representatives, One Hundred Eleventh Congress, First Session, Hearing Held May 14, 2009. 2009. (Illus.). v, 160p. (978-0-16-083946-7(7), 552-070-39635-7) United States Government Printing Office.

Thygerson, Alton L. Injury Prevention: Competencies for Unintentional Injury Prevention Professionals. 3rd rev. ed. 2008. 298p. pap. 90.95 (978-0-7637-5383-2(1)) Jones & Bartlett Learning, LLC.

Tideiksaar, Rein. Falls in Older People: Prevention & Management. 4th ed. 2010. (ENG., Illus.). 376p. pap. 34.95 (978-1-932529-44-9(6)) Health Professions Pr.

Turner, Joe M. Excavation Systems: Planning, Design & Safety. 2008. (ENG., Illus.). 509p. (C). 89.95 (978-0-07-149869-2(9), 0071498699) McGraw-Hill Professional Publishing.

Tzeng, Huey-Ming & Yin, Chang-Yi. Patient Unit Safety & Care Quality: Promotion of Self-Healing Systems During Hospital Stays. 2008. 235.00 (978-1-60456-670-3(1)) Nova Science Pubs., Inc.

United States, Congress House Committee on Transportation and Infrastructure Subcommittee on Aviation Staff, contrib. by. Oversight of Federal Aviation Administration Safety Programs: Hearing Before the Subcommittee on Aviation of the Committee on Transportation & Infrastructure, House of Representatives, One Hundred Ninth Congress, Second Session, September 20, 2006. 2007. (Illus.). v, 194p. (978-0-16-078468-2(9), 552-070-35754-8) United States Government Printing Office.

Urbonavicius, Egidijus, et al. Accident Management for NPPS with RBMK Reactors. 2010. (978-1-56700-267-6(6)) Begell Hse. Pubs., Inc.

WHO Regional Office for Europe Staff, et al. Preventing Injuries in Europe: From International Collaboration to Local Implementation. 2010. (Euro Non Serial Publications). 95p. pap. 36.00 (978-92-890-4196-6(X)) World Health Organization.

Williams, Kimberly & Lebrun, Marcel. Keeping Kids Safe, Healthy, & Smart: An Educator's Guide to Child Health & Safety. 2009. (ENG.). 304p. 45.00 (978-1-57886-971-8(4)) Rowman & Littlefield Education.

World Health Organization, Ageing and Life Course Unit Staff, contrib. by. WHo Global Report on Falls: Prevention in Older Age. 2008. (Nonserial Publication Ser.). (Illus.). 51p. pap. 18.00 (978-92-4-156353-6(2)) World Health Organization.

ACCIDENTS, INDUSTRIAL

see Industrial Accidents

ACCIDENTS, SPACECRAFT

see Astronautics—Accidents

ACCIDENTS, TRAFFIC

see Traffic Accidents

ACCLIMATIZATION

see also Altitude, Influence Of; Animal Introduction; Human Beings—Effect of Climate on; Tropical Medicine

Angilletta Jr., Michael J. Thermal Adaptation: A Theoretical & Empirical Synthesis. 2009. (ENG., Illus.). 302p. 150.00 (978-0-19-857087-5(2)); 304p. pap. 65.00 (978-0-19-857088-2(0)) Oxford Univ. Pr., Inc.

Bell, Elanor. Life at Extremes: Environments, Organisms, & Strategies for Survival. 2012. 576p. 180.00 **(978-1-84593-814-7(3))** CABI GBR. Dist: Stylus Publishing, LLC.

Griffiths, Jenny, et al, eds. Climate Change: Diagnosis & Cure. 2009. (ENG., Illus.). 256p. 112.00 (978-1-84407-728-1(4)) Routledge.

—Health Practitioner's Guide to Climate Change: Diagnosis & Cure. 2009. (ENG., Illus.). 256p. pap. 30.95 (978-1-84407-729-8(2)) Routledge.

Hannah, Lee. Climate Change Biology. 2010. (ENG., Illus.). 416p. (C). pap. 59.95 (978-0-12-374182-0(3), Academic Pr.) Elsevier Science & Technology Bks.

Heldmaier, Gerhard, et al, eds. Life in the Cold: Eleventh International Hibernation Symposium. 2010. (Illus.). x, 546p. pap. 219.00 (978-3-642-08682-3(9), 3642086829) Springer.

Ruf, Thomas, et al, eds. Living in a Seasonal World: Thermoregulatory & Metabolic Adaptations. 2012. (ENG., Illus.). xiv, 563p. 239.00 **(978-3-642-28677-3(1)**, 3642286771) Springer.

Seidl, Amy. Finding Higher Ground: Adaptation in the Age of Warming. 2011. (ENG.). 208p. 24.95 (978-0-8070-8598-1(7)) Beacon Pr.

ACCLIMATIZATION (PLANTS)

see also Plant Introduction

Gunin, P. D., et al, eds. Vegetation Dynamics of Mongolia. 2011. (Geobotany Ser.). (ENG., Illus.). 233p. pap. 249.00 (978-90-481-5174-5(0), 9048151740) Springer.

Guthrie-Smith, H. Tutira: The Story of a New Zealand Sheep Station. 2011. (Cambridge Library Collection - Life Sciences Ser.). (ENG., Illus.). 502p. pap. 37.99 **(978-1-108-04001-3(2))** Cambridge Univ. Pr.

ACCOMAC COUNTY (VA.)

Badger, Tom & Badger, Curtis. Accomack County. 2009. (Images of America Ser.). (ENG., Illus.). 128p. pap. 21.99 (978-0-7385-6784-6(1)) Arcadia Publishing.

Miles, Barry & Miles, Moody K., compiled by. Civil War Soldiers & Sailors on the Eastern Shore. 2007. (Illus.). per. 35.00 (978-1-886706-75-0(1)) Hickory Hse.

Smith, Richard H., Jr. Accomack County, Virginia Free Negro Records. 2007. 116p. per. 36.50 net. (978-0-9796857-0-5(2)) Accomac Roots.

Wise, Jennings Cropper. Ye Kingdome of Accawmacke: The Eastern Shore of Virginia in the Seventeenth Century. (Illus.). 406p. reprint ed. lib. bdg. 98.00 (978-0-7222-4643-6(9)) Library Reprints, Inc.

ACCOMMODATION (PSYCHOLOGY)

see Adjustment (Psychology)

ACCOMPANIMENT, MUSICAL

see Musical Accompaniment

ACCOMPLICES

see also Receiving Stolen Goods

Habenicht, Arne. Die Beteiligung an sexuellen Gewalttaten: Unter besonderer Berücksichtigung der Doktrin von den sogenannten eigenhändigen Delikten. 2009. (Schriften zum Strafrecht und Strafprozeßrecht Ser.). (GER.). 240p. 69.95 (978-3-631-59179-6(9)) Lang, Peter GmbH, Europaischer Verlag der Wissenschaften DEU. Dist: Lang, Peter.

Kolbe, Dagmar. Strafbarkeit im Vorfeld und im Umfeld der Teilnahme (§§ 88a, 110, 111, 130a und 140 StGB) Reformdiskussion und Gesetzgebung seit dem 19. Jahrhundert. 2011. (Juristische Zeitgeschichte / Abteilung 3 Ser.).Tr. of Criminal Liability in the Context of Participation (sections 88a, 110, 111, 130a & 140 German Criminal Code - StGB). (GER.). XIV, 244p. 70.00 **(978-3-11-024857-9(3))** De Gruyter, Walter Inc.

Lehto, Marja. Indirect Responsibility for Terrorist Acts: Redefinition of the Concept of Terrorism Beyond Violent Acts. 2009. 535p. (978-90-04-17807-6(4)) BRILL.

Poppe, Andreas. Die Akzessorietät der Teilnahme: Eine Kritische Analyse der Dogmatischen Grundlagen. 2011. (Schriften zum Strafrecht und Strafprozeßrecht Ser.). (GER.). 502p. 121.95 (978-3-631-61164-7(1)) Lang, Peter GmbH, Europaischer Verlag der Wissenschaften DEU. Dist: Lang, Peter.

Roxin, Claus. Täterschaft und Tatherrschaft. (Hamburger Rechtsstudien Ser.). (GER.). XVI, 625p. 240.00 **(978-3-11-121998-1(4))**; 3rd ed. XVI, 644p. 248.00 **(978-3-11-004959-6(7))** De Gruyter, Walter Inc.

Suárez Sánchez, Alberto. Autoría. 3rd ed. 2006. (SPA.). 572p. pap. 48.00 (978-958-710-176-8(6)) Universidad Externado de Colombia COL. Dist: Siglo del Hombre.

Welz, Markus. Zum Verhältnis von Anstiftung und Beihilfe: Überlegungen insbesondere zur Abgrenzung von Anstiftung und psychischer Beihilfe sowie zur Durchführung einer Wahlfeststellung zwischen den Teilnahmeformen. 2010. (Strafrecht und Rechtsphilosophie in Geschichte und Gegenwart Ser.).

(GER.). 252p. 72.95 (978-3-631-59881-8(5)) Lang, Peter GmbH, Europaischer Verlag der Wissenschaften DEU. Dist: Lang, Peter.

ACCORDION

Alexander, Tim. Tim Alexander - Tex-Mex Accordion Bundle Pack: Tex-Mex Accordion Practice Session (Book/CD Pack) with Tex-Mex Accordion (DVD) 2009. (ENG.). 12p. pap. 44.95 incl. audio compact disk (978-1-4234-3670-6(9), 1423436709) Homespun Video.

Bollerud, Bruce. International Accordion Favorites: Waltzes, Polkas, Tangos, Hornpipes, Two-Steps & More!, 1 vol. 2007. (ENG., Illus.). 74p. pap. 19.95 (978-0-7866-0732-7(7)) Mel Bay Pubns., Inc.

Dahl, Gary. Getting Into... Accordion, 1 vol. 2007. (Getting Into Ser.). (ENG., Illus.). 104p. pap. 17.95 (978-0-7866-6725-3(7), 99926BCD) Mel Bay Pubns., Inc.

Deiro, Count Guido & Doktorski, Henry. Complete Works of Guido Deiro, 1 vol. 2008. (ENG.). 192p. pap. 25.00 (978-0-7866-7825-9(9)) Mel Bay Pubns., Inc.

Hal Leonard Corp., creator. Classic Songs: Accordion Play-along Volume 3. 2010. (ENG.). 48p. pap. 14.99 incl. audio compact disk (978-1-4234-9559-8(4), 1423495594) Leonard, Hal Corp.

—Light Classical Pieces for Accordion. 2011. (ENG.). 56p. pap. 9.99 (978-1-4234-9928-2(X), 142349928X) Leonard, Hal Corp.

—Polka Favorites: Accordion Play-along Volume 1. 2010. (ENG.). 48p. pap. 14.99 incl. audio compact disk (978-1-4234-9557-4(8), 1423495578) Leonard, Hal Corp.

Hal Leonard Corp., creator. 3-Chord Songs for Accordion. 2011. (ENG.). 48p. pap. 9.99 **(978-1-61780-472-4(X)**, 161780472X) Leonard, Hal Corp.

Jacobson, Marion S. Squeeze This! A Cultural History of the Accordion in America. 2012. E-Book **(978-0-252-09385-2(2))**; (ENG., Illus.). 304p. 29.95 **(978-0-252-03675-0(1))** Univ. of Illinois Pr.

Zucco, Frank. Mel Bay's Deluxe Accordion Method, 1 vol. 2007. (ENG., Illus.). 100p. spira bd. 19.95 (978-0-7866-7751-1(1)) Mel Bay Pubns., Inc.

ACCOUNTABILITY

see Criminal Liability; Liability (Law); Responsibility

ACCOUNTANTS

see also Accounting—Law and Legislation; Accounting—Vocational Guidance; Accounting Firms; Tax Consultants; Women Accountants

Aicpa. Independence & Ethics Alert 2007/2008. 2007. pap. 36.25 (978-0-87051-701-3(5)) American Institute of Certified Public Accountants.

Balkaran, Lal. Directory of Global Professional Accounting & Business Certifications. 2007. (ENG.). 288p. per. 40.00 (978-0-470-12486-4(5), Wiley) Wiley, John & Sons, Inc.

Bisk, Nathan M. Auditing & Attestation. 40th ed. 2010. (Bisk Comprehensive CPA Review Ser.). pap. 49.95 (978-1-57961-846-9(4)) Bisk Education, Inc.

Brown, Richard. History of Accounting & Accountants. 2006. (ENG., Illus.). xvi, 459p. 37.95 (978-1-59605-961-0(3), Cosimo Classics) Cosimo, Inc.

Cooper, Cynthia & Cooper. Extraordinary Circumstances: The Journey of a Corporate Whistleblower. 2009. (ENG.). 416p. pap. 16.95 (978-0-470-44331-6(6), Wiley) Wiley, John & Sons, Inc.

Cram101 Textbook Reviews & Cram101 Textbook Reviews. Outlines & Highlights for Ethical Obligations & Decision Making in Accounting: Text & Cases by Steven Mintz. 2011. 174p. pap. 29.95 **(978-1-61830-413-1(5))** Cram101 Inc.

Cram101 Textbook Reviews Staff. Outlines & Highlights for Business & Professional Ethics for Directors, Executives & Accountants by Brooks & Dunn, Isbn: 9780324594553. 2009. 108p. pap. 28.95 (978-1-4288-7613-2(8)) Cram101 Inc.

Crawford, Micheal & Loyd, D. Scot. CPA's Multistate Guide to Ethics & Professional Conduct 2008. 2008. 600p. pap. 215.00 (978-0-8080-9176-9(X)) Toolkit Media Group.

Criscione, Richard. Abraham H. (Abe) Briloff: A Biography. 2009. (Illus.). 258p. 134.95 (978-1-84855-588-4(1)) Emerald Group Publishing Ltd. GBR. Dist: Turpin Distribution Services Ltd.

Cynthia Jeffrey Staff. Research on Professional Responsibility & Ethics in Accounting Volume 13. 2009. (Illus.). 177p. 114.95 (978-1-84855-376-7(5)) Emerald Group Publishing Ltd. GBR. Dist: Turpin Distribution Services Ltd.

Edwards, Stewart. My First Forty Years. 2010. 187p. pap. 21.50 (978-1-4452-6710-4(1)) Lulu Enterprises Inc.

Fiorini, Karen. Work-Life Balance & Well-Being in Public Practice Accounting. 2008. 100p. pap. (978-3-639-02349-7(8)) VDM Verlag Dr. Mueller e.K.

Garrett, Nathan. A Palette, Not a Portrait: Stories from the life of Nathan Garrett. 2010. 240p. 28.95 (978-1-4502-4876-1(4)); pap. 18.95 (978-1-4502-4875-4(6)) iUniverse, Inc.

Gill, Matthew. Accountants' Truth: Knowledge & Ethics in the Financial World. 2011. (ENG.). 208p. pap. 35.00 (978-0-19-960310-7(3)) Oxford Univ. Pr., Inc.

Gotbetter Cpa, Edward. And You Thought Accounting Was Boring: Or the Debit Is the Side Towards the Window. 2011. 148p. pap. 12.95 (978-1-4620-3536-6(1)) iUniverse, Inc.

Hawkins, Sheeka Nyqula. The Scars Will Heal. 2011. 64p. pap. 19.95 **(978-1-4626-2409-6(X))** PublishAmerica, Inc.

Huang, Angela. The CPA Woman: An Insider's Guide to Success in a Global Accounting Career (Mandarin-Chinese Edition) 2009.Tr. of CPA nu zi: bei mei zhi chang Plan. (CHI & ENG.). 116p. pap. (978-0-9812420-0-2(6)) ABL Publishing, Inc.

International Federation of Accountants Staff, contrib. by. Statements of Membership Obligations 1-7. 2006. 48p. pap. (978-1-931949-30-9(1)) International Federation of Accountants (IFAC).

Jeffrey, Cynthia. Research on Professional Responsibility & Ethics in Accounting. (Research on Professional Responsibility & Ethics in Accounting Ser.). 2011. (Illus.). 192p. (978-1-78052-004-9(2)) 2010. 260p. (978-1-84950-723-3(6)) Emerald Group Publishing Ltd.

—Research on Professional Responsibility & Ethics in Accounting. 2010. 260p. 114.95 (978-1-84950-722-6(8)) Emerald Group Publishing Ltd. GBR. Dist: Turpin Distribution Services Ltd.

Jeffrey, Cynthia, ed. Research on Professional Responsibility & Ethics in Accounting. (Research on Professional Responsibility & Ethics in Accounting (formerly Research on Accounting Ethics) Ser.). 2008. 232p. 99.95 (978-0-7623-1393-8(5)) 2006. (Illus.). 228p. 111.95 (978-0-7623-1367-9(6)) Emerald Group Publishing Ltd. GBR. Dist: Turpin Distribution Services Ltd.

Kinross-Kennedy, John. How the Value over 100 Closely Held Businesses: Fifth Edition. 2007. 626p. per. 105.00 net. (978-0-9786460-6-6(1)) National Assn. of Certified Valuation Analysts, Inc.

Lange, Gerhard H. F. How i became an Australian. 2007. 68p. pap. 6.50 (978-1-84753-884-0(3)) Lulu Enterprises Inc.

Lazar, Zachary. Evening's Empire: The Story of My Father's Murder. 2010. (ENG., Illus.). 256p. pap. 14.99 (978-0-316-03769-3(9), Back Bay Bks.) Little Brown & Co.

Lee, T. A. The Development of the American Public Accounting Profession: Scottish Chartered Accountants & the Early American Public Accountancy Profession. 2006. (Routledge New Works in Accounting History: Vol. 7). (ENG., Illus.). 192p. (C). 168.00 (978-0-415-40394-8(4)) Routledge.

Loosvelt, Derek & Vault Editors. Vault Guide to the Top 40 Accounting Firms. 6th ed. 2008. (Vault Career Library). (ENG., Illus.). 128p. pap. 29.95 (978-1-58131-567-7(8)) Vault.com.

Mintz, Steven & Morris, Roselyn. Ethical Obligations & Decision-Making in Accounting: Text & Cases. 2nd ed. 2010. (ENG., Illus.). 512p. (C). pap. 79.33 (978-0-07-802528-0(1), 0078025281, McGraw-Hill/Irwin) McGraw-Hill Higher Education.

Mintz, Steven M. & Morris, Roselyn E. Ethical Obligations & Decision Making in Accounting: Text & Cases. 2007. (ENG., Illus.). 304p. (C). per. 79.33 (978-0-07-340399-1(7), 0073403997, McGraw-Hill/Irwin) McGraw-Hill Higher Education.

Partners Financial. Life Insurance: How to Use It to Your Clients' Advantage. Schick, Bryan, ed. 2010. 182p. pap. 72.00 (978-0-87051-897-3(6)) American Institute of Certified Public Accountants.

Practising Law Institute Staff, contrib. by. Basics of Accounting for Lawyers: What Every Practicing Lawyer Needs to Know. 2007. (Corporate Law & Practice Course Handbook Ser.: No. 1613). (Illus.). 476p. (978-1-4024-0925-7(7)) Practising Law Institute.

Previts, Gary, et al, eds. Research in Accounting Regulation. 2006. (Research in Accounting Regulation Ser.). (ENG., Illus.). 380p. 94.95 (978-0-7623-1290-0(4), Elsevier Science) Elsevier Science & Technology Bks.

Previts, Gary & Robinson, Tom, eds. Research in Accounting Regulation. 2007. (ENG.). 338p. 99.95 (978-0-08-045380-4(5), JAI Pr.) Elsevier Science & Technology Bks.

Ross, Stan & Carberry, James. The Inside Track to Careers in Accounting. 2010. 364p. pap. 73.75 (978-0-87051-872-0(0)) American Institute of Certified Public Accountants.

Rossouw, Deon, et al. Ethics for Accountants & Auditors. 2nd ed. 2010. (Illus.). 352p. pap. 29.95 (978-0-19-599046-1(3)) Oxford Univ. Pr., Inc.

Russell, Michael. QuickBooks Made Fast & Simple: Why pay high-priced Accountant fees when you can do the work your Self? 2011. (ENG.). 240p. pap. 39.99 (978-1-4609-4061-7(X)) CreateSpace.

Shenkman, Martin M. Life Cycle Planning for the CPA Practice: Practical Strategies & Forms. 2007. 184p. pap. 98.75 (978-0-87051-677-1(9)) American Institute of Certified Public Accountants.

Stainbank, Lesley. Employee Reporting in South Afric. 2010. 360p. pap. (978-3-8383-1475-4(1)) Lambert Academic Publishing.

Sunday, Ogunode & Arifalo S.O. From Servitude to Greatness. 2011. 132p. pap. **(978-3-8443-3152-3(2))** Lambert Academic Publishing.

Udemezue. Nigerian Accounting Practices: An Examination of Their Social, Economic, Cultural, Technological, & Political Implications. 2008. 172p. pap. 15.99 (978-1-4389-2969-9(2)) AuthorHouse.

Udemezue, Chike C. The Role & Obligations of Accountants in the Development of Nigeria. 2006. 118p. per. 10.95 (978-1-59824-424-3(8)) E-BookTime LLC.

ACCOUNTANTS—MALPRACTICE

Rufus, Robert. Effects of Decision-Aid Use on Evaluations of Tax Preparer Liability. 2010. 96p. pap. (978-3-8383-1546-1(4)) Lambert Academic Publishing.

Watson-Gandy, Mark. Watson-Gandy on Accountants: Law, Practice & Precedents. 2nd ed. 2008. 340p. (978-1-85811-600-6(7)) EMIS Professional Publishing.

ACCOUNTING

see also Amortization; Auditing; Bookkeeping; Business Losses; Business Mathematics; Card System in Business; Comparative Accounting; Cost Accounting; Depreciation; Financial Statements; Forensic Accounting; Income Accounting; Inventories; Managerial Accounting; Productivity Accounting; Social Accounting; Tax Accounting

also subdivision Accounting under names of industries, professions, trades, etc., e.g. Printing—Accounting

Abdallah, Wagdy M. Accounting, Finance, & Taxation in the Gulf Countries. 2008. (ENG., Illus.). 288p. 116.00 (978-1-4039-7798-4(4)) Palgrave Macmillan.

Abdel-Kader, Magdy G. & Lin, Erin Yu-Ching. Performance Measurement of New Product Development Teams: A Case of the High-Tech Sector. 2009. (ENG., Illus.). 272p. 105.00 (978-0-230-57384-0(3)) Palgrave Macmillan.

Accounting: A Foundation. 2008. 512p. pap. 61.99 (978-1-84480-805-2(X)) Cengage Learning GBR. Dist: CENGAGE Learning.

Accounting & Auditing for Nonprofit: Companies-Products-Services. 600p. (978-0-7605-0650-9(7)) Rector Pr., Ltd.

Accounting Disclosure. (978-0-7021-2684-0(5)) Juta & Co., Ltd.

Adhikari, Pawan. Nepalese Government Accounting Development. 2010. 224p. pap. (978-3-639-25931-5(9)) VDM Verlag Dr. Mueller e.K.

Advani, Reuben. The Wall Street MBA, Second Edition. 2nd rev. ed. 2011. (ENG., Illus.). 272p. pap. 22.00 **(978-0-07-178831-1(X)**, 007178831X) McGraw-Hill Cos., The.

Aicpa. Accounting Trends & Techniques. 61st ed. 2007. pap. 148.75 (978-0-87051-693-1(0)) American Institute of Certified Public Accountants.

—AICPA Audit & Accounting Guide: Brokers & Dealers in Securities. 2007. pap. 86.25 (978-0-87051-685-6(X)) American Institute of Certified Public Accountants.

—AICPA Audit & Accounting Guide: Common Interest Realty Associations. 2007. pap. 73.75 (978-0-87051-689-4(2)) American Institute of Certified Public Accountants.

—AICPA Audit & Accounting Guide: Personal Financial Statements Guide. 2007. pap. 61.25 (978-0-87051-691-7(4)) American Institute of Certified Public Accountants.

—AICPA Real Estate Industry Developments 2007/08. 2007. pap. 29.00 (978-0-87051-709-9(0)) American Institute of Certified Public Accountants.

—Independence & Ethics Alert 2007/2008. 2007. pap. 36.25 (978-0-87051-701-3(5)) American Institute of Certified Public Accountants.

Ainsworth, Penne & Deines, Dan. Introduction to Accounting: an Integrated Approach: An Integrated Approach. 6th ed. 2010. (ENG., Illus.). 672p. (C). 235.33 (978-0-07-813660-3(1), 0078136601, McGraw-Hill/Irwin) McGraw-Hill Higher Education.

Ainsworth, Penne & Deines, Dan S. Introduction to Accounting: an Integrated Approach: An Integrated Approach. 6th ed. 2011. (Illus.). xxi, 647p. pap. (978-0-07-122058-3(5), Irwin Professional Publishing) McGraw-Hill Schl. Education Group.

Akasie, Godwin. Accounting Essentials: Concepts, Terms & Meaning. 2010. 316p. pap. 17.99 (978-1-4520-4305-0(1)) AuthorHouse.

Al-Adeem, Khalid & Fogarty, Timothy. Accounting Theory. 2010. 256p. pap. (978-3-8383-3916-0(9)) Lambert Academic Publishing.

Albrecht, Stice. Accounting Concepts & Applications. 2006. pap. 19.95 (978-1-4288-1198-0(2)) Cram101 Inc.

—Financial Accounting. 2006. pap. 14.95 (978-1-4288-1164-5(8)) Cram101 Inc.

Albrecht, W. Steve, et al. Accounting: Concepts & Applications. 11th ed. 2010. (ENG.). (C). 320p. pap., wbk. ed. 82.95 (978-0-538-75019-6(7)); 1344p. 225.95 (978-0-538-74548-2(7)); 1344p. 256.95 (978-0-538-47818-2(7)) Cengage South-Western.

—Financial Accounting. 11th ed. 2010. (Available Titles CengageNOW Ser.). (ENG.). 832p. (C). 238.95 (978-0-538-74695-3(5)) Cengage South-Western.

—K&A General Software for Albrecht/Stice/Stice/Swain's Accounting: Concepts & Applications, 11th & Financial Accounting, 11th ed. 2010. (ENG.). (C). 44.95 (978-0-538-75083-7(9)) Cengage South-Western.

Alexander, David. Comparative International Accounting. 2008. (ENG.). 576p. (gr. 8-8). 33.90 **(978-0-03-099001-4(7))** Houghton Mifflin Harcourt Publishing Co.

Alexander, David & Nobes, Christopher. Financial Accounting: An International Introduction. 4th rev. ed. 2010. (ENG.). 496p. pap. 115.00 (978-0-273-72164-2(X)) FT Press.

Allen, James R., et al. PPC's 1120 Deskbook, 2 vols. Incl. Vol. 1. ring bd. 150.00 (978-0-7646-0311-2(6)); Vol. 2. ring bd. 150.00 (978-0-7646-0312-9(4)); 1997. Set ring bd. 150.00 (978-0-7646-0310-5(8)) Practitioners Publishing Co.

Anandarajan, Murugan, et al, eds. Business Intelligence Techniques: A Perspective from Accounting & Finance. 2010. (Illus.). x, 268p. pap. 149.00 (978-3-642-07403-5(0), 3642074030) Springer.

Anthony, Breitner. Core Concepts of Accounting. 2006. pap. 9.95 (978-1-4288-1257-4(1)) Cram101 Inc.

Anthony, Robert N. & Breitner, Leslie K. Essentials of Accounting. 10th ed. 2009. (ENG.). 360p. (C). pap. 86.67 (978-0-13-607182-2(1), Prentice Hall) Prentice Hall PTR.

Anthony, Robert N., et al. Accounting: Texts & Cases. 13th ed. 2010. (ENG., Illus.). 944p. (C). 225.67 (978-0-07-337959-3(X), 007337959X, McGraw-Hill/Irwin) McGraw-Hill Higher Education.

—Core Concepts of Accounting. 10th ed. 2009. (ENG., Illus.). 208p. (C). pap. 60.00 (978-0-13-602944-1(2), Prentice Hall) Prentice Hall PTR.

Antle, Garstka. Financial Accounting. 2006. pap. 12.95 (978-1-4288-1162-1(1)) Cram101 Inc.

Antle, Rick, et al, eds. Essays in Accounting Theory in Honour of Joel S. Demski. (ENG.). xx, 326p. 2010. pap. 139.00 (978-1-4419-4021-6(9), 1441940219) 2006. (Illus.). 139.00 (978-0-387-30397-0(9), 0387303979) Springer.

Arnold, Vicky, ed. Advances in Accounting Behavioral Research. 2007. (ENG.). 234p. 120.00 (978-0-7623-1454-6(0), JAI Pr.) Elsevier Science & Technology Bks.

—Advances in Accounting Behavioral Research Vol. 9. 2006. (Advances in Accounting Behavioral Research Ser.). (Illus.). 235p. 106.95 (978-0-7623-1353-2(6)) Emerald Group Publishing Ltd. GBR. Dist: Turpin Distribution Services Ltd.

Arnold., Vicky, ed. Advances in Accounting in Behavioural Research, Vol. 13. 2010. (Advances in Accounting in Behavioural Research). (Illus.). 250p. 114.95 (978-0-85724-137-5(0)) Emerald Group Publishing Ltd. GBR. Dist: Turpin Distribution Services Ltd.

Arnold, Vicky, ed. & contrib. by. Advances in Accounting Behavioral Research. 2011. (Advances in Accounting Behavioral Research Ser.). 250p. (978-1-78052-086-5(7)) Emerald Group Publishing Ltd.

Ashton, Robert H. & Ashton, Alison Hubbard, eds. Judgment & Decision-Making Research in Accounting & Auditing. 2007. (Cambridge Series on Judgment & Decision Making). (ENG., Illus.). 312p. pap. 61.00 (978-0-521-66439-7(1)) Cambridge Univ. Pr.

Asia Law and Practice Staff. Building Value in Asia. 125.00 (978-962-936-087-0(X)) Asia Law & Practice Ltd. HKG. Dist: Book Clearing Hse.

Atrill, Peter. Financial Management for Decision Makers. 5th ed. 2009. (ENG., Illus.). 624p. pap. 117.50 (978-0-273-71764-5(2)) Financial Times/Prentice Hall.

—Financial Management for Decision Makers. 6th rev. ed. 2012. (ENG., Illus.). 609p. pap. 120.00 **(978-0-273-75693-4(1))** Pearson Education, Ltd. GBR. Dist: Trans-Atlantic Pubns., Inc.

Atrill, Peter & McLaney, Eddie. Accounting & Finance for Non-Specialist. 7th rev. ed. 2011. (Illus.). 576p. pap. 99.50 (978-0-273-74596-9(4)) FT Press.

—Accounting & Finance for Non-Specialists. 6th ed. 2008. (Illus.). 592p. pap. 97.50 (978-0-273-71694-5(8)) Financial Times/Prentice Hall.

—Financial Accounting for Decision Makers. 6th rev. ed. 2010. (ENG., Illus.). 568p. pap. 107.50 (978-0-273-74039-1(3)) Pearson Education, Ltd. GBR. Dist: Trans-Atlantic Pubns., Inc.

Baginski and, Hassell. Management Decisions & Financial Accou. 2006. pap. 11.95 (978-1-4288-0727-3(6)) Cram101 Inc.

Baker, Lembke. Advanced Financial Accounting. 2006. pap. 16.95 (978-1-4288-1178-2(8)) Cram101 Inc.

Baker, Richard, et al. Advanced Financial Accounting. 8th ed. 2008. (ENG., Illus.). 1088p. (C). 204.69 (978-0-07-352691-1(6), 0073526916) McGraw-Hill Professional Publishing.

—Essentials of Advanced Financial Accounting. 2011. (ENG., Illus.). 864p. (C). 211.33 (978-0-07-802564-8(8), 0078025648, McGraw-Hill/Irwin) McGraw-Hill Higher Education.

—Loose-Leaf Essentials of Advanced Financial Accounting. 2011. (ENG.). (C). ring bd. 148.00 (978-0-07-750526-4(3), 0077505263, McGraw-Hill/Irwin) McGraw-Hill Higher Education.

Baker, Richard E., et al. Advanced Financial Accounting. 7th rev. ed. 2007. (ENG., Illus.). 1072p. (C). 204.69 (978-0-07-352674-4(6), 0073526746) McGraw-Hill Cos., The.

—Advanced Financial Accounting. 9th ed. 2010. (ENG., Illus.). 1120p. (C). 236.33 (978-0-07-811092-4(0), 0078110920, McGraw-Hill/Irwin) McGraw-Hill Higher Education.

Balkaran, Lal. Directory of Global Professional Accounting & Business Certifications. 2007. (ENG.). 288p. per. 40.00 (978-0-470-12486-4(5), Wiley) Wiley, John & Sons, Inc.

BarCharts, Inc. Accounting 2. 2011. (ENG.). 6p. 5.95 (978-1-4232-1631-5(8)) Barcharts, Inc.

Barich, Thomas. QuickBooks 2012 QuickSteps. 2011. (Quick Guides). (ENG., Illus.). 240p. pap. 22.00 **(978-0-07-177594-6(3)**, 0071775943) McGraw-Hill Osborne.

Barker, Richard. Short Introduction to Accounting Dollar Edition. 2011. (Cambridge Short Introductions to Management Ser.). (ENG.). 176p. (C). 75.00 **(978-1-107-01551-7(0))**; pap. 25.99 **(978-1-107-61011-8(7))** Cambridge Univ. Pr.

Barndorff-Nielsen, Ole & Shephard, Neil. Continuous Time Approach to Financial Volatility. 2008. (Mathematics, Finance & Risk Ser.: Vol. 4). 400p. 80.00 (978-0-521-83440-7(6)) Cambridge Univ. Pr.

Barnes, P., et al. Financial Accounting. 563p. pap. (978-0-908237-60-9(X), UNSW Press) NewSouth Publishing.

Beams and Antho Staff. Advanced Accounting. 2006. pap. 15.95 (978-1-4288-0766-2(7)) Cram101 Inc.

Beams, Floyd A., et al. Advanced Accounting. 10th ed. 2008. (ENG., Illus.). 864p. (C). 221.33 (978-0-13-603397-4(0)) Prentice Hall Higher Education.

—Advanced Accounting. 11th rev. ed. 2011. (ENG.). 840p. (C). 220.00 **(978-0-13-256896-8(9)**, Prentice Hall) Prentice Hall PTR.

Beasley and, Buckless. How Accounting Helped Make the Differenc. 2006. pap. 8.95 (978-1-4288-0711-2(X)) Cram101 Inc.

Beaver, William, et al. Financial Statement Analysis & the Prediction of Financial Distress. 2011. 84p. pap. 65.00 net. **(978-1-60198-424-1(3))** Now Pubs.

Bebbington, Jan. Accounting for Sustainable Development Performance. 2007. (ENG., Illus.). 144p. pap. 49.95 (978-0-7506-8559-7(X), CIMA Publishing) Elsevier Science & Technology Bks.

Beckett, Thomas. The Accountant's Assistant. 2008. 156p. pap. 21.95 (978-1-4370-5854-3(X)) Kessinger Publishing, LLC.

Benedict, Augustine & Elliott, Barry. Financial Accounting: An Introduction. (ENG., Illus.). 2008. 776p. pap. 132.50 (978-0-273-68885-3(5)) 2nd rev. ed. 2011. 752p. pap. 112.50 (978-0-273-73765-0(1)) Pearson Education, Ltd. GBR. Dist: Trans-Atlantic Pubns., Inc.

Benz, Christine. Morningstar Guide to Mutual Funds: Five-Star Strategies for Success. 2nd rev. ed. 2007. (ENG., Illus.). 304p. pap. 16.95 (978-0-470-13753-6(3), Wiley) Wiley, John & Sons, Inc.

Beretta Zanoni, Andrea. Accounting for Goodwill. 2009. (Routledge Studies in Accounting Ser.). (ENG., Illus.). 208p. (C). 186.00 (978-0-415-45149-9(3)) Routledge.

Berry, Aidan (Aidan Berry) & Jarvis, Robin. Accounting in a Business Context. 5th ed. 2011. (ENG., Illus.). 576p. pap. 75.99 *(978-1-4080-3047-9(0))* Cengage Learning GBR. Dist: CENGAGE Learning.

Berry, Leonard Eugene. Financial Accounting DeMYSTiFieD. 2010. (Demystified Ser.). (ENG., Illus.). 352p. pap. 22.00 *(978-0-07-174102-6(X)*, 007174102X) McGraw-Hill Cos., The.

Bettner, Mark S., et al. Financial Accounting/Financial & Managerial Accounting Study Guide: Volume 1, Chapters 1-14. 14th ed. 2006. (ENG., Illus.). 230p. (C). per. 72.33 *(978-0-07-326815-6(1)*, 0073268151, McGraw-Hill/Irwin) McGraw-Hill Higher Education.

Biafore, Bonnie. Quickbooks 2010. 2009. (Missing Manual Ser.). (ENG., Illus.). 702p. pap. 29.99 *(978-0-596-80402-2(4)*, Pogue Pr.) O'Reilly Media, Inc.

—QuickBooks 2011. 2010. (ENG., Illus.). 724p. pap. 29.99 *(978-1-4493-9245-1(8)*, Pogue Pr.) O'Reilly Media, Inc.

Biafore, Bonnie. QuickBooks 2012: the Missing Manual. 2011. (ENG.). 760p. pap. 34.99 ***(978-1-4493-9851-4(0)***, Pogue Pr.) O'Reilly Media, Inc.

Biebel, Andrew R., et al. PPC's 1120S Deskbook, 2 vols. Incl. Vol. 1. ring bd. 150.00 *(978-0-7646-0345-7(0))*; Vol. 2. ring bd. 150.00 *(978-0-7646-0346-4(9))*; 1997. Set ring bd. 150.00 *(978-0-7646-0344-0(2))* Practitioners Publishing Co.

Biondi, Yuri, et al, eds. The Firm as an Entity: Implications for Economics, Accounting & the Law. 2007. (Economics of Legal Relationships Ser.). (Illus.). 387p. 160.00 *(978-0-415-41443-2(1))* Routledge.

Biondi, Yuri & Zambon, Stefano, eds. Accounting & Business Economics: Insights from National Traditions. 2012. (Routledge Studies in Accounting Ser.). (ENG., Illus.). 456p. (C). 125.00 *(978-0-415-88702-1(X))* Routledge.

Bissessur, Sanjay. Earnings Quality & Earnings Management: The Role of Accounting Accruals. 2008. 216p. pap. *(978-3-639-05544-3(6))* VDM Verlag Dr. Mueller e.K.

Bizell, Allen. Financial Accounting & Reporting - Advanced. 2007th ed. 2008. (ENG.). 208p. per. *(978-0-9771658-2-7(5))* Efficient Learning Systems, Inc.

Bloom, Martin. Double Accounting for Goodwill. 2009. 232p. pap. 41.95 *(978-0-415-57852-3(3))* Routledge.

—Double Accounting for Goodwill: A Problem Redefined. 2008. (Routledge New Works in Accounting History Ser.). (Illus.). X, 238p. 138.00 *(978-0-415-43748-6(2))* Routledge.

Bodnar and, Hopwood. Accounting Information Systems. 2006. pap. 12.95 *(978-1-4288-0778-5(0))* Cram101 Inc.

Bonin, Holger. Generational Accounting: Theory & Application. 2010. (Population Economics Ser.). (Illus.). x, 268p. pap. 117.00 *(978-3-642-07601-5(7)*, 3642076017) Springer.

Bragg, Steven M. Accounting Best Practices. 6th ed. 2010. (ENG., Illus.). 512p. 99.95 *(978-0-470-56165-2(3)*, Wiley) Wiley, John & Sons, Inc.

—Accounting Policies & Procedures Manual: A Blueprint for Running an Effective & Efficient Department. 5th rev. ed. 2007. (ENG., Illus.). 544p. 183.95 *(978-0-470-14662-0(1)*, Wiley) Wiley, John & Sons, Inc.

—Just-in-Time Accounting: How to Decrease Costs & Increase Efficiency. 3rd ed. 2009. (ENG., Illus.). 354p. 73.95 *(978-0-470-40372-3(1)*, Wiley) Wiley, John & Sons, Inc.

—Throughput Accounting: A Guide to Constraint Management. 2007. (ENG., Illus.). 192p. 84.50 *(978-0-471-25109-5(7)*, Wiley) Wiley, John & Sons, Inc.

—The Vest Pocket Controller. 2010. (ENG., Illus.). 448p. pap. 29.95 *(978-0-470-59373-8(3)*, Wiley) Wiley, John & Sons, Inc.

Bragg, Steven M. & Bragg. Accounting Control Best Practices. 2nd ed. 2009. (ENG., Illus.). 304p. 84.50 *(978-0-470-40542-0(2)*, Wiley) Wiley, John & Sons, Inc.

Brammertz, Willi, et al. Unified Financial Analysis: The Missing Links of Finance. 2009. (Wiley Finance Ser.: 557). (ENG., Illus.). 460p. 80.00 *(978-0-470-69715-3(6)*, Wiley) Wiley, John & Sons, Inc.

Breitner, Leslie K. & Anthony, Robert N. Core Concepts of Accounting. 11th rev. ed. 2012. (ENG.). 208p. (C). pap. 60.00 ***(978-0-13-274439-3(2)***, Prentice Hall) Prentice Hall PTR.

—Essentials of Accounting. 11th rev. ed. 2012. (ENG.). 384p. (C). pap. 86.67 ***(978-0-13-274437-9(6)***, Prentice Hall) Prentice Hall PTR.

Brinton, Willard C. Graphic Methods for Presenting Facts. 2007. (ENG.). 388p. per. 33.95 *(978-1-4325-2633-7(2))* Kessinger Publishing, LLC.

Britton, Anne & Waterston, Chris. Financial Accounting. 5th ed. 2009. (ENG.). 448p. pap. 117.50 *(978-0-273-71930-4(0))* Pearson Education, Ltd. GBR. Dist: Trans-Atlantic Pubns., Inc.

Britton, Anne & Waterston, Christopher. Financial Accounting. 4th rev. ed. 2006. (Illus.). 368p. pap. 99.50 *(978-0-273-70360-0(9))* Financial Times/Prentice Hall.

Brown, Richard. History of Accounting & Accountants. 2006. (ENG., Illus.). xvi, 459p. 37.95 *(978-1-59605-961-0(3)*, Cosimo Classics) Cosimo, Inc.

Brugger, Katrin. Accounting for Pension Liabilities. 2010. 80p. pap. *(978-3-639-24202-7(5))* VDM Verlag Dr. Mueller e.K.

Brunsdon, Terri. Learning Quickbooks 2010. 4th ed. 2010. (ENG.). 992p. (C). spiral bd. 153.33 *(978-0-13-216658-4(5)*, Prentice Hall) Prentice Hall PTR.

Brunsdon, Terri E. Learning Quickbooks 2009: A Practical Approach. 2nd ed. 2009. (ENG., Illus.). 1008p. (C). spiral bd. 146.67 *(978-0-13-612320-0(1)*, Prentice Hall) Prentice Hall PTR.

Brunsdon, Terri E. Learning QuickBooks Pro & Premier Accountant 2011: A Practical Approach & QuickBooks 2011 Software. 5th rev. ed. 2011. (ENG.). 992p. (C). spiral bd. 153.33 ***(978-0-13-274325-9(6)***, Prentice Hall) Prentice Hall PTR.

Buffett, Warren E. The Essays of Warren Buffett: Lessons for Investors & Managers. Cunningham, Lawrence A., ed. 2nd ed. 2008. pap. 32.50 *(978-0-9664461-2-8(7))* Carolina Academic Pr.

Burke, Gary T., et al. Risk & Management Accounting: Best Practice Guidelines for Enterprise-Wide Internal Control Procedures. 2006. (ENG., Illus.). 188p. per. 64.95 *(978-0-7506-8040-0(7)*, CIMA Publishing) Elsevier Science & Technology Bks.

Cagan, Michele. The Everything Accounting Book: Balance Your Budget, Manage Your Cash Flow, & Keep Your Books in the Black. 2006. (ENG., Illus.). 304p. per. 15.95 *(978-1-59337-718-2(5))* Adams Media Corp.

Capachietti, Leslie. QuickBooks 2010 the Official Guide. 2009. (Quicken Press Ser.). (Illus.). 608p. pap. 29.99 *(978-0-07-163338-3(3)*, 0071633383) McGraw-Hill Osborne.

—QuickBooks 2011 the Official Guide. 2010. (Official Guide Ser.). (ENG., Illus.). 608p. pap. 30.00 *(978-0-07-174859-9(8)*, 0071748598) McGraw-Hill Osborne.

Capachietti, Leslie. QuickBooks 2012 the Official Guide. 2011. (Quick Guides). (ENG., Illus.). 656p. pap. 30.00 ***(978-0-07-177621-9(4)***, 0071776214) McGraw-Hill Osborne.

Caplan, Suzanne. Streetwise Finance & Accounting for Entrepreneurs: Set Budgets, Manage Costs, Keep Your Business Profitable. 2006. (ENG., Illus.). 384p. per. 19.95 *(978-1-59337-609-3(X))* Adams Media Corp.

Carey, Mary, et al. Accounting: A Smart Approach. 2011. (ENG., Illus.). 400p. pap. 65.00 *(978-0-19-958741-4(8))* Oxford Univ. Pr., Inc.

Carmichael, D. R. & Graham, Lynford. Accountants' Handbook, 2 vols., Set. 12th ed. 2012. (ENG.). 1920p. pap. 240.00 ***(978-1-118-17180-6(2)***, Wiley) Wiley, John & Sons, Inc.

Carmichael, D. R. & Graham, Lynford. Accountants' Handbook 2011. 11th ed. 2011. (ENG.). 560p. pap., suppl. ed. 125.00 *(978-0-470-61080-0(8)*, Wiley) Wiley, John & Sons, Inc.

Carter, Clairmont. Computer Applications Accounting Practice Set with IBM 3. (C). pap. 27.56 *(978-0-395-49451-6(6))* CENGAGE Learning.

Cases from Management Accounting Practice. *(978-0-86641-161-5(5))* Institute of Management Accountants.

CCH Editors. CCH Accounting for Financial Assets & Liabilities. 2007. 820p. pap. 210.00 *(978-0-8080-9117-2(4))* Toolkit Media Group.

Cengage Learning, (Cengage Learning). Course360 Principles of Accounting I. 2nd ed. 2011. (ENG.). (C). 100.00 *(978-1-111-74750-3(4))* Cengage South-Western.

Cengage Learning Staff. Course 360. 2nd ed. 2011. (ENG.). (C). 90.00 *(978-1-111-74747-3(4))* Cengage South-Western.

Chapman, Christopher S., et al. Accounting, Organizations, & Institutions: Essays in Honour of Anthony Hopwood. 2012. (ENG.). 464p. pap. 45.00 ***(978-0-19-964460-5(8))*** Oxford Univ. Pr., Inc.

Chorafas, Dimitris N. Strategic Business Planning for Accountants: Methods, Tools & Case Studies. 2006. (ENG., Illus.). 632p. 83.95 *(978-0-7506-8132-2(2)*, CIMA Publishing) Elsevier Science & Technology Bks.

Christensen, Peter Ove & Feltham, Gerald. Economics of Accounting: Performance Evaluation. 2007. (Springer Series in Accounting Scholarship Ser.). (Illus.). 688p. per. 139.00 *(978-0-387-74577-0(7))* Springer.

Church, Nancy. Not-for-Profit Accounting: A Very Practical Manual for Bookkeepers, Accountants & Finance Directors of Small Nonprofits. 2nd ed. 2007. 250p. spiral bd. 50.00 *(978-0-9801041-0-3(6))* Church, Nancy.

Clay, John R., et al. Guide to Compilation & Review Engagements, 4 vols. Incl. Vol. 4. ring bd. 156.00 *(978-0-7646-0232-0(2))*; Vol. 1. ring bd. 156.00 *(978-0-7646-0229-0(2))*; Vol. 2. ring bd. 156.00 *(978-0-7646-0230-6(6))*; Vol. 3. ring bd. *(978-0-7646-0231-3(4))*; 1997. 156.00 *(978-0-7646-0228-3(4))* Practitioners Publishing Co.

Collis, Jill & Hussey, Roger. Business Accounting. 2nd ed. 2006. (ENG., Illus.). 400p. pap. 42.50 *(978-1-4039-4886-1(0))* Palgrave Macmillan.

Collis, Jill, et al. Business Accounting: An Introduction to Financial & Management Accounting. 2nd rev. ed. 2012. (ENG., Illus.). 472p. (C). pap. 55.00 ***(978-0-230-27623-9(7))*** Palgrave Macmillan.

Connor, Chun-Mei. A Study of Traditional & Online Accounting Education Systems. 2010. 156p. pap. 79.00 *(978-3-8383-5993-9(3))* Lambert Academic Publishing.

Copeland, Tom. Family Child Care Record-Keeping Guide. 8th ed. 2010. (Redleaf Business Ser.). (ENG.). 216p. pap. 17.95 *(978-1-933653-89-1(2))* Redleaf Pr.

Costa, Carol. Alpha Teach Yourself Bookkeeping in 24 Hours. 2008. (ENG., Illus.). 368p. (gr. 12-18). 19.95 *(978-1-59257-695-1(8)*, Alpha Bks.) Penguin Group (USA) Inc.

Cote, Raymond. Understanding Hospitality Accounting I. 2011. *(978-0-86612-035-7(1))* Educational Institute of the American Hotel & Motel Assn.

Crabtree, Greg & Harzog, Beverly Blair. Simple Numbers, Straight Talk, Big Profits! 4 Keys to Unlock Your Business Potential. 2011. (Illus.). 178p. 21.95 *(978-1-60832-056-1(1))* Greenleaf Book Group.

Cram101 Textbook Reviews. Outlines & Highlights for Advanced Financial Accounting by Richard E Baker, Isbn: 9780073526744. 2010. 204p. pap. 30.95 *(978-1-61698-066-5(4))* Cram101 Inc.

—Outlines & Highlights for Financial & Managerial Accounting: Information for Decisions by Wild, ISBN. 2010. 390p. pap. 34.95 *(978-1-61698-067-2(2))* Cram101 Inc.

Cram101 Textbook Reviews & Cram101 Textbook Reviews. Outlines & Highlights for Intermediate Accounting by Donald E Kieso. 2011. 444p. pap. 36.95 ***(978-1-61830-377-6(5))*** Cram101 Inc.

Cram101 Textbook Reviews Staff. Outlines & Highlights for Accounting for Decision Making & Control by Jerold L Zimmerman, Isbn: 9780073379487. 2009. 92p. pap. 27.95 *(978-1-4288-2027-2(2))* Cram101 Inc.

—Outlines & Highlights for Accounting Principles by Jerry J Weygandt, Isbn: 9780471980193. 2009. 228p. pap. 31.95 *(978-1-4288-2419-5(7))*; 210p. pap. 30.95 *(978-1-4288-9207-1(9))* Cram101 Inc.

—Outlines & Highlights for Cornerstones of Financial & Managerial Accounting, Current Trends Update by Rich, Jones, Mowen, Hansen, & Heitger, Isbn: 9. 2009. 228p. pap. 31.95 *(978-1-4288-7603-3(0))* Cram101 Inc.

—Outlines & Highlights for Financial Accounting: A Business Process Approach by Jane L. Reimers, ISBN. 2009. 118p. pap. 28.95 *(978-1-4288-2169-9(4))* Cram101 Inc.

—Outlines & Highlights for Financial Accounting: A New Perspective by Solomon, ISBN. 2009. 186p. pap. 30.95 *(978-1-4288-3888-8(0))* Cram101 Inc.

—Outlines & Highlights for Financial Accounting: An Introduction to Concepts, Methods & Uses by Stickney, Weil, Schipper, & Francis, ISBN. 2009. 252p. pap. 31.95 *(978-1-4288-2837-7(0))*; 254p. pap. 31.95 *(978-1-4288-7608-8(1))* Cram101 Inc.

—Outlines & Highlights for Financial Accounting: Media Enhanced by Belverd E. Needles, ISBN. 2009. 66p. pap. 27.95 *(978-1-4288-9917-9(0))* Cram101 Inc.

—Outlines & Highlights for Financial Accounting: The Impact on Decision Makers by Gary A. Porter, ISBN. 2009. 154p. pap. 29.95 *(978-1-4288-2497-3(9))*; 156p. pap. 29.95 *(978-1-4288-8960-6(4))* Cram101 Inc.

—Outlines & Highlights for Financial Accounting: Tools for Business by Paul D. Kimmel, Jerry J. Weygandt, Donald E. Kieso, ISBN. 2009. 172p. pap. 29.95 *(978-1-4288-3423-1(0))* Cram101 Inc.

—Outlines & Highlights for Financial Accounting: Tools for Business Decision Making by Paul D. Kimmel, Jerry J. Weygandt, Donald E. Kieso, ISBN. 2009. 178p. pap. 29.95 *(978-1-4288-3369-2(2))* Cram101 Inc.

—Outlines & Highlights for Financial Accounting by Carl S Warren, Isbn: 9780324663785. 2009. 192p. pap. 30.95 *(978-1-4288-2663-2(7))* Cram101 Inc.

—Outlines & Highlights for Financial Accounting by Harrison & Horngren, Isbn: 9780136129349. 2009. 238p. pap. 31.95 *(978-1-4288-3826-0(0))* Cram101 Inc.

—Outlines & Highlights for Financial Accounting by Kieso, Weygandt, Kimmel, Isbn: 9780470128848. 2009. 144p. pap. 28.95 *(978-1-4288-2833-9(8))*; 142p. pap. 28.95 *(978-1-4288-7607-1(3))* Cram101 Inc.

—Outlines & Highlights for Financial Accounting by Needles, Jr , & Powers, Isbn: 9780547193281. 2009. 112p. pap. 28.95 *(978-1-4288-2921-3(0))*; 220p. pap. 30.95 *(978-1-4288-7805-1(X))* Cram101 Inc.

—Outlines & Highlights for Financial Accounting by Robert Libby, Daniel G Short, Patricia Libby, Isbn: 9780073526881. 2009. 68p. pap. 27.95 *(978-1-4288-3431-6(1))* Cram101 Inc.

—Outlines & Highlights for Financial Accounting by Robert Libby, Isbn: 9780072931174. 2009. 240p. pap. 31.95 *(978-1-4288-2749-3(8))*; 222p. pap. 30.95 *(978-1-4288-8679-7(6))* Cram101 Inc.

—Outlines & Highlights for Financial Accounting by W Steve Albrecht, Earl K Stice, James D Stice, Isbn: 9780324645576. 2009. 150p. pap. 29.95 *(978-1-4288-3411-8(7))* Cram101 Inc.

—Outlines & Highlights for Financial Accounting by Walter T Harrison, Isbn: 9780135012840. 2009. 242p. pap. 31.95 *(978-1-4288-2395-2(6))*; 74p. pap. 27.95 *(978-1-4288-9714-4(3))* Cram101 Inc.

—Outlines & Highlights for Financial Accounting by Werner & Jones, Isbn: 013032759x. 2009. 146p. pap. 29.95 *(978-1-4288-3886-4(4))* Cram101 Inc.

—Outlines & Highlights for Financial Accounting by Williams, Haka, Bettner, & Carcello, Isbn: 9780073526980. 2009. 266p. pap. 31.95 *(978-1-4288-2811-7(7))* Cram101 Inc.

—Outlines & Highlights for Financial Accounting Theory & Analysis by Jack M Cathey, Richard G Schroeder, Myrtle W Clark, Isbn: 9780470128817. 2009. 82p. pap. 27.95 *(978-1-4288-3339-5(0))* Cram101 Inc.

—Outlines & Highlights for Financial Accounting Theory by William Scott, Isbn: 9780132072861. 2009. 190p. pap. 30.95 *(978-1-4288-2671-7(8))*; 158p. pap. 29.95 *(978-1-4288-8737-4(7))* Cram101 Inc.

—Outlines & Highlights for Healthcare Finance by Gapenski, Isbn: 9781567932805. 2009. 172p. pap. 29.95 *(978-1-4288-3810-9(4))*; 162p. pap. 29.95 *(978-1-4288-6828-1(3))* Cram101 Inc.

—Outlines & Highlights for Intermediate Accounting by Donald E Kieso, Isbn: 9780470374948. 2009. 308p. pap. 32.95 *(978-1-4288-2563-5(0))*; 314p. pap. 33.95 *(978-1-4288-9116-6(1))* Cram101 Inc.

—Outlines & Highlights for Intermediate Accounting by J David Spiceland, Isbn: 9780073526874. 2009. 272p. pap. 32.95 *(978-1-4288-3409-5(5))* Cram101 Inc.

—Outlines & Highlights for Intermediate Accounting by Spiceland Isbn: 0072994029. 2007. 240p. pap. 14.95 *(978-1-4288-5702-5(8))* Cram101 Inc.

—Outlines & Highlights for Intermediate Accounting, Volume I - Updated by Donald E Kieso, Isbn: 9780470128756. 2009. 198p. pap. 30.95 *(978-1-4288-2373-0(5))*; 64p. pap. 27.95 *(978-1-4288-9759-5(3))* Cram101 Inc.

—Outlines & Highlights for Rethinking the Rules of Financial Accounting: Examining the Rules for Accurate Financial Reporting by Anthony, ISBN. 2008. 68p. per. 10.95 *(978-1-4288-5799-5(0))* Cram101 Inc.

—Outlines & Highlights for Using Financial Accounting Information: The Alternative to Debits & Credits by Gary A. Porter, ISBN. 2009. 142p. pap. 28.95 *(978-1-4288-2173-6(2))* Cram101 Inc.

—Outlines & Highlights for Wiley Pathways Small Business Accounting by Lita Epstein, Isbn: 9780470198636. 2009. 110p. pap. 28.95 *(978-1-4288-8984-2(1))* Cram101 Inc.

Crosson, Susan V. & Needles, Belverd E. Managerial Accounting. 9th ed. 2011. (Illus.). xxx, 616p. ***(978-0-538-74281-8(X))*** 2010. (ENG.). 656p. (C). 252.95 *(978-0-538-74280-1(1))* Cengage South-Western.

Curtis, James W. Mark to Market & Fair Value Accounting: An Examination. 2009. (Business Economics in a Rapidly-Changing World Ser.). 79.00 *(978-1-60741-996-9(3))* Nova Science Pubs., Inc.

Cynthia Jeffrey Staff. Research on Professional Responsibility & Ethics in Accounting Volume 13. 2009. (Illus.). 177p. 114.95 *(978-1-84855-376-7(5))* Emerald Group Publishing Ltd. GBR. Dist: Turpin Distribution Services Ltd.

Dansby, Robert. Paradigm College Accounting: Annotated Instructor's Edition 1, 11. 3rd rev. ed. 59.95 *(978-0-7638-0037-6(6))* EMC/Paradigm Publishing.

Dansby, Robert L., et al. College Accounting: 1-12. 4th ed. 54.95 *(978-0-7638-0274-5(3))* EMC/Paradigm Publishing.

—College Accounting: 1-18. 4th ed. 59.95 *(978-0-7638-0275-2(1))* EMC/Paradigm Publishing.

—College Accounting: 1-29. 4th ed. 73.90 *(978-0-7638-0276-9(X))* EMC/Paradigm Publishing.

—College Accounting: Annotated Instructor's Edition 1-29. 4th ed. 79.95 *(978-0-7638-0161-8(5))* EMC/Paradigm Publishing.

—College Accounting: Chapters 1-11. 421p. 33.95 *(978-0-7638-0034-5(1))* EMC/Paradigm Publishing.

—College Accounting: Chapters 1-12. 4th ed. 457p. stu. ed. 35.95 *(978-0-7638-0157-1(7)*, 01322) EMC/Paradigm Publishing.

—College Accounting: Charters 1-18. 4th ed. 677p. stu. ed. 39.95 *(978-0-7638-0159-5(3)*, 27322) EMC/Paradigm Publishing.

—College Accounting: Complete Text, Chapters 1-27. 3rd rev. ed. 962p. 49.75 *(978-0-7638-0033-8(3))* EMC/Paradigm Publishing.

—College Accounting: Study Guide & Working Papers. 4th ed. 564p. 24.95 *(978-0-7638-0162-5(3)*, 21322) EMC/Paradigm Publishing.

—College Accounting: Study Guide & Working Papers 1-18. 4th ed. 747p. 24.95 *(978-0-7638-0163-2(1))* EMC/Paradigm Publishing.

—College Accounting: Study Guide & Working Papers, 19-29. 339p. 20.95 *(978-0-7638-0164-9(X))* EMC/Paradigm Publishing.

—Paradigm College Accounting: Annotated Instructor's Edition 1,29. 3rd ed. 79.95 *(978-0-7638-0036-9(8))* EMC/Paradigm Publishing.

Davidoff, Howard, et al. Accounting. 4th ed. 2007. (McGraw-Hill 36-Hour Courses Ser.). (ENG.). 416p. per. 19.95 *(978-0-07-148603-3(8)*, 0071486038) McGraw-Hill Cos., The.

Davis, Charles. Financial Accounting & Reporting - Intermediate, Vol. 1. 6th ed. 2008. 504p. per. *(978-0-9771658-1-0(7))* Efficient Learning Systems, Inc.

Davis, Maria K. Accounting for Real Estate Transactions: A Guide for Public Accountants & Corporate Financial Professionals. 2nd ed. 2012. (Wiley Corporate F&a Ser.: 4). (ENG., Illus.). 474p. 150.00 ***(978-0-470-60338-3(0)***, Wiley) Wiley, John & Sons, Inc.

De Bondt, Werner F., ed. Financial Accounting & Investment Management, 2 vols. 2009. (International Library of Critical Writings in Financial Economics Ser.). (Illus.). 1200p. 595.00 *(978-1-84844-039-5(1))* Elgar, Edward Publishing, Inc.

Dellinger, Jeffrey K. The Handbook of Variable Income Annuities. 2006. (Wiley Finance Ser.: 311). (ENG., Illus.). 776p. 185.00 *(978-0-471-73382-9(2)*, Wiley) Wiley, John & Sons, Inc.

DeMarco, Shari L. Who-Dun-It Practice Set. (ENG.). 200p. (C). 10th ed. 2006. pap. 60.00 *(978-0-13-228641-1(6))* 11th ed. 2009. pap. 60.00 *(978-0-13-606570-8(8))* Prentice Hall PTR. (Prentice Hall).

Derstine, Robert. Intermediate Accounting Ready Notes. 2011. (C). pap. 19.95 ***(978-1-118-12123-8(6)***, Wiley) Wiley, John & Sons, Inc.

Devi, S. Susela & Hooper, Keith, eds. Accounting in Asia. 2011. 319p. ***(978-1-78052-444-3(7))*** Emerald Group Publishing Ltd. GBR. Dist: Ebsco Publishing.

Dirksen, Michelle. Fair Value Measurement. 2011. 72p. pap. ***(978-3-8443-0858-7(X))*** Lambert Academic Publishing.

Donovan, 6E Six Easy Steps for Transformational Account Management Marc. 6E Six Easy Steps for Transformational Account Management. 2009. 108p. pap. 13.88 *(978-0-557-05081-9(2))* Lulu Enterprises Inc.

Doupnik, Timothy, et al. Advanced Accounting. 11th ed. 2012. (ENG., Illus.). 912p. (C). 236.33 ***(978-0-07-802540-2(0)***, 0078025400, McGraw-Hill/Irwin) McGraw-Hill Higher Education.

—Fundamentals of Advanced Accounting. 5th ed. 2012. (ENG., Illus.). 640p. (C). 211.33 ***(978-0-07-802539-6(7)***, 0078025397, McGraw-Hill/Irwin) McGraw-Hill Higher Education.

Duchac, Jonathan, et al. Blank Working Papers - Accounting. 22nd ed. 2006. (ENG., Illus.). 384p. (C). per. 46.95 *(978-0-324-38260-0(X))* Cengage South-Western.

Dummies Technical Press Staff, et al. Cash Flow for Dummies. 2011. (ENG.). 384p. pap. 26.99 ***(978-1-118-01850-7(8)***, For Dummies) Wiley, John & Sons, Inc.

Duska, Brenda Shay, et al. Accounting Ethics. 2nd ed. 2011. (CourseSmart Ser.: 21). (ENG.). 256p. pap. 39.95 *(978-1-4051-9613-0(0)*, Wiley-Blackwell) Wiley, John & Sons, Inc.

Duvall, James. Osha 1926 Subpartg/signs,signals,barricades: Master study guide & Workbook. 2009. (ENG.). 20p. wbk. ed. *(978-0-9769489-6-4(6))* Ficus Tree Publishing, LLC.

Dyer, Andrea L., et al. PPC's 5500 Deskbook, 2 vols. Incl. Vol. 1. ring bd. *(978-0-7646-0135-4(0))*; Vol. 2. ring bd. *(978-0-7646-0136-1(9))*; 1997. 150.00 *(978-0-7646-0134-7(2))* Practitioners Publishing Co.

Dyson, John R. Accounting for Non-Accounting Students. 8th ed. 2010. (ENG., illus.). 544p. pap. 99.50 (978-0-273-72297-7(2)) FT Press.

Dzamba, Andy, ed. Accounting Essentials for AP Professionals. 2006. (Illus.). 104p. pap. 179.00 (978-1-58673-174-8(2)) Institute of Management & Administration, IOMA.

Eades, Kenneth M., et al. The Portable MBA. 5th ed. 2010. (Portable MBA Ser.: 34). (ENG., Illus.). 358p. 34.95 (978-0-470-48129-5(3), Wiley) Wiley, John & Sons, Inc.

Easton, Peter D., et al. Student Solutions Manual to Accompany Financial Accounting for MBAs, 3rd Edition. 2007. (C). per. 25.00 net. (978-0-9787279-4-9(0)) Cambridge Business Pubs.

Edmonds, et al. Fundamental Financial Accounting Concepts. 6th ed. 2007. (McGraw-Hill's Homework Manager Ser.). 65.00 (978-0-07-321846-5(4), 9780073218465, McGraw-Hill/Irwin) McGraw-Hill Higher Education.

—Fundamental Financial Accounting Concepts with Connect Plus. 7th ed. 2010. (ENG.). (C). 253.33 (978-0-07-740014-9(3), 0077400143, McGraw-Hill/Irwin) McGraw-Hill Higher Education.

Edmonds, McNair. Fundamental Financial Accounting Concept. 2006. pap. 12.95 (978-1-4288-0514-9(1)) Cram101 Inc.

Edmonds, Thomas. Working Papers for Fundamental Financial Accounting Concepts. 8th ed. 2012. (ENG.). 1024p. (C). pap. 74.00 (978-0-07-743388-8(2), 0077433882, McGraw-Hill/Irwin) McGraw-Hill Higher Education.

Edmonds, Thomas & McNair, Frances. Fundamental Financial Accounti. 6th ed. 2007. 704p. 116.75 (978-0-07-352678-2(9)) McGraw-Hill Professional Publishing.

—Fundamental Financial Accounting Concepts. 7th ed. 2010. (ENG.). 256p. (C). pap., pupil's gde. ed. 79.00 (978-0-07-726985-2(3), 0077269853, McGraw-Hill/Irwin) McGraw-Hill Higher Education.

Edmonds, Thomas, et al. Fundamental Financial Accounting Concepts. 8th ed. 2012. (ENG., Illus.). 832p. (C). 237.67 (978-0-07-802536-5(2), 0078025362, McGraw-Hill/Irwin) McGraw-Hill Higher Education.

—Loose-Leaf Fundamental Financial Accounting Concepts. (ENG.). (C). 7th ed. 2010. ring bd. 166.67 (978-0-07-740516-8(1), 0077405161) 8th ed. 2012. ring bd. 166.67 (978-0-07-743380-2(7), 0077433807) McGraw-Hill Higher Education. (McGraw-Hill/Irwin).

—Loose-Leaf Survey of Accounting 3e. 3rd ed. 2011. (ENG.). (C). ring bd. 162.00 (978-0-07-749083-6(5), 0077490835, McGraw-Hill/Irwin) McGraw-Hill Higher Education.

—Study Guide for Fundamental Financial Accounting Concepts. 8th ed. 2012. (ENG.). 256p. (C). pap. 79.00 (978-0-07-743387-1(4), 0077433874, McGraw-Hill/Irwin) McGraw-Hill Higher Education.

Edmonds, Thomas, et al. Survey of Accounting with Connect Plus. 3rd ed. 2011. (ENG.). (C). 246.67 (978-0-07-750395-6(3), 0077503953, McGraw-Hill/Irwin) McGraw-Hill Higher Education.

Edmonds, Thomas P. & McNair, Frances M. Fundamental Financial Accounting Concepts. 6th ed. 2007. (ENG., Illus.). 282p. (C). per. 79.00 (978-0-07-321833-5(2), 0073218332) McGraw-Hill Professional Publishing.

Edmonds, Thomas P., et al. Fundamental Financial Accounting Concepts. 6th ed. 2007. pap. 186.88 (978-0-07-336777-4(X), 9780073367774) 7th ed. 2010. (ENG., Illus.). 800p. (C). 237.67 (978-0-07-352712-3(2), 0073527122) McGraw-Hill Higher Education. (McGraw-Hill/Irwin).

—Working Papers for Use with Fundamental Financial Accounting Concepts. 6th ed. 2007. (ENG.). (C). per. 74.00 (978-0-07-321832-8(4), 0073218324, McGraw-Hill/Irwin) McGraw-Hill Higher Education.

Eisen, Peter & Eisen, Peter J. E-Z Accounting. 5th rev. ed. 2009. (Barron's E-Z Ser.). (ENG.). 480p. pap. 16.99 (978-0-7641-4256-7(9)) Barron's Educational Series, Inc.

Elbannan, Mohamed. Earnings Management & Environmental Remediation Costs. 2010. 148p. pap. (978-3-8383-0668-1(6)) Lambert Academic Publishing.

Elliott, Barry & Elliott, Jamie. Financial Accounting & Reporting. 14th rev. ed. 2010. 897p. pap. 117.50 (978-0-273-74453-5(4)) FT Press.

—Financial Accounting & Reporting. 11th rev. ed. 2006. (Illus.). 896p. (C). pap. 115.00 (978-0-273-70870-4(8), Financial Times/Prentice Hall) Pearson Education, Ltd. GBR. Dist: Trans-Atlantic Pubns., Inc.

Englard, Baruch. Intermediate Accounting II. 2nd ed. 2009. (Schaum's Outline Ser.). (ENG.). 288p. (C). pap. 20.00 (978-0-07-161166-4(5), 0071611665) McGraw-Hill Cos., The.

Enyi, Enyi. Detecting, Predicting & Preventing Corporate Failure. 2010. 140p. pap. (978-3-8383-4863-6(X)) Lambert Academic Publishing.

Epstein, Lita, MBA & Moore, Shellie L., CPA. Accounting - The Complete Idiot's Guide. 3rd ed. 2011. (Complete Idiot's Guide Ser.). (ENG.). 352p. (gr. 12). 19.95 (978-1-61564-065-2(7), Alpha Bks.) Penguin Group (USA) Inc.

Epstein, Lita. Wiley Pathways Small Business Accounting. 2008. (ENG., Illus.). 410p. (C). pap. 71.95 (978-0-470-19863-5(X), Wiley) Wiley, John & Sons, Inc.

Esquerre, Paul-Joseph. The Applied Theory of Accounts. 2008. 524p. 55.95 (978-1-4374-1942-9(9)); pap. 40.95 (978-1-4373-3350-3(8)) Kessinger Publishing, LLC.

Faciane, Kirby. International Accounting. 2007. 381p. pap. 389.95 (978-0-9788208-3-1(5)) Henry Carey Baird & Co.

FASB Staff. 2006 FARS. 2006. (ENG.). (C). 2000.00 (978-0-470-05259-4(7)) Wiley, John & Sons, Inc.

Feldman, Matan & Libman, Arkady. Crash Course in Accounting & Financial Statement Analysis. 2nd rev. ed. 2007. (ENG., Illus.). 292p. per. 29.95 (978-0-470-04701-9(1), Wiley) Wiley, John & Sons, Inc.

Fields, Edward. The Essentials of Finance & Accounting for Nonfinancial Managers, 1 vol. 2nd ed. 2011. (ENG.). 320p. pap. 19.95 (978-0-8144-1624-2(1)) Amacom.

Financial Accounting: an Introduction to Concepts, Methods & Uses Solutions Manual. 13th ed. pap. (978-0-324-78901-0(7)) CENGAGE Learning.

Financial Accounting Standards Board Staff. 2006 fars cd- for set Pkg. 2006. cd-rom 32.95 (978-0-470-05261-7(9), Wiley) Wiley, John & Sons, Inc.

Fischer, Paul M., et al. Advanced Accounting. 11th ed. 2011. (ENG.). 1152p. (C). 277.95 (978-0-538-48028-4(9)) Cengage South-Western.

Fishman, Jay E., et al. Standards of Value: Theory & Applications. 2006. (ENG., Illus.). 368p. 131.50 (978-0-471-69483-0(5), Wiley) Wiley, John & Sons, Inc.

Follett, Robert. How to Keep Score in Business: Accounting & Financial Analysis for the Non-Accountant. 2nd ed. 2012. (ENG., Illus.). 192p. pap. 19.99 (978-0-13-284925-5(9)) FT Press.

Fortes, Hilary. Accounting Simplified. 2011. (ENG., Illus.). 664p. pap. 77.50 (978-0-273-73446-8(6)) Pearson Education, Ltd. GBR. Dist: Trans-Atlantic Pubns., Inc.

Fortin, Henri, et al. Accounting for Growth in Latin America & the Caribbean: Improving Corporate Financial Reporting to Support Regional Economic Development. 2009. (Directions in Development Ser.). (ENG., Illus.). 196p. pap. 29.95 (978-0-8213-8108-3(3), 9780821381083) World Bank Pubns.

Freytag, Gustav. Debit & Credit. 2008. 672p. 35.99 (978-0-554-36784-2(X)); 39.99 (978-0-554-27481-2(7)) BiblioBazaar.

—Debit & Credit. 2010. 212p. pap. 19.75 (978-1-152-22797-2(1)) Books LLC.

—Debit & Credit. L. C. C., tr. 2009. 370p. pap. (978-1-4099-6714-9(X)); 372p. pap. (978-1-4099-6717-0(4)) Dodo Pr.

—Debit & Credit. 2010. 192p. pap. 14.84 (978-1-152-22799-6(8)) 2009. 416p. pap. 14.84 (978-1-151-08275-6(9)) General Bks. LLC.

Freytag, Gustav & Cummings, L. C. Debit & Credit. 2010. 564p. pap. 43.75 (978-1-141-99516-5(6)) BiblioBazaar.

Gachihi, James & Spuring, David. An Introduction to Accounting. 2006. 228p. per. (978-1-84549-143-7(2)) arima publishing.

Garey, Regan W. Business Literacy Survival Guide for HR Professionals. 2011. (ENG.). 160p. pap. 26.95 (978-1-58644-205-7(8)) Society for Human Resource Management.

Gasking, Terry. Accounting Keys for Success. 2008. (Illus.). 168p. pap. (978-0-9547236-6-8(X)) TwigBooks.

Gerber, Michael E. & Root, M. Darren. The E-Myth Accountant: Why Most Accounting Practices Don't Work & What to Do about It. 2011. (ENG., Illus.). 182p. 24.95 (978-0-470-50366-9(1), Wiley) Wiley, John & Sons, Inc.

Get Going with QuickBooks 2007 for Windows: Et84745sm. 2007. spiral bd. (978-1-4246-0532-3(5)) Element K Content LLC.

Gilbertson. Century 21 Accounting. 9th ed. 2008. (ENG.). 592p. (C). 89.95 (978-0-538-44764-5(8)) Cengage South-Western.

Gilbertson & Lehman. Fundamentals of Accounting. 9th ed. 2008. (ENG.). 256p. (C). pap. 34.95 (978-0-538-44833-8(4)) Cengage South-Western.

Gilbertson, Claudia & Lehman, Mark W. Century 21 Accounting: Multicolumn Journal, Introductory Course. 9th ed. 2011. (ENG.). 608p. (C). 89.95 (978-1-111-98867-8(6)) Cengage South-Western.

Gilbertson Claudia B. & Lehman, Mark W. Fundamentals of Accounting. 9th ed. 2008. (ENG.). 480p. (C). pap. 34.95 (978-0-538-44832-1(6)) Cengage South-Western.

—Fundamentals of Accounting: Course 1. 9th ed. 2008. (ENG., Illus.). 592p. (C). pap. 106.95 (978-0-538-44826-0(1)) Cengage South-Western.

—Fundamentals of Accounting: Course 2. 9th ed. 2008. (ENG., Illus.). 272p. (C). pap. 106.95 (978-0-538-44827-7(X)) Cengage South-Western.

Gilbertson, Claudia Bienias. Accounting: 9th ed. 2009. (ENG.). (C). 26.95 (978-0-538-44807-9(5)) Cengage South-Western.

Gilbertson, Claudia Bienias & Lehman, Mark W. Century 21 Accounting: General Journal. 9th rev. ed. 2008. (ENG., Illus.). 816p. (C). 106.95 (978-0-538-44756-0(7)) Cengage South-Western.

—Century 21 Accounting: General Journal, 2012 Copyright Update. 9th ed. 2011. (Accounting I Ser.). (ENG.). 832p. (C). 106.95 (978-1-111-98862-3(5)) Cengage South-Western.

—Century 21 Accounting: General Journal, Introductory Course, Chapters 1-16, 2012 Update. 9th ed. 2011. (ENG.). 608p. (C). 89.95 (978-1-111-98863-0(3)) Cengage South-Western.

—Century 21 Accounting: Multicolumn Journal, Copyright Update. 9th ed. 2011. (Accounting Applications Ser.). (ENG.). 832p. (C). 106.95 (978-1-111-98866-1(8)) Cengage South-Western.

Gilbertson, Claudia Bienias, et al. Accounting: Multicolumn Journal. 9th ed. 2008. (ENG.). 592p. (C). 91.95 (978-0-538-44707-2(9)) Cengage South-Western.

—Century 21 Accounting Advanced 2012. 9th ed. 2011. (Accounting II Ser.). (ENG.). 848p. (C). 106.95 (978-1-111-98905-7(2)) Cengage South-Western.

Gill, Matthew. Accountants' Truth: Knowledge & Ethics in the Financial World. (ENG.). 2011. 208p. pap. 35.00 (978-0-19-960310-7(3)) 2009. 200p. 110.00 (978-0-19-954714-2(9)) Oxford Univ. Pr., Inc.

Gillespie, Janet. Finacial Accounting & Reporting: Governmental & Not-for-Profit Organizations. 2008. (ENG.). 164p. per. (978-0-9771658-3-4(3)) Efficient Learning Systems, Inc.

Gillett, Mark R., et al. Fiduciary Accounting: Principles, Modern Applications, Illustrations. 2010. 256p. pap. (978-0-8318-9978-3(6)) American Law Institute.

Global Economics Crisis Resource Center. Global Economic Watch: Impact on Accounting. 2009. (ENG.). 32p. (C). pap. 21.95 (978-1-4240-5966-9(6)) Cengage South-Western.

Godwin, Norman H. & Alderman, C. Wayne. Financial ACCT 2010. 2010. (Available Titles CengageNOW Ser.). (ENG.). 336p. pap. 97.75 (978-0-538-79896-9(3)) Cengage South-Western.

Gonnerman, Michael. Ask Mike. 2006. pap. 24.95 (978-1-84728-936-0(3)) Lulu Enterprises Inc.

Goodman, Philip E. Accounting Savvy for Business Owners: A Guide to the Bare Essentials. 2010. (ENG.). 272p. pap. 34.95 (978-1-932925-18-0(X)) CPA911 Publishing.

Granof, Michael H. Core Concepts of Accounting. 2nd ed. 2008. 59.95 (978-0-470-38338-4(0)) Wiley, John & Sons, Inc.

—Government & Not-for-Profit Accounting. 3rd ed. 2006. pap. 15.95 (978-1-4288-1112-6(5)) Cram101 Inc.

—Government & Not-for-Profit Accounting: Concepts & Practices. 4th rev. ed. 2007. (ENG., Illus.). 768p. (C). 221.95 (978-0-470-08734-3(X), Wiley) Wiley, John & Sons, Inc.

Granof, Michael H. & Khumawala, Saleha B. Government & Not-for-Profit Accounting: Concepts & Practices. 5th ed. 2010. (ENG., Illus.). 802p. (C). 221.95 (978-0-470-39078-8(6), Wiley) Wiley, John & Sons, Inc.

Grasso, Lawrence P. Practical Lean Accounting: A Proven System for Measuring & Managing the Lean Enterprise. 2nd rev. ed. 2011. (ENG., Illus.). 475p. pap. 59.95 (978-1-4398-1716-2(2)) Productivity Pr.

Green, James. CCH Accounting for Derivatives & Hedging. 2008. 1300p. pap. 225.00 (978-0-8080-9209-4(X)) Toolkit Media Group.

Griffin, Michael & Hovey, Craig. MBA Fundamentals Accounting & Finance. 2009. (Kaplan MBA Fundamentals Ser.). (ENG., Illus.). 352p. pap. 19.95 (978-1-4277-9719-3(6)) Kaplan Publishing.

Gross, Malvern J. Financial & Accounting Guide for Not-for-Profit Organizations. 7th ed. 2010. (ENG.). 272p. pap. 130.00 (978-0-470-45706-1(6), Wiley) Wiley, John & Sons, Inc.

Grossman, Theodore & Livingstone, John Leslie. The Portable MBA in Finance & Accounting. 4th ed. 2009. (ENG., Illus.). 624p. 34.95 (978-0-470-48130-1(7), Wiley) Wiley, John & Sons, Inc.

Haddock, M. David. Quickbooks Pro 2008 Templates for use with College Accounting. 2009. (ENG.). 160p. (C). pap. 29.75 (978-0-07-731194-0(9), 0077311949, McGraw-Hill/Irwin) McGraw-Hill Higher Education.

—Student Guide for Quickbooks Pro 2008 for College Accounting. 2nd ed. 2011. 480p. (C). pap. 42.19 (978-0-07-743073-3(5), 0077430735, McGraw-Hill/Irwin) McGraw-Hill Higher Education.

—Study Guide/ Working Papers for College Accounting. 2nd ed. 2011. (ENG.). 384p. (C). pap. 46.67 (978-0-07-743074-0(3), 0077430743, McGraw-Hill/Irwin) McGraw-Hill Higher Education.

—Study Guide/ Working Papers to accompany College Accounting. 2009. (ENG.). 384p. (C). pap. 19.75 (978-0-07-731195-7(7), 0077311957, McGraw-Hill/Irwin) McGraw-Hill Higher Education.

Haddock, M. David, et al. College Accounting: A Contemporary Approach with Home Depot 2006 Annual Report. 2010. (Illus.). xxxix, 453p. (978-0-07-339694-1(X)) McGraw-Hill Cos., The.

—College Accounting: A Contemporary Approach. 2nd ed. 2011. (ENG., Illus.). 528p. (C). 114.00 (978-0-07-339695-8(8), 0073396958, McGraw-Hill/Irwin) McGraw-Hill Higher Education.

—College Accounting: A Contemporary Approach with Connect Plus. 2nd ed. 2011. (ENG.). (C). 129.67 (978-0-07-750398-7(8), 0077503988, McGraw-Hill/Irwin) McGraw-Hill Higher Education.

Hagigi. International Accounting. Date not set. (C). (978-0-395-68832-8(9)) CENGAGE Learning.

Haines, Thomas M. Reading Proxy Statements: A Guide to the New SEC Disclosure Rules for Executive & Director Compensation. 2007. 70p. pap. (978-1-57963-164-2(9)) WorldatWork.

Harrison and, Horngren. Financial Accounting. 2006. pap. 13.95 (978-1-4288-0804-1(3)) Cram101 Inc.

Harrison, Walter T., et al. Accounting: Global Edition. 9th rev. ed. 2012. (ENG.). 1315p. pap. 137.50 (978-0-273-77026-8(8)) Pearson Education, Ltd. GBR. Dist: Trans-Atlantic Pubns., Inc.

Harrison, Walter T., Jr., et al. Financial Accounting. (ENG.). 960p. (C). 8th ed. 2009. 233.33 (978-0-13-610886-3(5)) 9th rev. ed. 2012. 233.33 (978-0-13-275112-4(7)) Prentice Hall PTR. (Prentice Hall).

Harrison, Walter T., et al. Student Value Edition for Financial Accounting. 9th ed. 2012. (ENG.). 960p. (C). ring bd. 151.67 (978-0-13-275121-6(6), Prentice Hall) Prentice Hall PTR.

Hart, Leita A. Accounting. 2nd ed. 2011. (Demystified Ser.). (ENG., Illus.). 352p. pap. 22.00 (978-0-07-176373-8(2), 0071763732) McGraw-Hill Cos., The.

Haskins, Mark E. The Secret Language of Financial Reports: The Back Stories That Can Enhance Your Investment Decisions. 2007. (ENG., Illus.). 288p. per. 24.95 (978-0-07-154553-2(0), 0071545530) McGraw-Hill Cos., The.

Haslam, Colin, et al. Redefining Business Models: Strategies for a Financialized World. 2012. (ENG., Illus.). 296p. (C). 145.00 (978-0-415-67440-9(9)) Routledge.

Headley, Glyden. Elements of Accounting & Financial Management in the Government of Canada. 2010. 392p. pap. 50.00 (978-1-4251-6267-2(3)) Trafford Publishing.

Heidhues, Eva & Patel, Christopher, eds. Globalisation & Contextual Factors in Accounting: The Case of Germany, Vol. 23. 2011. (Studies in Managerial & Financial Accounting Ser.). 256p. (978-1-78052-244-9(4)) Emerald Group Publishing Ltd.

Heintz, James A. & Parry, Robert W. College Accounting. (Available Titles CengageNOW Ser.). (ENG., (C). 19th ed. 2007. Illus.). 704p. 175.95 (978-0-324-38249-5(9)) 20th ed. 2011. 46.95 (978-0-538-47616-4(8)) 20th ed. 2010. 48.95 (978-0-538-75069-1(3)) 20th ed. 2010. 742.95 (978-0-538-75358-6(7))Chapters 1-15. 20th ed. 2010. 704p. 175.95 (978-0-538-74521-5(5))Chapters. 1-27. 20th ed. 2010. 1168p. 193.95 (978-0-538-74519-2(3))Chapters 10-15. 20th ed. 2010. 96p. pap., stu. ed. 29.95 (978-0-538-75072-1(3))Chs. 1-9. 20th ed. 2010. 96p. pap., stu. ed. 29.95 (978-0-538-75071-4(5))Chs. 1-9. 20th ed. 2010. 552p. pap., stu. ed. 69.95 (978-0-538-73705-0(0))Chs. 1-9. 20th ed. 2010. 416p. pap. 150.95 (978-0-538-74522-2(3))Chs. 16-27. 20th ed. 2010. 576p. pap., pupil's gde. ed. 72.95 (978-0-538-75070-7(7))Chs. 16-27. 20th ed. 2010. 128p. pap., stu. ed. 29.95 (978-0-538-75073-8(1)) Cengage South-Western.

Henderson & Peirson. Financial Accounting Theory. Date not set. 268p. pap. 9.95 (978-0-582-71482-3(6)) Addison-Wesley Longman, Ltd. GBR. Dist: Trans-Atlantic Pubns., Inc.

Henderson, Perry M. Top Auditing Issues for CPE Course. 2007. 241p. per. 22.50 (978-0-8080-1530-7(3)) Toolkit Media Group.

Henderson, Perry M., contrib. by. TOP Auditing Issues for 2009 CPE Course. 2008. 200p. pap. 31.00 (978-0-8080-1887-2(6)) Toolkit Media Group.

Henderson, Perry M. & Ulvog, James. TOP Auditing Issues for 2009 CPE Course. 2008. 250p. pap. 0.00 (978-0-8080-1874-2(4)) Toolkit Media Group.

Hendrix, R. Blake. Accounting, Finance & Presentation for Small Business: Commerce Is King. 2007. 204p. per. 18.95 (978-0-595-42734-5(0)) iUniverse, Inc.

Herbert, Kyle. Hospital Reimbursement: Concepts & Principles. 2012. (ENG., Illus.). 269p. 69.95 (978-1-4398-9894-9(4)) Productivity Pr.

Herwitz, David R. & Barrett, Matthew J. Accounting for Lawyers. 4th rev. ed. 2011. 224p. pap. 26.00 (978-1-59941-939-8(4), Foundation Pr.) West.

Herwitz, David R. & Barrett, Matthew J. Accounting for Lawyers, 4th Edition, 2009 Supplement. 4th rev ed. 2009. 132p. pap. 23.00 (978-1-59941-628-1(X), Foundation Pr.) West.

Hightower, Rose. Accounting & Finance Policies & Procedures. 2008. (ENG., Illus.). 336p. pap. 84.50 (978-0-470-25962-7(0), Wiley) Wiley, John & Sons, Inc.

Hkib. Fundamentals of Accounting & Law in Banking. 2011. 256p. pap. 50.50 (978-0-470-82659-1(2), Wiley) Wiley, John & Sons, Inc.

Hocking, Deborah. Accounting in Action: Learning in the Field. 2009. 216p. pap. (978-3-639-16207-3(2)) VDM Verlag Dr. Mueller e.K.

Hopper, T., et al, eds. Handbook of Accounting & Development. 2012. (Elgar Original Reference Ser.). 352p. 210.00 (978-1-84844-816-2(3)) Elgar, Edward Publishing, Inc.

Horne, Janet. QuickBooks Pro 2006 with Update 2007: A Complete Course. 9th ed. 2007. (ENG., Illus.) (C). pap. 113.33 (978-0-13-242407-3(X), Prentice Hall) Prentice Hall PTR.

—Quickbooks Pro 2008/2009: Simplified. 2009. (ENG.). 469p. (C). pap. 120.00 (978-0-13-611602-8(7), Prentice Hall) Prentice Hall PTR.

—Quickbooks Pro 2009: A Complete Course. 2009. (ENG.). 800p. (C). pap. 146.67 (978-0-13-612325-5(2), Prentice Hall) Prentice Hall PTR.

—Quickbooks Pro 2010: A Complete Course & QuickBooks 2010 Software. 11th ed. 2010. (ENG.). 816p. (C). spiral bd. 146.67 (978-0-13-216663-8(1), Prentice Hall) Prentice Hall PTR.

—QuickBooks Pro 2011: A Complete Course & QuickBooks 2011 Software. 12th rev. ed. 2011. (ENG.). 800p. (C). spiral bd. 153.33 (978-0-13-274334-1(5), Prentice Hall) Prentice Hall PTR.

Horne, Janet. Runners Corporation: A Merchandise Distributor. 6th ed. 2009. (ENG.). (C). 53.67 (978-0-13-509590-4(5), Prentice Hall) Prentice Hall PTR.

Horngren, Charles, et al. Financial & Managerial Accounting, 2 vols., Chapters 16-24. 2nd ed. 2008. (ENG., Illus.). 528p. (C). 173.33 (978-0-13-504576-3(2), Prentice Hall) Prentice Hall PTR.

Horngren, Charles T. Introduction to Financial Accounting. 10th ed. 2010. (ENG.). 656p. (C). ring bd. 151.67 (978-0-13-139342-4(1), Prentice Hall) Prentice Hall PTR.

—Study Guide for for Introduction to Financial Accounting. 10th ed. 2010. (ENG.). 216p. (C). pap. 46.67 (978-0-13-612299-9(X)) Pearson Education Canada CAN. Dist: Pearson Education.

Horngren, Charles T., et al. Accounting. (ENG.). (C). 9th ed. 2011. 1328p. 240.00 (978-0-13-256905-7(1)) 9th ed. 2011. 912p. pap. 173.33 (978-0-13-256901-9(9)) 9th ed. 2011. 624p. pap. 173.33 (978-0-13-256904-0(3)) 9th ed. 2011. 1328p. ring bd. 156.00 (978-0-13-256930-9(2))Chapters 14-23. 8th ed. 2008. 576p. 173.33 (978-0-13-607301-7(8)) Prentice Hall PTR. (Prentice Hall).

—Accounting, Chapters 1-15 (Financial chapters), Student Value Edition. 9th ed. 2011. (ENG.). 912p. (C). ring bd. 112.67 (978-0-13-256920-0(5), Prentice Hall) Prentice Hall PTR.

—Financial & Managerial Accounting. 3rd ed. 2011. (ENG.). (C). 1280p. 240.00 (978-0-13-249799-2(9)); 624p. pap. 173.33 (978-0-13-249792-3(1)); 896p. pap. 173.33 (978-0-13-249794-7(8)) Prentice Hall PTR. (Prentice Hall).

—Financial & Managerial Accounting Ch 1-15 (Financial Chapters), Student Value Edition. 3rd ed. 2011. (ENG.). 396p. (C). ring bd. 112.67 (978-0-13-249793-0(X), Prentice Hall) Prentice Hall PTR.

—Financial & Managerial Accounting Ch 14-24 (Managerial Chapters), Student Value Edition. 3rd ed. 2011. (ENG.). 624p. (C). ring bd. 112.67 (978-0-13-249791-6(3), Prentice Hall) Prentice Hall PTR.

—Financial & Managerial Accounting, Chapters 1-15, 2 vols. 2nd ed. 2008. (ENG., Illus.). 936p. (C). pap. 173.33 (978-0-13-504575-6(4), Prentice Hall) Prentice Hall PTR.

—Financial & Managerial Accounting, Chapters 15-23 & MyAccountingLab Student Access Code Card Package. 2nd ed. 2010. (ENG.). (C). 180.00 *(978-0-13-248681-1(4)*, Prentice Hall) Prentice Hall PTR.

—Financial & Managerial Accounting, Student Value Edition. 3rd ed. 2011. (ENG.). 1344p. (C). ring bd. 156.00 *(978-0-13-249802-9(2)*, Prentice Hall) Prentice Hall PTR.

—Introduction to Financial Accounting. 10th rev. ed. 2010. (ENG.). 656p. (C). 233.33 *(978-0-13-612297-5(3)*, Prentice Hall) Prentice Hall PTR.

—Study Guide for Accounting, Chapter 14-24 (Managerial Chapters) 9th rev. ed. 2011. (ENG.). 408p. (C). pap. 46.67 *(978-0-13-256929-3(9)*, Prentice Hall) Prentice Hall PTR.

—Study Guide for Accounting, Chapters 1-15 (Financial Chapters) 9th rev. ed. 2011. (ENG.). 576p. (C). pap. 46.67 *(978-0-13-256919-4(1)*, Prentice Hall) Prentice Hall PTR.

—Vango Notes for Accounting. 7th ed. 2006. (Charles T. Horngren Series in Accounting Ser.). (Illus.). 1297p. per. 133.33 *(978-0-13-239912-8(1))* Prentice Hall PTR.

Horngren, Harrison. Accounting. 2006. pap. 17.95 *(978-1-4288-1191-1(5))* Cram101 Inc.

Horngren, Sundem. Introduction to Financial Accounting. 2006. pap. 14.95 *(978-1-4288-1196-6(6))* Cram101 Inc.

Hoskin, Robert E., et al. WP Course Financial Accounting, Sixth Canadian Edition. 6th ed. 2011. (C). 75.50 ***(978-1-118-00066-3(8)***, Wiley) Wiley, John & Sons, Inc.

Hovey, Craig. The Accountant's Guide to the Universe: Heaven & Hell by the Numbers. 2010. (ENG.). 176p. 21.99 *(978-0-312-37624-6(3)*, Dunne, Thomas Bks.) St. Martin's Pr.

Howard, Malcolm K. Accounting & Business Valuation Methods: How to Interpret IFRS Accounts. 2007. (ENG., Illus.). 312p. pap. 54.95 *(978-0-7506-8468-2(2)*, CIMA Publishing) Elsevier Science & Technology Bks.

Hoyle, Joe Ben, et al. Advanced Accounting. 9th ed. 2008. (ENG., Illus.). 928p. (C). 204.69 *(978-0-07-337945-6(X)*, 007337945X, McGraw-Hill/Irwin) McGraw-Hill Higher Education.

—Fundamentals of Advanced Accounting. (ENG.). (C). 2nd ed. 2007. 182.81 *(978-0-07-724057-8(X)*, 007724057X) 4th ed. 2010. (Illus.). 616p. 211.33 *(978-0-07-813663-4(6)*, 0078136636) McGraw-Hill Higher Education. (McGraw-Hill/Irwin).

—Fundamentals of Advanced Accounting with Connect Plus 1 Semester Access Card. 4th ed. 2010. (ENG.). (C). 227.00 *(978-0-07-743915-6(5)*, 0077439155, McGraw-Hill/Irwin) McGraw-Hill Higher Education.

—Loose-Leaf Fundamentals of Advanced Accounting. 4th ed. 2010. (ENG.). (C). ring bd. 111.00 *(978-0-07-743181-5(2)*, 0077431812, McGraw-Hill/Irwin) McGraw-Hill Higher Education.

—Study Guide & Working Papers to accompany Advanced Accounting. 10th ed. 2010. (ENG.). 256p. (C). pap. 82.67 *(978-0-07-726804-6(0)*, 0077268040, McGraw-Hill/Irwin) McGraw-Hill Higher Education.

Hoyle, Schaefer. Advanced Accounting. 2006. pap. 13.95 *(978-1-4288-0498-2(6))* Cram101 Inc.

Hsu, Audrey Wenhsin. Asymmetric Timeliness of Earnings. 2011. 260p. pap. ***(978-3-8383-7505-2(X))*** Lambert Academic Publishing.

Huefner, Ronald J., et al. Advanced Financial Accounting. 10th ed. 2006. (ENG.). 1100p. (C). 182.95 *(978-0-7593-6426-4(5))* CENGAGE Learning Custom Publishing.

Humphrey, Christopher & Lee, Bill H. K., eds. The Real Life Guide to Accounting Research: A Behind-the-Scenes View of Using Qualitative Research Methods. 2007. (ENG., Illus.). 544p. pap. 57.95 *(978-0-08-048992-6(3)*, CIMA Publishing) Elsevier Science & Technology Bks.

Hunter, Christopher. Hybrid Derivatives - Modeling & Pricing. 2007. 448p. pap. 140.00 *(978-0-470-02661-8(8))* Wiley, John & Sons, Inc.

Ingram. Financial Accounting: Information for Decisions Working Papers. (SWC-Accounting Ser.). pap. 7.00 net. *(978-0-538-85830-4(3))* Cengage South-Western.

Ingram & Albright. Ie, Financial Accounting: Bridge to Decision Making. 6th ed. 2007. (Illus.). xxix, 603p. *(978-0-324-37466-7(6))* Cengage South-Western.

Ingram, et al. Ie, Financial Accounting-Information for Decisions. 6th ed. 2007. (Illus.). xxix, 603p. *(978-0-324-37464-3(X))* Cengage South-Western.

Intermediate Accounting CengageNOW Express Printed Access Card. 11th ed. *(978-0-324-78837-2(1))* Cengage South-Western.

Intermediate Accounting Reporting Analysis Study Guide, Volume 2. 2011. (ENG.). (C). pap. 46.95 ***(978-1-133-18919-0(9))*** Cengage South-Western.

Introductory Accounting. (Proficiency Examination Program Ser.). (C). 49.95 *(978-0-8373-5560-3(5)*, PEP-10, Passbooks) National Learning Corp.

Isert, Dietmar. The Accounting Treatment of Derivates on a Reporting Entity's Own Shares: Adding the New Category Equity Derivates. 2009. 231p. pap. 49.00 *(978-3-8329-4504-6(0))* Nomos Verlagsgesellschaft DEU. Dist: International Specialized Bk. Services.

Ivens, Kathy & Barich, Tom. Running QuickBooks 2012 Premier Editions: The Only Definitive Guide to the Premier Editions. 2011. (ENG.). 640p. pap. 36.95 ***(978-1-932925-34-0(1))*** CPA911 Publishing.

Jack, Lisa, et al, eds. The Routledge Companion to Accounting Communication. 2012. (ENG., Illus.). 480p. (C). 165.00 *(978-0-415-61714-7(6))* Routledge.

Jagels, Martin G., et al. Hospitality Management Accounting. 10th ed. 2013. (ENG., Illus.). 640p. 77.95 *(978-0-470-05243-3(0)*, Wiley) Wiley, John & Sons, Inc.

Jansen, Ewoud. Accounting & Finance: A Basic Introduction. 2011. 336p. pap. 51.50 *(978-90-5931-628-7(2))* Eleven International Publishing NLD. Dist: International Specialized Bk. Services.

Jeffrey, Cynthia. Research on Professional Responsibility & Ethics in Accounting. (Research on Professional Responsibility & Ethics in Accounting Ser.). 2011. (Illus.). 192p. *(978-1-78052-004-9(2))* 2010. 260p. *(978-1-84950-723-3(6))* Emerald Group Publishing Ltd.

—Research on Professional Responsibility & Ethics in Accounting. 2010. 260p. 114.95 *(978-1-84950-722-6(8))* Emerald Group Publishing Ltd. GBR. Dist: Turpin Distribution Services Ltd.

Jeffrey, Cynthia, ed. Research on Professional Responsibility & Ethics in Accounting. (Research on Professional Responsibility & Ethics in Accounting (formerly Research on Accounting Ethics) Ser.). 2008. 232p. 99.95 *(978-0-7623-1393-8(5))* 2006. (Illus.). 228p. 111.95 *(978-0-7623-1367-9(6))* Emerald Group Publishing Ltd. GBR. Dist: Turpin Distribution Services Ltd.

Jeter and, Chaney. Advanced Accounting. 2006. pap. 15.95 *(978-1-4288-0882-9(5))* Cram101 Inc.

Jeter, Debra C. Advanced Accounting. 5th ed. 2011. (C). pap., pupil's gde. ed. 59.95 *(978-1-118-10852-9(3)*, Wiley) Wiley, John & Sons, Inc.

Jeter, Debra C. & Chaney, Paul. Advanced Accounting. 4th ed. (ENG.). (C). 2010. 312p. pap., pupil's gde. ed. 66.95 *(978-0-470-59084-3(X))* 2009. 1032p. 233.95 *(978-0-470-50698-1(9))* Wiley, John & Sons, Inc. (Wiley).

Jeter, Debra C. & Chaney, Paul K. Advanced Accounting. (ENG.). (C). 3rd ed. 2007. 400p. pap., pupil's gde. ed. 66.95 *(978-0-470-13040-7(7))* 3rd ed. 2007. (Illus.). 976p. 242.95 *(978-0-470-08736-7(6))* 5th ed. 2011. 1072p. 224.95 ***(978-1-118-02229-0(7))*** Wiley, John & Sons, Inc. (Wiley).

—Advanced Accounting, Professional Simulations. 2007. 10.00 *(978-0-470-19113-2(9)*, Wiley) Wiley, John & Sons, Inc.

—Online Practice Set Reg. Card Advanced Accounting. 3rd ed. 2007. (ENG.). (C). 10.00 *(978-0-470-19853-7(2)*, Wiley) Wiley, John & Sons, Inc.

Jiambalvo, James. Accounting for Managers for Ohio University Main Campus. 2011. (Wiley Custom Select Ser.). (C). pap. 77.95 ***(978-0-470-95591-8(0)***, Wiley) Wiley, John & Sons, Inc.

Jiambalvo, James. Managerial Accounting. 3rd rev. ed. 2006. (ENG., Illus.). 624p. (C). 233.95 *(978-0-470-03815-4(2)*, Wiley) Wiley, John & Sons, Inc.

Johal, Parminder, et al. Unlocking Financial Accounting. 2010. (Illus.). 416p. pap. 37.99 *(978-1-4441-1210-8(4))* Hodder Education GBR. Dist: Oxford Univ. Pr., Inc.

Jones, Michael. Financial Accounting. 2006. (ENG., Illus.). 500p. per. 70.95 *(978-0-470-05898-5(6)*, Wiley) Wiley, John & Sons, Inc.

Kamoroff, Bernard. Small Time Operator: How to Start Your Own Business, Keep Your Books, Pay Your Taxes & Stay Out of Trouble. 11th ed. 2010. 240p. pap. 18.95 *(978-0-917510-30-4(5))* Bell Springs Publishing.

Keegan, Karl. Biotechnology Valuation: An Introductory Guide. 2009. (Wiley Finance Ser.). (ENG., Illus.). 216p. instr.'s gde. ed. 90.00 *(978-0-470-51178-7(8)*, Wiley) Wiley, John & Sons, Inc.

Keiso, Weygandt. Fundamentals of Intermediate Accounting. 2006. pap. 17.95 *(978-1-4288-0875-1(2))* Cram101 Inc.

Kelly, Jane. Sage 50 Accounts for Dummies. (ENG., Illus.). 2009. 388p. pap. 32.99 ***(978-0-470-71558-1(8))*** 2nd ed. 2012. 424p. pap. 24.99 ***(978-1-118-30858-5(1))*** Wiley, John & Sons, Inc. (For Dummies).

Kew, Jacqui & Watson, Alex. Financial Accounting: an Introduction 3e. 3rd ed. 2011. (ENG.). 736p. pap. 65.00 ***(978-0-19-598835-2(3))*** Oxford Univ. Pr., Inc.

Khondaker, Mizanur Rahman. Development of Business Organization & Accounting. 2011. 96p. pap. ***(978-3-8443-1277-5(3))*** Lambert Academic Publishing.

Kieso. Intermediate Accounting for University of Texas Dallas, Vol. 2. 14th ed. 2011. 776p. (C). pap. 128.95 ***(978-1-118-10711-9(X)***, Wiley) Wiley, John & Sons, Inc.

Kieso, Donald E. Accounting: Tools for Business Decision Making. 4th ed. 2011. 148p. (C). pap. 24.95 ***(978-1-118-11491-9(4)***, Wiley) Wiley, John & Sons, Inc.

—Intermediate Accounting. 13th ed. 2009. 960p. (C). 102.95 *(978-0-470-46769-5(X))* Wiley, John & Sons, Inc.

—Intermediate Accounting, 13th edition Volume 1. 2011. 790p. (C). pap. 143.95 ***(978-1-118-03807-9(X)***, Wiley) Wiley, John & Sons, Inc.

—Intermediate Accounting 13th Edition Volume 2 CUE. 2011. 696p. (C). pap. 143.95 ***(978-1-118-03806-2(1)***, Wiley) Wiley, John & Sons, Inc.

—Intermediate Accounting 14E Volume 1 for the University of Texas at Dallas. 14th ed. 2011. 954p. (C). pap. 128.95 ***(978-1-118-10712-6(8)***, Wiley) Wiley, John & Sons, Inc.

—(WCS)Intermediate Accounting 12th Edition Binder Ready with Binder, Problem Solving Survival Guide Volume 1 & Wiley Plus Set. 2006. pap. 155.95 *(978-0-470-10801-7(0))* Wiley, John & Sons, Inc.

—(WCS)Intermediate Accounting 12th Edition Custom for Brooklyn College. 2007. pap. 61.95 *(978-0-470-14418-3(1)*, Wiley) Wiley, John & Sons, Inc.

Kieso, Donald E. & Weygandt, Jerry J. Intermediate Accounting Volume 1. 2006. pap. 16.95 *(978-1-4288-1295-6(4))* Cram101 Inc.

—Intermediate Accounting Volume 2. 2006. pap. 14.95 *(978-1-4288-1296-3(2))* Cram101 Inc.

—Rockford Practice Set to accompany Intermediate Accounting Vol. 1. 2006. pap. 15.95 *(978-1-4288-0500-2(1))* Cram101 Inc.

—Rockford Practice Set to accompany Intermediate Accounting Vol. 1. 11th ed. 2006. pap. 78.95 *(978-0-470-07588-3(0))* Wiley, John & Sons, Inc.

Kieso, Donald E., et al. Accounting: Tools for Business Decision Making. 4th ed. 2011. (ENG., Illus.). 1408p. (C). 241.95 *(978-0-470-53478-6(8)*, Wiley) Wiley, John & Sons, Inc.

—Fundamentals of Intermediate Accounting. (Wiley Plus Products Ser.). 2007. pap. 0.01 *(978-0-470-17523-1(0)*, Wiley) 22nd ed. 2008. pap. 39.95 *(978-0-471-73797-1(6))* Wiley, John & Sons, Inc.

—Fundamentals of Intermediate Accounting, w/Take Action! CD & 3M Annual Report, Rockford Computerized Practice Set. 2006. cd-rom 44.95 *(978-0-471-74956-1(7))* Wiley, John & Sons, Inc.

—Intermediate Accounting. 13th ed. 2009. (ENG.). (C). 66.95 *(978-0-470-38062-8(4))*; 224.95 *(978-0-470-46767-1(3))* Wiley, John & Sons, Inc. (Wiley).

—Intermediate Accounting. 14th ed. 2011. (C). pap. 109.95 *(978-0-470-91909-5(4))*; (ENG.). 1640p. 254.95 *(978-0-470-58723-2(7))* Wiley, John & Sons, Inc. (Wiley).

—Intermediate Accounting. (ENG.). 384p. (C). 13th Edition, Volume 1. 13th ed. 2009. pap., pupil's gde. ed. 66.95 *(978-0-470-38059-8(4))* Vol. 1. 2010. pap., pupil's gde. ed. 74.95 *(978-0-470-61330-6(0))* Wiley, John & Sons, Inc. (Wiley).

—Intermediate Accounting, 2 vols., Vol. 1. (ENG., (C). 11th ed. 2010. Illus.). 800p. 146.95 *(978-0-470-61630-7(X))* 14th ed. 2011. 888p. 192.95 *(978-0-470-58728-7(8))* Wiley, John & Sons, Inc. (Wiley).

—Intermediate Accounting, Vol. 1, Chs. 1-14. 2010. (ENG.). 608p. (C). pap. 77.95 *(978-0-470-61346-7(7)*, Wiley) Wiley, John & Sons, Inc.

—Intermediate Accounting, Vol. 2. (ENG., (C). 13th ed. 2009. Illus.). 688p. 143.95 *(978-0-470-42369-1(2))* 14th ed. 2011. 792p. 143.95 *(978-0-470-58729-4(6))* Wiley, John & Sons, Inc. (Wiley).

—Intermediate Accounting. 13th ed. 2009. (ENG.). 384p. (C). Vol. 2, Chapters 15-24. pap. 66.95 *(978-0-470-38058-1(6))* Vol. 2, Chs. 15-24. pap., stu. ed. 78.95 *(978-0-470-38060-4(8))* Wiley, John & Sons, Inc. (Wiley).

—Intermediate Accounting, Volume 2. 14th ed. 2011. (ENG.). (C). 384p. pap., pupil's gde. ed. 78.95 *(978-1-118-01450-9(2))*; 704p. pap. 60.95 *(978-1-118-01453-0(7))* Wiley, John & Sons, Inc. (Wiley).

—Intermediate Accounting: International Finanacial Reporting. 2010. 1416p. (C). 217.95 *(978-0-470-48595-8(7)*, Wiley) Wiley, John & Sons, Inc.

—Intermediate Accounting: International Finanacial Reporting Standards. 2010. (ENG.). (C). cd-rom 57.95 *(978-0-470-61348-1(3)*, Wiley) Wiley, John & Sons, Inc.

—Intermediate Accounting: Principles & Analysis. 2nd ed. 2007. (ENG., Illus.). 1136p. (C). 231.95 *(978-0-471-73793-3(3)*, Wiley) Wiley, John & Sons, Inc.

—Intermediate Accounting Chs. 1-14, Vol. 1. 13th ed. 2009. (ENG.). 576p. (C). pap., wbk. ed. 75.95 *(978-0-470-38061-1(6)*, Wiley) Wiley, John & Sons, Inc.

—Intermediate Accounting Vol. 1. (ENG.). (C). 13th ed. 2009. 1440p. 254.95 *(978-0-470-37494-8(2))*Volume 1. 14th ed. 2011. 384p. pap., pupil's gde. ed. 66.95 *(978-1-118-01449-3(9))* Wiley, John & Sons, Inc. (Wiley).

—Intermediate Accounting Vol. 1: Problem Solving Survival Guide, Volume 1. 14th ed. 2011. (ENG.). 504p. (C). pap. 66.95 *(978-1-118-01447-9(2)*, Wiley) Wiley, John & Sons, Inc.

—Intermediate Accounting Vol. 1: Working Papers, Volume 1. 14th ed. 2011. (ENG.). 632p. (C). pap. 75.95 *(978-1-118-01451-6(0)*, Wiley) Wiley, John & Sons, Inc.

—Intermediate Accounting Vol. 1, Chs. 1-14: Problem Solving Survival Guide, 13th Edition, Volume 1. 13th ed. 2009. (ENG.). 480p. (C). pap. 66.95 *(978-0-470-38057-4(8)*, Wiley) Wiley, John & Sons, Inc.

—Intermediate Accounting Vol. 2, 2 vols. 21st ed. 2010. (ENG., Illus.). 656p. (C). 140.95 *(978-0-470-61631-4(8)*, Wiley) Wiley, John & Sons, Inc.

—Intermediate Accounting Vol. 2, Vol. 2, Chapters 15-24. 2010. (ENG.). 342p. (C). pap., pupil's gde. ed. 74.95 *(978-0-470-61331-3(9)*, Wiley) Wiley, John & Sons, Inc.

—Intermediate Accounting Vol. II: Problem Solving Survival Guide, Volume 2. 14th ed. 2011. (ENG.). 408p. (C). pap. 66.95 *(978-1-118-01448-6(0)*, Wiley) Wiley, John & Sons, Inc.

—Intermediate Accounting Vol. 2: Working Papers - Chapters 15-24. 2011. (ENG.). 544p. (C). pap. 66.95 *(978-0-470-61347-4(5)*, Wiley) Wiley, John & Sons, Inc.

—Intermediate Accounting 12th edition, no end of chapter material Version. 12th rev. ed. 2008. 772p. 89.95 *(978-0-470-12877-0(1))* Wiley, John & Sons, Inc.

—Intermediate Accounting 14E Chapter 18 Only for Northern Illinois University. 2011. 84p. (C). pap. 23.95 ***(978-1-118-10082-0(4)***, Wiley) Wiley, John & Sons, Inc.

—Intermediate Accounting, 14th edition Binder Ready Version. 2011. 1640p. (C). ring bd. 159.95 *(978-0-470-91783-1(0)*, Wiley) Wiley, John & Sons, Inc.

—Intermediate Accounting 14th Edition Volume 1 CUE. 2011. (C). ring bd. 118.95 ***(978-1-118-12182-5(1)***, Wiley) Wiley, John & Sons, Inc.

—Intermediate Accounting 14th Edition Volume 1 Selected Chapters for University of NE Omaha. 14th ed. 2011. 810p. (C). ring bd. 83.95 ***(978-1-118-11611-1(9)***, Wiley) Wiley, John & Sons, Inc.

—Intermediate Accounting 14th Edition Volume 2 CUE. 2011. (C). ring bd. 118.95 ***(978-1-118-12184-9(8)***, Wiley) Wiley, John & Sons, Inc.

—Intermediate Accounting 14th Edition Volume 2 Selected Chapters for University of NE Omaha. 14th ed. 2011. 908p. (C). ring bd. 83.95 ***(978-1-118-11612-8(7)***, Wiley) Wiley, John & Sons, Inc.

—Intermediate Accounting, Instructor's Manual Volume II: IFRS Edition. 2011. 258p. (C). pap. 9.95 ***(978-0-470-61342-9(4)***, Wiley) Wiley, John & Sons, Inc.

—Intermediate Accounting, Professional Simulations. 12th ed. 2007. 10.00 *(978-0-470-19112-5(0)*, Wiley) Wiley, John & Sons, Inc.

—Rockford Practice Set to Accompany Intermediate Accounting, 2 vols., Vol. 1. 13th ed. 2009. (ENG., Illus.). 784p. (C). 192.95 *(978-0-470-42368-4(4)*, Wiley) Wiley, John & Sons, Inc.

—Rockford Practice Set to accompany Intermediate Accounting Vol. 1. 12th ed. 2007. 1416p. pap., ring bd. 123.95 *(978-0-470-27972-4(9)*, Wiley) Wiley, John & Sons, Inc.

—Wiley Plus/Blackboard Stand-alone to accompany Intermediate Accounting. 12th ed. 2006. (Wiley Plus Products Ser.). pap. 77.95 *(978-0-470-07715-3(8))* Wiley, John & Sons, Inc.

—Working Papers to Accompany Fundamentals of Intermediate Accounting. 2nd ed. 2008. 816p. pap. 39.95 *(978-0-471-73795-7(X))* Wiley, John & Sons, Inc.

Kimmel. Accounting: Tools for Business Decision Makers 4E Custom Edition Volume 1. 4th ed. 2011. 928p. (C). pap. 114.95 ***(978-1-118-10635-8(0)***, Wiley) Wiley, John & Sons, Inc.

—Accounting: Tools for Business Decision Makers 4E Custom Edition Volume 2. 4th ed. 2011. 662p. (C). pap. 101.95 ***(978-1-118-10634-1(2)***, Wiley) Wiley, John & Sons, Inc.

Kimmel, et al. Financial Accounting: Tools for Business Decision Making. 6th ed. 2011. (ENG.). 880p. (C). 232.95 *(978-0-470-53477-9(X)*, Wiley) Wiley, John & Sons, Inc.

Kimmel, Paul D. Accounting Tools for Business Decision Makers. 4th ed. 2011. (C). pap. 109.95 *(978-0-470-92038-1(6)*, Wiley) Wiley, John & Sons, Inc.

—Financial Accounting Tools for Business Decision Making. 6th ed. 2011. (C). pap. 109.95 *(978-0-470-92036-7(X)*, Wiley) Wiley, John & Sons, Inc.

—Wiley Plus/Blackboard Stand-alone Premium to Accompany Accounting, 2nd Edition. 2nd ed. 2007. (Wiley Plus Products Ser.). pap., pap. 0.01 *(978-0-470-11205-2(0))* Wiley, John & Sons, Inc.

—Wiley Plus/Blackboard Stand-alone to Accompany Accounting, 2nd Edition. 2nd ed. 2007. (Wiley Plus Products Ser.). pap., pap. 0.01 *(978-0-470-11204-5(2))* Wiley, John & Sons, Inc.

—Wiley Plus/WebCT Stand-alone to Accompany Accounting, 2nd Edition. 2nd ed. 2007. (Wiley Plus Products Ser.). pap. 0.01 *(978-0-470-11202-1(6))* Wiley, John & Sons, Inc.

Kimmel, Paul D., et al. Accounting. (ENG., (C). 3rd ed. 2008. Illus.). 1360p. 241.95 *(978-0-470-37785-7(2))* 4th ed. 2011. 26.95 ***(978-0-470-93868-3(4))*** Wiley, John & Sons, Inc. (Wiley).

—Accounting, Vol. 1. 3rd ed. 2009. (ENG.). 296p. (C). pap., stu. ed. 61.95 *(978-0-470-47603-1(6)*, Wiley) Wiley, John & Sons, Inc.

—Accounting: Binder Ready Version. 3rd ed. 2008. (ENG.). 1360p. (C). ring bd. 149.95 *(978-0-470-41833-8(8)*, Wiley) Wiley, John & Sons, Inc.

—Accounting: Tools for Business Decision Makers. 4th ed. 2011. (C). 107.95 ***(978-0-470-92037-4(8)***, Wiley) Wiley, John & Sons, Inc.

—Accounting: Tools for Business Decision Making. 2007. pap. 0.01 *(978-0-470-12666-0(3))* 3rd ed. 2010. (ENG.). 312p. (C). pap., stu. ed. 61.95 *(978-0-470-47604-8(4)*, Wiley) 3rd ed. 2009. (ENG.). 500p. (C). pap. 59.95 *(978-0-470-38784-9(X)*, Wiley) Wiley, John & Sons, Inc.

—Accounting Vol. 1: Tools for Business Decision Making. 3rd ed. 2009. (ENG.). 772p. (C). pap. 59.95 *(978-0-470-38783-2(1)*, Wiley) Wiley, John & Sons, Inc.

—Accounting, Working Papers VI. 3rd ed. 2009. (C). pap., stu. ed. 14.95 *(978-0-470-38782-5(3)*, Wiley) Wiley, John & Sons, Inc.

—Beacon Lumber Practice Set. 5th ed. 2009. (ENG.). 48p. (C). pap. 47.95 *(978-0-470-44925-7(X)*, Wiley) Wiley, John & Sons, Inc.

—Essentials of Accounting: Tools for Business Decision Making. 3rd ed. 2007. (Illus.). 510p. 115.95 *(978-0-470-14440-4(8)*, Wiley) Wiley, John & Sons, Inc.

—Essentials of Accounting for Business. 2008. (Illus.). 390p. pap. 75.00 *(978-0-470-89900-7(X))* Wiley, John & Sons, Inc.

—Essentials of Accounting for Business: Accounting 203 College of Business Administration School of Accounting Central Michigan University; Financial Accounting: Tools for Business Decision Making 4/E & Managerial Accounting: Tools for Business Decision Making 3/E. 2006. (Illus.). 390p. per. 122.95 *(978-0-470-13889-2(0)*, Wiley) Wiley, John & Sons, Inc.

—Financial Accounting. 8th ed. 2012. (ENG.). (C). 858p. pap. 57.95 *(978-1-118-10298-5(3))*; 400p. pap., pupil's gde. ed. 57.95 *(978-1-118-10295-4(9))* Wiley, John & Sons, Inc. (Wiley).

—Financial Accounting: Problem Solving Survival. 8th ed. 2012. (ENG.). (C). pap. 57.95 *(978-1-118-10292-3(4)*, Wiley) Wiley, John & Sons, Inc.

—Financial Accounting: Tools for Business Decision Making. (Wiley Plus Products Ser.). 3rd ed. 2006. pap. 60.95 *(978-0-470-07923-2(1))* 4th ed. 2006. pap. 73.95 *(978-0-470-07719-1(0))* 5th ed. 2009. (ENG.). (C). 33.95 *(978-0-470-55128-8(3)*, Wiley) 5th ed. 2009. (ENG.). (C). wbk. ed. 70.95 *(978-0-470-37977-6(4)*, Wiley) 5th ed. 2008. (ENG.). 848p. (C). 232.95 *(978-0-470-23980-3(8)*, Wiley) Wiley, John & Sons, Inc.

—Financial Accounting: Tools for Business Decision Making. 6th ed. 2011. (ENG.). (C). 57.95 *(978-0-470-88796-7(6))*; 272p. pap., pupil's gde. ed. 55.95 *(978-0-470-88792-9(3))* Wiley, John & Sons, Inc. (Wiley).

—Financial Accounting: Tools for Business Decision Making Excel Working Papers. 6th ed. 2010. (ENG.). (C). 66.95 *(978-0-470-88794-3(X)*, Wiley) Wiley, John & Sons, Inc.

—Financial Accounting: Tools for Business Decision Making Working Papers. 6th ed. 2011. (ENG.). 696p. (C). pap. 74.95 *(978-0-470-88793-6(1)*, Wiley) Wiley, John & Sons, Inc.

—Financial Accounting 6E for Nassau Community College. 6th ed. 2011. 888p. (C). pap. 119.95 ***(978-1-118-11482-7(5)***, Wiley) Wiley, John & Sons, Inc.

—Financial Accounting 6th Edition for Brigham Young Univ - Idaho. 2011. 888p. (C). pap. 115.95 ***(978-1-118-10008-0(5)***, Wiley) Wiley, John & Sons, Inc.

—Financial Accounting 6th Edition for Corning Community College. 6th ed. 2011. (Wiley Custom Select Ser.). 760p. (C). ring bd. 83.95 ***(978-1-118-11489-6(2)***, Wiley) Wiley, John & Sons, Inc.

—Financial Accounting 6th Edition for Monmouth University. 6th ed. 2011. 888p. (C). pap. 150.95 ***(978-1-118-12125-2(2)***, Wiley) Wiley, John & Sons, Inc.

—Financial Accounting 6th Edition for Oakton CC. 6th ed. 2011. 890p. (C). pap. 91.95 ***(978-1-118-11363-9(2)***, Wiley) Wiley, John & Sons, Inc.

—Financial Accounting, Excel Working Papers. 8th ed. 2012. (ENG.). (C). 57.95 *(978-1-118-10285-5(1)*, Wiley) Wiley, John & Sons, Inc.

—Financial Accounting, Study Guide: Tools for Business Decision Making. 5th ed. 2009. (ENG.). 288p. (C). pap., stu. ed., wbk. ed. 75.95 *(978-0-470-37976-9(6)*, Wiley) Wiley, John & Sons, Inc.

—Managerial Accounting: Tools for Business Decision Makers. 6th ed. 2011. (ENG.). 336p. (C). pap., pupil's gde. ed. 74.95 *(978-1-118-06451-1(8)*, Wiley) Wiley, John & Sons, Inc.

—Managerial Accounting: Tools for Business Decision Makers Excel Working Papers. 6th ed. 2011. (ENG.). (C). 61.95 *(978-1-118-06453-5(4)*, Wiley) Wiley, John & Sons, Inc.

—Managerial Accounting: Tools for Business Decision Making. 6th ed. 2011. (ENG.). 542p. (C). pap., wbk. ed. 77.95 *(978-1-118-06452-8(6)*, Wiley) Wiley, John & Sons, Inc.

—Principles of Accounting. (Wiley Plus Products Ser.). 2006. pap. 73.95 *(978-0-470-07720-7(4))* Vol. 1. 2nd rev. ed. 2007. 920p. pap. 76.95 *(978-0-470-08747-3(1)*, Wiley) Vol. 2. 2nd ed. 2007. pap., stu. ed., wbk. ed. 31.95 *(978-0-470-08742-8(0)*, Frommers) Vol. 2. 2nd rev. ed. 2007. 512p. pap. 74.95 *(978-0-470-08748-0(X)*, Wiley) Wiley, John & Sons, Inc.

Kimmel, Wygandt. Financial Accounting Tools for Business. 2006. pap. 11.95 *(978-1-4288-0482-1(X))* Cram101 Inc.

King, Alfred M. Executive's Guide to Fair Value: Profiting from the New Valuation Rules. 2008. (ENG.). 272p. 63.50 *(978-0-470-17329-9(7)*, Wiley) Wiley, John & Sons, Inc.

—Internal Control of Fixed Assets: A Controller & Auditor's Guide. 2011. (Wiley Corporate F&a Ser.: 564). (ENG., Illus.). 192p. 68.50 *(978-0-470-53940-8(2)*, Wiley) Wiley, John & Sons, Inc.

Klerks-van de Nouland, C. A. M. & van Sten-van 't Hoff, H. J. M. Introduction to the Accounting Process. 2010. (ENG.). 152p. (C). pap. 64.95 *(978-90-01-78923-7(4))* Routledge.

Kochanek, Richard F. & Hillman, A. Douglas. Financial Accounting: A Focus on Interpretation & Analysis. 7th ed. 2010. (ENG.). 800p. (C). 134.95 *(978-1-111-06175-3(0))* CENGAGE Learning Custom Publishing.

Kochanek, Richard F., et al. Financial Accounting DataBase/Disk. 9th ed. 2006. (ENG.). 54p. (C). pap. 56.95 *(978-0-7593-6712-8(4))* CENGAGE Learning Custom Publishing.

Kolitz, D. L., et al. Concepts-Based Introduction to Financial Accounting. 4th ed. 2009. (ENG., Illus.). 372p. pap. 46.95 *(978-0-7021-7749-1(0))* Juta Academic ZAF. Dist: Independent Pubs. Group.

Koskay, Kenneth A., et al. Guide to Health Care Consulting, 2 vols. Incl. Vol. 1. ring bd. *(978-0-7646-0146-0(6))*; Vol. 2. ring bd. *(978-0-7646-0147-7(4))*; 1997. 190.00 *(978-0-7646-0145-3(8))* Practitioners Publishing Co.

Kühne, Ralph. Self-Configurable Accounting Systems for Next-Generation Charging & Billing. 2011. 210p. pap. ***(978-3-8325-2924-6(1))*** Logos Verlag Berlin.

Label, Wayne. Accounting for Non-Accountants, 2E: The Fast & Easy Way to Learn the Basics. 2nd ed. 2010. (Quick Start Your Business Ser.). (ENG.). 240p. pap. 16.99 *(978-1-4022-2263-4(7))* Sourcebooks, Inc.

Larsen, E. John. Modern Advanced Accounting. 2006. (ENG.). pap. 14.95 *(978-1-4288-0879-9(5))*; 10th ed. pap. 14.95 *(978-1-4288-1224-6(5))* Cram101 Inc.

Larson, Charles B. 30. 2011. (Illus.). 53p. pap. 14.95 ***(978-0-9815875-1-6(8))*** Condor Publishing Foundation Inc.

Larson, Kermit D. & Wild, John J. Fundamental Accounting Principles. 17th ed. 2006. pap. 17.95 *(978-1-4288-1081-5(1))* Cram101 Inc.

Lawrence, Michael & Ryan, Joan. Essentials of Accounting. 10th ed. 2007. (ENG.). 314p. (C). 105.95 *(978-0-7593-9246-5(3))* Cengage South-Western.

—Essentials of Accounting, Study Guide / Working Papers. 10th ed. 2007. (ENG.). 346p. (C). pap. 66.95 *(978-0-7593-9592-3(6))* Cengage South-Western.

Leach, Robert. Accounts Made Simple: A beginner's guide to company Accounts. 2012. (ENG.). 196p. pap. 22.99 *(978-1-906659-85-1(0))* Harriman Hse. Publishing GBR. Dist: Ingram Pub. Services.

—Ratios Made Simple: A beginner's guide to the key financial Ratios. 2010. (ENG.). 196p. pap. 22.99 *(978-1-906659-84-4(2))* Harriman Hse. Publishing GBR. Dist: Ingram Pub. Services.

Lee, Cheng-Few. Advances in Quantitative Analysis of Finance & Accounting, Vol. 6. 2008. (Illus.). 280p. 121.00 *(978-981-279-168-9(X))* World Scientific Publishing Co., Inc.

Lee, Cheng-Few, ed. Advances in Quantitative Analysis of Finance & Accounting: Volume 4. 2006. (Advances in Quantitative Analysis of Finance & Accounting Ser.). (Illus.). 358p. 124.00 *(978-981-270-021-6(8))* World Scientific Publishing Co., Inc.

—Advances in Quantitative Analysis of Finance & Accounting, Volume 5. 2007. (Advances in Quantitative Analysis of Finance & Accounting Ser.). (Illus.). 326p. 121.00 *(978-981-270-628-7(3))* World Scientific Publishing Co., Inc.

Lehman, Cheryl R., ed. Envisioning a New Accountability. 2007. (ENG.). 286p. 99.95 *(978-0-7623-1462-1(1)*, JAI Pr.) Elsevier Science & Technology Bks.

—Ethics, Equity, & Regulation. 2010. (Advances in Public Interest Accounting Ser.). (Illus.). 250p. 114.95 *(978-1-84950-728-8(7))* Emerald Group Publishing Ltd. GBR. Dist: Turpin Distribution Services Ltd.

—Independent Accounts: The Possibilities for Auditor Independence in the Age of Financial Scandal. 2006. (Advances in Public Interest Accounting Ser.). (Illus.). 186p. 111.95 *(978-0-7623-1382-2(X))* Emerald Group Publishing Ltd. GBR. Dist: Turpin Distribution Services Ltd.

Lerner, Joel, et al. Schaum's Outline of Bookkeeping & Accounting, Fourth Edition. 4th ed. 2009. (Schaum's Outline Ser.). (ENG.). 480p. (C). pap. 20.00 *(978-0-07-163536-3(X)*, 007163536X) McGraw-Hill Cos., The.

Leung, David. The Truth about Accounting Researching Financial Reporting & Auditing. 2011. 158p. 114.95 ***(978-1-4094-2049-1(3)***, Gower Publishing Co., Ltd.) Ashgate Publishing, Ltd. GBR. Dist: Ashgate Publishing Co.

Lewis, Lawrence D. The Power Magic & Beauty of Accounting. 2012. (ENG., Illus.). 264p. 120.00 ***(978-0-415-88430-3(6))***; pap. 79.95 ***(978-0-415-88431-0(4))*** Routledge.

Libby, Libby. Financial Accounting. 2006. pap. 12.95 *(978-1-4288-0477-7(3))*; pap. 11.95 *(978-1-4288-0509-5(5))* Cram101 Inc.

Libby, Patricia A. Principles of Accounting. 2009. *(978-0-07-327397-6(X))*; *(978-0-07-327396-9(1))*; *(978-0-07-327395-2(3))*; *(978-0-07-327408-9(9))*; *(978-0-07-327398-3(8))*; *(978-0-07-352684-3(3))* McGraw-Hill Schl. Education Group. (Irwin Professional Publishing).

Libby, Robert, et al. Financial Accounting. 7th ed. 2010. (ENG., Illus.). 880p. (C). 237.67 *(978-0-07-811102-0(1)*, 0078111021, McGraw-Hill/Irwin) McGraw-Hill Higher Education.

—Financial Accounting with Connect Plus. 7th ed. 2010. (ENG.). (C). 253.33 *(978-0-07-748001-1(5)*, 0077480015, McGraw-Hill/Irwin) McGraw-Hill Higher Education.

—Loose Leaf for Financial Accounting. 7th ed. 2010. (ENG.). (C). ring bd. 125.00 *(978-0-07-746686-2(1)*, 0077466861, McGraw-Hill/Irwin) McGraw-Hill Higher Education.

—Principles of Accounting Volume 1 Ch 1-12 with Annual Report. 2008. (ENG.). (C). pap. 169.67 *(978-0-07-730041-8(6)*, 0077300416, McGraw-Hill/Irwin) McGraw-Hill Higher Education.

Lisle, George. Accounting in Theory & Practice. 2010. 450p. pap. 36.75 *(978-1-178-43812-3(0))* BiblioBazaar.

—Accounting in Theory & Practice. 2010. 198p. pap. 26.43 *(978-1-151-86076-1(6))* General Bks. LLC.

—Accounting in Theory & Practice. 2008. 440p. pap. *(978-1-4097-7128-9(8))* Read Bks.

Loughran, Maire. Financial Accounting for Dummies. 2011. (ENG., Illus.). 360p. pap. 24.99 *(978-0-470-93065-6(9)*, For Dummies) Wiley, John & Sons, Inc.

Loughran, Maire. Intermediate Accounting for Dummies. 2012. (ENG.). 384p. pap. 26.99 ***(978-1-118-17682-5(0)***, For Dummies) Wiley, John & Sons, Inc.

Lunt, Henry. Fundamentals of Financial Accounting. 6th ed. 2009. (ENG., Illus.). 750p. (C). pap. 55.95 *(978-1-85617-785-6(8)*, CIMA Publishing) Elsevier Science & Technology Bks.

Lunt, Henry & Kaplan Higher Education Staff. Fundamentals of Financial Accounting, Kit. 3rd ed. 2010. (ENG., Illus.). 258p. (C). pap. 28.95 *(978-1-85617-786-3(6)*, CIMA Publishing) Elsevier Science & Technology Bks.

Lymer, Andy & Lloyd, David. Small Business Accounting. 2010. (Teach Yourself Ser.). (ENG., Illus.). 224p. pap. 19.95 *(978-1-4441-0024-2(6)*, Hodder & Stoughton) Hodder General Publishing Div. GBR. Dist: Independent Pubs. Group.

Lynch, Nancy. Study Guide & PowerNotes for Financial Accounting: Business Process Approach. 3rd ed. 2010. (ENG.). 202p. (C). pap. 46.67 *(978-0-13-611530-4(6)*, Prentice Hall) Prentice Hall PTR.

Madeira, Laura. QuickBooks 2009: Solutions Guide for Business Owners & Accountants. 2008. (ENG., Illus.). 600p. pap. 39.99 *(978-0-7897-3834-9(1))* Que.

Madishetti, Sri Nivas. Accounting for Managers of Non-Corporate Undertakings. 2011. (Illus.). 432p. pap. ***(978-3-8443-2675-8(8))*** Lambert Academic Publishing.

Mahboob, Faisal. Integration of Materials Management with Financial Accounting in SAP. 2010. (ENG., Illus.). 429p. 79.95 *(978-1-59229-337-7(9)*, SAP PR.) Galileo Pr., Inc.

Malynes, Gerard, et al. Consuetudo, Vel, Lex Mercatoria: In Three Parts, According to the Essentials of Traffick... . Whereunto are Annexed the Following Tracts, viz. I. the Collection of Sea Laws. II. Advice Concerning Bills of Exchange. by John Marius. III. the Merchants Mirrour: or, Directions for the Perfect Ordering of Keeping of His Accompts. by Way of Debtor & Creditor, after the Italian Manner. by R. Dassome. IV. an Introduction to Merchants, 2 vols. 3rd ed. 2008. 395.00 *(978-1-58477-871-4(7))* Lawbook Exchange, Ltd., The.

Marshall and Mc, Viele. Accounting What the Numbers Mean. 2006. pap. 14.95 *(978-1-4288-0870-6(1))* Cram101 Inc.

Marshall, David, et al. Accounting: What the Numbers Mean with Connect Plus. 9th ed. 2010. (ENG.). (C). 246.67 *(978-0-07-739827-9(0)*, 0077398270, McGraw-Hill/Irwin) McGraw-Hill Higher Education.

Marshall, Peter. Mastering Book-Keeping. 8th ed. 2009. (Illus.). 192p. pap. 26.00 *(978-1-84528-324-7(4))* How To Books GBR. Dist: Parkwest Pubns., Inc.

—Mastering Book-Keeping: A Complete Guide to the Principles & Practice of Business Accounting. 9th ed. 2010. (ENG., Illus.). 541p. pap. 34.00 *(978-1-84528-446-6(1))* How To Books GBR. Dist: Parkwest Pubns., Inc.

Maskell, Brian Henry. Lean Accounting: A Concise Guide to Lean Management. 2007. 166p. pap. 19.99 *(978-0-9789760-1-9(0))* BMA Inc.

Mason, Roger. Bookkeeping & Accounting. 2008. (Instant Manager Ser.). (ENG.). 224p. pap. 19.95 *(978-0-340-97286-1(6)*, Hodder & Stoughton) Hodder General Publishing Div. GBR. Dist: Independent Pubs. Group.

Masui, John. Excel for Accounting & Finance Professionals. 2009. 84p. pap. 11.55 *(978-1-4269-1718-9(X))* Trafford Publishing.

Mather, J., et al. Financial Accounting. 8th ed. 2011. (ENG.). 960p. (C). 236.95 *(978-0-470-92938-4(3)*, Wiley) Wiley, John & Sons, Inc.

Matis. Irs for Lawyers & Other Dorks: Beating the IRS at their own damn Game. 2010. 172p. pap. 14.95 *(978-1-60844-411-3(2))* Dog Ear Publishing, LLC.

May, Claire B. & May, Gordon S. Effective Writing. 9th ed. 2011. (ENG.). 288p. (C). pap. 60.00 *(978-0-13-256724-4(5)*, Prentice Hall) Prentice Hall PTR.

Mayzler, Alexandra & Daniele, Joseph. ACT Demystified. 2012. (Demystified Ser.). (ENG., Illus.). 672p. (C). pap. 20.00 ***(978-0-07-175443-9(1)***, 0071754431) McGraw-Hill Cos., The.

McCrary, Stuart A. Mastering Financial Accounting Essentials: The Critical Nuts & Bolts. 2009. (Wiley Finance Ser.: 485). (ENG., Illus.). 159p. 49.95 *(978-0-470-39332-1(7)*, Wiley) Wiley, John & Sons, Inc.

McGee, Robert W., ed. Accounting Reform in Transition & Developing Economies. 2008. (ENG., Illus.). 600p. 189.00 *(978-0-387-25707-5(1)*, 0387257071) Springer.

McGee, Robert W. & Preobragenskaya, Galina G. Accounting & Financial System Reform in a Transition Economy: A Case Study of Russia: A Case Study of Russia. 2010. (ENG.). vii, 182p. pap. 139.00 *(978-1-4419-3667-7(X)*, 144193667X) Springer.

—Accounting & Financial System Reform in Eastern Europe & Asia. 2010. (ENG.). vii, 352p. pap. 159.00 *(978-1-4419-3822-0(2)*, 1441938222) Springer.

McGraw-Hill Staff & Wild, John. Study Guide to accompany Financial Accounting. 5th ed. 2010. (ENG.). 384p. (C). pap. 76.00 *(978-0-07-726898-5(9)*, 0077268989, McGraw-Hill/Irwin) McGraw-Hill Higher Education.

McLaney, Eddie & Atrill, Peter. Accounting: An Introduction. 5th ed. 2010. (ENG., Illus.). 856p. pap. *(978-0-273-73320-1(6))* Financial Times Business Enterprises, Ltd.

McManus, Wayne William, et al. Accounting: What the Numbers Mean. 8th ed. 2007. (ENG., Illus.). 768p. (C). 195.63 *(978-0-07-337941-8(7)*, 0073379417, McGraw-Hill/Irwin) McGraw-Hill Higher Education.

McMurrian, Howard P., et al. Guide to Physicians & Other Health Care Professionals, 3 vols. Incl. Vol. 3. ring bd. 146.00 *(978-0-7646-0306-8(X))*; Vol. 1. ring bd. 146.00 *(978-0-7646-0304-4(3))*; Vol. 2. ring bd. 146.00 *(978-0-7646-0305-1(1))*; 1997. Set ring bd. 140.00 *(978-0-7646-0303-7(5))* Practitioners Publishing Co.

Mcquaig College Accounting General Ledger Software & Electronicworking Papers Access Card for Sales Ninth Edition. 9th ed. 2007. (YA). 38.36 *(978-0-547-06469-7(1)*, 1040160) CENGAGE Learning.

McQuaig, Douglas. College Accounting. 9th ed. 2007. (ENG.). (C). 58.95 *(978-0-618-85541-4(6)*, 336155); 2.95 *(978-0-618-85536-0(X)*, 336150); 96p. pap. 46.95 *(978-0-618-85535-3(1)*, 336149) Cengage South-Western.

McQuaig, Douglas, et al. College Accounting. 10th ed. 2010. (Available Titles CengageNOW Ser.). (ENG.). 592p. (C). 120.95 *(978-1-4390-3878-9(3))* Cengage South-Western.

McQuaig, Douglas J. College Accounting 1-29: Exams, 4 vols. Date not set. (C). 50.36 *(978-0-395-49433-2(8))* CENGAGE Learning.

—College Accounting Chapters 1 - 26 9e. 9th ed. 2007. (ENG.). 1040p. (C). 169.95 *(978-0-618-82417-5(0)*, 336140) CENGAGE Learning.

McQuaig, Douglas J. & Bille, Patricia A. College Accounting. 2006. pap. 14.95 *(978-1-4288-1195-9(8))*; 7th ed. pap. 13.95 *(978-1-4288-1117-1(6))* Cram101 Inc.

—College Accounting: 1-13. 9th ed. 2007. (ENG., Illus.). 576p. (C). 120.95 *(978-0-618-82418-2(9)*, 336141) CENGAGE Learning.

Meise, Eric. Momentum Accounting for Trends. 2010. 316p. pap. *(978-3-639-16051-2(7))* VDM Verlag Dr. Mueller e.K.

Merchant, Kenneth & Chen, Clara Xiaoling. Strategy Mapping: an Interventionist Examination of a Homebuilder's Performance Measurement & Incentive Systems. 2010. (ENG., Illus.). 80p. pap. 67.95 *(978-0-08-096594-9(6)*, CIMA Publishing) Elsevier Science & Technology Bks.

Messier, William F., et al. Auditing & Assurance Services: A Systematic Approach. 5th rev. ed. 2006. (Illus.). 800p. 171.88 incl. cd-rom *(978-0-07-333720-3(X)*, 9780073337203, McGraw-Hill/Irwin) McGraw-Hill Higher Education.

Miller, Roger LeRoy & Jentz, Gaylord A. Accounting Taxation & E-Commerce. 2006. pap. 10.95 *(978-1-4288-0691-7(1))* Cram101 Inc.

Mintz, Steven M. & Morris, Roselyn E. Ethical Obligations & Decision Making in Accounting: Text & Cases. 2007. (ENG., Illus.). 304p. (C). per. 79.33 *(978-0-07-340399-1(7)*, 0073403997, McGraw-Hill/Irwin) McGraw-Hill Higher Education.

Mohr, Angie. Bookkeepers' Boot Camp: Get a Grip on Accounting Basics. 2nd ed. 2010. (ENG.). 204p. pap. 18.95 *(978-1-77040-044-3(3))* Self-Counsel Pr., Inc. CAN. Dist: National Bk. Network.

—Financial Management 101: Get a Grip on Your Business Numbers. 2nd ed. 2008. (Numbers 101 for Small Business Ser.). (ENG., Illus.). 160p. pap. 16.95 *(978-1-55180-805-5(6))* Self-Counsel Pr., Inc. CAN. Dist: Midpoint Trade Bks., Inc.

Monger, Rod. Financial Accounting: A Global Perspective. 2010. (ENG., Illus.). 800p. pap. 88.95 *(978-0-470-51840-3(5)*, Wiley) Wiley, John & Sons, Inc.

Mostyn, Gregory. Basic Accounting Concepts, Principles, & Procedures: Applying Principles & Procedures, 2 vols., Vol. 2. 2007. (Illus.). 939p. per. 34.95 *(978-0-9791494-9-8(5))* Worthy & James Publishing.

—Basic Accounting Concepts, Principles, & Procedures: Building the Conceptual Foundation, 2 vols., Vol. 1. 2007. (Illus.). 693p. per. 31.95 *(978-0-9791494-8-1(7))* Worthy & James Publishing.

Mullis, Darrell & Orloff, Judith. The Accounting Game: Basic Accounting Fresh from the Lemonade Stand. 2nd ed. 2008. (ENG., Illus.). 192p. pap. 19.95 *(978-1-4022-1186-7(4))* Sourcebooks, Inc.

Murray, George R. & Murray, Kathleen. Accounting at Your Fingertips. 2007. (ENG., Illus.). 416p. (gr. 12-18). 18.95 *(978-1-59257-649-4(4)*, Alpha Bks.) Penguin Group (USA) Inc.

Myddelton, David R. & Office for National Statistics Staff. Margins of Error in Accounting. 2009. (ENG., Illus.). 200p. 100.00 *(978-0-230-21991-5(8))* Palgrave Macmillan.

NAIC Staff, creator. Accounting Practices & Procedures Manual (2008), 3 vols. 2008. 3266p. pap., pap. 465.00 *(978-1-59917-139-5(2))* National Assn. of Insurance Commissioners.

Namusonge, Gregory & ANYANGU, Moses. Business Finance. 2010. 316p. pap. *(978-3-639-20917-4(6))* VDM Verlag Dr. Mueller e.K.

Napier. Islamic Accounting. 2012. (Elgar Mini Ser.). 768p. 425.00 ***(978-1-84844-220-7(3))*** Elgar, Edward Publishing, Inc.

Needles, et al. Principles of Accounting & Principles of Financial Accounting. 11th ed. 2010. (ENG.). (C). 26.95 *(978-0-538-45133-8(5))* CENGAGE Learning.

—Principles of Accounting & Principles of Financial Accounting. 11th ed. 2010. (ENG.). (C). 33.95 *(978-0-538-75585-6(7))* Cengage South-Western.

Needles, Belverd E., Jr. Peachtree Education Software 2007. 9th ed. 2007. (ENG.). (C). 13.95 *(978-0-618-62683-0(2)*, 339507) Cengage South-Western.

Needles, Belverd E. Principles of Accounting. 10th ed. 2007. (ENG.). (C). 33.95 *(978-0-618-99066-5(6)*, 1027366) Cengage South-Western.

Needles, Belverd E. Working Papers. 8th ed. 2007. (ENG.). (C). pap. 78.95 ***(978-0-618-91002-1(6))*** Cengage South-Western.

Needles, Belverd E. & Powers, Marian. Electronic Working Papers for Needles/Powers' Financial Accounting, 10th. 10th ed. 2009. (C). 33.95 *(978-1-4390-3609-9(8))* Cengage South-Western.

Needles, Belverd E., Jr. & Powers, Marian. Financial Accounting. 2006. pap. 15.95 *(978-1-4288-0954-3(6))* Cram101 Inc.

Needles, Belverd E. & Powers, Marian. Financial Accounting. 10th ed. 2010. (Illus.). xxiv, 840p. *(978-0-324-83004-0(1))* 2008. (ENG.). 864p. (C). 258.95 *(978-0-547-19328-1(9))* Cengage South-Western.

Needles, Belverd E., Jr. & Powers, Marian. Principles of Financial Accounting. 10th ed. 2007. (ENG., Illus.). 928p. (C). 224.95 *(978-0-618-73641-6(7)*, 339082) CENGAGE Learning.

Needles, Belverd E. & Powers, Marian. Principles of Financial Accounting. 11th ed. 2010. (Financial Accounting Ser.). (ENG.). 864p. (C). 252.95 *(978-0-538-75516-0(4))*; ring bd. 166.95 *(978-0-538-75524-5(5))* Cengage South-Western.

—Working Papers for Needles' Financial Accounting, 10th. 10th ed. 2008. (ENG.). 720p. (C). pap. 76.95 *(978-0-547-19452-3(8))* Cengage South-Western.

Needles, Belverd E., Jr., et al. Financial & Managerial Accounting, Vol. 2. 8th ed. 2007. (ENG.). 560p. (C). pap. 70.95 *(978-0-618-77724-2(5)*, 339114) Cengage South-Western.

—Principles of Accounting. 10th ed. 2007. (Available Titles CengageNOW Ser.). (ENG., Illus.). 1344p. (C). 260.95 *(978-0-618-73661-4(1)*, 339081) CENGAGE Learning.

Needles, Belverd E., et al. Principles of Accounting. 11th ed. 2010. (Available Titles CengageNOW Ser.). (ENG.). 1328p. (C). 260.95 *(978-1-4390-3774-4(4))*; (Illus.). ring bd. 173.95 *(978-0-538-75519-1(9))* Cengage South-Western.

—Principles of Accounting. 11th ed. 2011. (Illus.). xxxii, 1295p. *(978-0-538-75528-3(8))* Course Technology.

—Principles of Financial Accounting. 11th ed. 2010. (ENG.). (C). 869.95 *(978-0-538-75783-6(3))*; Vol. 2, Chs. 18-27. 528p. pap. 42.95 *(978-0-538-75527-6(X))* Cengage South-Western.

—Working Papers, Chapters 1-17 for Needles/Powers/Crosson's Principles of Accounting, 11th & Principles of Financial Accounting. 11th ed. 2010. (ENG.). 744p. (C). pap. 42.95 *(978-0-538-75526-9(1))* Cengage South-Western.

Needles Financial & Managerial Accounting & Managerial Accountinggeneral Ledger Software & Electronic Working Papers Access Card Forsales Eighth Edition. 8th ed. 2007. (YA). 43.56 *(978-0-547-06496-3(9)*, 1040191) CENGAGE Learning.

Needles, Powers. Financial Accounting. 2006. pap. 15.95 *(978-1-4288-1274-1(1))* Cram101 Inc.

Needles Principles of Accounting & Principles of Financial Accountinggeneral Ledger Software & Electronic Working Papers Access Card Forsales Tenth Edition. 10th ed. 2007. (YA). 43.56 *(978-0-547-06472-7(1)*, 1040159) CENGAGE Learning.

Nelson, Stephen L. QuickBooks 2007 for Dummies. 14th ed. 2006. (ENG., Illus.). 408p. per. 21.99 *(978-0-470-07278-3(4)*, For Dummies) Wiley, John & Sons, Inc.

—QuickBooks 2009 All-in-One for Dummies. 5th ed. 2009. (ENG., Illus.). 624p. pap. 34.99 *(978-0-470-39652-0(0)*, For Dummies) Wiley, John & Sons, Inc.

—QuickBooks 2009 for Dummies. 16th ed. 2008. (ENG., Illus.). 408p. pap. 24.99 *(978-0-470-39181-5(2)*, For Dummies) Wiley, John & Sons, Inc.

—QuickBooks for Dummies 2012. 19th ed. 2011. (ENG.). 408p. pap. 24.99 *(978-1-118-09120-3(5)*, For Dummies) Wiley, John & Sons, Inc.

Nelson, Stephen L. Quicken 2012 for Dummies. 2011. (ENG.). 384p. pap. 24.99 ***(978-1-118-09121-0(3)***, For Dummies) Wiley, John & Sons, Inc.

Nelson, Stephen L. & Nelson, Stephen L., Jr. QuickBooks 2008 All-in-One Desk Reference for Dummies. 4th ed. 2008. (ENG., Illus.). 648p. per. 36.99 *(978-0-470-18471-4(X)*, For Dummies) Wiley, John & Sons, Inc.

Nessel, John K. Restaurant Operators Complete Guide to QuickBooks 2nd Edition. 2007. 317p. ring bd. 89.00 *(978-0-9724998-4-2(9))* Restaurant Resources Group, Inc.

Newton, Grant W. Bankruptcy & Insolvency Accounting, 2 vols., Vols. 1 & 2, Set. 7th ed. 2009. (ENG., Illus.). 2016p. 283.95 *(978-0-471-78763-1(9)*, Wiley) Wiley, John & Sons, Inc.

—Bankruptcy & Insolvency Accounting: Forms & Exhibits, 2 vols. 7th ed. 2009. (ENG., Illus.). 1128p. 157.95 *(978-0-471-78762-4(0)*, Wiley) Wiley, John & Sons, Inc.

—Bankruptcy & Insolvency Accounting Vol. 1: Practice & Procedure, 2 vols., Volume 1. 7th ed. 2009. (ENG., Illus.). 888p. 157.95 *(978-0-471-78761-7(2)*, Wiley) Wiley, John & Sons, Inc.

Nikolai, et al. le, Intermediate Accounting 11 E. 2010. *(978-0-324-65914-6(8))* Cengage South-Western.

Nikolai, Loren A. Problem Solving Strategy Guides for Nikolai/Bazley/Jones' Intermediate Accounting. 11th ed. 2009. (ENG.). (C). pap. 36.95 *(978-0-538-74247-4(X))* Cengage South-Western.

Nikolai, Loren A. & Bazley, John D. Intermediate Accounting. 9th ed. 2006. pap. 20.95 *(978-1-4288-1057-0(9))* Cram101 Inc.

Nikolai, Loren A., et al. Accounting: Information for Business Decisions, Volume 1. 2006. (Illus.). 990p. per. 91.95 *(978-0-7593-9542-8(X))* Cengage South-Western.

—Intermediate Accounting. 11th ed. 2009. (Available Titles CengageNOW Ser.). (ENG.). 1440p. (C). 270.95 *(978-0-324-65913-9(X))* Cengage South-Western.

—Intermediate Accounting Update. 11th ed. 2009. (ENG.). 1440p. (C). 270.95 *(978-0-538-46708-7(8))* Cengage South-Western.

—Intermediate Accounting (with Business & Company Resource Center & Chapter 20, 2007) 10th rev. ed. 2006. (ENG.). 1408p. (C). 252.95 *(978-0-324-65192-8(9))* Cengage South-Western.

—Problem Solving Strategy Guide, Volume 2 for Nikolai/Bazley/Jones' Intermediate Accounting, 10th. 10th ed. 2006. (ENG.). 320p. (C). per. 87.95 *(978-0-324-37429-2(1))* Cengage South-Western.

Nobes, Christopher W. Current Debates in International Accounting. 2011. (Illus.). 224p. 110.00 *(978-1-84844-838-4(4))* Elgar, Edward Publishing, Inc.

Nobles, Tracie L., et al. College Accounting, Chapters 1-12. 11th ed. 2012. (ENG.). 576p. (C). 120.95 ***(978-1-111-52812-6(8))*** Cengage South-Western.

O'Bryan, David W. Financial Accounting: A Course for All Majors. 2010. (Illus.). 236p. *(978-1-61735-096-2(6))*; pap. *(978-1-61735-095-5(8))* Information Age Publishing, Inc.

O'Connor, Kevin. The International Dictionary of Accounting Acronyms. 2013. 200p. pap. 45.00 *(978-1-906403-35-5(X))* Lessons Professional Publishing GBR. Dist: Stylus Publishing, LLC.

Okezie, Stella Ogechukwu. Income Tax Administration in Ikenne Lga, Nigeria: Evaluation of Income Tax Administration in Ikenne Local Government Area, Nigeria: Effects on Revenue Generation: Problems & Prospects. 2011. 76p. pap. ***(978-3-639-23793-1(5))*** VDM Verlag Dr. Mueller e.K.

O'Regan, Philip. Financial Information Analysis. 2nd rev. ed. 2006. (ENG., Illus.). 634p. per. 79.95 *(978-0-470-86572-9(5)*, Wiley) Wiley, John & Sons, Inc.

O'Regan, Philip. Financial Information Analysis: The Role of Accounting Information in Modern Society. 2012. (ENG., Illus.). 624p. (C). 160.00 ***(978-0-415-69584-8(8))***; pap. 71.95 ***(978-0-415-69585-5(6))*** Routledge.

Organisation for Economic Co-operation and Development. National Accounts of OECD Countries: Detailed Tables. 2011. (Illus.). 322p. pap. 5.00 ***(978-92-64-10693-2(6))*** Organization for Economic Cooperation & Development.

Owen, Glenn. Using Quickbooks Pro for Accounting 2004. 3rd ed. 2006. pap. 8.95 *(978-1-4288-1102-7(8))* Cram101 Inc.

Pallais, Don. Audits & Other Accountants' Services. 2011. (ENG.). 240p. pap. 74.95 *(978-1-60442-810-0(4))* American Bar Assn.

Panel to Advance a Research Program on the Design of National Health Accounts & National Research Council. Accounting for Health & Health Care: Approaches to Measuring the Sources & Costs of Their Improvement. 2011. (ENG.). 238p. pap. 49.00 *(978-0-309-15679-0(3))* National Academies Pr.

Paradigm College Accounting: Solutions Manual 1,27. 3rd ed. 49.95 *(978-0-7638-0038-3(4))* EMC/Paradigm Publishing.

Patel, Chris. A Comparative Study of Professional Accountants' Judgements. 2006. (Studies in Managerial & Financial Accounting). 220p. 110.95 *(978-0-7623-1062-3(6))* Emerald Group Publishing Ltd. GBR. Dist: Turpin Distribution Services Ltd.

Pearson/Prentice Hall, creator. Accounting Chapters 1-13. 7th ed. 2007. pap., pap. *(978-0-13-242455-4(X))* Pearson Education Canada.

—Peachtree Complete Accounting 2007 Educational Version. 3rd ed. 2007. cd-rom 14.67 *(978-0-13-612869-4(6))* Prentice Hall PTR.

Peck, Sarah. Investment Ethics. 2010. (ENG., Illus.). 304p. (C). pap. 93.95 *(978-0-470-43453-6(8)*, Wiley) Wiley, John & Sons, Inc.

Penman, Stephen. Accounting for Value. 2010. (Columbia Business School Publishing Ser.). (ENG., Illus.). 264p. (gr. 17). 44.95 *(978-0-231-15118-4(7))* Columbia Univ. Pr.

Permanent Court of Arbitration, The Hague, The Hague, compiled by. The Rhine Chlorides Arbitration Concerning the Auditing of Accounts (Netherlands-France) Award Of 2004. 2008. (Permanent Court of Arbitration Award Ser.). (FRE & ENG.). 196p. 69.95 *(978-90-6704-266-6(8))* T.M.C. Asser Pr. NLD. Dist: Springer.

Perry, Gail & Madeira, Laura. QuickBooks 2009. 2009. (On Demand Ser.). (ENG., Illus.). 456p. pap. 29.99 *(978-0-7897-3935-3(6))* Que.

—QuickBooks 2010 on Demand. 2009. (On Demand Ser.). (ENG., Illus.). 456p. pap. 34.99 *(978-0-7897-4323-7(X)*, Que Publishing) Pearson Education, Ltd. GBR. Dist: Pearson Education.

Peter G Peterson Institute for International Economics, creator. Working Papers Volume I. 2007. (Working Papers). (Illus.). 467p. per. 24.95 *(978-0-88132-388-7(8))* Peterson Institute for International Economics.

Phillips, Fred & Libby, Robert. Annual Report to accompany Fundamentals of Financial Accounting, 2/e. 2009. 64p. pap. 72.19 *(978-0-07-726959-3(4)*, McGraw-Hill/Irwin) McGraw-Hill Higher Education.

—Fundamentals of Financial Acco. 2nd ed. 2007. 768p. 116.75 *(978-0-07-313648-6(4))* McGraw-Hill Professional Publishing.

—Fundamentals of Financial Accounting. 2nd ed. 2007. (ENG.). 448p. (C). pap., pupil's gde. ed. 66.67 *(978-0-07-313658-5(1)*, 0073136581, McGraw-Hill/Irwin) McGraw-Hill Higher Education.

Phillips, Fred, et al. Fundamentals of Financial Accounting. 3rd ed. 2011. xxiv, 654p. *(978-0-07-352710-9(6)*, Irwin Professional Publishing) McGraw-Hill Schl. Education Group.

—Fundamentals of Financial Accounting with Annual Report. 3rd ed. 2010. (ENG.). (C). pap. 237.67 *(978-0-07-734493-1(6)*, 0077344936, McGraw-Hill/Irwin) McGraw-Hill Higher Education.

—Loose-Leaf Fundaments of Financial Accounting. 3rd ed. 2010. (ENG.). (C). ring bd. 166.67 *(978-0-07-740517-5(X)*, 007740517X, McGraw-Hill/Irwin) McGraw-Hill Higher Education.

—Study Guide for Fundamentals of Financial Accounting. 3rd ed. 2010. (ENG.). 448p. (C). pap. 66.67 *(978-0-07-726969-2(1)*, 0077269691, McGraw-Hill/Irwin) McGraw-Hill Higher Education.

Pinson, Linda. Keeping the Books: Basic Recordkeeping & Accounting for the Successful Small Business. 7th rev. ed. 2007. (ENG.). 224p. pap. 22.95 *(978-1-4195-8438-1(3))* Kaplan Publishing.

Pischke, J. D. von, ed. Greening the Financial Sector: How to Mainstream Environmental Finance in Developing Countries. 2011. (ENG., Illus.). xiv, 250p. 89.95 *(978-3-642-05086-2(7)*, 3642050867) Springer.

Pizzey, Alan. Accounting & Finance: A Firm Foundation. 4th ed. (Illus.). viii, 549p. pap. *(978-0-304-33128-4(7)*, Burns & Oates) Continuum International Publishing Group, Ltd.

Poe, Brannon. Accountant's Flight Plan: Best Practices for Today's Firms. 2010. 90p. 34.95 *(978-0-615-38935-6(X))* Blackman, Lynne F.

Polino, Mark. Microsoft Dynamics Gp 2010 Cookbook: LITE Edition. 2011. 116p. pap. ***(978-1-84968-380-7(8))*** Packt Publishing, Ltd.

Porter & Norton. Aie, Financial Accounting, 5e. 5th ed. 2007. (Illus.). xxiv, 695p. *(978-0-324-37578-7(6))* Cengage South-Western.

Porter, Brenda, et al. Principles of External Auditing. 3rd ed. 2008. (ENG., Illus.). 816p. pap. 65.95 *(978-0-470-01825-5(9)*, Wiley) Wiley, John & Sons, Inc.

Porter, Gary A. & Norton, Curtis L. Financial Accounting. 7th ed. 2010. (ENG.). 928p. (C). ring bd. 156.95 *(978-0-538-45265-6(X))* Cengage South-Western.

—Financial Accounting: The Impact on Decision Makers, 2 vols. (C). 6th ed. 2009. (Illus.). 204.95 *(978-0-324-82781-1(4))* 7th ed. 2010. (ENG.). 928p. 270.95 *(978-1-4390-8052-8(6))* Cengage South-Western.

—Financial Accounting: The Impact on Decision Makers (with 2009 IFRS Update), 2 vols. 6th ed. 2008. (ENG., Illus.). 832p. (C). 270.95 *(978-1-4390-3711-9(6))* Cengage South-Western.

—Using Financial Accounting. 6th ed. 2010. (ENG.). 1p. (C). pap. 187.95 *(978-1-111-52796-9(2))* Cengage South-Western.

—Using Financial Accounting Information: The Alternative to Debits & Credits. (Available Titles CengageNOW Ser.). (ENG.). (C). 6th ed. 2009. 800p. 259.95 *(978-0-324-59374-7(0))* 7th ed. 2010. 864p. 259.95 *(978-0-538-45274-8(9))* 7th ed. 2010. 864p. ring bd. 155.95 *(978-0-538-46808-4(4))* Cengage South-Western.

Poullaos, Chris. Accounting & Empire: The British Legacy of Professional Organization. Sian, Suki, ed. 2010. (Routledge New Works in Accounting History Ser.). (ENG., Illus.). 282p. (C). 125.00 *(978-0-415-45771-2(8))* Routledge.

Powers. Accounting. Date not set. (C). *(978-0-395-63680-0(9))* CENGAGE Learning.

—Financial Accounting. Date not set. (C). *(978-0-395-63681-7(7))* CENGAGE Learning.

Practitioners Publishing Co. Staff. PPC's Guide to Accounting & Reporting for Estates & Trusts, 2 vols., Vol. 2. 2006. *(978-0-7646-3768-1(1))* Practitioners Publishing Co.

Pratt, Jamie. Financial Accounting in an Economic Context. 7th ed. 2008. (ENG., Illus.). 792p. (C). 221.95 *(978-0-470-12882-4(8)*, Wiley) Wiley, John & Sons, Inc.

—Financial Accounting in an Economic Context. 8th ed. 2010. (ENG.). (C). 826p. 221.95 *(978-0-470-63529-2(0))*; 248p. pap., pupil's gde. ed. 66.95 *(978-0-470-65037-0(0))* Wiley, John & Sons, Inc. (Wiley).

—Financial Accounting in an Economic Context, Study Guide. 7th ed. 2008. (ENG.). 272p. (C). pap. 66.95 *(978-0-470-34331-9(1)*, Wiley) Wiley, John & Sons, Inc.

Pratt, Jamie, et al. Financial Reporting for Managers: A Value-Creation Perspective. 2008. (ENG., Illus.). 430p. (C). pap. 133.95 *(978-0-471-45749-7(3)*, Wiley) Wiley, John & Sons, Inc.

Prentice, Robert, et al, texts. Business Environment & Concepts. 2007th ed. 2008. (ENG.). 420p. per. *(978-0-9746541-0-2(8))* Efficient Learning Systems, Inc.

Previts, Gary, et al. A Global History of Accounting, Financial Reporting & Public Policy: Europe, 3 vols., Vol. 14. 2010. (Studies in the Development of Accounting Thought). (Illus.). 220p. *(978-0-85724-671-4(2))* Emerald Group Publishing Ltd.

Price, John, et al. College Accounting (Chapters 1-30) 13th ed. 2011. (ENG., Illus.). 1136p. (C). 185.67 *(978-0-07-802527-3(3)*, 0078025273, McGraw-Hill/Irwin) McGraw-Hill Higher Education.

—College Accounting Chapters -13 with Connect Plus. 13th ed. 2011. (ENG.). (C). pap., pap. 131.33 *(978-0-07-750403-8(8)*, 0077504038, McGraw-Hill/Irwin) McGraw-Hill Higher Education.

—College Accounting (Chapters 1-13) 13th ed. 2011. (ENG., Illus.). 560p. (C). pap. 115.67 *(978-0-07-743062-7(X)*, 007743062X, McGraw-Hill/Irwin) McGraw-Hill Higher Education.

—College Accounting (Chapters 1-24) 13th ed. 2011. (ENG., Illus.). 976p. (C). 162.67 *(978-0-07-743063-4(8)*, 0077430638, McGraw-Hill/Irwin) McGraw-Hill Higher Education.

—College Accounting Chapters 1-24 with Connect Plus. 13th ed. 2011. (ENG.). (C). 178.33 *(978-0-07-750404-5(6)*, 0077504046, McGraw-Hill/Irwin) McGraw-Hill Higher Education.

—College Accounting Chapters 1-30 with Connect Plus. 13th ed. 2011. (ENG.). (C). 201.33 *(978-0-07-750405-2(4)*, 0077504054, McGraw-Hill/Irwin) McGraw-Hill Higher Education.

—Loose Leaf Version for College Accounting. 13th ed. 2011. (ENG.). (C). ring bd. 130.00 *(978-0-07-743077-1(8)*, 0077430778, McGraw-Hill/Irwin) McGraw-Hill Higher Education.

Price, John Ellis. Study Guide & Working Papers to accompany College Accounting (Chapters 1-13) 13th ed. 2011. (ENG.). 384p. (C). pap. 71.33 *(978-0-07-743057-3(3)*, 0077430573, McGraw-Hill/Irwin) McGraw-Hill Higher Education.

Price, John Ellis, et al. College Accounting. 11th ed. 2007. (Illus.). xlviii, 1119p. *(978-0-07-321537-2(6))* McGraw-Hill Cos., The.

—College Accounting: Chapters 1-30. 12th ed. 2009. lv, 1034p. *(978-0-07-336560-2(2))* McGraw-Hill Cos., The.

—College Accounting: Chapters 1-30. 13th ed. 2012. xxxii, 485p. *(978-0-07-743045-0(X)*, Irwin Professional Publishing) McGraw-Hill Schl. Education Group.

—College Accounting Ch 1-13 w/Home Depot 2007 Annual Report. 12th ed. 2008. (ENG.). (C). pap., pap. 115.67 *(978-0-07-726433-8(9)*, 0077264339, McGraw-Hill/Irwin) McGraw-Hill Higher Education.

—College Accounting Ch 1-25 w/Home Depot 2007 Annual Report. 12th ed. 2008. (ENG.). (C). pap. 162.67 *(978-0-07-726432-1(0)*, 0077264320, McGraw-Hill/Irwin) McGraw-Hill Higher Education.

—Home Team Advantage Practice, Set. 12th ed. 2008. (ENG.). 128p. (C). pap. 71.33 *(978-0-07-336557-2(2)*, 0073365572, McGraw-Hill/Irwin) McGraw-Hill Higher Education.

—Student Guide for Quickbooks Pro 2008 for use with College Accounting. 12th ed. 2008. 1280p. (C). pap. 31.00 *(978-0-07-336568-8(8)*, 0073365688, McGraw-Hill/Irwin) McGraw-Hill Higher Education.

—Study Guide & Working Papers Chapters to accompany College Accounting (14-24) 13th ed. 2011. (ENG.). 256p. (C). pap. 71.33 *(978-0-07-743060-3(3)*, 0077430603, McGraw-Hill/Irwin) McGraw-Hill Higher Education.

—Study Guide & Working Papers to accompany College Accounting (Chapters 1-30) 13th ed. 2011. (ENG.). 768p. (C). pap. 71.33 *(978-0-07-743058-0(1)*, 0077430581, McGraw-Hill/Irwin) McGraw-Hill Higher Education.

Prince, Russ Alan & Rogers, Bruce H. In the Line of Money: Branding Yourself Strategically to the Financial Elite. 2011. 152p. 49.95 ***(978-1-4634-4225-5(4))***; pap. 29.95 ***(978-1-4634-4224-8(6))*** AuthorHouse.

PuzzlePro. Crossword Puzzles - Anything Accounting. 2007. 4.99 net. *(978-1-60402-384-8(8))* Independent Pub.

PwC. Manual of Accounting: Financial Instruments 2012. 2011. 1000p. pap. 115.00 ***(978-1-84766-905-6(0)***, Bloomsbury Professional) Bloomsbury Publishing Plc GBR. Dist: International Specialized Bk. Services.

—Manual of Accounting: IFRS 2012. 2011. 1000p. 130.00 ***(978-1-84766-906-3(9)***, Bloomsbury Professional) Bloomsbury Publishing Plc GBR. Dist: International Specialized Bk. Services.

Questions Answered on Being a Naturopathic Practioner. 2006. (C). per. 14.99 *(978-0-9788069-1-0(3))* Laurel Lane Publishing.

Quinn, Martin. Book-keeping & Accounts for Entrepreneurs. 2009. (ENG., Illus.). 208p. (C). pap. 24.99 *(978-0-273-72395-0(2))* FT Press.

—Brilliant Accounting: Everything You Need to Know to Manage the Success of Your Accounts. 2011. (ENG., Illus.). 248p. pap. 39.50 *(978-0-273-73537-3(3))* Prentice Hall PTR.

—Brilliant Book-Keeping: How to Keep Your Business Efficient & Cost-Effective. 2010. (ENG., Illus.). 232p. (C). pap. 19.99 *(978-0-273-73178-8(5))* FT Press.

Raiborn, Cecily A. Core Concepts of Accounting. 2nd ed. 2009. (ENG., Illus.). 426p. (C). pap. 100.95 *(978-0-470-49947-4(8)*, Wiley) Wiley, John & Sons, Inc.

Raman, Bhavani. Document Raj: Writing & Scribes in Early Colonial South India. 2012. (South Asia Across the Disciplines Ser.). (Illus.). 296p. 45.00 ***(978-0-226-70327-5(4))*** Univ. of Chicago Pr.

Rauf, S. Bobby. Finance & Accounting for Energy Engineers. 2010. *(978-0-88173-643-4(0))*; *(978-0-88173-642-7(2))*; (ENG.). 129.95 *(978-1-4398-5193-7(X))* Fairmont Pr., Inc.

Reckers, Philip M. J., et al, eds. Advances in Accounting. (Advances in Accounting Ser.: 22). (ENG.) Vol. 22. 2006. 288p. 99.95 *(978-0-7623-1360-0(9))* Vol. 23. 2007. (Illus.). 334p. 99.95 *(978-0-7623-1425-6(7))* Elsevier Science & Technology Bks. (JAI Pr.).

Reeve, James M., et al. Accounting. 22nd ed. 2006. (ENG.). 1280p. (C). ring bd. 136.95 *(978-0-324-38185-6(9))* Cengage South-Western.

—Financial Accounting. 10th ed. 2007. (ENG.). (C). 28.95 *(978-0-324-65548-3(7))* Cengage South-Western.

Reimers. Financial Accounting A Business Process. 2006. pap. 10.95 *(978-1-4288-0503-3(6))* Cram101 Inc.

Reimers, Jane L. Financial Accounting: A Business Process Approach. (MyAccountingLab Ser.). (ENG., (C). 2nd rev. ed. 2007. Illus.). 656p. 213.33 *(978-0-13-147386-7(7))* 3rd ed. 2010. 648p. 233.33 *(978-0-13-611527-4(6))* Prentice Hall PTR. (Prentice Hall).

—Financial Accounting: A Business Process Approach: International Edition. 2nd ed. 2008. (Illus.). 656p. pap. *(978-0-13-233504-1(2))* Prentice Hall PTR.

—Financial Accounting: Business Process Approach, Student Value Edition. 3rd ed. 2010. (ENG.). 648p. (C). ring bd. 151.67 *(978-0-13-611539-7(X)*, Prentice Hall) Prentice Hall PTR.

Rezaee, Zabihollah & Riley, Richard. Financial Statement Fraud: Prevention & Detection. 2nd ed. 2009. (CourseSmart Ser.). (ENG., Illus.). 332p. 75.00 *(978-0-470-45570-8(5)*, Wiley) Wiley, John & Sons, Inc.

Rice, Anthony. Accounts Demystified: The Astonishingly Simple Guide to Accounting. 6th rev. ed. 2011. (ENG., Illus.). 280p. pap. 47.50 ***(978-0-273-74470-2(4))*** Pearson Education, Ltd. GBR. Dist: Trans-Atlantic Pubns., Inc.

Rich, Jay, et al. Cornerstones of Financial Accounting. 2nd ed. 2011. (ENG.). 816p. (C). ring bd. 153.95 *(978-1-111-52915-4(9))* Cengage South-Western.

—Cornerstones of Financial Accounting, Current Trends Update. 2010. (ENG.). (C). ring bd. 143.95 *(978-1-111-52795-2(4))* Cengage South-Western.

—Cornerstones of Financial & Managerial Accounting. 2nd ed. 2011. (ENG.). 1408p. (C). ring bd. 139.95 *(978-1-111-52914-7(0))* Cengage South-Western.

Rikhardsson, Pall M., et al, eds. Implementing Environmental Management Accounting: Status & Challenges. 2007. (Eco-Efficiency in Industry & Science Ser.: Vol. 18). (Illus.). 374p. 219.00 *(978-1-4020-3371-1(0))* Springer.

Robinson, Canaan W. E. J. Actor's Wallet: Income & Expense Accounting for Today's Aspiring Actor. 2009. 155p. pap. 14.95 *(978-1-4327-4426-7(7))* Outskirts Pr., Inc.

Romney and, Steinbart. Accounting Information Systems. 2006. pap. 14.95 *(978-1-4288-0911-6(2))* Cram101 Inc.

Rudman, Jack. Principles of Financial Accounting. (Dantes Subject Standardized Tests Ser.: Vol. 47). 49.95 *(978-0-8373-6547-3(3))* National Learning Corp.

Ryals, Lynette & McDonald, Malcolm. Key Account Plans: The Practitioners' Guide to Profitable Planning. 2007. (ENG., Illus.). 408p. (C). pap. 54.95 *(978-0-7506-8367-8(8))* Routledge.

Ryan, Bob. Finance & Accounting for Business. 2nd ed. 2008. (Illus.). 544p. (C). 64.99 *(978-1-84480-897-7(1))* Cengage Learning GBR. Dist: CENGAGE Learning.

Salter, Stephen B. & Sharp, David J. Advances in International Accounting. Sale, J. Timothy, ed. (ENG.). 2007. 308p. 99.95 *(978-0-7623-1399-0(4))* 2006. (Illus.). 274p. 99.95 *(978-0-7623-1361-7(7))* Elsevier Science & Technology Bks. (JAI Pr.).

Sands, Jack. Accounting for Business: What the Numbers Mean & How to Use Them. 2nd ed. 2008. (Illus.). 312p. pap. 19.95 *(978-0-9702461-2-7(9))* Arena Bks., Inc.

Sangster, Alan & Wood, Frank. Frank Wood's Business Accounting, Vol. 1. 12th rev. ed. 2011. (ENG., Illus.). 779p. pap. 107.50 ***(978-0-273-75928-7(0))*** Pearson Education, Ltd. GBR. Dist: Trans-Atlantic Pubns., Inc.

Sapovadia, Vrajlal, et al. Accounting for Non-Accountants. 2010. 160p. pap. *(978-3-639-26559-0(9))* VDM Verlag Dr. Mueller e.K.

Schadewitz, Hannu. Financial & Nonfinancial Information in Interim Reports. 2010. 276p. pap. *(978-3-8383-0187-7(0))* Lambert Academic Publishing.

Schaltegger, Stefan, et al, eds. Sustainability Accounting & Reporting: Selected Papers. 2006. (Eco-Efficiency in Industry & Science Ser.). (Illus.). X, 716p. 379.00 *(978-1-4020-4079-5(2)*, 1402040792) Springer.

Schiehll, Eduardo. Corporate Governance & Accountability. 2009. 152p. pap. *(978-3-639-18382-5(7))* VDM Verlag Dr. Mueller e.K.

Schmeisser, Wilhelm, et al, eds. Innovation performance Accounting: An innovation management approach of financial costs & earning patents, research & development, production & marketing Planning. 2010. (ENG., Illus.). xx, 480p. 169.00 *(978-3-642-01352-2(X)*, 364201352X) Springer.

Scott, Peter. Accounting for Business: An Integrated Print & Online Solution. 2012. (ENG.). 550p. pap. 75.00 ***(978-0-19-958653-0(5))*** Oxford Univ. Pr., Inc.

Scott, William R. Financial Accounting Theory. (ENG., Illus.). (C). 5th ed. 2009. 560p. 186.67 *(978-0-13-207286-1(6))* 6th ed. 2011. 592p. 186.67 ***(978-0-13-511915-0(4))*** Prentice Hall PTR. (Prentice Hall).

Selected Readings 2007 — Management of a Practice. 2007. cd-rom *(978-0-87051-658-0(2))* American Institute of Certified Public Accountants.

Serra Salvador, Vicente & Salvador, Vicente Serra. Plan General de Contabilidad y Plan General de Contabilidad de Pequeñas y Medianas Empresas: Incluye Criterios Contables para Microempresas. 2008. (SPA., Illus.). 550p. *(978-84-8002-476-1(3))* Tirant lo Blanch.

Shah, Paresh. Financial Accounting for Management. 2007. (ENG., Illus.). 544p. pap. 60.00 *(978-0-19-569009-5(5))* Oxford Univ. Pr., Inc.

Shapland, Julie & Turner, Cynthia. Shapland & Turner Cases in Financial Accounting. 2012. (ENG.). 240p. (C). pap. 40.00 ***(978-0-13-275281-7(6)***, Prentice Hall) Prentice Hall PTR.

—Shapland & Turner Cases in Financial Accounting, Student Value Edition. 2012. (ENG.). 500p. (C). ring bd. 26.00 ***(978-0-13-297142-3(9)***, Prentice Hall) Prentice Hall PTR.

Shim, Jae, et al. Corporate Controller's Handbook of Financial Management (2008-2009) 2008. 1900p. pap. 189.00 *(978-0-8080-9172-1(7))* Toolkit Media Group.

Shim, Jae K. & Siegel, Joel G. Budgeting Basics & Beyond. 3rd ed. 2008. (ENG., Illus.). 448p. pap. 105.50 *(978-0-470-38968-3(0)*, Wiley) Wiley, John & Sons, Inc.

Shiver, John M. & Eitel, David R. Maximizing Emergency Department Productivity. 2009. (ENG., Illus.). 260p. pap. 75.95 *(978-1-4200-8377-4(5))* Productivity Pr.

Siegel, Joel G., et al. The Vest Pocket CPA. 4th ed. 2008. (ENG., Illus.). 768p. per. 34.95 *(978-0-470-16813-4(7)*, Wiley) Wiley, John & Sons, Inc.

Siegel, Paul, et al. Credit Derivatives: Techniques to Manage Credit Risk for Financial Professionals. 2006. (McGraw-Hill Financial Education Ser.). (ENG., Illus.). 304p. 59.95 *(978-0-07-145314-1(8)*, 0071453148) McGraw-Hill Cos., The.

Simmons, Anthony & Hardy, Richard. Essential VCE Accounting Units 1&2. 2006. (ENG.). pap., stu. ed. 38.95 *(978-0-521-67127-9(2))* Cambridge Univ. Pr.

—Essential VCE Accounting Units 3&4. 2006. pap., stu. ed. 39.95 *(978-0-521-67128-6(0))* Cambridge Univ. Pr.

Simpson, Kemper. Economics for the Accountant. 2009. 132p. pap. *(978-0-217-46660-3(5))* Books LLC.

—Economics for the Accountant. 2009. 220p. 39.95 *(978-1-120-22995-3(2))*; pap. 24.95 *(978-1-120-19122-9(X))* Kessinger Publishing, LLC.

Sitarz, Daniel. Small Business Accounting Simplified. 5th rev. ed. 2010. Orig. Title: Simplified Small Business Accounting. (ENG.). 272p. pap. 29.95 incl. cd-rom *(978-1-892949-50-9(4))* Nova Publishing Co.

Slater, Jeffrey. College Accounting. (ENG.). (C). 11th ed. 2009. 272p. pap., instr.'s gde. ed. 53.33 *(978-0-13-606571-5(5))* 11th ed. 2009. 928p. 186.67 *(978-0-13-606380-3(2))* 12th rev. ed. 2012. 936p. 186.67 ***(978-0-13-277206-3(X))*** Prentice Hall PTR. (Prentice Hall).

—College Accounting: A Practical Approach. 9th ed. 2006. pap. 12.95 *(978-1-4238-1247-5(4))* Cram101 Inc.

—College Accounting Chapers 1-12 Student Value Edition. 12th ed. 2012. (ENG.). 984p. (C). ring bd. 76.27 ***(978-0-13-277324-9(4)***, Prentice Hall) Prentice Hall PTR.

—College Accounting, Chapters 1-12 with Study Guide & Working Papers. 11th ed. 2009. (ENG.). 984p. (C). pap. 117.33 *(978-0-13-606566-1(X)*, Prentice Hall) Prentice Hall PTR.

—College Accounting Chapters 1-12 with Study Guide & Working Papers. 12th rev. ed. 2012. (ENG.). 992p. (C). pap. 117.33 ***(978-0-13-277217-4(5)***, Prentice Hall) Prentice Hall PTR.

—College Accounting, Chapters 1-25: A Practical Approach. 10th ed. 2006. (ENG., Illus.). 960p. (C). 186.67 *(978-0-13-228638-1(6)*, Prentice Hall) Prentice Hall PTR.

—College Accounting Chapters 1-25, Student Value Edition. 12th ed. 2012. (ENG.). 928p. (C). ring bd. 121.33 ***(978-0-13-277230-3(2)***, Prentice Hall) Prentice Hall PTR.

—Study Guide & Working Papers for College Accounting Chapters 1-12. 12th rev. ed. 2012. (ENG.). 464p. (C). pap. 53.33 ***(978-0-13-277215-0(9)***, Prentice Hall) Prentice Hall PTR.

—Study Guide & Working Papers for College Accounting Chapters 13 - 25. 12th rev. ed. 2012. (ENG.). 224p. (C). pap. 53.33 ***(978-0-13-277216-7(7)***, Prentice Hall) Prentice Hall PTR.

Slater, Jeffrey & DeMarco, Shari L. Who-Dun-It Practice Set for College Accounting. 12th rev. ed. 2012. (ENG.). 180p. (C). pap. 60.00 ***(978-0-13-277253-2(1)***, Prentice Hall) Prentice Hall PTR.

Sleeter. Quickbooks Fundamentals 2009. 2009. *(978-1-932487-50-3(6))* Sleeter Group, Inc., The.

Smith, Blake T., et al. PPC's 706/709 Deskbook, 2 vols. Incl. Vol. 1. ring bd. *(978-0-7646-0156-9(3))*; Vol. 2. ring bd. *(978-0-7646-0157-6(1))*; 1997. 150.00 *(978-0-7646-0155-2(5))* Practitioners Publishing Co.

Smith, James. Keeping It Simple: Small Business Bookkeeping, Cash Flow, Tax & VAT. (Illus.). 2011. 224p. pap. ***(978-1-907302-34-3(4))*** 2010. 226p. pap. *(978-1-907302-24-4(7))* 2010. 226p. pap. *(978-1-907302-16-9(6))* 2009. 224p. pap. *(978-1-904608-89-9(2))* Taxcafe UK Ltd.

Smith, James. Keeping It Simple: Small Business Bookkeeping, Self-Assessment & VAT. 2008. (Illus.). 184p. pap. *(978-1-904608-82-0(5))* 2007. 188p. per. *(978-1-904608-31-8(0))* Taxcafe UK Ltd.

Smith, Malcolm. Research Methods in Accounting. 2nd ed. 2011. (Illus.). 240p. (C). 135.00 *(978-1-84920-796-6(8)*, 307966C); pap. 54.00 *(978-1-84920-797-3(6)*, B07966P) SAGE Pubns., Ltd. GBR. Dist: SAGE Pubns., Inc.

Smith, Ralph E. & Birney, Patrick. Financial Accounting Basics. 3rd ed. 2006. pap. 11.95 *(978-1-4288-1040-2(4))* Cram101 Inc.

Snowden, P. N. Emerging Risk in International Banking (RLE Banking & Finance) Origins of Financial Vulnerability in The 1980s, Volume 31. 2012. (ENG.). 160p. 100.00 ***(978-0-415-52942-6(5))*** Routledge.

Solomon, Jerrold M. & Fullerton, Rosemary. Acccunting for World Class Operations: A Practical Guide for Providing Relevant Information in Support of the Lean Enterprise. 2007. (Making Companies Globally Competitive Ser.). (Illus.). xii, 280p. *(978-0-9793331-0-1(5))* WCM Assocs.

Sondhi, Ashwinpaul C. & Scott, Taub. Revenue Recognition Guide. 2007th rev. ed. 2006. (Miller Ser.). (Illus.). 624p. per. 222.00 *(978-0-8080-9066-3(6))* Toolkit Media Group.

Soule, George. Soule's New Science & Practice of Accounts. 2010. 786p. 54.36 *(978-1-169-37575-8(8))* 2010. 786p. 67.95 *(978-1-161-97413-3(X))* 2009. 788p. pap. 52.95 *(978-1-104-47053-1(5))* Kessinger Publishing, LLC.

Spall, Jonathan. Investing in Gold: The Essential Safe Haven Investment for Every Portfolio. 2008. (ENG., Illus.). 240p. 27.95 *(978-0-07-160346-1(8)*, 0071603468) McGraw-Hill Cos., The.

Spiceland, Davi & Sepe, James. Intermediate Accounting Update. 2010. 1248p. 174.06 *(978-0-07-332466-1(3))* McGraw-Hill Professional Publishing.

Spiceland, J. David. Intermediate Accounting. 5th ed. 2009. (Illus.). *(978-0-07-332465-4(5))*; *(978-0-07-332464-7(7))* McGraw-Hill Cos., The.

Spiceland, J. David & Sepe, James. Intermediate Accounting. 6th ed. 2010. 1280p. 203.75 *(978-0-07-811083-2(1))*; (ENG.). 224p. (C). pap. 48.00 *(978-0-07-732887-0(6)*, 0077328876) McGraw-Hill Higher Education. (McGraw-Hill/Irwin).

—Intermediate Accounting, (ch 1-12) 6th ed. 2010. 736p. 158.75 *(978-0-07-732891-7(4)*, McGraw-Hill/Irwin) McGraw-Hill Higher Education.

—Intermediate Accounting, (ch. 13-21) 6th ed. 2010. 640p. 112.50 *(978-0-07-732890-0(6)*, McGraw-Hill/Irwin) McGraw-Hill Higher Education.

Spiceland, J. David, et al. Financial Accounting. 2nd ed. 2010. (ENG., Illus.). 736p. (C). 237.67 *(978-0-07-811082-5(3)*, 0078110823, McGraw-Hill/Irwin) McGraw-Hill Higher Education.

—Financial Accounting: A Decision Maker's Perspective. 2009. (Illus.). *(978-0-07-337933-3(6)*, Irwin Professional Publishing) McGraw-Hill Schl. Education Group.

—Financial Accounting: Making the Connection. 2012. (ENG.). (C). 199.33 ***(978-0-07-786226-3(0)***, 0077862260, Irwin Professional Publishing) McGraw-Hill Higher Education.

—Financial Accounting: Making the Connection with Connect Plus & LearnSmart1Se. 2012. (ENG.). (C). 214.99 ***(978-0-07-760619-0(1)***, 0077606191, McGraw-Hill/Irwin) McGraw-Hill Higher Education.

—Financial Accounting w/Buckle Annual Report. 2008. (ENG.). 750p. (C). 198.44 *(978-0-07-728228-3(0)*, 0077282280, McGraw-Hill/Irwin) McGraw-Hill Higher Education.

—Financial Accounting with Connect Plus. 2nd ed. 2010. (ENG.). (C). 253.33 *(978-0-07-748000-4(7)*, 0077480007, McGraw-Hill/Irwin) McGraw-Hill Higher Education.

—Intermediate Accounting. 5th ed. 2009. 1280p. *(978-0-07-352687-4(8))* McGraw-Hill Cos., The.

—Intermediate Accounting, Vol. 2. 6th ed. 2010. (ENG.). 224p. (C). pap. 48.00 *(978-0-07-732888-7(4)*, 0077328884, McGraw-Hill/Irwin) McGraw-Hill Higher Education.

—Intermediate Accounting Vol 1 (Ch 1-12) with British Airways Annual Report. 6th ed. 2010. (ENG.). (C). 199.33 *(978-0-07-739583-4(2)*, 0077395832, McGraw-Hill/Irwin) McGraw-Hill Higher Education.

—Intermediate Accounting Vol 1 (Ch 1-12) with British Airways Report + Connect Plus. 6th ed. 2010. (ENG.). (C). 215.00 *(978-0-07-740016-3(X)*, 007740016X, McGraw-Hill/Irwin) McGraw-Hill Higher Education.

—Intermediate Accounting Vol 2 (Ch 13-21) with British Airways Annual Report + Connect Plus. 6th ed. 2010. (ENG.). (C). 157.33 *(978-0-07-740017-0(8)*, 0077400178, McGraw-Hill/Irwin) McGraw-Hill Higher Education.

—Intermediate Accounting Volume 1 Ch 1-12 w/Google Annual Report. 5th ed. 2008. (ENG.). (C). 168.75 *(978-0-07-728469-5(0)*, 0077284690, McGraw-Hill/Irwin) McGraw-Hill Higher Education.

—Intermediate Accounting Volume 2 Ch 13-21 w/Google Annual Report. 5th ed. 2008. (ENG.). (C). 119.69 *(978-0-07-728471-8(2)*, 0077284712, McGraw-Hill/Irwin) McGraw-Hill Higher Education.

—Intermediate Accounting Volume 2 (Ch 13-21) with Annual Report. 7th ed. 2012. (ENG.). (C). 137.33 ***(978-0-07-761406-5(2)***, 0077614062, McGraw-Hill/Irwin) McGraw-Hill Higher Education.

—Intermediate Accounting Volume 2 (Ch 13-21) with British Airways Report. 6th ed. 2010. (ENG.). (C). 141.67 *(978-0-07-739582-7(4)*, 0077395824, McGraw-Hill/Irwin) McGraw-Hill Higher Education.

—Intermediate Accounting Volume I (Ch 1-12) with Annual Report. 7th ed. 2012. (ENG.). (C). 193.33 ***(978-0-07-761405-8(4)***, 0077614054, McGraw-Hill/Irwin) McGraw-Hill Higher Education.

—Intermediate Accounting w/Google Annual Report. 5th ed. 2008. (ENG.). (C). 216.25 *(978-0-07-728207-3(8)*, 0077282078, McGraw-Hill/Irwin) McGraw-Hill Higher Education.

—Intermediate Accounting with Annual Report. 7th ed. 2012. (ENG.). 1280p. (C). 260.99 ***(978-0-07-761404-1(6)***, 0077614046, McGraw-Hill/Irwin) McGraw-Hill Higher Education.

—Intermediate Accounting with British Airways Annual Report. 6th ed. 2010. (ENG.). (C). 261.00 *(978-0-07-739581-0(6)*, 0077395816, McGraw-Hill/Irwin) McGraw-Hill Higher Education.

—Intermediate Accounting with British Airways Annual Report + Connect Plus 6th ed. 2010. (ENG.). (C). 276.67 *(978-0-07-740349-2(5)*, 0077403495, McGraw-Hill/Irwin) McGraw-Hill Higher Education.

—Loose-leaf Intermediate Accounting. 6th ed. 2010. (ENG., Illus.). (C). ring bd. 183.00 *(978-0-07-740359-1(2)*, 0077403592, McGraw-Hill/Irwin) McGraw-Hill Higher Education.

—Loose-leaf Intermediate Accounting, Volume 1 (ch. 1-12) 6th ed. 2010. (ENG.). (C). ring bd. 139.67 *(978-0-07-740361-4(4)*, 0077403614, McGraw-Hill/Irwin) McGraw-Hill Higher Education.

—Loose-leaf Intermediate Accounting, Volume 2 (ch. 13-21) 6th ed. 2010. (ENG.). (C). ring bd. 99.33 *(978-0-07-740360-7(6)*, 0077403606, McGraw-Hill/Irwin) McGraw-Hill Higher Education.

—Loose Leaf Intermediate Accounting with Annual Report. 7th ed. 2012. (ENG.). (C). ring bd., ring bd. 183.00 ***(978-0-07-761407-2(0)***, 0077614070, McGraw-Hill/Irwin) McGraw-Hill Higher Education.

—Loose-Leaf version Financial Accounting: Making the Connection w/ Connect Plus. 2012. (ENG.). (C). ring bd., ring bd. 162.00 ***(978-0-07-760618-3(3)***, 0077606183, McGraw-Hill/Irwin) McGraw-Hill Higher Education.

—Study Guide Volume 1 for Intermediate Accounting. 7th ed. 2012. (ENG.). 224p. (C). pap. 48.00 ***(978-0-07-744643-7(7)***, 0077446437, McGraw-Hill/Irwin) McGraw-Hill Higher Education.

—Study Guide Volume 1 to accompany Intermediate Accounting. 5th ed. 2008. (ENG.). 224p. (C). pap. 40.63 *(978-0-07-332459-3(0)*, 0073324590, McGraw-Hill/Irwin) McGraw-Hill Higher Education.

—Study Guide Volume 2 for Intermediate Accounting. 7th ed. 2012. (ENG.). 224p. (C). pap. 48.00 ***(978-0-07-744644-4(5)***, 0077446445, McGraw-Hill/Irwin) McGraw-Hill Higher Education.

—Study Guide, Volume 2 to accompany Intermediate Accounting. 5th ed. 2008. (ENG.). 224p. (C). pap. 40.63 *(978-0-07-332460-9(4)*, 0073324604, McGraw-Hill/Irwin) McGraw-Hill Higher Education.

Spiceland, J. David, et al. Working Papers for Intermediate Accounting. 7th ed. 2012. (ENG.). 736p. (C). pap. 79.00 ***(978-0-07-744645-1(3)***, 0077446453 McGraw-Hill/Irwin) McGraw-Hill Higher Education.

Spiceland, Sepe. Intermediate Accounting. 2006. pap. 19.95 *(978-1-4288-1194-2(X))* Cram101 Inc.

Spitters, Thomas Heaton. Accounting Essays. 2011. 370p. 39.50 ***(978-1-257-37406-9(0))*** Lulu Enterprises Inc.

Sprague, Charles E. The Philosophy of Accounts. 2009. 216p. 24.99 *(978-1-113-86691-2(8))*; 32.99 *(978-1-113-86693-6(4))*; pap. 17.99 *(978-1-113-86687-5(X))* BiblioBazaar.

Sprunt, Hugh H., et al. PPC's 1041 Deskbook, 2 vols. Incl. Vol. 2. 1996. ring bd. *(978-0-7646-0047-0(8))*; 150.00 o.p. *(978-0-7646-0045-6(1))*; 150.00 *(978-0-7646-0328-0(0))* Practitioners Publishing Co.

Stice, James D. & Stice, Earl K. Intermediate Accounting. 18th ed. 2011. (ENG.). 1632p. (C). 283.95 *(978-0-538-47973-8(6))*; ring bd. 198.95 *(978-1-111-53509-4(4))* Cengage South-Western.

Stickney, Clyde P., et al. Financial Accounting: An Introduction to Concepts, Methods & Uses. 13th ed. 2009. (Available Titles CengageNOW Ser.). (ENG.). 960p. (C). 243.95 *(978-0-324-65114-0(7))* Cengage South-Western.

—Financial Reporting, Financial Statement Analysis & Valuation. 7th ed. 2010. (ENG., Illus.). 1296p. (C). 257.95 *(978-0-324-78941-6(6))* Cengage South-Western.

Stittle, John & Wearing, Robert T. Financial Accounting. 2008. (SAGE Course Companions Ser.). 176p. (C). 76.00 *(978-1-4129-3502-9(4)*, B35024C) SAGE Pubns., Ltd. GBR. Dist: SAGE Pubns., Inc.

Stittle, John, et al. Financial Accounting. 2008. (SAGE Course Companions Ser.). (Illus.). 176p. (C). pap. 32.00 *(978-1-4129-3503-6(2)*, B35024P) SAGE Pubns., Ltd. GBR. Dist: SAGE Pubns., Inc.

Stolowy, Herve & Lebas, Michel. Financial Acc Rep 3E. 3rd ed. 2010. (Illus.). 800p. pap. 79.99 *(978-1-4080-2113-2(7))* Cengage Learning GBR. Dist: CENGAGE Learning.

Stott, J. Randall & Truman, Mike. Basic Accounting. 2010. (Teach Yourself Ser.). (ENG., Illus.). 330p. pap. 19.95 *(978-1-4441-0023-5(8)*, Hodder & Stoughton) Hodder General Publishing Div. GBR. Dist: Independent Pubs. Group.

Stroup, et al. QuickBooks 2012 for Dummies. 2nd ed. 2012. (ENG.). 428p. pap. 24.99 ***(978-1-119-96894-8(1)***, For Dummies) Wiley, John & Sons, Inc.

Sundaram, Rangarajan K. & Das, Sanjiv. Derivatives. 2010. (ENG., Illus.). 940p. (C). 199.33 *(978-0-07-294931-5(7)*, 0072949317, McGraw-Hill/Irwin) McGraw-Hill Higher Education.

Sundem, Gary L., et al. Introduction to Financial Accounting: Global Edition. 10th rev. ed. 2012. (ENG.). 611p. pap. 129.50 ***(978-0-273-77017-6(9))*** Pearson Education, Ltd. GBR. Dist: Trans-Atlantic Pubns., Inc.

Tan, Rebecca Chyi Woan. Accounting for Financial Instruments. 2008. 184p. pap. *(978-3-639-05167-4(X))* VDM Verlag Dr. Mueller e.K.

Taylor, William James, et al. Fundamentals of Advanced Accounting. 2007. (ENG., Illus.). 696p. (C). 260.95 *(978-0-324-37890-9(4))* Cengage South-Western.

Teixeira. Accounting in New Zealand. 922p. *(978-0-471-33455-2(3))* Wiley, John & Sons, Inc.

Tiffin, Ralph. The Finance & Accounting: Accounting Literacy for the Non-Financial Manager. 2nd rev. ed. 2007. 323p. pap., instr.'s gde. ed. 33.00 *(978-1-85418-309-5(5))* Thorogood GBR. Dist: Stylus Publishing, LLC.

Titman, Sheridan, et al. Financial Management: Principles & Applications with MyFinanceLab with Pearson eText Student Access Code Card Package. 11th ed. 2011. (ENG.). (C). 233.33 *(978-0-13-275708-9(7)*, Prentice Hall) Prentice Hall PTR.

Tolson, David A., et al. PPC's Controllership Guide, 4 vols. Incl. Vol. 1. ring bd. 170.00 *(978-0-7646-0370-9(1))*; Vol. 2. ring bd. 170.00 *(978-0-7646-0371-6(X))*; Vol. 3. ring bd. 170.00 *(978-0-7646-0372-3(8))*; Vol. 4. ring bd. 170.00 *(978-0-7646-0373-0(6))*; 1997. 140.00 *(978-0-7646-0369-3(8))* Practitioners Publishing Co.

Tracy, John. Accounting for Dummies. 4th ed. 2008. (ENG., Illus.). 408p. pap. 21.99 *(978-0-470-24600-9(6)*, For Dummies) Wiley, John & Sons, Inc.

Tracy, John A. Accounting Workbook for Dummies. 2006. (ENG., Illus.). 320p. pap. 19.99 *(978-0-471-79145-4(8)*, For Dummies) Wiley, John & Sons, Inc.

Tracy, John A. & Laurin, Cecile. Accounting for Canadians for Dummies. 2007. (ENG.). 416p. pap. 29.99 ***(978-0-470-83878-5(7)***, For Dummies) Wiley, John & Sons, Inc.

Tsay, Bor-Yi, et al. Survey of Accounting. 3rd ed. 2011. (ENG., Illus.). 672p. (C). 231.00 *(978-0-07-811085-6(8)*, 0078110858, McGraw-Hill/Irwin) McGraw-Hill Higher Education.

Tweedie, David, et al. The Debate on Inflation Accounting. 2009. (Cambridge Studies in Management Ser.). (ENG.). 420p. pap. 42.00 *(978-0-521-11765-4(8))* Cambridge Univ. Pr.

Uddin, Shahzad & Tsamenyi, Mathew, eds. Research in Accounting in Emerging Economies. 2010. (Research in Accounting in Emerging Economies Ser.). 300p. 134.95 *(978-0-85724-451-2(5))* Emerald Group Publishing Ltd. GBR. Dist: Turpin Distribution Services Ltd.

Ulmer, Donna. Computer Accounting with QuickBooks Pro 2009. 2009. 704p. pap. 86.50 *(978-0-07-337950-0(6))* McGraw-Hill Professional Publishing.

United Nations. Accounting & Financial Reporting Guidelines for Small & Medium-sized Enterprises (SMEGA) Level 3 Guidance. 2009. (ENG.). 20p. pap. 10.00 *(978-92-1-112764-5(5))* United Nations Pubns.

University of North Carolina-Wilmington Staff. Applications of Accounting: 201 Lab Manual. 5th rev. ed. 2009. (ENG.). 170p. spiral bd. 50.53 *(978-0-7575-6391-1(0))* Kendall Hunt Publishing Co.

Venezia, Itzhak & Wiener, Zvi. Bridging the GAAP: Recent Advances in Finance & Accounting. 2012. 304p. 1?0.00 ***(978-981-4350-00-6(1))*** World Scientific Publishing Co., Inc.

Vicky Arnold Staff. Advances in Accounting Behavioral Research, Vol. 11. 2008. (Advances in Accounting Behavioral Research Ser.). (Illus.). 132p. 99.95 *(978-1-84663-960-9(3))* Emerald Group Publishing Ltd. GBR. Dist: Turpin Distribution Services Ltd.

—Advances in Accounting Behavioral Research Volume 12. 2009. (Advances in Accounting Behavioral Research Ser.). (Illus.). xii, 200p. 114.95 *(978-1-84855-738-3(8))* Emerald Group Publishing Ltd. GBR. Dist: Turpin Distribution Services Ltd.

Villani, Kathleen & Rosa, James B. Computerized Accounting with QuickBooks Pro 2007. 2008. (Illus.). *(978-0-7638-3044-1(5))* Paradigm Pubs.

Wahlen, James M., et al. Financial Reporting, Financial Statement Analysis & Valuation: A Strategic Perspective. 7th ed. 2010. (ENG.). 1296p. (C). 246.95 *(978-0-324-78942-3(4))* Cengage South-Western.

Wahlen, James M., et al. Intermediate Accounting: Reporting & Analysis. 2012. (ENG.). 1356p. (C). 231.95 ***(978-1-111-82236-1(0))*** Cengage South-Western.

Walker, Janet. Accounting in a Nutshell: Accounting for the Non-Specialist. 3rd ed. 2008. (CIMA Professional Handbook Ser.). (ENG., Illus.). 368p. pap. 40.95 *(978-0-7506-8738-6(X)*, CIMA Publishing) Elsevier Science & Technology Bks.

Wallace, Wanda A. Mastery of the Financial Accounting Research System (FARS) Through Cases. 2nd ed. 2007. (ENG., Illus.). 352p. (C). pap. 84.95 *(978-0-471-74161-9(2)*, Wiley) Wiley, John & Sons, Inc.

Walston-Dunham, Beth. Accounting & Tax Principles for Legal Professionals. 2007. (ENG., Illus.). 448p. (C). per. 80.95 *(978-1-4180-1107-9(X))* Delmar Cengage Learning.

Walters, Diane & McPhail, Ken. Accounting & Business Ethics. (Illus.). 2009. (ENG.). 240p. (C). 45.95 *(978-0-415-36236-8(9))* 2007. 320p. 155.00 *(978-0-415-36235-1(0))* Routledge.

Wang, Jun & Jun, Wang. Accounting with Heart: China's Role in International Finance & Business. 2010. (ENG.). 256p. pap. 39.95 *(978-0-470-82570-9(7)*, Wiley) Wiley, John & Sons, Inc.

Warfield, Terry D., et al. Excel Working Papers CD, Intermediate Accounting: Principles & Analysis. 2nd ed. 2008. (ENG.). (C). 78.95 *(978-0-470-27957-1(5)*, Wiley) Wiley, John & Sons, Inc.

Warren, et al. Accounting, Chapters 1-13. 24th ed. 2011. pap. *(978-0-538-47896-0(9))* Cengage South-Western.

Warren, Carl & Reeve, James M. Financial Acccunting for Future Business Leaders. 2006. pap. 13.95 *(978-1-4288-1074-7(9))* Cram101 Inc.

Warren, Carl S. Survey of Accounting. 5th ed. 2010. (Available Titles CengageNOW Ser.). (ENG.). 720p. (C). 244.95 *(978-0-538-74909-1(1))* Cengage South-Western.

Warren, Carl S. & Reeves, M. Financial & Managerial Accounting. 8th ed. 2006. (ENG.). pap. 17.95 *(978-1-4288-1093-8(5))* Cram101 Inc.

Warren, Carl S., et al. Accounting. Orig. Title: Accounting Principles. (ENG., (C). 22nd ed. 2006. Illus.). 288p. per., pupil's gde. ed. 46.95 *(978-0-324-38258-7(8))* 22nd ed. 2006. 416p. pap. 91.95 *(978-0-324-38261-7(8))* 22nd ed. 2006. (Illus.). 1280p. 256.95 *(978-0-324-40184-4(1))* 23rd ed. 2008. 1328p. 256.95 *(978-0-324-66296-2(3))* 24th ed. 2011. 1360p. 256.95 *(978-0-538-47500-6(5))* 24th ed. 2011. 720p. pap. 42.95 *(978-0-538-47853-3(5))* 24th ed. 2011. 320p. pap., pupil's gde. ed. 44.95 *(978-0-538-47907-3(8))* 24th ed. 2011. 1352p. ring bd. 179.95 *(978-0-538-47850-2(0))* Cengage South-Western.

—Accounting Working Papers. 24th ed. 2011. (ENG.). 448p. (C). pap. 46.95 *(978-0-538-47854-0(3))* Cengage South-Western.

—Corporate Financial Accounting. 11th ed. 2011. (ENG.). 880p. (C). ring bd. 165.95 *(978-1-111-52747-1(4))* Cengage South-Western.

—Financial Accounting. 12th ed. 2011. (Financial Accounting Ser.). (ENG.). (C). 944p. 214.95 *(978-0-538-47851-9(9))*; 960p. ring bd. 150.95 *(978-0-538-47995-0(7))* Cengage South-Western.

—Financial & Managerial Accounting. 11th ed. 2011. (ENG.). 1424p. (C). ring bd. 172.95 *(978-1-111-52712-9(1))* Cengage South-Western.

—Financial & Managerial Accounting General Ledger Software. 11th ed. 2011. (ENG.). (C). 48.95 *(978-1-111-52916-1(7))* Cengage South-Western.

—General Ledger Software for Financial Accounting. 24th ed. 2011. (ENG.). (C). 39.95 *(978-1-111-52837-9(3))* Cengage South-Western.

—Study Guide for Accounting, Finincial Accounting. 24th ed. 2011. (ENG.). 384p. (C). pap. 46.95 *(978-0-538-47855-7(1))* Cengage South-Western.

Watson, Alex. Accounting. 2nd ed. 2008. 784p. pap. 60.00 *(978-0-19-576051-4(4))* Oxford Univ. Pr., Inc.

Waybright, Jeffrey. Financial Accounting, Student Value Edition. 2010. (ENG.). 768p. (C). ring bd. 151.67 (978-0-13-212678-6(8), Prentice Hall) Prentice Hall PTR.

Waybright, Jeffrey & Kemp, Robert. Financial Accounting. (ENG.). (C). 2009. 768p. pap. 233.33 (978-0-13-606048-2(X)) 2nd rev. ed. 2012. (Illus.). 816p. 233.33 **(978-0-13-277158-0(6))** Prentice Hall PTR. (Prentice Hall).

Waybright, Jeffrey & Kemp, Robert. Financial Accounting, Student Value Edition. 2nd ed. 2012. (ENG.). 816p. (C). ring bd. 151.67 **(978-0-13-277180-1(2),** Prentice Hall) Prentice Hall PTR.

Waybright, Jeffrey & Street, Rick. Study Guide with DemoDocs for Financial Accounting. 2010. (ENG.). 504p. (C). pap. 46.67 (978-0-13-605141-1(3), Prentice Hall) Prentice Hall PTR.

Weetman, Pauline. Financial Accounting: An Introduction. (Illus.). (Orig.). 4th rev. ed. 2006. 504p. (C). pap. 97.50 (978-0-273-70340-2(4), Financial Times/Prentice Hall) 5th rev. ed. 2010. (ENG.). 512p. pap. 117.50 (978-0-273-71840-6(1)) Pearson Education, Ltd. GBR. Dist: Trans-Atlantic Pubns., Inc.

Weiner, David P. Financial Accounting as a Second Language. 2008. (ENG.). 320p. (C). pap. 46.95 (978-0-470-04388-2(1), Wiley) Wiley, John & Sons, Inc.

Weirich, Thomas R., et al. Accounting & Auditing Research: Tools & Strategies. 7th ed. 2009. (ENG., Illus.). 240p. (C). pap. 78.95 (978-0-470-50697-4(0), Wiley) Wiley, John & Sons, Inc.

Weiss, David. Financial Instruments: Equities, Debt, Derivatives, & Alternative Investments. 2009. (ENG.). 384p. (gr. 12-18). 65.00 (978-1-59184-227-9(1), Portfolio (Hardcover)) Penguin Group (USA) Inc.

Werner, Jones. Introduction to Accounting A User Perspe. 2006. pap. 14.95 (978-1-4288-1241-3(5)) Cram101 Inc.

Weygandt. Accounting Principles 10E Volume 1 for Paradise Valley Community College. 10th ed. 2011. 1690p. (C). pap. 89.95 **(978-1-118-10602-0(4),** Wiley) Wiley, John & Sons, Inc.

—Accounting Principles 9E for Columbia-chicago. 9th ed. 2011. 546p. (C). pap. 96.95 **(978-1-118-10639-6(3),** Wiley) Wiley, John & Sons, Inc.

—Accounting Principles 9E Volume 2 for Paradise Valley Community College. 10th ed. 2011. 760p. (C). pap. 89.95 **(978-1-118-10601-3(6),** Wiley) Wiley, John & Sons, Inc.

—Accounting Principles for Matc. 10th ed. 2011. 988p. (C). pap. 109.95 **(978-1-118-11117-8(6),** Wiley) Wiley, John & Sons, Inc.

Weygandt, et al. Accounting Principles. 9th ed. 2010. (Wiley Custom Select Ser.). (Illus.). (C). pap. 30.95 (978-0-470-73413-1(2)); pap. 30.95 (978-0-470-73412-4(4)) Wiley, John & Sons, Inc. (Wiley).

—Financial Accounting. 6th ed. 2007. (ENG.). 928p. (C). ring bd. 142.95 (978-0-470-27974-8(5), Wiley) Wiley, John & Sons, Inc.

Weygandt, J. J. Financial Accounting. 6th ed. 2008. (ENG., Illus.). 600p. (C). pap. 55.95 (978-0-470-39531-8(1), Wiley) Wiley, John & Sons, Inc.

Weygandt, Jerry J. Accounting Principles, Vol. 2. 10th ed. 2011. (ENG.). 736p. (C). pap. 165.95 (978-1-118-00928-4(2), Wiley) Wiley, John & Sons, Inc.

—Accounting Principles 10th Edition Volume 1 for Queensborough Community College. 10th ed. 2011. 584p. (C). pap. 83.53 **(978-1-118-10137-7(5),** Wiley) Wiley, John & Sons, Inc.

—Accounting Principles 10th Edition Volume 2 for Queensborough Community College. 10th ed. 2011. 508p. (C). pap. 77.10 **(978-1-118-10139-1(1),** Wiley) Wiley, John & Sons, Inc.

—Accounting Principles 7th Edition PAR Take Action CD & Student Access Card with WileyPLUS Set Set. 7th rev. ed. 2007. (Wiley Plus Products Ser.). 149.95 (978-0-470-19276-4(3)) Wiley, John & Sons, Inc.

—Accounting Principles Chapters 1-12, Vol. 1. 10th ed. 2011. 688p. (C). pap. 150.95 (978-1-118-00927-7(4), Wiley) Wiley, John & Sons, Inc.

—Financial Accounting 6E for Bergen Cc. 6th ed. 2011. 740p. (C). pap. 109.95 **(978-1-118-11085-0(4),** Wiley) Wiley, John & Sons, Inc.

—Intermediate Accounting 14E Volume 1 for Bergen Community College. 14th ed. 2011. 810p. (C). pap. 83.99 **(978-1-118-11119-2(2),** Wiley) Wiley, John & Sons, Inc.

—ISV Financial Accounting, a Focus on Fundamentals, 6E, International Student Version. 6th ed. 2008. (Illus.). 960p. pap. 158.95 (978-0-470-27671-6(1)) Wiley, John & Sons, Inc.

—(WCS)Financial Accounting 7th Edition Volume 1 with Wiley Plus & Wiley Plus Wrapper Set. 2006. pap. 50.95 (978-0-470-10817-8(7), Wiley) Wiley, John & Sons, Inc.

—(WCS)Financial Accounting Fundamentals volumes 1 & 2 with Fundamentals of Managerial Accounting, Wiley Plus & Wiley Plus Wrapper Set. 2006. pap. 140.95 (978-0-470-10816-1(9), Wiley) Wiley, John & Sons, Inc.

—(WCS)Principles of Financial Accounting Chapters 1-18, Eighth Edition with Campus Cycle Shop for University of Hawii - Leeward CC. 2007. 1074p. pap. 75.95 (978-0-470-89551-1(9)) Wiley, John & Sons, Inc.

—Wiley Plus/Blackboard Stand-alone to accompany Accounting Principles. 8th rev. ed. 2007. (Wiley Plus Products Ser.). pap., pap. 75.95 (978-0-470-11182-6(8)) Wiley, John & Sons, Inc.

—Wiley Plus/Webct Stand-Alone to Accompany Accounting Principles. 8th rev. ed. 2007. (Wiley Plus Products Ser.). pap. 75.95 (978-0-470-11188-8(7)) Wiley, John & Sons, Inc.

Weygandt, Jerry J. & Kieso, Donald E. Accounting Principles. 6th ed. 2006. pap. 17.95 (978-1-4288-1066-2(8)) Cram101 Inc.

Weygandt, Jerry J., et al. Accounting Principles. 7th ed. 2006. pap. 73.95 (978-0-470-07651-4(8)) 8th rev. ed. 2007. (ENG., Illus.). 1280p. (C). 241.95 (978-0-471-98019-3(6), Wiley) 9th ed. 2008. (ENG., Illus.). 1288p. (C). 232.95 (978-0-470-31754-9(X), Wiley) 10th ed. 2011. (ENG., Illus.). 864p. (C). 232.95 (978-0-470-53479-3(6), Wiley) 10th ed. 2011. (ENG.). (C). pap. 57.95 (978-0-470-88788-2(5), Wiley) 10th ed. 2011. (ENG.). 480p. (C). pap. 47.95 (978-0-470-88821-6(0), Wiley)Chapters 1-12, Vol. 1. 9th ed. 2008. (ENG.). 312p. (C). pap., pupil's gde. ed. 69.95 (978-0-470-38658-3(4), Wiley) Wiley, John & Sons, Inc.

—Accounting Principles, Vol. 1, Chapters 1-12. 9th ed. 2008. (ENG.). 656p. (C). pap. 150.95 (978-0-470-31755-6(8), Wiley) Wiley, John & Sons, Inc.

—Accounting Principles, Vol. 1, Chs. 1-12. 9th ed. 2008. (ENG.). 720p. (C). pap. 65.95 (978-0-470-38662-0(2), Wiley) Wiley, John & Sons, Inc.

—Accounting Principles, Vol. 2. 9th ed. 2008. (ENG.). 720p. (C). pap. 165.95 (978-0-470-31757-0(4), Wiley) Wiley, John & Sons, Inc.

—Accounting Principles. 9th ed. 2008. (ENG.). (C). Vol. 2, Chs. 13-26. 544p. pap. 64.95 (978-0-470-38663-7(0)) Vol. 2, Chs 13-26. 336p. pap., stu. ed. 62.95 (978-0-470-38659-0(2)) Wiley, John & Sons, Inc. (Wiley).

—Accounting Principles Chs. 1-7: Working Papers. 9th ed. 2008. (ENG.). 520p. (C). pap., wbk. ed. 46.95 (978-0-470-38668-2(1), Wiley) Wiley, John & Sons, Inc.

—Accounting Principles Chs. 1-26. 9th ed. 2009. (ENG.). (C). 55.95 (978-0-470-38664-4(9), Wiley) Wiley, John & Sons, Inc.

—Accounting Principles - Working Papers, Chs. 1-18. 9th ed. 2008. (ENG.). 896p. (C). pap. 56.95 (978-0-470-38669-9(X), Wiley) Wiley, John & Sons, Inc.

—Accounting Principles, , Problem Solving Guide. 8th ed. 2007. pap. 31.95 (978-0-470-12886-2(0), Wiley) Wiley, John & Sons, Inc.

—Accounting Principles, , Working Papers. 8th ed. 2007. pap. 31.95 (978-0-470-12885-5(2), Wiley) Wiley, John & Sons, Inc.

—Accounting Principles 10E Chapters 1-12 for University of North Dakota. 10th ed. 2011. 692p. (C). ring bd. 96.95 **(978-1-118-11486-5(8),** Wiley) Wiley, John & Sons, Inc.

—Accounting Principles 10th Edition Volume 2 for Danville Coummunty College. 10th ed. 2011. 796p. (C). pap. 65.95 **(978-1-118-09444-0(1),** Wiley) Wiley, John & Sons, Inc.

—Accounting Principles, Soft Cover. 10th ed. 2011. 1350p. (C). pap. 173.95 **(978-1-118-12180-1(5),** Wiley) Wiley, John & Sons, Inc.

—Annotated Instructor's Edition, Accounting Principles. 10th ed. 2011. 1360p. (C). 221.95 **(978-1-118-00930-7(4),** Wiley) Wiley, John & Sons, Inc.

—Financial Accounting. (ENG.). (C). 2010. 408p. pap., pupil's gde. ed. 74.95 (978-0-470-60726-8(2)) 2010. (Illus.). 848p. 222.95 (978-0-470-55200-1(X)) 6th ed. 2008. 55.95 (978-0-470-39688-9(1)) Wiley, John & Sons, Inc. (Wiley).

—Financial Accounting. 7th ed. 2009. (ENG.). 850p. (C). 232.95 (978-0-470-47715-1(6), Wiley) Wiley, John & Sons, Inc.

—Financial Accounting. 7th ed. 2010. (ENG.). 392p. (C). pap., pupil's gde. ed. 71.95 (978-0-470-50699-8(7), Wiley) Wiley, John & Sons, Inc.

—Financial Accounting: Excel Working Papers. 7th ed. 2010. (ENG.). (C). 57.95 (978-0-470-52440-4(5), Wiley) Wiley, John & Sons, Inc.

—Financial Accounting: IFRS Excel Working Papers. 2010. (C). 19.95 (978-0-470-60728-2(9), Wiley) Wiley, John & Sons, Inc.

—Financial Accounting: Working Papers. (ENG., (C). 6th ed. 2007. Illus.). 852p. pap. 101.95 (978-0-470-17590-3(7)) 7th ed. 2010. 870p. pap. 92.95 (978-0-470-50701-8(2)) Wiley, John & Sons, Inc. (Wiley).

—Financial Accounting - Problem Solving Survival Guide. 2006. pap. 14.95 (978-1-4288-0995-6(3)); 5th ed. pap. 12.95 (978-1-4288-1150-8(8)) Cram101 Inc.

—Financial Accounting - Problem Solving Survival Guide. 5th ed. 2006. pap. 73.95 (978-0-470-07652-1(6)) 6th rev. ed. 2007. (ENG., Illus.). 938p. (C). 232.95 (978-0-470-12884-8(4), Wiley) 7th ed. 2010. (ENG., Illus.). 562p. (C). pap. 61.95 (978-0-470-88184-2(4), Wiley) Wiley, John & Sons, Inc.

—Financial Accounting, Study Guide. 6th ed. 2007. (ENG., Illus.). 422p. (C). pap. 68.95 (978-0-470-17588-0(5), Wiley) Wiley, John & Sons, Inc.

—General Ledger Software CD to accompany Financial Accounting. 7th ed. 2010. (ENG.). (C). 32.95 (978-0-470-64366-2(8), Wiley) Wiley, John & Sons, Inc.

—Hospitality Financial Accounting. 2nd ed. 2008. (ENG., Illus.). 544p. 114.95 (978-0-470-08360-4(3), Wiley) Wiley, John & Sons, Inc.

—Hospitality Financial Accounting Working Papers. 2nd ed. 2008. (ENG.). 176p. pap. 41.95 (978-0-470-14057-4(7), Wiley) Wiley, John & Sons, Inc.

—Instuctor's Manual to Accompany Accounting Principles, 9th Edition, 2 vols. 9th ed. 2009. (Illus.). pap. **(978-0-470-38709-2(2));** pap. **(978-0-470-38708-5(4))** Wiley, John & Sons, Inc.

—Intermediate Accounting: Principles & Analysis. 2nd ed. 2007. (ENG.). 1140p. ring bd. 138.95 (978-0-470-27973-1(7), Wiley) Wiley, John & Sons, Inc.

—Principles of Financial Accounting. 10th ed. 2011. (ENG.). 976p. (C). pap. 174.95 (978-1-118-00931-4(2), Wiley) Wiley, John & Sons, Inc.

—Principles of Financial Accounting, Chapters 1-18. 9th ed. 2008. (ENG.). 944p. (C). pap. 174.95 (978-0-470-31758-7(2), Wiley) Wiley, John & Sons, Inc.

Wild, John. Excel Working Papers to accompany Financial Accounting. 5th ed. 2010. (ENG.). (C). cd-rom 74.00 (978-0-07-726891-6(1)) 0077268911, McGraw-Hill/Irwin) McGraw-Hill Higher Education.

—Excel Working Papers to accompany Financial Accounting Fundamentals. 2nd ed. 2008. (ENG.). (C). cd-rom 53.33 (978-0-07-336033-1(3), 0073360333, McGraw-Hill/Irwin) McGraw-Hill Higher Education.

—Financial Accounting Fundamentals. 3rd ed. 2010. (ENG., Illus.). 744p. (C). pap. 177.33 (978-0-07-352704-8(1), 0073527041, McGraw-Hill/Irwin) McGraw-Hill Higher Education.

—Financial Accounting: Information for Decisions with Connect Plus. 6th ed. 2012. (ENG.). (C). 253.33 **(978-0-07-763585-5(X),** 007763585X, McGraw-Hill/Irwin) McGraw-Hill Higher Education.

—Financial Accounting with IFRS Fold Out Primer. 5th ed. 2010. (ENG., Illus.). 736p. (C). 237.67 (978-0-07-740877-0(2), 0077408772, McGraw-Hill/Irwin) McGraw-Hill Higher Education.

—Loose-leaf Financial Accounting with IFRS FO Primer. 5th ed. 2010. (ENG.). (C). ring bd. 166.67 (978-0-07-741414-6(4), 0077414144, McGraw-Hill/Irwin) McGraw-Hill Higher Education.

—Loose-leaf for Financial Accounting: Information for Decisions. 6th ed. 2012. (ENG.). (C). ring bd. 166.67 **(978-0-07-743001-6(8),** 007743001 8, McGraw-Hill/Irwin) McGraw-Hill Higher Education.

—Study Guide to accompany Financial Accounting Fundamentals. 3rd ed. 2010. (ENG.). 288p. (C). pap. 76.00 (978-0-07-731793-5(9), 0077317939, McGraw-Hill/Irwin) McGraw-Hill Higher Education.

—Working Papers to accompany Financial Accounting. 5th ed. 2010. (ENG.). 672p. (C). pap. 75.00 (978-0-07-726899-2(7), 0077268997, McGraw-Hill/Irwin) McGraw-Hill Higher Education.

Wild, John, et al. College Accounting Ch. 1-14 with Annual Report + Connect Plus. 2nd ed. 2010. (ENG.). (C). pap., pap. 133.33 (978-0-07-739818-7(1), 0077398181, McGraw-Hill/Irwin) McGraw-Hill Higher Education.

—College Accounting Ch. 1-29 with Annual Report + Connect Plus. 2nd ed. 2010. (ENG.). (C). 201.33 (978-0-07-739817-0(3), 0077398173, McGraw-Hill/Irwin) McGraw-Hill Higher Education.

—Excel Working Papers for FAP (CH 1-25) 20th ed. 2010. (ENG.). (C). cd-rom 74.33 (978-0-07-733808-4(1), 0077338081, McGraw-Hill/Irwin) McGraw-Hill Higher Education.

—Fundamental Accounting Principles Vol 1 Softcover with Conect Plus. 20th ed. 2011. (ENG.). (C). pap. 189.00 (978-0-07-750603-2(0), 0077506030, McGraw-Hill/Irwin) McGraw-Hill Higher Education.

—Fundamental Accounting Principles Vol 1 with Connect Plus. 20th ed. 2011. (ENG.). (C). 189.00 (978-0-07-750600-1(6), 0077506006, McGraw-Hill/Irwin) McGraw-Hill Higher Education.

—Fundamental Accounting Principles Vol 2 Softcover with Connect Plus. 20th ed. 2011. (ENG.). (C). pap. 152.33 (978-0-07-750604-9(9), 0077506049, McGraw-Hill/Irwin) McGraw-Hill Higher Education.

—Loose-leaf College Accounting CHAPTERS 1-14. 2nd ed. 2010. (ENG.). (C). ring bd. 82.67 (978-0-07-740401-7(7), 0077404017, McGraw-Hill/Irwin) McGraw-Hill Higher Education.

—Loose-leaf College Accounting CHAPTERS 1-29. 2nd ed. 2010. (ENG.). (C). ring bd. 130.00 (978-0-07-740405-5(X), 007740405X, McGraw-Hill/Irwin) McGraw-Hill Higher Education.

—MP: Student Guide for QuickBooks Pro 2010 with Edu Ver. Software & Templates for College Accounting. 2nd ed. 2010. (ENG.). (C). 39.33 incl. cd-rom (978-0-07-742693-4(2), 0077426932, McGraw-Hill/Irwin) McGraw-Hill Higher Education.

—Principles of Financial Accounting (Ch 1-17) with Connect Plus. 20th ed. 2011. (ENG.). (C). 223.33 (978-0-07-750602-5(2), 0077506022, McGraw-Hill/Irwin) McGraw-Hill Higher Education.

—Study Guide & Working Papers Ch 1-14 to accompany College Accounting. 2nd ed. 2010. (ENG.). 672p. (C). pap. 71.33 (978-0-07-726885-5(7), 0077268857, McGraw-Hill/Irwin) McGraw-Hill Higher Education.

—Study Guide to accompany Financial & Managerial Accounting. 4th ed. 2010. (ENG.). 608p. (C). pap. 39.67 (978-0-07-731834-5(X), 007731834X, McGraw-Hill/Irwin) McGraw-Hill Higher Education.

—Study Guide Vol 1 for FAP Volume 1 (CH 1-12) 20th ed. 2010. (ENG.). 256p. (C). pap. 72.33 (978-0-07-733816-9(2), 0077338162, McGraw-Hill/Irwin) McGraw-Hill Higher Education.

—Study Guide Vol 2 for FAP Volume 2 (CH 12-25) 20th ed. 2010. (ENG.). 288p. (C). pap. 72.33 (978-0-07-733817-6(0), 0077338170, McGraw-Hill/Irwin) McGraw-Hill Higher Education.

—Working Papers (print) to accompany Principles of Financial Accounting (CH 1-17) 19th ed. 2008. (ENG.). 768p. (C). pap. 88.33 (978-0-07-336634-0(X), 007336634X, McGraw-Hill/Irwin) McGraw-Hill Higher Education.

Wild, John J. Financial Accounting: Information for Decisions. 3rd ed. 2006. pap. 34.95 (978-1-4288-1135-5(4)) Cram101 Inc.

—Financial Accounting: Information for Decisions. 4th rev. ed. 2008. (Illus.). 736p. (978-0-07-304375-3(3)) McGraw-Hill Cos., The.

—Financial Accounting: Information for Decisions. (ENG., Illus.). (C). 4th rev. ed. 2006. xxxii, 580p. pap. 196.25 (978-0-07-333502-5(9), 0073335029) 6th ed. 2012. 736p. 237.67 **(978-0-07-802538-9(9),** 0078025389) McGraw-Hill Higher Education. (McGraw-Hill/Irwin).

—Financial Accounting: Information for Decisions: Information for Decisions. 5th ed. 2010. (Illus.). 736p. 185.00 (978-0-07-352701-7(7), McGraw-Hill/Irwin) McGraw-Hill Higher Education.

Wild, John J. & Chiappetta, Barbara. Financial & Managerial Accounting: Information for Decisions. 2nd ed. 2007. (Illus.). 975p. (978-0-07-352668-3(1)) McGraw-Hill Cos., The.

Wild, John J., et al. College Accounting. 2nd ed. 2010. (ENG.). 512p. (C). pap., pap. 117.67 (978-0-07-734610-2(6), 0077346106, McGraw-Hill/Irwin) McGraw-Hill Higher Education.

—College Accounting. 2008. (Illus.). (978-0-07-337944-9(1)); (978-0-07-333669-5(6)) McGraw-Hill Schl. Education Group. (Irwin Professional Publishing).

—College Accounting: Chapters 1-29. 2nd ed. 2011. (Illus.). xxxii, 837p. (978-0-07-726873-2(3)); (978-0-07-813667-2(9)) McGraw-Hill Cos., The.

—College Accounting: Chapters1-29. 2nd ed. 2010. (ENG.). 1056p. (C). 185.67 (978-0-07-734609-6(2), 0077346092, McGraw-Hill/Irwin) McGraw-Hill Higher Education.

—Electronic Study Guide & Working Papers Ch 1-30 for use with College Accounting. 2007. (ENG.). (C). cd-rom 70.00 (978-0-07-333670-1(X), 007333670X, McGraw-Hill/Irwin) McGraw-Hill Higher Education.

—FAP Volume 2 (CH 12-25) softcover with Working Papers. 19th ed. 2008. (ENG., Illus.). 704p. (C). pap. 136.67 (978-0-07-336631-9(5), 0073366315, McGraw-Hill/Irwin) McGraw-Hill Higher Education.

—Financial & Managerial Accounting: Information for Decisions. 3rd ed. 2008. (ENG., Illus.). 656p. (C). pap. 143.00 (978-0-07-336057-7(0), 0073360570, McGraw-Hill/Irwin) McGraw-Hill Higher Education.

—Financial & Managerial Accounting Vol. 2: Information for Decisions. 4th ed. 2010. (ENG., Illus.). 672p. (C). pap. 143.00 (978-0-07-731839-0(0), 0077318390, McGraw-Hill/Irwin) McGraw-Hill Higher Education.

—Fundamental Accounting Principles. (C). 18th rev. ed. 2007. (ENG.). pap. 198.44 incl. cd-rom (978-0-07-334316-7(1), 0073343161) 19th ed. 2008. 1188p. 168.75 (978-0-07-337954-8(9), 9780073379548) 20th ed. 2010. (ENG., Illus.). 1204p. 239.00 (978-0-07-811087-0(4), 0078110874) Vol. 1. 20th ed. 2010. (ENG., Illus.). 620p. pap. 173.33 (978-0-07-733826-8(X), 007733826X) Vol. 1. 20th ed. 2010. (ENG., Illus.). 620p. 173.33 (978-0-07-733825-1(1), 0077338251) Vol. 2. 20th ed. 2010. (ENG., Illus.). 712p. pap. 136.67 (978-0-07-733827-5(8), 0077338278) Vol. 2. 20th ed. 2010. (ENG., Illus.). 712p. 136.67 (978-0-07-733824-4(3), 0077338243) McGraw-Hill Higher Education. (McGraw-Hill/Irwin).

—Fundamental Accounting Principles. 19th ed. 2009. (Illus.). (978-0-07-336630-2(7)); (978-0-07-336627-2(7)) McGraw-Hill Schl. Education Group. (Irwin Professional Publishing).

—Fundamental Accounting Principles: Chapters 1-12. 18th ed. 2006. (Fundamental Accounting Principles with Working Papers). pap. 109.06 (978-0-07-332381-7(0), 9780073323817, McGraw-Hill/Irwin) McGraw-Hill Higher Education.

—Fundamental Accounting Principles 18e Phase 2. 18th rev. ed. 2008. (Illus.). 1156p. (978-0-07-326648-0(5)) McGraw-Hill Cos., The.

—Fundamental Accounting Principles, Vol 1 (Chapters 1-12) 19th ed. 2008. 620p. (C). 125.94 (978-0-07-336629-6(3), 9780073366296, McGraw-Hill/Irwin) McGraw-Hill Higher Education.

—Fundamental Accounting Principles, Vol 2 (Chapters 12-25) 19th ed. 2008. (ENG., Illus.). 704p. (C). 136.67 (978-0-07-336628-9(5), 0073366285, McGraw-Hill/Irwin) McGraw-Hill Higher Education.

—MP Fundamental Accounting Principles Volume 1 (Ch 1-12) Softcover with Working Papers & Best Buy Annual Report. 19th ed. 2008. (ENG.). (C). pap., pap. 173.33 (978-0-07-730324-2(5), 0077303245, McGraw-Hill/Irwin) McGraw-Hill Higher Education.

—MP Fundamental Accounting Principles Volume 1 (Ch 1-12) with Best Buy Annual Report. 19th ed. 2008. (ENG.). (C). pap. 173.33 (978-0-07-730323-5(7), 0077303237, McGraw-Hill/Irwin) McGraw-Hill Higher Education.

—Principles of Financial Accounting. 20th ed. 2010. (ENG., Illus.). 844p. (C). 207.67 (978-0-07-733823-7(5), 0077338235, McGraw-Hill/Irwin) McGraw-Hill Higher Education.

WileyPlus, creator. Wiley Plus/Blackboard Stand-Alone Chalk Cartridge Student Registration Code. 12th ed. 2006. (Wiley Plus Products Ser.). pap. 113.95 (978-0-470-11629-6(3)) Wiley, John & Sons, Inc.

Willand, Heinz. Account Management Key- Strategic- & Global Account Management. 2008. 176p. pap. (978-3-639-05606-8(X)) VDM Verlag Dr. Mueller e.K.

Williams, Jan, et al. Financial Accounting. 14th ed. 2009. (ENG., Illus.). 808p. (C). 237.67 (978-0-07-352698-0(3), 0073526983, McGraw-Hill/Irwin) McGraw-Hill Higher Education.

—Financial Accounting with Connect Plus. 15th ed. 2011. (ENG.). (C). 253.33 (978-0-07-750402-1(X), 007750402X, McGraw-Hill/Irwin) McGraw-Hill Higher Education.

—Financial & Managerial Accounting. 15th ed. 2009. (ENG., Illus.). 1264p. (C). 240.33 (978-0-07-352699-7(1), 0073526991, McGraw-Hill/Irwin) McGraw-Hill Higher Education.

—Loose-leaf version Financial Accounting. 15th ed. 2011. (ENG.). (C). ring bd. 166.67 (978-0-07-748457-6(6), 0077484576, McGraw-Hill/Irwin) McGraw-Hill Higher Education.

—Loose-Leaf Version Financial & Managerial Accounting. 16th ed. 2011. (ENG.). (C). ring bd. 168.33 (978-0-07-748456-9(8), 0077484568, McGraw-Hill/Irwin) McGraw-Hill Higher Education.

—Study Guide, Volume 1, Chapters 1-15 to accompany Financial Accounting & Financial & Managerial Accounting. 16th ed. 2011. (ENG.). 192p. (C). pap. 72.33 (978-0-07-732866-5(3), 0077328663, McGraw-Hill/Irwin) McGraw-Hill Higher Education.

—Study Guide, Volume 2, Chapters 15-26 for Use with Financial & Managerial Accounting 14th Edition. 14th ed. 2006. (ENG., Illus.). (C). per. 72.33 (978-0-07-326816-3(X), 007326816X, McGraw-Hill/Irwin) McGraw-Hill Higher Education.

—Study Guide, Volume 2, Chapters 16-26 to accompany Financial Accounting & Financial & Managerial Accounting. 16th ed. 2011. (ENG.). 256p. (C). pap. 72.33 (978-0-07-732867-2(1), 0077328671, McGraw-Hill/Irwin) McGraw-Hill Higher Education.

—Working Papers, Volume 1, Chapters 1-15 to accompany Financial & Managerial Accounting. 16th ed. 2011. (ENG.). 576p. (C). pap. 76.33

(978-0-07-732868-9(X), 007732868X, McGraw-Hill/Irwin) McGraw-Hill Higher Education.

—Working Papers, Volume 2, Chapters 16-26 to accompany Financial & Managerial Accounting. 16th ed. 2011. (ENG.). 480p. (C). pap. 76.33 (978-0-07-732869-6(8), 0077328698, McGraw-Hill/Irwin) McGraw-Hill Higher Education.

Williams, Jan R., et al. Financial Accounting. 15th ed. 2011. (ENG., Illus.). 800p. (C). 237.67 (978-0-07-732870-2(1), 0077328701, McGraw-Hill/Irwin) McGraw-Hill Higher Education.

—Financial & Managerial Accounting: The Basis for Business Decisions. 16th ed. 2011. (ENG., Illus.). 1264p. (C). 240.33 (978-0-07-811104-4(8), 0078111048, McGraw-Hill/Irwin) McGraw-Hill Higher Education.

Wilmington, Unc. Applications of Accounting: 201 Lab Manual. 6th rev. ed. 2010. (ENG.). 170p. spiral bd. 50.53 (978-0-7575-7992-9(2)) Kendall Hunt Publishing Co.

Wilmington, Unc & University of North Carolina-Wilmington. Applications of Accounting: 201 Lab Manual. 7th rev. ed. 2011. (ENG.). 170p. spiral bd. 47.95 **(978-0-7575-9179-2(5))** Kendall Hunt Publishing Co.

Wink, Geri B. & Corradino, Laurie. Intermediate Accounting DeMYSTiFieD. 2010. (Demystified Ser.). (ENG., Illus.). 400p. pap. 22.00 (978-0-07-173885-9(1), 0071738851) McGraw-Hill Cos., The.

Wolk, Harry I. Accounting Theory, 4 vols. Wolk, Harry I., ed. 2009. (SAGE Library in Accounting & Finance Ser.). (Illus.). 1584p. 995.00 (978-1-84787-609-6(9), B76096C) SAGE Pubns., Ltd. GBR. Dist: SAGE Pubns., Inc.

Wolk, Harry I., et al. Accounting Theory: Conceptual Issues in a Political & Economic Environment. 7th ed. 2007. (Illus.). 696p. (C). 129.00 (978-1-4129-5345-0(6), B53456C) SAGE Pubns., Inc.

Wood, Frank & Horner, David. Business Accounting Basics. 2010. (ENG., Illus.). 328p. pap. 57.50 (978-0-273-72500-8(9)) Pearson Education, Ltd. GBR. Dist: Trans-Atlantic Pubns., Inc.

Wood, Frank & Robinson, Sheila. Book-keeping & Accounts. 7th ed. 2009. (ENG., Illus.). 640p. pap. 87.50 (978-0-273-71805-5(3)) Financial Times/Prentice Hall.

Wood, Frank & Sangster, Alan H. Frank Wood's Business Accounting, Vol. 1. 11th ed. 2008. (Illus.). 792p. pap. (978-0-273-71212-1(8)) Financial Times Business Enterprises, Ltd.

Yacht, Carol & Crosson, Susan. Computer Accounting Essentials Using Quickbooks w/Quickbooks 2008 Educational Trial Software. 4th ed. 2008. (ENG.). (C). pap., pap. 79.33 incl. cd-rom (978-0-07-729309-3(6), 0077293096, McGraw-Hill/Irwin) McGraw-Hill Higher Education.

Yacht, Carol, et al. MP Computer Accounting Essentials with Microsoft Dynamics GP 10. 0. 2nd ed. 2008. (ENG.). (C). pap. 76.00 (978-0-07-729939-2(6), 0077299396, McGraw-Hill/Irwin) McGraw-Hill Higher Education.

—MP Computer Accounting with Microsoft Dynamics GP 10. 0. 2nd ed. 2008. (ENG.). (C). spiral bd. 141.33 (978-0-07-729938-5(8), 0077299388, McGraw-Hill/Irwin) McGraw-Hill Higher Education.

Zimmermann, Jochen, et al. Global Governance in Accounting: Rebalancing Public Power & Private Commitment. 2008. (Transformations of the State Ser.). (ENG., Illus.). 264p. 95.00 (978-0-230-51814-8(1)) Palgrave Macmillan.

ACCOUNTING—CASE STUDIES

Anthony, et al. Accounting: Texts & Cases. 13th ed. 2011. (Illus.). 960p. pap. (978-0-07-128909-2(7)) McGraw-Hill Cos., The.

Bierman. Accounting/Finance Lessons of Enron. 2008. ix, 204p. 69.00 (978-981-279-030-9(6)) World Scientific Publishing Co., Inc.

David R.Herwitz & Matthew J.Barrett. Accounting for Lawyers. 4th rev. ed. 2006. (Illus.). 594p. 80.00 (978-1-59941-202-3(0)) West.

Deslauriers, Sylvie. Comptabilisez Vos Succès! Le Guide à la Rédaction de Cas. (FRE.). x, 273p. (978-0-9738038-3-9(5)) Editions AB+.

Grabski, Severin, et al. Management Accounting in Enterprise Resource Planning Systems. 2009. (ENG., Illus.). 176p. pap. 50.95 (978-1-85617-679-8(7), CIMA Publishing) Elsevier Science & Technology Bks.

Hamilton, Stewart & Micklethwait, Alicia. Greed & Corporate Failure: The Lessons from Recent Disasters. 2006. (ENG.). 256p. 59.00 (978-1-4039-8636-8(3)) Palgrave Macmillan.

Sandretto, Michael J. Cases in Financial Reporting. 2011. (ENG.). 576p. (C). pap. 78.95 (978-0-538-47679-9(6)) Cengage South-Western.

Timoshenko, Konstantin. Accounting Norms for the State. 2010. 100p. pap. (978-3-639-25465-5(1)) VDM Verlag Dr. Mueller e.K.

ACCOUNTING—COMPUTER PROGRAMS

Arif, Naeem & Tauseef, Sheikh. Integrating SAP ERP Financials: Configuration & Design. 2010. (Illus.). 394p. 79.95 (978-1-59229-300-1(X), SAP PR.) Galileo Pr., Inc.

—SAP ERP Financials: Configuration & Design. 2nd ed. 2011. (Illus.). 664p. 79.95 (978-1-59229-393-3(X), SAP PR.) Galileo Pr., Inc.

Barich, Thomas. QuickBooks 2011 QuickSteps. 2nd ed. 2010. (ENG., Illus.). 240p. pap. 22.00 (978-0-07-175135-3(1), 0071751351) McGraw-Hill Osborne.

Bauer, Eric & Siebert, Jörg. The SAP General Ledger. 2nd ed. 2010. (Illus.). 450p. 79.95 (978-1-59229-350-6(6), SAP PR.) Galileo Pr., Inc.

Biafore, Bonnie. Quickbooks 2008. 2007. (Missing Manual Ser.). (ENG., Illus.). 706p. per. 29.99 (978-0-596-51514-0(6), Pogue Pr.) O'Reilly Media, Inc.

Brunsdon, Terri E. Learning Peachtree Complete 2007. 2007. (Illus.). 832p. pap. (978-0-13-233175-3(6)) Prentice Hall PTR.

Cable, Sandra. New Perspectives on Microsoft Office Accounting 2009: Introductory. 2009. (Available Titles Skills Assessment Manager (SAM) - Office 2007 Ser.). (ENG.). 432p. pap. 131.95 (978-0-495-80642-4(0)) Course Technology.

—New Perspectives on Microsoft Office Accounting. Brief. 2009. (New Perspectives Ser.). (ENG.). 272p. pap. 88.95 (978-0-495-80645-5(5)) Course Technology.

Capachietti / Sleeter Group, Leslie. QuickBooks Point of Sale - Best Practices for Success (Version 6) (CD-ROM Version) 2007. cd-rom 79.95 (978-1-932487-91-6(3)) Sleeter Group, Inc., The.

Cram101 Textbook Reviews. Outlines & Highlights for Computer Accounting with Peachtree Complete 2007 - with Cd by Carol Yacht, Isbn: 9780073365916. 2010. 68p. pap. 27.95 (978-1-4288-5623-3(4)) Cram101 Inc.

Faleiros, Rogerio & Kreis Ryan, Alison. Configuring Controlling in SAP ERP. 2012. (ENG., Illus.). 550p. 79.95 (978-1-59229-401-5(4), SAP PR.) Galileo Pr., Inc.

Frye, Curtis & Pearson, William E., II. Microsoft Office Accounting Professional 2007. 2007. (ENG., Illus.). 400p. pap. 24.99 (978-0-7356-2420-7(8)) Microsoft Pr.

Ivens, Kathy. QuickBooks 2009. 2008. (ENG.). 656p. pap. 29.99 (978-0-07-159859-0(6), 0071598596) McGraw-Hill Osborne.

Jacobs, Kathy, et al. Excel 2007 Charts Made Easy. 2008. (ENG., Illus.). 207p. pap. 21.99 (978-0-07-160006-4(X), 007160006X) McGraw-Hill Osborne.

Jordan, John. 100 Things You Should Know about Controlling with SAP ERP Financials. 2010. (Illus.). 300p. 49.95 (978-1-59229-341-4(7), SAP PR.) Galileo Pr., Inc.

Kay, Donna. Computer Accounting with Quickbooks 2011 MP -wQBPremAccCD, wStudent CD. 13th ed. 2011. (ENG.). (C). spiral bd. 146.67 incl. cd-rom (978-0-07-749986-0(7), 0077499867, McGraw-Hill/Irwin) McGraw-Hill Higher Education.

Keep Going with QuickBooks 2007 for Windows: Et84746sm. 2007. spiral bd. (978-1-4246-0534-7(2)) Element K Content LLC.

Klooster, Dale & Allen, Warren. Integrated Accounting for Windows. 7th ed. 2010. (ENG.). (C). 281.95 (978-0-538-45144-4(0)); 592p. pap. 131.95 (978-0-538-74798-1(6)) Cengage South-Western.

Madeira, Laura. QuickBooks 2008 Solutions Guide: For Business Owners & Accountants. 2007. (ENG., Illus.). 528p. per. 34.99 (978-0-7897-3711-3(6)) Que.

—QuickBooks 2010 Solutions Guide for Business Owners & Accountants. 2009. (ENG., Illus.). 528p. pap. 39.99 (978-0-7897-4322-0(1), Que Publishing) Pearson Education, Ltd. GBR. Dist: Pearson Education.

Madeira, Laura. QuickBooks 2012 in Depth. 2012. (In Depth Ser.). (ENG.). 960p. pap. 39.99 **(978-0-7897-4918-5(1))** Que.

Marmel, Elaine J. & Koers, Diane. Peachtree for Dummies. 3rd rev. ed. 2007. (ENG., Illus.). 432p. per. 24.99 (978-0-470-17988-8(0), For Dummies) Wiley, John & Sons, Inc.

Mazza, Jim & Chavez, Gary. Computerized Accounting with Peachtree 2007. 2008. (Illus.). x, 622p. (978-0-7638-3030-4(5)); (978-0-7638-3031-1(3)) Paradigm Publishing, Inc.

Mucha-Aydlott, Julie. I have QuickBooks, Now What? For the Self-Employed. 2007. 342p. per. 29.95 (978-0-9794124-0-0(4)) San Diego Business Accounting Solutions a Non CPA Firm.

Narayanan, Veeriah. Customizing Financial Accounting in SAP. 2011. (ENG., Illus.). 765p. 79.95 (978-1-59229-377-3(8), SAP PR.) Galileo Pr., Inc.

Needles, Belverd E. Principles of Accounting. 10th ed. 2007. (ENG.). (C). 33.95 (978-0-618-99066-5(6), 1027366) Cengage South-Western.

Nelson, Stephen L. QuickBooks 2011 All-in-One for Dummies. 2010. (ENG., Illus.). 624p. pap. 34.99 (978-0-470-64650-2(0), For Dummies) Wiley, John & Sons, Inc.

—QuickBooks 2011 for Dummies. 18th ed. 2010. (ENG., Illus.). 408p. pap. 24.99 (978-0-470-64649-6(7), For Dummies) Wiley, John & Sons, Inc.

Nelson, Stephen L. QuickBooks 2012 All-in-One for Dummies. 7th ed. 2011. (ENG.). 648p. pap. 34.99 **(978-1-118-09119-7(1)**, For Dummies) Wiley, John & Sons, Inc.

Ovigele, Paul. 100 Things You Should Know about Financial Accounting with SAP. 2011. (Illus.). 300p. 49.95 (978-1-59229-364-3(6), SAP PR.) Galileo Pr., Inc.

Owen, Glenn. Using Excel & Access for Accounting 2010 (with Student Data CD-ROM) 3rd ed. 2011. (ENG., Illus.). 384p. (C). pap. 97.95 (978-1-111-53267-3(2)) Cengage South-Western.

—Using Peachtree 2009: Comlete For Accounting. 3rd ed. 2008. (ENG.). 416p. (C). pap. 136.95 (978-0-324-66551-2(2)) Cengage South-Western.

—Using Peachtree Complete 2010 for Accounting. 4th ed. 2010. (ENG.). (C). pap. 125.95 (978-0-538-47428-3(9)) Cengage South-Western.

—Using Peachtree Complete 2011 for Accounting. 6th ed. 2012. (ENG.). 432p. (C). pap. 146.95 **(978-1-133-62728-9(5))** Cengage South-Western.

—Using Peachtree Complete 2011 for Accounting (with Data File & Accounting CD-ROM) 5th ed. 2011. (Accounting II Ser.). (ENG., Illus.). 448p. (C). pap. 136.95 (978-1-111-82240-8(9)) Cengage South-Western.

—Using Quickbooks Pro 2011 for Accounting. 10th ed. 2011. (Accounting II Ser.). (ENG., Illus.). 384p. (C). pap. 131.95 (978-1-111-82254-5(9)) Cengage South-Western.

Patel, Manish. Account Determination in SAP. 2nd ed. 2011. (ENG., Illus.). 268p. 84.95 (978-1-59229-392-7(4), SAP PR.) Galileo Pr., Inc.

Pearson Education Staff. Getting Started with Peachtree Complete 2009. 2009. (ENG.). 100p. (C). pap. 13.33 (978-0-13-611557-1(8), Prentice Hall) Prentice Hall PTR.

Perry, Gail. Excel 2007 Macros Made Easy. 2008. (ENG., Illus.). 208p. pap. 21.99 (978-0-07-159958-0(4), 0071599584) McGraw-Hill Osborne.

—QuickBooks X on Demand. 2006. (On Demand Ser.). (ENG., Illus.). 448p. pap. 39.99 (978-0-7897-3632-1(2)) Que.

Pierce, Pamela. Microsoft Office Accounting Express 2007 Starter Kit. 2007. (Starter Kit Ser.). (ENG., Illus.). 432p. pap. 34.99 (978-0-7897-3685-7(3)) Que.

Purbhoo, M. Using Simply Accounting by Sage 2007, Trade Version. 2007. (ENG., Illus.). xiii, 799p. (C). spiral bd. (978-0-321-49510-5(1)) Pearson Education Canada.

QuickBooks 2007 - Level 1: Nh84745s. 2007. spiral bd. (978-1-4246-0533-0(4)) Element K Content LLC.

QuickBooks 2007 - Level 2: Nh84746s. 2007. spiral bd. (978-1-4246-0535-4(0)) Element K Content LLC.

QuickBooks Consultant's Reference Guide - Version 2007 (CD ROM Only) 2007. cd-rom 89.95 (978-1-932487-98-5(0)) Sleeter Group, Inc., The.

QuickBooks Consultant's Reference Guide - Version 2007 (Printed Book) 2007. per. 89.95 (978-1-932487-99-2(9)) Sleeter Group, Inc., The.

Reis, Vanda. Actual Costing with the SAP Material Ledger. 2011. (Illus.). 504p. 79.95 (978-1-59229-378-0(6), SAP PR.) Galileo Pr., Inc.

Romney, Marshall B. & Steinbart, Paul John. Accounting Information Systems. 11th ed. 2008. (ENG., Illus.). 832p. (C). 233.33 (978-0-13-601518-5(2), Prentice Hall) Prentice Hall PTR.

Sage Software. Peachtree Complete Accounting 2011 CD. 2011. (C). cd-rom 28.00 **(978-0-13-285820-5(7)**, Prentice Hall) Prentice Hall PTR.

Schneider, Thomas. SAP Performance Optimization Guide. 6th ed. 2010.Tr. of SAP(r)-Performanceoptimierung. (Illus.). 789p. 79.95 (978-1-59229-368-1(9), SAP PR.) Galileo Pr., Inc.

Sharma, Shivesh. Maximizing the SAP General Ledger. 2009. (Illus.). 500p. 79.95 (978-1-59229-306-3(9), SAP PR.) Galileo Pr., Inc.

Sisfontes-Monge, Marco. Controlling-Profitability Analysis with SAP. 2nd ed. 2012. (ENG., Illus.). 560p. 79.95 (978-1-59229-386-5(7), SAP PR.) Galileo Pr., Inc.

Sopracolle, Vincenzo. Financial Accounting with SAP. 2010. (Illus.). 650p. 69.95 (978-1-59229-313-1(1), SAP PR.) Galileo Pr., Inc.

The Sleeter Group, S. S. leeter, reader. QuickBooks Point of Sale - Best Practices for Success (Version 6) 2007. spiral bd. 79.95 (978-1-932487-94-7(8)) Sleeter Group, Inc., The.

Theobald, Paul. Transitioning to IFRS in SAP ERP Fincancials. 2009. (Illus.). 209p. 79.95 (978-1-59229-319-3(0), SAP PR.) Galileo Pr., Inc.

Tredennick, John C. The Lawyer's Guide to Microsoft Excel 2007. 2009. (ENG.). 250p. pap. 69.95 incl. cd-rom (978-1-60442-209-2(2)) American Bar Assn.

Ulmer, Donna. Computer Accounting with QuickBooks Pro 2010. 12th ed. 2010. 704p. spiral bd. 116.25 (978-0-07-352715-4(7), McGraw-Hill/Irwin) McGraw-Hill Higher Education.

van Ortega, Eleazar. Maximizing Cash Management with SAP ERP Financials. 2010. (Illus.). 460p. 79.95 (978-1-59229-324-7(7), SAP PR.) Galileo Pr., Inc.

Weygandt, Jerry J., et al. Accounting Principles: Peachtree Complete Accounting. 9th ed. 2010. (ENG.). 432p. (C). pap., wbk. ed. 55.95 (978-0-470-38667-5(3), Wiley) Wiley, John & Sons, Inc.

—Financial Accounting. annuals 6th ed. 2008. (ENG.). (C). 55.95 (978-0-470-39688-9(1), Wiley) Wiley, John & Sons, Inc.

—Financial Accounting: Excel Working Papers. 6th ed. 2008. (ENG.). (C). 56.95 (978-0-470-24521-7(2), Wiley) Wiley, John & Sons, Inc.

—General Ledger Software to accompany Accounting Principles. 8th ed. 2009. (ENG., Illus.). (C). 37.95 (978-0-470-38670-5(3), Wiley) Wiley, John & Sons, Inc.

Yacht, Carol. Carol Yacht's General Ledger & Peachtree Complete Software on CD-ROM t/a Financial & Managerial Accounting. 14th ed. 2007. (ENG.). (C). cd-rom 76.33 (978-0-07-326812-5(7), 0073268127, McGraw-Hill/Irwin) McGraw-Hill Higher Education.

—Computer Accounting with Peachtree by Sa Ge Complete Accounting 2012 Cd. 16th ed. 2012. (ENG.). (C). pap. 146.33 incl. audio compact disk **(978-0-07-763402-5(0)**, 0077634020, McGraw-Hill/Irwin) McGraw-Hill Higher Education.

Yacht, Carol. Computer Accounting with Peachtree Complete 2008 for Microsoft Windows, Release 15. 12th ed. 2008. (Illus.). 736p. spiral bd. 129.06 incl. cd-rom (978-0-07-726181-8(X), 9780077261818, McGraw-Hill/Irwin) McGraw-Hill Higher Education.

Yacht, Carol & Crosson, Susan. Computer Accounting Essentials Using QuickBooks. 224p. 4th ed. 2008. (C). pap. 63.44 (978-0-07-337938-8(7), 9780073379388) 5th ed. 2010. (Illus.). pap. 69.69 (978-0-07-811076-4(9)) McGraw-Hill Higher Education. (McGraw-Hill/Irwin).

—Computer Accounting Essentials Using Quickbooks Pro 2012 with CD. 6th ed. 2012. (ENG.). (C). spiral bd. 123.66 incl. cd-rom **(978-0-07-763686-9(4)**, 0077636864, McGraw-Hill/Irwin) McGraw-Hill Higher Education.

—Computer Accounting Essentials with Microsoft Office Accounting 2010. 2nd ed. 2010. 320p. pap. 50.63 (978-0-07-813661-0(X), McGraw-Hill/Irwin) McGraw-Hill Higher Education.

—Computer Accounting Essentials with QuickBooks Pro 2010. 5th ed. 2010. (ENG.). (C). pap., pap. 89.00 incl. cd-rom (978-0-07-740895-4(0), 0077408950, McGraw-Hill/Irwin) McGraw-Hill Higher Education.

—Computer Accounting Using Microsoft Small Business Accounting. 2007. 512p. (C). 101.56 (978-0-07-312972-3(0), 9780073129723, McGraw-Hill/Irwin) McGraw-Hill Higher Education.

—Computer Accounting with Microsoft Office Accounting 2010. 2nd ed. 2010. 512p. spiral bd. 121.56 (978-0-07-813665-8(2), McGraw-Hill/Irwin) McGraw-Hill Higher Education.

Yacht, Carol & Crosson, Susan V. Computer Accounting Essentials with Microsoft Office Accounting 2007. 2007. (ENG.). (C). pap. 63.33 (978-0-07-723374-7(3), 0077233743, McGraw-Hill/Irwin) McGraw-Hill Higher Education.

Yacht, Carol & Peachtree Software. Computer Accounting with Peachtree by Sage Complete Accounting 2011. 15th ed. 2011. (ENG.). (C). spiral bd. 160.67 incl. cd-rom (978-0-07-750503-5(4), 0077505034, McGraw-Hill/Irwin) McGraw-Hill Higher Education.

Yacht, Carol & Peachtree Software Staff. Computer Accounting with Peachtree COMPL 2009, Release 16. 0. 2009. 704p. pap. 95.00 (978-0-07-337951-7(4)) McGraw-Hill Professional Publishing.

—Computer Accounting with Peachtree Complete 2007, Release 14. 0. 11th rev. ed. 2008. 704p. spiral bd. (978-0-07-352662-9(7)) McGraw-Hill Cos., The.

—Computer Accounting with Peachtree Complete 2010, Release 17. 0. 14th ed. 2010. (Illus.). 704p. spiral bd. 127.50 (978-0-07-352714-7(9), McGraw-Hill/Irwin) McGraw-Hill Higher Education.

ACCOUNTING—DATA PROCESSING

Alton, William. Cloud Accounting. 2011. (ENG.). 159p. 19.95 **(978-0-9771659-8-8(1))** Smyth Barnabas Publishing.

Alsmadi, Izzat. Building a Gui Test Automation Framework Using the Data Model. 2008. 168p. pap. (978-3-639-04347-1(2)) VDM Verlag Dr. Mueller e.K.

Arif, Naeem & Tauseef, Sheikh. Integrating SAP ERP Financials: Configuration & Design. 2010. (Illus.). 394p. 79.95 (978-1-59229-300-1(X), SAP PR.) Galileo Pr., Inc.

—SAP ERP Financials: Configuration & Design. 2nd ed. 2011. (Illus.). 664p. 79.95 (978-1-59229-393-3(X), SAP PR.) Galileo Pr., Inc.

Bagranoff, Simkin and Str. Core Concepts of Accounting Information. 2006. pap. 13.95 (978-1-4288-1151-5(6)) Cram101 Inc.

Bauer, Eric & Siebert, Jörg. The SAP General Ledger. 2nd ed. 2010. (Illus.). 450p. 79.95 (978-1-59229-350-6(6), SAP PR.) Galileo Pr., Inc.

Bodnar, George H. & Hopwood, William S. Accounting Information Systems. (ENG., Illus.). 544p. (C). 10th ed. 2009. pap. 173.33 (978-0-13-609712-9(X)) 11th rev. ed. 2012. pap. 173.33 **(978-0-13-287193-8(9))** Prentice Hall PTR. (Prentice Hall).

Brechner, Robert A. Contemporary Mathematics for Business & Consumers. 5th ed. 2008. (ENG., Illus.). 880p. (C). pap. 209.95 (978-0-324-56816-5(9)) Cengage South-Western.

Bride, Mac. Get Started in Sage 50. 2010. (Teach Yourself Ser.). (ENG., Illus.). 224p. pap. 19.95 (978-1-4441-0066-2(1), Hodder & Stoughton) Hodder General Publishing Div. GBR. Dist: Independent Pubs. Group.

Brunsdon, Terri E. Learning Peachtree Complete Accounting 2009. 3rd ed. 2009. (ENG., Illus.). 864p. (C). pap. 146.67 (978-0-13-611603-5(5), Prentice Hall) Prentice Hall PTR.

Brunsdon, Terri J., et al. Introduction to Microsoft Dynamics GP 10.0: Focus on Internal Controls. 2nd ed. 2009. (ENG.). 600p. (C). pap. 77.33 (978-0-13-609804-1(5), Prentice Hall) Prentice Hall PTR.

Cameron, Melanie. Oracle Self-Service Applications. 2010. (Osborne ORACLE Press Ser.). (ENG., Illus.). 320p. pap. 39.99 (978-0-07-171330-6(1), 0071713301) McGraw-Hill Osborne.

Carlberg, Conrad. Excel for Accountants. 2nd ed. 2011. (ENG.). 300p. pap. 36.95 (978-1-932925-26-5(0)) CPA911 Publishing.

Cram101 Textbook Reviews. Outlines & Highlights for Accounting Information Systems by James a Hall. 2011. 64p. pap. 27.95 **(978-1-61905-568-1(6))** Cram101 Inc.

Cram101 Textbook Reviews. Outlines & Highlights for Core Concepts of Accounting Information System by Bagranoff, Isbn: 9780470045596. 2010. 162p. pap. 29.95 (978-1-61654-366-2(3)) Cram101 Inc.

Cram101 Textbook Reviews & Cram101 Textbook Reviews. Outlines & Highlights for Accounting Information Systems by Cynthia D Heagy. 2011. 144p. pap. 28.95 **(978-1-61830-429-2(1))** Cram101 Inc.

Cram101 Textbook Reviews Staff. Outlines & Highlights for Accounting Information Systems by Gelinas & Dull, Isbn: 9780324663808. 2009. 56p. pap. 26.95 (978-1-4288-8462-5(9)) Cram101 Inc.

—Outlines & Highlights for Accounting Information Systems by Marshall B Romney, Isbn: 9780131475915. 2009. 86p. pap. 27.95 (978-1-4288-2021-0(3)) Cram101 Inc.

—Outlines & Highlights for Accounting Information Systems by Marshall B Romney, Isbn: 9780136015185. 2009. 56p. pap. 26.95 (978-1-4288-8911-8(6)) Cram101 Inc.

—Outlines & Highlights for Corporate Accounting Information Systems by Tony Boczko, Isbn: 9780273684879. 2009. 166p. pap. 29.95 (978-1-4288-1943-6(6)) Cram101 Inc.

—Outlines & Highlights for Integrated Accounting for Windows by Dale Klooster, Isbn: 9780324664850. 2009. 58p. pap. 26.95 (978-1-4288-2327-3(1)) Cram101 Inc.

FASB Staff. 2008 FARS Network. 2008. (C). cd-rom 2827.95 (978-0-470-39695-7(4), Wiley) Wiley, John & Sons, Inc.

Freedman, Harvey C. Simply Accounting: Service Business, Version 8. (978-1-55232-083-9(9)) Norbry Publishing Ltd.

Gelinas, Ulric J. (Ulric J. Gelinas), et al. Accounting Information Systems. 9th ed. 2011. (ENG.). 744p. (C). 260.95 (978-0-538-46931-9(5)) Cengage South-Western.

Gilert, Gillian. Sage 50 Accounts 2012 in Easy Steps. 2012. (In Easy Steps Ser.). (ENG., Illus.). 192p. pap. 14.99 **(978-1-84078-530-2(6))** Computer Step GBR. Dist: Perseus-PGW.

Gottlieb, Isaac. Next Generation Excel: Modeling in Excel for Analysts & MBAs. 2009. (Wiley Finance Ser.: 623). (ENG., Illus.). 250p. 115.00 *(978-0-470-82473-3(5)*, Wiley) Wiley, John & Sons, Inc.

Grabski, Severin, et al. Management Accounting in Enterprise Resource Planning Systems. 2009. (ENG., Illus.). 176p. pap. 50.95 *(978-1-85617-679-8(7)*, CIMA Publishing) Elsevier Science & Technology Bks.

Hall, James A. Accounting Information Systems. 7th ed. 2010. (ENG.). 840p. (C). 249.95 *(978-1-4390-7857-0(2))* Cengage South-Western.

Heagy, Cynthia D. & Lehmann, Constance M. Accounting Information Systems: A Practitioner Emphasis. 7th ed. 2010. (ENG., Illus.). 544p. (C). pap. 141.95 *(978-1-111-21951-2(6))* CENGAGE Learning Custom Publishing.

Heagy, Cynthia Donnell, et al. Accounting Information Systems: A Practitioner Emphasis. 6th ed. 2008. (Illus.). xix, 504p. pap. *(978-1-4266-2883-2(8))* CENGAGE Learning Custom Publishing.

Horngren, Charles T. Runners Corporation PT Lab Manual. 7th ed. 2007. (ENG.). 120p. (C). pap. 46.67 *(978-0-13-243998-5(0))* Pearson Education Canada CAN. Dist: Pearson Education.

Howlett, Lloyd S., et al. Guide to Installing Microcomputer Accounting Systems, 2 vols. Incl. Vol. 1. 145.00 *(978-0-7646-0325-9(6))*; Vol. 2. 145.00 *(978-0-7646-0326-6(4))*; 1997. Set ring bd. 140.00 *(978-0-7646-0324-2(8))* Practitioners Publishing Co.

Hurt, Robert. Accounting Information Systems. (ENG., Illus.). (C). 2007. 368p. 158.00 *(978-0-07-319555-1(3)*, 0073195553) 2nd ed. 2009. 448p. 158.00 *(978-0-07-811105-1(6)*, 0078111056) McGraw-Hill Higher Education. (McGraw-Hill/Irwin).

Hurt, Robert L. Accounting Information Systems: Basic Concepts & Current Issues. 3rd ed. 2012. (ENG., Illus.). 368p. (C). 158.00 ***(978-0-07-802533-4(8)***, 0078025338) McGraw-Hill Cos., The.

IDEA & Mueller, John Paul. Mastering IDEAScript: The Definitive Guide. 2011. (ENG., Illus.). 504p. pap. 195.00 *(978-1-118-00448-7(5)*, Wiley) Wiley, John & Sons, Inc.

Jumbe, Rehema. Information & Communication Technology. 2011. 64p. pap. ***(978-3-8433-9262-4(5))*** Lambert Academic Publishing.

Kay, Donna. Computer Accounting with Quickbooks 2012 & Student CD. 14th ed. 2012. (ENG.). (C). spiral bd. 146.00 incl. cd-rom, cd-rom ***(978-0-07-762453-8(X)***, 007762453X, McGraw-Hill/Irwin) McGraw-Hill Higher Education.

Kholeif, Ahmed, et al. Enterprise Resource Planning: Implementation & Management Accounting Change in a Transitional Country. 2008. (ENG., Illus.). 320p. 105.00 *(978-0-230-51601-4(7))* Palgrave Macmillan.

Kieso, Donald E. Windows Vista Rockford GLS Practice Package. 12th ed. 2008. (C). pap. 56.95 incl. cd-rom *(978-0-470-40474-4(4)*, Wiley) Wiley, John & Sons, Inc.

Kieso, Donald E., et al. Intermediate Accounting: Excel. 14th ed. 2011. (ENG.). (C). wbk. ed. 66.95 *(978-1-118-01452-3(9)*, Wiley) Wiley, John & Sons, Inc.

King, David. International Journal of Accounting Information Science & Leadership (Ijaisl) 2008. pap. 75.00 *(978-0-9800418-8-0(0))* Intellectbase International Consortium.

King, David, ed. International Journal of Accounting Information Science & Leadership. 2008. 104p. pap. 55.00 *(978-0-9800418-4-2(8))* Intellectbase International Consortium.

Klooster, Dale & Allen, Warren. Integrated Accounting for Windows. 7th ed. 2010. (ENG.). (C). 281.95 *(978-0-538-45144-4(0))*; 592p. pap. 131.95 *(978-0-538-74798-1(6))* Cengage South-Western.

—Integrated Accounting for Windows (with Integrated Accounting Software CD-ROM) 7th ed. 2010. (ENG.). 592p. (C). pap. 184.95 *(978-0-538-74797-4(8))* Cengage South-Western.

Korolev, Sergey. ABAP Development for SAP ERP Financials: Custom Enhancements. 2011. (Illus.). 240p. 84.95 *(978-1-59229-370-4(0)*, SAP PR.) Galileo Pr., Inc.

Liley, Christopher & Duncan, David. Microsoft Dynamics GP 2010 Reporting. 2011. 333p. pap. ***(978-1-84968-218-3(6))*** Packt Publishing, Ltd.

Marchetti, Anne M. Sarbanes-Oxley Ongoing Compliance Guide: Key Processes & Summary Checklists. 2007. (ENG., Illus.). 96p. pap. 35.00 *(978-0-471-74686-7(X)*, Wiley) Wiley, John & Sons, Inc.

Marshall, Peter. Computerised Book-Keeping: An Accredited Textbook of the Institute of Certified Bookkeepers. 2010. (ENG., Illus.). 375p. pap. 34.00 *(978-1-84528-397-1(X))* How To Books GBR. Dist: Parkwest Pubns., Inc.

Narayanan, Veeriah. Customizing Financial Accounting in SAP. 2011. (ENG., Illus.). 765p. 79.95 *(978-1-59229-377-3(8)*, SAP PR.) Galileo Pr., Inc.

Needles, Belverd E. & Powers, Marian. Financial Accounting - K & a General Ledger Software. 11th ed. 2012. (ENG.). (C). 40.95 *(978-1-111-52880-5(2))* Cengage South-Western.

—Financial Accounting - Peachtree. 11th ed. 2012. (ENG.). (C). 15.95 *(978-1-111-52881-2(0))* Cengage South-Western.

Needles, Belverd E. (Belverd E. Needles) & Powers, Marian. K & A General Ledger Software, Network Version for Needles/Powers' Financial Accounting, 11th. 11th ed. 2011. (C). 686.95 *(978-1-111-52879-9(9))* Cengage South-Western.

Nehmer. Algebraic Models for Accounting Systems. 2010. 256p. 65.00 *(978-981-4287-11-1(3))* World Scientific Publishing Co., Inc.

Norman, Carolyn Strand, et al. Core Concepts of Accounting Information Systems. Moscove, Stephen A., ed. (ENG., Illus.). (C). 10th rev. ed. 2007. 528p. per. 143.95 *(978-0-470-04559-6(0))* 11th ed. 2009. 544p. pap. 143.95 *(978-0-470-50702-5(0))* Wiley, John & Sons, Inc. (Wiley).

Ovigele, Paul. 100 Things You Should Know about Financial Accounting with SAP. 2011. (Illus.). 300p. 49.95 *(978-1-59229-364-3(6)*, SAP PR.) Galileo Pr., Inc.

Owen, Glenn. Using Quickbooks Pro 2008 for Accounting. 7th ed. 2008. (ENG.). 384p. (C). pap. 131.95 *(978-0-324-56081-7(8))* Cengage South-Western.

—Using Quickbooks Pro 2011 for Accounting. 10th ed. 2011. (Accounting II Ser.). (ENG., Illus.). 384p. (C). pap. 131.95 *(978-1-111-82254-5(9))* Cengage South-Western.

Patel, Manish. Account Determination in SAP. 2nd ed. 2011. (ENG., Illus.). 268p. 84.95 *(978-1-59229-382-7(4)*, SAP PR.) Galileo Pr., Inc.

Peachtree Software Staff & Sage Software Staff. CD Peachtree Complete 2009. 2009. (ENG.). (C). cd-rom 28.00 *(978-0-13-611485-7(7)*, Prentice Hall) Prentice Hall PTR.

Perry, James & Newmark, Richard. Building Accounting Systems Using Access 2010. 8th ed. 2011. (ENG.). 672p. (C). pap. 161.95 *(978-1-111-53099-0(8))* Cengage South-Western.

Perry, James T., et al. Building Accounting Systems Using Access 2007. 7th ed. 2010. (ENG.). 624p. (C). pap. 161.95 *(978-0-324-66527-7(X))* Cengage South-Western.

Reeve, James, et al. Accounting Using Excel for Success. 2nd ed. 2011. (Managerial Accounting Ser.). (ENG.). 1368p. (C). 244.95 *(978-1-111-53521-6(3))* Cengage South-Western.

—Financial & Managerial Accounting Using Excel for Success (with Accounting CourseMate with eBook Printed Access Card) 2011. (ENG.). 1424p. (C). 212.95 *(978-1-111-53522-3(1))* Cengage South-Western.

Romney, Marshall B. & Steinbart, Paul John. Accounting Information Systems. (ENG., (C). 11th ed. 2008. (Illus.). 832p. 233.33 *(978-0-13-601518-5(2))* 12th ed. 2011. 720p. 233.33 *(978-0-13-255262-2(0))* Prentice Hall PTR. (Prentice Hall).

Rosa, James & Villani, Kathleen. Integrated Accounting: Using Simply Accounting for Windows Version 3.0. 464p. (C). pap. 79.96 *(978-0-395-88389-1(X))* CENGAGE Learning.

Sharma, Shivesh. Maximizing the SAP General Ledger. 2009. (Illus.). 500p. 79.95 *(978-1-59229-306-3(9)*, SAP PR.) Galileo Pr., Inc.

Silverstein, Sam. No More Excuses: The Five Accountabilities for Personal & Organizational Growth. 2010. (ENG., Illus.). 182p. 24.95 *(978-0-470-53192-1(4)*, Wiley) Wiley, John & Sons, Inc.

Simkin, Mark G. & Norman, Carolyn A. Strand. Core Concepts of Accounting Information Systems. 12th ed. 2011. (ENG.). 532p. (C). pap. 137.95 ***(978-1-118-02230-6(0)***, Wiley) Wiley, John & Sons, Inc.

Smith, Gaylord N. Excel Applications for Accounting Principles. 4th ed. 2011. (ENG.). 208p. (C). pap. 106.95 *(978-1-111-58156-5(8))* Cengage South-Western.

Sopracolle, Vincenzo. Financial Accounting with SAP. 2010. (Illus.). 650p. 69.95 *(978-1-59229-313-1(1)*, SAP PR.) Galileo Pr., Inc.

Sullivan, Richard J. Risk Management & Nonbank Participation in the U. S. Retail Payments System: A Reprint from the Federal Reserve Bank of Kansas City Economic Review. 2007. (Illus.). 35p. (C). pap. 20.00 *(978-1-4223-1743-3(9))* DIANE Publishing Co.

Turner, Leslie & Weickgenannt, Andrea. Accounting Information Systems: Controls & Processes, 2 vols. 11th ed. 2008. (ENG., Illus.). 672p. (C). 178.95 *(978-0-471-47951-2(9)*, Wiley) Wiley, John & Sons, Inc.

Uhr, Wolfgang, et al. Retail Information Systems Based on SAP Products. 2010. (SAP Excellence Ser.). (Illus.). xii, 246p. pap. 109.00 *(978-3-642-08654-0(3)*, 3642086543) Springer.

Ulmer, Donna. Computer Accounting with QuickBooks Pro 2007. 9th ed. 2007. 712p. spiral bd. 99.38 *(978-0-07-352683-6(5)*, 9780073526836, McGraw-Hill/Irwin) McGraw-Hill Higher Education.

Ulmer, Donna, et al. Accounting Information Systems: The Crossroads of Accounting & IT. 2011. (ENG., Illus.). 496p. (C). 206.67 *(978-0-13-213252-7(4)*, Prentice Hall) Prentice Hall PTR.

Vaassen, Eddy, et al. Accounting Information Systems & Internal Control. 2nd ed. 2009. (ENG., Illus.). 396p. pap. 77.95 *(978-0-470-75395-8(1)*, Wiley) Wiley, John & Sons, Inc.

Vanderbeck, Edward J. Klooster & Allen Gnrl Ldgr Sftwre Princ Cost Accounting, 14e. 14th ed. 2007. (ENG.). (C). 48.95 *(978-0-324-65521-6(5))* Cengage South-Western.

Warren, Carl S., et al. Accounting: Using Microsoft(r) Accounting Pro & Excel(r). 2010. (ENG.). 1312p. (C). 209.95 *(978-0-324-59656-4(1))* Cengage South-Western.

Weygandt. Financial & Managerial Accounting. 2011. (ENG.). (C). 51.95 ***(978-1-118-28564-0(6)***, Wiley) Wiley, John & Sons, Inc.

—General Ledger Software T/a for Weygandt Financial & Managerial Accounting. 2011. (ENG.). (C). 32.95 ***(978-1-118-28563-3(8)***, Wiley) Wiley, John & Sons, Inc.

Weygandt, Jerry J., et al. Financial Accounting, General Ledger Software CD. 8th ed. 2011. (ENG.). (C). cd-rom 28.95 ***(978-1-118-10286-2(X)***, Wiley) Wiley, John & Sons, Inc.

—General Ledger Software to Accompany Accounting Principles. 10th ed. 2011. (ENG., Illus.). (C). 21.95 ***(978-0-470-93858-4(7)***, Wiley) Wiley, John & Sons, Inc.

Wittenberg, David, ed. Paperless Accounts Payable: The AP Department's Complete Guide to Electronic Invoicing. 2007. (Illus.). 174p. pap. 459.00 *(978-1-58673-250-9(1))* Institute of Management & Administration, IOMA.

Yacht, Carol. Computer Accounting with Peachtree by Sage Complete Accounting 2010. 14th ed. 2010. (ENG., Illus.). xix, 813p. (C). pap., spiral bd. 158.67 incl. cd-rom *(978-0-07-740874-9(8)*, 007740874B, McGraw-Hill/Irwin) McGraw-Hill Higher Education.

—Computer Accounting with Peachtree Complete 2008 for Microsoft Windows, Release 15. 12th ed. 2008. (Illus.). 736p. spiral bd. 129.06 incl. cd-rom *(978-0-07-726181-8(X)*, 9780077261818, McGraw-Hill/Irwin) McGraw-Hill Higher Education.

Yacht, Carol & Crosson, Susan. Computer Accounting Essentials Using QuickBooks. 224p. 4th ed. 2008. (C). pap. 63.44 *(978-0-07-337938-8(7)*, 9780073379388) 5th ed. 2010. (Illus.). pap. 69.69 *(978-0-07-811076-4(9))* McGraw-Hill Higher Education. (McGraw-Hill/Irwin).

—Computer Accounting with Microsoft Office Accounting 2007 w/ CD. 2007. (ENG.). (C). spiral bd. 151.00 *(978-0-07-333796-8(X)*, 007333796X, McGraw-Hill/Irwin) McGraw-Hill Higher Education.

ACCOUNTING—DICTIONARIES

Carmichael, D. R., et al. Accountants' Handbook: Financial Accounting & General Topics. 12th ed. 2012. (ENG.). 944p. pap. 120.00 ***(978-1-118-17182-0(9)***, Wiley) Wiley, John & Sons, Inc.

Carmichael, D. R., et al. Accountants' Handbook 2009, 2 vols., Set. 11th rev. ed. 2007. (ENG.). 1944p. pap. 252.50 *(978-0-471-79041-9(9)*, Wiley) Wiley, John & Sons, Inc.

Clubb, Colin, ed. Accounting, 13 vols., Vol. 1. 2nd rev. ed. 2006. (Blackwell Encyclopaedia of Management Ser.: Vol. 1). (ENG., Illus.). 456p. 157.95 *(978-1-4051-1827-9(X)*, Wiley-Blackwell) Wiley, John & Sons, Inc.

Collin, S. M. H. & Russell, Jane. Dictionary of Accounting: Over 6,000 Terms Clearly Defined. 4th rev. ed. 2007. (ENG.). 256p. pap. 16.95 *(978-0-7136-8286-1(8))* A & C Black GBR. Dist: Macmillan.

Esposito, Marie-Claude. Dictionnaire de L'économie, de la Finance et de la Comptabilité (Anglais/Français et Français/Anglais) 5th ed. 2010. (FRE & ENG.). 554p. *(978-2-7178-5892-1(X))* Economica, Editions.

Ferraino, Cindy. The Complete Dictionary of Accounting & Bookkeeping Terms Explained Simply. 2010. (ENG.). 288p. pap. 24.95 *(978-1-60138-325-9(8))* Atlantic Publishing Co.

Garza Bores, Jaime. Diccionario Tecnico de Terminologia Comercial Cantable y Bancaria. (SPA.). 19.95 *(978-0-7859-0707-7(6)*, S-25235) French & European Pubns., Inc.

Gilbertson, Claudia B. & Lehman, Mark W. Accounting. 9th ed. 2008. (ENG.). 32p. (C). pap. 11.95 *(978-0-538-44745-4(1))* Cengage South-Western.

—Accounting: Multicolumn Journal. 9th ed. 2008. (ENG.). 32p. (C). pap. 11.95 *(978-0-538-44747-8(8))* Cengage South-Western.

Harrison, Ian. A-Z Accounting Handbook. 3rd ed. 2010. (Illus.). 288p. 22.99 *(978-0-340-99105-3(4))* Hodder Education GBR. Dist: Oxford Univ. Pr., Inc.

Law, Jonathan. A Dictionary of Accounting. 4th ed. 2010. (Oxford Paperback Reference Ser.). (ENG., Illus.). 448p. pap. 19.99 *(978-0-19-956305-0(5))* Oxford Univ. Pr., Inc.

Magoon, Linda M. Dictionary of Financial Formulas & Ratios. 2008. 200p. pap. 35.00 *(978-1-906403-03-4(1))* Lessons Professional Publishing GBR. Dist: Stylus Publishing, LLC.

Mooney, Kate. Dictionary of Essential Accounting Terms. 2008. (ENG.). 624p. pap. 21.99 *(978-1-57248-651-5(1)*, Sphinx Publishing) Sourcebooks, Inc.

Siegel CPA, Joel G. & Shim, Jae K. Dictionary of Accounting Terms. 5th rev. ed. 2010. (Barron's Business Dictionaries Ser.). (ENG., Illus.). 536p. pap. 14.99 *(978-0-7641-4310-6(7))* Barron's Educational Series, Inc.

Various Authors. Qfinance: The Dictionary of Accounting & Finance. 2011. (ENG.). 320p. pap. 25.00 *(978-1-84930-011-7(9))* Bloomsbury Publishing.

ACCOUNTING—EXAMINATIONS, QUESTIONS, ETC.

Here are entered collections of questions actually set in examinations. Problems for classroom use or private study are entered under Accounting—Problems, Exercises, etc.

Allan, Walter. CIMA Official Exam Practice Kit Fundamentals of Management Accounting: CIMA Certificate in Business Accounting, 2006 Syllabus. 3rd ed. 2010. (ENG., Illus.). 258p. (C). pap. 28.95 *(978-1-85617-778-8(5)*, CIMA Publishing) Elsevier Science & Technology Bks.

Balla, Donald. CLEP Financial Accounting. 2007. (CLEP Test Preparation Ser.). (ENG.). 416p. (C). pap. 27.95 *(978-0-7386-0313-1(9))*; pap. 34.95 *(978-0-7386-0314-8(7))* Research & Education Assn.

Balla, Donald. CLEP Financial Accounting with Online Practice Tests. 2012. (CLEP Test Preparation Ser.). (ENG.). 416p. pap. 34.95 ***(978-0-7386-1029-0(1))*** Research & Education Assn.

Berkun, S., et al. Wiley CPA Exam Review 2012: Regulation, 4 vols. 9th ed. 2011. (ENG.). 813p. pap. 65.00 ***(978-0-470-92393-1(8)***, Wiley) Wiley, John & Sons, Inc.

Billingsley, Randall S., et al, eds. Professional Exam Review Candidate Study Notes. 2009. (CFA Exam Review: Level 1 Ser.). (Illus.). 258p. pap. 141.95 *(978-0-324-78363-6(9)*, South-Western) Cengage South-Western.

Bisk, Nathan M. Auditing & Attestation. 40th ed. 2010. (Bisk Comprehensive CPA Review Ser.). pap. 49.95 *(978-1-57961-846-9(4))* Bisk Education, Inc.

—Bisk Comprehensive CPA Review: Business Environment & Concepts. 39th ed. 2009. (Bisk Comprehensive CPA Review Ser.). 608p. pap. 49.95 *(978-1-57961-736-3(0))* Bisk Education, Inc.

—Bisk Comprehensive CPA Review: Financial Accounting & Reporting. 39th ed. 2009. (Bisk Comprehensive CPA Review Ser.). 1088p. pap. 49.95 *(978-1-57961-733-2(6))* Bisk Education, Inc.

—Bisk Comprehensive CPA Review: Regulation. 39th ed. 2009. (Bisk Comprehensive CPA Review Ser.). pap. 49.95 *(978-1-57961-735-6(2))* Bisk Education, Inc.

—Bisk Comprehensive Exam Review: Auditing & Attestation. 39th ed. 2009. (Bisk Comprehensive CPA Review Ser.). 912p. pap. 49.95 *(978-1-57961-734-9(4))* Bisk Education, Inc.

—Bisk CPA Comprehensive Exam Review: Business Environment & Concepts. 38th ed. 2008. (Illus.). 576p. pap. 46.95 *(978-1-57961-681-6(X))* Bisk Education, Inc.

—Bisk CPA Comprehensive Exam Review: Financial Accounting & Reporting. 38th ed. 2008. (Illus.). 1056p. pap. 46.95 *(978-1-57961-678-6(X))* Bisk Education, Inc.

—Bisk CPA Comprehensive Exam Review: Regulation. 38th ed. 2008. (Illus.). 928p. pap. 46.95 *(978-1-57961-680-9(1))* Bisk Education, Inc.

—Business Environment & Concepts. 40th ed. 2010. (Bisk Comprehensive CPA Review Ser.). pap. 49.95 *(978-1-57961-848-3(0))* Bisk Education, Inc.

—Financial Accounting & Reporting. 40th ed. 2010. (Bisk Comprehensive CPA Review Ser.). pap. 49.95 *(978-1-57961-845-2(6))* Bisk Education, Inc.

Delaney, Patrick R. Wiley CPA Examination Review: Outlines & Study Guides, 2 vols. 39th ed. 2012. (ENG.). 1344p. pap. 59.95 ***(978-1-118-25449-3(X)***, Wiley) Wiley, John & Sons, Inc.

—Wiley CPA Examination Review Vol. 2: Problems & Solutions, 2 vols. 39th ed. 2012. (ENG.). 1392p. pap. 59.95 ***(978-1-118-25450-9(3)***, Wiley) Wiley, John & Sons, Inc.

Delaney, Patrick R. & Whittington, O. Ray. CPA Exam Review 2011, 4 vols., Set. 8th ed. 2010. (ENG.). pap. 220.00 *(978-0-470-55438-8(X)*, Wiley) Wiley, John & Sons, Inc.

—CPA Examination Review 2009-2010, 2 vols., Volumes 1 and 2. 3rd ed. 2010. (ENG.). pap. 119.90 *(978-0-470-55426-5(6)*, Wiley) Wiley, John & Sons, Inc.

—Wiley CPA Exam Review 2012 Test Bank: Auditing & Attestation. 17th ed. 2012. (ENG.). 105.00 ***(978-0-470-92385-6(7)***, Wiley) Wiley, John & Sons, Inc.

—Wiley CPA Exam Review 2012 Test Bank: Business Environment & Concepts. 17th ed. 2012. (ENG.). 105.00 ***(978-0-470-92386-3(5)***, Wiley) Wiley, John & Sons, Inc.

—Wiley CPA Exam Review 2012 Test Bank Set: Over 4,300 Questions & 164 Simulations!, 4 vols. 17th ed. 2012. (ENG.). 299.00 ***(978-0-470-92389-4(X)***, Wiley) Wiley, John & Sons, Inc.

—Wiley Cpa Exam Review 2012 Test Bank - Regulation. 17th ed. 2012. (ENG.). 105.00 ***(978-0-470-92388-7(1)***, Wiley) Wiley, John & Sons, Inc.

—Wiley CPA Exam Review 2012 Test Banks: Financial Accounting & Reporting. 17th ed. 2012. (ENG.). 105.00 ***(978-0-470-92387-0(3)***, Wiley) Wiley, John & Sons, Inc.

—Wiley Cpa Examination Review, 2 vols., Set. 3rd ed. 2011. (ENG.). pap. 119.90 *(978-0-470-92382-5(2)*, Wiley) Wiley, John & Sons, Inc.

—Wiley CPA Examination Review 2010-2011, 2 vols., Volume 1. 3rd ed. 2011. (ENG.). 1344p. pap., pupil's gde. ed. 59.95 *(978-0-470-92383-2(0)*, Wiley) Wiley, John & Sons, Inc.

—Wiley CPA Examination Review 2011-2012: Problems & Solutions, Volume 2. 3rd ed. 2011. (ENG.). 1383p. pap. 59.95 *(978-0-470-92384-9(9)*, Wiley) Wiley, John & Sons, Inc.

Dickinson, K. C. & Sanders, F. A. Selected Questions in Accounting. 657p. *(978-0-7021-2622-2(5))* Juta & Co., Ltd.

Dobrynskaya, Victoria. Financial Accounting: A Key to Your Success in the Exam. 2011. 112p. pap. ***(978-3-8433-8971-6(3))*** Lambert Academic Publishing.

Epstein, Barry J. & Saafir, Nadira M. GAAP: Practical Implementation Guide. 2nd ed. 2010. (ENG.). 368p. pap., wbk. ed. 95.00 *(978-0-470-59906-8(5)*, Wiley) Wiley, John & Sons, Inc.

The ExamMatrix CPA Exam Review - Financial Accounting & Reporting. 2007. per. 995.00 net. *(978-1-933366-08-1(7))* ExamMatrix.

The ExamMatrix CPA Exam Review - Regulation. 2007. per. 995.00 net. *(978-1-933366-06-7(0))* ExamMatrix.

Feller, Anita L. Mastering Accounting Research for the CPA Exam. 2nd ed. 2008. (ENG., Illus.). 208p. pap. 39.95 *(978-0-470-29338-6(1)*, Wiley) Wiley, John & Sons, Inc.

Friel, H., et al. Wiley CPA Exam Review 2012: Financial Accounting & Reporting, 4 vols. 9th ed. 2011. (ENG.). 1054p. pap. 65.00 ***(978-0-470-92392-4(X)***, Wiley) Wiley, John & Sons, Inc.

Gmac. GMAT Business Ready, Accounting Module. 2011. (ENG.). 89.95 ***(978-1-118-11183-3(4)***, Wiley) Wiley, John & Sons, Inc.

Harris, David. CIMA: Pass First Time! 2nd ed. 2009. (ENG.). 160p. pap. 24.95 *(978-1-85617-798-6(X)*, CIMA Publishing) Elsevier Science & Technology Bks.

Hopkins, Debra R. & Hopkins. You Can Pass the CPA Exam: Get Motivated! 3rd ed. 2009. (ENG., Illus.). 243p. pap. 34.95 *(978-0-470-45002-4(9)*, Wiley) Wiley, John & Sons, Inc.

Joehnk, Michael D. CFA Advantage Premier: Candidate Study Notes, Print Exams, Online D&P, Video. 2008. (C). pap. 905.95 *(978-0-324-66089-0(8))* Cengage South-Western.

Joehnk, Michael D., et al, eds. CFA Exam Review Level 1, Volume 1: Candidate Study Notes. 2nd ed. 2009. (Illus.). 187p. pap. 141.95 *(978-0-324-78361-2(2))* Delmar Cengage Learning.

Joyce, Tim. Cambridge Checkpoints VCE Accounting Unit 3 2007. 2006. (Cambridge Checkpoints Ser.). pap. 16.00 *(978-0-521-69742-2(5))* Cambridge Univ. Pr.

—Cambridge Checkpoints VCE Accounting Unit 3 2009. 2008. (Cambridge Checkpoints Ser.). pap. 15.95 *(978-0-521-75940-3(4))* Cambridge Univ. Pr.

—Cambridge Checkpoints VCE Accounting Unit 4 2008. 2007. pap. 19.95 *(978-0-521-71578-2(4))* Cambridge Univ. Pr.

—Cambridge Checkpoints VCE Accounting Unit 4 2009. 2008. (Cambridge Checkpoints Ser.). pap. 15.95 *(978-0-521-75941-0(2))* Cambridge Univ. Pr.

Kaplan CPA Education Staff. CPA Exam: Quick Review Flash Cards Business Environments & Concepts. 2006. n/ap. 98.95 *(978-1-4195-9107-5(X))* Dearborn Financial Publishing.

—CPA Exam: Quick Review Flash Cards Financial Accounting & Reporting. 2006. n/ap. 98.95 *(978-1-4195-9108-2(8))* Dearborn Financial Publishing.

—CPA Exam: Quick Review Flash Cards Regulation. 2006. n/ap. 98.95 *(978-1-4195-9109-9(6))* Dearborn Financial Publishing.

—Kaplan CPA Exam Set: Quick Review Flash Cards, 4 Nos. 2006. n/ap. 145.00 *(978-1-4195-9145-7(2))* Dearborn Financial Publishing.

Kaplan CPA Review. CPA Exam Study Manual: Auditing & Attestation 2009/2010. 2009. (ENG.). 576p. pap. 49.95 **(978-1-4277-8869-6(3))** Kaplan Publishing.

—CPA Exam Study Manual: Business Environment & Concepts 2009/2010. 2009. (ENG.). 752p. pap. 49.95 **(978-1-4277-8861-0(8))** Kaplan Publishing.

—CPA Exam Study Manual: Financial Accounting & Reporting 2009/2010. 2009. (ENG.). 736p. pap. 49.95 *(978-1-4277-8863-4(4))* Kaplan Publishing.

—CPA Exam Study Manual: Regulation 2009/2010. 2009. (ENG.). 688p. pap. 49.95 *(978-1-4277-8865-8(0))* Kaplan Publishing.

Kieso, Donald E., et al. Rockford Practice Set to accompany Intermediate Accounting, Set. 13th ed. 2009. (ENG.). 144p. (C). pap. 61.95 *(978-0-470-38063-5(2),* Wiley) Wiley, John & Sons, Inc.

Mackenzie, Bruce, et al. Applying IFRS for SMEs. 2010. (ENG., Illus.). 484p. pap. 95.00 *(978-0-470-60337-6(2),* Wiley) Wiley, John & Sons, Inc.

McAnarney, Amy & The Tax Institute at H&R Block. Wiley Registered Tax Return Preparer Exam Review 2012. 2012. (ENG.). 552p. pap. 59.95 **(978-0-470-90561-6(1),** Wiley) Wiley, John & Sons, Inc.

McCaulay, Philip Martin. McCaulay's Cfa Level I Mock Exam. 2009. 98p. pap. 24.95 *(978-0-557-09945-0(5))* Lulu Enterprises Inc.

—McCaulay's CFA Level I Practice Exams Volume I of V. 2009. 364p. pap. 49.95 *(978-0-557-09122-5(5))* Lulu Enterprises Inc.

—McCaulay's CFA Level I Practice Exams Volume II of V. 2009. 364p. pap. 49.95 *(978-0-557-09176-8(4))* Lulu Enterprises Inc.

—McCaulay's CFA Level I Practice Exams Volume III of V. 2009. 364p. pap. 49.95 *(978-0-557-09168-1(8))* Lulu Enterprises Inc.

—McCaulay's CFA Level I Practice Exams Volume IV of V. 2009. 364p. pap. 49.95 *(978-0-557-09149-2(7))* Lulu Enterprises Inc.

—McCaulay's CFA Level I Practice Exams Volume V of V. 2009. 364p. pap. 49.95 *(978-0-557-09260-4(4))* Lulu Enterprises Inc.

—McCaulay's CFA Level I Sample Exam. 2009. 63p. pap. 19.95 *(978-0-557-09725-8(8))* Lulu Enterprises Inc.

Melamed, Leo, et al. Wiley CPA Exam Review 2012: Business Environment & Concepts, 4 vols. 9th ed. 2011. (ENG.). 432p. pap. 65.00 **(978-0-470-92391-7(1),** Wiley) Wiley, John & Sons, Inc.

Randall, Harold & Stephens-James, Lystra B. CAPE Accounting. 2007. (ENG.). 352p. pap. *(978-0-521-70116-7(3))* Cambridge Univ. Pr.

Rattiner, Jeffrey H. & Rattiner. CFP Certification Examination. 3rd ed. 2009. (ENG., Illus.). 456p. pap., stu. ed. 75.00 *(978-0-470-43628-8(X),* Wiley) Wiley, John & Sons, Inc.

Robinson, Scott, ed. VCE Accounting Assessment Handbook 2007¿2010. 2006. 40p. *(978-1-920992-93-4(6))* Victorian Government - Victorian Curriculum & Assessment Authority.

Rudman, Jack. Accounting II. (Regents External Degree Ser.: Vol. 2). (C). 49.95 *(978-0-8373-5652-5(0),* Passbooks) National Learning Corp.

—Accounting III. (Regents External Degree Ser.: Vol. 3). (C). 49.95 *(978-0-8373-5653-2(9),* Passbooks) National Learning Corp.

—Auditing. (ACT Proficiency Examination Program Ser.: Vol. 14). (C). 49.95 *(978-0-8373-5564-1(8)); (Dantes Subject Standardized Tests Ser.: Vol. 69).* 49.95 *(978-0-8373-6569-5(4))* National Learning Corp. (Passbooks).

—Certified Public Accountant Examination (CPA) (Admission Test Ser.: Vol. 71). 89.95 *(978-0-8373-5171-1(5))* National Learning Corp.

Shain, Daniel H., et al. Wiley CPA Exam Review 2012, 4 vols., Set. 9th ed. 2011. (ENG.). ix, 676p. pap. 260.00 **(978-0-470-92394-8(6),** Wiley) Wiley, John & Sons, Inc.

Shim, Jae K. Financial Reporting: A User's Perspective. 2009. 200p. pap. 55.00 *(978-1-906403-43-0(0))* Lessons Professional Publishing GBR. Dist: Stylus Publishing, LLC.

Simmons, Anthony & Hardy, Richard. Cambridge VCE Accounting Units 1&2 Workbook. 2007. (ENG.). pap., stu. ed. *(978-0-521-71973-5(9))* Cambridge Univ. Pr.

—Cambridge VCE Accounting Units 3&4 Workbook. 2007. pap., stu. ed. *(978-0-521-71974-2(7))* Cambridge Univ. Pr.

Smith, C, et al. Wiley CPA Exam Review 2012: Auditing & Attestation. 9th ed. 2011. (ENG.). 676p. pap. 65.00 **(978-0-470-92390-0(3),** Wiley) Wiley, John & Sons, Inc.

Stevens, Kevin. Business Environment & Concepts 2012. 7th ed. 2011. (ENG.). 179p. pap. 40.00 **(978-1-118-12132-0(5),** Wiley) Wiley, John & Sons, Inc.

—Focus Notes Regulation 2012. 7th ed. 2011. (ENG.). 264p. pap. 40.00 **(978-1-118-12134-4(1),** Wiley) Wiley, John & Sons, Inc.

Stevens, Kevin & Wiley, Ann. Financial Accounting & Reporting 2012. 7th ed. 2011. (ENG.). 336p. pap. 40.00 **(978-1-118-12133-7(3),** Wiley) Wiley, John & Sons, Inc.

Stevens, Kevin & Wiley Staff. Wiley CPA Exam Review - Focus Notes 2012, 4 vols., Set. 7th ed. 2011. (ENG.). 240p. pap. 160.00 **(978-1-118-12135-1(X),** Wiley) Wiley, John & Sons, Inc.

Tidrick, Donald. Auditing & Attestation - Supplemental Outlines. 2008. (ENG.). 244p. per. *(978-0-9746541-7-1(5),* Efficient Learning Systems, Inc.

Twyman, Daniel. Flashpoint CPA Review - Audit 2010. 2010. 66p. pap. 99.99 *(978-0-557-28343-9(4))* Lulu Enterprises Inc.

—Flashpoint CPA Review - Business Environment & Concepts 2010. 2010. 78p. pap. 99.99 *(978-0-557-28964-6(5,)* Lulu Enterprises Inc.

—Flashpoint CPA Review - Financial Accounting & Reporting 2010. 2010. 106p. pap. 99.99 *(978-0-557-30331-1(1,)* Lulu Enterprises Inc.

—Flashpoint CPA Review - Regulation 2010. 2010. 116p. pap. 99.99 *(978-0-557-32226-8(X))* Lulu Enterprises Inc.

Vessey, Jane. A-Plus Study Notes for 2011 Cfa Level I. 2011. 622p. pap. 99.95 **(978-1-59095-956-5(6))** TotalRecall Pubns., Inc.

—Examwise (r) Volume 1 for 2011 Cfa (r) Level I Certification the Candidates Question & Answer Workbook with Preliminary Reading Assignments for Charter. 2011. 544p. pap. 64.95 **(978-1-59095-960-2(4))** TotalRecall Pubns., Inc.

Wasser, Al & Kimble, Donna. Mastering the CPAT: A Comprehensive Guide. 2006. (ENG., Illus.). 176p. per. 79.95 *(978-1-4180-1229-8(7))* Delmar Cengage Learning.

Weygandt, Jerry J., et al. Accounting Principles, Vol. 2. 9th ed. 2009. (ENG.). 432p. (C). pap. 60.95 *(978-0-470-38661-3(4),* Wiley) Wiley, John & Sons, Inc.

—Problem Solving Survival Guide Vol. I, Chs. 1-12 to Accompany Accounting Principles Vol. 1, Vol. 1, Chs. 1-12. 9th ed. 2008. (ENG.). 408p. (C). pap. 66.95 *(978-0-470-38660-6(6),* Wiley) Wiley, John & Sons, Inc.

Whittington, O. Ray. Wiley CPA Exam Review Fast Track Study Guide. 4th ed. 2008. (ENG.). 384p. pap., stu. ed. 29.95 *(978-0-470-19609-0(2),* Wiley) Wiley, John & Sons, Inc.

Whittington, O. Ray & Hopkins, Debra R. Wiley CPA Exam: How to Master Simulations. 2nd ed. 2009. (ENG.). 166p. pap. 45.00 *(978-0-470-50537-3(0),* Wiley) Wiley, John & Sons, Inc.

Yaeger. CPA Reg MP3 Download 1. 2007. 20.00 *(978-0-470-22655-1(2),* Wiley) Wiley, John & Sons, Inc.

—CPA Reg MP3 Download 2. 2007. 20.00 *(978-0-470-22656-8(0),* Wiley) Wiley, John & Sons, Inc.

—CPA Reg MP3 Download 3. 2007. 20.00 *(978-0-470-22657-5(9),* Wiley) Wiley, John & Sons, Inc.

—CPA Reg MP3 Download 4. 2007. 20.00 *(978-0-470-22658-2(7),* Wiley) Wiley, John & Sons, Inc.

—CPA Reg MP3 Download 5. 2007. 20.00 *(978-0-470-22659-9(5),* Wiley) Wiley, John & Sons, Inc.

ACCOUNTING—FORMS

Swain, Bert L. CPA's Guide to Management Letter Comments. 2007. (CPA Guides). 314p. pap. 290.00 incl. cd-rom *(978-0-8080-9126-4(3))* Toolkit Media Group.

ACCOUNTING—HANDBOOKS, MANUALS, ETC.

Aicpa. AICPA Audit & Accounting Manual 2007. 2007. pap. 148.75 *(978-0-87051-708-2(2))* American Institute of Certified Public Accountants.

—Checklist Supplement & Illustrative Financial Statements for Real Estate Ventures. 2007. pap. 31.25 *(978-0-87051-703-7(1))* American Institute of Certified Public Accountants.

—Checklist Supplement & Illustrative Financial Statements for State & Local Government. 2007. pap. 48.75 *(978-0-87051-705-1(8))* American Institute of Certified Public Accountants.

—Checklists & Illustrative Financial Statements for Corporations. 2007. pap. 48.75 *(978-0-87051-702-0(3))* American Institute of Certified Public Accountants.

—Checklists & Illustrative Financial Statements for Not-for-Profit Organizations. 2007. pap. 48.75 *(978-0-87051-680-1(9))* American Institute of Certified Public Accountants.

Anis I. Milad, D. B. A. Financial Accounting Handbook. 2009. 96p. pap. 21.45 *(978-1-4389-7760-7(3))* AuthorHouse.

Atwood, E. Barrett, Sr., et al. Guide to Preparing Governmental Financial Statements, 2 vols. Incl. Vol. 1. 1997. ring bd. *(978-0-7646-0165-9(7));* Set pap. 156.00 *(978-0-7646-0184-2(9))* Practitioners Publishing Co.

Bragg, Steven M. The Vest Pocket Guide to GAAP. 3rd ed. 2010. (ENG., Illus.). 418p. pap. 34.95 *(978-0-470-76782-5(0),* Wiley) Wiley, John & Sons, Inc.

Carmichael, D. R., et al, eds. Special Industries & Special Topics, 2 vols., Volume 2. 11th rev. ed. 2007. (ENG., Illus.). 864p. pap. 126.50 *(978-0-471-79039-6(7),* Wiley) Wiley, John & Sons, Inc.

Carmichael, D. R., et al. Accountants' Handbook 2009, 2 vols., Set. 11th rev. ed. 2007. (ENG.). 1944p. pap. 252.50 *(978-0-471-79041-9(9),* Wiley) Wiley, John & Sons, Inc.

Dansby, Robert L., et al. College Accounting: Solutions Manual 1-29. 4th ed. 953p. 49.95 *(978-0-7638-0165-6(8))* EMC/Paradigm Publishing.

Delves, Donald P. CCH Accounting for Compensation Arrangements (2008) 2008th rev. ed. 2007. 368p. pap. 225.00 *(978-0-8080-9124-0(7))* Toolkit Media Group.

Easton, Peter D., et al. Solution Manual to Accompany Financial Accounting for MBAs, 3rd Edition. 2007. (C). per. 200.00 net. *(978-1-934319-07-9(4))* Cambridge Business Pubs.

—Solution Manual to Accompany Financial & Managerial Accounting for MBAs, 1st Edition. 2007. (C). per. 200.00 net. *(978-1-934319-12-3(0))* Cambridge Business Pubs.

—Student Solutions Manual to Accompany Financial & Managerial Accounting for MBAs, 1st Edition. 2007. (C). per. 25.00 net. *(978-1-934319-09-3(0))* Cambridge Business Pubs.

Eisen, Peter J. Accounting. 5th ed. 2007. (Barron's Business Review Ser.). (ENG., Illus.). 448p. per. 18.99 *(978-0-7641-3547-7(3))* Barron's Educational Series, Inc.

Graham, Lynford, et al, eds. Financial Accounting & General Topics, Vol. 1. 11th rev. ed. 2007. (ENG., Illus.). 1056p. pap. 126.50 *(978-0-471-79038-9(9),* Wiley) Wiley, John & Sons, Inc.

Griffith, J. Clifford, et al. Guide to Managing an Accounting Practice, 3 vols. Incl. Vol. 1. ring bd. 138.00 *(978-0-7646-0423-2(6)); Vol. 2. ring bd. 138.00 (978-0-7646-0424-9(4)); Vol. 3. ring bd. 138.00 (978-0-7646-0425-6(2));* 1998. Set pap. 138.00 *(978-0-7646-0422-5(8))* Practitioners Publishing Co.

—A Guide to Managing an Accounting Practice, 3 vols. Incl. Vol. 1. Guide to Managing an Accounting Practice. ring bd. *(978-0-7646-0127-9(X)); Vol. 2. ring bd. (978-0-7646-0128-6(8)); Vol. 3. ring bd. (978-0-7646-0129-3(6));* 1997. Set pap. 130.00 *(978-0-7646-0126-2(1))* Practitioners Publishing Co.

Guide to Divorce Engagements, 2 vols. Incl. Vol. 1. Great Beginnings. ring bd. 156.00 *(978-0-7646-0342-6(6)); Vol. 2. Great Beginnings. ring bd. 156.00 (978-0-7646-0343-3(4));* 1997. Set ring bd. 150.00 *(978-0-7646-0341-9(8))* Practitioners Publishing Co.

Harlow, Gwen. Simplified Accounts. 2007. 196p. pap. 25.50 *(978-1-84753-638-9(7))* Lulu Enterprises Inc.

Hopwood, Anthony G., et al, eds. Handbook of Management Accounting Research, 3 vols., 3. 2008. (Handbooks of Management Accounting Research Ser.: 3). (ENG., Illus.). 280p. 225.00 *(978-0-08-055450-1(4),* Elsevier Science) Elsevier Science & Technology Bks.

Horngren, Charles T. Accounting, Chapters 1-23. 8th ed. 2008. (ENG.). 384p. (C). pap., pupl's gde. ed. 46.67 *(978-0-13-606482-4(5),* Prentice Hall) Prentice Hall PTR.

—Runners Corporation PT Lab Manual. 7th ed. 2007. (ENG.). 120p. (C). pap. 46.67 *(978-0-13-243998-5(0))* Pearson Education Canada CAN. Dist: Pearson Education.

International Business Publications Staff & Global Investment and Business Center, Inc. Staff. Global Offshore Tax Handbook: Tax Regulations Guidelines for 33 Offshore Countries & Territories. pap. *(978-0-7397-3935-8(2))* International Business Pubns., USA.

Koltz, D. L. Questions, Exercises & Problems in Financial Accounting. 4th ed. 2010. (ENG., Illus.). 464p. pap. 45.00 *(978-0-7021-7737-8(7))* Juta Academic ZAF. Dist: Independent Pubs. Group.

Langdon, Ken & Bonham, Alan. Understanding Accounts. 2nd rev. ed. 2006. (ENG., Illus.). 126p. per. 13.95 *(978-1-84112-709-5(4),* Capstone) Wiley, John & Sons, Inc.

Maskell, Brian & Lilly, Susan. Life's Little Lean Accounting Instruction Book. 2006. pap. 12.99 *(978-0-9789760-0-2(2))* BMA Inc.

Meyer, Charles H. Accounting & Finance for Lawyers in a Nutshell. 3rd rev. ed. 2006. (In a Nutshell Ser.). (Illus.). 511p. per. 32.00 *(978-0-314-16295-3(X),* West Legalworks) West.

Practitioners Publishing Co. Staff. PPC's Guide to Nontraditional Engagements, 3 vols., Vol. 2. 2006. *(978-0-7646-3782-7(7))* Practitioners Publishing Co.

Rudman, Jack. Accounting. (National Teacher Examination Ser.: NT-51). pap. 29.95 *(978-0-8373-8471-9(0)); (Regents College Proficiency Examination Ser.: Vol. 1). (C).* 49.95 *(978-0-8373-5451-4(X))* National Learning Corp. (Passbooks).

Ruppel, Warren. Not-for-Profit Accounting Made Easy. 2nd rev. ed. 2007. (ENG., Illus.). 256p. 29.95 *(978-0-471-78979-6(8),* Wiley) Wiley, John & Sons, Inc.

Shim, Jae K. & Dauber, Nick A. The Complete CPA Reference. 5th ed. 2012. (ENG.). 725p. pap. 65.00 **(978-1-118-11588-6(0),** Wiley) Wiley, John & Sons, Inc.

Siegel, Joel G. & Shim, Jae K. Barron's Accounting Handbook. 5th rev. ed. 2010. (ENG.). 1056p. pap. 39.99 *(978-0-7641-6270-1(5))* Barron's Educational Series, Inc.

Singer, Michael. Pocket MBA 2: Everything an Attorney Needs to Know about Finance. 2nd rev. ed. 2008. (ENG.). 305p. pap. 49.00 *(978-1-4024-1094-9(8))* Practising Law Institute.

Swain, Bert L. CPA's Guide to Management Letter Comments. 2007. (CPA Guides). 314p. pap. 290.00 incl. cd-rom *(978-0-8080-9126-4(3))* Toolkit Media Group.

Weygandt, Jerry J., et al. Payroll Accounting Supplement to accompany Accounting Principles, Fourth Canadian Edition, Part 1. 2007. pap. 9.45 *(978-0-470-15360-4(1),* Wiley) Wiley, John & Sons, Inc.

Wisdom, John C. & Hasselback, James R. U. S. Master Accounting Guide (2008) 2008. 140p. pap. 99.00 *(978-0-8080-1866-7(3))* Toolkit Media Group.

—2006 US Master Accounting Guide. 2006th rev. ed. 2006. 1400p. pap. 82.50 *(978-0-8080-1436-2(6),* 0-5966-400) Toolkit Media Group.

ACCOUNTING—HISTORY

Barfitt, Laurie. The Contributions of John Lansing Carey to the Profession of Accountancy. 2007. 250p. 111.95 *(978-0-7623-1394-5(3))* Emerald Group Publishing Ltd. GBR. Dist: Turpin Distribution Services Ltd.

Brown, Richard. History of Accounting & Accountants. 2006. (ENG., Illus.). xvi, 459p. 37.95 *(978-1-59605-961-0(3),* Cosimo Classics) Cosimo, Inc.

Edwards, John Richard & Walker, Stephen, eds. The Routledge Companion to Accounting History. 2008. (Routledge Companions in Business, Management & Accounting Ser.). (ENG., Illus.). 640p. (C). 220.00 *(978-0-415-41094-6(0))* Routledge.

Ezzamel, Mahmoud. Accounting & Order. 2012. (Routledge New Works in Accounting History Ser.). (ENG., Illus.). 502p. (C). 150.00 *(978-0-415-48261-5(5))* Routledge.

Fleischman, Richard K., et al, eds. Critical Histories of Accounting: Sinister Inscriptions in the Modern Era. 2012. (Routledge New Works in Accounting History Ser.). (ENG., Illus.). 256p. (C). 125.00 *(978-0-415-88670-3(3))* Routledge.

Gomes, Delfina. Accounting Change in Central Government. 2009. 308p. pap. *(978-3-639-20070-6(5))* VDM Verlag Dr. Mueller e.K.

Green, Duncan & Neu, Dean. Truth or Profit? The Ethics & Business of Public Accounting. 2006. (ENG.). 160p. pap. 21.95 *(978-1-55266-190-1(3))* Fernwood Publishing Co., Ltd. CAN. Dist: Independent Pubs. Group.

King, Thomas A. More Than a Numbers Game: A Brief History of Accounting. 2006. (ENG., Illus.). 256p. 29.95 *(978-0-470-00873-7(3),* Wiley) Wiley, John & Sons, Inc.

Lee, T. A. The Development of the American Public Accounting Profession: Scottish Chartered Accountants & the Early American Public Accountancy Profession. 2006. (Routledge New Works in Accounting History: Vol. 7). (ENG., Illus.). 192p. (C). 168.00 *(978-0-415-40394-8(4))* Routledge.

Levant, Yves & de la Villarmois, Olivier, eds. French Accounting History: New Contributions. 2011. (ENG.). 192p. (C). 125.00 *(978-0-415-67588-8(X))* Routledge.

Mattesich. Two Hundred Years of Accounting Research. 2007. (Routledge New Works in Accounting History Ser.). (ENG.). 640p. (C). 208.00 *(978-0-415-77256-3(7))* Routledge.

Previts, Gary, et al, eds. A Global History of Accounting, Financial Reporting & Public Policy: Asia & Oceania, 3 vols., Vol. 14. 2011. (Studies in the Development of Accounting Thought Ser.). (Illus.). 205p. **(978-0-85724-813-8(8))** Emerald Group Publishing Ltd.

Previts, Gary, et al. A Global History of Accounting, Financial Reporting & Public Policy: Americas, 3 vols., Vol. 14. 2011. 205p. **(978-0-85724-811-4(1))** Emerald Group Publishing Ltd. GBR. Dist: Ebsco Publishing.

Starkman, Jay. The Sex of a Hippopotamus: A Unique History of Taxes & Accounting. 2008. 456p. 28.95 *(978-0-9818063-0-3(9))* Twinset, Inc.

Waymire, Gregory & Basu, Sudipto. Accounting Is an Evolved Economic Institution, Vol. 2. 2008. (ENG.). 184p. pap. 99.00 *(978-1-60198-160-8(0))* Now Pubs.

Whittington, Geoffrey. Profitability, Accounting Theory & Methodology: The Selected Essays of Geoffrey Whittington. 2007. (Routledge Historical Perspectives in Accounting Ser.). (ENG., Illus.). 480p. (C). 198.00 *(978-0-415-37644-0(0))* Routledge.

Zeff, Stephen A. Insights from Accounting History. 2010. (Routledge Historical Perspectives in Accounting Ser.). (ENG., Illus.). 558p. (C). 125.00 *(978-0-415-55429-9(2))* Routledge.

ACCOUNTING—LAW AND LEGISLATION

see also Tax Accounting

Aboody, David & Kasznik, Ron. Executive Compensation & Financial Accounting, Vol. 4. 2010. (Illus.). 100p. pap. 70.00 *(978-1-60198-342-8(5))* Now Pubs.

Afterman, Allan B. Handbook of SEC Accounting & Disclosure 1993 Annual. 172.00 *(978-0-7913-0309-2(8))* Warren, Gorham & Lamont, Inc.

Althoff, Frank. Rechtsgeschäfte zwischen Gesellschaften und ihren Gesellschaftern in der externen Rechnungslegung nach HGB und IFRS unter besonderer Berücksichtigung gesellschaftsrechtlicher Kapitalerhaltung. 2009. (UniDO. FACTS. Universität Dortmund Financial Accounting & Taxation Studies). (GER.). 542p. 130.95 *(978-3-631-59515-2(8))* Lang, Peter GmbH, Europaischer Verlag der Wissenschaften DEU. Dist: Lang, Peter.

Arena, Christopher M. & Carreras, Eduardo M. The Business of Intellectual Property. 2008. (ENG., Illus.). 500p. pap. 225.50 *(978-0-19-533838-6(3))* Oxford Univ. Pr., Inc.

Aspatore Books Staff, compiled by. IT's Role in Successfully Managing Sarbanes-Oxley Compliance: Leading CTOs & CIOs on Communicating with Management, Reducing Risks, & Controlling the Cost of Compliance (Inside the Minds) 2008. 72p. pap. 65.00 *(978-0-314-98680-1(4))* Aspatore Bks.

Botzem, S. The Politics of Accounting Regulation: Organizing Transnational Standard Setting in Financial Reporting. 2012. (Illus.). 232p. 110.00 **(978-1-84980-177-5(0))** Elgar, Edward Publishing, Inc.

BVR's Guide to Discounts for Lack of Marketability. 2008. ring bd. 329.00 *(978-0-9758668-9-4(3))* Business Valuation Resources, LLC.

CCH Editorial Staff. TOP Accounting Issues for 2009 CPE Course. 2008. 250p. pap. 0.00 *(978-0-8080-1873-5(6))* Toolkit Media Group.

CCH Editors. TOP Accounting Issues for 2009 CPE Course. 2008. 200p. pap. 31.00 *(978-0-8080-1886-5(8))* Toolkit Media Group.

Hershman, Stuart & Mazero, Joyce G. Financial Performance Representations: The New & Updated Earnings Claims. 2009. (ENG.). pap. 135.00 *(978-1-60442-279-5(3))* American Bar Assn.

Hoerning, Andreas. Hybrides Kapital im Jahresabschluss: Zugleich zum Begriff des Eigenkapitals in Insolvenzrecht, Bankaufsichtsrecht und Ratingmethodik. 2011. (Schriften zum Europäischen und Internationalen Privat-, Bank- und Wirtschaftsrecht Ser.).Tr. of Hybrid Capital in Annual Financial Statements. (GER., Illus.). XXIV, 234p. 98.00 **(978-3-11-026149-3(9))** De Gruyter, Walter Inc.

Holgate, Peter A. & Buckley, Elizabeth. Accounting Principles for Non-Executive Directors. 2009. (Law Practitioner Ser.). (ENG.). 276p. 169.00 *(978-0-521-50978-7(5))* Cambridge Univ. Pr.

Jackson, Peggy M. Sarbanes-Oxley for Small Businesses: Leveraging Compliance for Maximum Advantage. 2006. (ENG., Illus.). 176p. 39.95 *(978-0-471-99825-9(7),* Wiley) Wiley, John & Sons, Inc.

King, Thomas A. More Than a Numbers Game: A Brief History of Accounting. 2006. (ENG., Illus.). 256p. 29.95 *(978-0-470-00873-7(3)*, Wiley) Wiley, John & Sons, Inc.

Lang, Yvonne. Accounts & Audits of Limited Liability Partnerships: Third Edition. 3rd ed. 2009. 223p. pap. 145.00 *(978-1-84766-503-4(9)*, Bloomsbury Professional) Bloomsbury Publishing Plc GBR. Dist: International Specialized Bk. Services.

McGill, Ross, et al. Sarbanes Oxley: Building Working Strategies for Compliance. 2007. (Finance & Capital Markets Ser.). (ENG., Illus.). 320p. 228.00 *(978-0-230-00678-2(7))* Palgrave Macmillan.

Mulli, Boniface Kalinda & F.Ali (Illinois USA), Prof. Hamdi. Review of Internal Control Systems. 2011. 72p. pap. ***(978-3-8443-0499-2(1))*** Lambert Academic Publishing.

Office of the Federal Register (U.S.), compiled by. Code of Federal Regulations, Title 4, Accounts, Revised as of January 1 2011. rev. ed. 2011. (ENG.). 164p. pap. 13.00 *(978-0-16-087521-2(8)*, Office of the Federal Register) United States Government Printing Office.

Office of the Federal Register (U.S.), compiled by. Code of Federal Regulations, Title 4, Accounts, Revised as of January 1 2012. rev. ed. 2012. (ENG.). 165p. pap. 13.00 ***(978-0-16-090054-9(9)***, Office of the Federal Register) United States Government Printing Office.

Practising Law Institute Staff, contrib. by. Basics of Accounting for Lawyers: What Every Practicing Lawyer Needs to Know. 2007. (Corporate Law & Practice Course Handbook Ser.: No. 1613). (Illus.). 476p. *(978-1-4024-0925-7(7))* Practising Law Institute.

Previts, Gary, et al, eds. Research in Accounting Regulation. 2006. (Research in Accounting Regulation Ser.). (ENG., Illus.). 380p. 94.95 *(978-0-7623-1290-0(4)*, Elsevier Science) Elsevier Science & Technology Bks.

Previts, Gary & Robinson, Tom, eds. Research in Accounting Regulation. 2007. (ENG.). 338p. 99.95 *(978-0-08-045380-4(5)*, JAI Pr.) Elsevier Science & Technology Bks.

Price Water House Coopers Staff. Manual of Accounting - IFRS for the UK 2012, 4 vols., Pack. 2011. pap. 180.00 ***(978-1-84766-912-4(3)***, Bloomsbury Professional) Bloomsbury Publishing Plc GBR. Dist: International Specialized Bk. Services.

—Manual of Accounting IFRS 2012, 3 vols., Pack. 2011. (ENG.). pap. 175.00 ***(978-1-84766-913-1(1)***, Bloomsbury Professional) Bloomsbury Publishing Plc GBR. Dist: International Specialized Bk. Services.

—Manual of Accounting UK GAAP 2012, 4 vols., Pack. 2011. pap. 135.00 ***(978-1-84766-911-7(5)***, Bloomsbury Professional) Bloomsbury Publishing Plc GBR. Dist: International Specialized Bk. Services.

PwC. Manual of Accounting: IFRS for the UK 2012. 2011. 1000p. 130.00 ***(978-1-84766-904-9(2)***, Bloomsbury Professional) Bloomsbury Publishing Plc GBR. Dist: International Specialized Bk. Services.

—Manual of Accounting: UK GAAP 2012. 2011. 1000p. 155.00 ***(978-1-84766-903-2(4)***, Bloomsbury Professional) Bloomsbury Publishing Plc GBR. Dist: International Specialized Bk. Services.

Ramos, Michael. The Sarbanes-Oxley Section 404 Implementation Toolkit: Practice AIDS for Managers & Auditors. 2nd ed. 2008. (ENG., Illus.). 396p. 94.95 *(978-0-470-16931-5(1)*, Wiley) Wiley, John & Sons, Inc.

Robinson, Thomas R. & Chandar, Nandini. Research in Accounting Regulation. Previts, Gary, ed. 2008. (ENG.). 338p. 99.95 *(978-0-08-045393-4(7)*, Elsevier Science) Elsevier Science & Technology Bks.

Rosen, Louis I. Cost Accounting Standards Board Rules & Procedures. 2007. xxviii, 1160p. pap. *(978-0-314-97825-7(9))* West Publishing Co., College & Schl. Div.

Scheel, Michael. Rechnungsabgrenzungsposten und steuerliche Gewinnermittlung. 2010. (Europäische Hochschulschriften. Reihe 5: Volks- und Betriebswirtschaft Ser.). (GER.). 248p. pap. 69.95 *(978-3-631-59432-2(1))* Lang, Peter GmbH, Europaischer Verlag der Wissenschaften DEU. Dist: Lang, Peter.

SEC Compliance Best Practices: Leading Lawyers on Understanding Disclosure Requirements, Developing Compliance Procedures, & Advising Clients on Reporting Practices (Inside the Minds) 2009. 176p. pap. *(978-0-314-20608-4(6))* Aspatore Bks.

Shamrock, Steven E. IFRS & US GAAP: A Comprehensive Comparison. 2012. (Wiley Regulatory Reporting Ser.: 5). (ENG.). 213p. pap. 110.00 ***(978-1-118-14430-5(9)***, Wiley) Wiley, John & Sons, Inc.

Shekel, Moshe. The Timing of Income Recognition in Tax Law & the Time Value of Money. 2012. (ENG.). 368p. pap. 44.95 ***(978-0-415-63163-1(7)***, Routledge Cavendish) Taylor & Francis Group GBR. Dist: Taylor & Francis Group.

Stevens, Kevin. Focus Notes Regulation 2012. 7th ed. 2011. (ENG.). 264p. pap. 40.00 ***(978-1-118-12134-4(1)***, Wiley) Wiley, John & Sons, Inc.

Stolle, Ron. White-Collar Crime & Punishment - Corporate Codes & the Sarbanes-Oxley Act. 2008. 228p. pap. *(978-3-639-07857-2(8))* VDM Verlag Dr. Mueller e.K.

Watson, Robert & Watson, Louise. Business Accountibg for Solicitors: A Guide to Scottish Law. 2nd rev. ed. 2013. (ENG.). 414p. pap. 105.00 *(978-1-84592-206-1(9)*, Bloomsbury Professional) Bloomsbury Publishing Plc GBR. Dist: International Specialized Bk. Services.

Weilep, Jan-Henning. Die Nichtigkeit des Jahresabschlusses: Eine Umfassende Analyse: Tatbestandsvoraussetzungen und Rechtsfolgen Sowie Straf- und Zivilrechtliche Konsequenzen FüR Vorstand, Aufsichtsrat und AbschlussprüFer. 2011. (GER.). 446p. 112.95 ***(978-3-631-60735-0(0))*** Lang, Peter GmbH, Europaischer Verlag der Wissenschaften DEU. Dist: Lang, Peter.

ACCOUNTING—OUTLINES, SYLLABI, ETC.

Cram101 Textbook Reviews. Outlines & Highlights for Accounting: Concepts & Applications by W. Steve Albrecht, ISBN. 2011. 274p. pap. 32.95 ***(978-1-4288-2996-1(2))*** Cram101 Inc.

—Outlines & Highlights for Accounting: Tools for Business Decision Makers by Paul D. Kimmel, ISBN. 2011. 450p. pap. 36.95 ***(978-1-4288-2986-2(5))*** Cram101 Inc.

—Outlines & Highlights for Accounting & Finance for Your Small Business by Steven M Bragg, Isbn: 9780471771562. 2011. 80p. pap. 27.95 ***(978-1-4288-0438-8(2))*** Cram101 Inc.

—Outlines & Highlights for Accounting Fundamentals by Jr Curran, Isbn: 9780073193519. 2011. 58p. pap. 26.95 ***(978-1-4288-3010-3(3))*** Cram101 Inc.

—Outlines & Highlights for Accounting Information Systems & Internal Control by Eddy Vaassen, Isbn: 9780470753958. 2011. 56p. pap. 26.95 ***(978-1-4288-2984-8(9))*** Cram101 Inc.

—Outlines & Highlights for Accounting Information Systems by Cengage South-Western, Isbn: 9780538469319. 2011. 130p. pap. 28.95 ***(978-1-4288-5647-9(1))*** Cram101 Inc.

—Outlines & Highlights for Accounting Information Systems by Robert Hurt, Isbn: 9780078111051. 2011. 120p. pap. 28.95 ***(978-1-4288-2988-6(1))*** Cram101 Inc.

—Outlines & Highlights for Accounting Principles, Volume 2 by Jerry J Weygandt, Isbn: 9780470081976. 2010. 110p. pap. 28.95 *(978-1-4288-9416-7(0))* Cram101 Inc.

—Outlines & Highlights for Advanced Accounting by Debra C Jeter, Isbn: 9780470087367. 2010. 104p. pap. 28.95 *(978-1-61698-065-8(6))* Cram101 Inc.

—Outlines & Highlights for Advanced Financial Accounting by Richard Baker, Isbn: 9780078110924. 2011. 238p. pap. 31.95 ***(978-1-4288-3002-8(2))*** Cram101 Inc.

—Outlines & Highlights for Advanced Financial Accounting by Ronald J Huefner, Isbn: 9780759364264. 2011. 294p. pap. 32.95 ***(978-1-4288-3176-6(2))*** Cram101 Inc.

—Outlines & Highlights for Auditing & Assurance Services: An Applied Approach by Iris Stuart, ISBN. 2011. 168p. pap. 29.95 ***(978-1-4288-0420-3(X))*** Cram101 Inc.

—Outlines & Highlights for College Accounting , Chapter 1-27 by James a Heintz, Isbn: 9780324376166. 2010. 264p. pap. 31.95 *(978-1-61654-560-4(7))* Cram101 Inc.

—Outlines & Highlights for College Accounting, Chapter 1-25 by John Price, Isbn: 9780073365503. 2010. 280p. pap. 32.95 *(978-1-61654-628-1(X))* Cram101 Inc.

—Outlines & Highlights for College Accounting Chapters 1-24 by John Ellis Price. 2011. 520p. pap. 34.95 ***(978-1-4288-1907-8(X))*** Cram101 Inc.

—Outlines & Highlights for College Accounting Chapters 1-30 by John Price, M David Haddock, Michael Farina, Isbn: 9780073401669 9780073365602 97800772. 2011. 390p. pap. 34.95 ***(978-1-4288-3405-7(2))*** Cram101 Inc.

—Outlines & Highlights for Computer Accounting with Peachtree Complete 2007 - with Cd by Carol Yacht, Isbn: 9780073365916. 2010. 68p. pap. 27.95 *(978-1-4288-5623-3(4))* Cram101 Inc.

—Outlines & Highlights for Core Concepts of Accounting by Cecily Raiborn, Isbn: 9780470499474. 2011. 210p. pap. 30.95 ***(978-1-4288-0379-4(3))*** Cram101 Inc.

—Outlines & Highlights for Cornerstones of Cost Accounting by Don R Hansen, Isbn: 9780538469081. 2011. 178p. pap. 29.95 ***(978-1-4288-0357-2(2))*** Cram101 Inc.

—Outlines & Highlights for Cornerstones of Financial Accounting by Jay Rich, Isbn: 9780324657739. 2010. 188p. pap. 30.95 *(978-1-61654-297-9(7))* Cram101 Inc.

—Outlines & Highlights for Cornerstones of Financial Accounting by Jay Rich, Isbn: 9780538473453. 2011. 144p. pap. 28.95 ***(978-1-4288-0437-1(4))*** Cram101 Inc.

—Outlines & Highlights for Cornerstones of Managerial Accounting by Cengage South-Western, Isbn: 9780538473460. 2011. 130p. pap. 28.95 ***(978-1-4288-0424-1(2))*** Cram101 Inc.

—Outlines & Highlights for Cost Accounting by Charles T Horngren, Isbn: 9780132109178. 2011. 170p. pap. 29.95 ***(978-1-4288-0423-4(4))*** Cram101 Inc.

—Outlines & Highlights for Finance & Accounting for Business by Bob Ryan, Isbn: 9781844808977. 2011. 244p. pap. 31.95 ***(978-1-4288-0398-5(X))*** Cram101 Inc.

Cram101 Textbook Reviews & Cram101 Textbook Reviews. Outlines & Highlights for Accounting Best Practices by Steven M Bragg. 2011. 82p. pap. 27.95 ***(978-1-61830-430-8(5))*** Cram101 Inc.

—Outlines & Highlights for Accounting Principles by Jerry J Weygandt. 2011. 366p. pap. 34.95 ***(978-1-61830-538-1(7))*** Cram101 Inc.

—Outlines & Highlights for Century 21 Accounting: Advanced by Claudia Bienias Gilbertson. 2011. 226p. pap. 30.95 ***(978-1-61830-403-2(8))*** Cram101 Inc.

—Outlines & Highlights for College Accounting, Chapters 1-24 by Douglas Mcquaig. 2011. 214p. pap. 30.95 ***(978-1-61830-533-6(6))*** Cram101 Inc.

—Outlines & Highlights for College Accounting, Chapters 1-27, Edition by James a Heintz. 2011. 186p. pap. 30.95 ***(978-1-61830-534-3(4))*** Cram101 Inc.

—Outlines & Highlights for Computer Accounting by Carol Yacht. 2011. 142p. pap. 28.95 ***(978-1-61830-536-7(0))*** Cram101 Inc.

—Outlines & Highlights for Cornerstones of Financial & Managerial Accounting by Jay Rich. 2011. 304p. pap. 32.95 ***(978-1-61830-424-7(0))*** Cram101 Inc.

—Outlines & Highlights for Essentials of Advanced Financial Accounting by Richard Baker. 2011. 168p. pap. 29.95 ***(978-1-61830-416-2(X))*** Cram101 Inc.

—Outlines & Highlights for Financial Accounting: A Focus on Interpretation & Analysis by Richard F. Kochanek. 2011. 192p. pap. 30.95 ***(978-1-61830-395-0(3))*** Cram101 Inc.

—Outlines & Highlights for Financial Accounting: A Global Approach by Rod Monger. 2011. 254p. pap. 31.95 ***(978-1-61830-394-3(5))*** Cram101 Inc.

—Outlines & Highlights for Financial Accounting: IFRS Edition by Jerry J. Weygandt. 2011. 324p. pap. 33.95 ***(978-1-61830-408-7(9))*** Cram101 Inc.

—Outlines & Highlights for Financial Accounting, 11th Edition by W Steve Albrecht. 2011. 168p. pap. 29.95 ***(978-1-61830-404-9(6))*** Cram101 Inc.

—Outlines & Highlights for Financial Accounting by Carl S Warren. 2011. 242p. pap. 31.95 ***(978-1-61830-388-2(0))*** Cram101 Inc.

—Outlines & Highlights for Financial Accounting by Jan Williams. 2011. 200p. pap. 30.95 ***(978-1-61830-400-1(3))*** Cram101 Inc.

—Outlines & Highlights for Financial Accounting by Thomas R Dyckman. 2011. 406p. pap. 35.95 ***(978-1-61830-418-6(6))***; 400p. pap. 35.95 ***(978-1-61830-401-8(1))*** Cram101 Inc.

—Outlines & Highlights for Financial Accounting for Executives & Mbas by Kenneth R Ferris. 2011. 342p. pap. 33.95 ***(978-1-61830-279-3(5))*** Cram101 Inc.

—Outlines & Highlights for Financial Accounting for Executives by Kenneth R Ferris. 2011. 124p. pap. 28.95 ***(978-1-61830-255-7(8))*** Cram101 Inc.

—Outlines & Highlights for Financial Accounting in an Economic Context by Jamie Pratt. 2011. 350p. pap. 33.95 ***(978-1-61830-402-5(X))*** Cram101 Inc.

—Outlines & Highlights for Financial Accounting Theory & Analysis: Text & Cases by Richard G. Schroeder. 2011. 248p. pap. 31.95 ***(978-1-61830-399-8(6))*** Cram101 Inc.

—Outlines & Highlights for Financial & Managerial Accounting: Information for Decisions by John Wild. 2011. 548p. pap. 38.95 ***(978-1-61830-532-9(8))*** Cram101 Inc.

—Outlines & Highlights for Financial & Managerial Accounting by Charles T Horngren. 2011. 402p. pap. 35.95 ***(978-1-61830-419-3(4))*** Cram101 Inc.

—Outlines & Highlights for Fundamental Accounting Principles by John Wild. 2011. 552p. pap. 38.95 ***(978-1-61830-396-7(1))*** Cram101 Inc.

—Outlines & Highlights for Fundamentals of Accounting: Course 2 by Claudia B. Gilbertson. 2011. 84p. pap. 27.95 ***(978-1-61830-374-5(0))*** Cram101 Inc.

—Outlines & Highlights for Principles of Financial Accounting by John Wild. 2011. 412p. pap. 35.95 ***(978-1-61830-387-5(2))*** Cram101 Inc.

Cram101 Textbook Reviews Staff. Outlines & Highlights for Accounting: What the Numbers Mean by Marshall ISBN. 2007. 164p. pap. 12.95 *(978-1-4288-5693-6(5))* Cram101 Inc.

—Outlines & Highlights for Accounting by Carl S Warren, James M Reeve, Jonathan Duchac, Isbn: 9780324662962. 2009. 246p. pap. 31.95 *(978-1-4288-3371-5(4))* Cram101 Inc.

—Outlines & Highlights for Accounting by Paul D Kimmel, Jerry J Weygandt, Donald E Kieso, Isbn: 9780470377857. 2009. 236p. pap. 31.95 *(978-1-4288-3403-3(6))* Cram101 Inc.

—Outlines & Highlights for Accounting by Robert Anthony, Isbn: 9780073100913. 2009. 226p. pap. 30.95 *(978-1-4288-2689-2(0))*; 230p. pap. 31.95 *(978-1-4288-8715-2(6))* Cram101 Inc.

—Outlines & Highlights for Accounting Chap 13-23 by Charles T Horngren, Walter T Harrison Jr , M Suzanne Oliver, Isbn: 9780136073017. 2009. 108p. pap. 28.95 *(978-1-4288-7682-8(0))* Cram101 Inc.

—Outlines & Highlights for Accounting-Chapter 1-13 by Charles T Horngren, Isbn: 9780132249959. 2009. 166p. pap. 29.95 *(978-1-4288-2019-7(1))* Cram101 Inc.

—Outlines & Highlights for Accounting Concepts & Applications by Albrecht, Stice, Stice, Swain, Isbn: 0324187564. 2009. 220p. pap. 30.95 *(978-1-4288-3921-2(6))* Cram101 Inc.

—Outlines & Highlights for Advanced Accounting by Floyd a Beams, Isbn: 9780136033974. 2009. 210p. pap. 30.95 *(978-1-4288-2017-3(5))* Cram101 Inc.

—Outlines & Highlights for Advanced Accounting by Joe Ben Hoyle, Isbn: 9780073379456. 2009. 146p. pap. 29.95 *(978-1-4288-2473-7(1))*; 136p. pap. 28.95 *(978-1-4288-8983-5(3))* Cram101 Inc.

—Outlines & Highlights for Advanced Accounting by Paul M Fischer, William J Taylor, Rita H Cheng, Isbn: 9780324379051. 2009. 166p. pap. 29.95 *(978-1-4288-3375-3(7))* Cram101 Inc.

—Outlines & Highlights for Advanced Financial Accounting by Richard Baker, Isbn: 9780073526911. 2009. 194p. pap. 30.95 *(978-1-4288-2615-1(7))* Cram101 Inc.

—Outlines & Highlights for Business & Professional Ethics for Directors, Executives & Accountants by Brooks & Dunn, Isbn: 9780324594553. 2009. 108p. pap. 28.95 *(978-1-4288-7613-2(8))* Cram101 Inc.

—Outlines & Highlights for Century 21 Accounting: General Journal by Gilbertson & Lehman, ISBN. 2009. 226p. pap. 30.95 *(978-1-4288-2915-2(6))*; 228p. pap. 31.95 *(978-1-4288-7809-9(2))* Cram101 Inc.

—Outlines & Highlights for College Accounting: A Practical Approach by Slater, ISBN. 2009. 154p. pap. 29.95 *(978-1-4288-3919-9(4))* Cram101 Inc.

—Outlines & Highlights for College Accounting: A Practical Approach Chapters 1-12 with Study Guide & Working Papers by Jeffrey Slater, ISBN. 2009. 78p. pap. 27.95 *(978-1-4288-1971-9(1))* Cram101 Inc.

—Outlines & Highlights for College Accounting , Chapter 1-15 by James a Heintz, Isbn: 9780324382495. 2009. 138p. pap. 28.95 *(978-1-4288-2215-3(1))* Cram101 Inc.

—Outlines & Highlights for College Accounting 1-13 by Douglas Mcquaig, Patricia Bille, Isbn: 9780618824182. 2009. 94p. pap. 27.95 *(978-1-4288-3419-4(2))* Cram101 Inc.

—Outlines & Highlights for College Accounting by Mcquaig, Bille, Isbn: 0618507132. 2009. 142p. pap. 28.95 *(978-1-4288-3922-9(4))* Cram101 Inc.

—Outlines & Highlights for College Accounting, Chapter 1-9 by James a Heintz, Robert W Parry, Isbn: 9780324382488. 2009. 90p. pap. 27.95 *(978-1-4288-3427-9(3))* Cram101 Inc.

—Outlines & Highlights for College Acct: PRAC APPR 1-25 by Jeffrey Slater, ISBN. 2009. 156p. pap. 29.95 *(978-1-4288-3393-7(5))* Cram101 Inc.

—Outlines & Highlights for Financial Accounting: A New Perspective by Solomon, ISBN. 2008. 88p. per. 10.95 *(978-1-4288-5776-6(1))* Cram101 Inc.

—Outlines & Highlights for Financial Accounting by Porter, Gary a / Norton, Curtis L , Isbn: 9780324655230. 2009. 76p. pap. 27.95 *(978-1-4288-3343-2(9))* Cram101 Inc.

—Outlines & Highlights for Financial Accounting with Annual Report by Robert Libby, Isbn: 9780077300333. 2009. 196p. pap. 30.95 *(978-1-4288-2657-1(2))*; 192p. pap. 30.95 *(978-1-4288-8743-5(1))* Cram101 Inc.

—Outlines & Highlights for Financial & Managerial Accounting by John J Wild, Kermit D Larson, Barbara Chiappetta, Ken Shaw, Isbn: 9780073379524. 2009. 122p. pap. 28.95 *(978-1-4288-3355-5(2))* Cram101 Inc.

—Outlines & Highlights for Financial & Managerial Accounting by Warren, Isbn: 9780324401882. 2008. 176p. pap. 12.95 *(978-1-4288-6586-0(1))* Cram101 Inc.

—Outlines & Highlights for Financial & Managerial Accounting by Warren, Reeve, & Duchac, Isbn: 9780324663815. 2009. 240p. pap. 31.95 *(978-1-4288-2839-1(7))* Cram101 Inc.

—Outlines & Highlights for Financial Management of Health Care Organizations: An Introduction to Fundamental Tools, Concepts, & Applications by Micha. 2009. 60p. pap. 26.95 *(978-1-4288-9039-8(4))* Cram101 Inc.

—Outlines & Highlights for Fundamental Accounting Principles: 9780073366289. 2009. 220p. pap. 30.95 *(978-1-4288-2595-6(9))*; 206p. pap. 30.95 *(978-1-4288-9094-7(7))* Cram101 Inc.

—Outlines & Highlights for Fundamental Accounting Principles by John J Wild, Barbara Chiappetta, Ken W Shaw, Isbn: 9780073366272. 2009. 316p. pap. 33.95 *(978-1-4288-3361-6(7))* Cram101 Inc.

—Outlines & Highlights for Fundamentals of Advanced Accounting by Hoyle Isbn: 9780073379463. 2008. 80p. pap. 10.95 *(978-1-4288-6587-7(X))* Cram101 Inc.

—Outlines & Highlights for Fundamentals of Advanced Accounting by John J Wild, Kermit D Larson, Barbara Chiappetta, Isbn: 9780073379548. 2009. 436p. pap. 36.95 *(978-1-4288-3373-9(0))* Cram101 Inc.

—Outlines & Highlights for Fundamentals of Financial Accounting by Phillips, Isbn: 9780077214555. 2009. 180p. pap. 29.95 *(978-1-4288-2719-6(6))*; 158p. pap. 29.95 *(978-1-4288-8515-8(3))* Cram101 Inc.

—Outlines & Highlights for Intermediate Accounting: 2007 FASB Update by Donald E. Kieso, ISBN. 2009. 128p. pap. 28.95 *(978-1-4288-2151-4(1))* Cram101 Inc.

—Outlines & Highlights for Intermediate Accounting by Nikolai, Loren a / Bazley, John D / Jones, Jeffe Nikolai, Loren a / Bazley, John D / Jones, J. 2009. 88p. pap. 27.95 *(978-1-4288-9737-3(2))* Cram101 Inc.

—Outlines & Highlights for Introduction to Accounting: An Integrated Approach by Penne Ainsworth, ISBN. 2009. 340p. pap. 33.95 *(978-1-4288-2585-7(1))* Cram101 Inc.

—Outlines & Highlights for Introduction to Management Accounting - Chapters 1-14 by Charles T Horngren, Isbn: 9780136141501. 2009. 194p. pap. 30.95 *(978-1-4288-2271-9(2))* Cram101 Inc.

—Outlines & Highlights for Introduction to Management Accounting by Horngren / Sundem / Stratton / Schatzberg / Burgstahler, Isbn: 9780136129219. 2009. 56p. pap. 26.95 *(978-1-4288-2983-1(0))* Cram101 Inc.

—Outlines & Highlights for Introduction to Managerial Accounting by Peter C Brewer, Isbn: 9780073379357. 2009. 114p. pap. 28.95 *(978-1-4288-2557-4(6))*; 110p. pap. 28.95 *(978-1-4288-8888-3(8))* Cram101 Inc.

—Outlines & Highlights for Managerial Accounting by Garrison Isbn: 9780073526706. 2007. 120p. pap. 11.95 *(978-1-4288-5687-5(0))* Cram101 Inc.

—Outlines & Highlights for Managerial Accounting by Hansen, Isbn: 0324376006. 2007. 76p. pap. 10.95 *(978-1-4288-5699-8(4))* Cram101 Inc.

—Outlines & Highlights for Managerial Accounting by Hilton, Isbn: 9780073022857. 2007. 128p. pap. 11.95 *(978-1-4288-5689-9(7))* Cram101 Inc.

—Outlines & Highlights for Mp Financial Accounting: Information for Decisions by Wild, ISBN. 2009. 236p. pap. 31.95 *(978-1-4288-3898-7(8))* 2007. 168p. pap. 12.95 *(978-1-4288-5704-9(4))* Cram101 Inc.

—Outlines & Highlights for Mp Financial Accounting by Libby Isbn: 9780073208145. 2007. 144p. pap. 11.95 *(978-1-4288-5692-9(7))* Cram101 Inc.

—Outlines & Highlights for Principles of Accounting by Robert Libby, Patricia Libby, Fred Phillips, Stacey M Whitecotton, Isbn: 9780077251031. 2009. 264p. pap. 31.95 *(978-1-4288-3391-3(9))* Cram101 Inc.
—Outlines & Highlights for Principles of Accounting Volume 2 Ch 12-25 by Patricia Libby, Robert Libby, Fred Phillips, Stacey M Whitecotton, Isbn: 9780. 2009. 140p. pap. 28.95 *(978-1-4288-3367-8(6))* Cram101 Inc.
—Outlines & Highlights for Rethinking the Rules of Financial Accounting by Anthony, Isbn: 0071423877. 2009. 150p. pap. 29.95 *(978-1-4288-3889-5(9))* Cram101 Inc.
—Outlines & Highlights for Survey of Accounting by Thomas P Edmonds, Isbn: 9780073379555. 2009. 188p. pap. 30.95 *(978-1-4288-2143-9(0))* Cram101 Inc.
—Outlines & Highlights for Wiley Pathways Small Business Accounting by Lita Epstein, Isbn: 9780470198636. 2009. 102p. pap. 27.95 *(978-1-4288-2471-3(5))* Cram101 Inc.
Ingram and Albr, Baldwin. Financial Accounting. 2006. pap. 13.95 *(978-1-4288-0892-8(2))* Cram101 Inc.
Lerner, Joel. Schaum's Easy Outline of Bookkeeping & Accounting, Revised Edition. 2011. (Schaum's Easy Outlines Ser.). (ENG.). 144p. (C). pap. 11.00 ***(978-0-07-177975-3(2)**, 0071779752)* McGraw-Hill Cos., The.
Lerner, Joel & Cashin, James. Schaum's Easy Outline of Accounting, Revised Edition. 2011. (Schaum's Easy Outlines Ser.). (ENG.). 160p. (C). pap. 11.00 ***(978-0-07-177752-0(0)**, 0071777520)* McGraw-Hill Cos., The.
Lerner, Joel, et al. Schaum's Outline of Principles of Accounting I, Fifth Edition. 5th ed. 2009. (Schaum's Outline Ser.). (ENG., Illus.). 408p. (C). pap. 20.00 *(978-0-07-163538-7(6), 0071635386)* McGraw-Hill Cos., The.
Pahler. Advanced Accounting. 2006. pap. 19.95 *(978-1-4288-0980-2(5))* Cram101 Inc.
Porter and, Norton. Financial Accounting the Impact on Decis. 2006. pap. 13.95 *(978-1-4288-0937-6(6))* Cram101 Inc.
Shim, Jae & Siegel, Joel G. Financial Accounting. 2nd ed. 2011. (Schaum's Outline Ser.). (ENG.). 360p. (C). pap. 19.00 ***(978-0-07-176250-2(7)**, 0071762507)* McGraw-Hill Cos., The.
Tidrick, Donald. Auditing & Attestation - Supplemental Outlines. 2008. (ENG.). 244p. per. *(978-0-9746541-7-1(5))* Efficient Learning Systems, Inc.

ACCOUNTING—PROBLEMS, EXERCISES, ETC.

Berkun, S., et al. Wiley CPA Exam Review 2012: Regulation, 4 vols. 9th ed. 2011. (ENG.). 813p. pap. 65.00 ***(978-0-470-92393-1(8)**, Wiley)* Wiley, John & Sons, Inc.
Bragg, Steven M. The Vest Pocket Guide to GAAP. 3rd ed. 2010. (ENG., Illus.). 418p. pap. 34.95 *(978-0-470-76782-5(0), Wiley)* Wiley, John & Sons, Inc.
Cram101 Textbook Reviews & Cram101 Textbook Reviews. Outlines & Highlights for Financial Accounting Theory & Analysis: Text & Cases by Richard G. Schroeder. 2011. 248p. pap. 31.95 ***(978-1-61830-399-8(6))*** Cram101 Inc.
Cram101 Textbook Reviews Staff. Outlines & Highlights for Cornerstones of Financial Accounting, Current Trends Update by Rich, Jones, Mowen, & Hansen, Isbn: 9780538751265. 2009. 158p. pap. 29.95 *(978-1-4288-2865-0(6))*; 144p. pap. 29.95 *(978-1-4288-7595-1(6))* Cram101 Inc.
Davies, Tony & Crawford, Ian. Business Accounting & Finance. rev. ed. 2011. (ENG., Illus.). 772p. pap. 115.00 ***(978-0-273-72312-7(X)**, Financial Times/Prentice Hall)* Pearson Education, Ltd. GBR. Dist: Trans-Atlantic Pubns., Inc.
Delaney, Patrick R. Wiley CPA Examination Review Vol. 2: Problems & Solutions, 2 vols. 39th ed. 2012. (ENG.). 1392p. pap. 59.95 ***(978-1-118-25450-9(3)**, Wiley)* Wiley, John & Sons, Inc.
Delaney, Patrick R. & Whittington, O. Ray. CPA Exam Review 2011, 4 vols., Set. 8th ed. 2010. (ENG.). pap. 220.00 *(978-0-470-55438-8(X), Wiley)* Wiley, John & Sons, Inc.
Dyson, John. Accounting for Non-Accounting Students. 7th rev. ed. 2007. (ENG., Illus.). 528p. pap. 99.50 *(978-0-273-70922-0(4))* Financial Times/Prentice Hall.
Elliott, Barry & Elliott, Jamie. Financial Accounting & Reporting. 15th rev. ed. 2012. (ENG.). 919p. pap. 117.50 ***(978-0-273-76088-7(2)**, Financial Times/Prentice Hall)* Pearson Education, Ltd GBR. Dist: Trans-Atlantic Pubns., Inc.
Elliott, Barry, et al. Financial Accounting & Reporting. 13th ed. 2009. 926p. pap. 117.50 *(978-0-273-73004-0(5), Prentice Hall)* Pearson Education, Ltd. GBR. Dist: Trans-Atlantic Pubns., Inc.
Elliott, Jamie & Elliott, Barry. Financial Accounting & Reporting 12e. 12th rev. ed. 2007. 920p. pap. 115.00 *(978-0-273-71231-2(4), Financial Times/Prentice Hall)* Pearson Education, Ltd. GBR. Dist: Trans-Atlantic Pubns., Inc.
Englard, Baruch. Intermediate Accounting I: More Than 500 Fully Solved Problems. 2nd ed. 2011. (Schaum's Outline Ser.). (ENG., Illus.). 360p. (C). pap. 19.00 *(978-0-07-175606-8(X), 007175606X)* McGraw-Hill Cos., The.
Godwin, Norman H. & Alderman, C. Wayne. Financial ACCT: 2013 Student Edition (with Printed Access Card) 2nd ed. 2012. (Acct Ser.). (ENG.). 352p. pap. 99.95 ***(978-1-111-53076-1(9))*** Cengage South-Western.
Heintz, James A. & Parry, Robert W. Study Guide with Working Papers, Chapters 1-9 & 10-15 (with Combination Journal Module) for Heintz/Parry's College Accounting. 20th ed. 2010. (ENG.). 1064p. (C). pap. 69.95 *(978-0-538-73704-3(2))* Cengage South-Western.
Howard University, creator. Accounting Principles II. 2007. (Illus.). 446p. per. 76.95 *(978-0-470-14462-6(9))* Wiley, John & Sons, Inc.
Ingram and Albr, Baldwin. Financial Accounting. 2006. pap. 13.95 *(978-1-4288-0892-8(2))* Cram101 Inc.
Jeter, Debra C. & Chaney, Paul K. Advanced Accounting. 5th ed. 2012. (ENG.). 904p. (C). pap. 161.95 ***(978-1-118-09861-5(7)**, Wiley)* Wiley, John & Sons, Inc.
Joyce, Tim. Cambridge Checkpoints VCE Accounting Unit 3 2008. 2007. (Cambridge Checkpoints Ser.). pap. *(978-0-521-71577-5(6))* Cambridge Univ. Pr.
—Cambridge Checkpoints VCE Accounting Unit 3 2009. 2008. (Cambridge Checkpoints Ser.). pap. 15.95 *(978-0-521-75940-3(4))* Cambridge Univ. Pr.
—Cambridge Checkpoints VCE Accounting Unit 4 2008. 2007. pap. 19.95 *(978-0-521-71578-2(4))* Cambridge Univ. Pr.
—Cambridge Checkpoints VCE Accounting Unit 4 2009. 2008. (Cambridge Checkpoints Ser.). pap. 15.95 *(978-0-521-75941-0(2))* Cambridge Univ. Pr.
Kaplan CPA Review. CPA Exam Study Manual: Regulation 2009/2010. 2009. (ENG.). 688p. pap. 49.95 *(978-1-4277-8865-8(0))* Kaplan Publishing.
Kelly, Jane. Accounting. 2010. (ENG., Illus.). 296p. pap., wbk. ed. 26.50 ***(978-0-470-74716-2(1)**, For Dummies)* Wiley, John & Sons, Inc.
Kieso, Donald E., et al. Intermediate Accounting, Set. 14th ed. 2011. (ENG.). 144p. (C). pap. 61.95 *(978-1-118-01454-7(5), Wiley)* Wiley, John & Sons, Inc.
—Rockford Practice Set to accompany Intermediate Accounting Vol. 1, 2 vols. 7th rev. ed. 2007. (ENG.). 664p. 69.95 *(978-0-470-83373-5(4))* Wiley, John & Sons, Inc.
Kimmel, Paul D. Wiley Plus Stand-Alone Premium to Accompany Accounting. 2nd ed. 2007. (Wiley Plus Products Ser.). pap. 0.01 *(978-0-470-11207-6(7))* Wiley, John & Sons, Inc.
Kimmel, Paul D., et al. Accounting Vol. 2: Tools for Business Decision Makers - Working Papers. 4th ed. 2011. (ENG.). 422p. (C). pap. 61.95 *(978-0-470-93119-6(1), Wiley)* Wiley, John & Sons, Inc.
—Financial Accounting: Tools for Business Decision Making. 5th ed. 2009. (ENG.). 688p. (C). pap., pupil's gde. ed. 75.95 *(978-0-470-37975-2(8), Wiley)* Wiley, John & Sons, Inc.
—Financial Accounting Set: Tools for Business Decision Making. 6th ed. 2011. (ENG.). (C). pap. 48.95 *(978-0-470-88795-0(8), Wiley)* Wiley, John & Sons, Inc.
—Wiley Plus/WebCT Premium to Accompany Accounting. 2nd ed. 2007. (Wiley Plus Products Ser.). pap. 65.95 *(978-0-470-11203-8(4))* Wiley, John & Sons, Inc.
Larson, Raymond L. & Schattke Rudolph W. Practice Set to Accompany Financial Accounting _ Concepts & Uses, Second Edition. 10th ed. 2010. (ENG., Illus.). (C). ring bd. 77.33 *(978-0-205-05904-1(X))* Longman Publishing Group.
Lymer, Andy, et al. Get to Grips with Book Keeping. 2010. (Teach Yourself Ser.). (ENG., Illus.). 484p. pap. 23.95 *(978-1-4441-0298-7(2), Hodder & Stoughton)* Hodder General Publishing Div. GBR. Dist: Independent Pubs. Group.
McLaney, Eddie, et al. Accounting Pack: An Introduction. 5th ed. 2010. (ENG., Illus.). pap. 115.00 *(978-0-273-73365-2(6))* FT Press.
McMahon, Daniel. Comptabilité Intermédiaire: Analyse Théorique et Pratique. (FRE.). *(978-2-7651-0433-9(6))* Chenelière/McGraw-Hill.
Melamed, Leo, et al. Wiley CPA Exam Review 2012: Business Environment & Concepts, 4 vols. 9th ed. 2011. (ENG.). 432p. pap. 65.00 ***(978-0-470-92391-7(1)**, Wiley)* Wiley, John & Sons, Inc.
Mirza, Abbas A., et al. Wiley IFRS: Practical Implementation Guide & Workbook. 3rd ed. 2011. (Wiley Regulatory Reporting Ser.: 3). (ENG.). 584p. pap., wbk. ed. 95.00 *(978-0-470-64791-2(4), Wiley)* Wiley, John & Sons, Inc.
Morris, Deigan, et al. Accounting: Theory & Practice. 8th rev. ed. 2011. (ENG., Illus.). 864p. pap. 112.50 *(978-0-273-69385-7(9))* Pearson Education, Ltd. GBR. Dist: Trans-Atlantic Pubns., Inc.
Needles, Belverd E. Principles of Financial Accounting. 10th ed. 2007. (ENG.). (C). 66.95 *(978-0-618-73649-2(2), 339090)* Cengage South-Western.
Olson, William. Adviser's Guide to the Tax Consequences of the Purchase & Sale of a Business. 2nd ed. 2007. pap. 61.25 *(978-0-87051-692-4(2))* American Institute of Certified Public Accountants.
Pahler. Advanced Accounting. 2006. pap. 19.95 *(978-1-4288-0980-2(5))* Cram101 Inc.
Porter and, Norton. Financial Accounting the Impact on Decis. 2006. pap. 13.95 *(978-1-4288-0937-6(6))* Cram101 Inc.
Price, John Ellis, et al. Study Guide & Working Papers Chapters 14-24 for Use with College Accounting. 12th ed. 2008. (ENG.). 256p. (C). pap., stu. ed., instr.'s gde. ed. 71.33 *(978-0-07-336570-1(X), 007336570X, McGraw-Hill/Irwin)* McGraw-Hill Higher Education.
Reid Clyne, Carole, et al. Accounting Principles, Pt. 1 & 2. 3rd rev. ed. 2008. (ENG., Illus.). 1p. pap., stu. ed. 27.95 *(978-0-470-83456-5(0))* Wiley, John & Sons, Inc.
Rich, Jay, et al. Cornerstones of Financial Accounting. 2nd ed. 2011. (Cornerstones Ser.). (ENG.). 816p. (C). 249.95 *(978-0-538-47345-3(2))* Cengage South-Western.
Schroeder, Jeanne Lorraine. Schroeder Financial Accounting Theory: Text & Cases 9e BRV. 2008. 640p. pap., ring bd. 57.95 *(978-0-470-38686-6(X), Wiley)* Wiley, John & Sons, Inc.
Schroeder, Richard G., et al. Financial Accounting Theory & Analysis: Text & Cases. 10th ed. 2010. (ENG., Illus.). 612p. (C). 214.95 *(978-0-470-64628-1(4), Wiley)* Wiley, John & Sons, Inc.
Shain, Daniel H., et al. Wiley CPA Exam Review 2012, 4 vols., Set. 9th ed. 2011. (ENG.). ix, 676p. pap. 260.00 ***(978-0-470-92394-8(6)**, Wiley)* Wiley, John & Sons, Inc.
Stickney, Clyde P., et al. Financial Accounting: An Introduction to Concepts, Methods & Uses. 13th ed. 2009. (ENG.). 320p. (C). pap. 46.95 *(978-0-324-78900-3(9))* Cengage South-Western.
Tidrick, Donald. Auditing & Attestation - Supplemental Outlines. 2008. (ENG.). 244p. per. *(978-0-9746541-7-1(5))* Efficient Learning Systems, Inc.
Weygandt, Jerry J., et al. Accounting Principles. (ENG.). (C). 10th ed. 2011. 984p. pap. 68.95 *(978-0-470-88791-2(5))*Set. 10th ed. 2011. 136p. pap. 23.95 *(978-0-470-88789-9(3))* Vol. 1. 10th ed. 2011. 402p. pap. 48.95 *(978-0-470-88784-4(2))* Vol. 1. 10th ed. 2011. (Illus.). 292p. pap., stu. ed. 70.95 *(978-0-470-88782-0(6))* Vol. 2. 9th ed. 2009. 432p. pap. 60.95 *(978-0-470-38661-3(4))* Vol. 2. 10th ed. 2011. 426p. pap., pupil's gde. ed. 46.95 *(978-0-470-88785-1(0))* Vol. 2. 10th ed. 2011. 560p. pap. 66.95 *(978-0-470-88787-5(7))* Vol. 2. 10th ed. 2011. (Illus.). 316p. pap., pupil's gde. ed. 65.95 *(978-0-470-88783-7(4))* Wiley, John & Sons, Inc. (Wiley).
—Accounting Principles Set: Narrative Practice. 10th ed. 2011. (ENG.). 82p. (C). pap. 23.95 *(978-0-470-88790-5(7), Wiley)* Wiley, John & Sons, Inc.
—Accounting Principles Vol. 1: Working Papers. 10th ed. 2011. (ENG.). 672p. (C). pap. 68.95 *(978-0-470-88786-8(9), Wiley)* Wiley, John & Sons, Inc.
—Campus Cycle Practice Set to accompany Accounting Principles. 9th ed. 2009. (ENG.). 134p. (C). pap. 55.95 *(978-0-470-38665-1(7), Wiley)* Wiley, John & Sons, Inc.
—Heritage Home Furniture: A Narrative Practice Set for use with Accounting Principles. 9th ed. 2009. (ENG.). 88p. (C). pap. 55.95 *(978-0-470-38666-8(5), Wiley)* Wiley, John & Sons, Inc.
—Problem Solving Survival Guide Vol. I, Chs. 1-12 to Accompany Accounting Principles Vol. 1, Vol. 1, Chs. 1-12. 9th ed. 2008. (ENG.). 408p. (C). pap. 66.95 *(978-0-470-38660-6(6), Wiley)* Wiley, John & Sons, Inc.
Whittington, O. Ray. Wiley CPA Exam Review Fast Track Study Guide. 4th ed. 2008. (ENG.). 384p. pap., stu. ed. 29.95 *(978-0-470-19609-0(2), Wiley)* Wiley, John & Sons, Inc.
Whittington, O. Ray & Hopkins, Debra R. Wiley CPA Exam: How to Master Simulations. 2nd ed. 2009. (ENG.). 166p. pap. 45.00 *(978-0-470-50537-3(0), Wiley)* Wiley, John & Sons, Inc.

ACCOUNTING—STANDARDS

Aamir, Suhaib & Farooq, Umar. Ifrs for Smes. 2010. 128p. pap. *(978-3-8383-9138-0(1))* Lambert Academic Publishing.
Accounting & Auditing Standards: Pending Proposals & Emerging Issues: Hearing Before the Subcommittee on Capital Markets, Insurance, & Government Sponsored Enterprises of the Committee on Financial Services, U.S. House of Representatives, One Hundred Eleventh Congress, Second Session, May 21, 2010. 2010. v, 118p. *(978-0-16-086767-5(3), 552-070-41688-9)* United States Government Printing Office.
Aicpa. Audit & Accounting Guide: Health Care Entities, with Conforming Changes as of June 1 2010. 2010. pap. 106.25 *(978-0-87051-915-4(8))* American Institute of Certified Public Accountants.
—Audit Risk Alert Compliation an Review Alert 2007/08. 2007. pap. 48.75 *(978-0-87051-706-8(6))* American Institute of Certified Public Accountants.
—Establishing & Maintaining a System of Quality Control for a CPA Firm's Accounting & Auditing Practice. 2007. pap. 50.00 *(978-0-87051-704-4(X))* American Institute of Certified Public Accountants.
—Independence & Ethics Alert 2007/2008. 2007. pap. 36.25 *(978-0-87051-701-3(5))* American Institute of Certified Public Accountants.
AICPA Staff. AICPA Professional Standards 2010: Cch#04585404, vols. 2 set. *(978-0-87051-869-0(0))* American Institute of Certified Public Accountants.
Alexander, David & Archer, Simon. International Accounting/Financial Reporting Standards Guide. 2007th rev. ed. 2007. (Illus.). per. 180.00 *(978-0-8080-9064-9(X))* Toolkit Media Group.
—International Accounting/Financial Reporting Standards Guide 2009. 2008. 800p. pap. 218.50 *(978-0-8080-9226-1(X))* Toolkit Media Group.
Alexander, David & Nobes, Christopher, eds. International Financial Reporting Standards: Critical Perspectives on Business & Management, 4 vols. 2008. (Critical Perspectives on Business & Management Ser.). (ENG.). 2016p. (C). 1315.00 *(978-0-415-38097-3(9))* Routledge.
Antill, Nick & Lee, Kenneth. Company Valuation under Ifrs, 2nd Edition Interpreting & Forecasting Accounts Using International Financial. 2nd ed. 2008. (ENG., Illus.). 406p. 78.95 *(978-1-905641-77-2(X))* Harriman Hse. Publishing GBR. Dist: Ingram Pub. Services.
Beasley, Mark & Carcello, Joseph. GAAS Guide, 2012 eBook (with CD-ROM) 2011. 1600p. E-Book 226.00 ***(978-0-8080-2793-5(X))*** Toolkit Media Group.
Becker, Howard & Terrano, Richard J. Not-for-Profit Reporting: GAAP, Plus Tax, Financial, & Regulatory Requirements. 2007. (Illus.). 544p. per. 179.00 *(978-0-8080-9133-2(6))* Toolkit Media Group.
—Not-for-Profit Reporting: GAAP Plus Tax, Financial, & Regulatory Requirements. 2007th rev. ed. 2006. (Illus.). per. 169.00 *(978-0-8080-9065-6(8))* Toolkit Media Group.
Bettermann, Constantin. Finanzierung von Familiengesellschaften nach Basel II und IFRS: Kautelarjuristische und betriebswirtschaftliche Betrachtung. 2009. (GER.). 328p. 86.95 *(978-3-631-59483-4(6))* Lang, Peter GmbH, Europäischer Verlag der Wissenschaften DEU. Dist: Lang, Peter.
Botzem, S. The Politics of Accounting Regulation: Organizing Transnational Standard Setting in Financial Reporting. 2012. (Illus.). 232p. 110.00 ***(978-1-84980-177-5(0))*** Elgar, Edward Publishing, Inc.
Bragg, Steven M. GAAP 2012: Interpretation & Application of Generally Accepted Accounting Principles. 10th ed. 2011. (ENG.). 110.00 ***(978-0-470-92397-9(0)**, Wiley)* Wiley, John & Sons, Inc.
—IFRS Made Easy. 2010. (ENG.). 266p. 49.95 *(978-0-470-89070-7(3), Wiley)* Wiley, John & Sons, Inc.
—Practitioner's Guide to GAAS 2012: Including all SASs, SSAEs, SSARSs, & Interpretations. 9th ed. 2011. (ENG.). 979p. pap. 95.00 ***(978-0-470-92395-5(4)**, Wiley)* Wiley, John & Sons, Inc.
—The Ultimate Accountants' Reference: Including GAAP, IRS & SEC Regulations, Leases, & More. 3rd ed. 2010. (ENG., Illus.). 816p. 183.95 *(978-0-470-57254-2(X), Wiley)* Wiley, John & Sons, Inc.
—The Vest Pocket Guide to GAAP. 3rd ed. 2010. (ENG., Illus.). 418p. pap. 34.95 *(978-0-470-76782-5(0), Wiley)* Wiley, John & Sons, Inc.
—The Vest Pocket Guide to IFRS. 3rd ed. 2010. (ENG., Illus.). 405p. pap. 29.95 *(978-0-470-61947-6(3), Wiley)* Wiley, John & Sons, Inc.
—Wiley GAAP 2012: Interpretation & Application of Generally Accepted Accounting Principles CD-ROM & Book. 10th ed. 2011. (ENG., Illus.). pap. 235.00 ***(978-0-470-92398-6(9)**, Wiley)* Wiley, John & Sons, Inc.
Bragg, Steven M. Wiley GAAP Policies & Procedures. 2nd rev. ed. 2007. (ENG., Illus.). 432p. per. 115.95 *(978-0-470-08183-9(X), Wiley)* Wiley, John & Sons, Inc.
Bragg, Steven M., et al. IFRS Policies & Procedures. 2008. (ENG., Illus.). 470p. pap. 94.95 *(978-0-471-69958-3(6), Wiley)* Wiley, John & Sons, Inc.
Butler, Cormac. Accounting for Financial Instruments. 2009. (ENG., Illus.). 296p. 90.00 *(978-0-470-69980-5(9), Wiley)* Wiley, John & Sons, Inc.
Camfferman, Kees & Zeff, Stephen A. Financial Reporting & Global Capital Markets: A History of the International Accounting Standards Committee, 1973-2000. 2007. (ENG., Illus.). 704p. 175.00 *(978-0-19-929629-3(4))* Oxford Univ. Pr., Inc.
Carcello, Joseph & Beasley, Mark. GAAS Guide, 2007. 2007th rev. ed. 2006. 1136p. pap. 159.00 *(978-0-8080-9048-9(8), CCH)* Wolters Kluwer Tax & Accounting.
Catty, James P. & Catty. Fair Value under IFRS. 2010. (ENG., Illus.). 624p. pap. 115.95 *(978-0-470-47708-3(3), Wiley)* Wiley, John & Sons, Inc.
CCH Editors. Cost Accounting Standards REcord REgulations as Of 2008. 2008. 250p. pap. 40.00 *(978-0-8080-1726-4(8))* Wolters Kluwer Law & Business.
—OCBOA Guide, 2008 Edition. 2007. 754p. pap. 179.00 *(978-0-8080-9115-8(8))* Toolkit Media Group.
Ceylan, Petra. Rechnungslegung über Restrukturierungs- verpflichtungen: UGB/HGB, US-GAAP und IFRS im Vergleich. 2009. 116p. pap. *(978-3-639-19703-7(8))* VDM Verlag Dr. Mueller e.K.
CFA Institute Centre. Self-Regulation in Today's Securities Markets: Outdated System or Work in Progress? 2007. 37p. per. *(978-1-932495-71-3(1))* CFA Institute.
Chairas, Ira Yuta & E.D. Radianto, Wirawan. Accounting Harmonization in Asean. 2010. 148p. pap. *(978-3-639-25457-0(0))* VDM Verlag Dr. Mueller e.K.
Chatham, Michael. Is Compliance with International Accounting Standards Beneficial? 2008. 120p. pap. *(978-3-639-03661-9(1))* VDM Verlag Dr. Mueller e.K.
Clikeman, Paul M. Called to Account: Fourteen Financial Frauds That Shaped the American Accounting Profession. 2008. (ENG., Illus.). 360p. (C). 190.00 *(978-0-415-99697-6(X))* Routledge.
—Called to Account: Fourteen Financial Frauds that Shaped the American Public Accounting Profession. 2008. (ENG., Illus.). 360p. (C). 59.95 *(978-0-415-99698-3(8))* Routledge.
Collings, Steven. The Core Aspects of International Financial Reporting Standards & International Accounting Standards. 2009. (Illus.). 104p. pap. 18.99 *(978-1-4389-9319-5(6))* AuthorHouse.
Cotter, Derry. Advanced Financial Reporting: A Complete Guide to IFRS. rev. ed. 2012. (ENG., Illus.). 487p. pap. 92.50 ***(978-0-273-73235-8(8)**, Financial Times/Prentice Hall)* Pearson Education, Ltd. GBR. Dist: Trans-Atlantic Pubns., Inc.
Cram101 Textbook Reviews & Cram101 Textbook Reviews. Outlines & Highlights for Wiley Gaap: Interpretation & Application of Generally Accepted Accounting Principles 2011 by Steven M. Bragg. 2011. 186p. pap. 30.95 ***(978-1-61830-241-0(8))*** Cram101 Inc.
Cram101 Textbook Reviews Staff. Outlines & Highlights for Wiley Ifrs 2009: Interpretation & Application of International Accounting & Financial Reporting Standards 2009 by Barry. 2009. 212p. pap. 30.95 *(978-1-4288-2453-9(7))*; 222p. pap. 30.95 *(978-1-4288-9000-8(9))* Cram101 Inc.
Crawford, Michael A. & Loyd, D. Scot. Governmental GAAP Practice Manual: Including GASB 34 Guidance. 2007th rev. ed. 2006. per. 199.00 *(978-0-8080-9063-2(1))* Toolkit Media Group.
—Governmental GAAP Practice Manual (2009) 2008. 1100p. pap. 245.00 *(978-0-8080-9225-4(1))* Toolkit Media Group.
Crawford, Micheal & Loyd, D. Scot. CPA's Multistate Guide to Ethics & Professional Conduct 2008. 2008. 600p. pap. 215.00 *(978-0-8080-9176-9(X))* Toolkit Media Group.
Dauber, Nick A. & Dauber. Wiley the Complete Guide to Auditing Standards, & Other Professional Standards for Accountants 2009. 5th ed. 2009. (ENG.). 549p. pap. 95.00 *(978-0-470-41152-0(X), Wiley)* Wiley, John & Sons, Inc.
Dauber, Nick A., et al. The Complete Guide to Auditing Standards & Other Professional Standards for Accountants 2008. 4th ed. 2008. (ENG.). 532p. pap. 95.00 *(978-0-470-18397-7(7), Wiley)* Wiley, John & Sons, Inc.
Dennis, Ian. The Nature of Accounting Regulation. 2012. (Routledge Studies in Accounting Ser.). (ENG.). 176p. (C). 125.00 *(978-0-415-89195-0(7))* Routledge.
Dick, Wolfgang & Missonier-Piera, Franck. Financial Reporting under IFRS: A Topic Based Approach. 2nd ed. 2010. (Wiley Regulatory Reporting Ser.: 1).

A

(ENG., Illus.). 360p. pap. 65.00 *(978-0-470-68831-1(9)*, Wiley) Wiley, John & Sons, Inc.

Dong, Bei. Noncontrolling Interests. 2010. 72p. pap. *(978-3-8383-0135-8(8))* Lambert Academic Publishing.

Eamon McNicholas Staff. Accounting Standards: A Guide for Lawyers. 2011. 96p. pap. 44.95 *(978-1-904905-47-9(1))* Spiramus Pr. GBR. Dist: International Specialized Bk. Services.

Ellis, Jeffrey & Accounting and Research Manager Staff. CCH Accounting for Leases. 2007th rev. ed. 2006. (Illus.). 816p. *(978-0-8080-9068-7(2))* Wolters Kluwer Law & Business.

Ellis, Jeffrey & Pippin, Ronald G. CCH Accounting for Leases: Interpretations of FASB Statement No. 13, Accounting for Leases, as Amended. 2008th rev. ed. 2007. (Cch Accounting Ser.). (Illus.). 571p. per. 225.00 *(978-0-8080-9135-6(2))* Toolkit Media Group.

Epstein, Barry J. & Jermakowicz, Eva K. IFRS 2009: Interpretation & Application of International Accounting & Financial Reporting Standards 2009. 2009. pap. 250.00 incl. cd-rom *(978-0-470-48774-7(7)*, Wiley) Wiley, John & Sons, Inc.

Epstein, Barry J. & Saafir, Nadira M. GAAP: Practical Implementation Guide. 2nd ed. 2010. (ENG.). 368p. pap., wbk. ed. 95.00 *(978-0-470-59906-8(5)*, Wiley) Wiley, John & Sons, Inc.

Epstein, Barry J., et al. IFRS for SMEs: Practical Implementation Guide. 2010. (Wiley Regulatory Reporting Ser.). (ENG.). 384p. pap., wbk. ed., instr.'s gde. ed. 95.00 *(978-0-470-61471-6(4)*, Wiley) Wiley, John & Sons, Inc.

Ernst & Young. International GAAP 2012: Generally Accepted Accounting Practice under International Financial Reporting Standards, 3 vols. 2nd ed. 2012. (ENG.). 3806p. pap. 220.00 ***(978-1-119-96245-8(5)***, Wiley) Wiley, John & Sons, Inc.

Ernst and Young Staff & Berger, Thomas Müller-Marqués. IPSAS Explained: A Summary of International Public Sector Accounting Standards. 2009. (ENG., Illus.). 208p. 70.00 *(978-0-470-68392-7(9)*, Wiley) Wiley, John & Sons, Inc.

Fatumo, Olubukola. International Financial Reporting Standards. 2010. 108p. pap. *(978-3-639-26259-9(X))* VDM Verlag Dr. Mueller e.K.

Financial Accounting Standards Board (FASB). 2007 Fars Cd- Network Version. 2007. cd-rom 2000.00 *(978-0-470-18543-8(0)*, Wiley) Wiley, John & Sons, Inc.

Financial Accounting Standards Board Staff & American Institute of Certified Public Accountants Staff, contrib. by. FASB Codification Developments 2008: Strengthening Financial Management & Reporting. 2008. (Illus.). vi, 57p. pap. ***(978-0-87051-757-0(0))*** American Institute of Certified Public Accountants.

Flower, John. Accounting & Distributive Justice. 2010. (Routledge Studies in Accounting Ser.). (ENG., Illus.). 216p. (C). 150.00 *(978-0-415-87177-8(8))* Routledge.

Friedlich, Mark. FIN 48 Answer Book. 2010. 700p. pap. 238.00 *(978-0-8080-2094-3(3))* Toolkit Media Group.

—FIN 48 Answer Book (2009) 2008. 700p. pap. 258.00 *(978-0-8080-9178-3(6))* Toolkit Media Group.

Georgiades, George. GAAP Financial Statement Disclosures Manual 2008-2009. 2008. 1460p. 199.00 *(978-0-8080-9181-3(6))* Toolkit Media Group.

Georgiades, George B. GAAS Practice Manual, 2007. 2007th rev. ed. 2006. 1536p. pap. 159.00 *(978-0-8080-9039-7(9)*, CCH) Wolters Kluwer Tax & Accounting.

Godfrey. Globalisation of Accounting Standards. 2007. (Monash Studies in Global Movements Ser.). (Illus.). 328p. 140.00 *(978-1-84542-852-5(8))* Elgar, Edward Publishing, Inc.

Granof, Michael H. Government & Not-for-Profit Accounting, Professional Simulations: Concepts & Practices. 2007. 10.00 *(978-0-470-19114-9(7)*, Wiley) Wiley, John & Sons, Inc.

Greuning, Hennie van. International Financial Reporting Standards: A Practical Guide. 6th rev. ed. 2011. (World Bank Training Ser.). (ENG., Illus.). 448p. pap. 49.95 *(978-0-8213-8428-2(7)*, 9780821384282) World Bank Pubns.

Greuning, Hennie van, et al. International Financial Reporting Standards: A Practical Guide. 6th ed. 2011. (Illus.). xii, 434p. E-Book ***(978-0-8213-8555-5(0))*** World Bank Pubns.

Hicks, Douglas. I May Be Wrong, but I Doubt It: How Accounting Information Undermines Profitability. 2008. 116p. pap. 19.99 *(978-0-557-03159-7(1))* Lulu Enterprises Inc.

Holgate, Peter A. & Buckley, Elizabeth. Accounting Principles for Non-Executive Directors. 2009. (Law Practitioner Ser.). (ENG.). 276p. 169.00 *(978-0-521-50978-7(5))* Cambridge Univ. Pr.

Hussey, Roger. Fundamentals of International Financial Accounting & Reporting. 2010. 600p. 89.00 *(978-981-4280-23-5(2))* World Scientific Publishing Co., Inc.

Ismail, Tariq. Perspectives in Accounting Practices. 2010. 328p. pap. *(978-3-639-24967-5(4))* VDM Verlag Dr. Mueller e.K.

Jamagin, Bill D. U. S. Master GAAP Guide. 2007th rev. ed. 2006. (U. S. Master Ser.). (Illus.). 1305p. per. 93.00 *(978-0-8080-9081-6(X))* Toolkit Media Group.

—2001 U.S. Master GAAP Guide. rev. ed. 1400p. pap. 69.00 *(978-0-8080-0510-0(3))* Toolkit Media Group.

Jentleson, Bruce & Bragg, Steven M. Wiley GAAP 2012: Interpretation & Application of Generally Accepted Accounting Principles. 10th ed. 2011. (ENG., Illus.). 1344p. pap. 125.00 *(978-0-470-92396-2(2)*, Wiley) Wiley, John & Sons, Inc.

King, Thomas A. More Than a Numbers Game: A Brief History of Accounting. 2006. (ENG., Illus.). 256p. 29.95 *(978-0-470-00873-7(3)*, Wiley) Wiley, John & Sons, Inc.

Kothari, Jagdish & Barone, Elisabetta. Advanced Financial Accounting: An International Approach. 2011. (ENG., Illus.). 704p. pap. 112.50 *(978-0-273-71274-9(8))* Pearson Education, Ltd. GBR. Dist: Trans-Atlantic Pubns., Inc.

Kotlikoff, Laurence J. & Burns, Scott. The Clash of Generations: Saving Ourselves, Our Kids, & Our Economy. 2012. (ENG., Illus.). 288p. (gr. 17). 21.95 ***(978-0-262-01672-8(9))*** MIT Pr.

Krivogorsky, Victoria, ed. Law Corporate Governance & Accounting. 2011. (Routledge Studies in Accounting Ser.). (ENG., Illus.). 308p. (C). 125.00 *(978-0-415-87186-0(7))* Routledge.

Kumar, Gaurav. Voluntary Accounting Disclosures by Us-Listed Asian Companies - Does the Strictness of Mandatory Disclosures Matter? 2008. 104p. pap. *(978-3-639-04524-6(6))* VDM Verlag Dr. Mueller e.K.

KüTing, Ulrich. RüCkstellungsbilanzierung Nach Hgb und Ifrs: Normendeskription und Empirische Analysen Zur Deutschen und Internationalen Bilanzierungspraxis. 2011. (Betriebswirtschaftliche Forschung im Rechnungswesen Ser.). (GER.). 418p. 104.95 ***(978-3-631-61832-5(8))*** Lang, Peter GmbH, Europaischer Verlag der Wissenschaften DEU. Dist: Lang, Peter.

Last Name Staff. International Financial Reporting Standards, 4 vols. Alexander, David, ed. 2008. Vol. 1. XXX, 546p. 37.95 *(978-0-415-38098-0(7))* Vol. 2. XII, 324p. 37.95 *(978-0-415-38099-7(5))* Vol. 3. XII, 500p. 37.95 *(978-0-415-38100-0(2))* Vol. 4. XII, 580p. 37.95 *(978-0-415-38101-7(0))* Routledge.

Lee, Timothy R. & Hood, L. Paul. A Reviewer's Handbook to Business Valuation: Practical Guidance to the Use & Abuse of a Business Appraisal. 6th ed. 2011. (ENG., Illus.). 378p. 95.00 *(978-0-470-60340-6(2)*, Wiley) Wiley, John & Sons, Inc.

Loyd, D. Scot & Crawford, Michael A. Governmental GAAP Guide: For State & Local Governments. 2007. (Illus.). 920p. per. 189.00 *(978-0-8080-9130-1(1))* Toolkit Media Group.

Lubbe, Ilse, et al. Accounting GAAP. 3rd ed. 2011. (ENG., Illus.). 800p. pap. 99.00 ***(978-0-19-599811-5(1))*** Oxford Univ. Pr., Inc.

Madray, J. Russell. Compilations & Reviews. 2008. 1100p. pap. 209.00 incl. audio compact disk *(978-0-8080-9168-4(9))* Toolkit Media Group.

—OCBOA Guide, 2007. 2007th rev. ed. 2006. 1024p. pap. 169.00 *(978-0-8080-9049-6(6)*, CCH) Wolters Kluwer Tax & Accounting.

Maier, Michael Thomas. Der Management Approach: Herausforderungen für Controller und Abschlußprüfer im Kontext der IFRS-Finanzberichterstattung. 2009. (Controlling & Business Accounting Ser.). (GRE.). 518p. 122.95 *(978-3-631-59197-0(7))* Lang, Peter GmbH, Europaischer Verlag der Wissenschaften DEU. Dist: Lang, Peter.

Malik, Malieka Farah Deeba. Convergence of Ifrs & Us Gaap. 2011. 72p. pap. ***(978-3-8433-8860-3(1))*** Lambert Academic Publishing.

Mark-To-Market Accounting: Practices & Implications: Hearing Before the Subcommittee on Capital Markets, Insurance, & Government Sponsored Enterprises of the Committee on Financial Services, U.S. House of Representatives, One Hundred Eleventh Congress, First Session, March 12, 2009. 2009. (Illus.). vi, 412p. *(978-0-16-083965-8(3)*, 552-070-39648-9) United States Government Printing Office.

Melville, Alan. International Financial Reporting: A Practical Guide. 3rd rev. ed. 2012. (ENG., Illus.). 512p. (C). pap. 25.00 ***(978-0-273-75815-0(2)***, Prentice Hall) Prentice Hall PTR.

Mirza, Abbas A., et al. Wiley IFRS: Practical Implementation Guide & Workbook. 3rd ed. 2011. (Wiley Regulatory Reporting Ser.: 3). (ENG.). 584p. pap., wbk. ed. 95.00 *(978-0-470-64791-2(4)*, Wiley) Wiley, John & Sons, Inc.

Mirza, Abbas Ali, et al. Understanding IFRS Fundamentals: International Financial Reporting Standards. 2010. (ENG., Illus.). 432p. pap. 70.00 *(978-0-470-39914-9(7)*, Wiley) Wiley, John & Sons, Inc.

Mitra, Gautam & Ray, Amabdebnarayan. Accounting Standard Setting Process. 2010. 408p. pap. *(978-3-8383-3606-0(2))* Lambert Academic Publishing.

Nach, Ralph. IFRS for SMEs Implementation. 2010. (ENG.). 384p. pap. 90.00 *(978-0-470-63366-3(2)*, Wiley) Wiley, John & Sons, Inc.

Needles, Belverd E., Jr. & Powers, Marian. A International Financial Reporting Standards. 2nd ed. 2010. (ENG.). 64p. (C). pap. 26.95 *(978-0-538-47680-5(X))* Cengage South-Western.

Neelan, Michael H. Focus on Finance & Accounting Research. 2006. 175p. (C). 169.00 *(978-1-60021-380-9(4))* Nova Science Pubs., Inc.

Neu, Dean E. & Ocampo, Elizabeth. Doing Missionary Work: The World Bank & the Diffusion of Financial Practices. 2008. (ENG., Illus.). 150p. pap. 19.95 *(978-1-55266-261-8(6))* Fernwood Publishing Co., Ltd. CAN. Dist: Independent Pubs. Group.

Oppermann, HRB, et al. Accounting Standards. 12th ed. 2008. 721p. pap. 62.00 *(978-0-7021-7270-0(7))* Juta Academic ZAF. Dist: Independent Pubs. Group.

Pallais, Don, et al. Guide to Forecasts & Projections, 3 vols. Incl. Vol. 1. ring bd. 164.00 *(978-0-7646-0407-2(4))*; Vol. 2. ring bd. 164.00 *(978-0-7646-0408-9(2))*; Vol. 3. ring bd. 164.00 *(978-0-7646-0409-6(0))*; 1998. 164.00 *(978-0-7646-0406-5(6))*; Set ring bd. 156.00 *(978-0-7646-0163-7(6))* Practitioners Publishing Co.

Peng, Songlan. Chinese Accounting Standards. 2007. 184p. per. *(978-3-8364-3433-1(4))* VDM Verlag Dr. Mueller e.K.

Petersen, Richard. CCH Accounting for Income Taxes(2009) 2008. 36p. pap. 241.50 *(978-0-8080-9163-9(8))* Toolkit Media Group.

Prather-kinsey, Jenice. International Accounting & Developing Countries. 2012. (Routledge Studies in Accounting Ser.). (ENG.). 288p. (C). 170.00 *(978-0-415-77745-2(3))* Routledge.

Price Water House Coopers Staff. Manual of Accounting - IFRS for the UK 2012, 4 vols., Pack. 2011. pap. 180.00 ***(978-1-84766-912-4(3)***, Bloomsbury Professional) Bloomsbury Publishing Plc GBR. Dist: International Specialized Bk. Services.

—Manual of Accounting IFRS 2012, 3 vols., Pack. 2011. (ENG.). pap. 175.00 ***(978-1-84766-913-1(1)***, Bloomsbury Professional) Bloomsbury Publishing Plc GBR. Dist: International Specialized Bk. Services.

—Manual of Accounting UK GAAP 2012, 4 vols., Pack. 2011. pap. 135.00 ***(978-1-84766-911-7(5)***, Bloomsbury Professional) Bloomsbury Publishing Plc GBR. Dist: International Specialized Bk. Services.

Principles of Generally Accepted Accounting Practice. 2007. (Illus.). 357p. pap. 50.00 *(978-0-7021-6670-9(7))* Juta & Co., Ltd. ZAF. Dist: Gaunt, Inc.

Puncel, Luis. Audit Procedures, 2008 (with CD-ROM) 2008th rev. ed. 2007. 100p. pap. 190.00 incl. audio compact disk *(978-0-8080-9123-3(9))* Toolkit Media Group.

PwC. Manual of Accounting: UK GAAP 2012. 2011. 1000p. 155.00 ***(978-1-84766-903-2(4)***, Bloomsbury Professional) Bloomsbury Publishing Plc GBR. Dist: International Specialized Bk. Services.

Roberts, Clare, et al. International Corporate Reporting: A comparative Approach. 4th ed. 2008. (ENG., Illus.). 704p. (C). pap. 70.00 *(978-0-273-71473-6(2)*, Prentice Hall) Prentice Hall PTR.

Robinson, Thomas R. & Chandar, Nandini. Research in Accounting Regulation. Previts, Gary, ed. 2008. (ENG.). 338p. 99.95 *(978-0-08-045393-4(7)*, Elsevier Science) Elsevier Science & Technology Bks.

Rodgers, Paul. International Accounting Standards: From UK Standards to IAS, an Accelerated Route to Understanding the Key Principles of International Accounting Rules. 2007. (ENG., Illus.). 288p. pap. 54.95 *(978-0-7506-8203-9(5)*, CIMA Publishing) Elsevier Science & Technology Bks.

Rutherford, Brian A. Financial Reporting in the UK: A History of the Accounting Standards Committee, 1969-1990. 2007. (Illus.). 438p. 190.00 *(978-0-415-39421-5(X))* Routledge.

Sangiuolo, Rosemarie & Seidman CPA, Leslie F. Financial Instruments: A Comprehensive Guide to Accounting & Reporting. 2009. 1200p. pap. 299.00 *(978-0-8080-2095-0(1))* Toolkit Media Group.

Shamrock, Steven E. IFRS & US GAAP: A Comprehensive Comparison. 2012. (Wiley Regulatory Reporting Ser.: 5). (ENG.). 213p. pap. 110.00 ***(978-1-118-14430-5(9)***, Wiley) Wiley, John & Sons, Inc.

Siegel, Joel, et al. GAAP Handbook of Policies & Procedures. 1400p. 2009. pap. 159.00 incl. cd-rom *(978-0-8080-2098-1(6))* 2008. pap. 165.00 incl. audio compact disk *(978-0-8080-9182-0(4))* Toolkit Media Group.

Siegel, Joel G., et al. GAAP Handbook of Policies & Procedures. 2007th rev. ed. 2006. (GAAP Handbook of Policies & Procedures Ser.). (Illus.). 1290p. pap. 140.00 incl. cd-rom *(978-0-8080-9043-4(7))* Toolkit Media Group.

Singer, Michael. Pocket MBA 2: Everything an Attorney Needs to Know about Finance. 2nd rev. ed. 2008. (ENG.). 305p. pap. 49.00 *(978-1-4024-1094-9(8))* Practising Law Institute.

Solovyov, Aleksei & Kuznetsov, Ilia. International Accounting in the 21st Century. 2009. (Business Economics in a Rapidly-Changing World Ser.). 129.00 *(978-1-60876-018-3(9))* Nova Science Pubs., Inc.

svc, Pwc uk account cons. Pwc Manual of Accounting Ifrs 2010. 2010. *(978-90-411-3257-4(0))* Kluwer Law International.

Tafelmeier, Robert. Markenbilanzierung und Markenbewertung: Analyse und Eignung von Markenbewertungsverfahren in Hinblick auf die bilanzielle Behandlung von Marken nach HGB und IAS/IFRS. 2009. (GER.). 312p. 83.95 *(978-3-631-58584-9(5))* Lang, Peter GmbH, Europaischer Verlag der Wissenschaften DEU. Dist: Lang, Peter.

Theobald, Paul. Transitioning to IFRS in SAP ERP Financials. 2009. (Illus.). 209p. 79.95 *(978-1-59229-319-3(0)*, SAP PR.) Galileo Pr., Inc.

Tiffin, Ralph. The Complete Guide to International Financial Reporting Standards: Including IAS & Interpretation. 3rd rev. ed. 2010. (Thorogood Reports). 280p. pap. 157.00 *(978-1-85418-690-4(6))* Thorogood GBR. Dist: Stylus Publishing, LLC.

—International Financial Reporting Standards: Including IAS & Interpretation. 2nd rev. ed. 2007. 272p. per., instr.'s gde. ed. 39.95 *(978-1-85418-337-8(0))* Thorogood GBR. Dist: Stylus Publishing, LLC.

United Nations Conference on Trade and Development Staff. International Accounting & Reporting Issues: 2008 Review. 2011. (ENG., Illus.). 176p. pap. 75.00 ***(978-92-1-112824-6(2))*** United Nations Pubns.

Van Greuning, Hennie. International Financial Reporting Standards: A Practical Guide. (Stand Alones Ser.). (ENG.). 4th rev. ed. 2006. 312p. per. 39.95 *(978-0-8213-6768-1(4)*, 9780821367681) 5th rev. ed. 2010. pap. 37.50 *(978-0-8213-8106-9(7))* 5th rev. ed. 2009. (Illus.). 344p. pap. 49.95 *(978-0-8213-7727-7(2)*, 9780821377277) World Bank Pubns.

Wallace, Eric. Construction Guide: Accounting & Knowledge-Based Audits 2008. 2008. 998p. pap. 169.00 *(978-0-8080-9169-1(7))* Toolkit Media Group.

Walter, Andrew. Governing Finance: East Asia's Adoption of International Standards. 2008. (Cornell Studies in Money Ser.). (Illus.). 235p. 36.95 *(978-0-8014-4645-0(7))* Cornell Univ. Pr.

Weirich, Thomas R., et al. Mastering FASB Codification & EIFRS: A Casebook Approach. 2011. (ENG., Illus.). 112p. (C). pap. 100.95 ***(978-1-118-10729-4(2)***, Wiley) Wiley, John & Sons, Inc.

Weiss, Judith. GAAP Guide Levels B, C, & D (2009) 2008. 1200p. pap. 185.00 *(978-0-8080-9221-6(9))* Toolkit Media Group.

Weygandt, Jerry J., et al. Financial Accounting: Working Papers. 2010. (ENG.). 868p. (C). pap. 74.95 *(978-0-470-60727-5(0)*, Wiley) Wiley, John & Sons, Inc.

Wiecek, Irene M. & Young, Nicola M. IFRS Primer: International GAAP Basics. 2008. (ENG.). 376p. pap. 29.95 *(978-0-470-15888-3(3)*, Wiley) Wiley, John & Sons, Inc.

—IFRS Primer International GAAP Basics. 2009. (ENG., Illus.). 384p. (C). pap. 79.95 *(978-0-470-48317-6(2)*, Wiley) Wiley, John & Sons, Inc.

Wiehle, Ulrich, et al. 100 IFRS Kennzahlen / 100 IFRS Financial Ratios Dictionary - Deutsch / Englisch. 3rd ed. 2007. (GER & ENG.). 235p. pap. *(978-3-9809461-2-4(6))* cometis publishing GmbH.

Wiley-VCH Staff, ed. International Financial Reporting Standards (IFRS) 2009: Deutsch-Englische Textausgabe der von der EU gebilligten Standards. English & German Edition of the Official Standards Approved by the EU. 2009. (International Financial Reporting Standards (IFRS) Deutsche-Englische Ser.). 1174p. pap. 40.00 *(978-3-527-50469-5(9)*, Wiley-VCH) Wiley, John & Sons, Inc.

—International Financial Reporting Standards (IFRS) 2011: Deutsch-Englische Textausgabe der von der EU gebilligten Standards. English & German edition of the official standards approved by the EU. 2011. (International Financial Reporting Standards (IFRS) Deutsche-Englische Ser.). (ENG.). 1293p. pap. 39.95 *(978-3-527-50588-3(1)*, Wiley-VCH) Wiley, John & Sons, Inc.

Williams, Jan, et al. Complete GAAP Library 2007. 2007th rev. ed. 2006. 3500p. pap. 269.00 *(978-0-8080-9045-8(3))* Toolkit Media Group.

—Complete GAAP Library 2008. 2007. 3000p. pap. 285.00 *(978-0-8080-9125-7(5))* Toolkit Media Group.

Williams, Jan R. & Carcello, Joseph V. GAAP Guide Level A. 2008. 1400p. pap. 185.00 *(978-0-8080-9218-6(9))* Toolkit Media Group.

—GAAP Guide Level A. 2007th rev. ed. 2006. 1256p. pap. 149.00 *(978-0-8080-9046-5(1)*, CCH) Wolters Kluwer Tax & Accounting.

—GAAP Guide, Level A: Restatement & Analysis of Current FASB Standards. 2007. 1400p. pap. 253.00 incl. cd-rom *(978-0-8080-9128-8(X))* Toolkit Media Group.

—GAAP Guide Level A: Restatement & Analysis of Current FASB Standards. 2007th rev. ed. 2006. 1200p. pap. 239.00 incl. cd-rom *(978-0-8080-9060-1(7))* Toolkit Media Group.

Yip, Shu Wing, et al. Australian SME Readiness to adopt AIFRS: Australian SME Readiness to adopt Australian equivalents of International Financial Reporting Standards. 2008. 120p. pap. *(978-3-639-08913-4(8))* VDM Verlag Dr. Mueller e.K.

ACCOUNTING—STATISTICAL METHODS

Barrow, Michael. Statistics for Economics, Accounting & Business Studies, 2 vols. 5th ed. 2010. (ENG., Illus.). 480p. (C). pap. 180.00 *(978-0-273-71794-2(4)*, Prentice Hall) Prentice Hall PTR.

Monheiser-List, Lorraine. Referral Practice Chart of Accounts. 2009. (ENG.). pap. 39.95 *(978-1-58326-112-5(5)*, AAHA Pr.) American Animal Hospital Assn. Pr.

ACCOUNTING—STUDY AND TEACHING

Barnard, Marietjie & Gous, M.M. Introduction to Accounting for the Senior Phase Teacher's Guide. 2007. 184p. pap. *(978-0-521-71063-3(4))* Cambridge Univ. Pr.

—Introduction to Accounting for the Senior Phase Teacher's Guide (Afrikaans Translation) 2007. 184p. pap. *(978-0-521-71065-7(0))* Cambridge Univ. Pr.

Braun, Karen & Farmer, Amanda. Study Guide with DemoDocs for Managerial Accounting. 2nd ed. 2010. (ENG.). 504p. (C). pap., pupil's gde. ed. 46.67 *(978-0-13-602322-7(3)*, Prentice Hall) Prentice Hall PTR.

Brubeck, Helen. Accounting, Pack. 8th ed. 2009. (ENG.). (C). pap., stu. ed. 53.33 incl. cd-rom *(978-0-13-508174-7(2)*, Prentice Hall) Prentice Hall PTR.

—Financial & Managerial Accounting, Chs. 1-14. 2nd ed. 2009. (ENG.). (C). pap., stu. ed. 46.67 incl. cd-rom *(978-0-13-508171-6(8)*, Prentice Hall) Prentice Hall PTR.

Brubeck, Helen E., et al. Managerial Accounting. 2010. (ENG.). (C). pupil's gde. ed. 20.00 incl. cd-rom *(978-0-13-602280-0(4)*, Prentice Hall) Prentice Hall PTR.

Catanach, Anthony H. & Schwartz, Bill N., eds. Advances in Accounting Education Vol. 9: Teaching & Curriculum Innovations. 2008. (Advances in Accounting Education Teaching & Curriculum Innovations Ser.). 192p. 99.95 *(978-0-7623-1458-4(3))* Emerald Group Publishing Ltd. GBR. Dist: Turpin Distribution Services Ltd.

Catanach Jr, Anthony H. & Feldmann, Dorothy, eds. Advances in Accounting Education, Vol. 12. 2011. 250p. ***(978-1-78052-222-7(3))*** Emerald Group Publishing Ltd.

Cezair, Joan. Learning Style & Its Relationship to Success in Accounting Courses. 2009. 280p. pap. *(978-3-639-21735-3(7))* VDM Verlag Dr. Mueller e.K.

Cram101 Textbook Reviews Staff. Outlines & Highlights for Accounting Concepts & Applications by Albrecht, Stice, Stice, Swain, Isbn: 0324187564. 2009. 220p. pap. 30.95 *(978-1-4288-3921-2(6))* Cram101 Inc.

Crosson, Susan V. & Needles, Belverd E. Financial & Managerial Accounting. 9th ed. 2010. (ENG.). (C). 30.95 *(978-0-538-74296-2(8))*; 26.95 *(978-0-538-79191-5(8))* Cengage South-Western.

Eldenburg, Leslie G. & Wolcott, Susan K. Cost Management 2E Study Guide. 2nd ed. 2008. pap. 31.95 *(978-0-470-18232-1(6))* Wiley, John & Sons, Inc.

Evans, Elaine. Colleges of Advanced Education in Australi: A lasting Legacy. 2009. 104p. pap. *(978-3-639-14548-9(8))* VDM Verlag Dr. Mueller e.K.

Evans, Elaine, et al, eds. The Interface of Accounting Education & Professional Training. 2012. (ENG.). 160p. (C). 125.00 ***(978-0-415-69925-9(8))*** Routledge.

Feldman, Dorothy & Catanach, Anthony H., eds. Advances in Accounting Education Teaching & Curriculum Innovations. 2010. (Advances in

Accounting Education Ser.). (Illus.). 282p. (978-0-85724-291-4(1)) Emerald Group Publishing Ltd.

Gakunga, Daniel Komo. Determinants of Accounting Students' Performance. 2010. 68p. pap. (978-3-639-23945-4(8)) VDM Verlag Dr. Mueller e.K.

Harrison, Walter T. Study Guide with DemoDocs for Financial Accounting. 8th ed. 2009. (ENG.). 528p. (C). pap. 46.67 (978-0-13-602334-0(7), Prentice Hall) Prentice Hall PTR.

Heintz, James A. & Parry, Robert W. Study Guide with Working Papers, Chapters 1-9 & 10-15 (with Combination Journal Module) for Heintz/Parry's College Accounting. 20th ed. 2010. (ENG.). 1064p. (C). pap. 69.95 (978-0-538-73704-3(2)) Cengage South-Western.

Kimmel, Paul D., et al. Accounting - Excel Working Papers. 3rd ed. 2009. (ENG.). (C). 37.95 (978-0-470-37885-6(3), Wiley) Wiley, John & Sons, Inc.

MicroMash CPA Review Reference, 1998-1999, 5 vols. Incl. MicroMash CPA Review Reference Vol. 1: The MicroMash Way to Pass. 142p. (C). pap. 7.00 (978-0-926709-78-2(X)); MicroMash CPA Review Reference Vol. 2: Financial Accounting (FARE) Mann, M. Herschel. 432p. pap. 7.00 (978-0-926709-81-2(X)); MicroMash CPA Review Reference Vol. 3: Managerial/Governmental/Taxation (ARE) Cherrington, J. Owen. 386p. (C). pap. 7.00 (978-0-926709-82-9(8)); MicroMash CPA Review Reference Vol. 4: Auditing (AUDIT) Clay, Raymond J. 257p. (C). pap. 7.00 (978-0-926709-79-9(8)); MicroMash CPA Review Reference Vol. 5: Business Law & Professional Responsibilities (LPR) Jaeger, David G. 319p. (C). pap. 7.00 (978-0-926709-80-5(1)); (Illus.). 1998. (978-0-926709-77-5(1)) MicroMash.

Oliver, M. Suzanne. Demodocs for Managerial Accounting. 2010. (ENG.). 384p. (C). pap., stu. ed. 46.67 (978-0-13-602500-9(5), Prentice Hall) Prentice Hall PTR.

Phillips, et al. Fundamentals of Financial Accounting with Annual Report + Connect Plus. 3rd ed. 2010. (ENG.). (C). pap. 253.33 (978-0-07-739820-0(3), 0077398203, McGraw-Hill/Irwin) McGraw-Hill Higher Education.

Phillips, Fred, et al. Connect Accounting. 3rd ed. 2010. (ENG.). (C). pap. 110.75 (978-0-07-726965-4(9), 0077269659, McGraw-Hill/Irwin) McGraw-Hill Higher Education.

—Connect Accounting with LearnSmart 1-Semester to Accompany Fundamentals of Financial Accounting. 3rd ed. 2010. (ENG.). 32p. (C). pap. 49.99 (978-0-07-726963-0(2), 0077269632, McGraw-Hill/Irwin) McGraw-Hill Higher Education.

Price, John & Haddock, David. College Accounting. 2008. 608p. pap. 89.00 (978-0-07-336549-7(1)) McGraw-Hill Professional Publishing.

Price, John, et al. College Accounting. 12th ed. 2008. (Illus.). (C). 1008p. stu. ed. 132.67 (978-0-07-336550-3(5), 0073365505); 1176p. stu. ed. 151.67 (978-0-07-340166-9(8), 0073401668) McGraw-Hill Professional Publishing.

Rittner, Max. Accounting for the Twenty-First Century Classroom Workbook: An Integrated QuickBooks Perspective. 2011. 251p. pap. 58.95 (978-1-4327-6912-3(X)) Outskirts Pr., Inc.

Simmons, Anthony & Hardy, Richard. Cambridge VCE Accounting Units 3&4 Teacher CD-ROM. 2006. tchr. ed. 72.00 incl. cd-rom (978-0-521-67129-3(9)) Cambridge Univ. Pr.

Straney, Louis L. Securities Fraud: Detection, Prevention, & Control. 2010. (Wiley Finance Ser.: 584). (ENG., Illus.). 208p. 75.00 (978-0-470-60157-0(4), Wiley) Wiley, John & Sons, Inc.

Verduzco, David. Foundations of Accounting. rev. ed. 2010. (ENG.). 272p. pap. 65.24 (978-0-7575-6767-4(3)) Kendall Hunt Publishing Co.

Watty, Kim, et al, eds. Personal Transferable Skills in Accounting Education. 2012. (ENG.). 192p. (C). 125.00 **(978-0-415-69920-4(7))** Routledge.

Weygandt, Jerry J. Accounting Principles. 10th ed. 2011. (Illus.). (C). pap. 109.95 (978-0-470-92034-3(3), Wiley) Wiley, John & Sons, Inc.

Wild & Wild, John. Financial Accounting with IFRS FO Primer + Connect Plus. 5th ed. 2010. (ENG.). (C). 253.33 (978-0-07-741380-4(6), 0077413806, McGraw-Hill/Irwin) McGraw-Hill Higher Education.

ACCOUNTING—VOCATIONAL GUIDANCE

Joyce, Tim. Cambridge Checkpoints VCE Accounting Unit 3 2008. 2007. (Cambridge Checkpoints Ser.). pap. (978-0-521-71577-5(6)) Cambridge Univ. Pr.

Ross, Stan & Carberry, James. The Inside Track to Careers in Accounting. 2010. 364p. pap. 73.75 (978-0-87051-872-0(0)) American Institute of Certified Public Accountants.

Whiting, Rosalind. Gender, Family Responsibilities & Career Success in the Accountancy Profession. 2008. 416p. pap. (978-3-639-03871-2(1)) VDM Verlag Dr. Mueller e.K.

ACCOUNTING FIRMS

Clark, Lydia. How to Open & Operate a Financially Successful Bookkeeping Business: With Companion CD-ROM. 2011. (ENG.). 288p. pap. 39.95 (978-1-60138-277-1(4)) Atlantic Publishing Co.

Cottle, David. Bill What You're Worth, Second Edition. 2011. pap. 68.75 (978-0-87051-917-8(4)) American Institute of Certified Public Accountants.

Fligel, Robert. Supercharge Your Cpa Firm. 2011. 36p. pap. 21.99 **(978-1-4568-6495-8(5))** Xlibris Corp.

Gerber, Michael E. & Root, M. Darren. The E-Myth Accountant: Why Most Accounting Practices Don't Work & What to Do about It. 2011. (ENG., Illus.). 182p. 24.95 (978-0-470-50366-9(1), Wiley) Wiley, John & Sons, Inc.

Loosvelt, Derek & Vault Editors. Vault Guide to the Top 40 Accounting Firms. 5th ed. 2008. (Vault Career Library). (ENG., Illus.). 128p. pap. 29.95 (978-1-58131-567-7(8)) Vault.com.

Partners Financial. Life Insurance: How to Use It to Your Clients' Advantage. Schick, Bryan, ed. 2010. 182p. pap. 72.00 (978-0-87051-897-3(6)) American Institute of Certified Public Accountants.

Reed, William. Securing the Future 1: Succession Planning Basics. 2009. pap. 98.75 (978-0-87051-854-6(2)) American Institute of Certified Public Accountants.

—Securing the Future 2: Taking Succession to the Next Level. 2009. pap. 98.75 (978-0-87051-855-3(0)) American Institute of Certified Public Accountants.

Sandler, Susan F., ed. CPA Firm Statistical Analysis Reference Handbook 2007. 2006. 67p. pap. 379.00 (978-1-58673-204-2(8)) Institute of Management & Administration, IOMA.

Selected Readings 2007 — Management of a Practice. 2007. cd-rom (978-0-87051-658-0(2)) American Institute of Certified Public Accountants.

United States, General Accounting Office Staff, contrib. by. Audits of Public Companies. 2008. (Illus.). 133p. 82.00 (978-1-60456-503-4(9)) Nova Science Pubs., Inc.

ACCOUNTING STANDARDS

see Accounting—Standards

ACCOUNTS, COLLECTING OF

see Collecting of Accounts

ACCOUNTS, INDIVIDUAL RETIREMENT

see Individual Retirement Accounts

ACCOUNTS PAYABLE

Cokala. Aapa Guide to Accounts Payable 2010e. 2010. ring bd. 259.00 (978-0-7355-9183-7(0), Aspen Pubs.) Wolters Kluwer Law & Business.

Dzamba, Andrew, ed. Accounts Payable Compensation Report 2007. 2007. (Illus.). 94p. pap. 299.00 (978-1-58673-195-3(5)) Institute of Management & Administration, IOMA.

—Accounts Payable Policies & Procedures Guide. 2006. 42p. pap. 329.00 (978-1-58673-190-8(4)) Institute of Management & Administration, IOMA.

Dzamba, Andy, ed. AP Benchmarks Executive Summary 2007. 2006. (Illus.). 32p. pap. 179.60 (978-1-58673-202-8(1)) Institute of Management & Administration, IOMA.

—AP Department Benchmarks & Analysis 2007. 2006. (Illus.). 201p. pap. 495.00 (978-1-58673-194-6(7)) Institute of Management & Administration, IOMA.

Dzambq, Andy, ed. Imaging & Workflow Systems for Accounts Payable. 2007. 107p. pap. 349.00 (978-1-58673-198-4(X)) Institute of Management & Administration, IOMA.

Lanza, Richard B. & Lanza. Cost Recovery: Turning Your Accounts Payable Department into a Profit Center. 2009. (ENG., Illus.). 343p. 78.95 (978-0-470-32238-3(1), Wiley) Wiley, John & Sons, Inc.

Schaeffer, Mary S. Controller & CFO's Guide to Accounts Payable. 2006. (ENG.). 256p. 63.50 (978-0-471-78599-7(X), Wiley) Wiley, John & Sons, Inc.

—Fraud in Accounts Payable: How to Prevent It. 2008. (ENG.). 200p. 57.95 (978-0-470-26045-6(9), Wiley) Wiley, John & Sons, Inc.

Wittenberg, David, ed. Paperless Accounts Payable: The AP Department's Complete Guide to Electronic Invoicing. 2007. (Illus.). 174p. pap. 459.00 (978-1-58673-250-9(1)) Institute of Management & Administration, IOMA.

ACCOUNTS RECEIVABLE

Bernstein, Robert. Get P. A. I. D. A Guide to Getting Paid Faster. 2007. (Illus.). 34.95 (978-0-9801264-1-9(X)) Business Credit Pubns., LLC.

—Get P. A. I. D. A Guide to Getting Paid Faster (And What to Do If You Don'T) 2008. (Illus.). 212p. per. 19.95 (978-0-9801264-0-2(1)) Business Credit Pubns., LLC.

Cowger, Jim. Effective & Efficient Medical Billing, 1 vol. 2010. 60p. pap. 16.95 (978-1-4489-5573-2(4)) PublishAmerica, Inc.

Keegan, Deborah Walker, et al. The Physician Billing Process: 12 Potholes to Avoid in the Road to Getting Paid. 2nd ed. 2009. 128.00 net. (978-1-56829-339-4(9)) Medical Group Management Assn. (MGMA).

Patel, Manish. Maximizing SAP ERP Financials Accounts Receivable. 2010. (Illus.). 505p. 79.95 (978-1-59229-303-2(4), SAP PR.) Galileo Pr., Inc.

Stanley, Kay. Maximizing Billing & Collections in the Medical Practice. 2007. (Illus.). 145p. pap. 75.95 incl. cd-rom (978-1-57947-867-4(0)) American Medical Assn.

ACCOUNTS RECEIVABLE FINANCE COMPANIES

see Commercial Finance Companies

ACCREDITATION (EDUCATION)

see also subdivision Study and Teaching under specific subjects, e.g. Industrial Arts—Study and Teaching, as well as names of types of schools, e.g. High Schools, with or without the subdivision Accreditation

Alstete, Jeffrey W. & Alstete, Jeffrey. College Accreditation: Managing Internal Revitalization & Public Respect. 2006. (ENG.). 264p. 89.00 (978-1-4039-7420-4(9)) Palgrave Macmillan.

American Medical Association, creator. Graduate Medical Education Directory: Including Programs Accredited by the Accreditation Council for Graduate Medical Education. 2008. (Graduate Medical Education Directory Ser.). pap. 78.00 (978-1-60359-003-7(X)) American Medical Assn.

Breier, Mignonne. The RPL Conundrum: Recognition of Prior Learning in a Teacher Upgrading Programme. 2009. (Teacher Education in South Africa Ser.). (ENG.). 144p. pap. 22.95 (978-0-7969-2220-5(9)) Human Sciences Research Council ZAF. Dist: Independent Pubs. Group.

Burris, Robert T. The Impact of Significant Shifts. 2009. 140p. pap. (978-3-639-13728-6(0)) VDM Verlag Dr. Mueller e.K.

Cairns, Carol S. Verify & Comply: A Quick Reference Guide to the Joint Commission & NCQA Standards for Credentialing. 4th ed. 2007. xiv, 182p. spiral bd. (978-1-57839-980-2(7)) Opus Communications.

Community Colleges Staff. Institutional Effectiveness: New Directions for Community Colleges. Head, Ronald B., ed. 2011. (J-B CC Single Issue Community Colleges Ser.: 212). (ENG., Illus.). 112p. pap. 29.00 (978-1-118-08413-7(6), Jossey-Bass) Wiley, John & Sons, Inc.

Education Regulations: Federal Overreach into Academic Affairs: Hearing Before the Subcommittee on Higher Education & Workforce Training, Committee on Education & the Workforce, U.S. House of Representatives, One Hundred Twelfth Congress, First Session, Hearing Held in Washington, DC, March 11, 2011. 2011. iii, 85p. **(978-0-16-088794-9(1)**, 552-070-42934-4) United States Government Printing Office.

Esteban Anzoise, Esteban Anzoise. Higher Education Accreditation & Organizational Change. 2008. 256p. pap. (978-3-639-07209-9(X)) VDM Verlag Dr. Mueller e.K.

Fowler, Josephine. Insiders Guide to the ACGME Institutional Site Review. 2008. 118p. pap. 149.00 (978-1-60146-140-7(2)) Opus Communications.

Hamm, Vicki L. Graduate Medical Education Committee Handbook. 2008. 167p. pap. (978-1-60146-192-6(5)) HCPro, Inc.

Hamner, Candace J. J-Mail: Joint Commission Survey Prep Tool. 2009. cd-rom 149.00 (978-1-60146-250-3(6)) Opus Communications.

Hendricks, Mohamed Natheem. The Recognition of Prior Learning in Higher Education. 2009. 96p. pap. (978-3-639-13425-4(7)) VDM Verlag Dr. Mueller e.K.

Higher Education Staff. Accreditation: Assuring & Enhancing Quality 2009. O'Brien, Patricia M., ed. 2009. (J-B HE Single Issue Higher Education Ser.: 94). (ENG.). 112p. pap. 29.00 (978-0-470-48902-4(2), Jossey-Bass) Wiley, John & Sons, Inc.

Joko Wahyono & Toruan, Rayendra L. Sekolah Kaya Sekolah Miskin, Guru Kaya Guru Miskin. 2010. (IND., Illus.). xxiii, 156p. (978-979-27-7207-4(3)) Elex Media Komputindo.

Jung, Insung, et al, eds. Quality Assurance & Accreditation in Distance Education: Models, Policies & Research. 2011. (Open & Flexible Learning Ser.). (ENG., Illus.). 310p. 160.00 (978-0-415-88734-2(8)); pap. 44.95 (978-0-415-88735-9(6)) Routledge.

Miles, M. d. Development of an Accreditation Assessment Survey. 2011. 300p. pap. **(978-3-8454-1362-4(X))** Lambert Academic Publishing.

Mwenda, Kenneth Kaoma. Comparing American & British Legal Education Systems: Lessons for Commonwealth African Law Schools. 2007. (ENG.). 136p. (C). 79.95 (978-1-934043-51-6(6)) Cambria Pr.

Prados, John W., ed. A Proud Legacy of Quality Assurance in the Preparation of Technical Professionals: ABET 75th Anniversary Retrospective. 2007. 225p. (978-0-9799910-0-4(5)) ABET, Inc.

Rider, Elizabeth A. & Nawotniak, Ruth H. A Practical Guide to Teaching & Assessing the ACGME Core Competencies. 2nd ed. 2010. (Illus.). 394p. pap. (978-1-60146-740-9(0)) Opus Communications.

Rider, Elizabeth A., et al. A Practical Guide to Teaching & Assessing the ACGME Core Competencies. 2007. xx, 238p. pap. (978-1-57839-999-4(8)) Opus Communications.

Robertson, Rachel & Dressler, Miriam. Prove It! Achieving Quality Recognition for Your Early Childhood Program. 2009. (ENG.). 224p. pap. 39.95 (978-1-933653-77-8(9)) Redleaf Pr.

Schwartz, Sydney L. & Copeland, Sherry M. Connecting Emergent Curriculum & Standards in the Early Childhood Classroom: Strengthening Content & Teaching Practice. 2010. (ENG., Illus.). 208p. pap. 26.95 (978-0-8077-5109-1(X)); 58.00 (978-0-8077-5110-7(3)) Teachers College Pr., Teachers College, Columbia Univ.

SOAR to Success: Score Ongoing Accreditation Readiness, Behavioral Series. 5th ed. 2007. cd-rom 199.00 (978-0-9752634-9-5(8)) CBRCC, Inc.

SOAR to Success: Score Ongoing Accreditation Readiness, Hospital Series. 5th ed. 2007. cd-rom 199.00 (978-0-9752634-8-8(X)) CBRCC, Inc.

Swim, Terri Jo. Teacher National Accreditation As Community Dialogue: Transformative Reflections. 2010. (978-1-57273-912-3(6)); (978-1-57273-911-6(8)) Hampton Pr., Inc.

Twomey, Cordelia, et al. Teachers as Technology Leaders: A Guide to ISTE Technology Facilitation & Technology Leadership Accreditation. 2006. 176p. (C). pap. 29.95 (978-1-56484-226-8(6)) International Society for Technology in Education.

Whitten, Jeri L. & Hamm, Vicki L. Program Information Form Made Simple: A Guide to Completing the ACGME PIF. 2008. (Illus.). 111p. pap. 149.00 incl. cd-rom (978-1-60146-254-1(9)) Opus Communications.

Yilmaz, Harun. Systematic Approach to Accreditation. 2008. 136p. per. (978-3-8364-3511-6(X)) VDM Verlag Dr. Mueller e.K.

ACCULTURATION

see also Assimilation (Sociology); Diffusion of Innovations; Ethnic Relations; Indians of North America—Cultural Assimilation; Socialization

Abulafia, David. The Discovery of Mankind: Atlantic Encounters in the Age of Columbus. 2009. (ENG., Illus.). 408p. pap. 25.95 (978-0-300-15821-2(1)) Yale Univ. Pr.

Adams, Geoff W. Power & Religious Acculturation in Romano-Celtic Society: An Examination of Archaeological Sites in Gloucestershire. 2009. (Bar Ser.). (Illus.). 290p. (C). 112.50 (978-1-4073-0387-1(2)) British Archaeological Reports Ltd. GBR. Dist: Brown, David Bk. Co., The.

Ahmad, Imran. The Perfect Gentleman: A Muslim Boy Meets the West. 2012. (ENG.). 352p. 24.99 **(978-1-4555-0849-5(7))** Grand Central Publishing.

Akhtar, Salman. Immigration & Acculturation: Mourning, Adaptation, & the Next Generation. 2010. (ENG.). 310p. 70.00 (978-0-7657-0824-3(8)); xvi, 294p. (978-0-7657-0826-7(4)) Rowman & Littlefield Publishers, Inc. (Aronson, Jason).

Alvarez, Cecilia M. O. The Acculturation Process of Middle Income U S Hispanics. 2008. 144p. pap. (978-3-639-08106-0(4)) VDM Verlag Dr. Mueller e.K.

Barnouw, Victor. Acculturation & Personality among the Wisconsin Chippewa: American Anthropologist, V52, No. 4, Part 2, October 1950. Hoijer, Harry & Herskovits, Melville J., eds. 2011. 154p. 41.95 **(978-1-258-05884-5(7))** Literary Licensing, LLC.

Bell, Sinclair & Hansen, Inge Lyse. Role Models in the Roman World: Identity & Assimilation. 2008. (Supplements to the Memoirs of the American Academy in Rome Ser.). (ENG., Illus.). 328p. 90.00 (978-0-472-11589-1(8)) Univ. of Michigan Pr.

Berg, Ina. Negotiating Island Identities: The Active Use of Pottery in the Middle & Late Bronze Age Cyclades. 2007. (Gorgias Dissertations in Classics: 5). 78.00 (978-1-59333-725-4(6)) Gorgias Pr., LLC.

Bilde, Pia Guldager & Petersen, Jane Hjarl, eds. Meetings of Cultures in the Black Sea Region: Between Conflict & Coexistence. 2008. (Black Sea Studies). (ENG., Illus.). 422p. (C). 60.00 (978-87-7934-419-8(4)) Aarhus Universitetsforlag DNK. Dist: ISD.

Biswas, Debasish. International Students' Acculturation to a New Discourse Community. 2011. 108p. pap. **(978-3-8443-3079-3(8))** Lambert Academic Publishing.

Bletz, May E. Immigration & Acculturation in Brazil & Argentina: 1890-1929. 2010. (ENG.). 190p. 84.00 (978-0-230-10019-0(8)) Palgrave Macmillan.

Boatwright, Mary Taliaferro. Peoples of the Roman World. 2012. (Cambridge Introduction to Roman Civilization Ser.). (ENG.). 258p. 90.00 **(978-0-521-84062-0(7))**; (Illus.). pap. 25.99 **(978-0-521-54994-3(9))** Cambridge Univ. Pr.

Bodley, John H. Victims of Progress. 5th ed. 2008. (ENG.). 358p. pap. 44.95 (978-0-7591-1148-6(0)) AltaMira Pr.

Bonfante, Larissa, ed. The Barbarians of Ancient Europe: Realities & Interactions. 2011. (ENG., Illus.). 420p. 90.00 (978-0-521-19404-4(0)) Cambridge Univ. Pr.

Bourn, Douglas. Development Education: Debates & Dialogue. 2008. (ENG., Illus.). 134p. pap. 31.00 (978-0-85473-803-8(7)) Institute of Education GBR. Dist: Stylus Publishing, LLC.

Burnett, Kristin. Taking Medicine: Women's Healing Work & Colonial Contact in Southern Alberta, 1880-1930. 2011. (Women & Indigenous Studies Ser.). (ENG., Illus.). 248p. pap. 35.95 (978-0-7748-1829-2(8)) UBC Pr. CAN. Dist: Univ. of Washington Pr.

Burns, Robert I. Muslims Christians, & Jews in the Crusader Kingdom of Valencia: Societies in Symbiosis. 2009. (Cambridge Iberian & Latin American Studies). (ENG., Illus.). 338p. pap. 51.00 (978-0-521-09518-1(2)) Cambridge Univ. Pr.

Cameron, Rosalea. The Ecology of Third Culture Kids. 2008. 240p. pap. (978-3-639-01700-7(5)) VDM Verlag Dr. Mueller e.K.

Carson, James Taylor. Making an Atlantic World: Circles, Paths, & Stories from the Colonial South. 2007. (ENG.). 176p. 36.00 (978-1-57233-479-3(7)) Univ. of Tennessee Pr.

Chan, Kwok Bun, ed. Hybridity. 2012. (ENG.). 240p. (C). 125.00 **(978-0-415-69798-9(0))** Routledge.

Chytkova, Zuzana. Immigration, Gender & Consumer Acculturation. 2010. 228p. pap. (978-3-8383-6885-6(1)) Lambert Academic Publishing.

Codell, Julie F., ed. Transculturation in British Art, 1770-1930. 2012. (British Art: Global Contexts Ser.). (Illus.). 312 + 4 lourp. 119.95 **(978-1-4094-0977-9(5))** Ashgate Publishing Co.

Collins, Gregory. The Leadership Mind: Mastering the Superlative Qualities of Successful Leadership. 2010. 256p. 24.99 (978-1-4520-2798-2(6)); pap. 15.49 (978-1-4520-2799-9(4)) AuthorHouse.

Corfis, Ivy A. Al-Andalus, Sepharad, & Medieval Iberia: Cultural Contact & Diffusion. 2009. pap. (978-90-04-17919-6(4)) BRILL.

Cram101 Textbook Reviews Staff. Outlines & Highlights for Dominant-Minority Relations in Americ: Convergence in the New World by Myers, ISBN. 2008. 184p. pap. 12.95 (978-1-4288-6388-0(5)) Cram101 Inc.

Cumfer, Cynthia. Separate Peoples, One Land: The Minds of Cherokees, Blacks, & Whites on the Tennessee Frontier. 2007. (ENG., Illus.). 336p. (C). pap. 24.95 (978-0-8078-5844-8(7)) Univ. of North Carolina Pr.

Curet, L. Antonio & Hauser, Mark W. Islands at the Crossroads: Migration, Seafaring, & Interaction in the Caribbean. 2011. (Illus.). 352p. **(978-0-8173-8537-8(1))** Univ. of Alabama Pr.

Curet, L. Antonio & Hauser, Mark W., eds. Islands at the Crossroads: Migration, Seafaring, & Interaction in the Caribbean. 2011. (Caribbean Archaeology & Ethnohistory Ser.). (ENG., Illus.). 328p. pap. 35.00 (978-0-8173-5655-2(X)) Univ. of Alabama Pr.

Davis & Davis, Dorothy. Cultures in Contact. rev. ed. 2011. (ENG.). 186p. pap. 83.75 (978-0-7575-5243-4(9)) Kendall Hunt Publishing Co.

Dominguez, Silvia. Getting Ahead: Social Mobility, Public Housing, & Immigrant Networks. 2010. (ENG.). 288p. 45.00 (978-0-8147-2077-6(3)) New York Univ. Pr.

DuVal, Kathleen & DuVal, John. Interpreting a Continent: Voices from Colonial America. 2009. (ENG., Illus.). 312p. 95.00 (978-0-7425-5182-4(2)); pap. 35.00 (978-0-7425-5183-1(0)) Rowman & Littlefield Publishers, Inc.

Epstein, Beth. Collective Terms: Race, Culture, & Community in a State-Planned City in France. 2011. (BMFS Ser.). (Illus.). 220p. 75.00 (978-0-85745-084-5(0)) Berghahn Bks., Inc.

Eric, K. W. Desiring Hong Kong, Consuming South China: Transborder Cultural Politics, 1970-2010. 2011. (Hong Kong Culture & Society Ser.). (Illus.). 176p. ***(978-988-8053-93-3(0))*** Hong Kong Univ. Pr.
—Desiring Hong Kong, Consuming South China: Transborder Cultural Politics, 1970-2010. 2012. (Hong Kong Culture & Society Ser.). (ENG., Illus.). 220p. (gr. 17). pap. 25.00 ***(978-988-8083-46-6(5))*** Hong Kong Univ. Pr. HKG. Dist: Columbia Univ. Pr.
Garrett, Roger M., ed. Education & Development. 2011. (ENG.). 288p. 115.00 *(978-0-415-59494-3(4))* Routledge.
Gose, Peter. Invaders as Ancestors: On the Intercultural Making & Unmaking of Spanish Colonialism in the Andes. 2008. (Anthropological Horizons Ser.). (ENG., Illus.). 404p. *(978-0-8020-9876-4(2))*; pap. *(978-0-8020-9617-3(4))* Univ. of Toronto Pr.
Govor, E. V. Twelve Days at Nuku Hiva: Russian Encounters & Mutiny in the South Pacific. 2010. (C). 49.00 *(978-0-8248-3368-8(6))* Univ. of Hawaii Pr.
Green, Andrew. Transition & Acculturation. 2010. 280p. pap. *(978-3-8383-1837-0(4))* Lambert Academic Publishing.
Haun, Beverley. Inventing 'Easter Island' 2008. (Illus.). 320p. (ENG.). *(978-0-8020-9888-7(6))*; pap. *(978-0-8020-9353-0(1))* Univ. of Toronto Pr.
Higham, Carol L. & Katerberg, William H. Conquests & Consequences: The American West from Frontier to Region. 2009. (General American History Ser.). (Illus.). 475p. pap. 44.95 *(978-0-88295-270-3(6))* Davidson, Harlan Inc.
Hodges, Russell, et al. Teaching Study Strategies in Developmental Education: Readings on Theory, Research, & Best Practice. 2011. (ENG.). 480p. (C). pap. 12.95 *(978-0-312-66274-5(2))* Bedford/Saint Martin's.
Jacob, James. Policy Debates in Comparative, International, & Development Education. Hawkins, John N., ed. 2011. (International & Development Education Ser.). (ENG., Illus.). 320p. 85.00 *(978-0-230-62067-4(1))* Palgrave Macmillan.
Jolly, Margaret & MacIntyre, Martha, eds. Family & Gender in the Pacific: Domestic Contradictions & the Colonial Impact. 2010. (ENG.). 312p. pap. 33.99 *(978-0-521-13177-3(4))* Cambridge Univ. Pr.
Karam-Read, Daisy. From Manhattan to Mississippi: A New Yorker Falls in Love with the South. 2007. 112p. *(978-1-934193-09-9(7))* Quail Ridge Pr., Inc.
Knauft, Bruce. The Gebusi: Lives Transformed in a Rainforest World. 3rd ed. 2012. (ENG., Illus.). 208p. (C). pap. 47.00 ***(978-0-07-803492-3(2)***, 0078034922) McGraw-Hill Cos., The.
Knauft, Bruce M. The Gebusi: Lives Transformed in a Rainforest World. 2nd ed. 2009. (ENG., Illus.). 208p. (C). pap. 47.00 *(978-0-07-340537-7(X)*, 007340537X) McGraw-Hill Cos., The.
Lansford, Jennifer E., et al, eds. Immigrant Families in Contemporary Society. 2007. (Duke Series in Child Develpment & Public Policy Ser.). (ENG., Illus.). 336p. 60.00 *(978-1-59385-403-4(X))* Guilford Pubns., Inc.
Lansford, Jennifer E., et al. Immigrant Families in Contemporary Society. Lansford, Jennifer E. et al, eds. 2009. (Duke Series in Child Develpment & Public Policy Ser.). (ENG.). 336p. pap. 35.00 *(978-1-60623-247-7(9))* Guilford Pubns., Inc.
Ling, Huping. Voices of the Heart: Asian American Women on Immigration, Work, & Family. 2007. (Illus.). 424p. pap. 34.95 *(978-1-931112-68-0(1))* Truman State Univ. Pr.
Lomas, Kathryn. Rome & the Western Greeks 350 Bc - Ad 200. 2011. (ENG.). 272p. pap. 42.95 ***(978-0-415-62012-3(0))*** Routledge.
Lutz, John S. Myth & Memory: Stories of Indigenous-European Contact. Lutz, John Sutton, ed. 2007. (ENG., Illus.). 248p. *(978-0-7748-1262-7(1))* Univ. of British Columbia Pr.
Lutz, John Sutton, ed. Myth & Memory: Stories of Indigenous-European Contact. 2008. (ENG., Illus.). 248p. pap. 35.95 *(978-0-7748-1263-4(X))* Univ. of Washington Pr.
Ma, Jiewei. Desiring Hong Kong, Consuming South China: Transborder Cultural Politics, 1970-2010. 2012. (Hong Kong Culture & Society Ser.). (ENG., Illus.). 220p. (gr. 17). 60.00 ***(978-988-8083-45-9(7))*** Hong Kong Univ. Pr. HKG. Dist: Columbia Univ. Pr.
Mancall, Peter C., ed. The Atlantic World & Virginia, 1550-1624. 2007. (ENG., Illus.). 608p. per. 31.95 *(978-0-8078-5848-6(X))* Univ. of North Carolina Pr.
Marques, Lénia & Pimentel Biscaia, Maria Sofia, eds. Intercultural Crossings: Conflict, Memory & Identity. 2012. (Europe des cultures/Europe of cultures Ser.). 208p. pap. 40.95 ***(978-90-5201-816-4(2))*** PIE - Peter Lang BEL. Dist: Lang, Peter.
Marshall, Patricia. Stress & Coping among Professional Mediators: attributes & competencies. 2008. 420p. pap. *(978-3-639-09828-0(5))* VDM Verlag Dr. Mueller e.K.
Mathisen, Ralph W. & Shanzer, Danuta R., eds. Romans, Barbarians, & the Transformation of the Roman World: Cultural Interaction & the Creation of Identity in Late Antiquity. 2011. (Illus.). 398p. 99.95 *(978-0-7546-6814-5(2))* Ashgate Publishing Co.
Mattingly, D. J. Imperialism, Power & Identity: Experiencing the Roman Empire. 2010. (Miriam S. Balmuth Lectures in Ancient History & Archaeology Ser.). (ENG., Illus.). 366p. (C). 39.95 *(978-0-691-14605-8(5))* Princeton Univ. Pr.
Mccants, William. Founding Gods, Inventing Nations: Conquest & Culture Myths from Antiquity to Islam. 2011. (ENG.). 192p. (C). 35.00 *(978-0-691-15148-9(2))* Princeton Univ. Pr.
McElroy, Ann. Nunavut Generations: Change & Continuity in Canadian Inuit Communities. 2007. (Illus.). 187p. (C). pap. 18.50 *(978-1-57766-489-5(2))* Waveland Pr., Inc.
McGough, Todd. Cognition & Acculturation - Thinking about How We Adapt. 2007. 148p. per. *(978-3-8364-2662-6(5))* VDM Verlag Dr. Mueller e.K.
Migliazzo, Arlin C. To Make This Land Our Own: Community, Identity, & Cultural Adaptation in Purrysburg Township, South Carolina, 1732-1865. 2007. (Carolina Lowcountry & the Atlantic World Ser.). (Illus.). 435p. 59.95 *(978-1-57003-682-8(9))* Univ. of South Carolina Pr.
Miller, Gwenn A. Kodiak Kreol: Communities of Empire in Early Russian America. 2010. (Illus.). 248p. 55.00 *(978-0-8014-4642-9(2))* Cornell Univ. Pr.
Moran, Robert T., et al. Managing Cultural Differences: Global Leadership Strategies for Cross-Cultural Business Success. 8th rev. ed. 2011. (ENG., Illus.). 586p. (C). pap. 74.95 *(978-1-85617-923-2(0))* Routledge.
Nadeau, Carla. The Efficacy of Pre-Departure Cultural Orientation in Acculturation: An examination of employment as an element of acculturation success. 2008. 92p. pap. *(978-3-639-09637-8(1))* VDM Verlag Dr. Mueller e.K.
Nederveen Pieterse, Jan. Globalization & Culture: Global Mélange. 2nd ed. 2009. (Globalization Ser.). (ENG.). 196p. 79.00 *(978-0-7425-5605-8(0))*; pap. 24.95 *(978-0-7425-5606-5(9))* Rowman & Littlefield Publishers, Inc.
Nekvapil, Jiri & Sherman, Tamah, eds. Language Management in Contact Situations: Perspectives from Three Continents. 2009. (Prague Papers on Language, Society & Interaction / Prager Arbeiten zur Sprache, Gesellschaft und Interaktion Ser.). 272p. 72.95 *(978-3-631-58263-3(3))* Lang, Peter GmbH, Europaischer Verlag der Wissenschaften DEU. Dist: Lang, Peter.
Oers, Ricky van, et al. A Re-definition of Belonging? Language & Integration Tests in Europe. 2010. (Immigration & Asylum Law & Policy in Europe Ser.). 270p. *(978-90-04-17506-8(7))* BRILL.
Okeke, Amaka. The Acculturation Model: A Case Study of the Recent Adult Sudanese & Somalis English as a Second Language Learners. 2008. 320p. pap. *(978-3-639-07011-8(9))* VDM Verlag Dr. Mueller e.K.
Osburn, Katherine M. B. Southern Ute Women: Autonomy & Assimilation on the Reservation, 1887-1934. 2009. (ENG., Illus.). 184p. pap. 18.95 *(978-0-8032-2038-6(3))* Univ. of Nebraska Pr.
Park, Clara C. Asian American Education Acculturation, Literacy Development, & Learning. 2007. (Research on the Education of Asian & Pacific Americans Ser.). (ENG.). 232p. (C). *(978-1-59311-723-8(X))*; per. *(978-1-59311-722-1(1))* Information Age Publishing, Inc.
Parker, Charles H. Global Interactions in the Early Modern Age, 1400-1800. 2010. (Cambridge Essential Histories Ser.). (ENG., Illus.). 272p. (C). 85.00 *(978-0-521-86866-2(1))*; pap. 24.99 *(978-0-521-68867-3(1))* Cambridge Univ. Pr.
Paterson, Alistair. The Lost Legions: Culture Contact in Colonial Australia. 2008. (Indigenous Archaeologies Ser.). (ENG., Illus.). 288p. 90.00 *(978-0-7591-0683-3(5))*; per. 37.95 *(978-0-7591-0684-0(3))* AltaMira Pr.
Raw, Laurence, et al, eds. The Theme of Cultural Adaptation in American History, Literature, & Film: Cases When the Discourse Changed. 2009. (Illus.). vi, 553p. *(978-0-7734-3876-7(9))* Mellen, Edwin Pr., The.
Rebelo, Marcia. Acculturation Influences on the Self Concept of the Black Adolescent. 2009. 140p. pap. *(978-3-639-16237-0(4))* VDM Verlag Dr. Mueller e.K.
Restall, Matthew & Lane, Kris. Latin America in Colonial Times: Volume 1. 2011. (ENG., Illus.). (C). 304p. 90.00 *(978-0-521-76118-5(2))*; 320p. pap. 29.99 *(978-0-521-13260-2(6))* Cambridge Univ. Pr.
Reyes-Ruiz, Rafael, ed. Engaging Otherness. 2011. (ENG., Illus.). 272p. pap. 50.00 *(978-9948-15-750-2(8)*, Zayed University) I. B. Tauris & Co., Ltd. GBR. Dist: Macmillan.
Rodi, Robert. Seven Seasons in Siena: My Quixotic Quest for Acceptance among Tuscany's Proudest People. 2011. (Illus.). 272p. 25.00 *(978-0-345-52105-7(6)*, Ballantine Bks.) Random House Publishing Group.
Roth, R. E. & Keller, J. Roman by Integration: Dimensions of group identity in material culture & Text. Roth, R. E. & Keller, J., eds. 2007. (Journal of Roman Archaeology Ser.). (Illus.). 103p. 47.50 *(978-1-887829-66-3(0))* Journal of Roman Archaeology, LLC.
Rozbicki, Michal Jan & Ndege, George O. Cross-Cultural History & the Domestication of Otherness. 2011. (ENG., Illus.). 242p. 85.00 ***(978-0-230-33997-2(2))*** Palgrave Macmillan.
Samuel, Samantha. Living Two Lives & Two Cultures. 2009. 72p. pap. *(978-3-639-13551-0(2))* VDM Verlag Dr. Mueller e.K.
Sassen, Saskia, ed. Decphering the Global: Its Scales, Spaces & Subjects. 2007. (ENG., Illus.). 352p. 145.00 *(978-0-415-95732-8(X))*; per. 45.95 *(978-0-415-95733-5(8))* Routledge.
Schoina, Maria. Romantic 'Anglo-Italians' Configurations of Identity in Byron, the Shelleys, & the Pisan Circle. 2009. (Nineteenth Century Ser.). (Illus.). 202p. 99.95 *(978-0-7546-6292-1(6))* Ashgate Publishing Co.
Schwerin, Karl H. Oil & Steel: Processes of Karinya Culture Change in Response to Industrial Development. 2009. 288p. 68.00 *(978-1-59740-782-3(8))* ACLS Humanities E-Book.
Schwerin, Karl H. & Pleck, Elizabeth H. Oil & Steel: Processes of Karinya Culture Change in Response to Industrial Development. 2008. 288p. pap. 29.00 *(978-1-59740-659-8(7))* ACLS Humanities E-Book.
Small, Cathy A. Voyages: From Tongan Villages to American Suburbs. 2nd rev. ed. 2011. (Illus.). 312p. 65.00 ***(978-0-8014-5069-3(1))***; pap. 19.95 ***(978-0-8014-7739-3(5))*** Cornell Univ. Pr.
Spitta, Silvia. Misplaced Objects: Migrating Collections & Recollections in Europe & the Americas. 2009. (ENG., Illus.). 294p. 50.00 *(978-0-292-71897-5(7))* Univ. of Texas Pr.
Stein, Gil. The Archaeology of Colonial Encounters: Comparative Perspectives. (School of American Research Advanced Seminar Ser.). (Illus.). 464p. pap. 24.95 *(978-1-930618-44-2(1))* School for Advanced Research Pr./SAR Pr.
Tara M. Johnson. Acculturation: Implications for Individuals, Families & Societies. 2011. (Series: Social Issues, Justice & Status Ser.). xii, 246p. 89.00 *(978-1-61122-525-9(6))* Nova Science Pubs., Inc.
Thompson, Niobe. Settlers on the Edge: Identity & Modernization on Russia's Arctic Frontier. 2008. (ENG.). 320p. 85.00 *(978-0-7748-1467-6(5))* Univ. of British Columbia Pr. CAN. Dist: Univ. of Toronto Pr.
van Dommelen, P. & Terrenato, N. Articulating local Cultures: Power & identity under the expanding Roman Republic. van Dommelen, P. & Terrenato, N., eds. 2007. (International Roman Archaeology Conference Ser.). (Illus.). 144p. 65.50 *(978-1-887829-63-2(6))* Journal of Roman Archaeology, LLC.
van Tilburg, Miranda & Vingerhoets, A. J. J. M. Psychological Aspects of Geographical Moves: Homesickness & Acculturation Stress. 2007. (Amsterdam Academic Archive Ser.). 240p. pap. *(978-90-5356-860-6(3)*, Leiden Univ. Pr.) Amsterdam Univ. Pr.
Veth, Peter, et al, eds. Strangers on the Shore: Early Coastal Contact in Australia. 2008. (ENG.). 248p. pap. 29.95 *(978-1-876944-63-6(3))* National Museum of Australia AUS. Dist: Independent Pubs. Group.
Vishnevsky, Victor. The Magic Power of Life: Spiritual & Supernatural Stories of the Lovara Gypsies. 2008. (ENG.). 93p. pap. 20.00 *(978-0-9787728-1-9(4))* Salo Pr.
Westoby, Peter. The Sociality of Refugee Healing: In Dialogue with Southern Sudanese Refugees Resettling in Australia - Towards A Social Model of Healing. 2009. 220p. pap. 30.00 *(978-1-86335-625-1(8))* Common Ground Publishing Pty, Ltd.
Williams, Caroline A. Bridging the Early Modern Atlantic World: People, Products, & Practices on the Move. 2009. (Illus.). 276p. 124.95 *(978-0-7546-6681-3(6))* Ashgate Publishing Co.
Woolf, Greg. Tales of the Barbarians: Ethnography & Empire in the Roman West. 2011. (Blackwell-Bristol Lectures on Greece, Rome & the Classical Tradition Ser.: 2). (ENG.). 184p. 89.95 *(978-1-4051-6073-5(X)*, Wiley-Blackwell) Wiley, John & Sons, Inc.
Yoshimoto, Mika. Second-Language Learning & Identity: Cracking Metaphors in Ideological & Poetic Discourse in the Third Space. 2008. 336p. 109.95 *(978-1-60497-589-5(X))* Cambria Pr.
Young, Cynthia Y., et al. Ethics of Cultural Appropriation. Young, James O. & Brunk, Conrad G., eds. 2009. (Wiley Desktop Editions Ser.). (ENG., Illus.). 320p. 104.95 *(978-1-4051-6159-6(0)*, Wiley-Blackwell) Wiley, John & Sons, Inc.

ACCUMULATED EARNINGS TAX
see Undistributed Profits Tax

ACCUMULATIONS (LAW)
see Perpetuities

ACCUMULATORS
see Storage Batteries

ACD'S
see Adult Children of Divorced Parents

ACE
see Automatic Checkout Equipment

ACEPHALIA
see Bivalvia

ACETAL RESINS
Kiyota, Hiromasa, et al, contrib. by. Marine Natural Products. 2006. (Topics in Heterocyclic Chemistry Ser.: Vol. 5). (Illus.). XIV, 287p. 269.00 *(978-3-540-33728-7(8)*, 3540337288) Springer.

ACETAMINOPHEN
Jawale, Bhushan. Best Analgesics for Pain Associated with Separator Placement-A Study. 2011. 124p. pap. ***(978-3-8433-9130-6(0))*** Lambert Academic Publishing.
Mukhopadhyay, Debashis. Preparation & Evaluation of Novel Drug Alginate Granule Systems. 2009. 332p. pap. *(978-3-639-20332-5(1))* VDM Verlag Dr. Mueller e.K.

ACETYLENE
Bloor, D. & Chance, R. R., eds. Polydiacetylenes: Synthesis, Structure & Electronic Properties. 2010. (NATO Science Series E: (closed) Ser.). 432p. pap. 409.00 *(978-90-481-8294-7(8)*, 9048182948) Springer.
Have OSHA Standards Kept up with Workplace Hazards?: Hearing Before the Subcommittee on Workforce Protections, Committee on Education & Labor, U.S. House of Representatives, One Hundred Tenth Congress, First Session, Hearing Held in Washington, DC, April 24, 2007. 2007. (Illus.). iii, 72p. *(978-0-16-079769-9(1)*, 552-070-36684-9) United States Government Printing Office.
Inoue, Takashi. Diacetyl in Fermented Foods & Beverages. 2008. (Illus.). viii, 139p. *(978-1-881696-15-5(4))* American Society of Brewing Chemists.

ACETYLENE BLACK
see Carbon-Black

ACHAEMENIAN INSCRIPTIONS
see also Cuneiform Inscriptions; Cuneiform Writing
Williams Jackson, A. V. The Religion of the Achaemenian Kings. 2010. pap. 19.00 *(978-1-61719-551-8(0))* Gorgias Pr., LLC.

ACHALASIA OF THE CARDIA
see Cardiospasm

ACHEBE, CHINUA, 1930-
Abrahams, Kunle. A Study Guide to Chinua Achebe's Anthills of the Savannah. 2007. 64p. per. *(978-1-84549-258-8(7))* arima publishing.
Achebe, Chinua. The Education of a British-Protected Child: Essays. 2010. (ENG.). 192p. pap. 14.95 *(978-0-307-47367-7(8)*, Anchor) Knopf Doubleday Publishing Group.
Bloom, Harold, ed. & intro. Things Fall Apart. 2nd rev. ed. 2009. (Bloom's Modern Critical Interpretations Ser.). 232p. (C). (gr. 9-18). 45.00 *(978-1-60413-581-7(6)*, Chelsea Hse.) Facts On File, Inc.
Booker, M. Keith. Things Fall Apart, by Chinua Achebe. 2011. (Critical Insights Ser.). 322p. (YA). (gr. 9-18). 85.00 *(978-1-58765-711-5(2))* Salem Pr., Inc.
Chukwuma, Helen. Achebe's Women: Imagism & Power. 2011. ***(978-1-59221-869-1(5))***; pap. ***(978-1-59221-870-7(9))*** Africa World Pr.
Lindfors, Bernth. Early Achebe. 2009. *(978-1-59221-702-1(8))*; 224p. pap. *(978-1-59221-703-8(6))* Africa World Pr.
Morrison, Jago. The Fiction of Chinua Achebe. 2007. (Readers' Guides to Essential Criticism Ser.). (ENG.). 208p. 85.00 *(978-1-4039-8671-9(1))* Palgrave Macmillan.
—The Fiction of Chinua Achebe. Tredell, Nicolas, ed. 2007. (Readers' Guides to Essential Criticism Ser.). (ENG.). 208p. pap. 25.00 *(978-1-4039-8672-6(X))* Palgrave Macmillan.
Msiska & Whitaker. Chinua Achebe's Things Fall Apart. 2007. (Routledge Guides to Literature Ser.). (ENG.). 160p. (C). 95.00 *(978-0-415-34455-5(7))* Routledge.
Msiska, Mpalive-Hangson & Whittaker, David. Chinua Achebe's Things Fall Apart. 2007. (Routledge Guides to Literature Ser.). XIV, 146p. 28.95 *(978-0-415-34456-2(5))* Routledge.
Nwanyanwu, Augustine Uka. Chinua Achebe's Fiction. 2010. 232p. pap. *(978-3-8383-6362-2(0))* Lambert Academic Publishing.
Ogede, Ode & Ogede. Achebe's Things Fall Apart. 2007. (Reader's Guides (Continuum Paperback) Ser.). (ENG.). 136p. 19.95 *(978-0-8264-9084-1(0))* Continuum International Publishing Group, Ltd. GBR. Dist: National Bk. Network.
—Achebe's Things Fall Apart: A Reader's Guide. 2007. (Continuum Reader's Guides). (ENG.). 144p. 110.00 *(978-0-8264-9083-4(2))* Continuum International Publishing Group, Ltd. GBR. Dist: National Bk. Network.
Okolo, M. S. C. African Literature As Political Philosophy. 2007. (Africa in the New Millennium Ser.). (ENG.). 218p. 123.95 *(978-1-84277-894-4(3))*; per. 36.95 *(978-1-84277-895-1(1))* Zed Bks., Ltd. GBR. Dist: Macmillan.
Onyeozili, Gloria Nne. Shaken Wisdom: Irony & Meaning in Postcolonial African Fiction. 2011. (ENG., Illus.). 192p. (C). (gr. 13-17). pap. 21.50 *(978-0-8139-3187-6(8))* Univ. Pr. of Virginia.
Orobator, A. E. Theology Brewed in an African Pot. 2008. xiii, 162p. pap. *(978-1-57075-795-2(X))* Orbis Bks.
Shea, George. A Reader's Guide to Chinua Achebe's Things Fall Apart. 2008. (Multicultural Literature Ser.). (Illus.). 128p. (J). (gr. 9-12). lib. bdg. 31.93 *(978-0-7660-2831-9(3))* Enslow Pubs., Inc.

ACHESON, DEAN, 1893-1971
Beisner, Robert L. & Beisner, Robert. Dean Acheson: A Life in the Cold War. 2009. (ENG., Illus.). 832p. (J). pap. 19.95 *(978-0-19-538248-8(X))* Oxford Univ. Pr., Inc.
Chace, James. Acheson: The Secretary of State Who Created the American World. 2007. (ENG., Illus.). 512p. pap. 20.00 *(978-1-4165-4865-2(3))* Simon & Schuster.
McMahon, Robert J. Dean Acheson & the Creation of an American World Order. 2008. (Shapers of International History Ser.). (Illus.). 272p. 25.95 *(978-1-57488-926-0(5))*; pap. 16.95 *(978-1-57488-927-7(3))* Potomac Bks., Inc.
Truman, Harry S. & Acheson, Dean. Affection & Trust: The Personal Correspondence of Harry S. Truman & Dean Acheson, 1953-1971. Geselbracht, Ray & Acheson, David C., eds. 2010. (ENG., Illus.). 368p. 30.00 *(978-0-307-59354-2(1)*, Knopf) Knopf Doubleday Publishing Group.

ACHIEVEMENT, ACADEMIC
see Academic Achievement

ACHIEVEMENT MOTIVATION
see also Level of Aspiration
Anti, Lydia. Develop the Keys to Successful Living. 2010. 64p. pap. 13.95 *(978-1-4502-6195-1(7))* iUniverse, Inc.
Ball, Sharon. Reinventing Yourself Today: Step by Step Program to Discover Your True Self & Reinvent Your Life Accordingly. 2011. 148p. 29.99 ***(978-1-4568-9638-6(5))***; pap. 19.99 ***(978-1-4568-9637-9(7))*** Xlibris Corp.
Bartlett, Cynthia. Expectations, Encouragement & Empowerment - an Education: An alternative to Targets, Testing & Tables - a Tragedy. 2011. 148p. pap. 16.95 ***(978-1-4467-2616-7(9))*** Lulu Enterprises Inc.
Bembenutty, Héfer, ed. Self-Regulated Learning. No. 126. 2011. (J-B TL Single Issue Teaching & Learning Ser.: 126). (ENG.). 128p. pap. 29.00 *(978-1-118-09163-0(9)*, Jossey-Bass) Wiley, John & Sons, Inc.
Boggiano, Ann K. & Pittman, Thane S., eds. Achievement & Motivation: A Social-Developmental Perspective. 2011. (Cambridge Studies in Social & Emotional Development Ser.). (ENG.). 303p. pap. 39.99 *(978-0-521-17968-3(8))* Cambridge Univ. Pr.
Bruce Sr., James E. Life Is Like Climbing a Mountain. 2008. 160p. 24.95 *(978-1-4389-1710-8(4))*; pap. 18.95 *(978-1-4389-1711-5(2))* AuthorHouse.
Caffrey, Janine Walker. Nurturing Brilliance: Discovering & Developing Your Child's Gifts. 2011. 315p. pap. 19.95 ***(978-1-935067-12-2(5))*** Great Potential Pr., Inc.

Calipari, John. Bounce Back: Overcoming Setbacks to Succeed in Business & in Life. 2009. (ENG., Illus.). 304p. 26.00 *(978-1-4165-9750-6(6)*, Free Pr.) Free Pr.

Chaet, Mike, et al. Loops: The Seven Keys to Small Business Success. 2009. (ENG., Illus.). 144p. 19.95 *(978-0-07-162487-9(2)*, 0071624872) McGraw-Hill Cos., The.

Chapman, Stephen, et al. Improving Classroom Performance: Practical Applications for Effective Teaching & Learning. 2011. (Illus.). 176p. pap. **(978-1-84590-694-8(2))** Crown Hse. Publishing.

Charan, Ram. Leadership in the Era of Economic Uncertainty: The New Rules for Getting the Right Things Done in Difficult Times. 2008. (ENG.). 160p. 22.95 *(978-0-07-162616-3(6)*, 0071626166) McGraw-Hill Cos., The.

Chauncey, Caroline & Walser, Nancy, eds. Spotlight on Student Engagement, Motivation, & Achievement. 2009. 168p. lib. bdg. 39.95 *(979-1-934742-27-3(9)*, Harvard Education Pr.) Harvard Education Publishing Group (HEPG).

Choudhry, Salman. Seize the Day. 2008. 68p. pap. 9.99 *(978-1-59858-776-0(5))* Dog Ear Publishing, LLC.

Coman, Dumitru D. We Are Born to Fight to Win to Conquer & Overcome. 2011. 64p. pap. 19.95 **(978-1-4626-1353-3(5))** PublishAmerica, Inc.

Corfe, Robert. Populism Against Progress: And the Collapse of Aspirational Values. 2007. (ENG.). 170p. pap. 20.99 *(978-0-9543161-8-1(5))* Arena Bks. GBR. Dist: Lightning Source UK, Ltd.

Cram101 Textbook Reviews. Outlines & Highlights for Sport Psychology by Gellucci, Isbn: 9781841694863 184169486x. 2011. 252p. pap. 31.95 **(978-1-4288-9405-1(5))** Cram101 Inc.

Cram101 Textbook Reviews Staff. Outlines & Highlights for Seven Habits of Highly Effective People: Powerful Lessons in Personal Change by Stephen R. Covey, ISBN. 2009. 58p. pap. 26.95 *(978-1-4288-2261-0(5))* Cram101 Inc.

Cruz, Camilo. Factor X. 2009. 192p. pap. 13.95 *(978-1-60738-000-9(5))* Taller del Exito, Inc.

DeLong, Thomas J. Flying Without a Net: Turn Fear of Change into Fuel for Success. 2011. (ENG., Illus.). 288p. 29.95 *(978-1-4221-6229-3(X))* Harvard Business Review Pr.

Dembo, Myron H. & Seli, Helena. Motivation & Learning Strategies for College Success: A Self-Management Approach. 3rd rev. ed. 2007. (ENG., Illus.). 360p. per. 49.95 *(978-0-8058-6229-4(3))* Routledge.

—Motivation & Learning Strategies for College Success: A Self-Regulatory Approach. 4th rev. ed. 2012. (ENG., Illus.). 336p. 135.00 *(978-0-415-89419-7(0))*; pap. 49.95 *(978-0-415-89420-3(4))* Routledge.

Dembo/Seli. Motivation & Learning Strategies for College Success. 3rd rev. ed. 2007. 112p. *(978-0-8058-6230-0(7))* Erlbaum, Lawrence Assocs., Inc.

Dendrinos, Shirley. Unwritten. 2011. 288p. 29.99 **(978-1-4568-8705-6(X))**; pap. 19.99 **(978-1-4568-8704-9(1))** Xlibris Corp.

Duffy, Tim & Rimmer, Russell. Improving Students' Motivation to Study: A Photocopiable Resource for College & University Lecturers. 2008. 80p. (C). spiral bd. *(978-1-906052-11-9(5))* Lantern Publishing Limited.

Duncan, Kevin. Tick Achieve: How to Get Stuff Done. 2008. (ENG., Illus.). 235p. pap. 24.95 *(978-1-84112-795-8(7)*, Capstone) Wiley, John & Sons, Inc.

Durand, Dave. Perpetual Motivation: How to Light Your Fire & Keep It Burning in Your Career & in Life. 2010. (ENG.). 192p. pap. 16.95 *(978-0-8245-2592-7(2))* Crossroad Publishing Co., The.

Eikenberry, Kevin. Setting Goals & Supporting Goal Setting: Creating Remarkable Leaders. 2010. (ENG.). 16p. pap., wbk. ed. 15.00 *(978-0-470-50191-7(X)*, Pfeiffer) Wiley, John & Sons, Inc.

Elwins, Dannie. How to Set Goals & Start Achieving More in Life. 2009. 46p. pap. 16.99 *(978-0-557-15750-1(1))* Lulu Enterprises Inc.

Engeler, Martin. The Impact of International Experience on Football Team Performance. 2009. 88p. pap. *(978-3-639-20443-8(3))* VDM Verlag Dr. Mueller e.K.

Evensen, Dorothy H. & Pratt, Carla D., eds. The End of the Pipeline: A Journey of Recognition for African Americans Entering the Legal Profession. 2011. 344p. 40.00 **(978-1-59460-981-7(0))** Carolina Academic Pr.

Farnette, Cherrie & Jones, Jonathan. Strategies for Practicing Postive Choices: A Quick-Reference Resource for Helping Students with Self-Awareness, Proactivity, Perseverance, Goal Setting, Use of Support Systems, & Emotional Coping. 2007. (Greatest & Latest Teaching Tips Ser.). pap. 6.99 *(978-0-86530-706-3(7))* Incentive Pubns., Inc.

Frid, Marcia C. I Like You, I Like Me, Too! A Teacher/Parent Guide to Help Children Aged 6-10 Develop Self-Esteem Based on Choice Theory. 2008. (Illus.). 184p. pap. *(978-1-894431-25-5(1))* Your Nickel's Worth Publishing.

Glider, Jennifer L. What Do You Want in Life? 2008. 49p. pap. 16.95 *(978-1-60672-665-5(X))* PublishAmerica, Inc.

Glasper, Tamika & Jones, Valeria. Joy for a Lifetime. 2011. 108p. 22.00 **(978-1-4567-6237-7(0))**; pap. 12.00 **(978-1-4567-6236-0(2))** AuthorHouse.

Guerra, Bianca. A Woman's Guide to Manifestation Workbook. 2007. (Illus.). 135p. per. 13.95 *(978-0-9774499-3-4(9))* Living Life Publishing Co.

Gurian, Michael. The Purpose of Boys: Helping Our Sons Find Meaning, Significance, & Direction in Their Lives. (ENG.). 272p. 2010. pap. 16.95 *(978-0-470-40182-8(6))* 2009. 26.95 *(978-0-470-24337-4(6))* Wiley, John & Sons, Inc. (Jossey-Bass).

Gutman, Ross E. Pithy Truths, 4 vols., set. unabr. ed. Incl. 40 More Pithy Truths Vol. 2: A Self-Analysis Test. (Illus.). 1996. pap. 3.50 *(978-0-9652555-1-6(4))*; Vol. 1. 40 Pithy Truths: A Self-Analysis Test. (Illus.). 1996. pap. 3.50 *(978-0-9652555-0-9(6))*; Vol. 3. 40 Old Pithy Truths: A Self-Analysis Test. (Illus.). 1997. pap. 3.50 *(978-0-9652555-2-3(2))*; Vol. 4. 40 New Pithy Truths: A Self-Analysis Test to Test Thinking Skills Applying Personal Ananlysis to Varities of Pithy Truths. 1999. pap. 3.50 *(978-0-9652555-4-7(9))*; 96p. Set pap. 12.50 *(978-0-9652555-3-0(0))* Gutman, Ross.

Haley, Peter. Bury Me Across from the Burger King. 2008. 128p. 30.99 *(978-1-4257-3657-6(2))*; pap. 20.99 *(978-1-4257-3656-9(4))* Xlibris Corp.

Hallowell, Ned. Shine: Using Brain Science to Get the Best from Your People. 2011. (ENG., Illus.). 224p. 26.95 *(978-1-59139-923-0(8))* Harvard Business Review Pr.

Hart, Brig & Abraham, Ken. Why Not You, Why Not Now: The Brig Hart Story. 2011. (ENG., Illus.). 288p. 25.95 *(978-0-9826387-2-9(8)*, 0982638728) Franklin Green Publishing.

Hawkins, Mike. Activating Your Ambition: A Guide to Coaching the Best Out of Yourself & Others. 2009. (Illus.). xii, 314p. pap. *(978-1-934812-42-6(0))* Brown Bks. Publishing Group.

Hayden, Gene C. The Follow-Through Factor: Getting from Doubt to Done. 2010. (ENG., Illus.). 256p. pap. 17.99 *(978-0-7710-3817-4(8)*, McClelland & Stewart) McClelland & Stewart CAN. Dist: Random Hse., Inc.

Holroyd, Jane & Ross, Vicky. Improving Personal & Organisational Performance in Social Work. 2012. (ENG.). 128p. pap. **(978-0-85725-995-0(4))** Learning Matters Ltd.

Horton, Will. Teen Power: Wisdom for Greatness: Positive Thoughts on Hopes & Dreams. 2010. x, 97p. pap. *(978-1-892274-62-5(0))* Wisdom Bks. Inc.

Huff, Eane. Heads Up: Finding Possibility & Purpose with Head Injury. 2009. 289p. pap. 18.95 *(978-1-4327-3747-4(3))* Outskirts Pr., Inc.

Hunter, William. Dream Greatness Be Unstoppable: Live Your Dream & Leave a Legacy. 2008. (ENG.). 184p. per. 14.95 *(978-0-9792263-1-1(7))* William, Hunter.

Jackson, Yvette. The Pedagogy of Confidence: Inspiring High Intellectual Performance in Urban Schools. 2011. (ENG., Illus.). 208p. 27.95 *(978-0-8077-5224-1(X))*; pap. 27.95 *(978-0-8077-5223-4(1))* Teachers College Pr., Teachers College, Columbia Univ.

Kang, Ed. Re:LIFE & the Myth of Motivation. 2009. 138p. pap. 13.95 *(978-0-557-11694-2(5))* Lulu Enterprises Inc.

Kay, Susie. PROFESSIONALISM the ABC for Success. 2010. 92p. pap. 23.50 *(978-0-9565401-0-2(4))* Professionalism Bks. GBR. Dist: Lulu Enterprises Inc.

Klemmer, Brian. The Compassionate Samurai: Being Extraordinary in an Ordinary World. 2009. (ENG., Illus.). 245p. pap. 14.95 *(978-1-4019-2045-6(4))* Hay Hse., Inc.

Kofodimos, Joan. Your Executive Coaching Solution: Getting Maximum Benefit from the Coaching Experience. 2007. (ENG., Illus.). 120p. 22.95 *(978-0-89106-221-9(1))* Ebsco Publishing.

Lardon, Michael. Finding Your Zone: Ten Core Lessons for Achieving Peak Performance in Sports & Life. 2008. (ENG.). 192p. (gr. 12-18). 16.00 *(978-0-399-53427-0(X)*, Perigee Trade) Penguin Group (USA) Inc.

Lavoie, Richard. The Motivation Breakthrough: 6 Secrets to Turning on the Tuned-Out Child. 2008. (ENG.). 416p. pap. 16.00 *(978-0-7432-8961-0(7)*, Touchstone) Touchstone.

Lawson, Robert L. Destined for Greatness: Getting the Results You Desire from Yourself & Others. 160p. reprint ed. pap. 9.95 *(978-0-935979-01-5(8))* Professional Dynamics.

Lencioni, Patrick M. Managing for Employee Engagement: A Workshop Based on the Three Signs of a Miserable Job. 2011. (ENG.). 8p. ring bd. 20.00 *(978-0-470-52074-1(4)*, Pfeiffer) Wiley, John & Sons, Inc.

—Managing for Employee Engagement Set: A Workshop Based on the Three Signs of a Miserable Job. 2011. (ENG.). ring bd. 695.00 *(978-0-470-92706-9(2)*, Pfeiffer) Wiley, John & Sons, Inc.

—Managing for Employee Engagement Facilitator's Guide - Flash Drive Replacement Only. 2011. 130.00 *(978-0-470-62187-5(7)*, Pfeiffer) Wiley, John & Sons, Inc.

—The Three Signs of a Miserable Job: Anonymity, Irrelevance, Immeasurement. 2011. (J-B Lencioni Ser.: 39). (ENG.). 1p. pap. 10.00 *(978-0-470-92962-9(6)*, Pfeiffer) Wiley, John & Sons, Inc.

Lewis, Elaine M. Achieving Your Desires: Staying Focus on Your Direction in Life. 2011. 76p. pap. 12.95 *(978-1-4567-3676-7(0))* AuthorHouse.

London, Manuel. Employee Engagement Through Effective Performance Management: A Manager's Guide to Psychological Principles of Team Leadership. 2009. (ENG., Illus.). 272p. 49.95 *(978-1-84872-820-2(4)*, Routledge) Taylor & Francis Group GBR. Dist: Taylor & Francis Group.

Lovell, Sister Janet. Wisdom Speaks: The Power of the Blood, Thoughts, Words & Energy. 2011. 188p. 26.95 *(978-1-4620-0286-3(2))*; pap. 16.95 *(978-1-4620-0284-9(6))* iUniverse, Inc.

Maehr, Martin L. Encouraging a Continuing Personal Investment in Learning Motivation As an Instructional Outcome. 2012. **(978-1-61735-714-5(6))**; pap. **(978-1-61735-713-8(8))**; E-Book **(978-1-61735-715-2(4))** Information Age Publishing, Inc.

Margitics, Ferenc & Pauwlik, Zsuzsa, eds. Personal Strivings as a Predictor of Emotional Intelligence. 2010. (Psychology of Emotions, Motivations & Actions Ser.). (Illus.). ix, 79p. pap. 43.00 *(978-1-60876-620-8(9))* Nova Science Pubs., Inc.

Marin, Maria. Secretos de la Mujer Segura. 2010. audio compact disk 19.95 *(978-0-9745682-0-1(1))* Voice of Empowerment, Inc.

Marrone, Gerard. Unleash Your Amazing Potential: Find Your Perfect Grace. 2011. 323p. pap. 32.95 *(978-1-4327-6914-7(6))* Outskirts Pr., Inc.

McArthur, Ken. Impact: How to Get Noticed, Motivate Millions, & Make a Difference in a Noisy World. 2008. (ENG., Illus.). 1p. 24.99 *(978-1-56414-997-8(8))* Career Pr., Inc.

McClelland, David C. Achievement Motive. (Illus.). 42.50 *(978-0-8290-1167-8(6))* Irvington Pubs.

—The Achieving Society: With a New Introduction. 520p. (C). 50.50 *(978-0-8290-0870-8(5))* Irvington Pubs.

McMahon, Gladeana & Leimon, Averil. Performance Coaching for Dummies. 2012. (ENG., Illus.). 306p. pap. 29.99 **(978-0-470-51748-2(4)**, For Dummies) Wiley, John & Sons, Inc.

Men of Achievement, 4 vol., set. (Men of Achievement Ser.). reprint ed. 500.00 *(978-0-7222-8575-6(2))* Library Reprints, Inc.

Miller, Caroline Adams & Frisch, Michael B. Creating Your Best Life: The Ultimate Life List Guide. 2009. (ENG.). 288p. 19.95 *(978-1-4027-6259-8(3))* Sterling Publishing Co., Inc.

Munroe, Megan. Bitch, Please: How Nice Girls Can Succeed in a Bitch's World. 2011. (ENG.). 236p. 24.95 *(978-1-59652-806-2(0))* Turner Publishing Co.

Murphy, Mark. Hundred Percenters: Challenge Your Employees to Give It Their All & They'll Give You Even More. 2009. (ENG., Illus.). 240p. 27.95 *(978-0-07-163894-4(6)*, 0071638946) McGraw-Hill Cos., The.

Nakhid, Camille. "Intercultural" Perceptions & Institutional Responses: Explaining Pacific Islands Students Achievement in New Zealand Secondary Schools. 2010. (Illus.). 219p. pap. *(978-3-8383-2034-2(4))* Lambert Academic Publishing.

ón, Diego. Achievement Values: Puerto Rico & the United States. 2011. 158p. 23.00 **(978-1-4349-8556-9(3)**, RoseDog Bks.) Dorrance Publishing Co., Inc.

Ongong'a, Jared & APOPO, Yuanina. Motivating Learning at the Secondary School Level in Kenya. 2011. 84p. pap. **(978-3-8443-8838-1(9))** Lambert Academic Publishing.

Parker, Sam. 212: The Extra Degree. 2nd ed. 2011. pap. 10.95 *(978-1-885228-67-3(8)*, WalkTheTalk.com.

Perlus, Haley. The Ultimate Achievement Journal: Daily Inspiration for Peak Fitness Performance. 2009. (ENG.). 200p. 24.95 *(978-1-60037-636-8(3))* Morgan James Publishing.

Pettigrew, Karyn. The Invitation: The Secret to Creating Your Best Life. Bruce, Lynda, ed. 2007. 48p. pap. 6.95 *(978-1-59825-009-1(4)*, Highest Good Pubns.) EbonyEnergy Publishing, Inc.

Phillips, Lorraine, compiled by. Your Personal Success Quote Bible: Over 1,001 Inspirational Quotes for Daily Living! 2010. 176p. pap. 12.50 *(978-0-9822765-2-5(4))* 360 Bks., LLC.

Port, Michael, et al. The Think Big Manifesto: Think You Can't Change Your Life (And the World)? Think Again. 2009. (ENG.). 176p. 22.95 *(978-0-470-43237-2(3)*, Wiley) Wiley, John & Sons, Inc.

Quiñonez, Gustavo. Exito Integral. 2008. 122p. 26.95 *(978-0-557-01559-7(6))* Lulu Enterprises Inc.

Redinius, Don L. The New Era of Financial Success: Powered by the REACH Methodology. 2010. 368p. pap. 24.95 *(978-1-60911-587-6(2)*, Eloquent Bks.) AEG Literary Publishing Services, Inc.

Robbins, Alexandra. The Overachievers: The Secret Lives of Driven Kids. 2006. 448p. 24.95 *(978-1-4013-0201-6(7))* Hyperion Pr.

Robinson, A. Helene. Reading Achievement of Ninth Grade Students with Disabilities. 2009. 80p. pap. *(978-3-639-17343-7(0))* VDM Verlag Dr. Mueller e.K.

Robustelli, Stacy. There Is More Than One Yellow Brick Road to Achievement. 2008. 116p. pap. *(978-3-639-00513-4(9))* VDM Verlag Dr. Mueller e.K.

Sanborn, Mark. The Encore Effect: How to Achieve Remarkable Performance in Anything You Do. 2008. (ENG.). 160p. 15.95 *(978-1-4000-7306-1(5)*, WaterBrook Pr.) Doubleday Religious Publishing Group, The.

—The Encore Effect: How to Achieve Remarkable Performance in Anything You Do. 2008. (ENG.). 144p. 15.99 *(978-0-385-51905-2(2)*, Broadway Business) Knopf Doubleday Publishing Group.

Sanchez Ohep, Jesus A. Building a Nation One Person at a Time. 2008. 73p. pap. 16.95 *(978-1-60610-696-9(1))* PublishAmerica, Inc.

Scumaci, Dondi. Designed for Success: The 10 Commandments for Women in the Workplace. 2007. (ENG.). 256p. 21.99 *(978-1-59979-237-8(0))* Charisma Media.

Sharir, Eitan. Activate Your Power: How to Unlock Your Full Potential & Direct Your Own Success. 2010. 164p. 28.99 *(978-1-4520-1678-8(X))*; pap. 17.99 *(978-1-4520-1677-1(1))* AuthorHouse.

Sheard, Michael. Mental Toughness: The Mindset Behind Sporting Achievement. (ENG., Illus.). 2009. 160p. 59.95 *(978-0-415-49109-9(6))* 2009. 160p. pap. 29.95 *(978-0-415-49110-5(X))* 2nd rev. ed. 2012. 256p. 80.00 *(978-0-415-57895-0(7))* 2nd rev. ed. 2012. 256p. pap. 34.95 *(978-0-415-57896-7(5))* Routledge.

Smith, Jeffrey D. Assume the Victory! 2009. 100p. pap. 13.99 *(978-1-4389-4327-5(X))* AuthorHouse.

Stricker, Paul R. Sports Success RX! Your Child's Prescription for the Best Experience: How to Maximize Potential & Minimize Pressure. 2006. (ENG., Illus.). 200p. per. 15.95 *(978-1-58110-227-7(5))* American Academy of Pediatrics.

Sugar, Steve & Willett, Carol. Boost & Energize Set. 2006. (ENG., Illus.). 608p. pap. 90.00 *(978-0-7879-9523-2(1)*, Pfeiffer) Wiley, John & Sons, Inc.

Sullo, Robert. Activating the Desire to Learn. 2007. (Illus.). vii, 164p. pap. 23.95 *(978-1-4166-0423-5(5))* Assn. for Supervision & Curriculum Development.

Taylor, Les. Moving from Activity to Achievement: Keys for Transforming Your Life & Your Business. 2009. 120p. pap. 12.95 *(978-1-4401-6506-1(8))* iUniverse, Inc.

Terwilliger, Tom. 7 Rules of Achievement: From Vision to Action the Complete Guide to Programming Your Internal Success Mechanism. 2010. (ENG.). 182p. pap. 17.95 *(978-1-60037-737-2(8))* Morgan James Publishing.

Tolton, Frances. The Rainbow Factor - 7 Steps to Life Engagement. 2009. (Illus.). 142p. pap. *(978-1-907011-00-9(5))* Esteemworld Pubns.

Tynan, Bernadette. Make Your Child Brilliant: Uncovering Your Child's Hidden Talents. 2008. (ENG., Illus.). 1p. pap. 15.95 *(978-1-84400-579-6(6))* Quadrille Publishing, Ltd. GBR. Dist: Ingram Pub. Services.

Tynjälä, Päivi, et al, eds. Transitions & Transformations in Learning & Education. 2012. (ENG., Illus.). xi, 340p. 139.00 **(978-94-007-2311-5(3)**, 9400723113) Springer.

Ugba, David. Awaken the Riches Within: Creating Extraordinary Wealth Using the Powerful Imagination of a Poet. 2010. 240p. pap. 18.95 *(978-1-4401-4295-6(5))* iUniverse, Inc.

Um, Eun K. Motivation & Mathematics Achievement. 2008. 108p. pap. *(978-3-639-07111-5(5))* VDM Verlag Dr. Mueller e.K.

Umunnakwe, Chinelo Benny. Purpose of the Powerful. 2011. (ENG.). pap. 12.99 **(978-0-9836771-4-7(X))** Mindstir Media.

Wallace, Susan. Getting the Buggers Motivated in FE. 2007. (Essential FE Toolkit Ser.). (ENG.). 166p. 39.95 *(978-0-8264-9249-4(5))* Continuum International Publishing Group, Ltd. GBR. Dist: National Bk. Network.

Walter, Ryan. Off the Bench & into the Game: Eight Success Strategies from Professional Sport, 1 vol. 2010. (ENG., Illus.). 160p. per. *(978-1-894974-23-3(9))* Heritage Hse.

Williams, Nicole. Girl on Top: Your Guide to Turning Dating Rules into Career Success. 2012. (ENG.). 208p. pap. 15.99 *(978-1-4555-0716-0(4))* Center St.

Willmore, Joe. No Magic Bullet: Seven Steps to Better Performance. 2009. (ENG., Illus.). 192p. pap. 38.95 *(978-1-56286-509-2(9))* American Society for Training & Development.

Wooden, John & Jamison, Steve. Leadership Game Plan for Success: 12 Lessons for Extraordinary Performance & Personal Excellence. 2009. (ENG.). 208p. 26.95 *(978-0-07-162614-9(X)*, 007162614X) McGraw-Hill Cos., The.

Wright, John. How To Accomplish Anything You Want To Do In Life. 16.95 *(978-0-9720239-0-0(9))* Superior Bks.

ACHIEVEMENT TESTS

see also ACT Assessment; Criterion-Referenced Tests; General Educational Development Tests; Preliminary Scholastic Assessment Test

Ache, Paul, et al. PRAXIS II ParaPro Assessment 0755 & 1755. 2009. (PRAXIS Teacher Certification Test Prep Ser.). (ENG.). 416p. (C). pap. 39.95 *(978-0-7386-0413-8(5))* Research & Education Assn.

Ackroyd, Sarah. Pre-Intermediate Test Generator. 2010. (ENG.). cd-rom 154.00 *(978-0-521-74587-1(X))* Cambridge Univ. Pr.

ACT Inc. Staff. The Real ACT Prep Guide: The Only Official Prep Guide from the Makers of the ACT. Hammond, Wallie W., ed. 2nd ed. 2007. (ENG., Illus.). 623p. (YA). per. 24.95 *(978-0-7689-2675-0(0))* Peterson's.

ACTOrg Staff. The Real ACT Prep Guide. 2nd ed. 2010. (ENG.). 648p. (YA). pap., pap. 30.95 *(978-0-7689-3140-2(1))* Peterson's.

Allen, John & Stocks, Meagan. FCAT FL 2. 0 Reading & Writing. 3rd ed. 2012. (Florida FCAT Test Preparation Ser.). (ENG.). 368p. pap. 15.95 **(978-0-7386-1021-4(6))** Research & Education Assn.

Bobrow, Jerry. CBEST. 7th ed. 2010. (ENG., Illus.). 384p. pap. 19.99 *(978-0-470-45453-4(9)*, Cliff Notes) Wiley, John & Sons, Inc.

Brice, J. Language Arts Literacy. Research and Education Association Staff & Northeast Editing, Inc Staff, eds. 2nd ed. 2010. (New Jersey ASK Test Preparation Ser.). (ENG.). 224p. (gr. 3-3). pap. 15.95 *(978-0-7386-0797-9(5))* Research & Education Assn.

California Achievement Test (CAT) (Admission Test Ser.: ATS-101). 49.95 *(978-0-8373-5851-2(5)*, ATS-101) National Learning Corp.

CBASE Exam Secrets Test Prep Staff, ed. CBASE Practice Questions: CBASE Practice Tests & Exam Review for the College Basic Academic Subjects Examination. 2011. (C). 34.99 *(978-1-61403-492-6(3))* Mometrix Media LLC.

Cizek, Gregory J. & Bunch, Michael B. Standard Setting: A Guide to Establishing & Evaluating Performance Standards on Tests. 2006. (Illus.). 368p. (C). 101.00 *(978-1-4129-1682-0(8)*, B16828C); per. 53.00 *(978-1-4129-1683-7(6)*, B16828P) SAGE Pubns., Inc.

Cram101 Textbook Reviews. Outlines & Highlights for Assessment of Student Achievement by Norman E Gronlund, Isbn: 9780205597284 0205597289. 2011. 66p. pap. 27.95 **(978-1-61490-436-6(7))** Cram101 Inc.

Cram101 Textbook Reviews & Cram101 Textbook Reviews. Outlines & Facts101 for Handbook of Psychoeducational Assessment: A Practical HandbookA Volume in the EDUCATIONAL PSYCHOLOGY Series by Gary D. Phye. 2011. 122p. (C). pap. 28.95 **(978-1-61830-266-3(3))** Cram101 Inc.

Davis, A. L. & Research and Education Association Staff. ICTS: Basic Skills & Elementary - Middle Grades. O'Connell, Julie, ed. 2nd ed. 2010. (ICTS Teacher Certification Test Prep Ser.). (ENG.). 400p. (C). pap. 39.95 *(978-0-7386-0804-4(1))* Research & Education Assn.

Day, Erica. ACT(r) Mathematics Test Preparation Guide. 2008. pap. 24.00 *(978-1-59807-174-0(2))* American Bk. Co.

Digital Actuarial Resources. Headway Test Prep for ACT Math. 2008. 308p. (YA). pap. 39.99 *(978-0-9798071-8-3(2))* Digital Actuarial Resources, LLC.

DSST Exam Secrets Test Prep Staff, ed. DSST A History of the Vietnam War Exam Secrets Study Guide: DSST Test Review for the Dantes Subject Standardized Tests. 2011. 62.99 *(978-1-61403-521-3(0))* Mometrix Media LLC.

—DSST Art of the Western World Exam Secrets Study Guide: DSST Test Review for the Dantes Subject Standardized Tests. 2011. 62.99 *(978-1-61403-517-6(2))* Mometrix Media LLC.

—DSST Business Law II Exam Secrets Study Guide: DSST Test Review for the Dantes Subject Standardized Tests. 2011. 62.99 (978-1-61403-518-3(0)) Mometrix Media LLC.

—DSST Criminal Justice Exam Secrets Study Guide: DSST Test Review for the Dantes Subject Standardized Tests. 2011. 62.99 (978-1-61403-519-0(9)) Mometrix Media LLC.

—DSST Environment & Humanity Exam Secrets Study Guide: DSST Test Review for the Dantes Subject Standardized Tests. 2011. 62.99 (978-1-61403-520-6(2)) Mometrix Media LLC.

—DSST Human Resource Management Exam Flashcard Study System: DSST Test Practice Questions & Review for the Dantes Subject Standardized Tests. 2011. 62.99 (978-1-61403-523-7(7)) Mometrix Media LLC.

—DSST Human Resource Management Exam Secrets Study Guide: DSST Test Review for the Dantes Subject Standardized Tests. 2011. 62.99 (978-1-61403-522-0(9)) Mometrix Media LLC.

—DSST Introduction to Computing Exam Secrets Study Guide: DSST Test Review for the Dantes Subject Standardized Tests. 2011. 62.99 (978-1-61403-526-8(1)) Mometrix Media LLC.

—DSST Introduction to Law Enforcement Exam Flashcard Study System: DSST Test Practice Questions & Review for the Dantes Subject Standardized Tests. 2011. 62.99 (978-1-61403-525-1(3)) Mometrix Media LLC.

—DSST Introduction to Law Enforcement Exam Secrets Study Guide: DSST Test Review for the Dantes Subject Standardized Tests. 2011. 62.99 (978-1-61403-524-4(5)) Mometrix Media LLC.

Dulan, Steven. McGraw-Hill's 10 ACT Practice Tests. 3rd ed. 2010. (ENG., Illus.). 864p. (C). pap. 21.95 (978-0-07-173697-8(2), 0071736972) McGraw-Hill Cos., The.

DynaNotes Revised Exit Level Math TAKS Review Guide. 2007. (YA). pap. (978-1-933854-67-0(7)) DynaStudy, Inc.

DynaNotes Revised Grade 7 Math TAKS Review Guide. 2007. (J). pap. (978-1-933854-62-5(6)) DynaStudy, Inc.

DynaNotes Revised Grade 8 Math TAKS Review Guide. 2007. (YA). pap. (978-1-933854-64-9(2)) DynaStudy, Inc.

DynaNotes Revised Grade 9 Math TAKS Review Guide. 2007. (YA). pap. (978-1-933854-65-6(0)) DynaStudy, Inc.

DynaNotes Revised Guía de Repaso para TAKS 6 Grado Matematicas. 2007. (J). pap. (978-1-933854-59-5(6)) DynaStudy, Inc.

DynaNotes Revsied Grade 6 Math TAKS Review Guide. 2007. (J). pap. (978-1-933854-58-8(8)) DynaStudy, Inc.

Fletcher, Lauren & Brock, Erica. [NJ ASK Grade 4 Science. 2012. (New Jersey ASK Test Preparation Ser.). (ENG.). 256p. (J). (gr. 4-4). pap. 15.95 **(978-0-7386-1018-4(6))** Research & Education Assn.

Fowler & Coe. Quickcheck Placement Tests. Date not set. 16p. spiral bd. (978-0-17-555563-5(X)) Addison-Wesley Longman, Inc.

Friedman, Mel. NJ HSPA Mathematics. 3rd ed. 2010. (New Jersey HSPA Test Preparation Ser.). (ENG.). 288p. (gr. 10-12). pap. 15.95 (978-0-7386-0692-7(6)) Research & Education Assn.

Garrison, Mark J. A Measure of Failure: The Political Origins of Standardized Testing. 2009. 160p. 60.00 (978-1-4384-2777-5(8)); pap. 19.95 (978-1-4384-2778-2(6)) State Univ. of New York Pr.

Gronlund, Norman E. & Waugh, C. Keith. Assessment of Student Achievement. 10th rev. ed. 2012. (ENG.). 256p. (C). pap. 68.00 **(978-0-13-268963-2(4))** Addison Wesley.

—Assessment of Student Achievement. 9th ed. 2008. (ENG., Illus.). 240p. (C). per. 68.00 (978-0-205-59728-4(9)) Allyn & Bacon, Inc.

Gruber, Gary. Gruber's Complete ACT Guide 2010. 2010. (ENG.). 736p. pap. 19.99 (978-1-4022-2662-5(4)) Sourcebooks, Inc.

Hashemi, Louise & Thomas, Barbara. Objective PET Pack (Student's Book & PET for schools Practice Test Booklet without answers with Audio CD) Pack for New PET for Schools Exam. 2009. (Objective Ser.). (ENG.). 208p. pap. 43.68 (978-0-521-74459-1(8)) Cambridge Univ. Pr.

—PET for Schools: Practice Test Booklet with Answers. 2009. (Objective Ser.). (ENG.). 72p. pap. 13.10 incl. audio compact disk (978-0-521-74454-6(7)) Cambridge Univ. Pr.

Henkins, Kathryn & Reiss, Stephen A. Barron's CBEST: California Basic Educational Skills Test. 2008. (ENG., Illus.). 464p. pap. 16.99 (978-0-7641-3589-7(9)) Barron's Educational Series, Inc.

Jarrett, Mark, et al. Mastering the Ohio Grade 8 Science Achievement Test. 2007. pap. 9.95 (978-0-9795493-0-4(2)) Jarrett Publishing Co.

Kaplan. Kaplan SAT Subject Test Biology E/M 2011-2012. 2011. (Kaplan SAT Subject Test Ser.). (ENG.). 384p. pap. 18.99 (978-1-60714-868-5(4)) Kaplan Publishing.

Kaplan Publishing Staff, et al. Kaplan Spotlight ACT: 25 Lessons Illuminate the Most Frequently Tested Topics. 2007. (ENG.). 416p. pap. 16.95 (978-1-4277-5223-9(0)) Kaplan Publishing.

Kellaghan, Thomas, et al. Using the Results of a National Assessment of Educational Achievement. 2009. (National Assessments of Educational Achievement Ser.: 5). (ENG., Illus.). 192p. pap. 25.00 (978-0-8213-7929-5(1), 9780821379295) World Bank Pubns.

Kleinschmidt, Ulrich & Brown, Bill. Kaplan AP U. S. Government & Politics 2012. rev. ed. 2011. (Kaplan AP Ser.). (ENG.). 372p. pap. 17.99 (978-1-60978-072-2(8)) Kaplan Publishing.

Learning Hand Staff, creator. Math Study Guide, State Standardized Tests. 2007. 284p. per. 35.00 (978-1-934295-48-9(5), Learning Hand, The) Great Expressions Publishing.

LearningExpress Editors. CBEST. 5th ed. 2011. 256p. pap. 19.95 (978-1-57685-759-5(X)) LearningExpress, LLC.

Litton, Nancy & Wickett, Maryann. This Is Only a Test: Teaching for Mathematical Understanding in an Age of Standardized Testing. 2008. 128p. 24.95 (978-0-941355-87-2(X)) Math Solutions.

Madsen, Lucas E. Achievement Tests: Types, Interpretations, & Uses. 2011. (Education in a Competitive & Globalizing World Ser.). (Illus.). xi, 202p. 89.00 (978-1-61122-056-8(4)) Nova Science Pubs., Inc.

Morrison, Elizabeth & Carleton, Jodie. Florida End-of-Course Assessment - Algebra 1. 2012. (Florida FCAT Test Preparation Ser.). (ENG.). 336p. (J). (gr. 10-12). pap. 15.95 **(978-0-7386-1022-1(4))** Research & Education Assn.

Naglieri, Jack A. & Goldstein, Sam. Practitioner's Guide to Assessing Intelligence & Achievement. 2009. (ENG., Illus.). 600p. 90.00 (978-0-470-13538-9(7), Wiley) Wiley, John & Sons, Inc.

New Jersey HSPA Mathematics w/ TestWare. pap. 19.95 (978-0-7386-0691-0(X)) Research & Education Assn.

Organisation for Economic Co-operation and Development Staff. Take the Test: Sample Questions from OECD's PISA Assessments. 2009. (Illus.). 318p. pap. 63.00 (978-92-64-05080-8(9)) Organization for Economic Cooperation & Development.

Passananti, Dana & Magliacano, Karen. NJ ASK Grade 5 Language Arts Literacy (REA) 2012. (New Jersey ASK Test Preparation Ser.). (ENG.). 192p. (J). (gr. 5-5). pap. 15.95 **(978-0-7386-1020-7(8))** Research & Education Assn.

Peterson's Guides Staff & Prometric, Drake. Mastering Dsst. 2010. (ENG.). 480p. (YA). pap. 26.95 (978-0-7689-2832-7(X)) Peterson's.

Phelps, Richard P. Standardized Testing Primer. 2007. (Peter Lang Primer Ser.). 168p. (C). pap. 18.95 (978-0-8204-9741-9(X)) Lang, Peter Publishing, Inc.

Porter, Kathryn, et al. California Basic Educational Skills Test: Are You Ready to Pass the CBST? 7th ed. 2010. (CBEST Teacher Certification Test Prep Ser.). (ENG.). 400p. (C). pap. 19.95 (978-0-7386-0784-9(3)) Research & Education Assn.

REA Staff. Ga Ghsgt English Language Arts, w/Bonus Online Tests (REA) 2nd ed. 2010. pap. 15.95 (978-0-7386-0846-4(7)) Research & Education Assn.

Ready Set Show What You Know on the Ohio Achievement Test for Grade Kindergarten, Parent/Teacher Edition. 2007. (J). per. 16.95 (978-1-59230-235-2(1)) Englefield & Assocs., Inc.

Ready, Set, Show What You Know on the Ohio Achievement Test for Grade Kindergarten, Student Workbook. 2007. (J). per. 10.95 (978-1-59230-236-9(X)) Englefield & Assocs., Inc.

Research and Education Association Staff. NJ ASK Grade 4 Language Arts Literacy. Northeast Editing, Inc Staff, ed. 2nd ed. 2010. (New Jersey ASK Test Preparation Ser.). (ENG.). 304p. (gr. 4-4). pap. 15.95 (978-0-7386-0798-6(3)) Research & Education Assn.

—PRAXIS PLT. Davis, Anita Price, ed. 2nd ed. 2008. (PRAXIS Teacher Certification Test Prep Ser.). (ENG.). 448p. (C). pap. 31.95 (978-0-7386-0477-0(1)) Research & Education Assn.

—USMLE Step 2: U. S. Medical Licensing Examination. 2008. (Flash Card Bks.). (ENG.). 464p. pap. 17.95 (978-0-7386-0470-1(4)) Research & Education Assn.

Research and Education Association Staff & Friedman, Audrey A. Mass. Mtel General Curriculum. 2010. (Test Preps Ser.). (ENG.). 480p. (C). pap. 39.95 (978-0-7386-0410-7(0)) Research & Education Assn.

Research and Education Association Staff, et al. USMLE Step 1: U. S. Medical Licensing Examination. 2008. (Flash Card Bks.). (ENG.). 432p. pap. 17.95 (978-0-7386-0469-5(0)) Research & Education Assn.

Revised DynaNotes Exit Math TAKS Review Guide Transparency Set. 2007. (YA). trans. (978-1-933854-68-7(5)) DynaStudy, Inc.

Revised DynaNotes Grade 6 Math TAKS Review Guide Transparency Set. 2007. (J). trans. (978-1-933854-60-1(X)) DynaStudy, Inc.

Revised DynaNotes Grade 7 Math TAKS Review Guide Tranparency Set. 2007. (J). trans. (978-1-933854-63-2(4)) DynaStudy, Inc.

Revised DynaNotes Grade 8 Math TAKS Review Guide Tranpsarency Set. 2007. (YA). trans. (978-1-933854-71-7(5)) DynaStudy, Inc.

Revised DynaNotes Grade 9 Math TAKS Review Guide Transparency Set. 2007. (YA). trans. (978-1-933854-66-3(9)) DynaStudy, Inc.

Rochford, Edlin. Communication Studies: Preparing Students for CAPE. 2008. 136p. pap. 13.95 (978-0-595-53330-5(2)) iUniverse, Inc.

Rudman, Jack. Adult APL Survey (APL-A) (Admission Test Ser.: ATS-60B). 43.95 (978-0-8373-6989-1(4)); pap. 23.95 (978-0-8373-6964-8(9)) National Learning Corp. (Passbooks).

—Adult Performance Level Program (APL) (Admission Test Ser.: ATS-60). 43.95 (978-0-8373-5160-5(X)); pap. 23.95 (978-0-8373-5060-8(3)) National Learning Corp.

—California Achievement Test (CAT) (Admission Test Ser.: ATS-101). pap. 29.95 (978-0-8373-5801-7(9), ATS-101) National Learning Corp.

—Texas Academic Skills Program (TASP) (Admission Test Ser.: ATS-110). pap. 29.95 (978-0-8373-5810-9(8)) National Learning Corp.

Shavers-Sublett, Shawn. Special Eduation Students Academic Performance on Tests: The Performance of Special Edudation Students in Inclusive & Non-Inclusive Settings on Norm- Referenced Tests. 2008. 68p. pap. (978-3-639-09027-7(6)) VDM Verlag Dr. Mueller e.K.

Show What You Know Publishing, ed. Show What You Know on the CSAP 4, Parent/Teacher Edition. 2007. (J). per. 16.95 (978-1-59230-214-7(9)) Englefield & Assocs., Inc.

—Show What You Know on the CSAP 7, Reading/Writing Parent/Teacher Edition. 2007. (J). per. 16.95 (978-1-59230-245-1(9)) Englefield & Assocs., Inc.

Simmons, Bruce, et al. Kaplan AP Statistics 2012. 2011. (Kaplan AP Ser.). (ENG.). 464p. pap. 18.99 (978-1-60978-071-5(X)) Kaplan Publishing.

Simonyan, Lena. Constuction & Validation of a Task-Based Test in Armenian Context. 2011. 92p. pap. **(978-3-8443-8383-6(2))** Lambert Academic Publishing.

Stoddard, Lynn. Educating for Human Greatness. 2010. 212p. pap. 15.00 (978-1-936051-83-0(4)) Peppertree Pr., The.

TEAS Exam Secrets Test Prep Staff, ed. TEAS Exam Practice Questions: TEAS Practice Tests & Review for the Test of Essential Academic Skills. 2011. (C). 34.99 (978-1-61403-736-1(1)) Mometrix Media LLC.

Test Master Press. TEXAS TEST PREP Practice Test Book STAAR Reading Grade 4: Aligned to the 2011-2012 Texas STAAR Reading Test. 2011. (ENG.). 128p. pap. 15.95 **(978-1-4663-7443-0(8))** CreateSpace.

TExES Exam Secrets Test Prep Staff, ed. TExES (156) Journalism 8-12 Exam Flashcard Study System: TExES Test Practice Questions & Review for the Texas Examinations of Educator Standards. 2011. (C). 62.99 (978-1-61403-746-0(9)) Mometrix Media LLC.

Thompson, Frances McBroom. Math Essentials, Elementary School Level: Lessons & Activities for Test Preparation, Grades 3-5. 2006. (ENG., Illus.). 400p. per. 32.95 (978-0-7879-8880-7(4), Jossey-Bass) Wiley, John & Sons, Inc.

Whelan, Patrick. Kaplan AP World History 2012. 2011. (ENG.). 360p. pap. 17.99 (978-1-60978-184-2(8)) Kaplan Publishing.

Wickersham, Joy & Konzelmann, Ann. NJ Ask Mathematics. 2012. (New Jersey ASK Test Preparation Ser.). (ENG.). 304p. (J). (gr. 5-5). pap. 15.95 **(978-0-7386-1019-1(4))** Research & Education Assn.

Wiens, Kathryn L. Boys Who Achieve: An Examination of Single-Sex Classes in aCoeducational College Preparatory School. 2008. 192p. pap. (978-3-639-10419-6(6)) VDM Verlag Dr. Mueller e.K.

Williams, W. Kay & Williams, David E. Preparing for FCAT Mathematics Grade 10. 2nd ed. 2007. (YA). pap. (978-1-56765-591-9(2), R668W) AMSCO Schl. Pubns., Inc.

Wynne, Sharon. CBEST CA Basic Educational Skills Test Practice Test 1. 2011. (Cbest Ser.). (ENG.). 106p. pap. 14.99 (978-1-60787-165-1(3)) XAMonline, Inc.

—CBEST CA Basic Educational Skills Test Practice Test 2. 2011. (Cbest Ser.). (ENG.). 104p. pap. 14.99 (978-1-60787-166-8(1)) XAMonline, Inc.

Yeh, Stuart S. Raising Student Achievement Through Rapid Assessment & Test Reform. 2006. (ENG., Illus.). 208p. pap. 26.95 (978-0-8077-4723-0(8)); 53.00 (978-0-8077-4724-7(6)) Teachers College Pr., Teachers College, Columbia Univ.

ACID (DRUG)

see LSD (Drug)

ACID-BASE EQUILIBRIUM

Cook, Michelle Schoffro & Cook, Michelle S. The Ultimate PH Solution: Balance Your Body Chemistry to Prevent Disease & Lose Weight. 2007. (ENG., Illus.). 208p. pap. 14.99 (978-0-06-133643-0(2), Harper Paperbacks) HarperCollins Pubs.

Egginton, S., et al, eds. Regulation of Tissue pH in Plants & Animals: A Reappraisal of Current Techniques. 2007. (Society for Experimental Biology Seminar Ser.). (ENG.). 392p. pap. 79.00 (978-0-521-03938-3(X)) Cambridge Univ. Pr.

Faubel, Sarah & Topf, Joel. The Electrolyte & Acid-Base Companion: A Visual Guide to the Anatomy of the Stick Figure. Date not set. (Illus.). 550p. (Orig.). pap. 21.95 (978-0-9640124-2-4(1)) Alert & Oriented Publishing.

Gingrich, Margaret M. & Overby, Penny, eds. Fluids, Electrolytes, & Acid-Base Balance. 2nd ed. 2006. (ENG., Illus.). 240p. (C). per. 39.95 (978-0-13-224079-6(3), Prentice Hall) Prentice Hall PTR.

Graf, Jeannette & Bowman, Alisa. Stop Aging, Start Living: The Revolutionary 2-Week pH Diet That Erases Wrinkles, Beautifies Skin, & Makes You Feel Fantastic. 2008. (ENG.). 256p. pap. 13.95 (978-0-307-38237-5(0), Three Rivers Pr.) Crown Publishing Group.

Külpmann, Wolf-Rüdiger, et al. Electrolytes, Acid-Base Balance & Blood Gases: Clinical Aspects & Laboratory. 2nd rev. ed. 2007. (Illus.). VIII, 192p. pap. 49.95 (978-3-211-33127-9(1), 3211331271) Springer.

Longenecker, J. Craig. Acid-Base. 2nd rev. ed. 2006. (High-Yield Ser.). (ENG., Illus.). 128p. pap. 29.99 (978-0-7817-9655-2(5)) Lippincott Williams & Wilkins.

Putz, Mihai V. Absolute & Chemical Electronegativity & Hardness. 2008. pap. 29.00 (978-1-60456-937-7(9)) Nova Science Pubs., Inc.

Toney, Toni. Get Clean Go Green Ecodiet. 2010. 350p. pap. 19.95 (978-0-9827445-0-5(1)) New Earth Wisdom.

Vyas, Bharti & Le Quesne, Suzanne. The pH Balance Diet: Restore Your Acid-Alkaline Levels to Eliminate Toxins & Lose Weight. 2007. (ENG., Illus.). 208p. per. 14.95 (978-1-56975-607-2(4)) Ulysses Pr.

Young, Robert O. & Young, Shelley Redford. The pH Miracle: Balance Your Diet, Reclaim Your Health. 2008. (ENG.). 480p. mass mkt. 6.99 (978-0-446-53619-6(9), Wellness Central) Grand Central Publishing.

—The Ph Miracle: Balance Your Diet, Reclaim Your Health. rev. ed. 2010. (ENG.). 432p. pap. 16.99 (978-0-446-55618-7(1), Wellness Central) Grand Central Publishing.

ACID-BASE IMBALANCES

Cook, Michelle Schoffro & Cook, Michelle S. The Ultimate PH Solution: Balance Your Body Chemistry to Prevent Disease & Lose Weight. 2007. (ENG., Illus.). 208p. pap. 14.99 (978-0-06-133643-0(2), Harper Paperbacks) HarperCollins Pubs.

Graf, Jeannette & Bowman, Alisa. Stop Aging, Start Living: The Revolutionary 2-Week pH Diet That Erases Wrinkles, Beautifies Skin, & Makes You Feel Fantastic. 2008. (ENG.). 256p. pap. 13.95 (978-0-307-38237-5(0), Three Rivers Pr.) Crown Publishing Group.

Halperin, Mitchell L., et al. Fluid, Electrolyte, & Acid-Base Physiology: A Problem-Based Approach. 4th ed. 2010. (ENG., Illus.). 616p. pap. 69.95 (978-1-4160-2442-2(5), Saunders) Elsevier - Health Sciences Div.

Hasan, Ashfaq. Handbook of Blood Gas/Acid-Base Interpretation. 2009. (ENG., Illus.). x, 320p. pap. 69.95 (978-1-84800-333-0(1), 1848003331) Springer.

Jameson, J. Larry, et al. Harrison's Nephrology & Acid-Base Disorders. 2010. (ENG., Illus.). 320p. pap. 82.00 (978-0-07-166339-7(8), 0071663398) McGraw-Hill Professional Publishing.

Johnson, Ben & Trivieri, Larry, Jr. Healing Waters: The Powerful Benefits of Ionized H2O. 2011. 104p. pap. 14.95 (978-0-7570-0328-8(1)) Square One Pubs.

Kee, Joyce LeFever, et al. Fluids & Electrolytes with Clinical Applications. 8th ed. 2008. (ENG.). 576p. (C). pap. 67.95 (978-1-4354-5367-8(0)) Delmar Cengage Learning.

—Fluids, Electrolytes & Acid Base Imabalances. 3rd ed. 2009. (Nursing Reference Ser.). (ENG.). 432p. (C). pap., instr.'s hndbk. ed. 66.95 (978-1-4354-5368-5(9)) Delmar Cengage Learning.

Kellum, John A. & Elbers, Paul Wg. Stewart's Textbook of Acid-Base. 2009. 504p. pap. 97.95 (978-1-4092-5470-6(4)) Lulu Enterprises Inc.

Kliment, Felicia. The Acid Alkaline Balance Diet: An Innovative Program That Detoxifies Your Body's Acidic Waste to Prevent Disease & Restore Overall Health. 2nd ed. 2010. (ENG.). 256p. pap. 16.95 (978-0-07-170337-6(3), 0071703373) McGraw-Hill Cos., The.

Lippincott Williams and Wilkins Staff. Fluids & Electrolytes. Springhouse Publishing Company Staff, ed. 2nd rev. ed. 2009. (Incredibly Easy! Ser.). (ENG., Illus.). 256p. pap., instr.'s gde. ed. 32.99 (978-1-60547-252-2(2)) Lippincott Williams & Wilkins.

Longenecker, J. Craig. Acid-Base. 2nd rev. ed. 2006. (High-Yield Ser.). (ENG., Illus.). 128p. pap. 29.99 (978-0-7817-9655-2(5)) Lippincott Williams & Wilkins.

Moorthy, A. Vishnu, et al. Pathophysiology of Kidney Disease & Hypertension. 2008. (ENG., Illus.). 240p. (C). pap. 49.95 (978-1-4160-4391-1(8), Saunders) Elsevier - Health Sciences Div.

Morter, M. T. Your Health... your Choice. 2009. (ENG., Illus.). 224p. pap. 14.95 (978-0-88391-172-3(8)) Fell, Frederick Pubs., Inc.

Morter, Ted. Your Health Your Choice. 2011. **(978-0-88391-198-3(1))** Fell, Frederick Pubs., Inc.

Ross, Bonnie. The Amazing Acid Alkaline Cookbook: Balancing Taste, Nutrition, & Your PH Levels. 2010. 194p. 17.95 (978-0-7570-0316-5(8)) Square One Pubs.

Springhouse Corporation Staff, contrib. by. Metabolic Problems. 2011. (NurseReview Ser.). ring bd. (978-0-87434-148-5(5), Springhouse Corp.) Lippincott Williams & Wilkins.

Toney, Toni. Get Clean Go Green Ecodiet. 2010. 350p. pap. 19.95 (978-0-9827445-0-5(1)) New Earth Wisdom.

An Undetected Acid-Alkaline Imbalance: Is Slowly Killing You & Severely Hurting Your Children! 2006. per. 21.95 (978-0-9774917-2-8(2)) Vision Publishing, LLC.

Vasey, Christopher. The Acid-Alkaline Diet for Optimum Health: Restore Your Health by Creating pH Balance in Your Diet. Graham, Jon, tr. from FRE. 2nd rev. ed. 2006. (ENG., Illus.). 1p. per. 12.95 (978-1-59477-154-5(5)) Inner Traditions International, Ltd.

Vyas, Bharti & Le Quesne, Suzanne. The pH Balance Diet: Restore Your Acid-Alkaline Levels to Eliminate Toxins & Lose Weight. 2007. (ENG., Illus.). 208p. per. 14.95 (978-1-56975-607-2(4)) Ulysses Pr.

Young, Robert O. & Young, Shelley Redford. The pH Miracle: Balance Your Diet, Reclaim Your Health. 2008. (ENG.). 480p. mass mkt. 6.99 (978-0-446-53619-6(9), Wellness Central) Grand Central Publishing.

—The Ph Miracle: Balance Your Diet, Reclaim Your Health. rev. ed. 2010. (ENG.). 432p. pap. 16.99 (978-0-446-55618-7(1), Wellness Central) Grand Central Publishing.

ACID DEPOSITION

Brimblecombe, Peter, et al, eds. Acid Rain - Deposition to Recovery. (ENG.). viii, 420p. 2010. pap. 219.00 (978-90-481-7467-6(8), 9048174678) 2007. (Illus.). 219.00 (978-1-4020-5884-4(5), 1402058845) Springer.

Radojevic, M. & Harrison, R. M., eds. Atmospheric Acidity: Sources, Consequences & Abatement. 2007. (Illus.). 594p. 339.00 (978-1-85166-777-2(6)) Springer.

Visgilio, Gerald R. & Whitelaw, Diana M., eds. Acid in the Environment: Lessons Learned & Future Prospects. 2006. (Illus.). xiv, 332p. 99.00 (978-0-387-37561-8(9), 0387375619) Springer.

ACID POLLUTION OF RIVERS, LAKES, ETC.

Edwards, Anthony & Cresser, Malcolm. Acidification of Freshwaters. 2010. (Cambridge Environmental Chemistry Ser.). (ENG.). 146p. pap. 19.99 (978-0-521-15836-7(2)) Cambridge Univ. Pr.

Fott, J., ed. Limnology of Mountain Lakes. 2011. (Developments in Hydrobiology Ser.). (ENG.). 196p. pap. 229.00 (978-90-481-4351-1(9), 9048143519) Springer.

Mason, B. J., ed. The Surface Waters Acidification Programme. 2006. (ENG.). 536p. pap. 110.00 (978-0-521-03167-7(2)) Cambridge Univ. Pr.

Morris, R., et al, eds. Acid Toxicity & Aquatic Animals. 2008. (Society for Experimental Biology Seminar Ser.). (ENG., Illus.). 296p. pap. 58.00 (978-0-521-05762-2(0)) Cambridge Univ. Pr.

ACID PRECIPITATION (METEOROLOGY)

see Acid Rain

ACID RAIN

Adams, Mary Beth, et al, eds. The Fernow Watershed Acidification Study. 2010. (Environmental Pollution Ser.). xiii, 279p. pap. 159.00 (978-90-481-7153-3(9), 9048171539) Springer.

Bohera, Carme. La Lluvia Acida (Acid Rain) (Nuestro Mundo en Peligro Ser.). (SPA.). 32p. 10.50 (978-84-342-1904-5(2), CAR1904) Parramon Ediciones S.A. ESP. Dist: Continental Bk. Co., Inc.

Bright, M. La Lluvia Acida: La Lluvia Contaminada. (Nuestro Mundo en Peligro Ser.). (SPA., Illus.). 32p. 8.95 (978-84-342-1190-2(4)) Parramon Ediciones S.A. ESP. Dist: Distribuidora Norma, Inc.

Brimblecombe, Peter, et al, eds. Acid Rain - Deposition to Recovery. (ENG.). viii, 420p. 2010. pap. 219.00 (978-90-481-7467-6(8), 9048174678) 2007. (Illus.). 219.00 (978-1-4020-5884-4(5), 1402058845) Springer.

Jenkins, Jerry C., et al. Acid Rain in the Adirondacks: An Environmental History. 2007. (Illus.). 256p. 76.95 (978-0-8014-4651-1(1), Comstock Publishing Assocs.) Cornell Univ. Pr.

Jones, George. Acid Rain Legislation & Local Areas. 2011. 172p. pap. (978-3-8443-1086-3(X)) Lambert Academic Publishing.

Qasim, Shamaila & Mumtaz Hussain. Effect of Simulated Acid Rain on Plants. 2011. 96p. pap. (978-3-8443-0505-0(X)) Lambert Academic Publishing.

Radojevic, M. & Harrison, R. M., eds. Atmospheric Acidity: Sources, Consequences & Abatement. 2007. (Illus.). 594p. 339.00 (978-1-85166-777-2(6)) Springer.

Roglesfield, Lyman G. Acid Rain Research Focus. 2008. (C). 89.00 (978-1-60456-373-3(7)) Nova Science Pubs., Inc.

Roy, Karen, et al. Acid Rain in the Adirondacks: An Environmental History. 2007. (Illus.). 246p. pap. 32.95 (978-0-8014-7424-8(8), Comstock Publishing Assocs.) Cornell Univ. Pr.

Somerville, Richard. The Forgiving Air: Understanding Environmental Change. 2nd ed. 2008. (Illus.). 224p. pap. 22.00 (978-1-878220-85-1(3)) American Meteorological Society.

Visgilio, Gerald R. & Whitelaw, Diana M., eds. Acid in the Environment: Lessons Learned & Future Prospects. 2006. (Illus.). xiv, 332p. 99.00 (978-0-387-37561-8(9), 0387375619) Springer.

ACIDS

see also names of acids, e.g. Sulphuric Acid

Arata, Kazushi & Matsuhashi, Hiromi. Solid Superacids. 2011. (Chemistry Research & Applications Ser.). 208p. 69.00 (978-1-61209-649-0(2)) Nova Science Pubs., Inc.

Carolina Biological Staff, compiled by. Discovering Acids & Bases. 2009. (Inquiries in Science Chemistry Ser.). (978-1-4350-0410-8(8)) Carolina Biological Supply Co.

COLLEGE OF WILLIAM & MARY. Acid, Acid Everywhere: Student Pak. 2007. pap. 49.95 (978-0-7575-3891-9(6)) Kendall Hunt Publishing Co.

Laurence, Christian & Gal, Jean-François. Lewis Basicity & Affinity Scales: Data & Measurement. 2010. (ENG., Illus.). 476p. 190.00 (978-0-470-74957-9(1), Wiley) Wiley, John & Sons, Inc.

Mikhailov, Miroslav. Aspects of Acid Placement & Coverage in the Acid Jetting Process. 2010. 80p. pap. (978-3-8383-7555-7(5)) Lambert Academic Publishing.

Tojo, Gabriel & Fernández, Marcos I. Oxidation of Primary Alcohols to Carboxylic Acids: A Guide to Current Common Practice. 2006. (Basic Reactions in Organic Synthesis Ser.). (Illus.). xvi, 116p. 99.00 (978-0-387-35431-6(X), 038735431X) Springer.

Walker, Denise. Acids & Alkalis. 2006. (Core Chemistry/Evans Brothers Ser.). (Illus.). 48p. (YA). (gr. 5-9). 34.25 (978-1-58340-821-6(5)) Black Rabbit Bks.

Yamamoto, Hisashi & Ishihara, Kazuaki, eds. Acid Catalysis in Modern Organic Synthesis, 2 vols. 2008. (ENG., Illus.). 1136p. 505.00 (978-3-527-31724-0(4), Wiley-VCH) Wiley, John & Sons, Inc.

ACIDS, FATTY

see Fatty Acids

ACIDS, ORGANIC

Hall, Dennis G., ed. Boronic Acids: Preparation & Applications in Organic Synthesis, Medicine & Materials. 2nd ed. 2011. (ENG., Illus.). 726p. 260.00 (978-3-527-32598-6(0), Wiley-VCH) Wiley, John & Sons, Inc.

Madronova, Libuse, ed. Humic Acids from Raw Materials of the Czech Republic. 2010. (Environmental Science, Engineering & Technology Ser.). (Illus.). x, 133p. 75.00 (978-1-61668-965-0(X)) Nova Science Pubs., Inc.

Stone, Martin. Hyaluronic Acid: Powerful Antiarthritic & Antiwrinkle Supplement. 2007. (Woodland Health Ser.). 24p. pap. 4.95 (978-1-58054-458-0(4)) Woodland Publishing, Inc.

ACKNOWLEDGMENTS

see also Conveyancing; Deeds; Forms (Law); Justices of the Peace; Notaries

Govier, Trudy. Taking Wrongs Seriously: Acknowledgment, Reconciliation, & the Politics of Sustainable Peace. 2006. (ENG., Illus.). 300p. 42.98 (978-1-59102-425-5(0), Humanity Bks.) Prometheus Bks., Pubs.

ACNE

Bowser, Alison. Acne & Rosacea: The Complete Guide. 2010. (ENG.). 264p. pap. 19.95 (978-0-09-192970-1(9)) Random Hse. GBR. Dist: Independent Pubs. Group.

Goldberg, David J. & Berlin, Alexander. Acne & Rosacea: Epidemiology, Diagnosis & Treatment. 2011. (ENG., Illus.). 128p. 64.95 (978-1-84076-150-4(4)) Thieme Medical Pubs., Inc.

Herane, Maria Isabel, et al, eds. Acne Vol. 206: Symposium at the World Congress of Dermatology, Paris, July 2002. (Dermatology Ser.: Vol. 206, No. 1). (Illus.). 74p. (978-3-8055-7548-5(3)) Karger, S. AG.

Juettner, Bonnie. Acne. 2010. (Diseases & Disorders Ser.). (Illus.). 128p. (YA). (gr. 7-18). 32.45 (978-1-4205-0215-2(8), Lucent Bks.) Cengage Gale.

Leung, Alexander K. C. & Hon, K. L. E. Acne: Causes, Treatment & Myths. 2010. (Dermatology - Laboratory & Clinical Research Ser.). pap. 43.00 (978-1-61668-258-3(2)) Nova Science Pubs., Inc.

Logan, Alan C., et al. The Clear Skin Diet: How to Defeat Acne & Enjoy Healthy Skin. 2007. (ENG., Illus.). 304p. 22.95 (978-1-58182-574-9(9), Cumberland Hse.) Sourcebooks, Inc.

Mummery, Elaine. Spotless: The Essential Guide to Getting Rid of Spots & Acne. 2009. (ENG., Illus.). 192p. pap. (978-1-84876-109-4(0)) Troubadour Publishing Ltd.

parks, peggy. Acne & skin Disorders. 2011. (Compact Research Ser.). 96p. (YA). (gr. 7-12). lib. bdg. (978-1-60152-226-9(6)) ReferencePoint Pr., Inc.

Roth, David E., ed. Dermatology Research Focus on Acne, Melanoma & Psoriasis. 2010. (Dermatology - Laboratory & Clinical Research Ser.). 349p. 145.00 (978-1-60876-075-6(8), Nova Biomedical Bks.) Nova Science Pubs., Inc.

Shalita, Alan R., et al, eds. Acne Vulgaris. 2010. (ENG., Illus.). 240p. (978-1-84184-707-8(0)) Informa Healthcare.

Webster, Guy F. & Rawlings, Anthony V., eds. Acne & Its Therapy. 2006. (Basic & Clinical Dermatology Ser.: Vol. 40). (ENG., Illus.). 328p. 230.00 (978-0-8247-2971-4(4)) Taylor & Francis Group.

Zouboulis, Christos C., et al, eds. Pathogenesis & Treatment of Acne & Rosacea. 2011. (ENG., Illus.). 350p. 139.00 (978-3-540-69374-1(2), 3540693742) Springer.

ACOLYTES

Alcuin Club, the, compiled by. A Server's Manual for the Holy Communion. 2010. pap. 19.60 (978-1-61719-819-9(6)); pap. 19.60 (978-1-61719-834-2(X)) Gorgias Pr., LLC.

Grosenick, Conrad. You Are an Acolyte. (Illus.). 32p. pap. 3.00 (978-0-88028-232-1(0), 788) Forward Movement Pubns.

Laughlin, Corinna. Guide for Servers. 2009. (Illus.). ix, 95p. pap. (978-1-56854-803-6(6)) Liturgy Training Pubns.

Laughlin, Corinne, et al. Manual para Acolitos. 2010. (SPA.). 112p. pap. 7.95 (978-1-56854-901-9(6)) Liturgy Training Pubns.

Rosage, David E. Letters to an Altar Boy. 2011. (Illus.). 99p. (978-1-892331-88-5(8)) Bruce Pubng.

—Letters to an Altar Boy. 2011. 94p. 38.95 (978-1-258-09110-1(0)) Literary Licensing, LLC.

Thomas, Caroline M. The Ministry of the Altar Server. 2012. pap. (978-0-89390-712-9(X)) Resource Pubns., Inc.

ACOMA (N.M.)

Dillingham, Rick & Elliott, Melinda. Acoma & Laguna Pottery. O'Donnell, Joan K., ed. (Native America Ser.). (Illus.). 256p. pap. 29.95 (978-0-933452-32-9(2)) School for Advanced Research Pr./SAR Pr.

ACONCAGUA (MOUNTAIN)

Logan, Joy. Aconcagua: The Invention of Mountaineering on America's Highest Peak. 2011. (ENG., Illus.). 272p. pap. 35.00 (978-0-8165-2950-6(7)) Univ. of Arizona Pr.

ACOUSTIC ENGINEERING

see Acoustical Engineering

ACOUSTIC HOLOGRAPHY

Abraham, Dunstan, et al. Emergency Medicine Sonography: Sonographic Anatomy & Pathology. 2009. 308p. spiral bd. 42.95 (978-0-7637-6558-3(9)) Jones & Bartlett Learning, LLC.

Akiyama, Iwaki. Acoustical Imaging. 2008. (Acoustical Imaging Ser.). (Illus.). 564p. 299.00 (978-1-4020-8822-3(1)) Springer.

Atalick, Stefan. Confocal Acoustic Holography - Confocal Acoustic Holography for Non-Invasive 3d Temperature & Composition Measurement. 2008. 136p. pap. (978-3-8364-9360-4(8)) VDM Verlag Dr. Mueller e.K.

Baltgaile, G., et al, eds. European Society of Neurosonology & Cerebral Hemodynamics: 14th Meeting, Riga, May 2009: Abstracts. 2009. 44p. pap. (978-3-8055-9157-7(8)) Karger, S. AG.

Blondel, Philippe & Caiti, A. Buried Waste in the Seabed: Acoustic Imaging & Bio-Toxicity; Results from the European SITAR Project. 2006. (Springer Praxis Books / Geophysical Sciences Ser.). (Illus.). 202p. 259.00 (978-3-540-28120-7(7), 3540281207) Springer.

Caiti, Andrea, et al, eds. Acoustic Sensing Techniques for the Shallow Water Environment: Inversion Methods & Experiments. 2006. (Illus.). xiii, 332p. 209.00 (978-1-4020-4372-7(4), 1402043724) Springer.

Carmody, Kristin, et al. Handbook of Critical Care & Emergency Ultrasound. 2011. (ENG., Illus.). 352p. pap. 68.00 (978-0-07-160489-5(8), 0071604898) McGraw-Hill Professional Publishing.

Cheng, Xiaoyang. Capacitive Micromachined Ultrasonic Transducers. 2009. 124p. pap. (978-3-639-18633-8(8)) VDM Verlag Dr. Mueller e.K.

Dogra, Vikram & Saad, Wael E. A. Ultrasound-Guided Procedures. 2009. (ENG., Illus.). 344p. pap. 109.99 (978-1-60406-170-3(7)) Thieme Medical Pubs., Inc.

Fink, Mathias, et al. Imaging of Complex Media with Acoustic & Seismic Waves. 2010. (Topics in Applied Physics Ser.). (Illus.). xi, 336p. pap. 329.00 (978-3-642-07501-8(0), 3642075010) Springer.

Fox, J. Christian, ed. Atlas of Emergency Ultrasound. 2011. (ENG., Illus.). 202p. 75.00 (978-0-521-19168-5(8)) Cambridge Univ. Pr.

Frenkel, Victor, ed. Therapeutic Ultrasound: Mechanisms to Applications. 2010. (Public Health in the 21st Century Ser.). 235.00 (978-1-61668-599-7(9)) Nova Science Pubs., Inc.

Gill, Kathryn A. Breast Sonography Review: A Q&A Review for the ARDMS Breast Exam. 2009. spiral bd. 55.00 (978-0-941022-75-0(7)) Davies Publishing, Inc.

Hager, Nelson. Musculoskeletal Ultrasound, an Issue of Physical Medicine & Rehabilitation Clinics. 2010. (Clinics: Orthopedics Ser.: 21-3). (ENG., Illus.). xii, 462p. 105.00 (978-1-4377-2483-7(3), Saunders) Elsevier - Health Sciences Div.

Hedrick, Wayne R. & Wagner, Paul R. Technology for Diagnostic Sonography. 2012. (ENG., Illus.). 204p. pap. 59.95 (978-0-323-08197-9(5), Mosby) Elsevier - Health Sciences Div.

Katz, James D. & Brindle, Kathleen, eds. MRI & Ultrasound in the Diagnosis & Management of Rheumatological Diseases. 2009. (Annals of the New York Academy of Sciences Ser.). (ENG., Illus.). 352p. pap. 134.95 (978-1-57331-736-8(5), Wiley-Blackwell) Wiley, John & Sons, Inc.

Kawamura, Diane & Lunsford, Bridgette. Diagnostic Medical Sonography: A Guide to Clinical Practice Abdomen & Superficial Structures. 3rd rev. ed. 2012. (Diagnostic Medical Sonography Ser.). (ENG.). 864p. 179.95 (978-1-60547-995-8(0)) Lippincott Williams & Wilkins.

Nowicki, Andrzej, et al, eds. Acoustical Imaging: Volume 31. 2012. (Acoustical Imaging Ser.: 31). (ENG., Illus.). viii, 508p. 259.00 (978-94-007-2618-5(X), 940072618X) Springer.

O'Donnell, Paul & Bradley, Mike. Atlas of Musculoskeletal Ultrasound Anatomy. 2nd ed. 2009. (ENG., Illus.). 234p. pap. 66.00 (978-0-521-72809-6(6)) Cambridge Univ. Pr.

Odwin, Charles S. & Fleischer, Arthur C. Ultrasonography Examination. 4th ed. 2012. (LANGE Reviews Allied Health Ser.). (ENG., Illus.). 704p. pap. 85.00 incl. cd-rom (978-0-07-163424-3(X), 007163424X) McGraw-Hill Medical Publishing Div.

Parker, Barry. Good Vibrations: The Physics of Music. 2009. (ENG., Illus.). 288p. 29.95 (978-0-8018-9264-6(3)) Johns Hopkins Univ. Pr.

Taylor, Janelle S. The Public Life of the Fetal Sonogram: Technology, Consumption, & the Politics of Reproduction. 2008. (Studies in Medical Anthropology). (ENG., Illus.). (C). 222p. 62.00 (978-0-8135-4363-5(0)); 256p. pap. 23.95 (978-0-8135-4364-2(9)) Rutgers Univ. Pr.

Thrush, Abigail & Hartshorne, Timothy. Vascular Ultrasound: How, Why & When. Thrush, Abigail & Hartshorne, Timothy, eds. 3rd ed. 2009. (How, Why & When Ser.). (ENG., Illus.). 320p. (C). 85.95 (978-0-443-06918-5(2), Churchill Livingstone) Elsevier - Health Sciences Div.

ACOUSTIC IMAGING (HOLOGRAPHY)

see Acoustic Holography

ACOUSTIC MICROSCOPY

Briggs, Andrew & Kolosov, Oleg. Acoustic Microscopy. 2nd ed. 2009. (Monographs on the Physics & Chemistry of Materials Ser.: 67). (ENG., Illus.). 384p. 125.00 (978-0-19-923273-4(3)) Oxford Univ. Pr., Inc.

Maev, Roman Gr. Acoustic Microscopy: Fundamentals & Applications. 2008. (ENG., Illus.). 291p. 220.00 (978-3-527-40744-6(8), Wiley-VCH) Wiley, John & Sons, Inc.

Marinello, Francesco, et al, eds. Acoustic Scanning Probe Microscopy. 2012. (NanoScience & Technology Ser.). (ENG., Illus.). xiii, 557p. 169.00 (978-3-642-27493-0(5), 3642274935) Springer.

ACOUSTIC NERVE

Gill, Michael Gates. How Starbucks Saved My Life: A Son of Privilege Learns to Live Like Everyone Else. 2008. (CHI., Illus.). 323p. pap. (978-957-13-4855-1(4)) China Times Publishing Co.

—How Starbucks Saved My Life: A Son of Privilege Learns to Live Like Everyone Else. 2008. (ENG.). 272p. (gr. 12-18). 14.00 (978-1-59240-404-9(9), Gotham) Penguin Group (USA) Inc.

Hayat, M. A., ed. Tumors of the Central Nervous System, Volume 7: Meningiomas & Schwannomas. 2012. (Tumors of the Central Nervous System Ser.). (ENG., Illus.). xxxv, 359p. 209.00 (978-94-007-2893-6(X), 940072893X) Springer.

Kaga, Kimitaka & Starr, Arnold, eds. Neuropathies of the Auditory & Vestibular Eighth Cranial Nerves. (ENG.). xii, 160p. 2010. pap. 109.00 (978-4-431-99804-4(7), 4431998047) 2009. (Illus.). 109.00 (978-4-431-09432-6(6), 4431094326) Springer.

Sanna, Mario, et al. Atlas of Acoustic Neurinoma Microsurgery. 2nd ed. 2010. (ENG., Illus.). 320p. 199.99 (978-3-13-110282-9(9)) Thieme Medical Pubs., Inc.

ACOUSTIC PHENOMENA IN NATURE

see also Echo; Thunderstorms

Lemke, Helmut. Helmut Lemke: The Site the Sound Requires. 2009. (GER & ENG., Illus.). 120p. 48.00 (978-3-86678-126-9(1)) Kerber Verlag DEU. Dist: D.A.P./Distributed Art Pubs.

ACOUSTIC TUMORS

see Acoustic Nerve

ACOUSTICAL ENGINEERING

see also Architectural Acoustics; Electro-Acoustics; Noise Control; Soundproofing

Acoustic Emission 5 - Micro. 100.00 (978-0-87849-097-4(3)) Trans Tech Pubns., Ltd. CHE. Dist: Enfield Publishing & Distribution Co., Inc.

Acoustic Emission Micro. 6th ed. 100.00 (978-0-87849-102-5(3)) Trans Tech Pubns., Ltd. CHE. Dist: Enfield Publishing & Distribution Co., Inc.

Akiyama, Iwaki. Acoustical Imaging. 2008. (Acoustical Imaging Ser.). (Illus.). 564p. 299.00 (978-1-4020-8822-3(1)) Springer.

Allen, Christopher S., et al, told to. Aeroacoustic Measurements. 2010. (Experimental Fluid Mechanics Ser.). (ENG., Illus.). xiv, 313p. pap. 219.00 (978-3-642-07514-8(2), 3642075142) Springer.

American Society of Mechanical Engineers, Noise Control and Acoustics Division Staff, contrib. by. Proceedings of NoiseCon/ASME NCAD — 2008: Presented at NoiseCon2008/ASME NCAD July 28-30, 2008 Dearborn, Michigan USA. 2009. (Illus.). xiii, 423p. (978-0-7918-4839-5(6)) American Society of Mechanical Engineers, The.

—Proceedings of the ASME Noise Control & Acoustics Division — 2006: Presented at [the] 2006 ASME International Mechanical Engineering Congress & Exposition: November 5-10, 2006, Chicago, Illinois, USA. 2007. (Illus.). xv, 193p. (978-0-7918-4776-3(4)) American Society of Mechanical Engineers, The.

Amundson, Mark. Live Sound. 2007. (ENG., Illus.). 156p. pap. 34.95 (978-0-9798107-0-1(1), 0979810701) Timeless Communications.

André, Michael P. Acoustical Imaging. 2007. (Acoustical Imaging Ser.). (Illus.). xvi, 477p. 309.00 (978-1-4020-5720-5(2)) Springer.

André, Michael P., ed. Acoustical Imaging: Volume 28. 2010. (Acoustical Imaging Ser.). xvi, 478p. pap. 309.00 (978-90-481-7434-8(1), 9048174341) Springer.

Arnold, Walter K. & Hirsekorn, Sigrun, eds. Acoustical Imaging: Volume 27. 2010. (Acoustical Imaging Ser.). xviii, 774p. pap. 339.00 (978-90-481-6652-7(7), 9048166527) Springer.

Attenborough, Keith, et al. Predicting Outdoor Sound. 2006. (ENG., Illus.). 456p. (C). 170.00 (978-0-419-23510-1(8), RU29124, CRC Press) Taylor & Francis Group GBR. Dist: Taylor & Francis Group.

Audio Engineering Society (AES) Staff, compiled by. Audio Engineering Society 121st Convention Papers 2006. 2007. 1511p. pap. 243.00 (978-1-60423-663-7(9)) Curran Assocs., Inc.

—122nd Audio Engineering Society Convention 2007. 2007. 1669p. pap. 275.00 (978-1-60423-140-3(8)) Curran Assocs., Inc.

Baalman, Marije. On Wave Field Synthesis & Electro-Acoustic Music. 2008. (Illus.). 296p. pap. (978-3-639-07731-5(8)) VDM Verlag Dr. Mueller e.K.

Baine, Celeste. The Musical Engineer: A Music Enthusiast's Guide to Engineering & Technology Careers. 2007. (Illus.). 132p. per. 17.95 (978-0-9711613-7-5(2), Engineering Education Service Ctr.) Bonamy Publishing.

Ballou, Glen. Handbook for Sound Engineers. 4th ed. 2008. (ENG., Illus.). 1808p. 141.00 (978-0-240-80969-4(6), Focal Pr.) Elsevier Science & Technology Bks.

Beauchamp, James W., ed. Analysis, Synthesis, & Perception of Musical Sounds: The Sound of Music. 2006. (Modern Acoustics & Signal Processing Ser.). (Illus.). 325p. 109.00 (978-0-387-32496-8(8), 0387324968) Springer.

Benesty, J., et al. Advances in Network & Acoustic Echo Cancellation. 2010. (Digital Signal Processing Ser.). (ENG., Illus.). xi, 222p. pap. 129.00 (978-3-642-07507-0(X), 364207507X) Springer.

Benesty, Jacob, et al. Noise Reduction in Speech Processing. 2009. (Springer Topics in Signal Processing Ser.). (ENG., Illus.). x, 229p. 129.00 (978-3-642-00295-3(1), 3642002951) Springer.

Benesty, Jacob, et al. A Perspective on Stereophonic Acoustic Echo Cancellation. 2011. (Springer Topics in Signal Processing Ser.). (ENG., Illus.). vi, 142p. 129.00 (978-3-642-22573-4(X), 364222573X) Springer.

Beranek, Leo. Riding the Waves: A Life in Sound, Science, & Industry. 2010. (ENG., Illus.). 248p. (gr. 17). pap. 14.95 (978-0-262-51399-9(4)) MIT Pr.

Blauert, Jens, ed. Communication Acoustics. 2010. (ENG., Illus.). xiv, 379p. pap. 149.00 (978-3-642-06060-1(9), 3642060609) Springer.

Blauert, Jens & Xiang, Ning. Acoustics for Engineers: Troy Lectures. 2008. 250p. 84.95 (978-3-540-76346-8(5)) 2nd ed. 2009. (ENG., Illus.). x, 254p. 89.95 (978-3-642-03392-6(X), 364203392X) Springer.

Brandt, Anders. Noise & Vibration Analysis: Signal Analysis & Experimental Procedures. 2011. (ENG., Illus.). 464p. 120.00 (978-0-470-74644-8(0), Wiley) Wiley, John & Sons, Inc.

Caiti, Andrea, et al, eds. Acoustic Sensing Techniques for the Shallow Water Environment: Inversion Methods & Experiments. 2006. (Illus.). xiii, 332p. 209.00 (978-1-4020-4372-7(4), 1402043724) Springer.

Carpico, Bronwynne. Noise Reduction in a Hospital Setting Using a Cultural Change Model. 2008. 76p. pap. (978-3-639-05750-8(3)) VDM Verlag Dr. Mueller e.K.

Chen. Piezoelectricity, Acoustic Waves & Dev... 2007. (C). 184.00 (978-981-270-813-7(8)) World Scientific Publishing Co., Inc.

Corey, Jason. Audio Production & Critical Listening: Technical Ear Training. 2010. (ENG., Illus.). 191p. 56.95 (978-0-240-81295-3(6), Focal Pr.) Elsevier Science & Technology Bks.

Cox, Trevor & D'Antonio, Peter. Acoustic Absorbers & Diffusers: Theory, Design & Application. 2nd rev. ed. 2009. (ENG., Illus.). 496p. 160.00 (978-0-415-47174-9(5), CRC Press) Taylor & Francis Group GBR. Dist: Taylor & Francis Group.

Cremer, L., et al. Structure-Borne Sound: Structural Vibrations & Sound Radiation at Audio Frequencies. 3rd ed. 2010. (ENG.). xii, 607p. pap. 249.00 (978-3-642-06155-4(9), 3642061559) Springer.

Dittmar, Tim. Audio Engineering 101: A Beginner's Guide to Music Production. 2011. (ENG., Illus.). 256p. pap. 29.95 (978-0-240-81915-0(2), Focal Pr.) Elsevier Science & Technology Bks.

Egan, M. David. Architectural Acoustics. 2007. (J. Ross Publishing Classics Ser.). (Illus.). 411p. per. *(978-1-932159-78-3(9))* Ross, J. Publishing, Inc.

Emerick, Geoff & Massey, Howard. Here, There & Everywhere: My Life Recording the Music of the Beatles. 2007. (ENG.). 400p. (gr. 12-18). 17.00 *(978-1-59240-269-4(0),* Gotham) Penguin Group (USA) Inc.

Farquharson, Michael. Writer. Producer. Engineer: A Handbook for Creating Contemporary Commercial Music. Lindsay, Susan Gedutis & Feist, Jonathan, eds. 2007. (ENG., Illus.). 304p. per. 24.95 *(978-0-87639-053-5(X),* 087639053X, Berklee Pr.) Leonard, Hal Corp.

Gainey, Rob. Rockin' Your Stage Sound: Music Pro Guides, 1 vol. 2010. (ENG., Illus.). 256p. pap. 24.99 *(978-1-4234-9278-8(1),* 1423492781) Leonard, Hal Corp.

Gan, Woon Siong. Acoustical Imaging: Techniques & Applications for Engineers. 2012. (ENG.). 440p. 140.00 ***(978-0-470-66160-4(7),*** Wiley) Wiley, John & Sons, Inc.

Ginevsky, A. S., et al. Acoustic Control of Turbulent Jets. 2010. (Foundations of Engineering Mechanics Ser.). (ENG., Illus.). xiv, 232p. pap. 169.00 *(978-3-642-05764-9(0),* 3642057640) Springer.

Gottlieb, Gary. How Does It Sound Now? Legendary Engineers & Vintage Gear. 2009. (ENG., Illus.). 480p. pap. 24.99 *(978-1-59863-852-3(1))* Course Technology.

Große, Christian U. & Ohtsu, Masayasu, eds. Acoustic Emission Testing. 2008. (ENG., Illus.). x, 406p. 239.00 *(978-3-540-69895-1(7),* 3540698957) Springer.

Haase, Werner, et al, eds. DESider - A European Effort on Hybrid RANS-les Modelling: Results of the European-Union Funded Project, 2004 - 2007. 2009. (Notes on Numerical Fluid Mechanics & Multidisciplinary Design Ser.). (Illus.). xx, 454p. 339.00 *(978-3-540-92772-3(7))* Springer.

Hänsler, Eberhard & Schmidt, Gerhard, eds. Speech & Audio Processing in Adverse Environments. 2010. (Signals & Communication Technology Ser.). (Illus.). xx, 736p. pap. 179.00 *(978-3-642-08953-4(4),* 3642089534) Springer.

—Topics in Acoustic Echo & Noise Control: Selected Methods for the Cancellation of Acoustical Echoes, the Reduction of Background Noise, & Speech Processing. 2010. (Signals & Communication Technology Ser.). (Illus.). xix, 642p. pap. 179.00 *(978-3-642-06975-8(4),* 3642069754) Springer.

Harris, Ben. Home Studio Setup: Everything You Need to Know from Equipment to Acoustics. 2009. (Mastering Music Ser.). (ENG., Illus.). 200p. pap. 29.95 *(978-0-240-81134-5(8),* Focal Pr.) Elsevier Science & Technology Bks.

Havelock, David Ian, et al, eds. Handbook of Signal Processing in Acoustics, 2 vols. 2008. (Illus.). 1933p. 569.00 *(978-0-387-77698-9(2))* Springer.

IEEE Staff. 2007 IEEE Workshop on Applications of Signal Processing to Audio & Acoustics. 2007. pap. 246.00 *(978-1-4244-1618-9(3))* IEEE.

Institute of Acoustics (IOA) Staff, compiled by. Autumn Conference of the Institute of Acoustics 2007: Advances in Noise & Vibration Engineering. 2008. (Proceedings of the Institute of Acoustics Ser.). 227p. pap. 115.00 *(978-1-60423-938-6(7))* Curran Assocs., Inc.

—Institute of Acoustics Spring Conference 2007: Sound of Sustainability: Going for Gold! 2007. (Proceedings of the Institute of Acoustics Ser.). 206p. pap. 143.00 *(978-1-60423-816-7(X))* Curran Assocs., Inc.

—It's Practically a Quality Measurement! Are Your Acoustic Measurements Fit for Purpose? 2007. (Proceedings of the Institute of Acoustics Ser.). 64p. pap. 118.00 *(978-1-60423-348-3(6))* Curran Assocs., Inc.

—Planning & Noise 2005. 2007. (Proceedings of the Institute of Acoustics Ser.). 42p. pap. 85.00 *(978-1-60423-992-8(1))* Curran Assocs., Inc.

—Reproduced Sound 21: Feedback to the Future. 2007. (Proceedings of the Institute of Acoustics Ser.). 225p. pap. 115.00 *(978-1-60423-993-5(X))* Curran Assocs., Inc.

Jones, Douglas R. Sound of Worship: A Handbook of Acoustics & Sound System Design for the Church. 2010. (ENG., Illus.). 316p. pap. 49.95 *(978-0-240-81339-4(1),* Focal Pr.) Elsevier Science & Technology Bks.

Jones, Joie P. & Lee, Hua, eds. Acoustical Imaging: Volume 30. 2010. (Acoustical Imaging Ser.). (ENG.). 420p. 259.00 *(978-90-481-3254-6(1),* 9048132541) Springer.

Kerscher, Michael. Compact Spherical Loudspeaker Array. 2010. 92p. pap. *(978-3-639-27945-0(X))* VDM Verlag Dr. Mueller e.K.

Kuttruff, Heinrich. Acoustics. 2006. (ENG., Illus.). 480p. (C). 230.00 *(978-0-415-38679-1(9),* CRC Press) Taylor & Francis Group GBR. Dist: Taylor & Francis Group.

—Acoustics: An Introduction. 2006. (ENG., Illus.). 480p. per. 70.95 *(978-0-415-38680-7(2),* CRC Press) Taylor & Francis Group GBR. Dist: Taylor & Francis Group.

Lawrence, Bosiwah. Acoustic Study of Akan Nasals: Nasals at Different Word Positions, Duration & Gender Issues. 2011. 172p. pap. ***(978-3-639-32833-2(7))*** VDM Verlag Dr. Mueller e.K.

Lubin, Tom. Getting Great Sounds: The Microphone Book. 2009. (ENG.). 320p. pap. 39.99 *(978-1-59863-570-6(0))* Course Technology.

Magoules, F., ed. Computational Methods for Acoustics Problems. 2009. (ENG., Illus.). 338p. 195.00 *(978-1-874672-30-2(X))* Saxe-Coburg Pubns. GBR. Dist: Independent Pubs. Group.

Masters, Jerry L. Hanging from a Tree by My Knees: The Jerry Masters Story - Let It All Hang Out. 2010. 310p. pap. 14.95 *(978-0-9819657-4-1(1))* Crossover Pubns.

Mechel, F. P. Formulas of Acoustics. 2nd ed. 2008. 1500p. 339.00 *(978-3-540-76832-6(7))* Springer.

Mechel, Fridolin. Room Acoustical Fields. 2012. (ENG., Illus.). xiii, 595p. 229.00 ***(978-3-642-22355-6(9),*** 3642223559) Springer.

Menasche, Emile D. Your Sound Onstage. 2011. (ENG., Illus.). 256p. pap. 29.99 incl. disk *(978-1-61774-231-6(7),* 1617742317) In-Tune Bks. AUS. Dist: Leonard, Hal Corp.

Miller, Richard K. & Montone, Wayne V. Handbook of Acoustical Enclosures & Barriers. 33.00 *(978-0-915586-06-6(1))* Fairmont Pr., Inc.

Möser, Michael. Engineering Acoustics: An Introduction to Noise Control. Zimmermann, S. & Ellis, R., trs. from GER. 2nd ed. 2009. (ENG., Illus.). xiv, 536p. 129.00 *(978-3-540-92722-8(0),* 3540927220) Springer.

Möser, Michael & Müller, Gerhard, eds. Handbook of Engineering Acoustics: A Handbook. 650th ed. 2008. (Illus.). 650p. 279.00 *(978-3-540-24052-5(7),* 3540240527) Springer.

Moylan, William. Understanding & Crafting the Mix: The Art of Recording. 2nd ed. 2006. (ENG., Illus.). 424p. pap. 34.95 *(978-0-240-80755-3(3),* Focal Pr.) Elsevier Science & Technology Bks.

Newell, Philip. Recording Studio Design. 3rd ed. 2011. (ENG., Illus.). 832p. pap. 89.95 *(978-0-240-52240-1(0),* Focal Pr.) Elsevier Science & Technology Bks.

Newell, Philip & Holland, Keith. Loudspeakers: For Music Recording & Reproduction. 2006. (ENG., Illus.). 416p. 76.95 *(978-0-240-52014-8(9),* Focal Pr.) Elsevier Science & Technology Bks.

Overholt, Sara. Stockhausen's Musical Shapes: How a Master Composer Moves Sound. 2008. 168p. pap. *(978-3-639-08890-8(5))* VDM Verlag Dr. Mueller e.K.

Owsinski, Bobby & Moody, Dennis. The Drum Recording. 2009. (ENG.). 154p. pap., instr.'s hndbk. ed. 29.99 *(978-1-4234-4343-8(8),* 1423443438) Leonard, Hal Corp.

Rallabhandi, Sriram. Sonic Boom Minimization Through Shape Optimization & Acoustic Propagation. 2008. 224p. per. *(978-3-8364-6087-3(4))* VDM Verlag Dr. Mueller e.K.

Reynolds, Douglas D. Engineering Principles of Acoustics: Noise & Vibration Control. 5th ed. 2012. (Illus.). 641p. pap. ***(978-0-205-07283-5(6))*** Allyn & Bacon, Inc.

Rossing, Thomas D. & Fletcher, Neville H. Principles of Vibration & Sound. 2nd ed. 2010. (ENG., Illus.). viii, 330p. pap. 69.95 *(978-1-4419-2343-1(8),* 1441923438) Springer.

Sandberg, Göran & Ohayon, Roger, eds. Computational Aspects of Structural Acoustics & Vibration. 2010. (CISM International Centre for Mechanical Sciences Ser.). (ENG., Illus.). viii, 276p. pap. 179.00 *(978-3-211-99947-9(7),* 3211999477) Springer.

Sandberg, Göran & Ohayon, Roger. Computational Aspects of Structural Acoustics & Vibration. 2009. (CISM International Centre for Mechanical Sciences Ser.). (Illus.). viii, 276p. 179.00 *(978-3-211-89650-1(3))* Springer.

Santana Jr., Avandelino. Passive Control of Combustion Instability. 2010. 172p. pap. *(978-3-8383-6992-1(0))* Lambert Academic Publishing.

Self, Douglas. Small Signal Audio Design. 2010. (ENG., Illus.). 576p. pap. 73.95 *(978-0-240-52177-0(3),* Focal Pr.) Elsevier Science & Technology Bks.

Self, Douglas, ed. Audio Engineering Explained. 2009. (ENG., Illus.). 656p. pap. 51.95 *(978-0-240-81273-1(5),* Focal Pr.) Elsevier Science & Technology Bks.

Shin, Kihong & Hammond, Joseph K. Fundamentals of Signal Processing for Sound & Vibration Engineers. 2008. (ENG., Illus.). 416p. 110.00 *(978-0-470-51188-6(5),* Wiley) Wiley, John & Sons, Inc.

Simsekli, Umut. Bayesian Methods for Real-Time Pitch Tracking. 2011. 72p. pap. ***(978-3-8443-1251-5(X))*** Lambert Academic Publishing.

Sinclair, Ian, et al. Audio Engineering. 2008. (Newnes Know It All Ser.: 1). (ENG., Illus.). 936p. pap. 64.95 *(978-1-85617-526-5(X),* Newnes) Elsevier Science & Technology Bks.

Swallow, Dave. Live Audio: The Art of Mixing a Show. 2010. (ENG., Illus.). 256p. pap. 39.95 *(978-0-240-81604-3(8),* Focal Pr.) Elsevier Science & Technology Bks.

Swedien, Bruce & Hal Leonard Corporation Staff. Make Mine Music, 1 vol. 2009. (ENG., Illus.). 288p. pap. 22.99 *(978-1-4234-6494-5(X),* 142346494X) Leonard, Hal Corp.

Thomas, Richard K. The Designs of Abe Jacob. 2008. 127p. pap. 35.00 *(978-1-933348-14-8(3))* USITT.

Toole, Floyd. Sound Reproduction: The Acoustics & Psychoacoustics of Loudspeakers & Rooms. 2008. (ENG., Illus.). 568p. pap. 54.95 *(978-0-240-52009-4(2),* Focal Pr.) Elsevier Science & Technology Bks.

Trapp, Martin & Chen, Fang. Automotive Buzz, Squeak & Rattle: Mechanisms, Analysis, Evaluation & Prevention. Chen, Frank, ed. 2011. (ENG., Illus.). 296p. 99.95 *(978-0-7506-8496-5(8),* Butterworth-Heinemann) Elsevier Science & Technology Bks.

Vigran, Tor Erik. Building Acoustics. 2008. (ENG., Illus.). 384p. 170.00 *(978-0-415-42853-8(X),* CRC Press) Taylor & Francis Group GBR. Dist: Taylor & Francis Group.

Winer, Ethan. The Audio Expert: Everything You Need to Know about Audio. 2012. (ENG.). 696p. pap. 54.95 ***(978-0-240-82100-9(9),*** Focal Pr.) Elsevier Science & Technology Bks.

Zangi, K. C. & Oppenheim, Alan V. Active Noise Cancellation System Design Engineering. 2007. 152p. 89.95 *(978-1-934939-05-5(6))* Wexford College Pr.

Zhang, Lei. Underwater Acoustic Sensor Networks Protocol Design. 2010. 140p. pap. *(978-3-8383-8608-9(6))* Lambert Academic Publishing.

Zita, K. Lexikon der Schulphysik Vol. 1: Mechanik und Akustik. (GER.). 85.00 *(978-0-8288-8062-6(X),* M7222) French & European Pubns., Inc.

ACOUSTICAL HOLOGRAPHY

see Acoustic Holography

ACOUSTICS

see Hearing; Sound

ACOUSTICS, ARCHITECTURAL

see Architectural Acoustics

ACOUSTICS, MOLECULAR

see Molecular Acoustics

ACOUSTICS, UNDERWATER

see Underwater Acoustics

ACQUAINTANCE RAPE

see also Date Rape

Crabb, Cindy. Learning Good Consent. 2010. 48p. 3.00 *(978-1-934620-33-5(5))* Microcosm Publishing.

Sampson, Rana. Acquaintance Rape of College Students. 2009. pap. 43.00 *(978-1-60692-207-1(6))* Nova Science Pubs., Inc.

ACQUIRED IMMUNODEFICIENCY SYNDROME

see AIDS (Disease)

ACQUISITION OF CORPORATIONS

see Consolidation and Merger of Corporations

ACQUISITION OF LANGUAGE

see Language Acquisition

ACQUISITION OF SERIAL PUBLICATIONS

Lawson, Karen G., ed. Serials Collection Management in Recessionary Times. 2011. (ENG., Illus.). 216p. (C). 125.00 *(978-0-415-58961-1(4))* Routledge.

ACQUISITION OF PERIODICALS

see Acquisition of Serial Publications

ACQUISITION OF TERRITORY

see also Occupancy (International Law)

Blanken, Leo J. Rational Empires: Institutional Incentives & Imperial Expansion. 2012. (ENG., Illus.). 208p. pap. 27.50 ***(978-0-226-05674-6(0));*** 218p. 85.00 ***(978-0-226-05673-9(2))*** Univ. of Chicago Pr.

Fei, Yiwen. The Institutional Approach to Mergers. 2009. 256p. pap. *(978-3-639-08781-9(X))* VDM Verlag Dr. Mueller e.K.

ACQUISITIONS (LIBRARIES)

see also Searching, Bibliographical

Agee, Jim. Acquisitions Go Global: An Introduction to Library Collection Management in the 21st Century. 2007. (Illus.). 180p. *(978-1-84334-327-1(4));* pap. *(978-1-84334-326-4(6))* Woodhead Publishing Ltd. (Chandos Publishing).

Ashmore, Beth, et al. The Librarian's Guide to Negotiation: Winning Strategies for the Digital Age. 2012. 256p. pap. 39.50 ***(978-1-57387-428-1(0))*** Information Today, Inc.

Daniels, Tim. Charleston Conference Proceedings 2008, 1 vol. Bernhardt, Beth R. et al, eds. 2009. 242p. pap. 40.00 *(978-1-59158-933-4(9),* A2610P) Libraries Unlimited, Inc.

Data Acquisition Handbook: Companies-Products-Services. 200p. (Orig.). pap. 125.00 *(978-0-7605-1830-4(0))* Rector Pr., Ltd.

Dirik, Ahmet. New Techniques in Multimedia Forensics. 2011. 108p. pap. ***(978-3-8443-2076-3(8))*** Lambert Academic Publishing.

Holden, Jesse. Acquisitions in the New Information Universe: Core Competencies & Ethical Practices. 2010. (Illus.). xv, 135p. 80.00 *(978-1-55570-696-8(7))* Neal-Schuman Pubs., Inc.

Nixon, Judith M., et al, eds. Patron-Driven Acquisitions: Current Successes & Future Directions. 2011. (ENG., Illus.). 152p. (C). 125.00 *(978-0-415-61870-0(3))* Routledge.

Primary Research Group Staff. The Survey of Academic & Research Library Journal Purchasing Practices. 2008. (ESK.). 177p. pap. 89.50 *(978-1-57440-108-0(4))* Primary Research Group.

Tarulli, Laurel. The Library Catalogue as Social Space: Promoting Patron Driven Collections, Online Communities, & Enhanced Reference & Readers' Services, 1 vol. 150p. pap. 40.00 *(978-1-59884-629-4(9),* A3165P) Pearson Education GBR. Dist: ABC-CLIO, LLC.

Trompenaars, Fons & Nijhoff Asser, Maarten. The Global M&A Tango: How to Reconcile Cultural Differences in Mergers, Acquisitions, & Strategic Partnerships. 2010. (ENG.). 208p. 30.00 *(978-0-07-176115-4(2),* 0071761152) McGraw-Hill Cos., The.

ACRASIALES

Winston, Wayne L. Mathletics: How Gamblers, Managers, & Sports Enthusiasts Use Mathematics in Baseball, Basketball, & Football. 2009. (ENG., Illus.). 376p. 29.95 *(978-0-691-13913-5(X))* Princeton Univ. Pr.

ACRITARCHS

Moczydlowska, M. Fossils & Strata, Cambrian Acritarchs from Upper Silesia, Poland: Biochronology & Tectonic Implications, Number 46. 2006. (Fossils & Strata Monograph Ser.: 46). (ENG.). 120p. pap. 44.95 *(978-82-00-37692-7(3),* Wiley-Blackwell) Wiley, John & Sons, Inc.

ACROBATS AND ACROBATISM

see also Gymnastics; Tumbling

Heyman, Harriet. Private Acts: The Acrobat Sublime. 2011. (ENG., Illus.). 224p. 45.00 *(978-0-8478-3673-4(8))* Rizzoli International Pubns., Inc.

Petit, Philippe. Man on Wire: "By Evoking His Youthful Passion for the World Trade Center, Petit Brings the Towers' Awesomeness Back to Life." 2008. (ENG., Illus.). 256p. pap. 14.95 *(978-1-60239-332-5(X),* 239332) Skyhorse Publishing Co., Inc.

—To Reach the Clouds: My High-Wire Walk Between the Twin Towers. 2007. (Illus.). 288p. pap. 14.95 *(978-1-60239-128-4(9))* Skyhorse Publishing Co., Inc.

Rooyackers, Paul. 101 Circus Games for Children: Juggling - Clowning - Balancing Acts - Acrobatics - Animal Numbers. 2010. (SmartFun Activity Bks.). (ENG., Illus.). 160p. (gr. -1). pap. 14.95 *(978-0-89793-516-6(0));* spiral bd. 19.95 *(978-0-89793-517-3(9))* Hunter Hse., Inc.

Tong, Manny. Balancing Acts. 2008. pap. 22.95 *(978-0-7414-4721-0(5))* Infinity Publishing.

Yong, Johnny. A Balanced Life. 2011. 144p. 24.95 ***(978-1-936343-99-7(1));*** pap. 14.95 ***(978-1-936343-98-0(3))*** Peppertree Pr., The.

ACROGENS

see Cryptogams; Ferns; Mosses

ACROMEGALY

Kontogeorgos, G., et al, eds. Growth Hormones & Growth Factors in Acromegaly & Beyond: 4th International Workshop on Highlights in Basic & Clinical Neuroendocrinology, Athens, November 2005: Proceedings: Special Issue: Neuroendocrinology 2006, Vol. 83, No. 3-4. (Illus.). 144p. pap. *(978-3-8055-8198-1(X))* Karger, S. AG.

Ranke, M. B. & Abs, R., eds. The Role of IGF Parameters in the Management of Growth Disorders & Acromegaly - Diagnosis, Efficacy & Safety: 7th KIGS/KIMS Expert Meeting on Growth Hormone & Growth Disorders, Paris, France, January 16-17, 2004, Vol. 62. (Illus.). 4;16p. pap. *(978-3-8055-7837-0(7))* Karger, S. AG.

ACRONYMS

Acronyms, Initialisms & Abbreviations Dictionary, 4.0. 45th ed. 2011. 1404.00 *(978-1-4144-6817-4(2))* Cengage Gale.

Acronyms, Initialisms & Abbreviations Dictionary, 4 vols., Set 4 vols. 43rd rev. ed. 2010. (ENG.). 1404.00 *(978-1-4144-4537-3(7))* Cengage Gale.

American Heritage Dictionaries Editors, ed. The American Heritage Abbreviations Dictionary: A Compilation of Today's Acronyms & Abbreviations Including Cyberspeak. 3rd ed. 2007. (American Heritage Bks.). (ENG.). 304p. 6.95 *(978-0-618-85747-0(8))* Houghton Mifflin Harcourt Trade & Reference Pubs.

Harvey, John Ross. Acronymville Your One Stop Destination in the World of Acronyms. 2009. 251p. pap. 17.99 *(978-1-4357-3033-5(X))* Lulu Enterprises Inc.

International Encyclopedia of Abbreviations & Acronyms in Science & Technology Yearbook 2002. 700p. 241.00 *(978-3-598-23496-5(1))* Saur, K. G. Verlag GmbH & Co. DEU. Dist: Saur, K. G. Verlag GmbH & Co.

McGowan, Lee & Phinnemore, David. A Dictionary of the European Union. 4th rev. ed. 2008. VIII, 480p. 260.00 *(978-1-85743-485-9(4))* Routledge.

Reverse Acronyms Initialisms & Abbreviations Dictionary, 4.0. 45th ed. 2011. 926.00 *(978-1-4144-6908-9(X))* Cengage Gale.

Unterman, Alan. Historical Dictionary of the Jews. 2010. (Historical Dictionaries of Peoples & Cultures Ser.: 9). (ENG.). 276p. 70.00 *(978-0-8108-5525-0(9))* Scarecrow Pr., Inc.

ACRYLATES

Friedman, Mendel & Mottram, Don, eds. Chemistry & Safety of Acrylamide in Food. 2010. (Advances in Experimental Medicine & Biology Ser.). (Illus.). xii, 466p. pap. 229.00 *(978-1-4419-3672-1(6),* 1441936726) Springer.

Nik Hussain, Nik Hazlina, et al. Tissue Adhesive Versus Standard Wound Closure Technique. 2011. 84p. pap. ***(978-3-8443-1412-0(1))*** Lambert Academic Publishing.

ACRYLIC PAINTING

Adams, David. FairyArt: Painting Magical Fairies & Their Worlds. 2009. (ENG., Illus.). 128p. pap. 22.99 *(978-1-60061-089-9(7),* Impact) F&W Media, Inc.

Akib, Hashim. Vibrant Acrylics. 2012. (ENG., Illus.). 128p. pap. 29.95 ***(978-1-84448-697-7(4))*** Search Pr., Ltd. GBR. Dist: Independent Pubs. Group.

Arobateau, Red Jordan. Obedience to the Call of Art. 2010. 406p. pap. 24.50 *(978-0-615-22144-1(0))* Red Jordan Pr.

Barber, John. The Acrylic Paint Colour Wheel Book. 2011. (ENG., Illus.). 160p. pap. 19.95 *(978-1-84448-421-8(1))* Search Pr., Ltd. GBR. Dist: Independent Pubs. Group.

—Acrylics: A Visual Reference to Mixing Acrylic Colour. 2007. (Winsor & Newton Color Mixing Guides). (ENG., Illus.). 64p. spiral bd. 19.95 *(978-1-84448-227-6(8))* Search Pr., Ltd. GBR. Dist: Independent Pubs. Group.

Barron, Gill. Acrylic Secrets: 300 Tips & Techniques for Painting the Easy Way. 2011. (ENG.). 176p. (gr. 12). 19.95 *(978-1-60652-345-2(7))* Reader's Digest Assn., Inc., The.

Book Sales, Inc. Staff & Scott, Marilyn. Acrylic Artist's Bible. 2009. (Artist's Bibles Ser.). (ENG.). 192p. spiral bd. 14.99 *(978-0-7858-1944-8(4),* 0785819444, Chartwell) Book Sales, Inc.

Brady, Patti. Rethinking Acrylic: Radical Solutions for Exploiting the World's Most Versatile Medium. 2008. (ENG., Illus.). 160p. 29.99 *(978-1-60061-013-4(7),* North Light Bks.) F&W Media, Inc.

Bryan, Debra Jordan. Seasons & Other Reasons to Paint. 2006. 84p. 16.95 *(978-1-60140-140-3(X))* Leisure Arts, Inc.

Cross, Maureen. Mixing & Matching: Approaches to Retouching Paintings. Ellison, Rebecca, ed. 2010. (ENG., Illus.). 198p. pap. 80.00 *(978-1-904982-50-0(6))* Archetype Pubns. GBR. Dist: National Bk. Network.

Cuthbert, David. Acrylic Tips & Tricks: Getting the Best Results from Acrylics — Helping You to Paint with Confidence & Style. 2009. (Artist's Bibles Ser.).

(ENG., Illus.). 192p. spiral bd. 14.99 *(978-0-7858-2438-1(3)*, 0785824383, Chartwell) Book Sales, Inc.
Dewberry, Donna. Donna Dewberry's Essential One-Stroke Painting Reference. 2009. (ENG., Illus.). 160p. pap. 24.99 *(978-1-60061-131-5(1)*, North Light Bks.) F&W Media, Inc.
Evans, Charles. Landscapes in Acrylics. 2009. (Ready to Paint Ser.). (ENG., Illus.). 48p. pap. 19.95 *(978-1-84448-423-2(8))* Search Pr., Ltd. GBR. Dist: Independent Pubs. Group.
Fisher, Timothy, et al. Flowers in Acrylics. 2012. (How to Paint Ser.). (ENG., Illus.). 64p. pap. 17.95 ***(978-1-84448-582-6(X))*** Search Pr., Ltd. GBR. Dist: Independent Pubs. Group.
Fredericq, Suzanne. Artist Eugene J. Martin's 2000 Acrylic Paintings on Canvas. 2009. 75p. pap., pap. 31.50 *(978-0-9825704-7-0(3))* Estate of Eugene James Martin.
—Artist Eugene J. Martin's 2001 Acrylic Paintings on Canvas, Part 1. 2009. 93p. pap. 41.90 *(978-0-9825704-8-7(1))* Estate of Eugene James Martin.
—Artist Eugene J. Martin's 2002 Acrylic Paintings on Canvas, Part 1. 2010. 97p. pap. 43.10 *(978-0-9825704-9-4(X))* Estate of Eugene James Martin.
—Artist Eugene J. Martin's 2003-04 Acrylic Paintings on Canvas. 2010. 104p. pap. 42.70 *(978-0-9826351-2-4(5))* Estate of Eugene James Martin.
—Artist Eugene J. Martin's 2003 Acrylic Paintings on Canvas, Part 1. 2010. 99p. pap. 41.20 *(978-0-9826351-0-0(9))* Estate of Eugene James Martin.
—Transformations: Works on Paper by Artist Eugene J. Martin, Part I. 2010. 103p. pap. 44.90 *(978-0-9825704-6-3(5))* Estate of Eugene James Martin.
French, Soraya. Acrylics. 2008. (30 Minute Art Ser.). (Illus.). 96p. pap. 9.95 *(978-0-06-149183-2(7)*, HarperPerennial) HarperCollins Pubs.
—Dynamic Acrylics. 2009. (ENG.). 128p. 18.99 *(978-0-7641-6973-1(4))* Barron's Educational Series, Inc.
Garcia, Claire Watson. Painting for the Absolute & Utter Beginner. 2009. (ENG., Illus.). 160p. pap. 21.99 *(978-0-8230-9947-4(4)*, Watson-Guptill Pubns., Inc.
Gregory, Noel. Turner: In Acrylics. 2011. (Ready to Paint the Masters Ser.). (ENG., Illus.). 88p. pap. 19.95 *(978-1-84448-579-6(X))* Search Pr., Ltd. GBR. Dist: Independent Pubs. Group.
Guasch, Gemma & Asunción, Josep. Acrylics. 2011. (Creative Techniques Ser.). (ENG.). 144p. 26.99 *(978-0-7641-6390-6(6))* Barron's Educational Series, Inc.
Hammond, John. Capturing Light in Acrylics. 2006. (ENG., Illus.). 128p. pap. 19.95 *(978-0-7134-9027-5(6)*, Batsford, B. T. Ltd.) Anova Bks. GBR. Dist: Sterling Publishing Co., Inc.
—Free Expression in Acrylics. 2008. (ENG., Illus.). 128p. 27.95 *(978-0-7134-9043-5(8)*, Batsford, B. T. Ltd.) Anova Bks. GBR. Dist: Sterling Publishing Co., Inc.
Hammond, John & Capon, Robin. Painting Atmospheric Acrylics. 2011. (ENG., Illus.). 128p. pap. 17.95 *(978-1-84994-012-2(6)*, Batsford, B. T. Ltd.) Anova Bks. GBR. Dist: Sterling Publishing Co., Inc.
Hammond, Lee. Acrylic Painting with Lee Hammond. 2006. (ENG., Illus.). 128p. pap. 19.99 *(978-1-58180-709-7(0)*, North Light Bks.) F&W Media, Inc.
—Discover Acrylic Painting with Lee Hammond. 2009. (ENG.). cd-rom 35.00 *(978-1-60061-689-1(5)*, North Light Bks.) F&W Media, Inc.
—Lee Hammond's Big Book of Acrylic Painting: Fast, easy techniques for painting your favorite Subjects. 2012. (ENG., Illus.). 192p. pap. 24.99 *(978-1-4403-0858-1(6)*, North Light Bks.) F&W Media, Inc.
—Paint Landscapes in Acrylic with Lee Hammond. 2009. (ENG., Illus.). 144p. pap. 24.99 *(978-1-60061-309-8(8)*, North Light Bks.) F&W Media, Inc.
—Paint People in Acrylic with Lee Hammond. 2006. (ENG., Illus.). 128p. pap. 24.99 *(978-1-58180-798-1(6)*, North Light Bks.) F&W Media, Inc.
—Paint Realistic Animals in Acrylic with Lee Hammond. 2007. (ENG., Illus.). 128p. pap. 24.99 *(978-1-58180-912-1(3)*, North Light Bks.) F&W Media, Inc.
Hampton, Anita, et al. Oil & Acrylic: Landscapes: Learn to paint a collection of beautiful scenes-step by Step. 2011. (How to Draw & Paint Ser.). (ENG., Illus.). 32p. pap. 8.95 *(978-1-60058-222-6(2)*, 1600582222) Foster, Walter Publishing, Inc.
Harrison, Hazel. Encyclopedia of Acrylic Techniques: A Unique A-Z Directory of Acrylic Techniques with Step-by-Step Guidance on Their Use. 2009. (ENG., Illus.). 176p. pap. 19.95 *(978-0-85532-961-7(0))* Search Pr., Ltd. GBR. Dist: Independent Pubs. Group.
—Oils & Acrylics Made Easy. 2008. (ENG., Illus.). 64p. pap. 7.99 *(978-1-84476-590-4(3))* Anness Publishing GBR. Dist: National Bk. Network.
—Watercolor, Oil & Acrylic: A Practical Guide to Successful Painting: A Complete Step-by-Step Course in Techniques, from Getting Started to Achieving Excellence. 2006. (ENG., Illus.). 132p. pap. 10.99 *(978-1-84476-419-8(2))* Anness Publishing GBR. Dist: National Bk. Network.
Harrison, Terry. Painting Acrylic Landscapes the Easy Way. 2011. (ENG., Illus.). 128p. pap. 25.95 ***(978-1-84448-466-9(1))*** Search Pr., Ltd. GBR. Dist: Independent Pubs. Group.
—Terry's Greatest Tips: For Watercolour & Acrylic Artists. 2012. (ENG., Illus.). 192p. 29.95 ***(978-1-84448-802-5(0))*** Search Pr., Ltd. GBR. Dist: Independent Pubs. Group.
Harrison, Terry. Terry's Top Tips for Acrylic Artists: Over 100 Essential Tips to Improve Your Painting. 2010. (ENG., Illus.). 96p. spiral bd. 19.95 *(978-1-84448-463-8(7))* Search Pr., Ltd. GBR. Dist: Independent Pubs. Group.
Hederer, Marcus. Acrylic Painting for Beginners. 2008. 176p. 9.95 *(978-0-8416-0352-3(9))* American Map Corp.
Humberstone, Dani. Abstracts in Acrylics. 2011. (Ready to Paint Ser.). (ENG., Illus.). 72p. pap. 17.95 *(978-1-84448-489-8(0))* Search Pr., Ltd. GBR. Dist: Independent Pubs. Group.
Hyce, David, et al. Acrylic Painting. 2009. (ENG., Illus.). 144p. pap. 19.95 *(978-1-84448-411-9(4))* Search Pr., Ltd. GBR. Dist: Independent Pubs. Group.
Jay, Peter. Acrylics. 2009. (How to Paint Ser.). (ENG., Illus.). 64p. pap. 17.95 *(978-1-84448-295-5(2))* Search Pr., Ltd. GBR. Dist: Independent Pubs. Group.
Jelbert, Wendy. Creative Acrylic Landscapes. 2009. (Acrylic Tips & Techniques Ser.). (ENG., Illus.). 96p. pap. 19.95 *(978-1-84448-171-2(9))* Search Pr., Ltd. GBR. Dist: Independent Pubs. Group.
—Ready to Paint: Flowers in Acrylics. 2009. (Ready to Paint Ser.). (ENG., Illus.). 48p. pap. 17.95 *(978-1-84448-425-6(4))* Search Pr., Ltd. GBR. Dist: Independent Pubs. Group.
—Ready to Paint: Venice in Acrylics. 2009. (Ready to Paint Ser.). (ENG., Illus.). 48p. pap. 17.95 *(978-1-84448-413-3(0))* Search Pr., Ltd. GBR. Dist: Independent Pubs. Group.
—Wendy's Top Tips for Acrylic Artists: Over 130 Essential Tips to Improve Your Painting. 2011. (ENG., Illus.). 96p. spiral bd. 19.95 *(978-1-84448-485-0(8))* Search Pr., Ltd. GBR. Dist: Independent Pubs. Group.
Jelbert, Wendy, et al. Trace & Paint Flowers. 2012. (Trace & Paint Ser.). (ENG., Illus.). 128p. pap. 25.95 ***(978-1-84448-727-1(X))*** Search Pr., Ltd. GBR. Dist: Independent Pubs. Group.
Keller, Christoph, ed. Glen Rubsamen: Take All the Time You Need. 2010. (ENG., Illus.). 184p. 60.00 *(978-3-941185-48-7(9))* Verlag fur Moderne Kunst DEU. Dist: D.A.P./Distributed Art Pubs.
Lawrence, Rod. Animals / Acrylic: Learn to Paint Step by Step. 2009. (How to Draw & Paint Ser.). (ENG., Illus.). 32p. pap. 8.95 *(978-1-60058-123-6(4)*, 1600581234) Foster, Walter Publishing, Inc.
Lucio, Laura. Eastern Bluebird. 2007. (ENG., Illus.). 44p. spiral bd. 24.95 *(978-1-881982-54-6(8))* Stackpole Magazines.

Maday, Jane. Landscapes in Bloom: 10 Flower-Filled Scenes You Can Paint in Acrylics. 2009. (ENG., Illus.). 128p. pap. 24.99 *(978-1-60061-101-8(X)*, North Light Bks.) F&W Media, Inc.
McNeill, Suzanne. Painting for Patios for Home & Garden Decor. 2011. (Design Originals Ser.). (Illus.). 36p. pap. 11.99 ***(978-1-57421-758-2(5))*** Design Originals.
Odanaka, T. Secrets of Japanese Quick Stroke Paintin. 2006. pap. 15.95 *(978-1-4286-6187-5(5))* Kessinger Publishing, LLC.
of California, Phranc. Phranc: The Cardboard Cobbler. 2007. pap. 8.00 *(978-0-9797964-0-1(7))* CUE Art Foundation.
Olwin, Anne. Acrylic. 2007. 5.95 *(978-1-934396-03-2(6))* Creativity Pr.
Palliex, Laure. Fresh & Fabulous Flowers in Acrylics. 2008. (ENG., Illus.). 128p. pap. 24.99 *(978-1-58180-975-3(X)*, North Light Bks.) F&W Media, Inc.
Parramon Studios, ed. Acrylic Painting. 2010. (Painting Class Ser.). (ENG.). 160p. 29.99 *(978-0-7641-6274-9(6))* Barron's Educational Series, Inc.
—Acrylics. 2010. (Barron's Easel Ser.). (ENG.). 96p. pap. 16.99 *(978-0-7641-4549-0(5))* Barron's Educational Series, Inc.
Penney, Jacqueline. Paint Charming Seaside Scenes with Acrylics. 2008. (ENG., Illus.). 128p. pap. 24.99 *(978-1-60061-059-2(5)*, North Light Bks.) F&W Media, Inc.
Pitcher, Colette, et al. Acrylic Painting for Dummies. 2009. (ENG., Illus.). 320p. pap. 24.99 *(978-0-470-44455-9(X)*, For Dummies) Wiley, John & Sons, Inc.
Quiller, Stephen. Watermedia Painting with Stephen Quiller: The Complete Guide to Working in Watercolor, Acrylics, Gouache, & Casein. 2008. (ENG., Illus.). 176p. pap. 24.95 *(978-0-8230-9688-6(2))* Watson-Guptill Pubns., Inc.
Reyner, Nancy. Acrylic Innovation: Styles & Techniques Featuring 84 Visionary Artists. 2010. (ENG., Illus.). 144p. 29.99 *(978-1-60061-864-2(2)*, North Light Bks.) F&W Media, Inc.
—Acrylic Revolution: New Tricks & Techniques for Working with the World's Most Versatile Medium. 2007. (ENG., Illus.). 128p. 27.99 *(978-1-58180-804-9(6)*, North Light Bks.) F&W Media, Inc.
Roig, Gabriel Martin. Painting with Acrylics. 2007. (Beginner's Art Guides). (ENG., Illus.). 64p. 12.99 *(978-0-7641-6048-6(6))* Barron's Educational Series, Inc.
Sanders, Mike. Quick & Clever Acrylics. 2008. (ENG., Illus.). 128p. pap. 22.99 *(978-0-7153-2678-7(3))* David & Charles Pubs. GBR. Dist: F&W Media, Inc.
Schaper, Kristina & Zander, Ute. All about Acrylics: A Complete Guide to Painting Using This Versatile Medium. 2011. (ENG., Illus.). 176p. pap. 24.95 *(978-1-84448-605-2(2))* Search Pr., Ltd. GBR. Dist: Independent Pubs. Group.
Sidaway, Ian. Practical Encyclopedia of Acrylics, Oils And: Mixing Paint - Brush Strokes - Gouache - Masking Out - Glazing - Wet-into-Wet - Drybrush Painting - Stretching Canvas - Painting with Knives - Light to Dark. 2012. (ENG., Illus.). 256p. pap. 16.99 ***(978-1-78019-050-1(6))*** Anness Publishing GBR. Dist: National Bk. Network.
Silvers, William L. Painting Realistic Wildlife in Acrylic: 30 Step-by-Step Demonstrations. 2009. (ENG., Illus.). 144p. pap. 26.99 *(978-1-60061-135-3(4)*, North Light Bks.) F&W Media, Inc.
Smith, Roy C. Still Life in Acrylics. (Leisure Arts Ser.: No. 34). (Illus.). 32p. pap. 4.95 *(978-0-85532-633-3(6)*, 633-6) Search Pr., Ltd. GBR. Dist: Independent Pubs. Group.
Sundell, Lexi. The Acrylic Flower Painter's A-Z: An Illustrated Directory of Techniques for Painting 40 Popular Flowers. 2010. (ENG., Illus.). 128p. pap. 19.95 *(978-1-84448-294-8(4))* Search Pr., Ltd. GBR. Dist: Independent Pubs. Group.
—Painting Acrylic Flowers A to Z. 2007. (ENG.). 128p. 29.99 *(978-1-58180-987-9(5)*, North Light Bks.) F&W Media, Inc.
Swimm, Tom. Oil & Acrylic - Sunsets: Master the Art of Painting Colorful & Dramatic Skies. 2012. (How to Draw & Paint Ser.). (ENG., Illus.). 32p. pap. 8.95 *(978-1-60058-242-4(7)*, 1600582427) Foster, Walter Publishing, Inc.
Tauchid, Rheni. New Acrylics Essential Sourcebook: Materials, Techniques & Contemporary Applications for Today's Artist. 2009. (ENG., Illus.). 192p. pap. 24.95 *(978-0-8230-9926-9(1))* Watson-Guptill Pubns., Inc.
Tranberg, Dan. Acrylic Fusion: Experimenting with Alternative Methods for Painting, Collage, & Mixed Media. 2012. (ENG., Illus.). 128p. pap. 24.99 *(978-1-59253-752-5(9)*, 1592537529) Quayside.
Van Boxtel, Jean-Paul. Incredible Acrylics: Techniques, Ideas & New Ways to Use This Versatile Medium. 2010. (ENG., Illus.). 160p. pap. 29.95 *(978-1-84448-537-6(4))* Search Pr., Ltd. GBR. Dist: Independent Pubs. Group.
Walter Foster Creative Team. Oil & Acrylic: Oceans & Seascapes: Discover the secrets to painting waves, open seas, & coastal Scenes. 2012. (How to Draw & Paint Ser.). (ENG., Illus.). 32p. pap. 8.95 ***(978-1-60058-274-5(5)***, 1600582745) Foster, Walter Publishing, Inc.
Welford, Lin. Painted Garden Art: Anyone Can Do. 2009. (ENG., Illus.). 112p. pap. 22.99 *(978-0-9777065-1-8(6))* ArtStone Pr.

ACRYLONITRILE

Rahman, Rezaur, et al. Effect of Chemical Modification on Coir Fibre Polypropylene Composites. 2011. 64p. pap. ***(978-3-8443-8440-6(5))*** Lambert Academic Publishing.

ACT (PHILOSOPHY)

see also Agent (Philosophy); Intentionality (Philosophy)

Aguilar, Jess H., et al, eds. New Waves in Philosophy of Action. 2010. (New Waves in Philosophy Ser.). (ENG., Illus.). 320p. pap. 36.00 *(978-0-230-23060-6(1))* Palgrave Macmillan.
Aguilar, Jesús H. Causing Human Actions: New Perspectives on the Causal Theory of Action. Buckareff, Andrei A., ed. 2010. (ENG., Illus.). 336p. (gr. 17). 70.00 *(978-0-262-01456-4(4))* MIT Pr.
—New Waves in Philosophy of Action. Buckareff, Andrei A. & Frankish, Keith, eds. 2010. (New Waves in Philosophy Ser.). (ENG., Illus.). 320p. 100.00 *(978-0-230-58060-2(2))* Palgrave Macmillan.
Aguilar, Jesús H. & Buckareff, Andrei A., eds. Causing Human Actions: New Perspectives on the Causal Theory of Action. 2010. (ENG., Illus.). 336p. (gr. 17). pap. 35.00 *(978-0-262-51476-7(1))* MIT Pr.
Alvarez, Maria. Kinds of Reasons: An Essay in the Philosophy of Action. 2010. (ENG.). 240p. 60.00 *(978-0-19-955000-5(X))* Oxford Univ. Pr., Inc.
Bengson, John & Moffett, Marc A., eds. Knowing How: Essays on Knowledge, Mind, & Action. 1 vol. 2012. (ENG., Illus.). 416p. 85.00 *(978-0-19-538936-4(0))* Oxford Univ. Pr., Inc.
Berthoz, Alain & Petit, Jean-Luc. The Physiology & Phenomenology of Action. Macann, Christopher, tr. from FRE. 2008. (ENG., Illus.). 240p. 75.00 *(978-0-19-954788-3(2))* Oxford Univ. Pr., Inc.
Bishop, John. Natural Agency: An Essay on the Causal Theory of Action. 2008. (Cambridge Studies in Philosophy Ser.). (ENG.). 224p. pap. 46.00 *(978-0-521-06397-5(3))* Cambridge Univ. Pr.
Brewer, Talbot. The Retrieval of Ethics. 2011. (ENG.). 352p. pap. 35.00 *(978-0-19-969222-4(X))* Oxford Univ. Pr., Inc.
Corcilius, Klaus & Rapp, Christof, eds. Beiträge zur Aristotelischen Handlungstheorie: Akten der 8. Tagung der Karl und Gertrud Abel-Stiftung vom 08. 11. 07. 2004 in Blankensee. 2008. (Philosophie der Antike (PhA) Ser.). (GER., Illus.). 217p. (C). 68.00 *(978-3-515-09057-5(6))* Steiner, Franz Verlag Wiesbaden GmbH DEU. Dist: Brown, David Bk. Co., The.
Danto, Arthur C. Analytical Philosophy of Action. 2009. (ENG.). 240p. pap. 29.99 *(978-0-521-11751-7(8))* Cambridge Univ. Pr.

Davenport, Anne Ashley. Descartes's Theory of Action. 2006. (Brill's Studies in Intellectual History: Vol. 142). 310p. *(978-90-04-15205-2(9))* BRILL.
de Gaynesford, Maximilian. Agents & Their Actions. 2011. (Ratio Special Issues Ser.: 6). (ENG.). 152p. pap. 34.95 *(978-1-4443-3908-6(7)*, Wiley-Blackwell) Wiley, John & Sons, Inc.
González Lagier, Daniel. The Paradoxes of Action: (Human Action, Law & Philosophy) 2010. (Law & Philosophy Library). 146p. pap. 109.00 *(978-90-481-6443-1(5)*, 9048164435) Springer.
Haddock, Adrian & Macpherson, Fiona. Disjunctivism: Perception, Action, Knowledge. 2011. (ENG.). 422p. pap. 40.00 *(978-0-19-969308-5(0))* Oxford Univ. Pr., Inc.
Hanna, Robert & Maiese, Michelle. Embodied Minds in Action. 2009. (ENG., Illus.). 280p. 75.00 *(978-0-19-923031-0(5))* Oxford Univ. Pr., Inc.
Holmström-Hintikka, Ghita & Tuomela, R., eds. Contemporary Action Theory Volume 1: Individual Action: Individual Action. 2010. (Synthese Library). 372p. pap. 269.00 *(978-90-481-4914-8(2)*, 9048149142) Springer.
—Contemporary Action Theory Volume 2: Social Action: Social Action. 2010. (Synthese Library). 336p. pap. 239.00 *(978-90-481-4915-5(0)* 9048149150) Springer.
Kalis, Annemarie. Failures of Agency: Irrational Behavior & Self-Understanding. 2011. (ENG.). 194p. 60.00 ***(978-0-7391-4888-4(5))*** Lexington Bks.
Kanzian, Christian & Runggaldier, Edmund, eds. Cultures - Conflict - Analysis - Dialogue: Proceedings of the 29th International Ludwig Wittgenstein-Symposium in Kirchberg, Austria 2006. 2007. (ENG., Illus.). 431p. 89.95 *(978-3-938793-66-4(X))* Ontos Verlag DEU. Dist: Transaction Pubs.
Korsgaard, Christine M. Self-Constitution: Agency, Identity, & Integrity. 2009. (ENG.). 248p. 105.00 *(978-0-19-955279-5(7))* Oxford Univ. Pr., Inc.
Kozel, Susan. Closer: Performance, Technologies, Phenomenology. 2008. (Leonardo Bks.). (ENG., Illus.). 384p. (gr. 17). 39.00 *(978-0-262-11310-6(4))* MIT Pr.
Laitinen, Arto & Sandis, Constantine, eds. Hegel on Action. 2010. (Philosophers in Death Ser.). (ENG., Illus.). 320p. 89.00 *(978-0-230-22908-2(5))* Palgrave Macmillan.
Lumer, Christoph & Nannini, Sandro, eds. Intentionality Deliberation & Autonomy: The Action- Theoretic Basis of Practical Philosophy. 2007. 326p. 134.95 *(978-0-7546-6058-3(3))* Ashgate Publishing Co.
Marcus, Eric. Rational Causation. 2012. (ENG., Illus.). 280p. 45.00 ***(978-0-674-05990-0(5))*** Harvard Univ. Pr.
McCarty, Richard. Kant's Theory of Action. 2009. (ENG.). 256p. 85.00 *(978-0-19-956772-0(7))* Oxford Univ. Pr., Inc.
Nadelhoffer, Thomas. Intentions & Intentional Actions in Ordinary Language & the Law. 2008. 188p. pap. *(978-3-8364-3562-8(4))* VDM Verlag Dr. Mueller e.K.
Nordenfelt, L. Y. Action, Ability & Health: Essays in the Philosophy of Action & Welfare. 2010. (International Library of Ethics, Law, & the New Medicine Ser.). 192p. pap. 189.00 *(978-90-481-5412-8(X)*, 904815412X) Springer.
O'Brien, Lucy. Self-Knowing Agents. 2007. (ENG.). 256p. 85.00 *(978-0-19-926148-2(2))* Oxford Univ. Pr., Inc.
O'Brien, Lucy & Soteriou, Matthew, eds. Mental Actions. 2009. (ENG.). 296p. 99.00 *(978-0-19-922598-9(2))* Oxford Univ. Pr., Inc.
Ong, Andre. John Paul II's Philosophy of the Acting Person: A Personalistic Approach to Life. 2009. (Illus.). 356p. 119.95 *(978-0-7734-4893-3(4))* Mellen, Edwin Pr., The.
Oshana, Marina. The Importance of How We See Ourselves: Self-Identity & Responsible Agency. 2010. (ENG.). 186p. pap. 27.95 *(978-0-7391-2626-4(1))*; ix, 173p. E-Book *(978-0-7391-4935-5(0)*, Rowman & Littlefield Publishers, Inc.
Oshana, Marina A. L. The Importance of How We See Ourselves: Self-Identity & Responsible Agency. 2010. (ENG.). 184p. 65.00 *(978-0-7391-2625-7(3))* Rowman & Littlefield Publishers, Inc.
Rozmarin, Miri. Creating Oneself: Agency, Desire & Feminist Transformations. 2011. (ENG.). 184p. pap. 53.95 ***(978-3-0343-0707-9(1))*** Lang, Peter AG GBR. Dist: Lang, Peter.
Sandis, Constantine. Things We Do & Why We Do Them. 2012. (ENG.). 248p. 74.95 *(978-0-230-52212-1(2))* Palgrave Macmillan.
Sandis, Constantine, ed. New Essays on the Explanation of Action. 2009. (ENG., Illus.). 448p. 126.00 *(978-0-230-52202-2(5))* Palgrave Macmillan.
Sandis, Constantine & O'Connor, Timothy, eds. A Companion to the Philosophy of Action. 2010. (Blackwell Companions to Philosophy Ser.: 97). (ENG., Illus.). 664p. 209.95 *(978-1-4051-8735-0(2)*, Wiley-Blackwell) Wiley, John & Sons, Inc.
Sannino, Annalisa, et al, eds. Learning & Expanding with Activity Theory. 2009. (ENG., Illus.). 390p. (C). 98.00 *(978-0-521-76075-1(5))*; pap. 35.00 *(978-0-521-75810-9(6))* Cambridge Univ. Pr.
Schatzki, Theodore R. Timespace of Human Activity: On Performance, Society, & History as Indeterminate Teleological Events. 2010. (Toposophia: Sustainability, Dwelling, Design Ser.). (ENG., Illus.). 278p. 83.99 *(978-0-7391-4268-4(2))* Lexington Bks.
Segal, Jerome M. Agency Illusion & Well Being: Essays in Moral Psychology & Philosophical Economics. 2009. (ENG.). 260p. 78.99 *(978-0-7391-2968-5(6))* Lexington Bks.
—Agency, Illusion, & Well-Being: Essays in Moral Psychology & Philosophical Economics. 2008. (ENG.). 260p. pap. 31.50 *(978-0-7391-2969-2(4))* Lexington Bks.
Setiya, Kieran. Reasons Without Rationalism. (ENG.). 131p. (C). 2010. pap. 22.95 *(978-0-691-14652-2(7))* 2007. 35.00 *(978-0-691-12749-1(2))* Princeton Univ. Pr.
Shwayder, David. Statement & Referent: An Inquiry into the Foundations of our Conceptual Order. 2008. (Center for the Study of Language & Information - Lecture Notes Ser.). 878p. pap. 100.00 *(978-1-57586-540-9(8))* CSLI Pubns.
Sneddon, Andrew. Action & Responsibility. 2010. (Library of Ethics & Applied Philosophy Ser.). x, 198p. pap. 159.00 *(978-90-481-7008-1(7)*, 9048170087) Springer.
Soto-Morettini, Donna. Philosophical Actor: A Practical Meditation for Practicing Theatre Artists. 2010. (Illus.). 228p. pap. 30.00 *(978-1-84150-326-4(6))* Intellect, Ltd. GBR. Dist: Chicago Distribution Ctr.
Spurrett, David, et al, eds. Distributed Cognition & the Will: Individual Volition & Social Context. 2007. (ENG., Illus.). 384p. (gr. 17). 70.00 *(978-0-262-18261-4(0))*; per. 36.00 *(978-0-262-68169-8(2))* MIT Pr.
Stein, Edith, et al. Potency & ACT: Studies Toward a Philosophy of Being. Redmond, Walter, tr. from GER. 2009. (ENG.). pap. 19.95 *(978-0-935216-48-6(0))* I C S Pubns.
Thompson, Michael. Life & Action: Elementary Structures of Practice & Practical Thought. (Illus.). 240p. 2012. (ENG.). pap. 22.95 ***(978-0-674-06398-3(8))*** 2008. 44.00 *(978-0-674-01670-5(X))* Harvard Univ. Pr.
Timmons, Mark, et al, eds. Rationality & the Good: Critical Essays on the Ethics & Epistemology of Robert Audi. 2007. (ENG.). 272p. pap. 40.00 *(978-0-19-532602-4(4))* Oxford Univ. Pr., Inc.
Tsohatzidis, Savas L., ed. Intentional Acts & Institutional Facts: Essays on John Searle's Social Ontology. 2007. (Theory & Decision Library A: Ser.). 236p. (C). 189.00 *(978-1-4020-6103-5(X))* Springer.
Velleman, J. David. Practical Reflection. 2007. (Center for the Study of Language & Information - Lecture Notes Ser.). 332p. per. 32.50 *(978-1-57586-534-8(3))* CSLI Pubns.

Weaver, Darlene Fozard. The Acting Person & Christian Moral Life. 2011. (Moral Traditions Ser.). 226p. pap. 32.95 *(978-1-58901-772-6(2))* Georgetown Univ. Pr.

Wiland, Eric. Reasons. 2012. (ENG.). 200p. 100.00 ***(978-1-4411-4519-2(2))***; pap. 29.95 ***(978-1-4411-5308-1(X))*** Continuum International Publishing Group, Ltd. GBR. Dist: National Bk. Network.

ACT (PSYCHOTHERAPY)

see Acceptance and Commitment Therapy

ACT! (COMPUTER PROGRAM)

Act! 2007: 084743ie. 2007. spiral bd. *(978-1-4246-0640-5(3))* Element K Content LLC.

Act! 2007: 084743s3. 2007. spiral bd. *(978-1-4246-0641-2(1))* Element K Content LLC.

Act! 2007: 084744ie. 2007. spiral bd. *(978-1-4246-0638-2(1))* Element K Content LLC.

Act! 2007: 084744s3. 2007. spiral bd. *(978-1-4246-0639-9(X))* Element K Content LLC.

Clark, Susan. QuickStudy Guide for Swiftpage E-Marketing: Introduction. 2010. (ENG., Illus.). 173p. spiral bd. 35.00 *(978-0-9677658-0-8(3)*, ACTWOO-1) Cornerstone Solutions, Inc.

Fredricks, Karen S. ACT! by Sage for Dummies. 9th ed. 2007. (ENG., Illus.). 408p. per. 24.99 *(978-0-470-19225-2(9)*, For Dummies) Wiley, John & Sons, Inc.

Murphy, Indera. No Stress Tech Guide to ACT! 2007. 2007. (Illus.). 347p. pap. 49.95 *(978-0-9773912-5-7(6))* Tolana Publishing.

ACT ASSESSMENT

Ace Academics, ed. Act: Exam Prep Software on CD-ROM! Exambusters CD-ROM Study Cards. 2007. (Exambusters Ser.). cd-rom 12.95 *(978-1-57633-210-8(1)*, Exambusters) Ace Academics, Inc.

ACT All-Nighter. 2008. 212p. pap. *(978-1-4114-0522-6(6))* Spark Publishing Group.

ACT Exam Secrets Test Prep Staff, ed. ACT Exam Practice Questions: ACT Practice Tests & Review for the ACT Test. 2011. 34.99 *(978-1-61403-485-8(0))* Mometrix Media LLC.

ACT Inc. Staff. The Real ACT. 3rd ed. 2011. (ENG.). 672p. (YA). (gr. 7-17). pap. 34.95 ***(978-0-7689-3440-3(0))*** Peterson's.

—The Real ACT, 3rd Edition. 3rd ed. 2011. (ENG.). 672p. (YA). (gr. 7-17). pap. 30.95 ***(978-0-7689-3432-8(X))*** Peterson's.

ACT Inc. Staff. The Real ACT Prep Guide: The Only Official Prep Guide from the Makers of the ACT. Hammond, Wallie W., ed. 2nd ed. 2007. (ENG., Illus.). 623p. (YA). per. 24.95 *(978-0-7689-2675-0(0))* Peterson's.

ACTOrg Staff. The Real ACT Prep Guide. 2nd ed. 2010. (ENG.). 648p. (YA). pap., pap. 30.95 *(978-0-7689-3140-2(1))* Peterson's.

Brass, Charles O. ACT TestBuster with TestWare. 2011. (SAT PSAT ACT (College Admission) Prep Ser.). (ENG.). 448p. pap. 29.95 *(978-0-7386-0921-8(8))* Research & Education Assn.

Brass, Charles O., et al. ACT Assessment Plus Writing Test. 6th ed. 2011. (Test Preps Ser.). (ENG.). 1056p. (gr. 11). pap. 29.95 *(978-0-7386-0807-5(6))* Research & Education Assn.

Brody, Jay. How to Survive the SAT (And ACT) 2007. (Hundreds of Heads Survival Guides). (ENG., Illus.). 256p. pap. 14.95 *(978-1-933512-06-8(7))* Hundreds of Heads Bks., Inc.

Carnevale, Linda. Barron's ACT English, Reading, & Writing Workbook. 2008. (ENG.). 272p. pap. 14.99 *(978-0-7641-3982-6(7))* Barron's Educational Series, Inc.

Day, Erica. ACT(r) Mathematics Test Preparation Guide. 2008. pap. 24.00 *(978-1-59807-174-0(2))* American Bk. Co.

Digital Actuarial Resources. Headway Test Prep for ACT Math. 2008. 308p. (YA). pap. 39.99 *(978-0-9798071-8-3(2))* Digital Actuarial Resources, LLC.

Dulan, Steven. McGraw-Hill's 10 ACT Practice Tests. 3rd ed. 2010. (ENG., Illus.). 864p. (C). pap. 21.95 *(978-0-07-173697-8(2)*, 0071736972) McGraw-Hill Cos., The.

—McGraw-Hill's ACT. 6th ed. 2011. (ENG.). pap. 33.00 incl. cd-rom *(978-0-07-176357-8(0)*, 0071763570) McGraw-Hill Cos., The.

—McGraw-Hill's ACT, 2013 Edition. 7th ed. 2012. (ENG., Illus.). 560p. (C). pap. 20.00 ***(978-0-07-179292-9(9)***, 0071792929) McGraw-Hill Cos., The.

—McGraw-Hill's ACT with CD-ROM, 2013 Edition. 7th ed. 2012. (ENG.). 560p. pap. 33.00 incl. audio compact disk ***(978-0-07-179298-1(8)***, 0071792988) McGraw-Hill Cos., The.

—McGraw-Hill's Conquering ACT English Reading & Writing, 2nd Edition. 2nd ed. 2011. (ENG., Illus.). 352p. (C). pap. 16.00 ***(978-0-07-176908-2(0)***, 0071769080) McGraw-Hill Cos., The.

—McGraw-Hill's Conquering the ACT Math & Science, 2nd Edition. 2nd ed. 2011. (ENG., Illus.). 336p. (C). pap. 16.00 ***(978-0-07-176416-2(X)***, 007176416X) McGraw-Hill Cos., The.

Ehrenhaft, George. Grammar Workbook for the SAT, ACT, & More. 2nd rev. ed. 2010. (ENG.). 264p. pap. 14.99 *(978-0-7641-4489-9(8))* Barron's Educational Series, Inc.

Ehrenhaft, George, et al. Barron's ACT. 16th rev. ed. 2010. (ENG.). 696p. pap. 18.99 *(978-0-7641-4482-0(0))* Barron's Educational Series, Inc.

—Barron's ACT with CD-ROM. 16th rev. ed. 2010. (ENG.). 696p. 29.99 *(978-0-7641-9758-1(4))* Barron's Educational Series, Inc.

—Pass Key to the ACT. 8th rev. ed. 2010. (ENG.). 512p. pap. 9.99 *(978-0-7641-4483-7(9))* Barron's Educational Series, Inc.

Fodor, Jodi. The Sat Word Slam: Rhyme Your Way to a Better Vocabulary & Higher SAT & ACT Scores. 2009. (ENG.). 224p. pap. 12.95 *(978-1-60550-025-6(9))* Adams Media Corp.

Fredricks, Karen S. ACT! 2007 for Dummies. 2006. (ENG., Illus.). 392p. per. 26.99 *(978-0-470-05514-4(6)*, For Dummies) Wiley, John & Sons, Inc.

Gilman, Michelle Rose, et al. Act for Dummies. 5th ed. 2011. (ENG.). 528p. pap. 29.99 *(978-1-118-01260-4(7)*, For Dummies) Wiley, John & Sons, Inc.

Gruber, Gary. Gruber's Complete ACT Guide 2010. 2010. (ENG.). 736p. pap. 19.99 *(978-1-4022-2662-5(4))* Sourcebooks, Inc.

Kaplan. Kaplan ACT English, Reading, & Writing Workbook. 2nd rev. ed. 2011. (ENG.). 288p. pap. 16.99 *(978-1-60978-054-8(X))* Kaplan Publishing.

—Kaplan ACT Math & Science Workbook. 2nd rev. ed. 2011. (ENG.). 228p. pap. 16.99 *(978-1-60978-058-6(2))* Kaplan Publishing.

Kaplan Higher Education Staff. Kaplan ACT in a Box. 2nd ed. 2009. (ENG.). 1206p. 19.95 *(978-1-60714-478-6(6))* Kaplan Publishing.

Kaplan Publishing Staff, ed. Strategies for Super Busy Students: 15 Simple Steps to Tackle the Act While Keeping Your Life Together. 4th ed. 2011. (ENG.). 396p. pap. 16.99 *(978-1-4195-5017-1(9))* Kaplan Publishing.

Kaplan Publishing Staff, et al. Kaplan Spotlight ACT: 25 Lessons Illuminate the Most Frequently Tested Topics. 2007. (ENG.). 416p. pap. 16.95 *(978-1-4277-5223-9(0))* Kaplan Publishing.

Kittler, Jason M., et al. Interact with ACT: A Methodical Approach to the Compass/ACT Exam. 2009. (ENG.). (C). pap. 52.60 *(978-0-558-41821-2(X))* Pearson Learning Solutions.

Lampert, R. Brigham. Perfect 800: SAT Verbal: Advanced Strategies for Top Students. 2010. (ENG.). 200p. pap. 16.95 *(978-1-59363-434-6(X))* Prufrock Pr.

Leaf, Brian. Top 50 Skills for a Top Score: ACT Math. 2009. (ENG., Illus.). 208p. pap. 20.00 *(978-0-07-161376-7(5)*, 0071613765) McGraw-Hill Cos., The.

Learning Express Editors. ACT: Power Practice. 2011. (ENG.). 512p. pap. 25.99 *(978-1-57685-789-2(1))* LearningExpress, LLC.

Learning Express Llc. ACT Flash Review. 2012. (ENG.). 320p. pap. 12.95 ***(978-1-57685-896-7(0))*** LearningExpress, LLC.

LearningExpress Editors. ACT Word Games. 2011. (ENG.). 224p. pap. 13.95 *(978-1-57685-797-7(2))* LearningExpress, LLC.

LearningExpress Staff. ACT Essay Practice: Write Here, Write Now! 2007. (ENG.). 304p. per. 14.95 *(978-1-57685-591-1(0))* LearningExpress, LLC.

Martinson, Thomas H. ACT English Victory Classroom Text. 3rd ed. 2007. per. *(978-1-58894-058-2(6))* Cambridge Educational Services, Inc.

—ACT English Victory Teacher's Guide. 3rd ed. 2007. per. *(978-1-58894-059-9(4))* Cambridge Educational Services, Inc.

—ACT Mathematics Victory Classroom Text. 3rd ed. 2007. per. *(978-1-58894-060-5(8))* Cambridge Educational Services, Inc.

—ACT Mathematics Victory Teacher's Guide. 3rd ed. 2007. per. *(978-1-58894-061-2(6))* Cambridge Educational Services, Inc.

—ACT Reading Victory Classroom Text. 3rd ed. 2007. per. *(978-1-58894-062-9(4))* Cambridge Educational Services, Inc.

—ACT Reading Victory Teacher's Guide. 3rd ed. 2007. per. *(978-1-58894-063-6(2))* Cambridge Educational Services, Inc.

—ACT Science Reasoning Victory Classroom Text. 3rd ed. 2007. per. *(978-1-58894-064-3(0))* Cambridge Educational Services, Inc.

—ACT Science Reasoning Victory Teacher's Guide. 3rd ed. 2007. per. *(978-1-58894-065-0(9))* Cambridge Educational Services, Inc.

—ACT Writing Victory Classroom Text. 3rd ed. 2007. per. *(978-1-58894-066-7(7))* Cambridge Educational Services, Inc.

—ACT Writing Victory Teacher's Guide. 3rd ed. 2007. per. *(978-1-58894-067-4(5))* Cambridge Educational Services, Inc.

Pipkin, James. The Parent's Guide to the SAT & ACT: Preparing Your Child for College. 2007. 132p. per. *(978-0-9701058-3-7(5))* Upstream Pr., Inc.

Popham, W. James. College Entrance Exams: SAT & ACT, Mastering Assessment - A Self-Service System for Educators, Pamphlet. 2nd rev. ed. 2011. (Mastering Assessment Ser.). (ENG.). 32p. (C). pap. 10.99 *(978-0-13-273500-1(8))* Allyn & Bacon, Inc.

Prince, Patsy J. & Giovannini, James D. Barron's 6 ACT Practice Tests. 2012. (ENG.). 480p. pap. 12.99 ***(978-0-7641-4722-7(6))*** Barron's Educational Series, Inc.

Princeton Review. Cracking the ACT, 2013 Edition. 2012. (College Test Preparation Ser.). (ENG.). 640p. pap. 19.99 ***(978-0-307-94535-8(9)***, Princeton Review) Random Hse. Information Group.

—Cracking the ACT with DVD, 2013 Edition. 2012. (College Test Preparation Ser.). (ENG.). 640p. pap. 31.99 ***(978-0-307-94536-5(7)***, Princeton Review) Random Hse. Information Group.

—Crash Course for the ACT, 4th Edition. 2012. (College Test Preparation Ser.). (ENG.). 240p. pap. 9.99 ***(978-0-375-42762-6(7)***, Princeton Review) Random Hse. Information Group.

Princeton Review Staff. Cracking the ACT, 2012 Edition. 2011. (College Test Preparation Ser.). (ENG.). 640p. pap. 19.99 *(978-0-375-42744-2(9)*, Princeton Review) Random Hse. Information Group.

—Cracking the ACT with DVD, 2012 Edition. 2011. (College Test Preparation Ser.). (ENG.). 640p. pap. 31.99 *(978-0-375-42745-9(7)*, Princeton Review) Random Hse. Information Group.

—English & Reading Workout for the ACT. 2011. (College Test Preparation Ser.). 192p. pap. 16.99 *(978-0-375-42807-4(0)*, Princeton Review) Random Hse. Information Group.

—Math & Science Workout for the ACT. 2011. (College Test Preparation Ser.). 160p. pap. 16.99 *(978-0-375-42808-1(9)*, Princeton Review) Random Hse. Information Group.

—SAT or ACT? Choosing the Right Exam for You. 2009. (College Test Preparation Ser.). (ENG., Illus.). 256p. pap. 15.99 *(978-0-375-42924-8(7)*, Princeton Review) Random Hse. Information Group.

Roell, Kelly C. ACT Strategy Smart. 2012. (Test Preps Ser.). (ENG.). 400p. (YA). (gr. 12-13). pap. 11.95 ***(978-0-7386-1009-2(7))*** Research & Education Assn.

Rudman, Jack. ACT Assessment Examination for College Entrance (ACT) (Admission Test Ser.: Vol. 44). 49.95 *(978-0-8373-5144-5(8))* National Learning Corp.

SPANOTES Reading - Spanish CD: A Spanish language study aid for secondary school language Arts. 2009. (SPA.). cd-rom 24.95 *(978-1-884730-20-7(5)*, Interlingua Publishing) InterLingua.com, Inc.

Spark Publishing Staff, contrib. by. 5 Practice Tests for the ACT. 2009. *(978-1-4114-1775-5(5))* Spark Publishing Group.

Summers, Ann, et al. Barron's ACT 36, 2nd Edition: Aiming for the Perfect Score. 2nd rev. ed. 2012. (ENG.). 336p. pap. 16.99 ***(978-0-7641-4705-0(6))*** Barron's Educational Series, Inc.

—Barron's ACT 36 with CD-ROM, 2nd Edition: Aiming for the Perfect Score. 2nd rev. ed. 2012. (ENG.). 336p. pap. 29.99 ***(978-1-4380-7217-3(1))*** Barron's Educational Series, Inc.

SuryaChandra, Punit Raja. EZ ACT - Math Strategies: EZ ACT Math Test Taking Strategies. 2007. (Illus.). 160p. (YA). per. 29.95 *(978-0-9727790-5-0(1))* EZ Solutions.

Teukolsky, Roselyn. ACT Math & Science. 2009. (ENG.). 480p. pap., wbk. ed. 14.99 *(978-0-7641-4034-1(5))* Barron's Educational Series, Inc.

The DeaNell Institute. Ace ACT with Writing Option. 2007. 292p. pap. 28.95 *(978-1-4303-2380-8(9))* Lulu Enterprises Inc.

Vlk, Suzee, et al. ACT for Dummies. 5th ed. 2011. (ENG.). 528p. pap. 19.99 *(978-1-118-01259-8(3)*, For Dummies) Wiley, John & Sons, Inc.

Williamson, Lynette. On Demand Writing for Students: Coaching Yourself for the SAT1, ACT & AP Essays. 2011. (ENG.). 192p. (YA). pap. 25.95 ***(978-1-61770-027-9(4))*** International Debate Education Assn.

Zegarelli, Mark. ACT Math for Dummies. 2011. (ENG., Illus.). 360p. pap. 16.99 *(978-1-118-00154-7(0)*, For Dummies) Wiley, John & Sons, Inc.

ACT TESTS

see ACT Assessment

ACTIN

Gallo, Gianluca & Lanier, Lorene M., eds. Neurobiology of Actin: From Neurulation to Synaptic Function. 2010. (Advances in Neurobiology Ser.). (Illus.). viii, 282p. 209.00 *(978-1-4419-7367-2(2)*, 1441973672) Springer.

Lappalainen, Pekka, ed. Actin-Monomer-Binding Proteins. (Molecular Biology Intelligence Unit Ser.). (Illus.). 2010. xiv, 118p. pap. 199.00 *(978-1-4419-2362-2(4)*, 1441923624) 2006. 118p. 199.00 *(978-0-387-46405-3(0)*, 0387464050) Springer.

Pardee, Joel. The Actin Cytoskeleton in Cell Motility, Cancer, & Infection. Pardee, Joel, ed. 2010. (Colloquium Series on Cell Biology of Medicine Ser.). 57p. (C). pap., pap. 30.00 *(978-1-61504-006-3(4))* Morgan & Claypool Life Science Publishers.

Staiger, Christopher J., et al, eds. Actin: A Dynamic Framework for Multiple Plant Cell Functions: A Dynamic Framework for Multiple Plant Cell Functions. 2010. (Developments in Plant & Soil Sciences Ser.). 676p. pap. 459.00 *(978-90-481-5504-0(5)*, 9048155045) Springer.

ACTINARIA

see Sea-Anemones

ACTING

see also Acting for Television; Actors; Actresses; Amateur Theater; Commedia Dell'Arte; Drama; Expression; Gesture; Impersonation; Improvisation (Acting); Method Acting; Mime; Theater

Adrian, Barbara. Actor Training the Laban Way: An Integrated Approach to Voice, Speech, & Movement. 2008. (ENG., Illus.). 208p. pap. 24.95 *(978-1-58115-648-5(0)*, 115648, Allworth Pr.) Skyhorse Publishing Co., Inc.

Albright, H. D. Working up a Part: A Manual for the Beginning Actor. 2011. 244p. 46.95 ***(978-1-258-09215-3(8))*** Literary Licensing, LLC.

Ashenden, Andrew. Basics of Stage Combat: Unarmed. 2012. pap. ***(978-1-61233-071-6(1))*** Universal Pubs.

Astington, John H. Actors & Acting in Shakespeare's Time: The Art of Stage Playing. 2010. (ENG., Illus.). 260p. (C). 75.00 *(978-0-521-19250-7(1))*; pap. 26.99 *(978-0-521-14077-5(3))* Cambridge Univ. Pr.

Barnett, Daniel. Movement as Meaning: In Experimental Film. 2008. (Illus.). 240p. pap. 72.00 *(978-90-420-2385-7(6))* Rodopi.

Baron, Cynthia & Carnicke, Sharon Marie. Reframing Screen Performance. 2008. (ENG., Illus.). 310p. (C). 80.00 *(978-0-472-07025-1(8))*; pap. 27.95 *(978-0-472-05025-3(7))* Univ. of Michigan Pr.

Barton, Robert. Acting Reframes: Using NLP to Make Better Decisions in & Out of the Theatre. 2011. (ENG.). 176p. 115.00 *(978-0-415-59231-4(3))*; pap. 27.95 *(978-0-415-59232-1(1))* Routledge.

BARTON, Robert. Style for Actors: A Handbook for Moving Beyond Realism. 2nd ed. 2009. (ENG., Illus.). 360p. 39.95 *(978-0-415-48573-9(8))*; 115.00 *(978-0-415-48572-2(X))* Routledge.

Basil, John & Gunning, Stephanie. Will Power: How to Act Shakespeare in 21 Days. 2006. (Applause Bks.). (ENG., Illus.). 376p. per. 17.95 *(978-1-55783-666-3(3)*, 1557836663, Applause Theatre & Cinema) Leonard, Hal Corp.

Batson, Susan. Truth: Personas, Needs, & Flaws in the Art of Building Actors & Creating Characters. 2007. (ENG., Illus.). 301p. 29.95 *(978-1-59071-053-1(3))* Rugged Land.

Benedetti, Jean. The Art of the Actor: The Essential History of Acting, from Classical Times to the Present Day. 2007. (ENG.). 256p. 105.00 *(978-0-87830-203-1(4))*; per. 30.95 *(978-0-87830-204-8(2))* Routledge.

Benedetti, Robert. The Actor at Work. 10th ed. 2008. (ENG., Illus.). 224p. (C). pap. 125.40 *(978-0-205-54207-9(7))* Allyn & Bacon, Inc.

—The Actor in You: Sixteen Simple Steps to Understanding the Art of Acting. 4th ed. 2007. (ENG., Illus.). 160p. (C). per. 59.40 *(978-0-205-54208-6(5))* Allyn & Bacon, Inc.

Benedetti, Robert L. The Actor in You: Sixteen Simple Steps to Understanding the Art of Acting. 5th rev. ed. 2011. (ENG., Illus.). 160p. (C). pap. 59.40 *(978-0-205-78123-2(3))* Allyn & Bacon, Inc.

Better Homes and Gardens Books Staff & Hagen, Uta. Respect for Acting. 2nd ed. 2008. (ENG., Illus.). 240p. 19.95 *(978-0-470-22848-7(2)*, Wiley) Wiley, John & Sons, Inc.

Binnerts, Paul. Acting in Real Time. 2012. (ENG.). 272p. (C). 85.00 ***(978-0-472-11794-9(7))***; (Illus.). pap. 35.00 ***(978-0-472-03503-8(7))*** Univ. of Michigan Pr.

Blair, Rhonda. The Actor, Image, & Action: Acting & Cognitive Neuroscience. Blair, Rhonda, ed. 2007. XIV, 146p. 38.95 *(978-0-415-77417-8(9)*, 0415774179) Routledge.

—The Actor, Image, & Action: Acting & Cognitive Neuroscience. 2007. XIV, 146p. 125.00 *(978-0-415-77416-1(0)*, 0415774160) Routledge.

BLAIR, Rhonda L., ed. Acting: The First Six Lessons. 2nd rev. ed. 2010. (ENG.). 232p. 100.00 *(978-0-415-56385-7(2))*; pap. 26.95 *(978-0-415-56386-4(0))* Routledge.

Blix, Stina Bergman. Rehearsing Emotions: The Process of Creating a Role for the Stage. 2010. (Stockholm Studies in Sociology Ser.). (Illus.). 237p. pap. 87.50 *(978-91-86071-41-7(6))* Stockholms Universitet SWE. Dist: Coronet Bks.

Blumenfeld, Robert. Using the Stanislavsky System: A Practical Guide to Character Creation & Period Styles. 2008. (ENG.). 390p. per. 19.95 *(978-0-87910-356-9(6)*, 0879103566, Limelight Editions) Leonard, Hal Corp.

Bogart, Anne. And Then, You Act. 2007. (ENG.). 160p. 115.00 *(978-0-415-41141-7(6))* Routledge.

—And Then, You Act: Making Art in an Unpredictable World. 2007. (ENG.). 160p. per. 31.95 *(978-0-415-41142-4(4))* Routledge.

Boleslavsky, Richard. Acting: The First Six Lessons. 2011. 122p. 39.95 ***(978-1-258-01102-4(6))*** Literary Licensing, LLC.

Boughn, Jenn Zuko. Stage Combat: Fisticuffs, Stunts, & Swordplay for Theater & Film. 2006. (ENG., Illus.). 224p. per. 19.95 *(978-1-58115-461-0(5)*, 115461, Allworth Pr.) Skyhorse Publishing Co., Inc.

Brown, D. W. You Can Act! A Complete Guide for Actors. 2009. (ENG., Illus.). 338p. pap. 24.95 *(978-1-932907-56-8(4))* Wiese, Michael Productions.

Brown, John Russell, ed. The Routledge Companion to Actors' Shakespeare. 2011. (ENG.). 288p. 120.00 *(978-0-415-48302-5(6))*; pap. 31.95 *(978-0-415-48301-8(8))* Routledge.

Brownell, Mark & Miner, Sue, eds. Rhubarb! Rhubarb! An Actor's Guide to Theatrical Practices, Phrases, & Superstitions. 2011. 120p. pap. 16.95 *(978-1-897289-64-8(2))* Shillingford, J. Gordon Publishing CAN. Dist: Univ. of Toronto Pr.

Burgess, Thomas. The Singing & Acting Handbook: Games & Exercises for the Performer. 2nd ed. 2009. pap. 35.95 *(978-0-415-44146-9(3))* Routledge.

Burwick, Frederick. Romantic Drama: Acting & Reacting. 2009. (ENG., Illus.). 354p. 90.00 *(978-0-521-88967-4(7))* Cambridge Univ. Pr.

Buyer, Jason. Inside the Audition Room: The Essential Actor's Handbook for Los Angeles. 2011. 90p. pap. 12.95 ***(978-0-557-93943-5(7))*** Lulu Enterprises Inc.

Cairney, John. Greasepaint Monkey: An Actor on Acting. 2010. (ENG.). 156p. pap. 19.95 *(978-1-906817-42-8(1))* Luath Pr. Ltd. GBR. Dist: Ingram Pub. Services.

Calvert, Louis. Problems of the Actor. 2009. 138p. pap. 19.99 *(978-0-217-74397-6(8))* General Bks. LLC.

—Problems of the Actor. 2007. (ENG.). 304p. 43.95 *(978-0-548-10234-3(1))* Kessinger Publishing, LLC.

Campo, Giuliano. Voice & Body. 2010. (ENG., Illus.). 208p. 120.00 *(978-0-415-56846-3(3)*, Routledge) Taylor & Francis Group GBR. Dist: Taylor & Francis Group.

Campo, Giuliano, ed. Voice & Body. 2010. (ENG., Illus.). 208p. pap. 36.99 *(978-0-415-56847-0(1)*, Routledge) Taylor & Francis Group GBR. Dist: Taylor & Francis Group.

Cantrell, Tom & Luckhurst, Mary, eds. Playing for Real: Actors on Playing Real People. 2010. (ENG.). 176p. 75.00 *(978-0-230-23041-5(5))*; pap. 17.00 *(978-0-230-23042-2(3))* Palgrave Macmillan.

Carter, David. The Art of Acting: And How to Master It. 2011. (ENG.). 224p. pap. 23.95 *(978-1-84243-221-1(4))* Oldcastle Bks., Ltd. GBR. Dist: Independent Pubs. Group.

Chekhov, Michael. To the Actor on the Technique of Acting. 2011. 218p. 44.95 ***(978-1-258-09727-1(3))*** Literary Licensing, LLC.

Cherkasov, Nikolai Konstantinovich. Notes of a Soviet Actor. Ivano-Mumjiev, G. & Rosenberg, S., trs. 2011. 274p. 47.95 ***(978-1-258-03191-6(4))*** Literary Licensing, LLC.

Churcher, Mel. A Screen Acting Workshop. 2012. (ENG., Illus.). 2245p. (J). 30.95 ***(978-1-84842-055-7(2))*** Hern, Nick Bks., Ltd. GBR. Dist: Consortium Bk. Sales & Distribution.

Clayton. Introduction to Theatre & Dramatic Literature: An Anthology & Sourcebook - Text. 3rd rev. ed. 2010. 466p. ring bd. 68.84 *(978-0-7575-4735-5(4))* Kendall Hunt Publishing Co.

Cohen, Robert. Acting One. 5th rev. ed. 2007. (ENG., Illus.). 288p. (C). per. 98.00 (978-0-07-351416-1(0), 0073514160) McGraw-Hill Cos., The.

—Acting One/Acting Two. 5th ed. 2007. (ENG.). 552p. (C). 113.67 (978-0-07-328854-3(3), 0073288543) McGraw-Hill Cos., The.

Cole, Toby, ed. Acting: A Handbook of the Stanislavski Method. 224p. 2010. pap. 19.96 (978-1-163-16811-0(4)) 2008. 39.95 (978-1-4367-1148-7(7)) 2007. per. 24.95 (978-1-4325-6837-5(X)) Kessinger Publishing, LLC.

Cook, Rena. Voice & the Young Actor. 2012. (ENG., Illus.). 224p. pap., wbk. ed. 29.95 (978-1-4081-5460-1(9), Methuen Drama) A & C Black GBR. Dist: Macmillan.

Cram101 Textbook Reviews. Outlines & Highlights for Acting in Person & in Style by Crawford & Hurst & Lugering, Isbn: 0697201333. 2011. 262p. pap. 31.95 (978-1-61830-022-5(9)) Cram101 Inc.

—Outlines & Highlights for Acting One / Acting Two by Robert Cohen. 2011. 62p. pap. 27.95 (978-1-61812-142-4(1)) Cram101 Inc.

—Outlines & Highlights for Acting One by Robert Cohen. 2011. 64p. pap. 27.95 (978-1-61905-908-5(8)) Cram101 Inc.

—Outlines & Highlights for Acting with Style by Harrop & Epstein, Isbn: 0205295827. 2011. 298p. pap. 32.95 (978-1-61812-991-8(0)) Cram101 Inc.

—Outlines & Highlights for Actor at Work by Robert Benedetti. 2011. 56p. pap. 26.95 (978-1-61905-910-8(X)) Cram101 Inc.

Cram101 Textbook Reviews & Cram101 Textbook Reviews. Outlines & Highlights for Acting: Onstage & off by Robert Barton. 2011. 68p. pap. 27.95 (978-1-61830-678-4(2)) Cram101 Inc.

Csapo, Eric. Actors & Icons of the Ancient Theater. 2010. (ENG., Illus.). 248p. 128.95 (978-1-4051-3536-8(0), Wiley-Blackwell) Wiley, John & Sons, Inc.

Darley, C. The Space to Move. 2010. (ENG.). 224p. pap. 26.95 (978-1-84842-024-3(2)) Hern, Nick Bks., Ltd. GBR. Dist: Consortium Bk. Sales & Distribution.

Davis, Michael Ray. Camera, Speed... Action! An Insider's Secrets to the Real World of Acting. 2011. 248p. pap. 17.99 (978-1-4567-3577-7(2)) AuthorHouse.

Detrick, Erin, ed. Monologues for Men. 2008. (Actor's Choice Ser.). (ENG.). 152p. per. 14.95 (978-0-9709046-5-2(7)) Playscripts, Inc.

—Monologues for Teens. 2008. (Actor's Choice Ser.). (ENG.). 136p. (gr. 7-18). per. 14.95 (978-0-9709046-6-9(5)) Playscripts, Inc.

—Monologues for Women. 2008. (Actor's Choice Ser.). (ENG.). 152p. per. 14.95 (978-0-9709046-4-5(9)) Playscripts, Inc.

DiMarco, Damon. The Quotable Actor: 1001 Pearls of Wisdom from Actors Talking about Acting. 2009. (ENG.). 312p. pap. 16.95 (978-1-59580-044-2(1)) Santa Monica Pr.

Donnellan, Declan. The Actor & the Target. 2006. (ENG.). 300p. per. 18.95 (978-1-55936-285-6(5)) Theatre Communications Group, Inc.

Duncan, Anne. Performance & Identity in the Classical World. 2011. (ENG.). 252p. pap. 48.00 (978-0-521-31348-3(1)) Cambridge Univ. Pr.

Ebraham, Ti Em. Abhinayakala, Oramukham. 2008. (Illus.). 193p. (978-2-7710-1838-5(1), Library of Congress — New Delhi Overseas Office); (978-81-240-1838-5(3), Library of Congress — New Delhi Overseas Office) Current Bks.

Edelstein, Barry. Thinking Shakespeare: A How-To Guide for Student Actors, Directors, & Anyone Else Who Wants to Feel More Comfortable with the Bard. 2007. (Illus.). 455p. (978-1-4114-9872-3(0)) Spark Publishing Group.

Eichenbaum, Rose. The Actor Within: Intimate Conversations with Great Actors. Hirt-Manheimer, Aron, ed. 2011. (ENG., Illus.). 268p. 30.00 (978-0-8195-6952-3(6)) Wesleyan Univ. Pr.

Elsam, Paul. Acting Characters: 16 Simple Steps from Rehearsal to Performance. 2011. (ENG., Illus.). 192p. pap. 19.95 (978-0-7136-7586-3(1), Methuen Drama) A & C Black GBR. Dist: Macmillan.

Esper, William & DiMarco, Damon. The Actor's Art & Craft: William Esper Teaches the Meisner Technique. 2008. (ENG.). 304p. pap. 16.00 (978-0-307-27926-2(X), Anchor) Knopf Doubleday Publishing Group.

Eustis, Morton. Players at Work. 2007. (ENG.). 144p. per. (978-1-4067-4529-3(6)) Read Bks.

Evans, Mark. Movement Training for the Modern Actor. 2010. 212p. pap. 39.95 (978-0-415-88395-5(4)) Routledge.

Fulton, Julia. Acting for Camera: From the Actor's P. O. V. rev. ed. 2011. (ENG.). 108p. pap. 37.00 (978-0-7575-9074-0(8)) Kendall Hunt Publishing Co.

Gaskill, William. Words into Action: Finding the Life of the Play. 2011. (ENG.). 224p. pap. 22.95 (978-1-84842-100-4(1)) Hern, Nick Bks., Ltd. GBR. Dist: Consortium Bk. Sales & Distribution.

Gold, Nancy. Finding Your Funny Bone! The Actor's Guide to Physical Comedy & Characters. 2007. (ENG., Illus.). 182p. pap. 16.95 (978-1-57525-449-4(2)) Smith & Kraus Pubs., Inc.

Hall, Lyn, ed. Actors Speaking. 2008. (ENG., Illus.). 140p. pap. 26.95 (978-1-84002-776-1(2)) Theatre Communications Group, Inc.

Harris, Lani Michea e, et al. A Beginning Actor's Companion. 4th rev. ed. 2009. (ENG.). 140p. pap. 93.14 (978-0-7575-5171-0(8)) Kendall Hunt Publishing Co.

Hester, John. Performing Shakespeare. 2009. (ENG., Illus.). 192p. pap. 34.95 (978-1-84797-073-2(7)) Crowood Pr., Ltd. GBR. Dist: Independent Pubs. Group.

Hill, Kimberly Mohne, ed. Monologues in Dialect for Young Actors Volume 2, Vol. 2. 2007. (ENG.). 224p. (YA). pap. 14.95 (978-1-57525-577-4(4)) Smith & Kraus Pubs., Inc.

Hlavsa, David. An Actor Rehearses: What to Do When & Why. 2006. (ENG.). 224p. per. 19.95 (978-1-58115-462-7(3), 115462, Allworth Pr.) Skyhorse Publishing Co., Inc.

Hooks, Ed. The Ultimate Scene & Monologue Sourcebook: An Actor's Reference to over 1,000 Scenes & Monologues from More Than 300 Con Temporary Plays. Hooks, Ed, ed. exp. rev. ed. 2007. (ENG., Illus.). 336p. pap. 19.95 (978-0-8230-9949-8(0), Back Stage Bks.) Watson-Guptill Pubns., Inc.

Houseman, Barbara. Tackling Text: A Step-by-Step Guide for Actors. 2008. (ENG.). 288p. pap. 26.95 (978-1-85459-799-1(X)) Hern, Nick Bks., Ltd. GBR. Dist: Consortium Bk. Sales & Distribution.

Howell, Jonathan. Stage Fighting: A Practical Guide. 2009. (ENG., Illus.). 192p. pap., instr.'s gde. ed. 34.95 (978-1-84797-046-6(X)) Crowood Pr., Ltd. GBR. Dist: Independent Pubs. Group.

Igweonu, Kene. Trends in Twenty-First Century African Theatre & Performance. Igweonu, Kene, ed. 2011. (Illus.). 476p. 36.00 (978-90-420-3386-3(X)) Rodopi.

Irving, Dale. A Study of the Experience of Dramatic Performance for Drama Students. 2010. 348p. pap. (978-3-8383-2701-3(2)) Lambert Academic Publishing.

Jacobs, Martha. A Meisner Legacy. 2011. (ENG., Illus.). (C). pap. 32.00 (978-0-88734-982-9(X)) Players Pr., Inc.

Jbara, Rima. Muddy Minutes: Is When Soiled Souls Exist. 2011. 60p. pap. 15.67 (978-1-4567-7663-3(0)) AuthorHouse.

Johnston-Brown, Anne. The Ten Commandments of Theater for Young Actors: The Gospel According to Stanislavski. 2008. (Young Actors Ser.). (ENG.). 144p. (YA). pap. 14.95 (978-1-57525-584-2(7)) Smith & Kraus Pubs. Inc.

Johnston, Chris. Drama Games for Those Who Like to Say No. 2011. (ENG.). 224p. pap. 18.95 (978-1-84842-049-6(8)) Hern, Nick Bks., Ltd. GBR. Dist: Consortium Bk. Sales & Distribution.

Kahan, Stanley. Introduction to Acting. 2011. 322p. 50.95 (978-1-258-09305-1(7)) Literary Licensing, LLC.

Katselas, Milton. Acting Class: Take a Seat. 2008. 295p. 34.95 (978-1-59777-592-2(4)) Phoenix Bks., Inc.

Kemp, Rick. Embodied Acting: Cognitive Foundations of Performance. 2012. (ENG., Illus.). 224p. 120.00 (978-0-415-50787-5(1)); pap. 27.95 (978-0-415-50788-2(X)) Routledge.

King, T. J. Casting Shakespeare's Plays: London Actors & Their Roles, 1590-1642. 2009. (ENG.). 304p. pap. 38.99 (978-0-521-10721-1(0)) Cambridge Univ. Pr.

Kogan, Sam. The Science of Acting. 2009. (ENG., Illus.). 268p. 115.00 (978-0-415-48811-2(7)); pap. 31.95 (978-0-415-48812-9(5)) Routledge.

Krasner, David. An Actor's Craft: The Art & Technique of Acting. 2011. (ENG., Illus.). 224p. (C). 80.00 (978-0-230-27552-2(4)); pap. 27.00 (978-0-230-27553-9(2)) Palgrave Macmillan.

Kuhns, David F. German Expressionist Theatre: The Actor & the Stage. 2006. (ENG.). 324p. pap. 61.00 (978-0-521-03522-4(8)) Cambridge Univ. Pr.

Law, Alma. Meyerhold, Eisenstein & Biomechanics: Actor Training in Revolutionary Russia. alt. ed. 2012. (ENG., Illus.). 294p. pap. 25.00 (978-0-7864-6750-1(9)) McFarland & Co., Inc. Pubs.

Lay, Brandon C. 100 Monologues, Scenes & One Acts. 2011. 492p. pap. 22.99 (978-1-4567-2837-3(7)) AuthorHouse.

Leach, Robert. Theatre Studies. 2008. (Basics Ser.). (ENG., Illus.). 208p. (C). 100.00 (978-0-415-42638-1(3)); pap. 19.95 (978-0-415-42639-8(1)) Routledge.

Levy, Gavin. Acting Games for Individual Performers: A Comprehensive Workbook of 110 Acting Exercises, 1 vol. 2007. (ENG.). 250p. per. 17.95 (978-1-56608-146-7(7)) Meriwether Publishing, Ltd.

Liyanage, Saumya. Body Mind Dilemmas in Acting. 2011. 96p. pap. (978-3-8383-4685-4(8)) Lambert Academic Publishing.

Lubar, Deborah. For Love of the World: A Harangue with Practical Guidance on Writing & Performing Solo Dramas That Matter. 2007. (Illus.). 176p. per. 19.95 (978-0-325-00839-4(6), E00839, Drama) Heinemann.

Lugering, Michael. The Expressive Actor. 2012. (ENG., Illus.). 192p. 115.00 (978-0-415-66930-6(8)); pap. 27.95 (978-0-415-66931-3(6)) Routledge.

Lust, Annette. Bringing the Body to the Stage & Screen: Expressive Movement for Performers. 2011. (ENG., Illus.). 364p. 99.00 (978-0-8108-8124-2(1)); 352p. pap. 49.95 (978-0-8108-8212-6(4)) Scarecrow Pr., Inc.

Lutterbie, John. Toward a General Theory of Acting: Cognitive Science & Performance. 2011. (Cognitive Studies in Literature & Performance Ser.). (ENG.). 280p. 85.00 (978-0-230-11335-0(4)) Palgrave Macmillan.

Maniscalco-Blasi, Anna. Lights, Camera, Action! Former Casting Director for the Sopranos Helps Actors Break into the Film Industry. 2007. 48p. pap. 13.95 (978-1-60145-157-6(1)) Booklocker.com, Inc.

Marasco, Ron. Notes to an Actor. 2007. (ENG.). 224p. 24.95 (978-1-56663-757-2(0)) Dee, Ivan R. Pub.

Marsh, Mae. Screen Acting. 2010. 134p. (ENG.). pap. 20.75 (978-1-176-97392-3(4)); pap. 20.75 (978-1-144-85764-4(3)) BiblioBazaar.

—Screen Acting. 2009. 60p. pap. (978-0-217-86605-7(0)) Books LLC.

Mason, Marshall W. Creating Life on Stage: A Director's Approach to Working with Actors. 2006. (Illus.). 272p. pap. 19.95 (978-0-325-00919-3(8), E00919, Drama) Heinemann.

Matthews, John. Training for Performance: A Meta-Disciplinary Account. 2011. (Performance Bks.). (ENG., Illus.). 240p. 75.00 (978-1-4081-2918-0(3)); pap. 39.95 (978-1-4081-2917-3(5)) A & C Black GBR. (Methuen Drama). Dist: Macmillan.

McAsh, F. Braun. Fight Choreography: A Practical Guide for Stage, Film & Television, 1 vol. 2011. (ENG., Illus.). 192p. 27.95 (978-1-84797-223-1(3)) Crowood Pr., Ltd. GBR. Dist: Independent Pubs. Group.

McClellan, Deslie. Acting Magic: The Complete Guide to the Art of Acting. 2007. (Illus.). 540p. per. 18.95 (978-0-9790089-5-5(6)) Playhouse Bks.

McGaw, Charles, et al. Acting Is Believing. 11th ed. 2011. (ENG., Illus.). 320p. (C). 122.95 (978-0-495-89807-8(4)) Wadsworth.

McGaw, Charles J. Acting Is Believing: A Basic Method for Beginners. 2011. 192p. 42.95 (978-1-258-01946-4(9)) Literary Licensing, LLC.

Melton, Joan & Tom, Kenneth. One Voice: Integrating Singing & Theatre Voice Techniques. 2nd ed. 2011. 141p. (C). pap. 24.95 (978-1-57766-771-1(9)) Waveland Pr., Inc.

Merlin, Bella. Acting. 2010. (Basics Ser.). (Illus.). 256p. (C). 90.00 (978-0-415-46100-9(6), Routledge) Taylor & Francis Group GBR. Dist: Taylor & Francis Group.

—Acting: The Basics. 2010. (Basics Ser.). (ENG., Illus.). 256p. (C). pap. 19.95 (978-0-415-46101-6(4), Routledge) Taylor & Francis Group GBR. Dist: Taylor & Francis Group.

Miller, Bruce. The Actor As Storyteller: an Introduction to Acting. 2nd ed. 2012. (ENG.). 330p. pap. 24.99 (978-0-87910-386-6(8), 0879103868, Limelight Editions) Leonard, Hal Corp.

—Actor's Alchemy: Finding the Gold in the Script. 2011. (ENG.). 194p. pap. 16.99 (978-0-87910-383-5(3), 0879103833, Limelight Editions) Leonard, Hal Corp.

—The Scene Study Book: Roadmap to Success, 1 vol. 2010. (ENG.). 160p. pap. 16.99 (978-0-87910-371-2(X), 087910371X, Limelight Editions) Leonard, Hal Corp.

Morris, Clara. Stage Confidences. 2008. 164p. 25.99 (978-0-554-24535-0(X)) 2008. 164p. 22.99 (978-0-554-33888-0(2)) 2007. 144p. pap. 18.99 (978-1-4264-6896-4(2)) 2006. (ENG.). 160p. pap. 21.99 (978-1-4264-6978-7(0)) BiblioBazaar.

Morris, Eric. Freeing the Actor: An Actor's Desk Reference. 2011. (ENG.). 204p. pap. 16.95 (978-0-9629709-6-2(4)) Ermor Enterprises.

Moseley, Nick. Acting & Reacting: Tools for the Modern Actor. 2006. (Theatre Arts Book Ser.). (Illus.). 202p. 85.00 (978-0-87830-205-5(0), Theatre Arts Bks.) Routledge.

Murray, Joan & Keefe. Physical Theatres: A Critical Introduction. (ENG., Illus.). 248p. (C). 2008. 125.00 (978-0-415-36249-8(0)) 2007. pap. 36.95 (978-0-415-36250-4(4)) Routledge.

Murray, Simon & Keefe. Physical Theatres: A Critical Reader. 2007. (Illus.). XXVIII, 292p. 41.95 (978-0-415-36252-8(0)) Routledge.

Murray, Simon & Keefe, John, eds. Physical Theatres: A Critical Reader. 2007. (Illus.). XXVIII, 292p. 125.00 (978-0-415-36251-1(2)) Routledge.

Nascimento, Cláudia Tatinge. Crossing Cultural Borders Through the Actor's Work: Foreign Bodies of Knowledge. 2008. (Routledge Advances in Theatre & Performance Studies). (ENG., Illus.). 194p. (C). 125.00 (978-0-415-98887-2(X)) Routledge.

Neelands, Jonothan, et al. Advanced Drama & Theatre Studies. 2008. 288p. pap. 57.50 (978-0-340-97262-5(9)) Hodder Education GBR. Dist: Trans-Atlantic Pubns., Inc.

Newlove, Jean. Laban for Actors & Dancers: Putting Laban's Movement Theory into Practice: A Step-by-Step Guide. 2007. (ENG., Illus.). 160p. per. 22.95 (978-1-85459-160-9(6)) Hern, Nick Bks., Ltd. GBR. Dist: Consortium Bk. Sales & Distribution.

Niess, Christopher. Essence to Action. 2010. 68p. pap. (978-3-8383-4850-6(8)) Lambert Academic Publishing.

Noble, Adrian. How to Do Shakespeare. 2010. (ENG., Illus.). 272p. 95.00 (978-0-415-54926-4(4)); pap. 29.95 (978-0-415-54927-1(2)) Routledge.

Normington, Kathleen & Glazer, Amy. Simply Acting: A Handbook for Beginning Actors. rev. ed. 2012. (ENG.). 138p. pap. 29.51 (978-0-7575-8683-5(X)) Kendall Hunt Publishing Co.

Nystul, Daisy. Acting: Everything You Need to Know about Acting but Forgot to Ask. rev. ed. 2011. (ENG.). 210p. spiral bd. 89.00 (978-0-7575-9105-1(1)) Kendall Hunt Publishing Co.

Nystul, Daisy. Everything You Need to Know about Acting but Forgot to Ask. 2010. (ENG.). 74p. pap. 31.68 (978-0-7575-7457-3(2)) Kendall Hunt Publishing Co.

O'Dell, Leslie. The Charismatic Chameleon: The Actor as Creative Artist. 2010. (ENG.). 323p. pap. 29.95 (978-1-84519-412-3(8)) Sussex Academic Pr. GBR. Dist: International Specialized Bk. Services.

Oida, Yoshi & Marshall, Lorna. An Actor's Tricks. 2007. (Performance Bks.). (ENG.). 112p. per. 19.99 (978-0-413-77449-1(X), Methuen Drama) A & C Black GBR. Dist: Macmillan.

Olsen, Mark & Broadnax, Steve. Acting: Scene One. rev. ed. 2010. (ENG.). 114p. pap. 41.71 (978-0-7575-4557-3(2)) Kendall Hunt Publishing Co.

Panet, Brigid. Acting: Actors, Teachers & Directors. 2009. (ENG., Illus.). 296p. 105.00 (978-0-415-47677-5(1)); pap. 35.95 (978-0-415-47678-2(X)) Routledge.

Paterson, Ronan, ed. Stages to Outstanding Performance: In the Rehearsal Room. 2012. 288p. pap. 29.95 (978-1-904794-30-1(0)) Northumbria University Press GBR. Dist: Independent Pubs. Group.

Perks, Alan. A2 Drama & Theatre Studies: The Essential Introduction for Edexcel. 2009. (ENG., Illus.). 192p. stu. ed. 33.95 (978-0-415-43661-8(3)) Routledge.

Perks, Alan & Porteous, Jacqueline. A2 Drama & Theatre Studies. 2009. (ENG., Illus.). 192p. pap., stu. ed. 120.00 (978-0-415-43660-1(5)) Routledge.

Perrucci, Andrea & Heck, Thomas F. A Treatise on Acting, from Memory & by Improvisation (1699) Dell'arte Rappresentativa, Premeditata Ed All'improviso. Goodrich Heck, Anne, tr. from ITA. 2007. (ITA & ENG.). 256p. per. 60.00 (978-0-8108-6033-9(3)) Scarecrow Pr., Inc.

PETIT, Lenard. The Michael Chekhov Handbook: For the Actor. 2009. (ENG., Illus.). 192p. 115.00 (978-0-415-49671-1(3)); 37.95 (978-0-415-49672-8(1)) Routledge.

Pitches, Jonathan. Science & the Stanislavsky Tradition of Acting. 2009. 236p. pap. 34.00 (978-0-415-54403-0(3)) Routledge.

Playwrights Canada Press Staff & Theatre Direct Canada Staff, contrib. by. Acting Out: Monologues & Scenes from Theatre Direct (Canada's Plays For Young People) 2007. (ENG., Illus.). 116p. pap. 19.95 (978-0-88754-882-6(2)) Theatre Communications Group, Inc.

Rodgers, Janet B. & Armstrong, Frankie. Acting & Singing with Archetypes, 1 vol. 2009. (ENG.). 150p. pap. 18.99 incl. audio compact disk (978-0-87910-368-2(X), 087910368X, Limelight Editons) Leonard, Hal Corp.

Rokison, Abigail. Shakespearean Verse Speaking: Text & Theatre Practice. (ENG.). 2011. 250p. pap. 35.00 (978-1-107-40403-5(7)) 2010. (Illus.). 248p. 95.00 (978-0-521-76434-6(3)) Cambridge Univ. Pr.

Rozik, Eli. Generating Theatre Meaning: A Theory & Methodology of Performance Analysis. 2010. (Illus.). 304p. pap. 34.95 (978-1-84519-330-0(X)) Sussex Academic Pr. GBR. Dist: International Specialized Bk. Services.

Ruscio, Al. So Therefore... 2012. (ENG., Illus.). 168p. 115.00 (978-0-415-51671-6(4)); pap. 25.95 (978-0-415-51672-3(2)) Routledge.

Russell, Paul. Acting - Make It Your Business: How to Avoid Mistakes & Achieve Success As a Working Actor. 2008. (ENG., Illus.). 320p. pap. 19.95 (978-0-8230-9955-9(5), Back Stage Bks.) Watson-Guptill Pubns., Inc.

Saint-Denis, Michel. Theatre: The Rediscovery of Style & Other Writings. Baldwin, Jane, ed. 2008. (Illus.). X, 198p. pap. 30.95 (978-0-415-45048-5(9)) Routledge.

Saint-Denis, Michel & Baldwin, Jane. Theatre: The Rediscovery of Style & Other Writings. Baldwin, Jane, ed. 2008. (Illus.). X, 198p. 110.00 (978-0-415-45047-8(0)) Routledge.

Saklad, Nancy. Voice & Speech Training in the New Millennium: Conversations with Master Teachers. 2011. (ENG., Illus.). 304p. pap. 19.99 (978-1-61774-058-9(6), 1617740586, Applause Theatre & Cinema) Leonard, Hal Corp.

Sanderson, Michael. From Irving to Olivier. (Illus.). 375p. (978-0-485-11252-8(3)) Continuum International Publishing Group, Ltd.

Sapsis, Bill. HEADS! & Tales: Uncle Bill's Musings on the Theatrical Experience. 2007. (Illus.). 111p. per. 19.95 (978-0-9797039-0-4(3)) Sapsis Pubns.

Schulte, Philipp. IdentitäT Als Experiment: Ich-Performanzen Auf der GegenwartsbüHne. 2011. (Theaomai - Studien zu den performativen Künsten Ser.). (GER.). 444p. 105.95 (978-3-631-60350-5(9), Lang, Peter GmbH, Europaischer Verlag der Wissenschaften DEU. Dist: Lang, Peter.

Schwiebert, Jerald & Platt, Candace. Physical Expression & the Performing Artist: Moving Beyond the Plateau. 2011. E-Book (978-0-472-02796-5(4)) Univ. of Michigan Pr.

Schwiebert, Jerald C. Physical Expression & the Performing Artist: Moving Beyond the Plateau. 2011. (ENG., Illus.). 216p. (C). pap. 40.00 (978-0-472-03416-1(2)) Univ. of Michigan Pr.

Seldon, Samuel. First Steps in Acting. 2007. (ENG.). 358p. 46.95 (978-0-548-06069-8(X)) Kessinger Publishing, LLC.

Senelick, Laurence, ed. Theatre Arts on Acting. 2008. XVIII, 534p. 120.00 (978-0-415-77492-5(6)); 36.95 (978-0-415-77493-2(4)) Routledge.

Shurgot, Michael W. North American Players of Shakespeare: A Book of Interviews. 2007. (ENG.). 69.50 (978-1-61149-299-6(8)) Univ. of Delaware Pr.

Shurgot, Michael W., ed. North American Players of Shakespeare: A Book of Interviews. 2007. (Illus.). 425p. 60.00 (978-0-87413-953-2(8)) Univ. of Delaware Pr.

Sibony, Daniel. Le Jeu: Et la Passe: Identité et Théâtre. (FRE.). 309p. (978-2-02-032212-6(9)) Editions du Seuil.

Skinner, Edith. Speak with Distinction: The Classic Skinner Method to Speech for the Stage. Mansell, Lilene, ed. 2007. (Applause Acting Ser.). (ENG., Illus.). 40p. pap. 19.95 incl. audio compact disk (978-1-55783-724-0(4), 1557837244, Applause Theatre & Cinema) Leonard, Hal Corp.

Smith, Anthony. Acting Career Start-up 101: The Real First Steps. 2012. 268p. pap. 20.95 (978-0-595-51630-8(0)) iUniverse, Inc.

Smith, Gay. Lady Macbeth in America: From the Stage to the White House. 2010. (Palgrave Studies in Theatre & Performance History Ser.). (ENG.). 252p. 89.00 (978-0-230-62288-3(7)) Palgrave Macmillan.

Snow, Jackie. Movement Training for Actors. 2012. (Performance Bks.). (ENG., Illus.). 224p. pap. 34.95 (978-1-4081-2857-2(8), Methuen Drama) A & C Black GBR. Dist: Macmillan.

Sreenath, Nair. Restoration of Breath: Consciousness & Performance. 2007. (Illus.). 208p. per. 56.00 (978-90-420-2306-2(6)) Rodopi.

Stanislavski, Constantin. Actor Prepares. 2007. 28.95 (978-0-8488-1180-8(1)) Amereon LTD.

Swale, Jessica. Drama Games for Devising. 2012. (ENG.). 224p. pap. 18.95 (978-1-84842-037-3(4)) Hern, Nick Bks., Ltd. GBR. Dist: Consortium Bk. Sales & Distribution.

Swindall, Lindsey R. The Politics of Paul Robeson's Othello. (Margaret Walker Alexander Series in African American Studies). (ENG.). 224p. 2011. pap. 30.00 (978-1-61703-203-5(4)) 2010. 50.00 (978-1-60473-824-7(3)) Univ. Pr. of Mississippi.

Taylor, Aaron, ed. Theorizing Film Acting. 2012. (Routledge Advances in Film Studies). (ENG., Illus.). 304p. (C). 125.00 (978-0-415-50951-0(3)) Routledge.

Taylor, Philip. Theatre Behind Bars: Can the Arts Rehabilitate? Atkinson, Elizabeth & DePalma, Renee, eds. 2012. 188p. pap. 34.95 (978-1-85856-455-5(7)) Trentham Bks. Ltd. GBR. Dist: Stylus Publishing, LLC.

Taylor, Tom. To Parents & Guardians! at Jubilee House Establishment, Clapham, Young Gentlemen Are, & C & C an Original Comic Drama, in One Act, by the Author Of. 2011. 26p. pap. 11.99 ***(978-1-4181-9198-6(1))*** MPublishing.

Tichler, Rosemarie & Kaplan, Barry Jay. Actors at Work. 2007. (ENG.). 392p. pap. 17.00 *(978-0-86547-955-5(0))* Faber & Faber, Inc.

Tribble, Evelyn B. Cognition in the Globe: Attention & Memory in Shakespeare's Time. 2011. (Cognitive Studies in Literature & Performance Ser.). (ENG., Illus.). 216p. 80.00 *(978-0-230-11085-4(1))* Palgrave Macmillan.

Turner, J. Clifford & Boston, Jane. Voice & Speech in the Theatre. 6th rev. ed. 2007. (ENG., Illus.). 176p. per. 19.95 *(978-0-7136-8188-8(8)*, Methuen Drama) A & C Black GBR. Dist: Macmillan.

Ullmann, Lisa & Laban, Rudolf. The Mastery of Movement. 2011. (Illus.). 210p. pap. ***(978-1-85273-145-8(1))*** Dance Bks., Ltd.

Van Tassel, Wesley. Clues to Acting Shakespeare. 2nd rev. ed. 2006. (ENG.). 288p. pap. 18.95 *(978-1-58115-464-1(X)*, 115464, Allworth Pr.) Skyhorse Publishing Co., Inc.

Varley, Julia. Notes from an Odin Actress. 2010. (ENG., Illus.). 208p. 110.00 *(978-0-415-58628-3(3))*; pap. 32.95 *(978-0-415-58629-0(1))* Routledge.

Vaughn, Maura. The Anatomy of a Choice: An Actor's Guide to Text Analysis. 2010. (ENG.). 114p. pap. 20.99 *(978-0-7618-5109-7(7))* Univ. Pr. of America, Inc.

Velleman, J. David & Velleman, J. David. How We Get Along. 2009. (ENG.). 232p. 80.00 *(978-0-521-88853-0(0))*; pap. 26.99 *(978-0-521-04340-3(9))* Cambridge Univ. Pr.

Vergette, R. Drama & Theatre Studies. 2008. (Illus.). 264p. pap. 57.50 *(978-1-84489-447-5(9))* Hodder Education GBR. Dist: Trans-Atlantic Pubns., Inc.

—Edexcel Advanced Drama & Theatre Studies Textbook. 2008. 264p. pap. 59.50 *(978-1-84489-446-8(0))* Hodder Education GBR. Dist: Trans-Atlantic Pubns., Inc.

Warren, Deryn. How to Make Your Audience Fall in Love with You: Expert Advice on Acting Technique, Script Analysis, & Taking Risks. 2008. 240p. pap. 23.95 *(978-0-325-01393-0(4)*, E01393) Heinemann.

Weate, Cathy. Classic Voice. 2009. (ENG.). 210p. pap. 30.95 *(978-1-84002-827-0(0))* Oberon Bks., Ltd. GBR. Dist: Consortium Bk. Sales & Distribution.

West, Shearer. Image of the Actor. (Illus.). 196p. *(978-0-86187-182-7(0)*, Burns & Oates) Continuum International Publishing Group, Ltd.

White, Diz. The Comedy Group Book: How to Run One! How to Get Laughs! How to Make Money! 2006. (ENG., Illus.). 251p. pap. *(978-1-57525-452-4(2))* Smith & Kraus Pubs., Inc.

Wilsher, Toby. The Mask Handbook. 2006. (Illus.). 200p. 100.00 *(978-0-415-41436-4(9))* Routledge.

—The Mask Handbook: A Practical Guide. 2006. (Illus.). 188p. per. 31.95 *(978-0-415-41437-1(7))* Routledge.

Wyman, C. S. A. The Organic Actor. 2008. 280p. pap. 27.00 *(978-1-4343-6215-5(9))* AuthorHouse.

Yener, Setenay. The Svetlana in Me - How I Embraced My Turkish Identity in Order to Play a Russian/Estonian for an American Audience. 2008. 56p. pap. *(978-3-639-11134-7(6))* VDM Verlag Dr. Mueller e.K.

Young, Rebecca. 102 Monologues for Middle School Actors: Including duologues & Triologues, 1 vol. 2012. (ENG.). 160 pap. (YA). pap. 17.95 ***(978-1-56608-184-9(X))*** Meriwether Publishing, Ltd.

Zinder, David. Body Voice Imagination: A Training for the Actor Inspired by Chekhov. 2nd rev. ed. 2009. (ENG., Illus.). 320p. pap. 33.95 *(978-0-415-46198-6(7))* Routledge.

—Body Voice Imagination: Actor Training Inspired by Chekhov. 2nd rev. ed. 2009. (ENG., Illus.). 320p. 110.00 *(978-0-415-46197-9(9))* Routledge.

Zunshine, Lisa, ed. Acting Theory & the English Stage, 1700-1830, 5 vols., Set. 2008. (ENG., Illus.). 1808p. 795.00 *(978-1-85196-901-2(2))* Pickering & Chatto Pubs., Ltd. GBR. Dist: Ashgate Publishing Co.

ACTING—AUDITIONS

Audenreed Press. The Actor Takes a Meeting: How to Interview Successfully with Agents, Managers, Producers, & Casting Directors. 2006. (ENG.). 267p. per. 18.95 *(978-1-879505-89-6(4))* Silman-James Pr.

Belli, Mary Lou & Lenney, Dinah. Acting for Young Actors: For Money or Just for Fun. 2006. (ENG., Illus.). 224p. (gr. 7-13). pap. 16.95 *(978-0-8230-4947-9(7)*, Back Stage Bks.) Watson-Guptill Pubns., Inc.

Bishop, Nancy. Secrets from the Casting Couch: On Camera Strategies for Actors from a Casting Director. 2009. (ENG., Illus.). 224p. pap. 19.95 *(978-1-4081-1327-1(9)*, Methuen Drama) A & C Black GBR. Dist: Macmillan.

Boelter, Derrick. Demo Reel Secrets for Actors: How You Can Supercharge Your Reel & Book More Work. 2008. 156p. pap. 14.95 *(978-1-4327-3804-4(6))* Outskirts Pr., Inc.

Caldarone, Marina, intro. Classical Monologues for Men. 2006. (Good Audition Guides). (ENG.). 160p. per. 18.95 *(978-1-85459-869-1(4))* Hern, Nick Bks., Ltd. GBR. Dist: Consortium Bk. Sales & Distribution.

—Classical Monologues for Women. 2006. (Good Audition Guides). (ENG.). 160p. per. 18.95 *(978-1-85459-870-7(6))* Hern, Nick Bks., Ltd. GBR. Dist: Consortium Bk. Sales & Distribution.

Cobb, Abbie. Stuck on a Ferris Wheel: An Actor's Guide to Enjoying the Ride While Keeping Your Feet on the Ground. 2011. 219p. pap. 19.95 ***(978-1-4327-6554-5(X))*** Outskirts Pr., Inc.

Dabrowski, Kristen. The Ultimate Audition Book for Teens: 111 One-minute Monologues. 2011. 12.80 *(978-0-7848-3592-0(6)*, Everbind) Marco Bk. Co.

Depner, Mary. 50/50 Monologues for Student Actors: 100 monologues for guys & Girls, 1 vol. 2011. (ENG.). 200p. (YA). pap. 15.95 *(978-1-56608-176-4(9))* Meriwether Publishing, Ltd.

Dixon, Luke. Monos for Men (Shakespeare) 2010. (ENG.). 160p. pap. 18.95 *(978-1-84842-005-2(6))* Hern, Nick Bks., Ltd. GBR. Dist: Consortium Bk. Sales & Distribution.

—Monos for Women (Shakespeare) 2010. (ENG.). 160p. pap. 18.95 *(978-1-84842-007-6(2))* Hern, Nick Bks., Ltd. GBR. Dist: Consortium Bk. Sales & Distribution.

Evans, Richard. Auditions: A Practical Guide. 2009. (ENG.). 288p. 115.00 *(978-0-415-47034-6(X))*; (Illus.). pap. 31.95 *(978-0-415-47035-3(8))* Routledge.

Flom, Jonathan. Get the Callback: The Art of Auditioning for Musical Theatre. 2009. (ENG.). 162p. 42.00 *(978-0-8108-6398-9(7))* Scarecrow Pr., Inc.

Flom, null & Flom, Jonathan. Get the Callback: The Art of Auditioning for Musical Theatre. 2009. (ENG., Illus.). 162p. pap. 27.00 *(978-0-8108-6918-9(7))* Scarecrow Pr., Inc.

Freeman, Helen. So You Want to Go to Drama School? 2011. (ENG.). 150p. pap. 20.95 ***(978-1-84842-016-8(1))*** Hern, Nick Bks., Ltd. GBR. Dist: Consortium Bk. Sales & Distribution.

Frohnsdorff, Michael & Pickering, Kenneth. Great Neglected Speeches from the Elizabethan Stage, 4 vols., Vol. 3. 2011. 76p. pap. 10.00 *(978-0-88734-060-4(1))* Players Pr., Inc.

—Great Neglected Speeches from the Elizabethan Stage: A sourcebook for actors, students & Theatre-goers, 4 vols. 2011. 76p. Vol. 1. pap. 10.00 *(978-0-88734-058-1(X))* Vol. 2. (ENG.). pap. 10.00 *(978-0-88734-059-8(8))* Players Pr., Inc.

Goldenthal, Jolene. Describing Life: Monologs for Women. 2007. 126p. per. 11.99 *(978-0-9789087-0-6(8))* Bleich Bks.

Gordon, Robert. The Purpose of Playing: Modern Acting Theories in Perspective. 2006. (Theater: Theory/Text/Performance Ser.). (ENG., Illus.). 424p. per. 37.50 *(978-0-472-06887-6(3))* Univ. of Michigan Pr.

Hacker, Joseph. Auditioning for the Camera. 2011. (ENG.). 288p. pap. 25.95 *(978-0-415-61902-8(5))* Routledge.

—Auditioning for the Camera: An Actor's Guide. 2011. (ENG.). 288p. 100.00 *(978-0-415-61901-1(7))* Routledge.

Hester, John. Auditions: A Practical Guide, 1 vol. 2012. (ENG., Illus.). 144p. 22.95 ***(978-1-84797-333-7(7))*** Crowood Pr., Ltd. GBR. Dist: Independent Pubs. Group.

Hezlep, William. Past & Present: (Monologues & Scenes) 2010. 64p. pap. 10.00 *(978-0-88734-593-7(X))* Players Pr., Inc.

Holmes, Prudence Wright. Monologue Mastery: The Actor's Guide to Selecting & Performing Monologues, 1 vol. 2010. (ENG.). 118p. pap. 14.99 *(978-0-87910-370-5(1)*, 0879103701, Limelight Editions) Leonard, Hal Corp.

Jordan, Pat. Monologues for the Ages: Middle School through High School. 2010. (YA). pap. 10.00 *(978-0-88734-995-9(1))* Players Pr., Inc.

Kummel, Tamar. How to Run Auditions. 2009. pap. 11.50 *(978-0-615-14689-8(9))* Captain Purple.

Manderino, Ned. Stanislavski's Fourth Level. 192p. pap. 10.95 *(978-0-9601194-8-6(5))* Manderino Bks.

Marlow, Jean. Audition Speeches for 6-16 Year Olds: 50+ Audition Pieces for Actors & Actresses. 2nd ed. 2008. (Audition Speeches Ser.). (ENG.). 144p. pap. 16.95 *(978-0-7136-8772-9(X)*, Methuen Drama) A & C Black GBR. Dist: Macmillan.

—Audition Speeches for Men. 2011. (Audition Speeches Ser.). (ENG.). 125p. pap. 14.95 *(978-0-7136-5285-7(3)*, Methuen Drama) A & C Black GBR. Dist: Macmillan.

—Audition Speeches for Women. 2nd ed. 2011. (Audition Speeches Ser.). (ENG., Illus.). 128p. pap. 14.95 *(978-0-7136-7413-2(X)*, Methuen Drama) A & C Black GBR. Dist: Macmillan.

Master the Art of Cold Reading: An Actor's Guide to Making the Best of Cold Reading Workshops. 4th rev. ed. Date not set. 153p. pap. 17.95 *(978-0-9630551-2-5(7))* Heaven Sent Publishing.

Milstein, Karen. Hot Spots for Kids: One-Person Cold-Reading Copy for TV Commercial Auditioning Success. 2008. (Young Actors Ser.). (ENG.). 112p. (J). pap. 11.95 *(978-1-57525-574-3(X))* Smith & Kraus Pubs., Inc.

Newhouse, Miriam & Messaline, Peter. The Actor's Survival Kit. 4th ed. 2007. (ENG.). 264p. pap. 24.99 *(978-1-55002-678-8(X)*, Simon & Pierre) Dundurn CAN. Dist: Ingram Pub. Services.

Ortiz-Mackes, Liz. Ace Your Acting Audition: Using Iconic Specificity & Other Surefire Techniques. 2009. 109p. ***(978-0-9823462-0-4(4))*** S.O.M.E. Productions.

Ramirez, M. The Ultimate Audition Book for Teens Volume XIII: 111 One-Minute Monologues - Active Voices, Vol. 13. 2008. (Young Actors Ser.: Vol.XIII). (ENG.). 160p. (YA). pap. 11.95 *(978-1-57525-581-1(2))* Smith & Kraus Pubs., Inc.

Ramshur, Steve & Chandler, Wilma Marcus. Kiss or Kill: Contact Scenes of Love & Strife for Young Actors. 2007. (ENG.). 224p. (YA). pap. 16.95 *(978-1-57525-582-8(0))* Smith & Kraus Pubs., Inc.

Ratliff, Gerald Lee. Audition Monologues for Young Women: Contemporary audition pieces for aspiring Actresses. 2011. 174p. (YA). pap. 16.95 *(978-1-56608-180-1(7))* Meriwether Publishing, Ltd.

Ratliff, Gerald Lee, ed. The Theatre Audition, 1 vol., Bk. 2. 2009. (ENG.). 256p. (YA). pap. 17.95 *(978-1-56608-165-8(3))* Meriwether Publishing, Ltd.

—Young Women's Monologues from Contemporary Plays #2: Professional Auditions for Aspiring Actresses, 1 vol., 2. 2008. (ENG.). 248p. pap. 15.95 *(978-1-56608-153-5(X))* Meriwether Publishing, Ltd.

Schulman, John. Untitled Scenes & Monologues Book for Actors. Date not set. mass mkt. *(978-0-312-99203-3(3)*, St. Martin's Paperbacks) St. Martin's Pr.

Thompson, Ayanna. Colorblind Shakespeare: New Perspectives on Race & Performance. 2006. (Illus.). 262p. 95.00 *(978-0-415-97801-9(7))*; per. 27.95 *(978-0-415-97802-6(5))* Hudson Hills Pr. LLC.

Wallace, Craig. The Best of You: Winning Auditions Your Way. 2007. 123p. per. 17.95 *(978-0-9788362-0-7(0))* Oyster Mining Co., Inc.

Watson, Jamantha. Classical & Modern Monologues for Men. rev. ed. 2010. (ENG.). 228p. pap. 25.32 *(978-0-7575-8347-6(4))* Kendall Hunt Publishing Co.

—Classical & Modern Monologues for Women. rev. ed. 2010. (ENG.). 194p. pap. 25.32 *(978-0-7575-8348-3(2))* Kendall Hunt Publishing Co.

Weate, Catherine, ed. The Oberon Book of Modern Monologues for Men. 2008. (ENG.). 192p. pap. 18.95 *(978-1-84002-825-6(4))* Oberon Bks., Ltd. GBR. Dist: Consortium Bk. Sales & Distribution.

—The Oberon Book of Modern Monologues for Women. 2008. (ENG.). 192p. pap. 18.95 *(978-1-84002-826-3(2))* Oberon Bks., Ltd. GBR. Dist: Consortium Bk. Sales & Distribution.

Wilcox, Janet. Mastering Monologues & Acting Sides: How to Audition Successfully for Both Traditional & New Media. 2011. (ENG.). 256p. pap. 24.95 *(978-1-58115-866-3(1)*, 115866, Allworth Pr.) Skyhorse Publishing Co., Inc.

Zorich, Louis & Hal Leonard Corporation Staff. What Have You Done? The Inside Stories of Auditioning, from the Ridiculous to the Sublime, 1 vol. Zorich, Louis, ed. 2009. (ENG., Illus.). 320p. pap. 14.99 *(978-0-87910-365-1(5)*, 0879103655, Limelight Editions) Leonard, Hal Corp.

ACTING—COSTUME

see Costume

ACTING—JUVENILE LITERATURE

Levy, Gavin. 275 Acting Games: Theatre Games for Developing Acting Skills, 1 vol. 2010. (ENG.). 100p. (YA). pap., wbk. ed. 19.95 *(978-1-56608-169-6(6))* Meriwether Publishing, Ltd.

ACTING—MAKEUP

see Theatrical Makeup

ACTING—STUDY AND TEACHING

Arrighi, Gillian. The Neutral Mask. 2010. (Illus.). 108p. pap. *(978-3-639-22406-1(X))* VDM Verlag Dr. Mueller e.K.

Ashperger, Cynthia. The Rhythm of Space & the Sound of Time: Michael Chekhov's Acting Technique in the 21st Century. 2008. (Illus.). 396p. pap. 120.00 *(978-90-420-2387-1(2))* Rodopi.

Baldwin, Patrice & Baldwin, Patrice. The Primary Drama Handbook: A Practical Guide for Teaching Assistants & Teachers New to Drama. 2009. (Illus.). 168p. pap. 36.00 *(978-1-4129-2965-3(2)*, B29644P) SAGE Pubns., Ltd. GBR. Dist: SAGE Pubns., Inc.

—The Primary Drama Handbook: A Practical Guide for Teaching Assistants & Teachers New to Drama. 2009. (Illus.). 168p. 86.00 *(978-1-4129-2964-6(4)*, B29644C) SAGE Pubns., Ltd. GBR. Dist: SAGE Pubns., Inc.

Barker, Clive. Theatre Games: A New Approach to Drama Training. 2010. (Performance Bks.). (ENG., Illus.). 240p. pap. 29.95 *(978-1-4081-2519-9(6))* A & C Black GBR. Dist: Macmillan.

Bergman, Allison & Moore, Tracey. Acting the Song: Performance Skills for the Musical Theatre. 2008. (ENG.). 304p. pap. 24.95 *(978-1-58115-505-1(0)*, 115505, Allworth Pr.) Skyhorse Publishing Co., Inc.

Cameron, David, et al. Drama Education with Digital Technology. 2009. (Education & Digital Technology Ser.). (ENG., Illus.). 252p. 150.00 *(978-1-84706-266-6(0))* Continuum International Publishing Group, Ltd. GBR. Dist: National Bk. Network.

Chaulet, F. Emmanuelle. A Balancing Act: The development of Energize! a holistic approach to Acting. 2008. (Illus.). 336p. per. 24.95 *(978-0-9799063-0-5(X))* Starlight Acting Bks.

Cohen, Lola. The Lee Strasberg Notes. 2010. (ENG., Illus.). 232p. 100.00 *(978-0-415-55185-4(4))*; pap. 26.95 *(978-0-415-55186-1(2))* Routledge.

Cormier, J. Briggs. Learning to Listen. 2009. 156p. pap. *(978-3-639-19412-8(8))* VDM Verlag Dr. Mueller e.K.

Deckelbaum, Sheldon. The Actor's Lab Book: A Practical Supplement for the Beginning Actor. rev. ed. 2008. (ENG.). 92p. spiral bd. 42.89 *(978-0-7575-3132-3(6))* Kendall Hunt Publishing Co.

Fahay, Jessie. What Method? The Different Ways an Actor can Train. 2011. 56p. pap. 14.95 ***(978-1-4567-1463-5(5))*** AuthorHouse.

Farber, Vreneli. Stanislavsky in Practice: Actor Training in Post-Soviet Russia. 2008. (Artists & Issues in the Theatre Ser.: Vol. 16). 246p. (C). 79.95 *(978-1-4331-0315-5(X))* Lang, Peter Publishing, Inc.

Garfein, Jack. Life & Acting: Techniques for the Actor. 2010. (ENG.). 310p. pap. 19.95 *(978-0-8101-2673-2(7))* Northwestern Univ. Pr.

Hickman, Darryl. The Unconscious Actor: Out of Control, in Full Command - The Art of Performance in Acting & in Life. 2007. (ENG.). 312p. 24.95 *(978-0-9776809-2-4(4))* Small Mountain Pr.

Hill, Kimberly Mohne, ed. Scenes in Dialect for Young Actors, Vol. 2. 2007. 224p. (YA). pap. 14.95 *(978-1-57525-578-1(2))* Smith & Kraus Pubs., Inc.

Hodge, Ali. Core Training for Actors: The First Steps. 2012. (ENG., Illus.). 150.00 ***(978-0-415-60068-2(5))*** Routledge.

Hodge, Alison. Actor Training. 2nd rev. ed. 2010. (ENG., Illus.). 368p. 110.00 *(978-0-415-47167-1(2))*; pap. 38.95 *(978-0-415-47168-8(0))* Routledge.

Hubbard, Valorie & Brandenburg, Lea Tolub. The Actor's Workbook: How to Become a Working Actor. 2008. (ENG.). 160p. (C). pap. 29.40 *(978-0-205-59231-9(7))* Allyn & Bacon, Inc.

Hurley, Nancy. 175 Theatre Games: Warm-Up exercises for Actors, 1 vol. 2009. (ENG.). 136p. (J). pap. 17.95 *(978-1-56608-164-1(5))* Meriwether Publishing, Ltd.

Klö, et al. Heiße West- und kalte Ost-Schauspieler? Diskurse, Praxen, Geschichte(n) zur Schauspielausbildung in Deutschland nach 1945. 2008. (GER., Illus.). 291p. *(978-3-940737-27-4(5))* interessengemeinschaft theater der zeit.

Lecoq, Jacques. The Moving Body (le Corps Poetique) Teaching Creative Theatre. 2011. (Performance Bks.). (ENG., Illus.). 192p. pap. 22.95 *(978-1-4081-1146-8(2)*, Methuen Drama) A & C Black GBR. Dist: Macmillan.

Lugering, Michael. The Expressive Actor: Integrated Voice, Movement, & Acting Training. 2007. (Illus.). 240p. pap. 19.95 *(978-0-325-00963-6(5)*, E00963, Drama) Heinemann.

Malague, Rosemary. An Actress Prepares: Women & 'The Method' 2012. (ENG.). 264p. pap. 31.95 *(978-0-415-68157-5(X))* Routledge.

—An Actress Prepares: Women & the Method. 2012. (ENG.). 264p. 125.00 *(978-0-415-68156-8(1))* Routledge.

Marcus, Paul & Marcus, Gabriela. Theater As Life: Practical Wisdom Drawn from Great Acting Teachers, Actors & Actresses. 2011. (ENG.). 263p. 25.00 ***(978-0-87462-069-6(4))*** Marquette Univ. Pr.

Margolis, Ellen & Renaud, Lissa Tyler. The Politics of American Actor Training. Margolis, Ellen & Tyler Renaud, Lissa, eds. 2009. (Routledge Advances in Theatre & Performance Studies). (ENG.). 226p. (C). 125.00 *(978-0-415-80121-8(4))* Routledge.

Margolis, Ellen & Tyler Renaud, Lissa, eds. The Politics of American Actor Training. 2011. (ENG.). 218p. pap. 39.95 ***(978-0-415-89653-5(3))*** Routledge.

Mcnally, Tom. Acting: The Active Process. rev. ed. 2012. (ENG.). 112p. pap. 60.00 ***(978-0-7575-9721-3(1))*** Kendall Hunt Publishing Co.

Moseley, Nick. Acting & Reacting: Tools for the Modern Actor. 2006. (ENG.). 224p. per. 25.95 *(978-1-85459-803-5(1))* Hern, Nick Bks., Ltd. GBR. Dist: Consortium Bk. Sales & Distribution.

Pender, Judith Midyett. Acting: What to Do. rev. ed. 2012. (ENG.). 142p. pap. 53.00 *(978-0-7575-8628-6(7))* Kendall Hunt Publishing Co.

Rafael, Mark. Telling Stories: A Grand Unifying Theory of Acting Techniques. 2008. (Career Development Ser.). (ENG.). 208p. pap. 19.95 *(978-1-57525-565-1(0))* Smith & Kraus Pubs., Inc.

Rainer, John & Lewis, Martin. Drama at the Heart of the Secondary School. 2012. (ENG., Illus.). 208p. (C). 130.00 ***(978-0-415-57205-7(3))***; pap. 42.95 ***(978-0-415-57206-4(1))*** Routledge.

Rapkin, Mickey. Theater Geek: The Real Life Drama of a Summer at Stagedoor Manor. 2011. (ENG.). 272p. pap. 15.00 *(978-1-4391-4577-7(6)*, Free Pr.) Free Pr.

—Theater Geek: The Real Life Drama of a Summer at Stagedoor Manor, the Famous Performing Arts Camp. 2010. (ENG., Illus.). 240p. 25.00 *(978-1-4391-4576-0(8)*, Free Pr.) Free Pr.

Riley, Josephine. Chinese Theatre & the Actor in Performance. 2006. (Cambridge Studies in Modern Theatre Ser.). (ENG., Illus.). 364p. pap. 74.00 *(978-0-521-03523-1(6))* Cambridge Univ. Pr.

Shurin, Sande. Star Power: Defining Your Individual Signature. 2009. (ENG.). 168p. pap. 14.95 *(978-1-60037-651-1(7))* Morgan James Publishing.

Sloan, Gary. In Rehearsal. 2012. (ENG., Illus.). 280p. 115.00 *(978-0-415-67840-7(4))*; pap. 29.95 *(978-0-415-67841-4(2))* Routledge.

Soria Tomás, Guadalupe. La Formación Actoral en España: La Real Escuela Superior de Arte Dramático (1831-1857) 2010. (SPA., Illus.). 445p. *(978-84-245-1220-0(0))* Fundamentos, Editorial.

Swartz, Larry & Nyman, Debbie. Drama Schemes, Themes & Dreams: How to Plan, Structure, & Assess Classroom Strategies That Engage Young Adolescent Learners. 2010. (ENG.). 160p. (C). (gr. 6-12). pap. 22.00 ***(978-1-55138-253-1(9))*** Pembroke Pubs., Ltd. CAN. Dist: Stenhouse Pubs.

Tauber, Robert T. & Mester, Cathy Sargent. Acting Lessons for Teachers: Using Performance Skills in the Classroom, 1 vol. 2nd rev. ed. 2006. (Illus.). 240p. per. 34.95 *(978-0-275-99204-0(7)*, B9204); 54.95 *(978-0-275-99192-0(X)*, C9192) Greenwood Publishing Group, Inc. (Praeger Pubs.).

Tollefson, Donna & Fate, Fred. The Actor's Book: Study, Analysis, Rehearsal, Performance. rev. ed. 2007. (ENG.). 406p. pap. 80.51 *(978-0-7575-3819-3(3))* Kendall Hunt Publishing Co.

Watson, Jamantha. Don't Call Us We'll Call You: Ten Audition Tips for Actors. rev. ed. 2010. (ENG.). 218p. pap. 25.32 *(978-0-7575-8436-7(5))* Kendall Hunt Publishing Co.

Zimmerman, Suzi. Introduction to Theatre Arts: An Action Handbook for Middle Grade & High School Students & Teachers, 1 vol. 2007. (ENG., Illus.). 250p. tchr. ed., per. 29.95 *(978-1-56608-149-8(1))* Meriwether Publishing, Ltd.

ACTING—VOCATIONAL GUIDANCE

Alterman, Glenn. An Actor's Guide — Making It in New York City (Second Edition) 2nd ed. 2011. (ENG.). 344p. pap. 24.95 *(978-1-58115-763-5(0)*, 115763, Allworth Pr.) Skyhorse Publishing Co., Inc.

Audenreed Press. The Actor Takes a Meeting: How to Interview Successfully with Agents, Managers, Producers, & Casting Directors. 2006. (ENG.). 267p. per. 18.95 *(978-1-879505-89-6(4))* Silman-James Pr.

Barry, Carolyne. Hit the Ground Running First Years of Your Acting Career. 2009. 392p. pap. 22.95 *(978-0-9822360-0-0(X))* Barry, Carolyne Creative Entertainment.

Blumenfeld, Robert & Hal Leonard Corporation Staff. Blumenfeld's Dictionary of Acting & Show Business, 1 vol. 2009. (ENG.). 400p. pap. 19.99 (978-0-87910-363-7(9), 0879103639, Limelight Editions) Leonard, Hal Corp.

Brustein, Robert. Letters to a Young Actor. 2007. (Art of Mentoring (Paper) Ser.). (ENG.). 240p. per. 15.00 (978-0-465-00814-8(3)) Basic Bks.

Callan, K. The Los Angeles Agent Book: Get the Agent You Need for the Career You Want. 9th rev. ed. 2008. (Illus.). 254p. per. 20.00 (978-1-878355-20-1(1)) Sweden Pr.

Champion, Ian. Acting on Purpose. 2007. 204p. pap. 18.95 (978-1-84799-907-8(7)) Lulu Enterprises Inc.

Chaplin, Beth. The Acting Biz: A Career Guide to the Twin Cities. Chaplin, Beth, ed. 2009. (ENG.). 354p. pap. 35.00 (978-1-933794-17-4(8)) Kirk Hse. Pubs.

Cohen, Robert & Calleri, James. Acting Professionally: Raw Facts about Careers in Acting. 7th annot. rev. ed. 2009. (ENG., Illus.). 208p. pap. 31.00 (978-0-230-21724-9(9)) Palgrave Macmillan.

Cole, Della. Unraveling the Mystery of Monologues. 2008. 196p. pap. 15.95 (978-1-4357-1767-1(8)) Lulu Enterprises Inc.

Collier, Wayne Evans. An Actor's Primer: S. T. A. G. E. or a Simple Approach to Acting. 2007. 48p. per. 16.95 (978-1-4241-7625-0(5)) PublishAmerica, Inc.

Cram101 Textbook Reviews. Outlines & Highlights for Theatre in Your Life by Robert Barton, Isbn: 9780534640699 0534640699. 2011. 194p. pap. 30.95 **(978-1-61490-594-3(0))** Cram101 Inc.

Deer, Joe & Vera, Rocco dal. Acting in Musical Theatre: A Comprehensive Course. 2008. (ENG., Illus.). 480p. 115.00 (978-0-415-77318-8(0)); pap. 41.95 (978-0-415-77319-5(9)) Routledge.

Dunmore, Simon. An Actor's Guide to Getting Work. 5th ed. 2012. (ENG.). 256p. (C). pap. 22.95 **(978-1-4081-4554-8(5)**, Methuen Drama) A & C Black GBR. Dist: Macmillan.

Fava, Antonio. The Comic Mask in the Commedia Dell'arte: Actor Training, Improvisation, & the Poetics of Survival. 2007. (ENG., Illus.). 262p. per. 34.95 (978-0-8101-2358-7(1)) Northwestern Univ. Pr.

Fergason, Shannon. The New Actor's Guide: What Every New Actor Needs to Know about the Industry. rev. ed. 2007. (ENG.). 80p. pap. 26.41 (978-0-7575-3921-3(1)) Kendall Hunt Publishing Co.

Flanagan, Markus. One Less Bitter Actor: The Actor's Survival Guide. 2007. (Culture Tools Ser.). (ENG.). 130p. per. 15.95 (978-1-59181-063-6(9)) Sentient Pubns.

Fogelman, Bea. Copy Cats. 2008. 248p. pap. 19.99 (978-1-4363-2285-0(5)) Xlibris Corp.

Footsteps Toward Your Future. 2007. per. 19.95 (978-0-9792898-0-4(7)) Neal, Jolli.

Fridell, Squire. Acting in Television Commercials for Fun & Profit. 4th ed. 2009. (ENG., Illus.). 272p. pap. 14.99 (978-0-307-45024-1(4), Three Rivers Pr.) Crown Publishing Group.

Gillespie, Bonnie. Self-Management for Actors. 3rd rev. ed. 2008. 368p. pap. 29.95 (978-0-9723019-9-2(2)) Cricket Feet Publishing.

Gleason, Paul G. & Levy, Gavin. Acting for Love & Money: Connecting the craft to the industry, 1 vol. 2010. (ENG.). 100p. pap. 19.95 (978-1-56608-167-2(X)) Meriwether Publishing, Ltd.

Grady, Jame. Actor, Inc. How to Get the Next Gig — and Still Pay Your Rent. 2007. 160p. pap. 16.95 (978-0-325-01072-4(2), E01072) Heinemann.

Henry, Mari Lyn & Rogers, Lynne. How to Be a Working Actor, 5th Edition: The Insider's Guide to Finding Jobs in Theater, Film & Television. 5th rev. ed. 2007. (How to Be a Working Actor: the Insider's Guide to Finding Jobs Ser.). (ENG., Illus.). 432p. pap. 19.95 (978-0-8230-8895-9(2), Back Stage Bks.) Watson-Guptill Pubns., Inc.

How to Sell Yourself as an Actor. 6th rev. ed. 2008. 239p. pap. 20.00 (978-1-878355-21-8(X)) Sweden Pr.

Howl, Jona. 100 Projects to Strengthen Your Acting Skills. 2008. (Aspire Ser.). (ENG., Illus.). 128p. pap. 21.99 (978-0-7641-3949-9(5)) Barron's Educational Series Inc.

Joels, Merrill E. Acting Is a Business: How to Get into Television & Radio. 2011. 98p. 33.95 **(978-1-258-06035-0(3))** Literary Licensing, LLC.

Kaufman, Carrie L., ed. The Book: An Actor's Guide to Chicago, 7th Edition. 2007. m. lthr. 15.00 (978-1-892296-05-4(5)) Performink Bks., Ltd.

Kids in Show Business: How to Get Your Child into the Entertainment Industry. 2007. per. (978-0-9773099-2-4(4)) Quinn Entertainment.

Kummel, Tamar. How to Run Auditions. 2009. pap. 11.50 (978-0-615-14689-8(9)) Captain Purple.

Ladd, David. Footlight Dreams: Following Your Passion for a Career in Musical Theatre a Guide for Performers, Parents & Teachers. 2011. (ENG.). 96p. pap. 12.99 **(978-1-61780-464-9(9)**, 1617804649) Leonard, Hal Corp.

Lissenden, Hilary & Dunmore, Simon. Actors' Yearbook 2011: Essential Contacts for Stage, Screen & Radio. 2010. (ENG., Illus.). 512p. pap. 24.95 (978-1-4081-2840-4(3)) A & C Black GBR. Dist: Macmillan.

Newhouse, Miriam & Messaline, Peter. The Actor's Survival Kit. 5th ed. 2010. (ENG.). 272p. pap. 24.99 (978-1-55488-783-5(6)) Dundurn CAN. Dist: Ingram Pub. Services.

O'Neil, Brian. Acting As a Business: Strategies for Success. 4th ed. 2009. (Vintage Ser.). (ENG.). 192p. pap. 15.00 (978-0-307-47392-9(9), Vintage) Knopf Doubleday Publishing Group.

Pitman, Rod. Reel Extra Money: The Background Actor's Handbook. (Orig.). pap. (978-0-9642118-6-5(6)) Cascade Pr.

Powell, Michael. The Acting Bible: The Complete Resource for Aspiring Actors. 2010. (ENG.). 256p. 22.99 (978-0-7641-6358-6(2)) Barron's Educational Series, Inc.

Ramirez, M. The Ultimate Audition Book for Teens Volume XIII: 111 One-Minute Monologues - Active Voices, Vol. 13. 2008. (Young Actors Ser.: Vol.XIII). (ENG.). 160p. (YA). pap. 11.95 (978-1-57525-581-1(2)) Smith & Kraus Pubs., Inc.

Reinking, Cathy. How to Book Acting Jobs in TV & Film. 2009. 149p. pap. 18.00 (978-0-557-07547-8(5)) Lulu Enterprises Inc.

Robbins, Jon S. & Robbins. The Actor's Survival Guide: How to Make Your Way in Hollywood. 2008. (ENG., Illus.). 224p. pap. 22.95 (978-0-8264-2834-9(7)) Continuum International Publishing Group, Ltd. GBR. Dist: National Bk. Network.

Rosenberg, David. Abraham: The First Historical Biography. 2007. (ENG.). 368p. per. 18.00 (978-0-465-07095-4(7)) Basic Bks.

Sedita, Scott. Scott Sedita's Guide to Making It in Hollywood: Three Steps to Success, Three Steps to Failure. 2007. (ENG.). 259p. pap. 19.95 (978-0-9770641-1-3(5)) Atides Publishing.

Shurin, Sande. Star Power: Defining Your Individual Signature. 2009. (ENG.). 168p. pap. 14.95 (978-1-60037-651-1(7)) Morgan James Publishing.

Simpson, Fay. The Lucid Body: A Guide for the Physical Actor. 2008. (ENG., Illus.) 224p. pap. 19.95 (978-1-58115-651-5(0), 115651, Allworth Pr.) Skyhorse Publishing Co., Inc.

Swart, Tara & Tidmarsh, Andrew. An Attitude for Acting. 2012. (ENG.). 224p. pap. 26.95 **(978-1-84842-112-7(5))** Hern, Nick Bks., Ltd. GBR. Dist: Consortium Bk. Sales & Distribution.

Torrance, Ingrid. Act! a Step by Step Guide to Starting Your Acting Career. 2010. 100p. pap. 12.95 (978-1-60911-167-0(2), Eloquent Bks.) AEG Literary Publishing Services, Inc.

University of Toronto Press. Artistry: How to Achieve & Enjoy Great Performance. 2009. (ENG., Illus.). xviii, 199p. (978-1-4426-4130-3(4)) Univ. of Toronto Pr.

Wallach, Michael J. How to Get Arrested: A Motivational Story for Actors Breaking into Hollywood. 2007. (Illus.). 132p. per. 11.95 (978-0-9792711-0-6(X)) Arrested Pubns.

ACTING AS A PROFESSION

see Acting—Vocational Guidance

ACTING AUDITIONS

see Acting—Auditions

ACTING FOR TELEVISION

Fridell, Squire. Acting in Television Commercials for Fun & Profit. 4th ed. 2009. (ENG., Illus.). 272p. pap. 14.99 (978-0-307-45024-1(4), Three Rivers Pr.) Crown Publishing Group.

Joels, Merrill E. Acting Is a Business: How to Get into Television & Radio. 2011. 98p. 38.95 **(978-1-258-06035-0(3))** Literary Licensing, LLC.

Milstein, Karen. Hot Spots for Kids: One-Person Cold-Reading Copy for TV Commercial Auditioning Success. 2008. (Young Actors Ser.). (ENG.). 112p. (J). pap. 11.95 (978-1-57525-574-3(X)) Smith & Kraus Pubs., Inc.

Sedita, Scott. Scott Sedita's Guide to Making It in Hollywood: Three Steps to Success, Three Steps to Failure. 2007. (ENG.). 259p. pap. 19.95 (978-0-9770641-1-3(5)) Atides Publishing.

Swain, John Howard. The Science & Art of Commercial Acting. 2009. 94p. pap. 14.50 (978-0-578-01313-8(4)) 16 Coaches Long LLC.

ACTINIDE ELEMENTS

see also names of specific elements, e.g. Uranium

Al. Crystalline Materials for Actinide Immobilisation. 2010. (Illus.). xvi, 197p. 66.00 (978-1-84816-418-5(1)) World Scientific Publishing Co., Inc.

Albrecht-Schmitt, Thomas E. Organometallic & Coordination Chemistry of the Actinides. (Structure & Bonding Ser.). (Illus.). x, 191p. 249.00 (978-3-540-77836-3(5)) Springer.

American Nuclear Society, Materials Science and Technology Division Staff, contrib. by. Plutonium Futures — the Science 2010: [Topical Conference on Plutonium & Actinides], Keystone, Colorado, September 19-23, 2010. 2010. (Illus.). xxii, 426p. pap. **(978-0-89448-082-9(0))** American Nuclear Society.

Blobaum, K. J. M., et al, eds. Actinides 2006: Basic Science, Applications & Technology, 986. 2007. (MRS Symposium Proceedings Ser.). (Illus.). ix, 209p. 113.00 (978-1-55899-943-5(4)) Materials Research Society.

Bonnelle, Christiane & Spector, Nissan. Properties of nf electrons in lanthanide & actinide Materials. 2012. (Progress in Theoretical Chemistry & Physics Ser.). (ENG., Illus.). 250p. 289.00 (978-90-481-2878-5(1), 9048128781) Springer.

Edelstein, Norman M., et al, eds. The Chemistry of the Actinide & Transactinide Elements: Volume 6, 6 vols. 3rd ed. 2010. (ENG., Illus.). 850p. 379.00 (978-90-481-3146-4(4), 9048131464) Springer.

Gibson, J. K., et al, eds. Basic Actinide Science & Materials for Nuclear Applications: Volume 1264. 2010. (MRS Proceedings Ser.). (C). 115.00 **(978-1-60511-241-1(0))** Cambridge Univ. Pr.

Halka, Monica. Lanthanides & Actinides. Nordstrom, Brian, ed. 2011. (Periodic Table of the Elements Ser.). 224p. (C). (gr. 9-18). 40.00 (978-0-8160-7372-6(4)) Facts On File, Inc.

Kalmykov, Stepan N. & Denecke, Melissa A., eds. Actinide Nanoparticle Research. 2011. (ENG., Illus.). 388p. 189.00 (978-3-642-11431-1(8), 3642114318) Springer.

Krivovichev, Sergey, et al, eds. Structural Chemistry of Inorganic Actinide Compounds. 2006. (ENG.). 504p. 260.00 (978-0-444-52111-8(9), Elsevier Science) Elsevier Science & Technology Bks.

Morss, L. R., et al, eds. The Chemistry of the Actinide & Transactinide Elements (Volumes 1-6), 6 vols. 4th ed. 2011. (Illus.). 4514p. 2569.00 (978-94-007-0210-3(8), 9400702108) Springer.

Royal Society of Chemistry Staff. Recent Advances in Actinide Science. May, Iain et al, eds. 2006. (Special Publication). (ENG., Illus.). 836p. 192.00 (978-0-85404-678-2(X), 085404678X) Royal Society of Chemistry, The GBR. Dist: Ingram Pub. Services.

Soderholm, L., et al, eds. Actinides — Basic Science, Applications & Technology 802: 2003 MRS Fall Meeting Symposium Proceedings, Vol. 802. 2009. (Materials Research Society Symposium Proceedings Ser.: 802). (Illus.). 278p. 35.00 (978-1-55899-740-0(7), 802-C) Materials Research Society.

Sterne, P. A., et al, eds. Actinides & the Environment. 2010. (Nato Science Partnership Subseries: 2 (closed) Ser.). 500p. pap. 389.00 (978-90-481-5002-1(7), 9048150027) Springer.

ACTINIUM

see also Radioactivity

Fluck, Ekkehard & Heumann, Klaus G. The Ultimate Periodic Table - Look - Think - Learn. 2007. (ENG.). 1p. 29.99 (978-3-527-32082-0(2), Wiley-VCH) Wiley, John & Sons, Inc.

ACTINOMYCETALES

Mayo, Baltasar & Sinderen, Douwe Van, eds. Bifidobacteria: Genomics & Molecular Aspects. 2010. (Illus.). 274p. 319.00 (978-1-904455-68-4(9)) Caister Academic Pr. GBR. Dist: International Specialized Bk. Services.

Rushford, Jaime Salas & Benno DVM, Yoshimi. Morinaga BB536: Japan's Leading Clinically Proven Probiotic. 2011. (Woodland Health Ser.). 52p. pap. 4.95 **(978-1-58054-206-7(9))** Woodland Publishing, Inc.

Sonomoto, Kenji & Yokota, Atsushi, eds. Lactic Acid Bacteria & Bificobacteria: Current Progress in Advanced Research. 2011. (Illus.). 296p. 319.00 (978-1-904455-82-0(4)) Caister Academic Pr. GBR. Dist: International Specialized Bk. Services.

ACTINOMYCIN

Vekshin, N. L. Biophysics of DNA-Antibiotic Complexes. 2010. 75.00 (978-1-61761-199-5(9)) Nova Science Pubs., Inc.

ACTINOTHERAPY

see Phototherapy

ACTION, CATHOLIC

see Catholic Action

ACTION FRANCAISE

Dard, Olivier & Grunewald, Michel, eds. Charles Maurras et l'étranger - L'étranger et Charles Maurras: L'Action française - culture, politique, société II. 2009. (Convergences Ser.). (FRE.). 440p. pap. (978-3-0343-0039-1(5)) Lang, Peter.

Molnar, Thomas Steven. Bernanos: His Political Thought & Prophecy. 2011. 224p. 44.95 **(978-1-258-01842-9(X))** Literary Licensing, LLC.

ACTION IN ART

see also Futurism (Art)

Buddy Scalera. Comic & Fantasy Artist's Photo Reference: Colossal Collection of Action Poses. 2011. (ENG., Illus.). 320p. pap. 29.99 (978-1-4403-0922-9(1), Impact) F&W Media, Inc.

Cuneo, Terence T. Tanks & How to Draw Them. 2010. 66p. pap. 9.95 (978-1-61646-021-1(0)) Coachwhip Pubns.

Han, Heng-Gil & Ho, Christopher K. Jamaica Flux: Workspaces & Windows 2010: Art As Action, April 10, 2010-June 12, 2010. 2010. (978-0-9762853-7-3(1)) Jamaica Ctr. for Arts & Learning.

Plazer, Monika. Wiener Kinetismus: eine bewegte ModerneVienese Kineticism: Modernism in Motion: Eine Bewegte Moderne Viennese Kineticism: Modernism in Motion. Bast, Gerald, ed. 2011. (ENG.). 256p. 69.95 (978-3-211-99143-5(3)) Springer Wien AUT. Dist: Actar Birkhauser Distribution.

ACTION RESEARCH

Here are entered works about research concerned primarily with discovering the most effective means of bringing about a desired social change.

Berg, Anne Marie & Eikeland, Olav. Action Research & Organisation Theory. 2008. 190p. pap. 56.95 (978-3-631-56888-0(6)) Lang, Peter GmbH, Europäischer Verlag der Wissenschaften DEU. Dist: Lang, Peter.

Boog, Ben, et al, eds. Towards Quality Improvement of Action Research. 2008. 248p. (978-90-8790-593-4(9)); pap. (978-90-8790-592-7(0)) Sense Pubs.

Braben, Donald W. Scientific Freedom: The Elixir of Civilization. 2008. (ENG., Illus.). 184p. pap. 78.00 (978-0-470-22654-4(4), Wiley-Interscience) Wiley, John & Sons, Inc.

Brogger, Benedicte & Eikeland, Olav. Turning to Practice with Action Research. 2010. 286p. 72.95 (978-3-631-59446-9(1)) Lang, Peter GmbH, Europäischer Verlag der Wissenschaften DEU. Dist: Lang, Peter.

Butterworth, Kevin. Enhancing the Collection of Treatment Outcomes Data Through Canisc. 2010. 108p. pap. (978-3-8383-8665-2(5)) Lambert Academic Publishing.

Cameron, Helen. Talking about God in Practice: Theological Action Research & Practical Theology. 2010. (ENG., Illus.). 192p. pap. 29.99 (978-0-334-04363-8(8), SCM Pr.) Hymns Ancient & Modern Ltd GBR. Dist: Westminster John Knox Pr.

Campbell, Anne. An Ethical Approach to Practitioner Research. 2007. (ENG., Illus.). 208p. 47.95 (978-0-415-43088-3(7)) Routledge.

Campbell, Anne & Groundwater-Smith, S., eds. An Ethical Approach to Practitioner Research. 2007. (Illus.). 208p. 170.00 (978-0-415-43087-6(9)) Routledge.

Coghlan, David & Brannick, Teresa. Doing Action Research in Your Own Organization. 3rd ed. 2009. (Illus.). 184p. (C). 112.00 (978-1-84860-215-1(4), B02151C); pap. 52.00 (978-1-84860-216-8(2), B02151P) SAGE Pubns., Ltd. GBR. Dist: SAGE Pubns., Inc.

Cook, Douglas & Farmer, Lesley S. J. Using Qualitative Methods in Action Research: How Librarians Can Get to the Why of Data. 2011. pap. (978-0-8389-8576-2(9)) Assn. of College & Research Libraries.

Cooper, Susan. Action Research. 2010. 176p. pap. (978-3-8383-1266-2(6)) Lambert Academic Publishing.

Craig, Dorothy Valcarcel & Craig. Action Research Essentials. 2009. (Research Methods for the Social Sciences Ser.: 11). (ENG., Illus.). 272p. pap. 48.00 (978-0-470-18929-0(0), Jossey-Bass) Wiley, John & Sons, Inc.

Cram101 Textbook Reviews & Cram101 Textbook Reviews. Outlines & Highlights for Action Research by Ernest T Stringer, Isbn: 9781412952231 1412952239. 2011. 90p. pap. 27.95 **(978-1-61490-316-1(6))** Cram101 Inc.

Demusz, Kerry. Listening to the Displaced: Action Research in the Conflict Zones of Sri Lanka. (Working Papers). (ENG., Illus.). 80p. pap. 23.95 (978-0-85598-437-3(6)) Oxfam Publishing GBR. Dist: Stylus Publishing, LLC.

Fox, Mark, et al. Doing Practitioner Research. 2007. (Illus.). 224p. (C). 108.00 (978-1-4129-1233-4(4), B12334C); per. 53.00 (978-1-4129-1234-1(2), B12334P) SAGE Pubns., Ltd. GBR. Dist: SAGE Pubns., Inc.

Freshwater, Dawn & Lees, John. Practitioner Research in Healthcare: Transformational Research in Action. 2014. 224p. (C). 99.95 (978-1-4129-3023-9(5), B30235C); pap. 39.95 (978-1-4129-3024-6(3), B30235P) SAGE Pubns., Ltd. GBR. Dist: SAGE Pubns., Inc.

Hofman, Nila Ginger & Rosing, Howard, eds. Pedagogies of Praxis: Course-Based Action Research in the Social Sciences. 2006. (JB - Anker Ser.: 84). (ENG.). 202p. 40.00 (978-1-933371-09-2(9), Jossey-Bass) Wiley, John & Sons, Inc.

Hollenbach, Nicole & Tillmann, Klaus-Jürgen, eds. Teacher Research & School Development: German Approaches & International Perspectives. 2011. 259p. pap. 45.95 (978-3-86649-352-0(5)) Budrich-Esser Barbara DEU. Dist: International Specialized Bk. Services.

Holter, Anthony C. & Frabutt, James M. Action Research in Catholic Schools: A Step-By-Step Guide for Practitioners. 2009. pap. (978-0-9788793-8-9(4)) Alliance for Catholic Education Pr.

Holter, Anthony C. & Frabutt, James M. Action Research in Catholic Schools: Step-By-Step Guide for Practitioners. 2nd ed. 2011. pap. **(978-1-935788-07-2(8))** Alliance for Catholic Education Pr.

Johnson, Andrew P. What Every Teacher Should Know about Action Research. 2008. (What Every Student Should Know about... (WESSKA Series) Ser.). (ENG.). 32p. (C). pap. 7.80 (978-0-13-715584-2(0), Prentice Hall) Prentice Hall PTR.

Kapoor, Dip & Choudry, Aziz, eds. Learning from the Ground Up: Global Perspectives on Social Movements & Knowledge Production. 2010. (ENG., Illus.). 266p. 89.00 (978-0-230-62103-9(1)) Palgrave Macmillan.

Koch, Tina & Kralik, Debbie. Participatory Action Research in Health Care. 2006. (ENG., Illus.). 192p. pap. 65.99 (978-1-4051-2416-4(4), Wiley-Blackwell) Wiley, John & Sons, Inc.

Kock, Ned, ed. Information Systems Action Research: An Applied View of Emerging Concepts & Methods. 2010. (Integrated Series in Information Systems Ser.) (Illus.). xxv, 425p. pap. 149.00 (978-1-4419-4210-4(6), 1441942106) Springer.

Lehtonen, Jarmo & Kalliola, Satu, eds. Dialogue in Working Life Research & Development in Finland. 2008. (Arbeit, Bildung & Gesellschaft. Labour, Education & Society Ser.). (Illus.). 238p. pap. 61.95 (978-3-631-58277-0(3)) Lang, Peter GmbH, Europäischer Verlag der Wissenschaften DEU. Dist: Lang, Peter.

Levin, Morten & Greenwood, Davydd J. (James). Introduction to Action Research: Social Research for Social Change. 2nd rev. ed. 2006. (Illus.). 320p. (C). per. 61.00 (978-1-4129-2597-6(5), B25975P) SAGE Pubns., Inc.

Mac Naughton, Glenda & Hughes, Patrick. Doing Action Research in Early Childhood Studies. 2008. (ENG., Illus.). 208p. (C). pap. 45.00 (978-0-335-22862-1(3), 0335228623) McGraw-Hill Education GBR. Dist: McGraw-Hill Cos., The.

Macnaughton, Glenda & Hughes, Patrick. Doing Action Research in Early Childhood Studies. 2008. (Illus.). 208p. (C). 126.95 (978-0-335-22861-4(5), 0335228615, Open University Pr.) McGraw-Hill Education GBR. Dist: McGraw-Hill Cos., The.

Mangar, Eric. The Resettlement & Integration of la Pipe Community in Mauritius. 2011. 176p. pap. **(978-3-8443-9671-3(3))** Lambert Academic Publishing.

McIntosh, Paul. Action Research & Reflective Practice: Creative & Visual Methods to Facilitate Reflection & Learning. 2010. (ENG., Illus.). 196p. pap. 45.95 (978-0-415-46902-9(3), Routledge) Taylor & Francis Group GBR. Dist: Taylor & Francis Group.

—Action Research & Reflective Practice: Creative & Visual Methods to Facilitate Reflection & Learning. 2010. (ENG., Illus.). 208p. (C). 140.00 (978-0-415-46901-2(5)) Routledge.

McIntyre, Alice. Participatory Action Research. 2007. (Qualitative Research Methods Ser.: 52). (Illus.). 104p. (C). per. 23.00 (978-1-4129-5366-5(9), B53669P) SAGE Pubns., Inc.

Mckernan. Curriculum & Imagination. 2007. (Illus.). 264p. 170.00 (978-0-415-41337-4(0)) Routledge.

McKernan, James. Curriculum & Imagination: Process Theory, Pedagogy & Action Research. 2007. (ENG., Illus.). 264p. (C). per. 47.95 (978-0-415-41338-1(9)) Routledge.

Nnatuanya, Ifechukwu. Evolution of Living Information Systems Development. 2010. 148p. pap. (978-3-8383-7162-7(3)) Lambert Academic Publishing.

Rapoport, Robert Norman. New Interventions for Children & Youth: Action-Research Approaches. 2009. (ENG.). 284p. pap. 42.00 *(978-0-521-12494-2(8))* Cambridge Univ. Pr.

Rapoport, Robert Norman, ed. Children, Youth, & Families: The Action-Research Relationship. 2010. (ENG.). 332p. (C). pap. 34.99 *(978-0-521-14369-1(1))* Cambridge Univ. Pr.

Reason, Peter & Bradbury, Hilary, eds. The Sage Handbook of Action Research: Participative Inquiry & Practice. 2nd ed. 2007. (Illus.). 752p. 150.00 *(978-1-4129-2029-2(9)*, B20299C) SAGE Pubns., Ltd. GBR. Dist: SAGE Pubns., Inc.

Reeb, Roger N., ed. Community Action Research: Benifits to Community Members & Service Providers. 2006. (ENG.). 190p. 175.00 *(978-0-7890-3046-7(2))*; per. 49.95 *(978-0-7890-3047-4(0))* Routledge.

Slater, Tracesea, et al. Action Research for Business, Nonprofit, & Public Administration: A Tool for Complex Times. 2011. (Illus.). 376p. (C). pap. 45.00 ***(978-1-4129-9164-3(1)**, B91643P)* SAGE Pubns., Inc.

Stringer, Ernest T. Action Research. 3rd ed. 2007. (Action Research Ser.). (Illus.). 304p. (C). per. 63.00 *(978-1-4129-5223-1(9)*, B52220P) SAGE Pubns., Inc.

Whitehead, A. Jack & McNiff, Jean. All You Need to Know about Action Research. 2nd ed. 2011. (Illus.). 280p. (C). 125.00 *(978-0-85702-582-1(1)*, B25838C); pap. 47.00 *(978-0-85702-583-8(X)*, B25838P) SAGE Pubns., Ltd. GBR. Dist: SAGE Pubns., Inc.

Whitehead, A. Jack, et al. Doing & Writing Action Research. 2009. (Illus.). 208p. (C). 112.00 *(978-1-84787-174-9(7)*, B71749C); pap. 45.00 *(978-1-84787-175-6(5)*, B71749P) SAGE Pubns., Ltd. GBR. Dist: SAGE Pubns., Inc.

Zuber-Skerritt, Ortrun. Action Leadership: Towards a Participatory Paradigm. 2011. (Professional & Practice-based Learning Ser.). (ENG., Illus.). xxix, 210p. 139.00 *(978-90-481-3934-7(1)*, 9048139341) Springer.

—Action Learning & Action Research. 2009. (Illus.). 236p. *(978-90-8790-953-6(5))*; pap. *(978-90-8790-952-9(7))* Sense Pubs.

Zuber-Skerritt, Ortrun, ed. Action Research for Sustainable Development in a Turbulent World. 2012. 250p. 114.95 ***(978-1-78052-548-8(6))*** Emerald Group Publishing Ltd. GBR. Dist: Turpin Distribution Services Ltd.

ACTION RESEARCH IN EDUCATION

Alber, Sandra. Toolkit for Action Research. 2010. (ENG.). 214p. pap. 35.00 *(978-1-4422-0693-9(4))* Rowman & Littlefield Publishers, Inc.

Altrichter, Herbert, et al. Teachers Investigate Their Work. 2nd rev. ed. 2007. (Illus.). XII, 308p. 47.95 *(978-0-415-37794-2(3))*; 170.00 *(978-0-415-37795-9(1))* Routledge.

Anderson, Shona. No More Bystanders = No More Bullies: Activating Action in Educational Professionals. 2011. 176p. pap. 31.95 *(978-1-4129-9096-7(3)*, B90967P) Corwin Pr.

Baldwin, Shelia C., et al. Integrating Teaching, Learning, & Action Research: Enhancing Instruction in the K-12 Classroom. Stringer, Ernest T., ed. 2009. (Illus.). 200p. (C). pap. 32.00 *(978-1-4129-3975-1(5)*, B39747P) SAGE Pubns., Inc.

Ballenger, Cynthia. Puzzling Moments, Teachable Moments: Practicing Teacher Research in Urban Classrooms. 2010. (Practitioners Inquiry Ser.). (ENG., Illus.). 160p. 58.00 *(978-0-8077-4994-4(X))*; pap. 24.95 *(978-0-8077-4993-7(1))* Teachers College Pr., Teachers College, Columbia Univ.

Baumfield, Vivienne, et al. Action Research in the Classroom. 2008. (Illus.). 144p. (C). 112.00 *(978-1-4129-3039-0(1)*, B30391C); pap. 51.00 *(978-1-4129-3040-6(5)*, B30391P) SAGE Pubns., Ltd. GBR. Dist: SAGE Pubns., Inc.

Beeler, Linda, et al. Counseling Children & Adolescents in Schools. 2011. (Illus.). 440p. (C). pap. 60.00 ***(978-1-4129-9087-5(4)**,* B90875P) SAGE Pubns., Inc.

—Counseling Children & Adolescents in Schools Workbook. 2011. 128p. (C). pap. 30.00 ***(978-1-4129-9088-2(2)**,* B90875M) SAGE Pubns., Inc.

Blackburn, Mollie V. & Clark, Caroline T. Literacy Research for Political Action & Social Change. 2007. (Counterpoints: Studies in the Postmodern Theory of Education Ser.). (Illus.). 312p. (C). pap. 32.95 *(978-0-8204-8679-6(5))* Lang, Peter Publishing, Inc.

Bold, Christine, ed. Supporting Learning & Teaching. 2nd rev. ed. 2011. (ENG., Illus.). 224p. 135.00 *(978-0-415-58355-8(1))*; pap. 39.95 *(978-0-415-58356-5(X))* Routledge.

Brindley, Roger. Empowering the Voice of the Teacher Researcher: Achieving Success through a Culture of Inquiry. 2010. (ENG., Illus.). 110p. 55.00 *(978-1-60709-966-6(7))* Rowman & Littlefield Education.

Brindley, Roger & Crocco, Christine. Empowering the Voice of the Teacher Researcher: Achieving Success Through a Culture of Inquiry. 2010. (Illus.). x, 121p. *(978-1-60709-968-0(3))* Rowman & Littlefield Education.

Brindley, Roger & Crocco, Margaret Smith. Empowering the Voice of the Teacher Researcher: Achieving Success through a Culture of Inquiry. 2010. (ENG., Illus.). 110p. pap. 24.95 *(978-1-60709-967-3(5))* Rowman & Littlefield Education.

Bruce, Susan M. & Pine, Gerald J. Action Research in Special Education: An Inquiry Approach for Effective Teaching & Learning. 2010. (ENG., Illus.). 160p. 62.00 *(978-0-8077-5092-6(1))*; pap. 27.95 *(978-0-8077-5091-9(3))* Teachers College Pr., Teachers College, Columbia Univ.

Bucknall, Sue. Children as Researchers in Primary Schools: Choice, Voice & Participation. 2012. (ENG., Illus.). 232p. 155.00 *(978-0-415-61966-0(1))*; pap. 35.95 *(978-0-415-61970-7(X))* Routledge.

Burns, Anne. Doing Action Research in English Language Teaching. 2009. (ESL & Applied Linguistics Professional Ser.). (ENG., Illus.). 208p. pap., instr.'s gde. ed. 28.95 *(978-0-415-99145-2(5))* Routledge.

—Doing Action Research in English Language Teaching: A Guide for Practitioners. 2009. (ESL & Applied Linguistics Professional Ser.). (ENG., Illus.). 208p. 130.00 *(978-0-415-99144-5(7))* Routledge.

Campbell, Anne. An Ethical Approach to Practitioner Research. 2007. (ENG., Illus.). 208p. 47.95 *(978-0-415-43088-3(7))* Routledge.

Campbell, Anne & Groundwater-Smith, S., eds. An Ethical Approach to Practitioner Research. 2007. (Illus.). 208p. 170.00 *(978-0-415-43087-6(9))* Routledge.

Caro-Bruce, Cathy, et al, eds. Creating Equitable Classrooms Through Action Research. 2007. 328p. 90.95 *(978-1-4129-3666-8(7)*, B36667C); (Illus.). per. 41.95 *(978-1-4129-3667-5(5)*, B36667P) Corwin Pr.

Chambliss, Marilyn J. & Valli, Linda. Upper Elementary Reading Lessons: Case Studies of Real Teaching. 2011. (ENG.). 228p. (C). (gr. 13-17). pap. 22.95 *(978-1-4422-1193-3(8))* Rowman & Littlefield Publishers, Inc.

Cochran-Smith, Marilyn & Lytle, Susan L. Inquiry As Stance: Practitioner Research in the Next Generation. rev. ed. 2009. (Practitioners Inquiry Ser.). (ENG., Illus.). 392p. pap. 26.95 *(978-0-8077-4970-8(2))*; 60.00 *(978-0-8077-4971-5(0))* Teachers College Pr., Teachers College, Columbia Univ.

Costello, Patrick J. M. Effective Action Research: Developing Reflective Thinking & Practice. 2nd rev. ed. 2011. (Continuum Research Methods Ser.). (ENG., Illus.). 144p. 27.95 *(978-1-4411-6375-2(1))*; 90.00 *(978-1-4411-3326-7(7))* Continuum International Publishing Group, Ltd. GBR. Dist: National Bk. Network.

Cunningham, Diane. Improving Teaching with Collaborative Action Research: An ASCD Action Tool. 2011. 195p. pap. 69.00 *(978-1-4166-1162-2(2))* Assn. for Supervision & Curriculum Development.

Dana, Nancy Fichtman, ed. Leading with Passion & Knowledge: The Principal as Action Researcher. 2009. (Illus.). 240p. pap. 36.95 *(978-1-4129-6705-1(8)*, B67044P) Corwin Pr.

Dana, Nancy Fichtman & Yendol-Hoppey, Diane. The Reflective Educator's Guide to Professional Development: Coaching Inquiry-Oriented Learning Communities. 2008. (Illus.). 208p. 82.95 *(978-1-4129-5579-9(3)*, B55793C); pap. 36.95 *(978-1-4129-5580-5(7)*, B55793P) Corwin Pr.

Dana, Nancy Fichtman & Yendol-Silva, Diane. Facilitator's Guide: The Reflective Educator's Guide to Classroom Research: Learning to Teach & Teaching to Learn Through Practitioner Inquiry. 2nd ed. 2009. (Illus.). viii, 45p. pap. 16.95 *(978-1-4129-6654-2(X))* Corwin Pr.

Davies, Sue, et al. Improving the Context for Inclusion: How teachers & educational psychologists can use action research to work together to develop Inclusion. 2009. (Improving Learning Ser.). (ENG., Illus.). X, 198p. 41.95 *(978-0-415-47342-2(X))* Routledge.

—Improving the Context for Inclusion: Personalising Teacher Development through Collaborative Action Research. 2009. (Improving Learning Ser.). (ENG., Illus.). 208p. 130.00 *(978-0-415-47341-5(1))* Routledge.

DePino, Catherine. Who Says Bullies Rule? Common Sense Tips to Help Your Kids Cope. 2011. (ENG.). 126p. 17.95 *(978-1-61048-469-5(X))* Rowman & Littlefield Education.

Dexheimer Pharris. Community Based Collaborative Action Research. rev. ed. 2011. (Illus.). 434p. pap. 83.95 *(978-0-7637-7112-6(0))* Jones & Bartlett Learning, LLC.

Elliot, Dely, et al. A Guide to Practitioner Research in Education. 2011. (Illus.). 280p. (C). 104.00 *(978-1-84920-184-1(6)*, B01841C); pap. 39.00 *(978-1-84920-185-8(4)*, B01841P) SAGE Pubns., Ltd. GBR. Dist: SAGE Pubns., Inc.

Elliot, John. Reflecting Where the Action Is: The Selected Works of John Elliott. 2006. (World Library of Educationalists Ser.). (Illus.). 219p. per. 45.95 *(978-0-415-36993-0(2))* Routledge.

Farren, Margaret, et al, eds. Action Research in the Educational Workplace. 2010. (Illus.). 400p. lib. bdg. *(978-1-936320-05-9(3))* Academica Pr., LLC.

Finser, Torin M. Silence Is Complicity: A Call to Let Teachers Improve Our Schools through Action Research — Not NCLB. 2007. 112p. pap. 15.00 *(978-0-88010-580-4(1))* SteinerBooks, Inc.

Foreman-Peck, Lorraine. Using Educational Research to Inform Practice: A Practical Guide to Using Practitioner Research in Universities & Colleges. 2010. (ENG., Illus.). 160p. 125.00 *(978-0-415-45009-6(8))* Routledge.

Frabutt, James M., et al. Research, Action, & Change: Leaders Reshaping Catholic Schools. 2008. 304p. (ENG.). 20.00 *(978-0-9788793-7-2(6))*; pap. 15.00 *(978-0-9788793-6-5(8))* Alliance for Catholic Education Pr.

Goldring, Ellen B., et al. Leading with Inquiry & Action: How Principals Improve Teaching & Learning. Goldring, Ellen B. et al, eds. 2009. (Illus.). 168p. 72.95 *(978-1-4129-6413-5(X)*, B64135C); pap. 31.95 *(978-1-4129-6414-2(8)*, B64135P) Corwin Pr.

Goodnough, Karen. Taking Action in Science Classrooms Through Collaborative Action Research: A Guide for Educators. 2011. 114p. ***(978-94-6091-582-6(5))***; pap. ***(978-94-6091-581-9(7))*** Sense Pubs.

Gordon, Stephen P., ed. Collaborative Action Research: Developing Professional Learning Communities. 2008. (ENG.). 224p. 56.00 *(978-0-8077-4899-2(4))*; (Illus.). pap. 25.95 *(978-0-8077-4898-5(6))* Teachers College Pr., Teachers College, Columbia Univ.

Goswami, Dixie, et al. On Teacher Inquiry: Approaches to Language & Literacy Research. rev. ed. 2009. (Language & Literacy NCRLL Ser.). (ENG.). 128p. pap. 24.95 *(978-0-8077-4945-6(1))*; 56.00 *(978-0-8077-4946-3(X))* Teachers College Pr., Teachers College, Columbia Univ.

Groundwater-Smith, Susan & Campbell, Anne, eds. Action Research in Education, 3 vols. 2010. (Fundamentals of Applied Research Ser.). (Illus.). 1240p. 825.00 *(978-1-84860-683-8(4)*, B06838C) SAGE Pubns., Ltd. GBR. Dist: SAGE Pubns., Inc.

Groundwater-Smith, Susan & Mockler, Nicole. Teacher Professional Learning in an Age of Compliance: Mind the Gap. 2009. (Professional Learning & Development in Schools & Higher Education Ser.). (ENG., Illus.). 150p. 99.00 *(978-1-4020-9416-3(7))* Springer.

Groundwater-Smith, Susan, et al. Facilitating Practitioner Research. 2012. (ENG., Illus.). 176p. 128.00 ***(978-0-415-68441-5(2))***; pap. 39.95 ***(978-0-415-68442-2(0))*** Routledge.

Hawkes & Norton, Lin. L. Thinking about Reading. 2008. (ENG.). 224p. (C). 595.00 *(978-0-415-43793-6(8))* Routledge.

Hendricks, Cher. Improving Schools Through Action Research: A Comprehensive Guide for Educators. 2nd ed. 2008. (ENG., Illus.). 224p. (C). pap. 50.40 *(978-0-205-57846-7(2))* Allyn & Bacon, Inc.

Hendricks, Cher C. Improving Schools Through Action Research: A Reflective Practice Approach. 3rd rev. ed. 2012. (ENG., Illus.). 208p. (C). pap. 50.40 ***(978-0-13-286864-8(4))*** Addison Wesley.

Henning, John E., et al. Using Action Research to Improve Instruction. 2008. (Illus.). (ENG.). 224p. (C). 135.00 *(978-0-415-99173-5(0))*; XVIII, 206p. pap. 38.95 *(978-0-415-99174-2(9))* Routledge.

Hernandez-Tutop, Jeanne. Action Research: Teaching Improvement Method. 2009. 176p. pap. *(978-3-639-13773-6(6))* VDM Verlag Dr. Mueller e.K.

Herr, Kathryn, et al. Studying Your Own School: An Educator's Guide to Practitioner Action Research. Anderson, Gary L. & Nihlen, Ann Sigrid, eds. 2nd ed. 2007. (Illus.). 272p. 80.95 *(978-1-4129-4032-0(X)*, B4032XC); per. 36.95 *(978-1-4129-4033-7(8)*, B4032XP) Corwin Pr.

Hinchey, Patricia H. Action Research Primer. 2008. (Peter Lang Primers Ser.). (Illus.). 144p. (C). pap. 18.95 *(978-0-8204-9527-9(1))* Lang, Peter Publishing, Inc.

Holly, Mary Louise, et al. Action Research for Teachers: Traveling the Yellow Brick Road. 3rd ed. 2008. (ENG., Illus.). 416p. (C). pap. 60.80 *(978-0-13-515761-9(7)*, Prentice Hall) Prentice Hall PTR.

Hopkins, David. A Teacher's Guide to Classroom Research. 4th rev. ed. 2008. (ENG., Illus.). 240p. pap. 49.00 *(978-0-335-22174-5(2)*, 0335221742) McGraw-Hill Education GBR. Dist: McGraw-Hill Cos., The.

Hui, Ming-Fai & Grossman, David L., eds. Improving Teacher Education Through Action Research. 2008. (Routledge Research in Education Ser.). (ENG., Illus.). 210p. 125.00 *(978-0-415-95629-1(3))* Routledge.

Hymer, Barry, et al. Gifts, Talents & Education: A Living Theory Approach. 2009. (ENG., Illus.). 194p. 90.00 *(978-0-470-72539-9(7)*, Wiley) Wiley, John & Sons, Inc.

Johnson, Andrew P. A Short Guide to Action Research. 4th rev. ed. 2011. (ENG., Illus.). 304p. (C). pap. 53.60 ***(978-0-13-268586-3(8))*** Addison Wesley.

Jones, Phyllis, et al, eds. Creating Meaningful Inquiry in the Classroom: Teachers' Stories of Research. 2012. (ENG., Illus.). 160p. (C). 155.00 ***(978-0-415-67616-8(9))***; pap. 42.95 *(978-0-415-67617-5(7))* Routledge.

Khine, Myint Swe & Saleh, Issa M. Practitioner Research: Teachers' Investigations in Classroom Teaching. 2011. (Education in a Competitive & Globalizing World Ser.). (Illus.). xi, 213p. 129.00 *(978-1-61761-744-7(X))* Nova Science Pubs., Inc.

Klein, Sheri R., ed. Action Research Methods: Plain & Simple. 2012. (ENG., Illus.). 242p. 85.00 ***(978-0-230-11383-1(4))*** Palgrave Macmillan.

Koshy, Valsa. Action Research for Improving Educational Practice: A Step-by-Step Guide. 2nd ed. 2009. (Illus.). 176p. (C). 112.00 *(978-1-84860-159-8(X)*, B01598C); pap. 47.00 *(978-1-84860-160-4(3)*, B01598P) SAGE Pubns., Ltd. GBR. Dist: SAGE Pubns., Inc.

Laffey, Evelyn Hanna. Teacher Discourse Community. 2008. 276p. pap. *(978-3-8364-8846-4(9))* VDM Verlag Dr. Mueller e.K.

Lassonde, Cynthia A. & Israel, Susan E., eds. Teachers Taking Action: A Comprehensive Guide to Teacher Research. 2008. (Illus.). 248p. pap. 28.95 *(978-0-87207-463-7(3))* International Reading Assn.

Little, Mary E. Response to Intervention for Teachers: Classroom Instructional Problem Solving. 2009. (Illus.). 144p. (C). pap. *(978-0-89108-338-2(3))* Love Publishing Co.

Mcniff, Jean. You & Your Action Research Project. 3rd ed. 2009. (ENG., Illus.). 280p. 130.00 *(978-0-415-48708-5(0))*; pap. 42.95 *(978-0-415-48709-2(9))* Routledge.

Meier, Daniel R. & Henderson, Barbara. Learning from Young Children in the Classroom: The Art & Science of Teacher Research. 2007. (ENG., Illus.). 224p. 61.00 *(978-0-8077-4768-1(8))*; pap. 28.95 *(978-0-8077-4767-4(X))* Teachers College Pr., Teachers College, Columbia Univ.

Mercie, Julien, et al, eds. Collaborative & Individual Learning in Teaching. 2010. (Education in a Competitive & Globalizing World Ser.). 69.00 *(978-1-60876-889-9(9))* Nova Science Pubs., Inc.

Mertler, Craig A. Action Research: Improving Schools & Empowering Educators. 3rd ed. 2011. (Illus.). 328p. (C). pap. 47.00 *(978-1-4129-8889-6(6)*, B88896P) SAGE Pubns., Inc.

Metcalf, Linda. Solution-Focused RTI: A Positive & Personalized Approach to Response-to-Intervention. 2010. (ENG.). 224p. pap. 32.95 *(978-0-470-47042-8(9)*, Jossey-Bass) Wiley, John & Sons, Inc.

Milenkiewicz, Margaret T., et al. Participatory Action Research for Educational Leadership: Using Data-Driven Decision Making to Improve Schools. 2007. (Illus.). 248p. (C). per. 50.00 *(978-1-4129-3777-1(9)*, B37779P) SAGE Pubns., Inc.

Mills, Geoff E. Action Research: A Guide for the Teacher Researcher (with MyEducationLab) 4th ed. 2009. (ENG.). 264p. (C). pap. 59.27 *(978-0-13-802021-7(3)*, Prentice Hall) Prentice Hall PTR.

Mills, Geoffrey E. Action Research: A Guide for the Teacher Researcher. 4th rev. ed. 2010. (ENG.). 264p. (C). pap. 52.60 *(978-0-13-700314-3(5)*, Prentice Hall) Prentice Hall PTR.

Mockler, Nicole & Sachs, Judyth, eds. Rethinking Educational Practice Through Reflexive Inquiry: Essays in Honour of Susan Groundwater-Smith. 2011. (Professional Learning & Development in Schools & Higher Education Ser.). (ENG., Illus.). xix, 225p. 139.00 *(978-94-007-0804-4(1)*, 9400708041) Springer.

Moss, Glenda. Crossing Boundaries & Building Learning Communities: Critical Education & Narrative Research As Praxis. 2008. 216p. *(978-1-57273-720-4(4))*; ix, 205p. *(978-1-57273-719-8(0))* Hampton Pr., Inc.

Moss, Julianne, ed. Researching Education: Visually - Digitally - Spatially. 2007. 268p. per. *(978-90-8790-231-5(X))* Sense Pubs.

Murphy, Carlene U., et al, eds. Schoolwide Action Research for Professional Learning Communities: Improving Student Learning Through the Whole-Faculty Study Groups Approach. 2008. (Illus.). 304p. 95.95 *(978-1-4129-5207-1(7)*, B52077C); pap. 44.95 *(978-1-4129-5208-8(5)*, B52077P) Corwin Pr.

Noffke, Susan E. & Somekh, Bridget, eds. The SAGE Handbook of Educational Action Research. 2009. 568p. 150.00 *(978-1-4129-4708-4(1)*, B47084C) SAGE Pubns., Ltd. GBR. Dist: SAGE Pubns., Inc.

Norton, Lin. Action Research in Teaching & Learning: A Practical Guide to Conducting Pedagogical Research in Universities. 2008. 224p. 131.00 *(978-0-415-45093-5(4))* Routledge.

Norton, Lin S. Action Research in Teaching & Learning: A Practical Guide to Conducting Pedagogical Research in Universities. 2009. (Illus.). 224p. (ENG.). pap. 41.95 *(978-0-415-43794-3(6))*; 140.00 *(978-0-415-46846-6(9))* Routledge.

Pelton, Robert. Action Research for Teacher Candidates: Using Classroom Data to Enhance Instruction. 2010. (ENG., Illus.). 228p. pap. 32.95 *(978-1-60709-693-1(5))* Rowman & Littlefield Education.

—Making Classroom Inquiry Work: Techniques for Effective Action Research. 2010. (ENG.). 206p. pap. 37.95 *(978-1-60709-928-4(4))* Rowman & Littlefield Education.

Pelton, Robert P. Best Practices in Action Research for Teacher Candidates. 2010. (ENG.). 228p. 80.00 *(978-1-60709-692-4(7))*; (Illus.). xiii, 205p. *(978-1-60709-694-8(3))* Rowman & Littlefield Education.

Pelton, Robert P. Making Classroom Inquiry Work: Techniques for Effective Action Research. 2010. ***(978-1-60709-929-1(2))*** Rowman & Littlefield Education.

Pelton, Robert P., ed. Making Classroom Inquiry Work: Techniques for Effective Action Research. 2010. (ENG.). 206p. 95.00 *(978-1-60709-927-7(6))* Rowman & Littlefield Education.

Phillips, Donna Kalmbach & Carr, Kevin M. Becoming a Teacher Through Action Research: Process, Context, & Self-Study. 2nd rev. ed. 2010. (ENG., Illus.). 264p. pap. 44.95 *(978-0-415-80106-5(0))*; 135.00 *(978-0-415-80105-8(2))* Routledge.

Pine, Gerald J. Teacher Action Research: Building Knowledge Democracies. 2008. 416p. (C). 99.00 *(978-1-4129-6475-3(X)*, B64753C) Corwin Pr.; pap. 52.00 *(978-1-4129-6476-0(8)*, B64753P) SAGE Pubns., Inc.

Ponte, P. & Smit, B, eds. The Quality of Practitioner Research. 2007. 140p. per. *(978-90-8790-245-2(X))* Sense Pubs.

Ponte, Petra & Smit, Ben, eds. The Quality of Practitioner Research. 2008. 140p. *(978-90-8790-246-9(8))* Sense Pubs.

Roberts, Deborah, et al, eds. Teacher Research: Stories of Learning & Growing. 2007. (ENG.). 161p. pap. 21.95 *(978-1-933531-13-7(4))* National Science Teachers Assn.

Rodrigues, Susan, ed. Using Analytical Frameworks for Classroom Research: Collecting Data & Analysing Narrative. 2010. (ENG., Illus.). 224p. 130.00 *(978-0-415-55306-3(7))*; pap. 42.95 *(978-0-415-55307-0(5))* Taylor & Francis Group GBR. (Routledge). Dist: Taylor & Francis Group.

Ryan, Thomas. The Reflexive Classroom Manager. 2nd ed. 2006. (Illus.). 266p. pap. 27.95 *(978-1-55059-338-9(2))* Detselig Enterprises, Ltd. CAN. Dist: Temeron Bks., Inc.

Sagor, Richard. The Action Research Guidebook: A Four-Stage Process for Educators & School Teams. 2nd ed. 2010. (Illus.). 248p. pap. 38.95 *(978-1-4129-8128-6(X)*, B81286P) Corwin Pr.

—Collaborative Action Research for Professional Learning Communities. 2010. 176p. pap. 24.95 *(978-1-935249-61-0(4))*; lib. bdg. 54.95 *(978-1-935249-62-7(2))* Solution Tree Pr.

Samaras, Anastasia. Self-Study Teacher Research: Improving Your Practice Through Collaborative Inquiry. 2010. (Illus.). 344p. (C). pap. 48.00 *(978-1-4129-7207-9(8)*, B72079P) SAGE Pubns., Inc.

Shagoury, Ruth & Power, Brenda Miller. Living the Questions: A Guide for Teacher-Researchers. 2nd ed. 2011. pap. ***(978-1-57110-846-3(7))***; E-Book ***(978-1-57110-944-6(7))*** Stenhouse Pubs.

Shek, Daniel T.L., et al, eds. Positive Youth Development: Implementation of a Youth Program in a Chinese Context. 2010. (Health & Human Development Ser.). 129.00 *(978-1-61668-230-9(2))* Nova Science Pubs., Inc.

Sikes, Pat & Potts, Anthony, eds. Researching Education from the Inside: Investigating Institutions from Within. 2008. VIII, 192p. 45.95 *(978-0-415-43594-9(3))*; 150.00 *(978-0-415-43593-2(5))* Routledge.

Snyder, Alice. Research-Based Strategies for Literacy Instruction in Grades 3-5. rev. ed. 2010. (ENG.). 122p. pap. 40.96 *(978-0-7575-6231-0(0))* Kendall Hunt Publishing Co.

Spaulding, Dean T. & Falco, John. Action Research for School Leaders. 2011. (ENG.). 176p. (C). pap. 50.67 *(978-0-13-138104-9(0))*, Prentice Hall) Prentice Hall PTR.

Stringer, Ernie. Action Research in Education. 2nd ed. 2007. (ENG., Illus.). 256p. (C). per. 52.60 *(978-0-13-225518-9(9))*, Prentice Hall) Prentice Hall PTR.

Taylor, Claire, et al. Doing Action Research: A Guide for School Support Staff. 2006. (Supporting Learning Professionally Ser.). (Illus.). 112p. 69.00 *(978-1-4129-1277-8(6)*, B12776C); per. 28.00 *(978-1-4129-1278-5(4)*, B12776P) SAGE Pubns., Ltd. GBR. Dist: SAGE Pubns., Inc.

Tomal, Daniel R. Action Research for Educators. 2nd ed. 2010. (ENG., Illus.). 214p. 85.00 *(978-1-60709-646-7(3))*; pap. 35.00 *(978-1-60709-647-4(1))* Rowman & Littlefield Education.

Torres, Myriam & Reyes, Loui V. Research As Praxis: Democratizing Education Epistemologies. 2011. *(978-1-4331-1130-3(6))*; pap. *(978-1-4331-1129-7(2))* Lang, Peter GmbH, Europaischer Verlag der Wissenschaften.

Tunks, Jeanne & Neapolitan, Jane. A Framework for Research on Professional Development Schools. 2007. (ENG.). 108p. per. 26.50 *(978-0-7618-3822-7(8))* Univ. Pr. of America, Inc.

Wright, Robert J. Introduction to School Counseling. 2011. (Illus.). 664p. (C). pap. 78.00 *(978-1-4129-7871-2(8)*, B78712P) SAGE Pubns., Inc.

Yendol-Silva, Diane. The Reflective Educator's Guide to Classroom Research: Learning to Teach & Teaching to Learn Through Practitioner Inquiry. Dana, Nancy Fichtman & Yendol-Hoppey, Diane, eds. 2nd ed. 2008. (Illus.). 240p. pap. 36.95 *(978-1-4129-6657-3(4)*, B66566P) Corwin Pr.

Youth Development Staff. New Directions for Youth Development Issue 123: Youth in Participatory Action Research. Brown, Tara M. & Rodriguez, Louie F., eds. 2009. (J-B MHS Single Issue Mental Health Services Ser.: 97). (ENG.). 136p. pap. 29.00 *(978-0-470-57695-3(2)*, Jossey-Bass) Wiley, John & Sons, Inc.

Zeichner, Kenneth M. Teacher Education & the Struggle for Social Justice. 2009. 224p. (ENG.). 45.95 *(978-0-8058-5866-2(0))*; 145.00 *(978-0-8058-5865-5(2))* Erlbaum, Lawrence Assocs., Inc.

ACTION SONGS

see Games with Music

ACTIONS AND DEFENSES

see also Civil Procedure; Civil RICO Actions; Costs (Law); Defense (Civil Procedure); Equity; Evidence (Law); Extraordinary Remedies; Forms (Law); Frivolous Suits (Civil Procedure); Injunctions; Limitation of Actions; Matrimonial Actions; Pleading; Self-Defense (Law); Torts

ABA Publishing, creator. Criminal Antitrust Litigation Handbook. 2nd ed. 2006. (ENG., Illus.). 565p. per. 114.00 *(978-1-59031-369-5(0))* American Bar Assn.

Aspatore Books Staff, compiled by. Addressing a Client's Litigation Issues: Leading Lawyers on Educating Clients, Managing Expectations, & Developing a Case Strategy. 2008. (Inside the Minds Ser.). 184p. pap. 110.00 *(978-0-314-98966-4(2))* Aspatore Bks.

—Antitrust Litigation Best Practices: Leading Lawyers on Developing a Defense Strategy, Evaluating Settlement Opportunities, & Avoiding Common Client Mistakes. 2008. 192p. pap. 110.00 *(978-0-314-19475-6(4))* Aspatore Bks.

—Commercial Litigation Strategies: Leading Lawyers on Case Preparation, Settlement Opportunities, & Best Practices for Client Success. 2008. 192p. pap. 100.00 *(978-0-314-19476-3(2))* Aspatore Bks.

—Food, Beverage, & Drug Law Client Strategies: Leading Lawyers on Marketplace Considerations, Regulatory Compliance, & Dispute Resolution (Inside the Minds) 2008. 252p. pap. 135.00 *(978-0-314-99021-1(6))* Aspatore Bks.

—Government Contracts Law Client Strategies: Leading Lawyers on Counseling Clients During the Bidding Process, Negotiating Contracts, & Minimizing Litigation Liability. 2008. 344p. pap. 110.00 *(978-0-314-98987-1(0))* Aspatore Bks.

—Litigation Strategies for Government Contracts: Leading Lawyers on Exploring the Current State of Government Contracting, Developing an Effective Litigation Plan, & Collaborating with Clients & Officials (Inside the Minds) 2010. (Illus.). 348p. pap. 95.00 *(978-0-314-26357-0(X))* Aspatore Bks.

Aspatore Books Staff, compiled by. Representing Defendants in Personal Injury Cases: Leading Lawyers on Developing a Defense Strategy, Navigating the Discovery Process, & Litigating Disputes (Inside the Minds) 2011. 200p. pap. 85.00 *(978-0-314-27674-2(2))* Aspatore Bks.

Baker, Tom. The Medical Malpractice Myth. 2007. (ENG.). 222p. per. 14.00 *(978-0-226-03549-6(9))* Univ. of Chicago Pr.

Balboni, Jennifer M. Clergy Sexual Abuse Litigation: Survivors Seeking Justice. 2011. 170p. 59.95 *(978-1-935049-37-1(2))* FirstForumPress.

Ball, Carlos A. & Bronski, Michael. From the Closet to the Courtroom: Five LGBT Rights Lawsuits That Have Changed Our Nation. 2010. (ENG.). 296p. 27.95 *(978-0-8070-0078-6(7))* Beacon Pr.

Banking & Finance Litigation Strategies: Leading Lawyers on Working with Clients, Managing Documentation, & Negotiating Settlements (Inside the Minds) 2009. 120p. pap. 90.00 *(978-0-314-20736-4(8))* Aspatore Bks.

Barnes, John, et al, eds. The Politics of Legalism. 2013. (Law, Courts & Politics Ser.). (ENG.). 224p. (C). 130.00 *(978-0-415-63338-3(9))* Routledge.

Bartell, Laura B. Visualizing Secured Transactions. 2007. 40.00 *(978-1-4224-1551-1(1))* LexisNexis Matthew Bender.

Bensen, Eric E. & Myers, Rebecca K. Bensen & Myers on Litigation Management. 2009. pap. *(978-1-4224-2382-0(4))* LexisNexis Matthew Bender.

Bevans, Neal R. Civil Law & Litigation for Paralegals. 2007. (ENG., Illus.). 368p. (C). 54.67 *(978-0-07-352461-0(1)*, 0073524611) McGraw-Hill Higher Education.

Beveridge, Cathy. The Employment Litigation Handbook. 2nd ed. 2011. (ENG.). pap. 139.95 incl. cd-rom *(978-1-60442-912-1(7))* American Bar Assn.

Bhansali, Asim. Current Trends & Issues in Antitrust Litigation. 2010. (Illus.). 134p. pap. *(978-1-4024-1450-3(1))* Practising Law Institute.

Biggs, Keith. Lawyers Costs & Fees: Fees & Fixed Costs in Civil Actions. 17th rev. ed. 2011. 36p. pap. 35.00 *(978-1-84766-537-9(3)*, Bloomsbury Professional) Bloomsbury Publishing Plc GBR. Dist: International Specialized Bk. Services.

Biggs, Keith. Lawyers Costs & Fees: Fees & Fixed Costs in Civil Actions. 18th rev. ed. 2011. 44p. pap. 27.00 *(978-1-84766-942-1(5)*, Bloomsbury Professional) Bloomsbury Publishing Plc GBR. Dist: International Specialized Bk. Services.

Boston, John & Manville, Daniel E. Prisoners' Self Help Litigation Manual. 4th ed. 2010. (ENG., Illus.). 960p. pap. 39.95 *(978-0-19-537440-7(1))* Oxford Univ. Pr., Inc.

Brown, James J. & Fleishman, Wendy. Proving & Defending Damage Claims: A Fifty-State Guide. 2007. 26p. ring bd. 255.00 *(978-0-7355-6268-4(7)*, Aspen Pubs.) Wolters Kluwer Law & Business.

Cabrillo, Francisco & Fitzpatrick, Sean. The Economics of Courts & Litigation. 2008. (New Horizons in Law & Economics Ser.). (Illus.). 288p. (C). 125.00 *(978-1-84376-804-3(6))* Elgar, Edward Publishing, Inc.

Calif. Real Property Remedies & Damages: August 2006 Update, 2 vols. 2nd ed. 2006. 686p. ring bd. 126.00 *(978-0-7626-1151-5(0)*, RE-33445) Continuing Education of the Bar-California.

Campbell, Christian, Editor. International Product Liability [2007]. 2007. 566p. pap. 120.00 *(978-1-4357-0225-7(5))* Lulu Enterprises Inc.

Can We Sue Our Way to Prosperity? Litigation's Effect on America's Global Competitiveness: Hearing Before the Subcommittee on the Constitution of the Committee on the Judiciary, House of Representatives, One Hundred Twelfth Congress, First Session, May 24, 2011. 2011. (Illus.). iii, 55p. *(978-0-16-089061-1(6)*, 552-070-43093-8) United States Government Printing Office.

Carter, Samuel. The Infants Lawyer, or, the Law (Ancient & Modern) Relating to Infants. 2007. 431p. 135.00 *(978-1-58477-833-2(4))* Lawbook Exchange, Ltd., The.

Chappell, David. Building Contract Claims. 5th ed. 2011. (ENG.). 544p. 135.99 *(978-0-470-65738-6(3)*, Wiley) Wiley, John & Sons, Inc.

Cho, Kuk. ed. Litigation in Korea. 2010. (Elgar Korean Law Ser.). (Illus.). 256p. 130.00 *(978-1-84844-339-6(0))* Elgar, Edward Publishing, Inc.

Civil Causes of Action in Massachusetts. 2008. pap. 145.00 *(978-1-57589-477-5(7))* Massachusetts Continuing Legal Education, Inc.

Colombo, Rose. Fight Back Legal Abuse: How to Protect Yourself from Your Own Attorney. 2010. (ENG.). 296p. pap. 19.95 *(978-1-60037-709-9(2))* Morgan James Publishing.

Cook. Bankruptcy Litigation Manual 2010-2011e. 2010. ring bd. *(978-0-7355-9382-4(5)*, Aspen Pubs.) Wolters Kluwer Law & Business.

Cram101 Textbook Reviews. Outlines & Highlights for Civil Litigation in Comparative Context by Helen Hershkoff. 2011. 190p. pap. 30.95 *(978-1-61490-969-9(5))* Cram101 Inc.

Cram101 Textbook Reviews & Cram101 Textbook Reviews. Outlines & Highlights for Multi-Party Litigation: The Strategic Context by Wayne McIntosh, ISBN. 2011. 234p. pap. 31.95 *(978-1-61461-363-3(X))* Cram101 Inc.

Cumming, George. Civil Procedure in Eu Competition Cases Before the English & Dutch Courts. 2nd ed. 2009. xx, 395p. *(978-90-411-3192-8(2))* Kluwer Law International.

Cunningham-Hill, Susan & Elder, Karen. Civil Litigation Handbook 2008-2009. 2008. (Blackstone Legal Practice Course Guide Ser.). (Illus.). 496p. (C). pap. 89.95 *(978-0-19-953938-3(3)*, Blackstone Pr.) Oxford Univ. Pr. GBR. Dist: Oxford Univ. Pr., Inc.

—Civil Litigation Handbook 2010-11. 2010. (ENG.). 504p. pap. 80.00 *(978-0-19-958967-8(4))* Oxford Univ. Pr., Inc.

Cunningham-Hill, Susan & Elder, Karen. Civil Litigation Handbook 2011-12. 2011. (ENG.). 512p. pap. 70.00 *(978-0-19-960936-9(5))* Oxford Univ. Pr., Inc.

Dabbah, Maher M. & Hawk, Barry E. Anti-Cartel Enforcement Worldwide 3 Volume Set, 3 vols. 2009. (Antitrust & Competition Law Ser.). (ENG., Illus.). 3000p. 895.00 *(978-0-521-89721-1(1))* Cambridge Univ. Pr.

Dawson, Robert. How to Win (& Survive) a Lawsuit. 2006. pap. 15.95 *(978-0-9786107-4-6(1))* Arbor Bks.

Dickey, Jonathan C., et al. Securities Litigation: A Practitioner's Guide. 2006. (ENG.). 1144p. ring bd. 295.00 *(978-1-4024-0817-5(X))* Practising Law Institute.

Edgeworth, Dee R. Asset Forfeiture, Second Edition: Practice & Procedure in State & Federal Courts. 2nd ed. 2009. (ENG., Illus.). 325p. pap. 99.95 *(978-1-60442-063-0(4))* American Bar Assn.

Edwards, Harry T. & Elliott, Linda A. Federal Standards of Review: Review of District Court Decisions & Agency Actions. 2007. xix, 237p. pap. *(978-0-314-18809-0(6))* West.

Espinasse, Isaac. A Digest of the Law of Actions & Trials at Nisi Prius, 2 vols. 3rd ed. reprint ed. 276.00 *(978-1-56169-600-0(5))* Gaunt, Inc.

—A Digest of the Law of Actions & Trials at Nisi Prius. 2008. 340p. pap. 31.95 *(978-1-4367-2553-8(4))* Kessinger Publishing, LLC.

Eubanks, Sharon Y. & Glantz, Stanton A. Continuing Bad Acts. 2012. *(978-0-87553-017-8(6))* American Public Health Assn.

Examining the Federal Advisory Committee ACT: Current Issues & Developments: Hearing Before the Subcommittee on Information Policy, Census, & National Archives of the Committee on Oversight & Government Reform, House of Representatives, One Hundred Tenth Congress, Second Session, April 2, 2008. 2008. iii, 86p. *(978-0-16-082071-7(5)*, 552-070-38227-5) United States Government Printing Office.

False Claims ACT Correction ACT of 2007: Joint Hearing Before the Subcommittee on Courts, the Internet, & Intellectual Property & the Subcommittee on Commercial & Administrative Law of the Committee on the Judiciary, House of Representatives, One Hundred Tenth Congress, Second Session, on H.R. 4854, June 19, 2008. 2008. vi, 179p. *(978-0-16-082317-6(X)*, 552-070-38381-6) United States Government Printing Office.

Farhang, S. The Litigation State - Public Regulations & Private Law Suits in the United States. 2010. (Princeton Studies in American Politics: Historical, International, & Comparative Perspectives Ser.). (ENG., Illus.). 302p. (C). 75.00 *(978-0-691-14381-1(1))* Princeton Univ. Pr.

Farhang, Sean. The Litigation State - Public Regulations & Private Law Suits in the United States. 2010. (Princeton Studies in American Politics: Historical, International, & Comparative Perspectives Ser.). (ENG., Illus.). 302p. (C). pap. 27.95 *(978-0-691-14382-8(X))* Princeton Univ. Pr.

Felder, Barry G., et al. Information Technology Litigation. 2008. *(978-1-58852-146-0(X)*, Law Journal Pr.) Incisive Media.

Feldman, Joel, et al. The Pennsylvania Library of Personal Injury Forms. Shotsberger, Amanda, ed. 2009. (ENG.). 500p. pap. 179.00 *(978-1-57786-337-3(2))* Incisive Media.

Fischer, Markus. Die Verwaltungsprozessuale Klage Im Kraftfeld Zwischen Materiellem Recht und Prozessrecht. 2011. (GER.). 409p. 104.95 *(978-3-631-62028-1(4))* Lang, Peter GmbH, Europaischer Verlag der Wissenschaften DEU. Dist: Lang, Peter.

Fish, Barry, et al. The Family War: Winning the Inheritance Battle. 2006. 221p. per. *(978-0-9683513-8-3(7))* Continental Atlantic Pubns., Inc.

Flick, Martina. Organstreitverfahren vor den Landesverfassungsgerichten: Eine Politwissenschaftliche Untersuchung. 2011. (Europäische Hochschulschriften. Reihe 31: Politikwissenschaft Ser.). (GER.). 303p. pap. *(978-3-0343-0540-2(0))* Lang, Peter.

Florida Bar, Continuing Legal Education Staff, contrib. by. Business Litigation in Florida. 5th ed. 2007. 170.00 *(978-0-8205-8670-0(6))* Florida Bar Continuing Legal Education Pubns., The.

—Florida Real Property Litigation. (Illus.). 5th ed. 2009. *(978-1-4224-4110-7(5))* 6th ed. 2011. *(978-1-4224-9704-3(6))* Florida Bar Continuing Legal Education Pubns., The.

—Litigation under Florida Probate Code. 8th ed. 2011. (Illus.). *(978-1-4224-8538-5(2))* LEXIS Publishing.

—Litigation under Florida Probate Code. 7th ed. 2009. (Illus.). *(978-1-4224-5533-3(5))* LexisNexis Matthew Bender.

Friedman, Leon, ed. Brown V. Board: The Landmark Oral Argument before the Supreme Court. 2007. 347p. 30.00 *(978-1-4223-6630-1(8))* DIANE Publishing Co.

Fritzsche, Jörg. Unterlassungsanspruch und Unterlassungsklage. 2008. XXIX, 769p. pap. 153.69 *(978-3-540-67143-5(9)*, 3540671439) Springer.

Garza Barbosa, Roberto. International Copyright Law & Litigation. 2008. 284p. per. *(978-3-8364-3745-5(7))* VDM Verlag Dr. Mueller e.K.

Goldstein, Arnold S. So Sue Me! How to Protect Your Assets from the Lawsuit Explosion. 2006. xiv, 299p. 24.95 *(978-1-880539-63-7(2))* Garrett Publishing, Inc.

Grimm, Sebastian. Die Negative Konkurrentenklage Im Steuerrecht. 2011. (Finanz- und Steuerrecht in Deutschland und Europa Ser.). (GER.). 302p. 83.95 *(978-3-631-61583-6(3))* Lang, Peter GmbH, Europaischer Verlag der Wissenschaften DEU. Dist: Lang, Peter.

Hailing, Shan & Shan, Hailing. The Protection of Trade Secrets in China. 2008. xxiv, 323p. 231.00 *(978-90-411-2758-7(5))* Wolters Kluwer Law & Business.

Hanushek, Eric Alan, ed. Courting Failure: How School Finance Lawsuits Exploit Judges' Good Intentions & Harm Our Children. 2006. (Illus.). 366p. per. 15.00 *(978-0-8179-4782-8(5))* Cornell Univ. Pr.

—Courting Failure: How School Finance Lawsuits Exploit Judges' Good Intentions & Harm Our Children. 2006. (Hoover Inst Press Publication). (Illus.). 366p. 25.00 *(978-0-8179-4781-1(7))* Hoover Institution Pr.

Harder, Charles J., ed. Entertainment Litigation, 1 vol. 2011. (ENG., Illus.). 1104p. pap. 495.00 *(978-0-19-973343-9(0))* Oxford Univ. Pr., Inc.

Harper, Mark. International Trust & Divorce Litigation. 2007. (ENG.). 466p. pap. *(978-1-84661-018-9(4))* Jordan Publishing, Ltd.

Horowitz, Deborah. Letters of Credit & Demand Guarantees Defences to Payment. 2010. (ENG., Illus.). 350p. 337.50 *(978-0-19-958853-4(8))* Oxford Univ. Pr., Inc.

Humbach, John A. Whose Monet? An Introduction to the American Legal System. 2007. (Illus.). xvi, 232p. *(978-0-7355-7191-4(0)*, Aspen Pubs.) Wolters Kluwer Law & Business.

Intellectual Property Litigation Committee Section of Litigation. Model Jury Instructions: Copyright, Trademark & Trade Dress Litigation. 2009. (ENG.). pap. 120.00 incl. lp *(978-1-60442-102-6(9))* American Bar Assn.

Jordan, Hope M. & Willett, Henry. Leadership Bloopers & Blunders: How to Dodge Legal Minefields. 2009. (ENG.). 92p. 65.00 *(978-1-60709-133-2(X))* Rowman & Littlefield Education.

Jordan, Hope M. & Willett, Henry I., Jr. Leadership Bloopers & Blunders: How to Dodge Legal Minefields. 2009. (ENG.). 92p. pap. 21.95 *(978-1-60709-134-9(8))* Rowman & Littlefield Education.

Jorden. Erisa Litigation. 3rd ed. 2006. (Illus.). ring bd., instr.'s hndbk. ed. 299.00 *(978-0-7355-6311-7(X)*, Aspen Pubs.) Wolters Kluwer Law & Business.

Kaminsky, Alan. A Complete Guide to Premises Security Litigation. 3rd ed. 2007. *(978-1-59031-941-3(9))* American Bar Assn.

Kane, Siegrun D. Kane on Trademark Law: A Practitioner's Guide. 5th ed. 2007. (ENG.). 990p. ring bd. 345.00 *(978-1-4024-0958-5(3))* Practising Law Institute.

Karlsgodt, Paul G., ed. World Class Actions: A Guide to Group & Representative Actions around the Globe. 2012. (ENG.). 848p. pap. 225.00 *(978-0-19-973024-7(5))* Oxford Univ. Pr., Inc.

Kelly, Benjamin. Petitions, Litigation, & Social Control in Roman Egypt. 2011. (Oxford Studies in Ancient Documents Ser.). (ENG., Illus.). 448p. 150.00 *(978-0-19-959961-5(0))* Oxford Univ. Pr., Inc.

Kerger, Richard. The Client's Guide to Litigation. 2007. (ENG.). 160p. per. 24.95 *(978-1-4241-6888-0(0))* PublishAmerica, Inc.

Kessler, Daniel P. Regulation versus Litigation: Perspectives from Economics & Law. 2012. (National Bureau of Economic Research Conference Report). (ENG.). 344p. pap. 85.00 *(978-0-226-43220-5(3))* Univ. of Chicago Pr.

Kessler, Daniel P., ed. Regulation Versus Litigation: Perspectives from Economics & Law. 2011. (National Bureau of Economic Research Conference Report). (Illus.). 344p. 110.00 *(978-0-226-43218-2(1))* Univ. of Chicago Pr.

Ketterman, Travis J. Collecting Employer Contributions: The ERISA Litigation Guide. 2008. pap. 46.00 *(978-0-89154-647-4(2))* International Foundation of Employee Benefit Plans.

Kirkpatrick & Lockhart Preston Gates Ellis LLP, creator. The Securities Enforcement Manual: Tactics & Strategies. 2nd ed. 2007. (ENG.). 550p. per. 199.95 *(978-1-59031-729-7(7))* American Bar Assn.

LaFlura, Dennis & Towle, C. Griffith. Franchise Litigation Handbook. 2011. (ENG.). 320p. pap. 135.00 *(978-1-61632-028-7(1))* American Bar Assn.

Lang, John Franklin. The Executive's Guide to Depositions: A Practical Reference Explaining the Deposition Stage of Pre-Trial Discovery in Commercial Litigation. 2008. pap. *(978-0-314-98716-7(9))* Aspatore Bks.

Langsam, Henry I. & Romine, David E. Pennsylvania Causes of Action. 2011. xxiv, 253p. *(978-0-9839159-0-4(3))* Bisel, George T. Co.

Lawsuit Abuse Reduction ACT: Hearing Before the Subcommittee on the Constitution of the Committee on the Judiciary, House of Representatives, One Hundred Twelfth Congress, First Session, on H.R. 966, March 11, 2011. 2011. iii, 69p. *(978-0-16-088690-4(2)*, 552-070-42854-2) United States Government Printing Office.

LexisNexis Staff, compiled by. Mealey's Verdict Report: Patents 2005-2006. 2006. pap. 295.00 *(978-1-59579-423-9(9))* LexisNexis Mealey's.

Litigation by the Numbers - Substantive Companion. 2008. 210p. (C). spiral bd. *(978-0-9749361-2-3(X))* Lawdable Pr.

Maerowitz. Fundamentals of Litigation for Paralegals 7e W/ Cd. 7th ed. 2011. *(978-0-7355-9859-0(X)*, Aspen Pubs.) Wolters Kluwer Law & Business.

Maerowitz, Marlene A. & Mauet, Thomas A. Fundamentals of Litigation for Paralegals. 7th ed. 2012. (Illus.). xxx, 530p. *(978-0-7355-9870-6(3)*, Aspen Pubs.) Wolters Kluwer Law & Business.

Magnuson, Roger. Barracuda Bait: New & growing litigious risks to American Business. 2007. 16.95 *(978-0-9798498-0-0(2))* Dorsey & Whitney LLP.

Magratten, Brooks R. ERISA Survey of Federal Circuits. 2nd ed. 2007. *(978-1-59031-821-8(8))* American Bar Assn.

—Erisa Survey of the Federal Circuits, 2010. 2010th ed. 2011. (ENG.). 400p. pap. 139.95 *(978-1-60442-747-9(7))* American Bar Assn.

Magratten, Brooks R. & Allaire, Kristina H. ERISA Survey of Federal Circuits. 2011. *(978-1-61438-135-8(6))* American Bar Assn.

Malsberger, Brian M., et al. Tortious Interference in the Employment Context: A State-By-State Survey: Current Through December 2009. 3rd ed. 2010. *(978-1-57018-862-6(9))* BNA Bks.

Managing Construction Litigation: Leading Lawyers on Organizing Documentation, Developing a Case Strategy, & Overcoming Common Challenges (Inside the Minds) 2009. (Inside the Minds Ser.). 124p. pap. *(978-0-314-19947-8(0))* Aspatore Bks.

Mann, Charlie. How to Win Your Case in Small Claims Court Without a Lawyer. 2009. (ENG.). 288p. pap. 24.95 *(978-1-60138-305-8(1))* Atlantic Publishing Co.

Matthews, Paul. Trust & Estate Disputes: Practice & Procedure (Second Edition) 2011. 280p. *(978-1-85811-300-5(8))* EMIS Professional Publishing.

McClurg, Andrew, et al. Practical Global Tort Litigation: U. S., Germany & Argentina. 2007. pap. 27.00 *(978-1-59460-192-7(5))* Carolina Academic Pr.

Meister, Birte. Die Versagung der Akteneinsicht des Verletzten, § 406e Abs. 2 Stpo. 2011. (Bielefelder Rechtsstudien. Schriftenreihe für Gesetzgebungswissenschaft, Rechtstatsachenforschung und Rechtspolitik Ser.). (GER.). 222p. 69.95 *(978-3-631-61761-8(5))* Lang, Peter GmbH, Europaischer Verlag der Wissenschaften DEU. Dist: Lang, Peter.

Morriss, Andrew P., et al. Regulation by Litigation. 2008. (ENG.). 296p. 50.00 *(978-0-300-12002-8(8))* Yale Univ. Pr.

Orland, Leonard. A Final Accounting: Holocaust Survivors & Swiss Banks. 2010. 644p. 80.00 *(978-1-59460-769-1(9))* Carolina Academic Pr.

Puchniak, Dan W., et al. The Derivative Action in Asia: A Comparative & Functional Approach. 2012. (International Corporate Law & Financial Market Regulation Ser.). (ENG., Illus.). 476p. 130.00 *(978-1-107-01227-1(9))* Cambridge Univ. Pr.

Rees, Martin, ed. Cartel Enforcement Worldwide. 2010. x, 1082p. 330.00 *(978-1-907174-07-0(9))* Gaunt, Inc.

Reiche, Stefanie. Die prozessualen Folgen eines Betriebsübergangs nach § 613a BGB. 2009. (Schriften zum Verfahrensrecht Ser.). (GER.). 382p. 93.95 *(978-3-631-59429-2(1))* Lang, Peter GmbH, Europaischer Verlag der Wissenschaften DEU. Dist: Lang, Peter.

A

Reid, Paul H., Jr. The Edwin Mellen Press Versus Lingua Franca: A Case Study in the Law of Libel. 2007. (Illus.). 107p. (C). 89.95 (978-0-7734-5446-0(2)) Mellen, Edwin Pr., The.

Relis, Tamara. Perceptions in Litigation & Mediation: Lawyers, Defendants, Plaintiffs, & Gendered Parties. (ENG., Illus.). 304p. 2011. pap. 36.99 (978-0-521-28054-9(0)) 2009. 90.00 (978-0-521-51731-7(1)) Cambridge Univ. Pr.

Rosenne, Shabtai. Essays on International Law & Practice. 2007. 640p. (978-90-04-15536-7(8)) BRILL.

Saggerson, Alan. Travel Law & Litigation. 4th rev. ed. 2008. 768p. (978-1-85811-399-9(7)) EMIS Professional Publishing.

Salerno, Thomas J. Bankruptcy Litigation & Practice: Prac Gde 4e (2 Vol) W/Cd. 2007. ring bd. 450.00 (978-0-7355-6193-9(1), Aspen Pubs.) Wolters Kluwer Law & Business.

Sanchirico, Chris William, ed. Economics of Evidence, Procedure & Litigation. 2007. (Economic Approaches to Law Ser.). 1232p. (C). 590.00 (978-1-84542-939-3(7)) Elgar, Edward Publishing, Inc.

Schaffner, Joan E. Litigating Animal Law Disputes: A Complete Guide for Lawyers. 2009. (ENG., Illus.). 250p. pap. 129.95 (978-1-60442-001-2(4)) American Bar Assn.

Schapp, Hilke. Die Präklusion Von Gestaltungsrechten Nach § 767 Abs. 2 Zpo: Eine Kritische Untersuchung der Rechtsprechung Unter Besonderer Berücksichtigung der Rechtskraft und der Materiellen Rechtslage. 2011. (Schriften zum Verfahrensrecht Ser.). (GER.). 294p. 76.95 (978-3-631-60632-2(X)) Lang, Peter GmbH, Europaischer Verlag der Wissenschaften DEU. Dist: Lang, Peter.

Schilling, Alexander W. Passivlegitimation im gewerblichen Rechtsschutz und Urheberrecht: Die Bestimmung des Anspruchsgegners des urheber-, marken- und wettbewerbsrechtlichen Unterlassungsanspruchs anhand von Verkehrspflichten. 2010. (Schriften zum Handels- und Wirtschaftsrecht Ser.). (GER.). 152p. 50.95 (978-3-631-61034-3(3)) Lang, Peter GmbH, Europaischer Verlag der Wissenschaften DEU. Dist: Lang, Peter.

Schwartz, Martin A. Section 1983 Litigation: Fed Evid 4e V2. 2007. ring bd. 205.00 (978-0-7355-6774-0(3), Aspen Pubs.) Wolters Kluwer Law & Business.

Schwartz, Martin A. & Kirklin, John E. Section 1983 Litigation. 4th ed. 2011. (978-1-4548-0171-9(9)) Kluwer Law International.

Securities Litigation & the Economic Crisis: Leading Lawyers on Understanding the Current Legal Environment, Developing Litigation Best Practices, & Helping Clients Respond to a Changing Marketplace (Inside the Minds) 2009. 112p. pap. 100.00 (978-0-314-20738-8(4)) Aspatore Bks.

Shapo, Marshall. The Law of Products Liability. 2007. 3404p. pap. 145.00 (978-0-8080-1763-9(2)) Toolkit Media Group.

Shapo, Marshall S. An Injury Law Constitution. 2012. (ENG.). 310p. 85.00 (978-0-19-989636-3(4)) Oxford Univ. Pr., Inc.

Smith, Jessica. Emerging Issues in Confrontation Litigation: A Supplement to Crawford V. Washington: Confrontation One Year Later. 2007. 30p. 15.00 net. (978-1-56011-557-1(2)) Schl. of Government.

Statsky, William P. Torts: Personal Injury Litigation. 5th ed. 2010. (ENG., Illus.). 800p. (C). 171.95 (978-1-4018-7962-4(4)) Delmar Cengage Learning.

Thomas, Stephanie R. The Proactive Employer: Selected Readings on Compliance, Employment Discrimination & Litigation Avoidance. 2010. 261p. pap. 22.95 (978-0-557-59393-4(X)) Lulu Enterprises Inc.

Trial Lawyers Inc Illinois: A Report on the Lawsuit Industry in Illinois 2006. 2006. per. 5.00 net. (978-0-9726334-4-4(8)) Manhattan Institute.

Understanding Fair Labor Standards Act Violations: Leading Lawyers on Examining FLSA Trends & Developing Defense Strategies for Collective & Class Actions (Inside the Minds) 2010. 260p. pap. 95.00 (978-0-314-26246-2(6)) Aspatore Bks.

Verkerk, Remme. Fact-Finding in Civil Litigation: A Comparative Perspective. 2010. 464p. pap. 121.95 (978-94-000-0074-2(X)) Intersentia Uitgevers N.V. BEL. Dist: International Specialized Bk. Services.

Weismann, Miriam F. Parallel Proceedings: Navigating Multiple Case Litigation. 2012. (ENG.). 187p. pap. 89.95 (978-1-61438-107-5(0)) American Bar Assn.

Williamson, Deborah D., et al. Bankruptcy Litigation Manual: What Civil Litigators Need to Know. 2007. 100p. per. 25.00 (978-0-9792742-4-4(9)) American Bankruptcy Institute.

Wright, Bradley C. Drafting Patents for Litigation & Licensing. 2008. (978-1-57018-739-1(8)) BNA Bks.

Wu, Stephen S. A Guide to HIPAA Security & the Law. 2007. (ENG., Illus.). 372p. pap. 79.95 (978-1-59031-748-8(3)) American Bar Assn.

Yamin, Alicia Ely, et al. Litigating Health Rights: Can Courts Bring More Justice to Health? 2011. (Human Rights Program Ser.). (ENG., Illus.). 446p. pap. 24.95 (978-0-9796395-5-5(7)) Human Rights Program at Harvard Law School.

ACTIUM, BATTLE OF, 31 B.C.

Lange, Carsten Hjort. Res Publica Constituta: Actium, Apollo, & the Accomplishment of the Triumviral Assignment. 2009. (Impact of Empire Ser.). (Illus.). 250p. (978-90-04-17501-3(6)) BRILL.

Sheppard, Si. Actium 31 BC: Downfall of Antony & Cleopatra. 2009. (Campaign Ser.). (ENG., Illus.). 96p. pap. 19.95 (978-1-84603-405-3(1)) Osprey Publishing, Ltd. GBR. Dist: Random Hse., Inc.

ACTIVATED CARBON

see Carbon, Activated

ACTIVATION ANALYSIS, NUCLEAR

see Nuclear Activation Analysis

ACTIVE CHRONIC HEPATITIS

see Chronic Active Hepatitis

ACTIVE LEARNING

Here are entered works on any learning or teaching situation which is characterized by active participation on the part of the learner, as opposed to passive learning from listening or observation.

see also Experiential Learning

Abrams, Eleanor & Southerland, Sherry, eds. Inquiry in the Classroom: Realities & Opportunities (HC) 2007. (Contemporary Research in Education Ser.). 316p. 73.99 (978-1-59311-835-8(X)) Information Age Publishing, Inc.

—Inquiry in the Classroom: Realities & Opportunities (PB) 2007. (Contemporary Research in Education Ser.). 316p. per. 39.99 (978-1-59311-834-1(1)) Information Age Publishing, Inc.

Adams, Dennis M. Bringing Science & Mathematics to Life for All Learners. 2008. 96.00 (978-981-279-163-4(9)) World Scientific Publishing Co., Inc.

Adams, Dennis M. & Hamm, Mary. Bringing Science & Mathematics to Life for All Learners. 2008. (Illus.). 265p. pap. 60.00 (978-981-279-164-1(7)) World Scientific Publishing Co., Inc.

Allison, Sandra Boyd & James, Abigail Norfleet. Active Lessons for Active Brains: Teaching the Experiential Learner. McKenzie, Caitlin Z., ed. 2011. (Illus.). 248p. pap. 36.95 (978-1-4129-8665-6(6), B86656P) Corwin Pr.

Aubusson, Peter. Action Learning in Schools: Reframing Teacher Professional Learning & Development. 2009. (ENG., Illus.). 160p. 130.00 (978-0-415-47514-3(7)) Routledge.

—Action Learning in Schools: Reframing Teachers' Professional Learning & Development. 2008. (Illus.). 160p. 37.95 (978-0-415-47515-0(5)) Routledge.

Azer, Samy. Navigating Problem Based Learning. 2007. (ENG.). 200p. (C). pap. 32.95 (978-0-7295-3827-5(3), Churchill Livingstone) Elsevier - Health Sciences Div.

Baldwin, Amy, et al. NSSI Engaging Activities for Active Learning. 2009. (Engaging Activities For Ser.). (ENG.). 50p. (C). pap. 21.20 (978-0-13-705031-4(3), Prentice Hall) Prentice Hall PTR.

Barell, John. Problem-Based Learning: An Inquiry Approach. 2nd rev. ed. 2006. (Illus.). 192p. pap. 36.95 (978-1-4129-5004-6(X), B50031P) Corwin Pr.

Barell, John, ed. Why Are School Buses Always Yellow? Teaching for Inquiry, Prek-5. 2007. (Illus.). 216p. per. 36.95 (978-1-4129-5733-5(8), B5732XP) Corwin Pr.

Barell, John F. Problem-Based Learning: An Inquiry Approach. 2nd rev. ed. 2006. (Illus.). 192p. 80.95 (978-1-4129-5003-9(1), B50031C) Corwin Pr.

Barnier, Carol. The Big What Now Book of Learning Styles: A Fresh & Demystifying Approach. 2009. (Illus.). 192p. pap. 19.99 (978-1-932096-60-6(4)) Emerald Bks.

Barreca, Regina. Vital Ideas: Sex. 2011. (978-1-933147-81-9(4)) Great Bks. Foundation.

Barton, Angela Calabrese, et al. Empowering Science & Mathematics Education in Urban Communities. 2012. (ENG., Illus.). 224p. 75.00 (978-0-226-03797-4(5)); pap. 25.00 (978-0-226-03798-1(3)) Univ. of Chicago Pr.

Bath, Caroline. Learning to Belong: Young Children's Participation at School. 2009. (Illus.). 116p. 140.00 (978-0-415-48366-7(2)) Routledge.

Batsleer, Janet R. Informal Learning in Youth Work. 2008. 208p. (C). pap. 51.00 (978-1-4129-4619-3(0), B46182P) SAGE Pubns., Ltd. GBR. Dist: SAGE Pubns., Inc.

—Informal Learning in Youth Work. 2008. 208p. (C). 108.00 (978-1-4129-4618-6(2), B46182C) SAGE Pubns., Ltd. GBR. Dist: SAGE Pubns., Inc.

Beach, Richard, et al. Literacy Tools in the Classroom: Teaching Through Critical Inquiry, Grades 5-12. 2010. (Language & Literacy Ser.). (ENG., Illus.). 176p. pap. 24.95 (978-0-8077-5056-8(5)); 24.95 (978-0-8077-5057-5(3)) Teachers College Pr., Teachers College, Columbia Univ.

Bean, John C. Engaging Ideas: The Professor's Guide to Integrating Writing, Critical Thinking, & Active Learning in the Classroom. 2nd ed. 2011. (ENG., Illus.). 384p. pap. 40.00 (978-0-470-53290-4(4), Jossey-Bass) Wiley, John & Sons, Inc.

Beard, Colin. The Experiential Learning Toolkit: Blending Practice with Concepts. 2010. (ENG., Illus.). 288p. pap. 80.00 (978-0-7494-5078-6(9)) Kogan Page, Ltd. GBR. Dist: Ingram Pub. Services.

Becker, Shawnj. Object Lessons That Speak Louder Than Words: 70 Action-Based Activities That Teach. 2008. (ENG.). 88p. 16.95 (978-1-930572-53-9(0)) Educational Media Corp.

Bellanca, James A. 200+ Active Learning Strategies & Projects for Engaging Students' Multiple Intelligences. 2nd ed. 2008. (Illus.). 368p. pap. 44.95 (978-1-4129-6885-0(2), B68843P) Corwin Pr.

Berke, Kai-Lee, et al. The Creative Curriculum for Preschool Teaching Guide Featuring the Buildings Study. 2010. (978-1-60617-384-8(7)) Teaching Strategies, Inc.

Billingsley, Joanne M. Aim to Grow Your Brain. 2009. 152p. pap. 24.00 (978-1-60844-114-3(8)) Dog Ear Publishing, LLC.

Blanchard, John. Teaching, Learning & Assessment. 2009. (ENG.). 208p. 127.00 (978-0-335-23380-9(5), 0335233805); pap. 43.00 (978-0-335-23379-3(1), 0335233791, Open University Pr.) McGraw-Hill Education GBR. Dist: McGraw-Hill Cos., The.

Blaylock, Janet. My Family Activity Book. 2009. 44p. pap. 10.50 (978-0-557-04016-2(7)) Lulu Enterprises Inc.

Blindenbacher, Raoul & Nashat, Bidjan. The Black Box of Governmental Learning: The Learning Spiral — a Concept to Organize Learning in Governments. 2010. (ENG.). 192p. pap. 25.00 (978-0-8213-8453-4(8), 9780821384534) World Bank Pubns.

Boozer, Wesley. A Writing Teacher Learns from His Students. 2009. 204p. pap. (978-3-639-17056-6(3)) VDM Verlag Dr. Mueller e.K.

Boshyk, Yury & Dilworth, Robert, eds. Action Learning: History & Evolution. 2010. (ENG., Illus.). 300p. 105.00 (978-0-230-57640-7(0)) Palgrave Macmillan.

—Action Learning & Its Applications. 2010. (ENG., Illus.). 300p. 100.00 (978-0-230-57641-4(9)) Palgrave Macmillan.

Boufis, Christina. Vital Ideas: Work. 2011. (978-1-933147-78-9(4)) Great Bks. Foundation.

Boulton-Lewis, Gillian & Tam, Maureen, eds. Active Ageing, Active Learning: Issues & Challenges. 2011. (Education in the Asia-Pacific Region: Issues, Concerns & Prospects Ser.). (ENG., Illus.). xii, 180p. 139.00 (978-94-007-2110-4(2), 9400721102) Springer.

Bridges, Susan, et al, eds. Problem-Based Learning in Clinical Education: The Next Generation. 2012. (Innovation & Change in Professional Education Ser.). (ENG., Illus.). xxv, 255p. 139.00 (978-94-007-2514-0(0), 9400725140) Springer.

Brown, Steven & Smith, Dorolyn. Active Listening 1 Student's Book with Self-study Audio CD. 2nd rev. ed. 2006. (ENG., Illus.). 112p. pap. 26.25 incl. audio compact disk (978-0-521-67813-1(7)) Cambridge Univ. Pr.

Brutlag, Dan. Active Algebra: Strategies & Lessons for Successfully Teaching Linear Relationships, Grades 7-10. 2009. 166p. pap. 36.95 (978-1-935099-05-5(1)) Math Solutions.

Bucknall, Sue. Children as Researchers in Primary Schools: Choice, Voice & Participation. 2012. (ENG., Illus.). 232p. 155.00 (978-0-415-61966-0(1)); pap. 35.95 (978-0-415-61970-7(X)) Routledge.

Buehl, Doug. Classroom Strategies for Interactive Learning. 3rd ed. 2008. (ENG.). 232p. pap. 27.95 (978-0-87207-686-0(5)) International Reading Assn.

Burke, Heather & Smith, Claire, eds. Archaeology to Delight & Instruct: Active Learning in the University Classroom. 2007. (One World Archaeology Ser.). (ENG., Illus.). 288p. 94.00 (978-1-59874-256-5(6)); pap. 34.95 (978-1-59874-257-2(4)) Left Coast Pr., Inc.

Butler, Joy & Griffin, Linda, eds. More Teaching Games for Understanding. 2010. (ENG., Illus.). 296p. (gr. k-12). pap. 29.00 (978-0-7360-8334-8(0)) Human Kinetics Pubs.

Cain, James, et al. A Teachable Moment: A Facilitator's Guide to Activities for Processing Debriefing Reviewing & Reflection. rev. ed. 2012. (ENG.). 288p. pap. 39.27 (978-0-7575-1782-2(X), 075751782X) Kendall Hunt Publishing Co.

Campbell, Anne & Groundwater-Smith, Susan. Connecting Inquiry & Professional Learning in Education: International Perspectives & Practical Solutions. Campbell, Anne & Groundwater-smith, Susan, eds. 2009. (ENG., Illus.). 224p. 130.00 (978-0-415-47812-0(X)) Routledge.

Cernusca, Dan. Implementation of an Online Learning Environment in a Large Classroom. 2008. 172p. pap. (978-3-8364-3905-3(0)) VDM Verlag Dr. Mueller e.K.

Chalberg, Amie R. Reaching Young Children. 2011. 152p. pap. 23.95 (978-1-931061-40-7(8)) Jalmar Pr.

Chang, Maiga, et al, eds. Edutainment Technologies. Educational Games & Virtual Reality/Augmented Reality Applications: 6th International Conference on E-learning & Games, Edutainment 2011, Taipei, Taiwan, September 7-9, 2011, Proceedings. 2011. (Lecture Notes in Computer Science / Information Systems & Applications, incl. Internet/Web, & HCI Ser.). (ENG., Illus.). xxiv, 560p. pap. 107.00 (978-3-642-23455-2(0), 3642234550) Springer.

Chenoweth, Lillian & Bold, Mary. Reflections: Preparing for Your Practicum & Internship. 2007. (ENG., Illus.). 320p. (C). pap. 45.95 (978-1-4180-4083-3(5)) Delmar Cengage Learning.

Cheung, Chung Kwan Ackie. The Impact of Experiential Education on the Personal & Spiritual Development of Adolescents in Hong Kong: A Mixed-Method Study in the Secondary School Context. 2012. (ENG., Illus.). 400p. pap. 69.95 (978-3-531-18575-0(6), 3531185756) VS Verlag fur Sozialwissenschaften GmbH DEU. Dist: Springer.

Cheyne, Michele, et al. What Successful Science Teachers Do: 75 Research-Based Strategies. 2010. (Illus.). 272p. pap. 38.95 (978-1-4129-7234-5(5), B72338P) Corwin Pr.

Clarke, Shirley. Active Learning Through Formative Assessment. 2011. (ENG., Illus.). 184p. pap. 62.50 (978-0-340-97445-2(1)) Trans-Atlantic Pubns., Inc.

Claxton, Nancy. Teacher's Manual for Teaching & Learning Strategies for the Thinking Classroom: Melding Reading & Writing for Critical Thinking & Deliberative Methodology. 2007. 86p. pap. 19.95 (978-1-932716-28-3(9)) International Debate Education Assn.

Clouston, Teena, et al, eds. Problem Based Learning in Health & Social Care. 2010. (ENG., Illus.). 232p. pap. 72.99 (978-1-4051-8056-6(0), Wiley-Blackwell) Wiley, John & Sons, Inc.

Coffman, Teresa. Engaging Students Through Inquiry: Oriented Learning & Technology. 2009. (ENG.). 160p. 85.00 (978-1-60709-069-4(4)) Rowman & Littlefield Education.

—Engaging Students Through Inquiry-Oriented Learning & Technology. 2009. (ENG.). 160p. pap. 31.95 (978-1-60709-070-0(8)) Rowman & Littlefield Education.

Commodore, Carol, et al. Assessment Balance & Quality: An Action Guide for School Leaders. 3rd ed. 2010. (Assessment Training Institute, Inc Ser.). (ENG.). 240p. (C). pap. 38.99 (978-0-13-254878-6(X)) Allyn & Bacon, Inc.

Cooper, Paul W., et al. From Inclusion to Engagement: Helping Students Engage with Schooling Through Policy & Practice. 2011. (ENG., Illus.). 258p. pap. 45.00 (978-0-470-01946-7(8), Wiley) Wiley, John & Sons, Inc.

Coots, Jennifer J. & Stout, Kristin. Critical Reflections about Students with Special Needs: Stories from the Classroom. 2006. (ENG.). 128p. (C). pap. 31.80 (978-0-205-49606-8(7)) Allyn & Bacon, Inc.

Coppin, Charles, et al. The Moore Method: A Pathway to Learner-Centered Instruction. 2009. 245p. (C). pap. 57.50 net. (978-0-88385-185-2(7)) Mathematical Assn. of America.

Cordeiro, Paula G. & Cunningham, William G. Educational Leadership: A Bridge to Improved Practice, Student Value Edition. 5th ed. 2012. (ENG.). 456p. (C). ring bd. 97.00 (978-0-13-301483-9(5), Prentice Hall) Prentice Hall PTR.

Cornelius-White, Jeffrey H. D. & Harbaugh, Adam P. Learner-Centered Instruction: Building Relationships for Student Success. 2009. (Illus.). 240p. (C). pap. 55.00 (978-1-4129-5498-3(3), B54975P) SAGE Pubns., Inc.

Cram101 Textbook Reviews. Outlines & Highlights for Learning, Training, & Development in Organizations by Steve W J Kozlowski. 2011. 114p. pap. 28.95 (978-1-4672-6631-4(0)) Cram101 Inc.

Cram101 Textbook Reviews & Cram101 Textbook Reviews. Outlines & Highlights for Making Connections in Elementary & Middle School Social Studies by Andrew P Johnson, Isbn: 9781412968560 1412968569. 2011. 298p. pap. 32.95 (978-1-61654-114-9(8)) Cram101 Inc.

Crawford, Linda. The Advisory Book: Building a Community of Learners Grades 5-9. 2008. (Illus.). 296p. pap. 24.95 (978-0-938541-12-7(9)) Origins Program.

Crawford, Linda, et al. The Advisory Book Professional Development Guide. 2011. (Illus.). 80p. pap. 10.95 (978-0-938541-14-1(5)) Origins Program.

Daniels, Harvey, et al. Best Practice, Fourth Edition: Bringing Standards to Life in America's Classrooms. 4th ed. 2012. 304p. pap. 36.88 (978-0-325-04354-8(X), E04354) Heinemann.

de Graaf, Erik, et al. Research & Practice of Active Learning in Engineering Education. 2007. (ENG.). 224p. per. (978-90-8555-091-4(2), Leiden Univ. Pr.) Amsterdam Univ. Pr.

De Graaff, Erik & Kolmos, Anette, eds. Management of Change. 2009. 232p. (978-90-8790-014-4(7)) Sense Pubs.

de Silva, Mohan. Clinical Surgery Made Easy: A Companion to Problem-Based Learning. 2008. (Illus.). 274p. pap. 90.00 (978-1-903378-65-6(6)) TFM Publishing Ltd. GBR. Dist: JAMCO Distribution.

Dixon, Christopher. Transfer of Learning to the Organisation. 2011. 544p. pap. (978-3-8433-8444-5(4)) Lambert Academic Publishing.

Dorling Kindersley Publishing Staff, et al. Effective College Learning. 2nd ed. 2010. (ENG., Illus.). 368p. (C). pap. 72.00 (978-0-205-75013-9(3)) Longman Publishing Group.

Dowling, Jan Lavenger & Mitchell, Terri. I Belong: Active Learning for Children with Special Needs. 2007. (978-1-57379-322-3(1)) High/Scope Pr.

Doyle, Terry. Learner Centered Teaching: Putting the Research into Practice. 2011. 224p. 75.00 (978-1-57922-742-5(2)); pap. 24.95 (978-1-57922-743-2(0)) Stylus Publishing, LLC.

Du, Xiangyun, et al, eds. Research on Pbl Practice in Engineering Education. 2009. 246p. (978-90-8790-931-4(4)); pap. (978-90-8790-930-7(6)) Sense Pubs.

Egan, Kieran. Learning in Depth: A Simple Innovation That Can Transform Schooling. 2011. (Illus.). 232p. 25.00 (978-0-226-19043-3(9)) Univ. of Chicago Pr.

Epstein, Ann S. Essentials of Active Learning in Preschool: Getting to Know the High/Scope Curriculum. 2006. pap. (978-1-57379-300-1(0)) High/Scope Pr.

Falk, Beverly. Teaching the Way Children Learn. 2008. (On school reform Ser.). (ENG.). 208p. 54.00 (978-0-8077-4929-6(X)); pap. 23.95 (978-0-8077-4928-9(1)) Teachers College Pr., Teachers College, Columbia Univ.

Falk, John H., et al. Free-Choice Learning & the Environment. 2009. (Learning Innovations Ser.). (ENG., Illus.). 224p. pap. 29.95 (978-0-7591-1123-3(5)); 75.00 (978-0-7591-1122-6(7)) Rowman & Littlefield Publishers, Inc.

Feber, Jane. Student Engagement Is FUNdamental: Building a Learning Community with Hands-on Activities. 2011. (ENG.). pap. 19.95 (978-1-936700-47-9(6)) Maupin Hse. Publishing.

Fennessey, Sharon & Fennessey, Sharon M. Language Arts Lessons for Active Learning, Grades 3-8. 2008. (Illus.). 144p. pap. 27.50 (978-0-325-00984-1(8), E00984) Heinemann.

Fisher, Douglas & Frey, Nancy. Better Learning Through Structured Teaching: A Framework for the Gradual Release of Responsibility. 2008. (Illus.). 146p. per. 0.00 (978-1-4166-0635-2(1)) Assn. for Supervision & Curriculum Development.

Fitzler, Joe. Implementing Systems Engineering Techniques into Health Care - an Investigation into Using Problem Based Learning in Medical Schools to Teach Systems. 2008. 64p. pap. (978-3-8364-3782-0(1)) VDM Verlag Dr. Mueller e.K.

Flynn, Rosalind M. Dramatizing the Content with Curriculum-Based Readers Theatre, Grades 6-12. 2007. 170p. (YA). (gr. 6-12). 18.95 (978-0-87207-615-0(6)) International Reading Assn.

Forsten, Char & Hollas, Betty. Question Answer Relationships: A Simple Taxonomy of Questions. 2008. (ENG.). 112p. (C). (gr. 3-8). pap. 21.50 (978-1-934026-08-3(5), Crystal Springs Bks.) Staff Development for Educators.

Fowler, Susan. Multisensory Environments: A Guide to Controlled Sensory Experiences. 2007. (ENG., Illus.). 256p. pap. (978-1-84310-462-9(8)) Kingsley, Jessica Ltd.

—Sensory Stimulation: Sensory-Focused Activities for People with Physical & Multiple Disabilities. 2006. (ENG., Illus.). 176p. per. (978-1-84310-455-1(5)) Kingsley, Jessica Ltd.

Francis, Russell. Decentring & the Traditional University. 2010. (ENG., Illus.). 176p. (C). 120.00 *(978-0-415-55053-6(X))* Routledge.

Frey, Nancy, et al. Productive Group Work: How to Engage Students, Build Teamwork, & Promote Understanding. 2009. pap. 21.95 *(978-1-4166-0883-7(4))* Assn. for Supervision & Curriculum Development.

Gess-Newsome, Julie, et al, eds. Reforming Secondary Science Instruction. 2009. (ENG.). 127p. pap. 24.95 *(978-1-935155-03-4(2))* National Science Teachers Assn.

Glines, Don. Declaring War Against Schooling: Personalizing Learning Now. 2011. (ENG.). 206p. (gr. 17). 70.00 ***(978-1-61048-663-7(3))***; pap. 29.95 ***(978-1-61048-664-4(1))*** Rowman & Littlefield Education.

Glines, Don E. Declaring War Against Schooling: Personalizing Learning Now. 2012. E-Book ***(978-1-61048-665-1(X))*** Rowman & Littlefield Education.

Goeke, Jennifer L. Explicit Instruction: Strategies for Meaningful Direct Teaching. 2008. (ENG., Illus.). 144p. (C). pap. 22.99 *(978-0-205-53328-2(0))* Allyn & Bacon, Inc.

Grasberg, Lynn & Oldenburg, Gina. Great Group Skits: 50 Character-Building Scenarios for Teens. 2009. (ENG., Illus.). 172p. pap. 16.95 *(978-1-57482-265-6(9)*, 1304119) Search Institute.

Great Books Foundation (U.S.) Staff, contrib. by. Great Books Roundtable Planner: Using Shared Inquiry with Your Students. 2010. *(978-1-933147-56-7(3))*; *(978-1-933147-57-4(1))* Great Bks. Foundation.

Green, Linda Schwartz, et al. 40 Active Learning Strategies for the Inclusive Classroom. 2011. (Illus.). 176p. pap. 33.95 *(978-1-4129-8170-5(0)*, B81705P) Corwin Pr.

Habel, John & Bloom, Lisa. Constructing Positive Classrooms & Schools, Strategies for Promoting Learning, Responsibility, & Community. 2008. (ENG.). 442p. (C). pap. 62.67 *(978-0-13-088833-9(9)*, Prentice Hall) Prentice Hall PTR.

Haigh, Alan. Art of Creative Teaching: Primary Science:Big Ideas, Simple Rules. 2010. (Illus.). 184p. pap. 44.50 *(978-1-4082-2802-9(5))* Pearson Education, Ltd. GBR. Dist: Trans-Atlantic Pubns., Inc.

Hallinger, Philip & Bridges, Edwin M. A Problem-Based Approach for Management Education: Preparing Managers for Action. 2007. (ENG., Illus.). xvii, 320p. 219.00 *(978-1-4020-5755-7(5)*, 1402057555) Springer.

Hardaway, Karla. Active English: Learning Strategies That Will Have Your Students Asking, Is That the Bell Already? 2010. (ENG.). 144p. pap. 21.95 *(978-1-877673-96-2(X))* Cottonwood Pr., Inc.

Hazzan, Orit, et al. Guide to Teaching Computer Science: An Activity-Based Approach. 2011. (ENG., Illus.). xxvi, 260p. 89.95 *(978-0-85729-442-5(3)*, 0857294423) Springer.

Healey, Mick, et al, eds. Active Learning & Student Engagement: International Perspectives & Practices in Geography in Higher Education. 2012. (ENG.). 240p. (C). pap. 42.95 ***(978-0-415-63398-7(2))*** Routledge.

—Active Learning & Student Engagement: International Perspectives & Practices in Geography in Higher Education. 2010. 232p. 125.00 *(978-0-415-56492-2(1)*, Routledge) Taylor & Francis Group GBR. Dist: Taylor & Francis Group.

Heard, Georgia & McDonough, Jennifer. A Place for Wonder: Reading & Writing Nonfiction in the Primary Grades. 2009. (ENG.). 216p. (C). pap. 20.00 *(978-1-57110-432-8(1))* Stenhouse Pubs.

Heller, Dana A. & Pamplin, Claire. Vital Ideas: Money. 2011. ***(978-1-933147-80-2(6))*** Great Bks. Foundation.

Henning, John. The Art of Discussion-Based Teaching: Opening up Conversation in the Classroom. 2007. (ENG., Illus.). 240p. per. 33.95 *(978-0-415-95633-8(1))* Routledge.

Herrell, Adrienne L. & Jordan, Michael. 35 Classroom Management Strategies: Promoting Learning & Building Community. 2006. (50 Teaching Strategies Ser.). (ENG., Illus.). 256p. (C). spiral bd. 40.00 *(978-0-13-099076-1(0)*, Prentice Hall) Prentice Hall PTR.

Hewitt, Kimberly Kappler & Weckstein, Daniel J. Differentiation Is an Expectation: A School Leader's Guide to Building a Culture of Differentiation. 2010. 34.95 *(978-1-59667-164-5(5))* Eye On Education, Inc.

Himmele, Pérsida & Himmele, William. Total Participation Techniques: Making Every Student an Active Learner. 2011. 133p. pap. 24.95 *(978-1-4166-1294-0(7))* Assn. for Supervision & Curriculum Development.

Hohmann, Mary, et al. Educating Young Children: Active Learning Practices for Preschool & Child Care Programs. 3rd ed. 2008. *(978-1-57379-354-4(X))* High/Scope Pr.

Holschuh, Jodi Patrick & Nist-Olejnik, Sherrie L. Effective College Learning, Books a la Carte Edition. 2nd ed. 2011. (ENG.). 368p. (C). ring bd. 47.33 ***(978-0-205-07441-9(3))*** Longman Publishing Group.

Holt, Nicky. Bringing the High Scope Approach to Your Early Years Practice. 2nd rev. ed. 2010. (Bringing ... to your Early Years Practice Ser.). (ENG., Illus.). 136p. 115.00 *(978-0-415-56499-1(9))*; 24.95 *(978-0-415-56500-4(6))* Taylor & Francis Group GBR. (Routledge). Dist: Taylor & Francis Group.

Houff, Suzanne G. Classroom Facilitator: Special Issue Questions. 2010. (ENG., Illus.). 210p. 95.00 *(978-1-60709-491-3(6))* Rowman & Littlefield Education.

—The Classroom Facilitator: Special Issue Questions. 2010. (ENG., Illus.). 210p. pap. 39.95 *(978-1-60709-492-0(4))* Rowman & Littlefield Education.

Hughes, Marcia & Terrell, James Bradford. Emotional Intelligence in Action: Training & Coaching Activities for Leaders, Managers, & Teams. 2nd ed. 2012. (ENG., Illus.). 512p. pap., spiral bd. 50.00 ***(978-1-118-12804-6(4)***, Pfeiffer) Wiley, John & Sons, Inc.

Hunter, Alyce. Integrating Language Arts & Social Studies: 25 Strategies for K-8 Inquiry-Based Learning. Melber, Leah M., ed. 2009. 208p. (C). pap. 36.00 *(978-1-4129-7110-2(1)*, B71102P) SAGE Pubns., Inc.

Hutchinson, Steve & Lawrence, Helen. Playing with Purpose: How Experiential Learning Can Be More Than a Game. 2011. (Illus.). 216p. pap. 49.95 *(978-1-4094-0805-5(1)*, Gower Publishing Co., Ltd.) Ashgate Publishing, Ltd. GBR. Dist: Ashgate Publishing Co.

Hymer, Barry, et al. Gifts, Talents & Education: A Living Theory Approach. 2009. (ENG., Illus.). 194p. 90.00 *(978-0-470-72539-9(7)*, Wiley) Wiley, John & Sons, Inc.

Inquiry in Education Set V12 P, 2 vols. 2007. (ENG.). pap. 53.95 *(978-0-8058-6388-8(5))* Routledge.

Izuegbu, Vincent Emeka. Students As Designers of Their Own Life Curricula: The Reconstruction of Experience in Education. 2011. *(978-1-61735-349-9(3))*; pap. *(978-1-61735-348-2(5))*; E-Book *(978-1-61735-350-5(7))* Information Age Publishing, Inc.

Jarvela, Sanna. Affective Learning Together. 2012. (ENG.). 256p. (C). 155.00 ***(978-0-415-69687-6(9))***; pap. 51.95 ***(978-0-415-69688-3(7))*** Routledge.

Jeffrey, Bob & Woods, Peter. Creative Learning in the Primary School. 2009. (Illus.). (ENG.). 192p. (C). pap. 42.95 *(978-0-415-46472-7(2))*; VI, 186p. 150.00 *(978-0-415-46471-0(4))* Routledge.

Jin, Xiaoguang & Gobel, Stefan, eds. Technologies for E-Learning & Digital Entertainment: Second International Conference, Edutainment 2007, Hong Kong, China, June 11-13, 2007, Proceedings. 2007. (Lecture Notes in Computer Science Ser.). (Illus.). 974p. pap. 149.00 *(978-3-540-73010-1(9))* Springer.

Jowdy, Beth & McDonald, Mark. The Impact of Experience-Based Learning on Students' Emotional Competency. 2008. 312p. per. *(978-3-8364-3766-0(X))* VDM Verlag Dr. Mueller e.K.

Kalantzis, Mary & Cope, Bill. New Learning: Elements of a Science of Education. 2008. (Illus.). 304p. pap. 64.00 *(978-0-521-69124-6(9))* Cambridge Univ. Pr.

Kaplowitz, Joan R. Transforming Information Literacy Instruction Using Learner-Centered Teaching. 2011. ***(978-1-55570-765-1(3))*** Neal-Schuman Pubs., Inc.

Keiser, Debbie. Thinking Outside the Bean: All You Ever Wanted to Know about Mexican Jumping Beans & More. 2007. (ENG.). 64p. (gr. k-5). pap. 19.95 *(978-1-59363-252-6(5))* Prufrock Pr.

Knodt, Jean Sausele. Nine Thousand Straws: Teaching Thinking Through Open-Inquiry Learning, 1 vol. 2008. (Illus.). 340p. pap. 30.00 *(978-1-59158-640-1(2)*, TIP8640, Teacher Ideas Pr.) Libraries Unlimited, Inc.

Konicek-Moran, Richard. More Everyday Science Mysteries: Stories for Inquiry-Based Science Teaching. 2009. 207p. pap. 24.95 *(978-1-933531-44-1(4))* National Science Teachers Assn.

Lee, Joseph. Play in Education. 2009. 332p. pap. 23.00 *(978-1-150-58369-8(X))* General Bks. LLC.

—Play in Education. 2008. 528p. 55.95 *(978-1-4372-7736-4(5))*; pap. 40.95 *(978-1-4371-5206-7(6))* Kessinger Publishing, LLC.

Lee, Tae Bok. A Case Study of an Action Learning Program. 2009. 188p. pap. *(978-3-639-16893-8(3))* VDM Verlag Dr. Mueller e.K.

Lennex, Lesia C. & Nettleton, Kimberely Fletcher. Cases on Inquiry Through Instructional Technology in Math & Science. 2011. ***(978-1-4666-0068-3(3))***; ***(978-1-4666-0070-6(5))***; E-Book ***(978-1-4666-0069-0(1))*** IGI Global.

Levitov, Justin E. & Fall, Kevin A. Translating Theory into Practice: A Student Guide to Practicum & Internship. 2009. 268p. (C). pap. 29.95 *(978-1-57766-560-1(0))* Waveland Pr., Inc.

Lipton, Laura & Hubble, Deborah. More Than 100 Ways to Learner-Centered Literacy. 2nd ed. 2008. (Illus.). 200p. 72.95 *(978-1-4129-5784-7(2)*, B57830C); pap. 30.95 *(978-1-4129-5783-0(4)*, B57830P) Corwin Pr.

Luckin, Rosemary. Learning Context & the Role of Technology. 2010. (Foundations & Futures of Education Ser.). (ENG., Illus.). 208p. (C). 125.00 *(978-0-415-55441-1(1))* Routledge.

—Re-Designing Learning Contexts: Technology-Rich, Learner-Centred Ecologies. 2010. (Foundations & Futures of Education Ser.). (Illus.). 208p. (C). pap. 42.95 *(978-0-415-55442-8(X)*, Routledge) Taylor & Francis Group GBR. Dist: Taylor & Francis Group.

Lundy, Kathleen Gould. Leap into Literacy: Teaching the Tough Stuff So It Sticks! 2007. (ENG.). 160p. (C). (gr. 4-12). pap. 21.00 *(978-1-55138-212-8(1))* Pembroke Pubs., Ltd. CAN. Dist: Stenhouse Pubs.

—Teaching Fairly in an Unfair World. 2008. (ENG.). 144p. (C). (gr. 4-12). pap. 21.00 *(978-1-55138-231-9(8))* Stenhouse Pubs.

MacDonell, Colleen. Thematic Inquiry Through Fiction & Nonfiction, PreK to Grade 6, 1 vol. 2009. 200p. pap. 44.95 *(978-1-58683-350-3(2)*, A2456P) Linworth Publishing, Inc.

Mahurt, Sarah F., et al. Building Bridges from Early to Intermediate Literacy. 2007. (Illus.). 128p. 72.95 *(978-1-4129-4962-0(9)*, B49629C); per. 31.95 *(978-1-4129-4963-7(7)*, B49629P) Corwin Pr.

Malcom, Cliff. Learner-Centered Science Education. Dhunpath, Rubby ed. 2008. 292p. *(978-90-8790-662-7(5))*; pap. *(978-90-8790-661-0(7))* Sense Pubs.

March, Joe & McClure, Craig P. Introductory Chemistry: A Guided Inquiry. 2011. (ENG.). 272p. (C). pap. 42.95 *(978-0-8400-6221-5(4))* Brooks/Cole.

Marquardt, Michael J. Optimizing the Power of Action Learning: Real-Time Strategies for Developing Leaders, Building Teams & Transforming Organizations. 2nd ed. 2011. (ENG.). 240p. pap. 39.95 *(978-1-904838-33-3(2))* Ebsco Publishing.

Marquardt, Michael J. & Yeo, Roland K. Breakthrough Problem Solving with Action Learning: Concepts & Cases. 2012. (ENG.). 264p. 35.00 ***(978-0-8047-7412-3(9)***, Stanford Business Bks.) Stanford Univ. Pr.

Marquardt, Michael J., et al. Action Learning for Developing Leaders & Organizations: Principles, Strategies, & Cases. 2009. 392p. 59.95 *(978-1-4338-0435-9(2))* American Psychological Assn.

Marsh, Monica Miller & Turner-Vorveck, Tammy. (Mis)Understanding Families: Learning from Real Families in Our Schools. 2010. (ENG.). 224p. pap. 31.95 *(978-0-8077-5037-7(9))* Teachers College Pr., Teachers College, Columbia Univ.

Martin-Hansen, Lisa M. Inquiry Pedagogy & the Preservice Science Teacher. 2010. 244p. *(978-1-60497-666-3(7))* Cambria Pr.

Martin, Hope. Active Learning in the Mathematics Classroom, Grades 5-8. 2nd rev. ed. 2007. (Illus.). 208p. 85.95 *(978-1-4129-4977-4(7)*, B49777C); per. 38.95 *(978-1-4129-4978-1(5)*, B49777P) Corwin Pr.

Matthias, Catherine. Out the Door. 2011. (Rookie Ready to Learn Ser.). (Illus.). 40p. (J). (ENG.). pap. 5.95 *(978-0-531-26802-5(0))*; (gr. -1-k). lib. bdg. 22.00 *(978-0-531-25642-8(1))* Scholastic Library Publishing. (Children's Pr.).

Mayo, Marjorie & Annette, John. Taking Part? Active Learning for Active Citizenship, & Beyond. 2010. 328p. pap. 34.95 *(978-1-86201-435-0(3))* National Institute of Adult Continuing Education GBR. Dist: International Specialized Bk. Services.

McDevitt, Theresa R. Let the Games Begin! Engaging Students with Field-Tested Interactive Information Literacy Instruction. 2011. (Illus.). 150p. pap. 65.00 ***(978-1-55570-739-2(4))*** Neal-Schuman Pubs., Inc.

McDonald, Betty. Improving Teaching & Learning Through Assessment: A Problem-Based Learning (PBL) Approach. 2010. 134p. pap. 30.00 *(978-1-86335-669-5(X))* Common Ground Publishing Pty, Ltd.

McDonald, Lyn. Supervision of Student Teachers During Practicum. 2009. 60p. pap. *(978-3-639-05579-5(9))* VDM Verlag Dr. Mueller e.K.

McWhorter, Kathleen T. & Sember, Brette M. Active Reading Skills: Reading & Critical Thinking in College. 3rd ed. 2011. (ENG.). 544p. (C). pap. 88.00 *(978-0-205-02843-6(8))* Longman Publishing Group.

—Active Reading Skills: Reading & Critical Thinking in College, Books a la Carte Edition. 3rd ed. 2011. (ENG.). 512p. (C). ring bd. 57.33 *(978-0-205-10937-1(3))* Longman Publishing Group.

—Active Reading Skills: Reading & Critical Thinking in College (with MyReadingLab with Pearson eText Student Access Code Card) 3rd ed. 2011. (ENG.). 512p. (C). pap. 88.00 *(978-0-205-16774-6(8))* Longman Publishing Group.

—Active Reading Skills: Reading & Critical Thinking in College (with NEW MyReadingLab with Pearson eText Student Access Code Card) 3rd ed. 2012. (ENG.). 544p. (C). pap. 88.00 ***(978-0-321-85040-9(8))*** Addison Wesley.

McWhorter, Kathleen T. & Sember, Brette M. Active Reading Skills (with MyReadingLab Student Access Code Card) 2nd ed. 2008. (McWhorter Developmental Reading (Comprehensive) Ser.). (ENG.). 560p. (C). pap. 88.00 *(978-0-205-73442-9(1))* Longman Publishing Group.

McWhorter, Kathleen T. & Sember, Brette McWhorter. Active Reading Skills. 2nd ed. 2007. (ENG., Illus.). 560p. (C). per. 89.00 *(978-0-205-53249-0(7))* Longman Publishing.

Miller Marsh, Monica & Turner-Vorveck, Tammy. (Mis)Understanding Families: Learning from Real Families in Our Schools. 2010. (ENG.). 224p. 58.00 *(978-0-8077-5038-4(7))* Teachers College Pr., Teachers College, Columbia Univ.

Montoya, Juny. The Case for Active Learning in Legal Education. 2008. 264p. pap. *(978-3-639-05841-3(0))* VDM Verlag Dr. Mueller e.K.

Mulcahey, Christine. The Story in the Picture: Inquiry & Artmaking with Young Children. 2010. (Early Childhood Education Ser.). (ENG.). 120p. pap. 19.95 *(978-0-8077-5007-0(7))*; (Illus.). 42.00 *(978-0-8077-5008-7(5))* Teachers College Pr., Teachers College, Columbia Univ.

Murdoch, Kath & Wilson, Jeni. Creating a Learner-Centred Primary Classroom: Learner-Centered Strategic Teaching. 2008. (ENG., Illus.). 128p. pap. 31.95 *(978-0-415-45432-2(8))* Fulton, David Pubs. GBR. Dist: Taylor & Francis Group.

Nash, Ron. The Active Classroom: Practical Strategies for Involving Students in the Learning Process. 2008. 176p. 72.95 *(978-1-4129-6086-1(X)*, B60861C); (Illus.). pap. 31.95 *(978-1-4129-6087-8(8)*, B60861P) Corwin Pr.

—The Active Classroom Field Book: Success Stories from the Active Classroom. 2010. (Illus.). 152p. pap. 28.95 *(978-1-4129-8132-3(3)*, B81323P) Corwin Pr.

—The Active Teacher: Practical Strategies for Maximizing Teacher Effectiveness. 2009. (Illus.). 152p. pap. 28.95 *(978-1-4129-7387-8(2)*, B73878P) Corwin Pr.

Nash, Ronald (Ron) J. From Seatwork to Feetwork: Engaging Students in Their Own Learning. 2011. (Illus.). 152p. pap. 26.95 ***(978-1-4129-9794-2(1)***, B97942P) Corwin Pr.

Nevárez-LaTorre, Aida A. The Power of Learning from Inquiry. 2009. *(978-1-60752-281-2(0))*; pap. *(978-1-60752-280-5(2))* Information Age Publishing, Inc.

Nygaard, Claus, et al, eds. Improving Student's Learning Outcomes. 2009. 335p. pap. 63.00 *(978-87-630-0232-5(9))* Copenhagen Business Schl. Pr. DNK. Dist: International Specialized Bk. Services.

O'Neill, Judy E. & Marsick, Victoria J. Understanding Action Learning: Theory into Practice. 2007. (AMA Innovations in Adult Learning Ser.). (ENG., Illus.). 176p. per. 29.00 *(978-0-8144-7395-5(4))* Amacom.

Ovens, Peter. Developing Inquiry for Learning. 2011. (ENG., Illus.). 240p. 125.00 *(978-0-415-59876-7(1))* Routledge.

Ovens, Peter, et al. Developing Inquiry for Learning. 2011. (ENG., Illus.). 240p. pap. 44.95 *(978-0-415-59877-4(X))* Routledge.

Pagliaro, Marie. Exemplary Classroom Questioning: Practices to Promote Thinking & Learning. 2011. (ENG.). 172p. 50.00 ***(978-1-61048-456-5(8))***; pap. 24.95 ***(978-1-61048-457-2(6))*** Rowman & Littlefield Education.

Pagliaro, Marie Menna. Exemplary Classroom Questioning: Practices to Promote Thinking & Learning. 2011. E-Book ***(978-1-61048-458-9(4))*** Rowman & Littlefield Education.

Pan, Zhigeng, et al. Transactions on Edutainment II. 2009. (Lecture Notes in Computer Science / Transactions on Edutainment Ser.). (ENG., Illus.). xii, 313p. pap. 113.00 *(978-3-642-03269-1(9)*, 3642032699) Springer.

—Transactions on Edutainment III. 2010. (Lecture Notes in Computer Science / Transactions on Edutainment Ser.). x, 275p. pap. 99.00 *(978-3-642-11244-7(7)*, 3642112447) Springer.

—Transactions on Edutainment V. 2011. (Lecture Notes in Computer Science / Transactions on Edutainment Ser.). (Illus.). x, 271p. pap. 98.00 *(978-3-642-18451-2(0)*, 3642184510) Springer.

Pan, Zhigeng, et al, eds. Transactions on Edutainment VI. 2011. (Lecture Notes in Computer Science / Transactions on Edutainment Ser.). (ENG., Illus.). xi, 266p. pap. 98.00 ***(978-3-642-22638-0(8)***, 3642226388) Springer.

Parfitt, Vicki, et al. Maths Homework for Key Stage 2: Activity-based Learning. 2010. (Active Homework Ser.). (ENG., Illus.). 104p. 39.95 *(978-0-415-49625-4(X)*, Routledge) Taylor & Francis Group GBR. Dist: Taylor & Francis Group.

Parker, Diane. Planning for Inquiry: It's Not an Oxymoron. 2007. pap. *(978-0-8141-3560-0(9))* National Council of Teachers of English.

Parker, Jonathan. Effective Practice Learning in Social Work. 2nd ed. 2010. (Illus.). 174p. pap. *(978-1-84445-253-8(0))* Learning Matters Ltd.

Patel, Hina. Assessment of the Attributes of Educators Who Utilize Service-Learning. 2008. 268p. pap. *(978-3-639-07276-1(6))* VDM Verlag Dr. Mueller e.K.

Pearson, Joanne & Mitchell, Nick, eds. Inquiring in the Classroom: Asking the Questions that Matter about Teaching & Learning. 2012. (ENG.). 200p. 120.00 ***(978-1-4411-8237-1(3))***; pap. 34.95 ***(978-1-4411-5282-4(2))*** Continuum International Publishing Group, Ltd. GBR. Dist: National Bk. Network.

Pedler, Mike. Action Learning for Managers. 2nd rev. ed. 2008. (Illus.). 98p. pap. 19.95 *(978-0-566-08863-6(0)*, Gower Publishing Co., Ltd.) Ashgate Publishing, Ltd. GBR. Dist: Ashgate Publishing Co.

Pedler, Mike & Revans, Reg. Abc of Action Learning. 2011. 154p. pap. 24.95 ***(978-1-4094-2703-2(X)***, Gower Publishing Co., Ltd.) Ashgate Publishing, Ltd. GBR. Dist: Ashgate Publishing Co.

Peters, Erin. Thinking Like Scientists. 2009. 148p. pap. *(978-3-639-14703-2(0))* VDM Verlag Dr. Mueller e.K.

Pilliner, Eileen. Perceptions of & Attitudes Towards Adoption of Problem-Based Learning. 2008. 276p. pap. *(978-3-639-06116-1(0))* VDM Verlag Dr. Mueller e.K.

Pollman, Mary Jo. Blocks & Beyond: Strengthening Early Math & Science Skills Through Spatial Learning. 2010. (Illus.). 200p. pap. 29.95 *(978-1-59857-101-1(X))* Brookes, Paul H. Publishing Co.

Pope, Melanie & Shilvock, Kate, eds. Successful Teaching Placements in Secondary Schools. 2008. (Illus.). 128p. pap. *(978-1-84445-183-8(6))* Learning Matters Ltd.

Powell, Sara Davis. Wayside Teaching: Connecting with Students to Support Learning. 2010. 200p. pap. 33.95 *(978-1-4129-7290-1(6)*, B72895P) Corwin Pr.

Prensky, Marc, ed. Teaching Digital Natives: Partnering for Real Learning. 2010. (Illus.). 224p. pap. 36.95 *(978-1-4129-7541-4(7)*, B75414P) Corwin Pr.

Rabley, Jennifer. Displacement: The Impact of Forced Removal on Memory Reconstruction. 2008. 140p. pap. *(978-3-639-08033-9(5))* VDM Verlag Dr. Mueller e.K.

Ramer, Karin & Rose-Duckworth, Roxann. Fostering Learner Independence: An Essential Guide for K-6 Educators. 2008. (Illus.). 240p. pap. 36.95 *(978-1-4129-6607-8(8)*, B66061P) Corwin Pr.

—Fostering Learner Independence: An Essential Guide for K-6 Educators. 2008. (Illus.). 240p. 82.95 *(978-1-4129-6606-1(X)*, B66061C) Corwin Pr.

Redmond, Bairbre. Reflection in Action: Developing Reflective Practice in Health & Social Services. 2006. (Illus.). 172p. pap. 40.00 *(978-0-7546-4955-7(5))* Ashgate Publishing Co.

Reece, Jane B., et al. Inquiry in Action: Intrepreting Scientific Papers. 2nd ed. 2010. (ENG.). 128p. (C). pap. 17.20 *(978-0-321-68336-6(6))* Benjamin-Cummings Publishing Co.

Rickert, Cindy, et al, eds. High-Five Teaching, K-5: Using Green Light Strategies to Create Dynamic, Student-Focused Classrooms. 2010. (Illus.). 208p. pap. 36.95 *(978-1-4129-8112-5(3)*, B81125P) Corwin Pr.

Rigsbee, Cindi. Finding Mrs. Warnecke: The Difference Teachers Make. 2010. (ENG., Illus.). 160p. 19.95 *(978-0-470-48678-8(3)*, Jossey-Bass) Wiley, John & Sons, Inc.

Roberts, Deborah Fernald, contrib. by. Strengthening Your Foreign Language Instruction: Practical Strategies for Active Learning. 2006. (gr. 6-12). 89.00 *(978-1-886397-77-4(5))* Bureau of Education & Research.

Roberts, Jay W. Beyond Learning by Doing. 2011. (ENG., Illus.). 144p. pap. 41.95 *(978-0-415-88208-8(7))* Routledge.

Robertson, William H. P. Developing Problem-Based Curriculum: Unlocking Student Success Utilizing Critical Thinking & Inquiry. rev. ed. 2009. (ENG.). 162p. pap. 60.44 *(978-0-7575-5346-2(X))* Kendall Hunt Publishing Co.

Roubidoux, Susan. 101 Ways to Make Studying Easier & Faster for College Students: What Every Student Needs to Know Explained Simply. 2008. (ENG., Illus.). 288p. (C). per. 21.95 *(978-1-60138-249-8(9))* Atlantic Publishing Co.

Savin-Baden, Maggi. A Practical Guide to Problem-Based Learning Online. 2008. (Illus.). (ENG.). 168p. 46.95 (978-0-415-43788-2(1)); XII, 156p. 150.00 (978-0-415-43787-5(3)) Routledge.

Sawyer, R. Keith. Structure & Improvisation in Creative Teaching. 2011. (ENG., Illus.). 318p. (C). 95.00 (978-0-521-76251-9(0)) Cambridge Univ. Pr.

Sawyer, R. Keith, ed. Structure & Improvisation in Creative Teaching. 2011. (ENG., Illus.). 320p. (C). pap. 32.99 (978-0-521-74632-8(9)) Cambridge Univ. Pr.

Sbhatu, Desta. Metacognitive Instruction. 2009. 160p. pap. (978-3-639-19436-4(5)) VDM Verlag Dr. Mueller e.K.

Schmieder, June H. & McManus, John F. The Accreditors Are Coming! Are You Ready? rev. ed. 2006. (Illus.). 86p. pap. 47.08 (978-0-7575-3885-8(1)) Kendall Hunt Publishing Co.

Schultz, Brian D. Listening to & Learning from Students: Possibilities for Teaching, Learning, & Curriculum. 2011. (978-1-61735-172-3(5)); pap. (978-1-61735-171-6(7)); E-Book (978-1-61735-173-0(3)) Information Age Publishing, Inc.

Selwyn, Douglas. Following the Thread: Conducting Inquiry Research in the Social Studies Classroom. 2009. pap. 33.95 (978-1-4331-0607-1(8)) Lang, Peter Publishing, Inc.

Settles, Burr. Active Learning. 2011. (Synthesis Lectures on Artificial Intelligence & Machine Learning Ser.). 100p. pap. 35.00 **(978-1-60845-725-0(7))** Morgan & Claypool Pubs.

Silberman, Mel. Unforgettable Experiential Activities: An Active Training Resource. 2010. (ENG., Illus.). 320p. pap. 55.00 (978-0-470-53714-5(0), Pfeiffer) Wiley, John & Sons, Inc.

Silberman, Melvin L. The Best of Active Training II: 25 One-Day Workshops Guaranteed to Promote Involvement, Learning, & Change. 2007. (ENG.). 560p. ring bd. 175.00 (978-0-7879-9624-6(6), Pfeiffer) Wiley, John & Sons, Inc.

Silberman, Shoshana & Silberman, Mel. Active Jewish Learning. 2009. 212p. pap. 19.95 (978-1-934527-23-8(8)) Torah Aura Productions.

Simpson, Cynthia G., et al. Teacher's Survival Guide: The Inclusion Classroom. 2011. (ENG.). 250p. pap. 19.95 (978-1-59363-541-1(9)) Prufrock Pr.

Smith, Keri. How to Be an Explorer of the World. 2010. (KOR., Illus.). 210p. pap. (978-89-01-10497-3(0)) Woongjin.com Co., Ltd.

—How to Be an Explorer of the World: Portable Life Museum. 2008. (ENG., Illus.). 208p. (gr. 12-18). 14.95 (978-0-399-53460-7(1), Perigee Trade) Penguin Group (USA) Inc.

Spencer, Jill. Everyone's Invited! Interactive Strategies That Engage Young Adolescents. 2008. (978-1-56090-222-5(1)) National Middle Schl. Assn.

Springer, Mark. Soundings: A Democratic, Student-Centered Education. 2006. (Illus.). xii, 227p. (978-1-56090-200-3(0)) National Middle Schl. Assn.

Starkey, Theresa. Vital Ideas: Crime. 2011. **(978-1-933147-79-6(2))** Great Bks. Foundation.

Stephan, Elizabeth A., et al. Thinking Like an Engineer: An Active Learning Approach. 2nd rev. ed. 2012. (ENG., Illus.). 768p. (C). spiral bd. 157.00 **(978-0-13-276671-5(X)**, Prentice Hall) Prentice Hall PTR.

—Thinking like an engineer&myengbrglab Pkg. 2nd ed. 2012. (ENG.). (C). spiral bd. 190.33 **(978-0-13-298138-5(6)**, Prentice Hall) Prentice Hall PTR.

Stockton, Cally. Minds & Motion: Active Learning for the Creative Classroom. 2011. (978-1-56090-242-3(6)) National Middle Schl. Assn.

Sulla, Nancy. Students Taking Charge: Inside the Learner-Active, Technology-Infused Classroom. 2011. **(978-1-59667-185-0(8))** Eye On Education, Inc.

Swartz, Larry & Nyman, Debbie. Drama Schemes, Themes & Dreams: How to Plan, Structure, & Assess Classroom Strategies That Engage Young Adolescent Learners. 2010. (ENG.). 160p. (C). (gr. 6-12). pap. 22.00 **(978-1-55138-253-1(9))** Pembroke Pubs., Ltd. CAN. Dist: Stenhouse Pubs.

Talaro, Kathleen Park. Loose Leaf Version of Foundations in Microbiology. 7th ed. 2009. (ENG.). (C). ring bd., ring bd. 137.19 (978-0-07-736908-8(4), 0077369084, McGraw-Hill Science, Engineering & Mathematics) McGraw-Hill Higher Education.

Thomas, Carol M., et al. Inquiry: A Districtwide Approach to Staff & Student Learning. 2011. (Illus.). 200p. pap. 34.95 **(978-1-4129-9247-3(8)**, B92473P) Corwin Pr.

Tollefson, Kaia & Osborn, Monica K. Cultivating the Learner-Centered Classroom: From Theory to Practice. 2007. (Illus.). 216p. 72.95 (978-1-4129-4996-5(3), B49963C); per. 36.95 (978-1-4129-4997-2(1), B49963P) Corwin Pr.

Trentin, Guglielmo. Networked Collaborative Learning: Social Interaction & Active Learning. 2009. 200p. pap. 75.00 (978-1-84334-501-5(3), Chandos Publishing) Woodhead Publishing Ltd. GBR. Dist: Neal-Schuman Pubs., Inc.

Turville, Joni, et al. Differentiating by Readiness: Strategies & Lesson Plans for Tiered Instruction Grades K-8. 2009. 29.95 (978-1-59667-137-9(8)) Eye On Education, Inc.

Vascellaro, Salvatore. Out of the Classroom & into the World: Learning from Field Trips, Educating from Experience, & Unlocking the Potential of Our Students & Teachers. 2011. (ENG., Illus.). 272p. pap. 19.95 (978-1-59558-682-7(2)) New Pr., The.

Walsh, Andrew & Inala, Padma. Active Learning Techniques for Librarians: Practical Examples. 2010. 160p. pap. 75.00 (978-1-84334-592-3(7), Chandos Publishing) Woodhead Publishing Ltd. GBR. Dist: Neal-Schuman Pubs., Inc.

Walsh, Jackie A. (Acree) & Sattes, Elizabeth (Beth) D. (Dankert). Thinking Through Quality Questioning: Deepening Student Engagement. 2011. (Illus.). 208p. pap. 36.95 (978-1-4129-8902-2(7), B89022P) Corwin Pr.

Warren, Karen, et al. Theory & Practice of Experiential Education: A collection of articles addressing the historical, educational, philosophical, psychological, ethical, spiritual, & social justice foundations of Experiential Education. Warren, Karen et al, eds. 4th ed. 2008. (Illus.). 402p. (C). pap. 48.00 (978-0-929361-17-8(2)) Assn. for Experiential Education.

Wiltshire, Monica. Understanding the High Scope Approach. 2011. (Understanding the â€ Approach Ser.). (ENG., Illus.). 168p. 115.00 **(978-0-415-58357-2(8))**; pap. 37.95 **(978-0-415-58358-9(6))** Routledge.

Wood, Bonnie S. Lecture-Free Teaching: A Learning Partnership of Science Educators & Their Students. 2009. (978-1-933531-32-8(0)) National Science Teachers Assn.

Worrall. Cuckoo! Bk. 1: Activity. Date not set. pap. 72.95 (978-0-582-03068-8(4)) Addison-Wesley Longman, Ltd. GBR. Dist: Trans-Atlantic Pubns., Inc.

Wurdinger, Scot & Carlson, Julie. Teaching for Experiential Lear. 2009. (ENG.). 126p. pap. 28.95 (978-1-60709-368-8(5)) Rowman & Littlefield Publishers, Inc.

Wurdinger, Scott D. & Carlson, Julie A. Teaching for Experiential Learning: Five Approaches That Work. 2009. (ENG.). 126p. 74.95 (978-1-60709-367-1(7)) Rowman & Littlefield Education.

Zhang, Xiaopeng & Wong, Kevin, eds. Transactions on Edutainment IV. 2010. (Lecture Notes in Computer Science / Transactions on Edutainment Ser.). x, 277p. pap. 99.00 (978-3-642-14483-7(7), 3642144837) Springer.

Zuber-Skerritt, Ortrun. Action Leadership: Towards a Participatory Paradigm. 2011. (Professional & Practice-based Learning Ser.). (ENG., Illus.). xxix, 210p. 139.00 (978-90-481-3934-7(1), 9048139341) Springer.

—Action Learning & Action Research. 2009. (Illus.). 236p. (978-90-8790-953-6(5)); pap. (978-90-8790-952-9(7)) Sense Pubs.

ACTIVE OXYGEN

Akalan, Cengiz. Prediction of Aerobic Capacity from an Individualized Protocol. 2009. 132p. pap. (978-3-639-17301-7(5)) VDM Verlag Dr. Mueller e.K.

Aldini, Giancarlo, et al. Biomarkers for Antioxidant Defense & Oxidative Damage: Principles & Practical Applications. 2010. (ENG., Illus.). 380p. 220.95 (978-0-8138-1535-0(5), Wiley-Blackwell) Wiley, John & Sons, Inc.

Allison, William S. & Murphy, Anne. Mitochondrial Function, Part B: Mitochondrial Protein Kinases, Protein Phosphatases & Mitochondrial Diseases, 2 vols. 2009. (ENG., Illus.). 450p. 187.00 (978-0-12-374622-1(1), Academic Pr.) Elsevier Science & Technology Bks.

del Rio, Luis Alfonso & Puppo, Alain, eds. Reactive Oxygen Species in Plant Signaling. 2009. (Signaling & Communication in Plants Ser.). (ENG., Illus.). x, 245p. 239.00 (978-3-642-00389-9(3), 3642003893) Springer.

Duncan, C. J., ed. Calcium, Oxygen Radicals & Cellular Damage. 2008. (Society for Experimental Biology Seminar Ser.). (ENG., Illus.). 240p. pap. 53.00 (978-0-521-05761-5(2)) Cambridge Univ. Pr.

Forman, H. J., et al, eds. Signal Transduction by Reactive Oxygen & Nitrogen Species: Pathways & Chemical Principles: Pathways & Chemical Principles. 2011. 436p. pap. 189.00 (978-90-481-6216-1(5), 9048162165) Springer.

Gupta, S. Dutta. Reactive Oxygen Species & Antioxidants in Higher Plants. 2010. (ENG.). 380p. 149.95 (978-1-57808-686-3(8)) BIOS Scientific Publishers Ltd. GBR. Dist: Taylor & Francis Group.

Kozyrev, Dimitri, ed. Handbook of Free Radicals: Formation, Types & Effects. 2010. (Cell Biology Research Progress Ser.). 660p. 245.00 (978-1-60876-101-2(0)) Nova Science Pubs., Inc.

Li, Yunbo. Antioxidants in Biology & Medicine: Essentials, Advances, & Clinical Applications. 2011. (Medicine & Biology Research Developments (Series Editor - Tsisana Shartava, M. D. - Tbilisi, Georgia) Ser.). 195.00 (978-1-61122-502-0(7), Nova Novinka) Nova Science Pubs., Inc.

Naito, Y., et al, eds. Free Radical Biology in Digestive Diseases. 2010. (Frontiers of Gastrointestinal Research Ser.). (ENG., Illus.). 176p. (978-3-8055-9609-1(X)) Karger, S. AG.

Oberdanner, Christian. ROS & Antioxidant Systems in Apoptosis: Oxidant Balance in Cell Death & Cancer Therapy. 2008. 132p. pap. (978-3-8364-8211-0(8)) VDM Verlag Dr. Mueller e.K.

Prasad, Kedar N. Micronutrients in Health & Disease. 2010. (ENG., Illus.). 391p. 129.95 (978-1-4398-2106-0(2), CRC Press) Taylor & Francis Group GBR. Dist: Taylor & Francis Group.

Scheffler, Immo, et al. Mitochondrial Function, Part A: Mitochondrial Electron Transport Complexes & Reactive Oxygen Species, 2 vols. 2009. (ENG., Illus.). 502p. 187.00 (978-0-08-087776-1(1), Academic Pr.) Elsevier Science & Technology Bks.

ACTIVE SERVER PAGES (COMPUTER PROGRAM)

AL Zabir, Omar. Building a Web 2.0 Portal with ASP.NET 3.5. 2007. (ENG., Illus.). 320p. per. 44.99 (978-0-596-51050-3(0)) O'Reilly Media, Inc.

Aneel Allana, Sonal. ASP. NET jQuery Cookbook. 2011. (Illus.). 291p. pap. **(978-1-84969-046-1(4))** Packt Publishing, Ltd.

Arsenovski, Danijel. Professional Refactoring in C# & ASP. NET. 2009. (ENG., Illus.). 552p. pap. 59.99 (978-0-470-43452-9(X), Wrox) Wiley, John & Sons, Inc.

Bellinaso, Marco & Love, Chris. Asp. Net 3.5 Website Programming: Problem - Design - Solution. 2009. (ENG., Illus.). 648p. pap. 44.99 (978-0-470-18758-6(1), Wrox) Wiley, John & Sons, Inc.

Berardi, Nick, et al. ASP.NET MVC 1.0 Website Programming: Problem - Design - Solution. 2009. (ENG., Illus.). 552p. pap. 49.99 (978-0-470-41095-0(7), Wrox) Wiley, John & Sons, Inc.

Bochicchio, Daniele, et al. ASP. NET 4. 0 in Practice. 2011. (ENG., Illus.). 504p. pap. 54.99 (978-1-935182-46-7(3)) Manning Pubns. Co.

Boehm, Anne. Murach's ADO. NET 2. 0 Database Programming with VB 2005: Training & Reference. 2007. (Murach: Training & Reference Ser.). (Illus.). 764p. per. 52.50 (978-1-890774-43-1(X)) Murach, Mike & Assocs., Inc.

—Murach's ASP.NET 3.5 Web Programming with VB 2008. 2008. (Illus.). 974p. pap. 52.50 (978-1-890774-47-9(2)) Murach, Mike & Assocs., Inc.

Boehm, Anne & Murach, Joel. Murach's ASP.NET 4 Web Programming with C# 2010. 4th ed. 2011. (ENG., Illus.). 834p. pap. 54.50 (978-1-890774-61-5(8)) Murach, Mike & Assocs., Inc.

—Murach's ASP.NET 3.5 Web Programming with C# 2008. 2008. (Illus.). 1000p. pap. 52.50 (978-1-890774-48-6(0)) Murach, Mike & Assocs., Inc.

Brind, Mike & Spaanjaars, Imar. Beginning ASP. NET Web Pages with WebMatrix. 2011. (ENG.). 432p. pap. 39.99 (978-1-118-05048-4(7), Wrox) Wiley, John & Sons, Inc.

Calderon, Adam & Rumerman, Joel. Advanced ASP . NET AJAX Server Controls: For . NET 3. 5 Framework 3. 5. 2008. (ENG., Illus.). 648p. pap. 49.99 (978-0-321-51444-8(0)) Addison Wesley Professional.

Chadwick, Jess. Programming Razor. 2011. (ENG.). 120p. pap. 19.99 **(978-1-4493-0676-2(4))** O'Reilly Media, Inc.

Cheshire, Jim. The Expression Web Developer's Guide to ASP.NET 3.5: Learn to Create ASP.NET Applications Using Visual Web Developer 2008. 2007. (ENG., Illus.). 504p. per. 44.99 (978-0-7897-3665-9(9)) Que.

Chiaretta, Simone, et al. Beginning ASP. NET MVC 1. 0. 2009. (ENG., Illus.). 576p. pap. 49.99 (978-0-470-43399-7(X), Wrox) Wiley, John & Sons, Inc.

Connolly, Randy. Core Internet Application Development with ASP. Net 2. 0. 2007. (Core Ser.). (ENG., Illus.). 1088p. per. 64.99 (978-0-321-41950-7(2)) Prentice Hall PTR.

Cox, Ken. ASP. NET 3. 5 for Dummies. 2008. (ENG., Illus.). 432p. per. 29.99 (978-0-470-19592-5(4), For Dummies) Wiley, John & Sons, Inc.

Darie, Cristian & Barnett, Wyatt. Build Your Own ASP. NET 4 Web Site Using C# & VB. 4th ed. 2011. (ENG.). 776p. pap. 44.95 **(978-0-9870908-6-7(0))** SitePoint Pty, Ltd. AUS. Dist: Ingram Pub. Services.

Darie, Cristian & Brinzarea, Bogdan. Microsoft AJAX C# Essentials: A uniquely practical guide to working with the ASP. NET AJAX Control Toolkit, ASP. NET 2. 0 AJAX Extensions, & the Microsoft AJAX Library: Building Responsive ASP. NET 2. 0 Applications. 2007. (Illus.). 300p. per. (978-1-84719-098-7(7)) Packt Publishing, Ltd.

Darie, Cristian & Sirovich, Jaimie. Professional Search Engine Optimization with ASP.NET: A Developer's Guide to SEO. 2007. (ENG., Illus.). 410p. per. 39.99 (978-0-470-13147-3(0), Wrox) Wiley, John & Sons, Inc.

Darie, Cristian & Watson, Karli. Beginning ASP. NET E-Commerce in C# 2009. (ENG., Illus.). 736p. pap. 44.99 (978-1-4302-1074-0(5)) Apress L. P.

De Smet, Bart. C# 4. 0 Unleashed. rev. ed. 2011. (Unleashed Ser.). (ENG., Illus.). 1648p. pap. 59.99 (978-0-672-33079-7(2)) Sams.

DiMarzio, Jerome. Dynamic Control Survivability in ASP. NET. 2007. (Wrox Briefs Ser.). 33p. 6.99 (978-0-470-27934-2(6), Wrox) Wiley, John & Sons, Inc.

Dorrans, Barry. ASP. NET Security. 2010. (ENG., Illus.). 436p. pap. 44.99 (978-0-470-74365-2(4), Wrox) Wiley, John & Sons, Inc.

Dreamtech Software. ASP. Net 2. 0 Black Book. 2006. (Black Book (Paraglyph Press) Ser.). (ENG., Illus.). 1200p. pap. 49.99 (978-1-933097-17-6(5), Paraglyph Pr.) Paraglyph, Inc.

Ellis, Matthew. ASP.NET 3.5 AJAX Pocket Guide. 2008. 232p. pap. 10.95 (978-0-9703720-3-1(5)) Magma Interactive, LLC.

—ASP.NET AJAX Programming Tricks. 2007. 388p. pap. 34.99 (978-0-9703720-0-0(0)) Magma Interactive, LLC.

Esposito, Dino. Microsoft ASP.NET & AJAX: Architecting Web Applications. 2009. (ENG.). 352p. pap. 39.99 (978-0-7356-2621-8(9)) Microsoft Pr.

—Programming Microsoft ASP. NET 3. 5. 2008. (ENG., Illus.). 1152p. pap. 59.99 (978-0-7356-2527-3(1)) Microsoft Pr.

—Programming Microsoft ASP. NET 4. 2011. (ENG., Illus.). 992p. pap. 59.99 (978-0-7356-4338-3(5)) Microsoft Pr.

Esposito, Dino. Programming Microsoft ASP.NET MVC. 2nd ed. 2011. (ENG.). 464p. pap. 44.99 **(978-0-7356-6284-1(3))** Microsoft Pr.

Evjen, Bill, et al. ASP. NET 2. 0 Wrox Box: Professional ASP. NET 2. 0 Special Edition, ASP. NET 2. 0 Website Programming Problem-Design-Solution, Professional ASP. NET 2. 0 Server Controls & Component Development, Professional ASP. NET 2. 0 Security, Membership, & Role Management, & ASP. NET 2. 0 MVP Hacks & Tips. 2006. (ENG.). 4400p. pap. 189.99 (978-0-470-11757-6(5), Wrox) Wiley, John & Sons, Inc.

—ASP.NET 4 in C# & VB. 2010. (ENG., Illus.). 1536p. pap. 59.99 (978-0-470-50220-4(7), Wrox) Wiley, John & Sons, Inc.

—NET 3.5 Wrox Box: Professional Asp. NET 3.5, Professional C# 2008, Professional Linq, . NET Domain-Driven Design with C# 2008. (ENG.). 3600p. pap. 159.99 (978-0-470-38799-3(8), Wrox) Wiley, John & Sons, Inc.

—Professional ASP. NET 2. 0. 2006. (Wiley Desktop Editions Ser.). (ENG., Illus.). 1584p. 59.99 (978-0-470-04178-9(1), Wrox) Wiley, John & Sons, Inc.

—Professional ASP. Net 3. 5: In C# & VB. 2009. (ENG., Illus.). 1856p. 69.99 (978-0-470-47826-4(8), Wrox) Wiley, John & Sons, Inc.

—Professional ASP. NET 3.5: In C# & VB. 2008. (ENG., Illus.). 1704p. per. 54.99 (978-0-470-18757-9(3), Wrox) Wiley, John & Sons, Inc.

—Professional ASP.NET 3.5 AJAX. 2009. (ENG., Illus.). 552p. pap. 44.99 (978-0-470-39217-1(7), Wrox) Wiley, John & Sons, Inc.

Foster, Robert. ASP.NET 3.5 Ajax. 2008. (Unleashed Ser.). (ENG.). 264p. pap. 39.99 (978-0-672-32973-9(5)) Sams.

Freeman, Adam. Applied ASP. NET 4 in Context. 2011. (ENG., Illus.). 952p. pap. 59.99 (978-1-4302-3467-8(9)) Apress L. P.

Freeman, Adam & Sanderson, Steven. Pro ASP. NET MVC 3 Framework. 3rd ed. 2011. (ENG., Illus.). 852p. pap. 54.99 (978-1-4302-3404-3(0)) Apress L. P.

Freeman, Adam, et al. Beginning ASP. NET 2. 0 Web Services in C# From Novice to Professional. 400p. pap. 44.99 (978-1-59059-726-2(5)) Apress L. P.

Gallo, Alessandro, et al. ASP. Net Ajax in Action. 2007. (ENG., Illus.). 576p. per. 44.99 (978-1-933988-14-6(2)) Manning Pubns. Co.

Galloway, Jon, et al. Professional ASP. NET MVC 3. 2011. (ENG.). 432p. pap. 44.99 (978-1-118-07658-3(3), Wrox) Wiley, John & Sons, Inc.

Gibbs, Matt & Wahlin, Dan. Professional ASP.NET 2.0 AJAX. 2007. (ENG., Illus.). 336p. per. 39.99 (978-0-470-10962-5(9), Wrox) Wiley, John & Sons, Inc.

Gosselin, Don & Gosselin. ASP . NET Programming with C# & SQL Server. 2009. (Web Technologies Ser.). (ENG., Illus.). 672p. pap. 131.95 (978-1-4239-0324-6(2)) Course Technology.

Guay Paz, Jose Rolando. Pro Telerik ASP. NET & Silverlight Controls: Master Telerik Controls for Advanced ASP. NET & Silverlight Projects. 2010. (ENG.). 696p. pap. 59.99 (978-1-4302-2940-7(3)) Apress L. P.

Gupta, Atul, et al. ASP. NET 4 Social Networking. 2011. (Illus.). 457p. pap. **(978-1-84969-082-9(0))** Packt Publishing, Ltd.

Haack, Phil, et al. The ASP. Net 2. 0 Anthology: 101 Essential Tips, Tricks & Hacks. 2007. (ENG., Illus.). 500p. per. 39.95 (978-0-9802858-1-9(X)) SitePoint Pty, Ltd. AUS. Dist: Ingram Pub. Services.

Haager, Florian. Event-Driven Objects in .NET: Konzeption und Realisierung eines Framework zur Verteilung von Datenobjekten über Peer-to-Peer Systeme. 2010. 88p. pap. (978-3-639-24261-4(0)) VDM Verlag Dr. Mueller e.K.

Hanselman, Scott, et al. Professional ASP. NET MVC 2. 2010. (ENG., Illus.). 552p. pap. 44.99 (978-0-470-64318-1(8), Wrox) Wiley, John & Sons, Inc.

Harris, Alan. Pro ASP. NET 4 CMS: Advanced Techniques for C# Developers Using the . NET 4 Framework. 2010. (ENG.). 320p. pap. 42.99 (978-1-4302-2712-0(5)) Apress L. P.

Ibrahim, Emad & Goode, Troy. ASP. NET MVC 1.0 Test Driven Development: Problem - Design - Solution. 2009. (ENG.). 312p. pap. 49.99 (978-0-470-44762-8(1), Wrox) Wiley, John & Sons, Inc.

Itcookbook. Asp Net 20 Website Programming Interview. 2006. pap. 54.95 (978-1-933804-51-4(3)) Equity Pr.

Kalata, Kathleen. Introduction to ASP 2005. 3rd rev. ed. 2007. (ENG., Illus.). 688p. (C). per. 125.95 (978-1-4188-3765-5(2)) Course Technology.

Kanjilal, Joydip & Putrevu, Sriram. ASP.NET Ajax. 2008. (Sams Teach Yourself — Hours Ser.). (ENG., Illus.). 432p. pap. 39.99 (978-0-672-32967-8(0)) Sams.

Kauffman, John & Millington, Bradley. ASP. NET 2.0 & Databases. 2006. (ENG., Illus.). 535p. pap. 39.99 (978-0-471-78134-9(7), Wrox) Wiley, John & Sons, Inc.

Kaula, Rajeev. Oracle 11g: Developing AJAX Applications with PL/SQL Server Pages. 4th ed. 2008. (ENG.). 528p. (C). pap. 84.33 (978-0-07-340877-4(8), 0073408778) McGraw-Hill Cos., The.

Khosravi, Shahram. ASP.NET 2.0 & .NET 3.0 Programming: ASP.NET 2.0 Internals plus Atlas, IIS 7.0, Enterprise Library Application Blocks, Windows Workflow Foundation, & Windows Communication Foundation. 2008. 1100p. pap. 49.99 (978-0-470-10997-7(1), Wrox) Wiley, John & Sons, Inc.

—ASP.NET AJAX: With ASP. NET 2.0 & ASP.NET 3.5. 2007. (ENG., Illus.). 1522p. per. 59.99 (978-0-470-10998-4(X), Wrox) Wiley, John & Sons, Inc.

—Professional ASP. NET 2. 0 Server Control & Component Development. 2006. (ENG., Illus.). 1224p. pap. 49.99 (978-0-471-79350-2(7), Wrox) Wiley, John & Sons, Inc.

—Professional IIS 7 & ASP.NET Integrated Programming. 2007. (ENG.). 670p. pap. 49.99 (978-0-470-15253-9(2), Wrox) Wiley, John & Sons, Inc.

Kiessig, Rick. Ultra-Fast ASP. NET Building Ultra-Fast & Ultra-Scalable Websites Using ASP. NET & SQL Server. 2009. (ENG.). 496p. pap. 49.99 (978-1-4302-2383-2(9)) Apress L. P.

Kimmel, Paul T. DevExpress ASP.NET Controls. 2009. (ENG., Illus.). 672p. pap. 39.99 (978-0-470-50083-5(2), Wrox) Wiley, John & Sons, Inc.

Korol, Julitta. Access 2007 Programming by Example with VBA, XML, & ASP. 2007. (Illus.). 938p. per. 39.95 (978-1-59822-042-1(X)) Jones & Bartlett Learning, LLC.

—Excel 2007 VBA Programming with XML & ASP. 2008. (ENG., Illus.). 879p. pap. 43.95 (978-1-59822-043-8(8)) Jones & Bartlett Learning, LLC.

—Microsoft(r) Excel(r) 2010 Programming by Example: With VBA, XML, & ASP. 2011. 800p. pap. 49.95 (978-1-936420-03-2(1)) Mercury Learning & Information.

Liberty, Jesse, et al. ASP. NET 3.5. 2nd rev. annot. ed. 2008. (ENG., Illus.). 608p. pap. 44.99 (978-0-596-51845-5(5)) O'Reilly Media, Inc.

—Learning Asp. Net 2.0 with Ajax: A Practical Hands-On Guide. 2007. (ENG., Illus.). 528p. per. 44.99 (978-0-596-51397-9(6)) O'Reilly Media, Inc.

—Programming ASP.NET 3.5. 4th rev. ed. 2008. (ENG., Illus.). 1168p. pap. 59.99 (978-0-596-52956-7(2)) O'Reilly Media, Inc.

Love, Chris. Leveraging httpHandlers to Stream Custom Content in ASP. NET. 2008. (Wrox Briefs Ser.). 6.99 (978-0-470-37940-0(5), Wrox) Wiley, John & Sons, Inc.

—Leveraging httpModules for Better ASP. NET Applications. 2008. (Wrox Briefs Ser.). 40p. 6.99 (978-0-470-37939-4(1), Wrox) Wiley, John & Sons, Inc.

Lowe, Doug, et al. ASP. NET 2. 0. 2006. (ENG., Illus.). 936p. pap. 34.99 (978-0-471-78598-9(9), For Dummies) Wiley, John & Sons, Inc.

Lydford, Steve. Building ASP. NET Web Pages with Microsoft WebMatrix. 2011. (ENG.). 504p. pap. 39.99 **(978-1-4302-4020-4(2))** Apress L. P.

MacDonald, Matthew. Beginning ASP. NET 3. 5 in C# 2008. 2nd ed. 2007. (Expert's Voice in . Net Ser.). (ENG., Illus.). 954p. per. 49.99 (978-1-59059-891-7(1)) Apress L. P.

—Beginning ASP .NET 3.5 in VB 2008. 2nd ed. 2007. (Expert's Voice in .NET Ser.). (ENG., Illus.). 956p. per. 49.99 (978-1-59059-892-4(X)) Apress L. P.

—Beginning ASP. NET 4 in C# 2010. 2010. (ENG.). 1016p. pap. 49.99 *(978-1-4302-2608-6(0))* Apress L. P.

—Beginning ASP. NET 4 in VB 2010. 2010. (ENG.). 1080p. pap. 49.99 *(978-1-4302-2611-6(0))* Apress L. P.

—Pro Silverlight 5 in C# 4th ed. 2012. (ENG., Illus.). 700p. pap. 49.99 *(978-1-4302-3479-1(2))* Apress L. P.

—Pro Silverlight 5 in VB. 4th ed. 2012. (ENG.). 976p. pap. 59.99 *(978-1-4302-3518-7(7))* Apress L. P.

—Silverlight & ASP. NET Revealed. 2007. (ENG., Illus.). 50p. pap. 14.99 *(978-1-59059-939-6(X))* Apress L. P.

MacDonald, Matthew & Freeman, Adam. Pro ASP. NET 4 in C# 2010. 4th ed. 2010. (ENG.). 1616p. pap. 59.99 *(978-1-4302-2529-4(7))* Apress L. P.

MacDonald, Matthew & Szpuszta, Mario. ASP. NET 3. 5 in C# 2008. 2nd ed. 2007. (Expert's Voice In . Net Ser.). (ENG., Illus.). 1498p. per. 59.99 *(978-1-59059-893-1(8))* Apress L. P.

—Pro ASP. NET 3. 5 in C# 2008: Includes Silverlight 2. 3rd ed. 2008. (ENG.). 1520p. pap. 59.99 *(978-1-4302-1567-7(4))* Apress L. P.

—Pro ASP. NET 3. 5 in C# 2008: Includes Silverlight 2 & the ADO. NET Entity Framework. Third Edition. 2008. 1200p. pap. 59.99 *(978-1-4302-1566-0(6))* Apress L. P.

MacDonald, Matthew, et al. Pro ASP. NET 3. 5 in VB 2008: Includes Silverlight 2. 2008. (ENG.). 1500p. pap. 59.99 *(978-1-4302-1630-8(1))* Apress L. P.

—Pro ASP. NET 4 in VB 2010. 3rd ed. 2010. (ENG.). 1664p. pap. 59.99 *(978-1-4302-2511-9(4))* Apress L. P.

McClure, Wallace B., et al. Beginning Ajax with ASP. NET. 2006. (ENG., Illus.). 432p. pap. 39.99 *(978-0-471-78544-6(X),* Wrox) Wiley, John & Sons, Inc.

—Beginning ASP.NET 2.0 AJAX. 2007. (ENG., Illus.). 344p. per. 39.99 *(978-0-470-11283-0(2),* Wrox) Wiley, John & Sons, Inc.

McWherter, Jeff & Hall, Ben. Testing ASP. NET Web Applications. 2009. (ENG., Illus.). 432p. pap. 59.99 *(978-0-470-49664-0(9),* Wrox) Wiley, John & Sons, Inc.

Microsoft Official Academic Course Staff. Microsoft .NET Framework 3.5, ASP .NET Application Development: Exam 70-562, 2 vols. 2010. (ENG., Illus.). 624p. (C). pap. 146.95 *(978-0-470-55139-4(9),* Wiley) Wiley, John & Sons, Inc.

Millett, Scott. Professional ASP. NET Design Patterns. 2010. (ENG., Illus.). 720p. pap. 49.99 *(978-0-470-29278-5(4),* Wrox) Wiley, John & Sons, Inc.

Millett, Scott, et al. Pro Agile . NET Development with SCRUM. 2011. (ENG.). 392p. pap. 49.99 *(978-1-4302-3533-0(0))* Apress L. P.

Milner, Dave. Pro ASP. NET SharePoint 2010 Solutions: Techniques for Building Sharepoint Functionality into ASP. NET Applications. 2010. (ENG.). 368p. pap. 49.99 *(978-1-4302-3111-0(4))* Apress L. P.

Mitchell, Scott. ASP.NET 3.5, Kit. 2008. (Sams Teach Yourself — Hours Ser.). (ENG., Illus.). 648p. pap. 39.99 *(978-0-672-32997-5(2))* Sams.

—ASP.NET 4.0, Kit. 2010. (Sams Teach Yourself — Hours Ser.). (ENG., Illus.). 648p. pap. 34.99 *(978-0-672-33305-7(8))* Sams.

MOAC. 70-564: Designing & Developing ASP. NET Applications Using the Microsoft . Net Framework 3. 5, 2 vols. 2010. (ENG., Illus.). 384p. (C). pap. 127.95 *(978-0-470-57812-4(2),* Wiley) Wiley, John & Sons, Inc.

MOAC. 70-564: Designing & Developing ASP. NET Applications Using the Microsoft . Net Framework 3. 5 Lab Manual, 2 vols. 2010. (ENG., Illus.). 264p. (C). pap. 33.95 ***(978-0-470-57813-1(0),*** Wiley) Wiley, John & Sons, Inc.

Moroney, Laurence. Beginning Web Development, Silverlight, & ASP. NET AJAX. 2008. (Expert's Voice In . Net Ser.). (ENG., Illus.). 427p. per. 44.99 *(978-1-59059-959-4(4))* Apress L. P.

—Introducing Microsoft WebMatrix. 2011. (ENG., Illus.). 352p. pap. 39.99 *(978-0-7356-4970-5(7))* Microsoft Pr.

Moroney, Laurence & MacDonald, Matthew. Pro ASP. NET 2. 0 in VB 2005. ed. 2006. (Expert's Voice In . Net Ser.). (ENG., Illus.). 1360p. 64.99 *(978-1-59059-776-7(1))* Apress L. P.

Moroney, Laurence, et al. Foundations of ASP. NET AJAX. 2nd ed. 2007. (Expert's Voice In . Net Ser.). (ENG., Illus.). 268p. per. 39.99 *(978-1-59059-828-3(8))* Apress L. P.

Neese, Darren. DotNetNuke Skinning Tutorial. 2008. 156p. pap. *(978-1-84719-278-3(5))* Packt Publishing, Ltd.

Neimke, Darren. ASP. Net 2. 0 Web Parts in Action: Building Dynamic Web Portals. 2006. (In Action Ser.). (ENG., Illus.). 456p. per. 44.99 *(978-1-932394-77-1(X))* Manning Pubns. Co.

Niblack, Jeff & Nolan, Godfrey. ASP Application Performance & Tuning. 350p. 39.99 *(978-0-7357-1050-4(3))* New Riders Publishing.

Onion, Fritz. Essential ASP. Net 2. 0. 2nd ed. 2006. (Microsoft .NET Development Ser.). (ENG., Illus.). 384p. per. 54.99 *(978-0-321-23770-5(6))* Addison Wesley Professional.

Palermo, Jeffrey, et al. ASP. NET MVC 3 in Action. 3rd ed. 2012. (ENG.). 450p. pap. 49.99 ***(978-1-61729-041-1(6))*** Manning Pubns. Co.

—ASP.NET MVC 2. 2nd ed. 2010. (ENG., Illus.). 450p. pap. 49.99 *(978-1-935182-79-5(X))* Manning Pubns. Co.

—ASP.NET MVC in Action. 2009. (ENG., Illus.). 392p. pap. 44.99 *(978-1-933988-62-7(2))* Manning Pubns. Co.

Parsons, Doug. Migrating to LINQ to SQL in TheBeerHouse & ASP. NET 2. 0 Website Programming Problem Design Solution. 2008. (Wrox Briefs Ser.). 38p. 6.99 *(978-0-470-37501-3(9),* Wrox) Wiley, John & Sons, Inc.

Paterra, Chris, et al. Professional DotNetNuke Module Programming. 2009. (ENG., Illus.). 336p. pap. 49.99 *(978-0-470-17116-5(2),* Wrox) Wiley, John & Sons, Inc.

Preul, Wyatt, et al. Professional Community Server. 2007. (ENG., Illus.). 312p. per. 39.99 *(978-0-470-10828-4(2),* Wrox) Wiley, John & Sons, Inc.

Renner, Patrick & Hammond, Christopher J. DotNetNuke 5: Get Your Website up & Running. 2009. (ENG., Illus.). 312p. pap., instr.'s gde. ed. 44.99 *(978-0-470-46257-7(4),* Wrox) Wiley, John & Sons, Inc.

Sanders, William & Sanders, William B. ASP.NET 3.5. 2nd ed. 2008. (Beginner's Guide Ser.). (ENG., Illus.). 448p. pap. 39.99 *(978-0-07-159194-2(X),* 007159194X) McGraw-Hill Osborne.

Sanderson, Steven. Pro ASP. NET MVC 2 Framework. 2nd ed. 2010. (ENG.). 776p. pap. 54.99 *(978-1-4302-2886-8(5))* Apress L. P.

—Pro ASP. NET MVC Framework. 2009. (ENG.). 550p. pap. 49.99 *(978-1-4302-1007-8(9))* Apress L. P.

Sanderson, Steven E. ASP. NET MVC Framework Preview. 2008. (ENG.). 100p. pap. 19.99 *(978-1-4302-1646-9(8))* Apress L. P.

Sanford, Jacob J. Professional ASP. NET 2. 0 Design: CSS, Themes, & Master Pages. 2007. (ENG., Illus.). 474p. per. 39.99 *(978-0-470-12448-2(2),* Wrox) Wiley, John & Sons, Inc.

Sarknas, Paul. Pro ASP. NET 2. 0 E-Commerce in C# 2005. 2006. (Expert's Voice In . Net Ser.). (ENG., Illus.). 640p. pap. 59.99 *(978-1-59059-724-8(9))* Apress L. P.

Schackow, Stefan & Haidar, Bilal. Professional Asp. Net 3.5 Security, Membership, & Role Management with C# & VB. 2008. (ENG., Illus.). 936p. pap. 59.99 *(978-0-470-37930-1(8),* Wrox) Wiley, John & Sons, Inc.

Shaw, John & Evans, Simon. Pro Ado. Net Data Services: Working with Restful Data. 2008. (ENG.). 336p. pap. 49.99 *(978-1-4302-1614-8(X))* Apress L. P.

Shepherd, George. Microsoft ASP.NET 3.5. 2nd ed. 2008. (ENG., Illus.). 592p. pap. 39.99 *(978-0-7356-2426-9(7))* Microsoft Pr.

Sheriff, Paul D. Fundamentals of Asp Net. 2008. 244p. pap. 24.95 *(978-0-9793748-7-6(1))* PDSA, Inc.

Sheriff, Paul D. & Byrd, James H. Fundamentals of Asp Net Security. 2009. 228p. pap. 24.95 *(978-0-9816946-1-0(6))* PDSA, Inc.

Spaanjaars, Imar. ASP.NET 4.0: In C# & VB. 2010. (ENG., Illus.). 840p. pap. 44.99 *(978-0-470-50221-1(5),* Wrox) Wiley, John & Sons, Inc.

—Beginning ASP.NET 3.5: In C# & VB. 2008. (ENG., Illus.). 768p. pap. 44.99 *(978-0-470-18759-3(X),* Wrox) Wiley, John & Sons, Inc.

—A Blogging Application in ASP. NET 2. 0. 2007. (Wrox Briefs Ser.). 52p. 6.99 *(978-0-470-26121-7(8),* Wrox) Wiley, John & Sons, Inc.

Stehling, Brennan. Pro ASP. NET for SQL Server: High Performance Data Access for Web Developers. 2007. (Pro Ser.). (ENG., Illus.). 408p. per. 59.99 *(978-1-59059-860-3(1))* Apress L. P.

Swift, Jonathan, et al. Professional Silverlight 2 for ASP. NET Developers. 2009. (ENG., Illus.). 672p. pap. 49.99 *(978-0-470-27775-1(0),* Wrox) Wiley, John & Sons, Inc.

Sych, Oleg & Patterson, Randy. ASP. NET Dynamic Data Unleashed. 2012. (Unleashed Ser.). (ENG.). 544p. pap. 49.99 *(978-0-672-33565-5(4))* Sams.

Szpuszta, Mario & MacDonald, Matthew. Pro ASP. NET 2. 0 in C# 2005. ed. 2006. (ENG., Illus.). 1464p. 64.99 *(978-1-59059-768-2(0))* Apress L. P.

Thangarathinam, Thiru. Professional ASP. NET 2. 0 Databases. 2007. (ENG., Illus.). 504p. per. 49.99 *(978-0-470-04179-6(X),* Wrox) Wiley, John & Sons, Inc.

Walker, Shaun, et al. Professional DotNetNuke No. 5: Open Source Web Application Framework for ASP.NET. 2009. (ENG., Illus.). 600p. pap. 49.99 *(978-0-470-43870-1(3),* Wrox) Wiley, John & Sons, Inc.

—Professional DotNetNuke 4: Open Source Web Application Framework for ASP. NET 2. 0. 2006. (ENG., Illus.). 552p. pap. 39.99 *(978-0-471-78816-4(3),* Wrox) Wiley, John & Sons, Inc.

Walther, Stephen. ASP. NET 3. 5 Unleashed. 2011. (Unleashed Ser.). (ENG., Illus.). 1920p. pap. 59.99 *(978-0-672-33564-8(6))* Sams.

—ASP.NET MVC Framework. 2009. (Unleashed Ser.). (ENG., Illus.). 744p. pap. 54.99 *(978-0-672-32998-2(0))* Sams.

Walther, Stephen, et al. Agile ASP. NET Unleashed. 2012. (Unleashed Ser.). (ENG.). 400p. pap. 44.99 ***(978-0-672-33582-2(4))*** Sams.

Wenz, Christian. Programming ASP. Net AJAX. 2007. (ENG., Illus.). 480p. per. 39.99 *(978-0-596-51424-2(7))* O'Reilly Media, Inc.

White, Damien. ASP. NET AJAX Control Development with Visual Studio 2008 & . NET 3. 5 Framework. 2008. (Wrox Briefs Ser.). 40p. 6.99 *(978-0-470-28665-4(2),* Wrox) Wiley, John & Sons, Inc.

—Hands on ASP. NET AJAX Control Toolkit. 2008. (Wrox Briefs Ser.). 44p. 6.99 *(978-0-470-28664-7(4),* Wrox) Wiley, John & Sons, Inc.

Wittenkeller, Tracy. DotNetNuke Websites: Problem - Design - Solution. 2008. (ENG.). 360p. pap. 49.99 *(978-0-470-19064-7(7),* Wrox) Wiley, John & Sons, Inc.

Wright, Tol B., et al. ASP. NET 4 24-Hour Trainer. 2010. (ENG., Illus.). 552p. pap. 44.99 *(978-0-470-59691-3(0),* Wrox) Wiley, John & Sons, Inc.

Young, Mike. Programming Dynamic Websites Using ASP. 2009. 99p. pap. 25.50 *(978-0-9559877-1-7(7))* Young, Mike GBR. Dist: Lulu Enterprises Inc.

ACTIVE TRANSPORT

see Biological Transport

ACTIVEX (COMPUTER PROGRAM)

Boehm, Anne. Murach's ADO. NET 3. 5, LINQ, & the Entity Framework with VB 2008. 2009. (Illus.). 707p. pap. 52.50 *(978-1-890774-52-3(9))* Murach, Mike & Assocs., Inc.

Boehm, Anne & Mead, Ged. Murach's ADO. NET 4 Database Programming with VB 2010. 4th ed. 2011. (Illus.). 756p. pap. 54.50 *(978-1-890774-62-2(6))* Murach, Mike & Assocs., Inc.

Hamilton, Bill. ADO. NET 3. 5 Cookbook. 2nd rev. ed. 2008. (Cookbooks (o'Reilly) Ser.). (ENG., Illus.). 992p. pap. 54.99 *(978-0-596-10140-4(6))* O'Reilly Media, Inc.

Kimmel, Paul & Kimmel. ADO.NET Entity Framework. 2010. (Sams Teach Yourself — Hours Ser.). (ENG.). 400p. pap. 34.99 *(978-0-672-33053-7(9))* Sams.

Mostarda, Stefano, et al. Entity Framework 4 in Action. rev. ed. 2011. (ENG., Illus.). 576p. pap. 49.99 *(978-1-935182-18-4(8))* Manning Pubns. Co.

Riordan, Rebecca M. Fluent ADO. NET Entity Framework. 2012. (ENG.). 500p. pap. 49.99 ***(978-0-672-33592-1(1))*** Sams.

Sceppa, David. Programming Microsoft ADO. NET, No. 4. 2012. (ENG.). 770p. pap. 35.99 *(978-0-7356-4801-2(8))* Microsoft Pr.

ACTIVISM, STUDENT

see Student Movements

ACTIVISTS, ANIMAL RIGHTS

see Animal Rights Activists

ACTIVISTS, POLITICAL

see Political Activists

ACTIVITIES, STUDENT

see Student Activities

ACTIVITY COEFFICIENTS

International Society For Comparative Physical Education And Sport Staff. Physical Activity for Life: East & West, South & North. 550p. pap. *(978-3-89124-321-3(9))* Meyer & Meyer Fachverlag und Buchhandel GmbH.

ACTIVITY LEARNING

see Active Learning

ACTIVITY PROGRAMS IN EDUCATION

see also Creative Activities and Seat Work; Project Method in Teaching

Abbott, Lorraine. Friday Afternoon GCSE Religious Studies, Pack. 2010. (Illus.). 200p. 210.00 *(978-1-4441-1041-8(1))* Hodder Education GBR. Dist: Trans-Atlantic Pubns., Inc.

Abrahams, Ian, et al. Performing Science: Teaching Chemistry, Physics & Biology Through Drama & Role Play. Abrahams, Ian & Braund, Martin, eds. 2012. (ENG., Illus.). 160p. pap. 55.00 *(978-1-4411-6071-3(X))* Continuum International Publishing Group, Ltd. GBR. Dist: National Bk. Network.

Alexander, Kay. Art Activities with Paper, Clay, Fibers, & Printmaking: Using Masterworks As Inspiration. 2011. ***(978-1-56290-662-7(3))*** Crystal Productions.

Alkandari, Khaled. The Use of Posters & Perceived Values in Schools. 2010. 140p. pap. *(978-3-639-23946-1(6))* VDM Verlag Dr. Mueller e.K.

Allen, Marty. Hands-on Science Series Water. 2nd rev. ed. 2009. 156p. (YA). pap. 25.00 *(978-0-8251-6522-1(9))* Walch Education.

Alley, Kathleen M. Teaching Integrated Reading Strategies in the Middle School Library Media Center, 1 vol. 2008. (Illus.). 172p. pap. 35.00 *(978-1-59158-645-6(3),* LU8645) Libraries Unlimited, Inc.

Anderson, Laurie Halse. Speak: Activity Pack. 2008. 156p. spiral bd. 55.95 *(978-1-60389-057-1(2))* Prestwick Hse., Inc.

Anderson, Sally. Social Studies & Me! Using Children's Books to Learn about Our World. 2011. (ENG.). 224p. pap. 24.95 *(978-0-87659-331-8(7))* Gryphon Hse., Inc.

Andrews, Larry. Language Exploration & Awareness: A Resource Book for Teachers. 3rd rev. ed. 2006. (ENG., Illus.). 368p. per. 52.95 *(978-0-8058-4308-8(6))* Routledge.

Armstrong, Linda & Heitman, Jane. Jumpstarters for Analogies: Short Daily Warm-Ups for the Classroom. 2010. (Jumpstarters Ser.). (ENG., Illus.). 48p. (gr. 4-9). pap. 8.99 *(978-1-58037-533-7(2))* Twain, Mark Media, Inc. Pubs.

Athans, Sandra K. & Devine, Denise Ashe. Fun-Tastic Activities for Differentiating Comprehension Instruction, Grades 2-6. 2010. (ENG.). 192p. pap. 24.95 *(978-0-87207-476-7(5))* International Reading Assn.

Austen, Jane. Pride & Prejudice: Novel Test: Prestwick Premium Downloadable Resources. 2007. 7p. 5.99 *(978-1-60843-664-4(0))* Prestwick Hse., Inc.

Balkin, Alfred. Tune up to Literacy: Original Songs & Activities for Kids. 2009. 45.00 *(978-0-8389-0998-0(1))* American Library Assn.

Ball, Ann. Crafty Catholic Kids: Great Activities for Family Fun & Faith. 2008. (Illus.). 118p. pap. 19.95 *(978-1-59276-280-4(8))* Our Sunday Visitor, Publishing Div.

Bamberger, Honi Joyce & Oberdorf, Christine. Activities to Undo Math Misconceptions: Grades 3-5. 2010. 144p. pap. 25.00 *(978-0-325-02617-6(3),* E02617) Heinemann.

Bamberger, Honi Joyce & Schultz-Ferrell, Karren. Activities to Undo Math Misconceptions: PreK-Grade 2. 2010. 152p. pap. 25.00 *(978-0-325-02614-5(9),* E02614) Heinemann.

Bance, Linda. Musical Ideas for Early Learning. 2012. (ENG., Illus.). 112p. pap. 48.95 ***(978-0-415-67921-3(4))*** Routledge.

Bane, Rebecca C. Let's Pretend: 50 Start-To-Finish Preschooler Programs for the Busy Librarian That Foster Imagination. 2010. 143p. 55.00 *(978-1-55570-726-6(9))* Neal-Schuman Pubs., Inc.

Barbour, Ann C., ed. Learning at Home, PreK-3: Homework Activities That Engage Children & Families. 2009. (Illus.). 208p. 76.95 *(978-1-4129-6327-5(3),* B63275C); pap. 31.95 *(978-1-4129-6328-2(1),* B63275P) Corwin Pr.

Barron, Paul. Practical Ideas, Games & Activities for the Primary Lessons. 2008. (ENG., Illus.). 312p. pap. *(978-1-4058-5945-5(8))* Addison-Wesley Longman, Inc.

Beane, Allan L. The New Bully Free Classroom: Proven Prevention & Intervention Strategies for Teachers K-8. 3rd ed. 2011. (Bully Free Classroom Ser.). (ENG.). 192p. (gr. k-8). 39.99 *(978-1-57542-382-1(0))* Free Spirit Publishing, Inc.

Becker, Shawnj. Object Lessons That Speak Louder Than Words: 70 Action-Based Activities That Teach. 2008. (ENG.). 88p. 16.95 *(978-1-930572-53-9(0))* Educational Media Corp.

Bellanca, James A. 200+ Active Learning Strategies & Projects for Engaging Students' Multiple Intelligences. 2nd ed. 2008. (Illus.). 368p. pap. 44.95 *(978-1-4129-6885-0(2),* B68843P) Corwin Pr.

Beller, Joel & Magliore, Kim. Hands-on Science Series Electricity & Magnetism: Electricity & Magnetism. 2nd rev. ed. 2009. 148p. (YA). pap. 25.00 *(978-0-8251-6519-1(9))* Walch Education.

Benbow, Elaine. The Really Useful Art Book. 2012. (Really Useful Ser.). (ENG.). 144p. (C). pap. 44.95 *(978-0-415-67835-3(8))* Routledge.

Berke, Kai-Lee, et al. The Creative Curriculum for Preschool Teaching Guide Featuring the Reduce, Reuse, Recycle Study. 2010. *(978-1-60617-386-2(3))* Teaching Strategies, Inc.

—The Creative Curriculum for Preschool Teaching Guide Featuring the Trees Study. 2010. *(978-1-60617-387-9(1))* Teaching Strategies, Inc.

—El Currículo Creativo para Educación Preescolar Guía de Enseñanza Estudio de Cómo Reducir, Reutilizar y Reciclar. 2012. (SPA & ENG.). *(978-1-60617-413-5(4))* Teaching Strategies, Inc.

—El Currículo Creativo para Educación Preescolar Guía de Enseñanza Estudio de Las Pelotas, Bolas y Balones. 2012. (SPA & ENG.). *(978-1-60617-410-4(X))* Teaching Strategies, Inc.

Between the Lions Staff. L Is for Lion: And Other Playful Alphabet Fun. 2011. (ENG., Illus.). 72p. pap. 12.95 *(978-0-87659-354-7(6))* Gryphon Hse., Inc.

—Wild about Literacy: Fun Activities for Preschool. 2010. (ENG., Illus.). 224p. pap. 24.95 *(978-0-87659-306-6(6))* Gryphon Hse., Inc.

Bird, Ronit. The Dyscalculia Resource Book: Games & Puzzles for ages 7 To 14. 2011. (Illus.). 248p. 140.00 ***(978-1-4462-0167-1(8),*** B01671C); pap. 54.00 ***(978-1-4462-0168-8(6),*** B01671P) SAGE Pubns., Ltd. GBR. Dist: SAGE Pubns., Inc.

Blair, Sally Jo. Group Activities for Kids Who Hurt. 2011. 104p. pap. 21.95 ***(978-1-56499-077-8(X))*** Innerchoice Publishing.

Bland, Janice. Mini-Plays & Role Rhymes & Other Stepping Stones to English: Favourite Festivals. 2009. (J). *(978-0-88734-981-2(?))* Players Pr., Inc.

Boisvert, Christine & Gainsley, Suzanne. The Teacher's Idea Book Series: 50 Large-Group Activities for Active Learners. 2006. (Illus.). vii, 139p. *(978-1-57379-282-0(9))* High/Scope Pr.

Bouzoukis, Carol E. Encouraging Your Child's Imagination: A Guide & Stories for Play Acting. 2012. ***(978-1-4422-1289-3(6))*** 2011. (ENG.). 224p. 34.95 ***(978-1-4422-1287-9(X))*** Rowman & Littlefield Publishers, Inc.

Bower, Virginia. Games, Ideas & Activities for Primary Poetry. rev. ed. 2011. (ENG., Illus.). 352p. pap. 39.50 ***(978-1-4082-5934-4(6))*** Pearson Education, Ltd. GBR. Dist: Trans-Atlantic Pubns., Inc.

Bowkett, Wendy & Baillie, Christine. Activities for Individual Learning Through Rhyme: Resources for the Early Years Practitioner. 2010. (ENG., Illus.). 224p. 55.00 *(978-1-4411-6839-9(7))* Continuum International Publishing Group, Ltd. GBR. Dist: National Bk. Network.

—Activities for Individual Learning Through Shape & Colour: Resources for the Early Years Practitioner. 2010. (ENG., Illus.). 232p. 55.00 *(978-1-4411-5554-2(6))* Continuum International Publishing Group, Ltd. GBR. Dist: National Bk. Network.

Bradberry, Mary Ann. WEE Learn: Curriculum Guide for Pre-K. 2007. (Illus.). 688p. 219.95 *(978-1-4158-5202-6(2))* LifeWay Christian Resources.

Bray, Beth. Phonemic Awareness Activities & Games for Early Learners: Early Childhood. 2007. (Early Learner Ser.). (ENG., Illus.). 176p. (gr. k-1). pap., pap. 29.99 incl. cd-rom *(978-1-4258-0144-1(7))* Shell Educational Publishing.

Bray, Beth Anne. Early Childhood Phonemic Awareness Activities, Grades Pre-K-1: Literacy, Language, & Learning. 2010. (Early Childhood Activities Ser.). (Illus.). 176p. (gr. -1-1). pap. 29.99 *(978-1-4258-0697-2(X))* Shell Educational Publishing.

Briggs, Dianne. Toddler Storytimes II. 2008. (ENG.). 176p. pap. 55.00 *(978-0-8108-6057-5(0))* Scarecrow Pr., Inc.

Brodie, David & Parsonage, Max. Friday Afternoon AQA Science & Additional Science GCSE. Pack. 2010. (Illus.). 200p. 210.00 *(978-1-4441-0842-2(5))* Hodder Education GBR. Dist: Trans-Atlantic Pubns., Inc.

Bruce, Nefertiti & Cairone, Karen. Socially Strong, Emotionally Secure: 50 Activities to Promote Resilience in Young Children. 2011. (ENG.). 144p. pap. 16.95 *(978-0-87659-332-5(5))* Gryphon Hse., Inc.

Bruce, Tina. Learning Through Play: For Babies, Toddlers & Young Children. 2nd rev. ed. 2011. (ENG., Illus.). 144p. pap. 35.00 *(978-1-4441-3716-3(6))* Hodder Arnold Pubs.

Bryant, Sara Cone. How to Tell Stories to Children & Some Stories to Tell. 2008. 188p. 22.99 *(978-0-554-35069-1(6))* 2008. 188p. 25.99 *(978-0-554-25766-2(1))* 2007. (ENG.). 168p. pap. 19.99 *(978-1-4264-7496-5(2))* 2007. (ENG.). 186p. pap. 21.99 *(978-1-4264-9878-7(0))* BiblioBazaar.

—How to Tell Stories to Children & Some Stories to Tell. 2008. (Illus.). 176p. pap. *(978-1-4099-1287-3(6))* Dodo Pr.

—How to Tell Stories to Children & Some Stories to Tell. 2009. (ENG.). 180p. pap. 13.95 *(978-1-4357-4332-8(6))* Lulu Enterprises Inc.

Buffolano, Sandra. Coping with Tourette Syndrome: A Workbook for Kids with Tic Disorders. 2008. (Instant Help Ser.). (ENG.). 136p. (J). pap. 16.95 *(978-1-57224-632-4(4))* New Harbinger Pubns.

Burkins, Jan Miller & Croft, Melody. Preventing Misguided Reading: New Strategies for Guided Reading Teachers. 2010. 160p. pap. 24.95 *(978-978-087-207-6(8),* B72076P) Corwin Pr.

Burkins, Jan Miller & Croft, Melody M. Preventing Misguided Reading: New Strategies for Guided Reading Teachers. 2010. (ENG., Illus.). 160p. pap. 24.95 *(978-0-87207-828-4(0),* B72076P) International Reading Assn.

Butler, Heather. Literacy in Action: Football - 24 Flexible Lessons for Ages 9-11. 2010. (ENG., Illus.). 168p. 140.00 *(978-0-415-56486-1(7));* pap. 37.95 *(978-0-415-56485-4(9))* Taylor & Francis Group GBR. (Routledge). Dist: Taylor & Francis Group.

Calder, Hunter. Early Language Skills - Beginning to Read. 2008. (Early Language Skills Ser.). (ENG., Illus.). 96p. pap. 9.99 *(978-1-4206-8068-3(4))* Teacher Created Resources, Inc.

—Early Language Skills - Consonant Sounds. 2008. (Early Language Skills Ser.). (ENG., Illus.). 96p. pap. 9.99 *(978-1-4206-8065-2(X))* Teacher Created Resources, Inc.

—Reading with Sounds. 2008. (Early Language Skills Ser.). (ENG., Illus.). 96p. pap. 9.99 *(978-1-4206-8067-6(6))* Teacher Created Resources, Inc.

Callahan, Elisabeth & Callahan, Patrick. On My Own Two Feet: Helping Your Baby with Hypotonia Learn to Walk. 2010. 115p. pap. 24.95 *(978-0-578-05119-2(2))* Baby Walk LLC.

Çankaya, Dilek. Migration Within Turkey & Adult Education. 2010. 88p. pap. *(978-3-8383-5220-6(3))* Lambert Academic Publishing.

Carleton, Jessica Perich. Story Drama in the Special Needs Classroom: Step-by-Step Lesson Plans for Teaching Through Dramatic Play. 2012. 160p. pap. ***(978-1-84905-859-9(8))*** Kingsley, Jessica Ltd.

Carter, John Marshall. Gods, Heroes, Myths, & Legends: Activities for Elementary & Middle School Literature. 2009. 66p. pap. 10.64 *(978-0-557-07157-9(7))* Lulu Enterprises Inc.

Cataldo, Jodi L. Hugging the World: Children's Mission Study & Teacher's Guide: Faith, Hope, Love in Action. 2010. (Illus.). 48p. (J). pap. 8.00 *(978-1-933663-42-5(1),* WD/GBGM Bks.) General Board of Global Ministries, The United Methodist Church.

Cave, Sue. More Fun Ideas for Advancing Modern Foreign Languages in the Primary Classroom. 2010. (Illus.). 82p. pap. *(978-1-905780-72-3(9))* Brilliant Pubns.

Champion-Chupp, Nancy. Get Ready to Learn, 0 vols. 2008. 100p. pap. 8.99 *(978-0-8499-2884-0(2))* Nelson, Thomas Inc.

Champions Challenge Holiday Club Programme. 2007. 80p. pap. *(978-1-84427-270-9(2))* Scripture Union.

Chappell, Michaele F. & Thompson, Denisse R. Math, Culture, & Popular Media: Activities to Engage Middle School Students Through Film, Literature, & the Internet. 2009. 160p. pap. 26.25 *(978-0-325-02122-5(8),* E02122) Heinemann.

Charner, Kathy. Learn Every Day about Numbers. Charner, Kathy, ed. 2009. (Learn Every Day Ser.). (ENG., Illus.). 128p. pap. 12.95 *(978-0-87659-090-4(3))* Gryphon Hse., Inc.

—Learn Every Day about Seasons. 2011. (Learn Every Day Ser.). (ENG., Illus.). 128p. (gr. -1-k). pap. 12.95 ***(978-0-87659-364-6(3))*** Gryphon Hse., Inc.

—Learn Every Day about Shapes. Charner, Kathy, ed. 2009. (Learn Every Day Ser.). (ENG., Illus.). 128p. pap. 12.95 *(978-0-87659-092-8(X))* Gryphon Hse., Inc.

Charner, Kathy. Learn Every Day about Social Studies. 2011. (Learn Every Day Ser.). (ENG., Illus.). 128p. (gr. -1-k). pap. 12.95 ***(978-0-87659-363-9(5))*** Gryphon Hse., Inc.

Charner, Kathy, ed. Learn Every Day about Colors. 2009. (Learn Every Day Ser.). (ENG., Illus.). 128p. pap. 12.95 *(978-0-87659-088-1(1))* Gryphon Hse., Inc.

Church, Ellen Booth. Literacy-Building Transition Activities: Dozens of Quick & Easy Activities That Infuse Learning into Every Minute of the Day. 2008. (ENG.). 160p. pap. 18.99 *(978-0-439-65088-5(7),* Teaching Resources) Scholastic, Inc.

Clark Brack, Jenny. Learn to Move, Moving up! Sensorimotor Elementary-School Activity Themes. 2009. pap. 34.95 *(978-1-934575-38-3(0))* Autism Asperger Publishing Co.

Cohen, Arlene. Stories on the Move: Integrating Literature & Movement with Children, from Infants to Age 14, 1 vol. 2007. (Illus.). 248p. per. 32.00 *(978-1-59158-418-6(3),* LU4183) Libraries Unlimited, Inc.

Collins, Anne & Dacey, Linda. Zeroing in on Number & Operations: Key Ideas & Common Misconceptions, Grades 7-8. 2010. (ENG.). 64p. (C). spiral bd. 15.00 *(978-1-57110-799-2(1))* Stenhouse Pubs.

Collins, Margaret. Circle Time for the Very Young. 3rd ed. 2011. (Lucky Duck Bks.). (Illus.). 192p. pap. 42.00 *(978-0-85702-424-4(8),* B24244P) SAGE Pubns., Ltd. GBR. Dist: SAGE Pubns., Inc.

Colombo, Leone & Bianchi, Rachele. Preschool Children: Physical Activity, Behavioral Assessment & Developmental Challenges. 2010. (Children's Issues, Laws & Programs Ser.). (Illus.). 210p. 129.00 *(978-1-60876-026-8(X))* Nova Science Pubs., Inc.

Colston, Valerie. Teens Go Green! Tips, Techniques, Tools, & Themes for YA Programming. 2011. E-Book ***(978-1-59158-930-3(4))*** Libraries Unlimited, Inc.

Corbett, Pie. Jumpstart! Storymaking: Games & Activities for Ages 7-12. 2009. (Jumpstart! Ser.). (ENG., Illus.). 144p. pap. 23.95 *(978-0-415-46686-8(5))* Fulton, David Pubs. GBR. Dist: Taylor & Francis Group.

Corpus, Deborah & Giddings, Ann. Planning & Managing Effective Reading Instruction Across the Content Areas: A Strategic, Time-Saving Guide with Planning Sheets, Model Lessons, & More to Help You Boost Students' Comprehension & Learning. 2010. (ENG.). 176p. (gr. k-8). pap. 21.99 *(978-0-545-07480-3(0),* Teaching Resources) Scholastic, Inc.

Cory-Wright, Kate. Kid's Box American English, Pack. 2011. (ENG.). 144p. pap. 30.00 incl. audio compact disk *(978-0-521-17808-2(8))* Cambridge Univ. Pr.

—Kid's Box American English Level 6 Teacher's Resource Pack with Audio CD. 2011. (ENG.). 144p. pap. 30.00 incl. audio compact disk *(978-0-521-17818-1(5))* Cambridge Univ. Pr.

Coulson, Gill & Cousins, Lynn. Classroom Gems: Games, Ideas & Activities for Early Years Literacy. 2011. (ENG., Illus.). 368p. pap. ***(978-1-4082-5417-2(4))*** Longman Publishing Group.

Cram101 Textbook Reviews. Outlines & Highlights for Elementary Classroom Teachers As Movement Educators by Susan Kovar, Isbn: 9780073376462. 2011. 284p. pap. 32.95 ***(978-1-61812-478-4(1))*** Cram101 Inc.

Cram101 Textbook Reviews. Outlines & Highlights for Infants, Toddlers, & Caregivers: A Curriculum of Respectful, Responsive Care & Education by Janet Gonzalez-Mena, ISBN. 2010. 78p. pap. 27.95 *(978-1-61698-097-9(4))* Cram101 Inc.

Cram101 Textbook Reviews & Cram101 Textbook Reviews. Outlines & Highlights for Every Child Can Learn: Using Learning Tools & Play to Help Children with Developmental Delay by Katrin Stroh, ISBN. 2011. 60p. pap. 26.95 ***(978-1-4288-6133-6(5))*** Cram101 Inc.

—Outlines & Highlights for Planning Effective Instruction: Diversity Responsive Methods & Management by Kay M. Price, ISBN. 2011. 104p. pap. 28.95 ***(978-1-4288-7978-2(1))*** Cram101 Inc.

—Outlines & Highlights for Preschool Appropriate Practices by Janice J Beaty, Isbn: 9781428304482. 2011. 132p. pap. 28.95 ***(978-1-61744-304-6(2))*** Cram101 Inc.

Cross, Aerial. Nature Sparks: Connecting Children's Learning to the Natural World. 2011. (ENG.). 208p. pap. 29.95 ***(978-1-60554-041-2(2))*** Redleaf Pr.

Cunningham, Patricia M. & Cunningham, James W. What Really Matters in Writing: Research-Based Practices Across the Curriculum. 2009. (What Really Matters Ser.). (ENG.). 240p. (C). pap. 38.99 *(978-0-205-62742-4(0),* Allyn & Bacon) Pearson Education Canada CAN. Dist: Pearson Education.

Curran, Margaret. Speaking & Listening Games. 2007. (Illus.). 112p. spiral bd. *(978-1-903853-56-6(7))* Brilliant Pubns.

Dabell, John. Games, Ideas & Activities for Primary Science. 2010. (ENG., Illus.). 364p. pap. 37.50 *(978-1-4082-2323-9(6))* Pearson Education, Ltd. GBR. Dist: Trans-Atlantic Pubns., Inc.

Dacey, Linda & Collins, Anne. Zeroing in on Number & Operations: Key Ideas & Common Misconceptions. 2010. (ENG.). (C). 68p. (gr. 3-4). spiral bd. 15.00 *(978-1-57110-795-4(9));* 64p. (gr. 5-6). spiral bd. 15.00 *(978-1-57110-798-5(3))* Stenhouse Pubs.

Dacey, Linda Schulman & Collins, Anne. Zeroing in on Number & Operations: Key Ideas & Common Misconceptions, Grades 1-2. 2010. (ENG.). 64p. (C). (gr. 1-2). spiral bd. 15.00 *(978-1-57110-797-8(5))* Stenhouse Pubs.

D'Avanzo, Maria. Turn & Talk K Sound. 2007. (J). spiral bd. 27.95 *(978-1-58650-779-4(6))* Super Duper Pubns.

—Turn & Talk S Sound. 2007. (J). spiral bd. 27.95 *(978-1-58650-710-7(9))* Super Duper Pubns.

Davies, Dan. Teaching Science Creatively. 2011. (ENG., Illus.). 176p. (C). pap. 31.95 *(978-0-415-56132-7(9))* Routledge.

Davies, Dan & Milne, Ian. Teaching Science Creatively. 2011. (ENG., Illus.). 176p. (C). 120.00 *(978-0-415-56131-0(0))* Routledge.

Davies, Peter, et al. Enlivening Secondary History: 50 Classroom Activities for Teachers & Pupils. 2nd rev. ed. 2012. (ENG., Illus.). 224p. 160.00 *(978-0-415-67833-9(1));* pap. 42.95 *(978-0-415-67832-2(3))* Routledge.

Davis, E. Ann. Physical Activity in the Wheelchair & Out: An Illustrated Guide to Personalizing Participation. 2011. (Illus.). 136p. pap. 24.00 ***(978-1-4504-0199-9(6))*** Human Kinetics Pubs.

Davis, Stephen. Math Games Galore: Addition & Subtraction Facts. 2009. pap. 12.99 *(978-1-59198-985-1(X))* Creative Teaching Pr., Inc.

—Math Games Galore: Number Sense & Place Value. 2009. pap. 12.99 *(978-1-59198-984-4(1))* Creative Teaching Pr., Inc.

—Math Games Galore: Operations & Math Facts. 2009. pap. 12.99 *(978-1-59198-988-2(4))* Creative Teaching Pr., Inc.

—Math Games Galore: Time & Money. 2009. pap. 12.99 *(978-1-59198-989-9(2));* pap. 12.99 *(978-1-59198-983-7(3));* pap. 12.99 *(978-1-59198-986-8(8))* Creative Teaching Pr., Inc.

Dawes, Lyn. Talking Points: Discussion Activities in the Primary Classroom. 2011. (ENG., Illus.). 144p. 128.00 *(978-0-415-61458-0(9));* pap. 35.95 *(978-0-415-61459-7(7))* Routledge.

De las Casas, Dianne. A Is for Alligator: Draw & Tell Stories from A-Z. 2011. (Illus.). xii, 95p. E-Book *(978-1-59884-930-1(1))* Libraries Unlimited, Inc.

—Tell along Tales! Playing with Participation Stories. 2011. E-Book *(978-1-59884-636-2(1))* Libraries Unlimited, Inc.

De López, Jacqueline Salazar. Little Hands, Busy Minds: Daily Curriculum for Two's & Three's. 2011. 152p. pap. 38.97 ***(978-1-4520-9363-5(6))*** AuthorHouse.

DeBellis, Valerie A. Navigating Through Discrete Mathematics in Prekindergarten Through Grade 5. 2009. *(978-0-87353-608-0(8));* (Illus.). viii, 256p. *(978-0-87353-606-6(1))* National Council of Teachers of Mathematics.

Deed, Craig, et al. Using Circle Time to Learn about Stories. 2007. (Lucky Duck Bks.). (Illus.). 80p. pap. 27.00 *(978-1-4129-2252-4(6),* B22526P) SAGE Pubns., Ltd. GBR. Dist: SAGE Pubns., Inc.

Demers, Judy. Character-Building Activities: Teaching Responsibility, Interaction, & Group Dynamics. 2008. (ENG., Illus.). 168p. (gr. k-12). pap. 22.00 *(978-0-7360-7206-9(3))* Human Kinetics Pubs.

Depino, Catherine. 101 Activities to Help Presch. 2007. (ENG.). 158p. 55.00 *(978-1-57886-559-8(X));* pap. 24.95 *(978-1-57886-575-8(1))* Rowman & Littlefield Education.

Devine, Kay & Judd, Marsha. The Creative Classroom: The Elementary Experience. rev. ed. 2009. (ENG.). 256p. pap. 68.25 *(978-0-7575-6972-2(2))* Kendall Hunt Publishing Co.

Dolan, Dan, et al. Mathematics Activities for Elementary Teachers for Mathematical Reasoning for Elementary Teachers. 5th ed. 2008. (ENG.). 392p. (C). pap. 36.67 *(978-0-321-52862-9(X))* Addison Wesley Higher Education.

Doran, Patricia Rice & Mazur, Amy J. Teaching Diverse Learners: Principles for Best Practice. 2010. (Illus.). 200p. pap. 36.95 *(978-1-4129-7498-1(4),* B74981P) Corwin Pr.

Easton, Laurine M. Crafting Faith: 101 Crafts to Help Kids Grow in Their Faith. 2008. pap. 15.95 *(978-0-8294-2704-2(X))* Loyola Pr.

Edmunds, Tracy. Me & My World. Stanton, Ev, ed. 2008. (ENG., Illus.). 208p. pap. 19.99 *(978-1-4206-9269-3(0))* Teacher Created Resources, Inc.

Educa Vision Inc Staff, contrib. by. Syans Fizik: Physical Sciences in Haitian Creole. (Illus.). 183p. *(978-1-58432-220-7(9))* Educa Vision.

Ellis, Brian. Learning from the Land: Teaching Ecology Through Stories & Activities. 2011. E-Book ***(978-1-59884-919-6(0))*** Libraries Unlimited, Inc.

Ellis, Brian 'Fox'. Learning from the Land: Teaching Ecology through Stories & Activities, 1 vol. 2nd rev. ed. 228p. pap. 35.00 ***(978-1-59884-918-9(2),*** A3562P) Pearson Education GBR. Dist: ABC-CLIO, LLC.

Eriksson, Göta, ed. Special Education & Early Arithmetic Knowledge-Building. 2011. pap. ***(978-1-61209-779-4(0))*** Nova Science Pubs., Inc.

Escribano, Kathryn. Kid's Box 2 Teacher's Resource Pack. 2008. (ENG.). 144p. spiral bd. 32.76 incl. audio compact disk *(978-0-521-68810-9(8))* Cambridge Univ. Pr.

—Kid's Box American English Level 3 Teacher's Resource Pack with Audio CD. 2011. (ENG.). 144p. pap. 30.00 incl. audio compact disk *(978-0-521-17790-0(1))* Cambridge Univ. Pr.

—Kid's Box American English Level 4 Teacher's Resource Pack with Audio CD. 2011. (ENG.). 144p. pap. 30.00 incl. audio compact disk *(978-0-521-17797-9(9))* Cambridge Univ. Pr.

Evers, Betty Jo. Reading & Writing: 12 Irresistible & Easy-to-Make Centers That Help Students Practice & Strengthen Important Reading & Writing Skills. 2010. (Mini File-Folder Centers in Color Ser.). (ENG.). 112p. (gr. k-3). pap. 17.99 *(978-0-545-17693-4(X),* Teaching Resources) Scholastic, Inc.

Facey, Denis Fawcett. Social Studies Helper: Creative Assignments for Exam Success. 2010. (ENG.). 134p. pap. 29.95 *(978-1-60709-751-8(6))* Rowman & Littlefield Education.

Facey, Denise Fawcett. Social Studies Helper: Creative Assignments for Exam Success. 2010. (ENG.). 134p. 70.00 *(978-1-60709-750-1(8))* Rowman & Littlefield Education.

Fallin, Jana R. & Tower, Mollie G. Using Music to Enhance Student Learning: A Practical Guide for Elementary Classroom Teachers. 2011. E-Book *(978-0-203-83861-7(0))* Routledge.

Fast Start Prompts for Critical Thinking: Prestwick Premium Downloadable Resources. 2007. 15p. 9.99 *(978-1-60389-486-9(1))* Prestwick Hse., Inc.

Faurot, Kimberly K. Storytime Around the Year. 2008. (Illus.). 217p. (J). pap. 17.95 *(978-1-932146-50-9(4),* Upstart Bks.) Highsmith Inc.

Feasey, Rosemary. Jumpstart! Science: Games & activities for Ages 5-11. 2009. (Jumpstart! Ser.). (ENG., Illus.). 96p. (C). pap. 22.95 *(978-0-415-48212-7(7))* Fulton, David Pubs. GBR. Dist: Taylor & Francis Group.

Feber, Jane. Student Engagement Is FUNdamental: Building a Learning Community with Hands-on Activities. 2011. (ENG.). pap. 19.95 ***(978-1-936700-47-9(6))*** Maupin Hse. Publishing.

Febvre, L. & Dehn, Milton J. Helping Students Remember: Exercises & Strategies to Strengthen Memory. 2011. (ENG.). 276p. pap. 55.00 *(978-0-470-91997-2(3),* Wiley) Wiley, John & Sons, Inc.

Fenton, William E. & Reynolds, Barbara E. College Geometry: Using the Geometer's Sketchpad. 2011. (ENG., Illus.). 380p. (C). pap. 109.95 ***(978-0-470-53493-9(1),*** Wiley) Wiley, John & Sons, Inc.

Ferguson, Teresa. G. A. M. E. S. Games & Activities for Motivating & Educating Students. 2011. 138p. pap. 14.95 ***(978-1-4327-7657-2(6))*** Outskirts Pr., Inc.

Ferris, Jean. Bad: Downloadable Activity Pack. 2007. 101p. 35.95 *(978-1-60843-635-4(7))* Prestwick Hse., Inc.

Fishbaugh, Angela Schmidt. Celebrate Nature! Activities for Every Season. 2011. (ENG.). 304p. pap. 29.95 *(978-1-60554-034-4(X))* Redleaf Pr.

Flora, Sherrill B. Cut, Color, Trace, & Paste: Reproducible Activities for Learning & Practicing a Variety of Fine Motor Skills. 2010. (ENG., Illus.). 64p. pap. 11.99 *(978-1-60268-079-1(5),* Key Education Publishing Company, LLC) Carson-Dellosa Publishing, LLC.

Foster, John. Learning about Language: Activities for the Primary Classroom. 2012. (ENG., Illus.). 216p. 155.00 ***(978-0-415-53680-6(4));*** pap. 33.95 ***(978-0-415-53681-3(2))*** Routledge.

Franceschini, Debra. Romp in Room. 2009. 96p. pap. 16.95 *(978-1-4401-1283-6(5))* iUniverse, Inc.

Francis, Robert. Romeo & Juliet, Pack. 2010. (Illus.). 200p. spiral bd. 210.00 *(978-1-4441-1035-7(7))* Hodder Education GBR. Dist: Trans-Atlantic Pubns., Inc.

Frankel, Jill & Hobart, Christine. Activities for Young Children. Walker, Miranda, ed. 4th ed. 2009. (ENG., Illus.). 202p. pap., instr.'s gde. ed. 22.95 *(978-1-4085-0486-4(3))* Nelson Thornes Ltd. GBR. Dist: International Specialized Bk. Services.

Fredericks, Anthony D. Creative Activities for Gifted Readers Grades 3-6: Dynamic Investigations, Challenging Projects & Energizing Assignments. 2006. (Illus.). 121p. per. 14.95 *(978-1-59647-109-2(3))* Good Year Bks.

—MORE Science Adventures with Children's Literature: Reading Comprehension & Inquiry-Based Science, 1 vol. 2008. (Through Children's Literature Ser.). (Illus.). 456p. pap. 35.00 *(978-1-59158-619-7(4),* TIP8619, Teacher Ideas Pr.) Libraries Unlimited, Inc.

—Mother Goose Readers Theatre for Beginning Readers, 1 vol. 2007. (Readers Theatre Ser.). (SPA & ENG., Illus.). 188p. per. 25.00 *(978-1-59158-500-8(7),* TIP5007, Teacher Ideas Pr.) Libraries Unlimited, Inc.

Froschauer, Linda. The Frugal Science Teacher, 6-9: Strategies & Activities. 2010. xi, 168p. E-Book *(978-1-936137-77-0(1))* National Science Teachers Assn.

—The Frugal Science Teacher, Prek-5: Strategies & Activities. 2010. *(978-1-936137-01-5(1))* National Science Teachers Assn.

Frostig Center & Frostig Center. The 6 Success Factors for Children with Learning Disabilities: Ready-to-Use Activities to Help Kids with LD Succeed in School & in Life. 2009. (ENG., Illus.). 232p. pap. 29.95 *(978-0-470-38377-3(1),* Jossey-Bass) Wiley, John & Sons, Inc.

Fuqua, Blanche E., et al. English Activity Work Book: Grade 4. 2011. 100p. 38.95 ***(978-1-258-10283-8(8))*** Literary Licensing, LLC.

Gainsley, Suzanne & Hoelscher, Julie. Activities for Home Visits: Partnering with Preschool Families. 2010. *(978-1-57379-456-5(2))* High/Scope Pr.

Galindo, Linda. The Accountability Experience Facilitator's Guide, Set. 2010. (ENG.). ring bd. 225.00 *(978-0-470-60710-7(6),* Pfeiffer) Wiley, John & Sons, Inc.

Garcia Winner, Michelle & Crooke, Pamela. You Are A Social Detective: Explaining Social Thinking to Kids. 2010. (Illus.). (J). pap. 20.00 *(978-0-88427-200-7(1))* North River Pr. Publishing Corp., The.

Gavigan, Karen W. & Tomasevich, Mindy. Connecting Comics to Curriculum: Strategies for Grades 6 -12, 1 vol. 2011. (Illus.). 164p. pap. 40.00 ***(978-1-59884-768-0(6),*** A3385P) Pearson Education GBR. Dist: ABC-CLIO, LLC.

Gavigan, Karen W. & Tomasevich, Mindy. Connecting Comics to Curriculum: Strategies for Grades 6-12. 2011. E-Book ***(978-1-59884-769-7(4))*** Libraries Unlimited, Inc.

Gee, Martha Bettis. Piece Work / Peace Work: Working Together for Peace & Sudan: 2009-2010 Mission Study for Children (Teacher's Guide) 2009. (ENG.). 100p. (J). pap. 7.00 *(978-1-933663-34-0(0),* WD/GBGM Bks.) General Board of Global Ministries, The United Methodist Church.

Gentry, Marita & de Las Casas, Dianne. A Is for Alligator: Draw & Tell Stories from A-Z, 1 vol. 2011. (Illus.). 95p. pap. 32.00 *(978-1-59884-929-5(8),* A3578P) Pearson Education GBR. Dist: ABC-CLIO, LLC.

Gertz, Susan, et al. Wet Your Whistle! Drinking Water Activity Handbook. 2007. (Strive to Thrive Ser.). 72p. (YA). pap. 9.95 *(978-1-883822-43-9(2))* Terrific Science Pr.

Ghoting, Saroj Nadkarni & Martin-Díaz, Pamela. Art & Craft Activities for Early Literacy @ Your Fingertips. 2010. *(978-0-8389-1028-3(9))* American Library Assn.

—Early-Literacy-Enhanced Storytimes @ Your Fingertips. 2010. *(978-0-8389-1026-9(2))* American Library Assn.

—Songs & Movement Activities for Early Literacy @ Your Fingertips. 2010. *(978-0-8389-1029-0(7))* American Library Assn.

Glenn, David D. & Dickman, Donald I. Forestry Field Studies: A Manual for Science Teachers. 2009. *(978-1-935155-08-9(3))* National Science Teachers Assn.

Glynne, Hazel & Snowden, Amanda. Games, Ideas & Activities for Primary Literacy. 2010. (Illus.). 366p. pap. 37.50 *(978-1-4082-2551-6(4))* Pearson Education, Ltd. GBR. Dist: Trans-Atlantic Pubns., Inc.

Godin, Deirdre. Amazing Hands-on Literature Projects for Secondary Students. 2010. pap. 27.95 *(978-1-934338-76-6(1))* Maupin Hse. Publishing.

Goldberg, Merryl. Arts Integration: Teaching Subject Matter Through the Arts in Multicultural Settings. 4th rev. ed. 2011. (ENG.). 288p. (C). pap. 76.80 *(978-0-13-256556-1(0))* Allyn & Bacon, Inc.

Gonzalez-Mena, et al. Infants, Toddlers, & Caregivers: A Curriculum of Respectful, Responsive, Relationship-Based Care & Education. 9th ed. 2011. (ENG., Illus.). 416p. (C). pap. 102.33 *(978-0-07-802435-1(8),* 0078024358) McGraw-Hill Cos., The.

Gooch, C. Kay & Massey, Charlotte. Camp Summer Read: How to Create Your Own Summer Reading Camp, 1 vol. 2010. (Illus.). 108p. pap. 30.00 *(978-1-59884-447-4(4),* A2901P) Libraries Unlimited, Inc.

Green, Christine. 100+ Fun Ideas for Wet Playtimes That Are Easy to Prepare & That Children Will Love. 2009. (Illus.). 108p. pap. *(978-1-905780-32-7(X))* Brilliant Pubns.

Green, Linda Schwartz, et al. 40 Active Learning Strategies for the Inclusive Classroom. 2011. (Illus.). 176p. pap. 33.95 *(978-1-4129-8170-5(0),* B81705P) Corwin Pr.

Greene, Ellin, et al. Storytelling: Art & Technique, 1 vol. 4th rev. ed. 2009. (Illus.). 455p. 55.00 *(978-1-59158-600-5(3),* LU6003) Libraries Unlimited, Inc.

Griggs, Gerald, ed. Physical Education in the Primary School: An Introduction. 2012. (ENG., Illus.). 256p. (C). 145.00 *(978-0-415-61308-8(6));* pap. 44.95 *(978-0-415-61309-5(4))* Routledge.

Guillaume, Andrea M., et al. 50 Strategies for Active Teaching: Engaging K-12 Learners in the Classroom. 2006. (Merrill/Prentice Hall Teaching Strategies

The check digit for ISBN-10 appears in parentheses after the full ISBN-13

Ser.). (ENG., Illus.). 288p. (C). pap. 42.60 *(978-0-13-219272-9(1)*, Prentice Hall) Prentice Hall PTR.

Gunzenhauser, Kelly & Flora, Sherrill B. Creating Curriculum Using Children's Picture Books. 2007. (ENG., Illus.). 96p. pap. 13.99 *(978-1-60268-011-1(6)*, Key Education Publishing Company, LLC) Carson-Dellosa Publishing, LLC.

Guthrie, Dorothy Littlejohn. Integrating African American Literature in the Library & Classroom, 1 vol. 2011. 294p. pap. 40.00 *(978-1-59884-751-2(1)*, A3360P) Pearson Education GBR. Dist: ABC-CLIO, LLC.

Hagler, Kaye. Take Five! for Language Arts: 180 Bell-Ringers That Build Critical-thinking Skills. 2011. pap. 23.95 ***(978-1-937412-03-6(2))*** Maupin Hse. Publishing.

Hammett, Carol Totsky & Geigert, Nicki Collins. Read! Move! Learn! Active Stories for Active Learning. 2007. (ENG., Illus.). 232p. pap. 19.95 *(978-0-87659-058-4(X))* Gryphon Hse., Inc.

Hanko, Johanne. 100 Learning Games for Special Needs with Music, Movement, Sounds and...Silence. 2011. (ENG., Illus.). 128p. pap. ***(978-1-84905-247-4(6))*** Kingsley, Jessica Ltd.

Hannam, Nicolette & Williams, Michelle. Gute Idee: Time-saving Resources & Ideas for Busy German Teachers. 2009. (GER & ENG., Illus.). 150p. pap. *(978-1-905780-65-5(6))* Brilliant Pubns.

—Spanish Festivals & Traditions - Activities & Teaching Ideas for Primary Schools. 2010. (Illus.). 108p. pap. *(978-1-905780-53-2(2))* Brilliant Pubns.

Hannell, Glynis. Success with Inclusion: 1001 Teaching Strategies & Activities That Really Work. 2007. (Illus.). 184p. 44.95 *(978-0-415-44534-4(5))* Routledge.

Hansen, Alice. Games, Ideas, & Activities for Early Years Mathematics. 2012. (Illus.). 316p. pap. 37.50 ***(978-1-4082-8484-1(7))*** Pearson Education, Ltd. GBR. Dist: Trans-Atlantic Pubns., Inc.

Hansen, Mark Victor, et al. Chicken Soup for the Soul in the Classroom: Elementary: Grades 1-5. 2007. (Chicken Soup for the Soul in the Classroom Ser.). (ENG., Illus.). 416p. pap. 29.95 *(978-0-7573-0693-8(4))* Health Communications, Inc.

—Chicken Soup for the Soul in the Classroom: Lesson Plans & Students' Favorite Stories for:* Reading Comprehension*Writing Skills*Critical Thinking*Character Building. 2007. (Chicken Soup for the Soul in the Classroom Ser.). (ENG., Illus.). 418p. pap. 29.95 *(978-0-7573-0694-5(2))* Health Communications, Inc.

Hardaway, Karla. Active English: Learning Strategies That Will Have Your Students Asking, Is That the Bell Already? 2010. (ENG.). 144p. pap. 21.95 *(978-1-877673-96-2(X))* Cottonwood Pr., Inc.

Hart, Brian. English in Mind. 2nd rev. ed. 2011. 176p. spiral bd. 28.60 ***(978-0-521-18313-0(8))***; (ENG.). 184p. spiral bd. 28.60 ***(978-0-521-18318-5(9))*** Cambridge Univ. Pr.

Hart, Brian. English in Mind Level 4 Teacher's Resource Book. 2nd ed. 2011. (ENG.). 194p. spiral bd. 29.00 *(978-0-521-18450-2(9))* Cambridge Univ. Pr.

Hart, Brian, et al. English in Mind. 2nd ed. 2011. 184p. pap. 28.60 ***(978-0-521-18321-5(9))*** Cambridge Univ. Pr.

Haskill, Allison, et al. Months of Morphemes. 2007. per. 39.95 *(978-1-58650-742-8(7))* Super Duper Pubns.

Hastings, Kay, et al. Daily Preschool Experiences: For Learners at Every Level. Miller, Robert L., tr. 2008. (ENG., Illus.). 496p. pap. 29.95 *(978-0-87659-010-2(5))* Gryphon Hse., Inc.

Haynes, Joanna & Murris, Karin. Picturebooks & Pedagogy. 2011. (Routledge Research in Education Ser.). (ENG., Illus.). 284p. 125.00 *(978-0-415-88080-0(7))* Routledge.

Haysom, John & Bowen, Michael. Predict, Observe, Explain: Activities Enhancing Scientific Understanding. 2010. *(978-1-935155-23-2(7))* National Science Teachers Assn.

Head, Heno. Simple Science Object Talks: Over 100 Science Object Talks You Can Do. 2007. (Object Talks Ser.). (Illus.). 224p. (J). pap. 19.99 *(978-0-7847-1982-4(9))* Standard Publishing.

Helmrich, Erin & Schneider, Elizabeth. Create, Relate & Pop @ the Library: Services & Programs for Teens & Tweens. 2011. (Illus.). 220p. 60.00 *(978-1-55570-722-4(X))* Neal-Schuman Pubs., Inc.

Herbert, Sarah H. The Inclusion Toolkit. 2011. (Illus.). 120p. 100.00 ***(978-1-84920-759-1(3)***, B07591C); pap. 43.00 ***(978-1-84920-760-7(7)***, B07591P) SAGE Pubns., Ltd. GBR. Dist: SAGE Pubns., Inc.

Hewitt, Elaine, frwd. The Use of Psychomotor Activities in Teaching Children English As a Foreign Language: Empirical Research into the PEPA Method of Language Instruction. 2011. (ENG., Illus.). v, 380p. 129.95 *(978-0-7734-1468-6(1))* Mellen, Edwin Pr., The.

Hickam, Homer. October Sky: Activity Pack. 2007. 108p. spiral bd. 35.95 *(978-1-60389-043-4(2))* Prestwick Hse., Inc.

Holcombe, Garan. Interactive Level 1 Teacher's Book. 2011. (ENG.). 124p. pap. 35.00 *(978-0-521-71210-1(6))* Cambridge Univ. Pr.

—Interactive Level 2 Teacher's Book. 2011. (ENG.). 126p. pap. 35.00 *(978-0-521-71216-3(5))* Cambridge Univ. Pr.

—Interactive Level 3 Teacher's Book. 2012. (ENG.). 128p. pap. 35.00 ***(978-0-521-71221-7(1))*** Cambridge Univ. Pr.

—Interactive Level 4 Teacher's Book with Web Zone Access. 2012. (ENG.). 128p. 35.00 ***(978-0-521-71226-2(2))*** Cambridge Univ. Pr.

—Primary i-Dictionary 3 High Elementary Workbook. 2011. (ENG.). 88p. pap. 16.00 ***(978-0-521-17590-6(9))*** Cambridge Univ. Pr.

Horowitz, Gayle. International Games: Building Skills Through Multicultural Play. 2008. (ENG., Illus.). 128p. (gr. k-12). pap. 20.00 *(978-0-7360-7394-3(9))* Human Kinetics Pubs.

Horton, Michael. Take-Home Chemistry: 50 Low-Cost Activities to Extend Classroom Learning. 2011. (Illus.). xxix, 244p. ***(978-1-936137-39-8(9))*** National Science Teachers Assn.

Horton, Michael. Take-Home Physics: 65 High-Impact, Low-Cost Labs. 2009. *(978-1-935155-05-8(9))* National Science Teachers Assn.

Hoyt, Linda. Revisit, Reflect, Retell, Updated Edition: Time-Tested Strategies for Teaching Reading Comprehension. rev. ed. 2008. (Illus.). 256p. pap. 35.63 *(978-0-325-02579-7(7)*, E02579) Heinemann.

Huff, Mary Jo. Story Play: Building Language & Literacy One Story at a Time. 2011. (ENG.). 208p. pap. 16.95 *(978-0-87659-316-5(3))* Gryphon Hse., Inc.

Hughes, Anita M. Problem Solving, Reasoning & Numeracy in the Early Years Foundation Stage. 2009. (Practical Guidance in the EYFS Ser.). (ENG.). 160p. 120.00 *(978-0-415-47840-3(5))* Routledge.

—Problem Solving, Reasoning & Numeracy in the Early Years Foundation Stage, 7 vols. 2009. (Practical Guidance in the EYFS Ser.). (Illus.). 112p. pap. 31.95 *(978-0-415-47654-6(2))* Taylor & Francis Group.

Hughes, Giles. Creative Homework Tasks. 2010. (Illus.). 77p. pap. *(978-1-905780-55-6(9))*; 81p. pap. *(978-1-905780-56-3(7))* Brilliant Pubns.

Hutchins, Darcy J. Multicultural Partnerships: Involve All Families. 2012. ***(978-1-59667-210-9(2))*** Eye On Education, Inc.

Hutmacher, Kimberly. Picture Book Parties! 2011. E-Book *(978-1-59884-773-4(2))* Libraries Unlimited, Inc.

Hutmacher, Kimberly M. Picture Book Parties!, 1 vol. 2011. (Illus.). 128p. pap. 30.00 *(978-1-59884-772-7(4)*, A3393P) Pearson Education GBR. Dist: ABC-CLIO, LLC.

Hutson-Nechkash, Peg. Story Stunts. 2007. per. 34.95 *(978-1-58650-816-6(4))* Super Duper Pubns.

Ireson, Gren, et al. Secondary Science 11 to 16: A Practical Guide. 2010. (Illus.). 192p. (C). 112.00 *(978-1-84920-125-4(0)*, B01254C); pap. 43.00 *(978-1-84920-126-1(9)*, B01254P) SAGE Pubns., Ltd. GBR. Dist: SAGE Pubns., Inc.

Isenberg, Joan Packer & Jalongo, Mary R. Creative Thinking & Arts-Based Learning: Preschool Through Fourth Grade (with MyEducationLab) 5th ed. 2009. (ENG.). 456p. (C). pap. 100.67 *(978-0-13-610085-0(6)*, Prentice Hall) Prentice Hall PTR.

Jackson, Pamela A. & Sullivan, Patrick. International Students & Academic Libraries: Initiatives for Success. 2011. ***(978-0-8389-9377-4(X))*** pap. ***(978-0-8389-8593-9(9))***; E-Book ***(978-0-8389-9378-1(8))*** Assn. of College & Research Libraries.

Jantzen, Esther. Plus It! How to Easily Turn Everyday Activities into Learning Adventures for Kids. 2009. (ENG.). pap. 9.95 *(978-1-60037-566-8(9))* Morgan James Publishing.

Jenkins, Richard & Detamore, Debra, illus. Comics in Your Curriculum: Teacher-Friendly Activities for Making & Integrating Comics with Reading, Math, Science, & Other Subjects in Your Classroom. 2008. 128p. *(978-1-934358-15-3(0))* Pieces of Learning.

Johnson, Jeff A. Everyday Early Learning: Easy & Fun Activities & Toys Made from Stuff You Can Find Around the House. 2008. (ENG., Illus.). 200p. pap. 19.95 *(978-1-933653-42-6(6))* Redleaf Pr.

Johnson, LouAnne. Kick-Start Your Class: Academic Icebreakers to Engage Students. 2012. (ENG.). 288p. pap. 24.95 ***(978-1-118-10456-9(0)***, Jossey-Bass) Wiley, John & Sons, Inc.

Johnson, Paul F. & LoGiudice, Carolyn. Spotlight on Reasoning & Problem Solving Set (6) 2007. (J). 83.70 *(978-0-7606-9974-4(7))* LinguiSystems, Inc.

Johnstone, Jill A. & Ramon, Molly. Perceptual-Motor Activities for Children: An Evidence-Based Guide to Building Physical & Cognitive Skills. 2011. (Illus.). 240p. pap. 35.00 *(978-1-4504-0154-8(6))* Human Kinetics Pubs.

Jones, Eileen. 100+ Fun Ideas for Transition Times. 2009. (Illus.). 128p. pap. *(978-1-905780-34-1(6))* Brilliant Pubns.

Jones, M. Gail, et al. Extreme Science: From Nano to Galactic. 2009. 150p. pap. 29.95 *(978-1-933531-30-4(4))* National Science Teachers Assn.

Jones, Russell & Wyse, Dominic. Creativity in the Primary Curriculum. 2nd rev. ed. 2012. (ENG.). 224p. (C). 128.00 *(978-0-415-67546-8(4))*; pap. 35.95 *(978-0-415-67547-5(2))* Routledge.

Josephs, Kathie. All Aboard with Reading & Writing for Middle Grades. 2008. 64p. pap. 14.96 *(978-1-4357-0793-1(1))* Lulu Enterprises Inc.

Kafka, Franz. The Metamorphosis: Downloadable Activity Pack. 2008. 131p. 35.95 *(978-1-60389-265-0(6))* Prestwick Hse., Inc.

Kaltman, Gwen Snyder & Kaltman, Gwendolyn (Gwen) S. (Snyder). Hands-on Learning! More Than 1000 Activities for Young Children Using Everyday Objects. Kaltman, Gwendolyn (Gwen) S. (Snyder), ed. 2009. (Illus.) 152p. pap. 25.95 *(978-1-4129-7095-2(4)*, B70945P) Corwin Pr.

Kasten, Sarah & Newton, Jill. Reasoning & Sense Making for High School Mathematics: Activities from Mathematics Teacher. 2011. ***(978-0-87353-655-4(X))*** National Council of Teachers of Mathematics.

Kastens, Kim & Turrin, Margie. Earth Science Puzzles: Making Meaning from Data. 2010. *(978-1-935155-15-7(6))* National Science Teachers Assn.

Keane, Nancy J. & Cavanaugh, Terence W. The Tech-Savvy Booktalker: A Guide for 21st-Century Educators, 1 vol. 2008. (Illus.). 176p. pap. 35.00 *(978-1-59158-637-1(2)*, LU8637) Libraries Unlimited, Inc.

Keeley, Shannon, et al. The Complete Book of Sight Words: 220 Words Your Child Needs to Know to be a Successful Reader. 2011. (ENG., Illus.). 576p. (J). pap. 19.95 *(978-1-4114-4958-9(4))* Spark Publishing Group.

Keeling, Dave. Rocket up Your Class! 101 High Impact Activities to Start, Break & End Lessons. Gilbert, Ian, ed. 2009. (Illus.). 192p. pap. *(978-1-84590-134-9(7))* Crown Hse. Publishing.

Kempton, Susan L. The Literate Kindergarten: Where Wonder & Discovery Thrive. 2007. (Illus.). 208p. pap. 28.75 *(978-0-325-00833-2(7)*, E00833) Heinemann.

Kepler, Lynne. A Year of Hands-On Science: 100+ Standards-Based Activities Projects & Experiments That Help Students Develop Key Process Skills & Build Vocabulary & Content Knowledge. 2008. (Teaching Resources Ser.). (ENG., Illus.). 304p. (J). (gr. k-3). pap. 31.99 *(978-0-545-07475-9(4)*, Teaching Resources) Scholastic, Inc.

Kirby, Becky. Ways to Amaze & Engage Middle School Students. 2009. (Illus.). 174p. ***(978-1-57543-173-4(4))*** MAR*CO Products, Inc.

Kissling, Barbara. Cemeteries: Alive with Learning. 2010. *(978-1-56090-238-6(8))* National Middle Schl. Assn.

Klawitter, Pam. More, I'm Through! What Can I Do? 2009. pap. 14.99 *(978-1-59198-965-3(5))* Creative Teaching Pr., Inc.

Klobucka, Anna, et al. Brazilian Activities Manual. 2007. (ENG.). 456p. (C). pap. 75.60 *(978-0-13-189408-2(0)*, Prentice Hall) Prentice Hall PTR.

Klobucka, Anna, et al. European SAM Audio. 2007. (ENG.). (C). cd-rom 57.80 ***(978-0-13-157411-3(6)***, Prentice Hall) Prentice Hall PTR.

Kluth, Paula. Joyful Learning: Active & Collaborative Learning in Inclusive Classrooms. Udvari-Solner, Alice, ed. 2007. (Illus.). 160p. 76.95 *(978-1-4129-4173-0(3)*, B41733C); per. 33.95 *(978-1-4129-4174-7(1)*, B41733P) Corwin Pr.

Knoblock Kathleen & Knoblock, Kathleen. Primary Source Fluency Activities: World Cultures Through Time. 2007. (Primary Source Fluency Activities Ser.). (ENG., Illus.). 192p. (gr. 3-8). pap. 29.99 *(978-1-4258-0102-1(1))* Shell Educational Publishing.

Kohl, MaryAnn F., et al. First Art for Toddlers & Twos: Open-Ended Art Experiences. rev. ed. 2012. (ENG., Illus.). 128p. pap. 19.95 ***(978-0-87659-399-8(6))*** Gryphon Hse., Inc.

Kovar, Susan, et al. Elementary Classroom Teachers as Movement Educators. 4th ed. 2011. (ENG., Illus.). 608p. (C). pap. 98.00 ***(978-0-07-809576-4(X)***, 007809576X) McGraw-Hill Cos., The.

Kuhns, Catherine Jones. Building Number Sense: Games & Activities to Practice Combinations to 10. 2009. *(978-1-934026-59-5(X)*, Crystal Springs Bks.) Staff Development for Educators.

—Number Wonders: 160 Activities to Meet Math Standards & Inspire Students. 2006. (Illus.). 176p. *(978-1-884548-91-8(1)*, Crystal Springs Bks.) Staff Development for Educators.

Kummer, Ann. Oral & Nasal Listener. 2007. 89.95 *(978-1-58650-813-5(X))* Super Duper Pubns.

Kwitter, Karen & Souza, Steven. Hands-on Science Series: Force & Motion. 2nd rev. ed. 2009. (YA). pap. 25.00 *(978-0-8251-6518-4(0))* Walch Education.

Labrow, Mark. Creative Activities for the Secondary Classroom. 2009. (ENG.). 232p. pap. 44.50 *(978-1-4082-2557-8(3))* Pearson Education, Ltd. GBR. Dist: Trans-Atlantic Pubns., Inc.

Langstrom, Ray & Hodges, Jane. Teaching Terrific 5's. 2008. 232p. pap. 18.95 *(978-0-89334-449-8(4)*, Humanics Learning) Humanics Publishing Group.

Lappan, Glenda, compiled by. Rich & Engaging Mathematical Tasks: Grades 5-9. 2011. ***(978-0-87353-633-2(9))*** National Council of Teachers of Mathematics.

LaRose, Denise. Early Childhood Mathematics Activities, Grades PreK-1: Literacy, Language, & Learning. 2010. (Early Childhood Activities Ser.). (Illus.). 176p. pap. 29.99 incl. cd-rom *(978-1-4258-0699-6(6))* Shell Educational Publishing.

—Math Activities & Games for Early Learners. 2007. (Early Learner Ser.). (ENG., Illus.). 176p. (gr. k-1). pap., pap. 29.99 incl. cd-rom *(978-1-4258-0050-5(5))* Shell Educational Publishing.

Larsen, Stephanie & Bauman, Stephanie G. Storytimes for Children, 1 vol. 2010. (Illus.). 252p. pap. 30.00 *(978-1-59884-565-5(9)*, A3076P) Libraries Unlimited, Inc.

Le Messurier, Mark & Nawana Parker, Madhavi. What's the Buzz? Games & Activities to Improve Social Skills. 2011. (ENG., Illus.) 256p. 47.95 *(978-0-415-58382-4(9))* Routledge.

LeBeau, Patrick. Term Paper Resource Guide to American Indian History, 1 vol. 2009. (Term Paper Resource Guides). 376p. 65.00 *(978-0-313-35271-3(2)*, GR5271, Greenwood Pr.) Greenwood Publishing Group, Inc.

Ledbetter, Mary Ellen. The Writing Teacher's Activity-a-Day: 180+ Reproducible Prompts & Quick-Writes for the Secondary Classroom. 2010. (JB-Ed: 5 Minute FUNdamentals Ser.: 3). (ENG.). 224p. pap., tchr. ed., act. bk. ed. 19.95 *(978-0-470-46132-7(2)*, Jossey-Bass) Wiley, John & Sons, Inc.

Leicester, Mal & Taylor, Denise. Critical Thinking Across the Curriculum: Developing Philosophy, Reflection & Critical Thinking in the Primary Classroom. 2010. (ENG., Illus.). 160p. (C). pap. 47.00 *(978-0-335-23879-8(3)*, 0335238793) McGraw-Hill Education GBR. Dist: McGraw-Hill Cos., The.

—Environmental Learning for Classroom & Assembly at KS1 & KS2: Stories about the Natural World. 2009. (Illus.). 136p. 140.00 *(978-0-415-48461-9(8))* Fulton, David Pubs. GBR. Dist: Taylor & Francis Group.

Leleu, Sin Ad & Leleu, Sinead. German Speaking Activities - Fun Ways to Get Ks2 Pupils to Talk to Each Other in German. 2011. (GER & ENG., Illus.). 92p. pap. ***(978-1-905780-70-9(2))*** Brilliant Pubns.

Leleu, Sinead. French Speaking Activities-Fun Ways to Get Ks2 Pupils to Talk to Each Other in French. 2011. (FRE & ENG., Illus.). 92p. pap. ***(978-1-905780-66-2(4))*** Brilliant Pubns.

Leleu, Sinead & Kentish, Jo. Spanish Speaking Activities - Fun Ways to Get Ks2 Pupils to Talk to Each Other in Spanish. 2011. (Illus.). 90p. pap. ***(978-1-905780-68-6(0))*** Brilliant Pubns.

Levin, Freddie. Draw Plus Math. 2010. (ENG.). 64p. pap. 3.99 *(978-0-939217-90-8(2))* Peel Productions, Inc.

Levin, Freddie. Draw Plus Science: Enhance Science Learning Through Art Activities! 2012. pap. ***(978-0-939217-91-5(0))*** Peel Productions, Inc.

Levine MEd, Joni. The Everything Toddler Activities Book: Over 400 games & projects to entertain & Educate. 2nd ed. 2012. (ENG.). 320p. pap. 15.95 ***(978-1-4405-2978-8(7))*** Adams Media Corp.

Liftig, Inez Fugate. Tried & True: Time-Tested Activities for Middle School. 2010. *(978-1-936137-13-8(5))* National Science Teachers Assn.

Lingo, Susan L. Kids-Tell-'Em Bible Stories. 2008. 116p. pap. 14.99 *(978-1-935147-05-3(6))* Lingo, Susan Bks.

Livingston, Sue. Working Text: X-Word Grammar & Writing Activities for Students. 2010. (ENG.). 128p. pap. 19.95 *(978-1-56368-468-5(3))* Gallaudet Univ. Pr.

Logiudice, Carolyn & Johnson, Paul F. Spotlight on Social Skills Adolescent Conversations. 2008. (YA). per. 13.95 *(978-0-7606-0775-6(3))* LinguiSystems, Inc.

—Spotlight on Social Skills Adolescent Emotions. 2008. (YA). per. 13.95 *(978-0-7606-0776-3(1))* LinguiSystems, Inc.

—Spotlight on Social Skills Adolescent Getting Along. 2008. (YA). per. 13.95 *(978-0-7606-0777-0(X))* LinguiSystems, Inc.

—Spotlight on Social Skills Adolescent Interpersonal Negotiation. 2008. (YA). per. 13.95 *(978-0-7606-0778-7(8))* LinguiSystems, Inc.

—Spotlight on Social Skills Adolescent Making Social Inferences. 2008. (YA). per. 13.95 *(978-0-7606-0779-4(6))* LinguiSystems, Inc.

Lomba, Ana. Play & Learn Chinese with Audio CD. 2011. (ENG & CHI., Illus.). 64p. 20.00 incl. audio compact disk ***(978-0-07-175970-0(0)***, 0071759700) McGraw-Hill Cos., The.

Lord, Richard. Friday Afternoon GCSE, Pack. 2010. (Illus.). 200p. 210.00 *(978-1-4441-1040-1(3))* Hodder Education GBR. Dist: Trans-Atlantic Pubns., Inc.

Lord, Thomas R. & Travis, Holly J. Schoolyard Science: 101 Easy & Inexpensive Activities. 2011. ***(978-1-936137-16-9(X))*** National Science Teachers Assn.

Lucas, Robert W. Creative Learning: Activities & Games That Really Engage People. 2007. (ENG., Illus.). 260p. per. 45.00 *(978-0-7879-8740-4(9)*, Pfeiffer) Wiley, John & Sons, Inc.

Lushington, Nolan. Libraries Designed for Kids. 2008. 150p. 85.00 *(978-1-55570-631-9(2))* Neal-Schuman Pubs., Inc.

Maccagnano, Ann. Identifying & Enhancing the Strengths of Gifted Learners, K-8: Easy-to-Use Activities & Lessons. 2007. 136p. 72.95 *(978-1-4129-5198-2(4)*, B42535C); (Illus.). per. 31.95 *(978-1-4129-4253-9(5)*, B42535P) Corwin Pr.

Macintyre Latta, Margaret & Chan, Elaine. Teaching the Arts to Engage English Language Learners. 2010. (ENG., Illus.). 264p. 135.00 *(978-0-415-87385-7(1))*; pap. 36.95 *(978-0-415-87386-4(X))* Routledge.

MacMillan, Kathy & Kirker, Christine. Kindergarten Magic: Theme-Based Lessons for Building Literacy & Library Skills. 2011. 312p. pap. 50.00 *(978-0-8389-1069-6(6))* American Library Assn.

MacMillan, Kathy & Kirker, Christine. Multicultural Storytime Magic. 2012. 160p. ***(978-0-8389-1142-6(0))*** American Library Assn.

Mahood, Kristine. Booktalking with Teens, 1 vol. 2010. (Libraries Unlimited Professional Guides for Young Adult Librarians Ser.). 289p. pap. 45.00 *(978-1-59158-714-9(X)*, LU8714) Libraries Unlimited, Inc.

Maiden, Sabena C. & Pressnall, Debra Olson. Fun, Fitness & Learning: 55 Large Group Activites & 47 Hands-On Practice Pages to Energize & Teach Young Children. 2010. (ENG., Illus.). 64p. pap. 11.99 *(978-1-60268-081-4(7)*, Key Education Publishing Company, LLC) Carson-Dellosa Publishing, LLC.

Malenfant, Nicole. Routines & Transitions: A Guide for Early Childhood Professionals. 2006. (ENG.). 300p. pap. 34.95 *(978-1-933653-04-4(3))* Redleaf Pr.

Malnor, Carol L. How We Know What We Know about Our Changing Climate: Lessons, Resources, & Guidelines about Global Warming. 2008. (Illus.). 56p. (gr. 5-8). pap. 8.95 *(978-1-58469-105-1(0))* Dawn Pubns.

Margolin, Michael. Hands-on Science Series: Light & Color. 2nd rev. ed. 2009. (YA). pap. 25.00 *(978-0-8251-6520-7(2))* Walch Education.

—Hands-on Science Series ABCs of Chemistry. 2nd rev. ed. 2009. 170p. pap. 25.00 *(978-0-8251-6517-7(2))* Walch Education.

Martin, Ralph, et al. Teaching Science for All Children: An Inquiry Approach. 5th ed. 2008. (ENG.). 592p. (C). pap. 151.67 *(978-0-205-54314-1(0))* Allyn & Bacon, Inc.

Mayer, Brian & Harris, Christopher. Libraries Got Game: Aligned Learning Through Modern Board Games. 2009. (Illus.). 134p. 45.00 *(978-0-8389-1009-2(2))* American Library Assn.

Mayne, Laura. Great Teacher Projects: K-8. 2009. (ENG., Illus.). 160p. 35.00 *(978-1-55046-524-2(4))*; pap. 24.95 *(978-1-55046-510-5(4))* Boston Mills Pr. CAN. Dist: Firefly Bks., Ltd.

McCormick, Julie & Whyler, Robin. Games, Ideas & Activities for Primary PSHE. rev. ed. 2012. (ENG.). 376p. pap. ***(978-1-4082-6774-5(8))*** Pearson Education.

McEwan, Elaine K. & Bresnahan, Val. Vocabulary. 2008. (Reading Puzzle Ser.). (Illus.). 96p. (gr. -1-3). pap. 16.95 *(978-1-4129-5822-6(9)*, B58226P). (gr. 4-7). pap. 16.95 *(978-1-4129-5827-1(X)*, B58271P) Corwin Pr.

McEwan, Elaine K. & Nielsen, Linda M. The Reading Puzzle - Spelling. 2008. (Reading Puzzle Ser.). (Illus.). 96p. (gr. 4-7). pap. 16.95 *(978-1-4129-5826-4(1)*, B58264P) Corwin Pr.

McEwan, Elaine K., et al. Fluency. 2008. (Reading Puzzle Ser.). (Illus.). 96p. (gr. 4-7). pap. 16.95 *(978-1-4129-5828-8(8)*, B58288P) Corwin Pr.

—A Guide for Students & Practitioners - Comprehension. 2008. (Reading Puzzle Ser.). (Illus.). 96p. (gr. -1-3). pap. 16.95 *(978-1-4129-5824-0(5)*, B58240P) Corwin Pr.

—Phonemic Awareness. 2008. (Reading Puzzle Ser.). (Illus.). 96p. (gr. -1-3). pap. 16.95 *(978-1-4129-5820-2(2)*, B58202P) Corwin Pr.

—Phonics. 2008. (Reading Puzzle Ser.). (Illus.). 96p. (gr. -1-3). pap. 16.95 *(978-1-4129-5821-9(0)*, B58219P) Corwin Pr.

—The Reading Puzzle - Comprehension. 2008. (Reading Puzzle Ser.). (Illus.). 96p. (gr. 4-7). pap. 16.95 *(978-1-4129-5829-5(6)*, B58295P) Corwin Pr.

—The Reading Puzzle - Fluency. 2008. (Reading Puzzle Ser.). (Illus.). 96p. (gr. -1-3). pap. 16.95 *(978-1-4129-5823-3(7)*, B58233P) Corwin Pr.

McGowan, Andrea, et al. English Homework for Key Stage 2: Activity-Based Learning. 2009. (Active Homework Ser.). (ENG., Illus.). 96p. 47.95 *(978-0-415-47455-9(8))* Taylor & Francis Group.

McGregor, Debra. Practice & Perspectives: Learning in practical Science. 2010. 412p. pap. *(978-3-639-18762-5(8))* VDM Verlag Dr. Mueller e.K.

McGuire, Beth. Active Reading: Activities for Librarians & Teachers, 1 vol. 2008. (Illus.). 184p. pap. 35.00 *(978-1-59158-666-1(6)*, LU8666) Libraries Unlimited, Inc.

Melin, Jacqueline. Passport to Learn. 2008. (ENG.). 192p. (gr. 4-8). pap. 24.95 *(978-1-59363-339-4(4))* Prufrock Pr.

Melnick, Harold, et al. Math for All Participant Book Grade 3-5. 2011. (Illus.). 240p. pap. 38.95 *(978-1-4129-9521-4(7)*, B95221P) Corwin Pr.

Middle School Success Deluxe. 2009. 49.95 *(978-1-60077-575-8(6))* TOPICS Entertainment.

Middlewood, Gavin & Debenham, Andrew. 43 Team-Building Activities for Key Stage. 2009. (Illus.). 64p. pap. *(978-1-905780-49-5(4))* Brilliant Pubns.

Miller, Cathy Puett. Anytime Reading Readiness: Fun & Easy Family Activities That Prepare Your Child to Read. 2009. 96p. pap. 11.95 *(978-1-934338-74-2(5))* Maupin Hse. Publishing.

—Before They Read: Teaching Language & Literacy Development through Conversations, Interactive Read-alouds, & Listening Games. 2009. pap. 13.95 *(978-1-934338-75-9(3))* Maupin Hse. Publishing.

Miller, Mimi & Veatch, Nancy. Literacy in Context (Linc) Choosing Instructional Strategies to Teach Reading in Content Areas. 2011. (ENG.). 256p. (C). pap. 36.00 *(978-0-13-503484-2(1))* Allyn & Bacon, Inc.

Miller Thurston, Cheryl. Language Is Served: Games, Writing Prompts, & Other Language Arts Activities on the Yummy Topic of Food. 2008. (ENG.). 152p. (gr. 7). pap. 21.95 *(978-1-877673-79-5(X))* Cottonwood Pr., Inc.

Milofsky, Alison. Peacebuilding Toolkit for Educators: High School Lessons. 2011. ***(978-1-60127-106-8(9))*** U. S. Institute of Peace Pr. (USIP Pr.).

—Peacebuilding Toolkit for Educators: Middle School Lessons. 2011. ***(978-1-60127-105-1(0))*** U. S. Institute of Peace Pr. (USIP Pr.).

Montgomery, Paula. Paper Action Figures of the Imagination: Clip, Color & Create, 1 vol. 2009. 305p. pap. 25.00 *(978-1-59158-751-4(4)*, TIP8751) Libraries Unlimited, Inc.

Moomaw, Sally & Hieronymus, Brenda. More Than Counting: Math Activities for Preschool & Kindergarten. 2011. (More Than... Ser.). (ENG., Illus.). 304p. pap. 34.95 *(978-1-60554-029-0(3))* Redleaf Pr.

Murphy, Dominic. The Playground Potting Shed: Gardening with Children Made Simple. 2010. (ENG.). 272p. pap. 16.95 *(978-0-85265-209-1(7))* Random Hse. GBR. Dist: Independent Pubs. Group.

Muschla, Judith A. & Muschla, Gary Robert. Hands-on Math Projects with Real-Life Applications. (J-B Ed: Hands On Ser.: 30). (ENG., Illus.). 2009. 288p. pap. 29.95 *(978-0-470-26198-9(6))* 2nd rev. ed. 2006. 464p. per. 29.95 *(978-0-7879-8179-2(6))* Wiley, John & Sons, Inc. (Jossey-Bass).

Nagel, Michael & Lidstone, John. Green Doesn't Always Mean Go! 2008. 260p. pap. *(978-3-639-04830-8(X))* VDM Verlag Dr. Mueller e.K.

Nash, Marion & Lowe, Jackie. Supporting Early Language Development: Spirals for Babies & Toddlers. 2012. (ENG., Illus.). 176p. pap. 40.95 ***(978-0-415-69756-9(5))*** Routledge.

Nations, Susan & Waite, Sandy. Intermediate Literacy Stations. 2009. pap. 24.95 *(978-1-934338-42-1(7))* Maupin Hse. Publishing.

Nelson, Jennifer & Braafladt, Keith. Technology & Literacy: 21st Century Library Programming for Children & Teens. 2011. ***(978-0-8389-1108-2(0))*** American Library Assn.

Nijakowska, Joanna. Dyslexia in the Foreign Language Classroom. 2010. (Second Language Acquisition Ser.). (ENG., Illus.). 224p. 139.95 *(978-1-84769-280-1(X))*; pap. 49.95 *(978-1-84769-279-5(6))* Multilingual Matters GBR. Dist: Univ. of Toronto Pr.

Nixon, Caroline & Tomlinson, Michael. Kid's Box 5 Teacher's Book. 2009. (ENG., Illus.). 120p. pap. 32.76 *(978-0-521-68825-3(6))* Cambridge Univ. Pr.

—Primary Kid's Box Level 3 Activity Book with CD-ROM Polish Edition. 2010. 72p. pap. 8.00 incl. cd-rom *(978-0-521-75625-9(1))* Cambridge Univ. Pr.

Nixon, Caroline, et al. Primary Kid's Box Level 3 Pupil's Book with Songs CD & Parents' Guide Polish Edition. 2010. 88p. pap., pap. 12.00 incl. audio compact disk *(978-0-521-74993-0(X))* Cambridge Univ. Pr.

Norfolk, Sherry, et al. The Storytelling Classroom: Applications Across the Curriculum, 1 vol. 2006. (Illus.). 232p. pap. 35.00 *(978-1-59158-305-9(5)*, LU3055) Libraries Unlimited, Inc.

Novelli, Joan & Grundon, Holly. Week-by-Week Phonics Packets: 30 Independent Practice Packets That Help Children Learn Key Phonics Skills & Set the Stage for Reading Success. 2010. (ENG.). 160p. (gr. k-3). pap. 18.99 *(978-0-545-22304-1(0)*, Teaching Resources) Scholastic, Inc.

O'Connell, Susan & Croskey, Suzanne G. Introduction to Communication, Grades 6-8. 2008. (Math Process Standards Ser.). (Illus.). 176p. pap. 34.38 *(978-0-325-01732-7(8)*, E01732) Heinemann.

O'Driscoll, Denis. 100 Physical Education Activities. 2009. (Illus.). 62p. pap. *(978-1-84748-612-7(6))* Athena Pr.

Olson, Kathleen Dunn. What's up? Book 1: Integrated Skills & Culture for Adults. 2010. (ENG., Illus.). 128p. pap. 20.95 *(978-0-472-03291-4(7))* Univ. of Michigan Pr.

Oussoren, Ragnhild. More Write Dance: Extending Development of Write Dance for Children Age 5-9. 2nd ed. 2012. (Lucky Duck Bks.). (Illus.). 160p. 130.00 ***(978-1-4462-0112-1(0)***, B01121C) SAGE Pubns., Ltd. GBR. Dist: SAGE Pubns., Inc.

—Write Dance: Pack. 2nd ed. 2010. (Lucky Duck Bks.). (Illus.). 168p. pap. 104.00 *(978-1-84920-388-3(1)*, B03883P) SAGE Pubns., Ltd. GBR. Dist: SAGE Pubns., Inc.

—Write Dance in the Early Years, Pack. 2nd ed. 2010. (Lucky Duck Bks.). (Illus.). 128p. pap. 86.00 *(978-1-84920-392-0(X)*, B03920P) SAGE Pubns., Ltd. GBR. Dist: SAGE Pubns., Inc.

—Write Dance in the Early Years: A Pre-Writing Programme for Children 3 To 5. 2nd ed. 2010. (Lucky Duck Bks.). (Illus.). 128p. 130.00 *(978-1-84920-138-4(2)*, B01384C); pap. 54.00 *(978-1-84920-139-1(0)*, B01384P) SAGE Pubns., Ltd. GBR. Dist: SAGE Pubns., Inc.

Owen, Ruth. QEB Peek-a-Boo Penguin - Numbers & Counting. 2011. (Peek-a-Boo Penguin Ser.). 24p. (J). (gr. -1-k). 16.95 *(978-1-60992-056-2(2))* Amicus Publishing.

—QEB Peek-a-Boo Penguin - Ready for Reading. 2011. (Peek-a-Boo Penguin Ser.). 24p. (J). (gr. -1-k). 16.95 *(978-1-60992-058-6(9))* Amicus Publishing.

—QED Peek-a-Boo Penguin - Colours & Shapes. 2011. (Peek-a-Boo Penguin Ser.). 24p. (J). (gr. -1-k). 16.95 *(978-1-60992-055-5(4))* Amicus Publishing.

Oxford University Press Staff, ed. A2 Chemistry Planning & Resource Pack with Oxbox CD-ROM. 2009. (ENG., Illus.). 304p. (YA). cd-rom 900.00 *(978-0-19-915278-0(0))* Oxford Univ. Pr., Inc.

Palomares, Susanna & Schilling, Dianne. Educating the Whole Child: Social Development & Self-Awareness Activities for the Early Years. 2008. (Illus.). x, 168p. 27.00 *(978-1-4164-0370-8(1))* PRO-ED, Inc.

Pangrazi, Robert P. Dynamic Physical Education Curriculum Guide: Lesson Plans for Implementation. 17th rev. ed. 2012. (ENG.). 352p. (C). pap. 57.07 ***(978-0-321-79355-3(2))*** Benjamin-Cummings Publishing Co.

Parfitt, Vicki, et al. Maths Homework for Key Stage 2: Activity-based Learning. 2010. (Active Homework Ser.). (ENG., Illus.). 104p. 39.95 *(978-0-415-49625-4(X)*, Routledge) Taylor & Francis Group GBR. Dist: Taylor & Francis Group.

Parker, Christi. Primary Source Fluency Activities: My Community Then & Now. 2007. (Primary Source Fluency Activities Ser.). (ENG., Illus.). 176p. (gr. 1-3). pap. 29.99 *(978-1-4258-0368-1(7))* Shell Educational Publishing.

Parkin, Margaret. More Tales for Trainers: Using Stories & Metaphors to Influence & Encourage Learning. 2010. (ENG.). 192p. pap. 34.95 *(978-0-7494-6085-3(7))* Kogan Page, Ltd. GBR. Dist: Ingram Pub. Services.

Parratore, Phil. Wacky Science: Fun & Exciting Hands-On Activities for the Classroom. 2010. (ENG.). 172p. (gr. 5-8). pap. 17.95 *(978-1-59363-411-7(0))* Prufrock Pr.

Parsons, Cynthia. A Recipe Book for Tutors: Teaching the Kinesthetic Learner. 2008. (ENG.). 142p. 55.00 *(978-1-57886-790-5(8))*; pap. 20.95 *(978-1-57886-791-2(6))* Rowman & Littlefield Education.

Paterson, Anice, et al. 30 Fun Ways to Learn about Music. 2011. (30 Fun Ways Ser.). (ENG.). 80p. pap. 12.95 *(978-0-87659-368-4(6))* Gryphon Hse., Inc.

Paxson, Peyton. Media Literacy: Thinking Critically about Advertising. 2nd rev. ed. 2009. (YA). pap. 24.99 *(978-0-8251-6512-2(1))* Walch Education.

—Media Literacy: Thinking Critically about Television. 2nd rev. ed. 2009. (YA). pap. 24.99 *(978-0-8251-6511-5(3))* Walch Education.

—Media Literacy: Thinking Critically about the Internet. 2nd rev. ed. 2009. (YA). pap. 24.99 *(978-0-8251-6510-8(5))* Walch Education.

—Media Literacy: Thinking Critically about Video Games & Virtual Worlds. 2009. (YA). pap. 24.99 *(978-0-8251-6509-2(1))* Walch Education.

Pember, Richard. Friday Afternoon Chemistry, Pack. 2010. (Illus.). 140p. 225.00 *(978-0-340-99180-0(1))* Hodder Education GBR. Dist: Trans-Atlantic Pubns., Inc.

Petersen, Katia S. Activities for Building Character & Social-Emotional Learning Grades 6-8. 2012. (Safe & Caring Schools Ser.). (ENG.). 208p. (gr. 6-8). 29.99 ***(978-1-57542-394-4(4))*** Free Spirit Publishing, Inc.

—Activities for Building Character & Social-Emotional Learning Grades PreK-K. 2012. (Safe & Caring Schools Ser.). (ENG.). 160p. (gr. -1-k). 29.99 ***(978-1-57542-391-3(X))*** Free Spirit Publishing, Inc.

Petersen, Katia S. Safe & Caring Schools. 2008. (Safe & Caring Schools Ser.). (ENG.). 192p. (gr. 1-2). instr.'s gde. ed. 39.95 *(978-1-57542-288-6(3))* Free Spirit Publishing, Inc.

Phillips, Warren G. & Tate, Marcia L. Science Worksheets Don't Grow Dendrites: 20 Instructional Strategies That Engage the Brain. 2010. (Illus.). 192p. pap. 36.95 *(978-1-4129-7847-7(5)*, B78477P) Corwin Pr.

Polette, Keith. Teaching Grammar Through Writing: Activities to Develop Writer's Craft in All Students in Grades 4-12. 2nd ed. 2011. (ENG.). 192p. (C). pap. 42.80 *(978-0-13-256599-8(4))* Allyn & Bacon, Inc.

Polette, Nancy. Fairy Tale Fun! 2011. ***(978-1-55570-773-6(4))*** Neal-Schuman Pubs., Inc.

Polette, Nancy. Reading the World with Picture Books. 2010. E-Book *(978-1-59884-588-4(8))* Libraries Unlimited, Inc.

Polette, Nancy J. Reading the World with Picture Books, 1 vol. 2010. 348p. pap. 35.00 *(978-1-59884-587-7(X)*, A3100P) Libraries Unlimited, Inc.

Pool, Jessica. Why Buy the Cow? A Unit on Cohabitation. 2008. (Illus.). 40p. spiral bd. incl. audio compact disk *(978-0-9761349-3-0(4))* Dibble Institute for Marriage Education, The.

The Prairie Primer. 2006. pap. 45.00 *(978-0-9652511-3-6(6))* Cadron Creek Curriculum.

Preddy, Leslie B. Social Readers: Promoting Reading in the 21st Century, 1 vol. 2010. (Illus.). 223p. pap. 35.00 *(978-1-59158-869-6(3)*, LU8869) Libraries Unlimited, Inc.

Price, Kay M. & Nelson, Karna L. Planning Effective Instruction: Diversity Responsive Methods & Management. 4th ed. 2010. (Whatâ€(tm)s New in Education Ser.). (ENG.). 336p. (C). pap. 85.95 *(978-0-495-80949-4(7))* Wadsworth.

Pruitt, Eunice Z. Schools as Professional Learning Communities: Collaborative Activities & Strategies for Professional Development. Roberts, Sylvia M., ed. 2nd ed. 2008. (Illus.). 272p. 86.95 *(978-1-4129-6893-5(3)*, B68935C); pap. 39.95 *(978-1-4129-6894-2(1)*, B68935P) Corwin Pr.

Radd, Tommie R. & Brightman, Becky. The Grow with Guidance Classroom Activities File. 2nd ed. Date not set. *(978-1-878317-29-2(6))* Grow With Guidance.

Raines, Shirley C. & Smith, Brian Scott. Story Stretchers for the Primary Grades: Activities to Expand Children's Books. 2011. (Story S-t-r-e-t-c-h-e-r-s Ser.). (ENG., Illus.). 256p. (gr. k-4). pap. 29.95 ***(978-0-87659-309-7(0))*** Gryphon Hse., Inc.

Rakes, Celeste W. All American History Student Activity Book Vol. 1: The Explorers to the Jacksonians. 2007. (All American History Ser.). (Illus.). 224p. pap. 16.95 *(978-1-892427-11-3(7))* Bright Ideas! Educational Resources.

—All American History, Volume 1: The Explorers to the Jacksonians. 2007. (Illus.). 268p. per. 18.95 *(978-1-892427-10-6(9))* Bright Ideas! Educational Resources.

Read, Graham. Case Studies in Classification, Evolution & Biodiversity, Pack. 2009. (Illus.). 189p. spiral bd. 225.00 *(978-0-340-97247-2(5))* Hodder Education GBR. Dist: Trans-Atlantic Pubns., Inc.

Reid, Rob. What's Black & White & Reid All Over? Something Hilarious Happened at the Library. 2012. ***(978-0-8389-1147-1(1))*** American Library Assn.

Reynolds, Laureen. Catch Your Kids Before They Fall: 140+ Skill-Builders to Boost Academic Success. 2010. *(978-1-934026-83-0(2))* CSB Enterprises.

Rich, Steve. Bringing Outdoor Science In: Thrifty Classroom Lessons. 2012. ***(978-1-936959-04-4(6)***, Orbit Books) National Science Teachers Assn.

Rich, Steve A. Outdoor Science: A Practical Guide. 2010. *(978-1-935155-12-6(1))* National Science Teachers Assn.

Riley, Dave. Intellectual Development: Connecting Science & Practice in Early Childhood Settings. 2008. (Redleaf Professional Library). (ENG.). 160p. pap. 24.95 *(978-1-933653-63-1(9))* Redleaf Pr.

Roberts, Ann. 30 Fun Ways to Learn about Writing. 2011. (30 Fun Ways Ser.). (ENG.). 80p. (gr. -1-k). pap. 12.95 *(978-0-87659-366-0(X))* Gryphon Hse., Inc.

Robertson, William C. Companion Classroom Activities for Force & Motion: Stop Faking It! 2011. ***(978-1-936137-28-2(3))*** National Science Teachers Assn.

Robinson, Anne & Saxby, Karen. Fun for Movers Teacher's Book. 2nd ed. 2010. (ENG.). 160p. pap. 17.68 *(978-0-521-74829-2(1))* Cambridge Univ. Pr.

Rodwell, John. Activity-Based Training Design: Tools & Techniques for Transforming Existing Training Sessions into Accelerated Learning Activities. 2007. (Illus.). 194p. 114.95 *(978-0-566-08796-7(0)*, Gower Publishing Co., Ltd.) Ashgate Publishing, Ltd. GBR. Dist: Ashgate Publishing Co.

Roehlkepartain, Jolene. Spark Student Motivation: 101 Easy Activities for Cooperative Learning. 2012. (ENG.). 240p. pap. 16.95 ***(978-1-57482-494-0(5))*** Search Institute.

Rogers, David. Friday Afternoon Geography, Pack. 2010. (Illus.). 200p. 210.00 *(978-1-4441-0841-5(7))* Hodder Education GBR. Dist: Trans-Atlantic Pubns., Inc.

Rogers, Vanessa. A Little Book of Drugs: Activities to Explore Drug Issues with Young People. 2nd rev. ed. 2012. (ENG., Illus.). 128p. pap. ***(978-1-84905-304-4(9))*** Kingsley, Jessica Ltd.

Roman, Harry T. Energize Your Students with Creative Writing & Speaking Projects, 1 vol. 2009. 73p. pap. 16.95 *(978-1-4489-9835-7(2))* PublishAmerica, Inc.

Rosenberg, Mary. Math Problem of the Day Practice Mats: 180 Instant Activity Pages That Help Children Build the Essential Skills They Need to Meet the Math Standards. 2009. (ENG.). 208p. pap. 22.99 *(978-0-545-02813-4(2)*, Teaching Resources) Scholastic, Inc.

Rosenthal-Gazit, Roni. 101 Let's Have Fun: 101 fun activities that reinforce learning in the Hebrew Language. 2009. (Illus.). 148p. pap. 15.95 *(978-0-9792800-1-6(X))* StoryTime World Publishing Hse.

Ross, Mary H. Short & Sweet with a Treat: 52 Already Done, Ready-For Fun Family Home Evenings. 2008. (Illus.). 104p. pap. *(978-1-59811-505-5(7))* Covenant Communications.

Rozzelle, Jan & Scearce, Carol. Power Tools for Adolescent Literacy: Strategies for Learning. 2008. 232p. pap. 29.95 *(978-1-934009-35-2(0))* Solution Tree.

Saccardi, Marianne C. Art in Story: Teaching Art History to Elementary School Children, 1 vol. 2nd ed. 2006. (Illus.). 484p. pap. 35.00 *(978-1-59158-359-2(4)*, LU3594, Teacher Ideas Pr.) Libraries Unlimited, Inc.

Sang, David. Cambridge IGCSE Physics Teacher's Resource CD-ROM. 2010. (Cambridge International Examinations Ser.). cd-rom 42.00 *(978-0-521-17359-9(0))* Cambridge Univ. Pr.

Sang, David, et al. Cambridge International AS Level & A Level Physics Teacher's Resource CD-ROM. 2010. (Cambridge International Examinations Ser.). cd-rom 144.00 *(978-0-521-17915-7(7))* Cambridge Univ. Pr.

Santomauro, Josie, et al. Set for Success: Activities for Teaching Emotional, Social & Organizational Skills. 2011. 128p. pap. *(978-1-84905-058-6(9))* Kingsley, Jessica Ltd.

Saracho, Olivia N. & Spodek, Bernard. Contemporary Perspectives on Language & Cultural Diversity in Early Childhood Education. 2010. (Illus.). viii, 272p. *(978-1-60752-417-5(1))*; pap. *(978-1-60752-416-8(3))* Information Age Publishing, Inc.

Saunders-Smith, Gail. Non-Fiction Text Structures for Better Comprehension & Response. 2009. pap. 23.95 *(978-1-934338-38-4(9))* Maupin Hse. Publishing.

Sawyers, Karen, et al. Moving with Purpose: 54 Activities for Learning, Fitness, & Fun. 2010. *(978-1-57379-473-2(2))* High/Scope Pr.

Saxby, Karen. Storyfun for Flyers. 2010. (ENG.). 64p. pap., tchr. ed. 14.00 incl. audio compact disk ***(978-0-521-12667-0(3))*** Cambridge Univ. Pr.

Saxby, Karen. Storyfun for Movers. 2011. (ENG.). 64p. pap., tchr. ed. 13.00 incl. audio compact disk *(978-0-521-17023-9(0))* Cambridge Univ. Pr.

Schiller, Pam & Willis, Clarissa. Inclusive Literacy Lessons for Early Childhood. 2008. (ENG., Illus.). 297p. pap. 24.95 *(978-0-87659-299-1(X))* Gryphon Hse., Inc.

Schindler, Howard & Mucenski, Dennis. Science Sleuths: Solving Mysteries Using Scientific Inquiry. 2009. (ENG.). 150p. (gr. 6-9). pap. 19.95 *(978-1-59363-397-4(1))* Prufrock Pr.

Schiro, Michael S. & Schiro. Mega-Fun Math Games & Puzzles for the Elementary Grades: Over 125 Activities That Teach Math Facts, Concepts, & Thinking Skills. 2009. (ENG.). 336p. pap. 24.95 *(978-0-470-34475-0(X)*, Jossey-Bass) Wiley, John & Sons, Inc.

Scholastic Inc Staff, contrib. by. Expert 21: Teacher Implementation Guide. 2010. (Illus.). 208p. ***(978-0-545-20915-1(3))*** Scholastic, Inc.

Scholastic, Inc. Staff, contrib. by. Vowels. 2010. (Scholastic Success with Ser.). (ENG.). 48p. (gr. k-2). pap. 5.99 *(978-0-545-20113-1(6)*, Teaching Resources) Scholastic, Inc.

—Writing. 2010. (Scholastic Success with Ser.). (ENG.). 48p. (gr. 1-1). pap. 5.99 *(978-0-545-20079-0(2))*; (gr. 2-2). pap. 5.99 *(978-0-545-20078-3(4))*; (gr. 3-3). pap. 5.99 *(978-0-545-20077-6(6))*; (gr. 4-4). pap. 5.99 *(978-0-545-20076-9(8))*; (gr. 5-5). pap. 5.99 *(978-0-545-20075-2(X))* Scholastic, Inc. (Teaching Resources).

Scripture Union Staff, contrib. by. Matchday Programme: Holiday Club Resource Material for 5 to 11 Year-Olds. 2007. 64p. pap. ***(978-1-84427-333-1(4))*** Scripture Union.

Seefeldt, Carol, et al. Active Experiences for Active Children. 3rd ed. 2011. ***(978-0-13-265955-0(7))*** Pearson Bks.

—Active Experiences for Active Children: Mathmatics. 3rd rev. ed. 2011. (ENG., Illus.). 192p. (C). pap. 29.80 ***(978-0-13-237334-0(3)***, Prentice Hall) Prentice Hall PTR.

Selwyn, Douglas. Living History in the Classroom: Integrative Arts Activities for Making Social Studies Meaningful. 2008. (ENG., Illus.). 224p. (gr. 5-12). pap. 29.95 *(978-1-59363-336-3(X))* Prufrock Pr.

Senior, Claire. Getting the Buggers to Read. 2nd rev. ed. 2008. (Getting the Buggers Ser.). (ENG., Illus.). 216p. 29.95 *(978-1-84706-057-0(9))* Continuum International Publishing Group, Ltd. GBR. Dist: National Bk. Network.

Shahin, Gloria. Catholic Connections Student Activity Booklet. 2010. pap. 59.95 *(978-1-59982-043-9(9))* St. Mary's Pr.

Sharp, Stephen. New Look at the Interactive Writing Classroom: Methods, Strategies, & Activities to Engage Students. 2011. 224p. 55.00 *(978-1-61048-417-6(7))* Rowman & Littlefield Education.

—A New Look at the Interactive Writing Classroom: Methods, Strategies, & Activities to Engage Students. 2011. 224p. pap. 28.95 *(978-1-61048-418-3(5))* Rowman & Littlefield Education.

Shell-Gallasch, Amy, ed. Hands on History: A Resource for Teaching Mathematics. 2007. (MAA Notes Ser.). (ENG., Illus.). 190p. 55.00 *(978-0-88385-182-1(2))* Mathematical Assn. of America.

Sherwood, Elizabeth A., et al. Science Adventures: Nature Activities for Young Children. 2008. (ENG., Illus.). 272p. pap. 24.95 *(978-0-87659-015-7(6))* Gryphon Hse., Inc.

Shiotsu, Vicky. Build-A-Skill Instant Books: Compound Words. 2009. pap. 5.99 *(978-1-59198-973-8(6))* Creative Teaching Pr., Inc.

—Build-A-Skill Instant Books: Contractions. 2009. pap. 5.99 *(978-1-59198-971-4(X))* Creative Teaching Pr., Inc.

—Build-A-Skill Instant Books: Fractions. 2009. pap. 5.99 *(978-1-59198-980-6(9))* Creative Teaching Pr., Inc.

—Build-A-Skill Instant Books: Homophones. 2009. pap. 5.99 *(978-1-59198-970-7(1))* Creative Teaching Pr., Inc.

—Build-A-Skill Instant Books: Irregular Vowels. 2009. pap. 5.99 *(978-1-59198-972-1(8))* Creative Teaching Pr., Inc.

—Build-A-Skill Instant Books: Multiplication & Division. 2009. pap. 5.99 *(978-1-59198-977-6(9))* Creative Teaching Pr., Inc.

—Build-A-Skill Instant Books: Parts of Speech. 2009. pap. 5.99 *(978-1-59198-976-9(0))* Creative Teaching Pr., Inc.

—Build-A-Skill Instant Books: Plurals. 2009. pap. 5.99 *(978-1-59198-975-2(2))* Creative Teaching Pr., Inc.

—Build-A-Skill Instant Books: Prefixes & Suffixes. 2009. pap. 5.99 *(978-1-59198-974-5(4))* Creative Teaching Pr., Inc.

—Build-A-Skill Instant Books: Verb Forms. 2009. pap. 5.99 *(978-1-59198-979-0(5))* Creative Teaching Pr., Inc.

Siebert, Nicole. Innovative Art Projects for Children. 2010. (ENG.). 88p. (J). spiral bd. 19.95 *(978-1-56290-669-6(0))* Crystal Productions.

Silva, Nancy A. Sold on Mathematics: Using Real Estate Ads to Teach Key Skills. 2008. 14.95 (978-1-934026-14-4(X), Crystal Springs Bks.) Staff Development for Educators.

—Time for a Rhyme: Teaching Elapsed Time with Modern-Day Nursery Rhymes. 2008. 20.95 (978-1-934026-15-1(8), Crystal Springs Bks.) Staff Development for Educators.

Simpson, Cynthia G., et al. Teacher's Survival Guide: The Inclusion Classroom. 2011. (ENG.). 250p. pap. 19.95 (978-1-59363-541-1(9)) Prufrock Pr.

Simpson, Tim. No Object Object Talks. 2007. (Big Books (Gospel Light) Ser.). (ENG., Illus.). 224p. (J). 29.99 (978-0-8307-4358-2(8)) Gospel Light Pubns.

Sissel-Phelan, Peggy. All about Farmers' Markets: A Teaching Guide for Classrooms, Camps, & Community Programs. 2007. (ENG., Illus.). 106p. pap. 32.95 (978-0-9771010-2-3(9)) Brain Child Pr., Inc.

—A Very Purple Pepper: Colors to Know So You Can Grow. 2008. (ENG., Illus.). 18p. (J). 6.99 (978-0-9771010-4-7(5), Brain Child Bks.) Brain Child Pr., Inc.

Sissel-Phelan, Peggy, creator. Fruit & Vegetable Flashcards. 2007. (ENG.). (J). 24.95 (978-0-9771010-5-4(3)) Brain Child Pr., Inc.

Sissel-Phelan, Peggy, text. Let's All Eat Veggies! 2007. (ENG., Illus.). 16p. (J). (978-0-9771010-3-0(7)) Brain Child Pr., Inc.

Siwak, Karen. Library Programs for Teens: Mystery Theater. 3rd ed. 2010. (VOYA Guides). (ENG., Illus.). 266p. (gr. 17). pap. 45.00 (978-0-8108-4992-1(5)) Scarecrow Pr., Inc.

Smekens, Kristina. Trait-Based Writing: Lessons & Activities. 2009. (ENG.). 80p. pap. 14.99 (978-0-545-09659-1(6), Teaching Resources) Scholastic, Inc.

Smith, Jo. Exploring British Culture with Audio CD: Multi-level Activities about Life in the UK. 2012. (Cambridge Copy Collection). (ENG.). 128p. pap. 47.00 incl. audio compact disk **(978-0-521-18642-1(0))** Cambridge Univ. Pr.

Smith, Wallace P. & Smith, Wallace R. Baptism Ahead: A Road Map for Young Disciples. 2009. 128p. (J). pap. 15.00 (978-0-8170-1551-0(5)) Judson Pr.

Sousa, David A., ed. Brain-Compatible Activities for Mathematics, Grades 4-5. 2009. 200p. pap. 21.95 (978-1-4129-6787-7(2), B67877P) Corwin Pr.

Souza, Steven & Shorell, Joseph. Hands-on Science Series Simple Machines. 2nd rev. ed. 2009. 142p. pap. 25.00 (978-0-8251-6521-4(0)) Walch Education.

Spangler, David B. Strategies for Teaching Whole Number Computation: Using Error Analysis for Intervention & Assessment. 2010. (Illus.). 224p. pap. 38.95 (978-1-4129-8106-4(9), B81064P) Corwin Pr.

Spector, Cecile Cyrul. Sounds Like Fun: Activities for Developing Phonological Awareness, Revised Edition. 2009. 128p. 29.95 (978-1-59857-048-9(X)) Brookes, Paul H. Publishing Co.

Stanley, Nile & Dillingham, Brett. Performance Literacy Through Storytelling. 2009. (Illus.). ix, 22p. pap. 27.95 (978-1-934338-41-4(9)) Maupin Hse. Publishing.

Stanley, Sara. Why Think? Philosophical Play From 3-11. 2012. (ENG.). 208p. pap. 32.95 **(978-1-4411-9360-5(X))** Continuum International Publishing Group, Ltd. GBR. Dist: National Bk. Network.

—Why Think? Philosophical Play from 3-11. 2012. **(978-1-4411-6753-8(6)); (978-1-4411-8365-1(5))** Continuum International Publishing Group, Ltd.

Storm, Grace E. A Study of Indian Life. 2011. 66p. 36.95 **(978-1-258-01174-1(3))** Literary Licensing, LLC.

Super Duper Publications Staff. Elephone. 2007. 12.95 (978-1-58650-707-7(9)) Super Duper Pubns.

Sylvan Learning Staff. Fourth Grade Super Math Success. 2010. (Math Super Workbooks Ser.). (ENG.). 320p. (gr. 3-5). pap. 18.99 (978-0-307-47920-4(X), Sylvan Learning Publishing) Random Hse. Information Group.

—Super Math Success: Activities, Exercises, & Tips to Help Catch up, Keep up, & Get Ahead. 2010. (Math Super Workbooks Ser.). (ENG.). 320p. (gr. 1-3). pap. 18.99 (978-0-375-43050-3(4)); (gr. 4-7). pap. 18.99 (978-0-307-47921-1(8)) Random Hse. Information Group. (Sylvan Learning Publishing).

—Third Grade Super Math Success. 2010. (Math Super Workbooks Ser.). (ENG.). 320p. (gr. 2-4). pap. 18.99 (978-0-375-43051-0(2), Sylvan Learning Publishing) Random Hse. Information Group.

Tassoni & Thwaites, Alan. 100 Ideas for Teaching Knowledge & Understanding of the World. 2008. (100 Ideas for the Early Years Ser.). (ENG., Illus.). 144p. 24.95 (978-0-8264-9868-7(X)) Continuum International Publishing Group, Ltd. GBR. Dist: National Bk. Network.

Tate, Marcia L. Engage the Brain: Games, Science, Grades 6-8. 2008. (Engage the Brain: Games Ser.). (Illus.). 96p. (gr. 4-7). pap. 16.95 (978-1-4129-5925-4(X), B59254P) Corwin Pr.

—Engage the Brain - Games. 2008. (Engage the Brain: Games Ser.). (Illus.). 96p. (gr. -1-3). pap. 16.95 (978-1-4129-5930-8(6), B59308P); (gr. -1-3). pap. 16.95 (978-1-4129-5932-2(2), B59322P); (gr. -1-3). pap. 16.95 (978-1-4129-5931-5(4), B59315P); (gr. 4-7). pap. 16.95 (978-1-4129-5928-5(4), B59285P); (gr. 4-7). pap. 16.95 (978-1-4129-5929-2(2), B59292P) Corwin Pr.

—Games, Math. 2008. (Engage the Brain: Games Ser.). (Illus.). 96p. (gr. 4-7). pap. 16.95 (978-1-4129-5926-1(8), B59261P) Corwin Pr.

—Games, Social Studies. 2008. (Engage the Brain: Games Ser.). (Illus.). 96p. (gr. 4-7). pap. 16.95 (978-1-4129-5952-0(7), B59520P) Corwin Pr.

—Kindergarten. 2008. (Engage the Brain: Games Ser.). (Illus.). 96p. (gr. -1-3). pap. 16.95 (978-1-4129-5933-9(0), B59339P) Corwin Pr.

—Mathematics Worksheets Don't Grow Dendrites: 20 Numeracy Strategies That Engage the Brain, PreK-8. 2008. (Illus.). 200p. 80.95 (978-1-4129-5332-0(4), B53324C); pap. 36.95 (978-1-4129-5333-7(2), B53324P) Corwin Pr.

—Reading & Language Arts Worksheets Don't Grow Dendrites (Multimedia Kit) 20 Literacy Strategies That Engage the Brain. 2010. 48p. 360.00 (978-1-4129-7562-9(X), B75629K) Corwin Pr.

Taylor-Cox, Jennifer. Differentiating in Algebra, PreK-Grade 2: A Content Companion for Ongoing Assessment, Grouping Students, & Targeting Instruction. 2008. 96p. pap. 12.50 (978-0-325-02184-3(8), E02184) Heinemann.

—Differentiating in Geometry, PreK-Grade 2: A Content Companion for Ongoing Assessment, Grouping Students, & Targeting Instruction. 2008. 112p. pap. 12.50 (978-0-325-02186-7(4), E02186) Heinemann.

Taylor, Robert J. & Taylor, John. Maths Express Ages 7-9: 50+ Flexible Maths Activities. 2009. 112p. pap. 42.95 (978-0-415-47153-4(2)) Fulton, David Pubs. GBR. Dist: Taylor & Francis Group.

Teaford, Patricia & Wheat, Jan. HELP 3-6: Activities at Home. 2nd ed. 2010. (Illus.). xvi, 294p. **(978-0-89718-208-9(1))** VORT Corp.

Tegegne, Wondimu. Practical Implementation of Practicum Program. 2010. 100p. pap. (978-3-639-25779-3(0)) VDM Verlag Dr. Mueller e.K.

Tejas LEE Guía de Actividades de Intervención: Kindergarten Primer Grado Segundo Grado Tercer Grado. 2010. (SPA & ENG., Illus.). v, 198p. spiral bd. **(978-1-59857-155-4(9))** Brookes, Paul H. Publishing Co.

Terrill, Kelly & Marin, Portia. Summer Fit Fourth to Fifth Grade: Keeping Children Physically & Mentally Active During the Summer. 2011. (Summer Fit Ser.). (ENG.). 144p. pap. 12.95 (978-0-9762800-0-2(0)) Summer Fit Learning, Inc.

The Mailbox Books Staff. Everything Science: PreK-K. 2010. 176p. 19.95 (978-1-56234-931-6(7), Mailbox Bks., The) Education Ctr., Inc.

—Songs & Rhymes for Little Learners: PreK-K. 2010. 80p. 15.95 (978-1-56234-939-4(2), Mailbox Bks., The) Education Ctr., Inc.

Thomas, Nancy Pickering, et al. Information Literacy & Information Skills Instruction: Applying Research to Practice in the 21st Century School Library. 1 vol. 3rd rev. ed. 2011. 261p. pap. 40.00 (978-1-59884-490-0(3), A2995P) Libraries Unlimited, Inc.

Thombs, Margaret M., et al. Using WebQuests in the Social Studies Classroom: A Culturally Responsive Approach. 2008. (Illus.). 152p. 68.95 (978-1-4129-5950-6(0), B59506C); pap. 28.95 (978-1-4129-5951-3(9), B59506P) Corwin Pr.

Ticotsky, Alan. Science Giants: Physical Science: 27 Activities Exploring the World's Greatest Scientific Discoveries. 2007. (Illus.). 152p. (J). (gr. -1-3). per. 16.95 (978-1-59647-124-5(7)) Good Year Bks.

Totten, Kathryn. Storytime Crafts. 2009. (Illus.). 101p. pap. 16.95 (978-1-56472-229-4(5), Upstart Bks.) Highsmith Inc.

Tower, Mollie & Fallin, Jana R. Using Music to Enhance Student Learning, 2 vols. 2011. (ENG., Illus.). 256p. pap. 83.95 (978-0-415-87823-4(3)) Routledge.

Tower, Mollie Gregory & Fallin, Jana. Using Music to Enhance Student Learning. 2011. (Illus.). xvi, 290p. pap. **(978-0-415-89473-9(5))** Routledge.

Van Houten, Lori, et al. Developing an Effective School Plan: An Activity-Based Guide to Understanding Your School & Improving Student Outcomes, 2 vols. 2006. (ENG.). 336p. 129.95 (978-0-914409-26-7(3)) WestEd.

Van Zile, Susan & Napoli, Mary. Teaching Literary Elements with Picture Books: Engaging, Standards-Based Lessons & Strategies. 2009. (ENG.). 80p. pap. 14.99 (978-0-439-02799-1(3), Teaching Resources) Scholastic, Inc.

Vasquez, Anete, et al. Teaching Language Arts to English Language Learners. 2010. (ENG., Illus.). 216p. (C). 140.00 (978-0-415-99531-3(0)); pap. 36.95 (978-0-415-99532-0(9)) Routledge.

Walch Publishing Staff. Academic Support Program for Algebra. 2007. (J). lthr. 395.00 (978-0-8251-6376-0(5)) Walch Education.

—Academic Support Program for English Language Arts. 2008. (J). lthr. 395.00 (978-0-8251-6332-6(3)) Walch Education.

—Academic Support Program for Mathematics. 2007. (J). lthr. 395.00 (978-0-8251-6175-9(4)); (J). lthr. 395.00 (978-0-8251-6176-6(2)); (YA). lthr. 395.00 (978-0-8251-6177-3(0)) Walch Education.

—Academic Support Program for Science. 2008. (YA). lthr. 395.00 (978-0-8251-6466-8(4)) Walch Education.

—Differentiated Instruction for Language Arts. 2009. (YA). pap. 24.99 (978-0-8251-6514-6(8)) Walch Education.

—Expeditions in Your Classroom for English Language Arts. 2009. (J). pap. 26.00 (978-0-8251-6506-1(7)) Walch Education.

—Expeditions in Your Classroom for Mathematics. 2009. (J). pap. 26.00 (978-0-8251-6507-8(5)) Walch Education.

—Expeditions in Your Classroom for Science. 2009. (J). pap. 24.99 (978-0-8251-6508-5(3)) Walch Education.

—Hands-on Science: Forensics. 2009. (YA). pap. 23.99 (978-0-8251-6515-3(6)) Walch Education.

—Station Activities for English Language Arts. 2009. (J). pap. 31.00 (978-0-8251-6358-6(7)) Walch Education.

Walker, Pam & Wood, Elaine. The Science Teacher's Activity-a-Day: Over 180 Reproducible Pages of Quick, Fun Projects That Illustrate Basic Concepts. 2010. (JB-Ed: 5 Minute FUNdamentals Ser.: 18). (ENG., Illus.). 288p. pap. 19.95 (978-0-470-40881-0(2), Jossey-Bass) Wiley, John & Sons, Inc.

Wanamaker, Karen A. Farmer. Instant Library Lessons: Fall Fun. 2008. (Instant Library Lessons Ser.). (Illus.). 181p. (J). (gr. -1-3). pap. 17.95 (978-1-932146-78-3(4), Upstart Bks.) Highsmith Inc.

Ward, Jennifer. It's a Jungle Out There! 52 Nature Adventures for City Kids. 2011. (ENG., Illus.). 144p. pap. 14.00 (978-1-59030-908-7(1), Trumpeter) Shambhala Pubns., Inc.

Weatherhead, Yvonne. Creative Circle Time Lessons for the Early Years. 2008. (Lucky Duck Bks.). (Illus.). 160p. pap. 49.00 (978-1-4129-3533-3(4), B35334P) SAGE Pubns., Ltd. GBR. Dist: SAGE Pubns., Inc.

Webster, Maggie. Creative Activities & Ideas for Pupils with English as an Additional Language. rev. ed. 2011. (Classroom Gems Ser.). (ENG., Illus.). 258p. pap. 37.50 **(978-1-4082-6777-6(2))** Longman Publishing Group.

Webster, Maggie. Creative Approaches to Teaching Primary RE. 2010. (Illus.). 161p. pap. 49.95 (978-1-4082-0440-5(1)) Pearson Education, Ltd. GBR. Dist: Trans-Atlantic Pubns., Inc.

Widmaier, Rosemarie E., et al. Treffpunkt Deutsch. 5th ed. 2007. (ENG.). 408p. (C). pap., stu. ed., act. bk. ed. 73.33 (978-0-13-195581-3(0), Prentice Hall) Prentice Hall PTR.

Wieczorek, Anna. Primary i-Dictionary 2 Low Elementary Workbook. 2011. (ENG.). 88p. pap. 16.00 (978-0-521-17586-9(0)) Cambridge Univ. Pr.

—Primary i-Dictionary 3 High Elementary CD-ROM (Home User) 2011. (ENG.). 58.00 (978-0-521-17589-0(5)) Cambridge Univ. Pr.

—Primary i-Dictionary 3 High Elementary CD-ROM (Single Classroom) 2011. (ENG.). 200.00 (978-0-521-17587-6(9)) Cambridge Univ. Pr.

—Primary i-Dictionary 3 High Elementary CD-ROM (up to 10 Classrooms) 2011. (ENG.). 525.00 (978-0-521-17588-3(7)) Cambridge Univ. Pr.

Wilburne, Jane M., et al. Cowboys Count, Monkeys Measure, & Princesses Problem Solve: Building Early Math Skills Through Storybooks. 2011. (Illus.). 136p. pap. 24.95 (978-1-59857-106-6(0)) Brookes, Paul H. Publishing Co.

Will, Sab. Primary Music Box: Traditional Songs & Activities for Younger Learners. 2010. (Cambridge Copy Collection). (ENG., Illus.). 144p. pap. 62.40 incl. audio compact disk (978-0-521-72856-0(8)) Cambridge Univ. Pr.

Williams, Melanie. Kid's Box 2 Teacher's Book. 2008. (ENG.). 120p. pap. 34.94 (978-0-521-68809-3(4)) Cambridge Univ. Pr.

—Kid's Box American English Level 6 Teacher's Edition. 2011. (ENG.). 254p. pap. 32.00 (978-0-521-17817-4(7)) Cambridge Univ. Pr.

Williams, Michelle & Hannam, Nicolette. 100+ Fun Ideas for Teaching French Across the Curriculum in the Primary Classroom. 2011. (Illus.). 118p. pap. **(978-1-905780-79-2(6))** Brilliant Pubns.

Wilson, Ruth. Nature & Young Children. 2nd rev. ed. 2012. (ENG., Illus.). 136p. (C). 155.00 **(978-0-415-52673-9(6))** Routledge.

Wood, Piers. A2 Biology Planning & Resource Pack with Oxbox CD-ROM. 2009. (ENG.). 304p. (YA). cd-rom 900.00 (978-0-19-915272-8(1)) Oxford Univ. Pr., Inc.

Wright, Andrew. Storytelling with Children. Oxford University Press Staff, ed. 2nd ed. 2009. (ENG.). 196p. pap. 28.75 (978-0-19-442581-0(9)) Oxford Univ. Pr., Inc.

Wright, Craig, ed. We Won the Cup. 2010. (ENG., Illus.). 16p. act. bk. ed. 4.06 (978-0-19-440170-8(7)) Oxford Univ. Pr., Inc.

Young, Dolly, et al. ¡Vívelo! annot. ed. 2010. (SPA & ENG.). 614p. (C). tchr. ed. 147.95 (978-0-470-55497-5(5), Wiley) Wiley, John & Sons, Inc.

Young, Jonathan R., et al. Coyote's Guide to Connecting with Nature. 2nd ed. 2009. pap. 29.95 (978-1-57994-025-6(0)) Owlink Media Corp.

ACTIVITY TEACHING

see Active Learning

ACTIVITY THEORY

see Activity Coefficients

ACTON, JOHN EMERICH EDWARD DALBERG ACTON, BARON, 1834-1902

Altholz, Josef L., et al, eds. The Correspondence of Lord Acton & Richard Simpson: Volume 2, 3 vols. 2008. (ENG.). 356p. pap. 46.00 (978-0-521-08369-0(9)) Cambridge Univ. Pr.

—The Correspondence of Lord Acton & Richard Simpson: Volume 3, 3 vols. 2008. (ENG.). 384p. pap. 53.00 (978-0-521-08380-5(X)) Cambridge Univ. Pr.

Altholz, Josef L. & McElrath, Damian, eds. The Correspondence of Lord Acton & Richard Simpson: Volume 1, 3 vols. 2008. (ENG.). 260p. pap. 37.99 (978-0-521-08355-3(9)) Cambridge Univ. Pr.

The Cambridge Modern History: An Account of its Origin, Authorship & Production. 2011. (Cambridge Library Collection - History Ser.). (ENG., Illus.). 120p. pap. 19.99 **(978-1-108-03669-6(4))** Cambridge Univ. Pr.

Gasquet, Abbot, ed. Lord Acton & His Circle. 2007. (ENG.). 468p. 52.95 (978-0-548-10555-9(3)) Kessinger Publishing, LLC.

ACTORS

Here are entered general works on both men and women actors collectively, works on both men and women stage actors collectively and works on individual men and women stage actors. Works on women actors collectively are entered under Actresses. Works on actors, collectively or individually, specializing in particular media are entered under the appropriate specific heading, e.g. Television Actors and Actresses.

see also Acting; Actresses; Child Actors; Comedians; Female Impersonators; Motion Picture Actors and Actresses; Stunt Performers; Television Actors and Actresses; Theater

Astington, John H. Actors & Acting in Shakespeare's Time: The Art of Stage Playing. 2010. (ENG., Illus.). 260p. (C). 75.00 (978-0-521-19250-7(1)); pap. 26.99 (978-0-521-14077-5(3)) Cambridge Univ. Pr.

Benedetti, Jean. The Art of the Actor: The Essential History of Acting, from Classical Times to the Present Day. 2007. (ENG.). 256p. 105.00 (978-0-87830-203-1(4)); per. 30.95 (978-0-87830-204-8(2)) Routledge.

Berry, Cicely. From Word to Play: A Handbook for Directors. 2008. (ENG.). 240p. pap. 30.95 (978-1-84002-601-6(4)) Oberon Bks., Ltd. GBR. Dist: Consortium Bk. Sales & Distribution.

Chang, Chung-Ho & Chang, Kang-i Sun. Qu Ren Hong Zhao. 2010. (CHI & ENG., Illus.). 284p. (978-7-5633-9388-6(9)) Guangxi Teachers Univ. Pr.

Cherkasov, Nikolai Konstantinovich. Notes of a Soviet Actor. Ivano-Mumjev, G. & Rosenberg, S., trs. 2011. 274p. 47.95 **(978-1-258-03191-6(4))** Literary Licensing, LLC.

Curry, Julian. Shakespeare on Stage: Thirteen Leading Actors on Thirteen Key Roles. 2011. (ENG., Illus.). 220p. pap. 30.95 **(978-1-84842-077-9(3))**, Hern, Nick Bks., Ltd. GBR. Dist: Consortium Bk. Sales & Distribution.

De Miranda, Maria Brigida. Playful Training. 2010. 276p. pap. (978-3-8383-6041-6(9)) Lambert Academic Publishing.

DiMarco, Damon. The Quotable Actor: 1001 Pearls of Wisdom from Actors Talking about Acting. 2009. (ENG.). 312p. pap. 16.95 (978-1-59580-044-2(1)) Santa Monica Pr.

Dunn, K. Exit Through the Fireplace. (Illus.). xiv, 305p. pap. 22.95 (978-0-7195-5481-0(0)) Murray, John GBR. Dist: Trafalgar Square Publishing.

Fahay, Jessie. What Method? The Different Ways an Actor can Train. 2011. 56p. pap. 14.95 **(978-1-4567-1463-5(5))** AuthorHouse.

Fitzgerald, Percy Hetherington. The World Behind the Scenes. 2010. 202p. pap. 24.85 (978-1-152-14092-9(2)) General Bks. LLC.

Ford, James L. Forty Odd Years in the Literary Shop. 2007. (ENG.). 434p. 51.95 (978-0-548-02019-7(1)) Kessinger Publishing, LLC.

Hill, George Handel. Scenes from the Life of an Actor, Compiled from the Journals, Letters, & Memoranda of the Late Yankee Hill. 2006. 280p. per. 23.99 (978-1-4255-2514-9(8)) MPublishing.

Hill, John. The Actor. 2009. 174p. pap. (978-1-150-50871-4(X)) Books LLC.

Hubbard, Valorie & Brandenburg, Lea Tolub. The Actor's Workbook: How to Become a Working Actor. 2008. (ENG.). 160p. (C). pap. 29.40 (978-0-205-59231-9(7)) Allyn & Bacon, Inc.

Kemp, Rick. Embodied Acting: Cognitive Foundations of Performance. 2012. (ENG., Illus.). 224p. 120.00 **(978-0-415-50787-5(1))**; pap. 27.95 **(978-0-415-50788-2(X))** Routledge.

L.H., Victoria. Conquering the Haunting Memories of Ted Bundy. 2011. 30p. pap. 16.95 **(978-1-4626-2122-4(8))** PublishAmerica, Inc.

Loui, Annie. The Physical Actor: Exercises for Action & Awareness. 2009. (ENG., Illus.). 224p. 110.00 (978-0-415-46673-8(3)) Routledge.

Maher, Mary Z. & Hal Leonard Corporation Staff. Actors Talk about Shakespeare, 1 vol. 2009. (ENG., Illus.). 256p. pap. 18.99 (978-0-87910-364-4(7), 0879103647, Limelight Editions) Leonard, Hal Corp.

Martin, Bob. Highlights & Footlights: A Tribute to South African Stage & Screen. 2009. 164p. 33.95 (978-1-77013-064-7(0)); (Illus.). 33.35 (978-0-7021-7383-7(5)) Double Storey Bks. ZAF. Dist: International Publishers Marketing.

Mock, Roberta. Jewish Women on Stage, Film, & Television. 2007. (ENG., Illus.). 240p. 89.00 (978-1-4039-7989-6(8)) Palgrave Macmillan.

Morehouse, Ward & Morehouse III, Ward. Broadway after Dark. 2007. 376p. per. 24.95 (978-1-59393-081-3(X)) BearManor Media.

Mroz, Daniel. The Dancing Word: An Embodied Approach to the Preparation of Performers & the Composition of Performances. 2011. (ENG., Illus.). 219p. pap. 64.00 (978-90-420-3330-6(4)) Rodopi.

Mueller, Melissa. Das Madchen Anne Frank: Die Biographie. (GER., Illus.). 448p. (978-3-612-65006-1(8)) Econ-Verlag GmbH DEU. Dist: International Bk. Import Service, Inc.

Phillips, Willard. Death in Hollywood. 2012. (ENG.). 508p. pap. 17.99 **(978-1-4611-0632-6(X))** CreateSpace.

Symons, Arthur. Plays Acting & Music: A Book of Theory. 2007. (ENG.). 168p. pap. 19.99 (978-1-4346-2408-6(0)); 180p. pap. 21.99 (978-1-4346-2454-3(4)) BiblioBazaar.

Tichler, Rosemarie & Kaplan, Barry Jay. Actors at Work. 2007. (ENG.). 392p. pap. 17.00 (978-0-86547-955-5(0)) Faber & Faber, Inc.

Tune, Tommy. Footnotes: A Memoir. 2008. (ENG.). 233p. 24.00 (978-1-4379-5235-3(6)) DIANE Publishing Co.

Tyler, George C. Whatever Goes Up: The Hazardous Fortunes of a Natural Born Gambler. 2007. (ENG.). 350p. 46.95 (978-0-548-07344-5(9)) Kessinger Publishing, LLC.

Waldman, Berta. O Teatro Ídiche Em São Paulo: Memória. 2010. (POR., Illus.). 84p. (978-85-391-0071-2(1)) Annablume Editora Comunicacao Ltda.

Watson, Jamentha. Don't Call Us We'll Call You: Ten Audition Tips for Actors. rev. ed. 2010. (ENG.). 218p. pap. 25.32 (978-0-7575-8436-7(5)) Kendall Hunt Publishing Co.

Winter, William. Shadows of the Stage: Third Series. 2007. (ENG.). 374p. 48.95 (978-0-548-03292-3(0)) Kessinger Publishing, LLC.

—Vagrant Memories. 2009. 274p. pap. 19.99 (978-1-4589-9147-8(4)) General Bks. LLC.

—The Wallet of Time. 2009. 384p. pap. 25.88 (978-0-217-64502-7(X)) General Bks. LLC.

ACTORS—BIOGRAPHY

Aames, Willie, et al. Grace Is Enough. 2007. (ENG., Illus.). 307p. 19.99 (978-0-8054-4379-0(7), B&H Bks.) B&H Publishing Group.

Abd al-Karim, Lutas. Yusuf Wahbi Al-Sirah Al-Ukhra Li-Usturat Al-Masrah. 2010. (ARA., Illus.). 200p. (978-977-08-1465-9(2)) Akhbar al-Yawm Establishment.

Aguirre Carbaleira, Arantxa & Aguirre, Arantxa. 34 Actores Hablan de Su Oficio. (SPA., Illus.). 679p. (978-84-376-2505-8(X)) Ediciones Cátedra.

Alda, Alan. Never Have Your Dog Stuffed: And Other Things I've Learned. 2007. (Illus.). 224p. 25.00 (978-1-4223-6612-7(X)) DIANE Publishing Co.

—Things I Overheard While Talking to Myself. 2008. (ENG.). 256p. pap. 15.00 (978-0-8129-7752-3(1), Random Hse. Trade Paperbacks) Random House Publishing Group.

Alessio, Jim. The Eternal Flapper. 2009. 376p. 29.50 (978-1-4389-6129-3(4)) AuthorHouse.

—The Eternal Flapper: The Many Lives of Edna Wallace Hopper. 2009. 376p. pap. 19.95 (978-1-4389-6128-6(6)) AuthorHouse.

Allain, Paul, ed. Grotowski's Empty Room: A Challenge to the Theatre. 2009. (Enactments Ser.). (Illus.). 224p. 29.00 (978-1-906497-23-1(0)) Seagull Bks. London Ltd. GBR. Dist: Chicago Distribution Ctr.

Allen, Keith. Grow Up. 2008. (ENG., Illus.). 384p. pap. 15.95 (978-0-09-191071-6(4)) Ebury Publishing GBR. Dist: Independent Pubs. Group.

Andersen, Christopher. Somewhere in Heaven: The Remarkable Love Story of Dana & Christopher Reeve. 2009. (ENG.). 272p. mass mkt. 7.99 (978-0-7868-9130-6(0)) Hyperion Pr.

—Somewhere in Heaven: The Remarkable Love Story of Dana & Christopher Reeve. l.t. ed. 2008. (Illus.). 353p. (YA). 32.95 (978-1-4104-0905-8(8)) Thorndike Pr.

Anderson, Arthur. An Actor's Odyssey: From Orson Welles to Lucky the Leprechaun. 2010. 228p. pap. 19.95 (978-1-59393-522-1(6)) BearManor Media.

Anderson, Melissa. The Way I See It: A Look Back at My Life on Little House. 2011. (ENG., Illus.). 256p. pap. 16.95 (978-0-7627-7050-2(3)) Globe Pequot Pr., The.

Antoniades, Andrew & Siegel, Mike. Steve Mcqueen: The Actor & His Films. 2011. (ENG., Illus.). 492p. 69.00 (978-1-85443-253-7(2), 1854432532) Dalton Watson Fine Bks.

Appleton, William Worthen. Charles Macklin: An Actor's Life. 2011. 296p. 48.95 (978-1-258-07144-8(4)) Literary Licensing, LLC.

Archer, Stephen M. Junius Brutus Booth: Theatrical Prometheus. 2010. (Illus.). 364p. pap. 35.00 (978-0-8093-3000-3(8)); 346p. E-Book (978-0-8093-8592-8(9)) Southern Illinois Univ. Pr.

Archer, William. Henry Irving: Actor & Manager: A Critical Study. (Works of William Archer). 108p. reprint ed. lib. bdg. 59.00 (978-0-932051-21-9(9)) Reprint Services Co.

Arkin, Alan. An Improvised Life: A Memoir. l.t. ed. 2011. 233p. 31.99 (978-1-4104-4040-2(0)) Thorndike Pr.

Arness, James & Wise, James E., Jr. James Arness: An Autobiography. l.t. alt. ed. 2008. (ENG., Illus.). 344p. pap. 39.95 (978-0-7864-3316-2(7)) McFarland & Co., Inc. Pubs.

Astaire, Fred. Steps in Time: An Autobiography. 2008. (ENG., Illus.). 384p. pap. 13.99 (978-0-06-156756-8(6)) HarperCollins Pubs.

Atkins, Rick. Among the Rugged Peaks: An Intimate Biography of Carla Laemmle. 2009. (Illus.). 221p. pap. (978-1-887664-91-2(2)) Midnight Marquee Pr., Inc.

Bahr, Iris. Dork Whore: My Travels Through Asia as a Twenty-Year-Old Pseudo-Virgin. 2007. (ENG.). 224p. pap. 13.95 (978-1-59691-234-2(0)) Bloomsbury Publishing.

—Machu My Picchu: Searching for Sex, Sanity, & a Soul Mate in South America. 2011. (ENG., Illus.). 256p. pap. 14.95 (978-0-7627-7277-3(8), skirt!) Globe Pequot Pr., The.

Baker, Aaron. Steven Soderbergh. 2011. (Contemporary Film Directors Ser.). (ENG., Illus.). 152p. 65.00 (978-0-252-03605-7(0)); pap. 22.00 (978-0-252-07796-8(2)) Univ. of Illinois Pr.

Baker, Henry Barton. History of the London Stage & Its Famous Players 1576-1903. 2007. (ENG.). 596p. 59.95 (978-0-548-10334-0(8)) Kessinger Publishing, LLC.

Balbirer, Nancy. Take Your Shirt off & Cry: A Memoir of near-Fame Experiences. 2009. (ENG.). 256p. pap. 16.00 (978-1-59691-478-0(5)) Bloomsbury Publishing.

Barbe, Ryan E. The Life & Times of a Transitional Boyfriend: Vol. 1. 2010. 128p. (ENG.). pap. 15.00 (978-1-4520-1556-9(2)); 23.99 (978-1-4520-1555-2(4)) AuthorHouse.

Barnabee, Henry Clay. Reminiscences of Henry Clay Barnabee. Varney, George Leon, ed. 2007. (ENG.). 496p. 53.95 (978-0-548-07578-4(6)) Kessinger Publishing, LLC.

Barrault, Marie-Christine & Duroy, Lionel. Ce Long Chemin Pour Arriver Jusqu'à Toi. 2010. (FRE., Illus.). 397p. (978-2-84563-482-4(X)) XO Editions.

Barrowman, John & Barrowman, Carole E. Anything Goes. 2009. (ENG., Illus.). 256p. pap. 15.95 (978-1-84317-333-5(6)) O'Mara, Michael Bks., Ltd. GBR. Dist: Independent Pubs. Group.

—Anything Goes: The Autobiography. 2008. (ENG., Illus.). 256p. 29.95 (978-1-84317-289-5(5)) O'Mara, Michael Bks., Ltd. GBR. Dist: Independent Pubs. Group.

—I Am What I Am. 2009. (ENG., Illus.). 256p. 29.95 (978-1-84317-379-3(4)) O'Mara, Michael Bks., Ltd. GBR. Dist: Independent Pubs. Group.

Barton, Ruth. Hedy Lamarr: The Most Beautiful Woman in Film. 2010. (Screen Classics Ser.). (ENG., Illus.). 312p. 29.95 (978-0-8131-2604-3(5)) Univ. Pr. of Kentucky.

Batt, Bryan. She Ain't Heavy, She's My Mother: A Memoir. 2011. 288p. pap. 14.00 (978-0-307-58886-9(6), Three Rivers Pr.) Crown Publishing Group.

Beaver, Jim. Life's That Way. 2010. (ENG.). 336p. (gr. 12-18). 15.00 (978-0-425-23250-7(6), Berkley Trade) Penguin Group (USA) Inc.

Bending, Stephen, et al, eds. Women's Theatrical Memoirs, Part II, 5 vols., Vols. 6-10. 2008. (Chawton House Library Series: Women's Memoirs Ser.). (ENG.). 2000p. 750.00 (978-1-85196-875-6(X)) Pickering & Chatto Pubs., Ltd. GBR. Dist: Ashgate Publishing Co.

Bernhardt, Sarah. Memories of My Life: Being My Personal, Professional & Social. 2007. pap. 37.95 (978-1-4304-8099-0(8)) Kessinger Publishing, LLC.

Bertinelli, Valerie. Losing It: And Gaining My Life Back One Pound at a Time. 2008. (ENG., Illus.). 288p. pap. 15.00 (978-1-4165-6968-8(5), Free Pr.) Free Pr.

—Losing It: And Gaining My Life Back One Pound at a Time. l.t. ed. 2008. (Illus.). 415p. (YA). 31.95 (978-1-4104-0852-5(3)) Thorndike Pr.

Bierdz, Thom. Forgiving Troy. 2009. 288p. pap. 14.95 (978-1-61539-485-2(0)) Independent Pub.

Biographiq. Clark Gable - the King of Hollywood. 2008. 52p. pap. 9.99 (978-1-59986-026-8(0), Biographiq) Filiquarian Publishing, LLC.

—Frank Sinatra - Ol' Blue Eyes. 2008. 52p. pap. 9.99 (978-1-59986-044-2(9), Biographiq) Filiquarian Publishing, LLC.

—John Wayne - an American Icon. 2008. 52p. pap. 9.99 (978-1-59986-034-3(1), Biographiq) Filiquarian Publishing, LLC.

—Marlon Brando - Actor & Activist. 2008. 56p. pap. 9.99 (978-1-59986-049-7(X), Biographiq) Filiquarian Publishing, LLC.

Birkenhead, Peter. Gonville: A Memoir. 272p. 2011. pap. 15.00 (978-1-4165-9884-8(7)) 2010. (ENG.). 25.00 (978-1-4165-9883-1(9)) Free Pr. (Free Pr.).

Blackhall, Sue. Bill Nighy: The Unauthorised Biography. 2010. (ENG., Illus.). 278p. 29.95 (978-1-84454-867-5(8)) Blake, John Publishing, Ltd. GBR. Dist: Independent Pubs. Group.

Blackman, Joni. George Clooney: A Biography, 1 vol. 2009. (Greenwood Biographies Ser.). (Illus.). 158p. 35.00 (978-0-313-35826-5(5), GR5826) Greenwood Publishing Group, Inc.

Blake, Blue. Out of the Blue: Confessions of an Unlikely Porn Star. 2008. (ENG.). 304p. pap. 14.95 (978-0-7624-3388-9(4)) Perseus Bks. Group.

Blake, Bobby. My Life in Porn: The Bobby Blake Story. 2008. (ENG.). 280p. pap. 14.95 (978-0-7867-2096-5(4), Running Pr.) Running Pr. Bk. Pubs.

Blottner, Gene. Wild Bill Elliott: A Complete Filmography. 2007. (ENG., Illus.). 328p. 55.00 (978-0-7864-2986-8(0)) McFarland & Co., Inc. Pubs.

Booth, Rupert. Not a Number: Patrick McGoohan - A Life. 2011. (ENG.). 288p. pap. 28.95 (978-0-9566329-2-0(0)) Aurora Metro Pubns. Ltd. GBR. Dist: Consortium Bk. Sales & Distribution.

Booth, Tony. What's Left? (Illus.). 256p. pap. 20.00 (978-0-7538-1346-1(7), Phoenix) Orion Publishing Group, Ltd. GBR. Dist: Trafalgar Square Publishing.

Borgman, Albert S. & Mountfort, William. The Life & Death of William Mountfort. 2011. 242p. 46.95 (978-1-258-04877-8(9)) Literary Licensing, LLC.

Borgnine, Ernest. Ernie. 2009. (ENG.). 272p. 14.95 (978-0-8065-2942-4(3), Citadel Pr.) Kensington Publishing Corp.

—Ernie: The Autobiography. 2008. (ENG.). 288p. 24.95 (978-0-8065-2941-7(5), Citadel Pr.) Kensington Publishing Corp.

—Ernie: The Autobiography. l.t. ed. 2008. 396p. 31.50 (978-1-4104-1068-9(4)) Thorndike Pr.

Bowles, Hamish & Berenson, Marisa. Marisa Berenson: A Life in Pictures. Duzansky, Jason & Meisel, Steven, eds. 2011. (ENG., Illus.). 240p. 60.00 (978-0-8478-3654-3(1)) Rizzoli International Pubns., Inc.

Bowyer, Alison. Dawn French: The Unauthorized Biography. 2008. (ENG., Illus.). 320p. mass mkt. 16.95 (978-0-330-45452-0(8), Macmillan) Pan Macmillan GBR. Dist: Trans-Atlantic Pubns., Inc.

—Graham Norton: Laid Bare. 2009. (ENG., Illus.). 272p. pap. 15.95 (978-0-233-00268-2(5)) Andre Deutsch GBR. Dist: Independent Pubs. Group.

Brand, Russell. My Booky Wook: A Memoir of Sex, Drugs, & Stand-Up. (ENG.). 368p. 2010. pap. 14.99 (978-0-06-185780-5(7)) 2009. 25.99 (978-0-06-173041-2(6)) HarperCollins Pubs.

—My Booky Wook: A Memoir of Sex, Drugs, & Stand-Up. (Illus.). 2008. 416p. pap. 14.95 (978-0-340-93617-7(7)) 2007. 339p. 34.95 (978-0-340-93615-3(0)) 2007. 339p. pap. 24.95 (978-0-340-93616-0(9)) Hodder General Publishing Div. GBR. (Hodder & Stoughton). Dist: Independent Pubs. Group.

Bray, Christopher. Sean Connery: A Biography. 2011. (ENG., Illus.). 368p. 26.95 (978-1-60598-185-7(0), 605185) Pegasus Bks.

Bridges, Todd. Killing Willis: From Diff'rent Strokes to the Mean Streets to the Life I Always Wanted. 2010. (ENG., Illus.). 288p. 26.00 (978-1-4391-4898-3(8), Touchstone) Touchstone.

Brooke, W. H. The Biography of the British Stage: Being Correct Narratives of the Lives of All the Principal Actors & Actresses. 2007. (ENG.). 304p. 43.95 (978-0-548-14942-3(9)); (Illus.). per. 28.95 (978-1-4304-4253-0(0)) Kessinger Publishing, LLC.

Brooks, Lynn Matluck. John Durang: Man of the American Stage. 2011. (978-1-60497-775-2(2)) Cambria Pr.

Brooks, Riley. All Access: Totally Unauthorized! 2009. (Demi Lovato Ser.). (ENG.). 144p. (J). (gr. 4-7). 5.99 (978-0-545-17592-0(5), Scholastic Paperbacks) Scholastic, Inc.

Brown, Len. Jason Statham: Taking Stock. 2012. (ENG., Illus.). 256p. 19.95 (978-1-4091-3265-3(X)) Orion Bks. Ltd. GBR. Dist: Sterling Publishing Co., Inc.

Bruns, Phillip. The Character Actor's Do's, Don'ts & Anecdote. 2011. 328p. pap. 18.00 (978-0-615-44766-7(X)) PhillipBruns Publishing.

Brunström, Conrad. Thomas Sheridan's Career & Influence: An Actor in Earnest. 2011. ix, 151p. (978-0-8387-5777-2(4)) Bucknell Univ. Pr.

Burgoyne, Beckey. Perfectly Amanda: Gunsmoke's Miss Kitty: to Dodge & Beyond. 2010. (ENG.). 300p. pap. 29.95 (978-1-58985-163-4(3)) Five Star Pubns., Inc.

Burney, Fanny. Stage, Screen & Sandwiches: The Remarkable Life of Kenelm Foss. 2007. (Illus.). 196p. per. (978-1-84401-908-3(X)) Athena Pr.

Burnim, Kalman A. & Baskett, John. Brief Lives: Biographies of Sitters & Artists in the Garrick Club Collection. 2006. (ENG., Illus.). 192p. 65.00 (978-0-906290-73-6(2)) Unicorn Pr., London GBR. Dist: National Bk. Network.

Butters, Wes. Whatsisname: The Life & Death of Charles Hawtrey. 2010. (Illus.). 296p. 35.00 (978-0-9557670-7-4(5)) Tomahawk Pr. GBR. Dist: Midpoint Trade Bks., Inc.

Cairney, John. Greasepaint Monkey: An Actor on Acting. 2010. (ENG.). 156p. pap. 19.95 (978-1-906817-42-8(1)) Luath Pr. Ltd. GBR. Dist: Ingram Pub. Services.

Callan, Michael Feeney. Arise Sir Anthony Hopkins: The Biography. 2008. (ENG., Illus.). 466p. pap. 15.95 (978-1-84454-546-9(6)) Blake, John Publishing, Ltd. GBR. Dist: Independent Pubs. Group.

Callow, Simon. Love Is Where It Falls: An Account of a Passionate Friendship. 2007. (ENG.). 96p. per. 26.95 (978-1-85459-976-6(3)) Hern, Nick Bks., Ltd. GBR. Dist: Consortium Bk. Sales & Distribution.

—My Life in Pieces. 2011. (ENG.). 320p. 40.00 (978-1-84842-054-0(4)) Hern, Nick Bks., Ltd. GBR. Dist: Consortium Bk. Sales & Distribution.

—My Life in Pieces: An Alternative Autobiography. 2012. (ENG.). 448p. pap. 20.95 (978-1-84842-171-4(0)) Hern, Nick Bks., Ltd. GBR. Dist: Consortium Bk. Sales & Distribution.

Canatella, Ray. The Soul of My Past in New Orleans: A City of Many Dreams. 2011. 244p. pap. 24.95 (978-1-4560-1133-8(2)) PublishAmerica, Inc.

Canutt, Yakima & Crawford, John. My Rodeo Years: Memoir of a Bronc Rider's Path to Hollywood Fame. 2009. (ENG., Illus.). 218p. pap. 35.00 (978-0-7864-4389-5(8)) McFarland & Co., Inc. Pubs.

Capotorto, Carl. Twisted Head: An Italian American Memoir. 2009. (ENG.). 320p. pap. 14.00 (978-0-7679-2862-5(8)) Broadway Bks.

Capua, Michelangelo. Deborah Kerr: A Biography. 2010. (ENG., Illus.). 224p. pap. 35.00 (978-0-7864-5882-0(8)) McFarland & Co., Inc. Pubs.

Carlyle, John. Under the Rainbow: An Intimate Memoir of Judy Garland, Rock Hudson & My Life in Old Hollywood. Freeman, Chris, ed. 2007. (ENG.). 352p. per. 15.00 (978-0-7867-2034-7(4)) Da Capo Pr., Inc.

Caron, Leslie. Thank Heaven: A Memoir. 2010. (ENG.). 288p. (gr. 12). 16.00 (978-0-452-29662-6(5), Plume) Penguin Group (USA) Inc.

Carpenter, Amy. The Taylor Lautner Album. 2009. (ENG., Illus.). 96p. (gr. 3). pap. 16.95 (978-0-85965-453-1(2)) Plexus Publishing, Ltd. GBR. Dist: Perseus-PGW.

Carrigan, John. The Other Side of Harry: A schizophrenic Parent. 2008. 420p. pap. (978-1-84747-680-7(5)) Chipmunkapublishing.

Cassata, Mary Anne. The Essential Jim Carrey. 2010. 144p. pap. 19.95 (978-1-59393-517-7(X)) BearManor Media.

Cassin, Barry. I Never Had a Proper Job. 2012. (ENG.). 240p. pap. 29.95 (978-1-907593-40-6(3)) Liberties Pr. IRL. Dist: Dufour Editions, Inc.

Castellani, Raymond J. The End Was but a Beginning: A True Story. 2008. 140p. 29.95 (978-1-59858-831-6(1)); pap. 17.95 (978-1-59858-805-7(2)) Dog Ear Publishing, LLC.

Challen, Paul. The House That Hugh Laurie Built: An Unauthorized Biography & Episode Guide. 2007. (ENG., Illus.). 240p. pap. 17.95 (978-1-55022-803-8(X)) ECW Pr. CAN. Dist: Independent Pubs. Group.

Chamberlain, Tommy. A Spoon Full of Sugar. 2011. 252p. pap. 19.95 (978-1-4620-0140-8(8)) iUniverse, Inc.

Chandler, Charlotte. Ingrid: Ingrid Bergman, a Personal Biography. 2008. (ENG., Illus.). 336p. per. 16.95 (978-1-55783-735-6(X), 155783735X, Applause Theatre & Cinema) Leonard, Hal Corp.

—Marlene: Marlene Dietrich, A Personal Biography. 2012. (ENG.). 304p. pap. 19.99 (978-1-55783-838-4(0), 1557838380, Applause Theatre & Cinema) Leonard, Hal Corp.

—Marlene: Marlene Dietrich, A Personal Biography. l.t. ed. 2011. 459p. 31.99 (978-1-4104-3765-5(5)) Thorndike Pr.

—Not the Girl Next Door: Joan Crawford: A Personal Biography. l.t. ed. 2008. (Illus.). 537p. (YA). 31.95 (978-1-4104-0773-3(X)) Thorndike Pr.

Chemerka, William R. Fess Parker: Tv's frontier Hero. 2011. 416p. 34.95 (978-1-59393-210-7(3)); pap. 24.95 (978-1-59393-655-6(9)) BearManor Media.

Clary, Robert. From the Holocaust to Hogan's Heroes: An Autobiography of Robert Clary. 2007. (ENG., Illus.). 224p. per. 16.95 (978-1-58979-345-3(5)) Taylor Trade Publishing.

Clinton, Craig. Cora Urquhart Potter: The Victorian Actress as Provocateur. 2010. (ENG., Illus.). 262p. pap. 55.00 (978-0-7864-4957-6(8)) McFarland & Co., Inc. Pubs.

—Mrs. Leslie Carter: A Biography of the Early Twentieth Century American Stage Star. 2006. (ENG., Illus.). 228p. per. 45.00 (978-0-7864-2747-5(7)) McFarland & Co., Inc. Pubs.

Cloris, Cloris. l.t. ed. 2009. 360p. 31.95 (978-1-4104-1856-2(1)) Thorndike Pr.

Clover, Early. From Sawdust to Sawdust. 2010. 14.59 (978-0-578-05563-3(5)) Four Leaves Music.

Coghlan, Frank. They Still Call Me Junior: Autobiography of a Child Star; with a Filmography. alt. ed. 2011. (ENG., Illus.). 383p. pap. 29.95 (978-0-7864-6381-7(3)) McFarland & Co., Inc. Pubs.

Cole, Julie Dawn & Esslinger, Michael. I Want It Now! a Memoir of Life on the Set of Willy Wonka & the Chocolate Factory. 2011. 252p. pap. 21.95 (978-1-59393-074-5(7)) BearManor Media.

Collis, Rose. Coral Browne: This Effing Lady. 2008. (ENG., Illus.). 288p. 50.00 (978-1-84002-764-8(9)) Theatre Communications Group, Inc.

Cook, Judy. Loving Peter: My Life with Peter Cook & Dudley Moore. 2010. (ENG., Illus.). 320p. pap. 14.95 (978-0-7499-2947-3(2)) Piatkus Bks. GBR. Dist: Independent Pubs. Group.

Cook, Judy & Levin, Angela. Loving Peter: My Life with Peter Cook & Dudley Moore. 2008. (ENG., Illus.). 288p. 32.95 (978-0-7499-0966-6(8)) Piatkus Bks. GBR. Dist: Independent Pubs. Group.

Court, Hazel. Hazel Court — Horror Queen: An Autobiography. 2008. (Illus.). 258p. pap. 27.95 (978-0-9531926-8-7(7)) Tomahawk Pr. GBR. Dist: Midpoint Trade Bks., Inc.

Coward, Noël & Day, Barry. In His Own Words. 2008. (ENG., Illus.). 176p. pap. 14.95 (978-1-4081-0758-4(9), Methuen Drama) A & C Black GBR. Dist: Macmillan.

Cowie, Peter. Joan Crawford: The Enduring Star. 2009. (ENG., Illus.). 240p. 60.00 (978-0-8478-3066-4(7)) Rizzoli International Pubns., Inc.

—Joan Crawford: The Enduring Star. 2011. (Illus.). 240p. 19.98 (978-0-7893-2253-1(6), Rizzoli Universe Promotional Bks.) Rizzoli International Pubns., Inc.

Croall, Jonathan. Buzz Buzz! Playwrights, Actors & Directors at the National Theatre. 2008. (Plays & Playwrights Ser.). (ENG.). 240p. pap. 24.95 (978-1-4081-0520-7(9), Methuen Drama) A & C Black GBR. Dist: Macmillan.

—John Gielgud: Matinee Idol to Movie Star. 2011. (Biography & Autobiography Ser.). (ENG., Illus.). 688p. 45.00 (978-1-4081-3106-0(4), Methuen Drama) A & C Black GBR. Dist: Macmillan.

—Sybil Thorndike: A Star of Life. 2009. (ENG., Illus.). 550p. 30.00 (978-1-905791-92-7(5)) Haus Publishing GBR. Dist: Consortium Bk. Sales & Distribution.

Cunard, Garold B. Life & Times in the 20th Century. 2010. 324p. 42.95 (978-1-60594-445-6(9), Llumina Pr.) Aeon Publishing Inc.

Cunrad, Garold B. Life & Times in the 20th Century. 2010. 324p. pap. 19.95 (978-1-60594-444-9(0), Llumina Pr.) Aeon Publishing Inc.

Curtis, James. Spencer Tracy: A Biography. 2011. (ENG., Illus.). 1024p. 39.95 (978-0-307-26289-9(8), Knopf) Knopf Doubleday Publishing Group.

Davis, Warwick. Size Matters Not: The Extraordinary Life & Career of Warwick Davis. 2011. (ENG., Illus.). 416p. 24.95 (978-0-470-91466-3(1), Wiley) Wiley, John & Sons, Inc.

Davis, William B. Where There's Smoke... Musings of a Cigarette Smoking Man, a Memoir. 2011. (ENG., Illus.). 290p. pap. 19.95 (978-1-77041-052-7(X)) ECW Pr. CAN. Dist: Independent Pubs. Group.

De La Hoz, Cindy. A Touch of Grace: How to Be a Princess, the Grace Kelly Way. 2010. (ENG.). 256p. 17.95 (978-0-7624-3804-4(5), Running Pr.) Running Pr. Bk. Pubs.

De Lafayette, Maximillien. Bona Fide Divas & Femmes Fatales: The 700 Official Divas of the World in Cinema, Theater, Music, Opera, Jazz, Entertainment & Performing Arts. 2007. (Illus.). 400p. per. 69.95 (978-0-9799750-8-0(5)) Elite Assocs. International-Times Square Pr.

Deane, Pamala S. James Edwards: African American Hollywood Icon. 2009. (ENG., Illus.). 236p. pap. 45.00 (978-0-7864-4415-1(0)) McFarland & Co., Inc. Pubs.

Dearinger, Kevin Lane. Marie Prescott: A Star of Some Brilliancy. 2009. 55.00 (978-0-8386-4212-2(8)) Fairleigh Dickinson Univ. Pr.

Delmotte, Pascal & Delmotte, Annie. Bourvil: ça Va, Ils Sont Contents. 2010. (FRE., Illus.). 207p. (978-2-08-124124-4(2)) Flammarion et Cie.

Dench, Judi. And Furthermore. 2011. (ENG., Illus.). 288p. 26.99 (978-0-312-65906-6(7)) St. Martin's Pr.

—And Furthermore. l.t. ed. 2011. 351p. 32.99 (978-1-4104-3863-8(5)) Thorndike Pr.

Deneuve, Catherine. The Private Diaries of Catherine Deneuve: My Life Behind the Camera with Luis Bunuel, Francois Truffaut, Roman Polanski, & Lars Von Trier. 2008. (ENG.). 240p. pap. 14.95 (978-1-60598-019-5(6), 605019) Pegasus Bks.

Denton, Sally. The Pink Lady: The Many Lives of Helen Gahagan Douglas. 2009. (ENG.). 256p. 26.00 (978-1-59691-480-3(7)) Bloomsbury Publishing.

Dern, Bruce & Crane, Robert. Things I've Said, but Probably Shouldn't Have: An Unrepentant Memoir. 2007. (ENG., Illus.). 312p. 24.95 (978-0-470-10637-2(9), Wiley) Wiley, John & Sons, Inc.

DeSanto, John R. So, What about the Others? 2007. per. 24.95 (978-1-59712-059-3(6)) Catawba Publishing Co.

Dherbier, Yann-Brice. Steve McQueen. 2008. (Life in Pictures Ser.). (ENG., Illus.). 196p. 40.00 (978-1-86205-814-9(8)) Anova Bks. GBR. Dist: Independent Pubs. Group.

Diamond, Dustin. Behind the Bell. 2009. (ENG., Illus.). 311p. 25.00 (978-0-9812396-9-9(2)) Transit Publishing (Transit Editeur Inc.) CAN. Dist: Midpoint Trade Bks., Inc.

Dick, Bernard F. Forever Mame: The Life of Rosalind Russell. 2011. (Hollywood Legends Ser.). (ENG.). 320p. pap. 25.00 (978-1-60473-962-6(2)) Univ. Pr. of Mississippi.

Dickens, Charles. Memoirs of Joseph Grimaldi. 2008. (ENG.). 352p. pap. 22.95 (978-1-901285-94-9(4)) Pushkin Pr., Ltd. GBR. Dist: Consortium Bk. Sales & Distribution.

Donahue, Heather. Growgirl: How My Life after the Blair Witch Project Went to Pot. 2012. (ENG.). 304p. (gr. 12). 26.00 (978-1-59240-692-0(0), Gotham) Penguin Group (USA) Inc.

Douglas, Kirk. Let's Face It: 90 Years of Living, Loving, & Learning. 2007. (ENG., Illus.). 272p. 22.95 (978-0-470-08469-4(3), Wiley) Wiley, John & Sons, Inc.

Doyle, Mary. Life Was Like That. 2007. (ENG.). 276p. 42.95 (978-0-548-06326-2(5)) Kessinger Publishing, LLC.

Duncan, Paul, ed. Mae West. 2008. (Movie Icons Ser.). (FRE, GER & ENG., Illus.). 184p. pap. 9.99 *(978-3-8228-2321-7(X))* TASCHEN DEU. Dist: Ingram Pub. Services.
—Movie ICONS. Robert DeNiro. 2009. (Movie Icons Ser.). (ENG., Illus.). 192p. pap. 9.99 *(978-3-8365-0847-6(8))* TASCHEN DEU. Dist: Ingram Pub. Services.
Durang, Charles. The Theatrical Rambles of Mr & Mrs John Greene. Slout, William L., ed. 2007. 308p. 35.00 *(978-0-8095-0306-3(9))*; per. 19.95 *(978-0-8095-1306-2(4))* Wildside Pr., LLC. (Borgo Pr.).
Eaton, Gai. A Bad Beginning: The Path to Islam. 2009. (Illus.). 428p. 34.95 *(978-1-901383-32-4(6))* Archetype GBR. Dist: Midpoint Trade Bks., Inc.
Edelson, Loren. Danjuro's Girls: Women on the Kabuki Stage. 2009. (Palgrave Studies in Theatre & Performance History Ser.). (ENG., Illus.). 280p. 105.00 *(978-0-230-60946-4(5))* Palgrave Macmillan.
Eichenbaum, Rose. The Actor Within: Intimate Conversations with Great Actors. Hirt-Manheimer, Aron, ed. 2011. (ENG., Illus.). 268p. 30.00 *(978-0-8195-6952-3(6))* Wesleyan Univ. Pr.
Eliot, Marc. Reagan: The Hollywood Years. 2009. (ENG., Illus.). 384p. pap. 17.00 *(978-0-307-40513-5(3)*, Three Rivers Pr.) Crown Publishing Group.
—Reagan: The Hollywood Years. l.t. ed. 2009. 646p. 31.95 *(978-1-4104-1201-0(6))* Thorndike Pr.
Eliot, Marc. Steve McQueen: A Biography. 2012. (ENG., Illus.). 368p. pap. 15.00 ***(978-0-307-45322-8(7)**, Three Rivers Pr.) Crown Publishing Group.
Englund, Robert & Goldsher, Alan. Hollywood Monster: A Walk down Elm Street with the Man of Your Dreams. 2009. (ENG., Illus.). 304p. 26.00 *(978-1-4391-5048-1(6))* Gallery Pr., The. IRL. Dist: Simon & Schuster, Inc.
Enright, Diana & Hazelton, Tanya. Ten Chimneys. 2007. (ENG.). 384p. 38.95 *(978-1-59299-283-6(8))* Inkwater Pr.
Enss, Chris & Kazanjian, Howard. The Young Duke: The Early Life of John Wayne. 2009. (ENG., Illus.). 208p. pap. 14.95 *(978-0-7627-5101-3(0))* Globe Pequot Pr., The.
Essman, Susie. What Would Susie Say? Bullsh*t Wisdom about Love, Life & Comedy. 2009. (ENG.). 256p. 25.00 *(978-1-4391-5017-7(6))* Simon & Schuster.
Ewbank, Tim & Hildred, Stafford. Joanna Lumley: The Unauthorized Biography. 2nd ed. 2010. (ENG., Illus.). 262p. pap. 14.95 *(978-0-233-00305-4(3))* Andre Deutsch GBR. Dist: Independent Pubs. Group.
Eyre, Richard. Talking Theatre: Interviews with Theatre People. 2011. (ENG.). 352p. pap. 20.95 ***(978-1-84842-138-7(9))*** Hern, Nick Bks., Ltd. GBR. Dist: Consortium Bk. Sales & Distribution.
Fairbanks, Douglas, Jr. Laugh & Live. reprint ed. lib. bdg. 48.00 *(978-0-7426-1283-9(X))* Classic Bks.
Falk, Peter. Just One More Thing: Stories from My Life. 2007. (ENG., Illus.). 304p. per. 16.99 *(978-0-7867-1939-6(7))* Da Capo Pr., Inc.
Farley, Tom, Jr. & Colby, Tanner. The Chris Farley Show: A Biography in Three Acts. 2009. (ENG.). 368p. (gr. 12-18). 16.00 *(978-0-14-311556-4(1)*, Penguin (Non-Classics)) Penguin Group (USA) Inc.
Feder, Chris Welles. In My Father's Shadow: A Daughter Remembers Orson Welles. 2009. (ENG., Illus.). 304p. 24.95 *(978-1-56512-599-5(1)*, 1565125991) Algonquin Bks. of Chapel Hill.
Feeney, F. X. Movie ICONS. Johnny Depp. Duncan, Paul, ed. 2009. (Movie Icons Ser.). (ENG., Illus.). 192p. pap. 9.99 *(978-3-8365-0849-0(4))* TASCHEN DEU. Dist: Ingram Pub. Services.
Fonda, Jane. Jane Fonda's Words of Politics & Passion. Hershberger, Mary, ed. 2006. (ENG.). 161p. 22.95 *(978-1-59558-131-0(6))* New Pr., The.
Fontana, Ellen. Audrey 100: Eine traumhafte Reise in Bildern - ausgewählt von ihrer Familie. 2010. (ENG., Illus.). 192p. 40.00 *(978-1-4027-7836-0(8))* Sterling Publishing Co., Inc.
Ford, Peter. Glenn Ford: A Life. 2011. (Wisconsin Film Studies). (Illus.). (ENG.). 358p. pap. 24.95 *(978-0-299-28154-0(X))*; 312p. E-Book *(978-0-299-28153-3(1))* Univ. of Wisconsin Pr.
Foster, Michael & Foster, Barbara. A Dangerous Woman: The Life, Loves, & Scandals of Adah Isaacs Menken, 1835-1868, America's Original Superstar. 2011. (ENG., Illus.). 368p. 24.95 *(978-1-59921-602-7(7)*, Lyons Pr.) Globe Pequot Pr., The.
Fox, Michael J. Always Looking Up: The Adventures of an Incurable Optimist. 288p. 2010. (ENG.). pap. 14.99 *(978-1-4013-1016-5(8))* 2009. pap. 16.00 *(978-1-4013-0985-5(2))* 2009. (ENG.). 25.99 *(978-1-4013-0338-9(2))* 2009. 519.80 *(978-1-4013-2365-3(0))* Hyperion Pr.
—Always Looking Up: The Adventures of an Incurable Optimist. l.t. ed. 2010. (ENG.). 376p. pap. 16.99 *(978-1-59413-393-0(X)*, Large Print Pr.) Thorndike Pr.
—A Funny Thing Happened on the Way to the Future… Twists & Turns & Lessons Learned. 2010. (ENG.). 112p. 17.99 *(978-1-4013-2386-8(3))* Hyperion Pr.
Frankel, Art. Flew by the Seat of My Pants. 2010. 172p. 25.95 *(978-1-4502-6929-2(X))*; pap. 15.95 *(978-1-4502-6927-8(3))* iUniverse, Inc.
Friedman, Lauri S. Tina Fey. 2010. (People in the News Ser.). (Illus.). 128p. 32.45 *(978-1-4205-0238-1(7)*, Lucent Bks.) Cengage Gale.
Gale Editor & Greenhaven Editor, eds. Jon Stewart. 2011. (People in the News Ser.). (Illus.). 128p. (YA). (gr. 9-12). lib. bdg. 33.45 *(978-1-4205-0608-2(0))* Cengage Gale.
Gargiulo, Suzanne. Lon Chaney's Shadow - John Jeske & the Chaney Mystique. 2009. 184p. pap. 19.00 *(978-1-59393-330-2(4))* BearManor Media.
Garson, Helen S. Oprah Winfrey: A Biography. 2nd ed. 2011. E-Book *(978-0-313-35833-3(8)*, Greenwood Pr.); (Illus.). 212p. 35.00 *(978-0-313-35832-6(X)*, GR5832) Greenwood Publishing Group, Inc.
Gaston, Bibi & Gaston. The Loveliest Woman in America: A Tragic Actress, Her Lost Diaries, & Her Granddaughter's Search for Home. 2009. 352p. pap. 14.99 *(978-0-06-085771-4(4)*, HarperPerennial) HarperCollins Pubs.
Gill, Peter. Apprenticeship. 2009. (ENG.). 128p. 18.95 *(978-1-84002-871-3(8))* Oberon Bks., Ltd. GBR. Dist: Consortium Bk. Sales & Distribution.
Gillies, Isabel. Happens Every Day: An All-Too-True Story. 2010. (ENG., Illus.). 272p. pap. 15.00 *(978-1-4391-2662-2(3)*, Scribner) Scribner.
—A Year & Six Seconds: A Love Story. 2011. (ENG.). 256p. 21.99 *(978-1-4013-4162-6(4))* Hyperion Pr.
Gilvey, John Anthony. Jerry Orbach, Prince of the City: His Way from the Fantasticks to Law & Order. 2011. (ENG., Illus.). 192p. pap. 19.99 *(978-1-4234-8845-3(8)*, 1423488458, Applause Theatre & Cinema) Leonard, Hal Corp.
Gitlin, Martin. Audrey Hepburn: A Biography, 1 vol. 2008. (Greenwood Biographies Ser.). (Illus.). 152p. 35.00 *(978-0-313-35945-3(8)*, GR5945, Greenwood Pr.) Greenwood Publishing Group, Inc.
Godley, Janey. Handstands in the Dark: A True Story of Growing up & Survival. 2006. (ENG.). 416p. per. 14.95 *(978-0-09-190877-5(9))* Random Hse. GBR. Dist: Independent Pubs. Group.
Goodall, Nigel. David Tennant. 2011. (ENG., Illus.). 264p. pap. 12.95 *(978-1-84358-187-1(6))* Blake, John Publishing, Ltd. GBR. Dist: Independent Pubs. Group.
Gordon, Jeff. Foxy Lady: The Authorized Biography of Lynn Bari. 2010. 500p. pap. 29.95 *(978-1-59393-523-8(4))* BearManor Media.
Gordon, William A. The Ultimate Hollywood Tour Book: The Incomparable Guide to Movie Stars' Homes, Movie & TV Locations, Scandals, Murders, Suicides, & All the Famous Tourist Sites. 4th ed. 2007. 288p. pap. 16.95 *(978-0-937813-08-9(7))* North Ridge Bks.
Gossett, Louis, Jr. & Karas, Phyllis. An Actor & a Gentleman. 2010. (ENG., Illus.). 320p. 26.95 *(978-0-470-57471-3(2)*, Wiley) Wiley, John & Sons, Inc.
Gottfried, Gilbert. Rubber Balls & Liquor. 2011. (ENG., Illus.). 288p. 24.99 *(978-0-312-56811-2(2))* St. Martin's Pr.
Grace, Sherrill. Making Theatre: A Life of Sharon Pollock. Pollock, Sharon, ed. 2008. (ENG.). 480p. pap. 39.95 *(978-0-88922-586-2(9))* Talonbooks, Ltd. CAN. Dist: Consortium Bk. Sales & Distribution.
Granach, Alexander. From the Shtetl to the Stage: The Odyssey of a Wandering Actor. 2010. (ENG.). 304p. pap. 29.95 *(978-1-4128-1347-1(6))* Transaction Pubs.
Granger, Farley & Calhoun, Robert. Include Me Out: My Life from Goldwyn to Broadway. 2008. (ENG., Illus.). 288p. pap. 19.99 *(978-0-312-35774-0(5)*, St. Martin's Griffin) St. Martin's Pr.
Gray, Spalding. The Journals of Spalding Gray. Casey, Nell & Russo, Kathie, eds. 2011. (ENG., Illus.). 368p. 28.95 *(978-0-307-27345-1(8)*, Knopf) Knopf Doubleday Publishing Group.
Gray, Spalding. The Journals of Spalding Gray. Russo, Kathie & Casey, Nell, eds. 2012. (Vintage Ser.). (ENG.). 368p. pap. 16.00 ***(978-0-307-47491-9(7)**, Vintage) Knopf Doubleday Publishing Group.
Green, Paul. Pete Duel: A Biography. 2007. (ENG., Illus.). 229p. per. 35.00 *(978-0-7864-3062-8(1))* McFarland & Co., Inc. Pubs.
—Pete Duel: A Biography [LARGE PRINT]. l.t. alt. ed. 2008. (ENG., Illus.). 387p. pap. 45.00 *(978-0-7864-4117-4(8))* McFarland & Co., Inc. Pubs.
Grier, Pam. Foxy: My Life in Three Acts. 2011. (ENG., Illus.). 288p. pap. 14.99 *(978-0-446-54848-9(0))* Grand Central Publishing.
Griffin, Kathy. Official Book Club Selection: A Memoir According to Kathy Griffin. 2010. (ENG., Illus.). 384p. pap. 15.00 *(978-0-345-51856-9(X)*, Ballantine Bks.) Random House Publishing Group.
Griffin, Maggie. Tip It! The World According to Maggie. 2010. (ENG.). 256p. 23.99 *(978-1-4013-2404-9(5))* Hyperion Pr.
Grobel, Lawrence. Al Pacino: The Authorized Biography. l.t. ed. 2007. (Ulverscroft Nonfiction Ser.). 400p. 35.50 *(978-1-84617-803-0(7))* Ulverscroft Large Print Bks., Ltd.
—Conversations with Marlon Brando: Lawrence Grobel. 2009. (ENG.). 195p. pap. 25.00 *(978-0-9818056-2-7(0))* Rat Pr.
Grossman, Barbara Wallace. A Spectacle of Suffering: Clara Morris on the American Stage. 2nd ed. 2009. (Theater in the Americas Ser.). (Illus.). 344p. pap. 37.50 *(978-0-8093-2882-6(8))* Southern Illinois Univ. Pr.
Guttenberg, Steve. The Guttenberg Bible: A Memoir: From the Genesis of My Career to the Revelations. 2012. (ENG., Illus.). 352p. 25.99 ***(978-0-312-38345-9(2)**, Dunne, Thomas Bks.) St. Martin's Pr.
Hagen, Eva Maria. Eva und der Wolf. (GER.). *(978-3-612-26643-9(8))* Econ-Verlag GmbH DEU. Dist: International Bk. Import Service, Inc.
Hagman, Larry & Gold, Todd. Hello Darlin' Tall (and Absolutely True) Tales about My Life. 2011. (ENG.). 288p. pap. 18.99 ***(978-1-4516-4664-1(X))*** Simon & Schuster.
Hamlin, Harry. Full Frontal Nudity: The Making of an Accidental Actor. 2010. (ENG., Illus.). 288p. 24.00 *(978-1-4391-6999-5(3)*, Scribner) Scribner.
Hannah, Rufus & Soper, Barry. A Bum Deal: An Unlikely Journey from Hopeless to Humanitarian. 2010. (ENG.). 256p. 24.99 *(978-1-4022-4471-1(1))* Sourcebooks, Inc.
Hannsberry, Karen Burroughs. Bad Boys: The Actors of Film Noir, 2 vols. alt. ed. 2008. (ENG., Illus.). 797p. pap. 75.00 *(978-0-7864-3739-9(1))* McFarland & Co., Inc. Pubs.
Hansen, Kathryn. Stages of Life: Indian Theatre Autobiographies. 2011. (Anthem Studies in Theatre & Performance Ser.). (Illus.). 392p. 99.00 ***(978-0-85728-660-4(9))*** Anthem Pr. GBR. Dist: Books International, Inc.
Hansl, Art. Flashbacks. 2009. 280p. 25.95 *(978-1-935125-27-3(3))* Robertson Publishing.
Hanson, Dian. Vanessa del Rio: Fifty Years of Slightly Slutty Behavior. ltd. ed. 2007. (ENG.). 396p. 700.00 *(978-3-8228-2230-2(2))* TASCHEN DEU. Dist: Ingram Pub. Services.
Harbin, Billy J., et al, eds. The Gay & Lesbian Theatrical Legacy: A Biographical Dictionary of Major Figures in American Stage History in the Pre-Stonewall Era. 2007. (Triangulations: Lesbian/Gay/Queer Theater/Drama/Performance Ser.). (ENG., Illus.). 440p. pap. 37.50 *(978-0-472-06858-6(X))* Univ. of Michigan Pr.
Harbinson, W. A. Beauty & the Beast: the Story of Nastassja & Klaus Kinski. 2012. (ENG.). 158p. pap. 8.95 ***(978-1-4663-9674-6(1))*** CreateSpace.
Harrison, Cheung. Christian Bale: From Bad Man to Batman. 2011. 280p. pap. *(978-1-926745-72-5(8))* Transit Publishing (Transit Editeur Inc.).
Hatton, Joseph. Henry Irving's Impressions of America: Narrated in a Series of Sketches, Chronicles, & Conversations. 2007. (Travel in America Ser.). (ENG.). 496p. 49.95 *(978-1-4290-0456-5(8))*; per. 24.95 *(978-1-4290-0457-2(6))* Applewood Bks.
Haven, Kendall. Reluctant Heroes: True Five-Minute-Read Adventure Stories for Boys. 1 vol. 2008. 188p. pap. 30.00 *(978-1-59158-749-1(2)*, LU8749) Libraries Unlimited, Inc.
Hayat, Sofia. Dishonoured. 2009. (ENG., Illus.). 236p. pap. 14.95 *(978-1-84454-701-2(9))* Blake, John Publishing, Ltd. GBR. Dist: Independent Pubs. Group.
Hayter-Menzies, Grant. Charlotte Greenwood: The Life & Career of the Comic Star of Vaudeville, Radio & Film. 2007. (ENG., Illus.). 266p. per. 45.00 *(978-0-7864-2995-0(X))* McFarland & Co., Inc. Pubs.
—Mrs. Ziegfeld: The Public & Private Lives of Billie Burke. 2009. (ENG., Illus.). 245p. 55.00 *(978-0-7864-3800-6(2))* McFarland & Co., Inc. Pubs.
Heard, Christopher. Keifer Sutherland: Living Dangerously. 2010. 272p. 14.99 *(978-1-926745-04-6(3))* Transit Publishing (Transit Editeur Inc.) CAN. Dist: Midpoint Trade Bks., Inc.
Henderson, Jan Alan. Speeding Bullet: The life & bizarre death of George Reeves. 2nd exp. ed. 2007. pap. 24.95 *(978-0-9619596-7-8(3))* Bifulco, Michael.
Hershberger, Mary, ed. Jane Fonda's Words of Politics & Passion. 2008. (ENG.). 161p. per. 16.95 *(978-1-59558-217-1(7))* New Pr., The.
Herzogenrath, Bernd. The Films of Tod Browning. 2006. (ENG., Illus.). 238p. per. 45.00 *(978-1-904772-51-4(X))* Black Dog Publishing Ltd. GBR. Dist: Perseus Distribution.
Hickman, Darryl. The Unconscious Actor: Out of Control, in Full Command - The Art of Performance in Acting & in Life. 2007. (ENG.). 312p. 24.95 *(978-0-9776809-2-4(4))* Small Mountain Pr.
Hischak, Thomas S. Disney Voice Actors: A Biographical Dictionary. 2011. (ENG.). 290p. pap. 75.00 ***(978-0-7864-6271-1(X))*** McFarland & Co., Inc. Pubs.
Hoefling, Larry J. Nils Thor Granlund: Show Business Entrepreneur & America's First Radio Star. 2010. (ENG., Illus.). 243p. pap. 39.95 *(978-0-7864-4849-4(0))* McFarland & Co., Inc. Pubs.
Hoey, Michael. Elvis, Sherlock & Me. 2007. 336p. per. 24.95 *(978-1-59393-122-3(0))* BearManor Media.
Hogan, Hulk & Dagostino, Mark. My Life Outside the Ring. 2010. (ENG., Illus.). 336p. pap. 14.99 *(978-0-312-58890-8(9)*, St. Martin's Griffin) St. Martin's Pr.
Holbrook, Hal. Harold: The Boy Who Became Mark Twain. 2011. (ENG., Illus.). 480p. 30.00 *(978-0-374-28101-4(7))* Farrar, Straus & Giroux.
Holmes, Jessica. I Love Your Laugh: Finding the Light in My Screwball Life. (ENG., Illus.). 256p. 2011. pap. 17.95 *(978-0-7710-4135-8(7))* 2010. 27.99 *(978-0-7710-4134-1(9))* McClelland & Stewart CAN. (McClelland & Stewart). Dist: Random Hse., Inc.
Holmgren, Beth. Starring Madame Modjeska: On Tour in Poland & America. 2011. (ENG., Illus.). 432p. 39.95 *(978-0-253-35664-2(4)*, 0253356644) Indiana Univ. Pr.
Holroyd, Michael. A Strange Eventful History: The Dramatic Lives of Ellen Terry, Henry Irving, & Their Remarkable Families. 2010. (ENG., Illus.). 656p. pap. 28.00 *(978-0-312-42949-2(5))* Picador.
Holtz, Gunter. Ferdinand Raimund - der Geliebte Hypochonder: Sein Leben, sein Werk. 280p. 34.95 *(978-3-631-39162-4(5))* Lang, Peter Publishing, Inc.
Hordern, Michael. World Elsewhere: The Autobiography of a Well-Known British Character Actor. l.t. ed. 24.95 *(978-1-85695-186-9(3))* ISIS Large Print Bks. GBR. Dist: Transaction Pubs.
Howard, Tony. Women as Hamlet: Performance & Interpretation in Theatre, Film & Fiction. 2007. (ENG., Illus.). 341p. 109.99 *(978-0-521-86466-4(6))* Cambridge Univ. Pr.
Iannucci, Lisa. Will Smith: A Biography, 1 vol. 2009. (Greenwood Biographies Ser.). 133p. 35.00 *(978-0-313-37610-8(7)*, GR7610) Greenwood Publishing Group, Inc.
Ice-T & Century, Douglas. Ice: A Memoir of Gangster Life & Redemption-from South Central to Hollywood. 2011. (ENG., Illus.). 272p. 25.00 *(978-0-345-52328-0(8)*, One World/Ballantine) Random House Publishing Group.
Ignatieva, Maria. Stanislavsky & Female Actors: Women in Stanislavsky's Life & Art. 2008. (ENG.). 140p. pap. 29.50 *(978-0-7618-4103-5(2))* Univ. Pr. of America, Inc.
Jackson, Laura. Kiefer Sutherland: The Biography. 2008. (ENG., Illus.). 240p. 32.95 *(978-0-7499-5104-7(4))* Piatkus Bks. GBR. Dist: Independent Pubs. Group.
—Kiefer Sutherland - The Biography. 2007. (ENG., Illus.). 240p. 14.95 *(978-0-7499-5138-2(9))* Piatkus Bks. GBR. Dist: Independent Pubs. Group.
Jacobson, Laurie & Provost, Jon. Timmy's in the Well: The Jon Provost Story. 2010. (ENG.). 352p. pap. 18.95 *(978-0-9826387-3-6(6)*, 0982638736) Franklin Green Publishing.
James, Emmett. Admit One: My Life in Film. 2010. 19.95 *(978-0-9842581-0-9(8))* FizzyPop.
Jason, Sybil. 5 Minutes More. 2007. 144p. per. 19.95 *(978-1-59393-115-5(8))* BearManor Media.
Jodorowsky, Alejandro. The Spiritual Journey of Alejandro Jodorowsky: The Creator of El Topo. 2008. (ENG.). 1p. pap. 21.95 *(978-1-59477-173-6(1)*, Park Street Pr.) Inner Traditions International, Ltd.
Johns, Kevin. Oh Yes It Is! Read, Peter, ed. 2008. (ENG., Illus.). 188p. pap. 18.95 ***(978-1-84771-061-1(1))*** Y Lolfa GBR. Dist: Dufour Editions, Inc.
Johnson, Kim Howard. The Funniest One in the Room: The Lives & Legends of Del Close. 2008. (ENG., Illus.). 416p. 24.95 *(978-1-55652-712-8(8))* Chicago Review Pr., Inc.
Johnson, Michael A. Jamie Foxx & the Boycott Part. 2011. 64p. pap. 15.99 ***(978-1-4568-9093-3(X))*** Xlibris Corp.
Johnston, Kristen. Guts: The Endless Follies & Tiny Triumphs of a Giant Disaster. (ENG., Illus.). 288p. 2013. pap. 15.00 ***(978-1-4516-3506-5(0))*** 2012. 25.00 ***(978-1-4516-3505-8(2))*** Gallery Pr., The. IRL. Dist: Simon & Schuster, Inc.
Johnstone, Nick. George Clooney: The Illustrated Biography. 2009. (ENG., Illus.). 160p. pap. *(978-1-84732-145-9(3))* Carlton Bks., Ltd. GBR. Dist: Sterling Publishing Co., Inc.
Joncus, Berta & Barlow, Jeremy, eds. Stage's Glory: John Rich (1692-1761) 2011. *(978-0-87413-070-6(0))* Univ. of Delaware Pr.
Jordan, Leslie. My Trip down the Pink Carpet. 2009. (ENG.). 272p. pap. 15.00 *(978-1-4391-5348-2(5))* Gallery Pr., The. IRL. Dist: Simon & Schuster, Inc.
Kachmar, Diane C. Roy Scheider: A Film Biography. alt. ed. 2008. (ENG.). 256p. pap. 39.95 *(978-0-7864-4059-7(7))* McFarland & Co., Inc. Pubs.
Kafanova, Liudmila & Martinson, Sergei. Martinson S Dvukh Tochek Zreniia. 2009. (Illus.). 210p. pap. *(978-0-9821973-3-2(0))* Seagul Pr.
Kahan, Gerald. George Alexander Stevens & the Lecture on Heads. 2008. (ENG.). 232p. pap. 22.95 *(978-0-8203-3264-2(X))* Univ. of Georgia Pr.
Kahan, Jeffrey. The Cult of Kean. 2006. (Illus.). 204p. 110.00 *(978-0-7546-5650-0(0))* Ashgate Publishing Co.
Kanfer, Stefan. Somebody: The Reckless Life & Remarkable Career of Marlon Brando. 2009. (Vintage Ser.). (ENG., Illus.). 384p. pap. 16.00 *(978-1-4000-7804-2(0)*, Vintage) Knopf Doubleday Publishing Group.
Kauffmann, Stanley. About the Theater. 2010. 207p. pap. 17.95 *(978-1-931357-65-4(X))* Sheep Meadow Pr., The.
Kear, Lynn. Laurette Taylor, American Stage Legend. 2010. (ENG., Illus.). 286p. pap. 45.00 *(978-0-7864-5922-3(0))* McFarland & Co., Inc. Pubs.
Kear, Lynn & King, James. Evelyn Brent: The Life & Films of Hollywood's Lady Crook. 2009. (ENG., Illus.). 312p. pap. 45.00 *(978-0-7864-4363-5(4))* McFarland & Co., Inc. Pubs.
Kear, Lynn & Rossman, John. The Complete Kay Francis Career Record: All Film, Stage, Radio & Television Appearances. 2008. (ENG., Illus.). 295p. 55.00 *(978-0-7864-3198-4(9))* McFarland & Co., Inc. Pubs.
Kearns, Michael. Lasting Connections: Two Plays That Survived the Plague. 2009. 128p. pap. 18.59 *(978-0-325-02159-1(7)*, E02159) Heinemann.
Keesey, Douglas. Movie ICONS. Jack Nicholson. Duncan, Paul, ed. 2009. (ENG.). 192p. pap. 9.99 *(978-3-8365-0853-7(2))* TASCHEN DEU. Dist: Ingram Pub. Services.
Kelly, Michael. Reminiscences of Michael Kelly, of the King's Theatre, & Theatre Royal Drury Lane: Including a Period of Nearly Half a Century. 2011. (Cambridge Library Collection - Music Ser.). (ENG.). 386p. pap. 31.99 ***(978-1-108-03872-0(7))*** Cambridge Univ. Pr.
Kelly, Sherry. The Big Life of A Little Man: Michael Dunn Remembered. 2010. pap. 12.99 *(978-1-61566-442-9(4))* Tate Publishing & Enterprises, LLC.
Kemble, Fanny. Journal: Volume 1. 2009. (Cambridge Library Collection - History Ser.). (ENG.). 324p. pap. 19.99 *(978-1-108-00391-9(5))* Cambridge Univ. Pr.
—Journal: Volume 2. 2009. (Cambridge Library Collection - History Ser.) (ENG.). 296p. pap. 17.99 *(978-1-108-00392-6(3))* Cambridge Univ. Pr.
Kemble, Frances Anne. Records of a Girlhood. 2009. 744p. 36.99 *(978-0-559-08675-5(X))*; 40.99 *(978-0-559-08659-5(8))*; pap. 51.75 *(978-0-559-08663-2(6))*; pap. 27.99 *(978-0-559-08665-7(7))* BiblioBazaar.
—Records of a Girlhood. 2007. 640p. per. *(978-1-4065-1888-7(3))* Dodo Pr.
Kennedy, Matthew. Marie Dressler: A Biography; with a Listing of Major Stage Performances, a Filmography & a Discography. alt. ed. 2006. (ENG., Illus.). 279p. per. 39.95 *(978-0-7864-2844-1(9))* McFarland & Co., Inc. Pubs.
Kent, Gary. Shadows & Light: Journeys with Outlaws in Revolutionary Hollywood. 2009. (It's Just Lunch Guide to Dating Ser.). (Illus.). 400p. pap. 21.95 *(978-0-9817443-7-7(0))* Dalton Publishing GBR. Dist: Midpoint Trade Bks., Inc.
Keston, John. Expressions of Aging. 2011. 192p. pap. 15.95 *(978-0-615-44684-4(1))* 42K Books.
Kiškoumi, et al. Heiße West- und kalte Ost-Schauspieler? Diskurse, Praxen, Geschichte(n) zur Schauspielausbildung in Deutschland nach 1945. 2008. (GER., Illus.). 291p. *(978-3-940737-27-4(5))* interessengemeinschaft theater der zeit.
Knapp, Bettina. Marie Dorval: A Book for Actors: France's Theatrical Wonder. 2007. (Chiasma Ser.: 21). 234p. pap. 61.00 *(978-90-420-2132-7(2))* Rodopi.
Kobal Collection, photos by. ICONS Film - Marlene Dietrich. 2007. (Movie Icons Ser.). (FRE, GER & ENG., Illus.). 192p. per. 9.99 *(978-3-8228-2211-1(6))* TASCHEN DEU. Dist: Ingram Pub. Services.

A

Koestenbaum, Wayne. The Anatomy of Harpo Marx. 2012. (ENG., Illus.). 336p. 70.00 ***(978-0-520-26900-2(4))***; pap. 29.95 ***(978-0-520-26901-9(2))*** Univ. of California Pr.

Koestler-Grack, Rachel A. Bruce Lee. 2007. (Asian Americans of Achievement Ser.). (Illus.). 128p. (YA). (gr. 7-12). lib. bdg. 35.00 *(978-0-7910-9274-3(7))* Facts On File, Inc.

Kogan, Milt M. D. Second Act: Returning to College at Age 71. 2010. 88p. pap. 30.49 *(978-1-4520-0344-3(0))* AuthorHouse.

Koopmans, Andy. Seth Rogen. 2012. (People in the News Ser.). (Illus.). 128p. (YA). (gr. 7-12). 33.45 ***(978-1-4205-0616-7(1))*** Cengage Gale.

Kujawinska Courtney, Krystyna & Lukowska, Maria, eds. Ira Aldridge (1807-1867) The Great Shakespearean Tragedian on the Bicentennial Anniversary of his Birth. 2009. 168p. pap. 50.95 *(978-3-631-57734-9(6))* Lang, Peter GmbH, Europaischer Verlag der Wissenschaften DEU. Dist: Lang, Peter.

Lange, Artie & Bozza, Anthony. Too Fat to Fish. 2009. (ENG., Illus.). 336p. pap. 16.00 *(978-0-385-52657-9(1))* Spiegel & Grau.

Langella, Frank. Dropped Names: Famous Men & Women as I Knew Them. 2012. (ENG., Illus.). 374p. 25.99 ***(978-0-06-209447-6(5))*** HarperCollins Pubs.

Langley, Roger. Patrick Mcgoohan: Danger Man or Prisoner? 40th ed. 2007. (Illus.). 339p. pap. 32.00 *(978-0-9531926-4-9(4))* Tomahawk Pr. GBR. Dist: Midpoint Trade Bks., Inc.

Lapotaire, Jane. Everybody's Daughter, Nobody's Child. 2007. (ENG.). 384p. pap. 13.95 *(978-1-84408-416-6(7)*, Virago Press) Little, Brown Bk. Group Ltd. GBR. Dist: Independent Pubs. Group.

Larkins, Bob & Magers, Boyd. The Films of Audie Murphy. alt. ed. 2009. (ENG., Illus.). 240p. pap. 39.95 *(978-0-7864-4508-0(4))* McFarland & Co., Inc. Pubs.

Lauder, Harry. Between You & Me. 2008. 216p. 27.99 *(978-0-554-26990-0(2))* 2008. 216p. 24.99 *(978-0-554-36293-9(7))* 2007. (ENG.). 198p. pap. 19.99 *(978-1-4346-2286-0(X))* 2007. (ENG.). 212p. pap. 22.99 *(978-1-4346-2344-7(0))* BiblioBazaar.

—Between You & Me. 2007. (ENG.). 196p. per. *(978-1-4065-3580-8(X))* Dodo Pr.

Lawford, Christopher Kennedy. Moments of Clarity: Voices from the Front Lines of Addiction & Recovery. 2010. (ENG.). 304p. pap. 13.99 *(978-0-06-145622-0(5)*, William Morrow Paperbacks) HarperCollins Pubs.

—Symptoms of Withdrawal: A Memoir of Snapshots & Redemption. 2006. 320p. mass mkt. 7.99 *(978-0-06-073249-3(0))* HarperCollins Pubs.

Lawrence, Jeff & Lawrence, Shirley. Hollywood Be Thy Name: An Inside Look at Hollywood Actors & Extras. 2006. 440p. pap. 26.95 *(978-1-59800-155-6(8))* Outskirts Pr., Inc.

Lawson, Leigh. The Dream: An Actor's Tale. 2009. (ENG.). 200p. pap. 30.95 *(978-1-84002-867-6(X))* Oberon Bks., Ltd. GBR. Dist: Consortium Bk. Sales & Distribution.

le Gai Eaton, Charles. A Bad Beginning: The Path to Islam. 2009. (Illus.). 428p. pap. 19.95 *(978-1-901383-33-1(4))* Archetype GBR. Dist: Midpoint Trade Bks., Inc.

Lee, Anna & Roisman Cooper, Barbara. Anna Lee: Memoir of a Career on General Hospital & in Film. 2007. (ENG., Illus.). 322p. per. 35.00 *(978-0-7864-3161-8(X))* McFarland & Co., Inc. Pubs.

Leman, Walter Moore. Memories of an Old Actor. 2009. (ENG.). 421p. pap. 34.75 *(978-1-117-72715-8(7))* BiblioBazaar.

—Memories of an Old Actor. 2008. 428p. 51.95 *(978-1-4372-6760-0(2))*; 424p. pap. 36.95 *(978-1-4371-4127-6(7))* Kessinger Publishing, LLC.

Lemonier, Marc. L'intégrale de Funès: Louis de Funès de a à Z: Tout, Tout, Tout Sur Louis de Funès, Ses Films, Ses Partenaires, Ses Réalisateurs, les Lieux Associés à Sa Carrière et à Sa Vie Familiale, Ses Amis, Sa Carrière Au Cabaret et Au Théâtre, Etc. 2010. (FRE., Illus.). 295p. *(978-2-258-08333-2(8))* Hors collection.

Lennig, Arthur. The Immortal Count: The Life & Films of Bela Lugosi. 2010. (ENG., Illus.). 560p. pap. 30.00 *(978-0-8131-2661-6(4))* Univ. Pr. of Kentucky.

Life Magazine Editors. Life Remembering Liz, 1932-2011. 2011. (ENG., Illus.). 96p. 19.95 *(978-1-60320-223-7(4))* Time Home Entertainment, Inc.

—Life Ronald Reagan at 100. 2011. (ENG.). 144p. 24.95 *(978-1-60320-193-3(9))* Time Home Entertainment, Inc.

Lindfors, Bernth. Ira Aldridge: The Early Years, 1807-1833, 2 vols. 2011. (Rochester Studies in African History & the Diaspora Ser.: Volume 48). (Illus.). 402p. 55.00 *(978-1-58046-381-2(9))* Univ. of Rochester Pr.

—Ira Aldridge: The Early Years, 1807-1833 & the Vagabond Years, 1833-1852. 2011. (Rochester Studies in African History & the Diaspora Ser.). 660p. 99.00 *(978-1-58046-401-7(7))* Univ. of Rochester Pr.

—Ira Aldridge: The Vagabond Years, 1833-1852, 2 vols. 2011. (Rochester Studies in African History & the Diaspora Ser.: Volume 49). (Illus.). 258p. 55.00 *(978-1-58046-394-2(0))* Univ. of Rochester Pr.

Lipman, Maureen. Past-It Notes. 2008. (ENG., Illus.). 480p. 36.95 *(978-1-906217-75-4(0))* Aurum Pr., Ltd. GBR. Dist: Independent Pubs. Group.

Lithgow, John. Drama: An Actor's Education. (ENG.). 2012. 336p. pap. 14.99 ***(978-0-06-173498-4(5)***, HarperPerennial) 2011. 336p. 26.99 *(978-0-06-173497-7(7))* 2011. 448p. pap. 26.99 *(978-0-06-208874-1(2)*, HarperLuxe) HarperCollins Pubs.

Livingston, Barry. The Importance of Being Ernie: From My Three Sons to Mad Men, a Hollywood Survivor Tells All. 2011. (ENG., Illus.). 288p. 24.95 *(978-0-8065-3509-8(1)*, Citadel Pr.) Kensington Publishing Corp.

Lord, Graham. Arthur Lowe. (Illus.). 320p. pap. 16.00 *(978-0-7528-4229-5(3))* Orion Bks. Ltd. GBR. Dist: Trafalgar Square Publishing.

—Joan Collins: The Biography of an Icon. 2008. (ENG., Illus.). 424p. pap. 19.95 *(978-0-7528-9350-1(5))* Orion Publishing Group, Ltd. GBR. Dist: Independent Pubs. Group.

—NIV: The Authorized Biography of David Niven. pap. *(978-0-312-32864-1(8))* St. Martin's Pr.

Lord, Graham & Collins, Joan. Joan Collins: The Biography of an Icon. 2007. (ENG., Illus.). 400p. 37.95 *(978-0-7528-6753-3(9))* Orion Publishing Group, Ltd. GBR. Dist: Independent Pubs. Group.

Lumley, Joanna. Girl Friday: The Co-Star of "Absolutely Fabulous" Spends 9 Days on a Desert. l.t. ed. 196p. 23.95 *(978-1-85695-206-4(1))* ISIS Large Print Bks. GBR. Dist: Transaction Pubs.

LuPone, Patti. Patti Lupone: A Memoir. (ENG., Illus.). 336p. 2011. pap. 15.00 *(978-0-307-46074-5(6)*, Three Rivers Pr.) 2010. 25.99 *(978-0-307-46073-8(8)*, Harmony) Crown Publishing Group.

Lynch, Jane & Dickey, Lisa. Happy Accidents. 2011. (ENG.). 320p. 25.99 *(978-1-4013-4176-3(4))* Hyperion Pr.

Lyon, Nicola. Henry the Great: An Entertainment for Five Actors Celebrating the Life & Art of Sir Henry Irving. 2007. (Illus.). 81p. *(978-1-905886-79-1(9))* Troubadour Publishing Ltd.

Macken, Ultan. Walter Macken: Dreams on Paper. 2010. (ENG., Illus.). 448p. 47.95 *(978-1-85635-630-5(2))* Mercier Pr., Ltd., The IRL. Dist: Dufour Editions, Inc.

Malone, Greg. You Better Watch Out. 2009. (ENG., Illus.). 384p. 25.00 *(978-0-307-39674-7(6)*, Knopf Canada) Knopf Canada CAN. Dist: Random Hse., Inc.

—You Better Watch Out. 2010. (ENG., Illus.). 384p. pap. 18.00 *(978-0-307-39675-4(4)*, Vintage Canada) Random Hse. of Canada, Ltd. CAN. Dist: Random Hse., Inc.

Mandel, Howie & Young, Josh. Here's the Deal: Don't Touch Me. 2010. (Illus.). 240p. pap. 15.00 *(978-0-553-38665-3(4))* Random House Publishing Group.

Mank, Gregory William. Hollywood's Hellfire Club: The Misadventures of John Barrymore, W. C. Fields, Errol Flynn & the Bundy Drive Boys. 2007. (ENG., Illus.). 280p. per. 22.95 *(978-1-932595-24-6(4))* Feral Hse.

Marsh-Doll, Caren. Hollywood's Babe. 2007. 288p. per. 19.95 *(978-1-59393-107-0(7))* BearManor Media.

Marshall, Christabel. Ellen Terry's Memoirs. 2008. 380p. *(978-1-4437-4071-5(3)*, Obscure Pr.) Read Bks.

Marshall, David. Life among the Cannibals: The Life & Times of Marilyn Monroe 1962 - 2003. 2009. 508p. pap. 26.95 *(978-1-4401-2942-1(8))* iUniverse, Inc.

Marshall, Gail, ed. Lives of Shakespearian Actors, 3 vols., Vol. 1, Pt. II. 2009. (Lives of Shakespearian Actors Ser.). (ENG.). 1312p. 495.00 *(978-1-85196-852-7(0))* Pickering & Chatto Pubs., Ltd. GBR. Dist: Ashgate Publishing Co.

—Lives of Shakespearian Actors: Part I, 3 vols., Set. 2008. (Major Works Ser.). (ENG., Illus.). 1200p. 247.50 *(978-1-85196-853-4(9))* Pickering & Chatto Pubs., Ltd. GBR. Dist: Ashgate Publishing Co.

Marshall, Sarah. Daniel Craig: The Biography. (ENG., Illus.). 2009. 262p. pap. 13.95 *(978-1-84454-604-6(7))* 2008. 288p. 24.95 *(978-1-84454-454-7(0))* Blake, John Publishing, Ltd. GBR. Dist: Independent Pubs. Group.

—Sienna's Story: The Biography of Britain's Most Inspiring Star. 2007. (ENG., Illus.). 288p. 24.95 *(978-1-84454-296-3(3))* Blake, John Publishing, Ltd. GBR. Dist: Independent Pubs. Group.

Mask, Mia. Divas on Screen: Black Women in American Film. 2009. (ENG., Illus.). 320p. 75.00 *(978-0-252-03422-0(8))*; pap. 26.00 *(978-0-252-07619-0(2))* Univ. of Illinois Pr.

Matlin, Marlee. I'll Scream Later. 2010. (ENG., Illus.). 336p. pap. 16.00 *(978-1-4391-7151-6(3))* Gallery Pr., The IRL. Dist: Simon & Schuster, Inc.

McArthur, Benjamin. The Man Who Was Rip Van Winkle: Joseph Jefferson & Nineteenth-Century American Theatre. 2007. (ENG., Illus.). 464p. 45.00 *(978-0-300-12232-9(2))* Yale Univ. Pr.

McClanahan, Rue. My First Five Husbands. . & the Ones Who Got Away. 2008. (ENG., Illus.). 368p. pap. 14.95 *(978-0-7679-2694-2(3))* Broadway Bks.

McCormick, Maureen. Here's the Story: Surviving Marcia Brady & Finding My True Voice. 2009. (ENG., Illus.). 320p. pap. 14.99 *(978-0-06-149015-6(6))* HarperCollins Pubs.

McDonough, Mary. Lessons from the Mountain. 2012. (ENG.). 288p. pap. 15.00 ***(978-0-7582-6367-4(8))*** Kensington Publishing Corp.

McDougal, Dennis. Five Easy Decades: How Jack Nicholson Became the Biggest Movie Star in Modern Times. 2008. (ENG., Illus.). 512p. pap. 15.95 *(978-0-470-42282-3(3)*, Wiley) Wiley, John & Sons, Inc.

McGee, Garry. Breathless. 2008. 332p. per. 24.95 *(978-1-59393-127-8(1))* BearManor Media.

McKay, James. Dana Andrews: The Face of Noir. 2010. (ENG., Illus.). 256p. pap. 45.00 *(978-0-7864-4614-8(5))* McFarland & Co., Inc. Pubs.

McPhaul, Heather & Kelli, Colleen. Fire in the Hole: A Year in the Life of the World's Sorriest Stuntwoman. 2010. 220p. pap. 17.95 *(978-1-4502-1168-0(2))* iUniverse, Inc.

McShane, John. Heath Ledger: His Beautiful Life & Mysterious Death. 2008. (ENG., Illus.). 288p. pap. 17.95 *(978-1-84454-633-6(0))* Blake, John Publishing, Ltd. GBR. Dist: Independent Pubs. Group.

Mediane, creator. Tomas Milian: The Tough Bandit, the Rough Cop & the Filthy Rat in Italian Cinema. 2009. (Amarkord Ser.). (ENG., Illus.). 148p. 17.95 *(978-88-96042-12-0(7))* Mediane ITA. Dist: Ingram Pub. Services.

Meikle, Denis. Johnny Depp: The Bestselling Biography. rev. ed. 2011. (ENG., Illus.). 528p. pap. 14.95 *(978-0-85768-476-9(0)*, Titan Bks.) Titan Bks. Ltd. GBR. Dist: Random Hse., Inc.

Menefee, David. The First Male Stars Hb. 2007. 340p. 39.95 *(978-1-59393-109-4(3))* BearManor Media.

Menefee, David W. The First Male Stars: Men of the Silent ERA. 2007. *(978-1-59393-073-8(9))* BearManor Media.

—Sarah Bernhardt in the Theatre of Films & Sound Recordings. alt. ed. 2008. (FRE & ENG., Illus.). 168p. pap. 35.00 *(978-0-7864-3882-2(7))* McFarland & Co., Inc. Pubs.

Menefee, David W. Wally: The true wallace reid Story. 2011. 528p. pap. 34.95 ***(978-1-59393-623-5(0))*** BearManor Media.

Mercer, Rhona. Angelina Jolie: Portrait of a Superstar. 2009. (ENG., Illus.). 298p. pap. 14.95 *(978-1-84454-792-0(2))* Blake, John Publishing, Ltd. GBR. Dist: Independent Pubs. Group.

Michaud, Michael Gregg. Sal Mineo: A Biography. (Illus.). 432p. 2011. (ENG.). pap. 16.00 *(978-0-307-71667-5(8)*, Three Rivers Pr.) 2010. 25.99 *(978-0-307-71868-6(9)*, Harmony) Crown Publishing Group.

Mitchell, Molly. David Tennant Casebook. 2009. (ENG., Illus.). 64p. (J). (gr. 4). *(978-1-4091-0469-8(9))* Orion Bks. Ltd. GBR. Dist: Sterling Publishing Co., Inc.

Mitterrand, Frederic. The Bad Life: A Memoir. Browner, Jesse, tr. from FRE. 2010. (ENG.). 320p. pap. 16.95 *(978-1-59376-260-5(7)*, Soft Skull Pr.) Counterpoint LLC.

Miyao, Daisuke. Sessue Hayakawa: Silent Cinema & Transnational Stardom. 2007. (ENG., Illus.). 400p. 94.95 *(978-0-8223-3958-8(7))*; pap. 26.95 *(978-0-8223-3969-4(2))* Duke Univ. Pr.

Monetti, Sandro. Mickey Rourke: Wrestling with Demons. 2010. 272p. pap. 16.95 *(978-1-926745-40-4(X))* Transit Publishing (Transit Editeur Inc.) CAN. Dist: Midpoint Trade Bks., Inc.

Morrell, Roberta. Kenneth Sandford, Merely Corroborative Detail. 2009. 222p. pap. 29.03 *(978-1-4251-7829-1(4))* Trafford Publishing.

Morris, Eric. The Diary of a Professional Experiencer: An Autobiographical Journey into the Evolution of an Acting System. 2007. (Illus.). 400p. per. 18.95 *(978-0-9629709-5-5(6))* Ermor Enterprises.

Morse, Barry, et al. Remember with Advantages: Chasing the Fugitive & Other Stories from an Actor's Life. 2007. (ENG., Illus.). 258p. per. 35.00 *(978-0-7864-2771-0(X))* McFarland & Co., Inc. Pubs.

Munn, Michael. Lord Larry: Personal Portrait of Laurence Olivier. 2007. (ENG., Illus.). 320p. 24.95 *(978-1-86105-977-2(9))* Anova Bks. GBR. Dist: Independent Pubs. Group.

—Richard Burton: Prince of Players. 2008. (ENG.). 272p. 24.95 *(978-1-60239-355-4(9)*, 239355) Skyhorse Publishing Co., Inc.

Munn, Olivia & montandon, mac. Suck It, Wonder Woman! The Misadventures of a Hollywood Geek. 2011. (ENG., Illus.). 288p. pap. 14.99 *(978-0-312-58376-7(1)*, St. Martin's Griffin) St. Martin's Pr.

Murray, John B. Brett Halsey: Art or Instinct in the Movies. 2008. 284p. *(978-1-887664-83-7(1))* Midnight Marquee Pr., Inc.

Nagle, Jeanne. Oprah Winfrey: Profile of a Media Mogul. 2009. (Career Profiles Ser.). 112p. (gr. 9-10). 63.90 *(978-1-61511-798-7(9))* Rosen Publishing Group, Inc., The.

Nagle, Jeanne M. Oprah Winfrey: Profile of a Media Mogul. 2007. (Career Profiles Ser.). (Illus.). 112p. (YA). (gr. 7-12). lib. bdg. 31.95 *(978-1-4042-1908-3(0))* Rosen Publishing Group, Inc., The.

Napier, Charles & Renzulli, Jr. Square Jaw & Big Heart - the Life & Times of a Hollywood Actor. 2011. 192p. pap. 19.95 ***(978-1-59393-624-2(9))*** BearManor Media.

Naylor, Bob. Robert Naylor - the Life & Times of a Yorkshire Tenor. 2010. (Illus.). 292p. pap. *(978-1-904408-65-9(6))* Bank House Bks.

Neal, Patricia. As I Am. 2011. (ENG.). 384p. pap. 23.99 *(978-1-4516-2600-1(2))* Simon & Schuster.

Nealon, Kevin. Yes, You're Pregnant, but What about Me? 2009. 272p. pap. 13.99 *(978-0-06-121521-6(X))* HarperCollins Pubs.

Needham, Hal. Stuntman! My Car-Crashing, Plane-Jumping, Bone-Breaking, Death-Defying Hollywood Life. 2011. (ENG., Illus.). 320p. 25.99 *(978-0-316-07899-3(9))* Little Brown & Co.

Nicholls, Mark. Jeremy Irons & the Prince of Perversion. 2012. (ENG.). 198p. 70.00 ***(978-0-85745-443-0(9))*** Berghahn Bks., Inc.

Nicholls, Mark Desmond. Jeremy Irons & the Prince of Perversion. 2012. E-Book ***(978-0-85745-444-7(7))*** Berghahn Bks., Inc.

Norris, Chuck. The Official Chuck Norris Fact Book: 101 of Chuck's Favorite Facts & Stories. 2009. (ENG.). 320p. pap. 14.99 *(978-1-4143-3449-3(4))* Tyndale Hse. Pubs.

Nott, Robert. The Films of Randolph Scott. alt. ed. 2007. (ENG., Illus.). 245p. per. 39.95 *(978-0-7864-3759-7(6))* McFarland & Co., Inc. Pubs.

Nowak, Donna Marie. Just Joan: A Joan Crawford Appreciation. 2010. 580p. pap. 34.95 *(978-1-59393-542-9(0))* BearManor Media.

O'Brien, Daniel. Daniel Craig. 2008. (ENG., Illus.). 256p. pap. 16.95 *(978-1-905287-85-7(2))* Reynolds & Hearn GBR. Dist: Independent Pubs. Group.

O'Brien, Scott. Kay Francis. 2007. 380p. per. 24.95 *(978-1-59393-106-3(9))* BearManor Media.

O'Connell, Jay. Train Robber's Daughter: The Melodramatic Life of Eva Evans, 187601970. 2008. (Illus.). 320p. pap. 18.95 *(978-0-9673370-2-9(X))* Raven River Pr.

Oddie, Bill & Odie, Bill. One Flew into the Cuckoo's Egg: My Autobiography. 2009. (ENG., Illus.). 320p. pap. 15.95 *(978-0-340-95194-1(X)*, Hodder & Stoughton) Hodder General Publishing Div. GBR. Dist: Independent Pubs. Group.

Ogelsby, Greta. Mama 'n Nem: Handprints on My Life. 2012. ***(978-1-933794-48-8(8))*** Kirk Hse. Pubs.

Ohmart, Ben. Don Ameche: The Kenosha Comeback Kid. 2006. (Illus.). 220p. per. *(978-1-59393-045-5(3))* BearManor Media.

—Hold That Joan: The Life, Laughs & Films of Joan Davis. 2006. (Illus.). 172p. per. *(978-1-59393-046-2(1))* BearManor Media.

O'Neal, Ryan, et al. Both of Us: My Life with Farrah. 2012. (ENG., Illus.). 272p. 26.00 ***(978-0-307-95482-4(X)***, Crown Archetype) Crown Publishing Group.

O'Neal, Tatum & Liftin, Hilary. Found: A Daughter's Journey Home. 2012. (ENG.). 240p. pap. 15.99 ***(978-0-06-206657-2(9)***, William Morrow Paperbacks) HarperCollins Pubs.

Orbach, Jerry & Orbach, Elaine. Remember How I Love You: Love Letters from an Extraordinary Marriage. 2011. (ENG., Illus.). 208p. pap. 14.99 ***(978-1-4516-7208-4(X)***, Touchstone) Touchstone.

Orbi, Joseph. ¡DIPLO! ¿Por qué se reía la Gente? 2010. mass mkt. 30.00 *(978-0-9661619-2-2(0)*, I.O. Twomey) McQuicker & Company, Ltd.

Oswalt, Patton. Zombie Spaceship Wasteland. 2011. (ENG.). 208p. 24.00 *(978-1-4391-4908-9(9)*, Scribner) Scribner.

—Zombie Spaceship Wasteland: A Book by Patton Oswalt. 2011. (ENG.). 288p. pap. 14.00 *(978-1-4391-4909-6(7)*, Scribner) Scribner.

Otis, Carre & Schwyzer, Hugo. Beauty, Disrupted: A Memoir. 2012. (ENG., Illus.). 256p. pap. 15.99 ***(978-0-06-202446-6(9))*** HarperCollins Pubs.

Oumano, Elena. Paul Newman. 2010. 272p. pap. 19.95 *(978-1-4502-0641-9(7))* iUniverse, Inc.

Paige, Elaine. Memories. 2009. (ENG., Illus.). 144p. 50.00 *(978-1-84002-852-2(1))* Oberon Bks., Ltd. GBR. Dist: Consortium Bk. Sales & Distribution.

Palin, Michael. Diaries 1969-1979: the Python Years. 2008. (ENG., Illus.). 672p. pap. 21.99 *(978-0-312-38488-3(2)*, St. Martin's Griffin) St. Martin's Pr.

Pantoliano, Joey. Asylum: Hollywood Tales from My Great Depression - Brain Dis-Ease, Recovery, & Being My Mother's Son. 2012. (ENG.). 296p. 25.00 *(978-1-60286-135-0(8))* Perseus Bks. Group.

Parry, Edward Abbott. Eminent Actors Charles Macklin. 2006. pap. 24.95 *(978-1-4286-4239-3(0))* Kessinger Publishing, LLC.

Parvis, Sarah. Robert Pattinson. 2009. (ENG., Illus.). 80p. 5.99 *(978-0-7407-8597-9(4))* Andrews McMeel Publishing.

Paterson, Bill. Tales from the Back Green. (ENG., Illus.). 2009. 160p. pap. 13.95 *(978-0-340-93682-5(7))* 2008. 154p. 25.95 *(978-0-340-93681-8(9))* Hodder General Publishing Div. GBR. (Hodder & Stoughton). Dist: Independent Pubs. Group.

Patterson, Ada & Bateman, Victory. By the Stage Door. 2007. (ENG.). 228p. 41.95 *(978-0-548-02865-0(6))* Kessinger Publishing, LLC.

Pearson, Felicia 'Snoop' & Ritz, David. Grace after Midnight: A Memoir. 2009. (ENG.). 240p. pap. 13.99 *(978-0-446-19519-5(7))* Grand Central Publishing.

People Magazine Editors. People Elizabeth Taylor, 1932-2011. 2011. (ENG., Illus.). 128p. 19.95 *(978-1-60320-074-5(6)*, People Bks.) Time Home Entertainment, Inc.

Petro, Patrice, ed. & intro. Idols of Modernity: Movie Stars of the 1920s. 2010. (Star Decades Ser.). (ENG., Illus.). 328p. 72.00 *(978-0-8135-4731-2(8))*; pap. 25.95 *(978-0-8135-4732-9(6))* Rutgers Univ. Pr.

Philippe, Pierre. Maria Felix. 2006. (ENG., Illus.). 78p. 25.00 *(978-2-84323-888-8(9))* Assouline FRA. Dist: Perseus Distribution.

Phillips, Mackenzie. High on Arrival: A Memoir. 2011. (ENG.). 320p. pap. 15.00 *(978-1-4391-5386-4(8))* Gallery Pr., The IRL. Dist: Simon & Schuster, Inc.

Picerni, Paul & Weaver, Tom. Steps to Stardom Hb. 2007. 416p. 39.95 *(978-1-59393-200-8(6))* BearManor Media.

Pinsent, Gordon & Anthony, George. So Far So Good. 2012. (ENG., Illus.). 352p. 32.99 ***(978-0-7710-7137-9(X)***, McClelland & Stewart) McClelland & Stewart CAN. Dist: Random Hse., Inc.

Planché, J. R. The Recollections & Reflections of J. R. Planché: A Professional Autobiography. 2011. (Cambridge Library Collection - Music Ser.). (ENG.). 338p. pap. 28.99 ***(978-1-108-03883-6(2))***; (Illus.). 342p. pap. 28.99 ***(978-1-108-03882-9(4))*** Cambridge Univ. Pr.

Plummer, Christopher. In Spite of Myself. 2012. (Vintage Ser.). (ENG., Illus.). 656p. pap. 17.95 ***(978-0-345-80322-1(1)***, Vintage) Knopf Doubleday Publishing Group.

Porter, Darwin & Moseley, Roy. Damn You, Scarlett O'Hara: The Private Lives of Vivien Leigh & Laurence Olivier. 2011. (ENG., Illus.). 708p. 27.95 *(978-1-936003-15-0(5))* Blood Moon Productions, Ltd.

Postlethwaite, Pete. A Spectacle of Dust. 2011. (ENG., Illus.). 288p. 35.00 ***(978-0-297-86493-6(9))*** Orion Publishing Group, Ltd. GBR. Dist: Independent Pubs. Group.

—A Spectacle of Dust: The Autobiography. 2012. (ENG., Illus.). 288p. 16.95 ***(978-1-78022-003-1(0)***, Phoenix) Orion Publishing Group, Ltd. GBR. Dist: Independent Pubs. Group.

Power. Breaking Free. 2009. (ENG.). 112p. pap. 16.95 ***(978-1-84694-171-9(7))*** Hunt, John Publishing Ltd. GBR. Dist: National Bk. Network.

Powers, Stefanie. One from the Hart. 2011. (ENG., Illus.). 272p. pap. 15.00 *(978-1-4391-7211-7(0))* Gallery Pr., The IRL. Dist: Simon & Schuster, Inc.

Pressly, Jaime. It's Not Necessarily Not the Truth: Dreaming Bigger Than the Town You're From. 2009. 256p. 25.99 *(978-0-06-145414-1(1)*, Morrow, William & Co.) HarperCollins Pubs.

Rafiq, Fiaz. Bruce Lee: Conversations. 2010. (Illus.). 352p. 24.95 *(978-0-9552648-9-4(8))* Health 'n' Life Publishing GBR. Dist: Midpoint Trade Bks., Inc.

Rapp, Anthony. Without You: A Memoir of Love, Loss, & the Musical Rent. 2006. (ENG., Illus.). 320p. pap. 15.00 *(978-0-7432-6977-3(2))* Simon & Schuster.

Rathbone, Basil. In & Out of Character. 17.95 *(978-0-8488-1113-6(5))* Amereon LTD.

Rathbone, Basil. In & Out of Character: An Autobiography. 2011. 304p. 48.95 ***(978-1-258-00573-3(5))*** Literary Licensing, LLC.

Read, Piers Paul. Alec Guinness: The Authorised Biography. 2011. (ENG.). 640p. pap. 36.99 *(978-1-4516-3644-4(X))* Simon & Schuster.

Reed, Alan & Ohmart, Ben. Yabba Dabba Doo! the Alan Reed Story. 2009. 208p. pap. 19.95 *(978-1-59393-313-5(4))* BearManor Media.

Rees, James. The Life of Edwin Forrest with Reminiscences & Personal Recollections by James Rees with Portrait & Autograph. 2006. 516p. per. 29.99 *(978-1-4255-5737-9(6))* MPublishing.

Richard D. Jensen. The Nicest Fella - the Life of Ben Johnson: The world champion rodeo cowboy who became an Oscar-winning movie Star. 2010. 516p. pap. 30.95 *(978-1-4401-9678-2(8))* iUniverse, Inc.

Richards, Denise. The Real Girl Next Door. (ENG., Illus.). 288p. 2012. pap. 15.00 ***(978-1-4516-3322-1(X))*** 2011. 26.00 *(978-1-4516-3321-4(1))* Gallery Pr., The IRL. Dist: Simon & Schuster, Inc.

Rickles, Don. Rickles' Book. l.t. ed. 2007. (Thorndike Biography Ser.). 243p. 31.95 *(978-0-7862-9856-3(1))* Thorndike Pr.

Riley, Kathleen. The Astaires: Fred & Adele, 1 vol. 2012. (ENG., Illus.). 266p. 27.95 ***(978-0-19-973841-0(6))*** Oxford Univ. Pr., Inc.

Roach, Martin & Kaye, Liz. Gossip Boys: The Double Unauthorised Biography of Ed Westwick & Chace Crawford. 2012. (ENG., Illus.). 256p. (YA). (gr. 9). pap. 12.99 ***(978-0-7535-4028-2(2))*** Virgin Bks. Ltd. GBR. Dist: Independent Pubs. Group.

Robb, Brian J. Heath Ledger: Hollywood's Dark Star. 2008. (ENG., Illus.). 160p. pap. 19.95 *(978-0-85965-427-2(3))* Plexus Publishing, Ltd. GBR. Dist: Perseus-PGW.

Roberts, David. Thomas Betterton: The Greatest Actor of the Restoration Stage. 2010. (Illus.). 270p. 95.00 *(978-0-521-19584-3(5))* Cambridge Univ. Pr.

Roberts, Doris. Are You Hungry, Dear? Life, Laughs, & Lasagna. Date not set. mass mkt. *(978-0-312-98866-1(4)*, St. Martin's Paperbacks) St. Martin's Pr.

Robeson, Paul. The Undiscovered Paul Robeson Vol. 2: Quest for Freedom, 1939-1976. 2010. (ENG., Illus.). 432p. 35.00 *(978-0-471-40973-1(1)*, Wiley) Wiley, John & Sons, Inc.

Rode, Alan K. Charles Mcgraw: Biography of a Film Noir Tough Guy. 2007. (ENG., Illus.). 228p. 45.00 *(978-0-7864-3167-0(9))* McFarland & Co., Inc. Pubs.

Ross, Robert. Complete Sid James. 2007. (ENG., Illus.). 248p. 37.95 *(978-1-905287-55-0(0))* Reynolds & Hearn GBR. Dist: Independent Pubs. Group.

Rowell, Victoria. The Women Who Raised Me: A Memoir. 2008. (Illus.). 352p. pap. 14.99 *(978-0-06-124660-9(3)*, William Morrow Paperbacks) HarperCollins Pubs.

Rulli, Marti & Davern, Dennis. Goodbye Natalie, Goodbye Splendour. 2009. (ENG.). 352p. 24.95 *(978-1-59777-639-4(4))* Phoenix Bks., Inc.

Russell, Charles Edward. Julia Marlowe Her Life & Art. 2006. pap. 48.95 *(978-1-4286-5331-3(7))* Kessinger Publishing, LLC.

Sagala, Sandra K. Buffalo Bill on Stage. 2008. (ENG., Illus.). 319p. 19.95 *(978-0-8263-4427-4(5))* Univ. of New Mexico Pr.

Salem Press Staff, contrib. by. American Heroes, 3 vols. 2008. (Magill's Choice Ser.). (Illus.). 73.00 *(978-1-58765-459-6(8))*; 73.00 *(978-1-58765-458-9(X))*; 73.00 *(978-1-58765-460-2(1))* Salem Pr., Inc.

Schall, Ekkehard. The Craft of Theatre: Seminars & Discussions in Brechtian Theatre. Davis, John, tr. from GER. 2012. (Biography & Autobiography Ser.). (ENG., Illus.). 224p. pap. 70.00 ***(978-1-4081-5989-7(9)***, Methuen Drama) A & C Black GBR. Dist: Macmillan.

Schall, Ekkehard & Davis, John. The Craft of Theatre: Seminars & Discussions in Brechtian Theatre. 2008. (Biography & Autobiography Ser.). (ENG., Illus.). 224p. 70.00 *(978-1-4081-0069-1(X)*, Methuen Drama) A & C Black GBR. Dist: Macmillan.

Schanke, Robert A. Shattered Applause: The Lives of Eva le Gallienne. 2010. (ENG., Illus.). 344p. pap. 37.50 *(978-0-8093-3008-9(3))* Southern Illinois Univ. Pr.

Schickel, Richard. Clint Eastwood: Una Retrospectiva. 2011. (SPA.). 288p. 39.95 *(978-84-9801-471-6(9))* Blume ESP. Dist: Independent Pubs. Group.

Schnakenberg, Robert. The Encyclopedia Shatnerica: An A to Z Guide to the Man & His Universe. 2008. (ENG., Illus.). 288p. pap. 16.95 *(978-1-59474-230-9(8))* Quirk Bks.

Scott, Dee. Corbin Bleu: Up Close. 2006. (ENG., Illus.). 96p. pap. 12.95 *(978-1-4165-4114-1(4))* Gallery Pr., The IRL. Dist: Simon & Schuster, Inc.

Selfridge, Jack. Jack of All Trades, Mastered by One: Jack Selfridge's Adventures with God in Africa. (Illus.). 192p. reprint ed. *(978-1-85792-281-3(6))* Christian Focus Pubns. GBR. Dist: Riverside.

Sellers, Robert, et al. James Robertson Justice: "What's the Bleeding Time?": A Biography. 2010. (Illus.). 212p. pap. 25.00 *(978-0-9531926-7-0(9))* Tomahawk Pr. GBR. Dist: Midpoint Trade Bks., Inc.

Setzer, Sharon M., et al, eds. Women's Theatrical Memoirs, Part I, 5 vols., Vols. 1-5. 2007. (Chawton House Library Ser.). (ENG.). 2000p. 750.00 *(978-1-85196-861-9(X))* Pickering & Chatto Pubs., Ltd. GBR. Dist: Ashgate Publishing Co.

Shail, Robert. Stanley Baker: A Biography. 2008. (Illus.) 160p. 35.00 *(978-0-7083-2126-3(7))* Univ. of Wales Pr. GBR. Dist: Chicago Distribution Ctr.

Shatner, William. Up till Now: The Autobiography. l.t. ed. 2008. 581p. (YA). 31.95 *(978-1-4104-0869-3(8))* Thorndike Pr.

Shatner, William & Fisher, David. Up till Now: The Autobiography. 2009. (ENG., Illus.). 368p. pap. 15.95 *(978-0-312-56163-5(6)*, St. Martin's Griffin) St. Martin's Pr.

Shaw, Aiden. Sordid Truths: Selling My Innocence for a Taste of Stardom. 2009. (ENG.). 275p. pap. 15.95 *(978-1-59350-137-2(4))* Alyson Pubns.

Shearer, Stephen Michael. Beautiful: The Life of Hedy Lamarr. 2010. (ENG., Illus.). 480p. 29.99 *(978-0-312-55098-1(7)*, Dunne, Thomas Bks.) St. Martin's Pr.

—Patricia Neal: An Unquiet Life. 2011. (ENG., Illus.). 508p. pap. 24.95 *(978-0-8131-2971-6(0))* Univ. Pr. of Kentucky.

Sher, A. Beside Myself. 2010. (ENG., Illus.). 412p. pap. 22.95 *(978-1-84842-035-9(8))* Hern, Nick Bks., Ltd. GBR. Dist: Consortium Bk. Sales & Distribution.

Sherman, Kim. Fame: Taylor Lautner. 2010. (ENG.). 32p. pap. 3.99 *(978-1-4507-0883-8(8))* Bluewater Productions, Inc.

Shukert, Rachel. Everything Is Going to Be Great: An Underfunded & Overexposed European Grand Tour. 2010. (ENG.). 336p. pap. 13.99 *(978-0-06-178235-0(1)*, HarperPerennial) HarperCollins Pubs.

Sieve, Marx. Call Me Puke. 2009. 280p. pap. 14.95 *(978-1-935097-62-4(8))* Hillcrest Publishing Group, Inc.

Silver, Alain. Movie ICONS. Sean Connery. Duncan, Paul, ed. 2009. (ENG.). 192p. pap. 9.99 *(978-3-8365-0857-5(5))* TASCHEN DEU. Dist: Ingram Pub. Services.

Skal, David J. & Rains, Jessica. Claude Rains: An Actor's Voice. 2009. (Screen Classics Ser.). (ENG.). 304p. pap. 19.95 *(978-0-8131-9261-1(7))* Univ. Pr. of Kentucky.

Smeds, Dave. Chuck Norris. 2009. (Martial Arts Masters Ser.). 112p. (gr. 5-5). 63.90 *(978-1-61514-372-6(6))* Rosen Publishing Group, Inc., The.

Smith, Elaine C. Nothing Like a Dame: My Autobiography. 2010. (ENG., Illus.). 352p. pap. 14.95 *(978-1-84596-591-4(4))* Mainstream Publishing Co., Ltd. GBR. Dist: Independent Pubs. Group.

—Nothing Like a Dame: The Autobiography. 2010. (ENG., Illus.). 350p. 28.95 *(978-1-84596-455-9(1))* Mainstream Publishing Co., Ltd. GBR. Dist: Independent Pubs. Group.

Smith, Geddeth. Walter Hampden: Dean of the American Theatre. 2008. (Illus.). 430p. 45.00 *(978-0-8386-4166-8(0))* Fairleigh Dickinson Univ. Pr.

Smith, Glenn D. & Smith, Glenn D., Jr. Something on My Own: Gertrude Berg & American Broadcasting, 1929-1956. 2007. (Television Ser.). (Illus.). 293p. 24.95 *(978-0-8156-0887-5(X))* Syracuse Univ. Pr.

Sohrab Modi. 2009. (Illus.). 120p. 9.95 *(978-81-8328-108-9(7))* Wisdom Tree IND. Dist: SCB Distributors.

Sorbo, Kevin. True Strength: My Journey from Hercules to Mere Mortal — and How Nearly Dying Saved My Life. 2012. (ENG., Illus.). 296p. pap. 16.00 ***(978-0-7382-1602-7(X))*** Da Capo Pr., Inc.

Sorgi, Marcello. Le Amanti Del Vulcano: Bergman, Magnani, Rossellini: Un Triangolo Di Passioni Nell'Italia Del Dopoguerra. 2010. (ITA., Illus.). 202p. *(978-88-17-03999-4(3))* Rizzoli International Pubns., Inc.

Southern, Antonia. Player, Playwright & Preacher's Kid: The Story of Nathan Field 1587-1620. 2009. (Illus.). 252p. pap. *(978-1-84748-527-4(8))* Athena Pr.

Spelling, Tori. STORI Telling. 2009. (ENG., Illus.). 288p. pap. 16.00 *(978-1-4165-8700-2(4))* Gallery Pr., The IRL. Dist: Simon & Schuster, Inc.

Sperber, Ann. Bogart. 2011. (ENG.). 704p. pap. 16.99 *(978-0-06-210736-7(4))* HarperCollins Pubs.

Spicer, Chrystopher J. Clark Gable, in Pictures: Candid Images of the Actor's Life. 2011. (ENG., Illus.). 208p. 45.00 *(978-0-7864-4964-4(0))* McFarland & Co., Inc. Pubs.

Spinetti, Victor. Up Front: His Strictly Confidential Autobiography. 2009. (ENG., Illus.). 256p. pap. 15.95 *(978-1-905798-25-4(3))* Anova Bks. GBR. Dist: Independent Pubs. Group.

St Romain, Theresa & Romain, Theresa. Margarita Fischer: A Biography of the Silent Film Star. 2008. (ENG., Illus.). 207p. 55.00 *(978-0-7864-3552-4(6))* McFarland & Co., Inc. Pubs.

Stangeland, John. Warren William: Magnificent Scoundrel of Pre-Code Hollywood. 2010. (ENG., Illus.). 240p. pap. 45.00 *(978-0-7864-4878-4(4))* McFarland & Co., Inc. Pubs.

Starr, Michael. Black & Blue: The Redd Foxx Story. 2011. (ENG.). 328p. 27.99 *(978-1-55783-754-7(6)*, 1557837546, Applause Theatre & Cinema) Leonard, Hal Corp.

Starr, Michael Seth. Hiding in Plain Sight: The Secret Life of Raymond Burr, 1 vol. 2009. (ENG., Illus.). 270p. pap. 16.99 *(978-1-4234-7371-8(X)*, 142347371X, Applause Theatre & Cinema) Leonard, Hal Corp.

Steffans, Karrine. Confessions of a Video Vixen. 2006. (ENG., Illus.). 224p. pap. 14.95 *(978-0-06-089248-7(X)*, Harper Paperbacks) HarperCollins Pubs.

—The Vixen Diaries. 2009. (ENG.). 208p. pap. 15.99 *(978-0-446-19123-4(X))* Grand Central Publishing.

Stein, Lisa K. Syd Chaplin: A Biography. 2010. (ENG., Illus.). 279p. pap. 39.95 *(978-0-7864-6035-9(0))* McFarland & Co., Inc. Pubs.

Sterry, David Henry. Master of Ceremonies: A True Story of Love, Murder, Roller Skates & Chippendales. 2008. (ENG.). 304p. pap. 14.95 *(978-1-84195-876-7(X))* Canongate Bks. GBR. Dist: Perseus-PGW.

Stevens, Christopher. Born Brilliant: The Life of Kenneth Williams. (ENG., Illus.). 2011. 448p. pap. 16.95 *(978-1-84854-197-9(X))* 2010. 416p. pap. 22.95 *(978-1-84854-196-2(1))* Murray, John GBR. Dist: Independent Pubs. Group.

Stevens, Ronald Smokey. I Just Want to Tell Somebody. 2008. 181p. pap. 24.95 *(978-1-4241-9161-1(0))* PublishAmerica, Inc.

Strang, Lewis C. Famous Actresses of the Day in America. 2007. (ENG.). 360p. per. 31.95 *(978-1-4304-6184-5(5))* Kessinger Publishing, LLC.

Stumpf, Charles. ZaSu Pitts: The Life & Career. 2010. (ENG., Illus.). 224p. pap. 45.00 *(978-0-7864-4620-9(X))* McFarland & Co., Inc. Pubs.

Sunshine, Sandy. The One. 2008. 376p. pap. 20.99 *(978-1-60647-800-4(1))* Xulon Pr., Inc.

Tamblyn, Robin. Looking Closer: Kevin Spacey, the first 50 Years. 2010. 156p. pap. 14.95 *(978-1-4502-0438-5(4))* iUniverse, Inc.

Terry, Ellen. Ellen Terry's Memoirs. Craig, Edith & St. John, Christopher, eds. 2011. 406p. 54.95 ***(978-1-258-07315-2(3))*** Literary Licensing, LLC.

Terry, Ellen. The Story of My Life (Terry) Recollections & Reflections. 2007. (ENG.). 354p. pap. 25.99 *(978-1-4346-2309-6(2))*; 394p. pap. 26.99 *(978-1-4346-2367-6(X))* BiblioBazaar.

Thomas, Scott. All in This Together: The Unofficial Story of High School Musical. Hale, Jennifer, ed. 2007. (ENG., Illus.). 120p. (J). (gr. 4-7). pap. 14.95 *(978-1-55022-764-2(5))* ECW Pr. CAN. Dist: Independent Pubs. Group.

Thompson, Peter E. The Triumphant Juan Rana: A Gay Actor of the Spanish Golden Age. 2006. (University of Toronto Romance Ser.). (ENG.). 176p. *(978-0-8020-8969-4(0))* Univ. of Toronto Pr.

Thomson, David. Ingrid Bergman. 2010. (ENG., Illus.). 128p. pap. 14.00 *(978-0-86547-934-0(8))* Faber & Faber, Inc.

Tian, Min, ed. China's Greatest Operatic Male Actor of Female Roles: Documenting the Life & Art of Mei Lanfang 1894-1961. 2010. 428p. *(978-0-7734-3777-7(0))* Mellen, Edwin Pr., The.

Time-Life Books Staff, contrib. by. In the Time of War & Peace. (Illus.). 168p. 24.00 *(978-1-84447-143-0(8))* Time Life Value GBR. Dist: Mercury Bks. Ltd.

Titone, Nora. My Thoughts Be Bloody: The Bitter Rivalry That Led to the Assassination of Abraham Lincoln. 2011. (ENG.). 496p. pap. 16.00 *(978-1-4165-8606-7(7)*, Free Pr.) Free Pr.

Tonguette, Peter Prescott. Orson Welles Remembered: Interviews with His Actors, Editors, Cinematographers & Magicians. 2007. (ENG., Illus.). 216p. per. 35.00 *(978-0-7864-2760-4(4))* McFarland & Co., Inc. Pubs.

Tracy, Kathleen. Angelina Jolie: A Biography, 1 vol. 2008. (Greenwood Biographies Ser.). (Illus.). 132p. 35.00 *(978-0-313-36460-0(5)*, GR6460, Greenwood Pr.) Greenwood Publishing Group, Inc.

Tranberg, Charles. Fred MacMurray: A Biography. 2007. pap. *(978-1-59393-099-8(2))* BearManor Media.

—I Love the Illusion: The Life & Career of Agnes Moorehead. 2nd ed. 2007. *(978-1-59393-095-0(X))* BearManor Media.

Triumph Books Staff & Sprinkel, Katy. Elizabeth Taylor: The Life of a Hollywood Legend. 2011. (ENG.). 128p. pap. 14.95 *(978-1-60078-665-5(0))* Triumph Bks.

Tucker, David C. Eve Arden: A Chronicle of All Film, Television, Radio & Stage Performances. 2011. (ENG.). 205p. pap. 40.00 ***(978-0-7864-6131-8(4))*** McFarland & Co., Inc. Pubs.

Tucker, David C. Shirley Booth: A Biography & Career Record. 2008. (ENG., Illus.). 220p. pap. 39.95 *(978-0-7864-3600-2(X))* McFarland & Co., Inc. Pubs.

Tucker, Fredrick. Verna Felton. 2010. 768p. pap. 39.95 *(978-1-59393-524-5(2))* BearManor Media.

Tucker, Michael. Family Meals: Coming Together to Care for an Aging Parent. 2010. (ENG.). 256p. pap. 14.00 *(978-0-8021-4508-6(6)*, Grove Pr.) Grove/Atlantic, Inc.

Turner, Kathleen. Send Yourself Roses: Thoughts on My Life, Love, & Leading Roles. l.t. ed. 2008. (Thorndike Biography Ser.). (Illus.). 455p. 31.95 *(978-1-4104-0511-1(7))* Thorndike Pr.

Tweed, Shannon. Kiss & Tell. 2007. (Illus.). 200p. per. 15.95 *(978-1-59777-551-9(7))* Phoenix Bks., Inc.

Van Patten, Dick. Eighty Is Not Enough: One Actor's Journey Through American Entertainment. 2009. (ENG., Illus.). 288p. 22.95 *(978-1-60747-700-6(9))* Phoenix Bks., Inc.

Vance, Jeffrey & Maietta, Tony. Douglas Fairbanks. Cushman, Robert, ed. 2008. (Illus.). 376p. 50.00 *(978-0-520-25667-5(0))* Univ. of California Pr.

Vanderbilt, Gloria. It Seemed Important at the Time: A Romance Memoir. 2009. (ENG., Illus.). 176p. pap. 12.99 *(978-1-4391-8982-5(X))* Simon & Schuster.

Varley, Julia. Notes from an Odin Actress. 2010. (ENG., Illus.). 208p. 110.00 *(978-0-415-58628-3(3))*; pap. 32.95 *(978-0-415-58629-0(1))* Routledge.

Vaughn, Robert. A Fortunate Life. 2009. (ENG., Illus.). 352p. pap. 18.99 *(978-0-312-59043-7(1)*, St. Martin's Griffin) St. Martin's Pr.

—A Fortunate Life. l.t. ed. 2009. 512p. 31.50 *(978-1-4104-1324-6(1))* Thorndike Pr.

Venumadav. Mimicry & World Renowned. 2006. 132p. per. *(978-1-4067-2032-7(1)*, Hesperides Pr.) Read Bks.

Verlhac, Pierre-Henri & Dherbier, Yann-Brice, eds. Audrey Hepburn: A Life in Pictures. 2nd ed. 2009. (Life in Pictures Ser.). (ENG., Illus.). 192p. 27.95 *(978-1-86205-828-6(8)*, Pavilion Bks., Ltd.) Anova Bks. GBR. Dist: Independent Pubs. Group.

Vogel, Michelle. Marjorie Main: The Life & Films of Hollywood's Ma Kettle. alt. ed. 2011. (ENG., Illus.). 216p. pap. 38.00 *(978-0-7864-6443-2(7))* McFarland & Co., Inc. Pubs.

Voit, Jochen. Er rührte an den Schlaf der Welt. Ernst Busch: Die Biographie. 2010. (GER., Illus.). 515p. *(978-3-351-02716-2(8))* Aufbau-Verlag Gmbh.

Wagner, Robert J. & Eyman, Scott. Pieces of My Heart: A Life. (ENG.). 2009. 352p. pap. 15.99 *(978-0-06-137332-9(X))* 2008. 320p. pap. 25.95 *(978-0-06-166852-4(4)*, HarperLuxe) HarperCollins Pubs.

Wahl, Jan. Through a Lens Darkly. 2008. 272p. pap. 21.95 *(978-1-59393-311-1(8))* BearManor Media.

Walker, Jimmie. Dyn-O-Mite! Good Times, Bad Times ... & Our Times - A Memoir. 2012. (ENG.). 288p. 25.00 ***(978-0-306-82083-0(8))*** Da Capo Pr., Inc.

Walker, Jimmie & Manna, Sal. Dyn-O-Mite! Good Times, Bad Times, Our Times: A Memoir. 2012. E-Book ***(978-0-306-82110-3(9))*** Da Capo Pr., Inc.

Wallace, Dee. Bright Light: Spiritual Lessons from a Life in Acting. 2011. (ENG.). 218p. pap. 16.95 *(978-1-84694-598-4(4))* O Bks., John Hunt.

Wallace, Stone. George Raft. 2008. 252p. per. 19.95 *(978-1-59393-123-0(9))* BearManor Media.

—George Raft Hb. 2008. 252p. 39.95 *(978-1-59393-204-6(9))* BearManor Media.

Wallack, Lester. Memories of Fifty Years. 2009. 118p. pap. *(978-0-217-23573-0(5))* Books LLC.

Washington, Isaiah. A Man from Another Land: How Finding My Roots Changed My Life. 2011. (ENG., Illus.). 304p. 24.99 *(978-1-59995-318-2(8))* Center St.

Wayne, Aissa. John Wayne, My Father. l.t. ed. 23.95 *(978-1-85695-150-0(2))* ISIS Large Print Bks. GBR. Dist: Transaction Pubs.

Wayne, John. The Legend & the Man: An Exclusive Look Inside the Duke's Archives. 2012. (ENG., Illus.). 240p. 45.00 *(978-1-57687-590-2(3))* powerHouse Cultural Entertainment, Inc.

Weaver, Tom. John Carradine: The Films. alt. ed. 2008. (ENG., Illus.). 408p. per. 39.95 *(978-0-7864-3778-8(2))* McFarland & Co., Inc. Pubs.

—Science Fiction Stars & Horror Heroes: Interviews with Actors, Directors, Producers & Writers of the 1940s Through 1960s. alt. ed. 2006. (ENG., Illus.). 462p. per. 32.00 *(978-0-7864-2857-1(0))* McFarland & Co., Inc. Pubs.

West, Timothy. I'm Here, I Think, Where Are You? Letters from a Touring Actor. l.t. ed. 240p. 24.95 *(978-1-85695-144-9(8))* ISIS Large Print Bks. GBR. Dist: Transaction Pubs.

West, Timothy & West, Sherrie. A Moment Towards the End of the Play. 2011. (ENG., Illus.). 336p. pap. 20.95 ***(978-1-84842-109-7(5)***, Hern, Nick Bks., Ltd. GBR. Dist: Consortium Bk. Sales & Distribution.

Whaley, George. Leo 'Rumpole' McKern: The Accidental Actor. 2008. (ENG., Illus.). 312p. pap. 25.99 *(978-1-921410-89-5(2)*, UNSW Press) NewSouth Publishing AUS. Dist: Independent Pubs. Group.

Wheaton, Wil. Just a Geek: Unflinchingly Honest Tales of the Search for Life, Love, & Fulfillment Beyond the Starship Enterprise. 2009. (ENG.). 298p. pap. 16.99 *(978-0-596-80631-6(0))* O'Reilly Media, Inc.

White, Betty. If You Ask Me (and of Course You Won't) 2011. (ENG., Illus.). 272p. (gr. 12). 25.95 *(978-0-399-15753-0(0)*, Putnam Adult) Penguin Group (USA) Inc.

Wilkinson, Tate. Memoirs of His Own Life. 2009. 158p. pap. *(978-0-217-85097-1(9))* Books LLC.

—Memoirs of His Own Life. 2009. 118p. pap. 19.99 *(978-1-150-57345-3(7))*; 120p. pap. 19.99 *(978-1-150-36115-9(3))* General Bks. LLC.

Williams, Vanessa & Williams, Helen. You Have No Idea: A Famous Daughter, Her No-nonsense Mother, & How They Survived Pageants, Hollywood, Love, Loss (and Each Other) 2012. (ENG., Illus.). 304p. (gr. 12). 28.00 ***(978-1-59240-707-1(2)***, Gotham) Penguin Group (USA) Inc.

Willing, Sharon Lee. No One to Cry To: A Long, Hard Ride into the Sunset with Foy Willing. 2006. (ENG., Illus.). 264p. per. 19.95 *(978-1-58736-686-4(X))* Wheatmark.

Winterstein, Andrew P. Athletic Training Student Primer: A Foundation for Success. 2nd ed. 2009. (ENG., Illus.). 336p. (C). pap. 54.95 *(978-1-55642-804-3(9))* SLACK, Inc.

Wirz, Mario. It's Late, I Can't Breathe: A Nocturnal Narrative. Meyer, Alfred G., ed. 2007. 131p. pap. 12.95 *(978-0-9788691-1-3(7))* Meyer, G Bks.

Wise, James E., et al. Stars in Blue: Movie Actors in America's Sea Services. 2007. (Bluejacket Bks.). (Illus.). 316p. per. 19.95 *(978-1-59114-944-6(4))* Naval Institute Pr.

Witcover, Walt. My Road, Less Traveled: Becoming an Actor, a Director, a Teacher. 2011. 526p. 34.99 ***(978-1-4568-3540-8(8))***; pap. 23.99 ***(978-1-4568-3539-2(4))*** Xlibris Corp.

Wood, Henry & Fedo, Michael. A Sawdust Heart: My Vaudeville Life in Medicine & Tent Shows. 2011. (Illus.). 144p. pap. 16.95 *(978-0-8166-7230-1(X))* Univ. of Minnesota Pr.

Yeoman, JoAnn. Dream Dealer Stuart Walker & the Ameri. 2007. 164p. per. 14.95 *(978-1-932842-22-7(5)*, Star Cloud Pr.) Cloudbank Creations, Inc.

Young, Alan. Mister Ed & Me & More! 2007. pap. 19.95 *(978-0-9797404-0-4(1))* Geordie Pr.

—There's No Business Like Show Business... Was. 2006. (Illus.). 108p. per. *(978-1-59393-053-0(4))* BearManor Media.

Yowarski, Tom Nicholas. Costumes & Characters: Adventures on the fringe of Success. 2011. 264p. pap. 27.95 ***(978-1-4626-2131-6(7))*** PublishAmerica, Inc.

Zecher, Henry. William Gillette, America's Sherlock Holmes. 2011. 734p. 34.99 ***(978-1-4535-5581-1(1))***; pap. 23.99 ***(978-1-4535-5580-4(3))*** Xlibris Corp.

Zigman, Charles. World's Coolest Movie Star: Comeback/Patriarch: The Complete 95 Films (and Legend) of Jean Gabin, Vol. 2. 2008. (Illus.). 532p. 39.95 *(978-0-9799722-1-8(3))* Allenwood Pr.

—World's Coolest Movie Star: Tragic Drifter: The Complete 95 Films (and Legend) of Jean Gabin, Vol. 1. 2008. (Illus.). 576p. 39.95 *(978-0-9799722-0-1(5))* Allenwood Pr.

Zimmer, Kim & Morton, Laura. I'm Just Sayin'! Three Deaths, Seven Husbands, & a Clone! My Life as a Daytime Diva. (ENG.). 320p. (gr. 12). 2012. 15.00 ***(978-0-451-23490-2(1)***, N A L Trade) 2011. (Illus.). 26.95 *(978-0-451-23343-1(3)*, N A L Hardcover) Penguin Group (USA) Inc.

ACTORS—CORRESPONDENCE

Eames, J. H. Forty Years on the Stage: Others & Myself. 2007. (ENG.). 384p. 48.95 *(978-0-548-06091-9(6))* Kessinger Publishing, LLC.

Calvert, Louis. Problems of the Actor. 2009. 138p. pap. 19.99 *(978-0-217-74397-6(8))* General Bks. LLC.

—Problems of the Actor. 2007. (ENG.). 304p. 43.95 *(978-0-548-10234-3(1))* Kessinger Publishing, LLC.

Carson, William G. B. Letters of Mr & Mrs Charles Kean Relating to Their American Tours. 2011. 208p. 44.95 ***(978-1-258-03892-2(7))*** Literary Licensing, LLC.

Coward, Noël. The Letters of Noel Coward. Day, Barry, ed. 2009. (Vintage Ser.). (ENG., Illus.). 800p. pap. 19.95 *(978-0-307-39100-1(0)*, Vintage) Knopf Doubleday Publishing Group.

Freeman, Bill. Glory Days: A Play & History of the '46 Stelco Strike. 2007. (ENG., Illus.). 96p. per. 18.95 *(978-0-88754-668-6(4))* Playwrights Canada Pr. CAN. Dist: Consortium Bk. Sales & Distribution.

Lazarovich-Hrebelianovich, Eleanor Hulda Calhoun. Pleasures & Palaces: The Memoirs of Princess Lazarovich Hrebelianovich, Eleanor Calhoun. 2007. (ENG.). 370p. 48.95 *(978-0-548-03845-1(7))* Kessinger Publishing, LLC.

Martin, Pete & Hope, Bob. Have Tux Will Travel: Bob Hope's Own Story. 2011. 320p. 50.95 ***(978-1-258-00800-0(9))*** Literary Licensing, LLC.

Morris, Clara. Stage Confidences. 2008. 164p. 22.99 *(978-0-554-33888-0(2))* 2008. 164p. 25.99 *(978-0-554-24585-0(X))* 2007. 144p. pap. 18.99 *(978-1-4264-6896-4(2))* 2006. (ENG.). 160p. pap. 21.99 *(978-1-4264-6978-7(0))* BiblioBazaar.

Poitier, Sidney. Life Beyond Measure: Letters to My Great-Granddaughter. 2009. (ENG.). 304p. pap. 16.99 *(978-0-06-149620-2(0)*, HarperOne) 2008. (Illus.). 304p. 25.95 *(978-0-06-149618-9(9)*, HarperOne) 2008. (ENG., Illus.). 400p. pap. 25.95 *(978-0-06-156279-2(3)*, HarperLuxe) HarperCollins Pubs.

Robinson, Canaan W. E. J. So... You're an Actor?! Prove It! Branding & Marketing for Today's Aspiring Actor. 2009. 261p. pap. 25.95 *(978-1-4327-4085-6(7))* Outskirts Pr., Inc.

Vandenhoff, George. Dramatic Reminiscences or Actors & Act. 2006. pap. 31.95 *(978-1-4286-3606-4(4))* Kessinger Publishing, LLC.

—Leaves from an Actor's Note-Book; with Reminiscences & Chit-Chat of the Green-Room & the Stage, in England & America by George VanDenhoff. 2006. 360p. per. 26.99 *(978-1-4255-3663-3(8))* MPublishing.

Wilson, Emily Herring, ed. Becoming Elizabeth Lawrence: Discovered Letters of a Southern Gardener. 2010. 224p. 19.95 *(978-0-89587-375-0(3))* Blair, John F. Pub.

ACTORS—JUVENILE LITERATURE

Hillstrom, Laurie. Robert Downey, Jr. 2011. (People in the News Ser.). 128p. (J). lib. bdg. 33.45 *(978-1-4205-0569-6(6)*, Lucent Bks.) Cengage Gale.

Kennon, Michou. Queen Latifah. 2011. (Hip-Hop Headliners Ser.). (Illus.). 32p. (J). (gr. 3-8). pap. 10.50 *(978-1-4339-4809-1(5))* Stevens, Gareth Publishing LLLP.

Leavitt, Amie Jane. Victoria Justice. 2010. (Robbie Reader Ser.). (Illus.). 32p. (YA). (gr. 2-5). lib. bdg. 25.70 *(978-1-58415-902-5(2))* Mitchell Lane Pubs., Inc.

Yasuda, Anita. Johnny Depp. 2012. (J). pap. ***(978-1-61913-591-8(4))*** Weigl Pubs., Inc.

ACTORS—PORTRAITS

Arbus, Amy. The Fourth Wall. 2008. (ENG., Illus.). 160p. 50.00 *(978-1-59962-044-2(8)*, Welcome Bks.) Welcome Enterprises, Inc.

Brosnan, Pierce, et al, texts. Degrees°. 2007. (ENG., Illus.). 180p. *(978-0-9546843-6-5(2))* Lewis, Dewi Media, Ltd.

Burnim, Kalman A. & Baskett, John. Brief Lives: Biographies of Sitters & Artists in the Garrick Club Collection. 2006. (ENG., Illus.). 192p. 65.00 *(978-0-906290-73-6(2))* Unicorn Pr., London GBR. Dist: National Bk. Network.

Cibber, Colley. Apology for the Life of Colley Cibber Written by Himself, 2 vols. Lowe, R. W., ed. rev. ed. reprint ed. 125.00 *(978-0-404-01544-2(1))* AMS Pr., Inc.

Crist Steve. Marilyn, Andre de Dienes, 2 vols. 2011. (ENG., Illus.). 848p. 39.99 *(978-3-8365-2710-1(3))* TASCHEN DEU. Dist: Ingram Pub. Services.

Dherbier, Yann-Brice. Steve McQueen. 2008. (Life in Pictures Ser.). (ENG., Illus.). 196p. 40.00 *(978-1-86205-814-9(8))* Anova Bks. GBR. Dist: Independent Pubs. Group.

Fontana, Ellen. Audrey 100: Eine traumhafte Reise in Bildern - ausgewählt von ihrer Familie. 2010. (ENG., Illus.). 192p. 40.00 *(978-1-4027-7836-0(8))* Sterling Publishing Co., Inc.

Frangioni, David. Clint Eastwood Icon: The Ultimate Film Art Collection. 2009. (ENG., Illus.). 240p. 39.95 *(978-1-933784-96-0(2)*, Insight Editions) Palace Publishing Group, LP.

Gorman, Greg, photos by. Greg Gorman: in Their Youth, Limited Edition. 2010. (ENG., Illus.). 280p. 750.00 *(978-88-6208-141-2(3))* Damiani ITA. Dist: D.A.P./Distributed Art Pubs.

Greene, Milton. Marilyn Monroe. 2007. (ENG., Illus.). 120p. 40.00 *(978-3-940004-02-4(2)*, Earbooks) edel classics GmbH DEU. Dist: AtlasBooks Distribution.

Hermes Press. Elizabeth Taylor: the Most Beautiful Woman in the World - A Photographic Biography: The Most Beautiful Woman in the World - A Photographic Biography. 2012. (Illus.). 160p. (YA). 49.99 *(978-1-932563-39-9(3))* Hermes Pr.

Porter, Lucy. Hairy Hunks: A Celebration of Shaggy Stallions. 2009. (ENG., Illus.). 160p. 10.95 *(978-0-8109-0646-4(5)*, Abrams Image) Abrams.

Robinson, Jack, photos by. Jack Robinson Portraits in Vogue. 2011. (ENG.). 192p. 39.95 ***(978-0-9564942-2-1(6))*** Palazzo Editions, Ltd. GBR. Dist: Independent Pubs. Group.

Stern, Bert. Marilyn Monroe: The Last Sitting. 2007. (ENG., Illus.). 128p. pap. 39.95 *(978-0-307-39164-3(7))* Random House Mondadori ESP. Dist: Random Hse., Inc.

Van Sant, Gus. One Step Big Shot. 2010. (Illus.). 29p. ***(978-1-59005-287-7(0))*** Nazraeli Pr.

White, Timothy. Hollywood Pinups. 2008. (ENG., Illus.). 80p. 39.95 *(978-0-06-134959-1(3)*, Collins Design) HarperCollins Pubs.

ACTORS—AUSTRALIA

Collis, Rose. Coral Browne: This Effing Lady' 2008. (ENG., Illus.). 288p. 50.00 *(978-1-84002-764-8(9))* Theatre Communications Group, Inc.

McShane, John. Heath Ledger: His Beautiful Life & Mysterious Death. 2008. (ENG., Illus.). 288p. pap. 17.95 *(978-1-84454-633-6(0))* Blake, John Publishing, Ltd. GBR. Dist: Independent Pubs. Group.

Robb, Brian J. Heath Ledger: Hollywood's Dark Star. 2008. (ENG., Illus.). 160p. pap. 19.95 *(978-0-85965-427-2(3))* Plexus Publishing, Ltd. GBR. Dist: Perseus-PGW.

Whaley, George. Leo 'Rumpole' McKern: The Accidental Actor. 2008. (ENG., Illus.). 312p. pap. 25.99 *(978-1-921410-89-5(2)*, UNSW Press) NewSouth Publishing AUS. Dist: Independent Pubs. Group.

ACTORS—FRANCE

Bernhardt, Sarah. My Double Life. 2008. 504p. 33.99 *(978-0-554-22945-4(5))*; 31.99 *(978-0-554-32248-3(X))* BiblioBazaar.

Caron, Leslie. Thank Heaven: A Memoir. 2010. (ENG.). 288p. (gr. 12). 16.00 *(978-0-452-29662-6(5)*, Plume) Penguin Group (USA) Inc.

Delmotte, Pascal & Delmotte, Annie. Bourvil: ça Va, Ils Sont Contents. 2010. (FRE., Illus.). 207p. *(978-2-08-124124-4(2))* Flammarion et Cie.

Knapp, Bettina. Marie Dorval: A Book for Actors: France's Theatrical Wonder. 2007. (Chiasma Ser.: 21). 234p. pap. 61.00 *(978-90-420-2132-7(2))* Rodopi.

Lassez, Sarah. Psychic Junkie: A Memoir. 2006. (ENG.). 336p. pap. 14.95 *(978-1-4169-1838-7(8))* Gallery Pr., The IRL. Dist: Simon & Schuster, Inc.

Lemonier, Marc. L'intégrale de Funès: Louis de Funès de a à Z: Tout, Tout, Tout Sur Louis de Funès, Ses Films, Ses Partenaires, Ses Réalisateurs, les Lieux Associés à Sa Carrière et à Sa Vie Familiale, Ses Amis, Sa Carrière Au Cabaret et Au Théâtre, Etc. 2010. (FRE., Illus.). 295p. *(978-2-258-08333-2(8))* Hors collection.

Menefee, David W. Sarah Bernhardt in the Theatre of Films & Sound Recordings. alt. ed. 2008. (FRE & ENG., Illus.). 168p. pap. 35.00 *(978-0-7864-3882-2(7))* McFarland & Co., Inc. Pubs.

Mitterrand, Frederic. The Bad Life: A Memoir. Browner, Jesse, tr. from FRE. 2010. (ENG.). 320p. pap. 16.95 *(978-1-59376-260-5(7)*, Soft Skull Pr.) Counterpoint LLC.

Zigman, Charles. World's Coolest Movie Star: Comeback/Patriarch: The Complete 95 Films (and Legend) of Jean Gabin, Vol. 2. 2008. (Illus.). 532p. 39.95 *(978-0-9799722-1-8(3))* Allenwood Pr.

—World's Coolest Movie Star: Tragic Drifter: The Complete 95 Films (and Legend) of Jean Gabin, Vol. 1. 2008. (Illus.). 576p. 39.95 *(978-0-9799722-0-1(5))* Allenwood Pr.

ACTORS—GERMANY

Bauer, Karoline. Posthumous Memoirs of Karoline Bauer. 2009. 420p. pap. 19.99 *(978-0-217-73944-3(X))* General Bks. LLC.

Chandler, Charlotte. Marlene: Marlene Dietrich, A Personal Biography. 2012. (ENG.). 304p. pap. 19.99 ***(978-1-55783-838-4(0)***, 1557838380, Applause Theatre & Cinema) Leonard, Hal Corp.

—Marlene: Marlene Dietrich, A Personal Biography. l.t. ed. 2011. 459p. 31.99 *(978-1-4104-3765-5(5))* Thorndike Pr.

Granach, Alexander. From the Shtetl to the Stage: The Odyssey of a Wandering Actor. 2010. (ENG.). 304p. pap. 29.95 *(978-1-4128-1347-1(6))* Transaction Pubs.

Hagen, Eva Maria. Eva und der Wolf. (GER.). *(978-3-612-26643-9(8))* Econ-Verlag GmbH DEU. Dist: International Bk. Import Service, Inc.

Klö, et al. Heiße West- und kalte Ost-Schauspieler? Diskurse, Praxen, Geschichte(n) zur Schauspielausbildung in Deutschland nach 1945. 2008. (GER., Illus.). 291p. *(978-3-940737-27-4(5))* interessengemeinschaft theater der zeit.

Mikhailov, Boris, photos by. Maquette Braunschweig, 1 vol. 2009. (ENG., Illus.). 224p. 68.00 *(978-3-86521-834-6(2))* Steidl, Gerhard Druckerei und Verlag DEU. Dist: Innovative Logistics.

Schall, Ekkehard. The Craft of Theatre: Seminars & Discussions in Brechtian Theatre. Davis, John, tr. from GER. 2012. (Biography & Autobiography Ser.). (ENG., Illus.). 224p. pap. 70.00 ***(978-1-4081-5989-7(9)***, Methuen Drama) A & C Black GBR. Dist: Macmillan.

Schall, Ekkehard & Davis, John. The Craft of Theatre: Seminars & Discussions in Brechtian Theatre. 2008. (Biography & Autobiography Ser.). (ENG., Illus.). 224p. 70.00 *(978-1-4081-0069-1(X)*, Methuen Drama) A & C Black GBR. Dist: Macmillan.

Voit, Jochen. Er rührte an den Schlaf der Welt. Ernst Busch: Die Biographie. 2010. (GER., Illus.). 515p. *(978-3-351-02716-2(8))* Aufbau-Verlag Gmbh.

Wirz, Mario. It's Late, I Can't Breathe: A Nocturnal Narrative. Meyer, Alfred G., ed. 2007. 131p. pap. 12.95 *(978-0-9788691-1-3(7))* Meyer, G. Bks.

ACTORS—GREAT BRITAIN

Allen, Keith. Grow Up. 2008. (ENG., Illus.). 384p. pap. 15.95 *(978-0-09-191071-6(4))* Ebury Publishing GBR. Dist: Independent Pubs. Group.

Appleton, William Worthen. Charles MacKlin: An Actor's Life. 2011. 296p. 48.95 ***(978-1-258-07144-8(4))*** Literary Licensing, LLC.

Archer, William. Henry Irving: Actor & Manager: A Critical Study. (Works of William Archer). 108p. reprint ed. lib. bdg. 59.00 *(978-0-932051-21-9(9))* Reprint Services Co.

Asbury, Nick. Exit, Pursued by a Badger: One Actor's Journey Through History at the RSC. 2010. (ENG., Illus.). 256p. pap. 20.95 *(978-1-84002-892-8(0))* Oberon Bks., Ltd. GBR. Dist: Consortium Bk. Sales & Distribution.

Bainbridge, Beryl. Front Row: Evenings at the Theatre. 2006. (ENG., Illus.). 224p. 34.95 *(978-0-8264-8278-5(3))* Continuum International Publishing Group, Ltd. GBR. Dist: National Bk. Network.

Baker, Henry Barton. History of the London Stage & Its Famous Players 1576-1903. 2007. (ENG.). 596p. 59.95 *(978-0-548-10334-0(8))* Kessinger Publishing, LLC.

—Our Old Actors. 2007. (ENG.). 472p. 52.95 *(978-0-548-11077-5(8))* Kessinger Publishing, LLC.

Barratt, Mark. Ian Mckellen: An Unofficial Biography. 2006. (ENG., Illus.). 288p. pap. 12.95 *(978-0-7535-1074-2(X))* Virgin Bks. Ltd. GBR. Dist: Independent Pubs. Group.

Barrowman, John & Barrowman, Carole E. Anything Goes. 2009. (ENG., Illus.). 256p. pap. 15.95 *(978-1-84317-333-5(6))* O'Mara, Michael Bks., Ltd. GBR. Dist: Independent Pubs. Group.

—Anything Goes: The Autobiography. 2008. (ENG., Illus.). 256p. 29.95 *(978-1-84317-289-5(5))* O'Mara, Michael Bks., Ltd. GBR. Dist: Independent Pubs. Group.

Barrowman, John & Barrowman, Carole E. I Am What I Am. (ENG., Illus.). 2010. 272p. pap. 12.95 ***(978-1-84317-493-6(6))*** 2009. 256p. 29.95 *(978-1-84317-379-3(4))* O'Mara, Michael Bks., Ltd. GBR. Dist: Independent Pubs. Group.

Bending, Stephen, et al, eds. Women's Theatrical Memoirs, Part II, 5 vols., Vols. 6-10. 2008. (Chawton House Library Series: Women's Memoirs Ser.). (ENG.). 2000p. 750.00 *(978-1-85196-875-6(X))* Pickering & Chatto Pubs., Ltd. GBR. Dist: Ashgate Publishing Co.

Blackhall, Sue. Bill Nighy: The Unauthorised Biography. 2010. (ENG., Illus.). 278p. 29.95 *(978-1-84454-867-5(8))* Blake, John Publishing, Ltd. GBR. Dist: Independent Pubs. Group.

Borgman, Albert S. & Mountfort, William. The Life & Death of William Mountfort. 2011. 242p. 46.95 ***(978-1-258-04877-8(9))*** Literary Licensing, LLC.

Bowyer, Alison. Dawn French: The Unauthorized Biography. 2008. (ENG., Illus.). 320p. mass mkt. 16.95 *(978-0-330-45452-0(8)*, Macmillan) Pan Macmillan GBR. Dist: Trans-Atlantic Pubns., Inc.

Brooke, W. H. The Biography of the British Stage: Being Correct Narratives of the Lives of All the Principal Actors & Actresses. 2007. (ENG.). 304p. 43.95 *(978-0-548-14942-3(9))*; (Illus.). per. 28.95 *(978-1-4304-4253-0(0))* Kessinger Publishing, LLC.

Brown, Len. Jason Statham: Taking Stock. 2012. (ENG., Illus.). 256p. 19.95 ***(978-1-4091-3265-3(X))*** Orion Bks. Ltd. GBR. Dist: Sterling Publishing Co., Inc.

Butters, Wes. Whatsisname: The Life & Death of Charles Hawtrey. 2010. (Illus.). 296p. 35.00 *(978-0-9557670-7-4(5))* Tomahawk Pr. GBR. Dist: Midpoint Trade Bks., Inc.

Callan, Michael Feeney. Arise Sir Anthony Hopkins: The Biography. 2008. (ENG., Illus.). 466p. pap. 15.95 *(978-1-84454-546-9(6))* Blake, John Publishing, Ltd. GBR. Dist: Independent Pubs. Group.

Callow, Simon. Love Is Where It Falls: An Account of a Passionate Friendship. 2007. (ENG.). 96p. per. 26.95 *(978-1-85459-976-6(3))* Hern, Nick Bks., Ltd. GBR. Dist: Consortium Bk. Sales & Distribution.

—My Life in Pieces. 2011. (ENG.). 320p. 40.00 ***(978-1-84842-054-0(4))*** Hern, Nick Bks., Ltd. GBR. Dist: Consortium Bk. Sales & Distribution.

—My Life in Pieces: An Alternative Autobiography. 2012. (ENG.). 448p. pap. 20.95 ***(978-1-84842-171-4(0))*** Hern, Nick Bks., Ltd. GBR. Dist: Consortium Bk. Sales & Distribution.

Capua, Michelangelo. Deborah Kerr: A Biography. 2010. (ENG., Illus.). 224p. pap. 35.00 *(978-0-7864-5882-0(8))* McFarland & Co., Inc. Pubs.

Carrigan, John. The Other Side of Harry: A schizophrenic Parent. 2008. 420p. pap. *(978-1-84747-680-7(5))* Chipmunkapublishing.

Challen, Paul. The House That Hugh Laurie Built: An Unauthorized Biography & Episode Guide. 2007. (ENG., Illus.). 240p. pap. 17.95 *(978-1-55022-803-8(X))* ECW Pr. CAN. Dist: Independent Pubs. Group.

Cibber, Colley. Apology for the Life of Colley Cibber Written by Himself, 2 vols. Lowe, R. W., ed. rev. ed. reprint ed. 125.00 *(978-0-404-01544-2(1))* AMS Pr., Inc.

Cohn, Albert. Shakespeare in Germany in the Sixteenth & Seventeenth Centuries. 2010. 430p. pap. *(978-1-151-81782-2(1))* Books LLC.

Cole, Julie Dawn & Esslinger, Michael. I Want It Now! a Memoir of Life on the Set of Willy Wonka & the Chocolate Factory. 2011. 252p. pap. 21.95 ***(978-1-59393-074-5(7))*** BearManor Media.

Collis, Rose. Coral Browne: This Effing Lady' 2008. (ENG., Illus.). 288p. 50.00 *(978-1-84002-764-8(9))* Theatre Communications Group, Inc.

Cook, Judy. Loving Peter: My Life with Peter Cook & Dudley Moore. 2010. (ENG., Illus.). 320p. pap. 14.95 *(978-0-7499-2947-3(2))* Piatkus Bks. GBR. Dist: Independent Pubs. Group.

Cook, Judy & Levin, Angela. Loving Peter: My Life with Peter Cook & Dudley Moore. 2008. (ENG., Illus.). 288p. 32.95 *(978-0-7499-0966-6(8))* Piatkus Bks. GBR. Dist: Independent Pubs. Group.

Coward, Noël. The Letters of Noel Coward. Day, Barry, ed. 2009. (Vintage Ser.). (ENG., Illus.). 800p. pap. 19.95 *(978-0-307-39100-1(0)*, Vintage) Knopf Doubleday Publishing Group.

Croall, Jonathan. John Gielgud: Matinee Idol to Movie Star. 2011. (Biography & Autobiography Ser.). (ENG., Illus.). 688p. 45.00 *(978-1-4081-3106-0(4)*, Methuen Drama) A & C Black GBR. Dist: Macmillan.

Cunningham, Peter. The Story of Nell Gwyn & the Sayings of Charles II. 2009. 222p. 28.99 *(978-1-110-53562-0(7))*; pap. 23.75 *(978-1-110-53559-0(7))* BiblioBazaar.

Darbyshire, Alfred. The Art of the Victorian Stage. 2009. 126p. pap. 19.99 *(978-1-150-50949-0(X))* General Bks. LLC.

David, Deirdre. Fanny Kemble: A Performed Life. 2007. (Illus.). 376p. (C). 39.95 *(978-0-8122-4023-8(5))* Univ. of Pennsylvania Pr.

Davis, Warwick. Size Matters Not: The Extraordinary Life & Career of Warwick Davis. 2011. (ENG., Illus.). 416p. 24.95 ***(978-0-470-91466-3(1)***, Wiley) Wiley, John & Sons, Inc.

Dench, Judi. And Furthermore. 2011. (ENG., Illus.). 288p. 26.99 *(978-0-312-65906-6(7))* St. Martin's Pr.

—And Furthermore. l.t. ed. 2011. 351p. 32.99 ***(978-1-4104-3863-8(5))*** Thorndike Pr.

Dench, Judi & Miller, John. Scenes from My Life. 2007. (ENG., Illus.). 224p. pap. 24.95 *(978-1-84188-266-6(6)*, Weidenfeld & Nicolson) Orion Publishing Group, Ltd. GBR. Dist: Independent Pubs. Group.

Dickens, Charles. Memoirs of Joseph Grimaldi. 2008. (ENG.). 352p. pap. 22.95 *(978-1-901285-94-9(4))* Pushkin Pr., Ltd. GBR. Dist: Consortium Bk. Sales & Distribution.

Doran. Their Majesties' Servants or Annals of the English Stage from Thomas Betterton to Edmund Kean; Actors, Authors, Audiences. 2007. (ENG.). 468p. 52.95 *(978-0-548-03469-9(9))* Kessinger Publishing, LLC.

Doran, John. Their Majesties' Servants: Or Annals of the English Stage, 3 vols. Lowe, R. W., ed. reprint ed. 185.00 *(978-0-404-02170-2(0))* AMS Pr., Inc.

Ewbank, Tim & Hildred, Stafford. Joanna Lumley: The Unauthorized Biography. 2nd ed. 2010. (ENG., Illus.). 262p. pap. 14.95 *(978-0-233-00305-4(3))* Andre Deutsch GBR. Dist: Independent Pubs. Group.

Fisher, John. Tony Hancock: The Definitive Biography. 2009. (ENG., Illus.). 656p. pap. 16.95 *(978-0-00-726678-4(2))* HarperCollins Pubs. Ltd. GBR. Dist: Independent Pubs. Group.

Foulkes, Richard, ed. Henry Irving: A Re-Evaluation of the Pre-Eminent Victorian Actor Manager. 2008. (Nineteenth Century Ser.). (Illus.). 228p. 99.95 *(978-0-7546-5829-0(5))* Ashgate Publishing Co.

Gill, Peter. Apprenticeship. 2009. (ENG.). 128p. 18.95 *(978-1-84002-871-3(8))* Oberon Bks., Ltd. GBR. Dist: Consortium Bk. Sales & Distribution.

Goff, Moira. The Incomparable Hester Santlow: A Dancer-Actress on the Georgian Stage. 2007. (Performance in the Long Eighteenth Century: Studies in Theatre, Music, Dance Ser.). (Illus.). 218p. 114.95 *(978-0-7546-5805-4(8))* Ashgate Publishing Co.

Goodall, Nigel. David Tennant. 2011. (ENG., Illus.). 264p. pap. 12.95 *(978-1-84358-187-1(6))* Blake, John Publishing, Ltd. GBR. Dist: Independent Pubs. Group.

Haill, Lyn, ed. Actors Speaking. 2008. (ENG., Illus.). 140p. pap. 26.95 *(978-1-84002-776-1(2))* Theatre Communications Group, Inc.

Hanson, Bruce K. Peter Pan on Stage & Screen, 1904-2010. 2nd rev. ed. 2011. (ENG., Illus.). 417p. pap. 45.00 *(978-0-7864-4778-7(8))* McFarland & Co., Inc. Pubs.

Hatton, Joseph. Henry Irving's Impressions of America: Narrated in a Series of Sketches, Chronicles, & Conversations. 2007. (Travel in America Ser.). (ENG.). 496p. 49.95 *(978-1-4290-0456-5(8))*; per. 24.95 *(978-1-4290-0457-2(6))* Applewood Bks.

Holroyd, Michael. A Strange Eventful History: The Dramatic Lives of Ellen Terry, Henry Irving, & Their Remarkable Families. 2010. (ENG., Illus.). 656p. pap. 28.00 *(978-0-312-42949-2(5))* Picador.

James, Emmett. Admit One: My Life in Film. 2010. 19.95 *(978-0-9842581-0-9(8))* FizzyPop.

Johns, Kevin. Oh Yes It Is! Read, Peter, ed. 2008. (ENG., Illus.). 188p. pap. 18.95 ***(978-1-84771-061-1(1))*** Y Lolfa GBR. Dist: Dufour Editions, Inc.

Joncus, Berta & Barlow, Jeremy. Stage's Glory: John Rich (1692-1761) 2011. (ENG., Illus.). 296p. 75.00 *(978-1-61149-032-9(4))* Univ. of Delaware Pr.

Joncus, Berta & Barlow, Jeremy, eds. Stage's Glory: John Rich (1692-1761) 2011. *(978-0-87413-070-6(0))* Univ. of Delaware Pr.

Jones, Cambridge, et al. Off Stage: 100 Portraits Celebrating the Rada Centenary. 2006. (ENG., Illus.). 160p. 35.00 *(978-0-9546843-2-7(X))* Lewis, Dewi Publishing GBR. Dist: Consortium Bk. Sales & Distribution.

Kahan, Gerald. George Alexander Stevens & the Lecture on Heads. 2008. (ENG.). 232p. pap. 22.95 *(978-0-8203-3264-2(X))* Univ. of Georgia Pr.

Kahan, Jeffrey. Bettymania & the Birth of Celebrity Culture. 2010. (ENG.). 1p. 42.50 *(978-1-61146-069-8(7))*; (Illus.). 226p. 42.50 *(978-0-9821313-6-7(4))* Lehigh Univ. Pr.

—The Cult of Kean. 2006. (Illus.). 204p. 110.00 *(978-0-7546-5650-0(0))* Ashgate Publishing Co.

Kashner, Sam & Schoenberger, Nancy. Furious Love: Elizabeth Taylor, Richard Burton, & the Marriage of the Century. (ENG.). 320p. 2011. pap. 16.99 *(978-0-06-156285-3(8)*, Harper Paperbacks) 2010. (Illus.). 27.99 *(978-0-06-156284-6(X))* HarperCollins Pubs.

—Furious Love: Elizabeth Taylor, Richard Burton, & the Marriage of the Century. l.t. ed. 2010. (Illus.). 652p. 32.99 *(978-1-4104-2985-8(7))* Thorndike Pr.

Kelly, Michael. Reminiscences of Michael Kelly, of the King's Theatre, & Theatre Royal Drury Lane: Including a Period of Nearly Half a Century. 2011. (Cambridge Library Collection - Music Ser.). (ENG.). 386p. pap. 31.99 ***(978-1-108-03872-0(7))*** Cambridge Univ. Pr.

Kemble, Fanny. Journal: Volume 1. 2009. (Cambridge Library Collection - History Ser.). (ENG.). 324p. pap. 19.99 *(978-1-108-00391-9(5))* Cambridge Univ. Pr.

—Journal: Volume 2. 2009. (Cambridge Library Collection - History Ser.). (ENG.). 296p. pap. 17.99 *(978-1-108-00392-6(3))* Cambridge Univ. Pr.

Lapotaire, Jane. Everybody's Daughter, Nobody's Child. 2007. (ENG.). 384p. pap. 13.95 *(978-1-84408-416-6(7)*, Virago Press) Little, Brown Bk. Group Ltd. GBR. Dist: Independent Pubs. Group.

Lauder, Harry. Between You & Me. 2008. 216p. 24.99 *(978-0-554-36293-9(7))* 2008. 216p. 27.99 *(978-0-554-26990-0(2))* 2007. (ENG.). 198p. pap. 19.99 *(978-1-4346-2286-0(X))* 2007. (ENG.). 212p. pap. 22.99 *(978-1-4346-2344-7(0))* BiblioBazaar.

—Between You & Me. 2007. (ENG.). 196p. per. *(978-1-4065-3580-8(X))* Dodo Pr.

Lawson, Leigh. The Dream: An Actor's Tale. 2009. (ENG.). 200p. pap. 30.95 *(978-1-84002-867-6(X))* Oberon Bks., Ltd. GBR. Dist: Consortium Bk. Sales & Distribution.

Lee, Anna & Roisman Cooper, Barbara. Anna Lee: Memoir of a Career on General Hospital & in Film. 2007. (ENG., Illus.). 322p. per. 35.00 *(978-0-7864-3161-8(X))* McFarland & Co., Inc. Pubs.

Limon, Jerzy. Gentlemen of a Company: English Players in Central & Eastern Europe, 1590-1660. 2009. (ENG., Illus.). 204p. pap. 33.99 *(978-0-521-11509-4(4))* Cambridge Univ. Pr.

Lindfors, Bernth, ed. Ira Aldridge: The African Roscius. 2007. (Rochester Studies in African History & the Diaspora Ser.: Volume 28). (Illus.). 304p. 55.00 *(978-1-58046-258-7(8))* Univ. of Rochester Pr.

Lipman, Maureen. Past-It Notes. 2008. (ENG., Illus.). 480p. 36.95 *(978-1-906217-75-4(0))* Aurum Pr., Ltd. GBR. Dist: Independent Pubs. Group.

Lissenden, Hilary & Dunmore, Simon. Actors' Yearbook 2011: Essential Contacts for Stage, Screen & Radio. 2010. (ENG., Illus.). 512p. pap. 24.95 *(978-1-4081-2840-4(3))* A & C Black GBR. Dist: Macmillan.

Lord, Graham. Joan Collins: The Biography of an Icon. 2008. (ENG., Illus.). 424p. pap. 19.95 *(978-0-7528-9350-1(5))* Orion Publishing Group, Ltd. GBR. Dist: Independent Pubs. Group.

Lyon, Nicola. Henry the Great: An Entertainment for Five Actors Celebrating the Life & Art of Sir Henry Irving. 2007. (Illus.). 81p. *(978-1-905886-79-1(9))* Troubadour Publishing Ltd.

Macnee, Patrick & Rogers, Dave. The Avengers: The Inside Story. 2008. (ENG., Illus.). 144p. 24.95 *(978-1-84576-643-6(1)*, Titan Bks.) Titan Bks. Ltd. GBR. Dist: Random Hse., Inc.

Marshall, Christabel. Ellen Terry's Memoirs. 2008. 380p. *(978-1-4437-4071-5(3)*, Obscure Pr.) Read Bks.

Marshall, Gail, ed. Lives of Shakespearian Actors, 3 vols., Vol. 1, Pt. II. 2009. (Lives of Shakespearian Actors Ser.). (ENG.). 1312p. 495.00 *(978-1-85196-852-7(0))* Pickering & Chatto Pubs., Ltd. GBR. Dist: Ashgate Publishing Co.

—Lives of Shakespearian Actors: Part I, 3 vols., Set. 2008. (Major Works Ser.). (ENG., Illus.). 1200p. 247.50 *(978-1-85196-853-4(9))* Pickering & Chatto Pubs., Ltd. GBR. Dist: Ashgate Publishing Co.

Melville, Joy. Ellen Terry & Smallhythe Place (Kent) 2006. (National Trust Guidebooks Ser.). (ENG., Illus.). 32p. pap. 9.95 *(978-1-84359-134-4(0))* History Pr. Ltd.,The GBR. Dist: Independent Pubs. Group.

Munn, Michael. Lord Larry: Personal Portrait of Laurence Olivier. 2007. (ENG., Illus.) 320p. 24.95 *(978-1-86105-977-2(9))* Anova Bks. GBR. Dist: Independent Pubs. Group.

—Richard Burton: Prince of Players. 2008. (ENG.). 272p. 24.95 *(978-1-60239-355-4(9)*, 239355) Skyhorse Publishing Co., Inc.

Oddie, Bill & Odie, Bill. One Flew into the Cuckoo's Egg: My Autobiography. 2009. (ENG., Illus.). 320p. pap. 15.95 *(978-0-340-95194-1(X)*, Hodder & Stoughton) Hodder General Publishing Div. GBR. Dist: Independent Pubs. Group.

Paige, Elaine. Memories. 2009. (ENG., Illus.). 144p. 50.00 *(978-1-84002-852-2(1))* Oberon Bks., Ltd. GBR. Dist: Consortium Bk. Sales & Distribution.

Palin, Michael. Diaries 1969-1979: the Python Years. 2008. (ENG., Illus.). 672p. pap. 21.99 *(978-0-312-38488-3(2)*, St. Martin's Griffin) St. Martin's Pr.

—Halfway to Hollywood: Diaries, 1980-1988. 2011. (ENG., Illus.). 680p. 32.50 *(978-0-312-68202-6(6)*, Dunne, Thomas Bks.) St. Martin's Pr.

Paterson, Bill. Tales from the Back Green. (ENG., Illus.). 2009. 160p. pap. 13.95 *(978-0-340-93682-5(7))* 2008. 154p. 25.95 *(978-0-340-93681-8(9))* Hodder General Publishing Div. GBR. (Hodder & Stoughton). Dist: Independent Pubs. Group.

Pearson, Hesketh. Modern Men & Mummers. 2008. 224p. 24.99 *(978-0-559-52361-8(0))*; pap. 24.75 *(978-0-559-52360-1(2))* BiblioBazaar.

—Modern Men & Mummers. 2009. 112p. pap. *(978-1-150-08174-3(0))* Books LLC.

—Modern Men & Mummers. 2008. 220p. 39.95 *(978-1-4365-1360-9(X))* 2007. (ENG.). 224p. per. 24.95 *(978-0-548-74386-7(X))* Kessinger Publishing, LLC.

—Modern Men & Mummers. 2008. 220p. pap. *(978-1-4086-8806-9(9))* Read Bks.

Planché, J. R. The Recollections & Reflections of J. R. Planché: A Professional Autobiography. 2011. (Cambridge Library Collection - Music Ser.). (ENG.). 338p. pap. 28.99 ***(978-1-108-03883-6(2))***; (Illus.). 342p. pap. 28.99 ***(978-1-108-03882-9(4))*** Cambridge Univ. Pr.

Playfair, Giles. Kean: Paradoxical Genius. 2007. (ENG.). 376p. 48.95 *(978-0-548-06289-0(7))* Kessinger Publishing, LLC.

Porter, Darwin & Moseley, Roy. Damn You, Scarlett O'Hara: The Private Lives of Vivien Leigh & Laurence Olivier. 2011. (ENG., Illus.). 708p. 27.95 *(978-1-936003-15-0(5))* Blood Moon Productions, Ltd.

Postlethwaite, Pete. A Spectacle of Dust. 2011. (ENG., Illus.). 288p. 35.00 ***(978-0-297-86493-6(9))*** Orion Publishing Group, Ltd. GBR. Dist: Independent Pubs. Group.

—A Spectacle of Dust: The Autobiography. 2012. (ENG., Illus.). 288p. 16.95 ***(978-1-78022-003-1(0)***, Phoenix) Orion Publishing Group, Ltd. GBR. Dist: Independent Pubs. Group.

Power. Breaking Free. 2009. (ENG.). 112p. pap. 16.95 ***(978-1-84694-171-9(7))*** Hunt, John Publishing Ltd. GBR. Dist: National Bk. Network.

Rathbone, Basil. In & Out of Character: An Autobiography. 2011. 304p. 48.95 ***(978-1-258-00573-3(5))*** Literary Licensing, LLC.

Read, Piers Paul. Alec Guinness: The Authorised Biography. 2011. (ENG.). 640p. pap. 36.99 *(978-1-4516-3644-4(X))* Simon & Schuster.

Richards, Jeffrey. Sir Henry Irving: A Victorian Actor & His World. 2007. (ENG., Illus.). 508p. per. 29.95 *(978-1-85285-591-8(6)*, Hambledon Continuum) Continuum International Publishing Group, Ltd. GBR. Dist: National Bk. Network.

Roache, William. 50 Years on the Street: My Life with Ken Barlow. 2010. (ENG., Illus.). 240p. 27.95 *(978-1-84596-655-3(4))* Mainstream Publishing Co., Ltd. GBR. Dist: Independent Pubs. Group.

Roberts, David. Thomas Betterton: The Greatest Actor of the Restoration Stage. 2010. (Illus.). 270p. 95.00 *(978-0-521-19584-3(5))* Cambridge Univ. Pr.

Robins, Edward. The Palmy Days of Nance Oldfield. 2008. 240p. 24.99 *(978-0-554-33327-4(9))* 2008. 240p. 27.99 *(978-0-554-24024-4(6))* 2007. (ENG.). 208p. pap. 20.99 *(978-1-4264-5590-2(9))* 2006. 236p. pap. 22.99 *(978-1-4264-5638-1(7))* BiblioBazaar.

—The Palmy Days of Nance Oldfield. 2009. 228p. pap. *(978-1-4099-7984-5(9))* Dodo Pr.

—The Palmy Days of Nance Oldfield. 2007. (ENG.). 156p. per. *(978-1-4068-3948-7(5))* Echo Library.

Robinson, Mary. Beaux & Belles of England: Mrs. Mary Robinson, Written by Herself, with the lives of the Duchesses of Gordon & Devonshire. 2006. 222p. pap. 22.99 *(978-1-4264-3752-6(8))*; 200p. pap. 19.99 *(978-1-4264-3695-6(5))* BiblioBazaar.

Sanderson, Michael. From Irving to Olivier. (Illus.). 375p. *(978-0-485-11252-8(3))* Continuum International Publishing Group, Ltd.

Setzer, Sharon M., et al, eds. Women's Theatrical Memoirs, Part I, 5 vols., Vols. 1-5. 2007. (Chawton House Library Ser.). (ENG.). 2000p. 750.00 *(978-1-85196-861-9(X))* Pickering & Chatto Pubs., Ltd. GBR. Dist: Ashgate Publishing Co.

Sher, A. Beside Myself. 2010. (ENG., Illus.). 412p. pap. 22.95 *(978-1-84842-035-9(8))* Hern, Nick Bks., Ltd. GBR. Dist: Consortium Bk. Sales & Distribution.

Sher, Antony. Year of the King: An Actor's Diary & Sketchbook. 20th anniv. ed 2006. (ENG., Illus.). 254p. per. 19.99 *(978-0-87910-335-4(3)*, 0879103353, Limelight Editions) Leonard, Hal Corp.

Sinai, Anne. Reach for the Top: The Turbulent Life of Laurence Harvey. Sinai, Anne, ed. 2007. (Scarecrow Filmmakers Ser.). (ENG., Illus.). 408p. pap. 35.00 *(978-0-8108-5914-2(9))* Scarecrow Pr., Inc.

Southern, Antonia. Player, Playwright & Preacher's Kid: The Story of Nathan Field 1587-1620. 2009. (Illus.). 252p. pap. *(978-1-84748-527-4(8))* Athena Pr.

Stevens, Christopher. Born Brilliant: The Life of Kenneth Williams. (ENG., Illus.). 2011. 448p. pap. 16.95 *(978-1-84854-197-9(X))* 2010. 416p. pap. 22.95 *(978-1-84854-196-2(1))* Murray, John GBR. Dist: Independent Pubs. Group.

Susi, Lolly. Conversations with George Hall. 2010. (ENG., Illus.). 112p. 20.95 ***(978-1-84002-989-5(7))*** Oberon Bks., Ltd. GBR. Dist: Consortium Bk. Sales & Distribution.

Terry, Ellen. Ellen Terry's Memoirs. Craig, Edith & St. John, Christopher, eds. 2011. 406p. 54.95 ***(978-1-258-07315-2(3))*** Literary Licensing, LLC.

Terry, Ellen. The Story of My Life (Terry) Recollections & Reflections. 2007. (ENG.). 354p. pap. 25.99 *(978-1-4346-2309-6(2))*; 394p. pap. 26.99 *(978-1-4346-2367-6(X))* BiblioBazaar.

Varley, Julia. Notes from an Odin Actress. 2010. (ENG., Illus.). 208p. 110.00 *(978-0-415-58628-3(3))*; pap. 32.95 *(978-0-415-58629-0(1))* Routledge.

West, Timothy & West, Sherrie. A Moment Towards the End of the Play. 2011. (ENG., Illus.). 336p. pap. 20.95 ***(978-1-84842-109-7(5))*** Hern, Nick Bks., Ltd. GBR. Dist: Consortium Bk. Sales & Distribution.

Whaley, George. Leo 'Rumpole' McKern: The Accidental Actor. 2008. (ENG., Illus.). 312p. pap. 25.99 *(978-1-921410-89-5(2)*, UNSW Press) NewSouth Publishing AUS. Dist: Independent Pubs. Group.

Wilkinson, Tate. Memoirs of His Own Life. 2009. 158p. pap. *(978-0-217-85097-1(9))* Books LLC.

—Memoirs of His Own Life. 2009. 120p. pap. 19.99 *(978-1-150-36115-9(8))*; 118p. pap. 19.99 *(978-1-150-57345-3(7))* General Bks. LLC.

ACTORS—GREECE

Csapo, Eric. Actors & Icons of the Ancient Theater. 2010. (ENG., Illus.). 248p. 128.95 *(978-1-4051-3536-8(0)*, Wiley-Blackwell) Wiley, John & Sons, Inc.

Easterling, Pat & Hall, Edith, eds. Greek & Roman Actors: Aspects of an Ancient Profession. 2007. (ENG., Illus.). 544p. pap. 69.00 *(978-0-521-04550-6(9))* Cambridge Univ. Pr.

ACTORS—IRELAND

Brunström, Conrad. Thomas Sheridan's Career & Influence: An Actor in Earnest. 2011. ix, 151p. *(978-0-8387-5777-2(4))*; (ENG.). 168p. 60.00 *(978-1-61148-038-2(8))* Bucknell Univ. Pr.

Cassin, Barry. I Never Had a Proper Job. 2012. (ENG.). 240p. pap. 29.95 ***(978-1-907593-40-6(3))*** Liberties Pr. IRL. Dist: Dufour Editions, Inc.

Macken, Ultan. Walter Macken: Dreams on Paper. 2010. (ENG., Illus.). 448p. 47.95 *(978-1-85635-630-5(2))* Mercier Pr., Ltd., The IRL. Dist: Dufour Editions, Inc.

Membery, York. Pierce Brosnan: The Biography. 2nd ed. (Illus.). 272p. *(978-1-85227-967-7(2))* Virgin Bks. Ltd.

Terkel, Studs. The Studs Terkel Interviews: Film & Theater. 2008. (ENG.). 364p. pap. 16.95 *(978-1-59558-359-8(9))* New Pr., The.

ACTORS—ITALY

Csapo, Eric. Actors & Icons of the Ancient Theater. 2010. (ENG., Illus.). 248p. 128.95 *(978-1-4051-3536-8(0)*, Wiley-Blackwell) Wiley, John & Sons, Inc.

Easterling, Pat & Hall, Edith, eds. Greek & Roman Actors: Aspects of an Ancient Profession. 2007. (ENG., Illus.). 544p. pap. 69.00 *(978-0-521-04550-6(9))* Cambridge Univ. Pr.

McLeod, Addison. Plays & Players in Modern Italy. 2009. 396p. 38.99 *(978-1-117-05131-4(5))*; pap. 32.75 *(978-1-117-05132-1(3))* BiblioBazaar.

—Plays & Players in Modern Italy. 2009. 224p. pap. 19.84 *(978-1-150-69482-0(3))* General Bks. LLC.

—Plays & Players in Modern Italy. 2007. (ENG.). 392p. per. *(978-1-4067-4535-1(9))* Read Bks.

ACTORS—SOVIET UNION

Ignatieva, Maria. Stanislavsky & Female Actors: Women in Stanislavsky's Life & Art. 2008. (ENG.). 140p. pap. 29.50 *(978-0-7618-4103-6(2))* Univ. Pr. of America, Inc.

Kafanova, Liudmila & Martinson, Sergei. Martinson S Dvukh Tochek Zrenila. 2009. (Illus.). 210p. pap. *(978-0-9821973-3-2(0))* Seagul Pr.

Kotlerman, Ber Boris. In Search of Milk & Honey: The Theater of Soviet Jewish Statehood (1934-49) 2009. (ENG., Illus.). 318p. pap. 29.95 *(978-0-89357-347-8(7))* Slavica Pubs.

Stanislavski, Konstantin & Benedetti, Jean, trs. from RUS. My Life in Art. 2008. (Illus.). 452p. 40.95 *(978-0-415-43657-1(5))* Routledge.

ACTORS—JAPAN

Edelson, Loren. Danjuro's Girls: Women on the Kabuki Stage. 2009. (Palgrave Studies in Theatre & Performance History Ser.). (ENG., Illus.). 280p. 105.00 *(978-0-230-60346-4(5))* Palgrave Macmillan.

Miyao, Daisuke. Sessue Hayakawa: Silent Cinema & Transnational Stardom. 2007. (ENG., Illus.). 400p. 94.95 *(978-0-8223-3958-8(7))*; pap. 26.95 *(978-0-8223-3969-4(2))* Duke Univ. Pr.

ACTORS—SPAIN

Aguirre Carballeira, Arantxa & Aguirre, Arantxa. 34 Actores Hablan de Su Oficio. (SPA., Illus.). 679p. *(978-84-376-2505-8(X))* Ediciones Cátedra.

ACTORS—UNITED STATES

Aames, Willie, et al. Grace Is Enough. 2007. (ENG., Illus.). 307p. 19.99 *(978-0-8054-4379-0(7)*, B&H Bks.) B&H Publishing Group.

Alda, Alan. Never Have Your Dog Stuffed: And Other Things I've Learned. 2007. (Illus.). 224p. 25.00 *(978-1-4223-6612-7(X))* DIANE Publishing Co.

—Never Have Your Dog Stuffed: And Other Things I've Learned. 2006. (ENG., Illus.). 272p. per. 14.95 *(978-0-8129-7440-9(9)*, Random Hse. Trade Paperbacks) Random House Publishing Group.

—Things I Overheard While Talking to Myself. 2008. (ENG.). 256p. pap. 15.00 *(978-0-8129-7752-3(1)*, Random Hse. Trade Paperbacks) Random House Publishing Group.

Alessio, Jim. The Eternal Flapper. 2009. 376p. 29.50 *(978-1-4389-6129-3(4))* AuthorHouse.

—The Eternal Flapper: The Many Lives of Edna Wallace Hopper. 2009. 376p. pap. 19.95 *(978-1-4389-6128-6(6))* AuthorHouse.

Andersen, Christopher. Somewhere in Heaven: The Remarkable Love Story of Dana & Christopher Reeve. 2009. (ENG.). 272p. mass mkt. 7.99 *(978-0-7868-9130-6(0))* Hyperion Pr.

—Somewhere in Heaven: The Remarkable Love Story of Dana & Christopher Reeve. l.t. ed. 2008. (Illus.). 353p. (YA). 32.95 *(978-1-4104-0905-8(8))* Thorndike Pr.

Anderson, Arthur. An Actor's Odyssey: From Orson Welles to Lucky the Leprechaun. 2010. 228p. pap. 19.95 *(978-1-59393-522-1(6))* BearManor Media.

Anderson, Melissa. The Way I See It: A Look Back at My Life on Little House. 2011. (ENG., Illus.). 256p. pap. 16.95 *(978-0-7627-7050-2(3))* Globe Pequot Pr., The.

Antoniades, Andrew & Siegel, Mike. Steve Mcqueen: The Actor & His Films. 2011. (ENG., Illus.). 492p. 69.00 ***(978-1-85443-253-7(2)***, 1854432532) Dalton Watson Fine Bks.

Archer, Stephen M. Junius Brutus Booth: Theatrical Prometheus. 2010. 346p. E-Book *(978-0-8093-8592-8(9))* Southern Illinois Univ. Pr.

Arness, James & Wise, James E., Jr. James Arness: An Autobiography. l.t. alt. ed. 2008. (ENG., Illus.). 344p. pap. 39.95 *(978-0-7864-3316-2(7)*, McFarland & Co., Inc. Pubs.

Arngrim, Alison. Confessions of a Prairie Bitch: How I Survived Nellie Oleson & Learned to Love Being Hated. 2010. (ENG.). 320p. 25.99 *(978-0-06-196214-1(7))* HarperCollins Pubs.

Atkins, Rick. Among the Rugged Peaks: An Intimate Biography of Carla Laemmle. 2009. (Illus.). 221p. pap. ***(978-1-887664-91-2(2))*** Midnight Marquee Pr., Inc.

Bahr, Iris. Dork Whore: My Travels Through Asia as a Twenty-Year-Old Pseudo-Virgin. 2007. (ENG.). 224p. pap. 13.95 *(978-1-59691-234-2(0))* Bloomsbury Publishing.

—Machu My Picchu: Searching for Sex, Sanity, & a Soul Mate in South America. 2011. (ENG., Illus.). 256p. pap. 14.95 *(978-0-7627-7277-3(8)*, skirt!) Globe Pequot Pr., The.

Barton, Ruth. Hedy Lamarr: The Most Beautiful Woman in Film. 2010. (Screen Classics Ser.). (ENG., Illus.). 312p. 29.95 *(978-0-8131-2604-3(5))* Univ. Pr. of Kentucky.

Bean, Orson. Mail for Mikey. 2008. (ENG.). 128p. 18.95 *(978-1-56980-350-9(1))* Barricade Bks., Inc.

Beaver, Jim. Life's That Way. 2010. (ENG.). 336p. (gr. 12-18) 15.00 *(978-0-425-23250-7(6)*, Berkley Trade) Penguin Group (USA) Inc.

Beecher, Elizabeth. Roy Rogers, King of the Cowboys. 2011. 350p. 51.95 ***(978-1-258-03740-6(8))*** Literary Licensing, LLC.

Berg, Gertrude. Molly & Me. 22.95 *(978-0-88411-098-9(2))* Amereon LTD.

Birkenhead, Peter. Gonville: A Memoir. 272p. 2011. pap. 15.00 *(978-1-4165-9884-8(7))* 2010. (ENG.). 25.00 *(978-1-4165-9883-1(9))* Free Pr. (Free Pr.).

Black, Lewis. Me of Little Faith. 2008. (ENG.). 256p. (gr. 12-18). 24.95 *(978-1-59448-994-5(7)*, Riverhead Bks. (Hardcover)) Penguin Group (USA) Inc.

Blackman, Joni. George Clooney: A Biography, 1 vol. 2009. (Greenwood Biographies Ser.). (Illus.). 158p. 35.00 *(978-0-313-35826-5(5)*, GR5826) Greenwood Publishing Group, Inc.

Blitz, Michael & Krasniewicz, Louise. Arnold Schwarzenegger: A Biography, 1 vol. 2006. (Greenwood Biographies Ser.). (Illus.). 192p. 29.95 *(978-0-313-33810-6(8)*, GR3810, Greenwood Pr.) Greenwood Publishing Group, Inc.

Bonvillain, Keifer, told to. Ruthless: Media Mogul Call FBI to Silence Employee's Taped Confessions. 2008. 324p. pap. 24.99 *(978-0-9801049-0-5(4))* Keifer Publishing LLC.

Booth, Rupert. Not a Number: Patrick McGoohan - A Life. 2011. (ENG.). 238p. pap. 28.95 ***(978-0-9566329-2-0(0))*** Aurora Metro Pubns. Ltd. GBR. Dist: Consortium Bk. Sales & Distribution.

Borgnine, Ernest. Ernie. 2009. (ENG.). 272p. 14.95 *(978-0-8065-2942-4(3)*, Citadel Pr.) Kensington Publishing Corp.

—Ernie: The Autobiography. l.t. ed. 2008. 396p. 31.50 *(978-1-4104-1068-9(4))* Thorndike Pr.

Brooks, Lynn Matluck. John Durang: Man of the American Stage. 2011. ***(978-1-60497-775-2(2))*** Cambria Pr.

Brooks, Riley. All Access: Totally Unauthorized! 2009. (Demi Lovato Ser.). (ENG.). 144p. (J). (gr. 4-7). 5.99 *(978-0-545-17592-0(5)*, Scholastic Paperbacks) Scholastic, Inc.

Brown, Charles, ed. Russell Kirk: A Bibliography. 2nd ed. 2011. (ENG.). 240p. pap. 30.00 *(978-1-933859-80-4(6))* ISI Bks.

Burgoyne, Beckey. Perfectly Amanda: Gunsmoke's Miss Kitty: to Dodge & Beyond. 2010. (ENG.). 300p. pap. 29.95 *(978-1-58985-163-4(3))* Five Star Pubns., Inc.

Buyer, Jason. Inside the Audition Room: The Essential Actor's Handbook for Los Angeles. 2011. 90p. pap. 12.95 ***(978-0-557-93943-5(7))*** Lulu Enterprises Inc.

Canutt, Yakima & Crawford, John. My Rodeo Years: Memoir of a Bronc Rider's Path to Hollywood Fame. 2009. (ENG., Illus.). 218p. pap. 35.00 *(978-0-7864-4389-5(8))* McFarland & Co., Inc. Pubs.

Capotorto, Carl. Twisted Head: An Italian American Memoir. 2009. (ENG.). 320p. pap. 14.00 *(978-0-7679-2862-5(8))* Broadway Bks.

Carlyle, John. Under the Rainbow: An Intimate Memoir of Judy Garland, Rock Hudson & My Life in Old Hollywood. Freeman, Chris, ed. 2007. (ENG.). 352p. per. 15.00 *(978-0-7867-2034-7(4))* Da Capo Pr., Inc.

Carpenter, Amy. The Taylor Lautner Album. 2009. (ENG., Illus.). 96p. (gr. 3). pap. 16.95 *(978-0-85965-453-1(2))* Plexus Publishing, Ltd. GBR. Dist: Perseus-PGW.

Castellani, Raymond J. The End Was but a Beginning: A True Story. 2008. 140p. 29.95 *(978-1-59858-831-6(1))*; pap. 17.95 *(978-1-59858-805-7(2))* Dog Ear Publishing, LLC.

Cave, Lucie. God's Gift: Over 100 Studs, Stallions & Dreamboats from the 70s & 80s. 2007. (ENG., Illus.). 158p. 9.95 *(978-0-8109-9451-5(8)*, Abrams Image) Abrams.

Cave, Mark & Leopold, David. Drawn to Life: Al Hirschfeld & the Theater of Tennessee Williams. 2010. *(978-0-917860-58-4(6))* Univ. Pr. of Florida.

Channing, Carol. Just Lucky I Guess: A Memoir of Sorts. 2007. (ENG., Illus.). 272p. pap. 19.95 *(978-1-4165-6768-4(2))* Simon & Schuster.

Clary, Robert. From the Holocaust to Hogan's Heroes: An Autobiography of Robert Clary. 2007. (ENG., Illus.). 224p. per. 16.95 *(978-1-58979-345-3(5))* Taylor Trade Publishing.

Clinton, Craig. Cora Urquhart Potter: The Victorian Actress as Provocateur. 2010. (ENG., Illus.). 262p. pap. 55.00 *(978-0-7864-4957-6(8))* McFarland & Co., Inc. Pubs.

—Mrs. Leslie Carter: A Biography of the Early Twentieth Century American Stage Star. 2006. (ENG., Illus.). 228p. per. 45.00 *(978-0-7864-2747-5(7))* McFarland & Co., Inc. Pubs.

Cover, Early. From Sawdust to Sawdust. 2010. 14.59 *(978-0-578-05563-3(5))* Four Leaves Music.

Colacello, Bob. Ronnie & Nancy: Their Path to the White House, 1911 to 1980, Vol. 2. Date not set. *(978-0-446-57704-5(9))* Grand Central Publishing.

Curtis, James. Spencer Tracy: A Biography. 2011. (ENG., Illus.) 1024p. 39.95 *(978-0-307-26289-9(8)*, Knopf) Knopf Doubleday Publishing Group.

Davis, William B. Where There's Smoke... Musings of a Cigarette Smoking Man, a Memoir. 2011. (ENG., Illus.). 290p. pap. 19.95 *(978-1-77041-052-7(X))* ECW Pr. CAN. Dist: Independent Pubs. Group.

Deane, Pamala S. James Edwards: African American Hollywood Icon. 2009. (ENG., Illus.). 236p. pap. 45.00 (978-0-7864-4415-1(0)) McFarland & Co., Inc. Pubs.

Dearinger, Kevin Lane. Marie Prescott: A Star of Some Brilliancy. 2009. 55.00 (978-0-8386-4212-2(8)) Fairleigh Dickinson Univ. Pr.

Del Vecchio, Deborah & Johnson, Tom. Peter Cushing: The Gentle Man of Horror & His 91 Films. alt. ed. 2009. (ENG., Illus.). 485p. pap. 39.95 (978-0-7864-4495-3(9)) McFarland & Co., Inc. Pubs.

Denton, Sally. The Pink Lady: The Many Lives of Helen Gahagan Douglas. 2009. (ENG.). 256p. 26.00 (978-1-59691-480-3(7)) Bloomsbury Publishing.

Dherbier, Yann-Brice. Steve McQueen. 2008. (Life in Pictures Ser.). (ENG., Illus.). 196p. 40.00 (978-1-86205-814-9(8)) Anova Bks. GBR. Dist: Independent Pubs. Group.

Dherbier, Yann-Brice & Verlhac, Pierre-Henri, eds. Grace Kelly: A Life in Pictures. 2007. (Life in Pictures Ser.). (ENG., Illus.). 208p. 27.95 (978-1-86205-776-0(1)) Anova Bks. GBR. Dist: Independent Pubs. Group.

Dick, Bernard F. Forever Mame: The Life of Rosalind Russell. 2011. (Hollywood Legends Ser.). (ENG.). 320p. pap. 25.00 (978-1-60473-962-6(2)) Univ. Pr. of Mississippi.

Donahue, Heather. Growgirl: How My Life after the Blair Witch Project Went to Pot. 2012. (ENG.). 304p. (gr. 12). 26.00 (978-1-59240-692-0(0), Gotham) Penguin Group (USA) Inc.

Doyle, Mary. Life Was Like That. 2007. (ENG.). 276p. 42.95 (978-0-548-06326-2(5)) Kessinger Publishing, LLC.

Durang, Charles. The Theatrical Rambles of Mr & Mrs John Greene. Slout, William L., ed. 2007. 308p. 35.00 (978-0-8095-0306-3(9)); per. 19.95 (978-0-8095-1306-2(4)) Wildside Pr., LLC. (Borgo Pr.).

Eichenbaum, Rose. The Actor Within: Intimate Conversations with Great Actors. Hirt-Manheimer, Aron, ed. 2011. (ENG., Illus.). 268p. 30.00 (978-0-8195-6952-3(6)) Wesleyan Univ. Pr.

Eliot, Marc. Reagan: The Hollywood Years. 2009. (ENG., Illus.). 384p. pap. 17.00 (978-0-307-40513-5(3), Three Rivers Pr.) Crown Publishing Group.

—Reagan: The Hollywood Years. l.t. ed. 2009. 646p. 31.95 (978-1-4104-1201-0(6)) Thorndike Pr.

Englund, Robert & Goldsher, Alan. Hollywood Monster: A Walk down Elm Street with the Man of Your Dreams. 2009. (ENG., Illus.). 304p. 26.00 (978-1-4391-5048-1(6)) Gallery Pr., The IRL. Dist: Simon & Schuster, Inc.

Essman, Susie. What Would Susie Say? Bullsh*t Wisdom about Love, Life & Comedy. 2009. (ENG.). 256p. 25.00 (978-1-4391-5017-7(6)) Simon & Schuster.

Eustis, Morton. Players at Work. 2007. (ENG.). 144p. per. (978-1-4067-4528-3(6)) Read Bks.

Falk, Peter. Just One More Thing: Stories from My Life. 2007. (ENG., Illus.). 304p. per. 16.99 (978-0-7867-1939-6(7)) Da Capo Pr., Inc.

Farrell, Mike. Just Call Me Mike: A Journey to Actor & Activist. 2007. (ENG., Illus.). 368p. 21.95 (978-1-933354-08-8(9), RDV Bks.) Akashic Bks.

Fernandez, Yvonne. The Untold Story: Angelina Jolie, Brad Pitt & Jennifer Aniston. 2007. 208p. pap. 18.00 (978-1-4251-1241-7(2)) Trafford Publishing.

Ford, Peter. Glenn Ford: A Life. 2011. (Wisconsin Film Studies). (Illus.). (ENG.). 358p. pap. 24.95 (978-0-299-28154-0(X)); 312p. E-Book (978-0-299-28153-3(1)) Univ. of Wisconsin Pr.

Foster, Michael & Foster, Barbara. A Dangerous Woman: The Life, Loves, & Scandals of Adah Isaacs Menken, 1835-1868, America's Original Superstar. 2011. (ENG., Illus.). 368p. 24.95 (978-1-59921-602-7(7), Lyons Pr.) Globe Pequot Pr., The.

Gale Editor & Greenhaven Editor, eds. Jon Stewart. 2011. (People in the News Ser.). (Illus.). 128p. (YA). (gr. 9-12). lib. bdg. 33.45 (978-1-4205-0608-2(0)) Cengage Gale.

Gaston, Bibi & Gaston. The Loveliest Woman in America: A Tragic Actress, Her Lost Diaries, & Her Granddaughter's Search for Home. 2009. 352p. pap. 14.99 (978-0-06-085771-4(4), HarperPerennial) HarperCollins Pubs.

Gillies, Isabel. Happens Every Day: An All-Too-True Story. 2010. (ENG., Illus.). 272p. pap. 15.00 (978-1-4391-2662-2(3), Scribner) Scribner.

—A Year & Six Seconds: A Love Story. 2011. (ENG.). 256p. 21.99 (978-1-4013-4162-6(4)) Hyperion Pr.

Gilvey, John Anthony. Jerry Orbach, Prince of the City: His Way from the Fantasticks to Law & Order. 2011. (ENG., Illus.). 192p. pap. 19.99 (978-1-4234-8845-3(8), 1423488458, Applause Theatre & Cinema) Leonard, Hal Corp.

Gossett, Louis, Jr. & Karas, Phyllis. An Actor & a Gentleman. 2010. (ENG., Illus.). 320p. 26.95 (978-0-470-57471-3(2), Wiley) Wiley, John & Sons, Inc.

Grandinetti, Fred. Jack Mercer, the Voice of Popeye. 2007. 208p. per. 19.95 (978-1-59393-096-7(8)) BearManor Media.

Granger, Farley & Calhoun, Robert. Include Me Out: My Life from Goldwyn to Broadway. 2008. (ENG., Illus.). 288p. pap. 19.99 (978-0-312-35774-0(5), St. Martin's Griffin) St. Martin's Pr.

Gray, Spalding. The Journals of Spalding Gray. Casey, Neil & Russo, Kathie, eds. 2011. (ENG., Illus.). 368p. 28.95 (978-0-307-27345-1(8), Knopf) Knopf Doubleday Publishing Group.

Gray, Spalding. The Journals of Spalding Gray. Russo, Kathie & Casey, Nell, eds. 2012. (Vintage Ser.). (ENG.). 368p. pap. 16.00 (978-0-307-47491-9(7), Vintage) Knopf Doubleday Publishing Group.

Green, Paul. Pete Duel: A Biography. 2007. (ENG., Illus.). 229p. per. 35.00 (978-0-7864-3062-8(1)) McFarland & Co., Inc. Pubs.

—Pete Duel: A Biography [LARGE PRINT]. l.t. alt. ed. 2008. (ENG., Illus.). 387p. pap. 45.00 (978-0-7864-4117-4(8)) McFarland & Co., Inc. Pubs.

Grier, Pam. Foxy: My Life in Three Acts. 2011. (ENG., Illus.). 288p. pap. 14.99 (978-0-446-54848-9(0)) Grand Central Publishing.

Griffin, Maggie. Tip It! The World According to Maggie. 2010. (ENG.). 256p. 23.99 (978-1-4013-2404-9(5)) Hyperion Pr.

Grobel, Lawrence. Conversations with Marlon Brando: Lawrence Grobel. 2009. (ENG.). 195p. pap. 25.00 (978-0-9818056-2-7(0)) Rat Pr.

Grossman, Barbara Wallace. A Spectacle of Suffering: Clara Morris on the American Stage. 2nd ed. 2009. (Theater in the Americas Ser.). (Illus.). 344p. pap. 37.50 (978-0-8093-2882-6(8)) Southern Illinois Univ. Pr.

Hagman, Larry & Gold, Todd. Hello Darlin' Tall (and Absolutely True) Tales about My Life. 2011. (ENG.). 288p. pap. 18.99 (978-1-4516-4664-1(X)) Simon & Schuster.

Hanson, Bruce K. Peter Pan on Stage & Screen, 1904-2010. 2nd rev. ed. 2011. (ENG., Illus.). 417p. pap. 45.00 (978-0-7864-4778-7(8)) McFarland & Co., Inc. Pubs.

Harbin, Billy J., et al, eds. The Gay & Lesbian Theatrical Legacy: A Biographical Dictionary of Major Figures in American Stage History in the Pre-Stonewall Era. 2007. (Triangulations: Lesbian/Gay/Queer Theater/Drama/Performance Ser.). (ENG., Illus.). 440p. pap. 37.50 (978-0-472-06858-6(X)) Univ. of Michigan Pr.

Harriman, Margaret Case. The Vicious Circle: The Story of the Algonquin Round Table. 2011. 320p. 50.95 (978-1-258-10551-8(9)) Literary Licensing, LLC.

Hayter-Menzies, Grant. Charlotte Greenwood: The Life & Career of the Comic Star of Vaudeville, Radio & Film. 2007. (ENG., Illus.). 266p. per. 45.00 (978-0-7864-2995-0(X)) McFarland & Co., Inc. Pubs.

—Mrs. Ziegfeld: The Public & Private Lives of Billie Burke. 2009. (ENG., Illus.). 245p. 55.00 (978-0-7864-3800-6(2)) McFarland & Co., Inc. Pubs.

Heard, Christopher. Keifer Sutherland: Living Dangerously. 2010. 272p. 14.99 (978-1-926745-04-6(3)) Transit Publishing (Transit Editeur Inc.) CAN. Dist: Midpoint Trade Bks., Inc.

—Mickey Rourke: High & Low. 2006. (ENG., Illus.). 192p. per. 19.95 (978-0-85965-386-2(2)) Plexus Publishing, Ltd. GBR. Dist: Perseus-PGW.

Henderson, Jan Alan. Speeding Bullet: The life & bizarre death of George Reeves. 2nd exp. ed. 2007. pap. 24.95 (978-0-9619596-7-8(3)) Bifulco, Michael.

Hickman, Darryl. The Unconscious Actor: Out of Control, in Full Command - The Art of Performance in Acting & in Life. 2007. (ENG.). 312p. 24.95 (978-0-9776809-2-4(4)) Small Mountain Pr.

Hoefling, Larry J. Nils Thor Granlund: Show Business Entrepreneur & America's First Radio Star. 2010. (ENG., Illus.). 243p. pap. 39.95 (978-0-7864-4849-4(0)) McFarland & Co., Inc. Pubs.

Holbrook, Hal. Harold: The Boy Who Became Mark Twain. 2011. (ENG., Illus.). 480p. 30.00 (978-0-374-28101-4(7)) Farrar, Straus & Giroux.

Holmgren, Beth. Starring Madame Modjeska: On Tour in Poland & America. 2011. (ENG., Illus.). 432p. 39.95 (978-0-253-35664-2(4), 0253356644) Indiana Univ. Pr.

Hutton, Laurence. Plays & Players by Laurence Hutton. 2006. 288p. per. 23.99 (978-1-4255-2609-2(8)) MPublishing.

Iannucci, Lisa. Will Smith: A Biography, 1 vol. 2009. (Greenwood Biographies Ser.). 133p. 35.00 (978-0-313-37610-8(7), GR7610) Greenwood Publishing Group, Inc.

Jacobson, Laurie & Provost, Jon. Timmy's in the Well: The John Provost Story. 2010. (ENG.). 352p. pap. 18.95 (978-0-9826387-3-6(6), 0982638736) Franklin Green Publishing.

Jewell, Geri & Nichelson, Ted. I'm Walking as Straight as I Can: Transcending Disability in Hollywood & Beyond. 2011. (ENG., Illus.). 264p. pap. 19.95 (978-1-55022-883-0(8)) ECW Pr. CAN. Dist: Independent Pubs. Group.

Johnson, Kim Howard. The Funniest One in the Room: The Lives & Legends of Del Close. 2008. (ENG., Illus.). 416p. 24.95 (978-1-55652-712-8(8)) Chicago Review Pr., Inc.

Johnston, Kristen. Guts: The Endless Follies & Tiny Triumphs of a Giant Disaster. (ENG., Illus.). 288p. 2013. pap. 15.00 (978-1-4516-3506-5(0)) 2012. 25.00 (978-1-4516-3505-8(2)) Gallery Pr., The IRL. Dist: Simon & Schuster, Inc.

Johnstone, Nick. George Clooney: The Illustrated Biography. 2009. (ENG., Illus.). 160p. pap. (978-1-84732-145-9(3)) Carlton Bks., Ltd. GBR. Dist: Sterling Publishing Co., Inc.

Jordan, Leslie. My Trip down the Pink Carpet. 2009. (ENG.). 272p. pap. 15.00 (978-1-4391-5348-2(5)) Gallery Pr., The IRL. Dist: Simon & Schuster, Inc.

Jordan, Stephen C. Hollywood's Original Rat Pack: The Bards of Bundy Drive. 2008. (ENG., Illus.). 238p. per. 55.00 (978-0-8108-6032-2(5)) Scarecrow Pr., Inc.

Kanfer, Stefan. Somebody: The Reckless Life & Remarkable Career of Marlon Brando. 2009. (Vintage Ser.). (ENG., Illus.). 384p. pap. 16.00 (978-1-4000-7804-2(0), Vintage) Knopf Doubleday Publishing Group.

Kear, Lynn. Laurette Taylor, American Stage Legend. 2010. (ENG., Illus.). 286p. pap. 45.00 (978-0-7864-5922-3(0)) McFarland & Co., Inc. Pubs.

Kear, Lynn & King, James. Evelyn Brent: The Life & Films of Hollywood's Lady Crook. 2009. (ENG., Illus.). 312p. pap. 45.00 (978-0-7864-4363-5(4)) McFarland & Co., Inc. Pubs.

Kearns, Michael. Lasting Connections: Two Plays That Survived the Plague. 2009. 128p. pap. 18.69 (978-0-325-02159-1(7), E02159) Heinemann.

Kennedy, Matthew. Marie Dressler: A Biography; with a Listing of Major Stage Performances, a Filmography & a Discography. alt. ed. 2006. (ENG., Illus.). 279p. per. 39.95 (978-0-7864-2844-1(9)) McFarland & Co., Inc. Pubs.

Kent, Gary. Shadows & Light: Journeys with Outlaws in Revolutionary Hollywood. 2009. (It's Just Lunch Guide to Dating Ser.). (Illus.). 400p. pap. 21.95 (978-0-9817443-7-7(0)) Dalton Publishing GBR. Dist: Midpoint Trade Bks., Inc.

Keston, John. Expressions of Aging. 2011. 192p. pap. 15.95 (978-0-615-44684-4(1)) 42K Books.

Kippola, Karl M. Acts of Manhood: The Performance of Masculinity on the American Stage, 1828-1865. 2012. (Palgrave Studies in Theatre & Performance History Ser.). (ENG., Illus.). 272p. 85.00 (978-0-230-34045-9(8)) Palgrave Macmillan.

Kobbé, Gustav. Famous Actors & Actresses & Their Homes. 2007. (ENG.). 370p. 48.95 (978-0-548-04528-2(3)) Kessinger Publishing, LLC.

Koestler-Grack, Rachel A. Bruce Lee. 2007. (Asian Americans of Achievement Ser.). (Illus.). 128p. (YA). (gr. 7-12). lib. bdg. 35.00 (978-0-7910-9274-3(7)) Facts On File, Inc.

Koopmans, Andy. Seth Rogen. 2012. (People in the News Ser.). (Illus.). 128p. (YA). (gr. 7-12). 33.45 (978-1-4205-0616-7(1)) Cengage Gale.

Langella, Frank. Dropped Names: Famous Men & Women as I Knew Them. 2012. (ENG., Illus.). 374p. 25.99 (978-0-06-209447-6(5)) HarperCollins Pubs.

Lawford, Christopher Kennedy. Moments of Clarity: Voices from the Front Lines of Addiction & Recovery. 2010. (ENG.). 304p. pap. 13.99 (978-0-06-145622-0(5), William Morrow Paperbacks) HarperCollins Pubs.

Lawford, Christopher Kennedy & Lawford, Christopher K. Symptoms of Withdrawal: A Memoir of Snapshots & Redemption. 2006. (ENG., Illus.). 464p. pap. 14.99 (978-0-06-113123-3(7), William Morrow Paperbacks) HarperCollins Pubs.

Lee, Anna & Roisman Cooper, Barbara. Anna Lee: Memoir of a Career on General Hospital & in Film. 2007. (ENG., Illus.). 322p. per. 35.00 (978-0-7864-3161-8(X)) McFarland & Co., Inc. Pubs.

Life Magazine Editors. Life Ronald Reagan at 100. 2011. (ENG.). 144p. 24.95 (978-1-60320-193-3(9)) Time Home Entertainment, Inc.

Lindfors, Bernth. Ira Aldridge: The Early Years, 1807-1833 & the Vagabond Years, 1833-1852. 2011. (Rochester Studies in African History & the Diaspora Ser.). 660p. 99.00 (978-1-58046-401-7(7)) Univ. of Rochester Pr.

—Ira Aldridge: The Vagabond Years, 1833-1852, 2 vols. 2011. (Rochester Studies in African History & the Diaspora Ser.: Volume 49). (Illus.). 258p. 55.00 (978-1-58046-394-2(0)) Univ. of Rochester Pr.

Lithgow, John. Drama: An Actor's Education. (ENG.). 2012. 336p. pap. 14.99 (978-0-06-173498-4(5), HarperPerennial) 2011. 336p. 26.99 (978-0-06-173497-7(7)) 2011. 448p. pap. 26.99 (978-0-06-208874-1(2), HarperLuxe) HarperCollins Pubs.

Lucci, Susan. All My Life: A Memoir. 2011. (ENG.). 256p. 25.99 (978-0-06-206184-3(4)); 496p. pap. 25.99 (978-0-06-206530-8(0), HarperLuxe) HarperCollins Pubs.

Lucci, Susan & Morton, Laura. All My Life: A Memoir. 2011. (ENG., Illus.). 256p. pap. 15.99 (978-0-06-206185-0(2)) HarperCollins Pubs.

LuPone, Patti. Patti Lupone: A Memoir. 2010. (ENG., Illus.). 336p. 25.99 (978-0-307-46073-8(8), Harmony) Crown Publishing Group.

Lynch, Jane & Dickey, Lisa. Happy Accidents. 2011. (ENG.). 320p. 25.99 (978-1-4013-4176-3(4)) Hyperion Pr.

Mandel, Howie & Young, Josh. Here's the Deal: Don't Touch Me. 2010. (Illus.). 240p. pap. 15.00 (978-0-553-38665-3(4)) Random House Publishing Group.

Mask, Mia. Divas on Screen: Black Women in American Film. 2009. (ENG., Illus.). 320p. 75.00 (978-0-252-03422-0(8)); pap. 26.00 (978-0-252-07619-0(2)) Univ. of Illinois Pr.

McArthur, Benjamin. The Man Who Was Rip Van Winkle: Joseph Jefferson & Nineteenth-Century American Theatre. 2007. (ENG., Illus.). 464p. 45.00 (978-0-300-12232-9(2)) Yale Univ. Pr.

McCarthy, Jenny. Life Laughs: The Naked Truth about Motherhood, Marriage, & Moving On. 2007. (ENG., Illus.). 240p. (gr. 12-18). 13.95 (978-0-452-28829-4(0), Plume) Penguin Group (USA) Inc.

McClanahan, Rue. My First Five Husbands. . & the Ones Who Got Away. 2008. (ENG., Illus.). 368p. pap. 14.95 (978-0-7679-2694-2(3)) Broadway Bks.

McCormick, Maureen. Here's the Story: Surviving Marcia Brady & Finding My True Voice. 2009. (ENG., Illus.). 320p. pap. 14.99 (978-0-06-149015-6(6)) HarperCollins Pubs.

McDonough, Mary. Lessons from the Mountain. 2012. (ENG.). 288p. pap. 15.00 (978-0-7582-6367-4(8)) Kensington Publishing Corp.

McKay, James. Dana Andrews: The Face of Noir. 2010. (ENG., Illus.). 256p. pap. 45.00 (978-0-7864-4614-8(5)) McFarland & Co., Inc. Pubs.

McKinney, Devin. The Man Who Saw a Ghost: The Life & Work of Henry Fonda. 2012. (ENG., Illus.). 448p. 29.99 (978-1-250-00841-1(7)) St. Martin's Pr.

McShane, John. Heath Ledger: His Beautiful Life & Mysterious Death. 2008. (ENG., Illus.). 288p. pap. 17.95 (978-1-84454-633-6(0)) Blake, John Publishing, Ltd. GBR. Dist: Independent Pubs. Group.

Mediane, creator. Tomas Milian: The Tough Bandit, the Rough Cop & the Filthy Rat in Italian Cinema. 2009. (Amarkord Ser.). (ENG., Illus.). 148p. 17.95 (978-88-96042-12-0(7)) Mediane ITA. Dist: Ingram Pub. Services.

Menefee, David W. The First Male Stars: Men of the Silent ERA. 2007. (978-1-59393-073-8(9)) BearManor Media.

Menefee, David W. Wally: The true wallace reid Story. 2011. 528p. pap. 34.95 (978-1-59393-623-5(0)) BearManor Media.

Michaud, Michael Gregg. Sal Mineo: A Biography. (Illus.). 432p. 2011. (ENG.). pap. 16.00 (978-0-307-71667-5(8), Three Rivers Pr.) 2010. 25.99 (978-0-307-71868-6(9), Harmony) Crown Publishing Group.

Morse, Barry, et al. Remember with Advantages: Chasing the Fugitive & Other Stories from an Actor's Life. 2007. (ENG., Illus.). 258p. per. 35.00 (978-0-7864-2771-0(X)) McFarland & Co., Inc. Pubs.

Munn, Olivia & montandon, mac. Suck It, Wonder Woman! The Misadventures of a Hollywood Geek. 2011. (ENG., Illus.). 288p. pap. 14.99 (978-0-312-58376-7(1), St. Martin's Griffin) St. Martin's Pr.

Murray, John B. Brett Halsey: Art or Instinct in the Movies. 2008. 284p. (978-1-887664-83-7(1)) Midnight Marquee Pr., Inc.

Nagle, Jeanne. Oprah Winfrey: Profile of a Media Mogul. 2009. (Career Profiles Ser.). 112p. (gr. 9-10). 63.90 (978-1-61511-798-7(9)) Rosen Publishing Group, Inc., The.

Nagle, Jeanne M. Oprah Winfrey: Profile of a Media Mogul. 2007. (Career Profiles Ser.). (Illus.). 112p. (YA). (gr. 7-12). lib. bdg. 31.95 (978-1-4042-1908-3(0)) Rosen Publishing Group, Inc., The.

Neal, Patricia. As I Am. 2011. (ENG.). 384p. pap. 23.99 (978-1-4516-2600-1(2)) Simon & Schuster.

Nealon, Kevin. Yes, You're Pregnant, but What about Me? 2009. 272p. pap. 13.99 (978-0-06-121521-6(X)) HarperCollins Pubs.

Needham, Hal. Stuntman! My Car-Crashing, Plane-Jumping, Bone-Breaking, Death-Defying Hollywood Life. 2011. (ENG., Illus.). 320p. 25.99 (978-0-316-07899-3(9)) Little Brown & Co.

Norris, Chuck. The Official Chuck Norris Fact Book: 101 of Chuck's Favorite Facts & Stories. 2009. (ENG.). 320p. pap. 14.99 (978-1-4143-3449-3(4)) Tyndale Hse. Pubs.

Norris, Chuck & Abraham, Ken. Against All Odds: My Story. 2006. (ENG., Illus.). 246p. per. 14.99 (978-0-8054-4421-6(1), B&H Bks.) B&H Publishing Group.

O'Brien, Scott. Kay Francis. 2007. 380p. per. 24.95 (978-1-59393-106-3(9)) BearManor Media.

Ogelsby, Greta. Mama 'n Nem: Handprints on My Life. 2012. (978-1-933794-48-8(8)) Kirk Hse. Pubs.

Ohmart, Ben. Hold That Joan: The Life, Laughs & Films of Joan Davis. 2006. (Illus.). 172p. per. (978-1-59393-046-2(1)) BearManor Media.

O'Neal, Ryan, et al. Both of Us: My Life with Farrah. 2012. (ENG., Illus.). 272p. 26.00 (978-0-307-95482-4(X), Crown Archetype) Crown Publishing Group.

O'Neal, Tatum & Liftin, Hilary. Found: A Daughter's Journey Home. 2012. (ENG.). 240p. pap. 15.99 (978-0-06-206657-2(9), William Morrow Paperbacks) HarperCollins Pubs.

Orbach, Jerry & Orbach, Elaine. Remember How I Love You: Love Letters from an Extraordinary Marriage. 2011. (ENG., Illus.). 208p. pap. 14.99 (978-1-4516-7208-4(X), Touchstone) Touchstone.

Orbi, Joseph. ¡DIPLO! ¿Por qué se reía la Gente? 2010. mass mkt. 30.00 (978-0-9661619-2-2(0), I.O. Twomey) McQuicker & Company, Ltd.

Oswalt, Patton. Zombie Spaceship Wasteland. 2011. (ENG.). 208p. 24.00 (978-1-4391-4908-9(9), Scribner) Scribner.

—Zombie Spaceship Wasteland: A Book by Patton Oswalt. 2011. (ENG.). 288p. pap. 14.00 (978-1-4391-4909-6(7), Scribner) Scribner.

Otis, Carre & Schwyzer, Hugo. Beauty, Disrupted: A Memoir. 2012. (ENG., Illus.). 256p. pap. 15.99 (978-0-06-202446-6(9)) HarperCollins Pubs.

Oumano, Elena. Paul Newman. 2010. 272p. pap. 19.95 (978-1-4502-0641-9(7)) iUniverse, Inc.

Pacheco, Manny. Forgotten Hollywood Forgotten History: Starring the Great Character Actors of Hollywood's Golden Age. 2009. (ENG., Illus.). 121p. pap. 18.95 (978-1-935359-16-6(9)) Book Pubs. Network.

Pantoliano, Joey. Asylum: Hollywood Tales from My Great Depression - Brain Dis-Ease, Recovery, & Being My Mother's Son. 2012. (ENG.). 296p. 25.00 (978-1-60286-135-0(8)) Perseus Bks. Group.

Phillips, Mackenzie. High on Arrival: A Memoir. 2011. (ENG.). 320p. pap. 15.00 (978-1-4391-5386-4(8)) Gallery Pr., The IRL. Dist: Simon & Schuster, Inc.

Picerni, Paul & Weaver, Tom. Steps to Stardom Hb. 2007. 416p. 39.95 (978-1-59393-200-8(6)) BearManor Media.

Poitier, Sidney. Life Beyond Measure: Letters to My Great-Granddaughter. (ENG.). 2009. 304p. pap. 16.99 (978-0-06-149620-2(0), HarperOne) 2008. (Illus.). 400p. pap. 25.95 (978-0-06-156279-2(3), HarperLuxe) HarperCollins Pubs.

Porter, Lucy. Hairy Hunks: A Celebration of Shaggy Stallions. 2009. (ENG., Illus.). 160p. 10.95 (978-0-8109-0646-4(5), Abrams Image) Abrams.

Powers, Stefanie. One from the Hart. 2011. (ENG., Illus.). 272p. pap. 15.00 (978-1-4391-7211-7(0)) Gallery Pr., The IRL. Dist: Simon & Schuster, Inc.

Pressly, Jaime. It's Not Necessarily Not the Truth: Dreaming Bigger Than the Town You're From. 2009. 256p. 25.99 (978-0-06-145414-1(1), Morrow, William & Co.) HarperCollins Pubs.

Rapkin, Mickey. Theater Geek: The Real Life Drama of a Summer at Stagedoor Manor. 2011. (ENG.). 272p. pap. 15.00 (978-1-4391-4577-7(6), Free Pr.) Free Pr.

—Theater Geek: The Real Life Drama of a Summer at Stagedoor Manor, the Famous Performing Arts Camp. 2010. (ENG., Illus.). 240p. 25.00 (978-1-4391-4576-0(8), Free Pr.) Free Pr.

Rapp, Anthony. Without You: A Memoir of Love, Loss, & the Musical Rent. 2006. (ENG., Illus.). 320p. pap. 15.00 (978-0-7432-6977-3(2)) Simon & Schuster.

Reed, Alan & Ohmart, Ben. Yabba Dabba Doo! the Alan Reed Story. 2009. 208p. pap. 19.95 (978-1-59393-313-5(4)) BearManor Media.

Rees, James. The Life of Edwin Forrest with Reminiscences & Personal Recollections by James Rees with Portrait & Autograph. 2006. 516p. per. 29.99 (978-1-4255-5737-9(6)) MPublishing.

Rickles, Don. Rickles' Book. 2008. (ENG., Illus.). 256p. pap. 14.00 (978-0-7432-9306-8(1)) Simon & Schuster.

—Rickles' Book. l.t. ed. 2007. (Thorndike Biography Ser.). 243p. 31.95 (978-0-7862-9856-3(1)) Thorndike Pr.

Riley, Kathleen. The Astaires: Fred & Adele, 1 vol. 2012. (ENG., Illus.). 266p. 27.95 **(978-0-19-973841-0(6))** Oxford Univ. Pr., Inc.
Rivers, Victor Rivas. Asunto de Familia: Memorias. Echerri, Vicente, tr. 2006. (SPA., Illus.). 432p. pap. 14.00 *(978-1-4165-3729-8(5),* Beyond Words/Atria Bks.) Atria Bks.
Ross, Murray. Stars & Strikes: Unionization of Hollywood. reprint ed. 20.00 *(978-0-404-05408-3(0))* AMS Pr., Inc.
Rowell, Victoria. The Women Who Raised Me: A Memoir. 2008. (Illus.). 352p. pap. 14.99 *(978-0-06-124660-9(3),* William Morrow Paperbacks) HarperCollins Pubs.
Russell, Charles Edward. Julia Marlowe Her Life & Art. 2006. pap. 48.95 *(978-1-4286-5331-3(7))* Kessinger Publishing, LLC.
Sagala, Sandra K. Buffalo Bill on Stage. 2008. (ENG., Illus.). 319p. 19.95 *(978-0-8263-4427-4(5))* Univ. of New Mexico Pr.
Salem Press Staff, contrib. by. American Heroes, 3 vols. 2008. (Magill's Choice Ser.). (Illus.). 73.00 *(978-1-58765-458-9(X));* 73.00 *(978-1-58765-459-6(8));* 73.00 *(978-1-58765-460-2(1))* Salem Pr., Inc.
Schechter, Joel. Messiahs of 1933: How American Yiddish Theatre Survived Adversity Through Satire. 2008. (ENG., Illus.). 304p. 46.50 *(978-1-59213-872-2(1))* Temple Univ. Pr.
Schneider, Jerry L. Corriganville Movie Ranch. 2007. 500p. pap. 39.95 *(978-1-4303-1224-6(6))* Lulu Enterprises Inc.
Schnitzspahn, Karen. Stars of the Jersey Shore: A Theatrical History. 2007. (Illus.). 240p. pap. 19.95 *(978-0-7643-2719-3(4))* Schiffer Publishing, Ltd.
Scott, Dee. Corbin Bleu: Up Close. 2006. (ENG., Illus.). 96p. pap. 12.95 *(978-1-4165-4114-1(4))* Gallery Pr., The. IRL. Dist: Simon & Schuster, Inc.
Segrave, Kerry. Actors Organize: A History of Union Formation Efforts in America, 1880-1919. 2007. (ENG.). 215p. per. 39.95 *(978-0-7864-3283-7(7))* McFarland & Co., Inc. Pubs.
—Film Actors Organize: Union Formation Efforts in America, 1912-1937. 2009. (ENG.). 215p. pap. 39.95 *(978-0-7864-4276-8(X))* McFarland & Co., Inc. Pubs.
Shaffer, David W. Footprints on Broadway: My Journey to the Feet of the Stars. 2009. 484p. 30.99 *(978-1-4389-8463-6(4));* pap. 20.49 *(978-1-4389-8462-9(6))* AuthorHouse.
Shatner, William & Kreski, Chris. Star Trek Memories. 2009. (ENG., Illus.). 336p. pap. 14.99 *(978-0-06-166469-4(3))* HarperCollins Pubs.
Shearer, Stephen Michael. Beautiful: The Life of Hedy Lamarr. 2010. (ENG., Illus.). 480p. 29.99 *(978-0-312-55098-1(7),* Dunne, Thomas Bks.) St. Martin's Pr.
—Patricia Neal: An Unquiet Life. 2011. (ENG., Illus.). 508p. pap. 24.95 *(978-0-8131-2971-6(0))* Univ. Pr. of Kentucky.
Sherman, Kim. Fame: Taylor Lautner. 2010. (ENG.). 32p. pap. 3.99 *(978-1-4507-0883-8(8))* Bluewater Productions, Inc.
Skal, David J. & Rains, Jessica. Claude Rains: An Actor's Voice. 2009. (Screen Classics Ser.). (ENG.). 304p. pap. 19.95 *(978-0-8131-9261-1(7))* Univ. Pr. of Kentucky.
Smeds, Dave. Chuck Norris. 2009. (Martial Arts Masters Ser.). 112p. (gr. 5-5). 63.90 *(978-1-61514-372-6(6))* Rosen Publishing Group, Inc., The.
Smith, Geddeth. Walter Hampden: Dean of the American Theatre. 2008. (Illus.). 430p. 45.00 *(978-0-8386-4166-8(0))* Fairleigh Dickinson Univ. Pr.
Smith, Glenn D. & Smith, Glenn D., Jr. Something on My Own: Gertrude Berg & American Broadcasting, 1929-1956. 2007. (Television Ser.). (Illus.). 293p. 24.95 *(978-0-8156-0887-5(X))* Syracuse Univ. Pr.
Sorbo, Kevin. True Strength: My Journey from Hercules to Mere Mortal — and How Nearly Dying Saved My Life. 2012. (ENG., Illus.). 296p. pap. 16.00 **(978-0-7382-1602-7(X))** Da Capo Pr., Inc.
Stangelanc, John. Warren William: Magnificent Scoundrel of Pre-Code Hollywood. 2010. (ENG., Illus.). 240p. pap. 45.00 *(978-0-7864-4878-4(4))* McFarland & Co., Inc. Pubs.
Starr, Michael. Black & Blue: The Redd Foxx Story. 2011. (ENG.). 328p. 27.99 *(978-1-55783-754-7(6),* 1557837546, Applause Theatre & Cinema) Leonard, Hal Corp.
Starr, Michael Seth. Hiding in Plain Sight: The Secret Life of Raymond Burr, 1 vol. 2009. (ENG., Illus.). 270p. pap. 16.99 *(978-1-4234-7371-8(X),* 142347371X, Applause Theatre & Cinema) Leonard, Hal Corp.
Steen, M. F. Celebrity Death Certificates 3. 2010. (ENG., Illus.). 267p. pap. 39.95 *(978-0-7864-5935-3(2))* McFarland & Co., Inc. Pubs.
Steffans, Karrine. Confessions of a Video Vixen. 2006. (ENG., Illus.). 224p. pap. 14.95 *(978-0-06-089248-7(X),* Harper Paperbacks) HarperCollins Pubs.
—The Vixen Diaries. 2009. (ENG.). 208p. pap. 15.99 *(978-0-446-19123-4(X))* Grand Central Publishing.
Stein, Lisa K. Syd Chaplin: A Biography. 2010. (ENG., Illus.). 279p. pap. 39.95 *(978-0-7864-6035-9(0))* McFarland & Co., Inc. Pubs.
Stevens, Ronald Smokey. I Just Want to Tell Somebody. 2008. 181p. pap. 24.95 *(978-1-4241-9161-1(0))* PublishAmerica, Inc.
Strang, Lewis C. Famous Actresses of the Day in America. 2007. (ENG.). 360p. per. 31.95 *(978-1-4304-6184-5(5))* Kessinger Publishing, LLC.
Stumpf, Charles. ZaSu Pitts: The Life & Career. 2010. (ENG., Illus.). 224p. pap. 45.00 *(978-0-7864-4620-9(X))* McFarland & Co., Inc. Pubs.
Tamblyn, Robin. Looking Closer: Kevin Spacey, the first 50 Years. 2010. 156p. pap. 14.95 *(978-1-4502-0438-5(4))* iUniverse, Inc.
Thomas, François & Berthomé, Jean-Pierre. Orson Wells at Work. 2008. (ENG., Illus.). 320p. 79.95 *(978-0-7148-4583-8(3))* Phaidon Pr. Ltd. GBR. Dist: Hachette Bk. Group.
Thomas, Mike. The Second City Unscripted: Revolution & Revelation at the World-Famous Comedy Theater. 2012. (ENG.). 302p. pap. 16.95 **(978-0-8101-2844-6(6))** Northwestern Univ. Pr.
—The Second City Unscripted: Revolution & Revelation at the World-Famous Comedy Theater. 2009. (Illus.). 288p. 26.00 *(978-0-345-51422-6(X),* Villard Bks.) Random House Publishing Group.
Thomas, Scott. All in This Together: The Unofficial Story of High School Musical. Hale, Jennifer, ed. 2007. (ENG., Illus.). 120p. (J). (gr. 4-7). pap. 14.95 *(978-1-55022-764-2(5))* ECW Pr. CAN. Dist: Independent Pubs. Group.
Titone, Nora. My Thoughts Be Bloody: The Bitter Rivalry That Led to the Assassination of Abraham Lincoln. 2011. (ENG.). 496p. pap. 16.00 *(978-1-4165-8605-7(7),* Free Pr.) Free Pr.
Tonguette, Peter Prescott. Orson Welles Remembered: Interviews with His Actors, Editors, Cinematographers & Magicians. 2007. (ENG., Illus.). 216p. per. 35.00 *(978-0-7864-2760-4(4))* McFarland & Co., Inc. Pubs.
Tranberg, Charles. I Love the Illusion: The Life & Career of Agnes Moorehead. 2nd ed. 2007. *(978-1-59393-095-0(X))* BearManor Media.
Triumph Books Staff & Sprinkel, Katy. Elizabeth Taylor: The Life of a Hollywood Legend. 2011. (ENG.). 128p. pap. 14.95 *(978-1-60078-665-5(0))* Triumph Bks.
Tucker, David C. Eve Arden: A Chronicle of All Film, Television, Radio & Stage Performances. 2011. (ENG.). 205p. pap. 40.00 **(978-0-7864-6131-8(4))** McFarland & Co., Inc. Pubs.
Tucker, David C. Shirley Booth: A Biography & Career Record. 2008. (ENG., Illus.). 220p. pap. 39.95 *(978-0-7864-3600-2(X))* McFarland & Co., Inc. Pubs.
Tucker, Michael. Family Meals: Coming Together to Care for an Aging Parent. 2010. (ENG.). 256p. pap. 14.00 *(978-0-8021-4508-6(6),* Grove Pr.) Grove/Atlantic, Inc.
Turan, Kenneth & Papp, Joseph. Free for All: Joe Papp, the Public, & the Greatest Theater Story Every Told. 2010. (ENG., Illus.). 640p. pap. 18.00 *(978-0-7679-3169-4(6),* Anchor) Knopf Doubleday Publishing Group.
Turner, Kathleen. Send Yourself Roses: Thoughts on My Life, Love, & Leading Roles. l.t. ed. 2008. (Thorndike Biography Ser.). (Illus.). 455p. 31.95 *(978-1-4104-0511-1(7))* Thorndike Pr.
Tweed, Shannon. Kiss & Tell. 2007. (Illus.). 200p. per. 15.95 *(978-1-59777-551-9(7))* Phoenix Bks., Inc.
Vaughn, Robert. A Fortunate Life. 2009. (ENG., Illus.). 352p. pap. 18.99 *(978-0-312-59043-7(1),* St. Martin's Griffin) St. Martin's Pr.
—A Fortunate Life. l.t. ed. 2009. 512p. 31.50 *(978-1-4104-1324-6(1))* Thorndike Pr.
Vogel, Michelle. Marjorie Main: The Life & Films of Hollywood's Ma Kettle. alt. ed. 2011. (ENG., Illus.). 216p. pap. 38.00 *(978-0-7864-6443-2(7))* McFarland & Co., Inc. Pubs.
Wagner, Robert J. & Eyman, Scott. Pieces of My Heart: A Life. 2009. (ENG.). 352p. pap. 15.99 *(978-0-06-137332-9(X))* HarperCollins Pubs.
Wahl, Jan. Through a Lens Darkly. 2008. 272p. pap. 21.95 *(978-1-59393-311-1(8))* BearManor Media.
Walker, Jimmie. Dyn-O-Mite! Good Times, Bad Times ... & Our Times - A Memoir. 2012. (ENG.). 288p. 25.00 **(978-0-306-82083-0(8))** Da Capo Pr., Inc.
Walker, Jimmie & Manna, Sal. Dyn-O-Mite! Good Times, Bad Times, Our Times: A Memoir. 2012. E-Book **(978-0-306-82110-3(9))** Da Capo Pr., Inc.
Wallace, Stone. George Raft. 2008. 252p. per. 19.95 *(978-1-59393-123-0(9))* BearManor Media.
—George Raft Hb. 2008. 252p. 39.95 *(978-1-59393-204-6(9))* BearManor Media.
Warde, Frederick. Fifty Years of Make Believe. 2007. (ENG.). 376p. 48.95 *(978-0-548-01097-6(8))* Kessinger Publishing, LLC.
Washington, Isaiah. A Man from Another Land: How Finding My Roots Changed My Life. 2011. (ENG., Illus.). 304p. 24.99 *(978-1-59995-318-2(8))* Center St.
Weaver, Tom. John Carradine: The Films. alt. ed. 2008. (ENG., Illus.). 408p. per. 39.95 *(978-0-7864-3778-8(2))* McFarland & Co., Inc. Pubs.
Williams, Vanessa & Williams, Helen. You Have No Idea: A Famous Daughter, Her No-nonsense Mother, & How They Survived Pageants, Hollywood, Love, Loss (and Each Other) 2012. (ENG., Illus.). 304p. (gr. 12). 28.00 **(978-1-59240-707-1(2),** Gotham) Penguin Group (USA) Inc.
Wilson, Emily Herring, ed. Becoming Elizabeth Lawrence: Discovered Letters of a Southern Gardener. 2010. 224p. 19.95 *(978-0-89587-375-0(3))* Blair, John F. Pub.
Winter, William. Brief Chronicles. 2010. (ENG.). 414p. pap. 34.75 *(978-1-171-62390-8(9))* BiblioBazaar.
—Brief Chronicles. 2010. (Illus.). 174p. pap. 19.99 *(978-1-150-87266-2(7))* General Bks. LLC.
—Brief Chronicles. 2010. 394p. pap. 27.16 *(978-1-163-98465-9(5))* 2008. 392p. 48.95 *(978-0-548-99173-2(1))* 2007. (ENG.). 396p. per. 33.95 *(978-0-548-65538-2(3))* Kessinger Publishing, LLC.
—Henry Irving. 2009. 138p. pap. 20.75 *(978-1-115-79112-0(5));* 24.99 *(978-1-115-79111-3(7));* 28.99 *(978-1-115-79110-6(9));* pap. 19.75 *(978-1-115-79113-7(3))* BiblioBazaar.
—Henry Irving. 2009. 90p. pap. *(978-1-4589-5214-1(2))* Books LLC.
—Henry Irving. 123p. reprint ed. 48.00 *(978-0-7950-2339-2(1))* New Library Press LLC.
—The Jeffersons. 2009. 304p. 25.99 *(978-1-103-20164-8(6));* pap. 19.99 *(978-1-103-20160-0(3))* BiblioBazaar.
—The Jeffersons. 252p. reprint ed. 48.00 *(978-0-7950-2434-4(7))* New Library Press LLC.
Wood, Henry & Fedo, Michael. A Sawdust Heart: My Vaudeville Life in Medicine & Tent Shows. 2011. (Illus.). 144p. pap. 16.95 *(978-0-8166-7230-1(X))* Univ. of Minnesota Pr.
Yeoman, JoAnn. Dream Dealer Stuart Walker & the Ameri. 2007. 164p. per. 14.95 *(978-1-932842-22-7(5),* Star Cloud Pr.) Cloudbank Creations, Inc.
Young, Alan. There's No Business Like Show Business... Was. 2006. (Illus.). 108p. per. *(978-1-59393-053-0(4))* BearManor Media.
Zecher, Henry. William Gillette, America's Sherlock Holmes. 2011. 734p. 34.99 **(978-1-4535-5581-1(1));** pap. 23.99 **(978-1-4535-5580-4(3))** Xlibris Corp.
Zimmer, Kim & Morton, Laura. I'm Just Sayin'! Three Deaths, Seven Husbands, & a Clone! My Life as a Daytime Diva. (ENG.). 320p. (gr. 12). 2012. 15.00 **(978-0-451-23490-2(1),** N A L Trade) 2011. (Illus.). 26.95 *(978-0-451-23343-1(3),* N A L Hardcover) Penguin Group (USA) Inc.

ACTORS, AFRICAN AMERICAN

see African American Actors

ACTORS, BLACK

Lindfors, Bernth, ed. Ira Aldridge: The African Roscius. 2007. (Rochester Studies in African History & the Diaspora Ser.: Volume 28). (Illus.). 304p. 55.00 *(978-1-58046-258-7(8))* Univ. of Rochester Pr.

ACTRESSES

Here are entered works about women actors collectively. General works on both men and women actors collectively, works on both men and women stage actors collectively and works on individual men and women stage actors are entered under Actors. Works on actors, collectively or individually, specializing in particular media are entered under appropriate specific heading, e.g. Television Actors and Actresses.

see also Motion Picture Actors and Actresses; Television Actors and Actresses; Women Comedians

Alm, Sara & McDevitt, Hannah. Famous Frocks: Patterns & Instructions for Recreating Fabulous Iconic Dresses - 10 Patterns for 20 Dresses in All! 2011. (ENG.). 156p. 29.95 *(978-0-8118-7791-6(4))* Chronicle Bks. LLC.
Andersen, Christopher. Barbra: The Way She Is. 2007. (Illus.). 436p. 26.00 *(978-1-4223-6608-0(1))* DIANE Publishing Co.
Astington, John H. Actors & Acting in Shakespeare's Time: The Art of Stage Playing. 2010. (ENG., Illus.). 260p. (C). 75.00 *(978-0-521-19250-7(1));* pap. 26.99 *(978-0-521-14077-5(3))* Cambridge Univ. Pr.
Barranger, Milly S. Unfriendly Witnesses: Gender, Theater, & Film in the Mccarthy Era. 2008. (Theater in the Americas Ser.). (ENG., Illus.). 224p. pap. 37.50 *(978-0-8093-2876-5(3))* Southern Illinois Univ. Pr.
Beauclerk, Charles. Nell Gwyn: Mistress to a King. 2006. (ENG., Illus.). 448p. per. 18.00 *(978-0-8021-4274-0(5),* Grove Pr.) Grove/Atlantic, Inc.
Berg, Gertrude. Molly & Me. 22.95 *(978-0-88411-098-9(2))* Amereon LTD.
Bjornstad, Ketil. Wenche Foss: Diva Og Medmenneske. 2009. (Illus.). *(978-82-516-2426-8(6))* Schibsted.
Blackburne, E. Owens. Illustrious Irishwomen. 2009. (ENG.). 426p. 41.99 *(978-1-117-58697-7(9));* 428p. pap. 34.75 *(978-1-117-58698-4(7))* BiblioBazaar.
—Illustrious Irishwomen. 2009. 246p. pap. *(978-0-217-22976-0(X));* 214p. pap. *(978-1-4590-8801-6(8))* Books LLC.
—Illustrious Irishwomen, 2 Vols. reprint ed. 250.00 *(978-0-7222-1717-7(X))* Library Reprints, Inc.
—Illustrious Irishwomen: Being Memoirs of Some of the Most Noted Irishwomen from the Earliest Ages to the Present Century. 2010. (Cambridge Library Collection - Women's Writing Ser.). (ENG.). 372p. pap. 29.99 *(978-1-108-02107-4(7));* 430p. pap. 32.99 *(978-1-108-02106-7(9))* Cambridge Univ. Pr.
Bodeen, De Witt. Ladies of the Footlights. 2007. (ENG.). 134p. 35.95 *(978-0-548-06299-2(6))* Kessinger Publishing, LLC.
Booth, Michael, et al. Three Tragic Actresses: Siddons, Rachel, Ristori. 2007. (ENG., Illus.). 212p. pap. 48.00 *(978-0-521-03555-2(4))* Cambridge Univ. Pr.
Borkowski, Alina. The Actress & the Pope. 2006. 13.00 *(978-0-8059-9195-6(6))* Dorrance Publishing Co., Inc.
Brown, Pamela Allen & Parolin, Peter, eds. Women Players in England 1500-1660: Beyond the All-Mail Stage. 2008. (Studies in Performance & Early Modern Drama Ser.). (Illus.). 352p. pap. 29.95 *(978-0-7546-6535-9(6))* Ashgate Publishing Co.
—Women Players in England, 1500-1660: Beyond the All-Male Stage. 2006. (Studies in Performance & Early Modern Drama). (Illus.). 352p. 130.00 *(978-0-7546-0953-7(7))* Ashgate Publishing Co.
Carotenuto, Marinella. Sophia Loren: The Quintessence of Being an Italian Woman. 2009. (Photocult Ser.). (ENG., Illus.). 208p. 24.95 *(978-88-96042-10-6(0))* Mediane ITA. Dist: Ingram Pub. Services.
Chang, Chung-Ho & Chang, Kang-I Sun. Qu Ren Hong Zhao. 2010. (CHI & ENG., Illus.). 284p. *(978-7-5633-9388-6(9))* Guangxi Teachers Univ. Pr.
Chenoweth, Kristin. A Little Bit Wicked: Life, Love, & Faith in Stages. 2010. (ENG., Illus.). 256p. pap. 15.00 *(978-1-4165-8056-0(5),* Touchstone) Touchstone.
Cockin, Katharine, ed. The Collected Letters of Ellen Terry, Volume 1, 1 vol. 2010. (Pickering Masters Ser.). (ENG., Illus.). 288p. 180.00 *(978-1-85196-145-0(3))* Pickering & Chatto Pubs., Ltd. GBR. Dist: Ashgate Publishing Co.
—The Collected Letters of Ellen Terry, Volume 2, 1 vol. 2011. (Pickering Masters Ser.). (ENG., Illus.). 232p. 180.00 *(978-1-85196-146-7(1))* Pickering & Chatto Pubs., Ltd. GBR. Dist: Ashgate Publishing Co.
—The Collected Letters of Ellen Terry, Volume 3, 1 vol. 2012. (Pickering Masters Ser.). (ENG.). 416p. 180.00 *(978-1-85196-147-4(X))* Pickering & Chatto Pubs., Ltd. GBR. Dist: Ashgate Publishing Co.
Curry, Julian. Shakespeare on Stage: Thirteen Leading Actors on Thirteen Key Roles. 2011. (ENG., Illus.). 220p. pap. 30.95 **(978-1-84842-077-9(3))** Hern, Nick Bks., Ltd. GBR. Dist: Consortium Bk. Sales & Distribution.
De La Hoz, Cindy. Elizabeth Taylor: Her Place in the Sun - A Shining Legacy on Film. 2012. (ENG.). 304p. 30.00 *(978-0-7624-4045-0(7))* Running Pr. Bk. Pubs.
Deneuve, Catherine. The Private Diaries of Catherine Deneuve: Close up & Personal. 2007. (ENG.). 240p. 24.00 *(978-1-933648-36-1(8),* 933636) Pegasus Bks.
Downing, Lisa & Harris, Sue, eds. From Perversion to Purity: The Stardom of Catherine Deneuve. 2011. (ENG., Illus.). 194p. pap. 19.99 *(978-0-7190-7339-7(1))* Manchester Univ. Pr. GBR. Dist: Macmillan.
Dupree, Mary. The Mask & the Quill: Actress-Writers in Germany from Enlightenment to Romanticism. 2011. (New Studies in the Age of Goethe Ser.). (ENG.). 200p. 60.00 *(978-1-61148-024-5(8))* Bucknell Univ. Pr.
Dupree, Mary Helen. The Mask & the Quill: Actress-Writers in Germany from Enlightenment to Romanticism. 2011. *(978-0-8387-5800-7(2))* Bucknell Univ. Pr.
Elwood-Akers, Virginia. Caroline Severance. 2010. 400p. 35.95 *(978-1-4502-3627-0(8));* pap. 25.95 *(978-1-4502-3626-3(X))* iUniverse, Inc.
Engel, Laura. Fashioning Celebrity: Eighteenth-Century British Actresses & Strategies for Image Making. 2011. 216p. 44.95 *(978-0-8142-1148-9(8));* cd-rom 14.95 *(978-0-8142-9247-1(X))* Ohio State Univ. Pr.
Farrar, J. Maurice. Mary Anderson. 2007. 68p. per. *(978-1-4065-1668-3(0))* Dodo Pr.
Fitzgerald, Michael G. & Magers, Boyd. Ladies of the Western: Interviews with 25 Actresses from the Silent Era to the Television Westerns of the 1950s & 1960s. l.t. abr. alt. ed. 2009. (ENG., Illus.). 312p. pap. 39.95 *(978-0-7864-3938-6(6))* McFarland & Co., Inc. Pubs.
Foster, Michael & Foster, Barbara. A Dangerous Woman: The Life, Loves, & Scandals of Adah Isaacs Menken, 1835-1868, America's Original Superstar. 2011. (ENG., Illus.). 368p. 24.95 *(978-1-59921-602-7(7),* Lyons Pr.) Globe Pequot Pr., The.
Gale, Maggie B., ed. The Cambridge Companion to the Actress. 2007. (Cambridge Companions to Literature Ser.). (ENG., Illus.). 354p. per. 36.00 *(978-0-521-60854-1(6));* 364p. 101.99 *(978-0-521-84606-6(4))* Cambridge Univ. Pr.
Gold, Muriel. The Dramatic Legacy of Dorothy Davis & Violet Walters: The Montreal Children's Theatre, 1933-2009. 2010. 272p. pap. 20.95 *(978-1-4502-6070-1(5))* iUniverse, Inc.
Gottlieb, Robert. Sarah: The Life of Sarah Bernhardt. 2010. (Jewish Lives Ser.). (ENG., Illus.). 256p. 25.00 *(978-0-300-14127-6(0))* Yale Univ. Pr.
Grey, Sasha. Neu Sex. 2011. (ENG., Illus.). 192p. 30.00 *(978-1-57687-556-8(3),* powerHouse Bks.) powerHouse Cultural Entertainment, Inc.
Hanks, Tara. The Mmm Girl: Marilyn Monroe, by Herself. 2007. 348p. per. *(978-1-905796-13-7(7))* Boho Pr., The.
Hannsberry, Karen Burroughs. Femme Noir: Bad Girls of Film, 2 vols. alt. ed. 2009. (ENG., Illus.). 643p. pap. 75.00 *(978-0-7864-4682-7(X))* McFarland & Co., Inc. Pubs.
Hanson, Bruce K. Peter Pan on Stage & Screen, 1904-2010. 2nd rev. ed. 2011. (ENG., Illus.). 417p. pap. 45.00 *(978-0-7864-4778-7(8))* McFarland & Co., Inc. Pubs.
Hanson, Dian. Vanessa del Rio: Fifty Years of Slightly Slutty Behavior. 2007. (ENG.). 396p. 1800.00 *(978-3-8228-4651-3(1))* TASCHEN DEU. Dist: Ingram Pub. Services.
Havoc, June. Early Havoc. 2011. 328p. 50.95 **(978-1-258-07813-3(9))** Literary Licensing, LLC.
Howard, Tony. Women as Hamlet: Performance & Interpretation in Theatre, Film & Fiction. 2007. (ENG., Illus.). 341p. 109.99 *(978-0-521-86466-4(6))* Cambridge Univ. Pr.
Irvin, Sam. Kay Thompson: From Funny Face to Eloise. 2011. (ENG., Illus.). 432p. pap. 16.00 *(978-1-4391-7654-2(X))* Simon & Schuster.
Katritzky, M. A. Women, Medicine & Theatre, 1550-1750: Literary Mountebanks & Performing Quacks. 2007. (Studies in Performance & Early Modern Drama). (Illus.). 384p. 124.95 *(978-0-7546-5084-3(7))* Ashgate Publishing Co.
Kemble, Frances. Records of a Girlhood. 2007. 612p. per. 34.95 *(978-1-60206-806-3(2))* Cosimo, Inc.
Kruger, Petra E. Acting Lady Macbeth. 2010. 228p. pap. 25.50 *(978-1-4457-3458-3(3))* Lulu Enterprises Inc.
LaSalle, Mick. The Beauty of the Real: What Hollywood Can Learn from Contemporary French Actresses. 2012. (ENG., Illus.). 248p. 24.95 **(978-0-8047-6854-2(4),** Stanford General Bks.) Stanford Univ. Pr.
Leachman, Cloris. Cloris. 2010. (ENG.). 288p. pap. 15.00 *(978-0-7582-2964-9(X))* Kensington Publishing Corp.
Leachman, Cloris & Englund, George. Cloris. 2009. (ENG.). 384p. 24.00 *(978-0-7582-2963-2(1))* Kensington Publishing Corp.
Lisanti, Tom. Glamour Girls of Sixties Hollywood: Seventy-Five Profiles. 2007. (ENG., Illus.). 252p. 45.00 *(978-0-7864-3172-4(5))* McFarland & Co., Inc. Pubs.
Majumdar, Neepa. Wanted Cultured Ladies Only! Female Stardom & Cinema in India, 1930s-1950s. 2009. (ENG., Illus.). 272p. pap. 25.00 *(978-0-252-07628-2(1))* Univ. of Illinois Pr.
—Wanted Cultured Ladies Only! Female Stardom & Cinema in India, 1930s-50s. 2009. (ENG., Illus.). 272p. 65.00 *(978-0-252-03432-9(5))* Univ. of Illinois Pr.
Marshall, Gail. Actresses on the Victorian Stage: Feminine Performance & the Galatea Myth. 2006. (Cambridge Studies in Nineteenth-Century Literature & Culture Ser.). (ENG.). 252p. pap. 50.00 *(978-0-521-02746-5(2))* Cambridge Univ. Pr.

McKechnie, Donna & Lawrence, Greg. Time Steps: My Musical Comedy Life. 2009. (ENG.). 308p. pap. 19.99 *(978-1-4391-9191-0(3))* Simon & Schuster.
Mock, Roberta. Jewish Women on Stage, Film, & Television. 2007. (ENG., Illus.). 240p. 89.00 *(978-1-4039-7989-6(8))* Palgrave Macmillan.
Moore, Mary Tyler. Growing up Again: Life, Loves, & Oh Yeah, Diabetes. l.t. ed. 2009. 284p. 32.95 *(978-1-4104-1639-1(9))* Thorndike Pr.
Morris, Clara. Life on the Stage. 2007. 35.00 *(978-1-4344-9193-0(5))*; pap. 19.95 *(978-1-4344-9099-5(8))* Wildside Pr., LLC. (Borgo Pr.).
Nissen, Axel. Actresses of a Certain Character: Forty Familiar Hollywood Faces from the Thirties to the Fifties. alt. ed. 2011. (ENG., Illus.). 256p. pap. 35.00 *(978-0-7864-6110-3(1))* McFarland & Co., Inc. Pubs.
Nussbaum, Felicity. Rival Queens: Actresses, Performance, & the Eighteenth-Century British Theater. 2010. (Illus.). 376p. (C). 55.00 *(978-0-8122-4233-1(5))* Univ. of Pennsylvania Pr.
Olszewski, Gary. Marjorie White: Her Life & Work. 2011. 118p. pap. 19.95 ***(978-1-59393-625-9(7))*** BearManor Media.
Onika Pointer. Humble Bastard: A Memoir. 2010. 376p. 34.95 *(978-1-4502-1272-4(7))*; pap. 24.95 *(978-1-4502-1274-8(3))* iUniverse, Inc.
Otis, Carre & Schwyzer, Hugo. Beauty, Disrupted: A Memoir. 2011. (ENG.). 256p. 25.99 *(978-0-06-202445-9(0))* HarperCollins Pubs.
Pacheco, Manny. Forgotten Hollywood Forgotten History: Starring the Great Character Actors of Hollywood's Golden Age. 2009. (ENG., Illus.). 121p. pap. 18.95 *(978-1-935359-16-6(9))* Book Pubs. Network.
Paesel, Brett. Mommies Who Drink: Sex, Drugs, & Other Distant Memories of an Ordinary Mom. 2007. (ENG.). 352p. per. 22.99 *(978-0-446-69940-2(3))* Grand Central Publishing.
Pagett & Swannell. Diamonds Behind My Eyes. 252p. pap. 13.99 *(978-0-575-60267-0(8))* Gollancz, Victor Ltd. GBR. Dist: Trafalgar Square Publishing.
Perry, Gill. Spectacular Flirtations: Viewing the Actress in British Art & Theatre 1768-1820. 2008. (ENG., Illus.). 248p. (C). 75.00 *(978-0-300-13544-2(0))* Yale Univ. Pr.
Petkevich, T. V. Memoir of a Gulag Actress. 2010. (ENG., Illus.). 495p. 35.00 *(978-0-87580-428-6(4))* Northern Illinois Univ. Pr.
Phillips, Willard. Death in Hollywood. 2012. (ENG.). 508p. pap. 17.99 ***(978-1-4611-0632-6(X))*** CreateSpace.
Pope, Peggy. Atta Girl: Tales from A Life in the Trenches of Show Business. 2011. 192p. 23.95 ***(978-1-4620-4100-8(0))***; pap. 13.95 ***(978-1-4620-4098-8(5))*** iUniverse, Inc.
Powers, Stefanie. One from the Hart. 2010. (ENG., Illus.). 272p. 26.00 *(978-1-4391-7210-0(2))* Gallery Pr., The IRL. Dist: Simon & Schuster, Inc.
Pressly, Jaime. It's Not Necessarily Not the Truth: Dreaming Bigger Than the Town You're From. 2009. 256p. 25.99 *(978-0-06-145414-1(1)*, Morrow, William & Co.) HarperCollins Pubs.
Rhodes, Richard. Hedy's Folly: The Life & Breakthrough Inventions of Hedy Lamarr, the Most Beautiful Woman in the World. 2011. (ENG., Illus.). 272p. 26.95 *(978-0-385-53438-3(8)*, Doubleday) Knopf Doubleday Publishing Group.
Richards, Kyle. Life Is Not a Reality Show: Keeping It Real with the Housewife Who Does It All. 2011. (ENG., Illus.). 256p. 25.99 ***(978-0-06-211348-1(8)***, HarperOne) HarperCollins Pubs.
Riley, Kathleen. The Astaires: Fred & Adele, 1 vol. 2012. (ENG., Illus.). 266p. 27.95 ***(978-0-19-973841-0(6))*** Oxford Univ. Pr., Inc.
Ritchie, Anna Cora Ogden Mowatt. Mimic Life; or, Before & Behind the Curtain a Series of Narratives, by Anna Cora Ritchie. 2006. 436p. per. 26.99 *(978-1-4255-4763-9(X))* MPublishing.
Ritschel, Nelson O'Ceallaigh. Performative & Textual Imaging of Women on the Irish Stage, 1820-1920: M. A. Kelly to J. M. Synge & the Allgoods. 2006. 216p. 109.95 *(978-0-7734-5492-7(6))* Mellen, Edwin Pr., The.
Rock, Crissy. This Heart Within Me Burns: Crissy Rock - From Bedlam to Benidorm. 2011. (ENG., Illus.). 264p. 24.95 ***(978-1-84358-343-1(7))*** Blake, John Publishing, Ltd. GBR. Dist: Independent Pubs. Group.
Ryan, Kate. Old Boston Museum Days. 2009. 92p. pap. 20.00 *(978-1-151-53588-7(5))* General Bks. LLC.
—Old Boston Museum Days. 2008. 308p. 43.95 *(978-1-4365-6106-8(X))* 2007. (ENG.). 312p. per. 28.95 *(978-0-548-76111-3(6))* Kessinger Publishing, LLC.
—Old Boston Museum Days. 2007. (ENG.). 312p. per. *(978-1-4067-4168-1(X))* Read Bks.
Schickel, Richard & Perry, George. Bette Davis: Larger Than Life. 2009. (ENG., Illus.). 264p. 35.00 *(978-0-7624-3688-0(3)*, Running Pr.) Running Pr. Bk. Pubs.
Scott, Virginia. Women on the Stage in Early Modern France, 1540-1750. 2010. 336p. 95.00 *(978-0-521-89675-7(4))* Cambridge Univ. Pr.
Setzer, Sharon M., et al, eds. Women's Theatrical Memoirs, Part I, 5 vols., Vols. 1-5. 2007. (Chawton House Library Ser.). (ENG.). 2000p. 750.00 *(978-1-85196-861-9(X))* Pickering & Chatto Pubs., Ltd. GBR. Dist: Ashgate Publishing Co.
Shean, Nava. To Be an Actress. 2010. (ENG.). 196p. pap. 31.99 *(978-0-7618-5027-4(9))* Hamilton Bks.
Sherman, Charles Austin. Exciting Stories of My Personal Brushes with Greatness: Memoirs of Another Time (1922 To 1956) Stories of an Incredible Anglo/American Family who Lived in a Golden Era; of Relations with Royalty, Heads of State, Celebrities, Heroes & Heroines, Scoundre. 2011. 380p. pap. 21.72 *(978-1-4567-4199-0(3))* AuthorHouse.
Skin. Mr. Skin's Skincyclopedia: The A-to-Z Guide to Finding Your Favorite Actresses Naked. 2nd rev. ed. 2009. (ENG., Illus.). 704p. pap. 29.99 *(978-0-312-58402-3(4)*, St. Martin's Griffin) St. Martin's Pr.
Sokoowska-Gwizdka, Joanna. What I Received from God & from People: A Story of Helena Modjeska. 2009.Tr. of Co otrzymalam od Boga i Ludzi. (ENG & POL., Illus.). 63p. pap. 23.95 *(978-0-615-29344-8(1))* BoRey Publishing.
Statman, Alisa & Tate, Brie. Restless Souls: The Sharon Tate Family's Account of Stardom, the Manson Murders, & a Crusade for Justice. 2012. ***(978-0-06-200805-3(6))***; ***(978-0-06-210949-1(9))***; ***(978-0-06-211551-5(0))***; ***(978-0-06-213186-7(9))*** HarperCollins Pubs.
Statman, Alisa R. & Tate, Brie. Restless Souls: The Sharon Tate Family's Account of Stardom, Murder & a Crusade. l.t. ed. 2012. (ENG.). 400p. pap. 26.99 ***(978-0-06-210729-9(1)***, HarperLuxe) HarperCollins Pubs.
—Restless Souls: The Sharon Tate Family's Account of Stardom, the Mason Murders, & a Crusade for Justice. 2012. (ENG., Illus.). 384p. 26.99 ***(978-0-06-200804-6(8))*** HarperCollins Pubs.
Stokes, John. The French Actress & her English Audience. 2011. (ENG.). 236p. pap. 48.00 *(978-0-521-29261-0(1))* Cambridge Univ. Pr.
Tucker, David C. The Women Who Made Television Funny: Ten Stars of 1950s Sitcoms. 2007. (ENG., Illus.). 215p. per. 39.95 *(978-0-7864-2900-4(3))* McFarland & Co., Inc. Pubs.
Tyler, George C. Whatever Goes Up: The Hazardous Fortunes of a Natural Born Gambler. 2007. (ENG.). 350p. 46.95 *(978-0-548-07344-5(9))* Kessinger Publishing, LLC.
Victor, Barbara. Charlotte Rampling: A Biography. 2010. (ENG.). 256p. 26.00 *(978-1-59691-547-3(1))* Bloomsbury Publishing.
Williams, Hugh Noel. Queens of the French Stage. 2007. (ENG.). 390p. 48.95 *(978-0-548-04844-3(4))* Kessinger Publishing, LLC.
Winter, William. Shadows of the Stage: Third Series. 2007. (ENG.). 374p. 48.95 *(978-0-548-03292-3(0))* Kessinger Publishing, LLC.
Zakreski, Patricia. Representing Female Artistic Labour, 1848-1890: Refining Work for the Middle-Class Woman. 2006. (Illus.). 230p. 110.00 *(978-0-7546-5103-1(7))* Ashgate Publishing Co.

ACTRESSES—JUVENILE LITERATURE

Gale, ed. Sandra Bullock. 2011. (People in the News Ser.). 128p. (YA). (gr. 7-12). lib. bdg. 33.45 *(978-1-4205-0428-6(2))* Cengage Gale.

ACTUARIAL SCIENCE

see Insurance—Mathematics; Life Insurance; Life Insurance—Mathematics

ACTUARIAL STATISTICS

see Insurance—Rates and Tables

ACULEATA

see Ants; Bees; Wasps

ACUPRESSURE

Anderson, Sandra K. The Practice of Shiatsu. 2007. (Mosby's Massage Career Development Ser.). (ENG., Illus.). 256p. (C). pap. 51.95 *(978-0-323-04580-3(4)*, Mosby) Elsevier - Health Sciences Div.
Beresford-Cooke, Carola. Shiatsu Theory & Practice. 3rd ed. 2010. (ENG., Illus.). 400p. 79.95 *(978-0-7020-2963-9(7)*, Churchill Livingstone) Elsevier - Health Sciences Div.
Chia, Mantak. Taoist Foreplay. 2010. (ENG., Illus.). 1p. pap. 16.95 *(978-1-59477-188-0(X)*, Destiny Bks.) Inner Traditions International, Ltd.
Cook, Earl & Cook, Gail. ETouch for Health - the Complete Edition (Mac OS X) The Electronic Companion to Touch for Health. 2nd ed. 2006. cd-rom 69.95 *(978-0-9769669-5-1(6))* Laser Solutions, Inc.
—ETouch for Health - the Complete Edition (Windows) The Electronic Companion to Touch for Health. 2nd ed. 2006. cd-rom 69.95 *(978-0-9769669-4-4(8))* Laser Solutions, Inc.
Cossé, Anne. The Do-It-Yourself Acupressure Face Lift. 2008. 48p. pap. 29.00 *(978-1-4357-2673-4(1))* Lulu Enterprises Inc.
Cross, John. Healing with the Chakra Energy System: Acupressure, Bodywork, & Reflexology for Total Health. 2006. (ENG., Illus.). 332p. pap. 22.95 *(978-1-55643-625-3(4))* North Atlantic Bks.
Dempsey, Bobbi & Andrews, Synthia. Acupressure & Reflexology for Dummies. 2007. (ENG., Illus.). 360p. per. 19.99 *(978-0-470-13942-4(0)*, For Dummies) Wiley, John & Sons, Inc.
Evans, Mark, et al. Book of Step-by-Step Massage & Aromatherapy: The Power of Massage, Aromatherapy, Shiatsu & Reflexology for Health & Wellbeing, Shown in More Than 200 Colour Photographs. 2010. (ENG., Illus.). 96p. pap. 16.99 *(978-1-84476-765-6(5))* Anness Publishing GBR. Dist: National Bk. Network.
Fleming, Tapas. TAT Professional's Manual. 2007. spiral bd. 20.00 *(978-1-893412-14-9(8))* TAT International.
Franzen, Susanne. A Step-by-Step Guide to Shiatsu: A Simple Introduction to the Ancient Therapy of Pressure & Nurturing Touch, with 170 Easy-to-Follow Photographs. 2007. (ENG., Illus.). 64p. pap. 9.99 *(978-1-84476-443-3(5))* Anness Publishing GBR. Dist: National Bk. Network.
Goldstein, Shellie. Your Best Face Now: Look Younger in 20 Days with the Do-It-Yourself Acupressure Facelift. 2012. (ENG.). 272p. (gr. 12). 20.00 ***(978-1-58333-440-9(8)***, Avery) Penguin Group (USA) Inc.
Hecker, Hans-Ulrich & Liebchen, Kay. Acupressure Taping: The Practice of Acutaping for Chronic Pain & Injuries. Lueders, Katja & Lorenzo, Rafael, trs. from GER. 2007. (ENG., Illus.). 1p. pap. 16.95 *(978-1-59477-148-4(0)*, Healing Arts Pr.) Inner Traditions International, Ltd.
Jarmey, Chris & Bouratinos, Ilaira. Practical Guide to Acu-Points. 2008. (ENG., Illus.). 360p. pap. 39.95 *(978-1-55643-696-3(3))* North Atlantic Bks.
Karcher, Stephen L. & Kawada, Yuichi. Essential Shiatsu: Essential Shiatsu for Troubled Times. 2010. (ENG., Illus.). 208p. pap. 14.95 *(978-0-7499-4017-1(4))* Piatkus Bks. GBR. Dist: Independent Pubs. Group.
Kircher, Nora. Gemstone Reflexology. Myint, Nikolas Win, tr. from GER. 2006. (ENG., Illus.). 1p. pap. 16.95 *(978-1-59477-121-7(9))* Inner Traditions International, Ltd.
Kishi, Akinobu & Whieldon, Alice. Sei-Ki: Life in Resonance - The Secret Art of Shiatsu. 2011. (ENG., Illus.). 160p. pap. *(978-1-84819-042-9(5))* Kingsley, Jessica Ltd.
Koblin, Seymour A. Zen-Touch & the Art of Shiatsu: Fundamental Applications in Acupressure Massage. rev. ed. (Illus.). 147p. reprint ed. pap. 15.95 *(978-0-9625000-2-2(X))* Soulstar Creations.
Kolster, Bernard C. & Waskowiak, Astrid. The Acupressure Atlas. 2007. (ENG., Illus.). 1p. pap. 29.95 *(978-1-59477-207-8(X)*, Healing Arts Pr.) Inner Traditions International, Ltd.
—The Acupressure Atlas. Myint, Nikolas Win, tr. from GER. 2007. (ENG., Illus.). 1p. 39.95 *(978-1-59477-175-0(8)*, Healing Arts Pr.) Inner Traditions International, Ltd.
Mogilner, Victoria J. Ancient Secrets of Facial Rejuvenation: A Holistic, Nonsurgical Approach to Youth & Well-Being. 2006. (ENG., Illus.). 160p. per. 15.95 *(978-1-57731-552-0(9))* New World Library.
—Ancient Secrets of Facial Rejuvenation: A Holistic, Nonsurgical Approach to Youth & Well-Being'. 2010. (ENG.). 158p. pap. 15.00 *(978-1-4379-7341-9(8))* DIANE Publishing Co.
Rappenecker, Wilfried & Kockrick, Meike. Atlas of Shiatsu: The Meridians of Zen Shiatsu. 2008. (ENG., Illus.). 192p. 62.95 *(978-0-7020-2962-2(9)*, Churchill Livingstone) Elsevier - Health Sciences Div.
Ridolfi, Ray. Shiatsu. (Terapias Naturales Ser.). (SPA.). 128p. 6.70 *(978-84-89920-01-9(X)*, 86404) Ediciones Oniro S.A. ESP. Dist: Lectorum Pubns., Inc.
Roberts, Julie. Change Works with CLEAR, Clearing Limits Energetically with Acupressure Release. 2007. (Illus.). 105p. spiral bd. 15.00 *(978-0-9796033-0-3(7))* Change Works.
Schwarz, A. & Schweppe, R. P. Guia Facil de Shiatsu. (SPA., Illus.). 137p. *(978-84-7927-324-8(0))* Robinbk., Ediciones S.L. ESP. Dist: Lectorum Pubns., Inc.
Teeguarden, Iona Marsaa. The Joy of Feeling: Bodymind Acupressure - Jin Shin Do(r). 2006. (ENG., Illus.). 364p. per. 34.00 *(978-0-9785412-0-0(0))* Jin Shin Do(r) Foundation for Bodymind Acupressure.
Thompson, Gerry. Shiatsu Box. 2009. (Book-in-A-Box Ser.). (ENG.). 208p. 14.95 *(978-1-85906-263-0(6))* Connections Bk. Publishing, Ltd. GBR. Dist: Red Wheel/Weiser.
Wells, Steve & Lake, David. Enjoy Emotional Freedom: Simple techniques for living life to the Full. 2010. (ENG., Illus.). 240p. pap. 27.95 *(978-1-921497-48-3(3))* Exisle Publishing Pty Limited AUS. Dist: BookMasters Distribution Services (BDS).

ACUPUNCTURE

Abbate, Skya. Advanced Techniques in Oriental Medicine. 2006. (ENG., Illus.). 183p. 64.99 *(978-1-58890-493-5(8))* Thieme Medical Pubs., Inc.
Acupuncture Simplified for the Practicing Physician. 2007. per. 129.00 *(978-0-9793641-0-5(8))* Taus,, Stephen D. M.D., Inc.
Adams, Cheryl, et al. Proceedings of the 32nd Annual International Congress on Veterinary Acupuncture. 2006. (Illus.). 220p. 40.00 *(978-0-9616627-6-9(X))* International Veterinary Acupuncture Society.
Alexander, Skye. Acupressure Card Deck: 50 Pressure Points That Alleviate Pain, Ease Stress & Anxiety, & Restore Health. 2010. (ENG., Illus.). 52p. 14.99 *(978-1-59233-297-7(8)*, 1592332978) Quayside.
Aung, Steven K. H. & Chen, William P. D. Clinical Introduction to Medical Acupuncture. 2007. (ENG., Illus.). 336p. 129.99 *(978-1-58890-221-4(8))* Thieme Medical Pubs., Inc.
Aung, Steven K. H. & Chen, William Pai-Dei. Clinical Introduction to Medical Acupuncture. 2006. (Illus.). xii, 324p. 114.95 *(978-3-13-138271-9(6))* Thieme Medical Pubs., Inc.
Backer, Marcus & Hammes, Michael G., eds. Acupuncture in the Treatment of Pain: An Integrative Approach. 2010. (ENG., Illus.). 560p. 97.95 *(978-0-443-06869-0(0)*, Churchill Livingstone) Elsevier - Health Sciences Div.
Baldwin, Dean. Odic Energy in Acupuncture, Qi, & Energy Medicine. 2007. 32p. 6.95 *(978-0-9776512-1-4(5))* Odic Energy Research Institute.
Bauer, L. Ac. Making Acupuncture Pay: Real-World Advice for Successful Private Practice. 2011. 192p. pap. 22.50 ***(978-1-4575-0279-8(8))*** Dog Ear Publishing, LLC.
Beach, Phillip. Muscles & Meridians: The Manipulation of Shape. 2010. (ENG., Illus.). 220p. pap. 66.95 *(978-0-7020-3109-0(7)*, Churchill Livingstone) Elsevier - Health Sciences Div.
Bereder, Antoine. The Photographic Atlas of Acupuncture. 2011. (ENG., Illus.). 576p. 149.00 *(978-1-84409-538-4(X))* Findhorn Pr. GBR. Dist: Independent Pubs. Group.
Birch, Stephen. Shonishin: Japanese Pediatric Acupuncture. 2011. (ENG., Illus.). 272p. 79.99 *(978-3-13-150061-8(1))* Thieme Medical Pubs., Inc.
Bosch, Peggy M. P. C. & Van den Noort, Maurits W. M. L., eds. Schizophrenia, Sleep, & Acupuncture. 2008. (Illus.). 348p. 54.00 *(978-0-88937-355-6(8))* Hogrefe Publishing.
Campbell, Anthony. Medical Acupuncture: A Practical Guide. 2009. 82p. pap. 46.50 *(978-1-4452-3253-9(7))* Lulu Enterprises Inc.
Campbell, Joan. Acupuncture Channels & Points. 2008. (ENG., Illus.). xxiv, 264p. (C). pap. 79.95 *(978-0-7295-3866-4(4)*, Churchill Livingstone) Elsevier - Health Sciences Div.
Chen, Decheng. Single Point Acupuncture & Moxibustion for 100 Diseases. 2010. 148p. pap. 39.90 *(978-1-4269-3721-7(0))* Trafford Publishing.
Chen, Yu. The Voice of Medicine: An Integration of Traditional Chinese Medicine & Western Medicine. Munson, Alexander A., ed. 2007. 197p. per. 25.00 *(978-0-615-14630-0(9))* Jadestone Medical Supplies.
Choi, Jeung. Essentials of Electroacupuncture. 2011. 342p. 78.99 ***(978-1-4535-7867-4(6))***; pap. 59.99 ***(978-1-4535-7866-7(8))*** Xlibris Corp.
Connelly, Diane M. Traditional Acupuncture: The Law of Five Elements. 3rd ed. (Illus.). 157p. pap. 12.00 *(978-0-912379-01-2(4))* Ctr. for Traditional Acupuncture, Inc.
Cooper, Grant, et al. Acupuncture for Musculoskeletal Medicine. 2009. (ENG., Illus.). 176p. pap. 62.99 *(978-0-7817-8198-5(1))* Lippincott Williams & Wilkins.
Cross, John R. Acupuncture & the Chakra Energy System: Treating the Cause of Disease. 2008. (ENG., Illus.). 208p. pap. 19.95 *(978-1-55643-721-2(8))* North Atlantic Bks.
Cygler, Bernard, ed. Nerz, Gorge, Oreilles en Médecine Traditionelle Chinoise. 2007. (Médecines d'Asie: Savoirs et Pratique Ser.). XIII, 124p. pap. 39.95 *(978-2-287-33709-3(1)*, 2287337091) Springer.
Dalet, Roger. The Encyclopedia of Healing Points. 2010. (ENG., Illus.). 1p. pap. 24.95 *(978-1-59477-335-8(1)*, 1309802, Healing Arts Pr.) Inner Traditions International, Ltd.
Deadman, Peter & Al-Khafaji, Mazin. Acupuncture Point Cards. 2nd ed. 2008. (Illus.). 384p. 85.00 *(978-0-9559096-0-3(0))* Eastland Pr.
Dolowich, Gary. Archetypal Acupuncture: Healing with the Five Elements. 2011. (ENG., Illus.). 336p. pap. 19.95 *(978-1-58394-310-6(2))* North Atlantic Bks.
Eckman, Peter. In the Footsteps of the Yellow Emperor: Tracing the History of Traditional Acupuncture. 2007. (ENG., Illus.). 248p. per. 18.95 *(978-1-59265-074-3(0))* Long River Pr.
Ergil, Marnae C. Pocket Atlas of Chinese Medicine. Ergil, Kevin, ed. 2009. (ENG., Illus.). 415p. pap. 54.99 *(978-3-13-141611-7(4))* Thieme Medical Pubs., Inc.
Faso, W. Scott. A Student Manual to Chinese Acupuncture Differentiation of Syndromes. 2007. spiral bd. 60.00 net. *(978-1-60402-039-7(3))* Independent Pub.
Fedder, Michelle & Elkin, James L., eds. Acupuncture & Traditional Chainese Medicine in New York: Bi-lingual book Written in both English & Chinese. Chen, Doreen et al, trs. 2007. per. *(978-0-9793814-0-9(1))* United Alliance of NYS Licensed Acupuncturists, INC (UANYSLA).
Feely, Richard A. & Yamamoto, Toshikatsu. Yamamoto New Scalp Acupuncture: Principles & Practice. 2nd ed. 2010. (ENG.). 168p. 89.99 ***(978-3-13-141832-6(X))*** Thieme Medical Pubs., Inc.
Filshie, Jacqueline, et al. An Introduction to Western Medical Acupuncture. 2008. (ENG., Illus.). 320p. pap. 62.95 *(978-0-443-07177-5(2)*, Churchill Livingstone) Elsevier - Health Sciences Div.
Finando, Donna. Acupoint & Trigger Point Therapy for Babies & Children: A Parent's Healing Touch. 2008. (ENG., Illus.). 1p. per. 19.95 *(978-1-59477-189-7(8)*, Healing Arts Pr.) Inner Traditions International, Ltd.
Fleischman Omd, Gary F. Healthcare Solutions with Acupuncture. 2009. 236p. 28.95 *(978-1-4401-3643-6(2))*; pap. 18.95 *(978-1-4401-3641-2(6))* iUniverse, Inc.
Focks, Claudia. Acupuncture Points Trainer CD-ROM. 2009. (ENG., Illus.). cd-rom 59.95 *(978-0-7020-3415-2(0)*, Churchill Livingstone) Elsevier - Health Sciences Div.
—Atlas of Acupuncture. Schuster, Johanna, tr. from GER. 2008. (ENG., Illus.). 732p. 102.00 *(978-0-443-10028-4(4)*, Churchill Livingstone) Elsevier - Health Sciences Div.
Fornia, Larry & Mary Frances Lyles-Fornia. An Old-New Treatment for Health in the 21st Century, 1 vol. 2009. 90p. pap. 16.95 *(978-1-60749-904-6(5))* PublishAmerica, Inc.
Frantzis, Bruce. Dragon & Tiger Medical Qigong: A Miracle Health System for Developing Chi. 2010. (ENG., Illus.). 262p. pap. 23.95 *(978-1-55643-921-6(0))* North Atlantic Bks.
Gaffney, Debra. Keys to a Vibrantyl Healthy, Long Life: Insights & Information on Healing, Health & Well-Being. 2011. 212p. pap. 14.95 *(978-0-615-42602-0(6))* Serenity Pass Pr.
—Sensitivities: The Subtle Cause of Suffering, the Hidden Cause of Illness. 2008. (Illus.). 221p. pap. 19.95 *(978-0-9801824-0-8(9))* Smarketing.
Gilbert, Chris Elisabeth. Dr. Chris's A, B, C's of Health: When Your Body Screams, Listen to It! 2010. 148p. pap. 14.95 *(978-1-4502-4816-7(0))* iUniverse, Inc.
Godwin, Jacob. Acupuncture in Black & White: Qi, Yin-Yang, & the Cosmology of the Yijing. 2009. (ENG.). 494p. pap. 49.95 *(978-0-615-31188-3(1))* Godwin AOM.
Golding, Roisin. The Complete Stems & Branches: Time & Space in Traditional Acupuncture. 2008. (ENG., Illus.). 320p. 102.00 *(978-0-7020-2961-5(0)*, Churchill Livingstone) Elsevier - Health Sciences Div.
Hammer, Leon. The Patient-Practitioner Relationship in Acupuncture. 2008. (ENG.). 126p. pap. 44.99 *(978-3-13-148841-1(7))* Thieme Medical Pubs., Inc.
Hartmann, David & Hartmann. Acupoint Dictionary. 2nd rev. ed. 2009. (ENG., Illus.). 130p. (C). spiral bd. 54.95 *(978-0-7295-3883-1(4)*, Churchill Livingstone) Elsevier - Health Sciences Div.
Hecker, Hans-Ulrich, et al. Color Atlas of Acupuncture: Body Points - Ear Points - Trigger Points. 2nd ed. 2008. (ENG., Illus.). 352p. pap. 49.99 *(978-3-13-125222-7(7))* Thieme Medical Pubs., Inc.
Helms, Joseph M. Acupuncture Energetics: A Clinical Approach for Physicians. 2009. (ENG., Illus.). 759p. 175.00 *(978-1-58890-407-2(5))* Thieme Medical Pubs., Inc.

—Getting to Know You: A Physician Explains How Acupuncture Helps You Be the Best YOU. 2007. (ENG., Illus.). 248p. 26.00 *(978-1-57250-712-8(8))* North Atlantic Bks.

Heming, Zhu, et al. Surface Anatomy of Acupuncture. 2009. 120p. pap. 61.99 *(978-1-4363-8516-9(4))* Xlibris Corp.

Hicks, Angela. The Acupuncture: How Acupuncture Works & How It Can Help You. 2011. (ENG., Illus.). 288p. pap., instr.'s hndbk. ed. 15.95 *(978-0-7499-4160-4(X))* Piatkus Bks. GBR. Dist: Independent Pubs. Group.

Hicks, Angela, et al. Five Element Constitutional Acupuncture. 2nd ed. 2011. (ENG., Illus.). 448p. (C). 79.95 *(978-0-7020-3175-5(5),* Churchill Livingstone) Elsevier - Health Sciences Div.

Hicks, Angela, et al. Five Element Constitutional Acupuncture Text & Evolve eBooks Package. 2nd ed. 2011. (ENG., Illus.). 420p. (C). 119.92 ***(978-0-7020-4461-8(X),*** Churchill Livingstone) Elsevier - Health Sciences Div.

International Veterinary Acupuncture Society (IVAS) Staff, compiled by. Annual International Congress on Veterinary Acupuncture 2007. 2007. 268p. pap. 90.00 *(978-1-60423-999-7(9))* Curran Assocs., Inc.

Jarmey, Chris & Bouratinos, Ilaira. Practical Guide to Acu-Points. 2008. (ENG., Illus.). 360p. pap. 39.95 *(978-1-55643-696-3(3))* North Atlantic Bks.

Jin, Guan-Yuan, et al. Contemporary medical Acupuncture. 2007. (Illus.). 97.00 *(978-0-387-71028-0(0))* Springer.

Kassam, Neemez & Gowan, Matthew. Fundamentals of Clinical Acupuncture. 2009. 320p. pap. 124.95 *(978-1-897025-28-4(9))* Canadian College of Naturopathic Medicine Pr. CAN. Dist: SCB Distributors.

Kidson, Ruth. Is Acupuncture Right for You? What It Is, Why It Works, & How It Can Help You. 2nd ed. 2008. (ENG., Illus.). 1p. pap. *(978-1-59477-267-2(3),* Healing Arts Pr.) Inner Traditions International, Ltd.

Kiesewalter, Katharina & Kiesewalter, Boris. Acupuncture Pocket. Keller, Gabriele, ed. 2008. (Pocket (Borm Bruckmeier Publishing) Ser.). (Illus.). 114p. pap. 12.95 *(978-1-59103-248-9(2))* Bruckmeier, Borm Publishing, LLC.

Kobayashi, Shoji. Acupuncture Core Therapy: Shakujyu Chiryo. Kenner, Dan, tr. from JPN. 2008. 212p. 49.95 *(978-0-912111-89-6(5))* Paradigm Pubns.

Kong, Haili & Goldblatt, Howard, trs. from CHI. Ward Four: A Novel of Wartime China. 2012. (ENG.). 225p. pap. 16.95 *(978-0-8351-0000-7(6))* China Bks. & Periodicals, Inc.

Kubiena, Gertrude, et al. Practice Handbook of Acupuncture. 3rd ed. 2009. (ENG., Illus.). 424p. pap. 79.95 *(978-0-443-10265-3(1),* Churchill Livingstone) Elsevier - Health Sciences Div.

Kuoch, David. Acupuncture Desk Reference. 2007. (ENG., Illus.). 416p. spiral bd. 44.95 *(978-0-615-15463-3(8))* Retired Hipster.

Lad, Vasant & Durve, Anisha. Marma Points of Ayurveda: The Energy Pathways for Healing Body, Mind & Consciousness with a Comparison to Traditional Chinese Medicine. 2008. (ENG., Illus.). 384p. 65.00 *(978-1-883725-08-2(9))* Ayurvedic Pr.

Landgren, Kajsa. Ear Acupuncture: A Practical Guide. 2008. (ENG., Illus.). 224p. 79.95 *(978-0-443-06899-7(2),* Churchill Livingstone) Elsevier - Health Sciences Div.

Lian, Yu-Lin, et al. Pictorial Atlas of Acupunture. 2012. (ENG., Illus.). 352p. 19.99 *(978-3-8331-6106-3(X))* h.f.ullmann DEU. Dist: Innovative Logistics.

Lippelt, Ulrich Wilhelm. The Five Elements & Other Essential Rules in Acupuncture Treatment. 2011. 108p. 27.49 ***(978-1-4567-3766-5(X))***; pap. 16.49 ***(978-1-4567-3765-8(1))*** AuthorHouse.

Longbottom, Jennie, ed. Acupuncture in Manual Therapy. 2010. (ENG., Illus.). 248p. pap. 67.95 *(978-0-443-06782-2(1),* Churchill Livingstone) Elsevier - Health Sciences Div.

Ma, Yun-Tao. Biomedical Acupuncture for Sports & Trauma Rehabilitation: Dry Needling Techniques. 2010. (ENG., Illus.). 384p. (C). 78.95 *(978-1-4377-0927-8(3),* Churchill Livingstone) Elsevier - Health Sciences Div.

Maciocia, Giovanni. The Channels of Acupuncture: Clinical Use of the Secondary Channels & Eight Extraordinary Vessels. 2006. (ENG., Illus.). 768p. 145.00 *(978-0-443-07491-2(7),* Churchill Livingstone) Elsevier - Health Sciences Div.

—The Channels of Acupuncture Cards: Clinical Use of the Secondary Channels & Eight Extraordinary Vessels. 2006. (ENG., Illus.). 226p. (C). spiral bd. 83.95 *(978-0-443-10379-7(8),* Churchill Livingstone) Elsevier - Health Sciences Div.

—The Psyche in Chinese Medicine: Treatment of Emotional & Mental Disharmonies with Acupuncture & Chinese Herbs. 2009. (ENG., Illus.). 688p. 119.00 *(978-0-7020-2988-2(2),* Churchill Livingstone) Elsevier - Health Sciences Div.

MacPherson, Hugh, et al, eds. Acupuncture Research: Strategies for Establishing an Evidence Base. 2007. (ENG., Illus.). 288p. per. 66.95 *(978-0-443-10029-1(2),* Churchill Livingstone) Elsevier - Health Sciences Div.

Matern, Christina. Acupuncture for Dogs & Cats: A Pocket Atlas. 2011. (ENG., Illus.). 384p. pap. 79.99 ***(978-3-13-154691-3(3))*** Thieme Medical Pubs., Inc.

Mayor, David F. Electroacupuncture: A Practical Manual & Resource. 2007. (ENG., Illus.). 404p. 99.95 *(978-0-443-06369-5(9),* Churchill Livingstone) Elsevier - Health Sciences Div.

Mei-Pochtler, Antonella. Acupuncture for Management: New Perspectives on Strategy & Leadership. 2006. (ENG & GER., Illus.). 240p. per. 45.00 *(978-3-8327-9132-2(9))* teNeues Publishing Co.

Milford, Francine. Tuning Fork Therapy(r) using tuning forks on dog's acupuncture Points. 2008. 62p. pap. 15.00 *(978-1-4357-4031-0(9))* Lulu Enterprises Inc.

Mole, Peter. Acupuncture. 2008. (Illus.). 224p. pap. 18.00 *(978-1-905862-13-9(X))* How To Books GBR. Dist: Parkwest Pubns., Inc.

Montakab, Hamid. Acupuncture for Insomnia: Sleep & Dreams in Chinese Medicine. 2012. (ENG., Illus.). 200p. 74.95 *(978-3-13-154331-8(0))* Thieme Medical Pubs., Inc.

Nambudripac, Devi S. The NAET Guide Book: The Companion to Say Good-Bye to Illness. 2009. (ENG.). 96p. pap. 12.00 *(978-1-934523-09-4(7))* Delta Publishing Co.

Nogier, Raphaël. Auriculotherapy. 2008. (ENG., Illus.). 186p. pap. 54.99 *(978-3-13-148001-9(7))* Thieme Medical Pubs., Inc.

Oleson, Terry. Auriculotherapy Manual: Chinese & Western Systems of Ear Acupuncture. 4th ed. 2012. (ENG., Illus.). 384p. 81.95 ***(978-0-7020-3572-2(6),*** Churchill Livingstone) Elsevier - Health Sciences Div.

Pedrali, Tiziana & Quirico, Piero Ettore. Teaching Atlas of Acupuncture Vol. 1: Channels & Points. 2007. (ENG., Illus.). 414p. 179.99 *(978-1-58890-567-3(5))* Thieme Medical Pubs., Inc.

Quirico, P. E. & Pedrali, Tiziana. Teaching Atlas of Acupuncture. 2007. (Illus.). 169.95 *(978-3-13-141251-5(8))* Thieme Medical Pubs., Inc.

Quirico, Piero Ettore. Teaching Atlas of Acupuncture: Clinical Indications. 2007. (ENG.). 288p. 169.99 *(978-1-58890-665-6(5))* Thieme Medical Pubs., Inc.

Reaves, Whitfield. The Acupuncture Handbook of Sports Injuries & Pain. 2009. (ENG., Illus.). 352p. spiral bd. 65.00 *(978-0-615-27440-9(4))* Hidden Needle Pr.

Rhyu, Paul H. Acupuncture Meridians & Acupuncture Points. 2010. 136p. pap. 45.49 *(978-1-4520-2136-2(8))* AuthorHouse.

Robinson, Bruce H. Biomedicine. 2007. (Illus.). xiii, 748p. *(978-1-891845-38-3(1))* Blue Poppy Pr.

Romoli, Marco. Auricular Acupuncture Diagnosis. 2009. (ENG., Illus.). 320p. 81.95 *(978-0-443-06866-9(6),* Churchill Livingstone) Elsevier - Health Sciences Div.

Sachs, Thomas C. Does It Hurt? Acupuncture Explained: Answers to the Most Frequently Asked Questions About Acupuncture & Traditional Chinese Medicine for the Prospective Patient & How Acupuncture & Traditional Chinese Medicine May be the Missing Link in America's Failing Healthcare System. 2006. (Illus.). 288p. pap. 19.95 *(978-1-59800-661-2(4))* Outskirts Pr., Inc.

Salomon, Sobeida. It Is in Your Hands: The Power to Eliminate Stress, Anxiety, & All Negative Emotions. 2nd ed. 2011. (Illus.). 109p. pap. 29.52 *(978-0-9655643-0-4(4),* SpiralPress) HydroScience, Inc.

Schreck, Joel Harvey. A Patient's Guide to Chinese Medicine: Dr. Shen's Handbook of Herbs & Acupuncture. 2008. (ENG.). 288p. pap. 18.95 *(978-0-9801758-0-6(1))* Bay Tree Publishing.

Science and Life Consultants Association Staff. Acupuncture in the United Stated with Index & Medical Analysis of New Research Information for all Nations. 2007. (Illus.). 160p. 69.95 *(978-0-7883-4544-9(3),* 0-7883-4544-3) ABBE Pubs. Assn. of Washington, D.C.

Shizhen, Li. Clinical Application of Commonly Used Acupuncture Points. Zhaoguo, Li et al, trs. 2007. (ENG., Illus.). 950p. 110.00 *(978-1-901149-06-7(4))* Donica Publishing Ltd. GBR. Dist: Elsevier - Health Sciences Div.

Smith, Alan E. How to Unbreak Your Health: Your Map to the World of Complementary & Alternative Therapies, 2nd Edition. 2010. 268p. pap. 21.95 *(978-1-61599-042-9(9))* Loving Healing Pr., Inc.

Strittmatter, Beate. Ear Acupuncture: A Precise Pocket Atlas Based on the Works of Nogier/Bahr. 2nd ed. 2011. (ENG., Illus.). 440p. pap. 59.99 ***(978-3-13-131962-3(3))*** Thieme Medical Pubs., Inc.

Sun, Peilin. Management of Post-Operative Pain with Acupuncture. 2007. (ENG., Illus.). 304p. 79.95 *(978-0-443-10361-2(5),* Churchill Livingstone) Elsevier - Health Sciences Div.

—The Treatment of Pain with Chinese Herbs & Acupuncture. 2nd ed. 2010. (ENG.). 704p. (C). 110.00 *(978-0-7020-3179-3(8),* Churchill Livingstone) Elsevier - Health Sciences Div.

Tan, Richard Teh-Fu. Acupuncture 1,2,3. 2007. pap. *(978-0-9759412-3-2(2))* Tan, Richard.

Thambirajah, Radha. Cosmetic Acupuncture: A TCM approach to cosmetic & dermatological Problems. 2008. (ENG., Illus.). 208p. pap. 66.95 *(978-0-443-06954-3(9),* Churchill Livingstone) Elsevier - Health Sciences Div.

—Energetics in Acupuncture: Five Element Acupuncture Made Easy. 2010. (ENG., Illus.). 496p. (C). 69.95 *(978-0-7020-3413-8(4),* Churchill Livingstone) Elsevier - Health Sciences Div.

Thieme Almanac Staff, et al, eds. Thieme Almanac 2008: Acupuncture & Chinese Medicine. 2007. (ENG.). 501p. pap. 59.99 *(978-1-58890-617-5(5))* Thieme Medical Pubs., Inc.

Tibshraeny-Morten, Lilian. Moving the Energy: Reflexology & Meridian Therapy. 2006. pap. 26.95 *(978-0-9768922-2-9(7))* JML Publishing Inc.

Tran, Robert. Internal Diseases in Chinese Medicine: B?Nh N?I Khoa ChM C?U Th?C D?Ng. 2011. 372p. 34.90 ***(978-1-4634-3454-0(5))***; pap. 25.99 ***(978-1-4634-3455-7(3))*** AuthorHouse.

Wager, Kim & Cox, Sue. Auricular Acupuncture & Addiction: Mechanisms, Methodology & Practice. 2008. (ENG., Illus.). 256p. pap. 66.95 *(978-0-443-06885-0(2),* Churchill Livingstone) Elsevier - Health Sciences Div.

Walsh, Malachy. A Life Interrupted: Insights & Cure of a Depressive. 2008. (ENG.). 151p. pap. 25.95 *(978-1-905172-68-9(0))* Collins Pr., The IRL. Dist: Dufour Editions, Inc.

Wang, Ju-Yi & Robertson, Jason D. Applied Channel Theory in Chinese Medicine: Wang Ju-Yi's Lectures on Channel Therapeutics. 2008. (Illus.). 718p. 75.00 *(978-0-939616-62-6(9))* Eastland Pr.

Wang, Yajuan. Micro-Acupuncture in Practice. 2008. (ENG., Illus.). 608p. (C). 110.00 *(978-0-443-06732-7(5),* Churchill Livingstone) Elsevier - Health Sciences Div.

West, Zita. Acupuncture in Pregnancy & Childbirth. Isaacs, Lyndsey, ed. 2nd ed. 2008. (ENG., Illus.). 272p. 89.95 *(978-0-443-10371-1(2),* Churchill Livingstone) Elsevier - Health Sciences Div.

Wilcox, Lorraine, tr. from CHI. The Great Compendium of Acupuncture & Moxibustion Vol. V: Zhen jiu Da Cheng Vol. V. 2010. (Illus.). 262p. pap. 40.00 *(978-0-9799552-4-2(6))* Chinese Medicine Database, The.

World Health Organization. WHO Standard Acupuncture Point Locations in the Western Pacific Region. 2008. (WPRO Nonserial Publication). (ENG., Illus.). 256p. pap. 24.00 *(978-92-9061-383-1(1))* World Health Organization.

Xia, Ying, et al, eds. Current Research in Acupuncture. 2012. (ENG., Illus.). x, 798p. 239.00 ***(978-1-4614-3356-9(8),*** 1461433568) Springer.

Xia, Ying, et al. Acupuncture Therapy for Neurological Diseases: A Neurobiological View. Cheng, Jieshi, ed. 2010. (ENG., Illus.). 400p. 249.00 *(978-3-642-10855-6(5),* 3642108555) Springer.

Xie, Huisheng. Canine Multiple Acupuncture Channel Chart. 2007. (Illus.). 10p. ring bd. 45.00 *(978-0-9720045-6-5(4))* Chi Institute of Chinese Medicine.

—Equine Multiple Acupuncture Channel Chart. 2007. 40.00 *(978-0-9720045-4-1(8))* Chi Institute of Chinese Medicine.

—Xie's TCVM Clinic Chart - Heart. 2007. 15.00 *(978-0-9720045-3-4(X))* Chi Institute of Chinese Medicine.

Xie, Huisheng & Preast, Vanessa. Xie's Veterinary Acupuncture. 2007. (ENG., Illus.). 374p. 164.99 *(978-0-8138-1247-2(X),* Wiley-Blackwell) Wiley, John & Sons, Inc.

Xu, Jun & Murray, Frank. Magic Needles: Feel Younger & Live Longer with Acupuncture, 1 vol. 2011. 300p. pap. ***(978-1-59120-222-6(1))*** Basic Health Pubns., Inc.

Young, Wei-Chieh & Dong, Jingchang. Lectures on Tung's Acupuncture: Therapeutic System. 2008. (CHI & ENG., Illus.). 265p. ***(978-0-9779026-5-1(X),*** Orbit Books) Wei Chieh Young.

Yuen, Mullins. Chinese Meridians, blueprints of Life, Part III: Becoming Uniquely Ourselves. 2009. pap. *(978-1-61623-383-9(4))* Independent Pub.

Zheng, Li. Acupuncture & Hormone Balance. 2008. 413p. pap. 39.97 *(978-0-557-01917-5(6))* Lulu Enterprises Inc.

ACURA AUTOMOBILE

Chilton. Chilton 2006 Asian Diagnostic Service Manual Series. 2006. (Chilton Diagnostic Manuals Ser.). 239.85 *(978-1-4180-2986-9(6))* Delmar Cengage Learning.

Freund, Ken. Honda Pilot Acura MDX: Honda Pilot - 2003 thru 2007 - Acura MDX - 2001 Thru 2007. 2008. (Haynes Repair Manual Ser.). (ENG., Illus.). 352p. pap. 26.95 *(978-1-56392-690-7(3),* 1563926903) Haynes Manuals, Inc.

Haynes Manuals Editors, ed. Acura TL 1999 Thru 2008. 2009. (Automotive Repair Manual Ser.). (ENG., Illus.). 336p. pap. 26.95 *(978-1-56392-744-7(6),* 1563927446) Haynes Manuals, Inc.

Maddox, Rob. Acura TL: 1999 Thru 2008. 2009. (ENG.). 400p. pap. 29.95 *(978-1-56392-757-7(8))* Haynes,Chilton.

Wegmann, John A. Chilton's Honda Pilot/Acura MDX 2001-07 Repair Manual: Covers All U.S. & Canadian Models of Honda Pilot (2003 Through 2007) & Acura MDX (2001 Through 2007) 2009. (ENG., Illus.). 432p. pap. 29.95 *(978-1-56392-692-1(X))* Haynes,Chilton.

ACUTE CATARRHAL JAUNDICE

see Hepatitis A

ACUTE CONFUSIONAL STATES

see Delirium

ACUTE IDIOPATHIC POLYNEURITIS

see Guillain-Barre Syndrome

ACUTE JUVENILE CIRRHOSIS

see Chronic Active Hepatitis

ACUTE PHASE REACTION

Asarian, Lori. Role of Mast Cells in the Acute Phase Response. 2008. 120p. pap. *(978-3-639-08227-2(3))* VDM Verlag Dr. Mueller e.K.

ACYCLOVIR

Katragadda, Suresh. Amino Acid Prodrugs of Acyclovir: Ocular herpes Infections. 2009. 160p. pap. *(978-3-639-15135-7(4))* VDM Verlag Dr. Mueller e.K.

AD VALOREM TARIFF

see Tariff

ADA

see United States—Americans with Disabilities Act, 1990

ADA (COMPUTER PROGRAM LANGUAGE)

Association for Computing Machinery Staff, contrib. by. SIGAda'07: Proceedings of the 2007 ACM SIGAda Annual International Conference, Fairfax, Virginia, USA, November 4-9, 2007. 2007. (Illus.). vii, 108p. pap. ***(978-1-59593-876-3(1))*** Assn. for Computing Machinery

Barnes, John. ADA 2005 Rationale: The Language, the Standard Libraries. 2008. (Lecture Notes in Computer Science / Programming & Software Engineering Ser.). (Illus.). 267p. spiral bd. 69.95 *(978-3-540-79700-5(9),* 3540797009) Springer.

Ben-Ari, Mordechai. Ada for Software Engineers 2005. 2nd ed. 2009. (ENG., Illus.). xiv, 510p. pap. 69.95 *(978-1-84882-313-6(4),* 1848823134) Springer.

Burns, Alan & Wellings, Andy. Concurrent & Real-Time Programming in ADA. 2007. (ENG., Illus.). 476p. 83.00 *(978-0-521-86697-2(9))* Cambridge Univ. Pr.

Dale, Nell B. & McCormick, John A. ADA Plus Data Structures: An Object-Oriented Approach. 2nd rev. ed. 2006. (Illus.). 900p. (C). pap. 186.95 *(978-0-7637-3794-8(1))* Jones & Bartlett Learning, LLC.

Goos, G., et al, eds. DIANA. An Intermediate Language for Ada: Revised Version. 2007. (Lecture Notes in Computer Science Ser.). 216p. per. 29.95 *(978-3-540-12695-9(3))* Springer.

Goos, G. & Hartmanis, eds. An Attribute Grammar for the Semantic Analysis of Ada. 2007. (Lecture Notes in Computer Science Ser.). 528p. per. 49.95 *(978-3-540-11571-7(4))* Springer.

McCormick, John W., et al. Building Parallel, Embedded, & Real-Time Applications with Ada. 2011. (ENG., Illus.). 386p. 90.00 *(978-0-521-19716-8(3))* Cambridge Univ. Pr.

Romanovsky, Alexander & Vardanega, Tullio, eds. Reliable Software Technologies - Ada-Europe 2011: 16th Ada-Europe International Conference on Reliable Software Technologies, Edinburgh, UK, June 20-24, 2011. Proceedings. 2011. (Lecture Notes in Computer Science / Programming & Software Engineering Ser.). (Illus.). xii, 227p. pap. 72.00 *(978-3-642-21337-3(5),* 3642213375) Springer.

SIGAda Staff & Association for Computing Machinery Staff, contrib. by. SIGAda'08: Proceedings of the 2008 ACM SIGAda Annual International Conference: Portland, Oregon, USA, October 26-30, 2008. 2008. (Illus.). viii, 140p. 99.00 *(978-1-60558-274-0(3))* Assn. for Computing Machinery.

Springer, ed. The Programming Language Ada: Reference Manual. Proposed Standard Document United States Department of Defense. 2007. (Lecture Notes in Computer Science Ser.). 260p. per. 49.95 *(978-3-540-10693-7(6))* Springer.

Taft, S. Tucker. ADA 2005 Reference Manual: Language & Standard Libraries: International Standard ISO/IEC 8652/1995 (e) with Technical Corrigendum 1 & Amendment 1. 2007. (Lecture Notes in Computer Science Ser.: Vol. 4348). (Illus.). XXIX, 765p. pap. 139.00 *(978-3-540-69335-2(1),* 3540693351) Springer.

ADAGES

see Maxims; Proverbs

ADAM (BIBLICAL FIGURE)

Almond, Philip C. Adam & Eve in Seventeenth-Century Thought. 2008. (ENG.). 252p. pap. 36.00 *(978-0-521-09084-1(9))* Cambridge Univ. Pr.

Arbel, Vita Daphna. Forming Femininity in Antiquity: Eve, Gender, & Ideologies in the Greek Life of Adam & Eve, 1 vol. 2012. (ENG., Illus.). 224p. 74.00 ***(978-0-19-983777-9(5))*** Oxford Univ. Pr., Inc.

Arches, Tess. Power of Freewill- Life or Death? 2011. 116p. pap. 19.95 ***(978-1-4626-1288-8(1))*** PublishAmerica, Inc.

Collins, C. John. Did Adam & Eve Really Exist? Who They Were & Why You Should Care. 2011. *(978-1-4335-2426-4(0))* Crossway.

Devenport, Donald. 7 Healthy Stages in Male & Female Relationships. 2008. 208p. per. 15.99 *(978-1-60477-362-0(6))* Xulon Pr., Inc.

Edwards, Patricia. Eve's Quest & the Battle for Eden. 2010. 167p. pap. 14.50 *(978-0-557-37316-1(6))* Lulu Enterprises Inc.

Halevi, Z'ev ben Shimon. Adam & the Kabbalistic Trees. 2007. (Illus.). 292p. pap. 18.95 *(978-1-56171-218-2(3))* SPI Bks.

Hughes, Mary Joy. Hey There Were People on Earth before Adam & Eve: The Creation before Adam & Eve. 2006. pap. 19.95 *(978-0-8059-7052-4(5))* Dorrance Publishing Co., Inc.

Ingram, Harvey. Adam, Israel, & Jesus. 2009. *(978-1-55452-229-3(3))* (ENG.). 320p. pap. *(978-1-55452-228-6(5),* Guardian Bks.) Essence Publishing.

Jawaid, Mahmood Nayyer Azam. Atom to Adam — How, When & Where? In the Light of Quran, Bible, & Science. 2007. per. 20.00 *(978-1-59872-562-7(4))* Instant Pub.

King, Sandra. Adam & the Woman. 2008. 204p. per. 14.99 *(978-1-60477-432-0(0))* Xulon Pr., Inc.

LaCocque, Andre. The Trial of Innocence: Adam, Eve, & the Yahwist. 2006. 324p. pap. 31.00 *(978-1-59752-620-3(7),* Cascade Bks.) Wipf & Stock Pubs.

Langer, Lawrence. Adam & Eve in the Art of Samuel Bak. Choi, Justine, ed. 2012. (Illus.). 120p. 50.00 ***(978-1-879985-25-4(X))*** Pucker Gallery.

Levster, David. The Great Escape. 2010. 256p. 27.99 *(978-1-4490-9239-9(X))*; pap. 15.99 *(978-1-4490-9241-2(1))* AuthorHouse.

Lowrie, John M. Adam & His Times. 2006. 292p. per. 23.99 *(978-1-4255-2745-7(0))* MPublishing.

Makuannen, Yaqob. Man Woman & Spirit. 2007. 27.95 *(978-0-9801297-3-1(7))*; pap. 19.95 *(978-0-9801297-2-4(9))* G Publishing LLC.

Mbugua, Eunice. Adam's Death Was Worthy: Life Had to Begin in the Deadly World. 2009. 168p. pap. 13.99 *(978-1-4389-9873-2(2))* AuthorHouse.

Neufeld, Dietmar, et al. And So They Went Out: The Lives of Adam & Eve as Cultural Transformative Story. 2010. (ENG.). 208p. 130.00 *(978-0-567-02679-8(5),* T&T Clark Int'l) Continuum International Publishing Group, Ltd. GBR. Dist: National Bk. Network.

Novak, Kevin P. Adam Versus Adam. 2007. 82p. per. 9.99 *(978-1-59886-835-7(7))* Tate Publishing & Enterprises, LLC.

Paul, G. Derek Neriah. What Happened in the Garden of Eden. 2010. 124p. pap. 14.95 *(978-1-4520-7367-5(8))* AuthorHouse.

Platt, Rutherford. First Book of Adam & Eve. 2008. 96p. pap. *(978-1-4068-6592-9(3))* Echo Library.

—First Book of Adam & Eve. 2006. (ENG.). 208p. per. 17.99 *(978-1-59547-950-1(3))* NuVision Pubns., LLC.

—First Book of Adam & Eve. 2009. (ENG.). 100p. pap. 10.45 *(978-1-4385-1934-0(6),* Book Jungle) Standard Pubns., Inc.

Platt, Rutherford Hayes. The First Book of Adam & Eve. 2008. 140p. 21.99 *(978-0-554-30855-5(X))* 2008. 140p. 24.99 *(978-0-554-21552-5(7))* 2006. 138p. pap. 18.99 *(978-1-4264-0343-9(7))* BiblioBazaar.

Postell, Seth D. Adam As Israel: Genesis 1-3 as the Introduction to the Torah & Tanakh. 2012. (ENG.). 216p. pap. 39.00 ***(978-0-227-68019-3(7))*** Clarke, James Co., Ltd. GBR. Dist: Brown, David Bk. Co., The.

Postell, Seth D. Adam as Israel: Genesis 1Ð3 as the Introduction to the Torah & Tanakh. 2011. 216p. pap. 24.00 *(978-1-61097-176-8(0)*, Pickwick Pubns.) Wipf & Stock Pubs.

Richards, Mitchell. Definitive Blues. 2010. 225p. pap. 15.00 *(978-0-557-35150-3(2))* Lulu Enterprises Inc.

Rosenberg, Paul A. A Second Look at Eden. 2007. 50p. per. 9.95 *(978-0-9796011-4-9(2))* Vera Verba, Inc.

Rutherford Platt. First Book of Adam & Eve. 2010. 104p. pap. 3.49 *(978-1-60386-363-6(X)*, Watchmaker Publishing) Wexford College Pr.

Sanders, Theresa. Approaching Eden: Adam & Eve in Popular Culture. 2009. (ENG.). 264p. 37.50 *(978-0-7425-6333-9(2))* Rowman & Littlefield Publishers, Inc.

Schillman, Gabe. War of God: Part One. 2008. 114p. pap. 19.95 *(978-1-60563-306-0(2))* PublishAmerica, Inc.

Swedenborg, Emanuel. Worship & Love of God. Shotwell, Stuart S., tr. 2009. (New Century Edition of the Works of Emanuel Swedenborg). 288p. 49.00 *(978-0-87785-479-1(3)*, 325-137) Swedenborg Foundation, Inc.

Taylor, Bill. Men of Like Passion: Six Men God Used to Bless His People. 2011. (ENG.). 209p. pap. 21.95 ***(978-1-4327-7921-4(4))*** Outskirts Pr., Inc.

Toepel, A. Die Adam- und Seth-Legenden im Syrischen Buch der Schatzhohle. eine quellenkritische Untersuching. 2006. (Corpus Scriptorum Christianorum Orientalium Ser.). (ENG.). 259p. (C). pap. 124.00 *(978-90-429-1739-2(3))* Peeters Pubs. & Booksellers BEL. Dist: Brown, David Bk. Co., The.

White, Ellen G. Creation's Couple: Adam & Eve. 2006. 110p. per. 11.95 *(978-1-57258-427-3(0)*, 945-6288) TEACH Services, Inc.

Williams, Winston. The World Before Adam & Eve. 2008. 56p. pap. 15.99 *(978-1-4363-4408-1(5))* Xlibris Corp.

ADAM, ADOLPHE CHARLES, 1803-1856

Smith, Marian. Ballet & Opera in the Age of Giselle. 2010. (Princeton Studies in Opera Ser.). (ENG., Illus.). 288p. (C). pap. 27.95 *(978-0-691-14649-2(7))* Princeton Univ. Pr.

ADAM, JAMES, 1730-1794

Kondo, Ariyuki. Robert & James Adam, Architects of the Age of Enlightenment, 1 vol. 2011. (Enlightenment World Ser.). (ENG., Illus.). 224p. 99.00 *(978-1-84893-179-4(4))* Pickering & Chatto Pubs., Ltd. GBR. Dist: Ashgate Publishing Co.

ADAM, ROBERT, 1728-1792

Kondo, Ariyuki. Robert & James Adam, Architects of the Age of Enlightenment, 1 vol. 2011. (Enlightenment World Ser.). (ENG., Illus.). 224p. 99.00 *(978-1-84893-179-4(4))* Pickering & Chatto Pubs., Ltd. GBR. Dist: Ashgate Publishing Co.

Tames, Richard. Robert Adam: An Illustrated Life of Robert Adam, 1728-92. 2008. (Lifelines Ser.). (ENG., Illus.). 48p. per. 12.95 *(978-0-7478-0603-5(9))* Shire Pubns., Ltd. GBR. Dist: Random Hse., Inc.

ADAMS, ABIGAIL, 1744-1818

Abigail Adams: An American Heroine. 2007. per. 10.00 net. *(978-1-893311-93-0(7))* Univ. of Wisconsin-Madison, General Library System.

Adams, Abigail. My Dearest Friend: Letters of Abigail & John Adams. Hogan, Margaret A. & Taylor, C. James, eds. 2007. (Illus.). 528p. 35.00 *(978-0-674-02606-3(3)*, Belknap Pr.) Harvard Univ. Pr.

Adams, Abigail S. The Quotable Abigail Adams. Kaminski, John P., ed. 2009. 448p. 26.95 *(978-0-674-03532-4(1)*, Belknap Pr.) Harvard Univ. Pr.

Adams, Abigail S., et al. My Dearest Friend: Letters of Abigail & John Adams. 2010. (ENG., Illus.). 528p. pap. 19.95 *(978-0-674-05705-0(8)*, Belknap Pr.) Harvard Univ. Pr.

Adams, Charles Francis. Letters of John Adams, Addressed to His Wife. 2009. 324p. 36.99 *(978-1-113-63761-1(7))*; 32.99 *(978-1-113-63760-4(9))*; pap. 30.75 *(978-1-113-63759-8(5))*; pap. 29.75 *(978-1-113-63758-1(7))* BiblioBazaar.

—Letters of John Adams, Addressed to His Wife. 2010. 120p. pap. 19.99 *(978-1-154-14034-7(2))* General Bks. LLC.

—Letters of John Adams, Addressed to His Wife. 2010. (ENG.). 312p. pap. 29.75 *(978-1-177-47633-1(9))*; (ENG.). 330p. pap. 31.75 *(978-1-176-54387-4(3))*; 300p. pap. 28.75 *(978-1-145-89874-5(2))*; 320p. pap. 30.75 *(978-1-145-60127-7(8))* BiblioBazaar.

—Letters of John Adams, addressed to his Wife. 2009. 323p. (ENG.). pap. 23.99 *(978-1-113-63756-7(0))*; pap. 24.99 *(978-1-113-63757-4(9))* BiblioBazaar. (BiblioLife).

Adams, Charles Francis, ed. Letters of John Adams Addressed to his Wife. 2011. (Cambridge Library Collection - History Ser.). (ENG.). 308p. pap. 24.99 ***(978-1-108-03275-9(3))***; 324p. pap. 24.99 ***(978-1-108-03274-2(5))*** Cambridge Univ. Pr.

Adams, Charles Francis, ed. Letters of John Adams, Addressed to His Wife V2. 304p. 2010. 35.16 *(978-1-166-65757-4(4))* 2010. pap. 23.16 *(978-1-166-60534-6(5))* 2009. 43.95 *(978-1-120-37297-0(6))* 2009. pap. 28.95 *(978-1-120-31494-9(1))* Kessinger Publishing, LLC.

Adams-Graf, John. Familiar Letters of John Adams & His Wife Abigail Adams, During the Revolution. with a Memoir of Mrs. Adams. 424p. reprint ed. 98.00 *(978-0-7222-8616-6(3))* Library Reprints, Inc.

Adams, John Francis, ed. Letters of John Adams Addressed to His Wife V1. 2010. 322p. pap. 24.76 *(978-1-163-90677-4(8))* 2010. 324p. 36.76 ***(978-1-164-34406-3(4))*** 2008. 320p. 45.95 *(978-0-548-92982-7(3))* 2007. (ENG.). 324p. per. 30.95 *(978-0-548-56822-4(7))* Kessinger Publishing, LLC.

Barker-Benfield, G. J. Abigail & John Adams: The Americanization of Sensibility. 2010. (ENG.). 520p. 32.50 *(978-0-226-03743-1(6))* Univ. of Chicago Pr.

Ellis, Joseph J. First Family: Abigail & John Adams. (Vintage Ser.). (ENG.). 320p. 2011. pap. 15.95 *(978-0-307-38999-2(5)*, Vintage) 2010. 27.95 *(978-0-307-26962-1(0)*, Knopf) Knopf Doubleday Publishing Group.

Gelles, Edith. Abigail & John: Portrait of a Marriage. 2010. 352p. pap. 14.99 *(978-0-06-135412-0(0)*, HarperPerennial) 2009. (ENG.). 320p. pap. 26.99 *(978-0-06-166836-4(2)*, HarperLuxe) HarperCollins Pubs.

Gelles, Edith Belle. Abigail & John: Portrait of a Marriage. 2009. (Illus.). 352p. 26.99 *(978-0-06-135387-1(6)*, Morrow, William & Co.) HarperCollins Pubs.

Holton, Woody. Abigail Adams. 2010. (ENG., Illus.). 512p. pap. 18.00 *(978-1-4165-4681-8(2)*, Free Pr.) Free Pr.

Letters of John Adams, Addressed to His Wife. 2010. 308p. pap. 29.75 *(978-1-142-93874-1(3))* 2010. 324p. pap. 30.75 *(978-1-142-79789-8(9))* 2008. 320p. 28.99 *(978-0-554-43991-4(3))* 2008. 320p. 29.99 *(978-0-554-43979-2(4))* 2008. 320p. pap. 30.75 *(978-0-554-43983-9(2))* 2008. 320p. pap. 29.75 *(978-0-554-43989-1(1))* BiblioBazaar.

Letters of John Adams, Addressed to His Wife. 2009. 150p. pap. *(978-1-150-67722-9(8))* Books LLC.

Letters of John Adams, Addressed to His Wife. 2009. 158p. pap. 19.99 *(978-1-150-67718-2(X))*; 160p. pap. 19.39 *(978-1-150-26894-6(8))* General Bks. LLC.

Richards, Laura E. Abigail Adams & Her Times. 2009. 300p. 30.99 *(978-1-113-59887-5(5))*; pap. 29.75 *(978-1-113-61000-3(X))*; pap. 28.75 *(978-1-113-59886-8(7))* BiblioBazaar.

—Abigail Adams & Her Times. 2007. (ENG.). 300p. 43.95 *(978-0-548-43735-3(1))*; per. 28.95 *(978-0-548-41536-8(6))* Kessinger Publishing, LLC.

—Abigail Adams & Her Times. 2008. 300p. pap. *(978-1-4097-7066-4(4))* Read Bks.

ADAMS, ANSEL, 1902-1984

Adams, Ansel. Ansel Adams: The National Park Service Photographs. 2008. (ENG.). 144p. 20.00 *(978-1-4379-5835-5(4))* DIANE Publishing Co.

—In the National Parks: Photographs from America's Wild Places. Stillman, Andrea G., ed. 2010. (ENG., Illus.). 344p. 40.00 *(978-0-316-07846-7(8)*, Ansel Adams) Little Brown & Co.

Frye, Michael. Digital Landscape Photography: in the Footsteps of Ansel Adams & the Masters. 2010. (ENG., Illus.). 192p. pap. 24.95 *(978-0-240-81243-4(3)*, Focal Pr.) Elsevier Science & Technology Bks.

Georgia O'Keeffe Museum Staff. Natural Affinities. 2008. (ENG., Illus.). 176p. 40.00 *(978-0-316-11832-3(X))* Little Brown & Co.

Morgan-Griffiths, Lauris. Ansel Adams: Landscapes of the American West. 2008. (Illus.). 224p. *(978-1-84724-502-1(1)*, Quercus) Quercus.

—Ansel Adams: Landscapes of the American West. 2011. (ENG., Illus.). 224p. 39.95 *(978-1-84724-659-2(1))* Quercus GBR. Dist: Independent Pubs. Group.

Stillman, Andrea G. Looking at Ansel Adams: The Photographs & the Man. 2012. (ENG., Illus.). 272p. 40.00 ***(978-0-316-21780-4(8))*** Little Brown & Co.

ADAMS, CHARLES FRANCIS, 1807-1886

Adams, Charles Francis. Charles Francis Adams. 2009. (ENG.). 455p. 42.99 *(978-1-117-36133-8(0))* 2009. (ENG.). 437p. 41.99 *(978-1-117-45506-8(8))* 2009. 438p. pap. 34.75 *(978-1-117-45507-5(6))* 2009. (ENG.). 455p. pap. 35.75 *(978-1-117-36134-5(9))* 2008. 456p. 31.99 *(978-0-559-59412-0(7))* 2008. 456p. pap. 35.75 *(978-0-559-59409-0(7))* BiblioBazaar.

—Charles Francis Adams. 2009. 166p. pap. *(978-1-150-33946-2(2))* Books LLC.

—Charles Francis Adams. 2007. (ENG.). 444p. 51.95 *(978-0-548-00799-0(3))* Kessinger Publishing, LLC.

—Charles Francis Adams. (American Statesmen Ser.). 426p. reprint ed. 98.00 *(978-0-7222-8979-2(0))*; 98.00 *(978-0-7222-8479-7(9))* Library Reprints, Inc.

—Charles Francis Adams. 2008. 444p. pap. *(978-1-4086-9930-0(3))* 2008. 448p. pap. *(978-1-4097-9596-4(9))* 2007. (ENG.). 444p. per. *(978-1-4067-5787-3(X))* Read Bks.

Adams, Charles Francis, ed. Charles Francis Adams. 2007. (ENG.). 452p. 52.95 *(978-0-548-11121-5(9))* Kessinger Publishing, LLC.

Welles, Gideon. Lincoln & Seward Remarks upon the Memorial Address of Chas Francis Adams, on the Late William H Seward, with Incidents & Comments Illustrative. 2006. 224p. per. 20.99 *(978-1-4255-1817-2(6))* MPublishing.

ADAMS, CHARLES FRANCIS, 1835-1915

Adams, Charles Francis. Charles Francis Adams, 1835-1915: An Autobiography. 288p. 2009. 24.99 *(978-1-103-08451-7(8))* 2009. pap. 18.99 *(978-1-103-08448-7(8))* 2008. 25.99 *(978-0-559-88026-1(X))* 2008. pap. 27.75 *(978-0-559-88024-7(3))* 2008. 25.99 *(978-0-559-26286-9(8))* 2008. pap. 27.75 *(978-0-559-26282-1(5))* BiblioBazaar.

—Charles Francis Adams, 1835-1915: An Autobiography. 224p. reprint ed. 98.00 *(978-0-7222-8980-8(4))* Library Reprints, Inc.

ADAMS, HENRY, 1838-1918

Adams, Henry. The Education of Henry Adams. Date not set. lib. bdg. 24.95 *(978-0-89190-844-9(7))* Amereon LTD.

—The Education of Henry Adams. 2009. 368p. pap. 9.99 *(978-1-60450-649-5(0)*, Serenity Pubs.) Arc Manor.

—The Education of Henry Adams. 2008. 504p. 35.99 *(978-0-554-26065-5(4))* 2008. 504p. 32.99 *(978-0-554-35368-5(7))* 2007. (ENG.). 456p. pap. 28.99 *(978-1-4346-0344-9(X))* BiblioBazaar.

—The Education of Henry Adams. 2007. (ENG.). 268p. per. 11.99 *(978-1-4209-2951-5(8))* Digireads.com.

—The Education of Henry Adams. 2007. (ENG.). 320p. *(978-1-4068-2261-8(2))* Echo Library.

—The Education of Henry Adams. 2007. (ENG.). 212p. per. *(978-956-8530-34-1(7))* Editorial Benei Noaj.

—The Education of Henry Adams. 380p. 2009. 42.99 *(978-1-59547-856-6(6))* 2007. (ENG.). per. 19.99 *(978-1-59547-539-8(7))* NuVision Pubns., LLC.

—The Education of Henry Adams. Nadel, Ira, ed. 2009. (Oxford World's Classics Ser.). (ENG.). 560p. 14.95 *(978-0-19-955236-8(3))* Oxford Univ. Pr., Inc.

—The Education of Henry Adams. 2007. (ENG.). 544p. per. *(978-1-4067-6490-1(6))* Read Bks.

—The Education of Henry Adams. 2009. 324p. pap. 9.49 *(978-1-60459-634-2(1))* Wilder Pubns., Ltd.

—The Education of Henry Adams. 2009. 532p. 39.95 *(978-1-4344-5417-1(7))*; pap. 24.95 *(978-1-4344-5416-4(9))* Wildside Pr., LLC.

—The Education of Henry Adams. Wieseltier, Leon, ed. 2009. (ENG.). 524p. (gr. 12-18). 13.95 *(978-1-59853-060-5(7))* Library of America, The.

—The Education of Henry Adams. l.t. ed. 2007. (ENG.). 502p. pap. 31.99 *(978-1-4346-0417-0(9))* BiblioBazaar.

—The Education of Henry Adams. (Best Sellers of 1919 Ser.). reprint ed. lib. bdg. 48.00 *(978-0-7426-1328-7(3))* Classic Bks.

—The Education of Henry Adams. 453p. reprint ed. 98.00 *(978-0-7222-8982-2(0))*; 98.00 *(978-0-7222-8220-5(6))* Library Reprints, Inc.

—The Education of Henry Adams: A Centennial Version. Chalfant, Edward, ed. 2008. (ENG.). 542p. pap. 19.95 *(978-0-934909-93-8(8))* Univ. Pr. of Virginia.

—Henry Adams in the Secession Crisis: Dispatches to the Boston Daily Advertiser, December 1860-March 1861. Stegmaier, Mark J., ed. 2012. 256p. 42.50 ***(978-0-8071-4351-3(0))*** Louisiana State Univ. Pr.

Adams, Henry. Letters to a Niece & Prayer to the Virgin of Chartres. 2007. (ENG.). 140p. 35.95 *(978-0-548-01948-1(7))* Kessinger Publishing, LLC.

—Letters to a Niece & Prayer to the Virgin of Chartres. 2007. 144p. per. *(978-1-4067-2971-9(X))* Read Bks.

Baym, Max Isaac & Adams, Henry. The French Education of Henry Adams. 2011. 372p. 53.95 ***(978-1-258-07847-8(3))*** Literary Licensing, LLC.

Dykstra, Natalie. Clover Adams: A Gilded & Heartbreaking Life. 2012. (ENG., Illus.). 336p. 26.00 *(978-0-618-87385-2(6))* Houghton Mifflin Harcourt Trade & Reference Pubs.

Kaplan, Harold. Henry Adams & the American Naturalist Tradition. 2010. (ENG.). 197p. pap. 24.95 *(978-1-4128-1423-2(5))* Transaction Pubs.

O'Brien, Michael. Henry Adams & the Southern Question. 2007. (Mercer University Lamar Memorial Lecture Ser.). (ENG., Illus.). 216p. per. 24.95 *(978-0-8203-2956-7(8))* Univ. of Georgia Pr.

Samuels, Jayne N., ed. The Education of Henry Adams. 2007. 736p. per. 51.95 *(978-0-548-74582-3(X))* Kessinger Publishing, LLC.

Taylor, Natalie Fuehrer, ed. & contrib. by. A Political Companion to Henry Adams. 2010. (Political Companions to Great American Authors Ser.). (ENG., Illus.). 284p. 40.00 *(978-0-8131-2590-9(1))* Univ. Pr. of Kentucky.

Wills, Garry. Henry Adams & the Making of America. annot. ed. 2007. (ENG.). 480p. pap. 15.95 *(978-0-618-87266-4(3))* Houghton Mifflin Harcourt Trade & Reference Pubs.

ADAMS, JAMES TRUSLOW, 1878-1949

Adams, James. Waffle Street: The Confession & Rehabilitation of a Financier. 2011. (ENG., Illus.). 288p. pap. 14.99 ***(978-1-937458-00-3(8))*** Sourced Media Bks.

Nevins, Allan & Adams, James Truslow. James Truslow Adams: Biography & Select Correspondence. 2012. (ENG.). 315p. pap. 34.95 ***(978-1-4128-4740-7(0))*** Transaction Pubs.

ADAMS, JOHN, 1735-1826

Adams, Abigail. My Dearest Friend: Letters of Abigail & John Adams. Hogan, Margaret A. & Taylor, C. James, eds. 2007. (Illus.). 528p. 35.00 *(978-0-674-02606-3(3)*, Belknap Pr.) Harvard Univ. Pr.

Adams, Abigail S., et al. My Dearest Friend: Letters of Abigail & John Adams. 2010. (ENG., Illus.). 528p. pap. 19.95 *(978-0-674-05705-0(8)*, Belknap Pr.) Harvard Univ. Pr.

Adams, Charles Francis. Letters of John Adams, Addressed to His Wife. 2009. 324p. 36.99 *(978-1-113-63761-1(7))*; 32.99 *(978-1-113-63760-4(9))*; pap. 29.75 *(978-1-113-63758-1(7))*; pap. 30.75 *(978-1-113-63759-8(5))* BiblioBazaar.

—Letters of John Adams, Addressed to His Wife. 2010. 120p. pap. 19.99 *(978-1-154-14034-7(2))* General Bks. LLC.

—Letters of John Adams, Addressed to His Wife. 2010. (ENG.). 312p. pap. 29.75 *(978-1-177-47633-1(9))*; (ENG.). 330p. pap. 31.75 *(978-1-176-54387-4(3))*; 300p. pap. 28.75 *(978-1-145-89874-5(2))*; 320p. pap. 30.75 *(978-1-145-60127-7(8))* BiblioBazaar.

—Letters of John Adams, addressed to his Wife. 2009. 323p. pap. 24.99 *(978-1-113-63757-4(9))*; (ENG.). pap. 23.99 *(978-1-113-63756-7(0))* BiblioBazaar. (BiblioLife).

—The Life of John Adams. 2008. 420p. 30.99 *(978-0-559-85285-5(1))*; pap. 33.75 *(978-0-559-85283-1(5))* BiblioBazaar.

—The Life of John Adams. 2009. 124p. pap. *(978-0-217-12695-3(2))* Books LLC.

—The Life of John Adams. 2009. 208p. pap. 20.31 *(978-1-150-84422-5(1))* General Bks. LLC.

—The Life of John Adams, 2 vol., set. reprint ed. 250.00 *(978-0-7222-8617-3(1))* Library Reprints, Inc.

Adams, Charles Francis, ed. Letters of John Adams Addressed to his Wife. 2011. (Cambridge Library Collection - History Ser.). (ENG.). 324p. pap. 24.99 ***(978-1-108-03274-2(5))***; 308p. pap. 24.99 ***(978-1-108-03275-9(3))*** Cambridge Univ. Pr.

Adams, Charles Francis, ed. Letters of John Adams, Addressed to His Wife V2. 304p. 2010. 35.16 *(978-1-166-65757-4(4))* 2010. pap. 23.16 *(978-1-166-60534-6(5))* 2009. 43.95 *(978-1-120-37297-0(6))* 2009. pap. 28.95 *(978-1-120-31494-9(1))* Kessinger Publishing, LLC.

Adams-Graf, John. Familiar Letters of John Adams & His Wife Abigail Adams, During the Revolution. with a Memoir of Mrs. Adams. 424p. reprint ed. 98.00 *(978-0-7222-8616-6(3))* Library Reprints, Inc.

—The Works of John Adams: Second President of the United States, 10 vol., set. reprint ed. 1250.00 *(978-0-7222-8618-0(X))* Library Reprints, Inc.

Adams, John Francis, ed. Letters of John Adams Addressed to His Wife V1. 2010. 322p. pap. 24.76 *(978-1-163-90677-4(8))* 2010. 324p. 36.76 ***(978-1-164-34406-3(4))*** 2008. 320p. 45.95 *(978-0-548-92982-7(3))* 2007. (ENG.). 324p. per. 30.95 *(978-0-548-56822-4(7))* Kessinger Publishing, LLC.

Adams, John Quincy & Adams, Charles Francis. The Life of John Adams, Vol. 1. 2007. pap. 38.95 *(978-1-4304-4432-9(0))* Kessinger Publishing, LLC.

Baron, Robert C. & Wright, Conrad Edick. The Libraries, Leadership, & Legacy of John Adams & Thomas Jefferson. 2010. (ENG.). 304p. 35.00 *(978-1-936218-08-0(9))* Fulcrum Publishing.

Briggs, Walter Benjamin. Two Letters of John Adams to Joseph Willard: Cambridge Historical Society, Publications 16, Proceedings for the Year 1922. Pottinger, David T., ed. 2011. 16p. pap. 35.95 ***(978-1-258-06239-2(9))*** Literary Licensing, LLC.

Burleigh, Anne & Burleigh, Anne Husted. John Adams. 2009. (ENG.). 449p. pap. 39.95 *(978-1-4128-1000-5(0))* Transaction Pubs.

Chamberlain, Mellen. John Adams: The Statesman of the American Revolution. 85p. reprint ed. 88.00 *(978-0-7222-8619-7(8))* Library Reprints, Inc.

—John Adams, the Statesman of the American Revolution. 2009. 242p. pap. *(978-1-4590-9096-5(9))* Books LLC.

—John Adams, the Statesman of the American Revolution. 85p. reprint ed. 88.00 *(978-0-7222-7273-2(1))* Library Reprints, Inc.

Cowley, Joseph. John Adams: Architect of Freedom (1735-1826) 2009. 224p. pap. 18.95 *(978-1-4401-4704-3(3))* iUniverse, Inc.

Ellis, Joseph J. First Family: Abigail & John Adams. (Vintage Ser.). (ENG.). 320p. 2011. pap. 15.95 *(978-0-307-38999-2(5)*, Vintage) 2010. 27.95 *(978-0-307-26962-1(0)*, Knopf) Knopf Doubleday Publishing Group.

Ferling, John. John Adams: A Life. 2010. (ENG., Illus.). 544p. pap. 21.95 *(978-0-19-539866-3(1))* Oxford Univ. Pr., Inc.

Gelles, Edith. Abigail & John: Portrait of a Marriage. 2010. 352p. pap. 14.99 *(978-0-06-135412-0(0)*, HarperPerennial) 2009. (ENG.). 320p. pap. 26.99 *(978-0-06-166836-4(2)*, HarperLuxe) HarperCollins Pubs.

Gelles, Edith Belle. Abigail & John: Portrait of a Marriage. 2009. (Illus.). 352p. 26.99 *(978-0-06-135387-1(6)*, Morrow, William & Co.) HarperCollins Pubs.

Gibbs, George. Memoirs of the Administrations of Washington & John Adams. 2009. 464p. pap. 30.43 *(978-0-217-73237-6(2))* General Bks. LLC.

Hill, John E. Democracy, Equality, & Justice: John Adams, Adam Smith, & Political Economy. 2nd ed. 2007. (ENG.). 286p. 99.99 *(978-0-7391-1762-0(9))*; per. 31.50 *(978-0-7391-1763-7(7))* Lexington Bks.

Hoffman, Karen S. Popular Leadership in the Presidency: Origins & Practice. 2010. (ENG.). 184p. 60.00 *(978-0-7391-4419-0(7))*; pap. 27.95 *(978-0-7391-4420-6(0))* Lexington Bks.

Holton, Woody. Abigail Adams. 2010. (ENG., Illus.). 512p. pap. 18.00 *(978-1-4165-4681-8(2)*, Free Pr.) Free Pr.

H.R. 2802, Commemorative Work to Honor Former President John Adams; H.R. 2806, Adjust Boundary of the Stephen Mather Wilderness & North Cascades National Park; & H.R. 3113, Upper Elk River Wild & Scenic Study ACT: Legislative Hearing Before the Subcommittee on National Parks, Forests, & Public Lands of the Committee on Natural Resources, U.S. House of Representatives, One Hundred Eleventh Congress, First Session, Thursday, July 30, 2009. 2009. iii, 43p. *(978-0-16-085064-6(9)*, 552-070-40421-0) United States Government Printing Office.

Kurtz, Stephen G. The Presidency of John Adams: The Collapse of Federalism, 1795-1800. 2011. 454p. 57.95 ***(978-1-258-05201-0(6))*** Literary Licensing, LLC.

Larson, Edward J. A Magnificent Catastrophe: The Tumultuous Election of 1800, America's First Presidential Campaign. 2008. (ENG., Illus.). 352p. pap. 16.99 *(978-0-7432-9317-4(7)*, Free Pr.) Free Pr.

Letters of John Adams, Addressed to His Wife. 2010. 324p. pap. 30.75 *(978-1-142-79789-8(9))* 2010. 308p. pap. 29.75 *(978-1-142-93874-1(3))* 2008. 320p. 29.99 *(978-0-554-43979-2(4))* 2008. 320p. 28.99 *(978-0-554-43991-4(3))* 2008. 320p. pap. 30.75 *(978-0-554-43983-9(2))* 2008. 320p. pap. 29.75 *(978-0-554-43989-1(1))* BiblioBazaar.

Letters of John Adams, Addressed to His Wife. 2009. 150p. pap. *(978-1-150-67722-9(8))* Books LLC.

Letters of John Adams, Addressed to His Wife. 2009. 160p. pap. 19.39 *(978-1-150-26894-6(8))*; 158p. pap. 19.99 *(978-1-150-67718-2(X))* General Bks. LLC.

Lint, Gregg L., et al. Papers of John Adams, Volume 16. 2012. (Adams Papers). (ENG., Illus.). 680p. 95.00 ***(978-0-674-06557-4(3)***, Belknap Pr.) Harvard Univ. Pr.

—Papers of John Adams Vol. 14: October 27, 1782 - May 31, 1783, Volume 14. 2008. (Adams Papers). (Illus.). 640p. 114.00 *(978-0-674-02607-0(1)*, Belknap Pr.) Harvard Univ. Pr.

—Papers of John Adams, June 1783 - January 1784, Volume 15. 2010. (Adams Papers). (Illus.). 592p. 105.00 (978-0-674-05123-2(8), Belknap Pr.) Harvard Univ. Pr.

Mackay, Charles. The Founders of the American Republic: A History And Biography, With A Supplementary Chapter on Ultra-Democracy. 434p. reprint ed. 98.00 (978-0-7222-8398-1(9)) Library Reprints, Inc.

McCullough, David. John Adams. 2008. (ENG., Illus.). 768p. pap. 20.00 (978-1-4165-7588-7(X)) Simon & Schuster.

Morse, John Torrey. John Adams. 2009. 346p. 32.99 (978-1-115-16992-9(0)); 36.99 (978-1-115-16994-3(7)); pap. 32.75 (978-1-115-16990-5(4)); pap. 31.75 (978-1-115-16989-9(0)) BiblioBazaar.

—John Adams. 2009. 140p. pap. 22.81 (978-1-150-07088-4(9)) General Bks. LLC.

—John Adams. (American Statesmen Ser.). 337p. reprint ed. 98.00 (978-0-7222-8620-3(1)); 98.00 (978-0-7222-8498-8(5)) Library Reprints, Inc.

—John Adams. 2008. 344p. pap. (978-1-4097-6498-4(2)) Read Bks.

Sharp, James Roger. Deadlocked Election of 1800. 2010. (Illus.). 34.95 (978-0-7006-1742-5(6)) Univ. of Kansas Pubns.

Smith, Page. John Adams: 1735-1784 Volume I. 2008. 640p. 95.00 (978-1-59740-348-1(2)); pap. 64.00 (978-1-59740-436-5(5)) ACLS Humanities E-Book.

—John Adams: 1784-1826 Volume II. 2008. 596p. 89.00 (978-1-59740-349-8(0)); pap. 59.00 (978-1-59740-563-8(9)) ACLS Humanities E-Book.

Staloff, Darren. Hamilton, Adams, Jefferson: The Politics of Enlightenment & the American Founding. 2007. (ENG., Illus.). 432p. pap. 17.00 (978-0-8090-5356-8(X), Hill & Wang) Farrar, Straus & Giroux.

Walsh, Correa Moylan. The Political Science of John Adams: A Study in the Theory of Mixed Government & the Bicameral System. 374p. reprint ed. 98.00 (978-0-7222-8622-7(8)) Library Reprints, Inc.

Wood, Gordon, ed. John Adams: Revolutionary Writings, 1755-1775. 2011. (ENG.). 750p. (gr. 12). 35.00 (978-1-59853-089-6(5)) Library of America, The.

—John Adams: Revolutionary Writings, 1775-1783. 2011. (ENG.). 750p. (gr. 12). 35.00 (978-1-59853-090-2(9)) Library of America, The.

Yoder, Carolyn P. John Adams, the Writer: A Treasury of Letters, Diaries, & Public Document. 2007. (ENG., Illus.). 144p. 16.95 (978-1-59078-247-7(X), Calkins Creek) Boyds Mills Pr.

Zarrow, Sheila Dickman. Friendship & Healing: The Dreams of John Adams & Benjamin Rush. 2010. (Illus.). 128p. pap. 24.95 (978-1-888602-50-0(3)) Chiron Pubns.

ADAMS, JOHN CAPEN, 1812-1860

Hittell, Theodore H. The Adventures of James Capen Adams. 2009. (ENG.). 410p. 41.99 (978-1-117-42613-6(0)); (ENG.). 410p. pap. 26.99 (978-1-117-42615-0(7), BiblioLife); 412p. pap. 33.75 (978-1-117-42614-3(9)) BiblioBazaar.

ADAMS, JOHN QUINCY, 1767-1848

Adams, John Quincy. Memoirs of John Quincy Adams, 12 vols. Adams, Charles Francis, Jr., ed. reprint ed. lib. bdg. 894.00 (978-0-404-00330-2(3)) AMS Pr., Inc.

—Memoirs of John Quincy Adams. 2009. 68p. pap. (978-0-217-86452-7(X)); 188p. pap. (978-0-217-85109-1(6)); 168p. pap. (978-0-217-85108-4(8)); 178p. pap. (978-0-217-96905-5(4)); 68p. pap. (978-0-217-01894-4(7)); 124p. pap. (978-0-217-96909-3(7)); 88p. pap. (978-0-217-96907-9(0)) Books LLC.

—Orations. 2008. 48p. pap. (978-1-4099-3382-3(2)) Dodo Pr.

—State of the Union Addresses of John Quincy Adams. 2006. (ENG.). 88p. pap. 16.99 (978-1-4264-0266-1(X)); 86p. pap. 18.99 (978-1-4264-0283-8(X)) BiblioBazaar.

—Writings of John Quincy Adams. 2009. 608p. 31.99 (978-1-103-04463-4(X)) 2009. 564p. 30.99 (978-0-559-90790-6(7)) 2009. 584p. 30.99 (978-0-559-95533-4(2)) 2009. 564p. 30.99 (978-0-559-98852-3(4)) 2009. 536p. 29.99 (978-1-103-05066-6(4)) 2009. 572p. 30.99 (978-1-103-18899-4(2)) 2009. 608p. pap. 25.99 (978-1-103-04459-7(1)) 2009. 564p. pap. 24.99 (978-0-559-90787-6(7)) 2009. 584p. pap. 24.99 (978-0-559-95531-0(6)) 2009. 564p. pap. 24.99 (978-0-559-98850-9(8)) 2009. 536p. pap. 23.99 (978-1-103-05061-1(3)) 2009. 572p. pap. 24.99 (978-1-103-18898-7(4)) 2008. 544p. 32.99 (978-0-559-74724-3(1)) 2008. 588p. 33.99 (978-0-559-87226-6(7)) 2008. 572p. 33.99 (978-0-559-87427-7(8)) 2008. 544p. pap. 40.75 (978-0-559-74722-9(5)) 2008. 588p. pap. 43.75 (978-0-559-87224-2(0)) 2008. 572p. pap. 42.75 (978-0-559-87424-6(3)) 2008. 584p. 33.99 (978-0-559-46536-9(X)) 2008. 588p. 33.99 (978-0-559-56601-1(8)) 2008. 544p. 32.99 (978-0-559-64896-0(0)) 2008. 584p. pap. 43.75 (978-0-559-46534-5(3)) 2008. 544p. pap. 40.75 (978-0-559-64893-9(6)) 2008. 588p. pap. 43.75 (978-0-559-56599-1(2)) BiblioBazaar.

—Writings of John Quincy Adams. 2009. 338p. pap. (978-1-151-30375-2(5)); 350p. pap. (978-1-151-30376-9(3)); 410p. pap. (978-0-217-33972-8(7)); 422p. pap. (978-0-217-65471-5(1)); 424p. pap. (978-0-217-65475-3(4)); 412p. pap. (978-0-217-14859-7(X)) Books LLC.

—Writings of John Quincy Adams, 7 vol., set. reprint ed. 875.00 (978-0-7222-8623-4(6)) Library Reprints, Inc.

Adams, Louisa Catherine. The Diary & Autobiographical Writings of Louisa Catherine Adams, 1778-1850, Volumes 1 and 2. Graham, Judith S. et al, eds. 2013. (Adams Papers). (ENG., Illus.). 920p. 175.00 (**978-0-674-05868-2(2)**, Belknap Pr.) Harvard Univ. Pr.

Ford, Worthington Chauncey. John Quincy Adams, His Connection with the Monroe Doctrine, 1823. 113p. reprint ed. 88.00 (978-0-7222-7575-7(7)) Library Reprints, Inc.

Ford, Worthington Chauncey & Adams, Charles Francis. John Quincy Adams: His Connection with the Monroe Doctrine (1823), 1 vol. 2008. 113p. 65.00 (978-1-56169-970-4(5)) Gaunt, Inc.

John Torrey Morse Jr. John Quincy Adams: American Statesmen Series. 2007. (ENG.). 164p. pap. 19.99 (978-1-4346-3866-3(9)); 206p. pap. 22.99 (978-1-4346-3867-0(7)) BiblioBazaar.

Lipsky, George A. John Quincy Adams: His Theory & Ideas. 2009. 362p. 46.95 (978-1-104-84203-1(3)) 2007. (ENG.). 360p. per. 31.95 (978-0-548-38957-7(8)) Kessinger Publishing, LLC.

Morse, John Torrey. John Quincy Adams. 2009. 324p. 32.99 (978-1-115-58926-0(1)); pap. 29.75 (978-1-115-58928-4(8)) BiblioBazaar.

—John Quincy Adams. (American Statesmen Ser.). 315p. reprint ed. 98.00 (978-0-7222-8499-5(3)); 98.00 (978-0-7222-8626-5(0)) Library Reprints, Inc.

O'Brien, Michael. Mrs. Adams in Winter: A Journey in the Last Days of Napoleon. 2010. (ENG., Illus.). 384p. 27.00 (978-0-374-21581-1(2)) Farrar, Straus & Giroux.

—Mrs. Adams in Winter: A Journey in the Last Days of Napoleon. 2011. (ENG., Illus.). 384p. pap. 16.00 (978-0-312-68114-2(3)) Picador.

Portolano, Marlana. The Passionate Empiricist: The Eloquence of John Quincy Adams in the Service of Science. 2010. 245p. pap. 24.95 (978-0-7914-7700-7(2), Suny Pr.) 2009. 240p. 70.00 (978-0-7914-7699-4(5)) State Univ. of New York Pr.

Quincy, Josiah. Memoir of the Life of John Quincy Adams. 2009. (ENG.). 442p. 41.99 (978-1-117-05754-5(2)) 2008. 360p. 31.99 (978-0-554-28033-2(7)) 2008. 360p. 29.99 (978-0-554-37336-2(X)) 2007. (ENG.). 324p. pap. 23.99 (978-1-4346-4555-5(X)) 2007. 358p. pap. 26.99 (978-1-4346-4556-2(8)) BiblioBazaar.

—Memoir of the Life of John Quincy Adams. 2009. 216p. pap. (978-1-150-15204-7(4)) Books LLC.

—Memoir of the Life of John Quincy Adams. 2007. (ENG.). 296p. per. (978-1-4065-3989-9(9)) Dodo Pr.

—Memoir of the Life of John Quincy Adams. 440p. 2008. 51.95 (978-0-548-96569-6(2)) 2007. (ENG.). per. 36.95 (978-0-548-64120-0(X)) 2007. (ENG.). 51.95 (978-0-548-16515-7(7)) 2007. (ENG.). per. 36.95 (978-1-4304-6168-5(3)) Kessinger Publishing, LLC.

Seward, William H. Life & Public Services of John Quincy Adams. 2008. 340p. 28.99 (978-0-554-33202-4(7)); 29.99 (978-0-554-23899-9(3)) BiblioBazaar.

—Life & Public Services of John Quincy Adams: Sixth President of the United States. 2007. (ENG.). 304p. pap. 23.99 (978-1-4264-5134-8(2)); 338p. pap. 24.99 (978-1-4264-5435-6(X)) BiblioBazaar.

—Life & Public Services of John Quincy Adams, Sixth President of the United States with the Eulogy Delivered Before the Legislature of New York. 2008. 408p. pap. 31.45 (978-1-4097-1708-9(9)) Audubon Pr. & Christian Bk. Service.

Seward, William Henry. The Life of John Quincy Adams: Sixth President of the United States. 404p. reprint ed. 98.00 (978-0-7222-8627-2(9)) Library Reprints, Inc.

Teed, Paul E. John Quincy Adams: Yankee Nationalist. 2011. (First Men, America's Presidents Ser.). pap. 43.00 (978-1-60876-914-8(3)) Nova Science Pubs., Inc.

Unger, Harlow Giles. John Quincy Adams: A Life. 2012. (ENG., Illus.). 400p. 27.50 (**978-0-306-82129-5(X)**) Da Capo Pr., Inc.

Wheelan, Joseph. Mr. Adams's Last Crusade: John Quincy Adams's Extraordinary Post-Presidential Life in Congress. 2009. (ENG., Illus.). 336p. pap. 15.95 (978-1-58648-689-1(6)) PublicAffairs.

ADAMS, JOHN QUINCY, 1767-1848—JUVENILE LITERATURE

Barker-Benfield, G. J. Abigail & John Adams: The Americanization of Sensibility. 2010. (ENG.). 520p. 32.50 (978-0-226-03743-1(6)) Univ. of Chicago Pr.

ADAMS, LOUISA CATHERINE, 1775-1852

Adams, Louisa Catherine. The Diary & Autobiographical Writings of Louisa Catherine Adams, 1778-1850, Volumes 1 and 2. Graham, Judith S. et al, eds. 2013. (Adams Papers). (ENG., Illus.). 920p. 175.00 (**978-0-674-05868-2(2)**, Belknap Pr.) Harvard Univ. Pr.

O'Brien, Michael. Mrs. Adams in Winter: A Journey in the Last Days of Napoleon. 2010. (ENG., Illus.). 384p. 27.00 (978-0-374-21581-1(2)) Farrar, Straus & Giroux.

—Mrs. Adams in Winter: A Journey in the Last Days of Napoleon. 2011. (ENG., Illus.). 384p. pap. 16.00 (978-0-312-68114-2(3)) Picador.

ADAMS, MAUDE, 1872-1953

Patterson, Ada. Maude Adams: a Biography. 2007. (ENG.). 116p. per. 19.95 (978-1-4304-4262-2(X)) Kessinger Publishing, LLC.

ADAMS, SAMUEL, 1722-1803

Alexander, John K. Samuel Adams: The Life of an American Revolutionary. 2011. (ENG., Illus.). 432p. 44.95 (978-0-7425-7033-7(9)) Rowman & Littlefield Publishers, Inc.

Francis, Annette. Samuel Adams - Father of the American Revolution. pap. 3.95 (978-1-889086-03-3(7), SA-203) Pan Productions.

Hosmer, James K. Samuel Adams. (American Statesmen Ser.). 442p. reprint ed. 98.00 (978-0-7222-8984-6(7)) Library Reprints, Inc.

—Samuel Adams. 2008. 468p. pap. (978-1-4097-1438-5(1)) Read Bks.

Hosmer, James Kendall. Samuel Adams. 2009. 280p. pap. (978-0-217-55059-7(X)) Books LLC.

—Samuel Adams. (American Statesmen Ser.). 442p. reprint ed. 98.00 (978-0-7222-8487-2(X)) Library Reprints, Inc.

—Samuel Adams. 2008. 460p. pap. (978-1-4097-1571-9(X)) Read Bks.

Knollenberg, Bernhard. Did Samuel Adams Provoke the Boston Tea Party & the Clash at Lexington: American Antiquarian Society, V70, No. 2. 2011. 16p. pap. 35.95 (**978-1-258-06979-7(2)**) Literary Licensing, LLC.

Puls, Mark. Samuel Adams: Father of the American Revolution. (ENG., Illus.). 288p. 2009. pap. 15.00 (978-0-230-61400-0(0)) 2006. 24.95 (978-1-4039-7582-9(5)) Palgrave Macmillan.

Stoll, Ira. Samuel Adams: A Life. 2009. (ENG., Illus.). 352p. pap. 16.00 (978-0-7432-9912-1(4), Free Pr.) Free Pr.

Wells, William. The Life & Public Services of Samuel Adams. 2009. (Revolutionary War Ser.). (ENG.). 548p. pap. 31.95 (978-1-4290-1758-9(9)) Applewood Bks.

Wells, William Vincent. The Life & Public Services of Samuel Adams: A Narrative of His Acts & Opinions, & of His Agency in Producing & Forwarding the American Revolution, 3 vol., set. reprint ed. 375.00 (978-0-7222-8985-3(5)) Library Reprints, Inc.

ADAMS, WILLIAM, 1564-1620

Giles, Milton. Samurai William: The Englishman Who Opened the East. Date not set. pap. (978-0-312-42204-2(0)) Picador.

ADAMS FAMILY

Adams, Abigail. The Adams Family in Auteuil, 1784-1785: As Told in the Letters of Abigail Adams. 2011. 34p. 35.95 (**978-1-258-04019-2(0)**) Literary Licensing, LLC.

Adams Family. Adams Family Correspondence Vol.10: January 1794-June 1795, Volume 10. Hogan, Margaret A. et al, eds. 2011. (Adams Papers). (Illus.). 608p. 105.00 (978-0-674-05784-5(8), Belknap Pr.) Harvard Univ. Pr.

—Adams Family Correspondence, March 1787-December 1789 Vol. 8, Volume 8. Hogan, Margaret A. et al, eds. 2007. (Adams Papers). (Illus.). 592p. 107.50 (978-0-674-02275-2(5), Belknap Pr.) Harvard Univ. Pr.

Adams Family Association Staff. Adams Family Correspondence, January 1790-December 1793, Volume 9. Hogan, Margaret A. et al, eds. 2009. (Adams Papers). (Illus.). 624p. 105.00 (978-0-674-03275-0(6), Belknap Pr.) Harvard Univ. Pr.

Clark, Eunice Newbold. Clarks from Pennsylvania & Allied Families form Early 1700s To 2008. 2nd rev. ed. 2008. (Illus.). 474p. (978-0-9614199-4-3(6)) Clark, Eunice Newbold.

ADAPTABILITY (PSYCHOLOGY)

see also Adjustment (Psychology); Dissonance (Psychology)

Adler, Patricia & Adler, Peter. The Tender Cut: Inside the Hidden World of Self-Injury. 2011. (ENG.). 264p. pap. 22.00 (978-0-8147-0507-0(3)) New York Univ. Pr.

Adler, Patricia A. & Adler, Peter. The Tender Cut: The Rise & Transformation of Self-Injury. 2011. 288p. E-Book (978-0-8147-0518-6(9)) New York Univ. Pr.

Becking, Bob. Orthodoxy, Liberalism, & Adaptation: Essays on Ways of Worldmaking in Times of Change from Biblical, Historical, & Systematic Perspectives. 2011 (Illus.). 230p. (**978-90-04-20869-8(0)**) BRILL.

Burgoon, Judee K., et al. Interpersonal Adaptation: Dyadic Interaction Patterns. 2007. (ENG., Illus.). 356p. pap. 74.00 (978-0-521-03314-5(4)) Cambridge Univ. Pr.

Calarco, Allan, et al. Adaptability: Responding Effectively to Change. 2007. (J-B CCL (Center for Creative Leadership) Ser.: 111). (ENG.). 32p. pap. 12.95 (978-1-882197-92-7(5), Pfeiffer) Wiley, John & Sons, Inc.

Deal, Jennifer J., et al. Developing Cultural Adaptability: How to Work Across Differences. 2007. (J-B CCL (Center for Creative Leadership) Ser.: 105). (ENG.). 32p. pap. 12.95 (978-1-882197-80-4(1), Pfeiffer) Wiley, John & Sons, Inc.

Flach, Frederic. Choices: Coping Creatively with Personal Change. 2009. (Little Book, Big Idea Ser.). (ENG.). 216p. 11.00 (978-1-57826-286-1(0)) Hatherleigh Co., Ltd., The.

Ford, Martyn. It Happened to Me. 2010. (ENG.). 256p. pap. 12.95 (**978-1-84953-016-3(5)**) Summersdale Pubs. GBR. Dist: Independent Pubs. Group.

Gigerenzer, Gerd, et al, eds. Heuristics: The Foundations of Adaptive Behavior, 1 vol. 2011. (ENG., Illus.). 912p. 99.95 (978-0-19-974428-2(9)) Oxford Univ. Pr., Inc.

Glad, Clarence E. Paul & Philodemus: Adaptability in Epicurean & Early Christian Psychagogy. 2010. (978-1-58983-502-3(6)) Society of Biblical Literature.

Gold, Stuart Avery. Ping. 2007. (ENG., Illus.). 90p. pap. 6.99 (978-1-55704-756-4(1)) Newmarket Pr.

—The Way of Ping: Journey to the Great Ocean. 2009. (ENG., Illus.). 96p. 15.00 (978-1-55704-820-2(7)) Newmarket Pr.

Grigsby, Jim. Don't Tick off the Gators! Managing Problems Before Problems Manage You. 2006. 168p. per. 16.95 (978-1-56825-106-6(8)) Rainbow Bks., Inc.

Hatum, Andrés. Adaptation or Expiration in Family Firms. 2007. (Illus.). 256p. (C). 119.00 (978-1-84542-834-1(X)) Elgar, Edward Publishing, Inc.

Hudson, Christopher G. Complex Systems & Human Behavior. 2009. (ENG.). pap. (978-0-925065-63-6(3)) Lyceum Bks., Inc.

Innis, Nancy K., ed. Reflections on Adaptive Behavior: Essays in Honor of J. E. R. Staddon. 2008. (ENG., Illus.). 408p. (gr. 17). 70.00 (978-0-262-09044-5(9)); pap. 35.00 (978-0-262-59026-6(3)) MIT Pr.

Koutstaal, Wilma. The Agile Mind. 2011. (ENG., Illus.). 784p. 99.95 (**978-0-19-536718-8(9)**) Oxford Univ. Pr., Inc.

Malabou, Catherine. What Should We Do with Our Brain? Rand, Sebastian & Jeannerod, Marc, trs. from FRE. 3rd ed. 2008. (Perspectives in Continental Philosophy Ser.). (ENG.). 120p. 55.00 (978-0-8232-2952-9(1)); pap. 20.00 (978-0-8232-2953-6(X)) Fordham Univ. Pr.

Marten, James. Sing Not War: The Lives of Union & Confederate Veterans in Gilded Age America. 2011. (Civil War America Ser.). (ENG., Illus.). 368p. 39.95 (978-0-8078-3476-3(9)) Univ. of North Carolina Pr.

McGraw, Phil. Real Life: Preparing for the 7 Most Challenging Days of Your Life. 2009. (ENG.). 336p. pap. 15.00 (978-1-4391-3156-5(2), Free Pr.) Free Pr.

—Real Life: Preparing for the 7 Worst Days of Your Life. l.t. ed. 2008. 32.95 (978-1-59722-842-8(7)) Thorndike Pr.

McKeown, Max. Adaptability: The Art of Winning in an Age of Uncertainty. 2012. (ENG.). 228p. pap. 19.95 (**978-0-7494-6524-7(7)**) Kogan Page, Ltd. GBR. Dist: Ingram Pub. Services.

Miller, Thomas W. Handbook of Stressful Transitions Across the Lifespan. 2010. (Illus.). xxiii, 691p. E-Book 249.00 (**978-1-4419-0748-6(3)**) Springer.

Murray, Williamson. Military Adaptation in War: With Fear of Change. 2011. (ENG.). 336p. 35.00 (**978-1-107-00659-1(7)**) Cambridge Univ. Pr.

Oakland, Thomas & Harrison, Patti L., eds. Adaptive Behavior Assessment System-II: Clinical Use & Interpretation. 2008. (Practical Resources for the Mental Health Professional Ser.). (ENG., Illus.). 432p. 61.95 (978-0-12-373586-7(6), Academic Pr.) Elsevier Science & Technology Bks.

Radjou, Navi, et al. Jugaad Innovation: Think Frugal, Be Flexible, Generate Breakthrough Growth. 2012. (ENG.). 288p. 27.95 (**978-1-118-24974-1(7)**, Jossey-Bass) Wiley, John & Sons, Inc.

Ramsey, Janet L. & Blieszner, Rosemary. Spiritual Resiliency & Aging: Hope, Relationality, & the Creative Self. 2012. (**978-0-89503-474-8(3)**); (**978-0-89503-387-1(9)**) Baywood Publishing Co., Inc.

Samson, Alain. Life Is Unfair. 2008. (ENG., Illus.). 176p. pap. 19.95 (978-0-9738355-8-8(3)) Transcontinental Bks. CAN. Dist: Random Hse., Inc.

Shelley, Arthur. The Organizational Zoo: A Survival Guide to Work Place Behavior. 2006. (Illus.). 152p. per. (978-0-944031-46-9(3)) Aslan Publishing.

Shemin, Robert. How Come That Idiot's Rich & I'm Not? 2009. (ENG.). 256p. pap. 13.95 (978-0-307-39508-5(1), Three Rivers Pr.) Crown Publishing Group.

—¿Por Qué ese Idiota es Rico y yo No? ¡No te Enojes, hazte Rico! 2008. (Vintage Espanol Ser.). (SPA.). 288p. pap. 14.95 (978-0-307-39081-3(0), Vintage) Knopf Doubleday Publishing Group.

Southwick, Steven M., et al, eds. Resilience in Psychiatric Clinical Practice: Responding to Challenges Across the Lifespan. 2011. (ENG., Illus.). 382p. 99.00 (**978-0-521-89839-3(0)**) Cambridge Univ. Pr.

Southwick, Steven M. & Charney, Dennis S. Resilience: The Science of Mastering Life's Greatest Challenges. 2012. (ENG.). 285p. pap. 22.99 (**978-0-521-19563-8(2)**) Cambridge Univ. Pr.

Watson, Irene & Volkman, Victor R., eds. The Story That Must Be Told: True Tales of Transformation. 2007. (ENG., Illus.). 204p. per. (978-1-932690-38-5(7)) Loving Healing Pr., Inc.

Weber, Janice G. Individual & Family Stress & Crises. 2010. (Illus.). 272p. (C). pap. 47.00 (978-1-4129-3691-0(8), B36913P) SAGE Pubns., Inc.

ADAPTATION (BIOLOGY)

see also Acclimatization; Genetics; Stress (Physiology)

Amils Pibernat, Ricardo, et al, eds. Life in Extreme Environments. 2010. (ENG.). viii, 452p. pap. 279.00 (978-90-481-7596-3(8), 9048175968) Springer.

Amils, Ricardo, et al, eds. Life in Extreme Environments. 2007. (ENG., Illus.). viii, 452p. 279.00 (978-1-4020-6284-1(2), 1402062842) Springer.

Anderson, Wendy. Animal Adaptations. 2007. 32p. pap. 10.95 (978-0-86431-526-7(0)) ACER Pr. AUS. Dist: International Specialized Bk. Services.

Ayala, Francisco J. & Avise, John C., eds. In the Light of Evolution Vol. 1: Adaptation & Complex Design. 2007. (ENG., Illus.). 380p. 59.95 (978-0-309-10405-0(X)) National Academies Pr.

Bateson, Patrick & Gluckman, Peter. Plasticity, Robustness, Development & Evolution. 2011. (ENG., Illus.). 166p. (C). 115.00 (978-0-521-51629-7(3)); pap. 45.00 (978-0-521-73620-6(X)) Cambridge Univ. Pr.

Battaglia, Bruno, et al, eds. Antarctic Communities: Species, Structure & Survival. 2009. (ENG., Illus.). 484p. pap. 61.00 (978-0-521-11179-9(X)) Cambridge Univ. Pr.

Begall, Sabine, et al, eds. Subterranean Rodents: News from Underground. 2010. (ENG., Illus.). xviii, 398p. pap. 215.00 (978-3-642-08876-6(7), 3642088767) Springer.

Bell, Elanor. Life at Extremes: Environments, Organisms, & Strategies for Survival. 2012. 576p. 180.00 (**978-1-84593-814-7(3)**) CABI GBR. Dist: Stylus Publishing, LLC.

Bissonette, John A. & Storch, Ilse, eds. Temporal Dimensions of Landscape Ecology: Wildlife Responses to Variable Resources. 2007. (Illus.). 284p. per. 59.95 (978-0-387-45445-0(4)); x, 286p. 129.00 (978-0-387-45444-3(6), 0387454446) Springer.

Brokaw, Nicholas, et al, eds. A Caribbean Forest Tapestry: The Multidimensional Nature of Disturbance & Response, 1 vol. 2012. (Long-Term Ecological Research Network Ser.). (ENG.). 464p. 74.99 (**978-0-19-533469-2(8)**) Oxford Univ. Pr., Inc.

Culver, Stephen J. & Rawson, Peter F., eds. Biotic Response to Global Change: The Last 145 Million Years. 2006. (ENG.). 516p. pap. 116.00 (978-0-521-03419-7(1)) Cambridge Univ. Pr.

Dar, Naomi. The Selection of the Organizing Self. 2010. 396p. pap. (978-3-639-22258-6(X)) VDM Verlag Dr. Mueller e.K.

Dieckmann, Ulf, et al, eds. Adaptive Speciation. 2012. (Cambridge Studies in Adaptive Dynamics Ser.: 3). (ENG., Illus.). 275p. pap. 71.00 ***(978-1-107-40418-2(5))*** Cambridge Univ. Pr.

Dieckmann, Ulf & Couvet, Denis. Evolutionary Conservation Biology. Ferriére, Régis & Dieckmann, Ulf, eds. Couvet, Denis, ed. 2009. (Cambridge Studies in Adaptive Dynamics Ser.). (ENG., Illus.). 448p. pap. 58.00 *(978-0-521-11608-4(2))* Cambridge Univ. Pr.

Doebeli, Michael. Adaptive Diversification. 2011. (Monographs in Population Biology Ser.). (ENG., Illus.). 392p. (C). 110.00 *(978-0-691-12893-1(6))*; pap. 49.50 *(978-0-691-12894-8(4))* Princeton Univ. Pr.

Eisenberg, John F. The Mammalian Radiations: An Analysis of Trends in Evolution, Adaptation & Behaviour. (Illus.). xx, 610p. *(978-0-485-30008-6(7))* Continuum International Publishing Group, Ltd.

Fodor, Jerry & Piattelli-Palmarini, Massimo. What Darwin Got Wrong. 2011. (ENG., Illus.). 320p. pap. 16.00 *(978-0-312-68066-4(X))* Picador.

Forum on Microbial Threats. Microbial Evolution & Co-Adaptation: A Tribute to the Life & Scientific Legacies of Joshua Lederberg. 2009. (ENG.). 332p. pap. 68.00 *(978-0-309-13121-6(9))* National Academies Pr.

Fothergill, Alastair & Berlowitz, Vanessa. Frozen Planet: A World Beyond Imagination. 2011. (ENG., Illus.). 312p. 39.95 ***(978-1-55407-991-9(8))*** Firefly Bks., Ltd.

Francis, Richard C. Epigenetics: How Environment Shapes Our Genes. 2012. (ENG., Illus.). 256p. pap. 15.95 ***(978-0-393-34228-4(X)***, 34228) Norton, W. W. & Co., Inc.

Francis, Richard C. Epigenetics: The Ultimate Mystery of Inheritance. 2011. (ENG., Illus.). 234p. 25.95 *(978-0-393-07005-7(0)*, 7005) Norton, W. W. & Co., Inc.

Frankham, Richard, et al, eds. Adaptation & Fitness in Animal Populations: Evolutionary & Breeding Perspectives on Genetic Resource Management. 2008. (ENG., Illus.). xii, 260p. 189.00 *(978-1-4020-9004-2(8)*, 1402090048) Springer.

Gissis, Snait. Transformations of Lamarckism: From Subtle Fluids to Molecular Biology. Jablonka, Eva, ed. 2011. (Vienna Series in Theoretical Biology Ser.). (ENG., Illus.). 480p. (gr. 17). 50.00 *(978-0-262-01514-1(5))* MIT Pr.

Glaubrecht, Matthias, ed. Evolution in Action: Case studies in Adaptive Radiation, Speciation & the Origin of Biodiversity. 2010. (ENG., Illus.). xxv, 586p. 239.00 *(978-3-642-12424-2(0)*, 3642124240) Springer.

Grime, J. Philip & Pierce, Simon. The Evolutionary Strategies That Shape Ecosystems. 7th ed. 2012. (ENG.). 264p. 149.95 ***(978-0-470-67481-9(4))***; pap. 79.95 ***(978-0-470-67482-6(2))*** Wiley, John & Sons, Inc. (Wiley-Blackwell).

Hawkesford, M. J. & Buchner, Peter, eds. Molecular Analysis of Plant Adaptation to the Environment. 2010. (Plant Ecophysiology Ser.). 292p. pap. 239.00 *(978-90-481-5826-3(5)*, 9048158265) Springer.

Held, Lewis I. Quirks of Human Anatomy: An Evo-Devo Look at the Human Body. 2009. (ENG., Illus.). (C). 280p. 127.00 *(978-0-521-51848-2(2))*; 272p. pap. 34.99 *(978-0-521-73233-8(6))* Cambridge Univ. Pr.

Helfman, Gene S., et al. The Diversity of Fishes: Biology, Evolution, & Ecology. 2nd ed. 2009. (ENG., Illus.). 736p. 129.95 *(978-1-4051-2494-2(6)*, Wiley-Blackwell) Wiley, John & Sons, Inc.

Hilleman, Terry Bruce. Environmental Biology: The Conditions of Life - Environmental Selection, Extinction, Creation, Adaptation & Overpopulation. 2009. (ENG.). 391p. 79.95 *(978-1-57808-576-7(4))* BIOS Scientific Publishers Ltd. GBR. Dist: Taylor & Francis Group.

Holland, John H. Signals & Boundaries: Building Blocks for Complex Adaptive Systems. 2012. ***(978-0-262-01783-1(0))*** MIT Pr.

Holmes, Martha, et al. Life: Extraordinary Animals, Extreme Behaviour. 2010. 312p. 39.95 *(978-0-520-26537-0(8))* Univ. of California Pr.

Hudson, Arthur J. The Evolution of the Eye from Algae & Jellyfish to Humans: How Vision Adapts to Environment. 2010. (Illus.). iv, 154p. *(978-0-7734-3699-2(5))* Mellen, Edwin Pr., The.

Little, Colin. The Colonisation of Land: Origins & Adaptations of Terrestrial Animals. 2009. (ENG.). 300p. pap. 55.00 *(978-0-521-10683-2(4))* Cambridge Univ. Pr.

Mahoney, Conner L. & Springer, Douglas A. Genetic Diversity. 2009. (Genetics - Research & Issues Ser.). (Illus.). xiii, 304p. 129.00 *(978-1-60741-176-5(8))* Nova Science Pubs., Inc.

Margesin, Rosa & Schinner, Franz, eds. Cold-Adapted Organisms: Ecology, Physiology, Enzymology & Molecular Biology. 2010. (ENG., Illus.). viii, 416p. pap. 389.00 *(978-3-642-08445-4(1)*, 3642084451) Springer.

Mauricio, Rodney, ed. Genetics of Adaptation. 2010. (Georgia Genetics Review Ser.). vi, 210p. pap. 219.00 *(978-90-481-6876-7(7)*, 9048168767) Springer.

Minelli, Alessandro & Mannucci, Maria Pia. Surviving: How Animals Adapt to Their Environments. 2009. (ENG., Illus.). 200p. 45.00 *(978-1-55407-520-1(3))* Firefly Bks., Ltd.

Pelling, Mark. Adaptation to Climate Change. 2010. (ENG., Illus.). 224p. (C). 125.00 *(978-0-415-47750-5(6))* Routledge.

—Adaptation to Climate Change: A Progressive Vision of Human Security. 2010. (ENG., Illus.). 224p. (C). pap. 44.95 *(978-0-415-47751-2(4))* Routledge.

Regato, Pedro & World Conservation Union Staff. Adapting to Global Change: Mediterranean Forests. 2008. (FRE, SPA & ENG., Illus.). 253p. pap. 25.00 ***(978-2-8317-1098-3(7))*** International League of Conservation Photographers.

Ritter, William E. The Natural History of Our Conduct. 2007. (ENG.). 348p. 46.95 *(978-0-548-07048-2(2))* Kessinger Publishing, LLC.

Rothman, Stephen. Life Beyond Molecules & Genes: How Our Adaptations Make Us Alive. 2009. (ENG.). 240p. (C). pap. 29.95 *(978-1-59947-250-8(3))* Templeton Pr.

Russell, Edmund. Evolutionary History: Uniting History & Biology to Understand Life on Earth. 2011. (Studies in Environment & History Ser.). (ENG., Illus.). (C). 238p. 90.00 *(978-0-521-76211-3(1))*; 230p. pap. 22.99 *(978-0-521-74509-3(8))* Cambridge Univ. Pr.

Sagarin, Raphael D. & Taylor, Terence, eds. Natural Security: A Darwinian Approach to a Dangerous World. 2008. (Illus.). 289p. 49.95 *(978-0-520-25347-6(7))* Univ. of California Pr.

Schafer, Susan. Adaptations. 2009. (Genetics Ser.). (ENG., Illus.). 96p. (gr. 6-18). lib. bdg. 38.95 *(978-0-7656-8137-9(4))* Sharpe, M.E. Inc.

—The Science of Life, 4 bks., Set. Incl. Adaptations. 96p. lib. bdg. 38.95 *(978-0-7656-8137-9(4))*; Cloning. 88p. lib. bdg. 38.95 *(978-0-7656-8138-6(2))*; DNA & Genes. 96p. lib. bdg. 38.95 *(978-0-7656-8135-5(8))*; Heredity. 96p. lib. bdg. 38.95 *(978-0-7656-8136-2(6))*; (Illus.). (gr. 6-18). (Genetics Ser.). (ENG.). 2009. 155.80 *(978-0-7656-8134-8(X))* Sharpe, M.E. Inc.

Schwab, Ivan R. Evolution's Witness: How Eyes Evolved, 1 vol. 2011. (ENG., Illus.). 328p. 75.00 *(978-0-19-536974-8(2))* Oxford Univ. Pr., Inc.

Seckbach, Joseph, ed. Algae & Cyanobacteria in Extreme Environments. 2007. (Cellular Origin, Life in Extreme Habitats & Astrobiology Ser.). (Illus.). 450p. 399.00 *(978-1-4020-6111-0(0)*, 1402061110) Springer.

Seidl, Amy. Finding Higher Ground: Adaptation in the Age of Warming. 2011. (ENG.). 208p. 24.95 *(978-0-8070-8598-1(7))* Beacon Pr.

Shanahan, Timothy. Evolution of Darwinism: Selection, Adaptation, & Progress in Evolutionary Biology. 2008. (ENG.). 342p. pap. 25.00 *(978-1-4379-5880-5(X))* DIANE Publishing Co.

Simmons, Adam. Encyclopedia of Adaptations in the Natural World. 2009. 208p. 85.00 *(978-0-313-35556-1(8)*, GR5556) Greenwood Publishing Group, Inc.

Sodhi, Navjot S., et al. Conservation of Tropical Birds. 2011. (ENG., Illus.). 312p. 134.95 *(978-1-4443-3482-1(4)*, Wiley-Blackwell) Wiley, John & Sons, Inc.

Tanino, Karen K. & Storey, Kenneth B., eds. Temperature Adaptation in a Changing Climate: Nature at Risk. 2012. (CABI Climate Change Ser.). (Illus.). 256p. 160.00 *(978-1-84593-822-2(4))* CABI GBR. Dist: Stylus Publishing, LLC.

Vermeij, Geerat J. The Evolutionary World: How Adaptation Explains Everything from Seashells to Civilization. 2010. (ENG.). 336p. 27.99 *(978-0-312-59108-3(X)*, Dunne, Thomas Bks.) St. Martin's Pr.

Walker, Denise. Adaptation & Survival. 2006. (Basic Biology Ser.). (Illus.). 48p. (YA). (gr. 5-9). lib. bdg. 34.25 *(978-1-58340-992-3(0))* Black Rabbit Bks.

Yadav, Shyam Singh, et al. Crop Adaptation to Climate Change. 2011. (ENG., Illus.). 632p. 249.95 ***(978-0-8138-2016-3(2)***, Wiley) Wiley, John & Sons, Inc.

ADAPTATION (MUSIC)
see Arrangement (Music)

ADAPTATION (PHYSIOLOGY)

Calow, P. Evolutionary Physiological Ecology. 2008. (ENG., Illus.). 252p. pap. 51.00 *(978-0-521-10165-3(4))* Cambridge Univ. Pr.

Cheung, Stephen S. Advanced Environmental Exercise Physiology. 2009. (ENG., Illus.). 272p. 71.00 *(978-0-7360-7468-1(6))* Human Kinetics Pubs.

Clment, Gilles & Bukley, Angelia. Artificial Gravity. 2007. (Space Technology Library). (Illus.). 364p. 189.00 *(978-0-387-70712-9(3))* Springer.

Enoka, Roger M. Neuromechanics of Human Movement. 4th ed. 2008. (ENG., Illus.). 560p. (C). 84.00 *(978-0-7360-6679-2(9))* Human Kinetics Pubs.

Garénaux, Amélie, et al. Better Understanding of the Campylobacter Conundrum. 2008. (Illus.). 151p. (C). pap. 29.00 *(978-1-60456-636-9(1))* Nova Science Pubs., Inc.

Johnston, Ian A. & Bennett, Albert F., eds. Animals & Temperature: Phenotypic & Evolutionary Adaptation. 2008. (Society for Experimental Biology Seminar Ser.). (Illus.). 436p. pap. 79.00 *(978-0-521-05061-6(8))* Cambridge Univ. Pr.

Kalueff, Allan V. & LaPorte, Justin L. Behavioral Models in Stress Research. 2008. (Illus.). (C). 89.00 *(978-1-60456-361-0(3))* Nova Science Pubs., Inc.

Kühn, Reimer, et al, eds. Adaptivity & Learning: An Interdisciplinary Debate. 2010. (ENG., Illus.). xii, 403p. pap. 72.95 *(978-3-642-05510-2(9)*, 3642055109) Springer.

Lester, Barry M., et al, eds. Resilience in Children, Vol. 1094. 2007. (Annals of the New York Academy of Sciences Ser.: 4). (ENG., Illus.). 400p. pap. 139.95 *(978-1-57331-643-9(1)*, Wiley-Blackwell) Wiley, John & Sons, Inc.

Lignelli, Alfredo V., ed. Circadian Rhythms & Health Research Trends. 2008. (Illus.). 222p. 129.00 *(978-1-60021-875-0(X))* Nova Science Pubs., Inc.

Lutz, P. L., et al. The Brain Without Oxygen: Causes of Failure - Physiological & Molecular Mechanisms for Survival. 3rd ed. 2010. 260p. pap. 159.00 *(978-90-481-6237-6(8)*, 9048162378) Springer.

Marshall, B. & Woodward, F. I. Society for Experimental Biology, Seminar Series: Volume 22, Instrumentation for Environmental Physiology. 2009. (Society for Experimental Biology Seminar Ser.). (ENG., Illus.). 256p. pap. 53.00 *(978-0-521-10166-0(2))* Cambridge Univ. Pr.

Milledge, James S., et al. High Altitude Medicine & Physiology. 4th ed. 2007. (ENG., Illus.). 480p. 149.50 *(978-0-340-91344-4(4))* Hodder Arnold Pubs.

Morrow, Katherine N. Mental Health of College Students. 2008. (Illus.). xi, 252p. 89.00 *(978-1-60456-394-8(X)*, Nova Biomedical Bks.) Nova Science Pubs., Inc.

Moss, Charles. Power of the Five Elements: The Chinese Medicine Path to Healthy Aging & Stress Resistance. 2010. (ENG., Illus.). 312p. pap. 18.95 *(978-1-55643-874-5(5))* North Atlantic Bks.

Oxnard. Ghostly Muscles, Wrinkled Brains, Heresi. . 2008. 300p. pap. 69.00 *(978-981-279-743-8(2))* World Scientific Publishing Co., Inc.

Oxnard, Charles. Ghostly Muscles, Wrinkled Brains, Heresies & Hobbits. 2008. 300p. 112.00 *(978-981-279-742-1(4))* World Scientific Publishing Co., Inc.

Palmer, Stephen & Cooper, Cary. How to Deal with Stress. 2nd ed. 2010. (Creating Success Ser.). (ENG.). 176p. pap. 14.95 *(978-0-7494-6039-6(3))* Kogan Page, Ltd. GBR. Dist: Ingram Pub. Services.

Portner, H O & Playle, R C, eds. Cold Ocean Physiology. 2007. (Society for Experimental Biology Seminar Ser.). (ENG.). 520p. per. 105.00 *(978-0-521-03968-0(1))* Cambridge Univ. Pr.

Power, Michael L. & Schulkin, Jay. The Evolution of Obesity. 2009. (ENG., Illus.). 408p. (gr. 17). 42.00 *(978-0-8018-9262-2(7))* Johns Hopkins Univ. Pr.

Schulkin, Jay. Cognitive Adaptation: A Pragmatist Perspective. 2008. (ENG., Illus.). 208p. 89.00 *(978-0-521-51791-1(5))* Cambridge Univ. Pr.

Siddiqui, Khawar Sohail & Thomas, Torsten. Protein Adaptation in Extremophiles. 2008. (Illus.). (C). 120.00 *(978-1-60456-019-0(3))* Nova Science Pubs., Inc.

Simpson, Stephen J. & Raubenheimer, David. The Nature of Nutrition: A Unifying Framework from Animal Adaptation to Human Obesity. 2012. (ENG., Illus.). 260p. (C). 49.50 ***(978-0-691-14565-5(2))*** Princeton Univ. Pr.

Storz, G. Bacterial Stress Responses. 2nd ed. 2011. (ENG., Illus.). 580p. ***(978-1-55581-621-6(5))*** ASM Pr.

Turner, J. Scott. The Tinkerer's Accomplice: How Design Emerges from Life Itself. 2010. (ENG., Illus.). 304p. pap. 17.95 *(978-0-674-05753-1(8))* Harvard Univ. Pr.

Williams, Tony. Physiological Adaptations for Breeding in Birds. 2012. (ENG., Illus.). 392p. (C). 65.00 ***(978-0-691-13982-1(2))*** Princeton Univ. Pr.

Xi, Lei, ed. Intermittent Hypoxia: from Molecular Mechanisms to Clinical Applications. 2009. (Physiology - Laboratory & Clinical Research Ser.). (Illus.). xxxi, 615p. 89.00 *(978-1-60876-127-2(4))* Nova Science Pubs., Inc.

Zubieta-Calleja, Gustavo. Human Adaptation to High Altitude & to Sea Level. 2010. 72p. pap. *(978-3-639-25276-7(4))* VDM Verlag Dr. Mueller e.K.

ADAPTATION (PSYCHOLOGY)
see Adjustment (Psychology)

ADAPTATIONS, FILM
see Film Adaptations

ADAPTATIONS, STAGE
see Stage Adaptations

ADAPTED PHYSICAL EDUCATION
see Physical Education for People with Disabilities

ADAPTIVE OPTICS
see Optics, Adaptive

ADAPTIVE CONTROL SYSTEMS
see also Feedback Control Systems

Antoniou, Constantinos. On-Line Calibration for Dynamic Traffic Assignment Models- Theory, Methods & Application. 2007. 160p. per. *(978-3-8364-2141-6(0))* VDM Verlag Dr. Mueller e.K.

Astolfi, A., et al. Nonlinear & Adaptive Control with Applications. 2008. (Communications & Control Engineering Ser.). (Illus.). 304p. 119.00 *(978-1-84800-065-0(0))* Springer.

Astolfi, Alessandro, et al. Nonlinear & Adaptive Control with Applications. 2010. (Communications & Control Engineering Ser.). (Illus.). xvi, 290p. pap. 119.00 *(978-1-84996-719-8(9)*, 1849967199) Springer.

Aström, Karl J. & Wittenmark, Bjorn. Adaptive Control: Second Edition. 2nd ed. 2008. (Dover Books on Electrical Engineering Ser.). (ENG.). 592p. pap. 32.95 *(978-0-486-46278-3(1))* Dover Pubns., Inc.

Balakrishna, Ramachandran. Off-Line Calibration of Dynamic Traffic Assignment-Analysis, Algorithms & Applications. 2007. pap. *(978-3-8364-2089-1(9))* VDM Verlag Dr. Mueller e.K.

Balla, Srinivasa Prasad. Development of Simulation. 2010. 68p. pap. *(978-3-8383-7789-6(3))* Lambert Academic Publishing.

Baños, Alfonso & Barreiro, Antonio. Reset Control Systems. 2011. (Advances in Industrial Control Ser.). (ENG., Illus.). xvii, 252p. 129.00 ***(978-1-4471-2216-6(X)***, 144712216X) Springer.

Beckerman, Martin. Adaptive Cooperative Systems. 2012. (Adaptive & Learning Systems for Signal Processing, Communications & Control Ser.). (ENG.). 440p. 54.95 ***(978-0-471-18512-3(4)***, Wiley-Interscience) Wiley, John & Sons, Inc.

Bobda, Christophe. Introduction to Reconfigurable Computing: Architectures, Algorithms & Applications. 2007. (ENG., Illus.). xxvi, 362p. 139.00 *(978-1-4020-6088-5(2)*, 1402060882) Springer.

Bouchachia, Abdelhamid. 2009 International Conference on Adaptive & Intelligent Systems; ICAIS 2009; Proceedings: 24-26 September 2009, Klagenfurt, Austria. 2009. (Illus.). xviii, 201p. pap. *(978-0-7695-3827-3(4))* IEEE Computer Society Pr.

Bussmann, Stefan, et al. Multiagent Systems for Manufacturing Control: A Design Methodology. 2010. (Springer Series on Agent Technology Ser.). (Illus.). xiv, 288p. pap. 149.00 *(978-3-642-05890-5(6)*, 3642058906) Springer.

Butenko, Sergiy, et al, eds. Cooperative Control: Models, Applications & Algorithms: Models, Applications & Algorithms. 2010. (Cooperative Systems Ser.). (Illus.). 376p. pap. 259.00 *(978-1-4419-5241-7(1)*, 1441952411) Springer.

Chokshi, Nirav & McFarlane, Duncan. A Distributed Coordination Approach to Reconfigurable Process Control. 2010. (Springer Series in Advanced Manufacturing Ser.). (Illus.). xii, 189p. pap. 149.00 *(978-1-84996-717-4(2)*, 1849967172) Springer.

Chokshi, Nirav N. & McFarlane, D. C. A Distributed Coordination Approach to Reconfigurable Process Control. 2007. (Springer Series in Advanced Manufacturing Ser.). (Illus.). XII, 189p. 149.00 *(978-1-84800-059-9(6)*, 1848000596) Springer.

Demkowicz, Leszek, et al. Computing with hp-ADAPTIVE FINITE ELEMENTS: Volume 2: Frontiers: Three Dimensional Elliptic & Maxwell Problems with Applications, Vol. 2. 2007. (Chapman & Hall/CRC Applied Mathematics & Nonlinear Science Ser.). (ENG., Illus.). 440p. 102.95 *(978-1-58488-672-3(2)*, Chapman & Hall/CRC) CRC Pr. LLC.

Dickmanns, Ernst D. Dynamic Vision for Perception & Control of Motion. 2007. (ENG., Illus.). xviii, 474p. 109.00 *(978-1-84628-637-7(9)*, 1846286379) Springer.

Dickmanns, Ernst Dieter. Dynamic Vision for Perception & Control of Motion. (Illus.). 2010. (ENG.). xviii, 474p. pap. 109.00 *(978-1-84996-633-7(8)*, 1849966338) 2007. xvii, 474p. 99.00 *(978-1-84628-638-4(7))* Springer.

Dolog, Peter. Engineering Adaptive Web Applications. 2008. 176p. pap. *(978-3-639-08152-7(8))* VDM Verlag Dr. Mueller e.K.

Dumke, Reiner. Quality Assurance of Agent-Based & Self-Managed Systems. 2009. (ENG., Illus.). 176p. 102.95 *(978-1-4398-1266-2(7)*, CRC Press) Taylor & Francis Group GBR. Dist: Taylor & Francis Group.

Fafrowicz, Magdalena, et al, eds. Neuroadaptive Systems: Theory & Applications. 2012. (ENG., Illus.). 384p. 129.95 *(978-1-4398-5745-8(8)*, CRC Press) Taylor & Francis Group GBR. Dist: Taylor & Francis Group.

Fei, Juntao. Advanced Control Design of MEMS Vibratory Gyroscope. 2011. (Nanotechnology Science & Technology Ser.). (Illus.). xi, 180p. 47.00 ***(978-1-61470-487-4(2))*** Nova Science Pubs., Inc.

Fradkov, A. L., et al. Nonlinear & Adaptive Control of Complex Systems. 2010. (Mathematics & Its Applications Ser.). (Illus.). 528p. pap. 139.00 *(978-90-481-5294-0(1)*, 9048152941) Springer.

Fröschl, Christoph. User Modeling & User Profiling in Adaptive. 2008. 176p. pap. *(978-3-8364-6307-2(5))* VDM Verlag Dr. Mueller e.K.

Fusco, Giuseppe & Russo, Mario. Adaptive Voltage Control in Power Systems: Modeling, Design & Applications. (Advances in Industrial Control Ser.). (Illus.). xiv, 166p. 2010. pap. 129.00 *(978-1-84996-620-7(6)*, 1849966206) 2006. 129.00 *(978-1-84628-564-6(X)*, 184628564X) Springer.

Gabrys, Bogdan, et al, eds. Do Smart Adaptive Systems Exist? Best Practice for Selection & Combination of Intelligent Methods. 2010. (Studies in Fuzziness & Soft Computing Ser.). (Illus.). x, 370p. pap. 239.00 *(978-3-642-06320-6(9)*, 3642063209) Springer.

Ge, S. S., et al. Stable Adaptive Neural Network Control. 2010. (International Series on Asian Studies in Computer & Information Science Ser.). 298p. pap. 319.00 *(978-1-4419-4932-5(1)*, 1441949321) Springer.

Gilbert, Robert C. & Schultz, Angela M., eds. Industrial Control Systems. 2011. (Mechanical Engineering Theory & Applications Ser.). (Illus.). xii, 249p. 95.00 *(978-1-61209-988-0(2))* Nova Science Pubs., Inc.

Gkikas, Nikolaos. Ergonomics of Intelligent Vehicle Braking Systems. 2011. (Illus.). 256p. pap. ***(978-3-8443-9392-7(7))*** Lambert Academic Publishing.

Greenwood, Garrison W. & Tyrrell, Andrew M. Introduction to Evolvable Hardware: A Practical Guide for Designing Self-Adaptive Systems. 2006. (IEEE Press Series on Computational Intelligence Ser.: 5). (ENG., Illus.). 208p. 105.00 *(978-0-471-71977-9(3)*, Wiley-IEEE Pr.) Wiley, John & Sons, Inc.

Gros, Claudius. Complex & Adaptive Dynamical Systems: A Primer. 2008. (Springer Complexity Ser.). (Illus.). 250p. pap. 69.95 *(978-3-540-71873-4(7))* Springer.

—Complex & Adaptive Dynamical Systems: A Primer. 2nd ed. 2010. (ENG., Illus.). xiv, 325p. pap. 79.95 *(978-3-642-04705-3(X)*, 364204705X) Springer DEU. Dist: Springer.

Grundel, Don A. Cooperative Systems: Control & Optimization. 2007. (Lecture Notes in Economics & Mathematical Systems Ser.: Vol. 588). (Illus.). X, 403p. pap. 139.00 *(978-3-540-48270-3(9)*, 3540482709) Springer.

Haas, Olivier C. L. & Burnham, Keith J., eds. Intelligent & Adaptive Systems in Medicine. 2008. (Series in Medical Physics & Biomedical Engineering). (ENG., Illus.). 400p. 162.95 *(978-0-7503-0994-3(6)*, IP385, Taylor & Francis) Taylor & Francis Group GBR. Dist: Taylor & Francis Group.

He, Haibo. Self-Adaptive Systems for Machine Intelligence. 2011. (ENG., Illus.). 248p. 84.95 *(978-0-470-34396-8(6)*, Wiley-Interscience) Wiley, John & Sons, Inc.

Hirsch, Michael J. Optimization & Cooperative Control Strategies. 2009. (Lecture Notes in Control & Information Sciences Ser.). (ENG., Illus.). viii, 462p. pap. 189.00 *(978-3-540-88062-2(3))* Springer.

Holland, John H. Signals & Boundaries: Building Blocks for Complex Adaptive Systems. 2012. ***(978-0-262-01783-1(0))*** MIT Pr.

Holzmann, Édéric. Adaptive Cooperation between Driver & Assistant System: Improving Road Safety. 2010. (ENG., Illus.). xiv, 226p. pap. 159.00 *(978-3-642-09388-3(4)*, 3642093884) Springer.

Holzmann, Frederic. Adaptive Cooperation Between Driver & Assistant System: Improving Road Safety. 2007. (ENG., Illus.). xiv, 226p. 159.00 *(978-3-540-74473-3(8)*, 3540744738) Springer.

Hovakimyan, Naira & Cao, Chengyu. L1 Adaptive Control Theory: Guaranteed Robustness with Fast Adaptation. 2010. (ENG., Illus.). 337p. pap. *(978-0-89871-704-4(3))* Society for Industrial and Applied Mathematics.

Hubbard, James E. Filtering for the Control of Smart Structures: An Introduction. 2009. (ENG., Illus.). xv, 209p. 129.00 *(978-3-642-03803-7(4)*, 3642038034) Springer.

IEEE Staff. 2007 46th IEEE Conference on Decision & Control. 2007. pap. 962.00 *(978-1-4244-1497-0(0))* IEEE.

Igelnik, Boris, ed. Computational Modeling & Simulation of Intellect: Current State & Future Perspectives. 2011. 350p. 180.00 *(978-1-60960-551-3(9)*, Information Science Reference) IGI Global.

Islam, Rafiqul. Focus on Information, Intelligence, & Knowledge. 2011. (978-1-61209-979-8(3)) Nova Science Pubs., Inc.
—Genetic Algorithms, Fuzzy Systems, & Website Classification. 2012. (Computer Science, Technology & Applications Mathematics Research Developments Ser.). 226p. 89.00 (978-1-61324-000-7(7)) Nova Science Pubs., Inc.
Kamalasadan, Sukumar. Novel Intelligent Adaptive Designs for the Control of Smart Systems. 2010. 248p. pap. (978-3-639-25510-2(0)) VDM Verlag Dr. Mueller e.K.
Khan Niazi, Yasir Amir. Modeling & Neural Control of Quadrotor Helicopter. 2010. 80p. pap. (978-3-8383-9298-1(1)) Lambert Academic Publishing.
Kiencke, Uwe & Nielsen, Lars. Automotive Control Systems: For Engine, Driveline, & Vehicle. 2nd ed. 2010. (ENG., Illus.). xviii, 512p. pap. 89.95 (978-3-642-06211-7(3), 3642062113) Springer.
Krikidis, Ioannis. An Iterative Reconfigurability Approach for 3g Communication Systems. 2009. 180p. pap. (978-3-639-16435-0(0)) VDM Verlag Dr. Mueller e.K.
Krstic, Miroslav. Delay Compensation for Nonlinear, Adaptive, & PDE Systems. 2009. (Illus.). xiv, 466p. E-Book **(978-0-8176-4877-0(1))** Birkhauser Verlag AG.
Kulkarni, Sandeep & Schiper, André. Stabilization, Safety, & Security of Distributed Systems: 10th International Symposium, SSS 2008, Detroit, MI, USA, November 21-23, 2008. Proceedings. 2008. (Lecture Notes in Computer Science / Theoretical Computer Science & General Issues Ser.). x, 265p. pap. 69.95 (978-3-540-89334-9(2)) Springer.
Landau, Ioan Doré, et al. Adaptive Control: Algorithms, Analysis & Applications. 2nd ed. 2011. (Communications & Control Engineering Ser.). (Illus.). xxii, 587p. 229.00 (978-0-85729-663-4(9), 0857296639) Springer.
Lavaei, Javad & Aghdam, Amir G. Decentralized Control of Interconnected Systems. 2008. 208p. pap. (978-3-639-03417-2(1)) VDM Verlag Dr. Mueller e.K.
McKee, Michael. Bio Inspired Adaptive Control of Nonlinear Systems. 2010. 112p. pap. (978-3-8383-4058-6(2)) Lambert Academic Publishing.
Nassirharand, Amir. Computer-aided Nonlinear Control System Design: Using Describing Function Models. 2012. (ENG., Illus.). xii, 180p. 129.00 **(978-1-4471-2148-0(1)**, 1447121481) Springer.
Nová, et al. Controller Design. 2010. 96p. pap. (978-3-8383-4046-3(9)) Lambert Academic Publishing.
Pardalos, Panos M., et al, eds. Advances in Cooperative Control & Optimization: Proceedings of the 7th International Conference on Cooperative Control & Optimization. 2007. (Lecture Notes in Control & Information Sciences Ser.). (Illus.). 422p. pap. 159.00 (978-3-540-74354-5(5)) Springer.
Popovskij, Vladimir, et al. Control & Adaptation in Telecommunication Systems: Mathematical Foundations. 2011. (Lecture Notes in Electrical Engineering Ser.). (Illus.). xii, 176p. 129.00 (978-3-642-20613-9(1), 3642206131) Springer.
Qu, Zhihua. Cooperative Control of Dynamical Systems: Applications to Autonomous Vehicles. 2009. (ENG., Illus.). xvi, 325p. 129.00 (978-1-84882-324-2(X), 184882324X) Springer.
Rajamani, Rajesh. Vehicle Dynamics & Control. 2011. (Mechanical Engineering Ser.). (ENG., Illus.). xxv, 471p. pap. 129.00 (978-1-4419-3889-3(3), 1441938893); 2nd ed. xxv, 496p. 139.00 **(978-1-4614-1432-2(6)**, 1461414326) Springer.
Rigatos, Gerasimos. Modelling & Control for Intelligent Industrial Systems: Adaptive Algorithms in Robotics & Industrial Engineering. 2011. (Intelligent Systems Reference Library). (Illus.). xxx, 382p. 179.00 (978-3-642-17874-0(X), 364217874X) Springer.
Sastry, Shankar & Bodson, Marc. Adaptive Control: Stability, Convergence & Robustness. 2011. (Dover Books on Electrical Engineering Ser.). (ENG.). 400p. pap. 24.95 (978-0-486-48202-6(2)) Dover Pubns., Inc.
Shi, Wenyu. Adaptive Control of a Total Artificial Heart. 2010. 108p. pap. (978-3-8383-1961-2(3)) Lambert Academic Publishing.
Smyshlyaev, Andrey & Krstic, Miroslav. Adaptive Control of Parabolic PDEs. 2010. (ENG., Illus.). 342p. (C). 55.00 (978-0-691-14286-9(6)) Princeton Univ. Pr.
Steer, Michael & Palmer, W. Devereux. Multifunctional Adaptive Microwave Circuits & Systems. 2008. (Illus.). 410p. (978-1-891121-77-7(4)) SciTech Publishing, Inc.
Stefanovic, Margareta & Safonov, Michael G. Safe Adaptive Control: Data-driven Stability Analysis & Robust Synthesis. 2011. (Lecture Notes in Control & Information Sciences Ser.). (Illus.). xii, 148p. pap. 109.00 (978-1-84996-452-4(1), 1849964521) Springer.
Stoica, Adrian. AT-EQUAL 2009: 2009 ECSIS Symposium on Advanced Technologies for Enhanced Quality of Life (LAB-RS & ARTIPED 2009): Proceedings, 22-26 July 2009, Iasi, Romania. 2009. (Illus.). xi, 172p. pap. **(978-0-7695-3753-5(7))** IEEE Computer Society Pr.
Stoica, Adrian. Proceedings, LAB-RS 2008: 2008 ECSIS Symposium on Learning & Adaptive Behaviors for Robotic Systems: Proceedings, 6-8 August 2008, Edinburgh, Scotland, United Kingdom. 2008. (Illus.). xi, 115p. (978-0-7695-3272-1(1)) IEEE Computer Society Pr.
Sundararajan, N., et al. Fully Tuned Radial Basis Function Neural Networks for Flight Control. 2010. (International Series on Asian Studies in Computer & Information Science Ser.). 176p. pap. 279.00 (978-1-4419-4915-8(1), 1441949151) Springer.
Tao, Gang & Lewis, Frank L., eds. Adaptive Control of Nonsmooth Dynamic Systems. 2010. (ENG., Illus.). xxi, 407p. pap. 179.00 (978-1-84996-869-0(1), 1849968691) Springer.
Tao, Gang, et al. Adaptive Control of Systems with Actuator Failures. 2010. (ENG., Illus.). xvi, 299p. pap. 159.00 (978-1-84996-917-8(5), 1849969175) Springer.
Tyukin, Ivan. Adaptation in Dynamical Systems. 2011. (ENG., Illus.). 428p. 120.00 (978-0-521-19819-6(4)) Cambridge Univ. Pr.
Van, M., ed. The Logic of Adaptive Behavior: Knowledge Representation & Algorithms for Adaptive Sequential Decision Making under Uncertainty in First-Order & Relational Domains - Volume 192 Frontiers in Artificial Intelligence & Applications. 2009. (Illus.). 215p. 217.00 (978-1-58603-969-1(5)) IOS Pr., Inc.
Vasilakos, Athanasios V., et al. Autonomic Computing & Communications Systems: Third International ICST Conference, Autonomics 2009, Limassol, Cyprus, September 9-11, 2009, Revised Selected Papers. 2010. (Lecture Notes of the Institute for Computer Sciences, Social-Informatics & Telecommunications Engineering Ser.). xii, 269p. pap. 72.00 (978-3-642-11481-6(4), 3642114814) Springer.
Wang, Weixun, et al. Dynamic Reconfiguration in Real-Time Systems: Energy, Performance, & Thermal Perspectives. 2012. (Embedded Systems Ser.). (ENG., Illus.). xiv, 213p. 129.00 (978-1-4614-0277-0(8), 1461402778) Springer.
Widrow, Bernard & Walach, Eugene. Adaptive Inverse Control: A Signal Processing Approach. (ENG., Illus.). rev. ed. 2007. 508p. 152.00 (978-0-470-22609-4(9)) 2nd ed. 2014. 544p. 125.00 (978-0-470-23329-0(X)) Wiley, John & Sons, Inc. (Wiley-IEEE Pr.).
Wong, W. Eric. Adaptive Control Approach for Software Quality Improvement. 2011. (Illus.). 280p. 99.00 (978-981-4340-91-5(X)) World Scientific Publishing Co., Inc.
Young-Dippold, Amanda. Adaptive Control of Nonaffine Systems for Flight Applications. 2009. 76p. pap. (978-3-639-18000-8(3)) VDM Verlag Dr. Mueller e.K.
Yusoff, Nooryusmiza & Ramasamy, Marappagounder. Profit Optimization. 2010. 208p. pap. (978-3-639-27630-5(2)) VDM Verlag Dr. Mueller e.K.
Zangl, K. C. & Oppenheim, Alan V. Active Noise Cancellation System Design Engineering. 2007. 152p. 89.95 (978-1-934939-05-5(6)) Wexford College Pr.
Zbikowski, Rafal & Subchan, S. Computational Optimal Control: Tools & Practice. 2009. (ENG., Illus.). 202p. 145.00 (978-0-470-71440-9(9), Wiley) Wiley, John & Sons, Inc.
Zhang, Jianlong. Practical Adaptive Control. 2008. 228p. pap. (978-3-639-04759-2(1)) VDM Verlag Dr. Mueller e.K.
Zhou, Jing & Wen, Changyun. Adaptive Backstepping Control of Uncertain Systems: Nonsmooth Nonlinearities, Interactions, or Time-Variations. 2008. (Lecture Notes in Control & Information Sciences Ser.). (Illus.). xiv, 241p. pap. 139.00 (978-3-540-77806-6(3)) Springer.

ADAPTIVE CONTROL SYSTEMS—MATHEMATICAL MODELS

Duflo, Marie. Random Iterative Models. Wilson, S. S., tr. from FRE. 2010. (Stochastic Modelling & Applied Probability Ser.). xvi, 385p. pap. 129.00 (978-3-642-08175-0(4), 3642081754) Springer.
Miller, J. H. & Page, Scott E. Complex Adaptive Systems - an Introduction to Computational Models of Social Life. 2007. (Princeton Studies in Complexity). (Illus.). 264p. (C). 65.00 (978-0-691-13096-5(5)) Princeton Univ. Pr.
Ogunfunmi, Tokunbo. Adaptive Nonlinear System Identification: The Volterra & Wiener Model Approaches. 2010. (Signals & Communication Technology Ser.). xv, 229p. pap. 124.00 (978-1-4419-3883-1(4), 1441938834) Springer.
Sayed, Ali H. Adaptive Filters. 2008. (ENG., Illus.). 824p. 153.00 (978-0-470-25388-5(6), Wiley-IEEE Pr.) Wiley, John & Sons, Inc.

ADAPTIVE MATERIALS
see Smart Materials

ADARI LANGUAGE
see Harari Language

ADC PROGRAMS
see Aid to Families with Dependent Children Programs

ADD (CHILD BEHAVIOR DISORDER)
see Attention-Deficit Hyperactivity Disorder

ADD ADULTS
see Attention-Deficit-Disordered Adults

ADD CHILDREN
see Attention-Deficit-Disordered Children

ADD YOUTH
see Attention-Deficit-Disordered Youth

ADDAMS, JANE, 1860-1935

Addams, Jane. Twenty Years at Hull-House. 2008. 164p. pap. 10.99 (978-1-4209-3042-9(7)) Digireads.com.
—Twenty Years at Hull-House. 2006. (Twelve-Point Ser.). lib. bdg. 25.00 (978-1-58287-282-4(8)); lib. bdg. 26.00 (978-1-58287-873-7(0)) North Bks.
—Twenty Years at Hull-House. 2009. 322p. 14.99 (978-1-4344-0564-7(8)); pap. 14.99 (978-1-4344-0515-9(X)) Wildside Pr., LLC.
—Twenty Years at Hull-House: With Autobiographical Notes. 2008. (ENG.). 272p. pap. 26.75 (978-1-4375-3539-6(9)); 302p. pap. 29.75 (978-1-4375-3540-2(2)) BiblioBazaar.
—Twenty Years at Hull-House: With Autobiographical Notes. 2008. (ENG., Illus.). 304p. pap. 11.95 (978-0-486-45749-9(4)) Dover Pubns., Inc.
—Twenty Years at Hull-House Set: And the Second Twenty Years at Hull House, 2 vols. (Illus.). reprint ed. lib. bdg. 250.00 (978-0-7222-0071-1(4)) Library Reprints, Inc.
—Twenty Years at Hull-House, with Autobiographical Notes. 2010. 524p. pap. 39.75 (978-1-149-57954-1(4)); 518p. pap. 39.75 (978-1-149-57953-4(6)) BiblioBazaar.
—Twenty Years at Hull-House, with Autobiographical Notes. 2010. 186p. pap. 26.53 (978-1-153-19313-9(2)) General Bks. LLC.
—Twenty Years at Hull House with Autobiographical Notes. 2009. 248p. pap. (978-0-217-94478-6(7)) Books LLC.
—Twenty Years at Hull House; with Autobiographical Notes. 2010. (Illus.). 180p. pap. 26.53 (978-1-153-74179-8(2)) General Bks. LLC.
—Venturing into Usefulness Vol. 2. Bryan, Mary Lynn et al, eds. 2009. (Selected Papers of Jane Addams Ser.). (ENG., Illus.). 808p. 78.00 (978-0-252-03349-0(3)) Univ. of Illinois Pr.
Brown, Victoria Bissell. The Education of Jane Addams. 2007. (Politics & Culture in Modern America Ser.). (Illus.). 432p. (C). per. 27.50 (978-0-8122-1952-4(X)) Univ. of Pennsylvania Pr.
Cracraft, James. Two Shining Souls: Jane Addams &. 2012. (ENG.). 206p. (gr. 17). 60.00 **(978-0-7391-7450-0(9))** Lexington Bks.
Fischer, Marilyn, et al. Jane Addams & the Practice of Democracy. Chmielewski, Wendy & Fischer, Marilyn, eds. Nackenoff, Carol, ed. (ENG.). 248p. 2009. 67.00 (978-0-252-03406-0(6)) 2008. pap. 26.00 (978-0-252-07612-1(5)) Univ. of Illinois Pr.
Hamington, Maurice. The Social Philosophy of Jane Addams. 2009. (ENG., Illus.). 240p. 50.00 (978-0-252-03476-3(7)) Univ. of Illinois Pr.
Hamington, Maurice, ed. Feminist Interpretations of Jane Addams. 2010. (Re-Reading the Canon Ser.). (ENG.). 304p. 36.95 (978-0-271-03693-9(1)); pap. 94.95 (978-0-271-03694-6(X)) Pennsylvania State Univ. Pr.
Joslin, Katherine. Jane Addams, a Writer's Life. 2009. (ENG., Illus.). 328p. pap. 20.95 (978-0-252-07634-3(6)) Univ. of Illinois Pr.
Knight, Louise W. Citizen: Jane Addams & the Struggle for Democracy. 2006. (Illus.). 598p. per. 22.50 (978-0-226-44700-1(6)) Univ. of Chicago Pr.
Lewis, Hunter, ed. & intro. Essence of Jane Addam's Twenty Years at Hull House. 2012. (ENG.). 221p. pap. 12.00 **(978-1-60419-054-0(X))** Axios Pr.
Opdycke, Sandra. Jane Addams & Her Vision of America. 2011. (Library of American Biography Ser.). (ENG.). 264p. (C). pap. 25.20 (978-0-205-59840-3(4), Prentice Hall) Prentice Hall PTR.
Pinar, William & Pinar, William F. The Worldliness of a Cosmopolitan Education: Passionate Lives in Public Service. 2009. (Studies in Curriculum Theory Ser.). (ENG.). 226p. 140.00 (978-0-415-99550-4(7)) Routledge.
Weaks-Baxter, Mary, et al. We Are a College at War: Women Working for Victory in World War II. 2010. (ENG.). 256p. (C). 29.95 (978-0-8093-2992-2(1)); Southern Illinois Univ. Pr.

ADDICTION, LOVE
see Relationship Addiction

ADDICTION, RELATIONSHIP
see Relationship Addiction

ADDICTION, RELIGIOUS
see Religious Addiction

ADDICTION, ROMANCE
see Relationship Addiction

ADDICTION, SEX
see Sex Addiction

ADDICTION, SUBSTANCE
see Substance Abuse

ADDICTION, WORK
see Workaholism

ADDICTION TO DRUGS
see Drug Addiction

ADDICTION TO THE INTERNET
see Internet Addiction

ADDICTIVE BEHAVIOR
see Compulsive Behavior; Substance Abuse

ADDICTIVE RELATIONSHIPS
see Relationship Addiction

ADDING MACHINES
see Calculators

ADDISON, JOSEPH, 1672-1719

Addison, Joseph. The Right Honorable Joseph Addison Vol. 1: His Works. 2006. pap. 40.95 (978-1-4286-3687-3(0)) Kessinger Publishing, LLC.
—The Right Honorable Joseph Addison Vol. 2: His Works. 2006. pap. 40.95 (978-1-4286-3688-0(9)) Kessinger Publishing, LLC.
—The Right Honorable Joseph Addison Vol. 3: His Works. 2006. pap. 38.95 (978-1-4286-3689-7(7)) Kessinger Publishing, LLC.
—The Right Honorable Joseph Addison Vol. 4: His Works. 2006. pap. 40.95 (978-1-4286-3690-3(0)) Kessinger Publishing, LLC.
—The Right Honorable Joseph Addison Vol. 5: His Works. 2006. pap. 40.95 (978-1-4286-3691-0(9)) Kessinger Publishing, LLC.
—The Right Honorable Joseph Addison Vol. 6: His Works. 2006. pap. 38.95 (978-1-4286-3692-7(7)) Kessinger Publishing, LLC.
—The Works of the Right Honourable Joseph Addison. 2009. 552p. pap. (978-0-217-28826-2(X)); 454p. pap. (978-0-217-89529-3(8)); 336p. pap. (978-0-217-96537-8(7)) Books LLC.
—The Works of the Right Honourable Joseph Addison. 2009. 432p. pap. 27.36 (978-0-217-61709-3(3)); 622p. pap. 28.66 (978-0-217-89530-9(1)); 390p. pap. 30.06 (978-1-4589-1077-6(6)); 440p. pap. 27.46 (978-1-4589-1082-0(2)); 424p. pap. 23.00 (978-1-4589-1084-4(9)); 68p. pap. 24.95 (978-1-4589-8672-6(1)) General Bks. LLC.
Courthope, William. Addison. 2011. (Cambridge Library Collection - English Men of Letters Ser.). (ENG.). 204p. pap. 22.99 **(978-1-108-03442-5(X))** Cambridge Univ. Pr.
Courthope, William J. Addison. Morley, John, ed. (English Men of Letters Ser.). reprint ed. lib. bdg. 41.50 (978-0-404-51707-6(2)) AMS Pr., Inc.
—Addison. 204p. 2008. 39.95 (978-1-4365-1176-6(3)) 2007. (ENG.). per. 24.95 (978-0-548-73705-7(3)) Kessinger Publishing, LLC.
Finger, Charles J. Joseph Addison & His Time. 2007. (ENG.). 108p. 33.95 (978-0-548-08896-8(9)) Kessinger Publishing, LLC.
Goodman, Kevis. Georgic Modernity & British Romanticism: Poetry & the Mediation of History. 2008. (Cambridge Studies in Romanticism Ser.). (ENG., Illus.). 248p. pap. 36.00 (978-0-521-05729-5(9)) Cambridge Univ. Pr.
Haldeman-Julius, E. Miscellaneous Essays. 2006. pap. 16.95 (978-1-4286-4635-3(3)) Kessinger Publishing, LLC.
Johnson, Samuel. Lives of the Poets: Addison, Savage & Swift. 2007. 152p. per. (978-1-4065-3502-0(8)) Dodo Pr.
Joseph Addison. The Poetical Works of Addison; Gay's Fables; & Somerville's Chase. 2007. (ENG.). 446p. pap. 26.99 (978-1-4264-4238-4(6)); 542p. pap. 31.99 (978-1-4264-4302-2(1)) BiblioBazaar.
Macaulay, Lord. The Life & Writings of Addison. 2008. 233p. 24.99 (978-0-554-70218-6(5)); 21.99 (978-0-554-70223-0(1)); pap. 19.75 (978-0-554-70220-9(7)); pap. 19.75 (978-0-554-70222-3(3)) BiblioBazaar.
—The Life & Writings of Addison. 2007. (ENG.). 112p. 34.95 (978-0-548-07837-2(8)); 118p. 34.95 (978-0-548-02542-0(8)) Kessinger Publishing, LLC.
—Macaulay's Essays on Milton & Addison. Thurber, Samuel, ed. 2007. (ENG.). 142p. 35.95 (978-0-548-02922-0(9)) Kessinger Publishing, LLC.
Oliphant, M. O. W. Historical Characters of the Reign of Qu. 2006. pap. 28.95 (978-1-4286-5759-5(2)) Kessinger Publishing, LLC.

ADDITION

Battista, Michael. Cognition-Based Assessment & Teaching of Addition & Subtraction: Building on Students' Reasoning. 2012. 112p. pap. 24.38 **(978-0-325-01271-1(7)**, E01271) Heinemann.
Caldwell, Janet H. Developing Essential Understanding of Addition & Subtraction for Teaching Mathematics in Prekindergarten-Grade 2. 2010. (978-0-87353-664-6(9)) National Council of Teachers of Mathematics.
Davis, Stephen. Math Games Galore: Addition & Subtraction Facts. 2009. pap. 12.99 (978-1-59198-985-1(X)) Creative Teaching Pr., Inc.
Eichhorn, Connie. Whole Numbers: Addition & Subtraction. pap. 10.50 (978-0-13-078882-5(1)) Globe Fearon Educational Publishing.
Fosnot, Catherine Twomey. Ages & Timelines. 2008. 80p. pap. 29.94 **(978-0-325-01014-4(5)**, E01014, Firsthand) Heinemann.
Jackson-Collins, Myrtice. Rap N' Facts Addition Rap Songs: The Easier Way to Learn. 2010. 40p. pap. 18.49 (978-1-4389-2027-6(X)) AuthorHouse.
O'Connell, Susan & SanGiovanni, John. Mastering the Basic Math Facts in Addition & Subtraction: Strategies, Activities, & Interventions to Move Students Beyond Memorization. 2011. 192p. pap. 31.25 (978-0-325-02963-4(6), E02963) Heinemann.
Seidman, Glenn. Making Addition & Subtraction Easier. 2011. 60p. pap. 14.98 **(978-1-4634-4128-9(2))** AuthorHouse.
SLAM-Addition, 30 wkbks., Set. 15.95 (978-0-86624-031-4(4), LWB6536TB) Bilingual Educational Services, Inc.

ADDITION POLYMERIZATION

Barner-Kowollik, Christopher, ed. Handbook of RAFT Polymerization. 2008. (ENG., Illus.). 556p. 280.00 (978-3-527-31924-4(7), Wiley-VCH) Wiley, John & Sons, Inc.
Caneba, Gerard. Free-Radical Retrograde-Precipitation Polymerization (FRRPP) Novel Concepts, Processes, Materials, & Energy Aspects. 2010. (Illus.). xi, 306p. 159.00 (978-3-642-03024-6(6), 3642030246) Springer.
Lowe, Andrew B. & McCormick, Charles L., eds. Polyelectrolytes & Polyzwitterions: Synthesis, Properties, & Applications. 2006. (ACS Symposium Ser.: Vol. 937). (ENG., Illus.). 200p. (C). 149.50 (978-0-8412-3958-6(4)) American Chemical Society.
Zaikov, G. E. & Babkin, V. A. Theoretical Estimation of Acidic Force of Linear Olefins of Cationic Polymerization. 2011. pap. (978-1-61209-578-3(X)) Nova Science Pubs., Inc.

ADDITION REACTIONS

Vicario, Jose L., et al. Organocatalytic Enantioselective Conjugate Addition Reactions: A Powerful Tool for the Stereocontrolled Synthesis of Complex Molecules. 2010. (RSC Catalysis Ser.). (ENG., Illus.). 368p. (C). 195.00 **(978-1-84973-024-2(5))** Royal Society of Chemistry, The GBR. Dist: Ingram Pub. Services.
Woolford, Jason. The Double [3+2] Photocycloaddition Reaction. 2011. (Springer Theses Ser.). (ENG., Illus.). xvi, 182p. 129.00 **(978-3-642-22859-9(3)**, 3642228593) Springer.

ADDITIVE PROCESS (PROBABILITY THEORY)
see Random Walks (Mathematics)

ADDITIVES, FOOD
see Food Additives

ADDRESS, FORMS OF
see Forms of Address

ADDRESS, TITLES OF
see Forms of Address; Titles of Honor and Nobility

ADDRESSES
see Lectures and Lecturing; Speeches, Addresses, etc.

ADE, GEORGE, 1866-1944
Kriebel, Robert C. Ross Ade: Their Purdue Stories, Stadium, & Legacies. 2009. (ENG.). 295p. pap. 22.95 *(978-1-55753-522-1(1))* Purdue Univ. Pr.

ADELAIDE (S. AUST.)
Chambers, Mason. Mason Chambers Adventures Through Life. 2010. (Illus.). 192p. pap. 14.49 *(978-1-4389-4759-4(3))* AuthorHouse.
Price, John. Memoir of George Swan Fowler Christian Merchant. 2009. 120p. pap. 26.45 *(978-1-4446-2276-8(5))* Audubon Pr. & Christian Bk. Service.

ADELAIDE (S. AUST.)—HISTORY
Jenkin, John. William & Lawrence Bragg, Father & Son: The Most Extraordinary Collaboration in Science. 2008. (ENG., Illus.). 500p. 85.00 *(978-0-19-923520-9(1))* Oxford Univ. Pr., Inc.

ADEN
Lord, Cliff & Birtles, David. The Armed Forces of Aden & the Protectorate 1839-1967: Revised & Expanded Edition. 2010. (Illus.). 160p. pap. 79.95 *(978-1-906033-96-5(X))* Helion & Co., Ltd. GBR. Dist: Casemate Pubs. & Bk. Distributors, LLC.

ADENAUER, KONRAD, 1876-1967
Brady, Steven. Eisenhower & Adenauer: Alliance Maintenance under Pressure, 1953-1960. 2009. (Harvard Cold War Studies Book Ser.). (ENG.). 290p. 83.99 *(978-0-7391-4225-7(9))* Lexington Bks.

ADENOIDS
Batti, James S. & Schoem, Scott R. Evaluation & Management of the Neck Mass & Adenopathy in Children. 2008. (Illus.). 48p. pap. *(978-1-56772-119-5(2))* American Academy of Otolaryngology-Head & Neck Surgery Foundation, Inc.
Zelinger, Laurie. The O, My in Tonsillectomy & Adenoidectomy: How to prepare your child for surgery, a parent's manual, 2nd Edition. 2010. 32p. pap. 19.95 *(978-1-61599-053-5(4))* Loving Healing Pr., Inc.

ADENOIDS—SURGERY
Coolidge, Algernon. Adenoids & Tonsils. 2009. 56p. pap. 13.99 *(978-1-103-51721-3(X))* BiblioBazaar.
Jonas, Nico. The Adenoid in Children. 2010. 64p. pap. *(978-3-8383-2125-7(1))* Lambert Academic Publishing.
Zelinger, Laurie E. The "O, My" in Tonsillectomy & Adenoidectomy: How to Prepare Your Child for Surgery, a Parent's Manual. 2008. pap. *(978-1-932690-74-3(3))* Loving Healing Pr., Inc.

ADENOSINE
Borea, Pierandrea, ed. A3 Adenosine Receptors from Cell Biology to Pharmacology & Therapeutics. 2009. (ENG., Illus.). xvi, 322p. 199.00 *(978-90-481-3143-3(X)*, 904813143X) Springer.
Cronstein, Bruce N. & Hasko, Gyorgy, eds. Adenosine Receptors: Therapeutic Aspects for Inflammatory & Immune Diseases. 2006. (ENG., Illus.). 363p. 205.95 *(978-0-8493-3999-8(5)*, 3999, CRC Press) Taylor & Francis Group GBR. Dist: Taylor & Francis Group.
Wilson, Constance N. & Mustafa, S. Jamal. Adenosine Receptors in Health & Disease. 2008. (Handbook of Experimental Pharmacology Ser.). (Illus.). 360p. 529.00 *(978-3-540-89614-2(7))* Springer.

ADENOSINE TRIPHOSPHATE
Abdelmoez, Wael. Performing Enzymatic Reactions Using Novel Polymer-Bound Atp. 2011. 120p. pap. ***(978-3-8443-0980-5(2))*** Lambert Academic Publishing.
Amat, Albert. Photochemistry of Non-Resonant Light on Adenosine Triphosphate. 2009. (Illus.). 128p. pap. *(978-3-639-14786-5(3))* VDM Verlag Dr. Mueller e.K.
Gerasimovskaya, Evgenia & Kaczmarek, Elzbieta, eds. Extracellular ATP & adenosine as regulators of endothelial cell Function: Implications for health & Disease. 2009. (ENG., Illus.). 300p. 189.00 *(978-90-481-3434-2(X)*, 904813434X) Springer.
Linden, Joel & Jacobson, Kenneth A. Pharmacology of Purine & Pyrimidine Receptors. 2011. (ENG., Illus.). 558p. 241.00 *(978-0-12-385526-8(8)*, Academic Pr.) Elsevier Science & Technology Bks.

ADHD (CHILD BEHAVIOR DISORDER)
see Attention-Deficit Hyperactivity Disorder

ADHERANCE, CELL
see Cell Adhesion

ADHESION
see also Cell Adhesion; Cohesion
Adhesion Aspects of Polymeric Coatings. 2nd ed. Date not set. (Illus.). pap. 30.00 *(978-0-934010-07-8(2))* American Coatings Assn.
Brockmann, Walter, et al. Adhesive Bonding: Materials, Applications & Technology. Mikhail, Bettina, tr. from GER. 2008. (ENG., Illus.). 432p. 250.00 *(978-3-527-31898-8(4)*, Wiley-VCH) Wiley, John & Sons, Inc.
Brown, H. R., et al, contrib. by. Molecular Simulation/Fracture/Gel Theory. 2010. (Advances in Polymer Science Ser.). (Illus.). x, 228p. pap. 249.00 *(978-3-642-07569-8(X)*, 364207569X) Springer.
Byern, Janek & Grunwald, Ingo, eds. Adhesion Phenomena in Nature: From Structure to Application. 2010. (ENG., Illus.). xi, 305p. 209.00 *(978-3-7091-0141-4(7)*, 3709101417) Springer.
Ebnesajjad, Sina. Surface Treatment of Materials for Adhesion Bonding. Ebnesajjad, Cyrus, ed. 2007. (ENG., Illus.). 276p. 205.00 *(978-0-8155-1523-4(5))* William Andrew, Inc.
Gorb, S., ed. Functional Surfaces in Biology: adhesion related Phenomena, 2 vols. 2009. (ENG., Illus.). xviii, 270p. 179.00 *(978-1-4020-6694-8(5)*, 1402066945) Springer.
Gorb, Stanislav, ed. Adhesion & Friction in Biological Systems. 2011. (Biologically-Inspired Systems Ser.). (ENG., Illus.). xiv, 282p. 209.00 *(978-94-007-1444-1(0)*, 9400714440) Springer.
Gorb, Stanislav S. N., ed. Functional Surfaces in Biology, 2 vols. 2009. xviii, 660p. 329.00 *(978-1-4020-9994-6(0)*, 1402099940) Springer.
Kendall, Kevin & Rehfeldt, Florian. Adhesion of Cells, Viruses & Nanoparticles. 2010. (ENG., Illus.). xv, 282p. 189.00 *(978-90-481-2584-5(7)*, 9048125847) Springer.
Kim, Seong H., et al. Adhesion Aspects in MEMS-NEMS. 2011. (ENG., Illus.). 420p. 260.00 ***(978-90-04-19094-8(5)***, CRC Press) Taylor & Francis Group GBR. Dist: Taylor & Francis Group.
Kinloch, Anthony J. Adhesion & Adhesives: Science & Technology. 2010. (ENG.). 460p. pap. 359.00 *(978-90-481-4003-9(X)*, 904814003X) Springer.
Lesoine, John. The Development of the Single Molecule Recycler & Data Analysis Techniques for Solution Based FRET Studies. 2010. 210p. pap. 77.50 *(978-0-557-64648-7(0))* Lulu Enterprises Inc.
Maugis, D. Contact, Adhesion & Rupture of Elastic Solids. 2010. (Springer Series in Solid-State Sciences Ser.). (Illus.). xiv, 417p. pap. 289.00 *(978-3-642-08538-3(5)*, 3642085385) Springer.
Mittal, K. L. Adhesion Aspects of Thin Films. 2007. (ENG.). 284p. 192.00 *(978-90-6764-455-6(2)*, CRC Press) Taylor & Francis Group GBR. Dist: Taylor & Francis Group.
—Contact Angle, Wettability & Adhesion, Volume 6. 2009. (ENG.). 400p. 288.00 *(978-90-04-16932-6(6)*, CRC Press) Taylor & Francis Group GBR. Dist: Taylor & Francis Group.
Mittal, K. L., ed. Contact Angle, Wettability & Adhesion, Volume 5. 2008. (ENG.). 300p. 193.00 *(978-90-04-15864-1(2)*, CRC Press) Taylor & Francis Group GBR. Dist: Taylor & Francis Group.
Pearce, Eli M., et al, eds. Progress in Chemistry & Biochemistry: Kinetics, Thermodynamics, Synthesis, Properties & Applications, Vol. 1. 2009. 139.00 *(978-1-60692-344-3(7))* Nova Science Pubs., Inc.
Smith, Andrew M. & Callow, James A., eds. Biological Adhesives. 2010. (ENG., Illus.). xvii, 284p. pap. 249.00 *(978-3-642-06821-8(9)*, 3642068219) Springer.
Tabrizi, Mahdi Farshchi. On the Adhesion Between Fine Particles & Nanocontacts. 2008. 128p. pap. *(978-3-639-03390-8(6))* VDM Verlag Dr. Mueller e.K.
Victor Sunday, Aigbodion, et al. Wear Characteristics of Recycled Low Density Polyethylene Composites. 2011. 60p. pap. ***(978-3-8443-9637-9(3))*** Lambert Academic Publishing.

ADHESIVES
see also Cement; Glue
Alam, M. O. & Bailey, C., eds. Advanced Adhesives in Electronics: Materials, Properties & Applications. 2011. (ENG., Illus.). 280p. 210.00 *(978-1-84569-576-7(3))* Woodhead Publishing Ltd. GBR. Dist: Ingram Pub. Services.
Baghdachi, J. Logistic Distribution. Balakrishnan, N., ed. 2nd rev. ed. 2010. (Statistics: A Series of Textbooks & Monographs). (ENG.). 600p. instr.'s hndbk. ed. 139.95 *(978-0-8247-9026-4(X)*, DK2380) CRC Pr. LLC.
Benedek, Istvan & Feldstein, Mikhail M. Fundamentals of Pressure Sensitivity. Benedek, Istvan & Feldstein, Mikhail M., eds. 2008. (Handbook of Pressure-Sensitive Adhesives & Products Ser.). (ENG., Illus.). 370p. 139.95 *(978-1-4200-5937-3(8)*, CRC Press) Taylor & Francis Group GBR. Dist: Taylor & Francis Group.
Benedek, Istvan & Feldstein, Mikhail M., eds. Applications of Pressure-Sensitive Products. 2008. (Handbook of Pressure-Sensitive Adhesives & Products Ser.). (ENG., Illus.). 384p. 129.95 *(978-1-4200-5935-9(1)*, CRC Press) Taylor & Francis Group GBR. Dist: Taylor & Francis Group.
—Pressure-Sensitive Adhesives & Products, 3 vols., Set. 2008. (Handbook of Pressure-Sensitive Adhesives & Products Ser.). (ENG., Illus.). 1100p. instr.'s hndbk. ed. 267.95 *(978-1-4200-5934-2(3)*, CRC Press) Taylor & Francis Group GBR. Dist: Taylor & Francis Group.
—Technology of Pressure-Sensitive Adhesives & Products. 2008. (Handbook of Pressure-Sensitive Adhesives & Products Ser.). (ENG., Illus.). 568p. 162.95 *(978-1-4200-5939-7(4)*, CRC Press) Taylor & Francis Group GBR. Dist: Taylor & Francis Group.
Brahma, Nitosh Kumar. Bacterial Adherence. 2011. (Immunology & Immune System Disorders Ser.). 145.00 *(978-1-61209-225-6(X))* Nova Science Pubs., Inc.
Brockmann, Walter, et al. Adhesive Bonding: Materials, Applications & Technology. Mikhail, Bettina, tr. from GER. 2008. (ENG., Illus.). 432p. 250.00 *(978-3-527-31898-8(4)*, Wiley-VCH) Wiley, John & Sons, Inc.
Cognard, Philippe, ed. Handbook of Adhesives & Sealants: General Knowledge, Application of Adhesives, New Curing Techniques. 2006. (Handbook of Adhesives & Sealants Ser.: 2). (ENG., Illus.). 512p. 225.00 *(978-0-08-044708-7(2)*, Elsevier Science) Elsevier Science & Technology Bks.
Cram101 Textbook Reviews. Outlines & Highlights for Materials for Conservation by C V Horie, Isbn: 9780750669054. 2011. 180p. pap. 29.95 ***(978-1-4288-0440-1(4))*** Cram101 Inc.
Deb, S., ed. Orthopaedic bone Cements. 2008. (Illus.). 320p. 289.95 *(978-1-4200-9302-5(9))* CRC Pr. LLC.
Dillard, D. Improvements in structural adhesive Bonding. 2010. (ENG., Illus.). 400p. 249.95 *(978-1-4398-0217-5(3))* CRC Pr. LLC.
Dillard, D., ed. Advances in structural adhesive Bonding. 2010. (Illus.). 648p. *(978-1-84569-435-7(X))* Woodhead Publishing Ltd.
dmg World Media Ltd Staff, compiled by. Asia Pacific Coatings Conference 2007: Novel Concepts & Materials within Organic Coatings. 2007. 254p. pap. 312.00 *(978-1-60423-346-9(X))* Curran Assocs., Inc.
—Asia Pacific Coatings Show 2006: New Advances in Organic Coatings Technologies & Science. 2007. 317p. pap. 343.00 *(978-1-60423-661-3(2))* Curran Assocs., Inc.
Doyle, Jack S. & O'Quinn, Ryan C., eds. Adhesives: Types, Mechanics & Applications. 2011. (Series: Materials Science & Technologies Ser.). (Illus.). 173p. 95.00 *(978-1-61324-703-7(6))* Nova Science Pubs., Inc.
Dunn, D. J. Engineering & Structural Adhesives, Vol. 15. 138p. pap. *(978-1-85957-436-2(X))* iSmithers Rapra Publishing.
Dunn, David, pseud. Update on Engineering & Structural Adhesives. 2010. (iSmithers Update Ser.). 198p. *(978-1-84735-480-8(7))* iSmithers Rapra Publishing.
Duong, Cong N. & Wang, Chun Hui. Composite Repair: Theory & Design. 2007. (ENG., Illus.). 480p. 230.00 *(978-0-08-045146-6(2)*, Elsevier Science) Elsevier Science & Technology Bks.
Ebnesajjad, Sina. Adhesives Technology Handbook. 2nd enl. ed. 2008. (ENG., Illus.). 475p. 205.00 *(978-0-8155-1533-3(2))* William Andrew, Inc.
—Handbook of Adhesives & Surface Preparation: Technology, Applications & Manufacturing. 2010. (Plastics Design Library). (ENG., Illus.). 448p. 249.00 *(978-1-4377-4461-3(3))* William Andrew, Inc.
Gomatam, R. & Mittal, K. L., eds. Electrically Conductive Adhesives. 2008. (ENG.). 426p. 230.00 *(978-90-04-16592-2(4)*, CRC Press) Taylor & Francis Group GBR. Dist: Taylor & Francis Group.
Goss, Bob. Practical Guide to Adhesive Bonding of Small Engineering Plastic & Rubber Parts. 2010. (Practical Guide Ser.). 194p. *(978-1-84735-139-5(5))*; (Illus.). vii, 181p. pap. *(978-1-84735-138-8(7))* iSmithers Rapra Publishing.
Habenicht, Gerd. Applied Adhesive Bonding: A Practical Guide for Flawless Results. 2009. (ENG.). 186p. pap. 95.00 *(978-3-527-32014-1(8)*, Wiley-VCH) Wiley, John & Sons, Inc.
Horie, C. V. Materials for Conservation: Organic consolidants, adhesives & Coatings. 2nd rev. ed. 2010. (ENG., Illus.). 504p. pap. 74.95 *(978-0-7506-6905-4(5))* Routledge.
Kinloch, Anthony J. Adhesion & Adhesives: Science & Technology. 2010. (ENG.). 460p. pap. 359.00 *(978-90-481-4003-9(X)*, 904814003X) Springer.
Laithy Hassan, Ahmed Ahmed, et al. Self-Etching Adhesives: Bond Strength & SEM Evaluation. 2011. 92p. pap. ***(978-3-8433-9370-6(2))*** Lambert Academic Publishing.
Licari, James J. & Swanson, Dale W. Adhesives Technology for Electronic Applications: Materials, Processing, Reliability. 2nd ed. 2011. (Materials & Processes for Electronic Applications Ser.). (ENG.). 512p. 199.00 *(978-1-4377-7889-2(5))* William Andrew, Inc.
Markkanen, Pia. Shoes, Glues, & Homework: Dangerous Work in the Global Footwear Industry. 2009. 120p. 34.95 *(978-0-89503-328-4(3))* Baywood Publishing Co., Inc.
Mowrey, D., et al. Bonding Elastomers: A Review of Adhesives & Processes, Vol. 15. 140p. pap. *(978-1-85957-495-9(5))* iSmithers Rapra Publishing.
Müller, Bodo & Rath, Walter. Formulating Adhesives & Sealants. 2010. (ENG.). 288p. 236.00 *(978-3-86630-858-9(2))* Vincentz, Curt R. DEU. Dist: Elsevier Science & Technology Bks.
Petrie, Edward M. Handbook of Adhesives & Sealants. 2nd rev. ed. 2006. (ENG., Illus.). 800p. 125.00 *(978-0-07-147916-5(3)*, 0071479163) McGraw-Hill Professional Publishing.
Pizzi, A & Mittal, K. L. Wood Adhesives. 2011. (ENG.). 462p. 260.00 ***(978-90-04-19093-1(7)***, CRC Press) Taylor & Francis Group GBR. Dist: Taylor & Francis Group.
Qian, Haiyang. Damage Tolerance of Adhesively Bonded Joints. 2010. 128p. pap. *(978-3-8383-5880-2(5))* Lambert Academic Publishing.
Rovensky, Yury A. Adhesive Interactions in Normal & Transformed Cells. 2011. (ENG., Illus.). xx, 225p. 189.00 ***(978-1-61779-303-5(5)***, 1617793035) Humana Pr.
Satas, Donatas, ed. Advances in Pressure Sensitive Adhesive Technology Two. (Illus.). 300p. (C). 69.00 *(978-0-9637993-1-9(2))* Satas & Assocs.
Silva, Lucas Filipe Martins, et al, eds. Handbook of Adhesion Technology, 2 vols. 2011. (ENG., Illus.). xxiv, 1544p. 679.00 *(978-3-642-01168-9(3)*, 3642011683) Springer.
Silva, Lucas Filipe Martins da, et al. Modeling of Adhesively Bonded Joints. 2008. (ENG., Illus.). x, 335p. 159.00 *(978-3-540-79055-6(1)*, 3540790551) Springer.
Smith, Andrew M. & Callow, James A., eds. Biological Adhesives. 2010. (ENG., Illus.). xvii, 284p. pap. 249.00 *(978-3-642-06821-8(9)*, 3642068219) Springer.
TAPPI Press Staff, compiled by. Place Conference 2006: Polymers, Laminations, Adhesives, Coatings, Extrusions. 2007. 1396p. pap. 118.00 *(978-1-60423-685-9(X))* Curran Assocs., Inc.
Technology Research Editors, ed. Adhesive Bonding for Aerospace Applications, 2007 Ed. 2007. pap. 128.50 *(978-1-60030-139-1(8)*, Search-In-Print) CSA Journal Division.
—Adhesive Bonding of Polymer Matrix Composites, 2007 Ed. 2007. pap. 128.50 *(978-1-60030-606-8(3)*, Search-In-Print) CSA Journal Division.
—Adhesives & Adhesive Bonding for Automotive Applications, 2007 Ed. 2007. pap. 128.50 *(978-1-60030-159-9(2)*, Search-In-Print) CSA Journal Division.
The Adhesive And Sealant Council, Inc. ASC 2009 Pressure Sensitive Adhesives. 2010. (Conference Proceedings Ser.). 450p. pap. *(978-1-84735-431-0(9))* iSmithers Rapra Publishing.
The Adhesive And Sealant Council, Inc, ed. Asc 2009 Spring Convention & Expo. 2010. (Conference Proceedings Ser.). 456p. pap. *(978-1-84735-420-4(3))* iSmithers Rapra Publishing.
Wilkinson, Keri A. & Ordonez, Daniel A. Adhesive Properties in Nanomaterials, Composites & Films. 2011. (Materials Science & Technologies Ser.). (Illus.). x, 188p. 129.00 *(978-1-61209-268-3(3))* Nova Science Pubs., Inc.
Wong, C., et al. Electrical Conductive Adhesives with Nanotechnologies. 2009. (ENG., Illus.). xi, 433p. 129.00 *(978-0-387-88782-1(2)*, 0387887822) Springer.

ADI-GRANTH
Jodha Singha. Applied Philosophy in Guru Granth Sahib. 2009. 156p. *(978-81-302-0215-0(8)*, Library of Congress — New Delhi Overseas Office) Publication Bureau.
Narotama, Tara Singha, et al. Guru Giraratha Kosha: Punara Sampadita: Nawina Shabada-Krama Anusara. 2010. (PAN.). *(978-81-302-0212-9(3))*, Library of Congress — New Delhi Overseas Office); *(978-81-302-0245-7(X)*, Library of Congress — New Delhi Overseas Office) Publication Bureau.
Singh, Pashaura. Life & Work of Guru Arjan. 2006. (Illus.). 448p. 65.00 *(978-0-19-567921-2(0))* Oxford Univ. Pr., Inc.

ADIPOSE TISSUES
see also Cellulite; Fat
Awad, Atif B. & Bradford, Peter G., eds. Adipose Tissue & Inflammation. 2009. (Oxidative Stress & Disease Ser.). (ENG., Illus.). 318p. 154.95 *(978-1-4200-9130-4(1)*, CRC Press) Taylor & Francis Group GBR. Dist: Taylor & Francis Group.
Bienertovaacute;-Vascaron;k?, Julie, ed. Body Fat: Composition, Measurements & Reduction Procedures. 2011. (Series: Nutrition & Diet Research Progress Ser.). (Illus.). 186p. 95.00 *(978-1-61324-332-9(4))* Nova Science Pubs., Inc.
Clé & ment, Karine. Novel Insights into Adipose Cell Functions. Clément, Karine et al, eds. 2010. (Research & Perspectives in Endocrine Interactions Ser.). (Illus.). x, 160p. 189.00 *(978-3-642-13516-3(1)*, 3642135161) Springer.
Coleman, Sydney & Mazzola, Riccardo F. Fat Injection: From Filling to Regeneration. 2008. *(978-1-57626-284-9(7))* Quality Medical Publishing, Inc.
Fantuzzi, Giamila & Mazzone, Theodore, eds. Adipose Tissue & Adipokines in Health & Disease. 2010. (Nutrition & Health Ser.). (Illus.). xxii, 402p. pap. 229.00 *(978-1-61737-741-9(4)*, 1617377414) Humana Pr.
Gimble, Jeffrey M. & Bunnell, Bruce A. Adipose-Derived Stem Cells: Methods & Protocols. 2011. (Illus.). xv, 473p. E-Book ***(978-1-61737-960-4(3))*** Humana Pr.
Gimble, Jeffrey M. & Bunnell, Bruce A., eds. Adipose-Derived Stem Cells: Methods & Protocols. 2010. (Methods in Molecular Biology Ser.). (ENG., Illus.). xv, 473p. 139.00 *(978-1-61737-959-8(X)*, 161737959X) Humana Pr.
Illouz, Yves-Gerard & Sterodimas, Aris, eds. Adipose Stem Cells & Regenerative Medicine. 2011. (ENG., Illus.). xii, 278p. 189.00 *(978-3-642-20011-3(7)*, 3642200117) Springer.
Jarrar, Mohammed, et al. Adipokines & Pathogenesis of Non Alcoholic Fatty Liver Disease: Pathogenesis of Non Alcoholic Fatty Liver Disease & Circulatory Levels of Adipocytokines. 2008. 192p. pap. *(978-3-639-09165-6(5))* VDM Verlag Dr. Mueller e.K.
Lam, Samuel M., et al. Complementary Fat Grafting. 2006. (Illus.). 144p. 305.99 *(978-0-7817-6424-7(6))* Lippincott Williams & Wilkins.
Leff, Todd & Granneman, James G., eds. Adipose Tissue in Health & Disease, 2 vols. 2010. (ENG., Illus.). 530p. 239.95 *(978-3-527-31857-5(7)*, Wiley-VCH) Wiley, John & Sons, Inc.
Levy-Marchal, C. & Pénicaud, L., eds. Adipose Tissue Development: From Animal Models to Clinical Conditions3rd ESPE Advanced Seminar in Developmental Endocrinology, Paris, March 2009. 2010. (Endocrine Development Ser.). (ENG., Illus.). 96p. *(978-3-8055-9450-9(X))* Karger, S. AG.
Mazzone, Theodore, ed. Adipose Tissue & Adipokines in Health & Disease. 2007. (Nutrition & Health Ser.). (Illus.). 397p. 229.00 *(978-1-58829-721-1(7)*, 1588297217) Humana Pr.
Mobbs, C., et al, eds. Body Composition & Aging. 2010. (Interdisciplinary Topics in Gerontology Ser.). (ENG., Illus.). 198p. *(978-3-8055-9521-6(2))* Karger, S. AG.
Power, Michael L. & Schulkin, Jay. The Evolution of Obesity. 2009. (ENG., Illus.). 408p. (gr. 17). 42.00 *(978-0-8018-9262-2(7))* Johns Hopkins Univ. Pr.
Preedy, Victor R. & Hunter, Ross J., eds. Adipokines. 2011. (ENG., Illus.). 458p. 169.95 *(978-1-57808-689-4(2))* BIOS Scientific Publishers Ltd. GBR. Dist: Taylor & Francis Group.
Shiffman, Melvin A. & Di Giuseppe, Alberto, eds. Liposuction: Principles & Practice. 2006. (Illus.). 568p. 439.00 *(978-3-540-28042-2(1)*, 3540280421) Springer.
Symonds, Michael E., ed. Adipose Tissue Biology. 2011. (ENG., Illus.). vi, 413p. 209.00 ***(978-1-4614-0964-9(0)***, 1461409640) Springer.
Vlachakis, Dimitrios. Adipocyte viability & Ldh. 2007. 40p. 16.90 *(978-0-615-15238-7(4))* Vlachakis, Dimitrios P.
Wood, Philip A. How Fat Works. 2009. 272p. pap. 21.00 *(978-0-674-03499-0(6))* Harvard Univ. Pr.
Yang, Kaiping. Adipose Tissue Protocols. 2nd ed. 2008. (Methods in Molecular Biology Ser.: Vol. 456). (Illus.). 400p. 129.00 *(978-1-58829-916-1(3))* Humana Pr.
Yang, Kaiping, ed. Adipose Tissue Protocols. 2nd ed. 2010. (Methods in Molecular Biology Ser.). (Illus.). xvi, 336p. pap. 129.00 *(978-1-61737-844-7(5)*, 1617378445) Humana Pr.

ADIPOSITY
see Obesity

ADIRONDACK IRON AND STEEL COMPANY

Hochschild, Harold K. The MacIntyre Mine: From Failure to Fortune. rev. ed. 2010. (Township Thirty-Four Ser.). (Illus.). reprint ed. 6.95 *(978-0-910020-10-7(8))* Adirondack Museum, The.

ADIRONDACK MOUNTAINS (N.Y.)

Angus, Christopher. The Extraordinary Adirondack Journey of Clarence Petty: Wilderness Guide, Pilot, & Conservationist. 2007. (Illus.). 265p. per. 19.95 *(978-0-8156-0870-7(5))* Syracuse Univ. Pr.

April, Dennis. Good Fishing in the Adirondacks: From Lake Champlain to the Streams of Tug Hill. 3rd ed. 2010. (ENG., Illus.). 224p. pap. 21.95 *(978-0-88150-891-8(8),* 150891) Countryman Pr.

Armour, Marylee. HeartWood: The Adirondack Homestead Life of W. Donald Burnap. 2007. (ENG., Illus.). 322p. (Orig.). pap. 21.95 *(978-0-9623390-1-1(6))* Armour, Marylee.

Brenan, Dan & Sears, George Washington. The Adirondack Letters of George Washington Sears: Whose Pen Name Was Nessmuk. 2011. 204p. 44.95 ***(978-1-258-04215-8(0))*** Literary Licensing, LLC.

Bronski, Peter. At the Mercy of the Mountains: True Stories of Survival & Tragedy in New York's Adirondacks. 2008. (ENG., Illus.). 336p. per. 15.95 *(978-1-59921-304-0(4),* Lyons Pr.) Globe Pequot Pr., The.

Danielson, Bill. Still Speaking of Nature: Further Explorations in the Natural World. 2011. (Illus.). x, 154p. pap. *(978-1-4384-3598-5(3))* State Univ. of New York Pr.

—Still Speaking of Nature: Further Explorations in the Natural World. Danielson, Bill, ed. 2011. (Excelsior Editions Ser.). (Illus.). 144p. 19.95 *(978-1-4384-3599-2(1))* State Univ. of New York Pr.

Folwell, Elizabeth. Short Carries: Essays from Adirondack Life. 2009. 213p. pap. 16.95 *(978-0-922595-38-9(0))* Adirondack Life.

McMartin, Barbara & Ingersoll, Bill. Discover the Central Adirondacks: Four-Season Adventures in the Heart of the North Woods. 4th ed. 2007. (Discover the Adirondacks Ser.). (Illus.). 218p. (Orig.). *(978-1-888374-29-2(2),* Wild River Pr.) Wild River Publishing.

McMartin, Barbara, et al. Discover the Northeastern Adirondacks: Four-Season Adventures from Lake Champlain to the Giant of the Valley. 3rd ed. 2009. (Illus.). 200p. *(978-1-888374-31-5(4),* Wild River Pr.) Wild River Publishing.

Murray, W. H. H. (William Henry Harrison). Adventures in the Wilderness; or, Camp-Life in the Adirondacks, William H H Murray. 2006. 256p. per. 23.99 *(978-1-4255-2172-1(X))* MPublishing.

Wardner, Charles A. Footprints & Sunset on Adirondack Trails: The Memoirs of James Manchester Wardner. 2010. (Illus.). 213p. pap. ***(978-0-9829503-0-2(6))*** Graphics North.

Weill, Larry. Pardon Me, Sir — There's a Moose in Your Tent: More Stories of the Life of a Wilderness Park Ranger in the Adirondack Mountains. 2007. *(978-1-59531-017-0(7))* North Country Bks., Inc.

Welsh, Caroline M., et al. The Adirondack World of A. F. Tait. 2011. (Illus.). 102p. pap. 24.95 ***(978-0-910020-53-4(1))*** Adirondack Museum, The.

ADIRONDACK MOUNTAINS (N.Y.)—DESCRIPTION AND TRAVEL

Bowie, Mark. The Adirondacks: In Celebration of the Seasons. 2009. *(978-1-59531-027-9(4))* North Country Bks., Inc.

Brown, Phil, ed. Bob Marshall in the Adirondacks: Writings of a Pioneering Peak-Bagger, Pond-Hopper & Wilderness Preservationist. 2006. 24.95 *(978-0-9789254-0-6(8))* Lost Pond Pr.

Dresser, Eric. Wildlife Images of the Adirondacks. 2010. (Illus.). 144p. 24.95 *(978-1-59531-026-2(6))* North Country Bks., Inc.

Farb, Nathan. Adirondack Wilderness. 2009. (ENG.). 208p. 19.98 *(978-0-7893-2008-7(8),* Rizzoli Universe Promotional Bks.) Rizzoli International Pubns., Inc.

Foundation, Adirondack Wilderness. Amazing Adirondack Wonders. 2011. 76p. pap. 12.00 ***(978-1-4583-6415-9(1))*** Lulu Enterprises Inc.

Gaaserud, Michaela. Lake Placid: With the Olympic Village, Lake George & New York's Adirondacks. 2011. (Tourist Town Guides). pap. 14.95 *(978-1-935455-15-8(X))* Channel Lake, Inc.

Hammond, Samuel H. Hunting Adventures in the Northern Wilds. 2006. pap. 31.95 *(978-1-4286-5483-9(6))* Kessinger Publishing, LLC.

Harris, Philip J. Adirondack, Lumber Capital of the World. 2008. 200p. pap. 24.95 *(978-1-60563-680-1(0))* PublishAmerica, Inc.

Headley, J. T. The Adirondack or Life in the Woods. (ENG.). 316p. 2007. 45.95 *(978-0-548-14296-7(3))* 2006. per. 30.95 *(978-1-4286-5530-0(1))* Kessinger Publishing, LLC.

Headley, Joel Tyler. The Adirondack; or, Life in the Woods by J T Headley. 2006. 488p. per. 29.99 *(978-1-4255-5415-6(6));* 320p. per. 23.99 *(978-1-4255-3052-5(4))* MPublishing.

Kalinowski, Tom. Adirondack Nature Notes: An Adirondack Almanac Sequel. 2010. (Illus.). 256p. pap. 19.95 *(978-1-59531-034-7(7))* North Country Bks., Inc.

Kraus, James. Adirondack Moments. 2009. (ENG., Illus.). 136p. 29.95 *(978-1-55407-466-2(5))* Firefly Bks., Ltd.

Macken, Lynda Lee. Adirondack Ghosts III: Historic Haunts in New York State's North Country. 2010. (Illus.). 128p. pap. 12.95 *(978-0-9755244-9-7(6))* Black Cat Pr.

Mackesey, Melinda. Adirondack Exploration for Kids & Families: History, Discovery & Fun. 2011. 128p. pap. 12.99 ***(978-1-60949-498-8(9))*** History Pr., The.

Mellor, Don. Adirondacks Alive. 2010. (Illus.). 176p. 34.95 *(978-0-9778490-0-0(7))* Horizon Editions, LLC.

Parenzan Smalley, Carol. Around Caroga Lake, Canada Lake, & Pine Lake. 2011. (Images of America Ser.). (Illus.). 128p. pap. 21.99 *(978-0-7385-7513-1(5))* Arcadia Publishing.

Rowland, Tim. High Peaks: A History of Hiking the Adirondacks from Noah to Neoprene. 2008. pap. 19.99 *(978-1-59629-541-4(4))* History Pr., The.

Sandiford, Victoria Verner, compiled by. Historic Images of the Adirondacks: From the Collection of the Adirondack Museum. 2008. *(978-1-59531-016-3(9))* North Country Bks., Inc.

Starmer, Timothy. Five-Star Trails in the Adirondacks: A Guide to the Most Beautiful Hikes. 2010. (Five-Star Trails Ser.). (ENG., Illus.). 304p. pap. 15.95 *(978-0-89732-683-4(0))* Menasha Ridge Pr., Inc.

Stoddard, Seneca Ray. In Stoddard's Footsteps: The Adirondacks Then & Now: Featuring the Photography of Seneca Ray Stoddard & Mark Bowie. 2008. *(978-1-59531-024-8(X));* pap. *(978-1-59531-022-4(3))* North Country Bks., Inc.

Street, Alfred Billings. Woods & Waters; or, the Saranacs & Racket. 2006. 380p. per. 26.99 *(978-1-4255-3965-8(3))* MPublishing.

Sulavik, Stephen B. Adirondack: Of Indians & Mountains, 1535-1838. 2007. (Illus.). 246p. per. 27.50 *(978-1-930098-79-4(0))* Purple Mountain Pr., Ltd.

Surprenant, Neil. Paul Smith's Adirondack Hotel & College. 2009. (Images of America Ser.). (ENG., Illus.). 128p. pap. 21.99 *(978-0-7385-6290-2(4))* Arcadia Publishing.

Weaver, Anne A. & Hoffman, Beverly. Lake Pleasant & Speculator in the Adirondacks. 2010. (Images of America Ser.). (ENG., Illus.). 128p. pap. 21.99 *(978-0-7385-7251-2(9))* Arcadia Publishing.

Weber, Sandra. Adirondack Roots: Stories of Hiking, History & Women. 2011. (Illus.). 130p. pap. 19.99 ***(978-1-60949-364-6(8))*** History Pr., The.

Williams, Donald R. Adirondack People & Places. 2012. (Images of America Ser.). (ENG., Illus.). 128p. pap. 21.99 ***(978-0-7385-9169-8(6))*** Arcadia Publishing.

ADIRONDACK MOUNTAINS (N.Y.)—GUIDEBOOKS

Case, Jeffrey & Case, Donna. Adirondack Trails: Northville-Placid Trail. Burdick, Neal, ed. 4th ed. 2007. (Illus.). pap. 19.95 *(978-1-931951-19-7(5))* Adirondack Mountain Club, Inc.

Densmore, Lisa. Best Easy Day Hikes Adirondacks. 2011. (Best Easy Day Hikes Ser.). (ENG., Illus.). 128p. pap. 9.95 *(978-0-7627-4525-8(6),* Falcon Guides) Globe Pequot Pr., The.

Dunn, Russell & Delaney, Barbara. Adirondack Trails with Tales: History Hikes through the Adirondack Park & the Lake George, Lake Champlain & Mohawk Valley Regions. 2009. (Illus.). 320p. pap. 17.95 *(978-1-883789-64-0(9))* Black Dome Pr. Corp.

Ingersoll, Bill. Snowshoe Routes: Adirondacks & Catskills. 2006. (Snowshoe Routes Ser.). (ENG., Illus.). 237p. pap. 16.95 *(978-1-59485-009-7(7))* Mountaineers Bks., The.

Landis, Norm. Adirondack Trails: West-Central Region. 4th ed. 2006. (Forest Preserve Ser.: Vol. 5). (ENG., Illus.). 304p. pap. 19.95 *(978-1-931951-16-6(0))* Adirondack Mountain Club, Inc.

Lawyer, Jim & Haas, Jeremy. Adirondack Rock: A Rock Climber's Guide. 2008. (ENG & FRE., Illus.). per. 36.99 *(978-0-9814702-0-7(3))* Adirondack Rock Pr., LLC.

Morrissey, Spencer. The Other 54: A Hiker's Guide to the Lower 54 Peaks of the Adirondack 100 Highest. 2007. 306p. pap. 18.95 *(978-0-9786554-1-9(9))* Dacksdescents Publishing.

Peterson, John M. C. & Lee, Gary. Adirondack Birding. 2008. (Illus.). pap. *(978-0-9789254-3-7(2))* Lost Pond Pr.

Podskoch, Marty. Adirondack Stories: Historical Sketches. 2007. (Illus.). 168p. per. 18.95 *(978-0-9794979-0-2(6))* Podskoch Pr.

Reiter, Clifford. Witness the Forever Wild, A Guide to Favorite Hikes around the Adirondack High Peaks. 2008. 113p. pap. 48.95 *(978-1-4357-1195-9(3))* Lulu Enterprises Inc.

Ryan, James M. Adirondack Wildlife: A Field Guide. 2009. (ENG., Illus.). 296p. pap. 24.95 *(978-1-58465-749-1(9))* Univ. Pr. of New England.

Stoddard, Seneca Ray. Adirondacks. 2008. (ENG., Illus.). 228p. pap. 12.95 *(978-1-55709-089-6(0))* Applewood Bks.

Stoltie, Annie & Folwell, Elizabeth. Explorer's Guide the Adirondack Book: Including Saratoga Springs. 6th ed. 2008. (Great Destinations Ser.). (ENG., Illus.). 320p. pap. 18.95 *(978-1-58157-085-4(6),* 157085) Countryman Pr.

Tba. Discover the Adirondacks. 2012. (AMC Discover Ser.). (ENG., Illus.). 288p. pap. 18.95 *(978-1-934028-31-5(2))* Appalachian Mountain Club Bks.

Via, Alan. The Catskill 67: A Hiker's Guide to the Catskill 100 Highest Peaks Under 3500' LeBrun, Fred, ed. 2011. pap. ***(978-1-931951-08-1(X))*** Adirondack Mountain Club, Inc.

Zuger, Sascha. Moon Spotlight Adirondacks. 2011. (Moon Spotlight Ser.). (ENG.). 70p. pap. 7.99 *(978-1-59880-825-4(7))* Avalon Travel Publishing.

ADIRONDACK MOUNTAINS (N.Y.)—HISTORY

Bond, Hallie E., et al. A Paradise for Boys & Girls: Children's Camps in the Adirondacks. 2006. (Illus.). 146p. 39.95 *(978-0-8156-0822-6(5))* Syracuse Univ. Pr.

Covey, Frances Alden. The Earl Covey Story: A Master Builder in the Adirondacks Who Made Buildings as Beautiful as Nature Herself. rev. ed. 2010. 178p. pap. 20.00 *(978-0-615-34671-7(5))* Hoffer, Terry.

Donaldson, Alfred L. A History of the Adirondacks. 2009. 412p. 41.99 *(978-1-115-78490-0(0));* pap. 34.75 *(978-1-115-78492-4(7));* pap. 33.75 *(978-1-115-78493-1(5))* BiblioBazaar.

Dunn, Russell & Delaney, Barbara. Adirondack Trails with Tales: History Hikes through the Adirondack Park & the Lake George, Lake Champlain & Mohawk Valley Regions. 2009. (Illus.). 320p. pap. 17.95 *(978-1-883789-54-0(8))* Black Dome Pr. Corp.

Elinskas, Robert J., Sr. Adirondack Camps & Hunts. 2008. (Illus.). 228p. pap. 21.00 *(978-0-9771017-1-9(1))* Elinskas, Robert.

Flynn, Andy. New York State's Mountain Heritage: Adirondack Attic 4. 2007. 240p. per. 18.00 *(978-0-9754007-3-9(8))* Hungry Bear Publishing.

Gooley, Lawrence P. Terror in the Adirondacks: The True Story of Serial Killer Robert F. Garrow. 2009. (ENG., Illus.). 216p. pap. 22.00 *(978-0-9795741-3-9(7))* Bloated Toe Publishing.

Hochschild, Harold K. An Adirondack Resort in the Nineteenth Century: Blue Mountain Lake, 1870-1900, Stagecoaches & Luxury Hotels. rev. ed. 2010. (Township Thirty-Four Ser.). (Illus.). reprint ed. 8.95 *(978-0-910020-07-7(8))* Adirondack Museum, The.

—The MacIntyre Mine: From Failure to Fortune. rev. ed. 2010. (Township Thirty-Four Ser.). (Illus.). reprint ed. 6.95 *(978-0-910020-10-7(8))* Adirondack Museum, The.

Jenkins, Jerry C., et al. Acid Rain in the Adirondacks: An Environmental History. 2007. (Illus.). 256p. 76.95 *(978-0-8014-4651-1(1),* Comstock Publishing Assocs.) Cornell Univ. Pr.

Jimapco Map Company Staff & Other Publisher Map Staff. Map Sa Adirondack Ny. 2011. 24.95 *(978-1-56914-022-2(7))* JIMAPCO, Inc.

Lewis, Randy. Actively Adirondack: Reflections on Mountain Life in the 21st Century. 2007. 184p. per. 16.95 *(978-0-9754007-4-6(6))* Hungry Bear Publishing.

Mackesey, Melinda. Adirondack Exploration for Kids & Families: History, Discovery & Fun. 2011. 128p. pap. 12.99 ***(978-1-60949-498-8(9))*** History Pr., The.

McMartin, Barbara. Perspectives on the Adirondacks: A Thirty-Year Struggle by People Protecting Their Treasure. 2007. (Illus.). 388p. per. 24.95 *(978-0-8156-0895-0(0))* Syracuse Univ. Pr.

O'Hern, William J. Noah John Rondeau's Adirondack Wilderness Days: A Year with the Hermit of Cold River Flow. 2009. (ENG., Illus.). 336p. pap. *(978-0-9743943-8-1(6))* Forager Pr., LLC, The.

O'Hern, William J. & Reehil, Roy E. Under an Adirondack Influence: The Life of A. L. Byron-Curtiss - 1371-1959. 2008. (Illus.). 352p. pap. 21.95 *(978-0-9743943-5-0(1));* 29.95 *(978-0-9743943-4-3(3))* Forager Pr., LLC, The.

Parenzan Smalley, Carol. Around Caroga Lake, Canada Lake, & Pine Lake. 2011. (Images of America Ser.). (Illus.). 128p. pap. 21.99 *(978-0-7385-7513-1(5))* Arcadia Publishing.

Podskoch, Marty J. Adirondack Stories: Historical Sketches. 2007. (Illus.). 168p. per. 18.95 *(978-0-9794979-0-2(6))* Podskoch Pr.

Porter, William F., et al, eds. The Great Experiment in Conservation: Voices from the Adirondack Park. 2009. (Illus.). 400p. 45.00 *(978-0-8156-3231-3(2))* Syracuse Univ. Pr.

Potter, Donald & Potter, Orlando. Brandreth: A History of Brandreth Park: 1851-2010. 2011. (ENG.). 35.00 *(978-0-615-43007-2(4))* Two Loon Media,LLC.

Reehil, Roy E. & O'Hern, William J. Adirondack Adventures: Bob Gillespie & Harvey Dunham on French Louie¿s Trail. 2012. (Illus.). 256p. 32.95 *(978-0-9743943-2-9(7));* (ENG., Illus.). pap. 24.95 *(978-0-9743943-3-6(5))* Forager Pr., LLC, The.

Roy, Karen, et al. Acid Rain in the Adirondacks: An Environmental History. 2007. (Illus.). 246p. pap. 32.95 *(978-0-8014-7424-8(8),* Comstock Publishing Assocs.) Cornell Univ. Pr.

Sandiford, Victoria Verner, compiled by. Historic Images of the Adirondacks: From the Collection of the Adirondack Museum. 2008. *(978-1-59531-016-3(9))* North Country Bks., Inc.

Stoddard, Seneca Ray. In Stoddard's Footsteps: The Adirondacks Then & Now: Featuring the Photography of Seneca Ray Stoddard & Mark Bowie. 2008. *(978-1-59531-024-8(X));* pap. *(978-1-59531-022-4(3))* North Country Bks., Inc.

Sulavik, Stephen B. Adirondack: Of Indians & Mountains, 1535-1838. 2007. (Illus.). 246p. per. 27.50 *(978-1-930098-79-4(0))* Purple Mountain Pr., Ltd.

Surprenant, Neil. Paul Smith's Adirondack Hotel & College. 2009. (Images of America Ser.). (ENG., Illus.). 128p. pap. 21.99 *(978-0-7385-6290-2(4))* Arcadia Publishing.

Terrie, Philip G. Contested Terrain: A New History of Nature & People in the Adirondacks. 2nd ed. 2009. (Illus.). 272p. pap. 22.95 *(978-0-8156-0904-9(3))* Syracuse Univ. Pr.

Warren, John. Historic Tales from the Adirondack Almanack. 2009. (American Chronicles Ser.). 128p. pap. 19.99 *(978-1-59629-727-2(1))* History Pr., The.

Weaver, Anne A. & Hoffman, Beverly. Lake Pleasant & Speculator in the Adirondacks. 2010. (Images of America Ser.). (ENG., Illus.). 128p. pap. 21.99 *(978-0-7385-7251-2(9))* Arcadia Publishing.

Weber, Sandra. Adirondack Roots: Stories of Hiking, History & Women. 2011. (Illus.). 130p. pap. 19.99 ***(978-1-60949-364-6(8))*** History Pr., The.

Weill, Larry & Weill, Kelly. Forgive Me, Ma'am — Bears Don't Wear Blue. 2009. 256p. 17.95 *(978-1-59531-030-9(4))* North Country Bks., Inc.

Weston, Harold & Foster, Rebecca Feldman. Freedom in the Wilds: An Artist in the Adirondacks. 3rd ed. 2009. (Illus.). 272p. 24.95 *(978-0-8156-0899-8(3))* Syracuse Univ. Pr.

Williams, Donald R. Adirondack Ventures. 2006. (Images of America Ser.). (ENG., Illus.). 128p. per. 19.99 *(978-0-7385-4560-8(0))* Arcadia Publishing.

Wu, Melvin & Kalma, Dennis. Wetland Plants of the Adirondacks: Ferns, Woody Plants, & Graminoids. 2011. 192p. 25.00 *(978-1-4269-6057-4(3));* pap. 15.00 *(978-1-4269-5840-3(4))* Trafford Publishing.

—Wetland Plants of the Adirondacks: Herbaceous Plants & Aquatic Plants. 2011. 176p. pap. 15.00 *(978-1-4269-5843-4(9));* pap. 25.00 *(978-1-4269-6062-8(X))* Trafford Publishing.

ADJECTIVE LAW
see Procedure (Law)

ADJOINING LANDOWNERS
see also Boundaries (Estates); Nuisances; Right of Way; Servitudes

Agnew, Donald & Morris, Amanda. Neighbour Disputes: A Guide to the Law & Practice. 2nd ed. 2011. (ENG., Illus.). 259p. pap. 66.50 ***(978-0-85490-059-6(4))*** Gaunt, Inc.

Benedek, Paul. Neighbour Disputes. 2011. 240p. pap. 33.50 ***(978-1-4467-1734-9(8))*** Lulu Enterprises Inc.

Doskow, Emily & Jordan, Cora. Neighbor Law: Fences, Trees, Boundaries & Noise. 7th ed. 2011. 403p. E-Book *(978-1-4133-1346-8(9));* (ENG.). 424p. pap. 29.99 *(978-1-4133-1320-8(5))* NOLO.

Kate Chatot. Parcel 141: A decade long property rights litigation chronicle involving an old Vermont country Road. 2010. 220p. 25.95 *(978-0-595-50367-4(5));* pap. 15.95 *(978-0-595-46337-4(1))* iUniverse, Inc.

Koch, Bernhard A., ed. Economic Loss Caused by Genetically Modified Organisms: Liability & Redress for the Adventitious Presence of GMOs in Non-GM Crops. 2011. (Tort & Insurance Law Ser.). (ENG.). xii, 747p. pap. 299.00 *(978-3-211-99924-0(8),* 3211999248) Springer.

Okamoto, Shoji. Tsukoken Saiban No Gendaiteki Kadai. 2010. (JPN.). xv, 425p. *(978-4-7972-5439-6(4))* Shinzan Bks. Corp.

Salmen-Everinghoff, Christoph. Zur cautio damni infecti: Die Rückkehr eines römisch-rechtlichen Rechtsinstituts in das moderne Zivilrecht. 2009. (Rechtshistorische Reihe Ser.). (GER.). 178p. 54.95 *(978-3-631-58729-4(5))* Lang, Peter GmbH, Europaischer Verlag der Wissenschaften DEU. Dist: Lang, Peter.

ADJUDICATION, ADMINISTRATIVE
see Administrative Procedure

ADJUSTMENT (PSYCHOLOGY)
see also Adaptability (Psychology); Conflict (Psychology); Culture Shock; Defense Mechanisms (Psychology); Student Adjustment

Abrams, Mitch. Anger Management in Sport: Understanding & Controlling Violence in Athletes. 2010. (ENG., Illus.). 296p. 54.00 *(978-0-7360-6168-1(1))* Human Kinetics Pubs.

Adam, Carole. Emotions: Psychology, logical formalisation, & agent Applications. 2009. 216p. pap. *(978-3-639-17739-8(8))* VDM Verlag Dr. Mueller e.K.

Aldwin, Carolyn M. Stress, Coping, & Development: An Integrative Perspective. 2nd ed. (ENG., Illus.). 432p. 2009. pap. 35.00 *(978-1-60623-559-1(1))* 2007. 60.00 *(978-1-57230-840-4(0))* Guilford Pubns., Inc.

Ali, Anees Janee & Ismail, Mahazir. Repatriates & Their Spouses. 2010. 128p. pap. *(978-3-8383-6489-6(9))* Lambert Academic Publishing.

Allen, Jen, et al. Helping Your Pupils to Be Resilient. 2007. (Illus.). vi, 66p. 21.95 *(978-0-415-44728-7(3))* Fulton, David Pubs. GBR. Dist: Taylor & Francis Group.

Baer, Greg. Real Love & Freedom for the Soul: Eliminating the Chains of Victimhood. 2007. 368p. pap. 22.95 *(978-1-892319-28-9(4))* Blue Ridge Pr.

Beach, Wayne A. A Natural History of Family Cancer: Interactional Resources for Managing Illness. 2009. *(978-1-57273-891-7(7)); (978-1-57273-890-0(9))* Hampton Pr., Inc.

Beattie, Melody. Make Miracles in Forty Days: Turning What You Have into What You Want. 2010. (ENG.). 192p. 23.00 *(978-1-4391-0215-2(5))* Simon & Schuster.

Becking, Bob. Orthodoxy, Liberalism, & Adaptation: Essays on Ways of Worldmaking in Times of Change from Biblical, Historical, & Systematic Perspectives. 2011. (Illus.). 230p. ***(978-90-04-20869-8(0))*** BRILL.

Beresford, Thomas P. Psychological Adaptive Mechanisms: Ego Defense Recognition in Practice & Research. 2012. (ENG., Illus.). 338p. 59.99 ***(978-0-19-979449-2(9))*** Oxford Univ. Pr., Inc.

Bevan, Lynda. Life after Betrayal: A Practical Guide. 2007. (ENG.). 108p. per. *(978-1-932690-31-6(X))* Loving Healing Pr., Inc.

—Life after Your Lover Walks Out: A Practical Guide. 2007. 84p. pap. *(978-1-932690-26-2(3))* Loving Healing Pr., Inc.

Bodach, Diane LaRae. Straw into Gold: Illness, Loss, & Hardship As a Path to Inner Peace. 340p. 2012. E-Book *(978-1-57733-332-6(2))* 2011. pap. 19.95 *(978-1-57733-223-7(7))* Blue Dolphin Publishing, Inc.

Boonstra, C. R. Dealing with Life when Hurt Happens. 2011. pap. 11.99 ***(978-1-61346-325-3(1))*** Tate Publishing & Enterprises, LLC.

Brafman. Fostering Independence: Helping & Caring in Psychodynamic Therapies. 2010. (Illus.). 240p. pap. 34.95 *(978-1-85575-828-5(8))* Karnac Bks. GBR. Dist: Stylus Publishing, LLC.

Brewer, Britton, ed. Sport Psychology. 2009. (Olympic Handbook of Sports Medicine Ser.: 14). (ENG., Illus.). 148p. pap. 63.95 *(978-1-4051-7363-6(7),* Wiley-Blackwell) Wiley, John & Sons, Inc.

Brown, Nina W. Uptight & in Your Face: Coping with an Anxious Boss, Parent, Spouse, or Lover. 1 vol. 2010. 179p. 34.95 *(978-0-313-38555-1(6),* A3002C, Praeger Pubs.) Greenwood Publishing Group, Inc.

Call Essert, Priscilla. MY LIFE AS A PANCREAS: Reflections on Raising a Child with Diabetes. 2007. 72p. pap. 15.00 *(978-1-4303-0521-7(5))* Lulu Enterprises Inc.

Cantrell, et al. Once a Warrior: Wired for Life. 2007. 126p. pap. *(978-0-615-14132-9(3))* Hearts Toward Home International, Inc.

Castagnini, John. Thank God I... Presents: How to Say I Love You in Every Language. 2011. (ENG.). 140p. pap. 12.99 *(978-0-9815453-5-6(1))* Inspired Authors, LLC.

Castagnini, John, ed. Thank God I... Volume 3: Short STories of Inspiration for Every Situation. 2011. (ENG.). 300p. pap. 19.99 *(978-0-9815453-2-5(7))* Inspired Authors, LLC.

Charles A. Moss. The Adaptation Diet: The Complete Prescription for Reducing Stress, Feeling Great & Protecting Yourself Against Obesity, Diabetes & Heart Disease. 2010. 248p. pap. 19.95 *(978-1-4401-9231-9(6))* iUniverse, Inc.

Clerc, Olivier. Invaluable Lessons from a Frog: Seven Life-Enhancing Metaphors. Marcelin-Rice, Louis, tr. 2009. (ENG.). 112p. pap. 14.95 *(978-0-9797908-3-6(2))* Dreamriver Pr.

Cohen, Leonora M. & Frydenberg, Erica. Coping for Capable Kids: Strategies for Parents, Teachers, & Students. 2nd rev. ed. 2007. (ENG., Illus.). 199p. pap. 27.95 *(978-1-59363-203-8(7))* Prufrock Pr.

Coskie, Dixie. Unthinkable: Tips for Surviving a Child's Traumatic Brain Injury: Tips. 2011. 94p. pap. 10.00 ***(978-1-936214-41-9(5))*** Wyatt-MacKenzie Publishing.

Cram101 Textbook Reviews. Outlines & Highlights for Self-Directed Behavior by David L Watson, Roland G Tharp. 2011. 130p. pap. 28.95 ***(978-1-61654-124-8(5))*** Cram101 Inc.

Cram101 Textbook Reviews & Cram101 Textbook Reviews. Outlines & Highlights for Becoming Aware: A Text/Workbook for Human Relations & Personal Adjustment by Velma Walker, ISBN. 2011. 72p. pap. 27.95 ***(978-1-4286-6488-7(1))*** Cram101 Inc.

—Outlines & Highlights for Psychology Applied to Modern Life: Adjustment in the 21st Century by Wayne Weiten, ISBN. 2011. 512p. pap. 37.95 ***(978-1-4288-4043-0(5))*** Cram101 Inc.

Cram101 Textbook Reviews Staff. Outlines & Highlights for Human Adjustment by Santrock, Isbn: 9780073111919. 2008. 200p. pap. 13.95 *(978-1-4288-6066-7(5))* Cram101 Inc.

—Outlines & Highlights for Human Relations: A Game Plan for Improving Personal Adjustment by Ford, ISBN. 2008. 124p. pap. 11.95 *(978-1-4288-6426-9(1))* Cram101 Inc.

—Outlines & Highlights for Psychology & the Challenges of Life: Adjustment to the New Millenium by Jeffrey S. Nevid, Spencer A. Rathus, Spencer A. R. 2009. 232p. pap. 31.95 *(978-1-4288-7398-8(8))* Cram101 Inc.

—Outlines & Highlights for Psychology Applied to Modern Life: Adjustment in the 21st Century by Wayne Weiten, Margaret A. Lloyd, Elizabeth Yost Hammer. 2009. 96p. pap. 27.95 *(978-1-4288-8032-0(1))* Cram101 Inc.

Davis, Deborah L. & Stein, Mara Tesler. Parenting Your Premature Baby & Child: The Emotional Journey. 2006. 903p. reprint ed. pap. 25.00 *(978-1-4223-5806-1(2))* DIANE Publishing Co.

Del Gatto, Susan J. Creating Balance in a World of Stress: Six Key Habits to Avoid in order to Reduce Stress. 2009. 240p. pap. 18.95 *(978-1-4401-4905-4(4))* iUniverse, Inc.

Delahanty, Douglas L. The Psychobiology of Trauma & Resilience Across the Lifespan. 2008. (ENG., Illus.). 294p. 83.99 *(978-0-7657-0536-5(2),* Aronson, Jason) Rowman & Littlefield Publishers, Inc.

Di Luzio, Linda. Going the Distance. 2008. 208p. pap. *(978-3-639-02297-1(1))* VDM Verlag Dr. Mueller e.K.

Duffy, Karen. Personal Growth & Behavior 07/08. 26th rev. ed. 2007. (Annual Editions Ser.). (ENG., Illus.). 208p. (C). per. 44.00 *(978-0-07-339731-3(8),* 0073397318, McGraw-Hill/Dushkin) McGraw-Hill Higher Education.

Dyer, Wayne W. Living the Wisdom of the Tao: The Complete Tao Te Ching & Affirmations. 2008. (ENG., Illus.). 192p. per. 9.95 *(978-1-4019-2149-1(3))* Hay Hse., Inc.

Eggink, John. Managing Energy Costs: A Behavioral & Non-Technical Approach. 2006. xi, 274p. *(978-0-88173-544-4(2))* Fairmont Pr., Inc.

Flach, Frederic. Choices: Coping Creatively with Personal Change. 2009. (Little Book. Big Idea Ser.). (ENG.). 216p. 11.00 *(978-1-57826-286-1(0))* Hatherleigh Co., Ltd., The.

Ford, Loren. Human Relations: A Game Plan for Improving Personal Adjustment. 4th rev. ed. 2006. (ENG., Illus.). 320p. (C). pap. 127.00 *(978-0-13-227563-7(5),* Prentice Hall) Prentice Hall PTR.

Ford, Loren & Arter, Judith. Human Relations: A Game Plan for Improving Personal Adjustment. 5th rev. ed. 2012. (ENG.). 312p. (C). pap. 127.00 ***(978-0-205-23305-2(8),*** Prentice Hall) Prentice Hall PTR.

Ford, Martyn. It Happened to Me. 2010. (ENG.). 256p. pap. 12.95 ***(978-1-84953-016-3(5))*** Summerdale Pubs. GBR. Dist: Independent Pubs. Group.

Forrester, Rachel & Broadhurst, Sarah, eds. Autism & Loss. 2007. (ENG., Illus.). 208p. per. *(978-1-84310-433-9(4))* Kingsley, Jessica Ltd.

Funke, Cornelia. International Assignments: Expatriate Adjustment & on-site Support - the Case Study of Expatriates in Portugal. 2008. 132p. per. *(978-3-8364-6072-9(6))* VDM Verlag Dr. Mueller e.K.

Giles, Howard, et al, eds. Contexts of Accommodation: Developments in Applied Sociolinguistics. 2010. (Studies in Emotion & Social Interaction Ser.). (ENG., Illus.). 332p. pap. 36.99 *(978-0-521-36960-2(6))* Cambridge Univ. Pr.

Gomez, Cathy. Coping with Sudden Job Loss. 2010. 112p. pap. *(978-3-639-23696-5(3))* VDM Verlag Dr. Mueller e.K.

Gow, Kathryn & Celinski, Marek J. Wayfinding Through Life's Challenges: Coping & Survival. 2011. (Psychology of Emotions, Motivations & Actions Ser.). (Illus.). 569p. 98.00 *(978-1-61122-866-3(2))* Nova Science Pubs., Inc.

Hasselkus, Betty Risteen. The Meaning of Everyday Occupation. 2nd ed. 2011. (ENG., Illus.). 216p. (C). 49.95 *(978-1-55642-934-7(7))* SLACK, Inc.

Hauser, Stuart T., et al. Out of the Woods: Tales of Resilient Teens. 2008. (Adolescent Lives Ser.: 4). 336p. pap. 21.00 *(978-0-674-02734-3(5))* Harvard Univ. Pr.

How to Heal after Heartbreak: How to Recover from a Breakup & Get Your Hopes & Dreams Back. 2012. (ENG.). 288p. pap. 24.95 *(978-1-60138-583-3(8))* Atlantic Publishing Co.

Innis, Nancy K., ed. Reflections on Adaptive Behavior: Essays in Honor of J. E. R. Staddon. 2008. (ENG., Illus.). 408p. (gr. 17). 70.00 *(978-0-262-09044-5(9));* pap. 35.00 *(978-0-262-59026-6(3))* MIT Pr.

Jacobs, Léa K., ed. Coping with Cancer. 2008. (Illus.). 154p. 129.00 *(978-1-60456-213-2(7),* Nova Biomedical Bks.) Nova Science Pubs., Inc.

Jacobs, Negar Nicole. Coping with Infertility: Clinically Proven Ways of Managing the Emotional Roller Coaster. 2006. (ENG., Illus.). 272p. per. 34.95 *(978-0-415-95421-1(5))* Routledge.

James, John W. & Cherry, Frank. The Grief Recovery Handbook: A Step-by-Step Program for Moving beyond Loss. 2006. 175p. reprint ed. pap. 11.00 *(978-1-4223-5495-7(4))* DIANE Publishing Co.

Johnson, Tiffany. Buffering Effects of Activities upon Community Violence Exposure. 2009. 76p. pap. *(978-3-639-16038-3(X))* VDM Verlag Dr. Mueller e.K.

Jones, Jean E., ed. Surviving & Transcending a Traumatic Childhood: The Dark Thread. 2007. (ENG.). 212p. per. 41.95 *(978-0-7890-3265-2(1))* Routledge.

Kahana, Boaz, et al. Holocaust Survivors & Immigrants: Late Life Adaptations. 2010. (Springer Series on Stress & Coping Ser.). xiv, 157p. pap. 74.95 *(978-1-4419-3565-6(7),* 1441935657) Springer.

Kaniasty, Krzysztof, et al, eds. Stress & Psychosocial Resources: Coping with life changes, occupational demands, educational challenges, & threats to physical & emotional Well-being. 2008. 180p. pap. *(978-3-8325-1971-1(8))* Logos Verlag Berlin.

Kapany, Navneet. Conflict & Single Women. 2011. 168p. pap. ***(978-3-8443-0358-2(8))*** Lambert Academic Publishing.

Kennedy, Paul. Coping Effectively with Spinal Cord Injuries: A Group Program Therapist Guide. 2008. (Treatments That Work Ser.). (ENG., Illus.). 80p. pap., instr.'s gde. ed. 29.95 *(978-0-19-533972-7(X))* Oxford Univ. Pr., Inc.

Kingma, Daphne Rose. The Ten Things to Do When Your Life Falls Apart: An Emotional & Spiritual Handbook. 2010. (ENG.). 240p. pap. 15.95 *(978-1-57731-698-5(3))* New World Library.

Langdell, Cheri Colby & Langdell, Tim. Coping with Vision Loss: Understanding the Psychological, Social, & Spiritual Effects, 1 vol. 2010. 177p. 34.95 *(978-0-313-34664-4(X),* C34664); *(978-0-313-34665-1(8))* Greenwood Publishing Group, Inc. (Praeger Pubs.).

Ledbetter, Carole. Who Am I Now? 2007. (ENG.). 180p. per. *(978-1-4141-0877-3(X))* Pleasant Word.

Lederman, Regina & Weis, Karen. Psychosocial Adaptation to Pregnancy: Seven Dimensions of Maternal Role Development. 3rd ed. 2010. (ENG., Illus.). xv, 340p. pap. 79.95 *(978-1-4419-8175-2(6),* 1441981756) Springer.

Levin, Pamela. Cycles of Power: A User's Guide to the Seven Seasons of Life. 2007. (Illus.). xi, 221p. *(978-0-9672718-4-2(3))* Health Communications, Inc.

Linville, Deanna & Hertlein, Katherine M. The Therapist's Notebook for Family Healthcare: Homework, Handouts, & Activites for Individuals, Couples, & Families Coping with Illness, Loss & Disability. 2007. (ENG., Illus.). 272p. per. 44.95 *(978-0-7890-2696-5(1))* Routledge.

Livneh, Hanoch, ed. Coping with Chronic Illness & Disability: Theoretical, Empirical, & Clinical Aspects. 2007. (ENG., Illus.). xxvi, 430p. 109.00 *(978-0-387-48668-0(2),* 0387486682) Springer.

Macartney, James W. Crisis to Creation: Our Power of Choice. 2010. 210p. pap. *(978-1-935359-32-6(0))* Book Pubs. Network.

Magee, Sherri. Picking up the Pieces: Moving Forward after Surviving Cancer. 2007. (ENG.). 326p. per. 19.95 *(978-0-8135-4036-8(4))* Rutgers Univ. Pr.

Malia, Kit & Brannagan, Anne. How to do Cognitive Rehabilitation Therapy: A Guide for All of Us Part One. 2nd ed. 2007. (Illus.). 177p. per. 60.00 *(978-1-931117-39-5(X),* CAT1) Lash & Assocs. Publishing/Training, Inc.

Manassis, Katharina. Keys to Parenting Your Anxious Child. 2nd rev. ed. 2008. (Barron's Parenting Keys Ser.). (ENG.). 192p. pap. 8.99 *(978-0-7641-3916-1(9))* Barron's Educational Series, Inc.

Marten, James. Sing Not War: The Lives of Union & Confederate Veterans in Gilded Age America. 2011. (Civil War America Ser.). (ENG., Illus.). 368p. 39.95 *(978-0-8078-3476-3(9))* Univ. of North Carolina Pr.

Martz, Erin & Livneh, Hanoch, eds. Coping with Chronic Illness & Disability: Theoretical, Empirical, & Clinical Aspects. 2010. (ENG., Illus.). xxvi, 430p. pap. 109.00 *(978-1-4419-4308-8(0),* 1441943080) Springer.

Matsumoto, David. Culture & Modern Life: With Weiten/Lloyd, Psychology Applied to Modern Life (6th) *(978-0-534-73213-4(5))* Wadsworth.

McCracken, Lance M. Mindfulness & Acceptance in Behavioral Medicine: Current Theory & Practice. 2011. (Context Press Mindfulness & Acceptance Practica Ser.). (ENG., Illus.). 400p. pap. 49.95 *(978-1-57224-731-4(2))* New Harbinger Pubns.

McGough, Todd. Cognition & Acculturation - Thinking about How We Adapt. 2007. 148p. per. *(978-3-8364-2662-6(5))* VDM Verlag Dr. Mueller e.K.

McGraw, Phil. Real Life: Preparing for the 7 Most Challenging Days of Your Life. 2009. (ENG.). 336p. pap. 15.00 *(978-1-4391-3156-5(2),* Free Pr.) Free Pr.

—Real Life: Preparing for the 7 Worst Days of Your Life. l.t. ed. 2008. 32.95 *(978-1-59722-842-8(7))* Thorndike Pr.

Mergen, Ö, et al. Resilience/Vulnerability Factors As Predictors of College Adjustment. 2010. 92p. pap. *(978-3-8383-6363-9(9))* Lambert Academic Publishing.

Messer, Mitchell H. Beyond the Boiling Point: Managing Anger in the Classroom. *(978-1-929305-01-8(X))* Anger Institute, The.

Milkman, Harvey & Sunderwirth, Stanley. Craving for Ecstasy & Natural Highs: A Positive Approach to Mood Alteration. 2009. (Illus.). 496p. (C). pap. 41.00 *(978-1-4129-5673-4(0),* B56730P) SAGE Pubns., Inc.

Miller, Thomas W. Handbook of Stressful Transitions Across the Lifespan. 2010. (Illus.). xxiii, 691p. E-Book 249.00 ***(978-1-4419-0748-6(3))*** Springer.

Moffatt, Gregory K. Survivors: What We Can Learn from How They Cope with Horrific Tragedy, 1 vol. 2010. (Illus.). 221p. 44.95 *(978-0-313-37664-1(6),* C37664, Praeger Pubs.) Greenwood Publishing Group, Inc.

Monat, Alan, et al, eds. The Praeger Handbook on Stress & Coping, 2 vols. 2007. (Illus.). 664p. 200.00 *(978-0-275-99197-5(0),* C9197, Praeger Pubs.) Greenwood Publishing Group, Inc.

Monroe, Barbara & Oliviere, David, eds. Resilience in Palliative Care: Achievement in Adversity. 2007. (ENG., Illus.). 272p. pap. 69.95 *(978-0-19-920641-4(4))* Oxford Univ. Pr., Inc.

Moore, Lynn. Inspirational Goaling: How Intuition, Passion & a Taste for Adventure Create Goal Victory When Other Methods Haven't. 2010. (ENG.). 198p. pap. 15.99 *(978-1-59932-197-4(1),* Messenger Hse.) Advantage Media Group.

Mungleng, Toreiphi. Attitude of the Nagas Towards the Non-Nagas. 2010. 76p. pap. *(978-3-639-24814-2(7))* VDM Verlag Dr. Mueller e.K.

Nevid, Jeffrey S. & Rathus, Spencer A. Psychology & the Challenges of Life. 11th ed. 2010. (ENG.). 456p. (C). pap., pupil's gde. ed. 46.95 *(978-0-470-59231-1(1),* Wiley) Wiley, John & Sons, Inc.

—Psychology & the Challenges of Life: Adjustment & Growth. 11th ed. 2009. (ENG., Illus.). 624p. (C). 173.95 *(978-0-470-38362-9(3),* Wiley) Wiley, John & Sons, Inc.

—Psychology & the Challenges of Life: Adjustment in the New Millennium. 10th ed. 2007. (Wiley Plus Products Ser.). pap. 52.95 *(978-0-470-13948-6(X))* Wiley, John & Sons, Inc.

—Psychology & the Challenges of Life: Adjustment to the New Millennium. 9th ed. 2006. (Wiley Plus Products Ser.). pap. 47.95 *(978-0-470-07940-9(1))* Wiley, John & Sons, Inc.

Osteen, Joel. Become a Better You: 7 Keys to Improving Your Life Every Day. 2010. (ENG.). 128p. 5.95 *(978-0-7624-3887-7(8))* Running Pr. Bk. Pubs.

Owen, Ray. Facing the Storm: Using CBT, Mindfulness & Acceptance to build resilience when your world's about to fall Apart. 2011. (ENG.). 216p. 112.00 *(978-0-415-67658-8(4));* pap. 19.99 *(978-0-415-67659-5(2))* Routledge.

Parens, Henri, et al. The Unbroken Soul: Tragedy, Trauma, & Human Resilience. 2008. (Margaret S. Mahler Ser.). (ENG.). 208p. 89.50 *(978-0-7657-0588-4(5));* pap. 39.99 *(978-0-7657-0589-1(3))* Rowman & Littlefield Publishers, Inc. (Aronson, Jason).

Park, Crystal L. Medical Illness & Positive Life Change: Can Crisis Lead to Personal Transformation? Park, Crystal L. et al, eds. 2008. (Decade of Behavior Ser.). (Illus.). 280p. 49.95 *(978-1-4338-0396-3(8))* American Psychological Assn.

Phillips, William D., Jr., et al. Religious Conflict & Accommodation in the Early Modern World. Phillips, William D., Jr. & Ragnow, Marguerite, eds. 2011. 257p. 55.00 ***(978-0-9797559-2-7(1))*** Ctr. for Early Modern History.

Pushkar, Dolores, et al, eds. Improving Competence Across the Lifespan: Building Interventions Based on Theory & Research. 2010. (ENG & ABK.). 216p. pap. 159.00 *(978-1-4419-3293-8(3),* 1441932933) Springer.

Roberts, S. Craig. Applied Evolutionary Psychology. 2012. (ENG., Illus.). 472p. 98.50 ***(978-0-19-958607-3(1))*** Oxford Univ. Pr., Inc.

Roy, Sister Callista & Andrews, Heather A. The Roy Adaptation Model. 3rd ed. 2008. (ENG., Illus.). 576p. (C). pap. 59.40 *(978-0-13-038497-3(6),* Prentice Hall) Prentice Hall PTR.

Sakoschek, Janita. Ladybird: My house burnt down, my head Is on Here! 2011. 304p. pap. 22.00 *(978-1-4152-0133-6(1))* Random Hse. Struik (Pty.), Ltd. ZAF. Dist: International Publishers Marketing.

Sandford, Paula & Sandford, John Loren. Growing Pains: How to Overcome Life's Earliest Experiences to Become All God Wants You to Be. 2008. (Transformation Ser.). (ENG.). 240p. pap. 14.99 *(978-1-59979-278-1(8),* Charisma Hse.) Charisma Media.

Schaefer, G. J. The Widower's Toolbox: Repairing Your Life after Losing Your Spouse. 2010. (ENG.). 224p. pap. 14.95 *(978-0-88282-345-4(0))* New Horizon Pr. Pubs., Inc.

Schwartz, Morrie. Morrie - In His Own Words: Life Wisdom from a Remarkable Man. 2008. (ENG., Illus.). 144p. pap. 11.00 *(978-0-8027-1717-7(9))* Walker & Co.

Seaward, Brian Luke. Managing Stress: Principles & Strategies for Health & Well-Being. 6th rev. ed. 2008. 600p. pap. 118.95 *(978-0-7637-5614-7(8))* Jones & Bartlett Learning, LLC.

Seligman, Milton & Darling, Rosalyn Benjamin. Ordinary Families, Special Children: A Systems Approach to Childhood Disability. 3rd rev. ed. 2007. (ENG., Illus.). 434p. 65.00 *(978-1-59385-362-4(9))* Guilford Pubns., Inc.

Skogrand, Linda, et al. Surviving & Transcending a Traumatic Childhood: The Dark Thread. 2007. (ENG.). 212p. 125.00 *(978-0-7890-3264-5(3))* Routledge.

Smallwood, Beverly. This Wasn't Supposed to Happen to Me, 0 vols. 2009. 336p. pap. 16.99 *(978-0-7852-9731-4(6))* Nelson, Thomas Inc.

Spring, Bonnie & Spring, Bonnie J. Smoking Cessation with Weight Gain Prevention: A Group Program Therapist Guide. 2008. (Treatments That Work Ser.). (ENG., Illus.). 160p. (C). pap. 35.00 *(978-0-19-531402-1(6))* Oxford Univ. Pr., Inc.

Sroufe, L. Alan, et al. The Development of the Person: The Minnesota Study of Risk & Adaptation from Birth to Adulthood. 2009. (ENG.). 384p. pap. 40.00 *(978-1-60623-249-1(5))* Guilford Pubns., Inc.

Stark, Cleveland A. & Bonner, Dylan C. Handbook on Spirituality: Belief Systems, Societal Impact, & Roles in Coping. 2012. ***(978-1-61942-475-3(4))*** Nova Science Pubs., Inc.

Stebnicki, Mark A. What Is Adolescent Mental Health? Helping Disconnected & at-Risk Youth to Become Whole. 2008. 252p. *(978-0-7734-5251-0(6))* Mellen, Edwin Pr., The.

Stern, Robin & Martin, Courtney E. Project Rebirth: Survival & the Strength of the Human Spirit from 9/11 Survivors. 2011. (ENG.). 256p. (gr. 12). 25.95 *(978-0-525-95226-8(8),* Dutton Adult) Penguin Group (USA) Inc.

Stuster, Jack. Bold Endeavors. 2011. (Illus.). 408p. pap. 24.95 *(978-1-59114-830-2(8))* Naval Institute Pr.

Terry Smith. Surviving Head Traum: A Guide to Recovery Written by a Traumatic Brain Injury Patient. 2009. 108p. 22.95 *(978-1-4401-7644-9(2));* pap. 12.95 *(978-1-4401-7642-5(6))* iUniverse, Inc.

Tharp, Roland G. Delta Theory & Psychosocial Systems: The Practice of Influence & Change. 2011. (ENG., Illus.). 206p. 90.00 ***(978-1-107-01491-6(3))*** Cambridge Univ. Pr.

Thomas, Sandra P. Transforming Nurses' Stress & Anger: Steps Toward Healing. 3rd ed. 2008. 800p. *(978-0-8261-2542-2(5))* Springer.

Thompson, Donna Marie. Bouncing Back from Loss: How to Learn from Your Past, Heal the Present, & Transform Your Future. 2011. (ENG.). 226p. pap. 17.95 *(978-1-60037-825-6(0))* Morgan James Publishing.

Toch, Hans. Men in Crisis: Human Breakdowns in Prison. 2007. (ENG.). 347p. pap. 29.95 *(978-0-202-30932-3(0))* Aldine Transaction.

Tommasi, Luca, et al, eds. Cognitive Biology: Evolutionary & Developmental Perspectives on Mind, Brain, & Behavior. 2009. (Vienna Series in Theoretical Biology). (ENG., Illus.). 352p. (gr. 17). 52.00 *(978-0-262-01293-5(6))* MIT Pr.

Wanberg, Connie, ed. The Oxford Handbook of Organizational Socialization. 2012. (Oxford Library of Psychology Ser.). (ENG.). 384p. 135.00 ***(978-0-19-976367-2(4))*** Oxford Univ. Pr., Inc.

Wathall, Paul. Cardiac Rehabilitation: Exercise. 2009. 526p. pap. *(978-3-639-17748-0(7))* VDM Verlag Dr. Mueller e.K.

Watson, Irene & Volkman, Victor R., eds. The Story That Must Be Told: True Tales of Transformation. 2007. (ENG., Illus.). 204p. per. *(978-1-932690-38-5(7))* Loving Healing Pr., Inc.

Weiss, Marisa C. & Weiss, Ellen. Living Well Beyond Breast Cancer: A Survivor's Guide for When Treatment Ends & the Rest of Your Life Begins. 2nd ed. 2010. (ENG., Illus.). 528p. pap. 20.00 *(978-0-307-46022-6(3),* Three Rivers Pr.) Crown Publishing Group.

Weiten, Wayne & Lloyd, Margaret A. Psychology Applied to Modern Life: Adjustment at the Turn of the Century. 6th ed. tchr. ed. *(978-0-534-36660-5(0))* Wadsworth.

Weiten, Wayne, et al. Cengage Advantage Books: Psychology Applied to Modern Life: Adjustment in the 21st Century. 10th ed. 2011. (ENG.). 688p. (C). ring bd. 99.95 *(978-1-111-29798-5(3))* Wadsworth.

—Psychology Applied to Modern Life: Adjustment in the 21st Century. 10th ed. 2011. (Available Titles CengageNOW Ser.). (ENG.). 688p. (C). 179.95 *(978-1-111-18663-0(4))* Wadsworth.

—Study Guide for Weiten/Dunn/Hammer's Psychology Applied to Modern Life: Adjustment in the 21st Century, 10th. 10th ed. 2011. (ENG.). 304p. (C). pap. 75.95 *(978-1-111-34496-2(5))* Wadsworth.

Wolchik, Sharlene & Sandler, Irwin N., eds. Handbook of Children's Coping: Linking Theory & Intervention. 2010. (Issues in Clinical Child Psychology Ser.). 566p. pap. 149.00 *(978-1-4419-3269-3(0),* 1441932690) Springer.

Wood, Eve A. The Gift of Betrayal: How to Heal Your Life When Your World Explodes. 2009. (ENG.). 240p. pap. 14.95 *(978-1-4019-1849-1(2));* 24.95 *(978-1-4019-1848-4(4))* Hay Hse., Inc.

Wyatt, Randall C. & Seid, Erika L. Couples & Infertility (Instructor's Version) 2007. 149.00 *(978-1-60124-055-2(4))* Psychotherapy.net.

Wynhausen, Elisabeth. On Resilience. 2010. (Little Books on Big Themes Ser.). (ENG.). 96p. 15.95 *(978-0-522-85663-7(2))* Melbourne Univ. Publishing AUS. Dist: Independent Pubs. Group.

Zahm, Mary. Create Your Ideal Life: Applied Psychology of Personal Adjustment & Growth. 2010. 316p. pap. 58.99 *(978-1-4520-2503-2(7))* AuthorHouse.

ADJUSTMENT (PSYCHOLOGY) IN CHILDREN

Allen, Jen, et al. Helping Your Pupils to Be Resilient. 2007. (Illus.). VI, 66p. 21.95 *(978-0-415-44728-7(3))* Fulton, David Pubs. GBR. Dist: Taylor & Francis Group.

Boston Process Study Group Staff. Change in Psychotherapy - A Unifying Paradigm. 2010. (ENG.). 368p. 35.00 *(978-0-393-70599-7(4),* 70599) Norton, W. W. & Co., Inc.

Corr, Charles A. & Balk, David E. Children's Encounters with Death, Bereavement, & Coping. 2010. (Illus.). 488p. 70.00 *(978-0-8261-3422-6(X))* Springer Publishing Co., Inc.

Deans, Jan, et al. Developing Everyday Coping Skills in the Early Years: Proactive Strategies for Supporting Social & Emotional Development. 2012. (Illus.). 128p. E-Book ***(978-1-4411-6010-2(8));*** E-Book ***(978-1-4411-8799-4(X))*** Continuum International Publishing Group, Ltd.

Downs, Jacqueline. Coping with Change. 2010. 456p. pap. *(978-3-8383-4679-3(3))* Lambert Academic Publishing.

Dutch, Dorris A. Thumb Suckers Come In All Colors: Thoughts, Memories & Feelings of Life in This Colorless World. 2011. 216p. pap. 14.03 *(978-1-4567-4291-1(4))* AuthorHouse.

Frydenberg, Erica. Adolescent Coping: Advances in Theory, Research & Practice. 2nd rev. ed. 2008. (Adolescence & Society Ser.). (ENG., Illus.). 360p. 44.95 *(978-0-415-40572-0(6))*; 110.00 *(978-0-415-40571-3(8))* Routledge.

Frydenberg, Erica, et al. Developing Everyday Coping Skills in the Early Years: Proactive Strategies for Supporting Social & Emotional Development. 2012. (ENG., Illus.). 172p. pap. 34.95 *(978-1-4411-6104-8(X))* Continuum International Publishing Group, Ltd. GBR. Dist: National Bk. Network.

Smith, John, et al. Helping Children with Autism Spectrum Conditions through Everyday Transitions: Small Changes - Big Challenges. 2012. (ENG., Illus.). 192p. pap. ***(978-1-84905-275-7(1))*** Kingsley, Jessica Ltd.

ADJUSTMENT (STUDENTS)
see Student Adjustment

ADJUSTMENT, ECONOMIC
see Economic Stabilization

ADJUSTMENT, SOCIAL
see Social Adjustment

ADJUSTMENT OF CLAIMS
see Insurance Claims

ADJUVANT ARTHRITIS
see Rheumatoid Arthritis

ADJUVANTS, IMMUNOLOGICAL
see Immunological Adjuvants

ADLER, ADOLF PETER, 1812-1869

Kierkegaard, Soren, et al. The Book on Adler. 2009. (Kierkegaard's Writings: Vol. 24). (ENG., Illus.). 424p. (C). pap. 40.00 *(978-0-691-14082-7(0))* Princeton Univ. Pr.

Perkins, Robert L., ed. The Book on Adler: International Kierkegaard Commentary Series, Vol. 24. 2008. 50.00 *(978-0-88146-127-5(X))* Mercer Univ. Pr.

ADLER, ALFRED, 1870-1937

Adler, Alfred. Understanding Life: An Introduction to the Psychology of Alfred Adler. Brett, Colin, ed. 2009. (ENG.). 256p. pap. 29.95 *(978-1-85168-697-1(5))* Oneworld Pubns. GBR. Dist: National Bk. Network.

—What Life Could Mean to You: The Psychology of Personal Development. Brett Colin, ed. & tr. by. from GER. 2009. (ENG.). 256p. pap. 29.95 *(978-1-85168-670-4(3))* Oneworld Pubns. GBR. Dist: National Bk. Network.

Carlson, Jon & Maniacci, Michael P., eds. Alfred Adler Revisited. 2011. (ENG., Illus.). 339p. 135.00 *(978-0-415-88446-4(2))*; pap. 39.95 *(978-0-415-88447-1(0))* Routledge.

Johansen & Johansen, Thor. Religion & Spirituality in Psychotherapy: An Individual Psychology Perspective. 2009. 240p. *(978-0-8261-0385-7(5))* Springer.

Odajnyk, V. Walter. Archetype & Character: Power, Eros, Spirit & Matter Personality Types. 2012. (ENG., Illus.). 272p. 85.00 ***(978-0-230-36401-1(2))*** Palgrave Macmillan.

Sweeney, Thomas. Adlerian Counseling & Psychotherapy: A Practitioner's Approach. 5th rev. ed. 2009. (ENG., Illus.). 438p. 51.95 *(978-0-415-99348-7(2))* Routledge.

Wahl, Pit, et al. Macht - Lust. 2010. (Beitrage zur Individualpsychologie Ser.). (ENG & GER., Illus.). 320p. (C). pap. 54.00 *(978-3-525-45016-1(8))* Vandenhoeck & Ruprecht GmbH & Co. KG DEU. Dist: ISD.

ADLER, DANKMAR, 1844-1900

Nickel, Richard, et al. The Complete Architecture of Adler & Sullivan. 2010. (Illus.). 472p. 95.00 *(978-0-9660273-2-7(9))* Nickel, Richard Committee, The.

ADLER, MORTIMER J. (MORTIMER JEROME), 1902-2001

Adler, Mortimer J. How to Prove There Is a God: Mortimer J. Adler's Writings & Thoughts about God. Dzugan, Ken, ed. 2011. (ENG.). 320p. pap. 29.95 *(978-0-8126-9689-9(1))* Open Court Publishing Co.

ADMINISTRATION, AGRICULTURAL
see Agricultural Administration

ADMINISTRATION, BUSINESS
see Business

ADMINISTRATION, NURSING SERVICE
see Nursing Services—Administration

ADMINISTRATION, PUBLIC
see Public Administration

ADMINISTRATION OF CRIMINAL JUSTICE
see Criminal Justice, Administration Of

ADMINISTRATION OF ESTATES
see also Executors and Administrators; Probate Law and Practice

Banaji, Jairus. Agrarian Change in Late Antiquity: Gold, Labour, & Aristocratic Dominance. 2nd rev. ed. 2007. (Oxford Classical Monographs). (ENG., Illus.). 336p. per. 65.00 *(978-0-19-922803-0(2))* Oxford Univ. Pr., Inc.

Before It's Too Late - Don't Leave Your Loved Ones Unprepared. 2008. 67p. spiral bd. *(978-0-9657016-2-4(X))* Before It's Too Late.

Bosworth, Jose, et al, eds. The Middleton Papers: The Financial Problems of a Yorkshire Recusant Family in the Sixteenth & Seventeenth Centuries. 2010. (Yorkshire Archaeological Soc Record Ser.: Volume 161). (Illus.). 220p. 90.00 *(978-1-903564-31-8(X))* Yorkshire Archaeological Society GBR. Dist: Boydell & Brewer, Inc.

Bouman, Thomas J. Arizona Estate Administration Answer Book. 2010. 193p. pap. 19.95 *(978-0-557-57184-0(7))* Lulu Enterprises Inc.

Bowyer, B. Gene. Handbook for Administrators & Executors of Estates. 2009. 84p. pap. 10.95 *(978-1-4401-1613-1(X))* iUniverse, Inc.

Broad, John. Transforming English Rural Society: The Verneys & the Claydons, 1600-1820. 2007. (Cambridge Studies in Population, Economy & Society in Past Time Ser.). (ENG., Illus.). 312p. pap. 61.00 *(978-0-521-04198-0(8))* Cambridge Univ. Pr.

Crouch, Holmes F. Organizing Your Estate: How to Purge & Direct Property Transfer to Chosen Family Members by Gift, Bequest, or in Trust While Thinkingly Alive. 2006. (Series 300: Retirees & Estates Ser.). (Illus.). 224p. per. 24.95 *(978-0-944817-81-0(5))* Allyear Tax Guides.

Dooley, Terence. The Big Houses & Landed Estates of Ireland: A Research Guide. 2007. (Maynooth Research Guides for Irish Local History Ser.: No. 11). (Illus.). 192p. (C). 45.00 *(978-1-84682-039-7(1))* Four Courts Pr. IRL. Dist: International Specialized Bk. Services.

Hall, Julie. The Boomer Burden: Dealing with Your Parents' Lifetime Accumulation of Stuff, 0 vols. 2008. 256p. pap. 14.99 *(978-0-7852-2825-7(X))* Nelson, Thomas Inc.

Hower, Dennis R. & Kahn, Peter. Wills, Trusts, & Estates Administration. 7th ed. 2011. (ENG.). 648p. (C). pap. 157.95 *(978-1-111-13778-6(1))* Delmar Cengage Learning.

Larson, P. L. Conflict & Compromise in the Late Medieval Countryside: Lords & Peasants in Durham, 1349-1400. 2006. (Studies in Medieval History & Culture). (Illus.). 293p. 131.00 *(978-0-415-97836-1(X))* Routledge.

Tindley, Annie. The Sutherland Estate, 1850-1920: Aristocratic Decline, Estate Management & Land Reform. 2010. (Scottish Historical Review Monographs). (ENG.). 256p. (gr. 17). 80.00 *(978-0-7486-4032-4(0))* Edinburgh Univ. Pr. GBR. Dist: Columbia Univ. Pr.

Wade Martins, Susanna. A Great Estate at Work: The Holkham Estate & its Inhabitants in the Nineteenth Century. 2008. (ENG.). 308p. pap. 42.00 *(978-0-521-08084-2(3))* Cambridge Univ. Pr.

Xenophon. The Economist. 2009. 122p. pap. 6.99 *(978-1-60450-719-5(5))*, Serenity Pubs.) Arc Manor.

—The Economist. 2008. 120p. per. *(978-1-4065-5563-9(0))* Dodo Pr.

ADMINISTRATION OF JUSTICE
see Justice, Administration of

ADMINISTRATION OF JUVENILE JUSTICE
see Juvenile Justice, Administration of

ADMINISTRATIVE ABILITY
see Executive Ability

ADMINISTRATIVE ACTS
see also Judicial Review of Administrative Acts

Congressional Review ACT: Hearing Before the Subcommittee on Commercial & Administrative Law of the Committee on the Judiciary, House of Representatives, One Hundred Tenth Congress, First Session, November 6, 2007. 2009. iii, 51p. *(978-0-16-082687-0(X)*, 552-070-38704-8) United States Government Printing Office.

Federal Rulemaking & the Regulatory Process: Hearing Before the Subcommittee on Commercial & Administrative Law of the Committee on the Judiciary, House of Representatives, One Hundred Eleventh Congress, Second Session, July 27, 2010. 2010. iii, 210p. ***(978-0-16-087413-0(0)***, 552-070-42106-8) United States Government Printing Office.

Full Committee Hearing on the Impact of Financial Regulatory Restructuring on Small Businesses & Community Lenders: Hearing Before the Committee on Small Business, United States House of Representatives, One Hundred Eleventh Congress, First Session, Hearing Held September 23, 2009. 2009. (Illus.). vi, 203p. *(978-0-16-085160-5(2)*, 552-070-40514-3) United States Government Printing Office.

Jois. Customs & Excise Laws & Administrative Justice the Dynamics of Indirect Taxation & State Power in India. 2009. (ENG.). 450p. 89.95 *(978-0-19-569441-3(4))* Oxford Univ. Pr., Inc.

Kresser, Daniel. Die Bedeutung der Form für Begriff und Rechtsfolgen des Verwaltungsakts. 2009. (Dresdner Schriften zum Öffentlichen Recht Ser.). (GER.). 348p. pap. 81.95 *(978-3-631-59060-7(1))* Lang, Peter GmbH, Europäischer Verlag der Wissenschaften DEU. Dist: Lang, Peter.

Matthews, Lisa & Fanning, Jason, eds. Federal Government & the REINS Act: Major Regulations. 2012. ***(978-1-62100-346-5(9))*** Nova Science Pubs., Inc.

Meyer, Marshall W. Limits to Bureaucratic Growth. (De Gruyter Studies in Organization Ser.). (ENG.). X, 228p. 196.00 ***(978-3-11-177565-4(8))*** De Gruyter, Walter Inc.

Regulations from the Executive in Need of Scrutiny ACT of 2011: Hearing Before the Subcommittee on Courts, Commercial & Administrative Law of the Committee on the Judiciary, House of Representatives, One Hundred Twelfth Congress, First Session, on H.R. 10, March 8, 2011. 2011. (Illus.). iii, 154p. ***(978-0-16-089012-3(8)***, 552-070-43044-0) United States Government Printing Office.

Reinheimer, Sandra. Das Verbindungskonzept der Bundeswasserstraßenverwaltung. 2008. (Studien zum Internationalen, Europäischen und Öffentlichen Recht Ser.). 242p. pap. 61.95 *(978-3-631-56996-2(3))* Lang, Peter GmbH, Europaischer Verlag der Wissenschaften DEU. Dist: Lang, Peter.

REINS ACT: Promoting Jobs & Expanding Freedom by Reducing Needless Regulations: Hearing Before the Subcommittee on Courts, Commercial & Administrative Law of the Committee on the Judiciary, House of Representatives, One Hundred Twelfth Congress, First Session, January 24, 2011. 2011. iv, 155p. ***(978-0-16-088594-5(9)***, 552-070-42770-8) United States Government Printing Office.

Singh, Mahendra P. German Administrative Law in Common Law Perspective. 2nd ed. 2010. (Beiträge Zum Ausländischen öffentlichen Recht und Völkerrecht Ser.). xxxi, 380p. pap. 119.00 *(978-3-642-07615-2(7)*, 3642076157) Springer.

ADMINISTRATIVE ADJUDICATION
see Administrative Procedure

ADMINISTRATIVE AGENCIES
see also Executive Advisory Bodies; Executive Departments; Independent Regulatory Commissions

Abramson, Mark A. Getting It Done. 2008. (IBM Center for the Business of Government Book Ser.). (ENG.). 152p. 65.00 *(978-0-7425-6600-2(5))*; pap. 21.95 *(978-0-7425-6601-9(3))* Rowman & Littlefield Publishers, Inc.

—Operator's Manual for the New Administration. 2008. (IBM Center for the Business of Government Ser.). (ENG., Illus.). 192p. 85.00 *(978-0-7425-6329-2(4))*; pap. 32.95 *(978-0-7425-6330-8(8))* Rowman & Littlefield Publishers, Inc.

Agency Budgets & Priorities for FY 2010: Hearing Before the Subcommittee on Water Resources & Environment of the Committee on Transportation & Infrastructure, House of Representatives, One Hundred Eleventh Congress, First Session, June 3, 16, 2009. 2009. (Illus.). xi, 174p. *(978-0-16-086425-4(9)*, 552-070-41486-0) United States Government Printing Office.

Albro, Robert, et al, eds. Anthropologists in the SecurityScape: Ethics, Practice, & Professional Identity. 2011. (ENG.). 277p. 89.00 *(978-1-61132-012-1(7))*; pap. 34.95 *(978-1-61132-013-8(5))* Left Coast Pr., Inc.

Are Agencies Playing It Safe & Secure? An Examination of Worker Protections Pre- & Post-Injury: Hearing Before the Subcommittee on Federal Workforce, Postal Service, & the District of Columbia of the Committee on Oversight & Government Reform, House of Representatives, One Hundred Eleventh Congress, Second Session, July 21, 2010. 2011. (Illus.). iii, 102p. ***(978-0-16-088572-3(8)***, 552-070-42748-1) United States Government Printing Office.

Aristigueta, Maria P., et al, eds. International Handbook of Practice-Based Performance Management. 2007. 560p. 150.00 *(978-1-4129-4012-2(5)*, B40125C) SAGE Pubns., Inc.

Arnold, William G. The Prompt Payment ACT Answer Book. 2009. *(978-1-56726-243-8(0))* Management Concepts, Inc.

Aspatore Books Staff, compiled by. Working with Government Agencies in White Collar Law: Leading Lawyers on Responding to Investigations, Overcoming Client Challenges, & Understanding Enforcement Trends (Inside the Minds) 2008. 128p. pap. 80.00 *(978-0-314-19557-9(2))* Aspatore Bks.

Balancing ACT: Efforts to Right-Size the Federal Employer-To-Contractor Mix: Hearing Before the Oversight of Government Management, the Federal Workforce, & the District of Columbia Subcommittee of the Committee on Homeland Security & Governmental Affairs, United States Senate, One Hundred Eleventh Congress, Second Session, May 20, 2010. 2010. (Illus.). iii, 150p. ***(978-0-16-086901-3(3)***, 552-070-41811-3) United States Government Printing Office.

Ballinas Valdes, Cristopher. Political Struggles & the Forging of Autonomous Government Agencies. 2011. (Public Sector Organizations Ser.). (ENG., Illus.). 272p. 85.00 *(978-0-230-29648-0(3))* Palgrave Macmillan.

Balutis, Alan, et al, eds. Transforming American Governance: Rebooting the Public Square. 2011. (ENG.). 384p. pap. 49.95 ***(978-0-7656-2771-1(X))***; (Illus.). 99.95 *(978-0-7656-2770-4(1))* Sharpe, M.E. Inc.

Baranzelli, John. Making Government Great Again: Mapping the Road to Success with ISO 9001:2008. 2009. 75.00 *(978-0-87389-779-2(X))* ASQ Quality Pr.

Baum, Jeeyang Rhee. Responsive Democracy: Increasing State Accountability in East Asia. 2011. (Illus.). xii, 192p. E-Book ***(978-0-472-02573-2(2))***; (ENG.), 204p. 70.00 *(978-0-472-11749-9(1))* Univ. of Michigan Pr.

Beattie, Rona S. Human Resource Management in the Public Sector. 2007. pap. 40.00 *(978-0-415-49141-9(X))* Routledge.

Beck, Joachim & Thedieck, Franz, eds. The European Dimension of Administrative Culture. 2008. 338p. pap. 86.00 *(978-3-8329-3861-1(3))* Nomos Verlagsgesellschaft DEU. Dist: International Specialized Bk. Services.

Bekkers, Victor, et al, eds. Innovation in the Public Sector: Linking Capacity & Leadership. 2011. (Governance & Public Management Ser.). (ENG., Illus.). 256p. 85.00 *(978-0-230-28452-4(3))* Palgrave Macmillan.

Belgium's Chairmanship of the OSCE: Hearing Before the Commission on Security & Cooperation in Europe, One Hundred Ninth Congress, Second Session, June 28, 2006. 2007. ii, 19p. *(978-0-16-079765-1(9)*, 552-070-36680-6) United States Government Printing Office.

Bissessar, Ann Marie. The Crisis of Public Sector Reform in the Carribean: An Analysis Through the Use of Game Theory. 2008. (Illus.). 280p. 109.95 *(978-0-7734-5054-7(8))* Mellen, Edwin Pr., The.

Blue, Gold, & Green: How Delaware State & Local Governments Are Cutting Their Energy Costs: Hearing Before the Federal Financial Management, Government Information, Federal Services, & International Security Subcommittee of the Committee on Homeland Security & Governmental Affairs, United States Senate, of the One Hundred Eleventh Congress, Second Session, Field Hearing in Wilmington, Delaware, February 19, 2010. 2010. (Illus.). iii, 53p. ***(978-0-16-087453-6(X)***, 552-070-42145-9) United States Government Printing Office.

Bouckaert, Geert, et al. The Coordination of Public Sector Organizations: Shifting Patterns of Public Management. 2010. (Public Sector Organizations Ser.). (ENG., Illus.). 256p. 89.00 *(978-0-230-24015-5(1))* Palgrave Macmillan.

Bourn, John. Public Sector Auditing: Is It Value for Money? 2008. (ENG., Illus.). 426p. 60.00 *(978-0-470-05722-3(X)*, Wiley) Wiley, John & Sons, Inc.

Box, Richard C. Public Administration & Society: Critical Issues in American Governance. 2nd rev. ed. 2009. 312p. (C). (ENG.). pap. 59.95 *(978-0-7656-2359-1(5))*; (Illus.). 89.95 *(978-0-7656-2358-4(7))* Sharpe, M.E. Inc.

Boyne, George A., et al, eds. Public Service Performance: Perspectives on Measurement & Management. 2010. (ENG.). 338p. pap. 39.99 *(978-0-521-17293-6(4))* Cambridge Univ. Pr.

Brander, Michael N. Social Media Use in the Federal Government. 2012. (Media & Communications - Technologies, Policies & Challenges Ser.). 118p. pap. 47.00 ***(978-1-62100-747-0(2))*** Nova Science Pubs., Inc.

Bressman. The Regulatory State. 2010. 152.00 *(978-0-7355-9417-3(1)*, Aspen Pubs.) Wolters Kluwer Law & Business.

Bressman, Lisa Schultz, et al. The Regulatory State. 2010. (Illus.). xxix, 861p. *(978-0-7355-9418-0(X)*, Aspen Pubs.) Wolters Kluwer Law & Business.

Buss, Terry F., et al, eds. Performance Management & Budgeting: How Governments Can Learn from Experience. 2008. (Transformational Trends in Governance & Democracy Ser.). (Illus.). 360p. 94.95 *(978-0-7656-2232-7(7))* Sharpe, M.E. Inc.

Bussell, Jennifer. Corruption & Reform in India: Public Services in the Digital Age. 2012. (ENG., Illus.). 346p. 99.00 ***(978-1-107-01905-8(2))*** Cambridge Univ. Pr.

A Case Study in National General Services Administration Policies for Federal Agencies: Hearing Before the Subcommittee on Economic Development, Public Buildings, & Emergency Management of the Committee on Transportation & Infrastructure, House of Representatives, One Hundred Tenth Congress, First Session, February 27, 2007 (Washington, DC) 2007. (Illus.). viii, 58p. *(978-0-16-079568-8(0)*, 552-070-36535-4) United States Government Printing Office.

Cheung, Anthony B. L., et al, eds. Public Service Reform in East Asia: Reform Issues & Challenges in Japan, Korea, Singapore & Hong Kong. 2006. (ENG.). 312p. (gr. 17). pap. 23.00 *(978-962-996-234-0(9))* Chinese Univ. of Hong Kong, The HKG. Dist: Columbia Univ. Pr.

Chhabra, Susheel & Kumar, Muneesh. Strategic Enterprise Resource Planning Models for E-Government: Applications & Methodologies. 2011. ***(978-1-60960-865-1(8))*** IGI Global.

Chhabra, Susheel & Kumar, Muneesh, eds. Integrating E-Business Models for Government Solutions: Citizen-Centric Service Oriented Methodologies & Processes. 2009. (Advances in Electronic Government Research Book Ser.). (Illus.). 338p. 195.00 *(978-1-60566-240-4(2))* IGI Global.

—Strategic Enterprise Resource Planning Models for E-Government: Applications & Methodologies. 2011. 495p. 195.00 *(978-1-60960-863-7(1)*, Information Science Reference) IGI Global.

Cohen, Joshua B., ed. Waste, Fraud & Mismanagement in the Federal Government: High Risk Areas. 2011. ***(978-1-61324-592-7(0))*** Nova Science Pubs., Inc.

Commerce, Justice, Science, & Related Agencies Appropriations for 2010: Hearings Before a Subcommittee of the Committee on Appropriations, House of Representatives, One Hundred Eleventh Congress, First Session. 2009. (Illus.). *(978-0-16-083301-4(9)*, 552-070-39129-1 (pt. 4)); *(978-0-16-083210-9(1)*, 552-070-39129-1 (pt. 4)) United States Government Printing Office.

Commerce, Justice, Science, & Related Agencies Appropriations for 2011: Hearings Before a Subcommittee of the Committee on Appropriations, House of Representatives, One Hundred Eleventh Congress, Second Session. 2010. (Illus.). *(978-0-16-085613-6(2)*, 552-070-40687-5 (pt. 1A)); *(978-0-16-085360-9(5)*, 552-070-40687-5 (pt. 1A)); ***(978-0-16-085343-2(5)***, 552-070-40687-5 (pt. 1A)); *(978-0-16-085467-5(9)*, 552-070-40687-5 (pt. 1A)); *(978-0-16-085547-4(0)*, 552-070-40687-5 (pt. 1A)) United States Government Printing Office.

Commerce, Justice, Science, & Related Agencies Appropriations for 2012: Hearings Before a Subcommittee of the Committee on Appropriations, House of Representatives, One Hundred Twelfth Congress, First Session. 2011. (Illus.). ***(978-0-16-088646-1(5)***, 552-070-42821-6 (pt. 1A)); ***(978-0-16-088558-7(2)***, 552-070-42821-6 (pt. 1A)); ***(978-0-16-088652-2(X)***, 552-070-42821-6 (pt. 1A)); ***(978-0-16-088650-8(3)***, 552-070-42821-6 (pt. 1A)); ***(978-0-16-088564-8(7)***, 552-070-42821-6 (pt. 1A)) United States Government Printing Office.

Committee on Evaluating the Efficiency of Research and Development Programs at the U.S. Environmental Protection Agency & National Research Council. Evaluating Research Efficiency in the U. S. Environmental Protection Agency. 2008. (ENG.). 152p. pap. 35.00 *(978-0-309-11684-8(8))* National Academies Pr.

Committee to Review the NIOSH Hearing Loss Research Program (U.S.) Staff, contrib. by. Hearing Loss Research at NIOSH: Reviews of Research Programs of the National Institute for Occupational Safety & Health. 2006. (ENG.). 224p. pap. 48.75 *(978-0-309-10274-2(X))* National Academies Pr.

Commonwealth Secretariat Staff. Commonwealth Ministers Reference Book 2008. 2008. (Commonwealth Ministers Reference Books Ser.). 266p. pap. 68.00 *(978-0-9554408-4-7(X))* Henley Media Group, Ltd. GBR. Dist: Stylus Publishing, LLC.

—Commonwealth Ministers Reference Book 2009. 2009. (Commonwealth Ministers Reference Books Ser.). 326p. pap. 68.00 *(978-0-9554408-9-2(0))* Commonwealth Secretariat GBR. Dist: Stylus Publishing, LLC.

Commonwealth Secretariat Staff, contrib. by. Commonwealth Ministers Reference Book 2010. 2010. (ENG.). 380p. pap. 57.95 *(978-0-9563722-4-6(4))* Commonwealth Secretariat GBR. Dist: Stylus Publishing, LLC.

Commonwealth Secretariat Staff, contrib. by. Commonwealth Ministers Reference Book 2011. 2011. 368p. pap. 57.95 ***(978-0-9563722-6-0(0))*** Commonwealth Secretariat GBR. Dist: Stylus Publishing, LLC.

Congressional Review ACT: Hearing Before the Subcommittee on Commercial & Administrative Law of the Committee on the Judiciary, House of Representatives, One Hundred Tenth Congress, First Session, November 6, 2007. 2009. iii, 51p. *(978-0-16-082687-0(X)*, 552-070-38704-8) United States Government Printing Office.

Copley, Paul A. Essentials of Accounting for Governmental & Not-For-Profit Organizations. 11th ed. 2012. (ENG., Illus.). 480p. (C). pap. 145.33 ***(978-0-07-802545-7(1)***, 0078025451) McGraw-Hill Cos., The.

Cram101 Textbook Reviews. Outlines & Highlights for Defending Government: Why Big Government Works [with Mysearchlab] by Max Neiman. 2011. 122p. pap. 28.95 ***(978-1-61905-066-2(8))*** Cram101 Inc.

—Outlines & Highlights for Managerial Discretion in Government Decision Making: Beyond the Street Level by Jacqueline Vaughn. 2011. 62p. pap. 27.95 ***(978-1-61905-025-9(0))*** Cram101 Inc.

Cullen, Roy. The Poverty of Corrupt Nations. 2008. (ENG.). 228p. pap. 19.95 *(978-0-9781600-9-8(6))* Dundurn CAN. Dist: Ingram Pub. Services.

Cutting the Federal Government's Energy Bill: An Examination of the Sustainable Federal Government Executive Order: Hearing Before the Federal Financial Management, Government Information, Federal Services, & International Security Subcommittee of the Committee on Homeland Security & Governmental Affairs, United States Senate, of the One Hundred Eleventh Congress, Second Session, January 27, 2010. 2011. (Illus.). iii, 106p. ***(978-0-16-087892-3(6)***, 552-070-42347-8) United States Government Printing Office.

Cyber Insecurity: Hackers Are Penetrating Federal Systems & Critical Infrastructure: Hearing Before the Subcommittee on Emerging Threats, Cybersecurity, & Science & Technology of the Committee on Homeland Security, House of Representatives, One Hundred Tenth Congress, First Session, April 19, 2007. 2009. (Illus.). iv, 69p. *(978-0-16-083561-2(5)*, 552-070-39279-3) United States Government Printing Office.

D'Agostino, Davi M. & Williams, McCoy. Hurricane Katrina: Comprehensive Policies & Procedures are Needed to Ensure Appropriate Use of & Accountability for International Assistance. 2006. (Illus.). 51p. (C). pap. 20.00 *(978-1-4223-0622-2(4))* DIANE Publishing Co.

De Lancer Julnes, Patria & Holzer, Marc, eds. Performance Measurement: Building Theory, Improving Practice. 2008. (ASPA Classics Ser.). (ENG.). 208p. 77.95 *(978-0-7656-2037-8(5))*; pap. 39.95 *(978-0-7656-2038-5(3))* Sharpe, M.E. Inc.

Departments of Labor, Health & Human Services, Education, & Related Agencies Appropriations for 2009: Hearings Before a Subcommittee of the Committee on Appropriations, House of Representatives, One Hundred Tenth Congress, Second Session. 2007. (Illus.). *(978-0-16-081317-7(4)*, 552-070-37665-8 (pt. 1)); *(978-0-16-081253-8(4)*, 552-070-37665-8 (pt. 1)); *(978-0-16-081315-3(8)*, 552-070-37665-8 (pt. 1)); *(978-0-16-081273-6(9)*, 552-070-37665-8 (pt. 1)); *(978-0-16-081227-9(5)*, 552-070-37665-8 (pt. 1)) United States Government Printing Office.

Departments of Labor, Health & Human Services, Education, & Related Agencies Appropriations for 2010: Hearings Before a Subcommittee of the Committee on Appropriations, House of Representatives, One Hundred Eleventh Congress, First Session. 2009. (Illus.). *(978-0-16-083638-1(7)*, 552-070-39255-6 (pt. 1)); *(978-0-16-083663-3(8)*, 552-070-39255-6 (pt. 1)); *(978-0-16-083532-2(1)*, 552-070-39255-6 (pt. 1)) United States Government Printing Office.

Departments of Labor, Health & Human Services, Education, & Related Agencies Appropriations for 2011: Hearings Before a Subcommittee of the Committee on Appropriations, House of Representatives, One Hundred Eleventh Congress, Second Session. 2010. (Illus.). *(978-0-16-085706-5(6)*, 552-070-40856-8 (pt. 1)); *(978-0-16-087203-7(0)*, 552-070-40856-8 (pt. 1)); *(978-0-16-086753-8(3)*, 552-070-40856-8 (pt. 1)); *(978-0-16-087230-3(8)*, 552-070-40856-8 (pt. 1)); *(978-0-16-085616-7(7)*, 552-070-40856-8 (pt. 1)); *(978-0-16-085617-4(5)*, 552-070-40856-8 (pt. 1)); *(978-0-16-085614-3(0)*, 552-070-40856-8 (pt. 1)); *(978-0-16-085615-0(9)*, 552-070-40856-8 (pt. 1)) United States Government Printing Office.

Departments of Transportation, & Housing & Urban Development, & Related Agencies Appropriations for 2009: Hearings Before a Subcommittee of the Committee on Appropriations, House of Representatives, One Hundred Tenth Congress, Second Session. 2008. (Illus.). *(978-0-16-080669-8(0)*, 552-070-37268-7 (pt. 1)); *(978-0-16-080668-1(2)*, 552-070-37268-7 (pt. 1)); *(978-0-16-080670-4(4)*, 552-070-37268-7 (pt. 1)) United States Government Printing Office.

Departments of Transportation, & Housing & Urban Development, & Related Agencies Appropriations for 2010: Hearings Before a Subcommittee of the Committee on Appropriations, House of Representatives, One Hundred Eleventh Congress, First Session. 2009. (Illus.). *(978-0-16-083308-3(6)*, 552-070-39136-3 (pt. 1)) United States Government Printing Office.

Departments of Transportation, & Housing & Urban Development, & Related Agencies Appropriations for 2011: Hearings Before a Subcommittee of the Committee on Appropriations, House of Representatives, One Hundred Eleventh Congress, Second Session. 2010. (Illus.). *(978-0-16-087430-7(0)*, 552-070-40673-5 (pt. 1)); *(978-0-16-085346-3(X)*, 552-070-40673-5 (pt. 1)); *(978-0-16-085347-0(8)*, 552-070-40673-5 (pt. 1)); *(978-0-16-085344-9(3)*, 552-070-40673-5 (pt. 1)) United States Government Printing Office.

Departments of Transportation, & Housing & Urban Development, & Related Agencies Appropriations for 2012: Hearings Before a Subcommittee of the Committee on Appropriations, House of Representatives, One Hundred Twelfth Congress, First Session. 2011. (Illus.). ***(978-0-16-088971-4(5)***, 552-070-43010-5 (pt. 1)); ***(978-0-16-088969-1(3)***, 552-070-43010-5 (pt. 1)); ***(978-0-16-088970-7(7)***, 552-070-43010-5 (pt. 1)) United States Government Printing Office.

Dimitrios, et al. Les Politiques Publiques Au Canada: Pouvoir, Conflits et Idéologies. (FRE.). xii, 392p. *(978-2-7637-8752-7(5))* Les Presses de l'Universite Laval.

Dumouchel, J. Robert & Abbey, Cherie D., eds. Government Assistance Almanac 2008-2009: The Guide to Federal Domestic Assistance. 21st rev. ed. 2009. 1201p. lib. bdg. 267.00 *(978-0-7808-0702-0(2))* Omnigraphics, Inc.

Dunsire, Andrew & Hood, Christopher. Cutback Management in Public Bureaucracies: Popular Theories & Observed Outcomes in Whitehall. 2010. (ENG.). 272p. pap. 41.00 *(978-0-521-13075-2(1))* Cambridge Univ. Pr.

Dutil, Patrice, et al. The Service State: Rhetoric, Reality & Promise. 2010. (Governance Ser.). (ENG.). 224p. pap. *(978-0-7766-0743-6(X))* Univ. of Ottawa Pr./Presses de l'Universite d'Ottawa.

Dziobek, Linda. Worldwide Government Directory with International Organizations 2010, 01 vols. Dziobek, Linda, ed. rev. ed. 2010. 1984p. pap. 559.00 *(978-0-87289-662-8(5))* CQ Pr.

Egeberg, Morten, ed. Multilevel Union Administration: The Transformation of Executive Politics in Europe. 2006. (Palgrave studies in European Union Politics Ser.). (ENG., Illus.). 248p. 95.00 *(978-1-4039-9765-4(9))* Palgrave Macmillan.

Eisner, Marc Allen, et al. Contemporary Regulatory Policy: 2nd Edition. 2nd ed. 2006. (Illus.). 340p. pap. 26.00 *(978-1-58826-411-4(4))* Rienner, Lynne Pubs.

Eliadis, Pearl, et al, eds. Evaluation: Seeking Truth or Power? 2011. (ENG.). 240p. 59.95 *(978-1-4128-1141-5(4))* Transaction Pubs.

Ellig, Jerry, et al. Government Performance Reports. 2011. (ASPA Series in Public Administration & Public Policy Ser.). (ENG., Illus.). 321p. 59.95 *(978-1-4398-4464-9(X)*, CRC Press) Taylor & Francis Group GBR. Dist: Taylor & Francis Group.

Emison, Gerald Andrews. Practical Program Evaluations: Getting from Ideas to Outcomes, 00 vols. rev. ed. 2006. (Illus.). 112p. per. 33.00 *(978-0-87289-302-3(2))* CQ Pr.

Encyclopedia of Governmental Advisory Organizations, 3.0. 26th ed. 2011. pap. 1073.00 *(978-1-4144-5900-4(9))* Cengage Gale.

Energy Efficiency at the U.S. Department of Veterans Affairs: Hearing Before the Committee on Veterans' Affairs, U.S. House of Representatives, One Hundred Eleventh Congress, First Session, September 30, 2009. 2010. (Illus.). iv, 104p. *(978-0-16-085896-3(8)*, 552-070-41092-9) United States Government Printing Office.

Ensuring a Merit-Based Employment System: An Examination of the Merit Systems Protection Board & the Office of Special Counsel: Hearing Before the Subcommittee on Federal Workforce, Postal Service, & the District of Columbia of the Committee on Oversight & Government Reform, House of Representatives, One Hundred Tenth Congress, First Session, July 12, 2007. 2009. iii, 176p. *(978-0-16-084568-0(8)*, 552-070-40090-7) United States Government Printing Office.

Ethridge, Marcus. The Case for Gridlock: Democracy, Organized Power, & the Legal Foundations of American Government. 2010. (ENG., Illus.). 240p. 68.50 *(978-0-7391-4237-0(2))* Lexington Bks.

Ethridge, Marcus E. The Case for Gridlock: Democracy, Organized Power, & the Legal Foundations of American Government. 2011. (ENG.). 240p. pap. 29.95 ***(978-0-7391-4238-7(0))*** Lexington Bks.

Europa Publications. International Directory of Government 2009. 6th ed. 2009. 728p. 760.00 *(978-1-85743-538-2(9))* Routledge.

Europa Publications, ed. The International Directory of Government 2010. 7th rev. ed. 2010. (ENG.). 750p. 760.00 *(978-1-85743-560-3(5))* Routledge.

—The International Directory of Government 2011. 8th rev. ed. 2011. (ENG.). 752p. 795.00 *(978-1-85743-615-0(6))* Routledge.

European Commission Staff, contrib. by. Labour Market Studies. (Illus.). 218p. *(978-92-827-8747-2(8))* European Commission BEL. Dist: Balogh International, Inc.

Examining the Federal Advisory Committee ACT: Current Issues & Developments: Hearing Before the Subcommittee on Information Policy, Census, & National Archives of the Committee on Oversight & Government Reform, House of Representatives, One Hundred Tenth Congress, Second Session, April 2, 2008. 2008. iii, 86p. *(978-0-16-082071-7(5)*, 552-070-38227-5) United States Government Printing Office.

Exploring the National Criminal Justice Commission ACT of 2009: Hearing Before the Subcommittee on Crime & Drugs of the Committee on the Judiciary, United States Senate, One Hundred Eleventh Congress, First Session, June 11, 2009. 2010. (Illus.). iv, 184p. *(978-0-16-086235-9(3)*, 552-070-41326-0) United States Government Printing Office.

Farrell, Ryan M. & Becker, Victoria D., eds. Opportunities for Federal Belt-Tightening. 2011. (Economic Issues, Problems & Perspectives Ser.). 215.00 *(978-1-61324-587-3(4))* Nova Science Pubs., Inc.

Federal Financial Statements for Fiscal Year 2006: Fiscal Outlook, Management Weaknesses & Consequences: Hearing Before the Subcommittee on Government Management, Organization, & Procurement of the Committee on Oversight & Government Reform, House of Representatives, One Hundred Tenth Congress, First Session, March 20, 2007. 2007. (Illus.). iii, 116p. *(978-0-16-079207-6(X)*, 552-070-36313-1) United States Government Printing Office.

Federal Financial Statements for Fiscal Year 2007: Fiscal Outlook, Management Weaknesses & Consequences: Hearing Before the Subcommittee on Government Management, Organization, & Procurement of the Committee on Oversight & Government Reform, House of Representatives, One Hundred Tenth Congress, Second Session, June 5, 2008. 2008. (Illus.). iii, 95p. *(978-0-16-082468-5(0)*, 552-070-38511-8) United States Government Printing Office.

The Federal Government's Human Resource Management: Hearing Before the Subcommittee on Federal Workforce, Postal Service, & the District of Columbia of the Committee on Oversight & Government Reform, House of Representatives, One Hundred Eleventh Congress, First Session, April 22, 2009. 2009. (Illus.). iv, 213p. *(978-0-16-083930-6(0)*, 552-070-39619-5) United States Government Printing Office.

Federal Information Security: Current Challenges & Future Policy Considerations: Hearing Before the Subcommittee on Government Management, Organization, & Procurement of the Committee on Oversight & Government Reform, House of Representatives, One Hundred Eleventh Congress, Second Session, March 24, 2010. 2011. (Illus.). iii, 106p. ***(978-0-16-089044-4(6)***, 552-070-43076-8) United States Government Printing Office.

Federal IT Security: A Review of H.R. 4791: Joint Hearing Before the Subcommittee on Information Policy, Census, & National Archives & the Subcommittee on Government Management, Organization, & Procurement of the Committee on Oversight & Government Reform, House of Representatives, One Hundred Tenth Congress, Second Session, on H.R. 4791 to Amend Title 44, United States Code, to Strengthen Requirements for Ens. 2008. (Illus.). iii, 121p. *(978-0-16-081988-9(1)*, 552-070-38160-1) United States Government Printing Office.

Federal Procurement & the Three-Percent Set Aside: Hearing Before the Subcommittee on Economic Opportunity of the Committee on Veterans' Affairs, U.S. House of Representatives, One Hundred Tenth Congress, First Session, July 12, 2007. 2008. iv, 107p. *(978-0-16-081453-2(7)*, 552-070-37818-9) United States Government Printing Office.

Federal Register Office, compiled by. The United States Government Manual 2009-2010. rev. ed. 2009. (ENG., Illus.). 682p. pap. 30.00 *(978-0-16-083949-8(1)*, Office of the Federal Register) United States Government Printing Office.

Federal Rulemaking & the Regulatory Process: Hearing Before the Subcommittee on Commercial & Administrative Law of the Committee on the Judiciary, House of Representatives, One Hundred Eleventh Congress, Second Session, July 27, 2010. 2010. iii, 210p. ***(978-0-16-087413-0(0)***, 552-070-42106-8) United States Government Printing Office.

Financial Regulators. 2008. 132p. (C). pap. 69.00 *(978-1-60692-042-8(1))* Nova Science Pubs., Inc.

Financial Services & General Government Appropriations for 2009: Hearings Before a Subcommittee of the Committee on Appropriations, House of Representatives, One Hundred Tenth Congress, Second Session. 2008. (Illus.). *(978-0-16-080665-0(8)*, 552-070-37263-6 (pt. 2)) United States Government Printing Office.

Financial Services & General Government Appropriations for 2010: Hearings Before a Subcommittee of the Committee on Appropriations, House of Representatives, One Hundred Eleventh Congress, First Session. 2009. (Illus.). *(978-0-16-083658-9(1)*, 552-070-39369-2 (pt. 1)); *(978-0-16-083657-2(3)*, 552-070-39369-2 (pt. 1)); *(978-0-16-083655-8(7)*, 552-070-39369-2 (pt. 1)) United States Government Printing Office.

Financial Services & General Government Appropriations for 2011: Hearings Before a Subcommittee of the Committee on Appropriations, House of Representatives, One Hundred Eleventh Congress, First Session. 2010. (Illus.). *(978-0-16-087442-0(4)*, 552-070-41017-1 (pt. 1)); *(978-0-16-087465-9(3)*, 552-070-41017-1 (pt. 1)); *(978-0-16-087464-2(5)*, 552-070-41017-1 (pt. 1)); *(978-0-16-085846-8(1)*, 552-070-41017-1 (pt. 1)); *(978-0-16-085800-0(3)*, 552-070-41017-1 (pt. 1)); *(978-0-16-087447-5(5)*, 552-070-41017-1 (pt. 1)); *(978-0-16-085818-5(6)*, 552-070-41017-1 (pt. 1)); *(978-0-16-085819-2(4)*, 552-070-41017-1 (pt. 1)) United States Government Printing Office.

Financial Services & General Government Appropriations for Fiscal Year 2009: Hearings Before a Subcommittee of the Committee on Appropriations, United States Senate, One Hundred Tenth Congress, Second Session, on H.R. 7323/S. 3260, an ACT Making Appropriations for Financial Services & General Government for the Fiscal Year Ending September 30, 2009, & for Other Purposes: Commodity Futures Trading Commission, Consumer Product Safety Commission, Department of the Treasur. 2009. (Illus.). iii, 418p. *(978-0-16-082781-5(7)*, 552-070-38780=3) United States Government Printing Office.

Flinders, Matthew. Delegated Governance & the British State: Walking without Order. 2008. (ENG., Illus.). 296p. 110.00 *(978-0-19-927160-3(7))* Oxford Univ. Pr., Inc.

Flynn, Norman. Public Sector Management. 5th ed. 2007. (Illus.). 328p. (C). 146.00 *(978-1-4129-2992-9(X)*, B2992XC); per. 60.00 *(978-1-4129-2993-6(8)*, B2992XP) SAGE Pubns., Ltd. GBR. Dist: SAGE Pubns., Inc.

Forje, John W. The Challenges of Administrative Political & Developmental Renewal in Africa: Emerging Issues. 2011. (African Political, Economic, & Security Issues Ser.). 214p. pap. 43.00 *(978-1-61209-026-9(5))* Nova Science Pubs., Inc.

—The Challenges of Administrative Political & Developmental Renewal in Africa: Essays on Rethinking Government & Reorganization. (African Political, Economic, & Security Issues Ser.). 2011. xvi, 285p. pap. 43.00 *(978-1-61209-027-6(3))* 2009. 69.00 *(978-1-60741-266-3(7))* Nova Science Pubs., Inc.

Formal Rulemaking & Judicial Review: Protecting Jobs & the Economy with Greater Regulatory Transparency & Accountability: Hearing Before the Subcommittee on Courts, Commercial & Administrative Law of the Committee on the Judiciary, House of Representatives, One Hundred Twelfth Congress, First Session, May 31, 2011. 2011. iii, 236p. ***(978-0-16-089656-9(8)***, 552-070-43545-0) United States Government Printing Office.

Friedman, Barry D. Regulation in the Regan-Bush Era: The Eruption of Presidential Influence. 2009. (ENG.). 272p. (C). pap. 26.95 *(978-0-8229-6052-2(4))* Univ. of Pittsburgh Pr.

Full Committee Hearing on Small Business Participation in the Federal Procurement Marketplace: Hearing Before the Committee on Small Business, United States House of Representatives, One Hundred Eleventh Congress, Second Session, Hearing Held March 24, 2010. 2010. (Illus.). v, 361p. *(978-0-16-086241-0(8)*, 552-070-41332-4) United States Government Printing Office.

Full Committee Hearing Reducing the Regulatory Burden on Small Business: Improving the Regulatory Flexibility ACT. 2007. (Illus.). v, 90p. *(978-0-16-080051-1(X)*, 552-070-36817-5) United States Government Printing Office.

Funkhouser, Mark. Honest, Competent Government: The Promise of Performance Auditing. 2008. 84p. *(978-0-89413-634-4(8))* Institute of Internal Auditors, Inc.

Gale Editor, ed. Government Research Directory, 2 vols. 27th ed. 2011. 1195p. pap. 960.00 *(978-1-4144-5961-5(0))* Cengage Gale.

GAO Report on Duplication of Government Programs; Focus on Welfare & Related Programs: Hearing Before the Subcommittee on Human Resources of the Committee on Ways & Means, U.S. House of Representatives, One Hundred Twelfth Congress, First Session, April 5, 2011. 2011. (Illus.). iii, 97p. ***(978-0-16-090124-9(3)***, 552-070-43831-9) United States Government Printing Office.

Gauld, Robin, et al. Dangerous Enthusiasms: E-Government, Computer Failure & Information System Development. 2006. (Illus.). 160p. (C). pap. 39.95 *(978-1-877372-34-6(X))* Otago University Pr. NZL. Dist: International Specialized Bk. Services.

Geiger, Dale. Cost Management & Control in Government: Leadership Driven Management's Role in Fighting the Cost War. 2011. 220p. pap. 29.95 *(978-1-60649-217-8(9))* Business Expert Pr.

George, Roger Z. & Rishikof, Harvey, eds. The National Security Enterprise: Navigating the Labyrinth. 2011. (ENG., Illus.). 384p. pap. 32.95 *(978-1-58901-698-9(X))* Georgetown Univ. Pr.

Getting to Better Government: Focusing on Performance: Hearing Before the Federal Financial Management, Government Information, Federal Services, & International Security Subcommittee of the Committee on Homeland Security & Governmental Affairs, United States Senate of the One Hundred Eleventh Congress, First Session, September 24, 2009. 2010. (Illus.). iii, 189p. *(978-0-16-087013-2(5)*, 552-070-41872-5) United States Government Printing Office.

Gilardi, Fabrizio. Delegation in the Regulatory State: Independent Regulatory Agencies in Western Europe. (Illus.). 200p. 2009. pap. 50.00 *(978-1-84844-812-4(0))* 2008. (C). 119.00 *(978-1-84720-447-9(3))* Elgar, Edward Publishing, Inc.

Ginsburg, Tom. Administrative Law & Governance in Asia: Comparative Perspectives. Chen, Albert H. Y., ed. 2008. (Routledge Law in Asia Ser.). (ENG., Illus.). 400p. (C). pap. 47.95 *(978-0-415-77731-5(3))* Routledge.

Goodsell, Charles T. Mission Mystique: Belief Systems in Public Agencies, 00 vols. rev. ed. 2010. (Illus.). pap. 35.00 *(978-1-933116-75-4(7))* CQ Pr.

Gormley, William T., Jr. & Balla, Steven J. Bureaucracy & Democracy: Accountability & Performance, 00 vols. 2nd rev. ed. 2007. 220p. (C). pap. 51.00 *(978-0-87289-347-4(2))* 3rd rev. ed. 2012. (Illus.). 336p. pap. 51.00 ***(978-1-60871-717-0(8))*** CQ Pr.

Government 2.0: Advancing America into the 21st Century & a Digital Future: Hearing Before the Federal Financial Management, Government Information, Federal Services, & International Security Subcommittee of the Committee on Homeland Security & Governmental Affairs, United States Senate, of the One Hundred Eleventh Congress, First Session, April 28, 2009. 2009. iii, 92p. (J). *(978-0-16-084478-2(9)*, 552-070-40001-0) United States Government Printing Office.

Government Accountability Office (U.S.) Staff, compiled by. Government Auditing Standards 2007. rev. ed. 2007. (ENG.). 228p. pap. 12.50 *(978-0-16-078028-8(4)*, Government Accountability Office) United States Government Printing Office.

Government Institutes Staff. Office of Management & Budget 2009, Vol. 5. 2009. pap. 82.00 *(978-1-60590-289-0(6))* Bernan Assocs.

Government Research Directory. 26th ed. 2011. pap. 914.00 *(978-1-4144-4722-3(1))* Cengage Gale.

Great Britain, National Audit Office Staff, contrib. by. The Efficiency Programme: A Second Review of Progress. 2007. (Illus.). 53p. pap. (978-0-10-294438-9(5)) Stationery Office, The.

Grisinger, Joanna L. The Unwieldy American State: Administrative Politics since the New Deal. 2012. (ENG.). 328p. 85.00 **(978-1-107-00432-0(2))** Cambridge Univ. Pr.

Halachmi, Arie & Boorsma, Peter B. Inter & Intra Government Arrangements for Productivity: An Agency Approach. 2010. (ENG.). 240p. pap. 159.00 (978-1-4419-5015-4(X), 144195015X) Springer.

Heinzerling, Lisa & Tushnet, Mark V. The Regulatory & Administrative State: Materials, Cases, Comments. 2006. (Twenty-First Century Legal Education Ser.). (Illus.). 672p. (C). 99.00 (978-0-19-518931-5(0)) Oxford Univ. Pr., Inc.

Henley Media Group Limited, creator. Commonwealth Ministers Reference Book 2006. 2007. (Commonwealth Ministers Reference Books Ser.). (Illus.). 224p. per. 65.00 (978-0-9546572-6-0(8)) Commonwealth Secretariat GBR. Dist: Stylus Publishing, LLC.

Heyen, Erk, ed. Yearbook of European Administrative History, Vol. 18: Colonial Administration in Africa between Central Policy & Local Reality. 2007. 419p. 89.00 (978-3-8329-2333-4(0)) Nomos Verlagsgesellschaft DEU. Dist: International Specialized Bk. Services.

Heyen, Erk Volkmar, et al, eds. Yearbook of European Administrative History Vol. 20: Technological Development Between Economy & Administration in Great Britain & Germany (19th/20th C.) 2008. 372p. 89.00 (978-3-8329-4073-7(1)) Nomos Verlagsgesellschaft DEU. Dist: International Specialized Bk. Services.

Ho, Henry W. L. Customer Value Delivery in B2b Virtual Network Organisations. 2010. 180p. pap. (978-3-8383-7812-1(1)) Lambert Academic Publishing.

H.R. 2635, the Carbon-Neutral Government ACT of 2007: Hearing Before the Subcommittee on Government Management, Organization, & Procurement of the Committee on Oversight & Government Reform, House of Representatives, One Hundred Tenth Congress, First Session, on H.R. 2635 ... May 17, 2007. 2008. (Illus.). iii, 100p. (978-0-16-081018-3(3), 552-070-37531-7) United States Government Printing Office.

H.R. 5840: The Insurance Information ACT of 2008: Hearing Before the Subcommittee on Capital Markets, Insurance, & Government Sponsored Enterprises of the Committee on Financial Services, U.S. House of Representatives, One Hundred Tenth Congress, Second Session, June 10, 2008. 2008. v, 123p. (978-0-16-081989-6(X), 552-070-38161-9) United States Government Printing Office.

Hume, Robert. How Courts Impact Federal Administrative Behavior. 2009. (Routledge Studies in North American Politics Ser.). (ENG., Illus.). 174p. 125.00 (978-0-415-99927-4(8)) Routledge.

Hume, Robert J. How Courts Impact Federal Administrative Behavior. 2012. (ENG., Illus.). 164p. pap. 39.95 **(978-0-415-80741-8(7))** Routledge.

ICC. Building Department Administration Workbook. 2009. pap. 38.00 (978-1-58001-793-0(2)) International Code Council.

Implementing FOIA: Does the Bush Administration's Executive Order Improve Processing?: Hearing Before the Subcommittee on Government Management, Finance, & Accountability of the Committee on Government Reform, House of Representatives, One Hundred Ninth Congress, Second Session, July 26, 2006. 2008. (Illus.). iii, 195p. (978-0-16-082054-0(5), 552-070-38213-5) United States Government Printing Office.

The Improper Payments Information ACT: Are Agencies Meeting the Requirements of the Law?: Hearing Before the Subcommittee on Government Management, Finance, & Accountability of the Committee on Government Reform, House of Representatives, One Hundred Ninth Congress, Second Session, April 5, 2006. 2008. iii, 87p. (978-0-16-081169-2(4), 552-070-37593-7) United States Government Printing Office.

Improving Federal Employment of People with Disabilities: Hearing Before the Oversight of Government Management, the Federal Workforce, & the District of Columbia Subcommittee of the Committee on Homeland Security & Governmental Affairs, United States Senate, One Hundred Twelfth Congress, First Session, February 16, 2011. 2011. iii, 100p. **(978-0-16-089357-5(7)**, 552-070-43344-9) United States Government Printing Office.

Improving Federal Program Management Using Performance Information: Hearing Before the Federal Financial Management, Government Information, Federal Services, & International Security Subcommittee of the Committee on Homeland Security & Governmental Affairs, United States Senate, One Hundred Tenth Congress, Second Session, July 24, 2008. 2009. (Illus.). iii, 138p. (978-0-16-083569-8(0), 552-070-39287-4) United States Government Printing Office.

Innovations in American Government, 1986-1996. 55p. pap. 30.00 (978-0-7881-4471-4(5)) DIANE Publishing Co.

Inspectors General: Independence & Integrity: Hearing Before the Subcommittee on Government Management, Organization, & Procurement of the Committee on Oversight & Government Reform, House of Representatives, One Hundred Tenth Congress, First Session, June 20, 2007. 2008. iii, 151p. (978-0-16-081023-7(X), 552-070-37536-8) United States Government Printing Office.

Inter-American Development Bank, Institutional Capacity and Finance Sector PRODEV Staff & Centro Latinoamericano de Administración para el Desarrollo Staff, contrib. by. Modelo Abierto de Gestión para Resultados en el Sector Público. 2007. (SPA., Illus.). 67p. (978-980-6125-49-0(5)) Inter-American Development Bank.

Interagency Coordination of Grants & Contracts in Iraq & Afghanistan: Progress, Obstacles, & Plans: Hearing Before the Oversight & Investigations Subcommittee of the Committee on Armed Services, House of Representatives, One Hundred Eleventh Congress, Second Session, Hearing Held March 23, 2010. 2010. (Illus.). iii, 78p. (978-0-16-086537-4(9), 552-070-41535-1) United States Government Printing Office.

Interagency National Security Reform: Pragmatic Steps Towards a More Integrated Future: Hearing Before the Oversight & Investigations Subcommittee of the Committee on Armed Services, House of Representatives, One Hundred Eleventh Congress, Second Session, Hearing Held June 9, 2010. 2010. (Illus.). iii, 87p. (978-0-16-086541-1(7), 552-070-41539-4) United States Government Printing Office.

International Directory of Government 2008. 5th rev. ed. 2008. 720p. 720.00 (978-1-85743-484-2(6), Europa Pubns.

IT Procurement & Disposal: Application of the Federal Government's Green Policies in the Life Cycle Management of IT Assets: Hearing Before the Subcommittee on Government Management, Organization, & Procurement of the Committee on Oversight & Government Reform, House of Representatives, One Hundred Eleventh Congress, First Session, October 27, 2009. 2010 (Illus.). ii, 128p. (978-0-16-086735-4(5), 552-070-41657-9) United States Government Printing Office.

IT Programs at Risk: Is It Too Late to Save $12 Billion?: Hearing Before the Federal Financial Management, Government Information, & International Security Subcommittee of the Committee on Homeland Security & Governmental Affairs, United States Senate, One Hundred Ninth Congress, Second Session, September 7, 2006. 2007. (Illus.). iii, 61p. (978-0-16-079516-9(8), 552-070-36494-3) United States Government Printing Office.

John P. McGovern MD Center for Environmental and Regulatory Affairs Staff, contrib. by. Shattered Dreams: 100 Stories of Government Abuse. 5th ed. 2007. (Illus.). 119p. (978-0-9665961-3-7(7)) National Ctr. for Public Policy Research.

Johnston, Michael, ed. Public Sector Corruption, 4 vols. 2010. (SAGE Library of Political Science Ser.). (Illus.). 1632p. 995.00 (978-1-84920-604-4(X), B06044C) SAGE Pubns., Ltd. GBR. Dist: SAGE Pubns., Inc.

Julnes, Patria de Lancer. International Handbook of Practice-Based Performance Management. 2007. 700p. pap. 69.95 (978-1-4129-4013-9(3)) SAGE Pubns., Inc.

Kanstrup, Anne Marie, et al, eds. Perspectives on E-Government: Technology & Infrastructure, Politics & Organisation, Interaction & Communication. 2007. 250p. pap. 43.95 (978-87-7307-786-3(0)) Aalborg Universitetsforlag DNK. Dist: International Specialized Bk. Services.

Kee, James Edwin & Newcomer, Kathryn E. Transforming Public & Nonprofit Organizations: Stewardship for Leading Change. 2008. (978-1-56726-227-8(9)) Management Concepts, Inc.

Keehley, Patricia & Abercrombie, Neil. Benchmarking in the Public & Nonprofit Sectors: Best Practices for Achieving Performance Breakthroughs. 2nd ed. 2008. (ENG., Illus.). 256p. 55.00 (978-0-7879-9831-8(1), Jossey-Bass) Wiley, John & Sons, Inc.

Kessler, Thomas G. & Kelley, Patricia. Federal IT Capital Planning & Investment Control. 2008. (978-1-56726-222-3(8)) Management Concepts, Inc.

Kettl, Donald F. The Next Government of the United States: Why Our Institutions Fail Us & How to Fix Them. 2008. (ENG., Illus.). 304p. 25.95 (978-0-393-05112-4(9), 5112) Norton, W. W. & Co., Inc.

Kim, Kwon-Jip & Pak, Su-Gyong. Han'guk Haengjong Chojingnon. 4th ed. 2009. (KOR., Illus.). 480p. (978-89-91165-89-2(3)) I-hwa Publishing Co.

Kimbrell, Jody D. Bankers: the Only Profession That Drove Jesus to Violence: A True Story of Lies, Deceit, & Deception. 2011. pap. 9.99 (978-1-61739-164-4(6)) Tate Publishing & Enterprises, LLC.

King, Roger. The Regulatory State in an Age of Governance: Soft Words & Big Sticks. 2007. (ENG.). 248p. 100.00 (978-0-230-50039-6(0)) Palgrave Macmillan.

Koontz, Linda D. Continuity of Operations: Selected Agencies Could Improve Planning for Use of Alternate Facilities & Telework During Disruptions. 2006. 67p. (C). pap. 20.00 (978-1-4223-0789-2(1)) DIANE Publishing Co.

—Electronic Government: Agencies Face Challenges in Implementing New Federal Employee Identification Standard. 2006. (Illus.). 55p. (C). pap. 20.00 (978-1-4223-0739-7(5)) DIANE Publishing Co.

—Personal Information: Agency & Reseller Adherence to Key Privacy Principles. 2006. (Illus.). 87p. (C). pap. 25.00 (978-1-4223-0714-4(X)) DIANE Publishing Co.

Koppell, Jonathan. The Politics of Quasi-Government: Hybrid Organizations & the Dynamics of Bureaucratic Control. 2006. (Theories of Institutional Design Ser.). (Illus.). 253p. pap. 38.99 (978-0-521-52560-2(8)) Cambridge Univ. Pr.

Lambsdorff, Johann Graf. The Institutional Economics of Corruption & Reform: Theory, Evidence, & Policy. 2007. (ENG., Illus.). 304p. 102.00 (978-0-521-87275-1(8)) Cambridge Univ. Pr.

Lee, Nancy R. & Kotler, Philip. Marketing in the Public Sector: A Roadmap for Improved Performance. 2006. (ENG., Illus.). 352p. pap. 39.99 (978-0-13-706086-3(6)) Wharton Schl. Publishing.

Lee, Paul. Federal Rulemaking & Regulations. 2009. (Congressional Policies, Practices & Procedures Ser.). 79.00 (978-1-60876-069-5(3)) Nova Science Pubs., Inc.

Lewis, David E. The Politics of Presidential Appointments: Political Control & Bureaucratic Performance. 2008. (Illus.). (C). 280p. 66.00 (978-0-691-13342-3(5)); (ENG., 312p. pap. 29.95 (978-0-691-13544-1(4)) Princeton Univ. Pr.

Loader. Beyond E-Government. 2007. 224p. 140.00 (978-0-415-37191-9(0)) Routledge.

—Beyond E-Government - Loader. 2007. 224p. 43.95 (978-0-415-37192-6(9)) Routledge.

Lægreid, Per & Verhoest, Koen, eds. Governance of Public Sector Organizations: Proliferation, Autonomy & Performance. 2010. (Governance & Public Management Ser.). (ENG., Illus.). 320p. 110.00 (978-0-230-23820-6(3)) Palgrave Macmillan.

Mabururu, Michael. Gender Discrimination. 2011. 140p. pap. **(978-3-8443-0751-1(6))** Lambert Academic Publishing.

Mahmood, Sohail. Good Governance Reforms Agenda in Pakistan: Current Challenges. 2006. 244p. 169.00 (978-1-60021-418-9(5)) Nova Science Pubs., Inc.

—Reform of the Public Services in Pakistan. 2008. vi, 169p. pap. 50.00 (978-1-60456-528-7(4)) Nova Science Pubs., Inc.

Management Reform: Agencies Initial Efforts to Restructure Personnel Operations. 62p. pap. 20.00 (978-0-7881-7958-7(6)) DIANE Publishing Co.

Marlow, Michael L. The Myth of Fair & Efficient Government: Why the Government You Want Is Not the One You Get, 1 vol. 2011. (Illus.). 214p. 34.95 (978-0-313-39291-7(9), A3312C) Greenwood Publishing Group, Inc.

Mars, Laura. Canadian Environmental Directory 2010. Lang, Robert, ed. 2010. pap. 350.00 (978-1-59237-569-1(3)) Grey Hse. Publishing.

Materialy Plenarnogo Zasedaniia "Aktual'nye Problemy Ekspertnoi Deiatel'nosti Obshchestvennoi Palaty Rossiiskoi Federatsii" 26 Marta 2009 Goda. 2009. (RUS.). 135p. (978-5-94103-372-0(9)) Jurist.

Mayne, John & Zapico-Goni, Eduardo, eds. Monitoring Performance in the Public Sector: Future Directions from International Experience. 2007. (ENG.). 293p. (gr. 11). pap. 29.95 (978-1-4128-0632-9(1)) Transaction Pubs.

Menzel, Donald C. & White, Harvey L., eds. The State of Public Administration: Issues, Challenges, & Opportunities. 2011. (Illus.). 528p. (ENG.). 119.95 (978-0-7656-2504-5(0)); pap. 59.95 (978-0-7656-2505-2(9)) Sharpe, M.E. Inc.

Meuleman, Louis. Public Management & the Metagovernance of Hierarchies, Networks & Markets. 2008. (Contributions to Management Science Ser.). (Illus.). xiv, 399p. (C). 169.00 (978-3-7908-2053-9(9)) Springer.

Minogue. Regulatory Governance in Developing Countries. 2007. (CRC Series on Competition, Regulation & Development). (Illus.). 352p. (C). 150.00 (978-1-84542-612-5(6)) Elgar, Edward Publishing, Inc.

Minogue, Martin & Cariño, Ledivina, eds. Regulatory Governance in Developing Countries. 2008. (CRC Series on Competition, Regulation & Development Ser.). (Illus.). 352p. pap. 66.00 (978-1-84720-621-3(2)) Elgar, Edward Publishing, Inc.

Moran, Michael. The British Regulatory State: High Modernism & Hyper-Innovation. 2007. (ENG.). 256p. per. 45.00 (978-0-19-921921-6(4)) Oxford Univ. Pr., Inc.

Moravitz, Carl & Breul, Jonathan D. Integrating Performance & Budgets: The Budget Office of Tomorrow. Moravitz, Carl & Breul, Jonathan D., eds. 2007. (IBM Center for the Business of Government Book Ser.). (ENG., Illus.). 496p. 88.95 (978-0-7425-5831-1(2)); per. 37.95 (978-0-7425-5832-8(0)) Rowman & Littlefield Publishers, Inc.

More Security, Less Waste: What Makes Sense for Our Federal Cyber Defense: Hearing Before the Federal Financial Management, Government Information, Federal Services, & International Security Subcommittee of the Committee on Homeland Security & Governmental Affairs, United States Senate of the One Hundred Eleventh Congress, First Session, October 29, 2009. 2010. (Illus.). iii, 100p. (978-0-16-087054-5(2), 552-070-41911-0) United States Government Printing Office.

Moynihan, Donald P. The Dynamics of Performance Management: Constructing Information & Reform. 2nd rev. ed. 2008. (Public Management & Change Ser.). (ENG., Illus.). 264p. pap. 29.95 (978-1-58901-194-6(5)) Georgetown Univ. Pr.

The National Archives' Ability to Safeguard the Nation's Electronic Records: Hearing Before the Subcommittee on Information Policy, Census, & National Archives of the Committee on Oversight & Government Reform, House of Representatives, One Hundred Eleventh Congress, First Session, November 5, 2009. 2010. iii, 88p. (978-0-16-085594-7(8), 552-070-41582-3) United States Government Printing Office.

National Archives and Records Administration, compiled by. The United States Government Manual. 2011. (United States Government Manual Ser.). (ENG., Illus.). 602p. pap. 35.00 **(978-1-60175-837-8(5))** National Archives & Records Administration.

National Research Council. The Future of Federal Household Surveys: A Workshop Summary. 2011. (ENG.). 120p. pap. 30.00 **(978-0-309-21497-1(1))** National Academies Pr.

National Research Council Staff. Public Participation in Environmental Assessment & Decision Making. Dietz, Thomas & Stern, Paul C., eds. 2008. (ENG.). 322p. pap. 59.00 (978-0-309-12398-3(4)) National Academies Pr.

Newell, Terry, et al. The Trusted Leader: Building the Relationships that Make Government Work. 00 vols. 2nd rev. ed. 2011. (Illus.). 464p. 45.00 (978-1-60871-276-2(1)) CQ Pr.

Niemann, Arne. Explaining Decisions in the European Union. 2010. (ENG., Illus.). 384p. pap. 42.00 (978-0-521-14227-4(X)) Cambridge Univ. Pr.

Nikolov, George I. Cloud Computing & Government: Background, Benefits, Risks. 2011. (978-1-61761-784-3(9)) Nova Science Pubs., Inc.

Niven, Paul R. Balanced Scorecard: Step-by-Step for Government & Nonprofit Agencies. 2nd ed. 2008. (ENG., Illus.). 384p. 57.95 (978-0-470-18002-0(1), Wiley) Wiley, John & Sons, Inc.

Ockenden, Jonathan, et al. Reform of International Institutions: Towards a Commonwealth Agenda. 2009. (Economic Paper Ser.). (ENG., Illus.). 104p. pap. 32.95 (978-0-85092-897-6(4)) Commonwealth Secretariat GBR. Dist: Stylus Publishing, LLC.

Office of the Federal Register. The United States Government Manual. 2011. (United States Government Manual Ser.). (Illus.). 602p. pap. 30.00 **(978-1-59804-562-8(8))** National Archives & Records Administration.

Office of the Federal Register (U.S.) Staff, ed. The United States Government Manual 2011. rev. ed. 2011. (ENG.). 612p. pap. 30.00 **(978-0-16-087470-3(X)**, Office of the Federal Register) United States Government Printing Office.

Offline & Off-Budget: The Dismal State of Information Technology Planning in the Federal Government: Hearing Before the Federal Financial Management, Government Information, Federal Services, & International Security Subcommittee of the Committee on Homeland Security & Governmental Affairs, United States Senate, One Hundred Tenth Congress, Second Session, July 31, 2008. 2009. (Illus.). iii, 136p. (J). (978-0-16-083568-1(2), 552-070-39286-6) United States Government Printing Office.

Olshfski, Dorothy F. & Cunningham, Robert B. Agendas & Decisions: How State Government Executives & Middle Managers Make & Administer Policy. 2009. 167p. pap. 24.95 (978-0-7914-7324-5(4)) 2008. (Illus.). 157p. 50.00 (978-0-7914-7323-8(6)) State Univ. of New York Pr.

Omnigraphics, creator. Web Site Source Book: A Guide to Major U. S. Businesses, Organizations, Agencies, Institutions, & Other Information Resources on the World Wide Web. 13th ed. 2007. 2127p. pap. 194.00 (978-0-7808-1024-2(4)) Omnigraphics, Inc.

Ongaro, E. Public Management Reform & Modernization: Trajectories of Administrative Change in Italy, France, Greece, Portugal & Spain. 2010. (Illus.). 336p. 140.00 (978-1-84720-810-1(X)) Elgar, Edward Publishing, Inc.

Organisation for Economic Co-operation and Development Staff. Oecd Public Management Review - the Irish Public Service: Success Story to Sustained Success. 2008. (Illus.). 373p. pap. 63.00 (978-92-64-04325-1(X)) Organization for Economic Cooperation & Development.

—The State of the Public Service. 2008. (Illus.). 93p. pap. 63.00 (978-92-64-05594-0(0)) Organization for Economic Cooperation & Development.

O'Toole, Laurence J. & Meier, Kenneth J. Public Management: Organizations, Governance, & Performance. 2011. (ENG., Illus.). 332p. 73.00 (978-1-107-00441-2(1)) Cambridge Univ. Pr.

Oversight of Federal Financial Management: Hearing Before the Subcommittee on Government Management, Organization, & Procurement of the Committee on Oversight & Government Reform, House of Representatives, One Hundred Eleventh Congress, First Session, July 8, 2009. 2010. (Illus.). iii, 123p. (978-0-16-086574-9(3), 552-070-41572-6) United States Government Printing Office.

Parmenter, David. Key Performance Indicators for Government & Nonprofit Agencies: Implementing Winning KPIS. 2012. (ENG.). 309p. 49.95 **(978-0-470-94454-7(4)**, Wiley) Wiley, John & Sons, Inc.

Pautz, Michelle C. & Rinfret, Sara R. The Lilliputians of Environmental Regulation: A State Perspective. 2012. (ENG.). 224p. (C). 125.00 **(978-0-415-80815-6(4))** Routledge.

Payan, Tony. Cops Soldiers & Diplomats: Exp. 2007. (ENG.). 220p. pap. 29.50 (978-0-7391-2064-4(6)) Lexington Bks.

Perry, Penny, ed. Federal Staff Directory 2008: White House, Departments, Agencies, Biographies, 00 vols. 54th rev. ed. 2008. (Federal Staff Directory Ser.). 1776p. pap. 288.00 (978-0-87289-249-1(2)) CQ Pr.

—Federal Staff Directory 2010/Summer, 00 vols. 63rd rev. ed. 2010. 1728p. pap. 348.00 (978-0-87289-452-5(5)) CQ Pr.

—Federal Staff Directory 2011/Fall, 00 vols. 67th rev. ed. 2011. 1712p. pap. 365.00 (978-0-87289-633-8(1)) CQ Pr.

—Federal Staff Directory 2012/Winter, 00 vols. 68th rev. ed. 2011. 1680p. pap. 399.00 (978-0-87289-634-5(X)) CQ Pr.

—Federal Staff Directory Summer 2009: White House, Departments, Agencies, Biographies, 00 vols. 60th rev. ed. 2009. (Federal Staff Directory Ser.). (Illus.). 1752p. pap. 331.00 (978-0-87289-449-5(5)) CQ Pr.

—Federal Staff Directory, Winter 2011, 00 vols. 65th rev. ed. 2010. pap. 365.00 (978-0-87289-454-9(1)) CQ Pr.

"Perry, Penny" & Perry, Penny, eds. Federal Staff Directory 2011/Summer, 00 vols. 66th rev. ed. 2011. 1712p. pap. 365.00 (978-0-87289-632-1(3)) CQ Pr.

Peters, B. Guy. Comparative Administration Change & Reform: Lessons Learned. Ingraham, Patricia W. & Pierre, Jon, eds. 2010. (ENG., Illus.). 352p. (C). (978-0-7735-3659-3(0)) McGill-Queen's Univ. Pr.

Peterson, James A., et al. Risk Management for Park, Recreation, & Leisure Services: 5th Edition. 5th ed. 2008. (Illus.). 179p. pap. **(978-1-57167-538-5(8))** Sagamore Publishing, L.L.C.

Petit, Philippe & Gardere, Anne. Anticiper la Réforme Territoriale. 2010. (FRE., Illus.). 192p. (978-2-35740-059-7(5)) Media Conseil Communication, Edition.

Philpott, Don. A Guide to Federal Terms & Acronyms, 2 vols. 2011. (ENG.). 1220p. 175.00 (978-1-60590-712-3(X)) 2010. (978-1-60590-744-4(8)) Government Institutes.

Piotrowski, Suzanne J. Governmental Transparency in the Path of Administrative Reform. (Illus.). 139p. 2008. per. 24.95 (978-0-7914-7086-2(5)) 2007. 56.00 (978-0-7914-7085-5(7)) State Univ. of New York Pr.

Policies Affecting High-Tech Growth & Federal Adoption of Industry Best Practices: Hearing Before the Committee on Oversight & Government

Reform, House of Representatives, One Hundred Twelfth Congress, First Session, April 18, 2011. 2011. iii, 55p. (978-0-16-089670-5(3), 552-070-43554-9) United States Government Printing Office.

Pollitt, Christopher. New Perspectives on Public Services: Place & Technology. 2012. (ENG., Illus.). 272p. 65.00 (978-0-19-960383-1(9)) Oxford Univ. Pr., Inc.

Pollitt, Christopher & Bouckaert, Geert. Public Management Reform: A Comparative Analysis - New Public Management, Governance, & the Neo-Weberian State. 3rd ed. 2011. (ENG., Illus.). 392p. 125.00 (978-0-19-959508-2(9)); pap. 55.00 (978-0-19-959509-9(7)) Oxford Univ. Pr., Inc.

Privacy: The Use of Commercial Information Resellers by Federal Agencies: Hearing Before the Subcommittee on Information Policy, Census, & National Archives of the Committee on Oversight & Government Reform, House of Representatives, One Hundred Tenth Congress, Second Session, March 11, 2008. 2009. (Illus.). iii, 109p. (978-0-16-082619-1(5), 552-070-38673-8) United States Government Printing Office.

Prosser, Tony. The Regulatory Enterprise: Government, Regulation, & Legitimacy. 2010. (ENG.). 240p. 110.00 (978-0-19-957983-9(0)) Oxford Univ. Pr., Inc.

Protecting the Public Interest: Understanding the Threat of Agency Capture: Hearing Before the Subcommittee on Administrative Oversight & the Courts of the Committee on the Judiciary, United States Senate, One Hundred Eleventh Congress, Second Session, August 8, 2010. 2011. iii, 89p. (978-0-16-088460-3(8), 552-070-42672-8) United States Government Printing Office.

Rabin, Jack & Berman, Evan M., eds. Encyclopedia of Public Administration & Public Policy, Second Edition - Online/Print Version. 2007. (978-1-4200-6294-6(8)) Auerbach Pubs., Inc.

Radin, Beryl A. Federal Management Reform in a World of Contradictions. 2012. (Public Management & Change Ser.). (ENG.). 208p. pap. 29.95 (978-1-58901-892-1(3)) Georgetown Univ. Pr.

Radin, Beryl A. & Chanin, Joshua M. Federal Government Reorganization: A Policy & Management Perspective. 2008. 404p. pap. 75.95 (978-0-7637-5560-7(5)) Jones & Bartlett Learning, LLC.

Rahman, Taiabur. Parliamentary Control & Government Accountability in South Asia: A Comparative Analysis of Bangladesh, India & Sri Lanka. (ENG., Illus.). 272p. 2012. pap. 42.95 (978-0-415-53318-8(X)) 2007. 160.00 (978-0-415-40498-3(3)) Routledge.

Raising the Agencies' Grades: Protecting the Economy, Assuring Regulatory Quality & Improving Assessments of Regulatory Need: Hearing Before the Subcommittee on Courts, Commercial & Administrative Law of the Committee on the Judiciary, House of Representatives, One Hundred Twelfth Congress, First Session, March 29, 2011. 2011. (Illus.). iii, 144p. (978-0-16-089239-4(2), 552-070-43236-1) United States Government Printing Office.

Reducing Federal Agency Overreach: Modernizing the Regulatory Flexibility ACT: Hearing Before the Committee on Small Business, United States House of Representatives, One Hundred Twelfth Congress, First Session, Hearing Held March 30, 2011. 2011. iii, 71p. (978-0-16-088689-8(9), 552-070-42853-4) United States Government Printing Office.

The Refuse of the Federal Spending Binge II: How U.S. Taxpayers Are Paying Double for Failing Government Programs: Hearing Before the Committee on Oversight & Government Reform, House of Representatives, One Hundred Twelfth Congress, First Session, March 3, 2011. 2011. iii, 77p. (978-0-16-089355-1(0), 552-070-43342-2) United States Government Printing Office.

REINS ACT: Promoting Jobs & Expanding Freedom by Reducing Needless Regulations: Hearing Before the Subcommittee on Courts, Commercial & Administrative Law of the Committee on the Judiciary, House of Representatives, One Hundred Twelfth Congress, First Session, January 24, 2011. 2011. iv, 155p. (978-0-16-088594-5(9), 552-070-42770-8) United States Government Printing Office.

Revesz, Richard L. & Livermore, Michael A. Retaking Rationality: How Cost-Benefit Analysis Can Better Protect the Environment & Our Health, 1 vol. (ENG.). 2011. 264p. pap. 21.95 (978-0-19-976895-0(1)) 2008. 200p. 39.95 (978-0-19-536857-4(6)) Oxford Univ. Pr., Inc.

Richmond Law & Tax Staff, contrib. by. Europe, Vol. 1. 2006. (ENG., Illus.). 1122p. 455.00 (978-1-904501-10-7(9)) Oxford Univ. Pr., Inc.

Rist, Ray C. & Stame, Nicoletta. From Studies to Streams: Managing Evaluation Systems. 2011. (ENG., Illus.). 314p. pap. 29.95 (978-1-4128-1837-7(0)) Transaction Pubs.

Rist, Ray C., et al. Influencing Change: Capacity Building in Development & Evaluation. 2011. (World Bank Training Ser.). (ENG., Illus.). 302p. 30.00 (978-0-8213-8403-9(1), 9780821384039) World Bank Pubns.

—Influencing Change: Evaluation & Capacity Building. 2011. (Illus.). xxi, 275p. (978-0-8213-8497-8(X)) World Bank Pubns.

Roadmap for a More Efficient & Accountable Federal Government: Implementing the GPRA Modernization ACT: Joint Hearing Before the Oversight of Government Management, the Federal Workforce, & the District of Columbia Subcommittee & the Federal Financial Management, Government Information, Federal Services, & International Security Subcommittee of the Committee on Homeland Security & Governmental Affairs, United States Senate, One Hundred Twelfth Congress, 2011. (Illus.). iii, 140p. (978-0-16-090171-3(5), 552-070-43874-2) United States Government Printing Office.

Robertson, Robert E. Workplace Safety & Health: OSHA Could Improve Federal Agencies' Safety Programs with a More Strategic Approach to Its Oversight. 2006. (Illus.). 61p. (C). pap. 20.00 (978-1-4223-0728-1(X)) DIANE Publishing Co.

Rockwell, Stephen J. Indian Affairs & the Administrative State in the Nineteenth Century. 2010. (ENG.). 374p. 100.00 (978-0-521-19363-4(X)) Cambridge Univ. Pr.

Routledge Staff, creator. The International Directory of Government. 4th rev. ed. 2007. 764p. 680.00 (978-1-85743-276-3(2), RX6961) Routledge.

Running Out of Time: Telecommunications Transition Delays Wasting Millions of Federal Dollars: Hearing Before the Committee on Oversight & Government Reform, House of Representatives, One Hundred Eleventh Congress, Second Session, May 20, 2010. 2011. iii, 131p. (978-0-16-088316-3(4), 552-070-42621-3) United States Government Printing Office.

Savage, Steve. Police Reform: Forces for Change. 2008. (ENG.). 270p. 150.00 (978-0-19-921864-6(1)); 70.00 (978-0-19-921863-9(3)) Oxford Univ. Pr., Inc.

Scheidemann, Heike. Zwischen zwei Welten? Eine organisationssoziologische Analyse der (Re-)Konstruktion kommunaler Selbstbeschreibungen. 2008. (GER., Illus.). 284p. pap. (978-3-531-16479-3(1)) Westdeutscher Verlag GmbH.

Schutte, Nico & Schutte, Nico Eric. Public Service Strategic Leadership: A Competence Based Approach: Contemporary Issues, Concepts & Ideas. 2011. (Illus.). 376p. pap. (978-3-8433-8520-6(3)) Lambert Academic Publishing.

Sistare, Hannah S., et al, eds. Innovations in Human Resource Management: Getting the Public's Work Done in the 21st Century. 2008. (Transformational Trends in Governance & Democracy Ser.). (ENG.). 352p. pap. 53.95 (978-0-7656-2315-7(3)); (Illus.). 94.95 (978-0-7656-2314-0(5)) Sharpe, M.E. Inc.

Sommer. Public Sector Erp Issues in Change Management. 2007. (Illus.). 224p. (C). 119.00 (978-1-84542-006-2(3)) Elgar, Edward Publishing, Inc.

Song, Sung-Je. "Konggong Kigwan Ui Unyong e Kwanhan Pomnyul" Pigyopochok Yon'gu. 2008. 174p. (978-89-8323-885-6(2)) Korea Legislation Research Institute.

Sriraman, Bharath & Freiman, Viktor. Interdisciplinarity for the Twenty-First Century: Proceedings of the Third International Symposium on Mathematics & Its Connections to Arts & Sciences, Moncton 2009. 2010. (978-1-61735-181-5(4)); pap. (978-1-61735-180-8(6)); E-Book (978-1-61735-182-2(2)) Information Age Publishing, Inc.

Stalcup, George H. Personnel Practices: Conversions of Employees from Noncareer to Career Positions May 2001 - April 2005. 2006. 77p. (C). pap. 20.00 (978-1-4223-0790-8(5)) DIANE Publishing Co.

The State of the FOIA: Assessing Agency Efforts to Meet FOIA Requirements: Hearing Before the Subcommittee on Information Policy, Census, & National Archives of the Committee on Oversight & Government Reform, House of Representatives, One Hundred Tenth Congress, First Session, February 14, 2007. 2008. (Illus.). iii, 193p. (978-0-16-081353-5(0), 552-070-37733-6) United States Government Printing Office.

Steinzor, Rena & Shapiro, Sidney. The People's Agents & the Battle to Protect the American Public: Special Interests, Government, & Threats to Health, Safety, & the Environment. 2010. (ENG., Illus.). 272p. 45.00 (978-0-226-77202-8(0)) Univ. of Chicago Pr.

Steuerle, C. Eugene & Boris, Elizabeth, eds. Nonprofits & Government, Second Edition: Collaboration & Conflict. 2nd ed. 2006. (Illus.). xii, 453p. pap. 29.50 (978-0-87766-732-2(2)) Urban Institute Pr.

Strengthening the Federal Acquisition Workforce: Government-Wide Leadership & Initiatives: Hearing Before the Oversight of Government Management, the Federal Workforce, & the District of Columbia Subcommittee of the Committee on Homeland Security & Governmental Affairs, United States Senate, One Hundred Eleventh Congress, First Session, August 5, 2009. 2010. iii, 131p. (978-0-16-085854-3(2), 552-070-41066-0) United States Government Printing Office.

Strengthening the Unique Role of the Nation's Inspectors General: Hearing Before the Committee on Homeland Security & Governmental Affairs, United States Senate, One Hundred Tenth Congress, First Session, July 11, 2007. 2008. iii, 147p. (978-0-16-082342-8(0), 552-070-38399-9) United States Government Printing Office.

Structuring National Security & Homeland Security at the White House: Hearing Before the Committee on Homeland Security & Governmental Affairs, United States Senate of the One Hundred Eleventh Congress, First Session, February 12, 2009. 2010. iii, 60p. (978-0-16-086875-7(0), 552-070-41785-1) United States Government Printing Office.

Swank, Melanie R. The Wisconsin Public Records & Open Meetings Handbook. 3rd ed. 2008. pap. (978-1-57862-230-6(1)) 4th ed. 2009. (978-1-57862-266-5(2)) State Bar of Wisconsin.

Talmon, Stefan, ed. The Occupation of Iraq Vol. 2: The Official Documents of the Coalition Provisional Authority & the Iraqi Governing Council. 2012. 1378p. 160.00 (978-1-84113-642-4(5)) Hart Publishing Ltd. GBR. Dist: International Specialized Bk. Services.

Teeuwen, Bert. Lean Tools for the Public Sector. 2010. (ENG., Illus.). 223p. pap. 31.95 (978-1-4398-4022-1(9)) Productivity Pr.

Telecommuting: A 21st Century Solution to Traffic Jams & Terrorism: Hearing Before the Subcommittee on the Federal Workforce & Agency Organization of the Committee on Government Reform, House of Representatives, One Hundred Ninth Congress, Second Session, July 18, 2006. 2007. iii, 121p. (978-0-16-079225-0(8), 552-070-36300-9) United States Government Printing Office.

Telework: Breaking New Ground?: Hearing Before the Subcommittee on Federal Workforce, Postal Service, & the District of Columbia of the Committee on Oversight & Government Reform, House of Representatives, One Hundred Tenth Congress, First Session, November 6, 2007. 2008. (Illus.). iii, 172p. (978-0-16-081963-6(6), 552-070-38136-8) United States Government Printing Office.

Teodoro, Manuel P. Bureaucratic Ambition: Careers, Motives, & the Innovative Administrator. 2011. (Johns Hopkins Studies in Governance & Public Management Ser.). (ENG., Illus.). 240p. (gr. 17). 45.00 (978-1-4214-0245-1(9)) Johns Hopkins Univ. Pr.

Thomas, Christopher. Standards for Success: GIS for Federal Progress & Accountability. 2007. (Case Studies in GIS Ser.). (ENG., Illus.). 100p. per. 24.95 (978-1-58948-047-6(3), ESRI Pr.) ESRI, Inc.

Thomas, Christopher & Humenik-Sappington, Nancy. GIS for Decision Support & Public Policy Making. 2009. (ENG., Illus.). 189p. pap. 24.95 (978-1-58948-231-9(X), ESRI Pr.) ESRI, Inc.

TIYM Publishing Company, Inc. Staff, ed. Anuario Hispano-Hispanic Yearbook. 20th ed. 2007. 400p. 29.95 (978-0-9777254-2-7(1)) TIYM Publishing Co., Inc.

Todnem, Rune. Managing Organizational Change in Public Services: International Issues, Challenges & Cases. Macleod, Calum, ed. 2009. (Understanding Organizational Change Ser.). (ENG., Illus.). 304p. pap. 45.95 (978-0-415-46759-9(4)) Routledge.

—Managing Organizational Change in Public Services: International Issues, Challenges & Cases. Macleod, Calum, ed. 2009. (Understanding Organizational Change Ser.). (ENG., Illus.). 304p. (C). 160.00 (978-0-415-46758-2(6)) Routledge.

Toharia, Luis & European Commission, Directorate-General for Employment, Industrial Relations and Social Affairs Staff, contrib. by. Labour Market Studies. (Illus.). 238p. (978-92-827-8759-5(1)) European Commission BEL. Dist: Balogh International, Inc.

Trondal, Jarle & Busuioc, Madalina. The Agency Phenomenon in the European Union: Emergence, Institutionalisation & Everyday Decision-Making. Groenleer, Martijn, ed. 2012. (European Policy Studies). (ENG.). 208p. 100.00 (978-0-7190-8554-3(3)) Manchester Univ. Pr. GBR. Dist: Macmillan.

Turbane, James F., ed. Quasi Government Organizations. 2008. pap. 69.00 (978-1-60692-300-9(5)) Nova Science Pubs., Inc.

Ugur, Mehmet & Sunderland, David. Does Economic Governance Matter? Governance Institutions & Outcomes. 2011. (New Directions in Modern Economics Ser.). (Illus.). 256p. 115.00 (978-0-85793-176-4(8)) Elgar, Edward Publishing, Inc.

United Nations. Competent National Authorities under the International Drug Control Treaties 2010. 2011. (ENG.). 192p. pap. 38.00 (978-92-1-048144-1(5)) United Nations Pubns.

United Nations: Department of Economic and Social Affairs. Governance in the Middle East, North Africa & Western Balkans: Challenges & priorities in reforming public administration in the Mediterranean Region. 2008. (ENG.). 428p. pap. 45.00 (978-92-1-123169-4(8)) United Nations Pubns.

United States, Congress House Committee on Appropriations Subcommittee on Commerce, Justice, Science, and Related Agencies Staff, contrib. by. Commerce, Justice, Science, & Related Agencies Appropriations for 2008: Hearings Before a Subcommittee of the Committee on Appropriations, House of Representatives, One Hundred Tenth Congress, First Session. 2007. (Illus.). (978-0-16-078636-5(3), 552-070-35880-3 (pt. 4A)); (978-0-16-078612-9(6), 552-070-35880-3 (pt. 4A)) United States Government Printing Office.

United States, Congress House Committee on Appropriations Subcommittee on the Departments of Labor, Health and Human Services, Education, and Related Agencies Staff, contrib. by. Departments of Labor, Health & Human Services, Education, & Related Agencies Appropriations for 2008: Hearings Before a Subcommittee of the Committee on Appropriations, House of Representatives, One Hundred Tenth Congress, First Session. 2007. (Illus.). (978-0-16-078356-2(9), 552-070-35658-4 (pt. 1)); (978-0-16-078377-7(1), 552-070-35658-4 (pt. 1)); (978-0-16-078220-6(1), 552-070-35658-4 (pt. 1)) United States Government Printing Office.

United States, Congress House Committee on Appropriations Subcommittee on Transportation, Housing and Urban Development, and Related Agencies Staff, contrib. by. Departments of Transportation, & Housing & Urban Development, & Related Agencies Appropriations for 2008: Hearings Before a Subcommittee of the Committee on Appropriations, House of Representatives, One Hundred Tenth Congress, First Session. 2007. (Illus.). (978-0-16-078297-8(X), 552-070-35586-3 (pt. 2)); (978-0-16-078195-7(7), 552-070-35586-3 (pt. 2)) United States Government Printing Office.

United States, Congress House Committee on Government Reform Subcommittee on Government Management, Finance, and Accountability Staff, contrib. by. OMB's Financial Management Line of Business Initiative, Do Recent Changes to the Implementation Guidance Clarify the Rules? Hearing Before the Subcommittee on Government Management, Finance, & Accountability of the Committee on Government Reform, House of Representatives, One Hundred Ninth Congress, Second Session, June 28, 2006. 2007. iii, 90p. (978-0-16-078510-8(3), 552-070-35791-2) United States Government Printing Office.

United States, Congress House Committee on Government Reform Subcommittee on the Federal Workforce and Agency Organization Staff, contrib. by. Establishing a Commission to Recommend Improvements for the Federal Employees Appeals Process: Hearing Before the Subcommittee on the Federal Workforce & Agency Organization of the Committee on Government Reform, House of Representatives, One Hundred Ninth Congress, Second Session, July 11, 2006. 2007. (Illus.). iii, 104p. (978-0-16-078624-2(X), 552-070-35868-4) United States Government Printing Office.

United States, Congress House Committee on the Judiciary Subcommittee on Commercial and Administrative Law Staff, contrib. by. Amending Executive Order 12866: Good Governance or Regulatory Usurpation?: Hearing Before the Subcommittee on Commercial & Administrative Law of the Committee on the Judiciary, House of Representatives, One Hundred Tenth Congress, First Session, February 13, 2007. 2007. iv, 312p. (978-0-16-078550-4(2), 552-070-35819-6) United States Government Printing Office.

—Interim Report on the Administrative Law, Process & Procedure Project for the 21st Century: Committee Print: Subcommittee on Commercial & Administrative Law of the Committee on the Judiciary, House of Representatives, One Hundred Ninth Congress, Second Session, December, 2006. 2007. viii, 1436p. (978-0-16-077978-7(2), 552-070-35411-5) United States Government Printing Office.

—Legal Services Corporation Improvement ACT: Hearing Before the Subcommittee on Commercial & Administrative Law of the Committee on the Judiciary, House of Representatives, One Hundred Ninth Congress, Second Session, on H.R. 6101, September 26, 2006. 2007. iii, 142p. (978-0-16-078050-9(0), 552-070-35458-1) United States Government Printing Office.

United States, Congress Senate Committee on Homeland Security and Governmental Affairs Subcommittee on Federal Financial Management, Government Information, and International Security Staff, contrib. by. Reporting Improper Payments: A Report Card on Agencies' Progress: Hearing Before the Federal Financial Management, Government Information, & International Security Subcommittee of the Committee on Homeland Security & Governmental Affairs, United States Senate, One Hundred Ninth Congress, Second Session, March 9, 2006. 2007. (Illus.). iii, 158p. (978-0-16-078029-5(2), 552-070-35459-0) United States Government Printing Office.

United States, Congress Senate Committee on the Judiciary Staff, contrib. by. Balancing Privacy & Security: The Privacy Implications of Government Data Mining Programs: Hearing Before the Committee on the Judiciary, United States Senate, One Hundred Tenth Congress, First Session, January 10, 2007. 2007. iv, 174p. (978-0-16-078370-8(4), 552-070-35675-4) United States Government Printing Office.

Van Der Meer Staff. Civil Service Systems in Western Europe. Van Der Meer, Frits M., ed. 2nd rev. ed. 2011. (Illus.). 296p. 125.00 (978-1-84844-243-6(2)) Elgar, Edward Publishing, Inc.

Van Dooren, Wouter & Van de Walle, Steven, eds. Performance Information in the Public Sector: How it Is Used. 2011. (Governance & Public Management Ser.). (ENG., Illus.). 296p. pap. 37.00 (978-0-230-30912-8(7)) Palgrave Macmillan.

Vaughn, Jacqueline & Otenyo, Eric E. Managerial Discretion in Government Decision Making: Beyond the Street Level. 2006. 171p. per. 75.95 (978-0-7637-4656-8(8)) Jones & Bartlett Learning, LLC.

Vault Editors. Vault Guide to the Top Government & Nonprofit Employers, 2007 Edition. 2008. 176p. pap. 19.95 (978-1-58131-443-4(4)) Vault.com.

Verhoest, Koen, et al, eds. Government Agencies: Practices & Lessons from 30 Countries. (Public Sector Organizations Ser.). (ENG., Illus.). 496p. 2012. 150.00 (978-0-230-35435-7(1)) 2011. pap. 50.00 (978-0-230-35436-4(X)) Palgrave Macmillan.

Verhoest, Koen, et al. Autonomy & Control of State Agencies: Comparing States & Agencies. 2010. (Public Sector Organizations Ser.). (ENG., Illus.). 288p. 100.00 (978-0-230-57765-7(2)) Palgrave Macmillan.

Veterans' Preference: Hearing Before the Subcommittee on Economic Opportunity of the Committee on Veterans' Affairs, U.S. House of Representatives, One Hundred Tenth Congress, First Session, September 6, 2007. 2008. v, 92p. (978-0-16-081016-9(7), 552-070-37529-5) United States Government Printing Office.

Villarreal, M. Angeles, et al. Commerce, Justice & Science Appropriations Agencies. 2008. viii, 108p. pap. 50.00 (978-1-60456-635-2(3)) Nova Science Pubs., Inc.

Voelz, Glenn J. Contractors in the Government Workplace: Managing the Blended Workforce. 2010. (ENG.). 180p. 65.00 (978-1-60590-698-0(0)) Scarecrow Pr., Inc.

Wakefield, Jill. The Right to Good Administration. 2007. 165.00 (978-90-411-2697-9(X)) Wolters Kluwer Law & Business.

Walker, David M. Federal Financial Management: Critical Accountability & Fiscal Stewardship Challenges Facing Our Nation. 2007. (Illus.). 41p. (C). pap. 20.00 (978-1-4223-1573-6(8)) DIANE Publishing Co.

Wallis, Joe L. International Handbook of Public Management Reform. Wallis, Joe L. & Goldfinch, Shaun, eds. 2009. (Elgar Original Reference Ser.). (Illus.). 400p. 215.00 (978-1-84720-404-2(X)) Elgar, Edward Publishing, Inc.

Walters, Jonathan. Measuring up 2.0: Governing's New, Improved Guide to Performance Measurement for Geniuses (and Other Public Managers) 2nd ed. 2007. (978-0-87289-575-1(0)) CQ Pr.

Warren & Cram101 Textbook Reviews Staff. Administrative Law in the Political System. 2007. 152p. per. 12.95 (978-1-4288-2510-9(X)) Cram101 Inc.

Warren, Kenneth F. Administrative Law in the Political System. 5th ed. 2010. (ENG., Illus.). 640p. (C). pap. 75.00 (978-0-8133-4456-0(5)) Westview Pr.

Watkins, Zina L. & Berry, Carla. Congressional Liason Offices. 2008. pap. 39.00 (978-1-60456-872-1(0)) Nova Science Pubs., Inc.

The check digit for ISBN-10 appears in parentheses after the full ISBN-13

Wells, Jim. Crude Oil: Uncertainty about Future Oil Supply Makes it Important to Develop a Strategy for Addressing a Peak & Decline in Oil Production. 2007. (Illus.). 76p. (C). pap. 25.00 *(978-1-4223-1576-7(2))* DIANE Publishing Co.

West, Darrell. Digital Government: Technology & Public Sector Performance. 2007. (ENG.). 256p. (C). per. 26.95 *(978-0-691-13407-9(3))* Princeton Univ. Pr.

Wilde, Ralph. International Territorial Administration: How Trusteeship & the Civilizing Mission Never Went Away. (ENG.). 2010. 640p. 60.00 *(978-0-19-957789-7(7))* 2008. (Illus.). 600p. 137.50 *(978-0-19-927432-1(0))* Oxford Univ. Pr., Inc.

Williams, Valerie L., et al. Demonstrating & Communicating Research Impact: Preparing NIOSH Programs for External Review. 2009. 102p. pap. 38.00 *(978-0-8330-4650-5(0)*, mg-809) RAND Corp., The.

Year 2000 Computing Challenge: Readiness Improving but Much Work Remains to Avoid Disruption of Critical Services (5 reports together) 151p. pap. 35.00 *(978-0-7881-8458-1(X))* DIANE Publishing Co.

ADMINISTRATIVE AND POLITICAL DIVISIONS

see also Election Districts; Gerrymander; Local Government

Beck, Joachim & Thedieck, Franz, eds. The European Dimension of Administrative Culture. 2008. 338p. pap. 86.00 *(978-3-8329-3861-1(3))* Nomos Verlagsgesellschaft DEU. Dist: International Specialized Bk. Services.

Cooke, Tim. Maps for Governments. 2010. (Understanding Maps of Our World Ser.). (ENG.). 48p. (gr. 6-8). pap. 14.05 *(978-1-4339-3516-9(3)*, Stevens, Gareth Secondary Library) Stevens, Gareth Publishing LLLP.

Fegley, Randall. Beyond Khartoum: A History of Sub-National Government in Sudan. 2010. *(978-1-56902-335-8(2))*; 388p. pap. *(978-1-56902-336-5(0))* Red Sea Pr.

Fesler, James W. Area & Administration. 2nd ed. 2008. (ENG.). 176p. pap. 19.95 *(978-0-8173-5506-7(5))* Univ. of Alabama Pr.

Fesler, James W., intro. Area & Administration. 2008. *(978-0-8173-4802-1(6))* Univ. of Alabama Pr.

Goddard, Stacie E. Indivisible Territory & the Politics of Legitimacy: Jerusalem & Northern Ireland. 2009. (ENG., Illus.). 304p. 88.00 *(978-0-521-43985-5(X))* Cambridge Univ. Pr.

Territories of the Russian Federation 2008. 9th rev. ed. 2008. 336p. 285.00 *(978-1-85743-456-9(0))* Europa Pubns.

ADMINISTRATIVE APPEALS

see Administrative Remedies

ADMINISTRATIVE COMMUNICATION

see Business Communication

ADMINISTRATIVE COURTS

see also Administrative Remedies; Judicial Review of Administrative Acts
also names of individual courts, e.g. France—Conseil d'Etat

Baderschneider, Maira Mildred Susanne. Der Bürger als Richter: Eine Empirische Untersuchung des Ehrenamtlichen Richters an den Allgemeinen Verwaltungsgerichten. 2010. (GER.). 326p. 86.95 *(978-3-631-61208-8(7))* Lang, Peter GmbH, Europaischer Verlag der Wissenschaften DEU. Dist: Lang, Peter.

Blakeley, Richard, et al. The New Tribunals Handbook. 2010. 500p. pap. 135.00 *(978-1-84766-535-5(7)*, Bloomsbury Professional) Bloomsbury Publishing Plc GBR. Dist: International Specialized Bk. Services.

Butler, Jonathan L. Mental Health Review Tribunal: Law, Practice & Procedure. 2009. (ENG.). 674p. pap. *(978-1-84661-139-1(3))* Jordan Publishing, Ltd.

Cane, Peter. Administrative Tribunals & Adjudication. (ENG.). 311p. 2010. pap. 50.00 *(978-1-84946-091-0(4))* 2009. 114.00 *(978-1-84113-009-5(5))* Hart Publishing Ltd. GBR. Dist: International Specialized Bk. Services.

Coppel, Philip, et al. Tribunals Practice. 2012. (ENG.). 1000p. 250.00 *(978-1-84661-216-9(0))* Jordan Publishing, Ltd. GBR. Dist: International Specialized Bk. Services.

Frost, Michael H. & Bateman, Paul A. Writing Deskbook for Administrative Law Judges: An Introduction. 2010. 130p. pap. 25.00 *(978-1-59460-666-3(8))* Carolina Academic Pr.

Hametz, Maura. In the Name of Italy: Nation, Family, & Patriotism in a Fascist Court. 2012. (ENG.). 288p. 45.00 ***(978-0-8232-4339-6(7))*** Fordham Univ. Pr.

Mulholland, Maureen & Pullan, Brian, eds. Judicial Tribunals in England & Europe, 1200-1700 Vol. 1: The Trial in History. 2011. (ENG.). 200p. pap. 26.95 ***(978-0-7190-6343-5(4))*** Manchester Univ. Pr. GBR. Dist: Macmillan.

Reviewing the Coast Guard's Administrative Law System: Hearing Before the Subcommittee on Coast Guard & Maritime Transportation of the Committee on Transportation & Infrastructure, House of Representatives, One Hundred Tenth Congress, First Session, July 31, 2007. 2007. xiv, 115p. *(978-0-16-083652-7(2)*, 552-070-39363-3) United States Government Printing Office.

Rozsnyai, Krisztina F. Közigazgatási Bíráskodás Prokrusztész-ágyban: A Közigazgatás Feletti Bírói Kontroll Változó Körülmények Között, Változatlan Formában. 2010. (Illus.). 281p. *(978-963-284-129-8(8))* Eotvos Lorand Tudomanyegyetem.

Schwartz, Bernard. French Administrative Law & the Common-Law World: Introduction by Author T. Vanderbilt. 2006. 389p. 59.95 *(978-1-58477-704-5(4))* Lawbook Exchange, Ltd., The.

Stebbings, Chantal. Legal Foundations of Tribunals in Nineteenth Century England. 2009. (Cambridge Studies in English Legal History Ser.). (ENG.). 380p. pap. 51.00 *(978-0-521-10751-8(2))* Cambridge Univ. Pr.

—Legal Foundations of Tribunals in Nineteenth-Century England. 2007. (Cambridge Studies in English Legal History Ser.). (ENG.). 376p. 141.00 *(978-0-521-86907-2(2))* Cambridge Univ. Pr.

Supperstone, Michael & Knapman, Lynne, eds. Administrative Court Practice. 2008. (ENG., Illus.). 450p. pap. 180.00 *(978-0-19-921708-3(4))* Oxford Univ. Pr., Inc.

Thomas, Robert. Administrative Justice & Asylum Appeals: A Study of Tribunal Adjudication. 2011. (ENG., Illus.). 342p. pap. 100.00 *(978-1-84113-936-4(X))* Hart Publishing Ltd. GBR. Dist: International Specialized Bk. Services.

ADMINISTRATIVE DISCRETION

Boyd-Caine, Tessa. Protecting the Public? Detention & Release of Mentally Disordered Offenders. 2012. (ENG.). 216p. 125.00 *(978-1-84392-527-9(3))* Willan Publishing GBR. Dist: Taylor & Francis Group.

Boyd-Caine, Tessa. Protecting the Public? Executive Discretion & the Release of Mentally Disordered Offenders. 2012. (ENG.). 216p. (C). pap. 42.95 ***(978-0-415-62796-2(6))*** Routledge.

Cram101 Textbook Reviews. Outlines & Highlights for Managerial Discretion in Government Decision Making: Beyond the Street Level by Jacqueline Vaughn. 2011. 62p. pap. 27.95 ***(978-1-61905-025-9(0))*** Cram101 Inc.

Mobley, Samantha & Denton, Ross, eds. Global Cartels Handbook: Leniency - Policies & Procedure. 2012. (ENG.). 816p. pap. 190.00 ***(978-0-19-964100-0(5))*** Oxford Univ. Pr., Inc.

Scarry, Elaine. Thinking in an Emergency. (Amnesty International Global Ethics Ser.). (ENG.). 2012. 176p. pap. 14.95 ***(978-0-393-34058-7(9)***, 34058) 2011. 157p. 23.95 *(978-0-393-07898-5(1)*, 7898) Norton, W. W. & Co., Inc.

Vaughn, Jacqueline & Otenyo, Eric E. Managerial Discretion in Government Decision Making: Beyond the Street Level. 2006. 171p. per. 75.95 *(978-0-7637-4656-8(8))* Jones & Bartlett Learning, LLC.

ADMINISTRATIVE LAW

see also Administrative Agencies; Administrative and Political Divisions; Administrative Courts; Administrative Discretion; Administrative Procedure; Administrative Remedies; Administrative Responsibility; Civil Service; Colonies—Administration; Constitutional Law; De Facto Doctrine; Delegation of Powers; Executive Advisory Bodies; Government Liability; Independent Regulatory Commissions; Judicial Review of Administrative Acts; Local Government; Mandamus; Municipal Corporations; Police Power; Public Administration; Public Contracts; Rule of Law

Abe, Yasutaka. Gyoseiho No Shinro. 2010. (JPN.). x, 399p. *(978-4-8057-1144-6(2))* Chuo Univ. Pr.

Akman, Pinar. The Concept of Abuse in Eu Competition Law: Law & Economic Approaches, 0 vols. 2012. (ENG.). 366p. 120.00 ***(978-1-84946-109-2(0))*** Hart Publishing Ltd. GBR. Dist: International Specialized Bk. Services

Anthony, Gordon, et al, eds. Values in Global Administrative Law. 2011. 446p. 130.00 *(978-1-84946-009-5(4))* Hart Publishing Ltd. GBR. Dist: International Specialized Bk. Services.

Arroyo Jiménez, Luis, et al, eds. Spanish Administrative Law under European Influence. 2010. 213p. pap. 72.00 *(978-90-8952-083-8(X))* Europa Law Publishing, Netherlands NLD. Dist: International Specialized Bk. Services.

Aspen Publishers Staff & Casenotes Publishing Co., Inc. Staff. Administrative Law: Courses Using Breyer, Stewart, Sunstein, & Vermeule's Administrative Law & Regulatory Policy - Problems Texts, & Cases. 6th ed. 2006. (Casenote Legal Briefs Ser.). 151p. stu. ed., per. 35.95 *(978-0-7355-5823-6(X)*, Aspen Pubs.) Wolters Kluwer Law & Business.

Ayana, Abate. Administrative Courts in Ethiopi. 2010. 76p. pap. *(978-3-639-26664-1(1))* VDM Verlag Dr. Mueller e.K.

Beal, Ronald L. Texas Administrative Practice & Procedure. 4th rev. ed. ring bd., ring bd. 138.00 *(978-0-327-01939-8(5))* LEXIS Publishing.

Beerman. Elo: Administrative Law 2010. 3rd ed. 2010. pap., stu. ed. 39.95 *(978-0-7355-9009-0(5)*, Aspen Pubs.) Wolters Kluwer Law & Business.

Bermann, George A., et al. Administrative Law of the European Union, 6 vols. 2009. (ENG.). 872p. 254.95 *(978-1-60442-248-1(3))*; 50p. pap. 29.95 *(978-1-60442-137-8(1))* American Bar Assn.

Boom, Willem H. van, et al, eds. Tort & Regulatory Law. 2010. (Tort & Insurance Law Ser.). xiii, 477p. pap. 219.00 *(978-3-211-99883-0(7)*, 3211998837) Springer.

Borokini, A. & Adeji, Olong. Administrative Law in Nigeri: An Introduction. 2007. 156p. (C). pap. *(978-978-023-228-3(1))* Malthouse Press Ltd, Nigeria NGA. Dist: Michigan State Univ. Pr.

Briefs, Casenote Legal. Administrative Law: Cass, Diver, & Beermann's Administrative Law. 3rd ed. 2006. (Casenote Legal Briefs Ser.). pap., stu. ed. 35.95 *(978-0-7355-5824-3(8)*, Aspen Pubs.) Wolters Kluwer Law & Business.

Brudner, Alan. Constitutional Goods. 2007. (ENG.). 464p. per. 70.00 *(978-0-19-922579-8(6))* Oxford Univ. Pr., Inc.

Cane, Peter. Administrative Tribunals & Adjudication. 2009. (ENG.). 311p. 114.00 *(978-1-84113-009-5(5))* Hart Publishing Ltd. GBR. Dist: International Specialized Bk. Services.

Caranta, Roberto, ed. Traditions & Change in European Administrative Law. 2011. (Illus.). 335p. pap. 110.00 *(978-90-8952-071-5(6))* Europa Law Publishing, Netherlands NLD. Dist: International Specialized Bk. Services.

Casalta Nabais, José. Estudos Sobre Autonomias Territoriais, Institucionais e Cívicas. 2010. 222p. *(978-972-40-4224-4(3))* Almedina, Livraria.

Casenotes Publishing Co., Inc. Staff. Administrative Law: Funk, Shapiro, & Weaver's Administrative Procedure & Practice. 3rd ed. 2006. (Casenote Legal Briefs Ser.). pap., stu. ed. 34.95 *(978-0-7355-6327-8(6)*, Aspen Pubs.) Wolters Kluwer Law & Business.

Chipeta, B. D. Administrative Law in Tanzania: A Digest of Cases. 2008. 280p. pap. *(978-9987-449-50-7(6))* Mkuki na Nyoka Pubs. TZA. Dist: Michigan State Univ. Pr.

Chiti, Edoardo & Mattarella, Bernardo Giorgio, eds. Global Administrative Law & EU Administratve Law: Relationships, Legal Issues & Comparison. 2011. (ENG.). xiii, 409p. 189.00 *(978-3-642-20263-6(2)*, 3642202632) Springer.

Ch'oe, Yu. Sijang Chayul Kyuje Wa Haengjong Chido Ui Kwan'gye e Kwanhan Yon'gu. 2008. (KOR.). 95p. *(978-89-8323-892-4(5))* Korea Legislation Research Institute.

Connery, Niamh & Hodnett, David. Regulatory Law in Ireland. 2009. 582p. 240.00 *(978-1-84766-254-5(4)*, Bloomsbury Professional) Bloomsbury Publishing Plc GBR. Dist: International Specialized Bk. Services.

Corder, Hugh, ed. Global Administrative Law: Innovation & Development, Vol. 1. 2009. 422p. 73.00 *(978-0-7021-8190-0(0))* Juta & Co., Ltd. ZAF. Dist: Gaunt, Inc.

Craig, Paul. EU Administrative Law. 2nd ed. 2012. (ENG.). 840p. 220.00 ***(978-0-19-956862-8(6))***; pap. 80.00 ***(978-0-19-956863-5(4))*** Oxford Univ. Pr., Inc.

Croley, Steven P. Regulation & Public Interests: The Possibility of Good Regulatory Government. 2007. 379p. 72.00 *(978-0-691-13085-9(X))*; (ENG., Illus.). 392p. (C). per. 32.95 *(978-0-691-13464-2(2))* Princeton Univ. Pr.

Curtin, Deirdre. Executive Power in the European Union: Law, Practice, & Constitutionalism. 2009. (Collected Courses of the Academy of European Law Ser.). (ENG., Illus.). 350p. pap. 60.00 *(978-0-19-926409-4(0))*; 132.00 *(978-0-19-926408-7(2))* Oxford Univ. Pr., Inc.

DeLeo, John D., Jr. Administrative Law. 2008. (ENG., Illus.). 512p. (C). pap. 98.95 *(978-1-4018-5877-3(5))* Delmar Cengage Learning.

Derwent & Parker. Fair Enough? Date not set. (Illus.). 352p. pap., stu. ed. 59.50 *(978-0-582-87582-1(X))* Addison-Wesley Longman, Ltd. GBR. Dist: Trans-Atlantic Pubns., Inc.

Dilling, Olaf, et al. Transnational Administrative Rule-Making: Performance, Legal Effects, & Legitimacy. 2011. (ENG.). 354p. 120.00 *(978-1-84113-222-8(5))* Hart Publishing Ltd. GBR. Dist: International Specialized Bk. Services.

Dowdle, Michael W., ed. Public Accountability: Designs, Dilemmas & Experiences. 2006. (Cambridge Studies in Law & Society). (ENG., Illus.). 474p. 115.00 *(978-0-521-85214-2(5))* Cambridge Univ. Pr.

—Rethinking Public Accountability: Designs, Dilemmas & Experiences. 2006. (Cambridge Studies in Law & Society). (ENG., Illus.). 474p. pap. 62.00 *(978-0-521-61761-1(8))* Cambridge Univ. Pr.

Duguit, Leon. Law in the Modern State. 2009. 154p. pap. *(978-0-217-49802-9(7))* Books LLC.

—Law in the Modern State. Laski, Frida And Harold, tr. 2008. 296p. 43.95 *(978-1-4369-5628-4(5))* Kessinger Publishing, LLC.

—Law in the Modern State. Laski, Frida & Laski, Harold, trs. 2008. 296p. pap. 28.95 *(978-1-4368-8450-1(0))* Kessinger Publishing, LLC.

Dyzenhaus, David, et al, eds. A Simple Common Lawyer. 2009. (ENG.). 334p. 94.00 *(978-1-84113-923-4(8))* Hart Publishing Ltd. GBR. Dist: International Specialized Bk. Services.

Echevarria-Varga, Javier. Derecho administrativo Puertorriqueño. 2007. pap. *(978-1-59608-299-1(2))* Biblio Services, Inc.

Eijsvoogel, Peter V. & Van Hooijdonk, Marieke. Litigation in the Netherlands: Civil Procedure, Arbitration & Administrative Litigation. 2009. (Dutch Business Law Ser.: Vol. 1). xix, 187p. 79.00 *(978-90-411-2855-3(7))* Wolters Kluwer Law & Business.

Eliantonio, Mariolina. Europeanisation of Administrative Justice? The Influence of the ECJ's Case Law in Italy, Germany & England. 2009. 416p. pap. 120.00 *(978-90-76871-97-4(3))* Europa Law Publishing, Netherlands NLD. Dist: International Specialized Bk. Services.

Federal Register Office. Administrative Personnel 5: Part 1200 to End. 2010. (Code of Federal Regulations Ser.). 1094p. pap. *(978-1-60946-007-5(3))* United States Government Printing Office.

Federal Register Office, creator. Administrative Personnel: Part 1200 to End. 2011. (Code of Federal Regulations Ser.). (ENG.). 1128p. pap. 67.00 ***(978-1-60946-302-1(1))*** United States Government Printing Office.

—Administrative Personnel Parts 1 To 699. 2010. (Code of Federal Regulations Ser.). (Illus.). 892p. pap. 66.00 *(978-1-60946-005-1(7))* United States Government Printing Office.

—Administrative Personnel Parts 700 To 1199. 2010. (Code of Federal Regulations Ser.). (Illus.). 681p. pap. 56.00 *(978-1-60946-006-8(5))* United States Government Printing Office.

Fenwick, Helen & Phillipson, Gavin. Q&A Constitutional & Administrative Law. 5th rev. ed. 2006. (Routledge-Cavendish Questions & Answers Ser.). (Illus.). 396p. per. 26.95 *(978-1-84568-006-0(5)*, Routledge) Taylor & Francis Group GBR. Dist: Taylor & Francis Group.

Fisher, Elizabeth. Risk Regulation & Administrative Constitutionalism. (ENG.). 2010. 322p. pap. 44.00 *(978-1-84946-088-0(4))* 2007. 290p. 100.00 *(978-1-84113-033-0(8))* Hart Publishing Ltd. GBR. Dist: International Specialized Bk. Services.

Fuke, Toshiro. Gendai Gyosei No Kokyosei to Ho: Gyosei No Hoteki Sonzai Riyu. 2010. 361p. *(978-4-535-51776-9(2))* Nihon Hyoron-Sha.

Ginsburg, Tom. Administrative Law & Governance in Asia: Comparative Perspectives. Chen, Albert H. Y., ed. 2008. (Routledge Law in Asia Ser.). (ENG., Illus.). 400p. (C). 190.00 *(978-0-415-77683-7(X))*; pap. 47.95 *(978-0-415-77731-5(3))* Routledge.

Glendenning, Dympna. Religion, Education & the Law: A Comparative Approach. 2008. 501p. pap. 195.00 *(978-1-84766-064-0(9)*, Bloomsbury Professional) Bloomsbury Publishing Plc GBR. Dist: International Specialized Bk. Services.

Guerrero, Yolanda Jaimes. Doctrina Contencioso Administrativa y Tributaria. 2007. (SPA.). 185p. *(978-980-6074-34-7(3))* Tribunal Supremo de Justicia, Fundacion Gaceta Forense.

Harlow, Carol & Rawlings, Richard. Law & Administration. 3rd rev. ed. 2009. (Law in Context Ser.). (ENG.). (C). 880p. pap. 74.00 *(978-0-521-70179-2(1))*; (Illus.). 879p. 158.00 *(978-0-521-19707-6(4))* Cambridge Univ. Pr.

Hayden, Ken. Administrative Process of Public Service Agencies, 1 vol. 2010. 194p. pap. 24.95 *(978-1-4489-5306-5(5))* PublishAmerica, Inc.

Hofmann, H. C. H. & Türk, A. H., eds. Legal Challenges to EU Administrative Law: Towards an Integrated Administration. 2009. 416p. 173.00 *(978-1-84720-788-3(X))* Elgar, Edward Publishing, Inc.

Hofmann, Herwig, et al. Administrative Law & Policy of the European Union. 2012. (ENG.). 1152p. 250.00 *(978-0-19-928648-5(5))* Oxford Univ. Pr., Inc.

Hülshörster, Stefan. Recht im Umbruch: Die Transformation des Rechtssystems in der Ukraine unter ausländischer Beratung. 2008. (Studien des Instituts für Ostrecht München Ser.). 218p. pap. 56.95 *(978-3-631-57510-9(6))* Lang, Peter GmbH, Europaischer Verlag der Wissenschaften DEU. Dist: Lang, Peter.

Jans, Jan, et al, eds. European Administrative Law: Top down & Bottom Up: Proceedings of the First REALaw Research Forum. 2010. (Illus.). 180p. pap. 64.00 *(978-90-8952-072-2(4))* Europa Law Publishing, Netherlands NLD. Dist: International Specialized Bk. Services.

Jansen, Oswald & SchöNdorf-Haubold, Bettina, eds. The European Composite Administration. 2011. 610p. pap. 139.00 *(978-94-000-0098-8(7))* Intersentia Uitgevers N.V. BEL. Dist: International Specialized Bk. Services.

Kang, Mun-Su. Haengjongpopsang Kumjonjok Chejae Sudan Ui Chokchongsong Chego Rul Wihan Chongbi Pangan Yon'gu. 2009. (KOR.). 289p. *(978-89-8323-404-9(0))* Korea Legislation Research Institute.

Keessen, Andrea. European Administrative Decisions: How the EU Regulates Products on the Internal Market. 2009. 271p. 112.00 *(978-90-8952-056-2(2))* Europa Law Publishing, Netherlands NLD. Dist: International Specialized Bk. Services.

Kennedy, Sheila Suess. V540 Law & Public Affairs. 2007. (C). spiral bd. 88.25 *(978-0-9786276-8-3(7))* Mentzer Printing Ink.

Kerski, Joseph J. & Clark, Jill. The GIS Guide to Public Domain Data. 2012. (ENG., Illus.). 350p. (gr. 12). pap. 49.95 ***(978-1-58948-244-9(1)***, ESRI Pr.) ESRI, Inc.

Krajewski, Markus, et al, eds. The Changing Legal Framework for Services of General Interest in Europe: Volume: Between Competition & Solidarity. 2009. (ENG.). 544p. 129.00 *(978-90-6704-308-3(7))* T.M.C. Asser Pr. NLD. Dist: Springer.

Küpper, Herbert & Brenn, Wolfgang, eds. Rechtstransfer und internationale rechtliche Zusammenarbeit: Deutsche und japanische Erfahrungen bei der Kooperation mit Osteuropa und Zentralasien. 2010. (Studien des Instituts für Ostrecht München Ser.). (GER.). 238p. 69.95 *(978-3-631-59899-3(8))* Lang, Peter GmbH, Europaischer Verlag der Wissenschaften DEU. Dist: Lang, Peter.

Leyland, Peter & Anthony, Gordon. Textbook on Administrative Law. 6th ed. 2008. (ENG.). 576p. (Orig.). 80.00 *(978-0-19-921776-2(9))* Oxford Univ. Pr., Inc.

Lindseth, Peter L. Power & Legitimacy: Reconciling Europe & the Nation-State, 1 vol. 2010. (ENG.). 342p. 80.00 *(978-0-19-539014-8(8))* Oxford Univ. Pr., Inc.

Luce, Henry R., et al. Comparative Administrative Law. Rose-Ackerman, Susan, ed. 2011. (Research Handbooks in Comparative Law Ser.). (Illus.). 688p. pap. 50.00 *(978-1-84844-642-7(X))*; 295.00 *(978-1-84844-635-9(7))* Elgar, Edward Publishing, Inc.

Luchtman, Michiel. European Cooperation between Financial Supervisory Authorities, Tax Authorities & Judicial Authorities. 2008. 244p. pap. 81.25 *(978-90-5095-862-2(1))* Intersentia Uitgevers N.V. BEL. Dist: International Specialized Bk. Services.

Lukas, Meinhard, et al, eds. Tort & Regulatory Law. 2008. (Tort & Insurance Law Ser.). 477p. 219.00 *(978-3-211-31133-2(5))* Springer.

Malagón Pinzón, Miguel Alejandro. Vivir en Policía: Una Contralectura de Los Orígenes Del Derecho Administrativo Colombiano. 2007. (SPA.). 334p. pap. 29.00 *(978-958-710-244-4(4))* Universidad Externado de Colombia COL. Dist: Siglo del Hombre.

McNeil, Christopher. Perceptions of Fairness in State Administrative Agency Proceedings. 2010. 180p. pap. *(978-3-8383-2249-0(5))* Lambert Academic Publishing.

Newman, Elizabeth L. Security Clearance Law & Procedure. 2nd ed. 2008. (Illus.). viii, 940p. pap. *(978-1-934651-18-6(4))* Dewey Pubns., Inc.

Nieto-Garrido, Eva & Delgado, Isaac Martín. European Administrative Law in the Constitutional Treaty. 2007. (Modern Studies in European Law Ser.). 190p. (C). pap. 100.00 *(978-1-84113-512-0(7))* Hart Publishing Ltd. GBR. Dist: International Specialized Bk. Services.

O'Connor, Bernard. Understanding EU Commission Tenders: A Practical Guide. 2010. 272p. pap. 84.00 *(978-94-000-0020-9(0))* Intersentia Uitgevers N.V. BEL. Dist: International Specialized Bk. Services.

Ortiz Serrano, Adriana Catalina. Particulares Vinculados por la Fuerza Normativa de la Moralidad Administrativa. 2010. (SPA.). pap. 7.00 *(978-958-710-537-7(0))* Universidad Externado de Colombia COL. Dist: Siglo del Hombre.

Pollard, David, et al. Constitutional & Administrative Law: Text with Materials. 4th rev. ed. 2007. (ENG.). 976p. pap. 99.00 *(978-0-19-928637-9(X))* Oxford Univ. Pr., Inc.

Read, James S. & Slinn, Peter, eds. Law Reports of the Commonwealth. xxix, 734p. 5977.00 *(978-0-406-99842-2(6)*, LRCMW) LEXIS Publishing.

Reauthorization of the Medical Device User Fee & Modernization ACT: Hearing Before the Subcommittee on Health of the Committee on Energy & Commerce, House of Representatives, One Hundred Tenth Congress, First Session, May 16, 2007. 2008. (Illus.). v, 150p. (978-0-16-081907-0(5), 552-070-38080-9) United States Government Printing Office.

Reshetnikova, I. V. & Kurgannikova, I. V. Sudebnye Raskhody V Arbitrazhnom Protsesse: Kommentarii I Postateinye Materialy K Glave 9 Arbitrazhnogo Protsessualnogo Kodeksa Rossiiskoi Federatsii. 2nd ed. 2010. (RUS.). v, 184p. (978-5-466-00662-9(9)) Volters Kluver.

Robalino Orellana, Javier & Rodríguez-Arana, Jaime. Global Administrative Law: Towards a Lex Administrativa. 2010. xvii, 398p. (978-1-907174-04-9(4)) Cameron May, Ltd.

Ruffert, Matthias, ed. Legitimacy in European Administrative Law: Reform & Reconstruction. 2011. 360p. pap. 95.00 (978-90-8952-098-2(8)) Europa Law Publishing, Netherlands NLD. Dist: International Specialized Bk. Services.

—The Public-Private Law Divide: Potential for Transformation? 2009. 332p. pap. 145.00 (978-1-905221-34-9(7)) British Institute of International & Comparative Law GBR. Dist: International Specialized Bk. Services.

Ruffert, Matthias & Steinecke, Sebastian. The Global Administrative Law of Science. 2011. (Beiträge zum ausländischen öffentlichen Recht und Völkerrecht Ser.). (ENG.). ix, 140p. 89.95 (978-3-642-21358-8(8), 3642213588) Springer.

Ryan, David L. Kansas Administrative Law with Federal References. 1991st ed. 125.00 (978-0-942357-25-7(6)) Kansas Bar Assn.

Scott, Colin, et al, eds. The Challenge of Transnational Private Regulation: Conceptual & Constitutional Debates. 2011. (Journal of Law & Society Special Issues Ser.: 5). (ENG.). 192p. pap. 39.95 (978-1-4443-3927-7(3), Wiley-Blackwell) Wiley, John & Sons, Inc.

Seerden, Rene J.G.H. & Stroink, F. A. M. Administrative Law of the European Union, Its Member States & the United States: A Comparative Analysis. 2nd ed. 2007. (Illus.). 419p. (C). pap. 110.75 (978-90-5095-720-5(X)) Intersentia Uitgevers N.V. BEL. Dist: International Specialized Bk. Services.

Spampinato, Biagio. Tipologia Degli Interessi Legittimi e Forme Di Tutela. 2010. (ITA.). xi, 150p. (978-88-348-0937-2(8)) Giappichelli.

Stationery Office, creator. Criminal Injuries Compensation Authority Annual Report & Accounts. 2010. (Criminal Injuries Compensation Authority Annual Report & Accounts Ser.). (Illus.). 54p. pap. (978-0-10-296447-9(5)) Stationery Office, The.

Stevenson, Wayne. Administrative Law. 2010. stu. ed. 40.95 (978-0-7355-7977-4(6)) Wolters Kluwer Law & Business.

Szyszczak, Erika, et al, eds. Developments in Services of General Interest. 2011. (Legal Issues of Services of General Interest Ser.). xviii, 266p. 109.00 (978-90-6704-733-3(3), 9067047333) T.M.C. Asser Pr. NLD. Dist: Springer.

Teubner, Gunther. Constitutional Fragments: Societal Constitutionalism & Globalization. 2012. (ENG.). 275p. 100.00 (978-0-19-964467-4(5)) Oxford Univ. Pr., Inc.

Wade, William, et al. Administrative Law: The Problem of Justice. 829p. 125.00 (978-88-14-02339-2(5)) Giuffre ITA. Dist: Juris Publishing, Inc.

Wakefield, Jill. The Right to Good Administration. 2007. 165.00 (978-90-411-2697-9(X)) Wolters Kluwer Law & Business.

Weatherill, Stephen, ed. Better Regulation. 2007. (Studies of the Oxford Institute of European & Comparative Law: 6). (ENG.). 437p. (C). 110.00 (978-1-84113-715-5(4)) Hart Publishing Ltd. GBR. Dist: International Specialized Bk. Services.

West Law School. Administrative Law, Keyed to Funk. 4th rev. ed. 2010. (High Court Case Summaries Ser.). 314p. 38.00 (978-0-314-26626-2(7), West Legalworks) West.

Winkler, Günther. Rechtswissenschaft und Rechtserfahrung: Methoden- und erkenntniskritische Gedanken über Hans Kelsens Lehre und das Verwaltungsrecht. 2011. (GER.). viii, 147p. (978-3-211-82581-5(9)) Springer Singapore Pte. Ltd.

Wu, Hao & Li, Xiangdong. Guo Wai Gui Zhi Ying Xiang Fen Xi Zhi Du= Regulatory Impact Analysis Practice Outside China. 2010. (CHI.). (978-7-5093-1697-9(9)) China Legal Publishing Hse.

ADMINISTRATIVE LAW—AUSTRALIA

Harlow, Carol, et al. Administrative Law in a Changing State: Essays in Honour of Mark Aronson. Harlow, Carol & Pearson, Linda, eds. 2008. (ENG.). 417p. 136.00 (978-1-84113-787-2(1)) Hart Publishing Ltd. GBR. Dist: International Specialized Bk. Services.

Lee, H. P. & Groves, Matthew. Australian Administrative Law: Fundamentals, Principles & Doctrines. 2007. 522p. pap. 87.00 (978-0-521-69790-3(5)) Cambridge Univ. Pr.

ADMINISTRATIVE LAW—CANADA

Mullan, David J. & Huscroft, Grant. Inside & Outside Canadian Administrative Law: Essays in Honour of David Mullan. Taggart, Michael, ed. 2006. (ENG.). 480p. (978-0-8020-9245-8(4)) Univ. of Toronto Pr.

Reid, Richard & Mercer. Administrative Law & Practice. 3rd ed. 704p. 137.00 (978-0-409-80933-6(0), MICHIE) LEXIS Publishing.

Savoie, Donald J. Court Government & the Collapse of Accountability in Canada & the United Kingdom. 2008. (IPAC Series in Public Management & Governance Ser.). (ENG.). 416p. (978-0-8020-9870-2(3)); pap. (978-0-8020-9579-4(8)) Univ. of Toronto Pr.

ADMINISTRATIVE LAW—CHINA

He, Haibo. Shi Zhi Fa Zhi: Xun Qiu Xing Zheng Pan Jue de He Fa Xing. 2009. (CHI.). (978-7-5118-0028-2(9)) Law Publishing Hse., The.

Li, Lin. Quan Mian Luo Shi Yi Fa Zhi Guo Ji Ben Fang Lüe: Quanmian Luoshi Yifa Zhiguo Jiben Fanglue. 2009. (CHI., Illus.). (978-7-5004-8275-8(2)) China Social Sciences Pr.

Lin, Yaochang, et al. Zhongguo Xing Zheng He Tong de Li Lun Yu Shi Jian Tan Suo. 2009. (978-7-5036-9775-3(X)) Law Publishing Hse., The.

Scott, Ian. Public Sector in Hong Kong. 2010. (ENG.). 412p. (gr. 17). pap. 35.00 (978-962-209-172-6(5)) Hong Kong Univ. Pr. HKG. Dist: Columbia Univ. Pr.

Scott, Ian. The Public Sector in Hong Kong. 2010. (Illus.). 412p. (978-988-220-757-8(X)) Hong Kong Univ. Pr.

Shi, Yajun. Zhongguo Xing Zheng Guan Li Ti Zhi Shi Zheng Yan Jiu: Wen Juan Diao Cha Shu Ju Fen Xi. 2010. (CHI., Illus.). (978-7-5620-3414-8(1)) China Univ. of Political Science and Law Pr.

Wu, Tianhao. Xin Zhongguo Xian Fa Xing Zheng Fa 60 Nian. 2010. (CHI.). 8p. (978-7-80745-618-6(3)) Shanghai Academy of Social Sciences Pr.

Yang, Jianshun. Bi Jiao Xing Zheng Fa: Ji Fu Xing Zheng de Fa Yuan Li Ji Shi Zheng Xing Yan Jiu = the Comparative Administrative Law: The Legal Principles of Leistende Verwaltung & Demonstrational Research. 2008. (CHI.). (978-7-300-10162-0(3)) China Renmin Univ.Pr.

ADMINISTRATIVE LAW—FRANCE

Latour, Bruno. Making of Law: An Ethnography of the Conseil D'Etat. 2010. (ENG., Illus.). 280p. 79.95 (978-0-7456-3984-0(4)); pap. 26.95 (978-0-7456-3985-7(2)) Polity Pr. GBR. Dist: Wiley, John & Sons, Inc.

Petit, Philippe & Gardere, Anne. Anticiper la Réforme Territoriale. 2010. (FRE., Illus.). 192p. (978-2-35740-059-7(5)) Media Conseil Communication, Edition.

Schwartz, Bernard. French Administrative Law & the Common-Law World: Introduction by Author T. Vanderbilt. 2006. 389p. 59.95 (978-1-58477-704-5(4)) Lawbook Exchange, Ltd., The.

ADMINISTRATIVE LAW—GERMANY

Benvindo, Juliano Zaiden. On the Limits of Constitutional Adjudication: Deconstructing Balancing & Judicial Activism. 2010. (ENG.). xx, 424p. 189.00 (978-3-642-11433-5(4), 3642114334) Springer.

Cupa, Jozef. The Media Freedom to Inform V Celebrities' Personality Rights. 2010. 68p. pap. (978-3-639-18334-4(7)) VDM Verlag Dr. Mueller e.K.

Ehlers, Dirk. Allgemeines Verwaltungsrecht. Ehlers, Dirk & Erichsen, Hans-Uwe, eds. 14th ed. 2010. (De Gruyter Lehrbuch Ser.).Tr. of General Administrative Law. (GER., Illus.). XL, 1066p. (C). 91.00 (978-3-89949-623-9(X)) De Gruyter Rechtswissenschaften Verlags GmbH DEU. Dist: de Gruyter, Walter GmbH & Co. KG.

Erichsen, Hans-Uwe, et al, eds. Allgemeines Verwaltungsrecht. (De Gruyter Lehrbuch Ser.).Tr. of General Administrative Law. (GER.). 5th ed. XXXII, 596p. 358.00 (978-3-11-217655-9(3)) 5th ed. (Illus.). XXXII, 596p. 236.00 (978-3-11-008619-5(0)) 6th ed. XXXVI, 611p. 358.00 (978-3-11-217454-8(2)) 6th ed. XXXVI, 611p. 243.00 (978-3-11-009825-9(3)) 7th ed. XXXVII, 633p. 374.00 (978-3-11-218100-3(X)) 7th ed. (Illus.). XXXVII, 633p. 251.00 (978-3-11-010663-3(9)) De Gruyter, Walter Inc.

Erichsen, Hans-Uwe & Badura, Peter, eds. Allgemeines Verwaltungsrecht. (De Gruyter Lehrbuch Ser.).Tr. of General Administrative Law. (GER.). XXIX, 505p. 300.00 (978-3-11-218735-7(0)); (Illus.). XXIX, 505p. 200.00 (978-3-11-004901-5(5)); 2nd ed. XXXII, 507p. 300.00 (978-3-11-218780-7(6)); 2nd ed. XXXII, 507p. 202.00 (978-3-11-006953-2(9)); 3rd ed. XXXII, 536p. 314.00 (978-3-11-216151-7(3)); 3rd ed. XXXII, 536p. 213.00 (978-3-11-007301-0(3)); 4th ed. XXXII, 536p. 314.00 (978-3-11-216152-4(1)); 4th ed. XXXII, 536p. 213.00 (978-3-11-007828-2(7)) De Gruyter, Walter Inc.

Grünewald, Benedikt. Die Betonung des Verfahrensgedankens im deutschen Verwaltungsrecht durch das Gemeinschaftsrecht. 2009. (Regensburger Beiträge zum Staats- und Verwaltungsrecht Ser.). (GER.). 344p. 86.95 (978-3-631-59474-2(7)) Lang, Peter GmbH, Europaischer Verlag der Wissenschaften DEU. Dist: Lang, Peter.

Kresser, Daniel. Die Bedeutung der Form für Begriff und Rechtsfolgen des Verwaltungsakts. 2009. (Dresdner Schriften zum Öffentlichen Recht Ser.). (GER.). 348p. pap. 81.95 (978-3-631-59060-7(1)) Lang, Peter GmbH, Europaischer Verlag der Wissenschaften DEU. Dist: Lang, Peter.

Künnecke, Marina. Tradition & Change in Administrative Law: An Anglo-German Comparison. 2010. (ENG.). xii, 266p. pap. 169.00 (978-3-642-08021-0(9), 3642080219) Springer.

Münch, Ingo & Badura, Peter, eds. Besonderes Verwaltungsrecht. (De Gruyter Lehrbuch Ser.). (GER.). 4th ed. XXI, 786p. 448.00 (978-3-11-218054-9(2)) 4th ed. XXI, 786p. 303.00 (978-3-11-006643-2(2)) 5th ed. XXI, 843p. 478.00 (978-3-11-217460-9(7)) 5th ed. XXI, 843p. 324.00 (978-3-11-007854-1(6)) 6th ed. (Illus.). XXIII, 1057p. 598.00 (978-3-11-216173-9(4)) 6th ed. (Illus.). XXIII, 1057p. 405.00 (978-3-11-008642-3(5)) 9th ed. XXIII, 759p. 434.00 (978-3-11-217927-7(7)) 9th ed. XXIII, 759p. 293.00 (978-3-11-127162-0(5)) De Gruyter, Walter Inc.

Papier, Hans-Jargen. Recht der Öffentlichen Sachen. (Sammlung Göschen Ser.). (GER.). 164p. 210.00 (978-3-11-218154-6(9)) De Gruyter, Walter Inc.

Papier, Hans-Jurgen. Recht der öffentlichen Sachen. (Sammlung Göschen Ser.). (GER.). 164p. 135.00 (978-3-11-007404-8(4)) De Gruyter, Walter Inc.

Puchert, Frank. Entscheidungsfaktoren in der öffentlichen Verwaltung am Beispiel der Windenergie im Landkreis Aurich. 2010. (Recht und Rhetorik Ser.). (GER.). 240p. 69.95 (978-3-631-60012-2(7)) Lang, Peter GmbH, Europaischer Verlag der Wissenschaften DEU. Dist: Lang, Peter.

Singh, Mahendra P. German Administrative Law in Common Law Perspective. 2nd ed. 2010. (Beiträge Zum Ausländischen öffentlichen Recht und Völkerrecht Ser.). xxxi, 380p. pap. 119.00 (978-3-642-07615-2(7), 3642076157) Springer.

ADMINISTRATIVE LAW—GREAT BRITAIN

Administrative Law. 3rd rev. ed. 1878.00 (978-0-8205-3729-0(2)) LexisNexis.

Arnheim, Michael & Taylor, Chris. Constitutional & Administrative Law. 2008. 168p. pap. 27.50 (978-1-4058-2191-9(4), Longman) Pearson Education, Ltd. GBR. Dist: Trans-Atlantic Pubns., Inc.

Barnett, Hilaire. Constitutional & Administrative Law. 9th rev. ed. 2011. (ENG., Illus.). 768p. (C). pap. 69.95 (978-0-415-61108-4(3)); 180.00 (978-0-415-66422-6(5)) Routledge.

—Constitutional & Administrative Law. (Illus.). 6th rev. ed. 2006. 870p. 199.95 (978-1-84568-066-4(9)) 7th rev. ed. 2008. 912p. 65.95 (978-0-415-45829-0(3)) Taylor & Francis Group GBR. (Routledge Cavendish). Dist: Taylor & Francis Group.

Barnett, Hilaire & Jago, Robert. Constitutional & Administrative Law. 8th rev. ed. 2010. (ENG., Illus.). 960p. (C). pap. 64.95 (978-0-415-56301-7(1)) Routledge.

Beer, Jason. Public Inquiries. Dingemans, James & Lissack, Richard, eds. 2011. (ENG.). 400p. 250.00 (978-0-19-928777-2(5)) Oxford Univ. Pr., Inc.

Bernett, Hilaire. Constitutional & Administrative Law. 6th rev. ed. 2006. (Illus.). 960p. 69.95 (978-1-84568-033-6(2), Routledge Cavendish) Taylor & Francis Group GBR. Dist: Taylor & Francis Group.

Bradley, A. & Ewing, K. Constitutional & Administrative Law. 15th rev. ed. 2010. (ENG.). 804p. pap. 97.50 (978-1-4058-7350-5(7)) Addison-Wesley Longman, Inc.

Bradley, A. W. & Ewing, K. Constitutional & Administrative Law. 14th rev. ed. 2007. lxxiv, 872p. (C). pap. 79.50 (978-1-4058-1207-8(9)) Pearson Education.

Cane, Peter. Administrative Law. 5th ed. 2011. (ENG.). 496p. 100.00 (978-0-19-969232-3(7)); pap. 50.00 (978-0-19-969233-0(5)) Oxford Univ. Pr., Inc.

Carroll, Alex. Constitutional & Administrative Law. (ENG.). 5th ed. 2009. 704p. pap. (978-1-4058-9911-6(5)) 6th rev. ed. 2011. 752p. pap. (978-1-4082-5353-3(4)) Addison-Wesley Longman, Inc.

—Constitutional & Administrative Law. 4th rev. ed. 2007. (Illus.). 680p. pap. 66.00 (978-1-4058-1231-3(1)) Pearson Education.

—Constitutional & Administrative Law, Pack. 6th rev. ed. 2012. (ENG.). 693p. pap. 87.50 (978-1-4082-6809-4(4)) Pearson Education, Ltd. GBR. Dist: Trans-Atlantic Pubns., Inc.

City Law School (London, England) Staff, contrib. by. Negotiation 2008-2009. 2009. (Blackstone Bar Manual Ser.). (Illus.). 272p. pap. 80.00 (978-0-19-955349-5(1), Blackstone Pr.) Oxford Univ. Pr. GBR. Dist: Oxford Univ. Pr., Inc.

Clements, Richard & Jones, Philip. Q & A Public Law 2011 & 2012. 6th ed. 2011. (ENG.). 256p. pap. 35.00 (978-0-19-959995-0(5)) Oxford Univ. Pr., Inc.

Cracknell, Douglas. Constitutional & Administrative Law 2008-2009. 2nd rev. ed. 2008. (Routledge-Cavendish Core Statutes Ser.). (ENG.). 564p. (C). pap. 27.00 (978-0-415-45830-6(7), Routledge Cavendish) Taylor & Francis Group GBR. Dist: Taylor & Francis Group.

Cracknell, Douglas, ed. Constitutional & Administrative Law 2007-2008. 2007. 512p. pap. 27.00 (978-0-415-45120-8(5), Routledge Cavendish) Taylor & Francis Group GBR. Dist: Taylor & Francis Group.

Elliott, Mark, et al. Beatson, Matthews & Elliott's Administrative Law Text & Materials. 4th ed. 2011. (ENG.). 808p. pap. 70.00 (978-0-19-923852-1(9)) Oxford Univ. Pr., Inc.

Endicott, Timothy. Administrative Law. 2nd ed. 2011. (ENG., Illus.). 696p. pap. 60.00 (978-0-19-960175-2(5)) Oxford Univ. Pr., Inc.

Fenwick, Helen & Phillipson, Gavin. Constitutional & Administrative Law 2009-2010. 6th rev. ed. 2009. (Questions & Answers Ser.). (Illus.). 440p. pap. 28.95 (978-0-415-48374-2(3), Routledge Cavendish) Taylor & Francis Group GBR. Dist: Taylor & Francis Group.

—Q & A Constitutional & Administrative Law 2011-2012. 7th rev. ed. 2011. (Questions & Answers Ser.). (ENG.). 288p. (C). pap. 24.95 (978-0-415-59909-2(1)) Routledge.

Forsyth, Christopher & Wade, William. Administrative Law. 10th ed. 2009. (ENG.). 1030p. (C). pap. 90.00 (978-0-19-921973-5(7)); 180.00 (978-0-19-923161-4(3)) Oxford Univ. Pr., Inc.

Hesperides. An Analysis of the System of Government Throughout the British Empire. 2007. 252p. per. (978-1-4067-5169-7(3), Hesperides Pr.) Read Bks.

Joanne, Coles. Constitutional & Administrative Law. 2nd ed. 2006. (Illus.). 136p. pap. 22.50 (978-0-340-92592-8(2), Hodder Arnold) Hodder Education GBR. Dist: Trans-Atlantic Pubns., Inc.

Künnecke, Marina. Tradition & Change in Administrative Law: An Anglo-German Comparison. 2010. (ENG.). xii, 266p. pap. 169.00 (978-3-642-08021-0(9), 3642080219) Springer.

Loveland, Ian. Constitutional Law, Administrative Law, & Human Rights: A critical Introduction. (ENG.). 5th ed. 2009. 872p. (C). pap. 79.95 (978-0-19-921974-2(5)) 6th ed. 2012. 848p. pap. 70.00 (978-0-19-960640-5(4)) Oxford Univ. Pr., Inc.

Norris, Julie & Phillips, Jeremy. The Law of Regulatory Enforcement & Sanctions: A Practical Guide. 2011. (ENG., Illus.). 280p. pap. 120.00 (978-0-19-959320-0(5)) Oxford Univ. Pr., Inc.

Oliver, Dawn. Common Values & the Public-Private Divide. 2010. 348p. pap. 37.99 (978-0-521-60599-1(7)) Cambridge Univ. Pr.

Palmer, Ellie. Judicial Review, Socio-Economic Rights & the Human Rights Act. 2007. 383p. 120.00 (978-1-84113-372-0(8)) Hart Publishing Ltd. GBR. Dist: International Specialized Bk. Services.

Parpworth, Neil. Constitutional & Administrative Law. 7th ed. 2012. (ENG.). 672p. pap. 45.00 (978-0-19-969833-2(3)) Oxford Univ. Pr., Inc.

Prosser, Tony. The Regulatory Enterprise: Government, Regulation, & Legitimacy. 2010. (ENG.). 240p. 110.00 (978-0-19-957983-9(0)) Oxford Univ. Pr., Inc.

Taylor, Chris. Constitutional & Administrative Law. 2nd ed. 2009. (Illus.). 184p. pap. 29.50 (978-1-4082-2522-6(0)) Pearson Education, Ltd. GBR. Dist: Trans-Atlantic Pubns., Inc.

Thompson, Brian & Allen, Michael. Cases & Materials on Constitutional & Administrative Law. 10th ed. 2011. (ENG., Illus.). 800p. pap. 65.00 (978-0-19-957904-4(0)) Oxford Univ. Pr., Inc.

Vincent-Jones, Peter. The New Public Contracting: Regulation, Responsiveness, Relationality. 2006. 440p. 139.95 (978-0-19-929127-4(6)) Oxford Univ. Pr., Inc.

ADMINISTRATIVE LAW—SOUTH AFRICA

Chikwanha, Annie Barbara. The Politics of Housing Delivery. 2009. 276p. pap. (978-3-639-14937-1(8)) VDM Verlag Dr. Mueller e.K.

Hoexter, Cora. Administrative Law in South Africa, Vol. 1. 2007. 592p. pap. 79.00 (978-0-7021-7671-5(0)) Juta & Co., Ltd. ZAF. Dist: Gaunt, Inc.

ADMINISTRATIVE LAW—UNITED STATES

Adams. Basic Administrative Law for Paralegals. 4th ed. 2009. pap. 99.95 (978-0-7355-9006-9(0), Aspen Pubs.) Wolters Kluwer Law & Business.

Adams, Anne. Basic Administrative Law for Paralegals. 4th ed. 2010. (Illus.). xvii, 362p. (978-0-7355-7774-9(9), Aspen Pubs.) Wolters Kluwer Law & Business.

Andersen, William R. Mastering Administrative Law. 2010. 286p. pap. 30.00 (978-1-59460-582-6(3)) Carolina Academic Pr.

Approaching Midnight: Oversight of the Bush Administration's Last Minute Rulemakings: Hearing Before the Select Committee on Energy Independence & Global Warming, House of Representatives, One Hundred Tenth Congress, Second Session, December 11, 2008. 2010. (Illus.). iii, 131p. (978-0-16-087415-4(7), 552-070-42108-4) United States Government Printing Office.

Araiza. Friedmans Administrative Law. 2010. pap., stu. ed. 32.95 (978-0-7355-9797-6(9), Aspen Pubs.) Wolters Kluwer Law & Business.

Asimow, Michael & Bonfield, Arthur E. State & Federal Administrative Law, 2d, 2007 Supplement. 2007th rev. ed. 2007. (American Casebook Ser.). 111p. pap. 20.00 (978-0-314-18468-9(6), West Legalworks) West.

Asimow, Michael & Levin, Ronald M. State & Federal Administrative Law. 3rd ed. 2009. xxxviii, 779p. (978-0-314-15929-8(0)) West Publishing Co., College & Schl. Div.

Baum, Daniel J. The Welfare Family & Mass Administrative Justice. 2007. 132p. per. 14.95 (978-0-595-47646-6(5), Backinprint.com) iUniverse, Inc.

Beckett, Julia. Public Management & the Rule of Law. 2010. (ENG.). 232p. (C). 89.95 (978-0-7656-2321-8(8)); pap. 43.95 (978-0-7656-2322-5(6)) Sharpe, M.E. Inc.

Beermann. Administrative Law Crunchtime 2010. 3rd ed. 2010. pap., stu. ed. (978-0-7355-9011-3(7), Aspen Pubs.) Wolters Kluwer Law & Business.

—Inside Administrative Law: What Matters & Why. 2010. pap., stu. ed. 38.95 (978-0-7355-7961-3(X)) Wolters Kluwer Law & Business.

Beermann, Jack M. Administrative Law, Pack. 2008. pap., stu. ed. 45.95 (978-0-7355-8330-6(7)) Wolters Kluwer Law & Business.

Breyer. Administrative Law & Regulatory Policy: Problems Text & Cases. 7th ed. 2011. (978-0-7355-8744-1(2)) Wolters Kluwer Law & Business.

Breyer, Stephen G. Administrative Law & Regulatory Policy 2009-2010. 2009. pap., suppl. ed. 29.50 (978-0-7355-8719-9(1)) Wolters Kluwer Law & Business.

Casenotes. Administrative Law: Breyer Stewart Sunstein & Vermeule 7e. 2011. pap., stu. ed. (978-0-7355-9912-3(2), Aspen Pubs.) Wolters Kluwer Law & Business.

—Administrative Law: Cass Diver & Beermann 6e. 2011. pap., stu. ed. (978-0-7355-9913-0(0), Aspen Pubs.) Wolters Kluwer Law & Business.

Cass. Administrative Law: Cases & Materials. 6th ed. 2011. (978-0-7355-9647-4(6), Aspen Pubs.) Wolters Kluwer Law & Business.

—Ll: Administrative Law: Cases & Materials 5e. 2009. ring bd. 93.00 (978-0-7355-8882-0(1)) Wolters Kluwer Law & Business.

Coleman, James K. State Administration in South Carolina. (Columbia University, Studies in the Social Sciences: No. 406). reprint ed. 29.50 (978-0-404-51406-8(5)) AMS Pr., Inc.

Cooper, Philip J. Public Law & Public Administration. 4th rev. ed. 2006. (ENG., Illus.). 784p. (C). 178.95 (978-0-495-00755-5(2)) Wadsworth.

Cram101 Textbook Reviews. Outlines & Highlights for Administrative Law: Bureaucracy in a Democracy by Daniel E. Hall, John Feldmeier, ISBN. 2010. 74p. pap. 27.95 (978-1-61698-274-4(8)) Cram101 Inc.

Cram101 Textbook Reviews Staff. Outlines & Highlights for Administrative Law: Bureaucracy in a Democracy by Daniel E. Hall, John Feldmeier, ISBN. 2009. 68p. pap. 27.95 (978-1-4288-7571-5(9)) Cram101 Inc.

Cupa, Jozef. The Media Freedom to Inform V Celebrities' Personality Rights. 2010. 68p. pap. (978-3-639-18334-4(7)) VDM Verlag Dr. Mueller e.K.

Dempsey, Paul S. Legalines on Administrative Law, 6th — Keyed to Breyer. 6th rev. ed. 2007. (Legalines Ser.). 224p. pap. 29.95 (978-0-314-17696-7(9)) West.

Durham, Blake I. & Pugh, Angelo E., eds. Cost-Benefit Analysis in the Federal Rulemaking Process. 2012. 230p. pap. (978-1-61942-397-8(9)) Nova Science Pubs., Inc.

Enhancing FTC Consumer Protection in Financial Dealings with Telemarketers & the Internet: Hearing Before the Subcommittee on Commerce, Trade, & Consumer Protection of the Committee on Energy & Commerce, House of

Representatives, One Hundred Tenth Congress, First Session, October 23, 2007. 2008. v, 46p. *(978-0-16-082427-2(3)*, 552-070-38471-5) United States Government Printing Office.

Finnigan, et al. Washington Administrative Law Practice Manual. Date not set. 470p. ring bd 105.00 *(978-0-409-20038-6(7)*, 82717, MICHIE) LEXIS Publishing.

Florida Bar, Continuing Legal Education Staff, contrib. by. Florida Administrative Practice. 9th ed. 2011. ***(978-1-4224-9709-8(7))*** Florida Bar Continuing Legal Education Pubns., The.

Fox, William F. Understanding Administrative Law. 5th rev. ed. 2009. xvi, 471p. (C). pap. 41.00 *(978-1-4224-1714-0(X))* LexisNexis Matthew Bender.

Frost, Michael H. & Bateman, Paul A. Writing Deskbook for Administrative Law Judges: An Introduction. 2010. 130p. pap. 25.00 *(978-1-59460-666-3(8))* Carolina Academic Pr.

Funk. Administrative Law. 3rd ed. 2009. pap., stu. ed. 46.95 *(978-0-7355-7827-2(3))* Wolters Kluwer Law & Business.

Funk, William F. & Seamon, Richard H. Administrative Law. 2011. ***(978-1-4548-0521-2(8))*** Kluwer Law International.

Gifford, Daniel J. Administrative Law: Cases & Materials. 2nd ed. 2010. *(978-1-4224-7687-1(1))* LexisNexis Matthew Bender.

Glicksman, Robert L. & Levy, Richard E. Administrative Law: Agency Action in Legal Context. 2010. (Illus.). lix, 1189p. *(978-1-59941-611-3(5)*, Foundation Pr.) West.

Goodnow, Frank Johnson. The Principles of the Administrative Law of the United States. 2009. 388p. pap. *(978-0-217-76812-2(1))*; 374p. pap. *(978-0-217-26237-6(7))*; 352p. pap. ***(978-1-4589-0357-0(5))*** Books LLC.

Grisinger, Joanna L. The Unwieldy American State: Administrative Politics since the New Deal. 2012. (ENG.). 328p. 85.00 ***(978-1-107-00432-0(2))*** Cambridge Univ. Pr.

Hall, Daniel E. Administrative Law: Bureaucracy in a Democracy. 5th rev. ed. 2011. (ENG., Illus.). 468p. (C). 129.80 *(978-0-13-510949-6(3)*, Prentice Hall) Prentice Hall PTR.

Hall, Daniel E. & Feldmeier, John. Administrative Law: Bureaucracy in a Democracy. 4th ed. 2008. (ENG., Illus.). 456p. (C). 140.40 *(978-0-13-500518-7(3)*, Prentice Hall) Prentice Hall PTR.

Harrington, Christine B. & Carter, Lief H. Administrative Law & Politics: Cases & Comments. 00 vols. 4th rev. ed. 2008. 429p. (C). pap. 110.00 *(978-0-87289-334-6(9))* CQ Pr.

Hickman, Kristin E. & Pierce, Richard J. Federal Administrative Law: Cases & Materials. 2010. (Illus.). xxix, 901p. ***(978-1-60930-017-3(3)***, Foundation Pr.) West.

ICC. 2009 North Carolina Administrative Code. 2009. bds. 54.00 *(978-1-58001-757-2(6))* International Code Council.

The Impact of the Presidential Signing Statement on the Department of Defense's Implementation of the Fiscal Year 2008 National Defense Authorization ACT: Hearing Before the Oversight & Investigations Subcommittee of the Committee on Armed Services, House of Representatives, One Hundred Tenth Congress, Second Session, Hearing Held, March 11, 2008. 2008. iii, 111p. *(978-0-16-082548-4(2)*, 552-070-38577-1) United States Government Printing Office.

Implementation of the U.S. Department of Justice's Special Counsel Regulation: Hearing Before the Subcommittee on Commercial & Administrative Law of the Committee on the Judiciary, House of Representatives, One Hundred Tenth Congress, Second Session, February 26, 2008. 2009. (Illus.). iii, 167p. *(978-0-16-083186-7(5)*, 552-070-39032-4) United States Government Printing Office.

Koch, Charles H., et al. Administrative Law: Cases & Materials. 6th ed. 2010. *(978-1-4224-7043-5(1))* LexisNexis Matthew Bender.

Law Officer's Pocket Manual 2002. spiral bd. 15.95 *(978-1-57018-293-8(0))* BNA Bks.

Lawson, Gary. Federal Administrative Law. 4th rev. ed. 2006. 1056p. 154.00 *(978-0-314-16739-2(0)*, West Legalworks) West.

—Federal Administrative Law. 4th ed. 2007. 1018p. *(978-0-314-16738-5(2))* West Publishing Co., College & Schl. Div.

Lifflander, Matthew L. The Impeachment of Governor Sulzer: A Story of American Politics. 2012. (Excelsior Editions Ser.). (ENG.). 336p. 24.95 ***(978-1-4384-4337-9(4))*** State Univ. of New York Pr.

Luce, Henry R. Economics of Administrative Law. Rose-Ackerman, Susan, ed. 2008. (Economic Approaches to Law Ser.). 672p. (C). 315.00 *(978-1-84542-972-0(9))* Elgar, Edward Publishing, Inc.

Mashaw, Jerry L. Creating the Administrative Constitution: The Lost One Hundred Years of American Administrative Law. 2012. (Yale Law Library Series in Legal History & Reference Ser.). (ENG.). 432p. 75.00 ***(978-0-300-17230-0(3))***; pap. 45.00 ***(978-0-300-18002-2(0))*** Yale Univ. Pr.

Mechem, Floyd R. A Treatise on the Law of Public Offices & Officers. 2009. 868p. 175.00 *(978-1-58477-973-5(X))* Lawbook Exchange, Ltd., The.

Midnight Rulemaking: Shedding Some Light: Hearing Before the Subcommittee on Commercial & Administrative Law of the Committee on the Judiciary, House of Representatives, One Hundred Eleventh Congress, First Session, February 4, 2009. 2009. (Illus.). iv, 303p. *(978-0-16-083388-5(4)*, 552-070-39203-3) United States Government Printing Office.

Model Compliant Standard Operating Procedures for Administrative Enforcement. Date not set. *(978-1-893091-72-6(4))* Parker-Wallace Publishing Co., LLC.

Office of the Federal Register (U.S.), compiled by. Code of Federal Regulations: CFR Index & Finding AIDS. 2007. (Code of Federal Regulations Ser.). (ENG.). 1087p. per. 62.00 *(978-0-16-077709-7(7)*, Office of the Federal Register) United States Government Printing Office.

—Code of Federal Regulations, Title 32, National Defense, Pt. 1-190, Revised as of July 1 2010. 2010. (ENG.). 859p. pap. 67.00 *(978-0-16-086004-1(0)*, Office of the Federal Register) United States Government Printing Office.

—Code of Federal Regulations, Title 32, National Defense, Pt. 1-190, Revised as of July 1 2011. 2011. (ENG.). 859p. pap. 67.00 ***(978-0-16-088882-3(4)***, Office of the Federal Register) United States Government Printing Office.

—Code of Federal Regulations, Title 32, National Defense, Pt. 191-399, Revised as of July 1 2010. rev. ed. 2010. (ENG.). 1101p. pap. 59.00 *(978-0-16-086005-8(9)*, Office of the Federal Register) United States Government Printing Office.

—Code of Federal Regulations, Title 32, National Defense, Pt. 191-399, Revised as of July 1 2011. rev. ed. 2011. (ENG.). 1115p. pap. 69.00 ***(978-0-16-088883-0(2)***, Office of the Federal Register) United States Government Printing Office.

—Code of Federal Regulations, Title 32, National Defense, Pt. 630-699, Revised as of July 1 2011. rev. ed. 2011. (ENG.). 420p. pap. 42.00 ***(978-0-16-088885-4(9)***, Office of the Federal Register) United States Government Printing Office.

—Code of Federal Regulations, Title 32, National Defense, Pt. 700-799, Revised as of July 1 2010. rev. ed. 2010. (ENG.). 569p. pap. 52.00 *(978-0-16-086008-9(3)*, Office of the Federal Register) United States Government Printing Office.

—Code of Federal Regulations, Title 32, National Defense, Pt. 700-799, Revised as of July 1 2011. rev. ed. 2011. (ENG.). 569p. pap. 52.00 ***(978-0-16-088886-1(7)***, Office of the Federal Register) United States Government Printing Office.

—Code of Federal Regulations, Title 32, National Defense, Pt. 800-End, Revised as of July 1 2010. rev. ed. 2010. (ENG.). 637p. pap. 53.00 *(978-0-16-086009-6(1)*, Office of the Federal Register) United States Government Printing Office.

—Code of Federal Regulations, Title 32, National Defense, Pt. 800-End, Revised as of July 1 2011. rev. ed. 2011. (ENG.). 639p. pap. 47.00 ***(978-0-16-088887-8(5)***, Office of the Federal Register) United States Government Printing Office.

—Code of Federal Regulations, Title 49, Transportation, Pt. 1-99, Revised as of October 1 2011. rev. ed. 2012. (ENG.). 767p. pap. 66.00 ***(978-0-16-089593-7(6)***, Office of the Federal Register) United States Government Printing Office.

—Code of Federal Regulations, Title 49, Transportation, Pt. 1000-1199, Revised as of October 1 2011. rev. ed. 2012. (ENG.). 346p. pap. 53.00 ***(978-0-16-089600-2(2)***, Office of the Federal Register) United States Government Printing Office.

Office of the Federal Register (U.S.), ed. Code of Federal Regulations, Title 49, Transportation, Pt. 100-177, Revised as of October 1 2011. 2012. (ENG.). 924p. pap. 70.00 ***(978-0-16-089594-4(4)***, Office of the Federal Register) United States Government Printing Office.

—Code of Federal Regulations, Title 49, Transportation, Pt. 1200-End, Revised as of October 1 2011. rev. ed. 2012. (ENG.). 494p. pap. 39.00 ***(978-0-16-089601-9(0)***, Office of the Federal Register) United States Government Printing Office.

—Code of Federal Regulations, Title 49, Transportation, Pt. 178-199, Revised as of October 1 2011. 2012. (ENG.). 688p. pap. 70.00 ***(978-0-16-089595-1(2)***, Office of the Federal Register) United States Government Printing Office.

Office of the Federal Register (U.S.), prod. Code of Federal Regulations, Title 1, General Provisions, Revised as of January 1 2012. rev. ed. 2012. (ENG.). 127p. pap. 11.00 ***(978-0-16-090051-8(4)***, Office of the Federal Register) United States Government Printing Office.

O'Reilly, James T. Careers in Administrative Law & Regulatory Practice. 2011. (ENG.). 161p. pap. 49.95 *(978-1-60442-797-4(3))* American Bar Assn.

Parker, Reginald. Administrative Law: Forrest Cool Law Review. 2011. 88p. 38.95 ***(978-1-258-06350-4(6))*** Literary Licensing, LLC.

Pennell, Jeffrey N. & Casner, A. James. Estate Planning. annuals 6th ed. 200.00 *(978-0-7355-0651-0(5)*, CCH Tax & Accounting) Toolkit Media Group.

Pennell, Jeffrey N. & Casner, James. Estate Planning, 3. 2010. 3024p. pap. 370.00 *(978-0-8080-2331-9(4))* Toolkit Media Group.

Pierce, Richard J. Administrative Law Treatise, 3 vols. 5th ed. 2010. xvi, 2241p. *(978-0-7355-8049-7(9))*; *(978-0-7355-8048-0(0))*; *(978-0-7355-8050-3(2))* Kluwer Law International.

—Administrative Law Treatise. 5th rev. ed. 2009. 740.00 *(978-0-7355-8047-3(2))* Wolters Kluwer Law & Business.

Popper, Andrew & McKee, Gwendolyn M. Administrative Law: A Contemporary Approach. 2008. (American Interactive Casebook Ser.). 1110p. 151.00 *(978-0-314-19103-8(8)*, West Legalworks) West.

Popper, Andrew F. & Mckee, Gwendolyn M. Popper, Mckee, Varona, & Harter's Administrative Law: A Contemporary Approach, 2d (Interactive Casebook Series) 2nd rev. ed. 2010. (Interactive Casebook Ser.). 1270p. 170.00 *(978-0-314-26557-0(5)*, West Legalworks) West.

Presidential Signing Statements under the Bush Administration: A Threat to Checks & Balances & the Rule of Law?: Hearing Before the Committee on the Judiciary, House of Representatives, One Hundred Tenth Congress, First Session, January 31, 2007. 2007. iv, 136p. *(978-0-16-079037-9(9)*, 552-070-36147-2) United States Government Printing Office.

Reauthorization of the Prescription Drug User Fee ACT: Hearing Before the Subcommittee on Health of the Committee on Energy & Commerce, House of Representatives, One Hundred Tenth Congress, First Session, April 17, 2007. 2008. (Illus.). v, 122p. *(978-0-16-081987-2(3)*, 552-070-38159-7) United States Government Printing Office.

Rochvarg, Arnold. Principles & Practice of Maryland Administrative Law. 2011. 396p. 150.00 *(978-1-61163-055-8(X))* Carolina Academic Pr.

Rogers, John M. Administrative Law. 2nd ed. 2008. xviii, 814p. 148.00 *(978-0-7355-7142-6(2))* Wolters Kluwer Law & Business.

Rogers, John M., et al. Administrative Law. 3rd ed. 2012. ***(978-1-4548-0704-9(0))*** Kluwer Law International.

—Administrative Law. 2nd ed. 2008. xviii, 814p. pap. *(978-0-7355-7143-3(0))* Wolters Kluwer Law & Business.

Rosenbloom, David H., et al. Public Administration & Law, Third Edition. 3rd rev. ed. 2010. (Public Administration & Public Policy Ser.). (ENG., Illus.). 353p. 79.95 *(978-1-4398-0398-1(6)*, CRC Press) Taylor & Francis Group GBR. Dist: Taylor & Francis Group.

Schwartz. Administrative Law Casebook 7e. 7th ed. 2010. 155.00 *(978-0-7355-8746-5(9))* Wolters Kluwer Law & Business.

Schwartz, Bernard. French Administrative Law & the Common-Law World: Introduction by Author T. Vanderbilt. 2006. 389p. 59.95 *(978-1-58477-704-5(4))* Lawbook Exchange, Ltd., The.

Seerden, Rene J.G.H. & Stroink, F. A. M. Administrative Law of the European Union, Its Member States & the United States: A Comparative Analysis. 2nd ed. 2007. (Illus.). 419p. (C). pap. 110.75 *(978-90-5095-720-5(X))* Intersentia Uitgevers N.V. BEL. Dist: International Specialized Bk. Services.

Signorelli, Walter P. The Crisis of Police Liability Lawsuits: Prevention & Management. 2006. xii, 162p. pap. 22.00 *(978-1-59460-228-3(X))* Carolina Academic Pr.

Strauss, Peter L. & Gellhorn, Walter. Gellhorn & Byse's Administrative Law: Cases & Comments. 11th ed. 2011. lxxxvii, 1508p. ***(978-1-60930-104-0(8)***, Foundation Pr.) West.

Strauss, Peter L. & Rakoff, Todd. Administrative Law, Cases & Comments, Revised 10th Edition, 2007 Supplement. rev. ed. 2007. (University Casebook Ser.). 204p. 25.00 *(978-1-59941-329-7(9)*, Foundation Pr.) West.

Strauss, Peter L. & Rakoff, Todd. Gellhorn & Byse's Administrative Law, Cases & Comments, by Strauss, Rakoff, Farina & Metzger. 11th rev. ed. 2011. 1450p. 190.00 ***(978-1-59941-429-4(5)***, Foundation Pr.) West.

Subcommittee Hearing on Plain Language in Paperwork: The Benefits to Small Business. 2008. iii, 69p. *(978-0-16-080913-2(4)*, 552-070-37448-5) United States Government Printing Office.

Szypszak, Charles. Understanding Law for Public Administration. rev. ed. 2009. 350p. pap. 88.95 *(978-0-7637-8011-1(1))* Jones & Bartlett Learning, LLC.

Title 17 Commodity 200-239. 2008. pap. 76.00 *(978-1-59191-319-1(5))* Government Institutes.

United States, Congress House Committee on the Judiciary Subcommittee on Commercial and Administrative Law Staff, contrib. by. Interim Report on the Administrative Law, Process & Procedure Project for the 21st Century: Committee Print: Subcommittee on Commercial & Administrative Law of the Committee on the Judiciary, House of Representatives, One Hundred Ninth Congress, Second Session, December, 2006. 2007. viii, 1436p. *(978-0-16-077978-7(2)*, 552-070-35411-5) United States Government Printing Office.

United States, Congress Senate Committee on the Judiciary Staff, contrib. by. Balancing Privacy & Security: The Privacy Implications of Government Data Mining Programs: Hearing Before the Committee on the Judiciary, United States Senate, One Hundred Tenth Congress, First Session, January 10, 2007. 2007. iv, 174p. *(978-0-16-078370-8(4)*, 552-070-35675-4) United States Government Printing Office.

Utah Administrative Code, 1994 Edition, 4 vols., Set. 195.00 *(978-1-55834-141-8(2)*, MICHIE) LEXIS Publishing.

Warren & Cram101 Textbook Reviews Staff. Administrative Law in the Political System. 2007. 152p. per. 12.95 *(978-1-4288-2510-9(X))* Cram101 Inc.

Warren, Kenneth F. Administrative Law in the Political System. 5th ed. 2010. (ENG., Illus.). 640p. (C). pap. 75.00 *(978-0-8133-4456-0(5))* Westview Pr.

Weaver, et al. Questions & Answers: Multiple Choice & Short Answer Questions & Answers. 2nd ed. 2010. ix, 169p. pap. *(978-1-4224-7710-6(X)*, Branch Line Video) LexisNexis Matthew Bender.

West. High Court Case Summaries on Administrative Law-Keyed to Funk, 3d. 3rd rev. ed. 2006. 469p. 38.00 *(978-0-314-17605-9(5)*, West Legalworks) West.

Williamson, Katherine R., ed. Revisiting & Evaluating the Congressional Review Act. 2009. 69.00 *(978-1-60692-687-1(X))* Nova Science Pubs., Inc.

ADMINISTRATIVE LIBRARIES

see Government Libraries

ADMINISTRATIVE PROCEDURE

see also Administrative Courts; Administrative Remedies; Judicial Review of Administrative Acts; Licenses

Adams, Barbara A. & Juge, Elizabeth. Roadmap to Becoming an Administrative Law Judge: How to Find ALJ Jobs, Determine Your Qualifications, & Develop Your Application. 2011. 115p. pap. 28.95 ***(978-0-9823222-1-5(6))*** CareerPro Global-Publishing Division.

Administrative Conference of the United States: Hearing Before the Subcommittee on Commercial & Administrative Law of the Committee on the Judiciary, House of Representatives, One Hundred Eleventh Congress, Second Session, May 20, 2010. 2010. (Illus.). iv, 117p. ***(978-0-16-087201-3(4)***, 552-070-42043-6) United States Government Printing Office.

Alvin Robert Thorup And Stephen G. Wood. Utah's Administrative Procedures Act. 2009. 292p. 29.99 *(978-1-4363-9693-6(X))*; pap. 19.99 *(978-1-4363-9692-9(1))* Xlibris Corp.

Amending Executive Order 12866: Good Governance or Regulatory Usurpation. 2007. v, 239p. *(978-0-16-079820-7(5)*, 552-070-36724-1) United States Government Printing Office.

Anker, Deborah E. The Law of Asylum in the United States. 4th ed. 2011. xxviii, 611p. pap. ***(978-0-314-90334-1(8))*** West Publishing Co., College & Schl. Div.

APA at 65: Is Reform Needed to Create Jobs, Promote Economic Growth, & Reduce Costs?: Hearing Before the Subcommittee on Courts, Commercial & Administrative Law of the Committee on the Judiciary, House of Representatives, One Hundred Twelfth Congress, February 28, 2011. 2011. iii, 90p. ***(978-0-16-088712-3(7)***, 552-070-42870-4) United States Government Printing Office.

Baderschneider, Maira Mildred Susanne. Der Bürger als Richter: Eine Empirische Untersuchung des Ehrenamtlichen Richters an den Allgemeinen Verwaltungsgerichten. 2010. (GER.). 326p. 86.95 *(978-3-631-61208-6(7))* Lang, Peter GmbH, Europaischer Verlag der Wissenschaften DEU. Dist: Lang, Peter.

Baldwin, Robert, et al, eds. The Oxford Handbook of Regulation. 2012. (ENG., Illus.). 680p. pap. 50.00 ***(978-0-19-965588-5(X))*** Oxford Univ. Pr., Inc.

Bowers QC, John & Misra, Eleena. Procedure in Civil Courts & Tribunals. 3rd rev. ed. 2010. 111p. pap. 51.00 *(978-0-85490-051-0(9))* Wildy, Simmonds & Hill GBR. Dist: Gaunt, Inc.

California Administrative Hearing Practice: October 2006 Update. 2nd ed. 2006. 352p. ring bd. 83.00 *(978-0-7626-1172-0(3)*, CP-32671) Continuing Education of the Bar-California.

Cave, Martin, et al, eds. The Oxford Handbook of Regulation. 2010. (Oxford Handbooks Ser.). (ENG.). 656p. 150.00 *(978-0-19-956021-9(8))* Oxford Univ. Pr., Inc.

Ch'oe, Yu. Sijang Chayul Kyuje Wa Haengjong Chido Ui Kwan'gye e Kwanhan Yon'gu. 2008. (KOR.). 95p. *(978-89-8323-892-4(5))* Korea Legislation Research Institute.

Congressional Review ACT: Hearing Before the Subcommittee on Commercial & Administrative Law of the Committee on the Judiciary, House of Representatives, One Hundred Tenth Congress, First Session, November 6, 2007. 2009. iii, 51p. *(978-0-16-082687-0(X)*, 552-070-38704-8) United States Government Printing Office.

Continuing Education of the Bar (CEB). California Administrative Hearing Practice: October 2007 Update. 2nd ed. 2007. 370p. ring bd. 88.00 *(978-0-7626-1322-9(X))* Continuing Education of the Bar-California.

CQ Press Editors & Segal, Jeffrey A., eds. Federal Regulatory Directory, 00 vols. 15th rev. ed. 2011. 960p. 195.00 *(978-1-60871-739-2(9))* CQ Pr.

CQ Press Staff, ed. Federal Regulatory Directory. 14th rev. ed. 2009. 878p. 195.00 *(978-1-60426-542-2(6))* CQ Pr.

Cram101 Textbook Reviews Staff. Outlines & Highlights for Rulemaking: How Government Agencies Write Law & Make Policy by Kerwin, ISBN. 2007. 64p. per. 9.95 *(978-1-4288-2402-7(2))* Cram101 Inc.

Dabbah, Maher M. & Hawk, Barry E. Anti-Cartel Enforcement Worldwide 3 Volume Set, 3 vols. 2009. (Antitrust & Competition Law Ser.). (ENG., Illus.). 3000p. 895.00 *(978-0-521-89721-1(1))* Cambridge Univ. Pr.

Davis, Christina L. Why Adjudicate? Enforcing Trade Rules in the WTO. 2012. (ENG., Illus.). 344p. (C). pap. 35.00 ***(978-0-691-15276-9(4))*** Princeton Univ. Pr.

Davis, Christina L., ed. Why Adjudicate? Enforcing Trade Rules in the WTO. 2012. (ENG., Illus.). 344p. (C). 80.00 ***(978-0-691-15275-2(6))*** Princeton Univ. Pr.

Durham, Blake I. & Pugh, Angelo E., eds. Cost-Benefit Analysis in the Federal Rulemaking Process. 2012. 230p. pap. ***(978-1-61942-397-8(9))*** Nova Science Pubs., Inc.

Eisner, Marc Allen, et al. Contemporary Regulatory Policy: 2nd Edition. 2nd ed. 2006. (Illus.). 340p. pap. 26.00 *(978-1-58826-411-4(4))* Rienner, Lynne Pubs.

Elgström, Ole. European Union Negotiations: Processes, Networks & Institutions. 2009. 234p. pap. 39.95 *(978-0-415-55003-1(3))* Routledge.

Federal Rulemaking & the Regulatory Process: Hearing Before the Subcommittee on Commercial & Administrative Law of the Committee on the Judiciary, House of Representatives, One Hundred Eleventh Congress, Second Session, July 27, 2010. 2010. iii, 210p. ***(978-0-16-087413-0(0)***, 552-070-42106-8) United States Government Printing Office.

Fischer, Markus. Die Verwaltungsprozessuale Klage Im Kraftfeld Zwischen Materiellem Recht und Prozessrecht. 2011. (GER.). 409p. 104.95 ***(978-3-631-62028-1(4))*** Lang, Peter GmbH, Europaischer Verlag der Wissenschaften DEU. Dist: Lang, Peter.

Formal Rulemaking & Judicial Review: Protecting Jobs & the Economy with Greater Regulatory Transparency & Accountability: Hearing Before the Subcommittee on Courts, Commercial & Administrative Law of the Committee on the Judiciary, House of Representatives, One Hundred Twelfth Congress, First Session, May 31, 2011. 2011. iii, 236p. ***(978-0-16-089656-9(8)***, 552-070-43545-0) United States Government Printing Office.

Fox, William F. Understanding Administrative Law. 5th rev. ed. 2009. xvi, 471p. (C). pap. 41.00 *(978-1-4224-1714-0(X))* LexisNexis Matthew Bender.

Friedman, Barry D. Regulation in the Regan-Bush Era: The Eruption of Presidential Influence. 2009. (ENG.). 272p. (C). pap. 26.95 *(978-0-8229-6052-2(4))* Univ. of Pittsburgh Pr.

Frost, Michael H. & Bateman, Paul A. Writing Deskbook for Administrative Law Judges: An Introduction. 2010. 130p. pap. 25.00 *(978-1-59460-666-3(8))* Carolina Academic Pr.

A

Full Committee Hearing Reducing the Regulatory Burden on Small Business: Improving the Regulatory Flexibility ACT. 2007. (Illus.). v, 90p. *(978-0-16-080051-1(X)*, 552-070-36817-5) United States Government Printing Office.

Funk, William F., et al. Federal Administrative Procedure Sourcebook. 4th ed. 2009. (ENG.). 1172p. pap. 79.95 *(978-1-59031-969-7(9))* American Bar Assn.

GAO's Undercover Investigation: Wage Theft of America's Vulnerable Workers: Hearing Before the Committee on Education & Labor, U.S. House of Representatives, One Hundred Eleventh Congress, First Session, Hearing Held in Washington, DC, March 25, 2009. 2009. iii, 76p. *(978-0-16-083265-9(9)*, 552-070-39092-8) United States Government Printing Office.

Ghosal, Vivek. Reforming Rules & Regulations: Laws, Institutions, & Implementation. 2011. (Illus.). x, 316p. E-Book *(978-0-262-28941-2(5))* MIT Pr.

Ghosal, Vivek, ed. Reforming Rules & Regulations: Laws, Institutions, & Implementation. 2010. (CESifo Seminar Ser.). (ENG., Illus.). 328p. (gr. 17). 35.00 *(978-0-262-01468-7(8))* MIT Pr.

Gibson, Bryan. The New Home Office: An Introduction (Second Edition) 2nd ed. 2008. (Introductory Ser.). 172p. pap. 36.95 *(978-1-904380-49-8(2))* Waterside Pr. GBR. Dist: International Specialized Bk. Services.

Glicksman, Robert L. & Levy, Richard E. Administrative Law: Agency Action in Legal Context. 2010. (Illus.). lix, 1189p. *(978-1-59941-611-3(5)*, Foundation Pr.) West.

Government Litigation Savings ACT: Hearing Before the Subcommittee on Courts, Commercial & Administrative Law of the Committee on the Judiciary, House of Representatives, One Hundred Twelfth Congress, First Session, on H.R. 1996, October 11, 2011. 2011. iv, 130p. ***(978-0-16-090002-0(6)***, 552-070-43786-0) United States Government Printing Office.

Grundmann, Karina. Das Recht auf Akteneinsicht im Besteuerungsverfahren. 2009. (Bochumer Schriften zum Steuerrecht Ser.). (GER.). 230p. 69.95 *(978-3-631-58983-0(2))* Lang, Peter GmbH, Europaischer Verlag der Wissenschaften DEU. Dist: Lang, Peter.

Grünewald, Benedikt. Die Betonung des Verfahrensgedankens im deutschen Verwaltungsrecht durch das Gemeinschaftsrecht. 2009. (Regensburger Beiträge zum Staats- und Verwaltungsrecht Ser.). (GER.). 344p. 86.95 *(978-3-631-59474-2(7))* Lang, Peter GmbH, Europaischer Verlag der Wissenschaften DEU. Dist: Lang, Peter.

Guerrero, Yolanda Jaimes. Doctrina Contencioso Administrativa y Tributaria. 2007. (SPA.). 185p. *(978-980-6074-34-7(3))* Tribunal Supremo de Justicia, Fundacion Gaceta Forense.

Heinzerling, Lisa & Tushnet, Mark V. The Regulatory & Administrative State: Materials, Cases, Comments. 2006. (Twenty-First Century Legal Education Ser.). (Illus.). 872p. (C). 99.00 *(978-0-19-518931-5(0))* Oxford Univ. Pr., Inc.

Hiring of Administrative Law Judges at the Social Security Administration: Hearing Before the Subcommittee on Social Security of the Committee on Ways & Means, U.S. House of Representatives, One Hundred Tenth Congress, First Session, May 1, 2007. 2009. iii, 46p. *(978-0-16-083577-3(1)*, 552-070-39295-5) United States Government Printing Office.

Hofmann, Herwig, et al. Administrative Law & Policy of the European Union. 2012. (ENG.). 1152p. 250.00 *(978-0-19-928648-5(5))* Oxford Univ. Pr., Inc.

H.R. 2837, Indian Tribal Federal Recognition Administrative Procedures ACT: Legislative Hearing Before the Committee on Natural Resources, U.S. House of Representatives, One Hundred Tenth Congress, First Session, Wednesday, October 3, 2007. 2008. iii, 119p. *(978-0-16-080684-1(4)*, 552-070-37280-6) United States Government Printing Office.

Huth, Siegfried A. Das Sekretariatshandbuch. (Duden Ser.). (GER.). 696p. *(978-3-411-05322-3(4))* Bibliographisches Institut & F. A. Brockhaus AG DEU. Dist: International Bk. Import Service, Inc.

Hutter, Bridget, ed. Anticipating Risks & Organizing Risk Regulation. 2010. (ENG., Illus.). 320p. 95.00 *(978-0-521-19309-2(5))* Cambridge Univ. Pr.

Iancu, Bogdan, ed. The Law/Politics Distinction in Contemporary Public Law Adjudication. 2009. 211p. 104.00 *(978-90-77596-65-4(8))* Eleven International Publishing NLD. Dist: International Specialized Bk. Services.

Improving & Reforming Our Nation's Surface Transportation Programs: Central Florida, Field Hearing: Hearing Before the Committee on Transportation & Infrastructure, House of Representatives, One Hundred Twelfth Congress, First Session, March 14, 2011. 2011. (Illus.). vii, 142p. ***(978-0-16-089206-6(6)***, 552-070-43203-5) United States Government Printing Office.

Improving & Reforming Our Nation's Surface Transportation Programs: Columbus, Ohio, Field Hearing: Hearing Before the Committee on Transportation & Infrastructure, House of Representatives, One Hundred Twelfth Congress, First Session, February 19, 2011. 2011. (Illus.). vii, 113p. ***(978-0-16-089482-4(4)***, 552-070-43446-1) United States Government Printing Office.

Jansen, Oswald & Langbroek, Philip, eds. Defence Rights During Administrative Investigations: A comparative study into defence rights during administrative investigations against EU fraud in England & Wales, Germany, Italy, the Netherlands, Romania, Sweden & Switzerland. 2007. 474p. pap. 129.50 *(978-90-5095-659-8(9))* Intersentia Uitgevers N.V. BEL. Dist: International Specialized Bk. Services.

Kerwin, Cornelius M. & Furlong, Scott R. Rulemaking: How Government Agencies Write Law & Make Policy, 4th Edition, 00 vols. 4th rev. ed. 2010. (Illus.). 344p. pap. 51.00 *(978-0-87289-337-5(5))* CQ Pr.

Kessler, Daniel P. Regulation versus Litigation: Perspectives from Economics & Law. 2012. (National Bureau of Economic Research Conference Report). (ENG.). 344p. pap. 85.00 ***(978-0-226-43220-5(3))*** Univ. of Chicago Pr.

Kessler, Daniel P., ed. Regulation Versus Litigation: Perspectives from Economics & Law. 2011. (National Bureau of Economic Research Conference Report). (Illus.). 344p. 110.00 *(978-0-226-43218-2(1))* Univ. of Chicago Pr.

Lee, Paul. Federal Rulemaking & Regulations. 2009. (Congressional Policies, Practices & Procedures Ser.). 79.00 *(978-1-60876-069-5(3))* Nova Science Pubs., Inc.

Magat, Wesley A., et al. Rules in the Making: A Statistical Analysis of Regulatory Agency Behavior. 2011. (RFF Policy & Governance Set Ser.). (ENG.). 182p. 99.95 *(978-1-61726-065-0(7)*, RFF Pr.) Earthscan LLC.

Manning, John & Stephenson, Matthew C. Legislation & Regulation: Cases & Materials. 2010. xli, 996p. *(978-1-59941-727-1(8)*, Foundation Pr.) West.

Manning, John F. & Stephenson, Matthew C. Legislation & Regulation. 2010. (University Casebook Ser.). 996p. 174.00 *(978-1-59941-726-4(X)*, Foundation Pr.) West.

Martin, Nie. Governance of Western Public Lands. 2009. 382p. pap. 22.50 *(978-0-7006-1676-3(4))* Univ. Pr. of Kansas.

Mashaw, Jerry L. Creating the Administrative Constitution: The Lost One Hundred Years of American Administrative Law. 2012. (Yale Law Library Series in Legal History & Reference Ser.). (ENG.). 432p. 75.00 ***(978-0-300-17230-0(3))***; pap. 45.00 ***(978-0-300-18002-2(0))*** Yale Univ. Pr.

McNeil, Christopher B. Administrative Agency Litigation. 2011. xv, 146p. pap. ***(978-1-60156-144-2(X))*** National Institute for Trial Advocacy.

Mendes, Joana. Participation in European Union Rulemaking: A Rights-Based Approach. 2011. (ENG.). 528p. 120.00 *(978-0-19-959976-9(9))* Oxford Univ. Pr., Inc.

Mitschang, Stephan, ed. Fach- und Rechtsprobleme der Baunutzungsverordnung. 2009. (Berliner Schriften zur Stadt- und Regionalplanung Ser.). (GER.). 224p. pap. 61.95 *(978-3-631-59151-2(9))* Lang, Peter GmbH, Europaischer Verlag der Wissenschaften DEU. Dist: Lang, Peter.

Morriss, Andrew P., et al. Regulation by Litigation. 2008. (ENG.). 296p. 50.00 *(978-0-300-12002-8(8))* Yale Univ. Pr.

Mulholland, Daniel, et al. Peer Review Guidebook. 4th ed. 2010. xii, 188p. *(978-1-4224-6951-4(4))* American Health Lawyers Assn.

National Research Council Staff. Public Participation in Environmental Assessment & Decision Making. Dietz, Thomas & Stern, Paul C., eds. 2008. (ENG.). 322p. pap. 59.00 *(978-0-309-12398-3(4))* National Academies Pr.

Nie, Martin. The Governance of Western Public Lands: Mapping Its Present & Future. 2008. (Illus.). 368p. *(978-0-7006-1558-2(X))* Univ. Pr. of Kansas.

Oecd Publishing. Better Regulation in Europe Better Regulation in Europe: Finland 2010. 2010. 146p. pap. 42.00 *(978-92-64-08561-9(0))* Organization for Economic Cooperation & Development.

—Better Regulation in Europe Better Regulation in Europe: Germany 2010. 2010. 164p. pap. 42.00 *(978-92-64-08587-9(4))* Organization for Economic Cooperation & Development.

Oecd Publishing, Publishing & Oecd Publishing. Better Regulation in Europe Better Regulation in Europe: Belgium 2010. 2010. 194p. pap. 42.00 *(978-92-64-08706-4(0))* Organization for Economic Cooperation & Development.

—Better Regulation in Europe Better Regulation in Europe: Sweden 2010. 2010. 188p. pap. 42.00 *(978-92-64-08781-1(8))* Organization for Economic Cooperation & Development.

Office of the Federal Register (U.S.), prod. Code of Federal Regulations, Title 1, General Provisions, Revised as of January 1 2011. rev. ed. 2011. (ENG.). 111p. pap. 11.00 *(978-0-16-087518-2(8)*, Office of the Federal Register) United States Government Printing Office.

Okitsu, Yukio. Iho Zesei to Hanketsuko: Gyosei Sosho No Kino to Kozo. 2010. (JPN.). x, 356p. *(978-4-335-31213-7(X))* Kobundo.

O'Reilly, James T. Careers in Administrative Law & Regulatory Practice. 2011. (ENG.). 161p. pap. 49.95 *(978-1-60442-797-4(3))* American Bar Assn.

Organisation for Economic Co-Operation and Development. Administrative Simplification in Viet Nam: Supporting the Competitiveness of the Vietnamese Economy. 2011. 108p. pap. ***(978-92-64-09663-9(9))*** Organization for Economic Cooperation & Development.

Organisation for Economic Co-operation and Development. Better Regulation in Europe: Denmark 2010. 2010. (Illus.). 140p. pap. 42.00 *(978-92-64-08450-6(9))* Organization for Economic Cooperation & Development.

Organisation for Economic Co-Operation and Development. Better Regulation in Europe: Ireland 2010. 2010. (Illus.). 176p. pap. 42.00 ***(978-92-64-09508-3(X))*** Organization for Economic Cooperation & Development.

Organisation for Economic Co-operation and Development. Better Regulation in Europe: Netherlands 2010. 2010. (Illus.). 146p. pap. 42.00 *(978-92-64-08451-3(7))* Organization for Economic Cooperation & Development.

—Better Regulation in Europe: Portugal 2010. 2010. (Illus.). 124p. pap. 42.00 *(978-92-64-08452-0(5))* Organization for Economic Cooperation & Development.

Organisation for Economic Co-operation and Development Staff. Administrative Simplification & e-Government in Portugal. 2009. 209p. pap. 61.00 *(978-92-64-04788-4(3))* Organization for Economic Cooperation & Development.

—Measuring & Comparing Administrative Burdens Across Countries: The Red Tape Scoreboard. 2007. pap. 65.00 *(978-92-64-00821-2(7))* Organization for Economic Cooperation & Development.

Ortiz Serrano, Adriana Catalina. Particulares Vinculados por la Fuerza Normativa de la Moralidad Administrativa. 2010. (SPA.). pap. 7.00 *(978-958-710-537-7(0))* Universidad Externado de Colombia COL. Dist: Siglo del Hombre.

Pérez, Aida Torres. Conflicts of Rights in the European Union: A Theory of Supranational Adjudication. 2009. (Oxford Studies in European Law Ser.). (ENG.). 300p. 120.00 *(978-0-19-956871-0(5))* Oxford Univ. Pr., Inc.

The Performance of Social Security Administration Appeals Hearing Offices: Hearing Before the Subcommittee on Social Security of the Committee on Ways & Means, U.S. House of Representatives, One Hundred Tenth Congress, Second Session, September 16, 2008. 2009. iii, 146p. *(978-0-16-083837-8(1)*, 552-070-39534-2) United States Government Printing Office.

Pitschas, Rainer & Walther, Harald. Mediation im Verwaltungsverfahren und Verwaltungsprozess: Beiträge der Speyrer Mediationsinitiative. 2008. (Speyerer Schriften zur Verwaltungswissenschaft Ser.). 188p. pap. 56.95 *(978-3-631-58078-3(9))* Lang, Peter GmbH, Europaischer Verlag der Wissenschaften DEU. Dist: Lang, Peter.

Radaelli, Claudio M. & Francesco, Fabrizio De. Regulatory Quality in Europe: Concepts, Measures & Policy Processes. 2012. (European Policy Studies). (ENG.). 272p. pap. 30.95 ***(978-0-7190-8670-0(1))*** Manchester Univ. Pr. GBR. Dist: Macmillan.

Radaelli, Claudio M., et al. Regulatory Quality in Europe: Concepts, Measures & Policy Processes. 2007. (European Policy Studies). (ENG., Illus.). 272p. 79.00 *(978-0-7190-7404-2(5))* Manchester Univ. Pr. GBR. Dist: Macmillan.

Raising the Agencies' Grades: Protecting the Economy, Assuring Regulatory Quality & Improving Assessments of Regulatory Need: Hearing Before the Subcommittee on Courts, Commercial & Administrative Law of the Committee on the Judiciary, House of Representatives, One Hundred Twelfth Congress, First Session, March 29, 2011. 2011. (Illus.). iii, 144p. ***(978-0-16-089239-4(2)***, 552-070-43236-1) United States Government Printing Office.

Ramji-Nogales, Jaya, et al. Refugee Roulette: Disparities in Asylum Adjudication & Proposals for Reform. (ENG.). 354p. 2011. pap. 24.00 *(978-0-8147-4106-1(1))* 2009. (Illus.). 65.00 *(978-0-8147-4074-3(X))* New York Univ. Pr.

Reducing Federal Agency Overreach: Modernizing the Regulatory Flexibility ACT: Hearing Before the Committee on Small Business, United States House of Representatives, One Hundred Twelfth Congress, First Session, Hearing Held March 30, 2011. 2011. iii, 71p. ***(978-0-16-088689-8(9)***, 552-070-42853-4) United States Government Printing Office.

Reducing Regulatory Burdens, Ensuring the Flow of Commerce, & Protecting Jobs: A Commonsense Approach to Ballast Water Regulation: Joint Hearing Before the Subcommittee on Coast Guard & Maritime Transportation & the Subcommittee on Water Resources & Environment of the Committee on Transportation & Infrastructure, House of Representatives, One Hundred Twelfth Congress, First Session, July 13, 2011. 2011. xiii, 94p. ***(978-0-16-090168-3(5)***, 552-070-43871-8) United States Government Printing Office.

Reviewing the Coast Guard's Administrative Law System: Hearing Before the Subcommittee on Coast Guard & Maritime Transportation of the Committee on Transportation & Infrastructure, House of Representatives, One Hundred Tenth Congress, First Session, July 31, 2007. 2007. xiv, 115p. *(978-0-16-083652-7(2)*, 552-070-39363-3) United States Government Printing Office.

Rochvarg, Arnold. Principles & Practice of Maryland Administrative Law. 2011. 396p. 150.00 *(978-1-61163-055-8(X))* Carolina Academic Pr.

Rogers, John M. Administrative Law. 2nd ed. 2008. xviii, 814p. 148.00 *(978-0-7355-7142-6(2))* Wolters Kluwer Law & Business.

Rogers, John M., et al. Administrative Law. 3rd ed. 2012. ***(978-1-4548-0704-9(0))*** Kluwer Law International.

—Administrative Law. 2nd ed. 2008. xviii, 814p. pap. *(978-0-7355-7143-3(0))* Wolters Kluwer Law & Business.

The Role of Science in Regulatory Reform: Hearing Before the Subcommittee on Investigations & Oversight, Committee on Science & Technology, House of Representatives, One Hundred Eleventh Congress, First Session, April 30, 2009. 2009. (Illus.). iv, 381p. *(978-0-16-083964-1(5)*, 552-070-39647-1) United States Government Printing Office.

Rulemaking Process & the Unitary Executive Theory: Hearing Before the Subcommittee on Commercial & Administrative Law of the Committee on the Judiciary, House of Representatives, One Hundred Tenth Congress, Second Session, May 6, 2008. 2009. iv, 171p. *(978-0-16-083382-3(5)*, 552-070-39197-5) United States Government Printing Office.

Schwartz, Bernard. French Administrative Law & the Common-Law World: Introduction by Author T. Vanderbilt. 2006. 389p. 59.95 *(978-1-58477-704-5(4))* Lawbook Exchange, Ltd., The.

Shen, Deyong. Xing Zheng Si Fa Jie Shi Li Jie Yu Shi Yong. 2009. (CHI.). 11p. *(978-7-5036-7014-5(2))* Law Publishing Hse., The.

Shleifer, Andrei. The Failure of Judges & the Rise of Regulators. 2012. (Walras-Pareto Lectures). (ENG., Illus.). 352p. (gr. 17). 40.00 ***(978-0-262-01695-7(8))*** MIT Pr.

Stevenson, Wayne. Administrative Law. 2010. stu. ed. 40.95 *(978-0-7355-7977-4(6))* Wolters Kluwer Law & Business.

United Nations. Report of the Ad Hoc Committee on the Administration of Justice at the United Nations, Second Session (20-24 April 2009) 2009. (ENG.). 16p. pap. 6.00 *(978-92-1-820106-5(9))* United Nations Pubns.

United States, Congress House Committee on the Judiciary Subcommittee on Commercial and Administrative Law Staff, contrib. by. Amending Executive Order 12866: Good Governance or Regulatory Usurpation?: Hearing Before the Subcommittee on Commercial & Administrative Law of the Committee on the Judiciary, House of Representatives, One Hundred Tenth Congress, First Session, February 13, 2007. 2007. iv, 312p. *(978-0-16-078550-4(2)*, 552-070-35819-6) United States Government Printing Office.

—Interim Report on the Administrative Law, Process & Procedure Project for the 21st Century: Committee Print: Subcommittee on Commercial & Administrative Law of the Committee on the Judiciary, House of Representatives, One Hundred Ninth Congress, Second Session, December, 2006. 2007. viii, 1436p. *(978-0-16-077978-7(2)*, 552-070-35411-5) United States Government Printing Office.

Weitz, Tobias Timo. Gerichtsnahe Mediation in der Verwaltungs-, Sozial- und Finanzgerichtsbarkeit. 2008. (Schriften zum deutschen und europäischen öffentlichen Recht Ser.). 548p. pap. 124.95 *(978-3-631-57965-7(9))* Lang, Peter GmbH, Europaischer Verlag der Wissenschaften DEU. Dist: Lang, Peter.

Yi, Chong-Han. P'yojun Piyong Model Ch'ukchong Sarye. 2009. (Illus.). 171p. *(978-89-8323-901-3(8))* Korea Legislation Research Institute.

Zhen, Zhen. Min Shi Xing Zheng Jian Cha Jian du Nan Dian Yu Dui Ce Yan Jiu. 2009. (CHI.). *(978-7-5036-9661-9(3))* Law Publishing Hse., The.

ADMINISTRATIVE REMEDIES

see also Ombudsman; Tax Protests and Appeals

Buck, Trevor, et al. The Ombudsman Enterprise & Administrative Justice. 2010. (Illus.). 308p. 134.95 *(978-0-7546-7556-3(4))* Ashgate Publishing Co.

Fowler, Renn C. & Vitaro, Samuel A. The Art of Advocacy: What to Do & How to Do It Before the MSPB & Arbitrators. 2011. (Illus.). viii, 241p. pap. ***(978-1-934651-53-7(2))*** Dewey Pubns., Inc.

—MSPB Charges & Penalties: A Charging Manual. 3rd ed. 2006. 150.00 *(978-1-932612-64-6(5))* Dewey Pubns., Inc.

Fowler, Renn C. & Vitaro, Samuel A. MSPB, Charges & Penalties: A Charging Manual. 4th ed. 2011. xx, 631p. pap. ***(978-1-934651-42-1(7))*** Dewey Pubns., Inc.

Ingenix, Inc. Staff. Appeals Made Easy 2001. spiral bd. 99.95 *(978-1-56337-384-8(X))* OptumInsight, Inc.

Juta's Statutes Editors, ed. Promotion of Equality & Prevention of Unfair Discrimination Act, Promotion of Equality Access to Information Act, Promotion of Administrative Justic Act & Related Materials. 2010. pap. 15.00 *(978-0-7021-8454-3(3))* Gaunt, Inc.

Kresser, Daniel. Die Bedeutung der Form für Begriff und Rechtsfolgen des Verwaltungsakts. 2009. (Dresdner Schriften zum Öffentlichen Recht Ser.). (GER.). 348p. pap. 81.95 *(978-3-631-59060-7(1))* Lang, Peter GmbH, Europaischer Verlag der Wissenschaften DEU. Dist: Lang, Peter.

Pitschas, Rainer & Walther, Harald. Mediation im Verwaltungsverfahren und Verwaltungsprozess: Beiträge der Speyrer Mediationsinitiative. 2008. (Speyerer Schriften zur Verwaltungswissenschaft Ser.). 188p. pap. 56.95 *(978-3-631-58078-3(9))* Lang, Peter GmbH, Europaischer Verlag der Wissenschaften DEU. Dist: Lang, Peter.

Scully-Hayes, Kathleen & Cody, Daniel A. A Practical Guide to Medicare Appeals. 2007. (Practical Guides (American Bar Association) Ser.). (ENG.). 410p. per. 79.95 *(978-1-59031-827-0(7))* American Bar Assn.

United States, Congress House Committee on Government Reform Subcommittee on the Federal Workforce and Agency Organization Staff, contrib. by. Establishing a Commission to Recommend Improvements for the Federal Employees Appeals Process: Hearing Before the Subcommittee on the Federal Workforce & Agency Organization of the Committee on Government Reform, House of Representatives, One Hundred Ninth Congress, Second Session, July 11, 2006. 2007. (Illus.). iii, 104p. *(978-0-16-078624-2(X)*, 552-070-35868-4) United States Government Printing Office.

Weitz, Tobias Timo. Gerichtsnahe Mediation in der Verwaltungs-, Sozial- und Finanzgerichtsbarkeit. 2008. (Schriften zum deutschen und europäischen öffentlichen Recht Ser.). 548p. pap. 124.95 *(978-3-631-57965-7(9))* Lang, Peter GmbH, Europaischer Verlag der Wissenschaften DEU. Dist: Lang, Peter.

ADMINISTRATIVE RESPONSIBILITY

Here are entered works on the personal liability of government officials to the state or to individuals for wrongful acts committed in office. Works on the liability of the state for wrongful acts of officials are entered under Government Liability. Works on criminal offenses committed by government officials in the performance of their duties are entered under Misconduct in Office. Works on specific offenses are entered under the name of the offense, e.g. Bribery.

see also Government Liability; Impeachments; Misconduct in Office

Accountability During Contingency Operations: Preventing & Fighting Corruption in Contracting & Establishing & Maintaining Appropriate Controls on Materiel. 2008. iii, 94p. *(978-0-16-082614-6(4)*, 552-070-38632-7) United States Government Printing Office.

Akoh, Harry. How a Country Treats Its Citizens No Longer Exclusive Domestic Concern. 2009. 252p. pap. *(978-3-639-16941-6(7))* VDM Verlag Dr. Mueller e.K.

Bonafe, Beatrice I. The Relationship Between State & Individual Responsibility for International Crimes. 2009. *(978-90-04-17331-6(5))* BRILL.

Cooper, Cynthia & Holtzman, Elizabeth. Cheating Justice: How Bush & Cheney Attacked the Rule of Law, Plotted to Avoid Prosecution, & What We Can Do about It. 2012. (ENG.). 224p. 26.95 **(978-0-8070-0321-3(2))** Beacon Pr.
Cornford, Tom. Towards a Public Law of Tort. 2008. 278p. 124.95 *(978-0-7546-4683-9(1))* Ashgate Publishing Co.
Davis, Jeffrey. Justice Across Borders: The Struggle for Human Rights in U. S. Courts. 2008. (ENG., Illus.). 318p. 85.00 *(978-0-521-87817-3(9))*; pap. 30.99 *(978-0-521-70240-9(2))* Cambridge Univ. Pr.
Epp, Charles R. Making Rights Real: Activists, Bureaucrats, & the Creation of the Legalistic State. 2010. (Chicago Series in Law & Society Ser.). (ENG., Illus.). 368p. 72.00 *(978-0-226-21164-0(9))*; pap. 24.00 *(978-0-226-21165-7(7))* Univ. of Chicago Pr.
Goodin, Robert E. Innovating Democracy: Democratic Theory & Practice after the Deliberative Turn. 2012. (ENG.). 336p. pap. 35.00 **(978-0-19-965055-2(1))** Oxford Univ. Pr., Inc.
Heyer, Barbara A. A Citizen's Right: Holding Law Enforcement Agencies Accountable. 2nd ed. 2011. v, 161p. pap. **(978-0-615-53070-3(2))** Duversity Pubns.
Hood, C. The Blame Game: Spin, Bureaucracy & Self-Preservation in Government. 2010. (ENG., Illus.). 242p. (C). 39.95 *(978-0-691-12995-2(9))* Princeton Univ. Pr.
Hussain, Nasser. When Governments Break the Law: The Rule of Law & the Prosecution of the Bush Administration. Sarat, Austin, ed. 2010. (ENG.). 240p. pap. 25.00 *(978-0-8147-3985-3(7))* New York Univ. Pr.
Lawrence, Rebecca. Shifting Responsibilities & Shifting Terrains: State Responsibility, Corporate Social Responsibility, & Indigenous Claims. 2009. (Stockholm Studies in Sociology Ser.). (Illus.). 311p. pap. 125.00 *(978-91-86071-19-6(X))* Stockholms Universitet SWE. Dist: Coronet Bks.
Mayer-Rieckh, Alexander & de Greiff, Pablo. Justice as Prevention: Vetting Public Employees in Transitional Societies. 2008. (Columbia / SSRC Book Ser.). (ENG., Illus.). 566p. (gr. 17). pap. 35.00 *(978-0-9790772-1-0(4))* Social Science Research Council, The.
Power, Timothy J. & Taylor, Matthew M., eds. Corruption & Democracy in Brazil: The Struggle for Accountability. 2011. (ND Kellogg Inst Int'l Studies). (ENG., Illus.). 344p. pap. 38.00 *(978-0-268-03894-6(5))* Univ. of Notre Dame Pr.
Rahman, Taiabur. Parliamentary Control & Government Accountability in South Asia: A Comparative Analysis of Bangladesh, India & Sri Lanka. (ENG., Illus.). 272p. 2012. pap. 42.95 **(978-0-415-53318-8(X))** 2007. 160.00 *(978-0-415-40498-3(3))* Routledge.
Savoie, Donald J. Court Government & the Collapse of Accountability in Canada & the United Kingdom. 2008. (IPAC Series in Public Management & Governance Ser.). (ENG.). 416p. *(978-0-8020-9870-2(3))*; pap. *(978-0-8020-9579-4(8))* Univ. of Toronto Pr.
Sheppard, Stephen. I Do Solemnly Swear: The Moral Obligations of Legal Officials. 2009. (ENG.). 304p. 93.00 *(978-0-521-51368-5(5))*; pap. 29.99 *(978-0-521-73508-7(4))* Cambridge Univ. Pr.
Stephens, Beth. International Human Rights Litigation in U.S. Courts. 2008. xxxiv, 619p. (C). *(978-1-57105-353-4(0))* BRILL.
Sullivan, John J. & Ranalli, Michael D. Civil Liabilities of New York State Law Enforcement Officers. 3rd ed. 2010. (ENG.). 90p. pap. 10.95 *(978-1-932777-98-7(9)*, LLP) Looseleaf Law Pubns., Inc.
Wilson, Valerie Plame. Fair Game: How a Top CIA Agent Was Betrayed by Her Own Government. 2010. (ENG.). 432p. mass mkt. 7.99 *(978-1-4516-2404-5(2)*, Pocket Star) Pocket Star.
—Fair Game: How a Top CIA Agent Was Betrayed by Her Own Government. (ENG., Illus.). 432p. 2008. pap. 16.00 *(978-1-4165-3762-5(7))* 2010. pap. 15.00 *(978-1-4516-2387-1(9))* Simon & Schuster.
—Fair Game: My Life as a Spy, My Betrayal by the White House. l.t. ed. 2008. (Thorndike Nonfiction Ser.). (Illus.). 635p. 32.95 *(978-1-4104-0542-5(7))* Thorndike Pr.

ADMINISTRATOR-TEACHER RELATIONSHIPS

see Teacher-Administrator Relationships

ADMINISTRATORS AND EXECUTORS

see Executors and Administrators

ADMIRALS

Adamson, Hans Christian. Admiral Thunderbolt: The Spectacular Career of Peter Wessel, Norway's Greatest Sea Hero. 2011. 356p. 51.95 **(978-1-258-06036-7(1))** Literary Licensing, LLC.
Aldrigde, David Denis. Admiral Sir John Norris: And the British Naval Expeditions to the Baltic Sea, 1715-1727. 2010. (ENG., Illus.). 384p. 59.95 *(978-91-85505-31-7(0))* Nordic Academic Pr., Sweden SWE. Dist: Independent Pubs. Group.
Allen, Thomas B. & Polmar, Norman. Rickover: Father of the Nuclear Navy, 56 vols. 2007. (Military Profiles Ser.). (Illus.). 128p. 21.95 *(978-1-57488-445-6(X))*; pap. 13.95 *(978-1-57488-704-4(1))* Potomac Bks., Inc.
Allison, Robert J. Stephen Decatur: American Naval Hero, 1779-1820. 2007. (Illus.). 253p. per. 22.95 *(978-1-55849-583-8(5))* Univ. of Massachusetts Pr.
Baker, Richard. The Terror of Tobermory: Vice Admiral Sir Gilbert Stephenson KBE, CB, CMG. rev. ed. 2006. (Illus.). 170p. per. 16.95 *(978-1-84341-023-2(0))* Birlinn, Ltd. GBR. Dist: Casemate Pubs. & Bk. Distributors, LLC.
Barker, A. J. & Orde, Denis. In the Shadow of Nelson. 2008. (Illus.). 304p. 60.00 *(978-1-84415-782-2(2))* Pen & Sword Bks. Ltd. GBR. Dist: Casemate Pubs. & Bk. Distributors, LLC.
Baste, Pierre. A Marine of the Imperial Guard: Eyewitness to the French Failure in Spain 1808. Mehon, Timothy, tr. 2009. 82p. pap. 15.38 *(978-1-934840-50-4(5))* Nimble Bks. LLC.
Beatty, William. Authentic Narrative of the Death of Lord Nelson. 2007. 56p. per. *(978-1-4065-3699-7(7))* Dodo Pr.
Black, Barry C. From the Hood to the Hill: A Story of Overcoming, 0 vols. 2006. 240p. 22.99 *(978-0-7852-1881-4(5))* Nelson, Thomas Inc.
Borneman, Walter R. The Admirals: Nimitz, Halsey, Leahey, & King — The 5-Star Admirals Who Won the War at Sea. 2012. (ENG., Illus.). 576p. 29.99 **(978-0-316-09784-0(5))** Little Brown & Co.
Buell, Thomas. Quiet Warrior. 2009. 0560p. pap. 24.95 *(978-1-59114-085-6(4))* Naval Institute Pr.
Bush, Elizabeth Kauffman. America's First Frogman: The Draper Kauffman Story. (Illus.). 240p. 29.95 *(978-1-59114-098-6(6))* Naval Institute Pr.
Callo, Joseph. John Paul Jones. 2009. (Illus.). 288p. pap. 18.95 *(978-1-59114-104-4(4))* Naval Institute Pr.
Clark, Charles E. My Fifty Years in the Navy. 2009. (ENG.). 379p. pap. 32.75 *(978-1-117-60709-2(7))* BiblioBazaar.
—My Fifty Years in the Navy. 2007. (ENG.). 380p. 48.95 *(978-0-548-33303-7(3))*; per. 33.95 *(978-1-4326-9195-0(3))* Kessinger Publishing, LLC.
—My Fifty Years in the Navy. 2007. (ENG.). 380p. per. *(978-1-4067-3955-8(3))* Read Bks.
Clarke, James Stanier & McArthur, John. The Life & Services of Horatio Viscount Nelson From His Lordship's Manuscripts. 2010. (Cambridge Library Collection - History Ser.). (ENG.). 442p. pap. 32.99 *(978-1-108-02218-7(9))*; 536p. pap. 39.99 *(978-1-108-02217-0(0))*; (Illus.). 558p. pap. 39.99 *(978-1-108-02216-3(2))* Cambridge Univ. Pr.
Clements, Jonathan. Admiral Togo: The Nelson of the East. 2010. (ENG., Illus.). 320p. pap. 19.95 *(978-1-906598-62-4(2))* Haus Publishing GBR. Dist: Consortium Bk. Sales & Distribution.
Cochrane, Thomas. The Life of Thomas, Lord Cochrane: Tenth Earl of Dundonald, G. C. B. , Admiral of the Re. 2006. (ENG.). 274p. pap. 21.99 *(978-1-4264-6927-5(6))*; 302p. pap. 24.99 *(978-1-4264-7009-7(5))* BiblioBazaar.
Cordingly, David. Cochrane: The Real Master & Commander. 2008. (ENG., Illus.). 448p. pap. 19.00 *(978-1-59691-587-9(0))* Bloomsbury Publishing.
Crowe, William J. Line of Fire. 2010. (ENG.). 368p. pap. 22.99 *(978-1-4516-1362-9(8))* Simon & Schuster.
David, Wragg. Fighting Admirals of Wwii. 2009. 224p. 39.95 *(978-1-59114-269-0(5))* Naval Institute Pr.
de Kay, James Tertius. A Rage for Glory: The Life of Commodore Stephen Decatur, USN. 2007. (ENG., Illus.). 256p. pap. 17.95 *(978-1-4165-6831-5(X)*, Free Pr.) Free Pr.
Delaforce, Patrick. Nelson's First Love. 2011. (Illus.). 288p. 30.00 **(978-1-4456-0365-0(9))** Amberley Publishing GBR. Dist: Casemate Pubs. & Bk. Distributors, LLC.
Dictionary of Admirals of the U. S. Navy Vol. III: 1919-1941. Date not set. 49.95 *(978-1-55750-123-3(8))* Naval Institute Pr.
Duffy, James P. Lincoln's Admiral: The Civil War Campaigns of David Farragut. 2008. (ENG. Illus.). 288p. 9.99 *(978-0-7858-2096-3(5)*, 0785820965) Book Sales, Inc.
Elson, Bryan. Nelson's Yankee Captain: The Life of Boston Loyalist Sir Benjamin Hallowell. 2008. (ENG., Illus.). 416p. 29.95 *(978-0-88780-751-0(9))* Formac Publishing Co., Ltd. CAN. Dist: Casemate Pubs. & Bk. Distributors, LLC.
Epkenhans, Michael. Tirpitz: Architect of the German High Seas Fleet. 2008. (Military Profiles Ser.). (Illus.). 136p. pap. 13.95 *(978-1-57488-732-7(7))* Potomac Bks., Inc.
—Tirpitz: Architect of the German High Seas Fleet. 2008. (Military Profiles Ser.). (Illus.). 136p. 21.95 *(978-1-57488-444-9(1))* Potomac Bks., Inc.
Fox, Stephen. Wolf of the Deep: Raphael Semmes & the Notorious Confederate Raider CSS Alabama. 2008. (Vintage Civil War Library). (ENG., Illus.). 336p. pap. 14.95 *(978-1-4000-9542-1(5)*, Vintage) Knopf Doubleday Publishing Group.
Freemen, Richard. Great Edwardian Naval Feud: Beresford's Vendetta Against 'Jackie' Fisher. 2009. (Illus.). 288p. 50.00 *(978-1-84884-083-6(7)*, Pen & Sword Bks. Ltd. GBR. Dist: Casemate Pubs. & Bk. Distributors, LLC.
Gravely, Samuel & Stillwell, Paul. Trailblazer: The U. S. Navy's First Black Admiral. 2010. (Illus.). 384p. 34.95 *(978-1-59114-338-3(1))* Naval Institute Pr.
Hannay, David. Rodney. 2010. (ENG.). 236p. pap. 26.75 *(978-1-171-58845-7(8))* 2010. (ENG.). 240p. pap. 26.75 *(978-1-177-96858-4(4))* 2010. (ENG.). 240p. pap. 26.75 *(978-1-176-95230-0(7))* 2009. 230p. 28.99 *(978-1-115-40148-7(3))* 2009. 230p. 32.99 *(978-1-115-40150-0(5))* 2009. 230p. pap. 25.75 *(978-1-115-40146-3(7))* 2009. (ENG.). 229p. pap. 22.99 *(978-1-115-40143-2(2)*, BiblioLife) 2009. (ENG.). 229p. pap. 20.99 *(978-1-115-40140-1(8)*, BiblioLife) 2009. 248p. 28.99 *(978-1-110-59063-6(6))* 2009. 248p. pap. 25.75 *(978-1-110-59060-5(1))* 2009. (ENG.). 246p. pap. 22.99 *(978-1-110-59058-2(X)*, BiblioLife) 2009. (ENG.). 246p. pap. 20.99 *(978-1-110-59057-5(1)*, BiblioLife) 2008. 232p. 24.99 *(978-0-559-39111-8(0))* 2008. 232p. pap. 24.75 *(978-0-559-39110-1(2))* 2008. 232p. 27.99 *(978-0-554-49244-5(X))* 2008. 232p. 24.99 *(978-0-554-49249-0(0))* 2008. 232p. pap. 25.75 *(978-0-554-49245-2(8))* 2008. 232p. pap. 24.75 *(978-0-554-49247-6(4))* BiblioBazaar.
—Rodney. 2009. (Illus.). 128p. pap. *(978-1-150-70181-8(1))* Books LLC.
—Rodney. (American Revolutionary Ser.). (Illus.). vi, 222p. reprint ed. lib. bdg. 40.50 *(978-0-8398-0805-3(4))* Irvington Pubs.
Hanser, Lawrence M., et al. Developing Senior Navy Leaders: Requirements for Flag Officer Expertise Today & in the Future. 2008. (Illus.). 176p. pap. 28.00 *(978-0-8330-4294-1(7)*, mg-618) RAND Corp., The.
Harper, Glyn & Hayward, Joel, eds. Born to Lead? Portraits of New Zealand Commanders. 2010. (ENG., Illus.). 252p. pap. 27.99 *(978-0-908988-33-4(8))* Exisle Publishing Ltd. NZL. Dist: BookMasters Distribution Services (BDS).
Harris, Brayton. Admiral Nimitz: The Commander of the Pacific Ocean Theater. 2012. (ENG., Illus.). 256p. 26.00 **(978-0-230-10765-6(6))** Palgrave Macmillan.
Harrison, James. The Life of the Right Honourable Horatio Lord Viscount Nelson. 2008. 308p. 29.99 *(978-0-554-26190-4(1))* 2008. 380p. 31.99 *(978-0-554-26191-1(X))* 2008. 308p. 28.99 *(978-0-554-35493-4(4))* 2008. 380p. 29.99 *(978-0-554-35494-1(2))* 2007. (ENG.). 266p. pap. 21.99 *(978-1-4346-0588-7(4))* Vol. 1. 2007. (ENG.). 304p. pap. 24.99 *(978-1-4346-0663-1(5))* BiblioBazaar.
—The Life of the Right Honourable Horatio Lord Viscount Nelson. 2007. 552p. per. *(978-1-4065-3279-1(7))* Dodo Pr.
—The Life of the Right Honourable Horatio Lord Viscount Nelson. 2007. 252p. per. *(978-1-4068-1697-6(3))* Echo Library.
—The Life of the Right Honourable Horatio Lord Viscount Nelson, Vol. 2. 2007. 348p. pap. 15.45 *(978-1-60424-795-4(9)*, Book Jungle) Standard Pubns., Inc.
Hattendorf, John B. & Elleman, Bruce A., eds. Nineteen-Gun Salute: Case Studies of Operational, Strategic, & Diplomatic Naval Leadership During the 20th & Early 21st Centuries. 2010. (ENG., Illus.). 284p. pap. 38.00 *(978-1-884733-66-6(2)*, Dept. of the Navy) United States Government Printing Office.
Headley, Phineas Camp. Old Salamander. (Heroes of the Rebellion Ser.). 342p. reprint ed. 98.00 *(978-0-7222-9417-8(4))* Library Reprints, Inc.
Hills, A-M. E. Nelson: A Medical Casebook. 2006. (ENG., Illus.). 320p. 39.95 *(978-1-86227-321-4(9))* History Pr. Ltd.,The GBR. Dist: Independent Pubs. Group.
Hoey, Brian. Mountbatten: The Private Story. 2008. (ENG., Illus.). 244p. pap. 22.95 *(978-0-7509-5036-7(6))* History Pr. Ltd.,The GBR. Dist: Independent Pubs. Group.
Holloway, James L. & Holloway, James L., III. Aircraft Carriers at War: A Personal Retrospective of Korea, Vietnam, & the Soviet Confrontation. 2007. (Illus.). 479p. 36.95 *(978-1-59114-391-8(8))* Naval Institute Pr.
Hoppin, J. M. (James Mason). Life of Andrew Hull Foote, Rear-Admiral United States Navy by James Mason Hoppin, with a Portrait & Illustrations. 2006. 448p. per. 26.99 *(978-1-4255-4924-4(1))* MPublishing.
Hoyt, Edwin P. How They Won the War in the Pacific: Nimitz & His Admirals. 2011. (ENG., Illus.). 512p. pap. 21.95 *(978-0-7627-7285-8(9)*, Lyons Pr.) Globe Pequot Pr., The.
—The Last Kamikaze: The Story of Admiral Matome Ugaki, 1 vol. 2009. 256p. pap. 20.00 *(978-0-313-36065-7(0)*, BC4067, Praeger Pubs.) Greenwood Publishing Group, Inc.
Joinville, Prince de. Memoirs of the Prince de Joinville. 2008. 268p. 28.99 *(978-0-554-22291-2(4))*; 25.99 *(978-0-554-31594-2(7))* BiblioBazaar.
—Memoirs of the Prince de Joinville. Loyd, Lady Mary, tr. 2007. 260p. per. *(978-1-4065-3531-0(1))* Dodo Pr.
Jones, Ken & Kelley Jr., Hubert. Admiral Arleigh, 31 Knot, Burke: The Story of A Fighting Sailor. 2011. 230p. 46.95 **(978-1-258-06162-3(7))** Literary Licensing, LLC.
Kelly, Patrick J. Tirpitz & the Imperial German Navy. 2011. (ENG., Illus.). 608p. 45.00 *(978-0-253-35593-5(1)*, 0253355931) Indiana Univ. Pr.
Langer, Howard J. The World War II 100: A Ranking of the Most Influential Figures of the Second World War. 2008. (ENG., Illus.). 336p. 12.99 *(978-0-7858-2366-7(2)*, 0785823662) Book Sales, Inc.
Laughton, John Knox. Nelson. 2009. 250p. 28.99 *(978-1-110-69762-5(7))* 2009. 250p. 28.99 *(978-1-110-69763-2(5))* 2009. 250p. pap. 25.75 *(978-1-110-69759-5(7))* 2009. 250p. pap. 25.75 *(978-1-110-69761-8(9))* 2008. 272p. 25.99 *(978-0-554-40891-0(0))* 2008. 272p. 28.99 *(978-0-554-40876-7(7))* 2008. 272p. pap. 26.75 *(978-0-554-40887-3(2))* 2008. 272p. pap. 27.75 *(978-0-554-40879-8(1))* BiblioBazaar.
—Nelson. 2007. (ENG.). 252p. 41.95 *(978-0-548-10810-9(2))* Kessinger Publishing, LLC.
—Nelson & His Companions in Arms. 2009. 184p. pap. *(978-0-217-51835-2(4))* Books LLC.
—Nelson & His Companions in Arms. 2007. (ENG.). 432p. 51.95 *(978-0-548-13798-7(6))* 2006. pap. 36.95 *(978-1-4286-4967-5(0))* Kessinger Publishing, LLC.
Laver, Harry S. & Matthews, Jeffrey J., eds. The Art of Command: Military Leadership from George Washington to Colin Powell. 2010. (ENG., Illus.). 294p. pap. 21.95 *(978-0-8131-2660-9(6))* Univ. Pr. of Kentucky.
Lavo, Carl. Galloping Ghost. 2011. 240p. pap. 19.95 **(978-1-61251-046-0(9))** Naval Institute Pr.
LaVO, Carl. The Galloping Ghost: The Extraordinary Life of Submarine Legend Eugene Fluckey. 2007. (Illus.). 206p. 28.95 *(978-1-59114-456-4(6))* Naval Institute Pr.
Lawrence, William P. & Rausa, Rosario. Tennessee Patriot: The Naval Career of Vice Admiral William P. Lawrence, U. S. Navy. 2006. (Illus.). 230p. 28.95 *(978-1-59114-700-8(X))* Naval Institute Pr.
Ledbury, Lady Biddulph of. Charles Philip Yorke, Fourth Earl of Hardwicke, Vice-Admiral R. N. 2006. 222p. pap. 20.99 *(978-1-4264-2182-2(6))* 2007. (ENG.). 214p. pap. 22.99 *(978-1-4264-2250-8(4))* BiblioBazaar.
Mackenzie, Alexander. The Life of Stephen Decatur: A Commodore in the Navy of the United States. 443p. reprint ed. 98.00 *(978-0-7222-8553-4(1))* Library Reprints, Inc.
Maffeo, Steven E. Seize, Burn, or Sink: The Thoughts & Words of Admiral Lord Horatio Nelson. 2006. (ENG., Illus.). 672p. per. 110.00 *(978-0-8108-5781-0(2))* Scarecrow Pr., Inc.
Mahan, Alfred Thayer. The Life of Nelson: The Embodiment of the Sea Power of Great Britain. 2007. 398p. pap. 25.99 *(978-1-4346-0590-0(6))*; Vol. 2. (ENG.). 344p. pap. 23.99 *(978-1-4346-0591-7(4))* BiblioBazaar.
—The Life of Nelson: The Embodiment of the Sea Power of Great Britain. 2011. (Cambridge Library Collection - History Ser.). (ENG.). 492p. pap. 35.99 *(978-1-108-02605-5(2))*; (Illus.). 526p. pap. 39.99 *(978-1-108-02604-8(4))* Cambridge Univ. Pr.
—The Life of Nelson: The Embodiment of the Sea Power of Great Britain. 2007. (ENG.). 820p. per. 55.95 *(978-1-4325-6334-9(3))* Kessinger Publishing, LLC.
Mahan, Alfred Thayer. Types of Naval Officers: Drawn from the History of the British Navy. 2007. (ENG.). 300p. pap. 21.99 *(978-1-4346-2939-5(2))*; 334p. pap. 24.99 *(978-1-4346-2963-0(5))* BiblioBazaar.
—Types of Naval Officers: Drawn from the History of the British Navy. 2008. (Illus.). 308p. pap. *(978-1-4065-7034-2(6))* Dodo Pr.
—Types of Naval Officers: Drawn from the History of the British Navy. 2010. 540p. pap. 34.36 *(978-1-162-99522-9(X))* 2010. 540p. 46.36 **(978-1-163-44760-4(9))** 2007. (ENG.). 540p. 57.95 *(978-0-548-14102-1(9))* 2006. pap. 42.95 *(978-1-4286-5301-6(5))* Kessinger Publishing, LLC.
Marder, Arthur J. & Richmond, Herbert. Portrait of an Admiral: The Life & Papers of Herbert Richmond. 2011. 408p. 54.95 **(978-1-258-08522-3(4))** Literary Licensing, LLC.
Marx, John Locke & Jones, Mary. A Naval Life: The Edited Diaries & Papers of Admiral John Locke Marx 1852-1939. 2007. (Illus.). 304p. pap. *(978-0-9553095-0-2(6))* Persona Pr.
Mayne, Richard O. Betrayed: Scandal, Politics, & Canadian Naval Leadership. 2007. (Studies in Canadian Military History Ser.). (ENG., Illus.). 296p. pap. *(978-0-7748-1296-2(6))* Univ. of British Columbia Pr.
Mayne, Richard O. & Mayne, Richard. Betrayed: Scandal, Politics, & Canadian Naval Leadership. 2006. (Studies in Canadian Military History). (ENG., Illus.). 296p. *(978-0-7748-1295-5(8))* Univ. of British Columbia Pr.
McGeoch, Ian. Mountbatten of Burma: Captain of War, Guardian of Peace. 2009. (ENG., Illus.). 288p. 34.95 *(978-1-84425-686-0(3)*, 1844256863) Haynes Publishing PLC GBR. Dist: MBI Distribution Services/Quayside Distribution.
Mould, Paul, ed. In Drake's Wake: The Later Voyages, 4 vols, Vol. 3. 2009. 268p. pap. 35.00 *(978-1-58690-092-2(7))* Mould, Paul Publishing GBR. Dist: Gazelle Bk.Services Ltd.
Mueller, Michael. Canaris: The Life & Death of Hitler's Spymaster. Brooks, Geoffrey, tr. from GER. 2007. (Illus.). 368p. 34.95 *(978-1-59114-101-3(X))* Naval Institute Pr.
Nelson, Horatio. Letters of Lord Nelson to Lady Hamilton. 2006. pap. *(978-1-4068-3451-2(3))* Echo Library.
—The Letters of Lord Nelson to Lady Hamilton. 2009. 236p. 23.99 *(978-0-559-10599-9(1))*; 27.99 *(978-0-559-10589-0(4))*; pap. 22.99 *(978-0-559-10592-0(4))*; pap. 24.75 *(978-0-559-10597-5(5))* BiblioBazaar.
—The Letters of Lord Nelson to Lady Hamilton. 2007. 184p. per. *(978-1-4065-3071-1(9))* Dodo Pr.
Olsen Cec, Usn (Ret). The King Bee: A Biography of Admiral Ben Moreell. 2007. 356p. 35.95 *(978-1-4251-5918-4(4))* Trafford Publishing.
Osler, Edward. The Life of Admiral Viscount Exmouth. 2008. 484p. 31.99 *(978-0-559-26939-4(0))* 2008. 484p. pap. 36.75 *(978-0-559-26936-3(6))* 2008. 240p. 27.99 *(978-0-554-26549-0(4))* 2008. 240p. 24.99 *(978-0-554-35852-9(2))* 2007. (ENG.). 216p. pap. 20.99 *(978-1-4346-1334-9(8))* 2007. (ENG.). 238p. pap. 22.99 *(978-1-4346-1386-8(0))* BiblioBazaar.
—The Life of Admiral Viscount Exmouth. 2009. 200p. pap. *(978-0-217-94234-8(2))*; 158p. pap. *(978-1-4589-2467-4(X))* Books LLC.
—The Life of Admiral Viscount Exmouth. 2009. 214p. pap. *(978-1-4099-7400-0(6))* Dodo Pr.
Pengelly, Colin. Sir Samuel Hood & the Battle of the Chesapeake. 2009. (New Perspectives on Maritime History & Nautical Archaeology Ser.). (ENG., Illus.). 368p. 69.95 *(978-0-8130-3313-6(6))* Univ. Pr. of Florida.
Persico, Joseph E. Roosevelt's Centurions: FDR & the Commanders He Led to Victory in World War II. 2012. (ENG., Illus.). 672p. 35.00 **(978-1-4000-6443-4(0)**, Random House) Random House Publishing Group.
Puryear, Edgar F., Jr. American Admiralship: The Art of Naval Command. 2008. (ENG.). 652p. pap. 24.95 *(978-0-7603-3220-7(7)*, 0760332207, Zenith Pr.) MBI Publishing Co. LLC.
Ramsay, David. 'Blinker' Hall: Spymaster: The Man Who Brought America into World War I. 2010. (ENG.). 320p. pap. 29.95 *(978-0-7524-5398-9(X))* History Pr. Ltd.,The GBR. Dist: Independent Pubs. Group.
Rodney, George Brydges Rodney. The Rodney Papers: Selections from the Correspondence of Admiral Lord Rodney, Vol. 2. Syrett, David, ed. 2007. (Navy Records Society Publications: Vol. 151). 750p. 154.95 *(978-0-7546-6007-1(9))* Ashgate Publishing Co.
Shenk, Robert, ed. Playships of the World: The Naval Diaries of Admiral Dan Gallery, 1920-1924. 2008. (Studies in Maritime History Ser.). (Illus.). 308p. 34.95 *(978-1-57003-722-1(1))* Univ. of South Carolina Pr.
Smith, Adrian. Mountbatten: Apprentice War Lord. 2010. (ENG., Illus.). 480p. 50.00 *(978-1-84885-374-4(2))* I. B. Tauris & Co., Ltd. GBR. Dist: Macmillan.
Southey, Robert. The Life of Horatio Lord Nelson. 2008. 240p. pap. *(978-1-4065-7508-8(9))* Dodo Pr.

—The Life of Horatio Lord Nelson. 2008. (ENG.). 228p. pap. 15.45 *(978-1-60597-790-4(X)*, Book Jungle) Standard Pubns., Inc.

—Life of Horatio Lord Nelson. 2008. 228p. 24.99 *(978-0-554-30830-2(4))* 2008. 228p. 27.99 *(978-0-554-21527-3(6))* 2006. (ENG.). 366p. pap. 15.99 *(978-1-4264-0359-0(3))* 2007. 324p. pap. 20.99 *(978-1-4264-0308-8(9))* BiblioBazaar.

—Life of Horatio Lord Nelson. 2006. pap. *(978-1-4068-3003-3(8))* Echo Library.

—Life of Nelson. 2009. 260p. 24.99 *(978-1-103-11232-6(5))*; pap. 18.99 *(978-1-103-11227-2(9))* BiblioBazaar.

—The Life of Nelson. 2009. 196p. 22.99 *(978-1-103-28524-2(6))* 2009. 196p. pap. 16.99 *(978-1-103-28521-1(1))* 2008. 282p. 28.99 *(978-0-554-98192-5(0))* 2008. 282p. 25.99 *(978-0-554-98196-3(3))* 2008. 282p. pap. 28.75 *(978-0-554-98193-2(9))* 2008. 282p. pap. 27.75 *(978-0-554-98195-6(5))* BiblioBazaar.

Spalding, Thomas Alfred. Life of Richard Badiley ViceAdmiral of T. 2006. pap. 31.95 *(978-1-4286-5214-9(0))* Kessinger Publishing, LLC.

Stavridis, James G. Destroyer Captain: Lessons of a First Command. 2008. 201p. 24.95 *(978-1-59114-849-4(9))* Naval Institute Pr.

Steely, Skipper. Pearl Harbor Countdown: Admiral James O. Richardson, 1 vol. 2008. (ENG., Illus.). 544p. 35.00 *(978-1-58980-592-7(5))* Pelican Publishing Co., Inc.

Stewart, William. Admirals of the World: A Biographical Dictionary, 1500 to the Present. 2009. (ENG., Illus.). 341p. pap. 55.00 *(978-0-7864-3809-9(6))* McFarland & Co., Inc. Pubs.

Stille, Mark. Yamamoto Isoroku. 2012. (Command Ser.). (ENG., Illus.). 64p. pap. 18.95 ***(978-1-84908-731-5(8))*** Osprey Publishing, Ltd. GBR. Dist: Random Hse., Inc.

Symmes, Weymouth. This Is Latch: The Story of Roy F. Hoffman. 2007. 544p. 29.95 *(978-1-57510-137-8(8))* Pictorial Histories Publishing Co., Inc.

Symonds, Craig L. Confederate Admiral. 2008. 312p. pap. 18.95 *(978-1-59114-846-3(4))* Naval Institute Pr.

Taussig, Joseph K. Three Splendid Little Wars: the Diary of Joseph K. Taussig, 1898-1901: The Diary of Joseph K. Taussig, 1898-1901. Naval War College Press (U.S.) Staff & Cherpak, Evelyn M., eds. 2009. (ENG., Illus.). 130p. pap. 27.00 *(978-1-884733-61-1(1)*, Dept. of the Navy) United States Government Printing Office.

Taussig, Joseph K. & Cherpak, Evelyn M. Three Splendid Little Wars: The Diaries of Joseph Knefler Taussig, 1898-1901. 2009. *(978-0-16-082792-1(2))* Naval War College Pr.

Trimble, William F. Admiral William A. Moffett: Architect of Naval Aviation. 2007. (Bluejacket Books). (Illus.). 338p. per. 19.95 *(978-1-59114-880-7(4))* Naval Institute Pr.

Turner, Michael. In Drake's Wake: The Early Voyages. 2007. (Illus.). 272p. (gr. 4-12). pap. *(978-1-58690-020-5(X))* Mould, Paul Publishing.

—In Drake's Wake: The Later Voyages, Vol. 3. 2009. (Illus.). pap. 33.00 *(978-1-58690-099-1(4))* Empire Publishing Service.

—In Drake's Wake: The World Voyage, Vol. 2. Mould, Paul, ed. 2007. (Illus.). 298p. (gr. 4-12). pap. *(978-1-58690-036-6(6))* Mould, Paul Publishing.

Walker, Frank. John Paul Jones Maverick Hero. 2007. (Illus.). 278p. 32.95 *(978-1-932033-82-3(3))* Casemate Pubs. & Bk. Distributors, LLC.

Ware, Chris. Admiral Byng: His Rise & Execution. 2008. (Illus.). 192p. 45.00 *(978-1-84415-781-5(4))* Pen & Sword Bks. Ltd. GBR. Dist: Casemate Pubs. & Bk. Distributors, LLC.

Weir, William. 50 Military Leaders Who Changed the World. 2006. (ENG., Illus.). 1p. 24.99 *(978-1-56414-866-7(1))* Career Pr., Inc.

White, Colin. Nelson: The Admiral. 2010. (ENG., Illus.). 256p. pap. 32.95 *(978-0-7524-5305-7(X))* History Pr. Ltd.,The GBR. Dist: Independent Pubs. Group.

White, Colin, ed. Nelson - the New Letters. 2007. (Illus.). 600p. pap. 24.95 *(978-1-84383-299-7(2)*, Boydell Press) Boydell & Brewer, Ltd. GBR. Dist: Boydell & Brewer, Inc.

Wilkinson, J. The Narrative of a Blockade-Runner. 2009. 256p. 24.99 *(978-1-103-62287-0(0))*; pap. 18.99 *(978-1-103-62285-6(4))* BiblioBazaar.

—The Narrative of a Blockade-Runner. 2009. 110p. pap. *(978-1-4588-8915-7(7))* Books LLC.

—The Narrative of a Blockade-Runner. 2007. (ENG.). 252p. 41.95 *(978-0-548-37330-9(2))*; per. 26.95 *(978-0-548-31647-4(3))* Kessinger Publishing, LLC.

Wilkinson, John. The Narrative of a Blockade-Runner. 2008. 156p. 22.99 *(978-0-554-37323-2(8))* 2008. 156p. 25.99 *(978-0-554-28020-2(5))* 2007. (ENG.). 138p. pap. 18.99 *(978-1-4346-4527-2(4))* 2007. (ENG.). 152p. pap. 21.99 *(978-1-4346-4528-9(2))* BiblioBazaar.

Woodworth, Steven E. Grant's Lieutenants. 2008. (Modern War Studies). *(978-0-7006-1589-6(X))* Univ. Pr. of Kansas.

Wragg, David W. Fisher: The Admiral Who Reinvented the Royal Navy. 2009. (ENG., Illus.). 320p. 45.00 *(978-0-7524-4847-3(1))* History Pr. Ltd.,The GBR. Dist: Independent Pubs. Group.

Wukovits, John. Admiral Bull Halsey: The Life & Wars of the Navy's Most Controversial Commander. 2010. (ENG., Illus.). 304p. 27.00 *(978-0-230-60284-7(3))* Palgrave Macmillan.

Zabecki, David. Dönitz: A Defense. 2008. 118p. 34.95 *(978-1-4357-5653-3(3))*; pap. 16.95 *(978-1-4357-5654-0(1))* Lulu Enterprises Inc.

ADMIRALTY

see also Liability for Marine Accidents

Aicher, Josef, et al, eds. Decisions of the Arbitration Panel for in Rem Restitution, Vol. 3. 2010. (GER & ENG.). 567p. 136.00 *(978-1-84946-111-5(2))* Hart Publishing Ltd. GBR. Dist: International Specialized Bk. Services.

Bee, Thomas & Hopkinson, Francis. Reports of Cases Adjudged in the District Court of South Carolina. 2006. *(978-1-57588-905-4(6))* Hein, William S. & Co., Inc.

Costello, Kevin. The Court of Admiralty of Ireland, 1575-1893. 2011. (Illus.). 313p. 70.00 *(978-1-84682-243-8(2))* Four Courts Pr. IRL. Dist: International Specialized Bk. Services.

Friedell, Steven F., et al. Admiralty & Maritime Law in the United States: Cases & Materials, 2007-2008 Statutory & Update Supplement. 2007. 92p. pap. 12.00 *(978-1-59460-475-1(4))* Carolina Academic Pr.

Hare, J. Shipping Law & Admiralty Jurisdiction in South Africa, Vol. 1. 2nd ed. 2009. 1108p. 172.50 incl. audio compact disk *(978-0-7021-7946-4(9))* Juta & Co., Ltd. ZAF. Dist: Gaunt, Inc.

Hofmeyr, Gys. Admiralty Jurisdiction. 2006. 564p. 94.00 *(978-0-7021-7109-3(3))* Juta Academic ZAF. Dist: Gaunt, Inc.

Kimbell, John & Meeson, Nigel. Admiralty Jurisdiction & Practice. 4th rev. ed. 2011. (Illus.). 740p. 702.00 *(978-1-84311-943-2(9))* Informa Professional GBR. Dist: International Specialized Bk. Services.

Mandaraka-Sheppard, Aleka. Modern Maritime Law & Risk Management. 2nd rev. ed. 2009. (Illus.). 1061p. 189.00 *(978-1-84311-823-7(8))* Informa Professional GBR. Dist: International Specialized Bk. Services.

Mandaraka-Sheppard, Alexandra. Modern Admiralty Law. 2nd rev. ed. 2007. (Illus.). 1152p. 190.00 *(978-1-85941-895-6(3)*, Routledge) Taylor & Francis Group GBR. Dist: Taylor & Francis Group.

Maraist, Frank L. & Galligan, Thomas C. Admiralty in a Nutshell, 6th. 6th rev. ed. 2010. (Nutshell Ser.). 487p. 38.00 *(978-0-314-92699-9(2)*, West Legalworks) West.

Prichard, M. J. & Yale, D. E. C., eds. Hale & Fleetwood on Admiralty Jurisdiction. (Selden Society Annual Ser.: Vol. 108, 1992). 100.00 *(978-0-85423-178-2(1))* Selden Society GBR. Dist: Hein, William S. & Co., Inc.

Robertson, David, et al. Admiralty & Maritime Law in the United States: Cases & Materials. 2nd ed. 2008. 75.00 *(978-1-59460-580-2(7))* Carolina Academic Pr.

Robertson, David W., et al. Admiralty & Maritime Law in the United States, Second Edition, 2011-12 Supplement. 2011. pap. ***(978-1-61163-100-5(9))*** Carolina Academic Pr.

Schoenbaum, Thomas J. Admiralty & Maritime Law, 2 vols. 5th ed. 2011. (Illus.). ***(978-0-314-20460-8(1))***; ***(978-0-314-20461-5(X))*** West Publishing Co., College & Schl. Div.

Schoenbaum, Thomas J. & Mcclellan, Jessica. Admiralty & Maritime Law, 5th. 5th rev. ed. 2012. (Hornbook Ser.). 1130p. 105.00 ***(978-0-314-91157-5(X))*** West.

Sing, Toh Kian. Admiralty Law & Practice. lxxx, 637p. *(978-0-409-99909-9(1)*, MICHIE) LEXIS Publishing.

Wiswall, F. L. The Development of Admiralty Jurisdiction & Practice Since 1800. 2008. (ENG.). 256p. pap. 37.99 *(978-0-521-08991-3(3))* Cambridge Univ. Pr.

ADMISSION TO COLLEGE

see Universities and Colleges—Admission

ADMISSION TO THE BAR

see also Bar Examinations

Campbell, Gordon. A Compendium of Roman Law: Founded on the Institutes of Justinian Together with Examination Questions Set in the University & Bar Examinations (with Solutions) & Definitions of Leading Terms in the Words of the Principal Authorities. 2007. 282p. 80.00 *(978-1-58477-756-4(7))* Lawbook Exchange, Ltd., The.

Danaher, Franklin Martin. Bar Examinations & Courses of Law Study, Containing the Statutes & Rules of Court Regulating Admission to the Bar in New York State And. 2010. (ENG.). 336p. pap. 31.75 *(978-1-176-34720-5(9))* BiblioBazaar.

Friedland, Steven. Friedland's Exam Pro Bar Prep Workbook. 2010. (Exam Pro Ser.). 256p. pap. 35.00 *(978-0-314-20514-8(4)*, West Legalworks) West.

Glazier, Holly. Michigan Bar Exam Essay Deconstruction. 2012. (Illus.). xii, 943p. pap. ***(978-0-7355-0995-5(6))*** Wolters Kluwer Law & Business.

Kramer, Adam. Bewigged & Bewildered? A Guide to Becoming a Barrister in England & Wales. 2nd ed. 2011. (ENG., Illus.). 240p. pap. 30.00 *(978-1-84946-164-1(3))* Hart Publishing Ltd. GBR. Dist: International Specialized Bk. Services.

La Puma, Rosemary. If I Don't Pass the Bar I'll Die: 73 Ways to Keep Stress & Worry from Affecting Your Performance on the Bar Exam. 2008. pap., stu. ed. 25.95 *(978-0-7355-7842-5(7))* Wolters Kluwer Law & Business.

Pierce, Carl A. & Cornett, Judy M. Professional Responsibility in the Life of the Lawyer. 2010. (American Casebook Ser.). 1137p. 175.00 *(978-0-314-15010-3(2)*, West Legalworks) West.

Pierce, Carl A., et al. Professional Responsibility in the Life of the Lawyer. 2011. xlvi, 1087p. ***(978-0-314-15009-7(9))*** West Publishing Co., College & Schl. Div.

ADOBE ACROBAT (COMPUTER PROGRAM)

Acrobat 8 Professional Beyond the Basics. 2006. cd-rom 99.95 *(978-1-59671-295-9(3))* Lynda.com, LLC.

Acrobat 8 Professional Essential Training. 2006. cd-rom 99.95 *(978-1-59671-294-2(5))* Lynda.com, LLC.

Acrobat Connect Professional Essential Training. 2007. cd-rom 99.95 *(978-1-59671-307-9(0))* Lynda.com, LLC.

Adobe(r) Acrobat(r) 8. 0 - Level 1: Nh3187lgeel. 2007. spiral bd. *(978-1-4246-0552-1(0))* Element K Content LLC.

Adobe(r) Acrobat(r) 8. 0 - Level 1: Nh84179i. 2007. spiral bd. *(978-1-4246-0461-6(3))* Element K Content LLC.

Adobe(r) Acrobat(r) 8. 0 - Level 1: Nh84179s. 2007. spiral bd. *(978-1-4246-0462-3(1))* Element K Content LLC.

Adobe(r) Acrobat(r) 8. 0 - Level 2: Nh3188lgeel. 2007. spiral bd. *(978-1-4246-0611-5(X))* Element K Content LLC.

Adobe(r) Acrobat(r) 8. 0 - Level 2: Nh84180i. 2007. spiral bd. *(978-1-4246-0467-8(2))* Element K Content LLC.

Adobe(r) Acrobat(r) 8. 0 - Level 2: Nh84180s. 2007. spiral bd. *(978-1-4246-0468-5(0))* Element K Content LLC.

Adobe Acrobat 8. 0 - New Features: Nh3148lgeel. 2007. spiral bd. *(978-1-4246-0501-9(6))* Element K Content LLC.

Adobe(r) Acrobat(r) 8. 0: 084179ie. 2007. spiral bd. *(978-1-4246-0457-9(5))* Element K Content LLC.

Adobe(r) Acrobat(r) 8. 0: 084179s3. 2007. spiral bd. *(978-1-4246-0458-6(3))* Element K Content LLC.

Adobe(r) Acrobat(r) 8. 0: 084180ie. 2007. spiral bd. *(978-1-4246-0463-0(X))* Element K Content LLC.

Adobe(r) Acrobat(r) 8. 0: 084180s3. 2007. spiral bd. *(978-1-4246-0464-7(8))* Element K Content LLC.

Adobe Acrobat 8. 0: 084185ie. 2007. spiral bd. *(978-1-4246-0450-0(8))* Element K Content LLC.

Adobe Acrobat 8. 0: 084185s3. 2007. spiral bd. *(978-1-4246-0451-7(6))* Element K Content LLC.

Adobe(r) Acrobat(r) 8. 0: ET84179IG. 2007. spiral bd. *(978-1-4246-0459-3(1))* Element K Content LLC.

Adobe(r) Acrobat(r) 8. 0: ET84179SM. 2007. spiral bd. *(978-1-4246-0460-9(5))* Element K Content LLC.

Adobe(r) Acrobat(r) 8. 0: ET84180IG. 2007. spiral bd. *(978-1-4246-0465-4(6))* Element K Content LLC.

Adobe(r) Acrobat(r) 8. 0: ET84180SM. 2007. spiral bd. *(978-1-4246-0466-1(4))* Element K Content LLC.

Adobe Acrobat 8. 0: ET84185IG. 2007. spiral bd. *(978-1-4246-0452-4(4))* Element K Content LLC.

Adobe Acrobat 8. 0: ET84185SM. 2007. spiral bd. *(978-1-4246-0453-1(2))* Element K Content LLC.

Adobe Acrobat 8. 0: NH84185I. 2007. spiral bd. *(978-1-4246-0454-8(0))* Element K Content LLC.

Adobe Acrobat 8. 0: NH84185S. 2007. spiral bd. *(978-1-4246-0455-5(9))* Element K Content LLC.

Adobe Acrobat 8. 0 Quick Source Guide. 2007. 6p. 4.95 *(978-1-932104-61-5(5))* Quick Source.

Adobe Creative Team. Adobe Acrobat 9. 2008. (Classroom in a Book Ser.). (ENG., Illus.). 368p. pap. 59.99 *(978-0-321-55297-6(0))* Pearson Higher Education & Professional Group.

—Adobe Acrobat X Classroom in a Book. rev. ed. 2010. (Classroom in a Book Ser.). (ENG., Illus.). 336p. pap. 54.99 *(978-0-321-75125-6(6))* Adobe Pr.

—Adobe Creative Suite 5 Design Premium Classroom in a Book. rev. ed. 2010. (Classroom in a Book Ser.). (ENG., Illus.). 336p. pap. 54.99 *(978-0-321-70450-4(9))* Adobe Pr.

Adobe Press, creator. Adobe Acrobat 3D Version 8. 2007. (Classroom in a Book Ser.). (ENG., Illus.). 240p. pap. 59.99 *(978-0-321-44946-7(0))* Adobe Pr.

AGI Creative Team Staff, et al. Adobe Creative Suite 5 Design Premium Digital Classroom. 2010. (Digital Classroom Ser.: 37). (ENG., Illus.). 832p. pap. 59.99 *(978-0-470-60779-4(3)*, Wiley) Wiley, John & Sons, Inc.

BarCharts, Inc. Adobe Acrobat 9. 2010. (ENG.). 6p. 5.95 *(978-1-4232-1415-1(3))* Barcharts, Inc.

Blank, R., et al. AdvancED Flex Application Development: Building Rich Media X. 2007. (Friends of ED Adobe Learning Library). (ENG., Illus.). 550p. per. 54.99 *(978-1-59059-896-2(2)*, Friends of Ed) Apress L. P.

Deubert, John. Adobe Acrobat 8 for Windows & Macintosh: Visual QuickStart Guide. 2006. (Visual QuickStart Guide Ser.). (ENG., Illus.). 264p. per. 29.99 *(978-0-321-47079-9(6))* Peachpit Pr.

—Adobe Acrobat X for Windows & Macintosh. 2010. (Visual QuickStart Guide Ser.). (ENG., Illus.). 288p. pap. 29.99 *(978-0-321-74375-6(X))* Peachpit Pr.

Dickeson, Linda. CLICKstep Teacher Training Series: Interactive PDFs in Education. 2007. 34.95 *(978-0-9798787-2-5(1))* FTC Publishing.

GABRIEL. Ybs Sports 01, 1 vol. 2011. 122p. 149.00 *(978-0-16-617010-6(0))* mode... information Heinz Kramer GmbH DEU. Dist: Innovative Logistics.

Hauser, Jürgen, et al. SAP Interactive Forms by Adobe. 2nd ed. 2011.Tr. of SAP Interactive Forms by Adobe. (Illus.). 790p. 89.95 *(978-1-59229-398-8(0)*, SAP PR.) Galileo Pr., Inc.

Kent, Lynette. Adobe Phop Visual Quick Tips. 2008. 288p. pap. 24.99 *(978-0-470-33847-6(4)*, Visual) Wiley, John & Sons, Inc.

Lowagie, Bruno. IText in Action: Creating & Manipulating PDF. 2006. (ENG., Illus.). 656p. per. 49.99 *(978-1-932394-79-5(6))* Manning Pubns. Co.

Martins, Filipe P. & Kobylinska, Anna. Adobe Acrobat 8 Standard, Professional, Connect And 3D. 2008. 1000p. 59.95 *(978-3-540-49501-7(0))* Springer.

Masters, David L. The Lawyer's Guide to Adobe Acrobat 8. 0, Third Edition. 3rd ed. 2008. (ENG.). 272p. pap. 79.95 *(978-1-59031-978-9(8))* American Bar Assn.

Padova, Ted. Adobe Acrobat 9 PDF. 2008. (Bible Ser.: 536). (ENG., Illus.). 1296p. pap. 44.99 *(978-0-470-37919-6(7)*, Wiley) Wiley, John & Sons, Inc.

—Adobe Acrobat X PDF Bible. 2011. (Bible Ser.: 668). (ENG., Illus.). 936p. pap. 44.99 *(978-0-470-61291-0(6)*, Wiley) Wiley, John & Sons, Inc.

Padova, Ted & Murdock, Kelly L. Adobe Creative Suite 5. 2010. (ENG., Illus.). 1272p. pap. 44.99 *(978-0-470-58476-7(9)*, Wiley) Wiley, John & Sons, Inc.

Padova, Ted & Okamoto, Angie. PDF Forms Using Acrobat & LiveCycle Designer. 2009. (Bible Ser.: 545). (ENG., Illus.). 1224p. pap. 49.99 *(978-0-470-40017-3(X)*, Wiley) Wiley, John & Sons, Inc.

Peachpit Press Staff & Baker, Donna L. Adobe Acrobat 9: 125 Essential Techniques. 2008. (How-Tos Ser.). (ENG., Illus.). 360p. pap. 39.99 *(978-0-321-55294-5(6))* Adobe Pr.

Peachpit Press Staff & Deubert, John. Adobe Acrobat 9 for Windows & Macintosh. 2008. (Visual QuickStart Guide Ser.). (ENG., Illus.). 280p. pap. 29.99 *(978-0-321-55295-2(4))* Pearson Higher Education & Professional Group.

Rotovision. Graphic Design to Beat the Clock: Time-saving software secrets, online resources, & desktop Tips. 2012. (ENG., Illus.). 208p. pap. 29.95 ***(978-0-240-82422-2(9)***, Focal Pr.) Elsevier Science & Technology Bks.

Sahlin, Doug. How to Do Everything Adobe Acrobat X. 2011. (ENG., Illus.). 384p. pap. 25.00 *(978-0-07-175293-0(5)*, 0071752935) McGraw-Hill Osborne.

—How to Do Everything with Adobe Acrobat 8. rev. ed. 2007. (How to Do Everything Ser.). (ENG., Illus.). 508p. per. 24.99 *(978-0-07-226393-0(8)*, 0072263938) McGraw-Hill Osborne.

Smith, Jennifer, et al. Adobe Creative Suite 4 Web Premium All-in-One for Dummies. 2009. (ENG., Illus.). 912p. pap. 39.99 *(978-0-470-41407-1(3)*, For Dummies) Wiley, John & Sons, Inc.

—Adober Creative Suiter 5. 2nd ed. 2010. (ENG., Illus.). 1008p. pap. 39.99 *(978-0-470-60746-6(7)*, For Dummies) Wiley, John & Sons, Inc.

Stepek, Zach. AIR: Creating Desktop Applications with the Adobe Integrated Runtime. 2008. 400p. pap. 36.99 *(978-1-59059-937-2(3)*, Friends of Ed) Apress L. P.

Terry, J. P. Paperless: Real-World Solutions with Adobe Technology. 2009. (Illus.). (ENG.). 336p. pap. 54.99 *(978-0-321-65887-6(6))*; xviii, 317p. ***(978-0-321-65932-3(5)***, CL0500000065) Adobe Pr.

ADOBE AFTER EFFECTS (COMPUTER PROGRAM)

Adobe Creative Team. Adobe after Effects CS4. 2008. (Classroom in a Book Ser.). (ENG., Illus.). 400p. pap. 54.99 *(978-0-321-57383-4(8))* Adobe Pr.

—Adobe after Effects CS5. 2010. (Classroom in a Book Ser.). (ENG., Illus.). 400p. pap. 59.99 *(978-0-321-70449-8(5))* Adobe Pr.

Adobe Press Staff. Adobe after Effects CS3 Professional Classroom in a Book. 2007. (Classroom in a Book Ser.). (ENG., Illus.). 496p. pap. 54.99 *(978-0-321-49979-0(4))* Adobe Pr.

After Effects 7 & Flash 8 Integration. 2006. cd-rom 49.95 *(978-1-59671-285-0(6))* Lynda.com, LLC.

After Effects 7 Title Design Techniques. 2006. cd-rom 99.95 *(978-1-59671-283-6(X))* Lynda.com, LLC.

Bolante, Antony. After Effects CS4 for Windows & Macintosh. 2008. (Visual QuickPro Guide Ser.). (ENG., Illus.). 528p. pap. 39.99 *(978-0-321-59152-4(6))* Peachpit Pr.

Christiansen, Mark. Adobe After Effects CS3 Professional Studio Techniques. 2007. (Studio Techniques Ser.). (Illus.). 480p. pap. 59.99 *(978-0-321-49978-3(6))* Adobe Pr.

—Adobe after Effects CS5 Visual Effects & Compositing Studio Techniques. 2010. (Studio Techniques Ser.). (ENG., Illus.). 496p. pap. 59.99 *(978-0-321-71962-1(X))* Adobe Pr.

Cram101 Textbook Reviews. Outlines & Highlights for Creating Motion Graphics with after Effects by Chris & Trish Meyer, Isbn: 9780240810102 0240810104. 2011. 90p. pap. 27.95 ***(978-1-61490-345-1(X))*** Cram101 Inc.

Geduld, Marcus. After Effects Expressions. 2008. (ENG., Illus.). 448p. pap. 49.95 *(978-0-240-80936-6(X)*, Focal Pr.) Elsevier Science & Technology Bks.

Geduld, Marcus & Harrington, Richard. After Effects for Flash - Flash for after Effects: Dynamic Animation & Video with Adobe after Effects CS4 & Adobe Flash CS4 Professional. 2009. (ENG., Illus.). 360p. pap. 54.99 *(978-0-321-60607-5(8))* Adobe Pr.

Green, Tom & Dias, Tiago. From after Effects to Flash: Poetry in Motion Graphics. 2006. (ENG., Illus.). 504p. pap. 49.99 *(978-1-59059-748-4(6)*, Friends of Ed) Apress L. P.

Harrington, Richard, ed. After Effects @ Work. 2006. (DV Expert Ser.). (ENG., Illus.). 224p. pap. 44.95 *(978-1-57820-267-6(1)*, Focal Pr.) Elsevier Science & Technology Bks.

Hough, Mickey & Nth Degree Design and Visual FX, Inc Staff. After Effects for Digital Editors Only. 2009. (ENG.). 400p. pap. 44.99 *(978-0-470-48458-6(6)*, Wiley) Wiley, John & Sons, Inc.

Jackson, Chris. Flash + after Effects: Add Broadcast Features to Your Flash Designs. 2nd ed. 2010. (ENG., Illus.). 312p. pap. 52.95 *(978-0-240-81351-6(0)*, Focal Pr.) Elsevier Science & Technology Bks.

Meyer, Chris & Meyer, Trish. After Effects Apprentice: Real World Skills for the Aspiring Motion Graphics Artist. 3rd ed. 2012. (ENG.). 352p. pap. 49.95 ***(978-0-240-81736-1(2)***, Focal Pr.) Elsevier Science & Technology Bks.

Meyer, Chris & Meyer, Trish. Creating Motion Graphics with after Effects: Essential & Advanced Techniques. 5th ed. 2010. (ENG., Illus.). 768p. pap. 69.95 *(978-0-240-81415-5(0)*, Focal Pr.) Elsevier Science & Technology Bks.

Meyer, Chris and Trish. After Effects Apprentice. 2nd ed. 2009. (ENG., Illus.). 336p. pap. 44.95 *(978-0-240-81136-9(4)*, Focal Pr.) Elsevier Science & Technology Bks.

Meyer, Trish & Meyer, Chris. After Effects Apprentice: Real-World Skills for the Aspiring Motion Graphics Artist. 2007. (DV Expert Ser.). (ENG., Illus.). 320p. pap. 39.95 *(978-0-240-80938-0(6)*, Focal Pr.) Elsevier Science & Technology Bks.

Perkins, Chad. How to Cheat in after Effects. 2010. (How to Cheat In Ser.). (ENG., Illus.). 352p. pap. 44.95 *(978-0-240-52202-9(8)*, Focal Pr.) Elsevier Science & Technology Bks.

Taylor, Angie. Creative after Effects 7: Workflow Techniques for Animation, Visual Effects & Motion Graphics. 2006. (ENG., Illus.). 584p. pap. 54.95 *(978-0-240-51992-0(2)*, Focal Pr.) Elsevier Science & Technology Bks.

Virtual Training Company, prod. Adobe Video Bundle Essentials. 2006. cd-rom 99.95 *(978-1-933736-49-5(6))* VTC, Inc.

Weinman, Lynda & Fahs, Chad. Adobe after Effects 7 Hands-on Training: Includes Exercise Files & Demo Movies. 2006. (Hands-on-Training Ser.). (ENG., Illus.). 528p. pap. 44.99 *(978-0-321-39775-1(4))* Peachpit Pr.

Yamazaki, Michele. Plug-in to after Effects: Third Party Plug-in Mastery. 2011. (ENG., Illus.). 517p. pap. 49.95 *(978-0-240-81565-7(3)*, Focal Pr.) Elsevier Science & Technology Bks.

ADOBE AUDITION (COMPUTER PROGRAM)

Adobe Audition 2. 2006. cd-rom 99.95 *(978-1-933736-38-9(0))* VTC, Inc.

Audition 2. 0 Essential Training. 2006. cd-rom 99.95 *(978-1-59671-266-9(X))* Lynda.com, LLC.

Jago, Maxim & Video2brain Staff. Introducing Adobe Audition CS5. 5: Learn by Video. 2011. (Learn by Video Ser.). (ENG.). 48p. 34.99 ***(978-0-321-78685-2(8))*** Peachpit Pr.

Riley, Richard. Audio Editing with Adobe Audition. 2nd ed. 2008. (ENG., Illus.). 192p. pap. 22.95 *(978-1-906005-03-0(6))* PC Publishing GBR. Dist: Ingram Pub. Services.

ADOBE CAPTIVATE (COMPUTER PROGRAM)

see Captivate (Computer Program)

ADOBE CONSTRUCTION

see Building, Adobe

ADOBE FLASH (COMPUTER PROGRAM)

see Flash (Computer Program)

ADOBE FRAMEMAKER (COMPUTER PROGRAM)

Adobe Creative Team. Adobe FrameMaker 9 Classroom in a Book. 2009. (Classroom in a Book Ser.). (ENG., Illus.). 288p. pap. 54.99 *(978-0-321-64750-4(5))* Adobe Pr.

Aschwanden, Bernard. Adobe FrameMaker 8: A Hands-on Guide to Creating DITA Compliant Documents. 2008. (ENG.). per. 49.95 *(978-0-9771222-3-3(9))* Above & Beyond Language Learning, Inc.

DITA Cookbook. 2007. per. *(978-0-9771222-2-6(0))* Above & Beyond Language Learning, Inc.

Heys, Jacquie, ed. XML & FrameMaker 9. 2008. 400p. per. 49.95 *(978-0-9771222-4-0(7))* Above & Beyond Language Learning, Inc.

Kazoun, Chafic, et al. Programming Flex 2: The Comprehensive Guide to Creating Rich Internet Applications with Adobe Flex. 2007. (ENG., Illus.). 512p. pap. 54.99 *(978-0-596-52689-4(X))* O'Reilly Media, Inc.

O'Keefe, Sarah S. & Loring, Sheila A. Publishing Fundamentals: FrameMaker 7. 2006. (Illus.). 878p. per. 59.99 *(978-0-9704733-3-2(8))* Scriptorium Publishing Services, Inc.

—Publishing Fundamentals: Unstructured FrameMaker 8. Pringle, Alan S., ed. 2008. 736p. per. 49.99 *(978-0-9704733-4-9(6))* Scriptorium Publishing Services, Inc.

ADOBE GOLIVE (COMPUTER PROGRAM)

Course Technology Staff & Botello, Chris. A Guided Tour of Creative Suite 3 Design Standard. 2007. (Guided Tour Ser.). (ENG.). 23.95 *(978-1-4239-2572-9(6))* Course Technology.

Padova, Ted & Murdock, Kelly L. Adobe Creative Suite 4 Bible. 2008. (Bible Ser.: 514). (ENG., Illus.). 1296p. pap. 44.99 *(978-0-470-34518-4(7)*, Wiley) Wiley, John & Sons, Inc.

ADOBE HOUSES

Adobe Press Staff, creator. Adobe Font Folio 11: Type Reference Guide. 3rd ed. 2007. (MUL & ENG., Illus.). 368p. per. 44.99 *(978-0-321-54472-8(2))* Adobe Pr.

Bourdier, Jean-Paul & Minh-ha, Trinh T. Vernacular Architecture of West Africa: A World in Dwelling. 2011. (ENG., Illus.). 192p. 74.95 *(978-0-415-58543-9(0))* Routledge.

Byrne, Michael & Larson, Dottie. The New Adobe Home, 1 vol. 2009. (ENG., Illus.). 160p. 35.00 *(978-1-4236-0273-6(0))* Gibbs Smith, Publisher.

Crews, Carole. Clay Culture: Plasters, Paints & Preservation. 2010. (ENG., Illus.). 224p. pap. 27.00 *(978-0-9842229-0-2(1))* Gourmet Adobe Pr.

Hannaford, Donald R. & Edwards, Revel. Spanish Colonial or Adobe Architecture of California: 1800-1850. 2012. (ENG., Illus.). 128p. pap. 24.95 ***(978-1-58979-684-3(5))*** Taylor Trade Publishing.

Rimmington, Pat. The Adobes of Twentynine Palms. 2nd ed. 2009. (Illus.). xii, 164p. (Orig.). pap. ***(978-0-9842373-0-2(5)***, Orbit Books) Desert Spirit Pr.

Sanchez, Laura & Sanchez, Alex. Adobe Houses for Today: Flexible Plans for Your Adobe Home. rev. ed. 2008. (ENG., Illus.). 228p. pap. 29.95 *(978-0-86534-662-8(3))* Sunstone Pr.

Schroder, Lisa Morey & Ogletree, Vince. Adobe Homes for All Climates: Simple, Affordable, & Earthquake-Resistant Natural Building Techniques. 2010. (ENG., Illus.). 272p. pap. 34.95 *(978-1-60358-257-5(6))* Chelsea Green Publishing.

Vassallo, Marc, intro. The Homestead Builder: Practical Hints for Handy-Men. 2nd ed. 2007. (ENG., Illus.). 152p. per. 12.95 *(978-1-59921-153-4(X)*, Lyons Pr.) Globe Pequot Pr., The.

Virtual Training Company, prod. Adobe Encore DVD. 2006. cd-rom 99.95 *(978-1-933736-59-4(3))* VTC, Inc.

ADOBE ILLUSTRATOR (COMPUTER PROGRAM)

Adobe Creative Team. Adobe Creative Suite 5 Design Premium Classroom in a Book. rev. ed. 2010. (Classroom in a Book Ser.). (ENG., Illus.). 336p. pap. 54.99 *(978-0-321-70450-4(9))* Adobe Pr.

—Adobe Illustrator CS4. 2008. (Classroom in a Book Ser.). (ENG., Illus.). 480p. pap., wbk. ed., training bk. ed. 54.99 *(978-0-321-57378-0(1))* Adobe Pr.

—Illustrator CS5. 2010. (Classroom in a Book Ser.). (ENG., Illus.). 480p. pap. 54.99 *(978-0-321-70178-7(X))* Adobe Pr.

Adobe Press Staff, creator. Adobe Illustrator CS3 Classroom in a Book: The Official Training Workbook from Adobe Systems. 2007. (Classroom in a Book Ser.). (ENG., Illus.). 488p. pap. 54.99 *(978-0-321-49200-5(5))* Adobe Pr.

AGI Creative Team Staff & Smith, Jennifer. Illustrator CS5 Digital Classroom. 2010. (Digital Classroom Ser.: 39). (ENG., Illus.). 368p. pap. 49.99 *(978-0-470-60783-1(1)*, Wiley) Wiley, John & Sons, Inc.

AGI Creative Team Staff, et al. Illustrator CS4 Digital Classroom: A Complete Training Package! 2009. (Digital Classroom Ser.: 6). (ENG., Illus.). 320p. pap. 49.99 *(978-0-470-43635-6(2)*, Wiley) Wiley, John & Sons, Inc.

Alspach, Ted. Illustrator CS3 Bible. 2007. (Bible Ser.: 418). (ENG., Illus.). 760p. pap. 44.99 *(978-0-470-12634-9(5)*, Wiley) Wiley, John & Sons, Inc.

—Illustrator CS4 Bible. 2008. (Bible Ser.: 515). (ENG., Illus.). 784p. pap. 44.99 *(978-0-470-34519-1(5)*, Wiley) Wiley, John & Sons, Inc.

—Illustrator CS4 for Dummies. 2008. (ENG., Illus.). 384p. pap. 29.99 *(978-0-470-39656-8(3)*, For Dummies) Wiley, John & Sons, Inc.

—Illustrator CS5. 2010. (Bible Ser.: 642). (ENG., Illus.). 760p. pap. 44.99 *(978-0-470-58475-0(0)*, Wiley) Wiley, John & Sons, Inc.

Axzo Press, creator. Illustrator CS5: Advanced, ACE Edition. 2011. (ILT (Axzo Press) Ser.). (ENG., Illus.). spiral bd. 19.00 incl. cd-rom ***(978-1-4260-2103-9(8))*** Thomson NETg.

—Illustrator CS5 Basic, ACE Edition. 2011. (ILT (Axzo Press) Ser.). (ENG., Illus.). spiral bd. 19.00 ***(978-1-4260-2100-8(3))*** Thomson NETg.

Botello, Chris. Adobe Illustrator CS3 Revealed. 2007. (Adobe Creative Suite Ser.). (ENG., Illus.). 592p. (C). pap. 87.95 *(978-1-4283-1961-5(1))*; pap. 57.95 incl. cd-rom *(978-1-4354-3286-4(X))* Delmar Cengage Learning.

—Adobe Illustrator CS4 Revealed. 2009. 68.95 *(978-1-4354-8261-6(1))* Course Technology.

—Adobe Illustrator CS5 Illustrated. 2010. (Illustrated Ser.). (ENG.). 224p. (C). pap. 51.95 *(978-1-111-22196-6(0))* Course Technology.

—Adobe Illustrator CS5 Illustrated (Book Only) 2010. (ENG.). 224p. (C). pap. 51.95 *(978-1-111-53090-7(4))* Course Technology.

—Adobe Illustrator CS5 Revealed. 2010. (Revealed Ser.). (ENG.). 720p. (C). pap. 82.95 *(978-1-111-13044-2(2))* Delmar Cengage Learning.

—Adobe Photoshop CS5 Illustrated. 2010. (Illustrated Ser.). (ENG.). 232p. pap. 51.95 *(978-0-538-47781-9(4))* Course Technology.

Botello, Chris & Botello. Adobe Illustrator CS4 Revealed. 2009. (Adobe Creative Suite Ser.). (ENG.). 608p. pap. 80.95 *(978-1-4354-4188-0(5))* Course Technology.

Botello, Chris & Reding, Elizabeth Eisner. The Design Collection Revealed: Adobe Indesign CS3, Photoshop CS3 & Illustrator CS3. 2007. (Adobe Creative Suite Ser.). (ENG., Illus.). 696p. (C). pap. 101.95 *(978-1-4283-1962-2(X))* Delmar Cengage Learning.

—The Design Collection Revealed: Adobe Indesign CS5, Photoshop CS5 & Illustrator CS5. 2010. (Revealed Ser.). (ENG.). 880p. (C). pap. 87.95 *(978-1-111-13061-9(2))* Delmar Cengage Learning.

—HC - the Design Collection Revealed: Adobe Indesign CS4, Adobe Photoshop CS4, & Adobe Illustrator CS4. 2009. (ENG., Illus.). 75.95 *(978-1-4354-8270-8(0))* Course Technology.

Botello, Chris, et al. The Design Collection: Adobe Indesign CS4, Adobe Photoshop CS4, & Adobe Illustrator CS4. 2009. (Adobe Creative Suite Ser.). (ENG., Illus.). 720p. pap. 85.95 *(978-1-4354-4190-3(7))* Course Technology.

Centner, Marianne & Vereker, Frances. Fashion Designer's Handbook for Adobe Illustrator. 2nd ed. 2011. (ENG., Illus.). 212p. pap. 50.00 ***(978-1-119-97811-4(4)***, Wiley) Wiley, John & Sons, Inc.

Chan, Ron & Obermeier, Barbara. How to Wow with Illustrator. 2006. (How to Wow Ser.). (ENG., Illus.). 224p. per. 39.99 *(978-0-321-43454-8(4))* Peachpit Pr.

Course Technology Staff & Botello, Chris. A Guided Tour of Creative Suite 3 Design Standard. 2007. (Guided Tour Ser.). (ENG.). 23.95 *(978-1-4239-2572-9(6))* Course Technology.

Element K Journals Creative Team. Adobe(r) Illustrator(r) CS3: 084207ie. 2007. spiral bd. *(978-1-4246-0642-9(X))* Element K Content LLC.

—Adobe(r) Illustrator(r) CS3: 084207s3. 2007. spiral bd. *(978-1-4246-0643-6(8))* Element K Content LLC.

Gatter, Mark. Software Essentials for Graphic Designers: Photoshop, Illustrator, Indesign, QuarkXPress, Dreamweaver, Flash + Acrobat. 2006. (Illus.). 240p. pap. incl. cd-rom *(978-0-300-11800-1(7))* Yale Univ. Pr.

Glitschka, Von R. Vector Basic Training: A Systematic Creative Process for Building Precision Vector Art Work. rev. ed. 2010. (Voices That Matter Ser.). (ENG., Illus.). 256p. pap. 44.99 *(978-0-321-74959-8(6))* New Riders Publishing.

Golding, Mordy. Real World Adobe Illustrator CS3. 2nd rev. ed. 2007. (Real World Ser.). (ENG., Illus.). 584p. per. 44.99 *(978-0-321-49621-8(3))* Peachpit Pr.

—Real World Adobe Illustrator CS5. rev. ed. 2010. (Real World Ser.). (ENG., Illus.). 528p. pap. 54.99 *(978-0-321-71306-3(0))* Peachpit Pr.

Goralski, Greg & Leon, Lordalex. Foundation Flash Catalyst. 2010. (ENG.). 264p. pap. 39.99 *(978-1-4302-2862-2(8)*, Friends of Ed) Apress L. P.

Hartman, Annesa. Adobe Illustrator CS4. 2008. (Adobe Creative Suite Ser.). (ENG., Illus.). 376p. pap. 62.95 *(978-1-4354-4202-3(4))* Delmar Cengage Learning.

—Exploring Adobe Illustrator CS5. 2010. (Design Exploration Ser.). (ENG., Illus.). 384p. pap. 57.95 *(978-1-111-13036-7(1))* Delmar Cengage Learning.

Hartman, Annesa & Sholar, Ken. Exploring Illustrator CS3. 2007. (Adobe Creative Suite Ser.). (ENG., Illus.). 352p. pap. 65.95 *(978-1-4180-5257-7(4))* Delmar Cengage Learning.

Illustrator CS2 & Flash 8 Integration. 2006. cd-rom 49.95 *(978-1-59671-292-8(9))* Lynda.com, LLC.

Illustrator CS2 Creative Techniques. 2006. cd-rom 99.95 *(978-1-59671-263-8(5))* Lynda.com, LLC.

Illustrator CS2 FAQs. 2006. cd-rom 49.95 *(978-1-59671-300-0(3))* Lynda.com, LLC.

Jenkins, Geraint H. & Jenkins, Sue. Adobe Illustrator CS4. 2009. (Illus.). 336p. pap. 39.99 *(978-0-07-160310-2(7)*, 0071603107) McGraw-Hill Osborne.

Johnson, Steve. Illustrator CS5. 2010. (Illus.). 528p. pap. 57.50 *(978-0-273-74064-3(4)*, Prentice Hall) Pearson Education, Ltd. GBR. Dist: Trans-Atlantic Pubns., Inc.

Johnson, Steve & Perspection, Inc. Staff. Adobe Illustrator CS5. 2010. (On Demand Ser.). (ENG., Illus.). 528p. pap. 29.99 *(978-0-7897-4445-6(7))* Que.

Karlins, David. Illustrator CS4: 100 Essential Techniques. 2008. (How-Tos Ser.). (ENG., Illus.). 256p. pap. 29.99 *(978-0-321-56290-6(9))* Adobe Pr.

Karlins, David & Hopkins, Bruce K. Adobe Illustrator CS3 How-Tos: 100 Essential Techniques. 2007. (How-Tos Ser.). (ENG., Illus.). 272p. per. 29.99 *(978-0-321-50894-2(7))* Adobe Pr.

Lazear, Susan M. Adobe Illustrator for Fashion Design. 2008. (ENG., Illus.). 384p. pap. 61.60 *(978-0-13-119274-4(4)*, Prentice Hall) Prentice Hall PTR.

Lott, Joseph, et al. Adobe AIR in Action. 2008. (ENG., Illus.). 336p. pap. 39.99 *(978-1-933988-48-1(7))* Manning Pubns. Co.

Lowery, Joseph W. & Lowery. Adobe CS4 Web Workflows: Building Websites with Adobe Creative Suite 4. 2nd ed. 2009. (ENG., Illus.). 416p. pap. 49.99 *(978-0-470-50434-5(X)*, Wiley) Wiley, John & Sons, Inc.

McClelland, Deke. Adobe Illustrator CS5 One-on-One. 2010. (ENG., Illus.). 512p. pap. 49.99 *(978-0-596-80801-3(1)*, Deke) O'Reilly Media, Inc.

Mordy, Golding. Realw Real Wrl Title 187. 2008. (Real World Ser.). (ENG., Illus.). 600p. pap. 59.99 *(978-0-321-57355-1(2))* Peachpit Pr.

Murray, Katherine. Learning Web Design with Adobe CS4. 2009. (ENG., Illus.). 416p. (C). pap. 70.33 *(978-0-13-507688-0(9)*, Prentice Hall) Prentice Hall PTR.

Noble Desktop. Adobe Illustrator CS3 Step by Step Training. 2007. 65p. ring bd. 65.00 *(978-1-934624-01-2(2))* Noble Desktop, LLC.

Portnoi, Emily. The Vector Brushes Sourcebook: 300 Unique Brushes for Digital Illustration. 2010. (ENG.). 256p. pap. 35.00 *(978-1-4403-0301-2(0)*, HOW Bks.) F&W Media, Inc.

Ralston, Rick. The Designer's Apprentice: Automating Photoshop, Illustrator, & Indesign in Adobe Creative Suite 3. 2007. (ENG., Illus.). 256p. per. 39.99 *(978-0-321-49570-9(5))* Adobe Pr.

Reding, Elizabeth Eisner & Botello, Chris. Adobe Indesign CS, Photoshop CS, & Illustrator CS-Design Professional. 2006. (ENG.). 328p. pap. 105.95 *(978-1-4180-6457-0(2))* Course Technology.

Ruiz, Lucio Alberto. Confessions of A Process Junkie: Adobe Illustrator Techniques. 2007. (C). per. 24.95 *(978-0-9793447-6-3(X))* Brandstudio Pr.

Skintik, Catherine. Learning Media Design with Adobe CS4. 2009. (ENG.). 608p. (C). pap. 69.33 *(978-0-13-507687-3(0)*, Prentice Hall) Prentice Hall PTR.

Skintik, Catherine & Emergent Learning LLC, . Learning Media Design with Adobe CS5. 2010. (ENG.). 608p. (C). pap. 70.33 *(978-0-13-138408-8(2)*, Prentice Hall) Prentice Hall PTR.

Steuer, Sharon. The Adobe Illustrator CS3 Wow! Book: Tips, Tricks, & Techniques from 100 Top Illustrator Artists. 2007. (Wow! Book Ser.). (ENG., Illus.). 480p. pap. 54.99 *(978-0-321-51842-2(X))* Peachpit Pr.

—The Adobe Illustrator CS5 Wow! Book. 2010. (Wow! Ser.). (ENG., Illus.). 304p. pap. 44.99 *(978-0-321-71244-8(7))* Peachpit Pr.

—Illustrator CS4. 2009. (Wow! Book Ser.). (Illus.). 496p. pap. 59.99 *(978-0-321-60558-0(6))* Peachpit Pr.

Tallon, Kevin. Creative Fashion Design with Illustrator. 2006. (ENG., Illus.). 176p. pap. 24.95 *(978-0-7134-9022-0(5)*, Batsford, B. T. Ltd.) Anova Bks. GBR. Dist: Sterling Publishing Co., Inc.

Tallon, Kevin. Digital Fashion Print. 2012. (ENG., Illus.). 176p. pap. 24.95 ***(978-1-84994-004-7(5)***, Batsford, B. T. Ltd.) Anova Bks. GBR. Dist: Sterling Publishing Co., Inc.

Toland, Toni. Best Practice: The Pros on Adobe Illustrator. 2006. (Adobe Creative Suite Ser.). (ENG., Illus.). 272p. pap. 76.95 *(978-1-4180-1144-4(4))* Delmar Cengage Learning.

Torta, Stephanie. Vector Graphics Using Adobe(r) Illustrator(r) CS5: Tutorials & Techniques. 2012. 350p. pap. 45.95 *(978-1-936420-06-3(6))* Mercury Learning & Information.

Video2brain Staff, et al. Adobe Illustrator CS5. 2010. (Learn by Video Ser.). (ENG.). 120p. 59.99 *(978-0-321-73481-5(5))* Adobe Pr.

Weinmann, et al. Illustrator CS4 for Windows & Macintosh. 2009. (Visual QuickStart Guide Ser.). (ENG., Illus.). 456p. pap. 34.99 *(978-0-321-56345-3(X))* Peachpit Pr.

Weinmann, Elaine & Lourekas, Peter. Illustrator CS3 for Windows & Macintosh: Visual QuickStart Guide. 2007. (Visual QuickStart Guide Ser.). (ENG., Illus.). 480p. per. 29.99 *(978-0-321-51045-7(3))* Peachpit Pr.

—Illustrator CS5 for Windows & Macintosh. 2010. (Visual QuickStart Guide Ser.). (ENG., Illus.). 456p. pap. 34.99 *(978-0-321-70661-4(7))* Peachpit Pr.

Williams, Robin & Tollett, John. Non-Designer's Illustrator Book. rev. ed. 2011. (Non-Designer's Ser.). (ENG., Illus.). 240p. pap. 34.99 ***(978-0-321-77287-9(3))*** Peachpit Pr.

Wood, Allan. The Graphic Designer's Digital Toolkit: A Project-Based Introduction to Adobe Photoshop CS5, Illustrator CS5 & Indesign CS5. 5th ed. 2010. (Adobe Creative Suite Ser.). (ENG., Illus.). 752p. (C). pap. 92.95 *(978-1-111-13801-1(X))* Delmar Cengage Learning.

ADOBE INDESIGN (COMPUTER PROGRAM)

Adobe Creative Team. Adobe Creative Suite 5 Design Premium Classroom in a Book. rev. ed. 2010. (Classroom in a Book Ser.). (ENG., Illus.). 336p. pap. 54.99 *(978-0-321-70450-4(9))* Adobe Pr.

—Indesign CS4. 2008. (Classroom in a Book Ser.). (ENG., Illus.). 432p. pap., wbk. ed. 54.99 *(978-0-321-57380-3(3))* Adobe Pr.

—Indesign CS5. 2010. (Classroom in a Book Ser.). (ENG., Illus.). 416p. pap. 54.99 *(978-0-321-70179-4(8))* Adobe Pr.

Aquent Graphics Institute AGI. Adobe Indesign CS3 Digital Classroom. Smith, Christopher E., ed. 2008. (Illus.). 352p. mass mkt. 10.99 *(978-0-9678737-1-8(1))* Cyber Solution Publishing, Inc.

Baker, Donna, et al. Adobe InDesign CS4. 2009. (Illus.). 384p. pap. 39.99 *(978-0-07-160634-9(3)*, 0071606343) McGraw-Hill Osborne.

Botello, Chris. Adobe Indesign CS3 Revealed. 2007. (Adobe Creative Suite Ser.). (ENG., Illus.). 544p. (C). pap. 87.95 *(978-1-4283-1960-8(3))* Delmar Cengage Learning.

—Adobe Indesign CS4 Revealed. 2009. (Adobe Creative Suite Ser.). (ENG.). 544p. pap. 84.95 *(978-1-4354-4185-9(0))* Course Technology.

—Adobe Indesign CS4 Revealed. 2009. (ENG.). 68.95 *(978-1-4354-8267-8(0))* Course Technology.

—Adobe Indesign CS5 Revealed. 2010. (Revealed Ser.). (ENG.). 660p. (C). pap. 82.95 *(978-1-111-13049-7(3))* Delmar Cengage Learning.

—Adobe Photoshop CS5 Illustrated. 2010. (Illustrated Ser.). (ENG.). 232p. pap. 51.95 *(978-0-538-47781-9(4))* Course Technology.

Botello, Chris & Reding, Elizabeth Eisner. The Design Collection Revealed: Adobe Indesign CS3, Photoshop CS3 & Illustrator CS3. 2007. (Adobe Creative Suite Ser.). (ENG., Illus.). 696p. (C). pap. 101.95 *(978-1-4283-1962-2(X))* Delmar Cengage Learning.

—The Design Collection Revealed: Adobe Indesign CS5, Photoshop CS5 & Illustrator CS5. 2010. (Revealed Ser.). (ENG.). 880p. (C). pap. 87.95 *(978-1-111-13061-9(2))* Delmar Cengage Learning.

—HC - the Design Collection Revealed: Adobe Indesign CS4, Adobe Photoshop CS4, & Adobe Illustrator CS4. 2009. (ENG., Illus.). 75.95 *(978-1-4354-8270-8(0))* Course Technology.

Botello, Chris, et al. The Design Collection: Adobe Indesign CS4, Adobe Photoshop CS4, & Adobe Illustrator CS4. 2009. (Adobe Creative Suite Ser.). (ENG., Illus.). 720p. pap. 85.95 *(978-1-4354-4190-3(7))* Course Technology.

Burke, Pariah S. Mastering Indesign CS3 for Print Design & Production. 2007. (ENG., Illus.). 512p. per. 49.99 *(978-0-470-11456-8(8)*, Sybex) Wiley, John & Sons, Inc.

—Mastering Indesign CS5 for Print Design & Production. 2010. (ACE & ENG., Illus.). 736p. pap. 49.99 *(978-0-470-65098-1(2)*, Sybex) Wiley, John & Sons, Inc.

Cohen, Sandee. InDesign CS3 for Macintosh & Windows. 2007. (Visual QuickStart Guide Ser.). (ENG., Illus.). 600p. pap. 29.99 *(978-0-321-50306-0(6))* Peachpit Pr.

—InDesign CS4 for Macintosh & Windows: Visual QuickStart Guide. 2008. (Visual QuickStart Guide Ser.). (ENG., Illus.). 576p. pap. 34.99 *(978-0-321-57357-5(9))* Peachpit Pr.

—InDesign CS5 for Macintosh & Win. 2010. (Visual QuickStart Guide Ser.). (ENG., Illus.). 552p. pap. 29.99 *(978-0-321-70520-4(3))* Peachpit Pr.

Converse, Chris. Create Interactive Documents using Adobe Indesign CS5. 2010. (ENG.). 48p. 49.99 *(978-0-321-73392-4(4))* Peachpit Pr.

Course Technology Staff & Botello, Chris. A Guided Tour of Creative Suite 3 Design Standard. 2007. (Guided Tour Ser.). (ENG.). 23.95 *(978-1-4239-2572-9(6))* Course Technology.

Course Technology Staff & Fisher, Ann. Adobe Indesign Cs3 Illustrated. 2008. (Illus.). pap. 34.95 *(978-1-4239-9939-3(8))* Course Technology.

Cruise, John & Anton, Kelly Kordes. Adobe Indesign CS3 How-Tos: 100 Essential Techniques. 2007. (ENG., Illus.). 272p. per. 24.99 *(978-0-321-50895-9(5))* Adobe Pr.

—Adobe InDesign CS4 How-Tos: 100 Essential Techniques. 2008. (How-Tos Ser.). (ENG., Illus.). 272p. pap. 24.99 *(978-0-321-59094-7(5))* Adobe Pr.

Deuchler, Rufus & Video2brain Staff. Adobe Indesign CS5. 5 for Electronic Publishing: Learn by Video. 2011. (Learn by Video Ser.). (ENG.). 48p. 34.99 ***(978-0-321-78684-5(X))*** Peachpit Pr.

Element K Journals Creative Team. Adobe(r) Indesign(r) CS3: 084490ie. 2007. spiral bd. *(978-1-4246-0662-7(4))* Element K Content LLC.

—Adobe(r) Indesign(r) CS3: 084490s3. 2007. spiral bd. *(978-1-4246-0663-4(2))* Element K Content LLC.

Fisher, Anne. Adobe Indesign CS5 Illustrated. 2010. (Illustrated Ser.). (ENG., Illus.). 216p. pap. 51.95 *(978-0-538-47787-1(3))* Course Technology.

—Adobe Indesign CS5 Illustrated (Book Only) 2010. (ENG.). 240p. (C). pap. 51.95 *(978-1-111-53088-4(2))* Course Technology.

French, Nigel. InDesign Type: Professional Typography with Adobe Indesign. 2nd rev. ed. 2010. (ENG., Illus.). 288p. pap. 44.99 *(978-0-321-68536-0(9))* Adobe Pr.

Gatter, Mark. Software Essentials for Graphic Designers: Photoshop, Illustrator, Indesign, QuarkXPress, Dreamweaver, Flash + Acrobat. 2006. (Illus.). 240p. pap. incl. cd-rom *(978-0-300-11800-1(7))* Yale Univ. Pr.
Gruman, Galen. Adobe InDesign CS3. 2007. (Bible Ser.: 414). (ENG., Illus.). 1040p. per. 44.99 *(978-0-470-11938-9(1),* Wiley) Wiley, John & Sons, Inc.
—InDesign CS3 for Dummies. 2007. (ENG., Illus.). 432p. per. 24.99 *(978-0-470-11865-8(2),* For Dummies) Wiley, John & Sons, Inc.
—InDesign CS4 for Dummies. 2008. (ENG., Illus.). 432p. pap. 24.99 *(978-0-470-38848-8(X),* For Dummies) Wiley, John & Sons, Inc.
Gruman, Galen & Gruman. InDesign CS4 Bible. 2009. (Bible Ser.: 550). (ENG., Illus.). 992p. pap. 49.99 *(978-0-470-40511-6(2),* Wiley) Wiley, John & Sons, Inc.
Johnson, Steve. Indesign CS5. 2010. (Illus.). 565p. pap. 57.50 *(978-0-273-74065-0(2),* Prentice Hall) Pearson Education, Ltd. GBR. Dist: Trans-Atlantic Pubns., Inc.
Johnson, Steve & Perspection, Inc. Staff. Indesign CS4. 2008. (On Demand Ser.). (ENG.). 528p. pap. 29.99 *(978-0-7897-3839-4(2))* Que.
—Indesign CS5. 2010. (On Demand Ser.). (ENG., Illus.). 576p. pap. 29.99 *(978-0-7897-4446-3(5))* Que.
Kvern, Olav Martin & Blatner, David. Adobe InDesign CS4. 2009. (Real World Ser.). (Illus.). 840p. pap. 59.99 *(978-0-321-59243-9(3))* Peachpit Pr.
Maivald, James J. & Palmer, Cathy. A Designer's Guide to Adobe InDesign & XML: Harness the Power of XML to Automate Your Print & Web Workflows. 2007. (ENG., Illus.). 336p. per. 49.99 *(978-0-321-50355-8(4))* Adobe Pr.
McClelland, Deke & Futato, David. Adobe InDesign CS4. 2008. (One-On-One Ser.). (ENG., Illus.). 560p. pap. 49.99 *(978-0-596-52191-2(X),* Deke) O'Reilly Media, Inc.
McCue, Claudia. Fearless Flash: How to Use Adobe Indesign CS5 & the Tools You Already Know to Create Engaging Web Experiences. 2010. (ENG., Illus.). 240p. pap. 44.99 *(978-0-321-73482-2(3))* Adobe Pr.
Murray, Katherine & Emergent Learning LLC Staff. Learning Web Design with Adobe CS5. 2010. (ENG., Illus.). 416p. (C). pap. 70.33 *(978-0-13-802490-1(1),* Prentice Hall) Prentice Hall PTR.
Noble Desktop. Adobe Indesign CS3 Step by Step Training. 2007. 101p. ring bd. 65.00 *(978-0-9777017-8-0(6))* Noble Desktop, LLC.
Powell, Gabriel. Instant InDesign: Designing Templates for Fast & Efficient Page Layout. 2007. (ENG., Illus.). 336p. per. 49.99 *(978-0-321-49571-6(3))* Adobe Pr.
Ralston, Rick. The Designer's Apprentice: Automating Photoshop, Illustrator, & Indesign in Adobe Creative Suite 3. 2007. (ENG., Illus.). 256p. per. 39.99 *(978-0-321-49570-9(5))* Adobe Pr.
Reding, Elizabeth Eisner & Botello, Chris. Adobe Indesign CS, Photoshop CS, & Illustrator CS-Design Professional. 2006. (ENG.). 328p. pap. 105.95 *(978-1-4180-6457-0(2))* Course Technology.
Rydberg, Terry. Adobe Indesign CS5. 2010. (Design Exploration Ser.). (ENG.). 384p. pap. 57.95 *(978-1-111-13032-9(9))* Delmar Cengage Learning.
—Exploring Adobe Indesign CS4. 2008. (Adobe Creative Suite Ser.). (ENG.). 376p. pap. 62.95 *(978-1-4354-4200-9(8))* Delmar Cengage Learning.
Shufflebotham, Robert. InDesign CS3: For Windows & Mac. 2008. (In Easy Steps Ser.). (ENG., Illus.). 192p. pap. 14.99 *(978-1-84078-349-0(4))* Computer Step GBR. Dist: Perseus-PGW.
—Indesign in Easy Steps: Covers CS3, CS4, & CS5. 2011. (In Easy Steps Ser.). (ENG., Illus.). 192p. pap. 14.99 *(978-1-84078-414-5(8))* Computer Step GBR. Dist: Perseus-PGW.
Skintik, Catherine. Learning Media Design with Adobe CS4. 2009. (ENG.). 608p. (C). pap. 69.33 *(978-0-13-507687-3(0),* Prentice Hall) Prentice Hall PTR.
Skintik, Catherine & Emergent Learning LLC, . Learning Media Design with Adobe CS5. 2010. (ENG.). 608p. (C). pap. 70.33 *(978-0-13-138408-8(2),* Prentice Hall) Prentice Hall PTR.
Smith, Christopher & AGI Creative Team. Adobe Indesign CS5: A Complete Training Package! 2010. (ENG., Illus.). 416p. pap. 49.99 *(978-0-470-60781-7(5),* Wiley) Wiley, John & Sons, Inc.
Smith, Christopher E., et al. Indesign Cs4. 2008. (CourseSmart Ser.: 3). (ENG., Illus.). 400p. pap. 49.99 *(978-0-470-41094-3(9),* Wiley) Wiley, John & Sons, Inc.
Torta, Stephanie. Digital Layout Using Adobe(r) Indesign(r) CS5: Tutorials & Techniques. 2012. 350p. pap. 45.95 *(978-1-936420-08-7(2))* Mercury Learning & Information.
Williams, Robin. The Non-Designer's Indesign Book. rev. ed. 2011. (Non-Designer's Ser.). (ENG.). 240p. pap. 34.99 *(978-0-321-77284-8(9))* Peachpit Pr.
Witchel, Jeff. The Best of Layers Magazine Tips of the Day: Indesign. 2011. 188p. pap. 25.45 ***(978-1-4634-0244-0(9))*** AuthorHouse.
Wood, Allan. The Graphic Designer's Digital Toolkit: A Project-Based Introduction to Adobe Photoshop CS5, Illustrator CS5 & Indesign CS5. 5th ed. 2010. (Adobe Creative Suite Ser.). (ENG., Illus.). 752p. (C). pap. 92.95 *(978-1-111-13801-1(X))* Delmar Cengage Learning.

ADOBE PAGEMAKER (COMPUTER PROGRAM)

Detienne, M. G. PageMaker 5.0: Basics & Beyond. (Illus.). 97p. pap. 29.00 *(978-1-887580-05-2(0))* Tec Trek Ltd.
Schwartz, Linda K. How to Use PageMaker 5 for Windows, Pt. II. Young, Natalie B., ed. unabr. ed. 95p. pap. 175.00 incl. audio, disk *(978-1-56562-035-3(6),* 520) OneOnOne Computer Training.

ADOBE PHOTOSHOP (COMPUTER PROGRAM)

Aaland, Mikkel. Photoshop CS3 Raw: Transform Your Raw Images into Works of Art. 2nd rev. ed. 2007. (ENG., Illus.). 272p. per. 34.99 *(978-0-596-51052-7(7))* O'Reilly Media, Inc.
—Photoshop Lightroom 2 Adventure: Mastering Adobe's Next-Generation Tool for Digital Photographers. 2007. (ENG., Illus.). 352p. per. 39.99 *(978-0-596-10099-5(X))* O'Reilly Media, Inc.
Adobe Creative Team. Adobe Creative Suite 5 Design Premium Classroom in a Book. rev. ed. 2010. (Classroom in a Book Ser.). (ENG., Illus.). 336p. pap. 54.99 *(978-0-321-70450-4(9))* Adobe Pr.
—Adobe Photoshop CS4 Classroom in a Book. 2008. (Classroom in a Book Ser.). (ENG., Illus.). 464p. pap., wbk. ed. 59.99 *(978-0-321-57379-7(X))* Adobe Pr.
—Adobe Photoshop Elements, No. 8. 2009. (Classroom in a Book Ser.). (ENG.). 448p. pap., wbk. ed. 44.99 *(978-0-321-66032-9(3))* Adobe Pr.
—Adobe Photoshop Elements 10 Classroom in a Book. 2011. (ENG., Illus.). 320p. pap. 44.99 ***(978-0-321-81100-4(3))*** Adobe Pr.
—Adobe Photoshop Elements 5.0. 2006. (Classroom in a Book Ser.). (ENG., Illus.). 360p. pap. 39.99 *(978-0-321-47674-6(3))* Adobe Pr.
—Adobe Photoshop Elements 7: Classroom in a Book. 2008. (Classroom in a Book Ser.). (ENG., Illus.). 400p. pap. 44.99 *(978-0-321-57390-2(0))* Adobe Pr.
—Adobe Photoshop Elements 7 & Adobe Premiere Elements 7. 2009. (Classroom in a Book Ser.). (ENG., Illus.). 720p. pap. 69.99 *(978-0-321-57384-1(6))* Adobe Pr.
—Adobe Photoshop Elements 9. 2010. (Classroom in a Book Ser.). (ENG., Illus.). 448p. pap. 44.99 *(978-0-321-74973-4(1))* Adobe Pr.
—Adobe Photoshop Lightroom 2. 2008. (Classroom in a Book Ser.). (ENG., Illus.). 384p. pap. 54.99 *(978-0-321-55560-1(0))* Peachpit Pr.
—Adobe Photoshop Lightroom 3. 2010. (Classroom in a Book Ser.). (ENG., Illus.). 400p. pap. 54.99 *(978-0-321-70093-3(7))* Adobe Pr.
—Adobe Photoshop Lightroom 4 Classroom in a Book. 2012. (ENG.). 384p. pap. 54.99 ***(978-0-321-81957-4(8))*** Adobe Pr.
—Adobe Premiere Elements, No. 8. 2009. (Classroom in a Book Ser.). (ENG., Illus.). 320p. pap. 54.99 *(978-0-321-68638-1(1))* Adobe Pr.
—Photoshop CS5. 2010. (Classroom in a Book Ser.). (ENG., Illus.). 464p. pap. 54.99 *(978-0-321-70176-3(3))* Adobe Pr.
Adobe PhotoShop Advanced Artistry II. 2006. cd-rom 99.95 *(978-1-933736-42-6(9))* VTC, Inc.
Adobe Photoshop CS2 Training, 1. 2006. 82p. ring bd. 200.00 incl. DVD *(978-0-9777017-1-1(9))* Noble Desktop, LLC.
Adobe(r) Photoshop(r) Elements 6.0: 084031s3. 2008. spiral bd. *(978-1-4246-1060-0(5))* Element K Content LLC.
Adobe Press Staff. Adobe Photoshop CS3: Classroom in a Book: The official training workbook from adobe Systems. 2007. (Classroom in a Book Ser.). (ENG., Illus.). 496p. pap. 54.99 *(978-0-321-49202-9(1))* Adobe Pr.
—Adobe Photoshop Elements 6 Classroom in a Book. 2007. (Classroom in a Book Ser.). (Illus.). 384p. pap. 39.99 *(978-0-321-52465-2(9))* Adobe Pr.
AGI Creative Team. Photoshop Elements 9 Digital Classroom. 2010. (Digital Classroom Ser.: 53). (ENG., Illus.). 416p. pap. 39.99 *(978-0-470-93230-8(9),* Wiley) Wiley, John & Sons, Inc.
AGI Creative Team Staff. Photoshop Elements 8. 2009. (Digital Classroom Ser.: 21). (ENG., Illus.). 432p. pap. 39.99 *(978-0-470-56692-3(2),* Wiley) Wiley, John & Sons, Inc.
AGI Creative Team Staff & Smith, Jennifer. Photoshop CS5. 2010. (Digital Classroom Ser.: 95). (ENG., Illus.). 416p. pap. 49.99 *(978-0-470-60777-0(7),* Wiley) Wiley, John & Sons, Inc.
AGI Creative Team Staff & Smith, Jerron. Adobe after Effects CS5. 2010. (Digital Classroom Ser.: 33). (ENG., Illus.). 384p. pap. 49.99 *(978-0-470-59524-4(8),* Wiley) Wiley, John & Sons, Inc.
AGI Creative Team Staff, et al. Adobe Creative Suite 5 Design Premium Digital Classroom. 2010. (Digital Classroom Ser.: 37). (ENG., Illus.). 832p. pap. 59.99 *(978-0-470-60779-4(3),* Wiley) Wiley, John & Sons, Inc.
Ahearn, Luke. 3D Game Textures: Create Professional Game Art Using Photoshop. 3rd ed. 2011. (ENG., Illus.). 416p. (C). pap. 49.95 ***(978-0-240-82077-4(0),*** Focal Pr.) Elsevier Science & Technology Bks.
Alsheimer, Leslie, et al. Black & White in Photoshop CS4 & Lightroom: A Complete Integrated Workflow Solution for Creating Stunning Monochromatic Images in Photoshop CS4, Photoshop Lightroom, & Beyond. 2009. (ENG., Illus.). 336p. pap. 39.95 *(978-0-240-52159-6(5),* Focal Pr.) Elsevier Science & Technology Bks.
Ames, Kevin. AdobePhotoshopCS2: The Art of Photographing Women. 2006. (ENG., Illus.). 416p. per. 34.99 *(978-0-470-04825-2(5),* Wiley) Wiley, John & Sons, Inc.
—The Digital Photographer's Notebook: A Pro's Guide to Adobe Photoshop CS3, Lightroom, & Bridge. 2007. (Illus.). 352p. per. 39.99 *(978-0-321-35841-7(4))* New Riders Publishing.
—Faces: The Complete Guide to Retouching Portraits with Phop. 2011. (ENG., Illus.). 416p. pap. 34.99 *(978-0-470-60363-5(1),* Wiley) Wiley, John & Sons, Inc.
Anderson, Andy, et al. Photoshop CS3. 2007. (On Demand Ser.). (ENG., Illus.). 592p. per. 39.99 *(978-0-7897-3691-8(8))* Que.
Andrews, Philip. Adobe Photoshop CS3 A-Z: Tools & Features Illustrated Ready Reference. 2007. (ENG., Illus.). 320p. pap. 29.95 *(978-0-240-52065-0(3),* Focal Pr.) Elsevier Science & Technology Bks.
—Adobe Photoshop Elements 10 for Photographers: The Creative Use of Photoshop Elements on Mac & PC. 2011. (ENG., Illus.). 504p. pap. 44.95 ***(978-0-240-52382-8(2),*** Focal Pr.) Elsevier Science & Technology Bks.
—Adobe Photoshop Elements 5. 0: Tools & Features Illustrated Ready Reference. 2007. (ENG., Illus.). 256p. pap. 29.95 *(978-0-240-52061-2(0),* Focal Pr.) Elsevier Science & Technology Bks.
—Adobe Photoshop Elements 6: A Visual Introduction to Digital Photography. 2007. (ENG., Illus.). 424p. pap. 39.95 *(978-0-240-52099-5(8),* Focal Pr.) Elsevier Science & Technology Bks.
—Adobe Photoshop Elements 9 for Photographers. 2010. (ENG., Illus.). 544p. pap. 49.95 *(978-0-240-52244-9(3),* Focal Pr.) Elsevier Science & Technology Bks.
—Advanced Photoshop Elements 5. 0 for Digital Photographers. 2006. (ENG., Illus.). 424p. pap. 36.95 *(978-0-240-52057-5(2),* Focal Pr.) Elsevier Science & Technology Bks.
—Advanced Photoshop Elements 6 for Digital Photographers. 2008. (ENG., Illus.). 424p. per. 39.95 *(978-0-240-52097-1(1),* Focal Pr.) Elsevier Science & Technology Bks.
—The Complete Raw Workflow Guide: How to Get the Most from Your Raw Images in Adobe Camera Raw, Lightroom, Photoshop & Elements. 2007. (ENG., Illus.). 368p. pap. 39.95 *(978-0-240-81027-0(9),* Focal Pr.) Elsevier Science & Technology Bks.
Asch, David. Focus on Photoshop Elements: Focus on the Fundamentals. 2011. (ENG., Illus.). 152p. pap. 19.95 *(978-0-240-81445-2(2),* Focal Pr.) Elsevier Science & Technology Bks.
Asch, David & Caplin, Steve. How to Cheat in Photoshop Elements 10: Release Your Imagination. 2011. (ENG., Illus.). 320p. pap. 39.95 ***(978-0-240-82047-7(9),*** Focal Pr.) Elsevier Science & Technology Bks.
Asch, David & Caplin, Steve. How to Cheat in Photoshop Elements 6: Create Stunning Photomontages on a Budget. 2007. (How to Cheat In Ser.). (ENG., Illus.). 264p. pap. 34.95 *(978-0-240-52083-4(1),* Focal Pr.) Elsevier Science & Technology Bks.
Ballew, Joli. Photoshop CS3 for Screen Printers. 2007. 584p. pap. 44.95 incl. cd-rom *(978-1-59822-036-0(5))* Jones & Bartlett Learning, LLC.
BarCharts, Inc. Photoshop Cs5. 2010. (ENG.). 6p. 5.95 *(978-1-4232-1507-3(9))* Barcharts, Inc.
Barker, Corey. Photoshop down & Dirty Tricks for Designers. 2011. (Down & Dirty Tricks Ser.). (ENG., Illus.). 384p. pap. 49.99 ***(978-0-321-82049-5(5))*** New Riders Publishing.
Batdorff, John. Plug in with Nik: A Photographer's Guide to Creating Dynamic Images with Nik Software. 2012. (ENG.). 312p. pap. 39.99 ***(978-0-321-83977-0(3))*** Peachpit Pr.
Bauer, Peter. Photoshop CS3 for Dummies. 2007. (ENG., Illus.). 416p. per. 24.99 *(978-0-470-11193-2(3),* For Dummies) Wiley, John & Sons, Inc.
—Photoshop CS4 for Dummies. 2008. (ENG., Illus.). 416p. pap. 29.99 *(978-0-470-32725-8(1),* For Dummies) Wiley, John & Sons, Inc.
—Photoshop CS5 for Dummies. 2010. (ENG., Illus.). 432p. pap. 29.99 *(978-0-470-61078-7(6),* For Dummies) Wiley, John & Sons, Inc.
Binder, Kate. Easy Adobe Photoshop Elements 7: 2008. (ENG., Illus.). 240p. pap. 19.99 *(978-0-7897-3926-1(7))* Que.
—Photoshop Elements 7: See It Done. Do It Yourself. 2009. (Illus.). 240p. pap. *(978-0-7897-3927-8(5))* Que.
Binder, Kate & Binder, Kate. Sams Teach Yourself Adobe Photoshop CS4 in 24 Hours. 5th ed. 2008. (Sams Teach Yourself Ser.). (ENG., Illus.). 552p. pap. 34.99 *(978-0-672-33042-1(3))* Sams.
Birnholz, Robert A., et al. Motion Graphics with Adobe Creative Suite 5 Studio Techniques. 2010. (Studio Techniques Ser.). (ENG., Illus.). 456p. pap. 59.99 *(978-0-321-71969-0(7))* Adobe Pr.
Bishop, Sherry, et al. The Web Collection Revealed Premium Edition: Adobe Dreamweaver CS5, Flash CS5 & Photoshop CS5. 2010. (Revealed Ser.). (ENG., Illus.). 896p. (C). pap. 87.95 *(978-1-111-13073-2(6))* Delmar Cengage Learning.
Blatner, David & Chavez, Conrad. Real World Adobe Photoshop CS4 for Photographers. 2008. (Real World Ser.). (ENG., Illus.). 600p. pap. 59.99 *(978-0-321-60451-4(2))* Peachpit Pr.
Bluttman, Ken. Photoshop Elements No. 8. 2010. (ENG., Illus.). 240p. pap. 32.50 *(978-0-273-73439-0(3),* Prentice Hall) Pearson Education, Ltd. GBR. Dist: Trans-Atlantic Pubns., Inc.
Bluttman, Ken. Photoshop Elements 9 in Simple Steps. rev. ed. 2011. (ENG., Illus.). 240p. pap. 39.50 ***(978-0-273-74995-0(1))*** Pearson Education, Ltd. GBR. Dist: Trans-Atlantic Pubns., Inc.
Bolante, Antony. Premiere Pro CS3: For Windows & Macintosh. 2007. (ENG., Illus.). 440p. per. 39.99 *(978-0-321-52635-9(X))* Peachpit Pr.
Botello. Adobe Photoshop Cs3 Illustrated. 2008. (Illustrated Ser.). pap. 38.95 *(978-1-4239-9940-9(1))* Course Technology.
Botello, Chris. Adobe Illustrator CS4. 2009. (Illustrated Ser.). (ENG.). 192p. (C). pap. 53.95 *(978-0-538-75090-5(1))* Course Technology.
—Adobe Photoshop CS5 Illustrated. 2010. (Illustrated Ser.). (ENG.). 232p. pap. 51.95 *(978-0-538-47781-9(4))* Course Technology.
—Adobe Photoshop CS5 Illustrated (Book Only) 2010. (ENG.). 232p. (C). pap. 51.95 *(978-1-111-53089-1(0))* Course Technology.
—Advanced Adobe Photoshop CS5 Revealed. 2010. (Revealed Ser.). (ENG.). 616p. (C). pap. 87.95 *(978-1-111-13625-3(4))* Delmar Cengage Learning.
Botello, Chris & Reding, Elizabeth Eisner. The Design Collection Revealed: Adobe Indesign CS3, Photoshop CS3 & Illustrator CS3. 2007. (Adobe Creative Suite Ser.). (ENG., Illus.). 696p. (C). pap. 101.95 *(978-1-4283-1962-2(X))* Delmar Cengage Learning.
—The Design Collection Revealed: Adobe Indesign CS5, Photoshop CS5 & Illustrator CS5. 2010. (Revealed Ser.). (ENG.). 880p. (C). pap. 87.95 *(978-1-111-13061-9(2))* Delmar Cengage Learning.
—HC - the Design Collection Revealed: Adobe Indesign CS4, Adobe Photoshop CS4, & Adobe Illustrator CS4. 2009. (ENG., Illus.). 75.95 *(978-1-4354-8270-8(0))* Course Technology.
Botello, Chris, et al. The Design Collection: Adobe Indesign CS4, Adobe Photoshop CS4, & Adobe Illustrator CS4. 2009. (Adobe Creative Suite Ser.). (ENG., Illus.). 720p. pap. 85.95 *(978-1-4354-4190-3(7))* Course Technology.
Bouton, Gary D. Photoshop(r) the L Line, the Express Line to Learning. 2007. (Illus.). 544p. pap. 39.99 *(978-0-470-09746-5(9))* Wiley, John & Sons, Inc.
Bouton, Gary David. Adobe Photoshop CS3 Extended: Retouching Motion Pictures. 2008. (ENG., Illus.). 608p. pap. 49.99 *(978-1-59863-461-7(5))* Course Technology.
Brundage, Barbara. Photoshop Elements, No. 9. 2010. (ENG., Illus.). 640p. pap. 44.99 *(978-1-4493-8967-3(8),* Pogue Pr.) O'Reilly Media, Inc.
—Photoshop Elements 10: The Missing Manual. 2011. (ENG., Illus.). 656p. pap. 44.99 *(978-1-4493-9850-7(2),* Pogue Pr.) O'Reilly Media, Inc.
—Photoshop Elements 5: The Missing Manual. 2006. (Missing Manual Ser.: Vol. 5). (ENG., Illus.). 576p. per. 39.99 *(978-0-596-52728-0(4),* Pogue Pr.) O'Reilly Media, Inc.
—Photoshop Elements 6 for Mac. 2008. (Missing Manual Ser.). (ENG., Illus.). 560p. pap. 44.99 *(978-0-596-51936-0(2),* Pogue Pr.) O'Reilly Media, Inc.
—Photoshop Elements 7: The Missing Manual. 2008. (Missing Manuals Ser.). (ENG., Illus.). 592p. pap. 44.99 *(978-0-596-52133-2(2),* Pogue Pr.) O'Reilly Media, Inc.
Brundage, Barbara & Brundage, Barbara. Photoshop Elements 8 for Mac. 2009. (Missing Manual Ser.). (ENG., Illus.). 592p. pap. 44.99 *(978-0-596-80496-1(2),* Pogue Pr.) O'Reilly Media, Inc.
Bucki, Lisa & Hosier-Bounar, Jane. New Perspectives on Adobe Photoshop CS5, Comprehensive. 2012. (ENG., Illus.). 520p. pap. ***(978-0-538-47335-4(5))*** Course Technology.
Bucki, Lisa A., et al. New Perspectives on Adobe Photoshop CS5, Comprehensive, Pack. 2011. (ENG.). (C). 12.95 *(978-0-538-75796-6(5))* Course Technology.
Burns, Stephen. Advanced Photoshop C4 Trickery & FX. 2009. (ENG.). 400p. pap. 49.99 *(978-1-58450-683-6(0))* Charles River Media.
—The Art of Poser & Photoshop: the Official e-frontier Guide. 2008. (ENG.). 488p. pap. 39.99 *(978-1-59863-431-0(3))* Course Technology.
—Photoshop CS5 Trickery & FX. 2010. (ENG.). 288p. pap. 49.99 *(978-1-4354-5757-7(9))* Course Technology.
Busch, David D. Adobe Photoshop CS3. 2007. (ENG., Illus.). 392p. per. 39.99 *(978-1-59863-400-6(3))* Course Technology.
Campbell, Marc. Adobe Photoshop & Photoshop Elements for Teens. 2007. (ENG., Illus.). 312p. pap. 34.99 *(978-1-59863-379-5(1))* Course Technology.
Caplin, Steve. Art & Design in Photoshop: How to Simulate Just about Anything from Great Works of Art to Urban Graffiti. 2008. (ENG., Illus.). 256p. pap. 39.95 *(978-0-240-81109-3(7),* Focal Pr.) Elsevier Science & Technology Bks.
—How to Cheat in Photoshop CS4: The Art of Creating Photorealistic Montages. 2008. (ENG., Illus.). 448p. pap. 44.95 *(978-0-240-52115-2(3),* Focal Pr.) Elsevier Science & Technology Bks.
—How to Cheat in Photoshop Cs5: The Art of Creating Realistic Photomontages. 2010. (ENG., Illus.). 464p. pap. 44.95 *(978-0-240-52204-3(4),* Focal Pr.) Elsevier Science & Technology Bks.
—100% Photoshop: Create Stunning Illustrations Without Using Any Photographs. 2010. (ENG., Illus.). 256p. pap. 39.95 *(978-0-240-81425-4(8),* Focal Pr.) Elsevier Science & Technology Bks.
Carey, Patrick, et al. Microsoft Office Excel 2010. 2010. (ENG.). (C). 12.95 *(978-0-538-74294-8(1))* Course Technology.
Carlson, Jeff. Photoshop Elements 10 for Windows & Mac OS X: Visual QuickStart Guide. 2011. (Visual QuickStart Guide Ser.). (ENG., Illus.). 400p. pap. 39.99 ***(978-0-321-80834-9(7))*** Peachpit Pr.
—Photoshop Elements 7 for Windows. 2008. (ENG., Illus.). 384p. pap. 29.99 *(978-0-321-56596-9(7))* Peachpit Pr.
—Photoshop Elements 8 for Mac OS X. 2009. (Visual QuickStart Guide Ser.). (ENG., Illus.). 336p. pap. 29.99 *(978-0-321-68410-3(9))* Peachpit Pr.
—Photoshop Elements 8 for Windows. 2009. (Visual QuickStart Guide Ser.). (ENG., Illus.). 384p. pap. 29.99 *(978-0-321-64908-9(7))* Peachpit Pr.
—Photoshop Elements 9 for Windows. 2010. (Visual QuickStart Guide Ser.). (ENG., Illus.). 384p. pap. 34.99 *(978-0-321-74131-8(5))* Peachpit Pr.
Carlson, Jeff & Hoeschen, Craig. Photoshop Elements 5 for Windows. 2007. (Visual QuickStart Guide Ser.). (ENG., Illus.). 416p. per. 21.99 *(978-0-321-47671-5(9))* Peachpit Pr.
Carucci, John. Nighttime Digital Photography with Adobe Photoshop CS3. 2007. (ENG., Illus.). 240p. per. 49.99 *(978-0-321-50354-1(6))* Peachpit Pr.
Cates, Stacy, et al. Adobe Photoshop CS4. 2009. (CourseSmart Ser.: 513). (ENG., Illus.). 1048p. pap. 44.99 *(978-0-470-34517-7(9),* Wiley) Wiley, John & Sons, Inc.
Chavez, Conrad. Color Management without the Jargon: A Simple Approach for Designers & Photographers Using the Adobe Creative Suite. 2009. (ENG.). 48p. 39.99 *(978-0-321-70313-2(8))* Peachpit Pr.
—Working Smart in Adobe Photoshop CS2: Time-Saving Techniques & Shortcuts to Boost Your Photoshop Productivity. 2006. (ENG., Illus.). 304p. per. 39.99 *(978-0-321-33539-5(2))* Adobe Pr.
Chavez, Conrad & Blatner, David. Photoshop CS5 for Photographers. 2010. (Real World Ser.). (ENG., Illus.). 600p. pap. 59.99 *(978-0-321-71983-6(2))* Peachpit Pr.
Chen, Mark. Creative Wedding Album Design with Adobe Photoshop: Step-by-Step Techniques for Professional Digital Photographers. 2009. (ENG., Illus.). 128p. pap. 34.95 *(978-1-58428-261-7(4))* Amherst Media, Inc.

Chipkin, Frederick. Adobe Photoshop for Textile Design. 2008. (Illus.). 109p. (C). spiral bd. 120.00 *(978-0-9727317-0-6(9),* 1000944) Chipkin, Frederick.
Chow, Garrick. Adobe Dreamweaver Cs3. 2007. (Hands-on Training Ser.). (ENG., Illus.). 528p. pap. 54.99 *(978-0-321-50985-7(4))* Peachpit Pr.
Christiansen, Mark. Adobe after Effects CS4 Visual Effects & Compositing Studio Techniques. 2008. (Studio Techniques Ser.). (ENG.). 496p. pap. 59.99 *(978-0-321-59201-9(8))* Adobe Pr.
Cleghorn, Mark. Photoshop in a Weekend. 2009. (ENG., Illus.). 176p. pap. 19.95 *(978-1-86108-557-3(5))* Sterling Publishing Co., Inc.
Coalson, Nat. Lightroom 3: Streamlining Your Digital Photography Process. 2010. (ENG., Illus.). 400p. pap. 39.99 *(978-0-470-60705-3(X),* Wiley) Wiley, John & Sons, Inc.
Course Technology. ACA Certification Prep Basics. 2011. (ENG.). (C). 10.95 *(978-1-111-82247-7(6))* Course Technology.
—Adobe Dreamweaver CS4 CourseNotes. 2009. (CourseNotes Ser.). (ENG.). 6p. 8.95 *(978-0-538-78619-5(1))* Course Technology.
—Adobe Flash CS4. 2009. (CourseNotes Ser.). (ENG.). 6p. (C). 8.95 *(978-0-538-74871-1(0))* Course Technology.
—Adobe Photoshop CS5 CourseNotes. 2010. (Shelly Cashman Ser.). (ENG.). 6p. 8.95 *(978-1-111-53007-5(6))* Course Technology.
—The Best Practices in Academic Web Research. 2009. (CourseNotes Ser.). (ENG.). 6p. (C). 8.95 *(978-0-538-74489-8(8))* Course Technology.
Course Technology Staff & Botello, Chris. A Guided Tour of Creative Suite 3 Design Standard. 2007. (Guided Tour Ser.). (ENG.). 23.95 *(978-1-4239-2572-9(6))* Course Technology.
Covey, Sylvie. Photoshop for Artists: A Complete Guide for Fine Artists, Photographers, & Printmakers. 2012. (ENG., Illus.). 304p. pap. 35.00 ***(978-0-8230-0671-7(9))*** Watson-Guptill Pubns., Inc.
Crawford, Mike. Mastering Advanced Photoshop Techniques for Professional Photography. 2008. (Illus.). 191p. *(978-2-940378-33-3(9))* RotoVision SA.
Daly, Tim. Digital Print Styles: Getting Professional Results with Photoshop Elements & Your Inkjet Printer. 2008. (ENG., Illus.). 224p. pap. 39.99 *(978-0-321-56936-3(9))* Peachpit Pr.
—Printing with Adobe Photoshop CS4. 2009. (ENG.). 302p. pap. 39.95 *(978-0-240-81138-3(0),* Focal Pr.) Elsevier Science & Technology Bks.
DaNae Dayley, Lisa & Dayley, Brad. Photoshop CS5 Bible. 2010. (ENG., Illus.). 1096p. pap. 44.99 *(978-0-470-58474-3(2),* Wiley) Wiley, John & Sons, Inc.
Davis, Harold & Davis, Phyllis. The Photoshop Darkroom: Creative Digital Post-Processing. 2009. (ENG.). 208p. pap. 39.95 *(978-0-240-81259-5(X),* Focal Pr.) Elsevier Science & Technology Bks.
—The Photoshop Darkroom 2: Creative Digital Transformations. 2011. (ENG., Illus.) 208p. pap. 39.95 *(978-0-240-81531-2(9),* Focal Pr.) Elsevier Science & Technology Bks.
Davis, Jack & Willmore, Ben. Photoshop CS3 for Photography. 3rd rev. ed. 2008. (How to Wow Ser.). (ENG., Illus.). 224p. pap. 44.99 *(978-0-321-50986-4(2))* Peachpit Pr.
Davis, Jack, et al. How to Wow with Photoshop Elements 5. 2006. (How to Wow Ser.). (ENG., Illus.). 192p. pap. 39.99 *(978-0-321-48615-8(3))* Peachpit Pr.
—The Photoshop CS/CS2 Wow! Book. 2006. (Wow! Book Ser.). (ENG., Illus.). 800p. pap. 64.99 *(978-0-321-21345-7(9))* Peachpit Pr.
Dayley, Brad & Dayley, Lisa DaNae. Photoshop Elements 7: After the Shoot. 2009. (ENG., Illus.). 320p. pap. 24.99 *(978-0-470-38985-0(0))* Wiley, John & Sons, Inc.
Dayton, Linnea & Gillespie, Cristen. The Photoshop CS3/CS4. 8th ed. 2010. (Wow! Book Ser.). (ENG., Illus.). 800p. pap. 59.99 *(978-0-321-51495-0(5))* Peachpit Pr.
Debowski, Patty. Digital & Hybrid Scrapbooking & Card-Making: With Photoshop Elements. 2007. 384p. per. 39.99 incl. DVD *(978-0-9796959-0-2(2))* Digital Scrapbook Teacher, The.
Dillard, Ted. RAW Pipeline: Revolutionary Techniques to Streamline Digital Photo Workflow. 2008. (Lark Photography Book Ser.). (ENG., Illus.). 224p. pap. 29.95 *(978-1-60059-279-9(1))* Lark Bks.
Drafahl, Jack & Drafahl, Sue. Adobe Photoshop for Underwater Photographers. 2006. (ENG., Illus.). 224p. pap. 39.95 *(978-1-58428-189-4(8))* Amherst Media, Inc.
duChemin, David. Vision & Voice: Refining Your Vision in Adobe Photoshop Lightroom. 2010. (Voices That Matter Ser.). (ENG.). 272p. pap. 44.99 *(978-0-321-67009-0(4))* New Riders Publishing.
Dykan, Amanda & McNeill, Suzanne. Digi-Scrappin 102 Brushes & Actions: Learn to Install, Incorporate & Design Using Brushes & Actions on Digital Scrapbook Pages. 2011. (Design Originals Ser.). (Illus.). 36p. pap. 19.99 ***(978-1-57421-628-8(7))*** Design Originals.
Earney, Richard. Inside Lightroom 2: The Serious Photographer's Guide to Lightroom Efficiency. 2008. (ENG., Illus.). 208p. pap. 34.95 *(978-0-240-81142-0(9),* Focal Pr.) Elsevier Science & Technology Bks.
Eismann, Katrin, et al. Photoshop Masking & Compositing. 2nd rev. ed. 2012. (Voices That Matter Ser.). (ENG.). 552p. pap. 59.99 ***(978-0-321-70100-8(3))*** New Riders Publishing.
Element K Journals Creative Team. Adobe(r) Dreamweaver(r) CS3: 084204ie. 2007. spiral bd. *(978-1-4246-0648-1(9))* Element K Content LLC.
—Adobe(r) Dreamweaver(r) CS3: 084204s3. 2007. spiral bd. *(978-1-4246-0649-8(7))* Element K Content LLC.
—Adobe(r) Flash(r) CS3: 084540ie. 2007. spiral bd. *(978-1-4246-0654-2(3))* Element K Content LLC.
—Adobe(r) Flash(r) CS3: 084540s3. 2007. spiral bd. *(978-1-4246-0655-9(1))* Element K Content LLC.
—Adobe(r) Photoshop(r) CS3: 084570ie. 2007. spiral bd. *(978-1-4246-0664-1(0))* Element K Content LLC.
—Adobe(r) Photoshop(r) CS3: 084570s3. 2007. spiral bd. *(978-1-4246-0665-8(9))* Element K Content LLC.
Elmansy, Rafiq. Photoshop 3D for Animators. 2010. (ENG., Illus.). 292p. pap. 49.95 *(978-0-240-81349-3(9),* Focal Pr.) Elsevier Science & Technology Bks.
Evans, Duncan & Shelbourne, Tim. Creative Photoshop Portrait Techniques. rev. ed. 2009. (Lark Photography Book Ser.). (ENG., Illus.). 192p. pap. 29.95 *(978-1-60059-085-6(3))* Lark Bks.
Evening, Martin. The Adobe Photoshop, Bk. 3. 2010. (ENG., Illus.). 672p. pap., instr.'s gde. ed. 59.99 *(978-0-321-68070-9(7))* Adobe Pr.
—Adobe Photoshop CS4 for Photographers: A Professional Image Editor's Guide to the Creative Use of Photoshop for the Macintosh & PC. 2008. (ENG., Illus.). 704p. pap. 49.95 *(978-0-240-52125-1(0),* Focal Pr.) Elsevier Science & Technology Bks
—Adobe Photoshop CS5 for Photographers: A Professional Image Editor's Guide to the Creative Use of Photoshop for the Macintosh & PC. 2010. (ENG., Illus.). 758p. pap. 54.95 *(978-0-240-52200-5(1),* Focal Pr.) Elsevier Science & Technology Bks.
Evening, Martin. The Adobe Photoshop Lightroom 4 Book: The Complete Guide for Photographers. 2012. (ENG.). 704p. pap. 54.99 ***(978-0-321-81959-8(4))*** Adobe Pr.
Fitzgerald, Mark. Adobe Photoshop Lightroom & Photoshop Workflow Bible. 2008. (Bible Ser.: 510). (ENG., Illus.). 560p. pap. 44.99 *(978-0-470-30309-2(3),* Wiley) Wiley, John & Sons, Inc.
—Photoshop CS3 Restoration & Retouching Bible. 2008. (Bible Ser.: 521). (ENG., Illus.). 439p. per. 39.99 *(978-0-470-22367-3(7),* Wiley) Wiley, John & Sons, Inc.
—Photoshop CS5: Restoration & Retouching for Digital Photographers Only. 2010. (For Only Ser.: 7). (ENG., Illus.). 384p. pap. 44.99 *(978-0-470-61816-5(7),* Wiley) Wiley, John & Sons, Inc.
—Photoshop Elements 8 after the Shoot No. 8. 2010. (ENG., Illus.). 272p. pap. 24.99 *(978-0-470-56509-4(8),* Wiley) Wiley, John & Sons, Inc.
Focal Press Staff & Andrews, Philip. Adobe Photoshop Elements 8 for Photographers. 2009. (ENG., Illus.). 544p. pap. 49.95 *(978-0-240-52189-3(7),* Focal Pr.) Elsevier Science & Technology Bks.
Focal Press Staff & Galer, Mark. Adobe Photoshop Elements 8: Maximum Performance - Unleash the Hidden Performance of Elements. 2009. (ENG., Illus.). 360p. pap. 45.95 *(978-0-240-52183-1(8),* Focal Pr.) Elsevier Science & Technology Bks.
Focal Press Staff, et al. How to Cheat in Photoshop Elements 8: Discover the Magic of Adobe's Best Kept Secret. 2009. (ENG., Illus.). 320p. pap. 39.95 *(978-0-240-52187-9(0),* Focal Pr.) Elsevier Science & Technology Bks.
Fraser, Bruce. Real World Image Sharpening with Adobe Photoshop CS2: Industrial-Strength Production Techniques. 2006. (Real World Ser.). (ENG., Illus.). 304p. per. 39.99 *(978-0-321-44991-7(6))* Peachpit Pr.
Fraser, Bruce & Schewe, Jeff. Real World Camera Raw with Adobe Photoshop CS3. 2007. (Real World Ser.). (ENG., Illus.). 384p. per. 44.99 *(978-0-321-51867-5(5))* Peachpit Pr.
—Real World Image Sharpening with Adobe Photoshop, Camera Raw, & Lightroom. 2nd ed. 2009. (Real World Ser.). (ENG., Illus.). 360p. pap. 49.99 *(978-0-321-63755-0(0))* Peachpit Pr.
French, Nigel. Adobe Photoshop Unmasked: The Art & Science of Selections, Layers, & Paths. 2006. (Illus.). 264p. per. 44.99 *(978-0-321-44120-1(6))* Adobe Pr.
Fuller, Laurie Ulrich & Fuller, Robert C. Photoshop CS3 Bible. 2007. (Bible Ser.: 410). (ENG., Illus.). 1216p. pap. 39.99 *(978-0-470-11541-1(6),* Wiley) Wiley, John & Sons, Inc.
GABRIEL. Ybs College 01, 2 vols. 2011. (ENG.). 122p. (C). 149.00 ***(978-3-86437-001-4(9))*** mode... information Heinz Kramer GmbH DEU. Dist: Innovative Logistics.
—Ybs Sports 01, 1 vol. 2011. (ENG.). 122p. 149.00 ***(978-3-86437-000-7(0))*** mode... information Heinz Kramer GmbH DEU. Dist: Innovative Logistics.
Galer, Mark & Andrews, Philip. Photoshop CS3 Essential Skills. 2007. (Photography Essential Skills Ser.). (ENG., Illus.). 448p. pap. 36.95 *(978-0-240-52064-3(5),* Focal Pr.) Elsevier Science & Technology Bks.
—Photoshop CS5: Essential Skills - A Guide to Creative Image Editing. 2010. (ENG., Illus.). 496p. pap. 44.95 *(978-0-240-52214-2(1),* Focal Pr.) Elsevier Science & Technology Bks.
Galer, Mark & Chattaraj, Abhijit. Adobe Photoshop Elements 10 - Maximum Performance: Unleash the Hidden Performance of Elements. 2011. (ENG., Illus.). 368p. pap. 34.95 ***(978-0-240-52379-8(2),*** Focal Pr.) Elsevier Science & Technology Bks.
Galer, Mark & Chattaraj, Abhijit. Adobe Photoshop Elements 9 - Maximum Performance: Unleash the Hidden Performance of Elements. 2010. (ENG., Illus.). 368p. pap. 39.95 *(978-0-240-52242-5(7),* Focal Pr.) Elsevier Science & Technology Bks.
Gatter, Mark. Software Essentials for Graphic Designers: Photoshop, Illustrator, Indesign, QuarkXPress, Dreamweaver, Flash + Acrobat. 2006. (Illus.). 240p. pap. incl. cd-rom *(978-0-300-11800-1(7))* Yale Univ. Pr.
Gee, Zorana & Falco, Pete. 3D in Photoshop: The Ultimate Guide for Creative Professionals. 2010. (ENG., Illus.). 224p. pap. 49.95 *(978-0-240-81377-6(4),* Focal Pr.) Elsevier Science & Technology Bks.
Grey, Christopher. Photoshop Effects for Portrait Photographers. 2006. (ENG., Illus.). 152p. per. 29.95 *(978-0-240-80894-9(0),* Focal Pr.) Elsevier Science & Technology Bks.
Grey, Tim & Burian, Peter K. Photoshop Elements 5 Workflow: The Digital Photographer's Guide. 2007. (ENG., Illus.). 286p. per. 34.99 *(978-0-470-10086-8(9),* Sybex) Wiley, John & Sons, Inc.
Hall, Susannah. Best Digital Brushes for Photoshop: A Unique Directory of over 4,000 Digital Brush Effects, & How to Achieve Them. 2010. (ENG., Illus.). 416p. pap. 44.99 *(978-0-321-73580-5(3))* Peachpit Pr.
Hall, Susannah. Best Photoshop Filters. 2011. (ENG., Illus.). 416p. pap. 49.99 ***(978-0-321-75422-6(0))*** Peachpit Pr.
Harrington, Richard. Adobe Photoshop CS4: The Essential Techniques for Imaging Professionals. 2nd ed. 2008. (ENG., Illus.). 360p. pap. 49.99 *(978-0-321-56366-8(2))* Peachpit Pr.
—Photoshop for Video. 3rd ed. 2007. (DV Expert Ser.). (ENG., Illus.). 432p. pap. 54.95 *(978-0-240-80926-7(2),* Focal Pr.) Elsevier Science & Technology Bks.
—Photoshop for Video. 4th rev. ed. 2010. (ENG., Illus.). 360p. pap. 54.99 *(978-0-321-70355-2(3))* Peachpit Pr.
—Understanding Adobe Photoshop CS5: The Essential Techniques for Imaging Professionals. 2010. (ENG., Illus.). 312p. pap. 54.99 *(978-0-321-71426-8(1))* Peachpit Pr.
Hartman, Annesa. Adobe Photoshop CS5. 2010. (Design Exploration Ser.). (ENG.). 328p. pap. 60.95 *(978-1-111-13034-3(5))* Delmar Cengage Learning.
Hartman, Annesa & Sholar, Ken. Exploring Photoshop CS3. 2007. (Adobe Creative Suite Ser.). (ENG., Illus.). 272p. pap. 65.95 *(978-1-4180-5259-1(0))* Delmar Cengage Learning.
Hester, Nolan. Photoshop Lightroom No. 3. 2010. (Visual QuickStart Guide Ser.). (ENG., Illus.). 288p. pap. 29.99 *(978-0-321-71310-0(9))* Peachpit Pr.
Hilgraves, Rebekkah & Busch, David D. Adobe Photoshop. com: An Instant Start-Up Manual for Editing & Sharing Your Photos Online. 2008. (ENG., Illus.). 232p. pap. 29.99 *(978-1-59863-815-8(7))* Course Technology.
Hilz, Corey. Focus on Adobe Photoshop: Focus on the Fundamentals. 2011. (ENG., Illus.). 232p. pap. 19.95 *(978-0-240-81220-5(4),* Focal Pr.) Elsevier Science & Technology Bks.
Hinkel, Brad & Laskevitch, Stephen. Photoshop CS3 Photographer's Handbook: An Easy Workflow. 2007. (ENG., Illus.). 213p. per. 35.95 *(978-1-933952-11-6(3))* Rocky Nook.
Hollywood, Calvin. Calvinize: Signature Techniques of Photoshop Artist Calvin Hollywood. rev. ed. 2011. (ENG., Illus.). 144p. pap. 54.99 *(978-0-321-77279-4(2))* Peachpit Pr.
Hosie-Bounar, Jane. New Perspectives on Photoshop CS5: Introductory. 2011. (New Perspectives Ser.). (ENG., Illus.). 368p. pap. 93.95 *(978-1-111-52647-4(8))* Course Technology.
Huss, Dave. Photoshop Lighting & Atmospheric Effects Gone Wild. 2006. (Illus.). 336p. pap. 34.99 *(978-0-470-04060-7(2),* Visual) Wiley, John & Sons, Inc.
Huss, David & Plotkin, David. Adobe Photoshop Lightroom 2: A Digital Photographer's Guide. 2008. (ENG., Illus.). 384p. pap. 39.95 *(978-0-240-52133-6(1),* Focal Pr.) Elsevier Science & Technology Bks.
Ireland, R. Scott. Photoshop Astronomy: Includes Full Res Tutorial Images on DVD. 2nd ed. 2009. *(978-0-943396-91-0(3))* Willmann-Bell, Inc.
Jenkins, Sue. Smashing Photoshop CS5: 100 Professional Techniques. 2010. (Smashing Magazine Book Ser.: 3). (ENG., Illus.). 432p. pap. 39.99 *(978-0-470-66153-6(4),* Wiley) Wiley, John & Sons, Inc.
Johnson, Steve. Photoshop CS5. 2010. (Illus.). 570p. pap. 57.50 *(978-0-273-74061-2(X),* Prentice Hall) Pearson Education, Ltd. GBR. Dist: Trans-Atlantic Pubns., Inc.
Johnson, Steve & Perspection, Inc. Staff. Adobe Photoshop CS5 on Demond. 2010. (On Demand Ser.). (ENG., Illus.). 576p. pap. 34.99 *(978-0-7897-4447-0(3))* Que.
—Adobe Photoshop Elements 6. 0 on Demand. 2008. (On Demand Ser.). (ENG., Illus.). 576p. per. 34.99 *(978-0-7897-3787-8(6))* Que.
—Photoshop CS4. 2008. (On Demand Ser.). (ENG.). 576p. pap. 29.99 *(978-0-7897-3835-6(X))* Que.
Johnson, Steve, et al. Adobe Photoshop Elements 7. 2008. (On Demand Ser.). (ENG.). 576p. pap. 29.99 *(978-0-7897-3931-5(3))* Que.
Joinson, Simon. Get the Most from Photoshop. 2009. (ENG., Illus.). 160p. pap. 24.99 *(978-0-7153-2962-7(6))* David & Charles Pubs. GBR. Dist: F&W Media, Inc.
Jordan, Larry. Adobe CS Production Premium for Final Cut Studio Editors. 2009. (ENG., Illus.). 312p. pap. 49.95 *(978-0-240-81223-6(9),* Focal Pr.) Elsevier Science & Technology Bks.
Kelby, Scott. The Adobe Photoshop CS3 Book for Digital Photographers. 2007. (Voices That Matter Ser.). (ENG., Illus.). 496p. per. 54.99 *(978-0-321-50191-2(8))* Peachpit Pr.
—The Adobe Photoshop CS4 Book for Digital Photographers. 2008. (Voices That Matter Ser.). (ENG., Illus.). 480p. pap. 54.99 *(978-0-321-58009-2(5))* Peachpit Pr.
—The Adobe Photoshop CS5 Book for Digital Photographers. 2010. (Voices That Matter Ser.). (ENG., Illus.). 408p. pap. 54.99 *(978-0-321-70356-9(1))* Peachpit Pr.
—The Adobe Photoshop Lightroom 3 Book for Digital Photographers. rev. ed. 2010. (Voices That Matter Ser.). (ENG., Illus.). 480p. pap. 54.99 *(978-0-321-70091-9(0))* Peachpit Pr.
—The Adobe Photoshop Lightroom 4 Book for Digital Photographers. rev. ed. 2012. (ENG.). 504p. pap. 49.99 ***(978-0-321-81958-1(6))*** New Riders Publishing.
—The Digital Photography Vols. 1-3, Set: The Step-by-Step Secrets for How to Make Your Photos Look Like the Pros? 2009. (ENG.). 720p. pap., pap., pap. 69.99 *(978-0-321-67873-7(7))* Peachpit Pr.
—Light It, Shoot It, Retouch It: Learn Step by Step How to Go from Empty Studio to Finished Image. rev. ed. 2011. (ENG., Illus.). 264p. pap. 44.99 *(978-0-321-78661-6(0))* Peachpit Pr.
—The Photoshop Elements 5 Book for Digital Photographers. 2006. (Voices Ser.). (ENG., Illus.). 512p. per. 44.99 *(978-0-321-47673-9(5))* Peachpit Pr.
—Professional Portrait Retouching Techniques for Photographers Using Photoshop. 2011. (Voices That Matter Ser.). (ENG., Illus.). 384p. pap. 49.99 *(978-0-321-72554-7(9))* Peachpit Pr.
—Scott Kelby's Digital Photography Boxed Set, Volumes 1 & 2 (Includes the Digital Photography Book Volume 1, the Digital Photography Book Volume 2, & Limited Signed Print) 2008. (ENG.). 480p. pap., pap. 74.99 *(978-0-321-60353-1(2))* Peachpit Pr.
—7-Point System for Adobe Photoshop CS3. 2007. (ENG., Illus.). 288p. per. 49.99 *(978-0-321-50192-9(6))* Peachpit Pr.
Kelby, Scott & Kelby, Scott. Photoshop CS4 down & Dirty Tricks. 2009. (Down & Dirty Tricks Ser.). (ENG., Illus.). 360p. pap. 49.99 *(978-0-321-56317-0(4))* Peachpit Pr.
Kelby, Scott & Kloskowski, Matt. The Photoshop Elements 6 Book for Digital Photographers. 2008. (Voices That Matter Ser.). (ENG., Illus.). 512p. pap. 44.99 *(978-0-321-52464-5(0))* Peachpit Pr.
—The Photoshop Elements 9: For Digital Photographers. 2010. (Voices That Matter Ser.). (ENG., Illus.). 456p. pap. 49.99 *(978-0-321-74133-2(1))* Peachpit Pr.
Kelby, Scott, et al. The Photoshop Elements 7. 2009. (Voices That Matter Ser.). (ENG., Illus.). 512p. pap. 49.99 *(978-0-321-56595-2(9))* Peachpit Pr.
Keller, Debra. Adobe Creative Suite 5 ACA Certification Preparation: Featuring Dreamweaver, Flash & Photoshop. 2011. (Origins Ser.). (ENG.). 416p. (C). pap. 62.95 *(978-1-111-53358-8(X))* Course Technology.
—Multimedia Projects Binder Basics. 2012. (ENG.). 175p. (C). ring bd. 701.95 incl. cd-rom *(978-1-111-53225-3(7))* Course Technology.
Kent, Lynette. Adobe Photoshop CS3: Top 100 Simplified Tips & Tricks. 2007. (Top 100 Simplified Tips & Tricks Ser.). (ENG., Illus.). 256p. per. 19.99 *(978-0-470-14476-3(9),* Visual) Wiley, John & Sons, Inc.
—Adobe Photoshop CS4. 2009. (Top 100 Simplified Tips & Tricks Ser.: 21). (ENG., Illus.). 288p. pap. 24.99 *(978-0-470-44254-8(9),* Visual) Wiley, John & Sons, Inc.
—Adobe Photoshop Lightroom, No. 2. 2008. (Teach Yourself VISUALLY (Tech) Ser.: 51). (ENG., Illus.). 352p. pap. 29.99 *(978-0-470-26435-5(7),* Visual) Wiley, John & Sons, Inc.
—Photoshop CS5. 2010. (Top 100 Simplified Tips & Tricks Ser.: 26). (ENG., Illus.). 288p. pap. 24.99 *(978-0-470-61265-1(7),* Visual) Wiley, John & Sons, Inc.
Kent, Lynette, et al. Photoshop Elements, No. 7. 2009. (Top 100 Simplified Tips & Tricks Ser.: 22). (ENG., Illus.). 272p. pap. 24.99 *(978-0-470-43636-3(0),* Visual) Wiley, John & Sons, Inc.
Kerr, Gordon, et al. Photoshop CS4 for Nature Photographers: A Workshop in a Book. 2009. (ENG., Illus.). 480p. pap. 39.99 *(978-0-470-38127-4(2),* Sybex) Wiley, John & Sons, Inc.
Kloskowski, Matt. Layers: The Complete Guide to Photoshop's Most Powerful Feature. (ENG., Illus.). 2008. 264p. per. 44.99 *(978-0-321-53416-3(6))* 2nd ed. 2010. 312p. pap. 44.99 *(978-0-321-74958-1(8))* Peachpit Pr.
Kloskowski, Matt. Photoshop Compositing Secrets: Unlocking the Key to Perfect Selections & Amazing Photoshop Effects for Totally Realistic Composites. 2011. (ENG., Illus.). 408p. pap. 49.99 ***(978-0-321-80823-3(1))*** Peachpit Pr.
Kloskowski, Matt & Kelby, Scott. The Photoshop Elements 10 Book for Digital Photographers. 2011. (Voices That Matter Ser.). (ENG., Illus.). 456p. pap. 49.99 ***(978-0-321-80824-0(X))*** New Riders Publishing.
Krause, Jim. Ex3 No. 9: Exquisite Expressions with Photoshop Elements 9. 2011. (ENG., Illus.). 400p. pap. 39.99 *(978-0-470-57800-1(9),* Wiley) Wiley, John & Sons, Inc.
Krogh, Peter & Krogh, P. The Dam Book: Digigal Asset Management for Photographers. 2nd ed. 2009. (ENG., Illus.). 496p. pap. 49.99 *(978-0-596-52357-2(2))* O'Reilly Media, Inc.
Laskevitch, Stephen. Photoshop CS & Lightroom: A Photographer's Handbook. 2010. (ENG., Illus.). 296p. pap., instr.'s hndbk. ed. 39.95 *(978-1-933952-67-3(9))* Rocky Nook.
—Photoshop CS4: Photographer's Handbook. 2009. (ENG., Illus.). 272p. pap. 39.95 *(978-1-933952-42-0(3))* Rocky Nook.
Lazear, Susan. Adobe Photoshop for Fashion Design. 2009. (ENG., Illus.). 504p. pap. 61.80 *(978-0-13-119193-8(4),* Prentice Hall) Prentice Hall PTR.
Lea, Derek. Beyond Photoshop: Advanced techniques integrating Photoshop with Illustrator, Poser, Painter, Cinema 4D & ZBrush. 2010. (ENG., Illus.). 368p. pap. 39.95 *(978-0-240-81190-1(9),* Focal Pr.) Elsevier Science & Technology Bks.
—Creative Photoshop CS4: Digital Illustration & Art Techniques. 2009. (ENG., Illus.). 424p. pap. 39.95 *(978-0-240-52134-3(X),* Focal Pr.) Elsevier Science & Technology Bks.
Lecarme, Olivier & Delvare, Karine. The Book of GIMP. 2012. (ENG.). 736p. pap. 49.95 *(978-1-59327-383-5(5))* No Starch Pr., Inc.
Ligon, Scott. Digital Art Revolution: Creating Fine Art with Photoshop. 2010. (ENG., Illus.). 256p. pap. 29.99 *(978-0-8230-9536-0(3))* Watson-Guptill Pubns., Inc.
LoCascio, Ted. Adobe Photoshop Lightroom 2 on Demand. 2009. (On Demand Ser.). (ENG., Illus.). 336p. pap. 29.99 *(978-0-7897-4215-5(2))* Que.

Long, Ben. Adobe Photoshop CS3 Beta First Look with Adobe Bridge & Camera Raw. 2007. (ENG., Illus.). 120p. per. 19.99 *(978-0-321-50813-3(0))* Peachpit Pr.

—Getting Started with Camera Raw: How to Make Better Pictures Using Photoshop & Photoshop Elements. 2nd ed. 2009. (ENG., Illus.). 264p. pap. 39.99 *(978-0-321-59213-2(1))* Peachpit Pr.

Long, Sara & Carlson, Jeff. Adobe Photoshop Express Beta. 2008. (Pocket Guide Ser.). (ENG.). 112p. pap. 9.99 *(978-0-321-56346-0(8))* Peachpit Pr.

Lynch, Richard. The Adobe Photoshop CS4 Layers Book: Harnessing Photoshop's most powerful Tool. 2009. (ENG., Illus.). 320p. pap. 39.95 *(978-0-240-52155-8(2),* Focal Pr.) Elsevier Science & Technology Bks.

—The Adobe Photoshop Layers Book. 2011. (ENG., Illus.). 280p. pap. 39.95 *(978-0-240-52252-4(4),* Focal Pr.) Elsevier Science & Technology Bks.

Madden, Chris. Create Art & Cartoons in Photoshop Elements 4. 2007. pap. *(978-0-9548551-3-0(2))* Inkline Pr.

Margulis, Dan. Professional Photoshop: The Classic Guide to Color Correction. 5th rev. ed. 2006. (ENG., Illus.). 528p. pap. 59.99 *(978-0-321-44017-4(X))* Peachpit Pr.

Matthews, Carole & Bouton, Gary David. Photoshop CS4 QuickSteps. 2009. (Illus.). 320p. pap. 29.99 *(978-0-07-162537-1(2),* 0071625372) McGraw-Hill Osborne.

McClelland, Deke. Adobe Photoshop CS3 One-on-One. 2007. (ENG., Illus.). 544p. pap. 49.99 *(978-0-596-52975-8(9))* O'Reilly Media, Inc.

—Adobe Photoshop CS5. 2010. (ENG., Illus.). 544p. pap. 49.99 *(978-0-596-80797-9(X),* Deke) O'Reilly Media, Inc.

McClelland, Deke & Grey, Tim. Photoshop CS4 Channels & Masks One-on-One. rev. ed. 2009. (One-On-One Ser.). (ENG., Illus.). 512p. pap. 49.99 *(978-0-596-51615-4(0),* Deke) O'Reilly Media, Inc.

McClelland, Deke & Wheeler, Colleen. Photoshop Elements 8. rev. ed. 2009. (One-On One Ser.). (ENG., Illus.). 400p. pap. 39.99 *(978-0-596-80239-4(0),* Deke) O'Reilly Media, Inc.

McCue, Claudia. Print Production with Adobe Creative Suite Applications. 2009. (Real World Ser.). (ENG., Illus.). 352p. pap. 54.99 *(978-0-321-63683-6(X))* Peachpit Pr.

Miller, Brian & Miller, Kristy. Master Digital Color: Styles - Tools - Techniques. 2010. (ENG., Illus.). 176p. pap. 26.99 *(978-1-60061-759-1(X),* Impact) F&W Media, Inc.

Miller, Kristy & Miller, Brian Glen. Hi-Fi Color for Comics: Digital Techniques for Professional Results. 2008. (ENG., Illus.). 160p. pap. 24.99 *(978-1-58180-992-3(1),* Impact) F&W Media, Inc.

Monroy, Bert. Photoshop Studio: Digital Painting. 2008. (Voices That Matter Ser.). (ENG., Illus.). 304p. pap. 49.99 *(978-0-321-51587-2(0))* New Riders Publishing.

—Photoshop Studio with Bert Monroy: Lessons in Digital Painting. 2008. (Voices That Matter Ser.). (ENG.). 34.99 *(978-0-321-60365-4(6))* New Riders Publishing.

Moughamian, Dan & Valentine, Scott. Real World Compositing with Adobe Photoshop CS4. 2009. (Real World Ser.). (ENG., Illus.). 288p. pap. 44.99 *(978-0-321-60453-8(9))* Peachpit Pr.

Murphy, Michael. Indesign CS4 Styles: How to Create Better, Faster Text & Layouts. 2009. (Illus.). 256p. pap. 44.99 *(978-0-321-60606-8(X))* Adobe Pr.

Nitzsche, Birgit & Rose, Karsten B. Bodyshop: The Photoshop Retouching Guide for the Face & Body. 2010. (ENG., Illus.). 480p. pap. 49.99 *(978-0-470-62438-8(8),* Wiley) Wiley, John & Sons, Inc.

Noble Desktop. Adobe Dreamweaver CS3 Step by Step Training. 2007. 66p. ring bd. 65.00 *(978-0-9777017-4-2(3))* Noble Desktop, LLC.

—Adobe Flash Advanced CS3 Step by Step Training. 2007. 76p. ring bd. 65.00 *(978-0-9777017-6-6(X))* Noble Desktop, LLC.

—Adobe Flash CS3 Step by Step Training. 2007. 103p. ring bd. 65.00 *(978-0-9777017-5-9(1))* Noble Desktop, LLC.

—Adobe Photoshop Advanced CS3 Step by Step Training. 2007. 89p. ring bd. 65.00 *(978-1-934624-00-5(4))* Noble Desktop, LLC.

—Adobe Photoshop CS3 Step by Step Training. 2007. 78p. ring bd. 65.00 *(978-0-9777017-7-3(8))* Noble Desktop, LLC.

Obermeier, Barbara. Photoshop CS3 All-in-One Desk Reference for Dummies. 2007. (ENG., Illus.). 720p. per. 39.99 *(978-0-470-11195-6(X),* For Dummies) Wiley, John & Sons, Inc.

—Photoshop CS4 All-in-One for Dummies. 2008. (ENG., Illus.). 720p. pap. 39.99 *(978-0-470-32726-5(X),* For Dummies) Wiley, John & Sons, Inc.

—Photoshop CS5: All-in-One for Dummies. 2010. (ENG., Illus.). 720p. pap. 39.99 *(978-0-470-60821-0(8),* For Dummies) Wiley, John & Sons, Inc.

Obermeier, Barbara & Padova, Ted. Photoshop Elements 10 All-in-One for Dummies. 2011. (ENG.). 672p. pap. 39.99 ***(978-1-118-10739-3(X),*** For Dummies) Wiley, John & Sons, Inc.

—Photoshop Elements 10 for Dummies. 2011. (ENG., Illus.). 432p. pap. 29.99 ***(978-1-118-10742-3(X),*** For Dummies) Wiley, John & Sons, Inc.

—Photoshop Elements 6 for Dummies. 2007. (ENG., Illus.). 400p. per. 24.99 *(978-0-470-19238-2(0),* For Dummies) Wiley, John & Sons, Inc.

—Photoshop Elements 7 for Dummies. 2008. (ENG., Illus.). 400p. pap. 29.99 *(978-0-470-39700-8(4),* For Dummies) Wiley, John & Sons, Inc.

—Photoshop Elements 8 All-in-One for Dummies. 2009. (ENG., Illus.). 656p. pap. 39.99 *(978-0-470-54302-3(7),* For Dummies) Wiley, John & Sons, Inc.

—Photoshop Elements 9 All-in-One for Dummies. 2010. (ENG., Illus.). 656p. pap. 39.99 *(978-0-470-88003-6(1),* For Dummies) Wiley, John & Sons, Inc.

—Photoshop Elements 9 for Dummies. 2010. (ENG., Illus.). 432p. pap. 29.99 *(978-0-470-87872-9(X),* For Dummies) Wiley, John & Sons, Inc.

—Photoshop Elements for Dummies, No. 8. 2009. (ENG., Illus.). 416p. pap. 29.99 *(978-0-470-52967-6(9),* For Dummies) Wiley, John & Sons, Inc.

Onstott, Scott. Enhancing Architectural Drawings & Models with Photoshop. 2nd ed. 2010. (ENG., Illus.). 376p. pap. 49.99 *(978-0-470-91656-8(7),* Sybex) Wiley, John & Sons, Inc.

Origin inc. Le Design Textile avec Adobe Photoshop: Adobe Photoshop for Textile Design. 2007. (FRE., Illus.). 99p. spiral bd. 120.00 *(978-0-9727317-1-3(7))* Chipkin, Frederick.

Orwig, Chris. Adobe Photoshop CS3 for Photographers. 2007. (Video Training Book Ser.). (Illus.). 168p. pap. 49.99 *(978-0-321-44547-6(3))* Peachpit Pr.

—Adobe Photoshop CS4: 100 Essential Techniques. 2008. (How-Tos Ser.). (ENG., Illus.). 288p. pap. 24.99 *(978-0-321-57782-5(5))* Adobe Pr.

—Adobe Photoshop Lightroom 2 How-Tos: 100 Essential Techniques. 2008. (ENG., Illus.). 248p. pap. 24.99 *(978-0-321-52637-3(6))* Adobe Pr.

Padova, Ted & Murdock, Kelly L. Adobe Creative Suite 4 Bible. 2008. (Bible Ser.: 514). (ENG., Illus.). 1296p. pap. 44.99 *(978-0-470-34518-4(7),* Wiley) Wiley, John & Sons, Inc.

Palmer, et al. Photoshop Elements 7 All-in-One for Dummies. 2009. (ENG., Illus.). 672p. pap. 39.99 *(978-0-470-43413-0(9),* For Dummies) Wiley, John & Sons, Inc.

Patterson, Jodie. Create Your Own Scrapbook Papers: 175 Design Templates to Use with Photoshop Elements. 2012. (ENG., Illus.). 112p. pap. 19.95 *(978-0-486-99171-9(7))* Dover Pubns., Inc.

Peachpit Press. Photoshop Lightroom: From Snapshots to Great Shots. 2012. (ENG.). 192p. pap. 24.99 ***(978-0-321-81962-8(4))*** Peachpit Pr.

Peachpit Press Staff & Gyncild, Brie. The Photoshop CS5. 2010. (Pocket Guide Ser.). (ENG., Illus.). 240p. pap. 14.99 *(978-0-321-71432-9(6))* Peachpit Pr.

—The Photoshop Elements, No. 8. 2009. (Pocket Guide Ser.). (ENG., Illus.). 216p. pap. 14.99 *(978-0-321-66952-0(5))* Peachpit Pr.

Peachpit Press Staff & Moughamian, Dan. Digital Imaging: Essential Techniques for Photoshop CS5, Lightroom 3, & Camera Raw. 6th rev. ed. 2010. (How-Tos Ser.). (ENG., Illus.). 288p. pap. 34.99 *(978-0-321-71987-4(5))* Adobe Pr.

Pearson, Renee. Digital Designs for Scrapbooking 1: Getting Started with Photoshop(tm) Elements, 1 vol. 2010. (ENG.). pap. 22.99 *(978-1-934176-27-6(3),* Creating Keepsakes Magazine) Primedia Scrapbooking.

Perkins, Chad. How to Do Everything Adobe Photoshop CS4. 2009. (ENG., Illus.). 287p. pap. 39.99 *(978-0-07-160522-9(3),* 0071605223) McGraw-Hill Osborne.

Perkins, Chad & Perkins, Chad. Adobe Photoshop CS3 Extended for 3D & Video. 2007. (ENG., Illus.). 336p. pap. 59.99 *(978-0-321-51434-9(3))* Adobe Pr.

Photoshop CS2 Actions & Automation. 2006. cd-rom 149.95 *(978-1-59671-274-4(0))* Lynda.com, LLC.

Photoshop CS2 Channels & Masks. 2006. cd-rom 149.95 *(978-1-59671-303-1(8))* Lynda.com, LLC.

Photoshop CS2 FAQs. 2006. cd-rom 49.95 *(978-1-59671-254-6(6))* Lynda.com, LLC.

Photoshop CS2 Mastering Camera Raw. 2006. cd-rom 149.95 *(978-1-59671-289-8(9))* Lynda.com, LLC.

Photoshop Elements 5 Essential Training. 2006. cd-rom 99.95 *(978-1-59671-293-5(7))* Lynda.com, LLC.

Photoshop Filters. 2006. cd-rom 49.95 *(978-1-59671-273-7(2))* Lynda.com, LLC.

Ralston, Rick. The Designer's Apprentice: Automating Photoshop, Illustrator, & Indesign in Adobe Creative Suite 3. 2007. (ENG., Illus.). 256p. per. 39.99 *(978-0-321-49570-9(5))* Adobe Pr.

Reding, Elizabeth Eisner. Adobe Photoshop CS3 Revealed. 2007. (Adobe Creative Suite Ser.). (ENG., Illus.). 584p. (C). pap. 87.95 *(978-1-4283-1959-2(X))* Delmar Cengage Learning.

—Adobe Photoshop CS4 Revealed. 2009. (Adobe Creative Suite Ser.). (ENG., Illus.). 608p. 80.95 *(978-1-4354-4187-3(7));* 71.95 *(978-1-4354-8277-7(8))* Course Technology.

—Adobe Photoshop CS5 Revealed. 2010. (Revealed Ser.). (ENG.). 688p. (C). pap. 82.95 *(978-1-111-13038-1(8))* Delmar Cengage Learning.

Reding, Elizabeth Eisner & Botello, Chris. Adobe Indesign CS, Photoshop CS, & Illustrator CS-Design Professional. 2006. (ENG.). 328p. pap. 105.95 *(978-1-4180-6457-0(2))* Course Technology.

Reis, George. Imaging Forensics: A Step-by-Step Guide using Adobe Photoshop. 2006. (Illus.). 275p. pap. 69.95 *(978-0-12-369382-2(9),* Academic Pr.) Elsevier Science & Technology Bks.

Resnick, Seth & Spritzer, Jamie. The Photoshop Lightroom: Workflow Not Workslow in Lightroom 2. 2008. (ENG., Illus.). 376p. pap., wbk. ed. 34.95 *(978-0-240-81067-6(8),* Focal Pr.) Elsevier Science & Technology Bks.

Revell, Jeff. Photoshop Elements: From Snapshots to Great Shots. 2011. (From Snapshots to Great Shots Ser.). (ENG., Illus.). 192p. pap. 24.99 ***(978-0-321-80831-8(2))*** Peachpit Pr.

Romaniello, Stephen. Photoshop CS3 Channels & Masks Bible. 2007. (Bible Ser.: 450). (ENG., Illus.). 544p. per. 49.99 *(978-0-470-10264-0(0),* Wiley) Wiley, John & Sons, Inc.

Rose, Carla & Binder, Kate. Adobe Photoshop CS3 in 24 Hours. 4th rev. ed. 2007. (Sams Teach Yourself Ser.). (Illus.). 552p. per. 29.99 *(978-0-672-32935-7(2))* Sams.

Rouse, Scott. Adobe Photoshop Lightroom X for Wedding & Portrait Photographers. 2012. (ENG.). 352p. pap. 39.99 ***(978-1-4354-6089-8(8))*** Course Technology.

Rubin, Mira. Interactive Indesign CS5: Take Your Print Skills to the Web & Beyond. 2010. (ENG., Illus.). 400p. pap. 49.95 *(978-0-240-81511-4(4),* Focal Pr.) Elsevier Science & Technology Bks.

Ruddick Bloom, Susan. Digital Collage & Painting: Using Photoshop & Painter to Create Fine Art. 2nd ed. 2010. (ENG., Illus.). 600p. pap. 54.95 *(978-0-240-81175-8(5),* Focal Pr.) Elsevier Science & Technology Bks.

—Digital Painting in Photoshop. 2009. (ENG., Illus.). 256p. pap. 39.95 *(978-0-240-81114-7(3),* Focal Pr.) Elsevier Science & Technology Bks.

Schewe, Jeff. Schewe: The Digital Negative. rev. ed. 2012. (ENG.). 336p. pap. 49.99 ***(978-0-321-83957-2(9))*** Peachpit Pr.

Schewe, Jeff & Fraser, Bruce. Camera Raw with Adobe Photoshop CS4. 2008. (Real World Ser.). (Illus.). 448p. pap. 44.99 *(978-0-321-58013-9(3))* Peachpit Pr.

—Camera Raw with Adobe Photoshop CS5. rev. ed. 2010. (Real World Ser.). (ENG., Illus.). 480p. pap. 49.99 *(978-0-321-71309-4(5))* Peachpit Pr.

Scott, Geoff & Tranberry, Jeffrey. Power, Speed & Automation with Adobe Photoshop: (the Digital Imaging Masters Series) 2012. (ENG.). 344p. pap. 39.95 ***(978-0-240-82083-5(5),*** Focal Pr.) Elsevier Science & Technology Bks.

Sedgewick, Jerry. Scientific Imaging with Photoshop: Methods, Measurement, & Output. 2008. (ENG., Illus.). 312p. pap. 75.00 *(978-0-321-51433-2(5))* New Riders Publishing.

Seelig, Tim, et al. How to Draw Digital Manga & Anime. 2012. (ENG., Illus.). 96p. pap. 15.99 ***(978-1-78019-141-6(3))*** Anness Publishing GBR. Dist: National Bk. Network.

Sharp, Vicki F. Adobe Photoshop Elements in One Hour: Windows & Macintosh Versions 8 & 9. 2011. (Illus.). 150p. pap. ***(978-1-56484-276-3(2))*** International Society for Technology in Education.

Shelbourne, Tim. Photoshop Cs3 Photo Effects Cookbook: 53 Easy-to-Follow Recipes for Digital Photographers, Designers, & Artists. 2nd ed. 2007. (ENG., Illus.). 176p. pap. 29.99 *(978-0-596-51504-1(9))* O'Reilly Media, Inc.

Shelly, Gary B. & Starks, Joy L. Adobe Photoshop CS4: Complete Concepts & Techniques. 2009. (SAM 2010 Compatible Products Ser.). (ENG.). 528p. pap. 93.95 *(978-1-4390-7930-0(7))* Course Technology.

—Adobe Photoshop CS4: Comprehensive Concepts & Techniques. 2009. (SAM 2010 Compatible Products Ser.). (ENG.). 736p. pap. 125.95 *(978-1-4390-7927-0(7))* Course Technology.

—Adobe Photoshop CS4: Introductory Concepts & Techniques. 2009. (SAM 2007 Compatible Products Ser.). (ENG.). 328p. pap. 59.95 *(978-1-4390-7928-7(5))* Course Technology.

—Adobe Photoshop CS5: Complete. 2010. (Adobe CS5 ï Shelly Cashman Seriesï Ser.). (ENG., Illus.). 488p. pap. 90.95 *(978-0-538-47388-0(6))* Course Technology.

—Adobe Photoshop CS5: Introductory. 2010. (Shelly Cashman Ser.). (ENG.). 296p. pap. 57.95 *(978-0-538-47389-7(4))* Course Technology.

Shelly, Gary B., et al. Adobe Photoshop CS2: Comprehensive Concepts & Techniques. 2007. (Shelly Cashman Ser.). (ENG., Illus.). 784p. (C). pap. 125.95 *(978-1-4188-5941-1(9))* Course Technology.

—Adobe Photoshop CS3: Complete Concepts & Techniques. 2008. (Shelly Cashman Ser.). (ENG., Illus.). 496p. pap. 93.95 *(978-1-4239-1237-8(3))* Course Technology.

—Adobe Photoshop CS3: Comprehensive Concepts & Techniques. 2008. (Shelly Cashman Ser.). (ENG., Illus.). 712p. pap. 125.95 *(978-1-4239-1238-5(1))* Course Technology.

—Adobe Photoshop CS3: Introductory Concepts & Techniques. 2008. (Shelly Cashman Ser.). (ENG., Illus.). 264p. pap. 59.95 *(978-1-4239-1236-1(5))* Course Technology.

—Adobe Photoshop CS5: Comprehensive. 2010. (Adobe CS5 ï Shelly Cashman Seriesï Ser.). (ENG., Illus.). 656p. pap. 120.95 *(978-0-538-47391-0(6))* Course Technology.

Sheppard, Rob. Adobe Camera Raw for Digital Photographers Only. 2nd ed. 2008. (For Only Ser.: 2). (ENG., Illus.). 362p. per. 39.99 *(978-0-470-22457-1(6),* Wiley) Wiley, John & Sons, Inc.

—Photoshop Elements 9: Top 100 Simplified Tips & Tricks. 2010. (Top 100 Simplified Tips & Tricks Ser.: 29). (ENG., Illus.). 272p. pap. 24.99 *(978-0-470-91960-6(4),* Visual) Wiley, John & Sons, Inc.

Shire, Stan. HandsOn Photoshop CS3: Tutorial Workshops. 4th ed. 2007. (Illus.). 107p. per. 41.97 *(978-0-9723061-5-7(3))* Shire, Stanley.

Shufflebotham, Robert. Photoshop CS3: For Windows & Mac. 2007. (In Easy Steps Ser.). (ENG., Illus.). 192p. per. 14.99 *(978-1-84078-343-8(5))* Computer Step GBR. Dist: Perseus-PGW.

—Photoshop CS4 in Easy Steps: For Windows & Mac. 2009. (In Easy Steps Ser.). (ENG., Illus.). 240p. pap. 14.99 *(978-1-84078-372-8(9))* Computer Step GBR. Dist: Perseus-PGW.

—Photoshop CS5: For Windows & Mac. 2010. (In Easy Steps Ser.). (ENG., Illus.). 240p. pap. 14.99 *(978-1-84078-406-0(7))* Computer Step GBR. Dist: Perseus-PGW.

Skintik, Catherine. Learning Media Design with Adobe CS4. 2009. (ENG.). 608p. (C). pap. 69.33 *(978-0-13-507687-3(0),* Prentice Hall) Prentice Hall PTR.

Skintik, Catherine & Emergent Learning LLC, . Learning Media Design with Adobe CS5. 2010. (ENG.). 608p. (C). pap. 70.33 *(978-0-13-138408-8(2),* Prentice Hall) Prentice Hall PTR.

Smith, Colin & Cooper, Tim. Complete Adobe Photoshop CS4 for Digital Photographers. 2009. (ENG., Illus.). 496p. pap. 44.99 *(978-1-58450-685-0(7))* Charles River Media.

—Complete Photoshop CS3 for Digital Photographers. 2007. (ENG., Illus.). 456p. pap. 44.99 *(978-1-58450-536-5(2))* Charles River Media.

Smith, Jennifer & AGI Creative Team Staff. Learning Photoshop CS3. 2007. (Dynamic Learning Ser.). (ENG., Illus.). 368p. pap. 44.99 *(978-0-596-51061-9(6))* O'Reilly Media, Inc.

—Photoshop CS4 Digital Classroom. 2008. (ENG., Illus.). 384p. pap. 44.99 *(978-0-470-41090-5(6),* Wiley) Wiley, John & Sons, Inc.

Smith, Jennifer, et al. Adobe Creative Suite 4 Web Premium All-in-One for Dummies. 2009. (ENG., Illus.). 912p. pap. 39.99 *(978-0-470-41407-1(3),* For Dummies) Wiley, John & Sons, Inc.

—Adober Creative Suiter 5. 2nd ed. 2010. (ENG., Illus.). 1008p. pap. 39.99 *(978-0-470-60746-6(7),* For Dummies) Wiley, John & Sons, Inc.

Smith, Jerron, et al. Adobe Photoshop Elements 7. 2009. (Digital Classroom Ser.: 8). (ENG., Illus.). 400p. pap. 44.99 *(978-0-470-41091-2(4),* Wiley) Wiley, John & Sons, Inc.

Snider, Lesa. Photoshop CS5. 2010. (ENG., Illus.). 816p. pap. 49.99 *(978-1-4493-8168-4(5),* Pogue Pr.) O'Reilly Media, Inc.

Sondermann, Horst. Photoshop in Architectural Graphics. 2009. (ENG., Illus.). 328p. 69.95 *(978-3-211-71591-8(6),* 3211715916) Springer.

Spencer, Scott. ZBrush Creature Design: Creating Dynamic Concept Imagery for Film & Games. 2012. (ENG., Illus.). 384p. pap. 49.99 *(978-1-118-02433-1(8),* Sybex) Wiley, John & Sons, Inc.

Steinmueller, Uwe, et al. Managing Your Photographic Workflow with Photoshop Lightroom. 2007. (ENG., Illus.). 220p. per. 29.95 *(978-1-933952-20-8(2))* Rocky Nook.

Story, Derrick. The Photoshop CS4 Companion for Photographers. 2008. (ENG., Illus.). 208p. pap. 24.99 *(978-0-596-52193-6(6))* O'Reilly Media, Inc.

Sylvan, Rob. Photoshop Lightroom 2 for Dummies. 2008. (ENG., Illus.). 368p. pap. 29.99 *(978-0-470-34539-9(X),* For Dummies) Wiley, John & Sons, Inc.

Tallon, Kevin. Digital Fashion Print. 2012. (ENG., Illus.). 176p. pap. 24.95 ***(978-1-84994-004-7(5),*** Batsford, B. T. Ltd.) Anova Bks. GBR. Dist: Sterling Publishing Co., Inc.

Tallon, Kevin. Fashion Illustration with Photoshop & Illustrator. 2008. (ENG., Illus.). 176p. pap. 24.95 *(978-0-7134-9058-9(6),* Batsford, B. T. Ltd.) Anova Bks. GBR. Dist: Sterling Publishing Co., Inc.

Tannenbaum, Lisa & Waxer, Barbara. Adobe Photoshop Elements 6. 0 - Illustrated. 2nd ed. 2009. (Illustrated Ser.). (ENG.). 232p. pap. 49.95 *(978-1-4239-9941-6(X))* Course Technology.

Tapp, Eddie. Photoshop Workflow Setups: Eddie Tapp on Digital Photography. 2006. (ENG., Illus.). 208p. per. 29.99 *(978-0-596-10168-8(6))* O'Reilly Media, Inc.

Tarantino, Chris. Mastering Beauty Retouching. 2012. (ENG.). 288p. pap. 39.99 *(978-1-4354-5638-9(6))* Course Technology.

Tench, Ian. Teach Yourself Dreamweaver CS3. 2009. (Teach Yourself: Computers Ser.). (ENG.). 384p. pap. 14.95 *(978-0-07-162580-7(1),* 0071625801) McGraw-Hill Cos., The.

Threinen-Pendarvis, Cher, et al. Beyond Digital Photography: Transforming Photos into Fine Art with Photoshop & Painter. 2009. (ENG., Illus.). 256p. pap. 44.99 *(978-0-321-41021-4(1))* Peachpit Pr.

Toland, Toni. Best Practice: The Pros on Adobe Photoshop. 2006. (Adobe Creative Suite Ser.). (ENG., Illus.). 256p. pap. 76.95 *(978-1-4180-1142-0(8))* Delmar Cengage Learning.

Toon, Steve & McCormack, Sean. Photoshop Lightroom 2. 2009. (ENG., Illus.). 160p. pap. 22.95 *(978-1-86108-536-8(2))* Sterling Publishing Co., Inc.

Torta, Stephanie. Pixel Graphics Using Adobe(r) Photoshop(r) CS5: Tutorials & Techniques. 2012. 350p. pap. 45.95 *(978-1-936420-07-0(4))* Mercury Learning & Information.

Vandome, Nick. Dreamweaver CS5. 2010. (In Easy Steps Ser.). (ENG., Illus.). 192p. pap. 14.99 *(978-1-84078-407-7(5))* Computer Step GBR. Dist: Perseus-PGW.

—Photoshop Elements 5: Edit, Organize & Share Your Photos. 4th ed. 2007. (In Easy Steps Ser.). (ENG., Illus.). 192p. per. 14.99 *(978-1-84078-333-9(8))* Computer Step GBR. Dist: Perseus-PGW.

—Photoshop Elements 7: For Windows & Mac. 2009. (In Easy Steps Ser.). (ENG., Illus.). 192p. pap. 14.99 *(978-1-84078-373-5(7))* Computer Step GBR. Dist: Perseus-PGW.

—Photoshop Elements 8: For Windows & Mac. 2010. (In Easy Steps Ser.). (ENG., Illus.). 192p. pap. 14.99 *(978-1-84078-392-6(3))* Computer Step GBR. Dist: Perseus-PGW.

Vandome, Nick, photos by. Photoshop Elements 9 in Easy Steps: For Windows & Mac. 2011. (In Easy Steps Ser.). (ENG., Illus.). 192p. pap. 14.99 *(978-1-84078-435-0(0))* Computer Step GBR. Dist: Perseus-PGW.

Versace, Vincent. From Oz to Kansas: Almost Every Black & White Technique Known to Man. 2012. (ENG.). 240p. pap. 44.99 ***(978-0-321-79402-4(8))*** New Riders Publishing.

Versace, Vincent. Welcome to Oz 2.0: A Cinematic Approach to Digital Still Photography with Photoshop CS5. 2nd rev. ed. 2010. (Voices That Matter Ser.). (ENG., Illus.). 320p. pap. 49.99 *(978-0-321-71476-3(8))* New Riders Publishing.

Video2brain Staff & Aaland, Mikkel. Image Editing with Camera Raw in Adobe Photoshop CS5: Learn by Video. 2011. (Learn by Video Ser.). (ENG.). 48p. 34.99 *(978-0-321-78688-3(2))* Peachpit Pr.

Video2brain Staff & Aaland, Mikkel. Work Like a Pro in Adobe Photoshop Lightroom: Learn by Video. 2011. (Learn by Video Ser.). (ENG.). 48p. 34.99 ***(978-0-321-80464-8(3))*** Peachpit Pr.

Video2brain Staff & Glermann, Olaf. Mastering Adobe Photoshop Filters: Learn by Video. 2011. (Learn by Video Ser.). (ENG.). 48p. 34.99 ***(978-0-321-80961-2(0))*** Peachpit Pr.

Video2brain Staff & Grey, Tim. Adobe Photoshop Elements 10: Learn by Video. 2011. (Learn by Video Ser.). (ENG.). 48p. pap. 49.99 ***(978-0-321-81081-6(3))*** Adobe Pr.

—Automate Image Editing in Adobe Photoshop CS5: Learn by Video. 2011. (Learn by Video Ser.). (ENG.). 48p. 34.99 ***(978-0-321-80463-1(5))*** Peachpit Pr.

Video2brain Staff & Grey, Tim. Using Layer Masks for Image Editing in Adobe Photoshop CS5: Learn by Video. 2011. (Learn by Video Ser.). (ENG.). 48p. 34.99 *(978-0-321-78689-0(0))* Peachpit Pr.

Video2brain Staff, et al. Adobe Photoshop Cs4: Learn by Video. 2009. (Learn by Video Ser.). (ENG.). 120p. 59.99 *(978-0-321-63453-1(4))* Adobe Pr.

—Learn Adobe Photoshop Elements 8 & Adobe Premiere Elements 8 by Video. 2009. (Learn by Video Ser.). (ENG.). 120p. 64.99 *(978-0-321-68577-3(6))* Adobe Pr.

Virtual Training Company, prod. Adobe Video Bundle Essentials. 2006. cd-rom 99.95 *(978-1-933736-49-5(6))* VTC, Inc.

Ward, Al. Photoshop for Right-Brainers: The Art of Photomanipulation. 3rd ed. 2009. (ENG., Illus.). 288p. pap. 39.99 *(978-0-470-39701-5(2),* Sybex) Wiley, John & Sons, Inc.

Watkins, Pete. Learning Photoshop CS2. 2007. (Illus.). 512p. 53.28 *(978-1-59070-773-9(7))* Goodheart-Willcox Pub.

—Learning Photoshop CS4. 3rd ed. 2009. (ENG.). 560p. (gr. 8-14). 62.64 *(978-1-60525-168-4(2))* Goodheart-Willcox Pub.

Waxer, Barbara. Adobe Flash CS4. 2009. (Illustrated Ser.). (ENG.). 216p. (C). pap. 51.95 *(978-1-4390-3965-6(8))* Course Technology.

Weinmann, Elaine & Lourekas, Peter. Photoshop CS3: Visual QuickPro Guide. 2008. (Visual QuickPro Guide Ser.). (Illus.). 384p. pap. 39.99 *(978-0-321-55310-2(1))* Peachpit Pr.

—Photoshop CS3 for Windows & Macintosh: Visual QuickStart Guide. 2007. (Visual QuickStart Guide Ser.). (ENG., Illus.). 456p. per. 34.99 *(978-0-321-47379-0(5))* Peachpit Pr.

—Photoshop CS4, Vol. 2. 2009. (Visual QuickPro Guide Ser.). (ENG., Illus.). 384p. pap. 39.99 *(978-0-321-63503-7(5))* Peachpit Pr.

—Photoshop CS4 for Windows & Macintosh: Visual QuickStart Guide. 2008. (Visual QuickStart Guide Ser.). (Illus.). 456p. pap. 34.99 *(978-0-321-56365-1(4))* Peachpit Pr.

—Photoshop CS5 for Windows & Macintosh. 2010. (Visual QuickStart Guide Ser.). (ENG., Illus.). 456p. pap., instr.'s gde. ed. 34.99 *(978-0-321-70153-4(4))* Peachpit Pr.

Weinrebe, Steven. Adobe Photoshop & the Art of Photography. 2007. (Adobe Creative Suite Ser.). (ENG.). 448p. pap. 72.95 *(978-1-4283-1209-8(9))* Delmar Cengage Learning.

Weller, Alan. Butterflies. 2009. (Electronic Clip Art Photoshop Brushes Ser.). (ENG.). 48p. pap. 19.95 *(978-0-486-99058-3(3))* Dover Pubns., Inc.

—Floral & Botanical. 2009. (Electronic Clip Art Photoshop Brushes Ser.). (ENG., Illus.). 64p. pap. 24.95 *(978-0-486-99059-0(1))* Dover Pubns., Inc.

—Photoshop Brushes & Creative Tools: Cats & Dogs. 2010. (Electronic Clip Art Photoshop Brushes Ser.). (ENG.). 48p. pap. 19.95 *(978-0-486-99091-0(5))* Dover Pubns., Inc.

—Photoshop Brushes & Creative Tools: Holidays. 2011. (Electronic Clip Art Photoshop Brushes Ser.). (ENG.). 48p. pap. 24.95 *(978-0-486-99090-3(7))* Dover Pubns., Inc.

—Photoshop Brushes & Creative Tools: Ornate Letters & Alphabets. 2011. (Electronic Clip Art Photoshop Brushes Ser.). (ENG., Illus.). 48p. pap. 24.95 *(978-0-486-99126-9(1))* Dover Pubns., Inc.

—Photoshop Brushes & Creative Tools: Day of the Dead Motifs. 2011. (Electronic Clip Art Photoshop Brushes Ser.). (ENG., Illus.). 48p. pap. 24.95 ***(978-0-486-99167-2(9))*** Dover Pubns., Inc.

—Photoshop Brushes & Creative Tools: Japanese Motifs. 2012. (Electronic Clip Art Photoshop Brushes Ser.). (ENG., Illus.). 48p. pap. 24.95 ***(978-0-486-99168-9(7))*** Dover Pubns., Inc.

—Photoshop Brushes & Creative Tools: Whimsical Book Illustrations. 2012. (Electronic Clip Art Photoshop Brushes Ser.). (ENG., Illus.). 48p. pap. 24.95 ***(978-0-486-99198-6(9))*** Dover Pubns., Inc.

—Photoshop Brushes & Creative Tools: Winter Motifs. 2011. (Electronic Clip Art Photoshop Brushes Ser.). (ENG., Illus.). 48p. pap. 24.95 ***(978-0-486-99199-3(7))*** Dover Pubns., Inc.

Weston, Chris. Photoshop Pro Photography Handbook: Advanced Post-Production Techniques. 2007. (Lark Photography Book Ser.). (Illus.). 256p. pap. 24.95 *(978-1-57990-975-8(2))* Lark Bks.

Williams, Robin & Tollett, John. The Non-Designer's Photoshop Book. 2011. (Non-Designer's Ser.). (ENG., Illus.). 240p. pap. 34.99 *(978-0-321-77283-1(0))* Peachpit Pr.

Willmore, Ben. Adobe Photoshop CS3: Up to Speed. 2nd rev. ed. 2007. (ENG., Illus.). 168p. per. 29.99 *(978-0-321-51429-5(7))* Peachpit Pr.

—Adobe Photoshop CS3 Studio Techniques. 6th rev. ed. 2007. (Studio Techniques Ser.). (ENG., Illus.). 592p. pap. 55.00 *(978-0-321-51046-4(1))* Adobe Pr.

—Adobe Photoshop CS4: Up to Speed. 2008. (ENG., Illus.). 144p. pap. 24.99 *(978-0-321-58005-4(2))* Peachpit Pr.

Willmore, Ben, et al. Adobe Photoshop CS4 Studio Techniques. 2009. (Studio Techniques Ser.). (ENG., Illus.). 480p. pap. 54.99 *(978-0-321-61310-3(4))* Adobe Pr.

Wood, Allan. The Graphic Designer's Digital Toolkit: A Project-Based Introduction to Adobe Photoshop CS5, Illustrator CS5 & Indesign CS5. 5th ed. 2010. (Adobe Creative Suite Ser.). (ENG., Illus.). 752p. (C). pap. 92.95 *(978-1-111-13801-1(X))* Delmar Cengage Learning.

Wooldridge, Linda & Wooldridge, Michael. Adobe Photoshop CS3. 2007. (Teach Yourself VISUALLY (Tech) Ser.: 78). (ENG., Illus.). 320p. per. 24.99 *(978-0-470-11452-0(5),* Visual) Wiley, John & Sons, Inc.

Wooldridge, Linda & Wooldridge, Mike. Adobe Photoshop CS4: The Fast & Easy Way to Learn. 2008. (CourseSmart Ser.: 16). (ENG., Illus.). 336p. pap. 29.99 *(978-0-470-33947-3(0),* Visual) Wiley, John & Sons, Inc.

Wooldridge, Mike. Photoshop CS5. 2010. (Teach Yourself VISUALLY (Tech) Ser.: 69). (ENG., Illus.). 352p. pap. 29.99 *(978-0-470-61263-7(0),* Visual) Wiley, John & Sons, Inc.

—Teach Yourself Visually Photoshop Elements 9. 2010. (Teach Yourself VISUALLY (Tech) Ser.: 76). (ENG., Illus.). 368p. pap. 29.99 *(978-0-470-91961-3(2),* Visual) Wiley, John & Sons, Inc.

Wynne-Powell, Rod. Mac OS X for Photographers: Optimized Image Workflow for the Mac User. 2008. (Digital Workflow Ser.). (ENG., Illus.). 328p. pap. 39.95 *(978-0-240-52027-8(0),* Focal Pr.) Elsevier Science & Technology Bks.

Youngjin.com Staff. Photoshop Elements Accelerated: A Full-Color Guide. 2nd rev. ed. 2006. (Illus.). 256p. pap. 24.99 *(978-981-05-3850-7(2),* Sybex) Wiley, John & Sons, Inc.

Zuckerman, Jim. Digital Photographer's Guide to Dramatic Photoshop Effects. 2012. (ENG., Illus.). 128p. pap. 19.95 ***(978-1-4547-0118-7(8),*** Pixiq) Sterling Publishing Co., Inc.

Zuckerman, Jim & Stulberg, Scott. Photoshop Plug-Ins. 2009. (Lark Photography Book Ser.). (Illus.). 160p. pap., instr.'s gde. ed. 24.95 *(978-1-60059-212-6(0))* Lark Bks.

500 Photoshop Hints, Tips, & Techniques: The Easy, All-in-One Guide to Those Inside Secrets for Better Photoshop Images. 2007. (Illus.). 127p. pap. *(978-2-940378-14-2(2))* RotoVision SA.

ADOBE PREMIERE (COMPUTER PROGRAM)

Adobe Creative Team. Adobe Photoshop Elements 7 & Adobe Premiere Elements 7. 2009. (Classroom in a Book Ser.). (ENG., Illus.). 720p. pap. 69.99 *(978-0-321-57384-1(6))* Adobe Pr.

—Adobe Premiere Elements 10 Classroom in a Book. 2011. (ENG., Illus.). 320p. pap. 54.99 ***(978-0-321-81101-1(1))*** Adobe Pr.

—Adobe Premiere Elements 9 Classroom in a Book. 2010. (Classroom in a Book Ser.). (ENG., Illus.). 320p. pap. 54.99 *(978-0-321-74972-7(3))* Adobe Pr.

—Adobe Premiere Pro CS4. 2008. (Classroom in a Book Ser.). (ENG., Illus.). 416p. pap., wbk. ed. 59.99 *(978-0-321-57385-8(4))* Adobe Pr.

Adobe Press Staff. Adobe Soundbooth CS3. 2007. (Classroom in a Book Ser.). (ENG., Illus.). 208p. pap. 54.99 *(978-0-321-49977-6(8))* Adobe Pr.

AGI Creative Team Staff & Smith, Jerron. Premiere Pro CS5 & CS5. 5 Digital Classroom. 2011. (Digital Classroom Ser.: 60). (ENG., Illus.). 368p. pap. 49.99 *(978-1-118-01617-6(3),* Wiley) Wiley, John & Sons, Inc.

Bolante, Antony. Premiere Pro 2 for Windows: Visual Quickpro Guide. 2006. (Visual Quickpro Guide Ser.). (ENG., Illus.). 624p. per. 34.99 *(978-0-321-38352-5(4))* Peachpit Pr.

Droblas, Adele & Greenberg, Seth. Adobe Premiere Pro CS3 Bible. 2007. (CourseSmart Ser.: 426). (ENG., Illus.). 973p. pap. 49.99 *(978-0-470-13064-3(4),* Wiley) Wiley, John & Sons, Inc.

Grover, Chris. Premiere Elements 8. 8th ed. 2009. (Missing Manual Ser.). (ENG., Illus.). 480p. pap. 34.99 *(978-0-596-80336-0(2),* Pogue Pr.) O'Reilly Media, Inc.

Harrington, Richard, et al. Adobe Premiere Pro Switchers Bundle. 2011. (ENG.). pap., pap. 112.00 ***(978-0-321-82019-8(3))*** Adobe Pr.

—An Editor's Guide to Adobe Premiere Pro. 2011. (ENG.). 352p. pap. 54.99 ***(978-0-321-77301-2(2))*** Peachpit Pr.

Jago, Maxim & Video2brain Staff. Video Production with Adobe Premiere Cs5. 5 & after Effects Cs5. 5: Learn by Video. 2011. (Learn by Video Ser.). (ENG.). 48p. 74.99 ***(978-0-321-78809-2(5))*** Adobe Pr.

Keller, Debra. The Video Collection Revealed: Adobe Premiere Pro, after Effects, Soundbooth & Encore CS5. 2010. (Revealed Ser.). (ENG.). 496p. (C). pap. 70.95 *(978-1-4390-5758-2(3))* Delmar Cengage Learning.

Plumer, Carl & Ekert, Paul. Creating Hollywood-Style Movies with Adobe Premiere Elements 7. movie tie-in ed. 2009. (ENG., Illus.). 360p. pap. 44.99 *(978-0-321-60621-1(3))* Peachpit Pr.

Underdahl, Keith. Premiere Elements 8 for Dummies. 2nd ed. 2009. (ENG., Illus.). 360p. pap. 29.99 *(978-0-470-45318-6(4),* For Dummies) Wiley, John & Sons, Inc.

video2brain & Jago, Maxim. Introducing Adobe Premiere Elements 10: Learn by Video. 2011. (Learn by Video Ser.). (ENG.). 48p. pap. 34.99 ***(978-0-321-81212-4(3))*** Adobe Pr.

Video2brain Staff, et al. Adobe Premiere Pro CS5. 2010. (Learn by Video Ser.). (ENG.). 120p. 69.99 *(978-0-321-73484-6(X))* Adobe Pr.

Virtual Training Company, prod. Adobe Video Bundle Essentials. 2006. cd-rom 99.95 *(978-1-933736-49-5(6))* VTC, Inc.

ADOBES

see Adobe Houses

ADOLESCENCE

see also Adolescent Psychiatry; Puberty; Youth

also headings beginning with the word Adolescent

Adelson, Joseph. Inventing Adolescence: The Political Psychology of Everyday Schooling. 2008. (ENG., Illus.). 305p. pap. 29.95 *(978-1-4128-0792-0(1))* Transaction Pubs.

Allgrove, J. & Shaw, N. J., eds. Calcium & Bone Disorders in Children & Adolescents. 2009. (Endocrine Development Ser.). (ENG., Illus.). 300p. *(978-3-8055-9161-4(6))* Karger, S. AG.

Allgrove, Jeremy, et al. Evidence-Based Paediatric & Adolescent Diabetes. Allgrove, Jeremy et al, eds. 2007. (Evidence-Based Medicine Ser.). (ENG., Illus.). 256p. 133.95 *(978-1-4051-5292-1(3))* Wiley, John & Sons, Inc.

Altopp, Whitney. The Adolescent Beloved Disciple. 2010. 52p. pap. *(978-3-639-26712-9(5))* VDM Verlag Dr. Mueller e.K.

Alvarez, Manuel Diaz. Forma Tu Personalidad. (SPA.). 112p. 4.95 *(978-958-607-276-2(2))* Sociedad de San Pablo COL. Dist: St Pauls/Alba Hse. Pubs.

Amsel, Eric & Smetana, Judith, eds. Adolescent Vulnerabilities & Opportunities: Constructivist Developmental Perspectives. 2011. (Interdisciplinary Approaches to Knowledge & Development Ser.). (ENG., Illus.). 224p. 85.00 *(978-0-521-76346-7(2))* Cambridge Univ. Pr.

Anfara, Vincent A. & Mertens, Steven B. The Young Adolescent & the Middle School. 2007. (ENG., Illus.). 408p. *(978-1-59311-663-7(2));* per. *(978-1-59311-662-0(4))* Information Age Publishing, Inc.

Arfin, Lesley. Dear Diary. 2008. (ENG., Illus.). 288p. pap. 14.00 *(978-1-57687-440-0(0))* powerHouse Cultural Entertainment, Inc.

Arnett, Jeffery J. & Arnett, Jeffrey Jensen. Adolescence & Emerging Adulthood: A Cultural Approach. 4th ed. 2009. (ENG., Illus.). 504p. (C). pap. 150.00 *(978-0-13-814458-6(3),* Prentice Hall) Prentice Hall PTR.

Arnett, Jeffery J. Adolescence & Emerging Adulthood: A Cultural Approach. 4th ed. 2010. (Illus.). 504p. pap. *(978-0-13-507479-4(7))* Prentice Hall PTR.

Arnett, Jeffrey Jensen. International Encyclopedia of Adolescence, 2 vols. 2006. (Illus.). 1312p. 400.00 *(978-0-415-96667-2(1))* Routledge.

—Readings on Adolescence & Emerging Adulthood. 2nd ed. 2007. 288p. (C). 30.00 *(978-0-13-232563-9(2),* Prentice Hall) Prentice Hall PTR.

Arnett, Jeffrey Jensen, ed. Adolescent Psychology Around the World. 2011. (ENG., Illus.). 432p. 105.95 *(978-1-84872-888-2(3));* pap. 45.95 *(978-1-84872-889-9(1))* Taylor & Francis Group GBR. (Psychology Press). Dist: Taylor & Francis Group.

Bainbridge, David. Teenagers: A Natural History, 1 vol. 2009. (ENG., Illus.). 364p. pap. 16.00 *(978-1-55365-437-7(4),* Greystone Bks.) D&M Pubs. Inc. CAN. Dist: Perseus-PGW.

Bassani, Cherylynn. Adolescent Behavior. 2012. ***(978-1-62100-700-5(6))*** Nova Science Pubs., Inc.

Baxter, Kent. The Modern Age: Turn-of-the-Century American Culture & the Invention of Adolescence. (ENG., Illus.). 200p. 2011. pap. 24.95 ***(978-0-8173-5698-9(3))*** 2008. 39.95 *(978-0-8173-1626-6(4))* Univ. of Alabama Pr.

Becker-Weidman, Arthur. The Dyadic Developmental Psychotherapy Casebook. 2011. *(978-0-7657-0817-5(5));* (ENG.). 250p. 60.00 *(978-0-7657-0815-1(9))* Rowman & Littlefield Publishers, Inc. (Aronson, Jason).

Beidel, Deborah C. & Alfano, Candice. Child Anxiety Disorders: Research & Treatment. 2nd rev. ed. 2011. (ENG., Illus.). 544p. instr.'s gde. ed. 52.95 *(978-0-415-87373-4(8))* Routledge.

Benton, Ann. Putting Parenting to Bed: Uncommon Sense for Modern Parents. 2010. 32p. pap., pupil's gde. ed. *(978-1-905564-89-7(9));* 96p. pap. *(978-1-905564-22-4(8))* Good Bk. Co.

Berger, Kathleen Stassen. The Developing Person. 5th ed. 2007. 160p. per. 11.95 *(978-1-4288-1940-5(1))* Cram101 Inc.

—Developing Person Through Childhood & Adolescence. (ENG.). (C). 8th ed. 2009. 608p. 87.35 *(978-1-4292-4437-4(2))* 9th ed. 2011. 672p. 149.95 ***(978-1-4292-4351-3(1))*** Worth Pubs., Inc.

Bergin, David & Bergin, Christi. Child Development in Your Classroom. 2011. (Whatâ€(tm)s New in Education Ser.). (ENG.). 704p. (C). pap. 135.95 *(978-1-111-18634-0(0))* Wadsworth.

Berk, Laura E. Infants, Children & Adolescents. 4th ed. 2006. pap. 12.95 *(978-1-4288-1305-2(5))* Cram101 Inc.

—Study Guide for Infants, Children & Adolescents. 7th rev. ed. 2011. (ENG.). 448p. (C). pap. 37.40 *(978-0-205-01051-6(2),* Prentice Hall) Prentice Hall PTR.

—A Window on Child Development DVD Guide for Child Development. 8th ed. 2008. 128p. (C). pap. 5.00 *(978-0-205-62680-9(7),* Allyn & Bacon) Pearson Education Canada CAN. Dist: Pearson Education.

Blau, Gary M. & Magrab, Phyllis R., eds. The Leadership Equation: Strategies for Individuals Who Are Champions for Children, Youth, & Families, SCCMH Series, 1, Vol. 10. 2010. (Illus.). 256p. pap. 49.95 *(978-1-59857-092-2(7))* Brookes, Paul H. Publishing Co.

Boesky, Lisa Melanie. Juvenile Offenders with Mental Health Disorders: Who Are They & What Do We Do with Them? 2nd ed. 2011. (ENG.). pap. 45.00 *(978-1-56991-312-3(9))* American Correctional Assn.

Brighton, Kenneth L. Coming of Age: The Education & Development of Young Adolescents: A Resource for Educators & Parents. 2007. *(978-1-56090-211-9(6))* National Middle Schl. Assn.

Brown, Dave F. & Knowles, Trudy. What Every Middle School Teacher Should Know, Second Edition. 2nd rev. ed. 2007. (Illus.). 320p. pap. 36.25 *(978-0-325-00953-7(8),* E00953) Heinemann.

Bukatko, Danuta. Child & Adolescent Development: A Chronological Approach. 2007. (ENG., Illus.). 720p. (C). 195.95 *(978-0-618-34920-3(0),* 308200) Wadsworth.

Buntman, Peter H. How to Live with Your Teenager, Vol. II. 176p. pap. 14.95 *(978-0-9623986-0-5(8))* Ctr. for Family Life, Inc.

Burek Pierce, Jennifer. Sex, Brains, & Video Games: A Librarian's Guide to Teens in the Twenty-First Century. 2007. 130p. pap. 35.00 *(978-0-8389-0951-5(5))* American Library Assn.

Cantu, Robert & Hyman, Mark. Concussions & Our Kids: America's Leading Expert on How to Protect Young Athletes & Keep Sports Safe. 2012. (ENG., Illus.). 208p. 25.00 ***(978-0-547-77394-0(3))*** Houghton Mifflin Harcourt Trade & Reference Pubs.

Carleton, C J. What Makes You Unique: Discover the Truth or Believe the Lie. 2007. (Illus.). 157p. per. 14.99 *(978-0-924748-82-0(6))* Milestones International Publishers.

Carter, Brian S., et al, eds. Palliative Care for Infants, Children, & Adolescents: A Practical Handbook. 2nd ed. 2011. (ENG., Illus.). 560p. (gr. 17). 70.00 *(978-1-4214-0148-5(7));* pap. 35.00 *(978-1-4214-0149-2(5))* Johns Hopkins Univ. Pr.

Chuang, Ying-Chih. Neighborhood Context, Parenting, & Adolescent Smoking & Drinking. 2009. 92p. pap. *(978-3-639-04269-6(7))* VDM Verlag Dr. Mueller e.K.

Cobb & Cram101 Textbook Reviews Staff. Adolescence: Continuity, Change, & Diversity. 2007. 160p. per. 12.95 *(978-1-4288-2072-2(8))* Cram101 Inc.

Cohen, Libby G. & Spenciner, Loraine J. Assessment of Children & Youth with Special Needs. 4th ed. 2010. (ENG.). 432p. (C). pap. 129.80 *(978-0-13-705453-4(X),* Prentice Hall) Prentice Hall PTR.

Coleman, John C. The Nature of Adolescence. 4th rev. ed. 2011. (Adolescence & Society Ser.). (ENG., Illus.). 288p. 95.00 *(978-0-415-56419-9(0));* pap. 31.95 *(978-0-415-56420-5(4))* Routledge.

Committee on Nutrition Standards for National School Lunch and Breakfast Programs & Institute of Medicine. School Meals: Building Blocks for Healthy Children. 2010. (ENG.). 252p. pap. 55.00 *(978-0-309-14436-0(1))* National Academies Pr.

Connolly, Mary. Skills Based Health Education. 2010. 440p. pap. 93.95 *(978-1-4496-3020-1(0))* Jones & Bartlett Learning, LLC.

Cram101 Textbook Reviews. Outlines & Highlights for Adolescence: Development During a Global Era by Dena Phillips Swanson. 2011. 174p. pap. 29.95 ***(978-1-4288-6505-1(5))*** Cram101 Inc.

—Outlines & Highlights for Adolescence by Paul S Kaplan, Isbn: 9780395908235. 2010. 90p. pap. 27.95 *(978-1-61698-733-6(2))* Cram101 Inc.

—Outlines & Highlights for Child & Adolescent Development: An Advanced Course by William Damon, ISBN. 2010. 174p. pap. 29.95 *(978-1-61654-494-2(5))* Cram101 Inc.

Cram101 Textbook Reviews & Cram101 Textbook Reviews. Outlines & Highlights for Adolescent Development by John Dacey, Isbn: 9780759359635 9780759359635. 2011. 98p. pap. 27.95 ***(978-1-4288-7765-8(7))*** Cram101 Inc.

—Outlines & Highlights for Constructing Adulthood: Agency & Subjectivity in Adolescence & Adulthood, Vol. 11 by Ross Macmillan, ISBN. 2011. 108p. pap. 28.95 ***(978-1-61744-943-7(1))*** Cram101 Inc.

—Outlines & Highlights for the Adolescent: Development, Relationships, & Culture by Kim Dolgin, ISBN. 2011. 282p. pap. 32.95 ***(978-1-61461-663-4(9))*** Cram101 Inc.

Cram101 Textbook Reviews Staff. Outlines & Highlights for Adolescence & Emerging Adulthood: A Cultural Approach by Arnett, ISBN. 2008. 160p. pap. 12.95 *(978-1-4288-5931-9(4))* Cram101 Inc.

—Outlines & Highlights for Adolescence by Paul S Kaplan, Isbn: 9780395903235. 2009. 78p. pap. 27.95 *(978-1-4288-8001-6(1))* Cram101 Inc.

—Outlines & Highlights for Adolescence by Santrock, Isbn. 2008. 136p. pap. 11.95 *(978-1-4288-5876-3(8))* Cram101 Inc.

—Outlines & Highlights for Adolescence by Steinberg, Isbn. 2008. 132p. pap. 11.95 *(978-1-4288-5873-2(3));* 140p. pap. 11.95 *(978-1-4288-5874-9(1))* Cram101 Inc.

—Outlines & Highlights for Adolescent: Development, Relationships, & Culture by Rice, ISBN. 2008. 164p. pap. 12.95 *(978-1-4288-5958-6(6))* Cram101 Inc.

—Outlines & Highlights for Child & Adolescent Development Childhood & Adolescence. 2008. 160p. pap. 12.95 *(978-1-4288-5815-2(6))* Cram101 Inc.

—Outlines & Highlights for Child Development by Feldman, Isbn: 0131732471. 2008. 176p. pap. 12.95 *(978-1-4288-5964-7(0))* Cram101 Inc.

—Outlines & Highlights for Childhood. 2008. 136p. pap. 11.95 *(978-1-4288-5816-9(4))* Cram101 Inc.

—Outlines & Highlights for Children by Santrock, Isbn: 9780073382609. 2008. 180p. pap. 12.95 *(978-1-4288-5953-1(5))* Cram101 Inc.

—Outlines & Highlights for Infants, Children, & Adolescents by Berk, Isbn: 0205511384. 2008. 396p. pap. 17.95 *(978-1-4288-5976-0(4))* Cram101 Inc.

Crockett, Lisa J. & Silbereisen, Rainer K., eds. Negotiating Adolescence in Times of Social Change. 2011. (ENG.). 322p. pap. 39.99 *(978-0-521-28310-6(6))* Cambridge Univ. Pr.

Crosnoe, Robert. Fitting in, Standing Out: Navigating the Social Challenges of High School to Get an Education. 2011. (ENG., Illus.). 280p. 85.00 *(978-1-107-00502-0(7));* pap. 25.99 *(978-0-521-18203-4(4))* Cambridge Univ. Pr.

David, Ronald B. Clinical Pediatric Neurology. 3rd ed. 2009. 399.00 *(978-1-933864-22-8(2))* Demos Medical Publishing, LLC.

Dehart & Sroufe & Cooper & Cram101 Textbook Reviews Staff. Child Development: Its Nature & Course. 2007. 188p. per. 12.95 *(978-1-4288-2042-5(6))* Cram101 Inc.

Delahanty, Douglas L. The Psychobiology of Trauma & Resilience Across the Lifespan. 2008. (ENG., Illus.). 294p. 83.99 *(978-0-7657-0536-5(2),* Aronson, Jason) Rowman & Littlefield Publishers, Inc.

Dolgin, Kim Gale. The Adolescent: Development, Relationships, & Culture. 13th rev. ed. 2010. (ENG., Illus.). 528p. (C). 150.00 *(978-0-205-73136-7(8),* Prentice Hall) Prentice Hall PTR.

—The Adolescent: Development, Relationships, & Culture, Books a la Carte Edition. 13th ed. 2011. (ENG.). 528p. (C). ring bd. 96.20 *(978-0-205-01127-8(6)*, Prentice Hall) Prentice Hall PTR.

—The Adolescent: Development, Relationships, & Culture, Books a la Carte Plus MyDevelopmentLab. 13th ed. 2011. (ENG.). (C). ring bd. 104.67 *(978-0-205-01226-8(4)*, Prentice Hall) Prentice Hall PTR.

D'Onofrio, Amelio A. Adolescent Self-Injury: A Comprehensive Guide for Counselors & Health Care Professionals. 2007. 50.00 *(978-0-8261-0278-2(6))* Springer Publishing Co., Inc.

Drysdale, Maureen & Rye, B. J. Clashing Views in Adolescence. 2nd ed. 2008. (Taking Sides Ser.). (ENG.). 480p. (C). pap. 48.00 *(978-0-07-351536-6(1)*, 0073515361, McGraw-Hill/Dushkin) McGraw-Hill Higher Education.

Duncan, Eric. Growing up Memories Bk. II: The Turmoil of Adolescence. Date not set. (Illus.). 350p. 25.00 *(978-1-888347-05-0(8))*; pap. 6.99 *(978-1-888347-06-7(6))* Donnchad Publishing, Inc. (Veritas Pr.).

Fass, Paula S. & Grossberg, Michael, eds. Reinventing Childhood after World War II. 2011. 200p. (C). 42.50 ***(978-0-8122-4367-3(6))*** Univ. of Pennsylvania Pr.

Feldman, Robert S. Adolescence (with MyVirtualTeen Student Access Code Card) 2010. (ENG.). 560p. (C). pap. 156.67 *(978-0-205-80149-7(8)*, Prentice Hall) Prentice Hall PTR.

—Child Development. 5th ed. 2008. (ENG.). 552p. (C). 167.60 *(978-0-205-65502-1(5)*, Prentice Hall) Prentice Hall PTR.

Field, Tiffany. Adolescents a to Z. 2011. 234p. pap. 19.99 ***(978-1-4653-5579-9(0))*** Xlibris Corp.

Flanagan, Caitlin. Girl Land. 2012. (ENG.). 224p. 25.99 *(978-0-316-06598-6(6))* Little Brown & Co.

Freud, Sigmund. A Young Girl's Diary. 2008. 288p. 25.99 *(978-0-559-59727-5(4))*; 288p. pap. 27.75 *(978-0-559-59725-1(8))*; 192p. 25.99 *(978-0-554-21528-0(4))*; 192p. 22.99 *(978-0-554-30831-9(2))* BiblioBazaar.

—A Young Girl's Diary. Eden & Paul, Cedar, trs. 2007. (ENG.). 200p. pap. 19.99 *(978-1-4264-0312-5(7))*; pap. 21.99 *(978-1-4264-0363-7(1))* BiblioBazaar.

—A Young Girl's Diary. Paul, Cedar & Paul, Eden, trs. 2007. (ENG.). 188p. per. *(978-1-4065-8162-1(3))* Dodo Pr.

Freud, Sigmund, pref. A Young Girl's Diary. 2007. (ENG.). 164p. per. 12.99 *(978-1-59547-835-1(3))* NuVision Pubns., LLC.

Frosch, Mary, ed. Coming of Age in the 21st Century: Growing up in America Today. 2008. (ENG.). 319p. pap. 17.95 *(978-1-59558-055-9(7))* New Pr., The.

Gaines, Donna. Teenage Wasteland: Suburbia's Dead End Kids. 2006. pap. 8.95 *(978-1-4288-1589-6(9))* Cram101 Inc.

Galanter, Cathryn A. & Jensen, Peter S. DSM-IV-TR Casebook & Treatment Guide for Child Mental Health. 2008. (Illus.). 752p. pap. 89.00 *(978-1-58562-310-5(5))* American Psychiatric Publishing, Inc.

Garrod, et al. Adolescent Portraits: Identity, Relationships, & Challenges. 7th rev. ed. 2011. (ENG.). 336p. (C). pap. 78.00 *(978-0-205-03623-3(6)*, Prentice Hall) Prentice Hall PTR.

Goldstein, Mark A., ed. The MassGeneral Hospital for Children Adolescent Medicine Handbook. 2010. (Illus.). xvii, 252p. pap. 34.95 *(978-1-4419-6844-9(X)*, 144196844X) Springer.

Greydanus, Donald E. The Pediatric Diagnostic Examination. 2008. (Illus.). xviii, 813p. *(978-0-07-128727-2(2))* McGraw-Hill Medical Publishing Div.

Grinyer, Anne. Life after Cancer in Adolescence & Young Adulthood: The Experience of Survivorship. 2009. (ENG., Illus.). 208p. 150.00 *(978-0-415-47702-4(6))*; pap. 45.95 *(978-0-415-47703-1(4))* Routledge.

Hagarty, Maura Thompson, ed. What I Wish I Had Known about Becoming a Teenager: Wisdom & Advice from Teens in High School. 2007. 108p. (YA). (gr. 7-14). per. 13.75 *(978-0-88489-662-3(5))* St. Mary's Pr.

Hall, G. Stanley. Youth: Its Education, Regimen, & Hygiene. 2006. 332p. pap. 23.99 *(978-1-4264-3414-3(6))* 2007. (ENG.). 366p. pap. 26.99 *(978-1-4264-3464-8(2))* BiblioBazaar.

—Youth Its Education Regimen & Hygiene. 2006. pap. *(978-1-4068-1090-5(8))* Echo Library.

—Youth: Its Education, Regimen, & Hygiene. 2007. (ENG.). 312p. per. *(978-1-4065-1591-6(4))* Dodo Pr.

Hanley, Terry, et al, eds. Adolescent Counselling Psychology. 2012. (ENG., Illus.). 184p. (C). 110.00 ***(978-0-415-58025-0(0))***; pap. 33.95 ***(978-0-415-58026-7(9))*** Routledge.

Harold, Rena D., et al. Smooth Sailing or Stormy Waters? Family Transitions Through Adolescence & Their Implications for Practice & Policy. 2007. (ENG., Illus.). 352p. 145.00 *(978-0-8058-4907-3(6))*; per. 52.95 *(978-0-8058-6305-5(2))* Taylor & Francis Group GBR. (Routledge). Dist: Taylor & Francis Group.

Hayman, Suzy. Raise a Happy Teenager. 2012. (Teach Yourself Ser.). (ENG.). 224p. pap. 15.95 ***(978-1-4441-0734-0(8)***, Hodder & Stoughton) Hodder General Publishing Div. GBR. Dist: Independent Pubs. Group.

Hoffman, Julian I. E. & Moller, James H., eds. Pediatric Cardiovascular Medicine. 2nd ed. 2012. (ENG.). 1094p. 324.95 ***(978-1-4443-3589-7(8)***, Wiley-Blackwell) Wiley, John & Sons, Inc.

Holstein, Barbara Becker. The Truth: I'm 10, I'm smart & I know Everything. 2007. 112p. per. 12.95 *(978-1-889409-35-1(9))* LadybugPress.

Isaacs, David. Evidence-Based Pediatric Infectious Diseases. Elliott, Elizabeth et al, eds. 2007. (Evidence-Based Medicine Ser.: 36). (ENG., Illus.). 344p. per. 159.95 *(978-1-4051-4858-0(6))* Wiley, John & Sons, Inc.

Jackson-Smith, Urana. Initiation Rights. 2010. 108p. pap. 14.95 *(978-0-557-27135-1(5))* Lulu Enterprises Inc.

James, Susan R., et al. Nursing Care of Children: Principles & Practice. 4th ed. 2012. (ENG., Illus.). 880p. (C). pap. 89.95 ***(978-1-4557-0366-1(4)***, Saunders) Elsevier - Health Sciences Div.

Jaoui, Sylvaine. For Girls Only: The Ultimate Guide to Being a Girl. Bussell, Andrea, ed. 2010. (Sunscreen Ser.). (ENG., Illus.). 112p. (YA). (gr. 7-11). pap. 10.95 *(978-0-8109-8432-5(6)*, Amulet Bks.) Abrams.

Johnson, M. W. Oops Things Not to Say to Your Teenager or Adolescent: Speaking to Your Teenager. 2009. 168p. pap. 18.95 *(978-1-4327-4154-9(3))* Outskirts Pr., Inc.

Jones, Harold E. Development in Adolescence - Approaches to the Study of the Individual. 2007. 196p. per. *(978-1-4067-6254-9(7))* Read Bks.

Kaplan, Paul S. A Child's Odyssey: Child & Adolescent Development, Including InfoTrac College Edition. *(978-0-534-74502-8(4))* Wadsworth.

Kastner, Laura, et al. Getting to Calm: Cool-Headed Strategies for Parenting Tweens & Teens. 2009. (ENG., Illus.). 304p. pap. 19.95 *(978-0-9823454-0-5(2))* ParentMap.

Kauder Nalebuff, Rachel. My Little Red Book. 2009. (ENG.). 240p. 14.99 *(978-0-446-54636-2(4)*, Twelve) Grand Central Publishing.

Kerr, Margaret, et al, eds. What Can Parents Do? New Insights into the Role of Parents in Adolescent Problem Behavior. 2008. (Hot Topics in Developmental Research - a Series of Three Edited Volumes Ser.: 4). (ENG., Illus.). 304p. pap. 219.95 *(978-0-470-72363-0(7)*, Wiley) Wiley, John & Sons, Inc.

Krassas, G. E., et al, eds. Diseases of the Thyroid in Childhood & Adolescence [Bibliography & Price not Definite.]. (Pediatric & Adolescent Medicine Ser.: Vol. 11). (Illus.). 320p. *(978-3-8055-8205-6(6))* Karger, S. AG.

Kunnen, Saskia Elske, ed. Adolescent Development. 2011. (Studies in Adolescent Development Ser.). (ENG., Illus.). 192p. 77.00 ***(978-1-84872-037-4(8)***, Psychology Press) Taylor & Francis Group GBR. Dist: Taylor & Francis Group.

LeCroy, Craig W. Parenting Mentally Ill Children: Faith, Caring, Support, & Surviving the System. 2011. x, 204p. E-Book *(978-0-313-35869-2(9)*, Praeger Pubs.) Greenwood Publishing Group, Inc.

LeCroy, Craig Winston. Parenting Mentally Ill Children: Faith, Caring, Support, & Surviving the System, 1 vol. 2011. (Illus.). 204p. 44.95 *(978-0-313-35868-5(0)*, C35868, Praeger Pubs.) Greenwood Publishing Group, Inc.

Lerner, Richard M. The Good Teen: Rescuing Adolescence from the Myths of the Storm & Stress Years. 2008. (ENG.). 272p. 14.95 *(978-0-307-34758-9(3)*, Three Rivers Pr.) Crown Publishing Group.

Lesko, Nancy. ACT Your Age! A Cultural Construction of Adolescence. 2nd ed. 2012. ***(978-0-203-12158-0(9))*** Routledge.

Lesko, Nancy. Act Your Age! A Cultural Construction of Adolescence. 2nd rev. ed. 2012. (Critical Social Thought Ser.). (ENG., Illus.). 248p. 140.00 *(978-0-415-88761-8(5))*; pap. 44.95 *(978-0-415-88762-5(3))* Routledge.

LeTendre, Gerald K. Learning to Be Adolescent: Growing up in U. S. & Japanese Middle Schools. 2011. 258p. pap. 26.00 ***(978-0-300-18267-5(8))*** Yale Univ. Pr.

Levesque, Roger J. R., ed. Encyclopedia of Adolescence, 5 vols. 2011. (ENG.). liv, 3363p. 2050.00 *(978-1-4419-1694-5(6)*, 1441916946) Springer.

Lifshitz Fima Staff. Pediatric Endocrinology Fifth Edition Volume Two Growth Adrenal S, 2 vols. 5th rev. ed. 2007. (Illus.). 787p. *(978-1-4200-5523-8(2))* Informa Pharmaceuticals & Healthcare.

Lue, Hung-Chi. ECG in the Child & Adolescent: Normal Standards & Percentile Charts. 2006. (ENG., Illus.). 104p. 62.95 *(978-1-4051-5899-2(9)*, Wiley-Blackwell) Wiley, John & Sons, Inc.

Ma'ayan, Hadar Dubowsky. Reading Girls: The Lives & Literacies of Adolescents. 2012. (Language & Literacy Ser.). (ENG.). 160p. 29.95 ***(978-0-8077-5314-9(9))***; pap. 66.00 ***(978-0-8077-5315-6(7))*** Teachers College Pr., Teachers College, Columbia Univ.

Macleod, Catriona I. Adolescence Pregnancy & Abortion: Constructing a Threat of Degeneration. 2010. (Women & Psychology Ser.). (ENG., Illus.). 184p. 80.00 *(978-0-415-55339-1(3)*, Routledge) Taylor & Francis Group GBR. Dist: Taylor & Francis Group.

Macmillan, Ross, ed. Constructing Adulthood: Agency & Subjectivity in Adolescence & Adulthood. 2006. (ENG.). 346p. 105.00 *(978-0-7623-1201-6(7)*, JAI Pr.) Elsevier Science & Technology Bks.

Madrine, King'Endo, et al. Incidence & Extent of Substance Abuse: Among Secondary School Students in Nairobi Province Kenya: Implications for Specialised Intervention. 2011. 128p. pap. ***(978-3-639-32340-5(8))*** VDM Verlag Dr. Mueller e.K.

Mash, Eric J. & Barkley, Russell A., eds. Assessment of Childhood Disorders. 4th rev. ed. 2007. (ENG., Illus.). 866p. 90.00 *(978-1-59385-493-5(5))* Guilford Pubns., Inc.

McCoy, Kathy & Wibbelsman, Charles. The Teenage Body Book: A New Edition for a New Generation. 2008. (ENG., Illus.). 320p. pap. 19.95 *(978-1-57826-277-9(1))* Hatherleigh Co., Ltd., The.

McKinnon, John A. To Change a Mind: Parenting to Promote Maturity in Teenagers. 2011. 207p. pap. 23.00 *(978-1-59056-234-5(8))* Lantern Bks.

McMahan, Ian. Adolescence. 2008. (ENG., Illus.). 624p. (C). pap. 145.60 *(978-0-205-48232-0(5))* Allyn & Bacon, Inc.

Meece, Judith L., et al. Child & Adolescent Development for Educators. 3rd rev. ed. 2007. (ENG., Illus.). 640p. (C). per. 107.67 *(978-0-07-352576-1(6)*, 0073525766) McGraw-Hill Cos., The.

Merrick, Joav. Child Health & Human Development Yearbook 2009. 2011. (Health & Human Development (Joav Merrick - Ser. Editor - National Institute of Child Health & Human Development, Ministry of Social Affairs, Jerusalem) Ser.). 295.00 *(978-1-61668-912-4(9))* Nova Science Pubs., Inc.

Metin, Özdemir. Adolescent Self-Efficacy Beliefs in Multiple Contexts: An Analysis of Individual, Peer, Family, & Neighborhood Factors. 2011. 132p. pap. ***(978-3-639-30531-9(0))*** VDM Verlag Dr. Mueller e.K.

Miller, David N. & Brock, Stephen E. Identifying, Assessing, & Treating Self-Injury at School. 2011. (Developmental Psychopathology at School Ser.). xi, 137p. pap. 34.95 *(978-1-4419-9512-4(9)*, 1441995129) Springer.

Moon, Sarah & Lecesne, James. The Letter Q: Queer Writers' Notes to Their Younger Selves. 2012. pap. ***(978-0-545-39933-3(5)***, Levine, Arthur A. Bks.) Scholastic, Inc.

Moon, Sarah & Lecesne, James, eds. The Letter Q: Queer Writers' Notes to Their Younger Selves. 2012. (ENG.). 288p. (J). (gr. 7). 17.99 ***(978-0-545-39932-6(7)***, Levine, Arthur A. Bks.) Scholastic, Inc.

Muris, Peter. Normal & Abnormal Fear & Anxiety in Children & Adolescents. 2007. (BRAT Series in Clinical Psychology Ser.). (ENG., Illus.). 400p. 109.00 *(978-0-08-045073-5(3)*, Elsevier Science) Elsevier Science & Technology Bks.

Nadelberg, David. Mortified: Love Is a Battlefield. 2008. (ENG.). 304p. pap. 14.95 *(978-1-4169-5479-8(1))* Gallery Pr., The IRL. Dist: Simon & Schuster, Inc.

Nakkula, Michael J. & Toshalis, Eric. Understanding Youth: Adolescent Development for Educators. 2006. 304p. pap. 29.95 *(978-1-891792-31-1(8))*; lib. bdg. *(978-1-891792-32-8(6))* Harvard Education Publishing Group (HEPG). (Harvard Education Pr.).

National Directory of Children Youth & Families Services, creator. The National Directory of Children, Youth, & Families Services: The Professionals' Reference. 2007. (National Directory of Children, Youth & Families Services Ser.). 1438p. per. 179.00 *(978-1-885461-18-6(6))* National Directory CYF.

Noller. Family Life in Adolescence. 2011. (Adolescence & Society Ser.). 216p. pap. 32.50 *(978-0-415-47033-9(1))* Routledge.

Noller, Patricia & Atkin, Sharon. Family Life in Adolescence. 2nd ed. 2011. (Adolescence & Society Ser.). (Illus.). 208p. 80.00 *(978-0-415-47032-2(3))* Routledge.

Omar, Hatim A. & Greydanus, Donald E., eds. Obesity & Adolescence: A Public Health Concern. 2009. xvii, 295p. 89.00 *(978-1-60692-821-9(X))* Nova Science Pubs., Inc.

Pagliaro, Ann Marie & Pagliaro, Louis A. The Handbook of Child & Adolescent Drug & Substance Abuse: Pharmacological, Developmental, & Clinical Considerations. 2nd ed. 2011. (ENG., Illus.). 528p. 65.00 ***(978-0-470-63906-1(7)***, Wiley) Wiley, John & Sons, Inc.

Palmer, Pat & Froehner, Melissa A. Teen Esteem: A Self-Direction Manual for Young Adults. 3rd rev. ed. 2010. (ENG., Illus.). 128p. (YA). pap. 11.95 *(978-1-886230-87-3(0))* Impact Pubs., Inc.

Papalia, Diane E. & Feldman, Ruth Duskin. A Child's World: Infancy Through Adolescence. 12th ed. 2010. (ENG., Illus.). 608p. (C). 178.33 *(978-0-07-353204-2(5)*, 0073532045) McGraw-Hill Cos., The.

Papalia, Diane E., et al. A Child's World: Infancy Through Adolescence. 11th ed. 2007. (ENG., Illus.). 640p. (C). 177.00 *(978-0-07-353197-7(9)*, 0073531979) McGraw-Hill Cos., The.

Parker, Valeria Hopkins. For Daughters & Mothers. 2011. 136p. 40.95 ***(978-1-258-08135-5(0))*** Literary Licensing, LLC.

Patel, Dilip R., et al. Behavioral Pediatrics. 3rd Edition. Greydanus, Donald E., ed. 2008. 89.00 *(978-1-60692-702-1(7))* Nova Science Pubs., Inc.

Paul, Eden & Paul, Cedar, trs. A Young Girl's Diary. 2008. 292p. 43.95 *(978-1-4369-5387-0(1))*; pap. 28.95 *(978-1-4367-5870-3(X))* Kessinger Publishing, LLC.

Porterfield, Sally F. & Baumlin, Tita French. Perpetual Adolescence: Jungian Analyses of American Media, Literature, & Pop Culture. Polette, Keith, tr. 2009. 240p. 70.00 *(978-1-4384-2799-7(9))*; pap. 24.95 *(978-1-4384-2800-0(6))* State Univ. of New York Pr.

Purvis, Kenneth. From Boys to Men: A Manual for Concerned Parents about Puberty & Adolescence. 2007. 176p. pap. 10.99 *(978-0-470-06078-0(6))* Wiley, John & Sons, Inc.

Ranke, M. B., ed. Diagnostics of Endocrine Function in Children & Adolescents. 3rd rev. enl. ed. (Illus.). *(978-3-8055-7497-6(5))* Karger, S. AG.

Rathus, Spencer A. Childhood: Voyages in Development. (ENG., (C). 3rd rev. ed. 2007. Illus.). 584p. per. 136.95 *(978-0-495-50461-0(0))* 4th ed. 2010. 560p. pap. 153.95 *(978-0-495-90433-5(3))* Wadsworth.

—Childhood & Adolescence: Voyages in Development. (ENG.). (C). 3rd ed. 2007. 712p. ring bd. 67.95 *(978-0-495-50458-0(0))* 3rd ed. 2007. (Illus.). 712p. per. 156.95 *(978-0-495-50390-3(8))* 4th ed. 2010. 672p. pap. 175.95 *(978-0-495-90408-3(2))* 4th ed. 2010. 672p. ring bd. 75.95 *(978-0-495-90436-6(8))* Wadsworth.

—Observation Worksheets for Rathus' Childhood & Adolescence: Voyages in Development, 4th. 4th ed. 2010. (ENG.). 64p. (C). pap. 41.95 *(978-0-8400-3240-9(4))* Wadsworth.

Researcher, C. Q. Childhood & Adolescence in Society: Selections from CQ Researcher. 2011. (Illus.). 336p. (C). pap. 36.00 *(978-1-4129-9434-7(9)*, B94347P) SAGE Pubns., Inc.

Rosenberg, David & Gershon, Samuel, eds. Pharmacotherapy of Child & Adolescent Psychiatric Disorders. 3rd ed. 2012. (ENG.). 474p. 100.00 ***(978-0-470-97376-9(5)***, Wiley-Blackwell) Wiley, John & Sons, Inc.

Rumbaut, Ruben G., et al, eds. On the Frontier of Adulthood: Theory, Research, & Public Policy. 2008. (MacArthur Foundation Ser.). (ENG., Illus.). 608p. pap. 29.00 *(978-0-226-74890-0(1))* Univ. of Chicago Pr.

Russell, Stephen T., et al, eds. Journal of Research on Adolescence: Decade in Review. 2011. (Journal of Research on Adolescence Ser.: 1). (ENG.). 200p. pap. 39.95 *(978-1-4443-3953-6(2)*, Wiley-Blackwell) Wiley, John & Sons, Inc.

Sachs, Brad. When No One Understands: Letters to a Teenager on Life, Loss, & the Hard Road to Adulthood. 2007. (ENG.). 144p. per. 14.00 *(978-1-59030-407-5(1)*, Trumpeter) Shambhala Pubns., Inc.

Santrock. Children. 12th ed. 2012. (ENG., Illus.). 640p. (C). pap. 176.67 ***(978-0-07-803512-8(0)***, 0078035120) McGraw-Hill Cos., The.

Santrock & Cram101 Textbook Reviews Staff. Children. 2007. 276p. per. 15.95 *(978-1-4288-2134-7(1))* Cram101 Inc.

Santrock, John. Adolescence. 14th ed. 2011. (ENG., Illus.). 624p. (C). pap. 172.00 ***(978-0-07-811716-9(X)***, 007811716X) McGraw-Hill Cos., The.

Santrock, John W. Adolescence. (Illus.). 11th ed. 2007. 475p. per. 89.00 *(978-0-07-331481-5(1))* 13th ed. 2009. (ENG., 624p. (C). pap. 172.00 *(978-0-07-337067-5(3)*, 0073370673) McGraw-Hill Cos., The.

Sartor, Margaret. Miss American Pie: A Diary of Love, Secrets, & Growing up in the 1970s. 2007. (ENG., Illus.). 288p. per. 11.95 *(978-1-59691-201-4(4))* Bloomsbury Publishing.

Saunders, John & Rey, Joseph, eds. Young People & Alcohol: Impact, Policy, Prevention, Treatment. 2011. (ENG., Illus.). 384p. pap. 61.99 *(978-1-4443-3598-9(7)*, Wiley-Blackwell) Wiley, John & Sons, Inc.

Schofield, Patricia & Merrick, Joav, eds. Pain in Children & Youth. 2008. 69.00 *(978-1-60456-951-3(4))* Nova Science Pubs., Inc.

Shannon, Joyce Brennfleck, ed. Adolescent Health Sourcebook. 2nd ed. 2007. (Health Reference Ser.). (Illus.). 683p. 87.00 *(978-0-7808-0943-7(2))* Omnigraphics, Inc.

Sider, Ron & Unruh, Heidi Rolland, eds. Hope for Children in Poverty: Profiles & Possibilities. 2007. 192p. pap. 16.00 *(978-0-8170-1505-3(1))* Judson Pr.

Sippell, W. G., ed. ESPE - the First 50 Years: A History of the European Society for Paediatric Endocrinology. 2011. (ENG., Illus.). 220p. ***(978-3-8055-9868-2(8))*** Karger, S. AG.

SMETANA & Smetana, Judith G. Adolescents, Families, & Social Development: How Teens Construct Their Worlds. 2010. (ENG.). 336p. 104.95 *(978-1-4443-3250-6(3)*, Wiley-Blackwell) Wiley, John & Sons, Inc.

Smetana, Judith G. Adolescents, Families, & Social Development: How Teens Construct Their Worlds. 2010. (ENG.). 336p. pap. 49.95 *(978-1-4443-3251-3(1)*, Wiley-Blackwell) Wiley, John & Sons, Inc.

Staley, Betty. Between Form & Freedom. 2nd ed. 2009. 288p. pap. *(978-1-903458-89-1(7))* Hawthorn Pr.

STALLARD & Stallard, Paul. Anxiety: Cognitive Behavioural Therapy with Children & Young People. 2009. (CBT with Children, Adolescents & Families Ser.). (ENG., Illus.). 224p. (C). pap. 34.95 *(978-0-415-37255-8(0))* Routledge.

Steinberg, Laurence. Adolescence. 9th ed. 2010. (ENG., Illus.). 576p. (C). 172.00 *(978-0-07-353203-5(7)*, 0073532037) McGraw-Hill Cos., The.

Steinberg, Laurence, et al. Steinberg's Development: Infancy Through Adolescence. 2010. (ENG.). 272p. (C). pap., pupil's gde. ed. 58.95 *(978-0-618-60990-1(3))* Wadsworth.

Stephens, Steve. Communicate Teens: 101 Questions to Help Connect with Your Teen. 2009. (ENG.). 130p. pap. 10.99 *(978-0-9816514-4-6(5))* Last Chapter Publishing.

Strahan, David B., et al. Promoting Harmony: Young Adolescent Development & Classroom Practices. 3rd ed. 2009. *(978-1-56090-230-0(2))* National Middle Schl. Assn.

Suarez, Oscar S. Papa, Acercate, Soy Adolescente. (SPA.). 112p. 4.95 *(978-958-607-946-4(5))* Sociedad de San Pablo COL. Dist: St Pauls/Alba Hse. Pubs.

Swanson, Dena Phillips, et al, eds. Adolescence: Development During a Global Era. 2010. (ENG.). 568p. (C). 99.95 *(978-0-12-374424-1(5)*, Academic Pr.) Elsevier Science & Technology Bks.

Taylor, Katharine Whiteside. Understanding & Guiding the Adolescent Child: Do Adolescents Need Parents? 2011. 390p. 53.95 ***(978-1-258-10227-2(7))*** Literary Licensing, LLC.

UNAIDS Inter-agency Task Team on Young People. Preventing HIV/AIDS in young People: A Systematic Review of the Evidence from Developing Countries. Ross, David A. et al, eds. 2006. (Who Technical Report Ser.). (ENG., Illus.). 353p. pap. 24.00 *(978-92-4-120938-0(0))* World Health Organization.

VanHoose & Strahan & L'Esperance & Cram101 Textbook Reviews Staff. Promoting Harmony: Young Adolescent Development & School Practices. 2007. 60p. per. 9.95 *(978-1-4288-2054-8(X))* Cram101 Inc.

Waters, Mary, et al. Coming of Age in America: The Transition to Adulthood in the Twenty-First Century. 2011. (ENG.). 240p. 60.00 *(978-0-520-27092-3(4))* Univ. of California Pr.

Waters, Mary C., et al, eds. Coming of Age in America: The Transition to Adulthood in the Twenty-First Century. 2011. (ENG.). 240p. pap. 24.95 *(978-0-520-27093-0(2))* Univ. of California Pr.

Whit, I. G. Anastasi. 2011. 164p. pap. 19.99 ***(978-1-4628-8320-2(6))*** Xlibris Corp.

Wolf, Anthony. I'D Listen to My Parents If They'd Just Shut Up: What to Say & Not Say When Parenting Teens Today. 2011. (ENG.). 368p. pap. 14.99 *(978-0-06-191545-1(9)*, William Morrow Paperbacks) HarperCollins Pubs.

Wolf, Anthony E. I'd Listen to My Parents If They'd Just Shut Up: What to Say & Not Say When Parenting Teens Today. 2011. 12.99 *(978-0-06-209250-2(2))* HarperCollins Pubs.

Wright, H. Norman. Respuesta a Relaciones Entre Padres y Adolescentes: Answer to Parent - Teen. (SPA.). *(978-84-7228-722-8(X)*, 220781) Clie, Editorial.

Yang, Zhiyong. The Parent-Self-Peer Model. 2008. 112p. pap. *(978-3-639-02591-0(1))* VDM Verlag Dr. Mueller e.K.

Yancwitz, Karen L. & Bukatko, Danuta. Child & Adolescent Development: A Chronological Approach. 2007. (ENG.). 256p. (C). per., pupil's gde. ed. 55.95 *(978-0-618-34922-7(7)*, 308202) Wadsworth.

Zackheim, Victoria. The Face in the Mirror: Writers Reflect on Their Dreams of Youth & the Reality of Age. Zacheim, Victoria, ed. 2009. (ENG., Illus.). 300p. 25.00 *(978-1-59102-752-2(7))* Prometheus Bks., Pubs.

ADOLESCENCE—HEALTH AND HYGIENE

see Youth—Health and Hygiene

ADOLESCENCE—PHOTOGRAPHY

see Photography of Children and Youth

ADOLESCENCE—PSYCHOLOGY

see Adolescent Psychology

ADOLESCENCE IN LITERATURE

Burt, Stephen. The Forms of Youth: Twentieth-Century Poetry & Adolescence. 2007. (ENG.) 280p. (gr. 17). 40.00 *(978-0-231-14142-0(4))* Columbia Univ. Pr.

Ferrall, Charles & Jackson, Anna. Juvenile Literature & British Society, 1850-1950: The Age of Adolescence. 2012. (ENG., Illus.). 194p. pap. 39.95 ***(978-0-415-63422-9(9))*** Routledge.

Gale. World Apart 2010. 58.00 *(978-0-8387-5730-7(8))* Bucknell Univ. Pr.

Gale, Beth W. World Apart: Female Adolescence in the French Novel, 1870-1930. 2010. (ENG.). 231p. 58.00 *(978-1-61148-325-3(5))* Bucknell Univ. Pr.

Gubar, Marah. Artful Dodgers: Reconceiving the Golden Age of Children's Literature, 1 vol. 2010. (ENG., Illus.). 272p. pap. 24.95 *(978-0-19-975674-2(0))* Oxford Univ. Pr., Inc.

Hilton, Mary & Nikolajeva, Maria. Contemporary Adolescent Literature & Culture: The Emergent Adult. 2012. 160p. ***(978-1-4094-3938-2(7))*** Ashgate Publishing, Ltd.

Hogan, Walter. Animals in Young Adult Fiction. 2009. (Scarecrow Studies in Young Adult Literature Ser.). (ENG.). 268p. 50.00 *(978-0-8108-5994-4(7))* Scarecrow Pr., Inc.

Holt, Jenny. Public School Literature, Civic Education & the Politics of Male Adolescence. 2008. (Ashgate Studies in Childhood, 1700 to the Present Ser.). 280p. 114.95 *(978-0-7546-5662-3(4))* Ashgate Publishing Co.

Johnson, Vernon. Coming of Age in William Shakespeare's Romeo & Juliet. 2009. (Social Issues in Literature Ser.). (ENG.). 224p. (gr. 10-12). 26.50 *(978-0-7377-4615-0(7))*; (Illus.). 38.45 *(978-0-7377-4614-3(9))* Cengage Gale. (Greenhaven Pr., Inc.).

Ligon, Alison D. Traversing Caribbean Thresholds: Coming of Age Stories in Selected Works of Anglophone Fiction. 2009. *(978-1-4331-0629-3(9))* Lang, Peter Publishing, Inc.

McLennan, Rachael & Mclennan, Rachael. Adolescence, America & Postwar Fiction: Developing Figures. 2008. (ENG.). 232p. 89.00 *(978-0-230-20551-2(8))* Palgrave Macmillan.

Terzioglu, Gnlsen. The Catcher in the Rye & Brown Girl, Brownstones. 2008. 116p. pap. *(978-3-639-07564-9(1))* VDM Verlag Dr. Mueller e.K.

Younger, Beth. Learning Curves: Body Image & Female Sexuality in Young Adult Literature. 35th ed. 2009. (Scarecrow Studies in Young Adult Literature Ser.) (ENG.). 166p. 45.00 *(978-0-8108-5986-9(6))* Scarecrow Pr., Inc.

Yu, Jennifer. Alienation & Loneliness. 2009. 124p. pap. *(978-3-639-15915-8(2))* VDM Verlag Dr. Mueller e.K.

ADOLESCENT BOYS

Barrowcliffe, Mark. The Elfish Gene: Dungeons, Dragons & Growing up Strange. 2009. (ENG.). 288p. pap. 14.00 *(978-1-56947-601-7(2))* Soho Pr., Inc.

Belgrave, Faye Z., et al. Brothers of Ujima: A Cultural Enrichment Program to Empower Adolescent African American Males. 2011. pap. 26.95 ***(978-0-87822-652-8(4))*** Research Pr.

Bond, Douglas. Fathers & Sons, Volume 1: Stand Fast in the Way of Truth. 2008. 331p. per. *(978-1-59638-076-9(4))* P & R Publishing.

—Fathers & Sons, Volume 2: Hold Fast in a Broken World. 2008. (Fathers & Sons Ser.). 285p. pap. 14.99 *(978-1-59638-077-6(2))* P & R Publishing.

Castro-Vazquez, Genaro. In the Shadows: Sexuality, Pedagogy, & Gender among Japanese Teenagers. 2007. (ENG., Illus.). 214p. 68.50 *(978-0-7391-1537-4(5))* Lexington Bks.

Conchas, Gilberto Q. & Vigil, James Diego. Streetsmart Schoolsmart: Urban Poverty & the Education of Adolescent Boys. 2012. (Multicultural Education Ser.). (ENG.). 216p. 76.00 ***(978-0-8077-5319-4(X))***; pap. 33.95 ***(978-0-8077-5318-7(1))*** Teachers College Pr., Teachers College, Columbia Univ.

Davis, Anthony & Jackson, Jeffrey. Yo, Little Brother ... Volume II: Basic Rules of Survival for Young African American Males. 2007. (ENG.). 140p. (YA). pap. 14.95 *(978-1-934155-01-1(2))* African American Images.

Dean, Jeffrey. One-Liner Wisdom for Today's Guys. 2006. (Between the Lines Ser.). (ENG., Illus.). 128p. per. 9.00 *(978-1-59052-971-3(5)*, Multnomah) Doubleday Religious Publishing Group, The.

—Watch This: A Getting-There Guide to Manhood for Teen Guys. 2007. (ENG., Illus.). 224p. (gr 3-7). per. 14.99 *(978-1-59052-984-3(7)*, Multnomah) Doubleday Religious Publishing Group, The.

Dykstra, Robert C., et al. The Faith & Friendships of Teenage Boys. 2012. (ENG.). 144p. pap. 20.00 ***(978-0-664-23340-2(6))*** Westminster John Knox Pr.

Dykstra, Robert C., et al. Losers, Loners, & Rebels: The Spiritual Struggles of Boys. 2007. (ENG.). 204p. per. 20.00 *(978-0-664-22961-0(1))* Westminster John Knox Pr.

Elissa P. Benedek, M. d., et al. Principles & Practice of Child & Adolescent Forensic Mental Health. 2009. (ENG., Illus.). 531p. 135.00 *(978-1-58562-336-5(9))* American Psychiatric Publishing, Inc.

Fenemore. Sex, Thugs & Rock 'N' Roll: Teenage Rebels in Cold-War East Germany. 2007. (Monographs in German History). (Illus.). 296p. (C). 90.00 *(978-1-57181-532-3(5))* Berghahn Bks., Inc.

Fenemore, Mark. Sex, Thugs & Rock 'N' Roll: Teenage Rebels in Cold-War East Germany. 2009. 296p. 32.50 *(978-1-84545-718-1(8))* Berghahn Bks., Inc.

Gillilanc, Cleburne. Halloween Vigilantes. 2007. 160p. pap. 17.95 *(978-0-99992-167-9(1))* Council for Indian Education.

Group Work Staff, compiled by. Page Unlimited: Innovations in Layout Design. 2011. (ENG., Illus.). 256p. *(978-84-92810-24-6(6))* Promotora de prensa internacional S.A.

Hatchell, Helen. Masculinities & Whiteness - Issues of Power, Prejudice, & Social Justice. 2008. 340p. pap. *(978-3-639-02551-4(2))* VDM Verlag Dr. Mueller e.K.

Hewitt-Taylor, Jaqueline. Providing Support at Home for Children & Young People Who Have Complex Health Needs. 2008. (ENG.). 216p. pap. 60.99 *(978-0-470-51731-4(X)*, Wiley) Wiley, John & Sons, Inc.

Honor Books Publishing Staff, creator. Faith Unplugged: Stories for Guys to Challenge What You Believe & How You Live. 2006. (Unplugged Ser.). (ENG.). 188p. (YA). per. 12.99 *(978-1-56292-709-7(4)*, 1562927094) Cook, David C.

Kunjufu, Jawanza. Reducing the Black Male Dropout Rate. 2010. (ENG., Illus.). 192p. pap. 15.95 *(978-1-934155-22-6(5))* African American Images.

Lashlie, Celia. He'll Be OK: Growing Gorgeous Boys into Good Men. 2007. 224p. *(978-0-7322-8450-3(3))* HarperCollins Pubs. Australia.

McCormack, Mark. The Declining Significance of Homophobia: How Teenage Boys Are Redefining Masculinity & Heterosexuality, 1 vol. 2012. (Sexuality, Identity, & Society Ser.). (ENG., Illus.). 166p. 49.99 ***(978-0-19-977824-9(8))*** Oxford Univ. Pr., Inc.

Meeker, Meg. Boys Should Be Boys: 7 Secrets to Raising Healthy Sons. 2009. (ENG.). 304p. pap. 15.00 *(978-0-345-51369-4(X)*, Ballantine Bks.) Random House Publishing Group.

Olshine, David. I Want to Talk with My Teen about Guy Stuff. 2006. (I Want to Talk with My Teen Ser.). 96p. pap. 9.99 *(978-0-7847-1894-0(6))* Standard Publishing.

Orcutt, Georgia. How to Feed a Teenage Boy: Recipes & Strategies. 2007. (ENG.). 240p. pap. 14.95 *(978-1-58761-279-4(8)*, Celestial Arts) Ten Speed Pr.

Owens, Timothy J. From Adolescence to Adulthood in the Vietnam Era. 2010. (Longitudinal Research in the Social & Behavioral Sciences: an Interdisciplinary Ser.). (Illus.). xvi, 195p. pap. 74.95 *(978-1-4419-3559-5(2)*, 1441935592) Springer.

Pascoe, C. J. Dude, You're a Fag: Masculinity & Sexuality in High School, with a New Preface. 2nd ed. 2011. (ENG.). 240p. pap. 22.95 *(978-0-520-27148-7(3))* Univ. of California Pr.

Perkins, James C. Playbook for Christian Manhood: 12 Key Plays for Black Teen Boys. Elster, Jean A., ed. 2008. 100p. pap. 14.00 *(978-0-8170-1525-1(6))* Judson Pr.

Plessis, Eric H du. The Life of a Teenage Schoolboy in Paris During the 1960s: A Personal Memoir. 2009. (Illus.). 256p. 109.95 *(978-0-7734-4750-9(4))* Mellen, Edwin Pr., The.

Rice, David Wall. Balance: Advancing Identity Theory by Engaging the Black Male Adolescent. 2008. (ENG., Illus.). 148p. 57.99 *(978-0-7391-1688-7(9))* Lexington Bks.

Ross, Michael & Shellenberger, Susie. What Your Son Isn't Telling You: Unlocking the Secret World of Teen Boys. 2010. 192p. pap. 13.99 *(978-0-7642-0749-5(0))* Bethany Hse. Pubs.

Runyon, Brent. The Burn Journals. 2011. 14.02 *(978-0-7848-3404-6(0)*, Everbind) Marco Bk. Co.

Saval, Malina. The Secret Lives of Boys: Inside the Raw Emotional World of Male Teens. 2010. (ENG.). 272p. (gr. 9). pap. 15.95 *(978-0-465-02032-4(1))* Basic Bks.

Sguera, Vincenzo & Studio, Styland Fashion. Teen Boy Graphics Vol. 1. 2011. (ENG., Illus.). 96p. 115.00 incl. DVD *(978-88-88766-22-5(7))* Arkivia Bks. ITA. Dist: National Bk. Network.

Shoemaker, Tim. Dangerous Devotions for Guys: Dare to Live Your Faith. 2008. pap. *(978-0-7644-3734-2(8)*, Group) Group Publishing, Inc.

Skoyles, John. Secret Frequencies: A New York Education. 2006. (American Lives Ser.). (ENG., Illus.). 1p. pap. 15.95 *(978-0-8032-9355-7(0)*, Bison Bks.) Univ. of Nebraska Pr.

Stephenson, Bret. From Boys to Men: Spiritual Rites of Passage in an Indulgent Age. 2006. (ENG., Illus.). 1p. per. 18.95 *(978-1-59477-140-8(5))* Inner Traditions International, Ltd.

Tebbutt, Melanie. Being Boys: Youth, Leisure & Identity in the Inter-War Years. 2012. (Gender in History Ser.). (ENG., Illus.). 352p. 110.00 ***(978-0-7190-6613-9(1))*** Manchester Univ. Pr. GBR. Dist: Macmillan.

Wannamaker, Annette. Mediated Boyhoods: Boys, Teens, & Young Men in Popular Media & Culture. 2011. (Illus.). ix, 267p. 129.95 *(978-1-4331-0541-8(1))* Lang, Peter Publishing, Inc.

Zbaracki, Matthew D. Best Books for Boys: A Resource for Educators, 1 vol. 2008. (Children's & Young Adult Literature Reference Ser.). (Illus.). 204p. 45.00 *(978-1-59158-599-2(6)*, LU8599) Libraries Unlimited, Inc.

ADOLESCENT GIRLS

see also Pregnant Schoolgirls

Arfin, Lesley. Dear Diary. (ENG., Illus.). 288p. 2008. pap. 14.00 *(978-1-57687-440-0(0))* 2007. 20.00 *(978-1-57687-383-0(8))* powerHouse Cultural Entertainment, Inc.

Ashton, Jennifer, et al. The Body Scoop for Girls: A Straight-Talk Guide to a Healthy, Beautiful You. 2009. (ENG.). 304p. (gr. 12-18). 18.00 *(978-1-58333-369-3(X)*, Avery) Penguin Group (USA) Inc.

Bartel, Cathy. Every Teen Girl's Little Pink Book. 2007. (LITTLE PINK BOOK Ser.). 242p. (YA). (gr. 8-12). 12.99 *(978-1-57794-909-1(9))* Harrison House Pubs.

Beck, Debra. My Feet Aren't Ugly: A Girl's Guide to Loving Herself from the Inside Out. 2011. 176p. pap. 12.95 *(978-0-8253-0602-0(7))* 2007. (Illus.). 144p. (J). per. 12.95 *(978-0-8253-0542-9(X))* Beaufort Bks., Inc.

Belgrave, Faye Z. African American Girls: Reframing Perceptions & Changing Experiences. 2009. (Advancing Responsible Adolescent Development Ser.). (ENG.). xiii, 178p. 79.95 *(978-1-4419-0089-0(6)*, 1441900896) Springer.

Bradley, Linda. Teen Sisters' Health: An African American Girls' Wellness Guide for Body, Mind & Spirit. 2008. (ENG.). 250p. (YA). pap. 14.95 *(978-1-59624-067-4(9))* Cleveland Clinic Pr.

Bratton, Angela R. An Anthropolotical Study of Factors Affecting the Construction of Sexuality in Ghana: Teenage Pregnancy, School Education, & Virgins' Clubs. 2010. vii, 210p. 109.95 *(978-0-7734-3597-1(2))* Mellen, Edwin Pr., The.

Cahn, Susan K. Sexual Reckonings: Southern Girls in a Troubling Age. (Illus.). 384p. 2012. (ENG.). pap. 19.95 ***(978-0-674-06393-8(7))*** 2007. 29.95 *(978-0-674-02452-6(4))* Harvard Univ. Pr.

Cairoli, M. Laetitia. Girls of the Factory: A Year with the Garment Workers of Morocco. 2011. (ENG., Illus.). 256p. 74.95 *(978-0-8130-3561-1(9))* Univ. Pr. of Florida.

Caton, Tzipi. Miracle Ride: A True Story of Illness, Faith, Humor - & Triumph. 2008. 314p. 22.99 *(978-1-4226-0757-2(7)*, Shaar Pr.) Mesorah Pubns., Ltd.

CHRISTIE, Chante. I Want to Live: A Teenager's Guide to Finding Self Love. 2008. (ENG.). 87p. pap. 9.95 *(978-0-9794827-3-1(9))* Infinite Love Publishing.

Chronicle Books Staff. How to Raise Your Parents: A Teen Girl's Survival Guide. 2008. (YA). 15.50 *(978-0-8118-5695-9(X))* Chronicle Bks. LLC.

Clercq Zubli, Rita la Fontaine de. Disguised: A War Memoir. 2nd ed. 2007. (Illus.). 366p. *(978-1-4287-6366-1(X))* Candlewick Pr.

Cohen, Kerry. Dirty Little Secrets: Breaking the Silence on Teenage Girls & Promiscuity. 2011. (ENG., Illus.). 256p. pap. 14.99 *(978-1-4022-6069-8(5))* Sourcebooks, Inc.

—Loose Girl: A Memoir of Promiscuity. 2009. (ENG.). 224p. pap. 13.99 *(978-1-4013-0992-3(5))* Hyperion Pr.

Coleman, Angela D. A Journey Toward Womanhood Curriculum Guide. 5th ed. 2006. per. 55.00 *(978-0-9786906-0-1(5))* Sisterhood Agenda Enterprises, LLC.

—A Journey Toward Womanhood Student Manual. 2006. spiral bd. 55.00 *(978-0-9786906-1-8(3))* Sisterhood Agenda Enterprises, LLC.

Corrie, Rachel & Corrie, R. Let Me Stand Alone: The Journals of Rachel Corrie. 2009. (ENG.). 256p. pap. 13.95 *(978-0-393-33390-9(6)*, 33390) Norton, W. W. & Co., Inc.

CosmoGIRL! Editors. CosmoGIRL! Freaky Deaky: 150 Really Scary Stories. 2008. (ENG., Illus.). 208p. (J). (gr. 8-14). pap. 7.95 *(978-1-58816-672-2(4))* Hearst Communications, Inc.

CosmoGIRL! Editors, ed. Ask Cosmogirl! about Nutrition & Fitness. 2008. (ENG., Illus.). 128p. (J). pap. 5.95 *(978-1-58816-645-6(7))* Hearst Communications, Inc.

Davis. Your Daughter's Sexual Wellness & Development. rev. ed. 2010. 166p. pap. 22.95 *(978-0-7637-8545-1(8))* Jones & Bartlett Learning, LLC.

Davis, Erin. Graffiti: Learning to See the Art in Ourselves. ldr.'s ed. 2008. (ENG., Illus.). 72p. pap. 9.99 *(978-0-8024-4586-5(1))* Moody Pubs.

Davis, Harold D. Talks Your Dad Never Had with You. 2008. (ENG.). 192p. (gr. 8-13). pap. 9.99 *(978-0-8024-6251-0(0))* Moody Pubs.

Deak, JoAnn. How Girls Thrive. 2010. 104p. pap. *(978-0-9845787-0-2(6))* Green Blanket Pr.

Dean, Jeffrey. One-Liner Wisdom for Today's Girls. 2006. (Between the Lines Ser.). (ENG., Illus.). 128p. per. 9.00 *(978-1-59052-972-0(3)*, Multnomah) Doubleday Religious Publishing Group, The.

DeLuzio, Crista. Female Adolescence in American Scientific Thought, 1830-1930. 2007. (New Studies in American Intellectual & Cultural History Ser.). (ENG.). 344p. (gr. 17). 57.00 *(978-0-8018-8699-7(6))* Johns Hopkins Univ. Pr.

DeMoss, Nancy Leigh, et al. Lies Young Women Believe: And the Truth That Sets Them Free. 2008. (ENG.). 160p. pap. 13.99 *(978-0-8024-7291-5(5))* Moody Pubs.

DeMuth, Patricia J. & DeMuth, Donna R. Backyard Bones. 2007. 200p. per. 16.95 *(978-0-595-45069-5(5))* iUniverse, Inc.

DiMarco, Hayley. Ask Hayley Vol. 2: Real Answers for Today's Teen. 2008. (Illus.). 144p. (gr. 8-14). pap. 12.99 *(978-0-8007-3236-3(7))* Revell.

—Mean. 2009. (Pocket Bible Study & Journal Ser.). 128p. (YA). pap. 7.99 *(978-0-8007-3413-8(0))* Revell.

Drummond, Wilhelmina. Women Grassroots Horizons: And Other Essays. (Illus.). *(978-0-908822-32-4(4))* Nagare Pr.

Dyhouse, Carol. Girls Growing up in Late Victorian & Edwardian England, Volume 14. 2012. (Routledge Library Editions). (ENG.). 236p. (C). 115.00 ***(978-0-415-62321-6(9))*** Routledge.

Eastham, Chad. Guys Like Girls Who..., 0 vols. 2008. 240p. (YA). pap. 14.99 *(978-1-4003-1300-6(7))* Nelson, Thomas Inc.

Engelbrecht, Kate. Please Read (If at All Possible) The Girl Project, 2007-2010. 2011. (Illus.). 224p. pap. 24.95 *(978-0-7893-2260-9(9))* Universe Publishing.

Farmer, Lesley S. J. Teen Girls & Technology: What's the Problem, What's the Solution? 2008. (ENG.). 192p. 52.00 *(978-0-8077-4876-3(5))*; (ENG.). 192p. pap. 22.95 *(978-0-8077-4875-6(7))*; vi, 180p. pap. 40.00 *(978-0-8389-0974-4(4))* Teachers College Pr., Teachers College, Columbia Univ.

Fields, Anna. Confessions of a Rebel Debutante: A Memoir. 2011. (ENG.). 288p. (gr. 12). 15.00 *(978-0-425-23874-5(1)*, Berkley Trade) Penguin Group (USA) Inc.

Fingerson, Laura. Girls in Power: Gender, Body, & Menstruation in Adolescence. 2006. 190p. 65.50 *(978-0-7914-6899-9(2))*; per. 29.95 *(978-0-7914-6900-2(X))* State Univ. of New York Pr.

Fisette, Jennifer. Adolescent Girls' Embodied Identities. 2009. 164p. pap. *(978-3-639-16083-3(5))* VDM Verlag Dr. Mueller e.K.

Flanagan, Caitlin. Girl Land. 2012. (ENG.). 224p. 25.99 *(978-0-316-06598-6(6))* Little Brown & Co.

Flies, Heather. I Want to Talk with My Teen about Girl Stuff. 2006. (I Want to Talk with My Teen Ser.). 96p. pap. 9.99 *(978-0-7847-1895-7(4))* Standard Publishing.

Flynn, Sarah Wassner. The Book of Happy Things! 2008. (Cosmogirl! Ser.). (ENG., Illus.). 288p. (J). (gr. 7-12). pap. 6.95 *(978-1-58816-700-2(3))* Hearst Communications, Inc.

Freud, Sigmund. A Young Girl's Diary. 2008. 288p. 25.99 *(978-0-559-59727-5(4))*; 288p. pap. 27.75 *(978-0-559-59725-1(8))*; 192p. 22.99 *(978-0-554-30831-9(2))*; 192p. 25.99 *(978-0-554-21528-0(4))* BiblioBazaar.

—A Young Girl's Diary. Eden & Paul, Cedar, trs. 2007. (ENG.). 200p. pap. 19.99 *(978-1-4264-0312-5(7))*; pap. 21.99 *(978-1-4264-0363-7(1))* BiblioBazaar.

—A Young Girl's Diary. Paul, Cedar & Paul, Eden, trs. 2007. (ENG.). 188p. per. *(978-1-4065-8162-1(3))* Dodo Pr.

Freud, Sigmund, pref. A Young Girl's Diary. 2007. (ENG.). 164p. per. 12.99 *(978-1-59547-835-1(3))* NuVision Pubns., LLC.

Gackle, Lynne. Finding Ophelia's Voice, Opening Ophelia's Heart: Nurturing the Adolescent Female Voice: an Exploration of the Physiological, Psychological, & Musical Developments of Female Students. 2011. (Illus.). 208p. pap. 44.95 ***(978-1-4291-1858-3(X))*** Heritage Music Pr.

Gailor-Loflin, Heidi, et al. Building Leadership Skills in Adolescent. 2006. 148p. pap. 24.95 *(978-1-4241-0589-2(7))* PublishAmerica, Inc.

Gender Matters - A manual on addressing gender-based violence affecting young People(2008) 2008. 176p. pap. 29.00 *(978-92-871-6393-6(6))* Council of Europe FRA. Dist: Manhattan Publishing Co.

George, Elizabeth. A Young Woman after God's Own Heart: A Devotional. 2008. 149p. (YA). (gr. 7-12). 9.99 *(978-0-7369-2297-5(0))* Harvest Hse. Pubs.

—A Young Woman's Guide to Making Right Choices: Your Life God's Way. 2009. 208p. pap. 10.99 *(978-0-7369-2107-7(9))* Harvest Hse. Pubs.

George, Rosalyn. Girls in a Goldfish Bowl: Moral Regulation, Ritual & the Use of Power amongst Inner City Girls. 2007. 184p. per. *(978-90-8790-185-1(2))* Sense Pubs.

Glasson, Aline. Cristaux de Sagesse. 2006. (FRE.). 157p. *(978-2-89431-363-3(2))* Editions JCL, Les.

Gibbs, Pam. Esther: The Role of a Life Time: A Bible Study for Teen Girls. 2008. (Illus.). 103p. pap. *(978-1-4158-6604-7(X))* B&H Publishing Group.

Gibson, Andrenna C. Girls Set the Ground Rule: I'm not an Ordinary Chick! I'm an Extraordinary Woman! 2009. 99p. pap. 14.95 *(978-1-4327-3468-8(7))* Outskirts Pr., Inc.

Gildiner, Catherine. After the Falls: Coming of Age in the Sixties. (ENG.). (gr. 12). 2011. 384p. 16.00 *(978-0-14-311985-2(0)*, Penguin (Non-Classics)) 2010. (Illus.). 368p. 25.95 *(978-0-670-02205-2(5)*, Viking Adult) Penguin Group (USA) Inc.

Goldstein, Nikki. GirlForce: Shine. 2009. (ENG., Illus.). 176p. (YA). (gr. 5-9). pap. 12.99 *(978-1-59990-355-2(5))* Bloomsbury Publishing.

Gordon, Catherine M. Menstrual Cycle & Adolescent Health. Welt, Corrine et al, eds. 2008. (Annals of the New York Academy of Sciences Ser.: Vol. 1135). (ENG., Illus.). 452p. pap. 159.95 *(978-1-57331-715-3(2)*, Wiley-Blackwell) Wiley, John & Sons, Inc.

Graves, Kelly. Aggression among Female Adolescents. 2009. 68p. pap. *(978-3-639-12870-3(2))* VDM Verlag Dr. Mueller e.K.

Greenspan-Goldberg, Arden. What Do You Expect? She's a Teenager! A Hope & Happiness Guide for Moms with Daughters Ages 11 ¿ 19. 2011. (ENG.). 352p. pap. 14.99 *(978-1-4022-5624-0(8))* Sourcebooks, Inc.

Gresh, Dannah. Secret Keeper: The Delicate Power of Modesty. 2011. (ENG.). 96p. pap. 9.99 *(978-0-8024-3977-2(2))* Moody Pubs.

Gross, Gretchen & Livingston, Patricia. But Dad! A Survival Guide for Single Fathers of Tween & Teen Daughters. 2012. E-Book ***(978-1-4422-1268-8(3))***; (ENG.). 192p. pap. 17.95 ***(978-1-4422-1267-1(5))*** Rowman & Littlefield Publishers, Inc.

Grover, Michelle. No Matter What: You Can Rejoice, Reflections for Teens. 2008. (Illus.). 115p. (YA). (gr. 8). pap. 8.99 *(978-1-59166-820-6(4))* BJU Pr.

Gwartney, Debra. Live Through This: A Mother's Memoir of Runaway Daughters & Reclaimed Love. 2009. (ENG.). 240p. 24.00 *(978-0-547-05447-6(5))* Houghton Mifflin Harcourt Publishing Co.

—Live Through This: A Mother's Memoir of Runaway Daughters & Reclaimed Love. 2010. (ENG.). 240p. pap. 14.95 *(978-0-547-24801-1(6)*, Mariner Bks.) Houghton Mifflin Harcourt Trade & Reference Pubs.

Harris, Anita. Next Wave Cultures: Feminism, Subcultures, Activism. Harris, Anita, ed. 2007. (Illus.). 283p. 150.00 *(978-0-415-95709-0(5))*; per. 37.95 *(978-0-415-95710-6(9))* Routledge.

Harris, Ashley Rae. Is This Really My Family? Relating to Your Relatives. 2008. (Essential Health: Strong Beautiful Girls Ser.). 112p. (YA). (gr. 7-12). 34.22 (978-1-60453-101-5(0)) ABDO Publishing Co.

Hensel, Jana. After the Wall: Confessions from an East German Childhood & the Life That Came Next. Chase, Jefferson, tr. 2008. (ENG., Illus.). 192p. pap. 14.95 (978-1-58648-559-7(8)) PublicAffairs.

Honor Books Publishing Staff, creator. Faith Unplugged: Stories for Girls to Challenge What You Believe & How You Live. 2006. (Unplugged Ser.). (ENG.). 192p. (YA). per. 12.99 (978-1-56292-715-8(9), 1562927159) Cook, David C.

Huebner, Mary. Deal with It: A 12 Week Study on Teenage Girls' Anger, 1 vol. 2009. (ENG.). 128p. pap. 12.99 (978-0-310-28510-6(0)) Zondervan.

Ikuenobe-Otaigbe, Eve. Help! I Have an Alien in My House! Girl, Let's Talk! 2010. 192p. pap. 25.95 (978-1-4502-6516-4(2)) iUniverse, Inc.

Ingram Powell, Rebecca. Get Real! 2007. (ENG.). 172p. per. 19.95 (978-1-4141-0952-7(0)) Pleasant Word.

Inyang, Mfrekemfon. Female Secondary School Adolescent Sexual Behaviour. 2010. 192p. pap. (978-3-8383-3547-6(3)) Lambert Academic Publishing.

Jamison, Heather. Keeping It Real. 2007. (Go Girl Ser.). 160p. (YA). (gr. 8-12). pap. 10.99 (978-0-8254-2932-3(3)) Kregel Pubns.

—Real Stuff: A Survivor's Guide. 2006. (Go Girl! Ser.). 160p. (YA). (gr. 8-12). pap. 10.99 (978-0-8254-2931-6(5)) Kregel Pubns.

Jaoui, Sylvaine. For Girls Only: The Ultimate Guide to Being a Girl. Bussell, Andrea, ed. 2010. (Sunscreen Ser.). (ENG., Illus.). 112p. (YA). (gr. 7-11). pap. 10.95 (978-0-8109-8432-5(6), Amulet Bks.) Abrams.

Jeon, Julia. My Korean Experience: A Road to the Future. 2010. 80.00 (978-1-59689-097-8(5)); (ENG.). pap. 45.00 (978-1-59689-101-2(7)) Hermit Kingdom Pr., The. (Koreani).

Johanna Wycoff. Dancing in Bomb Shelters: My Diary of Holland in World War II. 2010. 200p. 26.95 (978-1-4502-0759-1(6)); pap. 16.95 (978-1-4502-0757-7(X)) iUniverse, Inc.

Jones, Lind. Fighting for Girls: New Perspectives on Gender & Violence. 2010. (SUNY series in Women, Crime, & Criminology Ser.). 288p. 85.00 (978-1-4384-3293-9(3)) State Univ. of New York Pr.

—Fighting for Girls: New Perspectives on Gender & Violence. Chesney-Lind, Meda & Jones, Nikki, eds. 2010. (SUNY series in Women, Crime, & Criminology Ser.). (ENG., Illus.). 288p. pap. 27.95 (978-1-4384-3294-6(1)) State Univ. of New York Pr.

Jordan, Elizabeth. Daddy & I: A Chronicle of Small Town Life & Youth, As Seen Through the Eyes of an Ultra Modern Young Lady of Fifteen. 2011. 272p. 47.95 (**978-1-258-06969-8(5)**) Literary Licensing, LLC.

Kessler, Lauren. My Teenage Werewolf: A Mother, a Daughter, a Journey Through the Thicket of Adolescence. 2011. (ENG.). 256p. (gr. 12). 15.00 (978-0-14-311945-6(1), Penguin (Non-Classics)) Penguin Group (USA) Inc.

—My Teenage Werewolf: A Mother, a Daughter, a Journey Through the Thicket of Adolesence. 2010. (ENG.). 256p. (gr. 12). 25.95 (978-0-670-02169-7(5), Viking Adult) Penguin Group (USA) Inc.

Khalifa, Colleen. Fat Girls. 2010. 64p. pap. 29.80 (978-0-557-45640-6(1)) Lulu Enterprises Inc.

Kilpatrick, Haley & Joiner, Whitney. The Drama Years: Real Girls Talk about Surviving Middle School — Bullies, Brands, Body Image, & More. 2012. (ENG., Illus.). 288p. pap. 16.00 (**978-1-4516-2791-6(2)**, Free Pr.) Free Pr.

King, Helen. The Disease of Virgins. 2009. 208p. pap. 39.95 (978-0-415-55499-2(3)) Routledge.

Kleinleder, Peggy Ellen & Evensen, Kimber. The Thursday Group: A Story & Information for Girls Healing from Sexual Abuse. 2009. (Illus.). 272p. pap. 25.00 (978-1-929657-44-5(7)) Neari Pr.

Koirala, Uma. Nutritional Status of Adolescent Girls in Rural Kathmandu. 2011. 180p. pap. (**978-3-8454-0914-6(2)**) Lambert Academic Publishing.

Kranz, Rachel & Hinshaw, Stephen. The Triple Bind: Saving Our Teenage Girls from Today's Pressures & Conflicting Expectations. 2009. (ENG.). 256p. pap. 15.00 (978-0-345-50400-5(3), Ballantine Bks.) Random House Publishing Group.

Krost, Chelsea. Nineteen: A Reflection of My Teenage Experience in an Extraordinary Life - What I Have Learned & What I Have to Share. 2011. (ENG.). 188p. pap. 15.95 (978-0-9819311-6-6(2)) Burman Books, Inc. CAN. Dist: Innovative Logistics.

Lambert, E. V. Tugging on a Heartstring. 2nd ed. 2009. (Illus.). 204p. pap. (**978-0-9798008-2-5(X)**) Marine Techniques, Inc.

Leach, Connie M. Adolescent Girls at Risk. 2011. 152p. pap. (**978-3-8443-0740-5(0)**) Lambert Academic Publishing.

Macleod, Catriona Ida. Adolescence, Pregnancy & Abortion: Constructing a Threat of Degeneration. 2010. (Women & Psychology Ser.). (ENG., Illus.). 184p. pap. 27.50 (978-0-415-55338-4(5), Routledge) Taylor & Francis Group GBR. Dist: Taylor & Francis Group.

Mann, Joyce Elizabeth. Handbook of Prevention & Intervention Programs for Adolescent Girls. LeCroy, Craig Winston, ed. 11th rev. ed. 2008. (ENG., Illus.). 391p. 65.00 (978-0-471-67796-3(5), Wiley) Wiley, John & Sons, Inc.

Marsh, Robin & Nelson, Lauren. God, Girls, & Getting Connected: Spiritual Apps for a Teen's Life. 2012. (Illus.). 176p. pap. 11.99 (**978-0-7369-4521-9(0)**) Harvest Hse. Pubs.

Massoni, Kelley. Fashioning Teenagers: A Cultural History of Seventeen Magazine. 2010. (ENG., Illus.). 256p. (C). 79.00 (978-1-59874-503-0(4)); pap. 24.95 (978-1-59874-504-7(2)) Left Coast Pr., Inc.

Mazzarella, Sharon R. Girl Wide Web 2. 0: Revisiting Girls, the Internet, & the Negotiation of Identity. 2010. (Mediated Youth Ser.). (Illus.). (C). 304p. 129.95 (978-1-4331-0550-0(0)); 308p. pap. 34.95 (978-1-4331-0549-4(7)) Lang, Peter Publishing, Inc.

Mcleod. Learning from the Margins. 2007. (Illus.). 208p. 190.00 (978-0-415-41133-2(5)) Routledge.

Mendoza-Denton, Norma. Homegirls: Language & Cultural Practice among Latina Youth Gangs. 2008. (New Directions in Ethnography Ser.). (ENG., Illus.). 360p. 110.95 (978-0-631-23489-0(6)); pap. 40.95 (978-0-631-23490-6(X)) Wiley, John & Sons, Inc. (Wiley-Blackwell).

Minter, Kelly. Hannah's One Wish: A Bible Study for Teen Girls. 2007. 120p. 10.95 (978-1-4158-5254-5(5)) LifeWay Christian Resources.

Mitchell, Claudia & Goad, Kim. For Planning Events, Retreats, & Small Groups. ldr.'s ed. 2009. (One Girl Ser.). (ENG.). 144p. (YA). pap. 19.99 (978-0-7847-2231-2(5)) Standard Publishing.

—One Girl Can Change the World. 2009. (One Girl Ser.). (ENG.). 208p. (YA). pap. 16.99 (978-0-7847-2229-9(3)) Standard Publishing.

Mitchell, Claudia A. & Reid-Walsh, Jacqueline, eds. Girl Culture: An Encyclopedia, 2 vols., Set. 2007. (Illus.). 744p. 185.00 (978-0-313-33908-0(2), GR3908, Greenwood Pr.) Greenwood Publishing Group, Inc.

Monaque, Mathilde. Trouble in My Head: A Young Girl's Struggle with Depression. 2007. (ENG.). 176p. 15.95 (978-0-09-191723-4(9)) Random Hse. GBR. Dist: Independent Pubs. Group.

Mondragon, Dona M. Parents Companion. 2006. 23p. 8.00 (978-0-9746644-2-2(1)) Debu, Inc.

Moorland, Margarite T., ed. Cancer in Female Adolescents. 2008. 120.00 (978-1-60456-421-1(0)) Nova Science Pubs., Inc.

Morrison, Connie. Who Do They Think They Are? Teenage Girls & Their Avatars in Spaces of Social Online Communication. 2009. (New Literacies & Digital Epistemologies Ser.). (Illus.). 246p. pap. 32.95 (978-1-4331-0552-4(7)) Lang, Peter Publishing, Inc.

Moss & Moss, Haley. Middle School: The Stuff Nobody Tells You About. (Illus.). 160p. pap. (978-1-934575-62-8(3)) Autism Asperger Publishing Co.

Mossman, Helen Madamba. A Letter to My Father: Growing up Filipina & American. 2008. (ENG., Illus.). 184p. 24.95 (978-0-8061-3909-8(9)) Univ. of Oklahoma Pr.

Mousa, Tamara, et al. Eating & Body Image Disturbances among Adolescent Girls in Jordan. 2011. 100p. pap. (**978-3-8443-1387-1(7)**) Lambert Academic Publishing.

Munroe, Erin A. The Anxiety Workbook for Girls. 2010. (ENG.). 208p. (J). (gr. 4-7). pap. 14.95 (978-1-57749-232-0(3)) Taylor Trade Publishing.

Munthree, Crystal & Nzimande, Nompumelelo. Life Transitions of Young Women & the Influence of Older Sisters. 2010. 88p. pap. (978-3-8383-5837-6(6)) Lambert Academic Publishing.

Mutopo, Patience. A Rights Based Approach to Reproductive Health in Zimbabwe. 2011. 92p. pap. (**978-3-8433-7087-5(7)**) Lambert Academic Publishing.

Ness, Cindy. Why Girls Fight: Female Youth Violence in the Inner City. 2010. (ENG.). 280p. pap. 21.00 (978-0-8147-5841-0(X)) New York Univ. Pr.

O'Quinn, Elaine, ed. Girls' Literacy Experiences in & Out of School: Learning & Composing Gendered Identities. 2012. (ENG., Illus.). 176p. 135.00 (978-0-415-89736-5(X)); pap. 39.95 (978-0-415-89737-2(8)) Routledge.

Ott, Victoria E. Confederate Daughters: Coming of Age During the Civil War. 2008. (ENG., Illus.). 232p. 29.95 (978-0-8093-2828-4(3)) Southern Illinois Univ. Pr.

Palad, Thea. Mixed Messages: Interpreting Body Image & Social Norms. 2008. (Essential Health: Strong Beautiful Girls Ser.). 112p. (YA). (gr. 7-12). 34.22 (978-1-60453-102-2(9)) ABDO Publishing Co.

Papo, Rachel, photos by. Serial No. 3817131. 2008. (ENG.). 128p. 250.00 (978-1-57687-447-9(8), powerHouse Editions); (Illus.). 39.95 (978-1-57687-431-8(1)) powerHouse Cultural Entertainment, Inc.

Parker, Evelyn L., ed. The Sacred Selves of Adolescent Girls: Hard Stories of Race, Class, & Gender. 2006. 184p. per. (978-0-8298-1688-4(7)) Pilgrim Pr., The/United Church Pr.

—The Sacred Selves of Adolescent Girls: Hard Stories of Race, Class, & Gender. 2010. 188p. pap. 22.00 (978-1-60899-390-1(6), Wipf and Stock) Wipf & Stock Pubs.

Paul, Eden & Paul, Cedar, trs. A Young Girl's Diary. 2008. 292p. 43.95 (978-1-4369-5387-0(1)); pap. 28.95 (978-1-4367-5870-3(X)) Kessinger Publishing, LLC.

Perl, Elizabeth. Psychotherapy with Adolescent Girls & Young Women: Fostering Autonomy through Attachment. 2008. (ENG.). 198p. 30.00 (978-1-59385-651-9(2)) Guilford Pubns., Inc.

Pierce, David. Don't Let Me Go: What My Daughter Taught Me about the Journey Every Parent Must Make. 2009. (ENG.). 224p. 13.99 (978-0-307-44468-4(6), WaterBrook Pr.) Doubleday Religious Publishing Group, The.

Pipher, Mary. Que Pasa con las Ninas de Hoy. (SPA.). 20.00 (978-958-04-5301-7(2)) Norma S.A. COL. Dist: Distribuidora Norma, Inc.

—Reviviendo a Ofelia.Tr. of Reviving Ophelia. (SPA.). pap. 20.00 (978-958-04-3742-0(4), NR9047) Norma S.A. COL. Dist: Lectorum Pubns., Inc.

—Reviving Ophelia: Saving the Selves of Adolescent Girls. 2010. (ENG.). 303p. 26.10 (978-0-7569-8480-9(7)) Perfection Learning Corp.

Point Of Grace. Girls of Grace Daily Devotional: Start Your Day with Point of Grace. 2007. (ENG., Illus.). 224p. (J). pap. 14.99 (978-1-4165-5396-0(7), Howard Bks.) Howard Books.

Point of Grace Staff, et al. The Complete Girls of Grace: Devotional & Bible Study Workbook. 2009. (ENG., Illus.). 432p. (J). pap., stu. ed., wbk. ed. 16.99 (978-1-4391-1005-8(0), Howard Bks.) Howard Books.

Powers, Kimberly. Escaping the Vampire: Desperate for the Immortal Hero. 2009. 187p. (**978-1-4347-0072-8(0)**) Kingsway Pubns.

Primicerio, Shannon. Hagar: Target of a Jealous Beauty Queen. 2007. (Think Bible Studies). (ENG.). 128p. (YA). per. 8.99 (978-1-60006-113-4(3), Th1nk Bks.) NavPress Publishing Group.

—Leah: Confessions of a First Runner-up. 2007. (Think Bible Studies). (ENG.). 144p. (YA). per. 8.99 (978-1-60006-112-7(5), Th1nk Bks.) NavPress Publishing Group.

—Miriam: A Go-Getter Goes Too Far. 2007. (Think Bible Studies). (ENG.). 128p. (YA). pap. 8.99 (978-1-60006-114-1(1), Th1nk Bks.) NavPress Publishing Group.

Primicerio, Shannon Kubiak. The Divine Dancer: If the World Is Your Stage, Who Are You Performing For? 2006. (Illus.). 160p. (YA). (gr. 7-9). pap. 12.99 (978-0-7642-0343-5(6)) Bethany Hse. Pubs.

Prosperi, Whitney. Girls' Ministry 101: Ideas for Retreats, Small Groups, & Everyday Life with Teenage Girls, 1 vol. 2006. (ENG., Illus.). 160p. pap. 14.99 (978-0-310-26747-8(1)) Zondervan.

Prosperi, Whitney. Life STYLE: Real Perspectives from Radical Women in the Bible. rev. ed. 2011. (ENG.). 192p. pap. 14.99 (**978-1-59669-336-4(3)**) New Hope Pubs.

Redd, Nancy Amanda. Diet Drama: Feed Your Body! Love Your Body! Move Your Body! 2010. (ENG.). 256p. (gr. 12). 22.50 (978-1-59240-602-9(5), Gotham) Penguin Group (USA) Inc.

Reist, Melinda Tankard, ed. Getting Real: Challenging the Sexualisation of Girls. 2010. (ENG., Illus.). 180p. pap. 18.95 (978-1-876756-75-8(6)) Spinifex Pr. AUS. Dist: Independent Pubs. Group.

Resh, Evelyn. The Secret Lives of Teen Girls: What Your Mother Wouldn't Talk about but Your Daughter Needs to Know. 2009. (ENG.). 256p. pap. 14.95 (978-1-4019-2278-8(3)) Hay Hse., Inc.

Roberts, Tara, ed. What Your Mama Never Told You: True Stories about Sex & Love. 2007. (ENG.). 160p. (YA). (gr. 10-18). pap. 7.99 (978-0-618-64636-4(1)) Houghton Mifflin Harcourt Publishing Co.

Rosenwald, Laurie. All the Wrong People Have Self-Esteem: An Inappropriate Book for Young Ladies (Or, Frankly, Anybody Else) 2008. (ENG., Illus.). 128p. (YA). (gr. 7-12). pap. 16.99 (978-1-59990-240-1(0)) Bloomsbury Publishing.

Salandy, Laurenda. Far above Rubies: A Handbook for Growing Teenage Girls. 2008. 152p. per. 11.95 (978-1-4327-1777-3(4)) Outskirts Pr., Inc.

Sanguinetti, Alessandra. The Adventures of Guille & Belinda & the Enigmatic Meaning of Their Dreams. 2010. (Illus.). 120p. (978-1-59005-269-3(2)) Nazraeli Pr.

Sartor, Margaret. Miss American Pie: A Diary of Love, Secrets, & Growing up in the 1970s. 2007. (ENG., Illus.). 288p. per. 11.95 (978-1-59691-201-4(4)) Bloomsbury Publishing.

Schwarz, Susan. Coping with Cliques: A Workbook to Help Girls Deal with Gossip, Put-Downs, Bullying, & Other Mean Behavior. 2008. (Instant Help Ser.). (ENG.). 168p. (J). pap. 32.95 (978-1-57224-654-6(5)) Play2Grow.

Searcy, Titania. True Short Stories from a Girls Home. 2008. 60p. pap. 10.49 (978-1-4389-2087-0(3)) AuthorHouse.

Shalit, Wendy. The Good Girl Revolution: Young Rebels with Self-Esteem & High Standards. 2008. (ENG.). 352p. pap. 15.00 (978-0-8129-7536-9(7), Ballantine Bks.) Random House Publishing Group.

Shamoon, Deborah Michelle. Passionate Friendship: The Aesthetics of Girls' Culture in Japan. 2012. 60.00 (**978-0-8248-3542-2(5)**); pap. 27.00 (**978-0-8248-3638-2(3)**) Univ. of Hawaii Pr.

Sheen, Barbara. Girls' Guide to Feeling Fabulous! 2008. (Life Skills Ser.). (ENG.). 56p. 33.50 (978-1-4329-1361-8(1), NA-h) Heinemann-Raintree.

Shellenberger, Susie. Girl Talk with God. 2011. 240p. (YA). pap. 14.99 (978-1-4003-1700-4(2)) Nelson, Thomas Inc.

—Raising a Spiritually Strong Daughter: Guiding Her Toward a Faith That Lasts. 2009. 224p. pap. 13.99 (978-0-7642-0376-3(2)) Bethany Hse. Pubs.

Shellenberger, Susie & Gowler, Kathy. What Your Daughter Isn't Telling You: Expert Insight into the World of Teen Girls. 2007. 192p. pap. 15.00 (978-0-7642-0375-6(4)) Bethany Hse. Pubs.

Sheridan-Rabideau, Mary P. Girls, Feminism, & Grassroots Literacies: Activism in the GirlZone. (SUNY Series in Feminist Criticism & Theory). (Illus.). 2009. 218p. pap. 24.95 (978-0-7914-7298-9(1)) 2008. 204p. 60.00 (978-0-7914-7297-2(3)) State Univ. of New York Pr.

The Slave Across the Street: The true story of an American teen caught in human Trafficking. 2010. 160p. pap. 14.99 (978-0-9823286-8-2(0)) Ampelon Publishing, LLC.

Smith, Joanne & Meghan Huppuch. Hey, Shorty! A Guide to Combating Sexual Harassment & Violence in Schools & on the Streets. 2011. (ENG.). 160p. pap. 13.95 (978-1-55861-669-1(1)) Feminist Pr. at The City Univ. of New York.

Soulsby, Lucy H. M. Stray Thoughts for Girls. 2008. 152p. 24.99 (978-0-554-27097-5(8)) 2008. 152p. 21.99 (978-0-554-36400-1(X)) 2007. (ENG.). 136p. pap. 18.99 (978-1-4346-2497-0(8)) 2007. 148p. pap. 19.99 (978-1-4346-2539-7(7)) BiblioBazaar.

Sprague, Marsha M. & Keeling, Kara K. Discovering Their Voices: Engaging Adolescent Girls with Young Adult Literature. 2007. (Illus.). xii, 211p. (gr. 7-12). pap. 23.95 net. (978-0-87207-611-2(3)) International Reading Assn.

St Stephen's Community House, creator. The Little Black Book for Girlz: A Book on Healthy Sexuality. 2006. (ENG., Illus.). 200p. (YA). (gr. 9-12). pap. 8.95 (978-1-55037-954-9(2)) Annick Pr., Ltd. CAN. Dist: Firefly Bks., Ltd.

Stabiner, Karen. Reclaiming Our Daughters: What Parenting a Pre-Teen Taught Me about Real Girls. 2007. (ENG.). 280p. per. 14.95 (978-1-58005-213-9(4)) Seal Pr.

Stephens, Andrea. Happy Thoughts for Bad Hair Days. 164p. pap. 9.99 (978-0-8307-3438-2(4), Regal Bks.) Gospel Light Pubns.

Stern, Shayla Thiel. Instant Identity: Adolescent Girls & the World of Instant Messaging. 2007. (Mediated Youth Ser.: Vol. 2). (Illus.). 160p. (C). pap. 27.95 (978-0-8204-6325-4(6)) Lang, Peter Publishing, Inc.

Stevens, Sydney. Dear Medora: Child of Oysterville's Forgotten Years. 2007. (ENG., Illus.). 168p. per. 24.95 (978-0-87422-292-0(3)) Washington State Univ. Pr.

Strauman, Timothy J., et al, eds. Depression in Adolescent Girls: Science & Prevention. 2011. (Duke Series in Child Develpment & Public Policy Ser.). (ENG., Illus.). 353p. 55.00 (978-1-59385-563-5(X)) Guilford Pubns., Inc.

Straus, Martha B. Adolescent Girls in Crisis. 2007. 24.95 (978-0-7937-0447-7(2)) Norton, W. W. & Co., Inc.

—Adolescent Girls in Crisis: Intervention & Hope. 2007. (ENG.). 240p. 35.00 (978-0-393-70447-1(5), 70447) Norton, W. W. & Co., Inc.

Sturgeon, Ava. A Daughter's Worth: A Bible Study for Teenaged Girls. 2006. 186p. per. 15.95 (978-1-59886-398-7(3)) Tate Publishing & Enterprises, LLC.

Sweeney, Kathleen. Maiden USA: Girl Icons Come of Age. (Mediated Youth Ser.). (C). 2008. (Illus.). 340p. 119.95 (978-1-4331-0208-0(0)) 2007. pap. 32.95 (978-0-8204-8197-5(1)) Lang, Peter Publishing, Inc.

Tadano, Nobuaki. 7 Billion Needles, Volume 4. 2011. (Illus.). 204p. (gr. 10). pap. 10.95 (978-1-935654-16-2(0)) Vertical, Inc.

Taflinger, Nicole H. Season of Suffering: Coming of Age in Occupied France, 1940-45. 2010. (978-0-87422-305-7(9)) Washington State Univ. Pr.

Taft, Jessica. Rebel Girls: Youth Activism & Social Change Across the Americas. 2010. (ENG.). 256p. pap. 22.00 (978-0-8147-8325-2(2)) New York Univ. Pr.

Taylor, Julia V. & Trice-Black, Shannon. G. I. R. L. S. , Girls in Real Life Situations, Grades K-5 (Book & CD) Group Counseling Activities for Enhancing Social & Emotional Development: Grades K-5. 2007. 236p. spiral bd. 37.95 (978-0-87822-543-9(9)) Research Pr.

Thomas, Mary E. Multicultural Girlhood: Racism, Sexuality, & the Conflicted Spaces of American Education. 2011. (Global Youth Ser.). (Illus.). (ENG.). 216p. 75.50 (978-1-4399-0731-3(5)); (ENG., 218p. pap. 24.95 (978-1-4399-0732-0(3)); viii, 204p. E-Book (**978-1-4399-0733-7(1)**) Temple Univ. Pr.

Tomeo, Teresa & Dickow, Cheryl. All Things Girl Truth for Teens. 2nd ed. 2009. (Illus.). 239p. (YA). pap. 19.99 (978-0-9823388-3-4(X)) Bezalel Bks.

Trevathan, Melissa, et al. Raising Girls, 1 vol. annot. ed. 2007. (ENG.). 256p. pap. 12.99 (978-0-310-27289-2(0)) Zondervan.

Vigil, Tori. Surviving the Teenage Journey: Discovering Your Inner Voice. 2006. 112p. per. 15.00 (978-0-9763565-3-0(8), Sparkling Pr.) Dusty Spark Publishing.

Virk, Manjit. Reena: A Father's Story, 1 vol. rev. ed. 2009. (ENG., Illus.). 192p. (978-1-894974-51-6(4)) Heritage Hse.

Weisz, Arlene N. & Black, Beverly M. Programs to Reduce Teen Dating Violence & Sexual Assault: Perspectives on What Works. 2009. (ENG.). 336p. (gr. 17). pap. 35.00 (978-0-231-13453-8(3)); (Illus.). 89.50 (978-0-231-13452-1(5)) Columbia Univ. Pr.

Wiseman, Rosalind. Queen Bees & Wannabes: Helping Your Daughter Survive Cliques, Gossip, Boyfriends, & the New Realities of Girl World. 2009. (ENG.). 448p. pap. 16.00 (978-0-307-45444-7(4), Three Rivers Pr.) Crown Publishing Group.

A Young Woman's Survival Guide. 2007. (YA). per. 10.00 (978-0-9786867-1-0(3)) Health Initiatives for Youth.

Zaslow, Emilie. Feminism, Inc: Coming of Age in Girl Power Media Culture. 2011. (ENG., Illus.). 216p. pap. 25.00 (978-0-230-11996-3(4)) Palgrave Macmillan.

ADOLESCENT MEDICINE

see also Adolescent Psychiatry

Altchek, Albert & Deligdisch, Liane. Pediatric, Adolescent, & Young Adult Gynecology. 2009. (ENG., Illus.). 520p. 290.00 (978-1-4051-5347-8(4), Wiley-Blackwell) Wiley, John & Sons, Inc.

American Academy of Pediatrics Section on Adolescent Health Staff. E-Health, Vol. 18,No. 2. Cohall, Alwyn T. et al, eds. 2007. (Adolescent Medicine: State of the Art Re Ser.). (ENG., Illus.). 219p. per. 59.95 (978-1-58110-256-7(9)) American Academy of Pediatrics.

Berlan, Elise D., et al. Adolescent Medicine Today: A Guide to Caring for the Adolescent Patient. 2011. 650p. 180.00 (**978-981-4324-48-9(5)**) World Scientific Publishing Co., Inc.

Coding for Pediatrics 2006. 450p. spiral bd. 79.95 (978-1-58110-173-7(2), OP590406CSD) American Academy of Pediatrics.

Cook, Kerry & Langton, Helen, eds. Cardiothoracic Care for Children & Young People: A Multidisciplinary Approach. 2009. (ENG., Illus.). 240p. pap. 61.99 (978-0-470-51841-0(3), Wiley) Wiley, John & Sons, Inc.

Cram101 Textbook Reviews & Cram101 Textbook Reviews. Outlines & Highlights for Adolescence & Health by John Coleman, Isbn: 9780470092064. 2011. 76p. pap. 27.95 (**978-1-4288-3093-6(6)**) Cram101 Inc.

—Outlines & Highlights for Adolescent Health Care by Adolescent Health Care, Isbn: 9780781792561 0781792568. 2011. 560p. pap. 38.95 (**978-1-61490-425-0(1)**) Cram101 Inc.

Diamanti-Kandarakis, Evanthia & Gore, Andrea C., eds. Endocrine Disruptors & Puberty. 2011. (Contemporary Endocrinology Ser.). (ENG., Illus.). xvii, 378p. 219.00 (**978-1-60761-560-6(6)**, 1607615606) Humana Pr.

Fisher, Martin & Rosenfeld, Walter. Textbook of Adolescent Health Care. Elizabeth, Alderman & Kreipe, Richard E., eds. 2011. (ENG., Illus.). 1500p. 159.95 (**978-1-58110-269-7(0)**) American Academy of Pediatrics.

Goldstein, Mark A., ed. The MassGeneral Hospital for Children Adolescent Medicine Handbook. 2010. (Illus.). xvii, 252p. pap. 34.95 (978-1-4419-6844-9(X), 144196844X) Springer.

Greydanus, Donald E., et al, eds. Adolescent Medicine: Pharmacotherapeutics in General, Mental & Sexual Health. 2012. (ENG., Illus.). 450p. 140.00 (978-3-11-025522-5(7)) De Gruyter, Walter Inc.

—Adolescent Medicine: Pharmacotherapeutics in Medical Disorders: Pharmacotherapeutics in Medical Disorders. 2012. (Health, Medicine & Human Development Ser.). (ENG., Illus.). 390p. 140.00 (978-3-11-027580-3(5)) De Gruyter, Walter Inc.

Laugeson, Elizabeth A. & Frankel, Fred. Social Skills for Teenagers with Developmental & Autism Spectrum Disorders. 2010. (ENG., Illus.). 448p. pap. 49.95 (978-0-415-87203-4(0)) Routledge.

Neinstein, Lawrence S. Adolescent Health Care: A Practical Guide. Neinstein, Lawrence S., ed. 5th rev. ed. 2007. (ENG., Illus.). 1300p. pap. 134.99 (978-0-7817-9256-1(8)) Lippincott Williams & Wilkins.

—Handbook of Adolescent Health Care. 2008. (ENG., Illus.). 840p. pap., instr.'s hndbk. ed. 69.99 (978-0-7817-9020-8(4)) Lippincott Williams & Wilkins.

Omar, Hatim, et al, eds. Adolescence & Chronic Illness. A Public Health Concern. 2010. (Health & Human Development (Joav Merrick - Series Editor - National Institute of Child Health & Human Development, Ministry of Social Affairs, Jerusalem) Ser.). (Illus.). x, 477p. 195.00 (978-1-60876-628-4(4)) Nova Science Pubs., Inc.

Papemy, David M. Handbook of Adolescent Medicine & Health Promotion. 2011. 290p. 95.00 (978-981-4317-98-6(5)) World Scientific Publishing Co., Inc.

Parsian, Nasrin. Spirituality & Coping in Young Adults with Diabetes. 2010. 244p. pap. (978-3-8383-1997-1(4)) Lambert Academic Publishing.

Sanfilippo, Joseph, et al, eds. Pediatric & Adolescent Gynecology: Principles & Practice. 2008. (ENG., Illus.). 652p. 300.00 (978-0-415-44888-8(3), Informa Healthcare) Taylor & Francis Group.

Slap, Gail B. Adolescent Medicine. 2008. (Requisites in Pediatrics Ser.). (ENG., Illus.) 352p. pap. 79.95 (978-0-323-04073-0(X), Mosby) Elsevier - Health Sciences Div.

Sultan, Charles, ed. Pediatric & Adolescent Gynecology Vol. 7: Evidence-Based Clinical Practice. (Endocrine Development Ser.: Vol. 7). (Illus.). (978-3-8055-7623-9(4)) Karger, S. AG.

Walker-Smith, J. A., et al, eds. Pediatric Inflammatory Bowel Disease: Perspective & Consequences. 2009. (Pediatric & Adolescent Medicine Ser.). (ENG., Illus.). 204p. (978-3-8055-9134-8(9)) Karger, S. AG.

Zdanowicz, Nicolas. The Adolescent Today in Medicine. 2007. 79.00 (978-1-60021-764-7(8)) Nova Science Pubs., Inc.

Zelikovic, I. & Eisenstein, I., eds. Nephrology. 2008. (Illus.). 122p. spiral bd. (978-3-8055-8539-2(X)) Karger, S. AG.

ADOLESCENT PARENTS

Arai, Lisa. Teenage Pregnancy: The Making & Unmaking of a Problem. 2009. 192p. pap. 37.95 (978-1-84742-074-9(5)) Policy Pr. GBR. Dist: Chicago Distribution Ctr.

ARISE Foundation & Benson, Susan. Life Skills Curriculum: ARISE Sprouts, Book 4. 2011. (Parenting 101 Ser.). (ENG., Illus.). 130p. (YA). pap., wbk. ed. 16.95 (978-1-58614-051-9(5)) Arise Foundation.

Bhana, Arvin & Swartz, Sharlene. Teenage Tata: Voices of Young Fathers in South Africa. 2010. (ENG.). 136p. pap. 25.95 (978-0-7969-2287-8(X)) Human Sciences Research Council ZAF. Dist: Independent Pubs. Group.

Cardone, Ida, et al. Teenagers & Their Babies: A Perinatal Home Visitor's Guide. 2007. (978-1-934019-16-0(X)) Zero To Three Pr.

Cisnado, Juanita Hernandez. My Journey to Becoming a Mentor. 2008. 108p. 24.99 (978-1-4363-0316-3(8)); pap. 15.99 (978-1-4363-0315-6(X)) Xlibris Corp.

Echols, Celina & Blacher-Wilson, Felicia. Lessons Learned: Caregivers & Parents Sharing Stories about Adolescence. rev. ed. 2011. (ENG.). 140p. pap. 45.00 (978-0-7575-9292-8(9)) Kendall Hunt Publishing Co.

Evans, Roy, et al, eds. Teenage Pregnancy & Parenthood: Global Perspectives, Issues & Interventions. 2006. (Illus.). 303p. 160.00 (978-0-415-34625-2(8)); 203p. per. 47.95 (978-0-415-34626-9(6)) Routledge.

Friedman, Lauri S. Teen Pregnancy. 2010. (Writing the Critical Essay: an Opposing Viewpoints Guide Ser.). (Illus.). 128p. (J). 30.85 (978-0-7377-4804-8(4), Greenhaven Pr., Inc.) Cengage Gale.

Hoffman, Saul D. & Maynard, Rebecca A., eds. Kids Having Kids: Economic Costs & Social Consequences. 2nd rev. ed. 2008. (ENG., Illus.). 414p. pap. 34.50 (978-0-87766-745-2(4)) Urban Institute Pr.

Hoover, C. A. The Teenager Parent. 2011. 104p. pap. 19.95 (978-1-4560-5706-0(5)) PublishAmerica, Inc.

Klor, Ellin & Lapin, Sarah. Serving Teen Parents: From Literacy Skills to Life Skills. 2011. E-Book (978-1-59884-694-2(9)) Libraries Unlimited, Inc.

—Serving Teen Parents: From Literacy to Life Skills, 1 vol. 2011. (Libraries Unlimited Professional Guides for Young Adult Librarians Ser.). (Illus.). 200p. pap. 45.00 (978-1-59884-693-5(0), A3272P) Libraries Unlimited, Inc.

Lawton, Sandra Augustyn. Pregnancy Information for Teens: Health Tips about Teen Pregnancy & Teen Parenting: Including Facts about Prenatal Care, Pregnancy Complications, Labor & Delivery, Postpartum Care, Pregnancy-Related Lifestyle Concerns, & More. 2007. (Teen Health Ser.). (Illus.). 434p. 65.00 (978-0-7808-0984-0(X)) Omnigraphics, Inc.

Lindsay, Jeanne Warren. The P. A. R. E. N. T Approach: How to Teach Young Moms & Dads the Art & Skills of Parenting. 2008. (ENG., Illus.). 160p. per. 12.95 (978-1-932538-85-4(2)) Morning Glory Pr., Inc.

Magill, Elizabeth, ed. Pregnancy Information for Teens. 2nd rev. ed. 2012. (Teen Health Ser.). (YA). lib. bdg. 69.00 (978-0-7808-1220-8(4)) Omnigraphics, Inc.

Malin, Nigel. Evaluating Sure Start. 2008. (978-1-86177-054-7(5)) Whiting & Birch, Ltd.

Martin, A. Ninas Madres - Madres Adolescentes. (Serie Actualidades - Actualities Ser.).Tr. of Child Mothers - Teen Mothers. (SPA.). 2.29 (978-1-56063-660-1(2), 496253) Editorial Unilit.

Miller Coffel, Cynthia. Thinking Themselves Free: Teen Mothers, Literacy, & Education. 2010. viii, 169p. (978-1-4331-0973-7(5)); (978-1-4331-0972-0(7)) Lang, Peter GmbH, Europaischer Verlag der Wissenschaften.

Munro, Eileen & McKay, Carol. As I Lay Me down to Sleep. 2008. (ENG.). 272p. mass mkt. 13.95 (978-1-84596-344-6(X)) Mainstream Publishing Co., Ltd. GBR. Dist: Independent Pubs. Group.

PDR Staff. PDR Guide to Pediatric & Adolescent Mental Health. Thomson Reuters Staff, ed. 2009. (ENG.). 950p. pap. 39.95 (978-1-56363-729-2(4)) PDR Network, LLC.

Stapleton, Helen. Surviving Teenage Motherhood: Myths & Realities. 2010. (Studies in Childhood & Youth Ser.). (ENG., Illus.). 248p. 89.00 (978-0-230-57920-0(5)) Palgrave Macmillan.

Stroble, Chris. Teens & Moms Breaking the Cycle. 2006. 97p. pap. 14.95 (978-1-933559-01-8(2)) Empowering Teens.

Treat, Carol E. When Alex Asks Why? 2011. 70p. pap. 19.95 (978-1-4560-9421-8(1)) PublishAmerica, Inc.

Watson, Theresa. A Guide for Teenage Parents. 2008. 100p. (YA). pap. 15.95 (978-0-9794781-2-3(X), Aji Custom Publishing) Aji Publishing.

Wolfe, David A. Ce Que les Parents Doivent Savoir Sur les Comportements à Risque des Adolescents: Stratégies Pour Réduire les Problèmes Liés à L'alcool, Aux Drogues, Aux Jeux de Hasard et à Internet. 2011. (FRE.). (978-0-88868-613-8(7)) Centre for Addiction & Mental Health.

Worth, Richard. Frequently Asked Questions about Teen Fatherhood. 2009. (FAQ: Teen Life Ser.). (Illus.). 64p. (J). (gr. 5-6). lib. bdg. 29.25 (978-1-4358-5325-6(3)) Rosen Publishing Group, Inc., The.

ADOLESCENT PSYCHIATRY

see also Adolescent Psychopathology

American Academy of Child and Adolescent Psychiatry (AACAP). Attention-Deficit / Hyperactivity Disorder GUIDELINES Pocketcard: American Academy of Child & Adolescent Psychiatry (2011) 2011. (ENG.). 6p. 9.95 (978-0-9846667-0-6(2)) International Guidelines Ctr., Inc.

Amsel, Eric & Smetana, Judith, eds. Adolescent Vulnerabilities & Opportunities: Constructivist Developmental Perspectives. 2011. (Interdisciplinary Approaches to Knowledge & Development Ser.). (ENG., Illus.). 224p. 85.00 (978-0-521-76846-7(2)) Cambridge Univ. Pr.

Arden, John B. & Linford, Lloyd. Brain-Based Therapy with Children & Adolescents: Evidence-Based Treatment for Everyday Practice. 2008. (ENG.). 324p. pap. 45.00 (978-0-470-13891-5(2), Wiley) Wiley, John & Sons, Inc.

Arnold, Carrie. Next to Nothing: A Firsthand Account of One Teenager's Experience with an Eating Disorder. 2007. (Adolescent Mental Health Initiative Ser.). (ENG., Illus.). 208p. 35.00 (978-0-19-530965-2(0)) Oxford Univ. Pr., Inc.

Arnold, Carrie & Walsh, B. Timothy. Next to Nothing: A Firsthand Account of One Teenager's Experience with an Eating Disorder. 2007. (Adolescent Mental Health Initiative Ser.). (ENG.). 208p. per. 9.95 (978-0-19-530966-9(9)) Oxford Univ. Pr., Inc.

Bailey, Susan, et al. Adolescent Forensic Psychiatry. 155.00 (978-0-7506-4090-9(1), Butterworth-Heinemann) Elsevier Science & Technology Bks.

Bausch. Starving for Affection: A journey of eating disorders, drugs, & Sex. 2008. 256p. pap. 19.95 (978-1-4401-1151-8(0)) iUniverse, Inc.

Blum, Sasha. The Gothic Subculture. 2009. 164p. pap. (978-3-639-20760-6(2)) VDM Verlag Dr. Mueller e.K.

Bostic, Jeffrey Q. & Bagnell, Alexa L. Evidence-Based School Psychiatry - An Issue of Child & Adolescent Psychiatric Clinics of North America. 2012. (Clinics: Internal Medicine Ser.: 21-1). (ENG., Illus.). 960p. 115.00 (978-1-4557-3839-7(5), Saunders) Elsevier - Health Sciences Div.

Brambring, Michael, et al, eds. Children at Risk: Assessment, Longitudinal Research & Intervention. (Prevention & Intervention in Childhood & Adolescence Ser.). (ENG.). XIV, 490p. 196.00 (978-3-11-179122-7(X)) De Gruyter, Walter Inc.

Brockman, David Dean. From Late Adolescence to Young Adulthood. 2011. 322p. pap. 41.95 (978-1-78049-058-8(5)) Karnac Bks. GBR. Dist: Stylus Publishing, LLC.

Castell, Rolf. Hundert Jahre Kinder- und Jugendpsychiatrie. Castell, Rolf, ed. 2008. (GER.). 285p. (C). 60.00 (978-3-89971-509-5(8)) Vandenhoeck & Ruprecht GmbH & Co. KG DEU. Dist: ISD.

Cepeda, Claudio. Clinical Manual for the Psychiatric Interview of Children & Adolescents. 2009. 59.00 (978-1-58562-343-3(1)) American Psychiatric Publishing, Inc.

Cheng, Keith & Myers, Kathleen M., eds. Child & Adolescent Psychiatry: The Essentials. 2nd rev. ed. 2010. (ENG.). 560p. 94.99 (978-1-60547-443-4(6)) Lippincott Williams & Wilkins.

Claveirole, Anne & Gaughan, Martin, eds. Understanding Children & Young People's Mental Health. 2010. (ENG., Illus.). 328p. pap. 47.99 (978-0-470-72345-6(9), Wiley-Blackwell) Wiley, John & Sons, Inc.

Cobert. Tarascon Pediatric Psychiatrica. rev. ed. 2011. 298p. pap. 24.95 (978-0-7637-7640-4(8), Tarascon) Jones & Bartlett Learning, LLC.

Corcoran, Jacqueline. Mental Health Treatment for Children & Adolescents, 1 vol. 2010. (Evidence-Based Practice Ser.). (ENG., Illus.). 304p. 39.95 (978-0-19-537571-8(8)) Oxford Univ. Pr., Inc.

Cram101 Textbook Reviews & Cram101 Textbook Reviews. Outlines & Highlights for Camps & Mental Health, an Issue of Child & Adolescent Psychiatric Clinics by Alicia Mcauliffe-Fogarty, Isbn: 97814160504. 2011. 70p. pap. 27.95 (978-1-61461-273-5(0)) Cram101 Inc.

—Outlines & Highlights for Cultural Issues in Pediatric Mental Health, an Issue of Child & Adolescent Psychiatric Clinics of North America by Shashan. 2011. 86p. pap. 27.95 (978-1-61461-226-1(9)) Cram101 Inc.

—Outlines & Highlights for Infant & Early Childhood Mental Health, an Issue of Child & Adolescent Psychiatric Clinics of North America by Mary Marg. 2011. 98p. pap. 27.95 (978-1-61461-219-3(6)) Cram101 Inc.

Cram101 Textbook Reviews Staff. Outlines & Highlights for Abnormal Child & Adolescent Psychology by Rita Wicks-Nelson, Allen C Israel, Isbn: 9780132359788. 2009. 140p. pap. 28.95 (978-1-4288-7992-8(7)) Cram101 Inc.

Dehn, Milton J. Long-Term Memory Problems in Children & Adolescents: Assessment, Intervention, & Effective Instruction. 2010. (ENG., Illus.). 408p. pap. 48.00 (978-0-470-43831-2(2), Wiley) Wiley, John & Sons, Inc.

Dulcan, Mina K., ed. Dulcan's Textbook of Child & Adolescent Psychiatry. 2009. (Illus.). 1104p. 249.00 (978-1-58562-323-5(7)) American Psychiatric Publishing, Inc.

Dulcan, Mina K. & Lake, MaryBeth. Concise Guide to Child & Adolescent Psychiatry. 4th ed. 2011. (Illus.). 405p. pap. 53.00 (978-1-58562-416-4(0)) American Psychiatric Publishing, Inc.

Elissa P. Benedek, M. d., et al. Principles & Practice of Child & Adolescent Forensic Mental Health. 2009. (ENG., Illus.). 531p. 135.00 (978-1-58562-336-5(9)) American Psychiatric Publishing, Inc.

Flaherty, Lois, ed. Adolescent Psychiatry, Vol. 30. 2007. (ENG.). 224p. 78.00 (978-0-88163-462-4(X)) Routledge.

Garralda, M. Elena. Culture & Conflict in Child & Adolescent Mental Health. 2008. (ENG., Illus.). 292p. per. 39.99 (978-0-7657-0593-8(1), Aronson, Jason) Rowman & Littlefield Publishers, Inc.

—Increasing Awareness of Child & Adolescent Mental Health. 2010. (ENG., Illus.). 338p. 83.99 (978-0-7657-0661-4(X), Aronson, Jason) Rowman & Littlefield Publishers, Inc.

Garralda, M. Elena & Raynaud, Jean Philippe. Culture & Conflict in Child & Adolescent Mental Health. 2008. (ENG., Illus.). 292p. 89.50 (978-0-7657-0592-1(3), Aronson, Jason) Rowman & Littlefield Publishers, Inc.

—Increasing Awareness of Child & Adolescent Mental Health. 2010. (Illus.). xvii, 319p. 34.95 (978-0-7657-0663-8(6), Aronson, Jason) Rowman & Littlefield Publishers, Inc.

Garralda, M. Elena & Raynaud, Jean-Philippe. Increasing Awareness of Child & Adolescent Mental Health. 2010. (ENG., Illus.). 338p. pap. 36.99 (978-0-7657-0662-1(8), Aronson, Jason) Rowman & Littlefield Publishers, Inc.

Gillberg, Christopher, et al, eds. A Clinician's Handbook of Child & Adolescent Psychiatry. 2011. (ENG., Illus.). 764p. pap. 85.00 (978-0-521-29484-3(3)) Cambridge Univ. Pr.

Grant, Jon E. & Potenza, Marc N. Young Adult Mental Health. 2009. (ENG.). 464p. 79.95 (978-0-19-533271-1(7)) Oxford Univ. Pr., Inc.

Green, Wayne Hugo. Child & Adolescent Clinical Psychopharmacology. 4th rev. ed. 2006. (ENG., Illus.). 400p. per. 87.50 (978-0-7817-5950-2(1)) Lippincott Williams & Wilkins.

Grigorenko, Elena L., ed. Handbook of Juvenile Forensic Psychology & Psychiatry, 2 vols. 2012. (ENG., Illus.). 620p. 349.00 (978-1-4614-0904-5(7), 1461409047) Springer.

Gullotta, Thomas P. Handbook of Adolescent Behavioral Problems. 2008. (Illus.). 666p. spiral bd. 54.95 (978-0-387-88715-9(6)) Springer.

Hanbury, Martin. Positive Behaviour Strategies to Support Children & Young People with Autism. 2007. (Illus.). 120p. 65.00 (978-1-4129-2910-3(5), B29105C); per. 30.00 (978-1-4129-2911-0(3), B29105P) SAGE Pubns., Ltd. GBR. Dist: SAGE Pubns., Inc.

Handler, Leonard, ed. The Clinical Assessment of Children & Adolescents: A Practitioner's Handbook. 2006. (ENG., Illus.). 648p. per. 110.95 (978-0-8058-6075-7(4)) Routledge.

Hazen, Eric P., et al. Mental Health Disorders in Adolescents: A Guide for Parents, Teachers, & Professionals. 2010. (ENG., Illus.). 350p. 75.00 (978-0-8135-4893-7(4)); pap. 23.95 (978-0-8135-4894-4(2)) Rutgers Univ. Pr.

Hendren. Child & Adolescent Psychiatry for the Specialty Board Review. 3rd rev. ed. 2007. (Continuing Education in Psychiatry & Psychology Ser.). (ENG.). 184p. 39.95 (978-0-415-95598-0(X)) Routledge.

Ivanenko, Anna, ed. Sleep & Psychiatric Disorders in Children & Adolescents. 2008. (ENG., Illus.). 432p. 200.00 (978-1-4200-4807-0(4), Informa Healthcare) Taylor & Francis Group GBR. Dist: Taylor & Francis Group.

Ivanenko, Anna & Shatkin, Jess P. Pediatric Sleep Disorders, an Issue of Child & Adolescent Psychiatric Clinics of North America. 2009. (Clinics: Internal Medicine Ser.: 18-4). (ENG., Illus.). 240p. 99.00 (978-1-4377-1200-1(2), Saunders) Elsevier - Health Sciences Div.

James, Bevery. Treating Traumatized Children. 2009. (ENG.). 290p. pap. 19.95 (978-1-4391-5734-3(0), Free Pr.) Free Pr.

Maximilian T. Badoy. Uncommon Sense. 2009. 108p. pap. 16.49 (978-1-4389-0066-7(X)) AuthorHouse.

McDougall, Tim, ed. Child & Adolescent Mental Health Nursing. 2006. (ENG., Illus.). 328p. pap. 66.99 (978-1-4051-2801-8(1), Wiley-Blackwell) Wiley, John & Sons, Inc.

McKinnon, John A. An Unchanged Mind: The Problem of Immaturity in Adolescence. 2008. 272p. pap. 23.00 (978-1-59056-124-9(4)) Lantern Bks.

Perinpanayagam, K.Sounthy. Dossier of a Critical Closure of a Regional Adolescent Unit Brookside Young People's Unit 1975-1985: Psychodynamics in Practice - Relationship Therapy. 2010. (Illus.). 532p. pap. (978-1-84401-082-0(1)) Athena Pr.

Pleak, Richard R. Gender Variant Children & Transgender Adolescents, an Issue of Child & Adolescent Psychiatric Clinics of North America. 2011. (Clinics: Internal Medicine Ser.: 20-4). (ENG., Illus.). 240p. 110.00 (978-1-4557-1092-8(X), Saunders) Elsevier - Health Sciences Div.

Pradhan, Manas Ranjan. Sexual Behavior of Urban Youth. 2010. 100p. pap. (978-3-639-26634-4(X)) VDM Verlag Dr. Mueller e.K.

Rosoman, Clare. Therapy to Go: Gourmet Fast Food Handouts for Working with Child, Adolescent & Family Clients. 2008. (ENG., Illus.). 192p. pap. (978-1-84310-643-2(4)) Kingsley, Jessica Ltd.

Rutter, Michael. Rutter's Child & Adolescent Psychiatry. 5th ed. 2008. (978-1-4051-4592-3(7), Wiley-Blackwell) Wiley, John & Sons, Ltd.

Rutter, Michael, et al. Rutter's Child & Adolescent Psychiatry. 5th ed. (ENG.). 1248p. 2010. pap. 125.00 (978-1-4051-4593-0(5)) 2008. (Illus.). 315.00 (978-1-4051-4549-7(8)) Wiley, John & Sons, Inc. (Wiley-Blackwell).

Shen, Hong, et al. Study Guide to Child & Adolescent Psychiatry: A Companion to Dulcan's Textbook of Child & Adolescent Psychiatry. 2009. (Illus.). 350p. pap. 54.00 (978-1-58562-353-2(9)) American Psychiatric Publishing, Inc.

Sidhu, Tanvir Kaur. Psychiatric Morbidity in Adolescents Attending Tertiary Care Facility. 2011. 100p. pap. (978-3-8443-2117-3(9)) Lambert Academic Publishing.

Steiner, Hans. Handbook of Developmental Psychiatry. 2011. 600p. 158.00 (978-981-4324-81-6(7)) World Scientific Publishing Co., Inc.

—The Stanford University School of Medicine Handbook of Developmental Psychiatry for Children & Adolescents. 2009. 1120p. 175.00 (978-0-7879-8435-9(3), Jossey-Bass) Wiley, John & Sons, Inc.

Stubbe, Dorothy. Child & Adolescent Psychiatry. 2006. (Practical Guides in Psychiatry Ser.). (ENG.). 283p. per. 49.95 (978-0-7817-7831-2(X)) Lippincott Williams & Wilkins.

Trivedi, Harsh K. & Kershner, Jeryl Dansky. Practical Child & Adolescent Psychiatry for Pediatrics & Primary Care. 2009. (Illus.). 230p. spiral bd. 49.00 (978-0-88937-349-5(3)) Hogrefe Publishing.

Volkmar, Fred R., et al, eds. Lewis's Child & Adolescent Psychiatry: A Comprehensive Textbook. 4th rev. ed. 2007. (ENG., Illus.). 1088p. 245.99 (978-0-7817-6214-4(6)) Lippincott Williams & Wilkins.

Whitbeck, Les B. Mental Health & Emerging Adulthood among Homeless Young People. 2009. (ENG., Illus.). 312p. pap. 39.95 (978-1-84169-752-9(4), Psychology Press) Taylor & Francis Group GBR. Dist: Taylor & Francis Group.

—Mental Health & Emerging Adulthood among HomelessYoung People. 2009. (ENG., Illus.). 312p. 73.95 (978-1-84169-751-2(6), Psychology Press) Taylor & Francis Group GBR. Dist: Taylor & Francis Group.

ADOLESCENT PSYCHOLOGY

see also Anger in Adolescence; Stress in Adolescence

Akhtar, Salman & Parens, Henri. Lying, Cheating, & Carrying On: Developmental, Clinical, & Sociocultural Aspects of Dishonesty & Deceit. 2009. (Margaret S. Mahler Ser.). (ENG.). 180p. 68.50 (978-0-7657-0602-7(4)); pap. 31.50 (978-0-7657-0603-4(2)) Rowman & Littlefield Publishers, Inc. (Aronson, Jason).

Al-Rawashdeh, Ahmad. Runaway Youth - Psychosocial Characteristics. 2008. 52p. pap. (978-3-8364-7700-0(9)) VDM Verlag Dr. Mueller e.K.

Aldridge, Marion D. Overcoming Adolescence: Growing Beyond Childhood into Maturity. 2011. pap. (978-1-57312-577-2(6)) Smyth & Helwys Publishing, Inc.

Alexander, Theron. Children & Adolescents: A Biocultural Approach to Psychological Development. 2007. (ENG., Illus.). 381p. pap. 29.95 (978-0-202-30913-2(4)) Aldine Transaction.

Alfano, Candice A. & Beidel, Deborah C. Social Anxiety in Adolescents & Young Adults: Translating Developmental Science into Practice. 2011. (978-1-4338-0949-1(4)); (Illus.). 296p. 69.95 (978-1-4338-0948-4(6)) American Psychological Assn.

Allen, Mollie, et al. Discovering Type with Teens: A comprehensive leader's guide with materials for presenting psychological type to young People. 2009. (ENG.). 191p. pap. 37.95 incl. cd-rom (978-0-935652-89-5(2)) Center for Applications of Psychological Type, Inc.

Allen, Nicholas B. & Sheeber, Lisa B. Adolescent Emotional Development & the Emergence of Depressive Disorders. Allen, Nicholas & Sheeber, Lisa, eds. 2008. (ENG., Illus.). 378p. 99.00 (978-0-521-86939-3(0)) Cambridge Univ. Pr.

Allen, William W. Big Pistol, Bigger Habit, Bad Attitude: He Decided as a Teen Not to Be a Loser. 2012. (ENG., Illus.). 144p. (gr. 8). pap. 12.00 (978-1-935166-23-8(9)) Parkhurst Brothers, Inc., Pubs.

Allman, Toney. Cliques. 2010. (Hot Topics Ser.). (ENG.). 96-128p. (YA). (gr. 7-12). 33.45 (978-1-4205-0308-1(1)) Cengage Gale.

Anglada, Tracy. Intense Minds Through the Eyes of Young. 2007. (Illus.). 163p. 26.95 (978-1-4251-6701-1(2)) Trafford Publishing.

Archer, Margaret. The Reflexive Imperative in Late Modernity. 2012. (ENG., Illus.). 352p. 95.00 (978-1-107-02095-5(6)); pap. 36.99 (978-1-107-60527-5(X)) Cambridge Univ. Pr.

Ardino, Vittoria, ed. Post-Traumatic Syndromes in Childhood & Adolescence: A Handbook of Research & Practice. 2011. (ENG., Illus.). 486p. instr.'s hndbk. ed. 144.95 (978-0-470-99769-7(9), Wiley) Wiley, John & Sons, Inc.

Arnett, Jeffrey Jensen, ed. Adolescent Psychology Around the World. 2011. (ENG., Illus.). 432p. 105.95 *(978-1-84872-888-2(3))*; pap. 45.95 *(978-1-84872-889-9(1))* Taylor & Francis Group GBR. (Psychology Press). Dist: Taylor & Francis Group.

Arnold, Christopher, et al. Excluded from School: Complex Discourse & Psychological Perspectives. 2009. (Illus.). 190p. pap. 32.95 *(978-1-85856-439-5(5))* Trentham Bks. Ltd. GBR. Dist: Stylus Publishing, LLC.

—Gangs, Marginalised Youth & Social Capital. Mason, John & Houssart, Jenny, eds. 2009. 192p. pap. 32.95 *(978-1-85856-444-9(1))* Trentham Bks. Ltd. GBR. Dist: Stylus Publishing, LLC.

Ashby, Jeffrey S., et al. Active Interventions for Kids & Teens: Adding Adventure & Fun to Counseling! 2008. *(978-1-55620-256-8(3))* American Counseling Assn.

Assaye, Legesse. Early Adolescents' Perceived School Environment: Patterns of Cognitions, Affects & Behavior of Adolescents in Upper Primary Schools: A Path Analysis. 2011. 108p. pap. ***(978-3-639-33795-2(6))*** VDM Verlag Dr. Mueller e.K.

Attaway, Kenny. Potholes in my Lawn: (175 & More Effective Group Activities for Troubled Adolescent & Teens) 2010. 264p. 31.99 *(978-1-4520-8802-0(0))*; pap. 18.49 *(978-1-4520-8801-3(2))* AuthorHouse.

Bachman, Jerald G., et al. The Education-Drug Use Connection: How Successes & Failures in School Relate to Adolescent Smoking, Drinking, Drug Use, & Delinquency. 2007. (ENG., Illus.). 435p. 105.95 *(978-0-8058-6170-9(X))*; per. 52.95 *(978-0-8058-6171-6(8))* Taylor & Francis Group GBR. (Psychology Press). Dist: Taylor & Francis Group.

Baddeley, Gavin. Youth Cults: Teen Tribes & Subculture Style. 2011. (ENG., Illus.). 176p. pap. 19.95 *(978-0-85965-475-3(3))* Plexus Publishing, Ltd. GBR. Dist: Perseus-PGW.

Bagby, Daniel. Beyond the Myths: The Journey to Adulthood. 2007. 118p. per. 17.00 *(978-1-57312-488-1(5))* Smyth & Helwys Publishing, Inc.

Bailey, Deryl F. & Bradbury-Bailey, Mary. Project Gentlemen on the Move: Nurturing Excellence in African American Youth. 2012. (Routledge Series on Counseling & Psychotherapy with Boys & Men Ser.). (ENG.). 192p. 90.00 ***(978-0-415-88414-3(4))***; pap. 29.95 ***(978-0-415-88415-0(2))*** Routledge.

Bailey, Sue. The Young Mind: An Essential Guide to Mental Health for Young Adults, Parents & Teachers. Shooter, Mike, ed. 2012. (ENG.). 400p. pap. 14.95 *(978-0-553-82418-6(X))* Transworld Publishers Ltd. GBR. Dist: Independent Pubs. Group.

Bainbridge, David. Teenagers: A Natural History, 1 vol. 2009. (ENG., Illus.). 364p. pap. 16.00 *(978-1-55365-437-7(4)*, Greystone Bks.) D&M Pubs. Inc. CAN. Dist: Perseus-PGW.

Bakewell, Lisa, ed. Mental Health Information for Teens. 3rd rev. ed. 2010. (Teen Health Ser.). 448p. (YA). lib. bdg. 69.00 *(978-0-7808-1087-7(2))* Omnigraphics, Inc.

Baksh, Nadir & Murphy, Laurie. You Don't Know Anything...! A Manual for Parenting Your Teenagers. 2008. (ENG.). 224p. pap. 12.95 *(978-1-890772-82-6(8))* Hohm Pr.

Banaschewski, Tobias & Rohde, L. A. Biological Child Psychiatry: Recent Trends & Developments. 2008. (Advances in Biological Psychiatry Ser.). (Illus.). 256p. *(978-3-8055-8482-1(2))* Karger, S. AG.

Barankin, Tatyana & Khanlou, Nazilla. Growing up Resilient: Ways to Build Resilience in Children & Youth. 2007. ***(978-0-88868-504-9(1))*** Centre for Addiction & Mental Health.

Baris, Latif & Uzun, Özertan, eds. Psychology of Adolescence: New Research. 2012. ***(978-1-61942-860-7(1))*** Nova Science Pubs., Inc.

Barkley, Russell A., et al. Your Defiant Teen: 10 Steps to Resolve Conflict & Rebuild Your Relationship. 2008. (ENG., Illus.). 326p. 40.00 *(978-1-59385-584-0(2))* Guilford Pubns., Inc.

Bayat, Asef & Herrera, Linda. Being Young & Muslim: New Cultural Politics in the Global South & North, 1 vol. 2010. (Religion & Global Politics Ser.). (ENG., Illus.). 464p. pap. 29.95 *(978-0-19-536920-5(3))* Oxford Univ. Pr., Inc.

Bazant, Rick. The Family System Effects on Children Placed in Out-of-Home Care. 2010. 64p. pap. *(978-3-639-23427-5(8))* VDM Verlag Dr. Mueller e.K.

Beck, Debra. My Feet Aren't Ugly: A Girl's Guide to Loving Herself from the Inside Out. 2011. 176p. pap. 12.95 *(978-0-8253-0602-0(7))* Beaufort Bks., Inc.

Bellak-Adams, Kerin. AD/HD Success! Solutions for Boosting Self-Esteem the Diary Method for Ages 7-17. 2010. 146p. pap. *(978-1-61599-024-5(0))* Loving Healing Pr., Inc.

Berger, Kathleen Stassen. The Developing Person Through Childhood & Adolescence. 8th ed. 2008. (ENG., Illus.). 608p. (C). pap. 137.95 *(978-1-4292-2080-4(5))* Worth Pubs., Inc.

Berger, Kathleen Stassen & Straub, Richard O. The Developing Person Through Childhood & Adolescence. 8th ed. 2008. (ENG.). 404p. (C). pap., stu. ed. 30.95 *(978-1-4292-1782-8(0))* Worth Pubs., Inc.

Best, Amy L., ed. Representing Youth: Methodological Issues in Critical Youth Studies. 2007. (ENG.). 360p. 75.00 *(978-0-8147-9952-9(3))*; per. 24.00 *(978-0-8147-9953-6(1))* New York Univ. Pr.

Beth, Patti. Forgiveness & Implicit Theories in Early Adolescents. 2008. 68p. pap. *(978-3-8364-7492-4(1))* VDM Verlag Dr. Mueller e.K.

Biglan, Anthony, et al, eds. Preventing Youth Problems. 2010. (Issues in Children's & Families' Lives Ser.). 196p. pap. 84.95 *(978-1-4419-3398-0(0)*, 1441933980) Springer.

Bisagni, Francesco, et al. Jung Today: Volume 2- Childhood & Adolescence. 2009. (Advances in Psychology Research Ser.). 79.00 *(978-1-60741-894-8(0))* Nova Science Pubs., Inc.

Blowers, Jerimy. Together We Move Forward: Utilizing Positive Psychology & Prevention Science in the Advancement of Youth Development. 2008. 136p. pap. *(978-3-639-02611-5(X))* VDM Verlag Dr. Mueller e.K.

Blyth, Maggie & Soloman, Enver. Prevention & Youth Crime: Is Early Intervention Working? 2008. (Illus.). 136p. pap. 29.95 *(978-1-84742-263-7(2))* Policy Pr. GBR. Dist: Chicago Distribution Ctr.

Boles, Blake. College Without High School: A Teenager's Guide to Skipping High School & Going to College. 2009. (ENG.). 176p. pap. 16.95 *(978-0-86571-655-1(2)*, 9780865716551) New Society Pubs., Ltd. CAN. Dist: Consortium Bk. Sales & Distribution.

Bonino, Silvia, et al. Adolescents & Risk: Behaviors, functions & protective Factors. 2010. (ENG., Illus.). xii, 371p. pap. 139.00 *(978-88-470-1551-7(0)*, 8847015510) Springer.

Bowers, Edmond P., et al, eds. Thriving in Childhood & Adolescence - The Role of Self Regulation Processes. 2011. (J-B CAD Single Issue Child & Adolescent Development Ser.: 104). (ENG.). 112p. pap. 29.00 *(978-1-118-09410-5(7)*, Jossey-Bass) Wiley, John & Sons, Inc.

Bowers, Linda, et al. Tasks of Problem Solving Adolescent. 2007. (YA). per. 39.95 *(978-0-7606-0744-2(3))* LinguiSystems, Inc.

—TOPS 2 Adolescent Test Form. 2007. (YA). 41.95 *(978-0-7606-9999-7(2))* LinguiSystems, Inc.

—TOPS 2 Adolescent Test Manual. 2007. spiral bd. 80.00 *(978-0-7606-0712-1(5))* LinguiSystems, Inc.

—TOPS 2 Adolescent Test Reading Passages Book. 2007. spiral bd. 40.00 *(978-0-7606-0761-9(3))* LinguiSystems, Inc.

Branwhite, Tony, ed. Helping Adolescents in School. 2008. (Illus.). 200p. pap. 45.99 *(978-1-59311-310-0(2))* Information Age Publishing, Inc.

Bray, Peter. Hamlet's Crisis of Consciousness: The Deeper Dimensions of Adolescent Loss. 2008. 472p. pap. *(978-3-639-09998-0(2))* VDM Verlag Dr. Mueller e.K.

Brent, David A., et al. Treating Depressed & Suicidal Adolescents: A Clinician's Guide. 2011. (ENG.). 276p. 35.00 *(978-1-60623-957-5(0))* Guilford Pubns., Inc.

Brezina, Corona. Frequently Asked Questions about When a Friend Dies. 2009. (FAQ: Teen Life Ser.). 64p. (gr. 5-6). 58.50 *(978-1-61512-592-0(2))* Rosen Publishing Group, Inc., The.

—When a Friend Dies. 2007. (FAQ Ser.). (Illus.). 64p. (YA). (gr. 7-12). lib. bdg. 29.25 *(978-1-4042-1935-9(8))* Rosen Publishing Group, Inc., The.

Brodie, Bruce R. Adolescence & Delinquency: An Object Relations Theory Approach. 2007. (ENG., Illus.). 192p. 89.50 *(978-0-7657-0473-3(0))*; per. 36.99 *(978-0-7657-0474-0(9))* Rowman & Littlefield Publishers, Inc.

Brown, B. Bradford & Prinstein, Mitchell J., eds. Encyclopedia of Adolescence, Three-Volume Set, 3 vols. 2011. (ENG.). 1294p. 1175.00 *(978-0-12-373915-5(2)*, Academic Pr.) Elsevier Science & Technology Bks.

The BROWN UNIVERSITY CHILD & ADOLESCENT BEHAVIOR Letter, 27/5. 2011. 16.58 *(978-1-118-02027-2(8)*, Wiley) Wiley, John & Sons, Inc.

The BROWN UNIVERSITY CHILD & ADOLESCENT BEHAVIOR Letter, 27/6. 2011. 16.58 *(978-1-118-02028-9(6)*, Wiley) Wiley, John & Sons, Inc.

The BROWN UNIVERSITY CHILD & ADOLESCENT PSYCHOPHARMACOLOGY UPDATE 13/05. 2011. 16.58 *(978-1-118-02015-9(4)*, Wiley) Wiley, John & Sons, Inc.

The BROWN UNIVERSITY CHILD & ADOLESCENT PSYCHOPHARMACOLOGY UPDATE 13/06. 2011. 16.58 *(978-1-118-02016-6(2)*, Wiley) Wiley, John & Sons, Inc.

Browning, Deborah L., ed. Adolescent Identities: A Collection of Readings. 2007. (Relational Perspectives Book Ser.: Vol. 37). (ENG.). 377p. 66.95 *(978-0-88163-461-7(1))* Routledge.

Broyles, Dan. Helping Teens at Risk of Suicide. 2010. 52p. pap. *(978-3-8383-4407-2(3))* Lambert Academic Publishing.

Bulbeck, Chilla. Sex, Love & Feminism in the Asia Pacific: A Cross-Cultural Study of Young People's Attitudes. 2008. (ASAA Women in Asia Ser.). (Illus.). XVI, 272p. 150.00 *(978-0-415-47006-3(4))* Routledge.

Burnham, Simon. Let's Talk: Using Personal Construct Psychology to Support Children & Young People. 2008. (Lucky Duck Bks.). (Illus.). 96p. pap. 28.00 *(978-1-4129-2089-6(2)*, B20884P) SAGE Pubns., Ltd. GBR. Dist: SAGE Pubns., Inc.

Bytheway, John. You're Gonna Make It Through Junior High. 2006. (Illus.). 128p. (YA). pap. 10.95 *(978-1-59038-733-7(3))* Desert Bks.

CAD. Core Competencies to Prevent Problem Behaviors & Promote Positive Youth Development, No. 122. Bradshaw, Catherine P. & Guerra, Nancy G., eds. 2008. (J-B CAD Single Issue Child & Adolescent Development Ser.: 92). (ENG.). 112p. pap. 29.00 *(978-0-470-44216-6(6)*, Jossey-Bass) Wiley, John & Sons, Inc.

CAD Staff. The Development of Autobiographical Reasoning in Adolescence & Beyond, No. 131. Habermas, Tilmann, ed. 2011. (J-B CAD Single Issue Child & Adolescent Development Ser.: 102). (ENG.). 112p. pap. 29.00 *(978-1-118-00380-0(2)*, Jossey-Bass) Wiley, John & Sons, Inc.

Caevel, Henri de & Balasc-Variéras, Christophe. Pourquoi les Adolescents Nous Poussent-Ils à Inventer? 2008. (FRE.). 207p. *(978-2-7492-0948-7(X))* Eres Editions.

Callaizakis-Higgins, Georgane. Exploration of Remorse As a Transformative Experience for Young Adults - Restorative Justice & Homeless Youth. 2007. 164p. per. *(978-3-8364-2841-5(5))* VDM Verlag Dr. Mueller e.K.

Canovas Sanchez, Francisco. Psicologia Evolutiva del Adolescente. (SPA.). 128p. 5.95 *(978-958-607-338-7(6))* Sociedad de San Pablo COL. Dist: St Pauls/Alba Hse. Pubs.

Carlson, Dennis. The Education of Eros: A History of Education & the Problem of Adolescent Sexuality. 2012. (Studies in Curriculum Theory Ser.). (ENG.). 216p. 125.00 ***(978-0-415-80851-4(0))*** Routledge.

Carlson, Joanne E. The Parent Effect: How Parenting Style Affects Adolescent Behavior & Personality Development. 2011. *(978-0-87101-417-7(3)*, NASW Pr.) National Assn. of Social Workers/NASW Pr.

Carlson, Jon & Lewis, Judith A. Counseling the Adolescent: Individual, Family, & School Interventions. 5th ed. 2007. (Illus.). 528p. (C). pap. 70.00 *(978-0-89108-320-7(0))* Love Publishing Co.

Carpentier, Melissa Y. & Mullins, Larry Lee. Adolescents with Cancer: The Influence of Close Relationships on Quality of Life, Distress, & Health Behaviors. 2008. 172p. 94.95 *(978-1-60497-580-2(6))* Cambria Pr.

Carskadon, Mary A., ed. Adolescent Sleep Patterns: Biological, Social, & Psychological Influences. 2010. (ENG.). 318p. pap. 39.99 *(978-0-521-16869-4(4))* Cambridge Univ. Pr.

Case, Paul. What Now? How Teen Therapeutic Programs Could Save Your Troubled Child. 2008. (ENG.). 208p. per. 17.95 *(978-1-934314-30-2(7))* Common Thread Media, LLC.

—What Now? How Teen Therapeutic Programs Could Save Your Troubled Child. 2008. (ENG.). 208p. pap. 17.95 *(978-1-59186-358-8(9))* Cool Springs Pr.

Casterline, Roger. The Ike Disease: Your Name Is Tracy. 2009. 52p. pap. 9.95 *(978-1-60693-796-9(0)*, Eloquent Bks.) AEG Literary Publishing Services, Inc.

Cbl. The Brown University Child & Adolescent Behavior Letter. 2011. (ENG.). 16.58 *(978-1-118-02033-3(2))*; 16.58 *(978-1-118-02032-6(4)*, Wiley); 16.58 *(978-1-118-02030-2(8)*, Wiley) Wiley, John & Sons, Inc.

—The Brown University Child & Adolescent Behavior Letter, 27/11. 2011. 16.58 ***(978-1-118-02034-0(0)***, Wiley) Wiley, John & Sons, Inc.

Cbl. The BROWN UNIVERSITY CHILD & ADOLESCENT BEHAVIOR Letter, 27/7. 2011. 16.58 *(978-1-118-02029-6(4)*, Wiley) Wiley, John & Sons, Inc.

Chadwick, Dara. You'd Be So Pretty If... Teaching Our Daughters to Love Their Bodies - Even When We Don't Love Our Own. 2009. (ENG.). 256p. pap. 15.95 *(978-0-7382-1258-6(X))* Da Capo Pr., Inc.

Chalachew Wassie, Wollie. Causal Attributions for Poverty among Youths. 2010. 80p. pap. *(978-3-639-28298-6(1))* VDM Verlag Dr. Mueller e.K.

Chalmers, Phil. Inside the Mind of a Teen Killer, 0 vols. 2010. 248p. pap. 14.99 *(978-1-59555-977-7(9))* Nelson, Thomas Inc.

Child and Adolescent Development Staff (CAD). The Intersections of Personal & Social Identities: New Directions for Child & Adolescent Development. Radmacher, Kimberly Ann et al, eds. 2008. (J-B CAD Single Issue Child & Adolescent Development Ser.: 90). (ENG.). 112p. pap. 29.00 *(978-0-470-37283-8(4)*, Jossey-Bass) Wiley, John & Sons, Inc.

Chimunhu, Jephias. Late Adolescents' Perceptions of the Relevance of Domains of Identity. 2011. 80p. pap. ***(978-3-8443-2511-9(5))*** Lambert Academic Publishing.

Christopher, Combates A. & Combates, Christopher. The Law of Attraction for Teens: How to Attract More of the Good Stuff & Get Rid of the Bad Stuff. 2011. (ENG.). 120p. pap. 13.95 ***(978-1-936332-29-8(9))*** Youngs, Bettie Bks.

Clark, Chap & Rabey, Steve. When Kids Hurt: Help for Adults Navigating the Adolescent Maze, 1 vol. 2009. 208p. pap. 13.99 *(978-0-8010-7183-6(6))* Baker Bks.

Clark, Hireshemo. One Last Chance High. 2008. 224p. pap. *(978-3-639-07831-2(4))* VDM Verlag Dr. Mueller e.K.

Claycomb, Shedrick & Goodlet, Deidre. A Common Sense Guide Working with Teens Pocket Edition. 2008. 48p. pap. 15.95 *(978-1-4357-2688-8(X))* Lulu Enterprises Inc.

Cobb & Cram101 Textbook Reviews Staff. Adolescence: Continuity, Change, & Diversity. 2007. 160p. per. 12.95 *(978-1-4288-2072-2(8))* Cram101 Inc.

Cobb, Nancy J. Adolescence: Continuity, Change, & Diversity. 7th rev. ed. 2010. (Illus.). 600p. ***(978-0-87893-338-9(7))*** Sinauer Assocs., Inc.

Cobert. Tarascon Adult Psychiatrica. rev. ed. 2010. 344p. pap. 24.95 *(978-0-7637-7639-8(4)*, Tarascon) Jones & Bartlett Learning, LLC.

Coch, Donna, et al, eds. Human Behavior, Learning, & the Developing Brain: Typical Development. 2007. (ENG., Illus.). 412p. 60.00 *(978-1-59385-136-1(7))* Guilford Pubns., Inc.

Collins, W. Andrew & Laursen, Brett, eds. Relationship Pathways: From Adolescence to Young Adulthood. 2011. (Illus.). 360p. (C). pap. 56.00 ***(978-1-4129-8739-4(3)***, B87394P) SAGE Pubns., Inc.

Committee on the Science of Adolescence, et al. The Science of Adolescent Risk-Taking: Workshop Report. 2011. (ENG.). 144p. pap. 35.00 *(978-0-309-15852-7(4))* National Academies Pr.

Cooper, Barbara. The Social Success Workbook for Teens: Skill-Building Activities for Teens with Nonverbal Learning Disorder, Asperger's Disorder, & Other Social-Skill Problems. 2008. (Instant Help Ser.). (ENG.). 144p. (J). pap. 32.95 *(978-1-57224-653-9(7))* Play2Grow.

Corbin, Barry. Unleashing the Potential of the Teenage Brain: Ten Powerful Ideas. 2007. 168p. 62.95 *(978-1-4129-5762-5(1)*, B42497C); per. 31.95 *(978-1-4129-4249-2(7)*, B42497P) Corwin Pr.

Corijn, M. & Klijzing, Erik, eds. Transitions to Adulthood in Europe. 2010. (European Studies of Population Ser.). (Illus.). 364p. pap. 269.00 *(978-90-481-5701-3(3)*, 9048157013) Springer.

Cotterell, John. Social Networks in Youth & Adolescence. 2nd ed. 2007. (Adolescence & Society Ser.). (ENG., Illus.). 328p. per. 49.99 *(978-0-415-35950-4(3))* Routledge.

—Social Networks&Soc Influ Adol Ed2. 2nd ed. 2007. (Adolescence & Society Ser.). (ENG., Illus.). 328p. 110.00 *(978-0-415-35949-8(X))* Routledge.

Cozic, Charles. Teenage mental Illness. 2011. (Compact Research Ser.). 96p. (YA). (gr. 7-12). lib. bdg. 27.95 *(978-1-60152-167-5(7))* ReferencePoint Pr., Inc.

Cpu. The Brown University Child & Adolescent Psychopharmacology. 2011. 16.58 *(978-1-118-02020-3(0))*; 16.58 *(978-1-118-02019-7(7))*; 16.58 *(978-1-118-02018-0(9))*; 16.58 *(978-1-118-02017-3(0))* Wiley, John & Sons, Inc. (Wiley).

Cram101 Textbook Reviews. Outlines & Highlights for Adolescence by John W Santrock, Isbn: 9780073133720 0073133728 9780073228754 9780073314815. 2011. 234p. pap. 31.95 ***(978-1-61698-333-8(7))*** Cram101 Inc.

—Outlines & Highlights for Adolescence, Risk & Resilience: Against the Odds by Ann Hagell. 2011. 84p. pap. 27.95 ***(978-1-4288-2295-5(X))*** Cram101 Inc.

Cram101 Textbook Reviews. Outlines & Highlights for Child & Adolescent Development: An Advanced Course by William Damon, ISBN. 2010. 174p. pap. 29.95 *(978-1-61654-494-2(5))* Cram101 Inc.

Cram101 Textbook Reviews & Cram101 Textbook Reviews. Outlines & Highlights for Abnormal Child & Adolescent Psychology by Jean E Dumas. 2011. 138p. pap. 28.95 ***(978-1-61830-364-6(3))*** Cram101 Inc.

—Outlines & Highlights for Adolescent Development by John Dacey, Isbn: 9780759359635 9780759359635. 2011. 98p. pap. 27.95 ***(978-1-4288-7765-8(7))*** Cram101 Inc.

—Outlines & Highlights for Behavioral, Social, & Emotional Assessment of Children & Adolescents by Kenneth Merrell, Isbn: 9780805853704. 2011. 72p. pap. 27.95 ***(978-1-61698-263-8(2))*** Cram101 Inc.

—Outlines & Highlights for Constructing Adulthood: Agency & Subjectivity in Adolescence & Adulthood, Vol. 11 by Ross Macmillan, ISBN. 2011. 108p. pap. 28.95 ***(978-1-61744-943-7(1))*** Cram101 Inc.

—Outlines & Highlights for Romantic Relationships in Emerging Adulthood by Frank Fincham, Isbn: 9780521195300. 2011. 90p. pap. 27.95 ***(978-1-61461-584-2(5))*** Cram101 Inc.

—Outlines & Highlights for the Adolescent: Development, Relationships, & Culture by Kim Dolgin, ISBN. 2011. 282p. pap. 32.95 ***(978-1-61461-663-4(9))*** Cram101 Inc.

—Outlines & Highlights for the Handbook of Child & Adolescent Clinical Psychology: A Contextual Approach by Alan Carr. 2011. 94p. pap. 27.95 ***(978-1-61830-298-4(1))*** Cram101 Inc.

Cram101 Textbook Reviews Staff. Outlines & Highlights for Adolescence by Santrock, Isbn. 2008. 136p. pap. 11.95 *(978-1-4288-5876-3(8))* Cram101 Inc.

—Outlines & Highlights for Adolescence by Steinberg, Isbn. 2008. 132p. pap. 11.95 *(978-1-4288-5873-2(3))*; 140p. pap. 11.95 *(978-1-4288-5874-9(1))* Cram101 Inc.

—Outlines & Highlights for Adolescent: Development, Relationships, & Culture by Rice, ISBN. 2008. 164p. pap. 12.95 *(978-1-4288-5958-6(6))* Cram101 Inc.

—Outlines & Highlights for Child Development & Education by Mcdevitt, Isbn: 0131188178. 2008. 220p. pap. 13.95 *(978-1-4288-6011-7(8))* Cram101 Inc.

—Outlines & Highlights for Child Development by Feldman, Isbn: 0131732471. 2008. 176p. pap. 12.95 *(978-1-4288-5964-7(0))* Cram101 Inc.

—Outlines & Highlights for Developmental Psychology: Childhood & Adolescence by Shaffer, ISBN. 2008. 152p. pap. 12.95 *(978-1-4288-5789-6(3))* Cram101 Inc.

—Outlines & Highlights for Middle Childhood to Middle Adolescence: Development from Ages 8 to 18 by Blume, ISBN. 2008. 152p. pap. 12.95 *(978-1-4288-5975-3(6))* Cram101 Inc.

Crawford, Glenda Beamon. Brain-Based Teaching with Adolescent Learning in Mind. 2nd rev. ed. 2007. (Illus.). 208p. per. 33.95 *(978-1-4129-5019-0(8)*, B5018XP) Corwin Pr.

Crawford, Glenda Beamon, ed. Differentiation for the Adolescent Learner: Accommodating Brain Development, Language, Literacy, & Special Needs. 2008. (Illus.). 184p. pap. 36.95 *(978-1-4129-4054-2(0)*, B40532P) Corwin Pr.

Crenshaw, David A., ed. Child & Adolescent Psychotherapy: Wounded Spirits & Healing Paths. 2010. (ENG.). 178p. pap. 26.50 *(978-0-7657-0599-0(0)*, Aronson, Jason) Rowman & Littlefield Publishers, Inc.

Cross, Richard. The Effect of Chronic Trauma in Children & Adolescents. 2011. pap. 34.95 *(978-1-85575-499-7(1))* Karnac Bks. GBR. Dist: Stylus Publishing, LLC.

Curtis, Brian E. Wake up Young Brother. 2008. 160p. per. 13.99 *(978-1-60477-502-0(5))* Xulon Pr., Inc.

D' Ambrosio, Jay. Rethinking Adolescence: Using Story to Navigate Life's Uncharted Years. 2006. (ENG.). 166p. per. 29.95 *(978-1-57886-477-5(1))*; 55.00 *(978-1-57886-476-8(3))* Rowman & Littlefield Education.

Daniel. Adolescents' Perceptions of Deviance While Using the Internet. 2010. 152p. pap. *(978-3-639-22669-0(0))* VDM Verlag Dr. Mueller e.K.

Darlon, Earl B. Adolescent Behavior Research Advances. 2007. 235p. 129.00 *(978-1-60021-695-4(1))* Nova Science Pubs., Inc.

Davies, Chris & Eynon, Rebecca. Teenagers & Technology. 2012. (Adolescence & Society Ser.). (ENG.). 178p. 88.11 *(978-0-415-68457-6(9)*, Routledge) Taylor & Francis Group GBR. Dist: Taylor & Francis Group.

Davis, Christopher. Walk with Me, the Journey. 2008. 128p. pap. 10.95 *(978-1-4357-1460-1(1))* Lulu Enterprises Inc.

Davis, Joan. Past to Present: A Stitch in Time. 2011. 116p. pap. 16.00 *(978-1-4490-7208-7(9))* AuthorHouse.

Dawson, David Laing. The Adolescent Owner's Manual. 2010. 144p. *(978-0-9866522-0-2(2))* Bridgeross Communications Inc.

Dawson, Peg & Guare, Richard. Coaching Students with Executive Skills Deficits. 2012. (Guilford Practical Intervention in the Schools Ser.). (ENG., Illus.). 240p. (gr. k-12). pap. 35.00 (978-1-4625-0375-9(6)) Guilford Pubns., Inc.

Deed, Craig. School Based Early Intervention for Adolescents at Risk. 2011. 276p. pap. (978-3-8443-1553-0(5)) Lambert Academic Publishing.

Derevensky, Jeffrey L., et al, eds. Youth Gambling: The Hidden Addiction. 2011. (Health, Medicine & Human Development Ser.). (ENG., Illus.). XVIII, 265p. 210.00 (978-3-11-916694-2(4)); 140.00 (978-3-11-025520-1(0)) De Gruyter, Walter Inc.

Deutsch, Nancy. Pride in the Projects: Teens Building Identities in Urban Contexts. 2008. (ENG., Illus.). 312p. pap. 23.00 (978-0-8147-1992-3(9)) New York Univ. Pr.

DiClemente, Ralph J., et al, eds. Adolescent Health: Understanding & Preventing Risk Behaviors. 2009. (ENG., Illus.). 608p. 85.00 (978-0-470-17676-4(8), Jossey-Bass) Wiley, John & Sons, Inc.

DiMarco, Hayley. Mean. 2009. (Pocket Bible Study & Journal Ser.). 128p. (YA). pap. 7.99 (978-0-8007-3413-8(0)) Revell.

DiMarco, Hayley & Lookadoo, Justin. The Dirt on Breaking Up. 2008. (Dirt Ser.). 120p. reprint ed. pap. 7.99 (978-0-8007-3295-0(2)) Revell.

Dolgin, Kim Gale. The Adolescent: Development, Relationships, & Culture. 13th rev. ed. 2010. (ENG., Illus.). 528p. (C). 150.00 (978-0-205-73136-7(8), Prentice Hall) Prentice Hall PTR.

—The Adolescent: Development, Relationships, & Culture, Books a la Carte Edition. 13th ed. 2011. (ENG.). 528p. (C). ring bd. 96.20 (978-0-205-01127-8(6), Prentice Hall) Prentice Hall PTR.

—The Adolescent: Development, Relationships, & Culture, Books a la Carte Plus MyDevelopmentLab. 13th ed. 2011. (ENG.). (C). ring bd. 104.67 (978-0-205-01226-8(4), Prentice Hall) Prentice Hall PTR.

Drysdale, Maureen & Rye, B. J. Clashing Views in Adolescence. 2nd ed. 2008. (Taking Sides Ser.). (ENG.). 480p. (C). pap. 48.00 (978-0-07-351536-6(1), 0073515361, McGraw-Hill/Dushkin) McGraw-Hill Higher Education.

Duffy, John. The Available Parent: Radical Optimism for Raising Teens & Tweens. 2011. (ENG., Illus.). 252p. pap. 15.95 (978-1-57344-657-0(2), Viva Editions) Cleis Pr.

Dunkels, Elza, et al, eds. Interactive Media Use & Youth: Learning, Knowledge Exchange & Behavior. 2010. 350p. 180.00 (978-1-60960-206-2(4), Information Science Reference) IGI Global.

Eastham, Chad. Guys Like Girls Who..., 0 vols. 2008. 240p. (YA). pap. 14.99 (978-1-4003-1300-6(7)) Nelson, Thomas Inc.

Ebel, Deborah Clark. The Forgotten Future: Adolescents in Crisis. 2008. 276p. pap. 17.95 (978-1-4327-1935-7(1)) Outskirts Pr., Inc.

Edelston. The Problems of Adolescents. 192p. (978-0-8022-1956-5(X)) Philosophical Library, Inc.

Eder, Michael, et al. Portraying Identity Through Art: A Sourcebook for Middle-Grade Visual Arts Teachers. Cunningham, Jennifer & Rothman, Michael, eds. 2008. (Wisdom of Educators Ser.). (ENG., Illus.). 117p. spiral bd. (978-0-9763600-5-6(5)) Neighborhood Hse. Charter Schl.

Eisenberg, Nancy, et al. Understanding Mother-Adolescent Conflict Discussions: Concurrent & Across-Time Prediction from Youths' Dispositions on Parenting. 2008. (Monographs of the Society for Research in Child Development Ser.: 1). (ENG., Illus.). 300p. pap. 39.95 (978-1-4051-9214-9(3), Wiley-Blackwell) Wiley, John & Sons, Inc.

Elliott, Gregory C. Family Matters: The Importance of Mattering to Family in Adolescence. 2009. (ENG., Illus.). 288p. 116.95 (978-1-4051-6242-5(2), Wiley-Blackwell) Wiley, John & Sons, Inc.

Elliott, Gregory C. & Elliott, Gregory. Family Matters: The Importance of Mattering to Family in Adolescence. 2009. (ENG., Illus.). 288p. pap. 57.95 (978-1-4051-6243-2(0), Wiley-Blackwell) Wiley, John & Sons, Inc.

Elrod, Leslie. From Fat to Fabulous: Adolescent Obesity, Self-Esteem, & Coping Mechanisms. 2008. 132p. pap. (978-3-639-03299-4(3)) VDM Verlag Dr. Mueller e.K.

Enroth, Ronald M. Sectas y la Juventud: Youth Brainwashing - Extremist. (SPA.). 240p. (978-84-7228-516-3(2), 220807) Clie, Editorial.

Epstein, Robert. Teen 2.0: Saving Our Children & Families from the Torment of Adolescence. 2010. (ENG., Illus.). 500p. pap. 18.95 (978-1-884995-59-0(4)) Quill Driver Bks.

Evelyn, Veronica C. Adolescents, Television & the Internet: Subjective Responses to Objective Possibilities. 2010. 252p. pap. (978-3-639-27560-5(8)) VDM Verlag Dr. Mueller e.K.

Farmer, Lesley S. J. Teen Girls & Technology: What's the Problem, What's the Solution? 2008. (ENG.). 192p. 52.00 (978-0-8077-4876-3(5)); pap. 22.95 (978-0-8077-4875-6(7)) Teachers College Pr., Teachers College, Columbia Univ.

Farnfield, Steve. A Practical Guide to Using Attachment Theory & Research with Children & Young People. 2008. 240p. pap. (978-1-84310-100-0(9)) Kingsley, Jessica Ltd.

Feinstein, Sheryl. Inside the Teenage Brain: Parenting a Work in Progress. 2nd ed. 2009. (ENG.). 148p. 28.00 (978-1-60709-118-9(6)) Rowman & Littlefield Education.

—Parenting the Teenage Brain: Understanding a Work in Progress. 2007. (ENG.). 162p. 49.95 (978-1-57886-620-5(0)); per. 18.95 (978-1-57886-621-2(9)) Rowman & Littlefield Publishers, Inc.

—Teaching the at-Risk Teenage Brain. 2007. (ENG., Illus.). 162p. 55.00 (978-1-57886-646-5(4)); per. 23.95 (978-1-57886-647-2(2)) Rowman & Littlefield Education.

Feldman, Robert S. Adolescence. 2007. (ENG., Illus.). 560p. (C). per. 150.00 (978-0-13-175061-6(5), Prentice Hall) Prentice Hall PTR.

—Adolescence (with MyVirtualTeen Student Access Code Card) 2010. (ENG.). 560p. (C). pap. 156.67 (978-0-205-80149-7(8), Prentice Hall) Prentice Hall PTR.

Feldman, Robert S. Child Development. 6th ed. 2011. (ENG., Illus.). 552p. (C). 166.67 (978-0-205-25354-8(7), Prentice Hall) Prentice Hall PTR.

Fincham, Frank D. & Cui, Ming, eds. Romantic Relationships in Emerging Adulthood. 2010. (Advances in Personal Relationships Ser.). (ENG., Illus.). 352p. 90.00 (978-0-521-19530-0(6)) Cambridge Univ. Pr.

Fingerson, Laura. Girls in Power: Gender, Body, & Menstruation in Adolescence. 2006. 190p. 65.50 (978-0-7914-6899-9(2)); per. 29.95 (978-0-7914-6900-2(X)) State Univ. of New York Pr.

Fisher, Deborah & Rush, Lee. A Quick-Start Guide to Building Assets in Your Prevention Program. 2008. (ENG., Illus.). 28p. pap. 14.95 (978-1-57482-195-6(4)) Search Institute.

Fitzgerald, Susan & Ginsburg, Kenneth. Letting Go with Love & Confidence: Raising Responsible, Resilient, Self-Sufficient Teens in the 21st Century. 2011. (ENG.). 368p. (gr. 12). 18.00 (978-1-58333-429-4(7), Avery) Penguin Group (USA) Inc.

Flanagan, Caitlin. Girl Land. 2012. (ENG.). 224p. 25.99 (978-0-316-06598-6(6)) Little Brown & Co.

Fleeman, William. Managing Teen Anger & Violence: A Pathways to Peace Program. 2008. (ENG., Illus.). 230p. per. 19.95 (978-1-57023-276-3(8)) Impact Pubns.

Flores, Kim Sabo. Youth Participatory Evaluation: Strategies for Engaging Young People. 2007. (Research Methods for the Social Sciences Ser.: 14). (ENG.). 208p. per. 48.00 (978-0-7879-8392-5(6), Jossey-Bass) Wiley, John & Sons, Inc.

Foderaro, Al & Schmidt, Denise. It's Your Decision for Teens: A Commonsense Guide to Making Better Choices. 2011. 80p. pap. 12.50 (978-1-4634-4823-3(6)) AuthorHouse.

Fondren, Gloria. Adolescents' Perceptions about Ways They Develop Autonomy. 2010. 184p. pap. (978-3-8383-5252-7(1)) Lambert Academic Publishing.

Ford, Emily. What You Must Think of Me: A Firsthand Account of One Teenager's Experience with Social Anxiety Disorder. 2007. (Adolescent Mental Health Initiative Ser.). (ENG.). 208p. per. 9.95 (978-0-19-531303-1(8)) Oxford Univ. Pr., Inc.

Foust. Social Coping Strategy Endorsement of Gifted Adolescents. 2010. 60p. pap. (978-3-639-22360-6(8)) VDM Verlag Dr. Mueller e.K.

Fox, Annie. What's up with My Family? 2010. (Middle School Confidential Ser.). (ENG., Illus.). 96p. (YA). (gr. 6-9). pap. 9.99 (978-1-57542-333-3(2)) Free Spirit Publishing, Inc.

France, Alan. Understanding Youth in Late Modernity. 2007. 216p. pap. 39.95 (978-0-335-21534-8(3)); 203p. 119.95 (978-0-335-21535-5(1)) McGraw-Hill Professional Publishing.

Free Spirit Publishing. The Teen Guide to Global Action Cards. 2011. (ENG.). (gr. 6). 12.99 (978-1-57542-364-7(2)) Free Spirit Publishing, Inc.

Freeman, Arthur, et al. Guide to Early Psychological Evaluation: Children & Adolescents. 2010. (ENG., Illus.). 160p. pap. 18.95 (978-0-393-70539-3(0), 70539) Norton, W. W. & Co., Inc.

Fritsch, Sandra L. & Trivedi, Harsh K. Interface Between Pediatrics & Children's Mental Health: Pediatric Clinics. 2011. (Clinics: Internal Medicine Ser.: 58-4). (ENG.). 88.00 (978-1-4557-1229-8(9), Saunders) Elsevier - Health Sciences Div.

Frost, Nick & Shaw, Julie. Foster Care in Adolescence. 2012. (Adolescence & Society Ser.). (ENG.). (C). 80.00 (978-0-415-66522-3(1)); pap. 34.95 (978-0-415-66526-1(4)) Routledge.

Fuller, Andrew. Bright Kid Challenge: Ending Conflict & Unlocking the Potential of Smart, Challenging Children. 2008. (ENG.). 224p. pap. 14.95 (978-1-4022-1212-3(7)) Sourcebooks, Inc.

Furman, Wyndol, et al, eds. The Development of Romantic Relationships in Adolescence. 2011. (Cambridge Studies in Social & Emotional Development Ser.). (ENG.). 461p. pap. 55.00 (978-0-521-18125-9(9)) Cambridge Univ. Pr.

Gagnon, Justin. Bringing up the Dead. 2011. 112p. pap. (978-3-639-26551-4(3)) VDM Verlag Dr. Mueller e.K.

Gallup Youth Development Specialists Staff. Strengthsexplorer for Ages 10 to 14: From Gallup, the Creators of Strengthsfinder. 2nd ed. 2007. (ENG.). 28p. (J). (gr. 6-10). pap. 40.00 (978-1-59562-018-7(4)) Gallup Pr.

Garot, Robert. Who You Claim: Performing Gang Identity in School & on the Streets. 2010. (ENG.). 272p. pap. 22.00 (978-0-8147-3213-7(5)) New York Univ. Pr.

Garrod, et al. Adolescent Portraits: Identity, Relationships, & Challenges. 7th rev. ed. 2011. (ENG.). 336p. (C). pap. 78.00 (978-0-205-03623-3(6), Prentice Hall) Prentice Hall PTR.

Gavazzi, Stephen M. Families with Adolescents: Bridging the Gaps between Theory, Research, & Practice. 2011. (Advancing Responsible Adolescent Development Ser.). (ENG., Illus.). xvii, 197p. 129.00 (978-1-4419-8245-2(0), 1441982450) Springer.

Geldard, Kathryn, ed. Practical Interventions for Young People at Risk. 2009. 232p. (C). 112.00 (978-1-84787-561-7(0), B75617C); (Illus.). pap. 45.00 (978-1-84787-562-4(9), B75617P) SAGE Pubns., Ltd. GBR. Dist: SAGE Pubns., Inc.

Geldard, Kathryn & Geldard, David. Counselling Adolescents: The Proactive Approach for Young People. 3rd ed. 2009. (Illus.). 320p. (C). 124.00 (978-1-84860-642-5(7), B06425C); pap. 53.00 (978-1-84860-643-2(5), B06425P) SAGE Pubns., Ltd. GBR. Dist: SAGE Pubns., Inc.

Gevirtzman, Bruce J. An Intimate Understanding of America's Teenagers: Shaking Hands with Aliens, 1 vol. 2008. 288p. pap. 19.95 (978-0-313-34508-1(2), B34508, Praeger Pubs.) Greenwood Publishing Group, Inc.

Geyer, Roger. Internet-Savvy Youth. 2009. 176p. pap. (978-3-639-21150-4(2)) VDM Verlag Dr. Mueller e.K.

Gholam, Alain. Attachment Styles & Relationship Outcomes. 2011. 80p. pap. (978-3-8443-8654-7(8)) Lambert Academic Publishing.

Glick, Barry & Gibbs, John C. Aggression Replacement Training, Third Edition, Revised & Expanded (Book & CD) A Comprehensive Intervention for Aggressive Youth. 2010. pap. 35.95 (978-0-87822-637-5(0)) Research Pr.

Glicken, Morley D. Evidence-Based Practice with Emotionally Troubled Children & Adolescents. 2009. (Practical Resources for the Mental Health Professional Ser.). (ENG.). 664p. 72.95 (978-0-12-374523-1(3), Academic Pr.) Elsevier Science & Technology Bks.

Glover, William H. The Adolescent Owner's Manual: A Guide to Parenting Your Prodigal Teenager. 2007. (Illus.). 266p. per. 20.99 (978-1-60247-160-3(6)) Tate Publishing & Enterprises, LLC.

Godley, Susan Harrington. The Adolescent Community Reinforcement Approach for Adolescent Cannabis Users. 2006. (Cannabis Youth Treatment Ser.: Vol. 4). (Illus.). 252p. (C). reprint ed. pap. 40.00 (978-1-4223-0665-9(8)) DIANE Publishing Co.

Grant, Stephen, et al. BAM! Boys Advocacy & Mentoring: A Leader's Guide to Facilitating Strengths-Based Groups for Boys, Helping Boys Make Better Contact by Making Better Contact with Them. 2007. (Routledge Series on Counseling & Psychotherapy with Boys & Men). (ENG.). 192p. 39.95 (978-0-415-96318-3(4)) Routledge.

Graves, Kelly. Aggression among Female Adolescents. 2009. 68p. pap. (978-3-639-12870-3(2)) VDM Verlag Dr. Mueller e.K.

Greenberg, Michael. Hurry down Sunshine: A Father's Memoir of Love & Madness. 2009. (Vintage Ser.). (ENG.). 256p. pap. 14.95 (978-0-307-47354-7(6), Vintage) Knopf Doubleday Publishing Group.

—Hurry down Sunshine: A Father's Memoir of Love & Madness. 2008. (ENG.). 240p. 22.00 (978-1-59051-191-6(3)) Other Pr., LLC.

Greenberger, Robert. Frequently Asked Questions about Loneliness. (FAQ: Teen Life Ser.). 64p. 2009. (gr. 5-6). 58.50 (978-1-61512-581-4(7)) 2007. (Illus.). (YA). (gr. 7-12). lib. bdg. 29.25 (978-1-4042-1940-3(4)) Rosen Publishing Group, Inc., The.

Grenell, Rene S. Adolescent Behavior Research Studies. 2007. 129.00 (978-1-60021-696-1(X)) Nova Science Pubs., Inc.

Grigorenko, Elena L., ed. Handbook of Juvenile Forensic Psychology & Psychiatry, 2 vols. 2012. (ENG., Illus.). 620p. 349.00 (978-1-4614-0904-5(7), 1461409047) Springer.

Guilamo-Ramos, Vincent, et al, eds. Parental Monitoring of Adolescents: Current Perspectives for Researchers & Practitioners. 2010. (ENG., Illus.). 312p. (gr. 17). 90.00 (978-0-231-14080-5(0)); pap. 30.00 (978-0-231-14081-2(9)) Columbia Univ. Pr.

Hagell, Ann, ed. Changing Adolescence: Social Trends & Mental Health. 2012. 192p. 110.00 (978-1-4473-0104-2(8)) Policy Pr. GBR. Dist: Chicago Distribution Ctr.

Hagell, Ann, et al, eds. Changing Adolescence: Social Trends & Mental Health. 2012. 192p. pap. 34.95 (978-1-4473-0103-5(X)) Policy Pr. GBR. Dist: Chicago Distribution Ctr.

Hagell, Ann & Coleman, John, eds. Adolescence, Risk & Resilience: Against the Odds. 2008. (Understanding Adolescence Ser.). (ENG., Illus.). 210p. per. 55.95 (978-0-470-02503-1(4)); 134.95 (978-0-470-02502-4(6)) Wiley, John & Sons, Inc. (Wiley).

Hall, Georgia & Piha, Sam, eds. Preparing Youth for the Crossing from Adolescence to Early Adulthood No. 111: New Directions for Youth Development. 2006. (J-B MHS Single Issue Mental Health Services Ser.: 85). (ENG.). 144p. per. 29.00 (978-0-7879-9497-6(9), Jossey-Bass) Wiley, John & Sons, Inc.

Hangal, Suneetha & A Aminabhavi, Vijayalaxmi. Psychology of Adolescents. 2010. 192p. pap. (978-3-639-25312-2(4)) VDM Verlag Dr. Mueller e.K.

Harris, Alex & Harris, Brett. Do Hard Things: A Teenage Rebellion Against Low Expectations. 2008. (ENG.). 256p. 17.99 (978-1-60142-112-8(5), Multnomah) Doubleday Religious Publishing Group, The.

—Start Here: Doing Hard Things Right Where You Are. 2010. (ENG.). 176p. pap. 12.99 (978-1-60142-270-5(9), Multnomah) Doubleday Religious Publishing Group, The.

Harris, Ashley Rae. Is This Really My Family? Relating to Your Relatives. 2008. (Essential Health: Strong Beautiful Girls Ser.). 112p. (YA). (gr. 7-12). 34.22 (978-1-60453-101-5(0)) ABDO Publishing Co.

Harris, Jeffrey D. Yes, You Can Survive Adolescence & Beyond: Real Talk. 2011. 116p. 26.99 (978-1-4567-5637-6(0)); pap. 15.99 (978-1-4567-5636-9(2)) AuthorHouse.

Harris, Rita, et al. Engaging with Complexity: Child & Adolescent Mental Health & Education. 2011. 256p. pap. 34.95 (978-1-78049-003-8(8)) Karnac Bks. GBR. Dist: Stylus Publishing, LLC.

Hart, Angie & Blincow, Derek. Resilient Therapy: Working with Children & Families. 2007. (ENG., Illus.). 224p. (C). 95.00 (978-0-415-40384-9(7)); per. 37.50 (978-0-415-40385-6(5)) Routledge.

Hart, Archibald D. & Weber, Catherine Hart. Is Your Teen Stressed or Depressed? A Practical & Inspirational Guide for Parents of Hurting Teens, 0 vols. 2008. 320p. pap. 14.99 (978-0-7852-8940-1(2)) Nelson, Thomas Inc.

Harvey, Joel. Young Men in Prison: Surviving & Adapting to Life Inside. 2006. (ENG., Illus.). 240p. (C). 74.95 (978-1-84392-203-2(7)) Willan Publishing GBR. Dist: Taylor & Francis Group.

Haugen, David M. How Does Advertising Impact Teen Behavior? 2008. (At Issue Ser.). (ENG., Illus.). 88p. (YA). (gr. 10-12). 22.50 (978-0-7377-3923-7(1), Greenhaven Pr., Inc.) Cengage Gale.

Hauser, Stuart T., et al. Out of the Woods: Tales of Resilient Teens. 2008. (Adolescent Lives Ser.: 4). 336p. pap. 21.00 (978-0-674-02734-3(5)) Harvard Univ. Pr.

Hayman, Suzy. Raise a Happy Teenager. 2012. (Teach Yourself Ser.). (ENG.). 224p. pap. 15.95 (978-1-4441-0734-0(8), Hodder & Stoughton) Hodder General Publishing Div. GBR. Dist: Independent Pubs. Group.

Heemer, Art, et al. If You Love Me, Please Read This: A Challenge to the Men in Generation X & Y from the People Who Love Them. 2010. 124p. pap. 13.95 (978-1-4502-0582-5(8)) iUniverse, Inc.

Hermann, Mary. Ecstasy Use among Adolescents. 2009. 60p. pap. (978-3-639-06518-3(2)) VDM Verlag Dr. Mueller e.K.

Hewlett, Bonnie Lynn, ed. Adolescent Identity: Evolutionary, Developmental & Cultural Perspectives. 2012. (Routledge Studies in Anthropology Ser.). (ENG., Illus.). 328p. (C). 125.00 (978-0-415-89012-0(8)) Routledge.

Hoffmann, Willem. Being an Adolescent Suicide Survivor. 2008. 272p. per. (978-3-8364-6587-8(6)) VDM Verlag Dr. Mueller e.K.

Hoge, Dean & Jewell, Marti. The Next Generation of Pastoral Leaders: What the Church Needs to Know. 2010. (ENG.). 208p. pap. 11.95 (978-0-8294-2650-2(7)) Loyola Pr.

Hoge, Robert D., et al, eds. Treating the Juvenile Offender. 2008. (ENG., Illus.). 294p. (gr. 7-13). 40.00 (978-1-59385-639-7(3)) Guilford Pubns., Inc.

Holder, Christen & Robillard, Rachel. Self-Compassion, Self-Esteem, & Body Image. 2011. 68p. pap. (978-3-8443-9966-0(6)) Lambert Academic Publishing.

Homrich, Barbara J. Autonomy Disturbance As a Psychological Characteristic in Anorexi. 2008. 164p. pap. (978-3-639-02739-6(6)) VDM Verlag Dr. Mueller e.K.

Honor Books Publishing Staff, creator. Faith Unplugged: Stories for Girls to Challenge What You Believe & How You Live. 2006. (Unplugged Ser.). (ENG.). 192p. (YA). per. 12.99 (978-1-56292-715-8(9), 1562927159) Cook, David C.

—Faith Unplugged: Stories for Guys to Challenge What You Believe & How You Live. 2006. (Unplugged Ser.). (ENG.). 188p. (YA). per. 12.99 (978-1-56292-709-7(4), 1562927094) Cook, David C.

Horton, Will. Wisdom Keys for Greatness: Rules of Success for Teens. 2010. x, 112p. pap. (978-1-892274-74-8(4)) Wisdom Bks. Inc.

Hospice of the Valley, creator. Grief Speak: Hospice of the Valley Teen Grief Program. 2008. 32p. (YA). pap. 20.00 (978-0-9798490-2-2(0)) Hospice of the Valley.

Howe, Mark L. The Nature of Early Memory: An Adaptive Theory of the Genesis & Development of Memory, 1 vol. 2011. (ENG.). 272p. 59.95 (978-0-19-538141-2(6)) Oxford Univ. Pr., Inc.

Huberty, Thomas J. Anxiety & Depression in Children & Adolescents: Assessment, Intervention, & Prevention. 2012. (ENG., Illus.). xxv, 469p. 64.95 (978-1-4614-3108-4(5), 1461431085) Springer.

Hugger, Kai-Uwe. Junge Migranten online: Suche nach sozialer Anerkennung und Vergewisserung von Zugehörigkeit. 2009. (GER., Illus.). 321p. pap. (978-3-531-16151-8(2)) Westdeutscher Verlag GmbH.

Hume, Margee & Sullivan Mort, Gillian. At Odds: Examining the impact of on-line gambling on youth Wellbeing. 2011. 168p. pap. (978-3-8443-2859-2(9)) Lambert Academic Publishing.

Jackson, Sandy. Handbook of Adolescent Development. 2006. (ENG., Illus.). 440p. 110.00 (978-1-84169-200-5(X), Psychology Press) Taylor & Francis Group GBR. Dist: Taylor & Francis Group.

Jackson-Smith, Urana. Initiation Rights. 2010. 108p. pap. 14.95 (978-0-557-27135-1(5)) Lulu Enterprises Inc.

James, Allison & Christensen, Pia Monrad. Research with Children: Perspectives & Practices. Christensen, Pia & James, Allison, eds. 2nd rev. ed. 2008. (Illus.). (ENG.). 312p. (C). 45.95 (978-0-415-41684-9(1)); XVI, 296p. 150.00 (978-0-415-41683-2(3)) Routledge.

Jannette, Urciuoli. Community Violence & Post Traumatic Stress Symptoms (PTSS) An Urban Setting. 2011. 148p. pap. (978-3-639-34030-3(2)) VDM Verlag Dr. Mueller e.K.

Jaoui, Sylvaine. For Girls Only: The Ultimate Guide to Being a Girl. Bussell, Andrea, ed. 2010. (Sunscreen Ser.). (ENG., Illus.). 112p. (YA). (gr. 7-11). pap. 10.95 (978-0-8109-8432-5(6), Amulet Bks.) Abrams.

Jarvis, Ana C. & Jarvis, Peter. Learning to Be a Person in Society. 2008. (Illus.). 224p. pap. 42.95 (978-0-415-41903-1(4)) Routledge.

Jedding, Kenneth. Higher Education: On Life, Landing a Job, & Everything Else They Didn't Teach You in College. 2010. (ENG.). 256p. 19.99 (978-1-60529-676-0(7)) Rodale Pr., Inc.

Jensen, Lene Arnett & Mortimer, Jeylan T., eds. Social Class & Transitions to Adulthood: New Directions for Child & Adolescent Development. 2008. (J-B CAD Single Issue Child & Adolescent Development Ser.: 89). (ENG.). 112p. pap. 29.00 (978-0-470-29362-1(4), Jossey-Bass) Wiley, John & Sons, Inc.

Johnson & Barber. A Smoother Transition: Why Teenagers Make Rational & Irrational Choices. 2009. 120p. pap. 12.95 (978-1-4401-1661-2(X)) iUniverse, Inc.

Johnson, Patrick B. & Malow-Iroff, Micheline S. Adolescents & Risk: Making Sense of Adolescent Psychology, 1 vol. 2008. (Making Sense of Psychology

Ser.). (Illus.). 160p. 49.95 (978-0-313-33687-4(3), GR3687, Praeger Pubs.) Greenwood Publishing Group, Inc.

Jones, Gill. Youth. 2009. (Key Concepts Ser.: 17). (ENG.). 176p. 59.95 (978-0-7456-4094-5(X)) Polity Pr. GBR. Dist: Wiley, John & Sons, Inc.

Jones, Nick & Jones, Gill. Youth. 2009. (Key Concepts Ser.: 16). (ENG.). 176p. pap. 24.95 (978-0-7456-4095-2(8)) Polity Pr. GBR. Dist: Wiley, John & Sons, Inc.

Jongsma, Arthur E., Jr. Adolescent Set: Treatment 4th Edition, Homework 2nd Edition, Progress Notes 3rd Edition. 4th ed. 2006. (PracticePlanners Ser.: 232). (ENG.). 1184p. pap. 132.00 (978-0-470-06719-2(5), Wiley) Wiley, John & Sons, Inc.

Joronen, Katja. Adolescent Subjective Well-Being in Their Social Contexts. 2008. 160p. pap. (978-3-639-08557-0(4)) VDM Verlag Dr. Mueller e.K.

Joseph.Shipp. Momma's Only Son: An Urban Autobiography. 2011. 334p. pap. 29.95 (978-1-4560-9130-9(1)) PublishAmerica, Inc.

Joshi, Shashank & Pumariega, Andres. Cultural Issues in Pediatric Mental Health, an Issue of Child & Adolescent Psychiatric Clinics of North America. 2010. (Clinics: Internal Medicine Ser.: 19-4). (ENG., Illus.). xvii, 662p. 105.00 (978-1-4377-2433-2(7), Saunders) Elsevier - Health Sciences Div.

Jung, Hyang-Jin. Learning to Be an Individual: Emotion & Person in an American Junior High School. 2007. (Adolescent Cultures, School & Society Ser.: Vol. 41). 185p. (C). pap. 29.95 (978-0-8204-8655-0(8)) Lang, Peter Publishing, Inc.

Junger-Tas, Josine, et al. The Many Faces of Youth Crime: Contrasting Theoretical Perspectives on Juvenile Delinquency across Countries & Cultures. 2011. (ENG., Illus.). viii, 367p. 129.00 (978-1-4419-9454-7(8), 1441994548) Springer.

Junnarkar, Mohita, et al. Child Adoption: A study of Adopted Adolescents. 2011. 128p. pap. (978-3-8443-3207-0(3)) Lambert Academic Publishing.

Kahane, Reuven. The Origins of Postmodern Youth: Informal Youth Movements in a Comparative Perspective. (International Studies on Childhood & Adolescence Ser.). (ENG.). XIV, 266p. 196.00 (978-3-11-174284-7(9)) De Gruyter, Walter Inc.

Karg, Barb. The Girl's Guide to Werewolves: All You Need to Know about the Original Untamed Bad Boys. 2009. (ENG.). 192p. pap. 9.95 (978-1-4405-0221-7(8)) Adams Media Corp.

Kastner, Laura, et al. Getting to Calm: Cool-Headed Strategies for Parenting Tweens & Teens. 2009. (ENG., Illus.). 304p. pap. 19.95 (978-0-9823454-0-5(2)) ParentMap.

Kauder Nalebuff, Rachel. My Little Red Book. 2009. (ENG.). 240p. 14.99 (978-0-446-54636-2(4), Twelve) Grand Central Publishing.

Kearney, Christopher A. & Albano, Anne Marie. When Children Refuse School: A Cognitive-Behavioral Therapy Approach Therapist Guide. 2nd rev. ed. 2007. (Treatments That Work Ser.). (ENG., Illus.). 288p. (C). per. 42.95 (978-0-19-530830-3(1)) Oxford Univ. Pr., Inc.

Keck, Gregory C. Parenting Adopted Adolescents: Understanding & Appreciating Their Journeys. 2009. (Hollywood Nobody Ser.). (ENG.). 240p. pap. 17.99 (978-1-60006-281-0(4)) NavPress Publishing Group.

Kehily, Mary Jane, ed. Understanding Youth: Perspectives, Identities & Practices. 2007. (Published in Association with the Open University Ser.). (Illus.). 368p. (C). 146.00 (978-1-4129-3064-2(2), B30642C); pap. 60.00 (978-1-4129-3065-9(0), B30642P) SAGE Pubns., Ltd. GBR. Dist: SAGE Pubns., Inc.

Kenney, Shannon R. Adolescent Selves. 2008. 212p. per. (978-3-8364-3776-9(7)) VDM Verlag Dr. Mueller e.K.

Kerr, Margaret, et al, eds. What Can Parents Do? New Insights into the Role of Parents in Adolescent Problem Behavior. 2008. (Hot Topics in Developmental Research - a Series of Three Edited Volumes Ser.: 4). (ENG., Illus.). 304p. pap. 219.95 (978-0-470-72363-0(7), Wiley) Wiley, John & Sons, Inc.

Kim, Bunyoung. Stories of Adolescents in Remarried Families: A Pastoral-Narrative Approach. 2008. 272p. pap. (978-3-639-08554-9(X)) VDM Verlag Dr. Mueller e.K.

Kim, Jung-Mi & Lee, Chang-Hun. An Application of General Strain Theory to Korean Adolescents: A Test of the Relationship between Negative Stimuli at School & Delinquency. 2008. 100p. pap. (978-3-639-09639-2(8)) VDM Verlag Dr. Mueller e.K.

Kimes, Joanne, et al. Teenagers Suck: What to Do When Missed Curfews, Texting, & Mom, Can I Have the Keys Make You Miserable. 2009. (ENG.). 176p. pap. 9.95 (978-1-59869-898-5(2)) Adams Media Corp.

Kimokeo, Deborah. School-Based Suicide Prevention Program Planning. 2008. 240p. per. (978-3-8364-3814-8(3)) VDM Verlag Dr. Mueller e.K.

Kirchhubel, Julie. Adolescent Music Development. 2009. 616p. pap. (978-3-639-00088-7(9)) VDM Verlag Dr. Mueller e.K.

Kiselica, Mark, et al, eds. Counseling Troubled Boys: A Guidebook for Professionals. 2007. (Routledge Series on Counseling & Psychotherapy with Boys & Men: Vol. 1). (ENG., Illus.). 336p. 39.95 (978-0-415-95547-8(5)) Routledge.

Kollar, Diana. Perpetual Sojourning. 2010. 112p. pap. (978-3-8383-4502-4(9)) Lambert Academic Publishing.

Kramer, Laurie & Conger, Katherine J., eds. Siblings As Agents of Socialization: New Directions for Child & Adolescent Development, No. 126. 2009. (J-B CAD Single Issue Child & Adolescent Development Ser.: 97). (ENG.). 120p. pap. 29.00 (978-0-470-61459-4(5), Jossey-Bass) Wiley, John & Sons, Inc.

Kranz, Rachel & Hinshaw, Stephen. The Triple Bind: Saving Our Teenage Girls from Today's Pressures & Conflicting Expectations. 2009. (ENG.). 256p. pap. 15.00 (978-0-345-50400-5(3), Ballantine Bks.) Random House Publishing Group.

Kreyszig, Sheila. Imaginary Audience & Voice in Emerging Adulthood: the Undergraduate Student Experience: Foreword by Jeffrey Jensen Arnett. 2010. (Europäische Hochschulschriften. Reihe 6: Psychologie Ser.). 154p. pap. 49.95 (978-3-631-58330-2(3)) Lang, Peter GmbH, Europaischer Verlag der Wissenschaften DEU. Dist: Lang, Peter.

Krost, Chelsea. Nineteen: A Reflection of My Teenage Experience in an Extraordinary Life - What I Have Learned & What I Have to Share. 2011. (ENG.). 188p. pap. 15.95 (978-0-9819311-6-6(2)) Burman Books, Inc. CAN. Dist: Innovative Logistics.

Kumar, Sanjay, et al, eds. Indian Youth in a Transforming World: Attitudes & Perceptions. 2009. (Illus.). 208p. (C). pap. 29.95 (978-81-321-0171-0(5), B01710P) SAGE Pubns., Inc.

Kunnen, Saskia Elske, ed. Adolescent Development. 2011. (Studies in Adolescent Development Ser.). (ENG., Illus.). 192p. 77.00 (978-1-84872-037-4(8), Psychology Press) Taylor & Francis Group GBR. Dist: Taylor & Francis Group.

Lamke, Susan, et al. Safe & Healthy Secondary Schools: Strategies to Build Relationships, Teach Respect, & Deliver Meaningful Behavioral Support to Students. 2009. (ENG.). 220p. pap. 29.95 (978-1-934490-11-2(3)) Boys Town Pr.

Lampadari, Stavrina. I Love Myself, I Love Life: An Adolescent Sends 365 Love Messages to the World. Moutsopoulou, Christina & Tsilikidou, Eftychia, trs. 2010. (ENG., Illus.). 250p. pap. (978-1-84748-691-2(6)) Athena Pr.

Laser, Julie Anne & Nicotera, Nicole. Working with Adolescents: A Guide for Practitioners. 2010. (Social Work Practice with Children & Families Ser.). (ENG.). 311p. 40.00 (978-1-60918-035-5(6)) Guilford Pubns., Inc.

Latta, Nigel. Before Your Teenagers Drive You Crazy, Read This! Battlefield Wisdom for Stressed-Out Parents. 2008. (978-1-86950-713-8(4)) HarperCollins Pubs. Australia.

Le Messurier, Mark & Nawana Parker, Madhavi. What's the Buzz? Games & Activities to Improve Social Skills. 2011. (ENG., Illus.). 256p. 47.95 (978-0-415-58382-4(9)) Routledge.

Leake, Valerie. Steps Between, Steps Within. 2008. 136p. pap. (978-3-639-08567-9(1)) VDM Verlag Dr. Mueller e.K.

Leigh, Jennifer. Laid or Loved? The Secrets Guys Wish You Knew about Being a Dream Girl Instead of a Just-in-His-Jeans Girl. 2009. 253p. pap. 15.95 (978-0-9816258-3-6(5)) Ignite Reality.

—The Secrets Guys Wish You Knew about Love. 2009. (ENG.). 256p. pap. (978-0-9816258-5-0(1)) Ignite Reality.

Lerner, Richard M. The Good Teen: Rescuing Adolescence from the Myths of the Storm & Stress Years. 2008. (ENG.). 272p. 14.95 (978-0-307-34758-9(3), Three Rivers Pr.) Crown Publishing Group.

Lerner, Richard M. & Steinberg, Laurence. Handbook of Adolescent Psychology, 2 vols., Set. 3rd ed. 2009. (ENG., Illus.). 1000p. 296.00 (978-0-470-14920-1(5), Wiley) Wiley, John & Sons, Inc.

—Handbook of Adolescent Psychology: Contextual Influences on Adolescent Development, 2 vols., Volume 2. 3rd ed. 2009. (ENG., Illus.). 705p. 148.00 (978-0-470-14922-5(1), Wiley) Wiley, John & Sons, Inc.

Lerner, Richard M., et al. Handbook of Adolescent Psychology Vol. 1: Individual Bases of Adolescent Development, 2 vols. 3rd ed. 2009. (ENG., Illus.). 823p. 148.00 (978-0-470-14921-8(3), Wiley) Wiley, John & Sons, Inc.

—Thriving & Spirituality among Youth: Research Perspectives & Future Possibilities. 2011. (ENG., Illus.). 367p. pap. 70.00 (978-0-470-94830-9(2), Wiley) Wiley, John & Sons, Inc.

LeTendre, Gerald K. Learning to Be Adolescent: Growing up in U. S. & Japanese Middle Schools. 2011. 258p. pap. 26.00 (978-0-300-18267-5(8)) Yale Univ. Pr.

Levin, Judith. Frequently Asked Questions about When a Friendship Ends. 2009. (FAQ: Teen Life Ser.). 64p. (gr. 5-6). 58.50 (978-1-61512-593-7(0)) Rosen Publishing Group, Inc., The.

Liabo, Kristin & Richardson, Joanna. Conduct Disorder & Offending Behaviour in Young People: Findings from Research. 2007. (Child & Adolescent Mental Health Ser.). (ENG., Illus.). 144p. per. (978-1-84310-450-6(6)) Kingsley, Jessica Ltd.

Lincoln, Siân. Youth Cultures & Private Space. 2012. (ENG., Illus.). 272p. 85.00 (978-0-230-23326-3(0)) Palgrave Macmillan.

Lindahl, Lars. Reminders. 2011. 418p. pap. 23.99 (978-1-4628-6538-3(0)) Xlibris Corp.

Linderman, Mike & Brozek, Gary. The Teen Whisperer: How to Break Through the Silence & Secrecy of Teenage Life. 2008. (ENG.). 320p. pap. 14.95 (978-0-06-137374-9(5), William Morrow Paperbacks) HarperCollins Pubs.

Liu, Wenhao. Adolescents' Physical Activity Levels & Behaviorse. 2008. 124p. pap. (978-3-639-08169-5(2)) VDM Verlag Dr. Mueller e.K.

Livingston, Aiden. Secrets of Advertising to Gen Y Consumers. 2010. (ENG.). 136p. pap. 17.95 (978-1-77040-034-4(6)) Self-Counsel Pr., Inc. CAN. Dist: Midpoint Trade Bks., Inc.

Londergan, Betty. The Agony & the Agony: Raising Your Teenager Without Losing Your Mind. 2008. (ENG.). 272p. pap. 14.95 (978-1-60094-074-3(9), Da Capo Lifelong) Da Capo Pr., Inc.

Long, Nicholas James, et al. The Angry Smile: The Psychology of Passive-Aggressive Behavior in Families, Schools, & Workplaces. 2nd ed. 2008. 26.00 (978-1-4164-0423-1(6)) PRO-ED, Inc.

Lott, George M. The Story of Human Emotions from a Teenage Viewpoint. 2011. 248p. 46.95 (978-1-258-07598-9(9)) Literary Licensing, LLC.

lowry, michael. Teenagers: their care & maintenance in Captivity. 2008. 307p. pap. 20.95 (978-1-4092-4206-2(4)) Lulu Enterprises Inc.

Luxmoore, Nick. Feeling Like Crap: Young People & the Meaning of Self Esteem. 2007. (ENG.). 160p. pap. (978-1-84310-682-1(5)) Kingsley, Jessica Ltd.

Mabatho, Sedibe. The Role of the Family in the Development of the Adolescent: The Role of the Family in the Development & Education of the Adolescent in the Makapanstad Disadvantaded Area of the North-West Province. 2011. 80p. pap. (978-3-639-29446-0(7)) VDM Verlag Dr. Mueller e.K.

MacConville, Ruth & Rae, Tina. Building Happiness, Resilience & Motivation in Adolescents: A Positive Psychology Curriculum for Well-Being. 2012. (ENG.). 240p. pap. (978-1-84905-261-0(1)) Kingsley, Jessica Ltd.

MacDonald, Ryan. Social Context & Mental Health. 2008. 112p. per. (978-3-8364-6394-2(6)) VDM Verlag Dr. Mueller e.K.

MacDonald, Stephen James. Towards a Sociology of Dyslexi. 2009. 292p. pap. (978-3-639-13113-0(4)) VDM Verlag Dr. Mueller e.K.

Macmillan, Ross, ed. Constructing Adulthood: Agency & Subjectivity in Adolescence & Adulthood. 2006. (ENG.). 346p. 105.00 (978-0-7623-1201-6(7), JAI Pr.) Elsevier Science & Technology Bks.

Macneil, Craig A., et al. Bipolar Disorder in Young People: A Psychological Intervention Manual. 2009. (ENG., Illus.). 198p. pap. 59.00 (978-0-521-71936-0(4)) Cambridge Univ. Pr.

Maholmes, Valerie & Lomonaco, Carmela Gina. Applied Research in Child & Adolescent Development. 2010. (ENG.). 340p. 94.95 (978-1-84872-814-1(X)); pap., instr.'s gde. ed. 47.95 (978-1-84872-815-8(8)) Taylor & Francis Group GBR. (Psychology Press). Dist: Taylor & Francis Group.

Malliett, Gabrielle Jolie. Beautiful Messenger. 2009. 164p. pap. 12.95 (978-1-4490-0867-3(4)) AuthorHouse.

Mallon, Brenda. Working with Bereaved Children & Young People. 2010. 168p. (C). 104.00 (978-1-84920-370-8(9), B03708C); pap. 41.00 (978-1-84920-371-5(7), B03708P) SAGE Pubns., Ltd. GBR. Dist: SAGE Pubns., Inc.

Mallon, Gerald P. Social Work Practice with Transgender & Gender Variant Youth. Mallon, Gerald P., ed. 2nd rev. ed. 2009. 194p. 125.00 (978-0-415-99481-1(0)) Routledge.

Mangan, Tricia. How to Feel Good: 20 Things Teens Can Do. 2011. 96p. (YA). pap. 12.95 (978-1-4338-1040-4(9), Magination Pr.) American Psychological Assn.

Manis & Manis, Frank. MyVirtualTeen. 2010. (ENG.). (C). 30.00 (978-0-205-80082-7(3), Prentice Hall) Prentice Hall PTR.

Mansouri, Fethi, ed. Youth Identity & Migration: Culture, values & social Connectedness. 2009. 244p. pap. 30.00 (978-1-86335-621-3(5)) Common Ground Publishing Pty, Ltd.

Marcus, Robert. Aggression & Violence in Adolescence. 2007. (ENG., 200p. Illus.). per. 25.99 (978-0-521-68891-8(4)); 80.00 (978-0-521-86881-5(5)) Cambridge Univ. Pr.

Margalit, Malka. Lonely Children & Adolescents: Self-Perceptions, Social Exclusion, & Hope. (ENG., Illus.). xiv, 303p. 2011. pap. 44.95 (978-1-4614-2375-1(9), 1461423759) 2010. 169.00 (978-1-4419-6283-6(2), 1441962832) Springer.

Marte, Ricardo M. Adolescent Problem Behaviors: Delinquency, Aggression, & Drug Use. 2008. (Criminal Justice). 266p. 70.00 (978-1-59332-269-4(0)) LFB Scholarly Publishing LLC.

Martin, Magy, et al. When Devon Met Oz: Helping Children Cope with Depression. 2008. (Let's Talk Ser.). (ENG., Illus.). 48p. (J). (gr. -1-4). pap. 8.95 (978-0-88282-304-1(3)) New Horizon Pr. Pubs., Inc.

Massoni, Kelley. Fashioning Teenagers: A Cultural History of Seventeen Magazine. 2010. (ENG., Illus.). 256p. (C). 79.00 (978-1-59874-503-0(4)); pap. 24.95 (978-1-59874-504-7(2)) Left Coast Pr., Inc.

Mayo, Jeanne. Dating Declassified: The Uncensored Truth about Dating, Friendship, & Sex. 2010. 240p. pap. 14.99 (978-1-60683-001-7(5)) Harrison House Pubs.

Mayseless, Orfa & Scharf, Miri, eds. Attachment in Adolescence: Reflections & New Angles. 2007. (J-B CAD Single Issue Child & Adolescent Development Ser.: 87). (ENG., Illus.). 128p. per. 29.00 (978-0-470-22560-8(2), Jossey-Bass) Wiley, John & Sons, Inc.

Mazzarella, Sharon R. Girl Wide Web 2. 0: Revisiting Girls, the Internet, & the Negotiation of Identity. 2010. (Mediated Youth Ser.). (Illus.). (C). 304p. 129.95 (978-1-4331-0550-0(0)); 308p. pap. 34.95 (978-1-4331-0549-4(7)) Lang, Peter Publishing, Inc.

McDevitt, Teresa, et al. Child Development & Education. 4th ed. 2008. (MyEducationLab Ser.). (ENG.). 720p. (C). pap. 135.00 (978-0-13-713383-3(9), Prentice Hall) Prentice Hall PTR.

McDevitt, Teresa M. & Ormrod, Jeanne E. Child Development & Education (with MyEducationLab) 4th ed. 2008. (ENG.). 720p. (C). pap. 141.67 (978-0-13-601129-1(1), Prentice Hall) Prentice Hall PTR.

McDevitt, Teresa M. & Ormrod, Jeanne Ellis. Child Development & Education. 5th rev. ed. 2012. (ENG.). 768p. (C). pap. 140.00 (978-0-13-248620-0(2)) Allyn & Bacon, Inc.

—Child Development & Education, Student Value Edition. 5th ed. 2012. (ENG.). 672p. (C). ring bd. 91.00 (978-0-13-289301-5(0), Prentice Hall) Prentice Hall PTR.

McHugh, Orla. Celtic Cubs: Inside the Mind of the Irish Teenager. 2006. (ENG.). 227p. pap. 27.95 (978-1-905483-08-2(2)) Liberties Pr. IRL. Dist: Dufour Editions, Inc.

McIlhaney, Joe S., Jr. & Bush, Freda McKissic. Hooked: New Science on How Casual Sex Is Affecting Our Children. 2008. (ENG.). 176p. 17.99 (978-0-8024-5060-9(1)) Northfield Publishing.

McKinnon, John A. To Change a Mind: Parenting to Promote Maturity in Teenagers. 2011. 207p. pap. 23.00 (978-1-59056-234-5(8)) Lantern Bks.

—An Unchanged Mind: The Problem of Immaturity in Adolescence. 2008. 272p. pap. 23.00 (978-1-59056-124-9(4)) Lantern Bks.

McLean, Kate C. & Pasupathi, Monisha, eds. Narrative Development in Adolescence: Creating the Storied Self. 2011. (Advancing Responsible Adolescent Development Ser.). (ENG., Illus.). xxxiii, 237p. pap. 49.95 (978-1-4614-1516-9(0), 1461415160) Springer.

McWhirter, Benedict T., et al. At Risk Youth: A Comprehensive Response for Counselors, Teachers, Psychologists, & Human Services Professionals. 4th rev. ed. 2006. (ENG., Illus.). 400p. (C). per. 161.95 (978-0-534-27236-4(3)) Wadsworth.

Mecca, Andrew M. Lifeplan: Tools Every Teenager Needs to Thrive, Not Merely Survive. 2008. xvi, 131p. (978-0-9713680-3-3(1)) California Mentor Foundation, The.

Mellor, Ken & Mellor, Elizabeth. Teen Stages: The Breakthrough Year-by-Year Approach to Understanding Your Ever-Changing Teen. 2009. (ENG.). 224p. pap. 14.99 (978-1-4022-1529-2(0)) Sourcebooks, Inc.

Meltzer & Bick. Adolescence: Talks & Papers by Donald Meltzer & Martha Harris. 2011. (Harris Meltzer Trust Ser.). 256p. pap. 45.00 (978-1-78049-011-3(9)) Karnac Bks. GBR. Dist: Stylus Publishing, LLC.

Merrick, Joav & Omar, Hatim A. Adolescent Behavior Research: International Perspectives. 2007. (C). 169.00 (978-1-60021-649-7(8)) Nova Science Pubs., Inc.

Messurier, Mark Le. Teaching Tough Kids: Simple & Proven Strategies for Student Success. 2009. (ENG., Illus.). 240p. pap. 42.95 (978-0-415-46060-6(3)) Routledge.

Meyer, Joyce. El Campo de Batalla de la Mente para Jovenes. 2007. (ENG & SPA.). 160p. (gr. 5-9). 9.99 (978-1-59979-030-5(0), Casa Creacion) Charisma Media.

Miklowitz, David J. & George, Elizabeth L. The Bipolar Teen: What You Can Do to Help Your Child & Your Family. 2007. (ENG.). 356p. 40.00 (978-1-59385-596-3(6)); pap. 17.95 (978-1-59385-318-1(1)) Guilford Pubns., Inc.

Miller, Alice, text. Paths of Life: Six Case Histories. 2008. (ENG.). 192p. pap. 15.00 (978-0-465-01268-8(X)) Basic Bks.

Mondragon, Dona M. Parents Companion. 2006. 23p. 8.00 (978-0-9746644-2-2(1)) Debu, Inc.

Moore, Susan & Rosenthal, Doreen. Sexuality in Adolescence: Current Trends. 2nd rev. ed. 2006. (Adolescence & Society Ser.). (ENG.). 304p. 95.00 (978-0-415-34462-3(X)) Routledge.

Morris, Richard. Handbook of Child & Adolescent Behavior Disorders. 2008. 89.95 (978-0-8058-6110-5(6)); 195.00 (978-0-8058-6109-9(2)) Erlbaum, Lawrence Assocs., Inc.

Morrison, Betsy S. & Ruiz, Ruth Ann. Self Esteem. 2011. (Teen Mental Health Ser.). (YA). (gr. 7-12). lib. bdg. 27.95 (978-1-4488-4587-3(4)) Rosen Publishing Group, Inc., The.

Moshman, David. Adolescent Psychological Development: Cognition, Morality, & Identity. 3rd rev. ed. 2011. (ENG.). 302p. (C). pap. 44.95 (978-1-84872-861-5(1), Psychology Press) Taylor & Francis Group GBR. Dist: Taylor & Francis Group.

—Adolescent Rationality & Development: Cognition, Morality, & Identity. 3rd rev. ed. 2011. (ENG.). 302p. (C). 90.95 (978-1-84872-860-8(3), Psychology Press) Taylor & Francis Group GBR. Dist: Taylor & Francis Group.

Moss & Moss, Haley. Middle School: The Stuff Nobody Tells You About. (Illus.). 160p. pap. (978-1-934575-62-8(3)) Autism Asperger Publishing Co.

Mounts, Nina S. & Brown, B. Bradford, eds. Linking Parents & Family to Adolescent Peer Relations: Ethnic & Cultural Considerations - New Directions for Child & Adolescent Development. 2007. (J-B CAD Single Issue Child & Adolescent Development Ser.: 86). (ENG., Illus.). 120p. per. 29.00 (978-0-470-17801-0(9), Jossey-Bass) Wiley, John & Sons, Inc.

Munroe, Erin A. The Anxiety Workbook for Girls. 2010. (ENG.). 208p. (J). (gr. 4-7). pap. 14.95 (978-1-57749-232-0(3)) Taylor Trade Publishing.

Myers, Edward. When Will I Stop Hurting? Teens, Loss, & Grief. 2006. (It Happened to Me Ser.). (ENG., Illus.). 176p. pap. 20.00 (978-0-8108-5758-2(8)) Scarecrow Pr., Inc.

Nakkula, Michael J. & Toshalis, Eric. Understanding Youth: Adolescent Development for Educators. 2006. 304p. pap. 29.95 (978-1-891792-31-1(8)); lib. bdg. (978-1-891792-32-8(6)) Harvard Education Publishing Group (HEPG). (Harvard Education Pr.).

Negotiating Ethical Challenges in Youth Research. 2012. (Critical Youth Studies). (ENG.). 140.00 (978-0-415-80846-0(4)); pap. 44.95 (978-0-415-80847-7(2)) Routledge.

Neuman, Sharon & Marshall, Richard M. The Middle School Mind: Growing Pains in Early Adolescent Brains. 2011. (ENG.). 134p. 40.00 (978-1-61048-584-5(X)); pap. 19.95 (978-1-61048-585-2(8)) Rowman & Littlefield Education.

Noller. Family Life in Adolescence. 2011. (Adolescence & Society Ser.). 216p. pap. 32.50 (978-0-415-47033-9(1)) Routledge.

Noller, Patricia & Atkin, Sharon. Family Life in Adolescence. 2nd ed. 2011. (Adolescence & Society Ser.). (Illus.). 208p. 80.00 (978-0-415-47032-2(3)) Routledge.

Ntarangwi, Mwenda. East African Hip Hop: Youth Culture & Globalization. 2009. (Interp Culture New Millennium Ser.). (ENG.). 176p. 60.00 *(978-0-252-03457-2(0))*; pap. 20.00 *(978-0-252-07653-4(2))* Univ. of Illinois Pr.

Obegi, Joseph H. & Berant, Ety, eds. Attachment Theory & Research in Clinical Work with Adults. 2008. (ENG.). 529p. 65.00 *(978-1-59385-998-5(8))* Guilford Pubns., Inc.

Obinyan, Evaristus. Delinquency Tolerance: Juvenile Appetite for Criminal Behavior. 2011. 176p. pap. 15.95 *(978-1-4327-6967-3(7))* Outskirts Pr., Inc.

O'Brien, Catherine. Bullying Across in-Groups & Out-Groups. 2008. 268p. pap. *(978-3-639-01834-9(6))* VDM Verlag Dr. Mueller e.K.

O'Connor, Frances. Frequently Asked Questions about Being Gifted. (FAQ: Teen Life Ser.). 64p. 2009. (gr. 5-6). 58.50 *(978-1-61512-566-1(3))* 2007. (Illus.). (YA). (gr. 7-12). lib. bdg. 29.25 *(978-1-4042-1938-0(2))* Rosen Publishing Group, Inc., The.

O'Connor, Pat. Irish Children & Teenagers in a Changing World: The National Write Here, Write Now Project. 2008. (ENG., Illus.). 224p. 89.00 *(978-0-7190-7819-4(9))*; pap. 26.00 *(978-0-7190-7820-0(2))* Manchester Univ. Pr. GBR. Dist: Macmillan.

Omar, Hatim, et al, eds. Adolescence & Chronic Illness. A Public Health Concern. 2010. (Health & Human Development (Joav Merrick - Series Editor - National Institute of Child Health & Human Development, Ministry of Social Affairs, Jerusalem) Ser.). (Illus.). x, 477p. 195.00 *(978-1-60876-628-4(4))* Nova Science Pubs., Inc.

O'Neill, Terry. Secret Scars: What You Need to Know about Cutting, 1 vol. 2009. (What's the Issue? Ser.). (ENG.). 48p. (gr. 5-6). lib. bdg. 27.99 *(978-0-7565-4142-2(5)*, CPB Grades 4-8) Compass Point Bks.

Oppong Asante, Kwaku. Cognitive Abilities in Mathematics among Adolescents. 2011. 68p. pap. ***(978-3-8443-2928-5(5))*** Lambert Academic Publishing.

Osborne, Randall, et al. Case Analyses for Child & Adolescent Disorders. 2008. 224p. 34.95 *(978-1-84169-081-0(3))* CRC Pr. LLC.

Osborne, Robin, et al. Case Analyses for Child & Adolescent Disorders. 2008. 224p. 80.00 *(978-1-84169-080-3(5))* CRC Pr. LLC.

Ougrin, Dennis, et al. Self-Harm in Young People. 2009. (ENG., Illus.). 208p. pap. 59.95 *(978-0-340-98726-1(X)*, Hodder Arnold) Hodder Education GBR. Dist: Oxford Univ. Pr., Inc.

Pagels, Douglas. Required Reading for All Teenagers: (or at least for one who Is very important to Me!), 1 vol. 2011. 96p. pap. 13.95 *(978-1-59842-599-4(4))* Blue Mountain Arts Inc.

Pajares, Frank & Urdan, Timothy C. Self-Efficacy & Adolescents. 2009. (Adolescence & Education Ser.). (Illus.). xii, 367p. (C). *(978-1-59311-367-4(6))* Information Age Publishing, Inc.

—Self-Efficacy Beliefs of Adolescents. 2009. (Adolescence & Education Ser.). (Illus.). xii, 367p. (C). pap. *(978-1-59311-366-7(8))* Information Age Publishing, Inc.

Palad, Thea. Mixed Messages: Interpreting Body Image & Social Norms. 2008. (Essential Health: Strong Beautiful Girls Ser.). 112p. (YA). (gr. 7-12). 34.22 *(978-1-60453-102-2(9))* ABDO Publishing Co.

Parker, Howard, et al. Illegal Leisure Revisited: Changing Patterns of Alcohol & Drug Use in Adolescents & Young Adults. 2nd ed. 2011. (Adolescence & Society Ser.). (ENG., Illus.). 264p. 85.00 *(978-0-415-49552-3(0))* Routledge.

Parolari, Fernanda. Psicologia de la Adolescencia. (SPA.). 176p. 7.95 *(978-958-607-801-6(9))* Sociedad de San Pablo COL. Dist: St Pauls/Alba Hse. Pubs.

Peile, Ed. The Normal Child. Bellman, Martin, ed. 11th ed. 2006. (ENG., Illus.). 224p. (C). pap. 69.95 *(978-0-443-05707-6(9)*, Churchill Livingstone) Elsevier - Health Sciences Div.

Perito, John E. Adolescent Sexuality: Too Much, Too Soon: Spiritual & Sexual Guidance for Parents. 2008. (ENG.). 244p. pap. 19.95 *(978-1-58982-441-6(5)*, Millennial Mind Publishing) American Bk. Publishing Group.

Perrin-Wallqvist, Rente. Juvenile & Adolescent Fire Play & Fire Setting. 2009. 52p. pap. *(978-3-8364-8532-6(X))* VDM Verlag Dr. Mueller e.K.

Persaud, Raj. The Young Mind. Bailey, Sue & Shooter, Mike, eds. 2009. (ENG., Illus.). 420p. pap. 29.99 *(978-0-593-06138-1(1))* Transworld Publishers Ltd. GBR. Dist: Independent Pubs. Group.

Peterson, Jean Sunde. The Essential Guide to Talking with Teens: Ready-to-Use Discussions for School & Youth Groups. 2006. (Essential Guide Ser.). (ENG., Illus.). 288p. (gr. 7-12). 39.99 *(978-1-57542-218-3(2))* Free Spirit Publishing, Inc.

Phares, Vicky. Understanding Abnormal Child Psychology. 2nd rev. ed. 2007. (ENG., Illus.). 566p. (C). 186.95 *(978-0-471-72411-7(4)*, Wiley) Wiley, John & Sons, Inc.

Picus, Donna B., et al. Mastery of Anxiety & Panic for Adolescents Riding the Wave. 2008. (Treatments That Work Ser.). (ENG., Illus.). 176p. pap. 37.95 *(978-0-19-533580-4(5))* Oxford Univ. Pr., Inc.

Pipher, Mary. Que Pasa con las Ninas de Hoy. (SPA.). 20.00 *(978-958-04-5301-7(2))* Norma S.A. COL. Dist: Distribuidora Norma, Inc.

—Reviviendo a Ofelia.Tr. of Reviving Ophelia. (SPA.). pap. 20.00 *(978-958-04-3742-0(4)*, NR9047) Norma S.A. COL. Dist: Lectorum Pubns., Inc.

—Reviving Ophelia: Saving the Selves of Adolescent Girls. 2010. (ENG.). 303p. 26.10 *(978-0-7569-8480-9(7))* Perfection Learning Corp.

Plante, Lori G. Bleeding to Ease the Pain: Cutting, Self-Injury, & the Adolescent Search for Self, 1 vol. 2007. (Abnormal Psychology Ser.). 200p. 49.95 *(978-0-275-99062-6(1)*, C9062, Praeger Pubs.) Greenwood Publishing Group, Inc.

Poliner, Rachel A. & Roberts, Jennifer. The Me I See: A Guide for Teachers, Counselors, & Therapists to Help Teens Examine Life's Questions. 2nd rev. ed. 2007. 310p. spiral bd. 39.95 *(978-1-885473-74-5(5))* Wood 'N' Barnes.

Poncin, Yann B., et al. Lewis's Child & Adolescent Psychiatry Review: 1400 Questions to Help You Pass the Boards. 4th rev. ed. 2009. (ENG.). 272p. pap. 68.99 *(978-0-7817-9507-4(9))* Lippincott Williams & Wilkins.

Porterfield, Sally F. & Baumlin, Tita French. Perpetual Adolescence: Jungian Analyses of American Media, Literature, & Pop Culture. Polette, Keith, tr. 2009. 240p. 70.00 *(978-1-4384-2799-7(9))*; pap. 24.95 *(978-1-4384-2800-0(6))* State Univ. of New York Pr.

Pressley, Michael & McCormick, Christine B. Child & Adolescent Development for Educators. 2006. (ENG., Illus.). 498p. 65.00 *(978-1-59385-352-5(1))* Guilford Pubns., Inc.

Prever, Mark. Counselling & Supporting Children & Young People: A Person-Centred Approach. 2010. 208p. (C). 112.00 *(978-1-84787-934-9(9)*, B79349C); pap. 39.00 *(978-1-84787-935-6(7)*, B79349P) SAGE Pubns., Ltd. GBR. Dist: SAGE Pubns., Inc.

Proctor, Wesley. Footprints of the Future. 2009. 52p. pap. 10.99 *(978-1-58930-236-5(2))* Selah Publishing Group, LLC.

Quill, Charlie. Anger & Anger Management. 2008. (Teen Mental Health Ser.). (Illus.). 48p. (YA). (gr. 7-12). lib. bdg. 26.50 *(978-1-4042-1800-0(9))* Rosen Publishing Group, Inc., The.

Rainey, Michelle. Parenting Practices & Adolescent Sexuality. 2007. 140p. per. *(978-3-8364-2593-3(9))* VDM Verlag Dr. Mueller e.K.

Rathus, Spencer A. Childhood & Adolescence: Voyages in Development. 4th ed. 2010. (ENG.). (C). 123p. pap. 42.95 *(978-0-8400-3255-3(2))*; 224p. pap., pupil's gde. ed. 72.95 *(978-0-8400-3252-2(8))* Wadsworth.

Rebelo, Marcia. Acculturation Influences on the Self Concept of the Black Adolescent. 2009. 140p. pap. *(978-3-639-16237-0(4))* VDM Verlag Dr. Mueller e.K.

Reid, Hazel & Westergaard, Jane. Effective Counselling with Young People. 2011. (ENG., Illus.). 182p. pap. *(978-0-85725-295-1(X))* Learning Matters Ltd.

Reuer, Barbara. Music Therapy & Adolescent Populations. 2011. (Illus.). 94p. pap. 50.00 *(978-0-9814606-7-3(4))* MusicWorx, Inc.

Rey, Joseph M., et al. Treating Child & Adolescent Depression. Birmaher, Boris, ed. 2009. (ENG., Illus.). 312p. 78.99 *(978-0-7817-9569-2(9))* Lippincott Williams & Wilkins.

Reyna, Valerie F. & Chapman, Sandra B., eds. The Adolescent Brain: Learning, Reasoning, & Decision Making. 2011. (Illus.). xviii, 457p. 79.95 ***(978-1-4338-1070-1(0))*** American Psychological Assn.

Rhoads. Adolescent Substance Abuse & Violence. 2009. 104p. pap. *(978-3-639-13433-9(8))* VDM Verlag Dr. Mueller e.K.

Rhodes, Terry C. Focus on Adolescent Behavior Research. 2007. 285p. 129.00 *(978-1-60021-697-8(8))* Nova Science Pubs., Inc.

Rice, David Wall. Balance: Advancing Identity Theory by Engaging the Black Male Adolescent. 2008. (ENG.). 148p. pap. 29.50 *(978-0-7391-1889-4(7))*; (Illus.). 57.99 *(978-0-7391-1888-7(9))* Lexington Bks.

Rittberg, Ellen. 35 Things Your Teen Won't Tell You, So I Will. 2010. (Good Things to Know Ser.). (ENG.). 126p. pap. 9.99 *(978-1-59652-554-2(1))* Turner Publishing Co.

Rodgers, Beverly & Rodgers, Tom. Adult Children of Divorced Parents. 2008. 172p. pap. 19.95 *(978-1-58930-228-0(1))* Selah Publishing Group, LLC.

Roizen, Michael F. & Oz, Mehmet C. You: The Owner's Manual for Teens - A Guide to a Healthy Body & Happy Life. 2011. (Illus.). 464p. pap. 16.00 *(978-1-4516-3494-5(3)*, Free Pr.) Free Pr.

Rollins, Justin. The Lost Boyz: A Dark Side of Graffiti. 2011. 176p. pap. 39.95 *(978-1-904380-67-2(0))* Waterside Pr. GBR. Dist: International Specialized Bk. Services.

Rosado, Jose. Being Good at Being Bad: Troubled Teenagers Factor. 2007. 201p. pap. 13.95 *(978-0-7414-4248-2(5))* Infinity Publishing.

Rose, James. You & Your Mid-Adolescent: The Hour of the Stranger. 2007. (You & Your Child Ser.). (Illus.). 86p. per. 25.00 *(978-1-85575-451-5(7))* Karnac Bks. GBR. Dist: Stylus Publishing, LLC.

Ross, Michael & Shellenberger, Susie. What Your Son Isn't Telling You: Unlocking the Secret World of Teen Boys. 2010. 192p. pap. 13.99 *(978-0-7642-0749-5(0))* Bethany Hse. Pubs.

Rotenberg, Ken J., ed. Disclosure Processes in Children & Adolescents. 2006. (Cambridge Studies in Social & Emotional Development Ser.). (ENG., Illus.). 248p. pap. 48.00 *(978-0-521-02860-8(4))* Cambridge Univ. Pr.

Rotenberg, Ken J. & Hymel, Shelley, eds. Loneliness in Childhood & Adolescence. 2008. (ENG., Illus.). 416p. pap. 53.00 *(978-0-521-08892-3(5))* Cambridge Univ. Pr.

Rubin, Kenneth H., et al, eds. Handbook of Peer Interactions, Relationships, & Groups. 2011. (Social, Emotional, & Personality Development in Context Ser.). (ENG.). 654p. pap. 50.00 *(978-1-60918-222-9(7))* Guilford Pubns., Inc.

Rubin, Kenneth H., et al. Handbook of Peer Interactions, Relationships, & Groups. Rubin, Kenneth H. et al, eds. 2008. (Social, Emotional, & Personality Development in Context Ser.). (ENG., Illus.). 654p. 85.00 *(978-1-59385-441-6(2))* Guilford Pubns., Inc.

Rubin, Lawrence C. Using Superheroes in Counseling & Play Therapy. 2007. (Illus.). 333p. 60.00 *(978-0-8261-0269-0(7))* Springer Publishing Co., Inc.

Rutherford, Jesse Jayne & Nickerson, Kathleen. The Everything Parent's Guide to the Defiant Child: Reassuring advice to help your child manage explosive emotions & gain Self-control. 2010. (ENG.). 304p. pap. 14.95 *(978-1-60550-369-1(X))* Adams Media Corp.

Rydin, Ingegerd & Sjoberg, Ulrika, eds. Mediated Crossroads: Identity, Youth Culture & Ethnicity: Theoretical & Methodological Challenges. 2008. (Illus.). 223p. pap. 99.50 *(978-91-89471-65-8(2))* International Clearinghouse on Childrennordicom SWE. Dist: Coronet Bks.

Sadowski, Michael, ed. Adolescents at School: Perspectives on Youth, Identity, & Education. 2nd ed. 2008. xi, 247p. 54.95 *(978-1-891792-95-3(4))*; pap. 29.95 *(978-1-891792-94-6(6))* Harvard Education Publishing Group (HEPG). (Harvard Education Pr.).

Santrock, John. Adolescence. 14th ed. 2011. (ENG., Illus.). 624p. (C). pap. 172.00 ***(978-0-07-811716-9(X)***, 007811716X) McGraw-Hill Cos., The.

Santrock, John W. Adolescence. (Illus.). 11th ed. 2007. 475p. per. 89.00 *(978-0-07-331481-5(1))* 13th ed. 2009. (ENG., 624p. (C). pap. 172.00 *(978-0-07-337067-5(3)*, 0073370673) McGraw-Hill Cos., The.

Saval, Malina. The Secret Lives of Boys: Inside the Raw Emotional World of Male Teens. 2010. (ENG.). 272p. (gr. 9). pap. 15.95 *(978-0-465-02032-4(1))* Basic Bks.

Saxon, Al N. Ah, If Only Young Again: (Followed by Interior Decorating, Etc.), 1 vol. 2009. 52p. pap. 16.95 *(978-1-60836-935-5(8))* PublishAmerica, Inc.

Schö, et al. PSYCHOSOZIALE LEBENSHILFE IN JUGENDMAGAZINEN: Eine Untersuchung der Leserbriefberatung in Jugendzeitschriften am Beispiel von 'BRAVO' und 'Xpress' 2009. 300p. pap. *(978-3-639-21649-3(0))* VDM Verlag Dr. Mueller e.K.

Schab, Lisa. The Anxiety Workbook for Teens: Activities to Help You Deal with Anxiety & Worry. 2008. (Instant Help Ser.). (ENG.). 192p. (J). pap. 32.95 *(978-1-57224-661-4(8))* Play2Grow.

—Beyond the Blues: A Workbook to Help Teens Overcome Depression. 2008. (Instant Help Ser.). (ENG.). 184p. (J). pap. 32.95 *(978-1-57224-663-8(4))* Play2Grow.

—Divorce Workbook for Teens: Activities to Help You Move Beyond the Break Up. 2008. (Instant Help Ser.). 132p. pap. 14.95 *(978-1-931704-27-4(9))* Play2Grow.

Scheithauer, Herbert & Bondu, Rebecca. Amoklauf und School Shooting: Definition, Verbreitung, Hintergründe und Prävention. 2011. (GER., Illus.). 121p. (C). pap. 18.00 ***(978-3-525-40435-5(2))*** Vandenhoeck & Ruprecht GmbH & Co. KG DEU. Dist: ISD.

Schmidt, William. Teens One on One, 1 vol. 2009. 52p. pap. 16.95 *(978-1-60813-290-4(0))* PublishAmerica, Inc.

Schmukler, Anita G., et al. Ethical Practice in Child & Adolescent Analysis & Psychotherapy: Protecting Safety in a Therapeutic Environment. 2011. (ENG.). 132p. (gr. 17). 55.00 ***(978-0-7657-0818-2(3)***, Aronson, Jason) Rowman & Littlefield Publishers, Inc.

Scholfield, Sam. Awkward: What to Do When Life Makes You Cringe - A Survival Guide. 2011. (ENG.). 272p. pap. 12.95 *(978-1-61519-038-6(4)*, 1615190384) Experiment LLC, The.

Schwartz, Susan & New Harbinger Publications Staff. Coping with Cliques. 2008. 130p. pap. 16.95 *(978-1-931704-31-1(7))* Play2Grow.

Seginer, Rachel. Future Orientation: Developmental & Ecological Perspectives. (Springer Series on Human Exceptionality Ser.). (ENG.). xviii, 258p. 2010. pap. 109.00 ***(978-1-4419-4697-3(7)***, 1441946977) 2009. (Illus.). 109.00 *(978-0-387-88640-4(0))* Springer.

Seltzer, Vivian. Peer-Impact Diagnosis & Therapy: A Handbook for Successful Practice with Adolescents. 2009. (ENG.). 352p. 39.00 *(978-0-8147-4042-2(1))* New York Univ. Pr.

Shaffer, David R. & Kipp, Katherine. Developmental Psychology: Childhood & Adolescence. 8th ed. 2009. (Available Titles CengageNOW Ser.). (ENG.). 784p. (C). 195.95 *(978-0-495-60171-5(3))*; ring bd. 92.95 *(978-0-495-59688-2(4))* Wadsworth.

Shakeshaft, Blidi. The Psychological Sense Belonging in of Adolescents Boys. 2010. 208p. pap. *(978-3-639-06359-2(7))* VDM Verlag Dr. Mueller e.K.

Shannon, Joyce Brennfleck, ed. Adolescent Health Sourcebook. 2nd ed. 2007. (Health Reference Ser.). (Illus.). 683p. 87.00 *(978-0-7808-0943-7(2))* Omnigraphics, Inc.

Shapiro MA MFT, Frank. The Oppositional Teenager: A Parents' Survival Guide. 2007. 248p. per. 12.95 *(978-1-4327-1273-0(X))* Outskirts Pr., Inc.

Shatkin, Jess P. Treating Child & Adolescent Mental Illness: A Practical, All-in-One Guide for Clinicians. 2009. (ENG., Illus.). 408p. 35.00 *(978-0-393-70545-4(5)*, 70545) Norton, W. W. & Co., Inc.

Shechtman, Zipora. Group Counseling & Psychotherapy with Children & Adolescents: Theory, Research, & Practice. 2006. (ENG., Illus.). 312p. 135.00 *(978-0-8058-5685-9(4))*; per. 44.95 *(978-0-8058-5686-6(2))* Routledge.

Silbereisen, Rainer K. & Eye, Alexander von, eds. Growing up in Times of Social Change. (International Studies on Childhood & Adolescence Ser.). (ENG.). XVI, 344p. 210.00 ***(978-3-11-182665-3(1))*** De Gruyter, Walter Inc.

Silva, Itamar & Souto, Anna Luiza Salles, eds. Democracy, Citizenship & Youth: Towards Social & Political Participation in Brazil. 2009. (International Library of Political Studies). (ENG.). 336p. 98.50 *(978-1-84885-048-4(4)*, Tauris Academic Studies) I. B. Tauris & Co., Ltd. GBR. Dist: Macmillan.

Simmons, Roberta G. & Blyth, Dale. Moving into Adolescence: The Impact of Pubertal Change & School Context. 2008. (ENG., Illus.). 457p. pap. 49 95 *(978-0-202-36294-6(9))* Aldine Transaction.

Singh, Manoj Kumar & Singh, Manjari. Understanding Adolescence. 2011. 72p. pap. ***(978-3-8383-8328-6(1))*** Lambert Academic Publishing.

Sink, Christopher A. Mental Health Interventions for School Counselors. 2010. (School Counseling Ser.). (ENG.). 208p. (C). pap. 47.95 *(978-0-618-75458-8(X))* Wadsworth.

Sirin, Selcuk & Fine, Michelle. Muslim American Youth: Understanding Hyphenated Identities through Multiple Methods. 2008. (ENG., Illus.). 304p. 75.00 *(978-0-8147-4039-2(1))*; pap. 24.00 *(978-0-8147-4040-8(5))* New York Univ. Pr.

Slap, Gail B. Adolescent Medicine. 2008. (Requisites in Pediatrics Ser.). (ENG., Illus.). 352p. pap. 79.95 *(978-0-323-04073-0(X)*, Mosby) Elsevier - Health Sciences Div.

Smith, Joanne & Meghan Huppuch. Hey, Shorty! A Guide to Combating Sexual Harassment & Violence in Schools & on the Streets. 2011. (ENG.). 160p. pap. 13.95 *(978-1-55861-669-1(1))* Feminist Pr. at The City Univ. of New York.

Sokol, Leslie & Fox, Marci G. Think Confident, Be Confident for Teens: A Cognitive Therapy Guide to Overcoming Self-Doubt & Creating Unshakable Self-Esteem. 2011. (Instant Help Solutions Ser.). (ENG.). 200p. (J). (gr. 6-12). pap. 16.95 *(978-1-60882-113-6(7))* New Harbinger Pubns.

Sommer, Carl. Teen Success in Career & Life Skills: If You Don't Want the Truth Don't Read This! 2009. (ENG.). 240p. (YA). lib. bdg. 19.95 *(978-1-57537-353-9(X))*; pap. *(978-1-57537-354-6(8))* Advance Publishing, Inc.

Sommers-Flanagan, John & Sommers-Flanagan, Rita. Tough Kids, Cool Counseling: User-Friendly Approaches with Challenging Youth. 2nd ed. 2006. *(978-1-55620-274-2(1))* American Counseling Assn.

Spilsbury, Louise. Be Smart, Stay Safe! 2009. (Life Skills Ser.). (ENG.). 56p. (gr. 6-9). 33.50 *(978-1-4329-2724-0(8)*, NA-h) Heinemann-Raintree.

Sroufe, L. Alan, et al. The Development of the Person: The Minnesota Study of Risk & Adaptation from Birth to Adulthood. 2009. (ENG.). 384p. pap. 40.00 *(978-1-60623-249-1(5))* Guilford Pubns., Inc.

Steinberg, Laurence, et al. Development: Infancy Through Adolescense. 2010. (ENG.). 576p. (C). pap. 117.95 *(978-0-8400-3307-9(9))* Wadsworth.

Stephens, Hallie. An Examination of the Impact Peer Pressure Has on Young Adults. 2008. 108p. pap. *(978-3-639-07233-4(2))* VDM Verlag Dr. Mueller e.K.

Stephenson, Bret. From Boys to Men: Spiritual Rites of Passage in an Indulgent Age. 2006. (ENG., Illus.). 1p. per. 18.95 *(978-1-59477-140-8(5))* Inner Traditions International, Ltd.

Stickle, Fred. Adolescent Psychology. 7th ed. 2009. (Annual Editions Ser.). (ENG., Illus.). 192p. (C). pap. 44.00 *(978-0-07-812775-5(0)*, 0078127750, McGraw-Hill/Dushkin) McGraw-Hill Higher Education.

—Annual Editions: Adolescent Psychology, 8/e. 8th ed. 2011. (Annual Editions Ser.). (ENG., Illus.). 192p. (C). pap. 44.00 *(978-0-07-805099-2(5)*, 0078050995, McGraw-Hill/Dushkin) McGraw-Hill Higher Education.

Stiegler, Bernard. Taking Care of Youth & the Generations. 2010. (Meridian: Crossing Aesthetics Ser.). (ENG.). 264p. 75.00 *(978-0-8047-6272-4(4))*; pap. 27.95 *(978-0-8047-6273-1(2))* Stanford Univ. Pr.

Straus, Martha B. Adolescent Girls in Crisis. 2007. 24.95 ***(978-0-7937-0447-7(2))*** Norton, W. W. & Co., Inc.

—Adolescent Girls in Crisis: Intervention & Hope. 2007. (ENG.). 240p. 35.00 *(978-0-393-70447-1(5)*, 70447) Norton, W. W. & Co., Inc.

Swan, Anna. Statues Without Shadows: A Daughter's Search for the Truth about the Parents She Never Knew. 2006. (ENG., Illus.). 288p. per. 13.95 *(978-0-340-83539-5(7))* Hodder General Publishing Div. GBR. Dist: Independent Pubs. Group.

Swinburne, Clair. So What Do You Think? A Guide for the Teenage Mind. 2011. 112p. 22.95 ***(978-1-4620-2936-5(1))***; pap. 12.95 ***(978-1-4620-2935-8(3))*** iUniverse, Inc.

Sylwester, Robert. The Adolescent Brain: Reaching for Autonomy. 2007. (Illus.). 176p. 72.95 *(978-1-4129-2610-2(6)*, B26106C); per. 31.95 *(978-1-4129-2611-9(4)*, B26106P) Corwin Pr.

Talley, P. Forrest. Creating & Implementing: Evidence-Based Treatment Plans for Children & Adolescents. 2009. (ENG.). 320p. 50.00 *(978-0-470-12779-7(1)*, Wiley) Wiley, John & Sons, Inc.

Taylor, Julia V. & Trice-Black, Shannon. G. I. R. L. S. , Girls in Real Life Situations, Grades K-5 (Book & CD) Group Counseling Activities for Enhancing Social & Emotional Development: Grades K-5. 2007. 236p. spiral bd. 37.95 *(978-0-87822-543-9(9))* Research Pr.

Taylor, Rachel & Gozna, Lynsey. Deception. 2011. (Studies in Adolescent Development Ser.). (ENG., Illus.). 192p. 69.95 *(978-1-84169-876-2(8)*, Psychology Press) Taylor & Francis Group GBR. Dist: Taylor & Francis Group.

Tellett-Royce, Nancy. Supporting Youth: How to Care, Communicate, & Connect in Meaningful Ways. 2008. (ENG.). 128p. pap. 14.95 *(978-1-57482-253-3(5))* Search Institute.

Thomas, Bonnie. Creative Expression Activities for Teens: Exploring Identity through Art, Craft & Journaling. 2010. (ENG., Illus.). 178p. pap. *(978-1-84905-842-1(3))* Kingsley, Jessica Ltd.

Thompson, Charles L. & Henderson, Donna A. Counseling Children. 8th ed. 2010. (SW 360K Child Abuse & Neglect Ser.). (ENG.). 768p. (C). 167.95 *(978-0-495-90338-3(8))* Brooks/Cole.

Thomsen, Kate. Parenting Preteens with a Purpose: Navigating the Middle Years. 2008. (ENG.). 216p. per. 13.95 *(978-1-57482-199-4(7))* Search Institute.

Thonnissen, Jorg. The Effects of Camp Interventions on Adolescent Self-Esteem. 2010. 64p. pap. *(978-3-8383-7681-3(1))* Lambert Academic Publishing.

Toschi, Luca. Sociologia e Sessualità: Modelli Relazionali Giovanili e Ricerca Empirica. 2009. (ITA.). 181p. *(978-88-7796-571-4(1))* Bonanno.

Trowell, Judith. Standing on Their Own Feet: You & Your Younger Adolescent. 2008. 118p. pap. 22.95 *(978-1-85575-531-4(9))* Karnac Bks. GBR. Dist: Stylus Publishing, LLC.

Tudor, Keith, ed. The Adult is Parent to the Child: Transactional Analysis with Children & Young People. 2008. 300p. pap. 69.95 *(978-1-905541-17-1(1))*

Russell Hse. Publishing Ltd. GBR. Dist: International Specialized Bk. Services.

Uhlenkamp, Jeannie. The Guide to Dating for Teenagers with Asperger Syndrome. 2009. (Illus.). xii, 129p. (YA). pap. 19.95 *(978-1-934575-53-6(4))* Autism Asperger Publishing Co.

Umeh, Kanayo. Understanding Adolescent Health Behaviour: A Decision Making Perspective. 2009. (ENG., Illus.). 318p. (C). pap. 49.99 *(978-0-521-69802-3(2))* Cambridge Univ. Pr.

Umeh, Kanayo & Umeh, Kanayo F. Understanding Adolescent Health Behaviour: A Decision Making Perspective. 2009. (ENG., Illus.). 318p. (C). 117.00 *(978-0-521-87526-4(9))* Cambridge Univ. Pr.

Underwood, Marion K. & Rosen, Lisa H., eds. Social Development: Relationships in Infancy, Childhood, & Adolescence. 2011. (ENG., Illus.). 480p. 65.00 *(978-1-60918-233-5(2))* Guilford Pubns., Inc.

Ungar, Michael. Playing at Being Bad: The Hidden Resilience of Troubled Teens. 2007. (ENG., Illus.). 272p. per. 16.95 *(978-0-7710-8711-0(X))* McClelland & Stewart CAN. Dist: Random Hse., Inc.

Vaccaro, Annemarie, et al. Safe Spaces: Making Schools & Communities Welcoming to LGBT Youth, 1 vol. 2011. 192p. 37.00 ***(978-0-313-39368-6(0),*** A3368C); xi, 192p. E-Book ***(978-0-313-39369-3(9),*** Praeger Pubs.) Greenwood Publishing Group, Inc.

Verhulst, Frank C. & van der Ende, Jan. Assessment Scales in Child & Adolescent Psychiatry. 2006. (ENG., Illus.). 232p. 140.00 *(978-1-84184-534-0(5),* DU5345) Taylor & Francis Group.

Vernon, Ann. Counseling Children & Adolescents. 4th ed. 2009. 528p. (C). 90.00 *(978-0-89108-340-5(5))* Love Publishing Co.

Vincent Cml Ma, Jeff. 1 250 Teen Advancement Strategies: Tactical Protocols for Today's Successful Teen. 2008. 376p. pap. 26.95 *(978-1-4327-3652-1(3))* Outskirts Pr., Inc.

Wahl, Lothar. Anti-Social & Young: Interventions: Interventions with Adolescents Diagnosed with Severe Conduct Disorder in Out-of-Home Care. 2008. 256p. pap. *(978-3-639-06584-8(0))* VDM Verlag Dr. Mueller e.K.

Watkins, Heidi, ed. Risky Teen Behavior. 2012. (Issues that Concern You Ser.). (ENG., Illus.). 144p. (gr. 7-10). lib. bdg. 36.80 ***(978-0-7377-5698-2(5),*** Greenhaven Pr., Inc.) Cengage Gale.

Westman, Jack C. & Costello, Victoria. Child & Adolescent Psychology - Complete Idiot's Guide. 2011. (Complete Idiot's Guide Ser.). (ENG.). 400p. (gr. 12). 19.95 *(978-1-61564-063-8(0),* Alpha Bks.) Penguin Group (USA) Inc.

Whelan, Christine B. Generation WTF: What the #$%&! to a Wise, Tenancious, & Fearless You - Advice on How to Get There from Experts & WTFers Just Like You. 2011. (ENG.). 240p. pap. 15.95 *(978-1-59947-347-5(X))* Templeton Pr.

Whitaker, Leighton C. & Cooper, Stewart Edwin. Pharmacological Treatment of College Students with Psychological Problems. 2007. (ENG.). 298p. pap. 54.50 *(978-0-7890-3679-7(7))* Routledge.

Whitbeck, Les B. Mental Health & Emerging Adulthood among Homeless Young People. 2009. (ENG., Illus.). 312p. pap. 39.95 *(978-1-84169-752-9(4),* Psychology Press) Taylor & Francis Group GBR. Dist: Taylor & Francis Group.

—Mental Health & Emerging Adulthood among HomelessYoung People. 2009. (ENG., Illus.). 312p. 73.95 *(978-1-84169-751-2(6),* Psychology Press) Taylor & Francis Group GBR. Dist: Taylor & Francis Group.

Wilkins, Amy C. Wannabes, Goths, & Christians: The Boundaries of Sex, Style, & Status. 2008. (ENG.). 294p. 55.00 *(978-0-226-89842-1(3));* pap. 22.00 *(978-0-226-89843-8(1))* Univ. of Chicago Pr.

Williams, Heidi. Teen Suicide. 2009. (Issues that Concern You Ser.). (ENG., Illus.). 144p. (gr. 7-10). 35.75 *(978-0-7377-4497-2(9),* Greenhaven Pr., Inc.) Cengage Gale.

Williams, Lisa. Changing lives, changing drug Journeys: Drug taking decisions from adolescence to Adulthood. 2012. (Routledge Advances in Ethnography Ser.). (ENG., Illus.). 232p. (C). 135.00 ***(978-1-84392-894-2(9))*** Routledge.

Wilson, Gary & Wilson, Gary B. Breaking Through Barriers to Boys' Achievement: Developing a Caring Masculinity. 2007. (ENG., Illus.). 152p. per. 49.95 *(978-1-85539-211-3(9),* Network Continuum Education) Continuum International Publishing Group, Ltd. GBR. Dist: National Bk. Network.

Wiseman, Rosalind. Owning up Curriculum (book & CD Rom) Empowering Adolescents to Confront Social Cruelty, Bullying & Injustice. 2009. (YA). pap. 64.95 *(978-0-87822-609-2(5))* Research Pr.

Wolf, Msw. I Still Dream Big: Stories of Teens Living with Chronic Illness. 2009. 160p. pap. 13.99 *(978-1-4490-3096-4(3))* AuthorHouse.

Wolfe, David A. Acting Out: Understanding & Reducing Aggressive Behaviour in Children & Youth. 2007. ***(978-0-88868-532-2(7))*** Centre for Addiction & Mental Health.

—What Parents Need to Know about Teen Risk Taking: Strategies for Reducing Problems Related to Alcohol, Other Drugs, Gambling & Internet Use. 2011. ***(978-0-88868-610-7(2))*** Centre for Addiction & Mental Health.

Wolfe, David A. & Mash, Eric J. Behavioral & Emotional Disorders in Adolescents: Nature, Assessment, & Treatment. Wolfe, David A. & Mash, Eric J., eds. 2008. (ENG.). 719p. pap. 55.00 *(978-1-60623-115-9(4))* Guilford Pubns., Inc.

Woolfolk, et al. Child & Adolescent Development, Student Value Edition. 2011. (ENG.). 592p. (C). ring bd. 84.00 ***(978-0-13-277939-5(0))*** Allyn & Bacon, Inc.

Worth, Richard. Frequently Asked Questions about Teen Fatherhood. 2009. (FAQ: Teen Life Ser.). (Illus.). 64p. (J). (gr. 5-6). lib. bdg. 29.25 *(978-1-4358-5325-6(3))* Rosen Publishing Group, Inc., The.

Yang, Sora, ed. My Korean Identity & Quest for Understanding: Essays by Korean Youth around the World. 2008. (Illus.). 136p. pap. 28.00 *(978-1-59689-147-0(5),* Koreani) Hermit Kingdom Pr., The.

—My Korean Identity & Quest for Understanding: Essays by Korean Youth around the World (Hardcover) 2008. (Illus.). 136p. 55.00 *(978-1-59689-062-6(2),* Koreani) Hermit Kingdom Pr., The.

Yarrow, Kit & O'Donnell, Jayne. Gen Buy: How Tweens, Teens, & Twenty-Somethings Are Revolutionizing Retail. 2009. (ENG., Illus.). 272p. 24.95 *(978-0-470-40091-3(9),* Jossey-Bass) Wiley, John & Sons, Inc.

Youth Development Staff. Afterschool Around the Globe No. 116: Policy, Practices, & Youth Voice - New Directions for Youth Development. Capece, Jen Hilmer et al, eds. 2008. (J-B MHS Single Issue Mental Health Services Ser.: 90). (ENG.). 168p. pap. 29.00 *(978-0-470-28239-7(8),* Jossey-Bass) Wiley, John & Sons, Inc.

—Cultural Agents & Creative Arts No. 125: New Directions for Youth Development. Sanin, Andres & Sommer, Doris, eds. 2010. (J-B MHS Single Issue Mental Health Services Ser.: 99). (ENG.). 168p. pap. 29.00 *(978-0-470-63384-7(0),* Jossey-Bass) Wiley, John & Sons, Inc.

Youth Development Staff. Expanded Learning Time & Opportunities: New Directions for Youth Development. Malone, ed. 2011. (J-B MHS Single Issue Mental Health Services Ser.: 105). (ENG.). 152p. pap. 29.00 ***(978-1-118-16753-3(8),*** Jossey-Bass) Wiley, John & Sons, Inc.

Youth Development Staff, et al. The Case for Twenty-First Century Learning, Number 110 No. 110: New Directions for Youth Development. 2006. (J-B MHS Single Issue Mental Health Services Ser.: 84). (ENG., Illus.). 136p. pap. 29.00 *(978-0-7879-8827-2(8),* Jossey-Bass) Wiley, John & Sons, Inc.

Zambo, Debby & Hansen, Cory Cooper. Child Development Through the Eyes of Children's Authors: Using Picture Books to Understand Theory. 2006. (Illus.). 78p. per. 10.00 *(978-0-13-199363-1(1))* Prentice Hall PTR.

Zdanowicz, Nicolas. The Adolescent Today in Medicine. 2007. 79.00 *(978-1-60021-764-7(8))* Nova Science Pubs., Inc.

Zheng, Robert, et al, eds. Adolescent Online Social Communication & Behavior: Relationship Formation on the Internet. 2009. (Illus.). 390p. 180.00 *(978-1-60566-926-7(1))* IGI Global.

ADOLESCENT PSYCHOPATHOLOGY

see also Adolescent Psychiatry

Achenbach, Thomas M. & Rescorla, Leslie A. Multicultural Understanding of Child & Adolescent Psychopathology: Implications for Mental Health Assessment. 2006. (ENG., Illus.). 322p. 45.00 *(978-1-59385-348-8(3))* Guilford Pubns., Inc.

Alexander, June & Le Grange, Daniel. My Kid Is Back. 2010. (ENG.). 272p. pap. 17.95 *(978-0-415-58115-8(X))* Routledge.

Austin, Vance L. & Sciarra, Daniel T. Children & Adolescents with Emotional & Behavioral Disorders. 2009. (ENG.). 504p. (C). pap. 123.60 *(978-0-205-50176-2(1),* Prentice Hall) Prentice Hall PTR.

Banaschewski, Tobias, et al. Attention-Deficit Hyperactivity Disorder & Hyperkinetic Disorder. 2010. (Oxford Poetry Library). (ENG., Illus.). 128p. pap. 24.95 *(978-0-19-957765-1(X))* Oxford Univ. Pr., Inc.

Beauchaine, Theodore P. & Hinshaw, Stephen P., eds. Child & Adolescent Psychopathology. 2008. (ENG., Illus.). 720p. 110.00 *(978-0-470-00744-0(3),* Wiley) Wiley, John & Sons, Inc.

Capuzzi, David & Gross, Douglas R. Youth at Risk: A Prevention Resource for Counselors, Teachers, & Parents. 5th ed. 2007. *(978-1-55620-275-9(X))* American Counseling Assn.

Claveirole, Anne & Gaughan, Martin, eds. Understanding Children & Young People's Mental Health. 2010. (ENG., Illus.). 328p. pap. 47.99 *(978-0-470-72345-6(9),* Wiley-Blackwell) Wiley, John & Sons, Inc.

Cooper, Sue & Norton, Peggy. Conquering Eating Disorders: How Family Communication Heals. 2008. (ENG.). 225p. pap. 16.95 *(978-1-58005-260-3(6))* Seal Pr.

Cram101 Textbook Reviews. Outlines & Highlights for Assessment of Childhood Disorders by Eric J Mash. 2011. 162p. pap. 29.95 ***(978-1-61905-143-0(5))*** Cram101 Inc.

—Outlines & Highlights for Child & Adolescent Psychopathology by Stephen P Hinshaw, Isbn: 9780470007440. 2011. 150p. pap. 29.95 ***(978-1-61698-020-7(6))*** Cram101 Inc.

Cram101 Textbook Reviews & Cram101 Textbook Reviews. Outlines & Highlights for Introduction to Abnormal Child & Adolescent Psychology by Robert Weis, Isbn: 9781412926577 1412926572. 2011. 188p. pap. 30.95 ***(978-1-61654-234-4(9))*** Cram101 Inc.

Cram101 Textbook Reviews Staff. Outlines & Highlights for Children & Adolescents with Emotional & Behavioral Disorders by VanCe L Austin, Isbn: 9780205501762. 2009. 118p. pap. 28.95 *(978-1-4286-8818-0(7))* Cram101 Inc.

Elliott, Julian & Place, Maurice. Children in Difficulty: A Guide to Understanding & Helping. 3rd rev. ed. 2012. (ENG., Illus.). 296p. (C). 160.00 *(978-0-415-67255-9(4));* pap. 44.95 *(978-0-415-67263-4(5))* Routledge.

Fanti, Kostas Andrea. Development & Co-Development of Aggressive & Depressive Psychopathology - Infancy to Early Adolescence. 2008. 128p. pap. *(978-3-639-00391-8(8))* VDM Verlag Dr. Mueller e.K.

Federman, Russ & Thomson, J. Anderson. Facing Bipolar: The Young Adult's Guide to Dealing with Bipolar Disorder. 2010. (ENG., Illus.). 176p. pap. 16.95 *(978-1-57224-642-3(1))* New Harbinger Pubns.

Garralda, M. Elena & Flament, Martine. Working with Children & Adolescents: An Evidence-Based Approach to Risk & Resilience. annot. ed. 2006. (Book Series of the International Association for Child & Adolescent Psychiatry & Allied Professions). (ENG.). 224p. 63.99 *(978-0-7657-0443-6(9),* Aronson, Jason) Rowman & Littlefield Publishers, Inc.

Gowers, Simon G. Eating Disorders: Cognitive Behaviour Therapy with Children & Young People. 2009. (CBT with Children, Adolescents & Families Ser.). (ENG., Illus.). 200p. (C). 128.00 *(978-0-415-44462-0(4))* Routledge.

Gullotta, Thomas P. Handbook of Adolescent Behavioral Problems. 2008. (Illus.). 666p. spiral bd. 54.95 *(978-0-387-88715-9(6))* Springer.

Hazen, Eric P., et al. Mental Health Disorders in Adolescents: A Guide for Parents, Teachers, & Professionals. 2010. (ENG., Illus.). 350p. 75.00 *(978-0-8135-4893-7(4));* pap. 23.95 *(978-0-8135-4894-4(2))* Rutgers Univ. Pr.

Hudziak, James J. Developmental Psychopathology & Wellness: Genetic & Environmental Influences. 2008. (Illus.). 320p. pap. 74.00 *(978-1-58562-279-5(6))* American Psychiatric Publishing, Inc.

Kauffman, James M. & Landrum, Timothy J. Cases in Emotional & Behavioral Disorders of Children & Youth. 2nd ed. 2008. (ENG.). 128p. (C). pap. 20.80 *(978-0-13-500263-6(X))* Prentice Hall Higher Education.

Kazdin, Alan E. Parent Management Training: Treatment for Oppositional, Aggressive, & Antisocial Behavior in Children & Adolescents. 2008. (ENG., Illus.). 424p. pap. 29.95 *(978-0-19-538600-4(0))* Oxford Univ. Pr., Inc.

Kerig & Wenar & Cram101 Textbook Reviews Staff. Developmental Psychopathology. 2007. 316p. per. 16.95 *(978-1-4288-2100-2(7))* Cram101 Inc.

Latzer, Yael & Tzischinsky, Orna, eds. The Dance of Sleeping & Eating among Adolescents: Normal & Pathological Perspectives. 2011. (Health & Human Development Ser.). 335p. 145.00 *(978-1-61209-710-7(3))* Nova Science Pubs., Inc.

Marcus, Robert. Aggression & Violence in Adolescence. 2007. (ENG., 200p. Illus.). per. 25.99 *(978-0-521-68891-8(4));* 80.00 *(978-0-521-86881-5(5))* Cambridge Univ. Pr.

Martin, Magy, et al. When Devon Met Oz: Helping Children Cope with Depression. 2008. (Let's Talk Ser.). (ENG., Illus.). 48p. (J). (gr. -1-4). pap. 8.95 *(978-0-88282-304-1(3))* New Horizon Pr. Pubs., Inc.

Mash, Eric J. & Barkley, Russell A., eds. Assessment of Childhood Disorders. 4th rev. ed. 2007. (ENG., Illus.). 866p. 90.00 *(978-1-59385-493-5(5))* Guilford Pubns., Inc.

Miller, David N. & Brock, Stephen E. Identifying, Assessing, & Treating Self-Injury at School. 2011. (Developmental Psychopathology at School Ser.). xi, 137p. pap. 34.95 *(978-1-4419-9512-4(9),* 1441995129) Springer.

Monteverde, Matt. Making Smart Choices about Violence, Gangs, & Bullying. 2009. (Making Smart Choices Ser.). 48p. (gr. 5-5). 53.00 *(978-1-61514-343-6(2),* Rosen Central) Rosen Publishing Group, Inc., The.

Mufson, Laura, et al. Interpersonal Psychotherapy for Depressed Adolescents, Second Edition. 2nd rev. ed. 2011. (ENG.). 315p. pap. 26.00 *(978-1-60918-226-7(X))* Guilford Pubns., Inc.

Nardone, Giorgio, et al. The Evolution of Family Patterns & Indirect Therapy with Adolescents. 2008. 126p. per. 39.95 *(978-1-85575-551-2(3))* Karnac Bks. GBR. Dist: Stylus Publishing, LLC.

Nurcombe, Barry, et al, eds. The Mental Health of Children & Adolescents: An Area of Global Neglect. 2007. (World Psychiatric Association Ser.). (ENG., Illus.). 256p. 110.95 *(978-0-470-51245-6(8),* Wiley) Wiley, John & Sons, Inc.

O'Neill, Terry. Secret Scars: What You Need to Know about Cutting, 1 vol. 2009. (What's the Issue? Ser.). (ENG.). 48p. (gr. 5-6). lib. bdg. 27.99 *(978-0-7565-4142-2(5),* CPB Grades 4-8) Compass Point Bks.

Romer, Daniel & Walker, Elaine F., eds. Adolescent Psychopathology & the Developing Brain: Integrating Brain & Prevention Science. 2007. (Illus.). 544p. *(978-0-19-530625-5(2))* Oxford Univ. Pr.

—Adolescent Psychopathology & the Developing Brain: Integrating Brain & Prevention Science. 2007. (ENG., Illus.). 544p. pap. 37.95 *(978-0-19-530626-2(0))* Oxford Univ. Pr., Inc.

Roth, Jeffrey D. Approaches to Substance Abuse & Addiction in Education Communities: A Guide to Practices that Support Recovery in Adolescents & Young Adults. 2008. (Illus.). vi, 299p. 130.00 *(978-0-7890-3696-4(7));* pap. 45.95 *(978-0-7890-3697-1(5))* Routledge.

Scheff, Sue. Wit's End: Advice & Resources for Saving Your Out-of-Control Teen. 2008. (ENG.). 224p. pap. 14.95 *(978-0-7573-0697-6(7))* Health Communications, Inc.

Selg, Peter. A Grand Metamorphosis: Contributions to the Spiritual-Scientific Anthropology & Education of Adolescents. 2008. 120p. pap. *(978-0-88010-598-9(4))* SteinerBooks, Inc.

Smith, Walter, Jr. & Smith, Bettye. Tell Our Story. 2007. 60p. (YA). per. 7.99 *(978-0-9796925-0-5(4))* Young People Pr.

Spalding, Frank. Antisocial Behavior. 2011. (Teen Mental Health Ser.). (YA). (gr. 7-12). lib. bdg. 27.95 *(978-1-4488-4585-9(8))* Rosen Publishing Group, Inc., The.

Stebnicki, Mark A. What Is Adolescent Mental Health? Helping Disconnected & at-Risk Youth to Become Whole. 2008. 252p. *(978-0-7734-5251-0(6))* Mellen, Edwin Pr., The.

Van Dijk, Sheri & Guindon, Karma. The Bipolar Workbook for Teens: DBT Skills to Help You Control Mood Swings. 2010. (Instant Help Ser.). (ENG., Illus.). 160p. (J). (gr. 6-12). pap. 16.95 *(978-1-57224-696-6(0))* Play2Grow.

Warley, Raquel Maria. Juvenile Homicide: Fatal Assault or Lethal Intent? 2011. 65.00 ***(978-1-59332-480-3(4))*** LFB Scholarly Publishing LLC.

Wilmshurst, Linda, ed. Child & Adolescent Psychopathology: A Casebook. 2nd ed. 2010. (Illus.). 384p. (C). pap. 42.00 *(978-1-4129-8249-8(9),* B82498P) SAGE Pubns., Inc.

World Health Organisation. Multiaxial Classification of Child & Adolescent Psychiatric Disorders: The ICD-10 Classification of Mental & Behavioural Disorders in Children & Adolescents. 2008. 312p. pap. 46.00 *(978-0-521-06577-1(1))* Cambridge Univ. Pr.

ADOLESCENT PSYCHOTHERAPY

Aguirre, Blaise A. Borderline Personality Disorder in Adolescents: A Complete Guide to Understanding & Coping When Your Adolescent Has BPD. 2007. (ENG., Illus.). 288p. per. 16.95 *(978-1-59233-287-8(0),* 1592332870) Quayside.

Alvarez, Anne. Levels of Therapeutic Work & Levels of Pathology. 2012. (ENG., Illus.). 232p. (C). 128.00 ***(978-0-415-55486-2(1));*** pap. 36.95 ***(978-0-415-55487-9(X))*** Routledge.

Apsche, Jack & DiMeo, Lucia R. Mode Deactivation Therapy for Aggression & Oppositional Behavior in Adolescents: An Integrative Methodology Using ACT, DBT, & CBT. 2012. (ENG.). 216p. pap. 59.95 ***(978-1-60882-107-5(2))*** New Harbinger Pubns.

Barton, Susan, et al. Therapeutic Residential Care for Children & Young People: An Attachment & Trauma-Informed Model for Practice. 2011. (ENG., Illus.). 288p. pap. ***(978-1-84905-255-9(7))*** Kingsley, Jessica Ltd.

Bertolino, Bob. Thriving on the Front Lines: A Guide to Strengths-Based Youth Care Work. 2012. (ENG.). 240p. pap. 36.95 *(978-0-415-89521-7(9))* Routledge.

Blake. Child & Adolescent Psychotherapy. 2011. 340p. pap. 46.95 ***(978-1-85575-898-8(9))*** Karnac Bks. GBR. Dist: Stylus Publishing, LLC.

Blom, Rinda. The Handbook of Gestalt Play Therapy: Practical Guidelines for Child Therapists. 2006. (ENG., Illus.). 288p. per. *(978-1-84310-459-9(8))* Kingsley, Jessica Ltd.

Boxmeyer, Caroline. Youth & Family Outcomes of Community Mental Health Treatment. 2008. 88p. pap. *(978-3-639-07714-8(8))* VDM Verlag Dr. Mueller e.K.

Briggs, Stephen. Working with Adolescents & Young Adults: A Contemporary Psychodynamic Approach. Frosh, Stephen, ed. 2nd rev. ed. 2008. (ENG.). 224p. pap. 39.00 *(978-0-230-55141-1(6))* Palgrave Macmillan.

Bromfield, Richard. Doing Child & Adolescent Psychotherapy: Adapting Psychodynamic Treatment to Contemporary Practice. 2nd ed. 2007. (ENG., Illus.). 320p. 78.00 *(978-0-470-12181-8(5),* Wiley) Wiley, John & Sons, Inc.

Capuzzi, David & Gross, Douglas R. Youth at Risk: A Prevention Resource for Counselors, Teachers, & Parents. 5th ed. 2007. *(978-1-55620-275-9(X))* American Counseling Assn.

Castro-Blanco, David & Karver, Marc S. Elusive Alliance: Treatment Engagement Strategies with High-Risk Adolescents. 2010. 272p. 59.95 *(978-1-4338-0811-1(0))* American Psychological Assn.

Christner, Ray W. & Stewart, Jessica, eds. Handbk Cbt Group Children & Adolescents: Specific Stteing & Popul. 2007. (ENG., Illus.). 552p. 65.95 *(978-0-415-95254-5(9))* Routledge.

Cram101 Textbook Reviews & Cram101 Textbook Reviews. Outlines & Highlights for Counseling & Psychotherapy with Children & Adolescents: Theory & Practice for School & Clinical Settings by H. Thom. 2011. 112p. pap. 28.95 ***(978-1-61744-885-0(0))*** Cram101 Inc.

Crenshaw, David A. Child & Adolescent Psychotherapy: Wounded Spirits & Healing Paths. 2008. (ENG., Illus.). 174p. 62.99 *(978-0-7657-0598-3(2),* Aronson, Jason) Rowman & Littlefield Publishers, Inc.

—Evocative Strategies in Child & Adolescent Psychotherapy. (ENG., Illus.). 312p. 2007. per. 39.99 *(978-0-7657-0580-8(X))* 2006. 18.95 *(978-0-7657-0414-6(5))* Rowman & Littlefield Publishers, Inc. (Aronson, Jason).

—Therapeutic Engagement of Children & Adolescents: Play, Symbol, Drawing, & Storytelling Strategies. 2008. (ENG., Illus.). 176p. 78.99 *(978-0-7657-0570-9(2));* per. 39.99 *(978-0-7657-0571-6(0))* Rowman & Littlefield Publishers, Inc. (Aronson, Jason).

DeGangi, Georgia. Kids' Club Letters: Narrative Tools for Stimulating Process & Dialogue in Therapy Groups for Children & Adolescents. 2009. (ENG., Illus.). 256p. 52.95 *(978-0-415-99432-3(2))* Routledge.

Dittoff, M. S. Mark. Understanding Issues of Power & Control: A Therapeutic Guide to Working with Adolescent Sex Offenders. 2008. 185p. pap. 24.95 *(978-1-4241-8320-3(0))* PublishAmerica, Inc.

Elliott, Julian & Place, Maurice. Children in Difficulty: A Guide to Understanding & Helping. 3rd rev. ed. 2012. (ENG., Illus.). 296p. (C). 160.00 *(978-0-415-67255-9(4));* pap. 44.95 *(978-0-415-67263-4(5))* Routledge.

Ellis, Rodney A. Best Practices in Residential Treatment. 2008. (Illus.). 168p. (C). 41.95 *(978-0-7890-3789-3(0));* 150.00 *(978-0-7890-3788-6(2))* Routledge.

Erk, Robert R. Counseling Treatment for Children & Adolescents with DSM-IV-TR Disorders. 2nd ed. 2007. (ENG., Illus.). 480p. (C). pap. 129.80 *(978-0-13-230262-3(4),* Prentice Hall) Prentice Hall PTR.

Gallo-Lopez, Loretta, ed. Play Therapy with Adolescents. 2010. (ENG.). 306p. pap. 44.95 *(978-0-7657-0802-1(7),* Aronson, Jason) Rowman & Littlefield Publishers, Inc.

Goldstein, Stanley. Shopping for A Shrink: Finding the Right Psychotherapist for You or Your Child /Sound Advice & Stories to Change Your Life. 2011. 358p. pap. 12.95 ***(978-0-9717705-5-3(7))*** Wyston Bks., Inc.

Gowers, Simon G. Eating Disorders: Cognitive Behaviour Therapy with Children & Young People. 2009. (CBT with Children, Adolescents & Families Ser.). (ENG., Illus.). 200p. (C). 128.00 *(978-0-415-44462-0(4))* Routledge.

Greco, Laurie A. Acceptance & Mindfulness Treatments for Children & Adolescents. Hayes, Steven C., ed. 2008. (Context / NHP Ser.). (ENG., Illus.). 312p. 59.95 *(978-1-57224-541-9(7))* New Harbinger Pubns.

Gunter, Michael. Winnicott's Squiggle Technique Practi. 2007. 223p. pap. 38.95 *(978-1-85575-419-5(3))* Karnac Bks. GBR. Dist: Stylus Publishing, LLC.

The check digit for ISBN-10 appears in parentheses after the full ISBN-13

Hanley, Terry, et al, eds. Adolescent Counselling Psychology. 2012. (ENG., Illus.). 184p. (C). 110.00 *(978-0-415-58025-0(0))*; pap. 33.95 *(978-0-415-58026-7(9))* Routledge.

Hardy, Kenneth V & Laszloffy, Tracey A. Teens Who Hurt: Clinical Interventions to Break the Cycle of Adolescent Violence. 2006. (ENG., Illus.). 280p. (gr. 5-13). pap. 30.00 *(978-1-59385-440-9(4))* Guilford Pubns., Inc.

Jongsma, Arthur E. & Bruce, Timothy J. Treatment Planning for Disruptive Child & Adolescent Behavior. 2011. (Evidence-Based Psychotherapy Treatment Planning Video Ser.: 7). (ENG.). mass mkt. 40.00 *(978-0-470-41789-8(7))*; Set. mass mkt., wbk. ed. 55.25 *(978-1-118-02894-0(5))* Wiley, John & Sons, Inc. (Wiley).

Jongsma, Arthur E., Jr., et al. The Adolescent Psychotherapy Progress Notes Planner. 3rd ed. 2006. (ENG.). (PracticePlanners Ser.). cd-rom 125.00 *(978-0-471-78788-4(4))*; (PracticePlanners Ser.: 214). 432p. pap. 55.00 *(978-0-471-78538-5(5))* Wiley, John & Sons, Inc. (Wiley).

—The Adolescent Psychotherapy Treatment Planner. 4th ed. 2006. (ENG.). (PracticePlanners Ser.). cd-rom 175.00 *(978-0-471-78786-0(8))*; (PracticePlanners Ser.: 215). 368p. pap. 55.00 *(978-0-471-78539-2(3))* Wiley, John & Sons, Inc. (Wiley).

—Adolescent Therapy Homework Planner. 2nd ed. 2006. (PracticePlanners? Ser.). (ENG.). cd-rom 100.00 *(978-0-471-78787-7(5))*, Wiley) Wiley, John & Sons, Inc.

Jurich, Anthony P. Family Therapy with Suicidal Adolescents. 2007. (ENG., Illus.). 288p. 44.95 *(978-0-415-96086-1(X))* Routledge.

Kendall, Philip C., ed. Child & Adolescent Therapy, Fourth Edition: Cognitive-Behavioral Procedures. 4th rev. ed. 2011. (ENG., Illus.). 538p. 65.00 *(978-1-60623-561-4(3))* Guilford Pubns., Inc.

Kratochwil, Thomas R. Handbook of Psychotherapy with Children & Adolescents, Second Edition. 2nd ed. 2009. pap. 89.95 *(978-0-8058-6226-3(9))* Erlbaum, Lawrence Assocs., Inc.

Lanyado, Monica. The Handbook of Child & Adolescent Psychotherapy: Psychoanalytic Approaches. 2nd ed. 2009. (ENG., Illus.). 480p. (C). instr.'s hndbk. ed. 105.00 *(978-0-415-46368-3(8))* Routledge.

—The Handbook of Child & Adolescent Psychotherapy: Psychoanalytic Approaches. Lanyado, Monica & Horne, Ann, eds. 2nd rev. ed. 2009. (ENG., Illus.). 480p. (C). 39.95 *(978-0-415-46369-0(6))* Routledge.

LeCroy, Craig Winston. Handbook of Evidence-Based Treatment Manuals for Children & Adolescents. 2nd ed. 2008. (ENG., Illus.). 560p. (C). 65.00 *(978-0-19-517741-1(X))* Oxford Univ. Pr., Inc.

Leigh, Lauraine, et al, eds. Dramatherapy with Children, Young People & Schools: Enabling creativity, sociability, communication & Learning. 2012. (ENG., Illus.). 304p. (C). 112.00 *(978-0-415-67076-0(4))*; pap. 36.99 *(978-0-415-67077-7(2))* Routledge.

Lines, Dennis. Brief Counselling in Schools: Working with Young People from 11 To 18. 3rd ed. 2012. (Illus.). 296p. (C). 115.00 ***(978-0-85702-511-1(2)***, B25111C); pap. 44.00 ***(978-0-85702-512-8(0)***, B25111P) SAGE Pubns., Ltd. GBR. Dist: SAGE Pubns., Inc.

Manassis, Katharina. Problem Solving in Child & Adolescent Psychotherapy: A Skills-Based, Collaborative Approach. 2012. (ENG.). 208p. 30.00 ***(978-1-4625-0370-4(5))*** Guilford Pubns., Inc.

McGinn, Christopher. Reducing the Use of Physical Restraints - the Effect of Federal Legislation. 2008. 92p. pap. *(978-3-639-10401-1(3))* VDM Verlag Dr. Mueller e.K.

Micucci, Joseph A. & Hnatov, Nina. The Adolescent in Family Therapy: Harnessing the Power of Relationships. 2nd rev. ed. 2009. (Guilford Family Therapy Ser.). (ENG., Illus.). 368p. 40.00 *(978-1-60623-330-6(0))* Guilford Pubns., Inc.

Mufson, Laura, et al. Interpersonal Psychotherapy for Depressed Adolescents, Second Edition. 2nd rev. ed. 2011. (ENG.). 315p. pap. 26.00 *(978-1-60918-226-7(X))* Guilford Pubns., Inc.

Nixon, Mary K. & Heath, Nancy L., eds. Self-Injury in Youth: The Essential Guide to Assessment & Intervention. 2008. (ENG.). 368p. 52.95 *(978-0-415-95725-0(7))* Routledge.

Norton, Christine L. Innovative Interventions in Child & Adolescent Mental Health. 2010. (ENG., Illus.). 208p. 135.00 *(978-0-415-87984-2(1))*; pap. 35.95 *(978-0-415-87985-9(X))* Routledge.

Oaklander, Violet. Hidden Treasure: A Map to the Child's Inner Self. 2007. 256p. per. 39.95 *(978-1-85575-490-4(8))* Karnac Bks. GBR. Dist: Stylus Publishing, LLC.

O'Donohue, William T. Behavioral Approaches to Chronic Disease in Adolescence: A Guide to Integrative Care. 2009. (ENG., Illus.). xi, 354p. 179.00 *(978-0-387-87686-3(3)*, 0387876863) Springer.

Office of Management and Budget (U.S.), compiled by. Cases of Child Neglect & Abuse at Private Residential Treatment Facilities: Hearing Before the Committee on Education & Labor, U. S. House of Representatives, One Hundred Tenth Congress, First Session, Hearing Held in Washington, DC, October 10, 2007. 2008. (ENG., Illus.). iii, 138p. pap. 102.00 *(978-0-16-080875-3(8)*, 552-070-37425-6, Office of Management & Budget) United States Government Printing Office.

Painter, Kirstin. Evidence-Based Practice Model for Youth with Externalizing Disorders. 2010. 140p. pap. *(978-3-8383-0253-9(2))* Lambert Academic Publishing.

Pazaratz, Don. Residential Treatment of Adolescents: Integrative Principles & Practices. 2009. (ENG., Illus.). 242p. 125.00 *(978-0-415-99708-9(9))* Routledge.

Perl, Elizabeth. Psychotherapy with Adolescent Girls & Young Women: Fostering Autonomy through Attachment. 2008. (ENG.). 198p. 30.00 *(978-1-59385-651-9(2))* Guilford Pubns., Inc.

Peters, Todd & Freeman, Jennifer. Cognitive Behavioral Therapy - An Issue of Child & Adolescent Psychiatric Clinics of North America. 2011. (Clinics: Internal Medicine Ser.: 20-2). (ENG., Illus.). xvi, 180p. 110.00 *(978-1-4557-0428-6(8)*, Saunders) Elsevier - Health Sciences Div.

Plant, Kathryn. Personal Development Matters: A Guide & Step-by-Step Educational Workbook for Helping Young People Aged Roughly 11-16 with Complex Needs to Get to Know Themselves Better. 2011. (Illus.). 224p. pap. 59.95 *(978-1-905541-69-0(4))* Russell Hse. Publishing Ltd. GBR. Dist: International Specialized Bk. Services.

Prout, H. Thompson & Brown, Douglas T., eds. Counseling & Psychotherapy with Children & Adolescents: Theory & Practice for School & Clinical Settings. 4th rev. ed. 2007. (ENG., Illus.). 480p. 152.00 *(978-0-471-77091-6(4)*, Wiley) Wiley, John & Sons, Inc.

Reamer, Frederic G. & Siegel, Deborah H. Teens in Crisis: How the Industry Serving Struggling Teens Helps & Hurts Our Kids. 2008. (ENG.). 192p. (gr. 17). 74.50 *(978-0-231-14462-9(8))*; pap. 26.50 *(978-0-231-14463-6(6))* Columbia Univ. Pr.

Rispoli, Luciano. The Basic Experience & the Development of the Self: Development from the Point of View of Functional Psychotherapy. 2008. 460p. pap. *(978-3-03911-750-5(5))* Lang, Peter.

Rodenhiser, Roy W. Assessment in Residential Care for Children & Youth. 2008. 228p. 150.00 *(978-0-7890-3838-8(2))*; 45.95 *(978-0-7890-3839-5(0))* Routledge.

Rosenfeld, George W. Beyond Evidence-Based Psychotherapy: Fostering the Eight Sources of Change in Child & Adolescent Treatment. 2008. (Counseling & Psychotherapy Ser.). (ENG.). 284p. 42.50 *(978-0-415-99336-4(9))*; 125.00 *(978-0-415-99335-7(0))* Routledge.

Rubin, Lawrence C., ed. Popular Culture in Counseling, Pschotherpay, & Play-Based Interventions. 2008. (Illus.). 372p. 48.00 *(978-0-8261-0118-1(6))* Springer Publishing Co., Inc.

Saxe, Glenn N., et al. Collaborative Treatment of Traumatized Children & Teens: The Trauma Systems Therapy Approach. (ENG., Illus.). 338p. 2009. pap. 35.00 *(978-1-60623-349-8(1))* 2006. 60.00 *(978-1-59385-315-0(7))* Guilford Pubns., Inc.

Selekman, Matthew D. Pathways to Change, Second Edition: Brief Therapy with Difficult Adolescents. 2nd ed. 2008. (ENG.). 292p. pap. 30.00 *(978-1-59385-979-4(1))* Guilford Pubns., Inc.

Selekman, Matthew D., et al. The Adolescent & Young Adult Self-Harming Treatment Manual: A Collaborative Strengths-Based Brief Therapy Approach. 2009. (ENG., Illus.). 256p. 33.95 *(978-0-393-70567-6(6)*, 70567) Norton, W. W. & Co., Inc.

Silverman, Wendy K. & Field, Andy, eds. Anxiety Disorders in Children & Adolescents. 2nd ed. 2011. (Cambridge Child & Adolescent Psychiatry Ser.). (ENG., Illus.). 436p. pap. 80.00 *(978-0-521-72148-5(2))* Cambridge Univ. Pr.

Smith, Steven R. & Handler, Leonard, eds. The Clinical Assessment of Children & Adolescents: A Practitioner's Handbook. 2006. (ENG., Illus.). 648p. 257.95 *(978-0-8058-5791-7(5))* Routledge.

Society for the Study of Inborn Errors of Metabolism Staff, ed. JIMD Reports - Case & Research Reports, 2011/2. 2011. (JIMD Reports). (ENG., Illus.). vii, 123p. pap. 139.00 ***(978-3-642-24757-6(1)***, 3642247571) Springer.

Sori, Catherine Ford & Hecker, Lorna L. The Therapist's Notebook Vol. 3: More Homework, Handouts, & Activities for Use in Psychotherapy. 2008. (ENG., Illus.). 248p. 54.50 *(978-0-7890-3522-6(7))* Routledge.

Steele, Ric G., et al, eds. Handbook of Evidence-Based Therapies for Children & Adolescents: Bridging Science & Practice. (Issues in Clinical Child Psychology Ser.). 2010. x, 585p. pap. 114.00 *(978-1-4419-4469-6(9)*, 1441944699) 2007. (Illus.). 585p. 114.00 *(978-0-387-73690-7(5))* Springer.

Steele, William & Malchiodi, Cathy A. Trauma-Informed Practices with Children & Adolescents. 2011. (ENG., Illus.). 279p. pap. 39.95 *(978-0-415-89052-6(7))* Routledge.

Straus, Martha B. Adolescent Girls in Crisis. 2007. 24.95 *(978-0-7937-0447-7(2))* Norton, W. W. & Co., Inc.

Taffel, Ron. Breaking Through to Teens: Psychotherapy for the New Adolescence. 2010. (ENG.). 292p. pap. 28.00 *(978-1-60623-944-5(9))* Guilford Pubns., Inc.

Thomas, Bonnie. Creative Expression Activities for Teens: Exploring Identity through Art, Craft & Journaling. 2010. (ENG., Illus.). 178p. pap. *(978-1-84905-842-1(3))* Kingsley, Jessica Ltd.

Tuber, Steven & Caflisch, Jane M. Beginning Treatment with Children & Adolescents: A Process-Oriented Guide for Therapists. 2011. (ENG.). 324p. 130.00 *(978-0-415-88557-7(4))* Routledge.

—Beginning Treatment with Children & Adolescents: The Clinician's Guide to Psychodynamic Approaches. 2011. (ENG.). 324p. pap. 34.95 *(978-0-415-88558-4(2))* Routledge.

Tudor, Keith, ed. The Adult is Parent to the Child: Transactional Analysis with Children & Young People. 2008. 300p. pap. 69.95 *(978-1-905541-17-1(1))* Russell Hse. Publishing Ltd. GBR. Dist: International Specialized Bk. Services.

Verduyn, Chrissie, et al. Depression. 2009. (CBT with Children, Adolescents & Families Ser.). (ENG., Illus.). 216p. (C). pap. 35.99 *(978-0-415-39978-4(5))* Routledge.

Vernon, Ann. More What Works When with Children & Adolescents (Book & CD) 2009. pap. 44.95 *(978-0-87822-614-6(1))* Research Pr.

Wanberg, Kenneth W. (Wayne) & Milkman, Harvey B. Criminal Conduct & Substance Abuse Treatment for Adolescents: Pathways to Self-Discovery & Change: The Provider's Guide. 2nd ed. 2012. 640p. pap. 80.00 ***(978-1-4522-0580-9(9)***, B05809P) SAGE Pubns., Inc.

Weisz, John R. & Kazdin, Alan E., eds. Evidence-Based Psychotherapies for Children & Adolescents. 2nd ed. 2010. (ENG., Illus.). 602p. 75.00 *(978-1-59385-974-9(0))* Guilford Pubns., Inc.

ADOPTED CHILDREN

Amend, Deborah. A Dress for Anna: The Story of the Redemption of the Life of a Ukranian Orphan. 2009. *(978-0-7880-2632-4(1))* FaithWalk Publishing.

Armah, Collins. Intercountry Child Adoption. 2011. 108p. pap. ***(978-3-8454-0733-3(6))*** Lambert Academic Publishing.

Ayres, Mary. In His Hands: (A Journey of an Adopted Child) 2011. 152p. 23.99 ***(978-1-4670-7280-9(X))***; pap. 14.95 ***(978-1-4670-7281-6(8))*** AuthorHouse.

Bay, Jane. Love & Loss: A Story about Life, Death & Rebirth. 2006. 415p. pap. *(978-1-57416-088-8(5))* Clear Light Pubs.

Bentovim. Assessing the Support Needs of Adoptive Children & Their Famili. 2006. (ENG., Illus.). 192p. (C). 150.00 *(978-0-415-40944-5(6))* Routledge.

Bentovim, Arnon & Miller, Liza Bingley. Assessing the Support Needs of Adopted Children & Their Families: Building Secure New Lives. 2006. (Illus.). 176p. per. 43.95 *(978-0-415-40945-2(4))* Routledge.

Blomquist, Barbara Taylor. Insight into Adoption: Uncovering & Understanding the Heart of Adoption. 2nd ed. 2009. pap. 27.95 *(978-0-398-07846-1(7))* Thomas, Charles C. Pub., Ltd.

Brian, Kristi. Reframing Transracial Adoption: Korean Adoptees, White Parents, & the Politics of Kinship. 2012. (ENG.). 220p. 82.50 ***(978-1-4399-0183-0(X))***; pap. 27.95 ***(978-1-4399-0184-7(8))*** Temple Univ. Pr.

Brown, Wain Karl & Seita, John Robert, eds. Growing up in the Care of Strangers: The Experiences, Insights & Recommendations of Eleven Former Foster Kids. 2009. 192p. pap. 27.95 *(978-0-9824510-0-7(6))* Gladden, William Foundation.

Carangelo, Lori. The Ultimate Search Book 2011 Edition Worldwide Adpotion, Genealogy & Other Search Secrets from the Files of Americans for Open Records. 2011. 306p. pap. 39.95 ***(978-0-8063-5515-3(8))*** Clearfield Co.

Cashin, Claire. Will You Be Here When I Get Home? 2006. (ENG.). 222p. pap. 24.95 *(978-1-85635-521-6(7))* Mercier Pr., Ltd., The IRL. Dist: Dufour Editions, Inc.

Comfort, Randy Lee. Searching to Be Found: Understanding & Helping Adopted & Looked after Children with Attention Difficulties. 2008. 206p. pap. 36.95 *(978-1-85575-464-5(9))* Karnac Bks. GBR. Dist: Stylus Publishing, LLC.

Cremer-Vogel, Kate, et al. What Every Adoptive Parent Needs to Know: Healing Your Child's Wounded Heart. 2008. xi, 269p. pap. *(978-0-615-18845-4(1))* Mountain Ridge Publishing.

Crossen, Jan. 9 Lives, Cat Tales. 2008. 168p. pap. 12.25 *(978-0-9798686-3-4(7))* Dragonpublishing.net.

Culberson, Sarah & Trivas, Tracy. A Princess Found: An American Family, an African Chiefdom, & the Daughter Who Connected Them All. 2010. (ENG., Illus.). 384p. pap. 16.99 *(978-0-312-62839-0(0)*, St. Martin's Griffin) St. Martin's Pr.

Dö, et al. Adoption: Adoptivkinder, ihre leiblichen Mütter und ihre Adoptiveltern: Ergebnisse einer Adoptionsvermittlung zwischen 1947-1987. 2011. 116p. pap. ***(978-3-8381-2372-1(7))*** Südwestdeutscher Verlag für Hochschulschriften AG & Co. KG.

Ellis, Titia. The Search: A Memoir of an Adopted Woman. 2010. 232p. pap. 18.95 *(978-1-4502-5296-6(6))* iUniverse, Inc.

Fern, Kelly & Fern, Brad. Songs of My Families: A Thirty-Seven Year Odyssey from Korea to America & Back. 2012. ***(978-1-59056-320-5(4))***; E-Book ***(978-1-59056-321-2(2))*** Lantern Bks.

Foster, Celia. Big Steps for Little People: Parenting Your Adopted Child. 2008. (ENG., Illus.). 176p. pap. *(978-1-84310-620-3(5))* Kingsley, Jessica Ltd.

Gerstenzang, Sarah. Another Mother: Co-Parenting with the Foster Care System, 1 vol. 2007. (ENG.). 224p. per. 27.95 *(978-0-8265-1549-0(5))*; (Illus.). 59.95 *(978-0-8265-1548-3(7))* Vanderbilt Univ. Pr.

Gibbons, Judith L. & Rotabi, Karen Smith, eds. Intercountry Adoption: Policies, Practices, & Outcomes. 2012. (Contemporary Social Work Studies). (Illus.). 350p. 119.95 ***(978-1-4094-1054-6(4))*** Ashgate Publishing Co.

Golding, Kim S. Nurturing Attachments: Supporting Children Who Are Fostered or Adopted. 2007. (ENG., Illus.). 240p. (C). pap. *(978-1-84310-614-2(0))* Kingsley, Jessica Ltd.

Gowan, Barbara Ann. Blending In: Crisscrossing the Lines of Race, Religion, Family, & Adoption. 2007. 208p. (ENG.). 27.95 *(978-0-595-69834-9(4))*; per. 17.95 *(978-0-595-44385-7(0))* iUniverse, Inc.

Gray, Deborah D. Attaching in Adoption: Practical Tools for Today's Parents. 2012. (ENG., Illus.). 400p. pap. ***(978-1-84905-890-2(3))*** Kingsley, Jessica Ltd.

—Nurturing Adoptions: Creating Resilience after Neglect & Trauma. 2012. (ENG., Illus.). 514p. pap. ***(978-1-84905-891-9(1))*** Kingsley, Jessica Ltd.

Greene, Melissa Fay. No Biking in the House Without a Helmet, 1 vol. 2011. (ENG., Illus.). 368p. 26.00 *(978-0-374-22306-9(8))* Farrar, Straus & Giroux.

Hamm, Regie. Angels & Idols: The Rise, Fall, & Redemption of a Would-Be Pop Star. 2010. pap. 14.99 *(978-1-61663-440-7(5))* Tate Publishing & Enterprises, LLC.

Herlem, Fanny Cohen. Great Answers to Difficult Questions about Adoption: What Children Need to Know. 2008. (ENG., Illus.). 112p. pap. *(978-1-84310-671-5(X))* Kingsley, Jessica Ltd.

—Great Answers to Difficult Questions about Divorce: What Children Need to Know. 2008. (ENG., Illus.). 96p. pap. *(978-1-84310-672-2(8))* Kingsley, Jessica Ltd.

Holman, William R. The Orphans' Nine Commandments: A Memoir. 2007. (ENG., Illus.). 238p. 24.50 *(978-0-87565-355-6(3))* Texas Christian Univ. Pr.

Holman, William Roger. The Orphans' Nine Commandments. 2009. (ENG., Illus.). 246p. pap. 19.95 *(978-0-87565-403-4(7))* Texas Christian Univ. Pr.

Homes, A. M. The Mistress's Daughter. 2008. (ENG., Illus.). 256p. (gr. 12-18). 14.00 *(978-0-14-311331-7(3)*, Penguin (Non-Classics)) Penguin Group (USA) Inc.

Hopgood, Mei-Ling. Lucky Girl. (ENG.). 2010. 272p. pap. 13.95 *(978-1-56512-982-5(2)*, 1565129822) 2009. 244p. 23.95 *(978-1-56512-600-8(9)*, 1565126009) Algonquin Bks. of Chapel Hill.

Hughes, Daniel. Building the Bonds of Attachment: Awakening Love in Deeply Troubled Children. 2nd ed. 2006. (ENG.). 272p. per. 46.50 *(978-0-7657-0404-7(8)*, Aronson, Jason) Rowman & Littlefield Publishers, Inc.

Hwa-Froelich, Deborah A. Supporting Development in Internationally Adopted Children. 2011. (ENG.). 256p. pap. 39.95 ***(978-1-59857-191-2(5))*** Brookes, Paul H. Publishing Co.

Jones, Lisa A. Images & Remembrances from My Life: The Autobiography of Lisa A. Jones. 2011. 90p. pap. 19.95 ***(978-1-4512-7643-5(5))*** PublishAmerica, Inc.

Josephs, Ian. Forced Adoption (shortened Version) 2009. 170p. pap. 12.50 *(978-1-4092-7362-2(8))* Lulu Enterprises Inc.

Katch, Jane. Far Away from the Tigers: A Year in the Classroom with Internationally Adopted Children. 2011. (ENG.). 176p. 22.50 *(978-0-226-42578-8(9))* Univ. of Chicago Pr.

Keck, Gregory C. Parenting Adopted Adolescents: Understanding & Appreciating Their Journeys. 2009. (Hollywood Nobody Ser.). (ENG.). 240p. pap. 17.99 *(978-1-60006-281-0(4))* NavPress Publishing Group.

Lacher, Denise B., et al. Connecting with Kids Through Stories: Using Narratives to Facilitate Attachment in Adopted Children. 2nd rev. ed. 2012. (ENG., Illus.). 240p. pap. ***(978-1-84905-869-8(5))*** Kingsley, Jessica Ltd.

Lancaster, Kathy. Keys to Parenting an Adopted Child. 2nd rev. ed. 2009. (Barron's Parenting Keys Ser.). (ENG.). 208p. pap. 8.99 *(978-0-7641-4097-6(3))* Barron's Educational Series, Inc.

Land, Judith & Land, Martin. Adoption Detective: Memoir of an Adopted Child. 2011. 46.95 ***(978-1-60494-571-3(0))***; pap. 21.95 ***(978-1-60494-570-6(2))*** Wheatmark.

Lehner, Olga. The Episodes of Olg. 2009. 112p. 29.99 *(978-1-4257-7085-3(1))*; pap. 19.99 *(978-1-4257-7060-0(6))* Xlibris Corp.

Lewis, Gaye. Bittersweet: The Restoration Continues. 2008. 256p. pap. 14.95 *(978-1-57921-944-4(6))* WinePress Publishing.

Lierow, Diane, et al. Dani's Story: A Journey from Neglect to Love. 2011. (ENG., Illus.). 272p. 24.95 *(978-0-470-59133-8(1)*, Wiley) Wiley, John & Sons, Inc.

Lifton, Betty Jean. Lost & Found: The Adoption Experience. 3rd ed. 2009. (ENG.). 344p. pap. 17.95 *(978-0-472-03328-7(X))* Univ. of Michigan Pr.

Macrae, Sheena & MacLeod, Jean, eds. Adoption Parenting: Creating a Toolbox, Building Connections. 2006. (Illus.). 503p. per. 29.95 *(978-0-9726244-5-9(7))* EMK Pr.

McCabe, Nancy. Crossing the Blue Willow Bridge: A Journey to My Daughter's Birthplace in China. 2nd ed. 2011. (ENG.). 216p. (gr. 3). pap. 19.95 *(978-0-8262-1942-8(X))* Univ. of Missouri Pr.

McKoy, Sandra H. God's Diamond among Rocks: Rewards & Challenges of Single Parent Adoption While Facing a Physical Challenge. 2009. 256p. pap. 16.99 *(978-1-4389-7909-0(6))* AuthorHouse.

Oakwater, Helen. Bubble Wrapped Children: How social networking is transforming the face of 21st century Adoption. 2012. 202p. pap. ***(978-1-78092-097-9(0))*** MX Publishing, Ltd.

Philps, Alan & Lahutsky, John. The Boy from Baby House 10: From the Nightmare of a Russian Orphanage to a New Life in America. 2011. (ENG., Illus.). 312p. pap. 14.99 *(978-0-312-65648-5(3)*, St. Martin's Griffin) St. Martin's Pr.

Player, Corrie Lynn, et al. The Everything Parent's Guide to Raising Your Adopted Child: A Complete Handbook to Welcoming Your Adopted Child into Your Heart & Home. 2008. (ENG., Illus.). 304p. pap. 14.95 *(978-1-59869-606-6(3))* Adams Media Corp.

Pool, Hannah. My Fathers' Daughter: A Story of Family & Belonging. 2012. (ENG.). 288p. pap. 18.99 *(978-1-4165-9490-1(6)*, Free Pr.) Free Pr.

Proctor, Curtis. Behavioral Indicators As Attachment Difficulties. 2008. 100p. pap. *(978-3-639-07119-1(0))* VDM Verlag Dr. Mueller e.K.

Rauhala, Ann, ed. The Lucky Ones: Our Stories of Adopting Children from China. 2008. (ENG., Illus.). 350p. per. 19.95 *(978-1-55022-823-6(4))* ECW Pr. CAN. Dist: Independent Pubs. Group.

Roberson, Nicole M. Sacred Trust Betrayed. 2008. 148p. 27.99 *(978-0-88144-295-3(X))* Yorkshire Publishing Group.

Rollings, Julia. Love Our Way: A Courageous Mother's Story That Gives New Meaning to the Word Family. 2008. 320p. *(978-0-7322-8813-6(4))* HarperCollins Pubs. Australia.

Sally Bacchetta. What I Want My Adopted Child to Know: An Adoptive Parent's Perspective. 2010. 124p. 23.95 *(978-1-4401-9438-2(6))* iUniverse, Inc.

Savarese, Ralph James. Reasonable People: A Memoir of Autism & Adoption: on the Meaning of Family & the Politics of Neurological Difference. annot. ed. 2007. (ENG.). 496p. 25.95 *(978-1-59051-129-9(8))* Other Pr., LLC.

Seven Rhinos. 2007. 197p. pap. 15.95 *(978-0-615-17552-2(X))* Navark, Jo Publishing LLC.

Smith, Susan Livingston & Silverstein, Deborah N. Siblings in Adoption & Foster Care: Traumatic Separations & Honoured Connections. Silverstein, Deborah & Smith, Susan Livingston, eds. Silverstein, Deborah N., ed. 2008. (Illus.). 216p. 49.95 *(978-0-313-35143-3(0)*, C35143, Praeger Pubs.) Greenwood Publishing Group, Inc.

Tripp, Paul David. Helping Your Adopted Child: Understanding Your Child's Unique Identity. 2008. (ENG.). 24p. 3.99 *(978-1-934885-31-4(2))* New Growth Pr.

Wilkinson, Sook & Fox, Nancy. After the Morning Calm: Reflections of Korean Adoptees. pap. 16.95 *(978-0-8187-0286-0(9))* Harlo Pr.

Williams, Mary Beth. Trauma & the Internationally Adopted Child. 2007. 224p. 34.95 *(978-0-415-95498-3(3))* Taylor & Francis Group.

Woodwyk, Carissa & Tebos, Susan. Before You Were Mine: Discovering Your Adopted Child's Lifestory. 2007. (Illus.). 176p. per. *(978-1-932902-69-3(4))* FaithWalk Publishing.

ADOPTED PERSONS

see Adoptees

ADOPTEES

Here are entered works on adults adopted as children.

Ahn-Redding, Heather & Simon, Rita J. Intercountry Adoptees Tell Their Stories. 2007. (ENG., Illus.). 350p. 89.50 *(978-0-7391-1855-9(2))*; per. 41.99 *(978-0-7391-1856-6(0))* Lexington Bks.

Bennett, Susan. Late Discoveries: An Adoptee's Quest for Truth. 2011. (ENG.). 176p. pap. 14.95 *(978-1-56474-513-2(9)*, Fithian Pr) Daniel & Daniel, Pubs., Inc.

Birne, Eleanor. Black by Design. 2012. (ENG., Illus.). 320p. pap. 18.95 ***(978-1-84668-790-7(X))*** Serpent's Tail Ltd. GBR. Dist: Consortium Bk. Sales & Distribution.

Briccetti, Katherine A. Blood Strangers: A Memoir. 2010. 300p. pap. 16.95 *(978-1-59714-130-7(5))* Heyday.

Carangelo, Lori. The Ultimate Search Book 2011 Edition Worldwide Adpotion, Genealogy & Other Search Secrets from the Files of Americans for Open Records. 2011. 306p. pap. 39.95 ***(978-0-8063-5515-3(8))*** Clearfield Co.

Champnella, Cindy. One Voice Was Heard. mass mkt. *(978-0-312-98741-1(2)*, St. Martin's Paperbacks) St. Martin's Pr.

Crumpacker, Bunny & Picariello, Jil. Jessica Lost: A Story of Birth & Adoption. 2011. (ENG., Illus.). 224p. 24.95 *(978-1-4027-7570-3(9))* Union Square Pr.

DeVrye, Catherine. Serendipity Road: A Memoir. 2008. (ENG., Illus.). 356p. pap. 24.95 *(978-1-55278-645-1(5))* McArthur & Co. CAN. Dist: National Bk. Network.

Eldridge, Sherrie. Questions Adoptees Are Asking: About Beginnings - About Birth Family - About Searching - About Finding Peace. 2009. (Maya Davis Ser.). (ENG.). 288p. pap. 15.99 *(978-1-60006-595-8(3))* NavPress Publishing Group.

Greenie. Greenie's Path: The Search for Christopher Hiltaychuk. 2011. 452p. 37.95 ***(978-1-4620-4983-7(4))***; pap. 27.95 ***(978-1-4620-4982-0(6))*** iUniverse, Inc.

Hess, Mary Anne, et al. Once They Hear My Name: Korean Adoptees & Their Journeys Toward Identity. 2008. (ENG., Illus.). 200p. pap. 14.95 *(978-0-9793756-0-6(6))* Tamarisk Bks. LLC.

Holloway, Sara, ed. Family Wanted: Stories of Adoption. 2006. (ENG.). 320p. per. 14.95 *(978-0-8129-7547-5(2)*, Random Hse. Trade Paperbacks) Random House Publishing Group.

Kay, Jackie. Red Dust Road: An Autobiographical Journey. 2011. (ENG.). 304p. 24.00 *(978-1-935633-34-1(1)*, 935634) Atlas & Co.

Kim, Eleana J. Adopted Territory: Transnational Korean Adoptees & the Politics of Belonging. 2010. (ENG., Illus.). 344p. 84.95 *(978-0-8223-4683-8(4))*; pap. 23.95 *(978-0-8223-4695-1(8))* Duke Univ. Pr.

Lancaster, Kathy. Keys to Parenting an Adopted Child. 2nd rev. ed. 2009. (Barron's Parenting Keys Ser.). (ENG.). 208p. pap. 8.99 *(978-0-7641-4097-6(3))* Barron's Educational Series, Inc.

Lauck, Jennifer. Found: A Memoir. (ENG.). 2012. 280p. pap. 17.00 ***(978-1-58005-395-2(5))*** 2011. 272p. 24.95 *(978-1-58005-367-9(X))* Seal Pr.

Leinaweaver, Jeffrey J. The Coordinated Management of a Culturally Diffused Identity: Internationally Adopted People & the Narrative Burden of Self. 2011. 202p. pap. 25.95 ***(978-1-61233-761-6(9)***, Dissertation.com) Universal Pubs.

Lifton, Betty Jean. Twice Born: Memoirs of an Adopted Daughter. 2006. (ENG.). 288p. pap. 16.95 *(978-1-59051-244-9(8))* Other Pr., LLC.

Lipton, William Lawrence. Grandpa Was A Deity: How A Tribal Assertion Created Modern Culture. 2011. 140p. 21.95 ***(978-1-4620-5304-9(1))***; pap. 11.95 ***(978-1-4620-5303-2(3))*** iUniverse, Inc.

Martin, Ross. A Mother to Kill a Son: A Childhood View of Cruelty. 2009. 176p. pap. *(978-1-84991-035-4(9))* Chipmunkapublishing.

McCaslin, Nikki. Finding Our Place: 100 Memorable Adoptees, Fostered Persons, & Orphanage Alumni, 1 vol. 2009. (Illus.). 363p. 85.00 *(978-0-313-34270-7(9)*, GR4270) Greenwood Publishing Group, Inc.

Meyers, Julia I. Coffee & Cake: An Adoptee in Search of Her Past. 2010. ***(978-1-935001-57-7(4))*** Acclaim Pr., Inc.

Miro, Asha. Daughter of the Ganges: The Story of One Girl's Adoption & Her Return Journey to India. Mahjoub, Jamal, tr. from CAT. 2007. (ENG., Illus.). 288p. pap. 19.95 *(978-0-7432-8673-2(1)*, Beyond Words/Atria Bks.) Atria Bks.

Movsisian Foess, Mary L. My Armenian Genesis: The last Survivor. 2010. 268p. pap. 23.98 *(978-0-557-26888-7(5))* Lulu Enterprises Inc.

Palmer, John D. The Dance of Identities: Korean Adoptees & Their Journey Toward Empowerment. 2010. (Illus.). 224p. 49.00 *(978-0-8248-3371-8(6))* Univ. of Hawaii Pr.

Patton, Stacey. That Mean Old Yesterday: A Memoir. 2008. (ENG.). 336p. pap. 20.99 *(978-0-7432-9311-2(8)*, Washington Square Pr.) Washington Square Pr.

Phillips, Zara H. Mother Me: An Adopted Woman's Journey to Motherhood. 2011. (ENG.). 224p. pap. 14.95 *(978-1-934848-36-4(0))* GemmaMedia.

Pool, Hannah. My Fathers' Daughter: A Story of Family & Belonging. 2012. (ENG.). 288p. pap. 18.99 *(978-1-4165-9490-1(6)*, Free Pr.) Free Pr.

Reed, Mary Mustard. Oceans Apart: A Voyage of International Adoption. 2008. (Illus.). 276p. pap. 18.95 *(978-0-9799327-0-0(X))* JKD Enterprise.

Renshaw, Jessica Shaver. Gianna: Aborted ... & Lived to Tell about It. 2010. (ENG.). 272p. pap. 12.99 *(978-1-58997-600-9(2))* Tyndale Hse. Pubs.

Renshaw, Jessica Shaver & Jessen, Gianna. Gianna: Aborted, & Lived to Tell about It. rev. ed. 2011. (ENG.). 224p. pap. 14.99 *(978-1-58997-639-9(8))* Tyndale Hse. Pubs.

Sharp, Dave. Complete Surrender. 2009. (ENG., Illus.). 264p. pap. 14.95 *(978-1-84454-767-8(1))* Blake, John Publishing, Ltd. GBR. Dist: Independent Pubs. Group.

—Complete Surrender: The True Story of a Family's Dark Secret & the Brothers It Tore Apart at Birth. 2008. (ENG., Illus.). 288p. 29.95 *(978-1-84454-582-7(2))* Blake, John Publishing, Ltd. GBR. Dist: Independent Pubs. Group.

Simon, Rita J. & Hernandez, Sarah. Native American Transracial Adoptees Tell Their Stories. 2008. (ENG., Illus.). 380p. 83.99 *(978-0-7391-2492-5(7))*; per. 38.99 *(978-0-7391-2493-2(5))* Lexington Bks.

Szara, Nicholas. My Life Adopted, 1 vol. 2009. 123p. pap. 19.95 *(978-1-60813-898-2(4))* PublishAmerica, Inc.

Trenka, Jane Jeong. Fugitive Visions: An Adoptee's Return to Korea. 2009. (ENG.). 192p. pap. 16.00 *(978-1-55597-529-6(1))* Graywolf Pr.

Tuan, Mia & Shiao, Jiannbin Lee. Choosing Ethnicity, Negotiating Race: Korean Adoptees in America. 2011. 213p. 35.00 *(978-0-87154-875-7(5))* Russell Sage Foundation.

ADOPTEES—IDENTIFICATION

Here are entered works that describe the search for the identity of persons who are adoptees.

Slaton, Pamela & Marshall, Samantha. Reunited: An Investigative Genealogist Unlocks Some of Life's Greatest Family Mysteries. 2012. (ENG.). 272p. pap. 14.99 ***(978-0-312-61732-5(1)***, St. Martin's Griffin) St. Martin's Pr.

ADOPTION

Here are entered works on adoption of children by gay men or lesbians.

see also Adoptees; Foster Home Care; Gay Adoption; Intercountry Adoption; Interracial Adoption

Allen Lassiter, Nancy. Proud Racer. 2008. 162p. pap. 19.50 *(978-1-4116-8986-2(0))* Lulu Enterprises Inc.

Amend, Deborah. A Dress for Anna: The Story of the Redemption of the Life of a Ukranian Orphan. 2009. *(978-0-7880-2632-4(1))* FaithWalk Publishing.

Antion, Majesta. We Chose You. 2010. 16p. 12.99 *(978-1-4520-1965-9(7))* AuthorHouse.

Baden, Amanda L., et al. Handbook of Adoption: Implications for Researchers, Practitioners, & Families. 2006. (Illus.). 584p. per. 74.95 *(978-1-4129-2751-2(X)*, B27501P) SAGE Pubns., Inc.

Baines, Christopher. Adoption - Double Identity: A Mother's Love. 2009. 88p. pap. 15.99 *(978-1-4415-1892-7(4))* Xlibris Corp.

Bakker, Geeri. Adoption Handbook: Stress During the Adoption Period. 2006. 208p. pap. *(978-90-5911-315-2(2))* Aspekt B. V., Uitgeverij.

Beeke, Joel R. Heirs with Christ: The Puritans on Adoption. 2008. 134p. 13.00 *(978-1-60178-040-9(0))* Reformation Heritage Bks.

Bemrose, Alex. Our Son from Afar: The Long Road to Adoption. 2010. (Illus.). 218p. 34.95 *(978-1-84624-491-9(9))* Book Guild, Ltd. GBR. Dist: Trans-Atlantic Pubns., Inc.

Bentley, Lisa Misraje. Saving Levi: Left to Die ... Destined to Live. 2006. (ENG., Illus.). 176p. per. 13.99 *(978-1-58997-449-4(2))* Tyndale Hse. Pubs.

Berg, Thomas V. & Furton, Edward James. Human Embryo Adoption: Biotechnology, Marriage, & the Right to Life. 2009. (ENG.). 361p. pap. 24.95 *(978-0-935372-50-2(4))* National Catholic Bioethics Ctr., The.

Biscontini, Tracey Vasil. Adoption. 2009. (Issues on Trial Ser.). (ENG.). 240p. (J). (gr. 10-12). 39.70 *(978-0-7377-4342-5(5)*, Greenhaven Pr., Inc.) Cengage Gale.

Bogach, Alexander. How to adopt from ukraine Successfully. 2009. 128p. pap. 24.97 *(978-1-4092-7940-2(5))* Lulu Enterprises Inc.

Bolme, Sarah. The Adoption Option: A Solution for an Unplanned Pregnancy. 2007. 120p. (YA). pap. 11.99 *(978-0-9725546-6-4(1))* CREST Pubns.

Brakman, Sarah-Vaughan & Fozard Weaver, Darlene, eds. The Ethics of Embryo Adoption & the Catholic Tradition: Moral Arguments, Economic Reality & Social Analysis. (Philosophy & Medicine / Catholic Studies in Bioethics Ser.). 2010. x, 326p. pap. 189.00 *(978-90-481-7568-0(2)*, 9048175682) 2008. (Illus.). 326p. 189.00 *(978-1-4020-6210-0(9))* Springer.

Bridgeford, Marci. Zachary's Story: A Boy's Journey into His Adopted Family. 2010. 28p. pap. 15.60 *(978-1-4490-5079-5(4))* AuthorHouse.

Brooks, Thomas. A Wealth of Family: An Adopted Son's International Quest for Heritage, Reunion, & Enrichment. 2006. (Family Success Ser.). (Illus.). 250p. (Orig.). per. 17.95 *(978-0-9774629-3-3(5))* Alpha Multimedia, Inc.

Buffington, Lois Gamblin. The China Miracle. 2008. 84p. pap. 16.95 *(978-1-60563-638-2(X))* PublishAmerica, Inc.

Burden, Linda. Where's My Sister? My Little Sister's Struggle with Addiction, Adoption, & Mental Illness. 2011. 196p. 26.95 *(978-1-4620-0382-2(6))*; pap. 16.95 *(978-1-4620-0381-5(8))* iUniverse, Inc.

Burke, Trevor J. The Message of Sonship. 2011. (Bible Speaks Today Bible Themes Ser.). (ENG.). 244p. pap. 20.00 ***(978-0-8308-2413-7(8)***, IVP Acad.) InterVarsity Pr.

Burns, Susan. Fast Track Infant Adoption. mass mkt. *(978-0-312-98572-1(X)*, St. Martin's Paperbacks) St. Martin's Pr.

Caldwell, Mardie. Adoption: Your Step-by-Step Guide: Using Technology & Time-Tested Techniques to Expedite a Safe, Successful Adoption. 2nd rev. ed. 2006. (ENG., Illus.). 424p. per. 34.95 *(978-0-9705734-2-1(1)*, 5000) American Carriage Hse. Publishing.

Canfield, Jack L., et al. Chicken Soup for the Adopted Soul: Stories Celebrating Forever Families. 2008. (Chicken Soup for the Soul Ser.). (ENG.). 320p. pap. 14.95 *(978-0-7573-0673-0(X))* Health Communications, Inc.

Caughman, Susan & Motley, Isolde. You Can Adopt: The Adoptive Families Guide. 2009. (ENG., Illus.). 320p. pap. 16.00 *(978-0-345-50401-2(1)*, Ballantine Bks.) Random House Publishing Group.

Chartrand, Jane W. From the Ground Up. 2007. 183p. pap. 15.95 *(978-1-4303-1127-0(4))* Lulu Enterprises Inc.

Choice Mom Guide to Adoption. 2008. pap. *(978-0-9772042-3-6(5))* Be-Mondo Publishing.

Christianson, Laura. The Adoption Network: Your Guide to Starting a Support System. 2007. 111p. per. 9.99 *(978-1-57921-902-4(0))* WinePress Publishing.

Collier, Victoria & Collier, Jennifer. Getting to Baby: Creating your Family Faster, Easier & Less Expensive through Fertility, Adoption, or Surrogacy. 2011. (ENG.). 220p. pap. 17.95 *(978-0-9828590-9-4(0)*, Glazer Kennedy Pub.) Morgan James Publishing.

Coventry, Brian L. Adopted at Age Four. 2010. 144p. 23.95 *(978-1-4520-3615-1(2))*; pap. 14.95 *(978-1-4520-3614-4(4))* AuthorHouse.

Crawshaw, Marilyn & Balen, Rachel, eds. Adopting after Infertility: Messages from Practice, Research & Personal Experience. 2010. (ENG.). 192p. pap. *(978-1-84905-028-9(7))* Kingsley, Jessica Ltd.

Cremer-Vogel, Kate, et al. What Every Adoptive Parent Needs to Know: Healing Your Child's Wounded Heart. 2008. xi, 269p. pap. *(978-0-615-18845-4(1))* Mountain Ridge Publishing.

Dö, et al. Adoption: Adoptivkinder, ihre leiblichen Mütter und ihre Adoptiveltern: Ergebnisse einer Adoptionsvermittlung zwischen 1947-1987. 2011. 116p. pap. ***(978-3-8381-2372-1(7))*** Südwestdeutscher Verlag für Hochschulschriften AG & Co. KG.

Dail, Laura. Truly Yours: The Miracle of Adoption. 2011. (ENG.). 128p. 14.00 *(978-1-9346467-14-3(3)*, vantage*Point) Vantage Pr., Inc.

Danzig, Alyssa. How Alyssa & Arianna Became a Family: Our Adoption Story. 2008. 40p. pap. 15.99 *(978-1-4389-0148-0(8))* AuthorHouse.

Dessalegn, Negeri. Guddifachaa Practice: As Community Based Child Problem Intervention in Oromo of Ada'A Liban. 2011. 120p. pap. ***(978-3-639-33841-6(3))*** VDM Verlag Dr. Mueller e.K.

Dormon, Sara & Graham, Ruth. So You Want to Adopt... Now What? A Practical Guide for Navigating the Adoption Process. 2006. (ENG., Illus.). 160p. per. 12.99 *(978-0-8307-3899-1(1))* Gospel Light Pubns.

Eldridge, Sherrie. 20 Things Adoptive Parents Need to Succeed. 2009. (ENG.). 320p. pap. 16.00 *(978-0-385-34162-2(8)*, Delta) Random House Publishing Group.

Falker, Elizabeth Swire. The Ultimate Insider's Guide to Adoption: Everything You Need to Know about Domestic & International Adoption. 2006. (ENG., Illus.). 368p. per. 22.99 *(978-0-446-69730-9(3))* Grand Central Publishing.

Fitzpatrick, Mary. Adoption: Insights, Inspiration & Information. Blandino, James, ed. Date not set. 161p. pap. 14.95 *(978-0-9673858-0-8(6))* New Horizons Pr.

Gair, Susan. Adoption: A different road to Mothering. 2010. 408p. pap. *(978-3-639-23593-7(2))* VDM Verlag Dr. Mueller e.K.

Gillespie, Natalie Nichols. Successful Adoption: A Guide for Christian Families, 0 vols. 2006. (Illus.). 414p. per. 19.99 *(978-1-59145-412-0(3))* Nelson, Thomas Inc.

Gormally, Eleanor. Little Lucy's Family: A Story about Adoption. 2008. (Illus.). 36p. (J). pap. 14.95 *(978-0-87946-373-1(2))* ACTA Pubns.

Gottlieb, Bernice. Take My Children: A Love Story. 2010. 188p. pap. 16.95 *(978-1-4502-7547-7(8))* iUniverse, Inc.

—Take My Children: An Adoption Story. 2010. 188p. 26.95 *(978-1-4502-7546-0(X))* iUniverse, Inc.

Gray, Deborah D. Attaching in Adoption: Practical Tools for Today's Parents. 2012. (ENG., Illus.). 400p. pap. ***(978-1-84905-890-2(3))*** Kingsley, Jessica Ltd.

—Nurturing Adoptions: Creating Resilience after Neglect & Trauma. 2012. (ENG., Illus.). 514p. pap. ***(978-1-84905-891-9(1))*** Kingsley, Jessica Ltd.

Green, Joanne. To My Child Concerning Your Birth Mother. 2008. 60p. pap. *(978-1-897512-13-5(9))* Saga Bks.

Gritter, James L. Hospitious Adoption. 2009. pap. *(978-1-58760-123-1(0)*, CWLA Pr.) Child Welfare League of America, Inc.

Grubb, Bobbi. Masterpiece of Joy: From the Despair of Infertility to the Joy of Adoption. 2007. 256p. per. 14.95 *(978-1-4327-1614-1(X))* Outskirts Pr., Inc.

Hart, Christine Joanna. Searching for Daddy: Looking for a Family, Longing for Love. 2008. (ENG.). 304p. pap. 25.95 *(978-0-340-96227-5(5)*, Hodder & Stoughton) Hodder General Publishing Div. GBR. Dist: Independent Pubs. Group.

Herlem, Fanny Cohen. Great Answers to Difficult Questions about Adoption: What Children Need to Know. 2008. (ENG., Illus.). 112p. pap. *(978-1-84310-671-5(X))* Kingsley, Jessica Ltd.

—Great Answers to Difficult Questions about Divorce: What Children Need to Know. 2008. (ENG., Illus.). 96p. pap. *(978-1-84310-672-2(8))* Kingsley, Jessica Ltd.

Hogg, Lori A. Between You & Me: Adoption. 2007. (Illus.). 24p. per. 9.99 *(978-0-9794976-2-9(0))* Bezalel Bks.

Holbrook, Nicholas. 16 Manor Way: The Story of Our Fated Adoptions. 2010. 160p. pap. *(978-1-84991-270-9(X))* Chipmunkapublishing.

Holloway, Sara, ed. Family Wanted: Stories of Adoption. 2006. (ENG.). 320p. per. 14.95 *(978-0-8129-7547-5(2)*, Random Hse. Trade Paperbacks) Random House Publishing Group.

Holmes, Patricia Lynn. Supporting an Adoption. Holmes, Steve, ed. 23p. reprint ed. pap. 4.50 *(978-0-9611872-1-7(2))* Our Child Pr.

Hood, Karen Jean Matsko. My Adoption Celebration: A Daily Journal. 2008. (J). *(978-1-59649-494-7(8))*; (J). per. *(978-1-59649-495-4(6))*; spiral bd. 22.95 *(978-1-59808-808-3(4))*; spiral bd. *(978-1-59649-496-1(4))* Whispering Pine Pr. International, Inc.

—My Holiday Memories: A Daily Journal. 2008. (J). spiral bd. 19.95 *(978-1-59434-085-7(4))* Whispering Pine Pr. International, Inc.

Jack, William F. The Little Russians: an Ailing Father's Letters to His Children. 2010. 463p. pap. 27.95 *(978-0-557-44579-0(5))* Lulu Enterprises Inc.

Johnston, Patricia Irwin. Adopting: Sound Choices, Strong Families. 2008. 544p. 26.95 *(978-0-944934-34-0(X))* Perspectives Pr., Inc.

Jones, Lynne. Caroline & Just Me, Vol. 1. Davis, Beverly, ed. Date not set. pap. 12.95 *(978-0-9661404-0-8(0))* Harvest Media, Inc.

Josephs, Ian. Forced Adoption. 2008. 240p. pap. 13.95 *(978-1-84799-798-2(8))* Lulu Enterprises Inc.

—Forced Adoption (shortened Version) 2009. 170p. pap. 12.50 *(978-1-4092-7362-2(8))* Lulu Enterprises Inc.

Junnarkar, Mohita, et al. Child Adoption: A study of Adopted Adolescents. 2011. 128p. pap. ***(978-3-8443-3207-0(3))*** Lambert Academic Publishing.

Kastello, Deana Coreen. Conceiving in the Heart. 2009. pap. 14.99 *(978-1-59955-262-0(0))* Cedar Fort, Inc./CFI Distribution.

Kay, Irene. Not for the Likes of Us: The Story of Luke's Adoption & Then Some. 2010. 180p. pap. 14.49 *(978-1-4520-5431-5(2))* AuthorHouse.

Kimutis, Susan T. Receiving Birth. 2011. 292p. 28.50 ***(978-1-59330-727-1(6))***; pap. 16.50 ***(978-1-59330-726-4(8))*** Aventine Pr.

Kruger, Pamela & Smolowe, Jill, eds. A Love Like No Other: Stories from Adoptive Parents. 2006. (ENG.). 272p. (gr. 12-18). 16.00 *(978-1-59448-215-1(2)*, Riverhead Trade (Paperbacks)) Penguin Group (USA) Inc.

Kuzman, Beverly. Maxi's Story. 2010. 36p. pap. 13.95 *(978-1-936343-27-0(4))* Peppertree Pr., The.

Lang, Gregory E. Why I Chose You: 100 Reasons Why Adopting You Made Us a Family. 2007. (ENG., Illus.). 128p. 14.95 *(978-1-58182-433-5(3)*, Cumberland Hse.) Sourcebooks, Inc.

Leinaweaver, Jessaca B. The Circulation of Children: Kinship, Adoption, & Morality in Andean Peru. 2008. (Latin America Otherwise Ser.). (ENG., Illus.). 248p. 79.95 *(978-0-8223-4181-9(6))*; pap. 22.95 *(978-0-8223-4197-0(2))* Duke Univ. Pr.

Limon, Miriam. Anything Impossible Is Possible. 2011. 74p. 24.99 ***(978-1-4653-4821-0(2))***; pap. 15.99 ***(978-1-4653-4820-3(4))*** Xlibris Corp.

Lindsay, Hugh. Adoption in the Roman World. 2009. (ENG., Illus.). 256p. 98.00 *(978-0-521-76050-8(X))* Cambridge Univ. Pr.

Longshore, Gracie. Infertility, Adoption & Say, How's the Weather? 2008. 352p. 32.99 *(978-1-60647-464-8(2))*; pap. 20.99 *(978-1-60647-463-1(4))* Xulon Pr., Inc.

Macrae, Sheena & MacLeod, Jean, eds. Adoption Parenting: Creating a Toolbox, Building Connections. 2006. (Illus.). 503p. per. 29.95 *(978-0-9726244-5-9(7))* EMK Pr.

Martin, W. C. Small Town, Big Miracle: How Love Came to the Least of These. 2007. (ENG., Illus.). 168p. pap. 13.99 *(978-1-58997-443-2(3))* Tyndale Hse. Pubs.

McCaslin, Nikki. Finding Our Place: 100 Memorable Adoptees, Fostered Persons, & Orphanage Alumni, 1 vol. 2009. (Illus.). 363p. 85.00 *(978-0-313-34270-7(9)*, GR4270) Greenwood Publishing Group, Inc.

McMahon, Kathleen A. Family: Finding a Way... 2011. 20p. 14.00 *(978-1-4269-5527-3(8))* Trafford Publishing.

Meadows, Sadie Olivia. Grandparents Adopting Their Grandchildren: And How It Can Affect Their Relationship with Their Children, 1 vol. 2010. 52p. pap. 16.95 *(978-1-4512-0013-3(7))* PublishAmerica, Inc.

Merino, Faith. Adoption & Surrogate Pregnancy. 2010. (Global Issues Ser.). (Illus.). 352p. (C). (gr. 9-18). 45.00 *(978-0-8160-8087-8(9))* Facts On File, Inc.

Milton, Michael A. What Is the Doctrine of Adoption? 2012. pap. ***(978-1-59638-391-3(7))*** P & R Publishing.

Momin, Elfreeda. Sociology of Adoption. 2008. 235p. 30.00 *(978-81-316-0137-2(4))* Rawat Pubns. IND. Dist: International Specialized Bk. Services.

Muldoon, Timothy. Longing to Love: A Memoir of Desire, Relationships, & Spiritual Transformation. 2010. (ENG.). 160p. pap. 13.95 *(978-0-8294-2805-6(4))* Loyola Pr.

Neil, E. International Advances in Adoption Research for Practice. Neil, Elsbeth & Wrobel, Gretchen Miller, eds. 2009. (ENG., Illus.). 358p. 144.95 *(978-0-470-99817-5(2)*, Wiley) Wiley, John & Sons, Inc.

Neil, Elsbeth & Wrobel, Gretchen Miller, eds. International Advances in Adoption Research for Practice. 2009. (ENG., Illus.). 358p. pap. 57.95 *(978-0-470-99818-2(0)*, Wiley) Wiley, John & Sons, Inc.

Nice, Dennis. Exploring the Spirit of Adoption: Healing the Heart of the Fatherless. 2006. 96p. per. 9.99 *(978-0-9778614-3-9(0))* Partnership Pubns.

Oblander, JoAnna Weekes. A Glimpse of Heaven: One Woman's Life-Altering Visit with God. 2011. ***(978-1-59955-976-6(5))*** Cedar Fort, Inc./CFI Distribution.

O'Brien, M. J. Beaten down by the System, but Not Beaten. 2011. 388p. pap. 29.95 (978-1-4560-6549-2(1)) PublishAmerica, Inc.

Pan, Yi, et al. Young Women with Unplanned Pregnancies in Bangkok, Thailand: Wireless Sensor Networks Security. 2008. (Illus.). viii, 101p. pap. 50.00 (978-1-60456-458-7(X)) Nova Science Pubs., Inc.

Pedley, Jennifer Joyce. Secrets to Your Successful Domestic Adoption: Insider Advice to Create Your Forever Family Faster. 2010. (ENG.). 240p. pap. 15.95 (978-0-7573-1468-1(6)) Health Communications, Inc.

Peppard, Michael. The Son of God in the Roman World: Divine Sonship in its Social & Political Context. (ENG.). 304p. 2012. pap. 27.95 (978-0-19-993365-5(0)) 2011. 74.00 (978-0-19-975370-3(9)) Oxford Univ. Pr., Inc.

Perez-Sebastian, Fidel. Innovation & Use. 2010. 96p. pap. (978-3-639-23343-8(3)) VDM Verlag Dr. Mueller e.K.

Powers, David S. Muhammad Is Not the Father of Any of Your Men: The Making of the Last Prophet. (Divinations: Rereading Late Ancient Religion Ser.). (Illus.). 376p. (C). 2011. pap. 29.95 (978-0-8122-2149-7(4)) 2009. 65.00 (978-0-8122-4178-5(9)) Univ. of Pennsylvania Pr.

Pratt, Stephanie & Carocci, Max, eds. Native American Adoption, Captivity, & Slavery in Changing Contexts. 2011. (Studies of the Americas Ser.). (ENG., Illus.). 278p. 90.00 (978-0-230-11505-7(5)) Palgrave Macmillan.

Puttere, Ladonna. My Black & White Family. 2010. 52p. pap. 11.49 (978-1-4520-6879-4(8)) AuthorHouse.

Quigley, Mary Lenore. Indelible Ink. 2008. 181p. pap. 24.95 (978-1-60441-560-5(6)) PublishAmerica, Inc.

Riley, Liliana. Rising from the Ashes: A Journey of Self-Discovery. 2011. 56p. pap. 8.95 (978-1-4620-1099-8(7)) iUniverse, Inc.

Rillera, Mary J. The Adoption Searchbook: Techniques for Tracing People. 15.95 (978-0-941770-02-6(8)) Triadoption Library, Inc.

Ross, Bridget. My Nephew, My Son. 2008. 124p. 10.99 (978-1-60462-825-8(1)) Tate Publishing & Enterprises, LLC.

Ruggiero, Josephine A. Eastern European Adoption: Policies, Practice, & Strategies for Change. 2007. (ENG., Illus.). 238p. (gr. 11). 39.95 (978-0-202-30976-7(2)) Aldine Transaction.

—Eastern European Adoption: Policies, Practice, & Strategies for Change. 2007. (978-0-7658-0371-9(2)) Transaction Pubs.

Sales, Sally. Adoption, Family & the Paradox of Origins: A Foucauldian History. 2012. (Palgrave Macmillan Studies in Family & Intimate Life Ser.). (ENG., Illus.). 232p. 85.00 (978-0-230-27625-3(3)) Palgrave Macmillan.

Sally Bacchetta. What I Want My Adopted Child to Know: An Adoptive Parent's Perspective. 2010. 124p. 23.95 (978-1-4401-9438-2(6)); pap. 13.95 (978-1-4401-9436-8(X)) iUniverse, Inc.

Schooler, Jayne E. & Atwood, Thomas C. The Whole Life Adoption Book: Realistic Advice for Building a Healthy Adoptive Family. 2008. (Real Life Stuff for Couples Ser.). (ENG.). 272p. pap. 17.99 (978-1-60006-165-3(6)) NavPress Publishing Group.

Sheasby, John. The Birthright: Out of the Servant's Quarters into the Father's House, 1 vol. 2010. (ENG.). 176p. 16.99 (978-0-310-32746-2(6)) Zondervan.

Simon, Scott. Baby, We Were Meant for Each Other: In Praise of Adoption. 2010. (Illus.). 192p. 22.00 (978-1-4000-6849-4(5), Random House) Random House Publishing Group.

Sinclair, Skye. Runaway. 2008. (ENG.). 320p. 25.95 (978-0-340-95336-5(5), Hodder & Stoughton) Hodder General Publishing Div. GBR. Dist: Independent Pubs. Group.

Sone, John. My Three Sons: The Birth of a New Family. 2009. 208p. 27.95 (978-1-4401-3420-3(0)); pap. 17.95 (978-1-4401-3419-0(9)) iUniverse, Inc.

Stolley, Kathy Shepherd & Bullough, Vern L., eds. The Praeger Handbook of Adoption, Vol. 2. 2006. 916p. 275.00 (978-0-313-33335-4(1), GR3335, Praeger Pubs.) Greenwood Publishing Group, Inc.

Tripp, Paul David. Helping Your Adopted Child: Understanding Your Child's Unique Identity. 2008. (ENG.). 24p. 3.99 (978-1-934885-31-4(2)) New Growth Pr.

United Nations. Child Adoption: Trends & Policies. 2010. (ENG.). 484p. pap. 58.00 (978-92-1-151466-7(5)) United Nations Pubns.

United Nations. Guidelines for Improving Data on Child Adoption. 2010. (Population Studies Ser.). (ENG.). 26p. pap. 10.00 (978-92-1-151477-3(0)) United Nations Pubns.

United States. Congress Senate Committee on Foreign Relations Subcommittee on East Asian and Pacific Affairs Staff, contrib. by. Asian Adoptions in the United States: Hearing Before the Subcommittee on East Asian & Pacific Affairs of the Committee on Foreign Relations, United States Senate, One Hundred Ninth Congress, Second Session, June 8, 2006. 2007. iii, 45p. (978-0-16-078380-7(1), 552-070-35685-1) United States Government Printing Office.

Urs And Evelyne Ribary. Samanta's Journey of Hope. 2009. (Illus.). 44p. pap. 21.95 (978-1-4389-6550-5(8)) AuthorHouse.

Violo, Linda. Home: A Story of Adoption. 2011. 28p. 14.95 (978-1-4520-9822-7(0)) AuthorHouse.

Vrooman, Joyce. Before You Finalize the Adoption - the Pre-Adoption Workbook. 2009. 296p. pap. 29.95 (978-0-595-45005-3(9)) iUniverse, Inc.

Walker, Marjorie. Pain No More. 2010. 92p. pap. 12.49 (978-1-4520-3143-9(6)) AuthorHouse.

Watson, Edward W. Paul, His Roman Audience, & the Adopted People of God: Understanding the Pauline Metaphor of Adopton in Romans as Authorial Audience. 2008. 252p. 109.95 (978-0-7734-4927-5(2)) Mellen, Edwin Pr., The.

White, Garry. My Quest to Be a Single Dad: Thirty-Plus Years Trying to Adopt. 2009. pap. 12.99 (978-1-60799-987-4(0)) Tate Publishing & Enterprises, LLC.

Winkel, Janet. Adoption Romanian Style. 2007. (ENG.). 188p. per. 24.95 (978-1-4241-6177-5(0)) PublishAmerica, Inc.

Wolff, Jana. Secret Thoughts of an Adoptive Mother. 3rd rev. ed. 2010. (ENG.). 166p. pap. 14.95 (978-0-9672143-1-3(9)) Vista Communications.

Wood, Mary A. Living with the Father: Abba Father. 2011. 186p. 29.99 (978-1-4653-3982-9(5)); pap. 19.99 (978-1-4653-3981-2(7)) Xlibris Corp.

Woods, Valeria. Olives for Breakfast: A Book for Prospective Foster/Adoptive Parents. 2010. 60p. pap. 9.95 (978-1-60911-700-9(X), Eloquent Bks.) AEG Literary Publishing Services, Inc.

ADOPTION—BIOGRAPHY

see also Adoptees

Anderson, Elliott. Answers in Abundance: A Miraculous Adoption Journey as Told from a Father's Heart. 2007. (ENG.). per. 16.95 (978-1-60037-232-2(5)) Morgan James Publishing.

Anderson, Elliott J. Answers in Abundance: A Miraculous Adoption Journey as Told from a Father's Heart. 2007. (ENG., Illus.). 248p. 24.95 (978-1-60037-233-9(3)) Morgan James Publishing.

Berger, M. And This Is My Adopted Daughter. 2007. pap. (978-1-84747-189-5(7)) Chipmunkapublishing.

—From the Prison of My Mind. 2007. 412p. per. (978-1-84747-162-8(5)) Chipmunkapublishing.

Bowman, J. L. He Did It Even for Me: Bringing Sarah Home. 2011. pap. 13.99 (978-1-61739-622-9(2)) Tate Publishing & Enterprises, LLC.

Bruch, Devereaux R. No Mama, I Didn't Die: My Life as A Stolen Baby. 2010. 136p. 22.87 (978-1-4269-4369-0(5)); pap. 12.87 (978-1-4269-4368-3(7)) Trafford Publishing.

Burton, Nicole. Swimming up the Sun: A Memoir of Adoption. 2008. 208p. pap. 14.95 (978-0-9798992-0-1(6)) Apippa Publishing Co.

Cade, Frances. Birds of Uncertain Passage. 2006. pap. (978-1-904623-57-1(3)) WritersPrintShop.

Champion, Edwina Holman. Silent Journey: A True Adoption Miracle. 2011. 128p. 28.95 (978-1-61507-907-0(6)); pap. 11.95 (978-1-61507-906-3(8)) Cross Bks. Publishing.

Champnella, Cindy. One Voice Was Heard. mass mkt. (978-0-312-98741-1(2), St. Martin's Paperbacks) St. Martin's Pr.

Child, Miss Paramount. A Baby God without a Name. 2007. pap. 9.00 (978-0-8059-7437-9(7)) Dorrance Publishing Co., Inc.

Cooper, Linda Ivy. She Ain't My Sister. 2011. 180p. 24.99 (978-1-4567-2992-9(6)); pap. 19.99 (978-1-4567-2993-6(4)) AuthorHouse.

Cox, Heidi. Darkness on a Sunny Day: The Struggle of an Adopted Child to Find Herself, 1 vol. 2009. 96p. pap. 16.95 (978-1-60813-582-0(9)) PublishAmerica, Inc.

Denise, Tonya. Stuck in the Middle but Never Alone. 2009. 112p. pap. 14.99 (978-1-4259-8297-3(2)) AuthorHouse.

Diggs, Roberta. Blessings from China: An Adoption Story. 2007. (Illus.). 95p. per. 9.99 (978-1-60247-280-8(7)) Tate Publishing & Enterprises, LLC.

DuGahl, Helene. The Puppies Find a Home. 2011. 28p. 13.54 (978-1-4567-2336-1(7)) AuthorHouse.

Gammage, Jeff. China Ghosts: My Daughter's Journey to America, My Passage to Fatherhood. 2008. 272p. pap. 14.95 (978-0-06-124030-0(3), HarperPerennial) HarperCollins Pubs.

Grossman, Kari Grady. Bones That Float: A Story of Adopting Cambodia. 2007. (Illus.). 256p. 24.95 (978-0-9792493-0-3(9), BTF-HC) Wild Heaven Pr.

Harding, Jeremy. Mother Country: Memoir of an Adopted Boy. 2010. (ENG.). 224p. pap. 17.95 (978-1-84467-657-6(9), 844657) Verso Bks. GBR. Dist: Norton, W. W. & Co., Inc.

Homes, A. M. The Mistress's Daughter. 2008. (ENG., Illus.). 256p. (gr. 12-18). 14.00 (978-0-14-311331-7(3), Penguin (Non-Classics)) Penguin Group (USA) Inc.

Howard, Sara M. Tuesday s Grace. 2011. 222p. pap. 15.99 (978-1-61215-589-0(8)) Xulon Pr., Inc.

Juntunen, Craig. Both Ends Burning: My Story of Adopting Three Children from Haiti. 2009. 232p. 24.95 (978-1-4327-3872-3(0)); (ENG.). pap. 16.95 (978-1-4327-3486-2(5)) Outskirts Pr., Inc.

Klein, George C. The Adventure: The Quest for My Romanian Babies. 2007. (ENG.). 192p. per. 26.50 (978-0-7618-3704-6(3)) Hamilton Bks.

Law, Leslie William. The Adopted Prisoner. 2010. 160p. pap. 18.95 (978-1-4452-5750-1(5)) Lulu Enterprises Inc.

Lee, Ellen, et al. Once They Hear My Name: Korean Adoptees & Their Journeys Toward Identity. 2008. (Illus.). 183p. 21.95 (978-0-9793756-1-3(4)) Tamarisk Bks. LLC.

Lifton, Betty Jean. Twice Born: Memoirs of an Adopted Daughter. 2006. (ENG.). 288p. pap. 16.95 (978-1-59051-244-9(8)) Other Pr., LLC.

McCallum, Susannah D. A Random Figurine. 2008. 160p. 29.99 (978-1-4363-2709-1(1)) Xlibris Corp.

McCullough, Nancy. Adoption Is for A Lifetime: God's Plan for A Family Through All the Phases of Adoption. 2008. 132p. pap. 13.99 (978-1-60647-655-0(6)) Xulon Pr., Inc.

Mock, Betty Jean. Persimmon Days: A Real Adoption Story. 2008. 252p. pap. 15.99 (978-1-60477-937-0(3)) Xulon Pr., Inc.

Pighin, Sonia. A Feather in the Wind. 2009. 92p. pap. 15.99 (978-1-4363-5607-7(5)) Xlibris Corp.

Popke, Suzanne L. The Buryat Journey Continues Overland: Siberian Pearls at Culture Camp, 1 vol. 2009. 372p. pap. 29.95 (978-1-60703-665-4(7)) PublishAmerica, Inc.

Rogers, Randy T. From the Bench: A Heartwarming Collection of Adoption Stories. 2007. (Illus.). 63p. 8.95 (978-0-9796502-0-8(8)) ProWriters Plus.

Rosemary, Kate. Raising Shane: Foster Care & Adoption of the Special-Needs Child. 2008. 180p. per. 24.95 (978-1-933912-49-3(9)) Westview Publishing Co., Inc.

Scott, Betty Sue. Shared Heartbeats. 2009. 269p. 19.95 (978-1-934363-40-9(5)) Zoe Life Publishing.

Sember, Brette McWhorter. Adoption Answer Book: Your Compete Guide to a Successful Adoption. 2007. (Answer Book Ser.). (ENG.). 256p. pap. 19.99 (978-1-57248-607-2(4), Sphinx Publishing) Sourcebooks, Inc.

Shanker, David. Elizabeth Song Shanker: An adoption Journey. 2007. 72p. per. 9.95 (978-0-595-43127-4(5)) iUniverse, Inc.

Skidmore, Kate & Skidmore, Mark. The Invitation: An Adoptive Family's Memoir. 2011. 136p. 28.95 (978-1-4497-0907-5(9)); pap. 11.95 (978-1-4497-0906-8(0)) Author Solutions, Inc. (WestBow Pr.).

Stock, Bracha. Bracha Means Blessing: Scenes from a Bi-Cultural Adoption. 2007. 104p. per. 11.95 (978-0-595-46338-1(X)) iUniverse, Inc.

Sydes, Stephanie. Journey for Julie: Witnessing God's Glory Through Toddler Adoption in China. 2011. 140p. pap. 15.99 (978-1-4567-3574-6(8)) AuthorHouse.

Thompson, Kimberly. Gypsy Phoenix: A Birthright of Hope. 2010. pap. 19.99 (978-1-61566-192-3(1)) Tate Publishing & Enterprises, LLC.

Tiffany, Neal. Bachelor Father Pioneer. 2007. 300p. pap. 15.95 (978-0-7414-4271-0(X)) Infinity Publishing.

Weidling, Mary J. In Search of an Angel. 2007. 99p. pap. 10.95 (978-0-7414-3994-9(8)) Infinity Publishing.

Welch, Debra. Son of My Soul - the Adoption of Christopher. 2007. 140p. per. (978-1-894936-93-4(0)) Saga Bks.

Woodwyk, Carissa & Tebos, Susan. Before You Were Mine: Discovering Your Adopted Child's Lifestory. 2007. (Illus.). 176p. per. (978-1-932902-69-3(4)) FaithWalk Publishing.

ADOPTION—CORRUPT PRACTICES

Archuletta, David. Odyssey of an Unknown Father: The Complete Book on Wrongful Adoption. 2008. pap. 18.95 (978-1-60494-161-6(8)) Wheatmark.

Cahill, Bette L. Butterbox Babies: Baby Sales, Baby Deaths-New Revelations 15 Years Later. 2nd ed. 2007. (ENG., Illus.). 224p. pap. 22.95 (978-1-55266-213-7(6)) Fernwood Publishing Co., Ltd. CAN. Dist: Independent Pubs. Group.

Milotte, Mike. Banished Babies: The Secret History of Ireland's Baby Export Business (Revised Edition) 2011. 272p. pap. 27.50 (978-1-84840-125-9(6)) New Island Books IRL. Dist: International Specialized Bk. Services.

Raymond, Barbara Bisantz. The Baby Thief: The Untold Story of Georgia Tann, the Baby Seller Who Corrupted Adoption. 2008. (ENG., Illus.). 320p. pap. 12.95 (978-1-4027-5863-8(4)) Union Square Pr.

Raymond, Barbara Bisantz & Da Capo Press, Inc. Staff. The Baby Thief: The Untold Story of Georgia Tann, the Baby Seller Who Corrupted Adoption. 2007. (ENG., Illus.). 320p. 26.95 (978-0-7867-1944-0(3)) Da Capo Pr., Inc.

ADOPTION—LAW AND LEGISLATION

Allen, Nick. Making Sense of the New Adoption Law: A Guide for Social & Welfare Services. 2nd rev. ed. 2007. 157p. pap. 39.95 (978-1-905541-08-9(2)) Russell Hse. Publishing Ltd. GBR. Dist: International Specialized Bk. Services.

Appleton, Susan Frelich. Adoptions & Assisted Reproduction: Families under Construction. 2009. xx, 368p. pap. 48.00 (978-0-7355-7813-5(3)) Wolters Kluwer Law & Business.

Archuletta, David. Odyssey of an Unknown Father: The Complete Book on Wrongful Adoption. 2008. pap. 18.95 (978-1-60494-161-6(8)) Wheatmark.

Atwood, Barbara Ann. Children, Tribes, & States: Adoption & Custody Conflicts over American Indian Children. 2010. pap. 42.00 (978-1-59460-522-2(X)) Carolina Academic Pr.

Fairfax, Jennifer. Adoption Law Handbook: Practice, Resources, & Forms for Family Law Professionals. 2012. (ENG., Illus.). 495p. pap. 139.95 incl. cd-rom (978-1-61438-115-0(1)) American Bar Assn.

—Adoption Resource Guide. 2011. (978-1-61438-116-7(X)) American Bar Assn.

Florida Bar, Continuing Legal Education Staff, contrib. by. Adoption, Paternity, & Other Florida Family Practice. (Illus.). 7th ed. 2007. 130.00 (978-1-4224-4124-4(5)) 8th ed. 2009. (978-1-4224-5383-4(9)) 9th ed. 2011. (978-1-4224-9047-1(5)) Florida Bar Continuing Legal Education Pubns., The.

Goodwin, Michele. Baby Markets: Money & the New Politics of Creating Families. 2010. (ENG., Illus.). 336p. 94.99 (978-0-521-51373-9(1)) Cambridge Univ. Pr.

Goodwin, Michele Bratcher. Baby Markets: Money & the New Politics of Creating Families. 2010. (ENG., Illus.). 336p. pap. 28.99 (978-0-521-73510-0(6)) Cambridge Univ. Pr.

Hague Conference on Private International Law Staff, contrib. by. Hague Conference Guide to Good Practice on Intercountry Adoption. 2008. (ENG., Illus.). 216p. pap. (978-1-84661-144-5(X)) Jordan Publishing, Ltd.

Hearing on the Implementation of the Fostering Connections to Success & Increasing Adoptions ACT: Hearing Before the Subcommittee on Income Security & Family Support of the Committee on Ways & Means, U.S. House of Representatives, One Hundred Eleventh Congress, First Session, September 15, 2009. 2010. (Illus.). iii, 103p. (978-0-16-085205-3(6), 552-070-40558-5) United States Government Printing Office.

Hicks, Randall. Adopting in America: How to Adopt Within One Year. 5th rev. ed. 2011. (ENG.). 368p. pap. 16.95 (978-0-9839425-0-4(1)) Wordslinger Pr.

Jasper, Margaret C. The Law of Adoption. 2008. (Legal Almanac Ser.). (ENG., Illus.). 224p. 47.00 (978-0-19-533902-4(9)) Oxford Univ. Pr., Inc.

Jones, B. J., et al. The Indian Child Welfare ACT Handbook: A Legal Guide to the Custody & Adoption of Native American Children. 2nd ed. 2008. (ENG.). pap. 79.95 incl. lp (978-1-59031-858-4(7)) American Bar Assn.

Lind, Craig & Keating, Heather, eds. Children, Family Responsibilities & the State. 2008. (Journal of Law & Society Special Issues Ser.). (ENG., Illus.). 192p. pap. 39.95 (978-1-4051-8301-7(2), Wiley-Blackwell) Wiley, John & Sons, Inc.

Lynch, Catherine. The Metaphor of an Adopted Body. 2009. 404p. pap. (978-3-639-14672-1(7)) VDM Verlag Dr. Mueller e.K.

Mabry, Cynthia R. & Kelly, Lisa. Adoption Law: Theory, Policy & Practice. 2006. xxxi, 808p. (978-0-8377-3448-4(7)) Hein, William S. & Co., Inc.

—Adoption Law: Theory, Policy, & Practice. 2nd ed. 2010. (Illus.). xxxi, 842p. (978-0-8377-3844-4(X)) Hein, William S. & Co., Inc.

Markus, Kent. Adoption Law: Cases, Materials, & Problems. 2007. (978-0-89089-576-4(7)) Carolina Academic Pr.

Mitchell, John. Adoption & Special Guardianship. 2009. (ENG.). 888p. pap., instr.'s hndbk. ed. (978-1-84661-114-8(8)) Jordan Publishing, Ltd.

Newton, Judith Sperling. Voluntary Termination of Parental Rights & Adoption: A Practical Handbook for Judges, Lawyers, & Human Services Providers. 2nd ed. 2009. (978-1-57862-263-4(8)) State Bar of Wisconsin.

O'Halloran, Kerry. The Politics of Adoption: International Perspectives on Law, Policy & Practice. 2nd ed. (ENG.). xxii, 498p. 2010. pap. 169.00 (978-90-481-8081-3(3), 9048180813) 2009. 169.00 (978-1-4020-9151-3(6), 1402091516) Springer.

Osorio, Wendelyn D. Stepparent Adoption: A Resource Book. 2011. 272p. pap. 39.99 (978-1-257-62508-6(X)) Lulu Enterprises Inc.

Roberson, Nicole M. Sacred Trust Betrayed. 2008. 148p. 27.99 (978-0-88144-295-3(X)) Yorkshire Publishing Group.

Sandra, Ferreira. Interracial & Intercultural Adoption. 2010. 388p. pap. (978-3-8383-4813-1(3)) Lambert Academic Publishing.

Solsberry, Victoria. Adoption for Singles 2008-2009. 2008. 288p. pap. 29.95 (978-0-557-02973-0(2)) Lulu Enterprises Inc.

Song, Minkyoung. Termination of Parental Rights & Adoption in Foster Care - a Foster Care Decision on Child Maltreatment. 2007. 180p. per. (978-3-8364-2728-9(1)) VDM Verlag Dr. Mueller e.K.

Steck, B. Adoption - ein lebenslanger Prozess. 2007. (Illus.). 242p. pap. (978-3-8055-8285-8(4)) Karger, S. AG.

van den Hoogen, Peter & Van Den Hoogen, Peter. An Inquiry Focussing on Identity Development of Adopted Individuals. 2010. 120p. pap. (978-3-639-28294-8(9)) VDM Verlag Dr. Mueller e.K.

Vité, Sylvain & Boéchat, Hervé. Commentary on the United Nations Convention on the Rights of the Child, Volume 21 Article 21: Adoption. 2008. (Commentary on the United Nations Convention on the Rights of the Child Ser.). (ENG & FRE.). 49p. pap. (978-90-04-14874-1(4)) BRILL.

When Adoptions Go Wrong: Psychological & Legal Issues of Adoption Disruption. 2006. (ENG., Illus.). 148p. (C). 34.95 (978-0-7890-3181-5(7)); per. 18.95 (978-0-7890-3182-2(5)) Routledge.

ADOPTION—PSYCHOLOGICAL ASPECTS

Adams, Lori. Fresh Paint. 2007. 64p. per. 9.99 (978-1-60266-754-9(3)) Xulon Pr., Inc.

Alessia, Kate. It's Quite a Journey. 2010. 240p. pap. (978-3-8383-9054-3(7)) Lambert Academic Publishing.

Blomquist, Barbara Taylor. Insight into Adoption: Uncovering & Understanding the Heart of Adoption. 2nd ed. 2009. pap. 27.95 (978-0-398-07846-1(7)) Thomas, Charles C. Pub., Ltd.

Brooks Hansen. The Brotherhood of Joseph: A Father's Memoir of Infertility & Adoption in the 21st Century. 2008. 17.50 (978-1-60529-923-5(5), Modern Times) Rodale Pr., Inc.

Caldwell, Mardie. The Healthcare Professional's Adoption Guide: A resource guide for clinicians, social workers, & healthcare providers, covering the many aspects of adoption Today. 2008. (ENG., Illus.). 16p. 3.95 (978-0-9705734-6-9(4)) American Carriage Hse. Publishing.

Cram101 Textbook Reviews & Cram101 Textbook Reviews. Outlines & Highlights for Understanding Adoption: Clinical Work with Adults, Children, & Parents by Kathleen Hushion, ISBN. 2011. 120p. pap. 28.95 (978-1-4288-4343-1(4)) Cram101 Inc.

Cross, David R., et al. The Connected Child: Bring Hope & Healing to Your Adoptive Family. 2007. (ENG., Illus.). 288p. per. 16.95 (978-0-07-147500-6(1), 0071475001) McGraw-Hill Cos., The.

Eldridge, Sherrie. Questions Adoptees Are Asking: About Beginnings - About Birth Family - About Searching - About Finding Peace. 2009. (Maya Davis Ser.). (ENG.). 288p. pap. 15.99 (978-1-60006-595-8(3)) NavPress Publishing Group.

Ellerby, Janet Mason. Following the Tambourine Man: A Birthmother's Memoir. 2007. (Writing American Women Ser.). (Illus.). 289p. (978-0-8156-0889-9(6)) Syracuse Univ. Pr.

Fessler, Ann. The Girls Who Went Away: The Hidden History of Women Who Surrendered Children for Adoption in the Decades Before Roe V. Wade. 2007. (ENG.). 368p. (gr. 12-18). 16.00 (978-0-14-303897-9(4), Penguin (Non-Classics)) Penguin Group (USA) Inc.

Foster, Celia. Big Steps for Little People: Parenting Your Adopted Child. 2008. (ENG., Illus.). 176p. pap. (978-1-84310-620-3(5)) Kingsley, Jessica Ltd.

Guarendi, Raymond. Adoption: Choosing It, Living It, Loving It. 2009. ix, 182p. pap. 14.99 (978-0-86716-913-3(3), Servant Bks.) Franciscan Media.

Hansen, Brooks. The Brotherhood of Joseph: A Father's Memoir of Infertility & Adoption in the 21st Century. 2008. (ENG.). 288p. 24.95 *(978-1-59486-827-6(1),* Modern Times) Rodale Pr., Inc.
Hindle, Debbie & Shulman, Graham, eds. Psycho Adoption - Hindle Shulm. 2008. (ENG.). 304p. (C). 170.00 *(978-0-415-37275-6(5))* Routledge.
—Psycho Adoption - Hindle/Shulm. 2008. (ENG.). 304p. (C). 49.95 *(978-0-415-37276-3(3))* Routledge.
Hushion, Kathleen. Understanding Adoption: Clinical Work with Adults, Children, & Parents. 2006. (ENG., Illus.). 268p. 86.50 *(978-0-7657-0425-2(0))* Rowman & Littlefield Publishers, Inc.
Hushion, Kathleen, ed. Understanding Adoption: Clinical Work with Adults, Children, & Parents. 2006. (ENG., Illus.). 268p. per. 36.99 *(978-0-7657-0426-9(9))* Rowman & Littlefield Publishers, Inc.
Keck, Gregory C. Parenting Adopted Adolescents: Understanding & Appreciating Their Journeys. 2009. (Hollywood Nobody Ser.). (ENG.). 240p. pap. 17.99 *(978-1-60006-281-0(4))* NavPress Publishing Group.
Lindsey, Caroline. Creating New Families: Therapeutic Approaches to Fostering & Adoption. 2007. (Tavistock Clinic Ser.). 250p. pap. 35.00 *(978-1-85575-935-0(7))* Karnac Bks. GBR. Dist: Stylus Publishing, LLC.
Luo, Nili. The Adoptive Parenting Process: A Study of the Experiences of Parents who Adopt Infant Girls from China. 2008. 116p. pap. *(978-3-639-09061-1(6))* VDM Verlag Dr. Mueller e.K.
Miller, Rhonda Y. Unveiling the Adoption Process: Seven Families' Adventures & Insights. 2010. pap. 14.99 *(978-1-61663-624-1(6))* Tate Publishing & Enterprises, LLC.
National Center for Health Statistics (U.S.) Staff, contrib. by. Adoption Experiences of Women & Men, & Demand for Children to Adopt by Women Ages 18-44 in the United States: Data from Cycle 6 (2002) of the National Survey of Family Growth. 2008. (DHHS Publication Ser.: Nos. 2008-1979). (Illus.). v, 36p. *(978-0-8406-0624-2(9))* National Ctr. for Health Statistics.
Owusu-Bempah, Kwame. The Wellbeing of Children in Care: A New Approach for Improving Developmental Outcomes. 2010. (ENG.). 192p. (C). 125.00 *(978-0-415-47939-4(8))*; pap. 39.95 *(978-0-415-47940-0(1))* Routledge.
Richardson, Meri. My Soul's Desire. 2007. 112p. per. 14.95 *(978-1-4327-0523-7(7))* Outskirts Pr., Inc.
Shipitsyna, Ludmila M. Psychology of Orphans. 2007. 244p. per. 18.95 *(978-0-595-43018-5(X))* iUniverse, Inc.
Steck, B. Adoption - ein lebenslanger Prozess. 2007. (Illus.). 242p. pap. *(978-3-8055-8285-8(4))* Karger, S. AG.
Stryker, Rachael. The Road to Evergreen: Adoption, Attachment Therapy, & the Promise of Family. 2010. (Illus.). 208p. 59.95 *(978-0-8014-4687-0(2))*; pap. 19.95 *(978-0-8014-7686-0(0))* Cornell Univ. Pr.
Talmen, Nina. Special Skills in International Adoptive Parenting. 2008. 80p. pap. *(978-3-639-02891-1(0))* VDM Verlag Dr. Mueller e.K.
van den Hoogen, Peter & Van Den Hoogen, Peter. An Inquiry Focussing on Identity Development of Adopted Individuals. 2010. 120p. pap. *(978-3-639-28294-8(9))* VDM Verlag Dr. Mueller e.K.
When Adoptions Go Wrong: Psychological & Legal Issues of Adoption Disruption. 2006. (ENG., Illus.). 148p. (C). 34.95 *(978-0-7890-3181-5(7))*; per. 18.95 *(978-0-7890-3182-2(5))* Routledge.
Whitten, Kathleen L. Labor of the Heart: A Parent's Guide to the Decisions & Emotions in Adoption. 2008. (ENG., Illus.). 240p. per. 16.95 *(978-1-59077-133-4(8))* Evans, M. & Co., Inc.
Williams, Mary Beth. Trauma & the Internationally Adopted Child. 2007. 224p. 34.95 *(978-0-415-95498-3(3))* Taylor & Francis Group.

ADOPTION—CANADA

Brennan, Deborah A. Labours of Love: Canadians Talk about Adoption. 2008. (ENG., Illus.). 272p. pap. 28.99 *(978-1-55002-845-4(6))* Dundurn CAN. Dist: Ingram Pub. Services.
Coulter, Myrl. The House with the Broken Two: A Birthmother Remembers. 2011. (ENG., Illus.). 160p. pap. 18.00 *(978-1-897535-72-1(4))* Anvil Pr. CAN. Dist: Univ. of Toronto Pr.
Dickerson, James L. & Allen, Mardi. The Basics of Adoption: A Guide for Building Families in the U. S. & Canada, 1 vol. 2006. 304p. 44.95 *(978-0-275-98799-2(X),* C8799, Praeger Pubs.) Greenwood Publishing Group, Inc.
Strong-Boag, Veronica. Finding Families, Finding Ourselves: A History of Adoption in Canada. 2006. (ENG.). 352p. 65.00 *(978-0-19-542492-8(1))* Oxford Univ. Pr., Inc.

ADOPTION—GREAT BRITAIN

Allen, Nick. Making Sense of the New Adoption Law: A Guide for Social & Welfare Services. 2nd rev. ed. 2007. 157p. pap. 39.95 *(978-1-905541-08-9(2))* Russell Hse. Publishing Ltd. GBR. Dist: International Specialized Bk. Services.
Bentovim. Assessing the Support Needs of Adoptive Children & Their Famili. 2006. (ENG., Illus.). 192p. (C). 150.00 *(978-0-415-40944-5(6))* Routledge.
Bentovim, Arnon & Miller, Liza Bingley. Assessing the Support Needs of Adopted Children & Their Families: Building Secure New Lives. 2006. (Illus.). 176p. per. 43.95 *(978-0-415-40945-2(4))* Routledge.
Clapton, Gary & Hoggan, Pauline. Adoption & Fostering in Scotland: Policy & Practice in Health & Social Care No. 16. 2011. (Illus.). 112p. pap. 29.99 *(978-1-906716-35-6(8))* Dunedin Academic Pr. GBR. Dist: International Specialized Bk. Services.
Harding, Jeremy. Mother Country: Memoir of an Adopted Boy. 2010. (ENG.). 224p. pap. 17.95 *(978-1-84467-657-6(9),* 844657) Verso Bks. GBR. Dist: Norton, W. W. & Co., Inc.
Pati, Jagannath, ed. Adoption: Global Perspectives & Ethical Issues. 2007. 314p. *(978-81-8069-442-4(9))* Concept Publishing Co.

ADOPTION—UNITED STATES

Adamec, Christine A. & Miller, Laurie C. The Encyclopedia of Adoption. 3rd rev. ed. 2006. (Facts on File Library of Health & Living). (Illus.). 432p. (C). (gr. 9). 75.00 *(978-0-8160-6329-1(X))* Facts On File, Inc.
Atwood, Barbara Ann. Children, Tribes, & States: Adoption & Custody Conflicts over American Indian Children. 2010. pap. 42.00 *(978-1-59460-522-2(X))* Carolina Academic Pr.
Barlin, Paul. In White America: Interracial Children & Adoption. 2011. 184p. 26.95 *(978-1-4502-4141-0(7))*; pap. 16.95 *(978-1-4502-4140-3(9))* iUniverse, Inc.
Barrington, Fiona. Not Your Normal Family. 2008. 180p. pap. *(978-0-7552-0421-2(2))* Authors OnLine, Ltd.
Barth, Richard P., et al. From Child Abuse to Foster Care: Child Welfare Services Pathways & Placements. 2010. (ENG., Illus.). 310p. pap. 29.95 *(978-0-202-36397-4(X))* Transaction Pubs.
Bramlett, Matthew D. Design & Operation of the National Survey of Adoptive Parents, 2007. 2010. *(978-0-8406-0633-4(8))* National Ctr. for Health Statistics.
Briggs, Laura. Somebody's Children: The Politics of Transracial & Transnational Adoption. 2012. (ENG., Illus.). 384p. 94.95 ***(978-0-8223-5147-4(1))***; pap. 25.95 ***(978-0-8223-5161-0(7))*** Duke Univ. Pr.
Brooks Hansen. The Brotherhood of Joseph: A Father's Memoir of Infertility & Adoption in the 21st Century. 2008. 17.50 *(978-1-60529-923-5(5),* Modern Times) Rodale Pr., Inc.
Caldwell, Mardie. The Healthcare Professional's Adoption Guide: A resource guide for clinicians, social workers, & healthcare providers, covering the many aspects of adoption Today. 2008. (ENG., Illus.). 16p. 3.95 *(978-0-9705734-6-9(4))* American Carriage Hse. Publishing.
—So I Was Thinking about Adoption... Considering Your Choices. 2008. (ENG., Illus.). 112p. 8.95 *(978-0-9705734-5-2(6))* American Carriage Hse. Publishing.
Caldwell, Mardie & Featherston, Heather. Called to Adoption: A Christian's Guide to Answering the Call: A Christian's Guide to Answering the Call. 2011. (ENG.). 128p. pap. 12.95 *(978-1-935176-09-1(9))* American Carriage Hse. Publishing.
Caring for Children in Out-of-Home Placement. 23p. pap. 30.00 *(978-0-7881-4180-5(5))* DIANE Publishing Co.
Carlisle, Ginger & Carlisle, Kevin. In Search of a Family: A Story of an International Adoption. 2009. (ENG.). 144p. pap. 19.95 *(978-1-60138-511-6(0))* Atlantic Publishing Co.
Carson, Bradley J. Barriers & Success Factors in Adoptions from Foster Care. 2011. (Children's Issues, Laws & Programs Ser.). 147p. 89.00 *(978-1-61209-740-4(5))* Nova Science Pubs., Inc.
Christianson, Laura. The Adoption Decision: 15 Things You Want to Know Before Adopting. 2007. 250p. per. 13.99 *(978-0-7369-2000-1(5))* Harvest Hse. Pubs.
Davis, Dixie van de Flier. Adoption: Stories of Lives Transformed. 2008. 232p. pap. 24.95 *(978-1-893815-42-1(0))* Pie in the Sky Publishing, LLC.
Dickerson, James L. & Allen, Mardi. The Basics of Adoption: A Guide for Building Families in the U. S. & Canada, 1 vol. 2006. 304p. 44.95 *(978-0-275-98799-2(X),* C8799, Praeger Pubs.) Greenwood Publishing Group, Inc.
Duxbury, Micky. Making Room in Our Hearts: Keeping Family Ties Through Open Adoption. 2006. (ENG., Illus.). 192p. per. 23.95 *(978-0-415-95502-7(5))* Routledge.
Ellerby, Janet Mason. Following the Tambourine Man: A Birthmother's Memoir. 2007. (Writing American Women Ser.). (Illus.). 289p. *(978-0-8156-0889-9(6))* Syracuse Univ. Pr.
Fairfax, Jennifer. Adoption Law Handbook: Practice, Resources, & Forms for Family Law Professionals. 2012. (ENG., Illus.). 495p. pap. 139.95 incl. cd-rom ***(978-1-61438-115-0(1))*** American Bar Assn.
—Adoption Resource Guide. 2011. ***(978-1-61438-116-7(X))*** American Bar Assn.
Florida Bar, Continuing Legal Education Staff, contrib. by. Adoption, Paternity, & Other Florida Family Practice. (Illus.). 7th ed. 2007. 130.00 *(978-1-4224-4124-4(5))* 9th ed. 2011. ***(978-1-4224-9047-1(5))*** Florida Bar Continuing Legal Education Pubns., The.
Gailey, Christine Ward. Blue-Ribbon Babies & Labors of Love: Race, Class, & Gender in U. S. Adoption Practice. 2010. (ENG.). 199p. pap. 19.95 *(978-0-292-72570-6(1))* Univ. of Texas Pr.
Goodwin, Michele. Baby Markets: Money & the New Politics of Creating Families. 2010. (ENG., Illus.). 336p. 94.99 *(978-0-521-51373-9(1))* Cambridge Univ. Pr.
Goodwin, Michele Bratcher. Baby Markets: Money & the New Politics of Creating Families. 2010. (ENG., Illus.). 336p. pap. 28.99 *(978-0-521-73510-0(6))* Cambridge Univ. Pr.
Hall, David. Taking Sides: Clashing Views in Family & Personal Relationships. 9th ed. 2012. (Taking Sides Ser.). (ENG.). 416p. (C). pap. 48.00 ***(978-0-07-805038-1(3)***, 0078050383, McGraw-Hill/Dushkin) McGraw-Hill Higher Education.
Harness, Susan/Devan. Mixing Cultural Identities Through Transracial Adoption: Outcomes of the Indian Adoption Project (1958-1967) 2009. (Illus.). 200p. 99.95 *(978-0-7734-4885-8(3))* Mellen, Edwin Pr., The.
Hart, Patricia Susan. A Home for Every Child: The Washington Children's Home Society in the Progressive Era. 2010. (Emil & Kathleen Sick Lecture-Book Series in Western History & Biography Ser.). (ENG., Illus.). 272p. pap. 26.95 *(978-0-295-99064-4(3))* Univ. of Washington Pr.
Herman, Ellen. Kinship by Design: A History of Adoption in the Modern United States. 2008. (ENG., Illus.). 368p. 70.00 *(978-0-226-32759-4(0))*; pap. 25.00 *(978-0-226-32760-0(4))* Univ. of Chicago Pr.
Hicks, Randall. Adopting in America: How to Adopt Within One Year. 5th rev. ed. 2011. (ENG.). 368p. pap. 16.95 ***(978-0-9839425-0-4(1))*** Wordslinger Pr.
Homes, A. M. The Mistress's Daughter. 2008. (ENG., Illus.). 256p. (gr. 12-18). 14.00 *(978-0-14-311331-7(3),* Penguin (Non-Classics)) Penguin Group (USA) Inc.
Hopkins-Best, Mary. Toddler Adoption: The Weaver's Craft. rev. ed. 2012. (ENG., Illus.). 272p. pap. ***(978-1-84905-894-0(6))*** Kingsley, Jessica Ltd.
Horn, Joseph & Loehlin, John. Heredity & Environment in 300 Adoptive Families: The Texas Adoption Project. 2010. (ENG., Illus.). 218p. 49.95 *(978-0-202-36345-5(7))* Aldine Transaction.
Howe, Doris. Adoption Joys: They Expected a Miracle. 2011. 144p. 28.95 *(978-1-4497-1293-8(2))*; pap. 11.95 *(978-1-4497-1292-1(4))* Author Solutions, Inc. (WestBow Pr.).
Jasper, Margaret C. The Law of Adoption. 2008. (Legal Almanac Ser.). (ENG., Illus.). 224p. 47.00 *(978-0-19-533902-4(9))* Oxford Univ. Pr., Inc.
Juntunen, Craig. Both Ends Burning: My Story of Adopting Three Children from Haiti. 2009. 232p. 24.95 *(978-1-4327-3872-3(0))*; (ENG.). pap. 16.95 *(978-1-4327-3486-2(5))* Outskirts Pr., Inc.
Keck, Gregory C., et al. Adopting the Hurt Child: Hope for Families with Special-Needs Kids - A Guide for Parents & Professionals. 3rd ed. 2009. (Hollywood Nobody Ser.). (ENG.). 264p. pap., instr.'s gde. ed. 17.99 *(978-1-60006-289-6(X))* NavPress Publishing Group.
Kordalewski, Lydia M. The Mom with the Red Lipstick: An Adoption Memory of a Little Bulgarian Boy. 2008. 36p. pap. 16.99 *(978-1-4343-8473-7(X))* AuthorHouse.
Lawrence, J. L. Nobody's Child: Memories of a Childhood Lost. 2008. 656p. pap. 20.95 *(978-1-60264-228-7(1))* Virtualbookworm.com Publishing, Inc.
Lee, Ellen, et al. Once They Hear My Name: Korean Adoptees & Their Journeys Toward Identity. 2008. (Illus.). 183p. 21.95 *(978-0-9793756-1-3(4))* Tamarisk Bks. LLC.
Lifton, Betty Jean. Lost & Found: The Adoption Experience. 3rd ed. 2009. (ENG.). 344p. pap. 17.95 *(978-0-472-03328-7(X))* Univ. of Michigan Pr.
Mabry, Cynthia R. & Kelly, Lisa. Adoption Law: Theory, Policy, & Practice. 2nd ed. 2010. (Illus.). xxxi, 842p. *(978-0-8377-3844-4(X))* Hein, William S. & Co., Inc.
Mallon, Gerald P. Lesbian & Gay Foster & Adoptive Parents: Recruiting, Assessing, & Supporting an Untapped Resource for Children & Youth. 2006. (Illus.). 131p. pap. 18.95 *(978-1-58760-104-0(4))* Child Welfare League of America, Inc.
Merino, Noël. Adoption. 2008. (Introducing Issues with Opposing Viewpoints Ser.). (Illus.). 112-144p. (J). (gr. 7-10). 35.75 *(978-0-7377-4165-0(1),* Greenhaven Pr., Inc.) Cengage Gale.
Miranda, May'lon. Love Is Blind. 2011. 180p. 27.99 ***(978-1-4670-7017-1(3))***; pap. 16.95 ***(978-1-4670-7018-8(1))*** AuthorHouse.
Moe, Barbara A. Adoption: A Reference Handbook. 2nd rev. ed. 2007. (Contemporary World Issues Ser.). (Illus.). 342p. 55.00 *(978-1-59884-029-2(0))* ABC-CLIO, LLC.
National Center for Health Statistics (U.S.) Staff, contrib. by. Adoption Experiences of Women & Men, & Demand for Children to Adopt by Women Ages 18-44 in the United States: Data from Cycle 6 (2002) of the National Survey of Family Growth. 2008. (DHHS Publication Ser.: Nos. 2008-1979). (Illus.). v, 36p. *(978-0-8406-0624-2(9))* National Ctr. for Health Statistics.
—Design & Operation of the National Survey of Adoptive Parents of Children with Special Health Care Needs, 2008. 2010. *(978-0-8406-0634-1(6))* National Ctr. for Health Statistics.
Newton, Judith Sperling. Voluntary Termination of Parental Rights & Adoption: A Practical Handbook for Judges, Lawyers, & Human Services Providers. 2nd ed. 2009. *(978-1-57862-263-4(8))* State Bar of Wisconsin.
Pertman, Adam. Adoption Nation: How the Adoption Revolution Is Transforming America. 2009. *(978-1-55832-715-3(0))* Harvard Common Pr.
—Adoption Nation: How the Adoption Revolution Is Transforming Our Families — & America. 2nd ed. 2011. (ENG.). 352p. pap. 16.95 *(978-1-55832-716-0(9))* Harvard Common Pr.
Poston, Dudley L., et al. Children for Families or Families for Children: The Demography of Adoption Behavior int he U. S. 2010. (Springer Series on Demographic Methods & Population Analysis Ser.). 300p. 139.00 *(978-90-481-8971-7(3),* 9048189713) Springer.
Quiroz, Pamela Anne. Adoption in a Color-Blind Society. 2007. (Perspectives on a Multiracial America Ser.). (ENG.). 144p. 65.00 *(978-0-7425-5941-7(6))*; per. 21.95 *(978-0-7425-5942-4(4))* Rowman & Littlefield Publishers, Inc.
Raymond, Barbara Bisantz. The Baby Thief: The Untold Story of Georgia Tann, the Baby Seller Who Corrupted Adoption. 2008. (ENG., Illus.). 320p. pap. 12.95 *(978-1-4027-5863-8(4))* Union Square Pr.
Raymond, Barbara Bisantz & Da Capo Press, Inc. Staff. The Baby Thief: The Untold Story of Georgia Tann, the Baby Seller Who Corrupted Adoption. 2007. (ENG., Illus.). 320p. 26.95 *(978-0-7867-1944-0(3))* Da Capo Pr., Inc.
Register, Cheri. Are Those Kids Yours? American Families with Children Adopted from Other. 2010. (ENG.). 256p. pap. 16.99 *(978-1-4391-9995-4(7),* Free Pr.) Free Pr.
Riley, Nancy E. & Van Vleet, Krista E. Making Families Through Adoption. 2011. (Contemporary Family Perspectives (CFP) Ser.). (Illus.). 168p. (C). pap. 27.00 *(978-1-4129-9800-0(X),* B98000P) SAGE Pubns., Inc.
Russell, Beth Nonte. Forever Lily: An Unexpected Mother's Journey to Adoption in China. 2007. (ENG., Illus.). 240p. pap. 14.00 *(978-0-7432-9297-9(9),* Touchstone) Touchstone.
Selkow, Aaron. Robust Cloud: A Father's Journey to China. 2011. 90p. pap. 19.95 ***(978-1-4560-4024-6(3))*** PublishAmerica, Inc.
Simon, Rita James & Roorda, Rhonda M. In Their Siblings' Voices: White Non-Adopted Siblings Talk about Their Experiences Being Raised with Black & Biracial Brothers & Sisters. 2009. (ENG.). 248p. (gr. 17). pap. 24.50 *(978-0-231-14851-1(8))*; (Illus.). 74.50 *(978-0-231-14850-4(X))* Columbia Univ. Pr.
Sinclair, Skye & Taylor, Diane. Runaway. 2008. (ENG.). 303p. pap. 24.95 *(978-0-340-96229-9(1),* Hodder & Stoughton) Hodder General Publishing Div. GBR. Dist: Independent Pubs. Group.
Solsberry, Victoria. Adoption for Singles 2008-2009. 2008. 288p. pap. 29.95 *(978-0-557-02973-0(2))* Lulu Enterprises Inc.
Stryker, Rachael. The Road to Evergreen: Adoption, Attachment Therapy, & the Promise of Family. 2010. (Illus.). 208p. 59.95 *(978-0-8014-4687-0(2))* Cornell Univ. Pr.
Taylor, Kimberley Raunikar. The Intentional Family: Celebrating Adoption. annot. ed. 2007. (ENG.). 192p. per. 14.99 *(978-0-8341-2313-7(4),* 083-412-3134) Beacon Hill Pr. of Kansas City.
Tuan, Mia & Shiao, Jiannbin Lee. Choosing Ethnicity, Negotiating Race: Korean Adoptees in America. 2011. 213p. 35.00 *(978-0-87154-875-7(5))* Russell Sage Foundation.
Wegar, Katarina, ed. Adoptive Families in a Diverse Society. 2006. (ENG.). 304p. 68.00 *(978-0-8135-3841-9(6))* Rutgers Univ. Pr.

ADOPTIVE PARENTS

Allen, Mardi & Dickerson, James L. Adoptive & Foster Parent Screening: A Professional Guide for Evaluations. 2006. (ENG.). 224p. 42.95 *(978-0-415-95268-2(9))* Routledge.
Amend, Deborah. A Dress for Anna: The Story of the Redemption of the Life of a Ukranian Orphan. 2009. *(978-0-7880-2632-4(1))* FaithWalk Publishing.
Bemrose, Alex. Our Son from Afar: The Long Road to Adoption. 2010. (Illus.). 218p. 34.95 *(978-1-84624-491-9(9))* Book Guild, Ltd. GBR. Dist: Trans-Atlantic Pubns., Inc.
Bentley, Lisa Misraje. Saving Levi: Left to Die ... Destined to Live. 2006. (ENG., Illus.). 176p. per. 13.99 *(978-1-58997-449-4(2))* Tyndale Hse. Pubs.
Bentovim. Assessing the Support Needs of Adoptive Children & Their Famili. 2006. (ENG., Illus.). 192p. (C). 150.00 *(978-0-415-40944-5(6))* Routledge.
Bentovim, Arnon & Miller, Liza Bingley. Assessing the Support Needs of Adopted Children & Their Families: Building Secure New Lives. 2006. (Illus.). 176p. per. 43.95 *(978-0-415-40945-2(4))* Routledge.
Blomquist, Barbara Taylor. Insight into Adoption: Uncovering & Understanding the Heart of Adoption. 2nd ed. 2009. pap. 27.95 *(978-0-398-07846-1(7))* Thomas, Charles C. Pub., Ltd.
Bogach, Alexander. How to adopt from ukraine Successfully. 2009. 128p. pap. 24.97 *(978-1-4092-7940-2(5))* Lulu Enterprises Inc.
Brooks Hansen. The Brotherhood of Joseph: A Father's Memoir of Infertility & Adoption in the 21st Century. 2008. 17.50 *(978-1-60529-923-5(5),* Modern Times) Rodale Pr., Inc.
Caughman, Susan & Motley, Isolde. You Can Adopt: The Adoptive Families Guide. 2009. (ENG., Illus.). 320p. pap. 16.00 *(978-0-345-50401-2(1),* Ballantine Bks.) Random House Publishing Group.
Cremer-Vogel, Kate, et al. What Every Adoptive Parent Needs to Know: Healing Your Child's Wounded Heart. 2008. xi, 269p. pap. *(978-0-615-18845-4(1))* Mountain Ridge Publishing.
Dickerson, James, et al. How to Screen Adoptive & Foster Parents: A Workbook for Professionals & Students. 2011. 39.99 *(978-0-87101-415-3(7),* NASW Pr.) National Assn. of Social Workers/NASW Pr.
Eldridge, Sherrie. 20 Things Adoptive Parents Need to Succeed. 2009. (ENG.). 320p. pap. 16.00 *(978-0-385-34162-2(8),* Delta) Random House Publishing Group.
Elkins, Richard A. Finding Maria, the Secret Mother. 2009. 208p. pap. 15.99 *(978-1-61579-483-6(2))* Xulon Pr., Inc.
Elwins, Dannie. How to Become an Adoptive Parent & Adopt A Baby. 2009. 32p. pap. 16.99 *(978-0-557-15404-3(9))* Lulu Enterprises Inc.
Foster, Celia. Big Steps for Little People: Parenting Your Adopted Child. 2008. (ENG., Illus.). 176p. pap. *(978-1-84310-620-3(5))* Kingsley, Jessica Ltd.
Gair, Susan. Adoption: A different road to Mothering. 2010. 408p. pap. *(978-3-639-23593-7(2))* VDM Verlag Dr. Mueller e.K.
Greene, Melissa Fay. No Biking in the House Without a Helmet, 1 vol. 2011. (ENG., Illus.). 368p. 26.00 *(978-0-374-22306-9(8))* Farrar, Straus & Giroux.
Gritter, James L. Hospitious Adoption. 2009. pap. *(978-1-58760-123-1(0),* CWLA Pr.) Child Welfare League of America, Inc.
Hansen, Brooks. The Brotherhood of Joseph: A Father's Memoir of Infertility & Adoption in the 21st Century. 2008. (ENG.). 288p. 24.95 *(978-1-59486-827-6(1),* Modern Times) Rodale Pr., Inc.
Herlem, Fanny Cohen. Great Answers to Difficult Questions about Adoption: What Children Need to Know. 2008. (ENG., Illus.). 112p. pap. *(978-1-84310-671-5(X))* Kingsley, Jessica Ltd.
—Great Answers to Difficult Questions about Divorce: What Children Need to Know. 2008. (ENG., Illus.). 96p. pap. *(978-1-84310-672-2(8))* Kingsley, Jessica Ltd.
Holloway, Sara, ed. Family Wanted: Stories of Adoption. 2006. (ENG.). 320p. per. 14.95 *(978-0-8129-7547-5(2),* Random Hse. Trade Paperbacks) Random House Publishing Group.
Jack, William F. The Little Russians: an Ailing Father's Letters to His Children. 2010. 463p. pap. 27.95 *(978-0-557-44579-0(5))* Lulu Enterprises Inc.
Jacobson, Heather. Culture Keeping: White Mothers, International Adoption, & the Negotiation of Family Difference. 2008. (ENG.). 216p. (C). pap. 22.95

(978-0-8265-1618-3(1)); lib. bdg. 49.95 *(978-0-8265-1617-6(3))* Vanderbilt Univ. Pr.

Keck, Gregory C. Parenting Adopted Adolescents: Understanding & Appreciating Their Journeys. 2009. (Hollywood Nobody Ser.). (ENG.). 240p. pap. 17.99 *(978-1-60006-281-0(4))* NavPress Publishing Group.

Keck, Gregory C., et al. Parenting the Hurt Child: Helping Adoptive Families Heal & Grow. 2009. (Hollywood Nobody Ser.). (ENG.). 304p. pap. 17.99 *(978-1-60006-290-2(3))* NavPress Publishing Group.

Kruger, Pamela & Smolowe, Jill, eds. A Love Like No Other: Stories from Adoptive Parents. 2006. (ENG.). 272p. (gr. 12-18). 16.00 *(978-1-59448-215-1(2)*, Riverhead Trade (Paperbacks)) Penguin Group (USA) Inc.

Lierow, Diane, et al. Dani's Story: A Journey from Neglect to Love. 2011. (ENG., Illus.). 272p. 24.95 *(978-0-470-59133-8(1)*, Wiley) Wiley, John & Sons, Inc.

Likins, Peter W. A New American Family: A Love Story. 2011. (ENG., Illus.). 200p. 29.95 *(978-0-8165-2931-5(0))* Univ. of Arizona Pr.

Luo, Nili. The Adoptive Parenting Process: A Study of the Experiences of Parents who Adopt Infant Girls from China. 2008. 116p. pap. *(978-3-639-09061-1(6))* VDM Verlag Dr. Mueller e.K.

Macrae, Sheena & MacLeod, Jean, eds. Adoption Parenting: Creating a Toolbox, Building Connections. 2006. (Illus.). 503p. per. 29.95 *(978-0-9726244-5-9(7))* EMK Pr.

McCabe, Nancy. Crossing the Blue Willow Bridge: A Journey to My Daughter's Birthplace in China. 2nd ed. 2011. (ENG.). 216p. (gr. 3). pap. 19.95 *(978-0-8262-1942-8(X))* Univ. of Missouri Pr.

Monroe, Debra. On the Outskirts of Normal: Forging a Family Against the Grain. 2010. 248p. 22.50 *(978-0-87074-560-7(3))* Southern Methodist Univ. Pr.

O'Dwyer, Jessica. Mamalita: An Adoption Memoir. 2010. (ENG., Illus.). 312p. pap. 16.95 *(978-1-58005-334-1(3))* Seal Pr.

Patty, Sandi. Life in the Blender. 0 vols. 2009. 192p. pap. 13.99 *(978-0-7852-9735-2(9))* Nelson, Thomas Inc.

Rauhala, Ann, ed. The Lucky Ones: Our Stories of Adopting Children from China. 2008. (ENG., Illus.). 350p. per. 19.95 *(978-1-55022-823-6(4))* ECW Pr. CAN. Dist: Independent Pubs. Group.

Roorda, Rhonda M. & Simon, Rita J. In Their Parents' Voices: Reflections on Raising Transracial Adoptees. 2007. (ENG.). 240p. (gr. 17). pap. 24.50 *(978-0-231-14137-6(8))* Columbia Univ. Pr.

Russell, Beth Nonte. Forever Lily: An Unexpected Mother's Journey to Adoption in China. 2007. (ENG., Illus.). 240p. pap. 14.00 *(978-0-7432-9297-9(9)*, Touchstone) Touchstone.

Sally Bacchetta. What I Want My Adopted Child to Know: An Adoptive Parent's Perspective. 2010. 124p. 23.95 *(978-1-4401-9438-2(6))*; pap. 13.95 *(978-1-4401-9436-8(X))* iUniverse, Inc.

Sanford, David & Sanford, Renee S., eds. Handbook on Thriving As an Adoptive Family: Real-Life Solutions to Common Challenges. 2008. (ENG.). 288p. pap. 14.99 *(978-1-58997-338-1(0))* Tyndale Hse. Pubs.

Savarese, Ralph James. Reasonable People: A Memoir of Autism & Adoption: on the Meaning of Family & the Politics of Neurological Difference. annot. ed. 2007. (ENG.). 496p. 25.95 *(978-1-59051-129-9(8))* Other Pr., LLC.

Sell, Colleen, ed. A Cup of Comfort for Adoptive Families: Stories that celebrate a special gift of Love. 2009. (ENG.). 336p. pap. 11.95 *(978-1-59869-870-1(2))* Adams Media Corp.

Seven Rhinos. 2007. 197p. pap. 15.95 *(978-0-615-17552-2(X))* Navark, Jo Publishing LLC.

Simon, Rita James, et al. In Their Parents' Voices: Reflections on Raising Transracial Adoptees. 2007. (ENG.). 240p. (gr. 17). 74.50 *(978-0-231-14136-9(X))* Columbia Univ. Pr.

Talmen, Nina. Special Skills in International Adoptive Parenting. 2008. 80p. pap. *(978-3-639-02891-1(0))* VDM Verlag Dr. Mueller e.K.

Taylor, Kimberley Raunikar. The Intentional Family: Celebrating Adoption. annot. ed. 2007. (ENG.). 192p. per. 14.99 *(978-0-8341-2313-7(4)*, 083-412-3134) Beacon Hill Pr. of Kansas City.

Tuohy, Leigh Anne, et al. In a Heartbeat: Sharing the Power of Cheerful Giving. 2010. (ENG., Illus.). 288p. 24.00 *(978-0-8050-9339-4(9))* Holt, Henry & Co.

—In a Heartbeat: Sharing the Power of Cheerful Giving. 2011. (ENG., Illus.). 288p. pap. 14.99 *(978-0-312-57718-6(4)*, St. Martin's Griffin) St. Martin's Pr.

—In a Heartbeat: Sharing the Power of Cheerful Giving. Lt. ed. 2010. 32.99 *(978-1-4104-2922-3(9))* Thorndike Pr.

Wegar, Katarina, ed. Adoptive Families in a Diverse Society. 2006. (ENG.). 304p. 68.00 *(978-0-8135-3841-9(6))*; per. 25.95 *(978-0-8135-3842-6(4))* Rutgers Univ. Pr.

Whitten, Kathleen L. Labor of the Heart: A Parent's Guide to the Decisions & Emotions in Adoption. 2008. (ENG., Illus.). 240p. per. 16.95 *(978-1-59077-133-4(8))* Evans, M. & Co., Inc.

ADORNO, THEODOR W., 1903-1969

Adorno, Theodor W. Correspondence, 1925-1935. Lonitz, Henri, ed. Hoban, Wieland, tr. 2012. (ENG.). 168p. pap. 14.95 ***(978-0-7456-2336-8(0))*** Polity Pr. GBR. Dist: Wiley, John & Sons, Inc.

Adorno, Theodor W. Dream Notes. Godde, Christoph & Lonitz, Henri, eds. Livingstone, Rodney, tr. from GER. 2007. (ENG.). 128p. 17.95 *(978-0-7456-3830-0(9))* Polity Pr. GBR. Dist: Wiley, John & Sons, Inc.

Adorno, Theodor W., et al. Minima Moralia, Culture & Materialism, for Marx, Aesthetics & Politics, 4 vols. 2010. (Radical Thinkers Classics Ser.: No. 4). (ENG.). 320p. 74.95 *(978-1-84467-665-1(X)*, 844665) Verso Bks. GBR. Dist: Norton, W. W. & Co., Inc.

Benzer, Matthias. The Sociology of Theodor Adorno. 2011. (ENG.). 278p. 95.00 *(978-1-107-00009-4(2))* Cambridge Univ. Pr.

Bernstein, Jay M., et al. Art & Aesthetics after Adorno. 2010. (Townsend Papers in the Humanities Ser.). 160p. pap. 18.95 *(978-0-9823294-2-9(3))* Townsend Ctr. For The Humanities.

Brittain, Christopher. Adorno & Theology. 2010. (Philosophy & Theology Ser.). (ENG.). 256p. 29.95 *(978-0-567-26108-3(5))*; 100.00 *(978-0-567-56929-5(2))* Continuum International Publishing Group, Ltd. GBR. (T&T Clark Int'l). Dist: National Bk. Network.

Burke, Donald A. Adorno & the Need in Thinking: New Critical Essays. Kiloh, Kathy et al, eds. 2007. (ENG.). 352p. *(978-0-8020-9214-4(4))* Univ. of Toronto Pr.

Cavalletto, George. Crossing the Psycho-Social Divide: Freud, Weber Adorno & Elias. 2007. (Rethinking Classical Sociology Ser.). (Illus.). 300p. 124.95 *(978-0-7546-4772-0(2))* Ashgate Publishing Co.

Claussen, Detlev. One Last Genius. Livingstone, Rodney, tr. from GER. 2010. Orig. Title: Theodor W. Adorno: ein letztes Genie. (ENG., Illus.). 464p. pap. 22.95 *(978-0-674-05713-5(9)*, Belknap Pr.) Harvard Univ. Pr.

—Theodor W. Adorno: One Last Genius. Livingstone, Rodney, tr. from GER. 2008. Orig. Title: Theodor W. Adorno: ein letztes Genie. (Illus.). 464p. 35.00 *(978-0-674-02618-6(7)*, Belknap Pr.) Harvard Univ. Pr.

Cook, Deborah. Adorno Habermas & the Search for A Rational Society. 2012. (ENG.). 240p. (C). pap. 42.95 ***(978-0-415-61922-6(X))*** Routledge.

—Adorno on Nature. 2011. (ENG.). 240p. (C). 90.00 *(978-1-84465-255-6(6))*; pap. 29.95 *(978-1-84465-262-4(9))* Acumen Publishing, Ltd. GBR. Dist: McGill-Queen's Univ. Pr.

—Theodor Adorno: Key Concepts. 2008. (ENG.). 224p. (C). pap. *(978-1-84465-120-7(7))* McGill-Queen's Univ. Pr.

Corse, Sandra. Craft Objects, Aesthetic Contexts: Kant, Heidegger, & Adorno on Craft. 2008. (ENG.). 110p. pap. 26.50 *(978-0-7618-4287-3(X))* Univ. Pr. of America, Inc.

Cunningham, David & Mapp, Nigel, eds. Adorno & Literature. 2009. (ENG.). 224p. 39.95 *(978-0-8264-0368-1(9))* Continuum International Publishing Group, Ltd. GBR. Dist: National Bk. Network.

Dineen, Murray. Friendly Remainders: Essays in Music Criticism after Adorno. 2011. (ENG., Illus.). 256p. (C). ***(978-0-7735-3884-9(4))***; pap. ***(978-0-7735-3919-8(0))*** McGill-Queen's Univ. Pr.

Djerassi, Carl. Four Jews on Parnassus - A Conversation Vol. 1: Benjamin, Adorno, Scholem, Schönberg. 2008. (ENG., Illus.). 232p. (gr. 17). 29.50 *(978-0-231-14654-8(X))* Columbia Univ. Pr.

Foster, Roger. Adorno: The Recovery of Experience. 2008. x, 236p. pap. 29.95 *(978-0-7914-7210-1(8))* 2007. 236p. 70.00 *(978-0-7914-7209-5(4))* State Univ. of New York Pr.

Gerhardt, Christina, et al, contrib. by. Adorno & Ethics, Vol. 33. 2006. (ENG.). 192p. (C). pap. 14.00 *(978-0-8223-6659-1(2))* Duke Univ. Pr.

Glazer, Aubrey L. A New Physiognomy of Jewish Thinking: Critical Theory after Adorno as Applied to Jewish Thought. 2011. (Continuum Studies in Jewish Thought Ser.). (ENG.). 224p. 130.00 *(978-1-4411-3398-4(4))* Continuum International Publishing Group, Ltd. GBR. Dist: National Bk. Network.

Hainz, Martin. Entgöttertes Leid: Zur Lyrik Rose Ausländers unter Berücksichtigung der Poetologie von Theodor W. Adorno, Peter Szondi und Jaques Derrida. 2007. (Conditio Judaica Ser.). (GER.). VI, 468p. pap. *(978-3-484-65165-4(2))* Verlag Max Niemeyer.

Hansen, Miriam Bratu. Cinema & Experience: Siegfried Kracauer, Walter Benjamin, & Theodor W. Adorno. Dimendberg, Edward, ed. 2011. (Weimar & Now: German Cultural Criticism Ser.). (ENG.). 368p. 70.00 *(978-0-520-26559-2(9))*; pap. 29.95 *(978-0-520-26560-8(2))* Univ. of California Pr.

Helmling, Steven. Adorno's Poetics of Critique. 2011. (ENG.). 210p. pap. 44.95 ***(978-1-4411-1964-3(7))*** Continuum International Publishing Group, Ltd. GBR. Dist: National Bk. Network.

Helmling, Steven & Helmling. Adorno's Poetics of Critique. 2009. (Continuum Studies in Continental Philosophy Ser.). (ENG.). 224p. 130.00 *(978-0-8264-4888-6(4))* Continuum International Publishing Group, Ltd. GBR. Dist: National Bk. Network.

Hullot-Kentor, Robert. Things Beyond Resemblance: Collected Essays on Theodor W. Adorno. (Columbia Themes in Philosophy, Social Criticism, & the Arts Ser.). (ENG.). 344p. (gr. 17). 2008. pap. 27.00 *(978-0-231-13659-4(5))* 2006. (Illus.). 85.00 *(978-0-231-13658-7(7))* Columbia Univ. Pr.

Jameson, Fredric & Jameson, Fredric. Late Marxism: Adorno or the Persistence of the Dialectic. 2007. (Radical Thinkers Ser.: Vol. 18). (ENG.). 270p. per. 12.95 *(978-1-84467-575-3(0)*, 844575) Verso Bks. GBR. Dist: Norton, W. W. & Co., Inc.

Jarvis, Ana C. Theodor Adorno, 4 vols. 2006. (Illus.). Vol. 1. 288p. *(978-0-415-30465-8(2))* Vol. 2. 464p. *(978-0-415-30466-5(0))* Vol. 4. 384p. *(978-0-415-30468-9(7))* Routledge.

—Theodor Adorno Vol. 3: Critical Evaluations Cultural Theory, 4 vols. 2006. (Illus.). 448p. *(978-0-415-30467-2(9))* Routledge.

Jarvis, Simon, ed. Theodor Adorno, 4 vols. 2006. (Critical Evaluations in Cultural Theory Ser.). (Illus.). 1584p. 1440.00 *(978-0-415-30464-1(4))* Routledge.

Jenemann, David. Adorno in America. 2007. (Illus.). 320p. 66.00 *(978-0-8166-4808-5(5))*; 280p. per. 22.95 *(978-0-8166-4809-2(3))* Univ. of Minnesota Pr.

Lawrence, Nick. How to Read Adorno & Horkheimer's Dialectic of Enlightenment, 1 vol. 2012. (How to Read Theory Ser.). (ENG.). 150p. 22.00 ***(978-0-7453-3034-1(7))***; lib. bdg. 75.00 ***(978-0-7453-3035-8(5))*** Pluto Pr. GBR. Dist: Macmillan.

League, Kathleen. Adorno, Radical Negativity, & Cultural Critique: Utopia in the Map of the World. 2010. (ENG.). 174p. 60.00 *(978-0-7391-5037-5(5))* Lexington Bks.

Lonitz, Henri, et al. Correspondence, 1943-1955. 2006. (ENG., Illus.). 144p. pap. 14.95 *(978-0-7456-3200-1(9))* Polity Pr. GBR. Dist: Wiley, John & Sons, Inc.

Macdonald, Iain & Ziarek, Krzysztof, eds. Adorno & Heidegger: Philosophical Questions. 2007. (ENG.). 240p. 60.00 *(978-0-8047-5635-8(X))* Stanford Univ. Pr.

McNamara, Andrew. An Apprehensive Aesthetic: The Legacy of Modernist Culture. 2009. (Illus.). 293p. pap. *(978-3-03911-720-8(3))* Lang, Peter.

Morgan, Alastair. Adorno's Concept of Life. 2007. (Continuum Studies in Continental Philosophy). (ENG.). 176p. 140.00 *(978-0-8264-9613-3(X))* Continuum International Publishing Group, Ltd. GBR. Dist: National Bk. Network.

Muller-Doohm, Stefan. Adorno: A Biography. Livingstone, Rodney, tr. from GER. 2009. (ENG., Illus.). 648p. pap. 29.95 *(978-0-7456-3109-7(6))* Polity Pr. GBR. Dist: Wiley, John & Sons, Inc.

O'Connor, Brian. Adorno. 2012. (Routledge Philosophers Ser.). (ENG.). 224p. (C). 120.00 *(978-0-415-36735-6(2))*; pap. 29.95 *(978-0-415-36736-3(0))* Routledge.

Ombrosi, Orietta. The Twilight of Reason: Benjamin, Adorno, Horkheimer & Levinas Tested by the Catastrophe. 2011. (Emunot: Jewish Philosophy & Kabbalah Ser.). (ENG.). 200p. 65.00 ***(978-1-936235-75-9(7))*** Academic Studies Pr.

Osborne, Thomas. The Structure of Modern Cultural Theory. 2011. (ENG.). 192p. pap. 24.95 ***(978-0-7190-8646-5(9))*** Manchester Univ. Pr. GBR. Dist: Macmillan.

Plass, Ulrich. Language & History in Adorno's Notes to Literature. 2012. (ENG.). 160p. pap. 39.95 ***(978-0-415-53590-8(5))*** Routledge.

Plass, Ulrich. Language & History in Theodore W. Adorno's Notes to Literature. annot. ed. 2006. (ENG.). 160p. 125.00 *(978-0-415-97837-8(8))* Routledge.

Rensmann, Lars & Gandesha, Samir. Arendt & Adorno: Political & Philosophical Investigations. 2012. (ENG.). 368p. 85.00 ***(978-0-8047-7539-7(7))***; pap. 24.95 ***(978-0-8047-7540-3(0))*** Stanford Univ. Pr.

Richter, Gerhard. Thought-Images: Frankfurt School Writers' Reflections from Damaged Life. 2007. (Cultural Memory in the Present Ser.). (ENG., Illus.). 256p. 65.00 *(978-0-8047-5616-7(3))*; per. 24.95 *(978-0-8047-5617-4(1))* Stanford Univ. Pr.

Richter, Gerhard, ed. Language Without Soil: Adorno & Late Philosophical Modernity. 2009. (ENG.). 288p. 80.00 *(978-0-8232-3126-3(7))*; pap. 28.00 *(978-0-8232-3127-0(5))* Fordham Univ. Pr.

Savage, Robert. Hölderlin after the Catastrophe: Heidegger - Adorno - Brecht. 2008. (Studies in German Literature Linguistics & Culture Ser.: Volume 24). 250p. 80.00 *(978-1-57113-320-5(8))* Camden Hse.

Schmidt, James, ed. Theodor Adorno. 2007. (International Library of Essays in the History of Social & Political Thought Ser.). 566p. 300.00 *(978-0-7546-2699-2(7))* Ashgate Publishing Co.

Schweppenhäuser, Gerhard. Theodor W. Adorno: An Introduction. Rolleston, James, tr. from GER. 2009. (Post-Contemporary Interventions Ser.). (ENG.). 200p. 79.95 *(978-0-8223-4454-4(8))*; pap. 22.95 *(978-0-8223-4471-1(8))* Duke Univ. Pr.

Sharma, B. R. The Death of Art. 2006. (ENG.). 106p. per. 27.50 *(978-0-7618-3466-3(4))* Univ. Pr. of America, Inc.

Sherman, David. Sartre & Adorno: The Dialectics of Subjectivity. 2008. x, 328p. pap. 29.95 *(978-0-7914-7116-6(0))* 2007. 328p. 85.00 *(978-0-7914-7115-9(2))* State Univ. of New York Pr.

Sherratt, Yvonne. Adorno's Positive Dialectic. 2007. (ENG.). 272p. pap. 58.00 *(978-0-521-03888-1(X))* Cambridge Univ. Pr.

Tarr, Zoltan. The Frankfurt School: The Critical Theories of Max Horkheimer & Theodor W. Adorno. 2011. (ENG., Illus.). 271p. pap. 34.95 *(978-1-4128-1834-6(6))* Transaction Pubs.

Wilson, Ross. Theodor Adorno. 2007. (Routledge Critical Thinkers Ser.). (ENG.). 160p. (C). 100.00 *(978-0-415-41818-8(6)*, 04154`8186); XIV, 146p. 22.95 *(978-0-415-41819-5(4)*, 0415418194) Routledge.

Wu, Jing. The Logic of Difference in Deleuze & Adorno. 2011. 160p. pap. ***(978-3-8443-8054-5(X))*** Lambert Academic Publishing.

Ziarek, Krzysztof & MacDonald, Iain, eds. Adorno & Heidegger: Philosophical Questions. 2007. (ENG.). 240p. per. 21.95 *(978-0-8047-5636-5(8))* Stanford Univ. Pr.

Zuidervaart, Lambert. Social Philosophy after Adorno. 2007. (ENG.). 232p. (C). 88.99 *(978-0-521-87027-6(5))*; per. 28.99 *(978-0-521-69038-6(2))* Cambridge Univ. Pr.

ADR (DISPUTE RESOLUTION)

see Dispute Resolution (Law)

ADRENAL CORTEX

see also Adrenocortical Hormones

Bronstein, Marcello D., ed. Cushing's Syndrome: Pathophysiology, Diagnosis & Treatment. 2010. (Contemporary Endocrinology Ser.). (ENG., Illus.). 350p. 259.00 *(978-1-60327-448-7(0)*, 1603274480) Humana Pr.

Flück, C. E. & Miller, W. L., eds. Disorders of the Human Adrenal Cortex. 2008. (Endocrine Development Ser.). (Illus.). 96p. *(978-3-8055-8580-4(2))* Karger, S. AG.

Inoue, Yuuki & Watanabe, Kouki. Adverse Effects of Steroids. 2008. 129.00 *(978-1-60456-880-6(1))* Nova Science Pubs., Inc.

Margioris, Andrew N. & Chrousos, George P., eds. Adrenal Disorders. 2010. (Contemporary Endocrinology Ser.). (Illus.). 416p. pap. 199.00 *(978-1-61737-029-8(0)*, 1617370290) Humana Pr.

ADRENAL CORTEX HORMONES

see Adrenocortical Hormones

ADRENAL GLANDS

see also Adrenal Cortex

Azziz, Ricardo, ed. Androgen Excess Disorders in Women. 2010. (Contemporary Endocrinology Ser.). (Illus.). 488p. pap. 209.00 *(978-1-61737-704-4(X)*, 161737704X) Humana Pr.

Azziz, Ricardo, et al. Androgen Excess Disorders in Women: Polycystic Ovary Syndrome & Other Disorders. 2nd ed. 2006. (Contemporary Endocrinology Ser.). (Illus.). 466p. 209.00 *(978-1-58829-663-4(6)*, 1588296636) Humana Pr.

Blake, Michael A. & Boland, Giles W. L. Adrenal Imaging. 2009. (Contemporary Medical Imaging Ser.). (Illus.). x, 224p. 199.00 *(978-1-934115-86-2(X))* Humana Pr.

Hammer, Gary D. Adrenocortical Carcinoma: Basic Science & Clinical Concepts. 2010. (ENG., Illus.). xv, 546p. 209.00 *(978-0-387-77235-6(9)*, 0387772359) Springer.

Harvey, Philip W., et al. Adrenal Toxicology. Harvey, Philip W. et al, eds. 2008. (Target Organ Toxicology Ser.: Vol. 26). (ENG., Illus.). 352p. 250.00 *(978-1-4200-5129-1(1))* CRC Pr. LLC.

Kiessling, Silke. Functional Analysis of the Adrenal Circadian Clock. 2011. 164p. pap. ***(978-3-8381-2306-6(9))*** Südwestdeutscher Verlag für Hochschulschriften AG & Co. KG.

Kohn, Taylor. Anp Inhibits the Production of Aldosterone in Rat Adrenal Glands. 2011. 68p. pap. ***(978-3-8454-0885-9(5))*** Lambert Academic Publishing.

Linos, Dimitrios A. & Heerden, Jon A. van, eds. Adrenal Glands: Diagnostic Aspects & Surgical Therapy. 2010. (Illus.). xv, 362p. pap. 289.00 *(978-3-642-07432-5(4)*, 3642074324) Springer.

Margioris, Andrew N. & Chrousos, George P., eds. Adrenal Disorders. 2010. (Contemporary Endocrinology Ser.). (Illus.). 416p. pap. 199.00 *(978-1-61737-029-8(0)*, 1617370290) Humana Pr.

Pick, Marcelle. Are You Tired & Wired? Your Proven 30-Day Program for Overcoming Adrenal Fatigue & Feeling Fantastic Again. 2011. (ENG.). 256p. 24.95 *(978-1-4019-2819-3(6))* Hay Hse., Inc.

Simpson, Kathryn R. Overcoming Adrenal Fatigue: How to Restore Hormonal Balance & Feel Renewed, Energized, & Stress Free. 2011. (ENG.). 160p. pap. 21.95 *(978-1-57224-952-3(8))* New Harbinger Pubns.

Valeri, Andrea, et al, eds. Surgery of the Adrenal Gland. 2012. (ENG., Illus.). ix, 175p. 189.00 ***(978-88-470-2585-1(0)***, 8847025850) Springer.

ADRENAL STEROIDS

see Adrenocortical Hormones; Steroids

ADRENALINE

see also Adrenergic Mechanisms

Lawson, Arnold G. & Gorman, Roger I. Research Progress on Epinephrine. 2008. (Illus.). xii, 161p. (C). 185.00 *(978-1-60456-443-3(1))* Nova Science Pubs., Inc.

ADRENERGIC AGENTS

see Sympathomimetic Agents

ADRENERGIC MECHANISMS

see also Adrenaline

Perez, Dianne M., ed. The Adrenergic Receptors: In the 21st Century. 2010. (Receptors Ser.). (Illus.). 416p. pap. 189.00 *(978-1-61737-559-0(4)*, 1617375594) Humana Pr.

ADRENOCORTICAL HORMONES

see also Aldosterone; Cortisone

Azziz, Ricardo, et al. Androgen Excess Disorders in Women: Polycystic Ovary Syndrome & Other Disorders. 2nd ed. 2006. (Contemporary Endocrinology Ser.). (Illus.). 466p. 209.00 *(978-1-58829-663-4(6)*, 1588296636) Humana Pr.

Inoue, Yuuki & Watanabe, Kouki. Adverse Effects of Steroids. 2008. 129.00 *(978-1-60456-880-6(1))* Nova Science Pubs., Inc.

Judd, Lewis L. & Sternberg, Esther M., eds. Glucocorticoids & Mood: Clinical Manifestations, Risk Factors & Molecular Mechanisms. 2009. (Annals of the New York Academy of Sciences Ser.: 37). (ENG., Illus.). 352p. pap. 134.95 *(978-1-57331-748-1(9)*, Wiley-Blackwell) Wiley, John & Sons, Inc.

Krakoff, Lawrence. Endocrine Hypertension , an Issue of Endocrinology Clinics. 2011. (Clinics: Internal Medicine Ser.: 40-2). (ENG.). 213p. 110.00 *(978-1-4557-0441-5(5)*, Saunders) Elsevier - Health Sciences Div.

Krane, Stephen M., ed. Advances in Corticosteroids: A Seminar in Print. (Illus.). 80p. (Orig.). pap. *(978-0-941741-04-0(4))* Adis Pr. International, Inc.

Maibach, Howard I. & Surber, C., eds. Topical Corticosteroids. (Illus.). *(978-3-8055-5332-2(3))* Karger, S. AG.

Pelt, Annemarie C., ed. Glucocorticoids: Effects, Action Mechanisms, & Therapeutic Uses. 2010. (Biochemistry Research Trends Ser.). 129.00 *(978-1-61728-758-9(X)*, Nova Biomedical Bks.) Nova Science Pubs., Inc.

Shirtcliff, Elizabeth. A Latent State Trait Model of Cortisol in Normally Developing Youth. 2009. 180p. pap. *(978-3-8364-9158-7(3))* VDM Verlag Dr. Mueller e.K.

Watson, Ronald Ross, ed. Dhea in Human Health & Aging. 2011. (ENG., Illus.). 472p. 149.95 *(978-1-4398-3883-9(6)*, CRC Press) Taylor & Francis Group GBR. Dist: Taylor & Francis Group.

ADULT-CHILD RELATIONSHIPS

see Children and Adults

ADRIATIC SEA

Cushman-Roisin, Benoit, et al, eds. Physical Oceanography of the Adriatic Sea: Past, Present & Future. 2010. 320p. pap. 129.00 *(978-90-481-5921-5(0),* 9048159210) Springer.

Forenbaher, Staso. A Connecting Sea: Maritime Interaction in Adriatic Prehistory. 2009. (Bar S Ser.). (ENG., Illus.). 155p. (C). pap. 87.50 *(978-1-4073-0614-8(6))* British Archaeological Reports Ltd. GBR. Dist: Brown, David Bk. Co., The.

Luni, Mario. I Greci in Adriatico Nell'età Dei Kouroi. 2007. (Quaderni Di Archeologia Nelle Marche Ser.: Vol. 13). (FRE & ITA., Illus.). 418p. *(978-88-392-0819-4(4))* Quattroventi.

Petri, Rolf. Nostalgia: Memoria e Passaggi Tra le Sponde Dell'Adriatico. 2010. (ITA.). xii, 276p. *(978-88-6372-113-3(0))* Storia e Letteratura.

Romanis, Giorgio De. The Bridge on the Adriatic Sea. 2010. (ENG., Illus.). 176p. *(978-88-7685-176-6(3),* Edizioni L'archivolto (Acc)) Antique Collectors' Club.

Whallon, Robert, ed. Late Paleolithic Environments & Cultural Relations Around the Adriatic / Environements du Paleolithique Final et Rapports Culturels Autour de L'Adriatique. 2007. (Bar S Ser.) (Illus.). 65p. (C). 62.50 *(978-1-4073-0160-0(8))* British Archaeological Reports Ltd. GBR. Dist: Brown, David Bk. Co., The.

Zaccaroni, Annalisa, et al, eds. Heavy Metals in Dolphins from the Northern Adriatic Sea & Potential Subtle Toxic Effects. 2011. (Marine Biology Ser.). 68p. pap. 43.00 *(978-1-61209-935-4(1))* Nova Science Pubs., Inc.

ADSORPTION

see also Adhesion; Carbon, Activated; Ion Exchange; Permeability; Porosity; Wetting Agents

Bottani, Eduardo J. & Tascón, Juan, eds. Adsorption by Carbons. 2008. (ENG., Illus.). 776p. 250.00 *(978-0-08-044464-2(4),* Elsevier Science) Elsevier Science & Technology Bks.

Byern, Janek & Grunwald, Ingo, eds. Adhesion Phenomena in Nature: From Structure to Application. 2010. (ENG., Illus.). xi, 305p. 209.00 *(978-3-7091-0141-4(7),* 3709101417) Springer.

Condon, James B. Surface Area & Porosity Determinations by Physisorption: Measurements & Theory. 2006. (ENG., Illus.). 296p. 205.00 *(978-0-444-51964-1(5),* Elsevier Science) Elsevier Science & Technology Bks.

Davankov, Vadim & Tsyurupa, Maria P. Hypercrosslinked Polymeric Networks & Adsorbing Materials: Synthesis, Properties, Structure, & Applications. 2010. (Comprehensive Analytical Chemistry Ser.: 56). (ENG., Illus.). 672p. 255.00 *(978-0-444-53700-3(7))* Elsevier Science & Technology Bks.

Davison, Sydney G. & Sulston, Kenneth. W. Green Function Theory of Chemisorption. 2006. (Illus.). xx, 212p. 199.00 *(978-1-4020-4404-5(6),* 1402044046) Springer.

Déjardin, Philippe, ed. Proteins at Solid-Liquid Interfaces. 2010. (Principles & Practice Ser.). (Illus.). xvi, 330p. pap. 279.00 *(978-3-642-06913-0(4),* 3642069134) Springer.

Dunne, Lawrence J. & Manos, George. Adsorption & Phase Behaviour in Nanochannels & Nanotubes. 2009. (ENG., Illus.). x, 295p. 199.00 *(978-90-481-2480-0(8),* 9048124808) Springer.

Interfacial Rheology. 2009. (ENG.). 680p. 284.00 *(978-90-04-17586-0(5),* CRC Press) Taylor & Francis Group GBR. Dist: Taylor & Francis Group.

Karge, H. G. & Weitkamp, J. Adsorption & Diffusion. 2008. (Molecular Sieves Ser.). (Illus.). xiii, 400p. 419.00 *(978-3-540-73965-4(3))* Springer.

Karge, Hellmut G. & Weitkamp, Jens, eds. Adsorption & Diffusion. 2010. (Molecular Sieves Ser.). (Illus.). xv, 400p. pap. 419.00 *(978-3-642-09326-5(4),* 3642093264) Springer.

Knerr, Robert. Integrin-Mediated Interactions Between Cells & Biomimetic Materials. 2008. 232p. pap. *(978-3-639-04200-9(X))* VDM Verlag Dr. Mueller e.K.

Kosmulski, Marek. Surface Charging & Points of Zero Charge. 2009. (Surfactant Science Ser.). (ENG., Illus.). 1092p. 205.95 *(978-1-4200-5188-9(1),* CRC Press) Taylor & Francis Group GBR. Dist: Taylor & Francis Group.

Lam, Koon Fung. Selective Adsorption of Metal Ions by Nano- Structured Materials. 2010. 236p. pap. *(978-3-8383-0191-4(9))* Lambert Academic Publishing.

Lambert, R. M. & Pacchioni, Gianfranco, eds. Chemisorption & Reactivity on Supported Clusters & Thin Films: Towards an Understanding of Microscopic Processes in Catalysis. 2010. (NATO Science Series E: (closed) Ser.). 526p. pap. 449.00 *(978-90-481-4807-3(3),* 9048148073) Springer.

Liu, Yu & Wang, Jianlong, eds. Fundamentals & Applications of Biosorption Isotherms, Kinetics & Thermodynamics. 2009. (Illus.). vii, 294p. 89.00 *(978-1-60741-169-7(5))* Nova Science Pubs., Inc.

Lyubchik, Svetlana & Mota, José P. B. Recent Advances in Adsorption Processes for Environmental Protection & Security: [proceedings of the NATO Advanced Research Workshop on Recent Advances in Adsorption Processes for Environmental Protection & Security, Kyiv, Ukraine, 9-12 September 2006]. Mota, José Paulo & Lyubchik, Svetlana, eds. 2007. (NATO Science for Peace & Security Series / NATO Science for Peace & Security Series C: Environmental Security Ser.). (Illus.). XIV, 192p. 189.00 *(978-1-4020-6803-4(4),* 1402068034) Springer.

Miller, R. & Liggieri, L. Bubble & Drop Interfaces. 2011. (ENG.). 560p. 277.00 *(978-90-04-17495-5(8),* CRC Press) Taylor & Francis Group GBR. Dist: Taylor & Francis Group.

Mota, José Paulo & Lyubchik, Svetlana, eds. Recent Advances in Adsorption Processes for Environmental Protection & Security. 2007. (NATO Science for Peace & Security Series / NATO Science for Peace & Security Series C: Environmental Security Ser.). (ENG., Illus.). XIV, 192p. pap. 79.95 *(978-1-4020-6804-1(2),* 1402068042) Springer.

Ng, Kim Choon & Saha, Budyut Baran, eds. Advances in Adsorption Technology. 2010. (Chemistry Research & Applications Ser.). (Illus.). 567p. 145.00 *(978-1-60876-833-2(3))* Nova Science Pubs., Inc.

Richard, Buamah. Adsorptive Removal of Manganese Arsenic & Iron from Groundwater. 2009. (ENG., Illus.). 198p. pap. 75.95 *(978-0-415-57379-5(3),* CRC Press) Taylor & Francis Group GBR. Dist: Taylor & Francis Group.

Roque-Malherbe, Rolando. Adsorption & Diffusion in Nanoporous Materials. 2007. (ENG., Illus.). 288p. 144.95 *(978-1-4200-4675-5(6),* CRC Press) Taylor & Francis Group GBR. Dist: Taylor & Francis Group.

Ruette, F., ed. Quantum Chemistry Approaches to Chemisorption & Heterogeneous Catalysis. 2010. (Understanding Chemical Reactivity Ser.). 388p. pap. 319.00 *(978-90-481-4109-8(5),* 9048141095) Springer.

Ruso, Juan & Piñeiro, Ángel. Proteins in Solution & at Interfaces: Properties & Applications. 2012. (Wiley Series on Surface & Interfacial Chemistry Ser.). (ENG.). 508p. 149.95 ***(978-0-470-95251-1(2),*** Wiley) Wiley, John & Sons, Inc.

Sun, Shi-Gang, et al, eds. In-Situ Spectroscopic Studies of Adsorption at the Electrode & Electrocatalysis. 2007. (ENG., Illus.). 558p. 250.00 *(978-0-444-51870-5(3),* Elsevier Science) Elsevier Science & Technology Bks.

Zhou & Zhou, Li. Adsorption: Progress in Fundamental & Application Research: Selected Reports at the 4th Pacific Basin Conference on Adsorption Science & Technology: Tianjin, China, 22-26 May 2006. 2007. (Illus.). 137.00 *(978-981-277-025-7(9))* World Scientific Publishing Co., Inc.

ADSORPTION IN SOILS

see Soil Absorption and Adsorption

ADSORPTION OF GASES

see Gases—Absorption and Adsorption

ADULT ADOPTEES

see Adoptees

ADULT AND CHILD

see Children and Adults

ADULT ATTENTION-DEFICIT DISORDER

see Attention-Deficit Disorder in Adults

ADULT CHILD ABUSE VICTIMS

Here are entered works on adults who were abused as children. Works on children who are victims of child abuse are entered under Abused Children.

see also Abused Children; Adult Child Sexual Abuse Victims

Anderson, Kim M. Enhancing Resilience in Survivors of Family Violence. 2009. 264p. *(978-0-8261-1139-5(4))* Springer.

Andrews, Sophie. Scarred: How One Girl Triumphed over Shocking Abuse & Self-Harm. 2008. (ENG.). 270p. 25.95 *(978-0-340-93735-8(1),* Hodder & Stoughton) Hodder General Publishing Div. GBR. Dist: Independent Pubs. Group.

—Scarred: She Was a Slave to Her Father, Pain Was Her Only Escape. 2009. (ENG.). 336p. pap. 12.95 *(978-0-340-93737-2(8),* Hodder & Stoughton) Hodder General Publishing Div. GBR. Dist: Independent Pubs. Group.

Ann Cathrine. Beautiful Buttons: A Memoir of Survival & Triumph. 2011. 334p. pap. ***(978-1-926645-62-9(6))*** BPS Bks.

Atkinson, Sue. Breaking the Chains of Abuse: A Practical Guide for Survivors. 2006. (ENG., Illus.). 208p. per. 13.95 *(978-0-7459-5135-5(X))* Lion Hudson PLC GBR. Dist: Independent Pubs. Group.

Baadsgaard, Janene Wolsey. Healing from Abuse: How the Atonement of Jesus Christ Can Heal Broken Lives & Broken Hearts. 2007. pap. 16.95 *(978-1-59038-714-6(7))* Deseret Bk. Co.

Banyard, Victoria L. Trauma & Physical Health: Understanding the Effects of Extreme Stress & of Psychological Harm. Edwards, Valerie J. & Kendall-Tackett, Kathleen A., eds. 2009. (Illus.). XIV, 258p. 140.00 *(978-0-415-48078-9(7));* pap. 39.95 *(978-0-415-48079-6(5))* Routledge.

Barth, Amy. 101 Tips for Survivors of Sexual Abuse: A Pocket Book of Wisdom. 2009. pap. *(978-1-932690-94-1(8))* Loving Healing Pr., Inc.

Bass, Ellen & Davis, Laura. The Courage to Heal: A Guide for Women Survivors of Child Sexual Abuse. 4th anniv. ed. 2008. (ENG.). 640p. pap. 22.99 *(978-0-06-128433-5(5),* HarperPerennial) HarperCollins Pubs.

Bennett, Lori. Dynamic Psychotherapy with Adult Survivors: Living Past Neglect. 2012. (ENG.). 220p. (gr. 17). 65.00 ***(978-0-7657-0892-2(2),*** Aronson, Jason) Rowman & Littlefield Publishers, Inc.

Borgstedt, John. I Love You Mom: Please Don't Break My Heart. 2009. 108p. 24.99 *(978-1-4490-4443-5(3))* AuthorHouse.

Bratcher, Sarah. Freed to Tell. 2009. 216p. pap. 15.99 *(978-1-60791-366-5(6))* Xulon Pr., Inc.

Brightwell, Lanette Hill. Caught up in Life's Web. 2008. 68p. pap. 38.60 *(978-1-4357-3507-1(2))* Lulu Enterprises Inc.

Brown, Annette. The Most Hateful Child God Ever Put Breath Into. 2006. 188p. pap. *(978-1-84401-770-6(2))* Athena Pr.

Caulkett, Lynne M. Requiem of Innocence: Fortitude of a Champion. 2007. 231p. per. 18.99 *(978-1-59824-465-6(5))* E-BookTime LLC.

Cedeno, Elna V. Stop the Silence: Can You Hear Us? 2006. 15.95 *(978-0-9773476-0-5(5))* Cedeno, Elna V.

Chivell, Rachel & Chapel, Alix. The Throwaway Boy. 2008. (ENG.). 288p. 29.95 *(978-1-84454-565-0(2))* Blake, John Publishing, Ltd. GBR. Dist: Independent Pubs. Group.

Chu, James A. Rebuilding Shattered Lives: Treating Complex PTSD & Dissociative Disorders. 2nd ed. 2011. (ENG., Illus.). 366p. pap. 58.00 *(978-0-470-76874-7(6),* Wiley) Wiley, John & Sons, Inc.

Coates, Jan. Set Free: God's Healing Power for Abuse Survivors & Those Who Love Them. 2007. 184p. per. 13.99 *(978-1-57921-912-3(8))* WinePress Publishing.

Cohn, Ruth. Coming Home to Passion: Restoring Loving Sexuality in Couples with Histories of Childhood Trauma & Neglect, 1 vol. 2011. (Sex, Love, & Psychology Ser.). 167p. 34.95 *(978-0-313-39212-2(9),* A3233C, Praeger Pubs.) Greenwood Publishing Group, Inc.

Colarusso, Calvin A. The Long Shadow of Sexual Abuse: Developmental Effects Across the Life Cycle. 2010. (ENG.). 202p. 55.00 *(978-0-7657-0766-6(7),* Aronson, Jason) Rowman & Littlefield Publishers, Inc.

Connolly, Paul. Against All Odds. 2010. (ENG.). 278p. pap. 12.95 *(978-1-84454-905-4(4))* Blake, John Publishing, Ltd. GBR. Dist: Independent Pubs. Group.

Coppinger, Maureen. Annie's Girl: How an Abandoned Orphan Finally Discovered the Truth about Her Mother. 2010. (ENG., Illus.). 432p. pap. 14.95 *(978-1-84596-579-2(5))* Mainstream Publishing Co., Ltd. GBR. Dist: Independent Pubs. Group.

—Annie's Girl: How an Abandoned Orphan Finally Found the Truth about Her Mother. 2009. (ENG., Illus.). 432p. pap. 22.95 *(978-1-84596-493-1(4))* Mainstream Publishing Co., Ltd. GBR. Dist: Independent Pubs. Group.

Cram101 Textbook Reviews & Cram101 Textbook Reviews. Outlines & Highlights for Introduction to Working with Adult Survivors of Childhood Traum: Technique by Carolyn Knight, ISBN. 2011. 60p. pap. 26.95 ***(978-1-4288-7924-9(2))*** Cram101 Inc.

Crittenden, Patricia McKinsey. Raising Parents: Attachment, Parenting & Child Safety. 2008. (ENG., Illus.). 400p. 210.00 *(978-1-84392-499-9(4))* Routledge.

Daniel, Sarah. Leaving Abuse Behind. 2007. 56p. per. 12.95 *(978-1-59858-479-0(0))* Dog Ear Publishing, LLC.

Davis, Gerry. A Promise to Protect: The Abuse Survivor's Handbook. 2011. 210p. pap. 19.99 ***(978-1-257-01487-3(0))*** Lulu Enterprises Inc.

Degun-Mather, Marcia. Hypnosis, Dissociation & Survivors of Child Abuse: Understanding & Treatment. 2006. (ENG., Illus.). 256p. 155.00 *(978-0-470-03254-1(5));* per. 62.95 *(978-0-470-01945-0(X))* Wiley, John & Sons, Inc. (Wiley).

Dickson Wright, Clarissa. Spilling the Beans: The Autobiography of One of Television's Two Fat Ladies. 2010. (ENG.). 336p. (gr. 12). 29.95 *(978-1-59020-296-8(1))* Overlook Pr., The.

Doyle, Kenneth, et al. Mother from Hell: Two Brothers; A Sadistic Mother; A Childhood Destroyed. 2009. (ENG., Illus.). 254p. pap. 18.95 ***(978-1-84717-143-6(5))*** O'Brien Pr., Ltd., The IRL. Dist: Dufour Editions, Inc.

Elliott, Jane & Crofts, Andrew. The Little Prisoner: A Memoir. 2008. 288p. pap. 13.99 *(978-0-06-156131-3(2),* Harper Paperbacks) HarperCollins Pubs.

Estrup, Carole. Barefoot Girl Out of Ohio. 2007. 408p. per. 25.95 *(978-0-595-43694-1(3))* iUniverse, Inc.

Fieldhouse, C. Why Do Monsters Come Out at Night. 2007. xi, 281p. *(978-1-4019-1544-5(2),* 463) Hay Hse. UK, Ltd. GBR. Dist: Grantham Bk. Services.

Ford, Donna. The Step Child. l.t. ed. 2007. (Ulverscroft Nonfiction Ser.). 352p. 32.50 *(978-1-84617-705-7(7))* Ulverscroft Large Print Bks., Ltd.

—What Daddy Did: The Shocking True Story of a Little Girl Betrayed. 2009. (ENG.). 288p. pap. 13.95 *(978-0-09-192403-4(0))* Random Hse. GBR. Dist: Independent Pubs. Group.

Ford, Donna & Watson-Brown, Linda. The Step Child: A True Story of a Broken Childhood. 2007. (ENG.). 224p. pap. 14.95 *(978-0-09-191049-5(8))* Random Hse. GBR. Dist: Independent Pubs. Group.

—What Daddy Did: The Shocking True Story of a Little Girl Betrayed. 2008. (ENG.). 208p. 23.95 *(978-0-09-192402-7(2))* Random Hse. GBR. Dist: Independent Pubs. Group.

Fournier, Delaine C. Cracked Vessel. 14.00 *(978-0-9719152-0-6(2))* Fournier, Delaine C.

Garner, The Greatest Painful Blessings Scott. The Greatest PAINFUL Blessings. 2010. 71p. pap. 10.60 *(978-0-557-10981-4(7))* Lulu Enterprises Inc.

Gilbert, Alloma. Deliver Me from Evil: A Sadistic Foster Mother, a Childhood Torn Apart. 2009. (ENG., Illus.). 288p. 17.95 *(978-0-330-45731-6(4),* Macmillan) Pan Macmillan GBR. Dist: Trans-Atlantic Pubns., Inc.

Gold, Jacqueline. Please Let It Stop: The True Story of My Abused Childhood. 2008. (ENG., Illus.). 288p. mass mkt. 13.95 *(978-0-09-192527-7(4))* Ebury Publishing GBR. Dist: Independent Pubs. Group.

Grey, William. The Devil Within. 2011. (Illus.). 107p. pap. 39.17 ***(978-1-4567-8589-5(3))*** AuthorHouse.

Hague, Gill, et al. The Experiences of Adult Survivors of Domestic Violence in Childhood: Strategies for Recovery for Children & Adults. 2012. (ENG.). 160p. pap. ***(978-1-84905-096-8(1))*** Kingsley, Jessica Ltd.

Hammond, Izzy & Potter, Robert. Someone to Watch over Me: The True Tale of a Survivor Haunted by the Demons of Abuse. 2007. (ENG.). 288p. mass mkt. 13.95 *(978-1-84596-258-6(3))* Mainstream Publishing Co., Ltd. GBR. Dist: Independent Pubs. Group.

Hart, Christine. Searching for Daddy: Looking for a Family, Longing for Love. 2008. (ENG.). 304p. 25.95 *(978-0-340-96226-8(7),* Hodder & Stoughton) Hodder General Publishing Div. GBR. Dist: Independent Pubs. Group.

Hart, Christine Joanna. Searching for Daddy. 2010. (ENG.). 320p. pap. *(978-0-340-91924-8(8))* Hodder & Stoughton Canada CAN. Dist: Hachette Bk. Group.

Hartzenberg, Joshua. Harry's Troubled Life. 2006. (ENG.). 96p. pap. 11.95 ***(978-0-86243-869-2(1))*** Y Lolfa GBR. Dist: Dufour Editions, Inc.

Heine, Steve. Lord, Please Don't Let Her See Me Cry. 2007. 242p. per. 14.99 *(978-1-60247-270-9(X))* Tate Publishing & Enterprises, LLC.

Henderson, Leon. Leon: A Lost Childhood. 2009. 224p. pap. 14.49 *(978-1-4389-8672-2(6))* AuthorHouse.

Holcy, Latasha. In His Hands. 2010. pap. 16.99 *(978-1-61566-400-9(9))* Tate Publishing & Enterprises, LLC.

Howarth, Stuart. I Just Wanted to Be Loved: A Boy Eager to Please - The Man Who Destroyed His Childhood - The Love That Overcame It. 2009. (ENG.). 288p. pap. 13.95 *(978-0-00-727170-2(0))* HarperCollins Pubs. Ltd. GBR. Dist: Independent Pubs. Group.

—Please, Daddy, No: A Boy Betrayed. 2007. (ENG.). 306p. pap. 13.95 *(978-0-00-723639-8(5))* HarperCollins Pubs. Ltd. GBR. Dist: Independent Pubs. Group.

Itzin, Catherine, et al. Domestic & Sexual Violence & Abuse. 2010. (ENG., Illus.). 240p. (C). pap. 42.95 *(978-0-415-55532-6(9))* Routledge.

—Domestic & Sexual Violence & Abuse: Tackling the Health & Mental Health Effects. 2010. (ENG., Illus.). 240p. (C). 125.00 *(978-0-415-55531-9(0))* Routledge.

Jackson, Brian W. From the Streets to the Pulpit. 2009. 112p. 29.99 *(978-1-4363-9140-5(7));* pap. 19.99 *(978-1-4363-9139-9(3))* Xlibris Corp.

Johnson, Mark. Wasted: A Childhood Stolen, an Innocence Betrayed, A Life Redeemed. 2009. (ENG.). 320p. pap. 14.95 *(978-1-60598-041-6(2),* 605041) Pegasus Bks.

Karras, Debra. Jagged Memories. 2007. 110p. pap. 12.95 *(978-0-7414-4251-2(5))* Infinity Publishing.

Kiser, Roger Dean. A Better Yesterday: Living Life after Abuse. 2010. (ENG.). 240p. pap. 12.95 *(978-0-7573-1360-8(4))* Health Communications, Inc.

Knight, Carolyn. Introduction to Working with Adult Survivors of Childhood Trauma: Techniques & Strategies. 2008. (Mental Health Practice Ser.). (ENG.). 256p. (C). per. 89.95 *(978-0-495-00618-3(1))* Wadsworth.

Knight, Michele. Touched by Evil: The True Story of the Psychic Powers That Saved Me from a Life of Abuse. 2008. (ENG.). 438p. pap. 13.95 *(978-0-340-95129-3(X),* Hodder & Stoughton) Hodder General Publishing Div. GBR. Dist: Independent Pubs. Group.

Landler, Christine & Martin, Sue. No Way Home: The Terrifying Story of Life in a Children's Home & a Little Girl's Struggle to Survive. 2007. (ENG.). 288p. pap. 14.95 *(978-0-09-191737-1(9))* Random Hse. GBR. Dist: Independent Pubs. Group.

Landon, Maria. Daddy's Little Earner: A Heartbreaking True Story of a Brave Little Girl's Escape from Violence. 2008. (ENG.). 352p. pap. 12.95 *(978-0-00-726877-1(7))* HarperCollins Pubs. Ltd. GBR. Dist: Independent Pubs. Group.

Lavett, Diane. A Still, Small Voice: Healing from Abuse. 2010. 332p. pap. 22.95 *(978-1-4502-1937-2(3))* iUniverse, Inc.

Lemoncelli, John J. Healing from Childhood Abuse: Understanding the Effects, Taking Control to Recover, 1 vol. 2012. 171p. 37.00 ***(978-0-313-39788-2(0),*** A3599C) Greenwood Publishing Group, Inc.

Madden, Amy. Stolen Beauty: Healing the Scars of Child Abuse: One Woman's Journey. 2007. 196p. per. 14.95 *(978-0-929636-74-0(0))* Syren Bk. Co.

Mahill, Wendy. Growing a Passionate Heart. 2007. 212p. per. 16.99 *(978-1-60266-461-6(7))* Xulon Pr., Inc.

Marie, Ellen. The Big Ugly: No Excuse for Murder? 2010. pap. 17.00 *(978-1-4349-9900-9(9),* RoseDog Bks.) Dorrance Publishing Co., Inc.

McCann, Richard. The Boy Grows Up: The Inspirational Story of His Journey from Broken Boy to Family Man. 2007. (ENG., Illus.). 304p. per. 12.95 *(978-0-09-190864-5(7))* Random Hse. GBR. Dist: Independent Pubs. Group.

Mccann, Richard. Into the Light. l.t. ed. 2007. 256p. 35.50 *(978-1-84617-693-7(X),* Charnwood) Ulverscroft Large Print Bks. GBR. Dist: Ulverscroft Large Print Bks., Ltd.

McDermott, Joe. Medical Mystery. 2010. 52p. pap. *(978-1-84748-550-2(2))* Athena Pr.

McLaren, Andy & Guidi, Mark. Tormented: The Andy McLaren Story. 2007. (ENG., Illus.). 224p. per. 19.95 *(978-1-84596-274-6(5))* Mainstream Publishing Co., Ltd. GBR. Dist: Independent Pubs. Group.

Miller, Alice. The Body Never Lies: The Lingering Effects of Hurtful Parenting. Jenkins, Andrew, tr. from GER. 2006. (ENG.). 224p. per. 15.95 *(978-0-393-32863-9(5),* 32863) Norton, W. W. & Co., Inc.

—Breaking down the Wall of Silence: The Liberating Experience of Facing Painful Truth. 2008. (ENG.). 186p. pap. 16.99 *(978-0-465-01504-7(2))* Basic Bks.

—Free from Lies: Discovering Your True Needs. Jenkins, Andrew, tr. from GER. 2010. (ENG.). 282p. pap. 15.95 *(978-0-393-33850-8(9),* 33850) Norton, W. W. & Co., Inc.

Miller, Alice, text. The Drama of the Gifted Child: The Search for the True Self. 2008. (ENG.). 144p. 22.00 *(978-0-465-01261-9(2))* Basic Bks.

Milligan, Gregg Tyler. A Beautiful World: One Son's Escape from the Snares of Abuse & Devotion. 2009. 152p. pap. 14.95 *(978-1-60844-051-1(6))* Dog Ear Publishing, LLC.

Murphey, Cecil. When a Man You Love Was Abused: A Woman's Guide to Helping Him Overcome Childhood Sexual Molestation, 1 vol. 2010. 256p. pap. 13.99 *(978-0-8254-3353-5(3))* Kregel Pubns.

Ndoro, Samuel. Community Psychological Exploration on Abuse of Vulnerable Adults. 2010. 100p. pap. *(978-3-639-25957-5(2))* VDM Verlag Dr. Mueller e.K.

Òe Rís, Pádraig. Dare to Dream. 2009. (Illus.). 240p. pap. 14.49 *(978-1-4490-4624-8(X))* AuthorHouse.

The check digit for ISBN-10 appears in parentheses after the full ISBN-13

Owen, Sue. Sue's Story: How I Survived a Lost Childhood. 2007. (ENG., Illus.). 288p. per. 15.95 (978-1-84358-166-6(3)) Blake, John Publishing, Ltd. GBR. Dist: Independent Pubs. Group.

Paivio, Sandra C. & Pascual-Leone, Antonio. Emotion-Focused Therapy for Complex Trauma: An Integrative Approach. 2010. (Illus.). 296p. 59.95 (978-1-4338-0725-1(4)) American Psychological Assn.

Past, Stormy. Caution: Surviving Your Childhood. 2010. 92p. pap. 13.99 (978-1-4520-1286-5(5)) AuthorHouse.

Patton, Stacey. That Mean Old Yesterday: A Memoir. 2008. (ENG.). 336p. pap. 20.99 (978-0-7432-9311-2(8)), Washington Square Pr.) Washington Square Pr.

Pelzer, Richard B. A Teenager's Journey: Overcoming a Childhood of Abuse. 2007. (ENG.). 240p. per. 13.99 (978-0-446-69835-1(0)) Grand Central Publishing.

Phelps, Shirley Itim Melo. We Women of Many Shades & Hues: Daily Common Ground for Survivors of Childhood Sexual Abuse, Incest, & Rape. 2008. 404p. pap. 25.00 (978-0-9798633-8-7(4)) Robertson Publishing.

Pittelli, Renee. Breaking the Bonds of Adult Child Abuse: A Biblical Textbook on Abusive Narcissistic Families, How they Operate, & How to Deal with Them. 2011. 649p. pap. 25.95 (978-1-4327-6656-6(2), Outskirts Pr., Inc.

Powell, Cheryl. Grand Larceny. 2007. (ENG.). 188p. per. 24.95 (978-1-4241-4719-9(0)) PublishAmerica, Inc.

Powlison, David. Recovering from Child Abuse: Healing & Hope for Victims. 2008. (ENG.). 24p. 3.99 (978-1-934885-47-5(9)) New Growth Pr.

Preston, Robin L. Journey of a Lost Child: Cries of a Child. 2007. 124p. per. 8.95 (978-1-4327-0405-6(2)) Outskirts Pr., Inc.

Randall, Jeff. Love Hurts: The True Story of a Life Destroyed. 2008. (ENG.). 240p. pap. 13.95 (978-1-84596-298-2(2)) Mainstream Publishing Co., Ltd. GBR. Dist: Independent Pubs. Group.

Reyome, Nancy Dodge, ed. The Effect of Childhood Emotional Maltreatment on Later Intimate Relationships. 2010. (ENG.). 264p. (C). 125.00 (978-0-415-59369-4(7)) Routledge.

Richards, Nancy. Heal & Forgive II: The Journey from Abuse & Estrangement to Reconciliation. 2008. 172p. pap. 16.00 (978-1-57733-220-6(2)) Blue Dolphin Publishing, Inc.

Rider, Tanya, et al. Missing Without a Trace: 8 Days of Horror. 2010. 234p. pap. 18.95 (978-0-9823008-6-2(7)) Titletown Publishing, LLC.

Rivera, Al. The Barefoot Shoeshine Boy. 2008. 156p. 22.49 (978-1-4389-2121-1(7)); pap. 15.49 (978-1-4389-2120-4(9)) AuthorHouse.

Rivers, Victor Rivas. Asunto de Familia: Memorias. Echerri, Vicente, tr. 2006. (SPA., Illus.). 432p. pap. 14.00 (978-1-4165-3729-8(5), Beyond Words/Atria Bks.) Atria Bks.

Ross, Tracy. The Source of All Things: A Memoir. (ENG.). 2012. 320p. pap. 15.00 (978-1-4391-7298-8(6)) 2011. 304p. 26.00 (978-1-4391-7297-1(8)) Free Pr. (Free Pr.).

Sabbagh, Karl. Remembering our Childhood: How Memory Betrays Us. 2011. (ENG., Illus.). 240p. pap. 19.95 (978-0-19-921841-7(2)) Oxford Univ. Pr., Inc.

Salcido, Carmina & Jackson, Steve. Not Lost Forever: My Story of Survival. 2011. (ENG., Illus.). 368p. mass mkt. 7.99 (978-0-06-204494-5(X)) HarperCollins Pubs.

Seed, Michael & Botham, Noel. Nobody?'s Child. 2008. (ENG.). 288p. pap. 15.95 (978-1-84454-588-9(1)) Blake, John Publishing, Ltd. GBR. Dist: Independent Pubs. Group.

—Nobody's Child. 2007. (ENG., Illus.). 288p. 27.95 (978-1-84454-343-4(9)) Blake, John Publishing, Ltd. GBR. Dist: Independent Pubs. Group.

Settles, Linda. The Girl among Thorns: Why Did She Stay So Long. 2010. (ENG.). 290p. pap. 12.99 (978-0-9790238-6-6(6)) Edict House Publishing Group, LLC.

—Redeeming Our Treasures: Finding Joy in the Shadows of an Abusive Past. 2009. (ENG.). 320p. pap. 19.99 (978-0-9790238-3-5(1)) Edict House Publishing Group, LLC.

Sontag, Rachel. House Rules: A Memoir. 2009. (P. S. Ser.). 288p. pap. 13.99 (978-0-06-134123-5(1), HarperPerennial) HarperCollins Pubs.

Spry, Christopher. Child C: Surviving a Foster Mother's Reign of Terror. 2008. (ENG.). 320p. pap. 12.95 (978-1-84739-189-6(3)) Simon & Schuster, Ltd. GBR. Dist: Independent Pubs. Group.

St. Clair, Chip. The Butterfly Garden: Surviving Childhood on the Run with One of America's Most Wanted. 2008. (ENG.). 304p. pap. 15.95 (978-0-7573-0695-2(0)) Health Communications, Inc.

Steel, Vanessa. Punished: A Mother's Cruelty - A Daughter's Survival - A Secret That Couldn't Be Told. 2009. (ENG.). 352p. pap. 13.95 (978-0-00-725581-5(7)) HarperCollins Pubs. Ltd. GBR. Dist: Independent Pubs. Group.

Strength Within Surviving by the Grace of God. 2nd rev. ed. 2008. 288p. pap. 15.00 (978-0-615-21031-5(7)) Tyler, Roland Vincent.

Taiwo, Lydia Ola. A Broken Childhood: A True Story of Abuse. 2011. 94p. 22.50 (978-1-84624-590-9(7)) Book Guild, Ltd. GBR. Dist: Trans-Atlantic Pubns., Inc.

Thomas, David. Tell Me Why, Mummy: A Little Boy's Struggle to Survive - A Mother's Shameful Secret. 3rd ed. 2008. (ENG.). 320p. pap. 11.95 (978-0-00-725637-2(X)) HarperCollins Pubs. Ltd. GBR. Dist: Independent Pubs. Group.

Touher, Patrick. Fear of the Collar: The True Story of the Boy They Couldn't Break. 2007. (ENG., Illus.). 272p. pap. 12.95 (978-0-09-191766-1(2)) Ebury Publishing GBR. Dist: Independent Pubs. Group.

Trujillo, Olga R. The Sum of My Parts: A Survivor's Story of Dissociative Identity Disorder. 2011. (ENG.). 256p. pap. 18.95 (978-1-57224-991-2(9)) New Harbinger Pubns.

Turko, Sadie. Healing Through Forgiveness. 2007. 139p. 24.95 (978-1-4241-5294-0(1)) PublishAmerica, Inc.

Vranceanu, Ana-Maria & Robert Johnson / Stevan Hobfoll, /. Sequelae of Child Abuse. 2010. 76p. pap. (978-3-8383-0227-0(3)) Lambert Academic Publishing.

Warner, Sam. Understanding the Effects of Child Sexual Abuse: Feminist Revolutions in Theory, Research & Practice. Warner, Sam, ed. 2009. (Women & Psychology Ser.). (ENG., Illus.). 304p. 34.95 (978-0-415-36028-9(5), RU60285) Routledge.

Watson, Tom. Man Shoes. 2011. (ENG.). 228p. 21.99 (978-1-59932-174-5(2)) Advantage Media Group.

Western Schools. The Body Never Lies. 2007. wbk. ed. 69.95 (978-1-57801-206-0(6)) Western Schls.

Westwater, Judy. Nowhere to Run: Where Do You Go When There's Nowhere Left to Hide? 2008. (ENG.). 280p. pap. 15.95 (978-0-00-726664-7(2)) HarperCollins Pubs. Ltd. GBR. Dist: Independent Pubs. Group.

Whelan, David. No More Silence: He Thought He'D Got Away with It - But One Day Little David Would Find the Strength to Speak Out. McBeth, Jim & Scott, Marion, eds. 2011. (ENG.). 304p. 11.95 (978-0-00-733890-5(X)) HarperCollins Pubs. Ltd. GBR. Dist: Independent Pubs. Group.

When Love Hurts: A True Story of Abuse & Addiction. 2006. per. (978-0-9785553-2-0(5)) DMT Publishing.

Wright, Clarissa. Spilling the Beans. 2007. (Illus.). 320p. 34.95 (978-0-340-93388-6(7), Hodder & Stoughton) Hodder General Publishing Div. GBR. Dist: Independent Pubs. Group.

Wright, Clarissa Dickson. Spilling the Beans. 2009. (ENG., Illus.). 336p. pap. 15.95 (978-0-340-93389-3(5), Hodder & Stoughton) Hodder General Publishing Div. GBR. Dist: Independent Pubs. Group.

ADULT CHILD AND PARENTS

see Parent and Adult Child

ADULT CHILD SEXUAL ABUSE VICTIMS

see also Sexually Abused Children

Adams, Kenneth. Silently Seduced, Revised & Updated: When Parents Make Their Children Partners. 2011. (ENG.). 192p. pap. 12.95 (978-0-7573-1587-9(9)) Health Communications, Inc.

Allen-Kelly, Kandie. Steel Magnolias Healing Journeys. 2008. 192p. pap. (978-3-639-05366-1(4)) VDM Verlag Dr. Mueller e.K.

Allender, Dan B. The Wounded Heart: A Companion Workbook for Personal or Group Use. 2008. (Maranatha Novels Ser.). (ENG.). 208p. pap., wbk. ed. 16.99 (978-1-60006-308-4(X)) NavPress Publishing Group.

—The Wounded Heart: Hope for Adult Victims of Childhood Sexual Abuse. 2008. (Real Life Stuff for Women Ser.). (ENG.). 272p. pap. 16.99 (978-1-60006-307-7(1)) NavPress Publishing Group.

Armstrong, Mary K. Confessions of a Trauma Therapist: A Memoir of Healing & Transformation. 2010. (978-1-926645-19-3(7)) BPS Bks.

Bonnie Lis Norris & John Norris, Lis No & Bonnie Lis Norris & John Norris. Keeper of Secrets: My story of childhood sexual abuse. 2009. 92p. pap. 11.95 (978-1-4401-8111-5(X)) iUniverse, Inc.

Brand, Julie A. A Mother's Touch: Surviving Mother-Daughter Sexual Abuse. 2007. (Illus.). 208p. per. 19.95 (978-1-4251-0564-8(5)) Trafford Publishing.

Bromley, Nicole Braddock. Breathe: Finding Freedom to Thrive in Relationships after Childhood Sexual Abuse, 1 vol. 2009. (ENG.). 192p. pap. 12.99 (978-0-8024-4865-1(8)) Moody Pubs.

—Hush: Moving from Silence to Healing after Childhood Sexual Abuse. 2007. (ENG.). 192p. per. 12.99 (978-0-8024-4864-4(X)) Moody Pubs.

Brooke, Stephanie L., ed. The use of the creative therapies with sexual abuse Survivors. 2007. (Illus.). 342p. pap. 49.95 (978-0-398-07702-0(9)) Thomas, Charles C. Pub., Ltd.

—The Use of the Creative Therapies with Sexual abuse Survivors. 2007. (Illus.). 342p. 74.95 (978-0-398-07701-3(0)) Thomas, Charles C. Pub., Ltd.

Brown, Nancy. Facing Life. 2008. 183p. per. 24.95 (978-1-897323-07-6(7)) Penumbra Pr. CAN. Dist: Michigan State Univ. Pr.

Callaghan, Linda Y. & DeLaMartre, Audrey E. Inrage: Healing the Hidden Rage of Child Sexual Abuse. 3rd ed. 2009. 326p. pap. 29.00 (978-0-9706926-9-6(2), 91-0010-03) Tyborne Hill Pubs., LLC.

Carethers, DeVona. My Battle Through Life. 2011. pap. 10.99 (978-1-61346-576-9(9)) Tate Publishing & Enterprises, LLC.

Cashman, Hilary. Christianity & Child Sexual Abuse. 144p. 12.00 (978-0-281-04647-8(6)) SPCK Publishing GBR. Dist: Pilgrim Pr., The/United Church Pr.

Clemenger, Michael. The Tyranny of Memories: Little Feet That Walked in Fear. 2009. (ENG., Illus.). 412p. pap. 18.95 (978-1-84717-187-0(7)) O'Brien Pr., Ltd., The IRL. Dist: Dufour Editions, Inc.

Culbreth, Sallie. No Longer Alone: Rising above Childhood Sexual Abuse. 2009. (Modern Girl's Bible Study Ser.). (ENG.). 128p. pap. 11.99 (978-1-60006-362-3(6)) NavPress Publishing Group.

Daniel, Sarah. Leaving Abuse Behind. 2007. 56p. per. 12.95 (978-1-59858-479-0(0)) Dog Ear Publishing, LLC.

Daugherty, Lynn B. Why Me? Help for Victims of Child Sexual Abuse (Even if they are adults now), Fourth Edition. 4th rev. ed. 2007. 128p. per. 12.95 (978-0-9771614-3-0(9)) Cleanan Pr., Inc.

Davies, Sara. Running from the Devil. 2006. (ENG.). 288p. 29.95 (978-1-84454-284-0(X)) Blake, John Publishing, Ltd. GBR. Dist: Independent Pubs. Group.

—Running from the Devil: How I Survived a Stolen Childhood. 2007. (ENG.). 257p. per. 14.95 (978-1-84454-413-4(3)) Blake, John Publishing, Ltd. GBR. Dist: Independent Pubs. Group.

de Milly, Walter A., III. In My Father's Arms: A True Story of Incest. 2012. (Living Out: Gay & Lesbian Autobiog Ser.). (ENG.). 152p. pap. 21.95 (978-0-299-16514-7(0)) Univ. of Wisconsin Pr.

Drake, Debra J. An Uncommon Dialogue. 2006. (ENG.). 314p. (Orig.). per. 19.95 (978-1-86254-679-0(7)) Wakefield Pr. Pty, Ltd. AUS. Dist: Independent Pubs. Group.

Duncan, Karen A. Healing from the Trauma of Childhood Sexual Abuse: The Journey for Women, 1 vol. 2008. (Illus.). 264p. pap. 19.95 (978-0-313-36321-4(8), B36321, Praeger Trade) Greenwood Publishing Group, Inc.

Fleury, Theo & Day, Kirstie Mclellan. Playing with Fire. 2011. (ENG.). 336p. pap. 14.95 (978-1-60078-637-2(5)) Triumph Bks.

Forsyth, Sarah. Slave Girl. 2009. (ENG.). 256p. pap. 14.95 (978-1-84454-685-5(3)) Blake, John Publishing, Ltd GBR. Dist: Independent Pubs. Group.

Fournier, Delaine C. Cracked Vessel. 14.00 (978-0-9719152-0-6(2)) Fournier, Delaine C.

Gould, Lynette & Richards, Stephen. Heart of Darkness: How I Triumphed over a Childhood of Abuse. (ENG.). 2008. 254p. pap. 15.95 (978-1-84454-605-3(5)) 2007. 288p. 34.95 (978-1-84454-321-2(8)) Blake, John Publishing, Ltd. GBR. Dist: Independent Pubs. Group.

Harrison, Sarah. You Love Your Daddy, Don't You? A True Tragedy about Sexual Abuse. 2008. (Illus.). 316p. pap. (978-0-9809191-4-1(2), CCB Publishing) CCB Publishing.

Jameel, Issam. Iraq Through a Bullet Hole: A Civilian Returns Home. 2008. 212p. pap. 19.95 (978-1-932690-70-5(0), Modern History Fr.) Loving Healing Pr., Inc.

James, Nikola T. The Price of Love. 2007. (ENG.). 224p. per. 20.95 (978-0-283-07056-3(0)) Macmillan Pubs., Ltd. GBR. Dist: Independent Pubs. Group.

Johnson, Victoria. Children & Sexual Abuse. 2007. (IVP Booklets Ser.). (ENG.). 32p. 1.50 (978-0-87784-040-4(7), IVP Bks.) InterVarsity Pr.

Keeling, Frank D. Nobody's Son. 2007. (Illus.). 321p. 24.99 (978-1-4251-1710-8(4)) Trafford Publishing.

Keenan, Shy. Broken. 2008. (ENG.). 320p. pap. 13.95 (978-0-340-93744-0(0), Hodder & Stoughton) Hodder General Publishing Div. GBR. Dist: Independent Pubs. Group.

Kemp, Martin & Lowe, Matt. The Family Friend: Sometimes the Danger Is Closer Than You Think. 2008. (ENG.). 348p. pap. 13.95 (978-0-09-191226-0(1)) Ebury Publishing GBR. Dist: Independent Pubs. Group.

Lowe, Anna. Wake Up, Mummy: An Abused Little Girl - A Mother Too Drunk to Notice. 2011. (ENG.). 320p. pap. 12.95 (978-0-09-194051-5(6)) Ebury Publishing GBR. Dist: Independent Pubs. Group.

Lukara, Alssa. Riding Grace: A Triumph of the Soul. 2006. (ENG., Illus.). 192p. per. (978-0-9744890-3-2(4)) Silver Light Pubns.

Lumsden, Raymond E. Stronger by the Day: A Gripping Story of Abuse, Neglect, Courage & Redemption. 2007. 286p. per. 16.95 (978-0-9790628-0-3(2)) Lighthouse Publishing.

Madden, Amy. Stolen Beauty: Healing the Scars of Child Abuse: One Woman's Journey. 2007. 196p. per. 14.95 (978-0-929636-74-0(0)) Syren Bk. Co.

Maguire, Toni. Don't Tell Mummy: True Story of the Ultimate Betrayal. 2007. (ENG.). 352p. pap. 12.95 (978-0-00-722376-3(5)) HarperCollins Pubs. Ltd. GBR Dist: Independent Pubs. Group.

Maltz, Wendy. Sexual Healing Journey: A Guide for Survivors of Sexual Abuse (Third Edition) 3rd ed. 2012. (ENG., Illus.). 368p. pap. 14.99 (978-0-06-213073-0(0), William Morrow Paperbacks) HarperCollins Pubs.

Marie, Ellen. The Big Ugly: No Excuse for Murder? 2010. pap. 17.00 (978-1-4349-9900-9(9), RoseDog Bks.) Dorrance Publishing Co., Inc.

McCall, Catherine. When the Piano Stops: A Memoir of Healing from Sexual Abuse. 2009. (ENG.). 280p. pap. 16.95 (978-1-58005-267-2(3)) Seal Pr.

Mccollum, Hilary. Funny Peculiar. 2009. 224p. pap. 22.95 (978-0-86322-372-3(9)) Brandon/Mount Eagle Pubns., Ltd. IRL. Dist: Dufour Editions, Inc.

McGovern, Sharon. Afraid. 2008. (ENG.). 240p. 27.95 (978-1-4091-0022-5(7)) Orion Publishing Group, Ltd. GBR. Dist: Independent Pubs. Group.

McGregor, Kim. Surviving & Moving On: Self-Help for Survivors of Childhood Sexual Abuse. 2010. (ENG.). 464p. pap. 38.00 (978-1-84392-507-1(9)) Willan Publishing GBR. Dist: Taylor & Francis Group.

McKinnon, Margie. Repair Your Life: A Bridge of Recovery from Incest & Childhood Sexual Abuse. 2008. 196p. pap. (978-1-932690-52-1(2)) Loving Healing Pr., Inc.

McKinnon, Marjorie. Repair Your Life: A Program for Recovery from Incest & Childhood Sexual Abuse. 2011. 196p. 32.95 (978-1-61599-103-7(4)) Loving Healing Pr., Inc.

—Repair Your Life Workbook: Supporting a Program of Recovery from Incest & Childhood Sexual Abuse. 2011. 46p. pap. 8.95 (978-1-61599-101-3(8)) Loving Healing Pr., Inc.

Munro, Eileen. If I Should Die Before I Wake. 2012. (ENG.). 272p. pap. 14.95 (978-1-84596-616-4(3)) Mainstream Publishing Co., Ltd. GBR. Dist: Independent Pubs. Group.

O'Gorman, Colm. Beyond Belief: Abused by His Priest, Betrayed by His Church, the Story of the Boy Who Sued the Pope. 2011. (ENG.). 320p. pap. 12.95 (978-0-340-92528-7(0), Hodder & Stoughton) Hodder General Publishing Div. GBR. Dist: Independent Pubs. Group.

Oz, Sheri & Ogiers, Sarah-Jane. Overcoming Childhood Sexual Trauma: A Guide to Breaking Through the Wall of Fear for Practitioners & Survivors. 2006. (ENG., Illus.). 338p. 145.00 (978-0-7890-2979-9(0)); per. 44.95 (978-0-7890-2980-5(4)) Routledge.

Rabbitt, Karen. Trading Fathers: Forgiving Dad, Embracing God. 2009. 336p. pap. 15.95 (978-1-57921-995-6(0)) WinePress Publishing.

Reid, Gregory. The Color of Pain: Boys Who Are Sexually Abused & the Men They Become. 2010. pap. (978-0-9824881-7-1(3)) Lighthouse Trails Publishing Co.

Richard, Sycelle. Dear Mama. 2006. per. 12.95 (978-0-9786235-0-0(9)) Glory Bks Publishing, LLC.

Rock, Crissy. This Heart Within Me Burns. 2012. (ENG., Illus.). 266p. pap. 12.95 (978-1-84358-753-8(X)) Blake, John Publishing, Ltd. GBR. Dist: Independent Pubs. Group.

—This Heart Within Me Burns: Crissy Rock - From Bedlam to Benidorm. 2011. (ENG., Illus.). 264p. 24.95 (978-1-84358-343-1(7)) Blake, John Publishing, Ltd. GBR. Dist: Independent Pubs. Group.

Rose, Prophetess Gail. My Past Was Just a Set up for My Future. 2007. 208p. per. 16.95 (978-1-4327-1479-6(1)) Outskirts Pr., Inc.

Sandford, Paula. Healing Victims of Sexual Abuse: How to Counsel & Minister to Hearts Wounded by Abuse. 2009. (ENG.). 176p. pap. 14.99 (978-1-59979-753-3(4), Charisma Hse.) Charisma Media.

Scharff, David & Scharff, Jill. Object Relations Therapy of Physical & Sexual Trauma. 2008. (Library of Object Relations Ser.). (ENG.). 390p. pap. 41.99 (978-0-7657-0406-1(4), Aronson, Jason) Rowman & Littlefield Publishers, Inc.

Schmutzer, Andrew J., ed. The Long Journey Home: Understanding & Ministering to the Sexually Abused. 2011. 524p. pap. 57.00 (978-1-60899-395-6(7), Wipf and Stock) Wipf & Stock Pubs.

Settles, Linda. The Girl among Thorns: Why Did She Stay So Long. 2010. (ENG.). 290p. pap. 12.99 (978-0-9790238-6-6(6)) Edict House Publishing Group, LLC.

—Redeeming Our Treasures: Finding Joy in the Shadows of an Abusive Past. 2009. (ENG.). 320p. pap. 19.99 (978-0-9790238-3-5(1)) Edict House Publishing Group, LLC.

Sherrie Watkins. Touching Temptation. 2010. 468p. pap. 28.95 (978-1-4502-0220-6(9)) iUniverse, Inc.

Silverman, Sue William. Love Sick: One Woman's Journey Through Sexual Addiction. 2008. (ENG.). 304p. per. 14.95 (978-0-393-33300-8(0), 33300) Norton, W. W. & Co., Inc.

Smith, Megan J. Child Sexual Abuse: Issues & Challenges. 2008. (Illus.). (C). 89.00 (978-1-60021-999-3(3)) Nova Science Pubs., Inc.

Stefanowicz, Dawn. Out from Under: The Impact of Homosexual Parenting. 2007. 245p. per. 14.95 (978-1-59977-011-6(3)) Annotation Pr.

Sullivan, Felicia C. The Sky Isnt Visible from Here. 2008. 288p. (978-0-7322-8805-1(3)) HarperCollins Pubs. Australia.

Thomas, Anna F. Fire & Water: A Safe Journey Through Multiple Personality Disorder. Rakini, Kate, ed. 2009. (Illus.). 164p. pap. 14.95 (978-1-934759-18-9(X)) Reed, Robert D. Pubs.

Thornton, Sara Jane. Facing the Sunshine: A Young Women's Emergence from the Shadows of Sexual Abuse & Anorexia. 2007. 224p. pap. 19.95 (978-0-9763694-6-2(X)) Appelstein Training Resources.

Tracy, Steven R. Mending the Soul: Understanding & Healing Abuse. 2008. (ENG., Illus.). 272p. pap. 16.99 (978-0-310-26529-8(1)) Zondervan.

VanLiere, Donna. Finding Grace: A True Story about Losing Your Way in Life... & Finding It Again. 2009. (ENG.). 224p. 21.95 (978-0-312-38051-9(8)) St. Martin's Pr.

Wallace, Sharon. A House Full of Whispers. 2010. pap. (978-1-61599-065-8(8), Modern History Pr.) Loving Healing Pr., Inc.

—Surviving a House Full of Whispers. 2009. 168p. pap. (978-1-932690-90-3(5), Modern History Pr.) Loving Healing Pr., Inc.

Williams, Dan. Above His Shoulders: A True Account of Sexual Abuse,Its Impact on Relationships, & the Emotional Survival & Healing. 2009. (Illus.). 242p. pap. 15.95 (978-1-4327-3749-8(X)) Outskirts Pr., Inc.

Williamson-Taylor, James. They Can't Touch Him Now. 2007. pap. (978-0-9554101-0-9(X)) Anodyne Pubs.

Willows, Jonathan. Moving on after Childhood Sexual Abuse: Understanding the Effects & Preparing for Therapy. 2008. (ENG., Illus.). 200p. 95.00 (978-0-415-42482-0(8)); pap. 24.95 (978-0-415-42483-7(6)) Routledge.

Wilmer, Graham. Conspiracy of Faith: Fighting for Justice after Child Abuse. 2007. (ENG.). 160p. per. 28.00 (978-0-7188-3058-8(X)) Lutherworth Pr., The GBR. Dist: Brown, David Bk. Co., The.

Yapko, Michael. Suggestions of Abuse. 2009. (ENG.). 272p. pap. 18.95 (978-1-4391-7099-1(1)) Simon & Schuster.

Young, Richard. Joyce Meyer: A Life of Redemption & Destiny. 2009. 192p. pap. 13.99 (978-1-60374-112-5(7), 771125) Whitaker Hse.

ADULT CHILDREN

Here are entered works on adults who have middle-aged or elderly parents.

Baker, Amy J. L. Adult Children of Parental Alienation Syndrome. 2007. 32.00 (978-0-7937-0519-1(3)) Norton, W. W. & Co., Inc.

—Adult Children of Parental Alienation Syndrome: Breaking the Ties That Bind. 2007. (ENG.). 320p. 32.00 (978-0-393-70519-5(6), 70519) Norton, W. W. & Co., Inc.

Benor, Roberta Schultz. The Keys to Senior Housing: A Guide for Two Generations, 1 vol. 2009. 195p. pap. 24.95 (978-1-60749-025-8(0)) PublishAmerica, Inc.

Bottke, Allison. Setting Boundaries with Your Adult Children. 2008. 218p. per. 12.99 (978-0-7369-2135-0(4)) Harvest Hse. Pubs.

—Setting Boundaries with Your Aging Parents: Finding Balance Between Burnout & Respect. 2010. 240p. pap. 12.99 (978-0-7369-2674-4(7)) Harvest Hse. Pubs.

Brown, Nina W. Children of the Self-Absorbed: A Grown-Up's Guide to Getting over Narcissistic Parents. 2nd rev. ed. 2008. (ENG.). 240p. pap. 16.95 (978-1-57224-561-7(1)) New Harbinger Pubns.

Budd, Ken. The Voluntourist: A Six-Country Tale of Love, Loss, Fatherhood, Fate, & Singing Bon Jovi in Bethlehem. 2012. (ENG.). 464p. pap. 15.99 **(978-0-06-194646-2(X)**, William Morrow Paperbacks) HarperCollins Pubs.

Butler, Lynne. Estate Planning Through Family Meetings. 2010. (ENG.). 160p. pap. 23.95 (978-1-77040-036-8(2)) Self-Counsel Pr., Inc. CAN. Dist: Midpoint Trade Bks., Inc.

Currier, Mary L. Fact, Fiction & Family: A Sister's Perspective on Conflict, Communication & Care Giving. 2010. 144p. (ENG.). 24.95 (978-1-4520-1281-0(4)); pap. 17.99 (978-1-4520-1280-3(6)) AuthorHouse.

Delehanty, Hugh & Ginzler, Elinor. Caring for Your Parents: The Complete Family Guide. 2008. (AARP Ser.). (ENG., Illus.). 256p. per. 12.95 (978-1-4027-5857-7(X)) Sterling Publishing Co., Inc.

Dodds, Monica. A Catholic Guide to Caring for Your Aging Parent. 2006. (ENG.). 360p. per. 14.95 (978-0-8294-1872-9(5)) Loyola Pr.

Edelman, Hope. Motherless Mothers: How Losing a Mother Shapes the Parent You Become. 2007. (ENG.). 432p. pap. 14.95 (978-0-06-053246-8(7), HarperPerennial) HarperCollins Pubs.

Fuller, Cheri & Plum, Ali D. Mother-Daughter Duet: Getting to the Relationship You Want with Your Adult Daughter. 2010. (ENG.). 240p. pap. 13.99 (978-1-60142-162-3(1), Multnomah) Doubleday Religious Publishing Group, The.

Gibson, Margaret. The Prodigal Daughter: Reclaiming an Unfinished Childhood. 2008. (ENG., Illus.). 216p. (gr. 9). per. 19.95 (978-0-8262-1783-7(4)) Univ. of Missouri Pr.

Gilbert, Allison. Always Too Soon: Voices of Support for Those Who Have Lost Both Parents. 2006. (ENG.). 200p. per. 14.95 (978-1-58005-176-7(6)) Seal Pr.

Gross, Jane. A Bittersweet Season: Caring for Our Aging Parents — and Ourselves. 2011. (ENG.). 368p. 26.95 (978-0-307-27182-2(X), Knopf) Knopf Doubleday Publishing Group.

Harvest USA Staff. Your Gay Child Says I Do. Black, R. Nicholas, ed. 2012. (ENG.). 24p. 3.99 **(978-1-936768-95-0(X))** New Growth Pr.

Highe, Jackie. Now Where Did I Put My Glasses? Caring for Your Elder Parents - A Practical & Emotional Lifeline. 2007. (ENG.). 276p. pap. 23.95 (978-0-7432-9531-4(5)) Simon & Schuster, Ltd. GBR. Dist: Independent Pubs. Group.

Isay, Jane. Walking on Eggshells: Navigating the Delicate Relationship Between Adult Children & Parents. 2008. (ENG.). 256p. pap. 15.00 (978-0-7679-2085-8(6)) Broadway Bks.

—Walking on Eggshells: Navigating the Delicate Relationship Between Adult Children & Their Parents. l.t. ed. 2007. (Thorndike Health, Home & Learning Ser.). 315p. 29.95 (978-0-7862-9663-7(1)) Thorndike Pr.

Koslow, Sally. Slouching Toward Adulthood: Observations from the Not-So-Empty Nest. 2012. (ENG.). 272p. (gr. 12). 25.95 **(978-0-670-02362-2(0)**, Viking Adult) Penguin Group (USA) Inc.

Kuttner, Robert & Trotter, Sharland. Family Re-Union: Reconnecting Parents & Children in Adulthood. 2007. (ENG.). 288p. pap. 19.95 (978-1-4165-6778-3(X), Free Pr.) Free Pr.

Luxenberg, Steve. Annie's Ghosts: A Journey into a Family Secret. 2010. (ENG.). 432p. pap. 15.99 (978-1-4013-1019-6(2)) 2009. 416p. 24.99 (978-1-4013-2247-2(6)) Hyperion Pr.

Madden, Amy. Stolen Beauty: Healing the Scars of Child Abuse: One Woman's Journey. 2007. 196p. per. 14.95 (978-0-929636-74-0(0)) Syren Bk. Co.

Milton, Colin. Recollections of an Adult Baby. 2008. 154p. pap. 20.95 (978-1-4092-2849-3(5)) Lulu Enterprises Inc.

Nemzoff, Ruth. Don't Bite Your Tongue: How to Foster Rewarding Relationships with Your Adult Children. 2008. (ENG.). 256p. pap. 14.95 (978-0-230-60518-3(4)) Palgrave Macmillan.

Newheiser, Jim & Fitzpatrick, Elyse. You Never Stop Being a Parent: Thriving in Relationship with Your Adult Children. 2010. pap. (978-1-59638-174-2(4)) P & R Publishing.

Newman, Katherine S. The Accordion Family: Boomerang Kids, Anxious Parents, & the Private Toll of Global Competition. (ENG.). 2013. pap. 18.00 **(978-0-8070-0745-7(5))** 2012. 320p. 25.95 (978-0-8070-0743-3(9)) Beacon Pr.

Nielsen, Linda. Between Fathers & Daughters: Enriching & Rebuilding Your Adult Relationship. 2008. (ENG.). 256p. pap. 16.95 (978-1-58182-661-6(3)) Turner Publishing Co.

Omartian, Stormie. The Power of Praying for Your Adult Children. l.t. ed. 2010. (ENG.). 420p. pap. 17.99 (978-1-59415-317-4(5)) Cengage Gale.

—The Power of Praying for Your Adult Children. 2009. 240p. pap. 13.99 (978-0-7369-2086-5(2)) Harvest Hse. Pubs.

Owens, Virginia Stem. Caring for Mother: A Daughter's Long Goodbye. 2007. (ENG.). 163p. per. 17.00 (978-0-664-23152-1(7)) Westminster John Knox Pr.

Parent, Gail & Ende, Susan. How to Raise Your Adult Children: Because Big Kids Have Even Bigger Problems. 2010. (ENG.). 304p. (gr. 12). 25.95 (978-1-59463-069-9(0), Hudson Street Pr.) Penguin Group (USA) Inc.

Perry, Greg. An Other Road into the Heartland: after Basho, Buddha, & Japan. 2009. 148p. pap. 15.95 (978-0-557-04480-1(4)) Lulu Enterprises Inc.

Phillips, Kathy J. The Moon in the Water: Reflections on an Aging Parent. 2008. (Illus.). (ENG.). 160p. 19.95 (978-0-8265-1586-5(X)); xiii, 139p. pap. (978-0-8265-1587-2(8)) Vanderbilt Univ. Pr.

Pittelli, Renee. Narcissistic Predicaments: A Biblical Guide to Navigating the Schemes, Snares, & No-Win Situations Unique to Abusive Families. 2010. 368p. pap. 22.95 (978-1-4327-5044-2(5)) Outskirts Pr., Inc.

Pope, Alan. From Child to Elder: Personal Transformation in Becoming an Orphan at Midlife. 2006. (American University Studies: Vol. 24). 294p. (C). 73.95 (978-0-8204-7941-5(1)) Lang, Peter Publishing, Inc.

Reid, Iain. One Bird's Choice: A Year in the Life of an Overeducated, Underemployed Twenty-Something Who Moves Back Home, 1 vol. 2011. (ENG.). 264p. 24.95 (978-0-88784-243-6(7)) House of Anansi Pr. CAN. Dist: Perseus-PGW.

Russert, Tim. Wisdom of Our Fathers: Lessons & Letters from Daughters & Sons. 2008. (ENG.). 273p. 23.00 (978-1-4223-9341-3(0)) DIANE Publishing Co.

—Wisdom of Our Fathers: Lessons & Letters from Daughters & Sons. 2007. (ENG., Illus.). 320p. pap. 13.95 (978-0-8129-7543-7(X), Random Hse. Trade Paperbacks) Random House Publishing Group.

—The Wisdom of Our Fathers: Lessons & Letters from Daughters & Sons. l.t. ed. 2010. (ENG.). 480p. pap. 23.00 (978-0-7393-7752-9(3)) Random Hse. Large Print.

Safer, Jeanne. Death Benefits: How Losing a Parent Can Change an Adult's Life — for the Better. 2010. (ENG.). 240p. pap. 15.95 (978-0-465-01857-4(2)) Basic Bks.

Shaffer, Susan Morris & Gordon, Linda Perlman. Too Close for Comfort? Questioning the Intimacy of Today's New Mother-Daughter Relationship. 2009. (ENG.). 304p. (gr. 12-18). pap. 16.00 (978-0-425-22960-6(2), Berkley Trade) Penguin Group (USA) Inc.

Silin, Jonathan G. My Father's Keeper: The Story of a Gay Son & His Aging Parents. 2007. (ENG.). 184p. per. 16.00 (978-0-8070-7965-2(0)) Beacon Pr.

Silverstone, Barbara, et al. You & Your Aging Parent: A Family Guide to Emotional, Social, Health, & Financial Problems. 4th ed. 2008. (ENG.). 400p. per. 17.95 (978-0-19-531316-1(X)) Oxford Univ. Pr., Inc.

Tucker, Michael. Family Meals: Coming Together to Care for an Aging Parent. 2010. (ENG.). 256p. pap. 14.00 (978-0-8021-4508-6(6), Grove Pr.) Grove/Atlantic, Inc.

Wickersham, Joan & Hochman, Gail. The Suicide Index: Putting My Father's Death in Order. 2009. (ENG.). 336p. pap. 14.95 (978-0-15-603380-0(1), Mariner Bks.) Houghton Mifflin Harcourt Trade & Reference Pubs.

Wright, Margaret O'Dougherty, ed. Childhood Emotional Abuse: Mediating & Moderating Processes Affecting Long-Term Impact. 2008. (Journal of Emotional Abuse Ser.: No. 7). (Illus.). 148p. pap. 51.95 (978-0-7890-3712-1(2)) Routledge.

ADULT CHILDREN AND PARENTS

see Parent and Adult Child

ADULT CHILDREN OF ALCOHOLICS

Al-Anon Family Group Headquarters, Inc Staff, contrib. by. Opening Our Hearts: Transforming Our Losses. 2007. x, 193p. pap. (978-0-910034-47-0(8)) Al-Anon Family Group Headquarters, Inc.

Bey, Douglas & Bey, Deborah. Loving an Adult Child of an Alcoholic. 2007. (ENG.). 240p. per. 16.95 (978-1-59077-117-4(6)) Evans, M. & Co., Inc.

Dickson Wright, Clarissa. Spilling the Beans: The Autobiography of One of Television's Two Fat Ladies. 2010. (ENG.). 336p. (gr. 12). 29.95 (978-1-59020-296-8(1)) Overlook Pr., The.

Goolrick, Robert. The End of the World as We Know It: Scenes from a Life. 2007. (ENG.). 224p. 22.95 (978-1-56512-481-3(2), 1565124812) Algonquin Bks. of Chapel Hill.

Gwilliam, J. Gary. Getting a Winning Verdict in My Personal Life: A Trial Lawyer Finds His Soul. 2007. (978-1-4243-4283-9(X)) Pavior Publishing.

Middelton-Moz, Jane & Dwinell, Lorie. After the Tears: Helping Adult Children of Alcoholics Heal Their Childhood Trauma. 2nd rev. ed. 2010. (ENG., Illus.). 312p. pap. 14.95 (978-0-7573-1513-8(5)) Health Communications, Inc.

Wright, Clarissa. Spilling the Beans. 2007. (Illus.). 320p. 34.95 (978-0-340-93388-6(7), Hodder & Stoughton) Hodder General Publishing Div. GBR. Dist: Independent Pubs. Group.

Wright, Clarissa Dickson. Spilling the Beans. 2009. (ENG., Illus.). 336p. pap. 15.95 (978-0-340-93389-3(5), Hodder & Stoughton) Hodder General Publishing Div. GBR. Dist: Independent Pubs. Group.

ADULT CHILDREN OF DIVORCED PARENTS

Abbas, Jen. Generation Ex: Adult Children of Divorce & the Healing of Our Pain. 2007. 220p. per. 12.99 (978-1-57229-975-7(4)) FamilyLife.

Das, Chaitali. British-Indian Adult Children of Divorce: Context Impact & Coping. 2011. (Illus.). 204p. 99.95 (978-1-4094-0824-6(8)) Ashgate Publishing Co.

Flowerdew & Neale. Moving on Chang Live Youn Peop Aft. 2007. (Relationships & Resources Ser.). (ENG.). 176p. (C). 140.00 (978-0-415-36789-9(1)); pap. 43.95 (978-0-415-36790-5(5)) Routledge.

Piorkowski, Geraldine K. Adult Children of Divorce: Confused Love Seekers, 1 vol. 2008. 208p. 39.95 (978-0-313-34600-2(3), C34600, Praeger Pubs.) Greenwood Publishing Group, Inc.

Rodgers, Beverly & Rodgers, Tom. Adult Children of Divorced Parents. 2008. 172p. pap. 19.95 (978-1-58930-228-0(1)) Selah Publishing Group, LLC.

Schab, Lisa. Divorce Workbook for Teens: Activities to Help You Move Beyond the Break Up. 2008. (Instant Help Ser.). 132p. pap. 14.95 (978-1-931704-27-4(9)) Play2Grow.

ADULT CHILDREN OF DRUG ADDICTS

Sullivan, Felicia C. The Sky Isnt Visible from Here. 2008. 288p. (978-0-7322-8805-1(3)) HarperCollins Pubs. Australia.

—The Sky Isn't Visible from Here: A Memoir. 2009. (P. S. Ser.). 288p. pap. 13.99 (978-0-06-176532-2(5), HarperPerennial) HarperCollins Pubs.

ADULT CHILDREN OF DYSFUNCTIONAL FAMILIES

Celani, David P. Leaving Home: The Art of Separating from Your Difficult Family. 2011. (ENG.). 176p. (gr. 17). pap. 22.50 (978-0-231-13477-4(0)) Columbia Univ. Pr.

Estrup, Carole. Barefoot Girl Out of Ohio. 2007. 408p. per. 25.95 (978-0-595-43694-1(3)) iUniverse, Inc.

Harvest USA Staff. Your Gay Child Says I Do. Black, R. Nicholas, ed. 2012. (ENG.). 24p. 3.99 **(978-1-936768-95-0(X))** New Growth Pr.

Hoich, John L. From the Ground Up: It's Not Just Business! 2007. pap. (978-1-930819-53-5(6)) Tapestry Pr.

McCracken, Mary. A Legacy of Hope: Rescued from the Quicksand of Dysfunction. 2008. (ENG.). 144p. pap. 16.95 (978-1-932124-93-4(4)) ACW Pr.

Mitchell, R. B. Castaway Kid: One Man's Search for Hope & Home. 2007. (ENG., Illus.). 272p. per. 13.99 (978-1-58997-434-0(4)) Tyndale Hse. Pubs.

Powlison, David/Arthur. Life Beyond Your Parents' Mistakes: The Transforming Power of God's Love. 2009. 24p. 3.99 (978-1-935273-18-9(3)) New Growth Pr.

Reinhold, Margaret. How to Survive in Spite of Your Parents. Date not set. pap. 5.99 (978-0-7493-2198-7(9)) Heinemann.

Rivers, Victor Rivas. Asunto de Familia: Memorias. Echerri, Vicente, tr. 2006. (SPA., Illus.). 432p. pap. 14.00 (978-1-4165-3729-8(5), Beyond Words/Atria Bks.) Atria Bks.

Rosenthal, Sarah S. The Unavailable Father: Seven Ways Women Can Understand, Heal, & Cope with a Broken Father-Daughter Relationship. 2010. (ENG.). 192p. pap. 16.95 (978-0-470-61414-3(5), Jossey-Bass) Wiley, John & Sons, Inc.

Sipp, Carey. The Turnaround Mom: How an Abuse & Addiction Survivor Stopped the Toxic Cycle for Her Family — and How You Can, Too! 2007. (ENG., Illus.). 200p. pap. 14.95 (978-0-7573-0596-2(2)) Health Communications, Inc.

Sontag, Rachel. House Rules: A Memoir. 2009. (P. S. Ser.). 288p. pap. 13.99 (978-0-06-134123-6(1), HarperPerennial) HarperCollins Pubs.

Stoop, David. Forgiving Our Parents, Forgiving Ourselves: Healing Adult Children of Dysfunctional Families. 2011. (ENG.). 256p. pap. 16.99 (978-0-8307-5723-7(6)) Gospel Light Pubns.

ADULT CHILDREN OF NARCOTIC ADDICTS

see Adult Children of Drug Addicts

ADULT DAY CARE CENTERS

Davis, Charlene & Lynn, Jacquelyn. Start Your Own Senior Services Business: Adult Day Care, Relocation Services, Homecare, Transportation Service, Concierge, Travel Service & More. 2nd ed. 2010. (ENG.). 224p. pap. 17.95 (978-1-59918-359-6(5), 1599183595) Entrepreneur Pr. dba Entrepreneur Media, Inc.

Moore, Keith Diaz, et al. Designing a Better Day: Guidelines for Adult & Dementia Day Services Centers. 2006. (ENG., Illus.). 216p. (gr. 17). per. 43.00 (978-0-8018-8415-3(2)) Johns Hopkins Univ. Pr.

Sonnet, Helen & Taylor, Ann. Activities for Adults with Learning Disabilities: Having Fun, Meeting Needs. 2009. (ENG., Illus.). 144p. pap. (978-1-84310-975-4(1)) Kingsley, Jessica Ltd.

Tideiksaar, Rein. Managing Falls in Adult Day Services. 2006. (Essential Falls Management Ser.). cd-rom 69.95 (978-1-932529-19-7(5)) Health Professions Pr.

ADULT EDUCATION

see also Elementary Education of Adults; Non-Formal Education; Older People—Education; Religious Education of Adults; Television in Adult Education

Abbagidi, Fadil Jihad. Conceptions & Traditions of Adult Literacy Curriculum in Ethiopi. 2010. 136p. pap. (978-3-639-27281-9(1)) VDM Verlag Dr. Mueller e.K.

Abdi, Ali A. & Kapoor, Dip. Global Perspectives on Adult Education. Abdi, Ali A. & Kapoor, Dip, eds. 2008. (ENG.). 284p. 100.00 (978-0-230-60795-8(0)) Palgrave Macmillan.

Ace. Meeting Adult Learner Needs Through the Nontraditional Doctoral Degree. Jerman, Jerry & Pappas, James P., eds. 2010. (J-B ACE Single Issue Adult & Continuing Education Ser.: 107). (ENG.). 112p. pap. 29.00 (978-1-118-02763-9(9), Jossey-Bass) Wiley, John & Sons, Inc.

ACE (Adult and Continuing Education) Staff & Reed Books Staff. Third Update on Adult Learning Theory No. 119: New Directions for Adult & Continuing Education. Merriam, Sharan B., ed. 2008. (J-B ACE Single Issue Adult & Continuing Education Ser.: 94). (ENG.). 96p. pap. 29.00 (978-0-470-41785-0(4), Jossey-Bass) Wiley, John & Sons, Inc.

Ace Staff. Adult Education for Health & Wellness. Hill, Lilian H., ed. 2011. (J-B ACE Single Issue Adult & Continuing Education Ser.: 108). (ENG.). 112p. pap. 29.00 (978-1-118-08878-4(6), Jossey-Bass) Wiley, John & Sons, Inc.

Ace Staff & Carnton. Challenging Homophobia & Heterosexism No. 112: Lesbian, Gay, Bisexual, Transgender & Queer Issues in Organizational Settings. Hill, Robert J., ed. 2007. (J-B ACE Single Issue Adult & Continuing Education Ser.: 83).Tr. of . (ENG., Illus.). 96p. pap. 29.00 (978-0-7879-9495-2(2), Jossey-Bass) Wiley, John & Sons, Inc.

ACEC Staff. Adult Education & the Pursuit of Wisdom No. 131: New Directions for Adult & Continuing Education. Swartz, Ann L. & Tisdell, Elizabeth J., eds. 2011. (J-B ACE Single Issue Adult & Continuing Education Ser.: 109). (ENG.). 112p. pap. 29.00 **(978-1-118-13327-9(7)**, Jossey-Bass) Wiley, John & Sons, Inc.

Adelson-Goldstein, Jayme. Professional Development Program. 2006. (Step Forward Ser.). (ENG., Illus.). 32p. pap. 25.94 (978-0-19-439877-0(3)) Oxford Univ. Pr., Inc.

Adult and Continuing Education (ACE) Staff. Narrative Perspectives on Adult Education: New Directions for Adult & Continuing Education. Clark, M. Carolyn & Rossiter, Marsha, eds. 2010. (J-B ACE Single Issue Adult & Continuing Education Ser.: 102). (ENG.). 112p. pap. 29.00 (978-0-470-87465-3(1), Jossey-Bass) Wiley, John & Sons, Inc.

Adult and Continuing Education Staff. Adult Education in the Rural Context: People, Place, & Change - New Directions for Adult & Continuing Education. Ritchey, Jeffrey A., ed. 2008. (J-B ACE Single Issue Adult & Continuing Education Ser.: 92). (ENG., Illus.). 96p. pap. 29.00 (978-0-470-28975-4(9), Jossey-Bass) Wiley, John & Sons, Inc.

—Bringing Community to the Adult ESL Classroom, No. 121. Brooks, Ann K. & Larrotta, Clarena, eds. 2009. (J-B ACE Single Issue Adult & Continuing Education Ser.: 96). (ENG., Illus.). 96p. pap. 29.00 (978-0-470-47955-1(8), Jossey-Bass) Wiley, John & Sons, Inc.

—Negotiating Ethical Practice in Adult Education No. 123: New Directions for Adult & Continuing Education. Burge, Elizabeth J., ed. 2009. (J-B ACE Single Issue Adult & Continuing Education Ser.: 98). (ENG.). 96p. pap. 29.00 (978-0-470-53971-2(2), Jossey-Bass) Wiley, John & Sons, Inc.

—Social Capital & Women's Support Systems No. 122: Networking, Learning, & Surviving - New Directions for Adult & Continuing Education. Nanton, Carmela R. & Alfred, Mary V., eds. 2009. (J-B ACE Single Issue Adult & Continuing Education Ser.: 97). (ENG.). 100p. pap. 29.00 (978-0-470-53734-3(5), Jossey-Bass) Wiley, John & Sons, Inc.

—White Privilege & Racism - Perceptions & Actions: New Directions for Adult & Continuing Education. Colin, Scipio A. J. & Lund, Carole L., eds. 2010. (J-B ACE Single Issue Adult & Continuing Education Ser.: 100). (ENG.). 104p. pap. 29.00 (978-0-470-63162-1(7), Jossey-Bass) Wiley, John & Sons, Inc.

Albertson, Gerald. E., ed. Issues in English Language Learning. 2010. (Education in a Competitive & Globalizing World Ser.). 89.00 (978-1-60876-848-6(1)) Nova Science Pubs., Inc.

Alder, Ann. Pattern Making, Pattern Breaking: Using Past Experience & New Behaviour in Training, Education & Change Management. 2010. (Illus.). 240p. 99.95 (978-0-566-08853-7(3), Gower Publishing Co., Ltd.) Ashgate Publishing, Ltd. GBR. Dist: Ashgate Publishing Co.

Aldridge, Fiona & Tuckett, Alan. Practice Makes Perfect. 2007. (978-1-86201-328-5(4)) National Institute of Adult Continuing Education.

Anastasiades, Panagiotes S. Blended Learning Environments for Adults: Evaluations & Frameworks. 2012. **(978-1-4666-0941-9(9))** IGI Global.

Anastasiades, Panagiotes S., ed. Blended Learning Environments for Adults: Evaluations & Frameworks. 2012. 365p. 175.00 **(978-1-4666-0939-6(7)**, Information Science Reference) IGI Global.

Andersson, Per-Ake & Harris, Judy. Re-Theorising the Recognition of Prior Learning. 2006. (Illus.). 342p. pap. 34.95 (978-1-86201-265-3(2)) National Institute of Adult Continuing Education GBR. Dist: International Specialized Bk. Services.

Antikainen, A. In from the Margins Adult Education Work. 2006. 372p. (978-90-77874-47-9(X)) Sense Pubs.

Appleby, Yvon & Barton, David. Developing Adult Teaching & Learning Practitioner Guides: Responding to People's Lives. 2007. (Illus.). 43p. (978-1-86201-330-8(6)) National Institute of Adult Continuing Education.

Aspin, David N., ed. Philosophical Perspectives on Lifelong Learning. 2010. (Lifelong Learning Book Ser.). xvii, 332p. pap. 279.00 (978-90-481-7561-1(5), 9048175615) Springer.

Aspin, David N., et al, eds. Second International Handbook of Lifelong Learning, 2 vols. 2012. (Springer International Handbooks of Education Ser.). (ENG., Illus.). lxxxiv, 958p. 679.00 **(978-94-007-2359-7(8)**, 9400723598) Springer.

Aspin, David N. & Chapman, Judith D., eds. Values Education & Lifelong Learning: Principles, Policies, Programmes. (Lifelong Learning Book Ser.). 2010. xv, 446p. pap. 189.00 (978-90-481-7558-1(5), 9048175585) 2007. (Illus.). 446p. 189.00 (978-1-4020-6183-7(8)) Springer.

Athanasou, James A., ed. Adult Educational Psychology. 2008. 436p. (978-90-8790-554-5(8)); pap. (978-90-8790-553-8(X)) Sense Pubs.

Balistrieri, Edmondo & DeNino, Giustino. New Research in Education: Adult, Medical, & Vocational. 2009. 110.00 (978-1-60741-873-3(8)) Nova Science Pubs., Inc.

Barlow, Adrian. Extramural: Literature & Lifelong Learning. 2012. (ENG.). 204p. pap. 39.00 **(978-0-7188-9279-1(8))** Lutherworth Pr., The GBR. Dist: Brown, David Bk. Co., The.

Barton, George E. Ordered Pluralism: A Philosophical Plan of Action for Teaching. 2.50 *(978-0-8156-7022-3(2)*, NES 42) Syracuse Univ. Pubns. in Continuing Education.

Bean, Tom. Multimodal Learning for the 21st Century Adolescent. 2010. (N/A Ser.). (Illus.). 136p. (gr. 6-12). pap. 24.99 *(978-1-4258-0517-3(5))* Shell Educational Publishing.

BéLanger, Paul. Theories in Adult Learning & Education: Study Guides in Adult Education. 2011. 106p. pap. 19.95 *(978-3-86649-362-9(2))* Budrich-Esser, Barbara DEU. Dist: International Specialized Bk. Services.

Belzer, Alisa, ed. Toward Defining & Improving Quality in Adult Basic Education. 2007. (Rutgers Invitational Symposium on Education Ser.). (ENG., Illus.). 344p. (C). 105.00 *(978-0-8058-5545-6(9))* Routledge.

Beyene, Temeschen (Thomas). Teaching English to Adult Immigrants. 2011. 68p. pap. ***(978-3-8454-1347-1(6))*** Lambert Academic Publishing.

Bitterlin, Gretchen, et al. Add Ventures 4. 2008. (Ventures Ser.). (ENG.). pap. 36.88 *(978-0-521-67586-4(3))* Cambridge Univ. Pr.

Blakely, Patricia N. & Tomlin, Anna H., eds. Adult Education: Issues & Developments. 2008. 69.00 *(978-1-60456-272-9(2))* Nova Science Pubs., Inc.

Borthwick, Arlene & Pierson, Melissa. Transforming Classroom Practice: Professional Development Strategies in Educational Technology. 2008. (Illus.). xiii, 241p. pap. 44.95 *(978-1-56484-246-6(0))* International Society for Technology in Education.

Bostick, Nan. Consumer Spending. 2011. (21st Century Lifeskills Ser.). (ENG.). 48p. (gr. 9-12). pap., stu. ed. 14.95 *(978-1-61651-117-3(6))* Saddleback Educational Publishing.

—Managing Money. 2011. (21st Century Lifeskills Ser.). (ENG.). 48p. (gr. 9-12). pap., stu. ed. 14.95 *(978-1-61651-122-7(2))* Saddleback Educational Publishing.

Bowl, Marion, et al, eds. Gender, Masculinities & Lifelong Learning. (ENG., Illus.). 192p. (C). 2013. 155.00 *(978-0-415-66758-6(5))* 2012. pap. 44.95 *(978-0-415-56759-3(3))* Routledge.

Boylston, Mary T. & Blair, Anthony L. Minimizing the Stress of Accelerated Adult Education. 2009. 53p. pap. 37.00 *(978-1-60692-859-2(7))* Nova Science Pubs., Inc.

Branch, Kirk. Eyes on the Ought to Be: What We Teach about When We Teach about Literacy. 2007. (Research & Teaching in Rhetoric & Composition Ser.). 62.50 *(978-1-57273-713-6(1))*; (ENG.). 256p. pap. 21.95 *(978-1-57273-714-3(X))* Hampton Pr., Inc.

Brookfield, Stephen D. & Holst, John D. Radicalizing Learning: Adult Education for a Just World. 2010. (ENG.). 288p. 40.00 *(978-0-7879-9825-7(7)*, Jossey-Bass) Wiley, John & Sons, Inc.

Buckner, Dwayne. Balance: How to Stay Happily Married While a Student in Law School. 2009. 55p. pap. 17.95 *(978-0-557-04427-6(8))* Lulu Enterprises Inc.

Camenson, Blythe. Opportunities in Adult Education. 2008. (ENG.). 160p. pap. 14.95 *(978-0-07-149306-2(9)*, 0071493069) McGraw-Hill Cos., The.

Çankaya, Dilek. Migration Within Turkey & Adult Education. 2010. 88p. pap. *(978-3-8383-5220-6(3))* Lambert Academic Publishing.

Carroll, Michael. Developing a New Curriculum for Adult Learners. 2007. (Illus.). ix, 254p. *(978-1-931185-45-5(X))* Teachers of English to Speakers of Other Languages, Inc. (TESOL).

Chancellor, John. The Library in the TVA Adult Education Program. 75p. reprint ed. lib. bdg. 88.00 *(978-0-7222-0389-7(6))* Library Reprints, Inc.

Chapman, Judith, et al, eds. Lifelong Learning, Participation & Equity. 2010. (Lifelong Learning Book Ser.). xxvi, 365p. pap. 219.00 *(978-90-481-7339-6(6)*, 9048173396) Springer.

Church, Kathryn, et al, eds. Learning Through Community: Exploring Participatory Practices. 2008. (ENG.). xvi, 216p. 129.00 *(978-1-4020-6653-5(8)*, 1402066538) Springer.

Cloutier, Yvon J. Participation in Adult Learning Activities. 2010. 192p. pap. *(978-3-8383-2160-8(X))* Lambert Academic Publishing.

Coben, D., et al, eds. Perspectives on Adults Learning Mathematics: Research & Practice. 2010. (Mathematics Education Library). 376p. pap. 279.00 *(978-90-481-5506-4(1)*, 9048155061) Springer.

Comings, John, et al, eds. Review of Adult Learning & Literacy: Connecting Research, Policy, & Practice. 2007. 363p. 110.00 *(978-0-8058-6164-8(5))* Erlbaum, Lawrence Assocs., Inc.

Comings, John, et al. National Center for the Study of Adult Learning & Literacy, Vol. 2. 2009. (J-B Annual Review of Adult Learning & Literacy Ser.: 8). (ENG.). 320p. pap. 40.00 *(978-0-470-62305-3(5)*, Jossey-Bass) Wiley, John & Sons, Inc.

Conceição, Simone C. O., ed. Teaching Strategies in the Online Environment: New Directions for Adult & Continuing Education. 2007. (J-B ACE Single Issue Adult & Continuing Education Ser.: 86). (ENG., Illus.). 96p. per. 29.00 *(978-0-7879-9674-1(2)*, Jossey-Bass) Wiley, John & Sons, Inc.

Cooper, Natasha. Scripts for Winning Jobs: Job Search - Negotiations - Interviews - Promotions, 4 vols. 2007. (Power English Ser.). 160p. 79.99 incl. audio compact disk *(978-1-932521-48-1(8))* Cooper Learning Systems.

Corder & Corder, Nicholas. Learning to Teach Adults: An Introduction. 2nd rev. ed. 2007. (Illus.). XVI, 160p. 160.00 *(978-0-415-42362-5(7))* Routledge.

Corder, Nicholas. Learning to Teach Adults: An Introduction. 2nd rev. ed. 2007. (ENG., Illus.). 176p. pap. 41.95 *(978-0-415-42363-2(5))* Routledge.

Cranton, Patricia. Planning Instruction for Adult Learners, 1 vol. 3rd ed. 2012. (ENG.). 228p. pap. 19.50 ***(978-1-895131-25-3(1))*** Wall & Emerson, Inc. CAN. Dist: Univ. of Toronto Pr.

Cross, Sue. Adult Teaching & Learning: A Guide to Effective Practice. 2009. (ENG.). 184p. (C). 127.00 *(978-0-335-23467-7(4)*, 0335234674) McGraw-Hill Education GBR. Dist: McGraw-Hill Cos., The.

—Adult Teaching & Learning: Developing Your Practice. 2009. (ENG.). 184p. (C). pap. 45.00 *(978-0-335-23466-0(6)*, 0335234666) McGraw-Hill Education GBR. Dist: McGraw-Hill Cos., The.

Daffron, Sandra Ratcliff & North, Mary Wehby. Successful Transfer of Learning. 2011. *(978-1-57524-298-9(2))* Krieger Publishing Co.

Dahlstedt, Magnus & Fejes, Andreas. The Confessing Society: Foucault, Confession & Practices of Lifelong Learning. 2012. (ENG.). 160p. (C). 155.00 *(978-0-415-58166-0(4))* Routledge.

Danks, Sharon. Asphalt to Ecosystems: Design Ideas for Schoolyard Transformation. 2010. (ENG., Illus.). 288p. pap. 39.95 *(978-0-9766054-8-5(1))* New Village Pr.

Davis, Cecil. I Got My Ged At 53. 2009. 78p. pap. 14.95 *(978-1-4327-3932-4(8))* Outskirts Pr., Inc.

Davis, Deborah. Adult Learner's Companion. 2007. xv, 191p. *(978-0-618-47467-7(6))*; *(978-0-618-73134-3(2))* Houghton Mifflin Harcourt Publishing Co.

—The Adult Learner's Companion: A Guide for the Adult College Student. 2nd ed. 2011. (ENG.). 144p. (C). spiral bd. 49.95 *(978-0-495-91383-2(9))* Wadsworth.

Derrick, et al. Remaking Adult Learning. 2011. (ENG., Illus.). 296p. pap. 39.95 *(978-0-85473-885-4(1))* Institute of Education GBR. Dist: Stylus Publishing, LLC.

Doghonadze, Natela. Esp Course Book for Adult Learners. 2011. 164p. pap. ***(978-3-8443-0374-2(X))*** Lambert Academic Publishing.

Doyle, Lesley, et al, eds. Building Stronger Communities: Connecting Research, Policy & Practice. 2008. (Illus.). 320p. pap. 34.95 *(978-1-86201-345-2(4))* National Institute of Adult Continuing Education GBR. Dist: International Specialized Bk. Services.

Draves, Bill. How-to-Teach Adults in One Hour. 67p. 7.95 *(978-0-914951-33-9(5))* Learning Resources Network, Inc.

Drury, Sharon. Systems of Excellence in Adult Higher Education. 2007. (Illus.). 91p. *(978-1-931283-29-8(X)*, Wiley-Blackwell) Triangle Publishing.

Duus Henriksen, Thomas. A Little More Conversation, a Little Less Action, Please. 2010. 344p. pap. *(978-3-8383-5528-3(8))* Lambert Academic Publishing.

Egetenmeyer, Regina & Nuissl, Ekkehard, eds. Teachers & Trainers in Adult & Lifelong Learning: Asian & European Perspectives. 2010. 224p. 43.95 *(978-3-631-61298-9(2))* Lang, Peter GmbH, Europaischer Verlag der Wissenschaften DEU. Dist: Lang, Peter.

English, Leona. International Encyclopedia of Adult Education. English, Leona M., ed. 2008. (ENG.). 768p. pap. 61.00 *(978-0-230-20171-2(7))* Palgrave Macmillan.

Esparza, June F. Los Hombres Hablan de Seguir Adelante: A Guide for Men Returning to School. Montalvo, Maria, tr. Date not set. (Illus.). 240p. (Orig.). (C). pap. 16.95 *(978-0-9647161-5-5(1))* Thoughts in Motion.

Fairclough, Marilyn. Supporting Learners in the Lifelong Learning Sector. 2008. (ENG., Illus.). 176p. 132.00 *(978-0-335-23363-2(5)*, 0335233635); pap. 40.00 *(978-0-335-23362-5(7)*, 0335233627) McGraw-Hill Education GBR. Dist: McGraw-Hill Cos., The.

Feldman & Mcphee. 88 Proven Classroom Practices for Adult Educators. 2007. (ENG.). 224p. (C). pap. 49.95 *(978-1-4180-1617-3(9))* Delmar Cengage Learning.

Field. Adult & Continuing Education. (Taking Responsibility Ser.). 80p. (C). pap. 8.95 *(978-0-7453-0932-3(1))* Pluto Pr. GBR. Dist: Stylus Publishing, LLC.

Field, Jane. Evaluating Community Projects. (Illus.). 35p. pap. *(978-1-86201-152-6(4))* National Institute of Adult Continuing Education.

Field, John, et al. Researching Transitions in Lifelong Learning. Field, John et al, eds. 2009. (ENG., Illus.). 230p. 42.95 *(978-0-415-49599-8(7))*; 150.00 *(978-0-415-49598-1(9))* Routledge.

FitzSimons, Gail E., ed. Lifelong Learning: Theoretical & Practical Perspectives on Adult Numeracy & Vocational Mathematics. 2010. (Education in a Competitive & Globalizing World Ser.). pap. 43.00 *(978-1-61668-291-0(4)*, Nova Science Pubs., Inc.

Fleming, et al. Brief Guide for Teaching Adult Learners. 2009. (Illus.). 92p. *(978-1-931283-40-3(0)*, Nicholson) Triangle Publishing.

Fuller, Alison, et al, eds. Widening Participation for Reluctant Students. 2011. (ENG., Illus.). 176p. (C). 120.00 *(978-0-415-57563-8(X))*; pap. 36.95 *(978-0-415-57564-5(8))* Routledge.

Garner, Barbara, et al, eds. Connecting Research, Policy, & Practice. 2007. 363p. per. 36.95 *(978-0-8058-6165-5(3))* Erlbaum, Lawrence Assocs., Inc.

Garson, Kyra. Applying Transformative Learning to Cross-Cultural Training Endeavours. 2009. 132p. pap. *(978-3-639-16168-7(8))* VDM Verlag Dr. Mueller e.K.

Gast, Natalie. For ESL Advancing Your Career. 2010. (Perfect Phrases Ser.). (ENG.). 176p. pap. 11.95 *(978-0-07-160836-7(2)*, 0071608362) McGraw-Hill Cos., The.

Gathers, Victor, et al, eds. TABE Fundamentals: Language & Spelling, Level M. 2nd ed. 2008. (Tabe Fundamentals Ser.). (Illus.). 99p. pap. 20.40 *(978-1-4190-5353-5(1))* Houghton Mifflin Harcourt Supplemental Pubs.

Georgina, David. Re-visioning Pedagogy for Adult Learners: Designing a Computer Lab-Based Education Technology Course to be Inclusive of Non-Traditional Students. 2008. 72p. pap. *(978-3-639-09448-0(4))* VDM Verlag Dr. Mueller e.K.

Giordani, Tania. All Children Are Our Children. 2009. 188p. pap. *(978-3-639-02154-7(1))* VDM Verlag Dr. Mueller e.K.

González, Arturo. California's Commitment to Adult English Learners: Caught Between Funding & Need. 2007. *(978-1-58213-123-8(6))* Public Policy Institute of California.

Harrell, Jack. The Adult Creative Writer. 2008. 164p. pap. *(978-3-639-03609-1(3))* VDM Verlag Dr. Mueller e.K.

Harrison, J. F. C. Learning & Living 1790-1960. 10th ed. 2007. 448p. 200.00 *(978-0-415-43237-5(5))* Routledge.

Hayes. Teaching Adults. 2006. (Essential FE Toolkit Ser.). (ENG.). 158p. 31.95 *(978-0-8264-8707-0(6))* Continuum International Publishing Group, Ltd. GBR. Dist: National Bk. Network.

Hayes Ed.D., William D. In Their Own Words: How Simply Asking Adult English as a Second Language Students How They Preferred to Learn How to Speak & Write in English Change. 2009. 134p. pap. 13.95 *(978-1-4401-5939-8(4))* iUniverse, Inc.

Heaney, Thomas, et al, eds. The Struggle for Democracy in Adult Education No. 128: New Directions for Adult & Continuing Education. 2011. (J-B ACE Single Issue Adult & Continuing Education Ser.: 106). (ENG.). 112p. pap. 29.00 *(978-1-118-00302-2(0)*, Jossey-Bass) Wiley, John & Sons, Inc.

Henry, George. Malcolm Shepherd Knowles: A History of his Thought. 2011. (Education in a Competitive & Globalizing World Ser.). (Illus.). 217p. 129.00 *(978-1-61209-451-9(1))* Nova Science Pubs., Inc.

Hillier Yvonne & Hillier, Yvonne. Reflective Teaching in Further & Adult Education. 3rd ed. 2012. (ENG., Illus.). 304p. pap. 44.95 *(978-1-4411-7550-2(4))* Continuum International Publishing Group, Ltd. GBR. Dist: National Bk. Network.

Houghton, Peggy M. & Houghton, Timothy J. Adult Learning: The Easy Way. 2007. *(978-0-923568-80-1(8))* Baker College Publishing Co.

Hunt, Rachael. What Is the Virtual Water Cooler? 2008. 100p. pap. *(978-3-639-00395-6(0))* VDM Verlag Dr. Mueller e.K.

Hutchinson, Emily. Everyday Household Tasks. 2011. (21st Century Lifeskills Ser.). (ENG.). 48p. (gr. 9-12). pap., stu. ed. 14.95 *(978-1-61651-118-0(4))* Saddleback Educational Publishing.

Hutchinson, Emily & Bostick, Nan. Moving Out on Your Own. 2011. (21st Century Lifeskills Ser.). (ENG.). 48p. (gr. 9-12). pap., stu. ed. 14.95 *(978-1-61651-123-4(0))* Saddleback Educational Publishing.

Jackson, Sue, et al, eds. Gendered Choices: Learning, Work, Identities in Lifelong Learning. 2011. (Lifelong Learning Book Ser.). xviii, 259p. 139.00 *(978-94-007-0646-0(4)*, 9400706464) Springer.

Jacobsen, Yola. E-Guidelines 11 Usine E-Learning for Adults with Learning Difficulties. 2007. (Illus.). 61p. pap. *(978-1-86201-319-3(5))* National Institute of Adult Continuing Education.

Jameson & Steward, Angela. FE Lecturer's Survival Guide. 2006. (Essential FE Toolkit Ser.). (ENG.). 128p. 29.95 *(978-0-8264-8550-2(2))* Continuum International Publishing Group, Ltd. GBR. Dist: National Bk. Network.

Jarvis, Peter. Adult Education & Lifelong Learning: Theory & Practice. 4th rev. ed. 2010. (ENG., Illus.). 352p. (C). 145.00 *(978-0-415-49478-6(8))*; pap. 51.95 *(978-0-415-49481-6(8))* Routledge.

—Adult Learning in the Social Context (Rle Edu G) 2011. (Routledge Library Editions: Education Ser.). (ENG.). 234p. 115.00 ***(978-0-415-68486-6(2))*** Routledge.

—From Adult Education to the Learning Society. 2012. (ENG.). 456p. pap. 44.95 ***(978-0-415-50945-9(9))*** Routledge.

—The Routledge International Handbook of Lifelong Learning. 2008. (ENG., Illus.). 560p. (C). 205.00 *(978-0-415-41904-8(2))* Routledge.

Jarvis, Peter. The Sociology of Adult & Continuing Education. 2012. (Routledge Library Editions: Education Ser.). (ENG.). 294p. 115.00 ***(978-0-415-68485-9(4))*** Routledge.

Jarvis, Peter, ed. The Routledge International Handbook of Lifelong Learning. 2010. (Illus.). 560p. (C). pap. 69.95 *(978-0-415-58165-3(6)*, Routledge) Taylor & Francis Group GBR. Dist: Taylor & Francis Group.

Johnson, Glenn R. & Magnan, Robert. Beyond Subject Matter Expertise: Strategies for Instructing Adults. 2009. pap. *(978-1-891859-78-6(1))* Atwood Publishing.

Johnson, Shilene. Using Volunteers to Enhance Reading. 2011. 68p. pap. 9.95 ***(978-1-61507-827-1(4))*** Cross Bks. Publishing.

Jones, Bill. Issues in Rural ACL. 2006. *(978-1-86201-255-4(5))* National Institute of Adult Continuing Education.

Jude, Chris. Consulting Adults. (Illus.). 45p. pap. *(978-1-86201-149-6(4))* National Institute of Adult Continuing Education.

Kaufman, Maurice. The Literacy Tutor's Handbook: A Guide for Planning, Assessment, & Instruction. 2007. 312p. 42.95 *(978-1-929024-96-4(7))* Christopher-Gordon Pubs., Inc.

Kejawa, Iwasan D. Strategic Analysis of Education Fundamentals for Modern Society. 2008. pap. 10.00 *(978-1-4349-6020-7(X))* Dorrance Publishing Co., Inc.

Kidd, Terry T. Adult Learning in the Digital Age: Perspectives on Online Technologies & Outcomes. Kidd, Terry T. & Keengwe, Jared, eds. 2009. 342p. 180.00 *(978-1-60566-828-4(1)*, Information Science Reference) IGI Global.

Kidd, Terry T., ed. Online Education & Adult Learning: New Frontiers for Teaching Practices. 2009. 374p. 180.00 *(978-1-60566-830-7(3))* IGI Global.

Knowles,, Malcolm S., Malcolm S, et al. The Adult Learner: The definitive classic in adult education & human resource Development. 7th rev. ed. 2011. (ENG., Illus.). 416p. (C). pap. 49.95 *(978-1-85617-811-2(0))* Routledge.

Knowles & Holton Ii & Swanson & Cram101 Textbook Reviews Staff. The Adult Learner. 2007. 80p. per. 10.95 *(978-1-4288-2048-7(5))* Cram101 Inc.

Kosbab, Derek. Lifetime Goal-Setting Effects for Adult Vocational Learners. 2010. 292p. pap. *(978-3-8383-1993-3(1))* Lambert Academic Publishing.

Krasemann, Keith W. The Role of Time Consciousness in Lifelong Learning: A Theoretical Framework for Adult Education. 2006. 240p. *(978-0-7734-5534-4(5))* Mellen, Edwin Pr., The.

Lakey, George. Facilitating Group Learning: Strategies for Success with Diverse Adult Learners. 2010. (ENG.). 304p. 40.00 *(978-0-470-75863-1(0)*, Jossey-Bass) Wiley, John & Sons, Inc.

Lucio-Villegas, Emilio, ed. Citizenship As Politics. 2009. 180p. *(978-94-6091-039-5(4))*; pap. *(978-94-6091-033-8(6))* Sense Pubs.

Lukenchuk, Antonina. Reflections on the Nature of Self in the World & Adult Education. 2009. 260p. pap. *(978-3-639-15774-1(5))* VDM Verlag Dr. Mueller e.K.

Ma, Cheng. Perfect Phrases for ESL Advancing Your Career. 2010. 96p. pap. 10.95 *(978-0-07-160386-7(7))* McGraw-Hill Professional Publishing.

Mageehon, Alexandria. Value, Belief & Experience in Women's Jail Based Adult Education. 2008. 326p. lib. bdg. *(978-1-933146-33-1(8)*, Sheridan, W.B. Law Publishers) Academica Pr., LLC.

Martin, Allan. Older Adulthood, Education & Social Change- Education & the Potential for Social Change in Later Life. 2007. pap. *(978-3-8364-2595-7(5))* VDM Verlag Dr. Mueller e.K.

Materna, Laurie. Jump-Start the Adult Learner: How to Engage & Motivate Adults Using Brain-Compatible Strategies. 2007. (Illus.). 232p. 85.95 *(978-1-4129-5293-4(X)*, B5293XC); per. 38.95 *(978-1-4129-5294-1(8)*, B5293XP) Corwin Pr.

Mathison, Sandra, ed. Enduring Issues in Evaluation: The 20th Anniversary of the Collaboration Between NDE & AEA - New Directions for Evaluation. 2007. (J-B PE Single Issue (Program) Evaluation Ser.: 83). (ENG., Illus.). 144p. per. 29.00 *(978-0-470-17900-0(7)*, Jossey-Bass) Wiley, John & Sons, Inc.

Merriam, Sharan B. & Brockett, Ralph G. The Profession & Practice of Adult Education: An Introduction. 2007. (CourseSmart Ser.). (ENG.). 400p. pap. 42.00 *(978-0-470-18153-9(2)*, Jossey-Bass) Wiley, John & Sons, Inc.

Merriam, Sharan B. & Grace, Andre P., eds. The Jossey-Bass Reader on Contemporary Issues in Adult Education. 2011. (ENG., Illus.). 512p. pap. 45.00 *(978-0-470-87356-4(6)*, Jossey-Bass) Wiley, John & Sons, Inc.

Millard, Robert. Developing a Collaborative Learning Community. 2010. 152p. pap. *(978-3-639-23266-0(6))* VDM Verlag Dr. Mueller e.K.

Miller, Mev & King, Kathleen P., eds. Empowering Women Through Literacy: Views from Experience (HC) 2009. (Illus.). 340p. *(978-1-60752-084-9(2))* Information Age Publishing, Inc.

—Empowering Women Through Literacy: Views from Experience (PB) 2009. (Illus.). 340p. pap. *(978-1-60752-083-2(4))* Information Age Publishing, Inc.

Miller, Susan. The Study of a State Initiative. 2010. 80p. pap. *(978-3-639-19829-4(8))* VDM Verlag Dr. Mueller e.K.

Mojab, Shahrzad & Carpenter, Sara. Educating from Marx: Race, Gender, & Learning. 2011. (Marxism & Education Ser.). (ENG., Illus.). 288p. 90.00 *(978-0-230-11581-1(0))* Palgrave Macmillan.

Molka-Danielsen, Judith & Deutschmann, Mats, eds. Learning & Teaching in the Virtual World of Second Life. 2009. (Illus.). 210p. pap. 60.00 *(978-82-519-2353-8(0))* Tapir Forlag NOR. Dist: International Specialized Bk. Services.

Morgan-Klein, Brenda & Osborne, Michael. The Concepts & Practices of Lifelong Learning. 2008. (Illus.). VIII, 160p. 37.95 *(978-0-415-42861-3(0))* Routledge.

Morris, Barranco. Linking Learning to Strategy Formation. 2010. 232p. pap. *(978-3-639-17171-6(3))* VDM Verlag Dr. Mueller e.K.

Moses, James, et al. The Adult & Continuing Education Business Report. Date not set. 156p. 295.00 *(978-1-57440-007-6(X))* Primary Research Group.

Nicoll, Katherine & Fejes, Andreas, eds. Foucault & Lifelong Learning: Governing the Subject. 2008. 208p. 150.00 *(978-0-415-42402-8(X))*; 47.95 *(978-0-415-42403-5(8))* Routledge.

Nisheducator. The Native Literacy Source of Medicine: Taking Care of the Care Givers. 2009. 128p. pap. 10.99 *(978-1-4490-2089-7(5))* AuthorHouse.

Nordstrom, Nancy Merz & Merz, Jon F. Learning Later, Living Greater: The Secret for Making the Most of Your after-50 Years. 2006. (Culture Tools Ser.). (ENG.). 240p. per. 16.95 *(978-1-59181-047-6(7))* Sentient Pubns.

Olson, Kathleen Dunn. What's up? Book 1: Integrated Skills & Culture for Adults. 2010. (ENG., Illus.). 128p. pap. 20.95 *(978-0-472-03291-4(7))* Univ. of Michigan Pr.

Organisation for Economic Co-operation and Development Staff. Formative Assessment: Improving Learning of Adults with Foundation Skills. 2008. pap. 63.00 *(978-92-64-03990-2(2))* Organization for Economic Cooperation & Development.

O'Rourke, Liz. Teacher, Trainer, Tutor: Empowering the Learning Process by Improving the Relationships between Learners, Teachers, Trainers & Tutors, 1 vol. 2011. (ENG.). 208p. pap. 19.95 *(978-1-61110-019-8(4))* Global Management Enterprises.

Osborne, Michael & Longworth, Norman. Perspectives on Learning Cities & Regions (PASCAL) Policy, Practice & Participation. 2010. 371p. pap. 34.95 *(978-1-86201-448-0(5))* National Institute of Adult Continuing Education GBR. Dist: International Specialized Bk. Services.

Osborne, Mike. The Concepts & Practices of Lifelong Learning. 2008. (Illus.). VIII, 160p. 160.00 *(978-0-415-42860-6(2))* Routledge.

Parent, Neil A. A Concise Guide to Adult Faith Formation. 2009. 192p. pap. 16.95 *(978-1-59471-208-1(5))* Ave Maria Pr.

Paterson, R. W. K. Values, Education & the Adult. 2010. (ENG.). 320p. 140.00 *(978-0-415-55359-8(3))* Routledge.

Paton, Anne & Wilkins, Meryl. Teaching Adult ESOL. 2009. (ENG., Illus.). 296p. (C). 117.00 *(978-0-335-23737-1(1)*, 0335237371) McGraw-Hill Education GBR. Dist: McGraw-Hill Cos., The.

—Teaching Adult ESOL: Principles & Practice. 2009. (ENG., Illus.). 296p. (C). pap. 47.00 *(978-0-335-23738-8(X)*, 033523738X) McGraw-Hill Education GBR. Dist: McGraw-Hill Cos., The.

Penketh, Claire. A Clumsy Encounter: Dyspraxia & Drawing. 2011. 184p. ***(978-94-6091-456-0(X))***; pap. ***(978-94-6091-455-3(1))*** Sense Pubs.

Peterson's Guides Staff. GED Basics 2011. Schwartz, Jill, ed. 4th ed. 2010. (ENG.). 240p. (YA). pap. 15.95 *(978-0-7689-2883-9(4)*, Arco) Peterson's.

Powell, Scott. Appalachian Educational Realization. 2008. 212p. pap. *(978-3-639-04378-5(2))* VDM Verlag Dr. Mueller e.K.

Preece, Julia. Lifelong Learning & Development: A Southern Perspective. (ENG.). 200p. 2011. pap. 44.95 ***(978-1-4411-1175-3(1))*** 2009. 150.00 *(978-1-84706-291-8(1))* Continuum International Publishing Group, Ltd. GBR. Dist: National Bk. Network.

Primary Research Group Staff. Profiles of College & University Distance Learning Programs. Date not set. 100p. 80.00 *(978-1-57440-009-0(6))* Primary Research Group.

Princeton Review Staff. GED Basics: An Introduction to All 5 Tests. 2012. (College Test Preparation Ser.). (ENG.). 544p. pap. 17.99 *(978-0-375-42836-4(4)*, Princeton Review) Random Hse. Information Group.

Qi, Sun. East Meets West: Perennial Wisdom for the Ends/Means Issue of Modern Adult Ecucation. 2011. 140p. pap. ***(978-3-639-32520-1(6))*** VDM Verlag Dr. Mueller e.K.

RamdehoII, Dianne. Adult Literacy in a New Era: Oral Histories from the Open Book. 2011. (Series in Critical Narrative Ser.). 192p. 98.00 *(978-1-59451-848-5(3))* Paradigm Pubs.

Regan, Jeannette. The Dance of Learning: On Encounters in Adult Second-Language Learning. 2009. (Illus.). 332p. pap. *(978-3-0343-0017-9(4))* Lang, Peter.

Reischmann, Jost & Bron jr, Michal, eds. Comparative Adult Education 2008: Experiences & Examples. 2008. (Studien zur Pädagogik, Andragogik und Gerontagogik. Studies in Pedagogy, Andragogy, & Gerontagogy Ser.). 282p. pap. 57.95 *(978-3-631-58235-0(8))* Lang, Peter GmbH, Europäischer Verlag der Wissenschaften DEU. Dist: Lang, Peter.

Remtulla, Karim A. Socio-Cultural Impacts of Workplace E-Learning: Epistemology, Ontology & Pedagogy. 2010. (Illus.). 350p. 180.00 *(978-1-61520-835-7(6))* IGI Global.

Rimanoczy, Isabel & Turner, Ernie. Action Reflection Learning: Solving Real Business Problems by Connecting Learning with Earning. 2008. (ENG., Illus.). 214p. 36.95 *(978-0-89106-240-0(8))* Ebsco Publishing.

Roberson, Donald. Wiregrass Wisdom. 2009. 324p. pap. *(978-3-639-14432-1(5))* VDM Verlag Dr. Mueller e.K.

Rocco, Tonette S. & Grace, Andre, eds. Challenging the Professionalization of Adult Education: John Ohliger & Contradictions in Modern Practice. 2009. (ENG.). 384p. 40.00 *(978-0-7879-7827-3(2)*, Jossey-Bass) Wiley, John & Sons, Inc.

Rogers, Alan & Horrocks, Naomi. Teaching Adults. 4th ed. 2010. (ENG., Illus.). 360p. (C). pap. 49.00 *(978-0-335-23539-1(5)*, 0335235395) McGraw-Hill Education GBR. Dist: McGraw-Hill Cos., The.

Rogers, Jenny. Adults Learning. 5th rev. ed. 2007. (ENG., Illus.). 272p. pap. 49.00 *(978-0-335-22535-4(7)*, 0335225357) McGraw-Hill Education GBR. Dist: McGraw-Hill Cos., The.

Rogers, Rebecca. Adult Education Teachers. Kramer, Mary Ann, ed. 2007. 352p. 150.00 *(978-0-8058-6242-3(0))* Erlbaum, Lawrence Assocs., Inc.

—Adult Education Teachers. 2007. (ENG.). 352p. (C). pap. 50.95 *(978-0-8058-6243-0(9))* Routledge.

Rogers, Stephen D. My First Year in the Classroom: 50 Stories That Celebrate the Good, the Bad, & the Most Unforgettable Moments. 2009. (ENG.). 224p. pap. 9.95 *(978-1-60550-654-8(0))* Adams Media Corp.

Rose, Amy D., et al, eds. Handbook of Adult & Continuing Education. 2010. 512p. 88.00 *(978-1-4129-6050-2(9)*, B60502C) SAGE Pubns., Inc.

Rossiter, Marsha & Clark, M. Carolyn. Narrative & the Practice of Adult Education. 2006. *(978-1-57524-222-4(2))* Krieger Publishing Co.

Rubenson, Kjell, ed. Adult Learning & Education. 2011. (ENG., Illus.). 326p. 99.95 *(978-0-12-381489-0(8)*, Academic Pr.) Elsevier Science & Technology Bks.

Sample, John. Legal Reference for Adult Educators, Human Resource Developers, & Instructional Designers. 2007. *(978-1-57524-273-6(7))* Krieger Publishing Co.

Schmidt, Steven W. Case Studies & Activities in Adult Education & Human Resource Development. 2010. E-Book *(978-1-61735-075-7(3))*; (Illus.). 198p. *(978-1-61735-074-0(5))*; (Illus.). 198p. pap. *(978-1-61735-073-3(7))* Information Age Publishing, Inc.

Schütze, Hans Georg & Slowey, Maria. Global Perspectives on Higher Education & Lifelong Learners. 2012. E-Book ***(978-0-203-12249-5(6))*** Routledge.

Seddon, Terri, et al, eds. Learning & Work & the Politics of Working Life: Global Transformations & Collective Identities in Teaching, Nursing & Social Work. 2010. (ENG.). 243p. 140.00 *(978-0-415-55752-8(6))* Routledge.

Seddon, Terri, et al. Learning & Work & the Politics of Working Life: Global Transformations & Collective Identities in Teaching, Nursing & Social Work. 2010. (ENG.). 243p. pap. 47.95 *(978-0-415-55753-5(4))* Routledge.

Sheared, Vanessa, et al, eds. The Handbook of Race & Adult Education: A Resource for Dialogue on Racism. 2010. (ENG., Illus.). 416p. 57.00 *(978-0-470-38176-2(0)*, Jossey-Bass) Wiley, John & Sons, Inc.

Singh, M., ed. Meeting Basic Learning Needs in the Informal Sector: Integrating Education & Training for Decent Work, Empowerment & Citizenship. 2010. (Technical & Vocational Education & Training: Issues, Concerns & Prospects Ser.). xv, 250p. pap. 169.00 *(978-90-481-6862-0(7)*, 9048168627) Springer.

Smith, Cristine, et al. How Teachers Change: A Study of Professional Development in Adult Education. 2008. (Illus.). 209p. pap. 37.00 *(978-1-60692-922-3(4))* Nova Science Pubs., Inc.

Smith, M. Cecil. Handbook of Research on Adult Learning & Development. 2008. (ENG., Illus.). 832p. 285.00 *(978-0-8058-5819-8(9))*; pap. 109.95 *(978-0-8058-5820-4(2))* Routledge.

Smith, Ray B. The Child in the Voting Booth: When Grown People Elect Parents into Political Office. 2009. 231p. pap. 14.99 *(978-1-60696-538-2(7))* Tate Publishing & Enterprises, LLC.

Solomon, Amy & Quantum Integrations. Faculty Development Workbook Module 1: Understanding the Adult Learner. 2006. (ENG.). 200p. (C). pap. 33.50 *(978-1-4180-3723-9(0))* Delmar Cengage Learning.

Solomon, Amy & Quantum Integrations Staff. Faculty Development Workbook Module 12: Creating an Innovated Learning Environment. 2006. (ENG.). 160p. (C). per. 33.50 *(978-1-4180-4798-6(8))* Delmar Cengage Learning.

St Clair, Ralf. Why Literacy Matters: Understanding the Effects of Literacy Education for Adults. 2010. (ENG., Illus.). 224p. pap. 34.95 *(978-1-86201-450-3(7))* National Institute of Adult Continuing Education GBR. Dist: International Specialized Bk. Services.

Staudacher, Carol. Getting Ahead at Work. 2011. (21st Century Lifeskills Ser.). (ENG.). 48p. (gr. 9-12). pap., stu. ed. 14.95 *(978-1-61651-119-7(2))* Saddleback Educational Publishing.

Stenberg, Anders. Adult Education for a Better Society? 2008. 112p. pap. *(978-3-639-04418-8(5))* VDM Verlag Dr. Mueller e.K.

Steward, Angela. A to Z of Teaching in Fe. 2007. (Essential FE Toolkit Ser.). (ENG.). 144p. 39.95 *(978-0-8264-9080-3(8))* Continuum International Publishing Group, Ltd. GBR. Dist: National Bk. Network.

Suter, Joanne. Community Resources. 2011. (21st Century Lifeskills Ser.). (ENG.). 48p. (gr. 9-12). pap., stu. ed. 14.95 *(978-1-61651-116-6(8))* Saddleback Educational Publishing.

—Health & Safety. 2011. (21st Century Lifeskills Ser.). (ENG.). 48p. (gr. 9-12). pap., stu. ed. 14.95 *(978-1-61651-120-3(6))* Saddleback Educational Publishing.

TABE Exam Secrets Test Prep Staff, ed. TABE Practice Questions: TABE Practice Tests & Exam Review for the Test of Adult Basic Education. 2011. 34.99 *(978-1-61403-735-4(3))* Mometrix Media LLC.

Tanabe, Kelly & Tanabe, Gen. Adult Students: A Painless Guide to Going Back to College. 2nd ed. 2007. (ENG., Illus.). 224p. per. 14.95 *(978-1-932662-21-4(9))* SuperCollege LLC.

Tanner, Lori. Critical Challenges & Barriers to Online Learning- Nontraditional Adult Students in a Nontraditional Teacher Licensing Program. 2007. 188p. per. *(978-3-8364-1757-0(X))* VDM Verlag Dr. Mueller e.K.

Taylor, Edward W. Nonformal Education: Teaching Adults in Public Places. 2011. *(978-1-57524-291-0(5))* Krieger Publishing Co.

Taylor, Edward W. & Cranton, Patricia. The Handbook of Transformative Learning: Theory, Research, & Practice. 2012. (ENG.). 624p. 75.00 ***(978-0-470-59072-0(6)***, Jossey-Bass) Wiley, John & Sons, Inc.

Tesol. Standards for ESL/EFL Teachers of Adults: Adult/Community, Workplace, College/University, Intensive English, English As a Foreign Language. 2008. (Illus.). x, 187p. *(978-1-931185-50-9(6)*, Debolsillo) Teachers of English to Speakers of Other Languages, Inc. (TESOL).

Thompson, Jane. More Words in Edgeways. 2007. 200p. pap. 29.95 *(978-1-86201-344-5(6))* National Institute of Adult Continuing Education GBR. Dist: International Specialized Bk. Services.

Thompson, Patricia M. & Tisdell, Elizabeth J., eds. Popular Culture & Entertainment Media in Adult Education: New Directions for Adult & Continuing Education. 2007. (J-B ACE Single Issue Adult & Continuing Education Ser.: 88). (ENG.). 96p. pap. 29.00 *(978-0-470-24870-6(X)*, Jossey-Bass) Wiley, John & Sons, Inc.

Tight, Malcolm, ed. Education for Adults (Rle Edu G) 2012. (Routledge Library Editions: Education Ser.). (ENG.). 336p. 130.00 ***(978-0-415-68517-7(6))***; 314p. 130.00 ***(978-0-415-68515-3(X))*** Routledge.

Tuckett, Alan, ed. Participation & the Pursuit of Equality: Essays in Adult Learning, Widening Participation & Achievement. 2007. 192p. pap. 34.95 *(978-1-86201-256-1(3))* National Institute of Adult Continuing Education GBR. Dist: International Specialized Bk. Services.

Tuttle, Sonia. Journal Bites. 2009. 72p. pap. 16.50 *(978-1-4389-6055-5(7))* AuthorHouse.

University of Toronto Press. Health & Adult Education. 2009. (ENG.). *(978-1-4426-4024-5(3))*; pap. *(978-1-4426-0998-3(2))* Univ. of Toronto Pr.

Usher, Robin & Bryant, Ian. Adult Education As Theory, Practice & Research: The Captive Triangle. 2012. (Routledge Library Editions: Education Ser.). (ENG.). 220p. 115.00 ***(978-0-415-68439-2(0))*** Routledge.

Usher, Robin & Edwards, Richard. Lifelong Learning - Signs, Discourses, Practices. 2010. (Lifelong Learning Book Ser.). ix, 182p. pap. 189.00 *(978-90-481-7400-3(7)*, 9048174007) Springer.

Van Dijk, Lutz & Van Driel, Barry, eds. Challenging Homophobia: Teaching about Sexual Diversity. 2007. 204p. per. 32.95 *(978-1-85856-413-5(1))* Trentham Bks. Ltd. GBR. Dist: Stylus Publishing, LLC.

Vella, Jane. On Teaching & Learning: Putting the Principles & Practices of Dialogue Education into Action. 2007. (ENG., Illus.). 272p. 40.00 *(978-0-7879-8699-5(2)*, Jossey-Bass) Wiley, John & Sons, Inc.

Wallace, Susan & Gravells, Jonathan. A to Z for All Managers in FE. 2007. (Essential FE Toolkit Ser.). (ENG., Illus.). 162p. 39.95 *(978-0-8264-9170-1(7))* Continuum International Publishing Group, Ltd. GBR. Dist: National Bk. Network.

Wang, Victor C. X. Assessing & Evaluating Adult Learning in Career & Technical Education. 2010. (Illus.). 350p. 180.00 *(978-1-61520-745-9(7))* IGI Global.

—Pedagogical & Andragogical Teaching & Learning with Information Communication Technologies. 2011. *(978-1-60960-793-7(7))* IGI Global.

Wang, Victor C. X. Vocational Education Technologies & Advances in Adult Learning: New Concepts. 2012. ***(978-1-4666-0254-0(6))*** IGI Global.

Wang, Victor C. X., ed. Encyclopedia of Information Communication Technologies & Adult Education Integration, 3 vols. 2010. (Illus.). 1535p. 1495.00 *(978-1-61692-906-0(5)*, Information Science Reference) IGI Global.

—Integrating Adult Learning & Technologies for Effective Education: Strategic Approaches. 2010. 391p. 180.00 *(978-1-61520-694-0(9)*, Information Science Reference) IGI Global.

Wang, Victor C. X., ed. Vocational Education Technologies & Advances in Adult Learning: New Concepts. 2012. 355p. 175.00 ***(978-1-4666-0252-6(X)***, Information Science Reference) IGI Global.

Wang, Victor C. X., et al. Pedagogical & Andragogical Teaching & Learning with Information Communication Technologies. 2011. 362p. 195.00 *(978-1-60960-791-3(0)*, Information Science Reference) IGI Global.

Warren, Clay, ed. Democracy is Born in Conversations: N.F.S Grundtvig for Lifelong Learners Around the World. (Illus.). 221p. pap. 17.00 *(978-1-891592-05-8(X))* Circumstantial Productions.

Weatherholt, Anne. Breaking the Silence: The Church Responds to Domestic Violence. 2008. 136p. pap. 16.00 *(978-0-8192-2320-3(4)*, Morehouse Publishing) Church Publishing, Inc.

Whalley, Welch. E-learning in FE. 2006. (Essential FE Toolkit Ser.). (ENG., Illus.). 128p. 29.95 *(978-0-8264-8862-6(5))* Continuum International Publishing Group, Ltd. GBR. Dist: National Bk. Network.

Withnall, Alexandra. Improving Learning in Later Life. 2008. (Improving Learning Ser.). (Illus.). 176p. 41.95 *(978-0-415-46172-6(3))* Routledge.

Witte, James E. & Martinez, Witte Maria. Sources of Adult Education. rev. ed. 2009. (ENG.). 220p. pap. 60.44 *(978-0-7575-5929-7(8))* Kendall Hunt Publishing Co.

Wlodkowski, Raymond J. Enhancing Adult Motivation to Learn: A Comprehensive Guide for Teaching All Adults. 3rd ed. 2008. (CourseSmart Ser.). (ENG., Illus.). 528p. 52.00 *(978-0-7879-9520-1(7)*, Jossey-Bass) Wiley, John & Sons, Inc.

Wodlinger, Michael. Adult Education. 2007. 212p. per. 14.99 *(978-1-60266-069-4(7))* Xulon Pr., Inc.

Wolf, Alison & Evans, Karen. Improving Literacy at Work. 2010. (Improving Learning Ser.). (ENG., Illus.). 216p. pap. 36.95 *(978-0-415-54872-4(1))* Routledge.

Wright, Hazel. Women Studying Childcare: Integrating Lives Through Adult Education. 2011. (Illus.). 188p. pap. 34.95 *(978-1-85856-485-2(9))* Trentham Bks. Ltd. GBR. Dist: Stylus Publishing, LLC.

Yi, Pu-Il. Noin P'yongsaeng Kyoyuk Sisol P'uroguraem Ch'amyo Tonggi Wa Pich'amyo Yoin. 2010. (KOR., Illus.). 201p. pap. *(978-89-26-81193-1(X))*; E-Book *(978-89-26-81194-8(8))* Korean Studies Information Co., Ltd.

Yuzer, T. Volkan & Kurubacak, Gulsun, eds. Transformative Learning & Online Education: Aesthetics, Dimensions & Concepts. 2010. (Illus.). 386p. 180.00 *(978-1-61520-985-9(9))* IGI Global.

ADULT EDUCATION—DIRECTORIES

National Institute of Adult Continuing Education (England and Wales) Staff, contrib. by. Adult Learning Yearbook 2007. 2007. 327p. *(978-1-86201-257-8(1))* National Institute of Adult Continuing Education.

National Institute of Adult Continuing Education Staff. Adult Learning Yearbook 2008. 310p. *(978-1-86201-334-6(9))* National Institute of Adult Continuing Education.

ADULT EDUCATION—RESEARCH

Harris, Judy, et al, eds. Researching the Recognition of Prior Learning: International Perspectives. 2011. (ENG.). 358p. pap. 34.95 *(978-1-86201-460-2(4))* National Institute of Adult Continuing Education GBR. Dist: International Specialized Bk. Services.

King, Kathleen & Wang, Victor. Comparative Adult Education around the Globe: International Portraits & Readings of the History, Practice, Philosophy, & Theories of Adult Learning. King, Kathleen & Wang, Victor, eds. 2006. 69.99 *(978-7-308-04892-7(6))* Zhejiang Science & Techology Publishing Hse. CHN. Dist: BX Media LLC.

Oliver, Esther. Research & Development in Adult Education: Fields & Trends. 2010. 136p. pap. 41.95 *(978-3-86649-304-9(5))* Budrich-Esser, Barbara DEU. Dist: International Specialized Bk. Services.

West, Linden, et al, eds. Using Biographical & Life History Approaches in the Study of Adult & Lifelong Learning: European Pespectives. 310p. pap. 62.95 *(978-3-631-56286-4(1))* Lang, Peter Publishing, Inc.

Withnall, Alexandra. Improving Learning in Later Life. 2009. (Improving Learning Ser.). (Illus.). 176p. 150.00 *(978-0-415-46171-9(5))* Routledge.

ADULT EDUCATION—AFRICA

Alemayehu Hailu Gebre. Everyday Literacies in Africa: Enthnographic Studies of Literacy & Numeracy Practices in Ethiopia. (Illus.). 162p. pap. *(978-9970-02-975-4(4))* Fountain Pubs. Ltd.

Likando, Gilbert. Conceptualising the Benefits of Adult Literacy Programme. 2011. 316p. pap. ***(978-3-8443-8683-7(1))*** Lambert Academic Publishing.

Mareng, Chuei. Human Rights Roles in Shaping Policy: A Motivation of the International Rescue Committee's Policy of Adult Education Programs in the Kakuma Refugee Camp, Kenya, 1 vol. 2010. 187p. pap. 24.95 *(978-1-4489-5271-7(9))* PublishAmerica, Inc.

Oketch, Moses O. & Amutabi, Maurice N., eds. Studies in Lifelong Learning in Africa: From Ethnic Traditions to Technological Innovations. 2009. (Illus.). 428p. 129.95 *(978-0-7734-4757-8(1))* Mellen, Edwin Pr., The.

Preece, J. Adult Education & Poverty Reduction. 2007. pap. ***(978-99912-71-36-1(8))*** Lentswe La Lesedi.

Riutta, Satu. Democratic Participation in Rural Tanzania & Zambia: The Impact of Civic Education. 2009. (Illus.). 200p. 59.95 *(978-1-935049-14-2(3))* FirstForumPress.

Wainaina, Michael. Gender in Nascent Module II Programmes in Kenyan Public Universities: A Descriptive Survey. 2008. (Illus.). 96p. pap. 19.95 *(978-99944-55-31-7(1))* African Bks. Collective, Ltd. GBR. Dist: Lightning Source, Inc.

ADULT EDUCATION—CANADA

Adult and Continuing Education Staff. Reaching Out Across the Border: Canadian Perspectives in Adult Education. Cranton, Patricia & English, Leona M., eds. 2010. (J-B ACE Single Issue Adult & Continuing Education Ser.: 99). (ENG.). 112p. pap. 29.00 *(978-0-470-59259-5(1)*, Jossey-Bass) Wiley, John & Sons, Inc.

Bitterlin, Gretchen, et al. Ventures Canadian Teacher's Guide. 2008. (Ventures Ser.). pap. 19.00 *(978-0-521-73974-0(8))* Cambridge Univ. Pr.

Church, Kathryn, et al, eds. Learning through Community: Exploring Participatory Practices. 2010. (ENG.). xvi, 216p. pap. 129.00 *(978-90-481-7691-5(3)*, 9048176913) Springer.

Hodgkins, Andrew. Marketing Adult Education for Mega-Projects in Canada'S North. 2008. 116p. pap. *(978-3-639-02733-4(7))* VDM Verlag Dr. Mueller e.K.

Livingstone, D. W., ed. Lifelong Learning in Paid & Unpaid Work: Survey & Case Study Findings. 2010. (ENG., Illus.). 272p. (C). 140.00 *(978-0-415-56564-6(2))* Routledge.

Merriam, Sharan B. & Brockett, Ralph G. The Profession & Practice of Adult Education: An Introduction. 2007. (CourseSmart Ser.). (ENG.). 400p. pap. 42.00 *(978-0-470-18153-9(2)*, Jossey-Bass) Wiley, John & Sons, Inc.

Willment, Jo-Anne Helen. Learners in Midlife: Graduate Education & Workplaces in Canada. 2008. (FRE & ENG., Illus.). 208p. 29.95 *(978-1-55059-354-9(4))* Detselig Enterprises, Ltd. CAN. Dist: Temeron Bks., Inc.

ADULT EDUCATION—CHINA

Liu, Ning Rong, ed. Decentralization & Marketization: the Changing Landscape of China's Adult & Continuing Education. 2010. (Education in a Competitive & Globalizing World Ser.). 89.00 *(978-1-60876-835-6(X))* Nova Science Pubs., Inc.

ADULT EDUCATION—EUROPE

Ankers, Anne & Gladdish, Lois. Learning, Participation & Choice: A Guide for Facilitating Older Learners. 2010. 88p. spiral bd. 39.95 *(978-1-86201-194-6(X))* National Institute of Adult Continuing Education GBR. Dist: International Specialized Bk. Services.

Baacke, Dieter, et al. Neue Medien und Erwachsenenbildung. (GER., Illus.). XX, 310p. 210.00 ***(978-3-11-179138-8(6))*** De Gruyter, Walter Inc.

Bron Jr, Michal & Guimarães, Paula, eds. The State, Civil Society & the Citizen: Exploring Relationships in the Field of Adult Education in Europe. 2009. (European Studies in Lifelong Learning & Adult Learning Research Ser.). 230p. pap. 61.95 *(978-3-631-58593-1(4))* Lang, Peter GmbH, Europaischer Verlag der Wissenschaften DEU. Dist: Lang, Peter.

Clark, Alistair. Learning Centres in Europe. Hesse, Claudia & Stang, Richard, eds. 2006. (Illus.). 192p. pap. 29.95 *(978-1-86201-314-8(4))* National Institute of Adult Continuing Education GBR. Dist: International Specialized Bk. Services.

English, Mildred E. College in the Country: A Program of Education for Adults. 2010. (ENG., Illus.). 154p. pap. 22.95 *(978-0-8203-3535-3(5))* Univ. of Georgia Pr.

Hake, Barry J. & Laot, Françoise F., eds. The Social Question & Adult Education la question sociale et l'éducation des Adultes: European Perspectives in the 19th & 20th Centuries Perspectives européennes, XIXe - XXe Siecles. 2009. (European Studies in Lifelong Learning & Adult Learning Research Ser.). (ENG & FRE.). 234p. pap. 61.95 *(978-3-631-57632-8(3))* Lang, Peter GmbH, Europaischer Verlag der Wissenschaften DEU. Dist: Lang, Peter.

Theile, Elke E. Erinnerungskultur und Erwachsenenbildung. 2009. (GER.). 417p. *(978-3-89974-466-8(7))* Wochenschau Verlag Dr. Kurt Debus GmbH.

van Wieringen, Fons & Attwell, Graham, eds. Vocational & Adult Education in Europe. 2010. (Illus.). 448p. pap. 279.00 *(978-90-481-5323-7(9)*, 9048153239) Springer.

West, Linden, et al, eds. Using Biographical & Life History Approaches in the Study of Adult & Lifelong Learning: European Pespectives. 2007. 310p. pap. 62.95 *(978-3-631-56286-4(1))* Lang, Peter Publishing, Inc.

Wolter, Stefan C., ed. Empirical Research in Vocational Education & Training. 2011. 80p. pap. ***(978-94-6091-574-1(4))*** Sense Pubs.

ADULT EDUCATION—GREAT BRITAIN

Aldridge, Fiona & Tuckett, Alan. Tough Times for Adult Learners: The NIACE Survey on Adult Participation in Learning 2011. 2011. (Illus.). 40p. pap. 16.95 ***(978-1-86201-510-4(4))*** National Institute of Adult Continuing Education GBR. Dist: International Specialized Bk. Services.

Armstrong, Paul, et al, eds. New Uses of Literacy: Popular Culture in the Learning Society. 2007. pap. (978-1-86201-287-5(3)) National Institute of Adult Continuing Education.

Barr, Jean. The Stranger Within. 2008. 244p. (978-90-8790-530-9(0)); pap. (978-90-8790-529-3(7)) Sense Pubs.

Biesta, Gert, et al. Improving Learning Life Course. 2011. (Improving Learning Ser.). (ENG., Illus.). 152p. (C). 120.00 (978-0-415-57372-6(6)); pap. 36.95 (978-0-415-57373-3(4)) Routledge.

Clarke, Alan. The Minimum Core for Information & Communication Technology: Knowledge, Understanding & Personal Skills. 2009. (Illus.). 109p. pap. (978-1-84445-269-9(7)) Learning Matters Ltd.

Fryer, R. H. Promises of Freedom: Citizenship, Belonging & Lifelong Learning. 2010. (ENG.). 288p. pap. 34.95 (978-1-86201-442-8(6)) National Institute of Adult Continuing Education GBR. Dist: International Specialized Bk. Services.

Hillier. Everything you need to know about FE Policy. 2006. (Essential FE Toolkit Ser.). (ENG., Illus.). 144p. 65.00 (978-0-8264-8807-7(2)) Continuum International Publishing Group, Ltd. GBR. Dist: National Bk. Network.

Hole, James. An Essay on the History & Management of Literary, Scientific, & Mechanics' Institutions: And Especially How Far They May Be Developed & Combined so as to Promote the Moral Well-Being & Industry of the Country. 2010. (Cambridge Library Collection - Printing & Publishing History Ser.). (ENG.). 196p. pap. 19.99 (978-1-108-00937-9(9)) Cambridge Univ. Pr.

Ingleby, Ewan & Powell, Sharon. Learning to Teach in the Lifelong Learning Sector. 2011. (ENG., Illus.). 192p. 39.95 (978-1-4411-8296-8(9)) Continuum International Publishing Group, Ltd. GBR. Dist: National Bk. Network.

Jarvis, Peter, ed. Inquiry into the Future of Lifelong Learning in the Uk. 2011. (ENG.). 128p. (C). 125.00 **(978-0-415-69323-3(3))** Routledge.

Jones, Bill, et al. University Continuing Education 1981-2006: Twenty-Five Turbulent Years. 2010. 220p. pap. 34.95 (978-1-86201-446-6(9)) National Institute of Adult Continuing Education GBR. Dist: International Specialized Bk. Services.

Kirkwood, Gerri & Kirkwood, Colin. Living Adult Education: Freire in Scotland. 2011. 216p. **(978-94-6091-551-2(5))**; pap. **(978-94-6091-550-5(7))** Sense Pubs.

Livingstone, Richard Winn. On Education. 2006. 240p. per. (978-1-4067-3253-5(2), Hesperides Pr.) Read Bks.

Malone, Kate. Promoting Learning. (Illus.). 38p. pap. (978-1-86201-151-9(6)) National Institute of Adult Continuing Education.

McNair, Stephen. Older people's learning: An Action Plan. 2009. 40p. pap. 14.95 (978-1-86201-430-5(2)) National Institute of Adult Continuing Education GBR. Dist: International Specialized Bk. Services.

Molyneux, Frank H. & R., ed. Learning for Life: Politics & Progress in Recurrent Education. 2012. (Routledge Library Editions: Education Ser.). (ENG.). 344p. 130.00 (978-0-415-67561-1(8)) Routledge.

Nance, Barbara, ed. Platforms for Success: A Guide for Managers Implementing a Learning Platform Strategy. 2008. (Illus.). 48p. cd-rom (978-1-86201-325-4(X)) National Institute of Adult Continuing Education.

National Institute of Adult Continuing Education (England and Wales) Staff, contrib. by. Adult Learning Yearbook 2007. 2007. 327p. (978-1-86201-257-8(1)) National Institute of Adult Continuing Education.

National Institute of Adult Continuing Education Staff. Adult Learning Yearbook 2008. 310p. (978-1-86201-334-6(9)) National Institute of Adult Continuing Education.

Powell, Stuart. Returning to Study for a Research Degree. 2nd ed. 192p. 2009. 119.95 (978-0-335-23351-9(1), Open University Pr.) 2008. (ENG.). (C). pap. 43.00 (978-0-335-23353-3(8), 0335233538) McGraw-Hill Education GBR. Dist: McGraw-Hill Professional Publishing, McGraw-Hill Cos., The.

Quinn, Jocey. Learning Communities & Imagined Social Capital: Learning to Belong. 2011. (ENG.). 176p. pap. 44.95 **(978-1-4411-2420-3(9))** Continuum International Publishing Group, Ltd. GBR. Dist: National Bk. Network.

Routledge Library Editions: Education Mini-Set G Higher & Adult Education, 11 vols. 2012. (Routledge Library Editions: Education Ser.). (ENG.). 3592p. 1255.00 **(978-0-415-68518-4(4))** Routledge.

Southwood, Sue & Swift, Judith. Lifelines 24 Working with Unions to Support Literacy, Language & Numeracy in the Workplace. (Illus.). 44p. (978-1-86201-355-1(1)) National Institute of Adult Continuing Education.

Steward, Angela. How to Teach in FE with a Hangover: A Practical Survival Guide. 2007. (Essential FE Toolkit Ser.). (ENG.). 104p. 29.95 (978-0-8264-9566-2(4)) Continuum International Publishing Group, Ltd. GBR. Dist: National Bk. Network.

Ward, Kevin & Taylor, Richard. Adult Education & the Working Class: Education for the Missing Millions. 2012. (Routledge Library Editions: Education Ser.). (ENG.). 210p. 115.00 **(978-0-415-68445-3(5))** Routledge.

Weyers, Mark. Teaching the FE Curriculum: Encouraging active learning in the Classroom. 2006. (Essential FE Toolkit Ser.). (ENG., Illus.). 128p. 29.95 (978-0-8264-8804-6(8)) Continuum International Publishing Group, Ltd. GBR. Dist: National Bk. Network.

Wright, Abdi-Jama. FE Lecturer's Guide to Diversity & Inclusion. 2007. (Essential FE Toolkit Ser.). (ENG.). 122p. 65.00 (978-0-8264-8844-2(7)) Continuum International Publishing Group, Ltd. GBR. Dist: National Bk. Network.

ADULT EDUCATION—INDIA

Bhattacharya, Asoke. Education for the People: Concepts of Grundtvig, Tagore,Gandhi & Freire. 2010. 176p. (978-94-6091-265-8(6)); pap. (978-94-6091-264-1(8)) Sense Pubs.

ADULT EDUCATION AND LIBRARIES

see Libraries and Adult Education

ADULT ELEMENTARY EDUCATION

see Elementary Education of Adults

ADULT LEARNING

ACE (Adult and Continuing Education). Arts & Societal Learning No. 116: Transforming Communities Socially, Politically, & Culturally - New Directions for Adult & Continuing Education. Hayes, Sandra & Yorks, Lyle, eds. 2007. (J-B ACE Single Issue Adult & Continuing Education Ser.: 91). (ENG.). 96p. pap. 29.00 (978-0-470-27852-9(8), Jossey-Bass) Wiley, John & Sons, Inc.

ACE (Adult and Continuing Education) Staff. Adult Learning & the Emotional Self 2008 No. 120: New Directions in Adult & Community Education. Dirkx, John M., ed. 2009. (J-B ACE Single Issue Adult & Continuing Education Ser.: 95). (ENG.). 96p. pap. 29.00 (978-0-470-44674-4(9), Jossey-Bass) Wiley, John & Sons, Inc.

Al-Osaimi, Saleh. Beliefs about Second Language Learning. 2010. 264p. pap. (978-3-8383-8921-9(2)) Lambert Academic Publishing.

Allen, Dianne. Contributing to Learning to Change. 2008. (Illus.). 180p. pap. (978-3-639-06165-9(9)) VDM Verlag Dr. Mueller e.K.

Andrew, Patricia. The Social Construction of Age: Adult Foreign Language Learners. 2012. (Second Language Acquisition Ser.). (ENG., Illus.). 200p. 129.95 **(978-1-84769-614-4(7))**; pap. 39.95 **(978-1-84769-613-7(9))** Multilingual Matters GBR. Dist: Univ. of Toronto Pr.

Athanasou, James A., ed. Adult Educational Psychology. 2008. 436p. (978-90-8790-554-5(8)); pap. (978-90-8790-553-8(X)) Sense Pubs.

Bjerkaker, Sturla & Summers, Judtih. Learning Democratically: Using Study Circles. 2006. (Illus.). 128p. 19.95 (978-1-86201-284-4(9)) National Institute of Adult Continuing Education GBR. Dist: International Specialized Bk. Services.

Boshier, Peter. Perspectives of Quality in Adult Learning. 2011. (ENG., Illus.). 238p. pap. 44.95 (978-1-4411-3931-3(1)) Continuum International Publishing Group, Ltd. GBR. Dist: National Bk. Network.

Boshier, Peter & Boshier. Perspectives of Quality in Adult Learning. 2006. (ENG., Illus.). 220p. 130.00 (978-0-8264-8127-6(2)) Continuum International Publishing Group, Ltd. GBR. Dist: National Bk. Network.

Boulton-Lewis, Gillian & Tam, Maureen, eds. Active Ageing, Active Learning: Issues & Challenges. 2011. (Education in the Asia-Pacific Region: Issues, Concerns & Prospects Ser.). (ENG., Illus.). xii, 180p. 139.00 **(978-94-007-2110-4(2)**, 9400721102) Springer.

Boyer, Naomi Rose. Learning Contracts. 2009. (978-1-57922-104-1(1)); pap. (978-1-57922-105-8(X)) Stylus Publishing, LLC.

Boys. The E-Revolution & Post-Compulsory Education: Using E-Business Models to Deliver Quality Education. 2008. CLXp. pap. 46.95 (978-0-415-41987-1(5)); 145.00 (978-0-415-41986-4(7)) Routledge.

Brennan, Drew. Older Adults in Adventure Education. 2008. 196p. pap. (978-3-8364-3912-1(3)) VDM Verlag Dr. Mueller e.K.

Brockfield, Stephen D. & Holst, John D. Radicalizing Learning: Adult Education for a Just World. 2010. (ENG.). 288p. 40.00 (978-0-7879-9825-7(7), Jossey-Bass) Wiley, John & Sons, Inc.

Carter, Carol, et al. Keys to College Studying: Becoming an Active Thinker & Pearson Guide to Research Navigator Package. 2nd ed. 2008. (ENG.). (C). pap., pap. 74.40 (978-0-13-508665-0(5), Prentice Hall) Prentice Hall PTR.

—Keys to Effective Learning: Study Skills & Habits for Success. 6th ed. 2010. (ENG.). 400p. (C). pap. 78.80 (978-0-13-700750-9(7), Prentice Hall) Prentice Hall PTR.

Castillo, Diana. Hybrid Course Effectiveness. 2009. 184p. pap. (978-3-639-16242-4(0)) VDM Verlag Dr. Mueller e.K.

Clark, Alistair. Learning Centres in Europe. Hesse, Claudia & Stang, Richard, eds. 2006. (Illus.). 192p. pap. 29.95 (978-1-86201-314-8(4)) National Institute of Adult Continuing Education GBR. Dist: International Specialized Bk. Services.

Cole, Lisa. Adult Learning on the Internet: Engaging the seniornet Process. 2010. 380p. pap. (978-3-639-23013-0(2)) VDM Verlag Dr. Mueller e.K.

Comings, John, et al, eds. Review of Adult Learning & Literacy: Connecting Research, Policy, & Practice. 2007. 363p. 110.00 (978-0-8058-6164-3(5)) Erlbaum, Lawrence Assocs., Inc.

Comings, John, et al. National Center for the Study of Adult Learning & Literacy, Vol. 2. 2009. (J-B Annual Review of Adult Learning & Literacy Ser.: 8). (ENG.). 320p. pap. 40.00 (978-0-470-62305-3(5), Jossey-Bass) Wiley, John & Sons, Inc.

Connolly, Brid. Adult Learning in Groups. 2008. (ENG.). 192p. (C). 120.00 (978-0-335-22859-1(3), 0335228593); pap. 40.00 (978-0-335-22860-7(7), 0335228607) McGraw-Hill Education GBR. Dist: McGraw-Hill Cos., The.

Cooper, Linda & Walters, Shirley, eds. Learning - Work: Turning Work & Lifelong Learning Inside Out. 2009. (ENG.). 384p. pap. 34.95 (978-0-7969-2233-0(7)) Human Sciences Research Council ZAF. Dist: Independent Pubs. Group.

Cram101 Textbook Reviews & Cram101 Textbook Reviews. Outlines & Highlights for Leading Adult Learning: Supporting Adult Development in Our Schools by Eleanor Drago-Severson, ISBN. 2011. 156p. pap. 29.95 **(978-1-4288-1979-5(7))** Cram101 Inc.

Dar-El, Ezey M. Human Learning: from Learning Curves to Learning Organizations: From Learning Curves to Learning Organizations. 2010. (International Series in Operations Research & Management Science Ser.). 256p. pap. 209.00 (978-1-4419-4997-4(6), 1441949976) Springer.

Dochy, Filip, et al. Psychological Theories of Learning in the Workplace: Building Blocks for Training & Professional Development Programs. 2011. (Routledge Psychology in Education Ser.). (ENG., Illus.). 168p. (C). pap. 44.95 (978-0-415-61894-6(0)) Routledge.

—Theories of Learning for the Workplace: Buiding Blocks for Training & Professional Development Programs. 2011. (Routledge Psychology in Education Ser.). (ENG., Illus.) 168p. (C). 155.00 (978-0-415-61893-9(2)) Routledge.

Doghonadze, Natela. Esp Course Book for Adult Learners. 2011. 164p. pap. **(978-3-8443-0374-2(X))** Lambert Academic Publishing.

Drago-Severson, Eleanor. Leading Adult Learning: Supporting Adult Development in Our Schools. 2009. (Illus.). 368p. 95.95 (978-1-4129-5071-8(6), B50716C); pap. 44.95 (978-1-4129-5072-5(4), B50716P) Corwin Pr.

Dron, Jon. Control & Constraint in E-Learning: Choosing When to Choose. 2007. (Illus.). 300p. 94.95 (978-1-59904-390-6(4)); xxii, 340p. pap. 94.95 (978-1-59904-391-3(2)) IGI Global. (Information Science Publishing).

Edwards, Richard, et al. Rethinking Contexts for Learning & Teaching: Communities, Activites & Networks. 2009. (ENG., Illus.). 192p. pap. 42.95 (978-0-415-46776-6(4)); 180p. 150.00 (978-0-415-46775-9(6)) Routledge.

Fairclough, Marilyn. Supporting Learners in the Lifelong Learning Sector. 2008. (ENG., Illus.). 176p. 132.00 (978-0-335-23363-2(5), 0335233635); pap. 40.00 (978-0-335-23362-5(7), 0335233627) McGraw-Hill Education GBR. Dist: McGraw-Hill Cos., The.

Fisher-Yoshida, Beth, et al. Innovations in Transformative Learning: Space, Culture, & the Arts. 2008. (Counterpoints: Studies in the Postmodern Theory of Education Ser.). (Illus.). xii, 308p. pap. 34.95 (978-1-4331-0291-2(9), Lang, Peter Publishing, Inc.

Foord, Kathleen A. & Haar, Jean M. Professional Learning Communities. 2008. (ENG.). 204p. pap. 39.95 (978-1-59667-088-4(6)) Eye On Education, Inc.

Fragoso, António & Kurantowicz, Ewa, eds. Between Global & Local: Adult Learning & Development. 2011. (European Studies in Lifelong Learning & Adult Learning Research Ser.). 244p. 57.95 (978-3-631-60499-1(8)) Lang, Peter GmbH, Europaischer Verlag der Wissenschaften DEU. Dist: Lang, Peter.

Garner, Barbara, et al, eds. Connecting Research, Policy, & Practice. 2007. 363p. per. 36.95 (978-0-8058-6165-5(3)) Erlbaum, Lawrence Assocs., Inc.

Garson, Kyra. Applying Transformative Learning to Cross-Cultural Training Endeavours. 2009. 132p. pap. (978-3-639-16168-7(8), VDM Verlag Dr. Mueller e.K.

Gravells, Ann. Preparing to Teach in the Lifelong Learning Sector. 4th rev. ed. 2011. (ENG., Illus.). 144p. pap. (978-0-85725-053-7(1)) Learning Matters Ltd.

Gravells, Ann. What Is Teaching in the Lifelong Learning Sector? 2012. (ENG., Illus.). 112p. pap. **(978-0-85725-729-1(3))** Learning Matters Ltd.

Gray-Schlegel, Mary Ann, et al. Read! Write! Discuss! Learn! A Workbook of Interactive Handouts to Support the College Literacy Course. rev. ed. 2010. (ENG.). 166p. pap. 67.43 (978-0-7575-5634-0(5)) Kendall Hunt Publishing Co.

Haggart, Jeanne & Spacey, Rachel. Adding Value. 2007. (Illus.). 40p. pap. (978-1-86201-356-8(X)) National Institute of Adult Continuing Education.

Harrison, Connie & Cathcart, Susan. Brain-Based Study Strategies: A Guide for Adult Learners. 2009. (978-1-935356-02-8(X)) Baker College Publishing Co.

Hayes. Teaching Adults. 2006. (Essential FE Toolkit Ser.). (ENG.). 158p. 31.95 (978-0-8264-8707-0(6)) Continuum International Publishing Group, Ltd. GBR. Dist: National Bk. Network.

Hayes, Charles D. September University: Summoning Passion for an Unfinished Life. 2010. 312p. pap. 16.95 net. (978-0-9621979-7-0(1)) Autodidactic Pr.

Hillier Yvonne & Hillier, Yvonne. Reflective Teaching in Further & Adult Education. 3rd ed. 2012. (ENG., Illus.). 304p. pap. 44.95 (978-1-4411-7550-2(4)) Continuum International Publishing Group, Ltd. GBR. Dist: National Bk. Network.

Hinken, Brian. The Learner's Path: Practices for Recovering Knowers. 2007. per. 39.95 (978-1-883823-53-5(6)) Pegasus Communications.

Hoare, Carol, ed. The Oxford Handbook of Reciprocal Adult Development & Learning, 1 vol. 2nd ed. 2011. (Oxford Library of Psychology Ser.). (ENG., Illus.). 624p. 150.00 **(978-0-19-973630-0(8))** Oxford Univ. Pr., Inc.

Illeris, Knud. The Fundamentals of Workplace Learning. 2011. (ENG., Illus.). 192p. (C). 128.00 (978-0-415-57906-3(6)); pap. 36.95 (978-0-415-57907-0(4)) Routledge.

Illeris, Knud, ed. Contemporary Theories of Learning: Learning Theorists... In Their Own Words. 2009. (ENG., Illus.). 256p. 150.00 (978-0-415-47343-9(8)); pap. 37.95 (978-0-415-47344-6(6)) Routledge.

Isenberg, Susan Kay. Applying Andragogical Principles to Internet Learning. 2007. (ENG.). 356p. 114.95 (978-1-934043-19-6(2)) Cambria Pr.

Jackson, Patrick Thaddeus. Reconceptualising LI. 2007. (ENG., Illus.). 248p. 45.95 (978-0-415-37615-0(7)); 170.00 (978-0-415-37614-3(9)) Routledge.

Jacobs, Frederic & Hundley, Stephen P. Understanding & Supporting Adult Learners: A Guide for Colleges & Universities. 2010. (Wiley Desktop Editions Ser.). (ENG., Illus.). 240p. 40.00 (978-0-470-59254-0(0), Jossey-Bass) Wiley, John & Sons, Inc.

Jarvis, Peter. Paradoxes of Learning (Rle Edu G) 2012. (Routledge Library Editions: Education Ser.). (ENG.). 292p. 115.00 **(978-0-415-68491-0(9))** Routledge.

Jarvis, Peter. The Routledge International Handbook of Lifelong Learning. 2008. (ENG., Illus.). 560p. (C). 205.00 (978-0-415-41904-8(2)) Routledge.

Jude, Chris. Consulting Adults. (Illus.). 45p. pap. (978-1-86201-149-6(4)) National Institute of Adult Continuing Education.

Knowles,, Malcolm S., Malcolm S, et al. The Adult Learner: The definitive classic in adult education & human resource Development. 7th rev. ed. 2011. (ENG., Illus.). 416p. (C). pap. 49.95 (978-1-85617-811-2(0)) Routledge.

Knowles & Holton Iii & Swanson & Cram101 Textbook Reviews Staff. The Adult Learner. 2007. 80p. per. 10.95 (978-1-4283-2048-7(5)) Cram101 Inc.

Krasemann, Keith W. The Role of Time Consciousness in Lifelong Learning: A Theoretical Framework for Adult Education. 2006. 240p. (978-0-7734-5534-4(5)) Mellen, Edwin Pr., The.

Kruse, Nathan B. Andragogy & Music: Canadian & American Models of Music Learning Among Adults. 2008. 220p. pap. (978-3-639-10745-6(4)) VDM Verlag Dr. Mueller e.K.

Lakey, George. Facilitating Group Learning: Strategies for Success with Diverse Adult Learners. 2010. (ENG.). 304p. 40.00 (978-0-470-76863-1(0), Jossey-Bass) Wiley, John & Sons, Inc.

Leberman, Sarah, et al. The Transfer of Learning: Participants Perspectives of Adult Education & Training. 2006. (Illus.). 146p. 90.00 (978-0-566-08734-9(0), Gower Publishing Co., Ltd.) Ashgate Publishing, Ltd. GBR. Dist: Ashgate Publishing Co.

Lucas, Robert W. Creative Learning: Activities & Games That Really Engage People. 2007. (ENG., Illus.). 260p. per. 45.00 (978-0-7879-8740-4(9), Pfeiffer) Wiley, John & Sons, Inc.

Malone, Kate. Promoting Learning. (Illus.). 38p. pap. (978-1-86201-151-9(6)) National Institute of Adult Continuing Education.

Mangino, Christine. A Statistical Analysis of the Dunn & Dunn Learning Style with Adult Populations: What We Discovered about How Adults Learn. 2009. (Illus.). 312p. 119.95 (978-0-7734-4771-4(7)) Mellen, Edwin Pr., The.

McDermott, Dana. Developing Caring Relationships among Parents, Children, Schools, & Communities. 2007. (Illus.). 304p. (C). per. 51.00 (978-1-4129-2786-4(2), B27862P) SAGE Pubns., Inc.

McDermott, Dana R. Developing Caring Relationships among Parents, Children, Schools, & Communities. 2007. 304p. (C). 79.00 (978-1-4129-5408-2(8), B27862C) SAGE Pubns., Inc.

Mcewan, Bruce. Applying Adult Learning Principles to Employee Training: The Employees' Perspective of Effectiveness. 2008. 140p. pap. (978-3-639-08630-0(9)) VDM Verlag Dr. Mueller e.K.

Merriam, Sharan B., et al. Learning in Adulthood: A Comprehensive Guide. 3rd rev. ed. 2006. (CourseSmart Ser.). (ENG., Illus.). 560p. 62.00 (978-0-7879-7588-3(5), Jossey-Bass) Wiley, John & Sons, Inc.

Merrill, Barbara, ed. Learning to Change? The Role of Identity & Learning Careers in Adult Education. 2009. (European Studies in Lifelong Learning & Adult Learning Research Ser.). (Illus.). 252p. pap. 65.95 (978-3-631-58279-4(X)) Lang, Peter GmbH, Europaischer Verlag der Wissenschaften DEU. Dist: Lang, Peter.

Od Cohen, Yehudit. Effective Mentoring Via the Interpersonal Dimension. 2010. 340p. pap. (978-3-639-25591-1(7)) VDM Verlag Dr. Mueller e.K.

Olson, Kathleen Dunn. What's up? Book 1: Integrated Skills & Culture for Adults. 2010. (ENG., Illus.). 128p. pap. 20.95 (978-0-472-03291-4(7)) Univ. of Michigan Pr.

Organisation for Economic Co-operation and Development Staff. Education & Training Policy Qualifications Systems: Bridges to Lifelong Learning. 2007. pap. 60.00 (978-92-64-01367-4(9)) Organization for Economic Cooperation & Development.

Ostrouch, Joanna & Ollagnier, Edmée, eds. Researching Gender in Adult Learning. 2008. (European Studies in Lifelong Learning & Adult Learning Research Ser.). (Illus.). 252p. pap. 65.95 (978-3-631-58251-0(X)) Lang, Peter GmbH, Europaischer Verlag der Wissenschaften DEU. Dist: Lang, Peter.

Remtulla, Karim A. Socio-Cultural Impacts of Workplace E-Learning: Epistemology, Ontology & Pedagogy. 2010. (Illus.). 350p. 180.00 (978-1-61520-835-7(6)) IGI Global.

Ritz, Aixa. Transformative Learning International Students in an American University. 2008. 260p. pap. (978-3-639-07667-7(2)) VDM Verlag Dr. Mueller e.K.

Roberson, Donald. Wiregrass Wisdom. 2009. 324p. pap. (978-3-639-14432-1(5)) VDM Verlag Dr. Mueller e.K.

Roisko, Hilkka. Adult Learners' Learning in a University Setting. 2008. 196p. pap. (978-3-639-09758-0(0)) VDM Verlag Dr. Mueller e.K.

Rossiter, Marsha, ed. Possible Selves & Adult Learning: Perspectives & Potential, Summer 2007. 2007. (J-B ACE Single Issue Adult & Continuing Education Ser.: 87). (ENG.). 96p. per. 29.00 (978-0-470-18329-8(2), Jossey-Bass) Wiley, John & Sons, Inc.

Rossiter, Marsha & Clark, M. Carolyn. Narrative & the Practice of Adult Education. 2006. (978-1-57524-222-4(2)) Krieger Publishing Co.

Rothwell, William J. Adult Learning Basics. 2008. (ENG., Illus.). 176p. pap. 29.95 (978-1-56286-533-7(1)) American Society for Training & Development.

Rowden, Robert W. Workplace Learning: Principles & Practice. 2007. (Professional Practices in Adult Education & Lifelong Learning Ser.). (Illus.). 146p. (C). (978-1-57524-258-2(0)) Krieger Publishing Co.

Roßnagel, Christian Stamov, et al, eds. A Competence Perspective on Lifelong Workplace Learning. 2010. (Professions - Training, Education & Demographics Ser.). pap. 49.00 (978-1-61668-686-4(3), Nova Novinka) Nova Science Pubs., Inc.

Rubenson, Kjell, ed. Adult Learning & Education. 2011. (ENG., Illus.). 326p. 99.95 (978-0-12-381489-0(8), Academic Pr.) Elsevier Science & Technology Bks.

Siebert, Al & Karr, Mary. The Adult Student's Guide to Survival & Success. 6th ed. 2008. (ENG.). 176p. pap. 15.00 (978-0-944227-38-1(4)) Practical Psychology Pr.

Simon, Linda. New Beginnings: A Reference Guide for Adult Learners. 4th ed. 2009. (ENG.). 176p. (C). pap. 33.20 (978-0-13-715230-8(2), Prentice Hall) Prentice Hall PTR.

Sinnott, Jan D. The Development of Logic in Adulthood: Postformal Thought & its Applications. 2010. (Springer Series in Adult Development & Aging Ser.). 392p. pap. 109.00 (978-1-4419-3286-0(0), 1441932860) Springer.

Smith, Ann F. V. & Strong, Gregory E. Adult Language Learners: Context & Innovation. 2009. (Illus.). x, 175p. (978-1-931185-61-5(1)) Teachers of English to Speakers of Other Languages, Inc. (TESOL).

Smith, M. Cecil. Handbook of Research on Adult Learning & Development. 2008. (ENG., Illus.). 832p. 285.00 (978-0-8058-5819-8(9)); pap. 109.95 (978-0-8058-5820-4(2)) Routledge.

Sonnheim, Moshe & Lehman, Shlomit. The Andragogic Learning Center: A Field Study in Social Work Education. 2009. (ENG.). 128p. pap. 28.50 (978-0-7618-4947-6(5)) Univ. Pr. of America, Inc.

Stembera, Katarina. Recomposing Life & Career: Exploring Effective Academic Advising for Mature Immigrant Women. 2008. 136p. pap. (978-3-639-02193-6(2)) VDM Verlag Dr. Mueller e.K.

Steward, Angela & Steward. Getting the Buggers to Learn in FE: Dealing with the Headaches & Realities of College Life. 2008. (Essential FE Toolkit Ser.). (ENG., Illus.). 152p. 29.95 (978-0-8264-9567-9(2)) Continuum International Publishing Group, Ltd. GBR. Dist: National Bk. Network.

Strom, Paris & Strom, Robert D. Adult Learning & Relationships. 2011. (978-1-61735-388-8(4)); pap. (978-1-61735-387-1(6)); E-Book (978-1-61735-389-5(2)) Information Age Publishing, Inc.

Swan, Malcolm. Collaborative Learning in Mathematics: A Challenge to Our Beliefs & Practices. 2006. (Illus.). 368p. 54.95 (978-1-86201-316-2(0)) National Institute of Adult Continuing Education GBR. Dist: International Specialized Bk. Services.

Tanchanpong, Pawalai. Teaching Piano for Senior Citizen. 2009. 60p. pap. (978-3-639-12805-5(2)) VDM Verlag Dr. Mueller e.K.

Taylor, Edward W. & Cranton, Patricia. The Handbook of Transformative Learning: Theory, Research, & Practice. 2012. (ENG.). 624p. 75.00 **(978-0-470-59072-0(6)**, Jossey-Bass) Wiley, John & Sons, Inc.

Tennant, Mark C. The Learning Self: Understanding the Potential for Transformation. 2012. (ENG.). 224p. 38.00 **(978-0-470-39336-9(X)**, Jossey-Bass) Wiley, John & Sons, Inc.

Tight, Malcolm, ed. Education for Adults (Rle Edu G) 2012. (Routledge Library Editions: Education Ser.). (ENG.). 336p. 130.00 **(978-0-415-68517-7(6))**; 314p. 130.00 **(978-0-415-68515-3(X))** Routledge.

Tusting, Karin & Barton, David. Models of Adult Learning. 2006. 56p. pap. 14.95 (978-1-86201-280-6(6)) National Institute of Adult Continuing Education GBR. Dist: International Specialized Bk. Services.

VanDerbilt, Kathi. Online Professional Development. 2009. 164p. pap. (978-3-639-10319-9(X)) VDM Verlag Dr. Mueller e.K.

Vella, Jane. On Teaching & Learning: Putting the Principles & Practices of Dialogue Education into Action. 2007. (ENG., Illus.). 272p. 40.00 (978-0-7879-8699-5(2), Jossey-Bass) Wiley, John & Sons, Inc.

Wang, Victor & King, Kathleen, eds. Innovations in Career & Technical Education: Strategic Approaches Towards Workforce Competencies Around the Globe (HC) 2007. (Adult Education Special Topics Ser.). 308p. 73.99 (978-1-59311-840-2(6)) Information Age Publishing, Inc.

—Innovations in Career & Technical Education: Strategic Approaches Towards Workforce Competencies Around the Globe (PB) 2007. (Adult Education Special Topics Ser.). 308p. per. 39.99 (978-1-59311-839-6(2)) Information Age Publishing, Inc.

Wang, Victor C. X. Assessing & Evaluating Adult Learning in Career & Technical Education. 2010. (Illus.). 350p. 180.00 (978-1-61520-745-9(7)) IGI Global.

—Curriculum Development for Adult Learners in the Global Community. 2008. (978-1-57524-296-5(6)); (978-1-57524-300-9(8)) Krieger Publishing Co.

Wang, Victor C. X. Vocational Education Technologies & Advances in Adult Learning: New Concepts. 2012. **(978-1-4666-0254-0(6))** IGI Global.

Wang, Victor C. X., ed. Vocational Education Technologies & Advances in Adult Learning: New Concepts. 2012. 355p. 175.00 **(978-1-4666-0252-6(X)**, Information Science Reference) IGI Global.

Wesley, Karry D. The Best Is yet to Come: A Study of the Book of Ruth. 2007. 189p. per. 16.99 (978-1-57921-886-7(5)) WinePress Publishing.

Withnall, Alexandra. Improving Learning in Later Life. 2009. (Improving Learning Ser.). (Illus.). 176p. 150.00 (978-0-415-46171-9(5)) Routledge.

Yi, Pu-Il. Noin P'yongsaeng Kyoyuk Sisol P'urogurаem Ch'amyo Tonggi Wa Pich'amyo Yoin. 2010. (KOR., Illus.). 201p. pap. (978-89-26-81193-1(X)); E-Book (978-89-26-81194-8(8)) Korean Studies Information Co., Ltd.

ADULT LITERACY

see Functional Literacy

ADULT ONSET DIABETES

see Non-Insulin-Dependent Diabetes

ADULT SURVIVORS OF CHILD ABUSE

see Adult Child Abuse Victims

ADULT SURVIVORS OF CHILD SEXUAL ABUSE

see Adult Child Sexual Abuse Victims

ADULTERY

see also Mistresses; Paramours

Alan, Richard. First Aid for the Betrayed: Recovering from the Devastation of an Affair: A Personal Guide to Healing. 2006. 168p. per. 22.00 (978-1-4251-0356-9(1)) Trafford Publishing.

Barnes, H. Cameron. Affair! How to Manage Every Aspect of Your Extramarital Relationship with Passion, Discretion & Dignity. 3rd ed. 2011. pap. **(978-1-61233-065-5(7))** Universal Pubs.

Baucom, Donald H., et al. Helping Couples Get Past the Affair: A Clinician's Guide. (ENG.). 351p. 2011. pap. 30.00 (978-1-60918-239-7(1)) 2009. 55.00 (978-1-60623-067-1(0)) Guilford Pubns., Inc.

Beall, Cindy. Healing Your Marriage When Trust Is Broken: Finding Forgiveness & Restoration. 2011. 208p. pap. 12.99 (978-0-7369-4315-4(3)) Harvest Hse. Pubs.

Caprio, Frank Samuel. Marital Infidelity. 2011. 282p. 47.95 **(978-1-258-08602-2(6))** Literary Licensing, LLC.

Carder, Dave. Close Calls: What Adulterers Want You to Know about Protecting Your Marriage. 2008. (ENG., Illus.). 208p. pap. 14.99 (978-0-8024-4211-6(0)) Northfield Publishing.

—Torn Asunder: Recovering from an Extramarital Affair. 2008. (ENG.). 160p. pap., wbk. ed. 16.99 (978-0-8024-7136-9(6)); 3rd rev. ed. 320p. pap. 16.99 (978-0-8024-7135-2(8)) Moody Pubs.

Clouthier, Greg & Clouthier, Ann. A Woman's Guide to Revenge. 2nd ed. 2010. 256p. per. 14.95 (978-1-59079-071-7(5)) Select Bks.

Collins, Maria Antonieta & Collins, Maria A. Dijiste Que Me Querías: Como Sobrellevar lo Impensable. 2007. (SPA., Illus.). 304p. pap. 14.95 (978-0-06-088471-0(1), Rayo) HarperCollins Pubs.

Currin, Liz. The Essential Guide to Surviving Infidelity. 2012. (ENG.). 288p. (gr. 12). 14.95 **(978-1-61564-119-2(X)**, Alpha Bks.) Penguin Group (USA) Inc.

Davidson, Ruth. Out of the Ashes. 2007. 14.95 (978-0-9795690-0-5(1)) Gatehouse Media.

Dobson, James C. Love Must Be Tough: New Hope for Marriages in Crisis. 2007. (ENG., Illus.). 272p. per. 14.99 (978-1-4143-1745-8(X)) Tyndale Hse. Pubs.

Druckerman, Pamela. Lust in Translation: Infidelity from Tokyo to Tennessee. 2008. (ENG.). 304p. (gr. 12-18). 15.00 (978-0-14-311329-4(1), Penguin (Non-Classics)) Penguin Group (USA) Inc.

Falk, Petra. Being the Other Woman. 2009. 238p. pap. 25.50 (978-1-4092-8684-4(3)) Lulu Enterprises Inc.

Fenster, Julie M. The Case of Abraham Lincoln: A Story of Adultery, Murder & the Making of a Great President. (ENG., Illus.). 256p. 2008. pap. 14.95 (978-0-230-60809-2(4)) 2007. 24.95 (978-1-4039-7635-2(X)) Palgrave Macmillan.

Ferraro, Joanne Marie. Nefarious Crimes, Contested Justice: Illicit Sex & Infanticide in the Republic of Venice, 1557-1789. 2008. (ENG., Illus.). 272p. (gr. 17). 49.00 (978-0-8018-8987-5(1)) Johns Hopkins Univ. Pr.

Gallagher, Steve. En el Altar de la Idolatria Sexual, 1 vol. 2006. (SPA.). 320p. (gr. 11). per. 12.99 (978-0-8297-4587-0(4)) Vida Pubs.

Gough, Elissa. A Betrayed Husband's guide from Infidelity: A journal for husband's who were/are Betrayed. 2007. 82p. 19.95 (978-1-891863-11-0(8)) Face Reality, Inc.

—A Betrayed Wife's guide from Infidelity. 2007. 88p. 19.95 (978-1-891863-09-7(6)) Face Reality, Inc.

—An Unfaithful Husband's guide from Infidelity: A journal for husband's who were/are Unfaithful. 2007. 82p. 19.95 (978-1-891863-12-7(6)) Face Reality, Inc.

—An Unfaithful Wife's guide from Infidelity: A journal for wives who were/are Unfaithful. 2007. 92p. 19.95 (978-1-891863-10-3(X)) Face Reality, Inc.

Gray, T. J. The Lives Some People Live: Uncovering One Family Killer. 2009. 232p. pap. 15.95 (978-1-4401-1844-9(2)) iUniverse, Inc.

Hibbler, Darrick. He cheats the collateral damage of a cheating Spouse. 2011. 172p. pap. 15.95 (978-1-4502-3685-0(5)) iUniverse, Inc.

Hirsch, Jennifer S., et al. The Secret: Love, Marriage, & HIV. 2010. (ENG., Illus.). 320p. pap. 29.95 (978-0-8265-1683-1(1)); lib. bdg. 69.95 (978-0-8265-1682-4(3)) Vanderbilt Univ. Pr.

Hitchcock, Colleen & Wood, Denise. Inside the Cheater's Mind: Why He Cheats & Why She Cheats. 2010. 300p. pap. 19.95 (978-0-9723441-6-6(0), Leopard Spot Pr.) Leopard Spot Press, Inc.

Holtz, Lyndell Hetrick. Confessions of an Adulterous Christian Woman: Lies That Got Me There Truths That Brought Me Back. 2007. (ENG.). 192p. per. 14.99 (978-0-8341-2328-1(2), 0834123282) Beacon Hill Pr. of Kansas City.

Horsler, Val. All for Love: Seven Centuries of Illicit Liaison. 2007. (Illus.). 256p. 34.95 (978-1-903365-97-7(X)) National Archives (PRO), The GBR. Dist: International Publishers Marketing.

Jones, Robert. After Adultery. 2007. (ENG.). 24p. per. 3.99 (978-0-9770807-9-3(X)) New Growth Pr.

Jones, Robert David. Restoring Your Broken Marriage: Healing after Adultery. 2nd rev. ed. 2009. 24p. 3.99 (978-1-934885-95-6(9)) New Growth Pr.

Kennedy, Erskine. Adultery Prevention: It's up to You Ladies. Johnson, Denise M., ed. 2011. 164p. pap. 14.95 (978-0-9817111-7-1(0)) Blackcurrant Pr. Co.

Kent-Ferraro, Jay & Kent-Ferraro, Julie. Surprised by Love: One Couple's Journey from Infidelity to True Love. 2011. (ENG., Illus.). 256p. pap. 16.95 (978-1-936487-03-5(9), 1936487039) Franklin Green Publishing.

Kirshenbaum, Mira. When Good People Have Affairs: Inside the Hearts & Minds of People in Two Relationships. 2009. (ENG.). 272p. pap. 15.99 (978-0-312-56344-8(2), St. Martin's Griffin) St. Martin's Pr.

Kleven, Arthur. Memoirs of a Smoking Jacket. 2011. 126p. 40.95 **(978-1-258-08815-6(0))** Literary Licensing, LLC.

Laaser, Debra. Shattered Vows: Hope & Healing for Women Who Have Been Sexually Betrayed, 1 vol. 2008. (ENG., Illus.). 240p. (gr. 13). pap. 12.99 (978-0-310-27394-3(3)) Zondervan.

Libaire, Jardine. French Women Don't Get Caught: The Secret Art of Infidelity Revealed. 2008. (Illus.). 200p. 24.95 (978-1-59921-346-0(X), Lyons Pr.) Globe Pequot Pr., The.

Lucich, John Paul. Cyber Lies: When Finding the Truth Matters. 2006. pap. 35.00 (978-0-9774894-0-4(X)) StarPath Bks., LLC.

Mannarelli, Maria Emma. Private Passions & Public Sins: Men & Women in Seventeenth-Century Lima. Evans, Sidney & Dodge, Meredith D., trs. from SPA. 2007. (Dialogos Ser.). (SPA & ENG., Illus.). 220p. (C). pap. 29.95 (978-0-8263-2279-1(4)) Univ. of New Mexico Pr.

Metz, Julie. Perfection: A Memoir of Betrayal & Renewal. (ENG.). 2010. 352p. pap. 14.99 (978-1-4013-4135-0(7)) 2009. 240p. 23.99 (978-1-4013-2255-7(7)) Hyperion Pr.

Millet, Catherine. Jealousy: The Other Life of Catherine M. Stevenson, Helen, tr. (ENG.). 192p. 2011. pap. 14.00 (978-0-8021-4519-2(1)) 2010. 23.00 (978-0-8021-1915-5(8)) Grove/Atlantic, Inc. (Grove Pr.).

Moore, Shirley. This Change Is Crucial: We Change or Suffer Loss, 1 vol. 2009. 91p. pap. 16.95 (978-1-60836-565-4(4)) PublishAmerica, Inc.

Mrkvicka, Edward F. No Innocent Affair: Making Right the Wrong of Adultery. 2011. pap. 15.99 **(978-1-61777-768-4(4))** Tate Publishing & Enterprises, LLC.

Nacho, Prince Eze. Hard Hitting! The Real Truth about Men, Marriage & Infidelity (the Three Minute Factor) 2010. (Illus.). 108p. pap. 13.99 (978-1-4520-6340-9(0)) AuthorHouse.

Natori. Dealing with Unfinished Business: Secrets & Lies. 2011. 86p. pap. 19.95 **(978-1-4512-8105-7(6))** PublishAmerica, Inc.

Neuman, M. Gary. The Truth about Cheating: Why Men Stray & What You Can Do to Prevent It. 2008. (ENG.). 240p. 24.95 (978-0-470-11463-6(0), Wiley) Wiley, John & Sons, Inc.

Neuman, M. Gary & Neuman. The Truth about Cheating: Why Men Stray & What You Can Do to Prevent It. 2009. (ENG.). 240p. pap. 14.95 (978-0-470-50213-6(4), Wiley) Wiley, John & Sons, Inc.

Nogales, Ana & Nogales,, Ana, Ana. Parents Who Cheat: How Children & Adults Are Affected When Their Parents Are Unfaithful. 2009. (ENG.). 271p. pap. 14.95 (978-0-7573-0652-5(7)) Health Communications, Inc.

Ortman, Dennis C. Transcending Post-Infidelity Stress Disorder: The Six Stages of Healing. 2009. (ENG.). 256p. pap. 16.99 (978-1-58761-334-0(4)) Ten Speed Pr.

Peluso, Paul R., ed. Infidelity: A Practitioner's Guide to Working with Couples in Crisis. 2007. (Family Therapy & Counseling Ser.). (ENG.). 352p. 54.95 (978-0-415-95390-0(1)) Routledge.

Potter-Efron, Ronald T. & Potter-Efron, Patricia S. The Emotional Affair: How to Recognize Emotional Infidelity & What to Do about It. 2009. (ENG.). 184p. pap. 16.95 (978-1-57224-570-9(0)) New Harbinger Pubns.

Price, Betty R. Warning to Ministers, Their Wives, & Mistresses: Avoid the Road to Destruction. 2009. (ENG.). 80p. 13.99 (978-1-59979-774-8(7), Creation Hse.) Charisma Media.

Rickman, Johanna. Love, Lust, & License in Early Modern England: Illicit Sex & the Nobility. 2008. (Women & Gender in the Early Modern World Ser.). (Illus.). 244p. 124.95 (978-0-7546-6135-1(0)) Ashgate Publishing Co.

Rosewarne, Lauren. Cheating on the Sisterhood: Infidelity & Feminism, 1 vol. 2009. 272p. 49.95 (978-0-313-36031-2(6), C36031, Praeger Pubs.) Greenwood Publishing Group, Inc.

Rubenhold, Hallie. The Lady in Red: An Eighteenth-Century Tale of Sex, Scandal, & Divorce. 2010. (ENG., Illus.). 320p. pap. 18.99 (978-0-312-62416-3(6), St. Martin's Griffin) St. Martin's Pr.

Sahebjam, Freidoune. The Stoning of Soraya M. A Story of Injustice in Iran. Seaver, Richard, tr. from FRE. 2011. (ENG.). 160p. pap. 12.95 (978-1-61145-025-5(X), 611025, Arcade Publishing) Skyhorse Publishing Co., Inc.

Samuelson, Laura. Out of Ruins: Healing after Adultery. 2011. 120p. pap. 11.95 **(978-1-4627-0590-0(1))** Cross Bks. Publishing.

Sandford, John Loren. Why Good People Mess Up: Keys to Upright Living in a Seductive World. 2007. (ENG., Illus.). 224p. pap. 14.99 (978-1-59979-208-8(7), Charisma Hse.) Charisma Media.

Schweninger, Loren. Families in Crisis in the Old South: Divorce, Slavery, & the Law. 2012. (ENG., Illus.). 264p. 49.95 **(978-0-8078-3569-2(2))** Univ. of North Carolina Pr.

Shriver, Gary & Shriver, Mona. Unfaithful: Hope & Healing after Infidelity, 1 vol. 2009. (ENG.). 256p. pap. 14.99 (978-1-4347-6533-8(4)) Cook, David C.

Smith, Sierra N. Did He Cheat? You Tell Me! A Woman's Instruction Manual to Deal with Her Cheating Man. 2008. 80p. pap. 10.95 (978-0-595-52748-9(5)) iUniverse, Inc.

Smith, Winston T. Help! My Spouse Committed Adultery: First Steps for Dealing with Betrayal. 2008. 24p. 3.99 (978-1-934885-38-3(X)) New Growth Pr.

Snyder, Douglas K., et al. Getting Past the Affair: A Program to Help You Cope, Heal, & Move on — Together or Apart. 2007. (ENG.). 342p. 40.00 (978-1-59385-357-0(2)); pap. 15.95 (978-1-57230-801-5(X)) Guilford Pubns., Inc.

Solomon, Joyce M. Healing Hurting Hearts: Surviving the Onslaught of Adultery. 2009. 64p. pap. 10.95 (978-1-4389-8163-5(5)) AuthorHouse.

Spring, Janis A. After the Affair, Revised & Updated Edition: Healing the Pain & Rebuilding Trust When a Partner Has Been Unfaithful. 2012. (ENG.). 320p. pap. 14.99 **(978-0-06-212270-4(3)**, William Morrow Paperbacks) HarperCollins Pubs.

Subotnik, Rona. Why Did He Cheat on Me? The Truth Behind Why Men Stray. 2010. (ENG.). 240p. pap. 14.95 (978-1-4405-0054-1(1)); xi, 227p. E-Book **(978-1-4405-0713-7(9))** Adams Media Corp.

Turner, David M. Fashioning Adultery: Gender, Sex & Civility in England, 1660-1740. 2007. (Past & Present Publications). (ENG.). 252p. pap. 56.00 (978-0-521-04270-3(4)) Cambridge Univ. Pr.

Vaughan, Peggy. Preventing Affairs. 2008. 198p. pap. 14.95 (978-0-936390-21-5(2)) Dialog Pr.

—To Have & to Hold: A Personal Handbook For Building a Strong Marriage & Preventing Affairs. 2010. (ENG.). 208p. pap. 14.95 (978-1-55704-851-6(7), William Morrow Paperbacks) HarperCollins Pubs.

Whalum, Sheila. The Stimulus Package: Why men Cheat. 2011. 74p. 24.99 **(978-1-4628-5185-0(1))**; pap. 15.99 **(978-1-4628-5184-3(3))** Xlibris Corp.

Williams, Glenn A. Betrayal in the Church: The Bishop & My Wife-A True Story of Surviving Adultery. 2008. 156p. pap. 11.99 (978-1-4343-0632-6(1)) AuthorHouse.

Wynn. After the Affair. 2008. 48p. pap. 9.95 (978-0-595-53394-7(9)) iUniverse, Inc.

Young, Christina. A Woman's Guide to Forgiving Infidelity - How to Save Your Self-esteem & Restore Trust. 2011. 180p. pap. **(978-1-907498-59-6(1))** Lean Marketing Pr.

Zackheim, Victoria. The Other Woman: Twenty-One Wives, Lovers, & Others Talk Openly about Sex, Deception, Love, & Betrayal. 2008. (ENG.). 288p. pap. 13.99 (978-0-446-69882-5(2)) Grand Central Publishing.

ADULTERY IN LITERATURE

Amann, Elizabeth. Importing Madame Bovary: The Politics of Adultery. 2006. (ENG.). 284p. 89.00 (978-1-4039-7606-2(6)) Palgrave Macmillan.

Utell, Janine. James Joyce & the Revolt of Love: Marriage, Adultery, Desire. 2010. (New Directions in Irish & Irish American Literature Ser.). (ENG.). 192p. 79.00 (978-0-230-10512-6(2)) Palgrave Macmillan.

White, Nicholas. The Family in Crisis in Late Nineteenth-Century French Fiction. 2006. (Cambridge Studies in French Ser.). (ENG.). 232p. pap. 50.00 (978-0-521-02680-2(6)) Cambridge Univ. Pr.

ADULTHOOD

see also Adult Children; Old Age

Anderson, Mary Louise, et al. Counseling Adults in Transition: Linking Schlossberg's Theory with Practice in a Diverse World. 4th ed. 2011. **(978-0-8261-0635-3(8))**; E-Book **(978-0-8261-0636-0(6))** Springer Publishing Co., Inc.

Arnett, Jeffrey Jensen, et al. Debating Emerging Adulthood: Stage or Process?, 1 vol. 2011. (ENG., Illus.). 192p. 34.95 (978-0-19-975717-6(8)) Oxford Univ. Pr., Inc.

Becerra. Death of a Parent in Childhood & Resilience in Adulthood. 2010. 148p. pap. (978-3-639-25650-5(6)) VDM Verlag Dr. Mueller e.K.

Bee, Bjorklund. Journey of Adulthood. 2006. pap. 9.95 (978-1-4288-1800-2(6)) Cram101 Inc.

Bentley, Evie. Adulthood. 2007. (Modular Psychology Ser.). (ENG., Illus.). 136p. (C). 18.00 (978-0-415-25824-1(3)); 59.95 (978-0-415-25823-4(5)) Routledge.

Bjorklund, Barbara R. & Bee, Helen L. Journey of Adulthood. 7th ed. 2010. (ENG., Illus.). 456p. (C). 160.00 (978-0-205-01805-5(X), Prentice Hall) Prentice Hall PTR.

Blatterer. Coming of Age in Times of Uncertainty. 2009. 160p. 24.95 (978-1-84545-628-3(9)) Berghahn Bks., Inc.

Blatterer, Harry. Coming of Age in Times of Uncertainty: Redefining Contemporary Adulthood. 2007. 160p. (C). 90.00 (978-1-84545-285-8(2)) Berghahn Bks., Inc.

Bricker, J. Timothy, et al, eds. Adults with Childhood Illnesses: Considerations for Practice. 2011. (Health, Medicine & Human Development Ser.). (ENG., Illus.). XXII, 299p. 210.00 **(978-3-11-916189-3(6))**; 140.00 **(978-3-11-025521-8(9))** De Gruyter, Walter Inc.

Burnett, Judith, ed. Contemporary Adulthood: Calendars, Cartographies & Constructions. 2010. (ENG., Illus.). 208p. 89.00 (978-0-230-58103-6(X)) Palgrave Macmillan.

Cameron, Rosalea. The Ecology of Third Culture Kids. 2008. 240p. pap. (978-3-639-01700-7(5)) VDM Verlag Dr. Mueller e.K.

Charles, Susan T. & Association for Psychological Science Staff. Current Directions in Adulthood & Aging. 2008. (Association for Psychological Science Readers Ser.). (ENG., Illus.). 224p. (C). per. 53.60 (978-0-205-59749-9(1)) Allyn & Bacon, Inc.

Coker, Suzanne. Gender Role Schema, Childhood Trauma, & Well-Beingin Adulthood: A Positive Psychological Perspective. 2008. 236p. pap. (978-3-8364-7187-9(6)) VDM Verlag Dr. Mueller e.K.

Collins, W. Andrew & Laursen, Brett, eds. Relationship Pathways: From Adolescence to Young Adulthood. 2011. (Illus.). 360p. (C). pap. 56.00 **(978-1-4129-8739-4(3)**, B87394P) SAGE Pubns., Inc.

Cram101 Textbook Reviews. Outlines & Highlights for Adulthood & Aging by Marion G Mason, Isbn: 9780205433513. 2011. 160p. pap. 29.95 **(978-1-61461-902-4(6))** Cram101 Inc.

Cram101 Textbook Reviews & Cram101 Textbook Reviews. Outlines & Highlights for Adult Development & Aging by John C Cavanaugh, Isbn: 9780495601746. 2011. 116p. pap. 28.95 **(978-1-4288-8825-8(X))** Cram101 Inc.

—Outlines & Highlights for Constructing Adulthood: Agency & Subjectivity in Adolescence & Adulthood, Vol. 11 by Ross Macmillan, ISBN. 2011. 108p. pap. 28.95 **(978-1-61744-943-7(1))** Cram101 Inc.

—Outlines & Highlights for Counseling Adults in Transition: Linking Practice with Theory by Jane Goodman, ISBN. 2011. 102p. pap. 27.95 **(978-1-4288-4819-1(3))** Cram101 Inc.

—Outlines & Highlights for Journey of Adulthood by Barbara R Bjorklund. 2011. 78p. pap. 27.95 **(978-1-61830-465-0(8))** Cram101 Inc.

—Outlines & Highlights for Psychology Applied to Modern Life: Adjustment in the 21st Century by Wayne Weiten, ISBN. 2011. 512p. pap. 37.95 ***(978-1-4288-4043-0(5))*** Cram101 Inc.

Cram101 Textbook Reviews Staff. Outlines & Highlights for Adult Development & Aging by Cavanaugh, Isbn: 0534520669. 2008. 140p. per. 11.95 *(978-1-4288-5766-7(4))* Cram101 Inc.

—Outlines & Highlights for Journey of Adulthood, the by Bjorklund, Isbn: 0131888323. 2008. 100p. pap. 10.95 *(978-1-4288-5927-2(6))* Cram101 Inc.

Crudup, Sylvia & Bethea, James. Lifted A Young Person's Guide to Self-Motivation & Success. 2011. pap. 8.99 *(978-1-61739-528-4(5))* Tate Publishing & Enterprises, LLC.

Danziger, Sheldon & Rouse, Cecilia Elena. The Price of Independence: The Economics of Early Adulthood. 2007. (Illus.). 313p. *(978-0-87154-316-5(8))* Russell Sage Foundation.

Donohue, Brad & Allen, Daniel N. Treating Adult Substance Abuse Using Family Behavior Therapy: A Step-by-Step Approach. 2011. (ENG., Illus.). 264p. pap. 55.00 *(978-0-470-62193-6(1),* Wiley) Wiley, John & Sons, Inc.

Evans C.H., Trudy W. The Root of the Tree: The Foundation of Truth, 1 vol. 2009. 74p. pap. 16.95 *(978-1-4489-2074-7(4))* PublishAmerica, Inc.

Galpin, Diane & Bates, Nathalie. Social Work Practice with Adults. 2009. (ENG., Illus.). 124p. pap. *(978-1-84445-292-7(1))* Learning Matters Ltd.

George, Carol & West, Malcolm L. The Adult Attachment Projective Picture System: Attachment Theory & Assessment in Adults. 2012. (ENG.). 304p. 45.00 ***(978-1-4625-0425-1(6))*** Guilford Pubns., Inc.

Harwood, T. Mark, et al. Integrative Assessment of Adult Personality. 3rd rev. ed. 2011. (ENG.). 475p. 70.00 *(978-1-60918-650-0(8))* Guilford Pubns., Inc.

Hayslip, Bert & Hicks-Patrick, Julie. Adult Development & Aging. 5th ed. 2011. ***(978-1-57524-308-5(3))*** Krieger Publishing Co.

Hayslip, Bert, et al. Adult Development & Aging. 4th ed. 2007. *(978-1-57524-245-3(1))* Krieger Publishing Co.

Heemer, Art, et al. If You Love Me, Please Read This: A Challenge to the Men in Generation X & Y from the People Who Love Them. 2010. 124p. pap. 13.95 *(978-1-4502-0582-5(8))* iUniverse, Inc.

Heischman, Daniel R. Good Influence: Teaching the Wisdom of Adulthood. 2009. 160p. pap. 16.00 *(978-0-8192-2363-0(8),* Morehouse Publishing) Church Publishing, Inc.

Hendry, Leo & Kloep, Marion. Adolescence & Adulthood: Transitions & Transformations. 2012. (Palgrave Insights in Psychology Ser.). (ENG., Illus.). 216p. (C). pap. 16.00 ***(978-0-230-29640-4(8))*** Palgrave Macmillan.

Hoare, Carol, ed. The Oxford Handbook of Reciprocal Adult Development & Learning. 1 vol. 2nd ed. 2011. (Oxford Library of Psychology Ser.). (ENG., Illus.). 624p. 150.00 ***(978-0-19-973630-0(8))*** Oxford Univ. Pr., Inc.

Horne, Ann & Lanyado, Monica, eds. Through Assessment to Consultation: Independent Psychoanalytic Approaches with Children & Adolescents. 2009. (ENG.). 208p. (C). pap. 34.95 *(978-0-415-46290-7(8))* Routledge.

Hoyer, William J. & Roodin, Paul A. Adult Development & Aging. 6th ed. 2007. (C). 118.75 *(978-0-07-319184-3(1),* 9780073191843, McGraw-Hill Humanities, Social Sciences & World Languages) McGraw-Hill Higher Education.

James Swift. How I Survived Three Years at a Two-Year Community College: A Junior Memoir of Epic Proportions. 2009. 588p. 43.95 *(978-1-4401-8328-7(7))* iUniverse, Inc.

Jay, Meg. The Defining Decade: Why Your Twenties Matter — and How to Make the Most of Them Now. 2012. (ENG.). 272p. 22.99 ***(978-0-446-56176-1(2),*** Twelve) Grand Central Publishing.

Jongsma, Arthur E., Jr. & Berghuis, David J. The Adult Psychotherapy Progress Notes Planner. 3rd rev. ed. 2006. (PracticePlanners Ser.: 206). (ENG.). 400p. pap. 55.00 *(978-0-471-76344-4(6),* Wiley) Wiley, John & Sons, Inc.

Kaiser, Stacy. How to Be a Grown Up: The Ten Secret Skills Everyone Needs to Know. 2011. (ENG.). 272p. pap. 14.99 *(978-0-06-194119-1(0),* HarperOne) HarperCollins Pubs.

Kardener, Sheldon H. & Kardener, Monika Olofsson. Breaking Free: How Chains from Childhood Keep Us from What We Want. 2009. (ENG.). 216p. pap. 18.95 *(978-1-60037-645-0(2))* Morgan James Publishing.

Kotre, John. Make It Count: How to Generate a Legacy That Gives Meaning to You. 2011. (ENG.). 256p. pap. 16.99 ***(978-1-4516-8236-6(0),*** Free Pr.) Free Pr.

Lemme, Barbara H. Development in Adulthood. 2006. 3rd ed. pap. 9.95 *(978-1-4288-1715-9(8))* 4th ed. pap. 11.95 *(978-1-4288-1322-9(5))* Cram101 Inc.

Lindeman, Gary. Early Adulthood Transition - Personal Perspectives from Working Class Males. 2008. 216p. per. *(978-3-8364-5928-0(0))* VDM Verlag Dr. Mueller e.K.

MacKinnon, Donna. Becoming an Adult in Rural Scotland. 2008. 368p. pap. *(978-3-639-10533-9(8))* VDM Verlag Dr. Mueller e.K.

Macmillan, Ross, ed. Constructing Adulthood: Agency & Subjectivity in Adolescence & Adulthood. 2006. (ENG.). 346p. 105.00 *(978-0-7623-1201-6(7),* JAI Pr.) Elsevier Science & Technology Bks.

Magolda, Marcia B. Baxter. Authoring Your Life: Developing an Internal Voice to Navigate Life's Challenges. 2009. 400p. 29.95 *(978-1-57922-271-0(4))* Stylus Publishing, LLC.

Mason, Marion G. Adulthood & Aging. 2010. (ENG.). 480p. (C). 160.00 *(978-0-205-43351-3(0),* Prentice Hall) Prentice Hall PTR.

McCray, Walter A. Get Grown & Keep Growing! The Self-Help Adult Maturity Handbook. 2010. 160p. (Orig.). (YA). pap. 5.95 *(978-1-889303-00-0(3))* Yama Twenty-first Publishers, Inc.

Mellor, Christie. Raised by Wolves: Everything You Need to Know to Live a Happy & Civilized Life. 2010. (ENG.). 256p. pap. 13.99 *(978-0-06-193873-3(4),* Harper Paperbacks) HarperCollins Pubs.

Modica Myers, Amy. The Difference Between a Boy & a Man: 75 Words that Illustrate the Gap. 2009. 168p. 25.95 *(978-0-595-50745-0(X));* pap. 15.95 *(978-0-595-51306-2(9))* iUniverse, Inc.

New Passages. *(978-0-8041-1823-1(X))* Random House Publishing Group.

Okano, Kaori H. Young Women in Japan: Transitions to Adulthood. 2010. (ENG.). pap. 39.95 *(978-0-415-59051-8(5),* Routledge.

O'Murchu, Diarmuid. Adult Faith: Growing in Wisdom & Understanding. 2010. 224p. pap. 20.00 *(978-1-57075-886-7(7))* Orbis Bks.

Papalia, Sterns & Cram101 Textbook Reviews Staff. Adult Development & Aging. 2007. 176p. per. 12.95 *(978-1-4288-2114-9(7))* Cram101 Inc.

Pickhardt, Carl. Boomerang Kids: A Revealing Look at Why So Many of Our Children Are Failing on Their Own, & How Parents Can Help. 2011. (ENG.). 336p. pap. 14.99 *(978-1-4022-4858-0(X))* Sourcebooks, Inc.

Riekers, J. A. Living with the Dead. 2011. 120p. pap. 19.95 ***(978-1-4512-7862-0(4))*** PublishAmerica, Inc.

Rumbaut, Ruben G., et al, eds. On the Frontier of Adulthood: Theory, Research, & Public Policy. 2008. (MacArthur Foundation Ser.). (ENG., Illus.). 608p. pap. 29.00 *(978-0-226-74890-0(1))* Univ. of Chicago Pr.

Salandy, Laurenda. Far above Rubies: A Handbook for Growing Teenage Girls. 2008. 152p. per. 11.95 *(978-1-4327-1777-3(4))* Outskirts Pr., Inc.

Schouela, Daniel. The Gift & the Labor of Gratitude. 2008. 116p. per. *(978-3-8364-3540-6(3))* VDM Verlag Dr. Mueller e.K.

Sironi, Maria. A Century of Transitions to Adulthood in Europe. 2010. 140p. pap. *(978-3-639-24310-9(2))* VDM Verlag Dr. Mueller e.K.

Weiten, Wayne & Lloyd, Margaret A. Psychology Applied to Modern Life: Adjustment at the Turn of the Century. 6th ed. tchr. ed. *(978-0-534-36660-5(0))* Wadsworth.

Weiten, Wayne, et al. Cengage Advantage Books: Psychology Applied to Modern Life: Adjustment in the 21st Century. 10th ed. 2011. (ENG.). 688p. (C). ring bd. 99.95 *(978-1-111-29798-5(3))* Wadsworth.

—Psychology Applied to Modern Life: Adjustment in the 21st Century. 10th ed. 2011. (Available Titles CengageNOW Ser.). (ENG.). 688p. (C). 179.95 *(978-1-111-18663-0(4))* Wadsworth.

West, Diana. The Death of the Grown-Up: How America's Arrested Development Is Bringing down Western Civilization. 2008. (ENG.). 272p. pap. 15.99 *(978-0-312-34049-0(4),* St. Martin's Griffin) St. Martin's Pr.

Whitbourne, Susan Krauss. Adult Development & Aging: Biopsychosocial Perspectives. 3rd ed. 2007. (ENG., Illus.). 496p. (C). 172.95 *(978-0-470-11860-3(1),* Wiley) Wiley, John & Sons, Inc.

Whitbourne, Susan Krauss & Sliwinski, Martin J., eds. The Wiley-Blackwell Handbook of Adulthood & Aging. 2012. (Blackwell Handbooks of Developmental Psychology Ser.: 30). (ENG., Illus.). 584p. 199.95 ***(978-1-4443-3147-9(7),*** Wiley-Blackwell) Wiley, John & Sons, Inc.

Whitbourne, Susan Krauss & Whitbourne, Stacey B. Adult Development & Aging: Biopsychosocial Perspectives. 4th ed. 2010. (ENG., Illus.). 404p. (C). 172.95 *(978-0-470-64697-7(7),* Wiley) Wiley, John & Sons, Inc.

Yates, Alan J. Figs of the Imagination: Tales of bairns, wee men, lads & Lassies. 2010. 428p. pap. 22.77 *(978-1-4269-3226-7(X))* Trafford Publishing.

Young, Richard A. Transition to Adulthood: Action, Projects, & Counseling. 2011. ix, 235p. E-Book *(978-1-4419-6238-6(7))* Springer.

Young, Richard A., et al, told to. Active Transition to Adulthood: A New Approach for Counseling. 2010. (ENG., Illus.). x, 238p. 129.00 *(978-1-4419-6237-9(9),* 1441962379) Springer.

ADULTS, EDUCATION OF

see Adult Education

ADULTS ABUSED AS CHILDREN

see Adult Child Abuse Victims

ADULTS AND CHILDREN

see Children and Adults

ADULTS SEXUALLY ABUSED AS CHILDREN

see Adult Child Sexual Abuse Victims

ADVAITA

Adi Da Samraj & Adi Da Samraj. The Ancient Reality-Teachings: The Single Transcendental Truth Taught by the Great Sages of Buddhism & Advaitism - As Revealed by the Avataric Great Sage, Adi Da Samraj. 2006. (Perfect Knowledge Ser.). (Illus.). 278p. per. *(978-1-57097-198-3(6))* Dawn Horse Pr.

Anslow, Maurice. I Am Brahman: A Personal Quest into the Advaita Reality. 2010. (ENG.). 126p. pap. 16.95 *(978-1-84694-366-9(3))* O Bks., John Hunt.

Balasubramanian, R., ed. Advaita Vedanta, Vols. 2 , Pts. 2. 2010. 747p. 77.50 *(978-81-87586-04-3(4))* Munshiram Manoharlal Pubs. Private, Ltd. IND. Dist: Coronet Bks.

Balsekar, Ramesh & Jacobs, Alan. The Wisdom of Balsekar: The World's Leading Teacher of Advaita, co. 2006. 240p. pap. 16.95 *(978-1-84293-079-3(6),* Watkins Publishing) Duncan Baird Pubs. GBR. Dist: Sterling Publishing Co., Inc.

Balsekar, Ramesh S. The Ultimate Understanding. 2006. (Illus.). 256p. 22.95 *(978-1-84293-045-8(1),* Watkins Publishing) Duncan Baird Pubs. GBR. Dist: Sterling Publishing Co., Inc.

Bhaskarananda, Swami. Journey from Many to One: Essentials of Advaita Vedanta. 2009. pap. 15.95 *(978-1-884852-12-1(2))* Viveka Pr.

Bradford, G. Kenneth, et al, eds. Listening from the Heart of Silence. 2007. (Nondual Wisdom & Psychotherapy Ser.). (ENG.). 300p. pap. 19.95 *(978-1-55778-862-7(6))* Paragon Hse. Pubs.

Cee. The Way of Knowledge. 2007. 124p. pap. 14.95 *(978-1-60145-170-5(9))* Booklocker.com, Inc.

Cover, Jennifer. Understanding Bodhasar. 2009. 256p. pap. *(978-3-639-19147-9(1))* VDM Verlag Dr. Mueller e.K.

Davis, Leesa S. Advaita Vedanta & Zen Buddhism: Deconstructive Modes of Spiritual Inquiry. (ENG.). 246p. 2011. pap. 44.95 ***(978-1-4411-2109-7(9))*** 2010. 120.00 *(978-0-8264-2068-8(0))* Continuum International Publishing Group, Ltd. GBR. Dist: National Bk. Network.

Douglas, Paul. Language & Truth: A Study of the Sanskrit Language & Its Relationship with Principles of Truth. 2010. (ENG & SAN.). 124p. 25.00 *(978-0-85683-271-0(5))* Shepheard-Walwyn Pubs., Ltd. GBR. Dist: Independent Pubs. Group.

Grimes, John A. Ramana Maharshi: The Crown Jewel of Advaita. 2010. 320p. *(978-81-86569-95-5(2),* Library of Congress — New Delhi Overseas Office) Indica Bks.

Gupta, Sanjukta. Advaita Vedanta & Vaisnavism: The Philosophy of Madhusudana Sarasvati. 2006. (Hindu Studies). 176p. 160.00 *(978-0-415-39535-9(6))* Routledge.

Hyde, Unmani Liza. I am Life Itself. 2007. 104p. per. 17.95 *(978-1-4303-1552-0(0))* Lulu Enterprises Inc.

Klein, Jean. I Am. 2006. (ENG.). 164p. (Orig.). per. *(978-0-9551762-7-2(1))* Non-Duality Bks.

Koutha Mohanram, Sastry. Secret of Man & World. 2006. 244p. per. *(978-1-4067-2051-8(8),* Hesperides Pr.) Read Bks.

Mazumdar, P. J. The Circle of Fire: The Metaphysics of Yoga. 2009. (ENG.). 400p. pap. 22.95 *(978-1-55643-670-3(X))* North Atlantic Bks.

Puligandla, Ramakrishna. Jnana-Yoga: The Way of Knowledge. 2007 140p. per. 20.00 *(978-0-87573-091-2(4))* Jain Publishing Company, Inc.

Rajagopalachari, C. Bhaja Govindam: A Song of Sri Sankara. 2007. (Golden Thread Ser.). 64p. (C). pap. 14.95 *(978-1-55921-356-1(6),* Asphodel Pr.) Moyer Bell.

Rambachan, Anantanand. The Advaita Worldview: God, World, & Humanity. 2006. (SUNY Series in Religious Studies). 145p. per. 24.95 *(978-0-7914-6852-4(6))* State Univ. of New York Pr.

Rao, Srinivasa. Advaita: A Contemporary Critique. 2012. (ENG.). 240p. 55.00 ***(978-0-19-807981-1(8))*** Oxford Univ. Pr., Inc.

Samraj, Adi. Reality Is All the God There Is. 2008. (ENG.). 1p. pap. *(978-1-59477-257-3(6),* Inner Traditions) Inner Traditions International, Ltd.

Schoch, Manuel. Bitten by the Black Snake: The Ancient Wisdom of Ashtavakra. 2007. (ENG.). 110p. per. 12.95 *(978-1-59181-060-5(4))* Sentient Pubns.

Shankara, Panchikaranam. pap. 2.50 *(978-0-87481-068-4(X))* Vedanta Pr.

Sharma, Arvind. A Guide to Hindu Spirituality. 2006. (Perennial Philosophy Ser.). (ENG., Illus.). 136p. per. 17.95 *(978-1-933316-17-8(9))* World Wisdom, Inc.

Timalsina, Sthaneshwar. Consciousness in Indian Philosophy: The Advaita Doctrine of 'Awareness Only' 2008. (Routledge Hindu Studies Ser.). XXII, 186p. 150.00 *(978-0-415-77677-6(5))* Routledge.

Victor, P. George. Life & Teachings of AAdi Sanckaraacaarya. 2008. (Andhra University Philosophical Studies Ser.: No. 1). xii, 172p. *(978-81-246-0194-5(1))* D. K. Print World (P) Ltd.

—Life & Teachings of Adi Sankaracarya. 2008. (Andhra University Philosophical Studies Ser.: No. 1). 172p. pap. *(978-81-246-0407-6(X))* D. K. Print World (P) Ltd.

Waite, Dennis. Back to the Truth: 5000 Years of Advaita. 2007. (ENG.). 600p. per. 49.95 *(978-1-905047-61-1(4))* O Bks. GBR. Dist: National Bk. Network.

—The Book of One. 2010. (ENG.). 320p. pap. 13.95 *(978-1-84694-347-8(7))* O Bks., John Hunt.

—Enlightenment: the Path Through the Jungle: A Criticism of Non-Traditional Teaching Methods in Advaita. 2008. (ENG.). 176p. pap. 22.95 *(978-1-84694-118-4(0))* O Bks., John Hunt.

ADVANCED PLACEMENT PROGRAMS (EDUCATION)

Ace Academics, ed. AP: Exam Prep Software on CD-ROM! Exambusters CD-ROM Study Cards. 2007. (Exambusters Ser.). cd-rom 12.95 *(978-1-57633-211-5(X),* Exambusters) Ace Academics, Inc.

Amiry, Laila. Barron's AP French. 3rd ed. 2007. (ENG., Illus.). 416p. 26.99 *(978-0-7641-9337-8(6));* 34.99 *(978-0-7641-9336-1(8))* Barron's Educational Series, Inc.

Anestis, Mark. AP Biology 2012. 4th ed. 2011. (5 Steps to a 5 on the Advanced Placement Examinations Ser.). (ENG.). pap. 27.95 incl. cd-rom *(978-0-07-175183-4(1),* 0071751831) McGraw-Hill Cos., The.

—AP Biology 2012-2013. 4th ed. 2011. (5 Steps to a 5 on the Advanced Placement Examinations Ser.). (ENG., Illus.). 384p. (C). pap. 18.95 *(978-0-07-175179-7(3),* 0071751793) McGraw-Hill Cos., The.

AP Exam Secrets Test Prep Staff, ed. AP European History Exam Flashcard Study System: AP Test Practice Questions & Review for the Advanced Placement Exam. 2011. 62.99 *(978-1-61403-488-9(5))* Mometrix Media LLC.

—AP European History Exam Secrets Study Guide: AP Test Review for the Advanced Placement Exam. 2011. 62.99 *(978-1-61403-487-2(7))* Mometrix Media LLC.

—AP Psychology Exam Secrets Study Guide: AP Test Review for the Advanced Placement Exam. 2011. 62.99 *(978-1-61403-489-6(3))* Mometrix Media LLC.

Armstrong, Stephen. AP U. S. History. 4th ed. 2011. (5 Steps to a 5 on the Advanced Placement Examinations Ser.). (ENG.). 432p. pap. 27.95 incl. cd-rom *(978-0-07-175217-6(X),* 007175217X) McGraw-Hill Cos., The.

—5 Steps to a 5 AP US History, 2012-2013 Edition. 4th ed. 2011. (5 Steps to a 5 on the Advanced Placement Examinations Ser.). (ENG., Illus.). 432p. (C). pap. 18.95 *(978-0-07-175213-8(7),* 0071752137) McGraw-Hill Cos., The.

Asch, Gayle A. AP Art History Crash Course. 2012. (Advanced Placement (AP) Crash Course Ser.). (ENG.). 224p. (C). (gr. 10-12). pap. 12.95 ***(978-0-7386-1004-7(6))*** Research & Education Assn.

Asher, Randy J., et al. 5 Steps to a 5 500 AP Calculus AB/BC Questions to Know by Test Day. 2012. (5 Steps to a 5 on the Advanced Placement Examinations Ser.). (ENG., Illus.). 288p. (C). pap. 14.00 *(978-0-07-175370-8(2),* 0071753702) McGraw-Hill Cos., The.

Audio CD for Level 1-AP Italian Track. 2007. (ITA.). cd-rom *(978-0-9786016-4-5(5))* Edizioni Farinelli.

Barker, Brett & Peterson's Guides Staff. Chemistry. 2nd ed. 2007. (ENG., Illus.). 640p. pap. 18.00 *(978-0-7689-2472-5(3))* Peterson's.

Bentley, Jerry. Traditions & Encounters: A Global Perspective on the Past ©2008, 4E w/ AP Achiever Package. 4th ed. 2009. (ENG.). 167.66 *(978-0-07-892755-3(2),* 0078927552) McGraw-Hill Higher Education.

Bergman, Michael & Preis, Kevin. Barron's AP United States History: 500 Flash Cards. 2nd rev. ed. 2011. (ENG.). 504p. 18.99 *(978-0-7641-6264-0(0))* Barron's Educational Series, Inc.

Berman, Stacie Brensilver & Epstein, Mark. Preparing for the AP United States History Examination. 2012. (ENG.). 483p. pap. 18.99 ***(978-1-4354-6130-7(4))*** Course Technology.

Bernstein, Jared. Psychology Advanced Placement HM Testing. 8th ed. 2007. (YA). 140.76 *(978-0-547-01624-5(7),* 1031444) CENGAGE Learning.

Bernstein Psychology Advanced Placement Edition Eighth Edition. 8th ed. 2007. (YA). 128.36 *(978-0-547-01615-3(8),* 1031435) CENGAGE Learning.

Bloom, Lynn Z. The Essay Connection: Advanced Placement Edition. 8th ed. 2007. (YA). 63.56 *(978-0-547-05800-9(4),* 1037230) CENGAGE Learning.

Bobrow Test Preparation Services & Thorpe, Gary S. CliffsAP Chemistry. 4th ed. 2007. (ENG., Illus.). 480p. pap. 16.99 *(978-0-470-13500-6(X),* Cliff Notes) Wiley, John & Sons, Inc.

Bobrow Test Preparation Services Production Staff. CliffsNotes AP Chemistry. 4th ed. 2009. (ENG., Illus.). 480p. pap. 29.99 *(978-0-470-40034-0(X),* Cliff Notes) Wiley, John & Sons, Inc.

Boyle, Bruna Petrarca. AP Italian Track - Level 1 with Audio CD. 2007. (ITA., Illus.). 120p. stu. ed., per. 46.95 *(978-0-9786016-1-4(0))* Edizioni Farinelli.

Brand, Genevieve. AP World History All Access. 2012. (Advanced Placement (AP) All Access Ser.). (ENG.). 480p. (gr. 10-12). pap. 18.95 ***(978-0-7386-1025-2(9),)*** Research & Education Assn.

Brautigam, Jeffrey. 5 Steps to a 5 AP European History, 2012-2013 Edition. 3rd ed. 2011. (5 Steps to a 5 on the Advanced Placement Examinations Ser.). (ENG., Illus.). 352p. (C). pap. 18.95 *(978-0-07-175160-5(2),* 0071751602) McGraw-Hill Cos., The.

Brun-Ozuna, Barbara, et al. Preparing for the AP World History Examination. 2012. (ENG.). 486p. pap. 18.99 ***(978-1-4354-6126-0(6))*** Course Technology.

Bryan, Kevin, et al. CliffsNotes AP Environmental Science. 2011. (ENG., Illus.). 360p. pap. 16.99 *(978-0-470-88975-6(6),* Cliff Notes) Wiley, John & Sons, Inc.

Cade, Sharon, et al. Preparing for the AP Calculus AB & Calculus BC Examinations. 2012. (ENG.). 342p. pap. 18.99 ***(978-1-4354-6128-4(2))*** Course Technology.

Callihan, Laurie Ann, et al. AP Biology. 8th ed. 2009. (Advanced Placement (AP) Test Preparation Ser.). (ENG.). 496p. (gr. 12-12). pap. 24.95 *(978-0-7386-0786-3(X))* Research & Education Assn.

Campbell, M. W., et al. AP European History. Link, Jere, ed. 2009. (Advanced Placement (AP) Test Preparation Ser.). (ENG.). 640p. (gr. 9-12). pap. 29.95 *(978-0-7386-0626-2(X));* 10th ed. pap. 20.95 *(978-0-7386-0627-9(8))* Research & Education Assn.

Carroll, Anne & Bock, David E. Preparing for the Statistics AP Exam: With Stats, Modeling the World, Third Edition [by] Bock, Velleman, de Veaux. 3rd ed. 2009. *(978-0-321-57058-1(8))* Addison-Wesley Longman, Inc.

Casson, Allan & Eggenschwiler, Jean. English Literature & Composition. 3rd ed. 2010. (ENG., Illus.). 312p. pap. 16.99 *(978-0-470-60757-2(2),* Cliff Notes) Wiley, John & Sons, Inc.

Center for Learning Staff. AP U. S. Government & Politics. 2006. (Social Studies Ser.). (YA). Bk. 1. 124p. spiral bd. 10.95 *(978-1-56077-811-0(3))*Bk. 1. (Illus.). 214p. spiral bd. 39.95 *(978-1-56077-810-3(5))*Bk. 2. 180p. spiral bd. 10.95 *(978-1-56077-831-8(8))*Bk. 2. (Illus.). 270p. spiral bd. 39.95 *(978-1-56077-830-1(X))* Center for Learning, The.

Chasey, James. Multiple Choice & Free Response Questions in Preparation for the AP Economics Examination. 3rd ed. 2007. (YA). pap. 21.55 net. *(978-0-9787199-8-2(0))* D & S Marketing Systems, Inc.

Chmiel, Frank, et al. AP Art History. 2012. (Advanced Placement (AP) Test Preparation Ser.). (ENG.). 512p. (gr. 11-12). pap. 29.95 ***(978-0-7386-1075-7(5))*** Research & Education Assn.

D'Alessio, Michael. AP Chemistry Crash Course. 2010. (Advanced Placement (AP) Crash Course Ser.). (ENG.). 224p. (gr. 10-12). pap. 11.95 *(978-0-7386-0697-2(9))* Research & Education Assn.

—AP Statistics Crash Course. 2011. (Advanced Placement (AP) Crash Course Ser.). (ENG.). 240p. (gr. 11-12). pap. 11.95 *(978-0-7386-0888-4(2))* Research & Education Assn.

Demeter, Scott & Evangelist, Thomas A. 500 AP U.S. History Questions to Know by Test Day. 2010. (ENG., Illus.). 240p. (C). pap. 14.00 *(978-0-07-174207-8(7),* 0071742077) McGraw-Hill Cos., The.

Dickison, Sheila & Ricks, Patsy. Cicero: De Amicitia Selections. 2006. 82p. tchr. ed. 29.00 *(978-0-86516-641-7(2));* pap., stu. ed. 20.00 *(978-0-86516-639-4(0))* Bolchazy-Carducci Pubs.

Digital Actuarial Resources. Headway Test Prep for AP Calculus AB. 2008. 154p. (YA). pap. 19.99 *(978-0-9798071-9-0(0))* Digital Actuarial Resources, LLC.

Dodge, Eric. AP Microeconomics/Macroeconomics: 2012-2013. 4th ed. 2011. (5 Steps to a 5 on the Advanced Placement Examinations Ser.). (ENG., Illus.). 384p. (C). pap. 18.95 *(978-0-07-175122-3(X)*, 007175122X) McGraw-Hill Cos., The.

—Steps to a 5 AP Microeconomics/Macroeconomics 2012-2013. 4th ed. 2011. (5 Steps to a 5 on the Advanced Placement Examinations Ser.). (ENG.). 384p. pap. 27.95 incl. cd-rom *(978-0-07-175126-1(2)*, 0071751262) McGraw-Hill Cos., The.

Doltar, Robert, et al. Preparing for the AP Biology Examination: Fast Track to A 5. 2012. (ENG.). 339p. pap. 18.99 ***(978-1-4354-6124-6(X))*** Course Technology.

Dornbush, Krista. Kaplan AP U. S. History 2012. 2011. (Kaplan AP Ser.). (ENG.). 480p. pap. 17.99 *(978-1-60978-073-9(6))* Kaplan Publishing.

Dumas, P. E., et al. AP Chemistry. Fikar, R. M., ed. 10th ed. 2008. (Advanced Placement (AP) Test Preparation Ser.). (ENG., Illus.). 500p. (gr. 11-12). pap. 18.95 *(978-0-7386-0427-5(5))* Research & Education Assn.

Dzamba, Andy & Goodman, Nat, eds. IOMA's Complete Guide to AP Best Practices. 2008. (Illus.). 318p. pap. 379.00 *(978-1-58673-281-3(1))* Institute of Management & Administration, IOMA.

Eder, James M. & Roberts, Seth A. Barron's AP European History. 4th ed. 2008. (ENG., Illus.). 416p. per. 16.99 *(978-0-7641-3680-1(1))* Barron's Educational Series, Inc.

Evangelist, Thomas A. & Ambrose, Allyson. 5 Steps to a 5 500 AP English Language Questions to Know by Test Day. 2010. (5 Steps to a 5 on the Advanced Placement Examinations Ser.). (ENG., Illus.). 224p. (C). pap. 14.00 *(978-0-07-175368-5(0)*, 0071753680) McGraw-Hill Cos., The.

Evangelist, Thomas A. & Stevens, Adam. 5 Steps to a 5 500 AP World History Questions to Know by Test Day. 2010. (ENG., Illus.). 176p. (C). pap. 14.00 *(978-0-07-174209-2(3)*, 0071742093) McGraw-Hill Cos., The.

Evans, Gayle. AP Environmental Science Crash Course. 2011. (Advanced Placement (AP) Crash Course Ser.). (ENG.). 288p. (gr. 9-12). pap. 11.95 ***(978-0-7386-0931-7(5))*** Research & Education Assn.

Feldmeth, Gregory. AP U.S. History 2012-2013 Edition. 2011. pap. 16.95 ***(978-0-7386-1011-5(9))*** Research & Education Assn.

Feldmeth, Gregory, et al. AP U. S. History All Access. 2012. (Advanced Placement (AP) All Access Ser.). (ENG.). 576p. (gr. 10-12). pap. 18.95 ***(978-0-7386-1057-3(7))*** Research & Education Assn.

Fenton, Nancy & Flitter, Jessica. AP Psychology All Access. 2012. (Advanced Placement (AP) All Access Ser.). (ENG.). 528p. (gr. 10-12). pap. 18.95 ***(978-0-7386-1026-9(7))*** Research & Education Assn.

Ferguson, Stephanie K., et al. Advanced Placement Programs & Gifted Students. 2009. (ENG.). pap. 12.95 *(978-1-59363-378-3(5))* Prufrock Pr.

Freudenrich, Craig C., et al. Kaplan AP Environmental Science 2012. 2011. (Kaplan AP Ser.). (ENG.). 396p. pap. 17.99 *(978-1-60978-065-4(5))* Kaplan Publishing.

Gava, Rita, et al. AP Chemistry All Access. 2012. (Advanced Placement (AP) All Access Ser.). (ENG.). 272p. (gr. 10-12). pap. 18.95 ***(978-0-7386-1027-6(5))*** Research & Education Assn.

Godat, Chris. Barriers Removed. 2010. 168p. pap. *(978-3-639-06066-9(0))* VDM Verlag Dr. Mueller e.K.

Goldberg M.S., Deborah T. Barron's AP Biology: 500 Flash Cards. 2nd rev. ed. 2011. (ENG.). 492p. 18.99 *(978-0-7641-6265-7(9))* Barron's Educational Series, Inc.

Hakala, Chris. Kaplan AP Psychology 2012. 2011. (Kaplan AP Ser.). (ENG.). 300p. pap. 17.99 *(978-1-60978-070-8(1))* Kaplan Publishing.

Heckert, Paul, et al. Kaplan AP Physics B & C 2012. 2011. (Kaplan AP Ser.). (ENG.). 552p. pap. 17.99 *(978-1-60978-069-2(8))* Kaplan Publishing.

Hinders, Duane. Ap Statistics: 2012-2013. 4th ed. 2011. (5 Steps to a 5 on the Advanced Placement Examinations Ser.). (ENG., Illus.). 384p. (C). pap. 18.95 *(978-0-07-175118-6(1)*, 0071751181) McGraw-Hill Cos., The.

Hogue, Dawn. AP English Language & Composition Crash Course. 2011. (Advanced Placement (AP) Crash Course Ser.). (ENG.). 288p. (gr. 10-12). pap. 12.95 *(978-0-7386-0783-2(5))* Research & Education Assn.

—AP English Literature & Composition Crash Course. 2010. (Advanced Placement (AP) Crash Course Ser.). (ENG.). 240p. (gr. 10-12). pap. 11.95 *(978-0-7386-0782-5(7))* Research & Education Assn.

Horstmann, Cay S. Java Concepts for AP Computer Science. 5th ed. 2007. (ENG., Illus.). 880p. (C). 133.95 *(978-0-470-18160-7(5)*, Wiley) Wiley, John & Sons, Inc.

Horstmann, Cay S. & Trees, Frances P. Java Concepts: Advanced Placement Computer Science Study Guide. 5th ed. 2007. (ENG.). 480p. (C). per. 53.95 *(978-0-470-18161-4(3)*, Wiley) Wiley, John & Sons, Inc.

Horwitz, Susan. AP Computer Science. 4th ed. 2011. *(978-0-13-213351-7(2))* Prentice Hall PTR.

Horwitz, Susan & Sudol, Leigh Ann. Pearson Education's Review for the AP Computer Science A & AB. 3rd ed. 2008. (ENG.). 408p. (C). pap. 20.80 *(978-0-13-606861-7(8))* Addison Wesley Higher Education.

Hostage, David W. & Fossett, Martin. AP Advantage Laboratory Investigations: AP Chemistry. 2006. (AP Advantage Ser.). (C). pap. 27.99 *(978-1-4138-0489-8(6))* Peoples Education.

Howell, Rebecca & Banu, F. AP Physics B Crash Course. 2012. (Advanced Placement (AP) Crash Course Ser.). (ENG.). 240p. (gr. 10-12). pap. 12.95 ***(978-0-7386-0934-8(X))*** Research & Education Assn.

Hughes, Erica, et al. AP Spanish Language. 7th ed. 2009. (Advanced Placement (AP) Test Preparation Ser.). (ENG.). 512p. (gr. 9-12). pap. 27.95 *(978-0-7386-0630-9(8))* Research & Education Assn.

Jacobs, Greg & Schulman, Joshua. AP Physics B&C ,2012-2013. 4th ed. 2011. (5 Steps to a 5 on the Advanced Placement Examinations Ser.). (ENG., Illus.). 416p. (C). pap. 18.95 *(978-0-07-175120-9(3)*, 0071751203) McGraw-Hill Cos., The.

James, William & McLane, Michael. Preparing for the AP Psychology Exam: Fast Track to A 5. 2012. (ENG.). 404p. pap. 18.99 ***(978-1-4354-6134-5(7))*** Course Technology.

Jespersen, Neil D. Barron's AP Chemistry Flash Cards. 2008. (ENG.). 504p. 18.99 *(978-0-7641-6116-2(4))* Barron's Educational Series, Inc.

Jones, David. AP Physics B & C. Kinard, John, ed. 6th ed. 2009. (Test Preps Ser.). (ENG.). 480p. (gr. 11-12). pap. 18.95 *(978-0-7386-0480-0(1))* Research & Education Assn.

Kaplan Higher Education Staff. Kaplan AP English Language & Composition Express. 2010. (ENG.). 120p. pap. 11.99 *(978-1-60714-789-3(0))* Kaplan Publishing.

—Kaplan AP World History Express. 2010. (ENG.). 108p. pap. 11.99 *(978-1-60714-787-9(4))* Kaplan Publishing.

—Kaplan AP World History in a Box. 2010. (ENG.). 1204p. 19.99 *(978-1-60714-783-1(1))* Kaplan Publishing.

Kaplan Publishing Staff. Kaplan AP European History 2007. 2007. 416p. pap. 18.00 *(978-0-7432-6063-3(5))* Kaplan Publishing.

—Kaplan AP Physics B & C 2007: An Apex Learning Guide. 2007. 360p. pap. 19.00 *(978-0-7432-7904-8(2))* Kaplan Publishing.

—Kaplan AP U. S. History in a Box. 2nd ed. 2010. (ENG.). 1204p. 19.95 *(978-1-60714-552-3(9))* Kaplan Publishing.

Kaplan Publishing Staff, ed. Kaplan AP Human Geography. 2007. 256p. pap. 18.00 *(978-1-4277-0602-7(6))* Dearborn Financial Publishing.

—Kaplan AP Psychology 2008. 2007. 264p. pap. 18.00 *(978-1-4277-5171-3(4))* Dearborn Financial Publishing.

Kelley, W. Michael, et al. Master AP Calculus AB & BC. 2nd ed. 2007. (ENG., Illus.). 720p. pap. 19.00 *(978-0-7689-2470-1(7))* Peterson's.

King, Julie Adair, et al. *AP Environmental Science. 2011. (ENG.). 360p. pap. 29.99 *(978-0-470-88977-0(2)*, Cliff Notes) Wiley, John & Sons, Inc.

Kleinschmidt, Ulrich & Brown, Bill. Kaplan AP U. S. Government & Politics 2012. rev. ed. 2011. (Kaplan AP Ser.). (ENG.). 372p. pap. 17.99 *(978-1-60978-072-2(8))* Kaplan Publishing.

—Kaplan AP US Government & Politics 2007: An Apex Learning Guide. 2007. 408p. pap. 18.00 *(978-0-7432-7912-3(3))* Kaplan Publishing.

Knauer, Ellen. AP French Language, 3rd Edition plus 3 Audio CDs. 2012. pap. 27.95 ***(978-0-7386-1005-4(4))*** Research & Education Assn.

Krieger, Larry. AP Psychology Crash Course. 2010. (Advanced Placement (AP) Crash Course Ser.). (ENG.). 272p. (gr. 11-12). pap. 11.95 *(978-0-7386-0781-8(9))* Research & Education Assn.

—AP U. S. History: The Test Prep APTeachers Recommend. 2nd ed. 2010. (Advanced Placement (AP) Crash Course Ser.). (ENG.). 240p. (gr. 10-12). pap. 12.95 *(978-0-7386-0813-6(0))* Research & Education Assn.

—U. S. Government & Politics. 2009. (Advanced Placement (AP) Crash Course Ser.). (ENG.). 192p. (gr. 11-12). pap. 11.95 *(978-0-7386-0809-9(2))* Research & Education Assn.

Krieger, Larry & Harmon, Jay P. AP World History Crash Course (REA) 2011. (Advanced Placement (AP) Crash Course Ser.). (ENG.). 320p. (gr. 10-12). pap. 11.95 *(978-0-7386-0696-5(0))* Research & Education Assn.

Lamb, Pamela. AP U. S. Government & Politics 2012-2013. 4th ed. 2011. (5 Steps to a 5 on the Advanced Placement Examinations Ser.). (ENG.). 304p. (C). pap. 18.95 *(978-0-07-175163-6(7)*, 0071751637); pap. 27.95 incl. cd-rom *(978-0-07-175167-4(X)*, 007175167X) McGraw-Hill Cos., The.

—5 Steps to a 5 AP U. S. Government & Politics Flashcards for your iPod with MP3/CD-ROM Disk. 2010. (5 Steps to a 5 on the Advanced Placement Examinations Ser.). (ENG.). pap. 18.95 incl. cd-rom *(978-0-07-170096-2(X)*, 007170096X) McGraw-Hill Cos., The.

Langley, Richard H. & Moore, John. 5 Steps to a 5 AP Chemistry 2012-2013. 4th ed. 2011. (5 Steps to a 5 on the Advanced Placement Examinations Ser.). (ENG., Illus.). 400p. (C). pap. 18.95 *(978-0-07-175168-1(8)*, 0071751688) McGraw-Hill Cos., The.

Lavoie, Dennis. 5 Steps to a 5 AP Spanish Language with MP3 Disk, 2012-2013 Edition. 4th ed. 2011. (5 Steps to a 5 on the Advanced Placement Examinations Ser.). (SPA & ENG.). 400p. pap. 26.95 incl. cd-rom *(978-0-07-175231-2(5)*, 0071752315) McGraw-Hill Cos., The.

Lebitz, Mina & Evangelist, Thomas A. AP Biology Questions to Know by Test Day. 2010. (5 Steps to a 5 on the Advanced Placement Examinations Ser.). (ENG., Illus.). 176p. (C). pap. 14.00 *(978-0-07-174201-6(8)*, 0071742018) McGraw-Hill Cos., The.

Lederman, David & Wood, Ethel. Multiple-Choice & Free-Response Questions in Preparation for the AP Calculus AB Examination. 2011. pap. 24.14 net. ***(978-1-934780-08-4(1))*** D & S Marketing Systems, Inc.

Levine-Wissing, Robin. AP Statistics 2012-2013 Edition. 2011. pap. 16.95 ***(978-0-7386-1012-2(7))*** Research & Education Assn.

Levine-Wissing, Robin & Thiel, David. AP Statistics. 4th ed. 2009. (Advanced Placement (AP) Test Preparation Ser.). (ENG.). 496p. (gr. 10-12). pap. 24.95 *(978-0-7386-0790-0(8))* Research & Education Assn.

Levine-Wissing, Robin, et al. AP Statistics All Access. 2012. (Advanced Placement (AP) All Access Ser.). (ENG.). 320p. (gr. 10-12). pap. 18.95 ***(978-0-7386-1058-0(5))*** Research & Education Assn.

Levy, Norman. AP Calculus AB & BC. 2nd ed. 2009. (Advanced Placement (AP) Test Preparation Ser.). (ENG.). 544p. (gr. 9-12). pap. 24.95 *(978-0-7386-0628-6(6))* Research & Education Assn.

Link, Jere, et al. AP European History All Access. 2012. (Advanced Placement (AP) All Access Ser.). (ENG.). 576p. (gr. 10-12). pap. 18.95 ***(978-0-7386-1023-8(2))*** Research & Education Assn.

Ma, William. AP Calculus AB & BC, 2012-2013. 4th ed. 2011. (5 Steps to a 5 on the Advanced Placement Examinations Ser.). (ENG., Illus.). 480p. (C). pap. 18.95 *(978-0-07-175172-8(6)*, 0071751726) McGraw-Hill Cos., The.

Maitland, Laura. AP Psychology 2012-2013. 4th ed. 2011. (5 Steps to a 5 on the Advanced Placement Examinations Ser.). (ENG.). pap. 27.95 incl. cd-rom *(978-0-07-175190-2(4)*, 0071751904); (Illus.). 352p. (C). pap. 18.95 *(978-0-07-175186-5(6)*, 0071751866) McGraw-Hill Cos., The.

Martin, Peggy. 5 Steps to a 5 AP World History, 2012-2013 Edition. 4th ed. 2011. (5 Steps to a 5 on the Advanced Placement Examinations Ser.). (ENG., Illus.). 352p. (C). pap. 18.95 *(978-0-07-175097-4(5)*, 0071750975) McGraw-Hill Cos., The.

Martin, Peggy. 5 Steps to a 5 AP World History Flashcards. 2011. (5 Steps to a 5 on the Advanced Placement Examinations Ser.). (ENG.). 624p. (C). 19.00 ***(978-0-07-178064-3(5)***, 0071780645) McGraw-Hill Cos., The.

Mayer, David. AP Microeconomics Crash Course. 2011. (Advanced Placement (AP) Crash Course Ser.). (ENG.). 208p. (gr. 10-12). pap. 11.95 *(978-0-7386-0972-0(2))* Research & Education Assn.

McConnell, Campbell & Brue, Stanley L. Economics: Principles, Problems, & Policies. 17th ed. 2006. (Illus.). 716p. 154.06 *(978-0-07-329392-9(X)*, 9780073293929, McGraw-Hill/Irwin) McGraw-Hill Higher Education.

McDuffie, J. A., et al. AP United States History W/CD-ROM (REA) Feldmeth, Gregory, ed. 2011. (Test Preps Ser.). 864p. pap. 29.95 *(978-0-7386-0885-3(8))* Research & Education Assn.

McKay, John P., et al. A History of Western Society since 1300. 9th ed. 2008. (ENG.). pap., pupil's gde. ed. 31.95 *(978-0-312-68323-8(5))* Bedford/Saint Martin's.

Mendez, Juan & Fairchild, Ana Laura Tello. Spanish Grammar. Knickerbocker, Dale F., ed. 2nd ed. 2006. (Collins College Outlines Ser.). (ENG & SPA.). 256p. per. 15.95 *(978-0-06-088157-3(7))* HarperCollins Pubs.

Miller, Shveta Verma & Evangelist, Thomas A. 5 Steps to a 5 500 AP English Literature Questions to Know by Test Day. 2010. (5 Steps to a 5 on the Advanced Placement Examinations Ser.). (ENG., Illus.). 224p. (C). pap. 14.00 *(978-0-07-175410-1(5)*, 0071754105) McGraw-Hill Cos., The.

Monahan, Chris. My Max Score SAT Math 1 & 2 Subject Test: Maximize Your Score in Less Time. 2012. (My Max Score Ser.). (ENG.). 272p. pap. 14.99 *(978-1-4022-5601-1(9))* Sourcebooks, Inc.

Moore, Martha. Kaplan AP European History 2012. 2011. (Kaplan AP Ser.). (ENG.). 480p. pap. 17.99 *(978-1-60978-066-1(3))* Kaplan Publishing.

Moran, Margaret C., et al. The AP U. S. History: Everything You Need to Get AP* & a Head Start on College. 2nd ed. 2006. (ENG., Illus.). 300p. (YA). pap. 18.00 *(978-0-7689-2469-5(3))* Peterson's.

—Master AP English Literature & Composition. 2nd ed. 2007. (ENG.). 300p. pap. 18.00 *(978-0-7689-2473-2(1))* Peterson's.

Murphy, Barbara & Rankin, Estelle. AP English Language 2012-2013. 4th ed. 2011. (5 Steps to a 5 on the Advanced Placement Examinations Ser.). (ENG.). 272p. pap. 27.95 incl. cd-rom *(978-0-07-175158-2(0)*, 0071751580) McGraw-Hill Cos., The.

—AP English Literature 2012-2013. 4th ed. 2011. (5 Steps to a 5 on the Advanced Placement Examinations Ser.). (ENG.). 256p. pap. 27.95 incl. cd-rom *(978-0-07-175178-0(5)*, 0071751785) McGraw-Hill Cos., The.

—5 Steps to a 5 AP English Language 2012-2013. 4th ed. 2011. (5 Steps to a 5 on the Advanced Placement Examinations Ser.). (ENG.). 272p. (C). pap. 18.95 *(978-0-07-175154-4(8)*, 0071751548) McGraw-Hill Cos., The.

Murphy, Barbara & Rankin, Estelle M. 5 Steps to a 5 Writing the AP English Essay, 2012-2013 Edition. 2nd ed. 2011. (5 Steps to a 5 on the Advanced Placement Examinations Ser.). (ENG.). 208p. (C). pap. 18.95 *(978-0-07-176054-6(7)*, 0071760547) McGraw-Hill Cos., The.

Myers, David G. Psychology for AP. 2010. (ENG.). 944p. 130.95 *(978-1-4292-4436-7(4))* Worth Pubs., Inc.

Pack, Phillip E. Biology. 3rd ed. 2009. (ENG., Illus.). 360p. pap. 29.99 *(978-0-470-40035-7(6)*, Cliff Notes) Wiley, John & Sons, Inc.

—CliffsAP Biology. 3rd rev. ed. 2007. (ENG., Illus.). 360p. pap. 16.99 *(978-0-470-09764-9(7)*, Cliff Notes) Wiley, John & Sons, Inc.

Palma, Ronald B. & Benediktson, D. Thomas. AP Latin Vergil Exam. 2nd ed. 2010. (Advanced Placement (AP) Test Preparation Ser.). (ENG.). 640p. (gr. 10-12). pap. 29.95 *(978-0-7386-0706-1(1))* Research & Education Assn.

Perfect Score Software, compiled by. CLEP / AP Courseware ¿ Principles of Marketing. 2007. 400p. cd-rom 25.95 *(978-0-9798516-2-9(9))* Perfect Score Software, Inc.

Peterson, Hiromi, et al. Strive for a 5: AP Japanese Practice Tests. 2009. (Illus.). 247p. pap. *(978-0-88727-649-1(0)*, Debolsillo) Cheng & Tsui Co.

Peterson's Guides Staff, et al. Master AP U. S Government & Politics: Everything You Need to Get AP* Credit & a Head Start on College. 2nd ed. 2007. (ENG.). 384p. (YA). pap. 17.00 *(978-0-7689-2471-8(5))* Peterson's.

Pfirrmann, Cynthia. Barron's New Jersey Biology Competency Test. 2012. (ENG.). 400p. pap. 16.99 *(978-0-7641-4378-6(6))* Barron's Educational Series, Inc.

Pivarnik-Nova, Denise. Kaplan AP English Language & Composition 2012. 2011. (Kaplan AP Ser.). (ENG.). 360p. pap. 17.99 *(978-1-60978-063-0(9))* Kaplan Publishing.

—Kaplan AP English Literature & Composition 2012. 2011. (Kaplan AP Ser.). (ENG.). 360p. pap. 17.99 *(978-1-60978-064-7(7))* Kaplan Publishing.

Princeton Review. Cracking the AP Biology Exam, 2013 Edition. 2012. (College Test Preparation Ser.). (ENG.). 384p. pap. 18.99 ***(978-0-307-94508-2(1)***, Princeton Review) Random Hse. Information Group.

—Cracking the AP Calculus AB & BC Exams, 2013 Edition. 2012. (College Test Preparation Ser.). (ENG.). 896p. pap. 19.99 ***(978-0-307-94486-3(7)***, Princeton Review) Random Hse. Information Group.

—Cracking the AP Chemistry Exam, 2013 Edition. 2012. (College Test Preparation Ser.). (ENG.). 464p. pap. 18.99 ***(978-0-307-94488-7(3)***, Princeton Review) Random Hse. Information Group.

—Cracking the AP Economics Macro & Micro Exams, 2013 Edition. 2012. (College Test Preparation Ser.). (ENG.). 256p. pap. 18.00 ***(978-0-307-94509-9(X)***, Princeton Review) Random Hse. Information Group.

—Cracking the AP English Language & Composition Exam, 2013 Edition. 2012. (College Test Preparation Ser.). (ENG.). 272p. pap. 18.00 ***(978-0-307-94511-2(1)***, Princeton Review) Random Hse. Information Group.

—Cracking the AP English Literature & Composition Exam 2012. 2012. (College Test Preparation Ser.). (ENG.). 240p. pap. 18.00 ***(978-0-307-94512-9(X)***, Princeton Review) Random Hse. Information Group.

—Cracking the AP Environmental Science Exam, 2013 Edition. 2012. (College Test Preparation Ser.). (ENG.). 336p. pap. 18.99 ***(978-0-307-94513-6(8)***, Princeton Review) Random Hse. Information Group.

—Cracking the AP European History Exam, 2013 Edition. 2012. (College Test Preparation Ser.). (ENG.). 464p. pap. 18.99 ***(978-0-307-94489-4(1)***, Princeton Review) Random Hse. Information Group.

—Cracking the AP Human Geography Exam, 2013 Edition. 2012. (College Test Preparation Ser.). (ENG.). 400p. pap. 18.00 ***(978-0-307-94514-3(6)***, Princeton Review) Random Hse. Information Group.

—Cracking the AP Psychology Exam, 2013 Edition. 2012. (College Test Preparation Ser.). (ENG.). 320p. pap. 18.00 ***(978-0-307-94517-4(0)***, Princeton Review) Random Hse. Information Group.

—Cracking the AP Spanish Exam with Audio CD, 2013 Edition. 2012. (College Test Preparation Ser.). (ENG.). 288p. pap. 24.99 ***(978-0-307-94518-1(9)***, Princeton Review) Random Hse. Information Group.

—Cracking the AP Statistics Exam, 2013 Edition. 2012. (College Test Preparation Ser.). (ENG.). 416p. pap. 19.99 ***(978-0-307-94519-8(7)***, Princeton Review) Random Hse. Information Group.

—Cracking the AP U. S. Government & Politics Exam, 2013 Edition. 2012. (College Test Preparation Ser.). (ENG.). 320p. pap. 18.99 ***(978-0-307-94520-4(0)***, Princeton Review) Random Hse. Information Group.

—Cracking the AP U. S. History Exam, 2013 Edition. 2012. (College Test Preparation Ser.). (ENG.). 432p. pap. 18.99 ***(978-0-307-94490-0(5)***, Princeton Review) Random Hse. Information Group.

—Cracking the AP World History Exam, 2013 Edition. 2012. (College Test Preparation Ser.). (ENG.). 416p. pap. 18.99 ***(978-0-307-94491-7(3)***, Princeton Review) Random Hse. Information Group.

Princeton Review Staff. Cracking the AP Biology Exam, 2012 Edition. 2011. (College Test Preparation Ser.). (ENG.). 384p. pap. 18.99 *(978-0-375-42725-1(2)*, Princeton Review) Random Hse. Information Group.

—Cracking the AP Calculus AB & BC Exams, 2012 Edition. 2011. (College Test Preparation Ser.). (ENG.). 896p. pap. 19.99 *(978-0-375-42720-6(1)*, Princeton Review) Random Hse. Information Group.

—Cracking the AP Chemistry Exam, 2012 Edition. 2011. (College Test Preparation Ser.). (ENG.). 464p. pap. 18.99 *(978-0-375-42721-3(X)*, Princeton Review) Random Hse. Information Group.

—Cracking the AP English Language & Composition Exam, 2012 Edition. 2011. (College Test Preparation Ser.). (ENG.). 272p. pap. 18.00 *(978-0-375-42727-5(9)*, Princeton Review) Random Hse. Information Group.

—Cracking the AP English Literature & Composition Exam, 2012 Edition. 2011. (College Test Preparation Ser.). (ENG.). 240p. pap. 18.00 *(978-0-375-42728-2(7)*, Princeton Review) Random Hse. Information Group.

—Cracking the AP Environmental Science Exam, 2012 Edition. 2011. (College Test Preparation Ser.). (ENG.). 336p. pap. 18.99 *(978-0-375-42729-9(5)*, Princeton Review) Random Hse. Information Group.

—Cracking the AP Human Geography Exam, 2012 Edition. 2011. (College Test Preparation Ser.). (ENG.). 384p. pap. 18.00 *(978-0-375-42730-5(9)*, Princeton Review) Random Hse. Information Group.

—Cracking the AP Psychology Exam, 2012 Edition. 2011. (College Test Preparation Ser.). (ENG.). 320p. pap. 18.00 *(978-0-375-42733-6(3)*, Princeton Review) Random Hse. Information Group.

—Cracking the AP Spanish Exam with Audio CD, 2012 Edition. 2011. (College Test Preparation Ser.). (ENG.). 288p. pap. 24.99 *(978-0-375-42734-3(1)*, Princeton Review) Random Hse. Information Group.

—Cracking the AP Statistics Exam, 2012 Edition. 2011. (College Test Preparation Ser.). (ENG.). 416p. pap. 19.99 *(978-0-375-42735-0(X)*, Princeton Review) Random Hse. Information Group.

—Cracking the AP U. S. Government & Politics Exam, 2012 Edition. 2011. (College Test Preparation Ser.). (ENG.). 320p. pap. 18.99 *(978-0-375-42736-7(8)*, Princeton Review) Random Hse. Information Group.

—Cracking the AP World History Exam, 2012 Edition. 2011. (College Test Preparation Ser.). (ENG.). 416p. pap. 18.99 *(978-0-375-42724-4(4)*, Princeton Review) Random Hse. Information Group.

—Essential AP Biology (flashcards) 2010. (College Test Preparation Ser.). (ENG.). 450p. 18.99 *(978-0-375-42803-6(8)*, Princeton Review) Random Hse. Information Group.

—Essential AP Psychology. 2010. (College Test Preparation Ser.). (ENG.). 450p. 18.99 *(978-0-375-42801-2(1)*, Princeton Review) Random Hse. Information Group.

—Essential AP U. S. Government & Politics. 2010. (College Test Preparation Ser.). (ENG.). 450p. 18.99 *(978-0-375-42804-3(6),* Princeton Review) Random Hse. Information Group.
—Essential AP U. S. History: 450 Flashcards. 2010. (College Test Preparation Ser.). (ENG.). 450p. 18.99 *(978-0-375-42800-5(3),* Princeton Review) Random Hse. Information Group.
—Essential AP World History. 2010. (College Test Preparation Ser.). (ENG.). 450p. 18.99 *(978-0-375-42802-9(X),* Princeton Review) Random Hse. Information Group.
Rankin, Estelle & Murphy, Barbara. 5 Steps to a 5 AP English Literature 2012-2013. 4th ed. 2011. (5 Steps to a 5 on the Advanced Placement Examinations Ser.). (ENG.). 256p. (C). pap. 18.95 *(978-0-07-175174-2(2),* 0071751742) McGraw-Hill Cos., The.
REA Staff, et al. AP Calculus AB & BC Crash Course. 2011. (Advanced Placement (AP) Crash Course Ser.). (ENG.). 224p. (gr. 11-12). pap. 11.95 *(978-0-7386-0887-7(4))* Research & Education Assn.
Reedy, Tyler, et al. AP English Language & Composition. Raulston, Dwight & Wood, Sally, eds. 8th ed. 2011. (Advanced Placement (AP) Test Preparation Ser.). (ENG.). 304p. (gr. 10-12). pap. 24.95 *(978-0-7386-0901-0(3))* Research & Education Assn.
Reel, Kevin R. AP Environmental Science. 2nd ed. 2009. (Advanced Placement (AP) Test Preparation Ser.). (ENG.). 560p. pap. 24.95 *(978-0-7386-0788-7(6))* Research & Education Assn.
Research and Education Association Staff, et al. AP French Language & Culture All Access. 2012. (Advanced Placement (AP) All Access Ser.). (ENG.). 448p. (gr. 10-12). pap. 26.95 ***(978-0-7386-1060-3(7))*** Research & Education Assn.
Resnick, Eugene V. Barron's AP United States History. 2nd ed. 2012. (ENG.). 480p. pap. 18.99 *(978-0-7641-4682-4(3))* Barron's Educational Series, Inc.
—Barron's AP United States History with CD-ROM. 2nd ed. 2012. (ENG.). 480p. pap. 29.99 *(978-1-4380-7115-2(9))* Barron's Educational Series, Inc.
Romano, Michael J. CliffsNotes AP European History. 2nd ed. 2010. (ENG., Illus.). 408p. pap. 29.99 *(978-0-470-55106-4(3),* Cliff Notes) Wiley, John & Sons, Inc.
—European History. 2nd ed. 2010. (ENG., Illus.). 408p. pap. 16.99 *(978-0-470-55099-1(6),* Cliff Notes) Wiley, John & Sons, Inc.
Sadler, Philip M., et al, eds. AP: A Critical Examination of the Advanced Placement Program. 2010. 286p. pap. 29.95 *(978-1-934742-55-6(4));* lib. bdg. 54.95 *(978-1-934742-56-3(2))* Harvard Education Publishing Group (HEPG). (Harvard Education Pr.).
Sattora, Richard. AP Microeconomics & Macroeconomics. 2009. (Advanced Placement (AP) Test Preparation Ser.). (ENG.). 336p. (gr. 10-12). pap. 24.95 *(978-0-7386-0789-4(4))* Research & Education Assn.
Sawyer, Christian. AP Human Geography. 2nd ed. 2009. (Advanced Placement (AP) Test Preparation Ser.). (ENG.). 512p. (gr. 9-12). pap. 24.95 *(978-0-7386-0631-6(6))* Research & Education Assn.
—AP Human Geography 2012-2013 Edition. 2011. pap. 16.95 ***(978-0-7386-1013-9(5))*** Research & Education Assn.
—AP Human Geography All Access. 2012. (Advanced Placement (AP) All Access Ser.). (ENG.). 352p. (gr. 10-12). pap. 18.95 ***(978-0-7386-1059-7(3))*** Research & Education Assn.
Sawyer, Christian. AP Human Geography Crash Course. 2011. (Advanced Placement (AP) Crash Course Ser.) (ENG.). 240p. (gr. 9-12). pap. 11.95 *(978-0-7386-0932-4(3))* Research & Education Assn.
Schultz, Susan. Twice-Exceptional Students Participating in Advanced Placement. 2009. 200p. pap. *(978-3-639-12719-5(6))* VDM Verlag Dr. Mueller e.K.
Scoggin, Nancy. AP Music Theory. 2010. (ENG.). 648p. 34.99 *(978-0-7641-9631-7(6))* Barron's Educational Series, Inc.
Simmons, Bruce, et al. Kaplan AP Statistics 2012. 2011. (Kaplan AP Ser.). (ENG.). 464p. pap. 18.99 *(978-1-60978-071-5(X))* Kaplan Publishing.
Singh, Benwari, et al. Preparing for the AP U. S. Government & Politics Examination: Fast Track to A 5. 2012. (ENG.). 372p. pap. 18.99 ***(978-1-4354-6132-1(0))*** Course Technology.
Sisson, Jocelyn. My Max Score AP English Language & Composition: Maximize Your Score in Less Time. 2011. (ENG.). 208p. pap. 14.99 *(978-1-4022-4312-7(X))* Sourcebooks, Inc.
Soifer, Paul. U. S. History. 2008. (ENG.). 1000p. pap. 19.99 *(978-0-470-28279-3(7),* Cliff Notes) Wiley, John & Sons, Inc.
SparkNotes Staff, contrib. by. SparkNotes Guide to AP U.S. History. 2008. (Illus.). xii, 417p. pap. *(978-1-4114-0517-2(X))* Spark Publishing Group.
Springer, Alice G. Barron's AP Spanish, 5 vols. 7th rev. ed. 2011. (ENG & SPA.). 600p. pap. 26.99 *(978-1-4380-7029-2(2))* Barron's Educational Series, Inc.
—Barron's AP Spanish with Audio CDs & CD-ROM. 7th rev. ed. 2011. (ENG & SPA.). 600p. pap. 34.99 *(978-1-4380-7030-8(6))* Barron's Educational Series, Inc.
—How to Prepare for the AP Advanced Placement Exam. 5th ed. 2006. (ENG & SPA.). 538p. 26.95 *(978-0-7641-3466-9(8))* Barron's Educational Series, Inc.
Sternstein, Martin. Barron's AP Statistics. 4th ed. 2007. (ENG., Illus.). 608p. 29.99 *(978-0-7641-9333-0(3))* Barron's Educational Series, Inc.
Stewart, Robert. My Max Score AP Biology: Maximize Your Score in Less Time. 2012. (My Max Score Ser.). (ENG.). 432p. pap. 14.99 *(978-1-4022-4315-8(4))* Sourcebooks, Inc.
Thorpe, Gary. Barron's AP Environmental Science. 4th rev. ed. 2011. (ENG.). 544p. pap. 18.99 *(978-0-7641-4571-1(1));* pap. 29.99 *(978-1-4380-7036-0(5))* Barron's Educational Series, Inc.
Thorpe, Gary S. AP Environmental Science. 3rd ed. 2009. *(978-0-7641-8630-1(2))* Barron's Educational Series, Inc.
Velm, Greg. AP U. S. History for Dummies. 2008. (ENG., Illus.). 384p. pap. 16.99 *(978-0-470-24758-7(4),* For Dummies) Wiley, John & Sons, Inc.
Vess, Deborah & Jones, Preston. AP World History. Knight, Theodore, ed. 2nd ed. 2009. (Advanced Placement (AP) Test Preparation Ser.). (ENG.). 768p. (gr. 9-12). pap. 24.95 *(978-0-7386-0791-7(6))* Research & Education Assn.
Vivion, Nichole. AP Biology Flashcards. 2008. (ENG.). 1000p. pap. 19.99 *(978-0-470-28281-6(9),* Cliff Notes) Wiley, John & Sons, Inc.
Vogel, Richard. Teacher's Manual for the AP English Language & Compostion 6th Edition. 6th ed. 2006. (Multiple Choice Questions in Preparation for the AP Examinations Ser.). *(978-1-878621-74-0(2))* D & S Marketing Systems, Inc.
Wadsworth. Fast Track to A5: Kirszner's Preparing for the AP* English Literature & Composition Examination. 2009. (ENG.). 192p. (C). pap. 37.95 *(978-0-495-90876-0(2))* Wadsworth.
Walker. Physics: AP* Instructors Resource CD W/TestGen. 3rd ed. 2006. 1120p. cd-rom 18.97 *(978-0-13-153635-7(4))* Prentice Hall (Schl. Div.).
—Physics: Test Item File. 2nd rev. ed. 692p. per. 18.97 *(978-0-13-101480-0(3))* Prentice Hall (Schl. Div.).
Wasowski, Richard P. AP English Language. 2008. (ENG.). 1000p. pap. 19.99 *(978-0-470-26985-5(5),* Cliff Notes) Wiley, John & Sons, Inc.
—AP English Literature. 2008. (ENG.). 1000p. pap. 19.99 *(978-0-470-27010-3(1),* Cliff Notes) Wiley, John & Sons, Inc.
Waterman, Edward *, et al. Chemistry: The Central Science. 11th ed. 2008. (ENG.). 464p. (C). pap. 19.96 *(978-0-13-600284-0(6))* Benjamin-Cummings Publishing Co.
Welker, Jason. AP Macroeconomics Crash Course. 2011. (Advanced Placement (AP) Crash Course Ser.). (ENG.). 304p. (gr. 10-12). pap. 11.95 *(978-0-7386-0971-3(4))* Research & Education Assn.
Weseley, Allyson & McEntarffer, Robert. AP(r) Psychology. 4th ed. 2010. *(978-0-7641-8607-3(8))* Barron's Educational Series, Inc.
Weseley, Allyson J. & McEntarffer, Robert. Barron's AP Psychology Flash Cards. 2009. (ENG.). 502p. 18.99 *(978-0-7641-9613-3(8))* Barron's Educational Series, Inc.
Wheater, Carolyn. My Max Score AP Calculus AB/BC: Maximize Your Score in Less Time. 2011. (ENG.). 352p. pap. 14.99 *(978-1-4022-4313-4(8))* Sourcebooks, Inc.
Whelan, Patrick. Kaplan AP World History 2012. 2011. (ENG.). 360p. pap. 17.99 *(978-1-60978-184-2(8))* Kaplan Publishing.
Whitehead, Kirby. My Max Score AP World History: Maximize Your Score in Less Time. 2012. (My Max Score Ser.). (ENG.). 400p. pap. 14.99 *(978-1-4022-4317-2(0))* Sourcebooks, Inc.
Wien, Howard D. My Max Score AP European History: Maximize Your Score in Less Time. 2012. (My Max Score Ser.). (ENG.). 320p. pap. 14.99 *(978-1-4022-4318-9(9))* Sourcebooks, Inc.
Williams, Lauren & Evangelist, Thomas A. AP Psychology Questions to Know by Test Day. 2010. (ENG., Illus.). 208p. (C). pap. 14.00 *(978-0-07-174203-0(4),* 0071742034) McGraw-Hill Cos., The.
Williams, Linda D. 5 Steps to a 5 AP Environmental Science, 2012-2013 Edition. 2nd ed. 2011. (5 Steps to a 5 on the Advanced Placement Examinations Ser.). (ENG., Illus.). 304p. (C). pap. 18.95 *(978-0-07-175199-5(8),* 0071751998) McGraw-Hill Cos., The.
Williamson, Lynette. On Demand Writing for Students: Coaching Yourself for the SAT1, ACT & AP Essays. 2011. (ENG.). 192p. (YA). pap. 25.95 ***(978-1-61770-027-9(4))*** International Debate Education Assn.
Wilson, David. Kaplan AP Chemistry 2012. 2011. (Kaplan AP Ser.). (ENG.). 396p. pap. 17.99 *(978-1-60978-062-3(0))* Kaplan Publishing.
Wilson, Todd, et al. College Physics: Test Item File. 6th ed. 2006. 1056p. 18.97 *(978-0-13-149713-9(8))* Prentice Hall (Schl. Div.).
Wolf, Jonathan. Barron's AP Physics B. 5th rev. ed. 2011. (ENG.). 480p. pap. 18.99 *(978-0-7641-4568-1(1));* pap. 29.99 *(978-1-4380-7037-7(3))* Barron's Educational Series, Inc.
Wolf, Jonathan S. Barron's AP Physics B. 4th ed. 2008. (Illus.). ix, 509p. *(978-0-7641-8484-0(9))* Barron's Educational Series, Inc.
Woods, Geraldine. AP English Literature & Composition for Dummies. 2008. (ENG., Illus.). 363p. per. 16.99 *(978-0-470-19425-6(1),* For Dummies) Wiley, John & Sons, Inc.
Xu, Weiman. Cheng & Tsui Strive for a 5: AP Chinese Practice Tests. 2009. pap. 29.99 *(978-0-88727-764-1(0))* Cheng & Tsui Co.
Zanfardino, Michael, et al. AP U. S Government & Politics All Access. 2012. (Advanced Placement (AP) All Access Ser.). (ENG.). 288p. (gr. 10-12). pap. 18.95 ***(978-0-7386-1024-5(0))*** Research & Education Assn.

ADVANCED ROAD TRAFFIC SYSTEMS

see Intelligent Vehicle Highway Systems

ADVENT

see also Advent Sermons; Second Advent

Abbott, Candy, ed. Christ Is Here; Very Soon Christ Will Appear. 2011. 32p. pap. 5.00 *(978-1-886068-11-7(9))* Fruitbearer Publishing, LLC.
Adamsbaum, Beryl. Light of the World, 1 vol. 2009. (Cover to Cover Advent Guide Ser.). (ENG.). 98p. pap. *(978-1-85345-525-4(3))* Crusade for World Revival.
Alonso, Tony. Waiting in Hope: Praying & Living Advent. 2006. 47p. pap. 6.25 *(978-0-88489-948-8(9))* St. Mary's Pr.
Andrew, Gawrych, ed. Gift of Hope. 2009. 96p. pap. 3.50 *(978-1-59471-221-0(2))* Ave Maria Pr.
Arnold, Eberhard, et al. When the Time Was Fulfilled: Christmas Meditations. 2nd ed. 2007. xxv, 141p. *(978-0-87486-940-8(4))* Plough Publishing Hse.
Arthur, Ginny, ed. Best of Blessings: Advent, Christmas, & Epiphany. 152p. pap. 19.95 *(978-1-55126-220-8(7),* 1509) Forward Movement Pubns.
Baker, Kevin. Hail the Heaven Born: An Advent Study Based on the Revised Common Lectionary. 2007. (Scriptures for the Church Seasons Ser.). 53p. per. 6.50 *(978-0-687-49095-0(2))* Abingdon Pr.
Basi, Kathleen & Basi, Kathleen M. Joy to the Word: Advent Activities for Your Family. 2010. pap. *(978-0-7648-1937-7(2))* Liguori Pubns.
becker, ellen c. & barnes, mary t. Advent in the Home: Activities for Families. 2008. (Illus.). 120p. pap. 14.95 *(978-1-59276-430-3(4))* Our Sunday Visitor, Publishing Div.
Blasé, John. Touching Wonder: Recapturing the Awe of Christmas, 1 vol. 2009. (ENG.). 128p. 12.99 *(978-1-4347-6465-2(6))* Cook, David C.
Bonhoeffer, Dietrich. God Is in the Manger: Reflections on Advent & Christmas. 2012. (ENG.). 112p. 16.00 ***(978-0-664-23887-2(4))*** Westminster John Knox Pr.
Bonhoeffer, Dietrich & Riess, Jana. God Is in the Manger: Reflections on Advent & Christmas. 2010. (ENG.). 96p. pap. 13.00 *(978-0-664-23429-4(1))* Westminster John Knox Pr.
Bozzuti-Jones, Mark. The Womb of Advent. 2007. 128p. per. 13.00 *(978-0-89869-567-0(8))* Church Publishing, Inc.
Brown, Timothy. Coming Home: Devotions for Advent. 2009. *(978-1-59255-516-1(0))* Faith Alive Christian Resources.
Bullis, Marty A. The Miraculous Journey: Anticipating God in the Christmas Season. 2007. (ENG.). 144p. 14.99 *(978-0-8307-4278-3(6))* Gospel Light Pubns.
Burch, Cindy, ed. Advent of the Savior. 2009. (LifeGuide Bible Studies). (ENG., Illus.). 64p. pap. 8.00 *(978-0-8308-3136-4(3),* IVP Conn.) InterVarsity Pr.
Butler, Carolyn. Under African Skies: Reflections for Advent & Christmas. 2011. 96p. pap. 9.95 *(978-0-7963-0850-4(0))* NB Pubs. Ltd. ZAF. Dist: International Publishers Marketing.
Campbell, Jeffrey. Christ, Light of the World: Advent Wreath Blessing & Prayers. 2007. 14p. 3.95 *(978-0-9796766-7-3(3))* Tau Publishing.
Center for the Study of C. S. Lewis and Friends Staff, contrib. by. Advent & Christmas Wisdom. 2007. 114p. per. 10.99 *(978-0-7648-1628-4(4))* Liguori Pubns.
Champlin, Joseph M. Daily Reflections for Advent 2007: Prepare Your Heart. 2007. 43p. pap. 1.95 *(978-0-86716-832-7(3))* Franciscan Media.
Chandler, Paul-Gordon. Songs in Waiting: Spiritual Reflections on Christ's Birth. 2009. (Illus.). 128p. 20.00 *(978-0-8192-2360-9(3),* Morehouse Publishing) Church Publishing, Inc.
Coco, Lucio. Preparing for Christmas with Pope Benedict Xvi. 2009. 0064p. pap. 2.50 *(978-1-59471-233-3(6))* Ave Maria Pr.
Cormier, Jay. Waiting in Joyful Hope. 2011. 112p. pap. 2.00 ***(978-0-8146-3361-8(7))*** Liturgical Pr.
—Waiting in Joyful Hope: Daily Reflections for Advent & Christmas 2007-2008 Year A. 2007. 101p. per. 2.00 *(978-0-8146-3080-8(4),* Liturgical Pr. Bks.) Liturgical Pr.
Cormier, Jay. Waiting in Joyful Hope Large Print. 2011. 112p. pap. 5.95 ***(978-0-8146-3398-4(6))*** Liturgical Pr.
Cotter, Jim. Expectant: Verses for Advent. 2008. (Illus.). 57p. *(978-1-870652-38-4(X))* Cairns Pubns.
D'Avila-Latourrette, Victor-Antoine. A Monastery Journey to Christmas. 2011. (Illus.). 208p. ***(978-0-7648-2081-6(8))*** Liguori Pubns.
Davis, Jeanne, et al, eds. Worship Resources Year B: Beginning Advent 2011 up to Advent 2012. 2011. 240p. pap. 21.95 ***(978-0-8309-1514-9(1),*** Herald Publishing Hse.) Herald Publishing Hse.
Doherty, Catherine. Donkey Bells: Advent & Christmas. 156p. pap. *(978-0-921440-38-3(3))* Madonna Hse. Pubns.
Dolan, Timothy M. Advent Reflections: Come Lord Jesus. 2007. 64p. per. 41.95 *(978-1-59276-394-8(4),* Our Sunday Visitor, Publishing Div.
—Advent Reflections: Come, Lord Jesus! 2007. (Illus.). 63p. per. 6.95 *(978-1-59276-393-1(6))* Our Sunday Visitor, Publishing Div.
Dudley, Martin. A Herald Voice: The Work of God in Advent & Christmas. 160p. 12.00 *(978-0-281-05280-6(8))* SPCK Publishing GBR. Dist: Pilgrim Pr., The/United Church Pr.
Dunnam, Maxie D. The Grace-Filled Life: 52 Devotions to Warm Your Heart & Guide Your Path. 2010. 175p. pap. 12.00 *(978-1-4267-0682-0(0))* Abingdon Pr.
Edwards, Joel. Advent Hope. 2007. 98p. *(978-1-85345-426-4(5))* Crusade for World Revival.
Fadness, Arley K. Blueprints for Advent & Christmas: Dynamic Sketches, Scenes, & Scripts for the Season. 2008. (Illus.). 168p. pap. *(978-0-7880-2556-3(2))* CSS Publishing Co.
Finley, Jeanne Torrence. Blessings of the Manger Student: An Advent Study Based on the Revised Common Lectionary. 2010. (Sftcs Ser.). pap. 7.00 *(978-0-687-46696-2(2))* Abingdon Pr.
Finley, Mitch. Season of Promises: Praying Through Advent with Julian of Norwich, Thomas ç Kempis, Caryll Houselander, Thomas Merton, Brother Lawrence, Max Picard. 2010. 64p. pap. 9.00 *(978-1-60899-263-8(2),* Wipf and Stock) Wipf & Stock Pubs.
Fisher, Susan, ed. Looking, Longing & Living: Readying Ourselves for Advent. 2007. 60p. per. *(978-1-57383-416-2(5),* Regent College Publishing) Regent College Publishing.
Foulger, Sarah M. Yards of Purple: Stories for Advent. 2008. 128p. pap. 16.00 *(978-1-60608-452-6(6),* Wipf and Stock) Wipf & Stock Pubs.
Francis. Advent & Christmas Wisdom from Saint Francis of Assisi: Daily Scripture & Prayers Together with Saint Francis of Assisi's Own Words. 2008. 10.99 *(978-0-7648-1756-4(6))* Liguori Pubns.
Freelan, Rebekah J. His Advent: Still His Greatest Gift. 2010. 108p. pap. 11.95 *(978-1-4497-0181-9(7),* WestBow Pr.) Author Solutions, Inc.
Friedman, Greg. Advent with the Saints: Daily Reflections. 2011. (Illus.). x, 70p. ***(978-1-61636-132-7(8))*** Franciscan Media.
George, Cathy H. The Stillness We Seek: Daily Meditations for Advent. 2011. ***(978-0-88028-327-4(0))*** Forward Movement Pubns.
Gleddiesmith, Stacey. Welcoming the Stranger: Readying Ourselves for Christmas. 2010. ***(978-1-57383-452-0(1))*** Regent College Publishing.
Gleddiesmith, Stacey, ed. God with Us, Always. 2008. 60p. pap. *(978-1-57383-430-8(0))* Regent College Publishing.
Gooder, Paula. The Meaning Is in the Waiting: The Spirit of Advent. 2009. (ENG.). 144p. (gr. 13). pap. 14.99 *(978-1-55725-662-1(4))* Paraclete Pr., Inc.
Guthrie, Nancy. Let Every Heart Prepare Him Room: Daily Family Devotions for Advent. 2010. (ENG.). 112p. 9.99 *(978-1-4143-3909-2(7))* Tyndale Hse. Pubs.
Hakes, Derek K. Advent Hope: 2 or 3 Octaves (Handbells or Handchimes), Level 2. 2011. 7p. pap. 4.50 ***(978-1-4291-2331-0(1))*** Lorenz Corp., The.
Harnish, James A. Rejoicing in Hope: An Advent Study for Adults. 2007. 38p. per. 6.50 *(978-0-687-49075-2(8))* Abingdon Pr.
Hawkins, Pamela C. Behold! Cultivating Attentiveness in the Season of Advent. 2011. 112p. 14.00 *(978-0-8358-1062-3(3))* Upper Room Bks.
—Simply Wait: Cultivating Stillness in the Season of Advent. 2007. 112p. per. 14.00 *(978-0-8358-9917-8(9))* Upper Room Bks.
Hemrich-Skomer, Denise & Tyrtania, Joachim. Let the Children Come: A Family Guide to the Liturgy of the Word Cycle A. 2007. 64p. (J). per. 6.95 *(978-0-9787087-1-9(7))* Bound by Grace Pr., LLC.
Huntsman, Eric D. Good Tidings of Great Joy: An Advent Celebration of the Savior's Birth. 2011. 160p. 27.99 ***(978-1-60641-659-4(6))*** Deseret Bk. Co.
Jarboe, Robert S. More Services for the Advent Wreath: For Lectionary Cycle A. 2007. (Illus.). 64p. pap. 14.95 *(978-0-7880-2460-3(4))* CSS Publishing Co.
Jars of Clay. Peace Is Here: Christmas Reflections. 2007. (Illus.). 57p. *(978-1-894160-08-7(8))* Gray Matters Pr.
John Paul II, pseud. Advent & Christmas Wisdom from Pope John Paul II: Daily Scripture & Prayers Together with Pope John Paul II's Own Words, 1 vol. 2006. (Advent & Christmas Wisdom Ser.). (Illus.). 112p. per. 9.95 *(978-0-7648-1510-2(5))* Liguori Pubns.
Johnson, Bruce. Come & Behold. 48p. mass mkt., stu. ed. 5.50 *(978-0-687-74170-0(X))* Abingdon Pr.
Joiner, F. Belton. Advent, Christmas, & Epiphany Services. 2010. 97p. pap. 12.00 *(978-1-4267-0680-6(4))* Abingdon Pr.
Kalas, J. Ellsworth. The Best Songs Come at Night: And Other Christmas Proverbs: An Advent Study for Adults. 2009. pap. 7.00 *(978-0-687-65980-7(9))* Abingdon Pr.
Keefe, Rachael A. A Circle in the Dark: Daily Meditations for Advent. 2011. 124p. pap. 15.00 ***(978-1-61097-339-7(9),*** Wipf and Stock) Wipf & Stock Pubs.
Kelly, Matthew. Rediscover Advent. 2011. ***(978-1-61636-164-8(6))*** Franciscan Media.
Larson, Lloyd. Light a Candle in the Night: Unison or Two-Part Any Combination with Opt. Congregation & Narration. 2011. 12p. pap. 1.95 ***(978-1-4291-2554-3(3))*** Lorenz Corp., The.
Larson, Lloyd, contrib. by. Joy of Every Longing Heart: SATB with Opt. C-Instrument & Cello. 2011. 11p. pap. 1.95 ***(978-1-4291-2584-0(5))*** Lorenz Corp., The.
Leo, Jason. We Shall All Be Changed: Daily Meditations for Advent. 2010. *(978-0-88028-322-9(X))* Forward Movement Pubns.
Liguori, Alfonso Maria de'. Advent & Christmas Wisdom from Saint Alphonsus Liguori: Daily Scripture & Prayers Together with Saint Alphonsus Liguori's Own Words. 2011. *(978-0-7648-1909-4(7))* Liguori Pubns.
Luchterhand, Lyle L. The Lord's Anointed: Advent & Christmas Devotions for Young & Old. 2009. pap. *(978-0-8100-2234-8(6))* Northwestern Publishing Hse.
Masters, Henry L. Makin' Room in the Inn: Christmas Hospitality Through an African American Experience. 2010. 64p. 7.00 *(978-1-4267-0371-3(6))* Abingdon Pr.
Mathson, Patricia L. Live Advent at Home: Daily Prayers & Activities for Families. 2011. *(978-0-7648-2035-9(4))* Liguori Pubns.
Maul, Derek. In My Heart I Carry a Star: Stories for Advent. 2008. 144p. 14.00 *(978-0-8358-9966-6(7))* Upper Room Bks.
McGarry, William J. He Cometh: Devotion & the Liturgy, V1, Advent. 2011. 344p. 51.95 ***(978-1-258-09611-3(0))*** Literary Licensing, LLC.
McKenna, Megan. Advent, Christmas, & Epiphany: Stories & Reflections on the Daily Readings. 2008. 256p. pap. 19.95 *(978-1-56548-301-9(4))* New City Pr.
—Advent, Christmas & Epiphany: Stories & Reflections on the Sunday & Daily Readings. 2008. 512p. pap. 39.90 *(978-1-55548-302-6(2))* New City Pr.
—Advent, Christmas, & Epiphany: Stories & Reflections on the Sunday Readings. 2008. 256p. pap. 19.95 *(978-1-56548-300-2(6))* New City Pr.
Meeks, Blair Gilmer. Expecting the Unexpected: An Advent Devotional Guide. 2006. 125p. per. 15.00 *(978-0-8358-1004-3(6))* Upper Room Bks.
Merton Institute for Contemplative Living Staff. Advent & Christmas. Montaldo, Jonathan & Toth, Robert G., eds. 2010. (Illus.). 64p. 5.95 *(978-1-59471-195-4(X))* Ave Maria Pr.
Millar, Peter & Paynter, Neil. Good News of Great Joy. 2011. (Illus.). 123p. pap. *(978-1-84952-075-1(5))* Wild Goose Pubns. GBR. Dist: Novalis Publishing.

Miller, Calvin. The Christ of Christmas: Readings for Advent - 31 Days of Devotions. 2006. (ENG.). 144p. 9.99 *(978-0-8054-4419-3(X)*, B&H Bks.) B&H Publishing Group.

Moore, James W. Christmas Gifts That Won't Break: An Advent Study for Adults. 2010. 48p. 7.00 *(978-1-4267-0805-3(X))* Abingdon Pr.

—Christmas Gifts That Won't Break: An Advent Study for Children. 2010. 48p. 12.95 *(978-1-4267-0828-2(9))* Abingdon Pr.

—Christmas Gifts That Won't Break: An Advent Study for Youth. 2010. 64p. 7.00 *(978-1-4267-0827-5(0))* Abingdon Pr.

—The Miracle of Christmas: An Advent Study for Adults. 2006. 39p. pap. 6.50 *(978-0-687-33236-6(2))* Abingdon Pr.

—What Do You Want for Christmas? an Advent Study for Adults. 2008. 48p. pap. 6.50 *(978-0-687-65064-4(X))* Abingdon Pr.

Morneau, Robert. Waiting in Joyful Hope Advent & Christmas 2009-2010. 2009. 112p. pap. 2.00 *(978-0-8146-3082-2(0)*, Liturgical Pr. Bks.) Liturgical Pr.

Mueller, Joan. Praying Advent: Three Minute Reflections on Peace, Faithfulness, Joy, & Light. 2010. pap. *(978-1-56548-358-3(8))* New City Community Pr.

Oliver, Kara. Meeting the Messiah: Scriptures for the Advent Season with Leader's Guide. 2010. *(978-0-8358-1029-6(1))* Upper Room Bks.

Overman, Kathy M. Fun Family Christmas Devotions: Advent Guide for Busy Parents. 2007. per. 19.95 *(978-0-9743425-6-6(4))* Ablaze Pubns.

Pala, Ivo. The Christ. 2009. 608p. pap. *(978-1-84923-923-3(1))* YouWriteOn.

Pennoyer, Greg & Wolfe, Gregory, eds. God With Us: Rediscovering the Meaning of Christmas. 2007. 164p. *(978-1-57725-541-3(0))* Paraclete Pr.

Peterson, Eugene H. My First Message the Christmas Story. 2008. (Living the Letters Ser.). 24p. (J). 12.99 *(978-1-60006-276-6(8))* Message Bks. AUS. Dist: NavPress Publishing Group.

Pollard, Joseph. Waiting in Expectation: A Reflection for Each Day of Advent. 2006. (ENG.). 84p. pap. 13.95 *(978-1-85607-514-5(1))* Columba Pr. IRL. Dist: Dufour Editions, Inc.

Raab C.S.C., Ronald Patrick. The Unsheltered Heart: An at-Home Advent Retreat (Cycle B) 2011. 96p. 5.95 ***(978-1-59471-284-5(0))*** Ave Maria Pr.

Raab, Ronald Patrick. The Unsheltered Heart: An at Home Advent Retreat, Cycle A. 2010. 64p. 5.95 *(978-1-59471-254-8(9))* Ave Maria Pr.

Ratzinger, Joseph. The Blessing of Christmas: Meditations for the Season. 2007. 110p. 14.95 *(978-1-58617-172-8(0))* Ignatius Pr.

Read, Harry. Words of Life. 128p. pap. 5.99 *(978-0-340-71384-6(4)*, Hodder & Stoughton) Hodder General Publishing Div. GBR. Dist: Trafalgar Square Publishing.

Richardson, Beth A. The Uncluttered Heart: Making Room for God During Advent & Christmas. 2009. 13.00 *(978-0-8358-9994-9(2))* Upper Room Bks.

Rogers, Thomas. Advent, Christmas, Epiphany. (Church Year Bible Study Series B). pap., stu. ed. 5.50 *(978-0-570-09450-0(X)*, 20-2568); pap. 5.50 *(978-0-570-09451-7(8)*, 20-2569) Concordia Publishing Hse.

Rogne, David G. Advent Services. 2007. (Just in Time! (Abingdon Press) Ser.). 76p. per. 12.00 *(978-0-687-46581-1(8))* Abingdon Pr.

Rohr, Richard. Preparándose para Navidad con P. Richard Rohr, O.F.M: Reflexiones Diarias para Adviento. 2008. (SPA.). pap. *(978-0-86716-903-4(6))* Franciscan Media.

Savage, Warren, et al. Joyful Meditations for Every Day of Advent & the 12 Days of Christmas. 2010. 128p. pap. 6.99 *(978-0-7648-1940-7(2))* Liguori Pubns.

Sheneman, Paul. Illuminate: An Advent Experience. 2011. (ENG.). 96p. pap. 9.99 ***(978-0-8341-2772-2(5)***, 9780834127722) Beacon Hill Pr. of Kansas City.

Skidmore, Kerry A. Get Ready for Christmas. 2007. 60p. per. 9.99 *(978-1-60477-007-0(4))* Xulon Pr., Inc.

Spangler, Ann. Immanuel: Praying the Names of God Through the Christmas Season, 1 vol. 2007. (ENG.). 144p. 14.99 *(978-0-310-27614-2(4))* Zondervan.

Stevenson, Kenneth W. Watching & Waiting: A Guide to the Celebration of Advent. 2008. 119p. pap. 22.99 *(978-1-85311-834-0(6))* Canterbury Pr.

Stroble, Paul. Celebrate the Newborn Jesus St. 2009. (Sftcs Ser.). 64p. pap. 7.00 *(978-0-687-65893-0(4))* Abingdon Pr.

Sutera, Judith & Benedict. Advent & Christmas Wisdom from Saint Benedict: Daily Scripture & Prayers Together with Saint Benedict's Own Words. 2010. pap. *(978-0-7648-1883-7(X))* Liguori Pubns.

the Daughters of St. Paul. Advent Grace: Daily Gospel Reflections. 2009. 128p. pap. 7.95 *(978-0-8198-0787-8(7))* Pauline Bks. & Media.

Thomas. Advent & Christmas Wisdom from St. Thomas Aquinas. 2009. 10.99 *(978-0-7648-1819-6(8))* Liguori Pubns.

Thompson, Richard & Fisher, Susan Maxine. The Cradle & the Crown: A Regent College Advent Reader. 2006. (ENG.). 60p. per. *(978-1-57383-392-9(4)*, Regent College Publishing) Regent College Publishing.

Timmerman, John H. Light of the World: Daily Meditations for Advent. 2007. 120p. per. 10.95 *(978-0-7648-1621-5(7))* Liguori Pubns.

Tolhurst, James. Come Lord Jesus: Reflections on the Adve. 2006. 92p. per. *(978-0-85244-020-9(0))* Gracewing, Ltd.

Tyndale House Publishers Staff, prod. Devotions for Advent. 2009. (Holy Bible: Mosaic Ser.). (ENG.). 48p. pap. 1.99 *(978-1-4143-3578-0(4))* Tyndale Hse. Pubs.

Tyrtania, Joachim & Hemrich-Skomer, Denise. Let the Children Come: A Family Guide to the Liturgy of the Word. 2006. 65p. (J). per. 6.95 *(978-0-9787087-0-2(9))* Bound by Grace Pr., LLC.

Webber, Christopher L. Advent with Evelyn Underhill. 2006. 96p. per. 13.00 *(978-0-8192-2221-3(6)*, Morehouse Publishing) Church Publishing, Inc.

Wezeman, Phyllis. Advent: A Calendar of Devotions 2006. 2006. 48p. 65.00 *(978-0-687-33560-2(4))*; 1.65 *(978-0-687-33570-1(1))* Abingdon Pr.

Wilke, Julia Kitchens Trust, et al. Christmas: the Good, the Bad, & the Ugly: An Advent Study for Adults. 2010. 48p. pap. 7.00 *(978-0-687-66034-6(3))* Abingdon Pr.

Will, Julianne M. Adviento: Maneras Sencillas de Prepararse para el Nacimiento de Jesus. Estenger, Vilma G., tr. 2009. (SPA.). 1p. 14.95 *(978-1-59276-715-1(X))* Our Sunday Visitor, Publishing Div.

Williams, Marilyn. Advent Devotions, Keeping Christ in Your Christmas. 2009. 58p. pap. 24.00 *(978-0-557-11659-1(7))* Lulu Enterprises Inc.

Windell, John E. Advent Meditations. 2009. 84p. pap. 9.95 *(978-1-60860-577-4(9)*, Eloquent Bks.) AEG Literary Publishing Services, Inc.

Wolfe, Gregory, et al, eds. God with Us: Rediscovering the Meaning of Christmas. 2007. (Illus.). 185p. 29.95 *(978-1-55725-541-9(5))* Paraclete Pr., Inc.

Wren, Brian & Wren, Brian A. Advent, Christmas, & Epiphany: Liturgies & Prayers for Public Worship. 2008. (ENG., Illus.). 240p. pap. 30.00 *(978-0-664-23309-9(0))* Westminster John Knox Pr.

Wright, Ralph. Living the Days of Advent & the Christmas Season 2008. 2008. 48p. pap. 3.95 *(978-0-8091-4519-5(7))* Paulist Pr.

Young, Deanna & Young, York. Catholic Parent Know How: Advent. 2007. (Catholic Parent Know-How Ser.). per. 11.95 *(978-1-59276-390-0(1))* Our Sunday Visitor, Publishing Div.

Young, Deanna A. Something New for Advent. 2007. (Catholic Parent Know-How Ser.). (Illus.). 7p. pap. 1.95 *(978-1-59276-389-4(8))* Our Sunday Visitor, Publishing Div.

Ytreeide, Arnold. Jotham's Journey: A Storybook for Advent, 1 vol. 2008. 168p. pap. 13.99 *(978-0-8254-4174-5(9))* Kregel Pubns.

ADVENT SERMONS

Churcher, John & Bishop, Ted. Advent to Epiphany. 2010. 80p. pap. 10.50 *(978-1-4461-4398-8(8))* Lulu Enterprises Inc.

Cloud, Olivia, ed. Joy to the World: Inspirational Christmas Messages from America's Pr. 2013. (ENG.). 416p. pap. 24.99 *(978-1-4516-5633-6(5)*, Beyond Words/Atria Bks.) Atria Bks.

Cloud, Olivia M. & Cloud, Olivia, eds. Joy to the World: Inspirational Christmas Messages from America's Preachers. 2006. (ENG.). 416p. 25.00 *(978-1-4165-4000-7(8)*, Beyond Words/Atria Bks.) Atria Bks.

Concordia Pulpit. Sermons for Advent & Christmas. 2008. (Selections from Concordia Pulpit Resources Ser.). 168p. pap. 16.99 incl. cd-rom *(978-0-7586-1379-0(2))* Concordia Publishing Hse.

de Blas, Alonso. Prepare-Don't Wait: Scriptural Readings & Reflections for Advent. 2007. 72p. pap. 6.95 *(978-0-9796766-8-0(1))* Tau Publishing.

Delp, Alfred. Advent of the Heart: Seasonal Sermons & Prison Writings, 1941-1944. 2006. 233p. pap. 14.95 *(978-1-58617-081-3(3))* Ignatius Pr.

Doriani, Daniel M., et al. The Incarnation in the Gospels. 2008. v, 227p. *(978-1-59638-140-7(X))* P & R Publishing.

Hyson, Leon O. All along This Pilgrim Journey: Devotions & Reflections for the Way. 2007. per. *(978-0-9776555-6-4(3))* Emeth Pr.

Kaylor, Robert. Come to the Manger Scriptures for the Church Seasons Advent 2008. 2008. (Sftcs Ser.). 48p. pap., stu. ed. 6.50 *(978-0-687-64711-8(8))*; 24p. pap. 6.50 *(978-0-687-64721-7(5))* Abingdon Pr.

Leinenweber, John, ed. Bernard of Clairvaux: Sermons for Advent & the Christmas Season. Edmonds, Irene et al, trs. from LAT. 2007. (Cistercian Fathers Ser.). 202p. per. 24.95 *(978-0-87907-451-7(5)*, CF051P) Cistercian Pubns., Inc.

Motter, Alton M. Preaching the Nativity: Nineteen Great Sermons for Advent, Christmas, & Epiphany. Motter, Alton M., ed. 2011. 148p. 40.95 ***(978-1-258-03072-8(1))*** Literary Licensing, LLC.

Murray, Scott R. Away in a Manger: Resources for Advent & Christmas Preaching & Worship. 2008. 34.99 *(978-0-7586-1448-3(9))* Concordia Publishing Hse.

Smith, Timothy J. Christmas Grace & Other Cycle A Sermons for Advent, Christmas, & Epiphany: Based on the Second Readings of the Revised Common Lectionary. 2010. *(978-0-7880-2628-7(3))* CSS Publishing Co.

Wezeman, Phyllis. Advent: A Calendar of Devotions. 2007. 48p. pap. 0.65 *(978-0-687-64128-4(4))* Abingdon Pr.

—Advent 2007 LP/E: A Calendar of Devotions. 2007. 48p. pap. 1.65 *(978-0-687-64138-3(1))* Abingdon Pr.

ADVENTISTS

see also Seventh-Day Adventists

Andrews, John N. & James, David C. We Have This Hope: Timeless Adventist Sermons. 2008. *(978-0-8163-2271-8(6))*; *(978-0-8163-2279-4(1))* Pacific Pr. Pubns.

Anyaogu, Okore Chukwu. Manual on Adventist Pilot Project. 2011. 220p. pap. ***(978-3-8443-2233-0(7))*** Lambert Academic Publishing.

Bruinsma, Reinder. The Body of Christ: An Adventist Understanding of the Church. 2009. 222p. 19.99 *(978-0-8280-2488-4(X))* Review & Herald Publishing Assn.

Bullon, Alejandro. Signs of Hope. 2009. 126p. pap. 2.49 *(978-0-8280-2392-4(1))* Review & Herald Publishing Assn.

Churchill, John & Turner, Dwight. The Little Armageddon: The Great Controversy Within the Seventh-day Adventist Church. 2010. 220p. pap. 16.00 *(978-1-4269-3241-0(3))* Trafford Publishing.

King, William Peter. Adventism: The Second Coming of Christ. 2007. (ENG.). 132p. 35.95 *(978-0-548-05751-3(6))* Kessinger Publishing, LLC.

Knight, George R. The Apocalyptic Vision & the Neutering of Adventism. 2008. pap. 10.99 *(978-0-8280-2385-6(9))* Review & Herald Publishing Assn.

—William Miller & the Rise of Adventism. 2011. pap. 21.99 *(978-0-8163-2432-3(8))* Pacific Pr. Publishing Assn.

Kuromiya, Hiroaki. Conscience on Trial: The Fate of Fourteen Pacifists in Stalin's Ukraine, 1952-1953. 2012. (ENG., Illus.). 224p. ***(978-1-4426-4461-8(3))*** Univ. of Toronto Pr.

Lichtenwalter, Larry L. Revelation's Great Love Story: More Than I Ever Imagined. 2008. (ENG.). 141p. pap. 12.99 *(978-0-8127-0460-0(6))* Review & Herald Publishing Assn.

Mills, Charles D. Adventism Going Two Ways: Where Are You? 2011. (ENG.). 258p. pap. 24.95 ***(978-1-4327-7506-3(5))*** Outskirts Pr., Inc.

Rowe, David L. God's Strange Work: William Miller & the End of the World. 2008. (Library of Religious Biography). (Illus.). 280p. pap. 24.00 *(978-0-8028-0380-1(6))* Eerdmans, William B. Publishing Co.

Scriven, Charles. The Promise of Peace: Dare to Experience the Advent Hope. 2009. pap. 13.99 *(978-0-8163-2350-0(X))* Pacific Pr. Publishing Assn.

Thompson, Alden L. Beyond Common Ground: Why Liberals & Conservatives Need Each Other. 2009. 254p. pap. 16.99 *(978-0-8163-2340-1(2))* Pacific Pr. Publishing Assn.

White, Ellen G. The Spirit of Prophecy by Ellen G White + 2006. (ENG.). 416p. per. 26.99 *(978-1-4255-4477-5(0))*; (ENG.). 412p. per. 26.99 *(978-1-4255-4385-3(5))*; 404p. per. 26.99 *(978-1-4255-4284-9(0))* MPublishing.

White, James. Life Incidents, in Connection with the Great Advent Movement, As Illustrated by the Three Angels of Revelation Xiv by Elder James White. 2006. (Illus.). 376p. per. 26.99 *(978-1-4255-3930-6(0))* MPublishing.

Wohlberg, Steve & Lewis, Chris. The Character of God Controversy: A Close Look at the Intense Love & Justice of God Almighty. 2008. 159p. pap. 13.99 *(978-0-8163-2288-6(0))* Pacific Pr. Publishing Assn.

ADVENTURE AND ADVENTURERS

see also Escapes; Explorers; Filibusters; Frontier and Pioneer Life; Heroes; Safaris; Sea Stories; Seafaring Life; Shipwrecks; Voyages and Travels

Abushama- Rademaker, Anna Maria. The Dutch Ladies Tinne, in the Sudan: Nineteenth Century Adventurers. 2010. 224p. 25.86 *(978-1-4269-1403-4(2))* Trafford Publishing.

—The Dutch Ladies Tinne, in the Sudan: Nineteenth Century Adventurers. 2010. 224p. pap. 15.86 *(978-1-4269-1402-7(4))* Trafford Publishing.

Adventure, Knowledge. The Discoverers. pap. 22.00 *(978-1-56997-095-9(5))* Knowledge Adventure, Inc.

—Science Adventure II. pap. 22.00 net. *(978-1-56997-092-8(0))* Knowledge Adventure, Inc.

Allen, David. Colder Than A Fart in A Dead Eskimo. 2007. 228p. pap. 17.49 *(978-1-4303-1144-7(4))* Lulu Enterprises Inc.

Allen, Richard. Mud Running. 2011. 176p. pap. 10.95 ***(978-1-257-05514-2(3))*** Lulu Enterprises Inc.

Anderson, Dave & Absolon, Molly. NOLS Expedition Planning. 2011. (NOLS Ser.). (ENG., Illus.). 336p. pap. 21.95 *(978-0-8117-3551-3(6))* Stackpole Bks.

Anderson, Rocky. Maximum Risk: True Adventures of a Homeland Security Pilot. 2011. 192p. pap. 16.95 *(978-1-4502-8994-8(0))* iUniverse, Inc.

Andrews, Kenneth R., ed. The Last Voyage of Drake & Hawkins. 2008. (ENG., Illus.). 312p. pap. 42.00 *(978-0-521-07359-2(6))* Cambridge Univ. Pr.

Angus, Colin. Beyond the Horizon: The First Human-Powered Expedition to Circle the Globe. 2008. (ENG.). 384p. 24.95 *(978-0-89732-685-8(7))* Menasha Ridge Pr., Inc.

Baker, Timothy Louis. Where North Meets South & East Meets West, 1 vol. 2009. 176p. pap. 24.95 *(978-1-4489-1973-4(8))* PublishAmerica, Inc.

Baldwin, C. Stephen. Shadows over Sundials: Dark & Light. 2009. 376p. pap. 24.95 *(978-1-4401-5717-2(0))* iUniverse, Inc.

Balkan, Evan. Vanished! Explorers Forever Lost. 2007. (ENG., Illus.). 148p. per. 9.95 *(978-0-89732-983-5(X))* Menasha Ridge Pr., Inc.

Balkan, Evan L. Shipwrecked! Deadly Adventures & Disasters at Sea. 2008. (Dying to Explore Ser.). (ENG., Illus.). 188p. pap. 11.95 *(978-0-89732-653-7(9))* Menasha Ridge Pr., Inc.

Barney, Ollie O. The Life & Times of Ollie Barney: An Arizona Native Son. 2006. 357p. pap. 18.95 *(978-0-7414-3609-2(4))* Infinity Publishing.

Barrett, Frank. A Set of Rogues. 2008. 308p. 28.99 *(978-0-554-39695-8(5))* 2008. 308p. 29.99 *(978-0-554-30392-5(2))* 2007. (ENG.). 272p. pap. 26.75 *(978-1-4375-0154-4(0))* 2007. (ENG.). 304p. pap. 29.75 *(978-1-4375-0155-1(9))* BiblioBazaar.

Barton, O. S. Three Years with Quantrill. Date not set. 240p. 21.95 *(978-0-8488-2802-8(X))* Amereon LTD.

Beach, Rex E. North of Fifty-Three. 2007. (ENG.). 124p. 35.95 *(978-0-548-01817-0(0))* Kessinger Publishing, LLC.

Belden, Barbara. I'm Still Here. 2011. 150p. 29.99 ***(978-1-4628-9596-0(4))***; pap. 19.99 ***(978-1-4628-9595-3(6))*** Xlibris Corp.

Bennett, Chris. Rivermen of the Cumberland. 2009. 129p. pap. 13.95 *(978-0-557-05263-9(7))* Lulu Enterprises Inc.

Bentley, Anne. I Just Kissed Another Frog: Adventure in Online Dating. 2011. 24p. pap. 11.32 ***(978-1-4567-9997-7(5))*** AuthorHouse.

Bernstein, Josh. Digging for the Truth: A Real-Life Adventurer Uncovers the World's Greatest Ancient Mysteries. 2006. 224p. 26.95 *(978-0-06-117608-1(7))* HarperCollins Pubs.

Birnbaum, Bill. A Lifetime of Small Adventures: Stories of Adventure, Misadventure & Lessons Learned along the Way. 2011. 202p. pap. 14.95 *(978-1-932632-00-2(X))* Douglas Mountain Publishing.

Black, Larry. Survival in the Wild. 2011. 188p. 27.99 *(978-1-4520-8672-9(9))*; pap. 21.49 *(978-1-4520-8671-2(0))* AuthorHouse.

Bledsoe, Lucy Jane. The Ice Cave: A Woman's Adventures from the Mojave to the Antarctic. 2006. 182p. per. 19.95 *(978-0-299-21844-7(9)*, Terrace Bks.) Univ. of Wisconsin Pr.

Blondell, Anthony J. The Unpaid Piper. 2009. 146p. 39.95 *(978-1-55571-669-1(5)*, Hellgate Pr.) L & R Publishing.

Bluhm, William T., compiled by. Signaling the French: Adventures of a world war II american army Team. 2008. 168p. pap. 15.95 *(978-1-4401-0034-5(9))* iUniverse, Inc.

Blumenfeld, Jeff. You Want to Go Where? How to Get Someone to Pay for the Trip of Your Dreams. 2009. (ENG., Illus.). 244p. 24.95 *(978-1-60239-647-0(7)*, 239647) Skyhorse Publishing Co., Inc.

Boorman, Charley. By Any Means: The Brand New Adventure from Wicklow to Wollongong. 2010. (ENG., Illus.). 352p. pap. 12.95 *(978-0-7515-4173-1(7))* Little, Brown Bk. Group Ltd. GBR. Dist: Independent Pubs. Group.

Boyton, Paul. The Story of Paul Boyton: Voyages on All the Great Rivers of the World. 2007. (ENG.). 362p. pap. 25.99 *(978-1-4264-9629-5(X))*; 404p. pap. 28.99 *(978-1-4264-2502-8(3))* BiblioBazaar.

Brayman, James O. Thrilling Adventures by Land & Sea: Being Remarkable Historical Facts Gathered from Authentic Sources. 2007. (ENG.). 298p. pap. 21.99 *(978-1-4346-2169-6(3))*; 328p. pap. 24.99 *(978-1-4346-2229-7(0))* BiblioBazaar.

Brook, Richard. The Long & Wine-Ing Road. 2008. 264p. 24.99 *(978-1-4389-0810-6(5))*; pap. 14.49 *(978-1-4389-0809-0(1))* AuthorHouse.

Brooks, Noah & Adams, Francis A. First Across the Continent. 2008. 292p. 25.99 *(978-0-554-30740-4(5))*; 28.99 *(978-0-554-21437-5(7))* BiblioBazaar.

Brower, Kenneth. A Song for Satawal. 230p. 2010. 33.56 *(978-1-166-51609-3(1))* 2009. 41.95 *(978-1-120-23149-9(3))* 2009. pap. 26.95 *(978-1-120-13098-3(0))* Kessinger Publishing, LLC.

Brown, Bern Will. Free Spirits: Portraits from the North. 2007. (Illus.). 146p. per. *(978-2-89507-900-2(5))* Novalis Publishing.

Brown, Jim. Adventures in an Alternative Reality of Living in Louisian: Enter at Your Own Risk. 2008. 220p. 24.99 *(978-1-4389-1188-5(2))*; pap. 14.49 *(978-1-4389-1187-8(4))* AuthorHouse.

Bruton, Bill. Driven by Dreams: From the Mountains of Colorado to the Mysteries of Papua New Guinea. 2007. (ENG.). 376p. per. 29.95 *(978-0-9791704-0-9(0))* Wokabaut Publishing.

Burnham, Bill & Burnham, Mary. Car Camping: A Step-by-Step Guide to Planning Your Outdoor Adventure. 2009. (Knack: Make It Easy Ser.). (ENG., Illus.). 256p. pap. 19.95 *(978-1-59921-505-1(5)*, Knack) Globe Pequot Pr., The.

Callender, Michael. Leopard on a Razor Wire. 2011. 402p. ***(978-1-907722-65-3(3))***; pap. ***(978-1-907722-52-3(1))*** Ecademy Pr. Ltd.

Casanova de Seingalt, Jacques. The Memoirs of Casanova: Venetian Years. 2007. 432p. per. *(978-1-4068-4414-6(4))* Echo Library.

Chaapel, Barbary. Journey of the Snow Goose. 2006. (ENG.). 76p. per. 16.95 *(978-1-4241-5786-0(2))* PublishAmerica, Inc.

Chaffey, Will. Swimming with Crocodiles: The True Story of a Young Man in Search of Meaning & Adventure Who Finds Himself in an Epic Struggle for Survival. 2011. (ENG.). 328p. pap. 14.95 *(978-1-61145-021-7(7)*, 611021, Arcade Publishing) Skyhorse Publishing Co., Inc.

Chapin, Tom. More Poachers Caught. 2007. 214p. pap. 18.95 *(978-1-59193-207-9(6))* Adventure Pubns., Inc.

Cheney, Mark. Alask. 2011. 158p. pap. ***(978-1-84549-451-3(2)***, Swirl) arima publishing.

Chichester, Francis. The Lonely Sea & the Sky. 2012. (ENG., Illus.). 432p. pap. 15.95 ***(978-1-84953-201-3(X))*** Summerdale Pubs. GBR. Dist: Independent Pubs. Group.

Clark, D. W. (Davis Wasgatt). Travel & Adventure: Comprising Some of the Most Striking Narratives on Record. 2006. 420p. per. 26.99 *(978-1-4255-4549-9(1))* MPublishing.

Cobus Van Der Vlies. Southern Africa Wildlife & Adventure. 2010. 204p. pap. 55.49 *(978-1-4269-1932-9(8))* Trafford Publishing.

Coe, Steven R. Touching the Universe: My Favorite Twenty Nights Viewing the Sky. 2011. 248p. 32.95 *(978-1-4620-0249-8(8))*; pap. 22.95 *(978-1-4620-0247-4(1))* iUniverse, Inc.

Coile, Jon. Adventures in the Ditch: A Memoir of Family, Navigation, & Discovery on the Intracoastal Waterway. 2011. 208p. pap. 14.95 *(978-1-936236-51-0(6))* iUniverse, Inc.

Conefrey, Mick. The Adventurer's Handbook: From Surviving an Anaconda Attack to Finding Your Way Out of a Desert. 2010. (ENG.). 256p. pap. 12.00 *(978-0-230-10557-7(2))* Palgrave Macmillan.

Conlon, Dorothy S. At Home in the World: Memoirs of a Traveling Woman. 2007. 164p. per. 24.95 *(978-1-4137-9160-0(3))* PublishAmerica, Inc.

Coulton, Barry. A Cumbrian Lad: An Autobiography. 2007. (Illus.). 680p. *(978-1-905886-75-3(6))* Troubadour Publishing Ltd.

Courduff, William E. Butterfly on the Water. 2011. 304p. 25.74 ***(978-1-4567-3166-3(1))***; pap. 15.19 ***(978-1-4567-3165-6(3))*** AuthorHouse.

Cromarty, Jim. Pacific Adventures. 2009. (ENG., Illus.). 96p. pap. 8.99 *(978-1-84550-475-5(5))* Christian Focus Pubns. GBR. Dist: STL Distribution North America.

Dalton, Anthony. Alone Against the Arctic, 1 vol. 2007. (ENG., Illus.). 192p. per. *(978-1-894974-33-2(6))* Heritage Hse.

Dane, Ronald. Lost on the Way: Adventures in 40,000 Miles of Hitchhiking. 2011. 328p. pap. 19.95 ***(978-1-4620-4353-8(4))*** iUniverse, Inc.

Darwin, John. After Tamerlane: The Global History of Empire Since 1405. 2008. (ENG., Illus.). 592p. 34.95 *(978-1-59691-393-6(2))* Bloomsbury Publishing.

Davis, Jonathan W. The Adventures & Misadventures of Juan Loco. 2007. 172p. 25.95 *(978-1-59824-460-1(4))*; per. 12.95 *(978-1-59824-459-5(0))* E-BookTime LLC.

Dawson, Steven. Delusions of Immortality: Surviving an Unconventional Life. 2007. 372p. per. 16.95 *(978-1-59800-922-4(2))* Outskirts Pr., Inc.

De Nogales, Rafael. Memoirs of A Soldier of Fortune. 2006. pap. 34.95 *(978-1-4286-5834-9(3))* Kessinger Publishing, LLC.

Dean, Wildwood. River of Dreams. 2008. (Illus.). 252p. pap. 19.99 *(978-0-9798087-6-0(6))* Global Authors Pubns.

Delsi, Michael. The Ambush Master. 2011. 280p. pap. 14.16 ***(978-0-557-66757-4(7))*** Lulu Enterprises Inc.

Dixon, Joseph. Black Adventure. 2007. (ENG.). 208p. 39.95 *(978-0-548-05856-5(3))* Kessinger Publishing, LLC.

Douglas, George Mellis. Lands Forlorn: A Story of an Expedition to Hearne's Coppermine River. Hildebrand, Robert S., ed. & frwd. by. 2008. (Illus.). 452p. 39.00 *(978-0-615-19529-2(6))* Zancudo Pr.

Dowie, Menie M. Women Adventurers. 288p. reprint ed. 98.00 *(978-0-7222-1733-7(1))* Library Reprints, Inc.

Duncan, Nancy. The Nail That Sticks Up: An American Woman in Asia & Africa. 2007. 436p. per. 29.95 *(978-1-4241-7539-0(9))* PublishAmerica, Inc.

Eason, Randy. To Be Still & Know: Back Roads & Bridges. 2011. 116p. 28.95 ***(978-1-4497-1755-1(1))***; pap. 11.95 ***(978-1-4497-1754-4(3))*** Author Solutions, Inc. (WestBow Pr.).

East, Ben. Narrow Escapes & Wilderness Adventures. 2011. 334p. 50.95 ***(978-1-258-02900-5(6))*** Literary Licensing, LLC.

Ellis, Edward S. The Jungle Fugitives. 2007. 220p. per. *(978-1-4065-2476-5(X))* Dodo Pr.

Enright, Kelly. Osa & Martin. 2011. (ENG., Illus.). 240p. 24.95 *(978-0-7627-6360-3(4)*, Lyons Pr.) Globe Pequot Pr., The.

Farish, Blair. The Frolicking Physio. 2011. 232p. pap. 15.86 *(978-1-4269-6051-2(4))* Trafford Publishing.

Feller, R. A. Calington Castle II: Testing the Truth. 2011. 308p. pap. 15.19 ***(978-1-4634-1717-8(9))*** AuthorHouse.

Ferendo, Frank J. Spanish Lessons. 2008. pap. 19.95 *(978-0-9795180-1-0(6))* Process Publishing Co.

Foster, Nigel. Stepping Stones: Of Ungava & Labrador. 2009. 279p. (ENG.). 29.95 *(978-1-4327-4555-4(7))*; (Illus.). pap. 19.95 *(978-1-4327-4528-8(X))* Outskirts Pr., Inc.

Frazier, Gregory. Motorcycle Adventurer: Carl Stearns Clancy: First Motorcyclist to Ride Around the World 1912-1913. 2010. 324p. pap. 22.95 *(978-1-4502-2141-2(6))* iUniverse, Inc.

Freller, Thomas. The Last Corsairs of Malta. 2007. (ENG.). 191p. (C). pap. 15.75 *(978-99932-7-146-8(2))* Midsea Bks. Ltd. MLT. Dist: Brown, David Bk. Co., The.

Friedland, Lois, et al. Frommer's 500 Adrenaline Adventures. 2010. (500 Places Ser.: 7). (ENG., Illus.). 448p. pap. 19.99 *(978-0-470-52803-7(6)*, Frommers) Wiley, John & Sons, Inc.

Gallimore, Max. From Here to Caprock. 2009. 620p. pap. 23.99 *(978-1-4415-5655-4(9))* Xlibris Corp.

Galton, Francis & Mountaineers Books Staff. The Art of Rough Travel: From the Peculiar to the Practical Advice from a 19th Century Explorer. 2006. (ENG., Illus.). 124p. 15.95 *(978-1-59485-058-5(5))* Mountaineers Bks., The.

Games, Ben R. Adventures of Benny Bob. 2007. (ENG.). 128p. per. 9.95 *(978-1-60414-000-2(3)*, Celerus Bks.) Fideli Publishing, Inc.

Gates, Josh. Destination Truth. 2011. (ENG., Illus.). 272p. pap. 15.00 *(978-0-7434-9172-3(6))* Gallery Pr., The IRL. Dist: Simon & Schuster, Inc.

Gauthier, Tom. A Voyage Beyond Reason: An Epic of Survival Based on the Original Journals of Benjamin Wade. 2009. 408p. pap. 18.95 *(978-1-4327-1234-1(9))* Outskirts Pr., Inc.

Gehring, Abigail R. Dangerous Jobs: The Adventurer's Guide to High-Risk Careers. 2009. (ENG., Illus.). 224p. pap. 12.95 *(978-1-60239-620-3(5)*, 239620) Skyhorse Publishing Co., Inc.

Geiger, John. The Third Man Factor: Surviving the Impossible. 2010. (ENG.). 320p. pap. 14.95 *(978-1-60286-129-9(3))* Perseus Bks. Group.

Gerus, ed. The Long Ride: The Record Setting Journey by Horse Across the American Landscape. 2011. (ENG.). 212p. 35.00 ***(978-0-9835019-0-9(4))*** Green Rider.

Graddon, Nigel. Otto Rahn & the Quest for the Grail: The Amazing Life of the Real Indiana Jones. 2008. (Illus.). 369p. pap. 18.95 *(978-1-931882-82-8(7))* Adventures Unlimited Pr.

Grant, L. D. The Dream Thief Ant. 2008. 48p. pap. 49.95 *(978-1-4327-1318-8(3))* Outskirts Pr., Inc.

Graysmith, Robert. Black Fire: The True Story of the Original Tom Sawyer — and of the Mysterious Fires That Baptized Gold Rush-Era San Francisco. 2012. (ENG., Illus.). 336p. 26.00 ***(978-0-307-72056-6(X)***, Crown) Crown Publishing Group.

Grey, C. European Adventurers of Northern India 1785 To 1849. 2009. 466p. pap. *(978-1-84734-984-2(6))* Naval & Military Pr., The.

Grylls, Bear. Mud, Sweat, & Tears: The Autobiography. 2012. (ENG.). 416p. 26.99 ***(978-0-06-212419-7(6)***, Morrow, William & Co.) HarperCollins Pubs.

Hammack, Cheryl. Life & Times of a Pioneer Family. 2011. 72p. pap. 15.99 ***(978-1-4653-4717-6(8))*** Xlibris Corp.

Hanbury-Tenison, Robin, ed. The Seventy Great Journeys in History. 2006. (ENG., Illus.). 304p. 40.00 *(978-0-500-25129-4(0))* Thames & Hudson.

Hancock, Linda. Life Is an Adventure... Every Step of the Way. 2008. (ENG.). 138p. pap. 13.99 *(978-1-59932-041-0(X))* Advantage Media Group.

Harcum, Larry G. Dreamrider: Adventures on America's Great Loop. 2007. pap. 17.95 *(978-0-9787750-0-1(7))* HLH Pr.

Haskin, Jim. Jimmy & the Big Turtle. 2009. 112p. 22.95 *(978-1-4389-9761-2(2))*; pap. 12.95 *(978-1-4389-9760-5(4))* AuthorHouse.

Heavenrich, Charly. Unimagined Gifts. 2011. 304p. pap. 30.95 *(978-1-4620-0086-9(X))* iUniverse, Inc.

Hedley, Bungy. View from the Top of the Mast. 2008. 336p. 31.99 *(978-1-4343-7223-9(5))* AuthorHouse.

Herron, Al. Road to Adventure, 1 vol. 2009. 68p. pap. 16.95 *(978-1-60836-420-6(8))* PublishAmerica, Inc.

Hill, Roger & Bronski, Peter. Hunting Nature's Fury: A Storm Chaser's Obsession with Tornadoes, Hurricanes, & Other Natural Disasters. 2009. (ENG.). 206p. pap. 17.95 *(978-0-89997-511-5(9))* Wilderness Pr.

Hirst, Warwick. The Man Who Stole the Cyprus. 2008. (Illus.). 224p. pap. 29.95 *(978-1-877058-61-5(0))* Rosenberg Publishing Pty, Ltd. AUS. Dist: International Specialized Bk. Services.

Hobart-Hampden, Augustus Charles. Sketches from My Life. 2008. 188p. 25.99 *(978-0-554-25896-6(X))* 2008. 188p. 22.99 *(978-0-554-35199-5(4))* 2007. (ENG.). 168p. pap. 19.99 *(978-1-4346-0008-0(4))* 2007. (ENG.). 184p. pap. 21.99 *(978-1-4346-0093-6(9))* BiblioBazaar.

—Sketches from My Life. 2007. pap. *(978-1-4068-1350-0(8))* Echo Library.

Holcombe, R. The Boyz of Bradner. 2006. 108p. pap. 19.95 *(978-1-4241-4972-8(X))* PublishAmerica, Inc.

Hopkins, Howard. The Avenger: the Gray Nemesis. 2008. 79p. pap. 10.95 *(978-1-4357-5670-0(3))* Lulu Enterprises Inc.

Hornsby, Wade. How to Argue with God. 2007. 108p. per. 19.95 *(978-1-4241-6707-4(8))* PublishAmerica, Inc.

Hossack, Joei Carlton. Chasing the Lost Dream. Hossack, Joei Carlton & Montague-Bassett, Marian, eds. 2006. 256p. pap. 15.95 *(978-0-9657509-6-7(5))* Skeena Pr.

Hovey, Dave. Easy Money 1956. 2007. 74p. 16.95 *(978-1-4241-5557-6(6))* PublishAmerica, Inc.

Hoyle, Gwyneth. The Northern Horizons of Guy Blanchet: Intrepid Surveyor, 1884-1966. 2007. (ENG., Illus.). 224p. pap. 24.99 *(978-1-55002-759-4(X))* Natural Heritage/Natural History, Inc. CAN. Dist: Ingram Pub. Services.

Hulst, Sandra. If These Walls Could Laugh. 2008. 128p. 10.99 *(978-1-60462-824-1(3))* Tate Publishing & Enterprises, LLC.

Hutton, Dick. Northern Son: The Boy from the Bush. 2011. 146p. pap. 24.95 ***(978-1-4560-5140-2(7))*** PublishAmerica, Inc.

Ibanga, Ime. Rainbows in the Sky. 2011. 134p. pap. 19.99 ***(978-1-4568-6057-8(7))*** Xlibris Corp.

Ilott, Daniel. Depths of the Mind. 2007. 164p. per. *(978-1-84549-152-9(1))* arima publishing.

Intill, Henry. Travel Junkies: An Older Couple from Georgia Explores the World with Backpack & Canoe. 2008. 460p. pap. 29.95 *(978-1-60672-261-9(1))* PublishAmerica, Inc.

Isenberg, Robert. The Legend of Pangkor. 2008. 182p. pap. 15.50 *(978-1-4357-6029-5(8))* Lulu Enterprises Inc.

Jenle, Charley. Diving with Charley At 0500. 2007. 104p. per. 11.95 *(978-0-595-44821-0(6))* iUniverse, Inc.

Jenkinson, Clay S. The Character of Meriwether Lewis: Explorer in the Wilderness. 2011. (ENG.). 506p. 29.95 *(978-0-9825597-2-7(0))*; pap. 19.95 *(978-0-9825597-3-4(9))* Lewis.

Jewell, Douglas. Roadtrip: A Baby Boomer's Misadventures in Hitchhiking & Other Unconventional Travel. 2009. 228p. pap. 15.95 *(978-1-59858-902-3(4))* Dog Ear Publishing, LLC.

Johnson, Barbara. A Spirited Escape. 2007. 200p. per. 14.95 *(978-1-891386-93-0(X))* Plain View Pr.

Jones, Charles W. Childhood Adventures. 2009. 58p. pap. 9.95 *(978-1-4401-4901-6(1))* iUniverse, Inc.

Jones, Tammy. Alaska Bound: One Man's Dream, One Woman's Nightmare. 2011. (Illus.). 298p. pap. 15.95 *(978-0-615-44237-2(4))* Jones, Tammy.

Jones, Tom. Risky Living: The Fascinating Lives of People Who Work on the Edge. 2009. (ENG.). 400p. 24.95 *(978-1-60239-769-9(4)*, 239769) Skyhorse Publishing Co., Inc.

Judy Swain Garshelis. The Otter Spotters: A Wildlife Adventure in Alaska. 2009. 192p. 26.95 *(978-1-4401-6128-5(3))*; pap. 16.95 *(978-1-4401-6130-8(5))* iUniverse, Inc.

Kanigel, Robert. On an Irish Island. 2012. (ENG., Illus.). 336p. 26.95 ***(978-0-307-26959-1(0)***, Knopf) Knopf Doubleday Publishing Group.

Keay, John. The Mammoth Book of Travel in Dangerous Places. 2010. (ENG.). 480p. pap. 13.95 *(978-0-7624-3845-7(2))* Running Pr. Bk. Pubs.

Kelbaugh, Paul. Closure: My Life Backwards. 2011. 414p. 39.95 ***(978-1-257-85101-0(2))***; pap. 29.95 ***(978-1-257-85102-7(0))*** Lulu Enterprises Inc.

Kelly, Ian. Casanova: Actor, Lover, Priest, Spy. 2011. (ENG.). 416p. (gr. 12). 15.95 *(978-1-58542-844-1(2)*, Tarcher) Penguin Group (USA) Inc.

Kenerson, Ed. The Cabin in the Woods. 2008. 188p. 22.99 *(978-1-60647-632-1(7))*; pap. 14.99 *(978-1-60647-631-4(9))* Xulon Pr., Inc.

Kennedy, Meredith. Broken Glass Cake: Adventures off the Beaten Path. 2011. 362p. pap. 19.99 ***(978-1-61204-322-7(4)***, Strategic Bk. Publishing) AEG Literary Publishing Services, Inc.

Kiernan, Denise & D'Agnese, Joseph. The Indiana Jones Handbook: The Complete Adventurer's Guide. 2008. (ENG., Illus.). 176p. 18.95 *(978-1-59474-221-7(9))* Quirk Bks.

King, L. Jo & Janson, Lone. Bird in the Bush. 2008. 236p. pap. 17.50 *(978-1-933973-07-4(2))* KiwE Publishing, Ltd.

Kirchner, Paul. More of the Deadliest Men Who Ever Lived. 2009. (Illus.). 466p. pap. 39.00 *(978-1-58160-690-4(7))* Paladin Pr.

Kirkby, Bruce. The Dolphin's Tooth: A Decade in Search of Adventure. 2007. (ENG., Illus.). 384p. per. 17.95 *(978-0-7710-9567-2(8)*, McClelland & Stewart) McClelland & Stewart CAN. Dist: Random Hse., Inc.

Krakauer, Jon. Into the Wild. movie tie-in ed. 2007. (ENG., Illus.). 224p. pap. 14.95 *(978-0-307-38717-2(8)*, Anchor) Knopf Doubleday Publishing Group.

Krevald, Rein. The Adventures of Spanky & Rein: Peaks of the East. 2007. 302p. per. 20.00 *(978-0-9800310-0-3(1))* RAK Publishing, Inc.

Kubica, Kasey. Swine & Cheese. 2010. 264p. pap. 18.99 *(978-0-557-67972-0(9))* Lulu Enterprises Inc.

Kuhne, Cecil, ed. Near Death in the Desert: True Stories of Disaster & Survival. 2009. (Vintage Departures Original Ser.). (ENG.). 432p. pap. 16.00 *(978-0-307-27936-1(7)*, Vintage) Knopf Doubleday Publishing Group.

—Near Death in the Mountains: True Stories of Disaster & Survival. 2008. (Vintage Departures Original Ser.). (ENG.). 512p. pap. 16.00 *(978-0-307-27935-4(9)*, Vintage) Knopf Doubleday Publishing Group.

Kull, Irving Stoddard. Gold Rush: Jerseymen in California. 2006. Orig. Title: New Brunswick Adventurers Of '49. 24p. 3.95 *(978-1-58057-523-2(4)*, B25A3) Digital Antiquaria, Inc.

LaPierre, Alexandra. Women Travelers: A Century of Trailblazing Adventures, 1850-1950. Mouchard, Christel, ed. 2007. (ENG., Illus.). 240p. 45.00 *(978-2-08-030018-8(0))* Flammarion et Cie FRA. Dist: Random Hse., Inc.

Lawrence, Sarahlee. River House: A Memoir. 2010. (ENG.). 200p. pap. 16.95 *(978-0-9825691-3-9(0))* Tin Hse. Bks., LLC.

Leibfried, Philip. Rudyard Kipling & Sir Henry Rider Haggard on Screen, Stage, Radio & Television. alt. ed. 2008. (ENG.). 224p. pap. 39.95 *(978-0-7864-3746-7(4))* McFarland & Co., Inc. Pubs.

Leland, Doug. Alone on the Allagash. McGovern, Matt, ed. & des. by. 2007. per. 12.95 *(978-0-9725293-2-7(2))* SOAR Worldwide, Inc.

Lemon, David. Blood Sweat & Lions. 2008. 280p. per. *(978-1-906210-65-3(7))* Grosvenor Hse. Publishing Ltd.

Lewis, Jon E., ed. Survivor: True Tales of Danger, Discovery, & Endurance in the Words of Those Who Have Been to the Edge. 2011. (Best Stories Ever Told Ser.). (ENG.). 512p. pap. 12.95 *(978-1-61608-455-4(3)*, 608455) Skyhorse Publishing Co., Inc.

Lind, Paul & Ward, K P. End to End. 2007. 204p. per. *(978-1-897312-60-5(1))* Adlibbed, Ltd.

Little, James, ed. Way Out There: The Best of Explore. 2006. (ENG.). 376p. pap. 16.95 *(978-1-55365-164-2(2)*, Greystone Bks.) D&M Pubs. Inc. CAN. Dist: Perseus-PGW.

Littlepage, Dean. Steller's Island: Adventures of a Pioneer Naturalist in Alaska. 2006. (ENG., Illus.). 256p. per. 17.95 *(978-1-59485-057-8(7))* Mountaineers Bks., The.

Logothetis, Leon. Amazing Adventures of a Nobody. 2011. (ENG.). 268p. pap. 14.95 *(978-0-9843081-3-2(X))* Youngs, Bettie Bks.

Louis, John. From Tampa to the Cape: Eight Days Around the Florida Peninsula. 2008. 124p. pap. 12.95 *(978-0-595-50285-1(7))* iUniverse, Inc.

Maas, Deon. Witboy in Africa: Diary of a Troublemaker. 2010. 224p. pap. 23.95 *(978-0-624-04833-6(0))* NE Pubs. Ltd. ZAF. Dist: International Publishers Marketing.

—Witboy in Afrika. 2010. 224p. pap. 23.95 *(978-0-624-04778-0(4))* NB Pubs. Ltd. ZAF. Dist: International Publishers Marketing.

Maciejewski, Charles. Adventure, Self-Efficacy, & Students of Color. 2008. 76p. pap. *(978-3-639-05000-4(2))* VDM Verlag Dr. Mueller e.K.

Magee, Ken. Mudwatching: Adventuring with Grandpa. 2008. 136p. pap. 14.95 *(978-1-4327-2666-9(8))* Outskirts Pr., Inc.

Major, Joyce. Smiling at the World: A Woman's Passionate Yearlong Quest for Advneture & Love. 2008. (Illus.). 350p. 15.95 *(978-0-9799740-0-7(3))* Alegro Publishing.

Mapel, Tiffany. Lake Powell Tales: An Anthology of Adventure. 2007. 208p. per. 17.95 *(978-0-595-45126-5(8))* iUniverse, Inc.

Marcone, Massimo. Acquired Tastes: On the Trail of the World's Most Sought-after Delicacies. 2010. (ENG., Illus.). 256p. pap. 16.95 *(978-1-55470-279-4(8))* Key Porter Bks. CAN. Dist: Perseus-PGW.

Marcone, Massimo Francesco. In Bad Taste: The Adventures & Science Behind Food Delicacies. 2010. (ENG., Illus.). 198p. pap. 16.95 *(978-1-55470-288-6(7))* Key Porter Bks. CAN. Dist: Perseus-PGW.

Marryat, Frederick. Monsieur Violet. 2008. 436p. 30.99 *(978-0-554-33939-9(0))* 2008. 436p. 32.99 *(978-0-554-24636-9(8))* 2006. (ENG.). 392p. pap. 25.99 *(978-1-4264-7029-5(0))* 2006. (ENG.). 434p. pap. 28.99 *(978-1-4264-7105-6(X))* BiblioBazaar.

Marshall, Rowland Charles. Luck Was My Companion: Adventures of an Old Sea Dog. 2008. 410p. pap. *(978-1-897435-09-0(6))* Agio Publishing Hse.

Martel, Lynn. Expedition to the Edge: Stories of Worldwide Adventure, 1 vol. rev. ed. 2009. (ENG., Illus.). 352p. pap. *(978-1-897522-09-7(6))* Rocky Mountain Bks.

Max, Gerry. Horizon Chasers: The Lives & Adventures of Richard Halliburton & Paul Mooney. 2007. (ENG., Illus.). 320p. per. 39.95 *(978-0-7864-2671-3(3))* McFarland & Co., Inc. Pubs.

McCollum, Mary. Mighty Merry Too: About the Grandmother Who Went to Sea. 2007. (Illus.). 201p. pap. 15.95 *(978-0-9793797-0-3(9))* Merry Publishing.

McVicker, Mary F. Women Adventurers, 1750-1900: A Biographical Dictionary, with Excerpts from Selected Travel Writings. 2008. (ENG.). 224p. 55.00 *(978-0-7864-3205-9(5))* McFarland & Co., Inc. Pubs.

Mercer, Dena M. Campfires Remembered. 2011. 172p. pap. 14.95 ***(978-1-59330-728-8(4))*** Aventine Pr.

Merian, Dee. The Best Years of Flying: A Memoir of Howard Hughes, TWA, & Crew. 2010. *(978-0-929915-82-1(8))* Headline Bks.

Mills, Andi Rae. A Distant Drum. 2011. 172p. 29.99 ***(978-1-4653-4802-9(6))***; pap. 19.99 ***(978-1-4653-4801-2(8))*** Xlibris Corp.

Murphy, David Royce. Scenery, Curiosities, & Stupendous Rocks: William Quesenbury's Overland Sketches1850-1851. 2011. (ENG., Illus.). 304p. 45.00 *(978-0-8061-4219-7(7))* Univ. of Oklahoma Pr.

Murray, William Henry Harrison. Adventures in the Wilderness. 2009. 116p. pap. *(978-1-151-16854-2(8))* Books LLC.

Nash, Fred J. Utah's Low Points: A Guide to the Lowest Points in Utah's 29 Counties. 2008. (ENG., Illus.). 264p. (gr. 12). pap. 22.95 *(978-0-87480-932-9(0))* Univ. of Utah Pr.

Nash, Jill & Nash, Carlo. Family Adventures in Style. 2012. (Luxury Backpackers Ser.). pap. 24.95 ***(978-0-9557397-5-0(6))*** Luxury Backpackers, Ltd. GBR. Dist: Midpoint Trade Bks., Inc.

Negron, Stephen. False Dawn: Recollections of the Amazon. 2006. (Illus.). 88p. lib. bdg. 18.95 *(978-1-59715-015-6(0))* Chapel Hill Pr.

Neider, Susan M., ed. Wild Yosemite: Personal Accounts of Adventure, Discovery, & Nature. 2007. (Illus.). 283p. 24.95 *(978-1-60239-056-0(8))* Skyhorse Publishing Co., Inc.

Nelson, Richard. A Life Other Men Only Dream About. 2006. 530p. pap. 15.95 *(978-0-533-15349-7(2))* Vantage Pr., Inc.

Nelsson, Richard, ed. Those Who Dared: Stories from the Golden Age of Exploration. 2010. (ENG., Illus.). 250p. 26.95 *(978-0-85265-142-1(2))* Random Hse. GBR. Dist: Independent Pubs. Group.

Oh No! We're Gonna Die Too. 2009. 29.95 net *(978-1-57833-453-7(5))* Todd Communications.

Ondaatje, Christopher. The Last Colonial: Curious Adventures & Stories from a Vanishing World. 2011. (ENG., Illus.). 256p. 29.95 *(978-0-500-25186-7(X)*, 525186) Thames & Hudson.

O'Reilly, Edward S. Roving & Fighting: Adventures under Four Flags. 2007. (ENG.). 362p. 46.95 *(978-0-548-21550-0(2))*; 364p. per. 31.95 *(978-1-4325-3537-7(4))* Kessinger Publishing, LLC.

—Roving & Fighting: Adventures under Four Flags. 354p. reprint ed. 98.00 *(978-0-7222-7874-1(8))* Library Reprints, Inc.

Otterbacher, John. Sailing Grace: A True Story of Death, Life & the Sea. 2007. (Illus.). 258p. *(978-0-9793486-0-0(9))*; per. *(978-0-9793486-1-7(7))* Samadhi Pr.

Outerbridge, Gillian. Going About! A Waterway Adventure. 2007. per. 21.95 *(978-0-9789350-2-3(0))* Nautical Publishing Co.

Padel, Ruth. Tigers in Red Weather: A Quest for the Last Wild Tigers. 2006. (ENG., Illus.). 448p. 26.95 *(978-0-8027-1544-9(3))* Walker & Co.

Palmer, Ron. A Hole In The Ocean. 2006. 184p. per. 17.39 *(978-1-4251-0105-3(4))* Trafford Publishing.

Pasha, Hobart & Hobart, Augustus Charles. Sketches from My Life. 2008. 300p. 43.95 *(978-1-4372-3653-8(7))*; pap. 28.95 *(978-1-4371-0841-5(5))* Kessinger Publishing, LLC.

Patterson, R. M. The Dangerous River: Adventure on the Nahanni, 1 vol. 2009. (ENG., Illus.). 320p. pap. *(978-1-894898-86-7(9))* TouchWood Editions.

Pauly, Thomas H. Zane Grey: His Life, His Adventures, His Women. 2007. (Illus.). 408p. per. 24.95 *(978-0-252-07492-9(0))* Univ. of Illinois Pr.

Pearson, T. R. Seaworthy: Adrift with William Willis in the Golden Age of Rafting. 2007. (ENG., Illus.). 304p. per. 13.95 *(978-0-307-33595-1(X)*, Three Rivers Pr.) Crown Publishing Group.

Perretti, Angi. The Identity of Angiarts. 2008. 64p. pap. 25.49 *(978-1-4343-7754-8(7))* AuthorHouse.

Petzoldt, Patricia. On Top of the World: My Adventures with My Mountain Climbing Husband. 2011. 264p. 47.95 ***(978-1-258-09177-4(1))*** Literary Licensing, LLC.

Pierce, Kay D. Our Faith Adventure. 2008. 108p. pap. 10.99 *(978-1-4343-9600-6(2))* AuthorHouse.

Pinnock, Don. The Woman Who Lived in a Tree & Other Perfect Strangers. 2010. (ENG.). 289p. pap. 19.00 *(978-1-77009-692-9(2))* Jacana Media ZAF. Dist: Independent Pubs. Group.

Plant, Richard. Life's A Buzz (2) 2011. 276p. 30.95 ***(978-1-4620-4636-2(3))***; pap. 20.95 ***(978-1-4620-4637-9(1))*** iUniverse, Inc.

Plummer, Steve J. Salamander Dreaming. 2010. 200p. pap. 21.50 *(978-1-4452-9924-2(0))* Lulu Enterprises Inc.

Pocock, Geoffrey A. Outrider of Empire: The Life & Adventures of Roger Pocock. 2008. (ENG., Illus.). 400p. pap. 34.95 *(978-0-88864-448-0(5))* Univ. of Alberta Pr. CAN. Dist: Michigan State Univ. Pr.

Pond, Marilyn. Never Say Whoa in a Bad Place. 2010. (Illus.). 226p. pap. 19.95 *(978-1-57258-649-9(4))* TEACH Services, Inc.

Porter, Winton. Just Passin' Thru: A Vintage Store, the Appalachian Trail, & a Cast of Unforgettable Characters. 2009. (ENG., Illus.). 272p. pap. 14.95 *(978-0-89732-849-4(3))* Menasha Ridge Pr., Inc.

Price, Rod. Racing to the Yukon: A Lifetime of Adventure Racing from the Everglades to the Amazon to the World's Longest Canoe Race. 2010. 200p. pap. 19.95 *(978-1-934449-58-5(X))* Legacy Publishing Services, Inc.

Ralph & Phyllis Nansen. Stone Boat Odyssey. 2011. 322p. 29.99 ***(978-1-4628-7590-0(4))***; pap. 19.99 ***(978-1-4628-7589-4(0))*** Xlibris Corp.

Rasmus, John. The New Age of Adventure: Ten Years of Great Writing. 2009. (ENG.). 432p. pap. 16.95 *(978-1-4262-0545-0(5)*, National Geographic) National Geographic Society.

Reale, Rick. Tires Optional. 2011. 108p. pap. 13.95 *(978-1-4327-7127-0(2))* Outskirts Pr., Inc.

Redmond, Sean, tr. Spices, Saints, & Saracens: The Egyptian Wanderings of a Dominican Friar 1483. 2011. 384p. 24.95 *(978-977-416-396-8(6))* American Univ. in Cairo Pr. EGY. Dist: Oxford Univ. Pr., Inc.

Reed, Jim. Turning Final, A Life Complete. 2011. 228p. 25.86 *(978-1-4269-6322-3(X))*; pap. 15.86 *(978-1-4269-6319-3(X))* Trafford Publishing.

Richens, Marvin Gene. Dreams of Reality. 2008. 56p. pap. 15.49 *(978-1-4389-0470-2(3))* AuthorHouse.

Ridd, Michael F. Memoirs of a Mud-Puddler. 2006. (Illus.). 304p. *(978-1-905529-48-3(1))* Grosvenor Hse. Publishing Ltd.

Ridley, Rosamund. Dear Friends, Liebe Freunde. 2010. (Illus.). 266p. pap. 18.95 *(978-1-4457-1000-6(5))* Lulu Enterprises Inc.

Ridley, Scott. Morning of Fire: John Kendrick's Daring American Odyssey in the Pacific. 2010. 464p. 27.99 *(978-0-06-170012-5(6))*, Morrow, William & Co.) HarperCollins Pubs.

Rigby, Steven. 'Tears in the Sand' 2011. 132p. pap. 13.32 *(978-1-4567-7349-6(6))* AuthorHouse.

Righi, Brian. Spirits of Dallas: The Haunting of the Big D. 2008. (Illus.). 176p. pap. 14.99 *(978-0-7643-3036-0(5))* Schiffer Publishing, Ltd.

Rinehart, Rick & Rinehart, Amy. Dare to Survive: Death, Heartbreak, & Triumph in the Wild. 2008. (ENG.). 288p. 15.95 *(978-0-8065-2880-9(X)*, Citadel Pr.) Kensington Publishing Corp.

Robinson, Bob. God Don't Make Junk: From Ramblings of an Old Man. 2008. 286p. pap. 27.95 *(978-1-60610-353-1(9))* PublishAmerica, Inc.

Rock, Francis John. J Ross Browne: A Biography. 2011. 92p. 38.95 ***(978-1-258-08497-4(X))*** Literary Licensing, LLC.

Rogers, Stanley. Crusoes & Castaways. 2007. *(978-0-486-45600-3(5))* Dover Pubns., Inc.

—Crusoes & Castaways: True Stories of Survival & Solitude. 2011. (ENG., Illus.). 272p. pap. 10.95 *(978-0-486-47897-5(1))* Dover Pubns., Inc.

Rolde, Neil. Maine in the World: Stories of Some of Those from here Who Went Away. 2010. (Illus.). 384p. pap. 20.00 *(978-0-88448-320-5(7))* Tilbury Hse. Pubs.

Roosevelt, Theodore. The Hunting & Exploring Adventures of Theodore Roosevelt: Told in His Own Words. Day, Donald, ed. 2011. 444p. 56.95 ***(978-1-258-04808-2(6))*** Literary Licensing, LLC.

Rougemont, Louis de. Adventures of Louis de Rougemont. 2006. 254p. pap. 21.99 *(978-1-4264-0601-0(0))* BiblioBazaar.

Roybal, R. James. Summer Of '63. 2011. 326p. 29.99 ***(978-1-4568-5273-3(6))***; pap. 19.99 ***(978-1-4568-5272-6(8))*** Xlibris Corp.

Russell, Charles E. Wwi Adventures in Crime-Fighting & Spy-Hunting. 2011. 380p. pap. 14.95 ***(978-1-61646-096-9(2))*** Coachwhip Pubns.

Sabin, Edwin L. Adventuring with Carson & Fremont. 2007. (ENG.). 302p. 43.95 *(978-0-548-02035-7(3))* Kessinger Publishing, LLC.

Safont, Paul. True Adventures for Boys. rev. ed. 2007. (ENG., Illus.). 184p. 22.95 *(978-0-330-45294-6(0))* Macmillan Pubs., Ltd. GBR. Dist: Independent Pubs. Group.

Sammons, Edward. Justice... in Black & White: Tales of Retribution. 2008. 236p. pap. 11.95 *(978-1-4327-1808-4(8))* Outskirts Pr., Inc.

Sampey, Harry. Wizard of the Outer Lab: Adventures & Inventions of a Boy Who Would Never Amount to a Hill of Beans. 2007. 372p. per. 27.50 *(978-1-4251-0900-4(4))* Trafford Publishing.

Sanford, William. William Sanford, the Wanderer: An Autobiography. 2011. 146p. pap. 24.95 ***(978-1-4560-0510-8(3))*** PublishAmerica, Inc.

Santer, Lynn. Beyond World Safari. 2009. 236p. pap. 25.95 *(978-0-9803547-5-1(7))* JoJo Publishing AUS. Dist: International Publishers Marketing.

Schäffer, Mary T. S. Old Indian Trails of the Canadian Rockies, 1 vol. 2nd rev. ed. 2011. (Mountain Classics Collection). (ENG.). 200p. pap. *(978-1-897522-49-3(5))* Rocky Mountain Bks.

Schuler, Charles. The Schuler Sag. 2011. 326p. 39.95 ***(978-0-557-56579-5(0))*** Lulu Enterprises Inc.

Scott, Jeremy. Dancing on Ice: A Stirring Tale of Adventure, Risk & Reckless Folly. 2009. (ENG., Illus.). 272p. (gr. 6). 26.00 *(978-1-905847-50-1(5))* Old Street Publishing GBR. Dist: Consortium Bk. Sales & Distribution.

Seaver, Douglass J. Four Across the Atlantic: One Captain's Story of the Historic 2004 Nordhavn Atlantic Rally. 2007. per. 21.95 *(978-0-9789350-1-6(2))* Nautical Publishing Co.

Sherrod, Jane & Singer, Kurt. Great Adventures of the Se. 2011. 330p. 50.95 ***(978-1-258-07875-1(9))*** Literary Licensing, LLC.

Silverwood, Jean & Silverwood, John. Black Wave. 2008. 288p. *(978-0-7322-8831-0(2))* HarperCollins Pubs. Australia.

Simons, Janet Latshaw. Quest Over. 2008. 116p. pap. 19.95 *(978-1-60672-094-3(5))* PublishAmerica, Inc.

Skinner, Constance L. Adventurers of Oregon. 2010. 310p. pap. 29.75 *(978-1-117-88498-1(8))* BiblioBazaar.

Slivatz, Robert. True Tales from an Enigmatic Mind. 2006. (ENG.). 120p. per. 19.95 *(978-1-4241-2734-4(3))* PublishAmerica, Inc.

Smith, Rake. The Hard-Style Adventures of Rake Smith: A Masterpiece & a Trilogy (Minus One) 2009. 260p. pap. 14.95 *(978-1-60844-135-8(0))* Dog Ear Publishing, LLC.

Sobel, David. Wild Play: Parenting Adventures in the Great Outdoors. 2011. (ENG.). 224p. pap. 15.95 *(978-1-57805-176-2(2))* Sierra Club Bks.

Sorensen, Stacey. Go Green, Girlfriends: 10 Earth-Friendly Getaways for You & Your Friends. 2009. 160p. pap. 5.00 *(978-1-933102-74-0(8))* Capital Bks., Inc.

Sorrells, Margaret Frances. Adventures with Mr. Tape. Teen Travels. 2008. 131p. pap. 24.95 *(978-1-60441-438-7(3))* PublishAmerica, Inc.

Soyland, Eric I. Animals & Me of the Ocean, Land & Sky: 56 Selected Short Stories. 2009. 146p. 24.49 *(978-1-4490-0579-5(9))*; pap. 13.50 *(978-1-4490-0580-1(2))* AuthorHouse.

Speed. pap. 22.00 *(978-1-56997-096-6(3))* Knowledge Adventure, Inc.

Spieler, Abe. You Can Call Me Brooklyn. 2011. 263p. 14.95 ***(978-0-9717283-5-6(6))*** Telling Your Story, Inc.

Sprandel, Fritz T. Adventure on a Dare. 2009. 176p. 24.99 *(978-1-4389-5663-3(0))*; pap. 15.99 *(978-1-4389-5662-6(2))* AuthorHouse.

Stauffer, Ruth M. Joseph Conrad: His Romantic Realism. 2007. (ENG.). 120p. 34.95 *(978-0-548-04773-6(1))* Kessinger Publishing, LLC.

Steman, Caroline. Southern Alberta for City Folks. 2011. 44p. pap. 21.99 ***(978-1-4568-7472-8(1))*** Xlibris Corp.

Stoldt, Erling. Wind in My Hair. 2009. 172p. 23.50 *(978-1-60860-273-5(7))*, Eloquent Bks.) AEG Literary Publishing Services, Inc.

Stremba, Bob. Teaching Adventure Education Theory: Best Practices. Bisson, Christian A., ed. 2009. (ENG., Illus.). 408p. (gr. k-16). 52.00 *(978-0-7360-7126-0(1))* Human Kinetics Pubs.

Stroll, Norman. Two Strolls in the Wilderness. 2009. (ENG.). 208p. pap. 16.96 *(978-0-557-19445-2(8))*; 207p. pap. 16.95 *(978-0-557-09350-2(3))* Lulu Enterprises Inc.

Suffling, Ernest R. Jethou: Or Crusoe Life in the Channel Isles. 2007. 200p. pap. 19.99 *(978-1-4346-1182-6(5))*; (ENG.). 222p. pap. 22.99 *(978-1-4346-1253-3(8))* BiblioBazaar.

Talley, Jeannine. Lure of the Trade Winds: Two Women Sailing the Pacific Ocean. 2010. 244p. 29.95 *(978-1-4502-5175-4(7))*; pap. 19.95 *(978-1-4502-5173-0(0))* iUniverse, Inc.

Termini, Maria. Solitude & Splendor: Living in the Schoolhouse. 2007. 144p. per. 24.95 *(978-1-4241-6928-3(3))* PublishAmerica, Inc.

Terrill, James T. Joe Curtin: Memoirs Of A Construction Stiff. 2007. 96p. per. 9.95 *(978-1-4327-0651-7(9))* Outskirts Pr., Inc.

The Explorers Club Staff. They Lived to Tell the Tale: True Stories of Modern Adventure from the Legendary Explorers Club. Russell, Jan Jarboe, ed. 2007. (Explorers Club Book Ser.). (ENG., Illus.). 368p. 27.95 *(978-1-59228-991-2(6)*, Lyons Pr.) Globe Pequot Pr., The.

Thomas, E. Donnall, Jr. Have Bow, Will Travel: Around the World Adventure with Longbow & Recurve. 2011. (ENG., Illus.). 302p. pap. 22.00 *(978-0-9816584-6-9(6))* Raven's Eye Pr., LLC.

Thomas, Irv. Derelict Days ... Sixty-Six Years on the Roadside Path to Enlightenment. 2010. 252p. pap. 14.99 *(978-1-4520-2605-3(X))* AuthorHouse.

Thomas, William. Me & Benny. 2011. 162p. 35.00 ***(978-1-257-05258-5(6))*** Lulu Enterprises Inc.

Thompson, Chuck. To Hellholes & Back: Bribes, Lies, & the Art of Extreme Tourism. 2009. (ENG.). 336p. pap. 15.00 *(978-0-8050-8788-8(5)*, Holt Paperback) Holt, Henry & Co.

Thompson, F. M. "Punk". Living a Dream. 2007. 176p. per. 24.95 *(978-1-4241-8971-7(3))* PublishAmerica, Inc.

Thompson, James D. The Blackwater Philosopher. 2010. 134p. pap. 12.95 *(978-0-557-53891-1(2))* Lulu Enterprises Inc.

Thordahl, James Bjorn. On Side Roads. 2011. 210p. 26.95 ***(978-1-59330-721-9(7))***; pap. 13.95 ***(978-1-59330-720-2(9))*** Aventine Pr.

Time Out Guides Staff. Time Out 1000 Things for Kids to Do in the Holidays. 2009. (ENG., Illus.). 320p. 19.95 *(978-1-84670-090-3(6))* Time Out Guides Ltd. GBR. Dist: Perseus-PGW.

Toren, Bob. Fellow Travelers. 2008. 132p. pap. 11.50 *(978-1-59330-554-3(0))* Aventine Pr.

Trenck, Baron. Life & Adventures of Baron Trenck. 2007. (ENG.). 146p. pap. 18.99 *(978-0-9801439-1-1(8))* Town & Country Reprographics.

Trinh, D. J. Indefinite Ocean: Adventures of a Fifteen-Year-Old Vietnamese Fugitive. 2011. 372p. pap. 20.95 ***(978-1-4620-1716-4(9))*** iUniverse, Inc.

Venables, Stephen. First Ascent: Pioneering Mountain Climbs. 2008. (ENG., Illus.). 192p. 45.00 *(978-1-55407-403-7(7))* Firefly Bks., Ltd.

Voss, John Claus. The Venturesome Voyages of Captain Voss. 2011. 264p. ***(978-1-84902-378-8(6))*** Benediction Classics.

Wagner, Craig, et al. Small Boats Big Adventures. 2007. per. *(978-1-4346-5119-8(3))*; 148p. pap. 18.99 *(978-1-4346-5117-4(7))*; (ENG.). 162p. pap. 21.99 *(978-1-4346-5120-4(7))*; (ENG.). 162p. pap. 21.99 *(978-1-4346-5118-1(5))* BiblioBazaar.

Walker, Spike. On the Edge of Survival: A Shipwreck, a Raging Storm, & the Harrowing Alaskan Rescue That Became a Legend. 2010. (ENG., Illus.). 288p. 24.99 *(978-0-312-28634-7(1))* St. Martin's Pr.

Walkup, David. Voyage of Kabuki. 2007. 140p. per. 24.95 *(978-1-4241-8162-9(3))* PublishAmerica, Inc.

Waring, Rob. The Adventure Capital of the World (US) 2008. (ENG.). 24p. (C). pap. 10.95 *(978-1-4240-4457-3(X))* Cengage Heinle.

—Gliding Across the Gobi (US) 2008. (ENG.). 22p. (C). pap. 10.95 *(978-1-4240-4377-4(8))* Cengage Heinle.

Weaver, Alistair. A Drive on the Wild Side. 2007. (ENG., Illus.). 176p. 59.95 *(978-1-84584-100-3(X)*, 184584100X) Veloce Publishing Ltd. GBR. Dist: MBI Distribution Services/Quayside Distribution.

Wegley, H. L. Colby & Me: Growing up in The 50's. 2009. 296p. 25.99 *(978-1-4269-1819-3(4))*; pap. 15.99 *(978-1-4269-1818-6(6))* Trafford Publishing.

Weidemann, Dennis. This Water Goes North. 2008. (ENG.). 256p. 21.95 *(978-0-9796852-0-0(6))* Berens Hse.

When Gnats Swarm. 2011. 80p. pap. 27.99 ***(978-1-4634-0233-4(3))*** AuthorHouse.

White, Bob. Bannock & Beans: A Cowboy's Account of the Bedaux Expedition, 1 vol. Sherwood, Jay, ed. 2010. (ENG., Illus.). 224p. pap. *(978-0-7726-6060-2(3))* Royal British Columbia Museum.

Wiarda, Howard J. Adventures in Research Volume IV: Return Visits. 2007. 456p. per. 26.95 *(978-0-595-43284-4(0))* iUniverse, Inc.

Wiemert, Richard. High Seas, Bell Bottoms & Anchors Aweigh. 2008. 61p. pap. 16.95 *(978-1-60672-335-7(9))* PublishAmerica, Inc.

Wiese, Richard. Born to Explore: How to Be a Backyard Adventurer. 2009. (ENG.). 368p. pap. 18.99 *(978-0-06-144958-1(X)*, Harper Paperbacks) HarperCollins Pubs.

Wil Verhoeven Staff & Verhoeven, Wil. Gilbert Imlay: Citizen of the World, 1 vol. 2008. (ENG., Illus.). 320p. 99.00 *(978-1-85196-859-6(8))* Pickering & Chatto Pubs., Ltd. GBR. Dist: Ashgate Publishing Co.

Willis, Linda. Looking for Mr. Smith: Seeking the Truth Behind the Long Walk, the Greatest Survival Story Ever Told. 2010. (ENG., Illus.). 288p. 24.95 *(978-1-61608-158-4(9)*, 608158) Skyhorse Publishing Co., Inc.

Wilson, Brandon. Along the Templar Trail: Seven Million Steps for Peace. Rich, Bob, ed. 2008. (ENG., Illus.). 328p. 27.95 *(978-0-9770536-9-8(5))*; per. 14.95 *(978-0-9770536-8-1(7))* Pilgrim's Tales, Inc.

Winslow, A. D. The Real People: A True Story. 2008. 176p. pap. 13.95 *(978-0-595-51830-2(3))* iUniverse, Inc.

Winyard Sr., David C. Shore to Shore, A Father-and-Son Journey Across America. 2008. 284p. pap. 18.00 *(978-1-4303-1758-6(2))* Lulu Enterprises Inc.

Wood, Deborah. The Legend of River Mahay: Based on a true Alaska adventure story of love, survival & triumph over Adversity. 2007. per. 19.95 *(978-1-59433-057-5(3)*, Publishing Consultants) Publication Consultants.

Wood, Ginny & Brewster, Karen. Boots, Bikes, & Bombers: Adventures of Alaska Conservationist Ginny Hill Wood. 2012. (ENG., Illus.). 550p. pap. 29.95 ***(978-1-60223-173-3(7))***; E-Book ***(978-1-60223-174-0(5))*** Univ. of Alaska Pr.

Woods, Padraic. 30 Irish Adventures. 2008. (ENG., Illus.). 192p. pap. 33.95 *(978-1-85635-587-2(X))* Mercier Pr., Ltd., The IRL. Dist: Dufour Editions, Inc.

Wray, Marvin. Journeys. 2010. 224p. 24.95 *(978-1-4520-9972-9(3))*; pap. 15.95 *(978-1-4520-9971-2(5))* AuthorHouse.

Yamashita, Michael. Zheng He. 2006. (ENG., Illus.). 504p. 39.95 *(978-88-544-0164-8(1)*, White Star) Rizzoli International Pubns., Inc.

Yurk, Mike. Anatomy of an Adventure. 2011. 148p. pap. 24.95 ***(978-1-4560-1211-3(8))*** PublishAmerica, Inc.

ADVENTURE AND ADVENTURERS IN LITERATURE

Hasty, Will. Adventure as Social Performance: A Study of the German Court Epic. (Untersuchungen zur deutschen Literaturgeschichte Ser.). (ENG.). V, 143p. 210.00 ***(978-3-11-186454-9(5))*** De Gruyter, Walter Inc.

Hill, Jen. White Horizon: The Arctic in the Nineteenth-Century British Imagination. (SUNY Series, Studies in the Long Nineteenth Century). 2008. viii, 238p. pap. 24.95 *(978-0-7914-7230-9(2))* 2007. 238p. 60.00 *(978-0-7914-7229-3(9))* State Univ. of New York Pr.

Levin, Stephen M. The Contemporary Anglophone Travel Novel: The Aesthetics of Self-Fashioning in the Era of Globalization. 2012. (Literary Criticism & Cultural Theory Ser.). (ENG.). 200p. (C). pap. 42.95 ***(978-0-415-54233-3(2))*** Routledge.

Soupel, Serge, et al. Adventure: An Eighteenth-Century Idiom: Essays on the Daring & the Bold As a Pre-Modern Medium. 2007. xx, 343p. *(978-0-404-64858-9(4))* AMS Pr., Inc.

ADVENTURE AND BEAGLE EXPEDITION (1826-1830)

Nichols, Peter. Evolution's Captain: The Story of the Kidnapping That Led to Charles Darwin's Voyage Aboard the Beagle. 2009. 335p. pap. 15.00 *(978-1-4379-6778-4(7))* DIANE Publishing Co.

ADVENTURE TRAVEL

Here are entered works on travel to remote and sometimes dangerous places without normal tourist amenities.

see also Safaris

Buckley, Ralf. Adventure Tourism. 2006. (Illus.). 336p. per. 85.00 *(978-1-84593-122-3(X))* CABI GBR. Dist: Stylus Publishing, LLC.

—Adventure Tourism Management. 2009. (ENG., Illus.). 288p. (C). pap. 48.95 *(978-1-85617-834-1(X))* Routledge.

Castrodale, Mary L. The Water's Edge: A Walk Through My Life. 2009. 304p. pap. 25.66 *(978-0-615-18624-5(6))* Marylou Pubns.

Dosch, Dee Davidson. A Summer In '69. 2010. 140p. pap. 11.50 *(978-1-60911-207-3(5)*, Eloquent Bks.) AEG Literary Publishing Services, Inc.

Farnsworth, Janet Webb. Grandma Needs a Four-Wheel Drive: Adventure Travel for Seniors. 2011. (Illus.). pap. 12.95 *(978-1-60494-557-7(5))* Wheatmark.

Flint, Alexander. Highway Odyssey: Traveling to, or Running From. 2011. 263p. pap. 10.95 *(978-1-4327-6669-6(4))* Outskirts Pr., Inc.

George, Don. Lonely Planet Tales from Nowhere: Unexpected Stories from Unexpected Places. 2nd ed. 2011. (Travel Literature Ser.). (ENG.). 288p. pap. 14.99 *(978-1-74179-520-2(6))* Lonely Planet Pubns.

Goetz, Gregory. Hey You-How about a Road Trip? Vicarious literary adventures to get you to temporarily stop reading vicarious literary adventures, go out, & make Y. 2009. 128p. pap. 10.99 *(978-1-4389-7612-9(7))* AuthorHouse.

Hanson, Jennifer A. Hiking the Continental Divide Trail: One Woman's Journey. 2011. (ENG., Illus.). 275p. pap. 16.95 *(978-1-56825-120-2(3))* Rainbow Bks., Inc.

Hood, Karen Jean Matsko. Adventure Travel & Tours Submission Guidelines. 2008. pap. 6.95 *(978-1-59808-040-7(7))* Whispering Pine Pr. International, Inc.

—Adventure Travel & USA Submission Guidelines. 2008. 32p. pap. 6.95 *(978-1-59808-041-4(5))* Whispering Pine Pr. International, Inc.

—Adventure Travel International Submission Guidelines. 2008. 32p. pap. 6.95 *(978-1-59808-042-1(3))* Whispering Pine Pr. International, Inc.

—Adventure Travel Northwest Mini Trips Submission Guidelines. 2008. pap. 6.95 *(978-1-59808-044-5(X))* Whispering Pine Pr. International, Inc.

Hunter, B. T. The Maine Ide. 2011. 254p. pap. 14.98 ***(978-0-557-79185-9(5))*** Lulu Enterprises Inc.

Katchor, Bernie, photos by. Around the Next Bend: Exploring the Rivers of Guyana. 2008. (Illus.). 164p. pap. 18.50 *(978-0-9805363-0-0(6))* Katchor Enterprises P/L AUS. Dist: CreateSpace.

Kirkby, Bruce. The Dolphin's Tooth: A Decade in Search of Adventure. 2007. (ENG., Illus.). 384p. per. 17.95 *(978-0-7710-9567-2(8))*, McClelland & Stewart) McClelland & Stewart CAN. Dist: Random Hse., Inc.

Laviolette, Patrick. Extreme Landscapes of Leisure Not A Hap-Hazardsous Sport. 2010. (Illus.). 226p. 99.95 *(978-0-7546-7958-5(6))* Ashgate Publishing Co.

Mankin, Don, et al. Riding the Hulahula to the Arctic Ocean: A Guide to Fifty Extraordinary Adventures for the Seasoned Traveler. 2008. (ENG., Illus.). 304p. pap. 18.95 *(978-1-4262-0278-0(4))*, National Geographic) National Geographic Society.

Marais, Jacques. Great African Adventures. 2008. (Illus.). 224p. pap. 25.00 *(978-1-77007-279-4(9))* Struik Pubs. ZAF. Dist: International Publishers Marketing.

McCormick, Herb. One Island, One Ocean: The Epic Environmental Journey Around the Americas. 2011. (ENG.). 240p. 35.00 *(978-1-61628-171-7(5))* Weldon Owen, Inc.

Michels, Joseph W. Deck Passage. 2008. 172p. pap. 13.95 *(978-1-4401-1222-5(3))* iUniverse, Inc.

Nadda, Vipin. Adventure Tourism in the Central Himalayas. 2009. 288p. pap. *(978-3-639-17596-7(4))* VDM Verlag Dr. Mueller e.K.

Sparks, John. Walking the World's Natural Wonders. 2009. (ENG., Illus.). 192p. 39.95 *(978-0-7892-1020-3(7))* Abbeville Pr., Inc.

Stine, Sharon. Gypsy Boots: A Young Woman Hitchhikes through Europe, 1958-59. 2008. 352p. pap. 17.99 *(978-1-4389-2630-8(8))* AuthorHouse.

Tarolli, John. Road Warriors: Turning Business Travel into Exciting Adventures! 2008. 92p. pap. 34.95 *(978-1-4343-4791-6(5))* AuthorHouse.

Wicks, Robert. The World's Great Adventure Motorcycle Rides: The Essential Guide to the Greatest Motorcycle Rides in the World. 2012. (ENG., Illus.). 240p. 39.95 *(978-1-84425-945-8(5)*, 1844259455) Haynes Publishing PLC GBR. Dist: MBI Distribution Services/Quayside Distribution.

Wicks, Robert & Baker, Greg. Adventure Riding Techniques: The Essential Guide to All the Skills You Need for off-Road Adventure Riding. 2009. (ENG., Illus.). 176p. 39.95 *(978-1-84425-572-6(7)*, 1844255727) Haynes Publishing PLC GBR. Dist: MBI Distribution Services/Quayside Distribution.

Wolff, Stewart L. Growing up on Bishop Street: The Story of A Little Boy. 2011. 221p. 26.95 ***(978-1-4327-5813-4(6))***; pap. 15.95 ***(978-1-4327-5812-7(8))*** Outskirts Pr., Inc.

Wooldridge, Frosty. How to Live A Life of Adventure: The Art of Exploring the World. 2011. 380p. pap. 19.95 ***(978-1-4634-2028-4(5))*** AuthorHouse.

ADVERSARIA

see Commonplace-Books

ADVERSARY SYSTEM (LAW)

see also Trial Practice

Barnes, John, et al, eds. The Politics of Legalism. 2013. (Law, Courts & Politics Ser.). (ENG.). 224p. (C). 130.00 ***(978-0-415-63338-3(9))*** Routledge.

Tidmarsh, Jay H. & Trangsrud, Roger H. Tidmarsh & Trangsrud's Modern Complex Litigation, 2d Editon (University Casebook Series) 2nd rev. ed. 2010. (University Casebook Ser.). 1243p. 160.00 *(978-1-58778-537-5(4)*, Foundation Pr.) West.

ADVERSE DRUG REACTIONS

see Drugs—Side Effects

ADVERSE POSSESSION

Barlach, Lisete & Malvezzi, Sigmar. Human Resilience: What Is It? 2010. 68p. pap. *(978-3-639-24387-1(0))* VDM Verlag Dr. Mueller e.K.

Jourdan, Stephen & Radley-Gardner, Oliver. Adverse Possession. 2nd rev. ed. 2011. (ENG.). 890p. 280.00 *(978-1-84766-372-6(9))*, Bloomsbury Professional) Bloomsbury Publishing Plc GBR. Dist: International Specialized Bk. Services.

Stanley, Charles F. Advancing Through Adversity, 0 vols. 2008. (Life Principles Study Ser.). 128p. pap. 9.99 *(978-1-4185-3333-5(5))* Nelson, Thomas Inc.

ADVERTISEMENT WRITING

see Advertising Copy

ADVERTISING

see also Advertising, Point-of-Sale; Advertising Cards; Children in Advertising; Color in Advertising; Commercial Art; Coupons (Retail Trade); Deceptive Advertising; Display of Merchandise; Internet Advertising; Mailing Lists; Market Surveys; Packaging; Premiums (Retail Trade); Prize Contests in Advertising; Propaganda; Public Relations; Publicity; Radio Advertising; Sales Promotion; Selling; Slogans; Television Advertising; Women in Advertising; Women in the Advertising Industry

also subdivision by topic, e.g. Advertising—Banks and Banking

Acland, Charles R. Swift Viewing: The Popular Life of Subliminal Influence. 2011. (ENG., Illus.). 328p. 89.95 ***(978-0-8223-4924-2(8))***; pap. 24.95 ***(978-0-8223-4919-8(1))*** Duke Univ. Pr.

Al-Senaidi, Aisha. Effectiveness & Contribution of Public Relations & Advertisements. 2010. 60p. pap. *(978-3-8383-6704-0(9))* Lambert Academic Publishing.

Alozie, Emmanuel C. Advertising in Developing & Emerging Countries: The Economic, Political & Social Context. 2011. (Illus.). 348p. 119.95 *(978-0-566-09174-2(7)*, Gower Publishing Co., Ltd.) Ashgate Publishing, Ltd. GBR. Dist: Ashgate Publishing Co.

Altenberger, Philipp. Word-Of-Mouth-Marketing: Fakten, Theorie & Praxis. 2010. 136p. pap. *(978-3-639-14478-9(3))* VDM Verlag Dr. Mueller e.K.

Altstiel, Tom & Grow, Jean. Advertising Creative: Strategy, Copy, & Design. 2nd ed. 2009. (Illus.). 368p. (C). pap. 79.00 *(978-1-4129-7491-2(7)*, B74912P) SAGE Pubns., Inc.

Applebooks, ed. Brand Vision 2008. 2008. 272p. pap. *(978-988-99550-3-8(2))* Actar Birkhauser Distribution.

Applegate, Edd & Johnsen, Art. Cases in Advertising & Marketing Management: Real Situations for Tomorrow's Managers. 2006. (ENG.). 232p. 96.00 *(978-0-7425-3835-1(4))*; per. 32.95 *(978-0-7425-3836-8(2))* Rowman & Littlefield Publishers, Inc.

Arens, William, et al. M: Advertising. 2011. (ENG., Illus.). 512p. (C). pap. 73.00 *(978-0-07-802891-5(4)*, 0078028914, McGraw-Hill/Irwin) McGraw-Hill Higher Education.

—M: Advertising with Connect Plus. 2011. (ENG.). (C). pap., pap. 109.00 *(978-0-07-748421-7(5)*, 0077484215, McGraw-Hill/Irwin) McGraw-Hill Higher Education.

Arens, William F. Contemporary Advertising. 9th ed. 2006. (ENG.). pap. 15.95 *(978-1-4288-1165-2(6))* Cram101 Inc.

—Contemporary Advertising. 10th rev. ed. 2007. 133.75 *(978-0-07-313569-4(0))* McGraw-Hill Cos., The.

Arens, William F., et al. Contemporary Advertising. 13th ed. 2010. (ENG., Illus.). 736p. (C). ring bd. 87.33 *(978-0-07-353003-1(4)*, 0073530034, McGraw-Hill/Irwin) McGraw-Hill Higher Education.

Armelini, Guillermo & Villanueva, Julian. Marketing Expenditures & Word-of-Mouth Communication: Complements or Substitutes?, Vol. 5. 2010. (ENG.). 60p. pap. 55.00 net. *(978-1-60198-380-0(8))* Now Pubs.

Armstrong, J. Scott. Persuasive Advertising: Evidence-Based Principles. 2010. (ENG., Illus.). 350p. 89.00 *(978-1-4039-1343-2(9))* Palgrave Macmillan.

Arnott, David C., ed. Fundamentals of Marketing Communications. 2013. (SAGE Library in Marketing Ser.). 1248p. 825.00 *(978-1-4129-4491-5(0)*, B44910C) SAGE Pubns., Ltd. GBR. Dist: SAGE Pubns., Inc.

Arri. The Secrets of How to Advertise in the Yellow Pages: Without the Walking Fingers Walking All over You. Mecham, Robert, ed. (Illus.). 125p. stu. ed. 29.95 *(978-0-9638138-0-0(3))* Ad Response Research, Inc.

Art Directors Club of Europe, creator. Best of European Design & Advertising: The Annual of Annuals. 2007. (Best of European Design & Advertising Ser.). (Illus.). 373p. *(978-84-611-3759-6(C))* Actar Birkhauser Distribution.

Baaghil, Said Aghil. The Power of Belonging: The Marketing Strategy for Branding. 2010. 152p. 25.95 *(978-1-4502-4578-4(1))*; pap. 15.95 *(978-1-4502-4576-0(5))* iUniverse, Inc.

Barnum, Diana. Map: Move Ahead Plan - A Complete Business Plan Kit with Marketing & Advertising Plans, Downloadable Templates & More. 2006. 132p. pap. 12.95 *(978-1-60145-087-6(7))* Booklocker.com, Inc.

Barry, Pete. Advertising Concept Book. 2nd ed. 2012. (ENG.). 288p. pap. 31.95 ***(978-0-500-29031-6(8)**, 529031)* Thames & Hudson.

Beard, Fred K. Humor in the Advertising Business: Theory, Practice, & Wit. 2007. (ENG., Illus.). 220p. per. 26.95 *(978-0-7425-5426-9(0))* Rowman & Littlefield Publishers, Inc.

Becker, Tilman. Werbung für Produkte mit einem Suchtgefährdungspotential: Tabak-, Alkohol- und Glücksspielwerbung aus rechtlicher, ökonomischer und psychologischer Sicht. 2010. (Schriftenreihe zur Glücksspielforschung Ser.). (GER.). 194p. 64.95 *(978-3-631-60430-4(0))* Lang, Peter GmbH, Europaischer Verlag der Wissenschaften DEU. Dist: Lang, Peter.

Beckwith, Harry. What Clients Love: A Field Guide to Growing Your Business. 2010. (ENG.). 304p. pap. 14.99 *(978-0-446-55602-6(5)*, Business Plus) Grand Central Publishing.

Belch, et al. Advertising & Promotion with ConnectPlus. 9th ed. 2011. (ENG.). (C). 239.00 ***(978-0-07-749985-3(9)**, 0077499859, McGraw-Hill/Irwin)* McGraw-Hill Higher Education.

Belch and, Belch. Advertising & Promotion. 2006. pap. 14.95 *(978-1-4288-0495-1(1))* Cram101 Inc.

Belch, George & Belch, Michael. Loose-Leaf Advertising & Promotion. 9th ed. 2011. (ENG.). (C). ring bd. 156.33 *(978-0-07-742796-2(3)*, 0077427963, McGraw-Hill/Irwin) McGraw-Hill Higher Education.

Belch, George E. & Belch, Michael A. Advertising & Promotion: An Integrated Marketing Communications Perspective. 9th ed. 2011. (ENG., Illus.). 864p. (C). 223.33 *(978-0-07-340486-8(1)*, 0073404861, McGraw-Hill/Irwin) McGraw-Hill Higher Education.

Berger, Arthur Asa. Ads, Fads, & Consumer Culture: Advertising's Impact on American Character & Society. 4th ed. 2011. (ENG.). 258p. 85.00 *(978-1-4422-0668-7(3))*; pap. 24.95 *(978-1-4422-0669-4(1))* Rowman & Littlefield Publishers, Inc.

Berman, Margo. Street-Smart Advertising: How to Win the Battle of the Buzz. 2006. (ENG., Illus.). 250p. pap. 29.95 *(978-0-7425-4137-5(1))* Rowman & Littlefield Publishers, Inc.

Bernardin, Tom & Tutssel, Mark. HumanKind. 2010. (Illus.). 256p. 29.95 *(978-1-57687-549-0(0)*, powerHouse Bks.) powerHouse Cultural Entertainment, Inc.

Bernstein, Jack. The Siege of Kut-al-Amara. 2009. 300p. reprint ed. 24.95 *(978-0-9616226-0-2(1)*, Tristan/Isolde Publishing) InterLingua.com, Inc.

Bird, Harry Lewis. This Fascinating Advertising Business. 2011. 436p. 56.95 ***(978-1-258-08312-0(4))*** Literary Licensing, LLC.

Blakeman, Robyn. Strategic Uses of Alternative Media: Just the Essentials. 2011. (ENG., Illus.). 272p. (C). 79.95 *(978-0-7656-2555-7(5))*; pap. 39.95 ***(978-0-7656-2556-4(3))*** Sharpe, M.E. Inc.

Boden, Jeanne. Mindmapping China: Language, Discourse & Advertising in China. 2010. (ENG & CHI., Illus.). 228p. pap. 35.95 *(978-90-5487-690-8(5))* VUB Univ. Pr. BEL. Dist: Independent Pubs. Group.

Boggs, John. Advice by John Boggs: Common Sense Stories of Local Advertising & Sales. 2009. 268p. pap. 21.95 *(978-1-4401-7523-7(3))* iUniverse, Inc.

Bogusky, Alex & Winsor, John. Baked In: Creating Products & Businesses That Market Themselves. 2010. (ENG.). 152p. pap. 15.00 *(978-1-932841-57-2(1))* Agate Publishing, Inc.

Briggs, Rex & Stuart, Greg. What Sticks: Why Most Advertising Fails & How to Guarantee Yours Succeeds. 2006. (ENG., Illus.). 304p. 25.00 *(978-1-4195-8433-6(2))* Kaplan Publishing.

Bronner, Kai, et al, eds. (((ABA))) Audio Branding Academy Yearbook 2009/2010. 2010. 142p. pap. 33.00 *(978-3-8329-5531-1(3))* Nomos Verlagsgesellschaft DEU. Dist: International Specialized Bk. Services.

Brown, Melissa T. Enlisting Masculinity: The Construction of Gender in US Military Recruiting Advertising During the All-Volunteer Force. 2012. (Oxford Studies in Gender & International Relations Ser.). (ENG.). 240p. 74.00 ***(978-0-19-984282-7(5))*** Oxford Univ. Pr., Inc.

Bruner, Mike. Signs of Our Past: Porcelain Enamel Advertising in America. 2008. (Illus.). 256p. bds. 59.99 *(978-0-7643-3042-1(X))* Schiffer Publishing, Ltd.

Burns, Neal M., et al. Handbook of Research on Digital Media & Advertising: User Generated Content Consumption. 2010. (Illus.). 550p. 265.00 *(978-1-60566-792-8(7))* IGI Global.

Burtenshaw, Ken, et al. The Fundamentals of Creative Advertising. 2007. (Fundamentals Ser.). (ENG., Illus.). 176p. pap. 36.95 *(978-2-940373-18-5(3))* AVA Publishing GBR. Dist: Ingram Pub. Services.

—The Fundamentals of Creative Advertising. 2nd rev. ed. 2011. (ENG., Illus.). 184p. (C). pap. 38.50 *(978-2-940411-56-6(5))* Ava Publishing SA CHE. Dist: Ingram Pub. Services.

Burton, Philip W. & Purvis, Scott C. Which Ad Pulled Best? Answer Key. 8th ed. pap. 3.95 *(978-0-8442-3316-1(1))* McGraw-Hill/Contemporary.

Butt, Mohsin & de Run, Ernest. Ethnic Advertising: Beyond Minority Groups. 2011. 388p. pap. ***(978-3-639-33989-5(4))*** VDM Verlag Dr. Mueller e.K.

Cai, Liping A., 1st, et al. Tourism Branding: Communities in Action. 2009. (Illus.). 261p. 124.95 *(978-1-84950-720-2(1))* Emerald Group Publishing Ltd. GBR. Dist: Turpin Distribution Services Ltd.

Cakim, Idil M. Implementing Word of Mouth Marketing: Online Strategies to Identify Influencers, Craft Stories, & Draw Customers. 2010. (ENG., Illus.). 224p. 39.95 *(978-0-470-44255-5(7)*, Wiley) Wiley, John & Sons, Inc.

Calder, Bobby J., ed. Kellogg on Advertising & Media: The Kellogg School of Management. 2008. (ENG., Illus.). 304p. 29.95 *(978-0-470-11986-0(1)*, Wiley) Wiley, John & Sons, Inc.

Calkins, Earnest Elmo & Holden, Ralph. Modern Advertising. 2008. 384p. 48.95 *(978-1-4372-6062-5(4))*; pap. 33.95 *(978-1-4371-3373-8(8))* Kessinger Publishing, LLC.

Carozzi, Barry. I'm Sold! 2007. 32p. pap. 10.95 *(978-0-86431-566-3(X))* ACER Pr. AUS. Dist: International Specialized Bk. Services.

Ch. Communication & Knowledge Transfer: Theories & Cases in Journalism, Public Relations & Advertising. 2011. 65.00 *(978-981-4271-02-8(0))* World Scientific Publishing Co., Inc.

Chang, Kara & Cheng, Hong, eds. Advertising & Chinese Society: Impacts & Issues. 2009. (Illus.). 315p. pap. 63.00 *(978-87-630-0227-1(2))* Copenhagen Business Schl. Pr. DNK. Dist: International Specialized Bk. Services.

Chauhan, Gajendra Singh. Language, Media, & Society: Essence of Advertising Communication. 2010. (Illus.). 268p. 30.00 *(978-81-316-0310-9(5))* Rawat Pubns. IND. Dist: International Specialized Bk. Services.

Ciarlo, David. Advertising Empire: Race & Visual Culture in Imperial Germany. 2011. (Harvard Historical Studies: 171). (ENG., Illus.). 462p. 49.95 *(978-0-674-05006-8(1))* Harvard Univ. Pr.

Ciochetto, Lynne. Globalisation & Advertising in Emerging Economies: Brazil, Russia, India & China. 2011. (Routledge Studies in International Business & the World Economy Ser.). (ENG., Illus.). 200p. (C). 145.00 *(978-0-415-56200-3(7))* Routledge.

Clark, Eric. The Want Makers: Inside the World of Advertising: How They Make You Buy. 2011. 416p. pap. 25.95 ***(978-1-4502-3139-8(X))*** iUniverse, Inc.

Clow and, Baack. Integrated Advertising Promotion & Mar. 2006. pap. 13.95 *(978-1-4288-0759-4(4))* Cram101 Inc.

Clow, Kenneth E. & Baack, Donald. Integrated Advertising, Promotion, & Marketing Communications. 5th rev. ed. 2010. (ENG.). 464p. (C). 180.00 *(978-0-13-253896-1(2)*, Prentice Hall) Prentice Hall PTR.

Clow, Kenneth E. & Baack, Donald E. IMC Plan Pro Handbook for Integrated Advertising, Promotion & Marketing Communications. 4th ed. 2008. (ENG.). 200p. (C). pap. 73.33 *(978-0-13-715416-6(X)*, Prentice Hall) Prentice Hall PTR.

Conrad, Diane. Ads That Talk Back. 2010. 172p. pap. *(978-3-8383-7922-7(5))* Lambert Academic Publishing.

Cook, Guy. The Language of Advertising. 2007. *(978-0-415-41219-3(6))*; *(978-0-415-41218-6(8))*; *(978-0-415-41216-2(1))*; *(978-0-415-41217-9(X))* Routledge.

Cook, Guy, ed. The Language of Advertising, 4 vols., Set. 2007. 1656p. 1315.00 *(978-0-415-41215-5(3))* Routledge.

Cortese, Anthony J. Provocateur: Images of Women & Minorities in Advertising. 3rd ed. 2007. (ENG., Illus.). 192p. per. 24.95 *(978-0-7425-5539-6(9))* Rowman & Littlefield Publishers, Inc.

Cram101 Textbook Reviews. Outlines & Highlights for Advertising & Imc by Sandra E Moriarty, Isbn: 9780132163644. 2011. 230p. pap. 31.95 ***(978-1-61812-132-5(4))*** Cram101 Inc.

—Outlines & Highlights for Advertising Strategy: Creative Tactics from the Outside/in by Tom Altstiel, ISBN. 2011. 124p. pap. 28.95 ***(978-1-61812-133-2(2))*** Cram101 Inc.

Cram101 Textbook Reviews & Cram101 Textbook Reviews. Outlines & Highlights for Ads, Fads, & Consumer Culture: Advertisings Impact on American Character & Society by Arthur Berger, ISBN. 2011. 82p. pap. 27.95 ***(978-1-61461-677-1(9))*** Cram101 Inc.

—Outlines & Highlights for Advertising & Integrated Brand Promotion by Thomas Oguinn, Isbn: 9780538473323. 2011. 228p. pap. 31.95 ***(978-1-61461-152-3(1))*** Cram101 Inc.

—Outlines & Highlights for Advertising & Promotion: An Integrated Marketing Communications Perspective by George Belch. 2011. 210p. pap. 30.95 ***(978-1-61830-356-1(2))*** Cram101 Inc.

—Outlines & Highlights for Advertising by Design: Generating & Designing Creative Ideas Across Media by Robin Landa, ISBN. 2011. 58p. pap. 26.95 ***(978-1-61461-378-7(8))*** Cram101 Inc.

—Outlines & Highlights for Digital Signage Broadcasting: Broadcasting, Content Management, & Distribution Techniques by Lars-Ingemar Lundstrom, ISBN. 2011. 118p. pap. 28.95 ***(978-1-61461-365-7(6))*** Cram101 Inc.

—Outlines & Highlights for Practice of Advertising by Adrian MacKay. 2011. 78p. pap. 27.95 ***(978-1-61830-163-5(2))*** Cram101 Inc.

—Outlines & Highlights for the Interplay of Influence: News, Advertising, Politics & the Internet by Karlyn Kohrs Campbell, ISBN. 2011. 146p. pap. 29.95 ***(978-1-61461-552-1(7))*** Cram101 Inc.

Cram101 Textbook Reviews Staff. Outlines & Highlights for Advertising & Promotion: An Integrated Marketing Communications Perspective by Belch, ISBN. 2009. 176p. pap. 25.95 *(978-1-4288-6710-9(4))* 2008. 216p. pap. 13.95 *(978-1-4288-6269-2(2))* Cram101 Inc.

—Outlines & Highlights for Contemporary Advertising by Arens Isbn: 9780073381077. 2009. 220p. pap. 26.95 *(978-1-4288-6707-9(4))* Cram101 Inc.

—Outlines & Highlights for Contemporary Advertising by Arens Isbn: 9780073529912. 2008. 240p. pap. 14.95 *(978-1-4288-6271-5(4))* Cram101 Inc.

—Outlines & Highlights for Controversies in Contemporary Advertising by Kim Bartel Sheehan, Isbn: 9780761926351. 2009. 98p. pap. 27.95 *(978-1-4288-3911-3(9))* Cram101 Inc.

—Outlines & Highlights for Essentials of Contemporary Advertising by Arens & Schaefer, Isbn: 9780073136660. 2009. 258p. pap. 31.95 *(978-1-4288-3847-5(3))* Cram101 Inc.

—Outlines & Highlights for Essentials of Contemporary Advertising by Arens Isbn: 9780073380971. 2008. 168p. pap. 12.95 *(978-1-4288-6461-0(X))* Cram101 Inc.

—Outlines & Highlights for Hospitality & Tourism Marketing by William Lazer, Isbn: 9780866122696. 2009. 80p. pap. 27.95 *(978-1-4288-4044-7(3))* Cram101 Inc.

—Outlines & Highlights for Integrated Advertising, Promotion & Marketing Communications by Kenneth E Clow, Isbn: 9780136079422. 2009. 134p. pap. 28.95 *(978-1-4288-4014-0(1))* Cram101 Inc.

Crane-Freeman, Leigh. The Truth in Advertising: Produce Simple, Honest, Effective Advertising. 2009. 128p. pap. 11.95 *(978-1-4327-3463-3(6))* Outskirts Pr., Inc.

Cuno, Steve. Prove It Before You Promote It: How to Take the Guesswork Out of Marketing. 2008. (ENG.). 256p. 24.95 *(978-0-470-38118-2(3)*, Wiley) Wiley, John & Sons, Inc.

Cyril De Run, Ernest. Targeted Advertising Unintended Effects. 2008. 132p. pap. *(978-3-639-06100-0(4))* VDM Verlag Dr. Mueller e.K.

Dade, Penny. Drink Talking: 100 years of alcohol Advertising. 2008. (Popular Culture Ser.). 132p. pap. 23.00 *(978-1-904750-40-6(0))* Libri Publishing Ltd GBR. Dist: Independent Pubs. Group.

Dahl, Gary. Advertising for Dummies. 2nd rev. ed. 2007. (ENG., Illus.). 336p. per. 21.99 *(978-0-470-04583-1(3)*, For Dummies) Wiley, John & Sons, Inc.

Danesi, Marcel. Why It Sells: Decoding the Meanings of Brand Names, Logos, Ads, & Other Marketing & Advertising Ploys. 2007. (R&L Series in Mass Communication Ser.). (ENG.). 220p. 84.00 *(978-0-7425-5544-0(5))*; per. 29.95 *(978-0-7425-5545-7(3))* Rowman & Littlefield Publishers, Inc.

Davila-Montes, Jose M. La traduccion de la persuasion Publicitaria. 2009. (SPA.). *(978-0-7734-4914-5(0))* Mellen, Edwin Pr., The.

Davis, Martyn P. Successful Advertising: Key Alternative Approaches. (Illus.). 160p. pap. *(978-0-304-70097-4(5)*, Burns & Oates) Continuum International Publishing Group, Ltd.

de Grazia, Victoria, et al, eds. Selling Modernity: Advertising in Twentieth-Century Germany. 2007. (ENG., Illus.). 384p. (C). 94.95 *(978-0-8223-4047-8(X))* Duke Univ. Pr.

De Mooij, Marieke K. Global Marketing & Advertising: Understanding Cultural Paradoxes. 3rd ed. 2009. (Illus.). 344p. (C). pap. 65.00 *(978-1-4129-7041-9(5)* B70419P) SAGE Pubns., Inc.

Deland, Lorin F. Imagination in Business. 2007. (ENG.). 112p. 34.95 *(978-0-548-15157-0(1))*; 116p. per. 19.95 *(978-1-4304-4505-0(X))* Kessinger Publishing, LLC.

Dervak, Diana. Wait Marketing: Communicate at the Right Moment at the Right Place. 2007. per. *(978-90-811840-1-4(6))* Salt City Books.

Diamond, Jay. Retail Advertising & Promotion. 2011. (Illus.). 448p. pap. ***(978-1-56367-898-1(5))*** Fairchild Bks.

Dickinson, Don. The New Account Manager. 2nd ed. 2009. (ENG.). 488p. pap. 47.50 net. *(978-1-887229-37-1(X))* Copy Workshop, The.

Dooley, Roger. Brainfluence: 100 Ways to Persuade & Convince Consumers with Neuromarketing. 2011. (ENG.). 286p. 24.95 ***(978-1-118-11336-3(5)**, Wiley)* Wiley, John & Sons, Inc.

Eckberg, John. Have a Crumby: A Collection of Wit & Whimsy from Cincinnati's Favorite Bakery. 2007. (ENG., Illus.). 160p. pap. 17.95 *(978-1-57860-306-0(4))* Clerisy Pr.

Effertz, Tobias. Kindermarketing: Analyse und rechtliche Empfehlungen. 2008. (Schriftenreihe Ökonomische Analyse des Rechts. Law & Economics Ser.). 596p. pap. 124.95 *(978-3-631-57849-0(0))* Lang, Peter GmbH, Europaischer Verlag der Wissenschaften DEU. Dist: Lang, Peter.

Egelhoff, Tom C. How to Market, Advertise, & Promote Your Business or Service in Your Own Backyard. 2008. (ENG.). 272p. pap. 19.95 *(978-0-470-25821-7(7)*, Wiley) Wiley, John & Sons, Inc.

Ehrlich, David A., et al. Smokey, Rosie & You! The History & Practice of Marketing Public Programs. 2007. per. 17.95 *(978-1-934248-33-1(9))* Mill City Pr., Inc.

Espejo, Roman. Advertising. 2010. (Opposing Viewpoints Ser.). (Illus.). 240p. (J). 38.50 *(978-0-7377-4751-5(X))*; pap. 26.75 *(978-0-7377-4752-2(8))* Cengage Gale. (Greenhaven Pr., Inc.).

Espenhahn, Cornelia. Virales Marketing: Wirkungsstrategien zwischen sozialen Netzwerken und einzelnem Konsument. 2010. 132p. pap. *(978-3-639-25156-2(3))* VDM Verlag Dr. Mueller e.K.

Evans, W. Douglas & Hastings, Gerard. Public Health Branding: Applying Marketing for Social Change. Evans, W. Douglas & Hastings, Gerard, eds. 2008. (ENG., Illus.). 310p. pap. 69.95 *(978-0-19-923713-5(1))* Oxford Univ. Pr., Inc.

Facts On File, Inc. Advertising & Marketing. 2011. (Discovering Careers Ser.). 24.95 *(978-0-8160-8061-8(5)*, Ferguson Publishing Co.) Facts On File, Inc.

Falberg, Bill, ed. United States Multiple Advertising & Discount Postal Cards: A Handbook Originally in 1982 by David G. Nussmann, Charles A. Fricke & George S. Norton. 2007. (Illus.). 180p. *(978-0-9300112-0-3(5))* United Postal Stationery Society.

Faulconbridge, James, et al. The Globalization of Advertising: Agencies, Cities & Spaces of Creativity. 2011. (Routledge Studies in Human Geography Ser.). (ENG., Illus.). 208p. (C). 140.00 *(978-0-415-56716-9(5))* Routledge.

Fearn-Banks, Kathleen. Crisis Communication: A Casebook Approach. 3rd rev. ed. 2007. (Routledge Communication Ser.). (ENG., Illus.). 136p. stu. ed., per., wbk. ed. 31.95 *(978-0-8058-6257-7(9))* Routledge.

—Crisis Communications. 3rd ed. 2007. pap. 1.00 *(978-0-8058-6256-0(0))* Erlbaum, Lawrence Assocs., Inc.

—Crisis Communications. 4th rev. ed. 2010. (Routledge Communication Ser.). (ENG., Illus.). 400p. 120.00 *(978-0-415-88058-5(0))*; pap. 64.95 *(978-0-415-88059-6(9))* Routledge.

Fearon Staff. Be Ad Wise. 64p. pap. *(978-0-8224-4653-8(7))* Globe Fearon Educational Publishing.

Fernina, Jerry Della. From Those Wonderful Folks Who Gave You Pearl Harbor: Front-Line Dispatches from the Advertising War. 2010. (ENG.). 288p. pap. 14.00 *(978-1-4516-0990-5(6))* Simon & Schuster.

Fennis. The Psychology of Advertising. 2010. (ENG., Illus.). 344p. 62.95 *(978-0-415-44273-2(7)*, Psychology Press) Taylor & Francis Group GBR. Dist: Taylor & Francis Group.

Fields, Jill. An Intimate Affair: Women, Lingerie, & Sexuality. 2007. (Illus.). 382p. 60.00 *(978-0-520-22369-1(1))*; 375p. per. 28.95 *(978-0-520-25261-5(6))* Univ. of California Pr.

Finskud, Lars. Developing Winning Brand Strategies. 2009. (Illus.). 104p. pap. ***(978-1-60649-043-3(5))*** Business Expert Pr.

First, Anat. America in Jerusalem: Globalization, National Identity, & Israeli Advertising. 2009. (ENG.). 156p. 62.99 *(978-0-7391-3325-5(X))* Lexington Bks.

Fletcher, Winston. Advertising: A Very Short Introduction. 2010. (Very Short Introductions Ser.). (ENG., Illus.). 144p. pap. 11.95 *(978-0-19-956892-5(8))* Oxford Univ. Pr., Inc.

—Powers of Persuasion: The Inside Story of British Advertising. 2008. (ENG., Illus.). 304p. 35.00 *(978-0-19-922801-0(9))* Oxford Univ. Pr., Inc.

Flores, Carlos. Exito Total Mercadotecnia Evolutiva. 2010. 280p. pap. *(978-1-4507-4066-1(9))* Independent Pub.

For Know-It-Alls Staff. Advertising for Know-It-Alls. 2008. pap. 9.99 *(978-1-59986-209-5(3)*, For Know-It-Alls) Filiquarian Publishing, LLC.

—Billboard Advertising for Know-It-Alls. 2008. pap. 9.99 *(978-1-59986-221-7(2)*, For Know-It-Alls) Filiquarian Publishing, LLC.

Forsyth, Patrick. Empty When Half Full: A cantankerous consumer's compilation of mistakes, misprints & Misinformation. 2011. (ENG.). 180p. pap. ***(978-1-907498-78-7(8))*** Lean Marketing Pr.

Foster, Jack. How to Get Ideas. 2nd rev. ed. 2007. (BK Life Ser.). (ENG., Illus.). 214p. pap. 20.95 *(978-1-57675-430-6(8))* Berrett-Koehler Pubs., Inc.

Freitas, Elsa Simoes Lucas. Taboo in Advertising. 2008. (Pragmatics & Beyond New Ser.: Vol. 179). (Illus.). 210p. (C). 143.00 *(978-90-272-5423-8(0))* Benjamins, John Publishing Co.

Frith, Katherine Toland & Mueller, Barbara. Advertising & Societies: Global Issues. 2nd ed. 2010. 280p. (C). pap. 49.95 *(978-1-4331-0385-8(0))* Lang, Peter Publishing, Inc.

Frost, Malcolm, et al. Street Talk: The Rise & Fall of the Poster. 2006. (ENG., Illus.). 224p. 55.00 *(978-1-86470-123-4(4)*, Images Publishing Dist Ac) Antique Collectors' Club GBR. Dist: National Bk. Network.

Fueroghne, Dean. Always Leave Room for the Mouse. 2007. 292p. pap. 34.95 *(978-0-615-15125-0(6))* Yellow Cat Pr.

Gautam, Harish & SINGH, Gurmeet. Consumer Attitude Towards TV & Web Advertising. 2010. 184p. pap. *(978-3-8383-7151-1(8))* Lambert Academic Publishing.

Glazer, Bill. Outrageous Advertising That's Outrageously Successful: Created for the 99% of Small Business Owners Who are Dissatisfied with the Results They Get from Their Current Advertising. 2009. (ENG.). 344p. 19.95 *(978-0-9823793-1-8(5))* Morgan James Publishing.

Goldberg, Scott. An Overview of Buying Habits of America's Growing Demographic Segment. 2010. 168p. pap. *(978-3-8383-4272-6(0))* Lambert Academic Publishing.

Goldenberg, Jacob, et al. Cracking the Ad Code. 2009. (ENG., Illus.). 178p. 90.00 *(978-0-521-85905-9(0))*; pap. 51.00 *(978-0-521-67597-0(9))* Cambridge Univ. Pr.

Goodman, Walter. The Clowns of Commerce: An Irreverent Investigation into the Motives & Morals of the Professional Persuaders. 2011. 278p. 47.95 ***(978-1-258-04744-3(6))*** Literary Licensing, LLC.

Gospe, Mike. Marketing Campaign Development: What Marketing Executives Need to Know about Architecting Global Integrated Marketing Campaigns. 2008. 176p. per. 24.95 *(978-1-60005-077-0(8))* Happy About.

Grafton, Carol Belanger. 60 Great Bicycle Posters Platinum DVD & Book. 2012. (Dover Electronic Clip Art Ser.). (ENG., Illus.). 48p. pap. 19.95 *(978-0-486-99172-6(5))* Dover Pubns., Inc.

Grafton, Carol Belanger & Clip Art Staff. The Art of Snake Oil & Quackery CD-ROM & Book. 2012. (Dover Electronic Clip Art Ser.). (ENG., Illus.). 48p. pap. 19.95 *(978-0-486-99157-3(1))* Dover Pubns., Inc.

Graphis Inc., compiled by. Branding USA No. 3. 2009. (Illus.). 408p. 60.00 *(978-1-932026-36-8(3))* Graphis, U.S., Inc.

Graphis Inc. Staff. Branding USA No. 2, Vol. 2. 2008. (Illus.). 320p. 50.00 *(978-1-932026-06-1(1))* Graphis, U.S., Inc.

Griffin, Patrick & Flynn, Kevin. Pay No Attention to that Man Behind the Curtain: How Technology has made Traditional Advertising Obsolete. 2010. 212p. 28.95 *(978-1-4502-1949-5(7))*; pap. 18.95 *(978-1-4502-1947-1(0))* iUniverse, Inc.

Griffin, W. Glenn & Morrison, Deborah. The Creative Process Illustrated: How Advertising's Big Ideas Are Born. 2010. (ENG., Illus.). 176p. pap. 25.00 *(978-1-60061-960-1(6)*, HOW Bks.) F&W Media, Inc.

Griffiths, Andrew. 101 Ways to Advertise Your Business: Building a Successful Business with Smart Advertising. 2nd ed. 2006. (101 ... Ser.). (ENG.). 256p. mass mkt. 22.95 ***(978-1-74175-007-2(5))*** Allen & Unwin AUS. Dist: Independent Pubs. Group.

Gründ, Harald. The Death of Fashion: The Passage Rite of Fashion in the Show Window. 2007. (Illus.). 299p. *(978-3-211-49854-5(0)*, 3211498540) Actar Birkhauser Distribution.

Guertin, Bill & Corbus, Andrew. Reality Sells: How to Bring Customers Back Again & Again by Marketing Your Genuine Story. 2007. 129p. 19.95 *(978-0-8329-5008-7(4)*, WBusiness Bks.) New Win Publishing.

Guitton, Pedro. Packaging Identity, 1 vol. 2009. (ENG.). 354p. 17.95 *(978-84-92643-28-8(5))* Index Bks., Spain ESP. Dist: Innovative Logistics.

Gumas, John. Marketing Smart. 2010. 280p. pap. 19.95 *(978-0-557-42700-0(2))* Lulu Enterprises Inc.

Gunter, Barrie, et al. Alcohol Advertising & Young People's Drinking: Representation, Reception & Regulation. 2010. (ENG., Illus.). 248p. 89.00 *(978-0-230-23753-7(3))* Palgrave Macmillan.

Gupta, Seema. Branding & Advertising. 2009. 312p. pap. 29.50 *(978-81-907941-1-4(6))* M. D. Pubns. Pvt, Ltd. IND. Dist: Coronet Bks.

Hackley, Chris. Advertising & Promotion: An Integrated Marketing Communications Approach. 2nd ed. 2010. (Illus.). 360p. (C). 146.00 *(978-1-84920-145-2(5)*, B01452C); pap. 62.00 *(978-1-84920-146-9(3)*, B01452P) SAGE Pubns., Ltd. GBR. Dist: SAGE Pubns., Inc.

Hackley, Chris, ed. Advertising, 3 vols. 2009. (SAGE Library in Marketing Ser.). (Illus.). 1312p. 825.00 *(978-1-4129-3429-9(X)*, B3429XC) SAGE Pubns., Ltd. GBR. Dist: SAGE Pubns., Inc.

Hadland, Adrian, et al. Advertising in the News: Paid-for Content & the South African Print Media. 2008. (ENG., Illus.). 76p. pap. 16.95 *(978-0-7969-2183-3(0))* Human Sciences Research Council ZAF. Dist: Independent Pubs. Group.

Hallward, John. Gimme! the Human Nature of Successful Marketing. 2007. (ENG., Illus.). 240p. 24.95 *(978-0-470-10029-5(X)*, Wiley) Wiley, John & Sons, Inc.

Hancock, Joseph. Brand/Story: Ralph, Vera, Johnny, Billy, & Other Adventures in Fashion Branding. 2009. pap. 82.00 *(978-1-56367-623-9(0))* Fairchild Bks.

Hansen. Emotions, Advertising & Consumer Choice. 2007. 462p. pap. 80.00 *(978-87-630-0198-4(5))* Copenhagen Business Schl. Pr. DNK. Dist: International Specialized Bk. Services.

Hardie, Jamie. Get Noticed: A How-To Guide to Spectacular Advertising. 2006. (Illus.). 104p. per. 17.35 *(978-1-4251-0644-7(7))* Trafford Publishing.

Hardy, Jonathan, et al. The Advertising Handbook. 3rd rev. ed. 2009. (Media Practice Ser.). (ENG., Illus.). 264p. (C). 45.95 *(978-0-415-42311-3(2))*; 130.00 *(978-0-415-42312-0(0))* Routledge.

Harris, Godfrey. Word of Mouth Advertising in the Real World: How to Stimulate Customer Comments in the 21st Century. 2011. *(978-0-935047-67-7(0))* Americas Group, The.

Hasen, Jeff. Mobilize Marketing: How to Drive Sales, Engagement, & Loyalty Through Mobile Devices. 2012. (ENG.). 224p. 24.95 ***(978-1-118-24326-8(9)***, Wiley) Wiley, John & Sons, Inc.

Hatch, Steve & Taylor, Jim. Rigorous Magic: Communication Ideas & Their Application. 2007. (ENG., Illus.). 304p. 49.95 *(978-0-470-02601-4(4)*, Wiley) Wiley, John & Sons, Inc.

Haugen, David M. How Does Advertising Impact Teen Behavior? 2008. (At Issue Ser.). (ENG., Illus.). 88p. (YA). (gr. 10-12). 22.50 *(978-0-7377-3923-7(1)*, Greenhaven Pr., Inc.) Cengage Gale.

Haugtvedt, Curtis P., et al. Handbook of Consumer Psychology. Haugtvedt, Curtis P. et al, eds. 2008. (Marketing & Consumer Psychology Ser.). (ENG., Illus.). 1290p. 115.95 *(978-0-8058-5603-3(X)*, Psychology Press) Taylor & Francis Group GBR. Dist: Taylor & Francis Group.

Hegarty, John. Hegarty on Advertising: Turning Intelligence into Magic. 2011. (ENG., Illus.). 224p. 29.95 *(978-0-500-51556-3(5)*, 551556) Thames & Hudson.

Heimann, Jim, ed. 50s Fashion: Vintage Fashion & Beauty Ads. 2007. (FRE, GER & ENG., Illus.). 192p. per. 9.99 *(978-3-8228-4933-0(2))* TASCHEN DEU. Dist: Ingram Pub. Services.

Heindler, Maria. Male Consumer Behaviour- a Gender Perspective on Advertising Response & Information Processing. 2007. (Illus.). 220p. per. *(978-3-8364-2162-1(3))* VDM Verlag Dr. Mueller e.K.

Held, Gudrun & Bendel, Sylvia, eds. Werbung - Grenzenlos: Multimodale Werbetexte im interkulturellen Vergleich. 2008. (Sprache im Kontext Ser.). (GER., Illus.). 252p. pap. 65.95 *(978-3-631-56621-3(2))* Lang, Peter GmbH, Europaischer Verlag der Wissenschaften DEU. Dist: Lang, Peter.

Hendrickson, Richard H. & Kaminski, Edward S. Billboard Refrigerator Cars. 2008. (Illus.). 224p. ***(978-1-930013-22-3(1))*** Signature Pr.

Heyman, Jay H. All You Need Is a Good Idea! How to Create Marketing Messages That Actually Get Results. 2008. (ENG.). 272p. 24.95 *(978-0-470-23791-5(0)*, Wiley) Wiley, John & Sons, Inc.

Hill, Laura, ed. Coolbrands 2011/12. 2011. (Illus.). 150p. 115.00 ***(978-0-9565334-2-5(6))*** Superbrands (UK), Ltd. GBR. Dist: Trans-Atlantic Pubns., Inc.

Himpe, Tom. Advertising Is Dead: Long Live Advertising! 2006. (Illus.). 224p. 60.00 *(978-0-500-51314-9(7))* Thames & Hudson.

—Advertising Is Dead Long Live Advertising: Long Live Advertising! 2008. (ENG., Illus.). 224p. pap. 34.95 *(978-0-500-28687-6(6))* Thames & Hudson.

—Advertising Next: 150 Winning Campaigns for the New Communications Age. 2008. (ENG.). 400p. 60.00 *(978-0-8118-6539-5(8))* Chronicle Bks. LLC.

Hoffman, Bob. The Ad Contrarian: Getting Beyond the Fleeting Trends, False Goals, & Dreadful Jargon of Contemporary Advertising. 2nd ed. 2008. (ENG.). 65p. pap. *(978-0-9796885-1-5(5))* Hoffman/Lewis.

Holdren, Anastasia. Google Adwords: Setting Your Account up for Success. 2011. (ENG.). 194p. pap. 29.99 ***(978-1-4493-0838-4(4))*** O'Reilly Media, Inc.

Hollis, Tim. Selling the Sunshine State: A Celebration of Florida Tourism Advertising. 2008. (ENG., Illus.). 288p. 34.95 *(978-0-8130-3266-5(0))* Univ. Pr. of Florida.

Hopkins, Claude. Scientific Advertising: Crushing Your Compitition Like Ants on the Sidewalk. 2011. 154p. pap. 14.99 ***(978-0-9842827-0-8(X))*** Anderson-Noble Publishing.

Hopkins, Claude C. Scientific Advertising. 2007. (ENG.). 108p. 19.99 *(978-1-59986-724-3(9))*; 100p. pap. 9.99 *(978-1-59986-916-2(0)*, FQ Classics) Filiquarian Publishing, LLC.

—Scientific Advertising: Complete & Unabridged. 2010. 70p. pap. 8.49 *(978-1-60459-965-7(0))* Wilder Pubns., Ltd.

Horn, Sam. Pop! Create the Perfect Pitch, Title, & Tagline for Anything. 2009. (ENG.). 256p. (gr. 12-18). 16.00 *(978-0-399-53361-7(3)*, Perigee Trade) Penguin Group (USA) Inc.

Hovland, Roxanne, et al, eds. Readings in Advertising, Society, & Consumer Culture. 2007. (ENG.). 440p. per. 65.95 *(978-0-7656-1545-9(2))* Sharpe, M.E. Inc.

Hovland, Roxanne & Wolburg, Joyce. Advertising, Society, & Consumer Culture. 2010. (ENG.). 206p. (C). 89.95 *(978-0-7656-1546-6(0))* Sharpe, M.E. Inc.

Hovland, Roxanne & Wolburg, Joyce M. Advertising, Society, & Consumer Culture. 2010. (ENG., Illus.). 206p. (C). pap. 44.95 *(978-0-7656-1547-3(9))* Sharpe, M.E. Inc.

Hoxie, Mark. 90 Days to Success Marketing & Advertising Your Small Business. 2010. (ENG.). 224p. pap. 19.99 *(978-1-4354-5828-4(1))* Course Technology.

Hurley, Dan. Natural Causes: Death, Lies & Politics in America's Vitamin & Herbal Supplement Industry. 2007. (ENG.). 336p. pap. 19.00 *(978-0-7679-2043-8(0)*, Broadway) Broadway Bks.

Ihlenfeld, Dave. Dog Days: A Year in the Oscar Mayer Weinermobile. 2011. (ENG., Illus.). 232p. pap. 14.95 *(978-1-4027-7610-6(1))* Union Square Pr.

Ihlenfeld, Dave. Dog Days: A Year in the Oscar Mayer Wienermobile. 2011. (ENG., Illus.). 232p. pap. 14.95 ***(978-1-4027-9803-0(2))*** Sterling Publishing Co., Inc.

Jantsch, John. The Referral Engine: Teaching Your Business to Market Itself. 2010. (ENG.). 256p. (gr. 12). 25.95 *(978-1-59184-311-5(1)*, Portfolio (Hardcover)) Penguin Group (USA) Inc.

Jethwaney, Jaishri & Jain, Shruti. Advertising Management. 2nd ed. 2012. (ENG., Illus.). 684p. 35.00 ***(978-0-19-807412-0(3))*** Oxford Univ. Pr., Inc.

Jhally, Sut. The Spectacle of Accumulation: Essays in Culture, Media, & Politics. 2006. 320p. (C). pap. 32.95 *(978-0-8204-7904-0(7))* Lang, Peter Publishing, Inc.

Joachim, Jean C. 151 Quick Ideas for Advertising on a Shoestring. 2008. (151 Quick Ideas Ser.). (ENG.). 1p. per. 12.99 *(978-1-56414-982-4(X))* Career Pr., Inc.

Johnson, Jacqueline. Classic Perfume Advertising: 1920-1970. 2007. (Illus.). 192p. pap. 39.95 *(978-0-7643-2741-4(0))* Schiffer Publishing, Ltd.

Johnson, Jeffrey K. American Advertising in Poland: A Study of Cultural Interactions since 1990. 2008. (ENG.). 244p. pap. 45.00 *(978-0-7864-3797-9(9))* McFarland & Co., Inc. Pubs.

Jones, John Philip. When Ads Work: New Proof That Advertising Triggers Sales. 2nd ed. 2007. (Illus.). 232p. 94.95 *(978-0-7656-1738-5(2))*; pap. 42.95 *(978-0-7656-1739-2(0))* Sharpe, M.E. Inc.

Jones, Paul L. Public Service Announcement Campaigns: Activities & Financial Obligations for Seven Federal Departments. 2006. (Illus.). 68p. (C). pap. 25.00 *(978-1-4223-0581-2(3))* DIANE Publishing Co.

Jugenheimer, Donald W. & Kelley, Larry D. Advertising Management. 2009. (ENG., Illus.). 232p. (C). pap. 65.95 *(978-0-7656-2260-0(2))* Sharpe, M.E. Inc.

Kalmane, Ms Ruta. Advertising: using words as tools for Selling. 2010. (ENG.). 103p. pap. 52.50 *(978-1-4457-1431-8(0))* Lulu Enterprises Inc.

Kaufmann, Maria. Werbung als Orientierungsfaktor im medialen Programm: Der Einfluss von Webvertising auf die Wahrnehmung und Bewertung der politischen Berichterstattung im Internet. 2009. 176p. pap. *(978-3-639-13496-4(6))* VDM Verlag Dr. Mueller e.K.

Kaynak, Erdener & Alozie, Emmanuel. Advertising & Emerging Societies in A Technological & Global Economy: A Cultura: A Cultura. 2009. (Routledge Studies in International Business & the World Economy Ser.). (ENG., Illus.). 144p. 125.00 *(978-0-7890-0141-2(1))* Routledge.

Keller, Ed & Fay, Brad. Face-to-Face Book: Why Real Relationships Rule in a Digital Marketplace. 2012. (ENG., Illus.). 304p. 26.00 ***(978-1-4516-4006-9(4)***, Free Pr.) Free Pr.

Kelley, Larry D. & Jugenheimer, Donald W. Advertising Account Planning: Planning & Managing an IMC Campaign. 2nd rev. ed. 2010. (ENG., Illus.). 226p. (C). pap. 46.95 *(978-0-7656-2564-9(4))* Sharpe, M.E. Inc.

—Advertising Media Planning: A Brand Management Approach. 2nd rev. ed. 2008. (Illus.). 188p. 89.95 *(978-0-7656-2032-3(4))*; per. 39.95 *(978-0-7656-2033-0(2))* Sharpe, M.E. Inc.

—Cases in Advertising Management. 2009. (ENG., Illus.). 144p. pap. 43.95 *(978-0-7656-2261-7(0))* Sharpe, M.E. Inc.

Kelly, J. Steven, ed. The IMC Handbook Reading & Cases in Integrated Marketing Communications: 2nd Edition. 2011. 510p. pap. 49.95 ***(978-1-933199-34-4(2))*** Racom Communications.

Kelly, John. Railroad Freight Car Slogans & Heralds. 2011. (ENG., Illus.). 128p. pap. 32.95 *(978-1-58388-276-4(6)*, 1583882766) Iconografix, Inc.

Kelsen, Keith. Unleashing the Power of Digital Signage: Content Strategies for the 5th Screen. 2010. (ENG., Illus.). 264p. pap. 46.95 *(978-0-240-81302-8(2)*, Focal Pr.) Elsevier Science & Technology Bks.

Key Porter Books Staff. His! Men's Underwear in the Classic Age of Advertising. (Illus.). 31p. pap. 12.00 *(978-1-85375-442-5(0))* Prion GBR. Dist: Trafalgar Square Publishing.

Kirkpatrick, Jerry. In Defense of Advertising: Arguments from Reason, Ethical Egoism, & Laissez-Faire Capitalism. 2nd ed. 2007. 200p. reprint ed. pap. 16.95 *(978-0-9787803-0-2(2))* TLJ Bks.

Klassen, Michael L., et al. Ad'Mat: Using 25 Classic Advertising Formats. rev. ed. 2011. (ENG.). 78p. pap. 57.60 *(978-0-7575-6568-7(9))* Kendall Hunt Publishing Co.

Kolster, Thomas. Goodvertising: Creative Advertising That Cares. 2012. (ENG., Illus.). 256p. 50.00 ***(978-0-500-51626-3(X)***, 551626) Thames & Hudson.

Krishna, Ammani. Advertising Decision Making Process. 2011. 216p. pap. ***(978-3-8433-9079-8(7))*** Lambert Academic Publishing.

Krols, Birgit. Sensational Billboards in Advertising. 2008. (FRE, DUT & ENG., Illus.). 176p. pap. *(978-90-76886-46-6(6))* Tectum B.V.B.A.

Kupper, Sabine. Anglizismen in Deutschen Werbeanzeigen. (GER., Illus.). 442p. pap. 89.95 *(978-3-631-56726-5(X))* Lang, Peter GmbH, Europaischer Verlag der Wissenschaften DEU. Dist: Lang, Peter Publishing, Inc.

Kuzwayo, Muzi. There's a Tsotsi in the Boardroom: Winning in a Hostile World. 2007. (ENG., Illus.). 136p. per. 22.00 *(978-1-77009-087-3(8))* Jacana Media ZAF. Dist: Independent Pubs. Group.

Lance, Steve & Woll, Jeff. The Little Blue Book of Advertising: 52 Small Ideas That Can Make a Big Difference. 2006. (ENG., Illus.). 288p. (gr. 12-18). 19.95 *(978-1-59184-124-1(0)*, Portfolio (Hardcover)) Penguin Group (USA) Inc.

Landa, Robin. Advertising by Design: Generating & Designing Creative Ideas Across Media. 2nd ed. 2010. (ENG., Illus.). 288p. pap. 60.00 *(978-0-470-36268-6(5)*, Wiley) Wiley, John & Sons, Inc.

Lane, Ron, et al. Advertising Procedure. 18th ed. 2011. (ENG., Illus.). 840p. pap. *(978-0-13-246551-9(5))* Prentice Hall PTR.

—Kleppner's Advertising Procedure. 18th ed. 2010. (ENG., Illus.). 840p. (C). 213.33 *(978-0-13-611082-8(7)*, Prentice Hall) Prentice Hall PTR.

Lawrence, Kate. The Practical Peacemaker: How Simple Living Makes Peace Possible. 2009. 128p. pap. 16.00 *(978-1-59056-140-9(6))* Lantern Bks.

Lee, Jason W. Branded: Branding in Sport Business. 2010. 370p. pap. 40.00 *(978-1-59460-506-2(8))* Carolina Academic Pr.

leeclowsbeard, creator. Leeclowsbeard. 2012. (ENG., Illus.). 224p. 24.95 ***(978-1-57687-605-3(5))*** powerHouse Cultural Entertainment, Inc.

Levinson, Jay Conrad. Guerrilla Marketing: Easy & Inexpensive Strategies for Making Big Profits from Your Small Business. 4th ed. 2007. (ENG.). 384p. pap. 14.95 *(978-0-618-78591-9(4))* Houghton Mifflin Harcourt Trade & Reference Pubs.

Levinson, Jay Conrad & Frishman, Rick. Guerrilla Publicity: Hundreds of Sure-Fire Tactics to Get Maximum Sales for Minimum DollarsIncludes Podcasts, Blogs, & Media Training for the Digital Age. 2nd ed. 2008. (ENG., Illus.). 352p. pap. 14.95 *(978-1-59869-845-9(1))* Adams Media Corp.

Levinson, Jay Conrad & Lautenslager, Al. Guerilla Marketing in 30 Days. 2nd ed. 2009. (ENG.). 304p. pap. 21.95 *(978-1-59918-266-7(1)*, 1599182661) Entrepreneur Pr. dba Entrepreneur Media, Inc.

Levinson, Jay Conrad & Meyerson, Mitch. Guerrilla Marketing on the Front Lines: 35 World-Class Strategies to Send Your Profits Soaring. 2008. (Guerilla Marketing Press Ser.). (ENG.). 300p. pap. 19.95 *(978-1-60037-377-0(1))* Morgan James Publishing.

Levinson, Jeannie & Levinson, Jay Conrad. Startup Guide to Guerrilla Marketing: A Simple Battle Plan for First-Time Marketers. 2007. (ENG.). 288p. per. 21.95 *(978-1-59918-153-0(3)*, 1599181533) Entrepreneur Pr. dba Entrepreneur Media, Inc.

Linn, Susan. The Case for Make-Believe: Saving Play in Our Commercialized World. 2008. (ENG.). 258p. 24.95 *(978-1-56584-970-9(1)*, 84970) New Pr., The.

Loeck, Judith Antonia. Die Unzumutbare Belästigung Nach der UWG Novelle 2008 und Dem Gesetz Zur Bekämpfung Unerlaubter Telefonwerbung und Zur Verbesserung des Verbraucherschutzes Bei Besonderen Vertriebsformen. 2011. (Veröffentlichungen des Instituts für deutsches und europäisches Wirtschafts-, Wettbewerbs- und Regulierungsrecht der Freien Universität Berlin Ser.). (GER.). 190p. 64.95 *(978-3-631-61099-2(8))* Lang, Peter GmbH, Europaischer Verlag der Wissenschaften DEU. Dist: Lang, Peter.

Lois, George. On Creating the Big Idea. 2008. (ENG., Illus.). 225p. 50.00 *(978-2-7594-0299-1(1))* Assouline FRA. Dist: Perseus Distribution.

Lok, Dan & Richoux, D. J. Lies Salon Owners Believe: And the Truth That Sets them Free. 2011. (ENG.). 192p. 21.99 ***(978-1-59932-270-4(6))*** Advantage Media Group.

Lopata, Andy. Recommended: How to Sell Through Networking & Referrals. rev. ed. 2011. (Financial Times Ser.). (ENG., Illus.). 304p. pap. 24.99 ***(978-0-273-75796-2(2))*** FT Press.

Lowrey, Tina M. Psycholinguistic Phenomena in Marketing Communications. 2006. (ENG., Illus.). 312p. 90.00 *(978-0-8058-5690-3(0)*, Psychology Press) Taylor & Francis Group GBR. Dist: Taylor & Francis Group.

Lucas, Gavin & Dorrian, Michael. Guerrilla Advertising: Unconventional Brand Communication. 2006. (ENG., Illus.). 192p. pap. 40.00 *(978-1-85669-470-4(4))* King, Laurence Publishing GBR. Dist: Hachette Bk. Group.

Maas, Jane. Mad Women: The Other Side of Life on Madison Avenue in the '60s & Beyond. 2012. (ENG., Illus.). 272p. 24.99 ***(978-0-312-64023-1(4)***, Dunne, Thomas Bks.) St. Martin's Pr.

MacDougall, Robert C., ed. Drugs & Media: New Perspectives on Communication, Consumption & Consciousness. 2011. (ENG., Illus.). 368p. 130.00 *(978-1-4411-1988-9(4))* Continuum International Publishing Group, Ltd. GBR. Dist: National Bk. Network.

—Drugs & Media: New Perspectives on Communication Consumption & Consciousness. 2011. (ENG., Illus.). 368p. pap. 39.95 *(978-1-4411-3492-9(1))* Continuum International Publishing Group, Ltd. GBR. Dist: National Bk. Network.

MacManus, Theodore. Advertising: Sword Arm of Business. 9.50 *(978-0-8159-6832-0(9))* Devin-Adair Pubs., Inc.

MacManus, Theodore F. SwordArm of Business. 2006. pap. 24.95 *(978-1-4286-5674-1(X))* Kessinger Publishing, LLC.

MacRury, Iain, ed. Macrury - Advertising, 4 vols., Set. 2013. (Critical Concepts in Media & Cultural Studies). (ENG.). 1600p. (C). 995.00 ***(978-0-415-57711-3(X))*** Routledge.

Macrury, Iain & MacRury, Iain. Advertising. 2009. (Illus.). 318p. pap. 30.95 *(978-0-415-25126-6(5)*, RU22499) Routledge.

MacRury, Iain & Macrury, Iain. Advertising. 2009. (Illus.). 318p. 110.00 *(978-0-415-25125-9(7)*, RU22498) Routledge.

Maher, Michael J. The (7L) the Seven Levels of Communication: Go from Relationships to Referrals. 2010. (ENG.). 170p. 29.95 *(978-1-4520-3397-6(8))* AuthorHouse.

Mahon, Nik. Art Direction. 2010. (Basics Advertising Ser.). (ENG., Illus.). 184p. (C). pap. 32.95 *(978-2-940411-21-4(2))* Ava Publishing SA CHE. Dist: Ingram Pub. Services.

—Ideation. 2011. (Basics Advertising Ser.). (ENG., Illus.). 184p. (C). pap. 34.50 *(978-2-940411-50-4(6))* Ava Publishing SA CHE. Dist: Ingram Pub. Services.

Malefyt, Timothy de Waal & Morais, Robert J. Advertising & Anthropology: Ethnographic Practice & Cultural Perspectives. 2012. (ENG.). 192p. (C). 99.95 ***(978-0-85785-201-4(9)***, 134595); pap. 29.95 ***(978-0-85785-202-1(7)***, 134742) Berg Pubs. GBR. Dist: Macmillan.

Mandalapu, Jayakrishna & J Akhil, M. Effects of Advertising on Consumers in Indi. 2011. 252p. pap. ***(978-3-8443-8008-8(6))*** Lambert Academic Publishing.

Mann, Evelyn P., ed. Advertising: Types, Trends & Controversies. 2011. (Advertising: Media, Marketing & Consumer Demands Ser.). 156p. 95.00 ***(978-1-61324-679-5(X))*** Nova Science Pubs., Inc.

Marieke de, Mooij. Global Marketing & Advertising: Understanding Cultural Paradoxes (Course Outline) 2006. 77p. pap. 9.95 *(978-1-4288-0515-6(X))* Cram101 Inc.

The Marketer's Guide to Digital Out-of-Home Media. 2008. pap. 349.00 *(978-1-885747-10-5(1))* EPM Communications, Inc.

Marschall, Richard. Drawing Power: A Compendium of Cartoon Advertising. Bernard, Warren, ed. 2011. (ENG., Illus.). 128p. pap. 28.99 *(978-1-60699-399-6(2)*, 699399) Fantagraphics Bks.

McAllister, Matthew P. & West, Emily, eds. The Routledge Companion to Advertising & Promotional Culture. 2012. (ENG., Illus.). 608p. (C). 205.00 *(978-0-415-88801-1(8))* Routledge.

McLaren, Carrie & Torchinsky, Jason, eds. Ad Nauseam: A Survivor's Guide to American Consumer Culture. 2009. (ENG., Illus.). 368p. pap. 18.00 *(978-0-86547-987-6(9))* Faber & Faber, Inc.

McQuarrie, Edward F. & Phillips, Barbara J., eds. Go Figure! New Directions in Advertising Rhetoric. 2007. (ENG., Illus.). 336p. 88.95 *(978-0-7656-1801-6(X))* Sharpe, M.E. Inc.

McStay, Andrew. Digital Advertising. 2009. (ENG., Illus.). 208p. 95.00 *(978-0-230-22240-3(4))*; pap. 33.00 *(978-0-230-22241-0(2))* Palgrave Macmillan.

Medicare Advantage Marketing & Sales: Who Has the Advantage?: Hearing Before the Special Committee on Aging, United States Senate, One Hundred Tenth Congress, First Session, Washington, DC, May 16, 2007. 2007. (Illus.). iii, 282p. *(978-0-16-080114-3(1)*, 552-070-36855-8) United States Government Printing Office.

Mepham, John. Super Salesmanship + Convincing Advertising = Lucrative Business. 2011. 342p. pap. 25.50 ***(978-1-4466-0366-6(0))*** Lulu Enterprises Inc.

Michelet, John, Jr. Advertising: An Insider Exposes Advertising's Ten Fundamental Problems & Reveals the Secrets to Overcoming Them: Industry in Peril. 2006. (Illus.). 224p. per. 14.95 *(978-0-9778982-0-6(2))* Olympian Publishing.

Miller, Barbara Manning. Marketplace Advocacy Campaigns: Generating Public Support for Business & Industry. 2012. 186p. ***(978-1-60497-789-9(2))*** Cambria Pr.

Morgan, Nigel, et al. Destination Brands Managing Place Reputation. 3rd rev. ed. 2011. (ENG., Illus.). 392p. (C). pap. 57.95 *(978-0-08-096930-5(5))* Routledge.

Moriarty, Sandra, et al. Advertising & IMC: Principles & Practice. 9th ed. 2011. (ENG.). 688p. (C). 106.67 *(978-0-13-253912-8(8))*; stu. ed., ring bd. 138.60 *(978-0-13-216372-9(1))* Prentice Hall PTR. (Prentice Hall).

Moriarty, Sandra E., et al. Advertising & IMC: Principles & Practice. 9th ed. 2011. (ENG.). 688p. (C). 220.00 *(978-0-13-216364-4(0)*, Prentice Hall) Prentice Hall PTR.

Moskowitz, Marina. Testimonial Advertising in the American Marketplace: Emulation, Identity, Community. Moskowitz, Marina & Schweitzer, Marlis, eds. 2009. (ENG., Illus.). 248p. 89.00 *(978-0-230-61560-1(0))* Palgrave Macmillan.

Mueller, Barbara. Communicating with the Ethnic Consumer: Theoretical & Practical Perspectives. 2007. 352p. (C). pap. 49.95 *(978-0-8204-8119-7(X))* Lang, Peter Publishing, Inc.

—Communicating with the Multicultural Consumer: Theoretical & Practical Perspectives. 2007. 350p. (C). 129.95 *(978-1-4331-0204-2(8))* Lang, Peter Publishing, Inc.

—Dynamics of International Advertising: Theoretical & Practical Perspectives. 2nd ed. 2010. pap. 54.95 *(978-1-4331-0384-1(2))* Lang, Peter Publishing, Inc.

Müller, Jörg, et al, eds. Pervasive Advertising. 2011. (Humanâ€"Computer Interaction Ser.). (ENG., Illus.). ix, 364p. 124.00 *(978-0-85729-351-0(6)*, 0857293516) Springer.

Muller, Lars & Weiland, Karen. Lufthansa und Graphic Design: Visuelle Geschichte eienr Fluggesellschaft. 2012. (GER & ENG., Illus.). 128p. pap. 40.00 ***(978-3-03778-267-5(6))*** Lars Muller Pubs. CHE. Dist: Prestel Publishing.

Munusamy, Jayaraman, et al. Students'attitude Towards Advertising in Higher Education Institutions. 2011. 156p. pap. ***(978-3-8443-2666-6(9))*** Lambert Academic Publishing.

Nadeau, Raymond A. Living Brands: Collaboration + Innovation = Customer Fascination. 2006. (ENG., Illus.). 288p. 29.95 *(978-0-07-146614-1(2)*, 0071466142) McGraw-Hill Cos., The.

Necerato, Patrick A. Salesmanship.. the Yellow Brick Road to Advertising & Business Success. pap. 79.95 *(978-0-9719257-0-0(4))* Advantage1One Pubns.

Nelson, Okorie. The Role of Celebrity Advertising on Brand Loyalty & Patronage. 2011. 92p. pap. ***(978-3-8433-9011-8(8))*** Lambert Academic Publishing.

New York Festivals. New York Festivals 18. 2012. (ENG., Illus.). 500p. 65.00 ***(978-0-06-212727-3(6)***, Collins Design) HarperCollins Pubs.

Nieder, Alison A. Fashion of the 20th Century: 100 Years of Apparel Ads / 100 Jahre Mode in der WErbung / 100 Ans de Pubs de Mode. Heimann, Jim, ed. 2009. (FRE, GER & ENG., Illus.). 464p. 39.99 *(978-3-8365-1461-3(3))* TASCHEN DEU. Dist: Ingram Pub. Services.

Nikolaou, Ioanna. Advertising & Children, Adolescent Boys & Video Game Advertising. 2010. 116p. pap. *(978-3-8383-7783-4(4))* Lambert Academic Publishing.

Nowosenetz, Tessa. The Construction of Masculinity & Femininity in Alcohol Advertising: A discourse analysis. 2008. 84p. pap. *(978-3-639-10706-7(3))* VDM Verlag Dr. Mueller e.K.

Nyota, Shumirai & E Mutasa, Davie. Elements & Ilocutions of Shona Advertising Texts. 2010. 64p. pap. *(978-3-639-26011-3(2))* VDM Verlag Dr. Mueller e.K.

Nyota, Shumirai & E. Mutasa, Davie. The Structure & Communicative Impact of Shona Advertisements. 2010. 68p. pap. *(978-3-639-27205-5(6))* VDM Verlag Dr. Mueller e.K.

Nyren, Chuck. Advertising to Baby Boomers. 2007. 182p. per. 24.95 *(978-0-9786602-3-9(4)*, 1025) Paramount Market Publishing, Inc.

O Guinn, Allen. Advertising & Integrated Brand Promoti. 2006. pap. 13.95 *(978-1-4288-0699-3(7))* Cram101 Inc.

O'Boyle, Neil. New Vocabularies, Old Ideas: Culture, Irishness & the Advertising Industry. 2011. (Reimagining Ireland Ser.). 234p. pap. 58.95 *(978-3-03911-978-3(8))* Lang, Peter AG GBR. Dist: Lang, Peter.

Odih, Pamela. Advertising & Cultural Politics in Global Times. 2010. (Illus.). 300p. 124.95 *(978-0-7546-7711-6(7))* Ashgate Publishing Co.

Ogden, James R. & Rarick, Scott. The Entrepreneur's Guide to Advertising, 1 vol. 2009. (Entrepreneur's Guide Ser.). 122p. 39.95 *(978-0-313-36582-9(2)*, C36582, Praeger Pubs.) Greenwood Publishing Group, Inc.

O'Guinn, Thomas, et al. Advertising & Integrated Brand Promotion. 6th ed. 2011. (ENG.). 736p. (C). 242.95 *(978-0-538-47332-3(0))* Cengage South-Western.

O'Guinn, Thomas, et al. PROMO2 (with Marketing CourseMate with eBook Printed Access Card) 2nd ed. 2012. (ENG.). 368p. pap. 74.95 ***(978-1-133-62617-6(3))*** Cengage South-Western.

Omedo, James. How Culture & Technology Impact Coca-Cola's Advertising Strategies. 2010. (Illus.). 108p. pap. *(978-3-639-26319-0(7))* VDM Verlag Dr. Mueller e.K.

One Club Staff. One Show Boxed Set, 2009 Awards, 3 vols. 2010. (One Show Ser.). (ENG., Illus.). 928p. 150.00 *(978-0-929837-43-7(6)*, 0929837436) Quayside.

O'Reilly, Terry & Tennant, Mike. The Age of Persuasion: How Marketing Ate Our Culture. 2010. (ENG.). 304p. 26.00 *(978-1-58243-580-0(4)*, Counterpoint Pr.) Basic Bks. GBR. Dist: Perseus-PGW.

—The Age of Persuasion: How Marketing Ate Our Culture. 2011. (ENG.). 352p. pap. 16.95 *(978-1-58243-724-8(6)*, Counterpoint) Counterpoint LLC.

Orlik, Peter B. Broadcast/Broadband Copywriting. 8th ed. 2009. (ENG.). 496p. (C). pap. 127.00 *(978-0-205-67452-7(6))* Allyn & Bacon, Inc.

O'Shaughnessy, John & O'Shaughnessy, Nicholas Jackson. The Marketing Power of Emotion. 2006. (Illus.). 274p. reprint ed. 27.00 *(978-1-4223-5590-9(X))* DIANE Publishing Co.

Osterman, Jim. Excellence in Brand Advertising. 2008. (Illus.). 203p. 50.00 *(978-1-58471-081-3(0))* Visual Reference Pubns., Inc.

Osterman, Jim & Visual, Reference P. Excellence in Brand Advertising. 2007. (Illus.). 208p. 50.00 *(978-1-58471-082-0(9))* Visual Reference Pubns., Inc.

Pardun, Carol J., ed. Advertising & Society: Controversies & Consequences. 2009. (ENG., Illus.). 224p. 99.95 *(978-1-4051-4409-4(2)*, Wiley-Blackwell) Wiley, John & Sons, Inc.

Paxson, Peyton. Media Literacy: Thinking Critically about Advertising. 2nd rev. ed. 2009. (YA). pap. 24.99 *(978-0-8251-6512-2(1))* Walch Education.

Pedroza, Jorge Ramón. Creatividad Efectiva. 2007. 331p. pap. 39.99 *(978-1-4303-2825-4(8))* Lulu Enterprises Inc.

Pelsmacker, Patrick de, et al. Marketing Communicationsa European Pers. 3rd rev. ed. 2006. (Illus.). 648p. (C). pap. *(978-0-273-70693-9(4))* Prentice Hall PTR.

Pennock, Pamela E. Advertising Sin & Sickness: The Politics of Alcohol & Tobacco Marketing, 1950-1990. 2007. (Illus.). 290p. 36.00 *(978-0-87580-368-5(7))* Northern Illinois Univ. Pr.

Penny, Laura. Your Call Is Important to Us: The Truth about Bullshit. 288p. pap. 26.95 *(978-1-920769-67-3(6))* Scribe Pubns. AUS. Dist: Independent Pubs. Group.

Percy, Larry. Strategic Integrated Marketing Communication: Theory & Practice. 2011. (ENG., Illus.). 328p. (C). pap. 42.95 *(978-0-7506-7980-0(8))* Routledge.

Percy, Larry & Rosenbaum-Elliott, Richard. Strategic Advertising Management. 4th ed. 2012. (ENG., Illus.). 450p. (Orig.). (C). pap. 69.95 ***(978-0-19-960558-3(0))*** Oxford Univ. Pr., Inc.

Peters, Paula. The Ultimate Marketing Toolkit: Ads That Attract Customers - Blogs That Create Buzz - Web Sites That Wow. 2nd ed. 2009. (ENG., Illus.). 240p. pap. 14.95 *(978-1-59869-893-0(1))* Adams Media Corp.

Peterson, Daniel. Branding- How to Determine Your Brand & Channel Your Marketing Efforts Correctly. 2007. 172p. per. *(978-3-8364-1674-0(3))* VDM Verlag Dr. Mueller e.K.

Phillips, Robbin, et al. Brains on Fire: Igniting Powerful, Sustainable, Word of Mouth Movements. 2010. (ENG., Illus.). 224p. 24.95 *(978-0-470-61418-1(8)*, Wiley) Wiley, John & Sons, Inc.

Pie Books Staff. Ideas Unleashed. Nishioka, Emi, ed. 2009. (ENG & JPN., Illus.). 168p. 59.00 *(978-4-89444-693-9(6))* Rizzoli International Pubns., Inc.

Pont Council Soc Communication Staff. Ethics in Advertising. 32p. pap. 1.95 *(978-0-8198-2340-3(6)*, 332-078) Pauline Bks. & Media.

Pont, Simon. The Better Mousetrap: Brand Invention in a Media Democracy. 2012. (ENG., Illus.). 272p. pap. 34.95 ***(978-0-7494-6621-3(9))*** Kogan Page, Ltd. GBR. Dist: Ingram Pub. Services.

Popp, Richard K. The Holiday Makers: Magazines, Advertising, & Mass Tourism in Postwar America. 2012. (Illus.). 256p. 39.95 ***(978-0-8071-4284-4(0))*** Louisiana State Univ. Pr.

Poulsen, William L. Advertising: Developments & Issues in the Digital Age. 2011. 138p. *(978-1-61761-783-6(0))* Nova Science Pubs., Inc.

Pricken, Mario. Creative Advertising: Ideas & Techniques from the World's Best Campaigns. 2nd rev. ed. 2008. (ENG., Illus.). 272p. pap. 39.95 *(978-0-500-28733-0(3)*, 528733) Thames & Hudson.

—Creative Strategies: Idea Management for Marketing, Advertising, Media & Design. 2010. (ENG., Illus.). 312p. 65.00 *(978-0-500-51540-2(9)*, 551540) Thames & Hudson.

Pringle, Hamish & Marshall, Jim. Spending Advertising Money in the Digital Age: How to Navigate the Media Flow. 2012. (ENG., Illus.). 336p. pap. 44.95 *(978-0-7494-6305-2(8))* Kogan Page, Ltd. GBR. Dist: Ingram Pub. Services.

Prussakov, Evgenii. Affiliate Program Management: An Hour a Day. 2011. (ENG., Illus.). 456p. pap. 29.99 *(978-0-470-65173-5(3)*, Sybex) Wiley, John & Sons, Inc.

Purvis, Scott. Which Ad Pulled Best? 10th ed. 2010. (ENG., Illus.). 96p. (C). pap. 46.33 *(978-0-07-811207-2(9)*, 0078112079, McGraw-Hill/Irwin) McGraw-Hill Higher Education.

R&ostroke, et al. Get in the Game. 2011. 132p. pap. ***(978-3-8443-2587-4(5))*** Lambert Academic Publishing.

Ramakrishnan, Ruchika. Rural Marketing in India: Strategies & Challenges. 2006. 222p. 32.00 *(978-81-7708-120-6(9))* New Century Publications IND. Dist: International Specialized Bk. Services.

Reichert. Investigating the Use of Sex in Media Promotion & Advertising. 2008. 210p. 95.00 *(978-0-7890-3128-2(9))* Routledge.

Reichert, Tom. Investigating the Use of Sex in Media Promotion & Advertising. 2007. (Illus.). 198p. per. 49.95 *(978-0-7890-3129-9(7))* Routledge.

Rennert, Jack, text. Cappiello: The Posters of Leonetto Cappiello. 2007. (ENG., Illus.). 336p. 80.00 *(978-0-7570-0065-2(7))* Square One Pubs.

Research and Education Association Staff. How to Create Great Advertising by the Most Creative People in the Field. Date not set. 208p. pap. 29.95 *(978-0-87891-977-2(5))* Research & Education Assn.

Resnick, Lynda & Wilkinson, Francis. Rubies in the Orchard: The POM Queen's Secrets to Marketing Just about Anything. 2010. (ENG., Illus.). 240p. pap. 15.00 *(978-0-385-52579-4(6)*, Broadway Business) Knopf Doubleday Publishing Group.

Robert Collier Publications. The Robert Collier Letter Book. 2011. 466p. (C). pap. 26.75 *(978-0-912576-20-6(0)*, Conran Octopus) Collier, Robert Pubns., Inc.

Roberts, Kevin. The Lovemarks Effect: Winning in the Consumer Revolution. 2006. (ENG., Illus.). 264p. 29.95 *(978-1-57687-267-3(X)*, powerHouse Bks.) powerHouse Cultural Entertainment, Inc.

Roche, Mary M. Doyle. Children, Consumerism, & the Common Good. 2009. (ENG.). 158p. 62.99 *(978-0-7391-2947-0(3))* Lexington Bks.

Rodgers, Shelly & Thorson, Esther, eds. Advertising Theory. 2012. (Routledge Communication Ser.). (ENG., Illus.). 648p. (C). 200.00 *(978-0-415-88661-1(9))*; pap. 75.00 *(978-0-415-88662-8(7))* Routledge.

Roig, Pat. From Staple Guns to Thumbtacks: Flyer art from the 1982-1995 New Orleans Punk & Hardcore Scene. 2010. 416p. pap. 29.99 *(978-0-557-56356-2(9))* Lulu Enterprises Inc.

Roscam Abbing, Erik. Brand-Driven Innovation. 2010. (Required Reading Range Ser.). (ENG., Illus.). 192p. (C). pap. 49.95 *(978-2-940411-28-3(X))* Ava Publishing SA CHE. Dist: Ingram Pub. Services.

Rosen, Emanuel. The Anatomy of Buzz Revisited: Real-Life Lessons in Word-of-Mouth Marketing. 2009. (ENG.). 384p. pap. 15.95 *(978-0-385-52632-6(6)*, Broadway Business) Knopf Doubleday Publishing Group.

Rosenberg, Chaim M. Goods for Sale: Products & Advertising in the Massachusetts Industrial Age. 2007. (Illus.). 242p. per. 24.95 *(978-1-55849-580-7(0))* Univ. of Massachusetts Pr.

Rosenshine, Allen. Funny Business: Moguls, Mobsters, Megastars, & the Mad, Mad World of the Ad Game. 2010. 296p. 24.95 *(978-0-8253-0539-9(X))* Beaufort Bks., Inc.

Rubleski, Tony. Mind Capture: How to Generate New & Repeat Business in the Age of Advertising Overload. 2006. (ENG.). 172p. per. 17.95 *(978-1-933596-65-5(1)*, 1933596651) Morgan James Publishing.

—Mind Capture: How You Can Stand Out in the Age of Advertising Deficit Disorder. 2008. (ENG.). 196p. pap. 19.95 *(978-1-60037-457-9(3))* Morgan James Publishing.

Russel and, Lane. Kleppners Advertising Procedure. 2006. pap. 13.95 *(978-1-4288-0496-8(X))* Cram101 Inc.

Rutherford, David & Knowles, Jonathan. Vulcans, Earthlings & Marketing ROI: Getting Finance, Marketing & Advertising onto the Same Planet. 2007. (ENG.). 174p. pap. 34.95 *(978-1-55458-031-6(5))* Wilfrid Laurier Univ. Pr. CAN. Dist: Univ. of Toronto Pr.

Sáez, Natalia. Pragmatic & Argumentative Structures in Written Advertisements. 2010. 112p. pap. *(978-3-8383-4662-5(9))* Lambert Academic Publishing.

Salavetz, Judith, et al. Art of the Modern Movie Poster: International Postwar Style & Design. 2008. (ENG., Illus.). 516p. 75.00 *(978-0-8118-6171-7(6))* Chronicle Bks. LLC.

Salminen, Joni. Power of Google. 2010. 140p. pap. *(978-3-8383-7625-7(0))* Lambert Academic Publishing.

Salz, Nancy L. Salz Survey of Advertiser-Agency Relations: The Collective Wisdom of the Top 200 Advertisers & Top 100 Agencies: the Twenty Year Report. 2007. 69p. spiral bd. 95.00 *(978-0-615-17546-1(5))* Salz, Nancy L. Consulting.

Samuel, Lawrence R. Freud on Madison Avenue: Motivation Research & Subliminal Advertising in America. 2010. 232p. 29.95 *(978-0-8122-4251-5(3))* Univ. of Pennsylvania Pr.

Sanabra, Pep & Minguet, Eva. Big Format Advertising. Minguet, Josep Maria, ed. 2010. (ENG.). 223p. pap. 57.50 *(978-84-96823-77-8(6))* Instituto Monsa de Ediciones, S.A. ESP. Dist: Trans-Atlantic Pubns., Inc.

Santee, Spike. The Four Keys to Advertising Success: A 1-Hour Guide for Small Business Owners. 2011. 80p. pap. 15.99 ***(978-1-4628-6503-1(8))*** Xlibris Corp.

Saucier, Rick D. Marketing Ethics. 2008. (Illus.). 176p. 99.95 *(978-0-7734-5116-2(1))* Mellen, Edwin Pr., The.

Sayre, Shay. Campaign Planner for Integrated Brand Communications. 4th ed. 2010. (ENG.). (C). pap. 50.95 *(978-0-538-49855-5(2))* Cengage South-Western.

Schilling, Andrea. Bewerbungsgesprache in der Eigenen und Fremden Sprache Deutsch: Empirische Analysen. (Arbeiten zur Sprachanalyse: Bd. 40). (GER., Illus.). 43.95 *(978-3-631-38891-4(8))* Lang, Peter Publishing, Inc.

Schonfeld & Associates. Advertising Growth Trends: 2007 Edition. 2007. 260p. spiral bd. 395.00 *(978-1-932024-47-0(6))* Schonfeld & Assocs., Inc.

Schwimmer, Walter. What Have You Done for Me Lately? 2011. 256p. 47.95 ***(978-1-258-08944-3(0))*** Literary Licensing, LLC.

Scott, David Meerman. World Wide Rave: Creating Triggers That Get Millions of People to Spread Your Ideas & Share Your Stories. 2009. (ENG.). 208p. 22.95 *(978-0-470-39500-4(1)*, Wiley) Wiley, John & Sons, Inc.

Seddon, Tony & Herriott, Luke. Art Directing Projects for Print: Solutions & Strategies for Creative Success. 2009. (ENG., Illus.). 256p. pap. 40.00 *(978-2-88893-020-4(X)*, 288893020X) RotoVision SA CHE. Dist: Quaysice.

Sedivy, Julie & Carlson, Greg. Sold on Language: How Advertisers Talk to You & What This Says about You. 2011. (ENG., Illus.). 336p. pap. 26.95 *(978-0-470-68309-5(0)*, Wiley) Wiley, John & Sons, Inc.

Segrave, Kerry. America Brushes Up: The Use & Marketing of Toothpaste & Toothbrushes in the Twentieth Century. 2010. (ENG., Illus.). 238p. pap. 35.00 *(978-0-7864-4754-1(0))* McFarland & Co., Inc. Pubs.

Sennebogen, Waltraud. Zwischen Kommerz und Ideologie: Berührungspunkte von Wirtschaftswerbung und Propaganda im Nationalsozialismus. 2008. (GER., Illus.). 447p. *(978-3-89975-684-5(3))* Medenbauer, Martin Verlagsbuchhandlung GmbH & Co. KG.

Sethi, Raunica, et al. Marketing Communications Industry: Entrepreneurial Case Studies. 2008. 212p. (C). pap. 29.95 *(978-81-7829-868-9(6)*, B98689P) SAGE Pubns., Inc.

Sheridan, Jayne. Fashion, Media, Promotion: The New Black Magic. 2010. (ENG., Illus.). 264p. pap. 59.99 *(978-1-4051-9421-1(9)*, Wiley-Blackwell) Wiley, John & Sons, Inc.

Shimp. Advertising, Promotion, & Supplemental. 2006. (ENG.). 195p. pap. 12.95 *(978-1-4288-0670-2(9))* Cram101 Inc.

Shimp, Terence A. Advertising Promotion & Other Aspects of Integrated Marketing Communications. 8th ed. 2008. (Deca Ser.). (ENG., Illus.). 688p. (C). 256.95 *(978-0-324-59360-0(0))* Cengage South-Western.

Shurtleff, William & Aoyagi, Akiko, compiled by. Marketing Miso & Miso Products: Labels, Ads, Sell Sheets & Other Graphics, 1941-2006. 2007. 267p. 454.00 *(978-1-928914-13-6(6))* Soyinfo Ctr.

Silver, Allison. 20th Century Travel: 100 years of travel ads. Heimann, Jim, ed. 2010. (ENG.). 392p. 39.99 *(978-3-8365-1941-0(0))* TASCHEN DEU. Dist: Ingram Pub. Services.

Silverman, George. The Secrets of Word-of-Mouth Marketing: How to Trigger Exponential Sales Through Runaway Word of Mouth, 1 vol. 2nd ed. 2011. (ENG.). 272p. pap. 17.95 *(978-0-8144-1668-6(3))* Amacom.

Sinclair, John. Advertising, the Media & Globalisation: A World in Motion. 2012. (ENG., Illus.). 168p. (C). 125.00 *(978-0-415-66882-8(4))*; pap. 39.95 *(978-0-415-66883-5(2))* Routledge.

Slutsky, Jeff. Jeff Slutsky's Streetfighting: Low Cost Advertising & Promotions for PADI Professionals. Coleman, Bob et al, eds. (Illus.). 48p. pap. 79.95 *(978-1-878663-12-2(7))* PADI.

—Street Fighter Marketing Solutions: How One-on-One Marketing Will Help You Overcome the Sales Challenges of Modern-Day Business. 2007. (ENG., Illus.). 256p. 26.00 *(978-0-7432-9914-5(0)*, Free Pr.) Free Pr.

Smith, Kristene. Style Tips of the Week, Volume One: Advertise, Market & Brand with Style. 2008. (ENG.). 96p. pap. 12.95 *(978-0-9752983-0-5(5))* Smith, Kristene Inc.

Smith, William S. The Changing World of International Advertising. rev. ed. 2011. (ENG.). 110p. pap. 89.00 *(978-0-7575-8595-1(7))* Kendall Hunt Publishing Co.

Sokotch, Mel. Shortcuts to the Obvious: How to Get More Effective Advertising More Efficiently — an Insider's Guide. 2011. (ENG.). 105p. pap. 21.95 ***(978-0-9769357-1-1(6))*** Aspetuck River Publishing.

Soloman, Barry. Take Note in Principles of Advertising. 3rd rev. ed. 2011. (ENG.). 106p. spiral bd. 37.99 *(978-0-7575-8602-6(3))* Kendall Hunt Publishing Co.

Solomon, Barry. Take Note in Principles of Advertising. 2nd rev. ed. 2010. (ENG.). 122p. spiral bd. 33.08 *(978-0-7575-6151-1(9))* Kendall Hunt Publishing Co.

Solomon, Robert. The Art of Client Service, Revised & Updated Edition: 58 Things Every Advertising & Marketing Professional Should Know. rev. ed. 2008. (ENG., Illus.). 208p. 19.95 *(978-1-4277-9671-4(8))* Kaplan Publishing.

Stern, Gail F., ed. Ethnic Images in Advertising: An exhibition Co-Sponsored by the Balch Institute for Ethnic Studies & the Anti-Defamation League of B'Nai B'Rith. 2006. (Illus.). 51p. reprint ed. pap. 15.00 *(978-1-4223-5825-2(9))* DIANE Publishing Co.

Strachan, John. Advertising & Satirical Culture in the Romantic Period. 2007. (Cambridge Studies in Romanticism Ser.). (ENG., Illus.). 368p. 103.99 *(978-0-521-88214-9(1))* Cambridge Univ. Pr.

Strunck, Michael. Celebrity Endorsement. 2011. 88p. pap. ***(978-3-8443-0117-5(8))*** Lambert Academic Publishing.

Sutherland, Max & Sylvester, Alice. Advertising & the Mind of the Consumer: What Works, What Doesn't, & Why. 3rd ed. 2009. (ENG., Illus.). 352p. pap. 24.95 *(978-1-74175-599-2(9))* Allen & Unwin AUS. Dist: Independent Pubs. Group.

Swett, Pamela E., et al, eds. Selling Modernity: Advertising in Twentieth-Century Germany. 2007. (ENG., Illus.). 384p. per. 26.95 *(978-0-8223-4069-0(0))* Duke Univ. Pr.

Sylvestrová, Marta. 23. Mezinárodní Bienále Grafického Designu Brno 2008: Grafický Design, Ilustrace a Písmo V Knihách, Casopisech, Novinách a Digitálních Médiích, 17.6.-19.10.2008 = 23rd International Biennial of Graphic Design Brno 2008: Graphic Design, Illustration & Type in Books, Magazines, Newspapers & Digital Media. 2010. (CZE., Illus.). 253p. *(978-80-7027-184-1(1))* Moravska galerie v Brne.

Taflinger, Richard F. Taking Advantage. rev. ed. 2011. (ENG.). 160p. pap. 55.00 ***(978-0-7575-9295-9(3))*** Kendall Hunt Publishing Co.

Tag, Nancy R. Ad Critique: How to Deconstruct Ads in Order to Build Better Advertising. 2011. (Illus.). 216p. (C). pap. 40.00 ***(978-1-4129-8053-1(4),*** B80531P) SAGE Pubns., Inc.

Taubert, Bjö. Effects of Ingame-Advertising Within a Strategy Computer Game: An Experimental Study Based on the Advertising Effects Path Model Within a World in Conflict: Soviet Assault Mission. 2011. 124p. pap. ***(978-3-639-31471-7(9))*** VDM Verlag Dr. Mueller e.K.

Tellis, Gerard J. & Ambler, Tim. The Sage Handbook of Advertising. 2007. (Illus.). xvi, 491p. pap. *(978-1-4129-1887-9(1))* SAGE Pubns., Inc.

Tellis, Gerard J. & Ambler, Tim, eds. The SAGE Handbook of Advertising. 2007. (Illus.). 512p. 150.00 *(978-1-4129-1886-2(3),* B18863C) SAGE Pubns., Ltd. GBR. Dist: SAGE Pubns., Inc.

Thomas, Aubyn. Customer Inspired Marketing: Change the game & become the brand they REALLY Love. 2009. 148p. 23.49 *(978-1-4490-0498-9(9));* pap. 12.99 *(978-1-4490-0499-6(7))* AuthorHouse.

Thomas, Susan Gregory. Buy, Buy Baby: How Consumer Culture Manipulates Parents & Harms Young Minds. 2009. (ENG.). 288p. pap. 14.95 *(978-0-547-23795-4(2),* Mariner Bks.) Houghton Mifflin Harcourt Trade & Reference Pubs.

Thompson, Fred S. Innkeepers' Key to Success: Written by an Innkeeper for an Innkeeper. 2010. 292p. pap. 19.95 *(978-1-60844-251-5(9))* Dog Ear Publishing, LLC.

Thorson, Esther & Duffy, Margaret. Advertising Age: The Principles of Advertising & Marketing Communication at Work. 2011. (ENG.). 224p. (C). pap. 32.95 *(978-1-111-52875-1(6))* Cengage South-Western.

Torossian, Ronn. For Immediate Release: Shape Minds, Build Brands, & Deliver Results with Game-Changing Public Relations. 2011. (ENG.). 288p. 24.95 *(978-1-936661-16-9(0))* BenBella Bks.

Tracy, Marta, et al. Starring You! The Insiders' Guide to Using Television & Media to Launch Your Brand, Your Business, & Your Life. 2007. 288p. per. 14.95 *(978-0-06-117112-3(3))* HarperCollins Pubs.

Treves, Tomer. The Hidden Treasure in Your Website: The First Professional Guide to Monetizing Your Website with in-Text Advertising. 2011. 120p. pap. 13.95 ***(978-1-4502-8899-6(5))*** iUniverse, Inc.

Trout, Jack. In Search of the Obvious: The Antidote for Today's Marketing Mess. 2008. (ENG.). 224p. 27.95 *(978-0-470-28859-7(0),* Wiley) Wiley, John & Sons, Inc.

Trout, Jack & Rivkin, Steve. Differentiate or Die: Survival in Our Era of Killer Competition. 2nd ed. 2008. (ENG., Illus.). 272p. 24.95 *(978-0-470-22339-0(1),* Wiley) Wiley, John & Sons, Inc.

—REPOSITIONING: Marketing in an Era of Competition, Change & Crisis. 2009. (ENG.). 224p. 26.95 *(978-0-07-163559-2(9),* 0071635599) McGraw-Hill Cos., The.

Tuckwell, Keith J. Canadian Advertising in Action. 8th ed. 2008. (ENG.). 576p. (C). pap. *(978-0-13-240574-4(1))* Pearson Education Canada.

Tungate, Mark. Fashion Brands: Branding Style from Armani to Zara. (ENG., Illus.). 272p. 2nd ed. 2008. 39.95 *(978-0-7494-5305-3(2))* 3rd ed. 2012. pap. 39.95 ***(978-0-7494-6446-2(1))*** Kogan Page, Ltd. GBR. Dist: Ingram Pub. Services.

Turkel, Bruce. Construyendo Valor de Marca. 2007. (SPA., Illus.). 91p. per. 19.95 net. *(978-0-9797084-1-1(9))* TURKEL.

Turow, Joseph. The Daily You: How the New Advertising Industry Is Defining Your Identity & Your Worth. 2012. (ENG.). 256p. 28.00 *(978-0-300-16501-2(3))* Yale Univ. Pr.

Turow, Joseph & McAllister, Matthew P., eds. The Advertising & Consumer Culture Reader. 2009. (ENG., Illus.). 456p. (C). 52.95 *(978-0-415-96330-5(3));* 125.00 *(978-0-415-96329-9(X))* Routledge.

Updegraff, Robert R. Obvious Adams: The Story of a Successful Business Man. 2007. pap. 12.99 *(978-1-59986-924-7(1))* Filiquarian Publishing, LLC.

Valin, David. 101 Top Secret Techniques Used by Successful Part Time Advertisers! 2010. 200p. pap. 19.95 *(978-1-884939-05-1(8))* Antoine Versailles Publishing.

van Gaalen, Anneloes. The Medium Is the Message: And 50 Other Ridiculous Advertising Rules. 2010. (Ridiculous Design Rules Ser.). (ENG.). 160p. 18.00 *(978-90-6369-215-5(3))* Bis B.V., Uitgeverij(BIS Publishers) NLD. Dist: Consortium Bk. Sales & Distribution.

Vanwormer, Chrissie & Massey, Michael J. Your Ad Here: De-Mystifying the Business of Media & Advertising. 2010. 100p. pap. 17.95 *(978-1-60844-538-7(0))* Dog Ear Publishing, LLC.

Vellucci, Lawrence. Free Advertising for Small Businesses: Tried & True Methods to Gain New Customers. 2011. 118p. pap. 14.95 ***(978-1-4327-7394-6(1))*** Outskirts Pr., Inc.

Verklin, David & Kanner, Bernice. Watch This, Listen up, Click Here: Inside the 300 Billion Dollar Business Behind the Media You Constantly Consume. 2007. (ENG.). 221p. 24.95 *(978-0-470-05643-1(6),* Wiley) Wiley, John & Sons, Inc.

Vollmer, Christopher & Precourt, Geoffrey. Always On: Advertising, Marketing, & Media in an Era of Consumer Control. 2008. (ENG., Illus.). 192p. pap. 17.95 *(978-0-07-150828-5(7),* 0071508287) McGraw-Hill Cos., The.

Wang, Jing. Brand New China: Advertising, Media, & Commercial Culture. 2010. (Illus.). 432p. pap. 18.95 *(978-0-674-04708-2(7))* Harvard Univ. Pr.

Watson, Paul E. Ladies & Gentlemen, Start Your Business: Any Kind, Anywhere. 2011. pap. 11.99 ***(978-1-61777-375-4(1))*** Tate Publishing & Enterprises, LLC.

Wells, William, et al. Advertising. 6th ed. 2006. 333p. pap. 15.95 *(978-1-4288-1051-8(X))* Cram101 Inc.

Wheeler, Alina. Designing Brand Identity: An Essential Guide for the Whole Branding Team. (ENG., 320p. 3rd ed. 2009. Illus.). 45.00 *(978-0-470-40142-2(7))* 4th ed. 2012. 45.00 ***(978-1-118-09920-9(6))*** Wiley, John & Sons, Inc. (Wiley).

Wheeler, Alina & Katz, Joel. Brand Atlas: Branding Intelligence Made Visible. 2011. (ENG., Illus.). 144p. 29.95 *(978-0-470-43342-3(6),* Wiley) Wiley, John & Sons, Inc.

White, J. H., ed. Write List of Wrong Words. 2007. 53p. cd-rom *(978-1-889206-14-1(8))* White, J. H. Pubs. Co.

Why Bad Ads Happen to Good Causes. 2008. pap. *(978-0-9763027-4-2(8))* Cause Communications.

Wiedemann, Julius, ed. Brand Identity Now! 2009. (ENG., Illus.). 384p. 39.99 *(978-3-8365-1584-9(9))* TASCHEN DEU. Dist: Ingram Pub. Services.

Wilks, Nicoletta A., ed. Marketing Food to Children & Adolescents. 2009. 69.00 *(978-1-60692-913-1(5))* Nova Science Pubs., Inc.

Wilson, Tony. Global Advertising, Attitudes, & Audiences. 2010. (Routledge Advances in Management & Business Studies). (ENG.). 182p. (C). 125.00 *(978-0-415-87597-4(8))* Routledge.

Wolbers, Marian Frances. Uncovering Fashion: Fashion Communications Across the Media. 2009. (Illus.). 320p. pap. 88.00 *(978-1-56367-615-4(X))* Fairchild Bks.

Wolburg, Joyce, ed. Readings in Advertising, Society, & Consumer Culture. 2007. (ENG., Illus.). 440p. 116.95 *(978-0-7656-1544-2(4))* Sharpe, M.E. Inc.

Wood, Daniella. Advertising Culture. 2011. 56p. pap. ***(978-3-8443-2834-9(3))*** Lambert Academic Publishing.

Woodbury, Susan. Salon Solutions: Salon marketing made easy without pulling your hair Out. 2010. 58p. pap. 15.99 *(978-1-4415-9535-5(X))* Xlibris Corp.

Woods, Charlie. Visualising Advertising. 2008. 480p. pap. 73.95 *(978-0-470-03777-5(6))* Wiley, John & Sons, Inc.

Wright, Linda. Skip to the Loo: Bypass Big-Ticket Advertising & Build Business with Better Bathrooms or Marketing to Women with your Restroom using the Power of Authenticity, Cleanliness, Word of Mouth & Care. Gray, Linda, ed. 2007. (Illus.). 244p. pap. 18.95 *(978-0-9800923-0-1(2))* Lindaloo Enterprises.

Wurster, Andrea. Mobile Marketing als Instrument für Below-the-Line Advertisement: Entwicklungen in der mobilen B2C-Kommunikation im deutschen Markt. 2010. 100p. pap. *(978-3-639-23469-5(3))* VDM Verlag Dr. Mueller e.K.

Yaknin, Judy. Driving It Home: 100 years of car Advertising. 2008. (Popular Culture Ser.). 132p. pap. 23.00 *(978-1-904750-35-2(4))* Libri Publishing Ltd GBR. Dist: Independent Pubs. Group.

Young, Vash. A Fortune to Share. 2009. 102p. pap. 20.68 *(978-0-557-11225-8(7))* Lulu Enterprises Inc.

Zweig, C. Dianne. Hot Kitchen & Home Collectibles 2nd Edition. 2nd ed. 2010. (ENG., Illus.). 304p. 24.95 *(978-1-57432-639-0(2),* 1574326392) Collector Bks.

ADVERTISING—AGENTS

see Advertising Agencies

ADVERTISING—AUTOMOBILE INDUSTRY AND TRADE

Heimann, Jim, ed. Cars of the 50s. 25th ed. 2009. (ENG., Illus.). 192p. 7.99 *(978-3-8365-1427-9(3))* TASCHEN DEU. Dist: Ingram Pub. Services.

Holmes, Duncan. Car Ads Infinitum: over 500 Car Ads from the Baby Boomer Years 1949-67. Volume 1-General Motors I Cadillac-Buick-Oldsmobile. 2009. 320p. pap. 10.00 *(978-0-557-20851-7(3))* Lulu Enterprises Inc.

Patton, Phil. Cars of the 20th Century: 100 Years of Automotive Ads, 1900-1999. Heimann, Jim, ed. 2009. (FRE, GER & ENG., Illus.). 400p. 39.99 *(978-3-8365-1463-7(X))* TASCHEN DEU. Dist: Ingram Pub. Services.

Stevenson, Heon. American Automobile Advertising, 1930-1980: An Illustrated History. 2008. (ENG., Illus.). 294p. 75.00 *(978-0-7864-3685-9(9))* McFarland & Co., Inc. Pubs.

ADVERTISING—BANKS AND BANKING

Hicks, Tyler G. Million Dollar Guide to Business & Real Estate Loan Sources. 17th ed. 2007. pap. 25.00 *(978-1-56150-849-5(7))* International Wealth Success, Inc.

ADVERTISING—BIOGRAPHY

Cruikshank, Jeffrey L. & Schultz, Arthur W. The Man Who Sold America: The Amazing (But True!) Story of Albert D. Lasker & the Creation of the Advertising Century. 2010. (ENG., Illus.). 480p. 27.95 *(978-1-59139-308-5(6))* Harvard Business Review Pr.

Gilbert, Richard L. Marching up Madison Avenue: How I Beat the Entrepreneurial Odds Armed with a Pencil & My Imagination. 2008. (ENG.). 200p. pap. 14.95 *(978-1-933016-51-1(5))* Behler Pubns., LLC.

Gill, Michael Gates. How Starbucks Saved My Life: A Son of Privilege Learns to Live Like Everyone Else. l.t. ed. 2008. (Thorndike Biography Ser.). 353p. 31.95 *(978-1-4104-0360-5(2))* Thorndike Pr.

Gossage, Howard. The Book of Gossage. rev. ed. 2006. 364p. per. 50.00 net. *(978-1-887229-28-9(0))* Copy Workshop, The.

Gupta, Sunil. Living on the Adge in JWT. 2010. (Roli Bks.). (ENG.). 466p. pap. 17.95 *(978-81-7436-744-0(6))* Roli Bks. Private, Ltd. IND. Dist: Ingram Pub. Services.

Guthrie, Kay. Selling Alaska: The White Collar Adventures of an Advertising Pioneer. 2006. (ENG., Illus.). 160p. (gr. 9). per. 14.95 *(978-0-9745014-8-2(4))* Epicenter Pr., Inc.

Oxby, Richard. A Search for Survival. 2007. (Illus.). 336p. per. *(978-1-84748-092-7(6))* Athena Pr.

Padulo, Rick. I Can Get It for You Retail: Down & Dirty Tales from a Canadian Ad Man. 2012. (ENG., Illus.). 224p. 29.99 ***(978-1-4597-0500-5(9))*** Dundurn CAN. Dist: Ingram Pub. Services.

Young, James Webb. The Itch for Orders: Chapter III of an Ego-Biography. 2011. 34p. 35.95 ***(978-1-258-09206-1(9))*** Literary Licensing, LLC.

ADVERTISING—BOOKS

Farrell, Mike. Of Mule & Man. 2009. (ENG.). 200p. pap. 15.95 *(978-1-933354-75-0(5))* Akashic Bks.

Garner, Dwight. Read Me: A Century of Classic American Book Advertisements. 2009. (ENG.). 304p. 26.99 *(978-0-06-157219-7(5),* Ecco) HarperCollins Pubs.

Horowitz, Shel. Grassroots Marketing for Authors & Publishers. 2007. 290p. pap. 24.95 *(978-0-7414-3469-2(5))* Infinity Publishing.

Lord, Udis. Publicity for Authors. 2009. pap. *(978-0-937571-05-7(9))* Philippine-American Educational Pr.

ADVERTISING—CARBONATED BEVERAGES

Berts, Jean-Michel, et al. Coca Cola (Trade) 2011. (ENG.). 208p. 65.00 *(978-2-7594-0514-5(1))* Assouline FRA. Dist: Perseus Distribution.

Thomas, Mark. Belching Out the Devil: Global Adventures with Coca-Cola. 2009. (ENG.). 384p. pap. 16.95 *(978-1-56858-431-7(8))* Basic Bks.

ADVERTISING—CHURCHES

see also Church Bulletins; Journalism, Religious

Harvey, L. James. 701 Sentence Sermons: Attention-Getting Quotes for Church Signs, Bulletins, Newsletters, & Sermons, 1 vol., Vol. 4. 2007. 144p. pap. 10.99 *(978-0-8254-2883-8(1))* Kregel Pubns.

ADVERTISING—CIGARETTES

Fritschler & Hoefler & Cram101 Textbook Reviews Staff. Smoking & Politics. 2007. 60p. per. 9.95 *(978-1-4288-2264-1(X))* Cram101 Inc.

ADVERTISING—CLOTHING AND DRESS

see also Fashion Shows

Blaszczyk, Regina Lee, ed. Producing Fashion: Commerce, Culture, & Consumers. 2009. (Hagley Perspectives on Business & Culture Ser.). (Illus.). 376p. (C). pap. 26.50 *(978-0-8122-2066-7(8))* Univ. of Pennsylvania Pr.

Heiman, Jim. 60s Fashion: Vintage Fashion & Beauty Ads. 2007. (GER, FRE & ENG., Illus.). 172p. per. 9.99 *(978-3-8228-4935-4(9))* TASCHEN DEU. Dist: Ingram Pub. Services.

McEuen, Melissa A. Making War, Making Women: Femininity & Duty on the American Home Front, 1941-1945. 2011. (ENG., Illus.). 344p. 69.95 *(978-0-8203-2904-8(5));* pap. 24.95 *(978-0-8203-2905-5(3))* Univ. of Georgia Pr.

Roberts, Kevin, text. Diesel: XXX Years of Diesel Communication. 2008. (Illus.). 251p. ***(978-88-17-02392-4(2))*** Rizzoli International Pubns., Inc.

Teller, Juergen, photos by. Election Day, 1 vol. 2009. (ENG., Illus.). 36p. pap. 21.00 *(978-3-86521-906-0(3))* Steidl, Gerhard Druckerei und Verlag DEU. Dist: Innovative Logistics.

ADVERTISING—COSMETICS

Dade, Penny. All Made Up: 100 Years of Cosmetics Advertising. 2007. (Popular Culture Ser.). (Illus.). 112p. pap. 23.00 *(978-1-904750-13-0(3))* Libri Publishing Ltd GBR. Dist: Independent Pubs. Group.

Grafton, Carol Belanger, ed. The Art of Perfume CD-ROM & Book. 2009. (Dover Electronic Clip Art Ser.). (ENG., Illus.). 48p. pap. 19.95 *(978-0-486-99086-6(9))* Dover Pubns., Inc.

Heiman, Jim. 60s Fashion: Vintage Fashion & Beauty Ads. 2007. (GER, FRE & ENG., Illus.). 172p. per. 9.99 *(978-3-8228-4935-4(9))* TASCHEN DEU. Dist: Ingram Pub. Services.

McEuen, Melissa A. Making War, Making Women: Femininity & Duty on the American Home Front, 1941-1945. 2011. (ENG., Illus.). 344p. 69.95 *(978-0-8203-2904-8(5));* pap. 24.95 *(978-0-8203-2905-5(3))* Univ. of Georgia Pr.

Tungate, Mark. Branded Beauty: How Marketing Changed the Way We Look. 2011. (ENG.). 288p. 29.95 *(978-0-7494-6181-2(0))* Kogan Page, Ltd. GBR. Dist: Ingram Pub. Services.

ADVERTISING—DATA PROCESSING

Marolf, Gerald. Advergaming & in-Game Advertising: An Approach to the next Generation of Advertising. 2007. 176p. per. *(978-3-8364-0285-9(8))* VDM Verlag Dr. Mueller e.K.

ADVERTISING—DICTIONARIES

Daube, Jean-Michel. Lexique Bilingue des Techniques Commerciales, Anglais-Francais/Francais-Anglais. (ENG & FRE.). *(978-0-7859-9324-7(X))* French & European Pubns., Inc.

ADVERTISING—DIRECTORIES

Hicks, Tyler G. Million Dollar Guide to Business & Real Estate Loan Sources. 17th ed. 2007. pap. 25.00 *(978-1-56150-849-5(7))* International Wealth Success, Inc.

Maher, Barry. Getting the Most from Your Yellow Pages Advertising: Maximum Profits at Minimum Cost. 3rd rev. exp. ed. 2006. (ENG., Illus.). 300p. (Orig.). per. 69.95 *(978-0-9787321-0-3(3))* Barry Maher & Associates.

National Register Publishing Co. Staff. Standard Directory of Advertisers, 1999. Date not set. 575.00 *(978-0-87217-270-8(8))* National Register Publishing.

Plunkett, Jack W. Plunkett's Advertising & Branding Industry Almanac 2007: Advertising & Branding Industry Market Research, Statistics, Trends & Leading Companies. annuals Plunkett, Jack W., ed. 2007. 544p. pap. 279.99 incl. cd-rom *(978-1-59392-081-4(4))* Plunkett Research, Ltd.

—Plunkett's Advertising & Branding Industry Almanac 2007 (E-Book) Advertising & Branding Industry Market Research, Statistics, Trends & Leading Companies. annuals Plunkett, Jack W., ed. 2007. 555p. E-Book 279.99 incl. cd-rom *(978-1-59392-423-2(2))* Plunkett Research, Ltd.

—Plunkett's Advertising & Branding Industry Almanac 2008: Advertising & Branding Industry Market Research, Statistics, Trends & Leading Companies. annuals Plunkett, Jack W., ed. 2008. 538p. pap. 299.99 incl. cd-rom *(978-1-59392-109-5(8))* Plunkett Research, Ltd.

Schonfeld & Associates. U. S. Sourcebook of Advertisers: 2007 Edition. 2007. 280p. spiral bd. 395.00 *(978-1-932024-45-6(X))* Schonfeld & Assocs., Inc.

ADVERTISING—HISTORY

Ballotta, Mirko & Bulgarelli, Stefano. È l'Ora Della Spesa: Pubblicità e Consumi Negli Anni Cinquanta. 2012. (ITA & ENG., Illus.). 144p. pap. 30.00 ***(978-88-96408-07-0(5))*** Anniversary Bks. ITA. Dist: National Bk. Network.

Berts, Jean-Michel, et al. Coca Cola (Trade) 2011. (ENG.). 208p. 65.00 *(978-2-7594-0514-5(1))* Assouline FRA. Dist: Perseus Distribution.

Chambers, Jason. Madison Avenue & the Color Line: African Americans in the Advertising Industry. 2009. (Illus.). 328p. (C). pap. 24.95 *(978-0-8122-2060-5(9))* Univ. of Pennsylvania Pr.

Chaudhuri, Arun. Indian Advertising: 1780 to 1950 A.D. 2007. (Illus.). xiv, 285p. *(978-0-07-060461-2(4))* TATA McGraw-Hill Publishing Co.

Clymer, Floyd, compiled by. Those Were the Days: Weird & Wacky Ads of Yesteryear. 2010. (ENG., Illus.). 240p. pap. 9.95 *(978-0-486-47242-3(6))* Dover Pubns., Inc.

Cram101 Textbook Reviews. Outlines & Highlights for Advertising in Modern & Postmodern Times by Pamela Odih. 2011. 68p. pap. 27.95 ***(978-1-61905-428-8(0))*** Cram101 Inc.

—Outlines & Highlights for Soap, Sex, & Cigarettes: A Cultural History of American Advertising by Juliann Sivulka, ISBN. 2011. 136p. pap. 28.95 ***(978-1-61812-103-5(0))*** Cram101 Inc.

Crawford, Robert. But Wait, There's More... A History of Australian Advertising, 1900-2000. 2008. (ENG.). 224p. pap. 26.00 *(978-0-522-85322-3(6))* Melbourne Univ. Publishing AUS. Dist: Independent Pubs. Group.

Cruddas, Colin. 100 Years Advertising in British Aviation. 2008. (ENG., Illus.). 192p. 64.95 *(978-0-7524-4527-4(8))* History Pr. Ltd., The GBR. Dist: Independent Pubs. Group.

Cruikshank, Jeffrey L. & Schultz, Arthur W. The Man Who Sold America: The Amazing (But True!) Story of Albert D. Lasker & the Creation of the Advertising Century. 2010. (ENG., Illus.). 480p. 27.95 *(978-1-59139-308-5(6))* Harvard Business Review Pr.

Darwin, Bernard, ed. The Dickens Advertiser: A Collection of the Advertisements in the Original Parts of Novels by Charles Dickens. 2007. (ENG.). 212p. 39.95 *(978-0-548-01299-4(7))* Kessinger Publishing, LLC.

Grafton, Carol Belanger, ed. Children in Old-Time Trade Cards CD-ROM & Book. 2008. (Dover Electronic Clip Art Ser.). (ENG., Illus.). 48p. pap. 22.95 *(978-0-486-99897-8(5))* Dover Pubns., Inc.

Heiman, Jim, ed. American Ads of the 50s & 60s: 25 Jahre Taschen, 2 vols. 2012. (25 Ser.). (FRE, GER & ENG.). 800p. pap. 59.99 *(978-3-8365-2834-4(7))* TASCHEN DEU. Dist: Ingram Pub. Services.

Janser, Andres & Junod, Barbara, eds. Corporate Diversity: Swiss Graphic Design & Advertising by Geigy 1940 - 1970. 2009. (Illus.). 208p. pap. *(978-3-03778-160-9(2))* Lars Muller Pubs.

Jump, Frank. Fading Ads of New York City. 2011. 220p. 24.99 ***(978-1-60949-438-4(5))*** History Pr., The.

Lemire, Beverly, ed. The Force of Fashion in Politics & Society: Global Perspectives from Early Modern to Contemporary Times. 2010. (History of Retailing & Consumption Ser.). (Illus.). 298p. 119.95 *(978-1-4094-0492-7(7))* Ashgate Publishing Co.

Library of Advertising, 6 vols., Set. 2009. 2700p. 1095.00 *(978-4-86166-122-8(6))* Routledge.

Museum Fur Gestaltung Zurich, et al, eds. Corporate Diversity: Schweizer Grafik und Werbung für Geigy 1940 -1970. 2009. (GER., Illus.). 208p. pap. *(978-3-03778-161-6(0))* Lars Muller Pubs.

Parker, Kate. Outrageous Ads: Meet Your Father's Automobile, the Nervous Housewife, the Smoking Doctor & the Bearded Baby. 2008. (ENG., Illus.). 96p. 14.99 *(978-1-933176-20-8(2))* Red Rock Pr., Inc.

Parkin, Katherine J. Food Is Love: Advertising & Gender Roles in Modern America. 2007. (Illus.). 304p. (C). per. 26.50 *(978-0-8122-1992-0(9))* Univ. of Pennsylvania Pr.

Sivulka. Soap Sex & Cigarettes A Cultural Histo. 2006. pap. 10.95 *(978-1-4288-0941-3(4))* Cram101 Inc.

Sivulka, Juliann. Soap, Sex, & Cigarettes: A Cultural History of American Advertising. 2nd ed. 2011. (ENG., Illus.). 448p. (C). pap. 80.95 ***(978-1-133-31113-3(X))*** Wadsworth.

Stevenson, Heon. American Automobile Advertising, 1930-1980: An Illustrated History. 2008. (ENG., Illus.). 294p. 75.00 *(978-0-7864-3685-9(9))* McFarland & Co., Inc. Pubs.

Taylor, Timothy D. The Sounds of Capitalism: Advertising, Music, & the Conquest of Culture. 2012. (ENG., Illus.). 408p. 35.00 ***(978-0-226-79115-9(7))*** Univ. of Chicago Pr.

Thornton, Sara. Advertising, Subjectivity & the Nineteenth-Century Novel: Dickens, Balzac & the Language of the Walls. 2009. (Palgrave Studies in Nineteenth-Century Writing & Culture Ser.). (ENG., Illus.). 256p. 84.00 *(978-0-230-00832-8(1))* Palgrave Macmillan.

Tungate, Mark. Adland: A Global History of Advertising. 2007. (ENG., Illus.). 278p. 39.95 *(978-0-7494-4837-0(7))* Kogan Page, Ltd. GBR. Dist: Ingram Pub. Services.

Vaknin, Judy. Smoke Signals: 100 Years of Tobacco Advertising. 2007. (Popular Culture Ser.). (Illus.). 112p. pap. 23.00 *(978-1-904750-12-3(5))* Libri Publishing Ltd GBR. Dist: Independent Pubs. Group.

West, Sally. I Shop in Moscow: Advertising & the Creation of Consumer Culture in Late Tsarist Russia. 2011. (ENG., Illus.). 334p. 45.00 *(978-0-87580-648-8(1))* Northern Illinois Univ. Pr.

Whitaker, Jan. The World of Department Stores. 2011. (ENG., Illus.). 264p. 60.00 *(978-0-86565-264-4(3))* Vendome Pr., The.

Williams, Elizabeth, et al. This Is Advertising. 2010. (ENG., Illus.). 224p. pap. 40.00 *(978-1-85669-647-0(2))* King, Laurence Publishing GBR. Dist: Hachette Bk. Group.

ADVERTISING—HOTELS

Kesselskramer. The Worst Hotel in the World: The Hans Brinker Budget Hotel, Amsterdam. 2009. (ENG., Illus.). 280p. 35.00 *(978-1-86154-311-0(5))* Booth-Clibborn Editions GBR. Dist: Hachette Bk. Group.

ADVERTISING—LAW

see Advertising Laws

ADVERTISING—LAWYERS

Foonberg, Jay. How to Get & Keep Good Clients. 3rd rev. ed. 2007. (ENG., Illus.). 618p. pap. 179.95 *(978-0-9795671-0-0(6))* National Academy of Law Ethics & Management, Inc.

Haserot, Phyllis Weiss. The Rainmaking Machine: Marketing, Planning, Strategies, & Management for Law Firms. 2007. x, 760p. pap. *(978-0-314-97717-5(1))* West Publishing Co., College & Schl. Div.

MacDonagh, Catherine Alman, et al. The Law Firm Associate's Guide to Personal Marketing & Selling Skills. 2007. (ENG., Illus.). 120p. pap. 49.95 *(978-1-59031-830-0(7))*; 48p. per. 59.95 *(978-1-59031-833-1(1))* American Bar Assn.

Singer, Gerald M. How to Be a Wealthy Lawyer Through Salesmanship! 2006. pap. 69.95 *(978-1-58477-762-5(1))* Lawbook Exchange, Ltd., The.

Walker, Corey J. The Facts about Attorney Advertising: Myths & Mistakes Made by Injured Iowans Revealed. 2007. per. 24.95 *(978-1-59872-857-6(1))* Instant Pub.

Weiss Haserot, Pyhllis. The Rainmaking Machine: Marketing Planning, Strategies, & Management for Law Firms. 2008. 861p. pap. 275.00 *(978-0-314-99019-8(4))* West.

ADVERTISING—LIBRARIES

see also Libraries—Public Relations

Mathews, Brian. Marketing Today's Academic Library: A Bold New Approach to Communicating with Students. 2009. (Illus.). 136p. 48.00 *(978-0-8389-0984-3(1))* American Library Assn.

ADVERTISING—MEDICINE

Gideon, David, et al. Medicine Ave 2: The Story of Medical Advertising, 1990-2008. 2010. (Illus.). 301p. ***(978-0-615-32415-9(0))*** Mercy Medical Ctr.

Thompson, Bambi. Direct-to-Consumer Advertising of Prescription Products - Ethical Strategies That Make Good Business Sense. 2008. 132p. per. *(978-3-8364-5981-5(7))* VDM Verlag Dr. Mueller e.K.

ADVERTISING—MOTION PICTURES

Gray, Jonathan. Show Sold Separately: Promos, Spoilers, & Other Media Paratexts. 2010. (ENG., Illus.). 256p. pap. 22.00 *(978-0-8147-3195-6(3))* New York Univ. Pr.

Johnston, Keith M. Coming Soon: Film Trailers & the Selling of Hollywood Technology. 2009. (ENG., Illus.). 228p. pap. 39.95 *(978-0-7864-4432-8(0))* McFarland & Co., Inc. Pubs.

ADVERTISING—PERIODICALS

Azur Corporation Editors, creator. Display, Commercial Space & Sign Design, Vol. 33. 2007. (ENG., Illus.). 358p. 85.00 *(978-4-89737-549-6(5))* Azur Corp. JPN. Dist: Antique Collectors' Club.

LaFleur, Teresa & LaFleur, Bruce, eds. LaFleur's 1997 World Lottery Almanac. 5th ed. 425p. pap. *(978-1-883567-75-0(0))* TLF Pubns., Inc.

New, York Festivals, creator. New York Festivals 14: International Advertising Awards. 2006. (New York Festivals Annual of Advertising Ser.). (Illus.). 514p. 65.00 *(978-0-9774930-0-5(8)*, Collins Design) HarperCollins Pubs.

One Club Staff. One Show, Vol. 31. 2010. (One Show Ser.). (ENG., Illus.). 368p. 69.95 *(978-0-929837-40-6(1)*, 0929837401) Quayside.

—One Show Vol. 32: To Steal Is Genius. 2011. (ENG., Illus.). 448p. 69.95 *(978-0-929837-44-4(4)*, 0929837444) Quayside.

One Club Staff, ed. One Show, Volume 30 Vol. 30. 2009. (One Show Ser.). (ENG., Illus.). 416p. 69.95 *(978-0-929837-36-9(3)*, 0929837363) Quayside.

Schonfeld & Associates. Advertising Ratios & Budgets: 2007 Edition. 2007. 200p. per. 395.00 *(978-1-932024-43-2(3))* Schonfeld & Assocs., Inc.

The One Club. One Show Boxed Set, 2011 Awards, 3 vols. 2012. (ENG., Illus.). 928p. 155.00 *(978-0-929837-52-9(5)*, 0929837525) Quayside.

—One Show Interactive, Volume XIV. 2012. (ENG., Illus.). 296p. pap. 49.95 *(978-0-929837-51-2(7)*, 0929837517) Quayside.

—One Show, Volume 33. 2012. (One Show Ser.). (ENG., Illus.). 438p. 74.99 *(978-0-929837-49-9(5)*, 0929837495) Quayside.

ADVERTISING—PHARMACEUTICAL INDUSTRY

Jain, Shaili. Understanding Physician-Pharmaceutical Industry Interaction. 2007. (ENG.). 160p. 73.00 *(978-0-521-86364-8(5))* Cambridge Univ. Pr.

—Understanding Physician-Pharmaceutical Industry Interactions. 2007. (ENG.). 160p. per. 28.99 *(978-0-521-68866-6(3))* Cambridge Univ. Pr.

ADVERTISING—PSYCHOLOGICAL ASPECTS

see also Motivation Research (Marketing)

Clark, Eric. The Real Toy Story: Inside the Ruthless Battle for America's Youngest Consumers. 2007. (ENG.). 272p. 26.00 *(978-0-7432-4765-8(5)*, Free Pr.) Free Pr.

Committee on Sc. Subliminal Communication Technology. 2006. 304p. per. 29.50 *(978-1-4102-2590-0(9))* Univ. Pr. of the Pacific.

Cyril De Run, Ernest. Targeted Advertising Unintended Effects. 2008. 132p. pap. *(978-3-639-06100-0(4))* VDM Verlag Dr. Mueller e.K.

Davis, Alison & Brown, Paul. Your Attention Please: How to Appeal to Today's Distracted, Disinterested, Disengaged, Disenchanted, & Busy Consumer. 2006. (ENG., Illus.). 256p. per. 14.95 *(978-1-59337-687-1(1))* Adams Media Corp.

Delton, Yohan. A Scientific Investigation of Persuasive Appeals - Comparing the Effectiveness of Hedonistic & Virtue Ethics Messages in Advertisements. 2008. 96p. pap. *(978-3-639-10615-2(6))* VDM Verlag Dr. Mueller e.K.

du Plessis, Erik. The Advertised Mind: Groundbreaking Insights into How Our Brains Respond to Advertising. 2008. (ENG., Illus.). 256p. pap. 35.00 *(978-0-7494-5024-3(X))* Kogan Page, Ltd. GBR. Dist: Ingram Pub. Services.

Du Plessis, Erik. The Branded Mind: What Neuroscience Really Tells Us about the Puzzle of the Brain & the Brand. 2011. (ENG., Illus.). 272p. 34.95 *(978-0-7494-6125-6(X))* Kogan Page, Ltd. GBR. Dist: Ingram Pub. Services.

Faulkner, Joanne. The Importance of Being Innocent: Why We Worry about Children, 1 vol. 2010. 176p. pap. 32.99 *(978-0-521-14597-5(6))* Cambridge Univ. Pr.

Freedman, Robert. Quiet! the New Scarcity. 2009. (Illus.). xii, 205p. 32.95 *(978-0-87586-715-1(4))*; 188p. pap. 22.95 *(978-0-87586-714-4(6))* Algora Publishing.

Heath, Robert. Seducing the Subconscious: The Psychology of Emotional Influence in Advertising. 2012. (ENG., Illus.). 264p. 32.95 ***(978-0-470-97488-9(5)***, Wiley-Blackwell) Wiley, John & Sons, Inc.

Hill, Dan. About Face: The Secrets of Emotionally Effective Advertising. 2010. (ENG., Illus.). 212p. 29.95 *(978-0-7494-5757-0(0))* Kogan Page, Ltd. GBR. Dist: Ingram Pub. Services.

Hogshead, Sally. Fascinate: Your 7 Triggers to Persuasion & Captivation. 2010. (ENG.). 288p. 26.99 *(978-0-06-171470-2(4)*, Collins) HarperCollins Pubs.

Johnson, Fern & Johnson, Fern L. Imaging in Advertising: Verbal & Visual Codes of Commerce. 2007. (Illus.). XVI, 256p. 34.95 *(978-0-415-97882-8(3))* Taylor & Francis Group.

Johnson, Fern L. Imaging in Advertising: Verbal & Visual Codes of Commerce. 2007. (ENG., Illus.). 272p. 110.00 *(978-0-415-97881-1(5))* Routledge.

Kelsmark, Kevin Ann. Sexual Imagery Attitudes in Advertising - a Comparison Between Hispanics & Non-Hispanics. 2008. 120p. per. *(978-3-8364-5744-6(X))* VDM Verlag Dr. Mueller e.K.

Kingston University. The Effect of Advertising & Display: Assessing the Evidence. 2010. xiv, 136p. pap. 89.95 *(978-1-4419-5373-5(6)*, 1441953736) Springer.

Krugman, Edward. Consumer Behavior & Advertising Involvement: Selected Works of Herbert E. Krugman. 2008. (Marketing & Consumer Psychology Ser.). (ENG.). 354p. 73.95 *(978-0-8058-5786-7(5)*, Routledge) Taylor & Francis Group GBR. Dist: Taylor & Francis Group.

Kulpe, Oswald. Outlines of Psychology. Wozniak, Robert H., ed. (Classics in Psychology Ser.). (Illus.). 480p. *(978-1-85506-682-3(3)*, Burns & Oates) Continuum International Publishing Group, Ltd.

Lamb, Sharon & Brown, Lyn Mikel. Packaging Girlhood: Rescuing Our Daughters from Marketers' Schemes. annot. ed. 2007. (ENG., Illus.). 336p. pap. 14.95 *(978-0-312-37005-3(9)*, St. Martin's Griffin) St. Martin's Pr.

Lindstrom, Martin. Brand Sense: Sensory Secrets Behind the Stuff We Buy. 2010. (ENG.). 192p. pap. 15.00 *(978-1-4391-7201-8(3)*, Free Pr.) Free Pr.

Manca, Luigi, et al, eds. Utopian Images & Narratives in Advertising: Dreams for Sale. Sorci-Bradley, Dolores, tr. 2012. (ENG.). 296p. (gr. 17). 80.00 ***(978-0-7391-7326-8(X))*** Lexington Bks.

Packard, Vance. The Hidden Persuaders. 2007. (ENG.). 200p. reprint ed. per. 14.95 *(978-0-9788431-0-6(X))* Ig Publishing, Inc.

Scott, Walter D. The Psychology of Advertising. (Classics in Psychology Ser.). (Illus.). 294p. *(978-1-85506-694-6(7)*, Burns & Oates) Continuum International Publishing Group, Ltd.

Shrum, L. J., ed. The Psychology of Entertainment Media: Blurring the Lines Between Entertainment & Persuasion. 2nd rev. ed. 2012. (ENG.). 364p. 75.00 *(978-1-84872-944-5(8)*, Routledge) Taylor & Francis Group GBR. Dist: Taylor & Francis Group.

Stoklossa, Uwe & Rempen, Thomas. Advertising: New Techniques for Visual Seduction. 2010. (ENG., Illus.). 272p. pap. 39.95 *(978-0-500-28909-5(3)*, 528909) Thames & Hudson.

Sutherland, Max & Sylvester, Alice. Advertising & the Mind of the Consumer: What Works, What Doesn't, & Why. 3rd ed. 2009. (ENG., Illus.). 352p. pap. 24.95 *(978-1-74175-599-2(9))* Allen & Unwin AUS. Dist: Independent Pubs. Group.

Vitale, Joe. The Seven Lost Secrets of Success: Million Dollar Ideas of Bruce Barton, America's Forgotten Genius. 2007. (ENG.). 193p. 24.95 *(978-0-470-10810-9(X)*, Wiley) Wiley, John & Sons, Inc.

Wedel, Michel & Pieters, Rik. Eye Tracking for Visual Marketing. 2008. (ENG.). 100p. pap. 75.00 net. *(978-1-60198-154-7(6))* Now Pubs.

Wedel, Michel & Pieters, Rik, eds. Visual Marketing: From Attention to Action. 2007. (Marketing & Consumer Psychology Ser.). (ENG., Illus.). 328p. 94.95 *(978-0-8058-6292-8(7)*, Psychology Press) Taylor & Francis Group GBR. Dist: Taylor & Francis Group.

Whitman, Drew Eric. Cashvertising: How to Use More Than 100 Secrets of Ad-Agency Psychology to Make Big Money Selling Anything to Anyone. 2008. (ENG.). 1p. pap. 14.99 *(978-1-60163-032-2(8))* Career Pr., Inc.

ADVERTISING—REAL ESTATE BUSINESS

Blodgett, Jan. Land of Bright Promise: Advertising the Texas Panhandle & South Plains, 1870-1917. 2011. (ENG.). 166p. pap. 19.95 ***(978-0-292-74223-9(1))*** Univ. of Texas Pr.

ADVERTISING—RESEARCH

Cano, Cynthia. Advertising Ethnicity. 2008. 212p. pap. *(978-3-639-00296-6(2))* VDM Verlag Dr. Mueller e.K.

Chafai, Habiba. Gender & the Language of Advertising. 2010. 108p. pap. *(978-3-639-23332-2(8))* VDM Verlag Dr. Mueller e.K.

Davis, Joel J. Advertising Research: Theory & Practice. 2nd rev. ed. 2011. (ENG.). 704p. (C). 129.33 *(978-0-13-212832-2(2)*, Prentice Hall) Prentice Hall PTR.

De Pelsmacker, Patrick & Dens, Nathalie, eds. Advertising Research: Message, Medium & Context. 2009. (Illus.). 392p. pap. 127.50 *(978-90-441-2387-6(4))* Garant Uitgevers N.V. BEL. Dist: Coronet Bks.

du Plessis, Erik. The Advertised Mind: Groundbreaking Insights into How Our Brains Respond to Advertising. 2008. (ENG., Illus.). 256p. pap. 35.00 *(978-0-7494-5024-3(X))* Kogan Page, Ltd. GBR. Dist: Ingram Pub. Services.

Hill, Dan. About Face: The Secrets of Emotionally Effective Advertising. 2010. (ENG., Illus.). 212p. 29.95 *(978-0-7494-5757-0(0))* Kogan Page, Ltd. GBR. Dist: Ingram Pub. Services.

Jugenheimer, Donald W., et al. Advertising & Public Relations Research. 2010. (ENG., Illus.). 336p. (C). pap. 84.95 *(978-0-7656-2418-5(4))* Sharpe, M.E. Inc.

Lucas, Darrell Blaine & Britt, Steuart Henderson. Advertising Psychology & Research. 2011. 784p. 72.95 ***(978-1-258-01236-6(7))*** Literary Licensing, LLC.

Maex, Dimitri & Brown, Paul B. Sexy Little Numbers: How to Grow Your Business Using the Data You Already Have. 2012. (ENG.). 304p. 27.50 ***(978-0-307-88834-1(7)***, Crown Business) Crown Publishing Group.

Marshall, Stephen W. & Roberts, Marilyn Sue. Television Advertising That Works: An Analysis of Commercials from Effective Campaigns. 2008. 196p. 104.95 *(978-1-60497-513-0(X))* Cambria Pr.

Okazaki, S., ed. Handbook of Research on International Advertising. 2012. (Elgar Original Reference Ser.). (Illus.). 576p. 260.00 ***(978-1-84844-858-2(9))*** Elgar, Edward Publishing, Inc.

Sheehan, Kim Bartel, et al. Using Qualitative Research in Advertising: Strategies, Techniques, & Applications. 2nd ed. 2011. (Illus.). 240p. (C). pap. 40.00 ***(978-1-4129-8724-0(5)***, B87240P) SAGE Pubns., Inc.

Weerakkody, Niranjala. Research Methods for Media & Communication. 2008. (ENG., Illus.). x, 310p. (C). pap. 64.95 *(978-0-19-556044-2(2))* Oxford Univ. Pr., Inc.

ADVERTISING—RETAIL TRADE

see Advertising

ADVERTISING—SMALL BUSINESS

Sheehan, Kim & O'Leary, Steve. Building Buzz to Beat the Big Boys: Word of Mouth Marketing for Small Businesses. 1 vol. 2008. (Illus.). 200p. 39.95 *(978-0-313-34598-2(6)*, C34598, Praeger Pubs.) Greenwood Publishing Group, Inc.

ADVERTISING—VOCATIONAL GUIDANCE

Andrews, Brad. The Truth about Advertising & Public Relations Jobs - How to Job-Hunt & Career-Change for Advertising & Public Relations Jobs - the Facts You Should Know. 2009. (Illus.). 196p. pap. *(978-1-74244-169-6(6))* Emereo Pty Ltd.

Cram101 Textbook Reviews Staff. Outlines & Highlights for Pick Me: Breaking into Advertising & Staying There by Vonk, ISBN. 2009. 78p. pap. 27.95 *(978-1-4288-6833-5(X))* Cram101 Inc.

Elwins, Dannie. How to Turn Yourself into A World-Class Copywriter. 2009. 56p. pap. 16.99 *(978-0-557-15708-2(0))* Lulu Enterprises Inc.

Minsky, Laurence. How to Succeed in Advertising When All You Have Is Talent. 2nd ed. 2007. 457p. per. 47.50 net. *(978-1-887229-20-3(5))* Copy Workshop, The.

Paetro, Maxine. How to Put Your Book Together & Get a Job in Advertising. 2nd ed. 2010. (ENG., Illus.). 256p. pap. 32.95 *(978-0-393-73285-6(1)*, 73285) Norton, W. W. & Co., Inc.

Thorne, Lynn. Word of Mouth Advertising Online & Off: How to Spark Buzz, Excitement, & Free Publicity for Your Business or Organization. 2008. (ENG.). 288p. per. 24.95 *(978-1-60138-011-1(9))* Atlantic Publishing Co.

Tibbs, Andy. Advertising. 2010. (ENG., Illus.). 232p. (C). instr.'s gde. ed. 131.00 *(978-0-415-54468-9(9))*; instr.'s gde. ed. 52.95 *(978-0-415-54466-5(1))* Routledge.

Tymorek, Stan. Advertising & Public Relations. 2010. (Career Launcher Ser.). 176p. (C). (gr. 9-18). 34.95 *(978-0-8160-7961-2(7)*, Ferguson Publishing Co.); pap. 14.95 *(978-0-8160-7983-4(8)*, Checkmark Bks.) Facts On File, Inc.

Vault Editors. Vault Guide to the Top Advertising & Public Relations Employers, 2007 Edition. 2008. 176p. pap. 19.95 *(978-1-58131-455-7(8))* Vault.com.

Veksner, Simon, et al. How to Make It as an Advertising Creative. 2010. (ENG., Illus.). 160p. pap. 24.95 *(978-1-85669-657-9(X))* King, Laurence Publishing GBR. Dist: Hachette Bk. Group.

WetFeet Editorial Staff, ed. Careers in Advertising & Public Relations. 2007. 158p. pap. 24.95 *(978-1-58207-646-1(4))* WetFeet, Inc.

Wojak, Angie. Spark Your Career in Advertising. 2007. *(978-1-4114-9813-6(5))* Spark Publishing Group.

ADVERTISING—YEARBOOKS

Print Casebooks 9: The Best in Advertising, 1991-1992. (Illus.). 96p. 27.95 *(978-0-915734-70-2(2))* RC Pubns., Inc.

ADVERTISING, ART IN

see Art and Industry; Commercial Art

ADVERTISING, CLASSIFIED

Job Hunter's Sourcebook. 11th ed. 2011. pap. 220.00 *(978-1-4144-6889-1(X))* Cengage Gale.

Lloyd, Jenna & Gunter, Sherry Kinkoph. Craigslist 4 Everyone. 2008. (ENG., Illus.). 320p. pap. 19.99 *(978-0-7897-3826-8(7))* Que.

Rose, David. They Call Me Naughty Lola: Personal Ads from the London Review of Books. 2010. (ENG.). 176p. pap. 12.99 *(978-1-4165-4030-4(X)*, Scribner) Scribner.

ADVERTISING, COLOR IN

see Color in Advertising

ADVERTISING, CONSUMER

see Advertising

ADVERTISING, DIRECT-MAIL

see also Commercial Catalogs; Mail-Order Business; Sales Letters

Boers, Nicholas M. An Automation of Mail Channels to Eliminate Junk E-Mail. 2008. 92p. pap. *(978-3-639-02127-1(4))* VDM Verlag Dr. Mueller e.K.

Grensing-Pophal, Lin. Direct Mail in the Digital Age. 2011. (ENG.). 168p. pap. 18.95 *(978-1-77040-071-9(0))* Self-Counsel Pr., Inc. CAN. Dist: National Bk. Network.

Lehman, Erich. Data-Driven Print Teaching Supplements. 2006. cd-rom 49.00 *(978-1-933360-20-1(8))* Rochester Institute of Technology, Cary Graphic Arts Pr.

Miyazaki, Ami, ed. New Absolute Appeal: Direct Mail Design. 2010. (ENG., Illus.). 160p. 75.00 *(978-4-7562-4016-3(X)*, PIE Bks.) Rizzoli International Pubns., Inc.

Shepard, Judy. The Catalog Book: Designs for Catalogs & Direct Mail. 2007. (Illus.). 175p. 40.00 *(978-1-58471-097-4(7))* Visual Reference Pubns., Inc.

ADVERTISING, FRAUDULENT

see Deceptive Advertising

ADVERTISING, INDUSTRIAL

Hviid, Marlene & Lerhard Jakobsen, Britt. A Comparative Analysis of Four Chanel Advertisements. 2011. 64p. pap. ***(978-3-8443-2034-3(2))*** Lambert Academic Publishing.

Land, Bob. America's Greatest Brands. 2009. (Americas Greatest Brands Ser.). (ENG.). 113p. 45.00 *(978-0-9706860-6-0(4))* America's Greatest Brands.

Puttur, Hansraz. Innovation of the Advertising Industry As Kpo. 2010. 108p. pap. *(978-3-8383-4224-5(0))* Lambert Academic Publishing.

Ron Ploof. Read This: The Executive's Guide to New Media-from Blogs to Social Networks. 2009. 180p. 27.95 *(978-1-4401-6687-7(0))*; pap. 17.95 *(978-1-4401-6685-3(4))* iUniverse, Inc.

Schober, Johanna. Intercultural Influences in a Strategic Communication Process. 2010. 132p. pap. *(978-3-639-23741-2(2))* VDM Verlag Dr. Mueller e.K.

Stevens, Ruth. Maximizing Lead Generation: The Complete Guide for B2B Marketers. rev. ed. 2011. (Que Biz-Tech Ser.). (ENG., Illus.). 224p. pap. 24.99 *(978-0-7897-4114-1(8))* Que.

ADVERTISING, MAGAZINE

Adkins Covert, Tawnya J. Manipulating Images: World War II Mobilization of Women through Magazine Advertising. 2012. (Lexington Studies in Political Communication Ser.). (ENG.). 198p. pap. 29.99 ***(978-0-7391-7674-0(9))*** Lexington Bks.

Adkins, Tawnya. Manipulating Images: World War II Mobilization of Women through Magazine Advertising. 2011. (Lexington Studies in Political Communication Ser.). (ENG., Illus.). 204p. 65.00 *(978-0-7391-3911-0(8))* Lexington Bks.

Jones, John Bush. All-Out for Victory! Magazine Advertising & the World War II Home Front. 2009. (ENG., Illus.). 340p. lib. bdg. 50.00 *(978-1-58465-768-2(5)*, Brandeis University Press) Univ. Pr. of New England.

ADVERTISING, MAGAZINE—DIRECTORIES

see Advertising—Directories

ADVERTISING, MAIL

see Advertising, Direct-Mail

ADVERTISING, NEWSPAPER

see also Advertising, Classified

Oliver Jr, Sylvester W. Hidden Chronicles: Published Ads on Buying, Selling & Recapturing Enslaved Africans in Marshall County, Mississippi. 2008. 63p. pap. 10.95 *(978-1-59800-967-5(2))* Outskirts Pr., Inc.

Rogers, Jason. Building Newspaper Advertising. 2009. 290p. pap. *(978-1-150-43269-9(1))* Books LLC.

Stoltzfus, Duane C. S. Freedom from Advertising: E. W. Scripps's Chicago Experiment. 2007. (History of Communication Ser.). (Illus.). 208p. 42.00 *(978-0-252-03115-1(6))* Univ. of Illinois Pr.

Wigelsworth, Jeffrey R. Selling Science in the Age of Newton: Advertising & the Commoditization of Knowledge. 2010. (Science, Technology & Culture, 1700ndash;1945 Ser.). (Illus.). 218p. 119.95 *(978-1-4094-0075-2(1))* Ashgate Publishing Co.

ADVERTISING, NEWSPAPER—DIRECTORIES
see Advertising—Directories

ADVERTISING, OUTDOOR
see also Advertising Cards; Billboards; Posters; Show Windows; Sign Painting; Signs and Signboards

Cronin, Anne M. Advertising, Commercial Spaces & the Urban. 2010. (Consumption & Public Life Ser.). (ENG., Illus.). 224p. 89.00 *(978-0-230-21680-8(3))* Palgrave Macmillan.

Hollis, Tim. Wish You Were Here: Classic Florida Motel & Restaurant Advertising. 2011. (ENG., Illus.). 288p. 34.95 *(978-0-8130-3683-0(6))* Univ. Pr. of Florida.

Laufer, Peter & Swan, Sheila. Neon Nevada. 2011. (ENG., Illus.). 128p. 16.95 *(978-0-7627-7068-7(6))* Globe Pequot Pr., The.

Marin, Dan. Signs of Opportunity: How Lamar Advertising Company Became the Biggest Business of Its Kind in the U.S.A. 2007. *(978-0-925417-57-2(2))* Acadian Hse. Publishing.

—Signs of Opportunity: How Lamar Advertising Grew into the Biggest Billboard Business in America. 2008. (Illus.). 196p. per. 15.95 *(978-0-925417-61-9(0))* Acadian Hse. Publishing.

O'Hara, K., et al, eds. Public & Situated Displays: Social & Interactional Aspects of Shared Display Technologies. 2011. (Computer Supported Cooperative Work Ser.). (ENG.). 456p. pap. 269.00 *(978-90-481-6449-3(4),* 9048164494) Springer.

ADVERTISING, PICTORIAL
see Posters

ADVERTISING, POINT-OF-SALE
see also Display of Merchandise; Show Windows; Signs and Signboards

Alpha Planning Inc., Staff. Best POP Design. Planning, Alpha, ed. 2009. (ENG., Illus.). 256p. 70.00 *(978-4-568-50348-7(5))* Azur Corp. JPN. Dist: Antique Collectors' Club.

Azur Corporation Editors. New P. O. P. Design 2. 2007. (JPN & ENG., Illus.). 224p. 70.00 *(978-4-86267-015-1(6))* Azur Corp. JPN. Dist: Antique Collectors' Club.

The Power of Marketing At-Retail: 3rd Edition. 2008. (Illus.). per. *(978-0-9707099-2-9(7))* Point-Of-Purchase Advertising International.

Stahlberg, Markus & Maila, Ville. Shopper Marketing: How to Increase Purchase Decisions at the Point of Sale. 2010. (ENG., Illus.). 240p. 39.95 *(978-0-7494-5702-0(3))* Kogan Page, Ltd. GBR. Dist: Ingram Pub. Services.

Stahlberg, Markus & Maila, Ville, eds. Shopper Marketing: How to Increase Purchase Decisions at the Point of Sale. 2nd ed. 2012. (ENG., Illus.). 296p. 39.95 ***(978-0-7494-6471-4(2))*** Kogan Page, Ltd. GBR. Dist: Ingram Pub. Services.

ADVERTISING, POLITICAL
see also Radio in Politics; Television in Politics

Abrajano, Marisa. Campaigning to the New American Electorate: Advertising to Latino Voters. 2010. (ENG.). 216p. 60.00 *(978-0-8047-6895-5(1));* pap. 21.95 *(978-0-8047-6896-2(X))* Stanford Univ. Pr.

Baker, Frank W. Political Campaigns & Political Advertising: A Media Literacy Guide, 1 vol. 2009. (Illus.). 196p. 45.00 *(978-0-313-34755-9(7),* GR4755, Greenwood Pr.) Greenwood Publishing Group, Inc.

Brändle, Christian. Kopf an Kopf: Politikerporträts = Head to Head: Political Portraits. Museum für Gestaltung Zürich, ed. 2008. (Poster Collection). (GER & ENG., Illus.). 192p. pap. 39.95 *(978-3-03778-151-7(3),* 3037781513) Springer.

Corporate Governance after Citizens United: Hearing Before the Subcommittee on Capital Markets, Insurance, & Government Sponsored Enterprises of the Committee on Financial Services, U.S. House of Representatives, One Hundred Eleventh Congress, Second Session, March 11, 2010. 2010. (Illus.). v, 212p. *(978-0-16-086320-2(1),* 552-070-41407-0) United States Government Printing Office.

Dover, E. D. On Message: Television Advertising by the Presidential Candidates in Election 2008. 2010. (ENG.). 278p. 75.00 *(978-0-7391-4790-0(0))* Lexington Bks.

First Amendment & Campaign Finance Reform after Citizens United: Hearing Before the Subcommittee on the Constitution, Civil Rights, & Civil Liberties of the Committee on the Judiciary, House of Representatives, One Hundred Eleventh Congress, Second Session, February 3, 2010. 2010. (Illus.). iii, 175p. *(978-0-16-085790-4(2),* 552-070-41007-4) United States Government Printing Office.

For Know-It-Alls Staff. Propaganda for Know-It-Alls. 2008. pap. 9.99 *(978-1-59986-210-1(7),* For Know-It-Alls) Filiquarian Publishing, LLC.

Franz, Michael M. Choices & Changes: Interest Groups in the Electoral Process. 2008. (ENG., Illus.). 240p. 78.50 *(978-1-59213-673-5(7));* pap. 24.95 *(978-1-59213-674-2(5))* Temple Univ. Pr.

Franz, Michael M., et al. Campaign Advertising & American Democracy. 2007. (ENG., Illus.). 216p. 80.50 *(978-1-59213-455-7(6));* per. 26.95 *(978-1-59213-456-4(4))* Temple Univ. Pr.

Groeling, Tim. When Politicians Attack: Party Cohesion in the Media. 2010. (Communication, Society & Politics Ser.). (ENG., Illus.). 256p. pap. 28.99 *(978-0-521-60307-2(2))* Cambridge Univ. Pr.

Groeling, Tim J. When Politicians Attack: Party Cohesion in the Media. 2010. (Communication, Society & Politics Ser.). (ENG., Illus.). 264p. 85.00 *(978-0-521-84209-9(3))* Cambridge Univ. Pr.

Johansen, Helen P. M. Relational Political Marketing in Party-Centered Democracies: Because We Deserve It. 2012. (Illus.). 240p. 99.95 ***(978-1-4094-3905-9(4))*** Ashgate Publishing Co.

Lees-Marshment, Jennifer. Political Marketing: Principles & Applications. 2009. (ENG., Illus.). 320p. (C). 145.00 *(978-0-415-43128-6(X))* Routledge.

Maarek, Philippe J. Campaign Communication & Political Marketing. 2011. (ENG., Illus.). 288p. 99.95 *(978-1-4443-3234-6(1));* pap. 46.95 *(978-1-4443-3235-3(X))* Wiley, John & Sons, Inc. (Wiley-Blackwell).

Mann, Robert. Daisy Petals & Mushroom Clouds: LBJ, Barry Goldwater, & the Ad That Changed American Politics. 2011. (Illus.). 216p. 22.50 ***(978-0-8071-4293-6(X))*** Louisiana State Univ. Pr.

Mark, David. Going Dirty: The Art of Negative Campaigning. 2nd ed. 2009. (ENG.). 300p. pap. 27.50 *(978-0-7425-9981-9(7))* Rowman & Littlefield Publishers, Inc.

Mark, David, et al. American Constitutional Law: Essays, Cases, & Comparative Notes. 2nd ed. 2009. (ENG.). 300p. 79.00 *(978-0-7425-9986-4(8))* Rowman & Littlefield Publishers, Inc.

Mason, Thomas O. & James, Sophie A. Campaign Finance & the Citizens United Supreme Court Case. 2011. (Congressional Policies, Practices & Procedures Ser.). 115.00 *(978-1-61209-209-6(8))* Nova Science Pubs., Inc.

Packard, Vance. The Hidden Persuaders. 2007. (ENG.). 200p. reprint ed. per. 14.95 *(978-0-9788431-0-6(X))* Ig Publishing, Inc.

Pardun, Carol J., ed. Advertising & Society: Controversies & Consequences. 2009. (ENG., Illus.). 224p. 99.95 *(978-1-4051-4409-4(2),* Wiley-Blackwell) Wiley, John & Sons, Inc.

—Advertising & Society: Controversies & Consequences. 2008. (ENG., Illus.). 224p. pap. 39.95 *(978-1-4051-4410-0(6),* Wiley-Blackwell) Wiley, John & Sons, Inc.

Richardson, Glenn. Pulp Politics: How Political Advertising Tells the Stories of American Politics. 2nd ed. 2008. (ENG., Illus.). 196p. 77.00 *(978-0-7425-5627-0(1));* pap. 24.95 *(978-0-7425-5628-7(X))* Rowman & Littlefield Publishers, Inc.

Ridout, Travis N. & Franz, Michael M. The Persuasive Power of Campaign Advertising. 2011. (ENG., Illus.). 200p. 68.50 *(978-1-4399-0332-2(8));* pap. 23.95 *(978-1-4399-0333-9(6))* Temple Univ. Pr.

Seidman, Steven A. Posters, Propaganda, & Persuasion in Election Campaigns Around the World & Through History. 2007. (C). 109.95 *(978-0-8204-8617-8(5));* pap. 33.95 *(978-0-8204-8616-1(7))* Lang, Peter Publishing, Inc.

Shaw, Daron R. The Race To 270: The Electoral College & the Campaign Strategies of 2000 And 2004. 2006. (Illus.). 216p. 55.00 *(978-0-226-75133-7(3));* per. 22.50 *(978-0-226-75134-4(1))* Univ. of Chicago Pr.

West, Darrell M. Air Wars: Television Advertising in Election Campaigns, 1952-2008, 00 vols. 5th rev. ed. 2009. 187p. (C). pap. 42.00 *(978-0-87289-778-6(8))* CQ Pr.

Youn, Monica, ed. Money, Politics, & the Constitution: Beyond Citizens United. 2011. (ENG.). 279p. pap. 19.95 *(978-0-87078-521-4(4))* Century Foundation, The.

ADVERTISING, PRIZE CONTESTS IN
see Prize Contests in Advertising

ADVERTISING, RADIO
see Radio Advertising

ADVERTISING, RETAIL
see Advertising

ADVERTISING, TELEVISION
see Television Advertising

ADVERTISING, TRANSPORTATION
see Advertising Cards

ADVERTISING AGENCIES

Andrews, Brad. The Truth about Advertising & Public Relations Jobs - How to Job-Hunt & Career-Change for Advertising & Public Relations Jobs - the Facts You Should Know. 2009. (Illus.). 196p. pap. *(978-1-74244-169-6(6))* Emereo Pty Ltd.

Azzaro, Marian. Strategic Media Decisions: Understanding the Business End of the Advertising Business. 2nd rev. ed. 2008. (ENG.). 560p. (C). per. 67.50 net. *(978-1-887229-33-3(7))* Copy Workshop, The.

Beckwith, Harry & Clifford, Christine K. You, Inc: The Art of Selling Yourself. 2011. (ENG.). 336p. pap. 14.99 *(978-0-446-69581-7(5),* Business Plus) Grand Central Publishing.

Beckwith, Harry, et al. You, Inc: The Art of Selling Yourself. 2007. (ENG.). 336p. 23.99 *(978-0-446-57821-9(5),* Business Plus) Grand Central Publishing.

Burroughs, Augusten. Dry: A Memoir. Date not set. pap. *(978-0-312-31819-2(7));* mass mkt. *(978-0-312-99095-4(2))* St. Martin's Pr. (St. Martin's Paperbacks).

Chambers, Jason. Madison Avenue & the Color Line: African Americans in the Advertising Industry. 2007. (Illus.). 328p. (C). 39.95 *(978-0-8122-4047-4(2))* Univ. of Pennsylvania Pr.

Cracknell, Andrew. The Real Mad Men: The Renegades of Madison Avenue & the Golden Age of Advertising. 2012. (ENG., Illus.). 224p. 28.00 *(978-0-7624-4090-0(2))* Running Pr. Bk. Pubs.

Crispin Porter + Bogusky, et al. Hoopla. 2006. (ENG., Illus.). 272p. 45.00 *(978-1-57687-312-0(9))* powerHouse Cultural Entertainment, Inc.

Dru, Jean-Marie. How Disruption Brought Order: The Story of a Winning Strategy in the World of Advertising. 2007. (ENG., Illus.). 256p. 29.00 *(978-0-230-60069-0(7))* Palgrave Macmillan.

Fallon, Pat & Barrie, Bob, eds. The Work: 25 Years of Fallon. 2006. (ENG., Illus.). 252p. 49.95 *(978-0-9743806-5-0(2))* Easton Studio Pr., LLC.

Fredericks, Steven J. StrADegy: Advertising in the Digital Age. 2007. 200p. 21.95 *(978-0-9788630-0-5(3))* TNS Media Intelligence.

Gilbert, Richard L. Marching up Madison Avenue: How I Beat the Entrepreneurial Odds Armed with a Pencil & My Imagination. 2008. (ENG.). 200p. pap. 14.95 *(978-1-933016-51-1(5))* Behler Pubns., LLC.

Ibach, Howard. How to Write an Inspired Creative Brief. 2009. 112p. pap. 13.95 *(978-1-4401-5827-8(4))* iUniverse, Inc.

Le Book Staff. Le Book New York 2007, 1 vol. 2007. (ENG., Illus.). 1800p. 190.00 *(978-2-905190-57-4(4))* Le Book FRA. Dist: D.A.P./Distributed Art Pubs.

Lewis, Herschell Gordon. Asinine Advertising: How Stupid & Unethical Advertising Costs You Money. 2008. 129p. pap. 22.95 *(978-1-933199-00-9(8))* Racom Communications.

Marin, Dan. Signs of Opportunity: How Lamar Advertising Company Became the Biggest Business of Its Kind in the U.S.A. 2007. *(978-0-925417-57-2(2))* Acadian Hse. Publishing.

—Signs of Opportunity: How Lamar Advertising Grew into the Biggest Billboard Business in America. 2008. (Illus.). 196p. per. 15.95 *(978-0-925417-61-9(0))* Acadian Hse. Publishing.

Osterman, Jim. Excellence in Brand Advertising. 2008. (Illus.). 203p. 50.00 *(978-1-58471-081-3(0))* Visual Reference Pubns., Inc.

Othmer, James P. Adland: Searching for the Meaning of Life on a Branded Planet. 2010. (ENG.). 336p. pap. 15.95 *(978-0-7679-2897-7(0),* Anchor) Knopf Doubleday Publishing Group.

Roman, Kenneth. The King of Madison Avenue: David Ogilvy & the Making of Modern Advertising. (ENG., Illus.). 304p. 2010. pap. 18.00 *(978-0-230-10036-7(8))* 2009. 27.95 *(978-1-4039-7895-0(6))* Palgrave Macmillan.

Salz, Nancy L. Salz Survey of Advertiser-Agency Relations: The Collective Wisdom of the Top 200 Advertisers & Top 100 Agencies: the Twenty Year Report. 2007. 69p. spiral bd. 95.00 *(978-0-615-17546-1(5))* Salz, Nancy L. Consulting.

Steel. Truth Lies & Advertising the Art of Ac. 2006. pap. 8.95 *(978-1-4288-0999-4(6))* Cram101 Inc.

Sugiyama, Kotaro & Andree, Tim. The Dentsu Way: Secrets of Cross Switch Marketing from the World's Most Innovative Advertising Agency. 2010. (ENG., Illus.). 320p. 28.00 *(978-0-07-174812-4(1),* 0071748121) McGraw-Hill Cos., The.

Sutton, Denise H. Globalizing Ideal Beauty: How Female Copywriters of the J. Walter Thompson Advertising Agency Redefined Beauty for the Twentieth Century. 2009. (ENG., Illus.). 224p. 89.00 *(978-0-230-61174-0(5))* Palgrave Macmillan.

ADVERTISING AGENCIES—EUROPE

Book Industry Services Publishers Staff & Babinet, Remi. Paris: Global Advertising Agency. 2008. (ENG., Illus.). 288p. 85.00 *(978-90-6369-178-3(5))* Bis B.V., Uitgeverij(BIS Publishers) NLD. Dist: Consortium Bk. Sales & Distribution.

ADVERTISING ART
see Commercial Art

ADVERTISING AS A PROFESSION
see Advertising—Vocational Guidance

ADVERTISING ASSOCIATION OF THE WEST

Sivulka. Soap Sex & Cigarettes A Cultural Histo. 2006. pap. 10.95 *(978-1-4288-0941-3(4))* Cram101 Inc.

ADVERTISING BUSINESS
see Advertising Agencies

ADVERTISING CAMPAIGNS
see also Market Surveys

Abellán, Miguel & Abellán, Miquel. Eat Drink Graphics. Minguet, Josep Maria, ed. 2011. (ENG & SPA., Illus.). 192p. pap. 62.50 ***(978-84-96823-97-6(0))*** Instituto Monsa de Ediciones, S.A. ESP. Dist: Trans-Atlantic Pubns., Inc.

Alpha Books Staff & Books, Alpha, eds. Campaign Graphics. 2009. (JPN & ENG., Illus.). 272p. 80.00 *(978-4-568-50356-2(6))* Azur Corp. JPN. Dist: Antique Collectors' Club.

AVA Publishing Staff, ed. Epica Vol. 21: Europe's Best Advertising. 2008. (Epica: Europe's Best Advertising Ser.). (ENG., Illus.). 391p. 65.00 *(978-2-88479-106-9(X))* Ava Publishing SA CHE. Dist: Ingram Pub. Services.

Berman, Margo & Blakeman, Robyn. The Brains Behind Great Ad Campaigns: Creative Collaboration Between Copywriters & Art Directors. 2009. (ENG.). 224p. 80.00 *(978-0-7425-5550-1(X));* pap. 33.00 *(978-0-7425-5551-8(8))* Rowman & Littlefield Publishers, Inc.

Blakeman, Robyn. Advertising Campaign Design: Just the Essentials. 2011. (ENG., Illus.). 256p. (C). pap. 39.95 ***(978-0-7656-2553-3(9))*** Sharpe, M.E. Inc.

Burtenshaw, Ken, et al. The Fundamentals of Creative Advertising. 2nd rev. ed. 2011. (ENG., Illus.). 184p. (C). pap. 38.50 *(978-2-940411-56-6(5))* Ava Publishing SA CHE. Dist: Ingram Pub. Services.

Cohen, Barry H. 10 Ways to Screw up an Ad Campaign: A Guide to Planning & Creating Advertising That Works. 2006. (ENG.). 272p. per. 12.95 *(978-1-59869-082-8(5))* Adams Media Corp.

Cram101 Textbook Reviews Staff. Outlines & Highlights for Advertising Campaign Strategy: A Guide to Marketing Communication Plans by Donald Parente, ISBN. 2009. 140p. pap. 28.95 *(978-1-4288-4237-3(3))* Cram101 Inc.

Epica. Epica Bk. 24: Europe's Best Advertising. 2011. (ENG., Illus.). 400p. 65.00 ***(978-2-88479-109-0(4))*** Ava Publishing SA CHE. Dist: Ingram Pub. Services.

Epica. Europe's Best Advertising, Bk. 23. 2010. (ENG., Illus.). 400p. 65.00 *(978-2-88479-108-3(6))* Ava Publishing SA CHE. Dist: Ingram Pub. Services.

Epica, compiled by. Epica Bk. 22: Europe's Best Advertising. 2009. (Epica: Europe's Best Advertising Ser.). (ENG., Illus.). 400p. 65.00 *(978-2-88479-107-6(8))* Ava Publishing SA CHE. Dist: Ingram Pub. Services.

Glazer, Bill. Outrageous Advertising That's Outrageously Successful: Created for the 99% of Small Business Owners Who Are Dissatisfied with the Results They Get. 2009. (ENG.). 313p. pap. 19.95 *(978-0-9823793-0-1(7))* Morgan James Publishing.

Kelley, Larry D. & Jugenheimer, Donald W. Advertising Account Planning: Planning & Managing an IMC Campaign. 2nd rev. ed. 2010. (ENG., Illus.). (C). 224p. 99.95 *(978-0-7656-2563-2(6));* 226p. pap. 46.95 *(978-0-7656-2564-9(4))* Sharpe, M.E. Inc.

Kyselova&apos, et al. Unconevntional Communication Strategies. 2011. 100p. pap. ***(978-3-8443-9118-3(5))*** Lambert Academic Publishing.

Lahusen, Christian. The Rhetoric of Moral Protest: Public Campaigns, Celebrity Endorsement, & Political Mobilization. (De Gruyter Studies in Organization Ser.). (ENG.). XVI, 425p. 240.00 ***(978-3-11-174959-4(2))*** De Gruyter, Walter Inc.

Lucas, Gavin. Guerrilla Advertising 2: More Unconventional Brand Communications. 2011. (ENG., Illus.). 192p. pap. 40.00 ***(978-1-85669-747-7(9))*** King, Laurence Publishing GBR. Dist: Hachette Bk. Group.

McNally, Clare. Portfolio Class with Clare. 2009. (ENG., Illus.). 160p. pap. 27.00 *(978-90-6369-198-1(X))* Bis B.V., Uitgeverij(BIS Publishers) NLD. Dist: Consortium Bk. Sales & Distribution.

Oxer, Jonathan. Quickstart Guide to Google Adwords. 2008. 80p. pap. 12.95 *(978-1-84799-649-7(3))* Lulu Enterprises Inc.

Parente. Advertising Campaign Strategy A Guide to. 2006. pap. 11.95 *(978-1-4288-0629-0(6))* Cram101 Inc.

Pedersen, B. Martin. Graphis Advertising Annual 2008. Carnick, Anna N., ed. 2007. (Illus.). 256p. 70.00 *(978-1-932026-44-3(4))* Graphis, U.S., Inc.

—100 Best Advertising Annual 2011, 1 vol. 2010. (ENG., Illus.). 237p. 70.00 *(978-1-932026-62-7(2))* Graphis, U.S., Inc.

Pedersen, B. Martin & Rico. Graphis Advertising Annual 2009. 2009. (Illus.). 256p. 70.00 *(978-1-932026-52-8(5))* Graphis, U.S., Inc.

Pincas, Stéphane, et al. A History of Advertising. 2008. (ENG., Illus.). 336p. 39.99 *(978-3-8365-0212-2(7))* TASCHEN DEU. Dist: Ingram Pub. Services.

Riggs, Thomas, ed. Encyclopedia of Major Marketing Campaigns: Volume 2. 2nd ed. 2006. (ENG., Illus.). 1947p. 429.00 *(978-0-7876-7356-7(0))* Cengage Gale.

Roberts, Kevin, text. Diesel: XXX Years of Diesel Communication. 2008. (Illus.). 251p. ***(978-88-17-02392-4(2))*** Rizzoli International Pubns., Inc.

Ryan, Damian & Jones, Calvin. The Best Digital Marketing Campaigns in the World: Mastering the Art of Customer Engagement. 2011. (ENG.). 224p. pap. 29.95 *(978-0-7494-6062-4(8))* Kogan Page, Ltd. GBR. Dist: Ingram Pub. Services.

Sayre, Shay. Campaign Planner for Integrated Brand Communications. 4th ed. 2010. (ENG.). (C). pap. 50.95 *(978-0-538-49855-5(2))* Cengage South-Western.

Semenik. Promotion & Integrated Marketing Commu. 2006. pap. 13.95 *(978-1-4288-0586-6(9))* Cram101 Inc.

Shankman, Peter. Can We Do That?! Outrageous PR Stunts That Work - And Why Your Company Needs Them. 2006. (ENG., Illus.). 211p. per. 24.95 *(978-0-470-04392-9(X),* Wiley) Wiley, John & Sons, Inc.

Springer, Paul. Ads to Icons: How Advertising Succeeds in a Multimedia Age. 2nd ed. 2009. (ENG., Illus.). 400p. pap. 29.95 *(978-0-7494-5647-4(7))* Kogan Page, Ltd. GBR. Dist: Ingram Pub. Services.

Stamm, Kat. Just Ad Culture. 2008. 80p. pap. *(978-3-639-11426-3(4))* VDM Verlag Dr. Mueller e.K.

Steel. Truth Lies & Advertising the Art of Ac. 2006. pap. 8.95 *(978-1-4288-0999-4(6))* Cram101 Inc.

Stevens, Ruth. Maximizing Lead Generation: The Complete Guide for B2B Marketers. rev. ed. 2011. (Que Biz-Tech Ser.). (ENG., Illus.). 224p. pap. 24.99 *(978-0-7897-4114-1(8))* Que.

Sutherland, Max & Sylvester, Alice. Advertising & the Mind of the Consumer: What Works, What Doesn't, & Why. 3rd ed. 2009. (ENG., Illus.). 352p. pap. 24.95 *(978-1-74175-599-2(9))* Allen & Unwin AUS. Dist: Independent Pubs. Group.

Wiedemann, Julius. Advertising Now! TV Commercials: Werbespots heute! 2009. (FRE, GER & ENG., Illus.). 448p. pap. 39.99 *(978-3-8228-4029-0(7))* TASCHEN DEU. Dist: Ingram Pub. Services.

Williams, Eliza. How 30 Great Ads Were Made: From Idea to Campaign. 2012. (ENG., Illus.). 224p. pap. 40.00 ***(978-1-85669-821-4(1))*** King, Laurence Publishing GBR. Dist: Hachette Bk. Group.

ADVERTISING CARDS
see also Business Cards; Cigarette Cards

Dover. Vintage Labels. 2011. (Dover Postcards Ser.). (ENG., Illus.). 24p. pap. 6.95 *(978-0-486-48018-3(6))* Dover Pubns., Inc.

Grafton, Carol Belanger, ed. Children in Old-Time Trade Cards CD-ROM & Book. 2008. (Dover Electronic Clip Art Ser.). (ENG., Illus.). 48p. pap. 22.95 *(978-0-486-99897-8(5))* Dover Pubns., Inc.

—Old-Time Trade Cards. 2007. (Dover Electronic Clip Art Ser.). (ENG., Illus.). 48p. pap. 19.95 *(978-0-486-99836-7(3))* Dover Pubns., Inc.

Victionary Staff. Nice to Meet You Too: Visual Greetings from Business Cards to Identity Packages. 2010. 320p. pap. *(978-988-17327-8-1(6))* Victionary.

ADVERTISING CARDS—COLLECTORS AND COLLECTING

Roberts, Bruce D. Mechanical Bank Trade Cards. 2008. (Illus.). 56p. per. 29.95 net. *(978-0-9794697-1-8(6))* Roberts, Bruce D.

ADVERTISING COPY

see also Copy Writers

Ashton, Robert. Successful Copywriting: Learn in a Week, What the Leading Experts Learn in a Lifetime. 2012. (Teach Yourself: General Reference Ser.). (ENG., Illus.). 128p. pap. 12.00 ***(978-1-4441-5907-3(0)***, 1444159070) McGraw-Hill Cos., The.

Atkinson, Ian. Copy Righter: Become a Master Wordsmith & Harness Copywrighting Secrets That Will Win You Hearts, Minds — And Business. 2011. (ENG., Illus.). 224p. pap. 29.99 ***(978-1-907794-14-8(X))*** LID Publishing GBR. Dist: AtlasBooks Distribution.

Berman, Margo. The Copywriter's Toolkit: The Complete Guide to Strategic Advertising Copy. 2012. (ENG.). 424p. 99.95 ***(978-1-4051-9952-0(0))***; 400p. pap. 59.95 ***(978-1-4051-9953-7(9))*** Wiley, John & Sons, Inc. (Wiley-Blackwell).

Bowdery, Rob. Copywriting: The Creative Process of Writing Text for Advertisements or Publicity Material. 2008. (Basics Advertising Ser.). (ENG., Illus.). 175p. pap. 29.95 *(978-2-940373-68-0(X))* AVA Publishing GBR. Dist: Ingram Pub. Services.

Caples, John. Making Ads Pay: Timeless Tips for Successful Copywriting. 2011. (ENG.). 256p. pap. 14.95 ***(978-0-486-48601-7(X))*** Dover Pubns., Inc.

Cram101 Textbook Reviews Staff & Cram101 Textbook Reviews. Outlines & Highlights for Advertising & Satirical Culture in the Romantic Period by John Strachan, Isbn: 9780521882149. 2011. 74p. pap. 27.95 ***(978-1-61461-354-1(0))*** Cram101 Inc.

Cram101 Textbook Reviews Staff. Outlines & Highlights for Creative Strategy in Advertising by Drewniany, Isbn: 0495095699. 2008. 60p. pap. 9.95 *(978-1-4288-6344-6(3))* Cram101 Inc.

Cross, Geoffrey A. Envisioning Collaboration: Group Verbal-Visual Composing in a System of Creativity. 2010. (ENG., Illus.). 254p. 54.95 *(978-0-89503-400-7(X))* Baywood Publishing Co., Inc.

Designers and Art Directors Association of the United Kingdom Staff, contrib. by. D & Ad, the Copy Book. 2011. (ENG., Illus.). 368p. 59.99 *(978-3-8365-2832-0(0))* TASCHEN DEU. Dist: Ingram Pub. Services.

Drewniany, Bonnie L. & Jewler, A. Jerome. Creative Strategy in Advertising. 10th ed. 2010. (ENG.). 352p. (C). pap. 177.95 *(978-1-4390-8270-6(7))* Wadsworth.

Edwards, Ray. Writing Riches: Learn How to Boost Profits, Drive Sales & Master Your Financial Destiny with Results-Based Web Copy. 2010. (ENG.). 184p. pap. 17.95 *(978-1-60037-755-6(6))* Morgan James Publishing.

Gabay, J. Jonathan. Improve Your Copywriting: A Teach Yourself Guide. 4th ed. 2011. (Teach Yourself: General Reference Ser.). (ENG.). 336p. pap. 15.00 *(978-0-07-176984-6(6)*, 0071769846) McGraw-Hill Cos., The.

Gabay, Jonathan. Gabay's Copywriters' Compendium: The Definitive Professional Writers Guide. 2nd rev. ed. 2006. (ENG., Illus.). 712p. pap., instr.'s gde. ed. 40.95 *(978-0-7506-8320-3(1))* Routledge.

—Gabay's Copywriting Compendium. 2010th ed. 2010. (Teach Yourself Ser.). (ENG., Illus.). 712p. pap. 39.95 *(978-1-4441-1092-0(6)*, Hodder & Stoughton) Hodder General Publishing Div. GBR. Dist: Independent Pubs. Group.

Gordon Lewis, Herschell. On the Art of Writing Copy: The Best of Print, Broadcast, Internet, Direct Mail, Social Media. 2011. (Illus.). 402p. pap. 39.95 *(978-1-933199-32-0(8))* Racom Communications.

Gunawan, Fitri. A Study of Rolex Advertisement Translations. 2010. 84p. pap. *(978-3-8383-1832-0(X))* Lambert Academic Publishing.

Gunelius, Susan. Kick-Ass Copywriting in 10 Easy Steps: Build the Buzz & Sell the Sizzle. 2008. (ENG., Illus.). 304p. pap. 21.95 *(978-1-59918-253-7(X)*, 159918253X) Entrepreneur Pr. dba Entrepreneur Media, Inc.

Hershkowitz-Coore, Sue. Power Sales Writing: Using Communication to Turn Prospects into Clients. 2nd ed. 2012. xiii, 225p. E-Book ***(978-0-07-177030-4(1))*** McGraw-Hill Cos., The.

—Power Sales Writing: Using Communication to Turn Prospects into Clients. 2nd rev. exp. ed. 2011. (ENG.). 224p. pap. 16.00 ***(978-0-07-177014-9(3)***, 0071770143) McGraw-Hill Cos., The.

Hines, Randall & Lauterborn, Robert. Print Matters: How to Write Great Advertising. 2008. (Illus.). 223p. pap. 27.95 *(978-1-933199-10-8(5))* Racom Communications.

Horberry, Roger. Brilliant Copywriting: How to Craft the Most Interesting & Effective Copy Imaginable. 2009. (ENG., Illus.). 176p. (C). pap. 19.99 *(978-0-273-72734-7(6))* FT Press.

Jewler, A. Jerome & Drewniany, Bonnie L. Creative Strategy in Advertising. 9th ed. 2007. (ENG., Illus.). 352p. (C). per. 168.95 *(978-0-495-09569-9(9))* Wadsworth.

Kirt D. Cable Mba. Sweeten Your Pot: Proven Business Strategies for Top Producers. 2009. 276p. pap. 16.79 *(978-1-4389-7791-1(3))* AuthorHouse.

Konstant, Tina. Copywriting - Bullet Guides: The Answers You Need - Now. 2012. (Bullet Guides). (ENG.). 128p. pap. 6.95 ***(978-1-4441-3499-5(X)***, Hodder & Stoughton) Hodder General Publishing Div. GBR. Dist: Independent Pubs. Group.

Lewis, Herschell Gordon. Asinine Advertising: How Stupid & Unethical Advertising Costs You Money. 2008. 129p. pap. 22.95 *(978-1-933199-00-9(8))* Racom Communications.

Maslen, Andy. Copywriting Ideas: From Leading Companies Around the World. 2011. 224p. 19.50 *(978-0-462-09973-6(3))* Marshall Cavendish International (Asia) Private Ltd. SGP. Dist: Marshall Cavendish Corp.

—The Copywriting Sourcebook: How to Write Better Copy, Faster - For Everything from Ads to Websites. 2010. (Illus.). 224p. pap. 12.95 *(978-0-462-09974-3(1))* Marshall Cavendish GBR. Dist: Midpoint Trade Bks., Inc.

Maxwell, Otis. Copywriting That Gets Results! 2011. 170p. pap. 14.95 ***(978-1-60746-247-7(6))*** FastPencil, Inc.

Meeske, Milan D. Copywriting for the Electronic Media: A Practical Guide. 6th rev. ed. 2008. (ENG., Illus.). 336p. (C). per. 168.95 *(978-0-495-41117-8(5))* Wadsworth.

Schofield, Perry, ed. 100 Top Copy Writers & Their Favorite Ads. 2011. 220p. 44.95 ***(978-1-258-06011-4(6))*** Literary Licensing, LLC.

Scott, David. Poetics of the Poster: The Rhetoric of Image-Text. 2011. (ENG., Illus.). 119p. 95.00 *(978-1-84631-486-5(0))* Liverpool Univ. Pr. GBR. Dist: Chicago Distribution Ctr.

Shaw, Mark. Copywriting: Successful Writing for Design, Advertising & Marketing. 2009. (ENG., Illus.). 216p. pap. 24.95 *(978-1-85669-568-8(9))* King, Laurence Publishing GBR. Dist: Hachette Bk. Group.

Sheldon, George & Entrepreneur Press Staff. Start Your Own Freelance Writing Business & More: Copywriter, Proofreader, Copyeditor, Journalist. 2008. (ENG., Illus.). 156p. pap. 19.95 *(978-1-59918-175-2(4)*, 1599181754) Entrepreneur Pr. dba Entrepreneur Media, Inc.

Strachan, John. Advertising & Satirical Culture in the Romantic Period. 2011. (Cambridge Studies in Romanticism Ser.). (ENG.). 370p. pap. 45.00 *(978-0-521-29306-8(5))* Cambridge Univ. Pr.

Sugarman, Joseph. The Adweek Copywriting Handbook: The Ultimate Guide to Writing Powerful Advertising & Marketing Copy from One of America's Top Copywriters. 2006. (ENG., Illus.). 360p. per. 21.95 *(978-0-470-05124-5(8)*, Wiley) Wiley, John & Sons, Inc.

Sullivan, Luke. Hey, Whipple, Squeeze This: The Classic Guide to Creating Great Ads. 4th ed. 2012. (ENG., Illus.). 386p. pap. 19.95 ***(978-1-118-10133-9(2)***, Wiley) Wiley, John & Sons, Inc.

Taylor, Vickie. The Complete Guide to Writing Web-Based Advertising Copy to Get the Sale: What You Need to Know Explained Simply. 2008. 288p. per. 24.95 *(978-1-60138-232-0(4))* Atlantic Publishing Co.

ADVERTISING IN POLITICS

see Advertising, Political

ADVERTISING LAWS

see also Competition, Unfair

Aspatore Books Staff, compiled by. Managing Advertising & Marketing Legal Issues: Leading Lawyers on Preventing Claims, Handling Disputes, & Understanding Recent Trends & Developments. 2008. 260p. pap. 75.00 *(978-0-314-20002-0(9))* Aspatore Bks.

Bernstein, David H. & Keller, Bruce P. The Law of Advertising, Marketing, & Promotions. 2011. *(978-1-58852-172-9(9)*, Law Journal Pr.) Incisive Media.

Butterworth Staff. Code of Advertising Practice & Procedural Guide. Date not set. (Illus.). ring bd. *(979-0-409-01010-7(3)*, MICHIE) LEXIS Publishing.

Crown, Giles. Advertising Law & Regulation 2ed. 2nd ed. 2010. 1046p. 250.00 *(978-1-84592-451-5(7)*, Bloomsbury Professional) Bloomsbury Publishing Plc GBR. Dist: International Specialized Bk. Services.

Martínez Guerra, Amparo & Guerra, Amparo Martínez. Publicidad y Derecho Penal: Estudio Comparado Del Modelo Americano y Europeo. 2007. (SPA.). 422p. *(978-84-8456-755-4(9))* Tirant lo Blanch.

Model Compliant Standard Operating Procedures for Advertising & Promotional Literature. Date not set. *(978-1-893091-71-9(6))* Parker-Wallace Publishing Co., LLC.

Moore, James W. & Moore, Roy. Advertising & Public Relations Law. 2nd rev. ed. 2010. (Routledge Communication Ser.). (ENG., Illus.). 480p. pap. 80.00 *(978-0-415-96548-4(9))* Routledge.

Moore, Roy & Collins, Erik. Advertising & Public Relations Law. 2nd rev. ed. 2010. (Routledge Communication Ser.). (ENG., Illus.). 480p. 200.00 *(978-0-8058-5346-9(4))* Routledge.

Piety, Tamara R. Brandishing the First Amendment: Commercial Expression in America. 2011. E-Book ***(978-0-472-02772-9(7))*** Univ. of Michigan Pr.

Vagnoni, Anthony, et al. The Idea Writers: Copywriting in a New Media & Marketing Era. 2010. (ENG.). 224p. pap. 18.00 *(978-0-230-61386-1(8))* Palgrave Macmillan.

Williams, Thomas M. False Advertising & the Lanham Act: Litigating Section 43(a)(1)(B). 1 vol. 2012. (ENG.). 160p. pap. 195.00 ***(978-0-19-977258-2(4))*** Oxford Univ. Pr., Inc.

ADVERTISING LAYOUT AND TYPOGRAPHY

Arntson, Amy E. Graphic Design Basics. 6th ed. 2011. (ENG.). 272p. (C). pap. 142.95 *(978-1-111-34717-8(4))*; pap. 142.95 *(978-0-495-91207-1(7))* Wadsworth.

Campos, Christian, et al. The Layout Look Book. 2007. (ENG., Illus.). 256p. 45.00 *(978-0-06-114975-7(6)*, Collins Design) HarperCollins Pubs.

Cram101 Textbook Reviews Staff. Outlines & Highlights for Creative Strategy in Advertising by Drewniany, Isbn: 0495095699. 2008. 60p. pap. 9.95 *(978-1-4288-6344-6(3))* Cram101 Inc.

Cullen, Kristen. Layout Workbook: A Real-World Guide to Building Pages in Graphic Design. 2007. (ENG., Illus.). 240p. pap. 25.00 *(978-1-59253-352-7(3)*, 1592533523) Quayside.

Davis, Susan E., ed. Typography 28: The Annual of the Type Directors Club. 2007. (Typography Ser.). (ENG., Illus.). 304p. 60.00 *(978-0-06-117342-4(8)*, Collins Design) HarperCollins Pubs.

Drewniany, Bonnie L. & Jewler, A. Jerome. Creative Strategy in Advertising. 10th ed. 2010. (ENG.). 352p. (C). pap. 177.95 *(978-1-4390-8270-6(7))* Wadsworth.

Jewler, A. Jerome & Drewniany, Bonnie L. Creative Strategy in Advertising. 9th ed. 2007. (ENG., Illus.). 352p. (C). per. 168.95 *(978-0-495-09569-9(9))* Wadsworth.

Pedersen, B. Martin, et al. The Big Book of Layouts. 2009. (ENG., Illus.). 384p. pap. 35.00 *(978-0-06-162675-3(9)*, Collins Design) HarperCollins Pubs.

Swann, Alan. Layout Source Book. 9.98 *(978-1-55521-530-9(0))* Book Sales, Inc.

Type Directors Club Staff. Typography 30. 2010. (ENG., Illus.). 300p. 60.00 *(978-0-06-172631-6(1)*, Collins Design) HarperCollins Pubs.

ADVERTISING MEDIA PLANNING

Azzaro, Marian. Strategic Media Decisions: Understanding the Business End of the Advertising Business. 2nd rev. ed. 2008. (ENG.). 560p. (C). per. 67.50 net. *(978-1-887229-33-3(7))* Copy Workshop, The.

Berman, Margo. Street-Smart Advertising: How to Win the Battle of the Buzz. (ENG.). 2010. 238p. pap. 19.95 *(978-1-4422-0335-8(8))* 2006. (Illus.). 250p. pap. 29.95 *(978-0-7425-4137-5(1))* Rowman & Littlefield Publishers, Inc.

Cram101 Textbook Reviews Staff. Outlines & Highlights for Advertising & Integrated Brand Promotion by O. Isbn: 0324289561. 2008. 180p. pap. 12.95 *(978-1-4288-6274-6(9))* Cram101 Inc.

Geskey, Ronald. Media Planning & Buying in the 21st Century Workbook. 2012. (ENG.). 176p. pap. 39.95 *(978-1-4610-0953-5(7))* CreateSpace.

Jantsch, John. Duct Tape Marketing: The World's Most Practical Small Business Marketing Guide. 2011. 304p. pap. 16.99 *(978-1-59555-465-9(3))* Nelson, Thomas Inc.

Katz, Helen E. The Media: Advertising Media Selection, Planning, Research, & Buying. 4th ed. 2010. (ENG., Illus.). 232p. pap., instr.'s hndbk. ed. 42.95 *(978-0-415-87354-3(1))* Routledge.

—The Media: Advertising Media Selection, Planning, Research, & Buying. 4th ed. 2010. (Illus.). 228p. instr.'s gde. ed. 100.00 *(978-0-415-87353-6(3)*, Routledge) Taylor & Francis Group GBR. Dist: Taylor & Francis Group.

Kelley, Larry D. & Jugenheimer, Donald W. Advertising Media Workbook & Sourcebook. 2nd rev. ed. 2008. 336p. pap. 39.95 *(978-0-7656-2034-7(0))* Sharpe, M.E. Inc.

Kelley, Larry D., et al. Advertising Media: Workbook & Sourcebook. 3rd ed. 2011. (ENG.). 360p. pap. 49.95 *(978-0-7656-2638-7(1))* Sharpe, M.E. Inc.

Kelley, Larry D., et al. Advertising Media Planning: A Brand Management Approach. 3rd ed. 2011. (ENG., Illus.). 304p. (C). 99.95 *(978-0-7656-2635-6(7))*; pap. 49.95 ***(978-0-7656-2636-3(5))*** Sharpe, M.E. Inc.

Kim, Hyo Gyoo. A Canonical Sequential Aggregation Media Model. 2010. 224p. pap. *(978-3-639-22294-4(6))* VDM Verlag Dr. Mueller e.K.

Lehu, Jean-Marc. Branded Entertainment: Product Placement & Brand Strategy in the Entertainment Business. 2009. (ENG., Illus.). 272p. pap. 39.95 *(978-0-7494-5337-4(0))* Kogan Page, Ltd. GBR. Dist: Ingram Pub. Services.

Mandal, B. S. Cable Television, Marketing & Web Advertising. 2011. 392p. pap. 37.50 ***(978-93-80228-90-7(2))*** Global India Pubns. Pvt. Ltd. IND. Dist: Coronet Bks.

O'Mara, Angela. Lights! Camera! Action! the Power of PR: The Plastic & Cosmetic Surgeon's Guide to Obtaining Priceless TV, Magazine, & Other Media Exposure. 2010. 120p. pap. 24.99 *(978-1-4520-1155-4(9))* AuthorHouse.

Rödel, Tanja. Typisierung verschiedener Medien bei Cross-Media-Strategien: Analyse des Einsatzes bei verschiedenen Zielgruppen sowie Untersuchung der optimalen Kombination bei der Zielgruppe Kinder und Jugendliche. 2010. 72p. pap. *(978-3-639-25600-0(X))* VDM Verlag Dr. Mueller e.K.

Schweiger, Carsten. Media-Auditing: Eine Betrachtung des deutschen Marktes. 2009. 72p. pap. *(978-3-639-16354-4(0))* VDM Verlag Dr. Mueller e.K.

Sissors, Jack Z. & Baron, Roger. Advertising Media Planning, Seventh Edition. 7th ed. 2010. (ENG., Illus.). 496p. 89.95 *(978-0-07-170312-3(8)*, 0071703128) McGraw-Hill Cos., The.

Tanaka, Yuzuru. Knowledge Media Architecture & Its Application from Augmentation Media to Meme Media. 79.95 *(978-0-7803-6034-1(6))* IEEE.

Thorne, Lynn. Word of Mouth Advertising Online & Off: How to Spark Buzz, Excitement, & Free Publicity for Your Business or Organization. 2008. (ENG.). 288p. per. 24.95 *(978-1-60138-011-1(9))* Atlantic Publishing Co.

Warner, Charles & Warner. Media Selling: Television, Print, Internet, Radio. 4th ed. 2009. (Wiley Desktop Editions Ser.). (ENG., Illus.). 616p. pap. 68.95 *(978-1-4051-5839-8(5)*, Wiley-Blackwell) Wiley, John & Sons, Inc.

ADVERTISING PHOTOGRAPHY

see also Fashion Photography

Banier, François-Marie, photos by & text. Vive la Vie. 2009. (ENG., Illus.). 80p. 55.00 *(978-3-86521-821-6(0))* Steidl, Gerhard Druckerei und Verlag DEU. Dist: D.A.P./Distributed Art Pubs.

Bourdin, Guy, photos by. Stern Spezial Fotografie 61. Guy Bourdin: Stern Portfolio. 2010. (Illus.). 96p. 45.00 *(978-3-652-00002-4(1))* teNeues Publishing Co.

Clymer, Floyd, ed. Floyd Clymer's Historical Scrapbook of Early Advertising Art: Early Advertising Art at Its Best & Worst. 2011. 226p. 44.95 ***(978-1-258-07933-8(X))*** Literary Licensing, LLC.

Helleu, Jacques. Jacques Helleu & Chanel. Pickford, Susan, tr. from FRE. 2006. (ENG., Illus.). 280p. 125.00 *(978-0-8109-4312-4(3))* Abrams.

Keaney, Magdalene. Fashion & Advertising. 2007. (World's Top Photographers' Workshops Ser.). (Illus.). 176p. *(978-2-940378-24-1(X))* RotoVision SA.

Le Book Staff. Le Book New York 2007. 1 vol. 2007. (ENG., Illus.). 1800p. 190.00 *(978-2-905190-57-4(4))* Le Book FRA. Dist: D.A.P./Distributed Art Pubs.

Lesko, Lou. Advertising Photography: A Straightforward Guide to a Complex Industry. 2007. (ENG., Illus.). 256p. per. 39.99 *(978-1-59863-406-8(2))* Course Technology.

Ludwigson, Hakan. Taken Out of Context. 1 vol. 2008. (ENG., Illus.). 176p. 80.00 *(978-3-86521-082-1(1))* Steidl, Gerhard Druckerei und Verlag DEU. Dist: Innovative Logistics.

Pedersen, B. Martin, ed. Graphis Photography Annual 2007. 2007. (Illus.). 256p. 70.00 *(978-1-932026-39-9(8))* Graphis, U.S., Inc.

Shinn, Cobb & Clip Art. Retro Advertising Graphics CD-ROM & Book. 2013. (Dover Electronic Clip Art Ser.). (ENG.). 48p. pap. 19.95 ***(978-0-486-99233-4(0))*** Dover Pubns., Inc.

Singer, Bonnie & Clip Art. The Art of Poster Stamps CD-ROM & Book. 2013. (Dover Electronic Clip Art Ser.). (ENG.). 48p. pap. 19.95 ***(978-0-486-99209-9(8))*** Dover Pubns., Inc.

ADVERTISING RESEARCH

see Advertising—Research

ADVERTISING SPECIALTIES—COLLECTORS AND COLLECTING

Harris, Leo J. & Harris, Moira F. Minnesota on Paper: Collecting Our Printed History. 2006. (Illus.). 304p. pap. 24.95 *(978-0-8166-4555-8(8))* Univ. of Minnesota Pr.

Harris, Leo J., et al. Minnesota on Paper: Collecting Our Printed History. 2006. (Illus.). xxi, 221p. (C). *(978-0-8166-4554-1(X))* Univ. of Minnesota Pr.

Schmid, John W. Authoritative Guide to Lionel's Promotional Outfits 1960 - 1969. Carp, Roger & Schmid, George J., eds. 2007. (Illus.). 848p. 89.95 *(978-1-933500-03-1(9))*; per. 69.95 *(978-1-933600-02-4(0))* Project Roar Publishing.

ADVERTISING TYPOGRAPHY

see Advertising Layout and Typography

ADVICE-FOR-LIVING BOOKS

see Life Skills

ADVISORY OPINIONS

Aljaghoub, Mahasen M. The Advisory Function of the International Court of Justice 1946-2005. 2006. (ENG.). xxx, 285p. 169.00 *(978-3-540-35732-2(7)*, 3540357327) Springer.

Brenneis, Verena Maria. Rechtspolitische Implikationen von Gefährlichkeitsprognosen im Vollzug von Maßregeln nach § 63 StGB: Zum Subjektstatus von Eingewiesenen. 2010. (Frankfurter kriminalwissenschaftliche Studien Ser.). (GER.). 176p. 60.95 *(978-3-631-60377-2(0))* Lang, Peter GmbH, Europäischer Verlag der Wissenschaften DEU. Dist: Lang, Peter.

Hilpold, Peter. Das Kosovo-Gutachten des IGH vom 22. Juli 2010. 2011. (GER & ENG., Illus.). 275p. ***(978-90-04-20482-9(2))*** BRILL.

Holderness, A. Sidney & Wunnicke, Brooke. Legal Opinion Letters Formbook. 3rd ed. 2010. 245.00 *(978-0-7355-9323-2(0)*, Aspen Pubs.) Wolters Kluwer Law & Business.

Kriebisch, Angela. Die Spruchkörper Juristenfakultät und Schöppenstuhl zu Jena: Strukturen, Tätigkeit, Bedeutung und eine Analyse ausgewählter Spruchakten. 2008. (Rechtshistorische Reihe Ser.). (GER., Illus.). 376p. pap. 81.95 *(978-3-631-58127-8(0))* Lang, Peter GmbH, Europäischer Verlag der Wissenschaften DEU. Dist: Lang, Peter.

Ohlson, Clu. Waves of Change. 2009. 172p. pap. 19.95 *(978-1-4389-4907-9(3))* AuthorHouse.

Pedone, F. Stephen & Donlon, James L., eds. Roman Replies & CLSA Advisory Opinions, 1998. viii, 114p. pap. 14.00 *(978-0-943616-82-7(4))* Canon Law Society of America.

Topf, Mel A. A Doubtful & Perilous Experiment: Advisory Opinions, State Constitutions, & Judicial Supremacy. 1 vol. 2011. (ENG.). 238p. 85.00 *(978-0-19-975876-0(7))* Oxford Univ. Pr., Inc.

ADVOCACY, HEALTH CARE

see Patient Advocacy

ADVOCACY, PATIENT

see Patient Advocacy

ADVOCATES

see Lawyers

ADVOCATES, ANIMAL RIGHTS

see Animal Rights Activists

AEGEAN ISLANDS (GREECE AND TURKEY)

see also Cyclades (Greece); Samothrace Island (Greece)

Aruz, Joan. Marks of Distinction: Seals & Cultural Exchange Between the Aegean & the Orient (Ca. 2600-1360 B.C.) 2008. (FRE., Illus.). xiv, 438p. (C). 210.00 *(978-3-8053-3450-1(8))* Zabern, Philipp von Verlag, GmbH DEU. Dist: Brown, David Bk. Co., The.

Belavilas, Nikos & Papastephanake, Leda. Orycheia Sto Aigaio: Viomechanike Archaiologia Sten Hellada. 2009. (GRE., Illus.). 305p. (C). 100.00 ***(978-960-204-284-7(2))*** Ekdotikos Oikos Melissa GRC. Dist: ISD.

Betancourt, Philip P. Introduction to Aegean Art. 2007. (ENG., Illus.). 252p. (C). per. 36.00 *(978-1-931534-21-5(7))* Institute for Aegean Prehistory Pr.

Buttress, Robert. West Aegean: Cruising Companion. 2007. (ENG., Illus.). 240p. 49.95 (978-1-904358-26-8(8), Wiley) Wiley, John & Sons, Inc.
Catling, H. W. Some Problems in Aegean Prehistory, 1450-1380 BC. (Gr-gen Ser.). (ENG.). 21p. (C). pap. 7.00 (978-0-904920-16-1(X)) Brown, David Bk. Co., The.
Constantakopoulou, Christy. The Dance of the Islands: Insularity, Networks, the Athenian Empire, & the Aegean World. (Oxford Classical Monographs). (Illus.). 2010. (ENG.). 348p. pap. 45.00 (978-0-19-959117-6(2)) 2007. 350p. 150.00 (978-0-19-921595-9(2)) Oxford Univ. Pr., Inc.
Day, Peter M., et al. Transport Stirrup Jars of the Bronze Age Aegean & East Mediterranean. 2011. (Prehistory Monographs). (ENG., Illus.). 340p. (C). 80.00 (978-1-931534-62-8(4)) Institute for Aegean Prehistory Pr.
Dimitrova, Nora M. Theoroi & Initiates in Samothrace: The Epigraphical Evidence. 2008. (Hesperia Supplements Ser.). (ENG., Illus.). 296p. pap. 55.00 (978-0-87661-537-9(X)) American Schl. of Classical Studies at Athens.
Dubin, Marc & Dorling Kindersley Publishing Staff. Greek Islands - Eyewitness Travel Guide. 2011. (Eyewitness Travel Guides). (ENG.). 408p. 28.00 (978-0-7566-7020-7(9)) Dorling Kindersley Publishing, Inc.
Facaros, Dana & Pauls, Michael. The Greek Islands. Cadogan, ed. 9th ed. (Country & Regional Guides). (ENG., Illus.). 340p. pap. 19.95 (978-1-86011-325-3(7)) Cadogan Guides GBR. Dist: Globe Pequot Pr., The.
Fodor's Travel Publications, Inc. Staff. Fodor's Greek Islands, 3rd Edition: With Great Cruises & the Best of Athens. 2012. (Full-Color Gold Guides). (ENG.). 580p. pap. 24.99 **(978-0-307-92845-0(4)**, Fodor's) Fodor's Travel Pubns.
Gunning, Lucia Patrizio. The British Consular Service & the Collection of Antiquities in the Aegean. 2009. (Illus.). 234p. 124.95 (978-0-7546-6023-1(0)) Ashgate Publishing Co.
Harissis, Haralampos V. & Harissis, Anastasios V. Apiculture in the Prehistoric Aegean: Minoan & Mycenaean Symbols Revisited. 2009. (ENG., Illus.). 101p. (C). pap. 100.00 (978-1-4073-0454-0(2)) British Archaeological Reports Ltd. GBR. Dist: Brown, David Bk. Co., The.
Harvard Student Agencies Inc. Staff & Avalon Travel Publishing Staff. Let's Go Istanbul, Athens & the Greek Islands: The Student Travel Guide. 2011. (Let's Go Ser.). (ENG., Illus.). 248p. pap. 14.95 (978-1-59880-740-0(4), Let's Go) Avalon Travel Publishing.
Jackson, Caroline & Wager, Emma C., eds. Vitreous Materials in the Late Bronze Age Aegean: A Window to the East Mediterranean World. 2007. (Sheffield Studies in Aegean Archaeology Ser.). (ENG., Illus.). 255p. (C). pap. 64.00 (978-1-84217-261-2(1)) Oxbow Bks., Ltd. GBR. Dist: Brown, David Bk. Co., The.
Kakmi, Dmetri. Mother Land. 2010. (ENG., Illus.). 231p. 39.95 (978-1-906011-39-0(7)) Eland Bks. GBR. Dist: Dufour Editions, Inc.
McGilchrist, Nigel. Greece: The Aegean Islands. 2010. (Blue Guides). (ENG., Illus.). 700p. pap. 29.95 (978-1-905131-35-8(6), 913135) Blue Guides Ltd. GBR. Dist: Norton, W. W. & Co., Inc.
McGilchrist, Nigel. McGilchrist's Greek Islands, Set. 2011. 3400p. pap. 225.00 **(978-1-907859-20-5(9))** Interlink Publishing Group, Inc.
Simon, Jos. Greek Islands with Your Family: From Golden Beaches to Ancient Legends. 2008. (Frommers with Your Family Ser.: 6). (ENG., Illus.). 258p. pap. 18.99 (978-0-470-51861-8(8), Frommers) Wiley, John & Sons, Inc.
Smith, Peter C., et al. War in the Aegean: The Campaign for the Eastern Mediterranean in World War II. 2008. (Stackpole Military History Ser.). (ENG., Illus.). 296p. pap. 19.95 (978-0-8117-3519-3(2)) Stackpole Bks.
Thomas Cook Publishing Staff. Turkey: Aegean Coast. 3rd ed. 2010. (Thomas Cook Pocket Guides). (ENG., Illus.). 128p. pap. 9.95 (978-1-84848-262-3(0)) Cook, Thomas Publishing GBR. Dist: Globe Pequot Pr., The.
Uhl, Jason. A Brief Introduction to Ancient Aegean Art: Cycladic, Minoan, & Mycenaean Art & Architecture. 2007. 76p. per. 16.95 (978-1-4241-8204-6(2)) PublishAmerica, Inc.
Yasur-Landau, Assaf. The Philistines & Aegean Migration at the End of the Late Bronze Age. 2010. (ENG., Illus.). 412p. (C). 95.00 (978-0-521-19162-3(9)) Cambridge Univ. Pr.

AEGIDIUS, OF ASSISI, D. 1262
see Giles, of Assisi, d. 1262

AELFRIC, ABBOT OF EYNSHAM
Gneuss, Helmut. Ælfric of Eynsham: His Life, Times, & Writings. 2009. pap. 12.00 (978-1-58044-144-5(0)) Medieval Institute Pubns.
Gretsch, Mechthild. Aelfric & the Cult of Saints in Late Anglo-Saxon England. 2009. (Cambridge Studies in Anglo-Saxon England Ser.). (ENG.). 276p. pap. 38.00 (978-0-521-09307-1(4)) Cambridge Univ. Pr.
Jones, Christopher A. Ælfric's Letter to the Monks of Eynsham. 2007. (Cambridge Studies in Anglo-Saxon England Ser.). (ENG.). 268p. pap. 53.00 (978-0-521-03073-1(0)) Cambridge Univ. Pr.
Magennis, Hugh & Swan, Mary, eds. A Companion to Ælfric. 2009. (Brill's Companions to the Christian Tradition Ser.). 480p. (978-90-04-17681-2(0)) BRILL.
Upchurch, Robert, ed. Aelfric's Lives of the Virgin Spouses: With Modern English Parallel-Text Translations. 2007. (Medieval Studies). (ANG, LAT & ENG.). 297p. (C). 100.00 (978-0-85989-779-2(6)) Univ. of Exeter Pr. GBR. Dist: Chicago Distribution Ctr.
Upchurch, Robert K., ed. Aelfric's Lives of the Virgin Spouses: With Modern English Parallel-Text Translations. 2007. (Medieval Studies). (ANG, LAT & ENG.). 320p. per. 29.95 (978-0-85989-780-8(X)) Univ. of Exeter Pr. GBR. Dist: Chicago Distribution Ctr.

AELRED, OF RIEVAULX, SAINT, 1110-1167
Jusserand, J. J. English Essays from a French Pen. 2010. pap. 41.80 (978-1-61719-426-9(3)) Gorgias Pr., LLC.

AENEAS (LEGENDARY CHARACTER)
Cairns, Francis. Virgil's Augustan Epic. 2006. (ENG.). 296p. pap. 58.00 (978-0-521-03496-8(5)) Cambridge Univ. Pr.
Clarke, M. Story of Aeneas. 2007. (ENG.). 120p. per. (978-1-4065-1380-6(6)) Dodo Pr.
Clarke, Michael. Story of Aeneas. 2008. 132p. 21.99 (978-0-554-31240-8(9)) 2008. 132p. 24.99 (978-0-554-21937-0(9)) 2006. (ENG.). 130p. pap. 18.99 (978-1-4264-1289-9(4)) 2006. (ENG.). 130p. pap. 19.99 (978-1-4264-1294-3(0)) BiblioBazaar.
—Story of Aeneas. 2007. (ENG.). 100p. per. (978-1-4068-4617-1(1)) Echo Library.
Heil, Andreas. Alma Aeneis: Studien zur Vergil- und Statiusrezeption Dante Alighieris. (Studien Zur Klassischen Philologie Ser.: Vol. 135). (GER.). 33.95 (978-3-631-39842-5(5)) Lang, Peter Publishing, Inc.
Kallendorf, Craig. The Other Virgil: Pessimistic Readings of the Aeneid in Early Modern Culture. 2007. (Classical Presences Ser.). (Illus.). 280p. 99.00 (978-0-19-921236-1(8)) Oxford Univ. Pr., Inc.
Stahl, Hans-Peter, ed. & intro. Vergil's Aeneid: Augustan Epic & Political Context. 2009. (ENG.). 324p. (C). pap. 40.00 (978-1-905125-33-3(X)) Classical Pr. of Wales, The GBR. Dist: Brown, David Bk. Co., The.
Vergil. Vergil Aeneid No. 1. Ganiban, Randall, ed. 2008. (Focus Vergil Aeneid Commentaries Ser.). (ENG., Illus.). 170p. (C). pap. 15.95 (978-1-58510-225-9(3)) Focus Publishing/R. Pullins Co., Inc.
Virgil. Aeneid. 2006. (ENG.). 382p. pap. (978-1-4068-0751-6(6)) Echo Library.
—Aeneid. 2006. (ENG.). 348p. per. (978-1-905530-09-0(9)) InternationalMedia Pubn. & Literary Assocs.
—The Aeneid. 2009. 382p. pap. (978-1-4589-4774-1(2)); 402p. pap. (978-1-4589-4775-8(0)) Books LLC.
—The Aeneid. Fagles, Robert, tr. from LAT. 2006. (ENG., Illus.). 496p. (gr. 12-18). 40.00 (978-0-670-03803-9(2), Viking Adult) Penguin Group (USA) Inc.
Virgil & Fantham, Elaine. Aeneid. Ahl, Frederick, tr. from LAT. 2008. (Oxford World's Classics Ser.). (ENG., Illus.). 480p. pap. 15.95 (978-0-19-923195-9(8)) Oxford Univ. Pr., Inc.
Yunck, John A. & Baswell, Christopher. Eneas: A Twelfth-Century French Romance. 274p. 49.50 (978-0-231-13252-7(2)) Columbia Univ. Pr.

AEOLIAN PROCESSES
see Eolian Processes

AERIAL BOMBING
see Bombing, Aerial

AERIAL BOMBS
see Bombs

AERIAL GEOGRAPHY
see Aerial Photography in Geography

AERIAL LAW
see Aeronautics—Law and Legislation

AERIAL NAVIGATION
see Navigation (Aeronautics)

AERIAL PHOTOGRAPH READING
see Photographic Interpretation; Photographic Interpretation (Military Science)

AERIAL PHOTOGRAPHY
Here are entered works on the taking of aerial photographs. Works on the interpretation of aerial photographs are entered under Photographic Interpretation.
see also Photographic Interpretation; Photographic Interpretation (Military Science); Photographic Reconnaissance Systems
Aber, James S., et al. Small-Format Aerial Photography: Principles, Techniques & Geoscience Applications. 2010. (ENG.). 268p. 97.95 (978-0-444-53260-2(9), Elsevier Science) Elsevier Science & Technology Bks.
Abicht, Matthew J., et al. Landscapes Through the Lens: Aerial Photographs & the Historic Environment. 2010. (ENG., Illus.). 302p. (C). pap. 90.00 (978-1-84217-981-9(0)) Oxbow Bks., Ltd. GBR. Dist: Brown, David Bk. Co., The.
Arthus-Bertrand, Yann. Earth from Above. 10th anniv. ed. 2010. (ENG., Illus.). 440p. 60.00 (978-0-8109-9693-9(6)) Abrams.
—Home: A Hymn to the Planet & Humanity. 2009. (ENG., Illus.). 192p. pap. 16.95 (978-0-8109-8434-9(2)) Abrams.
—New Earth from Above. rev. ed. 2009. (365's Ser.). (ENG., Illus.). 792p. 32.50 (978-0-8109-8461-5(X)) Abrams.
Arthus-Bertrand, Yann, photos by. Earth from Above. ltd. ed. 2008. (ENG., Illus.). 216p. 2000.00 (978-0-8109-9385-3(6)) Abrams.
Attini, Antonio. Morocco. 2008. (Flying High Ser.). (ENG., Illus.). 432p. 24.95 (978-88-544-0342-0(3)) White Star ITA. Dist: Random Hse., Inc.
Attini, Antonio, photos by. Naples: In Flight over the City & Campania. 2009. (ENG., Illus.). 224p. 29.95 (978-88-544-0369-7(5)) White Star ITA. Dist: Random Hse., Inc.
Beaver, Marge. Above West Michigan: Aerial Photography of West Michigan. 2007. (ENG., Illus.). 128p. 45.00 (978-0-472-11640-9(1)) Univ. of Michigan Pr.
Boilin' & Bakin in Boogar Hollow. 2.95 (978-0-936672-55-7(2)) Aerial Photography Services, Inc.
Bridges, Marilyn, photos by. Flights Through Time. 2007. pap. 24.95 (978-1-888899-37-5(9)); 100.00 (978-1-888899-38-2(7)) Lodima Pr.
Cohen, Jean-Louis. Above Paris: The Aerial Survey of Roger Henrard. 2006. (ENG., Illus.). 320p. 50.00 (978-1-56898-613-5(0)) Princeton Architectural Pr.
Copello, Roberto. Jerusalem. 2008. (ENG., Illus.). 136p. 16.95 (978-88-6312-005-9(6)) White Star ITA. Dist: Random Hse., Inc.
Cosgrove, Denis & Fox, William L. Photography & Flight. 2010. (Reaktion Books - Exposures Ser.). (ENG., Illus.). 144p. pap. 29.95 (978-1-86189-398-7(1)) Reaktion Bks., Ltd. GBR. Dist: Chicago Distribution Ctr.
Elaksher, Ahmed. Detection & 3d Reconstruction of Urban Features from Aerial Images. 2009. 192p. pap. (978-3-639-19244-5(3)) VDM Verlag Dr. Mueller e.K.
Fortney, Bill & Kettenhofen, Mark. America from 500 Feet II. 2008. 39.95 (978-1-935001-06-5(X)) Acclaim Pr., Inc.
Fox, William L. Aereality: On the World from Above. 2009. (ENG., Illus.). 320p. 30.00 (978-1-58243-429-2(8), Counterpoint Pr.) Basic Bks. GBR. Dist: Perseus-PGW.
Gao, Jay. Digital Analysis of Remotely Sensed Imagery. 2008. (ENG., Illus.). 674p. (C). 150.00 (978-0-07-160465-9(0), 0071604650) McGraw-Hill Professional Publishing.
Gerster, Georg. Paradise Lost: Persia from Above. 2009. (ENG., Illus.). 184p. 59.95 (978-0-7148-4884-6(0)) Phaidon Pr., Inc.
Gerster, Georg, photos by. The Sites of Ancient Greece. 2012. (ENG., Illus.). 160p. 69.95 **(978-0-7148-6084-8(0))** Phaidon Pr., Inc.
Glenn, Frank & Muller, Daan. Charleston from Above: Aerial Photography of the Lowcountry. 2007. (ENG.). 143p. 39.99 (978-1-60194-007-0(6)) Advantage Media Group.
Grinberg, Itamar & Grintberg, Hanit. Israel from Above. 2008. (ENG., Illus.). 504p. 24.95 (978-88-6312-000-4(5)) White Star ITA. Dist: Random Hse., Inc.
Grintberg, Hanit Armonn & Grinberg, Itamar. Israel from Above. 2010. (ENG., Illus.). 464p. 19.95 (978-88-544-0429-8(2)) White Star ITA. Dist: Sterling Publishing Co., Inc.
Guignard, Philippe. Paris au Fil du Vent: Paris from the Sky. 2007. 160p. 49.95 (978-2-7537-0056-7(7)) Editions Crès FRA. Dist: Independent Pubs. Group.
Haas, Robert. Through the Eyes of the Vikings: An Aerial Vision of Arctic Lands. 2010. (Illus.). 224p. 50.00 (978-1-4262-0638-2(0), National Geographic) National Geographic Society.
Haas, Robert B. Through the Eyes of the Condor: An Aerial Vision of Latin America. 2007. (ENG., Illus.). 232p. 50.00 (978-1-4262-0132-5(X), National Geographic) National Geographic Society.
Laar, Anthonie van & Akça, Alparslan. Forest Mensuration. 2nd ed. 2010. (Managing Forest Ecosystems Ser.). xvi, 383p. pap. 129.00 (978-90-481-7497-3(X), 904817497X) Springer.
Leonard, Zoe, photos by. Zoe Leonard: Photographs, 1 vol. 2007. (ENG., Illus.). 264p. 65.00 (978-3-86521-494-2(0)) Steidl, Gerhard Druckerei und Verlag DEU. Dist: Innovative Logistics.
MacLean, Alex S. Over: The American Landscape at the Tipping Point. 2008. (ENG., Illus.). 336p. 50.00 (978-0-8109-7145-5(3)) Abrams.
Maisel, David, photos by. Oblivion. 2006. (Illus.). 48p. 60.00 (978-1-59005-182-5(3)) Nazraeli Pr.
Manfreto De Fabianis, Valeria, ed. Forests. 2011. (ENG., Illus.). 736p. 19.95 (978-88-544-0464-9(0)) White Star ITA. Dist: Random Hse., Inc.
Marcarini, Albano & Della Pietà, Cesare. Switzerland from Above. 2010. (ENG., Illus.). 408p. 50.00 (978-88-544-0406-9(3)) White Star ITA. Dist: Random Hse., Inc.
National Monuments Record (England) Staff, contrib. by. Mata Hari's Glass Eye & Other Stories: Pioneers of Aerial Photography. 2007. (Illus.). 20p. 50.00 (978-1-905624-01-0(8)) English Heritage GBR. Dist: Brown, David Bk. Co., The.
Paine, David P. & Kiser, James D. Aerial Photography & Image Interpretation. 3rd ed. 2012. (ENG., Illus.). 648p. 135.00 **(978-0-470-87938-2(6)**, Wiley) Wiley, John & Sons, Inc.
Poliza, Michael. Eyes over Africa. 2007. 2000.00 (978-3-8327-9221-3(X)) teNeues Publishing Co.
Poliza, Michael, photos by. Eyes over Africa. collector's ed. 2007. 5000.00 (978-3-8327-9223-7(6)) teNeues Publishing Co.
Potter, Tami. Designing Photo Mosaics & More: Fast & fabulous pages using a simple grid system. 2007. 96p. per. 19.95 (978-0-9719403-1-4(2)) Wish In The Wind.
Rossi, Guido Alberto. Italy from the Air. 2007. (From the Air Ser.). (Illus.). 240p. 14.99 (978-88-540-0830-4(3)) White Star ITA. Dist: Book Sales, Inc.
Ruggiero, Elisa. Fotografare Volando: Storia, Arte, Impresa. 2010. (ITA., Illus.). 156p. (978-88-548-3271-8(5)) Aracne.
Sandau, Rainer. Digital Airborne Camera: Introduction & Technology. 2009. (ENG., Illus.). xi, 338p. 169.00 (978-1-4020-8877-3(9), 1402088779) Springer.
Schneider, Sigfrid. Luftbild und Luftbildinterpretation. (GER.). XVI, 530p. 225.00 **(978-3-11-177458-9(9))** De Gruyter, Walter Inc.
Sichel, Kim. To Fly: Contemporary Aerial Photography. 2007. pap. 20.00 (978-1-881450-26-9(0)) Boston Univ., Art Gallery.
Stadler, Hilar, ed. Die kolorierten Lichtbilder des Ballonpioniers Eduard Spelterini. 2010. (GER & ENG., Illus.). 152p. 55.00 (978-3-85881-303-9(6)) Scheidegger und Spiess AG, Verlag CHE. Dist: Antique Collectors' Club.
Steinmetz, George. African Air. 2008. (ENG., Illus.). 208p. 45.00 (978-0-8109-8403-5(2)) Abrams.
—Empty Quarter: A Photographic Journey to the Heart of the Arabian Desert. 2009. (ENG., Illus.). 208p. 40.00 (978-0-8109-8381-6(8)) Abrams.
Stern, Ralph & Huber, Nicole, texts. Urbanizing the Mojave Desert: Las Vegas. 2008. (GER & ENG., Illus.). 192p. 35.00 (978-3-939633-50-1(X)) Jovis Verlag GmbH DEU. Dist: D.A.P./Distributed Art Pubs.
Tauranac, John. New York from the Air: A Story of Architecture. 2011. (ENG., Illus.). 216p. 60.00 (978-0-8109-9384-6(8)) Abrams.
Tomei, Karel. Over Holland. 2011. 577p. 38.95 **(978-90-5594-422-4(X)**, Scriptum Pubs.) Midpoint Trade Bks., Inc.
Verma, Kunal & Bhalla, Dipti. Ocean to Sky: India from the Air. 2007. (ENG., Illus.). 204p. 24.95 (978-81-7436-380-0(7)) Roli Bks. Private, Ltd. IND. Dist: Ingram Pub. Services.
Wilson, Craig, photos by. Hanging by a Thread: A Kite's View of Wisconsin. 2011. (SPA, ENG, CHI & GER., Illus.). 144p. pap. 24.95 **(978-0-299-28604-0(5))** Univ. of Wisconsin Pr.
Woodcock, David, photos by. From the Air: Olympic Peninsula. 2010. 49.95 net. (978-1-57833-473-5(X)); pap. 29.95 net. (978-1-57833-474-2(8)) Todd Communications.
Wynn, Jeffrey C. Mapping Ground Water in Three Dimensions: An Analysis of the Airborne Geophysical Surveys of the Upper San Pedro River Basin, Cochise County, Southeastern Arizona. 2006. (978-1-4113-0901-2(4)) United States Geological Survey.

AERIAL PHOTOGRAPHY IN ARCHAEOLOGY
Albanese, Marilia, et al, texts. Archaeology from Above: The World from the Air. 2010. (ENG., Illus.). 192p. 39.95 (978-88-544-0493-9(4)) White Star ITA. Dist: Sterling Publishing Co., Inc.
Barber, Martyn. A History of Aerial Photography & Archaeology: Mata Hari's Glass Eye & Other Tales. 2012. (ENG., Illus.). 256p. 50.00 (978-1-84802-036-8(8)) English Heritage GBR. Dist: Brown, David Bk. Co., The.
Hauser, Kitty. Bloody Old Britain: O. G. S. Crawford & the Archaeology of Modern Life. (ENG., Illus.). 2010. 286p. pap. 18.95 (978-1-84708-077-6(4)) 2008. 224p. pap. 32.95 (978-1-86207-873-4(4)) Granta Bks. GBR. Dist: Independent Pubs. Group.
Ingle, Caroline & Saunders, Helen. Aerial Archaeology in Essex: The Role of the National Mapping Programme in Interpreting the Landscape. 2011. (East Anglian Archaeology Ser.). (ENG., Illus.). 200p. (C). pap. 40.00 (978-1-84194-073-1(9)) East Anglian Archaeology GBR. Dist: Brown, David Bk. Co., The.
Light, Michael, photos by. Michael Light: Bingham Mine, Garfield Stack. 2009. (ENG., Illus.). 48p. 50.00 (978-1-934435-20-5(1)) Radius Bks.
Norman, E. R. & St Joseph, J. K. S. The Early Development of Irish Society: The Evidence of Aerial Photography. 2008. (Cambridge Air Surveys Ser.). (ENG.). 140p. pap. 24.99 (978-0-521-08935-7(2)) Cambridge Univ. Pr.
Ryder, Lucy. Change & Continuity: A Study in the Historic Landscape of Devon. 2012. (ENG., Illus.). 256p. pap. 60.00 (978-1-905119-38-7(0)) Windgather Pr. GBR. Dist: Brown, David Bk. Co., The.
Trümpler, Charlotte, ed. The Past from Above: Aerial Photographs of Archaeological Sites. 2007. (Illus.). 416p. pap. 39.95 (978-0-89236-875-4(6)) Oxford Univ. Pr., Inc.

AERIAL PHOTOGRAPHY IN GEOGRAPHY
Country Store. 2.95 (978-0-936672-50-2(1)) Aerial Photography Services, Inc.
Davidson, Cameron. Chesapeake: The Aerial Photography of Cameron Davidson. 2011. (ENG., Illus.). 152p. 39.95 (978-0-9841620-0-0(3)) Univ. Pr. of Virginia.

AERIAL PHOTOGRAPHY IN GEOLOGY
Collier, Michael. Over the Coasts: An Aerial View of Geology. 2009. (ENG., Illus.). 120p. 34.95 (978-1-931414-42-5(4)) Mikaya Pr.
—Over the Mountains. 2007. (Aerial View of Geology Ser.). (ENG., Illus.). 128p. 34.95 (978-1-931414-18-0(1)) Mikaya Pr.
—Over the Rivers. 2008. (Aerial View of Geology Ser.). (ENG., Illus.). 128p. 34.95 (978-1-931414-21-0(1)) Mikaya Pr.
Rivard, Lambert. Satellite Geology & Photogeomorphology: An Instructional Manual for Data Integration. 2011. (ENG., Illus.). viii, 270p. 129.00 (978-3-642-20607-8(7), 3642206077) Springer.

AERIAL PROPELLERS
see Propellers, Aerial

AERIAL ROCKETS
see Rockets (Aeronautics); Rockets (Ordnance)

AERIAL WARFARE
see Air Warfare

AEROBATICS
see Stunt Flying

AEROBIC BACTERIA
see Bacteria, Aerobic

AEROBIC DANCING
Bishop, Jan Galen. Fitness Through Aerobics. 8th ed. 2010. (ENG.). 272p. (C). pap. 51.33 (978-0-321-67828-7(1)) Benjamin-Cummings Publishing Co.
Dorling Kindersley Publishing Staff. 15-Minute Energizing Workout. 2011. (ENG.). 275p. pap. 19.95 **(978-0-7566-7466-3(2))** Dorling Kindersley Publishing, Inc.
Hayes, Kendra. Stomping Ground. 2009. 133p. pap. 12.00 (978-0-557-20143-3(8)) Lulu Enterprises Inc.
Perez, Beto & Greenwood-Robinson, Maggie. Zumba: Ditch the Workout, Join the Party! - The Zumba Weight Loss Program. 2009. (ENG., Illus.). 304p. 24.99 (978-0-446-54612-6(7), Wellness Central) Grand Central Publishing.

AEROBIC EXERCISES
see also Cycling; Running; Swimming; Walking
Akalan, Cengiz. Prediction of Aerobic Capacity from an Individualized Protocol. 2009. 132p. pap. (978-3-639-17301-7(5)) VDM Verlag Dr. Mueller e.K.

A

Bayer, Cary. The Prosperity Aerobics. 80p. pap. 7.95 (978-0-9644224-0-7(9)) Bayer Communications.

Bricker, Kathryn & Bonelli, Sabra. Traditional Aerobics/Step Training. 2nd ed. 2007. (Illus.). 113p. per. 19.95 (978-1-58518-965-6(0)) Coaches Choice.

Bui Xuan, Thanh. Aerobic Granulation with Support Medi. 2010. 88p. pap. (978-3-8383-8859-4(0)) Lambert Academic Publishing.

Craig, Colleen, et al. Get on It! BOSU Balance Trainer Workouts for Core Strength & a Super Toned Body. 2008. (ENG., Illus.). 144p. pap. 14.95 (978-1-56975-589-1(2)) Ulysses Pr.

Dorling Kindersley Publishing Staff. 15-Minute Energizing Workout. 2011. (ENG.). 275p. pap. 19.95 **(978-0-7566-7466-3(2))** Dorling Kindersley Publishing, Inc.

Easter, Ethel L. Resurrection Aerobics the Christian Based Sex Aerobics. 2008. 136p. pap. 14.99 (978-1-60647-881-3(8)) Xulon Pr., Inc.

Institute for Aerobic Research, Cooper. 30 Curl-up Measuring Strip. 3.25 (978-0-7360-0115-1(8)) Human Kinetics Pubs.

—45 Curl-up Measuring Strip. 3.50 (978-0-7360-0116-8(6)) Human Kinetics Pubs.

Jasper, Maura. Punk Rock Aerobics: 75 Killer Moves, 50 Punk Classics, & 25 Reasons to Get off Your Ass & Exercise. 2008. (ENG.). 173p. pap. 18.00 (978-1-4379-6387-8(0)) DIANE Publishing Co.

Jonas, Steven. Triathloning for Ordinary Mortals: And Doing the Duathlon Too. 2nd ed. 2006. (ENG., Illus.). 256p. per. 17.95 (978-0-393-32877-6(5), 32877) Norton, W. W. & Co., Inc.

Kamenju, Janet. Aerobic Capacity of Kenyan. 2010. 84p. pap. (978-3-639-24389-5(7)) VDM Verlag Dr. Mueller e.K.

Kumar, Harish. Comparison of Ecg Responses to Graded Treadmill Test. 2010. 56p. pap. (978-3-639-25137-1(7)) VDM Verlag Dr. Mueller e.K.

Lieberman, David C., ed. Aerobic Exercise & Athletic Performance: Types, Duration & Health Benefits. 2009. (Sports & Athletics Preparation, Performance, & Psychology Ser.). 195.00 (978-1-60876-217-0(3), Nova Biomedical Bks.) Nova Science Pubs., Inc.

Mazzeo, Karen S. & Mangili, Lauren M. Fitness Through Aerobics, Step Training, Walking. 5th ed. 2012. (ENG.). 192p. (C). pap. 51.95 **(978-0-8400-4809-7(2))** Wadsworth.

McAurthur, Emily, photos by & des. After Baby Abs: By BuffMother! 2008. (Illus.). 32p. 19.95 (978-0-9800363-1-2(3)) Generational Health Pubns. LLC.

Meyer-Anderson, Mervee. Aerobic. (SPA.). 160p. (978-84-270-0798-7(1)) Ediciones Martínez Roca.

Perez, Beto & Greenwood-Robinson, Maggie. Zumba: Ditch the Workout, Join the Party! - The Zumba Weight Loss Program. 2009. (ENG., Illus.). 304p. 24.99 (978-0-446-54612-5(7), Wellness Central) Grand Central Publishing.

Sharkey, Brian J. Fitness Illustrated. 2010. (ENG., Illus.). 328p. pap. 21.95 (978-0-7360-8158-0(5)) Human Kinetics Pubs.

Wright, Bill. Aerobic Tennis: Use Tennis for a Cardio Workout! 2010. (ENG., Illus.). 192p. pap. 16.95 (978-0-936070-50-6(1)) Shelter Pubns., Inc.

AEROBICS

see Aerobic Exercises

AEROBIOLOGY

see Air—Microbiology

AERODROMES

see Airports

AERODYNAMIC FORCES

see Drag (Aerodynamics)

AERODYNAMIC HEATING

see also Space Vehicles—Atmospheric Entry

Bednarz, Piotr. Finite Element Simulation of Stress Evolution in Thermal Barrier Coating Systems. 2007. (Schriften des Forschungszentrums Jülich: Vol. 60). 121p. pap. (978-3-89336-471-8(4)) Forschungszentrum Julich GmbH - Zentralbibliothek, Verlag.

AERODYNAMICS

see also Aerodynamics, Supersonic; Aerodynamics, Transonic; Aeroelasticity; Aeronautics; Boundary Layer; Drag (Aerodynamics); Flutter (Aerodynamics); Gas Flow; Turbulence; Wind Tunnels

Agrawal, Anmol. Hingeless Flow Control over an Airfoil. 2011. 84p. pap. **(978-3-8454-0293-2(8))** Lambert Academic Publishing.

Ali, Shahjahan. Ing of Multiple Jets in Crossflow. 2010. 164p. pap. (978-3-639-23592-0(4)) VDM Verlag Dr. Mueller e.K.

American Society of Mechanical Engineers Staff, ed. Aerodynamics of Turbomachinery. (Illus.). 146p. 96.00 (978-1-86058-051-2(3)) Professional Engineering Publishing GBR. Dist: SAE Intl.

—Turbo Compressor & Fan Stability. (Illus.). 64p. 78.00 (978-0-85298-864-0(8)) Professional Engineering Publishing GBR. Dist: SAE Intl.

Anderson, David, et al. Understanding Flight. 2nd ed. 2009. (ENG., Illus.). 306p. pap. 34.95 (978-0-07-162696-5(4), 0071626964) McGraw-Hill Professional Publishing.

Anderson, John Fundamentals of Aerodynamics. 5th ed. 2010. (ENG., Illus.). 1152p. (C). 225.67 (978-0-07-339810-5(1), 0073398101, McGraw-Hill Science, Engineering & Mathematics) McGraw-Hill Higher Education.

—Introduction to Flight. 7th ed. 2011. (ENG., Illus.). 944p. (C). 228.00 (978-0-07-338024-7(5), 0073380245, McGraw-Hill Science, Engineering & Mathematics) McGraw-Hill Higher Education.

Anderson, John D. & Anderson, John D., Jr. Introduction to Flight. 6th ed. 2007. (ENG., Illus.). 912p. (C). 197.50 (978-0-07-352939-4(7), 0073529397, McGraw-Hill Science, Engineering & Mathematics) McGraw-Hill Higher Education.

Bertin, John J. & Cummings, Russell M. Aerodynamics for Engineers. 5th ed. 2008. (ENG., Illus.). 752p. (C). 191.00 (978-0-13-227268-1(7), Prentice Hall) Prentice Hall PTR.

Bllushgens, G. S. & Chernyshev, S. L. TsAGI: Russia's Global Aerospace Research Center: History of the Establishment & Future. 2011. **(978-1-56700-272-0(2))** Begell Hse. Pubs., Inc.

Bloor, David. The Enigma of the Aerofoil: Rival Theories in Aerodynamics, 1909-1930. 2011. (Illus.). 608p. 110.00 (978-0-226-06094-1(2)); (ENG., pap. 35.00 (978-0-226-06095-8(0)) Univ. of Chicago Pr.

Bowles, Mark D. The Apollo of Aeronautics: NASA's Aircraft Energy Efficiency Program, 1973-1987: NASA's Aircraft Energy Efficiency Program, 1973-1987. National Aeronautics and Space Administration, ed. 2010. (ENG., Illus.). 201p. 24.00 (978-0-16-084295-5(6), U. S. National Aeronautics & Space Administration) United States Government Printing Office.

Braga de Costa Campos, Luis Manuel. Differential Equations with Applications to Vibrations & Waves. 2010. (ENG., Illus.). 450p. 89.95 (978-1-4200-7115-3(7)) CRC Pr. LLC.

Browand, Fred. Aerodynamics of Heavy Vehicles Ii. 2008. (Lecture Notes in Applied & Computational Mechanics Ser.). (Illus.). 480p. 209.00 (978-3-540-85069-4(4), 3540850694) Springer.

Cebeci, T., et al. Analysis of Low Speed Unsteady Airfoil Flows. 226p. 185.00 (978-0-9668461-8-8(4)) Horizons Publishing.

Cebeci, Tuncer. An Engineering Approach to the Calculation of Aerodynamic Flows. 2010. (Illus.). xv, 396p. pap. 209.00 (978-3-642-08543-7(1), 3642085431) Springer.

Cogdell, Christina. Eugenic Design: Streamlining America in The 1930s. 2010. (Illus.). 352p. (C). pap. 24.95 (978-0-8122-2122-0(2)) Univ. of Pennsylvania Pr.

Collicott, Steven, et al. Aerodynamics for Engineering Students. 6th ed. 2012. (ENG., Illus.). 740p. pap. 99.95 **(978-0-08-096632-8(2)**, Butterworth-Heinemann) Elsevier Science & Technology Bks.

Cook, Michael V. Flight Dynamics Principles: A Linear Systems Approach to Aircraft Stability & Control. 2nd ed. 2007. (Elsevier Aerospace Engineering Ser.). (ENG., Illus.). 486p. 91.95 (978-0-7506-6927-6(6), Butterworth-Heinemann) Elsevier Science & Technology Bks.

Cram101 Textbook Reviews & Cram101 Textbook Reviews. Outlines & Highlights for Introduction to Flight by John D Anderson. 2011. 298p. pap. 32.95 **(978-1-61830-956-3(0))** Cram101 Inc.

Cram101 Textbook Reviews Staff. Outlines & Highlights for Fundamentals of Aerodynamics by John D Anderson, Isbn: 9780072950465. 2009. 220p. pap. 30.95 (978-1-4288-9766-3(6)) Cram101 Inc.

Das, Abhijit & Mukhopadhyay, Siddhartha. Nonlinear Autopilot Design for Aerospace Vehicles. 2010. 228p. pap. (978-3-639-24120-4(7)) VDM Verlag Dr. Mueller e.K.

Délery, Jean. Compressible Aerodynamics. 2010. (Iste Ser.: 421). (ENG., Illus.). 796p. 205.00 (978-1-84821-141-4(4), Wiley-ISTE) Wiley, John & Sons, Inc.

Dillmann, Andreas, et al, eds. New Results in Numerical & Experimental Fluid Mechanics VII: Contributions to the 16th STAB/DGLR Symposium Aachen, Germany 2008. 2010. (Notes on Numerical Fluid Mechanics & Multidisciplinary Design Ser.). 610p. 339.00 (978-3-642-14242-0(7), 3642142427) Springer.

Dragos, LazÃ£r. Mathematical Methods in Aerodynamics. 2010. 580p. pap. 379.00 (978-90-481-6445-5(1), 9048164451) Springer.

Encyclopaedia Britannica, Inc., compiled by. Aerodynamic Generation of Sound. 2009. 49.00 (978-1-60835-055-1(X)) Encyclopaedia Britannica, Inc.

—Low-Reynolds-Number Flow. 2009. 49.00 (978-1-60835-047-6(9)) Encyclopaedia Britannica, Inc.

—Stratified Flow. 2009. 49.00 (978-1-60835-048-3(7)) Encyclopaedia Britannica, Inc.

Erwin, John R. & Vitale, Nicholas G. Radial Outflow Compressor Design. 2008. 456p. pap. 59.95 (978-1-934939-34-5(X)) Wexford College Pr.

Flandro, Gary A., et al. Basic Aerodynamics. 2008. (Cambridge Aerospace Ser.). (Illus.). 400p. (C). 125.00 (978-0-521-80582-7(1)) Cambridge Univ. Pr.

Ginevsky, A. S. & Zhelannikov, A. I. Vortex wakes of Aircrafts. 2009. (Foundations of Engineering Mechanics Ser.). (ENG., Illus.). xv, 154p. 179.00 (978-3-642-01759-9(2), 3642017592) Springer.

Gülçat, Ülgen. Fundamentals of Modern Unsteady Aerodynamics. 2010. (ENG.). xii, 350p. 179.00 (978-3-642-14760-9(7), 3642147607) Springer.

Gunston, Bill. World Encyclopedia of Aero Engines: From the Pioneers to the Present Day. 5th ed. 2006. (ENG., Illus.). 272p. 54.95 (978-0-7509-4479-3(X)) Sutton Publishing.

H S, Tsien. Collected Works of H. S. Tsien (1938-1956) 2012. (ENG.). 900p. 120.00 **(978-0-12-398277-3(4)**, Academic Pr.) Elsevier Science & Technology Bks.

Haase, Werner, et al, eds. DESider - A European Effort on Hybrid RANS-les Modelling: Results of the European-Union Funded Project, 2004 - 2007. 2009. (Notes on Numerical Fluid Mechanics & Multidisciplinary Design Ser.). (Illus.). xx, 454p. 339.00 (978-3-540-92772-3(7)) Springer.

Hall, Kenneth C., et al, eds. Unsteady Aerodynamics, Aeroacoustics & Aeroelasticity of Turbomachines. 2010. (ENG.). xi, 626p. pap. 239.00 (978-90-481-7091-3(5), 9048170915) Springer.

Hansen, Martin. Aerodynamics of Wind Turbine. 2008. 192p. 117.00 (978-1-84407-439-6(0)) Earthscan GBR. Dist: Stylus Publishing, LLC.

—Aerodynamics of Wind Turbines. 2nd rev. ed. 2007. (ENG., Illus.). 208p. (C). 117.00 (978-1-84407-438-9(2)) Routledge.

Hirschel, Ernst-Heinrich & Krause, Egon, eds. 100 Volumes NNFM & 40 Years Numerical Fluid Mechanics. 2009. (Notes on Numerical Fluid Mechanics & Multidisciplinary Design Ser.). 450p. 219.00 (978-3-540-70804-9(9)) Springer.

Huang, Xing Z. & Verhaagen, N. G. Vortex Flow Behavior over Slender Delta Wing Configurations: Experimental Studies, Numerical & Analytical Solutions. 2008. 516p. 289.00 (978-1-4020-9332-6(2)) Springer.

Hull, David. Fundamentals of Airplane Flight Mechanics. 2007. (ENG., Illus.). xiv, 298p. 109.00 (978-3-540-46571-3(5), 3540465715) Springer.

Hurt, H. H. Aerodynamics for Naval Aviators: NAVWEPS 00-8ct-80. 2012. (ENG., Illus.). 432p. pap. 14.95 **(978-1-61608-439-4(1)**, 608439) Skyhorse Publishing Co., Inc.

ICAS Secretariat Staff, compiled by. 25th Congress of the International Council of the Aeronautical Sciences 2006. 2007. 4671p. pap. 493.00 (978-1-60423-227-1(7)) Curran Assocs., Inc.

Kroll, Norbert, et al, eds. ADIGMA - A European Initiative on the Development of Adaptive Higher-Order Variational Methods for Aerospace Applications: Results of a Collaborative Research Project Funded by the European Union, 2006-2009. 2010. (Notes on Numerical Fluid Mechanics & Multidisciplinary Design Ser.). (Illus.). 480p. 339.00 (978-3-642-03706-1(2), 3642037062) Springer.

—MEGADESIGN & MegaOpt - German Initiatives for Aerodynamic Simulation & Optimization in Aircraft Design: Results of the closing symposium of the MEGADESIGN & MegaOpt projects, Braunschweig, Germany, May 23 And 24 2007. 2009. (Notes on Numerical Fluid Mechanics & Multidisciplinary Design Ser.). (Illus.). xii, 314p. 289.00 (978-3-642-04092-4(6), 3642040926) Springer.

Kroll, Norbert & Fassbender, Jens K., eds. MEGAFLOW - Numerical Flow Simulation for Aircraft Design: Results of the second phase of the German CFD initiative MEGAFLOW, presented during its closing symposium at DLR, Braunschweig, Germany, December 10 And 11 2002. 2010. (Notes on Numerical Fluid Mechanics & Multidisciplinary Design Ser.). xii, 313p. pap. 289.00 (978-3-642-06365-7(9), 3642063659) Springer.

Lab-Volt Staff. Aerodynamics: Tech-Design ESeries. 2010. 105p. 11.00 (978-1-60533-154-6(6)); 68p. ring bd. 8.00 (978-1-60533-155-3(4)) Lab-Volt Systems, Inc.

Lang, Peter R. & Lombargo, Frank S., eds. Atmospheric Turbulence, Meteorological Modeling & Aerodynamics. 2010. 738p. 129.00 (978-1-60741-091-1(5)) Nova Science Pubs., Inc.

Langley, S. P. Experiments in Aerodynamics. 2009. 158p. 26.99 (978-1-116-17319-2(0)); 30.99 (978-1-116-17318-5(2)); pap. 21.75 (978-1-116-17320-8(4)); pap. 20.75 (978-1-116-17321-5(2)) BiblioBazaar.

Liskiewicz, Grzegorz & Sobczak, Krzysztof. Numerical Analysis of the Sail Aerodynamics. 2010. 124p. pap. (978-3-8383-6231-1(4)) Lambert Academic Publishing.

Liu, N. Y. & Ng, Eddie Y. K. Compressor Instability: With Integral Methods. 2007. (ENG., Illus.). xxiv, 134p. 139.00 (978-3-540-72411-7(7), 3540724117) Springer.

Liu, Tianshu & Sullivan, John P. Pressure & Temperature Sensitive Paints. 2010. (Experimental Fluid Mechanics Ser.). (Illus.). xi, 328p. pap. 179.00 (978-3-642-06075-5(7), 3642060757) Springer.

Lorenz, Ralph D. Spinning Flight: Dynamics of Frisbees, Boomerangs, Samaras, & Skipping Stones. 2006. (ENG., Illus.). xxi, 346p. 69.95 (978-0-387-30779-4(6), 0387307796) Springer.

Maglev Vechiles Getting Started Teacher's Guide. 2007. spiral bd. 24.95 (978-1-58651-919-3(0)) Pitsco/Pitsco LEGO Dacta.

Mazzola, Andrea. Low Reynolds Number Aerodynamics. 2009. 124p. pap. (978-3-639-19084-7(X)) VDM Verlag Dr. Mueller e.K.

McCormick, Barnes Warnock & Schetz, Joseph A. Introduction to Flight Testing & Applied Aerodynamics. 2011. (Illus.). ix, 133p. **(978-1-60086-827-6(4))** Virginia Polytechnic Institute & State Univ. Pr.

Mehdi, Nakhjiri. Robust Evolutionary Design Optimization for Aerodynamic Applications: Robustness Against Environmental Uncertainties & Evolutionary Optimization Towards an Operating Range in Opposite to an Operating Point. 2011. 128p. pap. **(978-3-639-32042-8(5))** VDM Verlag Dr. Mueller e.K.

Mettler, Bernard. Identification Modeling & Characteristics of Miniature Rotorcraft. 2010. (ENG.). 256p. pap. 259.00 (978-1-4419-5311-7(6), 1441953116) Springer.

Mughal, Umair. Pressure Differential Angle of Attack Measuring System. 2010. 128p. pap. (978-3-8383-7530-4(0)) Lambert Academic Publishing.

Mukherjee, Rinku. Decambering: A numerical tool to predict post-stall aerodynamic Data. 2010. 108p. pap. (978-3-8383-0209-6(5)) Lambert Academic Publishing.

Napolitano, Marcello. Aircraft Dynamics: From Modeling to Simulation. 2011. (ENG., Illus.). 706p. (C). 213.95 **(978-0-470-62667-2(4)**, Wiley) Wiley, John & Sons, Inc.

Ng, Eddie Y. K. & Liu, N. Y. Compressor Instability with Integral Methods. 2010. (ENG., Illus.). xxiv, 134p. pap. 139.00 (978-3-642-09147-6(4), 3642091474) Springer.

Norstrud, Helge. Sport Aerodynamics. 2009. (CISM International Centre for Mechanical Sciences Ser.). (Illus.). vi, 331p. 229.00 (978-3-211-89296-1(6)) Springer.

Obert, E., ed. Aerodynamic Design of Transport Aircraft. 2009. (Illus.). 656p. pap. 109.00 (978-1-58603-970-7(9)) IOS Pr., Inc.

Phillips, Warren F. Mechanics of Flight. 2nd ed. 2009. (ENG., Illus.). 1152p. 155.00 (978-0-470-53975-0(5), Wiley) Wiley, John & Sons, Inc.

Philpott, D. R. & Barnard, R. H. Aircraft Flight: A Description of the Physical Principles of Aircraft Flight. 4th ed. 2010. (ENG., Illus.). 384p. pap. 97.50 (978-0-273-73098-9(3)) Pearson Education, Ltd. GBR. Dist: Trans-Atlantic Pubns., Inc.

Pope, Alan. Basic Wing & Airfoil Theory. 2009. (Dover Books on Aeronautical Engineering Ser.). (ENG.). 320p. pap. 14.95 (978-0-486-47188-4(8)) Dover Pubns., Inc.

—Basic Wing & Airfoil Theory. 2011. 312p. 50.95 **(978-1-258-10068-1(1))** Literary Licensing, LLC.

Prouty, Ray. Helicopter Aerodynamics Volume I. 2009. 592p. pap. 54.95 (978-0-557-08991-8(3)) Lulu Enterprises Inc.

—Helicopter Aerodynamics Volume I. 2009. 364p. pap. 44.95 (978-0-557-09044-0(X)) Lulu Enterprises Inc.

Raman, Ganesh. Computational Aeroacoustics. Raman, Ganesh, ed. 2009. (Illus.). 507p. pap. 159.95 (978-0-906522-55-4(2)) Multi Science Publishing Co., Ltd. GBR. Dist: Independent Pubs. Group.

Raol, Jitendra L. & Singh, Jatinder. Flight Mechanics Modeling & Analysis. 2008. (ENG., Illus.). 440p. (C). 159.95 (978-1-4200-6753-8(2), CRC Press) Taylor & Francis Group GBR. Dist: Taylor & Francis Group.

Rasheed, Zohaib. Analysis of Transonic Flow over an Airfoil Using Cfd. 2010. 132p. pap. (978-3-8383-3443-1(4)) Lambert Academic Publishing.

Rath, Hans Josef, et al, eds. New Results in Numerical & Experimental Fluid Mechanics V: Contributions to the 14th STAB/DGLR Symposium Bremen, Germany 2004. (Notes on Numerical Fluid Mechanics & Multidisciplinary Design Ser.). xiv, 528p. 2010. pap. 409.00 (978-3-642-06995-6(9), 3642069959) 2006. (Illus.). 409.00 (978-3-540-33286-2(3), 3540332863) Springer.

Sarkar, Sunetra & Venkatraman, Kartik. Unsteady Aerodynamics of a Flapping Airfoil. 2010. 204p. pap. (978-3-8383-4759-2(5)) Lambert Academic Publishing.

Schmidt, David K. Modern Flight Dynamics. 2011. (ENG., Illus.). 912p. (C). 206.00 (978-0-07-339811-2(X), 007339811X, McGraw-Hill Science, Engineering & Mathematics) McGraw-Hill Higher Education.

Sears, William Rees. Introduction to Theoretical Aerodynamics & Hydrodynamics. 2011. (Illus.). xiii, 203p. (978-1-60086-773-6(1)) American Institute of Aeronautics & Astronautics.

Shannon, Jack. The 58P. 2008. 91p. pap. 32.50 (978-0-557-00015-9(7)) Lulu Enterprises Inc.

Sheard, Geoff. Aerodynamic & Mechanical Performance. 2011. 280p. pap. **(978-3-8443-0204-2(2))** Lambert Academic Publishing.

Shrestha, Samir, et al. Aerodynamics Force on a Fiber. 2010. 56p. pap. (978-3-639-25659-8(X)) VDM Verlag Dr. Mueller e.K.

Shyy, Wei, et al. Aerodynamics of Low Reynolds Number Flyers. 2011. (Cambridge Aerospace Ser.). (ENG.). 212p. pap. 45.00 (978-0-521-20401-9(1)) Cambridge Univ. Pr.

—Aerodynamics of Low Reynolds Number Flyers: Wei Shyy ... [et Al.]. 2007. (Cambridge Aerospace Ser.). (ENG., Illus.). 196p. 94.00 (978-0-521-88278-1(8)) Cambridge Univ. Pr.

Strømmen, Einar. Theory of Bridge Aerodynamics. 2nd ed. 2010. 300p. 129.00 (978-3-642-13659-7(1), 3642136591) Springer.

Suryanarayana, Gargeshwari. Aerodynamic Drag Reduction of Bluff Bodies. 2010. 180p. pap. (978-3-8383-1103-6(5)) Lambert Academic Publishing.

Swatton, Peter J. Principles of Flight for Pilots. 2010. (Aerospace Ser.). (ENG., Illus.). 506p. pap. 85.00 (978-0-470-71073-9(X), Wiley) Wiley, John & Sons, Inc.

Tennekes, H & Tennekes, Henk. The Simple Science of Flight: From Insects to Jumbo Jets. 2nd rev. exp. ed. 2009. (ENG., Illus.). 216p. (gr. 17). pap. 22.95 (978-0-262-51313-5(7)) MIT Pr.

Thawley, Scott. Spatio-Temporal Characteristics of Spray from Liquid Jet in Crossflow. 2009. 92p. pap. (978-3-639-18299-6(5)) VDM Verlag Dr. Mueller e.K.

Tropea, Cameron, et al, eds. New Results in Numerical & Experimental Fluid Mechanics VI: Contributions to the 15th STAB/DGLR Symposium Darmstadt, Germany 2006. 2010. (Notes on Numerical Fluid Mechanics & Multidisciplinary Design Ser.). xiv, 472p. pap. 339.00 (978-3-642-09387-6(6), 3642093876) Springer.

Tropea, Carmen, et al, eds. New Results in Numerical & Experimental Fluid Mechanics VI: Contributions to the 15th STAB/DGLR Symposium Darmstadt, Germany 2006. 2007. (Notes on Numerical Fluid Mechanics & Multidisciplinary Design Ser.). 530p. 339.00 (978-3-540-74458-0(4)) Springer.

Ullrich, Gary M. & Dusenbury, Mark Joseph. Aerodynamics. rev. ed. 2012. (ENG.). 152p. pap. 43.59 **(978-0-7575-9932-3(X))** Kendall Hunt Publishing Co.

Wauquiez, Christian. Shape Optimization of Low Speed Airfoils. 2009. 68p. pap. (978-3-639-11623-6(2)) VDM Verlag Dr. Mueller e.K.

Weng, Chin-Tang Tom. Aerodynamic Analysis of A Landing Transport Airplane in Windshear. 2008. 120p. pap. (978-3-639-01661-1(0)) VDM Verlag Dr. Mueller e.K.

Woods, L. C. The Theory of Subsonic Plane Flow. 2011. (ENG.). 618p. pap. 75.00 (978-0-521-28319-9(1)) Cambridge Univ. Pr.

Yazdani, Md Gholam & Yazdani, Gholam. Aerodynamic Stability of Bluff Afterbodies. 2011. 152p. pap. **(978-3-8454-0948-1(7))** Lambert Academic Publishing.

Zipfel, Peter H. Modeling & Simulation of Aerospace Vehicle Dynamics. 2nd ed. 2007. (AIAA Education Ser.) (Illus.). 567p. (978-1-56347-875-8(7)) American Institute of Aeronautics & Astronautics.

AERODYNAMICS, HYPERSONIC

Bose, Tarit K. High Temperature Gas Dynamics. 2010. (ENG., Illus.). xv, 359p. pap. 139.00 *(978-3-642-07420-2(0),* 3642074200) Springer.

Golovachov, Y. P. Numerical Simulation of Viscous Shock Layer Flows. 2010. (Fluid Mechanics & Its Applications Ser.). 364p. pap. 329.00 *(978-90-481-4594-2(5),* 9048145945) Springer.

Hirschel, Ernst H. & Weiland, Claus. Selected Aerothermodynamic Design Problems of Hypersonic Flight Vehicles. 2009. (ENG., Illus.). xvi, 512p. 129.00 *(978-3-540-89973-0(1),* 3540899731) Springer.

Hirschel, Ernst-Heinrich. Basics of Aerothermodynamics. 2010. (ENG., Illus.). xiv, 413p. pap. 149.00 *(978-3-642-06050-2(1),* 3642060501) Springer.

Jenkins, Dennis R. X-15: Extending the Frontiers of Flight. 2007. *(978-0-16-079285-4(1))* United States Government Printing Office.

Jenkins, Dennis R. & Landis, Tony R. Hypersonic: The Story of the North American X-15. rev. ed. 2008. (Illus.). 276p. pap. 28.95 *(978-1-58007-131-4(7))* Specialty Pr. Pubs. & Wholesalers, Inc.

Lunev, Vladimir & Lunev, Vladimir V. Real Gas Flows with High Velocities. 2009. (ENG., Illus.). 751p. 164.95 *(978-1-4398-0465-0(6),* CRC Press) Taylor & Francis Group GBR. Dist: Taylor & Francis Group.

Murthy, T. K. S. Computational Methods in Hypersonic Aerodynamics. 2010. (Fluid Mechanics & Its Applications Ser.). 400p. pap. 449.00 *(978-90-481-4144-9(3),* 9048141443) Springer.

Peebles, Curtis. Road to Mach 10: Lessons Learned from the X-43A Flight Research Program. Allen, Ned, ed. 2008. (Illus.). 238p. pap. 39.95 incl. cd-rom *(978-1-56347-932-8(X))* American Institute of Aeronautics & Astronautics.

Peebles, Curtis & Allen, Ned. Eleven Seconds into the Unknown: A History of the Hyper-X Program. 2011. *(978-1-60086-776-7(6))* American Institute of Aeronautics & Astronautics.

Sockalingam, Subramani & Tabiei, Ala. Simulation of Hypersonic Reentry Vehicles. 2011. 80p. pap. ***(978-3-8443-8571-7(1))*** Lambert Academic Publishing.

Surah, Dr. D. & Surah, D. Investigation of Attachment Line Boundary Layers in Hypersonic Flows. 2010. 404p. pap. *(978-3-8383-6268-7(3))* Lambert Academic Publishing.

AERODYNAMICS, SUBSONIC

see Aerodynamics

AERODYNAMICS, SUPERSONIC

see also Aerodynamics, Hypersonic; Aerothermodynamics; Shock Waves; Supersonic Planes

Bogolepov, V V, et al. Asymptotic Theory of Supersonic Viscous Gas Flows. Neyland, Vladimir, ed. 2008. (Aerospace Engineering Ser.). (ENG., Illus.). 560p. 170.00 *(978-0-7506-8513-9(1),* Butterworth-Heinemann) Elsevier Science & Technology Bks.

Conway, Erik M. High-Speed Dreams: NASA & the Technopolitics of Supersonic Transportation, 1945-1999. 2008. (New Series in NASA History Ser.). (ENG., Illus.). 392p. (gr. 17). pap. 30.00 *(978-0-8018-9081-9(0))* Johns Hopkins Univ. Pr.

Encyclopaedia Britannica, Inc., compiled by. Channel Flow of a Compressible Fluid. 2009. 49.00 *(978-1-60835-046-9(0))* Encyclopaedia Britannica, Inc.

Gunston, Bill. Faster Than Sound: The Story of Supersonic Flight. 2nd ed. 2009. (ENG., Illus.). 256p. 49.95 *(978-1-84425-564-1(6),* 1844255646) Haynes Publishing PLC GBR. Dist: MBI Distribution Services/Quayside Distribution.

Nastase, Adriana. Computation of Supersonic Flow over Flying Configurations. 2008. (ENG., Illus.). 410p. 225.00 *(978-0-08-044957-9(3),* Elsevier Science) Elsevier Science & Technology Bks.

Smits, Alexander J. & Dussauge, Jean-Paul. Turbulent Shear Layers in Supersonic Flow. 2nd ed. 2010. (ENG., Illus.). xiv, 410p. pap. 159.00 *(978-1-4419-2083-6(8),* 1441920838) Springer.

AERODYNAMICS, TRANSONIC

see also Aerothermodynamics

Côté, Nicolas. Integral & Diagnostic Intrusive Prediction of Speech Quality. 2011. (T-Labs Series in Telecommunication Services Ser.). (Illus.). xvii, 248p. 129.00 *(978-3-642-18462-8(6),* 3642184626) Springer.

Goethert, Bernhard H. Transonic Wind Tunnel Testing. Nelson, Wilbur C., ed. 2007. (Dover Books on Engineering Ser.). (ENG., Illus.). 416p. per. 24.95 *(978-0-486-45881-6(4))* Dover Pubns., Inc.

Merlin, Peter W. & Allen, Ned. From Archangel to Senior Crown: Design & Development of the Blackbird. 2008. 165p. *(978-1-56347-933-5(8))* American Institute of Aeronautics & Astronautics.

Tony, Landis. Lockheed Blackbird Family: A-12, YF-12, D-21/M-21 & SR-71 Photo Scrapbook. 2010. 128p. pap. 26.95 *(978-1-58007-151-2(1))* Specialty Pr. Pubs. & Wholesalers, Inc.

AEROELASTICITY

Balakrishnan, A. V. Aeroelasticity: The Continuum Theory. 2012. (ENG., Illus.). xiv, 402p. 129.00 ***(978-1-4614-3608-9(7),*** 1461436087) Springer.

Cooper, Jonathan Edward & Wright, Jan Robert. Introduction to Aircraft Aeroelasticity & Loads. 2008. (Aerospace Ser.: 18). (ENG., Illus.). 524p. 155.00 *(978-0-470-85840-0(0),* Wiley) Wiley, John & Sons, Inc.

Fung, Y. C. An Introduction to the Theory of Aeroelasticity. 2008. (Dover Books on Aeronautical Engineering Ser.). (ENG.). 512p. (C). pap. 29.95 *(978-0-486-46936-2(0))* Dover Pubns., Inc.

Haase, Werner, et al, eds. DESider - A European Effort on Hybrid RANS-les Modelling: Results of the European-Union Funded Project, 2004 - 2007. 2009. (Notes on Numerical Fluid Mechanics & Multidisciplinary Design Ser.). (Illus.). xx, 454p. 339.00 *(978-3-540-92772-3(7))* Springer.

Hall, Kenneth C., et al, eds. Unsteady Aerodynamics, Aeroacoustics & Aeroelasticity of Turbomachines. 2010. (ENG.). xi, 626p. pap. 239.00 *(978-90-481-7091-3(5),* 9048170915) Springer.

Jurado, J. A, et al. Bridge Aeroelasticity: Sensitivity Analysis & Optimum Design. 2011. (High Performance Structures & Materials Ser.: 10). (ENG., Illus.). 368p. lib. bdg. 280.00 *(978-1-84564-056-9(X))* WIT Pr GBR. Dist: WIT Pr.

Niyongere, Abraham. Aeroservoelastic Prediction. 2011. 160p. pap. ***(978-3-8443-8516-8(9))*** Lambert Academic Publishing.

Rodden, William P. Theoretical & Computational Aeroelasticity. 2011. (Illus.). xvi, 814p. ***(978-0-692-01241-3(9))*** Bluecliff Publishing.

Wright, Jan R. & Cooper, Jonathan E. Introduction to Aircraft Aeroelasticity & Dynamic Loads. 2008. (Aerospace Series (PEP) Ser.). (Illus.). 488p. pap. 85.00 *(978-0-470-85841-7(9))* Wiley, John & Sons, Inc.

—Introduction to Aircraft Aeroelasticity & Loads. 2007. (AIAA Education Ser.). (Illus.). 499p. 179.95 *(978-1-56347-935-9(4))* American Institute of Aeronautics & Astronautics.

AEROFOILS

Davidson, Lars, et al, eds. LESFOIL: Large Eddy Simulation of Flow Around a High Lift Airfoil: Results of the Project LESFOIL Supported by the European Union 1998 - 2001. 2010. (Notes on Numerical Fluid Mechanics & Multidisciplinary Design Ser.). xii, 246p. pap. 299.00 *(978-3-642-05605-5(9),* 3642056059) Springer.

Eppler, Richard. Airfoil Design & Data. 2nd ed. 2006. (Illus.). 560p. 119.00 *(978-3-540-41124-6(0),* 3540411240) Springer.

Mazzola, Andrea. Low Reynolds Number Aerodynamics. 2009. 124p. pap. *(978-3-639-19084-7(X))* VDM Verlag Dr. Mueller e.K.

Pope, Alan. Basic Wing & Airfoil Theory. 2009. (Dover Books on Aeronautical Engineering Ser.). (ENG.). 320p. pap. 14.95 *(978-0-486-47188-4(8))* Dover Pubns., Inc.

—Basic Wing & Airfoil Theory. 2011. 312p. 50.95 ***(978-1-258-10068-1(1))*** Literary Licensing, LLC.

Sarkar, Sunetra & Venkatraman, Kartik. Unsteady Aerodynamics of a Flapping Airfoil. 2010. 204p. pap. *(978-3-8383-4759-2(5))* Lambert Academic Publishing.

AEROGASTRES

see Myxomycetes

AEROLITES

see Meteorites

AEROLOGY

see Meteorology

AERONAUTICAL ACCIDENTS

see Aircraft Accidents

AERONAUTICAL INSTRUMENTS

see also Automatic Pilot (Airplanes); Flight Engineering; Flight Recorders; Guidance Systems (Flight); Gyro Compass; Instrument Flying

Agarwal, Sandeep. Aeromechanical Stability Augmentation Through Semi-Active Control. 2009. 180p. pap. *(978-3-639-17532-5(8))* VDM Verlag Dr. Mueller e.K.

Bailey, Norman. Helicopter Pilot's Manual Vol. 2: Powerplants, Instruments & Hydraulics, 3 vols. 2nd rev. ed. 2008. (ENG., Illus.). 152p. pap. 34.95 *(978-1-86126-991-1(9),* 1861269919) Crowood Pr., Ltd. GBR. Dist: MBI Distribution Services/Quayside Distribution.

—Helicopter Pilot's Manual Vol. 3: Mountain Flying & Advanced Techniques, 3 vols. 2nd ed. 2010. (ENG., Illus.). 96p. pap. 24.95 *(978-1-84797-105-0(9),* 1847971059) Crowood Pr., Ltd. GBR. Dist: MBI Distribution Services/Quayside Distribution.

Brown, Randall W. Head- & Helmet-Mounted Displays XII: Design & Applications: 10-11 April, 2007, Orlando, Florida, USA. 2007. (Proceedings of SPIE Ser.). (Illus.). 296p. pap. 80.00 *(978-0-8194-6679-2(4))* SPIE.

—Head- & Helmet-Mounted Displays XIII: Design & Applications: 17-18 March, 2008, Orlando, Florida, USA. 2008. (Proceedings of SPIE Ser.). (Illus.). 256p. pap. 70.00 *(978-0-8194-7146-8(1))* SPIE.

Daniel, Schauer. Integration of a 3D Time of Flight Camera System into a Robot System: Integration, Validation & Comparison. 2011. 132p. pap. ***(978-3-639-31877-7(3))*** VDM Verlag Dr. Mueller e.K.

Dempsey, Michael W. Professional Instrument Flight Review Guide. 112p. pap. *(978-1-57087-067-5(5))* Professional Pr.

Federal Aviation Administration Staff. Instrument Flying & Procedures Handbook. 2007. (Illus.). 564p. pap. 29.95 *(978-1-60239-108-6(4))* Skyhorse Publishing Co., Inc.

Fisher, David. The Leading Edge of Safety: The Story of Safe Flight Instrument Corporation. 2008. (Illus.). 136p. ***(978-0-944641-73-6(3))*** Greenwich Publishing Group, Inc.

Kaajakari, Ville. Practical MEMS: Analysis & design of microsystems, MEMS sensors (accelerometers, pressure sensors, gyroscopes), sensor electronics, actuators, RF MEMS, optical MEMS, & microfluidic Systems. 2009. 98.00 *(978-0-9822991-0-4(9))* Small Gear Publishing.

Marasco, Peter & Havig, Paul. Head- & Helmet-Mounted Displays XVI: Design & Applications. 2011. (Proceedings of SPIE Ser.). pap. 70.00 ***(978-0-8194-8615-8(9))*** SPIE.

Marasco, Peter Louis. Head- & Helmet-Mounted Displays XIV: Design & Applications: 16 April 2009, Orlando, Florida, United States. 2009. (Proceedings of SPIE Ser.). (Illus.). 240p. pap. 70.00 *(978-0-8194-7592-3(0))* SPIE.

Marasco, Peter Louis & Havig, Paul R. Head- & Helmet-Mounted Displays XV: Design & Applications: 8 April 2010, Orlando, Florida, United States. 2010. (Proceedings of SPIE Ser.). (Illus.). 168p. pap. 60.00 ***(978-0-8194-8152-8(1))*** SPIE.

Moir, I. & Seabridge, A. G. Aircraft Systems: Mechanical, Electrical, & Avionics Subsystems Integration. 3rd ed. 2008. (AIAA Education Ser.). *(978-1-56347-952-6(4))* American Institute of Aeronautics & Astronautics.

Nagabhushana, S. & Sudha, L. K. Aircraft Instrumentation & Systems. 2010. (Illus.). 410p. (C). *(978-93-80578-35-4(0))* I.K. International Publishing House Pvt. Ltd.

Samy, Ihab & Gu, Da-Wei. Fault Detection & Flight Data Measurement: Demonstrated on Unmanned Air Vehicles using Neural Networks. 2011. (Lecture Notes in Control & Information Sciences Ser.). (ENG., Illus.). xx, 176p. pap. 109.00 ***(978-3-642-24051-5(8),*** 3642240518) Springer.

Shkel, Andrei M. Inertial Microsensors. 2010. (MEMS Reference Shelf Ser.). (Illus.). 400p. 129.95 *(978-0-387-35540-5(5),* 0387355405) Springer.

Wild & Wild, Thomas W. Transport Category Aircraft Systems. 3rd ed. 2008. (Illus.). pap. *(978-0-88487-486-7(9))* Jeppesen Sanderson.

Young-Dippold, Amanda. Adaptive Control of Nonaffine Systems for Flight Applications. 2009. 76p. pap. *(978-3-639-18000-8(3))* VDM Verlag Dr. Mueller e.K.

AERONAUTICAL NAVIGATION

see Navigation (Aeronautics)

AERONAUTICAL RADIO STATIONS

see also Loran

Anderson MSc, Lionel K. ACARS - A Users Guide. 2010. 142p. pap. 36.95 *(978-1-4457-8847-0(0))* Lulu Enterprises Inc.

AERONAUTICAL RESEARCH

see Aeronautics—Research

AERONAUTICAL SPORTS

see also Airplane Racing; Airplanes—Models; Ballooning; Gliding and Soaring; Parachuting; Skydiving

Goodrum, Alastair. Balloons, Bleriots & Barnstormers: 200 Years of Flying for Fun. 2009. (ENG., Illus.). 224p. pap. 34.95 *(978-0-7524-4516-8(2))* History Pr. Ltd., The GBR. Dist: Independent Pubs. Group.

Kennedy, Gregory P. Touching Space: The Story of Project Manhigh. 2007. (Illus.). 128p. pap. 24.95 *(978-0-7643-2788-9(7))* Schiffer Publishing, Ltd.

Sonntag, Allene Morrow. Rushing with the Wind. 2009. 136p. 29.99 *(978-1-4363-8675-3(6));* pap. 19.99 *(978-1-4363-8674-6(8))* Xlibris Corp.

AERONAUTICS

see also Aerodynamics; Aeronautics, Commercial; Air Pilots; Airplanes; Airports; Airships; Astronautics; Avionics; Balloon Ascensions; Ballooning; Balloons; Flight; Flying-Machines; Gliding and Soaring; Helicopters; High-Speed Aeronautics; Interplanetary Voyages; Kites; Meteorology in Aeronautics; Navigation (Aeronautics); Propellers, Aerial; Radio in Aeronautics; Rocketry; Rockets (Aeronautics); Seaplanes; Stability of Airplanes; Unidentified Flying Objects; Vibration (Aeronautics)

Abacus Staff. Flight Deck. pap. 39.95 incl. cd-rom *(978-1-55755-338-6(6))* Abacus.

Abeyratne, Ruwantissa. Aviation & the Carbon Trade. 2011. (Series: Climate Change & its Causes, Effects & Prediction Ser.). 195.00 *(978-1-61761-990-8(6))* Nova Science Pubs., Inc.

Abu-Taieh, Evon, et al, eds. Technology Engineering & Management in Aviation: Advancements & Discoveries. 2011. 361p. 195.00 *(978-1-60960-887-3(9),* Information Science Reference) IGI Global.

Ac-U-Kwik Staff. Acukwik World Edition 2007-2008. 2007. pap. 99.95 *(978-1-59969-155-8(8))* Penton Media, Inc.

Adey, Peter. Aerial Life: Spaces, Mobilities, Affects. 2010. (RGS-IBG Book Ser.). (ENG., Illus.). 296p. pap. 39.95 *(978-1-4051-8261-4(X));* 94.95 *(978-1-4051-8262-1(8))* Wiley, John & Sons, Inc. (Wiley-Blackwell).

Aerospace Engineering Workbook. 2011. (ENG.). 128p. (C). spiral bd. 24.95 *(978-1-4354-4754-7(9))* Delmar Cengage Learning.

Aim/Far. 7th rev. ed. 2006. (AIM/FAR: Airman's Information Manual/Federal Aviation Regulations Ser.). (Illus.). 1001p. per. 19.95 *(978-0-07-147924-0(4),* 9780071479240) McGraw-Hill Professional Publishing.

Air & Space Library, 6 bks. & 6 cass., Set. 39.95 incl. audio *(978-0-86545-117-9(6))* Spizzirri Pr., Inc.

Alber, Irwin E. Aerospace Engineering on the Back of an Envelope. 2012. (Springer Praxis Bks.). (ENG., Illus.). xxi, 326p. 179.00 ***(978-3-642-22536-9(5),*** 3642225365) Springer.

Alexander, David E. Why Don't Jumbo Jets Flap Their Wings? Flying Animals, Flying Machines, & How They Are Different. 2009. (ENG., Illus.). 296p. 26.95 *(978-0-8135-4479-3(3))* Rutgers Univ. Pr.

Alley, Bill. Aviation in Southern Oregon. 2011. (Images of Aviation Ser.). (Illus.). 128p. pap. 21.99 *(978-0-7385-8191-0(7))* Arcadia Publishing.

Aloni, Shlomo. Vultures over Israel: The Vautour in Israeli Service Squadron 110 1957-1971. 2012. (Illus.). 256p. 59.99 ***(978-0-7643-3960-8(5),*** Schiffer Publishing Ltd) Schiffer Publishing, Ltd.

American Institute of Aeronautics and Astronautics Staff, contrib. by. Managing the Use of Commercial off the Shelf (COTS) Software Components for Mission-Critical Systems: AIAA G-118-2006 Guide. 2006. *(978-1-56347-915-1(X))* American Institute of Aeronautics & Astronautics.

American Society of Mechanical Engineers Staff, ed. Aeroengines & Propulsion. (Illus.). 98p. 72.00 *(978-1-86058-027-7(0))* Professional Engineering Publishing GBR. Dist: SAE Intl.

Anton, Phillip S., et al. Advancing Aeronautics: A Decision Framework for Selecting Research Agendas. 2010. 160p. pap. 37.00 *(978-0-8330-5019-9(2),* mg-997) RAND Corp., The.

Aradag, Selin. Cfd for High Speed Flows in Engineering. 2008. 116p. pap. *(978-3-8364-8090-1(5))* VDM Verlag Dr. Mueller e.K.

Astronautics & Aeronautics. (Illus.). reprint ed. lib. bdg. *(978-0-7222-3104-3(0))* Library Reprints, Inc.

Belfiore, Michael P. Rocketeers: How a Visionary Band of Business Leaders, Engineers, & Pilots Is Boldly Privatizing Space. 2008. (ENG.). 320p. pap. 14.95 *(978-0-06-114903-0(9),* Harper Paperbacks) HarperCollins Pubs.

Benavides, S., ed. Corrosion Control in the Aerospace Industry. 2009. (Illus.). 320p. *(978-1-84569-345-9(0))* Woodhead Publishing Ltd.

Bennett, Simon A. A Sociology of Commercial Flight Crew. 2006. (Illus.). 224p. 130.00 *(978-0-7546-4317-3(4))* Ashgate Publishing Co.

Berrick, Cathleen A. Aviation Security: Progress Made to Set up Program Using Private-Sector Airport Screeners, but More Work Remains. 2006. 50p. (C). pap. 15.00 *(978-1-4223-0787-8(5))* DIANE Publishing Co.

Bleakley, Bruce A. Dallas Aviation. 2011. (Images of Aviation Ser.). (Illus.). 128p. pap. 21.99 *(978-0-7385-7988-7(2))* Arcadia Publishing.

Bolonkin, Alexander. New Concepts, Ideas, & Innovations in Aerospace & Technology & Human Science. 2007. 49.00 *(978-1-60021-787-6(7))* Nova Science Pubs., Inc.

British Standards Institute Staff. Aerospace series. Connectors, electrical, rectangular, modular. Operating temperature 175$0DC continuous. Flange mounting receptacle 2 & 4 modules, series 2. Product Standard. 12p. pap. 120.00 *(978-0-580-53306-8(9))* Artech Hse., Inc.

—Aerospace series. Connectors, electrical, rectangular, modular. Operating temperature 175$0DC continuous. Plug for 2 & 4 modules, series 2. Product Standard. 12p. pap. 96.00 *(978-0-580-53296-2(8))* Artech Hse., Inc.

—Aerospace series. Connectors, electrical, rectangular, modular. Operating temperature 175$0DC continuous. Tooling for assembly receptacle coding component. Product Standard. 8p. pap. 197.00 *(978-0-580-53299-3(2))* Artech Hse., Inc.

Brown, Randall W. Head- & Helmet-Mounted Displays XIII: Design & Applications: 17-18 March, 2008, Orlando, Florida, USA. 2008. (Proceedings of SPIE Ser.). (Illus.). 256p. pap. 70.00 *(978-0-8194-7146-8(1))* SPIE.

Browning-Freeman. Aviation Foundations I. 2011. (ENG.). 240.00 ***(978-0-7575-9626-1(6))*** Kendall Hunt Publishing Co.

Bussa, Michael. NOW BOARDING Confessions of a Stowaway. 2010. 140p. pap. 17.49 *(978-0-557-39049-6(4))* Lulu Enterprises Inc.

Buttazzo, Giuseppe & Frediani, Aldo. Variational Analysis & Aerospace Engineering. 2009. (Springer Optimization & Its Applications Ser.). (ENG., Illus.). xxvi, 518p. 194.00 *(978-0-387-95856-9(8),* 0387958568) Springer.

Çakici, Ferit. Tiltrotor Uav Design. 2010. 132p. pap. *(978-3-8383-5410-1(9))* Lambert Academic Publishing.

Cannon, James & Richey, Franklin D. Practical Applications in Business Aviation Management. 2011. (ENG.). 320p. (C). (gr. 13-17). 99.00 ***(978-1-60590-763-5(4))*** Government Institutes.

Cannon, James R. & Richey, Franklin D. Practical Applications in Business Aviation Management. 2011. ***(978-1-60590-764-2(2))*** Government Institutes.

Chen, Yi. Dynamical Modelling of Space Tether. 2010. 388p. pap. *(978-3-8383-6907-5(6))* Lambert Academic Publishing.

Clark, Joseph F., ed. Eagle Tales. 2007. per. 20.95 *(978-0-9727707-5-0(5))* BluewaterPress, LLC.

Claxton, William. The Mastery of the Air. 2006. (ENG.). 202p. pap. 20.99 *(978-1-4264-0072-8(1))* BiblioBazaar.

Claxton, William J. The Mastery of the Air. 2007. 148p. per. *(978-1-4065-1385-1(7))* Dodo Pr.

—The Mastery of the Air. 2007. (ENG.). 120p. per. *(978-1-4068-4626-3(0))* Echo Library.

Corn, Joseph J., ed. Into the Blue: American Writing on Aviation & Spaceflight. 2011. (ENG.). 750p. (gr. 12). 40.00 *(978-1-59853-108-4(5))* Library of America, The.

Cox, Jeremy R. C. St. Louis Aviation. 2011. (Images of Aviation Ser.). (Illus.). 128p. pap. 21.99 *(978-0-7385-8410-2(X))* Arcadia Publishing.

Cozby, Warren/Reynolds, Jr. Nuts & Bolts of Space Colonization: A Practical Plan for the Colonization of the Solar System. 2009. (Illus.). 80p. *(978-0-692-00562-0(5))* Cozby, Warren.

Cram101 Textbook Reviews & Cram101 Textbook Reviews. Outlines & Highlights for Aircraft Systems: Mechanical, Electrical & Avionics Subsystems Integration by Allan Seabridge. 2011. 180p. pap. 29.95 ***(978-1-61830-877-1(7))*** Cram101 Inc.

—Outlines & Highlights for Manufacturing Technology for Aerospace Structural Materials by Flake C Campbell Jr, Isbn: 9781856174954. 2011. 138p. pap. 28.95 ***(978-1-61461-315-2(X))*** Cram101 Inc.

Culliton, James & Deb, Sushant. The AS9100C Handbook, Second Edition: Understanding Aviation, Space, & Defense Best Practices. 2011. 160p. spiral bd. 69.00 ***(978-1-932828-41-2(9))*** Paton Professional.

Curtis, Howard, et al. Aerospace Engineering Desk Reference. 2009. (ENG., Illus.). 704p. 103.00 *(978-1-85617-575-3(8),* Butterworth-Heinemann) Elsevier Science & Technology Bks.

Cwerner, Saulo. Aeromobilities. 2010. (Illus.). 260p. pap. 42.95 *(978-0-415-58134-9(6))* Routledge.

Davis, Clayton. Aviation, How & Why. 2007. 222p. pap. 21.88 *(978-1-4303-2378-7(3))* Lulu Enterprises Inc.

Davis, L. Porter, et al. Industrial & Commercial Applications of Smart Structures Technologies 2007: 19-20 March 2007, San Diego, California, USA. 2007. (Proceedings of SPIE Ser.). (Illus.). 344p. pap. 80.00 *(978-0-8194-6648-8(4))* SPIE.

—Industrial & Commercial Applications of Smart Structures Technologies 2008: 10-11 March 2008, San Diego, California, USA. 2008. (Proceedings of SPIE Ser.). (Illus.). 346p. pap. 90.00 *(978-0-8194-7116-1(X))* SPIE.

De Haan, Alexander. Study on Sustainable Aircraft Technology. 2011. 232p. pap. ***(978-3-8443-0444-2(4))*** Lambert Academic Publishing.

De Petro, Thomas G. Selective Guide to Literature on Aerospace Engineering. 22p. *(978-0-87823-161-4(7))* Bow Historical Bks.

Dick, Ron. Aviation Century: War & Peace in the Air 2006. (Aviation Century Ser.). (ENG., Illus.). 352p. 49.95 *(978-1-55046-430-6(2))* Boston Mills Pr. CAN. Dist: Firefly Bks., Ltd.

Dingle, Lloyd & Tooley, Mike. Aircraft Engineering Principles. 2nd rev. ed. 2013. (ENG.). 640p. (C). pap. 62.95 *(978-0-08-097084-4(2))* Routledge.

Dismukes, R. Key. Human Error in Aviation. 2009. (Critical Essays on Human Factors in Aviation Ser.). (Illus.). 604p. 325.00 *(978-0-7546-2831-6(0))* Ashgate Publishing Co.

Diston, Dominic J. Computational Modelling of Aircraft & the Environment Vol. 1: Platform Kinematics & Synthetic Environment. 2009. (Aerospace Ser.: 8). (ENG., Illus.). 382p. 125.00 *(978-0-470-01840-8(2),* Wiley) Wiley, John & Sons, Inc.

Droste, Carl & Walker, James. The General Dynamics Case Study on the F-16 Fly-by-Wire Flight Control System. (Illus.). 113p. pap. 23.00 *(978-1-56347-307-4(0))* American Institute of Aeronautics & Astronautics.

Dye, William. Climbing into My Dream: An Aerospace Engineer's Journey. 2011. 200p. 24.95 ***(978-1-4620-2389-9(4))***; pap. 14.95 ***(978-1-4620-2388-2(6))*** iUniverse, Inc.

El-Genk, Mohamed S., ed. Space Technology & Applications International Forum-STAIF 2007: 11th Conference on Thermophysics Applications in Microgravity 24th Symposium on Space Nuclear Power & Propulsion 5th Symposium on Space Colonization 4th Symposium on New Frontiers & Future Concepts. 2007. (AIP Conference Proceedings Ser.). 1254p. 286.00 *(978-0-7354-0386-4(4))* American Institute of Physics.

Ellam, Patrick. Royal Flying Corps Technical Notes: On the Airplanes & Engines Of 1916. 2011. 132p. pap. 18.95 *(978-1-4502-9948-0(2))* iUniverse, Inc.

Eteiwi, Diana. Effect of Service Quality on Air Passenger's Overall Satisfaction. 2011. 76p. pap. ***(978-3-8383-9624-8(3))*** Lambert Academic Publishing.

Farinholt, Kevin & Griffin, Steve. Industrial & Commercial Applications of Smart Structures Technologies 2011. 2011. (Proceedings of SPIE Ser.). 242p. pap. 70.00 ***(978-0-8194-8541-0(1))*** SPIE.

Ferguson, Steve, illus. Aces & Wingman, 2 vols. Incl. Vol. 1. Morris, Danny. Frisque, Thomas A., ed. (C). 1989. 39.95 *(978-0-9623080-1-7(3))*; Vol. 2. Hess, Bill. Frisque, Tom, ed. 1999. 49.95 *(978-0-9623080-2-4(1))*; 256p. (Illus.). *(978-0-9623080-0-0(5))* Aviation Usk.

Fioriti, Marco & Chiesa, Sergio. Innovative Solutions for Light, Very Light & Unmanned Aircraft. 2011. 152p. pap. ***(978-3-8443-0971-3(3))*** Lambert Academic Publishing.

Flouris, Triant & Yilmaz, Ayse Kucuk. Risk Management & Corporate Sustainability in Aviation. 2011. (Illus.). 252p. 99.95 ***(978-1-4094-1199-4(0))*** Ashgate Publishing Co.

Flouris, Triant G. & Lock, Dennis. Managing Aviation Projects from Concept to Completion. 2009. (Illus.). 528p. 119.95 *(978-0-7546-7615-7(3))* Ashgate Publishing Co.

Flyer. 12p. *(978-3-8238-0685-1(8))* teNeues Publishing Co.

Freschi, Graziano. The BAC Three-Eleven: The Airbus That Should Have Been. 2006. (ENG., Illus.). 224p. per. 39.95 *(978-0-7524-3913-6(8))* History Pr. Ltd.,The GBR. Dist: Independent Pubs. Group.

Fried, Joel R. Polymers in Aerospace Applications. 2010. (Rapra Review Report). 148p. pap. *(978-1-84735-093-0(3))* iSmithers Rapra Publishing.

Fulgaro, Lou. Turns Around a Point. 2009. 148p. pap. 13.49 *(978-1-4490-0919-9(0))* AuthorHouse.

Garland, Daniel J., et al, eds. Aviation Human Factors. 2nd rev. ed. 2009. (ENG., Illus.). 704p. instr.'s hndbk. ed. 154.95 *(978-0-8058-5906-5(3),* CRC Press) Taylor & Francis Group GBR. Dist: Taylor & Francis Group.

George, Thomas & Cheng, Z. -Y. Micro (MEMS) & Nanotechnologies for Defense & Security: 10-12 April, 2007, Orlando, Florida, USA. 2007. (Proceedings of SPIE Ser.). (Illus.). 362p. pap. 120.00 *(978-0-8194-6678-5(6))* SPIE.

George, Thomas F. & Cheng, Zhong-Yang. Micro (MEMS) & Nanotechnologies for Space, Defense & Security II: 18-20 April, 2008, Orlando, Florida, USA. 2008. (Proceedings of SPIE Ser.). (Illus.). 312p. pap. 90.00 ***(978-0-8194-7150-5(X))*** SPIE.

Gonzales, Laurence. One Zero Charlie: Adventures in Grass Roots Aviation. 2007. (ENG.). 272p. pap. 18.95 *(978-1-4165-7641-9(X))* Simon & Schuster.

Gooch, Jan W. & Daher, John K. Electromagnetic Shielding & Corrosion Protection for Aerospace Vehicles. (ENG., Illus.). xii, 130p. 2011. pap. 109.00 *(978-1-4419-2358-5(6),* 1441923586) 2007. 109.00 *(978-0-387-46094-9(2),* 0387460942) Springer.

Gordon, Yefim & Rigmant, Vladimir. Tupolev Tu-104: Aeroflot's First Jet. Komissarov, Dmitriy, tr. from RUS. 2010. (Red Star Ser.). (ENG., Illus.). 127p. pap. 36.95 *(978-1-85780-265-8(9))* Allan, Ian Publishing GBR. Dist: BookMasters Distribution Services (BDS).

Gössling, Stefan & Upham, Paul, eds. Climate Change & Aviation: Issues, Challenges & Solutions. 2009. (ENG., Illus.). 408p. 166.00 *(978-1-84407-619-2(9))*; pap. 48.95 *(978-1-84407-620-8(2))* Routledge.

Grace, David & Mohorcic, Mihael. Broadband Communications Via High Altitude Platforms. 2010. (ENG., Illus.). 398p. 135.00 *(978-0-470-69445-9(9),* Wiley) Wiley, John & Sons, Inc.

Hajiyev, Chingiz, et al. Aircraft Icing Detection, Identification & Reconfigurable Control. 2011. 184p. pap. ***(978-3-8443-8874-9(5))*** Lambert Academic Publishing.

Hale, Wayne, et al, eds. Wings in Orbit: Scientific & Engineering Legacies of the Space Shuttle, 1971-2010. 2011. (ENG., Illus.). 565p. 70.00 *(978-0-16-086847-4(5),* Scientific & Technical Information Office) United States Government Printing Office.

—Wings in Orbit: Scientific & Engineering Legacies of the Space Shuttle 1971-2010: Scientific & Engineering Legacies of the Space Shuttle 1971-2010. 2011. (ENG., Illus.). 565p. pap. 50.00 *(978-0-16-086846-7(7),* U. S. National Aeronautics & Space Administration) United States Government Printing Office.

Harper, E. H. & Ferguson, Allan. Aerial Locomotion. 2012. (ENG., Illus.). 178p. pap. 19.99 ***(978-1-107-60592-3(X))*** Cambridge Univ. Pr.

Havers, Richard & Tiffney, Christopher. In-Flight Confidential. 2009. (Confidential Ser.). (ENG., Illus.). 304p. pap. 10.99 *(978-1-906635-43-5(9),* 1906635439) G2 Entertainment Ltd. GBR. Dist: MBI Distribution Services/Quayside Distribution.

Henderson, B. K. & McMickell, M. Brett. Industrial & Commercial Applications of Smart Structures Technologies 2009: 9-10 March 2009, San Diego, California, United States. 2009. (Proceedings of SPIE Ser.). (Illus.). 264p. pap. 80.00 *(978-0-8194-7550-3(5))* SPIE.

Hiscocks, Richard. A Case Study on the De Havilland Family of STOL Commuter Aircraft. (Illus.). 32p. pap. 23.00 *(978-1-56347-310-4(0))* American Institute of Aeronautics & Astronautics.

Holt, Laurence. Stikky Landings: In One Hour, Learn How to Land a Jet Airplane in an Emergency. 2010. (Stikky Ser.). 256p. pap. 12.00 *(978-1-932974-06-5(7))* Holt, Laurence Bks., Inc.

Hoppe, Elizabeth A. Ethical Issues in Aviation. 2011. (Illus.). 314p. 99.95 *(978-1-4094-1786-6(7))* Ashgate Publishing Co.

Ibold, Ken. Defying Gravity: A Look at Life from a Higher Plane. 2010. pap. 16.99 *(978-1-61663-877-1(X))* Tate Publishing & Enterprises, LLC.

ICAS Secretariat Staff, compiled by. 25th Congress of the International Council of the Aeronautical Sciences 2006. 2007. 4671p. pap. 493.00 *(978-1-60423-227-1(7))* Curran Assocs., Inc.

Inalhan, Gokhan. Decentralized Optimization with Independent Decision Makers: Applications on Aerospace Problems. 2008. 184p. pap. *(978-3-639-02579-8(2))* VDM Verlag Dr. Mueller e.K.

Index to AIA National Aerospace Standards (NAS) 2007. ring bd. 600.00 *(978-1-57053-119-4(6))* IHS, Inc.

International ABC Aerospace Directory: The World's Aerospace Organisations at Your Fingertips. 725.00 *(978-0-7106-2318-8(6))* Jane's Information Group, Inc.

International Aviation: DOT Needs More Information to Address U.S. Airlines' Problems in Doing Business Abroad. 44p. pap. 25.00 *(978-0-7881-2848-6(5))* DIANE Publishing Co.

Jane's All the World's Aircraft: The Authority on Aircraft under Development or in Production. 560.00 *(978-0-7106-2307-2(0))* Jane's Information Group, Inc.

Jane's All the World's Aircraft 1909. (Illus.). reprint ed. lib. bdg. *(978-0-7222-3105-0(9))* Library Reprints, Inc.

Jane's International ABC Aerospace Directory. 57th rev. ed. 2007. (Jane's International ABC Aerospace Directory Ser.). 1565p. *(978-0-7106-2802-2(1))* Jane's Information Group.

Jha, A. R. MEMS & Nanotechnology-Based Sensors & Devices for Communications, Medical & Aerospace Applications. 2008. (ENG., Illus.). 432p. 139.95 *(978-0-8493-8069-3(3),* CRC Press) Taylor & Francis Group GBR. Dist: Taylor & Francis Group.

Kalivarathan, G. & Aravind, C. Aero Space Engines. 2011. (Illus.). 494p. 99.95 *(978-1-4398-6179-0(X),* CRC Press) Taylor & Francis Group GBR. Dist: Taylor & Francis Group.

Kamata, E. S. Influence of Psychological Factors on Product Development: Lessons from Aerospace & Other Industries. 2010. (Space Technology Library). (Illus.). 432p. pap. 239.00 *(978-90-481-6098-9(0),* 9048160960) Springer.

Kashif, Muhammad, et al. Identification of Modal Parameters of a Rocket. 2010. 80p. pap. *(978-3-8383-5125-4(8))* Lambert Academic Publishing.

Kessner, Thomas. The Flight of the Century: Charles Lindbergh & the Rise of American Aviation. 2012. (Pivotal Moments in American History Ser.). (ENG., Illus.). 336p. pap. 17.95 ***(978-0-19-993117-0(8))*** Oxford Univ. Pr., Inc.

Khodabakhshi, Goodarz. Computational Modelling of Fluid-Porous Solid Interaction Systems. 2011. 152p. pap. ***(978-3-8443-9900-4(3))*** Lambert Academic Publishing.

Khoury, Gabriel, ed. Airship Technology. 2nd ed. 2012. (Cambridge Aerospace Ser.). (ENG., Illus.). 724p. 145.00 ***(978-1-107-01970-6(2))*** Cambridge Univ. Pr.

Kinney, Jeremy R. Airplanes: The Life Story of a Technology, 1 vol. 2006. (Greenwood Technographies Ser.). (Illus.). 184p. 45.00 *(978-0-313-33150-3(2),* GR3150, Greenwood Pr.) Greenwood Publishing Group, Inc.

Kitsche, Wolfgang. Test Facility for a Cryogenic Rocket Engine: An Outline with down-to-Earth & up-to-Space Remarks. 2010. (Springer Aerospace Technology Ser.). (Illus.). 150p. 129.00 *(978-3-642-10564-7(5),* 3642105645) Springer.

Kymal, Chad. AS9101D Auditing for Process Performance: Combining Conformance & Effectiveness to Achieve Customer Satisfaction. 2011. ***(978-0-87389-807-2(9))*** ASQ Quality Pr.

Lantos, James & Applewood Books Staff, compiled by. Balloons. 2009. (Applewood's Pictorial America Ser.). (ENG.). 56p. pap. 9.95 *(978-1-60889-018-7(X))* Applewood Bks.

Larkins, William T. & Reuther, Ronald T. San Francisco Bay Area Aviation. 2007. (Images of Aviation Ser.). (ENG., Illus.). 128p. per. 21.99 *(978-0-7385-4723-7(9))* Arcadia Publishing.

Laurie, Bobby. Planely Speaking: Inflight Insight from Thirty Thousand Feet. 2010. 138p. pap. 13.75 *(978-0-557-47713-5(1))* Lulu Enterprises Inc.

Lawrence, Harry W. Embry Riddle Aeronautical University Version of Aviation & the Role of Government. 2nd rev. ed. 2010. (ENG.). 516p. pap. 94.33 *(978-0-7575-5194-9(7))* Kendall Hunt Publishing Co.

Legal Advisory Panel of the Aviation Working Group. Advanced Contract & Opinion Practices under the Cape Town Convention. 2008. (Cape Town Paper Ser.). (ENG.). 66p. pap. 104.00 *(978-1-84113-987-6(4))* Hart Publishing Ltd. GBR. Dist: International Specialized Bk. Services.

Liebergot, Sy & Harland, David M. Apollo EECOM: Journey of a Lifetime. 2nd ed. 2008. (Apogee Books Space Ser.). (ENG., Illus.). 216p. pap. 21.95 *(978-1-894959-88-9(4))* Collector's Guide Publishing, Inc. CAN. Dist: Independent Pubs. Group.

Linehan, Dan. SpaceShipOne: An Illustrated History. 2008. (ENG., Illus.). 160p. 34.95 *(978-0-7603-3188-0(X),* 076033188X, Zenith Pr.) MBI Publishing Co. LLC.

Longuski, James. The Seven Secrets of How to Think Like a Rocket Scientist. 2010. (ENG., Illus.). x, 174p. pap. 29.95 *(978-1-4419-2159-8(1),* 1441921591) Springer.

Lougheed, Victor. Vehicles of the Air: A Popular Exposition of Modern Aeronautics with Working Drawings. 2010. 624p. pap. 45.75 *(978-1-143-25413-0(9))*; 628p. pap. 45.75 *(978-1-143-36451-8(1))*; 648p. pap. 46.75 *(978-1-143-97056-6(X))* BiblioBazaar.

Loukopoulos, Loukia D., et al. The Multitasking Myth: Handling Complexity in Real-World Operations. 2009. (Ashgate Studies in Human Factors for Flight Operations Ser.). 202p. pap. 44.95 *(978-0-7546-7997-4(7))* Ashgate Publishing Co.

Lukasiewicz, Julius. Rue Lukasiewicz: Glimpses of a Life. 2011. (ENG., Illus.). 392p. 40.00 *(978-1-894908-08-5(2))* Golden Dog Pr. CAN. Dist: Univ. of Toronto Pr.

Malayney, Norman. The 25th Bomb Group (Rcn) in World War II. 2011. (Illus.). 304p. 69.99 ***(978-0-7643-3950-9(8))*** Schiffer Publishing, Ltd.

Mangla, Niranjan & Sinha, Sumon. Controlling Dynamic Stall with an Electrically Actuated Flexible Wall. 2010. 140p. pap. *(978-3-639-22963-9(0))* VDM Verlag Dr. Mueller e.K.

Marasco, Peter & Havig, Paul. Head- & Helmet-Mounted Displays XVI: Design & Applications. 2011. (Proceedings of SPIE Ser.). pap. 70.00 ***(978-0-8194-8615-8(9))*** SPIE.

Marasco, Peter Louis. Head- & Helmet-Mounted Displays XIV: Design & Applications: 16 April 2009, Orlando, Florida, United States. 2009. (Proceedings of SPIE Ser.). (Illus.). 240p. pap. 70.00 *(978-0-8194-7592-3(0))* SPIE.

Marasco, Peter Louis & Havig, Paul R. Head- & Helmet-Mounted Displays XV: Design & Applications: 8 April 2010, Orlando, Florida, United States. 2010. (Proceedings of SPIE Ser.). (Illus.). 168p. pap. 60.00 ***(978-0-8194-8152-8(1))*** SPIE.

Marriott, John. Aerotowing Gliders: A Guide to Towing Gliders, with an Emphasis on Safety. 2011. 144p. pap. 31.33 ***(978-1-4567-7515-5(4))*** AuthorHouse.

Mcmickell, M. Brett & Farinholt, Kevin. Industrial & Commercial Applications of Smart Structures Technologies 2010. 2010. (Proceedings of SPIE Ser.). 222p. pap. 90.00 ***(978-0-8194-8060-6(6))*** SPIE.

Means, Kevin P. Tactical helicopter Missions: How to Fly Safe, Effective Airborne Law Enforcement Missions. 2007. (Illus.). 136p. *(978-0-398-07738-9(X))* Thomas, Charles C. Pub., Ltd.

Mercer, Joey. Airborne Spacing & Merging in the Terminal Are. 2008. 68p. pap. *(978-3-639-07060-6(7))* VDM Verlag Dr. Mueller e.K.

Miele, Angelo & Frediani, Aldo, eds. Advanced Design Problems in Aerospace Engineering: Volume 1: Advanced Aerospace Systems. 2010. (Mathematical Concepts & Methods in Science & Engineering Ser.). (Illus.). xii, 188p. pap. 155.00 *(978-1-4419-3448-2(0),* 1441934480) Springer.

Miller, Ron. Extreme Aircraft. 2007. (Extreme Wonders Ser.). (ENG., Illus.). 224p. pap. 15.95 *(978-0-06-089141-1(6),* HarperPerennial) HarperCollins Pubs.

Mills, Stephen E. & Phillips, James Wendell. Sourdough Sky: A Pictorial History of Flights & Flyers in the Bush Country. 2011. 178p. 42.95 ***(978-1-258-05235-5(0))*** Literary Licensing, LLC.

Milosavljevic, Vojislav. Rnp Approach Procedures for Tma Belgrade. 2011. (Illus.). 148p. pap. ***(978-3-8443-1398-7(2))*** Lambert Academic Publishing.

Mitigating the Impact of Volcanic Ash Clouds on Aviation: What Do We Need to Know?: Hearing Before the Subcommittee on Space & Aeronautics, Committee on Science & Technology, House of Representatives, One Hundred Eleventh Congress, Second Session, May 5, 2010. 2010. (Illus.). iii, 51p. *(978-0-16-086831-3(9),* 552-070-41745-1) United States Government Printing Office.

Moir, I. & Seabridge, A. G. Aircraft Systems: Mechanical, Electrical, & Avionics Subsystems Integration. 3rd ed. 2008. (AIAA Education Ser.). *(978-1-56347-952-6(4))* American Institute of Aeronautics & Astronautics.

Morelli, Eugene A. & Klein, Vladislav. Aircraft System Identification: Theory & Practice. 2006. (AIAA Education Ser.: Vol. 213). (Illus.). 484p. *(978-1-56347-832-1(3))* American Institute of Aeronautics & Astronautics.

Murdock, Shirley Woodhouse & Gillaspie, James A. The Longest Flight: Yuma's Quest for the Future. 2009. 152p. 24.95 *(978-1-4401-7360-8(5))*; pap. 14.95 *(978-1-4401-7358-5(3))* iUniverse, Inc.

Murray, Iain. Bouncing-Bomb Man: The Science of Sir Barnes Wallis. 2010. (ENG., Illus.). 288p. 42.95 *(978-1-84425-588-7(3),* 1844255883) Haynes Publishing PLC GBR. Dist: MBI Distribution Services/Quayside Distribution.

NASA at 50: Past Accomplishments & Future Opportunities & Challenges: Hearing Before the Committee on Science & Technology, House of Representatives, One Hundred Tenth Congress, Second Session, July 30, 2008. 2008. (Illus.). iii, 59p. *(978-0-16-082104-2(5),* 552-070-38251-8) United States Government Printing Office.

NASA's Fiscal Year 2009 Budget Request: Hearing Before the Committee on Science & Technology, House of Representatives, One Hundred Tenth Congress, Second Session, February 13, 2008. 2008. (Illus.). iv, 110p. *(978-0-16-081518-8(5),* 552-070-37874-0) United States Government Printing Office.

NASA's Fiscal Year 2011 Budget Request & Issues: Hearing Before the Committee on Science & Technology, House of Representatives, One Hundred Eleventh Congress, Second Session, February 25, 2010. 2010. (Illus.). iii, 120p. ***(978-0-16-087179-5(4),*** 552-070-42021-5) United States Government Printing Office.

Naslin, Mathieu. Design of an Attitude Determination Subsystem for Nanosatellites. 2010. 112p. pap. *(978-3-8383-1312-2(7))* Lambert Academic Publishing.

National Aeronautics and Space Administration, compiled by. NASA Systems Engineering Handbook. 2008. (ENG., Illus.). 356p. pap. 43.00 *(978-0-16-079747-7(0),* U. S. National Aeronautics & Space Administration) United States Government Printing Office.

Neufeld, Michael & Spencer, Alex M., eds. Smithsonian National Air & Space Museum: An Autobiography. 2010. (Illus.). 416p. 40.00 *(978-1-4262-0653-5(4),* National Geographic) National Geographic Society.

Nikolaishvili, George & Chama, Brian. Eads & the A380 Project. 2010. 96p. pap. *(978-3-8383-6893-1(2))* Lambert Academic Publishing.

Pacco, John. F-16 in Dienst Van de Belgische Luchtmacht. (Belgie Onder de Wapens Ser.: Vol. 1). (DUT., Illus.). 56p. pap. 18.95 *(978-90-72547-17-0(9))* De Krijger BEL. Dist: Casemate Pubs. & Bk. Distributors, LLC.

Peek & Goodhead. The Spartan Story. (Illus.). 150p. pap. 22.95 *(978-0-943591-16-9(8))* MBI Distribution Services/Quayside Distribution.

Pettigrew, James Bell. Animal Locomotion. 2006. 296p. per. 23.99 *(978-1-4255-2778-5(7))* MPublishing.

Phoenix Flight Publications. Aviation Scholarship Directory: E-Book. 2007. per. 19.99 *(978-0-9799374-1-5(8))* Phoenix Flight Publications.

—Aviation Scholarship Directory: Print Book. 2007. per. 24.99 *(978-0-9799374-0-8(X))* Phoenix Flight Publications.

Radespiel, Rolf, et al, eds. Hermann Schlichting — 100 Years: Scientific Colloquium Celebrating the Anniversary of His Birthday, Braunschweig, Germany 2007. 2009. (Notes on Numerical Fluid Mechanics & Multidisciplinary Design Ser.). (Illus.). x, 196p. 259.00 *(978-3-540-95997-7(1))* Springer.

Rae André. Take Back the Sky: Protecting Communities in the Path of Aviation Expansion. 2009. 252p. pap. 18.95 *(978-1-4401-7837-5(2))* iUniverse, Inc.

Ramnath, Rudrapatna V. Computation & Asymptotics. 2012. (SpringerBriefs in Applied Sciences & Technology / SpringerBriefs in Computational Mechanics Ser.). (ENG., Illus.). xv, 120p. pap. 49.95 ***(978-3-642-25748-3(8),*** 3642257488) Springer.

Ramnath, Rudrapatna V. Multiple Scales Theory & Aerospace Applications. 2010. (Illus.). xxiv, 587p. 99.95 *(978-1-60086-762-0(6))* American Institute of Aeronautics & Astronautics.

Rampini, Edoardo. Aviation Sector As the Fastest Growing Contributor to Climate Changes. 2011. 104p. pap. ***(978-3-8454-1890-2(7))*** Lambert Academic Publishing.

Rheinfurth, M. Probability & Statistics in Aerospace. 2006. 136p. per. 29.50 *(978-1-4102-2588-7(7))* Univ. Pr. of the Pacific.

Roesler, Jeff, et al, eds. Airfield & Highway Pavements: Efficient Pavements Supporting Transportation's Future: Proceedings of the 2008 Airfield & Highway Pavements Conference, October 15-18, 2008, Bellevue, Washington. 2008. (ENG.). 646p. 125.00 *(978-0-7844-1005-9(4))* American Society of Civil Engineers.

Salas, Eduardo & Dietz, Aaron S., eds. Situational Awareness. 2011. (Critical Essays on Human Factors in Aviation Ser.). 544p. 260.00 ***(978-0-7546-2973-3(2))*** Ashgate Publishing Co.

Salas, Eduardo & Maurino, Dan, eds. Human Factors in Aviation. 2nd ed. 2010. (ENG., Illus.). 744p. pap. 103.00 *(978-0-12-374518-7(7),* Academic Pr.) Elsevier Science & Technology Bks.

Schafroth, Dario. Aerodynamics, Modeling & Control of an Autonomous Micro Helicopter: Towards the design of a fully autonomous MAV the size & mass of a small bird. 2011. 188p. pap. ***(978-3-8381-0869-8(8))*** Südwestdeutscher Verlag für Hochschulschriften AG & Co. KG.

Schipske, Gerrie. Early Aviation in Long Beach. 2009. 128p. pap. 21.99 *(978-0-7385-7083-9(4))* Arcadia Publishing.

The Science of Flight: A Gateway to New Horizons. 2011. ***(978-1-4496-3065-2(0))*** Jones & Bartlett Publishers.
Science Opportunities Enabled by NASA's Constellation System Committee & National Research Board Staff. Launching Science: Science Opportunities Provided by NASA's Constellation System. 2009. (ENG.). 156p. pap. 37.25 *(978-0-309-11644-2(9))* National Academies Pr.
Senson, Ben (Ben Senson) & Ritter, Jasen. Aerospace Engineering: From the Ground Up. 2011. (ENG.). 320p. (C). 124.95 *(978-1-4354-4753-0(0))* Delmar Cengage Learning.
Short, Simine. Locomotive to Aeromotive: Octave Chanute & the Transportation Revolution. 2011. (ENG., Illus.). 360p. 38.00 *(978-0-252-03631-6(X))* Univ. of Illinois Pr.
Shull, Peter, et al. Nondestructive Characterization for Composite Materials, Aerospace Engineering, Civil Infrastructure, & Homeland Security 2010. 2010. (Proceedings of SPIE Ser.). 492p. pap. 130.00 ***(978-0-8194-8064-4(9))*** SPIE.
Shull, Peter J. Nondestructive Characterization for Composite Materials, Aerospace Engineering, Civil Infrastructure, & Homeland Security 2008: 11-13 March 2008, San Diego, California, USA. 2008. (Proceedings of SPIE Ser.). (Illus.). 380p. pap. 105.00 ***(978-0-8194-7120-8(8))*** SPIE.
Simpson, Rod. The General Aviation Handbook: A Guide to Postwar General Aviation Manufacturers & Their Aircraft. 3rd ed. 2010. (ENG., Illus.). 320p. pap. 54.95 *(978-1-85780-222-1(5))* Allan, Ian Publishing GBR. Dist: BookMasters Distribution Services (BDS).
Singleton, Billy J. Mobile Aviation. 2011. (Images of Aviation Ser.). (Illus.). 128p. pap. 21.99 *(978-0-7385-8683-0(8))* Arcadia Publishing.
Skaarup, Harold A. Florida Warplanes. 2010. 420p. pap. 36.95 *(978-1-4502-6444-0(1))* iUniverse, Inc.
Smithersrapra Technology, Technology. Polymers in Defence & Aerospace Applications 2010 Conference Proceedings. 2010. (Conference Proceedings Ser.). (Illus.). 180p. pap. *(978-1-84735-398-6(3))* iSmithers Rapra Publishing.
Sóbester, András. Stratospheric Flight: Aeronautics at the Limit. 2011. (Springer Praxis Books / Popular Science Ser.). (ENG., Illus.). xxiv, 215p. pap. 34.95 *(978-1-4419-9457-8(2),* 1441994572, Springer-Praxis) Springer.
Society of Allied Weight Engineers (SAWE) Staff, compiled by. 65th Annual International Conference on Mass Properties Engineering 2006. 2007. 408p. pap. 225.00 *(978-1-60423-974-4(3))* Curran Assocs., Inc.
—66th Annual International Conference on Mass Properties Engineering 2007. 2007. 612p. pap. 325.00 *(978-1-60423-973-7(5))* Curran Assocs., Inc.
Space Operations: Mission Management, Technologies, & Current Applications. 2007. (Illus.). 662p. 109.95 *(978-1-56347-919-9(2))* American Institute of Aeronautics & Astronautics.
Spitz, William & Golaszewski, Richard. Airport Aviation Activity Forecasting:: A Synthesis of Airport Practice. 2007. (ACRP Synthesis Ser.: Vol. 2). (Illus.). 32p. 44.00 *(978-0-309-09782-6(7))* Transportation Research Board.
Suitor, William P. Rocketbelt Pilot's Manual: A Guide by the Bell Test Pilot. 2009. (Apogee Books Space Ser.). (ENG.). 300p. pap. 27.95 *(978-1-926592-05-3(0))* Collector's Guide Publishing, Inc. CAN. Dist: Independent Pubs. Group.
Talbot, Frederick. Aeroplanes & Dirigibles of War. 2006. (ENG.). 184p. pap. 19.99 *(978-1-4264-0071-1(3))* BiblioBazaar.
Der Taschen Brockhaus Band 4: Luftfahrt. (GER., Illus.). *(978-3-7653-1791-0(8))* Brockhaus, F. A., GmbH DEU. Dist: International Bk. Import Service, Inc.
Technology Research Editors, ed. Metal Matrix Composites for Aerospace Components, 2007 Ed. 2007. pap. 128.50 *(978-1-60030-151-3(7),* Search-In-Print) CSA Journal Division.
The Gathering Foundation, compiled by. The Gathering of Mustangs & Legends: The Final Roundup. 2011. ***(978-0-615-53732-0(4))*** Creative Spot.
Torenbeek, Egbert & Wittenberg, H. Flight Physics: Essentials of Aeronautical Disciplines & Technology, with Historical Notes. 2009. (ENG., Illus.). xii, 536p. 89.95 *(978-1-4020-8663-2(6),* 1402086636) Springer.
Valasek, John, ed. Morphing Aerospace Vehicles & Structures. 2nd ed. 2012. (Aerospace Ser.). (ENG., Illus.). 310p. 135.00 ***(978-0-470-97286-1(6),*** Wiley) Wiley, John & Sons, Inc.
van Pelt, Michel. Into the Solar System on a String: Space Tethers & Space Elevators. 2009. (ENG., Illus.). x, 215p. 29.95 *(978-0-387-76555-6(7))* Springer.
Voegele, Amelia K. Airport & Aviation Security. 2010. (Transportation Issues, Policies & R&D Ser.). 347p. 195.00 *(978-1-61668-583-6(2))* Nova Science Pubs., Inc.
Wagg, David. Adaptive Structures: Engineering Applications. Friswell, Michael et al, eds. 2007. (ENG., Illus.). 314p. 140.00 *(978-0-470-05697-4(5),* Wiley) Wiley, John & Sons, Inc.
Weng, Chin-Tang Tom. Aerodynamic Analysis of A Landing Transport Airplane in Windshear. 2008. 120p. pap. *(978-3-639-01661-1(0))* VDM Verlag Dr. Mueller e.K.
Weston, Hartley A. Shadows on the Wind. 2010. 468p. pap. 24.99 *(978-1-4269-0189-8(5))* Trafford Publishing.
Whitehurst. Introduction to Aviation. rev. ed. 2011. (ENG.). 378p. pap. 72.95 ***(978-0-7575-8922-5(7))*** Kendall Hunt Publishing Co.
Wicks, T. Gary. Huntsville Air & Space. 2010. (Images of Aviation Ser.). (ENG., Illus.). 128p. pap. 21.99 *(978-0-7385-6607-8(1))* Arcadia Publishing.
Wigle, Garth. Basic Training for Flight Information Centres: Applying Best Practices in Adult Education. 2008. 104p. pap. *(978-3-8364-9143-3(5))* VDM Verlag Dr. Mueller e.K.
World Health Organization. A Guide to Hygiene & Sanitation in Aviation. 3rd rev. ed. 2010. (Nonserial Publication Ser.). 71p. pap. 24.00 *(978-92-4-154777-2(4))* World Health Organization.
Wright, A. Jordan. System Health Management: With Aerospace Applications. Mott, Charles et al, eds. 2011. (Aerospace Ser.: 34). (ENG., Illus.). 664p. 210.00 *(978-0-470-74133-7(3),* Wiley) Wiley, John & Sons, Inc.
Wu, H. Felix. Nondestructive Characterization for Composite Materials, Aerospace Engineering, Civil Infrastructure, & Homeland Security 2009: 9-11 March 2009, San Diego, California, United States. 2009. (Proceedings of SPIE Ser.). (Illus.). 386p. pap. 80.00 *(978-0-8194-7554-1(8))* SPIE.
Wu, H. Felix. Nondestructive Characterization for Composite Materials, Aerospace Engineering, Civil Infrastructure, & Homeland Security 2011. 2011. (Proceedings of SPIE Ser.). 1068p. pap. 190.00 ***(978-0-8194-8545-8(4))*** SPIE.
Wu, H. Felix, et al. Nondestructive Characterization for Composite Materials, Aerospace Engineering, Civil Infrastructure & Homeland Security: 20-22 March 2007, San Diego, California, USA. 2007. (Proceedings of SPIE Ser.). (Illus.). 352p. pap. 90.00 *(978-0-8194-6652-5(2))* SPIE.
Zarchan, Paul & Musoff, Howard. Fundamentals of Kalman Filtering: A Practical Approach. Lu, Frank K., ed. 3rd ed. (Progress in Astronautics & Aeronautics Ser.: 232). 852p. 134.95 *(978-1-60086-718-7(9))* American Institute of Aeronautics & Astronautics.

AERONAUTICS—ACCIDENTS

see Aircraft Accidents

AERONAUTICS—BIBLIOGRAPHY

Brockett, Paul. Bibliography of Aeronautics. 2010. (ENG.). 964p. pap. 63.75 *(978-1-171-63055-5(7));* 954p. pap. 62.75 *(978-1-174-18285-3(7));* 960p. pap. 62.75 *(978-1-149-87075-4(3));* 956p. pap. 62.75 *(978-1-174-55171-0(2))* BiblioBazaar.
Wilkinson, Ronald S., et al. Aeronautical & Astronautical Resources of the Library of Congress: A Comprehensive Guide. 2007. (Illus.). 463p. *(978-0-8444-1160-6(4))* Library of Congress.

AERONAUTICS—BIOGRAPHY

see also Air Pilots; Women in Aeronautics

Anderson, Nina E. Flying above the Glass Ceiling: Inspirational Stories of Success from the First Women Pilots to Fly Airline & Corporate Aircraft. Pratt, Bill, ed. 2009. (Illus.). 134p. pap. 14.95 *(978-1-884820-94-6(8))* SAFE GOODS/ATN Publishing.
Benjamin, Robert. A Gift of Dreams. 2007. (ENG.). 320p. per. 15.00 *(978-0-9792328-4-8(8))* Helm Publishing.
Briesmeister, Dave. In Search of Something. 2010. 124p. pap. 12.49 *(978-1-4520-8398-8(3))* AuthorHouse.
Brulle, Robert V. Engineering the Space Age: A Rocket Scientist Remembers. 2008. (Illus.). xviii, 268p. pap. *(978-1-58566-184-8(8))* Air University Pr.
Cooper, Middle Finger. Biography of Tsgt Kenneth Alvin Jolley, Usaf, Retired. 2011. 90p. pap. 19.95 ***(978-1-4560-6951-3(9))*** PublishAmerica, Inc.
Culick, Fred E. C. & Dunmore, Spencer. On Great White Wings: The Wright Brothers & the Race for Flight. 2010. (ENG.). 176p. pap. 39.95 *(978-1-897330-42-5(1))* Madison Pr. Bks. CAN. Dist: Independent Pubs. Group.
Driggs, Laurence La Tourette. The High Aces: French, American, British, Italian & Belgian Pilots of the First World War 1914-18. 2010. 280p. *(978-1-84677-956-5(1));* pap. *(978-1-84677-955-8(3))* Leonaur Ltd.
Fossett, Steve & Hasley, Will. Chasing the Wind: The Autobiography of Steve Fossett. 2006. (ENG., Illus.). 256p. 29.95 *(978-1-85227-234-0(1))* Virgin Bks. Ltd. GBR. Dist: Independent Pubs. Group.
Glines, Alan. A Kansan Conquers the Cosmos: Or, spaced Out All My Life!™ 2010. 108p. 22.95 *(978-1-4502-6443-3(3));* pap. 12.95 *(978-1-4502-6441-9(7))* iUniverse, Inc.
Hallock, Austin Bruce. Sky Full of Dreams: The Aviation Exploits, Creations, & Visions of Bruce K. Hallock (Tailless Aircraft Designer, Builder, & Pilot) 2010. (Illus.). 230p. pap. 16.00 *(978-0-9826390-0-9(7))* Elevon Bks.
Harwood, Craig S. & Fogel, Gary. Quest for Flight: John J. Montgomery & the Dawn of Aviation in the West. 2012. ***(978-0-8061-4264-7(2))*** Univ. of Oklahoma Pr.
Hoffman, Paul. Wings of Madness: Alberto Santos-Dumont & the Invention of Flight. 2008. (ENG.). 369p. pap. 20.00 *(978-1-4223-9411-3(5))* DIANE Publishing Co.
Kaplan, Ray. A Spark Within Me: A Memoir by Ray Kaplan. 2007. 212p. per. 24.95 *(978-1-4241-8639-6(0))* PublishAmerica, Inc.
Kelly, Fred C. The Wright Brothers: A Biography Authorized by Orville Wright. 2011. 368p. 53.95 ***(978-1-258-00951-9(X))*** Literary Licensing, LLC.
Kemball, Michael. Out of the Blue: A true story about learning to fly, discover your wings & set your spirit Free. 2010. 140p. pap. 17.99 *(978-1-4389-5562-9(6))* AuthorHouse.
King, Stephen H. The Passion that Left the Ground. 2007. pap. 24.95 *(978-1-59571-178-6(3))* Word Association Pubs.
Kuntz, Jerry. Baseball Fiends & Flying Machines: The Many Lives & Outrageous Times of George & Alfred Lawson. 2009. (ENG., Illus.). 238p. pap. 29.95 *(978-0-7864-4375-8(8))* McFarland & Co., Inc. Pubs.
Linehan, Dan. Burt Rutan's Race to Space: The Magician of Mojave & His Flying Innovations. 2011. (Illus.). 160p. 30.00 *(978-0-7603-3815-5(9),* 0760338159, Zenith Pr.) MBI Publishing Co. LLC.
Mann, Carl. Lightning in the Sky: The Story of Jimmy Doolittle. 2011. 256p. 47.95 ***(978-1-258-00609-9(X))*** Literary Licensing, LLC.
McCoy, Charles. Echoes of War. 2009. 176p. 22.49 *(978-1-4389-4839-3(5));* pap. 11.99 *(978-1-4389-4838-6(7))* AuthorHouse.
McHardy, Aimee. An Airman's Wife: A True Story of Lovers Separated by War. 2007. 315p. per. 19.95 *(978-1-904943-94-5(2))* Grub Street GBR. Dist: Casemate Pubs. & Bk. Distributors, LLC.
Read McLaughlin, Jean. My Log Was My Diary. 2009. 256p. pap. 14.49 *(978-1-4490-4572-2(3))* AuthorHouse.
Riley, Lodr Paul Allen. Near Misses: A Naval Aviator's Story. 2011. 112p. 21.23 *(978-1-4567-3423-7(7));* pap. 10.68 *(978-1-4567-3421-3(0))* AuthorHouse.
Ross, Norman. Memoirs of a Tail Gunner II. 2009. 370p. pap. 21.50 *(978-0-557-09629-9(4))* Lulu Enterprises Inc.
Schoneberger, William A. Aeronautic Pathfinders: Celebrating Thirty-Three Years of Honoring Aeronautic & Space Pioneers with the Howard Hughes Memorial Award of the Aero Club of Southern California. 2012. pap. ***(978-1-57864-740-8(1))*** Donning Co. Pubs.
Sellers, Barbara L. A Moment in Time; the Biography of Matthew B. Sellers, II, Aviation Pioneer, 1869-1932. 2009. 552p. pap. 49.95 *(978-1-935097-96-9(2))* Hillcrest Publishing Group, Inc.
Shagena, Jack L. How the Wright Brothers Got It Right: Engineering & Invention of the Airplane. 2007. (Illus.). 102p. *(978-0-9776866-5-0(5))* Shagena, Jack L. Publishing.
Trueblood, Wes. From a Land Far, Far Away: Letters from the Front Line of the War on Terror. 2010. pap. 20.99 *(978-1-61663-830-6(3))* Tate Publishing & Enterprises, LLC.
Verdon-Roe, Alliott. The World of Wings & Things. 2006. 284p. per. *(978-1-4067-0115-9(7),* Hesperides Pr.) Read Bks.

AERONAUTICS—DATA PROCESSING

Colgren, Richard. Basic MATLAB, Simulink, & Stateflow. 2006. (AIAA Education Ser.). (Illus.). 485p. *(978-1-56347-838-3(2))* American Institute of Aeronautics & Astronautics.
Copilot V2.0 MS Flight Simulator. pap. 39.95 incl. cd-rom *(978-1-55755-353-9(X))* Abacus.
Diston, Dominic. Computational Modelling of Aircraft & the Environment. 2009. (Illus.). *(978-1-60086-704-0(9))* American Institute of Aeronautics & Astronautics.
Grubesic. The Global Airline Network in the Information Age. 2009. 288p. 150.00 *(978-0-415-77535-9(3))* Routledge.
Kearns, Suzanne. E-Learning in Aviation. 2010. (Ashgate Studies in Human Factors for Flight Operations Ser.). (Illus.). 194p. 99.95 *(978-0-7546-7879-3(2))* Ashgate Publishing Co.
Rouff, Christopher, ed. Autonomous & Autonomic Systems: With Applications to NASA Intelligent Spacecraft Operations & Exploration Systems. 2009. (NASA Monographs in Systems & Software Engineering Ser.). (Illus.). 332p. 149.00 *(978-1-84628-232-4(2),* 1846282322) Springer.
Sinclair, Christine. FS Action Scenery. pap. 12.99 incl. cd-rom *(978-1-55755-343-0(2))* Abacus.

AERONAUTICS—DICTIONARIES

Aerospace Dictionary English - Russian: Companies-Products-Services. 600p. *(978-0-7605-0646-2(9))* Rector Pr., Ltd.
Anderson, Dale, et al. Flight & Motion: The History & Science of Flying. 2009. (ENG.). 640p. 325.00 *(978-0-7656-8100-3(5),* Sharpe Reference) Sharpe, M.E. Inc.
Blockley, Richard & Shyy, Wei. Encyclopedia of Aerospace Engineering, 9 vols., Set. 2010. (ENG., Illus.). 5810p. 3760.00 *(978-0-470-75440-5(0),* Wiley) Wiley, John & Sons, Inc.
Cobb, Paul. Air Force Navy Translator Soft Cover. 2009. 52p. pap. 11.96 *(978-0-557-03896-1(0))* Lulu Enterprises Inc.
Crane, Dale. Dictionary of Aeronautical Terms. 4th ed. 2006. (ENG., Illus.). 786p. per. 19.95 *(978-1-56027-610-4(X))* Aviation Supplies & Academics, Inc.
Crane, Dale, ed. Dictionary of Aeronautical Terms. 5th ed. 2012. (ENG., Illus.). 852p. pap. 19.95 ***(978-1-56027-864-1(1))*** Aviation Supplies & Academics, Inc.
Crocker, David. Dictionary of Aviation: Over 5,500 Terms Dlearly Defined. 2nd ed. 2007. (ENG.). 288p. 16.95 *(978-0-7136-8734-7(7))* A & C Black GBR. Dist: Macmillan.
Gunston, Bill. The Cambridge Aerospace Dictionary. 2nd rev. ed. (Cambridge Aerospace Ser.). (ENG.). 816p. (C). 2011. pap. 50.00 *(978-0-521-27967-3(4))* 2009. 160.00 *(978-0-521-19165-4(3))* Cambridge Univ. Pr.
—World Encyclopedia of Aero Engines: From the Pioneers to the Present Day. 5th ed. 2006. (ENG., Illus.). 272p. 54.95 *(978-0-7509-4479-3(X))* Sutton Publishing.
Klußmann, Niels & Malik, Arnim. Lexikon der Luftfahrt. 2006. VIII, 378p. pap. 69.95 *(978-3-540-20556-2(X),* 354020556X) Springer.
Mariner, Liz. Cleared for Takeoff: English for Pilots, 2 bks. 2007. (Illus.). Bk. 1. 175p. per., wbk. ed. 48.95 incl. audio compact disk *(978-0-9795068-0-2(8))*Bk. 1 and 2. (ENG., 342p. per. 74.95 incl. audio compact disk *(978-0-9795068-2-6(4))*Bk. 2. (ENG., 167p. per. 48.95 incl. audio compact disk *(978-0-9795068-1-9(6))* A-E-Link Pubns., Ltd.

AERONAUTICS—EXAMINATIONS, QUESTIONS, ETC.

ASA Test Prep Board Staff. Private Pilot Test Prep 2012: Study & Prepare for the Recreational & Private: Airplane, Helicopter, Gyroplane, Glider, Balloon, Airship, Powered Parachute, & Weight-Shift Control FAA Knowledge Exams. 2011. (Test Prep Ser.). (ENG.). 380p. pap. 16.95 *(978-1-56027-850-4(1))* Aviation Supplies & Academics, Inc.
ASA Test Prep Board Staff, ed. Airline Transport Pilot Test Prep 2012: Study & Prepare for the Aircraft Dispatcher & ATP Part 121, 135, Airplane & Helicopter FAA Knowledge Exams. 2011. (Test Prep Ser.). (ENG.). 502p. pap. 36.95 *(978-1-56027-854-2(4))* Aviation Supplies & Academics, Inc.
—Certified Flight Instructor Test Prep 2011: Study & Prepare for the Ground, Flight & Sport Instructor: Airplane, Helicopter, Glider, Weight-Shift Control, Powered Parachute, Add-on Ratings, & Fundamentals of Instructing FAA Knowledge Tests. 2010. (Test Prep Ser.). (ENG.). 472p. pap. 21.95 *(978-1-56027-767-5(X))* Aviation Supplies & Academics, Inc.
—Certified Flight Instructor Test Prep 2012: For the Ground, Flight, Military Competency & Sport Instructor: Airplane, Helicopter, Glider, Weight-Shift Control, Powered Parachute, Add-on Ratings, & Fundamentals of Instructing FAA Knowledge Exams. 2011. (Test Prep Ser.). (ENG.). 480p. pap. 21.95 *(978-1-56027-853-5(6))* Aviation Supplies & Academics, Inc.
—Instrument Rating Test Prep 2011: Study & Prepare for the Instrument Rating, Instrument Flight Instructor (CFII), Instrument Ground Instructor, & Foreign Pilot: Airplane & Helicopter FAA Knowledge Tests. 2010. (Test Prep Ser.). (ENG.). 328p. pap. 21.95 *(978-1-56027-765-1(3))* Aviation Supplies & Academics, Inc.
—Instrument Rating Test Prep 2012: Study & Prepare for the Instrument Rating, Instrument Flight Instructor (CFII), Instrument Ground Instructor, & Foreign Pilot: Airplane & Helicopter FAA Knowledge Exams. 2011. (Test Prep Ser.). (ENG.). 335p. pap. 21.95 *(978-1-56027-851-1(X))* Aviation Supplies & Academics, Inc.
Aviation Theory Centre Ltd., Staff, ed. The Pilot's Manual: Ground School: All the Aeronautical Knowledge Required to Pass the FAA Exams & Operate as a Private & Commercial Pilot. 3rd ed. 2007. (Pilot's Manual Ser.). (ENG., Illus.). 688p. 59.95 *(978-1-56027-677-7(0))* Aviation Supplies & Academics, Inc.
Crane, Dale, et al. General Test Guide 2009: The Fast-Track to Study for & Pass the FAA Aviation Maintenance Technician General & Designated Mechanic Examiner Knowledge Tests. 2008. (Fast Track Ser.). (ENG., Illus.). 160p. pap. 14.95 *(978-1-56027-697-5(5))* Aviation Supplies & Academics, Inc.
Dempsey, Michael W. Professional Instrument Flight Review Guide. 112p. pap. *(978-1-57087-067-5(5))* Professional Pr.
Federal Aviation Administration. Aviation Mechanic Practical Test Standards for General, Airframe & Powerplant: FAA-S-8081-26, -27, And -28. 2009. (Practical Test Standards Ser.). (ENG.). 96p. pap. 9.95 *(978-1-56027-751-4(3))* Aviation Supplies & Academics, Inc.
—Flight Instructor Instrument for Airplane & Helicopter Practical Test Standards: Faa-s-8081-9c. 2007. (Practical Test Standards Ser.). (ENG.). 62p. pap. 5.95 *(978-1-56027-675-3(4))* Aviation Supplies & Academics, Inc.
—Pilot's Handbook of Aeronautical Knowledge: Faa-h-8083-25a. 2009. (FAA Handbooks Ser.). (ENG.). 470p. pap. 24.95 *(978-1-56027-750-7(5))* Aviation Supplies & Academics, Inc.
—Private Pilot Test Prep 2009. 2008. 368p. pap. 12.95 *(978-1-60239-325-7(7))* Skyhorse Publishing Co., Inc.
—Sport Pilot Practical Test Standards for Airplane, Weight-Shift Control, Powered Parachute, & Flight Instructor: FAA-S-8081-29 And 31. 2008. (Practical Test Standards Ser.). (ENG.). 196p. pap. 9.95 *(978-1-56027-725-5(4))* Aviation Supplies & Academics, Inc.
Federal Aviation Administration Staff. Certified Flight Instructor Test Prep 2010: Study & Prepare for the Ground, Flight & Sport Instructor: Airplane, Helicopter, Glider, Weight-Shift Control, Powered Parachute, Add-on Ratings, Fundamentals of Instructing, & Designated Pilot Examiner FAA Knowledge Exams. ASA Test Prep Board Staff, ed. 2009. (Test Prep Ser.). (ENG.). 464p. pap. 21.95 *(978-1-56027-739-2(4))* Aviation Supplies & Academics, Inc.
—Federal Aviation Regulations / Aeronautical Information Manual 2011 (FAR/AIM) 2010. (ENG., Illus.). 896p. pap. 15.95 *(978-1-61608-148-5(1),* 608148) Skyhorse Publishing Co., Inc.
—Flight Instructor for Airplane Multi-Engine Land & Sea: FAA-S-8081-6cm November 2006. 2007. (Practical Test Standards Ser.). (ENG.). 100p. pap. 5.95 *(978-1-56027-673-9(8))* Aviation Supplies & Academics, Inc.
Federal Aviation Administration Staff & Federal Aviation Administration. Airline Transport Pilot & Type Rating Practical Test Standards: For Airplane FAA-S-8081-5F. 2009. (Practical Test Standards Ser.). (ENG.). 95p. pap. 5.95 *(978-1-56027-729-3(7))* Aviation Supplies & Academics, Inc.
Gardner, Bob. The Complete Advanced Pilot: A Combined Commercial & Instrument Course. 4th ed. 2008. (Complete Pilot Ser.). (ENG., Illus.). 480p. pap. 29.95 *(978-1-56027-718-7(1))* Aviation Supplies & Academics, Inc.
Hayes, Michael D. Certified Flight Instructor Oral Exam Guide: The Comprehensive Guide to Prepare You for the FAA Oral Exam. 5th ed. 2008. (Oral Exam Guide Ser.). (ENG.). 312p. per. 12.95 *(978-1-56027-690-6(8))* Aviation Supplies & Academics, Inc.
—Commercial Oral Exam Guide: The Comprehensive Guide to Prepare You for the FAA Checkride. 7th ed. 2010. (Oral Exam Guide Ser.). (ENG.). 240p. pap. 12.95 *(978-1-56027-796-5(3))* Aviation Supplies & Academics, Inc.
—Instrument Oral Exam Guide: The Comprehensive Guide to Prepare You for the FAA Oral Exam. 2009. (Oral Exam Guide Ser.). (ENG.). 176p. pap. 12.95 *(978-1-56027-757-6(2))* Aviation Supplies & Academics, Inc.
—Private Oral Exam Guide: The Comprehensive Guide to Prepare You for the FAA Oral Exam. 2009. (Oral Exam Guide Ser.). (ENG.). 208p. pap. 12.95 *(978-1-56027-723-1(8))* Aviation Supplies & Academics, Inc.
Kershner, William K. Student Pilot's Flight Manual: From First Flight to Private Certificate. 10th ed. 2010. (Flight Manuals Ser.). (ENG., Illus.). 450p. pap. 24.95 *(978-1-56027-719-4(X))* Aviation Supplies & Academics, Inc.
Spanitz, Jackie. Guide to the Flight Review: Complete Preparation for Issuing or Taking a Flight Review. (Oral Exam Guide Ser.). (ENG.). 2010. 148p. pap.

12.95 *(978-1-56027-778-1(5))* 5th ed. 2006. (Illus.). 134p. per. 12.95 *(978-1-56027-512-8(6))* Aviation Supplies & Academics, Inc.

Wingfield, William. The Aeromedical Certification Examinations Self-Assessment Test. 2008. 293p. pap. 64.94 *(978-0-615-19124-9(X))* ResO Shop, The.

AERONAUTICS—FLIGHTS

see also Space Flight

Air, Commodore. First over Everest. 2006. 400p. per. *(978-1-4067-3144-6(7),* Hesperides Pr.) Read Bks.

Aviation Consumer Issues: Emergency Contingency Planning & Outlook for Summer Travel: Hearing Before the Subcommittee on Aviation of the Committee on Transportation & Infrastructure, House of Representatives, One Hundred Eleventh Congress, First Session, May 20, 2009. 2009. (Illus.). xiii, 139p. *(978-0-16-084374-7(X),* 552-070-39917-8) United States Government Printing Office.

Aviation Delays & Consumer Issues: Hearing Before the Subcommittee on Aviation of the Committee on Transportation & Infrastructure, House of Representatives, One Hundred Tenth Congress, Second Session, April 9, 2008. 2008. (Illus.). xii, 194p. *(978-0-16-082967-3(4),* 552-070-38878-8) United States Government Printing Office.

Bak, Richard. The Big Jump: Lindbergh & the Great Atlantic Air Race. 2011. (ENG., Illus.). 336p. 27.95 *(978-0-471-47752-5(4),* Wiley) Wiley, John & Sons, Inc.

Beamish, Richard J. The Story of Lindbergh: The Lone Eagle. 2011. 320p. 50.95 **(978-1-258-00983-0(8))** Literary Licensing, LLC.

Cannon, James & Richey, Franklin D. Practical Applications in Business Aviation Management. 2011. (ENG.). 384p. (C). (gr. 13-17). pap. 50.00 **(978-1-60590-770-3(7))** Government Institutes.

Ebinger, Ginger. The World Connected: DFW International Airport - Taking Flight into the 21st Century. 2007. (ENG., Illus.). 272p. 39.95 *(978-0-9774451-4-1(3))* DSA Publishing & Design, Inc.

Gagliardi Kindlimann, Oscar Gregorio. Jorge Chávez Dartnell: Centenario de la Hazaña Del Cruce de Los Alpes (1910 - 2010) 2010. (SPA., Illus.). 171p. *(978-9972-210-89-1(8))* Universidad Alas Peruanas.

Hawker, H. G. & Grieve, Kenneth M. Our Atlantic Attempt. 2008. 152p. 36.95 *(978-0-548-97267-0(2))* 2007. (ENG.). 156p. per. 21.95 *(978-0-548-67537-3(6))* Kessinger Publishing, LLC.

Jackson, Joe. Atlantic Fever: Lindbergh, His Competitors, & the Race to Cross the Atlantic, 1 vol. 2012. (ENG., Illus.). 544p. 30.00 **(978-0-374-10675-1(4))** Farrar, Straus & Giroux.

Lindbergh, Gage, et al. Plucky Lindbergh: Incidents in the Life of Colonel Charles Lindbergh & Brief Biography. 2011. 76p. 37.95 **(978-1-258-00620-4(0))** Literary Licensing, LLC.

Lynch, Brendan. Yesterday We Were in America: Alcock & Brown - First to Fly the Atlantic Non-Stop. 2009. (ENG., Illus.). 256p. 39.95 *(978-1-84425-681-5(2),* 1844256812) Haynes Publishing PLC GBR. Dist: MBI Distribution Services/Quayside Distribution.

Nevin, David. Pathfinders. (Illus.). 176p. 24.00 *(978-1-84447-032-7(6))* Time Life Value GBR. Dist: Mercury Bks. Ltd.

Stinson, Patrick M. Around-the-World Flights: A History. 2011. (ENG., Illus.). 267p. pap. 40.00 *(978-0-7864-6282-7(5))* McFarland & Co., Inc. Pubs.

Trautman, James. Pan American Clippers: The Golden Age of Flying Boats. 2011. (ENG., Illus.). 272p. pap. 29.95 *(978-1-55407-894-3(6))* Boston Mills Pr. CAN. Dist: Firefly Bks., Ltd.

AERONAUTICS—HANDBOOKS, MANUALS, ETC.

Bishop, Robert H. Aerospace Engineering Handbook. 2008. (Electrical Engineering Handbook Ser.). (ENG., Illus.). 1200p. 229.95 *(978-0-8493-1627-2(8),* CRC Press) Taylor & Francis Group GBR. Dist: Taylor & Francis Group.

Bruckert, Danielle. Cessna 152 Training Manual. 2009. 79p. pap. 20.00 *(978-0-557-02280-9(0))* Lulu Enterprises Inc.

Bruckert, Danielle & Roud, Oleg. Cessna 172 Training Manual. 2009. 99p. pap. 20.01 *(978-0-557-01472-9(7))* Lulu Enterprises Inc.

Dept. of the Army, prod. ANVIS an/AVS-6(V)3 Technical Manual. 2007. (Illus.). 200p. per. 39.50 *(978-0-935856-17-0(X))* Lancer Militaria.

Federal Aviation Administration. Aircraft Weight & Balance Handbook: FAA-H-8083-1A. 2007. (FAA Handbook Ser.). (ENG., Illus.). 92p. per. 9.95 *(978-1-56027-676-0(2))* Aviation Supplies & Academics, Inc.

Federal Aviation Administration (FAA). Far/amt 2011: Federal Aviation Regulations for Aviation Maintenance Technicians. 2010. (FAR/AIM Ser.). (ENG.). 896p. pap. 24.95 *(978-1-56027-774-3(2))* Aviation Supplies & Academics, Inc.

Federal Aviation Administration (FAA) Staff, creator. Commercial Pilot & Flight Instructor for Helicopter for Practical Test Standards: FAA-S-8081-16A & -7B. 2007. (Practical Test Standards Ser.). (ENG.). 208p. pap. 5.95 *(978-1-56027-674-6(6))* Aviation Supplies & Academics, Inc.

Film.Com, Periscope. X-15 Rocket Plane Pilot's Flight Operati. 2007. 194p. pap. 24.95 *(978-1-4116-9824-6(X))* Lulu Enterprises Inc.

Ley, Wilfried, et al, eds. Handbook of Space Technology. 2009. (Illus.). 882p. 139.95 *(978-1-60086-701-9(4))* American Institute of Aeronautics & Astronautics.

Linney, Mark. North American F-86 Sabre Owners' Workshop Manual: An Insight into Owning, Flying & Maintaining the Usaf's Legendary Cold War Jet Fighter. 2011. (ENG., Illus.). 160p. 28.00 **(978-0-7603-4292-3(X)**, 076034292X, Zenith Pr.) MBI Publishing Co. LLC.

Newlon, Clarke. 1,001 Questions Answered about Space. 2011. 376p. 53.95 **(978-1-258-06455-6(3))** Literary Licensing, LLC.

Rioni, Al. All Time High: A Pilot's Memoirs. 2007. (Illus.). 300p. per. 15.95 *(978-0-9748065-2-5(8))* Rioni, Al.

Rossin-Arthiat, Andre S. Powered Paraglider Pilot Training Manual. (Illus.). 108p. spiral bd. *(978-1-894288-98-9(X))* Auslander Publishing.

Roud, Oleg & Bruckert, Danielle. C182 Training Manual. 2009. 113p. pap. 20.00 *(978-0-557-04524-2(X))* Lulu Enterprises Inc.

AERONAUTICS—HISTORY

Abbot, Willis J. The War MacHines: The Development of Aircraft & Submarines for Aerial & Undersea Warfare to the End of the First World War. 2010. (Illus.). 376p. *(978-0-85706-126-3(7))*; pap. *(978-0-85706-125-6(9))* Leonaur Ltd.

Abney, Arthur E. Wings over Illinois. 2007. (ENG., Illus.). 272p. 50.00 *(978-0-8093-2765-3(6))* Southern Illinois Univ. Pr.

Abrams, Michael. Birdmen, Batmen, & Skyflyers: Wingsuits & the Pioneers Who Flew in Them, Fell in Them, & Perfected Them. 2007. (ENG., Illus.). 320p. per. 13.95 *(978-1-4000-5492-3(3),* Three Rivers Pr.) Crown Publishing Group.

Air Force, U. S. Army. B-24 Liberator Pilot's Flight Operating Instructions. 2010. 160p. pap. 17.95 *(978-1-935327-88-2(7))* Periscope Film, LLC.

Aircraft, Douglas & USAAF. A-26 Invader Pilot's Flight Operating Instructions. 2010. 150p. pap. 16.95 *(978-1-935700-03-6(0))* Periscope Film, LLC.

Almond, Peter. Aviation: Die Anfänge der Luftfahrt, 1 vol. 2011. (ENG, FRE & GER.). 349p. 19.99 **(978-3-8331-6185-8(X))** h.f.ullmann DEU. Dist: Innovative Logistics.

Almond, Peter. Aviation: The Early Years/Di Engange der Luftfahrt/les Premieres Annees de L'Aeronautique. 2008. (Transportation: the Early Years Ser.). (Illus.). 349p. 49.95 *(978-0-8416-0278-6(6))* American Map Corp.

Anderson, Dale, et al. Flight & Motion: The History & Science of Flying. 2009. (ENG.). 640p. 325.00 *(978-0-7656-8100-3(5),* Sharpe Reference) Sharpe, M.E. Inc.

Arrighi, Robert S. Revolutionary Atmosphere: the Story of the Altitude Wind Tunnel & the Space Power Chambers: The Story of the Altitude Wind Tunnel & the Space Power Chambers. National Aeronautics and Space Administration, ed. 2010. (ENG., Illus.). 410p. 44.00 *(978-0-16-085641-9(8),* U. S. National Aeronautics & Space Administration) United States Government Printing Office.

Arrington, Charles W. & Nokes, Garry J. Wings over the Falls: A Century of Aviation in Southern Indiana. 2007. 160p. 24.95 *(978-1-58374-170-2(4))* Chicago Spectrum Pr.

Bacon, J. M. The Dominion of the Air. 2007. 176p. per. *(978-1-4068-2382-0(1))* Echo Library.

Bak, Richard. The Big Jump: Lindbergh & the Great Atlantic Air Race. 2011. (ENG., Illus.). 336p. 27.95 *(978-0-471-47752-5(4),* Wiley) Wiley, John & Sons, Inc.

Barrett, Richard E. Aviation in Columbus. 2012. (Images of Aviation Ser.). (ENG., Illus.). 128p. pap. 21.99 **(978-0-7385-9371-5(0))** Arcadia Publishing.

Batchelor, John & Lowe, Malcolm V. Flight, 1848-1939. 2009. (Complete Encyclopedia Ser.). (ENG.). 303p. 12.99 *(978-90-366-1600-3(X),* 903661600X) Rebo International B.V. NLD. Dist: Book Sales, Inc.

Bell, Dana. Smithsonian Atlas of World Aviation. 2008. (ENG., Illus.). 240p. 39.95 *(978-0-06-125144-3(5))* Smithsonian Institution Pr.

Bennett, Leon. Three Wings for the Red Baron: Von Richthofen, Strategy, Tactics & Airplanes. 2011. (Illus.). 272p. 49.95 *(978-1-907677-13-7(5))* Helion & Co., Ltd. GBR. Dist: Casemate Pubs. & Bk. Distributors, LLC.

Berliner, D. Airplane Racing: A History, 1909-2008. 2010. (ENG., Illus.). 266p. pap. 35.00 *(978-0-7864-4300-0(6))* McFarland & Co., Inc. Pubs.

Berliner, Don. The Paris Air Show. 2006. (Illus.). 68p. reprint ed. pap. 25.00 *(978-1-4223-5692-0(2))* DIANE Publishing Co.

Billberg, Rudy. In the Shadow of Eagles: From Barnstormer to Alaska Bush Pilot, a Pilots Story. 2009. (ENG., Illus.). 352p. pap. 16.95 *(978-0-88240-815-6(1),* Alaska Northwest Bks.) Graphic Arts Ctr. Publishing Co.

Bilstein, Roger E. Flight Patterns: Trends of Aeronautical Development in the United States, 1918-1929. 2008. (ENG.). 260p. pap. 22.95 *(978-0-8203-3214-7(3))* Univ. of Georgia Pr.

Blackburn, Gerald A. & Aerospace Legacy Foundation. Downey's Aerospace History: 1947-1999. 2009. (Images of America Ser.). (ENG., Illus.). 128p. pap. 21.99 *(978-0-7385-5953-6(4))* Arcadia Publishing.

Blackman, Tony. Flight Testing to Win. 2007. 336p. per. *(978-0-9553856-4-3(4))* Blackman Assocs.

Branigan, Michael. A History of Chicago's O'Hare Airport. 2011. 160p. pap. 19.99 **(978-1-60949-434-6(2))** History Pr., The.

Branson, Richard. Reach for the Skies: Ballooning, Birdmen, & Blasting into Space. 2011. (ENG.). 352p. (gr. 12). 26.95 *(978-1-61723-003-5(0),* Current) Penguin Group (USA) Inc.

Brinson, Ronald E. Fort Lauderdale Executive Control Tower Simulator (TSS) Lab Workbook. 2011. (ENG.). 214p. (C). pap. 112.40 *(978-0-558-79762-1(8))* Pearson Learning Solutions.

Broadnax, Samuel L. Blue Skies, Black Wings: African American Pioneers of Aviation. 2008. (ENG., Illus.). 208p. pap. 17.95 *(978-0-8032-1774-4(9),* Bison Bks.) Univ. of Nebraska Pr.

Burnett, Claudine. Soaring Skyward: A History of Aviation in & Around Long Beach, California. 2011. 308p. pap. 29.95 **(978-1-4670-3361-9(8))** AuthorHouse.

Burns, Benjamin J. The Flying Firsts of Walter Hinton: From the 1919 Transatlantic Flight to the Arctic & the Amazon. 2012. (ENG.). 256p. pap. 40.00 **(978-0-7864-6447-0(X))** McFarland & Co., Inc. Pubs.

Caire, Vincent. Louisiana Aviation: An Extraordinary History in Photographs. 2012. (Illus.). 144p. 39.95 **(978-0-8071-4210-3(7))** Louisiana State Univ. Pr.

Cockle, Doug. Manston Memories 1916-2006. 2007. (Illus.). 128p. pap. 24.95 *(978-0-7509-4542-4(7))* Sutton Publishing.

Cook, Lee. The Aces of Fighting 17: VF-17's Top Guns in World War II. 2011. (Illus.). 224p. 69.99 **(978-0-7643-3947-9(8))** Schiffer Publishing, Ltd.

Cooksley, Peter G. The Men Who Changed the World: The Aviation Pioneers, 1903-1914. 2006. (Illus.). 179p. reprint ed. 30.00 *(978-1-4223-5870-2(4))* DIANE Publishing Co.

Cruddas, Colin. In Dorset's Skies. 2006. (Images of Aviation Ser.). (ENG., Illus.). 128p. per. 27.50 *(978-0-7524-1734-9(7))* History Pr. Ltd.,The GBR. Dist: Independent Pubs. Group.

Curnock, David. Book of Flight. 2008. (DVDBook Ser.). (ENG., Illus.). 128p. 17.99 *(978-1-906229-84-9(8),* 1906229848) G2 Entertainment Ltd. GBR. Dist: MBI Distribution Services/Quayside Distribution.

Danelek, J. Allan & Davis, Chuck. Phantoms of the Skies: The Lost History of Aviation from Antiquity to the Wright Brothers. 2011. (ENG., Illus.). 328p. pap. 24.95 **(978-1-935487-38-8(8))** Adventures Unlimited Pr.

Davis, John D. Early Wings over Maine. 2011. (Illus.). vii, 181p. **(978-0-9766564-2-5(6))** Potts Point Bks.

Dick, Ron & Patterson, Dan. 50 Aircraft That Changed the World. 2010. (ENG., Illus.). 208p. pap. 29.95 *(978-1-55407-658-1(7))* Boston Mills Pr. CAN. Dist: Firefly Bks., Ltd.

E. Charles Vivian. A History of Aeronautics. 2007. (ENG.). 384p. pap. 25.99 *(978-1-4264-0064-3(0))*; pap. 26.99 *(978-1-4264-0193-0(0))* BiblioBazaar.

Ellis, Ken. Wrecks & Relics: The Biennial Survey of Preserved, Instructional & Derelict Airframes in the UK & Ireland. 20th rev. ed. 2007. (ENG., Illus.). 320p. 29.95 *(978-1-85780-235-1(7))* Midland Counties Publ.

Engel, Jeffrey A. Cold War at 30,000 Feet: The Anglo-American Fight for Aviation Supremacy. 2007. (Illus.). 384p. 35.00 *(978-0-674-02461-8(3))* Harvard Univ. Pr.

Evans, A. A. & Gibbons, David. The Compact Timeline of Aviation History. 2008. (Illus.). 240p. *(978-1-903025-74-1(5))* Worth Pr. Ltd.

Forney, Joyce Manley, et al, eds. Henry S. Manley (1892-1967) His Life & Writings. 2011. 340p. 33.95 *(978-1-4502-7565-1(6))*; pap. 23.95 *(978-1-4502-7548-4(6))* iUniverse, Inc.

Freudenthal, Elsbeth E. Flight into History: The Wright Brothers & the Air Age. 300p. 2008. 43.95 *(978-1-4367-1464-8(8))* 2007. (ENG.). per. 28.95 *(978-1-4304-8314-4(8))* Kessinger Publishing, LLC.

Gagliardi Kindlimann, Oscar Gregorio. Jorge Chávez Dartnell: Centenario de la Hazaña Del Cruce de Los Alpes (1910 - 2010) 2010. (SPA., Illus.). 171p. *(978-9972-210-89-1(8))* Universidad Alas Peruanas.

Gero, David. Aviation Disasters: The World's Major Civil Airliner Crashes Since 1950. 4th ed. 2006. (ENG., Illus.). 368p. 44.95 *(978-0-7509-3146-5(9))* Sutton Publishing.

Gibbs-Smith, Charles H. Aviation: An Historical Survey from Its Origins to the End of the Second World War. 2nd ed. 2007. (Illus.). 304p. reprint ed. 27.00 *(978-1-4223-6825-1(4))* DIANE Publishing Co.

Goddard, Stephen B. Race to the Sky: The Wright Brothers Versus the United States Government. alt. ed. 2009. (ENG.). 232p. pap. 39.95 *(978-0-7864-4332-1(4))* McFarland & Co., Inc. Pubs.

Grant, R. G. Flight: 100 Years of Aviation. rev. ed. 2007. (ENG., Illus.). 425p. (gr. 4-7). per. 29.95 *(978-0-7566-1902-2(5))* Dorling Kindersley Publishing, Inc.

Greenwood, John T. & Hardesty, Von. Milestones of Aviation. 2007. 320p. *(978-0-88363-530-8(5))* Levin, Hugh Lauter Assocs.

Gross, Malvern. Nine Lives: Adventures of a Lucky Pilot. 2009. (ENG., Illus.). 520p. *(978-0-9760328-4-7(8))* Island In The Sky Publishing Co.

Gross, Malvern J. Nine Lives: Adventures of a Lucky Pilot. 2009. (Illus.). 510p. pap. 19.95 *(978-0-9760328-0-9(5))* Island In The Sky Publishing Co.

Gully, Patti. Sisters of Heaven: China's Barnstorming Aviatrixes: Modernity, Feminism, & Popular Imagination in Asia & the West. 2007. (ENG., Illus.). 448p. per. 24.95 *(978-1-59265-075-0(9))* Long River Pr.

Guttman, Jon. SPAD VII vs Albatros D III: 1917-18. 2011. (Duel Ser.). (ENG., Illus.). 80p. pap. 17.95 *(978-1-84908-475-8(0))* Osprey Publishing, Ltd. GBR. Dist: Random Hse., Inc.

Hagedorn, Dan. Conquistadors of the Sky: A History of Aviation in Latin America. (ENG., Illus.). 2010. 616p. pap. 29.95 *(978-0-8130-3509-3(0))* 2008. 576p. 39.95 *(978-0-8130-3249-8(0))* Univ. Pr. of Florida.

Hart, Arthur A. Wings over Idaho: An Aviation History. 2008. (ENG.). 175p. pap. 22.95 *(978-0-87004-467-0(2))* Caxton Pr.

Holanda, Ray. A History of Aviation Safety: Featuring the U. S. Airline System. 2009. 396p. pap. 19.95 *(978-1-4490-0797-3(X))* AuthorHouse.

Hylander, Clarence J. Cruisers of the Air: The Story of Lighter Than Air Craft from the Days of Roger Bacon to the Making of the ZRS-4. 2011. 334p. 50.95 **(978-1-258-01611-1(7))** Literary Licensing, LLC.

Jackson, Joe. Atlantic Fever: Lindbergh, His Competitors, & the Race to Cross the Atlantic, 1 vol. 2012. (ENG., Illus.). 544p. 30.00 **(978-0-374-10675-1(4))** Farrar, Straus & Giroux.

Kenney, Kimberly A. Canton's Pioneers in Flight. 2008. (ENG., Illus.). 160p. per. 19.99 *(978-0-7385-2522-8(7))* Arcadia Publishing.

Kessner, Thomas. The Flight of the Century: Charles Lindbergh & the Rise of American Aviation, 1 vol. 2010. (Pivotal Moments in American History Ser.). (ENG., Illus.). 432p. 27.95 *(978-0-19-532019-0(0))* Oxford Univ. Pr., Inc.

Kinney, Jeremy R. Airplanes: The Life Story of a Technology. 2008. (ENG., Illus.). 184p. (C). (gr. 13-17). pap. 20.95 *(978-0-8018-9069-7(1))* Johns Hopkins Univ. Pr.

Knight, Clayton. The Story of Flight. 2011. 162p. 41.95 **(978-1-258-10437-5(7))** Literary Licensing, LLC.

Knight, Darrell. Artillery Flyers at War. 2010. 484p. (ENG.). 49.50 *(978-0-557-32964-9(7))*; pap. 32.50 *(978-0-557-32963-2(9))* Lulu Enterprises Inc.

Knight, Max E. Spinning Through Clouds: Tales of an Early Hoosier Aviator. 2007. *(978-0-87195-256-1(4))* Indiana Historical Society.

Lake, Deborah. Growling over the Oceans: Avro Shackleton, the Men & the Missions 1951-1991. 2011. (ENG., Illus.). 304p. 34.95 *(978-0-285-63876-1(9))* Souvenir Pr. Ltd. GBR. Dist: Independent Pubs. Group.

London, Joanne Gernstein. Fly Now! A Colorful Story of Flight from Hot Air Balloon to the 777 Worldliner. 2007. (ENG., Illus.). 192p. 25.00 *(978-1-4262-0088-5(9),* National Geographic) National Geographic Society.

—Fly Now! A Colorful Story of Flight from Hot Air Balloon to the 777 Worldliner -the Poster Collection of the Smithsonian National Air & Space Museum. 2008. (ENG., Illus.). 192p. pap. 15.95 *(978-1-4262-0290-2(3),* National Geographic) National Geographic Society.

Lord, Brigadier Dick. Standby! South African Air Force Search & Rescue. 2010. (Illus.). 352p. pap. 29.95 *(978-1-920143-44-2(0))* 30° South Pubs. ZAF. Dist: International Publishers Marketing.

Lynch, Brendan. Yesterday We Were in America: Alcock & Brown - First to Fly the Atlantic Non-Stop. 2009. (ENG., Illus.). 256p. 39.95 *(978-1-84425-681-5(2),* 1844256812) Haynes Publishing PLC GBR. Dist: MBI Distribution Services/Quayside Distribution.

Mann, Robert A. The B-29 Superfortress: A Comprehensive Registry of the Planes & Their Missions. alt. ed. 2009. (ENG.). 288p. pap. 39.95 *(978-0-7864-4458-8(4))* McFarland & Co., Inc. Pubs.

Mattioli, Marco. 53 Stormo. 2010. (Aviation Elite Units Ser.). (ENG., Illus.). 128p. pap. 25.95 *(978-1-84603-977-5(0))* Osprey Publishing, Ltd. GBR. Dist: Random Hse., Inc.

McGill, Earl J. Jet Age Man: SAC B-47 & B-52 Operations in the Early Cold War. 2011. (Illus.) 288p. 49.95 **(978-1-907677-46-5(1))** Helion & Co., Ltd. GBR. Dist: Casemate Pubs. & Bk. Distributors, LLC.

McGoldrick, James P., 2nd. The Spokane Aviation Story, 1910-1941. 2007. (Illus.). 243p. 29.95 *(978-0-9740881-8-1(8))* Tornado Creek Pubns.

McLachlan, Ian. Flights into History: Final Missions Retold by Research & Archaeology. 2007. (ENG., Illus.). 224p. 36.95 *(978-0-7509-4299-7(1))* Sutton Publishing.

McLelland, Tim. The Victor Story. 2012. (Story Ser.). (ENG., Illus.). 128p. 14.95 **(978-0-7524-6314-8(4))** History Pr. Ltd.,The GBR. Dist: Independent Pubs. Group.

Merlin, Peter W. & Allen, Ned. From Archangel to Senior Crown: Design & Development of the Blackbird. 2008. 165p. *(978-1-56347-933-5(8))* American Institute of Aeronautics & Astronautics.

Millbrooke, Anne. Aviation History. 2nd rev. ed. 2006. (Illus.). 636p. *(978-0-88487-433-1(8))* Jeppesen Sanderson.

Mortimer, Gavin. Chasing Icarus: The Seventeen Days in 1910 That Forever Changed American Aviation. 2010. (ENG., Illus.). 320p. pap. 17.00 *(978-0-8027-1993-5(7))* Walker & Co.

Mowthorpe, Ces. Sky Sailors: The Story of the World's Airshipmen. 2011. (ENG.). 192p. pap. 19.95 *(978-0-7524-5879-3(5))* History Pr. Ltd.,The GBR. Dist: Independent Pubs. Group.

Nevin, David. Pathfinders. (Illus.). 176p. 24.00 *(978-1-84447-032-7(6))* Time Life Value GBR. Dist: Mercury Bks. Ltd.

Niccoli, Riccardo. History of Flight: From the Flying Machine of Leonardo Da Vinci to the Conquest of the Space. 2007. (ENG., Illus.). 320p. 35.00 *(978-88-544-0211-9(7),* White Star) Rizzoli International Pubns., Inc.

Norberg, John. Wings of Their Dreams: Purdue in Flight. 2007. (Illus.). 432p. per. 24.95 *(978-1-55753-489-7(6))* Purdue Univ. Pr.

Perry, William B. Our Pilots in the Air. 2006. (ENG.). pap. *(978-1-84702-445-9(9))* Echo Library.

Pinnegar, Edward. Aviation in Alderney. 2011. (Illus.). 96p. pap. 19.95 *(978-1-84868-981-7(0))* Amberley Publishing GBR. Dist: Casemate Pubs. & Bk. Distributors, LLC.

Poberezny, Paul H., ed. Flying Manual, 1932. (Flying & Gliding Ser.). (Illus.). 75p. reprint ed. pap. 5.95 *(978-0-940000-85-8(7))* EAA Aviation Foundation.

—Flying Manual, 1933. (Flying & Gliding Ser.). (Illus.). 75p. reprint ed. pap. 5.95 *(978-0-940000-86-5(5))* EAA Aviation Foundation.

Prendergast, Curtis. The First Aviators. (Illus.). 176p. 24.00 *(978-1-84447-037-2(7))* Time Life Value GBR. Dist: Mercury Bks. Ltd.

Pyne, Stephen J. Voyager: Exploration, Space, & the Third Great Age of Discovery. 2011. (ENG.). 464p. (gr. 12). 17.00 *(978-0-14-311959-3(1),* Penguin (Non-Classics)) Penguin Group (USA) Inc.

—Voyager: Seeking Newer Worlds in the Third Great Age of Discovery. 2010. (ENG., Illus.). 464p. (gr. 12). 29.95 *(978-0-670-02183-3(0),* Viking Adult) Penguin Group (USA) Inc.

Renga, Alan & Mentges, Mark E. Pacific Southwest Airlines. 2010. (Images of Aviation Ser.). (ENG., Illus.). 128p. pap. 21.99 *(978-0-7385-8112-5(7))* Arcadia Publishing.

Rev. J. M. Bacon. The Dominion of the Air: The Story of Aerial Navigation. 2006. (ENG.). 252p. pap. 21.99 *(978-1-4264-0067-4(5))* BiblioBazaar.

Rinard, Judith E. Book of Flight: The Smithsonian National Air & Space Museum. 2nd ed. 2007. (ENG., Illus.). 128p. (J). (gr. 5-12). 24.95 *(978-1-55407-292-7(1))*; pap. 16.95 *(978-1-55407-275-0(1))* Firefly Bks., Ltd.

Rioni, Al. All Time High: A Pilot's Memoirs. 2007. (Illus.). 300p. per. 15.95 *(978-0-9748065-2-5(8))* Rioni, Al.

—Wings & Things: True Flying Stories. 2007. (Illus.). 305p. per. 15.95 *(978-0-9748065-5-6(2))* Rioni, Al.

Roberts, Michael L. Aircraft Histories of the Ling-Temco-Vought A-7 Corsair II. 2009. (Illus.). 400p. bds. 69.99 *(978-0-7643-3238-8(4))* Schiffer Publishing, Ltd.

Romanowski, David & Keiser, Melissa A. N. The Legacy of Flight: Images from the Archives of the Smithsonian National Air & Space Museum. 12th ed. 2010. 288p. 25.00 *(978-1-59373-083-3(7))* Bunker Hill Publishing, Inc.

Rossiter, Sean. Otter & Twin Otter: The Universal Airplanes, 1 vol. 2010. (ENG., Illus.). 208p. pap. 24.95 *(978-1-55365-494-0(3))* D&M Pubs. Inc. CAN. Dist: Perseus-PGW.

Rowe, Basil. Under My Wings. (Airlines History Project Ser.). reprint ed. 30.00 *(978-0-404-19333-1(1))* AMS Pr., Inc.

Salba, Michael. Aviation. 2009. pap. *(978-1-61584-082-3(6))* Independent Pub.

Scott, Robert & Heppenheimer, T. A. Flight. 2009. (ENG., Illus.). 256p. pap. 24.95 *(978-1-84732-340-8(5))* Carlton Bks., Ltd. GBR. Dist: Sterling Publishing Co., Inc.

Searle, Tex. Golden Years of Flying: As We Remember - Frontier Airlines, 1946-1986. 2008. (ENG.). 300p. pap. 19.95 *(978-1-56027-708-8(4))* Aviation Supplies & Academics, Inc.

Serling, Robert J. Character & Characters: The Spirit of Alaska Airlines. 2008. (ENG.). 528p. (gr. 12). 29.95 *(978-1-933245-11-9(5))* Documentary Media LLC.

Sherman, Janann. Walking on Air: The Aerial Adventures of Phoebe Omlie. 2011. (Willie Morris Books in Memoir & Biography Ser.). (ENG., Illus.). 196p. 30.00 *(978-1-61703-124-3(0))* Univ. Pr. of Mississippi.

Shilliday, Jim. A Memory of Sky: A Pilot's View of Canada's Century of Flight. 2009. (ENG.). 200p. 29.95 *(978-1-894283-95-3(3))* Great Plains Pubns. CAN. Dist: Univ. of Toronto Pr.

Slagley, P. E. (Retired). A Century of Aviation: Worldwide Commercial & Military. 2011. 228p. pap. 18.95 ***(978-1-61204-093-6(4)***, Strategic Bk. Publishing) AEG Literary Publishing Services, Inc.

Smith, Henry L. Airways Abroad: The Story of American World Air Routes. (Airlines History Project Ser.). reprint ed. 40.00 *(978-0-404-19336-2(6))* AMS Pr., Inc.

Thomas, Lowell. Famous First Flights That Changed History: Sixteen Dramatic Adventures. 2008. (ENG.). 340p. pap. 17.00 *(978-1-4223-9451-9(4))* DIANE Publishing Co.

Tise, Larry E. Conquering the Sky: The Secret Flights of the Wright Brothers at Kitty Hawk. 2009. (ENG., Illus.). 256p. 25.00 *(978-0-230-61490-1(6))* Palgrave Macmillan.

Tuttle, Jim. Eject! The Complete History of U. S. Aircraft Escape Systems. 2008. (ENG.). 256p. 30.00 *(978-1-4223-9175-4(2))* DIANE Publishing Co.

Vivian, E. Charles. A History of Aeronautics. 2008. 364p. 31.99 *(978-0-554-21459-7(8))*; 29.99 *(978-0-554-30762-6(6))* BiblioBazaar.

—A History of Aeronautics. 2009. 368p. pap. *(978-1-4099-7253-2(4))* Dodo Pr.

—A History of Aeronautics. 2009. (ENG.). 326p. pap. 20.95 *(978-1-4385-1925-8(7)*, Book Jungle) Standard Pubns., Inc.

Weber. lel International Civil Aviation Organization. 2011. (Illus.). 216p. pap. 103.00 ***(978-90-411-3880-4(3))*** Wolters Kluwer Law & Business.

Weinstein, Michael. On Folded Wings: Paper Airplanes for All Ages. 2012. (ENG.). pap. 16.95 *(978-1-879384-79-8(5))* Cypress Hse.

Wohl, Robert. The Spectacle of Flight: Aviation & the Western Imagination, 1920-1950. 2007. (ENG., Illus.). 376p. per. 22.00 *(978-0-300-12265-7(9))* Yale Univ. Pr.

Woolford, Stephen & Warner, Carl. The Story of Flight: The Development of Aviation Through the Ages. 2009. (ENG., Illus.). 64p. 39.95 *(978-1-84732-459-7(2))* Carlton Bks., Ltd. GBR. Dist: Sterling Publishing Co., Inc.

Wragg, David & Wragg, David W. Historical Dictionary of Aviation: From Earliest Times to Present Day. 2009. (ENG., Illus.). 384p. 44.95 *(978-0-7509-4527-1(3)*, 0750945273) Sutton Publishing.

Wright, Wilbur & Wright, Orville. The Papers of Wilbur & Orville Wright, V1, 1899-1905: Including the Chanute-Wright Letters & Other Papers of Octave Chanute. McFarland, Marvin Wilks, ed. 2011. 810p. 74.95 ***(978-1-258-09933-6(0))*** Literary Licensing, LLC.

—The Papers of Wilbur & Orville Wright, V2, 1906-1948: Including the Chanute-Wright Letters & Other Papers of Octave Chanute. McFarland, Marvin Wilks, ed. 2011. 682p. 69.95 ***(978-1-258-09965-7(9))*** Literary Licensing, LLC.

AERONAUTICS—LAW AND LEGISLATION

see also Space Law

Abeyratne, Ruwantissa. Air Law & Policy. 2007. 644p. per. 39.95 *(978-1-4241-8293-0(X))* PublishAmerica, Inc.

Abeyratne, Ruwantissa. Air Navigation Law. 2012. (ENG.). 288p. 139.00 ***(978-3-642-25834-3(4)***, 3642258344) Springer.

Adlam, J. C., ed. Iran-U. S. Claims Tribunal Reports, Vol. 5. (Iran-U. S. Claims Tribunal Reports Ser.). (ENG.). *(978-0-906496-47-3(0))* Cambridge Univ. Pr.

Airworthiness Directives Large Aircraft, 2000-2001: Federal Aviation Regulations, Bk. 4 pt. 39. 1262p. ring bd. 69.50 *(978-0-16-067477-8(8))* United States Government Printing Office.

Antwerpen, Niels Van. Cross-Border Provision of Air Navigation Services with Specific Reference to Europe: Safeguarding Transparent Lines of Responsibility & Liability. 2008. (Aviation Law & Policy Ser.). (Illus.). 145.00 *(978-90-411-2688-7(0))* Wolters Kluwer Law & Business.

Barrett, Sean. Deregulation & the Airline Business in Europe. 2011. (ENG., Illus.). 208p. (C). pap. 44.95 ***(978-0-415-69649-4(6))*** Routledge.

Diederiks-Verschoor, I. H. Philepina. An Introduction to Air Law. 8th rev. ed. 2006. (Illus.). 345p. *(978-90-411-2458-6(6))* Kluwer Law International.

Doberstein, Dick. Regulations Made Easy for Private Pilots. pap. 8.95 *(978-0-9607866-4-0(3))* Simplified Regulations.

Federal Aviation Administration Staff. Federal Aviation Regulations / Aeronautical Information Manual 2011 (FAR/AIM) 2010. (ENG., Illus.). 896p. pap. 15.95 *(978-1-61608-148-5(1)*, 608148) Skyhorse Publishing Co., Inc.

Fontoh, Niba. Liabilities Generated by Aircraft Lease Contracts. 2011. 176p. pap. ***(978-3-8383-7026-2(0))*** Lambert Academic Publishing.

Goeteyn. EC Competition Law & Its Application in the Aviation Sector. 2011. 198.00 *(978-90-411-3132-4(9))* Wolters Kluwer Law & Business.

Haanappel. Law & Policy of Air, Space & Outer Space, Second Edition Rev. 2nd rev. ed. 2010. 158.00 *(978-90-411-2804-1(2))* Wolters Kluwer Law & Business.

Organisation for Economic Co-operation and Development Staff & Joint Transport Research Centre Staff. Competitive Interaction Between Airports, Airlines & High-Speed Rail. 2009. 208p. pap. 63.00 *(978-92-821-0245-9(9))* Organization for Economic Cooperation & Development.

Schnitker, Ronald & van 't Kaar, Dick. Aviation Accident & Incident Investigation Concurrence of Technical & Judicial Inquiries in the Netherlands. 2010. 228p. 85.00 *(978-94-90947-01-9(6))* Eleven International Publishing NLD. Dist: International Specialized Bk. Services.

Sheth, Jagdish N., et al. Deregulation & Competition: Lessons from the Airline Industry. 2007. (Illus.). 348p. (C). 60.00 *(978-0-7619-3596-4(7)*, B35964C) SAGE Pubns., Inc.

Singh, Karan. Aviation & Environmental Pollution. 2010. 116p. pap. *(978-3-8383-4442-3(1))* Lambert Academic Publishing.

Smith, Lesley Jane & Baumann, Ingo. Contracting for Space: Contract Practice in the European Space Sector. 2011. (Illus.). 456p. 180.00 ***(978-1-4094-1923-5(1))*** Ashgate Publishing Co.

Tompkins, George. New Area of Air Carrier Liability Intl Air Transportation Warsaw. 2010. xxxiii, 432p. *(978-90-411-2646-7(5))* Kluwer Law International.

Unmanned Aircraft Systems Drones & Law. 2011. 268p. pap. ***(978-90-5850-645-0(2))*** Wolf Legal Pubs., W.L.P.

van Schyndel, Heiko. Aviation Code of the Russian Federation. 2010. 192p. 88.00 *(978-90-77596-80-7(1))* Eleven International Publishing NLD. Dist: International Specialized Bk. Services.

AERONAUTICS—LAW AND LEGISLATION—UNITED STATES

Banner, Stuart. Who Owns the Sky? The Struggle to Control Airspace from the Wright Brothers On. 2008. (Illus.). 360p. 29.95 *(978-0-674-03082-4(6))* Harvard Univ. Pr.

Beck, Bettina. Die Regelung slots (von Zeitnischen) im Luftverkehrsrecht: Vergabe, Übertragung und Anfechtung in der Schweiz und der EG unter rechtsvergleichender Berücksichtigung US-amerikanischer Normen. 2008. (Studies in Global Economic Law. Studien zum globalen Wirtschaftsrecht. Etudes en droit économique mondial Ser.). 255p. pap. *(978-3-03911-737-6(8))* Lang, Peter.

Chambers, Joseph & Chambers, Mark. Radical Wings & Wind Tunnels: Advanced Concepts Tested at Nasa Langley. 2008. (Illus.). 160p. 36.95 *(978-1-58007-116-1(3))* Specialty Pr. Pubs. & Wholesalers, Inc.

Cook, LeRoy. Flying the Light Retractables: A Guided Tour Through the Most Popular Complex Single-Engine Airplanes. 2007. (ENG., Illus.). 140p. pap. 19.95 *(978-1-56027-607-4(X))* Aviation Supplies & Academics, Inc.

Eichenberger, Jerry. General Aviation Law 3/E. 3rd ed. 2011. (ENG., Illus.). 288p. pap. 40.00 ***(978-0-07-177181-8(6)***, 0071771816) McGraw-Hill Professional Publishing.

Federal Aviation Administration. Far/amt 2012: Federal Aviation Regulations for Aviation Maintenance Technicians. 2011. (FAR/AIM Ser.). (ENG.). 925p. pap. 24.95 *(978-1-56027-860-3(9))* Aviation Supplies & Academics, Inc.

—Federal Aviation Regulations / Aeronautical Information Manual 2012 (FAR/AIM) 2011. (ENG., Illus.). 960p. pap. 15.95 *(978-1-61608-486-8(3)*, 608486) Skyhorse Publishing Co., Inc.

—Federal Aviation Regulations/Aeronautical Information Manual 2009 (FAR/AIM 2009) 2008. (ENG., Illus.). 948p. pap. 12.95 *(978-1-60239-298-4(6)*, 239298) Skyhorse Publishing Co., Inc.

Federal Aviation Administration (FAA). Far/aim 2012: Federal Aviation Regulations/Aeronautical Information Manual. 2011. (FAR/AIM Ser.). (ENG.). 1090p. pap. 16.95 *(978-1-56027-858-0(7))* Aviation Supplies & Academics, Inc.

—Far/amt 2011: Federal Aviation Regulations for Aviation Maintenance Technicians. 2010. (FAR/AIM Ser.). (ENG.). 896p. pap. 24.95 *(978-1-56027-774-3(2))* Aviation Supplies & Academics, Inc.

—Far/fc 2011: Federal Aviation Regulations for Flight Crew. 2010. (FAR/AIM Ser.). (ENG.). 528p. pap. 16.95 *(978-1-56027-773-6(4))* Aviation Supplies & Academics, Inc.

Goodman, Jon C., ed. Aviation & the Environment. 2008. (Illus.). x, 515p. 95.00 *(978-1-60692-320-7(X))* Nova Science Pubs., Inc.

Hamilton, J. Scott. Practical Aviation Law. 5th ed. 2011. (ENG., Illus.). 352p. 39.95 *(978-1-56027-763-7(7))* Aviation Supplies & Academics, Inc.

—Practical Aviation Law Workbook. 2011. (ENG., Illus.). 86p. pap. 24.95 *(978-1-56027-776-7(9))* Aviation Supplies & Academics, Inc.

Huang, J. Aviation Safety Through the Rule of Law. 2009. (Aviation Law & Policy Ser.). xxi, 256p. 145.00 *(978-90-411-3115-7(9))* Wolters Kluwer Law & Business.

Office of the Federal Register (U.S.), compiled by. Code of Federal Regulations, Title 14, Aeronautics & Space, Pt. 1-59, Revised as of January 1 2011. rev. ed. 2011. (ENG.). 1080p. pap. 69.00 *(978-0-16-087557-1(9)*, Office of the Federal Register) United States Government Printing Office.

—Code of Federal Regulations, Title 14, Aeronautics & Space, Pt. 110-199, Revised as of January 1 2011. rev. ed. 2011. (ENG.). 917p. pap. 35.00 *(978-0-16-087559-5(5)*, Office of the Federal Register) United States Government Printing Office.

—Code of Federal Regulations, Title 14, Aeronautics & Space, Pt. 200-1199, Revised as of January 1 2011. rev. ed. 2011. (ENG., Illus.). 941p. pap. 56.00 *(978-0-16-087560-1(9)*, Office of the Federal Register) United States Government Printing Office.

—Code of Federal Regulations, Title 14, Aeronautics & Space, Pt. 60-109, Revised as of January 1 2011. rev. ed. 2011. (ENG.). 971p. pap. 67.00 *(978-0-16-087558-8(7)*, Office of the Federal Register) United States Government Printing Office.

USGPO Staff. Civil Aeronautics Board (Authority) Annual Report, 10 bks. Date not set. reprint ed. 475.00 *(978-1-57588-480-6(1)*, 201330) Hein, William S. & Co., Inc.

Vacek, Joseph J., et al. Air Law Cases & Materials. rev. ed. 2008. (ENG.). 514p. pap. 44.06 *(978-0-7575-6000-2(8))* Kendall Hunt Publishing Co.

Woodring, Suanne & Woodring, Frank. Fairchild Aircraft. 2007. (Images of Aviation Ser.). (ENG., Illus.). 128p. per. 21.99 *(978-0-7385-4439-7(6))* Arcadia Publishing.

AERONAUTICS—MEDICAL ASPECTS

see Aviation Medicine

AERONAUTICS—NAVIGATION

see Navigation (Aeronautics)

AERONAUTICS—PICTORIAL WORKS

Almond, Peter. Aviation: Die Anfänge der Luftfahrt, 1 vol. 2011. (ENG, FRE & GER.). 349p. 19.99 ***(978-3-8331-6185-8(X))*** h.f.ullmann DEU. Dist: Innovative Logistics.

Almond, Peter. Aviation: The Early Years/Di Engange der Luftfahrt/les Premieres Annees de L'Aeronautique. 2008. (Transportation: the Early Years Ser.). (Illus.). 349p. 49.95 *(978-0-8416-0278-6(6))* American Map Corp.

Army Air Forces Training Command. Wings for Combat: The Story of the Training of an Air Force. 2011. 82p. 37.95 ***(978-1-258-06001-5(9))*** Literary Licensing, LLC.

Baca, Paul. T-28 Trojan; Oil, Smoke, & Noise. 2009. 109p. pap. 46.70 *(978-0-557-17092-0(3))* Lulu Enterprises Inc.

Berliner, Don. The Paris Air Show. 2006. (Illus.). 68p. reprint ed. pap. 25.00 *(978-1-4223-5692-0(2))* DIANE Publishing Co.

Caire, Vincent. Louisiana Aviation: An Extraordinary History in Photographs. 2012. (Illus.). 144p. 39.95 ***(978-0-8071-4210-3(7))*** Louisiana State Univ. Pr.

Causey, Gregory, ed. Denizens of the Desert: AMARC Photographs by Danny Causey. 2008. 124p. pap. 28.99 *(978-1-934446-15-7(7))* Romance Divine LLC.

Christopher, John. Tornado Story. 2009. (Story Ser.). (ENG., Illus.). 128p. 16.95 *(978-0-7524-5085-8(9))* History Pr. Ltd.,The GBR. Dist: Independent Pubs. Group.

—The Zeppelin Story. 2011. (Story Ser.). (ENG., Illus.). 128p. 15.95 *(978-0-7524-5175-6(8))* History Pr. Ltd.,The GBR. Dist: Independent Pubs. Group.

Coopman, David T. Quad City International Airport. 2011. (Images of Aviation Ser.). (Illus.). 128p. pap. 21.99 *(978-0-7385-8371-6(5))* Arcadia Publishing.

Coulson. A Proud Heritage. (Illus.). 96p. pap. 24.99 *(978-1-899808-10-6(8))* Royal Air Force Benevolent Fund Enterprises GBR. Dist: Trafalgar Square Publishing.

Davis, Larry, et al. P/F-80 Shooting Star. 2008. (Illus.). 51p. ***(978-0-89747-557-0(7))*** Squadron Signal Pubns.

Derry, Martin. Britain's Military Aircraft in Colour 1960-1970. 2010. 96p. pap. *(978-0-9554268-2-7(0))* Flight Recorder Pubns. Ltd.

Fisher, Scott M. Eastern Iowa's Aviation Heritage. 2011. (Images of Aviation Ser.). (Illus.). 128p. pap. 21.99 *(978-0-7385-8330-3(8))* Arcadia Publishing.

Forsyth, Robert & Creek, Eddie J. Heinkel He162 Volksjäger: From Drawing Board to Destruction - The Volksjäger Spatz. 2009. (ENG., Illus.). 208p. 64.95 *(978-1-906537-00-5(3))* Allan, Ian Publishing GBR. Dist: BookMasters Distribution Services (BDS).

Goodall, Jim. Nimitz Class Aircraft Carriers. 2009. (Illus.). 80p. pap. ***(978-0-89747-605-8(0))*** Squadron Signal Pubns.

Harold A. Skaarup. Canadian Warplanes. 2009. 640p. pap. 49.95 *(978-1-4401-6758-4(3))* iUniverse, Inc.

Havers, Richard. Classic Aircraft: Civilian Aviation from 1906 until the Present Day. 2010. (ENG., Illus.). 128p. 14.95 *(978-1-84425-707-2(X)*, 184425707X) Haynes Publishing PLC GBR. Dist: MBI Distribution Services/Quayside Distribution.

Hildebrandt, Erik. Front Row Center 3: Inside the Great American Air Show. 2007. (ENG., Illus.). 160p. 39.95 *(978-0-9674040-6-6(1)*, 0967404061) Cleared Hot Media.

Hoeveler, Patrick & Krämer, Adel. Desert Boneyards: Retired Aircraft Storage Facilities n the U. S. 2010. (Illus.). 160p. 45.00 *(978-0-7643-3662-1(2))* Schiffer Publishing, Ltd.

Holden, Henry M. Teterboro Airport. 2010. (Images of Aviation Ser.). (Illus.). 128p. pap. 21.99 *(978-0-7385-7217-8(9))* Arcadia Publishing.

Holden, Henry M. & Large, Darren S. Morristown Municipal Airport. 2010. (Images of Aviation Ser.). (Illus.). 128p. pap. 21.99 *(978-0-7385-7360-1(4))* Arcadia Publishing.

Humphreys, Roy, ed. Kent Aviation: A Century of Flight. 2009. (ENG., Illus.). 192p. pap. 29.95 *(978-0-7524-5121-3(9))* History Pr. Ltd.,The GBR. Dist: Independent Pubs. Group.

Jendsch, Wolfgang. Aerial Firefighting. 2008. (Illus.). 352p. bds. 49.99 *(978-0-7643-3068-1(3))* Schiffer Publishing, Ltd.

Jenkins, Dennis R., compiled by. U. S. Air Force Aviation, Vol. 1. 2007. (ENG., Illus.). 120p. pap. 19.95 *(978-1-58007-113-0(9))* Specialty Pr. Pubs. & Wholesalers, Inc.

—U. S. Naval Aviation Vol. 1: A Military Photo Logbook. 2007. (ENG., Illus.). 120p. pap. 19.95 *(978-1-58007-114-7(7))* Specialty Pr. Pubs. & Wholesalers, Inc.

Kraemer, Norma J. South Dakota's First Century of Flight. 2010. (Images of Aviation Ser.). (ENG., Illus.). 128p. pap. 21.99 *(978-0-7385-8425-6(8))* Arcadia Publishing.

Leek, Michael. Military Low-Flying Aircraft. 2011. (Illus.). 272p. 50.00 ***(978-1-84884-223-6(6))*** Pen & Sword Bks. Ltd. GBR. Dist: Casemate Pubs. & Bk. Distributors, LLC.

London, Joanne Gernstein. Fly Now! A Colorful Story of Flight from Hot Air Balloon to the 777 Worldliner. 2007. (ENG., Illus.). 192p. 25.00 *(978-1-4262-0088-5(9)*, National Geographic) National Geographic Society.

—Fly Now! A Colorful Story of Flight from Hot Air Balloon to the 777 Worldliner -the Poster Collection of the Smithsonian National Air & Space Museum. 2008. (ENG., Illus.). 192p. pap. 15.95 *(978-1-4262-0290-2(3)*, National Geographic) National Geographic Society.

Mandle, Robert H. Crystal Flight: A Celebration of Art & Air. 2008. (Illus.). 79p. pap. 15.00 *(978-1-933197-59-3(5))* Orange Frazer Pr.

Manning, Gerry. Military Aircraft of the 1970s. 2010. (ENG., Illus.). 144p. pap. 36.95 *(978-1-85780-263-4(2))* Allan, Ian Publishing GBR. Dist: BookMasters Distribution Services (BDS).

March, Peter R. The Spitfire Story DVD & Book Pack. 2011. (Story Ser.). (ENG.). 128p. incl. DVD *(978-0-7524-5723-9(3))* History Pr. Ltd.,The GBR. Dist: Independent Pubs. Group.

Martins, Edgar. When Light Casts No Shadow. 2010. (ENG., Illus.). 88p. 50.00 ***(978-1-904587-81-1(X))*** Lewis, Dewi Publishing GBR. Dist: Consortium Bk. Sales & Distribution.

Masser, Barry. The Combat Aircraft Picture Book. 2007. pap. 24.95 net. *(978-1-60402-118-9(7))* Independent Pub.

McLelland, Tim. Harrier. 2011. (ENG., Illus.). 337p. 74.95 *(978-1-906537-20-3(8))* Allan, Ian Publishing GBR. Dist: BookMasters Distribution Services (BDS).

Messersmith, Dan W. Kingman. 2010. (Images of America Ser.). (Illus.). 128p. pap. 21.99 *(978-0-7385-7930-6(0))* Arcadia Publishing.

Milstein, Jeffrey. Aircraft: The Jet As Art. 2007. (ENG., Illus.). 104p. 32.50 *(978-0-8109-9285-6(X))* Abrams.

Musgrave, Story, et al. The Nasa Northrop T-38: Photographic Art from an Astronaut Pilot. 2009. 264p. 49.95 *(978-0-9751873-2-6(5))* Lannistoria AUS. Dist: AtlasBooks Distribution.

National Air and Space Museum Staff. In the Cockpit II: Inside History-Making Aircraft of World War II. 2010. (Illus.). 144p. 26.99 *(978-0-06-168434-0(1)*, Collins Design) HarperCollins Pubs.

Nicolai, Leland M. & Carichner, Grant. Fundamentals of Aircraft & Airship Design. 2010. (Illus.). xxii, 883p. 119.95 *(978-1-60086-751-4(0))* American Institute of Aeronautics & Astronautics.

Parkstone Press Staff. Airport. 2012. (Our Earth Ser.). (ENG., Illus.). 192p. 24.95 *(978-1-84484-861-4(2))* Parkstone Pr. USA, Ltd.

Pelletier, Alain J. Boeing: The Complete Story. 2010. (ENG., Illus.). 256p. 44.95 *(978-1-84425-703-4(7)*, 1844257037) Haynes Publishing PLC GBR. Dist: MBI Distribution Services/Quayside Distribution.

Porcelli, Richard V. Naval Air Station Atlantic City. 2012. (Images of Aviation Ser.). (ENG., Illus.). 128p. pap. 21.99 ***(978-0-7385-7670-1(0))*** Arcadia Publishing.

Press, Ammonite, ed. 100 Years of Aviation. 2010. (ENG., Illus.). 300p. pap. 19.95 *(978-1-906672-54-6(7)*, Ammonite Pr.) AE Pubns. GBR. Dist: BookMasters Distribution Services (BDS).

Pulford, John & Winn, Allan. 100 Years of Brooklands: The Birthplace of British Motorsport & Aviation. Temple, Julian, ed. 2007. (ENG., Illus.). 192p. 45.00 *(978-0-9551020-6-6(5))* Touchstone Bks. Ltd. GBR. Dist: Independent Pubs. Group.

Robertson, Scott. Lift Off: Air Vehicle Sketches & Renderings from the Drawthrough Collection. 2006. (ENG., Illus.). 143p. pap. 29.95 *(978-1-933492-15-5(5))* Design Studio Pr.

Rockwell, allen@allenrockwellphoto. com Allen. The Aircraft of Red Flag 08-3. 2008. 52p. pap. 25.95 *(978-1-4357-5650-2(9))* Lulu Enterprises Inc.

—The Aircraft of Red Flag 08-4. 2008. 86p. pap. 34.95 *(978-1-4357-6053-0(0))* Lulu Enterprises Inc.

—The Aviation Photography of Allen Rockwell - Volume 1. 2008. 44p. pap. 24.95 *(978-1-4357-4970-2(7))* Lulu Enterprises Inc.

Romanowski, David & Keiser, Melissa A. N. The Legacy of Flight: Images from the Archives of the Smithsonian National Air & Space Museum. 12th ed. 2010. 288p. 25.00 *(978-1-59373-083-3(7))* Bunker Hill Publishing, Inc.

Russo, Carolyn, photos by. In Plane View: Abstractions of Flight. 2007. (ENG., Illus.). 144p. 39.95 *(978-1-57687-405-9(2))* powerHouse Cultural Entertainment, Inc.

Singleton, Billy J. Montgomery Aviation. 2007. (Images of Aviation Ser.). (ENG., Illus.). 128p. per. 21.99 *(978-0-7385-5259-0(3))* Arcadia Publishing.

Stapfer, Hans-Heiri & Tullis, Tom. Me 262 in Action. 2008. (Illus.). 51p. *(978-0-89747-554-9(2))* Squadron Signal Pubns.

Tony, Landis. Lockheed Blackbird Family: A-12, YF-12, D-21/M-21 & SR-71 Photo Scrapbook. 2010. 128p. pap. 26.95 *(978-1-58007-151-2(1))* Specialty Pr. Pubs. & Wholesalers, Inc.

Windle, Dave & Bowman, Martin. Profiles of Flight: Panavia Tornado: Strike, Anti-ship, Air Superiority, Air Defence, Reconnaissance & Electronic Warfare Fighter-bomber. 2010. (Illus.). 80p. 39.95 *(978-1-84884-235-9(X))* Pen & Sword Bks. Ltd. GBR. Dist: Casemate Pubs. & Bk. Distributors, LLC.

Yenne, Bill. The American Aircraft Factory in World War II. 2010. (ENG., Illus.). 192p. pap. 24.99 *(978-0-7603-3913-8(9)*, 0760339139, Zenith Pr.) MBI Publishing Co. LLC.

AERONAUTICS—PSYCHOLOGY

see Aviation Psychology

AERONAUTICS—RESEARCH

Arrighi, Robert S. Revolutionary Atmosphere: the Story of the Altitude Wind Tunnel & the Space Power Chambers: The Story of the Altitude Wind Tunnel & the Space Power Chambers. National Aeronautics and Space Administration, ed. 2010. (ENG., Illus.). 410p. 44.00 *(978-0-16-085641-9(8)*, U. S. National Aeronautics & Space Administration) United States Government Printing Office.

Bowles, Mark D. The Apollo of Aeronautics: NASA's Aircraft Energy Efficiency Program, 1973-1987: NASA's Aircraft Energy Efficiency Program, 1973-1987. National Aeronautics and Space Administration, ed. 2010. (ENG., Illus.). 201p. 24.00 *(978-0-16-084295-5(6)*, U. S. National Aeronautics & Space Administration) United States Government Printing Office.

Chambers, Joseph & Chambers, Mark. Radical Wings & Wind Tunnels: Advanced Concepts Tested at Nasa Langley. 2008. (Illus.). 160p. 36.95 *(978-1-58007-116-1(3))* Specialty Pr. Pubs. & Wholesalers, Inc.

Chambers, Joseph R. Modeling Flight: the Role of Dynamically Scaled Free-Flight Models in Support of NASA's Aerospace Programs: The Role of Dynamically Scaled Free-Flight Models in Support of NASA's Aerospace Programs. National Aeronautics and Space Administration, ed. 2010. (ENG., Illus.). 200p. pap. 35.00 *(978-0-16-084633-5(1)*, U. S. National Aeronautics & Space Administration) United States Government Printing Office.

Chambers, Mark A. Flight Research at NASA Langley Research Center. 2007. (Images of Aviation Ser.). (ENG., Illus.). 128p. per. 19.99 *(978-0-7385-4437-3(X))* Arcadia Publishing.

Committee for the Assessment of NASA's Aeronautics Research Program & National Research Council. NASA Aeronautics Research: An Assessment. 2008. (ENG.). 122p. pap. 31.75 *(978-0-309-11913-9(8))* National Academies Pr.

Committee on the Assessment of NASA Laboratory Capabilities & National Research Council. Capabilities for the Future: An Assessment of NASA Laboratories for Basic Research. 2010. (ENG., Illus.). 112p. pap. 29.75 *(978-0-309-15351-5(4))* National Academies Pr.

Committee to Review the NASA Institute for Advanced Concepts & National Research Council Staff. Fostering Visions for the Future: A Review of the NASA Institute for Advanced Concepts. 2009. (ENG.). 90p. pap. 21.00 *(978-0-309-14051-5(X))* National Academies Pr.

Darling, Kev. American X & Y Planes: Volume 1: Experimental Aircraft To 1945, 1 vol. 2010. (ENG., Illus.). 176p. 34.95 *(978-1-84797-141-8(5)*, 1847971415) Crowood Pr., Ltd. GBR. Dist: MBI Distribution Services/Quayside Distribution.

—American X & Y Planes Vol. 2: Experimental Aircraft since 1945, 2 vols. 2010. (ENG., Illus.). 176p. 34.95 *(978-1-84797-147-0(4)*, 1847971474) Crowood Pr., Ltd. GBR. Dist: MBI Distribution Services/Quayside Distribution.

Eickhoff, Jens. Simulating Spacecraft Systems. 2009. (Springer Aerospace Technology Ser.). (ENG., Illus.). xxii, 353p. 129.00 *(978-3-642-01275-4(2)*, 3642012752) Springer.

Elias, Bart, et al. Mathematics, Game Theory & Algebra Compendium, Vol. 1. Mathias, Jacob, ed. 2008. 95.00 *(978-1-60456-659-8(0))* Nova Science Pubs., Inc.

The Federal Aviation Administration's R & D Budget Priorities for Fiscal Year 2008: Hearing Before the Subcommittee on Space & Aeronautics, Committee on Science & Technology, House of Representatives, One Hundred Tenth Congress, First Session, March 22, 2007. 2007. (Illus.). iv, 74p. *(978-0-16-079025-6(5)*, 552-070-36135-9) United States Government Printing Office.

Hallion, Richard. NASA's Contributions to Aeronautics, 2 vols. 2010. (Illus.). *(978-0-16-084636-6(6))*; *(978-0-16-084635-9(8))* National Aeronautics & Space Administration Scientific & Technical Information Facility.

Hallion, Richard P. & Gorn, Michael H. On the Frontier: Experimental Flight at NASA Dryden. 2010. (ENG., Illus.). 584p. pap. 39.95 *(978-1-58834-289-8(1))* Smithsonian Institution Pr.

Hanle, Donald. Near Miss: The Army Air Forces' Guided Bomb Program in World War II. 2007. (ENG., Illus.). 368p. per. 76.00 *(978-0-8108-5776-6(6))* Scarecrow Pr., Inc.

IEEE Staff. 2007 22nd International Congress on Instrumentation in Aerospace Simulation Facilities. 2007. pap. 206.00 *(978-1-4244-1599-1(3))* IEEE.

Kellerer, Johannes. Panoramic Displays: Untersuchung zur Auswahl von Eingabeelementen für Großflächendisplays in Flugzeugcockpits. 2011. 212p. pap. ***(978-3-8381-1920-5(7))*** Südwestdeutscher Verlag für Hochschulschriften AG & Co. KG.

Kuchemann, D. Progress in Aerospace Sciences (Incorporating Progress in Astronautical Sciences), Vol. 8. pap. Franklin Bk. Co., Inc.

Marrett, George J. Contrails over the Mojave: The Golden Age of Jet Flight Testing at Edwards Air Force Base. 2008. (Illus.). 230p. 29.95 *(978-1-59114-511-0(2))* Naval Institute Pr.

Peebles, Curtis. Road to Mach 10: Lessons Learned from the X-43A Flight Research Program. Allen, Ned, ed. 2008. (Illus.). 238p. pap. 39.95 incl. cd-rom *(978-1-56347-932-8(X))* American Institute of Aeronautics & Astronautics.

A Review of the Federal Aviation Administration's Research & Development Program: Hearing Before the Subcommittee on Space & Aeronautics, Committee on Science, Space, & Technology, House of Representatives, One Hundred Twelfth Congress, First Session, February 16, 2011. 2011. (Illus.). iii, 67p. ***(978-0-16-088764-2(X)***, 552-070-42904-2) United States Government Printing Office.

Science Opportunities Enabled by NASA's Constellation System Committee & National Research Council. Science Opportunities Enabled by NASA's Constellation System: Interim Report. 2008. (ENG.). 70p. pap. 21.00 *(978-0-309-12010-4(1))* National Academies Pr.

Seenith, ed. Mathematical Problems in Engineering & Aerospace Sciences; Proceedings: Int'l Conference on Mathematical Problems in Engineering & Aerospace Sciences (6th: 2006: Budapest, Hungary) 2007. 853p. pap. *(978-1-904868-56-9(8))* Cambridge Scientific Pubs. Ltd.

Silva, Edmar Thomaz Da & Gonzaga Trabasso, Luís. Flight Test Campaigns Management. 2010. 108p. pap. *(978-3-8383-7105-4(4))* Lambert Academic Publishing.

Spenser, Jay. The Airplane: How Ideas Gave Us Wings. 2009. (ENG.). 320p. pap. 14.99 *(978-0-06-125920-3(9)*, HarperPerennial) HarperCollins Pubs.

Wright, Wilbur, et al. A History of Early Aviation. 2009. 168p. pap. 12.99 *(978-1-934941-56-0(5))* Red & Black Pubs.

AERONAUTICS—SAFETY MEASURES

see also Air Traffic Control; Airplanes—Ice Prevention; Pressure Suits; Radar in Aeronautics

Abbott, Ace. The Rogue Aviator: In the Back Alleys of Aviation. 2009. 188p. 26.95 *(978-1-4401-5663-2(8))*; pap. 16.95 *(978-1-4401-5664-9(6))* iUniverse, Inc.

Ahmed, Rashid. Bird Hazard in Aviation. 2009. 64p. pap. 12.99 *(978-1-4490-3334-7(2))* AuthorHouse.

American Society of Mechanical Engineers Staff, ed. Aircraft Health & Usage Monitoring Systems. (Illus.). 90p. 68.00 *(978-1-86058-043-7(2))* Professional Engineering Publishing GBR. Dist: SAE Intl.

Auvinen, Petra. Achievement of Intersubjectivity in Airline Cockpit Interaction. 2009. (Acta Universitatis Tamperensis Ser.). 191p. pap. 82.50 *(978-951-44-7879-6(7))* Tampere Univ. Pr. FIN. Dist: Coronet Bks.

Aviation Safety: Can NASA Do More to Protect the Public?: Hearings Before the Committee on Science & Technology, House of Representatives, One Hundred Tenth Congress, First Session, October 31, 2007. 2008. (Illus.). v, 404p. *(978-0-16-081270-5(4)*, 552-070-37662-3) United States Government Printing Office.

Aviation Safety: FAA Generally Agrees With but Is Slow in Implementing Safety Recommendations. 59p. pap. 30.00 *(978-0-7881-4058-7(2))* DIANE Publishing Co.

Aviation Safety: Pilot Fatigue: Hearing Before the Subcommittee on Aviation Operations, Safety, & Security of the Committee on Commerce, Science, & Transportation, United States Senate, One Hundred Eleventh Congress, First Session, December 1, 2009. 2010. (Illus.). iii, 49p. *(978-0-16-086182-6(9)*, 552-070-41280-8) United States Government Printing Office.

Aviation Security Research & Development at the Department of Homeland Security: Hearing Before the Subcommittee on Technology & Innovation, Committee on Science & Technology, House of Representatives, One Hundred Tenth Congress, Second Session, April 24, 2008. 2008. (Illus.). iv, 58p. *(978-0-16-081382-5(4)*, 552-070-37760-3) United States Government Printing Office.

Ayres, Manuel, Jr. Improved Models for Risk Assessment of Runway Safety Areas. 2011. (Illus.). pap. ***(978-0-309-21321-9(5))*** Transportation Research Board.

Barsotti, Matthew A., et al. Developing Improved Civil Aircraft Arresting Systems. 2009. (Illus.). 196p. pap. ***(978-0-309-11813-2(1))*** Transportation Research Board.

Civil Aviation Medical Institute Staff. Pilot Medical Handbook: Human Factors for Successful Flying. 2009. (ENG., Illus.). 100p. pap. 16.95 *(978-1-56027-717-0(3))* Aviation Supplies & Academics, Inc.

Committee on NASA's National Aviation Operations Monitoring Service (NAOMS) Project: An Independent Assessment & National Research Council. An Assessment of NASA's National Aviation Operations Monitoring Service. 2009. (ENG.). 160p. pap. 37.75 *(978-0-309-14646-3(1))* National Academies Pr.

Critical Lapses in Federal Aviation Administration Safety Oversight of Airlines: Abuses of Regulatory "Partnership Programs": Hearing Before the Committee on Transportation & Infrastructure, House of Representatives, One Hundred Tenth Congress, Second Session, April 3, 2008. 2008. (Illus.). xxi, 720p. *(978-0-16-083250-5(0)*, 552-070-39078-2) United States Government Printing Office.

Crittenden, Phyllis. Aviation Ground Operation Safety Handbook. 6th ed. 2007. *(978-0-87912-266-9(8))* National Safety Council.

Dalamagkidis, Konstantinos, et al. On Integrating Unmanned Aircraft Systems into the National Airspace System: Issues, Challenges, Operational Restrictions, Certification, & Recommendations. (Intelligent Systems, Control & Automation: Science & Engineering Ser.). (ENG.). 2010. xx, 200p. pap. 89.95 *(978-90-481-7948-0(3)*, 9048179483) 2nd ed. 2011. (Illus.). xx, 305p. 179.00 ***(978-94-007-2478-5(0)***, 9400724780) Springer.

D'Avirro, John & Chaput, Michael D. Optimizing the Use of Aircraft Deicing & Anti-Icing Fluids. 2011. (Illus.). 92p. ***(978-0-309-15551-9(7))*** Transportation Research Board.

Dillingham, Gerald L. Commercial Aviation: Potential Safety & Capacity Issues Associated with the Introduction of the New A380 Aircraft. 2007. (Illus.). 69p. (C). pap. 20.00 *(978-1-4223-1583-5(5))* DIANE Publishing Co.

FAA Reauthorization: Hearing Before the Committee on Commerce, Science, & Transportation, United States Senate, One Hundred Eighth Congress, First Session, April 10, 2003. 2010. (Illus.). iii, 74p. ***(978-0-16-086792-7(4)***, 552-070-41708-7) United States Government Printing Office.

Federal Aviation Administration Reauthorization ACT of 2009: Hearing Before the Subcommittee on Aviation of the Committee on Transportation & Infrastructure, House of Representatives, One Hundred Eleventh Congress, First Session, February 11, 2009. 2009. (Illus.). xxii, 598p. *(978-0-16-084367-9(7)*, 552-070-39910-1) United States Government Printing Office.

The Federal Aviation Administration's Call to Action on Airline Safety & Pilot Training: Hearing Before the Subcommittee on Aviation of the Committee on Transportation & Infrastructure, House of Representatives, One Hundred Eleventh Congress, First Session, September 23, 2009. 2009. xviii, 192p. *(978-0-16-085163-6(7)*, 552-070-40517-8) United States Government Printing Office.

The Federal Aviation Administration's R & D Budget Priorities for Fiscal Year 2008: Hearing Before the Subcommittee on Space & Aeronautics, Committee on Science & Technology, House of Representatives, One Hundred Tenth Congress, First Session, March 22, 2007. 2007. (Illus.). iv, 74p. *(978-0-16-079025-6(5)*, 552-070-36135-9) United States Government Printing Office.

Firman, Dorothy & Quirk, Kevin. Brace for Impact: Miracle on the Hudson Survivors Share Their Stories of near Death & Hope for New Life. 2010. (ENG.). 288p. pap. 14.95 *(978-0-7573-1357-8(4))* Health Communications, Inc.

Fisher, David. The Leading Edge of Safety: The Story of Safe Flight Instrument Corporation. 2008. (Illus.). 136p. ***(978-0-944641-73-6(3))*** Greenwich Publishing Group, Inc.

Flight Safety Foundation Staff, compiled by. 18th Annual European Aviation Safety Seminar (EASS 2006) Safety Means Participating. 2007. 688p. pap. 132.00 *(978-1-60423-384-1(2))* Curran Assocs., Inc.

—52nd Annual Corporate Aviation Safety Seminar (CASS 2007) The Foundation for Excellence. 2007. 747p. pap. 132.00 *(978-1-60423-385-8(0))* Curran Assocs., Inc.

—59th Annual International Air Safety Seminar & IFA 36th International Conference 2006: Enhancing Safety Worldwide. 2007. 1452p. pap. 125.00 *(978-1-60423-393-3(1))* Curran Assocs., Inc.

Foyle, David C. & Hooey, Becky L., eds. Human Performance Modeling in Aviation. 2007. (ENG., Illus.). 392p. 82.95 *(978-0-8058-5964-5(0)*, CRC Press) Taylor & Francis Group GBR. Dist: Taylor & Francis Group.

General Aviation Security: Assessing Risks & the Road Ahead: Hearing Before the Subcommittee on Transportation Security & Infrastructure Protection of the Committee on Homeland Security, House of Representatives, One Hundred Eleventh Congress, First Session, July 15, 2009. 2009. iv, 81p. *(978-0-16-084857-5(1)*, 552-070-40258-6) United States Government Printing Office.

Gero, David. Aviation Disasters: The World's Major Civil Airliner Crashes Since 1950. 4th ed. 2006. (ENG., Illus.). 368p. 44.95 *(978-0-7509-3146-5(9))* Sutton Publishing.

Government Printing Office Staff. Flying Safety. pap. 50.00 *(978-0-16-010208-0(1))* United States Government Printing Office.

Hall, Jim, et al. Analysis of Aircraft Overruns & Undershoots for Runway Safety Areas. 2008. (Illus.). 58p. 40.00 *(978-0-309-09939-4(0))* Transportation Research Board.

Harris, Don. Human Performance on the Flight Deck. 2011. (Illus.). 384p. 144.95 ***(978-1-4094-2339-3(5))***; pap. 69.95 ***(978-1-4094-2338-6(7))*** Ashgate Publishing Co.

Holanda, Ray. A History of Aviation Safety: Featuring the U. S. Airline System. 2009. 396p. pap. 19.95 *(978-1-4490-0797-3(X))* AuthorHouse.

Internet Spyware (I-SPY) Prevention ACT of 2007, & the Securing Aircraft Cockpits Against Lasers ACT of 2007: Hearing Before the Subcommittee on Crime, Terrorism, & Homeland Security of the Committee on the Judiciary, House of Representatives, One Hundred Tenth Congress, First Session, on H.R. 1525 & H.R. 1615, May 1, 2007. 2008. iii, 32p. *(978-0-16-081704-5(8)*, 552-070-37928-2) United States Government Printing Office.

Jamie N. Wright. Air Traffic Safety & Control Issues. 2011. (Series: Transportation Infrastructure - Roads, Highways, Bridges, Airports & Mass Transit Ser.). (Illus.). viii, 213p. 115.00 *(978-1-61761-937-3(X))* Nova Science Pubs., Inc.

Jenkins, Brian & Wilkinson, Paul, eds. Aviation Terrorism & Security. 2nd rev. ed. 2007. 202p. 130.00 *(978-0-7146-5288-7(1)*, RU33273) Routledge.

Kearns, Suzanne. E-Learning in Aviation. 2010. (Ashgate Studies in Human Factors for Flight Operations Ser.). (Illus.). 194p. 99.95 *(978-0-7546-7879-3(2))* Ashgate Publishing Co.

Kritzinger, Duane. Aircraft System Safety: Military & Civil Aeronautical Applications. 2006. (ENG., Illus.). 350p. 259.95 *(978-0-8493-9012-8(5)*, CRC Press) Taylor & Francis Group GBR. Dist: Taylor & Francis Group.

Lechevin, Nicolas & Rabbath, Camille Alain. Safety & Reliability in Cooperating Unmanned Aerial Systems. 2010. (Illus.). 236p. 85.00 *(978-981-283-699-1(3))* World Scientific Publishing Co., Inc.

Lockett, Brian. Flying Aircraft Carriers of the USAF: Mcdonnell XF-85 Goblin. 2009. 52p. pap. 16.95 *(978-0-578-03481-2(6))* Lockett, Brian.

Lowery, John. Professional Pilot: Proven Tactics & PIC Strategies. 3rd ed. 2008. (ENG.). 350p. pap. 34.95 *(978-1-56027-709-5(2))* Aviation Supplies & Academics, Inc.

Ludwig, Duane A. Safety Management Systems for Airports. 2007. (ACRP Report Ser.: Vol. 1). (Illus.). 30p. 32.00 *(978-0-309-09896-0(3))*; ***(978-0-309-11798-2(4))*** Transportation Research Board.

Lupoli, Luis. Organizational Accidents in an Air Force: Brazilian Squadron Commanders' Perceptions. 2008. 168p. pap. *(978-3-8364-8349-0(1))* VDM Verlag Dr. Mueller e.K.

Lutz, Michael C., ed. Aviation Safety. 2010. 137.00 *(978-1-61761-431-6(9))* Nova Science Pubs., Inc.

Mensen, Heinrich. Moderne Flugsicherung: Organisation, Verfahren, Technik. 3rd ed. 2006. (VDI-Buch Ser.). (Illus.). XXXII, 466p. 69.95 *(978-3-540-20581-4(0)*, 3540205810) Springer.

Motevalli, Vahid, et al. Evaluation & Mitigation of Aircraft Slide Evacuation Injuries. 2008. (ACRP Report Ser.: Vol. 2). (Illus.). 77p. pap. 47.00 *(978-0-309-09933-2(1))* Transportation Research Board.

National Research Council (U.S.), Committee for the Review of NASA's Aviation Safety-Related Programs Staff, et al, contrib. by. Advancing Aeronautical Safety: A Review of NASA's Aviation Safety-Related Research Programs. 2010. (Illus.). xii, 76p. pap. ***(978-0-309-15793-3(5))*** National Academies Pr.

National Research Council (U.S.), Committee on the Effects of Commuting on Pilot Fatigue Staff, et al, contrib. by. Issues in Commuting & Pilot Fatigue: Interim Report. 2011. ix, 29p. ***(978-0-309-18712-1(5))*** National Academies Pr.

Oversight of Helicopter Medical Services: Hearing Before the Subcommittee on Aviation of the Committee on Transportation & Infrastructure, House of Representatives, One Hundred Eleventh Congress, First Session, April 22, 2009. 2009. (Illus.). xxi, 319p. *(978-0-16-084363-1(4)*, 552-070-39906-2) United States Government Printing Office.

Patankar, Manoj S., et al. Safety Culture: Building & Sustaining a Cultural Change in Aviation & Healthcare. 2011. (Illus.). 250p. 99.95 ***(978-0-7546-7237-1(9))*** Ashgate Publishing Co.

A Pilot's Guide to Safety: How to Avoid Moments of Stark Terror. 2006. per. 17.00 net. *(978-0-934754-13-2(6))* Airguide Pubns., Inc.

Prabhu, Ghanashyam. Study of Headpaths & Hic Data for Aircraft Seat & Cabin Certification. 2010. 80p. pap. *(978-3-8383-5557-3(1))* Lambert Academic Publishing.

Rasson, Jean L. & Delipetrov, Todor, eds. Geomagnetics for Aeronautical Safety: A Case Study in & around the Balkans. 2006. (NATO Science for Peace & Security Series / NATO Science for Peace & Security Series C: Environmental Security Ser.). (Illus.). vii, 363p. 249.00 *(978-1-4020-5023-7(2)*, 1402050232) Springer.

Rickard, John. Air safety group: a brief History. 2010. 58p. pap. 16.95 *(978-1-4457-6276-0(5))* Lulu Enterprises Inc.

Rodrigues, Clarence C. & Cusick, Stephen. Commercial Aviation Safety. 5th ed. 2011. (ENG., Illus.). 382p. (C). 55.00 *(978-0-07-176305-9(8)*, 0071763058) McGraw-Hill Professional Publishing.

Roelen, A. L. C., ed. Causal Risk Models of Air Transport: Comparison of User Needs & Model Capabilities. 2008. 256p. pap. 87.00 *(978-1-58603-933-2(4))* IOS Pr., Inc.

Rowe, Chester D. & Davis, Stephen M. The Excellence Engine Tool Kit. 2008. 193p. pap. 99.40 *(978-0-615-24850-9(0))* Excellence Engine, LLC, The.

Runway Safety: An Update: Hearing Before the Subcommittee on Aviation of the Committee on Transportation & Infrastructure, House of Representatives, One Hundred Tenth Congress, Second Session, September 25, 2008. 2008. (Illus.). xiii, 217p. *(978-0-16-083849-1(5)*, 552-070-39546-6) United States Government Printing Office.

Runway Safety: Hearing Before the Subcommittee on Aviation of the Committee on Transportation & Infrastructure, House of Representatives, One Hundred Tenth Congress, Second Session, February 13, 2008. 2008. (Illus.). vi, 351p. *(978-0-16-082840-9(6)*, 552-070-38820-6) United States Government Printing Office.

Stolzer, Alan J., et al, eds. Implementation of Safety Management Systems in Aviation. 2011. (Ashgate Studies in Human Factors for Flight Operations Ser.). (Illus.). 464p. 99.95 *(978-1-4094-0165-0(0))* Ashgate Publishing Co.

Stolzer, Alan J., et al. Safety Management Systems in Aviation. 2008. (Ashgate Studies in Human Factors for Flight Operations Ser.). (Illus.). 322p. 119.95 *(978-0-7546-7304-0(9))* Ashgate Publishing Co.

Strong, Richard. StrongMobile Aircar Development Report. 2007. (Illus.). 64p. ring bd. 10.00 incl. audio compact disk *(978-0-615-15823-5(4))* Safety Analysis Systems Co.

Sturkey, Marion F. Mid-Air: Accident Reports & Voice Transcripts from Military & Airline Mid-Air Collisions. Sturkey, Marion F., ed. 2008. (ENG., Illus.). 477p. pap. 19.00 *(978-0-9650814-7-4(8))* Heritage Pr. International.

Technology Research Editors, ed. Protection of Aerospace Components, 2007 Ed. 2007. pap. 128.50 *(978-1-60030-153-7(3)*, Search-In-Print) CSA Journal Division.

Tsuruta, Giorge. The Analysis of Flight Operational Quality Assurance Dat. 2009. 124p. pap. *(978-3-639-18635-2(4))* VDM Verlag Dr. Mueller e.K.

Van Hemel, Susan B. & Federal Aviation Administration Aviation Safety Committee. Staffing Standards for Aviation Safety Inspectors. Howell, William C., ed. 2006. (ENG., Illus.). 138p. pap. 34.00 (978-0-309-10326-8(6)) National Academies Pr.

Voogt, Alex De & D'Oliveira, Teresa C. Mechanisms in the Chain of Safety: Research & Operational Experiences in Aviation Psychology. 2012. (Illus.). 150p. 99.95 **(978-1-4094-1254-0(7))** Ashgate Publishing Co.

Wilkinson, Paul & Jenkins, Brian. Aviation Terrorism & Security. 2nd rev. ed. 2007. (Political Violence Ser.: No. 6). (Illus.). 202p. pap. 39.95 (978-0-7146-8221-1(7), RU33795) Routledge.

Winston, Clifford & de Rus, Gines, eds. Aviation Infrastructure Performance: A Study in Comparative Political Economy. 2008. (ENG., Illus.). 237p. 59.95 (978-0-8157-9394-6(4)); pap. 24.95 (978-0-8157-9395-3(2)) Brookings Institution Pr.

Yan, Ruixia. Assessing English Language Proficiency in International Aviation Issues of Reliability, Validity, & Aviation Safety. 2009. 128p. pap. (978-3-639-10984-9(8)) VDM Verlag Dr. Mueller e.K.

AERONAUTICS—STUDY AND TEACHING

see also Flight Training

Arthurs, Susan. Aerospace Activities - Ideas & Resources Grades 7-12, 1. 2007. cd-rom 49.00 (978-0-9792025-8-2(2)) Arthurs, S Enterprises, LLC.

—Aerospace Activities - Ideas & Resources Grades K-3. 2007. 60p. cd-rom 49.00 (978-0-9792025-6-8(6)) Arthurs, S Enterprises, LLC.

—Aerospace Education - Activities & Ideas Grades 7-12. 2006. 95p. spiral bd. (978-0-9792025-5-1(8)); cd-rom 45.00 (978-0-9792025-4-4(X)) Arthurs, S Enterprises, LLC.

Arthurs, Susan, compiled by. Aerospace Activities - Ideas & Resources Grades 4-6, 1. 2007. 86p. cd-rom 49.00 (978-0-9792025-7-5(4)) Arthurs, S Enterprises, LLC.

Committee for the Review and Evaluation of NASA's Precollege Education Program & National Research Council. NASA's Elementary & Secondary Education Program: Review & Critique. Quinn, Helen R. et al, eds. 2008. (ENG.). 162p. pap. 38.25 (978-0-309-11551-3(5)) National Academies Pr.

Comollo, George, et al. Basic Aviation Fun-Damentals: Fun with Aviation Math & Other Cool Stuff. rev. ed. 2009. (ENG.). 152p. pap. 24.00 (978-0-7575-7042-1(9)) Kendall Hunt Publishing Co.

Embry-Riddle Aeronautical University Staff, contrib. by. Forever an Eagle: Embry-Riddle Aeronautical University: A Pictorial History. 2011. **(978-1-57864-723-1(1))** Donning Co. Pubs.

Erman, Nathaniel. Flying Airplanes: for Fun & Money! 2010. 108p. pap. 15.99 (978-0-578-03438-6(7)) HEFF Publishing.

Federal Aviation Administration. Aviation Instructor's Handbook. 2009. (ENG., Illus.). 160p. pap. 14.95 (978-1-60239-777-4(5), 239777) Skyhorse Publishing Co., Inc.

Federal Aviation Administration (U.S.), compiled by. Aviation Instructor's Handbook 2008. 2009. (ENG., Illus.). 218p. pap. 35.00 (978-0-16-082212-4(2), Federal Aviation Administration) United States Government Printing Office.

—Pilot's Handbook of Aeronautical Knowledge. 2009. (ENG.). 470p. pap. 57.00 (978-0-16-082367-1(6), Federal Aviation Administration) United States Government Printing Office.

Kearns, Suzanne. E-Learning in Aviation. 2010. (Ashgate Studies in Human Factors for Flight Operations Ser.). (Illus.). 194p. 99.95 (978-0-7546-7879-3(2)) Ashgate Publishing Co.

Manacapilli, Thomas & Bennett, Bart. A User's Guide to the Technical Training Schoolhouse Model. 2006. (Illus.). 98p. pap. 27.50 (978-0-8330-3997-2(0), tr378) RAND Corp., The.

Rodwell, et al. Essentials of Aviation Management: A Guide for Aviation Service Businesses. 7th rev. ed. 2011. (ENG.). pap. 79.95 (978-0-7575-7481-8(5)) Kendall Hunt Publishing Co.

Selph, Martin & Easton, Jim. Standard Lesson Plans for Private, Commercial & Flight Instructor: Airplane Single Engine Land. 320p. (978-0-9641922-0-1(9)) Johannsen Group.

University Aviation Association, prod. Collegiate Aviation Guide: Reference of Collegiate Aviation Programs. 5th ed. 2008. (YA). mass mkt. (978-0-9678602-2-0(9)) Univ. Aviation Assn.

AERONAUTICS—VOCATIONAL GUIDANCE

Gardner, Bryan. Hired Minds: A Career Guide for Engineering Students & Graduates. 2007. (Illus.). 137p. per. (978-1-56347-876-5(5)) American Institute of Aeronautics & Astronautics.

Jonz, Adam. A Guidebook on Becoming a Flight Attendant: The Original Airline Interview Guidebook. rev. ed. 144p. pap. 14.95 (978-0-9614689-0-3(4)) K&K Publishing.

Mark, Robert P. Professional Pilot's Career Guide. 2nd rev. ed. 2007. (ENG., Illus.). 455p. per. 24.95 (978-0-07-148553-1(8), 0071485538) McGraw-Hill Professional Publishing.

Randall, Craig & Penn, Rexford. Crew / Cockpit Resource Management, (CRM) A Guide for Professional Pilots. 2010. 73p. pap. 39.90 (978-0-557-26985-3(7)) Lulu Enterprises Inc.

AERONAUTICS—ALASKA

Barresi, Mark. The Encounter over Alaska. 2011. 128p. 21.23 **(978-1-4634-4857-8(0))**; pap. 11.99 **(978-1-4634-4856-1(2))** AuthorHouse.

Billberg, Rudy. In the Shadow of Eagles: From Barnstormer to Alaska Bush Pilot, a Pilots Story. 2009. (ENG., Illus.). 352p. pap. 16.95 (978-0-88240-815-6(1), Alaska Northwest Bks.) Graphic Arts Ctr. Publishing Co.

Bruder, Gerry. Heroes of the Horizon: Flying Adventures of Alaska's Legendary Bush Pilots. 2007. (ENG., Illus.). 279p. pap. 17.95 (978-0-88240-363-2(X)) Graphic Arts Ctr. Publishing Co.

Fitzgerald, Allistair. AIR CRASH INVESTIGATIONS: the Crash of Alaska Airlines Flight 261. 2009. 328p. pap. 32.50 (978-0-557-13911-8(2)) Lulu Enterprises Inc.

AERONAUTICS—AUSTRALIA

Farram, Steven. Charles 'Moth' Eaton: Pioneer Aviator of the Northern Territory. 2007. (Illus.). 70p. pap. (978-0-9803846-1-1(3)) Darwin, Charles Univ. Pr.

Lovell, Mike, ed. & compiled by. Arthur Lovell - Aviation Pioneer & Navigator. 2007. (978-0-9776414-5-1(7)) LifeReloaded.

Tradition of Integrity. pap. (978-0-86840-110-2(2)) NewSouth Publishing.

AERONAUTICS—CANADA

Christopher Weicht. Alberta Skies. 2009. 428p. pap. 46.00 (978-1-4269-0686-2(2)) Trafford Publishing.

Kearns, Suzanne. Canadian Aviation. rev. ed. 2011. (ENG.). 252p. pap. 65.60 (978-0-7575-6484-0(4)) Kendall Hunt Publishing Co.

Payne, Stephen. Canadian Wings: A Remarkable Century of Flight, 1 vol. 2009. (ENG.). 256p. pap. 35.00 (978-1-55365-496-4(X)) D&M Pubs. Inc. CAN. Dist: Perseus-PGW.

Pigott, Peter. Wingwalkers: The Rise & Fall of Canada's Other Airline. 2nd rev. unabr. ed. (ENG., Illus.). 448p. pap. 26.95 (978-1-55017-292-8(1)) Harbour Publishing Co., Ltd. CAN. Dist: Ingram Pub. Services.

Shilliday, Jim. A Memory of Sky: A Pilot's View of Canada's Century of Flight. 2009. (ENG.). 200p. 29.95 (978-1-894283-95-3(3)) Great Plains Pubns. CAN. Dist: Univ. of Toronto Pr.

Tattersall, Andrew & Stachiw, Anthony L. Canadair CF104 Starfighter. 2007. (In Canadian Service: Aircraft Ser.). (Illus.). 151p. per. 29.95 (978-1-55125-114-1(0)) Vanwell Publishing, Ltd. CAN. Dist: Casemate Pubs. & Bk. Distributors, LLC.

Ted Beaudoin. Pilot of Fortune. 2009. 344p. 28.99 (978-1-4269-2231-2(0)); pap. 18.99 (978-1-4269-2230-5(2)) Trafford Publishing.

University Aviation Association, prod. Collegiate Aviation Guide: Reference of Collegiate Aviation Programs. 5th ed. 2008. (YA). mass mkt. (978-0-9678602-2-0(9)) Univ. Aviation Assn.

AERONAUTICS—EUROPE

Alfonso-Gil, Javier, ed. European Aeronautics: The Southwestern Axis. (ENG., Illus.). x, 277p. 2010. pap. 149.00 (978-3-642-07135-5(X), 364207135X) 2006. 149.00 (978-3-540-35646-2(0), 3540356460) Springer.

Antwerpen, Niels Van. Cross-Border Provision of Air Navigation Services with Specific Reference to Europe: Safeguarding Transparent Lines of Responsibility & Liability. 2008. (Aviation Law & Policy Ser.). (Illus.). 145.00 (978-90-411-2688-7(0)) Wolters Kluwer Law & Business.

Barrett, Sean. Deregulation & the Airline Business in Europe. 2011. (ENG., Illus.). 208p. (C). pap. 44.95 **(978-0-415-69649-4(6))** Routledge.

Bartlik, Martin. The Impact of EU Law on the Regulation of International Air Transportation. 2007. 290p. 124.95 (978-0-7546-4951-9(2)) Ashgate Publishing Co.

Beck, Bettina. Die Regelung slots (von Zeitnischen) im Luftverkehrsrecht: Vergabe, Übertragung und Anfechtung in der Schweiz und der EG unter rechtsvergleichender Berücksichtigung US-amerikanischer Normen. 2008. (Studies in Global Economic Law. Studien zum globalen Wirtschaftsrecht. Études en droit économique mondial Ser.). 255p. pap. (978-3-03911-737-6(8)) Lang, Peter.

Becze, Csaba. Baptism of Fire: The First Combat Experiences of the Royal Hungarian Air Force & Slovak Air Force, March 1939. 2010. (Illus.). 96p. 49.95 (978-1-906033-93-4(5)) Helion & Co., Ltd. GBR. Dist: Casemate Pubs. & Bk. Distributors, LLC.

Cram101 Textbook Reviews & Cram101 Textbook Reviews. Outlines & Highlights for a Europe of the Air: The Airline Industry & European Integration by Martin Staniland. 2011. 520p. pap. 38.95 **(978-1-61830-836-8(X))** Cram101 Inc.

Forsyth, Peter, et al. Airport Competition: The European Experience. Müller, Jürgen, ed. 2010. (Illus.). 462p. 134.95 (978-0-7546-7746-8(X)) Ashgate Publishing Co.

Glud, Alexander & Wedding, Eivind. Fasten Your Seatbelts. 2011. 140p. pap. **(978-3-8433-9459-8(8))** Lambert Academic Publishing.

Golabek, Adam. MiG-29, 2 vols. 2010. (Illus.). 96p. pap. 25.00 (978-83-61421-12-2(2)) Stratus, Wydawnictwo, Juszczak, Artur POL. Dist: Casemate Pubs. & Bk. Distributors, LLC.

Grufeneder, Mario. Sales Increase Oppurtunities for Austrian Airlines in Russi. 2008. 108p. pap. (978-3-639-11323-5(3)) VDM Verlag Dr. Mueller e.K.

Guruprasad, Ramachandran & Nikam, Khaiser. Use Patterns of Electronic Information Resources. 2011. 540p. pap. **(978-3-639-32104-3(9))** VDM Verlag Dr. Mueller e.K.

Haas, Silke. The European Aviation Industry. 2009. 112p. pap. (978-3-639-13222-9(X)) VDM Verlag Dr. Mueller e.K.

Havel, Brian F. In Search of Open Skies: Law & Policy for a New Era in International Aviation. 2nd ed. 2009. xxxi, 712p. (978-90-411-2389-3(X)) Kluwer Law International.

Kuchta, Marek. Viability of the Premium Airline Business Model. 2009. 118p. pap. (978-3-639-18166-1(2)) VDM Verlag Dr. Mueller e.K.

Morgaa, Andrzej. Ex USAAF Aircraft 1945. 2011. (Illus.). 80p. pap. 25.00 **(978-83-61421-11-5(4))** Stratus, Wydawnictwo, Juszczak, Artur POL. Dist: Casemate Pubs. & Bk. Distributors, LLC.

Piccard, Bertrand, text. A Trace in the Sky. 2010. (ENG., Illus.). 234p. 24.00 (978-88-544-0471-7(3)) White Star ITA. Dist: Random Hse., Inc.

Viikari, Lotta. The Environmental Element in Space Law: Assessing the Present & Charting the Future: Assessing the Present & Charting the Future. 2008. (Studies in Space Law Ser.). (Illus.). 250p. (978-90-04-16744-5(7)) BRILL.

Wagner, Arthur & Braxton, Leon E. Glacier Gooney. 2010. (ENG., Illus.). 160p. pap. 18.00 (978-0-615-39033-8(1)) Printer's Ink.

AERONAUTICS—FRANCE

Feldman, Elliot J. Concorde & Dissent: Explaining High Technology Project Failures in Britain & France. 2009. (ENG., Illus.). 220p. (C). pap. 31.99 (978-0-521-10826-3(8)) Cambridge Univ. Pr.

Fernandez, Jose. French Wings No. 2: Nieuport Delage NiD 29 & NiD 62 Family. 2010. (French Wings Ser.). (Illus.). 80p. pap. 23.00 (978-83-61421-21-4(1)) Stratus, Wydawnictwo, Juszczak, Artur POL. Dist: Casemate Pubs. & Bk. Distributors, LLC.

Vivian, E. Charles. A History of Aeronautics. 2008. 364p. 29.99 (978-0-554-30762-6(6)); 31.99 (978-0-554-21459-7(6)) BiblioBazaar.

—A History of Aeronautics. 2009. 368p. pap. (978-1-4099-7253-2(4)) Dodo Pr.

—A History of Aeronautics. 2009. (ENG.). 326p. pap. 20.95 (978-1-4385-1925-8(7), Book Jungle) Standard Pubns., Inc.

AERONAUTICS—GERMANY

Bickenbach, Frank, et al. Ausbau der Flughafenstruktur: Konflikte und institutionelle Lösungsansätze. (Kieler Studien - Kiel Studies). (GER.). X, 251p. 119.00 (978-3-540-29418-4(X), 354029418X) Springer.

Boewe, Marius & Geisler, Markus. The German Civil Aviation Act. 2009. 134p. 88.00 (978-90-77596-72-2(0)) Eleven International Publishing NLD. Dist: International Specialized Bk. Services.

Forsyth, Robert. Fw 190 Sturmbock vs B-17: Europe 1944-45. 2009. (Duel Ser.). (ENG., Illus.). 80p. pap. 17.95 (978-1-84603-941-6(X)) Osprey Publishing, Ltd. GBR. Dist: Random Hse., Inc.

Goss, Chris. Sea Eagles Vol. 2: Luftwaffe Anti-Shipping Units, 1942-45, 2 vols. 2009. (Luftwaffe Colours Ser.). (ENG., Illus.). 96p. pap. 27.95 (978-1-903223-56-7(3)) Allan, Ian Publishing GBR. Dist: BookMasters Distribution Services (BDS).

Harvey, James. Sharks of the Air: Willi Messerschmitt & How He Built the World's First Operational Jet Fighter. 2010. (Illus.). 352p. 32.95 (978-1-935149-46-0(6)) Casemate Pubs. & Bk. Distributors, LLC.

Ketley, Barry. Fledgling Eagles: Luftwaffe Training Aircraft 1933. 2010. (ENG., Illus.). 96p. pap. 27.95 (978-1-906537-05-0(4)) Allan, Ian Publishing GBR. Dist: BookMasters Distribution Services (BDS).

Mensen, Heinrich. Moderne Flugsicherung: Organisation, Verfahren, Technik. 3rd ed. 2006. (VDI-Buch Ser.). (Illus.). XXXII, 466p. 69.95 (978-3-540-20581-4(0), 3540205810) Springer.

Mower, Mark. Zeppelin over Suffolk. 2009. pap. 25.99 (978-1-84415-737-2(7)) Pen & Sword Bks. Ltd. GBR. Dist: Casemate Pubs. & Bk. Distributors, LLC.

Neuscheler, Tillmann. Flughäfen zwischen Regulierung und Wettbewerb: Eine netzökonomische Analyse. 2008. (GER., Illus.). 379p. pap. (978-3-8329-3737-9(4)) Nomos Verlagsgesellschaft.

Revell, Alex. No 56 Sqn RAF/RFC. 2009. (Aviation Elite Units Ser.). (ENG., Illus.). 128p. pap. 25.95 (978-1-84603-428-2(0)) Osprey Publishing, Ltd. GBR. Dist: Random Hse., Inc.

Samuel, Wolfgang W. E. Watson's Whizzers: Operation Lusty & the Race for Nazi Aviation Technology. 2010. (Illus.). 208p. 39.99 (978-0-7643-3517-4(0)) Schiffer Publishing, Ltd.

Schmoll, Peter. Nest of Eagles: Messerschmitt Production & Flight-Testing at Regensburg 1936-1945. 2010. (ENG., Illus.). 192p. 49.95 (978-1-906537-12-8(7)) Classic Pubns. GBR. Dist: BookMasters Distribution Services (BDS).

Stapfer, Hans-Heiri & Tullis, Tom. Me 262 in Action. 2008. (Illus.). 51p. **(978-0-89747-554-9(2))** Squadron Signal Pubns.

Uziel, Daniel. Arming the Luftwaffe: The German Aviation Industry in World War II. 2011. (ENG., Illus.). 312p. pap. 45.00 **(978-0-7864-6521-7(2))** McFarland & Co., Inc. Pubs.

Warsitz, Lutz. The First Jet Pilot: The Story of German Test Pilot Erich Warsitz. 2009. (Illus.). 176p. 39.99 (978-1-84415-818-8(7)) Pen & Sword Bks. Ltd. GBR. Dist: Casemate Pubs. & Bk. Distributors, LLC.

Wollersheim, Christoph. On the Provision of Airport Infrastructure in Germany. 2011. 280p. pap. 80.00 (978-3-8329-6308-8(1)) Nomos Verlagsgesellschaft DEU. Dist: International Specialized Bk. Services.

Woowski, Krzysztof. Bf 109 Late Versions: Camouflage & Markings. 2010. (Illus.). 96p. pap. 37.00 (978-83-61421-13-9(0)) Stratus, Wydawnictwo, Juszczak, Artur POL. Dist: Casemate Pubs. & Bk. Distributors, LLC.

AERONAUTICS—GREAT BRITAIN

Balmforth, John. Virgin Atlantic. 2010. (ENG., Illus.). 96p. 32.95 (978-1-85780-303-7(5)) Allan, Ian Publishing GBR. Dist: BookMasters Distribution Services (BDS).

Blackman, Tony. Tony Blackman - Test Pilot: My extraordinary life in Flight. 2009. (Illus.). 224p. 39.95 (978-1-906502-36-2(6)) Grub Street GBR. Dist: Casemate Pubs. & Bk. Distributors, LLC, Littlehampton Bk Services, Ltd.

—Vulcan Test Pilot: My experiences in the cockpit of a Cold War Icon. 2009. (Illus.). 224p. pap. 26.95 (978-1-906502-30-0(7)) Grub Street GBR. Dist: Casemate Pubs. & Bk. Distributors, LLC.

Bluffield, Robert. Imperial Airways. 2010. (ENG., Illus.). 224p. 56.95 (978-1-906537-07-4(0)) Allan, Ian Publishing GBR. Dist: BookMasters Distribution Services (BDS).

Britten, Michael D. Flights of Inspiration. 2009. (Illus.). 256p. pap. 14.49 (978-1-4389-5223-9(6)) AuthorHouse.

Butler, Phil. Liverpool John Lennon Airport. 2008. (ENG.). 160p. pap. 39.95 (978-0-7524-4511-3(1)) History Pr. Ltd.,The GBR. Dist: Independent Pubs. Group.

Castle, Ian. British Airships 1905-30. 2009. (New Vanguard Ser.). (ENG., Illus.). 48p. pap. 17.95 (978-1-84603-387-2(X)) Osprey Publishing, Ltd. GBR. Dist: Random Hse., Inc.

Cockle, Doug. Manston Memories 1916-2006. 2007. (Illus.). 128p. pap. 24.95 (978-0-7509-4542-4(7)) Sutton Publishing.

Cooper, Geoffrey. Farnborough & the Fleet Air Arm. 2010. (ENG., Illus.). 296p. 54.95 (978-1-85780-306-8(X)) Allan, Ian Publishing GBR. Dist: BookMasters Distribution Services (BDS).

Coulson. A Proud Heritage. (Illus.). 96p. pap. 24.99 (978-1-899808-10-6(8)) Royal Air Force Benevolent Fund Enterprises GBR. Dist: Trafalgar Square Publishing.

Dagwell, Keith. Silver City Airways: Pioneers of the Skies. 2010. (ENG., Illus.). 160p. pap. 28.95 (978-0-7524-5362-0(9)) History Pr. Ltd.,The GBR. Dist: Independent Pubs. Group.

Delve, Ken. Military Airfields of Britain: Scotland & Northern Ireland. 2011. (ENG., Illus.). 272p. 29.95 (978-1-84797-027-5(3), 1847970273) Crowood Pr., Ltd. GBR. Dist: MBI Distribution Services/Quayside Distribution.

Forrester, Peter. Wings over Somerset: Aircraft Crashes since the End of World War II. 2012. (ENG., Illus.). 192p. pap. 24.95 **(978-0-7524-6579-1(1))** History Pr. Ltd.,The GBR. Dist: Independent Pubs. Group.

Fozard, John W., compiled by. The British Aerospace Harrier Case Study in Aircraft Design. (Illus.). 102p. pap. 23.00 (978-1-56347-306-7(2)) American Institute of Aeronautics & Astronautics.

Gardner, Robert. From Bouncing Bombs to Concorde: The Authorized Biography of Aviation Pioneer Sir George Edwards OM. 2006. (ENG., Illus.). 352p. 46.95 (978-0-7509-4389-5(0)) Sutton Publishing.

Green, Oliver & Anthony, Scott. British Aviation Posters: Art Design & Flight. 2012. (Illus.). 200p. 70.00 **(978-1-84822-084-3(7)**, Lund Humphries Pubs.) Ashgate Publishing, Ltd. GBR. Dist: Ashgate Publishing Co.

Halford-Macleod, Guy. Britain's Airlines Vol. 3: 1964 to Deregulation. 2010. (ENG., Illus.). 288p. pap. 36.95 (978-0-7524-5499-3(4)) History Pr. Ltd.,The GBR. Dist: Independent Pubs. Group.

—Britains Airlines, 1951-1964, 2 vols., Vol. 2. 2007. (ENG., Illus.). 264p. pap. 39.95 (978-0-7524-4276-1(7)) History Pr. Ltd.,The GBR. Dist: Independent Pubs. Group.

Holding, John D. The British Manual of International Air Carriage. 2009. (ENG.). 223p. (978-1-55221-160-1(6)) Irwin Law, Inc.

Humphreys, Roy, ed. Kent Aviation: A Century of Flight. 2009. (ENG., Illus.). 192p. pap. 29.95 (978-0-7524-5121-3(9)) History Pr. Ltd.,The GBR. Dist: Independent Pubs. Group.

Jackson, Robert. Britain's Greatest Aircraft. 2007. (Illus.). 320p. 50.00 (978-1-84415-600-9(1)) Pen & Sword Bks. Ltd. GBR. Dist: Casemate Pubs. & Bk. Distributors, LLC.

James, Derek. Westland: A History. (Illus.). 208p. pap. 35.00 (978-0-7524-2772-0(5)) History Pr. Ltd.,The GBR. Dist: Trafalgar Square Publishing.

Jones, Barry. British Experimental Turbojet Aircraft. rev. ed. 2007. (Crowood Aviation Ser.). (ENG., Illus.). 208p. pap. 34.95 (978-1-86126-860-0(2), 1861268602) Crowood Pr., Ltd. GBR. Dist: MBI Distribution Services/Quayside Distribution.

Jones, Ivor. Airfields & Landing Grounds of Wales. 2008. (ENG.). 192p. pap. 38.95 (978-0-7524-4510-6(3)) History Pr. Ltd.,The GBR. Dist: Independent Pubs. Group.

Jones, Lois. EasyJet: The Story of Britain's Biggest Low-Cost Airline. 2nd rev. ed. 2007. (ENG.). 256p. pap. 15.95 (978-1-84513-247-7(5)) Aurum Pr., Ltd. GBR. Dist: Independent Pubs. Group.

Kuntz, Jerry. A Pair of Shootists: The Wild West Story of S. F. Cody & Maud Lee. 2010. (ENG.). 224p. (C). 29.95 (978-0-8061-4149-7(2)) Univ. of Oklahoma Pr.

Lancaster, Nicholas. Brooklands: Cradle of British Motor Racing & Aviation. 2009. (Shire Library). (ENG., Illus.). 56p. pap. 12.95 (978-0-7478-0707-0(8)) Shire Pubns., Ltd. GBR. Dist: Random Hse., Inc.

Leek, Michael. Military Low-Flying Aircraft. 2011. (Illus.). 272p. 50.00 **(978-1-84884-223-6(6))** Pen & Sword Bks. Ltd. GBR. Dist: Casemate Pubs. & Bk. Distributors, LLC.

Lynch, Brendan. Yesterday We Were in America: Alcock & Brown - First to Fly the Atlantic Non-Stop. 2009. (ENG., Illus.). 256p. 39.95 (978-1-84425-681-5(2), 1844256812) Haynes Publishing PLC GBR. Dist: MBI Distribution Services/Quayside Distribution.

Millward, Liz. Women in British Imperial Airspace: 1922-1937. 2007. (ENG., Illus.). 264p. (C). (978-0-7735-3337-0(0)) McGill-Queen's Univ. Pr.

Ottaway, Susan & Ottaway, Ian. Fly with the Stars: British South American Airways: the Rise & Controversial Fall of a Long-Haul Trailblazer. 2007. (ENG., Illus.). 256p. 36.95 (978-0-7509-4448-9(X)) Sutton Publishing.

Philpott, Ian M. Royal Air Force 1918-1939, 2 vols., Vol. 2. 2006. (Illus.). 576p. 75.00 (978-1-84415-391-6(6)) Pen & Sword Bks. Ltd. GBR. Dist: Casemate Pubs. & Bk. Distributors, LLC.

Piccard, Bertrand, text. A Trace in the Sky. 2010. (ENG., Illus.). 234p. 24.00 (978-88-544-0471-7(3)) White Star ITA. Dist: Random Hse., Inc.

Pirie, Gordon. Cultures & Caricatures of British Imperial Flying. 2012. (Studies in Imperialism Ser.). (ENG., Illus.). 256p. 100.00 **(978-0-7190-8682-3(5))** Manchester Univ. Pr. GBR. Dist: Macmillan.

Pulford, John & Winn, Allan. 100 Years of Brooklands: The Birthplace of British Motorsport & Aviation. Temple, Julian, ed. 2007. (ENG., Illus.). 192p. 45.00 *(978-0-9551020-6-6(5))* Touchstone Bks. Ltd. GBR. Dist: Independent Pubs. Group.

Rech, Jean & Leyman, Clives. A Case Study by Aerospatiale & British Aerospace on the Concorde. (Illus.). 102p. pap. 23.00 *(978-1-56347-308-1(9))* American Institute of Aeronautics & Astronautics.

Rosie, George. Flight of the Titan: The Story of the R34. 2010. (ENG., Illus.). 224p. pap. 16.00 *(978-1-84158-863-6(6))*, Birlinn) Birlinn, Ltd. GBR. Dist: Interlink Publishing Group, Inc.

Shelton, John. Schneider Trophy to Spitfire: The Design Career of R. J. Mitchell. 2009. (ENG., Illus.). 256p. 49.95 *(978-1-84425-530-6(1)*, 1844255301) Haynes Publishing PLC GBR. Dist: MBI Distribution Services/Quayside Distribution.

Simons, Graham & Bowman, Martin. London's Airports: Useful information on Heathrow, Gatwick, Luton, Stansted & City. 2011. (Illus.). 138p. pap. 29.95 *(978-1-84884-394-3(1))* Pen & Sword Bks. Ltd. GBR. Dist: Casemate Pubs. & Bk. Distributors, LLC.

Skinner, Stephen. British Aircraft Corporation: A History, 1 vol. 2012. (ENG., Illus.). 192p. 39.95 ***(978-1-34797-318-4(3)***, 1847973183) Crowood Pr., Ltd. GBR. Dist: MBI Distribution Services/Quayside Distribution.

Slessor, John Cotesworth. Air Power & Armies. 2009. (ENG., Illus.). 272p. pap. 28.00 *(978-0-8173-5610-1(X))* Univ. of Alabama Pr.

Smith, David J. Air Traffic Control Handbook: The Complete Guide for all Aviation & Air Band Enthusiasts. 9th ed. 2010. (ENG., Illus.). 208p. pap. 29.95 *(978-1-84425-332-1(7)*, 1844258327) Haynes Publishing PLC GBR. Dist: MBI Distribution Services/Quayside Distribution.

Smith, Richard C. RAF Duxford: A History in Photographs from 1917 to the Present Day. 2006. (Illus.). 160p. 39.95 *(978-1-904943-59-4(4))* Grub Street GBR. Dist: Casemate Pubs. & Bk. Distributors, LLC.

Thomas, Andrew. RAF Mustang & Thunderbolt Aces. 2010. (Aircraft of the Aces Ser.). (ENG., Illus.). 96p. pap. 22.95 *(978-1-84603-979-9(7))* Osprey Publishing, Ltd. GBR. Dist: Random Hse., Inc.

Vacher, Polly. Wings Around the World. 2008. (Illus.). 160p. 29.95 *(978-1-904943-99-0(3))* Grub Street GBR. Dist: Casemate Pubs. & Bk. Distributors, LLC.

Venables, David. Brooklands: The Official Centenary History. 2007. (ENG., Illus.). 256p. 54.95 *(978-1-84425-329-6(5)*, 1844253295) Haynes Publishing PLC GBR. Dist: MBI Distribution Services/Quayside Distribution.

Verdon-Roe, Alliott. The World of Wings & Things. 2006. 284p. per. *(978-1-4067-0115-9(7)*, Hesperides Pr.) Read Bks.

AERONAUTICS—ITALY

Dunning, Chris. Regia Aeronautica: The Italian Air Force 1923-1945 - an Operational History. 2010. (ENG., Illus.). 224p. 56.95 *(978-1-906537-02-9(X))* Classic Pubns. GBR. Dist: BookMasters Distribution Services (BDS).

AERONAUTICS—JAPAN

Cea, Eduardo. Japanese Military Aircraft: Aircraft of the Imperial Japanese Navy. Land-Based Aviation, 1929-1945 (I) Nº4. 2009. (Air Collection Ser.). (Illus.). 104p. pap. 29.00 *(978-84-96935-10-5(8))* Quiron Ediciones ESP. Dist: Casemate Pubs. & Bk. Distributors, LLC.

—Japanese Military Aircraft: Special Attacj Units - Tokubetsu Kogeki Tai. 2011. (Illus.). 195p. pap. 49.00 ***(978-84-96935-37-2(X))*** Quiron Ediciones ESP. Dist: Casemate Pubs. & Bk. Distributors, LLC.

—Japanese Military Aircraft: Special Units of the Imperial Army. 2011. (Illus.). 135p. pap. 42.95 ***(978-84-96935-36-5(1))*** Quiron Ediciones ESP. Dist: Casemate Pubs. & Bk. Distributors, LLC.

Mays, Terry M. Night Hawks & Black Widows: 13th Air Force Night Fighters in the South & Southwest Pacific O 1943-1945. 2009. (Illus.). 240p. bds. 69.99 *(978-0-7643-3344-6(5))* Schiffer Publishing, Ltd.

Peattie, Mark R. Sunburst: The Rise of Japanese Naval Air Power, 1909-1941. 2007. (Illus.). 364p. per. 26.95 *(978-1-59114-664-3(X))* Naval Institute Pr.

Treadwell, Terry C. Setting of the Rising Sun: Japanese Military Aviation, 1877-1945. 2011. (Illus.). 224p. pap. 29.95 *(978-1-4456-0226-4(1))* Amberley Publishing GBR. Dist: Casemate Pubs. & Bk. Distributors, LLC.

AERONAUTICS—SOVIET UNION

Dranovsky, Mark L., et al. Combustion Instabilities in Liquid Rocket Engines: Testing & Development Practices in Russia. 2007. (Illus.). xix, 320p. ***(978-1-56347-921-2(4))*** American Institute of Aeronautics & Astronautics.

Dreer, Francis. Space Conquest: The complete history of manned Spaceflight. 2009. (ENG., Illus.). 208p. 49.95 *(978-1-84425-573-3(5)*, 1844255735) Haynes Publishing PLC GBR. Dist: MBI Distribution Services/Quayside Distribution.

Gordon, Yefim. Lavochkin's Last Jets. Komissarov, Dmitriy, tr. 2010. (Red Star Ser.). (ENG., Illus.). 127p. per. 36.95 *(978-1-85780-253-5(5))* Allan, Ian Publishing GBR. Dist: BookMasters Distribution Services (BDS).

—Soviet Strategic Aviation in the Cold War. 2009. (Illus.). 272p. 56.95 *(978-1-902109-08-4(2))* Hikoki Pubns. GBR. Dist: Partners Pubs. Group, Inc.

—Soviet/Russian Unmanned Aerial Vehicles. Komissarov, Dmitriy, tr. 2010. (Red Star Ser.). (ENG., Illus.). 127p. per. 34.95 *(978-1-85780-193-4(8))* Allan, Ian Publishing GBR. Dist: BookMasters Distribution Services (BDS).

—US Aircraft in the Soviet Union & Russia. 2010. (ENG., Illus.). 335p. 63.95 *(978-1-85780-308-2(6))* Allan, Ian Publishing GBR. Dist: BookMasters Distribution Services (BDS).

Gordon, Yefim & Buttler, Tony. Soviet Secret Projects Bombers Since 1945, Vol. 1. 2010. (ENG., Illus.). 176p. 44.95 *(978-1-85780-194-1(6))* Allan, Ian Publishing GBR. Dist: BookMasters Distribution Services (BDS).

Gordon, Yefim & Komissarov, Dmitriy. Antonov An-12: The Soviet Hercules. 2008. (Red Star Ser.). (Illus.). 143p. per. 32.95 *(978-1-85780-255-9(1))* Midland Publishing Ltd. GBR. Dist: Partners Pubs. Group, Inc.

—Russian Airliners: Outside Russia. 2008. (Illus.). 160p. per. 32.95 *(978-1-85780-252-8(7))* Midland Publishing Ltd. GBR. Dist: Partners Pubs. Group, Inc.

Gordon, Yefim & Komissarov, Dmitriy. OKB Sukhoi: A History of the Design Bureau & Its Aircraft. 2010. (ENG., Illus.). 592p. 79.95 *(978-1-85780-314-3(0))* Midland Publishing Ltd. GBR. Dist: BookMasters Distribution Services (BDS).

Gordon, Yefim & Komissarov, Dmitriy. Soviet & Russian Testbed Aircraft. 2011. (Illus.). 416p. ***(978-1-902109-18-3(X))*** Hikoki Pubns.

Gordon, Yefim, et al. OKB Yakovlev: A History of the Design Bureau & Its Aircraft. 2010. (ENG., Illus.). 384p. pap. 69.95 *(978-1-85780-203-0(9))* Allan, Ian Publishing GBR. Dist: BookMasters Distribution Services (BDS).

Korovin, Igor. Air Crash Investigations: The Crash of Aeroflot Flight 821. 2009. 180p. pap. 25.50 *(978-0-557-13216-4(9))* Lulu Enterprises Inc.

Palmer, Scott W. Dictatorship of the Air: Aviation Culture & the Fate of Modern Russia. 2009. (Cambridge Centennial of Flight Ser.). (ENG., Illus.). 328p. (C). pap. 27.00 *(978-0-521-13043-1(3))* Cambridge Univ. Pr.

Paloque, Gerard. Mikoyan-Gurevitch MIG 21: Fishbed 1955 - 2010. 2010. (Planes & Pilots 12 Ser.). (Illus.). 96p. pap. 19.95 *(978-2-35250-147-3(4))* Casemate Pubs. & Bk. Distributors, LLC.

van Schyndel, Heiko. Aviation Code of the Russian Federation. 2010. 192p. 88.00 *(978-90-77596-80-7(1))* Eleven International Publishing NLD. Dist: International Specialized Bk. Services.

AERONAUTICS, COMMERCIAL

see also Air Mail Service; Air Travel; Airlines; Airways; Transport Planes

Abdelghany, Ahmed F. & Abdelghany, Khaled. Modeling Applications in the Airline Industry. 2010. (Illus.). 290p. 99.95 *(978-0-7546-7874-8(1))* Ashgate Publishing Co.

Abeyratne, Ruwantissa. ed. Aeropolitics. 2009. (Transportation Issues, Policies & R&D Ser.). 79.00 *(978-1-60876-102-9(9))* Nova Science Pubs., Inc.

Airline Competition: Higher Fares & Less Competition Continue at Concentrated Airports. 44p. pap. 30.00 *(978-0-7881-4081-5(7))* DIANE Publishing Co.

Alam, Sameer. Air Traffic Simulation & Modelling. 2009. 288p. pap. *(978-3-639-02255-1(6))* VDM Verlag Dr. Mueller e.K.

Anderson, Nina E. Flying above the Glass Ceiling: Inspirational Stories of Success from the First Women Pilots to Fly Airline & Corporate Aircraft. Pratt, Bill, ed. 2009. (Illus.). 134p. pap. 14.95 *(978-1-884820-94-6(8))* SAFE GOODS/ATN Publishing.

Andrup, Norbert. Colorful Aircraft: Unique Paint Schemes on the World's Passenger Airliners. 2010. (Illus.). 144p. 45.00 *(978-0-7643-3656-0(8))* Schiffer Publishing Ltd.

Aviation & the Environment: Emissions [sic]: Hearing Before the Subcommittee on Aviation of the Committee on Transportation & Infrastructure, House of Representatives, One Hundred Tenth Congress, Second Session, May 6, 2008. 2008. (Illus.) xiii, 203p. *(978-0-16-083489-9(9)*, 552-070-39229-1) United States Government Printing Office.

Aviation Consumer Issues: Emergency Contingency Planning & Outlook for Summer Travel: Hearing Before the Subcommittee on Aviation of the Committee on Transportation & Infrastructure, House of Representatives, One Hundred Eleventh Congress, First Session, May 20, 2009. 2009. (Illus.). xiii, 139p. *(978-0-16-084374-7(X)*, 552-070-39917-8) United States Government Printing Office.

Aviation Consumer Issues: Hearing Before the Subcommittee on Aviation of the Committee on Transportation & Infrastructure, House of Representatives, One Hundred Tenth Congress, First Session, April 20, 2007. 2007. (Illus.). xii, 194p. *(978-0-16-079977-8(5)*, 552-070-36802-7) United States Government Printing Office.

Aviation Delays & Consumer Issues: Hearing Before the Subcommittee on Aviation of the Committee on Transportation & Infrastructure, House of Representatives, One Hundred Tenth Congress, Second Session, April 9, 2008. 2008. (Illus.). xii, 194p. *(978-0-16-082967-3(4)*, 552-070-38878-8) United States Government Printing Office.

Aviation Safety: FAA's Role in the Oversight of Commercial Air Carriers: Hearing Before the Subcommittee on Aviation Operations, Safety, & Security of the Committee on Commerce, Science, & Transportation, United States Senate, One Hundred Eleventh Congress, First Session, June 10, 2009. 2010. iii, 81p. *(978-0-16-085627-3(2)*, 552-070-40689-0) United States Government Printing Office.

Aviation Safety: One Year after the Crash of Flight 3407: Hearing Before the Subcommittee on Aviation Operations, Safety, & Security of the Committee on Commerce, Science, & Transportation, United States Senate, One Hundred Eleventh Congress, Second Session, February 25, 2010. 2010. (Illus.). iii, 46p. *(978-0-16-086805-4(X)*, 552-070-41721-4) United States Government Printing Office.

Balakrishna, Poornima. Approximate Dynamic Programming. 2010. 176p. pap. *(978-3-639-24102-0(9))* VDM Verlag Dr. Mueller e.K.

Balasubramaniam, Sangeetha & Huam Hon Tat. Airline Industry. 2011. 156p. pap. ***(978-3-8443-8275-4(5))*** Lambert Academic Publishing.

Bauer, Eugene E. Boeing: The First Century & Beyond. 2nd ed. 2006. (Illus.). 424p. 29.50 *(978-1-879242-09-8(5))* TABA Publishing, Inc.

Bazargan, Massoud. Airline Operations & Scheduling. 2nd rev. ed. 2010. (Illus.). 302p. 89.95 *(978-0-7546-7900-4(4))* Ashgate Publishing Co.

Benson, Erik. Aviator of Fortune: Lowell Yerex & the Anglo-American Commercial Rivalry, 1931-1946. 2006. (Louise Lindsey Merrick Natural Environment Ser.: No. 40). (ENG., Illus.). 280p. 45.00 *(978-1-58544-500-4(2))* Texas A&M Univ. Pr.

Beyer, Morten. Flying Higher. 2010. 236p. pap. 18.95 *(978-1-4251-6652-6(0))* Trafford Publishing.

Bluffield, Robert. Imperial Airways. 2010. (ENG., Illus.). 224p. 56.95 *(978-1-906537-07-4(0))* Allan, Ian Publishing GBR. Dist: BookMasters Distribution Services (BDS).

Blumenthal, George T., ed. Aviation & Climate Change. 2010. (Environmental Research Advances Ser.). 115.00 *(978-1-60876-757-1(4))* Nova Science Pubs., Inc.

Bodding, Gerald A. & Cass, William F. Alaska's Father Goose: Captain Gerald A. "Bud" Bodding: A Career in Aviation. 2010. 176p. pap. 19.95 ***(978-0-88839-651-8(1))*** Hancock Hse. Pubs.

Bruce, Peter J. Understanding Decision-Making Processes in Airline Operations Control. 2011. (Illus.). 206p. 99.95 ***(978-1-4094-1148-2(6))*** Ashgate Publishing Co.

Bubb, Daniel K. Landing in Las Vegas: Commercial Aviation & the Making of a Tourist City. 2012. (Shepperson Series in Nevada History Ser.). (Illus.). 176p. 34.95 ***(978-0-87417-872-2(X))*** Univ. of Nevada Pr.

Cassidy, Michael J. & Navarrete, Joseph. Airport Passenger-Related Processing Rates Guidebook. 2009. (Illus.). 116p. pap. *(978-0-309-11805-7(0))* Transportation Research Board.

Chen, Philip N. L. Great Cities of the World. 2010. (Illus.). 216p. pap. ***(978-962-8269-50-1(X))*** Hong Kong Univ. Pr.

Ciriani, Tito A., et al, eds. Operations Research in Space & Air. 2010. (Applied Optimization Ser.). 464p. pap. 339.00 *(978-1-4419-5242-4(X)*, 144195242X) Springer.

Clever, Reinhard & Hansen, Mark M. The Competitive Advantage of High Speed Rail: Airport & Station Accessibility as a Determinant of Mode Choice. 2008. 240p. pap. *(978-3-639-10376-2(9))* VDM Verlag Dr. Mueller e.K.

Cliff, Roger, et al. Ready for Takeoff: China's Advancing Aerospace Industry, 1 vol. 2011. (ENG.). 162p. (C). pap. 24.00 *(978-0-8330-5180-6(6))* RAND Corp., The.

Committee for the Assessment of NASA's Aeronautics Research Program & National Research Council. NASA Aeronautics Research: An Assessment. 2008. (ENG.). 122p. pap. 31.75 *(978-0-309-11913-9(8))* National Academies Pr.

Craig, Kodera, et al. From Props to Jets: Commercial Aviation's Transition to the Jet Age 1952-1962. 2010. 160p. 29.95 *(978-1-58007-146-8(5))* Specialty Pr. Pubs. & Wholesalers, Inc.

Cram101 Textbook Reviews & Cram101 Textbook Reviews. Outlines & Highlights for a Europe of the Air: The Airline Industry & European Integration by Martin Staniland. 2011. 520p. pap. 38.95 ***(978-1-61830-836-8(X))*** Cram101 Inc.

—Outlines & Highlights for Air Transportation: A Management Perspective by John Wensveen. 2011. 488p. pap. 37.95 ***(978-1-61830-851-1(3))*** Cram101 Inc.

Cronin, Mike. Doesn't Time Fly? Aer Lingus - Its History. 2011. (ENG., Illus.). 224p. 44.95 *(978-1-84889-111-1(3))* Collins Pr., The IRL. Dist: Dufour Editions, Inc.

Daley, Ben. Air Transport & the Environment. 2010. (Illus.). 274p. 69.95 *(978-0-7546-7286-9(7))* Ashgate Publishing Co.

Davies, R. E. G. Airline of the Jet Age: A History. 2011. (ENG., Illus.). 480p. 99.95 *(978-0-9788460-8-4(7))* Smithsonian Institution Scholarly Pr.

De Kuyffer, Erik. The Integration of Uavs into Controlled Airspace. 2009. 124p. pap. *(978-3-639-20081-2(0))* VDM Verlag Dr. Mueller e.K.

Deborah A. Boehm-Davis & National Research Council. Assessing the Research & Development Plan for the Next Generation Air Transportation System: Summary of a Workshop. 2008. (ENG.). 38p. pap. 15.00 *(978-0-309-12470-6(0))* National Academies Pr.

Dillingham, Gerald L. Commercial Aviation: Potential Safety & Capacity Issues Associated with the Introduction of the New A380 Aircraft. 2007. (Illus.). 69p. (C). pap. 20.00 *(978-1-4223-1583-5(5))* DIANE Publishing Co.

—Commercial Aviation: Programs & Options for Providing Air Service to Small Communities. 2007. (Illus.). 46p. (C). pap. 20.00 *(978-1-4223-1577-4(0))* DIANE Publishing Co.

—Joint Planning & Development Office: Progress & Key Issues in Planning the Transition to the Next Generation Air Transportation System. 2007. (Illus.). 20p. (C). pap. 15.00 *(978-1-4223-1477-7(4))* DIANE Publishing Co.

Dixon, Matthew. The Maintenance Costs of Aging Aircraft: Insights from Commercial Aviation. 2006. (Illus.). 104p. per. 20.00 *(978-0-8330-3941-5(5)*, mg-486) RAND Corp., The.

Doganis, Rigas. Flying off Course Fourth Edition. 4th ed. 2010. (ENG., Illus.). 352p. 64.95 *(978-0-415-44737-9(2))*; 190.00 *(978-0-415-44736-2(4))* Routledge.

Donald, David, ed. The Classic Civil Aircraft Guide: From 1920 to 1964. 2006. (Illus.). 111p. reprint ed. 25.00 *(978-1-4223-5513-8(6))* DIANE Publishing Co.

Donohue, George L., et al. Terminal Chaos: Why US Air Travel Is Broken & How to Fix It. 2008. (Library of Flight Ser.). (Illus.). 150p. *(978-1-56347-949-6(4))* American Institute of Aeronautics & Astronautics.

Duke, Graham. Air Band Radio Guide. 7th rev. ed. 2010. (ENG., Illus.). 110p. pap. 16.95 *(978-1-85780-319-8(1))* Allan, Ian Publishing GBR. Dist: BookMasters Distribution Services (BDS).

Effects of the Proposed Arrangement Between DHL & UPS on Competition, Customer Service, & Employment: Hearing Before the Committee on Transportation & Infrastructure, House of Representatives, One Hundred Tenth Congress, Second Session, September 16, 2008. 2008. (Illus.). xi, 255p. *(978-0-16-083399-1(X)*, 552-070-39212-2) United States Government Printing Office.

Eltaher, Hassan M. Aviation & Maritime Security Intelligence. 2012. (ENG., Illus.). 242p. pap. ***(978-0-9784760-1-4(8))*** E&W Communications.

Essential Air Service & Small Community Air Service Development Programs: Hearing Before the Subcommittee on Aviation of the Committee on Transportation & Infrastructure, House of Representatives, One Hundred Tenth Congress, First Session, April 25, 2007. 2007. (Illus.). xv, 306p. *(978-0-16-079630-2(X)*, 552-070-36587-7) United States Government Printing Office.

Falconer, Jonathan. Concorde: The Ultimate Photographic History. 2009. (ENG., Illus.). 256p. 59.95 *(978-1-84425-529-0(8)*, 1844255298) Haynes Publishing PLC GBR. Dist: MBI Distribution Services/Quayside Distribution.

Fallows, James. China Airborne. 2012. (ENG., Illus.). 288p. 25.95 ***(978-0-375-42211-9(0)***, Pantheon) Knopf Doubleday Publishing Group.

Federal Aviation Administration (FAA) Staff, creator. Commercial Pilot & Flight Instructor for Helicopter for Practical Test Standards: FAA-S-8081-16A & -7B. 2007. (Practical Test Standards Ser.). (ENG.). 208p. pap. 5.95 *(978-1-56027-674-6(6))* Aviation Supplies & Academics, Inc.

Federal Aviation Administration Reauthorization: Hearing Before the Subcommittee on Aviation of the Committee on Transportation & Infrastructure, House of Representatives, One Hundred Tenth Congress, First Session, March 14, 21, 22, 28, 2007. 2007. (Illus.). xxiii, 996p. *(978-0-16-079982-2(1)*, 552-070-36807-8) United States Government Printing Office.

The Federal Aviation Administration's R & D Budget Priorities for Fiscal Year 2008: Hearing Before the Subcommittee on Space & Aeronautics, Committee on Science & Technology, House of Representatives, One Hundred Tenth Congress, First Session, March 22, 2007. 2007. (Illus.). iv, 74p. *(978-0-16-079025-6(5)*, 552-070-36135-9) United States Government Printing Office.

Frawley, Gerard. The International Directory of Civil Aircraft: 2001/2002. 4th rev. ed. 2006. (Illus.). 207p. reprint ed. pap. 22.00 *(978-1-4223-5690-6(6))* DIANE Publishing Co.

Gesell, Laurence E. & Dempsey, Paul Stephen. Air Transportation: Foundations for the 21st Century. 3rd ed. 2010. 978p. (C). 98.00 *(978-1-890938-12-3(2))* Coast Aire Pubns. & Consulting.

Goedeking, Philipp. Networks in Aviation: Strategies & Structures. 2010. (ENG., Illus.). xvii, 145p. 109.00 *(978-3-642-13763-1(6)*, 3642137636) Springer.

Goodman, Jon C., ed. Aviation & the Environment. 2008. (Illus.). x, 515p. 95.00 *(978-1-60592-320-7(X))* Nova Science Pubs., Inc.

Government Printing Office Staff. FAA Aviation News. pap. 21.00 *(978-0-16-011812-8(3))* United States Government Printing Office.

Graham, Anne, et al, eds. Aviation & Tourism: Implications for Leisure Travel. 2008. (Illus.). 408p. 124.95 *(978-0-7546-7187-9(9))* Ashgate Publishing Co.

Green, Oliver & Anthony, Scott. British Aviation Posters: Art Design & Flight. 2012. (Illus.). 200p. 70.00 ***(978-1-84822-084-3(7)***, Lund Humphries Pubs.) Ashgate Publishing, Ltd. GBR. Dist: Ashgate Publishing Co.

Grounded: How the Air Transportation Crisis Is Hurting Entrepreneurs & the Economy. 2008. v, 70p. *(978-0-16-081793-9(5)*, 552-070-37999-1) United States Government Printing Office.

Haas, Silke. The European Aviation Industry. 2009. 112p. pap. *(978-3-639-13222-9(X))* VDM Verlag Dr. Mueller e.K.

Halford-Macleod, Guy. Britain's Airlines Vol. 3: 1964 to Deregulation. 2010. (ENG., Illus.). 288p. pap. 36.95 *(978-0-7524-5499-3(4))* History Pr. Ltd., The GBR. Dist: Independent Pubs. Group.

Harvey, Geraint. Management in the Airline Industry. 2008. (Routledge Research in Employment Relations Ser.). (Illus.). 158p. 143.00 *(978-0-415-39078-1(8))* Routledge.

Hayes, Michael D. Commercial Oral Exam Guide: The Comprehensive Guide to Prepare You for the FAA Checkride. 7th ed. 2010. (Oral Exam Guide Ser.). (ENG.). 240p. pap. 12.95 *(978-1-56027-796-5(3))* Aviation Supplies & Academics, Inc.

Hellemann, Rolf. Capacity Options for Revenue Management: Theory & Applications in the Air Cargo Industry. 2006. (Lecture Notes in Economics & Mathematical Systems Ser.). (Illus.). xv, 199p. pap. 139.00 *(978-3-540-34419-3(5)*, 3540344195) Springer.

Hirst, M. The Air Transport System. 2008. 352p. *(978-1-84569-325-1(6))* Woodhead Publishing Ltd.

Hirst, Mike. The Air Transport System. 2008. (Library of Flight). (Illus.). ix, 341p. *(978-1-56347-964-9(8))* American Institute of Aeronautics & Astronautics.

Hoeveler, Patrick & Krämer, Adel. Desert Boneyards: Retired Aircraft Storage Facilities n the U. S. 2010. (Illus.). 160p. 45.00 *(978-0-7643-3662-1(2))* Schiffer Publishing, Ltd.

Hofbauer, Philip. Market Opportunities for Low-Cost Carriers in Chin. 2010. 108p. pap. *(978-3-639-27857-6(7))* VDM Verlag Dr. Mueller e.K.

Holloway, Stephen. Straight & Level: Practical Airline Economics. 3rd rev. ed. 2008. (Illus.). 614p. 154.95 *(978-0-7546-7256-2(5))*; pap. 49.95 *(978-0-7546-7258-6(1))* Ashgate Publishing Co.

Hoppe, Elizabeth A. Ethical Issues in Aviation. 2011. (Illus.). 314p. 99.95 *(978-1-4094-1786-6(7))* Ashgate Publishing Co.

Hurst, Mike, ed. The Air Transport System. 2008. ring bd. 239.95 *(978-1-4200-7212-9(9))* CRC Pr. LLC.

The Joint Planning & Development Office & the Next Generation Air Transportation System: Status & Issues: Hearing Before the Subcommittee on Space & Aeronautics, Committee on Science & Technology, House of

A

Representatives, One Hundred Tenth Congress, First Session, March 29, 2007. 2007. (Illus.). iv, 78p. (978-0-16-080101-3(X), 552-070-36842-6) United States Government Printing Office.

Jones, Geoff. Cardiff Airport at Rhoose: 70 Years of Aviation History. 2012. (ENG., Illus.). 160p. pap. 29.95 (978-0-7524-5988-2(0)) History Pr. Ltd.,The GBR. Dist: Independent Pubs. Group.

Jones, Ivor. Airfields & Landing Grounds of Wales. 2008. (ENG.). 192p. pap. 38.95 (978-0-7524-4510-6(3)) History Pr. Ltd.,The GBR. Dist: Independent Pubs. Group.

Kassim, Hussein & Stevens, Handley. Air Transport & the European Union: Europeanization & Its Limits. 2010. (Palgrave Studies in European Union Politics Ser.). (ENG., Illus.). 240p. 95.00 (978-0-333-63127-0(7)) Palgrave Macmillan.

Kossmann, Mario. Delivering Excellent Service Quality in Aviation: A Practical Guide for Internal & External Service Providers. 2006. (Illus.). 208p. 120.00 (978-0-7546-4725-6(0)) Ashgate Publishing Co.

Lawton, Thomas C., ed. Strategic Management in Aviation: Critical Essays. 2007. (Illus.). 416p. 225.00 (978-0-7546-2651-0(2)) Ashgate Publishing Co.

Liguori, Michael J. Commercial Airlines: Passenger Fee Issues. 2011. (Illus.). 101p. pap. (978-1-61761-989-2(2)) Nova Science Pubs., Inc.

Macário, Rosário & Van de Voorde, Eddy, eds. Critical Issues in Air Transport Economics & Business. 2010. (Routledge Studies in the Modern World Economy Ser.). (ENG., Illus.). 432p. (C). 145.00 (978-0-415-57055-8(7)) Routledge.

Mancia, Wilson & Santoro, Miguel. Heuristics for Reverse Logistics of Non-Conform Material. 2010. 104p. pap. (978-3-639-24152-5(5)) VDM Verlag Dr. Mueller e.K.

Maxwell, David. Airbus A380: Superjumbo on World Tour. rev. ed. 2007. (ENG., Illus.). 160p. 29.95 (978-0-7603-3279-5(7), 0760332797, Zenith Pr.) MBI Publishing Co. LLC.

Metcalfe-Chenail, Danielle. For the Love of Flying: The Story of Laurentian Air Services. 2010. (Illus.). 224p. pap. 36.95 (978-1-896941-57-8(5)) Brass, Robin Studio, Inc. CAN. Dist: Midpoint Trade Bks., Inc.

Morrell, Peter S. Moving Boxes by Air: The Economics of International Air Cargo. 2011. (Illus.). 352p. 99.95 (978-1-4094-0252-7(5)) Ashgate Publishing Co.

Morris, Doug. From the Flight Deck: Plane Talk & Sky Science. 2007. (ENG., Illus.). 184p. per. 15.95 (978-1-55022-765-9(3)) ECW Pr. CAN. Dist: Independent Pubs. Group.

Mortimer, Gavin. Chasing Icarus: The Seventeen Days in 1910 That Forever Changed American Aviation. 2009. (ENG., Illus.). 320p. 26.00 (978-0-8027-1711-5(X)) Walker & Co.

Morton, John K. European Airlines. 2010. (ENG., Illus.). 111p. pap. 27.95 (978-1-85780-210-8(1)) Allan, Ian Publishing GBR. Dist: BookMasters Distribution Services (BDS).

National Research Council Staff. Decadal Survey of Civil Aeronautics: Foundation for the Future. 2006. (ENG., Illus.). 212p. pap. 46.75 (978-0-309-10158-5(1)) National Academies Pr.

The National Transportation Safety Board's Most Wanted Aviation Safety Improvements: Hearing Before the Subcommittee on Aviation of the Committee on Transportation & Infrastructure, House of Representatives, One Hundred Tenth Congress, First Session, June 6, 2007. 2007. xvi, 166p. (978-0-16-079953-2(8), 552-070-36780-2) United States Government Printing Office.

Neuscheler, Tillmann. Flughäfen zwischen Regulierung und Wettbewerb: Eine netzökonomische Analyse. 2008. (GER., Illus.). 379p. pap. (978-3-8329-3737-9(4)) Nomos Verlagsgesellschaft.

The Next Generation Air Transportation System: Status & Issues: Hearing Before the Committee on Science & Technology, House of Representatives, One Hundred Tenth Congress, Second Session, September 11, 2008. 2008. (Illus.). iv, 216p. (978-0-16-082502-6(4), 552-070-38540-1) United States Government Printing Office.

NextGen: Area Navigation (RNAV) 2009. (Illus.). xvi, 194p. (978-0-16-084676-2(5), 552-070-40169-5) United States Government Printing Office.

O'Connell, John F. & Williams, George, eds. Contemporary Issues in the Air Transport Industry. 2011. (Illus.). 508p. 124.95 (978-1-4094-0097-4(2)) Ashgate Publishing Co.

Ottaway, Susan & Ottaway, Ian. Fly with the Stars: British South American Airways: the Rise & Controversial Fall of a Long-Haul Trailblazer. 2007. (ENG., Illus.). 256p. 36.95 (978-0-7509-4448-9(X)) Sutton Publishing.

Oversight of the Joint Planning & Development Office: Hearing Before the Subcommittee on Aviation of the Committee on Commerce, Science, & Transportation, United States Senate, One Hundred Ninth Congress, Second Session, July 25, 2006. 2011. (Illus.). iii, 69p. (978-0-16-089027-7(6), 552-070-43059-8) United States Government Printing Office.

Pescador, Katrina, et al. San Diego International Airport Lindbergh Field. 2012. (Images of Aviation Ser.). (ENG., Illus.). 128p. pap. 21.99 (978-0-7385-8908-4(X)) Arcadia Publishing.

Pilarski, Adam M. Why Can't We Make Money in Aviation? 2007. (Illus.). 260p. 69.95 (978-0-7546-4911-3(3)) Ashgate Publishing Co.

Pirie, Gordon. Air Empire: British Imperial Civil Aviation, 1919-39. 2010. (Studies in Imperialism Ser.). (ENG., Illus.). 272p. 89.95 (978-0-7190-4111-2(2)) Manchester Univ. Pr. GBR. Dist: Macmillan.

Pirie, Gordon. Cultures & Caricatures of British Imperial Flying. 2012. (Studies in Imperialism Ser.). (ENG., Illus.). 256p. 100.00 (978-0-7190-8682-3(5)) Manchester Univ. Pr. GBR. Dist: Macmillan.

Poynter, Dan. Dan Poynter's Air Travel Handbook. 2011. 322p. pap. 14.95 (978-1-56860-150-2(6)) Para Publishing.

Redmond, Shirley Raye. Richard Branson: Virgin Mega-brand Mogul. 2011. (Innovators Ser.). 64p. lib. bdg. 28.75 (978-0-7377-5536-7(9), Kidhaven) Cengage Gale.

Reeves, Earl. Aviation's Place in Tomorrow's Business. (Airlines History Project Ser.). reprint ed. 35.00 (978-0-404-19331-7(5)) AMS Pr., Inc.

—Aviation's Place in Tomorrow's Business. 2010. 154p. pap. 24.21 (978-1-153-44622-8(7)) General Bks. LLC.

Restructuring Canada's Airline Industry. (978-0-660-61142-6(2)) Canadian Government Publishing.

A Review of the Federal Aviation Administration's Research & Development Program: Hearing Before the Subcommittee on Space & Aeronautics, Committee on Science, Space, & Technology, House of Representatives, One Hundred Twelfth Congress, First Session, February 16, 2011. 2011. (Illus.). iii, 67p. (978-0-16-088764-2(X), 552-070-42904-2) United States Government Printing Office.

Rural Air Service: Hearing Before the Subcommittee on Aviation of the Committee on Commerce, Science, & Transportation, United States Senate, One Hundred Ninth Congress, Second Session, September 14, 2006. 2011. (Illus.). iii, 62p. (978-0-16-089003-1(9), 552-070-43035-1) United States Government Printing Office.

Rust, Daniel L. Flying Across America: The Airline Passenger Experience. 2009. (ENG., Illus.). 272p. 45.00 (978-0-8061-3870-1(X)) Univ. of Oklahoma Pr.

Schlumberger, Charles E. Open Skies for Africa: Implementing the Yamoussoukro Decision. 2010. (Directions in Development Ser.). (ENG.). 260p. pap. 30.00 (978-0-8213-8205-9(5), 9780821382059) World Bank Pubns.

Shaw, Stephen. Airline Marketing & Management. 6th rev. ed. 2007. 336p. pap. 34.95 (978-0-7546-4820-8(6)) 7th rev. ed. 2011. 378p. pap. 34.95 (978-1-4094-0149-0(9)) Ashgate Publishing Co.

—Airline Marketing & Management. 6th rev. ed. 2007. 336p. 144.95 (978-0-7546-4819-2(2)) Ashgate Publishing, Ltd. GBR. Dist: Ashgate Publishing Co.

Shawcross, Philip. Flightpath Student's Book: Aviation English for Pilots & ATCOs. 2011. (ENG.). 192p. pap., stu. ed. 46.00 incl. DVD, audio compact disk (978-0-521-17871-6(1)) Cambridge Univ. Pr.

Smith, Henry L. Airways: The History of Commercial Aviation in the United States. (Airlines History Project Ser.). (Illus.). reprint ed. 52.50 (978-0-404-19335-5(8)) AMS Pr., Inc.

Sparaco, Pierre. Chroniques Aéronautiques. 2010. (FRE.). 379p. (978-2-35593-083-6(X), Spotlight Poets) Pascal Galodé éditeurs.

Springer, A. M., et al. America by Air. 2007. (ENG., Illus.). 40p. pap. 10.50 (978-0-16-079431-5(5), U. S. National Aeronautics & Space Administration) United States Government Printing Office.

Staniland, Martin. A Europe of the Air? The Airline Industry & European Integration. 2008. (Governance in Europe Ser.). (ENG.). 316p. 80.00 (978-0-7425-2651-8(8)) Rowman & Littlefield Publishers, Inc.

Starkie, David. Aviation Markets: Studies in Competition & Regulatory Reform. 2008. (Illus.). 246p. pap. 49.95 (978-0-7546-7388-0(X)) Ashgate Publishing Co.

Szurovy, Geza & Yenne, Bill. Classic American Airlines. 2007. 360p. pap. 12.99 (978-0-7603-3206-1(1), Zenith Pr.) MBI Publishing Co. LLC.

Taneja, Nawal K. Flying Ahead of the Airplane. 2008. 298p. 69.95 (978-0-7546-7579-2(3)) Ashgate Publishing Co.

—Looking Beyond the Runway: Airlines Innovating with Best Practices While Facing Realities. 2010. (Illus.). 354p. 64.95 (978-1-4094-0099-8(9)) Ashgate Publishing Co.

Taylor, Michael J. H. The World's Commercial Airlines: An Illustrated History of the Airlines & Their Insignia. 2007. (Illus.). 80p. reprint ed. 25.00 (978-1-4223-6840-4(8)) DIANE Publishing Co.

Tu, Yufeng. Air Transportation System Performance- Estimation & Comparative Analysis of Departure Delays. 2007. pap. (978-3-8364-2230-7(1)) VDM Verlag Dr. Mueller e.K.

United States, Congress House Committee on Transportation and Infrastructure Subcommittee on Aviation Staff, contrib. by. Commercial Jet Fuel Supply: Impact & Cost on the United States Airline Industry: Hearing Before the Subcommittee on Aviation of the Committee on Transportation & Infrastructure, House of Representatives, One Hundred Ninth Congress, Second Session, February 15, 2006. 2007. (Illus.). v, 124p. (978-0-16-078047-9(0), 552-070-35455-7) United States Government Printing Office.

—Next Generation Air Transportation System Financing Options: Hearing Before the Subcommittee on Aviation of the Committee on Transportation & Infrastructure, House of Representatives, One Hundred Ninth Congress, Second Session, September 27, 2006. 2007. (Illus.). v, 92p. (978-0-16-078133-9(7), 552-070-35533-2) United States Government Printing Office.

Varma, Amily. Aviation, a World of Growth & Change: Proceedings of the 29th International Air Transport Conference, August 19-22, 2007, Irving, Texas. 2007. (Illus.). 253p. pap. 79.00 (978-0-7844-0938-1(2)) American Society of Civil Engineers.

Vasigh, Bijan, et al. Foundations of Airline Finance: Methodology & Practice. 2010. (Illus.). 444p. 134.95 (978-0-7546-7769-7(9)); pap. 49.95 (978-0-7546-7770-3(2)) Ashgate Publishing Co.

—Introduction to Air Transport Economics: From Theory to Applications. 2008. (Illus.). 382p. 144.95 (978-0-7546-7079-7(1)); pap. 39.95 (978-0-7546-7081-0(3)) Ashgate Publishing Co.

Verhovek, Sam Howe. Jet Age: The Comet, the 707, & the Race to Shrink the World. 2011. (ENG., Illus.). 272p. (gr. 12). 16.00 (978-1-58333-436-2(X), Avery) Penguin Group (USA) Inc.

Wagner, Mark & Norris, Guy. Boeing 787 Dreamliner. 2009. (ENG., Illus.). 160p. 30.00 (978-0-7603-2815-6(3), 0760328153, Zenith Pr.) MBI Publishing Co. LLC.

Walsh, Connor R. Airline Industry: Strategies, Operations & Safety. 2011. (Transportation Infrastructure - Roads, Highways, Bridges, Airports & Mass Transit Ser.). (Illus.). x, 242p. 129.00 (978-1-61122-079-7(3)) Nova Science Pubs., Inc.

Weigang, Li & Romani, Italo. Computational Models, Software Engineering, & Advanced Technologies in Air Transportation: Next Generation Applications. Barros, Alexandre de, ed. 2009. (Illus.). 392p. 180.00 (978-1-60566-800-0(1), Engineering Science Reference) IGI Global.

Wensveen, John G. Air Transportation: A Management Perspective. 7th rev. ed. 2011. (Illus.). 604p. 149.95 (978-1-4094-3062-9(6)); pap. 69.95 (978-1-4094-3063-6(4)) Ashgate Publishing Co.

Wilkinson, Paul & Jenkins, Brian. Aviation Terrorism & Security. 2nd rev. ed. 2007. (Political Violence Ser.: No. 6). (Illus.). 202p. pap. 39.95 (978-0-7146-8221-1(7), RU33795) Routledge.

Williams, Alan. Contemporary Issues Shaping China's Civil Aviation Policy: Balancing International with Domestic Priorities. 2009. 258p. 124.95 (978-0-7546-7140-4(2)) Ashgate Publishing Co.

Wittmer, Andreas, et al, eds. Aviation Systems: Management of the Integrated Aviation Value Chain. 2011. (Springer Texts in Business & Economics Ser.). (ENG., Illus.). xvii, 236p. 139.00 (978-3-642-20079-3(6), 3642200796) Springer.

World Air Cargo Forecast (1993) 73p. pap. 50.00 (978-0-7881-1793-0(9)) DIANE Publishing Co.

Wragg, David. The World's Major Airlines. 2nd ed. 2007. (ENG., Illus.). 320p. 44.95 (978-0-7509-4481-6(1)) Sutton Publishing.

Youngblood, Dorothy F. The Open Skies. 2008. 160p. 17.99 (978-0-7858-2442-8(1), Chartwell) Book Sales, Inc.

AERONAUTICS, COMMERCIAL—COLLECTIVE BARGAINING

see Collective Bargaining—Aeronautics

AERONAUTICS, COMMERCIAL—LAW AND LEGISLATION

Abeyratne, Ruwantissa. Aviation Security Law. 2010. (ENG.). xii, 250p. 139.00 (978-3-642-11701-5(5), 3642117015) Springer.

Abeyratne, Ruwantissa. Strategic Issues in Air Transport: Legal, Economic & Technical Aspects. 2012. (ENG.). xiv, 424p. 139.00 (978-3-642-21959-7(4), 3642219594) Springer.

Bartlik, Martin. The Impact of EU Law on the Regulation of International Air Transportation. 2007. 290p. 124.95 (978-0-7546-4951-9(2)) Ashgate Publishing Co.

Boewe, Marius & Geisler, Markus. The German Civil Aviation Act. 2009. 134p. 88.00 (978-90-77596-72-2(0)) Eleven International Publishing NLD. Dist: International Specialized Bk. Services.

Clarke, Malcolm. Contracts of Carriage by Air. 2nd rev. ed. 2010. 303p. 595.00 (978-1-84311-887-9(4)) Informa Professional GBR. Dist: International Specialized Bk. Services.

Giemulla, Elmar & Schmid, Ronald, eds. Montreal Convention. 9041st ed. 2006. (Illus.). ring bd. (978-90-411-2456-2(X)) Kluwer Law International.

Goode, Roy. Official Commentary on the Convention on International Interests in Mobile Equipment & Protocol Thereto on Matters Specific to Aircraft Equipment. rev. ed. 2008. (ENG.). 572p. pap. 384.00 (978-88-86449-18-2(6)) UNIDROIT ITA. Dist: International Specialized Bk. Services.

Holding, John D. The British Manual of International Air Carriage. 2009. (ENG.). 223p. (978-1-55221-160-1(6)) Irwin Law, Inc.

Hongliang, Zang & Qingfen, Meng. Civil Aviation Law in the People's Republic of China. 2010. 228p. 91.00 (978-90-77596-91-3(7)) Eleven International Publishing NLD. Dist: International Specialized Bk. Services.

Klingmüller, Angela & Steppler, Ulrich. EU Emissions Trading Scheme & Aviation. 2010. 448p. 104.00 (978-90-77596-79-1(8)) Eleven International Publishing NLD. Dist: International Specialized Bk. Services.

Lissitzyn, Oliver J. International Air Transport & National Policy. (Airlines History Project Ser.). reprint ed. 52.00 (978-0-404-19327-0(7)) AMS Pr., Inc.

Mackenzie, David. Icao: A History of the International Civil Aviation Organization. 2010. (ENG., Illus.). 608p. (978-1-4426-4010-8(3)) Univ. of Toronto Pr.

Milde, Michael. International Air Law & ICAO. 2nd rev. ed. 2012. 448p. 135.00 (978-94-90947-35-4(0)) Eleven International Publishing NLD. Dist: International Specialized Bk. Services.

Mun, Chun-Jo. Hanggong Kwallyon Kukche Hyobyak Kwa Hanggong Popche Kaeson Pangan Yon'gu. 2009. (KOR.). 319p. (978-89-8323-402-5(4)) Korea Legislation Research Institute.

Rhoades, Dawna L. Evolution of International Aviation: Phoenix Rising. 2nd rev. ed. 2008. (Illus.). 296p. 59.95 (978-0-7546-7389-7(8)) Ashgate Publishing Co.

Smith, Sydney B. Air Transport in the Pacific Area. reprint ed. 39.50 (978-0-404-59561-6(8)) AMS Pr., Inc.

Starkie, David. Aviation Markets: Studies in Economic Policy. 2008. (Illus.). 246p. 124.95 (978-0-7546-7360-6(X)) Ashgate Publishing Co.

Truxal, Steven. Competition & Regulation in the Airline Industry: Puppets in Chaos. 2012. (Routledge Research in Competition Law Ser.). (ENG.). 208p. (C). 135.00 (978-0-415-67196-5(5)) Routledge.

Von Den Steinen, Erwin. National Interest & International Aviation. 2006. (Aviation Law & Policy Ser.). 225p. (978-90-411-2455-5(1)) Kluwer Law International.

Weber. Iel International Civil Aviation Organization. 2011. (Illus.). 216p. pap. 103.00 (978-90-411-3880-4(3)) Wolters Kluwer Law & Business.

Weber, et al. International Civil Aviation Organization: An Introduction. 2007. (Illus.). (978-90-411-2622-1(8)) Kluwer Law International.

World Trade Organization Staff, contrib. by. Air Transport & the GATS: Documentation for the Second Air Transport Review under the General Agreement on Trade in Services (GATS): 2000-2005 in Review. 2007. (Illus.). 156p. pap. (978-92-870-3384-0(6)) World Trade Organization.

AERONAUTICS, COMMERCIAL—LAW AND LEGISLATION—UNITED STATES

Aviation Theory Centre Ltd., Staff, ed. The Pilot's Manual: Ground School: All the Aeronautical Knowledge Required to Pass the FAA Exams & Operate as a Private & Commercial Pilot. 3rd ed. 2007. (Pilot's Manual Ser.). (ENG., Illus.). 688p. 59.95 (978-1-56027-677-7(0)) Aviation Supplies & Academics, Inc.

Benson, Erik. Aviator of Fortune: Lowell Yerex & the Anglo-American Commercial Rivalry, 1931-1946. 2006. (Louise Lindsey Merrick Natural Environment Ser.: No. 40). (ENG., Illus.). 280p. 45.00 (978-1-58544-500-4(2)) Texas A&M Univ. Pr.

Committee on NASA's National Aviation Operations Monitoring Service (NAOMS) Project: An Independent Assessment & National Research Council. An Assessment of NASA's National Aviation Operations Monitoring Service. 2009. (ENG.). 160p. pap. 37.75 (978-0-309-14646-3(1)) National Academies Pr.

Dobson, Alan P. FDR & Civil Aviation: Flying Strong, Flying Free. 2011. (World of the Roosevelts Ser.). (ENG.). 292p. 85.00 (978-0-230-10666-6(8)) Palgrave Macmillan.

Elias, Bartholomew. Airport & Aviation Security: U. S. Policy & Strategy in the Age of Global Terrorism. 2009. (ENG., Illus.). 439p. 82.95 (978-1-4200-7029-3(0)) Auerbach Pubs., Inc.

FAA's Oversight of On-Demand Aircraft Operators: Hearing Before the Subcommittee on Aviation of the Committee on Transportation & Infrastructure, House of Representatives, One Hundred Eleventh Congress, Second Session, March 17, 2010. 2010. (Illus.). xiv, 116p. (978-0-16-086769-9(X), 552-070-41690-1) United States Government Printing Office.

Federal Aviation Administration. Far/fc 2010: Federal Aviation Regulations for Flight Crew. 2009. (FAR/AIM Ser.). (ENG.). 496p. pap. 16.95 (978-1-56027-745-3(9)) Aviation Supplies & Academics, Inc.

—Risk Management Handbook: Faa-h-8083-2. 2009. (FAA Handbooks Ser.). (ENG.). 112p. pap. 16.95 (978-1-56027-754-5(8)) Aviation Supplies & Academics, Inc.

Federal Aviation Administration (FAA). Far/fc 2012: Federal Aviation Regulations for Flight Crew. 2011. (FAR/AIM Ser.). (ENG.). 542p. pap. 19.95 (978-1-56027-859-7(5)) Aviation Supplies & Academics, Inc.

Federal Aviation Administration Reauthorization ACT of 2009: Hearing Before the Subcommittee on Aviation of the Committee on Transportation & Infrastructure, House of Representatives, One Hundred Eleventh Congress, First Session, February 11, 2009. 2009. (Illus.). xxii, 598p. (978-0-16-084367-9(7), 552-070-39910-1) United States Government Printing Office.

Gesell, Laurence E. & Dempsey, Paul Stephen. Aviation & the Law, 5th Ed. 5th ed. 2011. (Illus.). 938p. (C). 98.00 (978-1-890938-13-0(0)) Coast Aire Pubns. & Consulting.

Harakas, Andrew J. Litigating the Aviation Case. 3rd ed. 2008. (978-1-59031-996-3(6)) American Bar Assn.

Havel, Brian F. In Search of Open Skies: Law & Policy for a New Era in International Aviation. 2nd ed. 2009. xxxi, 712p. (978-90-411-2389-3(X)) Kluwer Law International.

Lawrence, Harry W. Aviation & the Role of Government. 2nd rev. ed. 2010. (ENG.). 516p. pap. 94.33 (978-0-7575-4803-1(2)) Kendall Hunt Publishing Co.

Navigating the Legal Impact of Airport Security Measures: An In-Depth Look at Passenger Profiling & Its Effect on the Public. 2011. 34p. pap. (978-0-314-27854-8(0)) Aspatore Bks.

United States, Congress House Committee on Transportation and Infrastructure Subcommittee on Aviation Staff, contrib. by. Oversight of Federal Aviation Administration Safety Programs: Hearing Before the Subcommittee on Aviation of the Committee on Transportation & Infrastructure, House of Representatives, One Hundred Ninth Congress, Second Session, September 20, 2006. 2007. (Illus.). v, 194p. (978-0-16-078468-2(9), 552-070-35754-8) United States Government Printing Office.

—Reforming the Wright Amendment: Hearing Before the Subcommittee on Aviation of the Committee on Transportation & Infrastructure, House of Representatives, One Hundred Ninth Congress, Second Session, July 12, 2006. 2007. vi, 314p. (978-0-16-078168-1(X), 552-070-35566-9) United States Government Printing Office.

Weber. Handbook on Aviation Law. 2011. (978-90-411-2645-0(7)) Kluwer Law International.

AERONAUTICS, COMMERCIAL—SECURITY MEASURES

Abeyratne, Ruwantissa. Aviation Security Law. 2010. (ENG.). xii, 250p. 139.00 (978-3-642-11701-5(5), 3642117015) Springer.

Aircraft Icing: Hearing Before the Subcommittee on Aviation of the Committee on Transportation & Infrastructure, House of Representatives, One Hundred

Eleventh Congress, Second Session, February 24, 2010. 2010. (Illus.). xv, 170p. ***(978-0-16-086345-5(7)***, 552-070-41429-1) United States Government Printing Office.

Altarescu, Joseba & Bai, Taro. Aviation & Passenger Security. 2012. (Transportation Issues, Policies & R & D Ser.). 147p. 95.00 ***(978-1-62100-155-3(5))*** Nova Science Pubs., Inc.

Assessment of Checkpoint Security: Are Our Airports Keeping Passengers Safe?: Hearing Before the Subcommittee on Transportation Security & Infrastructure Protection of the Committee on Homeland Security, House of Representatives, One Hundred Eleventh Congress, Second Session, March 17, 2010. 2011. (Illus.). iv, 86p. ***(978-0-16-089070-3(5)***, 552-070-43102-1) United States Government Printing Office.

Auvinen, Petra. Achievement of Intersubjectivity in Airline Cockpit Interaction. 2009. (Acta Universitatis Tamperensis Ser.). 191p. pap. 82.50 *(978-951-44-7879-6(7))* Tampere Univ. Pr. FIN. Dist: Coronet Bks.

Aviation Security: An Update: Hearing Before the Subcommittee on Aviation of the Committee on Transportation & Infrastructure, House of Representatives, One Hundred Tenth Congress, Second Session, July 24, 2008. 2008. xv, 193p. *(978-0-16-084017-3(1)*, 552-070-39689-6) United States Government Printing Office.

Aviation Security: Are We Truly Protected?, Part I & a Frontline Perspective on the Need for Enhanced Human Resources & Equipment, Part II: Hearing Before the Subcommittee on Transportation Security & Infrastructure Protection of the Committee on Homeland Security, House of Representatives, One Hundred Tenth Congress, First Session, October 16, 2007 & November 1, 2007. 2009. (Illus.). iv, 117p. *(978-0-16-084141-5(0)*, 552-070-39748-5) United States Government Printing Office.

Ballesteros, Jose Sanchez-Alarcos. Improving Air Safety through Organizational Learning: Consequences of a Technology-Led Model. 2007. 188p. 124.95 *(978-0-7546-4912-0(1))* Ashgate Publishing Co.

Closing the Gaps in Air Cargo Security: Hearing Before the Committee on Homeland Security & Governmental Affairs, United States Senate, One Hundred Eleventh Congress, Second Session, November 16, 2010. 2011. iii, 64p. ***(978-0-16-090027-3(1)***, 552-070-43804-1) United States Government Printing Office.

Committee on Assessment of Security Technologies for Transportation & National Research Council. Fusion of Security System Data to Improve Airport Security. 2007. (ENG.). 82p. pap. 21.00 *(978-0-309-10748-8(2))* National Academies Pr.

Elias, Bartholomew. Airport & Aviation Security: U. S. Policy & Strategy in the Age of Global Terrorism. 2009. (ENG., Illus.). 439p. 82.95 *(978-1-4200-7029-3(0))* Auerbach Pubs., Inc.

Ensuring America's Security: Cleaning up the Nation's Watchlists: Hearing Before the Subcommittee on Transportation Security & Infrastructure Protection of the Committee on Homeland Security, House of Representatives, One Hundred Tenth Congress, Second Session, September 9, 2008. 2008. iii, 62p. *(978-0-16-084351-8(0)*, 552-070-39894-5) United States Government Printing Office.

FAA Reauthorization: Hearing Before the Committee on Commerce, Science, & Transportation, United States Senate, One Hundred Eighth Congress, First Session, April 10, 2003. 2010. (Illus.). iii, 74p. ***(978-0-16-086792-7(4)***, 552-070-41708-7) United States Government Printing Office.

The Future of TSA's Registered Traveler Program: Hearing Before the Subcommittee on Economic Security, Infrstructure [i.e. Infrastructure] Protection, & Cybersecurity of the Committee on Homeland Security, House of Representatives, One Hundred Ninth Congress, First Session, November 3, 2005. 2007. (Illus.). iv, 84p. *(978-0-16-079483-4(8)*, 552-070-36476-5) United States Government Printing Office.

Goldenkoff, Robert. Aviation Security: TSA¿s Change to its Prohibited Items List Has Not Resulted in any Reported Security Incidents, but the Impact of the Change on Screening Oper. Is Inconclusive. 2007. 18p. (C). pap. 15.00 *(978-1-4223-1550-7(9))* DIANE Publishing Co.

Harrison, John. International Aviation & Terrorism: Evolving Threats, Evolving Security. 2009. (Cass Series on Political Violence Ser.). (ENG.). 224p. 140.00 *(978-0-415-48541-8(X))* Routledge.

Hawley, Kip & Means, Nathan. Permanent Emergency: Inside the TSA & the Fight for the Future of American Security. 2012. (ENG., Illus.). 272p. 27.00 ***(978-0-230-12095-2(4))*** Palgrave Macmillan.

Irwin, Ron. The FAA Will KILL You. 2007. 182p. pap. 14.96 *(978-0-615-14885-4(9))* Irwin, Ronald.

Managing Risk & Increasing Efficiency: An Examination of the Implementation of the Registered Traveler Program: Hearing Before the Subcommittee on Transportation Security & Infrastructure Protection of the Committee on Homeland Security, House of Representatives, One Hundred Tenth Congress, First Session, July 31, 2007. 2009. iii, 44p. *(978-0-16-083977-1(7)*, 552-070-39649-7) United States Government Printing Office.

Markarian, Garik, et al. Aviation Security Engineering: A Holistic Approach. 2011. (Illus.). 280p. 109.00 *(978-1-60807-072-5(7))* Artech Hse., Inc.

Moving Beyond the First Five Years: How the Transportation Security Administration (TSA) Will Continue to Enhance Security for All Modes of Transportation: Hearing Before the Subcommittee on Transportation Security & Infrastructure Protection of the Committee on Homeland Security, House of Representatives, One Hundred Tenth Congress, Second Session, April 15, 2008. 2008. iii, 78p. *(978-0-16-081436-5(7)*, 552-070-37803-1) United States Government Printing Office.

Mun, Chun-Jo. Hanggong Kwallyon Kukche Hyobyak Kwa Hanggong Popche Kaeson Pangan Yon'gu. 2009. (KOR.). 319p. *(978-89-8323-402-5(4))* Korea Legislation Research Institute.

Nath, R. Aircraft Repossession & Enforcement. 2009. xxx, 1155p. *(978-90-411-2648-1(1))* Kluwer Law International.

National Research Council (U.S.), Committee on Assessment of Security Technologies for Transportation Staff, contrib. by. Assessment of Millimeter-Wave & Terahertz Technology for Detection & Identification of Concealed Explosives & Weapons. 2007. (ENG., Illus.). 88p. pap. 21.00 *(978-0-309-10469-2(6))* National Academies Pr.

Navigating the Legal Impact of Airport Security Measures: An In-Depth Look at Passenger Profiling & Its Effect on the Public. 2011. 34p. pap. ***(978-0-314-27854-8(0))*** Aspatore Bks.

The Next Step in Aviation Security — Cargo Security: Is DHS Implementing the Requirements of the 9/11 Law Effectively?: Hearing Before the Subcommittee on Transportation Security & Infrastructure Protection of the Committee on Homeland Security, House of Representatives, One Hundred Tenth Congress, Second Session, July 15, 2008. 2008. iii, 91p. *(978-0-16-082113-4(4)*, 552-070-38260-7) United States Government Printing Office.

One Year Later: Have TSA Airport Security Checkpoints Improved?: Hearing Before the Committee on Oversight & Government Reform, House of Representatives, One Hundred Tenth Congress, First Session, November 15, 2007. 2008. iii, 68p. *(978-0-16-082167-7(3)*, 552-070-38302-6) United States Government Printing Office.

Organisation for Economic Co-operation and Development Staff. Itf Round Tables Terrorism & International Transport: Towards Risk-Based Security Policy. 2009. (Illus.). 148p. pap. 63.00 *(978-92-821-0231-2(9))* Organization for Economic Cooperation & Development.

Osbourne, David L. & Offenhauer, Priscilla. The History of the U. S. Army Battle Command Training Program, 1986-2003. 2007. (ENG., Illus.). 198p. (gr. 9). per. 17.00 *(978-0-16-077797-4(6)*, 552-070-35247-3, Defense Dept.) United States Government Printing Office.

Passenger Screening RandD: Responding to President Obama's Call to Develop & Deploy the Next Generation of Screening Technologies: Hearing Before the Subcommittee on Technology & Innovation, Committee on Science & Technology, House of Representatives, One Hundred Eleventh Congress, Second Session, February 3, 2010. 2010. (Illus.). iii, 70p. *(978-0-16-086200-7(0)*, 552-070-41298-1) United States Government Printing Office.

The President's FY 2007 Budget: Risked-Based Spending at the Transportation Security Administration: Hearing Before the Subcommittee on Economic Security, Infrastructure Protection, & Cybersecurity of the Committee on Homeland Security, House of Representatives, One Hundred Ninth Congress, Second Session, February 16, 2006. 2007. iii, 28p. *(978-0-16-079636-4(9)*, 552-070-36588-5) United States Government Printing Office.

Price, Jeffrey & Forrest, Jeffrey. Practical Aviation Security: Predicting & Preventing Future Threats. 2008. (ENG., Illus.). 416p. 82.95 *(978-1-85617-610-1(X)*, Butterworth-Heinemann) Elsevier Science & Technology Bks.

The Progress & Pitfalls of the Terrorist Watch List: Field Hearing of the Committee on Homeland Security, House of Representatives, One Hundred Tenth Congress, First Session, November 8, 2007. 2009. (Illus.). iii, 70p. *(978-0-16-084558-1(0)*, 552-070-40080-0) United States Government Printing Office.

Protecting the Protectors: Examining the Personnel Challenges Facing the Federal Air Marshal Service: Hearing Before the Subcommittee on Management, Investigations, & Oversight of the Committee on Homeland Security, House of Representatives, One Hundred Eleventh Congress, First Session, July 23, 2009. 2010. iii, 43p. *(978-0-16-086291-5(4)*, 552-070-41377-4) United States Government Printing Office.

Seidenstat, Paul & Splane, Francis X., eds. Protecting Airline Passengers in the Age of Terrorism, 1 vol. 2009. (Praeger Security International Ser.). (Illus.). 326p. 59.95 *(978-0-313-35453-3(7)*, C35453, Praeger Pubs.) Greenwood Publishing Group, Inc.

Sharing & Analyzing Information to Prevent Terrorism: Hearing Before the Committee on the Judiciary, House of Representatives, One Hundred Eleventh Congress, Second Session, March 24, 2010. 2010. iii, 103p. *(978-0-16-087088-0(7)*, 552-070-41944-6) United States Government Printing Office.

The State of Aviation Security: Is Our Current System Capable of Meeting the Threat?: Hearing Before the Committee on Commerce, Science, & Transportation, United States Senate, One Hundred Eleventh Congress, Second Session, January 20, 2010. 2010. iv, 91p. *(978-0-16-086668-5(5)*, 552-070-41646-3) United States Government Printing Office.

Sweet, Kathleen. Aviation & Airport Security: Terrorism & Safety Concerns, Second Edition. 2nd ed. 2008. (ENG., Illus.). 384p. (C). 83.95 *(978-1-4200-8816-8(5)*, CRC Press) Taylor & Francis Group GBR. Dist: Taylor & Francis Group.

The Transportation Security Administration's Airline Passenger & Baggage Screening: Hearing Before the Committee on Commerce, Science, & Transportation, United States Senate, One Hundred Ninth Congress, Second Session, April 4, 2006. 2011. iii, 73p. ***(978-0-16-087971-5(X)***, 552-070-42422-9) United States Government Printing Office.

Turrión, Pierre. Air Cargo Security. 2011. (Defense, Security & Strategies Ser.). 172p. 95.00 ***(978-1-62100-054-9(0))*** Nova Science Pubs., Inc.

United States, Congress House Committee on Homeland Security Subcommittee on Economic Security, Infrastructure Protection, and Cybersecurity Staff, contrib. by. The Promise of Registered Traveler: Hearing Before the Subcommittee on Economic Security, Infrastructure Protection, & Cybersecurity of the Committee on Homeland Security, House of Representatives, One Hundred Ninth Congress, First Session, June 9, 2005 & June 16, 2005. 2007. iv, 81p. *(978-0-16-078345-6(3)*, 552-070-35646-1) United States Government Printing Office.

United States, Congress House Committee on Homeland Security Subcommittee on Intelligence, Information Sharing, and Terrorism Risk Assessment Staff, contrib. by. Transportation Security Administration's Office of Intelligence: Progress & Challenges: Hearing Before the Subcommittee on Intelligence, Information Sharing, & Terrorism Risk Assessment of the Committee on Homeland Security, U.S. House of Representatives, One Hundred Ninth Congress, Second Session, June 14, 2006. 2007. (Illus.). iii, 64p. *(978-0-16-078439-2(5)*, 552-070-35730-1) United States Government Printing Office.

University of Texas at Austin Staff, contrib. by. Helicopter Safety. 2007. *(978-0-88698-219-5(7))* Petroleum Extension Service (PETEX).

US Airways Flight 1549 Accident: Hearing Before the Subcommittee on Aviation of the Committee on Transportation & Infrastructure, House of Representatives, One Hundred Eleventh Congress, First Session, February 24, 2009. 2009. (Illus.). xvi, 251p. *(978-0-16-084260-3(3)*, 552-070-39830-9) United States Government Printing Office.

Visa Security & Passenger Pre-Screening Efforts in the Wake of Flight 253: Hearing Before the Subcommittee on Border, Maritime, & Global Counterterrorism of the Committee on Homeland Security, House of Representatives, One Hundred Eleventh Congress, Second Session, March 11, 2010. 2011. iii, 40p. ***(978-0-16-090137-9(5)***, 552-070-43840-8) United States Government Printing Office.

100 Percent Air Cargo Screening: Remaining Steps to Secure Passenger Aircraft: Hearing Before the Subcommittee on Transportation Security & Infrastructure Protection of the Committee on Homeland Security, House of Representatives, One Hundred Eleventh Congress, Second Session, June 30, 2010. 2011. (Illus.). iii, 70p. ***(978-0-16-088765-9(8)***, 552-070-42905-1) United States Government Printing Office.

AERONAUTICS, HIGH-SPEED

see High-Speed Aeronautics

AERONAUTICS, MILITARY

see also Air Power; Air Warfare; Aircraft Carriers; Airplanes, Military; Parachute Troops

also subdivision Aerial Operations under names of wars, e.g. World War, 1939-45—Aerial Operations

Abbot, Willis J. The War Machines: The Development of Aircraft & Submarines for Aerial & Undersea Warfare to the End of the First World War. 2010. (Illus.). 376p. *(978-0-85706-126-3(7))*; pap. *(978-0-85706-125-6(9))* Leonaur Ltd.

Alkire, Brien, et al. Applications for Navy Unmanned Aircraft Systems. 2010. 94p. pap. 26.00 *(978-0-8330-4965-0(8)*, mg-957) RAND Corp., The.

Arbatov, Alexei & Dvorkin, Vladimir, eds. Outer Space: Weapons, Diplomacy, & Security. 2010. (ENG., Illus.). 144p. 49.95 *(978-0-87003-251-6(8))*; pap. 19.95 *(978-0-87003-250-9(X))* Carnegie Endowment for International Peace.

Aubert, Paul. La Base Aérienne 132, L'adieu. 2010. (FRE., Illus.). 167p. *(978-2-84960-224-9(8))* Bentzinger, Jerome Do., Editeur.

Becze, Csaba. Baptism of Fire: The First Combat Experiences of the Royal Hungarian Air Force & Slovak Air Force, March 1939. 2010. (Illus.). 96p. 49.95 *(978-1-906033-93-4(5))* Helion & Co., Ltd. GBR. Dist: Casemate Pubs. & Bk. Distributors, LLC.

Birkler, John, et al. Keeping a Competitive U. S. Military Aircraft Industry Aloft: Findings from an Analysis of the Industrial Base. 2012. (ENG.). 142p. pap. 32.50 ***(978-0-8330-5864-5(9))*** RAND Corp., The.

Buhl, Willard A. Sea-Based Airpower - the Decisive Factor in Expeditionary Operations? 2010. 64p. pap. 16.55 *(978-1-60888-023-2(0))* Nimble Bks. LLC.

Caldwell, Douglas R., et al, eds. Studies in Military Geography & Geology. 2010. xiv, 348p. pap. 179.00 *(978-90-481-6793-7(0)*, 9048167930) Springer.

Castle, Ian. British Airships 1905-30. 2009. (New Vanguard Ser.). (ENG., Illus.). 48p. pap. 17.95 *(978-1-84603-387-2(X))* Osprey Publishing, Ltd. GBR. Dist: Random Hse., Inc.

Chardkoff, Richard. World War II Aerial Navigation Training & the Flyboy Heroes of Selman Field. 2008. *(978-1-887366-81-6(4))* Univ. of Louisiana at Lafayette Pr.

Cole, Ben. Four down on OLd Peachtree Road. 2006. per. 18.95 *(978-0-9738967-0-6(X))* Crosswind Pubns., Ltd.

Committee on Evaluation of U.S. Air Force Preacquisition Technology Development & National Research Council. Evaluation of U. S. Air Force Preacquisition Technology Development. 2011. (ENG.). 154p. pap. 33.75 *(978-0-309-16275-3(0))* National Academies Pr.

Corbin, Jimmy. Last of the Ten Fighter Boys. 2010. (ENG., Illus.). 252p. pap. 18.95 *(978-0-7524-5643-0(1))* History Pr. Ltd.,The GBR. Dist: Independent Pubs. Group.

Cost Effective Airlift in the 21st Century: Hearing Before the Federal Financial Management, Government Information, Federal Services, & International Security Subcommittee of the Committee on Homeland Security & Governmental Affairs, United States Senate, One Hundred Tenth Congress, First Session, September 27, 2007. 2008. (Illus.). iii, 117p. *(978-0-16-081121-0(X)*, 552-070-37556-2) United States Government Printing Office.

Craft, Stephen G. Embry-Riddle at War: Aviation Training during World War II. 2010. (Florida History & Culture Ser.). (ENG., Illus.). 344p. pap. 24.95 *(978-0-8130-3503-1(1))* Univ. Pr. of Florida.

Crosby, Francis. The World Encyclopedia of Naval Aircrafts: An Illustrated History of Shipborne Fighters, Bombers & Helicopters, Including the Sopwith Pup, B-25 Mitchell II, Westland Lynx, Sikorsky Sea King & Many More. 2009. (ENG., Illus.). 256p. (J). 35.00 *(978-0-7548-1670-6(2))* Anness Publishing GBR. Dist: National Bk. Network.

David, Hobbs. Century of Carrier Aviation. 2009. 304p. 74.95 *(978-1-59114-023-8(4))* Naval Institute Pr.

Davies, Richard Bell. Sailor in the Air. 2010. (Illus.). 264p. pap. 19.95 *(978-1-84832-011-6(6))* Pen & Sword Bks. Ltd. GBR. Dist: Casemate Pubs. & Bk. Distributors, LLC.

Dept. of Defense. Army Aviation Operations. 2009. per. 15.95 *(978-1-60170-035-3(0))* Pentagon Publishing.

—Aviation Brigades. 2009. per. 17.95 *(978-1-60170-036-0(9))* Pentagon Publishing.

Drucker, Graham. Wings over the Waves: The Biography & Letters of Lieut. Com. Roy Baker-Falkner DSO DSC RN. 2010. (Illus.). 256p. 50.00 *(978-1-84884-305-9(4))* Pen & Sword Bks. Ltd. GBR. Dist: Casemate Pubs. & Bk. Distributors, LLC.

Dutcher, Russell K. Union Army Balloon Corps: Operations During the War of the Rebellion, 1861-1863. 2009. (Illus.). xx, 186p. *(978-0-7884-8062-1(6))*; 206p. pap. 22.00 *(978-0-7884-4785-3(8))* Heritage Bks.

The Economic Viability of the Civil Reserve Air Fleet (CRAF) Program: Hearing Before the Subcommittee on Aviation of the Committee on Transportation & Infrastructure, House of Representatives, One Hundred Eleventh Congress, First Session, May 13, 2009. 2009. xix, 133p. *(978-0-16-084011-1(2)*, 552-070-39683-7) United States Government Printing Office.

Erickson, Andrew. Chinese Aerospace Power. Goldstein, Lyle, ed. 2011. 512p. 52.96 *(978-1-59114-241-6(5))* Naval Institute Pr.

Evans, Tom Parry. Squadron Leader Tommy Broom Dfc** 2012. (Illus.). 192p. pap. 24.95 ***(978-1-84884-582-4(0))*** Pen & Sword Bks. Ltd. GBR. Dist: Casemate Pubs. & Bk. Distributors, LLC.

Farram, Steven. Charles 'Moth' Eaton: Pioneer Aviator of the Northern Territory. 2007. (Illus.). 70p. pap. *(978-0-9803846-1-1(3))* Darwin, Charles Univ. Pr.

Faulkner, William. Westover: Man, Base & Mission. (Illus.). 160p. pap. 10.00 *(978-0-9616486-1-9(9))* MBI Distribution Services/Quayside Distribution.

Federal Aviation Administration. Aviation Instructor's Handbook. 2009. (ENG., Illus.). 160p. pap. 14.95 *(978-1-60239-777-4(5)*, 239777) Skyhorse Publishing Co., Inc.

Federal Aviation Administration (U.S.), compiled by. Aviation Instructor's Handbook 2008. 2009. (ENG., Illus.). 218p. pap. 35.00 *(978-0-16-082212-4(2)*, Federal Aviation Administration) United States Government Printing Office.

Federal Aviation Administration Staff. Aviation Instructor's Handbook. 2007. (Illus.). 160p. pap. 14.95 *(978-1-60239-151-2(3))* Skyhorse Publishing Co., Inc.

Fox, Michael C. Knights of the Skies: Armour Protection for British Fighting Aeroplanes. 2006. (ENG., Illus.). 304p. per. *(978-1-871187-50-2(8)*, 1871187508) Air Research Pubns. GBR. Dist: MBI Distribution Services/Quayside Distribution.

Fredriksen, John C. The United States Air Force: A Chronology. 2011. E-Book *(978-1-59884-683-6(3))*; (Illus.). 351p. 85.00 *(978-1-59884-682-9(5)*, A3260C) ABC-CLIO, LLC.

Glass, Andrzej & Kopanski, Tomasz J. Polish Air Force 1939 Through German Eyes, Vol. 2. 2011. (Illus.). 320p. pap. 59.00 *(978-83-61421-33-7(5))* Stratus, Wydawnictwo, Juszczak, Artur POL. Dist: Casemate Pubs. & Bk. Distributors, LLC.

Gordon, Yefim. Soviet Strategic Aviation in the Cold War. 2009. (Illus.). 272p. 56.95 *(978-1-902109-08-4(2))* Hikoki Pubns. GBR. Dist: Partners Pubs. Group, Inc.

Gordon, Yefim & Komissarov, Sergey. German Aircraft in the Soviet Union & Russia. 2010. (ENG., Illus.). 320p. 59.95 *(978-1-85780-292-4(6))* Allan, Ian Publishing GBR. Dist: BookMasters Distribution Services (BDS).

Government Printing Office Staff. Air & Space Power Journal. per. 32.00 *(978-0-16-010138-0(7))* United States Government Printing Office.

—Citizen Airman, Official Magazine of the Air Force Reserve. pap. 19.00 *(978-0-16-010134-2(4))* United States Government Printing Office.

—Combat Edge: Air Combat Command Safety Magazine. pap. 51.00 *(978-0-16-010296-7(0))* United States Government Printing Office.

—Naval Aviation News. pap. 23.00 *(978-0-16-010253-0(7))* United States Government Printing Office.

Graff, Cory. Strike & Return: American Air Power & the Fight for Iwo Jima. 2006. (ENG., Illus.). 160p. pap. 29.95 *(978-1-58007-092-8(2))* Specialty Pr. Pubs. & Wholesalers, Inc.

Grod, Georges. When Art Keep Em Flying. 2010. (Illus.). 176p. 44.95 *(978-2-35250-133-6(4))* Histoire et Collections FRA. Dist: Casemate Pubs. & Bk. Distributors, LLC.

Hall, Malcolm. From Balloon to Boxkite. 2010. (ENG., Illus.). 256p. pap. 34.95 *(978-1-84868-992-3(6))* Amberley Publishing GBR. Dist: Casemate Pubs. & Bk. Distributors, LLC.

Hanle, Donald. Near Miss: The Army Air Forces' Guided Bomb Program in World War II. 2007. (ENG., Illus.). 368p. per. 76.00 *(978-0-8108-5776-6(6))* Scarecrow Pr., Inc.

Hearing on National Defense Authorization ACT for Fiscal Year 2010 & Oversight of Previously Authorized Programs Before the Committee on Armed Services, House of Representatives, One Hundred Eleventh Congress, First Session: Seapower & Expeditionary Forces Subcommittee Hearing on Budget Request for Department of the Navy Aviation Programs, Hearing Held, May 19, 2009. 2010. iii, 68p. pap. *(978-0-16-085974-8(3)*, 552-070-41165-8) United States Government Printing Office.

Higgs, Geoffrey. Front-Line & Experimental Flying with the Fleet Air Arm. 2010. (Illus.). 208p. 39.95 *(978-1-84884-262-5(7))* Pen & Sword Bks. Ltd. GBR. Dist: Casemate Pubs. & Bk. Distributors, LLC.

Hildebrandt, Erik. Fly Navy: Celebrating the First Century of Naval Aviation. 2011. (ENG., Illus.). 400p. 65.00 *(978-0-9674040-8-0(8)*, 0967404088) Cleared Hot Media.

Hone, Thomas C., et al. Innovation in Carrier Aviation. Naval War College Press (U.S.), ed. 2011. (Newport Paper Ser.). (ENG., Illus.). 235p. pap. 23.00 ***(978-1-884733-85-7(9)***, Dept. of the Navy) United States Government Printing Office.

Hurt, H. H. Aerodynamics for Naval Aviators: NAVWEPS 00-8ot-80. 2012. (ENG., Illus.). 432p. pap. 14.95 ***(978-1-61608-439-4(1)***, 608439) Skyhorse Publishing Co., Inc.

Jampoler, Andrew. Adak. 2011. (Illus.). 240p. pap. 17.95 ***(978-1-59114-410-6(8))*** Naval Institute Pr.

Jenkins, Dennis R., compiled by. U. S. Naval Aviation Vol. 1: A Military Photo Logbook. 2007. (ENG., Illus.). 120p. pap. 19.95 *(978-1-58007-114-7(7))* Specialty Pr. Pubs. & Wholesalers, Inc.

Jenkins, Dennis R. & Landis, Tony R. Valkyrie: North American's Mach 3 Superbomber. rev. ed. 2008. (Illus.). 246p. pap. 28.95 *(978-1-58007-130-7(9))* Specialty Pr. Pubs. & Wholesalers, Inc.

Johnson, E. R. United States Naval Aviation, 1919-1941: Aircraft, Airships & Ships Between the Wars. 2011. (ENG., Illus.). 352p. pap. 45.00 *(978-0-7864-4550-9(5))* McFarland & Co., Inc. Pubs.

Kennedy, Gregory P. Touching Space: The Story of Project Manhigh. 2007. (Illus.). 128p. pap. 24.95 *(978-0-7643-2788-9(7))* Schiffer Publishing, Ltd.

Killebrew, Tom. The Royal Air Force in Texas: Training British Pilots in Terrell During World War II. 2009. (War & the Southwest Ser.). (ENG., Illus.). 208p. pap. 19.95 *(978-1-57441-272-7(8))* Univ. of North Texas Pr.

Kritzinger, Duane. Aircraft System Safety: Military & Civil Aeronautical Applications. 2006. (ENG., Illus.). 350p. 259.95 *(978-0-8493-9012-8(5)*, CRC Press) Taylor & Francis Group GBR. Dist: Taylor & Francis Group.

Lord, Brigadier Dick. From Tailhooker to Mudmover: An Aviation Career in the Royal Naval Fleet Air Arm, United States Navy, & South African Air Force. 2010. 360p. pap. 29.95 *(978-0-620-30762-8(5))* 30° South Pubs. ZAF. Dist: International Publishers Marketing.

Manacapilli, Thomas & Bennett, Bart. A User's Guide to the Technical Training Schoolhouse Model. 2006. (Illus.). 98p. pap. 27.50 *(978-0-8330-3997-2(0)*, tr378) RAND Corp., The.

Manacapilli, Thomas, et al. Common Battlefield Training for Airmen. 2007. (Illus.). 166p. pap. 22.00 *(978-0-8330-4185-2(1)*, mg624) RAND Corp., The.

—Customized Learning: Potential Air Force Applications. 2011. 64p. pap. 17.00 *(978-0-8330-5061-8(3)*, TR880) RAND Corp., The.

—Finding the Balance Between Schoolhouse & on-the-Job Training. 2007. (Illus.). 148p. per. 25.00 *(978-0-8330-4045-9(6)*, mg555) RAND Corp., The.

Marrett, George J. Contrails over the Mojave: The Golden Age of Jet Flight Testing at Edwards Air Force Base. 2008. (Illus.). 230p. 29.95 *(978-1-59114-511-0(2))* Naval Institute Pr.

Marriott, Leo. Jets at Sea: Naval Aviation in Transition 1945 - 55. 2008. (Illus.). 224p. 39.95 *(978-1-84415-742-6(3))* Pen & Sword Bks. Ltd. GBR. Dist: Casemate Pubs. & Bk. Distributors, LLC.

Mars-Proietti, Laura & Grey House Publishing Staff, eds. Air Warfare: An International Encyclopeia 2008, 2 vols. 2nd rev. ed. 2011. 250.00 *(978-1-59237-295-9(3))* Grey Hse. Publishing.

Mason, Chris. Falling from Grace: The German Airborne (Fallschirmjager) in World War II. 2010. 60p. pap. 19.05 *(978-1-60888-032-4(X))* Nimble Bks. LLC.

Megee, Vernon E. Memoirs of a Marine - Old Corps - New Corps 1919 To 1959. 2011. 258p. pap. 19.95 ***(978-1-933177-28-1(4))*** Atriad Pr.

Meilinger, Phillip S. Hubert R. Harmon: Airman, Officer, Father of the Air Force Academy. 2009. (ENG., Illus.). 374p. 35.00 *(978-1-56373-184-6(3))* Fulcrum Publishing.

Merry, Lois K. Women Military Pilots of World War II: A History with Biographies of American, British, Russian & German Aviators. 2010. (ENG., Illus.). 220p. pap. 35.00 *(978-0-7864-4441-0(X))* McFarland & Co., Inc. Pubs.

Mitchell, William. Winged Defense: The Development & Possibilities of Modern Air Power — Economic & Military. 2nd ed. 2010. (Alabama Fire Ant Ser.). (ENG., Illus.). 302p. pap. 28.00 *(978-0-8173-5605-7(3))* Univ. of Alabama Pr.

Molter, Bennett A. Knights of the Air: An American Pilot's View of the Aerial War of the French Squadrons During the First World War. 2011. 112p. ***(978-0-85706-585-8(8))***; pap. ***(978-0-85706-586-5(6))*** Leonaur Ltd.

Morgaa, Andrzej. Ex USAAF Aircraft 1945. 2011. (Illus.). 80p. pap. 25.00 ***(978-83-61421-11-5(4))*** Stratus, Wydawnictwo, Juszczak, Artur POL. Dist: Casemate Pubs. & Bk. Distributors, LLC.

Musial, Marek. System Architecture of Small Autonomous Uavs. 2008. (Illus.). 240p. per. *(978-3-8364-6113-9(7))* VDM Verlag Dr. Mueller e.K.

Myers, Roger, et al. Fort Wayne Aviation: Baer Field & Beyond. 2012. (Images of Aviation Ser.). (ENG., Illus.). 128p. pap. 21.99 ***(978-0-7385-8860-5(1))*** Arcadia Publishing.

Nevin, David. Architects of Air Power. (Illus.). 176p. 24.00 *(978-1-84447-034-1(2))* Time Life Value GBR. Dist: Mercury Bks. Ltd.

Nijboer, Donald. Graphic War: The Secret Aviation Drawings & Illustrations of World War II. 2011. (Illus.). 272p. pap. 29.95 *(978-1-55407-892-9(X))* Boston Mills Pr. CAN. Dist: Firefly Bks., Ltd.

Olsen, John Andreas, ed. A History of Air Warfare. 2010. 522p. 55.00 *(978-1-59797-440-0(4))*; (Illus.). pap. 35.00 *(978-1-59797-433-2(1))* Potomac Bks., Inc.

O'Malley, Michael C. Military Aviation in Ireland, 1921-45. 2011. (ENG., Illus.). 367p. 104.95 *(978-1-906359-48-5(2))*; pap. 52.95 *(978-1-906359-49-2(0))* Univ. College Dublin Pr. IRL. Dist: Dufour Editions, Inc.

Owen, Robert C. & Mueller, Karl P. Airlift Capabilities for Future U. S. Counterinsurgency Operations. 2007. 88p. pap. 23.00 *(978-0-8330-4038-1(3)*, mg565) RAND Corp., The.

Pautigny, Bruno. Air Warfare 1914-1974: 60 Years of Aerial Warfare. 2010. (Illus.). 164p. 49.95 *(978-2-35250-117-6(2))* Histoire et Collections FRA. Dist: Casemate Pubs. & Bk. Distributors, LLC.

Philpott, Ian M. Royal Air Force 1918-1939, 2 vols., Vol. 2. 2006. (Illus.). 576p. 75.00 *(978-1-84415-391-6(6))* Pen & Sword Bks. Ltd. GBR. Dist: Casemate Pubs. & Bk. Distributors, LLC.

Pitchfork, Graham. The Royal Air Force Day by Day. 2009. (ENG., Illus.). 544p. 49.95 *(978-0-7509-4309-3(2))* History Pr. Ltd.,The GBR. Dist: Independent Pubs. Group.

Pocock, Chris. The Black Bats: CIA Spy Flights over China from Taiwan, 1951-1969. 2010. (Illus.). 208p. 39.99 *(978-0-7643-3513-6(8))* Schiffer Publishing, Ltd.

Poleskie, Stephen. The Balloonist: The Story of T. S. C. Lowe — Inventor, Scientist, Magician, & Father of the US Air Force. 2007. 338p. 24.95 *(978-1-929490-27-1(5))* Beil, Frederic C. Pub., Inc.

Reynolds, Clark G. The Carrier War. (Illus.). 176p. 24.00 *(978-1-84447-036-5(9))* Time Life Value GBR. Dist: Mercury Bks. Ltd.

Sachs, Dana. The Life We Were Given: Operation Babylift, International Adoption, & the Children of War in Vietnam. 2011. (ENG.). 280p. pap. 20.00 *(978-0-8070-0124-0(4))* Beacon Pr.

Section, Anti-Aircraft. Notes & Orders for Officers Anti-Aircraft Corps of the Royal Naval Air Service 1915. 2009. 88p. pap. *(978-1-84734-825-8(4))* Naval & Military Pr., The.

Simpson, R. W. Piper Aircraft. Date not set. (Images of Aviation Ser.). (Illus.). 128p. pap. *(978-0-7524-1742-4(8))* History Pr. Ltd.,The.

Slessor, John Cotesworth. Air Power & Armies. 2009. (ENG., Illus.). 272p. pap. 28.00 *(978-0-8173-5610-1(X))* Univ. of Alabama Pr.

Smith, David S. Lifting the Silence: A World War II RCAF Bomber Pilot Reunites with His Past. 2010. (ENG., Illus.). 248p. pap. 27.99 *(978-1-55488-774-3(7))* Dundurn CAN. Dist: Ingram Pub. Services.

Sparaco, Pierre. Chroniques Aéronautiques. 2010. (FRE.). 379p. *(978-2-35593-083-6(X)*, Spotlight Poets) Pascal Galodé éditeurs.

Staff, The. The Fighting in the Air, April 1918. 2009. 48p. pap. *(978-1-84734-851-7(3))* Naval & Military Pr., The.

Talbot, Frederick A. Aeroplanes & Dirigibles of War. 2009. 164p. pap. *(978-1-4099-0441-0(5))* Dodo Pr.

—Aeroplanes & Dirigibles of War. 2006. (ENG.). pap. *(978-1-4068-0763-9(X))* Echo Library.

—Aeroplanes & Dirigibles of War. 2008. 328p. pap. *(978-1-4097-8271-1(9))* Read Bks.

Terry, Michael Robert, ed. Winged Crusade: The Quest for American Air & Space Power. 2006. per. 24.95 *(978-1-879176-43-0(2))* Imprint Pubns., Inc.

Thomason, Tommy H. Strike from the Sea: U. S. Navy Attack Aircraft from Skyraider to Super Hornet, 1948-Present. 2009. (Illus.). 228p. 46.95 *(978-1-58007-132-1(5))* Specialty Pr. Pubs. & Wholesalers, Inc.

Tillman, Stephen F. Man Unafraid. 2007. (ENG.). 240p. 41.95 *(978-0-548-14493-0(1))* 2006. pap. 26.95 *(978-1-4286-5771-7(1))* Kessinger Publishing, LLC.

Towery, Tommy. We Were Crewdogs II: More B-52 Crewdog Tale. 2006. per. *(978-1-59872-656-5(0))* Instant Pub.

Treadwell, Terry C. Rocket & Jet Aircraft of the Third Reich. 2011. (ENG., Illus.). 192p. 29.95 ***(978-0-7524-6109-0(5))*** History Pr. Ltd.,The GBR. Dist: Independent Pubs. Group.

Treadwell, Terry C. Setting of the Rising Sun: Japanese Military Aviation, 1877-1945. 2011. (Illus.). 224p. pap. 29.95 *(978-1-4456-0226-4(1))* Amberley Publishing GBR. Dist: Casemate Pubs. & Bk. Distributors, LLC.

Tuttle, Jim. Eject! The Complete History of U. S. Aircraft Escape Systems. 2008. (ENG.). 256p. 30.00 *(978-1-4223-9175-4(2))* DIANE Publishing Co.

Uziel, Daniel. Arming the Luftwaffe: The German Aviation Industry in World War II. 2011. (ENG., Illus.). 312p. pap. 45.00 ***(978-0-7864-6521-7(2))*** McFarland & Co., Inc. Pubs.

Valavanis, Kimon P., et al, eds. Unmanned Aircraft Systems: International Symposium on Unmanned Aerial Vehicles, UAV-08. 2011. (ENG.). xx, 532p. pap. 109.00 ***(978-90-481-8076-9(7)***, 9048180767) Springer.

Vitarbo, Gregory. Army of the Sky: Russian Military Aviation Before the Great War, 1904-1914. 2012. E-Book ***(978-1-4539-0266-0(X))***; (C). 80.95 ***(978-1-4331-1490-8(9))*** Lang, Peter Publishing, Inc.

Warsitz, Lutz. The First Jet Pilot: The Story of German Test Pilot Erich Warsitz. 2009. (Illus.). 176p. 39.99 *(978-1-84415-818-8(7))* Pen & Sword Bks. Ltd. GBR. Dist: Casemate Pubs. & Bk. Distributors, LLC.

Winslow, Carroll Dana. With the French Flying Corps: The Experiences of an American Pilot During the First World War. 2011. 128p. ***(978-0-85706-713-5(3))***; pap. ***(978-0-85706-714-2(1))*** Leonaur Ltd.

Withington, Thomas. B-2A Spirit Units in Combat. 2006. (Osprey Combat Aircraft Ser.). (ENG., Illus.). 96p. pap. 22.95 *(978-1-84176-993-6(2))* Osprey Publishing, Ltd. GBR. Dist: Random Hse., Inc.

Wortman, Marc. Millionaires' Unit: The Aristocratic Flyboys Who Fought the Great War & Invented American Air Power. 2007. (ENG., Illus.). 320p. per. 15.95 *(978-1-58648-444-6(3))* PublicAffairs.

Yarsinske, Amy Waters. Flyboys over Hampton Roads: Glenn Curtiss's Southern Experiment. 2010. 160p. pap. 21.99 *(978-1-59629-972-6(X))* History Pr., The.

Zimmerman, W. Frederick. Cvn-72 Abraham Lincoln, U S Navy Aircraft Carrier. 2008. 32p. pap. 17.36 *(978-1-934840-23-8(8))* Nimble Bks. LLC.

AERONAUTICS, NAVAL

see Aeronautics, Military

AERONAUTICS, RADIO IN

see Radio in Aeronautics

AERONAUTICS AND CIVILIZATION

see also Astronautics and Civilization

Bowen, John. The Economic Geography of Air Transportation: Space, Time, & the Freedom of the Sky. 2010. (Illus.). xvi, 333p. (C). 145.00 *(978-0-203-85735-9(6))* Routledge.

Bowen, John T. The Economic Geography of Air Transportation: Space, Time, & the Freedom of the Sky. 2010. (Routledge Studies in the Modern World Economy Ser.). (ENG., Illus.). 352p. (C). 145.00 *(978-0-415-77805-3(0)*, Routledge) Taylor & Francis Group GBR. Dist: Taylor & Francis Group.

Wohl, Robert. The Spectacle of Flight: Aviation & the Western Imagination, 1920-1950. 2007. (ENG., Illus.). 376p. per. 22.00 *(978-0-300-12265-7(9))* Yale Univ. Pr.

AERONAUTICS AND STATE

see also Aeronautics—Law and Legislation

Bormann, Natalie & Sheehan, Michael, eds. Securing Outer Space: International Relations Theory & the Politics of Space. 2012. (ENG.). 272p. pap. 39.95 ***(978-0-415-62232-5(8))*** Routledge.

Cram101 Textbook Reviews & Cram101 Textbook Reviews. Outlines & Highlights for a Europe of the Air: The Airline Industry & European Integration by Martin Staniland. 2011. 520p. pap. 38.95 ***(978-1-61830-836-8(X))*** Cram101 Inc.

Deborah A. Boehm-Davis & National Research Council. Assessing the Research & Development Plan for the Next Generation Air Transportation System: Summary of a Workshop. 2008. (ENG.). 38p. pap. 15.00 *(978-0-309-12470-6(0))* National Academies Pr.

Decisions on the Future Direction & Funding for NASA: What Will They Mean for the U.S. Aerospace Workforce & Industrial Base?: Hearing Before the Committee on Science & Technology, House of Representatives, One Hundred Eleventh Congress, First Session, December 10, 2009. 2010. (Illus.). iv, 73p. ***(978-0-16-087771-1(7)***, 552-070-42282-0) United States Government Printing Office.

Dillingham, Gerald L. Commercial Aviation: Programs & Options for Providing Air Service to Small Communities. 2007. (Illus.). 46p. (C). pap. 20.00 *(978-1-4223-1577-4(0))* DIANE Publishing Co.

Dobson, Alan P. FDR & Civil Aviation: Flying Strong, Flying Free. 2011. (World of the Roosevelts Ser.). (ENG.). 292p. 85.00 *(978-0-230-10666-6(8))* Palgrave Macmillan.

Elias, Bart, et al. Mathematics, Game Theory & Algebra Compendium, Vol. 1. Mathias, Jacob, ed. 2008. 95.00 *(978-1-60456-659-8(0))* Nova Science Pubs., Inc.

Graham, Anne, et al, eds. Aviation & Tourism: Implications for Leisure Travel. 2008. (Illus.). 408p. 124.95 *(978-0-7546-7187-9(9))* Ashgate Publishing Co.

The Joint Planning & Development Office & the Next Generation Air Transportation System: Status & Issues: Hearing Before the Subcommittee on Space & Aeronautics, Committee on Science & Technology, House of Representatives, One Hundred Tenth Congress, First Session, March 29, 2007. 2007. (Illus.). iv, 78p. *(978-0-16-080101-3(X)*, 552-070-36842-6) United States Government Printing Office.

Lawrence, Harry W. Aviation & the Role of Government. 2nd rev. ed. 2010. (ENG.). 516p. pap. 94.33 *(978-0-7575-4803-1(2))* Kendall Hunt Publishing Co.

The Next Generation Air Transportation System: Status & Issues: Hearing Before the Committee on Science & Technology, House of Representatives, One Hundred Tenth Congress, Second Session, September 11, 2008. 2008. (Illus.). iv, 216p. *(978-0-16-082502-6(4)*, 552-070-38540-1) United States Government Printing Office.

Oster, Clinton V. & Strong, John S. Managing the Skies: Public Policy Organization & Financing of Air Traffic Management. 2007. 234p. pap. 99.95 *(978-0-7546-7045-2(7))* Ashgate Publishing Co.

Oversight of the Joint Planning & Development Office: Hearing Before the Subcommittee on Aviation of the Committee on Commerce, Science, & Transportation, United States Senate, One Hundred Ninth Congress, Second Session, July 25, 2006. 2011. (Illus.). iii, 69p. ***(978-0-16-089027-7(6)***, 552-070-43059-8) United States Government Printing Office.

Staniland, Martin. A Europe of the Air? The Airline Industry & European Integration. 2008. (Governance in Europe Ser.). (ENG.). 316p. 80.00 *(978-0-7425-2651-8(8))* Rowman & Littlefield Publishers, Inc.

Starkie, David. Aviation Markets: Studies in Competition & Regulatory Reform. 2008. (Illus.). 246p. pap. 49.95 *(978-0-7546-7388-0(X))* Ashgate Publishing Co.

—Aviation Markets: Studies in Economic Policy. 2008. (Illus.). 246p. 124.95 *(978-0-7546-7360-6(X))* Ashgate Publishing Co.

Vasigh, Bijan, et al. Foundations of Airline Finance: Methodology & Practice. 2010. (Illus.). 444p. 134.95 *(978-0-7546-7769-7(9))* Ashgate Publishing Co.

Williams, Alan. Contemporary Issues Shaping China's Civil Aviation Policy: Balancing International with Domestic Priorities. 2009. 258p. 124.95 *(978-0-7546-7140-4(2))* Ashgate Publishing Co.

AERONAUTICS AND STATE—GREAT BRITAIN

Benson, Erik. Aviator of Fortune: Lowell Yerex & the Anglo-American Commercial Rivalry, 1931-1946. 2006. (Louise Lindsey Merrick Natural Environment Ser.: No. 40). (ENG., Illus.). 280p. 45.00 *(978-1-58544-500-4(2))* Texas A&M Univ. Pr.

Feldman, Elliot J. Concorde & Dissent: Explaining High Technology Project Failures in Britain & France. 2009. (ENG., Illus.). 220p. (C). pap. 31.99 *(978-0-521-10826-3(8))* Cambridge Univ. Pr.

AERONAUTICS IN AGRICULTURE

Atwood, Bert L. My Father Was A Crop Duster: The Story of Atwood Crop Dusters. 2008. (Illus.). 192p. 39.95 *(978-0-9799287-2-7(9))* AAAA Publishing.

AERONAUTICS IN ART

see also Aeronautics—Pictorial Works

Graham, Thomas. Box Top Air Power: The Aviation Art of Model Airplane Boxes. 2008. (Illus.). 192p. pap. 29.99 *(978-0-7643-2964-7(2))* Schiffer Publishing, Ltd.

London, Joanne Gernstein. Fly Now! A Colorful Story of Flight from Hot Air Balloon to the 777 Worldliner. 2007. (ENG., Illus.). 192p. 25.00 *(978-1-4262-0088-5(9)*, National Geographic) National Geographic Society.

—Fly Now! A Colorful Story of Flight from Hot Air Balloon to the 777 Worldliner -the Poster Collection of the Smithsonian National Air & Space Museum. 2008. (ENG., Illus.). 192p. pap. 15.95 *(978-1-4262-0290-2(3)*, National Geographic) National Geographic Society.

Patterson, Dan. Gil Cohen: Aviation Artist. 2009. (ENG., Illus.). 144p. 49.95 *(978-1-55046-512-9(0))* Boston Mills Pr. CAN. Dist: Firefly Bks., Ltd.

Prelinger, Megan. Another Science Fiction: Advertising the Space Race 1957-1962. 2010. (ENG., Illus.). 240p. pap. 29.95 *(978-0-922233-35-9(7))* Blast Bks.

AERONAUTICS IN FORESTRY

Jendsch, Wolfgang. Aerial Firefighting. 2008. (Illus.). 352p. bds. 49.99 *(978-0-7643-3068-1(3))* Schiffer Publishing, Ltd.

Johnsen, Frederick. Fire Bombers in Action Videobook. 2010. (Illus.). 160p. pap. 34.95 incl. DVD *(978-1-58007-147-5(3))* Specialty Pr. Pubs. & Wholesalers, Inc.

AERONAUTICS IN LITERATURE

Erisman, Fred. Boys' Books, Boys' Dreams, & the Mystique of Flight. 2006. (ENG., Illus.). 300p. 29.95 *(978-0-87565-330-3(8))* Texas Christian Univ. Pr.

—From Birdwomen to Skygirls: American Girls' Aviation Stories. 2009. (ENG., Illus.). 192p. 29.95 *(978-0-87565-397-6(9))* Texas Christian Univ. Pr.

AERONAUTICS IN METEOROLOGY

see also Meteorology in Aeronautics

Olsen, W. Scott. Hard Air: Adventures from the Edge of Flying. 2008. (ENG., Illus.). 246p. pap. 19.95 *(978-0-8032-1144-5(9)*, Bison Bks.) Univ. of Nebraska Pr.

AEROPHYSICS

see Atmospheric Physics

AEROPLANES

see Airplanes

AEROSOL THERAPY

Gradon, Leon & Marijnissen, J. C., eds. Optimization of Aerosol Drug Delivery. 2010. 320p. pap. 239.00 *(978-90-481-6436-3(2)*, 9048164362) Springer.

AEROSOLS

see also Aerosol Therapy

Agranovski, Igor, ed. Aerosols: Science & Technology. 2010. (ENG., Illus.). 492p. 215.00 *(978-3-527-32660-0(X)*, Wiley-VCH) Wiley, John & Sons, Inc.

Alekseyev, Yakov & Plisetskaya, Klavdiy, eds. Aerosols: Properties, Sources & Management Practices. 2012. ***(978-1-61942-182-0(8))*** Nova Science Pubs., Inc.

Baron, Paul A., et al, eds. Aerosol Measurement: Principles, Techniques, & Applications. 3rd ed. 2011. (ENG., Illus.). 904p. 195.00 *(978-0-470-38741-2(6)*, Wiley) Wiley, John & Sons, Inc.

Basu, Tanaya. Coastline Identification & Shift Detection. 2010. 64p. pap. *(978-3-8383-4889-6(3))* Lambert Academic Publishing.

Bulut, Mevlut. Experimental & Theoretical Studies on Aerosol Nanoparticles: Understanding, Controlling & Using the Nanoparticles in Aerosols. 2008. 160p. pap. *(978-3-639-07970-8(1))* VDM Verlag Dr. Mueller e.K.

Cheng, Ming & Liu, Wen, eds. Airborne Particulates. 2009. 98.00 *(978-1-60692-907-0(0))* Nova Science Pubs., Inc.

Chu, Allen, et al. Remote Sensing of Aerosol & Chemical Gases, Model Simulation/Assimilation, & Applications to Air Quality: 13-14 August, 2006, San Diego, California, USDA. 2006. (Proceedings of SPIE Ser.). (Illus.). 176p. pap. 80.00 *(978-0-8194-6378-4(7))* SPIE.

Colbeck, Ian, ed. Environmental Chemistry of Aerosols. 2008. (ENG., Illus.). 272p. 135.00 *(978-1-4051-3919-9(6)*, Wiley-Blackwell) Wiley, John & Sons, Inc.

Committee on Determining a Standard Unit of Measure for Biological Aerosols & National Research Council. A Framework for Assessing the Health Hazard

Posed by Bioareosols. 2008. (ENG.). 100p. pap. 26.00 *(978-0-309-11150-8(1))* National Academies Pr.

Dawar, Saru. Migration of Liquid Drops on Fibers in Nonwoven Fibrous Filters. 2008. 216p. pap. *(978-3-8364-9574-5(0))* VDM Verlag Dr. Mueller e.K.

Ellis, Andrew M. & Monks, Paul S. Proton Transfer Reaction Mass Spectrometry & Related Techniques. 2013. (ENG.). 328p. 160.00 *(978-1-4051-7668-2(7),* Wiley) Wiley, John & Sons, Inc.

Gehr, Peter, et al, eds. Particle-Lung Interactions, Second Edition. 2nd rev. ed. 2009. (ENG., Illus.). 338p. 300.00 *(978-1-4200-7256-3(0),* Informa Healthcare) Taylor & Francis Group GBR. Dist: Taylor & Francis Group.

Gelencsér, András. Carbonaceous Aerosol. 2010. (Atmospheric & Oceanographic Sciences Library). ix, 350p. pap. 189.00 *(978-90-481-6740-1(X),* 904816740X) Springer.

Herman, Jay & Gao, Wei. Ultraviolet & Visible Ground- & Space-based Measurements, Trace Gases, Aerosols & Effects VI. 2009. (Proceedings of SPIE Ser.). 102p. pap. 70.00 ***(978-0-8194-7752-1(4))*** SPIE.

Hu, Xiao-Ming. Incorporation of an Aerosol Module into Wrf/Chem. 2011. 420p. pap. ***(978-3-8454-1776-9(5))*** Lambert Academic Publishing.

Khare, Puja & P Baruah, Bimala. Particulate Emissions from Coke Ovens. 2011. 116p. pap. ***(978-3-8443-1171-6(8))*** Lambert Academic Publishing.

Knox, Kerry J. Light-Induced Processes in Optically-Tweezed Aerosol Droplets. 2011. (Springer Theses Ser.). (ENG., Illus.). xii, 204p. 129.00 *(978-3-642-16347-0(5),* 3642163475) Springer.

Kokhanovsky, Alexander A. Aerosol Optics: Light Absorption & Scattering by Particles in the Atmosphere. 2010. (Springer Praxis Books / Environmental Sciences Ser.). viii, 148p. pap. 179.00 *(978-3-642-06268-1(7),* 3642062687) Springer.

—Satellite Aerosol Remote Sensing over Land. 2009. (Springer Praxis Books / Environmental Sciences Ser.). (Illus.). 300p. 239.00 *(978-3-540-69396-3(3))* Springer.

Kokhanovsky, Alexander A. & de Leeuw, Gerrit. Satellite Aerosol Remote Sensing over Land. 2010. (Springer Praxis Books / Environmental Sciences Ser.). (ENG., Illus.). xvii, 388p. pap. 239.00 *(978-3-642-08889-6(9),* 3642088899) Springer.

Kondratyev, Kirill Ya, et al. Atmospheric Aerosol Properties: Formation, Processes & Impacts. 2010. (Springer Praxis Books / Environmental Sciences Ser.). xxxiv, 572p. pap. 319.00 *(978-3-642-06577-4(5),* 3642065775) Springer.

Lenoble, Jacqueline, et al. Aerosol Remote Sensing. 2012. (ENG., Illus.). x, 300p. 179.00 *(978-3-642-17724-8(7),* 3642177247) Springer.

Levin, Zev & Cotton, William R. Aerosol Pollution Impact on Precipitation: A Scientific Review. 2008. (Illus.). 486p. 229.00 ***(978-1-4020-8689-2(X),*** 140208689X) Springer.

Levin, Zev & Cotton, William R., eds. Aerosol Pollution Impact on Precipitation: A Scientific Review. 2010. (Illus.). xxi, 386p. pap. 229.00 *(978-90-481-7953-4(X),* 904817953X) Springer.

Madl, Pierre. Development & Application of a Low-Flow Thermodenuder. 2009. 216p. pap. *(978-3-639-20747-7(5))* VDM Verlag Dr. Mueller e.K.

Massel, Stanislaw R. Ocean Waves Breaking & Marine Aerosol Fluxes. (Atmospheric & Oceanographic Sciences Library). (Illus.). xvi, 328p. 2010. pap. 189.00 *(978-1-4419-2269-4(5),* 1441922695) 2007. 189.00 *(978-0-387-36638-8(5),* 0387366385) Springer.

McDow, Stephen R. Atmospheric Organic Aerosols. Date not set. 75.00 *(978-1-56670-129-7(5))* Lewis Pubs.

O'Dowd, Colin & Wagner, Paul, eds. Nucleation & Atmospheric Aerosols: 17th International Conference, Galway, Ireland 2007. 2007. 1010p. 339.00 *(978-1-4020-6474-6(8),* 1402064748) Springer.

Peng, Yiran. Indirect Aerosol Effect & Modelling of Aerosol-Cloud Interactions. 2009. 132p. pap. *(978-3-639-20703-3(3))* VDM Verlag Dr. Mueller e.K.

Peretz, Daniel H., ed. Aerosols: Chemistry, Environmental Impact & Health Effects. 2008. 240p. 89.00 *(978-1-60692-925-4(9))* Nova Science Pubs., Inc.

Phalen, Robert F. Inhalation Studies: Foundations & Techniques. 2nd rev. ed. 2008. (ENG., Illus.). 288p. 180.00 *(978-0-8493-1400-1(3))* CRC Pr. LLC.

Ruzer, Lev S. & Harley, Naomi H., eds. Aerosols Handbook: Measurement, Dosimetry, & Health Effects, Second Edition. 2nd rev. ed. 2012. (ENG., Illus.). 668p. 179.95 *(978-1-4398-5510-2(2),* CRC Press) Taylor & Francis Group GBR. Dist: Taylor & Francis Group.

Serpenguzel, Ali. Optical Processes in Microparticles & Nanostructures: A Festschrift Dedicated to Richard Kounai Chang on His Retirement from Yale University. 2010. 488p. 140.00 *(978-981-4295-77-2(9))* World Scientific Publishing Co., Inc.

Shaw, D. T. Handbook of Aerosol Science & Technology. Date not set. *(978-0-8247-9597-9(0))* Dekker, Marcel Inc.

Sher, Rudolph & Hobbins, Richard R. Transport & Removal of Aerosols in Nuclear Power Plants Following Severe Accidents. 2011. ***(978-0-89448-043-0(X))*** American Nuclear Society.

Signorell, Ruth & Reid, Jonathan P., eds. Fundamentals & Applications in Aerosol Spectroscopy. 2010. (ENG., Illus.). 535p. 169.95 *(978-1-4200-8561-7(1),* CRC Press) Taylor & Francis Group GBR. Dist: Taylor & Francis Group.

Singh, Upendra. Lidar Remote Sensing for Environmental Monitoring XII. 2011. (Proceedings of SPIE Ser.). 214p. pap. 70.00 ***(978-0-8194-8769-8(4))*** SPIE.

Singh, Upendra N. Lidar Remote Sensing for Environmental Monitoring VIII: 29-30 August 2007, San Diego, California, USA. 2007. (Proceedings of SPIE Ser.). (Illus.). 276p. pap. 90.00 *(978-0-8194-6829-1(0))* SPIE.

—Lidar Remote Sensing for Environmental Monitoring X: 3 August 2009, San Diego, California, United States. 2009. (Proceedings of SPIE Ser.). (Illus.). 98p. pap. 60.00 *(978-0-8194-7750-7(8))* SPIE.

—Lidar Technologies, Techniques, & Measurements for Atmospheric Remote Sensing II: 13-14 September, 2006, Stockholm, Sweden. 2006. (Proceedings of SPIE Ser.). (Illus.). 298p. pap. 80.00 *(978-0-8194-6462-0(7))* SPIE.

Singh, Upendra N. & Pappalardo, Gelsomina. Lidar Technologies, Techniques, & Measurements for Atmospheric Remote Sensing IV: 16-18 September 2008, Cardiff, Wales, United Kingdom. 2008. (Proceedings of SPIE Ser.). (Illus.). 170p. pap. 80.00 *(978-0-8194-7342-4(1))* SPIE.

—Lidar Technologies, Techniques, & Measurements for Atmospheric Remote Sensing V: 31 August-1 September 2009, Berlin, Germany. 2009. (Proceedings of SPIE Ser.). (Illus.). 234p. pap. 80.00 *(978-0-8194-7784-2(2))* SPIE.

Singh, Upendra N. & Pappalardo, Gelsomina. Lidar Technologies, Techniques, & Measurements for Atmospheric Remote Sensing VI: 20-21 September 2010, Toulouse, France. 2010. (Proceedings of SPIE Ser.). (Illus.). 256p. pap. 80.00 ***(978-0-8194-8349-2(4))*** SPIE.

Singh, Upendra N., et al. Lidar Remote Sensing for Environmental Monitoring VII: 14-16 November 2006, Goa, India. 2006. (Proceedings of SPIE Ser.). (Illus.). 410p. pap. 130.00 *(978-0-8194-6516-0(X))* SPIE.

Tien, Chi & Ramarao, B. V. Granular Filtration of Aerosols & Hydrosols. 2nd ed. 2007. (ENG., Illus.). 512p. 205.00 *(978-1-85617-458-9(1),* Elsevier Science) Elsevier Science & Technology Bks.

Valsaraj, Kalliat T. & Kommalapati, Raghava R. Atmospheric Aerosols: Characterization, Chemistry, Modeling and Climate. 2009. (ACS Symposium Ser.). (ENG., Illus.). 216p. 150.00 *(978-0-8412-6973-6(4))* American Chemical Society.

Vincent, James H. Aerosol Sampling: Science, Standards, Instrumentation & Applications. 2007. (ENG., Illus.). 636p. 200.00 *(978-0-470-02725-7(8),* Wiley) Wiley, John & Sons, Inc.

AEROSPACE INDUSTRIES

see also Aircraft Industry

Alfonso-Gil, Javier, ed. European Aeronautics: The Southwestern Axis. 2010. (ENG., Illus.). x, 277p. pap. 149.00 *(978-3-642-07135-5(X),* 364207135X) Springer.

Apollo - Saturn Launch Vehicles: A Technological History. (Illus.). 525p. (Orig.). pap. 295.00 *(978-0-7605-1996-7(X))* Rector Pr., Ltd.

Ball, Jeffrey A. U. S. Manufacturing Dogfights: China's Steel & Foreign Aircraft Competition. 2012. (Manufacturing Technology Research Business Issues, Competition & Entrepreneurship Ser.). 92p. pap. 47.00 ***(978-1-62100-672-5(7))*** Nova Science Pubs., Inc.

Bauer, Eugene E. Boeing: The First Century & Beyond. 2nd ed. 2006. (Illus.). 424p. 29.50 *(978-1-879242-09-8(5))* TABA Publishing, Inc.

Beall, Donald R. The Formation, Evolution & Transformation of Rockwell. 2008. (Illus.). vi, 71p. pap. ***(978-0-615-22738-2(4))*** U. S. ISBN Agency.

Beattie, Donald A. ISScapades: The Crippling of America's Space Program. 2007. (Apogee Books Space Ser.). (ENG., Illus.). 227p. per. 23.95 *(978-1-894959-59-9(0))* Collector's Guide Publishing, Inc. CAN. Dist: Independent Pubs. Group.

Benavides, S., ed. Corrosion Control in the Aerospace Industry. 2009. 384p. 259.95 *(978-1-4200-7965-4(4))* CRC Pr. LLC.

Berik, Pelin. Nanotechnology Applications in Aerospace. 2008. 112p. pap. *(978-3-639-04255-9(7))* VDM Verlag Dr. Mueller e.K.

Brennan, Louis & Vecchi, Alessandra. The Business of Space: The Next Frontier of International Competition. 2011. (ENG., Illus.). 256p. 40.00 *(978-0-230-23175-3(X))* Palgrave Macmillan.

British Standards Institute Staff. Aerospace series. Electrical contacts used in elements of connection. Contacts, electrical, triaxial, size 08, male, type D, crimp, class R. Product Standard. 18p. pap. 144.00 *(978-0-580-53251-1(8))* Artech Hse., Inc.

—Aerospace series. Fibres & cables, optical, aircraft use. Test methods. Resistance to Fluids. pap. 135.00 *(978-0-580-53136-1(8))* Artech Hse., Inc.

Butterworth-Hayes, Philip. Future of Europe's Aerospace Industry. (Illus.). 160p. 695.00 *(978-0-7106-1364-6(4))* Jane's Information Group, Inc.

Cadogan, Richard S., ed. U. S. Aerospace Industry: Analysis & Prospects. 2011. (Transportation Infrastructure - Roads, Highways, Bridges, Airports & Mass Transit Business Issues, Competition & Entrepreneurship Ser.). 149p. 95.00 *(978-1-61324-234-6(4))* Nova Science Pubs., Inc.

Campbell, Flake C., Jr. Manufacturing Technology for Aerospace Structural Materials. 2006. (ENG., Illus.). 616p. 170.00 *(978-1-85617-495-4(6),* Elsevier Science) Elsevier Science & Technology Bks.

Cenkner, August A. Aerospace Technologies of Bell Aircraft Company: A Pictorial History (1935-1985) 2011. 312p. pap. 35.00 ***(978-1-4634-0213-6(9))*** AuthorHouse.

Chesley, Alfred T. Next Generation of Human Space Flight Systems. 2009. (Space Science, Exploration & Policies Ser.). 144p. 89.00 *(978-1-60692-726-7(4))* Nova Science Pubs., Inc.

Cliff, Roger, et al. Ready for Takeoff: China's Advancing Aerospace Industry, 1 vol. 2011. (ENG.). 162p. (C). pap. 24.00 *(978-0-8330-5180-6(6))* RAND Corp., The.

Committee on Meeting the Workforce Needs for the National Vision for Space Exploration. Building a Better NASA Workforce: Meeting the Workforce Needs for the National Vision for Space Exploration. 2007. (ENG., Illus.). 80p. pap. 21.00 *(978-0-309-10764-8(4))* National Academies Pr.

Darcy, Harry L., ed. Russian-English Aerospace Dictionary. (GER.). XVI, 407p. 240.00 ***(978-3-11-188931-3(9))***; 159.00 ***(978-3-11-114090-2(3))*** De Gruyter, Walter Inc.

Decisions on the Future Direction & Funding for NASA: What Will They Mean for the U.S. Aerospace Workforce & Industrial Base?: Hearing Before the Committee on Science & Technology, House of Representatives, One Hundred Eleventh Congress, First Session, December 10, 2009. 2010. (Illus.). iv, 73p. ***(978-0-16-087771-1(7),*** 552-070-42282-0) United States Government Printing Office.

Erickson, Andrew. Chinese Aerospace Power. Goldstein, Lyle, ed. 2011. 512p. 52.96 *(978-1-59114-241-6(5))* Naval Institute Pr.

Fallows, James. China Airborne. 2012. (ENG., Illus.). 288p. 25.95 ***(978-0-375-42211-9(0),*** Pantheon) Knopf Doubleday Publishing Group.

Gunn, Tom. Gunn Sights: Taking Aim on Selling in the High-Stakes Industry of International Aerospace. 2008. (Illus.). 256p. 29.95 *(978-1-59114-346-8(2))* Naval Institute Pr.

Gunther, Jocelyn S., ed. Commercial Space Transportation. 2010. (Space Science, Exploration & Policies Ser.). 195.00 *(978-1-61668-707-6(X))* Nova Science Pubs., Inc.

Harding Jr, Dale. Positional Leadership in Aerospace Organizations. 2010. 240p. pap. *(978-3-8383-7468-0(1))* Lambert Academic Publishing.

High Stakes Writing. Aerospace Studies: The Exploration of Space. 2010. (Illus.). xii, 588p. *(978-0-7637-8961-9(5))* Jones & Bartlett Learning, LLC.

Index to AIA National Aerospace Standards (NAS) 2007. ring bd. 600.00 *(978-1-57053-119-4(6))* IHS, Inc.

International ABC Aerospace Directory: The World's Aerospace Organisations at Your Fingertips. 725.00 *(978-0-7106-2318-8(6))* Jane's Information Group, Inc.

Kumar, Parvez. The Cry of the Eagle: The Life & Times of an Aerospace Engineer. 2008. (Illus.). xvi, 533p. 35.00 *(978-1-4251-3978-0(7))* Trafford Publishing.

Kymal, Chad. AS9101D Auditing for Process Performance: Combining Conformance & Effectiveness to Achieve Customer Satisfaction. 2011. ***(978-0-87389-807-2(9))*** ASQ Quality Pr.

Kymmell, Willem. Building Information Modeling: Planning & Managing Construction Projects. 2008. (Construction Ser.). (ENG., Illus.). 270p. 79.95 *(978-0-07-149453-3(7),* 0071494537) McGraw-Hill Professional Publishing.

Mancia, Wilson & Santoro, Miguel. Heuristics for Reverse Logistics of Non-Conform Material. 2010. 104p. pap. *(978-3-639-24152-5(5))* VDM Verlag Dr. Mueller e.K.

Moller, Rosa Maria. Aerospace States' Incentives to Attract the Industry: An Update. 2008. (Illus.). 117p. pap. *(978-1-58703-236-3(8))* California Research Bureau.

Myhrberg, Erik V., et al. A Practical Field Guide for AS9100C. 2010. 70.00 *(978-0-87389-793-8(5))* ASQ Quality Pr.

Smithersrapra Technology, Technology. Polymers in Defence & Aerospace Applications 2010 Conference Proceedings. 2010. (Conference Proceedings Ser.). (Illus.). 180p. pap. *(978-1-84735-398-6(3))* iSmithers Rapra Publishing.

SPACEPOL Academic Publishers Staff. Nordicspace 2012: Who's Who in the Nordic & Canadian Space Industry. 2012. (ENG., Illus.). 108p. pap. *(978-0-9812475-1-9(2),* SPACEPOL Academic Pubs.) SPACEPOL Editeurs Universitaires Academic Pubs.

Sparaco, Pierre. Chroniques Aéronautiques. 2010. (FRE.). 379p. *(978-2-35593-033-6(X),* Spotlight Poets) Pascal Galodé éditeurs.

Spreen, Wesley E. Marketing in the International Aerospace Industry. 2007. (Illus.). 308p. 99.95 *(978-0-7546-4975-5(X))* Ashgate Publishing Co.

A Strategic & Economic Review of Aerospace Exports: Hearing Before the Subcommittee on Terrorism, Nonproliferation, & Trade of the Committee on Foreign Affairs, House of Representatives, One Hundred Eleventh Congress, First Session, December 9, 2009. 2010. iii, 85p. *(978-0-16-085647-1(7),* 552-070-40884-3) United States Government Printing Office.

Technology Research Editors, ed. Adhesive Bonding for Aerospace Applications, 2007 Ed. 2007. pap. 128.50 *(978-1-60030-139-1(8),* Search-In-Print) CSA Journal Division.

—Advanced Materials for Aerospace Components: World Business Brief, 2007 Ed. 2007. pap. 68.50 *(978-1-60030-140-7(1),* Search-In-Print) CSA Journal Division.

—Delamination in Aerospace Components, 2007 Ed. 2007. pap. 128.50 *(978-1-60030-146-9(0),* Search-In-Print) CSA Journal Division.

—Weight Reduction in the Aerospace Industry, 2007 Ed. 2007. pap. 128.50 *(978-1-60030-158-2(4),* Search-In-Print) CSA Journal Division.

Teksen, Banu. Vibration Analysis of Pcbs & Electronic Components. 2010. 116p. pap. *(978-3-639-23375-9(1))* VDM Verlag Dr. Mueller e.K.

Torenbeek, E. Synthesis of Subsonic Airplane Design: An Introduction to the Preliminary Design of Subsonic General Aviation & Transport Aircraft, with Emphasis on Layout, Aerodynamic Design, Propulsion & Performance. 2010. (ENG.). 624p. pap. 109.00 *(978-90-481-8273-2(5),* 9048182735) Springer.

Tromaras, Alkiviadis. A Stakeholder Framework for Environmental Management. 2009. 232p. pap. *(978-3-639-13992-1(5))* VDM Verlag Dr. Mueller e.K.

Westwick, Peter J. & Deverell, William, eds. Blue Sky Metropolis: The Aerospace Century in Southern California. 2012. (Western Histories Ser.). (ENG., Illus.). 278p. 44.95 ***(978-0-87328-249-9(3))*** Huntington Library Pr.

Williamson, Mark. The Cambridge Dictionary of Space Technology. 2010. (ENG., Illus.). 476p. pap. 36.99 *(978-0-521-14231-1(8))* Cambridge Univ. Pr.

AEROSPACE INDUSTRIES—VOCATIONAL GUIDANCE

Andrews, Brad. How to Land a Top-Paying Aerospace Engineer, Aerospace Product & Parts Manufacturing Services Job: Your Complete Guide to Opportunities, Resumes & Cover Letters, Interviews, Salaries, Promotions, What to Expect from Recruiters & More! 2010. 160p. pap. *(978-1-74244-559-5(4))* Emereo Pty Ltd.

AEROSPACE LAW

see Aeronautics—Law and Legislation; Space Law

AEROSTATS

see Airships

AEROTHERMODYNAMICS

see also Aerodynamic Heating

Epstein, A. H. Aircraft & Rocket Turbines - Physics & Design. Vennard, J., ed. 2008. 156p. pap. 74.95 *(978-1-934939-18-5(8))* Wexford College Pr.

Hirschel, Ernst H. & Weiland, Claus. Selected Aerothermodynamic Design Problems of Hypersonic Flight Vehicles. 2009. (ENG., Illus.). xvi, 512p. 129.00 *(978-3-540-89973-0(1),* 3540899731) Springer.

Hirschel, Ernst-Heinrich. Basics of Aerothermodynamics. 2010. (ENG., Illus.). xiv, 413p. pap. 149.00 *(978-3-642-06050-2(1),* 3642060501) Springer.

Syred, Nick & Khalatov, Artem, eds. Advanced Combustion & Aerothermal Technologies: Environmental Protection & Pollution Reductions. 2007. (NATO Science for Peace & Security Series C: Environmental Security Ser.). 497p. 279.00 *(978-1-4020-6513-2(2))*; 129.00 *(978-1-4020-6514-9(0))* Springer.

AESCHYLUS

Aeschylus. Aeschylus: Fragments, 3 vols., Volume III. 2009. (Loeb Classical Library: 505). (GEC & ENG.). 384p. 24.00 *(978-0-674-99629-8(1))* Harvard Univ. Pr.

Ahrens, Robert H., Jr. Monarch Notes on Aeschylus' Plays. (C). 3.95 *(978-0-671-00801-7(3),* Arco) Peterson's.

Arkins, Brian. Irish Appropriation of Greek Tragedy. 2011. (ENG., Illus.). 150p. pap. 37.95 *(978-1-904505-47-1(3))* Carysfort Pr. IRL. Dist: Dufour Editions, Inc.

Beck, Martha Catherine. Interpreting Aeschylus' Agamemnon Through the Categories of Aristotle: How Greek Tragedy Shaped Ethical Citizens. 2011. 272p. 119.95 *(978-0-7734-1521-8(1))* Mellen, Edwin Pr., The.

Bowen, Anthony A. & Aeschylus. Aeschylus: Choephori. 2007. (Greek Texts Ser.). Tr. of Libation Bearers. (GRE.). 196p. pap. 19.95 *(978-0-86292-070-8(1))* Bristol Classical Pr. GBR. Dist: International Publishers Marketing.

Copleston, Reginald S. Aeschylus. 2007. (ENG.). 204p. 39.95 *(978-0-548-35558-9(4))*; per. 24.95 *(978-0-548-29818-3(1))* Kessinger Publishing, LLC.

Deforge, Bernard. Une Vie Avec Eschyle. 2010. (Verite des Mythes Ser.). (FRE.). 304p. (C). pap. 53.00 *(978-2-251-32458-6(5))* Societe d'edition Les Belles lettres FRA. Dist: ISD.

Doyle, Andrea. Archetypal Simulacr. 2010. 280p. pap. *(978-3-8383-5701-0(9))* Lambert Academic Publishing.

Ewans, Michael. Wagner & Aeschylus: the Ring & the Oresteia. 2009. (ENG.). 272p. (C). pap. 31.00 *(978-0-521-11753-1(4))* Cambridge Univ. Pr.

Garvie, A. F. & Garvie, Alex F. The Plays of Aeschylus. 2010. 128p. pap. 19.95 *(978-1-85399-707-5(2))* Duckworth Publishers GBR. Dist: International Publishers Marketing.

Goheen, Robert F. Aspects of Dramatic Symbolism: Three Studies in Oresteia. 2011. 32p. 35.95 ***(978-1-258-02243-3(5))*** Literary Licensing, LLC.

Griffith, Mark. The Authenticity of Prometheus Bound. 2007. (Cambridge Classical Studies). (ENG.). 432p. pap. 79.00 *(978-0-521-03814-0(6))* Cambridge Univ. Pr.

Headlam, Walter. On Editing Aeschylus: A Criticism. 2010. (Cambridge Library Collection - Cambridge Ser.). 208p. pap. 19.99 *(978-1-108-00964-5(6))* Cambridge Univ. Pr.

Heath, John. The Talking Greeks: Speech, Animals, & the Other in Homer, Aeschylus, & Plato. 2009. (ENG.). 404p. pap. 44.00 *(978-0-521-11778-4(X))* Cambridge Univ. Pr.

Kyriakou, Poulheria. The Past in Aeschylus & Sophocles. 2011. (Trends in Classics - Supplementary Volumes Ser.). (ENG.). IX, 606p. 154.00 *(978-3-11-025752-6(1))*; (Illus.). 238.00 ***(978-3-11-218869-9(1))*** De Gruyter, Walter Inc.

Lloyd, Michael, ed. Oxford Readings in Aeschylus. 2007. (Oxford Readings in Classical Studies). 434p. pap. 75.00 *(978-0-19-926524-4(0))* Oxford Univ. Pr., Inc.

Mikhailov, Boris, photos by. Maquette Braunschweig, 1 vol. 2009. (ENG., Illus.). 224p. 68.00 *(978-3-86521-834-6(2))* Steidl, Gerhard Druckerei und Verlag DEU. Dist: Innovative Logistics.

Otis, Brooks & Kopff, E. Christian. Cosmos & Tragedy: An Essay on the Meaning of Aeschylus. 2011. (ENG.). 137p. pap. 30.00 ***(978-0-8078-9744-7(2))*** Univ. of North Carolina Pr.

Papadopoulou, Thalia. Aeschylus: Suppliants. 2011. (Duckworth Companions to Greek & Roman Tragedy Ser.). 144p. pap. 24.95 *(978-0-7156-3913-9(7))* Duckworth Publishers GBR. Dist: International Publishers Marketing.

Pearson, A. C., ed. The Agamemnon of Aeschylus: With Verse Translation, Introduction & Notes. Headlam, W., tr. 2010. (Cambridge Library Collection - Classics Ser.). 284p. pap. 23.99 *(978-1-108-01209-6(4))* Cambridge Univ. Pr.

Rosenbloom, David. Aeschylus: Persians. 2007. (Duckworth Companions to Greek & Roman Tragedy Ser.). 144p. per. 24.95 *(978-0-7156-3286-4(8))* Duckworth Publishers GBR. Dist: International Publishers Marketing.

Ruffell, Ian. Aeschylus: Prometheus Bound. 2012. (Duckworth Companions to Greek & Roman Tragedy Ser.). 176p. pap. 24.95 *(978-0-7156-3476-9(3))* Duckworth Publishers GBR. Dist: International Publishers Marketing.

Seaford, Richard. Cosmology & the Polis: The Social Construction of Space & Time in the Tragedies of Aeschylus. 2012. (ENG., Illus.). 380p. 110.00 ***(978-1-107-00927-1(8))*** Cambridge Univ. Pr.

Sommerstein, Alan H. Aeschylean Tragedy. 2nd ed. 2011. 416p. pap. 44.95 (978-0-7156-3824-8(6)) Duckworth Publishers GBR. Dist: International Publishers Marketing.

Thoreau, Henry David. The Seven Against Thebes. Kaiser, Leo M., ed. (Emerson Society Quarterly Fifty-Nine, 1-30). reprint ed. 27.50 (978-0-404-19070-5(7)) AMS Pr., Inc.

Torrance, Isabel. Aeschylus: Seven Against Thebes. 2007. (Duckworth Companions to Greek & Roman Tragedy Ser.). (Illus.). 144p. per. 24.95 (978-0-7156-3466-0(6)) Duckworth Publishers GBR. Dist: International Publishers Marketing.

Tzanetou, Angeliki. City of Suppliants: Tragedy & the Athenian Empire. 2012. (ENG.). 236p. 55.00 **(978-0-292-73716-7(5))** Univ. of Texas Pr.

Van Steen, Gonda. Liberating Hellenism from the Ottoman Empire: Comte de Marcellus & the Last of the Classics. 2010. (ENG.). 264p. 89.00 (978-0-230-10023-7(6)) Palgrave Macmillan.

Zeitlin, Froma I. Under the Sign of the Shield: Semiotics & Aeschylus' Seven Against Thebes. 2nd ed. 2009. (Greek Studies: Interdisciplinary Approaches Ser.). (GEC & ENG.). 198p. 57.99 (978-0-7391-2589-2(3)) Lexington Bks.

AESCULAPIUS (GREEK DEITY)

de Waele, Ferdinand. The Sanctuary of Asklepios & Hygieia at Corinth. 2009. pap. 20.92 (978-1-60724-468-4(3)) Gorgias Pr., LLC.

Meier, Carl A. Healing Dream & Ritual (4th Edition) 2009. 176p. pap. 28.00 (978-3-85630-727-1(3)) Daimon Verlag CHE. Dist: AtlasBooks Distribution.

Petsalis-Diomidis, Alexia. Truly Beyond Wonders: Aelius Aristides & the Cult of Asklepios. 2010. (Oxford Studies in Ancient Culture & Representation Ser.). (ENG., Illus.). 380p. 135.00 (978-0-19-956190-2(7)) Oxford Univ. Pr., Inc.

Salaman, Clement. Asclepius: The Perfect Discourse of Hermes Trismegistus. 2007. (Illus.). 128p. per. 17.95 (978-0-7156-3564-3(6)) Duckworth Publishers GBR. Dist: International Publishers Marketing.

Walton, Alice. The Cult of Asklepios. 2010. 148p. pap. 21.75 (978-1-141-35612-6(0)) BiblioBazaar.

Wickkiser, Bronwen Lara. Asklepios, Medicine, & the Politics of Healing in Fifth-Century Greece: Between Craft & Cult. 2008. (ENG., Illus.). 192p. (gr. 17). 57.00 (978-0-8018-8978-3(2)) Johns Hopkins Univ. Pr.

AESOP

Carter, Steven. After Aesop: Improvisations on Aesop's Fables. 2010. (ENG.). 238p. pap. 35.99 (978-0-7618-5147-9(X)) Hamilton Bks.

de Weever, Jacqueline. Aesop & the Residue of Medieval Thought: A Study of Six Fables as Translated at the End of the Middle Ages. 2010. (ENG., Illus.). 217p. pap. 55.00 (978-0-7864-5955-1(7)) McFarland & Co., Inc. Pubs.

Kurke, Leslie. Aesopic Conversations: Popular Tradition, Cultural Dialogue, & the Invention of Greek Prose. 2010. (Martin Classical Lectures). (ENG., Illus.). 504p. (C). 75.00 (978-0-691-14457-3(5)); pap. 29.95 (978-0-691-14458-0(3)) Princeton Univ. Pr.

Perry, Ben Edwin, ed. Aesopica, Volume One: A Series of Texts Relating to Aesop or Ascribed to Him or Closely Connected with the Literary Tradition That Bears His Name: Greek & Latin Texts. 2nd ed. 2007. 792p. 129.00 (978-0-252-03192-2(X)) Univ. of Illinois Pr.

Springer, Carl P. E. Luther's Aesop. 2011. (ENG.). 264p. pap. 39.95 (978-1-61248-000-8(4)) Truman State Univ. Pr.

AESTHETIC MOVEMENT (ART)

see also Art Deco; Art Nouveau; Arts and Crafts Movement; Modernism (Art)

Comfort, Kelly. European Aestheticism & Spanish American Modernismo: Artist Protagonists & the Philosophy of Art for Art's Sake. 2011. (ENG., Illus.). 200p. 80.00 (978-0-230-27809-7(4)) Palgrave Macmillan.

Edwards, Jason & Hart, Imogen. Rethinking the Interior, C.1867-1896: Aestheticism & Arts & Crafts. 2010. (Illus.). 294p. 124.95 (978-0-7546-6817-6(7)) Ashgate Publishing Co.

Gere, Charlotte. Artistic Circles: Design & Decoration in the Aesthetic Movement. 2010. (ENG., Illus.). 240p. 60.00 (978-1-85177-602-3(8)) V & A Pubns. GBR. Dist: Hachette Bk. Group.

Iser, Wolfgang. Walter Pater: The Aesthetic Moment. Wilson, David H., tr. from GER. 2011. (European Studies in English Literature Ser.). 226p. pap. 30.99 (978-0-521-17928-7(9)) Cambridge Univ. Pr.

Lambourne, Lionel. The Aesthetic Movement. 2011. (ENG., Illus.). 240p. pap. 39.95 **(978-0-7148-6319-1(X))** Phaidon Pr., Inc.

Tsuji, Midori, ed. Aesthetic Movement in Victorian Life. 2008. (ENG.). 1665.00 (978-4-86166-019-1(X)) Synapse, Edition JPN. Dist: Taylor & Francis Group.

Ulrik, Christian, ed. Interface Criticism: Aesthetics Beyond the Buttons. 2011. (ENG., Illus.). 295p. (C). pap. 47.00 (978-87-7934-504-1(2)) Aarhus Universitetsforlag DNK. Dist: ISD.

AESTHETIC REALISM

Here are entered works on the philosophy founded in 1941 by American poet and critic Eli Siegel.

Thoreau, Henry David. Excursions. Moldenhauer, Joseph J., ed. 2007. (Writings of Henry D. Thoreau). (ENG., Illus.). 672p. (C). 72.00 (978-0-691-06450-5(4)) Princeton Univ. Pr.

—On the Duty of Civil Disobedience. 2007. (ENG.). 52p. per. 6.99 (978-1-59986-594-2(7), Filibust) Filiquarian Publishing, LLC.

—On the Duty of Civil Disobedience. 2008. pap. 4.95 (978-1-60545-127-5(4)) Quiet Vision Publishing.

—On the Duty of Civil Disobedience. 2007. (ENG.). 48p. per. 7.45 (978-1-59462-747-7(9)); per. 7.45 (978-1-59462-526-8(3), 562) Standard Pubns., Inc. (Book Jungle).

—On the Duty of Civil Disobedience. 2008. 48p. pap. 4.99 (978-1-60459-293-1(1)) Wilder Pubns., Ltd.

—Walking. 2008. 108p. 21.99 (978-1-60512-088-1(X)); pap. 10.99 (978-1-60512-188-8(6)) Akasha Publishing, LLC. (Akasha Classics).

—Walking. 2007. (ENG.). 60p. per. 3.99 (978-0-9786536-8-2(8)) Arc Manor.

—Walking. 2006. (ENG.). pap. 8.00 (978-1-59605-881-1(1), Cosimo Classics) Cosimo, Inc.

—Walking. 2008. (ENG.). 48p. per. 4.99 (978-1-59986-586-7(6)) Filiquarian Publishing, LLC.

—Walking. 2009. (ENG., Illus.). lthr. (978-1-55447-049-5(8)) Gaspereau Pr.

—Walking. 2007. (ENG.). 48p. per. 9.99 (978-1-59547-891-7(4)) NuVision Pubns., LLC.

—Walking. 2008. pap. 4.95 (978-1-60545-126-8(6)) Quiet Vision Publishing.

—Walking. 2009. (ENG.). 48p. pap. 8.45 (978-1-4385-2778-9(0), Book Jungle) Standard Pubns., Inc.

AESTHETICS

see also Art; Art—Philosophy; Art and Literature; Avant-Garde (Aesthetics); Classicism; Criticism; Cubism; Expressionism (Art); Feminine Beauty (Aesthetics); Form (Aesthetics); Futurism (Art); Grotesque; Harmony (Aesthetics); Idealism in Art; Idealism in Literature; Impressionism (Art); Literature—Aesthetics; Literature—Psychology; Modernism (Aesthetics); Motion Pictures—Aesthetics; Movement, Aesthetics of; Music—Philosophy and Aesthetics; Naturalism in Art; Naturalism in Literature; Nature (Aesthetics); Post-Impressionism (Art); Proportion; Realism in Art; Realism in Literature; Rhythm; Romanticism; Sublime, The; Symmetry; Ut Pictura Poesis (Aesthetics); Values

Acampora, Christa Davis & Cotten, Angela L. Unmaking Race, Remaking Soul: Transformative Aesthetics & the Practice of Freedom. 2007. (Illus.). 297p. 80.00 (978-0-7914-7161-6(6)) State Univ. of New York Pr.

Acampora, Christa Davis & Cotten, Angela L., eds. Unmaking Race, Remaking Soul: Transformative Aesthetics & the Practice of Freedom. 2008. (Illus.). xv, 297p. pap. 29.95 (978-0-7914-7162-3(4)) State Univ. of New York Pr.

Adorno, Theodor W. Aesthetic Theory. (Athlone Contemporary European Thinkers Ser.). (Illus.). 504p. pap. (978-0-485-30090-1(7)) Continuum International Publishing Group, Ltd.

Adorno, Theodor W. & Adorno. Aesthetic Theory. (Athlone Contemporary European Thinkers Ser.). (ENG.). 416p. 220.00 (978-0-485-30069-7(9)) Continuum International Publishing Group, Ltd. GBR. Dist: National Bk. Network.

Adorno, Theodor W., et al. Aesthetics & Politics. 2010. (Radical Thinkers Classics Ser.). (ENG.). 220p. 24.95 (978-1-84467-664-4(1), 844664) Verso Bks. GBR. Dist: Norton, W. W. & Co., Inc.

Agamben, Giorgio. Profanations. Fort, Jeff, tr. from ITA. 2007. (ENG., Illus.). 99p. (gr. 17). 25.95 (978-1-890951-82-5(X)) Zone Bks.

Ahrens, Rudiger & Stierstorfer, Klaus, eds. Symbolism: An International Annual of Critical Aesthetics, Vol. 7. 2007. 389p. 157.50 (978-0-404-63567-1(9)) AMS Pr., Inc.

Aldrich, Megan & Hutt, Julia. Understanding Art Objects: Thinking Through the Eye. Godfrey, Tony, ed. 2009. (Illus.). 176p. 50.00 (978-1-84822-016-4(2), Lund Humphries Pubs.) Ashgate Publishing, Ltd. GBR. Dist: Ashgate Publishing Co.

Allen, Grant. Physiological Aesthetics. 2009. 144p. pap. (978-0-217-53019-4(2)) Books LLC.

Ames, Van Meter. Aesthetics of the Novel. 2011. 230p. 46.95 **(978-1-258-01309-7(6))** Literary Licensing, LLC.

—The Function & Value of Aesthetics: The Journal of Aesthetics & Art Criticism, No. 1, Spring 1941. Runes, Dagobert D., ed. 2011. 16p. pap. 35.95 **(978-1-258-05505-9(8))** Literary Licensing, LLC.

Andina, Tiziana. Confini Sfumati: I Problemi Dell'arte, le Soluzioni Della Percezione. 2009. (ITA., Illus.). 199p. (978-88-8483-852-0(5)) Mimesis.

Andronescu, Serban. Bye Cadmos: A Journal of Aesthetic Analogies. (C). 5.00 (978-0-917944-00-0(3)) American Institute for Writing Research Corp.

Arora, Vipal. Winning Back Your Independence with Cosmetic Dermatology - Basics of Medical Aesthetics & Cosmetic Dermatology: Botox - A Cosmetic. 2008. 200p. 99.95 (978-1-4357-1397-0(4)) Lulu Enterprises Inc.

—Winning Back Your Independence with Cosmetic Dermatology - Basics of Medical Aesthetics & Cosmetic Dermatology: Dermal Fillers for Soft Tissue Augmentation. 2008. 244p. 99.95 (978-1-4357-1403-8(2)) Lulu Enterprises Inc.

—Winning Back Your Independence with Cosmetic Dermatology - Basics of Medical Aesthetics & Cosmetic Dermatology: Mesotheraphy, Pigmented Lesions & Photodynamic Therapy. 2008. 182p. 99.95 (978-1-4357-1426-7(1)) Lulu Enterprises Inc.

—Winning Back Your Independence with Cosmetic Dermatology: How to Start a Medical Aesthetic Practice. 2008. 70p. pap. 99.95 (978-1-4357-1336-9(2)) Lulu Enterprises Inc.

Arrault, Valérie. L'empire du Kitsch. 2010. (FRE.). 304p. (C). pap. 35.00 **(978-2-252-03752-2(0))** Klincksieck, Editions FRA. Dist: ISD.

The Art at Home (ES 4-vol. Set) 2011. 1025.00 (978-4-86166-100-6(5)) Synapse, Edition JPN. Dist: Taylor & Francis Group.

Ashbee, Charles Robert. Where the Great City Stands. 2008. 256p. pap. (978-1-905217-96-0(X)) Mills, Jeremy Publishing.

Astell, Ann W. Eating Beauty: The Eucharist & the Spiritual Arts of the Middle Ages. 2006. (Illus.). 296p. 39.95 (978-0-8014-4466-1(7)) Cornell Univ. Pr.

Babbitt, Irving. The New Laokoon: An Essay on the Confusion of the Arts. 2009. 276p. 24.99 (978-1-103-97814-4(4)); pap. 18.99 (978-1-103-97806-9(3)); 24.99 (978-1-103-19423-0(2)); pap. 18.99 (978-1-103-19420-9(8)) BiblioBazaar.

Balthasar, Hans Urs Von, et al. The Glory of the Lord: A Theological Aesthetics. 2nd ed. 2009. **(978-1-58617-321-0(9))** Ignatius Pr.

Bann, Stephen, et al, contrib. by. The Repeating Image: Multiples in French Painting from David to Matisse. 2007. (ENG., Illus.). 200p. 50.00 (978-0-300-12669-3(7)) Yale Univ. Pr.

Banta, Martha. One True Theory & the Quest for an American Aesthetic. 2007. (ENG.). 336p. (C). 38.00 (978-0-300-12297-8(7)) Yale Univ. Pr.

Barrett, Melanie Susan. Love's Beauty at the Heart of the Christian Moral Life: The Ethics of Catholic Theologian Hans Urs von Balthasar. 2009. 332p. (978-0-7734-4649-6(4)) Mellen, Edwin Pr., The.

Barwell, Michael John. Patterns of Redemption. 2008. 264p. pap. (978-3-639-07782-7(2)) VDM Verlag Dr. Mueller e.K.

Bascom, John. Aesthetics: Or the Science of Beauty. rev. ed. (Philosophy in America Ser.). reprint ed. 42.00 (978-0-404-59029-1(2)) AMS Pr., Inc.

—Aesthetics; or, the Science of Beauty by John Bascom. 2006. 280p. (ENG.). per. 23.99 (978-1-4255-2484-5(2)); per. 23.99 (978-1-4255-2483-8(4)) MPublishing.

Baudouin, Charles. Psychoanalysis & Aesthetics. Paul, Eden and Cedar, tr. 2007. (ENG.). 328p. 45.95 (978-0-548-02761-5(7)) Kessinger Publishing, LLC.

—Psychoanalysis & Aesthetics. 2007. (ENG.). 328p. per. (978-1-4067-4734-8(3)) Read Bks.

Bauer, Matthias, et al. Kunst und Kognition: Interdisziplinäre Studien zur Erzeugung von Bildsinn. 2008. (Illus.). 305p. pap. (978-3-7705-4451-6(X)) Wilhelm/Fink#GmbH & Co. Verlags-KG.

Baumeister, Martin, et al, eds. Die Kunst der Geschichte: Historiographie, Ästhetik, Erzählung. 2009. (GER., Illus.). 398p. (C). 68.00 (978-3-525-36384-3(2)) Vandenhoeck & Ruprecht GmbH & Co. KG DEU. Dist: ISD.

Bayley, Stephen. Ugly: The Aesthetics of Everything, 1 vol. 2011. (ENG., Illus.). 272p. 39.95 (978-1-906863-47-0(4)) FIELL Pubng. Ltd. GBR. Dist: D.A.P./Distributed Art Pubs.

Beer, Kenneth, et al, eds. Cosmetic Bootcamp Primer: Comprehensive Aesthetic Management. 2010. (Series in Cosmetic & Laser Therapy Ser.). (ENG., Illus.). 298p. (978-1-84184-698-9(8)) Informa Healthcare.

Beiser, Frederick. Schiller as Philosopher: A Re-Examination. 2008. (ENG.). 298p. pap. 45.00 (978-0-19-953231-5(1)) Oxford Univ. Pr., Inc.

Beistegui, Miguel. Aesthetics after Metaphysics: From Mimesis to Metaphor. 2012. (Routledge Studies in Contemporary Philosophy Ser.). (ENG.). 208p. (C). 125.00 **(978-0-415-53962-3(5))** Routledge.

Belknap, George N., ed. A Guide to Reading in Aesthetics & Theory of Poetry. 2011. 92p. 38.95 **(978-1-258-01256-4(1))** Literary Licensing, LLC.

Bell, Clive. Art. 2008. 188p. 22.99 (978-0-554-35410-1(1)) 2008. 188p. 25.99 (978-0-554-26107-2(3)) 2007. (ENG.). 168p. pap. 19.99 (978-1-4346-0389-0(X)) 2007. (ENG.). 186p. pap. 21.99 (978-1-4346-0462-0(4)) BiblioBazaar.

—Art. 2008. 320p. 45.95 (978-1-4366-4789-2(4)); pap. 30.95 (978-0-548-90130-4(9)) Kessinger Publishing, LLC.

—Art. 2008. (ENG.). 156p. pap. 12.45 (978-1-4385-0894-8(8)); pap. 11.95 (978-1-4385-0174-1(9)) Standard Pubns., Inc. (Book Jungle).

Ben-dor, Oren, ed. Law & Art: Ethics, Aesthetics, Justice. 2011. (ENG., Illus.). 336p. 125.00 (978-0-415-56021-4(7), Routledge Cavendish) Taylor & Francis Group GBR. Dist: Taylor & Francis Group.

Benjamin, Walter, et al. Aesthetics & Politics. 2007. (Radical Thinkers Ser.). (ENG.). 220p. per. 14.95 (978-1-84467-570-8(X), 844570) Verso Bks. GBR. Dist: Norton, W. W. & Co., Inc.

Berger, Arthur Asa. The Objects of Affection: Semiotics & Consumer Culture. 2010. (Semiotics & Popular Culture Ser.). (ENG., Illus.). 212p. 95.00 (978-0-230-10372-6(3)); pap. 27.00 (978-0-230-10373-3(1)) Palgrave Macmillan.

Berggruen, Olivier. The Writing of Art. 2012. (ENG.). 120p. pap. 16.00 **(978-1-906548-62-9(5))** Pushkin Pr., Ltd. GBR. Dist: Consortium Bk. Sales & Distribution.

Bergmann, Sigurd. In the Beginning Is the Icon: A Liberative Theology of Images, Visual Arts, & Culture. 2009. (ENG., Illus.). 208p. (C). 95.00 (978-1-84553-172-0(8)) Equinox Publishing Ltd. GBR. Dist: ISD.

Bergmann, Sigurd, ed. Theology in Built Environments: Exploring Religion, Architecture, & Design. (ENG.). 314p. 2011. pap. 29.95 **(978-1-4128-4580-9(7))** 2009. (Illus.). 49.95 (978-1-4128-1018-0(3)) Transaction Pubs.

Berleant, Arnold. Sensibility & Sense: The Aesthetic Transformation of the Human World. 2010. (St. Andrews Studies in Philosophy & Public Affairs Ser.). (ENG.). 232p. (gr. 10). 80.00 (978-1-84540-173-3(5)) Imprint Academic GBR. Dist: Ingram Pub. Services.

Bernier, Ronald R., ed. Beyond Belief. 2010. (Illus.). 150p. pap. 19.00 (978-1-60899-087-0(7), Pickwick Pubns.) Wipf & Stock Pubs.

Bleiker, Roland. Aesthetics & World Politics. Richmond, Oliver P., ed. 2009. (Rethinking Peace & Conflict Studies). (ENG.). 272p. 95.00 (978-1-4039-8976-5(1)) Palgrave Macmillan.

Bogue, Ronald. Deleuze's Way: Essays in Transverse Ethics & Aesthetics. 2007. 186p. 99.95 (978-0-7546-6032-3(X)) Ashgate Publishing Co.

Bonshek, Anna. The Big Fish: Consciousness as Structure, Body & Space. 2007. (Consciousness, Literature & the Arts Ser.: 6). 420p. 112.05 (978-90-420-2172-3(1)) Rodopi.

Bosanquet, Bernard. Three Lectures on Aesthetic. (Orig.). 2010. (ENG.). 136p. pap. 20.75 (978-1-177-03528-6(6)) 2009. 130p. 24.99 (978-1-110-90089-3(9)) 2009. 130p. pap. 19.75 (978-1-110-90086-2(4)) 2009. (ENG.). 129p. pap. 18.99 (978-1-110-90083-1(X), BiblioLife) 2009. (ENG.). 129p. pap. 19.99 (978-1-110-90085-5(6), BiblioLife) BiblioBazaar.

—Three Lectures on Aesthetic. (Orig.). 2008. 130p. 35.95 (978-1-4365-0316-7(7)) 2007. (ENG.). 132p. per. 20.95 (978-0-548-72086-8(X)) Kessinger Publishing, LLC.

Botz-Bornstein, Thorsten. Aesthetics & Politics of Space in Russia & Japan: A Comparative Philosophical Study. 2009. (Emerging Perspectives on Education in China Ser.). (ENG.). 190p. 62.99 (978-0-7391-3068-1(4)) Lexington Bks.

—The Cool-Kawaii: Afro-Japanese Aesthetics & New World Modernity. 2010. (ENG.). 224p. 65.00 (978-0-7391-4845-7(1)) Lexington Bks.

Bouleau, Nicolas. Risk & Meaning: Adversaries in Art, Science & Philosophy. 2011. (Illus.). vii, 302p. 79.95 (978-3-642-17646-3(1), 3642176461) Springer.

Bourdieu, Pierre. Distinction: A Social Critique of the Judgement of Taste. Nice, Richard, tr. from FRE. 2010. (Routledge Classics Ser.). (Illus.). 640p. pap. (978-0-415-56788-6(2), Routledge) Taylor & Francis Group.

Bourgeois, Jason Paul. The Aesthetic Hermeneutics of Hans-Georg Gadamer & Hans Urs Von Balthasar. 2007. (American University Studies VII: Theology & Religion Ser.: Vol. 268). 160p. (C). 59.95 (978-1-4331-0069-7(X)) Lang, Peter Publishing, Inc.

Boylan, Michael & Boylan. The Good, the True, & the Beautiful: A Quest for Meaning. 2008. (ENG., Illus.). 256p. 27.95 (978-1-84706-157-7(5)) Continuum International Publishing Group, Ltd. GBR. Dist: National Bk. Network.

Braiterman, Zachary. The Shape of Revelation: Aesthetics & Modern Jewish Thought. 2007. (Stanford Studies in Jewish History & C Ser.). (ENG., Illus.). 352p. 55.00 (978-0-8047-5321-0(0)) Stanford Univ. Pr.

Brand, Peg Zeglin, ed. Beauty Unlimited. 2012. (ENG.). 392p. pap. 28.00 **(978-0-253-00649-3(X)**, 025300649X); (Illus.). 80.00 **(978-0-253-00642-4(2)**, 0253006422) Indiana Univ. Pr.

Braziel, Jan Evans & Joseph, Young, eds. Erasing Public Memory: Race, Aesthetics, & Cultural Amnesia in the Americas. 2007. 350p. pap. 30.00 (978-0-88146-058-2(3)) Mercer Univ. Pr.

Braziel, Jan Evans & Young, Joseph, eds. Erasing Public Memory: Race, Aesthetics, & Cultural Amnesia in the Americas. 2007. 350p. 60.00 (978-0-88146-076-6(1)) Mercer Univ. Pr.

Brown, Frank Burch. Inclusive yet Discerning: Navigating Worship Artfully. 2009. (Illus.). 176p. pap. 20.00 (978-0-8028-6256-3(X)) Eerdmans, William B. Publishing Co.

Brown, Judith. Glamour in Six Dimensions: Modernism & the Radiance of Form. 2009. (Illus.). 224p. 39.95 (978-0-8014-4779-2(8)) Cornell Univ. Pr.

Bruner, Michael Lane. Repressive Regimes, Aesthetic States, & Arts of Resistance. 2012. **(978-1-4331-0108-3(4))** Lang, Peter Publishing, Inc.

Brunham, Hugh D., et al. The Aesthetics of Wine. 2012. (New Directions in Aesthetics Ser.: 28). (ENG.). 224p. 119.95 **(978-1-4443-3766-2(1)**, Wiley-Blackwell) Wiley, John & Sons, Inc.

Bucky, Louis P., et al. Aesthetic Breast Surgery. 2009. (Techniques in Aesthetic Surgery Ser.). (ENG., Illus.). 184p. 186.00 (978-0-7020-3091-8(0), Saunders) Elsevier - Health Sciences Div.

Budd, Malcolm. Aesthetic Essays. (ENG.). 2012. 290p. pap. 35.00 **(978-0-19-959626-3(3))** 2008. 272p. 75.00 (978-0-19-955617-5(2)) Oxford Univ. Pr., Inc.

Bulajic, Viktorija Vesna. Database Aesthetics: Art in the Age of Information Overflow. 2007. (Electronic Mediations Ser.). (Illus.). 336p. 75.00 (978-0-8166-4118-5(8)); per. 25.00 (978-0-8166-4119-2(6)) Univ. of Minnesota Pr.

Bullough, Edward. Aesthetics: Lectures & Essays. Wilkinson, Elizabeth M., ed. 2011. 202p. 44.95 **(978-1-258-01925-9(6))** Literary Licensing, LLC.

Burgin, Victor. Situational Aesthetics: Selected Writings by Victor Burgin. Streitberger, Alexander, ed. 2010. (Lieven Gevaert Ser.). 432p. pap. 55.00 (978-90-5867-768-6(0)) Leuven Univ. Pr. BEL. Dist: Cornell Univ. Pr.

Burgum, Edwin Berry, ed. The New Criticism: An Anthology of Modern Aesthetics & Literary Criticism. 2011. 368p. 53.95 **(978-1-258-05265-2(2))** Literary Licensing, LLC.

Burnham, Douglas & Jesinghausen, Martin. Nietzsche's 'the Birth of Tragedy' A Reader's Guide. 2010. (Reader's Guides). (ENG.). 208p. 24.95 (978-1-84706-585-8(6)); 80.00 (978-1-84706-584-1(8)) Continuum International Publishing Group, Ltd. GBR. Dist: National Bk. Network.

Bychkov, Oleg V. Aesthetic Revelation: Reading Ancient & Medieval Texts after Hans Urs von Balthasar. 2010. 368p. 79.95 (978-0-8132-1731-4(8)) Catholic Univ. of America Pr.

Bychkov, Oleg V. & Fodor, James, eds. Theological Aesthetics after Von Balthasar. 2008. (Ashgate Studies in Theology, Imagination & the Arts Ser.). (Illus.). 272p. 114.95 (978-0-7546-5834-4(1)) Ashgate Publishing Co.

Cahn, Steven M. & Meskin, Aaron, eds. Aesthetics: A Comprehensive Anthology. 2007. (Blackwell Philosophy Anthologies Ser.: 13). (ENG.). 704p. pap. 69.95 (978-1-4051-5435-2(7), Wiley-Blackwell) Wiley, John & Sons, Inc.

Calvert, George. Essays Aesthetical. 2007. 112p. per. (978-1-4068-4167-1(6)) Echo Library.

Calvert, George Henry. Essays Aesthetical, by George H Calvert. 2006. 268p. per. 23.99 (978-1-4255-2382-4(X)) MPublishing.

Cannon-Brown, Willie. Nefer: The Aesthetic Ideal in Classical Egypt. 2006. (African Studies: History, Politics, Economics & Culture Ser.). (Illus.). 116p. 138.00 (978-0-415-97994-8(3)) Routledge.

Carey, John. What Good Are the Arts?, 1 vol. 2010. (ENG.). 304p. pap. 17.95 (978-0-19-973597-6(2)) Oxford Univ. Pr., Inc.

Carpo, Mario. The Alphabet & the Algorithm. 2011. (Writing Architecture Ser.). (ENG., Illus.). 184p. (gr. 17). pap. 21.95 (978-0-262-51580-1(6)) MIT Pr.

Carr, Adrian & Hancock, Philip, eds. Work & Organization: The Aesthetic Dimension. 2009. (Illus.). x, 202p. pap. 24.99 (978-0-9817032-5-1(9)) Emergent Pubns.

Carr, Paul H. Beauty in Science & Spirit. 2007. (Illus.). xxiii, 171p. per. 18.00 (978-0-9776514-7-4(9)); (978-0-9793778-5-3(4)) Beech River Bks.

Carroll, Jerome. Art at the Limits of Perception: The Aesthetic Theory of Wolfgang Welsch. 2006. 288p. pap. (978-0-8204-7596-7(3)) Lang, Peter AG.

—Art at the Limits of Perception: The Aesthetic Theory of Wolfgang Welsch. 2006. 286p. pap. 68.95 (978-3-03910-569-4(8)) Lang, Peter Publishing, Inc.

Carroll, Noël. Art in Three Dimensions. 2010. 536p. 74.00 (978-0-19-955931-2(7)) Oxford Univ. Pr., Inc.

Carroll, Noel. Art in Three Dimensions. 2012. (ENG.). 548p. pap. 45.00 **(978-0-19-965592-2(8))** Oxford Univ. Pr., Inc.

Carroll, Noel. Living in an Art World. 2008. (ENG.). 272p. 20.95 (978-0-415-91938-8(X)); 74.95 (978-0-415-91937-1(1)) Routledge.

Castro, Sixto J. & Marcos, Alfredo. The Paths of Creation: Creativity in Science & Art. 2011. (Natur, Wissenschaft und die Künste/Nature, Science & the Arts/Nature, Science et les Arts Ser.). (ENG.). 277p. pap. **(978-3-0343-0511-2(7))** Lang, Peter.

Castronovo, Russ. Beautiful Democracy: Aesthetics & Anarchy in a Global Era. 2007. (Illus.). 272p. 65.00 (978-0-226-09628-5(9)); per. 27.50 (978-0-226-09629-2(7)) Univ. of Chicago Pr.

Cauvel, Jane & Li, Zehou. Four Essays on Aesthetics: Toward a Global View. 2006. (ENG., Illus.). 220p. per. 27.50 (978-0-7391-1321-9(6)) Lexington Bks.

Chandler, Albert R. Beauty & Human Nature: Elements of Psychological Aesthetics. reprint ed. 26.00 (978-0-404-59106-9(X)) AMS Pr., Inc.

Cheng, Francois. The Way of Beauty: Five Meditations for Spiritual Transformation. 2009. (ENG.). 1p. 18.95 (978-1-59477-287-0(8)) Inner Traditions International, Ltd.

Chytry, Josef. Unis Vers Cythère: Aesthetic-Political Investigations in Polis Thought & the Artful Firm. 2009. xii, 256p. 75.95 (978-1-4331-0732-0(5)) Lang, Peter Publishing, Inc.

Cixous, Hélène. Poetry in Painting: Writings on Contemporary Arts & Aesthetics. Segarra, Marta & Masó, Joana, eds. 2012. (Frontiers of Theory Ser.). (ENG., Illus.). 224p. (gr. 17). 105.00 **(978-0-7486-4744-6(9))** Edinburgh Univ. Pr. GBR. Dist: Columbia Univ. Pr.

Clark, Andrew H. Diderot's Part: Aesthetics & Physiology. 2008. (Illus.). 242p. 99.95 (978-0-7546-5438-4(9)) Ashgate Publishing Co.

Cleveland, Joseph. Nietzsche's Aesthetic Revaluation of Knowledge. 2008. 84p. pap. (978-3-639-04499-7(1)) VDM Verlag Dr. Mueller e.K.

Cohen, Michael. Interdisciplinary Treatment Planning: Principles, Design, Implementation. 2008. (Illus.). xx, 548p. (978-0-86715-474-0(8)) Quintessence Publishing Co., Inc.

Comfort, Kelly. European Aestheticism & Spanish American Modernismo: Artist Protagonists & the Philosophy of Art for Art's Sake. 2011. (ENG., Illus.). 200p. 80.00 (978-0-230-27809-7(4)) Palgrave Macmillan.

Computational Aesthetics 2007. 12th rev. ed. 2007. (ENG.). pap. 72.95 (978-1-56881-337-0(6)) AK Peters, Ltd.

Coohill, Patricia Trutty, ed. Art Inspiring Transmutations of Life. 2010. (Analecta Husserliana Ser.). (Illus.). x, 450p. 219.00 (978-90-481-9159-8(9), 9048191599) Springer.

Coomaraswamy, Ananda Kentish. Figures of Speech or Figures of Thought? The Traditional View of Art. Wroth, William, ed. 2007. (Perennial Philosophy Ser.). (ENG., Illus.). 288p. per. 24.95 (978-1-933316-34-5(9)) World Wisdom, Inc.

Cooper, David E. A Philosophy of Gardens. 2008. (ENG., Illus.). 192p. pap. 25.00 (978-0-19-923888-0(X)) Oxford Univ. Pr., Inc.

Corcoran, Steven & Rancière, Jacques. Dissensus: On Politics & Aesthetics. 2010. (ENG.). 240p. 19.95 (978-1-84706-445-5(0)) Continuum International Publishing Group, Ltd. GBR. Dist: National Bk. Network.

Costello, Diarmuid & Willsdon, Dominic, eds. The Life & Death of Images. 2008. (Illus.). 256p. 76.95 (978-0-8014-4698-6(8)) Cornell Univ. Pr.

—The Life & Death of Images: Ethics & Aesthetics. 2008. (Illus.). 255p. pap. 24.95 (978-0-8014-7455-2(8)) Cornell Univ. Pr.

Cousin, Victor. Lectures on the True, the Beautiful & the Good. 2006. 404p. per. 26.99 (978-1-4255-4300-6(6)) MPublishing.

—Lectures on the True, the Beautiful, & the Good by M V Cousin Increased by an Appendix on French Art Tr, with the Approbation of M Cousin, By. 2006. 404p. per. 25.99 (978-1-4255-4330-3(8)) MPublishing.

Cox, Caroline. How to Be Adored: A Girl's Guide to Hollywood Glamour. 2010. (ENG.). 256p. 19.99 (978-0-06-199291-9(7), Collins Design) HarperCollins Pubs.

Cram101 Textbook Reviews. Outlines & Highlights for Perceiving the Arts by Dennis J Sporre. 2011. 216p. pap. 30.95 **(978-1-4672-7001-4(6))** Cram101 Inc.

Crane, Lucy. Art & the Formation of Taste. 2009. 324p. 25.99 (978-1-103-29026-0(6)); pap. 19.99 (978-1-103-29023-9(1)) BiblioBazaar.

—Art & the Formation of Taste. 2009. 94p. pap. 14.14 (978-1-151-59185-2(8)) General Bks. LLC.

Crevel, M. van, ed. Chinese Poetry in Times of Mind, Mayhem & Money. 2008. (Sinica Leidensia Ser.). 500p. (C). (978-90-04-16382-9(4)) BRILL.

Crispin, Darla, ed. New Paths: Aspects of Music Theory & Aesthetics in the Age of Romanticism. 2009. (Collected Writings of the Orpheus Institute Ser.). (Illus.). 133p. pap. 39.50 (978-90-5867-734-1(6)) Leuven Univ. Pr. BEL. Dist: Cornell Univ. Pr.

Cristofovici, Anca. Touching Surfaces: Photographic Aesthetics, Temporality, Aging. 2009. (Illus.). 228p. pap. 67.00 (978-90-420-2513-4(1)) Rodopi.

Croce, Benedetto. Aesthetic As Science of Expression & General Linguistic. 2008. 320p. 29.99 (978-0-554-22984-3(6)); 28.99 (978-0-554-32287-2(0)) BiblioBazaar.

—Aesthetic As Science of Expression & General Linguistic. 2009. 354p. pap. (978-1-150-64065-0(0)) Books LLC.

—Aesthetic As Science of Expression & General Linguistic. Ainslie, Douglas, tr. 2009. 260p. pap. (978-1-4099-8267-8(X)) Dodo Pr.

—Aesthetic As Science of Expression & General Linguistic. 2008. 200p. pap. (978-1-4068-4950-9(2)) Echo Library.

—Aesthetic as Science of Expression & General Linguistic. Ainslie B. A., Douglas, tr. 2007. (ENG.). 284p. pap. 21.99 (978-1-4264-3483-9(9)); 318p. pap. 24.99 (978-1-4264-3518-8(5)) BiblioBazaar.

—Breviary of Aesthetics: Four Lectures. Fudemoto, Hiroko, tr. from ITA. 2007. (Lorenzo Da Ponte Italian Library). (ENG.). 144p. (978-0-8020-9771-2(5)) Univ. of Toronto Pr.

Crowther, Paul. Defining Art, Creating the Canon: Artistic Value in an Era of Doubt. 2007. (ENG.). 288p. 85.00 (978-0-19-921068-8(3)) Oxford Univ. Pr., Inc.

—The Kantian Aesthetic: From Knowledge to the Avant-Garde. 2010. (ENG.). 224p. 60.00 (978-0-19-957997-6(0)) Oxford Univ. Pr., Inc.

—Phenomenology of the Visual Arts (Even the Frame) 2009. (ENG., Illus.). 264p. 55.00 (978-0-8047-6214-4(7)) Stanford Univ. Pr.

—Phenomenology of Visual Arts. 2010. (ENG., Illus.). 264p. pap. 22.95 (978-0-8047-7602-8(4)) Stanford Univ. Pr.

Curtis, Neal, ed. The Pictorial Turn. 2011. (ENG.). 256p. (C). pap. 45.95 **(978-0-415-50874-2(6))** Routledge.

Dahnke, Michael D. Film, Art, & Filmart: An Introduction to Aesthetics Through Film. 2007. (ENG., Illus.). 140p. per. 29.50 (978-0-7618-3721-3(3)) Univ. Pr. of America, Inc.

Dallas, Enaeas S. The Gay Science V2. 2010. 348p. pap. 25.56 (978-1-163-28615-9(X)) 2010. 348p. 37.56 **(978-1-163-55934-5(2))** 2007. 346p. 46.95 (978-0-548-25835-4(X)) 2007. 348p. per. 31.95 (978-1-4326-6207-3(4)) Kessinger Publishing, LLC.

Dallas, Eneas Sweetland. The Gay Science. 2010. 360p. pap. 32.75 (978-1-144-61093-5(1)); 356p. pap. 32.75 (978-1-142-38899-7(9)); 356p. pap. 32.75 (978-1-142-28247-9(3)) BiblioBazaar.

—The Gay Science. 2011. (Cambridge Library Collection - Spiritualism & Esoteric Knowlege Ser.). (ENG.). 358p. pap. 29.99 (978-1-108-07312-7(3)); 356p. pap. 29.99 (978-1-108-07313-4(1)) Cambridge Univ. Pr.

—The Gay Science. 2010. 144p. pap. 19.99 (978-1-154-23430-5(4)) 2010. 178p. pap. 19.99 (978-1-150-87736-0(7)) 2009. 176p. pap. 19.99 (978-1-150-29542-3(2)) General Bks. LLC.

Dasilva, Fabio B. & Bompadre, Viviana A. How Does Language Communicate Through Drama: Television, Film, & Theater as Distinct Discourse Types. 204p. 109.95 (978-0-7734-5156-8(0)) Mellen, Edwin Pr., The.

Daverio, Philippe. The Ideal Museum. 2012. (ENG., Illus.). 288p. 50.00 **(978-0-8478-3755-7(6))** Rizzoli International Pubns., Inc.

Davies, Stephen & Stecker, Bob. Companion to Aesthetics. Cooper, David E. et al, eds. 2nd ed. 2009. (Blackwell Companions to Philosophy Ser.: 67). (ENG.). 640p. 209.95 (978-1-4051-6922-6(2), Wiley-Blackwell) Wiley, John & Sons, Inc.

Davis, Whitney. Queer Beauty: Sexuality & Aesthetics from Winckelmann to Freud & Beyond. 2010. (Columbia Themes in Philosophy, Social Criticism, & the Arts Ser.). (ENG., Illus.). 368p. (gr. 17). 40.00 (978-0-231-14690-6(6)) Columbia Univ. Pr.

Day, Henry Noble. The Science of Aesthetics; or, the Nature, Kinds, Laws, & Uses of Beauty by Henry N Day. 2006. 460p. per. 29.99 (978-1-4255-5067-7(3)) MPublishing.

De Bolla, Peter. Aesthetics & the Work of Art: Adorno, Kafka, Richter. De Bolla, Peter & Uhlig, Stefan H., eds. 2008. (Language, Discourse, Society Ser.). (ENG., Illus.). 280p. 100.00 (978-0-230-54919-7(5)) Palgrave Macmillan.

De Cortinas, Lia Pistiner. The Aesthetic Dimension of the Mind: Variations on a Theme of Bion. 2009. (Illus.). 340p. pap. 42.95 (978-1-85575-612-0(9)) Karnac Bks. GBR. Dist: Stylus Publishing, LLC.

De Maio, Mauricio & Rzany, Berthold. The Male Patient in Aesthetic Medicine. 2009. (ENG., Illus.). xxii, 239p. 189.00 (978-3-540-79045-7(4), 3540790454) Springer.

Del Nevo, Matthew. The Work of Enchantment. 2011. (ENG.). 178p. 34.95 (978-1-4128-1860-5(5)) Transaction Pubs.

Deleuze, Gilles & Parnet, Claire. Dialogues. 2nd ed. 184p. pap. (978-0-8264-5919-0(6)) Continuum International Publishing Group, Ltd.

—Dialogues II. Tomlinson, Hugh & Habberjam, Barbara, trs. from FRE. 2nd rev. ed. 2007. (ENG., Illus.). 192p. (gr. 17). pap. 26.50 (978-0-231-14135-2(1)) Columbia Univ. Pr.

Deleuze, Gilles, et al. Dialogues II. 2nd rev. ed. 2007. (ENG., Illus.). 192p. (gr. 17). 77.00 (978-0-231-14134-5(3)) Columbia Univ. Pr.

Dewey, John. The Later Works of John Dewey, Volume 10, 1925 - 1953: 1934, Art as Experience. Boydston, Jo Ann, ed. 2008. (Collected Works of John Dewey Ser.). (ENG., Illus.). 470p. pap. 40.00 (978-0-8093-2820-8(8)) Southern Illinois Univ. Pr.

DiBernardo, Barry, et al. Lasers & Non-Surgical Rejuvenation. 2009. (Techniques in Aesthetic Surgery Ser.). (ENG., Illus.). 256p. 186.00 (978-0-7020-3090-1(2), Saunders) Elsevier - Health Sciences Div.

Didi-Huberman, Georges. Confronting Images: Questioning the Ends of a Certain History of Art. (Illus.). 288p. pap. 35.00 (978-0-271-02472-1(0)) Pennsylvania State Univ. Pr.

Dudley, Sandra, ed. Museum Materialities: Objects, Engagements, Interpretations. 2009. (ENG., Illus.). 312p. (C). 44.95 (978-0-415-49218-8(1)); 140.00 (978-0-415-49217-1(3)) Routledge.

Duffy, John. Philosophy of Poetry Based on Thomistic. 2006. pap. 27.95 (978-1-4286-6137-0(9)) Kessinger Publishing, LLC.

Dufrenne, Mikel. In the Presence of the Sensuous: Essays in Aesthetics. Roberts, Mark S. & Gallagher, Dennis, eds. (Contemporary Studies in Philosophy & the Human Sciences Ser.). (ENG., Illus.). 238p. pap. 20.98 (978-1-57392-501-3(2), Humanity Bks.) Prometheus Bks., Pubs.

Dutton, Denis. The Art Instinct: Beauty, Pleasure, & Human Evolution. (ENG.). 288p. 2010. pap. 15.00 (978-1-60819-055-3(2)) 2008. 25.00 (978-1-59691-401-8(7)) Bloomsbury Publishing.

Dyrness, William A. Poetic Theology: God & the Poetics of Everyday Life. 2011. 341p. pap. 26.00 (978-0-8028-6578-6(X)) Eerdmans, William B. Publishing Co.

Eastham. Aesthetic Afterlives (h) 2011. (Continuum Literary Studies). (ENG.). 272p. 120.00 (978-0-8264-4398-4(2)) Continuum International Publishing Group, Ltd. GBR. Dist: National Bk. Network.

Eastman, Max. Enjoyment of Poetry. 2010. 274p. pap. 27.75 (978-1-141-83372-6(7)) 2010. 276p. pap. 27.75 (978-1-143-09953-3(2)) 2009. 246p. 28.99 (978-1-113-99666-4(8)) 2009. 246p. pap. 25.75 (978-1-113-99662-6(5)) 2009. 240p. 23.99 (978-1-103-83093-0(7)) 2009. 240p. pap. 17.59 (978-1-103-83087-9(2)) 2008. 272p. 25.99 (978-0-559-63565-6(6)) 2008. 272p. pap. 26.75 (978-0-559-63562-5(1)) BiblioBazaar.

—Enjoyment of Poetry. 2009. 130p. pap. (978-1-4588-2702-9(X)); pap. (978-0-217-71794-6(2)) Books LLC.

—Enjoyment of Poetry. 2008. 272p. 42.95 (978-1-4369-4774-9(X)); pap. 27.95 (978-1-4368-3650-0(6)) Kessinger Publishing, LLC.

Easton, Della. Aesthetics Matter. 2009. 52p. pap. 9.96 (978-0-557-03962-3(2)) Lulu Enterprises Inc.

Eddy, Arthur Jerome. Delight the Soul of Art: Five Lectures. 2007. (ENG.). 288p. 43.95 (978-0-548-09643-7(0)) Kessinger Publishing, LLC.

Egan, Ronald. The Problem of Beauty: Aesthetic Thought & Pursuits in Northern Song Dynasty China. 2006. (Harvard East Asian Monographs: 271). (Illus.). 382p. 49.95 (978-0-674-02264-5(5)) Harvard Univ., Asia Ctr.

Elbert, Monika & Drews, Marie, eds. Culinary Aesthetics & Practices in Nineteenth-Century American Literature. 2009. (Nineteenth-Century Major Lives & Letters Ser.). (ENG., Illus.). 276p. 84.00 (978-0-230-61628-8(3)) Palgrave Macmillan.

Elkins, Naef. What is an Image? Elkins, James & Naef, Maja, eds. 2011. (Stone Art Theory Institutes Ser.). (ENG., Illus.). 264p. 84.95 **(978-0-271-05064-5(0))** Pennsylvania State Univ. Pr.

Emmer, M. The Visual Mind II. 2006. (Leonardo Bks.). (ENG., Illus.). 712p. (gr. 17). per. 28.00 (978-0-262-55063-5(6)) MIT Pr.

Engström, Timothy & Selinger, Evan, eds. Rethinking Theories & Practices of Imaging. 2009. (ENG., Illus.). 320p. 116.00 (978-0-230-58065-7(3)) Palgrave Macmillan.

Erfani, Farhang. The Aesthetics of Autonomy: Ricœur & Sartre on Emancipation, Authenticity, & Selfhood. 2011. (ENG.). 166p. 60.00 (978-0-7391-1258-8(9)) Lexington Bks

Erman, Michel, ed. Le goût dans tous Ses états. 2009. (Littératures de langue française Ser.). (FRE.). 136p. pap. (978-3-03911-753-6(X)) Lang, Peter.

Esau, Erika. Images of the Pacific Rim: Australia & California, 1850-1935. 2011. (ENG., Illus.). 368p. pap. 59.95 (978-0-909952-39-6(6)) Power Pubns. AUS. Dist: Univ. of Washington Pr.

Eshelman, Raoul. Performatism, or the End of Postmodernism. 2008. (ENG., Illus.). 284p. pap. 27.00 (978-1-888570-41-0(5)) Davies Group Pubs., The.

Evans, Brad & Reid, Julian, eds. Deleuze & Guattari on Fascism. 2012. (Interventions Ser.). (ENG.). 208p. (C). 130.00 (978-0-415-58967-3(3)) Routledge.

Evans, Jill & Taliaferro, Charles. The Image in Mind: Theism, Naturalism, & the Imagination. 2010. (Continuum Studies in Philosophy of Religion Ser.). (ENG., Illus.). 224p. 130.00 (978-1-84706-482-0(5)) Continuum International Publishing Group, Ltd. GBR. Dist: National Bk. Network.

Falasca-Zamponi, Simonetta. Rethinking the Political: The Sacred, Aesthetic Politics, & the College de Sociologie. 2011. (McGill-Queen's Studies in the History of Religion Ser.). (ENG., Illus.). 296p. (C). **(978-0-7735-3900-6(X))**; pap. **(978-0-7735-3901-3(8))** McGill-Queen's Univ. Pr.

Farimani: Art Critical/Aesthetic Theory Music, No.1. 2008. (Illus.). 224p. (978-0-9801508-0-3(9)) Farimani.

Faulhaber, Christoph. Christoph Faulhaber - New York, NY 10047/48: Der öffentliche Prozess des Wiederaufbaus des World Trade Centers nach dem 11. September 2001. 2011. (ENG., Illus.). 76p. pap. 21.95 **(978-3-86678-454-3(6))** Kerber Verlag DEU. Dist: D.A.P./Distributed Art Pubs.

Feagin, Susan L., ed. Global Theories of the Arts & Aesthetics. 2006. (Journal of Aesthetics & Art Criticism Ser.). (ENG., Illus.). 140p. pap. 43.95 (978-1-4051-7355-1(6), Wiley-Blackwell) Wiley, John & Sons, Inc.

Federici, Corrado, et al. Beauty & the Abject: Interdisciplinary Perspectives. 2007. (Studies on Themes & Motifs in Literature: Vol. 88). (Illus.). xvi, 295p. (C). 78.95 (978-0-8204-8810-3(0)) Lang, Peter Publishing, Inc.

Fenner, David E. W. Art in Context: Understanding Aesthetic Value. 2008. (ENG.). 368p. 59.95 (978-0-8040-1104-4(4)); per. 29.95 (978-0-8040-1105-1(2)) Swallow Pr.

Ferguson, Kennan. The Politics of Judgment: Aesthetics, Identity, & Political Theory. Ferguson, Kennan, ed. 2007. (ENG.). 168p. pap. 27.50 (978-0-7391-2087-3(5)) Lexington Bks.

Ferre, Rosa, ed. Red Cavalry: Creation & Power in Soviet Russia between 1917 And 1945. 2011. 500p. 69.95 (978-84-96917-78-1(9)) Caja de Madrid ESP. Dist: Actar Birkhauser Distribution.

Ferrucci, Piero. Beauty & the Soul: The Extraordinary Power of Everyday Beauty to Heal Your Life. 2010. (ENG.). 304p. (gr. 12). 13.95 (978-1-58542-833-5(7), Tarcher) Penguin Group (USA) Inc.

Fishwick, Paul A., ed. Aesthetic Computing. 2008. (Leonardo Bks.). (ENG., Illus.). 480p. (gr. 17). pap. 26.00 (978-0-262-56237-9(5)) MIT Pr.

Flabpohler, Svenja, et al, eds. Kippfiguren der Wiederholung: Interdisziplinare Untersuchungen Zur Figu der Wiederholung in Literatur, Kunst und Wissenschaft. (GER., Illus.). 151p. pap. 32.95 (978-3-631-55955-0(0)) Lang, Peter GmbH, Europaischer Verlag der Wissenschaften DEU. Dist: Lang, Peter Publishing, Inc.

Fleming, Bruce. The Aesthetic Sense of Life: A Philosophy of the Everyday. 2007. (ENG.). 180p. per. 31.50 (978-0-7618-3916-3(X)) Univ. Pr. of America, Inc.

Fleming, Paul. Exemplarity & Mediocrity: The Art of the Average from Bourgeois Tragedy to Realism. 2008. (ENG.). 240p. 55.00 (978-0-8047-5890-1(5)) Stanford Univ. Pr.

Floistad, Guttorm, ed. Aesthetics & Philosophy of Art. 2007. (Contemporary Philosophy: A New Survey Ser.). viii, 416p. 239.00 (978-1-4020-5068-8(2), 1402050682) Springer.

Forte, Bruno. The Portal of Beauty: Towards a Theology of Aesthetics. Glenday, David & McPartian, Paul, trs. from ITA. 2008.Tr. of porta della bellezza: per un'estetica Teologica. 130p. pap. 30.00 (978-0-8028-3280-1(6)) Eerdmans, William B. Publishing Co.

Freeland, Cynthia A. Art Theory. 2007. (Very Short Introductions Ser.). (ENG., Illus.). 184p. pap. 11.95 (978-0-19-280463-1(4)) Oxford Univ. Pr., Inc.

Freeman, Damien. Art's Emotions: Ethics, Expression & Aesthetic Experience. 2012. (ENG.). 240p. (C). **(978-0-7735-4005-7(9))**; pap. **(978-0-7735-4006-4(7))** McGill-Queen's Univ. Pr.

Frers, Lars & Meier, Lars, eds. Encountering Urban Places: Visual & Material Performances in the City. 2007. (Re-Materialising Cultural Geography Ser.). (Illus.). 206p. 114.95 (978-0-7546-4929-8(6)) Ashgate Publishing Co.

Friend, Daniel S. The Pulse of Creation: Aesthetic Pleasures of Electron Micrographs. 2007. pap. 10.00 (978-0-8059-8779-9(7)) Dorrance Publishing Co., Inc.

Froschels, Emil. Philosophy & Aesthetics of Speech. Haskell, Joseph Noyes, tr. 2011. 176p. 42.95 **(978-1-258-03995-0(8))** Literary Licensing, LLC.

Gö, et al. Wenn Götzen dämmern: Formen ästhetischen Denkens bei Nietzsche. 2008. (GER.). 195p. (C). 98.00 (978-3-525-30160-9(X)) Vandenhoeck & Ruprecht GmbH & Co. KG DEU. Dist: ISD.

Gage, Mark Foster. Aesthetic Theory: Essential Texts for Architecture & Design. 2011. (ENG.). 208p. pap. 29.95 (978-0-393-73349-5(1), 73349) Norton, W. W. & Co., Inc.

Gaiger, Jason & Gaiger. Aesthetics & Painting. 2008. (Continuum Aesthetics Ser.). (ENG., Illus.). 192p. 29.95 (978-0-8264-8521-2(9)); 100.00 (978-0-8264-8520-5(0)) Continuum International Publishing Group, Ltd. GBR. Dist: National Bk. Network.

Gans, Eric Lawrence. A New Way of Thinking: Religion, Philosophy, Art. 2011. **(978-1-934542-25-5(3))** Davies Group Pubs., The.

Gaultier, Paul. The Meaning of Art: Its Nature, Role & Value. 2007. (ENG.). 304p. 43.95 (978-0-548-04337-0(X)) Kessinger Publishing, LLC.

Gaut, Berys. Art, Emotion & Ethics. 2009. (ENG.). 288p. pap. 37.95 (978-0-19-957152-9(X)) Oxford Univ. Pr., Inc.

Gayle, Addison, Jr. & Gayle, Addison. The Addison Gayle Jr. Reader. Norment, Nathaniel, Jr. & Norment, Nathaniel, eds. 2009. (ENG., Illus.). 504p. 78.00 (978-0-252-03408-4(2)) Univ. of Illinois Pr.

Gayley, Charles Mills. An Introduction to the Methods & Materials of Literary Criticism. 2008. 604p. 34.99 (978-0-559-86840-5(5)); pap. 44.75 (978-0-559-86837-5(5)) BiblioBazaar.

—An Introduction to the Methods & Materials of Literary Criticism. 2009. 478p. pap. (978-1-4588-1183-7(2)) Books LLC.

Gayley, Charles Mills & Scott, Fred Newton. An Introduction to the Methods & Materials of Literary Criticism. 2007. (ENG.). 600p. 59.95 (978-0-548-01043-3(9)) Kessinger Publishing, LLC.

Gerhardt, Christina, et al, contrib. by. Adorno & Ethics, Vol. 33. 2006. (ENG.). 192p. (C). pap. 14.00 (978-0-8223-6659-1(2)) Duke Univ. Pr.

Gibbons, Luke. Edmund Burke & Ireland: Aesthetics, Politics & the Colonial Sublime. 2009. (ENG., Illus.). 320p. pap. 44.00 (978-0-521-10094-6(1)) Cambridge Univ. Pr.

Gielen, Pascal, text. The Murmuring of the Artistic Multitude. 2010. (ENG., Illus.). 368p. pap. 28.95 (978-90-78088-34-9(6)) Valiz NLD. Dist: D.A.P./Distributed Art Pubs.

Gkogkas, Nikolaos. Nelson Goodman & the Case for a Kalological Aesthetics. 2008. (ENG.). 256p. 89.00 (978-0-230-57355-0(X)) Palgrave Macmillan.

Glover, Nicky. Psychoanalytic Aesthetics: An Introduction to the British School. 2009. (Harris Meltzer Trust Ser.). 300p. pap. 42.95 (978-1-85575-686-1(2)) Karnac Bks. GBR. Dist: Stylus Publishing, LLC.

Goizueta, Roberto S. Christ Our Companion: A Liberation Theological Aesthetic. 2009. 160p. pap. 30.00 (978-1-57075-853-9(0)) Orbis Bks.

Goldblatt, David & Brown, Lee. Aesthetics. 3rd ed. 2010. (ENG., Illus.). 480p. (C). pap. 84.00 (978-0-205-01703-4(7), Prentice Hall) Prentice Hall PTR.
Golec, Michael J. The Brillo Box Archive: Aesthetics, Design, & Art. 2008. (Interfaces: Studies in Visual Culture Ser.). (ENG., Illus.). 144p. pap. 25.00 (978-1-58465-701-9(4), Dartmouth College Press) Univ. Pr. of New England.
Gosetti-Ferencei, Jennifer. The Ecstatic Quotidian: Phenomenological Sightings in Modern Art & Literature. 2010. (Literature & Philosophy Ser.). 256p. pap. 27.95 (978-0-271-03228-3(6)) Pennsylvania State Univ. Pr.
Gosetti-Ferencei, Jennifer Anna. The Ecstatic Quotidian: Phenomenological Sightings in Modern Art & Literature. 2007. (Literature & Philosophy Ser.). (ENG.). 256p. 56.95 (978-0-271-03227-6(8)) Pennsylvania State Univ. Pr.
Granger, David A. John Dewey, Robert Pirsig, & the Art of Living: Revisioning Aesthetic Education. annot. ed. 2006. (ENG.). 384p. 95.00 (978-1-4039-7402-0(0)) Palgrave Macmillan.
Graves, David. The New Institutional Theory of Art. 2010. pap. (978-1-86335-721-0(1)) Common Ground Publishing Pty, Ltd.
Greanleaf, W. H. Ideological heritage Vol 2. 2012. (ENG.). 400p. 39.95 **(978-0-415-48956-0(3))** Routledge.
Green-Lewis, Jennifer, et al. Teaching Beauty in Delillo, Woolf, & Merrill. 2008. (ENG.). 224p. 84.00 (978-0-230-60124-6(3)) Palgrave Macmillan.
Griffin, John. On the Origin of Beauty: Ecophilosophy in the Light of Traditional Wisdom. 2011. (ENG.). 304p. pap. 23.95 (978-1-935493-98-3(1)) World Wisdom, Inc.
Griffiths, Annie. National Geographic Simply Beautiful Photographs. 2010. (ENG., Illus.). 504p. 35.00 (978-1-4262-0645-0(3)) National Geographic Society.
Griggs, Edward Howard. Art & the Human Spirit the Meaning and. 2006. pap. 16.95 (978-1-4286-3438-1(X)) Kessinger Publishing, LLC.
Gronstad, Asbjorn & Gustafsson, Henrik, eds. Ethics & Images of Pain. 2012. (Routledge Research in Cultural & Media Studies). (ENG., Illus.). 262p. (C). 125.00 (978-0-415-89382-4(8)) Routledge.
Grotting, James C. Reoperative Aesthetic & Reconstructive Plastic Surgery. 2nd ed. 2006. (978-1-57626-180-4(8)) Quality Medical Publishing, Inc.
Grudin, Louis. A Primer of Aesthetics: Logical Approaches to A Philosophy of Art. 2011. 262p. 47.95 **(978-1-258-01100-0(X))** Literary Licensing, LLC.
Guillen, Mauro F. The Taylorized Beauty of the Mechanical: Scientific Management & the Rise of Modernist Architecture. 2006. (Princeton Studies in Cultural Sociology). (ENG., Illus.). 232p. (C). 35.00 (978-0-691-11520-7(6)) Princeton Univ. Pr.
Gullestad, Anders M., et al, eds. Exploring Textual Action. 2010. (Text, Action & Space Ser.). (ENG.). 440p. (C). pap. 55.00 (978-87-7934-460-0(7)) Aarhus Universitetsforlag DNK. Dist: ISD.
Guter, Eran. Aesthetics A-Z. 2010. (Philosophy A-Z Ser.). (ENG.). 192p. (gr. 17). pap. 22.00 (978-0-7486-2340-2(X)) Edinburgh Univ. Pr. GBR. Dist: Columbia Univ. Pr.
—Aesthetics A-Z. 2010. (Philosophy A-Z Ser.). (ENG.). 192p. (gr. 17). 120.00 (978-0-7486-2339-6(6)) Edinburgh Univ. Pr. GBR. Dist: Columbia Univ. Pr.
Hagberg, Garry L., ed. Art & Ethical Criticism. 2008. (New Directions in Aesthetics Ser.: 11). (ENG., Illus.). 304p. 104.95 (978-1-4051-3483-5(6), Wiley-Blackwell) Wiley, John & Sons, Inc.
—Art & Ethical Criticism. 2010. (New Directions in Aesthetics Ser.: 19). (ENG.). 304p. pap. 34.95 (978-1-4443-3787-7(4), Wiley-Blackwell) Wiley, John & Sons, Inc.
Halliwell, Stephen. Aristotle's Poetics. 2009. 384p. pap. 34.95 (978-0-7156-2858-4(5)) Duckworth Publishers GBR. Dist: International Publishers Marketing.
Halsall, Francis, et al. Rediscovering Aesthetics: Transdisciplinary Voices from Art History, Philosophy, & Art Practice. Halsall, Francis et al, eds. 2008. (ENG.). 336p. 65.00 (978-0-8047-5990-8(1)); pap. 24.95 (978-0-8047-5991-5(X)) Stanford Univ. Pr.
Hamilton, Andy & Zangwill, Nick, eds. Scruton's Aesthetics. 2012. (ENG., Illus.). 288p. 85.00 **(978-0-230-25168-7(4))** Palgrave Macmillan.
Hamilton, G. Rostrevor. Poetry & Contemplation. 2006. 176p. per. (978-1-4067-3023-4(8), Hesperides Pr.) Read Bks.
Hamilton, Margaret. Transfigured Stages: Major Practitioners & Theatre Aesthetics in Australia. 2011. (ENG., Illus.). 244p. pap. 70.00 **(978-90-420-3356-6(8))** Rodopi.
Hansel, Joëlle, ed. Levinas in Jerusalem: Phenomenology, Ethics, Politics, Aesthetics. 2008. (Amsterdam Studies in Jewish Philosophy Ser.). (ENG.). xviii, 200p. 219.00 (978-1-4020-6247-6(8), 1402062478) Springer.
—Levinas in Jerusalem: Phenomenology, Ethics, Politics, Aesthetics: Phenomenology, Ethics, Politics, Aesthetics. 2010. (Amsterdam Studies in Jewish Philosophy Ser.). xviii, 200p. pap. 219.00 (978-90-481-7582-6(8), 9048175828) Springer.
Harrell, Jean Gabbert. Profundity. 2008. pap. 24.95 (978-0-271-02840-8(8)) Pennsylvania State Univ. Pr.
Harrison, Jane Ellen. Ancient Art & Ritual. 2009. 258p. 25.99 (978-0-559-65723-8(4)) 2009. 258p. pap. 25.75 (978-0-559-65720-7(X)) 2008. 152p. 21.99 (978-0-554-35539-9(6)) 2008. 152p. 24.99 (978-0-554-26236-9(3)) BiblioBazaar.
—Ancient Art & Ritual. 2007. (Illus.). 136p. per. (978-1-4065-3280-7(0)) Dodo Pr.
Haug, Wolfgang Fritz. Kritik der Warenästhetik, Gefolgt Von Warenästhetik Im High-Tech-Kapitalismus. 2009. 350p. pap. (978-3-518-12553-3(2)) Suhrkamp Verlag.
Hegel, Georg Wilhelm Friedrich. Introduction to Hegels Philosophy of Fin. 2006. pap. 28.95 (978-1-4286-3953-9(5)) Kessinger Publishing, LLC.
Heikkilä, Martta. At the Limits of Presentation: Coming-into-Presence & its Aesthetic Relevance in Jean-Luc Nancy's Philosophy. 2008. (Europäische Hochschulschriften. Reihe 20: Philosophie Ser.). 312p. pap. 74.95 (978-3-631-58105-6(X)) Lang, Peter GmbH, Europaischer Verlag der Wissenschaften DEU. Dist: Lang, Peter.
Heil, Reinhard, et al, eds. Tensions: Technological & Aesthetic (Trans)Formations of Society. 2006. (ENG.). 350p. (gr. 11). pap. 39.95 (978-3-89942-518-5(9)) Transcript Verlag DEU. Dist: Transaction Pubs.
Heller, Agnes & Rundell, John F. Aesthetics & Modernity: Essays. 2010. (978-0-7391-4133-5(3)) Lexington Bks.
Henninger, Katherine. Ordering the Facade: Photography & Contemporary Southern Women's Writing. 2007. (New Directions in Southern Studies). (ENG., Illus.). 256p. per. 22.00 (978-0-8078-5805-9(6)) Univ. of North Carolina Pr.
Herder, Johann Gottfried Von. Selected Writings on Aesthetics. annot. ed. 2006. (ENG.). 468p. (C). 82.50 (978-0-691-11595-5(8)) Princeton Univ. Pr.
Herwitz. Aesthetics. 2008. (Key Concepts in Philosophy Ser.). (ENG., Illus.). 200p. 120.00 (978-0-8264-8918-0(4)) Continuum International Publishing Group, Ltd. GBR. Dist: National Bk. Network.
Herwitz, Daniel. Aesthetics. 2008. (Key Concepts in Philosophy Ser.). (ENG., Illus.). 200p. 29.95 (978-0-8264-8919-7(2)) Continuum International Publishing Group, Ltd. GBR. Dist: National Bk. Network.
Herwitz, Daniel Alan. The Star as Icon: Celebrity in the Age of Mass Consumption. 2008. (ENG., Illus.). 176p. (gr. 17). 27.50 (978-0-231-14540-4(3)) Columbia Univ. Pr.
Heuer, Christopher. The City Rehearsed: Object, Architecture, & Print in the Worlds of Hans Vredeman de Vries. 2012. (Classical Tradition in Architecture Ser.). (ENG., Illus.). 312p. (C). pap. 42.95 **(978-0-415-54232-6(4))** Routledge.
Heyd, Thomas & Clegg, John. Aesthetics & Rock Art III Symposium. 2008. (Bar S Ser.). (ENG., Illus.). 102p. (C). pap. 70.00 (978-1-4073-0304-8(X)) British Archaeological Reports Ltd. GBR. Dist: Brown, David Bk. Co., The.
Heydt, Colin. Rethinking Mill's Ethics: Character & Aesthetic Education. 2006. (Continuum Studies in British Philosophy). (ENG.). 174p. 155.00 (978-0-8264-8639-4(8)) Continuum International Publishing Group, Ltd. GBR. Dist: National Bk. Network.
Heß, Gilbert, et al, eds. Raffael als Paradigma: Rezeption, Imagination und Kult im 19. Jahrhundert. 2011.Tr. of Raphael as Paradigm. (GER., Illus.). XXIX, 426p. 168.00 **(978-3-11-025562-1(6))** De Gruyter, Walter Inc.
Hick, Darren Hudson. Introducing Aesthetics & the Philosophy of Art. 2012. (ENG., Illus.). 248p. 110.00 **(978-1-4411-9820-4(2))**; pap. 32.95 **(978-1-4411-7103-0(7))** Continuum International Publishing Group, Ltd. GBR. Dist: National Bk. Network.
Hickey, Dave. The Invisible Dragon: Essays on Beauty. rev. exp. ed. 2009. (ENG., Illus.). 152p. 22.00 (978-0-226-33318-2(3)) Univ. of Chicago Pr.
Hickman, Larry A., et al, eds. The Continuing Relevance of John Dewey: Reflections on Aesthetics, Morality, Science, & Society. 2011. (Illus.). 328p. pap. 92.00 (978-90-420-3232-3(4)) Rodopi.
Hiebert, Ted. In Praise of Nonsense: Aesthetics, Uncertainty, & Postmodern Identity. 2012. (ENG., Illus.). 296p. (C). **(978-0-7735-3973-0(5))**; pap. **(978-0-7735-3974-7(3))** McGill-Queen's Univ. Pr.
Highmore, Ben. Ordinary Lives. 2010. (ENG., Illus.). 208p. (C). pap. 31.95 (978-0-415-46187-0(1)) Routledge.
—Ordinary Lives. 2010. (ENG., Illus.). 208p. (C). 115.00 (978-0-415-46186-3(3)) Routledge.
Hirn, Yrjo. The Origins of Art: A Psychological & Sociological Inquiry. 2007. (ENG.). 344p. per. 31.95 (978-1-4325-0438-0(X)) Kessinger Publishing, LLC.
Hobart, Angela & Kapferer, Bruce, eds. Aesthetics in Performance: Formations of Symbolic Construction & Experience. 2006. 252p. 27.50 (978-1-84545-315-2(8)) Berghahn Bks., Inc.
Hobson, Marian. The Object of Art: The Theory of Illusion in Eighteenth-Century France. 2009. (Cambridge Studies in French Ser.). (ENG.). 408p. pap. 46.00 (978-0-521-11502-5(7)) Cambridge Univ. Pr.
Hofer, Stefan O. P. Aesthetic Facial Reconstruction, an Issue of Clinics in Plastic Surgery. 2009. (Clinics: Surgery Ser.: 36-3). (ENG.). 99.00 (978-1-4377-1264-3(9), Saunders) Elsevier - Health Sciences Div.
Holmes, Tim. Beyond Faith & Reason. 2009. 114p. pap. 12.98 (978-0-557-04561-7(4)) Lulu Enterprises Inc.
Hontanilla, Ana. El Gusto de la Razón: Debates de Arte y Moral en el Siglo XVIII Español. 2010. (SPA., Illus.). 366p. pap. 56.00 (978-84-8489-523-7(8)) Iberoamericana Vervuert Publishing Corp.
Hopkins, Robert. Picture, Image & Experience: A Philosophical Inquiry. 2009. (ENG.). 216p. pap. 31.99 (978-0-521-10982-6(5)) Cambridge Univ. Pr.
Hosey, Lance. The Shape of Green: Aesthetics, Ecology, & Design. 2012. (ENG.). 208p. pap. 30.00 **(978-1-61091-032-3(X))**; (Illus.). 60.00 **(978-1-61091-031-6(1))** Island Pr.
Howes, Graham. The Art of the Sacred: An Introduction to the Aesthetics of Art & Belief. 2007. (ENG., Illus.). 200p. 85.00 (978-1-84511-005-5(6)); pap. 28.00 (978-1-84511-006-2(4)) I. B. Tauris & Co., Ltd. GBR. Dist: Macmillan.
Hughes, Fiona & Hughes. Kant's 'Critique of Aesthetic Judgement' 2010. (Reader's Guides). (ENG.). 208p. 80.00 (978-0-8264-9767-3(5)) Continuum International Publishing Group, Ltd. GBR. Dist: National Bk. Network.
—Kant's 'Critique of Judgement' 2010. (Reader's Guides). (ENG.). 208p. 24.95 (978-0-8264-9768-0(3)) Continuum International Publishing Group, Ltd. GBR. Dist: National Bk. Network.
Hutcheon, Linda. Formalism & the Freudian Aesthetic: The Example of Charles Mauron. 2006. (ENG.). 268p. pap. 55.00 (978-0-521-02795-3(0)) Cambridge Univ. Pr.
Hutcheson, Francis. An Inquiry into the Original of Our Ideas of Beauty & Virtue. (Scottish Enlightenment Ser.). reprint ed. 29.50 (978-0-404-17657-0(7)) AMS Pr., Inc.
Hyland, Drew A. Plato & the Question of Beauty. 2008. (Studies in Continental Thought). (ENG.). 168p. 55.00 (978-0-253-35138-8(3), 0253351383); (Illus.). pap. 21.95 (978-0-253-21977-0(9), 0253219779) Indiana Univ. Pr.
Iftodi Zamfir, Alexandra. Edgar Allan Poe's Gothic Interiors. 2011. 76p. pap. **(978-3-8433-8760-6(5))** Lambert Academic Publishing.
Imamichi, Tomonobu & Lenk, Hans, eds. Aesthetics in Contemporary Philosophy: Proceedings of the International Institute of Philosophy Conference. 2010. (FRE & ENG., Illus.). 296p. pap. 54.95 (978-3-8258-1912-5(4)) Lit Verlag DEU. Dist: Transaction Pubs.
Ingham, Mary Beth. Rejoicing in the Works of the Lord: Beauty in the Franciscan Tradition. 2009. v, 79p. (978-1-57659-205-2(7)) Franciscan Institute Pubns.
Inglis, David & Herrero, Marta, eds. Art & Aesthetics, 4 vols. 2009. (Critical Concepts in the Social Sciences Ser.). (ENG., Illus.). 1430p. (C). 1430.00 (978-0-415-45011-9(X)) Routledge.
JACKSON, Shannon. Social Works: Peforming Arts, Supporting Publics. 2011. (ENG., Illus.). 320p. pap. 35.95 (978-0-415-48601-9(7)) Routledge.
Jacques, Geoffrey. A Change in the Weather: Modernist Imagination, African American Imaginary. 2009. 240p. (ENG.). pap. 28.95 (978-1-55849-688-0(2)); lib. bdg. 80.00 net. (978-1-55849-687-3(4)) Univ. of Massachusetts Pr.
Jaeger, Stephen. Magnificence & the Sublime in Medieval Aesthetics: Art, Architecture, Literature, Music. Jaeger, Stephen, ed. 2010. (New Middle Ages Ser.). (ENG., Illus.). 320p. 84.00 (978-0-230-61898-5(7)) Palgrave Macmillan.
James, David. Art, Myth, & Society in Hegel's Aesthetics. 2009. (Continuum Studies in Philosophy Ser.). (ENG.). 160p. 130.00 (978-0-8264-2560-7(7)) Continuum International Publishing Group, Ltd. GBR. Dist: National Bk. Network.
James, David. Art, Myth & Society in Hegel's Aesthetics. 2012. (ENG.). 160p. pap. 34.95 **(978-1-4411-7210-5(6))** Continuum International Publishing Group, Ltd. GBR. Dist: National Bk. Network.
Jamieson, D., ed. Language, Mind, & Art: Essays in Appreciation & Analysis, in Honor of Paul Ziff. 2010. (Synthese Library). (Illus.). 236p. pap. 229.00 (978-90-481-4391-7(8), 9048143918) Springer.
Jantzen, Grace M. A Place of Springs. Carrette, Jeremy & Joy, Morny, eds. 2009. (Death & the Displacement of Beauty Ser.). XVI, 224p. 118.00 (978-0-415-46999-9(6)) Routledge.
Jaroszynski, Piotr. Beauty & Being: Thomistic Perspectives. 2011. (Etienne Gilson Ser.). (ENG.). 280p. 85.00 **(978-0-88844-733-3(7))** Pontifical Institute of Mediaeval Studies, Dept. of Pubns. CAN. Dist: Univ. of Toronto Pr.
Jdey, Adnen & Kuhn, Rolf, eds. Michel Henry et l'affect de L'art: Recherches sur l'esthétique de la phénoménologie Matérielle. 2010. (Studies in Contemporary Phenomenology Ser.). (978-90-04-18633-0(6)) BRILL.
Jimenez, Agustin, photos by. Agustin Jimenez: Memoirs of the Avant-Garde. 2008. (ENG., Illus.). 192p. 50.00 (978-968-9345-11-4(7)) R.M. Editorial, S.A. de C.V. MEX. Dist: D.A.P./Distributed Art Pubs.
Johnson, Mark. The Meaning of the Body: Aesthetics of Human Understanding. 2008. (ENG., Illus.). 328p. pap. 22.50 (978-0-226-40193-5(6)) Univ. of Chicago Pr.
Johnston, Jay. Angels of Desire: Esoteric Bodies, Aesthetics & Ethics. 2009. (Gnostica Ser.). (ENG., Illus.). (C). 297p. 110.00 (978-1-84553-307-6(0)); 300p. 34.95 (978-1-84553-308-3(9)) Equinox Publishing Ltd. GBR. Dist: ISD.
Jones, Omi Osun Joni L., et al, eds. Experiments in a Jazz Aesthetic: Art, Activism, Academia, & the Austin Project. 2010. (ENG., Illus.). 392p. 60.00 (978-0-292-72204-0(4)); pap. 24.95 (978-0-292-72287-3(7)) Univ. of Texas Pr.
Jones, Owen. Grammar of Ornament. 2006. 240p. pap. 34.95 (978-2-914199-49-0(X)) L'Aventurine FRA. Dist: Independent Pubs. Group.
Journal Editorial Collecive, Sr. Journal of Aesthetics & Protest #5. 2007. (Illus.). 122p. pap. 11.00 (978-0-9791377-1-6(3)) Journal of Aesthetics and Protest Pr./Herbst.
Jullien, Francois. The Great Image Has No Form, or on the Nonobject Through Painting. Todd, Jane Marie, tr. from FRE. 2nd ed. 2009. (ENG., Illus.). 288p. 48.00 (978-0-226-41530-7(9)) Univ. of Chicago Pr.
Jullien, François. In Praise of Blandness: Proceeding from Chinese Thought & Aesthetics. Varsano, Paula M., tr. from FRE. 2007. (ENG., Illus.). 169p. (gr. 17). pap. 18.95 (978-1-890951-42-9(0)) Zone Bks.
Jullien, Francois. This Strange Idea of the Beautiful. Fijalkowski, Krysztof & Richardson, Michael, trs. from FRE. 2012. (SB-the French List Ser.). (ENG.). 302p. 21.00 (978-0-85742-010-7(0)) Seagull Bks. GBR. Dist: Chicago Distribution Ctr.
Jullien, Francois & Todd, Jane Marie. The Great Image Has No Form, or, on the Nonobject Through Painting. 2012. (Illus.). 288p. pap. 35.00 (978-0-226-41531-4(7)) Univ. of Chicago Pr.
Kalar, Brent. Key Terms in Aesthetics. 2013. (Key Terms Ser.). (ENG.). 176p. 75.00 (978-0-8264-2162-3(8)); pap. 19.95 (978-0-8264-3527-9(0)) Continuum International Publishing Group, Ltd. GBR. Dist: National Bk. Network.
Kallen, Horace M. Indecency & the Seven Arts & Other Adventures of a Pragmatist in Aesthetics. reprint ed. 27.50 (978-0-404-59206-6(6)) AMS Pr., Inc.
Kamps, Toby, text. John Wood & Paul Harrison: Answers to Questions. 2011. (ENG., Illus.). 120p. pap. 24.95 (978-1-933619-31-6(7)) Contemporary Arts Museum, Houston.
Kandinsky, Wassily. The Art of Spiritual Harmony. Sadler, Michael T. H., tr. 2007. (ENG.). 96p. per. 9.95 (978-1-60206-428-7(8)) Cosimo, Inc.
—The Art of Spiritual Harmony. 2008. 164p. pap. (978-1-4097-8366-4(9)) Read Bks.
Kandinsky, Wassily. Concerning the Spiritual in Art. 2011. 92p. pap. 15.99 **(978-1-61279-057-2(7))** Publishing in Motion.
Kant, Immanuel. The Critique of Judgement. 2009. 232p. 27.99 (978-0-559-10553-1(3)); 24.99 (978-0-559-10568-5(1)); pap. 25.75 (978-0-559-10557-9(6)); pap. 17.99 (978-0-559-10564-7(9)) BiblioBazaar.
—The Critique of Judgement. Meredith, James Creed, tr. 2009. 184p. pap. (978-1-4099-6813-9(8)) Dodo Pr.
—The Critique of Judgement. 2008. 136p. pap. 7.99 (978-1-60459-273-3(7)) Wilder Pubns., Ltd.
Kanz, Roland & Schönwälder, Jürgen. Ästhetik des Charakteristischen: Quellentexte zu Kunstkritik und Streitkultur in Klassizismus und Romantik. 2008. (Super alta perennis. Studien zur Wirkung der Klassischen Antike Ser.). (GER.). 255p. (C). 62.00 (978-3-89971-466-1(0)) Vandenhoeck & Ruprecht GmbH & Co. KG DEU. Dist: ISD.
Kapor, Vladimir. Local Colour: A Travelling Concept. 2009. 262p. 55.95 (978-3-03911-415-3(8)) Lang, Peter AG GBR. Dist: Lang, Peter.
Katz, Adam, ed. The Originary Hypothesis: A Minimal Proposal for Humanistic Inquiry. 2007. (ENG.). 382p. pap. 28.00 (978-1-888570-36-6(9)) Davies Group Pubs., The.
Kaushik, Rajiv. Art & Institution: Aesthetics in the Late Works of Merleau-Ponty. 2011. (Continuum Studies in Continental Philosophy Ser.). (ENG.). 192p. 120.00 (978-1-4411-3663-3(0)) Continuum International Publishing Group, Ltd. GBR. Dist: National Bk. Network.
Keifer-Boyd, Karen & Maitland-Gholson, Jane. Engaging Visual Culture. Stewart, Marilyn, ed. 2007. (Art Education in Practice Ser.). (ENG.). 162p. 24.95 (978-0-87192-775-0(6)) Davis Pubns., Inc.
Kein, Li. The Liberation of Sensation from Reason. 2011. 160p. pap. **(978-3-8443-9280-7(7))** Lambert Academic Publishing.
Kelly, Michael. A Hunger for Aesthetics: Enacting the Demands of Art. 2012. (Columbia Themes in Philosophy, Social Criticism, & the Arts Ser.). (ENG., Illus.). 272p. (gr. 17). 50.00 **(978-0-231-15292-1(2))** Columbia Univ. Pr.
Kemal, Salim & Gaskell, Ivan, eds. Politics & Aesthetics in the Arts. 2010. (Cambridge Studies in Philosophy & the Arts Ser.). (ENG., Illus.). 284p. (C). pap. 30.99 (978-0-521-14196-3(6)) Cambridge Univ. Pr.
Kiaer, Christina. Imagine No Possessions: The Socialist Objects of Russian Constructivism. 2008. (ENG., Illus.). 344p. (gr. 17). pap. 28.95 (978-0-262-61221-0(6)) MIT Pr.
Kieran, Matthew & Lopes, Dominic McIver, eds. Knowing Art: Essays in Aesthetics & Epistemology. 2007. (Philosophical Studies Ser.). 161p. 149.00 (978-1-4020-5264-4(2), 1402052642) Springer.
Kim, Ha Poong. Beyond Words, Things, Thoughts, Feelings: Essays on Aesthetic Experience. 2011. 142p. 45.00 (978-1-84519-470-3(5)) Sussex Academic Pr. GBR. Dist: International Specialized Bk. Services.
Kingwell, Mark. Opening Gambits. 2009. (ENG., Illus.). 295p. pap. 19.95 (978-1-55470-205-3(4)) Key Porter Bks. CAN. Dist: Perseus-PGW.
—Opening Gambits: Essays on Art & Philosophy. 2009. (ENG., Illus.). 296p. 27.95 (978-1-55470-073-8(6)) Key Porter Bks. CAN. Dist: Perseus-PGW.
Kingwell, Mark & Turmel, Patrick, eds. Rites of Way: The Politics & Poetics of Public Space. 2009. (Canadian Commentaries Ser.). (ENG., Illus.). 210p. pap. 32.95 (978-1-55458-153-5(2)) Wilfrid Laurier Univ. Pr. CAN. Dist: Univ. of Toronto Pr.
Kirkpatrick, Graeme. Aesthetic Theory & the Video Game. 2011. (ENG., Illus.). 240p. pap. 25.95 (978-0-7190-7718-0(4)) Manchester Univ. Pr. GBR. Dist: Macmillan.
—Aesthetic Theory & the Video Game. 2011. (ENG., Illus.). 240p. 80.00 (978-0-7190-7717-3(6)) Manchester Univ. Pr. GBR. Dist: Macmillan.
Knapp, Peggy A. Chaucerian Aesthetics. 2008. (New Middle Ages Ser.). (ENG.). 252p. 85.00 (978-0-230-60668-5(7)) Palgrave Macmillan.
Koch, Erec R. The Aesthetic Body: Passion, Sensibility, & Corporeality in Seventeenth-Century France. 2008. 392p. (C). 75.00 (978-0-87413-010-2(7)) Univ. of Delaware Pr.
Koenig, Bernard. Art Matters: Art of Knowledge/Knowledge of Art. 2009. (Illus.). 264p. pap. (978-1-933146-58-4(3)) Academica Pr., LLC.
Korsmeyer, Carolyn. Savoring Disgust: The Foul & the Fair in Aesthetics. 2011. (ENG., Illus.). 208p. pap. 29.95 (978-0-19-975693-3(7)) Oxford Univ. Pr., Inc.
Kosnoski, John. John Dewey & the Habits of Ethical Life: The Aesthetics of Political Organizing in a Liquid World. 2010. (ENG.). 272p. 75.00 (978-0-7391-4464-0(2)) Lexington Bks.
Kratschmer, Edwin. Das Asthetische Monster Mensch: Fragmente zu einer Asthetik der Gewalt. (GER.). 317p. 39.95 (978-3-631-39580-6(9)) Lang, Peter Publishing, Inc.
Kraut, Robert. Artworld Metaphysics. (ENG.). 2010. 208p. pap. 35.00 (978-0-19-958742-1(6)) 2007. 176p. 75.00 (978-0-19-922812-6(4)) Oxford Univ. Pr., Inc.
Kronegger, M. & Tymieniecka, A-T., eds. The Aesthetics of Enchantment in the Fine Arts. 2010. (Analecta Husserliana Ser.). 352p. pap. 259.00 (978-90-481-5405-0(7), 9048154057) Springer.
Kubler, George. The Shape of Time: Remarks on the History of Things. 2008. (ENG., Illus.). 144p. per. 17.00 (978-0-300-10061-7(2)) Yale Univ. Pr.
Kukla, Rebecca, ed. Aesthetics & Cognition in Kant's Critical Philosophy. 2011. (ENG.). 324p. pap. 39.99 (978-0-521-18089-4(9)) Cambridge Univ. Pr.
Kul-Want, Christopher, ed. Philosophers on Art from Kant to the Postmodernists: A Critical Reader. 2010. (ENG., Illus.). 376p. (gr. 17). 89.50

(978-0-231-14094-2(0)); pap. 29.50 (978-0-231-14095-9(9)) Columbia Univ. Pr.

Kulwant, Christopher. Introducing Aesthetics: A Graphic Guide. 2010. (Introducing Ser.). (ENG., Illus.). 176p. 9.95 (978-1-84831-167-1(2)) Totem Bks. GBR. Dist: Consortium Bk. Sales & Distribution.

Kutzbach, Konstanze & Mueller, Monika, eds. The Abject of Desire: The Aestheticization of the Unaesthetic in Contemporary Literature & Culture. 2007. 312p. per. (978-90-420-2264-5(7)) Rodopi B.V. Editions.

Kyte-Coles, Robin, photos by. The Spirit of Buddha. 2009. 45.00 (978-3-8327-9315-9(1)) teNeues Publishing Co.

Lamarque, Peter. Work & Object: Explorations in the Metaphysics of Art. (ENG.). 2012. 264p. pap. 35.00 (978-0-19-965549-6(9)) 2010. 256p. 65.00 (978-0-19-957746-0(3)) Oxford Univ. Pr., Inc.

Lan, Shan. Postmodern Aesthetics in Six-Generation Chinese Films. 2010. 72p. pap. (978-3-8383-6129-1(6)) Lambert Academic Publishing.

Lane, Liv. Choosing Beauty. 2010. (978-1-57749-234-4(X)) Taylor Trade Publishing.

Langfeld, Herbert Sidney. The Aesthetic Attitude. 2007. (ENG.). 332p. 45.95 (978-0-548-04545-9(3)) Kessinger Publishing, LLC

László, Janos & Cupchik, Gerald C., eds. Emerging Visions of the Aesthetic Process: In Psychology, Semiology, & Philosophy. 2008. (ENG., Illus.). 348p. pap. 46.00 (978-0-521-08974-6(3)) Cambridge Univ. Pr.

Lee, Vernon. The Beautiful. 2011. 167p. pap. 19.99 (978-1-107-40166-2(6)) Cambridge Univ. Pr.

—The Beautiful: An Introduction to Psychological Aesthetics. 2008. 108p. pap. (978-1-4099-5094-3(8)) Dodo Pr.

Lehrer, Keith. Art, Self & Knowledge, 1 vol. 2011. (ENG., Illus.). 224p. pap. 24.95 (978-0-19-530499-2(3)) Oxford Univ. Pr., Inc.

Levinas, Emmanuel. Proper Names. 140p. (978-0-485-11466-9(6)) Continuum International Publishing Group, Ltd.

Levinson, Jerrold. Contemplating Art. 2006. 432p. 165.00 (978-0-19-920618-6(X)) Oxford Univ. Pr., Inc.

—Contemplating Art: Essays in Aesthetics. 2006. (ENG.). 432p. per. 55.00 (978-0-19-920617-9(1)) Oxford Univ. Pr., Inc.

—Music, Art, & Metaphysics. 2011. (ENG., Illus.). 440p. pap. 35.00 (978-0-19-959662-1(X)); 99.00 (978-0-19-959663-8(8)) Oxford Univ. Pr., Inc.

Lieu, Jee Woong. Cultural Aesthetic Codes Applied to the Visual Design of Products. 2010. 72p. pap. (978-3-639-26390-9(1)) VDM Verlag Dr. Mueller e.K.

Lin, Xiaoping. Children of Marx & Coca-Cola: Chinese Avant-Garde Art & Independent Cinema. 2009. (Illus.). 312p. (C). 47.00 (978-0-8248-3336-7(8)) Univ. of Hawaii Pr.

Livesey, Ruth. Socialism, Sex, & the Culture of Aestheticism in Britain, 1880-1914. 2007. (British Academy Postdoctoral Fellowship Monographs). (ENG., Illus.). 230p. 85.00 (978-0-19-726398-3(4)) Oxford Univ. Pr., Inc.

Loewen, G. V. The Role of Art in the Construction of Personal Identity: Toward a Phenomenology of Aesthetic Self-Consciousness. 2012. 180p. 129.95 (978-0-7734-3929-0(3)) Mellen, Edwin Pr., The.

Lopes, Dominic McIver & Kieran, Matthew, eds. Knowing Art: Essays in Aesthetics & Epistemology. 2007. (Philosophical Studies Ser.). XXIV, 168p. pap. 49.95 (978-1-4020-6785-3(2), 1402067852) Springer.

Loschek, Ingrid. When Clothes Become Fashion: Design & Innovation Systems. 2009. (ENG., Illus.). 1p. 99.95 (978-1-84788-367-4(2)); pap. 29.95 (978-1-84788-366-7(4)) Berg Pubs. GBR. Dist: Macmillan.

Ludovisi, Stefano Giacchetti & Saavedra, G. Agostini. Nostalgia for a Redeemed Future: Critical Theory. 2009. (ENG., Illus.). 280p. pap. 29.95 (978-0-87413-072-0(7)) Univ. of Delaware Pr.

Lukács, György. György Lukács: Notizen zu Georg Simmels Vorlesungen, 1906/07, und zur »Kunstsoziologie«, ca. 1909. 2011. (ENG., Illus.). 48p. pap. 10.00 (978-3-7757-2854-6(6)) Hatje Cantz Verlag GmbH & Co KG DEU. Dist: D.A.P./Distributed Art Pubs.

Lunde, Eric. The Commonplace of the Transfigurative. 2008. 122p. 34.96 (978-1-4357-3457-9(2)) Lulu Enterprises Inc.

Machon, Josephine. (Syn)aesthetics: Redefining Visceral Performance. 2009. (ENG., Illus.). 232p. 95.00 (978-0-230-22127-7(0)) Palgrave Macmillan.

—(Syn)Aesthetics: Redefining Visceral Performance. 2011. (ENG., Illus.). 240p. pap. 29.00 (978-0-230-33690-2(6)) Palgrave Macmillan.

Maciocco, Giovanni & Tagliagambe, Silvano. People & Space: New Forms of Interaction in the City. 2009. (Urban & Landscape Perspectives Ser.). (ENG., Illus.). vi, 246p. 139.00 (978-1-4020-9878-9(2)) Springer.

MacIver, Roderick. Art as a Way of Life. 2009. (ENG., Illus.). 96p. pap. 16.95 (978-1-55643-920-9(2)) North Atlantic Bks.

MacSwain, Robert & Worley, Taylor. Theology, Aesthetics, & Culture: Responses to the Work of David Brown. 2012. (ENG., Illus.). 320p. 125.00 (978-0-19-964682-1(1)) Oxford Univ. Pr., Inc.

Mair, Nancy. Grace: Freeing the Swan Within for a Beautiful Life. 272p. 50.85 (978-0-87596-544-4(X)) Rodale Pr., Inc.

Malecki, Wojciech. Embodying Pragmatism: Richard Shusterman's Philosophy & Literary Theory. 2010. (Literary & Cultural Theory Ser.). 204p. 57.95 (978-3-631-61217-0(6)) Lang, Peter GmbH, Europaischer Verlag der Wissenschaften DEU. Dist: Lang, Peter.

Maleuvre, Didier. The Religion of Reality: Inquiry into the Self, Art, & Transcendence. 2006. 318p. 79.95 (978-0-8132-1454-2(8)) Catholic Univ. of America Pr.

Mallat, Ernest. Protesis Fija Estetica: Enfoque Clinico y Multidisciplinario. 2007. (SPA.). 176.00 (978-84-8174-916-8(8), Elsevier Espana) Elsevier - Health Sciences Div.

Malone, Meredith. Chance Aesthetics. 2009. (Illus.). 160p. 35.00 (978-0-936316-27-7(6)) Washington Univ., Mildred Lane Kemper Art Museum.

Mancini, Daniele. Urban Fields. Aesthetic esperiments for urban appropriation. Volume 1 - 2009. 2010. 60p. pap. 30.95 (978-1-4461-4957-7(9)) Lulu Enterprises Inc.

Mandoki, Katya. Everyday Aesthetics: Prosaics, the Play of Culture & Social Identities. 2007. (Illus.). 344p. 134.95 (978-0-7546-5889-4(9)) Ashgate Publishing Co.

Mantle, Eric. A Visual Guide to Classical Art Theory for Drawing & Painting Students. 2009. (ENG.). 160p. pap. 22.50 (978-1-935166-12-2(3)) Parkhurst Brothers, Inc., Pubs.

Manzotti, Riccardo. Situated Aesthetics: Art Beyond the Skin. 2011. (ENG., Illus.). 250p. pap. 34.90 (978-1-84540-238-9(3)) Imprint Academic GBR. Dist: Ingram Pub. Services.

Margolis, Joseph. The Arts & the Definition of the Human: Toward a Philosophical Anthropology. 2008. (ENG.). 200p. 60.00 (978-0-8047-5953-3(7)); pap. 24.95 (978-0-8047-5954-0(5)) Stanford Univ. Pr.

—The Cultural Space of the Arts & the Infelicities of Reductionism. 2010. (Columbia Themes in Philosophy, Social Criticism, & the Arts Ser.). (ENG., Illus.). 232p. (gr. 17). 24.50 (978-0-231-14728-6(7)) Columbia Univ. Pr.

—On Aesthetics. 2008. (ENG.). 216p. (C). pap. 15.95 (978-0-495-00889-7(3)) Wadsworth.

Margolis, Joseph. Philosophy Looks at the Arts: Contemporary Readings in Aesthetics. 2011. 250p. 46.95 (978-1-258-03566-2(9)) Literary Licensing, LLC.

Marks, Laura U. Enfoldment & Infinity: An Islamic Genealogy of New Media Art. 2010. (Leonardo Bks.). (ENG., Illus.). 408p. (gr. 17). 39.95 (978-0-262-01421-2(1)) MIT Pr.

Marshall, Henry R. Pain, Pleasure & Aesthetics. reprint ed. 29.50 (978-0-404-59269-1(4)) AMS Pr., Inc.

Martindale, Charles. Latin Poetry & the Judgement of Taste: An Essay in Aesthetics. 2007. (ENG.). 276p. pap. 49.95 (978-0-19-921612-3(6)) Oxford Univ. Pr., Inc.

Martindale, Colin, et al, eds. Evolutionary & Neurocognitive Approaches to Aesthetics, Creativity & the Arts. 2007. (Foundations & Frontiers in Aesthetics Ser.). (Illus.). 256p. 49.95 (978-0-89503-306-2(2)) Baywood Publishing Co., Inc.

Marwick, Arthur. A History of Human Beauty. 2007. (ENG., Illus.). 276p. per. 27.95 (978-1-84725-050-6(5), Hambledon Continuum) Continuum International Publishing Group, Ltd. GBR. Dist: National Bk. Network.

Mazzalovo, Gerald. Brand Aesthetics. 2012. (ENG., Illus.). 240p. 95.00 (978-0-230-33673-5(6)) Palgrave Macmillan.

McDowall, Stewart A. Beauty & the Beast: An Essay in Evolutionary Aesthetic. 2012. (ENG.). 102p. pap. 36.99 (978-1-107-60495-7(8)) Cambridge Univ. Pr.

McFee, Graham. Artistic Judgement: A Framework for Philosophical Aesthetics. 2011. (Philosophical Studies Ser.). xii, 195p. 139.00 (978-94-007-0030-7(X), 940070030X) Springer.

McMahon, Jennifer A. Aesthetics & Material Beauty: Aesthetics Naturalized. 2007. (Routledge Studies in Contemporary Philosophy Ser.). (ENG.). 242p. (C). 156.00 (978-0-415-37830-7(3)) Routledge.

McNamara, Andrew. An Apprehensive Aesthetic: The Legacy of Modernist Culture. 2009. (Illus.). 293p. pap. (978-3-03911-720-8(3)) Lang, Peter.

McSweeney, Kerry. What's the Import? Nineteenth-Century Literary Works & Contemporary Critical Practice. 2007. (ENG.). 192p. (C). (978-0-7735-3202-1(1)) McGill-Queen's Univ. Pr.

Mead, Hunter. An Introduction to Aesthetics. 2011. 316p. 50.95 (978-1-258-01803-0(9)) Literary Licensing, LLC.

Mears, Patricia. American Beauty: Aesthetics & Innovation in Fashion. 2009. (ENG., Illus.). 192p. 55.00 (978-0-300-15535-8(2)) Yale Univ. Pr.

Melberg, Arne, ed. Aesthetics at Work. 2007. 176p. (C). pap. 29.00 (978-82-7477-294-6(6), Oslo Academic Pr.) Unipub forlag NOR. Dist: International Specialized Bk. Services.

Meltzer, Donald. Apprehension of Beauty. 2008. 260p. pap. 38.95 (978-1-85575-624-3(2)) Karnac Bks. GBR. Dist: Stylus Publishing, LLC.

Meskin, Aaron & Cahn, Steven M., eds. Aesthetics: A Comprehensive Anthology. 2007. (Blackwell Philosophy Anthologies Ser.: 19). (ENG.). 704p. 129.95 (978-1-4051-5434-5(9), Wiley-Blackwell) Wiley, John & Sons, Inc.

Mitscherling, Jeff. Aesthetic Genesis: The Origin of Consciousness in the Intentional Being of Nature. 2009. (ENG.). 174p. pap. 28.50 (978-0-7618-5021-2(X)) Univ. Pr. of America, Inc.

Monthoux, Pierre Guillet de, et al, eds. Aesthetic Leadership: Managing Fields of Flow in Art & Business. 2007. (ENG.). 288p. 110.00 (978-0-230-51558-1(4)) Palgrave Macmillan.

Morgan, Ed. The Aesthetics of International Law. 2007. (ENG.). 272p. (978-0-8020-9251-9(9)) Univ. of Toronto Pr.

Moriarty, Michael. Taste & Ideology in Seventeenth-Century France. 2009. (Cambridge Studies in French Ser.). (ENG.). 244p. pap. 36.99 (978-0-521-11336-6(9)) Cambridge Univ. Pr.

Mosobalaje, Adebayo. Ebenezer Obey & the Aesthetics of the Yoruba World. 2011. 120p. pap. (978-3-8443-9193-0(2)) Lambert Academic Publishing.

Mosset, Olivier & Armleder, John. John Armleder & Olivier Mosset. 2009. (ENG., Illus.). 56p. pap. 20.00 (978-0-9777528-5-0(2)) Contemporary Art Museum St. Louis.

Mossetto, Gianfranco. Aesthetics & Economics. 2010. (ENG.). 236p. pap. 183.00 (978-90-481-4277-4(6), 9048142776) Springer.

Mroz, Matilda. Temporality & Film Analysis. 2012. (ENG.). 240p. (gr. 17). 105.00 (978-0-7486-4346-2(X)) Edinburgh Univ. Pr. GBR. Dist: Columbia Univ. Pr.

Munk, Reinier W., ed. Moses Mendelssohn's Metaphysics & Aesthetics. 2011. (Studies in German Idealism Ser.). (ENG & GRE., Illus.). x, 379p. 189.00 (978-94-007-2450-1(0), 9400724500) Springer.

Munro, Thomas. The Journal of Aesthetics & Art Criticism, V20, No 2, Winter 1961. Munro, Thomas et al, eds. 2011. 112p. 39.95 (978-1-258-05481-6(7)) Literary Licensing, LLC.

—Toward Science in Aesthetics. 2011. 384p. 53.95 (978-1-258-05800-5(6)) Literary Licensing, LLC.

Munro, Thomas, ed. The Journal of Aesthetics & Art Criticism, V12, No 1, September 1953. 2011. 146p. 40.95 (978-1-258-08092-1(3)) Literary Licensing, LLC.

—The Journal of Aesthetics & Art Criticism, V15, No 3, March 1957. 2011. 124p. 40.95 (978-1-258-01048-5(8)) Literary Licensing, LLC.

Mura, Gianluca, ed. Metaplasticity in Virtual Worlds: Aesthetics & Semantic Concepts. 2010. (Illus.). 350p. 180.00 (978-1-60960-077-8(0), Information Science Reference) IGI Global.

Nancy, Jean-Luc. God, Justice, Love, Beauty: Four Little Dialogues. 2011. (ENG.). 150p. pap. 18.00 (978-0-8232-3426-4(6)) Fordham Univ. Pr.

—God, Justice, Love, Beauty: Four Little Dialogues. Clift, Sarah, tr. from FRE. 2011. (ENG.). 150p. 75.00 (978-0-8232-3425-7(8)) Fordham Univ. Pr.

Nasongkhla, Sirima. Aesthetics of Tai Cultural Landscapes. 2010. 420p. pap. (978-3-8383-0157-0(9)) Lambert Academic Publishing.

National Research Council (U.S.), Transportation Research Board Subcommittee on Bridge Aesthetics Staff & American Association of State Highway and Transportation Officials, Subcommittee on Bridges and Structures Staff, contrib. by. Bridge Aesthetics Sourcebook: Practical Ideas for Short- & Medium-Span Bridges. 2010. (Illus.). viii, 61p. (978-1-56051-485-5(X)) American Assn. of State Highway & Transportation Officials.

Nebelung, Tim. Sportästhetik: Sport Als ästhetisches Erlebnis. 2008. (GER., Illus.). 305p. (978-3-89665-457-1(8)) Academia Verlag Richarz GmbH.

Negri, Antonio. Art & Multitude. 2011. (ENG.). 224p. pap. 14.95 (978-0-7456-4900-9(9)); 49.95 (978-0-7456-4899-6(1)) Polity Pr. GBR. Dist: Wiley, John & Sons, Inc.

Nehamas, A. Only A Promise of Happiness - the Place of Beauty in A World. 2010. (ENG., Illus.). 208p. pap. 24.95 (978-0-691-14865-6(1)) Princeton Univ. Pr.

Ness, John / C. Anterior Anatomy & the Science of a Natural Smile, 10 vols., Vol. 1. 2007. (Illus.). 149p. 199.00 (978-0-9797402-0-6(7)) Productivity Training Corp.

—Contouring Anterior Bridges, 10 vols., Vol. 6. 2007. (Illus.). 59p. 199.00 (978-0-9797402-5-1(8)) Productivity Training Corp.

—Creating Natural Dentures, 10 vols., Vol. 9. 2007. (Illus.). 161p. 199.00 (978-0-9797402-4-4(X)) Productivity Training Corp.

Nguyen, Hong-Nguyen. The Haiku Approach for an Ideal Efl Literature Class in Vietnam. 2011. 148p. pap. (978-3-8443-8448-2(0)) Lambert Academic Publishing.

Nichols, Aidan. Redeeming Beauty: Soundings in Sacral Aesthetics. 2007. (Ashgate Studies in Theology, Imagination & the Arts Ser.). 168p. 89.95 (978-0-7546-5895-5(3)); pap. 39.95 (978-0-7546-6001-9(X)) Ashgate Publishing Co.

Nichols, Aidan Op. A Key to Balthasar: Hans Urs von Balthasar on Beauty, Goodness, & Truth. 2011. 128p. (C). pap. 17.99 (978-0-8010-3974-4(6)) Baker Academic.

Nietzsche, Friedrich Wilhelm. The Birth of Tragedy. Haussmann, Wm. A., tr. 2007. (ENG.). 100p. per. 7.99 (978-1-4209-2996-6(8)) Digireads.com.

—The Birth of Tragedy. 2010. 84p. 26.36 (978-1-169-68436-2(X)); pap. 14.36 (978-1-162-68895-4(5)); 32.95 (978-1-161-45760-5(7)) Kessinger Publishing, LLC.

—The Birth of Tragedy. 2009. 112p. 29.99 (978-1-59547-546-6(X)) NuVision Pubns., LLC.

—The Birth of Tragedy. Johnston, Ian C., tr. 2009. 145p. pap. 13.95 (978-0-9818162-2-7(3)) Richer Resources Pubns.

—The Birth of Tragedy. Johnston, Ian, tr. 2009. 145p. pap. 13.95 (978-1-935238-90-4(6), Debolsillo) Richer Resources Pubns.

—The Birth of Tragedy: Out of the Spirit of Music. 2007. (ENG.). 104p. per. 11.99 (978-1-59547-929-7(5)) NuVision Pubns., LLC.

—The Birth of Tragedy, or Hellenism & Pessimism. 2010. 238p. pap. 26.75 (978-1-177-69784-2(X)) BiblioBazaar.

—The Birth of Tragedy, or Hellenism & Pessimism. 2009. 96p. pap. 20.00 (978-1-151-44210-9(0)) General Bks. LLC.

—The Complete Works of Friedrich Nietzsche. 2008. 472p. pap. (978-1-4097-2889-4(7)) Read Bks.

—The Complete Works of Friedrich Nietzsche. 2007. 236p. per. 13.45 (978-1-59462-585-5(9), 621); per. 12.95 (978-1-59462-751-4(7)) Standard Pubns., Inc. (Book Jungle).

Nietzsche, Friedrich Wilhelm & Levy, Oscar. The Birth of Tragedy. Haussmann, William A., tr. from GER. 2006. (B&N Library of Essential Reading Ser.). (ENG., Illus.). 160p. pap. 7.95 (978-0-7607-8086-2(2)) Barnes & Noble, Inc.

Nietzsche, Friedrich Wilhelm & Smith, Douglas. The Birth of Tragedy. 2008. (Oxford World's Classics Ser.). (ENG.). 224p. pap. 10.95 (978-0-19-954014-3(4)) Oxford Univ. Pr., Inc.

Noyes, Carleton. The Gate of Appreciation: Studies in the Relation of Art to Life. 2008. 144p. pap. (978-1-4099-5785-0(3)) Dodo Pr.

—The Gate of Appreciation: Studies in the Relation of Art to Life. 2007. (ENG.). 290p. 43.95 (978-0-548-01774-6(3)) Kessinger Publishing, LLC.

Nuttall, Sarah, ed. Beautiful Ugly: African & Diaspora Aesthetics. 2007. (ENG., Illus.). 416p. pap. 29.95 (978-0-8223-3918-2(8)) Duke Univ. Pr.

—Beautiful/Ugly: African & Diaspora Aesthetics. 2007. (ENG., Illus.). 416p. 99.95 (978-0-8223-3907-6(2)) Duke Univ. Pr.

Nuttavuthisit, Krittinee. Consumer Aesthetic Experience in a Retail Context. 2010. 124p. pap. (978-3-639-22168-8(0)) VDM Verlag Dr. Mueller e.K.

Ogden, C. K., et al. Foundations aesthetics V 1. 2nd ed. 2011. (Illus.). 272p. 39.95 (978-0-415-48841-9(9)) Routledge.

O'Hear, Anthony. The Landscape of Humanity: Art, Culture & Society. 2008. (St. Andrews Studies in Philosophy & Public Affairs Ser.). (ENG.). 242p. pap. 34.90 (978-1-84540-112-2(3)) Imprint Academic GBR. Dist: Ingram Pub. Services.

Olivier, Bert. Philosophy & Art: Collected Essays. 2009. 255p. 49.95 (978-3-03911-903-5(6)) Lang, Peter AG GBR. Dist: Lang, Peter.

Oppo, Andrea. Philosophical Aesthetics & Samuel Beckett. 2008. 268p. pap. 66.95 (978-3-03911-824-3(2)) Lang, Peter AG GBR. Dist: Lang, Peter.

O'Reilly, Kevin E., ed. Aesthetic Perception: A Thomistic Perspective. 2007. 131p. (C). 55.00 (978-1-84682-027-4(8)) Four Courts Pr. IRL. Dist: International Specialized Bk. Services.

Osborne, Harold. Aesthetics & Criticism. 2011. 348p. 51.95 (978-1-258-01353-0(3)) Literary Licensing, LLC.

Osterkamp, Ernst. Wissensästhetik: Wissen über die Antike in ästhetischer Vermittlung. 2008. (Transformationen der Antike Ser.). (LAT, FRO, GER & ENG., Illus.). X, 386p. 119.00 (978-3-11-020491-9(6)) De Gruyter, Walter Inc.

O'Sullivan, Simon. Art Encounters Deleuze & Guattari: Thought Beyond Representation. 2008. (Renewing Philosophy Ser.). (ENG.). 256p. pap. 33.00 (978-0-230-57373-4(8)) Palgrave Macmillan.

Otto, Nina. Enargeia: Untersuchung zur Charakteristik alexandrinischer Dichtung. 2009. (Hermes - Einzelschriften Ser.). (Illus.). 254p. (C). pap. 79.00 (978-3-515-09335-4(4)) Steiner, Franz Verlag Wiesbaden GmbH DEU. Dist: Brown, David Bk. Co., The.

Palazón Mayoral, María Rosa. La Estética en México, Siglo XX: Diálogos Entre Filósofos. 2006. (Filosofia Ser.). (SPA.). 452p. pap. 25.99 (978-968-16-8112-8(6)) Fondo de Cultura Económica.

Pallasmaa, Juhani. The Eyes of the Skin: Architecture & the Senses. 3rd ed. 2012. (ENG.). 128p. 45.00 (978-1-119-94128-6(8), Wiley) Wiley, John & Sons, Inc.

Pandey, Upasana. Postmodernism & Gandhi. 2010. 264p. 45.00 (978-81-316-0372-7(5)) Rawat Pubns. IND. Dist: International Specialized Bk. Services.

Papel. Thomas Procedures in Facial Plastic Surgery: Blepharoplasty. 2011. (Illus.). 200p. (978-1-60795-151-3(7)) PMPH-USA. Ltd.

Pario Perra, Daniele. Low Cost Design. Pario Perra, Daniele, ed. 2011. (ENG & ITA., Illus.). 216p. pap. 50.00 (978-88-366-1665-7(8)) Silvana ITA. Dist: D.A.P./Distributed Art Pubs.

Parker, DeWitt H. The Principles of Aesthetics. 2007. (ENG.). 252p. per. (978-1-4065-4196-0(6)) Dodo Pr.

Parker, Henry W. Spirit of Beauty Essays Scientific & A. 2006. pap. 26.95 (978-1-4286-5407-5(0)) Kessinger Publishing, LLC.

Parker, Mina. Silver Linings: Meditations on Finding Joy & Beauty in Unexpected Places. 2008. (ENG., Illus.). 128p. 16.95 (978-1-57324-361-2(2), Conari Pr.) Red Wheel/Weiser.

Parsons, Glenn & Carlson, Allen. Functional Beauty. 2009. (ENG.). 240p. 75.00 (978-0-19-920524-0(8)) Oxford Univ. Pr., Inc.

Parussa, Gabriella, ed. Christine de Pizan: Epistre Othea. 2008. (Tlf Ser.). (FRE.). 544p. (C). pap. 90.00 (978-2-600-00376-6(2)) Droz, Librairie CHE. Dist: Brown, David Bk. Co., The.

Pasini, Roberto. Il Vuoto Nell'arte Contemporanea. 2010. (ITA., Illus.). 174p. (978-88-6464-051-8(7)) QuiEdit.

Paskow, Alan. The Paradoxes of Art: A Phenomenological Investigation. 2008. (ENG., Illus.). 272p. (C). pap. 34.99 (978-0-521-73318-2(9)) Cambridge Univ. Pr.

Pater, Walter. The Works of Walter Pater. 2011. (Cambridge Library Collection - Literary Studies). (ENG.). 292p. pap. 23.99 (978-1-108-03428-9(4)); 310p. pap. 24.99 (978-1-108-03429-6(2)); 234p. pap. 22.99 (978-1-108-03425-8(X)); 256p. pap. 23.99 (978-1-108-03424-1(1)); 264p. pap. 23.99 (978-1-108-03430-2(6)); 272p. pap. 23.99 (978-1-108-03427-2(6)); 332p. pap. 28.99 (978-1-108-03426-5(8)); (Illus.). 264p. pap. 23.99 (978-1-108-03423-4(3)) Cambridge Univ. Pr.

Pellizzi, Francesco. Absconding, Vol. 55/56. 2010. (Res: Anthropology & Aesthetics Ser.). (Illus.). 360p. pap. 50.00 (978-0-87365-854-6(X)) Peabody Museum of Archaeology & Ethnology, Harvard Univ., Pubns. Dept.

—Spring/Autumn 2006. 2006. (Res: Anthropology & Aesthetics Ser.). (Illus.). 272p. pap. 50.00 (978-0-87365-767-9(5)) Peabody Museum of Archaeology & Ethnology, Harvard Univ., Pubns. Dept.

Pellizzi, Francesco, ed. Res Vol. 52: Museums — Crossing Boundaries. 2008. (Res: Anthropology & Aesthetics Ser.). (Illus.). 240p. per. 50.00 (978-0-87365-790-7(X)) Peabody Museum of Archaeology & Ethnology, Harvard Univ., Pubns. Dept.

—Res 53/54 Spring/Autumn 2008: Anthropology & Aesthetics, Vol. 53. 2008. (Res: Anthropology & Aesthetics Ser.). (Illus.). 350p. pap. 50.00 (978-0-87365-840-9(X)) Peabody Museum of Archaeology & Ethnology, Harvard Univ., Pubns. Dept.

—Res, Volume 51: Anthropology & Aesthetics, Spring 2007. 2007. (Res: Anthropology & Aesthetics Ser.). (Illus.). 272p. per. 50.00 *(978-0-87365-775-4(6))* Peabody Museum of Archaeology & Ethnology, Harvard Univ., Pubns. Dept.

—West by Nonwest, Vol. 42. 2006. (Illus.). 272p. pap. 30.00 *(978-0-87365-842-3(6))* Peabody Museum of Archaeology & Ethnology, Harvard Univ., Pubns. Dept.

Pellizzi, Francesco, et al. Res 57/58: Anthropology & Aesthetics, Spring/Autumn 2010. 2011. (Res: Anthropology & Aesthetics Ser.). (Illus.). 376p. pap. 50.00 *(978-0-87365-861-4(2))* Peabody Museum of Archaeology & Ethnology, Harvard Univ., Pubns. Dept.

Penser L'art: Séminaire Interarts de Paris. 2009. (FRE.). 320p. (C). pap. 44.00 ***(978-2-252-03739-3(3))*** Klincksieck, Editions FRA. Dist: ISD.

Perry, Ellen. The Aesthetics of Emulation in the Visual Arts of Ancient Rome. 2011. (ENG., Illus.). 226p. pap. 45.00 *(978-0-521-28397-7(3))* Cambridge Univ. Pr.

Philipson, Morris, ed. Aesthetics Today. 2011. 478p. 58.95 ***(978-1-258-02906-7(5))*** Literary Licensing, LLC.

Polonsky, Rachel. English Literature & the Russian Aesthetic Renaissance. 2006. (Cambridge Studies in Russian Literature Ser.). (ENG., Illus.). 268p. pap. 50.00 *(978-0-521-02747-2(0))* Cambridge Univ. Pr.

Pomeroy, Trout. Swimming Downstream. 2008. (Illus.). 316p. per. 13.95 *(978-1-4327-2106-0(2))* Outskirts Pr., Inc.

Porter, James I. The Origins of Aesthetic Thought in Ancient Greece: Matter, Sensation, & Experience. 2010. (ENG., Illus.). 624p. 145.00 *(978-0-521-84180-1(1))* Cambridge Univ. Pr.

Porter, Kate Hatcher. Life in Beauty. 2009. (ENG.). *(978-1-894694-66-7(X))* Granville Island Publishing.

Porter, Robert. Deleuze & Guattari: Aesthetics & Politics. 2009. (University of Wales Press - Political Philosophy Now Ser.). (ENG.). 160p. 85.00 *(978-0-7083-2159-1(3))* Univ. of Wales Pr. GBR. Dist: Chicago Distribution Ctr.

Prasad, H. Buddhist Aesthetics & Ethics. 2011. 301p. pap. 35.00 ***(978-81-7533-348-2(0))*** M. D. Pubns. Pvt, Ltd. IND. Dist: Coronet Bks.

Puffer, Ethel D. The Psychology of Beauty. 2009. 156p. pap. *(978-1-4099-2190-5(5))* Dodo Pr.

Puolakka, Kalle. Relativism & Intentionalism in Interpretation: Davidson, Hermeneutics, & Pragmatism. 2011. (ENG.). 200p. 60.00 *(978-0-7391-5080-1(4))* Lexington Bks.

Pye, David. The Nature & Aesthetics of Design. 2008. (ENG., Illus.). 112p. per. 29.95 *(978-0-7136-5286-4(1))* A & C Black GBR. Dist: Macmillan.

Raizman, David Seth & Gorman, Carma. Objects, Audiences & Literatures: Alternative Narratives in the History of Design. 2007. (Illus.). 200p. *(978-1-84718-092-6(2))* Cambridge Scholars Pub.

Ranciere, Jacques. The Aesthetic Unconscious. 2010. (ENG.). 84p. 49.95 *(978-0-7456-4643-5(3))*; pap. 12.95 *(978-0-7456-4644-2(1))* Polity Pr. GBR. Dist: Wiley, John & Sons, Inc.

—Aesthetics & Its Discontents. 2009. (ENG.). 176p. 64.95 *(978-0-7456-4630-5(1))*; pap. 19.95 *(978-0-7456-4631-2(X))* Polity Pr. GBR. Dist: Wiley, John & Sons, Inc.

Rancière, Jacques. The Emancipated Spectator. 2011. (ENG., Illus.). 134p. pap. 16.95 *(978-1-84467-761-0(3)*, 844761) Verso Bks. GBR. Dist: Norton, W. W. & Co., Inc.

Raphael-Hernandez, Heike. The Utopian Aesthetics of Three African American Women (Toni Morrison, Gloria Naylor, Julie Dash) The Principle of Hope. 2008. 188p. 99.95 *(978-0-7734-4936-7(1))* Mellen, Edwin Pr., The.

Raussert, Wilfried & Jones, John Miller, eds. Traveling Sounds: Music, Migration, & Identity in the U. S. & Beyond. 2011. (ENG., Illus.). 360p. pap. 51.50 *(978-3-8258-1328-4(2))* Lit Verlag DEU. Dist: Transaction Pubs.

Rawes, Peg. Space, Geometry & Aesthetics: Through Kant & Towards Deleuze. 2008. (Renewing Philosophy Ser.). (ENG.). 256p. 89.00 *(978-0-230-55291-3(9))* Palgrave Macmillan.

Redeker, Mirjam-Christina. Wahrnehmung und Glaube: Zum Verhältnis von Theologie und Ästhetik in gegenwärtiger Zeit. 2011. (Theologische Bibliothek Töpelmann Ser.). (GER.). XII, 409p. 168.00 ***(978-3-11-024782-4(8))*** De Gruyter, Walter Inc.

Redfern, H. B. Questions in Aesthetic Education (Rle Edu K) 2012. (Routledge Library Editions: Education Ser.). (ENG.). 144p. 100.00 ***(978-0-415-69765-1(4))*** Routledge.

Rentsch, Thomas. Transzendenz und Negativität: Religionsphilosophische und ästhetische Studien. 2010. (GER., Illus.). XII, 459p. 126.00 ***(978-3-11-021496-3(2))*** De Gruyter, Walter Inc.

Rhodes, S. A. Cult of Beauty in Charles Baudelaire V1. 2006. pap. 28.95 *(978-1-4286-5372-6(4))* Kessinger Publishing, LLC.

—Cult of Beauty in Charles Baudelaire V2. 2006. pap. 31.95 *(978-1-4286-5373-3(2))* Kessinger Publishing, LLC.

Ribeiro, Aileen & Ribeiro, Anna Christina. The Continuum Companion to Aesthetics. 2012. (Continuum Companions Ser.). (ENG.). 368p. 170.00 *(978-1-84706-370-0(5))* Continuum International Publishing Group, Ltd. GBR. Dist: National Bk. Network.

Richards, I. A., et al. The Foundations of Aesthetics. 2011. 126p. 40.95 ***(978-1-258-05129-7(X))*** Literary Licensing, LLC.

Richter, Gerhard. Afterness: Figures of Following in Modern Thought & Aesthetics. 2011. (Columbia Themes in Philosophy, Social Criticism, & the Arts Ser.). (ENG., Illus.). 272p. (gr. 17). 50.00 ***(978-0-231-15770-4(3))*** Columbia Univ. Pr.

Ricioli, Terry, des. Vintage Impressions Jewelry. 2012. (ENG., Illus.). 64p. pap. 9.95 ***(978-1-59635-407-4(0))*** Annie's Publishing, LLC.

Rigakos, George S. Nightclub: Bouncers, Risk, & the Spectacle of Consumption. 2008. (ENG., Illus.). 288p. (C). pap. *(978-0-7735-3362-2(1))* McGill-Queen's Univ. Pr.

Rocha, João Cezar de Castro. Producing Presences: Branching Out from Gumbrecht's Work. Mendes, Victor K., ed. 2007. (Adamastor Ser.). 378p. 24.95 *(978-1-933227-22-1(2))* Tagus Pr.

Romano, Rafi, ed. The Art of the Smile: Integrating Prosthodontics, Orthodontics, Periodontics, Dental Technology, & Plastic Surgery in Esthetic Dental Treatment. (Illus.). 454p. 258.00 *(978-1-85097-096-5(3))* Quintessence Publishing Co., Inc.

Ronen, Ruth. Aesthetics of Anxiety. (SUNY series, Insinuations: Philosophy, Psychoanalysis, Literature Ser.). (Illus.). 2010. 195p. pap. 23.95 *(978-0-7914-7668-0(5)*, Suny Pr.) 2009. 208p. 65.00 *(978-0-7914-7667-3(7))* State Univ. of New York Pr.

Rongier, Sébastien. De L'ironie: Enjeux Critiques Pour la Modernité. 2007. (FRE.). 192p. (C). pap. 35.00 ***(978-2-252-03620-4(6))*** Klincksieck, Editions FRA. Dist: ISD.

Rook, Russell D. Rhyming Hope & History: Theology & Culture in the Work of Robert Jenson. 2011. 240p. pap. 26.00 ***(978-1-60899-600-1(X)***, Pickwick Pubns.) Wipf & Stock Pubs.

Rosen, Joseph. Symmetry Rules: How Science & Nature Are Founded on Symmetry. 2010. (Frontiers Collection). (Illus.). xiv, 305p. pap. 69.95 *(978-3-642-09508-5(9)*, 3642095089) Springer.

Rosenstein, Leon. Antiques: The History of an Idea. 2008. 280p. 36.95 *(978-0-8014-4734-1(8))* Cornell Univ. Pr.

Ross, Alison. The Aesthetic Paths of Philosophy: Presentation in Kant, Heidegger, Lacoue-Labarthe, & Nancy. 2007. (Cultural Memory in the Present Ser.). (ENG.). 256p. 65.00 *(978-0-8047-5487-3(X))*; per. 24.95 *(978-0-8047-5488-0(8))* Stanford Univ. Pr.

Ross, Bruce. Venturing upon Dizzy Heights: Lectures & Essays on Philosophy, Literature, & the Arts. 2008. (Illus.). 130p. (C). 59.95 *(978-1-4331-0287-5(0))* Lang, Peter Publishing, Inc.

Ross, Stephen David. The World As Aesthetic Phenomenon. 2007. *(978-1-58684-267-3(6))* Global Academic Publishing.

—The World As Aesthetic Phenomenon: The Image in Abundance, the Wonder of the Earth. 2006. *(978-1-58684-265-9(X))* Global Academic Publishing.

Rouhi, Katâyoun. L'ontologie du Lieu: Voyage Au Pays du "Non-Où" 2010. (FRE., Illus.). 157p. *(978-2-296-10339-9(1))* Harmattan Pr.

Rujivacharakul, Vimalin. Collecting China: The World, China, & a Short History of Collecting. (Illus.). 2011. (ENG.). 240p. 65.00 *(978-1-61149-006-0(5))* 2010. 210p. *(978-0-87413-096-6(4))* Univ. of Delaware Pr.

Rundell, John. Aesthetics & Modernity: Essays by Agnes Heller. 2010. (ENG.). 206p. 70.00 *(978-0-7391-4131-1(7))* Lexington Bks.

Rundell, John, ed. Aesthetics & Modernity: Essays by Agnes Heller. 2010. (ENG.). 206p. pap. 29.95 *(978-0-7391-4132-8(5))* Lexington Bks.

Ruskin, John. Modern Painters. 2009. 232p. 23.99 *(978-1-103-58661-5(0))*; pap. 17.99 *(978-1-103-58658-5(0))* BiblioBazaar.

Saggio, Antonino. Lo Strumento Di Caravaggio. 2010. (ITA.). 42p. pap. 18.81 *(978-1-4461-4730-6(4))* Lulu Enterprises Inc.

Saito, Yuriko. Everyday Aesthetics. 2010. (ENG.). 288p. pap. 30.00 *(978-0-19-957567-1(3))* Oxford Univ. Pr., Inc.

Sallis, John. Transfigurements: On the True Sense of Art. 204p. 2011. pap. 20.00 *(978-0-226-73418-7(8))* 2008. (ENG.). 25.00 *(978-0-226-73422-4(6))* Univ. of Chicago Pr.

Samuels, Jeffrey. Attracting the Heart: Social Relations & the Aesthetics of Emotion in Sri Lankan Monastic Culture. 2010. (C). 36.00 *(978-0-8248-3385-5(6))* Univ. of Hawaii Pr.

Sanders, T. Irene. Strategic Thinking in a Complex World. 2006. *(978-0-9788081-3-6(4))* Sanders & Co.

Sandrisser, Barbara. Exploring Environmental Aesthetics in Japan. 2009. *(978-1-4331-0141-0(6))* Lang, Peter Publishing, Inc.

Sandywell, Barry. Dictionary of Visual Discourse: A Dialectical Lexicon of Terms. 2011. 722p. 225.00 *(978-1-4094-0188-9(X))* Ashgate Publishing Co.

Sartwell, Crispin. Political Aesthetics. 2010. 272p. 35.00 *(978-0-8014-4890-4(5))* Cornell Univ. Pr.

Satz, Aura & Wood, Jon. Articulate Objects: Voice, Sculpture & Performance. 2009. (Illus.). 300p. 54.95 *(978-3-03910-747-6(X))* Lang, Peter AG GBR. Dist: Lang, Peter.

Schaeffer, Jean-Marie. Beyond Speculation: Art & Aesthetics without Myths. Roberts, Daffyd, tr. from FRE. 2012. (SB-the French List Ser.). (ENG.). 436p. 35.00 ***(978-0-85742-042-8(9))*** Seagull Bks. GBR. Dist: Chicago Distribution Ctr.

Scharfstein, Ben-Ami. Art Without Borders: A Philosophical Exploration of Art & Humanity. 2009. (ENG., Illus.). 558p. 35.00 *(978-0-226-73609-9(1))* Univ. of Chicago Pr.

Schellekens, Elisabeth & Goldie, Peter, eds. The Aesthetic Mind: Philosophy & Psychology. 2012. (ENG., Illus.). 420p. 99.00 ***(978-0-19-969151-7(7))*** Oxford Univ. Pr., Inc.

Schellekens, Elisabeth & Schellekens. Aesthetics & Morality. 2008. (Continuum Aesthetics Ser.). (ENG.). 172p. 29.95 *(978-0-8264-9762-8(4))*; 100.00 *(978-0-8264-8524-3(3))* Continuum International Publishing Group, Ltd. GBR. Dist: National Bk. Network.

Schiller, Frederick. Aesthetical & Philosophical Essays. 2006. pap. *(978-1-4068-2050-8(4))* Echo Library.

Schiller, Friedrich. Aesthetical & Philosophical Essays. 2007. (ENG.). 372p. pap. 25.99 *(978-1-4264-5002-0(8))*; 416p. pap. 28.99 *(978-1-4264-5303-8(5))* BiblioBazaar.

—Aesthetical & Philosophical Essays. 2007. 344p. per. *(978-1-4065-3891-5(4))* Dodo Pr.

Schmidt, Maurice. The Tabernacle of Exodus as a Work of Art: An Aesthetic of Monotheism. 2010. (Illus.). xiv, 338p. *(978-0-7734-3782-1(7))* Mellen, Edwin Pr., The.

Schnier, Jacques. Art Symbolism & the Unconscious: The Journal of Aesthetics & Art Criticism, V12, No. 1, September 1953. Munro, Thomas, ed. 2011. 12p. pap. 35.95 ***(978-1-258-08126-3(1))*** Literary Licensing, LLC.

Schor, Naomi. Reading in Detail: Aesthetics & the Feminine. 2006. (Illus.). 229p. per. 26.95 *(978-0-415-97945-0(5))* Routledge.

Scott, David. The Art & Aesthetics of Boxing. 2009. (ENG., Illus.). 224p. 40.00 *(978-0-8032-1386-9(7))* Univ. of Nebraska Pr.

Scott, David H. T. Pictorialist Poetics: Poetry & the Visual Arts in Nineteenth-Century France. 2009. (Cambridge Studies in French Ser.). (ENG.). 224p. pap. 33.99 *(978-0-521-11059-4(9))* Cambridge Univ. Pr.

Scott, Felicity & Scott, Felicity Dale Elliston. Ant Farm: Allegorical Time Warp - The Media Fallout of July 21, 1969. 2008. (Illus.). 320p. pap. *(978-84-96954-24-3(2))* Actar Birkhauser Distribution.

Scruton, Roger. Beauty. 2009. (ENG., Illus.). 176p. 19.95 *(978-0-19-955952-7(X))* Oxford Univ. Pr., Inc.

—Beauty: A Very Short Introduction. 2011. (ENG., Illus.). 160p. pap. 11.95 *(978-0-19-922975-8(9))* Oxford Univ. Pr., Inc.

Shaviro, Steven. Without Criteria: Kant, Whitehead, Deleuze, & Aesthetics. 2009. (Technologies of Lived Abstraction Ser.). (ENG.). 192p. (gr. 17). 29.00 *(978-0-262-19576-8(3))* MIT Pr.

Shaw, Theodore L. Art Reconstructed: A New Theory of Aesthetics. 2011. 286p. 48.95 ***(978-1-258-07199-8(1))*** Literary Licensing, LLC.

Shibles, Warren A. Emotion in Aesthetics. 2010. (Philosophical Studies Ser.). 288p. pap. 259.00 *(978-90-481-4593-5(7)*, 9048145937) Springer.

Shimamura, Arthur P. & Palmer, Stephen E., eds. Aesthetic Science: Connecting Minds, Brains, & Experience, 1 vol. 2012. (ENG., Illus.). 448p. 95.00 ***(978-0-19-973214-2(0))*** Oxford Univ. Pr., Inc.

Shockley, Evie. Renegade Poetics: Black Aesthetics & Formal Innovation in African American Poetry. 2011. (Contemporary North American Poetry Ser.). (ENG.). 264p. pap. 39.95 ***(978-1-60938-058-8(4))*** Univ. of Iowa Pr.

Shottenkirk, Dena. Nominalism & Its Aftermath: the Philosophy of Nelson Goodman: The Philosophy of Nelson Goodman. 2009. (Synthese Library). (ENG., Illus.). xiv, 174p. 159.00 *(978-1-4020-9930-4(4))* Springer.

Shugart, Helene A. & Waggoner, Catherine Egley. Making Camp: Rhetorics of Transgression in U. S. Popular Culture. 2nd ed. 2008. (Albma Rhetoric Cult & Soc Crit Ser.). (ENG.). 200p. 39.75 *(978-0-8173-1607-5(8))* Univ. of Alabama Pr.

Shusterman, Richard. Thinking through the Body: Essays in Somaesthetics. 2012. (ENG., Illus.). 374p. (C). 99.00 ***(978-1-107-01906-5(0))*** Cambridge Univ. Pr.

Shusterman, Richard, ed. Aesthetic Experience. 2007. (Routledge Studies in Contemporary Philosophy Ser.). (ENG.). 208p. (C). 131.00 *(978-0-415-37832-1(X))* Routledge.

Siebers, Tobin Anthony. Disability Aesthetics. 2010. (Corporealities: Discourses of Disability Ser.). (ENG., Illus.). 192p. pap. 25.95 *(978-0-472-05100-7(8))* Univ. of Michigan Pr.

—Disability Aesthetics. 2010. (Corporealities: Discourses of Disability Ser.). (ENG., Illus.). 192p. 75.00 *(978-0-472-07100-5(9))* Univ. of Michigan Pr.

Sinclair, Nathalie & Higginson, William, eds. Mathematics & the Aesthetic: New Approaches to an Ancient Affinity. 2010. (CMS Books in Mathematics Ser.). (Illus.). xvi, 288p. pap. 69.95 *(978-1-4419-2144-4(3)*, 1441921443) Springer.

Singer, Alan. The Self-Deceiving Muse: Notice & Knowledge in the Work of Art. 2010. (Literature & Philosophy Ser.). (ENG., Illus.). 248p. 74.95 *(978-0-271-03721-9(0))* Pennsylvania State Univ. Pr.

Siporin, Max. Artistry in Social Work Practice. 2009. 112p. pap. 12.95 *(978-1-4401-1090-0(5))* iUniverse, Inc.

Skov, Martin & Vartanian, Oshin, eds. Neuroaesthetics. 2009. (Illus.). 312p. 68.50 *(978-0-89503-336-9(4))* Baywood Publishing Co., Inc.

Smith, Matthew. The Total Work of Art. 2007. (ENG., Illus.). 240p. 120.00 *(978-0-415-97795-1(9))* Routledge.

Smith, Matthew Wilson. The Total Work of Art: From Bayreuth to Cyberspace. 2007. (ENG., Illus.). 240p. per. 33.95 *(978-0-415-97796-8(7))* Routledge.

Smith, Paul & Wilde, Carolyn, eds. A Companion to Art Theory. 2007. (Blackwell Companions in Cultural Studies: 21). (ENG., Illus.). 552p. 209.95 *(978-0-631-20762-7(7)*, Wiley-Blackwell) Wiley, John & Sons, Inc.

Smith, Robert Rowland. Death-Drive: Freudian Hauntings in Literature & Art. 2010. (Frontiers of Theory Ser.). (ENG., Illus.). 256p. (gr. 17). 115.00 *(978-0-7486-4039-3(8))* Edinburgh Univ. Pr. GBR. Dist: Columbia Univ. Pr.

Sonek, Krzysztof. Truth, Beauty, & Goodness in Biblical Narratives: A Hermeneutical Study of Genesis 21.1-21. 2009. (Beihefte zur Zeitschrift far die alttestamentliche Wissenschaft Ser.). (ENG.). 304p. 126.00 *(978-3-11-020974-7(8))* De Gruyter, Walter Inc.

Souza, Paulo de. Seara Vermelha: Estética e Ideologia Em Jorge Amado. 2008. (POR.). 151p. *(978-85-7315-483-2(7))* Universidade de Pernambuco.

Sparke, Penny. As Long As It's Pink: The Sexual Politics of Taste. 2010. (ENG., Illus.). 224p. pap. 25.00 *(978-0-919616-51-6(8))* Press of the Nova Scotia College of Art & Design CAN. Dist: D.A.P./Distributed Art Pubs.

Spitz, Ellen Handler. The Brightening Glance: Imagination & Childhood. 2007. (ENG.). 272p. pap. 14.95 *(978-0-385-72005-2(X)*, Anchor) Knopf Doubleday Publishing Group.

Spivak, Gayatri Chakravorty. An Aesthetic Education in the Era of Globalization. 2012. (Illus.). 624p. 35.00 *(978-0-674-05183-6(1))* Harvard Univ. Pr.

Sporre & Sporre, Dennis J. Perceiving the Arts: An Introduction to the Humanities with Music for the Humanities CD. 10th ed. 2011. (ENG.). (C). pap. 66.60 incl. cd-rom ***(978-0-205-23406-6(2)***, Prentice Hall) Prentice Hall PTR.

Sporre, Dennis J. Perceiving the Arts: An Introduction to the Humanities. 10th rev. ed. 2011. (ENG.). 272p. (C). pap. 66.60 *(978-0-205-09655-8(7)*, Prentice Hall) Prentice Hall PTR.

Spuybroek, Lars, text. The Sympathy of Things: Ruskin & the Ecology of Design. 2012. (ENG., Illus.). 400p. pap. 45.00 ***(978-90-5662-827-7(5))*** NAi Uitgevers / Publishers Stichting NLD. Dist: D.A.P./Distributed Art Pubs.

Stafford, Barbara Maria. Echo Objects: The Cognitive Work of Images. 2007. (ENG., Illus.). 296p. 47.50 *(978-0-226-77051-2(6))* Univ. of Chicago Pr.

Stecker, Robert. Aesthetics. Gracyk, Ted, ed. 2010. (Elements of Philosophy Ser.). (ENG.). 422p. 99.00 *(978-0-7425-6436-7(3))* Rowman & Littlefield Publishers, Inc.

—Aesthetics. Gracyk, Theodore, ed. 2010. (Elements of Philosophy Ser.). (ENG.). 422p. pap. 70.00 *(978-0-7425-6437-4(1))* Rowman & Littlefield Publishers, Inc.

—Aesthetics & the Philosophy of Art. 2nd ed. 2010. (Elements of Philosophy Ser.). (ENG.). 328p. 90.00 *(978-0-7425-6410-7(X))*; pap. 39.95 *(978-0-7425-6411-4(8))* Rowman & Littlefield Publishers, Inc.

Stock, Kathleen & Thomson-Jones, Katherine, eds. New Waves in Aesthetics. 2008. (New Waves in Philosophy Ser.). (ENG.). 368p. pap. 40.00 *(978-0-230-22047-8(9))* Palgrave Macmillan.

Stockwell, Peter. Texture: A Cognitive Aesthetics of Reading. (ENG.). 224p. (gr. 17). 2012. pap. 32.50 ***(978-0-7486-2582-6(8))*** 2009. (Illus.). 90.00 *(978-0-7486-2581-9(X))* Edinburgh Univ. Pr. GBR. Dist: Columbia Univ. Pr.

Stoneley, Peter. Mark Twain & the Feminine Aesthetic. 2008. (Cambridge Studies in American Literature & Culture Ser.). (ENG.). 224p. pap. 34.00 *(978-0-521-10228-5(6))* Cambridge Univ. Pr.

Storey, Nicholas. History of Men's Accessories: A Short Guide for Men about Town. 2011. (Illus.). 192p. 39.95 *(978-1-84468-115-0(7))* Pen & Sword Bks. Ltd. GBR. Dist: Casemate Pubs. & Bk. Distributors, LLC.

Strachan, Owen & Sweeney, Doug. Jonathan Edwards on Beauty, 1 vol. 2010. (Essential Edwards Collection). (ENG.). 160p. pap. 9.99 *(978-0-8024-2458-7(9))* Moody Pubs.

Sully, James. Sensation & Intuition. 2009. 340p. pap. 24.30 *(978-0-217-86923-2(8))* General Bks. LLC.

—Sensation & Intuition: Studies in Psychology & Aesthetics. 2007. (ENG.). 390p. 48.95 *(978-0-548-03507-8(5))* Kessinger Publishing, LLC.

Sutcliffe, Alistair. Designing for User Engagement: Aesthetic & Attractive User Interfaces. 2009. (Synthesis Lectures on Human-Centered Informatics Ser.). 55p. pap. 25.00 *(978-1-60845-023-7(6))* Morgan & Claypool Pubs.

Sychrava, Juliet. Schiller to Derrida: Idealism in Aesthetics. 2010. (ENG.). 264p. (C). pap. 27.99 *(978-0-521-13164-3(2))* Cambridge Univ. Pr.

Sykes-Davies, Hugh. Wordsworth & the Worth of Words. 2010. (ENG.). 340p. pap. 42.00 *(978-0-521-12914-5(1))* Cambridge Univ. Pr.

Symonds, John. Essays Speculative & Suggestive. 2007. (ENG.). 454p. 52.95 *(978-0-548-05093-4(7))* Kessinger Publishing, LLC.

Taliaferro, Charles. Aesthetics: A Beginner's Guide. 2011. (ENG., Illus.). 208p. 14.95 *(978-1-85168-820-3(X))* Oneworld Pubns. GBR. Dist: National Bk. Network.

Tallon, Philip. The Poetics of Evil: Toward an Aesthetic Theodicy, 1 vol. 2011. (ENG.). 288p. 74.00 *(978-0-19-977893-5(0))* Oxford Univ. Pr., Inc.

Tamme, Anne Mary. A Critique of John Dewey's Theory of Fine Art in the Light of the Principles of Thomism. 2011. 148p. 40.95 ***(978-1-258-01282-3(0))*** Literary Licensing, LLC.

Teilmann-Lock, Stina. British & French Copyright: A Historical Study of Aesthetic Implications. 2009. 265p. pap. 52.00 *(978-87-574-2213-9(3))* Djof Publishing DNK. Dist: International Specialized Bk. Services.

The University of Arizona Museum of Art. The Aesthetic Code: Unraveling the Secrets of Art. The University of Arizona Museum of Art, ed. 2010. (Illus.). 40p. (C). pap. 14.95 *(978-0-9814840-3-7(4))* Univ. of Arizona Museum of Art.

Thézé, Ariane. Le Corps à L'écran: La Mutation de L'image du Corps Par L'art écranique: Essai. (FRE., Illus.). 263p. *(978-2-89024-165-7(3))* Editions de la Pleine lune.

Thiam, Pascal Bokar. From Timbuktu to the Mississippi Delta. 2010. (C). pap. 0.00 *(978-1-60927-861-8(5))* Univ. Readers.

Thyssen, Ole. Aesthetic Communication. 2011. (ENG., Illus.). 336p. 110.00 *(978-0-230-24592-1(7))* Palgrave Macmillan.

Tidwell, John Edgar & Tracy, Steven C. After Winter: The Art & Life of Sterling A. Brown. Tidwell, John Edgar & Tracy, Steven C., eds. Tidwell, John Edar, ed. 2009. (ENG., Illus.). 464p. pap. 39.95 *(978-0-19-536580-1(1))* Oxford Univ. Pr., Inc.

Tidwell, John Edgar & Tracy, Steven C., eds. After Winter: The Art & Life of Sterling A. Brown. 2009. (ENG., Illus.). 464p. 99.00 *(978-0-19-536579-5(8))* Oxford Univ. Pr., Inc.

Tilghman, Benjamin. Reflections on Aesthetic Judgment & Other Essays. 2006. 186p. 99.95 *(978-0-7546-5707-1(8))* Ashgate Publishing Co.

Todd, Cain Samuel. The Philosophy of Wine: A Case of Truth, Beauty, & Intoxication. 2011. (ENG.). 200p. (C). *(978-0-7735-3838-2(0))* McGill-Queen's Univ. Pr.

Torevell, David. Liturgy & the Beauty of the Unknown: Another Place. 2007. 212p. 99.95 *(978-0-7546-3303-7(9))* Ashgate Publishing Co.

Townsend, Dabney. The A to Z of Aesthetics. 2010. (A to Z Guide Ser.). (ENG.). 418p. pap. 34.45 *(978-0-8108-7581-4(0))* Scarecrow Pr., Inc.

—Historical Dictionary of Aesthetics. 2006. (Historical Dictionaries of Religions, Philosophies, & Movements Ser.: No. 72). (ENG.). 416p. 99.00 *(978-0-8108-5539-7(9))* Scarecrow Pr., Inc.

Treier, Daniel J., et al, eds. The Beauty of God: Theology & the Arts. 2007. (ENG., Illus.). 233p. per. 22.00 *(978-0-8308-2843-2(5)*, IVP Acad.) InterVarsity Pr.

Trigg, Dylan. The Aesthetics of Decay: Nothingness, Nostalgia, & the Absence of Reason. 2006. (New Studies in Aesthetics: Vol. 37). (Illus.). 300p. (C). 76.95 *(978-0-8204-8646-8(9))* Lang, Peter Publishing, Inc.

Tsien, Jennifer. The Bad Taste of Others: Judging Literary Value in Eighteenth-Century France. 2011. 280p. (C). 47.50 ***(978-0-8122-4359-8(5))*** Univ. of Pennsylvania Pr.

Twitchett, Emily. Do Increases in Physical Fitness Affect Dance Aesthetics? 2010. 228p. pap. *(978-3-639-23498-5(7))* VDM Verlag Dr. Mueller e.K.

Tymieniecka, A-T., ed. Beauty's Appeal: Measure & Excess. 2010. (Analecta Husserliana Ser.). xxiii, 296p. pap. 219.00 *(978-90-481-7658-8(1)*, 9048176581) Springer.

—Gardens & the Passion for the Infinite. 2010. (Analecta Husserliana Ser.). 368p. pap. 189.00 *(978-90-481-6119-5(3)*, 9048161193) Springer.

—Human Creation Between Reality & Illusion. 2010. (Analecta Husserliana Ser.). xxvi, 300p. pap. 199.00 *(978-90-481-6902-3(X)*, 904816902X) Springer.

—Metamorphosis: Creative Imagination in Fine Arts Between Life-Projects & Human Aesthetic Aspirations. 2010. (Analecta Husserliana Ser.). xvi, 428p. pap. 319.00 *(978-90-481-6463-9(X)*, 904816463X) Springer.

Tymieniecka, Anna-Teresa, ed. Beauty's Appeal: Measure & Excess. 2007. (Analecta Husserliana Ser.). (Illus.). 296p. 219.00 *(978-1-4020-6520-0(5))* Springer.

Ulmer, Gregory L. Avatar Emergency. 2012. ***(978-1-60235-290-2(9))***; pap. ***(978-1-60235-289-6(5))*** Parlor Pr.

Urban, Otto. Decadence - In Morbid Colours Bohemia: Art & the Idea of Decadence in the Bohemian Lands, 1880-1914. 2011. (ENG., Illus.). 410p. 85.00 *(978-80-86300-84-9(6))* Nakladatelstvi Arbor vitae CZE. Dist: D.A.P./Distributed Art Pubs.

Van den Braembussche, Antoon & Kimmerle, Heinz, eds. Art & Worldviews: Towards an Intercultural Aesthetics. 2007. (Einstein Meets Magritte: an Interdisciplinary Reflection on Science, Nature, Art, Human Action & Society Ser.). (Illus.). vi, 217p. 139.00 *(978-1-4020-4507-3(7)*, 1402045077) Springer.

van Eck, Caroline, et al, eds. The Question of Style in Philosophy & the Arts. 2010. (Cambridge Studies in Philosophy & the Arts Ser.). (ENG.). 258p. pap. 37.00 *(978-0-521-15441-3(3))* Cambridge Univ. Pr.

van Gerwen, Rob, ed. Richard Wollheim on the Art of Painting: Art as Representation & Expression. 2007. (ENG., Illus.). 300p. pap. 62.00 *(978-0-521-03830-0(8))* Cambridge Univ. Pr.

van Maanen, Hans. How to Study Art Worlds: On the Societal Functioning of Aesthetic Values. 2010. 256p. pap. *(978-90-8964-152-6(1))* Amsterdam Univ. Pr.

Vattimo, Gianni. Art's Claim to Truth. Zabala, Santiago, ed. D'Isanto, Luca, tr. from ITA. (Columbia Themes in Philosophy, Social Criticism, & the Arts Ser.). (ENG.). 216p. (gr. 17). 2010. pap. 19.50 *(978-0-231-13851-2(2))* 2008. (Illus.). 29.50 *(978-0-231-13850-5(4))* Columbia Univ. Pr.

Vermeir, Koen & Funk Deckard, Michael, eds. The Science of Sensibility: Reading Burke's Philosophical Enquiry: Reading Burke's Philosophical Enquiry. 2011. (International Archives of the History of Ideas / archives internationales d'histoire des idées Ser.). (ENG., Illus.). xxii, 337p. 139.00 ***(978-94-007-2101-2(3)***, 9400721013) Springer.

Virilio, Paul. The Aesthetics of Disappearance. Beitchman, Philip, tr. from FRE. rev. ed. 2009. (Semiotext(e) / Foreign Agents Ser.). (ENG.). 128p. (gr. 17). pap. 14.95 *(978-1-58435-074-3(1))* Semiotexte/Smart Art.

Visser, Robin. Cities Surround the Countryside: Urban Aesthetics in Post-Socialist China. 2010. (ENG., Illus.). 376p. 89.95 *(978-0-8223-4709-5(1))*; pap. 25.95 *(978-0-8223-4728-6(8))* Duke Univ. Pr.

Voland, Eckart & Grammer, Karl, eds. Evolutionary Aesthetics. 2011. (ENG., Illus.). x, 377p. pap. 139.00 *(978-3-642-07822-4(2)*, 3642078222) Springer.

Von Teese, Dita & Nields, Sheryl. Dita: Stripteese. 2009. (ENG., Illus.). 256p. 30.00 *(978-0-06-176311-3(X))* HarperCollins Pubs.

von Vacano, Diego A. The Art of Power: Machiavelli, Nietzsche, & the Making of Aesthetic Political Theory. von Vacano, Diego A., ed. 2007. (ENG.). 288p. pap. 31.50 *(978-0-7391-2193-1(6))* Lexington Bks.

—The Art of Power: Machiavelli, Nietzsche, & the Making of Aesthetic Political Theory. 2006. (ENG.). 230p. 62.99 *(978-0-7391-1088-1(8))* Lexington Bks.

Walton, Kendall L. Marvelous Images: On Values & the Arts. 2008. (ENG., Illus.). 256p. 99.00 *(978-0-19-517794-7(0))*; pap. 24.95 *(978-0-19-517795-4(9))* Oxford Univ. Pr., Inc.

Ward Booth, Peter, et al. Maxillofacial Trauma & Esthetic Facial Reconstruction. 2nd ed. 2011. (ENG., Illus.). 640p. 369.00 ***(978-1-4377-2420-2(5)***, Saunders) Elsevier - Health Sciences Div.

Weber, Nicholas Fox. The Bauhaus Group: Six Masters of Modernism. 2011. (ENG., Illus.). 544p. pap. 27.50 *(978-0-300-16984-3(1))* Yale Univ. Pr.

Wegenstein, Bernadette. The Cosmetic Gaze: Body Modification & the Construction of Beauty. 2012. (ENG., Illus.). 240p. (gr. 17). 32.00 ***(978-0-262-23267-8(7))*** MIT Pr.

Weiermair, Peter. Image of the Body. 55.00 *(978-3-905514-08-7(7))* Edition Stemmle CHE. Dist: D.A.P./Distributed Art Pubs.

Weishan & Wu, Weishan. The Poetry of Sculpture. 2008. (Illus.). 250p. (C). 99.00 *(978-981-279-007-1(1))* World Scientific Publishing Co., Inc.

Weschler, Lawrence. Seeing Is Forgetting the Name of the Thing One Sees: Expanded Edition. exp. ed. 2009. (ENG., Illus.). 336p. pap. 26.95 *(978-0-520-25609-5(3))* Univ. of California Pr.

—Seeing Is Forgetting the Name of the Thing One Sees: Over Thirty Years of Conversations with Robert Irwin. exp. ed. 2009. (Illus.). 352p. 50.00 *(978-0-520-25608-8(5))* Univ. of California Pr.

Willems, Gottfried. Anschaulichkeit: Zu Theorie und Geschichte der Wort-Bild-Beziehungen und des literarischen Darstellungsstils. (Studien zur deutschen Literatur Ser.). (GER.). VIII, 484p. 195.00 ***(978-3-11-183806-9(4))*** De Gruyter, Walter Inc.

Williams, Dana. August Wilson & Black Aesthetics. Shannon, Sandra, ed. 2011. (ENG.). 240p. pap. 30.00 *(978-0-230-11301-5(X))* Palgrave Macmillan.

Williams, Terry Tempest. Finding Beauty in a Broken World. 2009. (Vintage Ser.). (ENG.). 432p. pap. 16.00 *(978-0-375-72519-7(9)*, Vintage) Knopf Doubleday Publishing Group.

Wilson, Anne. Anne Wilson: Wind/Rewind/Weave. 2011. (Illus.). 163p. pap. 30.00 ***(978-0-945323-22-8(0))*** WhiteWalls, Inc.

Wilson, Ross. Subjective Universality in Kant's Aesthetics. 2007. 236p. pap. 57.95 *(978-3-03911-106-0(X))* Lang, Peter Publishing, Inc.

Winston, Joe. Beauty & Education. 2011. (ENG., Illus.). 186p. pap. 39.95 ***(978-0-415-89664-1(9))*** Routledge.

Wiseman, Boris. Levi-Strauss, Anthropology, & Aesthetics. 2009. (Ideas in Context Ser.). 264p. pap. 38.99 *(978-0-521-12301-3(1))* Cambridge Univ. Pr.

Wittmann, Heiner. Aesthetics in Sartre & Camus. the Challenge of Freedom: Translated by Catherine Atkinson. 2009. (Dialoghi / Dialogues. Literatur und Kultur Italiens und Frankreichs Ser.). 170p. 50.95 *(978-3-631-58693-8(0))* Lang, Peter GmbH, Europaischer Verlag der Wissenschaften DEU. Dist: Lang, Peter.

Wolfe, Cary. What Is Posthumanism? 2009. (Posthumanities Ser.). (Illus.). 400p. pap. 24.95 *(978-0-8166-6615-7(6))* Univ. of Minnesota Pr.

Wolfe, Gregory. Beauty Will Save World: Recovering the Human in an Ideological Age. 2011. (ENG., Illus.). 320p. 29.95 *(978-1-933859-88-0(1))* ISI Bks.

Wolff, Janet. The Aesthetics of Uncertainty. 2008. (Columbia Themes in Philosophy, Social Criticism, & the Arts Ser.). (ENG., Illus.). 200p. (gr. 17). 40.00 *(978-0-231-14096-6(7))* Columbia Univ. Pr.

Wooddell, Joseph D. The Beauty of the Faith: Using Aesthetics for Christian Apologetics. 2010. 130p. pap. 16.00 *(978-1-60608-195-2(0)*, Wipf and Stock) Wipf & Stock Pubs.

Yeo, K. K. The Spirit Hovers: Journeying through Chaos with Prayers. 2011. 124p. pap. 15.00 ***(978-1-61097-506-3(5)***, Cascade Bks.) Wipf & Stock Pubs.

Yeo, K. K. The Spirit Intercedes. 2009. 132p. pap. 16.00 *(978-1-60608-794-7(0)*, Cascade Bks.) Wipf & Stock Pubs.

Zahnd, Brian. Beauty Will Save the World: Rediscovering the Allure & Mystery of Christianity. 2012. xviii, 234p. E-Book ***(978-1-61638-641-2(X))***; (ENG.). 256p. pap. 15.99 ***(978-1-61638-585-9(5))*** Charisma Media. (Charisma Hse.).

Zahoor, Asiya. Diaspora & the Caribbean Aesthetics. 2011. 104p. pap. ***(978-3-8383-7771-1(0))*** Lambert Academic Publishing.

Zargar, Cyrus Ali. Sufi Aesthetics: Beauty, Love, & the Human Form in the Writings of Ibn 'Arabi & 'Iraqi. 2011. (Studies in Comparative Religion Ser.). (ENG.). 248p. 59.95 *(978-1-57003-999-7(2))* Univ. of South Carolina Pr.

Zdebik, Jakub. Deleuze & the Diagram: Aesthetic Threads in Visual Organisation. 2012. (Continuum Studies in Continental Philosophy Ser.). (ENG.). 240p. 120.00 ***(978-1-4411-1560-7(9))*** Continuum International Publishing Group, Ltd. GBR. Dist: National Bk. Network.

—Deleuze & the Diagram: Aesthetic Threads in Visual Organization. 2012. E-Book ***(978-1-4411-7872-5(4))*** Continuum International Publishing Group, Ltd.

Ziff, Paul. Antiaesthetics: An Appreciation of the Cow with the Subtile Nose. 2010. (Synthese Library). (ENG.). 176p. pap. 219.00 *(978-90-481-8398-2(7)*, 9048183987) Springer.

Zijlstra, Onno. Language, Image & Silence: Kierkegaard & Wittgenstein on Ethics & Aesthetics. 2006. (Illus.). 193p. pap. 61.95 *(978-3-03910-842-8(5))*; x,183p. pap. 44.95 *(978-0-8204-8036-7(3))* Lang, Peter Publishing, Inc.

Zilberg, Jonathan. A New Theory & Method for the Study of Tourist Art. 2011. 108p. pap. ***(978-3-8443-1224-9(2))*** Lambert Academic Publishing.

Ziolkowski, Eric. The Literary Kierkegaard. 2011. (ENG., Illus.). 447p. 49.95 *(978-0-8101-2782-1(2))* Northwestern Univ. Pr.

Zock, T. H., ed. At the Crossroads of Art & Religion: Imagination, Commitment, Transcendence. 2008. (Groningen Studies in Cultural Change Ser.). (ENG.). 206p. (C). 70.00 *(978-90-429-2173-3(0))* Peeters Pubs. & Booksellers BEL. Dist: Brown, David Bk. Co., The.

Zuidervaart, Lambert. Artistic Truth: Aesthetics, Discourse, & Imaginative Disclosure. 2009. (ENG.). 296p. pap. 38.99 *(978-0-521-10124-0(7))* Cambridge Univ. Pr.

AESTHETICS—BIBLIOGRAPHY

Chandler, Albert R. & Barnhart, Edward Norton. Bibliography of Psychological & Experimental Aesthetics, 1864-1937. 2011. 196p. 42.95 ***(978-1-258-02191-7(9))*** Literary Licensing, LLC.

Herrmann. Gottfried Sempers theoretische Schriften an der ETH. (GER., Illus.). 271p. 50.95 *(978-3-7643-1239-8(4)*, 3764312394) Birkhauser Boston.

AESTHETICS—EARLY WORKS TO 1800

Aristotle. Aristotle on the Art of Poetry. 2006. pap. *(978-1-4065-1019-5(X))* Dodo Pr.

—Poetics. 2007. (ENG.). 88p. per. 7.99 *(978-1-59986-641-3(2))* Filiquarian Publishing, LLC.

—Rhetoric. 2008. (ENG.). 196p. per. 4.99 *(978-1-59986-566-9(1))* Filiquarian Publishing, LLC.

Aristotle & Butcher, S. H. The Poetics of Aristotle. 2011. 140p. pap. 6.95 ***(978-1-61427-036-2(8))*** Martino Publishing.

Baldwin, Charles Sears. Aristotle's Poetics & Longinus on the Sublime. Bywater, Ingram & Roberts, W. Rhys, trs. 2011. 146p. 40.95 ***(978-1-258-06921-6(0))*** Literary Licensing, LLC.

Bryant, Frank Egbert. On the Limits of Descriptive Writing Apropos of Lessing's Laocoon. 2009. 43p. pap. *(978-0-217-52314-1(5))* Books LLC.

Burke, Edmund. A Philosophical Enquiry into the Origin of Our Ideas of the Sublime & Beautiful. 2008. (ENG.). 160p. pap. 9.95 *(978-0-486-46166-3(1))* Dover Pubns., Inc.

—A Philosophical Enquiry into the Origin of Our Ideas of the Sublime & Beautiful. Phillips, Adam, ed. 2009. (Oxford World's Classics Ser.). (ENG.). 208p. 15.95 *(978-0-19-953788-4(7))* Oxford Univ. Pr., Inc.

—A Philosophical Enquiry into the Sublime & Beautiful. 2nd ed. 2008. (Routledge Classics Ser.). CXXX, 198p. 21.95 *(978-0-415-45326-4(7))* Routledge.

Bychkov, Oleg & Sheppard, Anne. Greek & Roman Aesthetics. 2010. (Cambridge Texts in the History of Philosophy Ser.). (ENG.). 294p. (C). pap. 30.99 *(978-0-521-54792-5(X))* Cambridge Univ. Pr.

Bychkov, Oleg V. & Sheppard, Anne. Greek & Roman Aesthetics. 2010. (Cambridge Texts in the History of Philosophy Ser.). (ENG.). 294p. (C). 95.00 *(978-0-521-83928-0(9))* Cambridge Univ. Pr.

Gerard, Alexander. An Essay on Taste. 2009. 126p. pap. 19.99 *(978-1-151-14955-8(1))* General Bks. LLC.

Hogarth, William. The Analysis of Beauty. 2008. 248p. 41.95 *(978-1-4373-8776-6(4))*; pap. 26.95 *(978-1-4372-9934-2(2))* Kessinger Publishing, LLC.

Hutcheson, Francis. An Inquiry into the Original of Our Ideas of Beauty & Virtue. 2009. 158p. (gr. 12-18). pap. *(978-0-217-68073-8(9))* Books LLC.

Hutcheson, Francis & Chamberlin, William Henry. America's Second Crusade. 2nd ed. 2008. (ENG., Illus.). 400p. (C). (gr. 12). pap. 12.00 *(978-0-86597-707-5(0))* Liberty Fund, Inc.

Hutcheson, Francis & Leidhold, W. Inquiry into the Original of Our Ideas of Beauty & Virtue. rev. ed. 2010. (Natural Law Cloth Ser.). (ENG.). 275p. (C). (gr. 12). 24.00 *(978-0-86597-773-0(9))* Liberty Fund, Inc.

—Inquiry into the Original of Our Ideas of Beauty & Virtue. 2nd rev. ed. 2008. (Natural Law Paper Ser.). (ENG., Illus.). 275p. (C). (gr. 12). pap. 14.50 *(978-0-86597-774-7(7))* Liberty Fund, Inc.

Telford, Kenneth A. Aristotle's Poetics: Translation & Analysis. 2011. 190p. 42.95 ***(978-1-258-06110-4(4))*** Literary Licensing, LLC.

Wellbery, David E. Lessing's Laocoon: Semiotics & Aesthetics in the Age of Reason. 2009. (Anglica Germanica Series 2 Ser.). (ENG.). 288p. pap. 38.99 *(978-0-521-10939-0(6))* Cambridge Univ. Pr.

AESTHETICS—HISTORY

Axelsson, Karl. The Sublime: Precursors & British Eighteenth-century Conceptions. 2007. 235p. pap. 63.95 *(978-0-8204-9389-3(9))* Lang, Peter Publishing, Inc.

Bosanquet, Bernard. A History of Aesthetic. 2009. 406p. pap. *(978-1-4432-8565-0(X))* Books LLC.

—A History of Aesthetic. 2011. (Cambridge Library Collection - Philosophy Ser.). (ENG.). 526p. pap. 37.99 ***(978-1-108-04022-8(5))*** Cambridge Univ. Pr.

Chambers, Frank P. Cycles of Taste: An Unacknowledged Problem in Ancient Art & Criticism. 2011. 148p. 40.95 ***(978-1-258-08488-2(0))*** Literary Licensing, LLC.

Damkjaer, Camilla. The Aesthetics of Movement. 2010. 272p. pap. *(978-3-8383-1653-6(3))* Lambert Academic Publishing.

Dickey, Colin, et al, eds. Failure! Experiments in Aesthetic & Social Practices, 1 vol. 2008. (ENG., Illus.). 218p. per. 15.00 *(978-0-9791377-0-9(5))* Journal of Aesthetics and Protest Pr./Herbst.

Eco, Umberto. On Ugliness. McEwen, Alastair, tr. from ITA.Tr. of Storia della Bruttezza. (Illus.). 456p. 2011. (ENG.). pap. 29.95 *(978-0-8478-3723-6(8))* 2007. 45.00 *(978-0-8478-2986-6(3))* Rizzoli International Pubns., Inc.

Eco, Umberto, ed. History of Beauty. 2010. (ENG., Illus.). 440p. pap. 29.95 *(978-0-8478-3530-0(8))* Rizzoli International Pubns., Inc.

—History of Beauty & on Ugliness, Set. 2008. (ENG., Illus.). 888p. 90.00 *(978-0-8478-3176-0(0))* Rizzoli International Pubns., Inc.

Filonov, Pavel Nikolaevich & Pravoverova, L. L. Pavel Filonov: Realnost I Mify. 2008. (RUS.). 670p. *(978-5-7784-0353-6(4))* Agraf, LTD, OOO.

Giovannelli, Alessandro. Aesthetics: The Key Thinkers. 2012. 240p. E-Book ***(978-1-4411-8027-8(3))*** Continuum International Publishing Group, Ltd.

—Aesthetics: The Key Thinkers. 2012. (Key Thinkers Ser.). (ENG.). 256p. 100.00 *(978-1-4411-9878-5(4))*; pap. 29.95 *(978-1-4411-8777-2(4))* Continuum International Publishing Group, Ltd. GBR. Dist: National Bk. Network.

Giovannelli, Alessandro, ed. Aesthetics: The Key Thinkers. 2012. 240p. E-Book ***(978-1-4411-4154-5(5))*** Continuum International Publishing Group, Ltd.

Gómez González, Concepción. Dau Al Set: Joan Brossa, Juan Eduardo Cirlot, Modest Cuixart, Jaon Ponç, Arnau Puig, Antoni Tàpies, Joan-Joseph Tharrats: Zaragoza, Ibercaja, Palio de la Infanta ... Del 6 de Octubre Al 13 de Diciembre de 2009. 2009. (SPA., Illus.). 139p. *(978-84-8324-283-4(4))* Caja de Ahorros y Monte de Piedad de Zaragoza, Aragon y Rioja.

Goncharova, Nataliella Sergeevna & Petrova, Yevgenia. Natalia Goncharova: The Russian Years. 2006. (MUL & ENG., Illus.). 342p. 85.00 *(978-3-935298-23-0(4)*, Palace Editions) Mandala Publishing.

Heller, Agnes. The Concept of the Beautiful. Morgan, Marcia S., ed. 2012. (ENG.). 220p. (gr. 17). 65.00 ***(978-0-7391-7047-2(3))*** Lexington Bks.

—The Concept of the Beautiful. 2011. ***(978-0-7391-7048-9(1))*** Lexington Bks.

Herman, Matthew D. Politics & Aesthetics in Contemporary Native American Literature: Across Every Border. 2009. (Indigenous Peoples & Politics Ser.). (ENG.). 154p. 125.00 *(978-0-415-80474-5(4))* Routledge.

Lang, Karen. Chaos & Cosmos: On the Image in Aesthetics & Art History. 2006. (Illus.). 320p. 68.95 *(978-0-8014-4166-0(8))*; 295p. per. 26.95 *(978-0-8014-8855-9(9))* Cornell Univ. Pr.

Leppanen-Guerra, Analisa. Children's Stories & 'Child-Time' in the Works of Joseph Cornell & the Trans-Atlantic Avant-Garde. 2011. (Ashgate Studies in Surrealism Ser.). (Illus.). 286p. 99.95 ***(978-1-4094-0156-8(1))*** Ashgate Publishing Co.

McDonough, Tom. The Situationists & the City. McDonough, Tom, ed. 2010. (ENG., Illus.). 288p. pap. 26.95 *(978-1-84467-364-3(2)*, 844364) Verso Bks. GBR. Dist: Norton, W. W. & Co., Inc.

McDonough, Tom, ed. The Situationists & the City. 2010. (ENG., Illus.). 288p. 110.00 *(978-1-84467-332-2(4)*, 844332) Verso Bks. GBR. Dist: Norton, W. W. & Co., Inc.

Nasir, Abdul Ghafoor. Preferences of Aesthetic Needs, Secondary School Students in Pakistan. 2011. 132p. pap. ***(978-3-8443-3286-5(3))*** Lambert Academic Publishing.

Olk, Claudia. Neuplatonismus und Aesthetik: Zur Transformationsgeschichte des Schoenen. Lobsien, Verena Olejniczak, ed. 2007. (Transformationen der Antike Ser.). (GER.). VIII, 256p. 126.00 *(978-3-11-019225-4(X))* De Gruyter, Walter Inc.

Peponi, Anastasia-Erasmia. Frontiers of Pleasure: Models of Aesthetic Response in Archaic & Classical Greek Thought. 2nd ed. 2012. (ENG., Illus.). 224p. 74.00 ***(978-0-19-979832-2(X))*** Oxford Univ. Pr., Inc.

Redner, Harry. Aesthetic Life: The Past & Present of Artistic Cultures. 2007. (ENG., Illus.). 516p. pap. 57.99 *(978-0-7618-3678-0(0))* Univ. Pr. of America, Inc.

—Aesthetic Life: The Past & Present of artistic Cultures. 2007. (ENG.). 516p. 89.50 *(978-0-7618-3677-3(2))* Univ. Pr. of America, Inc.

Robson, Mark. The Sense of Early Modern Writing: Rhetoric, Poetics, Aesthetics. 2007. (ENG., Illus.). 232p. 84.00 *(978-0-7190-6946-8(7))* Manchester Univ. Pr. GBR. Dist: Macmillan.

Sanouillet, Michel & Sanouillet, M. Dada in Paris. Ganguly, Sharmila, tr. from FRE. rev. ed. 2009. (ENG.). 720p. (gr. 17). 39.95 *(978-0-262-01303-1(7))* MIT Pr.

Staley, Allen. The New Painting of the 1860s: Between the Pre-Raphaelites & the Aesthetic Movement. 2011. (Paul Mellon Centre for Studies in British Art Ser.). (ENG., Illus.). 400p. 85.00 *(978-0-300-17567-7(1))* Yale Univ. Pr.

Stolzenberg, Jü, et al. Bildung als Kunst: Fichte, Schiller, Humboldt, Nietzsche. 2010. (GER.). VIII, 232p. 112.00 ***(978-3-11-022838-0(6))*** De Gruyter, Walter Inc.

Strother, Z. S. Pende: Visions of Africa. 2008. (Visions of Africa Ser.). (ENG., Illus.). 128p. pap. 34.95 *(978-88-7439-384-8(9))* 5 Continents ITA. Dist: Hachette Bk. Group.

Wark, McKenzie. 50 Years of Recuperation: Of the Situationist International. 2008. (ENG., Illus.). 80p. 24.95 *(978-1-56898-789-7(7))* Princeton Architectural Pr.

Zehou, Li. The Chinese Aesthetic Tradition. Samei, Maija Bell, tr. from CHI. 2009. 257p. *(978-0-8248-3307-7(4))* Univ. of Hawaii Pr.

AESTHETICS, BRITISH

see also Aesthetic Movement (Art)

Adelman, Richard. Idleness, Contemplation & the Aesthetic, 1750-1830. 2011. (Cambridge Studies in Romanticism Ser.). (ENG.). 220p. 85.00 *(978-0-521-19068-8(1))* Cambridge Univ. Pr.

Altholz, Josef L., ed. The Mind & Art of Victorian England. 2009. (ENG.). 206p. pap. 50.00 *(978-0-8166-5693-6(2))* Univ. of Minnesota Pr.

Anderson, Howard & Shea, John S., eds. Studies in Criticism & Aesthetics, 1660-1800: Essays in Honor of Samuel Holt Monk. 2009. (ENG.). 428p. pap. 60.00 *(978-0-8166-5694-3(0))* Univ. of Minnesota Pr.

Axelsson, Karl. The Sublime: Precursors & British Eighteenth-century Conceptions. 2007. 235p. pap. 63.95 *(978-0-8204-9389-3(9))* Lang, Peter Publishing, Inc.

Bernhart, Walter. "True Versifying" Studien Zur Elisabethanischen Verspraxis und Kunstideologie. Unter Einbeziehung der Zeitgenössischen Lautenlieder. (Studien zur englischen Philologie. Neue Folge Ser.). (GER., Illus.). VII, 401p. 210.00 ***(978-3-11-181385-1(1))*** De Gruyter, Walter Inc.

Casaliggi, Carmen & March-Russell, Paul, eds. The Legacies of Romanticism: Literature, Aesthetics, Landscape. 2012. (Routledge Studies in Romanticism Ser.). (ENG., Illus.). 304p. (C). 125.00 *(978-0-415-89008-3(X))* Routledge.

Chang, Elizabeth Hope. Britain's Chinese Eye: Literature, Empire, & Aesthetics in Nineteenth-Century Britain. 2010. (ENG., Illus.). 256p. 55.00 *(978-0-8047-5945-8(6))* Stanford Univ. Pr.

Cheetham, Mark A. Artwriting Nation & Cosmopolitanism in Britain: The Englishness of English Art Theory since the Eighteenth Century. 2012. (British Art: Global Contexts Ser.). (Illus.). 200p. 104.95 ***(978-1-4094-2073-6(6))*** Ashgate Publishing Co.

Clements, Elicia & Higgins, Lesley J., eds. Victorian Aesthetic Conditions: Pater Across the Arts. 2010. (ENG., Illus.). 288p. 84.00 *(978-0-230-23497-0(6))* Palgrave Macmillan.

Cottom, Daniel. The Civilized Imagination: A Study of Ann Radcliffe, Jane Austen & Sir Walter Scott. 2009. (ENG.). 240p. pap. 28.99 *(978-0-521-11097-6(1))* Cambridge Univ. Pr.

Flint, Kate. The Victorians & the Visual Imagination. 2008. (ENG., Illus.). 444p. pap. 58.00 *(978-0-521-08952-4(2))* Cambridge Univ. Pr.

Furniss, Tom. Edmund Burke's Aesthetic Ideology: Language, Gender & Political Economy in Revolution. 2008. (Cambridge Studies in Romanticism Ser.). (ENG.). 324p. (C). pap. 42.00 (978-0-521-05548-2(2)) Cambridge Univ. Pr.
Iser, Wolfgang. Walter Pater: The Aesthetic Moment. Wilson, David H., tr. from GER. 2011. (European Studies in English Literature Ser.). 226p. pap. 30.99 (978-0-521-17928-7(9)) Cambridge Univ. Pr.
Jones, Robert W. Gender & the Formation of Taste in Eighteenth-Century Britain: The Analysis of Beauty. 2009. (ENG., Illus.). 284p. pap. 42.00 (978-0-521-12129-3(9)) Cambridge Univ. Pr.
Komáromy, Zsolt. Figures of Memory: From the Muses to Eighteenth-Century British Aesthetics. 2011. (Transits: Literature, Thought & Culture, 1650ndash;1850 Ser.). (ENG.). 352p. 80.00 (978-1-61148-044-3(2)) Bucknell Univ. Pr.
Ledbetter, Kathryn. British Victorian Women's Periodicals: Beauty, Civilization, & Poetry. 2009. (Nineteenth-Century Major Lives & Letters Ser.). (ENG., Illus.). 252p. 95.00 (978-0-230-60126-0(X)) Palgrave Macmillan.
Orestano, Francesca & Frigerio, Francesca. Strange Sisters: Literature & Aesthetics in the Nineteenth Century. 2009. (Cultural Interactions: Studies in the Relationship between the Arts Ser.). (Illus.). 324p. 55.95 (978-3-03911-840-3(4)) Lang, Peter AG GBR. Dist: Lang, Peter.
Teskey, Gordon & Teskey, G. Delirious Milton: The Fate of the Poet in Modernity. 2009. 224p. pap. 16.00 (978-0-674-03509-6(7)) Harvard Univ. Pr.

AESTHETICS, COMMUNIST

see Communist Aesthetics

AESTHETICS, GERMAN

Beiser, Frederick C. Diotima's Children: German Aesthetic Rationalism from Leibniz to Lessing. (ENG.). 2011. 306p. pap. 35.00 (978-0-19-969465-5(6)) 2010. 288p. 70.00 (978-0-19-957301-1(8)) Oxford Univ. Pr., Inc.
Berhorst, Ralf. Anamorphosen der Zeit: Jean Pauls Romanästhetik und Geschichtsphilosophie. (Studien zur deutschen Literatur Ser.). (GER., Illus.). VII, 430p. 180.00 (978-3-11-183641-6(X)) De Gruyter, Walter Inc.
Bishop, Paul. Analytical Psychology & German Classical Aesthetics Vol. 2: Goethe, Schiller, & Jung: The Constellation of the Self. 2008. (ENG.). 264p. (C). 42.50 (978-0-415-43029-6(1)) Routledge.
Braungart, Georg. Leibhafter Sinn: Der andere Diskurs der Moderne. (Studien zur deutschen Literatur Ser.). (GER.). VI, 412p. 135.00 (978-3-11-182240-2(0)) De Gruyter, Walter Inc.
Haines, Brigid, et al. Aesthetics & Politics in Modern German Culture: Festschrift in Honour of Rhys W. Williams. 2010. (Illus.). 291p. 72.95 (978-3-03911-355-2(0)) Lang, Peter AG GBR. Dist: Lang, Peter.
Jacquette, Dale, ed. Schopenhauer, Philosophy & the Arts. 2007. (Cambridge Studies in Philosophy & the Arts Ser.). (ENG.). 324p. pap. 61.00 (978-0-521-04406-6(5)) Cambridge Univ. Pr.
Johnson, Laurie Ruth. Aesthetic Anxiety: Uncanny Symptoms in German Literature & Culture. 2010. (Illus.). 267p. pap. 69.00 (978-90-420-3113-5(1)) Rodopi.
Johnson, Laurie Ruth. The Art of Recollection in Jena Romanticism: Memory, History, Fiction, & Fragmentation in Texts by Friedrich Schlegel & Novalis. (Studien zur deutschen Literatur Ser.). (ENG.). VIII, 196p. 90.00 (978-3-11-183643-0(6)) De Gruyter, Walter Inc.
Kalar. Demands of Taste in Kant's Aesthetics. 2006. (Continuum Studies in Philosophy). (ENG.). 192p. 140.00 (978-0-8264-8890-9(0)) Continuum International Publishing Group, Ltd. GBR. Dist: National Bk. Network.
Koepnick, Lutz & McGlothlin, Erin, eds. After the Digital Divide? German Aesthetic Theory in the Age of New Media. 2009. (Screen Cultures: German Film & the Visual Ser.). (Illus.). 226p. 75.00 (978-1-57113-399-1(2)) Camden Hse.
Lang, Karen. Chaos & Cosmos: On the Image in Aesthetics & Art History. 2006. (Illus.). 320p. 68.95 (978-0-8014-4166-0(8)); 295p. per. 26.95 (978-0-8014-8855-9(9)) Cornell Univ. Pr.
Lifshitz, Mikhail. The Philosophy of Art of Karl Marx. Flores, Angel, ed. Winn, Ralph B., tr. 2011. 96p. 38.95 (978-1-258-05187-7(7)) Literary Licensing, LLC.
Martin, Alison E. Moving Scenes: The Aesthetics of German Travel Writing on England 1783-1830. 2008. (Legenda Studies in Comparative Literature Ser.). (Illus.). 200p. (C). 89.50 (978-1-906540-08-1(X)) European Humanities Research Ctr. GBR. Dist: Brown, David Bk. Co., The.
Moore, Evelyn K. & Simpson, Patricia Anne, eds. The Enlightened Eye: Goethe & Visual Culture. 2007. (Amsterdamer Beiträge Zur Neueren Germanistik Ser.: 62). 322p. 85.00 (978-90-420-2124-2(1)) Rodopi.
Richter, Sandra. A History of Poetics: German Scholarly Aesthetics & Poetics 1770-1960. 2010. (ENG., Illus.). XIV, 455p. 140.00 (978-3-11-022244-9(2)) De Gruyter, Walter Inc.
Rossol, Nadine. Performing the Nation in Interwar Germany: Sport, Spectacle & Political Symbolism, 1926-1936. 2010. (ENG., Illus.). 240p. 84.00 (978-0-230-21793-5(1)) Palgrave Macmillan.
Wabben, Yvonne. Gespenster und Gelehrte: Die Äthetische Lehrprosa Georg Friedrich Meiers (1718-1777) 2007. (Hallesche Beiträge Zur Europäischen Aufklärung Ser.).Tr. of Ghosts & Scholars. the Aesthetic Didactic Prose of Georg Friedrich Meier (1718â€"1777). (GER.). IX, 360p. pap. (978-3-484-81034-1(3)) Verlag Max Niemeyer.
Wegmann, Thomas. 'High' und 'low' Zur Interferenz von Hoch- und Populärkultur in der Gegenwartsliteratur. Wegmann, Thomas & Wolf, Norbert Christian, eds. 2011. (Studien und Texte zur Sozialgeschichte der Literatur Ser.).Tr. of High & Low. (GER.). VI, 238p. 126.00 (978-3-11-025560-7(X)) De Gruyter, Walter Inc.
Wegmann, Thomas & Wolf, Norbert Christian, eds. High und Low: Zur Interferenz Von Hoch- Und Populärkultur in der Gegenwartsliteratur. 2012. (Studien und Texte zur Sozialgeschichte der Literatur Ser.).Tr. of High & Low. (GER.). VI, 238p. (gr. 17). E-Book 196.00 (978-3-11-220448-1(4)) De Gruyter, Walter Inc.

AESTHETICS, GREEK

Acosta-Hughes, Benjamin & Stephens, Susan A. Callimachus in Context: From Plato to the Augustan Poets. 2012. (ENG., Illus.). 344p. 99.00 (978-1-107-00857-1(3)) Cambridge Univ. Pr.
Evangelista, Stefano-Maria. British Aestheticism & Ancient Greece: Hellenism, Reception, Gods in Exile. 2009. (Palgrave Studies in Nineteenth-Century Writing & Culture Ser.). (ENG., Illus.). 240p. 95.00 (978-0-230-54711-7(7)) Palgrave Macmillan.
Wood, John, ed. Odes of Pindar. Goins, Scott, tr. & notes by. 2007. (978-1-892733-36-8(6)) 21st Editions, Inc.

AESTHETICS, INDIC

Barlingay, Surendra Sheodas. A Modern Introduction to Indian Aesthetic Theory: The Development from Bharata to Jagannaltha. 2007. (SAN & ENG.). xxvi, 374p. (978-81-246-0377-2(4)); pap. (978-81-246-0378-9(2)) D. K. Print World (P) Ltd.
Bhadury, Poushali. Science, Literature, & Aesthetics. Dev, Amiya, ed. 2009. (Illus.). 851p. 175.00 (978-81-87586-39-5(7)) Centre for Studies in Civilizations IND. Dist: Coronet Bks.
Katsyayan, Kapila & Chattodhyaya, D. P., eds. Aesthetic Theories & Forms in Indian Tradition. 2008. (History of Science, Philosophy & Culture in Indian Civilization Ser.). (Illus.). 650p. 199.50 (978-81-87586-35-7(4)) Munshiram Manoharlal Pubs. Private, Ltd. IND. Dist: Coronet Bks.
Saxena, Sushil Kumar. Aesthetics: Approaches, Concepts, & Problems. 2010. viii, 446p. (978-81-246-0555-4(6), Library of Congress — New Delhi Overseas Office) D. K. Print World (P) Ltd.

AESTHETICS, JAPANESE

see also Sabi; Wabi

Francioli, Marco, et al, eds. Gutai. 2011. (ENG & ITA., Illus.). 264p. pap. 49.95 (978-88-366-1815-6(4)) Silvana ITA. Dist: D.A.P./Distributed Art Pubs.
Marra, Michael F. Essays on Japan: Between Aesthetics & Literature. 2010. (ENG.). XIV, 506p. (978-90-04-18977-5(7)) BRILL.
Sandrisser, Barbara. Exploring Environmental Aesthetics in Japan. 2009. (978-1-4331-0141-0(6)) Lang, Peter Publishing, Inc.
Tansman, Alan & Tansman, A. The Aesthetics of Japanese Fascism. 2009. (Studies of the Weatherhead East Asian Institute (temp) Ser.). (ENG.). 400p. 55.00 (978-0-520-24505-1(9)) Univ. of California Pr.
Visioning Eternity: Aesthetics, Politics, & History in the Early Modern Noh Theater. 2008. (Illus.). 325p. 66.00 (978-1-933947-08-2(X)); (ENG., pap. 33.00 (978-1-933947-38-9(1)) Cornell Univ. East Asia Program.
Wong, Yoke-Sum. The Aesthetics of Cute in Contemporary Japanese Art. 2012. (Critical Studies in Gender, Sexuality, & Culture Ser.). (ENG., Illus.). 256p. 85.00 (978-0-230-10539-3(4)) Palgrave Macmillan.

AESTHETICS, MODERN

Abbs, Peter. Aa Is for Aesthetic (Rle Edu K) 2012. (Routledge Library Editions: Education Ser.). (ENG.). 208p. 115.00 (978-0-415-69579-4(1)) Routledge.
Barrett, Terry. Why Is That Art? Aesthetics & Criticism of Contemporary Art, 1 vol. 2nd ed. 2011. (ENG., Illus.). 288p. (C). pap. 34.95 (978-0-19-975880-7(8)) Oxford Univ. Pr., Inc.
Berger, David. Kant's Aesthetic Theory: The Beautiful & Agreeable. 2011. (ENG.). 176p. pap. 44.95 (978-1-4411-2497-5(7)) Continuum International Publishing Group, Ltd. GBR. Dist: National Bk. Network.
Berger, David & Berger. Kant's Aesthetic Theory: The Beautiful & Agreeable. 2009. (Continuum Studies in Philosophy Ser.). (ENG.). 176p. 130.00 (978-0-8264-3580-4(7)) Continuum International Publishing Group, Ltd. GBR. Dist: National Bk. Network.
Bevin, Darren. Cultural Climbs. 2010. 200p. pap. (978-3-639-25295-8(0)) VDM Verlag Dr. Mueller e.K.
Biasi, Vittoria. Architetture Del Bianco: Viaggio Teorico-Creativo Attorno Alle Lingue Del Bianco. 2009. (ITA., Illus.). 238p. (978-88-492-1676-9(9)) Gangemi.
Bishop, Ryan & Phillips, John. Modernist Avant-Garde Aesthetics & Contemporary Military Technology: Technicities of Perception. (ENG., Illus.). 288p. (gr. 17). 2011. pap. 32.00 (978-0-7486-4319-6(2)) 2010. 115.00 (978-0-7486-3988-5(8)) Edinburgh Univ. Pr. GBR. Dist: Columbia Univ. Pr.
Bohn, Willard. Apollinaire on the Edge: Modern Art, Popular Culture, & the Avant-Garde. 2010. (Illus.). 143p. pap. 38.00 (978-90-420-3108-1(5)) Rodopi.
Brind, Susan, et al, eds. The State of the Real: Aesthetics in the Digital Age. 2007. (ENG., Illus.). 208p. pap. 34.00 (978-1-84511-077-2(3)) I. B. Tauris & Co., Ltd. GBR. Dist: Macmillan.
Carroll, Jerome, et al. Aesthetics & Modernity from Schiller to the Frankfurt School. 2011. (ENG.). 369p. pap. 71.95 (978-3-0343-0217-3(7)) Lang, Peter AG GBR. Dist: Lang, Peter.
Cheetham, Mark A. Kant, Art, & Art History: Moments of Discipline. 2009. (ENG., Illus.). 236p. pap. 34.99 (978-0-521-10756-3(3)) Cambridge Univ. Pr.
Cope, Kevin. 1650-1850 Vol. 13: Ideas, Aesthetics, & Inquiries in the Early Modern Era. 13th ed. 2006. (Ideas, Aesthetics, & Inquiries in the Early Modern Era Ser.). 139.50 (978-0-404-64413-0(9)) AMS Pr., Inc.
Cope, Kevin L. Ideas, Aesthetics & Inquiries in the Early Modern Era, 1650-1850, Vol. 14. 2007. 429p. 163.50 (978-0-404-64414-7(7)) AMS Pr., Inc.
Copley, Stephen & Garside, Peter, eds. The Politics of the Picturesque: Literature, Landscape & Aesthetics Since 1770. 2010. (ENG., Illus.). 320p. pap. 33.99 (978-0-521-13110-0(3)) Cambridge Univ. Pr.
Corse, Sandra. Craft Objects, Aesthetic Contexts: Kant, Heidegger, & Adorno on Craft. 2008. (ENG.). 110p. pap. 26.50 (978-0-7618-4287-3(X)) Univ. Pr. of America, Inc.
Costazza, Alessandro, et al, eds. Kunstreligion 01. Die Formulierung des Konzepts um 1800. 2010. (GER., Illus.). 269p. 140.00 (978-3-11-021780-3(5)) De Gruyter, Walter Inc.
Costelloe, Timothy M. Aesthetics & Morals in the Philosophy of David Hume. 2009. 144p. 39.95 (978-0-415-80298-7(9)) Routledge.
Deleuze, Gilles. The Fold: Leibniz & Baroq. Conley, Tom, tr. from FRE. (Illus.). 192p. (978-0-485-11421-8(6)) Continuum International Publishing Group, Ltd.
—The Fold: Leibniz & the Baroque. (Illus.). 192p. pap. (978-0-485-12087-5(9)) Continuum International Publishing Group, Ltd.
Disselkamp, Martin. Die Stadt der Gelehrten: Studien zu Johann Joachim Winckelmanns Briefen aus Rom. (Studien zur deutschen Literatur Ser.). (GER.). VII, 423p. 180.00 (978-3-11-182129-0(3)) De Gruyter, Walter Inc.
Dyhouse, Carol. Glamour: Women, History, Feminism. 2010. (ENG., Illus.). 238p. 30.00 (978-1-84813-407-2(X)) Zed Bks., Ltd. GBR. Dist: Macmillan.
Egginton, William. The Theater of Truth: The Ideology of (Neo)Baroque Aesthetics. 2009. (ENG.). 184p. 55.00 (978-0-8047-6954-9(0)) Stanford Univ. Pr.
Fortunato, Paul. Modernist Aesthetics & Consumer Culture in the Writings of Oscar Wilde. 2009. 168p. 39.95 (978-0-415-80302-1(0)) Routledge.
Fortunato, Paul L. Modernist Aesthetics & Consumer Culture in the Writings of Oscar Wilde. 2007. (Studies in Major Literary Authors Ser.). 162p. 131.00 (978-0-415-98103-3(4)) Routledge.
Hinderliter, Beth, et al, eds. Communities of Sense: Rethinking Aesthetics & Politics. 2009. (ENG., Illus.). 384p. 94.95 (978-0-8223-4497-1(1)); pap. 26.95 (978-0-8223-4513-8(7)) Duke Univ. Pr.
Johnson, Anthony. Ben Johnson. 2012. (Writers & Their Work Ser.). (ENG.). (C). pap. 26.00 (978-0-7463-0881-3(7)) Northcote Hse. Publishers, Ltd. GBR. Dist: Brown, David Bk. Co., The.
Jonas, Leah. Divine Science the Aesthetic of Some Rep. 2006. pap. 28.95 (978-1-4286-5336-8(8)) Kessinger Publishing, LLC.
Jones, Amelia. Seeing Differently. 2012. (ENG.). 288p. (C). 130.00 (978-0-415-54382-8(7)); pap. 39.95 (978-0-415-54383-5(5)) Routledge.
Jones, Robert W. Gender & the Formation of Taste in Eighteenth-Century Britain: The Analysis of Beauty. 2009. (ENG., Illus.). 284p. pap. 42.00 (978-0-521-12129-3(9)) Cambridge Univ. Pr.
Kreuzer, Stefanie. Katastrophe als Ubergangsmodus Kultureller Systeme im 20. Jahrhundert und das Phanomen des Ubergangs bei Wolfgang Max Faust. (Europaische Hochschulschriften Ser.). (GER., Illus.). 203p. 37.95 (978-3-631-38167-0(0)) Lang, Peter Publishing, Inc.
Levy-Navarro, Elena & Levy-navarro, Elena. The Culture of Obesity in Early & Late Modernity: Body Image in Shakespeare, Jonson, Middleton, & Skelton. 2008. (ENG.). 252p. 89.00 (978-0-230-60123-9(5)) Palgrave Macmillan.
Matthews, P. M. The Significance of Beauty: Kant on Feeling & the System of the Mind. 2010. (New Synthese Historical Library). 252p. pap. 167.00 (978-90-481-4921-6(5), 9048149215) Springer.
Mattick, Jr, Paul, Paul, ed. Eighteenth-Century Aesthetics & the Reconstruction of Art. 2008. (ENG.). 268p. pap. 37.99 (978-0-521-06683-9(2)) Cambridge Univ. Pr.
Ottmann, Klaus. Genius Decision: The Extraordinary & the Postmodern Condition. 2nd rev. exp. ed. 2013. (ENG & ACE.). 320p. pap. 24.00 (978-0-88214-592-1(4)) Spring Pubns., Inc.
Pericolo, Lorenzo & Nagel, Alexander. Subject as Aporia in Early Modern Art. 2010. (Illus.). 274p. 119.95 (978-0-7546-6493-2(7)) Ashgate Publishing Co.
Peterson, Gary R. The Intellectual Handyman on Art: A Compilation of Essays by Gary R. Peterson. 2011. 184p. pap. 16.95 (978-1-4620-5687-3(3)) iUniverse, Inc.
Rogerson, Kenneth F. The Problem of Free Harmony in Kant's Aesthetics. 2009. pap. 19.95 (978-0-7914-7626-0(X)) 2008. 138p. 45.00 (978-0-7914-7625-3(1)) State Univ. of New York Pr.
Schaeffer, Jean-Marie. Art of the Modern Age: Philosophy of Art from Kant to Heidegger. Rendall, Steven, tr. 2009. (New French Thought Ser.). (ENG., Illus.). 376p. (C). pap. 30.95 (978-0-691-14436-8(2)) Princeton Univ. Pr.
Schiller, Friedrich. Schiller's Philosophical Letters. 2007. 80p. per. (978-1-4065-3903-5(1)) Dodo Pr.
Schneider, Norbert. Geschichte der Ästhetik von der Aufklärung bis zur Postmoderne: Eine paradigmatische Einführung. (GER., Illus.). 352p. (978-3-15-009457-0(7)) Reclam, Philip jun., Verlag GmbH.
Schwartz, Regina. Sacramental Poetics at the Dawn of Secularism: When God Left the World. 2008. (Cultural Memory in the Present Ser.). (ENG.). 216p. 60.00 (978-0-8047-5667-9(8)); pap. 19.95 (978-0-8047-5833-8(6)) Stanford Univ. Pr.
Sepp, Hans Rainer & Embree, Lester, eds. Handbook of Phenomenological Aesthetics. 2009. (Contributions to Phenomenology Ser.). (ENG.). xxx, 383p. 319.00 (978-90-481-2470-1(0), 9048124700) Springer.
Stephenson, Roger H. Studies in Weimar Classicism: Writing As Symbolic Form. 2010. 495p. pap. 86.95 (978-3-03911-085-8(3)) Lang, Peter AG GBR. Dist: Lang, Peter.
Wachter, Alexander. Das Spiel in der Ästhetik: systematische Überlegungen zu Kants Kritik der Urteilskraft. 2006. (Kantstudien-Ergänzungshefte Ser.). (GER.). XI, 236p. 98.00 (978-3-11-019038-0(9)) De Gruyter, Walter Inc.
Wellbery, David E. Lessing's Laocoon: Semiotics & Aesthetics in the Age of Reason. 2009. (Anglica Germanica Series 2 Ser.). (ENG.). 288p. pap. 38.99 (978-0-521-10939-0(6)) Cambridge Univ. Pr.
Willis, Gary. Art As Mime. 2010. 232p. pap. (978-3-8383-1920-9(6)) Lambert Academic Publishing.
Wiseman, Boris. Lévi-Strauss, Anthropology & Aesthetics. 2007. (Ideas in Context Ser.). (ENG., Illus.). 264p. 95.00 (978-0-521-87529-5(3)) Cambridge Univ. Pr.
Wyss, Beat. Hegel's Art History & the Critique of Modernity: The 'Sorrow of Perfect' in the Aesthetics of German Idealism & Modern Art Criticism. 2008. (Res Monographs in Anthropology & Aesthetics). (ENG., Illus.). 308p. pap. 63.00 (978-0-521-06680-8(8)) Cambridge Univ. Pr.

AESTHETICS, MODERN—19TH CENTURY

Barker, Stephen. Autoaesthetics: Strategies of the Self after Nietzsche. (Philosophy & Literary Theory Ser.). (ENG.). 1p. 63.00 (978-1-57392-454-2(7), Humanity Bks.) Prometheus Bks., Pubs.
Calasso, Roberto. La La Folie Baudelaire, 1 vol. McEwen, Alastair, tr. from ITA. 2012. (ENG., Illus.). 352p. 35.00 (978-0-374-18334-9(1)) Farrar, Straus & Giroux.
Evangelista, Stefano-Maria. British Aestheticism & Ancient Greece: Hellenism, Reception, Gods in Exile. 2009. (Palgrave Studies in Nineteenth-Century Writing & Culture Ser.). (ENG., Illus.). 240p. 95.00 (978-0-230-54711-7(7)) Palgrave Macmillan.
Feldman, Jessica R. Victorian Modernism: Pragmatism & the Varieties of Aesthetic Experience. 2009. (ENG., Illus.). 276p. pap. 38.99 (978-0-521-12090-6(X)) Cambridge Univ. Pr.
Fendt, Astrid. Archäologie und Restaurierung: Die Skulpturenergänzungen in der Berliner Antikensammlung des 19. Jahrhunderts. 2011. (Transformationen der Antike Ser.).Tr. of Archaelogy & Restoration. (GER.). 1360p. 419.00 (978-3-11-219188-0(9)) De Gruyter, Walter Inc.
—Archäologie und Restaurierung. 3 Bände: Die Skulpturenergänzungen in der Berliner Antikensammlung des 19. Jahrhunderts, 3 vols. 2012. (Transformationen der Antike Ser.).Tr. of Archaelogy & Restoration. (GER.). 1360p. 280.00 (978-3-11-024743-5(7)) De Gruyter, Walter Inc.
Gray, Jeremy. Plato's Ghost: The Modernist Transformation of Mathematics. 2008. (ENG., Illus.). 526p. (C). 49.95 (978-0-691-13610-3(6)) Princeton Univ. Pr.
Haus, Andreas, et al. Material IM Prozess: Strategien Aesthetischer Produktivitaet. (GER & ENG., Illus.). 301p. (978-3-496-01227-6(7)) Reimer, Dietrich.
Leighton, Angela. On Form: Poetry, Aestheticism, & the Legacy of a Word. 2007. (ENG.). 304p. 75.00 (978-0-19-929060-4(1)) Oxford Univ. Pr., Inc.
Meindl, Matthias. Geschmack und Urteilskraft bei Pierre Bourdieu und Hannah Arendt. 2009. (Berliner Arbeiten zur Erziehungs- und Kulturwissenschaft Ser.). (GER.). 141p. pap. (978-3-8325-2334-3(0)) Logos Verlag Berlin.
Moggach, Douglas, ed. Politics, Religion, & Art: Hegelian Debates. 2011. (Topics in Historical Philosophy Ser.). (ENG.). 368p. 89.95 (978-0-8101-2729-6(6)) Northwestern Univ. Pr.
Ponton, Olivier. Nietzsche - Philosophie de la Legerete. 2007. (Monographien und Texte Zur Nietzsche-Forschung Ser.). (FRE.). XI, 343p. 154.00 (978-3-11-019346-6(9)) De Gruyter, Walter Inc.
Pothast, Ulrich. The Metaphysical Vision: Arthur Schopenhauer's Philosophy of Art & Life & Samuel Beckett's Own Way to Make Use of It. 2008. 260p. (C). 71.95 (978-1-4331-0286-8(2)) Lang, Peter Publishing, Inc.
Raspa, Venanzio, ed. Aesthetics of the Graz School. 2011. 279p. 131.95 (978-3-86838-076-7(0)) Ontos Verlag DEU. Dist: Transaction Pubs.
Shaw, W. David. The Lucid Veil: Poetic Truth in the Victorian Era. (ENG.). 336p. 170.00 (978-0-485-11293-1(0)) Continuum International Publishing Group, Ltd. GBR. Dist: National Bk. Network.
Teukolsky, Rachel. Literate Eye: Victorian Art Writing & Modernist Aesthetics. 2009. (ENG., Illus.). 336p. 35.00 (978-0-19-538137-5(8)) Oxford Univ. Pr., Inc.
Thain, Marion. 'Michael Field' Poetry, Aestheticism & the Fin de Siécle. 2010. (Cambridge Studies in Nineteenth-Century Literature & Culture Ser.). (ENG., Illus.). 286p. pap. 39.99 (978-0-521-14773-6(5)) Cambridge Univ. Pr.
Vandenabeele, Bart, ed. Companion to Schopenhauer. 2012. (Blackwell Companions to Philosophy Ser.: 85). (ENG.). 432p. 149.95 (978-1-4051-7103-8(0), Wiley-Blackwell) Wiley, John & Sons, Inc.

AESTHETICS, MODERN—20TH CENTURY

Adi Da Samraj. Transcendental Realism: The Image-Art of Egoless Coincidence with Reality Itself. 2nd ed. 2010. (Illus.). 265p. (978-1-57097-285-0(0)) Dawn Horse Pr.
Barlas, Seyda. Visions of Aesthetics & Culture in Yeni Adam. 2010. 184p. pap. (978-3-639-26956-7(X)) VDM Verlag Dr. Mueller e.K.
Beech, Dave. Beauty. 2009. (Documents of Contemporary Art Ser.). (ENG., Illus.). 239p. (gr. 17). pap. 24.95 (978-0-262-51238-1(6)) MIT Pr.
Bernstein, Jay M., et al. Art & Aesthetics after Adorno. 2010. (Townsend Papers in the Humanities Ser.). 160p. pap. 18.95 (978-0-9823294-2-9(3)) Townsend Ctr. For The Humanities.
Bjarnadottir, Birna. Recesses of the Mind: On Aesthetics Gubergur Bergsson's Work. 2012. (ENG.). 304p. (C). (978-0-7735-3910-5(7)) McGill-Queen's Univ. Pr.
Bonde, Hans. The Politics of the Male Body in Global Sport. 2010. (Sport in the Global Society - Historical Perspectives Ser.). (ENG.). 304p. (C). 125.00 (978-0-415-57176-0(6), Routledge) Taylor & Francis Group GBR. Dist: Taylor & Francis Group.
Brandt, Stefan L. The Culture of Corporeality: Aesthetic Experience & the Embodiment of America, 1945-1960. 2007. 448p. (978-3-8253-5353-7(2)) Universitatsverlag Winter GmbH Heidelberg.

Buch, Robert Caspar. The Pathos of the Real: On the Aesthetics of Violence in the Twentieth Century. 2010. (Rethinking Theory Ser.). (ENG.). 232p. (gr. 17). 60.00 *(978-0-8018-9756-6(4))* Johns Hopkins Univ. Pr.

Chillida, Eduardo. Eduardo Chillida: Writings. 2011. (ENG., Illus.). 160p. 40.00 *(978-3-941263-07-9(2))* Richter Verlag DEU. Dist: D.A.P./Distributed Art Pubs.

Colace-Scarabino, Gabrielle. Pourquoi Roue de Bicyclette Est une Uvre D'art. 2010. (FRE., Illus.). 214p. *(978-2-84301-293-8(7))* Aleas, Editeur.

Farebrother, Rachel. The College Aesthetic in the Harlem Renaissance: Discourses of Anthropology & Nationalism. 2009. (Illus.). 232p. 99.95 *(978-0-7546-6198-6(9))* Ashgate Publishing Co.

Friedman, Alice T. American Glamour & the Evolution of Modern Architecture. 2010. (Illus.). 272p. 55.00 *(978-0-300-11654-0(3))* Yale Univ. Pr.

Fuller, Matthew. Media Ecologies: Materialist Energies in Art & Technoculture. 2007. (Leonardo Bks.). (ENG., Illus.). 280p. (gr. 17). per. 22.95 *(978-0-262-56226-3(X))* MIT Pr.

Goncharova, Nataleiia Sergeevna & Petrova, Yevgenia. Natalia Goncharova: The Russian Years. 2006. (MUL & ENG., Illus.). 342p. 85.00 *(978-3-935298-23-0(4),* Palace Editions) Mandala Publishing.

Groys, Boris. Under Suspicion: A Phenomenology of Media. Strathausen, Carsten, tr. from GER. 2012. (Columbia Themes in Philosophy, Social Criticism, & the Arts Ser.). (ENG., Illus.). 232p. (gr. 17). 50.00 ***(978-0-231-14618-0(3))*** Columbia Univ. Pr.

Haus, Andreas, et al. Material IM Prozess: Strategien Aesthetischer Produktivitaet. (GER & ENG., Illus.). 301p. *(978-3-496-01227-6(7))* Reimer, Dietrich.

Jarzombek, Mark. The Psychologizing of Modernity: Art, Architecture & History. 2011. (ENG., Illus.). 340p. pap. 34.99 *(978-0-521-14763-7(8))* Cambridge Univ. Pr.

Martin, Jean-Clet & Dyrkton, Susan. Variations: The Philosophy of Gilles Deleuze. Boundas, Constantin V., tr. from FRE. 2010. (Plateaus — New Directions in Deleuze Studies). (ENG., Illus.). 280p. (gr. 17). 85.00 *(978-0-7486-3882-6(2))* Edinburgh Univ. Pr. GBR. Dist: Columbia Univ. Pr.

Masschelein, Anneleen. The Unconcept: The Freudian Uncanny in Late-Twentieth-Century Theory. 2011. (SUNY series, Insinuations: Philosophy, Psychoanalysis, Literature Ser.). (Illus.). 224p. 75.00 *(978-1-4384-3553-4(3),* Suny Pr.) State Univ. of New York Pr.

Mayo, Nuria Enguita. Afterall: Spring 2011, Issue 26. Lafuente, Pablo & Roelstraete, Dieter, eds. 2011. (Illus.). 130p. pap. 10.00 *(978-1-84638-075-4(8))* Univ. of Chicago Pr.

McKee, Alan, ed. Beautiful Things in Popular Culture. 2006. (ENG., Illus.). 248p. 99.95 *(978-1-4051-3190-2(X))*; pap. 35.95 *(978-1-4051-3191-9(8))* Wiley, John & Sons, Inc. (Wiley-Blackwell).

Menke, Christoph. Christoph Menke: Ästhetik der Gleichheit. 2011. (ENG., Illus.). 32p. pap. 10.00 ***(978-3-7757-2859-1(7))*** Hatje Cantz Verlag GmbH & Co KG DEU. Dist: D.A.P./Distributed Art Pubs.

Miles, Malcolm. Herbert Marcuse: An Aesthetics of Liberation, 1 vol. 2012. (Modern European Thinkers Ser.). (ENG., Illus.). 208p. 37.00 ***(978-0-7453-3038-9(X))***; lib. bdg. 105.00 ***(978-0-7453-3039-6(8))*** Pluto Pr. GBR. Dist: Macmillan.

Neill, Alex & Ridley, Aaron, eds. Arguing about Art: Contemporary Philosophical Debates. 3rd rev. ed. 2007. (Arguing about Philosophy Ser.). (ENG., Illus.). 504p. (C). 150.00 *(978-0-415-42450-9(X))*; per. 41.95 *(978-0-415-42451-6(8))* Routledge.

Papazian, Elizabeth Astrid. Manufacturing Truth: The Documentary Moment in Early Soviet Culture. 2008. (Illus.). 296p. 39.00 *(978-0-87580-389-0(X))* Northern Illinois Univ. Pr.

Raspa, Venanzio, ed. Aesthetics of the Graz School. 2011. 279p. 131.95 *(978-3-86838-076-7(0))* Ontos Verlag DEU. Dist: Transaction Pubs.

Ray, Gene. Terror & the Sublime in Art & Critical Theory: From Auschwitz to Hiroshima to September 11 & Beyond. 2011. (Studies in European Culture & History Ser.). (ENG.). 256p. pap. 28.00 *(978-0-230-11048-9(7))* Palgrave Macmillan.

Saksena, Divya. The Aesthetic Philosophy of D.H. Lawrence: 'The Shimmer, Not the Shape of Things' 2008. 180p. pap. *(978-3-639-09056-7(X))* VDM Verlag Dr. Mueller e.K.

Scheel, Werner & Bering, Kunibert. Kunst und Asthetik. (GER., Illus.). 208p. *(978-3-496-01168-2(8))* Reimer, Dietrich.

Short, Christopher. The Art Theory of Wassily Kandinsky, 1909-1928: The Quest for Synthesis. 2009. (Illus.). xiv, 241p. 61.95 *(978-3-03911-399-6(2))* Lang, Peter AG GBR. Dist: Lang, Peter.

Thain, Marion. 'Michael Field' Poetry, Aestheticism & the Fin de Siécle. 2010. (Cambridge Studies in Nineteenth-Century Literature & Culture Ser.). (ENG., Illus.). 286p. pap. 39.99 *(978-0-521-14773-6(5))* Cambridge Univ. Pr.

Watkinson, Gordon. Bauhaus Twenty-21: An Ongoing Legacy. Vrachliotis, Georg, ed. 2009. 232p. 89.95 *(978-3-0346-0054-5(2))* Springer.

Watson, Stephen. Crescent Moon over the Rational: Philosophical Interpretations of Paul Klee. 2009. (ENG., Illus.). 256p. 50.00 *(978-0-8047-6125-3(6))* Stanford Univ. Pr.

Zepke, Stephen. Art As Abstract Machine. 2011. (ENG., Illus.). 318p. pap. 39.95 ***(978-0-415-89006-9(3))*** Routledge.

AESTHETICS, MODERN—21ST CENTURY

Bernstein, Jay M., et al. Art & Aesthetics after Adorno. 2010. (Townsend Papers in the Humanities Ser.). 160p. pap. 18.95 *(978-0-9823294-2-9(3))* Townsend Ctr. For The Humanities.

Burda, Hubert. The Digital Wunderkammer: 10 Chapters on the Iconic Turn, 1 vol. 2011. (ENG., Illus.). 202p. 45.00 ***(978-3-7705-5193-4(1))*** Wilhelm/Fink#GmbH & Co. Verlags-KG DEU. Dist: D.A.P./Distributed Art Pubs.

Campanelli, Vito. Web Aesthetics. 2011. (ENG.). 276p. pap. 30.00 *(978-90-5662-770-6(8))* NAi Uitgevers / Publishers Stichting NLD. Dist: D.A.P./Distributed Art Pubs.

Costantino, Tracie & White, Boyd, eds. Essays on Aesthetic Education for the 21st Century. 2010 228p. *(978-94-6091-121-7(8))*; pap. *(978-94-6091-120-0(X))* Sense Pubs.

Koren, Leonard. Which Aesthetics Do You Mean? Ten Definitions. 2010. (ENG., Illus.). 96p. pap. 16.00 *(978-0-9814846-1-7(1))* Imperfect Publishing.

Murray, Scott. Translucent Skins: Contemporary Innovative Building Enclosure Systems. 2012. (ENG., Illus.). 208p. (C). 165.00 ***(978-0-415-68930-4(9))***; pap. 49.95 ***(978-0-415-68931-1(7))*** Routledge.

Pilis, Alexander. Architecture Parallax: the Blind Architect. 2008. 112p. pap. 38.00 *(978-1-4357-1660-5(4))* Lulu Enterprises Inc.

Taylor, Charles Thomas. Symbolism in Religion & Art. 2007. (ENG.). 100p. per. 25.50 *(978-0-7618-3875-3(9))* Univ. Pr. of America, Inc.

AESTHETICS, ORIENTAL

Behrstock, Barry B. The Way of the Artist: Reflections on Creativity & the Life, Home, Art, & Collections of Richard Marquis. 2007. (ENG., Illus.). 192p. *(978-0-935314-70-0(9))* Grand Central Pr.

McCabe, Ina Baghdiantz. Orientalism in Early Modern France: Eurasian Trade Exoticism & the Ancient Régime. 2008. (ENG., Illus.). 1p. 119.95 *(978-1-84520-374-0(7))* Berg Pubs. GBR. Dist: Macmillan.

AESTII

see Balts (Indo-European People)

AETA (JAPANESE PEOPLE)

see Buraku People

AETHELWOLD, SAINT, BISHOP OF WINCHESTER, CA. 908-984

Rumble, Alexander R., ed. Leaders of the Anglo-Saxon Church: From Bede to Stigand. 2012. (Publns Manchester Centre for Anglo-Saxon Studies: Volume 11). (Illus.). 216p. 95.00 ***(978-1-84383-700-8(5),*** Boydell Press) Boydell & Brewer, Ltd. GBR. Dist: Boydell & Brewer, Inc.

AFAN LANGUAGE

see Oromo Language

AFARA

see Limba

AFDC PROGRAMS

see Aid to Families with Dependent Children Programs

AFFECT (PSYCHOLOGY)

see also Emotions

Affect & Emotion in Human-Computer Interaction. 2008. (Lecture Notes in Computer Science / Information Systems & Applications, incl. Internet/Web, & HCI Ser.). spiral bd. 59.95 *(978-3-540-85098-4(8))* Springer.

Alsop, Steve. Beyond Cartesian Dualism. 2009. (Science & Technology Education Library). pap. 52.00 *(978-1-4020-5709-0(1))* Springer.

Biehl, Bobb. Why You Do What You Do. 2008. (ENG.). 192p. 20.00 *(978-0-9765040-6-1(5))* Aylen Publishing.

Bociurkiw, Marusya. Feeling Canadian: Television, Nationalism, & Affect. 2010. (Film & Media Studies). 196p. (C). pap. 32.95 *(978-1-55458-268-6(7))* Wilfrid Laurier Univ. Pr. CAN. Dist: Univ. of Toronto Pr.

Castiglia, Christopher. Interior States: Institutional Consciousness & the Inner Life of Democracy in the Antebellum United States. 2008. (New Americanists Ser.). (ENG.). 400p. (C). pap. 26.95 *(978-0-8223-4267-0(7))*; (Illus.). 94.95 *(978-0-8223-4244-1(8))* Duke Univ. Pr.

Catherall, Donald Roy. Emotional Safety: Viewing Couples Through the Lens of Affect. annot. ed. 2006. (Illus.). 282p. per. 42.50 *(978-0-415-95451-8(7))* Routledge.

Clough, Patricia Ticineto & Halley, Jean, eds. The Affective Turn: Theorizing the Social. 2007. (ENG.). 328p. (C). 89.95 *(978-0-8223-3911-3(0))*; per. 24.95 *(978-0-8223-3925-0(0))* Duke Univ. Pr.

Coan, James A. & Allen, John J. B., eds. Handbook of Emotion Elicitation & Assessment. 2007. (Series in Affective Science Ser.). (ENG., Illus.). 504p. 98.50 *(978-0-19-516915-7(8))* Oxford Univ. Pr., Inc.

Cram101 Textbook Reviews & Cram101 Textbook Reviews. Outlines & Highlights for Handbook of Affect & Social Cognition by Joseph P Forgas. 2011. 92p. pap. 27.95 ***(978-1-61830-529-9(8))*** Cram101 Inc.

Davidson, Richard J., et al, eds. Handbook of Affective Sciences. 2009. (ENG.). 1224p. pap. 89.99 *(978-0-19-537700-2(1))* Oxford Univ. Pr., Inc.

Eder, Andreas. B. & De Houwer Staff. Distinctiveness of Affective Processing. Hommel, Bernhard, ed. 2007. (Special Issues of Cognition & Emotion Ser.). (ENG., Illus.). 236p. 80.00 *(978-1-84169-814-4(8),* Psychology Press) Taylor & Francis Group GBR. Dist: Taylor & Francis Group.

Forgas, Joseph P., ed. Affect in Social Thinking & Behavior. 2006. (Frontiers of Social Psychology Ser.). (ENG., Illus.). 360p. 73.95 *(978-1-84169-454-2(1),* Psychology Press) Taylor & Francis Group GBR. Dist: Taylor & Francis Group.

Forgas, Joseph P. & Fitness, Julie, eds. Social Relationships: Cognitive, Affective & Motivational Processes. 2008. (Sydney Symposium of Social Psychology Ser.: Vol. 10). (ENG., Illus.). 368p. 89.95 *(978-1-84169-715-4(X),* Psychology Press) Taylor & Francis Group GBR. Dist: Taylor & Francis Group.

Garfield, David A. S. Unbearable Affect. 2nd ed. 2009. 224p. pap. 43.95 *(978-1-85575-547-5(5))* Karnac Bks. GBR. Dist: Stylus Publishing, LLC.

Gregg, Melissa & Seigworth, Gregory J., eds. The Affect Theory Reader. 2010. (ENG., Illus.). 416p. 89.95 *(978-0-8223-4758-3(X))*; pap. 24.95 *(978-0-8223-4776-7(8))* Duke Univ. Pr.

Heise, David R. Expressive Order: Confirming Sentiments in Social Actions. 2010. (ENG., Illus.). xiv, 164p. pap. 84.95 *(978-1-4419-4256-2(4),* 1441942564) Springer.

Hughes, Daniel A. Attachment-Focused Parenting: Effective Strategies to Care for Children. 2009. (ENG.). 272p. 29.95 *(978-0-393-70555-3(2),* 70555) Norton, W. W. & Co., Inc.

Humphrey, Ronald H. Affect & Emotion, New Directions in Management: Theory & Research. 2008. (Research in Management Ser.). 228p. (C). *(978-1-59311-960-7(7))*; pap. *(978-1-59311-959-1(3))* Information Age Publishing, Inc.

Karatzogianni, Athina & Kuntsman, Adi, eds. Digital Cultures & the Politics of Emotion: Feelings, Affect & Technological Change. 2012. (ENG., Illus.). 288p. 85.00 ***(978-0-230-29658-9(0))*** Palgrave Macmillan.

Khasnabish, Ashmita. Humanitarian Identity & the Political Sublime: Intervention of a Postcolonial Feminist. 2009. (ENG.). 190p. 62.99 *(978-0-7391-2292-1(4))* Lexington Bks.

LaMuth, John E. Challenges to World Peace: A Global Solution. 2009. (Illus.). 440p. pap. 28.95 *(978-1-929649-32-7(0),* Reference Bks. of America) Fairhaven Bk. Pubs.

Liljeström, Marianne & Paasonen, Susanna, eds. Working with Affect in Feminist Readings. 2012. (ENG.). 216p. (C). pap. 42.95 ***(978-0-415-52890-0(9))*** Routledge.

Liljeström, Marianne & Paasonen, Susanna, eds. Working with Affect in Feminist Readings: Disturbing Differences. 2010. (Transformations Ser.). (ENG.). 216p. (C). 160.00 *(978-0-415-48139-7(2))* Routledge.

MacKinnon, Neil J. & Heise, David R. Self, Identity, & Social Institutions. 2010. (ENG.). 278p. 89.00 *(978-0-230-62179-4(1))* Palgrave Macmillan.

Maharg, Paul & Maughan, Caroline. Affect & Legal Education: Emotion in Learning & Teaching the Law. 2011. (Emerging Legal Education Ser.). (Illus.). 338p. 134.95 ***(978-1-4094-1026-3(9))*** Ashgate Publishing Co.

Mannix, Elizabeth A. & Neale, Margaret Ann, eds. Affect & Groups. 2007. (Illus.). 364p. 134.95 *(978-0-7623-1413-3(3))* Emerald Group Publishing Ltd. GBR. Dist: Turpin Distribution Services Ltd.

Ouwerkerk, Martin, et al, eds. Sensing Emotions in Context: The impact of context on behavioral & physiological experience Measurements. 2010. (Philips Research Book Ser.). (ENG., Illus.). iv, 156p. 129.00 *(978-90-481-3257-7(6),* 9048132576) Springer.

Rottenberg, Jonathan & Johnson, Sheri L. Emotion & Psychopathology: Bridging Affective & Clinical Science. 2007. (Illus.). 336p. 49.95 *(978-1-59147-786-0(7))* American Psychological Assn.

Sander, David & Scherer, Klaus, eds. Oxford Companion to Emotion & the Affective Sciences. 2009. (Series in Affective Science Ser.). (ENG., Illus.). 408p. 98.50 *(978-0-19-856963-3(7))* Oxford Univ. Pr., Inc.

Schore, Allan & Schore, Judith Rothman. Reader's Guide to Affect Regulation & Neurobiology. 2008. 272p. 39.95 *(978-0-393-70480-8(7))* Norton, W. W. & Co., Inc.

Stewart, Charles T. Dire Emotions & Lethal Behaviors: Eclipse of the Life Instinct. 2007. (ENG., Illus.). 280p. (C). 110.00 *(978-0-415-40877-6(6))*; per. 42.50 *(978-0-415-40878-3(4))* Routledge.

Thiele, Leslie. The Heart of Judgment: Practical Wisdom, Neuroscience, & Narrative. 2006. (ENG., Illus.). 334p. 104.00 *(978-0-521-86444-2(5))* Cambridge Univ. Pr.

Thiele, Leslie Paul. The Heart of Judgment: Practical Wisdom, Neuroscience, & Narrative. 2010. (ENG.). 334p. pap. 65.00 *(978-0-521-24891-4(4))* Cambridge Univ. Pr.

Tomkins, Silvan S. Affect Imagery Consciousness: The Complete Edition. 2008. (C). 175.00 *(978-0-8261-4408-9(X))*; (Illus.). 1226p. 100.00 *(978-0-8261-4406-5(3))*; (Illus.). 614p. 100.00 *(978-0-8261-4404-1(7))* Springer Publishing Co., Inc.

Tracy, Jessica L., et al, eds. The Self-Conscious Emotions: Theory & Research. 2007. (ENG., Illus.). 493p. 65.00 *(978-1-59385-486-7(2))* Guilford Pubns., Inc.

West, Marcus. Feeling, Being, & the Sense of Self: A New Perspective on Identity, Affect, & Narcissistic Disorders. 2007. 280p. per. 43.95 *(978-1-85575-412-6(6))* Karnac Bks. GBR. Dist: Stylus Publishing, LLC.

Wilson, Elizabeth A. Affect & Artificial Intelligence. 2010. (In Vivo Ser.). (ENG., Illus.). 200p. (C). 60.00 *(978-0-295-99051-4(1))*; pap. 25.00 *(978-0-295-99047-7(3))* Univ. of Washington Pr.

AFFECTION

see Friendship; Kindness; Love

AFFECTIVE DISORDERS

see also Depression, Mental; Manic-Depressive Illness; Seasonal Affective Disorder

Amador, Xavier & Brondolo, Elizabeth. Break the Bipolar Cycle: A Day-by-Day Guide to Living with Bipolar Disorder. 2007. (ENG., Illus.). 304p. per. 16.95 *(978-0-07-148153-3(2),* 0071481532) McGraw-Hill Cos., The.

Anders, Silke, et al. Understanding Emotions. 2006. (Progress in Brain Research Ser.: Vol. 156). (ENG., Illus.). 522p. 268.00 *(978-0-444-52182-8(8),* Elsevier Science) Elsevier Science & Technology Bks.

Barlow, David H., et al. Unified Protocol for Transdiagnostic Treatment of Emotional Disorders: Therapist Guide, 1 vol. 2010. (Treatments That Work Ser.). (ENG.). 176p. pap. 39.95 *(978-0-19-977266-7(5))* Oxford Univ. Pr., Inc.

—Unified Protocol for Transdiagnostic Treatment of Emotional Disorders: Workbook, 1 vol. 2010. (Treatments That Work Ser.). (ENG., Illus.). 224p. pap. 29.95 *(978-0-19-977267-4(3))* Oxford Univ. Pr., Inc.

Borchard, Therese J. Beyond Blue: Surviving Depression & Anxiety & Making the Most of Bad Genes. lt. ed. 2010. (ENG.). 406p. 31.95 *(978-1-4104-2559-1(2))* Thorndike Pr.

Breggin, Peter. Medication Madness: The Role of Psychiatric Drugs in Cases of Violence, Suicide, & Crime. 2009. (ENG.). 400p. pap. 18.99 *(978-0-312-56550-3(X),* St. Martin's Griffin) St. Martin's Pr.

Coetzer, Rudi. Anxiety & Mood Disorders Following Traumatic Brain Injury: Clinical Assessment & Psychotherapy. 2010. 180p. pap. 30.95 *(978-1-85575-647-2(1))* Karnac Bks. GBR. Dist: Stylus Publishing, LLC.

Cram101 Textbook Reviews & Cram101 Textbook Reviews. Outlines & Highlights for Depression & Bipolar Disorder by Stephen M Stahl, Isbn: 9780521714129 0521714125. 2011. 104p. pap. 28.95 ***(978-1-61654-724-0(3))*** Cram101 Inc.

Czerbska, Martina T. Psychoneuroendocrinology Research Trends. 2007. 140.00 *(978-1-60021-665-7(X))* Nova Science Pubs., Inc.

Daley, Dennis C. Addiction & Mood Disorders: A Guide for Clients & Families. 2006. (ENG., Illus.). 232p. per. 23.95 *(978-0-19-530628-6(7))* Oxford Univ. Pr., Inc.

DeGangi, Georgia A. The Dysregulated Adult: Integrated Treatment Approaches. 2012. (Practical Resources for the Mental Health Professional Ser.). (ENG.). 518p. pap. 59.95 ***(978-0-12-385011-9(8),*** Academic Pr.) Elsevier Science & Technology Bks.

Dodds, Mary. Schizoaffective: A Happier & Healthier Life. 2007. 80p. per. 16.95 *(978-1-4241-9474-2(1))* PublishAmerica, Inc.

Edelman, Eva. Natural Healing for Bipolar Disorder: A Compendium of Nutritional Approaches. 2009. (Illus.). 392p. pap. 39.95 *(978-0-9650976-0-4(9))* Borage Bks.

Ghaemi, Nassir. A First-Rate Madness: Uncovering the Links Between Leadership & Mental Illness. 2011. (Playaway Adult Nonfiction Ser.). (ENG.). 59.99 ***(978-1-4551-2527-2(X))*** Blackstone Audio, Inc.

—A First-Rate Madness: Uncovering the Links Between Leadership & Mental Illness. (ENG.). 352p. (gr. 12). 2012. pap. 16.00 ***(978-0-14-312133-6(2),*** Penguin (Non-Classics)) 2011. 27.95 *(978-1-59420-295-7(8),* Penguin Pr. HC, The) Penguin Group (USA) Inc.

Ghaemi, S. Nassir. Mood Disorders: A Practical Guide. 2nd rev. ed. 2007. (Practical Guides in Psychiatry Ser.). (ENG., Illus.). 320p. per. 54.99 *(978-0-7817-6763-7(6))* Lippincott Williams & Wilkins.

Gould, Todd D., ed. Mood & Anxiety Related Phenotypes in Mice: Characterization Using Behavioral Tests, Volume II, 2 vols. 2011. (Neuromethods Ser.). (ENG., Illus.). xiii, 382p. 139.00 ***(978-1-61779-312-7(4),*** 1617793124) Humana Pr.

Hall, Will. Harm Reduction Guide to Coming off Psychiatric Drugs. 2007. (Illus.). 40p. 5.00 *(978-0-9800709-2-7(9),* Icarus Project, The.

Hart, Carol. Secrets of Serotonin: The Natural Hormone That Curbs Food & Alcohol Cravings, Reduces Pain, & Elevates Your Mood. rev. ed. 2008. (ENG., Illus.). 288p. pap. 14.99 *(978-0-312-37512-6(3),* St. Martin's Griffin) St. Martin's Pr.

Hirschfeld, Robert M.A. Advanced Mood Disorder Questionnaire (HA-MDQ) 2008. 48p. pap. 30.95 *(978-0-7637-6307-7(1))* Jones & Bartlett Learning, LLC.

Ingram, Rick E. & Price, Joseph M., eds. Vulnerability to Psychopathology, Second Edition: Risk across the Lifespan. 2nd ed. (ENG.). 524p. 2010. pap. 40.00 *(978-1-60918-148-2(4))* 2009. (Illus.). 65.00 *(978-1-60623-347-4(5))* Guilford Pubns., Inc.

Johnson, Merri Lisa & Mintz, Susannah B. On the Literary Nonfiction of Nancy Mairs: A Critical Anthology. 2011. (Critical Studies in Gender, Sexuality, & Culture Ser.). (ENG., Illus.). 240p. 85.00 *(978-0-230-11370-1(2))* Palgrave Macmillan.

Kaschka, W. P., ed. Perspectives in Affective Disorders: International Symposium '25 Years Weissenau Depression Unit', Weissenau, Germany, September 14-15, 2001, Vol. 21. (Advances in Biological Psychiatry Ser.: Vol. 21). (Illus.). *(978-3-8055-7439-6(8))* Karger, S. AG.

Laidlaw, Ken & Knight, Bob, eds. Handbook of Emotional Disorders in Later Life: Assessment & Treatment. 2008. (ENG., Illus.). 352p. pap. 69.95 *(978-0-19-856945-9(9))* Oxford Univ. Pr., Inc.

Lane, Andrew M. Mood & Human Performance: Conceptual, Measurement, & Applied Issues. 2006. (Illus.). 334p. 89.00 *(978-1-60021-269-7(7))* Nova Science Pubs., Inc.

Larsen, Stephen. The Neurofeedback Solution. 2012. 392p. pap. 19.95 ***(978-1-59477-366-2(1))*** Inner Traditions International, Ltd.

Loue, Sana, et al. Diversity Issues in the Diagnosis, Treatment, & Research of Mood Disorders. 2007. (ENG., Illus.). 352p. (C). 69.95 *(978-0-19-530818-1(2))* Oxford Univ. Pr., Inc.

Marneros, Andreas & Akiskal, Hagop, eds. The Overlap of Affective & Schizophrenic Spectra. 2006. (ENG., Illus.). 312p. 140.00 *(978-0-521-85858-8(5))* Cambridge Univ. Pr.

Marneros, Andreas & Akiskal, Hagop S., eds. The Overlap of Affective & Schizophrenic Spectra. 2009. (ENG., Illus.). 312p. pap. 58.00 *(978-0-521-10871-3(3))* Cambridge Univ. Pr.

McDonald, James J., Jr. Mental & Emotional Injuries in Employment Litigation, 1998 Supplement. 219p. pap. 55.00 *(978-1-57018-117-7(9),* 1117-PR8) BNA Bks.

McIntyre, Roger S. & Konarski, Jakub Z., eds. Psychiatric & Metabolic Disorders: Research Synthesis & Clinical Translation. 2008. (Illus.). 212p. 89.00 *(978-1-60021-842-2(3))* Nova Science Pubs., Inc.

Mohr, David. The Stress & Mood Management Program for Individuals with Multiple Sclerosis: Workbook, 1 vol. 2010. (Treatments that Work Ser.). (ENG., Illus.). 240p. pap. 32.99 *(978-0-19-536889-5(4))* Oxford Univ. Pr., Inc.

Mooney, Carla. Mood Disorders. 2010. (Compact Research Ser.). (YA). (gr. 7-12). 26.95 *(978-1-60152-119-4(7))* ReferencePoint Pr., Inc.

Moustafa. Depression: The Silent Screaming. 2009. 288p. pap. 21.95 *(978-1-935118-77-0(3))* Bellissima Publishing, LLC.

Nydegger, Rudy. Understanding & Treating Depression: Ways to Find Hope & Help, 1 vol. 2008. (Abnormal Psychology Ser.). (Illus.). 240p. 39.95 *(978-0-275-99856-1(8),* C9856, Praeger Pubs.) Greenwood Publishing Group, Inc.

Phillips-Goodnight, Dee. My Silent Scream: Finding Hope & Grace to Endure: Inside a Mother's Struggle to Raise a Child with OCD, ADHD, & Asperger's Syndrome. 2011. (ENG., Illus.). 148p. pap. 10.99 ***(978-1-936314-54-6(1))*** Word & Spirit Resources, LLC.

Postolache, Teodor T. & Merrick, Joav, eds. Environment, Mood Disorders & Suicide. 2010. (Health & Human Development (Joav Merrick); Ser.). 175.00 *(978-1-61668-505-8(0))* Nova Science Pubs., Inc.

Putman III, H. Paul. Rollercoaster: Finding & Treating Bipolar & Other Unstable Mood Disorders. 2008. 128p. pap. 12.50 *(978-1-4357-4731-9(3))* Lulu Enterprises Inc.

Radden, Jennifer. Moody Minds Distempered: Essays on Melancholy & Depression. 2009. (ENG.). 240p. 65.00 *(978-0-19-533828-7(6))* Oxford Univ. Pr., Inc.

Richard, Lucas. The Psychotic Wavelength: A Psychoanalytic Perspective for Psychiatry. 2009. (New Library of Psychoanalysis Ser.). (ENG., Illus.). 360p. (C). 110.00 *(978-0-415-48468-8(5));* pap. 38.95 *(978-0-415-48469-5(3))* Routledge.

Ritsner, Michael S. Brain Protection in Schizophrenia, Mood & Cognitive Disorders. 2010. (ENG., Illus.). xviii, 997p. 269.00 *(978-90-481-8552-8(1),* 9048185521) Springer.

Ritsner, Michael S. & Awad, A. George, eds. Quality of Life Impairment in Schizophrenia, Mood & Anxiety Disorders: New Perspectives on Research & Treatment. 2010. (ENG.). xiv, 388p. pap. 219.00 *(978-90-481-7443-0(0),* 9048174430) Springer.

Rothschild, Anthony J. Clinical Manual for the Diagnosis & Treatment of Psychotic Depression. 2008. 64.00 *(978-1-58562-292-4(3))* American Psychiatric Publishing, Inc.

Rush, A. John, ed. Mood Disorders Vol. 25: Systematic Medication Management. (Modern Problems of Pharmacopsychiatry Ser.: Vol. 25, 1996). (Illus.). *(978-3-8055-6223-2(3))* Karger, S. AG.

Sabotka, Cynthia M. Life Is Like a Line: A Memoir of Moods, Medication & Mania. 2008. 328p. *(978-0-9797792-0-6(0))* Silver Lining Publishing LLC.

Schou, Mogens. Lithium Treatment of Mood Disorders: A Practical Guide. 6th rev. ed. (Illus.). *(978-3-8055-7764-9(8))* Karger, S. AG.

Shawn, Allen. Twin: A Memoir. 2010. (ENG.). 240p. (gr. 12). 25.95 *(978-0-670-02237-3(3),* Viking Adult) Penguin Group (USA) Inc.

—Twin: A Memoir. l.t. ed. 2011. 315p. 31.99 *(978-1-4104-3616-0(0))* Thorndike Pr.

Shorter, Edward. Before Prozac: The Troubled History of Mood Disorders in Psychiatry. 2008. (ENG.). 336p. 31.99 *(978-0-19-536874-1(6))* Oxford Univ. Pr., Inc.

Shorter, Edward & Swartz, Conrad M. Psychotic Depression. 2007. (ENG.). 344p. 107.00 *(978-0-521-87822-7(5))* Cambridge Univ. Pr.

Stahl, Stephen & Stahl, Stephen M. Mood Stabilizers. 2009. (Stahl's Illustrated Ser.). (ENG., Illus.). 176p. pap. 41.99 *(978-0-521-75849-9(1))* Cambridge Univ. Pr.

Stahl, Stephen M. Antipsychotics & Mood Stabilizers. 3rd ed. 2008. (Essential Psychopharmacology Ser.). (ENG., Illus.). 248p. (C). pap. 52.00 *(978-0-521-71413-6(3))* Cambridge Univ. Pr.

—Depression & Bipolar Disorder: Stahl's Essential Psychopharmacology. 3rd ed. 2008. (Essential Psychopharmacology Ser.). (ENG., Illus.). 312p. (C). pap. 57.00 *(978-0-521-71412-9(5))* Cambridge Univ. Pr.

Stahl, Stephen M. & Stahl, S. M. The Prescriber's Guide, Antipsychotics & Mood Stabilizers. 3rd ed. 2009. (ENG.). 148p. pap. 36.99 *(978-0-521-75900-7(5))* Cambridge Univ. Pr.

Steffgen, Georges & Gollwitzer, Mario, eds. Emotions & Aggressive Behavior. 2007. (Illus.). 230p. 44.00 *(978-0-88937-343-3(4))* Hogrefe Publishing.

Taylor, Michael Alan & Fink, Max. Melancholia: The Diagnosis, Pathophysiology & Treatment of Depressive Illness. 2010. (ENG., Illus.). 564p. pap. 98.00 *(978-0-521-13124-7(3))* Cambridge Univ. Pr.

Thase, Michael E. & Lang, Susan S. Beating the Blues: New Approaches to Overcoming Dysthymia & Chronic Mild Depression. 2006. (Illus.). 192p. reprint ed. 23.00 *(978-1-4223-5757-6(0))* DIANE Publishing Co.

Thoele, Sue Patton. The Mindful Woman: Gentle Practices for Restoring Calm, Finding Balance & Opening Your Heart. 2008. (ENG.). 224p. per. 15.95 *(978-1-57224-542-6(5))* New Harbinger Pubns.

Westwood, S. A Moment Gone: Body dysmorphic Disorder. 2009. 156p. pap. *(978-1-84747-892-4(1))* Chipmunkapublishing.

Wilson, Daniel R., et al. The Evolutionary Epidemiology of Mania & Depression: A Theoretical & Empirical Interpretation of Mood Disorders. (Illus.). 412p. 129.95 *(978-0-7734-5209-1(5))* Mellen, Edwin Pr., The.

Wirz-Justice, A., et al. Chronotherapeutics for Affective Disorders: A Clinician's Manual for Light & Wake Therapy. 2009. (Illus.). 116p. pap. *(978-3-8055-9120-1(9))* Karger, S. AG.

Yip, Kam-Shing, ed. Schizoaffective Disorders: International Perspectives on Understanding, Intervention & Rehabilitation. 2008. 79.00 *(978-1-60456-948-3(4))* Nova Science Pubs., Inc.

Zittel, Kimberley. Postpartum Mood Disorders: A Guide for Medical, Mental Health, & Other Support Providers. 2010. *(978-0-87101-399-6(1))* National Assn. of Social Workers/NASW Pr.

AFFECTIVE DISORDERS IN CHILDREN

Cram101 Textbook Reviews & Cram101 Textbook Reviews. Outlines & Highlights for Treatment of Childhood Disorders by Eric Mash, Isbn: 9781572309210. 2011. 528p. pap. 38.95 ***(978-1-61461-094-6(0))*** Cram101 Inc.

Eagle, Rita. Help Him Make You Smile: The Development of Intersubjectivity in the Atypical Child. 2007. (Psychological Issues Ser.). (ENG.). 336p. 93.50 *(978-0-7657-0496-2(X));* pap. 41.99 *(978-0-7657-0497-9(8))* Rowman & Littlefield Publishers, Inc. (Aronson, Jason).

Kauffman, James M. & Landrum, Timothy J. Cases in Emotional & Behavioral Disorders of Children & Youth. 3rd rev. ed. 2012. (ENG.). 112p. (C). pap. 20.80 ***(978-0-13-268466-8(7),*** Prentice Hall) Prentice Hall PTR.

Papolos, Demitri & Papolos, Janice. The Bipolar Child: The Definitive & Reassuring Guide to Childhood's Most Misunderstood Disorder. 3rd ed. 2007. (ENG.). 496p. pap. 16.99 *(978-0-7679-2860-1(1))* Broadway Bks.

Pavuluri, Mani. What Works for Bipolar Kids: Help & Hope for Parents. 2008. (ENG.). 274p. pap. 15.95 *(978-1-59385-407-2(2));* (Illus.). (gr. -1-8). 40.00 *(978-1-59385-706-6(3))* Guilford Pubns., Inc.

AFFENPINSCHER

Cushman, Jerome. Affenpinscher. 2006. (Comprehensive Owners Guide Ser.). (ENG., Illus.). 155p. 19.95 *(978-1-59378-335-8(3))* Kennel Club Bks.

Linzy, Jan & Pata, Janae. German Pinscher Champions, 2001-2006. 2007. (Illus.). 145p. spiral bd. 46.95 *(978-1-55893-227-2(5))* Camino E.E. & Bk. Co.

AFFERENT PATHWAYS

see also Auditory Pathways; Visual Pathways

Jones, Edward G., et al. The Human Pain System: Experimental & Clinical Perspectives. 2010. (ENG., Illus.). 648p. 140.00 *(978-0-521-11452-3(7))* Cambridge Univ. Pr.

Lacquaniti, F. & Viviani, P., eds. Neural Bases of Motor Behaviour. 2010. (NATO Science Series D: (closed) Ser.). 356p. pap. 319.00 *(978-90-481-4695-6(X),* 904814695X) Springer.

Nuez, A. & Malmierca, E. Corticofugal Modulation of Sensory Information. 2007. (Advances in Anatomy, Embryology & Cell Biology Ser.). (Illus.). 74p. per. 149.00 *(978-3-540-36769-7(1),* 3540367691) Springer.

Singh, Bhopendra, et al. Detection & Classification of Hmv. 2011. 184p. pap. ***(978-3-8454-0797-5(2))*** Lambert Academic Publishing.

AFFINE GEOMETRY

see Geometry, Affine

AFFINITY, CHEMICAL

see Chemical Affinity

AFFIRMATIONS

Here are entered works on positive statements repeated to oneself in order to promote a desired attitude or behavior.

Affirmations from the Heart of God. 2007. Orig. Title: Affirmations from the Heart. 20.00 *(978-0-9793767-3-3(4))* SOFIA.

Allen, Marc. The Greatest Secret of All: Simple Steps to Abundance, Fulfillment, & a Life Well Lived. 2011. (ENG.). 128p. pap. 12.95 *(978-1-57731-963-4(X))* New World Library.

Banks, Mark M. A Song of Life, One Note at A Time: A Collection of Affirmations & Inspirational Quotes. 2011. 160p. pap. 9.99 ***(978-1-4567-5480-8(7))*** AuthorHouse.

Barnard, Tom. E-Couragement: Meditations for Leaders. 2008. (ENG.). 192p. pap. 14.99 *(978-0-8341-2358-8(4),* 083-412-3584) Beacon Hill Pr. of Kansas City.

Beckwith, Michael Bernard. 40 Day Mind Fast Soul Feast: A Guide to Soul Awakening & Inner Fulfillment. 2011. (ENG.). 176p. 12.95 ***(978-1-4019-3812-3(4))*** Hay Hse., Inc.

Branch, Susan. Drinks. (Illus.). 20p. pap. *(978-0-7683-2209-5(X))* CEDCO Publishing.

—Spring. (Illus.). 20p. pap. *(978-0-7683-2215-6(4))* CEDCO Publishing.

Brown, Vanessa Armstrong. Take It Personal: Reflecting on the Word of God, 1 vol. 2010. 128p. pap. 19.95 *(978-1-61582-849-4(4))* PublishAmerica, Inc.

Chickie-Wolfe, Louise A., ed. Lucky to Be a Teacher: Life-Changing Affirmations for Positive Classrooms. 2nd ed. 2009. 96p. pap. 24.95 *(978-1-4129-7262-8(0),* B72611P) Corwin Pr.

Day, Laura. The Circle: How the Power of a Single Wish Can Change Your Life. 2009. (ENG.). 192p. pap. 15.00 *(978-1-4391-1821-4(3),* Beyond Words/Atria Bks.) Atria Bks.

—The Circle: How the Power of a Single Wish Can Change Your Life. 2007. (ENG.). 160p. (gr. 12-18). 14.95 *(978-1-58542-598-3(2),* Tarcher) Penguin Group (USA) Inc.

Dean, Amy E. Morning Light: A Book of Meditations to Begin Your Day. 2011. (ENG.). 400p. pap. 14.95 *(978-1-61649-108-6(6))* Hazelden Publishing & Educational Services.

Dotson, Rev. Lewis. From Out of Chaos into the Light. 2010. 49p. pap. 14.51 *(978-0-557-39171-4(7))* Lulu Enterprises Inc.

Falikowski, Anthony. Higher Reality Therapy: Nine Pathways to Inner Peace. 2010. (ENG.). 400p. pap. 29.95 *(978-1-84694-257-0(8))* O Bks.,John Hunt.

Farber, Monte. Quantum Affirmations: The New Energy Science of Conscious Manifestation. 2012. (ENG.). 1p. pap. 16.95 ***(978-1-57863-514-6(4),*** Weiser Bks.) Red Wheel/Weiser.

Hansen, Mark Victor, et al. Chicken Soup for the Breast Cancer Survivor's Soul: Stories to Inspire, Support & Heal. 2006. (Chicken Soup for the Soul Ser.). (ENG., Illus.). 320p. pap. 14.95 *(978-0-7573-0521-4(0))* Health Communications, Inc.

Hay, Louise L. Experience Your Good Now! Learning to Use Affirmations. 2nd ed. 2010. (ENG.). 128p. 17.95 *(978-1-4019-2748-6(3))* Hay Hse., Inc.

—Letters to Louise: The Answers Are Within You (Updated Edition) 2011. (ENG.). 320p. pap. 12.95 *(978-1-4019-2727-1(0))* Hay Hse., Inc.

—The Present Moment: 365 Daily Affirmations. 2007. (ENG., Illus.). 384p. pap. 9.95 *(978-1-4019-1194-2(3))* Hay Hse., Inc.

Healing the Hurt Spirit: Daily Affirmations for People Who Have Lost a Loved One to Suicide. 2006. pap. 15.95 *(978-0-9778244-0-3(3))* St. Dymphna Press.

Hoffman, Jeffrey A. Living in Balance: 90 Meditations for Recovery from Addiction. 2011. (ENG.). 128p. pap. 7.95 *(978-1-61649-087-4(X))* Hazelden Publishing & Educational Services.

Hoolihan, Patricia. A Moment's Peace for Parents of Teens: 365 Rejuvenating Reflections. 2007. (ENG.). 384p. per. 9.95 *(978-1-57482-247-2(0))* Search Institute.

Inspiration House. Wish Book. 2010. 48p. pap. 20.45 *(978-1-4497-0840-5(4),* WestBow Pr.) Author Solutions, Inc.

Ivory, Stephanie Sampson. I Want to Be Like Me. 2008. 44p. pap. 18.49 *(978-1-4343-5792-2(9))* AuthorHouse.

James, N. A-Z of Positive Thinking. 80p. pap. *(978-0-340-73568-8(6),* Hodder & Stoughton) Hodder General Publishing Div.

Jay, Katie & Persing, Julia A. F. Small Bites: Daily Inspirations for Weight Loss Surgery Patients. 2007. 416p. per. 14.95 *(978-0-9772289-1-1(6))* Pink Sky, Inc.

Jinsei, Juna. Elevate Your Life: Achieve Success by Applying Positive Inspirational Affirmations. 2011. (ENG.). 415p. pap. 15.95 ***(978-1-4327-7990-0(7))*** Outskirts Pr., Inc.

Kroupa, Edward. Mind Healing: Affirmations to heal your mind & Soul. 2011. 52p. pap. 9.95 *(978-1-4502-8316-8(0))* iUniverse, Inc.

Leslie, Mary Ann. I AM Radiant: Beautiful affirmations to brighten your Day. 2007. (Illus.). 96p. 16.95 *(978-0-9779152-0-0(4))* I AM Manifest.

Logan, Jean. Unlocking the Power of Glyphs. 2009. 224p. spiral bd. *(978-1-60530-170-9(1))* Independent Pub.

Mastromarino, Diane. I Am Beautiful Affirmations for Women. 2007. 56p. 5.95 *(978-1-59842-200-9(6),* Blue Mountain Pr.) Blue Mountain Arts Inc.

Merritt, Daniel. A Sure Foundation: Eight Truths Affirming the Bible's Divine Inspiration. 2011. 228p. 33.95 ***(978-1-4627-0639-6(8));*** pap. 17.95 ***(978-1-4627-0637-2(1))*** Cross Bks. Publishing.

Miller, Brenda. Curiosity Expands Your Mind: A Resource Book for Truth Seekers. 2009. 164p. pap. 15.99 *(978-1-4251-8856-6(7))* Trafford Publishing.

Noel, Brook. Good Morning! 101 Positive Sticky Notes to Start the Day. 2010. (ENG.). 210p. pap. 8.99 *(978-1-4022-3923-6(8))* Sourcebooks, Inc.

—Good Morning: 365 Positive Ways to Start Your Day. 2008. (ENG.). 496p. pap. 18.95 *(978-1-4022-1224-6(0))* Sourcebooks, Inc.

Pringle, C. Edward. Message to a Friend: Secret Messages of Inner Healing. Date not set. 9.99 *(978-0-9711739-2-7(3))* JCI Productions.

Radmacher, Mary Anne. Courage Doesn't Always Roar. 2009. (ENG., Illus.). 96p. 14.95 *(978-1-57324-410-7(4),* Conari Pr.) Red Wheel/Weiser.

Reiter, Deanna, text. Dancing with Divinity: Positive Affirmations for Any Situation. 2007. (Illus.). 130p. pap. *(978-0-9800375-0-0(6))* Whistling Shade.

Richardson, Cheryl. My Daily Affirmations Cards: A 50-Card Deck. 2010. (ENG.). 50p. 15.95 *(978-1-4019-2751-6(3))* Hay Hse., Inc.

Rochelle, M. M. R S V P Journal: Recovery, Spirituality, Vision, Purpose. 2008. 124p. pap. 18.95 *(978-0-9787850-4-8(5))* Ambassador Pr.

Ross, Patricia A. & Armstrong, Scott Sharp. The Best Affirmations Handbook. 2009. (ENG.). pap. 14.00 *(978-1-60037-555-2(3))* Morgan James Publishing.

Rossman, Martin. The Worry Solution: Using Breakthrough Brain Science to Turn Stress & Anxiety into Confidence & Happiness. 2010. (ENG.). 256p. 23.99 *(978-0-307-71823-5(9))* Broadway Bks.

Spirit, In Nature. Affirmation Cards for Perfect Well-Being. 2008. (ENG.). 17.95 *(978-1-56589-238-5(0))* Crystal Clarity Pubs.

Staudt, Gail A. Nursing the Nurse-Affirmations. Date not set. (Illus.). 112p. *(978-0-9678555-1-6(9))* Staudt, Gail & Assocs., Inc.

Stein, Ben. The Eyes of Faith: How to Not Go Crazy - Thoughts to Bear in Mind to Get Through Even the Worst Days. 2009. (ENG.). 144p. pap. 9.95 *(978-1-4019-2552-9(9))* Hay Hse., Inc.

StrengthsQuest. 2006. (C). per. 35.00 *(978-1-59562-011-8(7))* Gallup Pr.

StrengthsQuest - Spanish Language Edition. 2006. (C). per. *(978-1-59562-013-2(3))* Gallup Pr.

Walker, David J. You Are Enough: Always Have Been... Always Will Be. 2007. 147p. per. 12.95 *(978-0-87516-826-5(4),* Devorss Pubns.) DeVorss & Co.

Yager, Jan. 365 Daily Affirmations for Happiness. 2011. (ENG.). 113p. 29.95 *(978-1-889262-58-1(7));* 118p. pap. 14.95 *(978-1-889262-59-8(5))* Hannacroix Creek Bks., Inc.

Yogananda, Paramhansa. Meditaciones Metafísicas: Oraciones, Afirmaciones y Visualizaciones Universales. rev. ed.Tr. of Metaphysical Meditations: Universal Prayers, Affirmations, & Visualizations. (SPA.). 170p. pap. 8.00 *(978-0-87612-048-4(6),* 1355) Self-Realization Fellowship Pubs.

AFFIRMATIVE ACTION PROGRAMS

see also Minorities—Employment

Anderson, E. The Imperative of Integration. 2010. (ENG.). 264p. (C). 29.95 *(978-0-691-13981-4(4))* Princeton Univ. Pr.

Anderson, Terry H. The Pursuit of Fairness: A History of Affirmative Action. 2007. (Illus.). 320p. reprint ed. 35.00 *(978-1-4223-6767-4(3))* DIANE Publishing Co.

Bonastia, Christopher. Knocking on the Door: The Federal Government's Attempt to Desegregate the Suburbs. 2008. (ENG.). 256p. (C). per. 27.95 *(978-0-691-13619-6(X))* Princeton Univ. Pr.

Boonin, David. Should Race Matter? Unusual Answers to the Usual Questions. 2011. (ENG.). 440p. (C). 99.00 ***(978-0-521-76086-7(0));*** pap. 34.99 ***(978-0-521-14980-8(0))*** Cambridge Univ. Pr.

Cargill, Jenny. Trick or Treat: Perspectives on Black Economic. 2010. (ENG.). 280p. pap. 24.00 *(978-1-77009-830-5(5))* Jacana Media ZAF. Dist: Independent Pubs. Group.

Cicalo, André. Urban Encounters: Affirmative Action & Black Identities in Brazil. 2012. (ENG., Illus.). 256p. 85.00 ***(978-0-230-33852-4(6))*** Palgrave Macmillan.

Civil Rights Services & Diversity Initiatives in the Coast Guard: Hearing Before the Subcommittee on Coast Guard & Maritime Transportation of the Committee on Transportation & Infrastructure, House of Representatives, One Hundred Eleventh Congress, First Session, April 1, 2009. 2009. (Illus.). xxv, 71p. *(978-0-16-084271-9(9),* 552-070-39836-8) United States Government Printing Office.

Cleveland, Darrell. When "Minorities Are Strongly Encouraged to Apply" Diversity & Affirmative Action in Higher Education. 2008. (Higher Ed: Questions about the Purpose(s) of Colleges & Universities Ser.). 336p. (C). 34.95 *(978-0-8204-7121-1(6))* Lang, Peter Publishing, Inc.

Connors, Paul. Affirmative Action. 2009. (At Issue Ser.). (ENG.). 128p. (gr. 10-12). 22.50 *(978-0-7377-4277-0(1));* No. 9. pap. 31.80 *(978-0-7377-4278-7(X))* Cengage Gale. (Greenhaven Pr., Inc.).

Cuttill, Lk. Locking Horns with the Federal Eeo. 2008. 56p. pap. 15.99 *(978-1-4363-8765-1(5))* Xlibris Corp.

Delton, Jennifer. Racial Integration in Corporate America, 1940-1990. 2009. (ENG.). 320p. 87.00 *(978-0-521-51509-2(2));* pap. 24.99 *(978-0-521-73080-8(5))* Cambridge Univ. Pr.

Deslippe, Dennis. Protesting Affirmative Action: The Struggle over Equality after the Civil Rights Revolution. 2012. (Reconfiguring American Political History Ser.). (ENG.). 296p. (gr. 17). 55.00 ***(978-1-4214-0358-8(7))*** Johns Hopkins Univ. Pr.

Djordjevich, Vera. Vault/MCCA Guide to Law Firm Diversity Programs, 2009 Edition: 4th Edition. 2008. 1344p. pap. 39.95 *(978-1-58131-607-0(0))* Vault.com.

Dobbin, Frank. Inventing Equal Opportunity. (ENG., Illus.). 360p. (C). 2011. pap. 24.95 *(978-0-691-14995-0(X))* 2009. 49.95 *(978-0-691-13743-8(9))* Princeton Univ. Pr.

Ensuring Diversity at the Senior Levels of the Federal Government & the U.S. Postal Service: Hearing Before the Subcommittee on Federal Workforce, Postal Service, & the District of Columbia of the Committee on Oversight & Government Reform, House of Representatives, One Hundred Tenth Congress, First Session, May 10, 2007. 2008. iv, 167p. *(978-0-16-080883-8(9),* 552-070-37429-9) United States Government Printing Office.

Featherman, David Lee, et al. The Next Twenty-five Years: Affirmative Action in Higher Education in the United States & South Africa. 2009. (ENG., Illus.). 416p. pap. 37.50 *(978-0-472-03377-5(8))* Univ. of Michigan Pr.

Federal Contractor Compliance: Hearing Before the Subcommittee on Economic Opportunity of the Committee on Veterans' Affairs, U.S. House of Representatives, One Hundred Eleventh Congress, First Session, May 14, 2009. 2009. iv, 56p. *(978-0-16-084350-1(2),* 552-070-39893-7) United States Government Printing Office.

Goldberg, David & Griffey, Trevor. Black Power at Work: Community Control, Affirmative Action, & the Construction Industry. 2010. 280p. pap. 24.95 *(978-0-8014-7431-6(0),* ILR Pr.) Cornell Univ. Pr.

Goldberg, David & Griffey, Trevor, eds. Black Power at Work: Community Control, Affirmative Action, & the Construction Industry. 2010. 280p. 65.00 *(978-0-8014-4658-0(9),* ILR Pr.) Cornell Univ. Pr.

Golland, David Hamilton. Constructing Affirmative Action: The Struggle for Equal Employment Opportunity. 2011. (Civil Rights & the Struggle for Black Equality in the Twentieth Century Ser.). (ENG., Illus.). 280p. 50.00 *(978-0-8131-2997-6(4))* Univ. Pr. of Kentucky.

Graham, Hugh Davis. Collision Course: The Strange Convergence of Affirmative Action & Immigration Policy in America. 2006. 246p. reprint ed. pap. 16.00 *(978-1-4223-5530-5(6))* DIANE Publishing Co.

Groschl, Stephan & Takagi, Junko. Diversity Quotas Diverse Perspectives: The Case of Gender. 2012. 154p. 114.95 ***(978-1-4094-3619-5(5),*** Gower Publishing Co., Ltd.) Ashgate Publishing, Ltd. GBR. Dist: Ashgate Publishing Co.

Hasan, Zoya & Nussbaum, Martha. Equalizing Access: Affirmative Action in Higher Education: India, US, & South Africa. 2012. (ENG., Illus.). 296p. 55.00 ***(978-0-19-807505-9(7))*** Oxford Univ. Pr., Inc.

Hill, Ann Maxwell & Zhou, Minglang, eds. Affirmative Action in China & the U. S. A Dialogue on Inequality & Minority Education. 2009. (Comparative & Developmental Education Ser.). (ENG.). 284p. 95.00 *(978-0-230-61235-8(0))* Palgrave Macmillan.

Johnson, John W. & Green, Robert P. Affirmative Action, 1 vol. 2009. (Historical Guides to Controversial Issues in America Ser.). 199p. 49.95 *(978-0-313-33814-4(0),* GR3814) Greenwood Publishing Group, Inc.

Jordaan, B., et al, eds. Understanding Broad-Based Black Economic Empowerment. 2010. 190p. pap. 17.50 *(978-0-7021-8187-0(0))* Gaunt, Inc.

Karr, Justin, ed. Affirmative Action. 2007. (Issues on Trial Ser.). (ENG., Illus.). 188p. (gr. 10-12). lib. bdg. 39.70 *(978-0-7377-3854-4(5),* Greenhaven Pr., Inc.) Cengage Gale.

Katznelson, Ira. When Affirmative Action Was White: An Untold History of Racial Inequality in Twentieth-Century America. 2006. (ENG.). 272p. pap. 16.95 *(978-0-393-32851-5(1)*, 32851) Norton, W. W. & Co., Inc.
Kennedy-Dubourdieu, Elaine, ed. Race & Inequality: World Perspectives on Affirmative Action. 2006. 214p. 120.00 *(978-0-7546-4839-0(7))* Ashgate Publishing Co.
King, Paul. Reflections on Affirmative Action in Construction. 2009. 292p. 25.99 *(978-1-4389-9565-5(2))*; 292p. pap. 15.99 *(978-1-4389-9564-9(4))*; (Illus.). xvii, 271p. E-Book *(978-1-4389-9566-3(0))* AuthorHouse.
Laird, Bob. The Case for Affirmative Action in University Admissions. 2006. (ENG.). 304p. 26.95 *(978-0-9720021-4-1(6))* Bay Tree Publishing.
Lapenson, Bruce P. Affirmative Action & the Meanings of Merit. 2009. (ENG.). 120p. pap. 20.99 *(978-0-7618-4347-4(7))* Univ. Pr. of America, Inc.
Lazin, Frederick A., et al. Higher Education & Equality of Opportunities: Cross-National Perspectives. 2010. (Illus.). xi, 355p. *(978-0-7391-4671-2(8))* Rowman & Littlefield Publishers, Inc.
Lazin/Jayaram/Evans. Higher Education & Equality of Opportunity: Cross-National Perspectives. 2010. (Studies in Public Policy Ser.). (ENG., Illus.). 346p. 80.00 *(978-0-7391-4669-9(6))* Rowman & Littlefield Publishers, Inc.
Leiter, William M. & Leiter, Samuel. Affirmative Action in Antidiscrimination Law & Policy: An Overview & Synthesis. 2nd ed. 2011. 464p. 85.00 *(978-1-4384-3513-5(4))* State Univ. of New York Pr.
—Affirmative Action in Antidiscrimination Law & Policy: An Overview & Synthesis, Second Edition. 2nd ed. 2011. 464p. pap. 29.95 *(978-1-4384-3514-5(2)*, Suny Pr.) State Univ. of New York Pr.
Lim, Nelson, et al. Planning for Diversity: Options & Recommendations for DoD Leaders. 2008. 130p. pap. 24.50 *(978-0-8330-4471-6(0)*, mg-743) RAND Corp., The.
Maclaury, Judson. To Advance Their Opportunities: Federal Policies Toward African American Workers from World War I to the Civil Rights Act Of 1964. 2008. (ENG.). 313p. pap. 24.95 *(978-0-9797292-3-2(8))* Univ. of Tennessee, Libraries of Newfound Pr.
Marin, Patricia & Horn, Catherine L., eds. Realizing Bakke's Legacy: Affirmative Action, Equal Opportunity, & Access to Higher Education. 2008. (Illus.). 278p. (C). 75.00 *(978-1-57922-267-3(6))*; pap. 29.95 *(978-1-57922-268-0(4))* Stylus Publishing, LLC.
Mbabane, Loyiso (Loy). Broad-Based Black Economic Empowerment in South Afric. 2011. 192p. pap. ***(978-3-8433-8019-5(8))*** Lambert Academic Publishing.
Niell, Russell K. Wounds That Will Not Heal: Affirmative Action & Our Continuing Racial Divide. 2012. (ENG.). 456p. 29.95 *(978-1-59403-582-1(2))* Encounter Bks.
Ondaatje, Michael. Black Conservative Intellectuals in Modern America. 232p. (C). 2012. pap. 22.50 ***(978-0-8122-2204-3(0))*** 2009. 34.95 *(978-0-8122-4206-5(8))* Univ. of Pennsylvania Pr.
Perry, Barbara A. The Michigan Affirmative Action Cases. 2007. (Landmark Law Cases & American Society Ser.). 210p. 35.00 *(978-0-7006-1548-3(2))*; per. 16.95 *(978-0-7006-1549-0(0))* Univ. Pr. of Kansas.
Richardson, Robin. Holding Together: Equalities, Difference & Cohesion. 2009. (Illus.). 112p. pap. 28.00 *(978-1-85856-453-1(0))* Trentham Bks. Ltd. GBR. Dist: Stylus Publishing, LLC.
Robles, Rowena. Asian Americans & the Shifting Politics of Race: The Dismantling of Affirmative Action at an Elite Public High School. 2009. 194p. 39.95 *(978-0-415-80575-9(9))* Routledge.
Sabbagh, Daniel. Equality & Transparency: A Strategic Perspective on Affirmative Action in American Law. 2007. (Sciences Po Series in International Relations & Political Economy Ser.). (ENG.). 268p. 95.00 *(978-1-4039-6382-6(7))* Palgrave Macmillan.
Schneider, Ann Christin. Affirmative Action in Higher Education. 2009. 124p. pap. *(978-3-639-11839-1(1))* VDM Verlag Dr. Mueller e.K.
Schneider, Susanne. Broad-based Black Economic Empowerment in der Republik Südafrika. 2008. (Schriften zum Arbeitsrecht und Wirtschaftsrecht Ser.). 174p. pap. 56.95 *(978-3-631-57310-5(3))* Lang, Peter GmbH, Europaischer Verlag der Wissenschaften DEU. Dist: Lang, Peter.
Smedley, Brian & Jenkins, Alan, eds. All Things Being Equal: Instigating Opportunity in an Inequitable Time. 2007. (ENG., Illus.). 246p. 24.95 *(978-1-59558-210-2(X))* New Pr., The.
Status of the Coas: Guard Civil Rights Programs & Diversity Initiatives: Hearing Before the Subcommittee on Coast Guard & Maritime Transportation of the Committee on Transportation & Infrastructure, House of Representatives, One Hundred Eleventh Congress, Second Session, April 27, 2010. 2010. (Illus.). xvi, 86p. *(978-0-16-086673-9(1)*, 552-070-41651-0) United States Government Printing Office.
Sterba, James P. Affirmative Action for the Future. 2009. (Illus.). 152p. 52.50 *(978-0-8014-4607-8(4))*; pap. 17.95 *(978-0-8014-7591-7(0))* Cornell Univ. Pr.
Sweet, Martin J. Merely Judgment: Ignoring, Evading, & Trumping the Supreme Court. 2010. (Constitutionalism & Democracy Ser.). (ENG., Illus.). 240p. (gr. 17). 35.00 *(978-0-8139-3058-9(8))* Univ. Pr. of Virginia.
Thorat, Sukhadeo & Kumar, Narender, eds. B. R. Ambedkar: Perspectives on Social Exclusion & Inclusive Policies. 2010. (ENG.). 436p. 31.95 *(978-0-19-806350-6(4))* Oxford Univ. Pr., Inc.
Transit Cooperative Research Program Staff, et al, contrib. by. Racial & Gender Diversity in State DOTs & Transit Agencies: A Benchmark Scoping. 2007. (Illus.). 51p. 36.00 *(978-0-309-09890-8(4))* Transportation Research Board.
Truesdell, William H. Secrets of Affirmative Action Compliance: 9th Edition. 9th rev. ed. 2010. (ENG.). 500p. pap. 125.00 *(978-1-879876-51-4(5))* Management Advantage, Inc., The.
Ward, Kevin & Taylor, Richard. Adult Education & the Working Class: Education for the Missing Millions. 2012. (Routledge Library Editions: Education Ser.). (ENG.). 210p. 115.00 ***(978-0-415-68445-3(5))*** Routledge.
World Bank Publications Staff, et al. Measuring Inequality of Opportunities in Latin America & the Caribbean. 2008. (Latin American Development Forum Ser.). (ENG., Illus.). 180p. 80.00 *(978-0-8213-7747-5(7)*, 9780821377475) World Bank Pubns.
Zamudio, Margaret, et al. Critical Race Theory Matters: Education & Ideology. 2010. (ENG.). 192p. 125.00 *(978-0-415-99673-0(2))*; pap. 31.95 *(978-0-415-99674-7(0))* Routledge.
Zhou, Minglang & Hill, Ann Maxwell, eds. Affirmative Action in China & the U. S. A Dialogue on Inequality & Minority Education. 2010. (Comparative & Developmental Education Ser.). (ENG.). 284p. pap. 29.00 *(978-0-230-61334-8(9))* Palgrave Macmillan.

AFFLICTION
see Suffering

AFFLUENT PEOPLE
see Rich People

AFFORESTATION
see also Forests and Forestry; Tree Planting
Blakesley, David & Buckley, G. Peter. Woodland Creation for Wildlife & People in a Changing Climate: Principles & Practice. 2010. (Illus.). xi, 171p. pap. *(978-1-874357-44-5(7))* Pisces Pubns.
Evans, Julian. Planted Forests: Uses, Impacts & Sustainability. 2010. (Illus.). 224p. 145.00 *(978-1-84593-564-1(0))* CABI GBR. Dist: Stylus Publishing, LLC.
Heil, Gerrit W., et al, eds. Environmental Effects of Afforestation in North-Western Europe: From Field Observations to Decision Support. 2007. (Plant & Vegetation Ser.: Vol. 1). (Illus.). 320p. 249.00 *(978-1-4020-4567-7(0)*, 1402045670) Springer.
Lewandrowski, Jan. Economics of Sequestering Carbon in the US Agricultural Sector. 2006. (Illus.). 61p. (C). reprint ed. pap. 25.00 *(978-1-4223-0694-9(1))* DIANE Publishing Co.
Mansourian, Stephanie & Vallauri, Daniel, eds. Forest Restoration in Landscapes: Beyond Planting Trees. 2010. (ENG., Illus.). xxviii, 437p. pap. 74.95 *(978-1-4419-2059-1(5)*, 1441920595) Springer.
Mercurio, Roberto. Restauro Della Foresta Mediterranea. 2010. (ITA., Illus.). 368p. *(978-88-491-3399-6(5))* CLUEB Editrice.
Miller, Debra A. Carbon Offsets. 2009. (Current Controversies Ser.). (ENG.). 240p. (gr. 10-12). 27.50 *(978-0-7377-4455-2(3))*; (Illus.). pap. 39.70 *(978-0-7377-4454-5(5))* Cengage Gale. (Greenhaven Pr., Inc.).

AFFREIGHTMENT
see Bills of Lading; Charter-Parties; Freight and Freightage

AFGHAN COOKING
see Cooking, Afghan

AFGHAN LANGUAGE
see Pushto Language

AFGHAN SONGS
see Songs, Afghan

AFGHAN WAR, 2001-
Addressing U.S. Strategy in Iraq & Afghanistan: Balancing Interests & Resources: Committee on Armed Services, House of Representatives, One Hundred Eleventh Congress, First Session, Hearing Held February 12, 2009. 2010. (Illus.). iii, 125p. *(978-0-16-086265-6(5)*, 552-070-41356-1) United States Government Printing Office.
Afghanistan: Getting the Strategy Right: Hearing Before the Full Committee of the Committee on Armed Services, House of Representatives, One Hundred Eleventh Congress, First Session, Hearing Held October 14, 2009. 2010. (Illus.). iii, 96p. *(978-0-16-086672-2(3)*, 552-070-41650-1) United States Government Printing Office.
Afghanistan: Governance & the Civilian Strategy: Hearing Before the Committee on Foreign Relations, United States Senate, One Hundred Eleventh Congress, Second Session, July 14, 2010. 2010. iii, 45p. ***(978-0-16-087186-3(7)***, 552-070-42028-2) United States Government Printing Office.
Afghanistan: Hearing Before the Committee on Armed Services, United States Senate, One Hundred Tenth Congress, First Session, March 1, 2007. 2008. iii, 91p. *(978-0-16-080354-3(3)*, 552-070-37050-1) United States Government Printing Office.
Afghanistan: Hearings Before the Committee on Armed Services, United States Senate, One Hundred Eleventh Congress, First Session, December 2 & 8, 2009. 2010. (Illus.). iii, 187p. *(978-0-16-085965-6(4)*, 552-070-41156-9) United States Government Printing Office.
Afghanistan: What Is an Acceptable End State, & How Do We Get There?: Hearing Before the Committee on Foreign Relations, United States Senate, One Hundred Twelfth Congress, First Session, May 3, 2011. 2011. iii, 53p. ***(978-0-16-089389-6(5)***, 552-070-43373-2) United States Government Printing Office.
Afghanistan & Iraq: Perspectives on U.S. Strategy. 2010. iii, 87p. *(978-0-16-086191-8(8)*, 552-070-41289-1); iii, 92p. ***(978-0-16-085979-3(4)***, 552-070-41170-4) United States Government Printing Office.
Afghanistan & Pakistan: Oversight of a New Interagency Strategy: Joint Hearing Before the Committee on Oversight & Government Reform & the Subcommittee on National Security & Foreign Affairs of the Committee on Oversight & Government Reform, House of Representatives, One Hundred Eleventh Congress, First Session, June 24, 2009. 2011. (Illus.). iii, 178p. ***(978-0-16-088215-9(X)***, 552-070-42577-2) United States Government Printing Office.
Afghanistan & Pakistan: Resourcing the Civilian Surge: Hearing Before the Subcommittee on National Security & Foreign Affairs of the Committee on Oversight & Government Reform, House of Representatives, One Hundred Eleventh Congress, First Session, May 19, 2009. 2010. iii, 79p. *(978-0-16-086593-0(X)*, 552-070-41581-5) United States Government Printing Office.
Afghanistan & Pakistan: Understanding & Engaging Regional Stakeholders: Hearing Before the Subcommittee on National Security & Foreign Affairs of the Committee on Oversight & Government Reform, House of Representatives, One Hundred Eleventh Congress, First Session, March 31, 2009. 2009. iii, 65p. *(978-0-16-084299-3(9)*, 552-070-39854-6) United States Government Printing Office.
Afghanistan Policy at the Crossroads: Hearing Before the Committee on Foreign Affairs, House of Representatives, One Hundred Eleventh Congress, First Session, October 15, 2009. 2009. iii, 89p. *(978-0-16-084992-3(6)*, 552-070-40371-0) United States Government Printing Office.
Afong, Milo S. Hunters: U. S. Snipers in the War on Terror. (ENG.). (gr. 12). 2011. 304p. 16.00 *(978-0-425-24112-7(2)*, Berkley Trade) 2010. 256p. 25.95 *(978-0-425-23436-5(3)*, Berkley Hardcover) Penguin Group (USA) Inc.
Allan, Alexander. Afghanistan: A Tour of Duty: A Photographic Portrait. 2009. (ENG., Illus.). 112p. pap. 19.95 *(978-1-906507-39-6(2)*, Third Millenium Pub Ltd, Antique Collectors' Club GBR. Dist: National Bk. Network.
Allen, Craig. With the Paras in Helmand: A Photographic Diary. 2010. (Illus.). 304p. 39.95 *(978-1-84884-300-4(3))* Pen & Sword Bks. Ltd. GBR. Dist: Casemate Pubs. & Bk. Distributors, LLC.
Allen, Nick. Embed: With the World's Armies in Afghanistan. 2011. (ENG., Illus.). 288p. 29.95 *(978-0-7524-5889-2(2))* History Pr. Ltd.,The GBR. Dist: Independent Pubs. Group.
Ambush Alley Games Staff, et al. Enduring Freedom: Afghanistan 2001-2010. 2011. (Force on Force Ser.). (ENG., Illus.). 176p. pap. 24.95 *(978-1-84908-532-8(3))* Osprey Publishing, Ltd. GBR. Dist: Random Hse., Inc.
Anderson, Terry H. Bush's Wars. 2011. (ENG., Illus.). 304p. 27.95 *(978-0-19-974752-8(0))* Oxford Univ. Pr., Inc.
Anonymous. Hunting Al Qaeda: A Take-No-Prisoners Account of Terror, Adventure, & Disillusionment. 2009. (ENG., Illus.). 256p. pap. 17.99 *(978-0-7603-3736-3(5)*, 0760337365, Zenith Pr.) MBI Publishing Co. LLC.
Archetti, Cristina. Explaining News: National Politics & Journalistic Cultures in Global Context. 2010. (Palgrave Macmillan Series in International Political Communication Ser.). (ENG., Illus.). 272p. 89.00 *(978-0-230-62282-1(8))* Palgrave Macmillan.
Armitage, Richard L., et al. U. S. Strategy for Pakistan & Afghanistan: Independent Task Force Report. 2010. (ENG.). 80p. pap. 15.00 *(978-0-87609-479-2(5))* Council on Foreign Relations.
Army & Marine Corps Force Protection Programs: Joint Hearing Before the Air & Land Forces Subcommittee Meeting Jointly with Seapower & Expeditionary Forces Subcommittee of the Committee on Armed Services, House of Representatives, One Hundred Eleventh Congress, First Session, Hearing Held, February 4, 2009. 2010. iv, 96p. *(978-0-16-085072-1(X)*, 552-070-4-429-5) United States Government Printing Office.
Assessing U.S. Foreign Policy Priorities & Needs Amidst Economic Challenges in South Asia: Hearing Before the Subcommittee on the Middle East & South Asia of the Committee on Foreign Affairs, House of Representatives, One Hundred Twelfth Congress, First Session, April 5, 2011. 2011. iii, 64p. ***(978-0-16-089126-7(4)***, 552-070-43138-1) United States Government Printing Office.
Assessment of U.S. Strategy & Operations in Afghanistan & the Way Ahead. 2009. (Illus.). iii, 107p. *(978-0-16-084208-5(5)*, 552-070-39785-0) United States Government Printing Office.
Barker, Kim. The Taliban Shuffle: Strange Days in Afghanistan & Pakistan. 2012. (ENG., Illus.). 320p. pap. 15.95 ***(978-0-307-47738-5(X)***, Anchor) Knopf Doubleday Publishing Group.
Barker, Kimberly. The Taliban Shuffle: Strange Days in Afghanistan & Pakistan. 2011. (ENG., Illus.). 320p. 25.95 *(978-0-385-53331-7(4)*, Doubleday) Knopf Doubleday Publishing Group.
Begg, Moazzam. Enemy Combatant: My Imprisonment at Guantanamo, Bagram, & Kandahar. 2007. (ENG.). 416p. per. 18.95 *(978-1-59558-206-5(1))* New Pr., The.
Begg, Moazzam & Brittain, Victoria. Enemy Combatant: My Imprisonment at Guantánamo, Bagram, & Kandahar. 2006. (ENG., Illus.). 397p. 26.95 *(978-1-59558-136-5(7))* New Pr., The.
Benitz, Max. Six Months Without Sundays: The Scots Guards in Afghanistan. 2011. (ENG., Illus.). 256p. 27.95 ***(978-1-84341-052-2(4))*** Birlinn, Ltd. GBR. Dist: Casemate Pubs. & Bk. Distributors, LLC.
Berger, John, et al. War with No End. 2007. (ENG., Illus.). 167p. per. 14.95 *(978-1-84467-184-7(4)*, 844184) Verso Bks. GBR. Dist: Norton, W. W. & Co., Inc.
Berlatsky, Noah. Afghanistan. 2010. (Opposing Viewpoints Ser.). (ENG.). 240p. 39.70 *(978-0-7377-5102-4(9))*; pap. 27.50 *(978-0-7377-5103-1(7))* Cengage Gale. (Greenhaven Pr., Inc.).
Bert, Wayne. American Military Intervention in Unconventional War: From the Philippines to Iraq. 2011. (ENG., Illus.). 284p. 85.00 *(978-0-230-11938-3(7))* Palgrave Macmillan.
Bird, Tim & Marshall, Alex. Afghanistan: How the West Lost Its Way. 2011. (Illus.). 303p. *(978-83-00-15457-9(4))*; 30.00 *(978-0-300-15457-3(7))* Yale Univ. Pr.
Blank, Stephen J. Challenges & Opportunities for the Obama Administration in Central Asia. 2009. ***(978-1-58487-391-4(4))*** Strategic Studies Institute, U.S. Army War College Commandant (AWCC-DSI/Pubns.).
Blatchford, Christie. Fifteen Days: Stories of Bravery, Friendship, Life & Death from Inside the New Canadian Army. 2008. (ENG., Illus.). 416p. pap. 19.00 *(978-0-385-66467-7(2)*, Anchor Can) Doubleday Canada, Ltd. CAN. Dist: Random Hse., Inc.
Blehm, Eric. The Only Thing Worth Dying For: How Eleven Green Berets Forged a New Afghanistan. 2011. (ENG., Illus.). 320p. pap. 15.99 *(978-0-06-166123-5(6)*, HarperPerennial) HarperCollins Pubs.
Bonds, Timothy M., et al. Army Deployments to OIF & OEF. 2010. 74p. pap. 30.00 *(978-0-8330-4920-9(8)*, db587) RAND Corp., The.
Bradley, Celeste. The Duke Next Door. l.t. ed. 2008. 532p. 31.95 *(978-1-4104-0884-6(1))* Thorndike Pr.
Bradley, Rusty & Maurer, Kevin. Lions of Kandahar: The Story of a Fight Against All Odds. 2011. (ENG., Illus.). 304p. 26.00 *(978-0-553-80757-8(9))* Random House Publishing Group.
Brahimi, Lakhdar & Pickering, Thomas Reeve. Afghanistan - Negotiating Peace The Report of the Century Foundation International Task Force on Afghanistan in Its Regional & Multilateral Dimensions. 2011. (ENG.). 104p. pap. 14.95 *(978-0-87078-520-7(6))* Century Foundation, The.
Brewster, Murray. The Savage War: The Untold Battles of Afghanistan. 8th ed. 2011. (ENG., Illus.). 384p. 34.95 ***(978-1-118-11593-0(7)***, Wiley) Wiley, John & Sons, Inc.
Briefing on Operation Moshtarak in Helmand Province, Afghanistan: Hearing Before the Committee on Armed Services, United States Senate, One Hundred Eleventh Congress, Second Session, February 22, 2010. 2011. iii, 36p. ***(978-0-16-088116-9(1)***, 552-070-42536-5) United States Government Printing Office.
Browder, Laura. When Janey Comes Marching Home: Portraits of Women Combat Veterans. 2010. (ENG., Illus.). 168p. 35.00 *(978-0-8078-3380-3(0))* Univ. of North Carolina Pr.
Brown, Seyom & Scales, Robert H., eds. US Policy in Afghanistan & Iraq: Lessons & Legacies. 2012. 235p. 55.00 ***(978-1-58826-809-9(8))*** Rienner, Lynne Pubs.
Burden, Matthew Currier. The Blog of War: Front-Line Dispatches from Soldiers in Iraq & Afghanistan. 2006. (ENG.). 304p. pap. 19.99 *(978-0-7432-9418-8(1))* Simon & Schuster.
Burke, John & Norfolk, Simon, photos by. Burke + Norfolk: Photographs from the War in Afghanistan. 2011. (ENG., Illus.). 168p. 65.00 ***(978-1-907893-11-7(3))*** Lewis, Dewi Publishing GBR. Dist: Consortium Bk. Sales & Distribution.
Butler, Michael J. Selling a Just War: Framing, Legitimacy & US Military Intervention. 2012. (ENG., Illus.). 304p. 95.00 ***(978-0-230-36064-8(5))*** Palgrave Macmillan.
Caldwell, Dan. Vortex of Conflict: U. S. Policy Toward Afghanistan, Pakistan, & Iraq. 2011. (ENG., Illus.). 408p. 75.00 *(978-0-8047-7665-3(2))*; pap. 25.95 *(978-0-8047-7666-0(0))* Stanford Univ. Pr.
Call, Steve. Danger Close: Tactical Air Controllers in Afghanistan & Iraq. (Williams-Ford Texas A&M University Military History Ser.). (ENG., Illus.). 2010. 250p. pap. 22.95 *(978-1-60344-142-1(5))* 2007. 272p. 50.00 *(978-1-58544-624-7(6))* Texas A&M Univ. Pr.
Camp, Dick. Boots on the Ground: The Fight to Liberate Afghanistan from Al-Qaeda & the Taliban, 2001-2002. 2012. (ENG., Illus.). 320p. 30.00 *(978-0-7603-4111-7(7)*, 0760341117, Zenith Pr.) MBI Publishing Co. LLC.
Carroll, Andrew, ed. Operation Homecoming: Iraq, Afghanistan, & the Home Front, in the Words of U. S. Troops & Their Families. 2008. (Illus.). 432p. pap. 16.00 *(978-0-226-09499-1(5))* Univ. of Chicago Pr.
Carter, Stephen. The Violence of Peace: America's Wars in the Age of Obama. 2011. (ENG.). 282p. (gr. 9). pap. 15.99 ***(978-0-9842951-8-0(6))*** Beast Bks.
Cartwright, Jamie. Sniper in Helmand. 2012. (Illus.). 192p. 39.95 ***(978-1-84884-663-0(0))*** Pen & Sword Bks. Ltd. GBR. Dist: Casemate Pubs. & Bk. Distributors, LLC.
Casscells, Samuel Ward. When It Mattered Most: Remembering Our Fallen Medical Personnel in Iraq-Afghanistan. 2009. (Illus.). xxx, 460p. *(978-0-16-081852-3(4)*, 008-000-01015-3) United States Government Printing Office.
Cawthorne, Nigel. On the Frontline: True Stories of Outstanding Bravery by British Forces in Iraq & Afghanistan. (ENG., Illus.). 280p. 2009. pap. 14.95 *(978-1-84454-733-3(7))* 2008. 34.95 *(978-1-84454-510-0(5))* Blake, John Publishing, Ltd. GBR. Dist: Independent Pubs. Group.
Chandrasekaran, Rajiv. Little America: The War Within the War for Afghanistan. 2012. (ENG., Illus.). 384p. 27.95 ***(978-0-307-95714-6(4)***, Knopf) Knopf Doubleday Publishing Group.
Chayes, Sarah. The Punishment of Virtue: Inside Afghanistan after the Taliban. 2007. (ENG., Illus.). 400p. (gr. 12-18). 16.00 *(978-0-14-311206-8(6)*, Penguin (Non-Classics)) Penguin Group (USA) Inc.
Clarke, Michael. The Afghan Papers. 2012. (Whitehall Papers). (ENG.). 160p. (C). pap. 42.95 ***(978-0-415-52593-0(4))*** Routledge.
Commission on Wartime Contracting in Iraq and Afghanistan (U.S.), ed. Transforming Wartime Contracting: Controlling Costs, Reducing Risks. 2011. (ENG., Illus.). 248p. pap. 48.00 ***(978-0-16-089317-9(8))*** United States Government Printing Office.

Committee on the Initial Assessment of Readjustment Needs of Military Personnel, Veterans, and Their Families, et al. Returning Home from Iraq & Afghanistan: Preliminary Assessment of Readjustment Needs of Veterans, Service Members, & Their Families. 2010. (ENG.). 192p. pap. 43.25 *(978-0-309-14763-7(8))* National Academies Pr.

Compton, Martyn, et al. Home from War: How Love Conquered the Horrors of a Soldier's Afghan Nightmare. (ENG., Illus.). 304p. 2010. pap. 14.95 *(978-1-84596-570-9(1))* 2009. 28.95 *(978-1-84596-450-4(0))* Mainstream Publishing Co., Ltd. GBR. Dist: Independent Pubs. Group.

Connor, Bill. Articles from War: The Writings of Lt. Col. Bill Connor. 2008. 127p. pap. 12.95 *(978-0-7414-4931-3(5))* Infinity Publishing.

Conrad, John. Ce que dit le Tonnerre: Reflexions d'un officier canadien a Kandahar. 2009. (FRE., Illus.). 280p. pap. 29.95 *(978-1-55488-419-3(5),* Dundurn Pr.) Dundurn CAN. Dist: Ingram Pub. Services.

—What the Thunder Said: Reflections of a Canadian Officer in Kandahar. 2009. (ENG., Illus.). 240p. pap. 29.95 *(978-1-55488-408-7(X),* Dundurn Pr.) Dundurn CAN. Dist: Ingram Pub. Services.

Contracting in a Counterinsurgency: An Examination of the Blackwater-Paravant Contract & the Need for Oversight: Hearing Before the Committee on Armed Services, United States Senate, One Hundred Eleventh Congress, Second Session, February 24, 2010. 2010. (Illus.). iv, 228p. *(978-0-16-086429-2(1),* 552-070-41490-8) United States Government Printing Office.

Corbett, Ron. First Soldiers Down: Canada's Friendly Fire Deaths in Afghanistan. 2012. (ENG., Illus.). 240p. pap. 28.99 ***(978-1-4597-0327-8(8))*** Dundurn CAN. Dist: Ingram Pub. Services.

Cortright, David. Ending Obama's War: Responsible Military Withdrawal from Afghanistan, 1 vol. 2011. (ENG.). 168p. 24.95 *(978-1-59451-984-0(6));* ix, 156p. pap. *(978-1-59451-985-7(4))* Paradigm Pubs.

Countering the Threat of Failure in Afghanistan: Hearing Before the Committee on Foreign Relations, United States Senate, One Hundred Eleventh Congress, First Session, September 17, 2009. 2010. iii, 55p. *(978-0-16-085307-4(9),* 552-070-40637-9) United States Government Printing Office.

Croucher, Matt. Bullet Proof. (ENG., 2011. Illus.). 288p. pap. 12.95 *(978-0-09-954308-4(7))* 2010. (Illus.). 272p. 34.95 *(978-1-84605-704-5(3))* 2009. 272p. pap. 24.95 *(978-1-84605-705-2(1))* Random Hse. GBR. Dist: Independent Pubs. Group.

Cucullu, Gordon & Fontana, Chris. Warrior Police: Rolling with America's Military Police in the World's Trouble Spots. (ENG.). 2012. 368p. pap. 15.99 ***(978-1-250-01313-2(5),*** St. Martin's Griffin) 2011. (Illus.). 352p. 25.99 *(978-0-312-65855-7(9))* St. Martin's Pr.

The Current Readiness of the U.S. Forces: Hearing Before the Subcommittee on Readiness & Management Support of the Committee on Armed Services, United States Senate, One Hundred Eleventh Congress, Second Session, April 14, 2010. 2011. iii, 112p. ***(978-0-16-088151-0(X),*** 552-070-42568-3) United States Government Printing Office.

The Current Status of U.S. Ground Forces: Hearing Before the Subcommittee on Readiness & Management Support of the Committee on Armed Services, United States Senate, One Hundred Eleventh Congress, First Session, April 22, 2009. 2009. (Illus.). iii, 92p. *(978-0-16-084691-5(9),* 552-070-40179-2) United States Government Printing Office.

Dale, Catherine & Bowman, Steve. War in Afghanistan: Strategy, Military Operations, & Issues for Congress. 2010. 78p. pap. 15.38 *(978-1-60888-068-3(0))* Nimble Bks. LLC.

Danziger, Danny. We Are Soldiers: Our Heroes - Their Stories - Real Life on the Frontline. 2010. (ENG., Illus.). 320p. 27.95 ***(978-1-84744-396-0(6))*** Little, Brown Bk. Group Ltd. GBR. Dist: Independent Pubs. Group.

—We Are Soldiers: Our Heroes. Their Stories. Real Life on the Front Line. 2010. (ENG.). 320p. pap. 22.95 ***(978-1-84744-397-7(4))*** Little, Brown Bk. Group Ltd. GBR. Dist: Independent Pubs. Group.

Darack, Ed. Victory Point: Operations Red Wings & Whalers - The Marine Corps' Battle for Freedom in Afghanistan. 2010. (ENG.). 336p. (gr. 12-18). 17.00 *(978-0-425-23259-0(X),* Berkley Trade) Penguin Group (USA) Inc.

Darman, Peter. Blood, Sweat & Steel: Frontline accounts from the Gulf, Afghanistan & Iraq, 1990-2010. 2011. (ENG., Illus.). 272p. pap. 14.95 *(978-1-84773-513-3(4))* New Holland Pubs., Ltd. GBR. Dist: Sterling Publishing Co., Inc.

De Paulo, Craig J. N. Augustinian Just War Theory & the Wars in Afghanistan & Iraq: Confessions, Contentions, & the Lust for Power. 2011. (C). pap. 34.95 ***(978-1-4331-1232-4(9))*** Lang, Peter Publishing, Inc.

Defeating the Improvised Explosive Device (IED) & Other Asymmetric Threats: Reviewing the Performance & Oversight of the Joint IED Defeat Organization (JIEDDO): Hearing Before the Oversight & Investigations Subcommittee of the Committee on Armed Services, House of Representatives, One Hundred Eleventh Congress, First Session, Hearing Held October 29, 2009. 2010. iii, 110p. *(978-0-16-085697-6(3),* 552-070-40929-7) United States Government Printing Office.

DeLong, Michael. Inside CentCom: The Unvarnished Truth about the Wars in Afghanistan & Iraq. 2008. (ENG.). 222p. 25.00 *(978-1-4379-5145-5(7))* DIANE Publishing Co.

Department of Defense Contracting in Iraq & Afghanistan: Hearing Before the Subcommittee on Readiness & Management Support of the Committee on Armed Services, United States Senate, One Hundred Tenth Congress, Second Session, April 2, 2008. 2008. iii, 49p. *(978-0-16-081856-1(7),* 552-070-38031-1) United States Government Printing Office.

Department of Defense Fiscal Year 2009 Budget: Hearing Before the Committee on the Budget, House of Representatives, One Hundred Tenth Congress, Second Session, Hearing Held in Washington, DC, February 27, 2008. 2008. (Illus.). iii, 57p. *(978-0-16-080984-2(3),* 552-070-37502-3) United States Government Printing Office.

Developments in Security & Stability in Afghanistan: Committee on Armed Services, House of Representatives, One Hundred Eleventh Congress, Second Session, Hearing Held May 5, 2010. 2010. iii, 57p. ***(978-0-16-088311-8(3),*** 552-070-42616-7) United States Government Printing Office.

Dilworth, Robert L. & Maital, Schlomo. Fogs of War & Peace: A Midstream Analysis of World War III, 1 vol. 2008. (Praeger Security International Ser.). (Illus.). 264p. 59.95 *(978-0-313-36049-7(9),* C36049, Praeger Security International) Greenwood Publishing Group, Inc.

Dinneen, Timothy W. An American Island. 2009. 228p. pap. 18.49 *(978-1-4490-1226-7(4))* AuthorHouse.

Doherty, Richard. Helmand Mission: With 1st Royal Irish Battlegroup in Afghanistan 2008. 2009. (Illus.). 176p. 39.95 *(978-1-84884-148-2(5))* Pen & Sword Bks. Ltd. GBR. Dist: Casemate Pubs. & Bk. Distributors, LLC.

Driscoll, Patricia & Straus, Celia. Hidden Battles on Unseen Fronts: Stories of American Soldiers with Traumatic Brain Injury & PTSD. 2010. (Illus.). 320p. pap. 18.95 *(978-1-935149-40-8(7))* Casemate Pubs. & Bk. Distributors, LLC.

Driscoll, Patricia P. & Straus, Celia. Hidden Battles on Unseen Fronts: Stories of American Soldiers with Traumatic Brain Injury & PTSD. 2009. (Illus.). 320p. 27.50 *(978-1-935149-01-9(6))* Casemate Pubs. & Bk. Distributors, LLC.

Duke of Rothesay [HRH Prince Charles], frwd. Aviation Assault Battlegroup in Afghanistan. 2011. (Illus.). 288p. 60.00 ***(978-1-84884-536-7(7))*** Pen & Sword Bks. Ltd. GBR. Dist: Casemate Pubs. & Bk. Distributors, LLC.

Duncan, Alex. Sweating the Metal: Flying under Fire. A Chinook Pilot's Blistering Account of Life, Death & Dust in Afghanistan. 2012. (ENG.). 352p. pap. 12.95 ***(978-1-4447-0800-4(7),*** Hodder & Stoughton) Hodder General Publishing Div. GBR. Dist: Independent Pubs. Group.

Edwards, Lucy Morgan. The Afghan Solution: The Inside Story of Abdul Haq, the CIA & How Western Hubris Lost Afghanistan. 2011. (ENG., Illus.). 368p. 29.95 *(978-0-9568449-0-3(1))* Pluto Pr. GBR. Dist: Macmillan.

Ehrhart, Hans-Georg & Pentland, Charles. The Afghanistan Challenge: Hard Realities & Strategic Choices. 2009. (ENG.). 250p. (C). pap. *(978-1-55339-241-5(8))* McGill-Queen's Univ. Pr.

Eide, Kai. The Power Struggle over Afghanistan: An Inside Look at What Went Wrong... & What We Can Do to Fix It. 2012. (ENG., Illus.). 320p. 24.95 *(978-1-61608-464-6(2),* 608464) Skyhorse Publishing Co., Inc.

Engelhardt, Tom. The American Way of War: How the Planet's Garrison State Brought Itself to Ruin. 2010. (ENG.). 269p. pap. 16.95 *(978-1-60846-071-7(1))* Haymarket Bks.

Evaluating Goals & Progress in Afghanistan & Pakistan: Hearing Before the Committee on Foreign Relations, United States Senate, One Hundred Twelfth Congress, First Session, June 23, 2011. 2011. iii, 55p. ***(978-0-16-089671-2(1),*** 552-070-43555-7) United States Government Printing Office.

Exoo, Calvin F. The Pen & the Sword: Press, War, & Terror in the 21st Century. 2009. (Illus.). 256p. (C). pap. 39.00 *(978-1-4129-5360-3(X),* B5360XP) SAGE Pubns., Inc.

Exploring Three Strategies for Afghanistan: Hearing Before the Committee on Foreign Relations, United States Senate, One Hundred Eleventh Congress, First Session, September 16, 2009. 2010. iii, 52p. *(978-0-16-085529-0(2),* 552-070-40752-9) United States Government Printing Office.

Farthing, Pen. One Dog at a Time: Saving the Strays of Afghanistan. (ENG.). 320p. 2012. pap. 14.99 ***(978-1-250-00195-5(1),*** St. Martin's Griffin) 2010. (Illus.). 24.99 *(978-0-312-60774-6(1),* Dunne, Thomas Bks.) St. Martin's Pr.

Faulder, Liane. The Long Walk Home: Paul Franklin's Journey from Afghanistan - A Soldier's Story, 1 vol. 2007. (ENG., Illus.). 224p. per. *(978-1-897142-25-7(0))* Brindle & Glass Publishing.

Fick, Nathaniel C. One Bullet Away: The Making of a Marine Officer. 2006. (ENG., Illus.). 400p. pap. 14.95 *(978-0-618-77343-5(6),* Mariner Bks.) Houghton Mifflin Harcourt Trade & Reference Pubs.

Fisher, Pete. Highway of Heroes: True Patriot Love. 2011. (ENG., Illus.). 184p. pap. 24.99 *(978-1-55488-971-6(5))* Dundurn CAN. Dist: Ingram Pub. Services.

Flank, Lenny. The Afghanistan Papers: A Selection of Leaked US Military Field Reports from the Afghan War. 2010. *(978-1-61001-000-9(0))* Red & Black Pubs.

Force Protection Equipment Programs for Operations in Iraq & Afghanistan: Joint Hearing Before the Seapower & Expeditionary Forces Subcommittee Meeting Jointly with Air & Land Forces Subcommittee of the Committee on Armed Services, House of Representatives, One Hundred Eleventh Congress, Second Session, Hearing Held March 17, 2010. 2010. (Illus.). iv, 97p. ***(978-0-16-087052-1(6),*** 552-070-41909-8) United States Government Printing Office.

Franzak, Michael. A Nightmare's Prayer: A Marine Harrier Pilot's War in Afghanistan. 2011. (ENG., Illus.). 432p. mass mkt. 7.99 *(978-1-4516-0807-6(1))* Pocket Books.

—A Nightmare's Prayer: A Marine Harrier Pilot's War in Afghanistan. 2010. (ENG., Illus.). 304p. 26.00 *(978-1-4391-9498-0(X),* Threshold Editions) Threshold Editions.

Freedman, Lawrence. A Choice of Enemies: America Confronts the Middle East. 2009. (ENG., Illus.). 640p. pap. 21.95 *(978-1-58648-701-0(9))* PublicAffairs.

Friedman, Lauri S., ed. The War in Afghanistan. 2012. (Writing the Critical Essay: an Opposing Viewpoints Guide Ser.). (ENG., Illus.). 128p. (gr. 6-10). lib. bdg. 32.75 ***(978-0-7377-5911-2(9),*** Greenhaven Pr., Inc.) Cengage Gale.

Friend, Robert Matthew. White Lies. 2008. 164p. pap. 11.99 *(978-1-4389-2259-1(0))* AuthorHouse.

Frisconalti, Michael. Friendly Fire: The Untold Story of the U. S. Bombing That Killed Four Canadian Soldiers in Afghanistan. 2006. (ENG.). 608p. pap. 24.95 *(978-0-470-83918-8(X),* Wiley) Wiley, John & Sons, Inc.

From Coalition to ISAF Command in Afghanistan: The Purpose & Impact of the Transition: Hearing Before the Committee on Foreign Relations, United States Senate, One Hundred Ninth Congress, Second Session, September 21, 2006. 2007. iii, 50p. *(978-0-16-078957-1(5),* 552-070-36075-1) United States Government Printing Office.

Furnich, Sergio. The 40-minute war - ipotesi di un atto di Terrorismo. 2008. 72p. pap. 13.50 *(978-1-4092-0684-2(X))* Lulu Enterprises Inc.

Gall, Sandy. War Against the Taliban: Why It All Went Wrong in Afghanistan. 2012. (ENG., Illus.). 320p. 42.00 ***(978-1-4088-0905-1(2))*** Bloomsbury Publishing.

Gannon, James. Obama's War: Avoiding a Quagmire in Afghanistan. 2011. (Illus.). 224p. 26.95 *(978-1-59797-537-7(0))* Potomac Bks., Inc.

Garcia, J. Malcolm. The Khaarijee: A Chronicle of Friendship & War in Kabul. 2009. (ENG.). 248p. 24.95 *(978-0-8070-0057-1(4))* Beacon Pr.

Garlasco, Marc E. "Troops in Contact" Airstrikes & Civilian Deaths in Afghanistan. 2008. (Illus.). 40p. *(978-1-56432-362-0(5))* Human Rights Watch.

Girardet, Edward. Killing the Cranes: A Reporter's Journey Through Three Decades of War in Afghanistan. 2011. (ENG.). 416p. 27.95 *(978-1-60358-342-8(4))* Chelsea Green Publishing.

Glantz, Aaron. The War Comes Home: Washington's Battle Against America's Veterans. (ENG.). 288p. 2010. pap. 21.95 *(978-0-520-26604-9(8))* 2009. 45.00 *(978-0-520-25612-5(3))* Univ. of California Pr.

Gonzalez, Roberto J. Militarizing Culture: Essays on the Warfare State. 2010. (ENG., Illus.). 209p. 79.00 *(978-1-59874-559-7(X));* pap. 24.95 *(978-1-59874-560-3(3))* Left Coast Pr., Inc.

Gould, Elizabeth. Crossing Zero: The Afpak War at the Turning Point of American Empire. 2011. (City Lights Open Media Ser.). (ENG.). 180p. pap. 16.95 *(978-0-87286-513-6(4))* City Lights Bks.

Grau, Lester & Billingsley, Dodge. Operation Anaconda. 2011. 464p. 39.95 ***(978-0-7006-1801-9(5))*** Univ. Pr. of Kansas.

Grover, Sonja C. Schoolchildren as Propaganda Tools in the War on Terror: Violating the Rights of Afghani Children under International Law. 2011. (ENG.). xix, 279p. 139.00 *(978-3-642-17899-3(5),* 3642178995) Springer.

Guantanamo: Implications for U.S. Human Rights Leadership: Hearing Before the Commission on Security & Cooperation in Europe, One Hundred Tenth Congress, First Session, June 21, 2007. 2010. (Illus.). iv, 80p. *(978-0-16-087030-9(5),* 552-070-41888-1) United States Government Printing Office.

Hastings, Michael. The Operators: The Wild & Terrifying Inside Story of America's War in Afghanistan. 2012. (ENG., Illus.). 432p. (gr. 12). 27.95 ***(978-0-399-15988-6(6),*** Blue Rider Pr.) Penguin Group (USA) Inc.

Hearing on National Defense Authorization ACT for Fiscal Year 2012 & Oversight of Previously Authorized Programs Before the Committee on Armed Services, House of Representatives, One Hundred Twelfth Congress, First Session: Full Committee Hearing on Budget Requests from the U.S. Central Command & U.S. Special Operations Command, Hearing Held March 3, 2011. 2011. (Illus.). iii, 121p. ***(978-0-16-089433-6(6),*** 552-070-43405-4) United States Government Printing Office.

Hennessey, Patrick. The Junior Officers' Reading Club: Killing Time & Fighting Wars. 2010. (ENG.). 336p. (gr. 12). 16.00 *(978-1-59448-479-7(1),* Riverhead Trade (Paperbacks)) Penguin Group (USA) Inc.

Herspring, Dale R. Rumsfeld's Wars: The Arrogance of Power. 2008. (Modern War Studies). 247p. 34.95 *(978-0-7006-1587-2(3))* Univ. Pr. of Kansas.

Hetherington, Tim, photos by. Infidel. 2010. (ENG., Illus.). 240p. pap. 35.00 *(978-1-905712-18-2(9))* Boot, Chris GBR. Dist: D.A.P./Distributed Art Pubs.

Hicks, Tyler, photos by. Histories Are Mirrors: The Path of Conflict Through Afghanistan & Iraq. 2008. (ENG., Illus.). 128p. 34.95 *(978-1-884167-44-7(6))* Umbrage Editions.

Hilton, D. Craig. Shaping Commitment: Resolving Canada's Strategic Gap in Afghanistan & Beyond. 2007. (Carlisle Papers Ser.). *(978-1-58487-299-3(3))* Strategic Studies Institute, U.S. Army War College Commandant (AWCC-DSI/Pubns.).

Hoehn, Andrew R. & Harting, Sarah. Risking NATO: Testing the Limits of the Alliance in Afghanistan. 2011. 108p. pap. 20.00 *(978-0-8330-5011-3(7),* mg-974) RAND Corp., The.

Horn, Bernd. From Cold War to New Millennium: The History of the Royal Canadian Regiment, 1953-2008. 2011. (Illus.). 424p. pap. 39.95 ***(978-1-55488-898-6(0));*** (ENG., lthr. 80.00 *(978-1-55488-897-9(2),* Dundurn Pr.) Dundurn CAN. Dist: Univ. of Toronto Pr., Ingram Pub. Services.

Horn, Bernd. No Lack of Courage: Operation Medusa, Afghanistan. 2010. (ENG., Illus.). 184p. pap. 30.00 *(978-1-55488-766-8(6))* Dundurn CAN. Dist: Ingram Pub. Services.

Horn, Bernd & Spencer, Emily, eds. No Easy Task: Fighting in Afghanistan. 2012. (ENG., Illus.). 352p. pap. 35.00 *(978-1-4597-0162-5(3))* Dundurn CAN. Dist: Ingram Pub. Services.

Hosek, James, ed. How Is Deployment to Iraq & Afghanistan: Affecting U. S. Service Members & Their Families? An Overview of Early Rand Research on the Topic. 2011. 60p. pap. 26.00 *(978-0-8330-5201-8(2))* RAND Corp., The.

Hunnicutt, Susan C. Casualties of War. 2011. (At Issue Ser.). 128p. pap. 22.50 *(978-0-7377-4881-9(8),* Greenhaven Pr., Inc.) Cengage Gale.

Implementing the Wounded Warrior Provisions of the National Defense Authorization ACT for Fiscal Year 2008: Hearing Before the Committee on Veterans' Affairs, U.S. House of Representatives, One Hundred Tenth Congress, Second Session, June 11, 2008. 2009. iv, 91p. *(978-0-16-082833-1(3),* 552-070-38813-3) United States Government Printing Office.

Investigation of Protection Payments for Safe Passage along Afghan Supply Chain: Hearing Before the Subcommittee on National Security & Foreign Affairs of the Committee on Oversight & Government Reform, House of Representatives, One Hundred Eleventh Congress, Second Session, June 22, 2010. 2011. (Illus.). iii, 212p. ***(978-0-16-089102-1(7),*** 552-070-43125-0) United States Government Printing Office.

Jalalzai, Zubeda & Jefferess, David, eds. Globalizing Afghanistan: Terrorism, War, & the Rhetoric of Nation Building. 2011. (American Encounters/Global Interactions Ser.). (ENG., Illus.). 232p. 79.95 *(978-0-8223-5001-9(7));* pap. 22.95 *(978-0-8223-5014-9(9))* Duke Univ. Pr.

Jamail, Dahr. Will to Resist: Soldiers Who Refuse to Fight in Iraq & Afghanistan. 2011. (ENG.). 240p. pap. 16.00 ***(978-1-60846-095-3(9))*** Haymarket Bks.

Jankowski, Jacob E. Corruption, Contractors, & Warlords in Afghanistan. 2011. (Politics & Economics of the Middle East; Ser.). 115.00 *(978-1-61761-598-6(6))* Nova Science Pubs., Inc.

Jobson, Robert. Harry's War: The True Story of the Soldier Prince. 2008. (ENG., Illus.). 252p. pap. 15.95 *(978-1-84454-672-5(1))* Blake, John Publishing, Ltd. GBR. Dist: Independent Pubs. Group.

Jones, Seth G. Counterinsurgency in Afghanistan. 2008. (ENG.). 176p. pap. 26.50 *(978-0-8330-4133-3(9),* MG-595) RAND Corp., The.

—In the Graveyard of Empires: America's War in Afghanistan. (ENG., Illus.). 2010. 464p. pap. 15.95 *(978-0-393-33851-5(7),* 33851) 2009. 448p. 27.95 *(978-0-393-06898-6(6),* 6898) Norton, W. W. & Co., Inc.

Joya, Malalai. A Woman among Warlords: The Extraordinary Story of an Afghan Who Dared to Raise Her Voice. 2011. (ENG.). 256p. pap. 16.00 *(978-1-4391-0947-2(8),* Scribner) Scribner.

Junger, Sebastian. War. (ENG.). 2011. 320p. pap. 15.99 *(978-0-446-55622-4(X))* 2010. 304p. 26.99 *(978-0-446-55624-8(6))* Grand Central Publishing. (Twelve).

Just World Books & Foust, Joshua. Afghanistan Journal: Selections from Registan. net. 2010. (Illus.). 240p. pap. 23.95 *(978-1-935982-02-9(8))* Just World Bks.

Katz, Mark N. Leaving Without Losing: The War on Terror after Iraq & Afghanistan. 2012. (ENG., Illus.). 160p. 19.95 ***(978-1-4214-0558-2(X))*** Johns Hopkins Univ. Pr.

Keillor, Garrison. Liberty: A Novel of Lake Wobegon. l.t. ed. 2008. 35.95 *(978-1-4104-0842-6(6))* Thorndike Pr.

Khan, Mahvish Rukhsana. My Guantanamo Diary: The Detainees & the Stories They Told Me. 2008. (ENG., Illus.). 320p. 25.95 *(978-1-58648-498-9(2))* PublicAffairs.

—My Guantanamo Diary: The Detainees & the Stories They Told Me. 2009. (ENG., Illus.). 320p. pap. 13.95 *(978-1-58648-707-2(8))* PublicAffairs.

Kilcullen, David. The Accidental Guerrilla: Fighting Small Wars in the Midst of a Big One, 1 vol. 2011. (ENG.). 384p. pap. 17.95 *(978-0-19-975409-0(8))* Oxford Univ. Pr., Inc.

Koontz, Christopher N., ed. Enduring Voices: Oral Histories of the U. S. Army Experience in Afghanistan, 2003-2005. 2009. (Center of Military History Publication). (ENG., Illus.). 577p. pap. 68.00 *(978-0-16-081737-3(4),* Dept. of the Army) United States Government Printing Office.

Krakauer, Jon. Where Men Win Glory: The Odyssey of Pat Tillman. (ENG., 2010. Illus.). 480p. pap. 15.95 *(978-0-307-38604-5(X),* Anchor) 2009. 416p. 27.95 *(978-0-385-52226-7(6))* Knopf Doubleday Publishing Group.

—Where Men Win Glory: The Odyssey of Pat Tillman. 2009. 15.42 ***(978-0-7848-3706-1(6),*** Everbind) Marco Bk. Co.

—Where Men Win Glory: The Odyssey of Pat Tillman. l.t. ed. 2009. (ENG.). 592p. pap. 28.00 *(978-0-7393-2763-0(1))* Random Hse. Large Print.

Kriner, Theresa Nolan. Your Personal Soldier: Emails from the Front. 2010. pap. 22.99 *(978-1-61663-829-0(X))* Tate Publishing & Enterprises, LLC.

Kyle, Chris, et al. American Sniper: The Autobiography of the Most Lethal Sniper in U. S. Military History. 2012. (ENG.). 336p. 26.99 ***(978-0-06-208235-0(3),*** Morrow, William & Co.); 400p. pap. 26.99 ***(978-0-06-210706-0(2),*** HarperLuxe) HarperCollins Pubs.

Lansford, Ph.D., Tom. 9/11 & the Wars in Afghanistan & Iraq: A Chronology & Reference Guide, 1 vol. 2011. 348p. 89.00 *(978-1-59884-419-1(9),* A2854C) ABC-CLIO, LLC.

Larsen, Matt & Cavallaro, Gina. Sniper: American Single-Shot Warriors in Iraq & Afghanistan. 2010. (ENG., Illus.). 240p. pap. 16.95 *(978-1-59921-855-7(0),* Lyons Pr.) Globe Pequot Pr., The.

Laxer, James. Mission of Folly: Canada & Afghanistan. 2008. 168p. pap. 22.95 *(978-1-897071-37-3(X))* Between the Lines CAN. Dist: Univ. of Toronto Pr.

Ledwidge, Frank. Losing Small Wars: British Military Failure in Iraq & Afghanistan. (ENG.). 304p. 2012. pap. 27.50 ***(978-0-300-18274-3(0))*** 2011. 38.00 *(978-0-300-16671-2(0))* Yale Univ. Pr.

—Losing Small Wars: British Military Failure in Iraq & Afghanstan. 2011. ***(978-83-00-16671-8(8))*** Yale Univ. Pr.

Lewis, Damien. Apache Dawn: Always Outnumbered, Never Outgunned. 2010. (ENG., Illus.). 304p. pap. 15.99 *(978-0-312-61089-0(0),* St. Martin's Griffin) St. Martin's Pr.

Libicki, Martin C., et al. Byting Back: Regaining Information Superiority Against 21st-Century Insurgents. 2007. (Rand Counterinsurgency Study Ser.). (ENG., Illus.). 156p. per. 23.00 (978-0-8330-4189-0(4)) RAND Corp., The.

The Long-Term Costs of the Current Conflict: Hearing Before the Committee on Veterans' Affairs, U.S. House of Representatives, One Hundred Tenth Congress, First Session, October 17, 2007. 2008. iii, 73p. (978-0-16-081754-0(4), 552-070-37962-2) United States Government Printing Office.

Loughran, David S. & Klerman, Jacob Alex. Explaining the Increase in Unemployment Compensation for Ex-Servicemembers During the Global War on Terror. 2008. 70p. pap. 24.00 (978-0-8330-4514-0(8), tr-588) RAND Corp., The.

Loveless, Antony. Blue Sky Warriors: The RAF in Afghanistan in Their Own Words. 2011. (ENG., Illus.). 256p. pap. 14.95 (978-0-85733-119-9(1), 0857331191) Haynes Publishing PLC GBR. Dist: MBI Distribution Services/Quayside Distribution.

Lowrey, Nathan S. U. S. Marines in Afghanistan, 2001-2002: from the Sea: From the Sea. Marine Corps (U.S.), ed. 2012. (ENG., Illus.). 420p. 75.00 (978-0-16-089557-9(X), Marine Corps) United States Government Printing Office.

Luttrell, Marcus. Lone Survivor: The Eyewitness Account of Operation Redwing & the Lost Heroes of SEAL Team 10. (ENG., Illus.). 2008. 416p. pap. 15.99 (978-0-316-06760-7(1), Back Bay Bks.) 2007. 400p. 24.99 (978-0-316-06759-1(8)) Little Brown & Co.

Luttrell, Marcus & Robinson, Patrick. Lone Survivor: The Eyewitness Account of Operation Redwing & the Lost Heroes of SEAL Team 10. 2009. (ENG., Illus.). 464p. mass mkt. 8.99 (978-0-316-04469-1(5)) Little Brown & Co.

Macy, Ed. Apache: Inside the Cockpit of the World's Most Deadly Fighting Machine. 2010. (ENG., Illus.). 400p. pap. 15.95 (978-0-8021-4478-2(0), Grove Pr.) Grove/Atlantic, Inc.

Maloney, Sean. Fighting for Afghanistan. 2011. (Illus.). 352p. 36.95 (978-1-59114-509-7(0)) Naval Institute Pr.

Maloney, Sean M. Enduring the Freedom: A Rogue Historian in Afghanistan. 2007. (Illus.). 320p. per. 18.95 (978-1-59797-049-5(2)) Potomac Bks., Inc.

Marsden, Peter. Afghanistan: Aid, Armies & Empires. 2009. (ENG.). 240p. pap. 26.00 (978-1-84511-751-1(4)) I. B. Tauris & Co., Ltd. GBR. Dist: Macmillan.

Martin, Matt J. & Sasser, Charles W. Predator: The Remote-Control Air War over Iraq & Afghanistan: A Pilot's Story. 2010. (ENG., Illus.). 320p. 28.00 (978-0-7603-3896-4(5), 0760338965, Zenith Pr.) MBI Publishing Co. LLC.

Mason, Whit, ed. The Rule of Law in Afghanistan: Missing in Inaction. 2011. (ENG., Illus.). 366p. 90.00 (978-1-107-00319-4(9)); pap. 39.99 (978-0-521-17668-2(9)) Cambridge Univ. Pr.

Mastrogiacomo, Daniele. Days of Fear: A Firsthand Account of Captivity under the New Taliban. Reynolds, Michael, tr. from ITA. 2010. (ENG.). 176p. (gr. 12-18). 15.00 (978-1-933372-97-6(4)) Europa Editions, Inc.

Maurer, Kevin. Gentlemen Bastards: On the Ground in Afghanistan with America's Elite Special Forces. 2012. (ENG., Illus.). 256p. (gr. 12). 26.95 (978-0-425-25269-7(8), Berkley Hardcover) Penguin Group (USA) Inc.

Meagher, Ilona. Moving a Nation to Care: Post-Traumatic Stress Disorder & America's Returning Troops. 2007. (ENG.). 200p. per. 14.95 (978-0-9771972-7-6(1)) Ig Publishing, Inc.

Medical Evidence of Torture by U.S. Personnel: Briefing of the Commission on Security & Cooperation in Europe. 2011. iv, 37p. (978-0-16-088052-0(1), 552-070-42474-1) United States Government Printing Office.

Melton, Stephen L. The Clausewitz Delusion: How the American Army Screwed up the Wars in Iraq & Afghanistan (A Way Forward) 2009. (ENG.). 320p. 30.00 (978-0-7603-3713-4(6), 0760337136, Zenith Pr.) MBI Publishing Co. LLC.

Mendelson, Sarah E. Closing Guantanamo: From Bumper Sticker to Blueprint. 2008. 32p. pap. 12.95 net. (978-0-89206-548-6(6), CSIS Pr., The) Ctr. for Strategic & International Studies.

Miller, Charles A. Endgame for the West in Afghanistan? Explaining the Decline in Support for the War in Afghanistan in the US, Great Britain, Canada, Australia, France, & Germany. 2010. (Letort Papers). pap. (978-1-58487-447-8(3)) Strategic Studies Institute, U.S. Army War College Commandant (AWCC-DSI/Pubns.).

Minear, Larry. Through Veterans' Eyes: The Iraq & Afghanistan Experience. 2010. 270p. 55.00 (978-1-59797-486-8(2)); pap. 21.95 (978-1-59797-490-5(0)) Potomac Bks., Inc.

Monahan, Patrick B. Memoirs of a Deployed Airman. 2009. (Illus.). xvi, 543p. (978-1-4401-2563-8(5), iUniverse, Inc.) iUniverse, Inc.

Moore, Christopher E. Contractors in Iraq & Afghanistan: Background & Issues. 2011. (Defense, Security & Strategies Ser.). 115.00 (978-1-61761-556-6(0)) Nova Science Pubs., Inc.

Mullaney, Craig M. The Unforgiving Minute: A Soldier's Education. 2010. (ENG.). 416p. (gr. 12-18). pap. 16.00 (978-0-14-311687-5(6), Penguin (Non-Classics)) Penguin Group (USA) Inc.

Munoz, Arturo. U. S. Military Information Operations in Afghanistan: Effectiveness of Psychological Operations 2001-2010. 2012. (ENG.). 202p. pap. 36.00 (978-0-8330-5151-6(2)) RAND Corp., The.

Neill, John Martin Bladen. With the Somersets in Afghanistan: The Recollections of an Officer of H. M. 40th Regiment During the First Afghan War 1838-42. 2011. 240p. (978-0-85706-489-9(4)); pap. (978-0-85706-490-5(8)) Leonaur Ltd.

Nessen, Shawn Christian, et al, eds. War Surgery in Afghanistan & Iraq: A Series of Cases, 2003-2007. 2008. (Textbooks of Military Medicine Ser.). (ENG., Illus.). 464p. (C). 71.00 (978-0-9818228-0-8(0), Dept. of the Army) United States Government Printing Office.

Neumann, Ronald E. The Other War: Winning & Losing in Afghanistan. 2009. (Illus.). 256p. 27.50 (978-1-59797-427-1(7)) Potomac Bks., Inc.

Neville, Leigh. Special Operations Forces in Afghanistan: Afganistan 2001-2007. 2008. (Elite Ser.). (ENG., Illus.). 64p. pap. 18.95 (978-1-84603-310-0(1)) Osprey Publishing, Ltd. GBR. Dist: Random Hse., Inc.

—Special Operations Patrol Vehicles: Afghanistan & Iraq. 2011. (New Vanguard Ser.). (ENG., Illus.). 48p. pap. 17.95 (978-1-84908-187-0(5)) Osprey Publishing, Ltd. GBR. Dist: Random Hse., Inc.

The New Strategy for Afghanistan & Pakistan & Developments in U.S. Central Command & Special Operations Command: Committee on Armed Services, House of Representatives, One Hundred Eleventh Congress, First Session, Hearing Held April 2, 2009. 2010. (Illus.). iii, 122p. (978-0-16-086605-0(7), 552-070-41593-9) United States Government Printing Office.

New York Times Staff. Open Secrets: WikiLeaks, War, & American Diplomacy. Star, Alexander, ed. 2011. (ENG., Illus.). 608p. pap. 16.95 (978-0-8021-4576-5(0), Grove Pr.) Grove/Atlantic, Inc.

Nuzum, Henry. Shades of CORDS in the Kush: The False Hope of Unity of Effort in American Counterinsurgency. 2010. (Letort Papers). (Illus.). xii, 132p. pap. (978-1-58487-435-5(X)) Strategic Studies Institute, U.S. Army War College Commandant (AWCC-DSI/Pubns.).

O'Hanlon, Michael E. & Sherjan, Hassina. Toughing It Out in Afghanistan. 2010. (ENG., Illus.). 164p. pap. 22.95 (978-0-8157-0409-6(7)) Brookings Institution Pr.

Olafsen, Jake. Wearing the Green Beret: A Canadian with the Royal Marine Commandos. (ENG., Illus.). 2012. 304p. pap. 19.95 (978-0-7710-6857-7(3)) 2011. 320p. 29.99 (978-0-7710-6852-2(2)) McClelland & Stewart CAN. (McClelland & Stewart). Dist: Random Hse., Inc.

Oversight Hearing on Traumatic Brain Injury (TBI) Progress in Treating the Signature Wounds of the Current Conflicts: Hearing Before the Committee on Veterans' Affairs, United States Senate, One Hundred Eleventh Congress, First [i.e. Second] Session, May 5, 2010. 2011. (Illus.). iv, 162p. (978-0-16-088322-4(9), 552-070-42627-2) United States Government Printing Office.

Owens, Brett & Belmont, Philip, Jr. Combat Orthopedic Surgery: Lessons Learned in Iraq & Afghanistan. 2011. (ENG.). 352p. 149.95 (978-1-55642-965-1(7)) SLACK, Inc.

Pakistan at the Crossroads; Afghanistan in the Balance: Hearing Before the Subcommittee on National Security & Foreign Affairs of the Committee on Oversight & Government Reform, House of Representatives, One Hundred Tenth Congress, First Session, July 12, 2007. 2009. iii, 61p. (978-0-16-083701-2(4), 552-070-39408-7) United States Government Printing Office.

Parnell, Sean & Bruning, John. Outlaw Platoon: Heroes, Renegades, Infidels, & the Brotherhood of War in Afghanistan. 2012. (ENG., Illus.). 384p. 26.99 (978-0-06-206639-8(0), Morrow, William & Co.) HarperCollins Pubs.

Parnell, Sean & Bruning, John R. Outlaw Platoon: Heroes, Renegades, Infidels, & the Brotherhood of War in Afghanistan. 2012. (Illus.). viii, 374p. pap. 14.99 (978-0-06-206640-4(4)); E-Book 21.99 (978-0-06-206641-1(2)) HarperCollins Pubs. (Morrow, William & Co.).

Pavlov, Andrea M. & Novikov, Stefan G., eds. Casualties of U. S. Wars. 2011. (Defense, Security & Strategies Ser.). (Illus.). ix, 74p. 47.00 (978-1-61209-986-6(6)) Nova Science Pubs., Inc.

Phillips, Jarett M. Iraq, Iran, & Afghanistan. 2011. (Series: Politics & Economics of the Middle East Ser.). 195.00 (978-1-61122-026-1(2)) Nova Science Pubs., Inc.

Pierrebourg, Fabrice de. Martyrs D'une Guerre Perdue D'avance: Le Canada en Afghanistan. 2010. (FRE., Illus.). 270p. (978-2-7604-1073-2(0)) Editions Internationales Alain Stanke, Limitee.

Pigott, Peter. Canada in Afghanistan: The War So Far. 2007. (ENG., Illus.). 240p. 35.00 (978-1-55002-674-0(7), Dundurn Pr.) Dundurn CAN. Dist: Ingram Pub. Services.

Platt, Stuart F. Letters from the Front Lines: Iraq & Afghanistan. 2006. (Illus.). 305p. 24.95 (978-1-894694-48-3(1)) Granville Island Publishing CAN. Dist: Greenleaf Book Group.

Poole, H. John. Expeditionary Eagles: Outmaneuvering the Taliban. 2010. (Illus.). 334p. pap. (978-0-9818659-2-8(5)) Posterity Pr.

The President's Fiscal Year 2009 War Supplemental Request: Hearing Before the Committee on Appropriations, United States Senate, One Hundred Eleventh Congress, First Session: Special Hearing, April 30, 2009, Washington, DC. 2009. iv, 81p. (978-0-16-084224-5(7), 552-070-39802-3) United States Government Printing Office.

Price, David H. Weaponizing Anthropology: Social Science in Service of the Militarized State. 2011. (Counterpunch Ser.). (ENG., Illus.). 208p. pap. 15.95 (978-1-84935-063-1(9)) AK Pr. GBR. Dist: Consortium Bk. Sales & Distribution.

Priorities of the Department of Defense in the New Administration: Hearing Before the Committee on Armed Services, House of Representatives, One Hundred Eleventh Congress, First Session, Hearing Held January 27, 2009. 2010. iv, 69p. (978-0-16-085090-4(3), 552-070-41200-0) United States Government Printing Office.

Pushies, Fred J. Deadly Blue: Battle Stories of the U. S. Air Force Special Operations Command, 1 vol. 2009. (ENG., Illus.). 256p. 24.95 (978-0-8144-1360-9(9)) Amacom.

Rashid, Ahmed. Pakistan on the Brink: The Future of America, Pakistan, & Afghanistan. 2012. (ENG., Illus.). 256p. (gr. 12). 26.95 (978-0-670-02346-2(9), Viking Adult) Penguin Group (USA) Inc.

Rayment, Sean. Bomb Hunters: In Afghanistan with Britain's Elite Bomb Disposal Unit. 2011. (ENG., Illus.). 304p. 12.95 (978-0-00-742796-3(4)) HarperCollins Pubs. Ltd. GBR. Dist: Independent Pubs. Group.

Richie-Melvan, Sharon & Vines, Diane. Angel Walk: Nurses at War. 2010. (ENG.). 192p. pap. 16.95 (978-0-9816822-0-4(0)) Amica Publishing, Inc.

Rico, Johnny. Blood Makes the Grass Grow Green: A Year in the Desert with Team America. 2007. (ENG., Illus.). 336p. per. 16.00 (978-0-89141-897-9(0), Presidio Pr.) Random House Publishing Group.

Ripley, Tim. Air War Afghanistan: NATO Air Operations From 2001. 2011. (Illus.). 272p. 60.00 (978-1-84884-356-1(9)) Pen & Sword Bks. Ltd. GBR. Dist: Casemate Pubs. & Bk. Distributors, LLC.

Ripley, Tim. Operation Enduring Freedom. 2011. (Illus.). 256p. 50.00 (978-1-84884-564-0(2)) Pen & Sword Bks. Ltd. GBR. Dist: Casemate Pubs. & Bk. Distributors, LLC.

Robbins, Bruce W. Perpetual War: Cosmopolitanism from the Viewpoint of Violence. 2012. (ENG.). 256p. 84.95 (978-0-8223-5198-6(6)); pap. 23.95 (978-0-8223-5209-9(5)) Duke Univ. Pr.

Robinson, Jacqueline R. & Miller, Francis. Wartime Contracting in Iraq & Afghanistan: Controlling Costs & Reducing Risks. 2012. (978-1-62100-984-9(X)) Nova Science Pubs., Inc.

Rohde, David & Mulvihill, Kristen. A Rope & a Prayer: A Kidnapping from Two Sides. 2010. (ENG., Illus.). 384p. (gr. 12). 26.95 (978-0-670-02223-6(3), Viking Adult) Penguin Group (USA) Inc.

—A Rope & a Prayer: The Story of a Kidnapping. 2011. (ENG.). 384p. (gr. 12). 16.00 (978-0-14-312005-6(0), Penguin (Non-Classics)) Penguin Group (USA) Inc.

Rothstein, Hy. Afghan Endgames: Strategy & Policy Choices for America's Longest War. Arquilla, John, ed. 2012. (South Asia in World Affairs Ser.). (ENG.). 248p. pap. 29.95 (978-1-58901-908-9(3)) Georgetown Univ. Pr.

Ryan, David. Frustrated Empire: US Foreign Policy, 9/11 to Iraq. 2007. (ENG.). 216p. per. 30.00 (978-0-7453-2388-6(X)) Pluto Pr. GBR. Dist: Macmillan.

—US Foreign Policy: 9/11 & After. 2007. (ENG.). 216p. 89.00 (978-0-7453-2389-3(8)) Pluto Pr. GBR. Dist: Macmillan.

Ryan, Mike. Battlefield Afghanistan. 2007. (ENG., Illus.). 192p. pap. 24.95 (978-1-86227-390-0(1)) History Pr. Ltd., The GBR. Dist: Independent Pubs. Group.

Ryan, Mike. Frontline Afghanistan: The Devil's Playground. 2009. (ENG., Illus.). 224p. pap. 22.95 (978-0-7524-5248-7(7)) History Pr. Ltd., The GBR. Dist: Independent Pubs. Group.

Sadeed, Suraya & Lewis, Damien. Forbidden Lessons in a Kabul Guesthouse: The True Story of a Woman Who Risked Everything to Bring Hope to Afghanistan. 2011. (ENG.). 304p. 24.99 (978-1-4013-4131-2(4)) Hyperion Pr.

Samuel-Azran, Tal. Al Jazeera & U. S. War Coverage. 2010. 176p. (C). 119.95 (978-1-4331-0865-5(8)) Lang, Peter Publishing, Inc.

—Al Jazeera & US War Coverage. 2010. 176p. (C). pap. 34.95 (978-1-4331-0864-8(X)) Lang, Peter Publishing, Inc.

Scannell-Desch, Elizabeth & Doherty, Mary Ellen. Nurses in War: Voices from Iraq & Afghanistan. 2012. 240p. pap. (978-0-8261-9383-4(8)) Springer.

Scheuer, Michael. Marching Toward Hell: America & Islam after Iraq. 2009. (ENG., Illus.). 400p. pap. 16.00 (978-0-7432-9971-8(X), Free Pr.) Free Pr.

Schmitt, Michael N. & Naval War College Press (U.S.) Staff, eds. The War in Afghanistan: A Legal Analysis. 2009. (International Law Studies). (ENG.). 604p. 58.00 (978-1-884733-64-2(6), Dept. of the Navy) United States Government Printing Office.

Schrock, Julie Burget. Missing Max. 2011. 100p. pap. 13.00 (978-1-59755-269-1(0), Advantage Inspirational) Advantage Bks.

Schroen, Gary. First In: An Insider's Account of How the CIA Spearheaded the War on Terror in Afghanistan. 2007. (ENG.). 416p. per. 7.99 (978-0-345-49661-4(2), Presidio Pr.) Random House Publishing Group.

Scott, Jake. Blood Clot. 2008. (Illus.). 200p. 49.95 (978-1-906033-31-6(5)) Helion & Co., Ltd. GBR. Dist: Casemate Pubs. & Bk. Distributors, LLC.

—Blood Clot: In Combat with the Patrols Platoon, 3 para, Afghanistan 2006. 2010. (Illus.). 232p. pap. 39.95 (978-1-906033-81-1(1)) Helion & Co., Ltd. GBR. Dist: Casemate Pubs. & Bk. Distributors, LLC.

—A Journey to Hell & Back: A Photographic Record of 3 para in Afghanistan 2006. 2009. (Illus.). 208p. 69.95 (978-1-906033-71-2(4)) Helion & Co., Ltd. GBR. Dist: Casemate Pubs. & Bk. Distributors, LLC.

Scott, Peter Dale. American War Machine: Deep Politics, the CIA Global Drug Connection, & the Road to Afghanistan. 2010. (War & Peace Library). (ENG.). 408p. 39.95 (978-0-7425-5594-5(1)) Rowman & Littlefield Publishers, Inc.

Security & Stability in Afghanistan: Status of U.S. Strategy & Operations & the Way Ahead. 2009. iii, 71p. (978-0-16-084302-0(2), 552-070-39857-1) United States Government Printing Office.

Self, Nate. Two Wars: One Hero's Fight on Two Fronts — Abroad & Within. (ENG.). 400p. 2009. pap. 14.99 (978-1-4143-2010-6(8)) 2008. (Illus.). 22.99 (978-1-4143-2009-0(4)) Tyndale Hse. Pubs.

Shaffer, Anthony. Operation Dark Heart: Spycraft & Special Ops on the Frontlines of Afghanistan — & the Path to Victory. 2010. (ENG.). 320p. 25.99 (978-0-312-60369-4(X), Dunne, Thomas Bks.) St. Martin's Pr.

—Operation Dark Heart: Spycraft & Special Ops on the Frontlines of Afghanistan — And the Path to Victory. 2011. (ENG.). 320p. pap. 15.99 (978-0-312-60691-6(5), St. Martin's Griffin) St. Martin's Pr.

Shinn, James & Dobbins, James. Afghan Peace Talks: A Primer, 1 vol. 2011. (Illus.). 126p. (C). pap. 24.50 (978-0-8330-5819-5(3)) RAND Corp., The.

Simons, Suzanne. Master of War: Blackwater USA's Erik Prince & the Business of War. 288p. 2010. (ENG.). pap. 15.99 (978-0-06-167271-2(8), Harper Paperbacks) 2009. 27.99 (978-0-06-165135-9(4)) HarperCollins Pubs.

Simonsen, Robert A., ed. Marines Dodging Death: Sixty-Two Accounts of Close Calls in World War II, Korea, Vietnam, Lebanon, Iraq & Afghanistan. 2008. (ENG., Illus.). 347p. pap. 35.00 (978-0-7864-3821-1(5)) McFarland & Co., Inc. Pubs.

The Situation in Afghanistan: Hearings Before the Committee on Armed Services, United States Senate, One Hundred Eleventh Congress, Second Session, June 15 & 16, 2010. 2011. iii, 86p. (978-0-16-088128-2(5), 552-070-42548-9) United States Government Printing Office.

Southby-Tailyour, Ewen. 3 Commando Brigade: Helmand Assault. 2011. (ENG., Illus.). 284p. pap. 14.95 (978-0-09-193776-8(0)) Ebury Publishing GBR. Dist: Independent Pubs. Group.

Stachan, Hew, et al. British Generals in Blair's Wars. 2012. (Military Strategy & Operational Art Ser.). (Illus.). 457p. pap. 59.95 (978-1-4094-3736-9(1)) Ashgate Publishing Co.

Stanton, Doug. Horse Soldiers: The Extraordinary Story of a Band of U. S. Soldiers Who Rode to Victory in Afghanistan. (ENG., Illus.). 2010. 432p. pap. 16.00 (978-1-4165-8052-2(2)) 2009. 416p. 28.00 (978-1-4165-8051-5(4)) Scribner. (Scribner).

—Horse Soldiers: The Extraordinary Story of a Band of U. S. Soldiers Who Rode to Victory in Afghanistan. Lt. ed. 2010. (ENG.). 790p. pap. 16.99 (978-1-59413-369-5(7), Large Print Pr.) Thorndike Pr.

Steps Needed for a Successful 2014 Transition in Afghanistan: Hearing Before the Committee on Foreign Relations, United States Senate, One Hundred Twelfth Congress, First Session, May 10, 2011. 2011. (Illus.). iii, 63p. (978-0-16-089390-2(9), 552-070-43374-1) United States Government Printing Office.

Stewart, Lyle, ed. Afghanistan & Canada: Is There an Alternative to the War? 2009. (ENG.). 224p. 44.99 (978-1-55164-329-8(4)); pap. 24.99 (978-1-55164-328-1(6)) Black Rose Bks. CAN. Dist: Consortium Bk. Sales & Distribution.

Stewart, Rory, pref. & text. Afghanistan: Broken Promise, 1 vol. 2007. (ENG., Illus.). 112p. pap. 39.95 (978-88-8158-646-2(0)) Charta ITA. Dist: D.A.P./Distributed Art Pubs.

Strachan, Hew, et al. British Generals in Blair's Wars. 2012. (Military Strategy & Operational Art Ser.). (Illus.). 457p. 59.95 (978-1-4094-3737-6(X)); 460p. 124.95 (978-1-4094-3735-2(3)) Ashgate Publishing Co.

Subcommittee Hearing: Is the Veterans Corporation Prepared to Provide Entrepreneurial Development Assistance to Service Men & Women Returning from Iraq & Afghanistan? 2007. iii, 72p. (978-0-16-080168-6(0), 552-070-36905-8) United States Government Printing Office.

Sullivan, Christine. Saving Cinnamon: The Amazing True Story of a Missing Military Puppy & the Desperate Mission to Bring Her Home. 2010. (ENG., Illus.). 256p. pap. 14.99 (978-0-312-64955-5(X), St. Martin's Griffin) St. Martin's Pr.

Supplemental Appropriations for Fiscal Year 2010: Hearing Before the Committee on Appropriations, United States Senate, One Hundred Eleventh Congress, Second Session, Special Hearing, March 25, 2010, Washington, DC. 2010. iv, 72p. (978-0-16-086835-1(1), 552-070-41749-4) United States Government Printing Office.

Sustaining the Force: Challenges to Readiness: Hearing Before the Subcommittee on Readiness of the Committee on Armed Services, House of Representatives, One Hundred Twelfth Congress, First Session, Hearing Held April 7, 2011. 2011. (Illus.). iii, 91p. (978-0-16-089733-7(5), 552-070-43612-0) United States Government Printing Office.

Tetreault, Stephan R., ed. Saluting American Valor: Selfless Courage at the Moment of Truth. 2010. (ENG.). 208p. 24.95 (978-1-935043-17-1(X)) Stephens Pr. LLC.

Tibbs, Brian. They Did Not Return: Honouring St. Catharines' War Dead: WWII 1939-1945 Korea 1950-1953 Afghanistan 2009. 2010. (Illus.). 185p. (978-0-9739629-3-2(3)) Mayholme Foundation.

Tillman, Marie. The Letter: My Journey Through Love, Loss, & Life. 2012. (ENG.). 272p. 23.99 (978-0-446-57145-6(8)) Grand Central Publishing.

Tillman, Mary. Boots on the Ground by Dusk: My Tribute to Pat Tillman. 2008. 18.50 (978-1-60529-924-2(3)); (ENG., Illus.). 368p. 25.95 (978-1-59486-880-1(8), Modern Times) Rodale Pr., Inc.

Time Magazine Editors. Time Beyond 9/11: Portraits of Resilience. 2011. (ENG., Illus.). 112p. 19.95 (978-1-60320-246-6(3), Time Bks.) Time Home Entertainment, Inc.

Training & Equipping Afghan Security Forces: Unaccounted Weapons & Strategic Challenges: Hearing Before the Subcommittee on National Security & Foreign Affairs of the Committee on Oversight & Government Reform, House of Representatives, One Hundred Eleventh Congress, First Session, February 12, 2009. 2011. (Illus.). iii, 75p. (978-0-16-088822-9(0), 552-070-42956-5) United States Government Printing Office.

Transition Assistance Program: Field Hearing Before the Subcommittee on Economic Opportunity of the Committee on Veterans' Affairs, U.S. House of Representatives, One Hundred Tenth Congress, Second Session, July 28, 2008, Field Hearing Held in Rapid City, SD. 2009. iv, 87p. (978-0-16-082813-3(9), 552-070-38795-1) United States Government Printing Office.

Transition Assistance Program for Guard & Reserve Forces: Field Hearing Before the Subcommittee on Economic Opportunity of the Committee on Veterans' Affairs, House of Representatives, One Hundred Tenth Congress, Second Session, May 16, 2008, Field Hearing Held in South Bend, IN. 2008. iii, 81p.

(978-0-16-082354-1(4), 552-070-38411-1) United States Government Printing Office.

Troops, Diplomats, & Aid: Assessing Strategic Resources for Afghanistan: Hearing Before the Subcommittee on National Security & Foreign Affairs of the Committee on Oversight & Government Reform, House of Representatives, One Hundred Eleventh Congress, First Session, March 26, 2009. 2010. iii, 107p. (978-0-16-087176-4(X), 552-070-42018-5) United States Government Printing Office.

Tucker, Spencer C., ed. The Encyclopedia of Middle East Wars: The United States in the Persian Gulf, Afghanistan, & Iraq Conflicts, 5 vols. 2010. (Illus.). 1887p. 495.00 (978-1-85109-947-4(6), MIDEWA1C) ABC-CLIO, LLC.

Tupper, Benjamin. Greetings from Afghanistan, Send More Ammo: Dispatches from Taliban Country. 2011. (ENG.). 272p. (gr. 12). 15.00 (978-0-451-23325-7(5), N A L Trade) Penguin Group (USA) Inc.

Turse, Nick, ed. The Case for Withdrawal from Afghanistan. 2010. (ENG., Illus.). 208p. pap. 14.95 (978-1-84467-451-0(7), 844451) Verso Bks. GBR. Dist: Norton, W. W. & Co., Inc.

U. S. Army Dept. Staff & Green, Daniel R. The Valley's Edge: A Year with the Pashtuns in the Heartland of the Taliban. 2011. (Illus.). 288p. 29.95 (978-1-59797-694-7(6)) Potomac Bks., Inc.

United States, Congress House Committee on Armed Services Staff, contrib. by. Afghanistan: Operations & Reconstruction: Hearing Before the Committee on Armed Services, House of Representatives, One Hundred Ninth Congress, First Session, Hearing Held, June 22, 2005. 2007. iii, 85p. (978-0-16-078161-2(2), 552-070-35559-6) United States Government Printing Office.

United States Senate. Tora Bora Revisited: How We Failed to Get Bin Laden & Why It Matters Today (Decisive Battles of the 21st Century) 2009. 50p. pap. 20.63 (978-1-60888-012-6(5)) Nimble Bks. LLC.

U.S. Department of Veterans Affairs/U.S. Department of Defense Cooperation in Reintegration of National Guard & Reserve: Hearing Before the Subcommittee on Oversight & Investigations of the Committee on Veterans' Affairs, U.S. House of Representatives, One Hundred Tenth Congress, Second Session, June 24, 2008. 2009. (Illus.). iii, 53p. (978-0-16-082727-3(2), 552-070-38737-4) United States Government Printing Office.

U.S. Promotion of the Afghan Economy: Impediments & Opportunities: Hearing Before the Subcommittee on National Security & Foreign Affairs of the Committee on Oversight & Government Reform, House of Representatives, One Hundred Eleventh Congress, First Session, July 14, 2009. 2010. (Illus.). iii, 83p. (978-0-16-086454-4(2), 552-070-41511-4) United States Government Printing Office.

U.S. Strategy for Afghanistan: Achieving Peace & Stability in the Graveyard of Empires: Hearing Before the Subcommittee on the Middle East & South Asia of the Committee on Foreign Affairs, House of Representatives, One Hundred Eleventh Congress, First Session, April 2, 2009. 2009. (Illus.). iii, 99p. (978-0-16-084272-6(7), 552-070-39837-6) United States Government Printing Office.

Ussery, Easton H. War in Afghanistan: Strategy, Military Operations & Congressional Issues. 2009. (Defense, Security & Strategies Ser.). 69.00 (978-1-60741-579-4(8)) Nova Science Pubs., Inc.

van Agtmael, Peter. 2nd Tour Hope I Don't Die. 2009. 112p. pap. 24.00 (978-1-934334-07-2(3)) Photolucida.

Verschueren, Paul. Picturing Afghanistan: The Photography of Foreign Conflict. 2012. (978-1-61289-038-8(5)); pap. (978-1-61289-039-5(3)) Hampton Pr., Inc.

Voice of Veterans of the Afghan War: Hearing Before the Committee on Foreign Relations, United States Senate, One Hundred Eleventh Congress, First Session, April 23, 2009. 2010. iii, 41p. (978-0-16-085191-9(2), 552-070-40544-5) United States Government Printing Office.

Warner, John, ed. Iraq, Afghanistan, & the Global War on Terrorism: Hearing before the Committee on Armed Services, U. S. Senate. 2007. (Illus.). 201p. (C). reprint ed. pap. 15.00 (978-1-4223-1713-6(7)) DIANE Publishing Co.

Warnock, John W. Creating a Failed State: The U. S. & Canada in Afghanistan. 2008. (ENG.). 192p. pap. 21.95 (978-1-55266-262-5(4)) Fernwood Publishing Co., Ltd. CAN. Dist: Independent Pubs. Group.

Wattie, Chris. Contact Charlie: The Canadian Army, the Taliban & the Battle That Saved Afghanistan. 2009. (ENG., Illus.). 304p. 28.95 (978-1-55470-084-4(1)) Key Porter Bks. CAN. Dist: Perseus-PGW.

—Contact Charlie: The Canadian Army, the Taliban, & the Battle That Saved Afghanistan. 2010. (ENG., Illus.). 304p. pap. 16.95 (978-1-55470-276-3(3)) Key Porter Bks. CAN. Dist: Perseus-PGW.

Webb, Brandon & Mann, John David. The Red Circle: My Journey into the Elite Navy SEAL Sniper Corps. 2012. (ENG., Illus.). 400p. 26.99 (978-0-312-60422-6(X)) St. Martin's Pr.

Weiss, Mitch & Maurer, Kevin. No Way Out: A Story of Valor in the Mountains of Afghanistan. 2012. (ENG., Illus.). 336p. (gr. 12). 26.95 (978-0-425-24526-2(8), Berkley Hardcover) Penguin Group (USA) Inc.

West, Bing. The Wrong War: Grit, Strategy, & the Way Out of Afghanistan. 2011. (Illus.). 336p. 28.00 (978-1-4000-6873-9(8), Random House) Random House Publishing Group.

Wildman, David & Bennis, Phyllis. Ending the US War in Afghanistan: A Primer. 2010. (ENG.). 272p. pap. 10.00 (978-1-56656-785-5(8), Olive Branch Pr.) Interlink Publishing Group, Inc.

Williams, Brian Glyn. Afghanistan Declassified: A Guide to America's Longest War. 2011. (Illus.). 264p. 34.95 (978-0-8122-4403-8(6)) Univ. of Pennsylvania Pr.

Williams, Gary. SEAL of Honor: Operation Red Wings & the Life of Lt. Michael P. Murphy, USN. (Illus.). 256p. 2011. pap. 18.95 (978-1-59114-965-1(7)) 2010. 29.95 (978-1-59114-957-6(6)) Naval Institute Pr.

Williams, M. J. The Good War: NATO & the Liberal Conscience in Afghanistan. 2011. (ENG., Illus.). 224p. 90.00 (978-0-230-29427-1(8)); pap. 32.00 (978-0-230-29428-8(6)) Palgrave Macmillan.

Williamson, Chaplain Don. Bringing Courage to the Courageous. 2010. 170p. pap. 14.99 (978-1-60957-687-5(X)) Xulon Pr., Inc.

Williamson, Janice. Omar Khadr, Oh Canada. 2012. (ENG., Illus.). 400p. (C). pap. (978-0-7735-4022-4(9)) McGill-Queen's Univ. Pr.

Windsor, Lee A., et al. Kandahar Tour: The Turning Point in Canada's Afghan Mission. 2010. (ENG., Illus.). 256p. 36.95 (978-0-470-15761-9(5), Wiley) Wiley, John & Sons, Inc.

Wise, James, Jr. & Baron, Scott. Women at War. 2011. (Illus.). 256p. pap. 19.95 (978-1-59114-972-9(X)) Naval Institute Pr.

Wise, James E., Jr. & Baron, Scott. Women at War: Iraq, Afghanistan, & Other Conflicts. 2006. (Illus.). 234p. 29.95 (978-1-59114-939-2(8)) Naval Institute Pr.

Wiss, Ray. A Line in the Sand: Canadians at War in Kandahar, 1 vol. 2011. (ENG., Illus.). 424p. pap. 18.95 (978-1-55365-926-6(0)); 29.95 (978-1-55365-592-3(3)) D&M Pubs. Inc. CAN. Dist: Perseus-PGW.

Wiss, Ray H. FOB Doc: A Doctor on the Front Lines in Afghanistan - A War Diary, 1 vol. 2010. (ENG., Illus.). 224p. 26.95 (978-1-55365-472-8(2)) D&M Pubs. Inc. CAN. Dist: Perseus-PGW.

Woodward, Bob. Obama's Wars. (ENG., Illus.). 464p. 2011. pap. 16.00 (978-1-4391-7250-6(1)) 2010. 30.00 (978-1-4391-7249-0(8)) Simon & Schuster.

Worrell, Mark P. Why Nations Go to War. 2010. (Framing 21st Century Social Issues Ser.). (ENG.). 80p. pap. 9.95 (978-0-415-89211-7(2)) Routledge.

Wright, Donald P., et al. A Different Kind of War: the United States Army in Operation ENDURING FREEDOM, October 2001 - September 2005: The United States Army in Operation ENDURING FREEDOM, October 2001 - September 2005. Combat Studies Institute (U.S.) & Contemporary Operations Study Team (U.S.), eds. 2010. (ENG., Illus.). 414p. pap. 44.00 (978-0-9823283-1-6(1), Dept. of the Army) United States Government Printing Office.

Zaeef, Abdul Salam. My Life with the Taliban. Kuehn, Felix & van Linschoten, Alex Strick, eds. & trs. by. from PUS. 2010. (Columbia/Hurst Ser.). (ENG., Illus.). 360p. (gr. 17). 29.95 (978-0-231-70148-8(9)) Columbia Univ. Pr.

Zakheim, Dov S. A Vulcan's Tale: How the Bush Administration Mismanaged the Reconstruction of Afghanistan. 2011. (ENG.). 335p. 32.95 (978-0-8157-2122-2(6)) Brookings Institution Pr.

Zhu, Yongbiao. "9.11" Zhi Hou de Afuhan. 2009. (Illus.). (978-7-5011-8879-6(3)) Xinhua Publishing Hse.

Zimmerman, Dwight Jon & Gresham, John D. Uncommon Valor: The Medal of Honor & the Warriors Who Earned It in Afghanistan & Iraq. 2011. (ENG., Illus.) 352p. pap. 15.99 (978-0-312-60456-1(4), St. Martin's Griffin) St. Martin's Pr.

AFGHAN WARS

Adamec, Ludwig W. The A to Z of Afghan Wars, Revolutions & Insurgencies. 2010. (A to Z Guide Ser.). (ENG.). 520p. pap. 34.45 (978-0-8108-7624-8(8)) Scarecrow Pr., Inc.

Adye, John. Indian Frontier Policy. 2006. (ENG.). 48p. pap. 16.99 (978-1-4264-0270-8(8)); 44p. pap. 12.99 (978-1-4264-0287-6(2)) BiblioBazaar.

—Indian Frontier Policy. 2009. 48p. pap. (978-0-217-48897-6(8)) Books LLC.

Adye, John. Sitan: A Mountain Campaign on the Borders of Afghanistan in 1863-the British Raj & Tribesmen on the Northwestern Frontier of India. 2011. 100p. (978-0-85706-639-8(0)); pap. (978-0-85706-640-4(4)) Leonaur Ltd.

Atkinson, James. Afghan Expedition - Notes & Sketches from the First British Afghan War Of 1839-1840. 2007. 304p. 40.00 (978-1-59048-280-3(8)) Long Riders' Guild Pr., The.

Atwood, Rodney. The March to Kandahar. (Illus.). 224p. 2012. pap. 24.95 (978-1-84884-672-2(X)) 2009. 39.99 (978-1-84415-848-5(9)) Pen & Sword Bks. Ltd. GBR. Dist: Casemate Pubs. & Bk. Distributors, LLC.

Barnes, Gregory & Fremont-Barnes, Gregory. Anglo-Afghan Wars, 1839-1919. 2009. (Essential Histories Ser.). (ENG., Illus.). 96p. pap. 19.95 (978-1-84603-446-6(9)) Osprey Publishing, Ltd. GBR. Dist: Random Hse., Inc.

Brooke, Henry. Brigade Commander: Afghanistan-the Journal of the Commander of the 2nd Infantry Brigade, Kandahar Field Force During the Second Afghan War. 2008. 152p. (978-1-84677-570-3(1)); pap. (978-1-84677-569-7(8)) Leonaur Ltd.

Burke, John & Norfolk, Simon, photos by. Burke + Norfolk: Photographs from the War in Afghanistan. 2011. (ENG., Illus.). 168p. 65.00 (978-1-907893-11-7(3)) Lewis, Dewi Publishing GBR. Dist: Consortium Bk. Sales & Distribution.

Eyre, Vincent. The Military Operations at Cabul-the Kabul Insurrection of 1841-42 & Rough Notes During Imprisonment in Afghanistan 1843. 2011. 272p. (978-0-85706-589-6(0)); pap. (978-0-85706-590-2(4)) Leonaur Ltd.

Forbes, Archibald. The Afghan Wars. 2009. (ENG.). 352p. 38.99 (978-1-117-26106-5(9)) BiblioBazaar.

—The Afghan Wars 1839-42 And 1878-80. 2008. 280p. 25.99 (978-0-554-32049-6(5)) 2008. 280p. 28.99 (978-0-554-22746-7(0)) 2007. (ENG.). 254p. pap. 21.99 (978-1-4264-2938-5(X)) BiblioBazaar.

—The Afghan Wars 1839-42 & 1878-80. l.t. ed. 2007. (ENG.). 278p. pap. 23.99 (978-1-4264-2991-0(6)) BiblioBazaar.

—Britain in Afghanistan: The First Afghan War 1839-42. 2007. 164p. (978-1-84677-304-4(0)); (Illus.). per. (978-1-84677-303-7(2)) Leonaur Ltd.

—Britain in Afghanistan: The Second Afghan War 1878-80. 2007. 172p. (978-1-84677-306-8(7)); per. (978-1-84677-305-1(9)) Leonaur Ltd.

Gleig, G. R. Afghanistan: The Beleaguered Brigade-an Account of Sale's Brigade During the First Afghan War. 2008. 212p. (978-1-84677-578-9(7)); pap. (978-1-84677-577-2(9)) Leonaur Ltd.

Glukhov, Nikolay. Risen from Hell. 2009. 240p. 36.99 (978-1-4389-7010-3(2)); pap. 21.49 (978-1-4389-7011-0(0)) AuthorHouse.

Hensman, Howard. The Afghan War Of 1879-80. 2009. 482p. pap. (978-0-217-88604-8(3)) Books LLC.

—The Afghan War Of 1879-80. 2007. (ENG.). 584p. 58.95 (978-0-548-15383-3(3)); pap. 43.95 (978-1-4304-4783-2(4)) Kessinger Publishing, LLC.

Holdsworth, T. W. E. Campaign of the Indus: A Series of Letters from an Officer of the Bombay Division. 2007. (ENG.). 146p. pap. 18.99 (978-1-4264-9215-0(4)); 166p. pap. 21.99 (978-1-4264-9272-3(3)) BiblioBazaar.

Holdsworth, Thomas. Campaign of the Indus Experiences of A. 2007. (ENG.). (978-1-84677-100-2(5)); pap. (978-1-84677-091-3(2)) Leonaur Ltd.

InterConsult, Lancer. The Afghan War Of 1879-1880. 2008. (Illus.). 570p. 27.95 (978-0-9815378-6-3(3)) Lancer International Inc., The.

—The First Afghan War & It's Causes. 2008. 484p. 27.95 (978-0-9815378-1-8(2)) Lancer International Inc., The.

Johnson, Robert. The Afghan Way of War: How & Why They Fight, 1 vol. 2011. (ENG., Illus.). 384p. 29.95 (978-0-19-979856-8(7)) Oxford Univ. Pr., Inc.

Kekewich, Margaret. Retreat & Retribution in Afghanistan 1842: Two Journals of the First Afghan War. 2011. (Illus.). 224p. 39.95 (978-1-84884-397-4(6)) Pen & Sword Bks. Ltd. GBR. Dist: Casemate Pubs. & Bk. Distributors, LLC.

Kingston, W. H. G. Blow the Bugle, Draw the Sword: The Wars, Campaigns, Regiments & Soldiers of the British & Indian Armies During the Victorian Era, 1839-1898. 2007. 364p. (978-1-84677-265-8(6)); per. (978-1-84677-266-5(4)) Leonaur Ltd.

Matthews, Matt. An Ever Present Danger: A Concise History of British Military Operations on the North-West Frontier, 1849-1947. 2010. (978-0-9841901-3-3(9)) United States Government Printing Office.

Norris, J. A. The First Afghan War, 1838-1842. 2010. (ENG.). 520p. pap. 39.99 (978-0-521-13096-7(4)) Cambridge Univ. Pr.

Robson, Brian. Crisis on the Frontier: The Third Afghan War & the Campaign in Waziristan 1919-20. 2007. (ENG., Illus.). 328p. pap. 38.00 (978-1-86227-403-7(7), Spellmount, Limited Pubs.) History Pr. Ltd.,The GBR. Dist: Independent Pubs. Group.

—The Road to Kabul: The Second Afghan War, 1878-1881. 2008. (ENG.). 416p. pap. 34.95 (978-1-86227-416-7(9), Spellmount, Limited Pubs.) History Pr. Ltd.,The GBR. Dist: Independent Pubs. Group.

Sale, Florentia. Lady Sale's Afghanistan: An Indomitable Victorian Lady's Account of the Retreat from Kabul During the First Afghan War. 2009. 288p. (978-1-84677-732-5(1)); pap. (978-1-84677-731-8(3)) Leonaur Ltd.

Stewart, Jules & Richards, David. The Crimson Snow: Britain's First Disaster in Afghanistan. 2008. (ENG., Illus.). 256p. 42.95 (978-0-7509-4825-8(6)) History Pr. Ltd.,The GBR. Dist: Independent Pubs. Group.

Taylor, William. With the Cavalry to Afghanistan: The Experiences of a Trooper of H. M. 4th Light Dragoons During the First Afghan War. 2008. 124p. (978-1-84677-568-0(X)); pap. (978-1-84677-567-3(1)) Leonaur Ltd.

AFGHANI, JAMAL AL-DIN, 1838-1897

Keddie, Nikki R. Sayyid Jamal Ad-Din Al-Afghani: A Political Biography. 2008. 508p. pap. 52.00 (978-1-59740-467-9(5)) ACLS Humanities E-Book.

Kedourie, Elie. Afghani & 'Abduh: An Essay on Religious Unbelief & Political Activism in Modern Islam. 2007. 112p. 165.00 (978-0-415-44289-3(3)) Routledge.

AFGHANISTAN

see also names of regions, cities, etc. in Afghanistan

Hamilton, Angus. Afghanistan. 2009. 344p. 32.99 (978-1-113-61130-7(8)); pap. 32.75 (978-1-113-61129-1(4)); pap. 31.75 (978-1-113-61128-4(6)) BiblioBazaar.

—Afghanistan. 2009. 180p. pap. (978-0-217-67676-2(6)) Books LLC.

Pigott, Peter. Canada in Afghanistan: The War So Far. 2007. (ENG., Illus.). 240p. 35.00 (978-1-55002-674-0(7), Dundurn Pr.) Dundurn CAN. Dist: Ingram Pub. Services.

Rotberg, Robert I., ed. Building a New Afghanistan. 2007. (ENG., Illus.). 242p. 44.95 (978-0-8157-7568-3(7)); per. 20.95 (978-0-8157-7569-0(5)) Brookings Institution Pr.

AFGHANISTAN—BIOGRAPHY

Ahmedi, Farah & Ansary, Mir Tamim. The Other Side of the Sky: A Memoir. 2008. (Illus.). v, 273p. (978-0-7362-3173-2(0)) Hampton-Brown Bks.

Akbari, Ali. The Illegal Journeys: From East to West. 2011. 326p. 29.99 (978-1-4628-9664-6(2)); pap. 19.99 (978-1-4628-9663-9(4)) Xlibris Corp.

Allen, Nick. Embed: With the World's Armies in Afghanistan. 2011. (ENG., Illus.). 288p. 29.95 (978-0-7524-5889-2(2)) History Pr. Ltd.,The GBR. Dist: Independent Pubs. Group.

Barker, Kim. The Taliban Shuffle: Strange Days in Afghanistan & Pakistan. 2012. (ENG., Illus.). 320p. pap. 15.95 (978-0-307-47738-5(X), Anchor) Knopf Doubleday Publishing Group.

Bloom, Harold, ed. Khaled Hosseini's the Kite Runner. 2009. (Bloom's Guides). 96p. (C). (gr. 9-18). 30.00 (978-1-60413-199-4(3), Chelsea Hse.) Facts On File, Inc.

Charkhi, Khaled Siddiq. From My Memories: Memoirs of political imprisonment from childhood in Afghanistan. 2010. 324p. (ENG.). 28.50 (978-1-4490-7277-3(1)); pap. 17.99 (978-1-4490-7276-6(3)) AuthorHouse.

Chavis, Melody E. Meena, Heroine of Afghanistan: The Martyr Who Founded RAWA, the Revolutionary Association of the Women of Afghanistan, ESS, ARK. Date not set. mass mkt. (978-0-312-98568-4(1), St. Martin's Paperbacks) St. Martin's Pr.

Davis, Russell. Ghost - a Story of Courage, Loyalty & Betrayal. 2010. 100p. pap. (978-1-907652-55-4(8)) Grosvenor Hse. Publishing Ltd.

Dobbins, James F. After the Taliban: Nation-Building in Afghanistan. 2008. (Illus.). 192p. 24.95 (978-1-59797-083-9(2)) Potomac Bks., Inc.

Farivar, Masood. Confessions of a Mullah Warrior. 2010. (ENG.). 336p. pap. 15.00 (978-0-8021-4454-6(3), Grove Pr.) Grove/Atlantic, Inc.

Geda, Fabio. In the Sea There Are Crocodiles: Based on the True Story of Enaiatollah Akbari. 2011. (ENG., Illus.). 224p. 22.95 (978-0-385-53473-4(6), Doubleday) Knopf Doubleday Publishing Group.

Glavin, Terry. Come from the Shadows: The Long & Lonely Struggle for Peace in Afghanistan, 1 vol. 2011. (ENG., Illus.). 256p. 26.95 (978-1-55365-782-8(9)) D&M Pubs. Inc. CAN. Dist: Perseus-PGW.

Inqita, Nasir. Yaqub Lays: Mard-I Bartar-I Tarikh-I Iran. 2010. (PER., Illus.). iii, 282p. (978-1-59584-257-2(8)) Ketab Corp.

Joya, Malalai. A Woman among Warlords: The Extraordinary Story of an Afghan Who Dared to Raise Her Voice. 2011. (ENG.). 256p. pap. 16.00 (978-1-4391-0947-2(8), Scribner) Scribner.

Karzai, Hamid. Letter from Kabul. 2006. 192p. 25.95 (978-0-470-04515-2(9), Wiley) Wiley, John & Sons, Inc.

Keeling, Philip C. Two Mountains to Climb. 2010. pap. 10.99 (978-1-61566-802-1(0)) Tate Publishing & Enterprises, LLC.

Koofi, Fawzia & Ghouri, Nadene. The Favored Daughter: One Woman's Fight to Lead Afghanistan into the Future. 2012. (ENG., Illus.). 272p. 26.00 (978-0-230-12067-9(9)) Palgrave Macmillan.

Lemmon, Gayle Tzemach. The Dressmaker of Khair Khana: Five Sisters, One Remarkable Family, & the Woman Who Risked Everything to Keep Them Safe. (P. S. Ser.). (ENG., Illus.). 2012. 272p. pap. 14.99 (978-0-06-173247-8(8), HarperPerennial) 2011. 288p. 24.99 (978-0-06-173237-9(0)) HarperCollins Pubs.

—The Dressmaker of Khair Khana: Five Sisters, One Remarkable Family, & the Woman Who Risked Everything to Keep Them Safe. l.t. ed. (ENG.). 287p. 2012. pap. 16.99 (978-1-59413-575-0(4), Large Print Pr.) 2011. 31.99 (978-1-4104-3965-9(8)) Thorndike Pr.

MacDonald, David & Macdonald, David. Drugs in Afghanistan: Opium, Outlaws & Scorpion Tales, 1 vol. 2007. (ENG., Illus.). 320p. 36.00 (978-0-7453-2617-7(X)); lib. bdg. 100.00 (978-0-7453-2618-4(8)) Pluto Pr. GBR. Dist: Macmillan.

Mastrogiacomo, Daniele. Days of Fear: A Firsthand Account of Captivity under the New Taliban. Reynolds, Michael, tr. from ITA. 2010. (ENG.). 176p. (gr. 12-18). 15.00 (978-1-933372-97-6(4)) Europa Editions, Inc.

Mills, Nick B. Karzai: The Failing American Intervention & the Struggle for Afghanistan. 2007. (ENG., Illus.). 256p. 25.95 (978-0-470-13400-9(3), Wiley) Wiley, John & Sons, Inc.

Minott, Janice. Letters from Kabul 1966-1968: A Memoir. 2008. (Illus.). xxxvi, 361p. 27.50 (978-1-4251-1349-0(4)) Trafford Publishing.

Monis, Haroon. Journey into Paradise from the Hell of Afghanistan. 2007. 73p. pap. 10.00 (978-1-4303-1445-5(1)) Lulu Enterprises Inc.

Neill, John Martin Bladen. With the Somersets in Afghanistan: The Recollections of an Officer of H. M. 40th Regiment During the First Afghan War 1838-42. 2011. 240p. (978-0-85706-489-9(4)); pap. (978-0-85706-490-5(8)) Leonaur Ltd.

Omidian, Patricia A. When Bamboo Bloom: An Anthropologist in Taliban's Afghanistan. 2010. 123p. (C). pap. 14.95 (978-1-57766-700-1(X)) Waveland Pr., Inc.

Qayumi, Shahnaz. Like You & Me. 2011. 40p. 16.99 (978-1-4520-8397-1(5)) AuthorHouse.

Rohde, David & Mulvihill, Kristen. A Rope & a Prayer: The Story of a Kidnapping. 2011. (ENG.). 384p. (gr. 12). 16.00 (978-0-14-312005-6(0), Penguin (Non-Classics)) Penguin Group (USA) Inc.

Scott, Jake. Blood Clot. 2008. (Illus.). 200p. 49.95 (978-1-906033-31-6(5)) Helion & Co., Ltd. GBR. Dist: Casemate Pubs. & Bk. Distributors, LLC.

—Blood Clot: In Combat with the Patrols Platoon, 3 para, Afghanistan 2006. 2010. (Illus.). 232p. pap. 39.95 (978-1-906033-81-1(1)) Helion & Co., Ltd. GBR. Dist: Casemate Pubs. & Bk. Distributors, LLC.

Shpoon, Wazir Akbar. Farangi - Autobiography of an Afghan Immigrant. 2011. 188p. pap. 14.00 (978-1-257-13377-2(2)) Lulu Enterprises Inc.

Sullivan, Christine. Saving Cinnamon: The Amazing True Story of a Missing Military Puppy & the Desperate Mission to Bring Her Home. 2010. (ENG., Illus.). 256p. pap. 14.99 (978-0-312-64955-5(X), St. Martin's Griffin) St. Martin's Pr.

Van Dyk, Jere. Captive: My Time as a Prisoner of the Taliban. 2011. (ENG., Illus.). 288p. pap. 14.99 (978-0-312-57342-3(1), St. Martin's Griffin) St. Martin's Pr.

Wahab, Saima. In My Father's Country. 2012. (978-0-307-88495-4(3)) Crown Publishing Group.

WAHAB, Saima. In My Father's Country: An Afghan Woman Defies Her Fate. 2012. (ENG.). 352p. 25.00 (978-0-307-88494-7(5), Crown) Crown Publishing Group.

Webb, Brandon & Mann, John David. The Red Circle: My Journey into the Elite Navy SEAL Sniper Corps. 2012. (ENG., Illus.). 400p. 26.99 ***(978-0-312-60422-5(X))*** St. Martin's Pr.

Whitteridge, Gordon. Charles Masson of Afghanistan: Explorer, Archaeologist, Numismatist & Intelligence Agent. 2006. (ENG., Illus.). 22.95 *(978-974-524-020-9(6))* Orchid Pr. THA. Dist: National Bk. Network.

Wiss, Ray. A Line in the Sand: Canadians at War in Kandahar, 1 vol. 2011. (ENG., Illus.). 424p. 29.95 *(978-1-55365-592-3(3))* D&M Pubs. Inc. CAN. Dist: Perseus-PGW.

Wiss, Ray H. FOB Doc: A Doctor on the Front Lines in Afghanistan - A War Diary, 1 vol. 2010. (ENG., Illus.). 224p. 26.95 *(978-1-55365-472-8(2))* D&M Pubs. Inc. CAN. Dist: Perseus-PGW.

Wuellner, Kira. Unsat: Letters from a Warrior in Afghanistan. 2011. 108p. pap. 15.99 ***(978-1-4628-9991-3(9))*** Xlibris Corp.

Zaeef, Abdul Salam. My Life with the Taliban. Kuehn, Felix & van Linschoten, Alex Strick, eds. & trs. by. from PUS. 2010. (Columbia/Hurst Ser.). (ENG., Illus.). 360p. (gr. 17). 29.95 *(978-0-231-70148-8(9))* Columbia Univ. Pr.

Zahrah Nasir, B. K. The Parwan Wind - Dust Motes. 2007. (ENG., Illus.). 250p. pap. 24.95 *(978-0-19-547402-2(3))* Oxford Univ. Pr., Inc.

AFGHANISTAN—ANTIQUITIES

Aruz, Joan & Fino, Elisabetta Valtz, eds. Afghanistan: Forging Civilizations along the Silk Road. 2012. (ENG., Illus.). 144p. pap. 35.00 ***(978-0-300-17954-5(5))*** Yale Univ. Pr.

Brancaccio, Pia & Behrendt, Kurt, eds. Gandharan Buddhism: Archaeology, Art, & Texts, 1 vol. 2007. (ENG., Illus.). 328p. pap. 34.95 *(978-0-7748-1081-4(5))* UBC Pr. CAN. Dist: Univ. of Washington Pr.

Chugg, Andrew. Alexander the Great in Afghanistan: A Reconstruction of Cleitarchus. 2011. 212p. pap. ***(978-0-9556790-3-2(6))*** AMC Pubns.

Errington, Elizabeth & Sarkhosh Curtis, Vesta. From Persepolis to the Punjab: Exploring the Past in in Iran, Afghanistan & Pakistan. 2011. (Illus.). 288p. (C). pap. 60.00 *(978-0-7141-1177-3(5))* British Museum Pr. GBR. Dist: Brown, David Bk. Co., The.

Hiebert, Fredrik. Afghanistan: Hidden Treasures from the National Museum, Kabul. Cambon, Pierre, ed. 2008. (ENG., Illus.). 304p. pap. 30.00 *(978-1-4262-0295-7(4))* National Geographic Society.

Hiebert, Fredrik T. & Cambon, Pierre. Afghanistan: Hidden Treasures from the National Museum, Kabul. 2008. (Illus.). 303p. *(978-1-4262-0374-9(8))* National Geographic Society.

Holt, Frank Lee. Lost World of the Golden King: In Search of Ancient Afghanistan. 2012. (Hellenistic Culture & Society Ser.). (ENG.). 304p. 39.95 ***(978-0-520-27342-9(7))*** Univ. of California Pr.

Krieken-Pieters, Juliette van. Art & Archaeology of Afghanistan: Its Fall & Survival: A Multi-Disciplinary Approach. 2006. (Handbook of Oriental Studies. Section Eight. Central Asia Ser.). (Illus.). 412p. *(978-90-04-15182-6(6))* BRILL.

Morgan, Llewelyn. The Buddhas of Bamiyan. 2012. (Wonders of the World Ser.). (Illus.). 256p. 19.95 ***(978-0-674-05788-3(0))*** Harvard Univ. Pr.

AFGHANISTAN—DESCRIPTION AND TRAVEL

Akbar, Said Hyder & Burton, Susan. Come Back to Afghanistan: Trying to Rebuild a Country with My Father, My Brother, My One-Eyed Uncle, Bearded Tribesmen, & PR. 2006. (ENG.). 352p. per. 16.00 *(978-1-59691-068-3(2))* Bloomsbury Publishing.

Allan, Alexander. Afghanistan: A Tour of Duty: A Photographic Portrait. 2009. (ENG., Illus.). 112p. pap. 19.95 *(978-1-906507-39-8(2)*, Trans Millenium Pub Ltd) Antique Collectors' Club GBR. Dist: National Bk. Network.

Amici, Giammarco. Afghanistan, a Country at War with Itself. 2009. 232p. pap. 53.25 *(978-1-60860-774-7(7)*, Eloquent Bks.) AEG Literary Publishing Services, Inc.

Atkinson, James. Afghan Expedition - Notes & Sketches from the First British Afghan War Of 1839-1840. 2007. 304p. 40.00 *(978-1-59048-280-3(8))* Long Riders' Guild Pr., The.

Beisler, Jerry. The Bandit of Kabul: Episode Two of the series: As the Prayer Wheel Turns. 2006. (Illus.). 250p. pap. 29.95 *(978-1-58790-094-5(7))* Regent Pr.

Briongos, Ana M. Winter in Kandahar. 2008. 224p. pap. *(978-1-906393-11-3(7))* Trotamundas Pr., Ltd.

Brophy, Kenneth Michael. A Photo Journal: Seldom Seen Sights: Afghanistan Edition. 2009. (Illus.). 257p. 141.99 *(978-1-4415-2935-0(7))*; pap. 131.99 *(978-1-4415-2934-3(9))* Xlibris Corp.

Burke, John & Norfolk, Simon, photos by. Burke + Norfolk: Photographs from the War in Afghanistan. 2011. (ENG., Illus.). 168p. 65.00 ***(978-1-907893-11-7(3))*** Lewis, Dewi Publishing GBR. Dist: Consortium Bk. Sales & Distribution.

Burslem, Rollo. Peep into Toorkisthan. 2006. 248p. per. *(978-1-4067-1043-4(1)*, Hesperides Pr.) Read Bks.

Byron, Robert. The Road to Oxiana. 2007. (ENG., Illus.). 320p. per. 15.95 *(978-0-19-532560-7(5))* Oxford Univ. Pr., Inc.

Clammer, Paul & Lonely Planet Staff. Afghanistan. 2007. (Country Guides). (ENG., Illus.). 244p. pap. 25.99 *(978-1-74059-642-8(0))* Lonely Planet Pubns.

Elliot, Jason. An Unexpected Light: Travels in Afghanistan. 2nd ed. 2011. (ENG., Illus.). 512p. pap. 18.00 *(978-0-312-62205-3(8))* Picador.

Garcia, J. Malcolm. The Khaarijee: A Chronicle of Friendship & War in Kabul. 2009. (ENG.). 248p. 24.95 *(978-0-8070-0057-1(4))* Beacon Pr.

Giacomelli, Gianni. The Face of Afghanistan. 2007. 101p. pap. 41.95 *(978-1-84753-856-7(8))* Lulu Enterprises Inc.

Girardet, Edward & Walter, Jonathan. Afghanistan: Essential Field Guide to Humanitarian & Conflict Zones. Norchi, Charles & Masood, Mirwais, eds. 3rd ed. 2007. (ENG.). 544p. pap. 29.95 *(978-2-9700176-2-2(8))* Media Action International CHE. Dist: Independent Pubs. Group.

Hafvenstein, Joel. Opium Season: A Year on the Afghan Frontier. 2009. (ENG.). 352p. pap. 16.95 *(978-1-59921-621-8(3)*, Lyons Pr.) Globe Pequot Pr., The.

Hartman, Fred. Window on Afghanistan Rebuilding Health. 2006. (Illus.). 325p. pap. 22.99 *(978-1-4251-0046-9(5))* Trafford Publishing.

Hetherington, Tim, photos by. Infidel. 2010. (ENG., Illus.). 240p. pap. 35.00 *(978-1-905712-18-2(9))* Boot, Chris GBR. Dist: D.A.P./Distributed Art Pubs.

Jubber, Nicholas. Drinking Arak off an Ayatollah's Beard: A Journey Through the Inside-Out Worlds of Iran & Afghanistan. 2010. (ENG., Illus.). 368p. pap. 15.95 *(978-0-306-81384-4(1))* Da Capo Pr., Inc.

Kandahar Provincial Handbook: A Guide to the People & the Province. 2011. 92p. spiral bd. ***(978-1-936336-46-3(4))*** IDS International.

Locken, E. Travel Journal Afghanistan. 2010. 192p. pap. 19.99 *(978-0-557-43253-0(7))* Lulu Enterprises Inc.

Loewen, Arley & McMichael, Josette. Images of Afghanistan: Exploring Afghan Culture through Art & Literature. 2010. (ENG., Illus.). 350p. 39.95 *(978-0-19-547795-5(2))* Oxford Univ. Pr., Inc.

Marine Corps (U.S.). ed. Afghanistan: Alone & Unafraid. 2010. (ENG., Illus.). 108p. (gr. 10). 47.00 *(978-0-16-086131-4(4)*, Dept. of the Navy) United States Government Printing Office.

Meissner, Ursula. Afghanistan: Hope & Beauty in a War-Torn Land. 2008. (Illus.). 189p. pap. *(978-3-7658-1688-8(4))* Bucher, C. J. Verlag GmbH.

Omrani, Bijan & Leeming, Matthew. Afghanistan: A Companion & Guide. 2nd ed. 2011. (Odyssey Illustrated Guides). (ENG., Illus.). 784p. pap. 37.95 *(978-962-217-816-8(2)*, 217816) Airphoto International/Odyssey HKG. Dist: Norton, W. W. & Co., Inc.

Richardson, Nan, ed. Great Game: Afghanistan Seen through Photographers Eyes. 2011. (ENG., Illus.). 200p. 60.00 ***(978-1-884167-79-9(9))*** Umbrage Editions.

Schwarzenbach, Annemarie. All the Roads Are Open: The Afghan Journey. Cole, Isabel Fargo, tr. from GER. 2011. (Seagull Books - the Swiss List Ser.). 124p. 15.00 *(978-0-85742-015-2(1))* Seagull Bks. GBR. Dist: Chicago Distribution Ctr.

Stark, Freya. The Minaret of Djam: An Excursion in Afghanistan. 2010. (Freya Stark Collection). (ENG., Illus.). 168p. pap. 16.00 *(978-1-84885-313-3(0)*, Tauris Parke Paperbacks) I. B. Tauris & Co., Ltd. GBR. Dist: Macmillan.

Weaver, John. A Flame on the Front Line: Journey from America to Afghanistan. 2009. 160p. pap. 14.99 *(978-1-61579-166-8(3))* Xulon Pr., Inc.

Willemsen, Roger. Afghan Journey. 2007. (ENG., Illus.). 148p. 24.95 *(978-1-905791-03-3(8))* Haus Publishing GBR. Dist: Consortium Bk. Sales & Distribution.

Williams, Brian Glyn. Afghanistan Declassified: A Guide to America's Longest War. 2011. (Illus.). 264p. 34.95 ***(978-0-8122-4403-8(6))*** Univ. of Pennsylvania Pr.

Wood, John. A Journey to the Source of the River Oxus. 2007. 374p. 48.95 *(978-0-548-25678-7(0))*; (ENG.). 376p. per. 33.95 *(978-1-4326-6034-5(9))* Kessinger Publishing, LLC.

WYLIE, Donavan. Outposts: Kandahar Province, 1 vol. 2011. (ENG., Illus.). 64p. 45.00 ***(978-3-86930-321-5(2))*** Steidl, Gerhard Druckerei und Verlag DEU. Dist: Innovative Logistics.

Yang, Sunny. Inside Afghanistan: Sunny Yang's Sketches in the Combat Zone. 2010. 180p. pap. 58.99 *(978-1-4269-3228-1(6))* Trafford Publishing.

AFGHANISTAN—FOREIGN RELATIONS

ABBE Scientist Research Division Staff. Afghanistan-U. S. War: Index, Reference & Medical Analysis of New Research Information. 2008. (Illus.). 160p. ring bd. 69.95 *(978-0-7883-3829-8(3))* ABBE Pubs. Assn. of Washington, D.C.

Afghanistan & Pakistan: Understanding & Engaging Regional Stakeholders: Hearing Before the Subcommittee on National Security & Foreign Affairs of the Committee on Oversight & Government Reform, House of Representatives, One Hundred Eleventh Congress, First Session, March 31, 2009. 2009. iii, 65p. *(978-0-16-084299-3(9)*, 552-070-39854-6) United States Government Printing Office.

Benard, Cheryl. Afghanistan: State & Society, Great Power Politics, & the Way Ahead: Findings from an International Conference, Copenhagen, Denmark 2007. 2008. 106p. pap. 26.00 *(978-0-8330-4415-0(X)*, cf-238) RAND Corp., The.

Bird, Tim & Marshall, Alex. Afghanistan: How the West Lost Its Way. 2011. (Illus.). 303p. 30.00 *(978-0-300-15457-3(7))* Yale Univ. Pr.

Blanchard, Christopher M. Afghanistan: Narcotics & U. S. Policy. 2008. (Illus.). viii, 66p. pap. 37.00 *(978-1-60692-918-6(6))* Nova Science Pubs., Inc.

Bromwich, Mark W. Captains Blog - the Chronicles of My Afghan Vacation. 2007. 192p. pap. 15.70 *(978-0-615-16909-5(0))* Bromwich, Mark W.

Deen, Robert P. & Burken, Allison D., eds. Fragile Mideest Countries: Afghanistan & Yemen. 2011. (Politics & Economics of the Middle East Ser.). (Illus.). 220p. 115.00 *(978-1-61209-709-1(X))* Nova Science Pubs., Inc.

Edwards, Lucy Morgan. The Afghan Solution: The Inside Story of Abdul Haq, the CIA & How Western Hubris Lost Afghanistan. 2011. (ENG., Illus.). 368p. 29.95 *(978-0-9568449-0-3(1))* Pluto Pr. GBR. Dist: Macmillan.

Ehrhart, Hans-Georg, et al. Afghanistan in the Balance: Counterinsurgency, Comprehensive Approach, & Political Order. 2012. (ENG.). 250p. (C). pap. ***(978-1-55339-353-5(8))*** McGill-Queen's Univ. Pr.

Emadi, Hafizullah. Dynamics of Political Development in Afghanistan: The British, Russian, & American Invasions. 2010. (ENG.). 316p. 95.00 *(978-0-230-10389-4(8))* Palgrave Macmillan.

Fowler, Corinne. Chasing Tales: Travel Writing, Journalism & the History of British Ideas about Afghanistan. 2007. (Illus.). 296p. per. 81.00 *(978-90-420-2262-1(0))* Rodopi.

Gould, Elizabeth. Crossing Zero: The Afpak War at the Turning Point of American Empire. 2011. (City Lights Open Media Ser.). (ENG.). 180p. pap. 16.95 *(978-0-87286-513-6(4))* City Lights Bks.

Hayes, Geoffrey & Sedra, Mark, eds. Afghanistan: Transition under Threat. 2008. (Studies in International Governance Ser.). (ENG., Illus.). 348p. pap. 42.95 *(978-1-55458-011-8(0))* Wilfrid Laurier Univ. Pr. CAN. Dist: Univ. of Toronto Pr.

Jalalzai, Zubeda & Jefferess, David, eds. Globalizing Afghanistan: Terrorism, War, & the Rhetoric of Nation Building. 2011. (American Encounters/Global Interactions Ser.). (ENG., Illus.). 232p. 79.95 *(978-0-8223-5001-9(7))*; pap. 22.95 *(978-0-8223-5014-9(9))* Duke Univ. Pr.

Johnson, Steve, et al. Afghanistan: The Mirage of Peace. 2nd ed. 2008. (ENG., Illus.). 272p. pap. 26.95 *(978-1-84277-956-9(7))* Zed Bks., Ltd. GBR. Dist: Macmillan.

Jones, Seth G. Securing Tyrants or Fostering Reform? U. S. Internal Security Assistance to Repressive & Transitioning Regimes. 2006. (Illus.). 234p. pap. 30.00 *(978-0-8330-4018-3(9))* RAND Corp., The.

Kalinovsky, Artemy. A Long Goodbye: The Soviet Withdrawal from Afghanistan. 2011. (ENG., Illus.). 320p. 27.95 *(978-0-674-05866-8(6))* Harvard Univ. Pr.

Katzman, Kenneth. Afghanistan: Post-War Governance, Security & U. S. Policy. 2008. (Illus.). 108p. pap. 39.00 *(978-1-60456-953-7(0))* Nova Science Pubs., Inc.

Khan, Ijaz. Pakistan Strategic Culture & Foreign Policy Making. 2007. 152p. (C). 125.00 *(978-1-60021-833-0(4))* Nova Science Pubs., Inc.

Khan, Ijaz. Pakistan's Strategic Culture & Foreign Policy Making. 2012. (Politics & Economics of the Middle East Ser.). 168p. pap. 47.00 ***(978-1-62100-678-7(6))*** Nova Science Pubs., Inc.

Khan, Riaz Mohammad. Afghanistan & Pakistan: Conflict, Extremism, & Resistance to Modernity. 2011. (ENG., Illus.). 400p. (gr. 17). 34.95 *(978-1-4214-0384-7(6))* Woodrow Wilson Ctr. Pr.

Khristoforov, V. S. Afganistan: Praviashchaia Partiia I Armiia: 1978-1989. 2009. (RUS.). 318p. *(978-5-98759-052-2(3))* Granica.

Kolhatkar, Sonali & Ingalls, James. Bleeding Afghanistan: Washington, Warlords, & the Propaganda of Silence. 2006. (Open Media Ser.). (ENG., Illus.). 336p. per. 18.95 *(978-1-58322-731-2(8))* Seven Stories Pr.

Malik, Hafeez. US Relations with Afghanistan & Pakistan: The Imperial Dimension. 2008. (Illus.). 350p. 35.00 *(978-0-19-547523-4(2))* Oxford Univ. Pr., Inc.

Marsden, Magnus & Hopkins, Benjamin D. Fragments of the Afghan Frontier. (Columbia/Hurst Ser.). 2012. (ENG.). 256p. (gr. 17). 35.00 *(978-0-231-70246-1(9))* 2011. ***(978-0-231-80006-8(1))*** Columbia Univ. Pr.

Mills, Nick B. Karzai: The Failing American Intervention & the Struggle for Afghanistan. 2007. (ENG., Illus.). 256p. 25.95 *(978-0-470-13400-9(3)*, Wiley) Wiley, John & Sons, Inc.

Mojtahed-Zadeh, Pirouz. The Small Players of the Great Game. 2007. 280p. 39.95 *(978-0-415-44452-1(7))* Routledge.

Qassem, Ahmad Shayeq. Afghanistan's Political Stability: A Dream Unrealised. 2009. 226p. 114.95 *(978-0-7546-7940-0(3))* Ashgate Publishing Co.

Rashid, Ahmed. Pakistan on the Brink: The Future of America, Pakistan, & Afghanistan. 2012. (ENG., Illus.). 256p. (gr. 12). 26.95 ***(978-0-670-02346-2(9)***, Viking Adult) Penguin Group (USA) Inc.

Riecke, Henning, ed. Partners for Stability: Involving Neighbors in Afghanistan's Reconstruction - Transatlantic Approaches. 2012. 200p. pap. 43.00 *(978-3-8329-6447-4(9))* Nomos Verlagsgesellschaft DEU. Dist: International Specialized Bk. Services.

Rothstein, Hy. Afghan Endgames: Strategy & Policy Choices for America's Longest War. Arquilla, John, ed. 2012. (South Asia in World Affairs Ser.). (ENG.). 248p. pap. 29.95 ***(978-1-58901-908-9(3))*** Georgetown Univ. Pr.

Rubin, Barnett R. Afghanistan's Uncertain Transition from Turmoil to Normalcy. 2006. (ENG., Illus.). 60p. per. 10.00 *(978-0-87609-356-6(X))* Council on Foreign Relations.

Simonelli, Mick. Riding a Donkey Backwards Through Afghanistan. 2009. 300p. pap. 16.95 *(978-1-934937-92-1(4))* Mill City Pr., Inc.

Smith, Richard & Twigge, Stephen, eds. The Invasion of Afghanistan & UK-Soviet Relations, 1979-82: Documents of British Policy Overseas, Series III, Volume VIII. 2012. (Whitehall Histories Ser.). (ENG.). 496p. (C). 145.00 *(978-0-415-67853-7(6))* Routledge.

Synnott, Hilary. Transforming Pakistan: Ways Out of Instability. 2009. (Adelphi Ser.). (ENG., Illus.). 186p. pap. 19.95 *(978-0-415-56260-7(0))* Routledge.

Thaler, David E. & Karasik, Theodore W. Future U. S. Security Relationships with Iraq & Afghanistan: U. S. Air Force Roles. 2008. 182p. pap. 32.00 *(978-0-8330-4197-5(5)*, MG-681) RAND Corp., The.

Tomsen, Peter. The Wars of Afghanistan: Messianic Terrorism, Tribal Conflicts, & the Failures of Great Powers. 2011. (ENG., Illus.). 912p. 39.99 *(978-1-58648-763-8(9))* PublicAffairs.

Training & Equipping Afghan Security Forces: Unaccounted Weapons & Strategic Challenges: Hearing Before the Subcommittee on National Security & Foreign Affairs of the Committee on Oversight & Government Reform, House of Representatives, One Hundred Eleventh Congress, First Session, February 12, 2009. 2011. (Illus.). ii, 75p. ***(978-0-16-088822-9(0)***, 552-070-42956-5) United States Government Printing Office.

Troops, Diplomats, & Aid: Assessing Strategic Resources for Afghanistan: Hearing Before the Subcommittee on National Security & Foreign Affairs of the Committee on Oversight & Government Reform, House of Representatives, One Hundred Eleventh Congress, First Session, March 26, 2009. 2010. iii, 107p. ***(978-0-16-087176-4(X)***, 552-070-42018-5) United States Government Printing Office.

United States Policy Toward Afghanistan & Pakistan: Hearing Before the Committee on Armed Services, United States Senate, One Hundred Eleventh Congress, First Session, April 7 [i.e. April 1], 2009. 2010. (Illus.). iii, 86p. *(978-0-16-085013-4(4)*, 552-070-40389-2) United States Government Printing Office.

Wilhite, Usar James. We Answered the Call: Building the Crown Jewel of Afghanistan. 2010. pap. 18.99 *(978-1-61566-779-6(2))* Tate Publishing & Enterprises, LLC.

Wissing, Douglas A. Funding the Enemy. 2012. (ENG.). 375p. 25.00 ***(978-1-61614-603-0(6))*** Prometheus Bks., Pubs.

Wyatt, Christopher M. Afghanistan & the Defence of Empire: Diplomacy & Strategy During the Great Game. 2011. (International Library of Twentieth Century History Ser.). (ENG., Illus.). 336p. 99.00 *(978-1-84885-610-3(5)*, Tauris Academic Studies) I. B. Tauris & Co., Ltd. GBR. Dist: Macmillan.

Yusafzai, Hamid Iqbal. The Us Factor in Pak-Afghan Relations. 2011. 160p. pap. ***(978-3-8443-9863-2(5))*** Lambert Academic Publishing.

Zakheim, Dov S. A Vulcan's Tale: How the Bush Administration Mismanaged the Reconstruction of Afghanistan. 2011. (ENG.). 335p. 32.95 *(978-0-8157-2122-2(6))* Brookings Institution Pr.

AFGHANISTAN—HISTORY

see also Afghan War, 2001-; Afghan Wars

Adamec, Ludwig. Historical Dictionary of Afghanistan. 4th rev. ed. 2011. (Historical Dictionaries of Asia, Oceania, & the Middle East Ser.). (ENG.). 666p. 95.00 ***(978-0-8108-7815-0(1))*** Scarecrow Pr., Inc.

Adamec, Ludwig W. The A to Z of Afghan Wars, Revolutions & Insurgencies. 2010. (A to Z Guide Ser.). (ENG.). 520p. pap. 34.45 *(978-0-8108-7624-8(8))* Scarecrow Pr., Inc.

Afghan Women & Girls: Building the Future of Afghanistan: Joint Hearing Before the Subcommittee on near Eastern & South & Central Asian Affairs & the Subcommittee on International Operations & Organizations, Human Rights, Democracy, & Global Women's Issues of the Committee on Foreign Relations, United States Senate, One Hundred Eleventh Congress, Second Session, February 23, 2010. 2010. iii, 49p. ***(978-0-16-086874-0(2)***, 552-070-41784-2) United States Government Printing Office.

Akbar, Said Hyder & Burton, Susan. Come Back to Afghanistan: Trying to Rebuild a Country with My Father, My Brother, My One-Eyed Uncle, Bearded Tribesmen & PR. 2006. (ENG.). 352p. per. 16.00 *(978-1-59691-068-3(2))* Bloomsbury Publishing.

Alexander, Chris. The Long Way Back: Afghanistan's Quest for Peace. 2011. 320p. 25.99 *(978-0-06-202037-6(4))* HarperCollins Pubs.

Alikuzai, Hamid Wahed. From Aryana-Khorasan to Afghanistan: Afghanistan History. 2011. 356p. pap. 93.54 ***(978-1-4269-6609-5(1))***; 368p. pap. 20.74 *(978-1-4269-6113-7(8))* Trafford Publishing.

Anderson, Ben. No Worse Enemy: The Inside Story of the Chaotic Struggle for Afghanistan. 2012. (ENG.). 304p. 24.95 ***(978-1-85168-852-4(8))*** Oneworld Pubns. GBR. Dist: National Bk. Network.

Atef, Said Shakib. Reservoir Operation Considering Environmental Flows. 2011. 84p. pap. ***(978-3-8443-0529-6(7))*** Lambert Academic Publishing.

Barfield, Thomas. Afghanistan: A Cultural & Political History. (Princeton Studies in Muslim Politics Ser.). (ENG., Illus.). 568p. 2012. pap. 16.95 ***(978-0-691-15441-1(4))*** 2010. 29.95 *(978-0-691-14568-6(7))* Princeton Univ. Pr.

Barker, Kim. The Taliban Shuffle: Strange Days in Afghanistan & Pakistan. 2012. (ENG., Illus.). 320p. pap. 15.95 ***(978-0-307-47738-5(X)***, Anchor) Knopf Doubleday Publishing Group.

Barker, Kimberly. The Taliban Shuffle: Strange Days in Afghanistan & Pakistan. 2011. (ENG., Illus.). 320p. 25.95 *(978-0-385-53331-7(4)*, Doubleday) Knopf Doubleday Publishing Group.

Barnes, Gregory & Fremont-Barnes, Gregory. Anglo-Afghan Wars, 1839-1919. 2009. (Essential Histories Ser.). (ENG., Illus.). 96p. pap. 19.95 *(978-1-84603-446-6(9))* Osprey Publishing, Ltd. GBR. Dist: Random Hse., Inc.

Blood, Peter, ed. Afghanistan: Past & Present /Comprised of Afghanistan, A Country Study & Country Profile. 2007. 232p. per. 24.95 *(978-1-60444-002-7(3))* IndoEuropeanPublishing.com.

Bradley, Rusty & Maurer, Kevin. Lions of Kandahar: The Story of a Fight Against All Odds. 2011. (ENG., Illus.). 304p. 26.00 *(978-0-553-80757-8(9))* Random House Publishing Group.

Briongos, Ana M. Winter in Kandahar. 2008. 224p. pap. *(978-1-906393-11-3(7))* Trotamundas Pr., Ltd.

Brooke, Henry. Brigade Commander: Afghanistan-the Journal of the Commander of the 2nd Infantry Brigade, Kandahar Field Force During the Second Afghan War. 2008. 152p. *(978-1-84677-570-3(1))*; pap. *(978-1-84677-569-7(8))* Leonaur Ltd.

Burroughs, Jim. Blood on the Lens: A Filmmaker's Quest for Truth in Afghanistan. 2007. (Illus.). 320p. 27.50 *(978-1-59797-124-9(3))* Potomac Bks., Inc.

Campbell, John. Lost among the Affghans Being the Adventures of John Campbell. Fry, Hubert Oswald, ed. 2007. (ENG.). 362p. 46.95 *(978-0-548-02131-6(7))* Kessinger Publishing, LLC.

Charkhi, Khaled Siddiq. From My Memories: Memoirs of political imprisonment from childhood in Afghanistan. 2010. 324p. (ENG.). 28.50 *(978-1-4490-7277-3(1))*; pap. 17.99 *(978-1-4490-7276-6(3))* AuthorHouse.

Chayes, Sarah. The Punishment of Virtue: Inside Afghanistan after the Taliban. 2007. (ENG., Illus.). 400p. (gr. 12-18). 16.00 (978-0-14-311206-8(6), Penguin (Non-Classics)) Penguin Group (USA) Inc.

Clarke, Michael. The Afghan Papers. 2012. (Whitehall Papers). (ENG.). 160p. (C). pap. 42.95 (978-0-415-52593-0(4)) Routledge.

Crews, Robert D. & Tarzi, Amin, eds. The Taliban & the Crisis of Afghanistan. 2009. (Illus.). 448p. pap. 20.00 (978-0-674-03224-8(1)) Harvard Univ. Pr.

Donnelly, Thomas. The War in Afghanistan & NATO's Future. 2011. (ENG.). 150p. 39.95 (978-0-8447-7212-7(7)) American Enterprise Institute for Public Policy Research.

Ehrhart, Hans-Georg & Pentland, Charles. The Afghanistan Challenge: Hard Realities & Strategic Choices. 2009. (ENG.). 250p. (C). pap. (978-1-55339-241-5(8)) McGill-Queen's Univ. Pr.

Elphinstone, Mountstuart. Account of the Kingdom of Caubul, & its Dependencies in Persia, Tartary, & India: Comprising a View of the Afghaun Nation, & a History of the Dooraunee Monarchy. 2011. (Cambridge Library Collection - History Ser.). (ENG., Illus.). 740p. pap. 48.00 (978-1-108-03671-9(6)) Cambridge Univ. Pr.

Fartash Barvarz. Islamic Atomic Bomb Cookbook. 2010. 116p. pap. 14.95 (978-1-4269-2366-1(X)) Trafford Publishing.

Fergusson, James. Taliban: The Unknown Enemy. (ENG., Illus.). 432p. 2012. pap. 17.50 (978-0-306-82077-9(3)) 2011. 27.50 (978-0-306-82033-5(1)) Da Capo Pr., Inc.

Firestone, Caroline Hudson. Afghanistan in Transition. 2009. 95.00 (978-1-61623-416-4(4)); pap. 45.00 (978-1-61623-417-1(2)) Independent Pub.

Fitzgerald, Paul & Gould, Elizabeth. Invisible History: Afghanistan's Untold Story. 2009. (ENG., Illus.). 300p. pap. 18.95 (978-0-87286-494-8(4)) City Lights Bks.

Friedman, Lauri S. Afghanistan. 2010. (Introducing Issues with Opposing Viewpoints Ser.). (Illus.). 144p. (J). 34.70 (978-0-7377-4729-4(3), Greenhaven Pr., Inc.) Cengage Gale.

Gannon, Kathy. I Is for Infidel: From Holy War to Holy Terror in Afghanistan. 2006. (ENG., Illus.). 208p. per. 12.95 (978-1-58648-452-1(4)) PublicAffairs.

Garlasco, Marc E. "Troops in Contact" Airstrikes & Civilian Deaths in Afghanistan. 2008. (Illus.). 40p. (978-1-56432-362-0(5)) Human Rights Watch.

Geda, Fabio. In the Sea There Are Crocodiles: Based on the True Story of Enaiatollah Akbari. 2011. (ENG., Illus.). 224p. 22.95 (978-0-385-53473-4(6), Doubleday) Knopf Doubleday Publishing Group.

Giustozzi, Antonio. Koran, Kalashnikov, & Laptop: The Neo-Taliban Insurgency in Afghanistan, 2002-2007. 2007. (Columbia/Hurst Ser.). (ENG., Illus.). 224p. (gr. 17). 24.95 (978-0-231-70009-2(1)) Columbia Univ. Pr.

—Koran, Kalashnikov, & Laptop: The Neo-Taliban Insurgency in Afghanistan, 2002-2207. 2009. (Columbia/Hurst Ser.). (ENG.). 224p. (gr. 17). pap. 18.50 (978-0-231-70010-8(5)) Columbia Univ. Pr.

Giustozzi, Antonio, ed. Decoding the New Taliban: Insights from the Afghan Field. 2012. (Columbia/Hurst Ser.). (ENG.). 420p. (gr. 17). pap. 26.00 (978-0-231-70113-6(6)) Columbia Univ. Pr.

Glatzer, Bernt. Afghanistan. 2008. (Contemporary Middle East Ser.). (Illus.). 192p. (gr. 13). 140.00 (978-0-415-27430-2(3)); 41.95 (978-0-415-28384-7(1)) Routledge.

Gleig, G. R. Afghanistan: The Beleaguered Brigade-an Account of Sale's Brigade During the First Afghan War. 2008. 212p. (978-1-84677-578-9(7)); pap. (978-1-84677-577-2(9)) Leonaur Ltd.

Green, Nile & Arbabzadah, Nushin, eds. Afghanistan in Ink: Literature Between Diaspora & Nation. 2012. (Columbia/Hurst Ser.). (ENG.). 288p. (gr. 17). 35.00 (978-0-231-70342-0(2)) Columbia Univ. Pr.

Grey, Stephen. Into the Viper's Nest: The First Pivotal Battle of the Afghan War. 2010. (Illus.). 352p. 28.00 (978-0-7603-3897-1(3), 0760338973, Zenith Pr.) MBI Publishing Co. LLC.

Griffiths, John C. Afghanistan: Land of Conflict & Beauty. 2009. (ENG., Illus.). 288p. pap. 16.95 (978-0-233-00275-0(8)) Andre Deutsch GBR. Dist: Independent Pubs. Group.

Griffiths, John Charles. Afghanistan: Land of Conflict & Beauty. 2011. (ENG., Illus.). 304p. pap. 16.95 (978-0-233-00315-3(0)) Andre Deutsch GBR. Dist: Independent Pubs. Group.

Hafvenstein, Joel. Opium Season: A Year on the Afghan Frontier. 2009. (ENG.). 352p. pap. 16.95 (978-1-59921-621-8(3), Lyons Pr.) Globe Pequot Pr., The.

Harpviken, Kristian Berg. Social Networks & Migration in Wartime Afghanistan. 2009. (ENG., Illus.). 272p. 100.00 (978-0-230-57655-1(9)) Palgrave Macmillan.

Hart, Howard P. Intelligence Thoughts: Afghanistan & Iran. 2011. 156p. pap. 15.99 (978-0-557-52746-5(5)) Lulu Enterprises Inc.

Hearing on National Defense Authorization ACT for Fiscal Year 2012 & Oversight of Previously Authorized Programs Before the Committee on Armed Services, House of Representatives, One Hundred Twelfth Congress, First Session: Full Committee Hearing on Budget Requests from the U.S. Central Command & U.S. Special Operations Command, Hearing Held March 3, 2011. 2011. (Illus.). iii, 121p. (978-0-16-089433-6(6), 552-070-43405-4) United States Government Printing Office.

Hodes, Cyrus & Sedra, Mark. The Search for Security in Post-Taliban Afghanistan. 2007. (Adelphi Ser.). (Illus.). 128p. 32.50 (978-0-415-43883-4(7)) Routledge.

Holt, Frank L. Into the Land of Bones: Alexander the Great in Afghanistan. 2006. (Hellenistic Culture & Society Ser.). (Illus.). 254p. pap. 19.95 (978-0-520-24993-6(3)) Univ. of California Pr.

Hopkins, B. D. The Making of Modern Afghanistan. 2012. (Cambridge Imperial & Post-Colonial Studies Ser.). (ENG., Illus.). 280p. (C). pap. 28.95 (978-0-230-30237-2(8)) Palgrave Macmillan.

Horn, Bernd & Spencer, Emily, eds. No Easy Task: Fighting in Afghanistan. 2012. (ENG., Illus.). 352p. pap. 35.00 (978-1-4597-0162-5(3)) Dundurn CAN. Dist: Ingram Pub. Services.

Isby, David. Afghanistan: Graveyard of Empires - A New History of the Borderland. (ENG.). 464p. 2011. pap. 16.95 (978-1-60598-189-5(3), 605189) 2010. (Illus.). 28.95 (978-1-60598-082-9(X), 605082) Pegasus Bks.

Jalalzai, Zubeda & Jefferess, David, eds. Globalizing Afghanistan: Terrorism, War, & the Rhetoric of Nation Building. 2011. (American Encounters/Global Interactions Ser.). (ENG., Illus.). 232p. 79.95 (978-0-8223-5001-9(7)); pap. 22.95 (978-0-8223-5014-9(9)) Duke Univ. Pr.

Johnson, Robert. The Afghan Way of War: How & Why They Fight, 1 vol. 2011. (ENG., Illus.). 384p. 29.95 (978-0-19-979856-8(7)) Oxford Univ. Pr., Inc.

Johnson, Steve & Leslie. Afganistan: The Mirage of Peace. 2nd ed. 2008. (ENG., Illus.). 272p. 108.95 (978-1-84277-955-2(9)) Zed Bks., Ltd. GBR. Dist: Macmillan.

Jones, Seth G. In the Graveyard of Empires: America's War in Afghanistan. 2009. (ENG., Illus.). 448p. 27.95 (978-0-393-06898-6(6), 6898) Norton, W. W. & Co., Inc.

Kolhatkar, Sonali & Ingalls, James. Bleeding Afghanistan: Washington, Warlords, & the Propaganda of Silence. 2006. (Open Media Ser.). (ENG., Illus.). 336p. per. 18.95 (978-1-58322-731-2(8)) Seven Stories Pr.

Leonard, Barry, ed. Afghanistan: Opium Rapid Assessment Survey. 2006. (Illus.). 51p. (C). pap. 20.00 (978-1-4223-0795-5(4)) DIANE Publishing Co.

Loyn, David. In Afghanistan: Two Hundred Years of British, Russian & American Occupation. 2009. (ENG.). 288p. 27.95 (978-0-230-61403-1(5)) Palgrave Macmillan.

Lumsden, H. B. The Mission to Kandahar, with Appendices. 2008. 95.00 (978-1-57898-711-5(3)) Martino Publishing.

MacPherson, Malcolm. Roberts Ridge: A Story of Courage & Sacrifice on Takur Ghar Mountain, Afghanistan. 2006. (ENG., Illus.). 384p. mass mkt. 7.99 (978-0-553-58680-0(7), Dell) Random House Publishing Group.

Mars-Proietti, Laura, ed. Conflict in Afghanistan: An Encyclopedia. 2nd ed. 2008. 135.00 (978-1-59237-296-6(1)) Grey Hse. Publishing.

Marsden, Magnus & Hopkins, Benjamin D. Fragments of the Afghan Frontier. 2012. (Columbia/Hurst Ser.). (ENG.). 256p. (gr. 17). 35.00 (978-0-231-70246-1(9)) Columbia Univ. Pr.

Marsden, Peter. Afghanistan: Aid, Armies & Empires. 2009. (ENG.). 240p. pap. 26.00 (978-1-84511-751-1(4)) I. B. Tauris & Co., Ltd. GBR. Dist: Macmillan.

McIntyre, Martin, et al. Maiwand: The Last Stand of the 66th (Berkshire) Regiment in Afghanistan, 1880. 2009. (ENG., Illus.). 192p. pap. 46.95 (978-0-7524-4537-3(5)) History Pr. Ltd.,The GBR. Dist: Independent Pubs. Group.

Meissner, Ursula. Afghanistan: Hope & Beauty in a War-Torn Land. 2008. (Illus.). 189p. pap. (978-3-7658-1688-8(4)) Bucher, C. J. Verlag GmbH.

Miller, Debra A. Afghanistan. 2010. (Current Controversies Ser.). 240p. pap. 26.75 (978-0-7377-4643-3(2)); (Illus.). 38.50 (978-0-7377-4642-6(4)) Cengage Gale. (Greenhaven Pr., Inc.).

Mirza, Aligholi. History of Afghanistan. Beykzadeh, Ghassem, ed. 2010. pap. 24.00 (978-1-4507-3202-4(X)) Independent Pub.

Murphy, Seamus. A Darkness Visible. 2008. (ENG., Illus.). 175p. 50.00 (978-0-86356-620-2(0)) Saqi Bks. GBR. Dist: Consortium Bk. Sales & Distribution.

Nivat, Anne. The Wake of War: Encounters with the People of Iraq & Afghanistan. Todd, Jane Marie, tr. from FRE. 2006. (ENG.). 320p. per. 16.00 (978-0-8070-0239-1(9)) Beacon Pr.

Patel, Seema, et al. Breaking Point: Measuring Progress in Afghanistan: A Report of the Post-Conflict Reconstruction Project, Center for Strategic & International Studies. 2007. pap. (978-0-89206-498-4(6), CSIS Pr., The) Ctr. for Strategic & International Studies.

Preston, Diana. The Dark Defile: Britain's Catastrophic Invasion of Afghanistan, 1838-1842. 2012. (ENG.). 352p. 28.00 (978-0-8027-7982-3(4)) Walker & Co.

Runion, Meredith L. The History of Afghanistan, 1 vol. 2007. (Greenwood Histories of the Modern Nations Ser.). (Illus.). 184p. 45.00 (978-0-313-33798-7(5), GR3798) Greenwood Publishing Group, Inc.

Sadeed, Suraya & Lewis, Damien. Forbidden Lessons in a Kabul Guesthouse: The True Story of a Woman Who Risked Everything to Bring Hope to Afghanistan. 2011. (ENG.). 304p. 24.99 (978-1-4013-4131-2(4)) Hyperion Pr.

Saikal, Amin. Modern Afghanistan: A History of Struggle & Survival. 2nd rev. ed. 2012. (ENG.). 368p. pap. 29.00 (978-1-78076-122-0(8)) I. B. Tauris & Co., Ltd. GBR. Dist: Macmillan.

Sale, Florentia. Lady Sale's Afghanistan: An Indomitable Victorian Lady's Account of the Retreat from Kabul During the First Afghan War. 2009. 288p. (978-1-84677-732-5(1)); pap. (978-1-84677-731-8(3)) Leonaur Ltd.

Samad, Rafi-us. The Grandeur of Gandhara: An Ancient Kingdom of Pakistan. 2011. 302p. pap. 23.95 (978-0-87586-859-2(2)) Algora Publishing.

—The Grandeur of Gandhara: An Ancient Kingdom of Pakistan. 2011. 302p. pap. 23.95 (978-0-87586-858-5(4)) Algora Publishing.

Schofield, Victoria. Afghan Frontier: At the Crossroads of Conflict. 2010. (ENG., Illus.). 392p. pap. 20.00 (978-1-84885-188-7(X), Tauris Parke Paperbacks) I. B. Tauris & Co., Ltd. GBR. Dist: Macmillan.

Sims-Williams, Nicholas. Bactrian Documents, Part II. 2007. (Studies in the Khalili Collections). 328p. (C). (978-1-874780-90-8(0), Khalili Collections) I. B. Tauris & Co., Ltd.

Sinno, Abdulkader H. Organizations at War in Afghanistan & Beyond. 2009. (Illus.). 352p. pap. 24.95 (978-0-8014-7578-8(3)) Cornell Univ. Pr.

Steeb, Randall, et al. Perspectives on the Battle of Wanat: Challenges Facing Small Unit Operations in Afghanistan. 2011. 40p. pap. 15.00 (978-0-8330-5322-0(1)) RAND Corp., The.

Steele, Jonathan. Ghosts of Afghanistan: Hard Truths & Foreign Myths. 2011. (ENG., Illus.). 256p. 26.00 (978-1-58243-787-3(4), Counterpoint) Counterpoint LLC.

Stewart, Jules. On Afghanistan's Plains: The Story of Britain's Afghan Wars. 2011. (ENG., Illus.). 272p. 35.00 (978-1-84885-717-9(9)) I. B. Tauris & Co., Ltd. GBR. Dist: Macmillan.

Stewart, Jules & Richards, David. The Crimson Snow: Britain's First Disaster in Afghanistan. 2008. (ENG., Illus.). 256p. 42.95 (978-0-7509-4825-8(6)) History Pr. Ltd.,The GBR. Dist: Independent Pubs. Group.

Sykes, Percy M. & McLane, Charles B. A History of Afghanistan, 2 vols. 2007. (ENG., Illus.). 256p. 395.00 (978-0-7103-1174-0(5)) Routledge.

Tanner, Stephen. Afghanistan: A Military History from Alexander the Great to the War Against the Taliban. rev. ed. 2009. (ENG., Illus.). 392p. pap. 17.95 (978-0-306-81826-4(4)) Da Capo Pr., Inc.

Tomsen, Peter. The Wars of Afghanistan: Messianic Terrorism, Tribal Conflicts, & the Failures of Great Powers. 2011. (ENG., Illus.). 912p. 39.99 (978-1-58648-763-8(9)) PublicAffairs.

Tripathi, Deepak. Breeding Ground: Afghanistan & the Origins of Islamist Terrorism. 2011. (Illus.). 256p. 26.95 (978-1-59797-530-8(3)) Potomac Bks., Inc.

van der Meulen, Jan, et al, eds. Mission Uruzgan: Collaborating in Multiple Coalitions for Afghanistan. 2012. (ENG.). 340p. pap. (978-90-8555-050-1(5), Pallas Publications) Amsterdam Univ. Pr.

Van Dyk, Jere. Captive: My Time as a Prisoner of the Taliban. 2011. (ENG., Illus.). 288p. pap. 14.99 (978-0-312-57342-3(1), St. Martin's Griffin) St. Martin's Pr.

Verma, N. K. Taliban. 2010. 535p. 92.50 (978-81-7533-270-6(0)) M. D. Pubns. Pvt, Ltd. IND. Dist: Coronet Bks.

Vogelsang, Willem. The Afghans. 2008. (Peoples of Asia Ser.: 7). (ENG., Illus.). 408p. pap. 35.95 (978-1-4051-8243-0(1), Wiley-Blackwell) Wiley, John & Sons, Inc.

Warikoo, K. Afghanistan: The Challenge. 2007. xxiii, 377p. (978-81-8274-254-3(4)) Pentagon Pr.

Wright, Donald P., et al. A Different Kind of War: the United States Army in Operation ENDURING FREEDOM, October 2001 - September 2005: The United States Army in Operation ENDURING FREEDOM, October 2001 - September 2005. Combat Studies Institute (U.S.) & Contemporary Operations Study Team (U.S.), eds. 2010. (ENG., Illus.). 414p. pap. 44.00 (978-0-9823283-1-6(1), Dept. of the Army) United States Government Printing Office.

Wyatt, Christopher M. Afghanistan & the Defence of Empire: Diplomacy & Strategy During the Great Game. 2011. (International Library of Twentieth Century History Ser.). (ENG., Illus.). 336p. 99.00 (978-1-84885-610-3(5), Tauris Academic Studies) I. B. Tauris & Co., Ltd. GBR. Dist: Macmillan.

Zaeef, Abdul Salam. My Life with the Taliban. van van Linschoten, Alex Strick & Kuehn, Felix, eds. 2012. (Columbia/Hurst Ser.). (ENG., Illus.). 360p. (gr. 17). pap. 19.95 (978-0-231-70149-5(7)) Columbia Univ. Pr.

Zahrah Nasir, B. K. The Parwan Wind - Dust Motes. 2007. (ENG., Illus.). 250p. pap. 24.95 (978-0-19-547402-2(3)) Oxford Univ. Pr., Inc.

Zhu, Yongbiao. "9.11" Zhi Hou de Afuhan. 2009. (Illus.). (978-7-5011-8879-6(3)) Xinhua Publishing Hse.

AFGHANISTAN—HISTORY—SOVIET OCCUPATION, 1979-1989

Braithwaite, Rodric. Afgantsy: The Russians in Afghanistan, 1979-1989, 1 vol. 2011. (ENG., Illus.). 432p. 29.95 (978-0-19-983265-1(X)) Oxford Univ. Pr., Inc.

Crile, George. Charlie Wilson's War: The Extraordinary Story of How the Wildest Man in Congress & a Rogue CIA Agent Changed the History of Our Times. 2007. (ENG., Illus.). 560p. per. 14.95 (978-0-8021-4341-9(5), Grove Pr.) Grove/Atlantic, Inc.

Farivar, Masood. Confessions of a Mullah Warrior. 2010. (ENG.). 336p. pap. 15.00 (978-0-8021-4454-6(3), Grove Pr.) Grove/Atlantic, Inc.

Feifer, Gregory. The Great Gamble: The Soviet War in Afghanistan. 336p. 2010. (ENG.). pap. 15.99 (978-0-06-114319-9(7), HarperPerennial) 2009. 27.99 (978-0-06-114318-2(9)) HarperCollins Pubs.

Girardet, Edward. Killing the Cranes: A Reporter's Journey Through Three Decades of War in Afghanistan. 2011. (ENG.). 416p. 27.95 (978-1-60358-342-8(4)) Chelsea Green Publishing.

Guibert, Emmanuel, et al. The Photographer: Into War-Torn Afghanistan with Doctors Without Borders. Siegel, Alexis, tr. from FRE. 2009. (ENG., Illus.). 288p. pap. 29.95 (978-1-59643-375-5(2), First Second Bks.) Roaring Brook Pr.

Kalinovsky, Artemy. A Long Goodbye: The Soviet Withdrawal from Afghanistan. 2011. (ENG., Illus.). 320p. 27.95 (978-0-674-05866-8(6)) Harvard Univ. Pr.

Khristoforov, V. S. Afganistan: Praviashchaia Partiia I Armiia: 1978-1989. 2009. (RUS.). 318p. (978-5-98759-052-2(3)) Granica.

Lessing, Doris. El Viento Se Llevara Nuestras Palabras. 2008. (Illus.). 190p. pap. (978-84-02-42065-7(6)) Bruguera, S.A.

Maley, William. The Afghanistan Wars. 2nd rev. ed. 2009. (Twentieth Century Wars Ser.). (ENG., Illus.). 288p. 80.00 (978-0-230-21313-5(8)); pap. 36.00 (978-0-230-21314-2(6)) Palgrave Macmillan.

Matthews, Matt. We Have Not Learned How to Wage War There: The Soviet Approach in Afghanistan 1979-1989. 2011. (978-0-9841901-9-5(8)) Combat Studies Institute Pr.

Oliker, Olga. Building Afghanistan's Security Forces in Wartime: The Soviet Experience, 1 vol. 2011. (ENG.). 126p. (C). pap. 20.00 (978-0-8330-5168-4(7)) RAND Corp., The.

Roselle, Laura. Media & the Politics of Failure: Great Powers, Communication Strategies, & Military Defeats. (Palgrave Series in International Political Communication). (ENG.). 2006. 200p. 89.00 (978-1-4039-7525-6(6)) 2011. (Illus.). 208p. pap. 30.00 (978-0-230-11677-1(9)) Palgrave Macmillan.

Rubin, Barnett R. Afghanistan in the Post-Cold War Era. 2012. (ENG.). 432p. 34.95 (978-0-19-979112-5(0)) Oxford Univ. Pr., Inc.

Sinno, Abdulkader H. Organizations at War in Afghanistan & Beyond. 2009. (Illus.). 352p. pap. 24.95 (978-0-8014-7578-8(3)) Cornell Univ. Pr.

Yousaf, Mohammad & Adkin, Mark. The Battle for Afghanistan: The Soviets Versus the Mujahideen During the 1980s. 2007. (Illus.). 243p. per. 24.95 (978-1-84415-616-0(8)) Pen & Sword Bks. Ltd. GBR. Dist: Casemate Pubs. & Bk. Distributors, LLC.

AFGHANISTAN—JUVENILE LITERATURE

Gale, ed. Hamid Karzai. 2011. (People in the News Ser.). 128p. (J). lib. bdg. 33.45 (978-1-4205-0425-5(8), Lucent Bks.) Cengage Gale.

AFGHANISTAN—POLITICS AND GOVERNMENT

Afghan Elections: What Happened & Where Do We Go from Here?: Hearing Before the Subcommittee on National Security & Foreign Affairs of the Committee on Oversight & Government Reform, House of Representatives, One Hundred Eleventh Congress, First Session, November 19, 2009. 2011. iii, 59p. (978-0-16-089001-7(2), 552-070-43033-4) United States Government Printing Office.

The Afghan Elections: Who Lost What?: Hearing Before the Subcommittee on the Middle East & South Asia of the Committee on Foreign Affairs, House of Representatives, One Hundred Eleventh Congress, First Session, October 1, 2009. 2010. (Illus.). iii, 87p. (978-0-16-085057-8(6), 552-070-40414-7) United States Government Printing Office.

Afghanistan & Pakistan: Oversight of a New Interagency Strategy: Joint Hearing Before the Committee on Oversight & Government Reform & the Subcommittee on National Security & Foreign Affairs of the Committee on Oversight & Government Reform, House of Representatives, One Hundred Eleventh Congress, First Session, June 24, 2009. 2011. (Illus.). iii, 178p. (978-0-16-088215-9(X), 552-070-42577-2) United States Government Printing Office.

Akbar, Said Hyder & Burton, Susan. Come Back to Afghanistan: Trying to Rebuild a Country with My Father, My Brother, My One-Eyed Uncle, Bearded Tribesmen, & PR. 2006. (ENG.). 352p. per. 16.00 (978-1-59691-068-3(2)) Bloomsbury Publishing.

Alexander, Chris. The Long Way Back: Afghanistan's Quest for Peace. 2011. 320p. 25.99 (978-0-06-202037-6(4)) HarperCollins Pubs.

Anderson, Ben. No Worse Enemy: The Inside Story of the Chaotic Struggle for Afghanistan. 2012. (ENG.). 304p. 24.95 (978-1-85168-852-4(8)) Oneworld Pubns. GBR. Dist: National Bk. Network.

Barfield, Thomas. Afghanistan: A Cultural & Political History. (Princeton Studies in Muslim Politics Ser.). (ENG., Illus.). 568p. 2012. pap. 16.95 (978-0-691-15441-1(4)) 2010. 29.95 (978-0-691-14568-6(7)) Princeton Univ. Pr.

Bashir, Shahzad & Crews, Robert D., eds. Under the Drones: Modern Lives in the Afghanistan-Pakistan Borderlands. 2012. (ENG., Illus.). 336p. 27.95 (978-0-674-06561-1(1)) Harvard Univ. Pr.

Benard, Cheryl. Afghanistan: State & Society, Great Power Politics, & the Way Ahead: Findings from an International Conference, Copenhagen, Denmark 2007. 2008. 106p. pap. 26.00 (978-0-8330-4415-0(X), cf-238) RAND Corp., The.

—Women & Nation-Building. 2008. (Illus.). 225p. pap. 31.50 (978-0-8330-4311-5(0), MG-579) RAND Corp., The.

Bergen, Peter & Tiedemann, Katherine, eds. Talibanistan: Negotiating the Borders Between Terror, Politics & Religion. 2012. 464p. 99.00 (978-0-19-989307-2(1)); (ENG.). 352p. pap. 18.95 (978-0-19-989309-6(8)) Oxford Univ. Pr., Inc.

Berlatsky, Noah. Afghanistan. 2010. (Opposing Viewpoints Ser.). (ENG.). 240p. 39.70 (978-0-7377-5102-4(9)); pap. 27.50 (978-0-7377-5103-1(7)) Cengage Gale. (Greenhaven Pr., Inc.).

Bhatia, Michael Vinay & Sedra, Mark. Afghanistan, Arms & Conflict: Armed Groups, Disarmament & Security in a Post-War Society. Sedra, Michael, ed. 2008. (Contemporary Security Studies). (Illus.). XXVIII, 324p. 140.00 (978-0-415-45308-0(9)) Routledge.

Bisogno, Enrico, ed. Corruption in Afghanistan: Bribery as Reported by the Victims. 2010. 42p. (C). pap. 20.00 (978-1-4379-2799-3(8)) DIANE Publishing Co.

Blanchard, Christopher M. Afghanistan: Narcotics & U. S. Policy. 2008. (Illus.). viii, 66p. pap. 37.00 (978-1-60692-918-6(6)) Nova Science Pubs., Inc.

Blehm, Eric. The Only Thing Worth Dying For: How Eleven Green Berets Forged a New Afghanistan. (Illus.). 320p. 2011. (ENG.). pap. 15.99 (978-0-06-166123-5(6), HarperPerennial) 2010. 25.99 (978-0-06-166122-8(8)) HarperCollins Pubs.

Block, Jeremy. Embracing the Occupiers: Conversations with the Future Leaders of Afghanistan & Iraq, 1 vol. 2009. (Praeger Security International Ser.). 196p. 75.00 (978-0-313-36534-8(2), C36534, Praeger Security International) Greenwood Publishing Group, Inc.

Brahimi, Lakhdar & Pickering, Thomas Reeve. Afghanistan - Negotiating Peace The Report of the Century Foundation International Task Force on Afghanistan in Its Regional & Multilateral Dimensions. 2011. (ENG.). 104p. pap. 14.95 (978-0-87078-520-7(6)) Century Foundation, The.

Brown, Jennifer L. Afghanistan National Development Strategies & Plans. 2011. (Politics & Economics of the Middle East Ser.). 446p. 225.00 (978-1-61209-637-7(9)) Nova Science Pubs., Inc.

Brzoska, Michael, et al, eds. Multi-Stakeholder Security Partnerships: A Critical Assessment with Case Studies from Afghanistan, Dr Congo & Kosovo. 2011. 276p. pap. 71.00 (978-3-8329-6794-9(X)) Nomos Verlagsgesellschaft DEU. Dist: International Specialized Bk. Services.

Carafano, James Jay. Private Sector, Public Wars: Contractors in Combat-Afghanistan, Iraq, & Future Conflicts. 2008. (Changing Face of War Ser.). 252p. 44.95 (978-0-275-99478-5(3), C9478, Praeger Security International) Greenwood Publishing Group, Inc.

Charkhi, Khaled Siddiq. From My Memories: Memoirs of political imprisonment from childhood in Afghanistan. 2010. 324p. (ENG.). 28.50 (978-1-4490-7277-3(1)); pap. 17.99 (978-1-4490-7276-6(3)) AuthorHouse.

Chin, Felix, ed. Political Developments & U. S. Policy in the Middle East. 2011. (Politics & Economics of the Middle East Ser.). 174p. 89.00 (978-1-61209-782-4(0)) Nova Science Pubs., Inc.

Coburn, Noah. Bazaar Politics: Power & Pottery in an Afghan Market Town. 2011. (Stanford Studies in Middle Eastern & I Ser.). (ENG., Illus.). 272p. 70.00 (978-0-8047-7671-4(7)); pap. 22.95 (978-0-8047-7672-1(5)) Stanford Univ. Pr.

Collmer, Sabine, ed. From Fragile State to Functioning State: Pathways to Democratic Transformation in a Comparative Perspective. 2011. (ENG., Illus.). 384p. pap. 44.95 (978-3-8258-1803-6(9)) Lit Verlag DEU. Dist: Transaction Pubs.

Connable, Ben. Embracing the Fog of War: Assessment & Metrics in Counterinsurgency. 1 vol. 2012. (ENG.). 340p. (C). pap. 36.50 (978-0-8330-5815-7(0)) RAND Corp., The.

Cordesman, Anthony H., et al. Winning in Afghanistan: Creating Effective Afghan Security Forces. 2009. (Illus.). 172p. pap. 22.95 (978-0-89206-566-0(4), CSIS Pr., The) Ctr. for Strategic & International Studies.

Cuccia, Phillip R. Implications of a Changing NATO. 2010. (978-1-58487-446-1(5)) Strategic Studies Institute, U.S. Army War College Commandant (AWCC-DSI/Pubns.).

Danspeckgruber, Wolfgang & Finn, Robert P., eds. Building State & Security in Afghanistan. 2010. 384p. (C). pap. 32.50 (978-0-9773544-4-3(X)) Princeton Univ., The Office of Communications.

Deconstructing Reconstruction: Problems, Challenges, & the Way Forward in Iraq & Afghanistan: Hearing Before the Committee on Homeland Security & Governmental Affairs, United States Senate, One Hundred Tenth Congress, First Session, March 22, 2007. 2008. (Illus.). iii, 417p. (978-0-16-080926-2(6), 552-070-37458-2) United States Government Printing Office.

Deen, Robert P. & Burken, Allison D., eds. Fragile Mideast Countries: Afghanistan & Yemen. 2011. (Politics & Economics of the Middle East Ser.). (Illus.). 220p. 115.00 (978-1-61209-709-1(X)) Nova Science Pubs., Inc.

Dobbins, James F. After the Taliban: Nation-Building in Afghanistan. 2008. (Illus.). 192p. 24.95 (978-1-59797-083-9(2)) Potomac Bks., Inc.

Dodge, Toby & Redman, Nicholas, eds. Afghanistan: to 2015 & Beyond. 2012. (Adelphi Ser.). (ENG.). 300p. (C). 78.00 (978-0-415-53257-0(4)) Routledge.

Döring, Sebastian. Mediator vs. Cowboy. 2008. 112p. pap. (978-3-639-07344-7(4)) VDM Verlag Dr. Mueller e.K.

Ehrhart, Hans-Georg, et al. Afghanistan in the Balance: Counterinsurgency, Comprehensive Approach, & Political Order. 2012. (ENG.). 250p. (C). pap. (978-1-55339-353-5(8)) McGill-Queen's Univ. Pr.

Eide, Kai. The Power Struggle over Afghanistan: An Inside Look at What Went Wrong... & What We Can Do to Fix It. 2012. (ENG., Illus.). 320p. 24.95 (978-1-61608-464-6(2), 608464) Skyhorse Publishing Co., Inc.

Emadi, Hafizullah. Dynamics of Political Development in Afghanistan: The British, Russian, & American Invasions. 2010. (ENG.). 316p. 95.00 (978-0-230-10389-4(8)) Palgrave Macmillan.

Fergusson, James. Taliban: The Unknown Enemy. 2012. (ENG., Illus.). 432p. pap. 17.50 (978-0-306-82077-9(3)) Da Capo Pr., Inc.

Firestone, Caroline Hudson. Afghanistan in Transition. 2009. 95.00 (978-1-61623-416-4(4)); pap. 45.00 (978-1-61623-417-1(2)) Independent Pub.

Fitzgerald, Paul & Gould, Elizabeth. Invisible History: Afghanistan's Untold Story. 2009. (ENG., Illus.). 300p. pap. 18.95 (978-0-87286-494-8(4)) City Lights Bks.

Fraser-Tytler, William K., Sr. Afghanistan: A Study of Political Developments in Central & Southern Asia. 5th ed. reprint ed. 42.50 (978-0-404-18962-4(8)) AMS Pr., Inc.

Girardet, Ed. Afghanistan: the Soviet War (Routledge Revivals) 2011. (Routledge Revivals Ser.). (ENG.). 274p. 120.00 (978-0-415-68480-4(3)) Routledge.

Giustozzi, Antonio. Empires of Mud: Wars & Warlords in Afghanistan. (Columbia/Hurst Ser.). (ENG.). 320p. (gr. 17). 2012. Illus.). pap. 28.00 (978-0-231-70081-8(4)) 2009. 35.00 (978-0-231-70080-1(6)) Columbia Univ. Pr.

Giustozzi, Antonio, ed. Decoding the New Taliban: Insights from the Afghan Field. (Columbia/Hurst Ser.). (ENG.). 420p. (gr. 17). 2012. pap. 26.00 (978-0-231-70113-6(6)) 2009. 40.00 (978-0-231-70112-9(8)) Columbia Univ. Pr.

Gladstone, Cary. Afghanistan Issues: Security, Narcotics & Political Currents. 2007. 79.00 (978-1-60021-587-2(4)) Nova Science Pubs., Inc.

Glatzer, Bernt. Afghanistan. 2008. (Contemporary Middle East Ser.). (Illus.). 192p. (gr. 13). 140.00 (978-0-415-27430-2(3)); 41.95 (978-0-415-28384-7(1)) Routledge.

Glavin, Terry. Come from the Shadows: The Long & Lonely Struggle for Peace in Afghanistan, 1 vol. 2011. (ENG., Illus.). 256p. 26.95 (978-1-55365-782-8(9)) D&M Pubs. Inc. CAN. Dist: Perseus-PGW.

Glaze, John A. Opium & Afghanistan: Reassessing U. S. Counternarcotics Strategy. 2007. (Carlisle Papers in Security Strategy). (978-1-58487-317-4(5)) Strategic Studies Institute, U.S. Army War College Commandant (AWCC-DSI/Pubns.).

Griffiths, John C. Afghanistan: Land of Conflict & Beauty. 2009. (ENG., Illus.). 288p. pap. 16.95 (978-0-233-00275-0(8)) Andre Deutsch GBR. Dist: Independent Pubs. Group.

Griffiths, John Charles. Afghanistan: Land of Conflict & Beauty. 2011. (ENG., Illus.). 304p. pap. 16.95 (978-0-233-00315-3(0)) Andre Deutsch GBR. Dist: Independent Pubs. Group.

Hafvenstein, Joel. The Opium Season: A Year on the Afghan Frontier. 2007. (ENG., Illus.). 352p. 24.95 (978-1-59921-131-2(9), Lyons Pr.) Globe Pequot Pr., The.

Hanifi, Shah Mahmoud. Connecting Histories in Afghanistan: Market Relations & State Formation on a Colonial Frontier. 2011. (ENG.). 288p. pap. 24.95 (978-0-8047-7411-6(0)) Stanford Univ. Pr.

Hodes, Cyrus & Sedra, Mark. The Search for Security in Post-Taliban Afghanistan. 2007. (Adelphi Ser.). (Illus.). 128p. 32.50 (978-0-415-43883-4(7)) Routledge.

Howk, Jason C. A Case Study in Security Sector Reform: Learning from Security Sector Reform/Building in Afghanistan. 2009. (PKSOI Papers). (978-1-58487-415-7(5)) Strategic Studies Institute, U.S. Army War College Commandant (AWCC-DSI/Pubns.).

Hussain, Imtiaz. Afghanistan, Iraq, & Post-Conflict Governance: Damoclean Democracy? 2010. (International Studies in Sociology & Social Anthropology Ser.). (Illus.). 314p. (978-90-04-18033-8(8)) BRILL.

Hynek, Nik & Marton, Peter, eds. Statebuilding in Afghanistan: Multinational Contributions to Reconstruction. 2011. (Routledge Studies in Intervention & Statebuilding Ser.). (ENG., Illus.). 296p. (C). 130.00 (978-0-415-62049-9(X)) Routledge.

Isby, David. Afghanistan: Graveyard of Empires - A New History of the Borderland. (ENG.). 464p. 2011. pap. 16.95 (978-1-60598-189-5(3), 605189) 2010. (Illus.). 28.95 (978-1-60598-082-9(X), 605082) Pegasus Bks.

Jalalzai, Musa Khan. Afghanistan Beyond 2014. 2011. 192p. pap. (978-3-8443-8044-6(2)) Lambert Academic Publishing.

Joes, Anthony James. Victorious Insurgencies: Four Rebellions that Shaped Our World. 2010. (ENG., Illus.). 336p. 40.00 (978-0-8131-2614-2(2)) Univ. Pr. of Kentucky.

Johnson, Steve & Leslie. Afganistan: The Mirage of Peace. 2nd ed. 2008. (ENG., Illus.). 272p. 108.95 (978-1-84277-955-2(9)) Zed Bks., Ltd. GBR. Dist: Macmillan.

Johnson, Steve, et al. Afganistan: The Mirage of Peace. 2nd ed. 2008. (ENG., Illus.). 272p. pap. 26.95 (978-1-84277-956-9(7)) Zed Bks., Ltd. GBR. Dist: Macmillan.

Jones, Seth G. Counterinsurgency in Afghanistan. 2008. (ENG.). 176p. pap. 26.50 (978-0-8330-4133-3(9), MG-595) RAND Corp., The.

—In the Graveyard of Empires: America's War in Afghanistan. 2010. (ENG., Illus.). 464p. pap. 15.95 (978-0-393-33851-5(7), 33851) Norton, W. W. & Co., Inc.

Jones, Seth G. Reintegrating Afghan Insurgents. 2011. 40p. pap. 15.00 (978-0-8330-5138-7(5)) RAND Corp., The.

Jones, Seth G. & Munoz, Arturo. Afghanistan's Local War: Building Local Defense Forces, 1 vol. 2010. 114p. pap. 20.00 (978-0-8330-4988-9(7), MG-1002) RAND Corp., The.

Just World Books & Foust, Joshua. Afghanistan Journal: Selections from Registan. net. 2010. (Illus.). 240p. pap. 23.95 (978-1-935982-02-9(8)) Just World Bks.

Kakar, Hasan Kawun. Government & Society in Afghanistan: The Reign of Amir 'Abd Al-Rahman Khan. 2011. (ENG.). 352p. pap. 30.00 (978-0-292-72900-1(6)) Univ. of Texas Pr.

Karzai, Hamid. Letter from Kabul. 2006. 192p. 25.95 (978-0-470-04515-2(9), Wiley) Wiley, John & Sons, Inc.

Katzman, Kenneth. Afghanistan: Post-War Governance, Security & U. S. Policy. 2008. (Illus.). 108p. pap. 39.00 (978-1-60456-953-7(0)) Nova Science Pubs., Inc.

Khalili, Wazhma. Rough Road: The Government Exists Only in Name in Afghanistan. 2010. 92p. pap. 12.99 (978-1-4269-4292-1(3)) Trafford Publishing.

Khristoforov, V. S. Afganistan: Praviashchaia Partiia I Armiia: 1978-1989. 2009. (RUS.). 318p. (978-5-98759-052-2(3)) Granica.

Krishnappa, V. & Singh, Priyanka, eds. Saving Afghanistan. 2009. (ENG., Illus.). 174p. 34.95 (978-81-7188-753-8(8)) Academic Foundation IND. Dist: Independent Pubs. Group.

Kumar, Sandeep. On Edge: The Afghan Passage. 2009. (Illus.). 242p. (978-81-212-1037-9(2), Library of Congress — New Delhi Overseas Office) Gyan Publishing Hse.

Leonard, Barry, ed. Afghanistan: Opium Rapid Assessment Survey. 2006. (Illus.). 51p. (C). pap. 20.00 (978-1-4223-0795-3(6)) DIANE Publishing Co.

Malkasian, Carter & Meyerle, Gerald. Provincial Reconstruction Teams: How Do We Know They Work? 2009. (Letort Papers). (978-1-58487-383-9(3)) Strategic Studies Institute, U.S. Army War College Commandant (AWCC-DSI/Pubns.).

Marsden, Magnus & Hopkins, Benjamin D. Fragments of the Afghan Frontier. 2011. (978-0-231-80006-8(1)) Columbia Univ. Pr.

Marsden, Peter. Afghanistan: Aid, Armies & Empires. 2009. (ENG.). 240p. pap. 26.00 (978-1-84511-751-1(4)) I. B. Tauris & Co., Ltd. GBR. Dist: Macmillan.

Mills, Nick B. Karzai: The Failing American Intervention & the Struggle for Afghanistan. 2007. (ENG., Illus.). 256p. 25.95 (978-0-470-13400-9(3), Wiley) Wiley John & Sons, Inc.

Misdaq, Nabi. Afghanistan: Political Frailty & External Interference. 2008. (Illus.). 380p. 39.95 (978-0-415-47024-7(2)) Routledge.

Montgomery, John D. & Rondinelli, Dennis A., eds. Beyond Reconstruction in Afghanistan: Lessons from Development Experience. 2007. (ENG., Illus.). 256p. pap. 32.00 (978-0-230-60220-5(7)) Palgrave Macmillan.

Morgan, Matthew J. A Democracy Is Born: An Insider's Account of the Battle Against Terrorism in Afghanistan, 1 vol. 2007. (Praeger Security International Ser.). (Illus.). 184p. 39.95 (978-0-275-99999-5(8), C9999, Praeger Security International) Greenwood Publishing Group, Inc.

Mujtaba, Bahaudin & Jawad, Sayed. Afghanistan: Realities of War & Rebuilding. 2006. 272p. pap. 17.95 (978-0-9774211-1-4(2)) ILEAD Academy, LLC.

Ohanyan, Anna. NGOs, IGOs, & the Network Mechanisms of Post-Conflict Global Governance in Microfinance. 2008. (ENG.). 256p. 89.00 (978-0-230-60769-9(1)) Palgrave Macmillan.

Peabody, Lawrence B., ed. Afghanistan Security. 2009. 59.00 (978-1-60692-149-4(5)) Nova Science Pubs., Inc.

Petrovic, Bojan. Afghanistan: The Political History of a Buffer State. rev. ed. 2011. (ENG.). 124p. pap. 44.40 (978-0-7575-8069-7(6)) Kendall Hunt Publishing Co.

Ponzio, Richard J. Democratic Peacebuilding: Aiding Afghanistan & other Fragile States. 2011. (ENG., Illus.). 288p. 99.00 (978-0-19-959495-5(3)) Oxford Univ. Pr., Inc.

Preston, Diana. The Dark Defile: Britain's Catastrophic Invasion of Afghanistan, 1838-1842. 2012. (ENG.). 352p. 28.00 (978-0-8027-7982-3(4)) Walker & Co.

Provincial Reconstruction Teams: Historical & Current Perspectives on Doctrine & Strategy: Hearing Before the Oversight & Investigations Subcommittee of the Committee on Armed Services, House of Representatives, One Hundred Tenth Congress, First Session, Hearing Held, December 5, 2007. 2008. iii, 81p. (978-0-16-081757-1(9), 552-070-37965-7) United States Government Printing Office.

Qassem, Ahmad Shayeq. Afghanistan's Political Stability: A Dream Unrealised. 2009. 226p. 114.95 (978-0-7546-7940-0(3)) Ashgate Publishing Co.

Rais, Rasul, et al. Recovering the Frontier State: War, Ethnicity, & the State in Afghanistan. 2009. (ENG.). 238p. pap. 31.50 (978-0-7391-3701-7(8)) Lexington Bks.

Rashid, Ahmed. Descent into Chaos: The United States & the Failure of Nation Building in Pakistan, Afghanistan, & Central Asia. (ENG.). 544p. (gr. 12-18). 2009. 18.00 (978-0-14-311557-1(X), Penguin (Non-Classics)) 2008. (Illus.). 27.95 (978-0-670-01970-0(4), Viking Adult) Penguin Group (USA) Inc.

—Pakistan on the Brink: The Future of America, Pakistan, & Afghanistan. 2012. (ENG., Illus.). 256p. (gr. 12). 26.95 (978-0-670-02346-2(9), Viking Adult) Penguin Group (USA) Inc.

Rashid, Ahmed. Taliban: Militant Islam, Oil & Fundamentalism in Central Asia. 2nd ed. 2010. (Illus.). 344p. pap. 17.95 (978-0-300-16368-1(1)) Yale Univ. Pr.

Redman, Nicholas & Dodge, Toby. The Future of Afghanistan After 2014. 2012. (Adelphi Ser.). (ENG.) 300p. (C). pap. 24.99 (978-0-415-69642-5(9)) Routledge.

Rognvik, Sylvia Rani. Warlords, Militias & Security Sector Reform in Afghanistan: Exploring the Constructive Potential of Non-State Armed Actors. 2011. 92p. pap. (978-3-639-32353-0(0)) VDM Verlag Dr. Mueller e.K.

The Role of the Department of Defense in Provincial Reconstruction Teams: Hearing Before the Oversight & Investigations Subcommittee of the Committee on Armed Services, House of Representatives, One Hundred Tenth Congress, First Session, Hearing Held, September 5, 2007. 2008. (Illus.). iii, 70p. (978-0-16-081472-3(3), 552-070-37834-1) United States Government Printing Office.

Rubin, Barnett R. Afghanistan's Uncertain Transition from Turmoil to Normalcy. 2006. (ENG., Illus.). 60p. per. 10.00 (978-0-87609-356-6(X)) Council on Foreign Relations.

Samad, Khorshied. Afghan Women, Media & Emerging Democracy. 2009. 116p. pap. (978-3-639-18206-4(5)) VDM Verlag Dr. Mueller e.K.

Schlenkhoff, Angela. Beyond the 'Wild Tribes' Understanding Modern Afghanistan & Its Diaspora. Oeppen, Ceri, ed. 2010. (Columbia/Hurst Ser.). (ENG.). 224p. (gr. 17). 40.00 (978-0-231-70210-2(8)) Columbia Univ. Pr.

Semple, Michael. Reconciliation in Afghanistan. 2009. (Perspectives Ser.). (Illus.). 104p. pap. 10.00 (978-1-60127-042-9(9)) U. S. Institute of Peace Pr. (USIP Pr.).

Shaaker, Wali. Democracy's Dilemma. 2010. 77p. pap. 12.86 (978-0-557-19712-5(0)) Lulu Enterprises Inc.

Shurkin, Michael. Subnational Government in Afghanistan. 2011. 40p. pap. 12.50 (978-0-8330-5229-2(2)) RAND Corp., The.

The Situation in Afghanistan: Hearings Before the Committee on Armed Services, United States Senate, One Hundred Eleventh Congress, Second Session, June 15 & 16, 2010. 2011. iii, 86p. (978-0-16-088128-2(5), 552-070-42548-9) United States Government Printing Office.

Skelly, Michael G. A Soldier's Tale: Living & Fighting with the Green Berets. 2010. 182p. 23.95 (978-1-60860-918-5(9), Eloquent Bks.) AEG Literary Publishing Services, Inc.

Smith, Scott Seward. Afghanistan's Troubled Transition: Politics, Peacekeeping, & the 2004 Presidential Election. 2010. 275p. 69.95 (978-1-935049-36-4(4)) FirstForumPress.

Stewart, Rory & Knaus, Gerald. Can Intervention Work? (Amnesty International Global Ethics Ser.). (ENG.). 2012. 272p. pap. 15.95 (978-0-393-34224-6(7), 34224) 2011. 236p. 23.95 (978-0-393-08120-6(6), 8120) Norton, W. W. & Co., Inc.

Suhrke, Astri. When More Is Less: The International Project in Afghanistan. 2012. (Columbia/Hurst Ser.). (ENG.). 256p. (gr. 17). 25.00 (978-0-231-70272-0(8)) Columbia Univ. Pr.

Tapper, Richard. Tribe & State in Iran & Afghanistan (Rle Iran A) 2011. (Routledge Library Editions: Iran Ser.). (ENG., Illus.). 496p. 150.00 (978-0-415-61056-8(7)) Routledge.

Thompson, Edwina A. Trust Is the Coin of Realm: Lessons from the Money Men in Afghanistan. 2011. (ENG.). 350p. 35.00 (978-0-19-547352-0(3)) Oxford Univ. Pr., Inc.

Tondini, Matteo. Statebuilding & Justice Reform: A Multidisciplinary Approach to Post-Conflict Reconstruction in Afghanistan. 2010. (Cass Series on Peacekeeping Ser.). (ENG., Illus.). 192p. (C). 130.00 (978-0-415-55894-5(8)) Routledge.

Troops, Diplomats, & Aid: Assessing Strategic Resources for Afghanistan: Hearing Before the Subcommittee on National Security & Foreign Affairs of the Committee on Oversight & Government Reform, House of Representatives, One Hundred Eleventh Congress, First Session, March 26, 2009. 2010. iii, 107p. (978-0-16-087176-4(X), 552-070-42018-5) United States Government Printing Office.

Tupper, Benjamin. Greetings from Afghanistan, Send More Ammo: Dispatches from Taliban Country. 2010. (ENG., Illus.). 272p. (gr. 12). 24.95 (978-0-451-23143-7(0), N A L Hardcover) Penguin Group (USA) Inc.

Turner, Christopher L. & Giordano, Denise M., eds. Assessments & Developments in the Security & Stability of Afghanistan. 2011. (Politics & Economics of the Middle East Ser.). 195.00 (978-1-61209-708-4(1)) Nova Science Pubs., Inc.

An Uneasy Relationship: U.S. Reliance on Private Security Firms in Overseas Operations: Hearing Before the Committee on Homeland Security & Governmental Affairs, United States Senate, One Hundred Tenth Congress, Second Session, February 27, 2008. 2010. iii, 162p. (978-0-16-085537-5(3), 552-070-40760-0) United States Government Printing Office.

United States, Congress House Committee on Armed Services Staff, contrib. by. Afghanistan: Operations & Reconstruction: Hearing Before the Committee on Armed Services, House of Representatives, One Hundred Ninth Congress, First Session, Hearing Held, June 22, 2005. 2007. iii, 85p. (978-0-16-078161-2(2), 552-070-35359-6) United States Government Printing Office.

United States, Congress House Committee on Foreign Affairs Staff, contrib. by. Afghanistan on the Brink: Where Do We Go from Here?: Hearing Before the Committee on Foreign Affairs, House of Representatives, One Hundred Tenth Congress, First Session, February 15, 2007. 2007. iii, 65p. (978-0-16-078641-9(X), 552-070-35383-8) United States Government Printing Office.

Verma, N. K. Taliban. 2010. 535p. 92.50 (978-81-7533-270-6(0)) M. D. Pubns. Pvt, Ltd. IND. Dist: Coronet Bks.

Wallis, Frank H. A History of the British Conquest of Afghanistan & Western India, 1838-1849. 2009. 384p. 119.95 (978-0-7734-4675-5(3)) Mellen, Edwin Pr., The.

Warnock, John W. Creating a Failed State: The U. S. & Canada in Afghanistan. 2008. (ENG.). 192p. pap. 21.95 (978-1-55266-262-5(4)) Fernwood Publishing Co., Ltd. CAN. Dist: Independent Pubs. Group.

Weaver, John. A Flame on the Front Line: Journey from America to Afghanistan. 2009. 160p. pap. 14.99 (978-1-61579-166-8(3)) Xulon Pr., Inc.

Williams, M. J. The Good War: NATO & the Liberal Conscience in Afghanistan. 2011. (ENG., Illus.). 224p. 90.00 (978-0-230-29427-1(8)); pap. 32.00 (978-0-230-29428-8(6)) Palgrave Macmillan.

Williamson, Myra. Terrorism, War & International Law: The Legality of the Use of Force Against Afghanistan in 2001. 2009. (Ashgate International Law Ser.). 294p. 124.95 (978-0-7546-7403-0(7)) Ashgate Publishing Co.

Zardushtian, Shukoor. Secularism in Afghanistan. 2011. 304p. 31.95 (978-1-4502-9082-1(5)); pap. 21.95 (978-1-4502-9083-8(3)) iUniverse, Inc.

Zhu, Yongbiao. "9.11" Zhi Hou de Afuhan. 2009. (Illus.). (978-7-5011-8879-6(3)) Xinhua Publishing Hse.

AFGHANISTAN—SOCIAL CONDITIONS

Ahmad, Khurram Maqsood. Talibanization in Afghanistan. 2011. 64p. pap. (978-3-8454-0654-1(2)) Lambert Academic Publishing.

Alexander, Chris. The Long Way Back: Afghanistan's Quest for Peace. 2011. 320p. 25.99 (978-0-06-202037-6(4)) HarperCollins Pubs.

Barfield, Thomas. Afghanistan: A Cultural & Political History. (Princeton Studies in Muslim Politics Ser.). (ENG., Illus.). 568p. 2012. pap. 16.95 (978-0-691-15441-1(4)) 2010. 29.95 (978-0-691-14568-6(7)) Princeton Univ. Pr.

Bhatia, Michael Vinay & Sedra, Mark. Afghanistan, Arms & Conflict: Armed Groups, Disarmament & Security in a Post-War Society. 2008. (Illus.). 352p. pap. 39.95 (978-0-415-47734-5(4)) Routledge.

Briongos, Ana M. Winter in Kandahar. 2008. 224p. pap. (978-1-906393-11-3(7)) Trotamundas Pr., Ltd.

Centlivres, Pierre & Centlivres-Demont, Micheline. Afghanistan on the Threshold of the 21st Century: Essays on Culture & Society. 2010. (Illus.). 320p. pap. 28.95 *(978-1-55876-524-5(7))* Wiener, Markus Pubs., Inc.

Chayes, Sarah. The Punishment of Virtue: Inside Afghanistan after the Taliban. 2007. (ENG., Illus.). 400p. (gr. 12-18). 16.00 *(978-0-14-311206-8(6)*, Penguin (Non-Classics)) Penguin Group (USA) Inc.

Coburn, Noah. Bazaar Politics: Power & Pottery in an Afghan Market Town. 2011. (Stanford Studies in Middle Eastern & I Ser.). (ENG., Illus.). 272p. 70.00 ***(978-0-8047-7671-4(7))***; pap. 22.95 ***(978-0-8047-7672-1(5))*** Stanford Univ. Pr.

Confronting Al-Qaeda: Understanding the Threat in Afghanistan & Beyond: Hearing Before the Committee on Foreign Relations, United States Senate, One Hundred Eleventh Congress, First Session, October 7, 2009. 2010. (Illus.). iii, 55p. *(978-0-16-085715-7(5)*, 552-070- 40944-1) United States Government Printing Office.

Contracting in a Counterinsurgency: An Examination of the Blackwater-Paravant Contract & the Need for Oversight: Hearing Before the Committee on Armed Services, United States Senate, One Hundred Eleventh Congress, Second Session, February 24, 2010. 2010. (Illus.). iv, 228p. *(978-0-16-086429-2(1)*, 552-070-41490-8) United States Government Printing Office.

Dodge, Toby & Redman, Nicholas, eds. Afghanistan: to 2015 & Beyond. 2012. (Adelphi Ser.). (ENG.). 300p. (C). 78.00 ***(978-0-415-53257-0(4))*** Routledge.

Duncan, Alex. Sweating the Metal: Flying under Fire. A Chinook Pilot's Blistering Account of Life, Death & Dust in Afghanistan. 2012. (ENG.). 352p. pap. 12.95 ***(978-1-4447-0800-4(7)***, Hodder & Stoughton) Hodder General Publishing Div. GBR. Dist: Independent Pubs. Group.

Emadi, Hafizullah. Dynamics of Political Development in Afghanistan: The British, Russian, & American Invasions. 2010. (ENG.). 316p. 95.00 *(978-0-230-10389-4(8))* Palgrave Macmillan.

Garcia, J. Malcolm. The Khaarijee: A Chronicle of Friendship & War in Kabul. 2009. (ENG.). 248p. 24.95 *(978-0-8070-0057-1(4))* Beacon Pr.

Girardet, Edward & Walter, Jonathan. Afghanistan: Essential Field Guide to Humanitarian & Conflict Zones. Norchi, Charles & Masood, Mirwais, eds. 3rd ed. 2007. (ENG.). 544p. pap. 29.95 *(978-2-9700176-2-2(8))* Media Action International CHE. Dist: Independent Pubs. Group.

Giustozzi, Antonio. Empires of Mud: Wars & Warlords in Afghanistan. 2009. (Columbia/Hurst Ser.). (ENG.). 320p. (gr. 17). 35.00 *(978-0-231-70080-1(6))* Columbia Univ. Pr.

Gladstone, Cary. Afghanistan Issues: Security, Narcotics & Political Currents. 2007. 79.00 *(978-1-60021-587-2(4))* Nova Science Pubs., Inc.

Glatzer, Bernt. Afghanistan. 2008. (Contemporary Middle East Ser.). (Illus.). 192p. (gr. 13). 140.00 *(978-0-415-27430-2(3))*; 41.95 *(978-0-415-28384-7(1))* Routledge.

Harpviken, Kristian Berg. Social Networks & Migration in Wartime Afghanistan. 2009. (ENG., Illus.). 272p. 100.00 *(978-0-230-57655-1(9))* Palgrave Macmillan.

Hopkins, Ben. The Making of Modern Afghanistan. 2008. (ENG., Illus.). 272p. 95.00 *(978-0-230-55421-4(0))* Palgrave Macmillan.

IntelCenter. IntelCenter Terrorism Incident Reference (TIR): Afghanistan: 2000-2007. 2008. 646p. pap. 59.95 *(978-0-9665437-8-0(5))* Tempest Publishing.

Johnson, Steve, et al. Afganistan: The Mirage of Peace. 2nd ed. 2008. (ENG., Illus.). 272p. pap. 26.95 *(978-1-84277-956-9(7))* Zed Bks., Ltd. GBR. Dist: Macmillan.

Jubber, Nicholas. Drinking Arak off an Ayatollah's Beard: A Journey Through the Inside-Out Worlds of Iran & Afghanistan. 2010. (ENG., Illus.). 368p. pap. 15.95 *(978-0-306-81884-4(1))* Da Capo Pr., Inc.

Kakar, Hasan Kawun. Government & Society in Afghanistan: The Reign of Amir 'Abd Al-Rahman Khan. 2011. (ENG.). 352p. pap. 30.00 *(978-0-292-72900-1(6))* Univ. of Texas Pr.

Kargar, Zarghuna. Dear Zari: The Secret Lives of the Women of Afghanistan. 2012. (ENG.). 272p. pap. 15.99 ***(978-1-4022-6837-3(8))*** Sourcebooks, Inc.

Kassimyar, Akhtar. The Truth of Terrorism. 2009. 176p. pap. 15.95 *(978-1-4401-5051-7(6))* iUniverse, Inc.

Keeling, Philip C. Afghanistan Why? 2009. 88p. pap. 16.95 *(978-1-60836-917-1(X))* PublishAmerica, Inc.

Lambers, William. The Spirit of the Marshall Plan: Taking Action Against World Hunger, Expanding the Mcgovern-Dole Global School Feeding Program. 2007. *(978-0-9724629-6-9(1))* Lambers, William.

Lyon, Peter D. S. A Solution for Ethnic Conflict. 2008. 320p. per. *(978-3-8364-3496-6(2))* VDM Verlag Dr. Mueller e.K.

Mack, Thomas J. Conceptual Model of Water Resources in the Kabul Basin, Afghanistan. 2010. (Illus.). x, 240p. *(978-1-4113-2671-2(7))* United States Geological Survey.

Mahmood, Waseem. Good Morning Afghanistan. Scott, Catriona, ed. 2010. (ENG.). 240p. pap. 13.95 *(978-1-903070-71-0(6))* Eye Bks. GBR. Dist: Independent Pubs. Group.

—Good Morning Afghanistan. 2007. (ENG., Illus.). 240p. 26.95 *(978-1-903070-53-6(8))* Eye Bks. GBR. Dist: Independent Pubs. Group.

Mazurana, Dyan E. & Nojumi, Neamatollah. After the Taliban: Life & Security in Rural Afghanistan. 2008. (ENG., Illus.). 338p. 85.00 *(978-0-7425-4032-3(4))* Rowman & Littlefield Publishers, Inc.

Meissner, Ursula. Afghanistan: Hope & Beauty in a War-Torn Land. 2008. (Illus.). 189p. pap. *(978-3-7658-1688-8(4))* Bucher, C. J. Verlag GmbH.

Mir, Ferrukh. Half Truth. 2011. 524p. pap. 30.95 *(978-1-4502-8644-2(5))* iUniverse, Inc.

Morgan, Matthew J. A Democracy Is Born: An Insider's Account of the Battle Against Terrorism in Afghanistan, 1 vol. 2007. (Praeger Security International Ser.). (Illus.). 184p. 39.95 *(978-0-275-99999-5(8)*, C9999, Praeger Security International) Greenwood Publishing Group, Inc.

Murphy, Seamus. A Darkness Visible. 2008. (ENG., Illus.). 175p. 50.00 *(978-0-86356-620-2(0))* Saqi Bks. GBR. Dist: Consortium Bk. Sales & Distribution.

Nojumi, Neamatollah, et al. Life & Security in Rural Afghanistan. 2010. (ENG.). 338p. pap. 37.50 *(978-0-7425-4033-0(2))* Rowman & Littlefield Publishers, Inc.

Peters, Gretchen. Seeds of Terror: How Drugs, Thugs, & Crime Are Reshaping the Afghan War. 2010. (ENG., Illus.). 352p. pap. 16.00 *(978-0-312-42963-8(0))* Picador.

Rais, Rasul Bakhsh. Recovering the Frontier State: War, Ethnicity, & State in Afghanistan. 2008. (ENG.). 252p. 83.99 *(978-0-7391-0956-4(1))* Lexington Bks.

Sadeed, Suraya & Lewis, Damien. Forbidden Lessons in a Kabul Guesthouse: The True Story of a Woman Who Risked Everything to Bring Hope to Afghanistan. 2011. (ENG.). 304p. 24.99 *(978-1-4013-4131-2(4))* Hyperion Pr.

Schlenkhoff, Angela. Beyond the 'Wild Tribes' Understanding Modern Afghanistan & Its Diaspora. Oeppen, Ceri, ed. 2010. (Columbia/Hurst Ser.). (ENG.). 224p. (gr. 17). 40.00 *(978-0-231-70210-2(8))* Columbia Univ. Pr.

Schofield, Victoria. Afghan Frontier: At the Crossroads of Conflict. 2010. (ENG., Illus.). 392p. pap. 20.00 *(978-1-84885-188-7(X)*, Tauris Parke Paperbacks) I. B. Tauris & Co., Ltd. GBR. Dist: Macmillan.

Shanty, Frank C. The Nexus: International Terrorism & Drug Trafficking from Afghanistan, 1 vol. 2011. (Praeger Security International Ser.). (Illus.). 288p. 49.95 *(978-0-313-38521-6(1)*, A2977C, Praeger Pubs.) Greenwood Publishing Group, Inc.

Sims-Williams, Nicholas. Bactrian Documents, Part II. 2007. (Studies in the Khalili Collections). 328p. (C). *(978-1-874780-90-8(0)*, Khalili Collections) I. B. Tauris & Co., Ltd.

Sutton, Jacqueline. Reconstructing Agriculture in Afghan: Agriculture & Food Security. 2008. (ENG.). 370p. (C). pap. 35.95 *(978-1-85339-634-2(6))* Intermediate Technology Development Group of North America.

Tripathi, Deepak. Breeding Ground: Afghanistan & the Origins of Islamist Terrorism. 2011. (Illus.). 256p. 26.95 *(978-1-59797-530-8(3))* Potomac Bks., Inc.

Tupper, Benjamin. Greetings from Afghanistan, Send More Ammo: Dispatches from Taliban Country. 2011. (ENG.). 272p. (gr. 12). 15.00 *(978-0-451-23325-7(5)*, N A L Trade) Penguin Group (USA) Inc.

United Nations. Global Afghan Opium Trade: A Threat Assessment. 2011. (ENG.). 280p. pap. 70.00 ***(978-92-1-148263-8(1))*** United Nations Pubns.

United States, Congress House Committee on Armed Services Staff, contrib. by. Afghanistan: Operations & Reconstruction: Hearing Before the Committee on Armed Services, House of Representatives, One Hundred Ninth Congress, First Session, Hearing Held, June 22, 2005. 2007. iii, 85p. *(978-0-16-078161-2(2)*, 552-070-35559-6) United States Government Printing Office.

Wahab, Saima. In My Father's Country. 2012. ***(978-0-307-88495-4(3))*** Crown Publishing Group.

WAHAB, Saima. In My Father's Country: An Afghan Woman Defies Her Fate. 2012. (ENG.). 352p. 25.00 ***(978-0-307-88494-7(5)***, Crown) Crown Publishing Group.

AFGHANISTAN—SOCIAL LIFE AND CUSTOMS

Amici, Giammarco. Afghanistan, a Country at War with Itself. 2009. 232p. pap. 53.25 *(978-1-60860-774-7(7)*, Eloquent Bks.) AEG Literary Publishing Services, Inc.

Burke, John & Norfolk, Simon, photos by. Burke + Norfolk: Photographs from the War in Afghanistan. 2011. (ENG., Illus.). 168p. 65.00 ***(978-1-907893-11-7(3))*** Lewis, Dewi Publishing GBR. Dist: Consortium Bk. Sales & Distribution.

Elliot, Jason. An Unexpected Light: Travels in Afghanistan. 2nd ed. 2011. (ENG., Illus.). 512p. pap. 18.00 *(978-0-312-62205-3(8))* Picador.

Garcia, J. Malcolm. The Khaarijee: A Chronicle of Friendship & War in Kabul. 2009. (ENG.). 248p. 24.95 *(978-0-8070-0057-1(4))* Beacon Pr.

Johnson, E. D. Serenity: 30 Days to Rebalance Mind-Body-Spirit. 2009. 80p. pap. 10.99 *(978-1-4490-1599-2(9))* AuthorHouse.

Kandahar Provincial Handbook: A Guide to the People & the Province. 2011. 92p. spiral bd. ***(978-1-936336-46-3(4))*** IDS International.

Klass, Rosanne. Land of the High Flags: Afghanistan When the Going Was Good. 2007. (Illus.). 344p. pap. 19.95 *(978-962-217-786-4(7))* Odyssey Pubns., Ltd. HKG. Dist: Norton, W. W. & Co., Inc.

Lemmon, Gayle Tzemach. The Dressmaker of Khair Khana: Five Sisters, One Remarkable Family, & the Woman Who Risked Everything to Keep Them Safe. 2011. (ENG., Illus.). 288p. 24.99 *(978-0-06-173237-9(0))* HarperCollins Pubs.

—The Dressmaker of Khair Khana: Five Sisters, One Remarkable Family, & the Woman Who Risked Everything to Keep Them Safe. l.t. ed. (ENG.). 287p. 2012. pap. 16.99 ***(978-1-59413-575-0(4)***, Large Print Pr.) 2011. 31.99 ***(978-1-4104-3965-9(8))*** Thorndike Pr.

Meissner, Ursula. Afghanistan: Hope & Beauty in a War-Torn Land. 2008. (Illus.). 189p. pap. *(978-3-7658-1688-8(4))* Bucher, C. J. Verlag GmbH.

Monis, Haroon. Life in Paradise: A Family's Struggles. 2008. 109p. pap. 15.99 *(978-0-557-02539-8(7))* Lulu Enterprises Inc.

Rodriguez, Deborah. Kabul Beauty School. 2011. 14.72 *(978-0-7848-3406-0(7)*, Everbind) Marco Bk. Co.

—Kabul Beauty School: An American Woman Goes Behind the Veil. l.t. ed. 2007. (Readers Circle Ser.). 351p. 32.95 *(978-1-60285-009-5(7))* Ctr. Point Large Print.

—Kabul Beauty School: An American Woman Goes Behind the Veil. 2008. (ENG.). 64.99 *(978-1-60640-750-9(3))* Findaway World, LLC.

Rodriguez, Deborah & Ohlson, Kristin. Kabul Beauty School: An American Woman Goes Behind the Veil. 2007. (ENG.). 320p. pap. 14.95 *(978-0-8129-7673-1(8))* Random House Publishing Group.

Rostami-Povey, Elaheh. Afghan Women: Identity & Invasion. 2007. (ENG., Illus.). 176p. 104.95 *(978-1-84277-855-5(2))*; per. 31.95 *(978-1-84277-856-2(0))* Zed Bks., Ltd. GBR. Dist: Macmillan.

Samad, Rafi-us. The Grandeur of Gandhara: An Ancient Kingdom of Pakistan. 2011. 302p. pap. 23.95 ***(978-0-87586-859-2(2))*** Algora Publishing.

—The Grandeur of Gandhara: An Ancient Kingdom of Pakistan. 2011. 302p. pap. 23.95 ***(978-0-87586-858-5(4))*** Algora Publishing.

Wilber, Donald N. Afghanistan: Its People, Its Society, Its Culture. 2011. 352p. 51.95 ***(978-1-258-06165-4(1))*** Literary Licensing, LLC.

AFGHANISTAN ART

see Art, Afghanistan

AFGHANS (COVERLETS)

Carter, Bendy. Charted Picture Afghans. Ellison, Connie, ed. 2011. (ENG., Illus.). 48p. pap. 8.95 *(978-1-59635-370-1(8)*, Annie's Attic, LLC) Annie's Publishing, LLC.

Chachula, Robyn. Unexpected Afghans: Innovative Crochet Designs with Traditional Techniques. 2012. (ENG., Illus.). 160p. pap. 22.95 ***(978-1-59668-299-3(X))*** Interweave Pr., LLC.

Chin, Lily, des. Lily Chin's Mosaic Magic Afghans. 2006. (ENG.). 144p. per. 24.95 *(978-1-60140-292-9(9))* Leisure Arts, Inc.

Creative Marketing Solutions, ed. More Herrschners(r) Blue-Ribbon Afghans. 2006. 128p. per. 24.95 *(978-1-60140-322-3(4))* Leisure Arts, Inc.

Crow, Judy. Heirloom Afghans. 2008. (Illus.). 175p. *(978-1-57367-307-5(2)*, Needlecraft Shop, The) Annie's Publishing, LLC.

DRG Publishing Staff. A Year of Afghans: 52 Projects to Keep You Knitting Every Week of the Year. Gott Warner, Kara, ed. 2011. (ENG., Illus.). 128p. pap. 19.95 *(978-1-59217-336-5(5)*, House of White Birches, Inc.) Annie's Publishing, LLC.

Ellison, Connie, ed. Geometric Afghans. 2011. 4p. 5.99 ***(978-1-59635-414-2(3)***, Annie's Attic, LLC) Annie's Publishing, LLC.

Gaughan, Norah, et al. Comfort Knitting & Crochet - Afghans: More Than 50 Beautiful, Affordable Designs Featuring Berroco's Comfort Yarn. 2010. (ENG., Illus.). 160p. pap. 19.95 *(978-1-58479-826-2(2))* Stewart, Tabori & Chang.

Gormley, Ellen. Go Crochet! Afghan Design Workshop: 50 Motifs, 10 Projects, 1 of a Kind Results. 2011. (ENG.). 128p. 24.99 *(978-1-4402-0907-9(3))* Krause Pubns.

Halliday, Anne, des. Baby Bubble Wraps. 2006. 28p. 9.95 *(978-1-60140-087-1(X))* Leisure Arts, Inc.

—Beauty of the Earth Afghans. 2007. 20p. 7.95 *(978-1-60140-415-2(8))* Leisure Arts, Inc.

Leapman, Mellissa, des. Fireside Afghans. 2006. 7.95 *(978-1-60140-312-4(7))* Leisure Arts, Inc.

Leisure Arts. Afghan Lover's Collection. 2011. (ENG.). 128p. pap. 24.95 *(978-1-60900-128-5(1))* Leisure Arts, Inc.

Leisure Arts, creator. Sweet & Soft Baby Afghans to Crochet: 5 Crochet Designs by Anne Halliday. 2006. (ENG.). 12p. pap. *(978-1-60140-262-2(7))* Leisure Arts, Inc.

—A Year of Q-Hook Afghans Book 3. 2006. (ENG.). 40p. pap. 10.95 *(978-1-60140-294-3(5))* Leisure Arts, Inc.

Leisure Arts Staff. Our Best Knit Baby Afghans. 2nd ed. 2010. (Our Best Knit Baby Afghans Ser.). (ENG.). 80p. pap. 14.95 *(978-1-60900-032-5(3))* Leisure Arts, Inc.

Lion Brand Yarn, ed. Homespun(r) Afghans: 4 Crochet Designs. 2006. 20p. 7.95 *(978-1-60140-410-7(7))* Leisure Arts, Inc.

Malcolm, Trisha, ed. Under Cover: 60 Afghans to Knit & Crochet. 2007. (ENG., Illus.). 160p. spiral bd. 17.95 *(978-1-933027-30-2(4))* Sixth&Spring Bks.

Matela, Bobbie. 50 Sensational Afghans & Throws. 2007. (Illus.). 176p. *(978-1-57367-277-1(7)*, Needlecraft Shop, The) Annie's Publishing, LLC.

Sims, Darla. 101 Granny Squares. Stratton, Ann, ed. 2008. (ENG.). 86p. pap. 14.95 *(978-1-59635-210-0(8)*, Annie's Attic, LLC) Annie's Publishing, LLC.

Weldon, Maggie. The Best of Maggie Weldon Crochet Afghans. 2007. (ENG., Illus.). 112p. pap. 22.95 *(978-1-57486-535-6(8))* Leisure Arts, Inc.

Weston, Angie & Batt, Angie. Mosaic Magic: Simple Creative Ideas for Sophisticated Home Style. 2008. (ENG., Illus.). 128p. pap. 22.99 *(978-0-7153-2798-2(4))* David & Charles Pubs. GBR. Dist: F&W Media, Inc.

White, Vanna. Color It Beautiful Afghans. 2008. (Vanna's Choice Ser.). (ENG., Illus.). 64p. per. 14.95 *(978-1-60140-685-9(1))* Leisure Arts, Inc.

AFICIONADOS

see Fans (Persons)

AFLATOXINS

Siantar, Darsa P., et al, eds. Food Contaminants: Mycotoxins & Food Allergens. 2008. (ACS Symposium Ser.). (ENG., Illus.). 560p. 195.00 *(978-0-8412-6954-5(8))* American Chemical Society.

Yourtee, D. Toxicology of Aflatoxins. Date not set. *(978-0-8247-0017-1(1))* Dekker, Marcel Inc.

AFL-CIO

see American Federation of Labor and Congress of Industrial Organizations

AFRICA

see also names of countries or regions of Africa, e.g. Egypt, Ghana, Sudan (Region), Zaire, etc.; also geographic subdivisions of Africa, e.g. Africa, East; Africa, Sub-Saharan

Bohannan, Paul & Curtin, Philip D. Africa & Africans. 4th ed. 2006. pap. 8.95 *(978-1-4288-1516-2(3))* Cram101 Inc.

Borrell, J. Exploring Ancient Africa. cd-rom 49.95 *(978-1-57047-027-1(8))* Sumeria, Inc.

Hoberman, Gerald. Namibia. 2009. (Dumpy Ser: Namibia Ser.). (ENG.). 248p. 29.95 *(978-1-919939-03-2(2))* Hoberman, Gerald Pubns. ZAF. Dist: Perseus Distribution.

Karugia, John Njenga. Africa Conflict Prevention: Early Warning & Early Response. 2008. 196p. pap. *(978-3-639-00473-1(6))* VDM Verlag Dr. Mueller e.K.

Maran, Rene. Batouala. 2008. 212p. 39.95 *(978-1-4369-2442-9(1))*; pap. 24.95 *(978-1-4367-8598-3(7))* Kessinger Publishing, LLC.

Remarks on the Country Extending from Cape Palmas to the River Congo. 2009. 98p. pap. 14.14 *(978-1-4589-6297-3(0))* General Bks. LLC.

Sislian, Jack. Think African. 2008. xix, 93p. pap. 39.00 *(978-1-60456-356-6(7))* Nova Science Pubs., Inc.

Tubenzele, Philippe Kanku. L'Afrique est a Construire: La Responsabilite Spirituelle. (FRE.). 252p. pap. 44.95 *(978-3-03911-427-6(1))* Lang, Peter Publishing, Inc.

Utas, Mats, et al. Young Female Fighters in African Wars: Conflict & Its Consequences. 2008. (Nordic Africa Institute Policy Dialogues Ser.). 54p. pap. 23.95 *(978-91-7106-627-5(6))* Nordiska Afrikainstitutet SWE. Dist: Stylus Publishing, LLC.

White, Arthur. The Development of Afric. 2007. 336p. per. 29.95 *(978-1-60206-900-8(X))* Cosimo, Inc.

AFRICA—ANTIQUITIES

Abed, Aicha Ben, ed. Stories in Stone: Conserving Mosaics of Roman Africa: Masterpieces from the National Museums of Tunisia. 2006. (Illus.). 200p. 75.00 *(978-0-89236-803-7(9))* Oxford Univ. Pr., Inc.

Arazi, N., et al. African Impressed Pottery: Roulette Decoration Past & Present. 2010. (ENG & FRE., Illus.). 208p. (C). pap. 50.00 *(978-1-84217-968-0(3))* Oxbow Bks., Ltd. GBR. Dist: Brown, David Bk. Co., The.

Arbousse-Bastide, Tristan. Du couteau au sabre / from Knife to Sabre: Armes Traditionnelles D'Afrique 2 / Traditional Arms of Africa 2. 2008. (Bar S Ser.). (FRE & ENG., Illus.). 63p. (C). pap. 82.50 *(978-1-4073-0253-9(1))* British Archaeological Reports Ltd. GBR. Dist: Brown, David Bk. Co., The.

Badenhorst, Shaw, et al, eds. Animals & People: Archaeozoological Papers in Honour of Ina Plug. 2008. (Bar S Ser.). (ENG., Illus.). 228p. (C). pap. 90.00 *(978-1-4073-0336-9(8))* British Archaeological Reports Ltd. GBR. Dist: Brown, David Bk. Co., The.

Barham, Lawrence & Mitchell, Peter J. The First Africans: African Archaeology from the Earliest Toolmakers to Most Recent Foragers. 2008. (Cambridge World Archaeology Ser.). (ENG., Illus.). 602p. (C). 103.99 *(978-0-521-84796-4(6))* Cambridge Univ. Pr.

Bastide, Tristan Arbousse. Traditional Weapons of Africa (Billhooks, Sickles & Scythes) Regional Approach & Technical, Morphological & Aesthetic Classification. 2012. (Bar S Ser.). (FRE & ENG., Illus.). 146p. (C). pap. 82.50 *(978-1-4073-0690-2(1))* British Archaeological Reports Ltd. GBR. Dist: Brown, David Bk. Co., The.

Beltrami, Vanni & Proto, Harry. Il Sahara Centro-Orientale Dalla Preistoria Ai Tempi Dei Nomadi Tubu: The Central-Oriental Sahara from Prehistory to the Times of the Nomadic Tubus. 2007. (Bar S Ser.). (ITA & ENG., Illus.). ii, 261p. (C). 90.00 *(978-1-4073-0102-0(0))* British Archaeological Reports Ltd. GBR. Dist: Brown, David Bk. Co., The.

Blue, Lucy, et al, eds. Connected Hinterlands. 2009. (Bar S Ser.). (Illus.). 232p. (C). pap. 107.50 *(978-1-4073-0631-5(6))* British Archaeological Reports Ltd. GBR. Dist: Brown, David Bk. Co., The.

Castiglioni, Angelo and Alfredo. Once upon a Time in Africa: 50 Years of Explorations & Adventures. 2010. (ENG., Illus.). 428p. 50.00 *(978-88-544-0485-4(3))* White Star ITA. Dist: Random Hse., Inc.

Colton, Danny. An Archaeological & Geomorphological Survey of the Luangwa Valley, Zambia. 2009. (Bar S Ser.). (ENG., Illus.). 200p. (C). pap. 100.00 *(978-1-4073-0597-4(2))* British Archaeological Reports Ltd. GBR. Dist: Brown, David Bk. Co., The.

David, Nicholas. Performance & Agency: The DGB Sites of Northern Cameroon. 2008. (Bar S Ser.). (Illus.). 155p. (C). 82.50 *(978-1-4073-0314-7(7))* British Archaeological Reports Ltd. GBR. Dist: Brown, David Bk. Co., The.

Delamarter, Steve & Terefe, Melaku. Ethiopian Scribal Practice 1: Plates for the Catalogue of the Ethiopic Manuscript Imaging Project. 2009. (Ethiopic Manuscripts, Texts, & Studies). 208p. pap. 67.00 *(978-1-60608-872-2(6)*, Pickwick Pubns.) Wipf & Stock Pubs.

Derricourt, Robin. Inventing Africa: History, Archaeology & Ideas, 1 vol. 2011. (ENG., Illus.). 256p. 28.00 *(978-0-7453-3105-8(X))*; lib. bdg. 90.00 *(978-0-7453-3106-5(8))* Pluto Pr. GBR. Dist: Macmillan.

Erbati, Elarbi & Trakadas, Athena. The Morocco Maritime Survey. 2009. (Bar S Ser.). (ARA & ENG., Illus.). 126p. (C). pap. 82.50 *(978-1-4073-0370-3(8))* British Archaeological Reports Ltd. GBR. Dist: Brown, David Bk. Co., The.

Gilbert, Elizabeth L. Tribes of the Great Rift Valley. 2007. (ENG., Illus.). 272p. 75.00 *(978-0-8109-9411-9(9))* Abrams.

Haviser, Jay B. & MacDonald, Kevin C., eds. African Re-Genesis: Confronting Social Issues in the Diaspora. (One World Archaeology Ser.). (ENG., Illus.).

290p. 2008. pap. 34.95 (978-1-59874-283-1(3)) 2007. 89.00 (978-1-59874-217-6(5)) Left Coast Pr., Inc.

Heckendorf, Renate. Bubalin und Bovidien in Sudmarokko: Kontext, Klassifikation und Chronologie der Felsbilder Im Mittleren Draa-Tal. 2008. (Forschungen zur Archaologie Aussereuropaischer Kulturen Ser.). (GER., Illus.). 332p. (C). 118.00 (978-3-89500-646-3(7)) Reichert, Ludwig Dr. DEU. Dist: Brown, David Bk. Co., The.

Hodder, Ian. Symbols in Action: Ethnoarchaeological Studies of Material Culture. 2009. (New Studies in Archaeology Ser.). (ENG., Illus.). 256p. pap. 36.99 (978-0-521-10508-3(0)) Cambridge Univ. Pr.

Howell, F. Clark, et al, eds. African Ecology & Human Evolution. 2007. (ENG., Illus.). 674p. (gr. 11). pap. 44.95 (978-0-202-36136-9(5)) Aldine Transaction.

Johnson, Steve. Afrikans of Antiquitya Coloring Book. per. 6.95 (978-0-86543-253-6(8)) Africa World Pr.

Mack, John. Preserving the Cultural Heritage of Africa: Crisis or Renaissance? Yoshida, Kenji, ed. 2010. (Illus.). 224p. pap. 29.95 (978-0-85255-982-6(8), Currey, James) Boydell & Brewer, Ltd. GBR. Dist: Boydell & Brewer, Inc.

Meredith, Martin. Born in Africa: The Quest for the Origins of Human Life. 2011. (ENG., Illus.). 288p. 26.99 (978-1-58648-663-1(2)) PublicAffairs.

Mitchell, Peter & Smith, Benjamin, eds. The Eland's People: New Perspectives in the Rock Art of the Maloti-Drakensberg Bushmen. 2011. (ENG., Illus.). 256p. pap. 60.00 (978-1-86814-498-3(4)) Witwatersrand Univ. Pr. Pubns. ZAF. Dist: Transaction Pubs.

Mitchell, Peter J. The First Africans: African Archaeology from the Earliest Toolmakers to Most Recent Foragers. 2008. (Cambridge World Archaeology Ser.). (ENG., Illus.). 602p. (C). pap. 37.99 (978-0-521-61265-4(9)) Cambridge Univ. Pr.

Notue, Jean-Paul & Triaca, Bianca. Mankon: Arts, Heritage & Culture from the Mankon Kingdom (Western Cameroon) 2008. (ENG., Illus.). 336p. pap. 35.00 (978-88-7439-200-1(1)) 5 Continents ITA. Dist: Hachette Bk. Group.

O'Brien, Terence P. The Prehistory of Uganda Protectorate. reprint ed. 34.50 (978-0-404-15874-3(9)) AMS Pr., Inc.

Peacock, David & Blue, Lucy, eds. The Ancient Red Sea Port of Adulis, Eritrea: Results of the Eritro-British Expedition, 2004-5. 2007. (ENG., Illus.). 160p. (C). per. 60.00 (978-1-84217-308-4(1)) Oxbow Bks., Ltd. GBR. Dist: Brown, David Bk. Co., The.

Pearson, Mike Parker, et al. Pastoralists, Warriors & Colonists: The Archaeology of Southern Madagascar. 2010. (Bar S Ser.). (Illus.). 725p. (C). pap. 237.50 (978-1-4073-0690-3(4)) British Archaeological Reports Ltd. GBR. Dist: Brown, David Bk. Co., The.

Schmidt, Peter. Historical Archaeology in Africa: Representation, Social Memory, & Oral Traditions. 2006. (African Archaeology Ser.). (ENG., Illus.). 240p. 93.00 (978-0-7591-0964-3(8)); per. 37.95 (978-0-7591-0965-0(6)) AltaMira Pr.

Schmidt, Peter R. Postcolonial Archaeologies in Africa. 2009. (ENG., Illus.). 304p. pap. 34.95 (978-1-930618-08-4(5)) School for Advanced Research Pr./SAR Pr.

Vinnicombe, Patricia. People of the Eland: Rock Paintings of the Drakensberg Bushmen as a Reflection of their Life & Thought. 2011. (ENG.). 400p. pap. 89.95 (978-1-86814-497-6(6)) Witwatersrand Univ. Pr. Pubns. ZAF. Dist: Transaction Pubs.

Willink, Robert Joost. Stages in Civilisation: Dutch Museums in Quest of West Central African Collections (1856-1889) 2011. (CNWS Publications). (Illus.). xiii, 389p. pap. (978-90-5789-113-7(1), Leiden Univ. Pr.) Amsterdam Univ. Pr.

Wright, Henry Tutwiler. Early State Formation in Central Madagascar: An Archaeological Survey of Western Avaradrano. 2007. (Illus.). 311p. 38.00 (978-0-915703-63-0(7)) Univ. of Michigan, Museum of Anthropology, Pubns. Dept.

AFRICA—ARMED FORCES

Abbott, Peter. Colonial Armies in Africa 1850-1918: Organisation, Warfare, Dress & Weapons. 2006. (Illus.). 222p. 59.95 (978-1-901543-07-0(2)) Foundry Bks. GBR. Dist: Casemate Pubs. & Bk. Distributors, LLC.

Adams, Mark & Cocks, Chris. Africa's Commandos. 2012. (Illus.). 544p. 99.95 (978-1-907677-75-5(5)) Helion & Co., Ltd. GBR. Dist: Casemate Pubs. & Bk. Distributors, LLC.

Africa Command. 2009. iii, 67p. (978-0-16-083684-8(0), 552-070-39390-1) United States Government Printing Office.

Aginam, Obijiofor & Rupiya, Martin R., eds. HIV/AIDS & the Security Sector in Africa. 2012. (ENG.). 296p. pap. 34.00 (978-92-808-1209-1(2)) United Nations Pubns.

Allen, Tim & Vlassenroot, Koen, eds. The Lord's Resistance Army: Myth & Reality. 2010. (ENG., Illus.). 288p. 125.95 (978-1-84813-562-8(9)) Zed Bks., Ltd. GBR. Dist: Macmillan.

Arnold, Guy. The A to Z of Civil Wars in Africa. 98th ed. 2009. (A to Z Guide Ser.: No. 98). (ENG.). 538p. pap. 34.45 (978-0-8108-6885-4(7)) Scarecrow Pr., Inc.

Baker, Deane-Peter & Evert, Evert. South Africa & Contemporary Counterinsurgency: Roots, Practices, Prospects. 2011. (Illus.). 288p. pap. 37.95 (978-1-919895-33-8(7)) International Publishers Marketing.

Binda, Alexandre. Masodja: The History of the Rhodesian African Rifles & its Forerunner, the Rhodesia Native Regiment. 2008. 480p. 90.00 (978-1-920143-03-9(3)) 30° South Pubs. ZAF. Dist: International Publishers Marketing.

Buss, Terry, et al, eds. African Security & the African Command: Viewpoints on the US Role in Africa. 2011. 288p. 75.00 (978-1-56549-413-8(X)); pap. 27.95 (978-1-56549-412-1(1)) Stylus Publishing, LLC.

Chau, Donovan C. Kenya. 2010. (Global Security Watch Ser.). (Illus.). 194p. 49.95 (978-0-313-37880-5(0), C37880, Praeger Pubs.) Greenwood Publishing Group, Inc.

Cherry, Janet. Umkhonto Wesizwe. 2011. (Pocket History Guides). 150p. pap. 15.99 (978-1-77009-961-6(1)) Jacana Media ZAF. Dist: Independent Pubs. Group.

Chun, Clayton K. S. Do Oil Exports Fuel Defense Spending? 2010. ix, 50p. (978-1-58487-420-1(1)) Strategic Studies Institute, U.S. Army War College Commandant (AWCC-DSI/Pubns.).

Cocks, Chris. Out of Action. 2009. (Illus.). 310p. pap. 30.00 (978-1-58160-707-9(5)) Paladin Pr.

Cordesman, Anthony H. & Nerguizian, Aram. The North African Military Balance: Force Developments in the Maghreb. 2009. (Illus.). pap. 22.95 (978-0-89206-552-5(4), CSIS Pr., The) Ctr. for Strategic & International Studies.

Croukamp, Dennis. The Bush War in Rhodesia. 2007. pap. 35.00 (978-1-58160-614-0(1)) Paladin Pr.

de Montfort, Pierre Juan & De Montfort, Pierre Juan. A Model of Co-Operative Education. 2010. 212p. pap. (978-3-8383-0127-3(7)) Lambert Academic Publishing.

Durand, Arn. Zulu Zulu Golf: Two Years with KOEVOET. 2011. (Illus.). 288p. pap. 27.95 (978-1-77022-148-2(4)) Random Hse. Struik (Pty.), Ltd. ZAF. Dist: International Publishers Marketing.

Falola, Toyin & Njoku, Raphael Chijioke, eds. War & Peace in Africa. 2010. pap. 65.00 (978-1-59460-745-5(1)) Carolina Academic Pr.

Fuhirott, Friederike. The Reintegration of Ex-Combatants: A Case Study of Burundi. 2008. 249p. pap. 61.00 (978-3-8329-3654-9(8)) Nomos Verlagsgesellschaft DEU. Dist: International Specialized Bk. Services.

Gillmore, Graham. Pathfinder Company: 44 Parachute Brigade - 'the Philistines' 2010. (Illus.). 224p. pap. 39.95 (978-1-920143-48-0(3)) 30° South Pubs. ZAF. Dist: International Publishers Marketing.

Haggett, Adrian & Tonder, Gerry van. Rhodesian Combined Forces Roll of Honour 1966-1981. 2012. 160p. pap. 49.95 (978-1-907677-79-3(8)) Helion & Co., Ltd. GBR. Dist: Casemate Pubs. & Bk. Distributors, LLC.

Jordan, David. The Balkans, Italy & Africa, 1914-1918: From Sarajevo to the Piave & Lake Tanganyika. 2012. (Illus.). 224p. 34.95 (978-1-906626-14-3(6)) Amber Bks. GBR. Dist: Casemate Pubs. & Bk. Distributors, LLC.

Korff, Granger. Nineteen with a Bullet: A South African Paratrooper in Angola. 2009. (Illus.). 352p. pap. 29.95 (978-1-920143-31-2(9)) 30° South Pubs. ZAF. Dist: International Publishers Marketing.

Larr, Frisky. Nigeria's Journalistic Militantism: Putting the Facts in Perspective on how the Press failed Nigeria Setting the Wrong Agenda & Excessively Attacking Ex-President Olusegun Obasanjo! 2011. 340p. pap. 26.32 (978-1-4567-7790-6(4)) AuthorHouse.

Lord, Brigadier Dick. From Fledgling to Eagle: The South African Air Force During the Border War. 2009. 544p. 39.95 (978-1-920143-30-5(0)) 30° South Pubs. ZAF. Dist: International Publishers Marketing.

—Vlamgat: The Story of the Mirage F1 in the South African Air Force. 2009. 368p. pap. 29.95 (978-1-920143-36-7(X)) 30° South Pubs. ZAF. Dist: International Publishers Marketing.

Malan, Mark. Security Sector Reform in Liberia: Mixed Results from Humble Beginnings. 2008. (YA). lib. bdg. (978-1-58487-345-7(0)) Strategic Studies Institute, U.S. Army War College Commandant (AWCC-DSI/Pubns.).

Mays, Terry M. Nigerian Peacekeeping Policy: The Application of Peacekeeping As a Foreign Policy Tool 1960-1990. 2010. (Illus.). x, 190p. 109.95 (978-0-7734-3588-9(3)) Mellen, Edwin Pr., The.

McLachlan, Sean. Armies of the Adowa Campaign 1896: The Italian Disaster in Ethiopia. 2011. (Men-at-Arms Ser.). (ENG., Illus.). 48p. pap. 17.95 (978-1-84908-457-4(2)) Osprey Publishing, Ltd. GBR. Dist: Random Hse., Inc.

Meharg, Sarah & Arnusch, Aleisha. Security Sector Reform: A Case Study Approach to Transition & Capacity Building. Merrill, Susan, ed. 2010. (PKSOI Papers). pap. (978-1-58487-418-8(X)) Strategic Studies Institute, U.S. Army War College Commandant (AWCC-DSI/Pubns.).

Moreman, Tim. Desert Rat, 1940-43: British Commonwealth Troops in North Africa. 2011. (Warrior Ser.). (ENG., Illus.). 64p. pap. 18.95 (978-1-84908-501-4(3)) Osprey Publishing, Ltd. GBR. Dist: Random Hse., Inc.

Mæland, Bård. Culture, Religion, & the Reintegration of Female Child Soldiers in Northern Uganda. 2010. (Bible & Theology in Africa Ser.). 332p. (C). 84.95 (978-1-4331-0951-5(4)) Lang, Peter Publishing, Inc.

Odetola, Olatunde. Military Regimes & Development: A Comparative Analysis in African Societies. 2011. (ENG.). 216p. 95.00 (978-0-415-60184-9(3)) Routledge.

Omitoogun, Wuyi & Hutchful, Eboe, eds. Budgeting for the Military Sector in Africa: The Process & Mechanisms of Control. 2006. (ENG., Illus.). 312p. 99.00 (978-0-19-926266-3(7)) Oxford Univ. Pr., Inc.

Peers, Chris. Central Africa: Tribal & Colonial Armies in the Congo, Gabon, Rwanda, Burundi, Northern Rhodesia & Nyasaland, 1800 To 1900. 2011. (Armies of the 19th Century: Africa Ser.). (Illus.). 200p. 63.00 (978-1-901543-23-0(4)) Foundry Bks. GBR. Dist: Casemate Pubs. & Bk. Distributors, LLC.

Reno, William. Warfare in Independent Africa. 2011. (New Approaches to African History Ser.). (ENG., Illus.). 294p. (C). 85.00 (978-0-521-85045-2(2)); pap. 27.99 (978-0-521-61552-5(6)) Cambridge Univ. Pr.

Scheepers, Marius. Striking Inside Angola with 32 Battalion. 2012. (Illus.). 176p. pap. 39.95 (978-1-907677-77-9(1)) Helion & Co., Ltd. GBR. Dist: Casemate Pubs. & Bk. Distributors, LLC.

Scott, Richard. Cities of Gold: Africa & the Americas, 1494-1698. 2011. (Field of Glory Renaissance Ser.). (ENG., Illus.). 132p. pap. 24.95 (978-1-84908-235-8(3)) Osprey Publishing, Ltd. GBR. Dist: Random Hse., Inc.

Stapleton, Timothy Joseph. A Military History of South Africa: From the Dutch-Khoi Wars to the End of Apartheid, 1 vol. 2010. (Praeger Security International Ser.). (Illus.). 229p. 49.95 (978-0-313-36589-8(X), C36589, Praeger Pubs.) Greenwood Publishing Group, Inc.

Thom, William. African Wars: A Defense Intelligence Perspective. 2010. (Illus.). 275p. pap. 34.95 (978-1-55238-273-8(7)) Univ. of Calgary Pr. CAN. Dist: Michigan State Univ. Pr.

Thompson, J. H. An Unpopular War: From Afkak to Bosbefok: Voices of South African National Servicemen. 2007. 256p. pap. 22.95 (978-1-77007-301-2(9), Zebra Pr.) Struik Pubs. ZAF. Dist: International Publishers Marketing.

United Nations University Staff. African Security Governance: Emerging Issues. Cawthra, Gavin, ed. 2010. (ENG.). 218p. pap. 32.00 (978-92-808-1177-3(0)) United Nations Univ. Pr. JPN. Dist: Brookings Institution Pr.

Wilsworth, Clive. First in, Last Out: The South African Artillery in Action: 1975-1988. 2010. (Illus.). 352p. pap. 29.95 (978-1-920143-40-4(8)) 30° South Pubs. ZAF. Dist: International Publishers Marketing.

Wonkeryor, Edward Lama. Liberia Military Dictatorship: A Fiasco Revolution (Reprint Edition with New Preface) 2011. (Illus.). 224p. 50.00 (978-0-9799537-1-2(5)); (ENG., per. 32.00 (978-0-9799537-2-9(3)) Africana Homestead Legacy Pubs., Inc.

Wood, J. R. T. Counter-Strike from the Sky: The Rhodesian All-Arms Fireforce in the War in the Bush, 1974-1980. Cocks, Chris, ed. 2009. 256p. 39.95 (978-1-920143-33-6(5)) 30° South Pubs. ZAF. Dist: International Publishers Marketing.

AFRICA—BIBLIOGRAPHY

Barringer, T. A. Africa Bibliography 2005. 2009. (ENG.). 400p. (gr. 17). pap. 150.00 (978-0-7486-2775-2(8), Edinburgh Univ. Pr. GBR. Dist: Columbia Univ. Pr.

—Africa Bibliography 2006. 2011. (ENG., Illus.). 372p. (gr. 17). pap. 160.00 (978-0-7486-3441-5(X)) Columbia Univ. Pr.

Betz, Richard L. The Mapping of Africa: A Cartobibliography of Printed Maps of the African Continent to 1700. 2007. (Illus.). 540p. 235.00 (978-90-5194-489-8(9)) HES & DE GRAAF Pubs. BV NLD. Dist: Oak Knoll Pr.

International African Bibliography Part 1. 36th rev. ed. 2006. (978-3-598-01341-6(8)) Saur, K. G. Verlag GmbH & Co.

Library Company of Philadelphia Staff & Historical Society of Pennsylvania Staff, contrib. by. Afro-Americana, 1553-1906: A Catalog of the Holdings of the Library Company of Philadelphia & the Historical Society of Pennsylvania. 2nd ed. 2008. 175.00 (978-1-58456-236-8(6)) Oak Knoll Pr.

McIlwaine, John. Africa: A Guide to Reference Material. 2nd ed. 2007. 666p. (978-0-9541029-3-7(2)) Hans Zell Publishing.

AFRICA—BIOGRAPHY

Abushama- Rademaker, Anna Maria. The Dutch Ladies Tinne, in the Sudan: Nineteenth Century Adventurers. 2010. 224p. 25.86 (978-1-4269-1403-4(2)) Trafford Publishing.

—The Dutch Ladies Tinne, in the Sudan: Nineteenth Century Adventurers. 2010. 224p. pap. 15.86 (978-1-4269-1402-7(4)) Trafford Publishing.

Adeuyan, Jacob Oluwatayo. The Journey of the First Black Bishop: Bishop Samuel Ajayi Crowther 1806 - 1891. 2011. 384p. 28.49 (978-1-4634-0733-9(5)); pap. 17.72 (978-1-4634-0734-6(3)) AuthorHouse.

Akpabio, Offonmbuk C. He Dared. 2011. 356p. 29.99 (978-1-4568-6738-6(5)); pap. 19.99 (978-1-4568-6737-9(7)) Xlibris Corp.

Akyeampong, Emmanuel K. & Niven, Steven J. Dictionary of African Biography, 6 vols., Set. Vols. 1-6. 2011. (ENG., Illus.). 3384p. 1200.00 (978-0-19-538207-5(2)) Oxford Univ. Pr., Inc.

Al-Sharif, William. The Dearest Quest: A Biography of Ibn Tumart. 2010. 175p. pap. 24.95 (978-1-4452-7625-4(1)) Lulu Enterprises Inc.

Allison, Peter. Don't Look Behind You! A Safari Guide's Encounters with Ravenous Lions, Stampeding Elephants, & Lovesick Rhinos. 2009. (ENG., Illus.). 256p. pap. 16.95 (978-1-59921-469-6(5), Lyons Pr.) Globe Pequot Pr., The.

—Whatever You Do, Don't Run: True Tales of a Botswana Safari Guide. 2007. (ENG., Illus.). 264p. per. 16.95 (978-0-7627-4565-4(7), Lyons Pr.) Globe Pequot Pr., The.

Amadou Nouhou Diallo. Male Circumcision & Initiation in Rural Afric: Autobiography, Culture & Traditions. 2009. 176p. pap. 12.99 (978-1-4389-9633-2(0)) AuthorHouse.

Angwafo, Fo. Royalty & Politics the Story of My Life. 2009. 148p. pap. (978-9956-558-31-5(1)) Langaa Research & Publishing Common Initiative Group CMR. Dist: Michigan State Univ. Pr.

Anyieth, Abraham Mayen. Then What. 2011. 58p. pap. 16.95 (978-1-4560-5273-7(X)) PublishAmerica, Inc.

Armes, Roy. Dictionary of African Filmmakers. 2008. (ENG.). 416p. 65.00 (978-0-253-35116-6(2), 0253351162) Indiana Univ. Pr.

Asante, Molefi K. Cheikh Anta Diop: An Intellectual Portrait. 2006. (978-0-943412-26-9(9)) Univ. of Sankore Pr., The.

Asong, Linus & Chi, Ndeh, eds. Ndeh Ntumazah: A Conversational Auto Biography. 2011. 442p. pap. (978-9956-579-32-7(7)) Langaa Research & Publishing Common Initiative Group.

Augustine, Saint & Augustine. The Confessions of St. Augustine: Modern English Version. 2008. 224p. reprint ed. 5.99 (978-0-8007-8762-2(5)) Revell.

Babou, Cheikh Anta & Babou, Cheikh Anta Mbacké. Fighting the Greater Jihad: Amadu Bamba & the Founding of the Muridiyya of Senegal, 1853-1913. 2007. (New African Histories Ser.). (ENG., Illus.). 320p. 59.95 (978-0-8214-1765-2(7)); per. 26.95 (978-0-8214-1766-9(5)) Ohio Univ. Pr.

Bagayoko, Amadou, et al. Away from the Light of Day. 2011. (ENG.). 176p. pap. 16.95 (978-1-901927-45-0(8)) Route GBR. Dist: Dufour Editions, Inc.

Baker, Heidi, et al. Expecting Miracles: True Stories of God's Supernatural Power & How You Can Experience It. 2007. (Illus.). 208p. pap. 14.99 (978-0-8007-9434-7(6)) Chosen Bks.

Bakkes, Johan. In Bushveld & Desert: A Game Ranger's Life. 2010. 296p. pap. 28.95 (978-0-7981-4928-0(0)) NB Pubs. Ltd. ZAF. Dist: International Publishers Marketing.

Balz-Cochois, Helgard. FUFU und Vergißmeinnicht: Die Afrika-Rundbriefe der Frau des Feldforschers. 2006. (GER., Illus.). 398p. pap. 34.90 (978-3-8334-4754-9(0)) Bks. on Demand.

Basil. The Darfurian: Road to Nowhere, 1 vol. 2010. 298p. pap. 27.95 (978-1-4489-3918-3(6)) PublishAmerica, Inc.

Battling Siki: A Tale of Ring Fixes, Race, & Murder in The 1920s. 2008. 360p. pap. 19.95 (978-1-55728-888-2(7)) Univ. of Arkansas Pr.

Baxter, Joan. Dust from Our Eyes: An Unblinkered Look at Africa. 2nd ed. 2010. (ENG.). 425p. pap. 25.00 (978-1-894987-47-9(0)) Wolsak & Wynn Pubs. Ltd. CAN. Dist: Univ. of Toronto Pr.

Beah, Ishmael. A Long Way Gone: Memoirs of a Boy Soldier. 240p. 2008. (ENG., Illus.). pap. 12.00 (978-0-374-53126-3(9)) 2007. 22.00 (978-0-374-95191-7(8)) 2007. (ENG., Illus.). 24.00 (978-0-374-10523-5(5)) Farrar, Straus & Giroux.

—A Long Way Gone: Memoirs of a Boy Soldier. 2008. (Illus.). 229p. (J). 19.65 (978-1-60686-094-6(1)) Perfection Learning Corp.

—A Long Way Gone: Memoirs of A Boy Soldier. 2008. 229p. lib. bdg. 23.30 (978-1-4178-2845-6(5), Turtleback) Turtleback Bks.

Beah, Ishmael. A Long Way Gone: Memoirs of a Boy Soldier. 2009. 11.21 (978-0-7848-2632-4(3), Everbind) Marco Bk. Co.

—A Long Way Gone: Memoirs of a Boy Soldier. lt. ed. 2008. 400p. (YA). pap. 13.95 (978-1-59413-267-4(4), Large Print Pr.) Thorndike Pr.

Bengtson, Harlan H. Tunakumbuka: Our Time in Tanzania as Peace Corps Volunteers, 1 vol. 2009. 68p. pap. 16.95 (978-1-60836-536-4(0)) PublishAmerica, Inc.

Benians, E. A., ed. Captain John Smith: Travels, History of Virginia: The True Travels, Adventures & Observations of Captain John Smith in Europe, Asia, Africa & America & the General History of Virginia, New England & the Summer Isles. Books I-III. 2012. (ENG.). 260p. pap. 35.99 (978-1-107-69811-6(1)) Cambridge Univ. Pr.

Bennett, Barbara. Soul of a Lion: One Woman's Quest to Rescue Africa's Wildlife Refugees. 2010. (Illus.). 320p. 26.00 (978-1-4262-0654-2(2), National Geographic) National Geographic Society.

Better Homes and Gardens Books Staff & Kinzer, Stephen. A Thousand Hills: Rwanda's Rebirth & the Man Who Dreamed It. 2008. (ENG., Illus.). 400p. 25.95 (978-0-470-12015-6(0), Wiley) Wiley, John & Sons, Inc.

Biographiq. Saint Augustine of Hippo - Philosopher & Theologian (Biography) 2008. 68p. pap. 9.99 (978-1-59986-387-0(1), Biographiq) Filiquarian Publishing, LLC.

Blackford, Jason. Why I'm Afraid to Poop in Public: A Memoir. 2011. 90p. pap. 19.95 (978-1-4626-0631-3(8)) PublishAmerica, Inc.

Boms, Alwell Chikwe. The African Village Boy: A True Life Story. 2011. 56p. pap. 10.99 (978-1-4567-6673-3(2)) AuthorHouse.

Bonna, Okyere. Africa's Football Legends: Soccer YTT Yesterday, Today & Tomorrow. 2009. 252p. pap. 21.99 (978-1-4415-4270-0(1)) Xlibris Corp.

Bourque, Peter. Tarnished Ivory: Reflections on Peace Corps & Beyond. 2011. 224p. pap. 19.99 (978-1-4628-7759-1(1)) Xlibris Corp.

Boyd, Mark. Reminiscences of Fifty Years by Mark Boyd. 2006. 400p. per. 26.99 (978-1-4255-4264-1(6)) MPublishing.

Brabazon, James & Brabazon, Tom. My Friend the Mercenary. 2011. (ENG., Illus.). 480p. 25.95 (978-0-8021-1975-9(1), Grove Pr.) Grove/Atlantic, Inc.

Brockman, Norbert C. An African Biographical Dictionary. 2nd ed. 2006. (Illus.). 667p. 75.00 (978-1-59237-112-9(4)) Grey Hse. Publishing.

Buor, Sel. No More War: Rebuilding Liberia through Faith, Determination & Education. 2009. 184p. pap. 16.95 (978-1-4401-5655-7(7)) iUniverse, Inc.

Buthelezi, Vusi. Wailing Dunes. 2011. 24p. pap. 4.99 (978-1-61667-195-2(5)) Raider Publishing International.

Butterworth, James & Marshall, Jane. Mokili in Congo: A Biography of William Millman. 2011. (Illus.). 348p. pap. 20.77 (978-1-4567-7104-1(3)) AuthorHouse.

Carter, Raymond B. How I Made It. 2008. 73p. pap. 16.95 (978-1-60672-855-0(5)) PublishAmerica, Inc.

Cass, Orion. Tales from the Kind African Rifles. (Illus.). 219p. 35.00 (978-0-304-35349-1(3)) Cassell P L C GBR. Dist: Trafalgar Square Publishing.

Cerew, Bruce. War Child. 2008. 320p. 28.49 (978-1-4389-0538-9(6)); pap. 19.99 (978-1-4389-0537-2(8)) AuthorHouse.

Chaaban. From Lebanon to Africa & America: My Roots. rev. ed. 2011. (ENG.). 66p. pap. 21.00 (978-0-7575-9262-1(7)) Kendall Hunt Publishing Co.

Chadwick, Henry. Augustine of Hippo: A Life. 2010. (ENG.). 208p. pap. 16.95 (978-0-19-958806-0(6)) Oxford Univ. Pr., Inc.

Chikanga, Everisto. My Journey to Americ: An Adventure of Faith. 2011. 108p. 28.95 ***(978-1-4627-0523-8(5))***; pap. 11.95 ***(978-1-4627-0522-1(7))*** Cross Bks. Publishing.

Chirwa, Vera & Chirwa, Vera Mlangazuwa. Fearless Fighter: An Autobiography. 2007. (ENG.). 216p. 65.95 *(978-1-84277-965-1(6))*; pap. 19.95 *(978-1-84277-966-8(4))* Zed Bks., Ltd. GBR. Dist: Macmillan.

Chishugi, Leah. A Long Way from Paradise: Surviving the Rwandan Genocide. 2012. (ENG.). 304p. pap. 13.95 ***(978-1-84408-657-3(7)***, Virago Press) Little, Brown Bk. Group Ltd. GBR. Dist: Independent Pubs. Group.

Chol, Abraham Biar. No Wings to Fly. 2011. 224p. 29.99 ***(978-1-4628-4525-5(8))***; pap. 19.99 ***(978-1-4628-4524-8(X))*** Xlibris Corp.

Chol Lual, Chagai. How Childhood Hardship Prepared Me for Life. 2009. 172p. 26.42 *(978-1-4251-8254-0(2))* Trafford Publishing.

Claire, Catherine & Larson, Catherine Claire. As We Forgive: Stories of Reconciliation from Rwanda, 1 vol. 2009. (ENG.). 272p. pap. 15.99 *(978-0-310-28730-8(8))* Zondervan.

Clelland, Santina. A Lost Childhood. 2008. 152p. pap. *(978-1-84549-297-7(8))* arima publishing.

Cochrane, Jane. A Figure in the Sand. 2011. (ENG., Illus.). 366p. pap. ***(978-1-907571-02-2(7))*** Rowe, Antony Ltd.

Cooper, Helene. The House at Sugar Beach: In Search of a Lost African Childhood. 2008. (Illus.). 517p. 31.95 *(978-1-4104-1038-2(2))* Thorndike Pr.

Cordell. The Human Tradition In Modern Africa. 2011. (Human Tradition around the World Ser.). (ENG.). 316p. pap. 29.95 ***(978-0-7425-3733-0(1))*** Rowman & Littlefield Publishers, Inc.

Cordell, Dennis D. The Human Tradition In Modern Africa. 2011. (Human Tradition around the World Ser.). (ENG.). 288p. 84.00 ***(978-0-7425-3732-3(3))*** Rowman & Littlefield Publishers, Inc.

Coughlan, Michael. Sundiata: The African King. 2007. (Timeline Ser.). (Illus.). 48p. pap. 8.99 *(978-1-4190-4409-0(5))* Steck-Vaughn.

Cristaudo, Wayne & Wong, Heung-Wah, eds. Augustine: His Legacy & Relevance. 2010. (University of Hong Kong European Studies in Philosophical Theology Ser.). (ENG.). 330p. (C). pap. 36.00 *(978-1-921511-73-8(7))* ATF Pr. AUS. Dist: Brown, David Bk. Co., The.

Crocker, Suzanne. Pig in a Taxi & Other African Adventures. 2006. 176p. pap. 10.99 *(978-0-8010-6632-0(8))* Baker Bks.

Dahl, Roald. Going Solo. 2009. (ENG.). 224p. (YA). (gr. 7-18). 6.99 *(978-0-14-241383-8(6)*, Puffin) Penguin Group (USA) Inc.

Dane, Ronald. Lost on the Way: Adventures in 40,000 Miles of Hitchhiking. 2011. 328p. pap. 19.95 ***(978-1-4620-4353-8(4))*** iUniverse, Inc.

Daponte, Lina. As I Walk Through Life: A Family's Struggle from the Azorean Islands to Africa. 2011. 72p. pap. 12.95 ***(978-1-4670-6197-1(2))*** AuthorHouse.

Dau, John Bul & Sweeney, Michael S. God Grew Tired of Us: A Memoir. (ENG., Illus.). 304p. 2008. per. 14.95 *(978-1-4262-0212-4(1))* 2007. 26.00 *(978-1-4262-0114-1(1)*, National Geographic) National Geographic Society.

Davies, Alberta. Raw Edge of Purgatory: I survived the Liberian Pogrom. 2011. 244p. pap. 19.99 ***(978-1-4568-4995-5(6))*** Xlibris Corp.

Davies, John Edward. Ramblings of a Rolling Stone. 2010. 336p. pap. *(978-1-906628-15-4(7))* Checkpoint Pr.

Deng, Francis Mading. The Man Called Deng Majok: A Biography of Power, Polygyny & Change. 2009. 338p. pap. *(978-1-56902-300-6(X))* Red Sea Pr.

—The Man Called Deng Majok: A Biography of Power, Polygyny, & Change. 2009. (Illus.). xvi, 321p. *(978-1-56902-299-3(2))* Red Sea Pr.

Diamant, Henri. Escape to Afric. 2011. 290p. pap. 18.95 ***(978-1-934074-68-8(3))*** Apprentice Hse.

Diamond, James. I Did What I Had to Do! 2010. 344p. pap. 14.95 *(978-0-533-16325-0(0))* Vantage Pr., Inc.

Donaldson, Ross. The Lassa Ward: One Man's Fight Against One of the World's Deadliest Diseases. 2010. (ENG.). 288p. pap. 14.99 *(978-0-312-37701-4(0)*, St. Martin's Griffin) St. Martin's Pr.

Douglas, Thomas. Sufism, Madhism & Nationalism: Limamou Laye & the Layennes of Senegal. 2012. (ENG., Illus.). 176p. 120.00 *(978-1-4411-6907-5(5))* Continuum International Publishing Group, Ltd. GBR. Dist: National Bk. Network.

Ekanem, Ita I. An Adventure Beyond Social Mobility: A Tribute to My Father. 2008. 356p. 31.99 *(978-1-4389-0710-9(9))*; pap. 19.99 *(978-1-4389-0711-6(7))* AuthorHouse.

Elizabeth. Rebecca's Mid-Life. 2010. 176p. (ENG.). 24.99 *(978-1-4490-8979-5(8))*; pap. 14.99 *(978-1-4490-8978-8(X))* AuthorHouse.

Elliott, Graham. Babylon Behind the Wire: A collection of true day-to-day short stories of a chef's life working in Iraq. 2011. 378p. pap. 29.95 ***(978-1-4626-0777-8(2))*** PublishAmerica, Inc.

Enrick, Nathan. A True South African Story. 2011. 210p. 29.99 ***(978-1-4628-7429-3(0))*** Xlibris Corp.

Farina, William. Perpetua of Carthage: Portrait of a Third-Century Martyr. 2008. (ENG., Illus.). 276p. pap. 39.95 *(978-0-7864-3713-9(8))* McFarland & Co., Inc. Pubs.

Fenn, Ronald A. Mirror Man: A Life of Entropy. 2011. 272p. 25.74 ***(978-1-4634-0438-3(7))***; pap. 15.19 ***(978-1-4634-0437-6(9))*** AuthorHouse.

Fischbach, Michael R. Biographical Encyclopedia of the Modern Middle East & North Africa, 2 vols. 2007. (Illus.). xxix, 929p. *(978-1-4144-1891-9(4))*; *(978-1-4144-1890-2(6))* Cengage Gale.

Fleteren, Frederick Van. Life of Augustine of Hippo: Child, Convert, Monk, Priest, 354-396, Volume 1. 2010. 410p. (C). 90.95 *(978-1-4331-0284-4(6))* Lang, Peter Publishing, Inc.

Flowers, Jane. Cooksie's Cake. 2008. 144p. 29.96 *(978-1-4092-0304-9(2))* Lulu Enterprises Inc.

For-mukwai, Gideon F. Facing Adversity with Audacity. 2010. 76p. pap. *(978-9956-616-00-8(1))* Langaa Research & Publishing Common Initiative Group CMR. Dist: Michigan State Univ. Pr.

Freemantle, D. M. A Hole in Our Lives Forever. 2011. 348p. 29.99 ***(978-1-4653-0007-2(4))***; pap. 19.99 ***(978-1-4653-0006-5(6))*** Xlibris Corp.

Fuller, Alexandra. EXP Cocktail Hour under the Tree of Forgetfulness. 2012. (ENG.). 304p. 7.99 ***(978-0-14-312186-2(3)***, Penguin (Non-Classics)) Penguin Group (USA) Inc.

Fundisi. The Monkey's Wedding. 2009. 254p. pap. 21.50 *(978-1-4092-8740-7(8))* Lulu Enterprises Inc.

Gai (Akuei Malueth), Jacob. Crossing the Barriers: Unending Journey. 2008. 213p. pap. 24.95 *(978-1-60441-430-1(8))* PublishAmerica, Inc.

Gibia, Roba. JOhn Garang: And the Vision of New Sudan. 2008. 237p. pap. 24.99 *(978-0-9782526-6-3(7))* Key Publishing Hse., Inc., The CAN. Dist: AtlasBooks Distribution.

Gooding Cornett, Jan. An Ordinary Guy. 2009. 68p. pap. 9.95 *(978-1-60693-939-0(4)*, Strategic Bk. Publishing) AEG Literary Publishing Services, Inc.

Haakonsen, Ray. An Arrested Heart. 2010. 264p. 29.99 *(978-1-4500-7919-8(9))*; pap. 19.99 *(978-1-4500-7918-1(0))* Xlibris Corp.

Haile, Ahmed Ali & Shenk, David W., told to. Teatime in Mogadishu: My Journey As a Peace Ambassador in the World of Islam. 2011. pap. *(978-0-8361-9557-6(4))* Herald Pr.

Happold, David. African Naturalist: The Life & Times of Rodney Carrington Wood, 1889-1962. 2011. (Illus.). 264p. 37.50 ***(978-1-84624-555-8(9))*** Book Guild, Ltd. GBR. Dist: Trans-Atlantic Pubns., Inc.

Hari, Daoud. The Translator: A Memoir. 2009. (ENG.). 224p. pap. 13.00 *(978-0-8129-7917-6(6)*, Random Hse. Trade Paperbacks) Random House Publishing Group.

—The Translator: A Tribesman's Memoir of Darfur. l.t. ed. 2008. 251p. (YA). 31.95 *(978-1-4104-0743-6(8))* Thorndike Pr.

Hassebu, Hiabu H. Padre from the Monastery to the Forest: A Memoir of My Life Journey in a War Torn Eitrea & My Immigrant Life in USA. 2010. 196p. pap. 16.95 *(978-1-4502-3682-9(0))* iUniverse, Inc.

Heavirland, Helen. My Enemy, My Brother: The Gripping, True Story of a Man Who Survived the Greatest Tragedy of the Twentieth Century. 2007. pap. 9.97 *(978-0-8163-2209-1(0))* Pacific Pr. Publishing Assn.

Herlocker, Dennis. Buffaloes by My Bedroom. 2009. 224p. 28.95 *(978-1-4401-4726-5(4))*; pap. 18.95 *(978-1-4401-4724-1(8))* iUniverse, Inc.

Hermansen, Michelle. Unexpected Journeys. 2010. (Illus.). 93p. pap. *(978-0-615-35476-7(9))* Unexpected Journeys LLC.

Hirsch, Susan F. In the Moment of Greatest Calamity: Terrorism, Grief, & a Victim's Quest for Justice. 2006. (ENG., Illus.). 310p. (C). 35.00 *(978-0-691-12136-9(2))* Princeton Univ. Pr.

Hogle, Norene. Are You Feeling a Little Finer, Miss Norene? A Personal Account of My Year as a Volunteer Teacher in Namibia, Africa In 2009. 2011. 192p. 24.59 ***(978-1-4634-0120-7(5))***; pap. 14.03 ***(978-1-4634-0121-4(3))*** AuthorHouse.

Holwerda, Luella Faith. Zamzam's Faith in the Middle: A True Story for Children. 2011. 40p. pap. 18.50 *(978-1-4567-3039-0(8))* AuthorHouse.

Hopwood, Tom. Cancer to Capricorn — - A Doctor in the Tropics. 2010. 214p. pap. 18.95 *(978-1-4457-0324-4(6))* Lulu Enterprises Inc.

Ilibagiza, Immaculée & Erwin, Steve. The Boy Who Met Jesus: Segatashya of Kibeho. 2011. (ENG., Illus.). 256p. 19.95 *(978-1-4019-3581-8(8))* Hay Hse., Inc.

—Sobrevivir para Contarlo: Como Descubri a Dios en Medio del Holocausto en Rwanda. Minino, Adriana, tr. 2007. (SPA & ENG., Illus.). 215p. per. 15.95 *(978-1-4019-1202-4(8))* Hay Hse., Inc.

Inman, Gina Hutchins & Pimot, Karen Hutchins. The Learners of Owamboland, the Children of Twaalulilwa School. 2008. 88p. pap. 10.95 *(978-0-9820479-9-6(1))* Peppertree Pr., The.

Jal, Emmanuel. War Child: A Child Soldier's Story. 2010. (ENG., Illus.). 272p. pap. 14.99 *(978-0-312-60297-0(9)*, St. Martin's Griffin) St. Martin's Pr.

Jal, Emmanuel & Davies, Megan Lloyd. War Child: A Memoir - A Child Soldier's Story. 2009. (ENG.). 272p. 24.95 *(978-0-312-38322-0(3))* St. Martin's Pr.

Jawara, Mohammed. Never End, 1 vol. 2009. 48p. pap. 16.95 *(978-1-61546-268-1(6))* PublishAmerica, Inc.

Kaldi, Leita. Roller Skating in the Desert. 2010. 226p. ***(978-1-4512-8056-2(4))***; 228p. pap. 24.95 ***(978-1-60749-180-4(X))*** PublishAmerica, Inc.

Kamara, Mariatu & McClelland, Susan. The Bite of the Mango. 2008. (ENG., Illus.). 224p. (YA). (gr. 9-12). 24.95 *(978-1-55451-159-4(3))*; pap. 12.95 *(978-1-55451-158-7(5))* Annick Pr., Ltd. CAN. Dist: Firefly Bks., Ltd.

Kamitanigawa, Osamu. A Way of Creating New Worlds. 2011. 60p. pap. 8.95 *(978-1-4620-1343-2(0))* iUniverse, Inc.

Karefa-Smart, John Albert Musselman. Rainbow Happenings. 2010. (ENG.). 188p. 29.99 *(978-1-4415-0168-4(1))* Xlibris Corp.

Kassum, Al Noor & Kassum, Al N. Africa's Winds of Change: Memoirs of an International Tanzanian. 2007. (ENG., Illus.). 288p. 37.00 *(978-1-84511-583-8(X))* I. B. Tauris & Co., Ltd. GBR. Dist: Macmillan.

Kemper, Steve. A Labyrinth of Kingdoms: 10,000 Miles Through Islamic Africa. 2012. (ENG., Illus.). 432p. 28.95 ***(978-0-393-07966-1(X)***, 7966) Norton, W. W. & Co., Inc.

Kennedy, Alfred Boymah Zinnah. The Journey from the Village: A Liberian Life. 2010. 368p. pap. 21.99 *(978-1-60844-478-6(3))* Dog Ear Publishing, LLC.

Kimambo, Samantha. Maazungu. 2007. 262p. pap. 27.50 *(978-1-84753-629-7(8))* Lulu Enterprises Inc.

Kluth, Andreas. Hannibal & Me: What History's Greatest Military Strategist Can Teach Us about Success & Failure. 2012. (ENG.). 336p. (gr. 12). 26.95 *(978-1-59448-812-2(6)*, Riverhead Bks. (Hardcover)) Penguin Group (USA) Inc.

Kormoh, Joseph Lansana & Bah, Ibrahim "Inspector". The Biography of Mohamed Kallon, the Gem of Sierra Leone. 2008. 176p. pap. 11.99 *(978-1-4343-9393-7(3))* AuthorHouse.

Koroma, Maligie. Dancing with the Devils. 2011. 104p. 24.99 ***(978-1-4568-5745-5(2))***; pap. 15.99 ***(978-1-4568-5744-8(4))*** Xlibris Corp.

Kryza, Frank T. The Race for Timbuktu: In Search of Africa's City of Gold. 2006. (ENG., Illus.). 352p. pap. 14.95 *(978-0-06-056065-2(7)*, HarperPerennial) HarperCollins Pubs.

Lemon, David. Blood Sweat & Lions. 2008. 280p. per. *(978-1-906210-66-3(7))* Grosvenor Hse. Publishing Ltd.

Linda K. Thomas. Grandma's Letters from Afric: Quaint I Ain't. 2010. 288p. 30.95 *(978-1-4401-9145-9(X))*; pap. 20.95 *(978-1-4401-9147-3(6))* iUniverse, Inc.

Livingstone, W. P. The Life of Robert Laws of Livingstonia: a Narrative of Missionary. 2006. (ENG.). 440p. per. 36.95 *(978-1-4286-5964-3(1))* Kessinger Publishing, LLC.

Logsdaile, Albert. While I Remember. 2010. (Illus.). 136p. pap. 10.99 *(978-1-4520-8013-0(5))* AuthorHouse.

Lovejoy, Paul & Law, Robin, eds. Biography of Baquaqua: His Passage from Slavery to Freedom in Africa & America. 2nd exp. ed. 2006. (Illus.). 298p. per. 24.95 *(978-1-55876-430-9(5))* Wiener, Markus Pubs., Inc.

Lungu, Edward Kavimba. The African Way: Struggle & Success of the Life of Lungu. 2010. 316p. pap. 14.95 *(978-0-9830232-0-3(4))* Lungu Publishing Co. Inc.

Lupton, Ken. Pascoe, Prince of Gobir. 2009. (Illus.). 364p. pap. 17.99 *(978-1-4389-2945-3(5))* AuthorHouse.

Macintosh, Donald. Gone Native. 2010. (ENG.). 224p. 21.95 ***(978-1-906122-26-3(1))*** Unwin, Merlin Bks. GBR. Dist: SCB Distributors.

Mahmoud, Mohamed A. Quest for Divinity: A Critical Examination of the Thought of Mahmud Muhammad Taha. 2006. (Modern Intellectual & Political History of the Middle East Ser.). (Illus.). 309p. 29.95 *(978-0-8156-3100-2(6))* Syracuse Univ. Pr.

Makura, Moky. Africa's Greatest Entrepreneurs. 2009. (ENG., Illus.). 300p. (gr. 12-18). 25.95 *(978-0-14-302430-9(2)*, Penguin Global) Penguin Group (USA) Inc.

Mamburay, Yankuba. The Search for a Lost Brother, 1 vol. 2009. 108p. pap. 16.95 *(978-1-60703-966-2(4))* PublishAmerica, Inc.

Martin, Kathleen. Kamakwie: Finding Peace, Love & Injustice in Sierra Leone, 1 vol. 2012. (ENG., Illus.). 176p. (J). pap. 19.95 ***(978-0-88995-472-4(0))*** Red Deer Pr. CAN. Dist: Ingram Pub. Services.

Massaquoi, Fatima & Tuchscherer, Konrad. The Autobiography of an African Princess. Seton, Vivian, ed. 2009. (Queenship & Power Ser.). (ENG.). 288p. 74.95 *(978-0-230-60958-7(9))* Palgrave Macmillan.

Mayer, Brantz. Captain Canot. 2008. (Civil War Ser.). (ENG.). 492p. pap. 29.95 *(978-1-4290-1500-4(4))* Applewood Bks.

Mbanga, Wilf, et al. Seretse & Ruth: The Love Story. 2011. 374p. pap. 29.95 ***(978-1-85425-101-5(5))*** Merlin Pr. Ltd. GBR. Dist: Independent Pubs. Group.

Mbile, Nerius Namaso. Cameroon Political Story Memories of an Authentic Eye Witness. 2011. 310p. pap. ***(978-9956-717-77-4(0))*** Langaa Research & Publishing Common Initiative Group.

McCall, Ian. All Youse That Want Pies & Other Pieces. 2010. 373p. pap. 30.50 *(978-1-4457-5560-1(2))* Lulu Enterprises Inc.

McCauley, Bob. The Still Small Voice. 2011. 340p. pap. 15.95 ***(978-1-60920-022-0(5))*** Ajoyin Publishing, Inc.

Melady, Thomas Patrick & Melady, Margaret Badum. Ten African Heroes: The Sweep of Independence in Black Africa. 2011. (Illus.). 240p. *(978-1-57075-929-1(4))* Orbis Bks.

Meyers, Marilyn. Through Fire & Sea: Adventures on the Mercy Ship: A Family's Journey to the World's Forgotten Poor. 2007. *(978-1-897213-33-9(6))* BayRidge Bks.

Michaels, Chidera. Coming Inside the Dream, 1 vol. 2009. 224p. pap. 24.95 *(978-1-60672-545-0(9))* PublishAmerica, Inc.

Millard, Mary Weeks. Emmanuel Kolini: The Unlikely Archbishop of Rwanda. 2009. (ENG.). 251p. pap. 16.99 *(978-1-934068-65-6(9))* Authentic Media.

Mirulla, Simone. Rumi; One in a Million: Volume 1. 2009. (Illus.). 372p. pap. 17.99 *(978-1-4389-5800-2(5))* AuthorHouse.

Mokeddem, Malika. My Men. Rice, Laura & Hamdy, Karim, trs. from FRE. 2009. (ENG.). 192p. 50.00 *(978-0-8032-3262-4(4))*; pap. 24.95 *(978-0-8032-8317-6(2)*, Bison Bks.) Univ. of Nebraska Pr.

Moodie, John. Hath the Lion Prevailed. (Illus.). (Orig.). pap. 6.95 *(978-1-56411-060-2(5))* UBUS Communications Systems.

Morris-Evans, Janet. Into Africa, a Vision of Hope & a Sanctuary Born. 2009. 80p. pap. 9.95 *(978-1-60693-630-6(1)*, Eloquent Bks.) AEG Literary Publishing Services, Inc.

Mowlem, Debrah. I Wonder. 2010. 364p. pap. 17.99 *(978-1-4490-9457-7(0))* AuthorHouse.

Mtei, Edwin. From Goatherd to Governor: The Autobiography of Edwin Mtei. 2008. 244p. pap. *(978-9987-08-030-4(8))* Mkuki na Nyoka Pubs. TZA. Dist: Michigan State Univ. Pr.

Munanga, Theresa. No Hurry in Africa: Life as A Peace Corps Volunteer in Kenya. 2010. 168p. pap. 15.95 *(978-1-4502-5155-6(2))* iUniverse, Inc.

Munya, Mbah Ferdinand. False Paradise, 1 vol. 2010. 239p. pap. 24.95 *(978-1-4489-8514-2(5))* PublishAmerica, Inc.

Munz, Jo, et al. Albert Schweitzer's Lambarene: A Legacy of Humanity for Our World Today. 2010. (Illus.). 359p. *(978-0-89725-872-2(X)*, Penobscot Pr.) Picton Pr.

Musabyimana, Jean De Dieu. Love above All: Forgiveness of a Young Rwandan Genocide Survivor. 2011. (Illus.). 128p. pap. 14.89 *(978-1-4567-0044-7(8))* AuthorHouse.

Mushimba, David. African Born, American Bound for Success. 2011. 96p. pap. 15.99 ***(978-1-4568-2428-0(7))*** Xlibris Corp.

Mwakikagile, Godfrey. Life under Nyerere. 2006. pap. *(978-0-9802587-2-1(3))* New Africa Pr.

—Tanzania under Mwalimu Nyerere Reflectio. 2006. pap. *(978-0-9802534-9-8(7))* New Africa Pr.

Nalumango, Keith. The African Journalist. 2010. 516p. 30.99 *(978-1-4490-5423-6(4))* AuthorHouse.

Nelson, Darryl. I'm Feeling Fine: Kidney Failure Is Not the End of Life. 2008. 116p. 22.95 *(978-0-595-49967-0(8))*; pap. 12.95 *(978-0-595-50653-8(4))* iUniverse, Inc.

Njoku, Charles. Images of a Native Son. 2011. 228p. pap. 22.11 *(978-1-4520-8642-2(7))* AuthorHouse.

Nkurunziza, Claver. Black Challenge. 2009. 88p. pap. 13.50 *(978-1-4490-3893-9(X))* AuthorHouse.

Nyang'oro, Julius Edo. JK: A Political Biography of Jakaya Mrisho Kikwete: President of the United Republic of Tanzania. 2010. 352p. *(978-1-59221-775-5(3))* Africa World Pr.

Nyigillo, Augustino L. Calamities. 2010. pap. 9.99 *(978-1-61663-671-5(8))* Tate Publishing & Enterprises, LLC.

Nzeyimana, Lucien. Upsetting Experiences Make My Heart Stronger: The Story of Occasions to Mark. 2011. 228p. pap. ***(978-1-4269-8170-8(8))*** Trafford Publishing (UK) Ltd.

Oden, Thomas C. The African Memory of Mark: Reassessing Early Church Tradition. 2011. (Early African Christianity Set Ser.). (ENG.). 279p. pap. 22.00 *(978-0-8308-3933-9(X)*, IVP Acad.) InterVarsity Pr.

Olufokunbi, Dotun. Sing Me a Dirge. 2010. 236p. 25.86 *(978-1-4269-3079-9(8))* Trafford Publishing.

Olverson, Eric. Eric on His Bike - a Home to Head For. 2011. (Illus.). 258p. pap. ***(978-0-7552-1343-6(2))*** Authors OnLine, Ltd.

Oonk, Gijsbert. The Karimjee Jivanjee Family: Merchant Princes of East Africa 1800-2000. 2010. (ENG., Illus.). 172p. *(978-90-8555-027-3(0)*, Pallas Publications) Amsterdam Univ. Pr.

Ottih, Mazi Ngozi. Reflections of a Glorious Life: Patrick Nwakamma Ottih. 2008. (Illus.). 51p. pap. 15.99 *(978-1-4363-5762-3(4))* Xlibris Corp.

Owens, Delia, et al. Secrets of the Savanna: Twenty-Three Years in the African Wilderness Unraveling the Mysteries of Elephants & People. 2007. (Twenty-Three Years in the African Wilderness Unraveling The Ser.). (ENG., Illus.). 272p. pap. 14.95 *(978-0-618-87250-3(7))* Houghton Mifflin Harcourt Trade & Reference Pubs.

Pal, Go. Gaddafi Up-Close. 2011. 196p. 27.99 ***(978-1-4670-4184-3(X))***; pap. 16.95 ***(978-1-4670-4185-0(8))*** AuthorHouse.

Parent, Elisabeth Anne. Learning to Be Someone: A Journey Toward the Light. 2011. 230p. pap. 14.95 ***(978-1-936780-22-8(4))*** Mill City Pr., Inc.

Peabody, Stanton B. I Was There. 2007. per. *(978-1-59916-270-6(9))* Printing Systems.

Pearson, Bettie Butler. A Hundredfold: Memoirs of Missionary Life in Africa. 2010. pap. *(978-1-4507-2055-7(2))* Independent Pub.

Perry, Dennis. Don't Run over a Snake's Tail, Slowly: A journal of my two years in Benin, West Africa with the Peace Corps. 2011. 202p. pap. 24.95 ***(978-1-4560-9735-6(0))*** PublishAmerica, Inc.

Perry, Joseph N., frwd. African Saints, African Stories: 40 Holy Men & Women. 2008. (Illus.). 145p. per. 14.95 *(978-0-86716-805-1(6))* Franciscan Media.

Perry, Michele. Love Has a Face: Mascara, a Machete & One Woman's Miraculous Journey with Jesus in Sudan. 2009. 224p. pap. 13.99 *(978-0-8007-9478-1(8))* Chosen Bks.

Piersma, Hida Jessie. The Gnawing Thoughts. 2010. (Illus.). 155p. pap. 14.95 *(978-1-4327-4571-4(9))* Outskirts Pr., Inc.

Pinnock, Don. The Woman Who Lived in a Tree & Other Perfect Strangers. 2010. (ENG.). 289p. pap. 19.00 *(978-1-77009-692-9(2))* Jacana Media ZAF. Dist: Independent Pubs. Group.

Plangesis, Esmeralda. In Search of Liberation. 2009. 380p. pap. 19.99 *(978-1-4389-9717-9(5))* AuthorHouse.

Polachic, Darlene. Keep on Standing: The Story of Krystaal: From African Affluence, to Refugee Camp, to World Acclaimed Musicians. 2007. *(978-1-894860-37-6(3))* Castle Quay Bks. Canada.

Pollecoff, Eve A. Pioneer Merchant Trader: The Life & Times of Otto Markus. 2012. (ENG., Illus.). 224p. 55.00 ***(978-1-84885-937-1(6)***, Radcliffe Pr., The) I. B. Tauris & Co., Ltd. GBR. Dist: Macmillan.

Price, John. When the White House Calls: From Immigrant Entrepreneur to U. S. Ambassador. 2011. (ENG., Illus.). 712p. (gr. 9). 30.00 *(978-1-60781-143-5(X))* Univ. of Utah Pr.

Prince, Alfred. My Life with Viruses, Friends & Enemies. 2008. 140p. 29.99 *(978-1-4363-4804-1(8))*; pap. 19.99 *(978-1-4363-4805-8(6))* Xlibris Corp.

Prince, Alfred M. The Poetry of Life: In Science in Africa & Manzee. 2010. 172p. 29.99 *(978-1-4500-5577-2(X))*; pap. 19.99 *(978-1-4500-5576-5(1))* Xlibris Corp.

Raal, Nadine. Mending a Broken Heart. 2011. (ENG.). 213p. pap. 29.95 (978-1-77009-909-8(3)) Jacana Media ZAF. Dist: Independent Pubs. Group.

Ramathal, Dorothy Charulata. A Continent Found: Memoirs of a Quarter Century in Africa, 1 vol. 2010. 63p. pap. 16.95 (978-1-4489-7691-1(X)) PublishAmerica, Inc.

Reeves, Terence. African Harvest. 2011. 374p. pap. (978-1-908447-57-9(5)) Grosvenor Hse. Publishing Ltd.

Robbins, Patrick K. & Dassac, René. Taulus. 2007. (ENG.). 516p. per. 30.00 (978-1-4303-0000-7(0)) Lulu Enterprises Inc.

Roberts, Gesue. Zammie Town: A Memior a Village Childhood in Liberia. 2011. 268p. 29.95 (978-1-60594-731-0(8), Llumina Pr.) Aeon Publishing Inc.

—Zammie Town: A Memoir of a Village Childhood in Liberia. 2011. 268p. pap. 14.95 (978-1-60594-730-3(X), Llumina Pr.) Aeon Publishing Inc.

Ruete, Emily. Memoirs of an Arabian Princess of Oman & Zanzibar. 2008. 308p. pap. (978-1-906393-09-0(5)) Trotamundas Pr., Ltd.

Rusesabagina, Paul. An Ordinary Man. l.t. ed. 2008. (Readers Circle Ser.). 271p. 31.95 (978-1-60285-154-2(9)) Ctr. Point Large Print.

—An Ordinary Man. l.t. ed. 2008. 272p. 29.99 (978-0-7531-9407-2(4)) ISIS Audio Bks. GBR. Dist: Ulverscroft Large Print Bks., Ltd.

Rusesabagina, Paul & Zoellner, Tom. An Ordinary Man: An Autobiography. 2007. (ENG., Illus.). 224p. (gr. 12-18). 15.00 (978-0-14-303860-3(5), Penguin (Non-Classics)) Penguin Group (USA) Inc.

Sacramento, Ange Miguel Do. Neither Black nor White: An Unconventional Life. 2011. 184p. 29.99 (978-1-4628-7607-5(2)); pap. 19.99 (978-1-4628-7606-8(4)) Xlibris Corp.

Santana, Zeca. Angol: Land of Shattered Dreams. 2009. 234p. 29.99 (978-1-4415-3113-1(0)); pap. 19.99 (978-1-4415-3112-4(2)) Xlibris Corp.

Saucier, C. A. P. The Lucy Man: The Scientist Who Found the Most Famous Fossil Ever! 2011. (ENG., Illus.). 136p. (J). pap. 16.00 (978-1-61614-433-3(5)) Prometheus Bks., Pubs.

Schofield-Childs, Joann Merritt. Take Me Home to Afrika: An Autobiography of A Returnee. 2011. 232p. 26.95 (978-1-4620-3701-8(1)); pap. 16.95 (978-1-4620-3699-8(0)) iUniverse, Inc.

Scott, Ivan. The Man from Somalia: Citizen of the World. 2011. 264p. 24.95 (978-0-533-16350-2(1)) Vantage Pr., Inc.

Scott, Robyn. Twenty Chickens for a Saddle: The Story of an African Childhood. 2009. (ENG.). 464p. (gr. 12-18). 15.00 (978-0-14-311509-0(X), Penguin (Non-Classics)) Penguin Group (USA) Inc.

Sebarenzi, Joseph. God Sleeps in Rwanda: A Journey of Transformation. 2009. (ENG., Illus.). 272p. 25.00 (978-1-4165-7573-3(1), Beyond Words/Atria Bks.) Atria Bks.

Sellin, Nancy. Avoid Mosquitoes-and Other Impossibilities. 2009. 248p. 29.95 (978-0-595-51897-5(4)); pap. 19.95 (978-0-595-52646-8(2)) iUniverse, Inc.

Shenk, Joseph C. Rafiki. 2007. 396p. per. 19.99 (978-1-4257-7171-3(8)) Xlibris Corp.

Shields, Bobby J. Safari Winds: A Whitetail Deer Hunter's First Safari. 2008. 170p. pap. 24.95 (978-1-60563-304-6(6)) PublishAmerica, Inc.

Simpson, Alistair. On the Wings of the Wind. 2007. 436p. per. 21.99 (978-1-60477-028-5(7)) Xulon Pr., Inc.

Skoda, Cp. Ogad: An African Passage. 2008. 336p. 42.49 (978-1-4389-1261-5(7)); pap. 26.99 (978-1-4389-1260-8(9)) AuthorHouse.

Starace, Chris. To Benin & Back: Short Stories, Essays, & Reflections about Life in Benin as A Peace Corps Volunteer & the Subsequent Readjustment Process. 2011. 324p. 29.95 (978-1-4620-4622-5(3)); pap. 19.95 (978-1-4620-4621-8(5)) iUniverse, Inc.

Stolen, Dennis. Stolen Moments in East Africa: A Safari with the African Touch. 2009. 104p. pap. 37.50 (978-1-4251-8627-2(0)) Trafford Publishing.

Stong, Paul A. My Years of Service to My Lord & Country. 2011. 48p. pap. 8.95 (978-1-4620-6022-1(6)) iUniverse, Inc.

Suleiman, Mahmoud. The Autobiography I Wrote Begins at a Zaghawa Village in Darfur. 2010. (Illus.). 256p. pap. 14.49 (978-1-4520-2587-2(8)) AuthorHouse.

Taku, Michael Fontem. Fontem Defang: Reminiscences of Leadership in a Post Colonial African Kingdom. 2008. (Illus.). 387p. pap. (978-0-9755261-5-6(4)) Nkemnji Global Tech.

Tamagnini, Miranda. A Life in Africa & Beyond. 2007. 168p. per. 24.95 (978-1-4241-8440-8(1)) PublishAmerica, Inc.

Thomas, Edward. Islam's Perfect Stranger: The Life of Mahmud Muhammad Taha, Muslim Reformer of Sudan. 2011. (International Library of African Studies). (ENG.). 288p. 92.50 (978-1-84885-004-0(2), Tauris Academic Studies) I. B. Tauris & Co., Ltd. GBR. Dist: Macmillan.

Thompson, David C. Hand on My Scalpel: Humorous & Heartbreaking Stories from a Jungle Operating Room. 2006. (Illus.). 167p. pap. 12.99 (978-1-60066-126-6(2)) WingSpread Publishers.

Tomaselli, Keyan G. Writing in the San/D: Autoethnography among Indigenous Southern Africans. 2007. (Crossroads in Qualitative Inquiry Ser.: Vol. 7). (AFR & ENG., Illus.). 190p. 80.00 (978-0-7591-0950-6(8)) AltaMira Pr.

Traore, Oumou. Buly Mother: The Story of Oumou Traore. 2011. 96p. pap. 11.99 (978-1-4634-0064-4(0)) AuthorHouse.

Tucker, Peter. The Mission Boy from Shebar: An Autobiography. 2011. (Illus.). 308p. pap. 18.81 (978-1-4567-8154-5(5)) AuthorHouse.

Tutton, Thomas. A Friend Thru Terror: The Liberian Civil War, 1989 — 1996. 2008. 164p. pap. 15.99 (978-1-4141-1107-0(X)) Pleasant Word.

Urey, Ernest Nanjeen. Fierce Memories. 2009. 108p. 24.99 (978-1-4415-1454-7(5)); pap. 15.99 (978-1-4415-1453-0(8)) Xlibris Corp.

Uzoka, Azubike. Growing up, Growing Old: Chronicle of an Ordinary Life. 2011. 172p. pap. 15.95 (978-1-4620-2079-9(8)) iUniverse, Inc.

van der Steen-Vorster, Antoinette. How Isaac Vanished. 2009. (ENG.). 411p. pap. 35.50 (978-1-4092-8578-6(2)) Lulu Enterprises Inc.

Waite, Robert Montrose. Haunted by Africa. 2007. 192p. per. 16.95 (978-0-595-44834-0(8)) iUniverse, Inc.

Walzer, Craig, ed. Out of Exile: Narratives from the Abducted & Displaced People of Sudan. 2009. (ENG.). 390p. pap. 16.00 (978-1-934781-28-9(2)) McSweeney's Publishing.

Watt, Nigel. Burundi: The Biography of a Small African Country. 2008. (Columbia/Hurst Ser.). (ENG.). 224p. (gr. 17). 55.00 (978-0-231-70090-0(3)) Columbia Univ. Pr.

Wek, Alek. Alek: My Life from Sudanese Refugee to International Supermodel. 2008. (ENG.). 224p. pap. 13.99 (978-0-06-124334-9(5), Amistad) HarperCollins Pubs.

Wessels, Hannes. PK van der Byl. 2010. (Illus.). 352p. pap. 29.95 (978-1-920143-49-7(1)) 30° South Pubs. ZAF. Dist: International Publishers Marketing.

weston, roger. A Smile on their Faces & Hope in their Hearts. 2009. 37p. pap. 18.50 (978-1-4452-4115-9(3)) Lulu Enterprises Inc.

Wheeler, Sara. Too Close to the Sun: The Audacious Life & Times of Denys Finch Hatton. 2009. (ENG., Illus.). 336p. pap. 18.00 (978-0-8129-6892-7(1), Random Hse. Trade Paperbacks) Random House Publishing Group.

Williams, Maggie. Waiting for Choo: A True Life Adventure. 2010. (Illus.). 224p. pap. 15.99 (978-1-4520-8724-5(5)) AuthorHouse.

Wills, Garry. Augustine's Confessions: The Biography of a Book. 2011. (Lives of Great Religious Bks.). (ENG.). 176p. 19.95 (978-0-691-14357-6(9)) Princeton Univ. Pr.

Wimmelbücker, Ludger & Wimmelbücker, Ludger. Mtoro bin Mwinyi Bakari: Swahili lecturer & author in Germany. 2008. 152p. pap. (978-9987-08-008-3(1)) Mkuki na Nyoka Pubs. TZA. Dist: Michigan State Univ. Pr.

Wulu, Sr. The Miracles & Riches of God: Autobiography of John Nimley Wulu, Sr. of Monrovia, Liberia, West Africa (Founder & Builder of Schools) 2008. 136p. 21.49 (978-1-4389-1799-3(6)) AuthorHouse.

Wylie, Dan. Myth of Iron: Shaka in History. 2008. (ENG., Illus.). 640p. pap. 29.95 (978-0-8214-1845-2(3)) Ohio Univ. Pr.

—Myth of Iron Shaka in History. 2008. (Illus.). 635p. pap. 34.95 (978-0-85255-441-8(9), Currey, James) Boydell & Brewer, Ltd. GBR. Dist: Boydell & Brewer, Inc.

Wylie, Dan. Shaka. 2011. (Pocket History Guides). (ENG., Illus.). 144p. pap. 15.99 (978-1-77009-962-3(0)) Jacana Media ZAF. Dist: Independent Pubs. Group.

Youmans, Roger L. When Bull Elephants Fight: An American Surgeon's Chronicle of Congo. 2011. 316p. 25.74 (978-1-4567-6776-1(3)); pap. 19.53 (978-1-4567-6777-8(1)) AuthorHouse.

Zhana. Black Success Stories Vol. 1: Celebrating People of African Heritage. 2006. (ENG.). per. (978-0-9525558-3-4(2)) Zhana Productions.

AFRICA—CIVILIZATION

see also Afrocentrism

Ajayi, S. Ademola. African Culture & Civilization. 2007. (Illus.). 456p. pap. (978-978-35454-5-6(0)) Ibadan Univ. Pr. NGA. Dist: Michigan State Univ. Pr.

Asante, Molefi Kete. The History of Africa: The Quest for Eternal Harmony. 2007. (Illus.). 397p. 110.00 (978-0-415-77138-2(2)); per. 31.95 (978-0-415-77139-9(0)) Routledge.

Bargna, Ivan. Africa. 2009. (Dictionaries of Civilization Ser.). (ENG., Illus.). 388p. pap. 26.95 (978-0-520-25974-4(2)) Univ. of California Pr.

Battle Michael. Ubuntu: I in You & You in Me. 2009. 176p. pap. 18.00 (978-1-59627-111-1(6), Seabury Bks.) Church Publishing, Inc.

Battle, Michael. Ubuntu: I in You & You in Me. 2009. 176p. 25.00 (978-1-59627-113-5(2), Seabury Bks.) Church Publishing, Inc.

Bausi, Alessandro. Languages & Literatures of Eastern Christianity: Ethiopian. 2012. (Worlds of Eastern Christianity, 300ndash;1500 Ser.). 450p. 225.00 (978-0-7546-6997-5(1)) Ashgate Publishing Co.

Beier, Ulli & Omodele, Remi. Weighing the Cost of Pin-Making: Ulli Beier in Conversations. 2011. (978-1-59221-859-2(8)); 276p. pap. (978-1-59221-860-8(1)) Africa World Pr.

Belcher, Wendy Laura. Abyssinia's Samuel Johnson: Ethiopian Thought in the Making of an English Author, 1 vol. 2012. (ENG., Illus.). 336p. 74.00 (978-0-19-979321-1(2)) Oxford Univ. Pr., Inc.

Belgrave, Allison. African American Psychology from Africa. 2006. pap. 10.95 (978-1-4288-1325-0(X)) Cram101 Inc.

Blundell, Geoffrey. Origins: The Story of the Emergence of Humans & Humanity in Africa. 2010. (Illus.). 168p. pap. 32.95 (978-1-77013-040-1(3)) Double Storey Bks. ZAF. Dist: International Publishers Marketing.

Bompani, Barbara & Frahm-Arp, Maria, eds. Development & Politics from Below: Exploring Religious Spaces in the African State. 2010. (Non-Governmental Public Action Ser.). (ENG., Illus.). 272p. 89.00 (978-0-230-23775-9(4)) Palgrave Macmillan.

Brown, Miles Shabazz. You Mountain You Lion: Science, Culture & Songs of Black Africa. 2009. (Illus.). 114p. pap. 11.95 (978-1-4327-3665-1(5), Outskirts Pr., Inc.

Campbell-Dunn, Gjk. The African Origins of Classical Civilisation. 2008. (Illus.). 332p. pap. 25.95 (978-1-4343-5080-0(0)) AuthorHouse.

Castiglioni, Angelo and Alfredo. Once upon a Time in Africa: 50 Years of Explorations & Adventures. 2010. (ENG., Illus.). 428p. 50.00 (978-88-544-0485-4(3)) White Star ITA. Dist: Random Hse., Inc.

CHE, Patrick. The african experience - Volume 1. 2009. 166p. pap. 58.80 (978-0-557-07617-8(X)) Lulu Enterprises Inc.

—The african experience - volume 1 part I. 2009. 77p. pap. 32.10 (978-0-557-07444-0(4)) Lulu Enterprises Inc.

—The african experience - volume 1 part II. 2009. 98p. pap. 38.40 (978-0-557-07694-9(3)) Lulu Enterprises Inc.

Cleary, Tim. Mauritius - Culture Smart! The Essential Guide to Customs & Culture. 2011. (Culture Smart! Ser.). (ENG., Illus.). 168p. pap. 9.95 (978-1-85733-542-2(2)) Kuperard Pubs. GBR. Dist: Random Hse., Inc.

Conant, Jonathan. Staying Roman: Conquest & Identity in Africa & the Mediterranean, 439-700. 2012. (Cambridge Studies in Medieval Life & Thought: Fourth Ser.). (ENG., Illus.). 456p. 99.00 (978-0-521-19697-0(3)) Cambridge Univ. Pr.

Corrado, Jacopo. The Creole Elite & the Rise of Angolan Proto-Nationalism (1870-1920) 2008. 109.95 (978-1-60497-529-1(6)) Cambria Pr.

Cossa, José. African Renaissance & Higher Education: A View Through the Lenses of Christian Higher Education. 2008. 88p. pap. (978-3-639-08733-3(X)) VDM Verlag Dr. Mueller e.K.

Cram101 Textbook Reviews. Outlines & Highlights for the Humanities: Cultural Roots & Continuities Volume 1 by Witt, Brown, Dunbar, Tirro. 2011. 402p. pap. 35.95 (978-1-61812-842-3(6)) Cram101 Inc.

Cumming, Heather Corinne. The Messages of Trees. 2008. Vol. 1. 572p. pap. 34.99 (978-1-60474-481-1(2)) Vol. 2. 588p. pap. 34.95 (978-1-60563-482-1(4)) Vol. 3. 504p. pap. 34.95 (978-1-60563-483-8(2)) PublishAmerica, Inc.

—The Messages of Trees: Volume IV. 2008. 487p. pap. 29.95 (978-1-60563-484-5(0)) PublishAmerica, Inc.

Dowden, Richard. Africa: Altered States, Ordinary Miracles. 2010. (ENG., Illus.). 592p. pap. 19.95 (978-1-58648-816-1(3)) PublicAffairs.

Dueck, Jennifer M. The Claims of Culture at Empire's End: Syria & Lebanon under French Rule. 2010. (British Academy Ser.). (ENG.). 250p. 85.00 (978-0-19-726447-8(6)) Oxford Univ. Pr., Inc.

Enworom, Sylvanus A. The Paragon of Civilization. 2011. 210p. pap. 24.95 (978-1-4626-1320-5(9)) PublishAmerica, Inc.

Falola, Toyin & Hassan, Salah, eds. Power & Nationalism in Modern Africa: Essays in Honor of Don Ohadike. 2008. 55.00 (978-1-59460-490-4(3)) Carolina Academic Pr.

Falola, Toyin & Ngom, Fallou. Facts, Fiction, & African Creative Imaginations. Falola, Toyin & Ngom, Fallou, eds. 2009. (Routledge African Studies). (ENG., Illus.). 348p. 125.00 (978-0-415-80316-8(0)) Routledge.

Gearon, Eamonn. The Sahara: A Cultural History. 2011. (Landscapes of the Imagination Ser.). (ENG.). 288p. 74.00 (978-0-19-986196-5(X)); pap. 16.95 (978-0-19-986195-8(1)) Oxford Univ. Pr., Inc.

Geary, Christraud M. Barnum: Visions of Africa Series. 2011. (Visions of Africa Ser.) (ENG., Illus.). 160p. pap. 34.95 (978-88-7439-573-6(6)) 5 Continents ITA. Dist: Hachette Bk. Group.

Geschiere. Readings in Modernity in Africa. 2008. (Illus.). 240p. pap. 26.95 (978-0-85255-898-0(8), Currey, James) Boydell & Brewer, Ltd. GBR Dist: Boydell & Brewer, Inc.

Geschiere, Peter, et al, eds. Readings in Modernity in Africa. 2008. (Readings in... Ser.). (ENG., Illus.). 256p. pap. 24.95 (978-0-253-21996-1(5), 0253219965) Indiana Univ. Pr.

Geschiere, Peter & Meyer, Birgit. Readings in Modernity in Africa. Geschiere, Peter & Meyer, Birgit, eds. Pels, Peter, ed. 2008. (Readings in... Ser.). (ENG., Illus.). 256p. 65.00 (978-0-253-35176-0(6), 0253351766) Indiana Univ. Pr.

Glasgow, Jacqueline & Rice, Linda J. Exploring African Life & Literature: Novel Guides to Promote Socially Responsive Learning. 2007. 376p. 34.95 (978-0-87207-609-5(1)) International Reading Assn.

Hespeler-Boultbee, J. J. A Story in Stones: Portugal's Influence on Culture & Architecture in the Highlands of Ethiopia 1493-1634. 2nd ed. 2011. (Illus.). 204p. pap. (978-1-926585-98-7(4), CCB Publishing) CCB Publishing.

Hewitt. Voices Out of Africa in Twentieth Century. 2009. (Illus.). 402p. 80.00 (978-0-8387-5729-1(4)) Bucknell Univ. Pr.

Hewlett, Barry S. & Hewlett, Bonnie L. Ebola, Culture, & Politics: The Anthropology of an Emerging Disease. 2007. (ENG., Illus.). 192p. (C). per. 44.95 (978-0-495-00918-4(0)) Wadsworth.

Hunwick, John. West Africa, Islam & the Arab World. 2006. per. 24.95 (978-1-55876-399-9(6)) Wiener, Markus Pubs., Inc.

Hunwick, John O. West Africa, Islam, & the Arab World: Studies in Honor of Basil Davidson. 2006. (Illus.). 147p. 88.95 (978-1-55876-398-2(8)) Wiener, Markus Pubs., Inc.

Hunwick, John O. & Boye, Alida Jay. The Hidden Treasures of Timbuktu: Rediscovering Africa's Literary Culture. 2008. (ENG., Illus.). 176p. 50.00 (978-0-500-51421-4(6), 551421) Thames & Hudson.

Imfeld, Al & Suter, Lotta. Elefanten in der Sahara: Agrar-Geschichten aus Afrika. 2009. (GER., Illus.). 255p. pap. (978-3-85869-404-1(5)) Rotpunktverlag.

Jeppie, Shamil & Diagne, Souleymane Bachir, eds. The Meanings of Timbuktu. 2008. (ENG., Illus.). 376p. 60.00 (978-0-7969-2204-5(7)) Human Sciences Research Council ZAF. Dist: Independent Pubs. Group.

Jones, Jeannette Eileen. In Search of Brightest Africa: Reimagining the Dark Continent in American Culture, 1884-1936. 2011. (Race in the Atlantic World, 1700-1900 Ser.). (ENG., Illus.). 260p. pap. 24.95 (978-0-8203-4029-6(4)) Univ. of Georgia Pr.

Joyce, Peter. Cultures of South Africa. 2009. (Illus.). 140p. pap. 19.95 (978-1-919938-99-8(0)) Sunbird Publishing ZAF. Dist: International Publishers Marketing.

K'Orinda-Yimbo, Akinyi von. Darkest Europe & Africa's Nightmare: A Critical Observation of the Neighbouring Continents. 2007. 34.95 (978-0-87586-519-5(4)); pap. 22.95 (978-0-87586-518-8(6)) Algora Publishing.

Larkin, Brian. Signal & Noise: Media, Infrastructure, & Urban Culture in Nigeria. 2008. (ENG., Illus.). 328p. (C). 89.95 (978-0-8223-4090-4(9)); pap. 24.95 (978-0-8223-4108-6(5)) Duke Univ. Pr.

Lewis-Williams, David & Challis, Sam. Deciphering Ancient Minds: The Mystery of San Bushman Rock Art. 2011. (ENG., Illus.). 224p. 29.95 (978-0-500-05169-6(0), 505169) Thames & Hudson.

Likaka, Osumaka. Naming Colonialism: History & Collective Memory in the Congo, 1870-1960. 2009. (Africa & the Diaspora Ser.). (ENG., Illus.). 216p. pap. 26.95 (978-0-299-23364-8(2)) Univ. of Wisconsin Pr.

Loutzenhiser, Mike. The Role of the Indigenous African Psyche in the Evolution of Human Consciousness. 2008. 172p. pap. 15.95 (978-0-595-50376-6(4), iUniverse, Inc.) iUniverse, Inc.

Manning, Patrick. The African Diaspora: A History Through Culture. (Columbia Studies in International & Global History Ser.). (ENG., Illus.). 424p. (gr. 17). 2010. pap. 24.50 (978-0-231-14471-1(7)) 2009. 29.95 (978-0-231-14470-4(9)) Columbia Univ. Pr.

Maspero, Gaston. The Dawn of Civilization - Map & over Four Hundred Seventy Illustrations & Places. (African Studies). reprint ed. 75.00 (978-0-938818-76-2(7)) ECA Assocs.

Mayson, Cedric. Why Africa Matters. 2010. 224p. pap. 20.00 (978-1-57075-869-0(7)) Orbis Bks.

Mazrui, Ali A., et al, eds. Africa's Islamic Experience: History, Culture & Politics. 2008. 278p. 29.95 (978-1-932705-78-2(3)) New Dawn Pr., Inc.

M'Bayo, Ritchard. Political Culture, Cultural Universals, & the Crisis of Identity in Africa: Essays in Ethnoglobalization. 2011. (ENG.). 444p. 139.95 (978-0-7734-1390-0(1)) Mellen, Edwin Pr., The.

McKinley, Catherine E. Indigo: In Search of the Color That Seduced the World. 2011. (ENG., Illus.). 256p. 27.00 (978-1-60819-505-3(8)) Bloomsbury Publishing.

Middleton, John & Miller, Joseph Calder. New Encyclopedia of Africa, 5 vols. 2007. (Illus.). (978-0-684-31455-6(X)); (978-0-684-31456-3(8)); (978-0-684-31457-0(6)); (978-0-684-31458-7(4)); (978-0-684-31459-4(2)) Cengage Gale. (Charles Scribner's Sons).

Mitchell, Peter, ed. Peoples & Cultures of Africa Nations & Personalities. 2006. (Peoples & Cultures of Africa Ser.) (Illus.). 112p. (gr. 6-12). 39.00 (978-0-8160-6266-9(8)) Facts On File, Inc.

—Peoples & Cultures of Central Africa. 2006. (Peoples & Cultures of Africa Ser.). (Illus.). 112p. (gr. 6-12). 39.00 (978-0-8160-6264-5(1)) Facts On File, Inc.

—Peoples & Cultures of East Africa. 2006. (Peoples & Cultures of Africa Ser.). (Illus.). 112p. (gr. 6-12). 39.00 (978-0-8160-6263-8(3)) Facts On File, Inc.

—Peoples & Cultures of North Africa. 2006. (Peoples & Cultures of Africa Ser.). (Illus.). 112p. (gr. 6-12). 39.00 (978-0-8160-6261-4(7)) Facts On File, Inc.

—Peoples & Cultures of Southern Africa. 2006. (Peoples & Cultures of Africa Ser.). (Illus.). 112p. (gr. 6-12). 39.00 (978-0-8160-6265-2(X)) Facts On File, Inc.

—Peoples & Cultures of West Africa. 2006. (Peoples & Cultures of Africa Ser.). (Illus.). 112p. (gr. 6-12). 39.00 (978-0-8160-6262-1(5)) Facts On File, Inc.

Moore, Lois Merriweather, ed. The Dispersion of Africans & African Culture Throughout the World: Essays on the African Diaspora. 2007. 225p. (978-0-7734-5309-8(1)) Mellen, Edwin Pr., The.

Moseley, William. Clashing Views on African Issues. 4th ed. 2011. (Taking Sides Ser.). (ENG., Illus.). 464p. (C). pap. 48.00 (978-0-07-805008-4(1), 0078050081, McGraw-Hill/Dushkin) McGraw-Hill Higher Education.

Moseley, William G. Clashing Views on African Issues. 3rd ed. 2008. (Taking Sides Ser.). (ENG.). 416p. (C). pap. 48.00 (978-0-07-351518-2(3), 0073515183, McGraw-Hill/Dushkin) McGraw-Hill Higher Education.

Mugo, Micere Githae. Writing & Speaking from the Heart of My Mind: Selected Essays & Speeches. 2011. (978-1-59221-853-0(9)); 300p. pap. (978-1-59221-854-7(7)) Africa World Pr.

Munene, Ishmael. An Interdisciplinary Primer in African Studies. 2011. (ENG., Illus.). 330p. 85.00 (978-0-7391-6597-3(6)) Lexington Bks.

Munene, Ishmael & Munene, Ishmael I. An Interdisciplinary Primer in African Studies. 2011. (ENG., Illus.). 330p. pap. 34.95 (978-0-7391-6598-0(4)) Lexington Bks.

Munene, Ishmael I. An Interdisciplinary Primer in African Studies. 2011. (Illus.). xiii, 308p. (978-0-7391-6887-5(8)) Lexington Bks.

Nabudere, W. Epistemology, Philosophy & Wholeness: An Epistemology. 2011. 178p. pap. (978-0-7983-0255-5(0)) Africa Institute of South Africa.

Nadel, S. F. A Black Byzantium: A Muslim Emirate in Northern Nigeria. 2008. 430p. 161.50 (978-0-7103-1224-2(5)) Kegan Paul International, Ltd. GBR. Dist: Columbia Univ. Pr.

Ngugi wa Thiong'o. Something Torn & New: An African Renaissance. 2009. (ENG.). 176p. pap. 25.00 (978-0-465-00946-6(8), Basic Civitas Bks.) Basic Bks.

Njoh, Ambe J. Tradition, Culture & Development in Africa: Historical Lessons for Modern Development Planning. 2006. (Heritage, Culture, & Identity Ser.). (Illus.). 240p. 130.00 (978-0-7546-4884-0(2)) Ashgate Publishing Co.

Ojaide, Tanure. Ordering the African Imagination. 2007. 184p. pap. (978-978-023-204-7(4)) Malthouse Press Ltd, Nigeria NGA. Dist: Michigan State Univ. Pr.

Ojakorotu, Victor. Fresh Dimensions on the Niger Delta Crisis of Nigeria. 2009. 277p. pap. 24.08 (978-0-557-06679-7(4)) Lulu Enterprises Inc.

Onunwa, Udobata R. A Critical Review of Methodologies of African Religion & Culture. 2006. 18.00 *(978-0-8059-8309-8(0))* Dorrance Publishing Co., Inc.

Phillipson, David W. Foundations of an African Civilisation: Aksum & the northern Horn, 1000 BC - AD 1300. 2012. (Eastern Africa Ser.). (Illus.). 312p. 70.00 ***(978-1-84701-041-4(5)***, Currey, James) Boydell & Brewer, Ltd. GBR. Dist: Boydell & Brewer, Inc.

Reid, Andrew & O'Connor, David, eds. Ancient Egypt in Africa. 2007. (Encounters with Ancient Egypt series, University College London Institute of Archaeology Publications). (ENG., Illus.). 233p. pap. 34.95 *(978-1-59874-205-3(1))* Left Coast Pr., Inc.

Schulz, Dorothea E. Culture & Customs of Mali, 1 vol. 2012. (Culture & Customs of Africa Ser.). (Illus.). 204p. 50.00 ***(978-0-313-35912-5(1)***, GR5912) Greenwood Publishing Group, Inc.

Schulz, Dorothea Elisabeth. Culture & Customs of Mali. 2012. (Illus.). xvi, 201p. E-Book ***(978-0-313-35913-2(X)***, Greenwood Pr.) Greenwood Publishing Group, Inc.

Senghor, Leopold S. Les Fondements de l'Africanite ou Negritude et Arabite. (FRE.). pap. 17.95 *(978-0-7859-5307-4(8))* French & European Pubns., Inc.

Sherman, Daniel J. French Primitivism & the Ends of Empire, 1945-1975. 2011. (Illus.). 312p. 45.00 *(978-0-226-75269-3(0))* Univ. of Chicago Pr.

Sims, Sedrick. Ancient AFRICAN History A Journey Highlighting Africa's Past. 2009. 117p. pap. 10.00 *(978-0-557-09694-7(4))* Lulu Enterprises Inc.

Stanton, Andrea L., et al, eds. Cultural Sociology of the Middle East, Asia, & Africa: An Encyclopedia. 2012. 1976p. 495.00 ***(978-1-4129-8176-7(X)***, B81767C) SAGE Pubns., Inc.

Taylor, Scott D. Culture & Customs of Zambia, 1 vol. 2006. (Culture & Customs of Africa Ser.). (Illus.). 168p. 49.95 *(978-0-313-33246-3(0)*, GR3246, Greenwood Pr.) Greenwood Publishing Group, Inc.

van Zyl, Ebben. Leadership in the African Context. 2010. (Illus.). 292p. pap. 51.95 *(978-0-7021-7770-5(9))* Double Storey Bks. ZAF. Dist: International Publishers Marketing.

Vaughan, Olufemi & Okome, Mojúbàolú Olúfúnké, eds. West African Migrations: Transnational & Global Pathways in a New Century. 2012. (ENG., Illus.). 294p. 90.00 ***(978-0-230-33867-8(4))*** Palgrave Macmillan.

Woodfork, Jacqueline. Culture & Customs of the Central African Republic, 1 vol. 2006. (Culture & Customs of Africa Ser.). (Illus.). 232p. 49.95 *(978-0-313-33203-6(7)*, GR3203, Greenwood Pr.) Greenwood Publishing Group, Inc.

Zank, Wolfgang. Clash or Cooperation of Civilizations? Overlapping Integration & Identities. 2009. (International Political Economy of New Regionalisms Ser.). 242p. 114.95 *(978-0-7546-7407-8(X))* Ashgate Publishing Co.

Zegeye, Abebe & Vambe, Maurice. Close to the Sources: Essays on Contemporary African Culture, Politics & Academy. 2011. (Routledge African Studies). 182p. 125.00 *(978-0-415-89595-8(2))* Routledge.

AFRICA—CLIMATE

Knox, Alexander. The Climate of the Continent of Africa. 2011. (ENG.). 576p. pap. 43.00 *(978-1-107-60071-3(5))* Cambridge Univ. Pr.

AFRICA—COLONIZATION

Agbodike, Chinedu. Colonial Conspiracies in Africa. 2009. 300p. 29.99 *(978-1-4415-1182-9(2))*; pap. 19.99 *(978-1-4415-1181-2(4))* Xlibris Corp.

Ahluwalia, Pal. Out of Africa: Post-Structuralism's Colonial Roots. 2010. (Postcolonial Politics Ser.). (ENG.). 208p. (C). 130.00 *(978-0-415-57069-5(7))*; pap. 47.95 *(978-0-415-57070-1(0))* Taylor & Francis Group GBR. (Routledge). Dist: Taylor & Francis Group.

Antwi-Boasiako, Kwame Badu & Bonna, Okyere. Traditional Institutions & Public Administration in Democratic Afric. 2009. 208p. 31.99 *(978-1-4415-2013-5(9))*; pap. 21.99 *(978-1-4415-2012-8(0))* Xlibris Corp.

Berenson, Edward. Heroes of Empire: Five Charismatic Men & the Conquest of Africa. 2012. (ENG.). 376p. pap. 24.95 ***(978-0-520-27258-3(7))*** Univ. of California Pr.

Brower, Benjamin C. A Desert Named Peace: The Violence of France's Empire in the Algerian Sahara, 1844-1902. 2009. (History & Society of the Modern Middle East Ser.). (ENG., Illus.). 480p. (gr. 17). 50.00 *(978-0-231-15492-5(5))* Columbia Univ. Pr.

Burroughs. Travel Writing & Atrocities: Eyewitness Accounts of Slavery in the Congo, Angola & the Putumayo. 2010. (Routledge Research in Travel Writing Ser.). (ENG., Illus.). 230p. (C). 125.00 *(978-0-415-99238-1(9))* Routledge.

Burroughs, Robert M. Travel Writing & Atrocities: Eyewitness Accounts of Colonialism in the Congo, Angola, & the Putumayo. 2010. (Illus.). xiv, 215p. 95.00 *(978-0-203-84916-3(7))* Routledge.

Campbell, Gwyn. An Economic History of Imperial Madagascar, 1750-1895: The Rise & Fall of an Island Empire. 2008. (African Studies). (ENG., Illus.). 436p. pap. 46.00 *(978-0-521-10391-6(6))* Cambridge Univ. Pr.

Chamberlain, M. E. The Scramble for Africa. 3rd ed. 2010. (Seminar Studies in History Ser.). (ENG., Illus.). 208p. (C). pap. 27.20 *(978-1-4082-2014-6(8))* Longman Publishing Group.

Delmas, Adrien & Penn, Nigel, eds. Written Culture in a Colonial Context: Africa & the Americas, 1500-1900. 2012. (African History Ser.). (ENG., Illus.). XXXII, 380p. pap. ***(978-90-04-22389-9(4))*** BRILL.

Etherington, Norman, ed. Mapping European Conquest: Australia & Southern Africa. 2007. (Illus.). 230p. (C). pap. 31.00 *(978-0-9802964-4-0(7))* UWA Publishing AUS. Dist: International Specialized Bk. Services.

Fowler, Ian & Fanso, Verkijika G., prefs. Encounter, Transformation & Identity: Peoples of the Western Cameroon Borderlands, 1891-2000. 2009. (Illus.). 254p. 95.00 *(978-1-84545-336-7(0))* Berghahn Bks., Inc.

Garrison, William Lloyd. Thoughts on African Colonization. 2009. 204p. pap. 20.12 *(978-1-4590-0767-3(0))* General Bks. LLC.

Hayward, Alan. Africa Called: Scientists & Development in Nigeria. 2008. (ENG., Illus.). 288p. 58.00 *(978-1-84511-494-7(9)*, Radcliffe Pr., The) I. B. Tauris & Co., Ltd. GBR. Dist: Macmillan.

Hélénon, Véronique. French Caribbeans in Africa: Diasporic Connections & Colonial Administration, 1880-1939. 2011. (ENG.). 214p. 80.00 *(978-0-230-10544-7(0))* Palgrave Macmillan.

Jagire, Jennifer M. Indigenous African Knowledge & Anticolonial Practice. 2010. 92p. pap. *(978-3-8383-6753-8(7))* Lambert Academic Publishing.

Jarrett, Alfred A. The Under-Development of Africa: Colonialism, Neo-Colonialism & Socialism. Date not set. 192p. (C). 57.00 *(978-0-7618-0105-4(7))*; pap. 29.50 *(978-0-7618-0106-1(5))* Univ. Pr. of America, Inc.

Johnston, Harry Hamilton. A History of the Colonization of Africa by Alien Races. 2nd ed. 2011. (ENG., Illus.). 538p. pap. 39.99 ***(978-0-521-23128-2(0))*** Cambridge Univ. Pr.

Kolapo, Femi James. African Agency & European Colonialism: Latitudes of Negotiations & Containment. 2007. (ENG., Illus.). 256p. pap. 41.99 *(978-0-7618-3846-3(5))* Univ. Pr. of America, Inc.

L'Ange, Gerald. The White Africans: From Colonisation to Liberation. 2009. (Illus.). 550p. pap. 28.95 *(978-1-86842-219-7(4))* International Publishers Marketing.

Larebo M. Haile Staff. Building of an Empire. (Illus.). 378p. 99.95 *(978-1-56902-230-6(5))* Red Sea Pr.

Limb, Peter & Midgely, Peter, eds. Grappling with the Beast: Indigenous Southern African Responses to Colonialism, 1840-1930. 2010. (European Expansion & Indigenous Response Ser.). 352p. *(978-90-04-17877-9(5))* BRILL.

Lingna Nafafé, José. Colonial Encounters: Issues of Culture, Hybridity & Creolisation: Portuguese Mercantile Settlers in West Africa. (Illus.). x, 215p. pap. 51.95 *(978-3-631-52779-5(9))* Lang, Peter GmbH, Europaischer Verlag der Wissenschaften DEU. Dist: Lang, Peter Publishing, Inc.

Mentan, Tatah. The Recolonization of Africa: Revised Edition. 2nd ed. 2011. (Illus.). 264p. lib. bdg. *(978-1-936320-17-2(7))* Academica Pr., LLC.

Omar, Musa Mohammad. Der Sklavenhandel und Die Kolonisierung in Afrika: Beiträge Zum Wesen und Den Auswirkungen Von Sklavenhandel und Kolonialisierung in Afrika. 2009. (GER., Illus.). 85p. pap. *(978-3-86573-426-6(X))* Gaudig, Olaf, u. Klaus-Peter Veit, wvb Wissenschaftlicher Verlag Berlin.

Peers, Chris. The African Wars: Warriors & Soldiers of the Colonial Campaigns. 2011. (Illus.). 240p. 39.95 *(978-1-84884-121-5(3))* Pen & Sword Bks. Ltd. GBR. Dist: Casemate Pubs. & Bk. Distributors, LLC.

Reinhard, Wolfgang. A Short History of Colonialism. 2011. (ENG., Illus.). 336p. 100.00 ***(978-0-7190-8327-3(3))***; pap. 38.95 ***(978-0-7190-8328-0(1))*** Manchester Univ. Pr. GBR. Dist: Macmillan.

Rich, Jeremy. A Workman Is Worthy of His Meat: Food & Colonialism in the Gabon Estuary. 2009. (France Overseas: Studies in Empire & D Ser.). (ENG.). 244p. pap. 24.95 *(978-0-8032-2497-1(4))* Univ. of Nebraska Pr.

Rodney, Walter. How Europe Underdeveloped Africa. 2011. 340p. 24.95 *(978-1-57478-048-2(4))* Black Classic Pr.

Sanderson, Edgar. Africa in the Nineteenth Century. 2009. 238p. pap. *(978-1-4590-2877-7(5))* Books LLC.

Saul, John S. Decolonization & Empire: Contesting the Rhetoric & Reality of Resubordination in Southern Africa & Beyond. 2008. (ENG.). 196p. pap. 22.95 *(978-0-85036-592-4(9))* Merlin Pr. Ltd. GBR. Dist: Independent Pubs. Group.

Schreier, Joshua. Arabs of the Jewish Faith: The Civilizing Mission in Colonial Algeria. 2010. (Jewish Cultures of the World Ser.). (ENG., Illus.). 256p. 49.95 *(978-0-8135-4794-7(6))* Rutgers Univ. Pr.

Taithe, Bertrand. The Killer Trail: A Colonial Scandal in the Heart of Africa. 2009. (ENG., Illus.). 304p. 34.95 *(978-0-19-923121-8(4))* Oxford Univ. Pr., Inc.

Thiessen, Inga. A History Forgotten, a Revolution Misunderstood. 2011. 60p. pap. ***(978-3-8433-9420-8(2))*** Lambert Academic Publishing.

Thomas, Martin. Empires of Intelligence: Security Services & Colonial Disorder after 1914. 2007. (Illus.). 486p. 55.00 *(978-0-520-25117-5(2))* Univ. of California Pr.

Thomas, Martin, ed. & intro. The French Colonial Mind Vol. 2: Violence, Military Encounters, & Colonialism, 2 vols. 2012. (France Overseas: Studies in Empire & D Ser.). (ENG., Illus.). 440p. pap. 45.00 *(978-0-8032-2094-2(4))* Univ. of Nebraska Pr.

—The French Colonial Mind, 2-volume Set, 2 vols. 2012. (France Overseas: Studies in Empire & D Ser.). (ENG.). 864p. pap. 75.00 *(978-0-8032-3815-2(0))* Univ. of Nebraska Pr.

Tilley, Helen. Africa as a Living Laboratory: Empire, Development, & the Problem of Scientific Knowledge, 1870-1950. 2011. (ENG., Illus.). 520p. 85.00 *(978-0-226-80346-3(5))*; pap. 29.00 *(978-0-226-80347-0(3))* Univ. of Chicago Pr.

Wariboko, Waibinte E. Race & the Civilizing Mission: The Impliations for the Framing of Blackness & African Personhood. 2010. 146p. pap. *(978-1-59221-770-0(2))* Africa World Pr.

AFRICA—COMMERCE

African Development Bank, creator. The African Development Report 2006: Aid, Debt Relief & Development in Africa. 2006. (ENG., Illus.). 176p. per. 39.95 *(978-0-19-929847-1(5))* Oxford Univ. Pr., Inc.

Ajakaiye, David Olusanya & Oyejide, T. Ademola, eds. Trade Infrastructure & Economic Development. 2011. (Routledge Studies in Development Economics Ser.). (ENG., Illus.). 368p. (C). 155.00 *(978-0-415-66913-9(8))* Routledge.

Alpers, Edward A. Ivory & Slaves: Changing Pattern of International Trade in East Central Africa to the Later Nineteenth Century. 2009. 320p. 47.00 *(978-1-59740-297-2(4))* ACLS Humanities E-Book.

Austen, Ralph A. Trans-Saharan Africa in World History. 2010. (New Oxford World History Ser.). (ENG., Illus.). 176p. pap. 19.95 *(978-0-19-533788-4(3))* Oxford Univ. Pr., Inc.

Baffoe, Abraham & Richard Vlosky, Prof. Forest Certification. 2011. 124p. pap. ***(978-3-8433-9306-5(0))*** Lambert Academic Publishing.

Bationo, Andre, et al, eds. Fighting Poverty in Sub-Saharan Africa: the Multiple Roles of Legumes in Integrated Soil Fertility Management: The Multiple Roles of Legumes in Integrated Soil Fertility Management. 2011. (ENG., Illus.). viii, 246p. 209.00 *(978-94-007-1535-6(8)*, 9400715358) Springer.

Bauer, P. T. West African Trade: A Study of Competition, Oligopoly & Monopoly in a Changing Economy. 2011. (ENG.). 480p. 130.00 *(978-0-415-59383-0(2))* Routledge.

Bernan Press Staff & World Trade Organization Staff. Trade Policy Review: Niger/Senegal 2009. 2010. (ENG.). 300p. pap. 75.00 *(978-1-59888-381-7(X))* Bernan Assocs.

Bigsten, Arne & Durevall, Dick. The African Economy & Its Role in the World Economy. 2008. (NAI Current African Issues Ser.). 66p. pap. 12.95 *(978-91-7106-625-1(X))* Nordiska Afrikainstitutet SWE. Dist: Stylus Publishing, LLC.

Boko, Sylvain Hounkponou & Seck, Diery. Back on Track: Sector-Led Growth in Africa & Implications for Development. 2009. *(978-1-59221-708-3(7))*; 480p. pap. *(978-1-59221-709-0(5))* Africa World Pr.

Broadman, Harry G. Africa's Silk Road: China & India's New Economic Frontier. 2006. (Stand Alones Ser.). (ENG., Illus.). 384p. per. 25.00 *(978-0-8213-6835-0(4)*, 9780821368350) World Bank Pubns.

Burnett, Patrick & Manji, Firoze, eds. From the slave trade to 'free' Trade: How trade undermines democracy & justice in Africa. 2007. (ENG.). 180p. pap. 19.95 *(978-0-9545637-1-4(9))* Pambazuka Pr. GBR. Dist: Independent Pubs. Group.

Chidoko, Clainos. Determinants of Intra-Industry Trade. 2011. 64p. pap. ***(978-3-8443-2585-0(9))*** Lambert Academic Publishing.

de Villiers, Les. Africa 2008. 2008. (Illus.). 400p. per. 28.95 *(978-0-916673-24-6(3))* Business Bks. International.

Dowler, Amelia & Galvin, Elizabeth R., eds. Money, Trade & Trade Routes in Pre-Islamic North Africa. 2011. (British Museum Research Publication). (ENG., Illus.). 86p. (C). pap. 40.00 *(978-0-86159-176-3(3))* British Museum Pr. GBR. Dist: Brown, David Bk. Co., The.

Endeley, RoseMarie-Rita & Thompson, Rosetta Bola. Management of Credit Schemes for Women Entrepreneurs in Africa. 2007. (Illus.). 407p. pap. 48.95 *(978-1-901127-32-4(X))* Studies Forum International GBR. Dist: Stylus Publishing, LLC.

Euromonitor International. African Marketing Data & Statistics. 3rd ed. 2011. (ENG.). 274p. (C). ***(978-1-84264-548-2(X))*** Euromonitor International PLC.

Eze, C. P. Don't Africa Me: 'Their' geo-branding war, 'Our' trade, tourism wounds, & Winning like China. 2008. 220p. 25.00 *(978-0-9800768-0-6(3)*, Expertz in PRINT) Brandwell Global Services.

Fiala, Natalie L. Sub-Saharan Africa: Economic Issues. 2011. pap. *(978-1-61761-891-8(8))* Nova Science Pubs., Inc.

Gibbon, Peter, et al, eds. Global Agro-Food Trade & Standards: Challenges for Africa. 2010. (International Political Economy Ser.). (ENG., Illus.). 256p. 105.00 *(978-0-230-57951-4(5))* Palgrave Macmillan.

Gomo, Kwashirai, et al. The Development of Informal Traders in Zimbabwe. 2011. 80p. pap. ***(978-3-8443-1877-7(1))*** Lambert Academic Publishing.

Green, Toby, ed. Brokers of Change: Atlantic Commerce & Cultures in Pre-Colonial Western Africa. 2012. (ENG., Illus.). 320p. 125.00 ***(978-0-19-726520-8(0))*** Oxford Univ. Pr., Inc.

Kaseke, Nyasha. Hyperinflation- Reasons for Staying in an Organisation. 2011. 68p. pap. ***(978-3-8433-8891-7(1))*** Lambert Academic Publishing.

Kea, Ray A. A Cultural & Social History of Ghana from the Seventeenth to the Nineteenth Century: The Gold Coast in the Age of Trans-Atlantic Slave Trade. 2011. 1024p. 199.95 ***(978-0-7734-3910-8(2))*** Mellen, Edwin Pr., The.

Kuada, John. African Journal of Business & Economic. 2006. (ENG.). 160p. per. *(978-1-905068-63-0(8))* Adonis & Abbey Publishers Ltd.

Kuada, John, ed. African Journal of Business & Economic Research. 2007. 124p. per. *(978-1-905068-93-7(X))* Adonis & Abbey Publishers Ltd.

—African Journal of Business & Economic Research, Volume 2, Nos 2 And. 2007. 116p. per. *(978-1-905068-14-2(X))* Adonis & Abbey Publishers Ltd.

Little, Peter D. & McPeak, John G. Pastoral Livestock Marketing in Eastern Africa: Research & Policy Challenges. Little, Peter D. & McPeak, John G., eds. 2006. (ENG., Illus.). 288p. per. 35.95 *(978-1-85339-631-1(1))* Intermediate Technology Development Group of North America.

Mahajan, Vijay & Gunther, Robert E. Africa Rising: How 900 Million African Consumers Offer More Than You Think. 2008. (ENG., Illus.). 288p. 34.99 *(978-0-13-233942-1(0))* Wharton Schl. Publishing.

Manda, Elizabeth Luhanga. Price Instability in the Maize Market in Malawi. 2011. 316p. pap. ***(978-3-8433-9440-6(7))*** Lambert Academic Publishing.

Mane, Damian Ondo. Oil & the Emergence of the Gulf of Guinea. 2007. 123p. pap. 11.95 *(978-0-7414-3816-4(X))* Infinity Publishing.

Mark, Peter & Horta, José da Silva. The Forgotten Diaspora: Jewish Communities in West Africa & the Making of the Atlantic World. 2011. (ENG., Illus.). 278p. (C). 80.00 *(978-0-521-19286-6(2))* Cambridge Univ. Pr.

Mawdsley, Emma & McCann, Gerard, eds. India in Africa: Changing Geographies of Power. 2011. (ENG.). 240p. pap. 27.95 ***(978-1-906387-65-5(6))*** Pambazuka Pr. GBR. Dist: Independent Pubs. Group.

McNeil, Mary & Malena, Carmen, eds. Demanding Good Governance: Lessons from Social Accountability Initiatives in Africa. 2010. (ENG., Illus.). 264p. pap. 25.00 *(978-0-8213-8380-3(9)*, 9780821383803) World Bank Pubns.

Melber, Henning, et al. Africa, Regional Cooperation & the World Market: Socio-Economic Strategies in Times of Global Trade Regimes. 2006. (NAI Discussion Papers). 72p. pap. 13.95 *(978-91-7106-559-9(8))* Nordiska Afrikainstitutet SWE. Dist: Stylus Publishing, LLC.

Mijere, Nsolo J. N. Informal & Cross-Border Trade in the Southern African Development Community. 2008. 116p. 22.95 *(978-99944-55-20-1(6))* African Bks. Collective, Ltd. GBR. Dist: Lightning Source, Inc.

Miller, Debra A. Aid to Africa. 2009. (Current Controversies Ser.). (ENG., Illus.). 240p. (gr. 10-12). pap. 39.70 *(978-0-7377-4316-6(6))*; pap. 27.50 *(978-0-7377-4315-9(8))* Cengage Gale. (Greenhaven Pr., Inc.).

Miran, Jonathan. Red Sea Citizens: Cosmopolitan Society & Cultural Change in Massawa. 2009. (ENG., Illus.). 400p. 75.00 *(978-0-253-35312-2(2)*, 0253353122); pap. 27.95 *(978-0-253-22079-0(3)*, 0253220793) Indiana Univ. Pr.

Misginaw, Tamirat. Cattle Commercial off-Take in Pastoral Areas of Hadiya Zone: Constraints & Opportunities of Cattle Commercial off-Take in Pastoral Areas of Hadiya Zone, Snnpr, Ethiopia. 2011. 96p. pap. ***(978-3-639-32787-8(X))*** VDM Verlag Dr. Mueller e.K.

Monroe, J. Cameron & Ogundiran, Akinwumi, eds. Power & Landscape in Atlantic West Africa: Archaeological Perspectives. 2012. (ENG., Illus.). 400p. 99.00 ***(978-1-107-00939-4(1))*** Cambridge Univ. Pr.

Moore, Geoff, ed. Fairness in International Trade. 2010. (International Society of Business, Economics, & Ethics Book Ser.). (ENG., Illus.). xv, 214p. 159.00 *(978-90-481-8839-0(3)*, 9048188393) Springer.

Mshomba, Richard E. Africa & the World Trade Organization. 2009. (ENG., Illus.). 384p. 84.00 *(978-0-521-51476-7(2))* Cambridge Univ. Pr.

Mutai, Henry. Compliance with International Trade Obligations: The Common Market for Eastern & Southern Africa. 2007. *(978-90-411-2664-1(3))* Kluwer Law International.

Ngangjoh-Hodu, Yenkong & Matambalya, Francis A. S. T. Trade Relations Between the EU & Africa: Development, Challenges & Options Beyond the Cotonou Agreement. 2009. (Illus.). xxvii, 291p. (C). E-Book 145.00 *(978-0-203-86452-4(2))* Routledge.

Ngangjoh-Hodu, Yenkong & Matambalya, Francis A. S. T., eds. Trade Relations Between the EU & Africa: Development, Challenges & Options Beyond the Cotonou Agreement. 2009. (Routledge Studies in Development Economics Ser.). (ENG., Illus.). 320p. 150.00 *(978-0-415-54981-3(7))* Routledge.

Niang, Abdoulaye. Globalization: The Key to Peace & Prosperity for Africa. 2008. (Illus.). 144p. pap. 12.95 *(978-1-57197-486-0(5)*, Ivy House Publishing Group) Pentland Pr., Inc.

Nicolini, Beatrice & Nicoline, Beatrice. Markran, Oman, & Zanzibar: Three-Terminal Cultural Corridor in the Western Indian Ocean (1799-1856) Watson, Penelope-Jane, tr. from ITA. 2011.Tr. of Sultanatodi Zanzibar nel XIX Secolo. (Illus.). 200p. pap. 26.95 *(978-1-55876-544-3(1))* Wiener, Markus Pubs., Inc.

Njinkeu, Dominique & English, Philip. African Countries in the New Trade Negotiations: Interest, Options, & Challenges. 2007. *(978-1-59221-622-2(6))* Africa World Pr.

Obst, Michael. Ghan: Enhancing Competitiveness Through Performance-Based Payment. 2009. 196p. pap. *(978-3-639-11949-7(5))* VDM Verlag Dr. Mueller e.K.

Organization, World Trade. Trade Policy Review: Malawi 2010. 2010. (ENG.). pap. 75.00 *(978-1-59888-444-9(1))* Bernan Assocs.

—Trade Policy Review: The Gambia 2010. 2010. (ENG.). 136p. pap. 75.00 *(978-1-59888-453-1(0))* Bernan Assocs.

Panini, Augusto. Middle Eastern & Venetian Glass Beads: Eighth to Twentieth Centuries. 2008. (ENG., Illus.). 312p. 100.00 *(978-88-6130-164-1(9))* Skira Editore ITA. Dist: Random Hse., Inc.

Pollecoff, Eve A. Pioneer Merchant Trader: The Life & Times of Otto Markus. 2012. (ENG., Illus.). 224p. 55.00 ***(978-1-84885-937-1(6)***, Radcliffe Pr., The) I. B. Tauris & Co., Ltd. GBR. Dist: Macmillan.

Razafimahefa, Ivohasina Fizara & Hamori, Shigeyuki. International Competitiveness in Africa: Policy Implications in the Sub-Saharan Region. 2007. (Advanced Studies in Theoretical & Applied Econometrics Ser.). (Illus.). xii, 170p. 109.00 *(978-3-540-68920-1(6))* Springer.

Reuvid, Jonathan. Morocco: Emerging Economy of the Mediterranean - An Authoritative Investment Guide. Reuvid, Jonathan, ed. 2009. (ENG., Illus.). 372p. pap. 54.99 *(978-1-906558-18-5(3))* Legend Pr. GBR. Dist: Innovative Logistics.

Rockel, Stephen J. Carriers of Culture: Labor on the Road in Nineteenth-Century East Africa, 1 vol. 2006. (Social History of Africa Ser.). (Illus.). 368p. per. 41.25 *(978-0-325-07133-6(0)*, E07133) Heinemann.

Rockel, Stephen J., ed. Carriers of Culture: Labor on the Road in Nineteenth-Century East Africa, 1 vol. 2006. (Social History of Africa Ser.). (Illus.). 368p. 124.95 *(978-0-325-07116-9(0)*, E07116, Praeger Pubs.) Greenwood Publishing Group, Inc.

Salih, M. A. Mohamed, et al. African E-Markets: Information & Economic Development. Opoku-Mensah, Aida & Salih, M. A. Mohamed, eds. 2007. (ENG.). 224p. pap. 27.95 *(978-90-5727-059-8(5))* International Bks. NLD. Dist: Independent Pubs. Group.

Sardanis, Andrew. A Venture in Africa: The Challenges of African Business. 2007. (ENG., Illus.). 320p. 51.00 *(978-1-84511-288-2(1))* I. B. Tauris & Co., Ltd. GBR. Dist: Macmillan.

Sereke-Brhan, Heran. Coffee, Culture & Intellectual Property: Lessons for African from the Ethiopian Fine Coffee Initiative, no. 11. 2010. 37p. 0.00 *(978-0-9825683-5-4(5))* Boston Univ.

Shipton, Parker. The Nature of Entrustment: Intimacy, Exchange, & the Sacred in Africa. 2007. (Yale Agrarian Studies). (ENG., Illus.). 312p. 60.00 *(978-0-300-11601-4(2))* Yale Univ. Pr.

Sungau, Joseph. Cross Border Trade & People Living Standard in Rukwa Region Borders. 2011. 64p. pap. ***(978-3-8443-3264-3(2))*** Lambert Academic Publishing.

The African Development Bank, ed. African Development Report 2007. 2007. (African Development Report). (ENG., Illus.). 336p. pap. 45.00 *(978-0-19-923886-6(3))* Oxford Univ. Pr., Inc.

United States, Office of the U.S. Trade Representative Staff, contrib. by. African Growth & Opportunity Act: An Implementation Guide. 2006. 131p. (C). 125.00 *(978-1-60021-389-2(8))* Nova Science Pubs., Inc.

Watkins, Ron. Doing Business in Africa: Myths & Realities. 200p. pap. 15.95 *(978-0-9640480-0-3(0))* Heritage Publishing.

Whitehouse, Bruce. Migrants & Strangers in an African City. 2012. (Illus.). x, 274p. ***(978-0-253-00075-0(0))***; (ENG., 288p. pap. 25.00 *(978-0-253-00082-8(3)*, 0253000823) Indiana Univ. Pr.

Whitehouse, Bruce. Migrants & Strangers in an African City: Exile, Dignity, Belonging. 2012. (ENG., Illus.). 288p. 70.00 *(978-0-253-00081-1(5)*, 0253000815) Indiana Univ. Pr.

World Trade Organization Staff & Bernan Press Staff. Trade Policy Review: Southern African Customs Union (SACU) 2009. 2010. (ENG.). 528p. pap. 75.00 *(978-1-59888-372-5(0))* Bernan Assocs.

AFRICA—COMMERCIAL POLICY

Ajakaiye, David Olusanya & Oyejide, T. Ademola, eds. Trade Infrastructure & Economic Development. 2011. (Routledge Studies in Development Economics Ser.). (ENG., Illus.). 368p. (C). 155.00 *(978-0-415-66913-9(8))* Routledge.

Allen, Rory & United Nations Conference on Trade and Development Staff. Investment Policy Review: Nigeria. 2009. (ENG., Illus.). 152p. pap. 20.00 *(978-92-1-112743-0(2))* United Nations Pubns.

Bernan Press Staff & World Trade Organization Staff. Trade Policy Review: Niger/Senegal 2009. 2010. (ENG.). 300p. pap. 75.00 *(978-1-59888-381-7(X))* Bernan Assocs.

Bernan Press/ WTO Staff. Trade Policy Review: Benin, Burkina Faso, & Mali 2010. 2011. (ENG.). pap. 75.00 ***(978-1-59888-459-3(X))*** Bernan Assocs.

Burnett, Patrick & Manji, Firoze, eds. From the slave trade to 'free' Trade: How trade undermines democracy & justice in Africa. 2007. (ENG.). 180p. pap. 19.95 *(978-0-9545637-1-4(9))* Pambuzuka Pr. GBR. Dist: Independent Pubs. Group.

Draper, Alves, et al, eds. Trade Reform in Southern Africa: Vision 2014? 2010. (ENG.). 170p. pap. 20.00 *(978-1-920196-20-2(X))* Jacana Media ZAF. Dist: Independent Pubs. Group.

Laurent, Edwin, ed. Trade Policy for Parliamentarians: A Guide for Sub-Saharan Africa. 2012. (ENG.). 100p. pap. 24.95 *(978-1-84929-039-5(3))* Commonwealth Secretariat GBR. Dist: Stylus Publishing, LLC.

López-Cálix, José R. & Walkenhorst, Peter, eds. Trade Competitiveness of the Middle East & North Africa: Policies for Export Diversification. 2010. (Directions in Development Ser.). (ENG., Illus.). 364p. pap. 30.00 *(978-0-8213-8074-1(5)*, 9780821380741) World Bank Pubns.

Nzioka, Charles. Market Integration in Mozambican Maize Markets. 2008. 116p. pap. 19.95 *(978-99944-55-26-3(5))* African Bks. Collective, Ltd. GBR. Dist: Lightning Source, Inc.

Organization, World Trade. Trade Policy Review: Malawi 2010. 2010. (ENG.). pap. 75.00 *(978-1-59888-444-9(1))* Bernan Assocs.

—Trade Policy Review: The Gambia 2010. 2010. (ENG.). 136p. pap. 75.00 *(978-1-59888-453-1(0))* Bernan Assocs.

Simo Tumnde, Martha, et al. Unified Business Laws for Africa: Common Law Perspectives on OHADA. 2009. (ENG.). 148p. pap. 110.00 *(978-1-84673-150-1(X)*, GMB Publishing Ltd.) Blue Ibex Ltd. GBR. Dist: Ingram Pub. Services.

United Nations Conference on Trade and Development. Economic development in Africa 2008: Export performance following trade liberalization; some patterns & policy Perspectives. 2008. (ENG., Illus.). 112p. pap. 30.00 *(978-92-1-112754-6(8))* United Nations Pubns.

United Nations Conference on Trade and Development Staff, contrib. by. Investment Policy Review. 2010. (ENG., Illus.). 124p. pap. 27.00 ***(978-92-1-112785-0(6))*** United Nations Pubns.

World Trade Organization Staff & Bernan Press Staff. Trade Policy Review: Southern African Customs Union (SACU) 2009. 2010. (ENG.). 528p. pap. 75.00 *(978-1-59888-372-5(0))* Bernan Assocs.

AFRICA—DESCRIPTION AND TRAVEL

Africanus, Leo. The History & Description of Africa: And of the Notable Things Therein Contained. Brown, Robert, ed. Pory, John, tr. 2010. (Cambridge Library Collection - Travel & Exploration Ser.). (ENG.). 488p. pap. 35.99 *(978-1-108-01289-8(2))*; 436p. pap. 32.99 *(978-1-108-01290-4(6))*; (Illus.). 364p. pap. 29.99 *(978-1-108-01288-1(4))* Cambridge Univ. Pr.

Antonson, Rick. To Timbuktu for a Haircut: A Journey Through West Africa. 2008. (ENG., Illus.). 256p. pap. 26.99 *(978-1-55002-805-8(7)*, Dundurn Pr.) Dundurn CAN. Dist: Ingram Pub. Services.

Association for Promoting the Discovery of the Interior Parts of Africa. African Researches: Or, Proceedings of the Association for Promoting the Discovery of the Interior Parts of Africa. 2011. (Cambridge Library Collection - Travel & Exploration Ser.). (ENG., Illus.). 460p. pap. 34.99 ***(978-1-108-03267-4(2))*** Cambridge Univ. Pr.

Bagnold, Ralph A. Libyan Sands: Travel in a Dead World. 2011. (ENG., Illus.). 228p. pap. 29.95 *(978-1-906011-33-8(8))* Eland Bks. GBR. Dist: Dufour Editions, Inc.

Bailey, Adrian, photos by. Safari: Journeys Through Wild Africa. 2007. (Illus.). 223p. 43.00 *(978-1-77007-394-4(9))* Struik Pubs. ZAF. Dist: International Publishers Marketing.

Balfour Baikie, William. Narrative of an Exploring Voyage up the Rivers Kwo'Ra & Bi'Nue In 1854. 2007. 480p. per. *(978-1-905748-43-3(4))* Rediscovery Bks.

Banning, Emile. Africa & the Brussels Geographical Conference. 2010. 162p. pap. 27.95 *(978-1-4460-0693-1(X))* Audubon Pr. & Christian Bk. Service.

Baraza, Patrick Wanakuta. Drumming up Dialogue: The Dialogic Philosophies of Martin Buber, Fred Iklé, & William Ury Compared & Applied to the Babukusu Community of Kenya. 2011. 420p. pap. 26.95 ***(978-1-4620-1620-4(0))*** iUniverse, Inc.

Benezet, Anthony. Some Historical Account of Guinea. 2008. (Civil War Ser.). (ENG.). 160p. pap. 13.95 *(978-1-4290-1478-6(4))* Applewood Bks.

Berhanu, Kassahun. Returnees, Resettlement & Power Relations: The Making of a Political Constituency in Humera, Ethiopia. (Illus.). 251p. (C). pap. 46.50 *(978-90-5383-700-9(0))* VU Univ. Pr. NLD. Dist: Independent Pubs. Group.

Beryl Doiron With Bernie Doiron. Rusticoriders Cycle Afric: From Cairo to Cape Town. 2009. 208p. 29.95 *(978-1-4490-4970-6(2))* AuthorHouse.

Bieber, David, ed. The Accurate Reloading Africa Book: Tales of & Tips for Hunting the Dark Continent. 2007. pap. 25.00 *(978-0-9792818-0-8(6))* Bieber, David.

Blackwood, Yvonne. Into Afric: The Return. 2009. 184p. pap. 18.95 *(978-1-4269-0265-9(4))* Trafford Publishing.

Bold, Edward. The Merchant's & Mariner's African Guide: Containing an Accurate Description of the Coast, Bays, Harbours, & Adjacent Islands of West Africa. 2011. (Cambridge Library Collection - History Ser.). (ENG., Illus.). 138p. pap. 19.99 *(978-1-108-03066-3(1))* Cambridge Univ. Pr.

Boorman, Charley. Race to Dakar. (ENG., Illus.). 320p. 2008. 14.95 *(978-0-7515-3817-5(5))* 2006. pap. 24.95 *(978-0-316-02711-3(1))* Little, Brown Bk. Group Ltd. GBR. Dist: Independent Pubs. Group.

Boorman, Charley, et al. Race to Dakar. 2006. (ENG., Illus.). 320p. 34.95 *(978-0-316-73192-8(7))* Little, Brown Bk. Group Ltd. GBR. Dist: Independent Pubs. Group.

Bosman, William. A New & Accurate Description of the Coast of Guinea: Divided into the Gold, the Slave, & the Ivory Coasts. 2011. (Cambridge Library Collection - Travel & Exploration Ser.). (ENG., Illus.). 550p. pap. 39.99 ***(978-1-108-03125-7(0))*** Cambridge Univ. Pr.

Bradt, Hilary. Madagascar. 10th rev. ed. 2011. (Bradt Travel Guide Ser.). (ENG., Illus.). 448p. pap. 27.99 *(978-1-84162-341-2(5))* Bradt Travel Guides GBR. Dist: Globe Pequot Pr., The.

Briggs, Philip. Africa: Continent of Contrasts. 2007. (Illus.). 296p. 43.95 *(978-1-77007-087-5(7))* Struik Pubs. ZAF. Dist: International Publishers Marketing.

—Mozambique. 5th ed. 2011. (Bradt Travel Guide Ser.). (ENG., Illus.). 352p. pap. 24.99 *(978-1-84162-342-9(3))* Bradt Travel Guides GBR. Dist: Globe Pequot Pr., The.

Brown, Neville & Gutteridge, William Frank. Africa, Volume 1, 2 vols., Vol. 1. 2006. (Adelphi Papers). (Illus.). 393p. 275.00 *(978-0-415-39821-3(5))* Routledge.

Burke, Mark. Glimmers of Hope: Memoir of a Volunteer in Africa. 2010. 304p. pap. 15.98 *(978-0-557-11209-8(5))* Lulu Enterprises Inc.

Bursi, Steven. Alone in Africa: A Wife Hunting Safari. 2008. 516p. pap. 19.95 *(978-1-4327-2222-7(0))* Outskirts Pr., Inc.

Burton, Richard. First Footsteps in East Africa: Or, an Exploration of Harar. 2011. (Cambridge Library Collection - Travel & Exploration Ser.). (ENG., Illus.). 706p. pap. 48.00 *(978-1-108-03030-4(0))* Cambridge Univ. Pr.

Burton, Richard F. Abeokuta & the Camaroons Mountains: An Exploration. 2011. (Cambridge Library Collection - Travel & Exploration Ser.). (ENG.). 332p. pap. 29.99 *(978-1-108-03028-1(9))*; (Illus.). 358p. pap. 29.99 *(978-1-108-03027-4(0))* Cambridge Univ. Pr.

Butchart, Duncan. Wild about the Lowveld. (Illus.). 128p. pap. 14.95 *(978-1-86812-596-8(3))* Southern Bk. Pubs. ZAF. Dist: Continental Enterprises Group, Inc. (CEG).

Cameron, Verney Lovett. Across Africa. 2007. (ENG.). 576p. per. 43.95 *(978-1-4326-8055-8(2))* Kessinger Publishing, LLC.

Campbell, James T. Middle Passages: African American Journeys to Africa, 1787-2005. 2008. (ENG.). 513p. 30.00 *(978-1-4379-5107-3(4))* DIANE Publishing Co.

—Middle Passages: African American Journeys to Africa, 1787-2005. 2007. (ENG., Illus.). 544p. (gr. 12-18). 17.00 *(978-0-14-311198-6(1)*, Penguin (Non-Classics)) Penguin Group (USA) Inc.

Carruthers, Vincent. The Wildlife of Southern Africa: The Larger Illustrated Guide to the Animals & Plants of the Region. 2008. (Illus.). 320p. pap. 31.00 *(978-1-77007-199-5(7))* Struik Pubs. ZAF. Dist: International Publishers Marketing.

Cassidy, Shelley-Maree. Great Escapes Africa. Taschen, Angelika, ed. 25th ed. 2009. (FRE, GER & ENG., Illus.). 360p. pap. 19.99 *(978-3-8365-1499-6(0))* TASCHEN DEU. Dist: Ingram Pub. Services.

Chipman, John, et al. Africa, Volume 2, 2 vols. 2006. (Adelphi Papers). (Illus.). 472p. 275.00 *(978-0-415-39822-0(3))* Routledge.

Clark, Des. Mountaineering in the Moroccan High Atlas. 2011. 256p. pap. 24.95 *(978-1-85284-611-4(9))* Cicerone Pr. GBR. Dist: Midpoint Trade Bks., Inc.

Cobus Van Der Vlies. Southern Africa Wildlife & Adventure. 2010. 204p. pap. 55.49 *(978-1-4269-1932-9(8))* Trafford Publishing.

Colley, Linda. The Ordeal of Elizabeth Marsh: A Woman in World History. 2008. (ENG., Illus.). 400p. pap. 16.95 *(978-0-385-72149-3(8)*, Anchor) Knopf Doubleday Publishing Group.

Copeland, Mike. Getaway Guide to Mozambique. 2009. (Illus.). 208p. pap. 17.95 *(978-1-919938-30-1(3))* International Publishers Marketing.

Copeland, Mike. Getaway Guide to Mozambique: 2nd Edition. 2011. (Illus.). 192p. pap. 23.00 ***(978-1-920289-09-6(7))*** Ball, Jonathan Pubs. ZAF. Dist: International Publishers Marketing.

Crowley, Lawrence. A Young Falconer's Walkabout: Hitchhiking Through Europe & Africa in the Sixties. 2010. 272p. 34.95 ***(978-0-88839-666-2(X))*** Hancock Hse. Pubs.

Crowther, Samuel. Journal of an Expedition up the Niger & Tshadda Rivers: Undertaken by Macgregor Laird, Esq. in Connection with the British Government, in 1854. 2010. (Cambridge Library Collection - Religion Ser.). (Illus.). 268p. pap. 23.99 *(978-1-108-01183-9(7))* Cambridge Univ. Pr.

Davis, Richard Harding. The Congo & Coasts of Africa. 2008. 148p. 24.99 *(978-0-554-29405-6(2))* 2007. (ENG.). 132p. per. 18.99 *(978-1-4346-7568-2(8))* 2007. (ENG.). 144p. per. 19.99 *(978-1-4346-7569-9(6))* BiblioBazaar.

—Congo & Coasts of Africa Illustrated E. 2006. pap. *(978-1-4065-1141-3(2))* Dodo Pr.

De Lope, Manuel. Jardines de Africa. (SPA.). 92p. pap. 5.95 *(978-84-204-8041-1(X))* Alfaguara, Ediciones, S.A.- Grupo Santillana ESP. Dist: Santillana USA Publishing Co., Inc.

Doerr, Ralph. Habari Safari. 2009. 212p. 26.99 *(978-1-4490-2282-2(0))*; pap. 17.49 *(978-1-4490-2278-5(2))* AuthorHouse.

Doiron, Beryl & Doiron, Bernie. Rusticoriders Cycle Afric: From Cairo to Cape Town. 2009. 208p. pap. 21.95 *(978-1-4490-4971-3(0))* AuthorHouse.

Du Bois, W. E. B. Africa, Its Geography, People, & Products: And, Africa, Its Place in Modern History. 2007. *(978-0-19-532580-5(X))* Oxford Univ. Pr., Inc.

Duncan, Nancy. The Nail That Sticks Up: An American Woman in Asia & Africa. 2007. 436p. per. 29.95 *(978-1-4241-7539-0(9))* PublishAmerica, Inc.

Eglin, Lorna. Missionary Stories on Safari. 2010. (ENG., Illus.). 176p. mass mkt. 9.99 *(978-1-84550-505-9(0))* Christian Focus Pubns. GBR. Dist: STL Distribution North America.

Fleminger, David. Lesotho. 2010. (Illus.). 176p. pap. 19.95 *(978-1-920143-26-8(2))* 30° South Pubs. ZAF. Dist: International Publishers Marketing.

Fletcher, Allen W. Heat, Sand & Friends. 2009. (ENG., Illus.). 158p. pap. 15.00 net. *(978-0-615-28598-6(8))* Worcester Publishing Ltd.

Garcetti, Gil. Water Is Key: A Better Future for Africa. 2007. (ENG., Illus.). 112p. 65.00 *(978-1-890449-45-2(8))* Balcony Pr.

Geldof, Bob. Geldof in Africa. 2007. (ENG., Illus.). 304p. pap. 16.95 *(978-0-09-949796-7(4)*, Arrow Bks., Ltd.) Random Hse. GBR. Dist: Independent Pubs. Group.

Geuka, Amefika. Reflections on My Pilgrimage: A Conscious Black Son of Africa returns to his Motherland. 2006. per. 9.95 *(978-0-9787394-2-3(6))* Protective Hands Communications.

Gibbons, Bob & Pritchard-Jones, Siân. Africa Overland, 5th: 4x4, Motorbike, Bicycle, Truck. 5th rev. ed. 2009. (ENG., Illus.). 320p. pap. 25.99 *(978-1-84162-283-5(4))* Bradt Travel Guides GBR. Dist: Globe Pequot Pr., The.

Goltz, Thomas. Assassinating Shakespeare: The True Confessions of a Bard in the Bush. 2006. (ENG., Illus.). 256p. per. 19.95 *(978-0-86356-718-6(5))* Saqi Bks. GBR. Dist: Consortium Bk. Sales & Distribution.

Grogan, Ewart S. & Sharp, Arthur H. From the Cape to Cairo: The First Traverse of Africa from South to North. 2007. (ENG.). 400p. 49.95 *(978-0-548-26663-2(8))*; per. 34.95 *(978-1-4326-7100-6(6))* Kessinger Publishing, LLC.

Hammond, Dorothy & Jablow, Alta. The Myth of Africa. 2012. 45.95 *(978-0-915042-03-6(7))* Library of Social Science.

Hank Wagner. Teachable Moments: Lessons from Africa. 2009. 124p. pap. 13.95 *(978-1-4401-9077-3(1))* iUniverse, Inc.

Haugen, David M., ed. Africa. 2008. (Opposing Viewpoints Ser.). (ENG., Illus.). 219p. (YA). (gr. 7-12). 27.50 *(978-0-7377-3989-3(4)*, LML02109-239957); pap. 39.70 *(978-0-7377-3988-6(6)*, LML02109-239949) Cengage Gale. (Greenhaven Pr., Inc.).

Hayes, Margaret Ann. Safarini- Many Journeys. 2007. (Illus.). 272p. 35.00 *(978-1-4251-2679-7(0))* Trafford Publishing.

Hepner, Tricia Redeker & O'Kane, David, eds. Biopolitics, Militarism, & Development: Eritrea in the Twenty-First Century. 2011. (DISL Ser.). 236p. 25.00 *(978-0-85745-289-4(4))* Berghahn Bks., Inc.

Hilton-Barber, Bridget. Travel Guide to Maputo & Southern Mozambique. 2012. (ENG., Illus.). 200p. (gr. 12). pap. 23.95 ***(978-0-14-352830-2(0))***, Penguin Global) Penguin Group (USA) Inc.

Hoare, Mike. Mike Hoare's Adventures in Africa. 2010. (Illus.). 226p. pap. 24.95 *(978-1-58160-732-1(6))* Paladin Pr.

Hoberman, Gerald. Wildlife of Africa. 2009. (Meridian Ser. - an imprint of the Hoberman Collection: Wildlife of Africa Ser.). (Illus.). 64p. 9.95 *(978-1-919939-47-6(4))* Hoberman, Gerald Pubns. ZAF. Dist: Perseus Bks. Group.

Hoberman, Gerald, photos by. Wildlife of Africa. 2010. (ENG.). 64p. 18.95 *(978-1-919939-61-2(X))* Hoberman, Gerald Pubns. ZAF. Dist: Perseus Distribution.

Holgate, Kingsley. Africa: In the Footsteps of the Great Explorers. 2006. (Illus.). 304p. 29.00 *(978-1-77007-147-6(4))* Struik Pubs. ZAF. Dist: International Publishers Marketing.

Huynh, Jean-Baptiste. Mali. 2006. (ENG & FRE., Illus.). *(978-88-7439-078-6(5))* 5 Continents.

Jackson, Bertha. Africa-A Pre-Trip Must! 2007. 64p. per. 9.99 *(978-1-60266-920-8(1))* Xulon Pr., Inc.

Jameson, Robert, et al. Narrative of Discovery & Adventure in Africa: From the Earliest Ages to the Present Time. 2007. (ENG.). 528p. per. 40.95 *(978-0-548-28663-0(9))* Kessinger Publishing, LLC.

Javins, Marie. Stalking the Wild Dik-Dik: One Woman's Solo Misadventures Across Africa. 2006. (ENG., Illus.). 288p. per. 15.95 *(978-1-58005-164-4(2))* Seal Pr.

Joubert, Dereck. Eye of the Leopard. 2009. (Illus.). 208p. 75.00 *(978-0-8478-3322-1(4))* Rizzoli International Pubns., Inc.

Khumalo, Sihle. Dark Continent, My Black Arse. 2010. 224p. pap. 18.00 *(978-1-4152-0036-0(X))* Random Hse. Struik (Pty.), Ltd. ZAF. Dist: International Publishers Marketing.

Kilgo, James. Colors of Africa. 2007. (Brown Thrasher Books Ser.). (ENG., Illus.). 224p. per. 19.95 *(978-0-8203-3017-4(5))* Univ. of Georgia Pr.

Kinvig, Noel. Beyond the Cabbage Tree. 2009. (Illus.). 240p. pap. 60.99 *(978-1-4490-1575-6(1))* AuthorHouse.

Knight, James & Manson, Katrina. Burkina Faso Bradt. 2nd rev. ed. 2012. (ENG., Illus.). 320p. pap. 25.99 *(978-1-84162-352-8(0))* Bradt Travel Guides GBR. Dist: Globe Pequot Pr., The.

Knight, Richard & Parmer, Alan. Moroccan Atlas. 2nd ed. 2011. (ENG., Illus.). 272p. pap. 22.95 *(978-1-873756-77-5(1))* Trailblazer Pubns. GBR. Dist: Globe Pequot Pr., The.

Koivunen, Leila. Visualizing Africa in Nineteenth-Century British Travel Accounts. (ENG., Illus.). (C). 2011. 350p. pap. 42.95 ***(978-0-415-69962-4(2))*** 2008. 368p. 125.00 *(978-0-415-99001-1(7))* Routledge.

Krakowiak, Fred. Africa: An Artist's Safari. 2007. (Illus.). 133p. 39.95 *(978-0-9787084-0-5(7))* Maverick Brush Strokes.

KuF Afrika 1: 12 000 000. Politische Karte: Mit Zeitzonen, Klimadiagramm und Flaggen. Deutsch, englisch, französisch, italienisch, Vol. 2. pap. 8.55 *(978-92-2-001667-1(2)*, ILO251) Bernan Assocs.

KuF Afrika 1: 12 000 000. Politische Karte: Mit Zeitzonen, Klimadiagramm und Flaggen. Deutsch, englisch, französisch, italienisch. tchr. ed. 41.95 *(978-0-382-44542-2(2))* Cobblestone Publishing Co.

KuF Afrika 1: 12 000 000. Politische Karte: Mit Zeitzonen, Klimadiagramm und Flaggen. Deutsch, englisch, französisch, italienisch. pap. 11.95 *(978-3-8283-0093-4(6))* Hallwag Verlag GmbH DEU. Dist: Rand McNally.

Lester, Rhoda Namwalizi. Cassava Is the Root. 2007. 115p. pap. 27.48 *(978-1-4116-7113-3(9))* Lulu Enterprises Inc.

Levitov, Betty. Africa on Six Wheels: A Semester on Safari. 2007. (ENG., Illus.). 184p. pap. 17.95 *(978-0-8032-8054-0(8)*, Bison Bks.) Univ. of Nebraska Pr.

Leyden, John. A Historical & Philosophical Sketch of the Discoveries & Settlements of the Europeans in Northern & Western Africa, at the Close of the Eighteenth Century. 2011. (Cambridge Library Collection - History Ser.). (ENG.). 434p. pap. 34.99 ***(978-1-108-03248-3(6))*** Cambridge Univ. Pr.

Lifshitz, Fima. An African Journey Through Its Art. 2009. 236p. pap. 75.99 *(978-1-4389-3450-1(5))* AuthorHouse.

Locken, E. Travel Journal Africa. 2009. 192p. pap. 20.95 *(978-0-557-08018-2(5))* Lulu Enterprises Inc.

—Travel Journal Angola. 2009. 192p. pap. 20.95 *(978-0-557-08821-8(6))* Lulu Enterprises Inc.

—Travel Journal Burundi. 2010. 192p. pap. 19.99 *(978-0-557-43281-3(2))* Lulu Enterprises Inc.

—Travel Journal Comoros. 2010. 192p. pap. 19.99 *(978-0-557-43458-9(0))* Lulu Enterprises Inc.

—Travel Journal Djibouti. 2010. 192p. pap. 19.99 *(978-0-557-43465-7(3))* Lulu Enterprises Inc.

—Travel Journal Malawi. 2010. 192p. pap. 19.99 *(978-0-557-43660-6(5))* Lulu Enterprises Inc.

—Travel Journal Mozambique. 2010. 192p. pap. 19.99 *(978-0-557-43676-7(1))* Lulu Enterprises Inc.

Lonely Planet Staff. Africa. 2nd rev. ed. 2008. (Healthy Travel Ser.). (ENG., Illus.). 440p. pap. 8.99 *(978-1-74059-143-0(7))* Lonely Planet Pubns.

Lonely Planet Staff & Fitzpatrick, Mary. Mozambique. 3rd ed. 2010. (Country Guide Ser.). (ENG., Illus.). 216p. pap. 25.99 *(978-1-74104-888-9(5))* Lonely Planet Pubns.

Lonely Planet Staff, et al. Africa. 12th ed. 2010. (Multi Country Guide Ser.). (ENG., Illus.). 1184p. pap. 36.99 *(978-1-74104-988-6(1))* Lonely Planet Pubns.

Lundy, Mike. Scenic Day Drives from Cape Town. 2011. 128p. pap. 21.95 *(978-0-7981-5119-1(6))* NB Pubs. Ltd. ZAF. Dist: International Publishers Marketing.

Luxton, James. Ecotourism & Island Ecology. 2010. 100p. pap. *(978-3-639-22745-1(X))* VDM Verlag Dr. Mueller e.K.

Maas, Deon. Witboy in Africa: Diary of a Troublemaker. 2010. 224p. pap. 23.95 *(978-0-624-04833-6(0))* NB Pubs. Ltd. ZAF. Dist: International Publishers Marketing.

—Witboy in Afrika. 2010. 224p. pap. 23.95 *(978-0-624-04778-0(4))* NB Pubs. Ltd. ZAF. Dist: International Publishers Marketing.

MacQueen, James. A Geographical Survey of Africa: Its Rivers, Lakes, Mountains, Productions, States, Population, Etc. 2011. (Cambridge Library Collection - Travel & Exploration Ser.). (ENG., Illus.). 432p. pap. 34.99 ***(978-1-108-03126-4(9))*** Cambridge Univ. Pr.

Magan, Manchan. Truck Fever: A Journey Through Africa. 2009. (ENG., Illus.). 278p. pap. 25.95 *(978-0-86322-389-1(3))* Brandon/Mount Eagle Pubns., Ltd. IRL. Dist: Dufour Editions, Inc.

Main, Mike. African Adventure's Guide: Botswana. 2011. 320p. pap. 24.95 *(978-1-77007-885-7(1))* Random Hse. Struik (Pty.), Ltd. ZAF. Dist: International Publishers Marketing.

Maitland, Alexander. Wilfred Thesiger in Africa: A Unique Collection of Essays & Personal Photographs. Morton, Chris & Grover, Philip, eds. 2010. (ENG., Illus.). 256p. 34.95 *(978-0-00-732524-5(X))* HarperCollins Pubs. Ltd. GBR. Dist: Independent Pubs. Group.

Manser, Riaan. Around Africa on my Bicycle. 2nd ed. 2009. 716p. pap. 18.00 *(978-1-86842-351-4(4))* Ball, Jonathan Pubs. ZAF. Dist: International Publishers Marketing.

—Around Africa on My Bike. 2009. 716p. pap. 23.95 *(978-1-86842-247-0(X))* International Publishers Marketing.

Marais, Jacques. Great African Adventures. 2008. (Illus.). 224p. pap. 25.00 *(978-1-77007-279-4(9))* Struik Pubs. ZAF. Dist: International Publishers Marketing.

Marryat, Frederick. The Mission or Scenes in Africa. 2006. (ENG.). 290p. pap. 21.99 *(978-1-4264-6895-7(4))*; 322p. pap. 24.99 *(978-1-4264-6977-0(2))* BiblioBazaar.

Matz, Peter. Lost in Transformation: Two years in Angola. 2008. 164p. pap. *(978-3-8334-7544-3(7))* Books on Demand GmbH.

Maurel, Martine. Mauritius. 4th ed. (Illus.). 128p. pap. 10.95 *(978-1-84330-840-9(1))* New Holland Pubs., Ltd. GBR. Dist: Globe Pequot Pr., The.

Mcelroy, C. J. African Safari of an Amateur Hunter. 2011. 82p. 37.95 ***(978-1-258-04062-8(X))*** Literary Licensing, LLC.

McGregor, Ewan & Boorman, Charley. Long Way Down: An African Adventure. 2009. (ENG., Illus.). 288p. 40.00 *(978-1-84744-249-9(8))* Little, Brown Bk. Group Ltd. GBR. Dist: Independent Pubs. Group.

—Long Way Down: An Epic Journey by Motorcycle from Scotland to South Africa. 2009. (ENG., Illus.). 352p. pap. 17.00 *(978-1-4165-7746-1(7)*, Beyond Words/Atria Bks.) Atria Bks.

McIntyre, Chris. Namibia/4 Bradt. 4th rev. ed. 2011. (Bradt Travel Guide Ser.). (ENG., Illus.). 560p. pap. 26.99 *(978-1-84162-335-1(0))* Bradt Travel Guides GBR. Dist: Globe Pequot Pr., The.

Mirandette, Erik. The Only Road North: 9,000 Miles of Dirt & Dreams, 1 vol. 2007. (ENG., Illus.). 304p. (gr. 13). pap. 12.99 *(978-0-310-27435-3(4))* Zondervan.

Montgomery, Denis. The Reflected Face of Africa. 2009. (ENG.). 496p. pap. 38.95 *(978-0-557-04055-1(8))* Lulu Enterprises Inc.

Moore, Peter. Swahili for broken Hearted. 2009. (ENG.). 320p. pap. 14.95 *(978-1-933572-06-2(X))* Centro Bks., LLC.

Murray, Martyn. The Storm Leopard. 2010. (ENG., Illus.). 272p. pap. *(978-1-84995-004-6(0))* Whittles Publishing.

Museyon Guides, ed. Film + Travel Asia, Oceania, Africa: Traveling the World Through Your Favorite Movies. 2009. (Film+ Ser.). (ENG., Illus.). 164p. pap. 15.95 *(978-0-9822320-1-9(2))* Museyon Inc.

Naipaul, V. S. The Masque of Africa: Glimpses of African Belief. (Vintage International Ser.). (ENG.). 256p. 2011. pap. 16.00 *(978-0-307-45499-7(1)*, Vintage) 2010. 26.95 *(978-0-307-27073-3(4)*, Knopf) Knopf Doubleday Publishing Group.

New, Jennifer & Eldon, Kathy. Dan Eldon: Safari as a Way of Life. 2011. (ENG., Illus.). 208p. (YA). (gr. 7-17). 24.99 *(978-0-8118-7091-7(X))* Chronicle Bks. LLC.

Ngowi, Epaphra P. M. Travellers Highlights: Setswana - Swahili - English Translations. 2011. 92p. pap. 17.24 ***(978-1-4567-8050-0(6))*** AuthorHouse.

Ngwa (Eds), Lydia and Wilfred. From Dust to Snow: the African Dream? 2006. 313p. pap. 20.52 *(978-0-615-13703-2(2))* African Renaissance Ambassador Corp.

Nolting, Mark W. African Safari Journal. 5th ed. 2008. (African Safari Journal Ser.). (ENG., Illus.). 320p. pap. 19.95 *(978-0-939895-11-3(0))* Global Travel Pubs., Inc.

—Africa's Top Wildlife Countries: Botswana, Kenya, Namibia, Rwanda, South Africa, Tanzania, Uganda, Zambia & Zimbabwe. 7th ed. 2008. (ENG., Illus.). 640p. pap. 29.95 *(978-0-939895-12-0(9))* Global Travel Pubs., Inc.

Ogbuji, Linus T. Seeing the World in Black & White. 2006. x, 239p. *(978-1-59221-486-0(X))* Africa World Pr.

Ondaatje, Christopher. Journey to the Source of the Nile. 2006. 388p. per. 19.99 *(978-1-59048-225-4(5))* Long Riders' Guild Pr., The.

Orford, Catja. Tracking Bubu: Or, How Threats of Disinheritance Caused Me to Set off for the Jungle in Search of Happiness, Gorillas & Perhaps a Husband. 2008. (ENG.). 196p. pap. 28.95 *(978-1-77009-238-9(2))* Jacana Media ZAF. Dist: Independent Pubs. Group.

O'Shea, Barbara. Postcards from Elsewhere: Travels in a Changing World. 2008. (ENG.). 320p. pap. *(978-1-903582-58-9(X))* Merlin Publishing, Dublin.

Overton, Cleve & Andreasen, Jude. The Doors of Senegal: Les Portes du Senegal. 2007. per. 16.95 *(978-0-9772393-1-3(4))* Diaspora Voices Pr.

Park, Mungo. The Journal of a Mission to the Interior of Africa,1805. 2007. 172p. per. *(978-1-84702-388-9(6))* Echo Library.

—Life & Travels of Mungo Park in Centra. 2006. pap. *(978-1-84702-391-9(6))* Echo Library.

—Travels in the Interior of Africa. 2007. (ENG.). 224p. per. *(978-1-4065-4085-7(4))* Dodo Pr.

—Travels in the Interior of Africa Two V. 2006. pap. *(978-1-84702-389-6(4))* Echo Library.

Patton, Gerald R. African Detour. 2011. 168p. 41.95 ***(978-1-258-06392-4(1))*** Literary Licensing, LLC.

Penfield, Marc. Horoscopes of Afric. 2009. 178p. pap. 23.95 *(978-0-86690-591-6(X))* American Federation of Astrologers, Inc.

Pickford, Peter & Pickford, Beverly. African Safari: Into the Great Game Reserves. 2011th ed. 2011. 300p. 49.95 ***(978-1-906780-44-9(7))*** Beaufoy, John Publishing GBR. Dist: Midpoint Trade Bks., Inc.

Poliza, Michael. Eyes over Africa. 2007. 408p. 125.00 *(978-3-8327-9209-1(0))* teNeues Publishing Co.

Poliza, Michael, photos by. Africa. 2006. (ENG, FRE, GER, SPA & ITA., Illus.). 408p. 125.00 *(978-3-8327-9127-8(2))*; 435.00 *(978-3-8327-9167-4(1))* teNeues Publishing Co.

Poussin, Alexandre & Poussin, Sonia. Africa Trek I: From the Cape of Good Hope to Mount Kilimanjaro. 2008. (Illus.). 496p. pap. 27.95 *(978-1-59299-357-4(5))* Inkwater Pr.

—Africa Trek II: From Mount Kilimanjaro to the Sea of Galilee. 2008. 672p. pap. 29.95 *(978-1-59299-358-1(3))* Inkwater Pr.

Powys, Llewelyn. Ebony & Ivory. 2007. (ENG.). 224p. 39.95 *(978-0-548-03990-8(9))* Kessinger Publishing, LLC.

Ramathal, Dorothy Charulata. A Continent Found: Memoirs of a Quarter Century in Africa, 1 vol. 2010. 63p. pap. 16.95 *(978-1-4489-7691-1(X))* PublishAmerica, Inc.

Rattray, Gordon. Access Africa: Safaris for People with Limited Mobility. 2009. (ENG., Illus.). 256p. pap. 24.99 *(978-1-84162-286-6(9))* Bradt Travel Guides GBR. Dist: Globe Pequot Pr., The.

Robbins, Sarah, et al. Nellie Arnott's Writings on Angola, 1905-1913: Missionary Narratives Linking Africa & America. 2010. *(978-1-60235-142-4(2))*; pap. *(978-1-60235-141-7(4))* Parlor Pr.

Roosevelt, Theodore. African Game Trails: An Account of the African Wanderings of an American Hunter-Naturalist. 2009. (ENG.). 529p. 49.95 *(978-1-57157-331-5(3))* Safari Pr., Inc.

Rough Guides Staff. The Rough Guide First-Time Africa 2. 2nd ed. 2011. (ENG., Illus.). 432p. 18.99 *(978-1-84836-481-3(4))* Rough Guides, Ltd. GBR. Dist: Dorling Kindersley Publishing, Inc.

Samson, Lisa & Samson, Ty. Love Mercy: A Mother & Daughter's Journey from the American Dream to the Kingdom of God, 1 vol. 2010. (ENG.). 176p. pap. 14.99 *(978-0-310-28477-2(5))* Zondervan.

Sandham, Fran. Traversa. 2009. (ENG., Illus.). 288p. (gr. 12). pap. 15.95 *(978-1-59020-164-0(7))* Overlook Pr., The.

—Traversa: A Solo Walk Across Africa, from the Skeleton Coast to the Indian Ocean. 2008. (ENG., Illus.). 320p. (gr. 12). 25.00 *(978-1-59020-036-0(5))* Overlook Pr., The.

Schaller, George B. The Year of the Gorilla. 2010. (ENG., Illus.). 290p. pap. 25.00 *(978-0-226-73647-1(4))* Univ. of Chicago Pr.

Schoeman, Amy. Skeleton Coast. 3rd ed. (Illus.). 176p. 27.95 *(978-1-86812-593-7(9))* Southern Bk. Pubs. ZAF. Dist: Continental Enterprises Group, Inc. (CEG).

Schramm, Katharina. African Homecoming: Pan-African Ideology & Contested Heritage. 2010. (Critical Cultural Heritage Ser.). (ENG., Illus.). 320p. 89.00 *(978-1-59874-513-9(1))*; pap. 36.95 *(978-1-59874-514-6(X))* Left Coast Pr., Inc.

Scott, Chris. Overlanders' Handbook: Worldwide Route & Planning Guide - Car, 4wd, Van, Truck. 2011. (ENG., Illus.). 672p. 39.95 *(978-1-905864-07-2(8))* Trailblazer Pubns. GBR. Dist: Globe Pequot Pr., The.

Shay, Don. Endangered Liaisons. 2008. (Illus.). 320p. 60.00 *(978-0-615-21345-3(6))* Alarus Pr.

Shields, Bobby J. Safari Winds: A Whitetail Deer Hunter's First Safari. 2008. 170p. pap. 24.95 *(978-1-60563-304-6(6))* PublishAmerica, Inc.

Skoda, Cp. Ogad: An African Passage. 2008. 336p. 42.49 *(978-1-4389-1261-5(7))*; pap. 26.99 *(978-1-4389-1260-8(9))* AuthorHouse.

Smith, Julian. Crossing the Heart of Africa: An Odyssey of Love & Adventure. 2010. (ENG.). 344p. pap. 14.99 *(978-0-06-187347-8(0)*, HarperPerennial) HarperCollins Pubs.

Souchon, Duncan. Mountains of Africa. 2008. (Illus.). 192p. 31.00 *(978-1-77007-218-3(7))* Struik Pubs. ZAF. Dist: International Publishers Marketing.

Speke, John Hanning. What Led to the Discovery of the Source. 2006. pap. *(978-1-4068-3009-5(7))* Echo Library.

—What Led to the Discovery of the Source of the Nile. 2008. 292p. 25.99 *(978-0-554-32045-8(2))* 2008. 292p. 28.99 *(978-0-554-22742-9(8))* 2007. (ENG.). 258p. pap. 21.99 *(978-1-4264-2934-7(7))* 2006. 288p. pap. 23.99 *(978-1-4264-2987-3(8))* BiblioBazaar.

—What Led to the Discovery of the Source of the Nile. 2009. 186p. pap. *(978-0-217-42054-9(0))* Books LLC.

—What Led to the Discovery of the Source of the Nile. 2009. (ENG.). 236p. pap. 15.95 *(978-1-4385-1760-5(2)*, Book Jungle) Standard Pubns., Inc.

Street, Donald M. Street's Guide to the Cape Verde Islands. 2011. pap. ***(978-1-892399-34-2(2))*** Seaworthy Pubns., Inc.

Streissguth, Thomas. Mozambique in Pictures. 2009. (Visual Geography Series, Second Ser.). (gr. 5-12). 30.60 *(978-1-57505-954-9(1))* Lerner Publishing Group.

Sullivan, James L. Gypsy on a Jet. 2008. 300p. per. 18.95 *(978-0-9798633-9-4(2))* Robertson Publishing.

Swan, G. P., et al. Hunting Africa: A Practical Guide. 2nd ed. 2009. (Illus.). 372p. pap. 30.95 *(978-1-919938-70-7(2))* International Publishers Marketing.

Taieb. Chroniques Abidjanes. (FRE.). 128p. *(978-2-907888-60-8(9))* Sepia, Editions.

Terrail, creator. Africa/Afrique Kharakter. 2006. (FRE & ENG., Illus.). 195p. pap. 23.50 *(978-2-87939-308-7(6))* Terrail, Pierre Editions FRA. Dist: Perseus-PGW.

Thompson, J. Lee. Theodore Roosevelt Abroad: Nature, Empire, & the Journey of an American President. 2010. (ENG., Illus.). 236p. 37.00 *(978-0-230-10277-4(8))* Palgrave Macmillan.

Tinker, Irene. Crossing Centuries: A Road Trip Through Colonial Africa. 2010. (ENG.). 544p. pap. 29.95 *(978-1-59299-471-7(7))* Inkwater Pr.

Toorawa, Shawkat, ed. The Western Indian Ocean: Essays on Islands & Islanders. 2012. (ENG., Illus.). 149p. (C). pap. 22.95 *(978-99949-22-32-1(7))* Hassam Toorawa Trust, The.

Travels, Tj. Visit the African Continent: Know the facts & figures of the african Countries. 2011. 88p. pap. 34.48 ***(978-1-4567-8712-7(8))*** AuthorHouse.

Tuthill, Cynthia Wales. Letters from Afric: Travel Stories from an Adventuresome Soul. 2008. 232p. pap. 18.95 *(978-0-595-53123-3(7))* iUniverse, Inc.

Vande weghe, Jean Pierre. Loango, Mayumba et le bas Ogooue. 2007. (FRE.). per. 40.00 *(978-0-9792418-1-9(2))* Wildlife Conservation Society.

Von Lossberg, Ann. 1089 Nights: An Odyssey Through the Middle East, Africa & Asia. 2008. 316p. pap. 18.95 *(978-1-4401-0520-3(0))* iUniverse, Inc.

Waring, Rob. A Disappearing World. 2008. (ENG.). 24p. (C). pap. 10.95 *(978-1-4240-4406-1(5))* Cengage Heinle.

—The Missing Snows of Kilimanjaro (US) 2008. (ENG.). 24p. (C). pap. 10.95 *(978-1-4240-4459-7(6))* Cengage Heinle.

Weis, Janet. Tourific: Travels in Asia, Africa, & Europe. 2007. 160p. 25.00 *(978-0-8387-5695-9(6))* Bucknell Univ. Pr.

West. Cameroon/3 Bradt. 3rd rev. ed. 2011. (ENG., Illus.). 272p. pap. 25.99 *(978-1-84162-353-5(9))* Bradt Travel Guides GBR. Dist: Globe Pequot Pr., The.

Whelan, Alan. African Brew Ha Ha. 2010. (ENG., Illus.). 352p. pap. 14.95 ***(978-1-84953-044-6(0))*** Summerdale Pubs. GBR. Dist: Independent Pubs. Group.

Wicksteed, Julian. A CATCH on AFRICA - an Angler's Walkabout Adventure. 2008. 421p. pap. 29.85 *(978-1-4092-0527-2(4))* Lulu Enterprises Inc.

Williams, Lizzie. Zimbabwe: Travel Guide to Zimbabwe. 2011. (Footprint - Handbooks Ser.). (ENG., Illus.). 282p. instr.'s hndbk. ed. 24.95 *(978-1-907263-21-7(7))* Footprint Handbooks GBR. Dist: Globe Pequot Pr., The.

Wilson, Steve. Short Way Up: A Classic Ride Through Southern Africa - 5,000 Solo Miles on a 1950s Ariel. 2011. (ENG., Illus.). 256p. 32.95 *(978-1-84425-685-3(5)*, 1844256855) Haynes Publishing PLC GBR. Dist: MBI Distribution Services/Quayside Distribution.

Witherby, Harry F. Bird Hunting on the White Nile - a Naturalist's Experience in the Soudan. 2009. 116p. pap. 26.45 *(978-1-4437-8791-8(4))* Harrison House Pubs.

Wolf, Vicente. Crossing Boundaries: A Global Vision of Design. 2006. (ENG., Illus.). 232p. 50.00 *(978-1-58093-181-6(2))* Monacelli Pr., Inc.

Wood, Adrian, ed. KuF Afrika 1: 12 000 000. Politische Karte: Mit Zeitzonen, Klimadiagramm und Flaggen. Deutsch, englisch, französisch, italienisch. 2009. (Sustainable Development Set Ser.). (ENG.). 228p. 110.00 *(978-1-84407-940-7(6))* Routledge.

AFRICA—DISCOVERY AND EXPLORATION

Baker, Samuel W. Albert N'yanzu: Great Basins of the Nile & Explorations of the Nile Sources, 2 vols. reprint ed. 79.00 *(978-0-7812-0732-4(0))* Reprint Services Co.

Beals, Herbert K., et al, eds. Four Travel Journals: The Americas, Antarctica & Africa, 1775-1874. 2008. (Hakluyt Society, Third Series: 18 Ser.). (Illus.). 414p. 99.95 *(978-0-904180-90-9(5))* Hakluyt Society GBR. Dist: Ashgate Publishing Co.

Betz, Richard L. The Mapping of Africa: A Cartobibliography of Printed Maps of the African Continent to 1700. 2007. (Illus.). 540p. 235.00 *(978-90-6194-489-8(9))* HES & DE GRAAF Pubs. BV NLD. Dist: Oak Knoll Pr.

Blake, John W. Europeans in West Africa 14501560. 2006. 288p. per. *(978-1-4067-2889-7(6)*, Hesperides Pr.) Read Bks.

Blake, John William, ed. Europeans in West Africa 1540-1560: Documents to Illustrate the Nature & Scope of Portuguese Enterprise in West Africa the Abortive Attempt to Castilians to Create an Empire There. 2010. (Hakluyt Society, Second Ser.). 506p. 120.00 *(978-1-4094-2486-4(3))* Hakluyt Society GBR. Dist: Ashgate Publishing Co.

—Europeans in West Africa 1540-1560 Documents to Illustrate the Nature & Scope of Portuguese Enterprise. 2010. (Hakluyt Society, Second Ser.). 224p. 69.95 *(978-1-4094-1454-4(X))*; 282p. 69.95 *(978-1-4094-1453-7(1))* Hakluyt Society GBR. Dist: Ashgate Publishing Co.

Bovill, E. W., ed. Missions to the Niger. 2010. (Hakluyt Society, Second Ser.). 948p. 240.00 *(978-1-4094-2494-9(4))* Hakluyt Society GBR. Dist: Ashgate Publishing Co.

—Missions to the Niger: The Bornu Mission 1822-25. 2010. (Hakluyt Society, Second Ser.). 210p. 69.95 *(978-1-4094-1496-4(5))*; 320p. 69.95 *(978-1-4094-1494-0(9))*; 336p. 69.95 *(978-1-4094-1495-7(7))* Hakluyt Society GBR. Dist: Ashgate Publishing Co.

—Missions to the Niger: The Journal of Friedrich Horneman's Travels from Cairo to Murzuk in the Years 1797-98; the Letters of Major Alexander Gordon Laing, 1824-26. 2010. (Hakluyt Society, Second Ser.). 418p. 69.95 *(978-1-4094-1489-6(2))* Hakluyt Society GBR. Dist: Ashgate Publishing Co.

Cliff, Nigel. Holy War: How Vasco da Gama's Epic Voyages Turned the Tide in a Centuries-Old Clash of Civilizations. 2011. (ENG.). 560p. 29.99 *(978-0-06-173512-7(4))* HarperCollins Pubs.

Crone, G. R., ed. The Voyages of Cadamosto & Other Documents on Western Africa in the Second Half of the Fifteenth Century. 2010. (Hakluyt Society, Second Ser.). 204p. 69.95 *(978-1-4094-1447-6(7))* Hakluyt Society GBR. Dist: Ashgate Publishing Co.

Dritsas, Lawrence. Zambesi: David Livingstone & Expeditionary Science in Africa. 2010. (ENG., Illus.). 256p. 85.00 *(978-1-84511-705-4(0))* I. B. Tauris & Co., Ltd. GBR. Dist: Macmillan.

Grant, Richard. Crazy River: Exploration & Folly in East Africa. 2011. (ENG.). 352p. pap. 15.00 *(978-1-4391-5414-4(7)*, Free Pr.) Free Pr.

Harries, Patrick. Butterflies & Barbarians: Swiss Missionaries & Systems of Knowledge in South-East Africa. 2007. (Illus.). (ENG.). 304p. pap. 26.95 *(978-0-8214-1777-5(0))*; 286p. 59.95 *(978-0-8214-1776-8(2))* Ohio Univ. Pr.

Holgate, Kingsley. Africa: In the Footsteps of the Great Explorers. 2006. (Illus.). 304p. 29.00 *(978-1-77007-147-6(4))* Struik Pubs. ZAF. Dist: International Publishers Marketing.

Jameson, Robert, et al. Narrative of Discovery & Adventure in Africa: From the Earliest Ages to the Present Time. 2007. (ENG.). 528p. per. 40.95 *(978-0-548-28663-0(9))* Kessinger Publishing, LLC.

Jeal, Tim. Explorers of the Nile: The Triumph & the Tragedy of a Great Victorian Adventure. 2011. (Illus.). 528p. 32.50 *(978-0-300-14935-7(2))* Yale Univ. Pr.

Kemper, Steve. A Labyrinth of Kingdoms: 10,000 Miles Through Islamic Africa. 2012. (ENG., Illus.). 432p. 28.95 ***(978-0-393-07966-1(X)***, 7966) Norton, W. W. & Co., Inc.

Koivunen, Leila. Visualizing Africa in Nineteenth-Century British Travel Accounts. (ENG., Illus.). (C). 2011. 350p. pap. 42.95 ***(978-0-415-69962-4(2))*** 2008. 368p. 125.00 *(978-0-415-99001-1(7))* Routledge.

Kryza, Frank T. The Race for Timbuktu: In Search of Africa's City of Gold. 2006. (ENG., Illus.). 352p. pap. 14.95 *(978-0-06-056065-2(7)*, HarperPerennial) HarperCollins Pubs.

Laird, MacGregor. Narrative of an Expedition into the Interior of Africa. 2008. 464p. 31.99 *(978-0-559-32723-0(4))*; pap. 36.75 *(978-0-559-32722-3(6))* BiblioBazaar.

Leyden, John. A Historical & Philosophical Sketch of the Discoveries & Settlements of the Europeans in Northern & Western Africa, at the Close of the Eighteenth Century. 2011. (Cambridge Library Collection - History Ser.). (ENG.). 434p. pap. 34.99 ***(978-1-108-03248-3(6))*** Cambridge Univ. Pr.

Library Company of Philadelphia Staff & Historical Society of Pennsylvania Staff, contrib. by. Afro-Americana, 1553-1906: A Catalog of the Holdings of the Library Company of Philadelphia & the Historical Society of Pennsylvania. 2nd ed. 2008. 175.00 *(978-1-58456-236-8(6))* Oak Knoll Pr.

Livingstone, David. Missionary Travels & Researches in South Africa. 2009. 412p. 32.99 *(978-0-559-11642-1(X))*; 412p. 30.99 *(978-0-559-11653-7(5))*; 432p. 32.99 *(978-0-559-11665-0(9))*; 432p. 30.99 *(978-0-559-11679-7(9))*; 412p. pap. 27.99 *(978-0-559-11645-2(4))*; 412p. pap. 33.75 *(978-0-559-11649-0(7))*; 432p. pap. 35.75 *(978-0-559-11668-1(3))*; 432p. pap. 34.75 *(978-0-559-11675-9(6))* BiblioBazaar.

Lockhart, Jamie Bruce. A Sailor in the Sahara: The Life & Travels in Africa of Hugh Clapperton, Commander RN. 2007. (ENG., Illus.). 344p. 52.00 *(978-1-84511-479-4(5))* I. B. Tauris & Co., Ltd. GBR. Dist: Macmillan.

MacQueen, Peter. In Wildest Africa. 2009. 230p. pap. *(978-0-217-48830-3(7))* Books LLC.

Moorehead, Alan. The White Nile. lib. bdg. 27.95 *(978-0-8488-2006-0(1))* Amereon LTD.

Newitt, Malyn, ed. The Portuguese in West Africa, 1415-1670. 2010. (ENG., Illus.). 264p. (C). 90.00 *(978-0-521-76894-8(2))*; pap. 27.99 *(978-0-521-15914-2(8))* Cambridge Univ. Pr.

Park, Mungo. The Journal of a Mission to the Interior of Africa, in the Year 1805. 2007. (ENG.). 238p. pap. 20.99 *(978-1-4264-3197-5(X))*; 386p. pap. 26.99 *(978-1-4264-3232-3(1))* BiblioBazaar.

—The Journal of a Mission to the Interior of Africa, in the Year 1805. 2009. 172p. pap. *(978-0-217-08671-4(3))* Books LLC.

—The Journal of a Mission to the Interior of Africa, in the Year 1805. 2011. (Cambridge Library Collection - Travel & Exploration Ser.). (Illus.). 402p. pap. 31.99 *(978-1-108-02767-0(9))* Cambridge Univ. Pr.

—Life & Travels of Mungo Park in Centra. 2006. pap. *(978-1-84702-391-9(6))* Echo Library.

—Life & Travels of Mungo Park in Central Africa. 2008. 428p. 32.99 *(978-0-554-22797-9(5))* 2007. (ENG.). 382p. pap. 25.99 *(978-1-4264-3061-9(2))* 2007. (ENG.). 424p. pap. 28.99 *(978-1-4264-3126-5(0))* BiblioBazaar.

—Travels in the Interior Districts of Africa: Performed under the Direction & Patronage of the African Association in the Years 1795, 1796, And 1797. 2011. (Cambridge Library Collection - Travel & Exploration Ser.). (Illus.). 536p. pap. 39.99 *(978-1-108-02597-3(8))* Cambridge Univ. Pr.

Pettitt, Clare. Dr. Livingstone, I Presume? Missionaries, Journalists, Explorers, & Empire. 2007. (Profiles in History Ser.). (Illus.). 264p. 22.95 *(978-0-674-02487-8(7))* Harvard Univ. Pr.

Pucci, Idanna, ed. Brazza in Congo: A Life & Legacy. 2009. (ENG., Illus.). 240p. 40.00 *(978-1-884167-94-2(2))* Umbrage Editions.

Ross, Andrew C. David Livingstone: Mission & Empire. 2006. (ENG., Illus.). 288p. per. 49.95 *(978-1-85285-565-9(7),* Hambledon Continuum) Continuum International Publishing Group, Ltd. GBR. Dist: National Bk. Network.

Smith, Fredrick S. Stanley, African Explorer. 21.95 *(978-0-89190-717-6(3))* Amereon LTD.

Speke, John Hanning. Journal of the Discovery of the Source of the Nile. 2009. 388p. pap. *(978-0-217-85687-4(X))* Books LLC.

—Journal of the Discovery of the Source of the Nile. 2007. (Illus.). 590p. pap. 51.00 *(978-1-55635-191-4(7),* Resource Pubns.) Wipf & Stock Pubs.

Stanley, Henry Morton. My African Travels. 2009. (Cambridge Library Collection - History Ser.). (ENG.). 56p. pap. 12.99 *(978-1-108-00411-4(3))* Cambridge Univ. Pr.

Taithe, Bertrand. The Killer Trail: A Colonial Scandal in the Heart of Africa. 2009. (ENG., Illus.). 304p. 34.95 *(978-0-19-923121-8(4))* Oxford Univ. Pr., Inc.

Zurara, Gomes Eanes de. The Chronicle of the Discovery & Conquest of Guinea. 2010. (Cambridge Library Collection - Travel & Exploration Ser.). (ENG., Illus.). 220p. pap. 22.99 *(978-1-108-01474-8(7))* Cambridge Univ. Pr.

—Chronicle of the Discovery & Conquest of Guinea. 2010. (Cambridge Library Collection - Travel & Exploration Ser.). (ENG., Illus.). 404p. pap. 31.99 *(978-1-108-01390-1(2))* Cambridge Univ. Pr.

AFRICA—ECONOMIC CONDITIONS

Abel, Martin. Doubling Aid to Africa. 2008. 96p. pap. *(978-3-639-01708-3(0))* VDM Verlag Dr. Mueller e.K.

Abraham, Kinfe. African Quest. the Transition from the Oau to Au. 2010. 714p. pap. 25.75 *(978-1-145-12003-7(2))* BiblioBazaar.

Adam, Rahma. What Needs to Be Done to Develop Local Food Markets in Tanzania? 2010. 72p. pap. *(978-3-8383-4982-4(2))* Lambert Academic Publishing.

Adebayo, Akanmu, et al. Marginality & Crisis: Globalization & Identity in Contemporary Africa. 2010. (ENG., Illus.). 294p. 78.99 *(978-0-7391-4556-2(8))* Lexington Bks.

Adeuyan, Jacob Oluwatayo. The Return of the Tidal Flow of the Middle Passage. 2011. 232p. 24.99 ***(978-1-4634-2409-1(4))***; pap. 16.99 ***(978-1-4634-2410-7(8))*** AuthorHouse.

Africa CD Business. 1400p. 4500.00 *(978-0-7605-4575-1(8))* Rector Pr., Ltd.

African Development Bank, creator. The African Development Report 2006: Aid, Debt Relief & Development in Africa. 2006. (ENG., Illus.). 176p. per. 39.95 *(978-0-19-929647-1(5))* Oxford Univ. Pr., Inc.

African Development Bank Group Staff, ed. African Development Report 2011. 2012. (ENG.). 220p. pap. 29.95 ***(978-0-19-958716-2(7))*** Oxford Univ. Pr., Inc.

African Development Bank Staff. African Development Report 2008/2009. Oxford University Press Staff, ed. 2009. (African Development Report). (ENG., Illus.). 336p. pap. 39.95 *(978-0-19-954894-1(3))* Oxford Univ. Pr., Inc.

—African Development Report 2009-2010: Ports, Logistics, & Trade in Africa. 2010. (African Development Report). (ENG., Illus.). 232p. pap. 35.00 *(978-0-19-956605-1(4))* Oxford Univ. Pr., Inc.

Agwuele, Augustine. ed. Development, Modernism & Modernity in Africa. 2011. (Routledge African Studies). (ENG., Illus.). 340p. (C). 125.00 ***(978-0-415-89924-6(9))*** Routledge.

Akintunde, Henry. Economic Development under Crises: An Econometric Analysis. 2011. 144p. 29.95 ***(978-1-4567-4228-7(0))***; pap. 17.95 ***(978-1-4567-4226-3(4))*** AuthorHouse.

Alagidede, Paul. Recession & Recovery: Whither Africa's Emerging Financial Markets? 2011. (Series: Global Recession - Causes, Impacts & Remedies Ser.). pap. 43.00 *(978-1-61209-531-8(3))* Nova Science Pubs., Inc.

Alderman, Harold & Haque, Trina. Insurance Against Covariate Shocks: The Role of Index-Based Insurance in Social Protection in Low-Income Countries of Africa. 2007. (World Bank Working Papers: 95). (ENG.). 44p. pap. 15.00 *(978-0-8213-7036-0(7),* 9780821370360) World Bank Pubns.

Allen, Christopher & Johnson, R. W., eds. African Perspectives: Papers in the History, Politics & Economics of Africa Presented to Thomas Hodgkin. 2008. (ENG.). 464p. pap. 58.00 *(978-0-521-10199-8(9))* Cambridge Univ. Pr.

Amin, Aloysius Aloysius & Dubois, Jean-Luc. Croissance et Dtveloppement Au Cameroun: D'une Croissance EquilibrTe a un DTveloppement Equitable. 2008. (FRE.). 440p. pap. *(978-9956-558-87-2(7))* Langaa Research & Publishing Common Initiative Group CMR. Dist: Michigan State Univ. Pr.

Amin, Samir. Maldevelopment: Anatomy of a Global Failure. 2nd ed. 2011. (ENG.). 350p. pap. 27.95 ***(978-1-906387-79-2(6))*** Pambazuka Pr. GBR. Dist: Independent Pubs. Group.

Ansoms, An & Marysse, Stefaan, eds. Natural Resources & Local Livelihoods in the Great Lakes Region in Africa: A Political Economy Perspective. 2011. (ENG., Illus.). 256p. 110.00 *(978-0-230-29025-9(6))* Palgrave Macmillan.

Artley, Oluwole &. Africation. 2007. 154p. pap. 11.95 *(978-0-7414-3932-1(8))* Infinity Publishing.

Aryeetey, Ernest, et al, eds. The Oxford Companion to the Economics of Africa. 2012. (ENG., Illus.). 696p. 150.00 ***(978-0-19-957597-8(5))*** Oxford Univ. Pr., Inc.

Atayi, Jane. Gender Discrimination under the Upe Program - a Ugandan Experience. 2011. 80p. pap. ***(978-3-8433-8460-5(6))*** Lambert Academic Publishing.

Ayadi, Felix, ed. Building New Strategic Partnerships for Africa's Economic Development, Volume 8. annuals 2007. 712p. per. 100.00 net. *(978-0-9765288-2-1(7),* IAABD) International Academy of African Business & Development.

Ayuk, Elias & Marouani, Mohamed Ali. The Policy Paradox in Africa: Strengthening Links Between Economic Research & Policymaking. 2007. *(978-1-59221-575-8(9))*; 320p. pap. *(978-1-59221-577-5(7))* Africa World Pr.

Baltissen, Gerard & Manyeh, Morie, eds. Strengthening Social Capital: The Gobifo Approach in Rural Sierra Leone. 2011. 72p. pap. 39.95 ***(978-94-6022-134-7(3))*** Royal Tropical Institute Pr. (KIT (Koninklijk Instituut voor de Tropen) NLD. Dist: Stylus Publishing, LLC.

Barrett, Christopher B. Understanding & Reducing Persistent Poverty in Africa. Carter, Michael & Little, Peter, eds. 2008. 256p. pap. 39.95 *(978-0-415-46389-8(0))* 2007. (ENG.). 224p. 150.00 *(978-0-415-41138-7(6))* Routledge.

Bayart, Jean-Francois. The State in Africa: The Politics of the Belly. 2nd ed. 2009. (ENG.). 420p. pap. 29.95 *(978-0-7456-4437-0(6))* Polity Pr. GBR. Dist: Wiley, John & Sons, Inc.

Beasley, Thomas W. Poverty in Africa. 2009. (Poverty in Africa Ser.). 98.00 *(978-1-60741-737-8(5))* Nova Science Pubs., Inc.

Bebelleh, Frederick Der. Ghana's Land Adminstration & Security of Land Tenure. 2011. 152p. pap. ***(978-3-8443-1446-5(6))*** Lambert Academic Publishing.

Beck, Thorsten & Maimbo, Samuel Munzele. Financing Africa: Through the Crisis & Beyond. 2011. (ENG., Illus.). 308p. pap. 40.00 *(978-0-8213-8797-9(9),* 9780821387979) World Bank Pubns.

Berg, Andrew. The Macroeconomics of Scaling up Aid: Lessons from Recent Experience. 2007. (Illus.). vii, 105p. *(978-1-58906-591-8(3))* International Monetary Fund.

Bigsten, Arne & Durevall, Dick. The African Economy & Its Role in the World Economy. 2008. (NAI Current African Issues Ser.). 66p. pap. 12.95 *(978-91-7106-625-1(X))* Nordiska Afrikainstitutet SWE. Dist: Stylus Publishing, LLC.

Binns, Tony. Africa Binns. 2012. (ENG., Illus.). 432p. (C). 160.00 *(978-0-415-41367-1(2))* Routledge.

Binns, Tony, et al. Africa: Diversity & Development. 2012. (ENG., Illus.). 432p. (C). pap. 59.95 *(978-0-415-41368-8(0))* Routledge.

Boko, Sylvain Hounkponou & Seck, Diery. Back on Track: Sector-Led Growth in Africa & Implications for Development. 2009. *(978-1-59221-708-3(7))*; 480p. pap. *(978-1-59221-709-0(5))* Africa World Pr.

Bolton, Giles. Africa Doesn't Matter: How the West Has Failed the Poorest Continent & What We Can Do about It. 2012. (ENG.). 368p. pap. 14.95 ***(978-1-61145-306-5(2),*** 611306, Arcade Publishing) Skyhorse Publishing Co., Inc.

Bond, Patrick. Looting Africa: The Economics of Exploitation. (Illus.). xx, 172p. *(978-1-86914-095-3(8))* University of Kwazulu-Natal Press ZAF. Dist: International Specialized Bk. Services.

—Looting Africa: The Economics of Exploitation. 2006. (ENG., Illus.). 224p. 79.95 *(978-1-84277-812-8(9))*; per. 25.95 *(978-1-84277-811-1(0))* Zed Bks., Ltd. GBR. Dist: Macmillan.

Boomsma, Marije J., et al, eds. Facilitating Pro-Poor Business: Why Advice Goes Further When It's Backed by Investment. 2011. (Bulletins of the Royal Tropical Institute Ser.). 72p. pap. 39.95 ***(978-94-6022-155-2(6))*** Royal Tropical Institute Pr. (KIT (Koninklijk Instituut voor de Tropen) NLD. Dist: Stylus Publishing, LLC.

Boyce, James & Ndikumana, Léonce. Africa's Odious Debt: How Foreign Loans & Capital Flight Bled a Continent. 2011. (African Arguments Ser.). (ENG., Illus.). 160p. (C). pap. 22.95 *(978-1-84813-459-1(2))* Zed Bks., Ltd. GBR. Dist: Macmillan.

Brautigam, Deborah. The Dragon's Gift: The Real Story of China in Africa. 2010. (ENG., Illus.). 224p. 29.95 *(978-0-19-955022-7(0))* Oxford Univ. Pr., Inc.

Bush, Ray. Poverty & Neoliberalism: Persistence & Reproduction in the Global South, 1 vol. 2007. (Third World in Global Politics Ser.). (ENG., Illus.). 237p. 36.00 *(978-0-7453-1960-5(2))*; 256p. lib. bdg. 100.00 *(978-0-7453-1961-2(0))* Pluto Pr. GBR. Dist: Macmillan.

Campbell, Gwyn. An Economic History of Imperial Madagascar, 1750-1895: The Rise & Fall of an Island Empire. 2008. (African Studies). (ENG., Illus.). 436p. pap. 46.00 *(978-0-521-10391-6(6))* Cambridge Univ. Pr.

Carmody, Padraig. Globalization in Africa: Recolonization or Renaissance? 2010. (Illus.). 175p. 55.00 *(978-1-58826-740-5(7))* Rienner, Lynne Pubs.

—The New Scramble for Africa. 2011. (ENG., Illus.). 240p. 69.95 *(978-0-7456-4784-5(7))*; pap. 24.95 *(978-0-7456-4785-2(5))* Polity Pr. GBR. Dist: Wiley, John & Sons, Inc.

Carmody, Padraig Risteard & Carmody, Padraig. Neoliberalism, Civil Society & Security in Africa. 2007. (ENG., Illus.). 224p. 105.00 *(978-0-230-52159-9(2))* Palgrave Macmillan.

Catley, Andy, et al, eds. Pastoralism & Development in Africa: Dynamic Change at the Margins. 2012. (Pathways to Sustainability Ser.). (ENG., Illus.). 320p. (C). 145.00 ***(978-0-415-54071-1(2))***; pap. 44.95 ***(978-0-415-54072-8(0))*** Routledge.

Cheru, Fantu. Africa's Development in the 21st Century: Reshaping the Research Agenda. 2008. (NAI Current African Issues Ser.). 50p. pap. 12.95 *(978-91-7106-628-2(4))* Nordiska Afrikainstitutet SWE. Dist: Stylus Publishing, LLC.

Cheru, Fantu & Obi, Cyril, eds. The Rise of China & India in Africa: Challenges, Opportunities & Critical Interventions. 2010. (Africa Now Ser.). (ENG., Illus.). 272p. 125.95 *(978-1-84813-436-2(3))*; pap. 37.95 *(978-1-84813-437-9(1))* Zed Bks., Ltd. GBR. Dist: Macmillan.

Chinje, Nathalie Beatrice. The Economic Impact of Mtn's Involvement. 2011. 108p. pap. ***(978-3-8443-2146-3(2))*** Lambert Academic Publishing.

Cholwe, Luonde. Exploring Youth Unemployment in a Re-structuredAfrican Economy: The Case of Zambia's University Graduates. 2008. 120p. pap. *(978-3-639-08555-6(8))* VDM Verlag Dr. Mueller e.K.

Chuhan-Pole, Punam & Angwafo, Manka, eds. Yes, Africa Can: Success Stories from a Dynamic Continent. 2011. (ENG., Illus.). 496p. pap. 49.95 *(978-0-8213-8745-0(6),* 9780821387450) World Bank Pubns.

Clarke, Duncan. Africa's Future - Darkness to Destiny: How the Past Is Shaping Africa's Economic Evolution. 2012. (ENG., Illus.). 320p. 32.95 ***(978-1-84668-569-9(9))*** Profile Bks. Ltd. GBR. Dist: Consortium Bk. Sales & Distribution.

Clément, Jean A. P. & Peiris, Shanaka J. Post-Stabilization Economics in Sub-Saharan Africa: Lessons from Mozambique. 2008. (Illus.). viii, 397p. pap. *(978-1-58906-677-9(4))* International Monetary Fund.

Columbus, Alexandra M., ed. Politics & Economics of Africa: Volume 9. 2011. (Politics & Economics of Africa Ser.). (Illus.). 171p. pap. 112.00 ***(978-1-61324-231-5(X))*** Nova Science Pubs., Inc.

Columbus, Frank, ed. Politics & Economics of Africa. Volume 7. 2010. (Politics & Economics of Africa Ser.). 115.00 *(978-1-61668-013-8(X))* Nova Science Pubs., Inc.

Coulter, G. W. Africa in Transition: The Journey from Tradition to Modern. 2011. 352p. 36.50 ***(978-1-84624-632-6(6))*** Trans-Atlantic Pubns., Inc.

Cram101 Textbook Reviews & Cram101 Textbook Reviews. Outlines & Highlights for Africa in the Century: Toward a New Future by Ama Mazama, ISBN. 2011. 114p. pap. 28.95 ***(978-1-61812-033-5(6))*** Cram101 Inc.

Crisafulli, Patricia & Redmond, Andrea. Rwanda, Inc: How a Devastated Nation Became an Economic Model for the Developing World. 2012. (ENG., Illus.). 256p. 27.00 ***(978-0-230-34022-0(9))*** Palgrave Macmillan.

Crush, Jonathan & Dodson, Belinda, eds. Migration, Remittances & Development in Lesotho. 2006. (Illus.). 96p. pap. *(978-1-920409-26-5(2))* IDASA Pubs. ZAF. Dist: Michigan State Univ. Pr.

Cunguara, Benedito. Pathways Out of Poverty in Rural Mozambique. 2010. 96p. pap. *(978-3-8383-2090-8(5))* Lambert Academic Publishing.

Dabula, Prince. Perceived Occupational Stress Amongst Female Nurses. 2010. 108p. pap. *(978-3-8383-4239-9(9))* Lambert Academic Publishing.

de Villiers, Les. Africa 2008. 2008. (Illus.). 400p. per. 28.95 *(978-0-916673-24-6(3))* Business Bks. International.

Deegan, Heather. Africa Today: Culture, Economics, Religion, Security. (Illus.). 2009. XVI, 240p. 170.00 *(978-0-415-41883-6(6))* 2008. (ENG., 256p. (C). pap. 42.95 *(978-0-415-41884-3(4))* Routledge.

Dramani, Latif. Integration & Convergence in Afric. 2010. 76p. pap. *(978-3-8383-8327-9(3))* Lambert Academic Publishing.

Effeh, Ubong. Why Sub-Saharan Africa Is Mired in Poverty: The Consequences of Misrule. 2008. 388p. 119.95 *(978-0-7734-5149-0(8))* Mellen, Edwin Pr., The.

Efretuei, Evobong. The New Partnership for Africa's Development. 2009. 296p. pap. *(978-3-639-17210-2(8))* VDM Verlag Dr. Mueller e.K.

Ekanem, Ita I. An Adventure Beyond Social Mobility: A Tribute to My Father. 2008. 356p. 31.99 *(978-1-4389-0710-9(9))*; pap. 19.99 *(978-1-4389-0711-6(7))* AuthorHouse.

Ekeha, George. Capital Budgeting Practices & Economic Development. 2011. 76p. pap. ***(978-3-8443-8259-4(3))*** Lambert Academic Publishing.

Ellis, Frank, et al. Social Protection in Africa. 2009. (Illus.). 304p. 155.00 *(978-1-84844-258-0(0))*; pap. 50.00 *(978-1-84844-364-8(1))* Elgar, Edward Publishing, Inc.

Ellis, Stephen. Season of Rains: Africa in the World. 2012. 224p. 25.00 ***(978-0-226-20559-5(2))*** Univ. of Chicago Pr.

Enga Awaseh, Stanley. Microfinance & Community Development in Cameroon. 2010. 84p. pap. *(978-3-8383-5860-4(0))* Lambert Academic Publishing.

Ensign, Margee & Bertrand, William E. Rwanda: History & Hope. 2009. (ENG.). 174p. 59.99 *(978-0-7618-4942-1(4))* Univ. Pr. of America, Inc.

Ensign, Margee M. & Bertrand, William E. Rwanda: History & Hope. 2010. (Illus.). xx, 154p. *(978-0-7618-4944-5(0))* Univ. Pr. of America, Inc.

Eric, Buah. Exploiting Opportunities in Africa Through Networking: A Road Map for Renewable Energy Sme's. 2011. 88p. pap. ***(978-3-639-33760-0(3))*** VDM Verlag Dr. Mueller e.K.

Etuk, Emma Samuel. Listen Africans! A Revolution Is Coming: Why It Must Come & How We Should Deal with It. 2011. 212p. 27.95 *(978-1-4502-7736-5(5))*; pap. 17.95 *(978-1-4502-7734-1(9))* iUniverse, Inc.

Euromonitor International. African Marketing Data & Statistics. 3rd ed. 2011. (ENG.). 274p. (C). ***(978-1-84264-548-2(X))*** Euromonitor International PLC.

Eze, C. P. Don't Africa Me: 'Their' geo-branding war, 'Our' trade, tourism wounds, & Winning like China. 2008. 220p. 25.00 *(978-0-9800768-0-6(3),* Expertz in PRINT) Brandwell Global Services.

Falloux, Francois & Talbot, Lee M. Crisis & Opportunity: Environment & Development in Africa. 2009. (Aid & Development Set Ser.). (ENG.). 380p. 110.00 *(978-1-84971-040-4(6))* Routledge.

Falola, Toyin & Brownell, Emily, eds. Africa, Empire & Globalization: Essays in Honor of A. G. Hopkins. 2011. 682p. 80.00 *(978-1-59460-915-2(2))* Carolina Academic Pr.

Falola, Toyin & House-Soremekun, Bessie, eds. Globalization & Sustainable Development in Africa. 2011. (Rochester Studies in African History & the Diaspora Ser.: Volume 51). (Illus.). 484p. 80.00 *(978-1-58046-392-8(4))* Univ. of Rochester Pr.

Farah, Hosh. Energy Security & Sustainable Development. 2011. 136p. pap. ***(978-3-8443-0807-5(5))*** Lambert Academic Publishing.

Fick, David. Africa: Continent of Economic Opportunity. 2007. (ENG.). 520p. pap. 80.00 *(978-1-919855-59-2(9))* STE Pubs. ZAF. Dist: Independent Pubs. Group.

Food and Agriculture Organization (Fao), creator. The 2007-2008 Food Price Swing: Impact & Policies in Eastern & Southern Africa. 2010. (Fao Commodities & Trade Technical Paper Ser.). (Illus.). 117p. pap. *(978-92-5-106343-9(5))* Food & Agriculture Organization of the United Nations.

Fox, M. Louise. Beating the Odds: Sustaining Inclusion in Mozambique's Growing Economy. 2008. (Directions in Development Ser.). (ENG., Illus.). 304p. pap. 35.00 incl. cd-rom *(978-0-8213-7565-5(2),* 9780821375655) World Bank Pubns.

Frindéthié, K. Martial. Globalization & the Seduction of Africa's Ruling Class: An Argument for a New Philosophy of Development. 2010. (ENG., Illus.). 204p. pap. 55.00 *(978-0-7864-4840-1(7),* McFarland & Co., Inc. Pubs.

Gaal, Melissa Sekkel, et al. Working Out of Poverty: Job Creation & the Quality of Growth in Africa. 2008. (Directions in Development Ser.). (ENG., Illus.). 96p. pap. 20.00 *(978-0-8213-7442-9(7),* 9780821374429) World Bank Pubns.

Gatsi, John. Venture Capital & Corporate Governance. 2010. 52p. pap. *(978-3-8383-7327-0(8))* Lambert Academic Publishing.

Gilliam, Tanji & Zuberi, Tukufu, eds. A Perspective on Africa & the World. 2011. (ANNALS of the American Academy of Political & Social Science Ser.: 632). 132p. (C). 47.00 *(978-1-4129-9395-1(4),* 295632C); pap. 34.00 *(978-1-4129-9394-4(6),* 295632P) SAGE Pubns., Inc.

Goffe, Leslie Gordon. When Banana Was King: The Life & Times of Jamaican Banana King Alfred Constantine Goffe. 2006. (ENG.). 332p. per. *(978-976-8202-23-9(8))* LMH Publishing, Ltd.

Gordon, April A. & Gordon, Donald L., eds. Understanding Contemporary Africa, 4th Edition. 4th ed. 2006. (Illus.). 475p. (C). pap. 27.50 *(978-1-58826-466-4(1))* Rienner, Lynne Pubs.

The Great Lakes Region: Current Conditions & U.S. Policy: Hearing Before the Subcommittee on Africa & Global Health of the Committee on Foreign Affairs, House of Representatives, One Hundred Eleventh Congress, Second Session, May 25, 2010. 2010. iii, 66p. *(978-0-16-086452-0(6),* 552-070-41509-2) United States Government Printing Office.

Gruffydd Jones, Branwen. Explaining Global Poverty: A Critical Realist Approach. 2009. 234p. pap. 39.95 *(978-0-415-56869-2(2))* Routledge.

Guseh, James S. & Oritsejafor, Emmanuel O. Governance, Democracy & Development in sub-Saharan Africa. 2011. (ENG., Illus.). 256p. 50.00 *(978-0-9770904-3-3(4))* Africana Homestead Legacy Pubs., Inc.

Hagen, Emlyn. The Digital Divide in Afric. 2007. 124p. per. *(978-3-8364-2562-9(9))* VDM Verlag Dr. Mueller e.K.

Hailu, Yitayal, et al. Domestic Solid Waste Quantity & Composition Analysis. 2010. 100p. pap. *(978-3-8383-4965-7(2))* Lambert Academic Publishing.

Hall, Linley Erin. Starvation in Africa. 2009. (In the News Ser.). 64p. (gr. 6-6). 58.50 *(978-1-61513-489-2(1))* Rosen Publishing Group, Inc., The.

Handa, Sudhanshu, et al, eds. Social Protection for Africas Children. 2010. (Routledge Studies in Development Economics Ser.). (ENG., Illus.). 272p. (C). 140.00 *(978-0-415-58333-6(0),* Routledge) Taylor & Francis Group GBR. Dist: Taylor & Francis Group.

Harrison, Graham. Neoliberal Africa: The Impact of Global Social Engineering. 2010. (ENG.). 192p. 116.95 *(978-1-34813-319-8(7))*; pap. 32.95 *(978-1-84813-320-4(0))* Zed Bks., Ltd. GBR. Dist: Macmillan.

Haugen, David M., ed. Africa. 2011. (Opposing Viewpoints Ser.). (Illus.). 240p. (ENG.). pap. 27.50 *(978-0-7377-5704-0(3),* Greenhaven Pr., Inc.); (YA). (gr. 9-12). 39.70 *(978-0-7377-5703-3(5))* Cengage Gale.

Herderschee, Han, et al. Resilience of an African Giant: Boosting Growth & Development in the Democratic Republic of Congo. 2011. ***(978-0-8213-8910-2(6))*** World Bank Pubns.

Herderschee, Johannes, et al. Resilience of an African Giant: Boosting Growth & Development in the Democratic Republic of Congo. 2011. (Directions in Development Ser.). (ENG.). 136p. pap. 25.00 ***(978-0-8213-8909-6(2),*** 9780821389096) World Bank Pubns.

Higher Education in Africa: Making the Link Between Intellectual Capital & Regional Development: Hearing Before the Subcommittee on Africa & Global Health of the Committee on Foreign Affairs, House of Representatives, One Hundred Tenth Congress, Second Session, May 6, 2008. 2009. iii, 50p. *(978-0-16-082688-7(8),* 552-070-38705-6) United States Government Printing Office.

Honwana, Alcinda Manuel. The Time of Youth: Work, Social Change, & Politics in Africa. 2012. 75.00 ***(978-1-56549-471-8(7))***; pap. 27.95 ***(978-1-56549-472-5(5))*** Stylus Publishing, LLC. (Kumarian Pr).

Hope, Kempe Ronald. Poverty, Livelihoods, & Governance in Africa: Fulfilling the Development Promise. 2008. (ENG.). 224p. 89.00 *(978-0-230-60834-4(5))* Palgrave Macmillan.

Horn of Africa: Current Conditions & U.S. Policy: Hearing Before the Subcommittee on Africa & Global Health of the Committee on Foreign Affairs, House of Representatives, One Hundred Eleventh Congress, Second Session, June 17, 2010. 2010. iii, 79p. *(978-0-16-086453-7(4),* 552-070-41510-6) United States Government Printing Office.

Hounhouigan, Joseph, ed. African Fermented Foods & Beverages. 2012. (Fermented Foods & Beverages Ser.). (ENG., Illus.). 584p. 179.95 ***(978-1-4398-4596-7(4),*** CRC Press) Taylor & Francis Group GBR. Dist: Taylor & Francis Group.

Icon Group International, Inc. Staff, compiled by. The 2006 Economic & Product Market Databook for Abeche, Chad. 2006. 605p. ring bd. 95.00 *(978-0-497-79941-0(3))* Icon Group International, Inc.

—The 2006 Economic & Product Market Databook for Algiers, Algeria. 2006. 618p. ring bd. 95.00 *(978-0-497-80030-7(6))* Icon Group International, Inc.
—The 2006 Economic & Product Market Databook for Annaba, Algeria. 2006. 618p. ring bd. 95.00 *(978-0-497-80059-8(4))* Icon Group International, Inc.
—The 2006 Economic & Product Market Databook for Anse Boileau, Seychelles. 2006. 618p. ring bd. 95.00 *(978-0-497-80060-4(8))* Icon Group International, Inc.
—The 2006 Economic & Product Market Databook for Anse Royale, Seychelles. 2006. 618p. ring bd. 95.00 *(978-0-497-80061-1(6))* Icon Group International, Inc.
—The 2006 Economic & Product Market Databook for Antananarivo, Madagascar. 2006. 618p. ring bd. 95.00 *(978-0-497-80063-5(2))* Icon Group International, Inc.
—The 2006 Economic & Product Market Databook for Antsirabe, Madagascar. 2006. 618p. ring bd. 95.00 *(978-0-497-80065-9(9))* Icon Group International, Inc.
—The 2006 Economic & Product Market Databook for Antsiranana, Madagascar. 2006. 618p. ring bd. 95.00 *(978-0-497-80066-6(7))* Icon Group International, Inc.
—The 2006 Economic & Product Market Databook for Atakpamé, Togo. 2006. 618p. ring bd. 95.00 *(978-0-497-80099-4(3))* Icon Group International, Inc.
—The 2006 Economic & Product Market Databook for Atar, Mauritania. 2006. 618p. ring bd. 95.00 *(978-0-497-80100-7(0))* Icon Group International, Inc.
—The 2006 Economic & Product Market Databook for Bambari, Central African Republic. 2006. 618p. ring bd. 95.00 *(978-0-497-80129-8(9))* Icon Group International, Inc.
—The 2006 Economic & Product Market Databook for Bata, Equatorial Guinea. 2006. 618p. ring bd. 95.00 *(978-0-497-80160-1(4))* Icon Group International, Inc.
—The 2006 Economic & Product Market Databook for Batna, Algeria. 2006. 618p. ring bd. 95.00 *(978-0-497-80161-8(2))* Icon Group International, Inc.
—The 2006 Economic & Product Market Databook for Beau Bassin, Mauritius. 2006. 618p. ring bd. 95.00 *(978-0-497-80166-3(3))* Icon Group International, Inc.
—The 2006 Economic & Product Market Databook for Bechar, Algeria. 2006. 618p. ring bd. 95.00 *(978-0-497-80167-0(1))* Icon Group International, Inc.
—The 2006 Economic & Product Market Databook for Bejaia, Algeria. 2006. 618p. ring bd. 95.00 *(978-0-497-80173-1(6))* Icon Group International, Inc.
—The 2006 Economic & Product Market Databook for Berberati, Central African Republic. 2006. 618p. ring bd. 95.00 *(978-0-497-80187-8(6))* Icon Group International, Inc.
—The 2006 Economic & Product Market Databook for Big Bend, Swaziland. 2006. 618p. ring bd. 95.00 *(978-0-497-80197-7(3))* Icon Group International, Inc.
—The 2006 Economic & Product Market Databook for Bissau, Guinea-Bissau. 2006. 618p. ring bd. 95.00 *(978-0-497-80205-9(8))* Icon Group International, Inc.
—The 2006 Economic & Product Market Databook for Blantyre, Malawi. 2006. 618p. ring bd. 95.00 *(978-0-497-80207-3(4))* Icon Group International, Inc.
—The 2006 Economic & Product Market Databook for Blida, Algeria. 2006. 618p. ring bd. 95.00 *(978-0-497-80208-0(2))* Icon Group International, Inc.
—The 2006 Economic & Product Market Databook for Bobonong, Botswana. 2006. 618p. ring bd. 95.00 *(978-0-497-80213-4(9))* Icon Group International, Inc.
—The 2006 Economic & Product Market Databook for Bongor, Chad. 2006. 618p. ring bd. 95.00 *(978-0-497-80222-6(8))* Icon Group International, Inc.
—The 2006 Economic & Product Market Databook for Bouar, Central African Republic. 2006. 618p. ring bd. 95.00 *(978-0-497-80230-1(9))* Icon Group International, Inc.
—The 2006 Economic & Product Market Databook for Chibuto, Mozambique. 2006. 618p. ring bd. 95.00 *(978-0-497-80355-1(0))* Icon Group International, Inc.
—The 2006 Economic & Product Market Databook for Conakry, Guinea. 2006. 618p. ring bd. 95.00 *(978-0-497-80401-5(8))* Icon Group International, Inc.
—The 2006 Economic & Product Market Databook for Cyangugu, Rwanda. 2006. 618p. ring bd. 95.00 *(978-0-497-80432-9(8))* Icon Group International, Inc.
—The 2006 Economic & Product Market Databook for Dikhil, Djibouti. 2006. 618p. ring bd. 95.00 *(978-0-497-80460-2(3))* Icon Group International, Inc.
—The 2006 Economic & Product Market Databook for Djibouti, Djibouti. 2006. 618p. ring bd. 95.00 *(978-0-497-80467-1(0))* Icon Group International, Inc.
—The 2006 Economic & Product Market Databook for Doba, Chad. 2006. 618p. ring bd. 95.00 *(978-0-497-80470-1(0))* Icon Group International, Inc.
—The 2006 Economic & Product Market Databook for Douala, Cameroon. 2006. 618p. ring bd. 95.00 *(978-0-497-80476-3(X))* Icon Group International, Inc.
—The 2006 Economic & Product Market Databook for Ech-Cheliff, Algeria. 2006. 618p. ring bd. 95.00 *(978-0-497-80500-5(6))* Icon Group International, Inc.
—The 2006 Economic & Product Market Databook for Fianarantsoa, Madagascar. 2006. 618p. ring bd. 95.00 *(978-0-497-80538-8(3))* Icon Group International, Inc.
—The 2006 Economic & Product Market Databook for Fomboni, Comoros. 2006. 618p. ring bd. 95.00 *(978-0-497-80544-9(8))* Icon Group International, Inc.
—The 2006 Economic & Product Market Databook for Garoua, Cameroon. 2006. 618p. ring bd. 95.00 *(978-0-497-80579-1(0))* Icon Group International, Inc.
—The 2006 Economic & Product Market Databook for Gitega, Burundi. 2006. 618p. ring bd. 95.00 *(978-0-497-80601-9(0))* Icon Group International, Inc.
—The 2006 Economic & Product Market Databook for Kiffa, Mauritania. 2006. 618p. ring bd. 95.00 *(978-0-497-81994-1(5))* Icon Group International, Inc.
—The 2006 Economic & Product Market Databook for Kigali, Rwanda. 2006. 618p. ring bd. 95.00 *(978-0-497-81995-8(3))* Icon Group International, Inc.
—The 2006 Economic & Product Market Databook for Koumra, Chad. 2006. 618p. ring bd. 95.00 *(978-0-497-80769-6(6))* Icon Group International, Inc.
—The 2006 Economic & Product Market Databook for Kumba, Cameroon. 2006. 618p. ring bd. 95.00 *(978-0-497-80782-5(3))* Icon Group International, Inc.
—The 2006 Economic & Product Market Databook for Lai, Chad. 2006. 618p. ring bd. 95.00 *(978-0-497-80817-4(X))* Icon Group International, Inc.
—The 2006 Economic & Product Market Databook for Luba, Equatorial Guinea. 2006. 618p. ring bd. 95.00 *(978-0-497-80887-7(0))* Icon Group International, Inc.
—The 2006 Economic & Product Market Databook for Machaze, Mozambique. 2006. 618p. ring bd. 95.00 *(978-0-497-80904-1(4))* Icon Group International, Inc.
—The 2006 Economic & Product Market Databook for Mafeteng, Lesotho. 2006. 618p. ring bd. 95.00 *(978-0-497-80912-6(5))* Icon Group International, Inc.
—The 2006 Economic & Product Market Databook for Mahajanga, Madagascar. 2006. 618p. ring bd. 95.00 *(978-0-497-80916-4(8))* Icon Group International, Inc.
—The 2006 Economic & Product Market Databook for Malabo, Equatorial Guinea. 2006. 618p. ring bd. 95.00 *(978-0-497-80927-0(3))* Icon Group International, Inc.
—The 2006 Economic & Product Market Databook for Mansoa, Guinea-Bissau. 2006. 618p. ring bd. 95.00 *(978-0-497-80946-1(X))* Icon Group International, Inc.
—The 2006 Economic & Product Market Databook for Manzini, Swaziland. 2006. 618p. ring bd. 95.00 *(978-0-497-80006-2(3))* Icon Group International, Inc.
—The 2006 Economic & Product Market Databook for Mbaiki, Central African Republic. 2006. 618p. ring bd. 95.00 *(978-0-497-80991-1(5))* Icon Group International, Inc.
—The 2006 Economic & Product Market Databook for Mbini, Equatorial Guinea. 2006. 618p. ring bd. 95.00 *(978-0-497-80996-6(6))* Icon Group International, Inc.
—The 2006 Economic & Product Market Databook for Mindelo, Cape Verde. 2006. 618p. ring bd. 95.00 *(978-0-497-81024-5(7))* Icon Group International, Inc.
—The 2006 Economic & Product Market Databook for Mitsamiouli, Comoros. 2006. 618p. ring bd. 95.00 *(978-0-497-81032-0(8))* Icon Group International, Inc.
—The 2006 Economic & Product Market Databook for Mochudi, Botswana. 2006. 618p. ring bd. 95.00 *(978-0-497-81035-1(2))* Icon Group International, Inc.
—The 2006 Economic & Product Market Databook for Molepolole, Botswana. 2006. 618p. ring bd. 95.00 *(978-0-497-81042-9(5))* Icon Group International, Inc.
—The 2006 Economic & Product Market Databook for Mopti, Mali. 2006. 618p. ring bd. 95.00 *(978-0-497-82016-9(1))* Icon Group International, Inc.
—The 2006 Economic & Product Market Databook for Moroni, Comoros. 2006. 618p. ring bd. 95.00 *(978-0-497-81057-3(3))* Icon Group International, Inc.
—The 2006 Economic & Product Market Databook for Moundou, Chad. 2006. 618p. ring bd. 95.00 *(978-0-497-81066-5(2))* Icon Group International, Inc.
—The 2006 Economic & Product Market Databook for Mutsamudu, Comoros. 2006. 618p. ring bd. 95.00 *(978-0-497-81074-0(3))* Icon Group International, Inc.
—The 2006 Economic & Product Market Databook for Mzuzu, Malawi. 2006. 618p. ring bd. 95.00 *(978-0-497-82026-8(9))* Icon Group International, Inc.
—The 2006 Economic & Product Market Databook for Nacala, Mozambique. 2006. 618p. ring bd. 95.00 *(978-0-497-82027-5(7))* Icon Group International, Inc.
—The 2006 Economic & Product Market Databook for N'Djamena, Chad. 2006. 618p. ring bd. 95.00 *(978-0-497-81077-1(8))* Icon Group International, Inc.
—The 2006 Economic & Product Market Databook for Oran, Algeria. 2006. 618p. ring bd. 95.00 *(978-0-497-81166-2(9))* Icon Group International, Inc.
—The 2006 Economic & Product Market Databook for Port-Bouet, Cote D'Ivoire. 2006. 618p. ring bd. 95.00 *(978-0-497-81277-5(0))* Icon Group International, Inc.
—The 2006 Economic & Product Market Databook for Port Gentil, Gabon. 2006. 618p. ring bd. 95.00 *(978-0-497-81272-0(X))* Icon Group International, Inc.
—The 2006 Economic & Product Market Databook for Port Louis, Mauritius. 2006. 618p. ring bd. 95.00 *(978-0-497-82079-4(X))* Icon Group International, Inc.
—The 2006 Economic & Product Market Databook for Sarh, Chad. 2006. 618p. ring bd. 95.00 *(978-0-497-81477-9(3))* Icon Group International, Inc.
—The 2006 Economic & Product Market Databook for Selebi-Phikwe, Botswana. 2006. 618p. ring bd. 95.00 *(978-0-497-81493-9(5))* Icon Group International, Inc.
—The 2006 Economic & Product Market Databook for Semara, Western Sahara. 2006. 618p. ring bd. 95.00 *(978-0-497-81495-3(1))* Icon Group International, Inc.
—The 2006 Economic & Product Market Databook for Serowe, Botswana. 2006. 618p. ring bd. 95.00 *(978-0-497-81503-5(6))* Icon Group International, Inc.
—The 2006 Economic & Product Market Databook for Setif, Algeria. 2006. 618p. ring bd. 95.00 *(978-0-497-81509-7(5))* Icon Group International, Inc.
—The 2006 Economic & Product Market Databook for Sidi-Bel-Abbes, Algeria. 2006. 618p. ring bd. 95.00 *(978-0-497-81533-2(8))* Icon Group International, Inc.
—The 2006 Economic & Product Market Databook for Skikda, Algeria. 2006. 618p. ring bd. 95.00 *(978-0-497-81547-9(8))* Icon Group International, Inc.
—The 2006 Economic & Product Market Databook for Tabligbo, Togo. 2006. 618p. ring bd. 95.00 *(978-0-497-81603-2(2))* Icon Group International, Inc.
—The 2006 Economic & Product Market Databook for Tadjourah, Djibouti. 2006. 618p. ring bd. 95.00 *(978-0-497-81609-4(1))* Icon Group International, Inc.
—The 2006 Economic & Product Market Databook for Tchibanga, Gabon. 2006. 618p. ring bd. 95.00 *(978-0-497-81238-6(X))* Icon Group International, Inc.
—The 2006 Economic & Product Market Databook for Tlemcen, Algeria. 2006. 618p. ring bd. 95.00 *(978-0-497-81688-9(1))* Icon Group International, Inc.
—The 2006 Economic & Product Market Databook for Toamasina, Madagascar. 2006. 618p. ring bd. 95.00 *(978-0-497-81691-9(1))* Icon Group International, Inc.
—The 2006 Economic & Product Market Databook for Toliara, Madagascar. 2006. 618p. ring bd. 95.00 *(978-0-497-81698-8(9))* Icon Group International, Inc.
—The 2006 Economic & Product Market Databook for Tutume, Botswana. 2006. 618p. ring bd. 95.00 *(978-0-497-81738-1(1))* Icon Group International, Inc.
—The 2006 Economic & Product Market Databook for Zomba, Malawi. 2006. 618p. ring bd. 95.00 *(978-0-497-81859-3(0))* Icon Group International, Inc.
—The 2006 Economic & Product Market Databook for Zouerate, Mauritania. 2006. 618p. ring bd. 95.00 *(978-0-497-81860-9(4))* Icon Group International, Inc.
Ilhem Baghdadli; Richard Harborne; Tania M. Rajadel, ed. Breaking the Cycle: A Strategy for Conflict-Sensitive Rural Growth in Burundi. 2008. (World Bank Working Papers: 147). (ENG.). 152p. pap. 28.00 *(978-0-8213-7561-7(X)*, 9780821375617) World Bank Pubns.
Jimu, Ignasio Malizani. Urban Appropriation & Transformation: Bicycle Taxi & Handcart Operators. 2008. 160p. pap. *(978-9956-558-75-9(3))* Langaa Research & Publishing Common Initiative Group CMR. Dist: Michigan State Univ. Pr.
Johnson, Omotunde E. G. African Economic Development: Cooperation, Ownership & Leadership. 2007. 286p. (C). 109.95 *(978-0-7734-5409-5(8))* Mellen, Edwin Pr., The.
Johnson, Sterling. Suffering & Smiling: A Diagnosis of African Impoverishment. 2008. (ENG., Illus.). 552p. pap. 68.50 *(978-0-7618-4351-1(5))* Univ. Pr. of America, Inc.
Jones, Branwen Gruffydd. Explaining Global Poverty: A Critical Realist Approach. 2006. (Routledge Studies in Critical Realism Ser.). 234p. *(978-0-415-39212-9(8))* Routledge, Chapman & Hall, Inc.
Kabbar, Reem, et al. Poverty in Khartoum State, Sudan. 2011. 84p. pap. ***(978-3-8443-9164-0(9))*** Lambert Academic Publishing.
Kalla, Britt. Utopia or Reality? - the Implementation of a Human Rights-Based Approach to the New Partnership for Africa's Development. 2008. 104p. pap. *(978-3-639-03238-3(1))* VDM Verlag Dr. Mueller e.K.
Kalu, Kelechi Amihe & Soyinka-Airewele, Peyi. Socio-Political Scaffolding & the Construction of Change: Constitutionalism & Democratic Governance in Africa. 2008. *(978-1-59221-634-5(X))*; 416p. pap. *(978-1-59221-635-2(8))* Africa World Pr.
Kaluya, Professor M. D. The Audacity to Change: Breaking the Berlin Wall in Africa. 2011. 148p. pap. 14.95 *(978-1-4502-8577-3(5))* iUniverse, Inc.
Kariuki, David Mureithi. Faith Based Project Sustainability in Afric. 2011. 80p. pap. ***(978-3-8443-3375-6(4))*** Lambert Academic Publishing.
Kieh, George Klay. Africa & the Third Millennium. 2007. *(978-1-59221-604-8(8))*; 326p. pap. *(978-1-59221-605-5(6))* Africa World Pr.
Kieh, George Klay, Jr. Beyond State Failure & Collapse: Making the State Relevant in Africa. 2007. (ENG., Illus.). 304p. 73.50 *(978-0-7391-0892-5(1))* Lexington Bks.
—Globalization & its Implications for Africa. Wonkeryor, Edward Lama, ed. 2011. (ENG.). 80.00 *(978-0-9770904-2-6(6))* Africana Homestead Legacy Pubs., Inc.
Kieh, George Klay, ed. Africa & the new Globalization. 2008. 206p. 114.95 *(978-0-7546-7138-1(0))* Ashgate Publishing Co.
Kihoza, Nou'el. Impact of Micro-Finance Institutions on Poverty Alleviation. 2011. 64p. pap. ***(978-3-8433-8528-2(9))*** Lambert Academic Publishing.
Kofi, Tetteh A. & Desta, Asayehgn. Saga of African Underdevelopment: A Viable Approach for Africa's Sustainable Development in the 21st Century. 2007. *(978-1-59221-582-9(3))*; 346p. pap. *(978-1-59221-583-6(1))* Africa World Pr.
Krabacher, Thomas, et al. Africa. 13th ed. 2010. (Global Studies). (ENG., Illus.). 320p. (C). pap. 50.00 *(978-0-07-352776-5(9)*, 0073527769, McGraw-Hill/Dushkin) McGraw-Hill Higher Education.
Krabacher, Thomas, et al. Global Studies: Africa. 14th ed. 2012. (Global Studies). (ENG., Illus.). 448p. (C). pap. 50.00 ***(978-0-07-802623-2(7)***, 0078026237, McGraw-Hill/Dushkin) McGraw-Hill Higher Education.
Krishna, Kamini. India's Brewing Support for Sub-Saharan Afric. 2011. 76p. pap. ***(978-3-8443-3444-9(0))*** Lambert Academic Publishing.
Krotz, Larry. The Uncertain Business of Doing Good: Outsiders in Africa. 2009. (ENG., Illus.). 220p. pap. 24.95 *(978-0-87013-852-2(9))* Michigan State Univ. Pr.
Kuada, John. African Journal of Business & Economic. 2006. (ENG.). 160p. per. *(978-1-905068-63-0(8))* Adonis & Abbey Publishers Ltd.
Kuada, John, ed. African Journal of Business & Economic Research. 2007. 124p. per. *(978-1-905068-93-7(X))* Adonis & Abbey Publishers Ltd.
—African Journal of Business & Economic Research, Volume 2, Nos 2 And. 2007. 116p. per. *(978-1-905068-14-2(X))* Adonis & Abbey Publishers Ltd.
—Challenges of Enterprise-Driven Economic Growth in Africa (African Journal of Business & Economic Research, Vol. 3. 2008. 120p. pap. *(978-1-906704-06-3(6))* Adonis & Abbey Publishers Ltd.
Lael Brainard & Chollet, Derek, eds. Too Poor for Peace? Global Poverty, Conflict, & Security in the 21st Century. annot. ed. 2007. (ENG.). 175p. per. 22.95 *(978-0-8157-1375-3(4))* Brookings Institution Pr.
Lall, Sanjaya & Kraemer-Mbula, Erika. Industrial Competitiveness in Africa: Lessons from East Asia. 2006. (Viewpoint Ser.). (ENG., Illus.). 136p. pap. 25.95 *(978-1-85339-618-2(4))* Practical Action Publishing GBR. Dist: Stylus Publishing, LLC.
Laouisset, Djamel Eddine. The Algerian Steel Industry Growth Decade: 1968-1978. 2010. pap. 47.00 *(978-1-61761-190-2(5))* Nova Science Pubs., Inc.
Latigo, Alfred A. R. The Best Options for Afric: 11 Political, Economic & Divine Principles. 2009. 236p. 35.00 *(978-1-4269-1918-3(2))* Trafford Publishing.
—The Best Options for Africa: 11 Political, Economic & Divine Principles. 2009. 236p. 35.00 *(978-1-4269-0767-8(2))* Trafford Publishing.
Lee, David R. & Ndulo, Muna. The Food & Financial Crises in Sub-Saharan Africa: Origins, Impacts & Policy Implications. 2012. 304p. 160.00 ***(978-1-84593-828-4(3))*** CABI GBR. Dist: Stylus Publishing, LLC.
Lemarchand, Rene. The Dynamics of Violence in Central Africa. 2009. (National & Ethnic Conflict in the 21st Century Ser.). (Illus.). 344p. (C). pap. 27.50 *(978-0-8122-2090-2(0))* Univ. of Pennsylvania Pr.
Lewanika, Lucas. Strategically Positioning Botswana Development Corporation in the Mkt. 2010. 108p. pap. *(978-3-8383-5844-4(9))* Lambert Academic Publishing.
Lituchy, Terri, et al, eds. Management in Africa: Macro & Micro Perspectives. 2012. (Routledge Advances in Management & Business Studies). (ENG.). 232p. (C). 125.00 ***(978-0-415-53646-2(4))*** Routledge.
Lockwood, Matthew. The State They're In: An Agenda for International Action on Poverty in Africa. 2nd rev. ed. 2006. (Viewpoints Ser.). (ENG.). 208p. pap. 24.95 *(978-1-85339-640-3(0))* Practical Action Publishing GBR. Dist: Stylus Publishing, LLC.
Lorentzen, Jo, ed. Resource Intensity, Knowledge & Development: Insights from Africa & South America. 2008. (ENG.). 272p. pap. 36.95 *(978-0-7969-2213-7(6))* Human Sciences Research Council ZAF. Dist: Independent Pubs. Group.
Lowi, Miriam R. Oil Wealth & the Poverty of Politics: Algeria Compared. 2009. (Cambridge Middle East Studies). (ENG., Illus.). 250p. 93.00 *(978-0-521-11318-2(0))* Cambridge Univ. Pr.
Lumumba-Kasongo, Tukumbi. Japan-Africa Relations. 2010. (ENG.). 294p. 89.00 *(978-0-230-61932-6(0))* Palgrave Macmillan.
Lundsgaarde, Erik, ed. Africa Toward 2030: Challenges for Development Policy. 2011. (Rethinking International Development Ser.). (ENG., Illus.). 320p. 95.00 ***(978-0-230-27990-2(2))*** Palgrave Macmillan.
Lushaba, Lwazi. Development As Modernity, Modernity As Development. 2009. (Illus.). 78p. pap. *(978-2-86978-252-5(7))* Council for the Development of Social Science Research in Africa SEN. Dist: Michigan State Univ. Pr.
Lust, Ellen M. & Ndegwa, Stephen N., eds. Governing Africa¿s Changing Societies: Dynamics of Reform. 2012. 180p. 55.00 ***(978-1-58826-834-1(9))*** Rienner, Lynne Pubs.
Lwemamu, Helen. Gender & Work Challenges in the Informal Sector of Ugand. 2011. 168p. pap. ***(978-3-8443-0093-2(7))*** Lambert Academic Publishing.
Maathai, Wangari. The Challenge for Africa. 2009. (ENG.). 336p. 25.00 *(978-0-307-37740-1(7)*, Pantheon) Knopf Doubleday Publishing Group.
Madichie, Nnamdi. The Economic Distintegration of Africa - Any Lessons from Europe? 2011. 68p. pap. ***(978-3-8454-0312-0(8))*** Lambert Academic Publishing.
Mahajan, Vijay & Gunther, Robert E. Africa Rising: How 900 Million African Consumers Offer More Than You Think. 2008. (ENG., Illus.). 288p. 34.99 *(978-0-13-233942-1(0))* Wharton Schl. Publishing.
Malunga, Chiku. Oblivion or Utopia: The Prospects for Africa. 2009. (ENG., Illus.). 148p. 52.50 *(978-0-7618-4985-8(8))*; pap. 26.50 *(978-0-7618-4986-5(6))* Univ. Pr. of America, Inc.
Malunga, Chiku Watchman. Oblivion or Utopia: The Prospects for Africa. 2010. (Illus.). viii, 136p. E-Book *(978-0-7618-4987-2(4))* Univ. Pr. of America, Inc.
Martinez, Luis. The Violence of Petrodollar Regimes: Algeria, Iraq & Libya. 2012. (Columbia/Hurst Ser.). (ENG.). 288p. (gr. 17). 50.00 ***(978-0-231-70302-4(3))*** Columbia Univ. Pr.
Mazama, Ama. Africa in the 21st Century: Toward a New Future. 2007. (African Studies: History, Politics, Economics & Culture Ser.). 286p. 138.00 *(978-0-415-95773-1(7))* Routledge.
Mbah, Emmanuel M. & Salm, Steven J. Globalization & the African Experience. 2012. pap. ***(978-1-61163-158-6(0))*** Carolina Academic Pr.
Mbaiwa, Joseph. Tourism, Livelihoods & Conservation. 2010. 212p. pap. *(978-3-8383-7023-1(6))* Lambert Academic Publishing.
Mbeseha, Timothy & Nkemnji, John. Bellah Ngeh Development Insight. 2008. (Illus.). 144p. *(978-0-9755261-6-3(2))* Nkemnji Global Tech.
McGowan, Patrick J., et al, eds. Power, Wealth & Global Equity: An International Relations Textbook for Africa. 3rd ed. 2007. (ENG., Illus.). 441p. pap. 67.95 *(978-1-919713-93-9(X))* Juta Academic ZAF. Dist: Independent Pubs. Group.
McQueen, Jeremy S. Economic, Political, & Social Issues of Africa. 2012. (Series: African Political, Economic, & Security Issues Ser.). 262p. 129.00 *(978-1-61209-957-6(2))* Nova Science Pubs., Inc.
Melber, Henning & Southall, Roger, eds. A New Scramble for Africa? Imperialism, Investment & Development. 2009. 440p. pap. 49.00 *(978-1-86914-171-4(7))* Univ. of Natal Pr. ZAF. Dist: International Specialized Bk. Services.

Melber, Henning, et al. Africa, Regional Cooperation & the World Market: Socio-Economic Strategies in Times of Global Trade Regimes. 2006. (NAI Discussion Papers). 72p. pap. 13.95 (978-91-7106-559-9(8)) Nordiska Afrikainstitutet SWE. Dist: Stylus Publishing, LLC.

Mensah, Joseph, ed. Understanding Economic Reforms in Africa: A Tale of Seven Nations. 2006. (ENG., Illus.). 312p. 116.00 (978-1-4039-8756-3(4)) Palgrave Macmillan.

Mentan, Tatah. The State in Africa: An Analysis of Impacts of Historical Trajectories of Global Capitalist Expansion & Domination in the Continent. 2010. 438p. pap. (978-9956-616-12-1(5)) Langaa Research & Publishing Common Initiative Group CMR. Dist: Michigan State Univ. Pr.

Meredith, Martin. The Fate of Africa: A History of the Continent since Independence. 2011. (ENG., Illus.). 816p. pap. 21.99 (978-1-61039-071-2(7)) PublicAffairs.

The Millennium Challenge Corporation in Africa: Promise Versus Progress: Hearing Before the Subcommittee on Africa & Global Health of the Committee on Foreign Affairs, House of Representatives, One Hundred Tenth Congress, First Session, June 28, 2007. 2007. (Illus.). iii, 87p. (978-0-16-079311-0(4), 552-070-36389-1) United States Government Printing Office.

Modi, Renu, ed. South-South Cooperation: Africa on the Centre Stage. 2011. (International Political Economy Ser.). (ENG., Illus.). 288p. 85.00 (978-0-230-24985-4(3)) Palgrave Macmillan.

Mohamoud, Abdullah, ed. Shaping a New Africa. 2007. 208p. per. 35.00 (978-90-6832-583-6(3)) Royal Tropical Institute Pr. (KIT (Koninklijk Instituut voor de Tropen) NLD. Dist: Stylus Publishing, LLC.

Mongo, Achiri. The State of Rural Roads in Cameroon: How Conscious Neglect of Infrastructure Has Perpetuated Economic Stagnation. 2010. 222p. pap. 23.95 (978-1-4327-4411-3(9)) Outskirts Pr., Inc.

Morton, Kathryn. Aid & Dependence. 2011. (ENG.). 208p. 95.00 (978-0-415-59275-8(5)) Routledge.

Moseley, William. Clashing Views on African Issues. 4th ed. 2011. (Taking Sides Ser.). (ENG., Illus.). 464p. (C). pap. 48.00 (978-0-07-805008-4(1), 0078050081, McGraw-Hill/Dushkin) McGraw-Hill Higher Education.

Moseley, William G. Clashing Views on African Issues. 3rd ed. 2008. (Taking Sides Ser.). (ENG.). 416p. (C). pap. 48.00 (978-0-07-351518-2(3), 0073515183, McGraw-Hill/Dushkin) McGraw-Hill Higher Education.

Moseley, William G. & Gray, Leslie C., eds. Hanging by a Thread: Cotton, Globalization, & Poverty in Africa. 2008. (Ohio RIS Global Ser.). (ENG., Illus.). 304p. pap. 24.00 (978-0-89680-260-5(4)) Ohio Univ. Pr.

Moss, Todd J. African Development: Making Sense of Issues & Actors. 2007. (Illus.). 250p. (C). pap. 23.50 (978-1-58826-472-5(6)); lib. bdg. 59.95 (978-1-58826-496-1(3)) Rienner, Lynne Pubs.

—African Development: Making Sense of the Issues & Actors. 2nd ed. 2011. (Illus.). 285p. (C). pap. 24.50 (978-1-58826-769-6(5)) Rienner, Lynne Pubs.

Moyo, Bhekinkosi, ed. Africa in Global Power Play: Debates, Challenges & Potential Reforms. 2007. 364p. per. (978-1-905068-62-3(X)) Adonis & Abbey Publishers Ltd.

—Africa in Global Power Play: Debates, Challenges & Potential Reforms (HB) 2007. 364p. (978-1-905068-61-6(1)) Adonis & Abbey Publishers Ltd.

Moyo, Dambisa. Dead Aid: Why Aid Is Not Working & How There Is a Better Way for Africa. (ENG., Illus.). 208p. 2010. pap. 14.00 (978-0-374-53212-3(5)) 2009. 24.00 (978-0-374-13956-8(3)) Farrar, Straus & Giroux.

Mshomba, Richard E. Africa & the World Trade Organization. 2011. (ENG., Illus.). 384p. pap. 34.99 (978-1-107-40153-2(4)) Cambridge Univ. Pr.

Munene, Ishmael. An Interdisciplinary Primer in African Studies. 2011. (ENG., Illus.). 330p. 85.00 (978-0-7391-6597-3(6)) Lexington Bks.

Munene, Ishmael & Munene, Ishmael I. An Interdisciplinary Primer in African Studies. 2011. (ENG., Illus.). 330p. pap. 34.95 (978-0-7391-6598-0(4)) Lexington Bks.

Munene, Ishmael I. An Interdisciplinary Primer in African Studies. 2011. (Illus.). xiii, 308p. (978-0-7391-6887-5(8)) Lexington Bks.

Mungai, Rose & World Bank. Africa Development Indicators 2011. 2011. (ENG.). cd-rom 50.00 (978-0-8213-8782-5(0), 9780821387825) World Bank Pubns.

Musoro, Raymond. The Impacts of Tourism in the Southwest Province of Cameroon. 2010. 128p. pap. (978-3-8383-0197-6(8)) Lambert Academic Publishing.

Mvula, Levi. Maternal Mortality As a Human Rights Issue in Malawi. 2011. 88p. pap. (978-3-8443-9639-3(X)) Lambert Academic Publishing.

Mwakikagile, Godfrey. Africa Is in A Mess What Went Wrong and. 2006. pap. (978-0-9802534-7-4(0)) New Africa Pr.

Nakku, Victoria Brenda. Capital Market Development & Market Efficiency. 2011. 92p. pap. (978-3-8433-9080-4(0)) Lambert Academic Publishing.

Ndiaye, Abdoulaye, ed. African Researchers & Decision-makers: Building Synergy for Development. 2009. 98p. pap. (978-2-86978-260-0(8)) Council for the Development of Social Science Research in Africa SEN. Dist: Michigan State Univ. Pr.

Ndikumana, Léonce & Boyce, James. Africa's Odious Debt. 2011. (African Arguments Ser.). (ENG., Illus.). 160p. 107.95 (978-1-84813-458-4(4)) Zed Bks., Ltd. GBR. Dist: Macmillan.

Ndulo, Muna, ed. Democartic Reform in Africa: The Impact on Governance & Poverty Alleviation. 2006. (Illus.). 320p. pap. 34.95 (978-0-85255-946-8(1), Currey, James) Boydell & Brewer, Ltd. GBR. Dist: Boydell & Brewer, Inc.

—Democratic Reform in Africa: The Impact on Governance & Poverty Alleviation. 2006. (Illus.). 320p. 90.00 (978-0-85255-945-1(3), Currey, James) Boydell & Brewer, Ltd. GBR. Dist: Boydell & Brewer, Inc.

Ndulu, Benno, et al. Challenges of African Growth: Opportunities, Constraints, & Strategic Directions. 2007. (Stand Alones Ser.). (ENG., Illus.). 276p. per. 29.95 (978-0-8213-6882-4(6), 9780821368824) World Bank Pubns.

Ndulu, Benno J., et al. eds. The Political Economy of Economic Growth in Africa, 1960-2000, 2 vols. 2007. (ENG., Illus.). 760p. 180.00 (978-0-521-87849-4(7)) Cambridge Univ. Pr.

Ndulu, Benno J., et al. The Political Economy of Economic Growth in Africa, 1960-2000, 2 vols., Vol. 1. 2009. (ENG., Illus.). 470p. pap. 52.00 (978-0-521-12775-2(0)) Cambridge Univ. Pr.

Nederlof, Suzanne & Heemskerk, Willem, eds. Access of the Poor to Agricultural Services: The Role of Farmers' Organizations in Social Inclusion. 2007. (Bulletins of the Royal Tropical Institute Ser.). (Illus.). 160p. per. 35.00 (978-90-6832-642-0(2)) Royal Tropical Institute Pr. (KIT (Koninklijk Instituut voor de Tropen) NLD. Dist: Stylus Publishing, LLC.

Newell, Sasha. The Modernity Bluff: Crime, Consumption, & Citizenship in Cote D'Ivoire. 2012. (ENG., Illus.). 296p. 85.00 (978-0-226-57519-3(5)); pap. 27.50 (978-0-226-57520-9(9)) Univ. of Chicago Pr.

Niang, Abdoulaye. Towards a Viable & Credible Development in Africa: The Push Factors. 2010. (Illus.). 120p. 18.95 (978-1-57197-455-6(5), Ivy House Publishing Group) Pentland Pr., Inc.

Nielinger, Olaf. Information & Communication Technologies for Development in Africa: An Assessment of ICT Strategies & ICT Utilisation in Tanzania, Vol. 533. 2006. (European University Studies Ser.: Vol. 31). (Illus.). 352p. pap. 62.95 (978-0-8204-9877-5(7)) Lang, Peter Publishing, Inc.

Njoh, Ambe J. Tradition, Culture & Development in Africa: Historical Lessons for Modern Development Planning. 2006. (Heritage, Culture, & Identity Ser.). (Illus.). 240p. 130.00 (978-0-7546-4884-0(2)) Ashgate Publishing Co.

Nketiah, Eric. Distance Forum: A multidisciplinary book of scholarly Articles. 2011. (Illus.). 192p. pap. 51.66 (978-1-4567-8926-8(0)) AuthorHouse.

Ohno, Kenichi & Ohno, Izumi, eds. Diversity & Complementarity in Development Aid: East Asian Lessons for African Growth. 2013. (Routledge-GRIPS Development Forum Studies). (ENG.). 256p. (C). 168.00 (978-0-415-68759-1(4)) Routledge.

Okoli, Chitu. Experts Speak on E-Business in Sub-Saharan Afric. 2010. (Illus.). 128p. pap. (978-3-639-23615-6(7)) VDM Verlag Dr. Mueller e.K.

Okonga Wabuyabo M , Brigitte. Benchmarking in the Kenyan & South African Electricity Sectors. 2011. 84p. pap. (978-3-8433-9219-8(6)) Lambert Academic Publishing.

Olawale, Akin. Perceived Effect of Internal Stakeholders on Project Success. 2010. 60p. pap. (978-3-8383-7176-4(3)) Lambert Academic Publishing.

Oluyi, Isaac. The Interplay of Literary Practice, Technology & Entrepreneurship. 2010. 72p. pap. (978-3-8383-5443-9(5)) Lambert Academic Publishing.

Onderc, Pete. Africa's Moment. 2010. 108p. pap., pap. 12.00 (979-0-615-22190-8(4)) Asset Capital, Ltd.

Onitiri-Abiola, Modupe. Farewell to Poverty: Let There Be Light in Africa. 2007. pap. 9.00 (978-0-8059-7377-8(X)) Dorrance Publishing Co., Inc.

Organisation for Economic Co-operation and Development Staff. African Economic Outlook 2008. 2008. (ENG.). 620p. pap. 124.00 (978-92-64-04585-9(6)) Organization for Economic Cooperation & Development.

Organisation for Economic Co-Operation and Development Staff. Economic Diversification in Africa: A Review of Selected Countries. 2011. (Illus.). 86p. pap. 33.00 (978-92-64-03805-9(1)) Organization for Economic Cooperation & Development.

Organisation for Economic Co-operation and Development Staff & African Development Bank Group Staff. African Economic Outlook 2009: Overview. 2009. (Illus.). 200p. pap. 63.00 (978-92-64-06170-5(3)) Organization for Economic Cooperation & Development.

Organisation for Economic Co-operation and Development: Development Centre & African Development Bank Group. African Economic Outlook 2011. 2011. (Illus.). 303p. pap. 77.00 (978-92-64-11175-2(1)) Organization for Economic Cooperation & Development.

Orji, Madukar. Lust for Corruption. 2009. 258p. 29.99 (978-1-4415-4940-2(4)); pap. 19.99 (978-1-4415-4939-6(0)) Xlibris Corp.

Oruonye, Emeka Daniel & S. Sanusi, S. Socio-Economic & Ecological Impact of Resattlement Scheme. 2011. 264p. pap. (978-3-8433-8541-1(6)) Lambert Academic Publishing.

An Overview of U.S. Policy in Africa: Hearing Before the Subcommittee on Africa & Global Health of the Committee on Foreign Affairs, House of Representatives, One Hundred Eleventh Congress, Second Session, March 24, 2010. 2010. (Illus.). iii, 122p. (978-0-16-086457-5(7), 552-070-41514-9) United States Government Printing Office.

Oxaal, Ivar, et al, eds. Beyond the Sociology of Development: Economy & Society in Latin America & Africa. 2011. (ENG.). 320p. 115.00 (978-0-415-60193-1(2)) Routledge.

Oxford Staff. Oil & Gas in Africa. 2009. (ENG., Illus.). 152p. 75.00 (978-0-19-956578-8(3)) Oxford Univ. Pr., Inc.

Padayachee, Vishnu, ed. The Political Economy of Africa. 2010. (ENG., Illus.). 456p. 67.95 (978-0-415-48039-0(6)); 200.00 (978-0-415-48038-3(8)) Routledge.

Patterson, Rubin, ed. African Brain Circulation: Beyond the Drain-Gain Debate. 2007. (International Studies in Sociology & Social Anthropology Ser.). 200p. pap. (978-90-04-15385-6(5)) BRILL.

Peterside, Chamberlain S. WEALTH EFFECT Africa in Midst of Global Economic Transformation. 2007. 156p. pap. 15.49 (978-1-4357-0096-3(1)) Lulu Enterprises Inc.

—WEALTH EFFECT Focus on Economic Reform & Sustainable Development in Nigeria. 2008. 288p. pap. 15.50 (978-1-4357-1201-0(3)) Lulu Enterprises Inc.

Prabhakar, Akhilesh Chandra. Globalisation & Afric. 2011. 388p. pap. (978-3-8433-9051-4(7)) Lambert Academic Publishing.

Rakiya Omaar & Ashamu, Elizabeth. A Second Chance: What Economic Opportunities Mean for Impoverished Women in Rwanda. 2008. (Illus.). 152p. pap. (978-1-60643-261-7(3)) Independent Pub.

Rasheed. Development, Participation & Democracy in Africa: Four Essays. xii, 148p. (978-0-7983-0127-5(9)) Africa Institute of South Africa.

Rhazaoui, Ahmed, et al. The Millennium Development Goals in Africa. 2008. (ENG., Illus.). 300p. pap. 28.95 (978-2-7178-4853-3(3)) Economica, Editions FRA. Dist: Brookings Institution Pr.

Rhodes, Terry, et al. Less Walk More Talk: How Celtel & the Mobile Phone Changed Africa. 2009. (ENG., Illus.). 236p. 39.95 (978-0-470-74320-1(4), Wiley) Wiley, John & Sons, Inc.

Roberts, Kofi J. The Sargasso Bridge: America Speaks, Africa Answers. 2009. 268p. 30.95 (978-0-595-48771-4(8)); pap. 20.95 (978-0-595-48645-8(2)) iUniverse, Inc.

ROBSON, Peter & Lury, D. A., eds. The Economies of Africa. 2011. (ENG.). 528p. 150.00 (978-0-415-59594-0(0)) Routledge.

Rodney, Walter. How Europe Underdeveloped Africa. 2011. 340p. 24.95 (978-1-57478-048-2(4)) Black Classic Pr.

Rugumamu, Severine M. Globalization Demystified: Africa's Possible Development Futures. 2006. 256p. pap. (978-9976-60-416-0(5)) Dar es Salaam Univ. Pr. TZA. Dist: Michigan State Univ. Pr.

Runge, Jurgen, ed. Geological Resources & Good Governance in Central Africa. 2011. (ENG., Illus.). 292p. 99.95 (978-0-415-58267-4(9), CRC Press) Taylor & Francis Group GBR. Dist: Taylor & Francis Group.

Russell, Margo & Russell, Martin. Afrikaners of the Kalahari: White Minority in a Black State. 2009. (African Studies). (ENG.). 184p. pap. 31.99 (978-0-521-10140-0(9)) Cambridge Univ. Pr.

S Kamara, Fouday. Economic & Social Crises in Sierra Leone. 2011. 328p. pap. (978-3-8443-1319-2(2)) Lambert Academic Publishing.

Sabwa, Jean-Marie. Modeling of Spaza Shop Operations. 2011. 112p. pap. (978-3-8443-1477-9(3)) Lambert Academic Publishing.

Samuel, Binuomote. Supply Response of Export & Food Crops in Some Ecowas Countries. 2011. 264p. pap. (978-3-8443-1873-9(9)) Lambert Academic Publishing.

Sardanis, Andrew. A Venture in Africa: The Challenges of African Business. 2007. (ENG., Illus.). 320p. 61.00 (978-1-84511-288-2(1)) I. B. Tauris & Co., Ltd. GBR. Dist: Macmillan.

Seck, Diery & Busari, Dipo T. Growth & Development in Africa. 2009. (978-1-59221-684-0(6)); 520p. pap. (978-1-59221-685-7(4)) Africa World Pr.

Seidman, Ann Willcox, et al. Africa's Challenge: Using Law for Good Governance & Development. 2006. (Illus.). viii, 228p. (978-1-59221-470-9(3)); 360p. pap. (978-1-59221-471-6(1)) Africa World Pr.

Sender, John & Smith, Sheila. The Development of Capitalism in Africa. 2011. (ENG.). 192p. 95.00 (978-0-415-60196-2(7)) Routledge.

Severino, Jean-Michel & Ray, Olivier. Africa's Moment. 2012. (ENG., Illus.). 352p. 25.00 (978-0-7456-5157-6(7)) Polity Pr. GBR. Dist: Wiley, John & Sons, Inc.

Shapiro, Brett. Nourishing the Land, Nourishing the People: The Story of One Rural Developmen[t] Project in the Deep South of Madagascar That Made a Difference. 2010. (FRE., Illus.). 202p. pap. (978-1-84593-740-9(6)) CABI.

—Nourishing the Land, Nourishing the People: The Story of One Rural Developmen[t] Project in the Deep South of Madagascar That Made a Difference. 2010. (FRE., Illus.). 210p. 125.00 (978-1-84593-739-3(2)) CABI GBR. Dist: Stylus Publishing, LLC.

Shivji, Issa G. Accumulation in an African Periphery: A Theoretical Framework. 2008. 110p. pap. (978-9987-08-031-1(6)) Mkuki na Nyoka Pubs. TZA. Dist: Michigan State Univ. Pr.

Sirleaf, Amos. African Liberation. 2010. 168p. 33.49 (978-1-4490-9344-0(2)) AuthorHouse.

Sirleaf, Amos M. "Deluxe". African Liberation. 2010. 168p. pap. 17.99 (978-1-4490-9343-3(4)) AuthorHouse.

Smith, Malinda S., ed. Beyond the 'African Tragedy' Discourses on Development & the Global Economy. 2006. (Illus.). 330p. 120.00 (978-0-7546-4824-6(9)) Ashgate Publishing Co.

Sodikoff, Genese Marie. Forest & Labor in Madagascar: From Colonial Concession to Global Biosphere. 2012. (ENG.). 208p. pap. 25.00 (978-0-253-00577-9(9), 0253005779); (Illus.). 70.00 (978-0-253-00309-6(1), 0253003091) Indiana Univ. Pr.

Sommers, Marc. Stuck: Rwandan Youth & the Struggle for Adulthood. 2012. (Studies in Security & International Affairs Ser.). (ENG., Illus.). 288p. 59.95 (978-0-8203-3890-3(7)) Univ. of Georgia Pr.

Soyinka-Airewele, Peyi & Edozie, Rita Kiki, eds. Reframing Contemporary Africa: Politics, Economics, & Culture in the Global Era. rev. ed. 2010. 412p. (C). pap. 44.00 (978-0-87289-407-5(X)) CQ Pr.

Spenceley, Anna. Responsible Tourism: Critical Issues for Conservation & Development. Spenceley, Anna, ed. 2008. (ENG., Illus.). 416p. (C). 135.00 (978-1-84407-639-0(3)) Routledge.

Stone, Lacey. Rwandan Genocide Economic Decline & Increased Willingness to Murder. 2008. 80p. pap. (978-3-8364-9781-7(6)) VDM Verlag Dr. Mueller e.K.

Strudsholm, Jasper, et al. Reality Bites: An African Decade. 2010. (Illus.). 144p. pap. 33.95 (978-1-919930-22-0(1)) Double Storey Bks. ZAF. Dist: International Publishers Marketing.

Sundaram, Jomo Kwame. Economic Liberalisation & Development in Afric. 2008. (FRE.). 76p. pap. (978-2-86978-257-0(8)) Council for the Development of Social Science Research in Africa SEN. Dist: Michigan State Univ. Pr.

Sunderland, David, ed. Communications in Africa, 1880-1939, 5 vols. 2012. (Britain & Africa Ser.). (ENG.). 2144p. 795.00 (978-1-84893-064-3(X)) Pickering & Chatto Pubs., Ltd. GBR. Dist: Ashgate Publishing Co.

Svare, Marte. Sudan & the Resource Curse. 2011. 96p. pap. (978-3-8443-0521-0(1)) Lambert Academic Publishing.

Taderera, Faustino. The Missing Dimension in Globalisation. 2010. 448p. pap. (978-3-8383-7170-2(4)) Lambert Academic Publishing.

Tandon, Yash & Tax Justice Network Africa. Tax Us if You Can: Why Africa Should Stand up for Tax Justice. 2011. (ENG.). 94p. pap. 14.95 (978-0-85749-042-1(7)) Pambuzuka Pr. GBR. Dist: Independent Pubs. Group.

Taylor, Scott D. Globalization & the Cultures of Business in Africa. 2012. (ENG., Illus.). 256p. 75.00 (978-0-253-00266-2(4), 0253002664); pap. 27.00 (978-0-253-00573-1(6), 0253005736) Indiana Univ. Pr.

Tesar, George & Kuada, John, eds. Marketing Management & Strategy: An African Casebook. 2012. (ENG.). 256p. (C). 155.00 (978-0-415-78333-0(X)); pap. 59.95 (978-0-415-78334-7(8)) Routledge.

The African Development Bank, ed. African Development Report 2007. 2007. (African Development Report). (ENG., Illus.). 336p. pap. 45.00 (978-0-19-923886-6(3)) Oxford Univ. Pr., Inc.

The World Bank. Sustaining Educational & Economic Momentum in Africa. 2010. (World Bank Working Papers: 195). (ENG.). 64p. pap. 15.00 (978-0-8213-8377-3(9), 9780821383773) World Bank Pubns.

Thorp, Rosemary, et al. The Developmental Challenges of Mining & Oil: Lessons from Africa & Latin America. 2012. (Conflict, Inequality & Ethnicity Ser.). (ENG., Illus.). 248p. 85.00 (978-1-137-00146-7(1)) Palgrave Macmillan.

Turshen, Meredeth. African Women: A Political Ecomony. Turshen, Meredeth, ed. 2010. (ENG., Illus.). 230p. 89.00 (978-0-230-10675-8(7)) Palgrave Macmillan.

Uko, Nung. Africa in the Ancient World & Today: The Wealth of a Nation Is the Excellent Education & Skills of Its Honestly Hardworking Citizens. 2009. 704p. pap. 25.99 (978-1-4490-0127-8(0)) AuthorHouse.

United Nations. African Statistical Yearbook 2009. 2011. (MUL & ENG., Illus.). 390p. pap. 55.00 (978-92-1-025164-8(4)) United Nations Pubns.

—Asia-Pacific Development Journal, June 2007. 2008. (ENG.). 162p. pap. 29.00 (978-92-1-120524-4(7)) United Nations Pubns.

—Economic Report on Africa 2010: Promoting High-level Sustainable Growth to Reduce Unemployment in Africa. 2010. (ENG.). 238p. pap. 40.00 (978-92-1-125113-5(3)) United Nations Pubns.

United Nations. Economic Report on Africa 2011: Governing Development in Africa - the Role of the State in Economic Transformation. 2011. (ENG.). 144p. pap. 40.00 (978-92-1-125116-6(8)) United Nations Pubns.

United Nations & United Nations: Economic Commission For Africa. African Statistical Yearbook 2010. 2011. (MUL., Illus.). 400p. pap. 55.00 (978-92-1-025165-5(2)) United Nations Pubns.

United Nations Conference on Trade and Development. Economic development in Africa 2008: Export performance following trade liberalization; some patterns & policy Perspectives. 2008. (ENG., Illus.). 112p. pap. 30.00 (978-92-1-112754-6(8)) United Nations Pubns.

United Nations Development Programme. Assessment of Development Results: Benin. 2009. 84p. pap. 23.00 (978-92-1-126239-1(9)) United Nations Pubns.

—Assessment of Development Results: Burkina Faso. 2010. 88p. pap. 15.00 (978-92-1-126274-2(7)) United Nations Pubns.

United Nations, Economic Commission for Africa Staff & African Union Staff, contrib. by. Assessing Regional Integration in Africa 2008: Towards Monetary & Financial Integration in Africa. 2009. (ENG., Illus.). 310p. pap. 55.00 (978-92-1-125109-8(5)) United Nations Pubns.

United Nations Publications Staff, contrib. by. Economic Report on Africa 2007: Accelerating Africa's Development through Diversification. 2007. (ENG.). 180p. pap. 35.00 (978-92-1-125104-3(4)) United Nations Pubns.

United Nations: Department of Economic and Social Affairs. Innovation for sustainable Development: Local case studies from Africa. 2008. (ENG., Illus.). 60p. pap. 15.00 (978-92-1-104578-5(9)) United Nations Pubns.

United Nations: Economic Commission for Africa & African Union. Economic report on Africa 2009: Developing African agriculture through regional value Chains. 2009. (ENG., Illus.). 210p. pap. 40.00 (978-92-1-125111-1(7)) United Nations Pubns.

Vudo, Emmanuel Yenshu, ed. Civil Society & the Search for Development Alternatives in Cameroon. 2008. 236p. pap. (978-2-86978-220-4(9)) Council for the Development of Social Science Research in Africa SEN. Dist: Michigan State Univ. Pr.

Vujicic, Marko, et al. Working in Health: Financing & Managing the Public Sector Health Workforce. 2009. (Directions in Development Ser.). (ENG.). 320p. pap. 35.00 (978-0-8213-7802-1(3), 9780821378021) World Bank Pubns.

Vulture Funds & the Threat to Debt Relief in Africa: A Call to Action at the G-8 & Beyond: Hearing Before the Subcommittee on Africa & Global Health of the Committee on Foreign Affairs, House of Representatives, One Hundred Tenth Congress, First Session, May 22, 2007. 2007. iii, 30p. (978-0-16-079140-6(5), 552-070-36236-3) United States Government Printing Office.

Wabuke, Mel. Eye on Africa. 2010. (Illus.) 544p. 29.95 (978-0-9820795-2-2(4)) Coltan Bks.

Wijngaarden, Vanessa. The World Bank & the Representation of Afric. 2010. 124p. pap. (978-3-639-27072-3(X)) VDM Verlag Dr. Mueller e.K.

Wilson, Ernest J., 3rd & Wong, Kelvin R., eds. Negotiating the Net in Africa: The Politics of Internet Diffusion. 2006. (Ipolitics Ser.). (Illus.). 230p. lib. bdg. 55.00 *(978-1-58826-421-3(1))* Rienner, Lynne Pubs.

Wilson Ramadhani, Selestine. Revision Economics: Micro ad Macroeconomics. 2008. (Illus.). 292p. pap. *(978-1-84748-039-2(X))* Athena Pr.

Wilson, Sigismond. The Spatial & Social Impacts of Sierra Leone's Civil War 1991-2001. 2011. 120p. pap. ***(978-3-8443-1741-1(4))*** Lambert Academic Publishing.

World Bank. Africa Development Indicators 2011. 2011. (Africa Development Indicators Ser.). (ENG.). 194p. pap. 100.00 incl. cd-rom *(978-0-8213-8731-3(6)*, 9780821387313) World Bank Pubns.

—Africa's Infrastructure: A Time for Transformation. 2009. (ENG., Illus.). 384p. pap. 39.95 *(978-0-8213-8041-3(9)*, 9780821380413) World Bank Pubns.

—The Little Data Book on Africa 2010. 2010. (Africa Development Indicators Ser.). (ENG.). 128p. pap. 15.00 *(978-0-8213-8255-4(1)*, 9780821382554) World Bank Pubns.

—Youth & Employment in Africa - The Potential, the Problem, the Promise 2008/2009. 2009. (Africa Development Indicators Ser.). (ENG.). 216p. pap. 100.00 incl. cd-rom *(978-0-8213-7787-1(6)*, 9780821377871) World Bank Pubns.

World Bank Center Staff. Africa's Future, Africa's Challenge: Early Childhood Care & Development in Sub-Saharan Africa. Garcia, Marito et al, eds. 2008. (Directions in Development Ser.). (ENG., Illus.). 556p. per. 25.00 *(978-0-8213-6886-2(9)*, 9780821368862) World Bank Pubns.

World Bank Staff. Africa Development Indicators 2007: Spreading & Sustaining Growth in Africa. 2008. (Africa Development Indicators Ser.). (ENG.). 176p. pap. 100.00 *(978-0-8213-7283-8(1)*, 9780821372838) World Bank Pubns.

—Angola: Oil, Broad-Based Growth, & Equity. 2007. (Country Studies). (ENG., Illus.). 214p. per. 25.00 *(978-0-8213-7102-2(9)*, 9780821371022) World Bank Pubns.

—The Little Data Book on Africa 2006. 2006th rev. ed. 2006. (Africa Development Indicators Ser.). (ENG.). 124p. per. 15.00 *(978-0-8213-6704-9(8)*, 9780821367049) World Bank Pubns.

—The Little Data Book on Africa 2007. rev. ed. 2007. (Africa Development Indicators Ser.). (ENG.). 120p. per. 15.00 *(978-0-8213-6971-5(7)*, 9780821369715) World Bank Pubns.

World Bank Staff, contrib. by. Little Data Book on Africa 2008-09. 2008. (ENG.). 128p. pap. 15.00 *(978-0-8213-7788-8(4)*, 9780821377888) World Bank Pubns.

World Bank Staff, creator. African Development Indicators 2006: From the World Bank Africa Database. 2006th rev. ed. 2006. (Africa Development Indicators Ser.). (ENG., Illus.). 160p. pap. 125.00 incl. cd-rom *(978-0-8213-6537-3(1)*, 9780821365373) World Bank Pubns.

World Bank Staff & Timofeev, Andrey. World Bank Africa Database 2006. 2006th rev. ed. 2006. (African Development Indicators Ser.). 220p. cd-rom 200.00 *(978-0-8213-6563-2(0))* World Bank Pubns.

Yartey, Charles Amo. Stock Market Development in Afric. 2008. 236p. pap. *(978-3-639-02820-1(1))* VDM Verlag Dr. Mueller e.K.

Yesigat, Habtamu. Impact of Input-Output Market Development Interventions in Ethiopi. 2011. 96p. pap. ***(978-3-8443-0713-9(3))*** Lambert Academic Publishing.

Young, Tom. Africa. 2010. (Beginners Guide (Oneworld) Ser.). (ENG., Illus.). 224p. pap. 14.95 *(978-1-85168-753-4(X))* Oneworld Pubns. GBR. Dist: National Bk. Network.

AFRICA—ECONOMIC INTEGRATION

Adejumobi, Said & Olukoshi, Adebayo O. The African Union & New Strategies for Development in Africa. 2008. *(978-1-59221-660-4(9))*; pap. *(978-1-59221-661-1(7))* Africa World Pr.

—The African Union & New Strategies for Development in Africa. 2008. 508p. 129.95 *(978-1-60497-574-1(1))* Cambria Pr.

Awoyiga, Babatunde. The Track to Deep Regional Integration. 2010. 104p. pap. *(978-3-639-23549-4(5))* VDM Verlag Dr. Mueller e.K.

Bobo, Benjamin F. & Sintim-Aboagye, Hermann. Neo-Liberalism, Interventionism & the Developmental State: Implementing the New Partnership for Africa's Development. 2011. ***(978-1-59221-790-8(7))***; ***(978-1-59221-789-2(3))*** Africa World Pr.

Calderisi, Robert. The Trouble with Africa: Why Foreign Aid Isn't Working. 2007. (ENG.). 256p. pap. 18.95 *(978-1-4039-7651-2(1))* Palgrave Macmillan.

Gathii, James Thuo. African Regional Trade Agreements as Legal Regimes. 2011. (Cambridge International Trade & Economic Law Ser.). (ENG., Illus.). 524p. 105.00 *(978-0-521-76983-9(3))* Cambridge Univ. Pr.

Kerekou, Monse Tchando. The Process of Integration in Afric. 2009. 96p. pap. *(978-3-639-15558-7(0))* VDM Verlag Dr. Mueller e.K.

Khamis, Kassim. Promoting the African Union. 2008. 450p. 34.95 *(978-0-936508-33-7(7))* Barber, Lilian Pr.

Kimbugwe, Kato, et al. Economic Development Through Regional Trade: A Role for the New East African Community? 2012. (ENG., Illus.). 288p. 100.00 ***(978-0-230-31421-4(X))*** Palgrave Macmillan.

Kufuor, Kofi Oteng. The Institutional Transformation of the Economic Coomunity of West African States. 2006. 190p. 130.00 *(978-0-7546-4488-0(X))* Ashgate Publishing Co.

Levitt, Jeremy, ed. Africa: Mapping New Boundaries in International Law. 2008. (ENG.). 355p. 104.00 *(978-1-84113-618-9(2))* Hart Publishing Ltd. GBR. Dist: International Specialized Bk. Services.

Loice, Natukunda. East African Customs Union & Foreign Direct Investment in Uganda: Economic Integration & Foreign Direct Investment for Developing Countries in Africa. 2011. 56p. pap. ***(978-3-639-33057-1(9))*** VDM Verlag Dr. Mueller e.K.

Maruba, James L. Globalization & Africa. 2008. (Illus.). xii, 168p. 79.00 *(978-1-60456-424-2(5))* Nova Science Pubs., Inc.

Melber, Henning, et al. Africa, Regional Cooperation & the World Market: Socio-Economic Strategies in Times of Global Trade Regimes. 2006. (NAI Discussion Papers). 72p. pap. 13.95 *(978-91-7106-559-9(8))* Nordiska Afrikainstitutet SWE. Dist: Stylus Publishing, LLC.

Nzioka, Charles. Market Integration in Mozambican Maize Markets. 2008. 116p. pap. 19.95 *(978-99944-55-26-3(5))* African Bks. Collective, Ltd. GBR. Dist: Lightning Source, Inc.

Oppong, Richard Frimpong. Legal Aspects of Economic Integration in Africa. 2011. (ENG.). 402p. 99.00 *(978-1-107-00717-8(8))* Cambridge Univ. Pr.

Oshikoya, Temitope W. Monetary & Financial Integration in West Africa. 2010. (Routledge Studies in Development Economics Ser.). (ENG., Illus.). 288p. (C). 145.00 *(978-0-415-58008-3(0)*, Routledge) Taylor & Francis Group GBR. Dist: Taylor & Francis Group.

Robson, Peter. Economic Integration in Africa. 2011. (ENG.). 328p. 115.00 *(978-0-415-59373-1(5))* Routledge.

—Integration, Development & Equity: Economic Integration in West Africa. 2011. (ENG.). 208p. 95.00 *(978-0-415-59572-8(X))* Routledge.

Rukato, Hesphina. Prospects for Democracy & Development under NEPAD. 2009. *(978-1-59221-734-2(6))*; (Illus.). 310p. pap. *(978-1-59221-735-9(4))* Africa World Pr.

United Nations, Economic Commission for Africa Staff & African Union Staff, contrib. by. Assessing Regional Integration in Africa 2008: Towards Monetary & Financial Integration in Africa. 2009. (ENG., Illus.). 310p. pap. 55.00 *(978-92-1-125109-8(5))* United Nations Pubns.

United Nations: Economic Commission for Africa & African Union. Economic report on Africa 2009: Developing African agriculture through regional value Chains. 2009. (ENG., Illus.). 210p. pap. 40.00 ***(978-92-1-125111-1(7))*** United Nations Pubns.

United Nations: Economic Commission for Europe. Assessing Regional Integration in Africa Iv: Enhancing Intra-African Trade. 2010. (ENG.). 524p. pap. 55.00 ***(978-92-1-125114-2(1))*** United Nations Pubns.

Welz, Martin. Decolonization Sovereignty & the African Union. 2012. (Global Institutions Ser.). (ENG., Illus.). 208p. (C). 130.00 ***(978-0-415-52201-4(3))*** Routledge.

AFRICA—ECONOMIC POLICY

Abbascia, Davide & Poggi, Giusto, eds. Cote D'Ivoire (Ivory Coast) Election Crisis & Aftermath. 2011. (African Political, Economic, & Security Issues Ser.). 95.00 ***(978-1-61470-457-7(0))*** Nova Science Pubs., Inc.

Adeleke, Oluwole, et al. Economics of Cassava-Based Production Systems in Osun State Nigeri. 2011. 60p. pap. ***(978-3-8443-2108-1(X))*** Lambert Academic Publishing.

African Development Bank, creator. The African Development Report 2006: Aid, Debt Relief & Development in Africa. 2006. (ENG., Illus.). 176p. per. 39.95 *(978-0-19-929847-1(5))* Oxford Univ. Pr., Inc.

African Development Bank Group Staff, ed. African Development Report 2011. 2012. (ENG.). 220p. pap. 29.95 ***(978-0-19-958716-2(7))*** Oxford Univ. Pr., Inc.

African Development Bank Staff. African Development Report 2008/2009. Oxford University Press Staff, ed. 2009. (African Development Report). (ENG., Illus.). 336p. pap. 39.95 *(978-0-19-954894-1(3))* Oxford Univ. Pr., Inc.

—African Development Report 2009-2010: Ports, Logistics, & Trade in Africa. 2010. (African Development Report). (ENG., Illus.). 232p. pap. 35.00 *(978-0-19-956605-1(4))* Oxford Univ. Pr., Inc.

Agyeman-Duah, Ivor, ed. Pilgrims of the Night: Development Challenges & Opportunities in Africa. 2011. (Illus.). 220p. 35.00 *(978-0-9562401-5-6(1))* Clarke, Ayebia Publishing, Ltd. GBR. Dist: Rienner, Lynne Pubs.

Ajakaiye, David Olusanya & Oyejide, T. Ademola, eds. Trade Infrastructure & Economic Development. 2011. (Routledge Studies in Development Economics Ser.). (ENG., Illus.). 368p. (C). 155.00 *(978-0-415-66913-9(8))* Routledge.

Akonor, Kwame. African Economic Institutions. 2009. (Global Institutions Ser.). (ENG., Illus.). 160p. (C). 126.00 *(978-0-415-77637-0(6))* Routledge.

Allen, Rory & United Nations Conference on Trade and Development Staff. Investment Policy Review: Nigeria. 2009. (ENG., Illus.). 152p. pap. 20.00 *(978-92-1-112743-0(2))* United Nations Pubns.

Amin, Aloysius Aloysius & Dubois, Jean-Luc. Croissance et Dtveloppement Au Cameroun: D'une Croissance EquilibrTe a un DTveloppement Equitable. 2008. (FRE.). 440p. pap. *(978-9956-558-87-2(7))* Langaa Research & Publishing Common Initiative Group CMR. Dist: Michigan State Univ. Pr.

Amutabi, Maurice N., ed. Studies in the Economic History of Kenya: Land, Water, Railways, Education, & Entrepreneurship. 2009. (Illus.). viii, 721p. *(978-0-7734-3907-8(2))* Mellen, Edwin Pr., The.

Anderson, Kym & Masters, William A., eds. Distortions to Agricultural Incentives in Africa. 2009. (Trade & Development Ser.). (ENG., Illus.). 656p. pap. 39.95 *(978-0-8213-7652-2(7)*, 9780821376522) World Bank Pubns.

Ayadi, Felix, ed. Building New Strategic Partnerships for Africa's Economic Development, Volume 8. annuals 2007. 712p. per. 100.00 net. *(978-0-9765288-2-1(7)*, IAABD) International Academy of African Business & Development.

Ayittey, George B. N. Defeating Dictators: Fighting Tyranny in Africa & Around the World. 2011. (ENG., Illus.). 288p. 28.00 *(978-0-230-10859-2(8))* Palgrave Macmillan.

Ayuk, Elias & Marouani, Mohamed Ali. The Policy Paradox in Africa: Strengthening Links Between Economic Research & Policymaking. 2007. *(978-1-59221-576-8(9))*; 320p. pap. *(978-1-59221-577-5(7))* Africa World Pr.

Bagia, Terry. Delta in Distress: The Politics & Perils of Petroleum Patronage in Nigeria. 2009. 176p. pap. 23.00 *(978-1-4490-0373-9(7))* AuthorHouse.

Barrett, Christopher B. Understanding & Reducing Persistent Poverty in Africa. Carter, Michael & Little, Peter, eds. 2007. (ENG.). 224p. 150.00 *(978-0-415-41138-7(6))* Routledge.

Bauer, Steffen & Scholz, Imme, eds. Adaptation to Climate Change in Southern Africa: New Boundaries for Development. 2010. (Climate & Development Ser.). (ENG., Illus.). 120p. 99.95 *(978-1-84971-163-0(1))* Routledge.

Beuret, Jean-Eudes & Fino, Daniel. Aide Au Développement et Conflit Armé Au Burundi: Pourquoi Rester, Comment Agir? 2009. (FRE., Illus.). 168p. *(978-2-8111-0173-2(X))* Editions-Diffusion Karthala.

Bhengu, Mfuniselwa J. African Economic Humanism: The Rise of an African Economic Philosophy. 2011. (Transformation & Innovation Ser.). 242p. 114.95 *(978-1-4094-0435-4(8)*, Gower Publishing Co., Ltd.) Ashgate Publishing, Ltd. GBR. Dist: Ashgate Publishing Co.

Bigsten, Arne & Durevall, Dick. The African Economy & Its Role in the World Economy. 2008. (NAI Current African Issues Ser.). 66p. pap. 12.95 *(978-91-7106-625-1(X))* Nordiska Afrikainstitutet SWE. Dist: Stylus Publishing, LLC.

Black, Philip, et al, eds. Public Economics. 5th ed. 2012. (ENG., Illus.). 348p. pap. 60.00 ***(978-0-19-599515-2(5))*** Oxford Univ. Pr., Inc.

Bobo, Benjamin F. & Sintim-Aboagye, Hermann. Neo-Liberalism, Interventionism & the Developmental State: Implementing the New Partnership for Africa's Development. 2011. ***(978-1-59221-789-2(3))***; ***(978-1-59221-790-8(7))*** Africa World Pr.

Boko, Sylvain Hounkponou & Seck, Diery. Back on Track: Sector-Led Growth in Africa & Implications for Development. 2009. *(978-1-59221-708-3(7))*; 480p. pap. *(978-1-59221-709-0(5))* Africa World Pr.

—NEPAD & the Future of Economic Policy in Africa. 2007. *(978-1-59221-558-4(0))*; 324p. pap. *(978-1-59221-559-1(9))* Africa World Pr.

Cheru, Fantu. Africa's Development in the 21st Century: Reshaping the Research Agenda. 2008. (NAI Current African Issues Ser.). 50p. pap. 12.95 *(978-91-7106-628-2(4))* Nordiska Afrikainstitutet SWE. Dist: Stylus Publishing, LLC.

Chuhan-Pole, Punam & Angwafo, Manka, eds. Yes, Africa Can: Success Stories from a Dynamic Continent. 2011. (ENG., Illus.). 496p. pap. 49.95 *(978-0-8213-8745-0(6)*, 9780821387450) World Bank Pubns.

Clément, Jean A. P. & Peiris, Shanaka J. Post-Stabilization Economics in Sub-Saharan Africa: Lessons from Mozambique. 2008. (Illus.). viii, 397p. pap. *(978-1-58906-677-9(4))* International Monetary Fund.

Engh, Ida-Eline. Developing Capacity to Realise Socio-Economic Rights: The Example of the Right to Food in the Context of HIV/AIDS in South Africa & Uganda. 2008. 500p. pap. 110.75 *(978-90-5095-766-3(8))* Intersentia Uitgevers N.V. BEL. Dist: International Specialized Bk. Services.

Ensign/Bertrand. Rwanda: History & Hope. 2009. (ENG.). 174p. pap. 28.50 *(978-0-7618-4943-8(2))* Univ. Pr. of America, Inc.

Falola, Toyin & House-Soremekun, Bessie, eds. Globalization & Sustainable Development in Africa. 2011. (Rochester Studies in African History & the Diaspora Ser.: Volume 51). (Illus.). 484p. 80.00 *(978-1-58046-392-8(4))* Univ. of Rochester Pr.

Falola, Toyin & Paddock, Adam, eds. Environment & Economics in Nigeria. 2011. (Routledge African Studies). (ENG., Illus.). 296p. (C). 125.00 *(978-0-415-89592-7(8))* Routledge.

Farole, Thomas. Special Economic Zones in Africa: Comparing Performance & Learning from Global Experiences. 2011. (Directions in Development Ser.). (ENG., Illus.). 324p. pap. 35.00 *(978-0-8213-8638-5(7)*, 9780821386385); *(978-0-8213-8639-2(5))* World Bank Pubns.

Foster, Vivien, et al. Batir des Ponts: Le Rôle Croissan Tde la Chine Dans le Financement des Infrastructures en Afrique Subsaharienne. 2009. (Trends & Policy Options (PPIAF) Ser.: 5). (FRE., Illus.). 120p. pap. 22.00 *(978-0-8213-7938-7(0)*, 9780821379387) World Bank Pubns.

Frindéthié, K. Martial. Globalization & the Seduction of Africa's Ruling Class: An Argument for a New Philosophy of Development. 2010. (ENG., Illus.). 204p. pap. 55.00 *(978-0-7864-4840-1(7))* McFarland & Co., Inc. Pubs.

Griffiths, Claire. Globalizing the Postcolony: Contesting Discourses of Gender & Development in Francophone Africa. 2010. (Illus.). xv, 323p. *(978-0-7391-4384-1(0))*; (ENG., 340p. 80.00 *(978-0-7391-4382-7(4))* Lexington Bks.

Gulde, Anne-Marie & Tsangarides, Charalambos G. The CFA Franc Zone: Common Currency, Uncommon Challenges. 2008. (Illus.). xi, 397p. *(978-1-58906-675-5(8))* International Monetary Fund.

Haan, Leo de & Engel, Ulf, eds. African Alternatives. 2007. (African-Europe Group for Interdisciplinary Studies). pap. *(978-90-04-16113-9(9))* BRILL.

Handley, Antoinette. Business & the State in Africa: Economic Policy-Making in the Neo-Liberal Era. 2008. (ENG., Illus.). 304p. 92.00 *(978-0-521-88605-5(8))*; pap. 40.00 *(978-0-521-71371-9(4))* Cambridge Univ. Pr.

Harrison. The World Bank & Africa. 2007. pap. 41.95 *(978-0-415-45983-9(4))* Routledge.

Harriss-White, Barbara & Heyer, Judith, eds. The Comparative Political Economy of Development. 2012. (ENG., Illus.). 358p. (C). pap. 44.95 ***(978-0-415-80995-5(9))*** Routledge.

Harriss-white, Barbara & Heyer, Judith, eds. The Comparative Political Economy of Development: Africa & South Asia. 2010. (Routledge Studies in Development Economics Ser.). (ENG., Illus.). 384p. (C). 145.00 *(978-0-415-55288-2(5))* Routledge.

Holmberg, Johan. Natural Resources in Sub-Saharan Africa: Assets & Vulnerabilities. 2008. (NAI Current African Issues Ser.). 52p. pap. 12.95 *(978-91-7106-624-4(1))* Nordiska Afrikainstitutet SWE. Dist: Stylus Publishing, LLC.

Hope, Kempe R. The Political Economy of Development in Kenya. 2011. (ENG., Illus.). 304p. (gr. 17). 130.00 ***(978-1-4411-9121-2(6))*** Continuum International Publishing Group, Ltd. GBR. Dist: National Bk. Network.

Hussein, Ashatu. Determinants of Firms' Export Performance. 2009. 100p. pap. *(978-3-639-19419-7(5))* VDM Verlag Dr. Mueller e.K.

Iskander, Natasha N. Creative State: Forty Years of Migration & Development Policy in Morocco & Mexico. 2010. (Illus.). 392p. 69.95 *(978-0-8014-4872-0(7))*; pap. 29.95 *(978-0-8014-7599-3(6))* Cornell Univ. Pr. (ILR Pr.).

Johnson, Omotunde E. G. African Economic Development: Cooperation, Ownership & Leadership. 2007. 286p. (C). 109.95 *(978-0-7734-5409-5(8))* Mellen, Edwin Pr., The.

Kabbar, Reem, et al. Poverty in Khartoum State, Sudan. 2011. 84p. pap. ***(978-3-8443-9164-0(9))*** Lambert Academic Publishing.

Kalla, Britt. Utopia or Reality? - the Implementation of a Human Rights-Based Approach to the New Partnership for Africa's Development. 2008. 104p. pap. *(978-3-639-03238-3(1))* VDM Verlag Dr. Mueller e.K.

Kargbo, Joseph M. Political Instability & Economic Recovery in Sierra Leone: Lessons in Applied Econometrics, Modeling, & Policy Making, Book 1, Book 2, 2 vols. 2011. (Illus.). 960p. ***(978-0-7734-1597-3(1))*** Mellen, Edwin Pr., The.

Kenday Samuel Kamara. Sierra Leone Policy Papers: Perspectives on Social Innovation & Change in Sierra Leone. 2009. 272p. pap. 28.95 *(978-1-4401-8073-6(3))* iUniverse, Inc.

Kerekou, Monse Tchando. The Process of Integration in Afric. 2009. 96p. pap. *(978-3-639-15558-7(0))* VDM Verlag Dr. Mueller e.K.

Kuada, John, ed. Challenges of Enterprise-Driven Economic Growth in Africa (African Journal of Business & Economic Research, Vol. 3. 2008. 120p. pap. *(978-1-906704-06-3(6))* Adonis & Abbey Publishers Ltd.

Kuteesa, Florence, et al, eds. Uganda's Economic Reforms: Insider Accounts. 2010. (ENG., Illus.). 304p. 99.00 *(978-0-19-955622-9(9))* Oxford Univ. Pr., Inc.

Lee, Rachel. Africa in the World Trade Organisation. 2012. (Routledge/RIPE Studies in Global Political Economy Ser.). (ENG.). 208p. (C). 140.00 *(978-0-415-42327-4(9))* Routledge.

Lowi, Miriam R. Oil Wealth & the Poverty of Politics: Algeria Compared. 2009. (Cambridge Middle East Studies). (ENG., Illus.). 250p. 93.00 *(978-0-521-11318-2(0))* Cambridge Univ. Pr.

Lule, Elizabeth & Haacker, Markus. The Fiscal Dimensions of HIV/AIDS in Botswana, South Africa, Swaziland, & Uganda. 2011. (ENG.). 308p. pap. 40.00 ***(978-0-8213-8807-5(X)***, 9780821388075) World Bank Pubns.

Mensah, Joseph, ed. Understanding Economic Reforms in Africa: A Tale of Seven Nations. 2006. (ENG., Illus.). 312p. 116.00 *(978-1-4039-8756-3(4))* Palgrave Macmillan.

Mogues, Tewodaj & Benin, Samuel E., eds. Public Expenditures for Agricultural & Rural Development in Africa. 2012. (Routledge Studies in Development Economics Ser.: 94). (ENG., Illus.). 304p. (C). 140.00 *(978-0-415-60367-6(6))* Routledge.

Mohan, Giles & Zack-Williams, Tunde, eds. The Politics of Transition: State, Democracy, & Economic Development in Africa. 288p. 99.95 *(978-1-59221-152-4(6))* Africa World Pr.

Moss, Todd J. African Development: Making Sense of the Issues & Actors. 2nd ed. 2011. (Illus.). 285p. (C). pap. 24.50 *(978-1-58826-769-6(5))* Rienner, Lynne Pubs.

Muhumuza, William. Credit & Reduction of Poverty in Uganda Structural Adjustment Reforms in Context. 2007. (Illus.). 328p. pap. *(978-9970-02-688-3(7))* Fountain Pubs. Ltd. UGA. Dist: Michigan State Univ. Pr.

Musafiri, Prosper. Budgeting for Effectiveness in Rwanda, 2003-07: From Reconstruction to Reform. 2010. *(978-0-8213-8561-6(5))*; (World Bank Working Papers: 205). (ENG., Illus.). 304p. pap. 35.00 *(978-0-8213-8558-6(5)*, 9780821385586) World Bank Pubns.

Mutai, Henry. Compliance with International Trade Obligations: The Common Market for Eastern & Southern Africa. 2007. *(978-90-411-2664-1(3))* Kluwer Law International.

Nagl, Florian & Nagengast, J. Adventure Tourism in Southern Africa: Development, Strategies & Opportunities for an Increasing Market. 2008. 96p. pap. *(978-3-639-10304-5(1))* VDM Verlag Dr. Mueller e.K.

Nanang, David M. Natural Resources in Ghana: Mangement, Policy & Economics. Nunifu, Thompson K., ed. 2010. (Environmental Science, Engineering & Technology Ser.). (Illus.). 372p. 89.00 *(978-1-61668-020-6(2))* Nova Science Pubs., Inc.

Ndulu, Benno J., et al, eds. The Political Economy of Economic Growth in Africa, 1960-2000, 2 vols. 2007. (ENG., Illus.). 760p. 180.00 *(978-0-521-87849-4(7))* Cambridge Univ. Pr.

Ndulu, Benno J., et al. The Political Economy of Economic Growth in Africa, 1960-2000, 2 vols., Vol. 1. 2009. (ENG., Illus.). 470p. pap. 52.00 *(978-0-521-12775-2(0))* Cambridge Univ. Pr.

Norcliffe, Glen & Pinfold, Tom, eds. Planning African Development. 2011. (ENG.). 208p. 95.00 *(978-0-415-59633-6(5))* Routledge.

Nord, Roger. Tanzania: The Story of an African Transition. 2009. (Illus.). v, 74p. *(978-1-58906-822-3(X))* International Monetary Fund.

Nzioka, Charles. Market Integration in Mozambican Maize Markets. 2008. 116p. pap. 19.95 *(978-99944-55-26-3(5))* African Bks. Collective, Ltd. GBR. Dist: Lightning Source, Inc.

Obadan, Mike I. The Economic & Social Impact of Privatisation of State-Owned Enterprises in Afric. 2008. 92p. pap. *(978-2-86978-228-0(4))* Council for the Development of Social Science Research in Africa SEN. Dist: Michigan State Univ. Pr.

Odetola, Olatunde. Military Regimes & Development: A Comparative Analysis in African Societies. 2011. (ENG.). 216p. 95.00 *(978-0-415-60184-9(3))* Routledge.

Odularu, Gbadebo Olusegun. The Impact of Agricultural Trade Liberalization on National Food Security in Nigeria, 1970-2000. 2010. 62p. pap. 19.95 *(978-1-59942-340-1(5)*, Dissertation.com) Universal Pubs.

Okanja, Otieno. Kenya at Forty-Five: 1963 - 2008 (Economic Performance, Problems & Prospects. 2010. (Illus.). 124p. pap. *(978-1-84748-696-7(7))* Athena Pr.

Okonjo-Iweala, Ngozi & Osafo-Kwaako, Philip. Nigeria's Economic Reforms: Progress & Challenges. 2007. 0.00 net. *(978-0-9790376-5-8(4))* Brookings Global Economy & Development.

Okpara, John. Management & Economic Development in Sub-Saharan Africa. 2007. 260p. *(978-1-905068-51-7(4))* Adonis & Abbey Publishers Ltd.

Oliveira, Ricardo Soares de. Oil & Politics in the Gulf of Guinea. 2007. (Columbia/Hurst Ser.). (ENG., Illus.). 400p. (gr. 17). 105.00 *(978-0-231-70027-6(X))* Columbia Univ. Pr.

Opoku, Darko Kwabena. The Politics of Government-Business Relations in Ghana, 1982-2008. 2010. (ENG., Illus.). 278p. 89.00 *(978-0-230-10556-0(4))* Palgrave Macmillan.

Organisation for Economic Co-operation and Development Staff. African Economic Outlook 2008. 2008. (ENG.). 620p. pap. 124.00 *(978-92-64-04585-9(6))* Organization for Economic Cooperation & Development.

Organisation for Economic Co-Operation and Development Staff. Economic Diversification in Africa: A Review of Selected Countries. 2011. (Illus.). 86p. pap. 33.00 ***(978-92-64-03805-9(1))*** Organization for Economic Cooperation & Development.

Organisation for Economic Co-operation and Development Staff & African Development Bank Group Staff. African Economic Outlook 2009: Overview. 2009. (Illus.). 200p. pap. 63.00 *(978-92-64-06170-5(3))* Organization for Economic Cooperation & Development.

Organisation for Economic Co-operation and Development Staff & Michel Colin, de Verdiàre. West African Perspectives: Resources for Development. 2009. (West African Studies). (Illus.). 112p. pap. 63.00 *(978-92-64-05975-7(X))* Organization for Economic Cooperation & Development.

Organisation for Economic Co-operation and Development: Development Centre & African Development Bank Group. African Economic Outlook 2011. 2011. (Illus.). 303p. pap. 77.00 ***(978-92-64-11175-2(1))*** Organization for Economic Cooperation & Development.

Otman, Waniss A. & Karlberg, Erling. The Libyan Economy: Economic Diversification & International Repositioning. 2007. (ENG., Illus.). xviii, 474p. 169.00 *(978-3-540-46460-0(3)*, 3540464603) Springer.

Otsuka, Keijiro. Rural Poverty & Income Dynamics in Asia & Africa. Estudillo, Jonna P. & Sawada, Yasuyuki, eds. 2008. (Routledge Studies in Development Economics Ser.). (Illus.). XXIV, 232p. 160.00 *(978-0-415-48009-3(4))* Routledge.

Padayachee, Vishnu, ed. The Political Economy of Africa. 2010. (ENG., Illus.). 456p. 67.95 *(978-0-415-48039-0(6))*; 200.00 *(978-0-415-48038-3(8))* Routledge.

Parsons, Raymond, ed. Zumanomics: Which Way to Shared Prosperity in South America? - Challenges for a New Government. 2010. (ENG.). 208p. pap. 22.95 *(978-1-77009-647-9(7))* Jacana Media ZAF. Dist: Independent Pubs. Group.

Pitcher, M. Anne. Party Politics & Economic Reform in Africa's Democracies. 2012. (African Studies: 119). (ENG.). 328p. 99.00 ***(978-0-521-44962-5(6))***; (Illus.). pap. 29.99 ***(978-0-521-73826-2(1))*** Cambridge Univ. Pr.

Quintyn, Marc & Verdier, Genevieve, eds. African Finance in the 21st Century. 2010. (ENG., Illus.). 176p. 116.00 *(978-0-230-58050-3(5))* Palgrave Macmillan.

Rasheed. Development, Participation & Democracy in Africa: Four Essays. xii, 148p. *(978-0-7983-0127-5(9))* Africa Institute of South Africa.

Razafimahefa, Ivohasina Fizara & Hamori, Shigeyuki. International Competitiveness in Africa: Policy Implications in the Sub-Saharan Region. 2007. (Advanced Studies in Theoretical & Applied Econometrics Ser.). (Illus.). xii, 170p. 109.00 *(978-3-540-68920-1(6))* Springer.

Rugumamu, Severine M. Globalization Demystified: Africa's Possible Development Futures. 2006. 256p. pap. *(978-9976-60-416-0(5))* Dar es Salaam Univ. Pr. TZA. Dist: Michigan State Univ. Pr.

S Kamara, Fouday. Economic & Social Crises in Sierra Leone. 2011. 328p. pap. ***(978-3-8443-1319-2(2))*** Lambert Academic Publishing.

Schneider, Susanne. Broad-based Black Economic Empowerment in der Republik Südafrika. 2008. (Schriften zum Arbeitsrecht und Wirtschaftsrecht Ser.). 174p. pap. 56.95 *(978-3-631-57310-5(3))* Lang, Peter GmbH, Europaischer Verlag der Wissenschaften DEU. Dist: Lang, Peter.

Seck, Diery & Busari, Dipo T. Growth & Development in Africa. 2009. *(978-1-59221-684-0(6))*; 520p. pap. *(978-1-59221-685-7(4))* Africa World Pr.

Sekkat, Khalid, ed. Market Dynamics & Productivity in Developing Countries. 2009. 180p. pap. *(978-1-4419-1208-4(8))* Springer Singapore Pte. Ltd.

Sender, John & Smith, Sheila. The Development of Capitalism in Africa. 2011. (ENG.). 192p. 95.00 *(978-0-415-60196-2(7))* Routledge.

Shaver, Lea & Rizk, Nagla, eds. Access to Knowledge in Egypt: New Research on Intellectual Property, Innovation & Development. 2010. (ENG.). 208p. 75.00 *(978-1-84966-008-2(5))* Bloomsbury Publishing.

Siwale, Mengo. Scenario Planning 2020 for Southern African Economic Empowerment. 2011. (Illus.). 100p. pap. ***(978-3-8443-2852-3(1))*** Lambert Academic Publishing.

Soares de Oliveira, Ricardo & Oliveira, Ricardo Soares de. Oil & Politics in the Gulf of Guinea. 2007. (Columbia/Hurst Ser.). (ENG., Illus.). 400p. (gr. 17). pap. 35.00 *(978-0-231-70029-0(6))* Columbia Univ. Pr.

Spenceley, Anna, ed. Responsible Tourism: Critical Issues for Conservation & Development. 2010. (ENG., Illus.). 416p. pap. 49.95 *(978-1-84971-070-1(8))* Routledge.

Taylor, Scott D. Globalization & the Cultures of Business in Africa. 2012. (ENG., Illus.). 256p. 75.00 ***(978-0-253-00266-2(4)***, 0253002664); pap. 27.00 ***(978-0-253-00573-1(6)***, 0253005736) Indiana Univ. Pr.

The African Development Bank, ed. African Development Report 2007. 2007. (African Development Report). (ENG., Illus.). 336p. pap. 45.00 *(978-0-19-923886-6(3))* Oxford Univ. Pr., Inc.

The World Bank. Fostering Technology Absorption in Enterprises in Southern Africa. 2011. (Directions in Development Ser.). (ENG.). 224p. pap. 30.00 ***(978-0-8213-8818-1(5)***, 9780821388181) World Bank Pubns.

Tripp, Aili Mari. Museveni's Uganda: Paradoxes of Power in a Hybrid Regime. 2010. (Illus.). 230p. (C). 59.95 *(978-1-58826-731-3(8))*; pap. 22.00 *(978-1-58826-707-8(5))* Rienner, Lynne Pubs.

United Nations Conference on Trade and Development Staff, contrib. by. Investment Policy Review. 2010. (ENG., Illus.). 124p. pap. 27.00 ***(978-92-1-112785-0(8))*** United Nations Pubns.

Weertman, Warren. Desperately Seeking Fdi. 2010. 228p. pap. *(978-3-639-15502-0(5))* VDM Verlag Dr. Mueller e.K.

Wodon, Quentin, ed. Growth & Poverty Reduction: Case Studies from West Africa. 2007. (World Bank Working Papers: 79). (ENG., Illus.). 150p. per. 20.00 *(978-0-8213-6629-5(7)*, 9780821366295) World Bank Pubns.

World Bank Staff. Tunisia's Global Integration: A Second Generation of Reforms to Boost Growth & Employment. 2008. (Country Studies). (ENG., Illus.). 154p. pap. 28.00 *(978-0-8213-7668-3(3)*, 9780821376683) World Bank Pubns.

Yago, Milton. Investment & Growth in Sub-Saharan Afric. 2010. 304p. pap. *(978-3-639-23551-7(7))* VDM Verlag Dr. Mueller e.K.

Zewde, Almaz. Sorting Africa's Developmental Puzzle: The Participatory Social Learning Theory as an Alternative Approach. 2010. (ENG.). 284p. pap. 39.99 *(978-0-7618-4907-0(6))* Univ. Pr. of America, Inc.

AFRICA—EMIGRATION AND IMMIGRATION

Adepoju, Aderanti. Migration in Sub-Saharan Africa, No. 37. 2008. (NAI Current African Issues Ser.). (Illus.). 80p. pap. 23.95 *(978-91-7106-620-6(9,)* Nordiska Afrikainstitutet SWE. Dist: Stylus Publishing, LLC.

Adepoju, Aderanti, ed. International Migration Within, to & from Africa in a Globalised World. 2009. (Illus.). 264p. pap. *(978-9988-647-42-1(5))* Sub-Saharan Pubs. & Traders GHA. Dist: Michigan State Univ. Pr.

Aissaoui, Rabah. Immigration & National Identity: North African Political Movements in Colonial & Postcolonial France. 2009. (ENG.). 320p. 97.00 *(978-1-84511-835-9(9)*, Tauris Academic Studies) I. B. Tauris & Co., Ltd. GBR. Dist: Macmillan.

Arthur, John A. African Diaspora Identities: Negotiating Culture in Transnational Migration. (ENG.). 318p. 2011. pap. 36.95 ***(978-0-7391-4638-5(6))*** 2010. (Illus.). 80.00 *(978-0-7391-4637-8(8))* Lexington Bks.

Arthur, John A. African Women Immigrants in the United States: Crossing Transnational Borders. 2009. (ENG.). 244p. 89.00 *(978-0-230-61778-0(6))* Palgrave Macmillan.

Asabir, Kwesi. International Migration of Shps-Project of Kwesi. 2009. 264p. pap. *(978-3-639-18946-9(9))* VDM Verlag Dr. Mueller e.K.

Attias-Donfut, Claudine, et al, eds. Citizenship, Belonging & Intergenerational Relations in African Migration. 2012. (ENG., Illus.). 224p. 85.00 ***(978-0-230-25274-5(5))*** Palgrave Macmillan.

Batalha, Luis & Carling, Jorgen, eds. Transnational Archipelago: Perspectives on Cape Verdean Migration & Diaspora. 2008. 288p. pap. *(978-90-5356-994-8(4)*, Leiden Univ. Pr.) Amsterdam Univ. Pr.

Brand, Laurie A. Citizens Abroad: Emigration & the State in the Middle East & North Africa. 2008. (Cambridge Middle East Studies). (ENG., Illus.). 268p. pap. 40.00 *(978-0-521-10091-5(7))* Cambridge Univ. Pr.

Chatty, Dawn & Finlayson, Bill, eds. Dispossession & Displacement: Forced Migration in the Middle East & North Africa. 2010. (British Academy Occasional Papers). (ENG., Illus.). 224p. 40.00 *(978-0-19-726459-1(X))* Oxford Univ. Pr., Inc.

Creese, Gillian Laura. The New African Diaspora in Vancouver: Migration, Exclusion, & Belonging. 2011. (ENG.). 288p. ***(978-1-4426-4295-9(5))***; pap. ***(978-1-4426-1159-7(6))*** Univ. of Toronto Pr.

Crush, Jonathan & Dodson, Belinda, eds. Migration, Remittances & Development in Lesotho. 2006. (Illus.). 96p. pap. *(978-1-920409-26-5(2))* IDASA Pubs. ZAF. Dist: Michigan State Univ. Pr.

Crush, Jonathan & Tevera, Daniel, eds. Zimbabwe's Exodus: Crisis, Migration, Survival. 2006. 432p. pap. *(978-1-920409-22-7(X))* IDASA Pubs. ZAF. Dist: Michigan State Univ Pr.

Crush, Jonathan, et al. Linking Migration, Hiv/Aids & Urban Food Security in Southern & Eastern Afric. 2007. (Illus.). 64p. (C). pap. *(978-1-920118-46-4(2))* IDASA Pubs. ZAF. Dist: Michigan State Univ. Pr.

de Silva Jaysuriya, Shihan. African Identity in Asia: Cultural Effects of Forced Migration. 2009. (Illus.). xiv, 164p. 89.95 *(978-1-55876-471-2(2))*; 26Cp. pap. 28.95 *(978-1-55876-472-9(0))* Wiener, Markus Pubs., Inc.

Ennaji, Moha & Sadiqi, Fatima. Migration & Gender in Morocco: The Impact of Migration on the Women Left Behind. 2008. *(978-1-56902-291-7(7))*; (Illus.). xi, 206p. pap. *(978-1-56902-292-4(5))* Red Sea Pr.

Falola, Toyin & Afolabi, Niyi, eds. The Human Cost of African Migrations. 2007. (African Studies: History, Politics, Economics & Culture Ser.). (Illus.). 401p. 128.00 *(978-0-415-95837-0(7))* Routledge.

—Trans-Atlantic Migration: The Paradoxes of Exile. (African Studies). (ENG.). 314p. 2012. pap. 42.95 ***(978-0-415-54249-4(9))*** 2007. (Illus.). 128.00 *(978-0-415-96091-5(6))* Routledge.

Falola, Toyin & Okpeh, Okpeh Ochayi. Population Movements, Conflicts, & Displacements in Nigeria. 2007. *(978-1-59221-598-0(X))*; pap. *(978-1-59221-599-7(8))* Africa World Pr.

Falola, Toyin, et al. Migrations & Creative Expressions in Africa & the African Diaspora. 2008. 510p. pap. 55.00 *(978-1-59460-460-7(6))* Carolina Academic Pr.

Fazzina, Alixandra. A Million Shillings: Escape from Somalia. 2010. (Illus.). 248p. *(978-1-904563-84-6(3))* Trolley.

Foner, Nancy & Holtzman, Jon D. Nuer Journeys, Nuer Lives: Sudanese Refugees in Minnesota. 2nd ed. 2007. (New Immigrants Ser.). (ENG., Illus.). 160p. (C). per. 37.40 *(978-0-205-54332-8(4))* Allyn & Bacon, Inc.

Freitag, Ulrike & Oppen, Achim Von. Translocality: The Study of Globalising Processes from a Southern Perspective. 2010. *(978-90-04-18116-8(4))* BRILL.

Gebrewold, Belachew, ed. Africa & Fortress Europe: Threats & Opportunites. 2007. 208p. 114.95 *(978-0-7546-7204-3(2))* Ashgate Publishing Co.

Gemignani, Regina. African Immigrant Religions in America. Olupona, Jacob K., ed. 2007. (ENG.). 368p. 75.00 *(978-0-8147-6211-0(5))*; per. 25.00 *(978-0-8147-6212-7(3))* New York Univ. Pr.

Getahun, Solomon Addis. The History of Ethiopian Immigrants & Refugees in America, 1900-2000: Patterns of Migration, Survival, & Adjustment. 2006. (New Americans). (Illus.). 342p. 80.00 *(978-1-59332-151-2(1))* LFB Scholarly Publishing LLC.

Gratz, Tilo. Mobility, Transnationalism & Contemporary African Societies. 2008. (MUL & ENG.). 199p. *(978-1-4438-1853-7(4))* Cambridge Scholars Pub.

Hahn, Hans Peter, et al. Cultures of Migration: African Perspectives. Hahn, Hans Peter & Klute, Georg, eds. 2008. (ENG.). 296p. pap. 49.95 *(978-3-8258-0668-2(5))* Lit Verlag DEU. Dist: Transaction Pubs.

Hassanen, Sadia. Repatriation, Integration, or Resettlement: The Dilemmas of Migration among Eritrean Refugees in Eastern Sudan. 2007. (Illus.). xiv, 220p. *(978-1-56902-273-3(9))*; pap. *(978-1-56902-274-0(7))* Red Sea Pr.

Iskander, Natasha N. Creative State: Forty Years of Migration & Development Policy in Morocco & Mexico. 2010. (Illus.). 392p. 69.95 *(978-0-8014-4872-0(7))*; pap. 29.95 *(978-0-8014-7599-3(6))* Cornell Univ. Pr. (ILR Pr.).

Itto, Dominic. Self Sufficiency & Adjustment among Sudanese Refugees in Tennessee. 2011. 124p. pap. ***(978-3-8443-8176-4(7))*** Lambert Academic Publishing.

Kane, Abdoulaye & Leedy, Todd H., eds. African Migrations: Patterns & Perspectives. 2012. (ENG.). 280p. 85.00 ***(978-0-253-00308-9(3)***, 0253003083); pap. 32.00 ***(978-0-253-00576-2(0)***, 0253005760) Indiana Univ. Pr.

Kifleyesus, Abbebe. Recollections of Return, Resettlement, & Reintegration from Gash Barka in Eritrea. 2010. (ENG.). 302p. pap. ***(978-99944-55-50-8(8))*** African Bks. Collective, Ltd.

Kothor, Djifa. Consciousness among Ewé Migrants in North Americ. 2010. 60p. pap. *(978-3-8383-7364-5(2))* Lambert Academic Publishing.

Lindley, Anna. The Early Morning Phonecall: Somali Refugees' Remittances. 2010. (FM Ser.). (Illus.). 192p. 70.00 *(978-1-84545-644-3(0))* Berghahn Bks., Inc.

Ludwig, Frieder & Asamoah-Gyadu, J. Kwabena. African Christian Presence in the West: New Immigrant Congregations & Transnational Networks in North America & Europe. 2011. *(978-1-59221-807-3(5))*; 238p. pap. *(978-1-59221-808-0(3))* Africa World Pr.

Manger, Leif & Assal, Munzoul. Diasporas Within & Without Africa: Dynamism, Heterogeneity, Variation. 2006. 200p. pap. 35.00 *(978-91-7106-563-6(6))* Nordiska Afrikainstitutet SWE. Dist: Stylus Publishing, LLC.

Migration en Mauritanie: Profil national 2009. 2009. 121p. pap. *(978-92-9068-558-6(1))* International Organization for Migration (IOM).

Migration in Ghana: A Country Profile 2009. 2009. 115p. pap. *(978-92-9068-557-9(3))* International Organization for Migration (IOM).

Mott, Tamar. African Refugee Resettlement in the United States. 2009. (New Americans). 322p. 80.00 *(978-1-59332-333-2(6))* LFB Scholarly Publishing LLC.

Nickanor, Ndeyapo. The Quality of Immigration & Citizenship Services in Namibia. 2008. 48p. pap. *(978-1-920118-67-9(5))* IDASA Pubs. ZAF. Dist: Michigan State Univ. Pr.

Nyiransekuye, Hadidja. At the Receiving End. 2008. 188p. pap. *(978-3-639-07723-0(7))* VDM Verlag Dr. Mueller e.K.

Okome, Mojúbàolú Olúfúnké & Vaughan, Olufemi, eds. Transnational Africa & Globalization. 2012. (ENG., Illus.). 274p. 90.00 ***(978-0-230-33866-1(6))*** Palgrave Macmillan.

Okpewho, Isidore & Nzegwu, Nkiru, eds. The New African Diaspora: The New African Immigrant Experience. 2009. (ENG., Illus.). 544p. 75.00 *(978-0-253-35337-5(8)*, 0253353378); pap. 29.95 *(978-0-253-22095-0(5)*, 0253220955) Indiana Univ. Pr.

Omondi, Charles Ochola. Fertility & Migration in Keny. 2010. 308p. pap. *(978-3-8383-8824-3(0))* Lambert Academic Publishing.

Onah, Sebastian. From Migrants to Transnationals - Cosmological & Religious Fundamentals among Igbo Migrants in an European Setting. 2007. 236p. per. *(978-3-8364-2648-0(X))* VDM Verlag Dr. Mueller e.K.

Organisation for Economic Co-operation and Development Staff. Regional Challenges of West African Migration: African & European Perspectives. Trâmoliàres, Marie, ed. 2009. (Illus.). 249p. pap. 63.00 *(978-92-64-05593-3(2))* Organization for Economic Cooperation & Development.

—West African Mobility & Migration Policies of OECD Countries. 2009. (West African Ser.). 139p. pap. 63.00 *(978-92-64-02943-9(5))* Organization for Economic Cooperation & Development.

Otero, Solimar. Afro-Cuban Diasporas in the Atlantic World. 2010. (Rochester Studies in African History & the Diaspora Ser.: Volume 45). (Illus.). 260p. 75.00 *(978-1-58046-326-3(6))* Univ of Rochester Pr.

Paoletti, Emanuela. The Migration of Power & North-South Inequalities: The Case of Italy & Libya. 2010. (ENG., Illus.). 320p. 95.00 *(978-0-230-24926-4(4))* Palgrave Macmillan.

Patterson, Rubin, ed. African Brain Circulation: Beyond the Drain-Gain Debate. 2007. (International Studies in Sociology & Social Anthropology Ser.). 200p. pap. *(978-90-04-15885-6(5))* BRILL.

Pex, Judith Galblum. A People Tall & Smooth: Stories of Escape from Sudan to Israel. 2011. (Illus.). 224p. pap. 13.99 *(978-0-9818929-3-1(0))* CLADACH Publishing.

Piguet, François. Moving People in Ethiopia: Development, Displacement & the State. Pankhurst, Alula & Piguet, François, eds. 2009. (Eastern Africa Ser.). (Illus.). 344p. 80.00 *(978-1-84701-613-3(8)*, Currey, James) Boydell & Brewer, Ltd. GBR. Dist: Boydell & Brewer, Inc.

Ratha, Dilip. Leveraging Migration for Africa: Remittances, Skills, & Investments. 2011. ***(978-0-8213-8718-4(9))*** World Bank Pubns.

Redeker Hepner, Tricia. Soldiers, Martyrs, Traitors, & Exiles: Political Conflict in Eritrea & the Diaspora. 2011. (Ethnography of Political Violence Ser.). (Illus.). 272p. (C). pap. 22.50 *(978-0-8122-2151-0(6))* Univ. of Pennsylvania Pr.

Sardinha. Immigrant Associations, Intergration. 2009. (IMISCOE Dissertations Ser.). pap. *(978-90-8964-036-9(3))* Amsterdam Univ. Pr.

Shandy, Dianna J. Nuer-American Passages: Globalizing Sudanese Migration. 2007. (New World Diasporas Ser.). (ENG., Illus.). 224p. 59.95 *(978-0-8130-3047-0(1))* Univ. Pr. of Florida.

Spickard, Jim. Religion Crossing Boundaries: Transnational Religious & Social Dynamics in Africa & the New African Diaspora. Adogame, Afe, ed. 2010. (Religion & the Social Order Ser.). 274p. *(978-90-04-18730-6(8))* BRILL.

Streiff-Fenart, Jocelyne & Kabwe-Segatti, Aurelia Wa. The Challenge of the Threshold: Border Closures & Migration Movements in Africa. 2011. (Illus.). xviii, 269p. E-Book ***(978-0-7391-6512-6(7))*** Lexington Bks.

Streiff-Fenart/Segat. Challenge of the Threshold: Border Closures & Migration Movements in Africa. 2011. (ENG., Illus.). 288p. 75.00 ***(978-0-7391-6510-2(0))*** Lexington Bks.

Talani, Leila Simona. From Egypt to Europe: Globalisation & Migration Across the Mediterranean. 2009. (ENG., Illus.). 288p. 92.50 *(978-1-84511-669-9(0)*, Tauris Academic Studies) I. B. Tauris & Co., Ltd. GBR. Dist: Macmillan.

Ureta, Ivan. Media, Migration & Public Opinion: Myths, Prejudices & the Challenge of Attaining Mutual Understanding Between Europe & North Africa. 2011. (Illus.). 290p. pap. ***(978-3-0343-0577-8(X))*** Lang, Peter Publishing, Inc.

Ureta, Ivan & Lutterbeck, Derek. Migration, Development ,and Diplomacy: Perspectives from the Southern Mediterranean. 2010. *(978-1-56902-329-7(8))* Red Sea Pr.

Vaughan, Olufemi & Okome, Mojúbàolú Olúfúnké, eds. West African Migrations: Transnational & Global Pathways in a New Century. 2012. (ENG., Illus.). 294p. 90.00 ***(978-0-230-33867-8(4))*** Palgrave Macmillan.

Whitehouse, Bruce. Migrants & Strangers in an African City. 2012. (Illus.). x, 274p. ***(978-0-253-00075-0(0))***; (ENG.). 288p. pap. 25.00 *(978-0-253-00082-8(3)*, 0253000823) Indiana Univ. Pr.

Whitehouse, Bruce. Migrants & Strangers in an African City: Exile, Dignity, Belonging. 2012. (ENG., Illus.). 288p. 70.00 *(978-0-253-00081-1(5)*, 0253000815) Indiana Univ. Pr.

World Bank. Migration, Remittances, & Development in Africa. 2011. (ENG., Illus.). 234p. pap. 39.95 *(978-0-8213-8257-8(3)*, 9780821382578) World Bank Pubns.

Yeboah, Ian E. a. Black African Neo-Diaspora: Ghanaian Immigrant Experiences in the Greater Cincinnati, Ohio, Area. 2008. (ENG., Illus.). 258p. 78.99 *(978-0-7391-1352-3(6))* Lexington Bks.

AFRICA—ENVIRONMENTAL CONDITIONS

Akaki, Tony. Mabira Forest Giveaway: A Path to Degenerative Development. 2011. 124p. 23.95 ***(978-1-4620-1730-0(4))***; pap. 13.95 ***(978-1-4620-1728-7(2))*** iUniverse, Inc.

Akingbade, Tunde. Niger: On the Trail of the Environment. 2009. 276p. pap. 15.49 *(978-1-4389-2777-0(0))* AuthorHouse.

Amakom, Chijioke. Radioactivity in Environmental Medi. 2011. 80p. pap. ***(978-3-8433-7338-8(8))*** Lambert Academic Publishing.

Amechi, Emeka. The Millennium Development Goals & Policy Reform. 2010. 256p. pap. (978-3-639-28575-8(1)) VDM Verlag Dr. Mueller e.K.

Amede, Tilahun, et al, eds. Integrated Natural Resource Management in the Highlands of Eastern Africa. 2012. (Earthscan Studies in Natural Resource Management Ser.). (ENG., Illus.). 340p. 99.95 **(978-1-84971-424-2(X))** Routledge.

Amofah, Kwaku & Kusi-Appiah, Twumasi A. Measuring Household Access to Environmental & Health Education. 2011. 76p. pap. **(978-3-8454-2063-9(4))** Lambert Academic Publishing.

Amori, Adeola. Resource & Learning Issues in Undergraduate Practical Geography. 2010. 340p. pap. (978-3-639-26661-0(7)) VDM Verlag Dr. Mueller e.K.

Arthur, Jones Lewis & AKYAA YEBOAH ARTHUR, Irene. Ghana's Environment in Retrospect. 2010. 64p. pap. (978-3-8383-9139-7(X)) Lambert Academic Publishing.

Awange, Joseph L. & Ong'ang'a, Obiero. Lake Victoria: Ecology, Resources, Environment. 2010. (ENG., Illus.). xviii, 354p. pap. 179.00 (978-3-642-06900-0(2), 3642069002) Springer.

Ayeh, Michael. Payment for Environmental Services & Institutional Arrangements. 2009. 152p. pap. (978-3-639-19051-9(3)) VDM Verlag Dr. Mueller e.K.

Ayorinde, Kolade. Assessing Wildfire Risk in West Africa Using Remote Sensing & Gis. 2010. 52p. pap. (978-3-639-25952-0(1)) VDM Verlag Dr. Mueller e.K.

Öztark, Manir, et al, eds. Sabkha Ecosystems: Africa & Southern Europe, Vol. III. 2010. (Tasks for Vegetation Science Ser.). (Illus.). xiii, 148p. 189.00 (978-90-481-9672-2(8), 9048196728) Springer.

Bass, Rick. The Black Rhinos of Namibia: Searching for Survivors in the African Desert. 2012. (ENG.). 288p. 25.00 (978-0-547-05521-3(8)) Houghton Mifflin Harcourt Trade & Reference Pubs.

Battarbee, Richard W., et al, eds. Past Climate Variability through Europe & Africa. 2010. (Developments in Paleoenvironmental Research Ser.). (Illus.). xxv, 638p. pap. 179.00 (978-90-481-6593-3(8), 9048165938) Springer.

Benjamin, Doglas. Biomass Combustion & Indoor Air Pollution in Tanzani. 2011. 92p. pap. **(978-3-8433-8885-6(7))** Lambert Academic Publishing.

Bennett, Barbara. Soul of a Lion: One Woman's Quest to Rescue Africa's Wildlife Refugees. 2010. (Illus.). 320p. 26.00 (978-1-4262-0654-2(2), National Geographic) National Geographic Society.

Boamponsem, Louis Kwame. Heavy Metal Levels in Lichens, Soils, Sediments & Water Bodies. 2011. 148p. pap. **(978-3-8443-3224-7(3))** Lambert Academic Publishing.

Bolaane, Benjamin. Constraints to Organized Recycling in Developing Countries. 2010. 268p. pap. (978-3-8383-6064-5(8)) Lambert Academic Publishing.

Bollig, Michael. Risk Management in a Hazardous Environment: A Comparative Study of two Pastoral Societies. 2010. (Studies in Human Ecology & Adaptation Ser.). (Illus.). xxiii, 324p. pap. 159.00 (978-1-4419-3902-9(4), 1441939024) Springer.

Bollig, Michael & Bubenzer, Olaf. African Landscapes: Interdisciplinary Approaches. 2008. (Studies in Human Ecology & Adaptation Ser.). (Illus.). 410p. 139.00 (978-0-387-78681-0(3)) Springer.

Boonman, G. East Africa's Grasses & Fodders: Their Ecology & Husbandry: Their Ecology & Husbandry. 2011. (Tasks for Vegetation Science Ser.). (Illus.). 360p. pap. 469.00 (978-90-481-4176-0(1), 9048141761) Springer.

Cartwright, Anton, et al, eds. Climate Change at the City Scale. 2012. (ENG., Illus.). 296p. 95.00 **(978-0-415-52758-3(9))** Routledge.

Chikozho, Claudious. The Realities & Challenges of Reforming the Water Sector in Zimbabwe. 2010. 208p. pap. (978-3-639-25585-0(2)) VDM Verlag Dr. Mueller e.K.

Chvatal, Jessica A. A Study of Waste Management Policy Implications. 2011. 148p. pap. **(978-3-8383-1995-7(8))** Lambert Academic Publishing.

Cicura, Donatien M. Identity & Historicity. 2009. 300p. pap. (978-3-639-14215-0(2)) VDM Verlag Dr. Mueller e.K.

Clack, Timothy A. R. Memory & the Mountain: Environmental Relations of the Wachagga of Kilimanjaro & Implications for Landscape Archaeology. 2007. (Bar S Ser.). (Illus.). 108p. (C). 72.50 (978-1-4073-0117-4(9)) British Archaeological Reports Ltd. GBR. Dist: Brown, David Bk. Co., The.

Cock, Jacklyn. The War Against Ourselves: Nature, Power & Justice. 2008. (ENG.). 256p. pap. 34.95 (978-1-86814-457-0(7)) Witwatersrand Univ. Pr. Pubns. ZAF. Dist: Transaction Pubs.

Codjoe, Samuel Nii Ardey. Population-Environment Nexus in Ghan. 2010. 176p. pap. (978-3-8383-6503-9(8)) Lambert Academic Publishing.

Combating Climate Change in Africa: Hearing Before the Subcommittee on Africa & Global Health of the Committee on Foreign Affairs, House of Representatives, One Hundred Eleventh Congress, Second Session, April 15, 2010. 2010. iii, 91p. (978-0-16-086539-8(5), 552-070-41537-8) United States Government Printing Office.

Critchley, William. More People, More Trees. 2011. (ENG., Illus.). 200p. pap. 29.95 incl. DVD (978-1-85339-717-2(2)) Practical Action Publishing GBR. Dist: Stylus Publishing, LLC.

Croitoru, Lelia & Sarraf, Maria. The Cost of Environmental Degradation in the Middle East & North Africa. 2010. (Directions in Development Ser.). (ENG., Illus.). 188p. pap. 30.00 (978-0-8213-8318-6(3), 9780821383186) World Bank Pubns.

Cumming, David & de Garine-Wichatitsky, Michel. Transfrontier Conservation Areas: People Living on the Edge. Gillet, Ken et al, eds. 2012. (ENG., Illus.). 256p. 99.95 (978-1-84971-208-8(5)) Routledge.

Dafalla, Mohamed Salih. Mapping & Assessment of Land Use/Land Cover Using Remote Sensing. 2008. 124p. pap. (978-3-8364-9632-2(1)) VDM Verlag Dr. Mueller e.K.

Davis, Diana K. Resurrecting the Granary of Rome: Environmental History & French Colonial Expansion in North Africa. 2007. (Ecology & History Ser.). (Illus.). 312p. 59.95 (978-0-8214-1751-5(7)); pap. 29.95 (978-0-8214-1752-2(5)) Ohio Univ. Pr.

Dean, W. Richard J. & Milton, Suzanne, eds. The Karoo: Ecological Patterns & Processes. 2009. 400p. pap. 42.00 (978-0-521-12687-8(8)) Cambridge Univ. Pr.

Descy, Jean-Pierre, et al, eds. Lake Kivu: Limnology & biogeochemistry of a tropical great Lake. 2012. (Aquatic Ecology Ser.: 5). (ENG., Illus.). x, 200p. 129.00 **(978-94-007-4242-0(8)**, 9400742428) Springer.

Draper, Peter & Mbirimi, Ivan, eds. Climate Change & Trade: The Challenges for Southern Africa. 2011. (ENG.). 290p. pap. 28.95 (978-1-920196-28-8(5)) Jacana Media ZAF. Dist: Independent Pubs. Group.

Eduvie, Martin. Groundwater Exploration & Development in Basement Complex Are. 2011. 220p. pap. **(978-3-8433-9172-6(6))** Lambert Academic Publishing.

Ekudu, Charity. The Legal Basis of the Clean Development Mechanism in Ugand. 2011. 72p. pap. **(978-3-8433-8775-0(3))** Lambert Academic Publishing.

Falola, Toyin & Paddock, Adam, eds. Environment & Economics in Nigeria. 2011. (Routledge African Studies). (ENG., Illus.). 296p. (C). 125.00 (978-0-415-89592-7(8)) Routledge.

Fanta, Gemechu, et al. Ultraviolet Radiation Measurement in Afric. 2010. 140p. pap. (978-3-639-28226-9(4)) VDM Verlag Dr. Mueller e.K.

Felix Olugbenga, Afolalu. Ground-Water Exploration. 2011. 80p. pap. **(978-3-8443-1700-8(7))** Lambert Academic Publishing.

Finting, Carolina. Flood Risk Perception in Tanzani. 2008. 48p. pap. (978-3-639-04657-1(9)) VDM Verlag Dr. Mueller e.K.

Fowler, Dennis. Zambian Plants: Their vernacular names & Uses. 2007. 308p. per. (978-1-84246-212-6(1)) Kew Publishing.

Fusco, Elizabeth M. Implications of Climate Change in North Africa. 2011. (African Political, Economic, & Security Issues Ser.). 89.00 (978-1-61122-850-2(6)) Nova Science Pubs., Inc.

Geddes, Gary. Drink the Bitter Root: A Search for Justice & Healing in Africa. 2011. (ENG.). 304p. 26.00 **(978-1-58243-788-0(2)**, Counterpoint) Counterpoint LLC.

Giresse, P. Tropical & Sub-Tropical West Africa: Marine & Continental Changes During the Late Quaternary. 2007. (Developments in Quaternary Science Ser.: 10). (ENG.). 406p. 275.00 (978-0-444-52984-8(5), Elsevier Science) Elsevier Science & Technology Bks.

Guerzoni, Stefano & Chester, R., eds. The Impact of Desert Dust Across the Mediterranean. 2010. (Environmental Science & Technology Library). (Illus.). 406p. pap. 229.00 (978-90-481-4764-9(6), 9048147646) Springer.

Gwambene, Brown. Climate Change & Variability Adaptation Strategies. 2011. 92p. pap. **(978-3-8443-2769-4(X))** Lambert Academic Publishing.

Hailemelekot, Abraham & Legesse, Dagnachew. Determination of Spatio-Temporal Differences of Water Hyacinth. 2010. 92p. pap. (978-3-639-08868-7(9)) VDM Verlag Dr. Mueller e.K.

Hallowes, David. Toxic Futures: South Africa in the Crises of Energy, Environment & Capital. 2011. 368p. pap. 42.00 **(978-1-86914-211-7(X))** University of Kwazulu-Natal Press ZAF. Dist: International Specialized Bk. Services.

Homewood, Katherine, et al. Staying Maasai? Livelihoods, Conservation & Development in East African Rangelands. Homewood, Katherine et al, eds. 2009. (Studies in Human Ecology & Adaptation Ser.). (ENG., Illus.). xvi, 418p. 139.00 (978-0-387-87491-3(7)) Springer.

Hubbard, Monique. Sub-Lethal Biomarker Responses to Cu in Oreochromis Mossambicus. 2011. 296p. pap. **(978-3-8383-2854-6(X))** Lambert Academic Publishing.

Inyang, Ekpe. Environmental Problems in the Bakossi Landscape: A Handbook for Environmental Educators. 2011. (Illus.). 62p. pap. **(978-9956-717-29-3(0))** Langaa Research & Publishing Common Initiative Group.

Isikwue, Bernadette. Solar Dynamic Effects on Stratospheric Ozone Variations in the Tropics. 2011. 80p. pap. **(978-3-8443-1442-7(3))** Lambert Academic Publishing.

Itai Offat, Manyanhaire. Impacts of Dam Construction in Zimbabwe. 2011. 100p. pap. **(978-3-8383-6632-6(8))** Lambert Academic Publishing.

Jaiteh, Malanding S. Land Cover Dynamics in Miombo Ecosystems. 2008. 92p. pap. (978-3-639-03737-1(5)) VDM Verlag Dr. Mueller e.K.

Janssen, Rainer & Rutz, Dominik, eds. Bioenergy for Sustainable Development in Africa. 2011. (ENG., Illus.). xxix, 413p. 179.00 **(978-94-007-2180-7(3)**, 9400721803) Springer.

Joubert, Leonie S. & Joubert, Leonie. Scorched: South Africa's Changing Climate. 2007. (ENG., Illus.). 240p. (gr. 11). pap. 29.95 (978-1-86814-437-2(2)) Witwatersrand Univ. Pr. Pubns. ZAF. Dist: Transaction Pubs.

Kachel, Anne Friederike. Habitat Use of Elephantulus Intufi - a Radiotracking Study in Northern Namibi. 2008. 60p. pap. (978-3-639-00761-9(1)) VDM Verlag Dr. Mueller e.K.

Karbo, Tony. Variations in Violent Conflicts in Africa: The Relative Influence of Political & Environmental Factors. 2008. 300p. pap. (978-3-8364-9068-9(4)) VDM Verlag Dr. Mueller e.K.

Kaskaoutis, D. G., et al, eds. Dust Storm Identification via Satellite Remote Sensing. 2010. (Natural Disaster Research, Prediction & Mitigation Ser.). pap. 43.00 (978-1-60876-906-3(2)) Nova Science Pubs., Inc.

Kebede, Banchiamlak & Mekonnen Ayana. Variability of Rainfall & Evapotranspiration. 2010. 92p. pap. (978-3-639-27600-8(0)) VDM Verlag Dr. Mueller e.K.

Kreike, Emmanuel. Deforestation & Reforestation in Namibia: The Global Consequences of Local Contradictions. 2009. (Illus.). 224p. (978-1-55876-497-2(6)); pap. (978-1-55876-498-9(4)) Wiener, Markus Pubs., Inc.

—Deforestation & Reforestation in Namibia the Global Consequences of Local Contradictions. 2009. pap. (978-90-04-17991-2(7)) BRILL.

Kruse, Thorben. In-Situ Conservation of Indigenous Trees. 2008. 88p. pap. (978-3-639-08189-3(7)) VDM Verlag Dr. Mueller e.K.

Lawley, Jonathan. Beyond the Malachite Hills: A Life of Colonial Service & Business in the New Africa. 2009. (ENG., Illus.). 256p. 55.00 (978-1-84885-049-1(2)) I. B. Tauris & Co., Ltd. GBR. Dist: Macmillan.

Lawson, Elaine Tweneboah. Inclusion of Ghanaian Women in Coastal Natural Resource Management. 2010. 188p. pap. (978-3-639-23414-5(6)) VDM Verlag Dr. Mueller e.K.

Leal Filho, Walter, ed. Experiences of Climate Change Adaptation in Africa. 2011. (Climate Change Management Ser.). (ENG., Illus.). ix, 315p. 139.00 **(978-3-642-22314-3(1)**, 3642223141) Springer.

Lehman, J. T., ed. Environmental Change & Response in East African Lakes. 2010. (Monographiae Biologicae Ser.). 250p. pap. 149.00 (978-90-481-5043-4(4), 9048150434) Springer.

Low, Pak Sum, ed. Climate Change & Africa. 2006. (ENG., Illus.). 412p. per. 79.00 (978-0-521-02995-7(3)) Cambridge Univ. Pr.

Ly, Oumou K., et al. Estimating the value of ecotourism in the Djoudj National Bird Park in Senegal. 2006. (Illus.). 34p. pap. 12.75 (978-2-8317-0968-0(7)) UICN Union Mondiale pour la Nature, Cecile Thiery CHE. Dist: Chicago Distribution Ctr.

Magrath, John. Africa - up in Smoke 2: The Second Report on Africa & Global Warming from the Working Group on Climate Change & Development. 2006. (Up in Smoke? Ser.). (ENG., Illus.). 20p. pap. 9.50 (978-1-904882-17-6(X)) Oxfam Publishing GBR. Dist: Stylus Publishing, LLC.

Magrath, John & Simms, Andrew. Africa-up in Smoke? Combined. 2007. (Up in Smoke? Ser.). (ENG.). 60p. 17.50 (978-0-85598-595-0(X)) Oxfam Publishing GBR. Dist: Stylus Publishing, LLC.

Marshall, Michael H. Palaeolimnology in Northern Ethiopi. 2010. 352p. pap. (978-3-8383-4844-5(3)) Lambert Academic Publishing.

Marzouk, Abdelkrim. Time Series Analysis of Environmental Ecosystems: Case of Morocco. 2009. 116p. pap. (978-3-639-13872-6(4)) VDM Verlag Dr. Mueller e.K.

Mosley, P. Green Revolution in Africa. 2011. pap. 49.95 (978-0-415-07464-3(9)) Routledge.

Moushabeck, Michel. Kilimanjaro: A Photographic Journey to the Roof of Africa. 2009. 160p. (ENG.). 30.00 (978-1-56656-781-7(5)); (Illus.). pap. 20.00 (978-1-56656-753-4(X)) Interlink Publishing Group, Inc. (Interlink Bks.).

Mushita, A. & Thompson, Carol B. Biopiracy of Biodiversity: Global Exchange As Enclosure. 2006. (978-1-59221-502-7(5)); pap. (978-1-59221-503-4(3)) Africa World Pr.

Muti, Simon. The June Winds on Rainfall & Food Security in Eastern Horn of Afric. 2011. 56p. pap. **(978-3-8443-8489-5(8))** Lambert Academic Publishing.

Ndenecho, Emmanuel Neba. Local Livelihoods & Protected Area Management Biodiversity Conservation Problems in Cameroon. 2011. 230p. pap. **(978-9956-717-54-5(1))** Langaa Research & Publishing Common Initiative Group.

Ndenecho, Neba. Climate Change & the Management of Natural Systems in Cameroon. 2011. 338p. pap. **(978-9956-717-78-1(9))** Langaa Research & Publishing Common Initiative Group.

Nhamo, Godwell & Inyang, Ekpe. Framework & Tools for Environmental Management in Africa. 2011. 234p. pap. **(978-2-86978-321-8(3))** Council for the Development of Social Science Research in Africa.

Ntow, William Joseph. The Use & Fate of Pesticides in Vegetable-Based Agro-Ecosystems. 2008. (ENG., Illus.). 120p. 62.95 (978-0-415-46274-7(6), Taylor & Francis) Taylor & Francis Group GBR. Dist: Taylor & Francis Group.

Odada, Eric O. & Olago, Daniel O., eds. The East African Great Lakes: Limnology, Palaeolimnology & Biodiversity: Limnology, Palaeolimnology & Biodiversity. 2010. (Advances in Global Change Research Ser.). 598p. pap. 279.00 (978-90-481-6083-9(9), 9048160839) Springer.

Odon, Akanimo & Guodadia, Sam. African Environmental Perspectives - Volume 1: An Academia for Green Africa Publication. 2011. 168p. pap. 21.57 **(978-1-4567-8444-7(7))** AuthorHouse.

Okoth, Peter. A Hierarchical Multi-Level Method for Spatially Assessing Soil Erosion. 2010. 228p. pap. (978-3-8383-1023-7(3)) Lambert Academic Publishing.

Omer, Abdeen Mustafa. Africa: The Driest Continent. 2010. (African Political, Economic, & Security Issues Ser.). (Illus.). x, 58p. pap. 43.00 (978-1-61728-854-8(3), Nova Novinka) Nova Science Pubs., Inc.

Omole, David. Development of Re-Aeration Coefficient for Rivers in Nigeri. 2011. 168p. pap. **(978-3-8443-3177-6(8))** Lambert Academic Publishing.

Ouma, George & Gottwald, Franz-Theo, eds. Agrarian Science for Sustainable Resource Management in Sub-Saharan Africa. 2009. (Studies in sub-Saharan Africa Ser.). 130p. pap. 39.95 (978-3-631-58524-5(1)) Lang, Peter GmbH, Europaischer Verlag der Wissenschaften DEU. Dist: Lang, Peter.

P, MOSLEY. Green Revolution in Africa. 2011. pap. 150.00 (978-0-415-07396-7(0)) Routledge.

Pachur, Hans-Joachim & Altmann, Norbert. Die Ostsahara im Spätquartär: Ökosystemwandel im größten hyperariden Raum der Erde. 2006. (Illus.). XII, 662p. 279.00 (978-3-540-20445-9(8), 3540204458) Springer.

Parker, Bismark Quarku. Biomass Burning in Ghan. 2011. 92p. pap. **(978-3-8443-9205-0(X))** Lambert Academic Publishing.

Pelling, Mark & Wisner, Ben, eds. Disaster Risk Reduction: Cases from Urban Africa. 2008. (ENG., Illus.). 200p. 97.50 (978-1-84407-556-0(7)) Routledge.

Prinsloo, Paul & Stoffberg, Hennie. Climate Change: A Guide for Corporates. 2009. 180p. pap. 39.00 (978-1-86888-564-0(X)) Unisa Press / Uitgewers GBR. Dist: International Specialized Bk. Services.

Purkitt, Helen E. African Environmental & Human Security in the 21st Century. 2010. 392p. (978-1-60497-646-5(2)) Cambria Pr.

Rozema, Jaap. Perceiving Risk Perceptions. 2011. 104p. pap. **(978-3-8383-7153-5(4))** Lambert Academic Publishing.

Runge, Jargen, ed. Evolution, Neotectonics & Quaternary Environmental Change in Southern Cameroon: An International Yearbook of Landscape Evolution & Palaeoenvironments. 2012. (Palaeoecology of Africa Ser.: 31). (ENG., Illus.). 300p. 139.95 (978-0-415-67735-6(1), CRC Press) Taylor & Francis Group GBR. Dist: Taylor & Francis Group.

S. Suleiman, Jokha. An Evaluation of the Role of Eia Database in Promoting Eia Practice. 2011. 108p. pap. **(978-3-8443-9385-9(4))** Lambert Academic Publishing.

Sankoh, Osman, et al. Environmental Factors & Malaria Transmission Risk: Modelling the Risk in a Holoendemic Area of Burkina Faso. 2008. (Illus.). 166p. 114.95 (978-0-7546-7570-9(X)) Ashgate Publishing Co.

Schabel, Hans G. Forest Entomology in East Africa: Forest Insects of Tanzania. 2010. (ENG.). lx, 328p. pap. 239.00 (978-90-481-7163-7(6), 9048171636) Springer.

Scholte, Paul. Floodplain Rehabilitation: Adaptive Management of Success in Waza-Logone, Cameroon. 2008. 344p. pap. (978-3-639-09750-4(5)) VDM Verlag Dr. Mueller e.K.

Seyoum, Aseffa. Costs of in-Situ Conservation of Arabica Coffee in Montane Rainforest of Ethiopia. 2008. 112p. pap. (978-3-639-00808-1(1)) VDM Verlag Dr. Mueller e.K.

Shackleton, Charlie M., ed. Livelihoods & Vulnerability in the Arid & Semi-Arid Lands of Southern Africa. 2010. (Hunger & Poverty: Causes, Impacts & Eradication Ser.). (Illus.). 267p. 89.00 (978-1-60876-940-7(2)) Nova Science Pubs., Inc.

Spinage, Clive Alfred. African Ecology: Benchmarks & Historical Perspectives. 2012. (Springer Geography Ser.). (ENG., Illus.). xxviii, 1300p. 279.00 **(978-3-642-22871-1(2)**, 3642228712) Springer.

Stoop, Aiden. A Framework Methodology for Cumulative Impact Assessment of Wetlands. 2010. 100p. pap. (978-3-8383-6327-1(2)) Lambert Academic Publishing.

Tadesse, Jemal Ahmed. Institutional Dimension of Payments for Environmental Services. 2010. 188p. pap. (978-3-639-27975-7(1)) VDM Verlag Dr. Mueller e.K.

Toulmin, Camilla. Climate Change in Africa. 2009. (ENG., Illus.). 160p. 72.95 (978-1-84813-014-2(7)); pap. 23.95 (978-1-84813-015-9(5)) Zed Bks., Ltd. GBR. Dist: Macmillan.

Twongyirwe, Ronald. Changing Forest Cover in & Around African Tropical Forests. 2010. 112p. pap. (978-3-639-28401-0(1)) VDM Verlag Dr. Mueller e.K.

Ufoegbune, Gideon. Rainfall Estimation. 2010. 188p. pap. (978-3-8383-7819-0(9)) Lambert Academic Publishing.

United Nations Environment Program. Kenya: Atlas of Our Changing Environment. 2009. (ENG., Illus.). 172p. 80.00 (978-92-807-2995-5(0)) United Nations Environment Programme KEN. Dist: National Bk. Network.

Urgessa, Getenet Kebede. Recent Climate Changes. 2010. 92p. pap. (978-3-639-23472-5(3)) VDM Verlag Dr. Mueller e.K.

Williams, Charles & Kniveton, Dominic R., eds. African Climate & Climate Change: Physical, Social & Political Perspectives. 2010. (Advances in Global Change Research Ser.). (Illus.). 200p. 129.00 (978-90-481-3841-8(8), 9048138418) Springer.

Workineh Kelbessa. Indigenous & Modern Environmental Ethics: A Study of the Indigenous Oromo Environmental Ethic & Modern Issues of Environment & Development. 2008. pap. (978-1-56518-253-0(7)) Council for Research in Values & Philosophy.

World Resources Institute Staff, contrib. by. Nature's Benefits in Kenya: An Atlas of Ecosystems & Human Well-Being. 2007. (Illus.). xii, 148p. (978-1-56973-642-5(1)) World Resources Institute.

Zereini, Fathi & Hötzl, Heinz. Climatic Changes & Water Resources in the Middle East & North Africa. 2008. (Environmental Science & Engineering / Environmental Science Ser.). (Illus.). xx, 552p. 239.00 (978-3-540-85046-5(5)) Springer.

AFRICA—ETHNIC RELATIONS

Adibe, Jideofor, ed. Ar: Consolidating the Democracy Project in Africa. 2007. 144p. per. (978-1-905068-00-5(X)) Adonis & Abbey Publishers Ltd.

Ahluwalia, Pal, et al, eds. Violence & Non-Violence in Africa. 2007. (Routledge Advances in International Relations & Global Politics Ser.). (Illus.). 213p. 150.00 (978-0-415-40514-0(9)) Routledge.

Akingbade, Tunde. Historical Studies on Global Scam & Nigeria's 419: How to Overcome Fraudsters & con Artists. 2009. 128p. pap. 10.99 (978-1-4389-7596-2(1)) AuthorHouse.

Araoye, Lasisi Ademola. Cote D'Ivoire: The Conundrum of a Still Wretched of the Earth. 2012. **(978-1-59221-863-9(6))**; (ENG., Illus.). 504p. pap. **(978-1-59221-864-6(4))** Africa World Pr.

Asante, Molefi Kete. An Afrocentric Manifesto. 2007. (ENG.). 192p. 69.95 (978-0-7456-4102-7(4)) Polity Pr. GBR. Dist: Wiley, John & Sons, Inc.

—An Afrocentric Manifesto: Toward an African Renaissance. 2007. (ENG.). 192p. pap. 19.95 *(978-0-7456-4103-4(2))* Polity Pr. GBR. Dist: Wiley, John & Sons, Inc.

Atanga, Mufor. The Anglophone Cameroon Predicament. 2011. 266p. pap. ***(978-9956-717-11-8(8))*** Langaa Research & Publishing Common Initiative Group.

Awedoba, A. K. & Martinon, C. A. Mumma. An Ethnographic Study of Northern Ghanaian Conflicts: Towards a Sustainable Peace. 2010. (ENG., Illus.). 342p. pap. ***(978-9988-647-38-4(7))*** Sub-Saharan Pubs. & Traders.

Bassey, Celestine. Conflict Resolution, Identity Crisis, & Development in Africa. 2007. (Illus.). 308p. (C). pap. *(978-978-023-219-1(2))* Malthouse Press Ltd, Nigeria NGA. Dist: Michigan State Univ. Pr.

Braeckman, Colette. Terreur Africaine: Burundi, Rwanda, Zaïre, les Racines de la Violence. (FRE., Illus.). 347p. *(978-2-213-59703-4(0))* Fayard, Artheme, Librairie.

Bruder, Edith. The Black Jews of Africa: History, Religion, Identity. 2008. (ENG., Illus.). 304p. 49.95 *(978-0-19-533356-5(X))* Oxford Univ. Pr., Inc.

Bruder, Edith. The Black Jews of Africa History, Religion, Identity. 2012. (ENG., Illus.). 304p. pap. 24.95 ***(978-0-19-993455-3(X))*** Oxford Univ. Pr., Inc.

Conyers, James, Jr., ed. Racial Structure & Radical Politics in the African Diaspora. 2009. (ENG., Illus.). 223p. pap. 29.95 *(978-1-4128-1045-6(0))* Transaction Pubs.

Daly, M. W. Darfur's Sorrow: The Forgotten History of a Humanitarian Disaster. 2nd rev. ed. 2010. (ENG., Illus.). 398p. (C). 85.00 *(978-0-521-19174-6(2))* Cambridge Univ. Pr.

Denis, Philippe & Ntsimane, Radikobo, eds. Oral History in a Wounded Country: Interactive Interviewing in South Africa. 2008. 208p. pap. 29.95 Univ. of Natal Pr. ZAF. Dist: International Specialized Bk. Services.

Duffy, Joanne L. The Politics of Ethnic Nationalism: Afrikaner Unity, the National Party, & the Radical Right in Stellenbosch, 1934-1948. 2006. (African Studies: History, Politics, Economics & Culture Ser.). (Illus.). 273p. 128.00 *(978-0-415-97986-3(2))* Routledge.

Egwaikhide, Festus O., et al. Federal Presence in Nigeria the 'sung' & 'Unsung' Basis for Ethnic Grievance. 2009. 126p. pap. *(978-2-86978-259-4(4))* Council for the Development of Social Science Research in Africa SEN. Dist: Michigan State Univ. Pr.

Elmaleh, Raphaël & Ricketts, George. Jews under Moroccan Skies: Two Thousand Years of Jewish Morocco. 2012. 280p. pap. 19.95 ***(978-1-935604-24-2(4))*** Gaon Bks.

Elsheikh, Elsadig. Darfur: Domesticating Coloniality: The Failure of the Nation-state Model inPost-colonial Sudan. 2008. 60p. pap. *(978-3-639-10549-0(4))* VDM Verlag Dr. Mueller e.K.

Fessha, Yonatan. Institutional Recognition & Accommodation of Ethnic Diversity: Federalism in South Africa & Ethiopia. 2010. 310p. 134.95 *(978-1-4094-0310-4(6))* Ashgate Publishing Co.

Fujii, Lee Ann. Killing Neighbors: Webs of Violence in Rwanda. 2011. (Illus.). 224p. pap. 21.95 *(978-0-8014-7713-3(1))* Cornell Univ. Pr.

Garuka Nsabimana, Christian. The Concept of Power Sharing. 2010. 60p. pap. *(978-3-639-25186-9(5))* VDM Verlag Dr. Mueller e.K.

Gatwa, Tharcisse. The Churches & Ethnic Ideology in the Rwandan Crises, 1900-1994. 2008. (Regnum Studies in Mission Ser.). 312p. pap. 36.00 *(978-1-59752-823-8(4))* Wipf & Stock Pubs.

Glassman, Jonathon War of Words, War of Stones: Racial Thought & Violence in Colonial Zanzibar. 2011. (ENG., Illus.). 414p. 80.00 *(978-0-253-35585-0(0)*, 0253355850); pap. 27.95 *(978-0-253-22280-0(X)*, 025322280X) Indiana Univ. Pr.

Hassan, Salah. Darfur & the Crisis of Governance in Sudan. 2009. (Illus.). 528p. pap. 39.95 *(978-0-8014-7594-8(5))* Cornell Univ. Pr.

Hull, Richard. Jews & Judaism in African History. 2009. (Illus.). 320p. 86.95 *(978-1-55876-495-8(X))*; pap. 26.95 *(978-1-55876-496-5(8))* Wiener, Markus Pubs., Inc.

Jalata, Asafa. Contending Nationalisms of Oromia & Ethiopia: Struggling for Statehood, Sovereignty, & Multinational Democracy. 2010. pap. *(978-1-58684-281-9(1))*; (ENG.). 237p. pap. 24.95 *(978-1-58684-280-2(3))* Global Academic Publishing.

Katongole, Emmanuel & Wilson-Hartgrove, Jonathan. Mirror to the Church: Resurrecting Faith after Genocide in Rwanda, 1 vol. 2009. (ENG.). 176p. pap. 15.99 *(978-0-310-28489-5(9))* Zondervan.

Keese, Alexander, ed. Ethnicity & the Long-Term Perspective: The African Experience. 2010. (CEAUP Studies on Africa Ser.). (Illus.). 216p. pap. *(978-3-0343-0337-8(8))* Lang, Peter.

Kibreab, Gaim. Critical Reflections on the Eritrean War of Independence: Social Capital, Associational Life, Religion, Ethnicity & Sowing Seeds of Dictatorship. 2007. *(978-1-56902-281-8(X))* Red Sea Pr.

Kohl, Ines. Beautiful Modern Nomads. 2009. (ENG.). 144p. pap. 39.95 *(978-3-496-02821-5(1)*, Art Stock Bks. Ltd/Csi) Continental Sales, Inc.

Krog, Antjie. Begging to be Black. 2011. 288p. pap. 28.00 *(978-1-77022-070-6(4))* Struik Pubs. ZAF. Dist: International Publishers Marketing.

Lentz, Carola. Ethnicity & the Making of History in Northern Ghana. 2006. (International African Library). (ENG., Illus.). 384p. (gr. 17). 72.00 *(978-0-7486-2401-0(5))* Edinburgh Univ. Pr. GBR. Dist: Columbia Univ. Pr.

Mamdani, Mahmood. Saviors & Survivors: Darfur, Politics, & the War on Terror. 2010. (ENG.). 416p. pap. 16.00 *(978-0-385-52596-1(6)*, Doubleday Religion) Doubleday Religious Publishing Group, The.

—Saviors & Survivors: Darfur, Politics, & the War on Terror. 2009. (ENG., Illus.). 416p. 26.95 *(978-0-307-37723-4(7)*, Pantheon) Knopf Doubleday Publishing Group.

Melvern, Linda & MELVERN, Linda. A People Betrayed: The Role of the West in Rwanda's Genocide. 2nd ed. 2009. (ENG.). 384p. 99.95 *(978-1-84813-244-3(1))* Zed Bks., Ltd. GBR. Dist: Macmillan.

—A People Betrayed: The Role of the West in Rwanda's Genocide, Second. 2nd ed. 2009. (ENG., Illus.). 384p. pap. 29.95 *(978-1-84813-245-0(X))* Zed Bks., Ltd. GBR. Dist: Macmillan.

Mogire, Edward. Victims as Security Threats: Refugee Impact on Host State Security in Africa. 2011. (Global Security in a Changing World Ser.). (Illus.). 228p. 99.95 *(978-0-7546-7820-5(2))* Ashgate Publishing Co.

Muhoozi, Francis Xavier Ndagabanye. A Deficit of Logic in the Great Lakes of Africa: The Floods of Innocent Human Blood that Could Have Been Spared. 2011. (Illus.). 340p. pap. 20.47 *(978-1-4567-7425-7(5))* AuthorHouse.

Ntsimane, Radikobo. Oral History in a Wounded Country: Interactive Interviewing in South Africa. Denis, Philippe, ed. 2008. 196p. pap. 29.95 *(978-1-86914-147-9(4))* Univ. of Natal Pr. ZAF. Dist: International Specialized Bk. Services.

Okeke, Okechukwu. A Political & Administrative History of Onitsha, 1917-1970. 2009. *(978-1-59221-730-4(3))*; 306p. pap. *(978-1-59221-731-1(1))* Africa World Pr.

Orji, Cyril U. Ethnic & Religious Conflict in Africa: An Analysis of Bias, Decline, & Conversion Based on the Works of Bernard Lonergan. 2008. pap. *(978-0-87462-736-7(2))* Marquette Univ. Pr.

Palmié, Stephan. Africas of the Americas: Beyond the Search for Origins in the Study of Afro-Atlantic Religions. Palmié, Stephan, ed. 2008. (Studies of Religion in Africa Ser.). 355p. *(978-90-04-16472-7(3))* BRILL.

Park, Yoon Jung. A Matter of Honour: Being Chinese in South Africa. 2009. (AsiaWorld Ser.). (ENG., Illus.). 248p. 70.00 *(978-0-7391-3553-2(8))* Lexington Bks.

Pinn, Anthony B. Black Religion & Aesthetics: Religious Thought & Life in Africa & the African Diaspora. Pinn, Anthony B., ed. 2009. (ENG., Illus.). 232p. 95.00 *(978-0-230-60550-3(8))* Palgrave Macmillan.

Piombo, Jessica. Institutions, Ethnicity, & Political Mobilization in South Africa. 2009. (ENG., Illus.). 276p. 89.00 *(978-0-230-61734-6(4))* Palgrave Macmillan.

Prunier, Gerard. Africa's World War: Congo, the Rwandan Genocide, & the Making of a Continental Catastrophe, 1 vol. 2011. (ENG., Illus.). 576p. pap. 19.95 *(978-0-19-975420-5(9))* Oxford Univ. Pr., Inc.

Rabasa, Angel & Rabasa. Radical Islam in East Africa. 2009. 110p. pap. 31.50 *(978-0-8330-4519-5(9)*, mg782) RAND Corp., The.

Reminick, Ronald A. Addis Ababa - the Evolution of an Urban African Cultural Landscape. 2010. (Illus.). 340p. *(978-0-7734-1387-0(1))* Mellen, Edwin Pr., The.

S. Alloy, Ihuah. The Ethics of Science & Technology. 2010. 276p. pap. *(978-3-8383-7405-5(3))* Lambert Academic Publishing.

Saha, Santosh C. Ethnicity & Socio-Political Change in Africa & Other Developing Countries: A Constructive Discourse in State Building. 2008. (ENG., Illus.). 266p. 68.50 *(978-0-7391-2332-4(7))* Lexington Bks.

Schilder Quest for Self-Esteem: State, Islam, & Mundang Ethnicity in Northern Cameroon. (Illus.). xiv, 283p. *(978-90-5448-021-1(1))* Afrika-Studiecentrum.

Schlee, Gunther & Watson, Elizabeth, eds. Changing Identifications & Alliances in Northeast Africa Vol. 2: Sudan, Uganda, & the Ethiopia-Sudan Borderlands, 2 vols. 2009. (Illus.). 268p. 95.00 *(978-1-84545-604-7(1))* Berghahn Bks., Inc.

Schreier Joshua. Arabs of the Jewish Faith: The Civilizing Mission in Colonial Algeria. 2010. (Jewish Cultures of the World Ser.). (ENG., Illus.). 253p. 49.95 *(978-0-8135-4794-7(6))* Rutgers Univ. Pr.

Seeman, Don. One People, One Blood: Ethiopian-Israelis & the Return to Judaism. (Jewish Cultures of the World Ser.). (ENG., Illus.). 2010. 250p. pap. 26.95 *(978-0-8135-4936-1(1))* 2009. 296p. 55.00 *(978-0-8135-4541-7(2))* Rutgers Univ. Pr.

Shoup, John A. Ethnic Groups of Africa & the Middle East: An Encyclopedia. 2011. E-Book ***(978-1-59884-363-7(X))***; (Illus.). 377p. 89.00 ***(978-1-59884-362-0(1)***, A2640C) ABC-CLIO, LLC.

Straus, Scott. The Order of Genocide: Race, Power, & War in Rwanda. 2008. (Illus.). 288p. pap. 19.95 *(978-0-8014-7492-7(2))* Cornell Univ. Pr.

Talton, Benjamin A. Politics of Social Change in Ghana: The Konkomba Struggle for Political Equality. 2009. (ENG., Illus.). 256p. 95.00 *(978-0-230-62278-4(X))* Palgrave Macmillan.

Totten, Samuel. Genocide by Attrition: The Nuba Mountains of Sudan. 2012. (ENG.). 148p. 29.95 ***(978-1-4128-4750-6(8))*** Transaction Pubs.

Totten, Samuel & Ubaldo, Rafiki, eds. We Cannot Forget: Interviews with Survivors of the 1994 Genocide in Rwanda. 2011. (Genocide, Political Violence, Human Rights Ser.). (ENG., Illus.). 220p. (C). 72.00 *(978-0-8135-4969-9(8))* Rutgers Univ. Pr.

Totten, Samuel & Ubaldo, Rifiki, eds. We Cannot Forget: Interviews with Survivors of the 1994 Genocide in Rwanda. 2011. (Genocide, Political Violence, Human Rights Ser.). (ENG., Illus.). 220p. (C). pap. 26.95 *(978-0-8135-4970-5(1))* Rutgers Univ. Pr.

Trovalla, Ulrika Andersson. Medicine for Uncertain Futures: A Nigerian City in the Wake of a Crisis. 2011. (Uppsala Studies in Cultural Anthropology Ser.). (Illus.). 214p. pap. 69.50 ***(978-91-554-8054-7(3))*** Uppsala Universitet/Acta Universitatis Uppsaliensis SWE. Dist: Coronet Bks.

Watson, R. L. Slave Emancipation & Racial Attitudes in Nineteenth-Century South Africa. 2012. (ENG., Illus.). 328p. 99.00 ***(978-1-107-02200-3(2))*** Cambridge Univ. Pr.

AFRICA—FOREIGN RELATIONS

Abd Allah, Muhammad Ibrahim Abdi. Mushkilat Al-Sumal Al-Gharbi Wa-Atharuha Alá Al-Alaqat Al-Arabiyah-Al-Ifriqiyah: 1960-1988 M. 2010. (ARA.). 223p. *(978-977-10-2566-5(X))* Dar al-Fikr al-Arabi.

Adam, al-Amin Abd al-Raziq. Ithyubiya: Al-Tatawwurat Al-Siyasiyah Wa-Al-Alaqah Maa Duwal Al-Jiwar Fi Al-Fatrah Min 1991-2009 M. 2009. (ARA., Illus.). 226p. *(978-99942-929-1-2(9))* Magyar ISBN Iroda, Orszagos Szechenyi Konyvtar.

Adebayo, Akanmu, et al. Marginality & Crisis: Globalization & Identity in Contemporary Africa. 2010. (ENG., Illus.). 294p. 78.99 *(978-0-7391-4556-2(8))* Lexington Bks.

Adem, Seifudein, ed. Japan, a Model & a Partner: Views & Issues in African Development. 2006. (International Studies in Sociology & Social Anthrooology Ser.: Vol. 98). (Illus.). 230p. per. *(978-90-04-15270-0(9))* BRILL.

Agyeman-Duah, Ivor, ed. Pilgrims of the Night: Development Challenges & Opportunities in Africa. 2011. (Illus.). 220p. 35.00 *(978-0-9562401-5-6(1))* Clarke, Ayebia Publishing, Ltd. GBR. Dist: Rienner, Lynne Pubs.

Akuffo, Edward Ansah. Canadian Foreign Policy in Africa: Regional Approaches to Peace Security & Development. 2012. (Global Security in a Changing World Ser.). 251p. 99.95 ***(978-1-4094-3452-8(4))*** Ashgate Publishing Co.

Alden, Chris. China in Africa: Partner, Competitor or Hegemon? 2007. (African Arguments Ser.). (ENG., Illus.). 180p. 81.00 *(978-1-84277-863-0(3))*; 154p. per. 23.00 *(978-1-84277-864-7(1))* Zed Bks., Ltd. GBR. Dist: Macmillan.

Ampiah, Kweku & Naidu, Sanusha. Crouching Tiger, Hidden Dragon? Africa & China. Ampiah, Kweku & Naidu, Sanusha, eds. 2008. (Illus.). 357p. (C). pap. 44.95 *(978-1-86914-150-9(4))* University of Kwazulu-Natal Press ZAF. Dist: International Specialized Bk. Services.

Ampwera, Meshach K. China's un Peacekeeping Experience in Afric. 2011 84p. pap. ***(978-3-8443-3012-0(7))*** Lambert Academic Publishing.

Beri, Ruchita & Sinha, Uttam Kumar, eds. Africa & Energy Security: Global Issues, Local Responses. 2009. (ENG.). 260p. 44.95 *(978-81-7188-754-5(6))* Academic Foundation IND. Dist: Independent Pubs. Group.

Bhengu, Mfuniselwa J. African Economic Humanism: The Rise of an African Economic Philosophy. 2011. (Transformation & Innovation Ser.). 242p. 114.95 *(978-1-4094-0435-4(8)*, Gower Publishing Co., Ltd.) Ashgate Publishing, Ltd. GBR. Dist: Ashgate Publishing Co.

Bigsten, Arne & Durevall, Dick. The African Economy & Its Role in the World Economy. 2008. (NAI Current African Issues Ser.). 66p. pap. 12.95 *(978-91-7106-625-1(X))* Nordiska Afrikainstitutet SWE. Dist: Stylus Publishing, LLC.

Blaine, Russell V., ed. Trade Barriers in Africa & the Middle East. 2008. (C). 98.00 *(978-1-60021-954-2(3))* Nova Science Pubs., Inc.

Boko, Sylvain Hounkponou & Seck, Diery. NEPAD & the Future of Economic Policy in Africa. 2007. *(978-1-59221-558-4(0))*; 324p. pap. *(978-1-59221-559-1(9))* Africa World Pr.

Boyce, James & Ndikumana, Léonce. Africa's Odious Debt: How Foreign Loans & Capital Flight Bled a Continent. 2011. (African Arguments Ser.). (ENG., Illus.). 160p. (C). pap. 22.95 *(978-1-84813-459-1(2))* Zed Bks., Ltd. GBR. Dist: Macmillan.

Broadman, Harry G. Africa's Silk Road: China & India's New Economic Frontier. 2006. (Stand Alones Ser.). (ENG., Illus.). 384p. per. 25.00 *(978-0-8213-6835-0(4)*, 9780821368350) World Bank Pubns.

Burr, J. Millard & Collins, Robert O. Darfur: The Long Road to Disaster. exp. ed. (Illus.). 2006. 400p. 89.95 *(978-1-55876-404-0(6))* 2008. 390p. 89.95 *(978-1-55876-469-9(0))* 2007. 390p. per. 28.95 *(978-1-55876-470-5(4))* Wiener, Markus Pubs., Inc.

Caplan, Gerald. The Betrayal of Africa. 2008. (Groundwork Guides). (ENG., Illus.). 144p. (gr. 9-12). 18.95 *(978-0-88899-824-8(4))* Groundwood Bks. CAN. Dist: Perseus-PGW.

—Betrayal of Africa. 2008. (Groundwork Guides). (ENG., Illus.). 144p. (gr. 9-18). pap. 10.00 *(978-0-88899-825-5(2))* Groundwood Bks. CAN. Dist: Perseus-PGW.

Cargill, Tom. Our Common Strategic Interests: Africa's Role in the Post-G8 World. 2010. (ENG., Illus.). 56p. pap. 15.00 *(978-1-86203-224-8(6))* Royal Institute of International Affairs GBR. Dist: Brookings Institution Pr.

Cathialam, Aam'pah-Katoh BaNtumpl. The African Remedy. 2008. 160p. 33.49 *(978-1-4389-0993-6(4))*; pap. 17.99 *(978-1-4389-0994-3(2))* AuthorHouse.

Caulker, Tcho Mbaimba. The African-British Long Eighteenth Century: An Analysis of African-British Treaties, Colonial Economics, & Anthropological Discourse. 2009. (ENG., Illus.). 216p. 68.50 *(978-0-7391-2743-8(8))* Lexington Bks.

Chan, Stephen. Grasping Africa: A Tale of Achievement & Tragedy. 2007. (ENG.). 224p. pap. 36.00 *(978-1-84511-295-1(7))* I. B. Tauris & Co., Ltd. GBR. Dist: Macmillan.

Cheru, Fantu. Africa's Development in the 21st Century: Reshaping the Research Agenda. 2008. (NAI Current African Issues Ser.). 50p. pap. 12.95 *(978-91-7106-628-2(4))* Nordiska Afrikainstitutet SWE. Dist: Stylus Publishing, LLC.

Cheru, Fantu & Obi, Cyril, eds. The Rise of China & India in Africa: Challenges, Opportunities & Critical Interventions. 2010. (Africa Now Ser.). (ENG., Illus.). 272p. 125.95 *(978-1-84813-436-2(3))*; pap. 37.95 *(978-1-84813-437-9(1))* Zed Bks., Ltd. GBR. Dist: Macmillan.

Columbus, Alexandra M., ed. Politics & Economics of Africa: Volume 9. 2011. (Politics & Economics of Africa Ser.). (Illus.). 171p. pap. 112.00 ***(978-1-61324-231-5(X))*** Nova Science Pubs., Inc.

Columbus, Frank. Politics & Economics of Africa. Volume 8. 2011. (Series: Politics & Economics of Africa Ser.). (Illus.). 326p. 165.00 *(978-1-61122-554-9(X))* Nova Science Pubs., Inc.

Columbus, Frank, ed. Politics & Economics of Africa. Volume 7. 2010. (Politics & Economics of Africa Ser.). 115.00 *(978-1-61668-013-8(X))* Nova Science Pubs., Inc.

Cooke, Jennifer. U. S. & Chinese Engagement in Africa: Prospects for Improving U. S. -China-Africa Cooperation. 2008. 68p. pap. 16.95 *(978-0-89206-538-7(9)*, CSIS Pr., The) Ctr. for Strategic & International Studies.

Cornelissen, Scarlett, et al, eds. Africa & International Relations in the 21st Century. 2011. (International Political Economy Ser.). (ENG., Illus.). 272p. 85.00 ***(978-0-230-23528-1(X))*** Palgrave Macmillan.

Dávila, Jerry. Hotel Troacute: Brazil & the Challenge of African Decolonization, 1950-1980. 2010. (ENG., Illus.). 328p. pap. 23.95 *(978-0-8223-4855-9(1))* Duke Univ. Pr.

—Hotel Tropico: Brazil & the Challenge of African Decolonization, 1950-1980. 2010. (ENG., Illus.). 328p. 84.95 *(978-0-8223-4867-2(5))* Duke Univ. Pr.

Dent, Christopher M., ed. China-Africa Development Relations. 2010. (Routledge Contemporary China Ser.). (ENG., Illus.). 208p. (C). 138.00 *(978-0-415-56933-0(8))* Routledge.

Dent, Christopher M., ed. China & Africa Development Relations. 2011. (Illus.). 208p. pap. 42.95 ***(978-0-415-69007-2(2))*** Routledge.

Dietz, Ton, et al, eds. African Engagements: Africa Negotiating an Emerging Multipolar World. 2011. (Africa-Europe Group for Interdisciplinary Studies). (Illus.). VIII, 392p. pap. ***(978-90-04-20988-6(3))*** BRILL.

Don Nanjira, Daniel. African Foreign Policy & Diplomacy: From Antiquity to the 21st Century, 2 vols. 2010. (Illus.). E-Book *(978-0-313-37983-3(1)*, Praeger Pubs.) Greenwood Publishing Group, Inc.

—African Foreign Policy & Diplomacy from Antiquity to the 21st Century, 2 vols. 2010. (Praeger Security International Ser.). (Illus.). 531p. 104.95 *(978-0-313-37982-6(3)*, A2037C, Praeger Pubs.) Greenwood Publishing Group, Inc.

Efretuei, Eyobong. The New Partnership for Africa's Development. 2009. 296p. pap. *(978-3-639-17210-2(8))* VDM Verlag Dr. Mueller e.K.

Egede, Edwin. Africa & the Deep Seabed Regime: Politics & International Law of the Common Heritage of Mankind: Politics & International Law of the Common Heritage of Mankind. 2011. (ENG., Illus.). xxxii, 271p. 139.00 *(978-3-642-17661-6(5)*, 3642176615) Springer.

Endeley, null & Endeley, Isaac N. Bloc Politics at the United Nations: The African Group. 2009. (ENG., Illus.). 60p. pap. 15.99 *(978-0-7618-4558-4(5))* Univ. Pr. of America, Inc.

Eze, C. P. Don't Africa Me: 'Their' geo-branding war, 'Our' trade, tourism wounds, & Winning like China. 2008. 220p. 25.00 *(978-0-9800768-0-6(3)*, Expertz in PRINT) Brandwell Global Services.

Francis, David J. Peace & Conflict in Africa. Francis, David J., ed. 2008. (ENG., Illus.). 224p. pap. 34.00 *(978-1-84277-954-5(0))* Zed Bks., Ltd. GBR. Dist: Macmillan.

Francis, David J., ed. Peace & Conflict in Africa. 2008. (ENG., Illus.). 224p. 117.00 *(978-1-84277-953-8(2))* Zed Bks., Ltd. GBR. Dist: Macmillan.

Gallagher, Julia. Britain & Africa under Blair: In Pursuit of the Good State. 2011. (ENG.). 240p. 100.00 *(978-0-7190-8500-0(4))* Manchester Univ. Pr. GBR. Dist: Macmillan.

Gilliam, Tanji & Zuberi, Tukufu, eds. A Perspective on Africa & the World. 2011. (ANNALS of the American Academy of Political & Social Science Ser.: 632). 132p. (C). 47.00 *(978-1-4129-9395-1(4)*, 295632C); pap. 34.00 *(978-1-4129-9394-4(6)*, 295632P) SAGE Pubns., Inc.

Githinji, Mwangi wa. Is That a Dragon or Elephant on Your Ladder: The Potential Impact of China & India on Export Led Growth in African Countries? 2009. (NAI Discussion Papers). 40p. pap. 12.95 *(978-91-7106-646-6(2))* Nordiska Afrikainstitutet SWE. Dist: Stylus Publishing, LLC.

Greenaway, David, ed. The World Economy: Global Trade Policy 2009. 2010. (World Economy Special Issues Ser.: 7). (ENG.). 176p. pap. 39.95 *(978-1-4051-9704-5(8)*, Wiley-Blackwell) Wiley, John & Sons, Inc.

Harneit-Sievers, Axel, et al. Chinese African Perspectives on China in Africa. 2010. (ENG., Illus.). 292p. pap. 27.95 ***(978-1-906387-33-4(8))*** Pambuzuka Pr. GBR. Dist: Independent Pubs. Group.

Hawley, John C., ed. India in Africa, Africa in India: Indian Ocean Cosmopolitanisms. 2008. (ENG., Illus.). 312p. 65.00 *(978-0-253-35121-0(9)*, 0253351219); pap. 24.95 *(978-0-253-21975-6(2)*, 0253219752) Indiana Univ. Pr.

Kieh, George & Kalu, Kelechi, eds. West Africa & the US War on Terror. 2012. (Routledge Studies in US Foreign Policy Ser.). (ENG., Illus.). 192p. 130.00 ***(978-0-415-53942-5(0))*** Routledge.

Kitissou, Marcel, ed. Africa in China's Global Strategy. 2007. 208p. *(978-1-905068-54-8(9))*; (ENG.). per. *(978-1-905068-88-3(3))* Adonis & Abbey Publishers Ltd.

Kopinski, Dominik, et al, eds. China's Rise in Africa. 2011. (ENG.). 120p. (C). 145.00 ***(978-0-415-68887-1(6))*** Routledge.

Krabacher, Thomas, et al. Africa. 12th ed. 2008. (Global Studies). (ENG., Illus.). 320p. (C). pap. 50.00 *(978-0-07-337977-7(8)*, 0073379778, McGraw-Hill/Dushkin) McGraw-Hill Higher Education.

Kuranga, David O. International & Regional Interdependency: Lessons from Africa. 2012. (ENG., Illus.). 208p. 90.00 ***(978-1-137-01992-9(1))***; pap. 30.00 ***(978-1-137-01995-0(6))*** Palgrave Macmillan.

Law, Robin, ed. Journals & Correspondence of Louis Fraser: British Vice-Consul to the Kingdom of Dahomey, West Africa, 1851-1852. 2012. (ENG., Illus.). 280p. 99.00 ***(978-0-19-726521-5(9))*** Oxford Univ. Pr., Inc.

Lee, Margaret C., et al. China in Africa. 2007. (NAI Current African Issues Ser.). (Illus.). 48p. pap. 14.95 *(978-91-7106-589-6(X))* Nordiska Afrikainstitutet SWE. Dist: Stylus Publishing, LLC.

Lee, Rachel. Africa in the World Trade Organisation. 2012. (Routledge/RIPE Studies in Global Political Economy Ser.). (ENG.). 208p. (C). 140.00 *(978-0-415-42327-4(9))* Routledge.

Levitt, Jeremy, ed. Africa: Mapping New Boundaries in International Law. 2008. (ENG.). 355p. 104.00 *(978-1-84113-618-9(2))* Hart Publishing Ltd. GBR. Dist: International Specialized Bk. Services.

Lohrmann, Ullrich. Voices from Tanganyika: Great Britian, the United Nations & the Decolonization of a Trust Territory, 1946-1961. 2008. (ENG., Illus.). 624p. pap. 84.95 *(978-3-8258-8082-8(6))* Lit Verlag DEU. Dist: Transaction Pubs.

Lumumba-Kasongo, Tukumbi. Japan-Africa Relations. 2010. (ENG.). 294p. 89.00 *(978-0-230-61932-6(0))* Palgrave Macmillan.

Makhulu, A. M. Hard Work, Hard Times - Global Volatility & African Subjectives. 2010. (Global, Area, & International Archive Ser.). 256p. pap. 29.95 *(978-0-520-09874-9(9))* Univ. of California Pr.

Manji, Firoze & Manji, F., eds. African Perspectives on China in Africa. 2007. (ENG.). 188p. pap. 19.95 *(978-0-9545637-3-8(5))* Pambuzuka Pr. GBR. Dist: Independent Pubs. Group.

Marafa, Lawal Mohammed. African Business & Development Relationship with China: Seeking Moral & Capital Values of the Last Economic Frontier. 2009. (NAI Discussion Papers). 30p. pap. 12.95 *(978-91-7106-645-9(4))* Nordiska Afrikainstitutet SWE. Dist: Stylus Publishing, LLC.

Maundi, Mohammed O., et al. Getting In: Mediators' Entry into the Settlement of African Conflicts. 2006. (Illus.). 256p. pap. 19.95 *(978-1-929223-62-6(5))* U. S. Institute of Peace Pr. (USIP Pr.).

Mawdsley, Emma & McCann, Gerard, eds. India in Africa: Changing Geographies of Power. 2011. (ENG.). 240p. pap. 27.95 ***(978-1-906387-65-5(6))*** Pambuzuka Pr. GBR. Dist: Independent Pubs. Group.

Mawuko-Yevugah, Lord. Developmentality. 2011. 208p. pap. ***(978-3-8433-9347-8(8))*** Lambert Academic Publishing.

Melber, Henning & Southall, Roger, eds. A New Scramble for Africa? Imperialism, Investment & Development. 2009. 440p. pap. 49.00 *(978-1-86914-171-4(7))* Univ. of Natal Pr. ZAF. Dist: International Specialized Bk. Services.

Melvern, Linda & MELVERN, Linda. A People Betrayed: The Role of the West in Rwanda's Genocide. 2nd ed. 2009. (ENG.). 384p. 99.95 *(978-1-84813-244-3(1))* Zed Bks., Ltd. GBR. Dist: Macmillan.

—A People Betrayed: The Role of the West in Rwanda's Genocide, Second. 2nd ed. 2009. (ENG., Illus.). 384p. pap. 29.95 *(978-1-84813-245-0(X))* Zed Bks., Ltd. GBR. Dist: Macmillan.

Men, Jing & Barton, Benjamin. China & the European Union in Africa: Partners or Competitors? 2011. (Illus.). 302p. 114.95 *(978-1-4094-2047-7(7))* Ashgate Publishing Co.

Michel, Serge & Beuret, Michel. China Safari: On the Trail of Beijing's Expansion in Africa. 2010. (ENG.). 336p. (gr. 9). pap. 17.50 *(978-1-56858-614-4(0),* Nation Bks.) Basic Bks.

Modi, Renu, ed. South-South Cooperation: Africa on the Centre Stage. 2011. (International Political Economy Ser.). (ENG., Illus.). 288p. 85.00 *(978-0-230-24885-4(3))* Palgrave Macmillan.

Monson, Jamie. Africa's Freedom Railway: How a Chinese Development Project Changed Lives & Livelihoods in Tanzania. 2011. (ENG., Illus.). 216p. pap. 24.95 *(978-0-253-22322-7(9),* 0253223229) Indiana Univ. Pr.

Moriah, Deborah J. Out of Egypt (and into Focus) A Year of Self-Discovery for People of African Descent. 2007. 140p. per. 24.95 *(978-1-4241-9106-2(8))* PublishAmerica, Inc.

Moyo, Bhekinkosi, ed. Africa in Global Power Play: Debates, Challenges & Potential Reforms. 2007. 364p. per. *(978-1-905068-62-3(X))* Adonis & Abbey Publishers Ltd.

—Africa in Global Power Play: Debates, Challenges & Potential Reforms (HB) 2007. 364p. *(978-1-905068-61-6(1))* Adonis & Abbey Publishers Ltd.

Mustapha, Ahmed Badawi. The China Factor in Ghana's Textile & Construction Industries. 2011. 128p. pap. ***(978-3-8443-9725-3(6))*** Lambert Academic Publishing.

Mutai, Henry. Compliance with International Trade Obligations: The Common Market for Eastern & Southern Africa. 2007. *(978-90-411-2664-1(3))* Kluwer Law International.

Ndikumana, Léonce & Boyce, James. Africa's Odious Debt. 2011. (African Arguments Ser.). (ENG., Illus.). 160p. 107.95 *(978-1-84813-458-4(4))* Zed Bks., Ltd. GBR. Dist: Macmillan.

Niang, Abdoulaye. Globalization Key Peace Prosperity Africa. 2008. 144p. pap. 12.95 *(978-1-57197-846-2(1))* Pentland Pr., Inc.

Nicolini, Beatrice & Nicoline, Beatrice. Markran, Oman, & Zanzibar: Three-Terminal Cultural Corridor in the Western Indian Ocean (1799-1856) Watson, Penelope-Jane, tr. from ITA. 2011.Tr. of Sultanatodi Zanzibar nel XIX Secolo. (Illus.). 200p. pap. 26.95 *(978-1-55876-544-3(1))* Wiener, Markus Pubs., Inc.

Njinkeu, Dominique & English, Philip. African Countries in the New Trade Negotiations: Interest, Options, & Challenges. 2007. *(978-1-59221-622-2(6))* Africa World Pr.

Ogalo, Jacob. The History of Informal Trade. 2010. 208p. pap. *(978-3-639-23010-9(8))* VDM Verlag Dr. Mueller e.K.

Parfitt, Trevor W. & Riley, Stephen P. The African Debt Crisis. 2011. (ENG.). 240p. 105.00 *(978-0-415-59278-9(X))* Routledge.

Porteous, Tom. Britain in Africa. 2008. ix, 158p. pap. *(978-1-86914-149-3(0))* Univ. of Natal Pr. ZAF. Dist: International Specialized Bk. Services.

—Britain in Africa. 2008. (African Arguments Ser.). (ENG.). 160p. 72.00 *(978-1-84277-975-0(3))*; pap. 23.00 *(978-1-84277-976-7(1))* Zed Bks., Ltd. GBR. Dist: Macmillan.

Provenzo, Jr, Eugene F, Eugene F & Abaka, Edmund, eds. W. E. B. du Bois on Africa. 2012. (ENG.). 200p. 94.00 ***(978-1-61132-180-7(8))***; pap. 34.95 ***(978-1-61132-181-4(6))*** Left Coast Pr., Inc.

Raine, Sarah. China's African Challenges. 2009. (Adelphi Ser.). (ENG., Illus.). 270p. pap. 19.95 *(978-0-415-55693-4(7))* Routledge.

Reid, Richard, ed. Eritrea's External Relations: Understanding Its Regional Role & Foreign Policy. 2009. (ENG., Illus.). 208p. pap. 26.95 *(978-1-86203-201-9(7))* Royal Institute of International Affairs GBR. Dist: Brookings Institution Pr.

—Eritrea's External Relations: Understanding Its Regional Role & Foreign Policy. 2009. (ENG., Illus.). 208p. 52.95 *(978-1-86203-200-2(9))* Royal Institute of International Affairs GBR. Dist: Brookings Institution Pr.

Rotberg, Robert I., ed. China into Africa: Trade, Aid, & Influence. 2008. (ENG., Illus.). 339p. pap. 29.95 *(978-0-8157-7561-4(X))* Brookings Institution Pr.

Senghor, Jeggan Colley. The Politics of Senegambian Integration, 1958-1994. 2008. (Illus.). 335p. pap. 79.95 *(978-3-03911-132-9(9))* Lang, Peter Publishing, Inc.

Shinn, David H. & Eisenman, Joshua. China & Africa: A Century of Engagement. 2012. (Illus.). 520p. (C). 69.95 ***(978-0-8122-4419-9(2))*** Univ. of Pennsylvania Pr.

Strauss, Julia & Saavedra, Martha, eds. China & Africa: Volume 9: Emerging Patterns in Globalization & Development. 2009. (China Quarterly Special Issues Ser.). (ENG., Illus.). 196p. (C). pap. 41.00 *(978-0-521-12200-9(7))* Cambridge Univ. Pr.

Taylor, Ian. China & Africa: Engagement & Compromise. 2009. 234p. pap. 39.95 *(978-0-415-54552-5(8))* 2006. (Routledge Contemporary China Ser.: Vol. 14). 233p. 160.00 *(978-0-415-39740-7(5))* Routledge.

Tillery, Alvin B. Between Homeland & Motherland: Africa, U. S. Foreign Policy, & Black Leadership in America. 2011. (Illus.). 216p. pap. 22.95 *(978-0-8014-7734-8(4))* Cornell Univ. Pr.

Torrent, Melanie. Diplomacy & Nation-Building in Africa: Franco-British relations & Cameroon at the End of Empire. 2012. (International Library of African Studies). (ENG.). 304p. 96.00 ***(978-1-84885-777-3(2))*** I. B. Tauris & Co., Ltd. GBR. Dist: Macmillan.

U.S.-Africa Trade Relations: Creating a Platform for Economic Growth: Joint Hearing Before the Subcommittee on Commerce, Trade, & Consumer Protection of the Committee on Energy & Commerce, & the Subcommittee on Africa & Global Health of the Committee on Foreign Relations, House of Representatives, One Hundred Eleventh Congress, First Session, June 24, 2009. 2011. (Illus.). v, 166p. ***(978-0-16-089250-9(3),*** 552-070-43247-7) United States Government Printing Office.

van Dijk, Meine Pieter, ed. The New Presence of China in Africa. 2010. (Eadi Ser.). (Illus.). 224p. pap. *(978-90-8964-136-6(X))* Amsterdam Univ. Pr.

Verschave, François-Xavier. La Françafrique: Le Plus Long Scandale de la République. (FRE.). 379p. *(978-2-234-04948-2(2))* Stock, Editions.

Waldron, Arthur N., ed. China in Africa. 2009. (ENG.). 135p. pap. 24.95 *(978-0-9816905-0-6(5))* Jamestown Foundation, The.

Welz, Martin. Decolonization Sovereignty & the African Union. 2012. (Global Institutions Ser.). (ENG., Illus.). 208p. (C). 130.00 ***(978-0-415-52201-4(3))*** Routledge.

Williams, A. Susan. Who Killed Hammarskjöld? The un, the Cold War, & White Supremacy in Africa. 2011. ***(978-0-231-80090-7(8))*** Columbia Univ. Pr.

Williams, Susan. Who Killed Hammarskjöld? The un, the Cold War, & White Supremacy in Africa. 2012. (Columbia/Hurst Ser.). (ENG.). 320p. (gr. 17). 37.50 ***(978-0-231-70320-8(1))*** Columbia Univ. Pr.

Winrow, Gareth M. The Foreign Policy of the GDR in Africa. 2009. (Cambridge Russian, Soviet & Post-Soviet Studies). (ENG.). 312p. pap. 42.00 *(978-0-521-12259-7(7))* Cambridge Univ. Pr.

Young, Tom. Africa. 2010. (Beginners Guide (Oneworld) Ser.). (ENG., Illus.). 224p. pap. 14.95 *(978-1-85168-753-4(X))* Oneworld Pubns. GBR. Dist: National Bk. Network.

AFRICA—FOREIGN RELATIONS—EUROPE

Ademola, Joji. Ft-Venturing West Africa vs Northern Europe. 2010. 88p. pap. *(978-3-8383-5353-1(6))* Lambert Academic Publishing.

Coller, Ian. Arab France: Islam & the Making of Modern Europe, 1798-1831. 2010. (ENG., Illus.). 304p. 60.00 *(978-0-520-26064-1(3))*; pap. 24.95 *(978-0-520-26065-8(1))* Univ. of California Pr.

Des Forges, Alison Liebhafsky & Newbury, David S. Defeat Is the Only Bad News: Rwanda under Musinga, 1897-1931. 2011. E-Book *(978-0-299-28143-4(4))* Univ. of Wisconsin Pr.

Dorman, Andrew. Blair's Successful War: British Military Intervention in Sierra Leone. 2009. (Military Strategy & Operational Art Ser.). (Illus.). 170p. 99.95 *(978-0-7546-7299-9(9))* Ashgate Publishing Co.

Goodwin, Stefan. Africa in Europe Vol. 2: Interdependencies, Relocations, & Globalization, 2 vols. 2008. (ENG.). 430p. 83.99 *(978-0-7391-2765-0(9))*; pap. 40.99 *(978-0-7391-2766-7(7))* Lexington Bks.

Kaluya, Professor M. D. The Audacity to Change: Breaking the Berlin Wall in Africa. 2011. 148p. pap. 14.95 *(978-1-4502-8577-3(5))* iUniverse, Inc.

Mann, Gregory. Native Sons: West African Veterans & France in the Twentieth Century. 2006. (Politics, History, & Culture Ser.). (ENG., Illus.). 344p. (C). 94.95 *(978-0-8223-3755-3(X))* Duke Univ. Pr.

—Native Sons: West African Veterans & France in the Twentieth Century. annot. ed. 2006. (Politics, History, & Culture Ser.). (ENG., Illus.). 344p. per. 25.95 *(978-0-8223-3768-3(1))* Duke Univ. Pr.

Mark, Peter & Horta, José da Silva. The Forgotten Diaspora: Jewish Communities in West Africa & the Making of the Atlantic World. 2011. (ENG., Illus.). 278p. (C). 80.00 *(978-0-521-19286-6(2))* Cambridge Univ. Pr.

Ngangjoh-Hodu, Yenkong & Matambalya, Francis A. S. T. Trade Relations Between the EU & Africa: Development, Challenges & Options Beyond the Cotonou Agreement. 2009. (Illus.). xxvii, 291p. (C). E-Book 145.00 *(978-0-203-86452-4(2))* Routledge.

Ngangjoh-Hodu, Yenkong & Matambalya, Francis A. S. T., eds. Trade Relations Between the EU & Africa: Development, Challenges & Options Beyond the Cotonou Agreement. 2009. (Routledge Studies in Development Economics Ser.). (ENG., Illus.). 320p. 150.00 *(978-0-415-54981-3(7))* Routledge.

Remacle, Eric. America, Europe, Africa 1945-1973 (L'Amérique, l'Europe, L'Afrique, 1945-1973) Winand, Pascaline, ed. 2009. (FRE & ENG.). 329p. pap. 58.95 *(978-90-5201-529-3(5))* PIE - Peter Lang BEL. Dist: Lang, Peter.

Rodney, Walter. How Europe Underdeveloped Africa. 2011. 340p. 24.95 *(978-1-57478-048-2(4))* Black Classic Pr.

Sesay, Amadu, ed. Africa & Europe: From Partition to Independence or Dependence? 2011. (ENG.). 272p. 105.00 *(978-0-415-60144-3(4))* Routledge.

Smith, Wynet. From Chainsaw to Chainstore. 2008. 236p. pap. *(978-3-639-02276-6(9))* VDM Verlag Dr. Mueller e.K.

Thompson, Ronald C. God-Forsaken Trends in Sub-Saharan Afric: Zimbabwean whites' farms Expropriated. 2008. 228p. pap. 14.99 *(978-0-60477-982-0(9))* Xulon Pr., Inc.

Thornton, John K. A Cultural History of the Atlantic World, 1250–1820. 2012. (ENG., Illus.). 350p. (C). 90.00 ***(978-0-521-89875-1(7))***; pap. 29.99 ***(978-0-521-72734-1(0))*** Cambridge Univ. Pr.

Worger, William, et al. Africa & the West: A Documentary History: Volume 2: from Colonialism to Independence, 1875 to the Present, 1 vol. 2nd ed. 2010. (ENG., Illus.). 328p. (C). pap. 24.95 *(978-0-19-537313-4(8))* Oxford Univ. Pr., Inc.

Worger, William H., et al. Africa & the West: A Documentary History: Volume 1: from the Slave Trade to Conquest, 1441-1905, 1 vol. 2nd ed. 2010. (ENG., Illus.). 312p. (C). pap. 24.95 *(978-0-19-537348-6(0))* Oxford Univ. Pr., Inc.

AFRICA—FOREIGN RELATIONS—SOVIET UNION

James, W. Martin. A Political History of the Civil War in Angola, 1974-1990. 2011. (ENG.). 327p. pap. 34.95 *(978-1-4128-1506-2(1))* Transaction Pubs.

Matusevich, Maxim, ed. Africa in Russia, Russia in Africa: 300 Years of Encounters. 2006. (Illus.). 324p. 99.95 *(978-1-59221-329-0(4))*; 29.95 *(978-1-59221-330-6(8))* Africa World Pr.

Mazov, S. V. A Distant Front in the Cold War: The USSR in West Africa & the Congo, 1956-1964. 2010. 288p. *(978-0-8047-6059-1(4))* Woodrow Wilson Ctr. Pr.

Patman, Robert G. The Soviet Union in the Horn of Africa: The Diplomacy of Intervention & Disengagement. 2009. (Cambridge Russian, Soviet & Post-Soviet Studies). (ENG., Illus.). 432p. pap. 55.00 *(978-0-521-10251-3(0))* Cambridge Univ. Pr.

AFRICA—FOREIGN RELATIONS—UNITED STATES

Afandi, Jolie. Primitive Liberation. 2010. 148p. pap. *(978-3-639-26429-6(0))* VDM Verlag Dr. Mueller e.K.

Bangura, Abdul. Assessing George W Bush's Africa Policy & Suggestions for Barack Obama & African Leaders. 2009. 304p. pap. 21.95 *(978-1-4401-5454-6(6))* iUniverse, Inc.

Bangura, Abdul K. Stakes in Africa-United States Relations: Proposals for Equitable Partnership. 2007. 264p. per. 19.95 *(978-0-595-45197-5(7))* iUniverse, Inc.

Barton, Myra, et al, eds. Foreign Relations of the United States, 1969-1976, Volume XXVIII, Southern Africa. 2011. (ENG.). 788p. 70.00 ***(978-0-16-083000-6(1),*** Bureau of Public Affairs, Office of the Historian) United States Government Printing Office.

Beyond Oil & Gas: African Growth & Opportunity Act's Benefits to Africa: Hearing Before the Subcommittee on Africa & Global Health of the Committee on Foreign Affairs, House of Representatives, One Hundred Tenth Congress, First Session, July 12, 2007. 2007. iii, 62p. *(978-0-16-079300-4(9),* 552-070-36378-5) United States Government Printing Office.

Cohen, Jared. One Hundred Days of Silence: America & the Rwanda Genocide. (ENG., Illus.). 2007. 272p. 79.00 *(978-0-7425-5236-4(5))* 2006. 232p. per. 24.95 *(978-0-7425-5237-1(3))* Rowman & Littlefield Publishers, Inc.

Copson, Raymond W. The United States in Africa: Bush Policy & Beyond. 2007. (African Arguments Ser.). (ENG.). 176p. 73.95 *(978-1-84277-914-9(1))*; per. 23.95 *(978-1-84277-915-6(X))* Zed Bks., Ltd. GBR. Dist: Macmillan.

Cotton, Deborah Helen. Africa Rising - a Response to U S Article 98 & the International Criminal Court. 2008. 88p. pap. *(978-3-8364-3788-2(0))* VDM Verlag Dr. Mueller e.K.

Council on Foreign Relations Staff. Beyond Humanitarianism: What You Need to Know about Africa & Why It Matters. 2007. 240p. pap. 17.95 *(978-0-87609-375-7(6))* Council on Foreign Relations.

Cram101 Textbook Reviews & Cram101 Textbook Reviews. Outlines & Highlights for Africa-U S Relations: Strategic Encounters by Donald Rothchild, ISBN. 2011. 372p. pap. 27.95 ***(978-1-61461-573-6(X))*** Cram101 Inc.

Djoumessi, Didier T. The Political Impact of the Sino-U. S. Oil Competition in Africa. 2009. *(978-1-906704-24-7(4))*; pap. *(978-1-906704-25-4(2))* Adonis & Abbey Publishers Ltd.

Exploring the U.S. Africa Command & a New Strategic Relationship with Africa: Hearing Before the Subcommittee on African Affairs of the Committee on Foreign Relations, United States Senate, One Hundred Tenth Congress, First Session, August 1, 2007. 2008. iii, 48p. *(978-0-16-081675-8(0),* 552-070-37906-1) United States Government Printing Office.

Ferro, Gregory D. U.S. Political & Trade Relations with Africa. 2011. *(978-1-61209-956-9(4))* Nova Science Pubs., Inc.

Francis, David J. US Strategy in Africa: AFRICOM, Terrorism & Security Challenges. 2010. (Routledge Global Security Studies). (ENG., Illus.). 224p. (C). 130.00 *(978-0-415-48510-4(X))* Routledge.

The Great Lakes Region: Current Conditions & U.S. Policy: Hearing Before the Subcommittee on Africa & Global Health of the Committee on Foreign Affairs, House of Representatives, One Hundred Eleventh Congress, Second Session, May 25, 2010. 2010. iii, 68p. *(978-0-16-086452-0(6),* 552-070-41509-2) United States Government Printing Office.

Horn of Africa: Current Conditions & U.S. Policy: Hearing Before the Subcommittee on Africa & Global Health of the Committee on Foreign Affairs, House of Representatives, One Hundred Eleventh Congress, Second Session, June 17, 2010. 2010. iii, 79p. *(978-0-16-086453-7(4),* 552-070-41510-6) United States Government Printing Office.

James, W. Martin. A Political History of the Civil War in Angola, 1974-1990. 2011. (ENG.). 327p. pap. 34.95 *(978-1-4128-1506-2(1))* Transaction Pubs.

Jones, Jeannette Eileen. In Search of Brightest Africa: Reimagining the Dark Continent in American Culture, 1884-1936. 2011. (Race in the Atlantic World, 1700-1900 Ser.). (ENG., Illus.). 260p. pap. 24.95 ***(978-0-8203-4029-6(4))*** Univ. of Georgia Pr.

Keenan, Jeremy. The Dark Sahara: America's War on Terror in Africa. 2009. (ENG.). 256p. 95.00 *(978-0-7453-2453-1(3))*; (Illus.). pap. 31.00 *(978-0-7453-2452-4(5))* Pluto Pr. GBR. Dist: Macmillan.

Lyman, Princeton N. & Dorff, Patricia, eds. Beyond Humanitarianism: What You Need to Know about Africa & Why It Matters. 2007. (ENG.). 252p. per. 19.95 *(978-0-87609-371-9(3))* Council on Foreign Relations.

Mathers, Kathryn Frances. Travel, Humanitarianism, & Becoming American in Africa. 2010. (ENG.). 236p. 84.00 *(978-0-230-10806-6(7))* Palgrave Macmillan.

Merrell, Brandon, et al. Up for Debate: U. S. Foreign Policy Options towards the Greater Horn of Africa. Cantrell, Daniel & Brickey, Brandy, eds. 2009. 195p. mass mkt. 14.99 *(978-0-9822898-0-8(4))* Picket Fence Memories.

Morrison, J. Stephen & Cooke, Jennifer G., eds. Africa Policy beyond the Bush Years: Critical Choices for the Obama Administration. 2009. (Illus.). 224p. pap. 24.95 *(978-0-89206-564-6(8),* CSIS Pr., The) Ctr. for Strategic & International Studies.

Muehlenbeck, Philip E. Betting on the Africans: John F. Kennedy's Courting of African Nationalist Leaders, 1 vol. 2012. (ENG., Illus.). 352p. 55.00 ***(978-0-19-539609-6(X))*** Oxford Univ. Pr., Inc.

Otenyo, Eric E. American Promotion of Democracy in Africa, 1988-2000: A Comparison of the Presidential Administrations of George H. W. Bush & William J. Clinton. 2009. (Illus.). 296p. 109.95 *(978-0-7734-4707-3(5))* Mellen, Edwin Pr., The.

Oudes, Bruce. Untitled on U. S. - Africa Policy. Date not set. 27.50 *(978-0-8050-4066-1(8))* Holt, Henry & Co.

An Overview of U.S. Policy in Africa: Hearing Before the Subcommittee on Africa & Global Health of the Committee on Foreign Affairs, House of Representatives, One Hundred Eleventh Congress, Second Session, March 24, 2010. 2010. (Illus.). iii, 122p. *(978-0-16-086457-5(7),* 552-070-41514-9) United States Government Printing Office.

Pham, J. Peter. India in Africa: Implications of an Emerging Power for AFRICOM & U. S. Strategy. 2011. 64p. *(978-1-58487-483-6(X))* Strategic Studies Institute, U.S. Army War College Commandant (AWCC-DSI/Pubns.).

Prospects for Peace in Guinea: Hearing Before the Subcommittee on Africa & Global Health of the Committee on Foreign Affairs, House of Representatives, One Hundred Tenth Congress, First Session, March 22, 2007. 2007. iii, 62p. *(978-0-16-078845-1(5),* 552-070-35980-0) United States Government Printing Office.

Roberts, Kofi J. The Sargasso Bridge: America Speaks, Africa Answers. 2009. 268p. 30.95 *(978-0-595-48771-4(8))*; pap. 20.95 *(978-0-595-48645-8(2))* iUniverse, Inc.

Rosser, James & Stevenson, Robert. The African Foreign Policy of Secretary of State Henry Kissinger: A Documentary Analysis. 2010. (ENG.). 298p. pap. 36.99 *(978-0-7391-1787-3(4))* Lexington Bks.

Strengthening U.S. Diplomatic Capacity in Africa: Hearing Before the Subcommittee on African Affairs of the Committee on Foreign Relations, United States Senate, One Hundred Eleventh Congress, First Session, April 21, 2009. 2009. iii, 43p. *(978-0-16-083558-2(5),* 552-070-39276-9) United States Government Printing Office.

Thornton, John K. A Cultural History of the Atlantic World, 1250–1820. 2012. (ENG., Illus.). 350p. (C). 90.00 ***(978-0-521-89875-1(7))***; pap. 29.99 ***(978-0-521-72734-1(0))*** Cambridge Univ. Pr.

Tillery, Alvin B. Between Homeland & Motherland: Africa, U.S. Foreign Policy, & Black Leadership in America. 2011. (Illus.). 216p. 69.95 *(978-0-8014-4897-3(2))* Cornell Univ. Pr.

Vestal, Ph.D., Theodore M. The Lion of Judah in the New World: Emperor Haile Selassie of Ethiopia & the Shaping of Americans' Attitudes toward Africa, 1 vol. 2011. (Illus.). 231p. 44.95 *(978-0-313-38620-6(X),* A3053C, Praeger Pubs.) Greenwood Publishing Group, Inc.

Vestal, Theodore M. The Lion of Judah in the New World: Emperor Haile SeLassie of Ethiopia & the Shaping of Americans' Attitudes Toward Africa.

2011. E-Book *(978-0-313-38621-3(8)*, Praeger Pubs.) Greenwood Publishing Group, Inc.
Walton, Hanes, Jr., et al. The African Foreign Policy of Secretary of State Henry Kissinger: A Documentary Analysis. 2007. (ENG., Illus.). 298p. 104.99 *(978-0-7391-1786-6(6))* Lexington Bks.
Waters, Robert. Historical Dictionary of United States-Africa Relations. 2009. (Historical Dictionaries of Diplomacy & Foreign Relations Ser.). (ENG.). 448p. 100.00 *(978-0-8108-5063-7(X))* Scarecrow Pr., Inc.
Waters, Robert Anthony, Jr. The A to Z of United States-Africa Relations. 2010. (A to Z Guide Ser.). (ENG.). 454p. pap. 34.45 *(978-0-8108-7551-7(9))* Scarecrow Pr., Inc.
Wonkeryor, Edward Lama, et al. American Democracy in Africa in the Twenty-First Century? 2012. (Illus.). 272p. per. 40.00 *(978-0-9653308-3-1(4))* Africana Homestead Legacy Pubs., Inc.

AFRICA—GENEALOGY

Amani, Athar. History of Ancient Afric. 2010. 64p. pap. *(978-3-8383-5706-5(X))* Lambert Academic Publishing.
Firstbrook, Peter. The Obamas: The Untold Story of an African Family. 2011. (ENG., Illus.). 352p. 26.00 *(978-0-307-59140-1(9)*, Crown) Crown Publishing Group.
Gates, Henry Louis, Jr. In Search of Our Roots: How 19 Extraordinary African Americans Reclaimed Their Past. 2009. (ENG., Illus.). 448p. 27.50 *(978-0-307-38240-5(0)*, Crown) Crown Publishing Group.
Oonk, Gijsbert. The Karimjee Jivanjee Family: Merchant Princes of East Africa 1800-2000. 2010. (ENG., Illus.). 172p. *(978-90-8555-027-3(0)*, Pallas Publications) Amsterdam Univ. Pr.
Pringle, Denys. An Expatriate Community in Tunis, 1648-1885: St George's Protestant Cemetery & Its Inscriptions. 2008. (Bar S Ser.). (Illus.). x, 178p. (C). pap. 112.50 *(978-1-4073-0222-5(1))* British Archaeological Reports Ltd. GBR. Dist: Brown, David Bk. Co., The.
Rogers, Douglas. The Last Resort: A Memoir of Mischief & Mayhem on a Family Farm in Africa. 2010. (ENG.). 336p. pap. 14.00 *(978-0-307-40798-6(5)*, Three Rivers Pr.) Crown Publishing Group.

AFRICA—HISTORIOGRAPHY

Afolabi, Niyi, ed. Toyin Falola: The Man, the Mask, the Muse. 2010. 1116p. 65.00 *(978-1-59460-754-7(0))* Carolina Academic Pr.
Asante, Molefi K. Cheikh Anta Diop: An Intellectual Portrait. 2006. *(978-0-943412-26-9(9))* Univ. of Sankore Pr., The.
Bala, Salisu. History of Jamaá Emirate, Circ. 2009. 204p. pap. *(978-3-639-21282-2(7))* VDM Verlag Dr. Mueller e.K.
Derricourt, Robin. Inventing Africa: History, Archaeology & Ideas, 1 vol. 2011. (ENG., Illus.). 256p. 28.00 *(978-0-7453-3105-8(X))*; lib. bdg. 90.00 *(978-0-7453-3106-5(8))* Pluto Pr. GBR. Dist: Macmillan.
Diawara, Mamadou, et al, eds. Historical Memory in Africa: Dealing with the Past, Reaching for the Future in an Intercultural Context. 2010. (MSH Ser.). (Illus.). 264p. 95.00 *(978-1-84545-652-8(1))* Berghahn Bks., Inc.
El Daly, Okasha. Egyptology: The Missing Millennium - Ancient Egypt in Medieval Arabic Writings. 2007. (University College London Institute of Archaeology Publications). (ENG., Illus.). 250p. 94.00 *(978-1-59874-210-7(8))* Left Coast Pr., Inc.
Eze, Michael Onyebuchi. The Politics of History in Contemporary Africa. 2010. (ENG.). 238p. 89.00 *(978-0-230-62357-6(3))* Palgrave Macmillan.
Falola, Toyin, et al. Emergent Themes & Methods in African Studies: Essays in Honor of Adiele E. Afigbo. 2008. *(978-1-59221-676-5(5))*; 708p. pap. *(978-1-59221-677-2(3)*, Africa World Pr.
Gam Nkwi, Walter. Voicing the Voiceless: Contributions to Closing Gaps in Cameroon History, 1958-2009. 2010. 200p. pap. *(978-9956-616-40-4(0))* Langaa Research & Publishing Common Initiative Group CMR. Dist: Michigan State Univ. Pr.
Haziza, Typhaine. Le Kaléidoscope Hérodotéen: Images, Imaginaire et Representations de L'Égypte à Travers le Livre II D'Hérodote. 2009. (Etudes anciennes Serie Grecque Ser.). (FRE., Illus.). 400p. (C). pap. 68.00 ***(978-2-251-32670-2(7))*** Societe d'edition Les Belles lettres FRA. Dist: ISD.
Jeffreys, David, ed. Views of Ancient Egypt since Napoleon Bonaparte: Imperialism, Colonialism & Modern Appropriations. 2007. (Encounters with Ancient Egypt series, University College London Institute of Archaeology Publications). (ENG., Illus.). 239p. pap. 34.95 *(978-1-59874-202-2(7))* Left Coast Pr., Inc.
Lipton, Merle. Liberals, Marxists, & Nationalists: Competing Interpretations of South African History. 2007. (ENG.). 240p. 89.00 *(978-0-230-60059-1(X))* Palgrave Macmillan.
Robertson, Clyde C. Africa Rising: Multidisciplinary Discussions on Africana Studies & History: From Ancient Times Through Modernity. 2009. *(978-1-59221-716-8(8))*; pap. *(978-1-59221-717-5(6))* Africa World Pr.
Rufer, Mario. La Nación en Escenas: Memoria Pública y Usos Del Pasado en Contextos Poscoloniales. 2010. (Estudios de Asia y Africa Ser.). (SPA., Illus.). 462p. pap. 41.99 *(978-607-462-062-7(8))* El Colegio de México, A.C., Biblioteca Miguel Cosio Villegas MEX. Dist: Fondo de Cultura Economica USA.
Stolten, Hans Erik. History Making & Present Day Politics: The Meaning of Collective Memory in South Africa. Stolten, Hans-Eric & Stolten, Hans Erik, eds. 2007. 376p. pap. 39.95 *(978-91-7106-581-0(4))* Nordiska Afrikainstitutet SWE. Dist: Stylus Publishing, LLC.
Tendi, Blessing-Miles. Making History in Mugabe's Zimbabwe: Politics, Intellectuals, & the Media. 2010. (Illus.). xviii, 286p. 63.95 *(978-3-03911-969-9(3))* Lang, Peter Publishing, Inc.
Yerxa, Donald A. Recent Themes in the History of Africa & the Atlantic World: Historians in Conversation. Yerxa, Donald A., ed. 2008. (Historians in Conversation Ser.). 120p. pap. 21.95 *(978-1-57003-758-0(2))* Univ. of South Carolina Pr.
Yerxa, Donald A., ed. Recent Themes in the History of Africa & the Atlantic World: Historians in Conversation. 2008. (Historians in Conversation Ser.). (ENG.). 120p. 39.95 *(978-1-57003-757-3(4))* Univ. of South Carolina Pr.

AFRICA—HISTORY

A. J. Ndeda, Mildred & Mildred, A. J. Ndeda. The Impact of Male Labour Migration on Rural Women: A Case of Central Nyanza in Colonial Kenya. 2011. 248p. pap. ***(978-3-639-32419-8(6))*** VDM Verlag Dr. Mueller e.K.
Abbott, Peter. Colonial Armies in Africa 1850-1918: Organisation, Warfare, Dress & Weapons. 2006. (Illus.). 222p. 59.95 *(978-1-901543-07-0(2))* Foundry Bks. GBR. Dist: Casemate Pubs. & Bk. Distributors, LLC.
Abroquah, Martin. Revelation: The Movement of the Akan People from Kanaan to Ghana. 2010. (Illus.). 532p. pap. 38.49 *(978-1-4490-6251-4(2))* AuthorHouse.
Adegbile, Isaiah. The African & African American History: An Introduction - The Political-Socio-Economic Context in Historical Perspective. 2008. (ENG.). 244p. per. 53.50 *(978-0-7618-3974-3(7))* Univ. Pr. of America, Inc.
Adelaar, K. Alexander & Himmelmann, Nikolaus, eds. The Austronesian Languages of Asia & Madagascar. 2011. (Routledge Language Family Ser.). 864p. (C). pap. 71.95 *(978-0-415-68153-7(7))* Routledge.
Adogbo, Michael P. Comparative Historical & Interpretative Study of Religions. 2010. 130p. pap. *(978-978-8422-23-5(3))* Malthouse Press, Stoke on Trent.
African Country Reports: Companies-Products-Services. 20p. (Orig.). pap. *(978-0-934393-60-7(5))* Rector Pr., Ltd.
Agbahowe, Nathaniel U. Wake up Africa! 2009. 460p. pap. 20.49 *(978-1-4389-1466-4(0))* AuthorHouse.
Agbodike, Chinedu. Colonial Conspiracies in Africa. 2009. 300p. 29.99 *(978-1-4415-1182-9(2))*; pap. 19.99 *(978-1-4415-1181-2(4))* Xlibris Corp.
Ajayi, S. Ademola. African Culture & Civilization. 2007. (Illus.). 456p. pap. *(978-978-35454-5-8(0))* Ibadan Univ. Pr. NGA. Dist: Michigan State Univ. Pr.
Allen, Christopher & Johnson, R. W., eds. African Perspectives: Papers in the History, Politics & Economics of Africa Presented to Thomas Hodgkin. 2008. (ENG.). 464p. pap. 58.00 *(978-0-521-10199-8(9))* Cambridge Univ. Pr.
Antwi Bosiakoh, Thomas. Nigerian Migration to Ghan. 2011. 128p. pap. ***(973-3-8443-0200-4(X))*** Lambert Academic Publishing.
Arnold-Forster, Forster Delafield. The Madagascar Pirates. 2011. 254p. 47.95 ***(978-1-258-05003-0(X))*** Literary Licensing, LLC.
Arnold, Guy. Historical Dictionary of Civil Wars in Africa. 2nd ed. 2007. (Historical Dictionaries of War, Revolution, & Civil Unrest Ser.). (ENG., Illus.). 536p. 133.00 *(978-0-8108-5766-7(9))* Scarecrow Pr., Inc.
Asante, Molefi Kete. The History of Africa: The Quest for Eternal Harmony. 2007. (Illus.). 397p. 110.00 *(978-0-415-77138-2(2))*; per. 31.95 *(978-0-415-77139-9(0))* Routledge.
Austen, Ralph A. Trans-Saharan Africa in World History. 2010. (New Oxford World History Ser.). (ENG., Illus.). 176p. pap. 19.95 *(978-0-19-533788-4(3))* Oxford Univ. Pr., Inc.
Bala, Salisu. History of Jamaá Emirate, Circ. 2009. 204p. pap. *(978-3-639-21282-2(7))* VDM Verlag Dr. Mueller e.K.
Barber, Karin, ed. Africa's Hidden Histories: Everyday Literacy & Making the Self. 2006. (African Expressive Cultures Ser.). (ENG., Illus.). 464p. 75.00 *(978-0-253-34729-9(7)*, 0253347297); pap. 29.95 *(978-0-253-21843-8(8)*, 0253218438) Indiana Univ. Pr.
Barwani, Naila. Gone Is Yesterday - Imepita Jan. 2011. 256p. pap. ***(978-0-7552-1327-6(0))*** Authors OnLine, Ltd.
Bates, Robert H. When Things Fell Apart: State Failure in Late-Century Africa. 2008. (Cambridge Studies in Comparative Politics). (ENG., Illus.). 218p. pap. 22.99 *(978-0-521-71525-6(3))*; 216p. 65.00 *(978-0-521-88735-9(6))* Cambridge Univ. Pr.
Batson, Roderick. Full Circle: AfricaAmerica. 2010. 352p. 29.99 *(978-1-4520-1992-5(4))*; pap. 25.99 *(978-1-4520-1991-8(6))* AuthorHouse.
Ben-Ze'ev, Efrat, et al, eds. Shadows of War: A Social History of Silence in the Twentieth Century. 2010. (ENG., Illus.). 234p. 85.00 *(978-0-521-19658-1(2))* Cambridge Univ. Pr.
Benjamin, Thomas. The Atlantic World: Europeans, Africans, Indians & Their Shared History, 1400-1900. 2009. (ENG., Illus.). (C). 752p. 99.00 *(978-0-521-85099-5(1))*; 750p. pap. 46.99 *(978-0-521-61649-2(2))* Cambridge Univ. Pr.
Bickford-Smith, Vivian & Mendelsohn, Richard, eds. Black & White in Colour: Africa's History on Screen. 2007. 400p. per. 26.95 *(978-0-8214-1747-8(9))* Ohio Univ. Pr.
Blackhall, Susan. Simon Mann: The Real Story. 2012. (Illus.). 192p. 39.95 ***(978-1-84884-577-0(4))*** Pen & Sword Bks. Ltd. GBR. Dist: Casemate Pubs. & Bk. Distributors, LLC.
Blake, Cecil. The African Origins of Rhetoric. 2010. 160p. pap. 39.95 *(978-0-415-88387-0(3))* Routledge.
Boaduo, Nana Adu-Pipim & Kofi Poku Quan-Baffour, Prof. Sankofaism: Reinventing Africa. 2011. 112p. pap. ***(978-3-8443-0045-1(7))*** Lambert Academic Publishing.
Boahen, A. Adu. African Perspectives on European Colonialism. 2011. (Illus.). 148p. pap. 15.00 ***(978-0-9660201-4-4(6))*** Diasporic Africa Pr.
Bogaerts, Els & Raben, Remco. Beyond Empire & Nation. 2010. 250p. pap. 31.00 *(978-90-6718-289-8(3))* KITLV Pr. NLD. Dist: Univ. of Hawaii Pr.
Bonn, Guillaume. Le Mal D'Afrique: A Journey into Old & New Africa. 2006. (Illus.). 149p. 45.00 *(978-0-9779008-3-1(5))* Empire Editions.
Booth, Joseph. Africa for the African. 2nd ed. 2007. 100p. pap. *(978-99908-87-23-5(3))* Kachere Series, Bks. on Religion, Theology & Society in Malawi MWI. Dist: Michigan State Univ. Pr.
Boyd, Herb. African History for Beginners. 2007. (For Beginners Ser.). (ENG., Illus.). 128p. per. 14.95 *(978-1-934389-18-8(8)*, For Beginners) Steerforth Pr.
Brown, Miles Shabazz. You Mountain You Lion: Science, Culture & Songs of Black Africa. 2009. (Illus.). 114p. pap. 11.95 *(978-1-4327-3665-1(5))* Outskirts Pr., Inc.
Bruder, Edith. The Black Jews of Africa: History, Religion, Identity. 2008. (ENG., Illus.). 304p. 49.95 *(978-0-19-533356-5(X))* Oxford Univ. Pr., Inc.
Bruder, Edith. The Black Jews of Africa History, Religion, Identity. 2012. (ENG., Illus.). 304p. pap. 24.95 ***(978-0-19-993455-3(X))*** Oxford Univ. Pr., Inc.
Campbell, Greg. Blood Diamonds, Revised Edition: Tracing the Deadly Path of the World's Most Precious Stones. 2nd ed. 2012. (ENG.). 336p. (gr. 9). pap. 16.99 ***(978-0-465-02991-4(4))*** Basic Bks.
Campbell, Gwyn. An Economic History of Imperial Madagascar, 1750-1895: The Rise & Fall of an Island Empire. 2008. (African Studies). (ENG., Illus.). 436p. pap. 46.00 *(978-0-521-10391-6(6))* Cambridge Univ. Pr.
Carey, Brian Todd. Hannibal's Last Battle: Zama & the Fall of Carthage. 2008. (ENG.). 232p. 26.00 *(978-1-59416-075-2(9))* Westholme Publishing.
Chamberlain, M. E. The Scramble for Africa. 3rd ed. 2010. (Seminar Studies in History Ser.). (ENG., Illus.). 208p. (C). pap. 27.20 *(978-1-4082-2014-6(8))* Longman Publishing Group.
Chamblee, Angela. An Ancient African Wisdom Book: Commentary on the Instruction of Ptahhotep. 2010. 224p. 28.95 *(978-0-595-62411-9(1))*; pap. 18.95 *(978-0-595-48011-1(X))* iUniverse, Inc.
CHE, Patrick. The african experience - Volume 1. 2009. 166p. pap. 58.80 *(978-0-557-07617-8(X))* Lulu Enterprises Inc.
—The african experience - volume 1 part I. 2009. 77p. pap. 32.10 *(978-0-557-07444-0(4))* Lulu Enterprises Inc.
—The african experience - volume 1 part II. 2009. 98p. pap. 38.40 *(978-0-557-07694-9(3))* Lulu Enterprises Inc.
Chem-Langhee, Bongfen & Fanso, Verkijika. Royal Susseccion in the African Kingdom of Nso' A Study in Oral Historiography. 2008. (Illus.). 156p. *(978-0-7734-5041-7(6))* Mellen, Edwin Pr., The.
Chetty, Suryakanthie. Gender under Fire. 2011. 180p. pap. ***(978-3-8433-8085-0(6))*** Lambert Academic Publishing.
Chijioke, F. A. Beginning History of Ancient Africa. Date not set. pap. 24.40 *(978-0-582-59501-9(0))* Addison-Wesley Longman, Ltd. GBR. Dist: Trans-Atlantic Pubns., Inc.
Chishugi, Leah. A Long Way from Paradise: Surviving the Rwandan Genocide. 2012. (ENG.). 304p. pap. 13.95 ***(978-1-84408-657-3(7)***, Virago Press) Little, Brown Bk. Group Ltd. GBR. Dist: Independent Pubs. Group.
Clark, J. Desmond & Gifford, D. P. Adrar Bous: Archaeology of a Central Saharan Granitic Ring Complex in Niger. 2008. (Illus.). 403p. *(978-90-74752-43-5(8))* Koninklijk Museum voor Midden-Afrika.
Clarke, Duncan. Africa's Future - Darkness to Destiny: How the Past Is Shaping Africa's Economic Evolution. 2012. (ENG., Illus.). 320p. 32.95 ***(978-1-84668-569-9(9))*** Profile Bks. Ltd. GBR. Dist: Consortium Bk. Sales & Distribution.
Clarke, John Henrik, ed. New Dimensions in African History: From the Nile Valley to the New World. 220p. 11.99 *(978-0-86543-227-7(9))*; 49.95 *(978-0-86543-226-0(0))* Africa World Pr.
Collins, Robert O. The A to Z of Pre-Colonial Africa. 2010. (A to Z Guide Ser.). (ENG.). 678p. pap. 34.45 *(978-0-8108-7580-7(2))* Scarecrow Pr., Inc.
Collins, Robert O., ed. Historical Problems of Imperial Africa. 2007. (Illus.). x, 318p. (C). pap. 28.95 *(978-1-55876-431-6(3))* Wiener, Markus Pubs., Inc.
—Problems in the History of Modern Africa. rev. enl. ed. 2007. (Illus.). 300p. (Orig.). (C). per. 28.95 *(978-1-55876-454-5(2))* Wiener, Markus Pubs., Inc.
Comaroff, John L., et al, eds. Picturing a Colonial Past: The African Photographs of Isaac Schapera. 2007. (Illus.). 234p. 65.00 *(978-0-226-11411-8(2))*; per. 30.00 *(978-0-226-11412-5(0))* Univ. of Chicago Pr.
Conant, Jonathan. Staying Roman: Conquest & Identity in Africa & the Mediterranean, 439-700. 2012. (Cambridge Studies in Medieval Life & Thought: Fourth Ser.). (ENG., Illus.). 456p. 99.00 ***(978-0-521-19697-0(3))*** Cambridge Univ. Pr.
Connell, Dan & Killion, Tom. Historical Dictionary of Eritrea. 2nd ed. 2010. (Historical Dictionaries of Africa Ser.). (ENG., Illus.). 688p. 115.00 *(978-0-8108-5952-4(1))* Scarecrow Pr., Inc.
Coquery-Vidrovitch, Catherine. Africa & the Africans in the Nineteenth Century: A Turbulent History. Baker, Mary, tr. from FRE. 2009. (ENG., Illus.). 336p. 79.95 *(978-0-7656-1696-8(3))*; pap. 36.95 *(978-0-7656-1697-5(1))* Sharpe, M.E. Inc.
Cordell. The Human Tradition In Modern Africa. 2011. (Human Tradition around the World Ser.). (ENG.). 316p. pap. 29.95 ***(978-0-7425-3733-0(1))*** Rowman & Littlefield Publishers, Inc.
Cordell, Dennis D. The Human Tradition In Modern Africa. 2011. (Human Tradition around the World Ser.). (ENG.). 288p. 84.00 ***(978-0-7425-3732-3(3))*** Rowman & Littlefield Publishers, Inc.
Coulter, G. W. Africa in Transition: The Journey from Tradition to Modern. 2011. 352p. 36.50 ***(978-1-84624-632-6(6))*** Trans-Atlantic Pubns., Inc.
Cram101 Textbook Reviews. Outlines & Highlights for a History of the African People by July, Isbn: 0881339806. 2011. 96p. pap. 27.95 ***(978-1-61812-896-6(5))*** Cram101 Inc.
—Outlines & Highlights for Africa in World History by Gilbert, Erik, Isbn: 9780136154389 0136154387. 2011. 144p. pap. 28.95 ***(978-1-61812-521-7(4))*** Cram101 Inc.
—Outlines & Highlights for African History: From Earliest Times to Independence by Curtin et al., ISBN. 2011. 84p. pap. 27.95 ***(978-1-61830-026-3(1))*** Cram101 Inc.
—Outlines & Highlights for Africana Studies: A Survey of Africa & the African Diaspora by Azevedo, ISBN. 2011. 122p. pap. 28.95 ***(978-1-61812-813-3(2))*** Cram101 Inc.
—Outlines & Highlights for Africana Studies: Survey of Africa & the African Diaspora by Azevedo, Mario, ISBN. 2011. 254p. pap. 31.95 ***(978-1-61812-522-4(2))*** Cram101 Inc.
—Outlines & Highlights for Modern Africa: A Social & Political History by Davidson, ISBN. 2011. 58p. pap. 26.95 ***(978-1-61812-953-6(8))*** Cram101 Inc.
—Outlines & Highlights for the African Experience: An Introduction by Vincent B. Khapoya. 2011. 100p. pap. 27.95 ***(978-1-61906-089-0(2))*** Cram101 Inc.
Cunningham, David E. Barriers to Peace in Civil War. 2011. (ENG., Illus.). 296p. 90.00 *(978-1-107-00759-8(3))* Cambridge Univ. Pr.
D-Kha'd. The Transformation Process of a People: From BC Africa up to 1619 America, with reference to modernity for comparative Analysis. 2011. 216p. 29.99 ***(978-1-4535-4911-7(0))***; pap. 19.99 ***(978-1-4535-4910-0(2))*** Xlibris Corp.
Dallaire, Roméo A. They Fight Like Soldiers, They Die Like Children: The Global Quest to Eradicate the Use of Child Soldiers. 2011. (ENG.). 320p. 26.00 *(978-0-8027-7956-4(5))* Walker & Co.
Dauge-Roth, Alexandr. Writing & Filming the Genoide. 2010. (After the Empire: the Francophone World & Postcolonial France Ser.). (ENG.). 304p. 78.99 *(978-0-7391-1229-8(5))* Lexington Bks.
Dauge-Roth, Alexandre. Writing & Filming the Genocide of the Tutsis in Rwanda: Dismembering & Remembering Traumatic History. 2011. (After the Empire: the Francophone World & Postcolonial France Ser.). (ENG.). 304p. pap. 34.95 ***(978-0-7391-7282-7(4))*** Lexington Bks.
Daymond, M. J. & Sandwith, Corinne, eds. Africa South: Viewpoints, 1956-1961. 2011. 431p. pap., pap. 55.00 *(978-1-86914-195-0(4))* University of Kwazulu-Natal Press ZAF. Dist: International Specialized Bk. Services.
de Villiers, Les. Africa 2007. annuals 7th ed. 2007. (Illus.). 400p. per. 28.95 *(978-0-916673-22-2(7))* Business Bks. International.
de Villiers, Lourens. Africa 2007. 2007. (Illus.). 400p. cd-rom 48.95 *(978-0-916673-23-9(5))* Business Bks. International.
Depelchin, Jacques. Reclaiming African History. 2011. 104p. pap. 20.95 ***(978-1-906387-98-3(2))*** Pambuzuka Pr. GBR. Dist: Independent Pubs. Group.
Derman, Bill, et al, eds. Conflicts over Land & Water in Africa. 2007. (Illus.). 256p. pap. 34.95 *(978-0-85255-888-1(0)*, Currey, James) Boydell & Brewer, Ltd. GBR. Dist: Boydell & Brewer, Inc.
Derman, Bill & Odgaard, Rie. Conflicts over Land & Water in Africa. 2007. (Illus.). 256p. pap. *(978-1-86914-129-5(6))* University of Kwazulu-Natal Press ZAF. Dist: International Specialized Bk. Services.
Derrick, Jonathan. Africa's 'Agitators' Militant Anti-Colonialism in Africa & the West, 1918-1939. 2012. (Columbia/Hurst Ser.). (ENG.). 320p. (gr. 17). pap. 27.50 *(978-0-231-70057-3(1))* Columbia Univ. Pr.
Des Forges, Alison Liebhafsky & Newbury, David S. Defeat Is the Only Bad News: Rwanda under Musinga, 1897-1931. 2011. E-Book *(978-0-299-28143-4(4))* Univ. of Wisconsin Pr.
Dibaba, Terfa. It Is a Long Way. 2011. 246p. pap. 24.90 ***(978-3-8423-5916-1(0))*** Bks. on Demand.
Dickovick, J. Tyler. Africa. 46th ed. 2011. (World Today Series: Africa Ser.). (ENG., Illus.). 344p. pap. 18.50 ***(978-1-935264-18-7(4))*** Stryker-Post Pubns.
Dowden, Richard. Africa: Altered States, Ordinary Miracles. 2010. (ENG., Illus.). 592p. pap. 19.95 *(978-1-58648-816-1(3))* PublicAffairs.
Du Bois, W. E. B. Africa, Its Geography, People, & Products: And, Africa, Its Place in Modern History. 2007. *(978-0-19-532580-5(X))* Oxford Univ. Pr., Inc.
—The Negro. 2009. 168p. 25.00 *(978-1-59740-364-1(4))*; 166p. pap. 17.00 *(978-1-59740-365-8(2))* ACLS Humanities E-Book.
—The Negro. 2008. 184p. 25.99 *(978-0-554-25278-0(3))* 2008. 188p. 25.99 *(978-0-554-29609-8(8))* 2008. 184p. 22.99 *(978-0-554-34581-9(1))* 2008. 188p. 22.99 *(978-0-554-38912-7(6))* 2007. (ENG.). 186p. pap. 21.99 *(978-1-4346-8015-0(0))* 2007. (ENG.). 170p. pap. 19.99 *(978-1-4346-8014-3(2))* 2007. (ENG.). 162p. pap. 19.99 *(978-1-4264-8576-3(X))* 2007. (ENG.). 182p. pap. 21.99 *(978-1-4264-8633-3(2))* BiblioBazaar.
—The Negro. 2007. (ENG.). 156p. per. 11.95 *(978-1-60206-814-8(3))* Cosimo, Inc.
—The Negro. 2006. (Illus.). pap. *(978-1-4065-1121-5(8))* Dodo Pr.
—The Negro. 2007. *(978-0-19-532576-8(1))* Oxford Univ. Pr., Inc.
—The Negro. 2009. 160p. pap. 11.95 *(978-1-4385-1906-7(0))*; (ENG.). pap. 14.45 *(978-1-4385-1287-7(2))* Standard Pubns., Inc. (Book Jungle).
—The Negro. 2008. 120p. pap. 7.99 *(978-1-60459-371-6(7))* Wilder Pubns., Ltd.
—The World & Africa: And, Color & Democracy. 2007. *(978-0-19-532584-3(2))* Oxford Univ. Pr., Inc.
DuBois, Gaylord. Tarzan: the Jesse Marsh Years Volume 9: The Jesse Marsh Years Volume 9. 2011. (Illus.). 240p. 49.99 *(978-1-59582-649-7(1))* Dark Horse Comics.
Dudley, Dean. History of the First Council of Nice. (African Heritage Classical Research Studies). 124p. reprint ed. 15.00 *(978-0-938818-63-2(5))* ECA Assocs.

Duffield, Mark. War & Famine in Africa. (Research Discussion Papers). (ENG.). 40p. (C). spiral bd. 23.95 *(978-0-85598-161-7(X))* Oxfam Publishing GBR. Dist: Stylus Publishing, LLC.

Eboe-Osuji, Chile. Protecting Humanity: Essays in International Law & Policy in Honour of Navanethem Pillay. 2010. (FRE & ENG.). 884p. *(978-90-04-18378-0(7))* BRILL.

Ellis, Stephen & Kessel, Ineke van. Movers & Shakers: Social Movements in Africa. 2009. pap. *(978-90-04-18013-0(3))* BRILL.

Ensign, Margee M. & Bertrand, William E. Rwanda: History & Hope. 2010. (Illus.). xx, 154p. *(978-0-7618-4944-5(0))* Univ. Pr. of America, Inc.

Etute, Joseph. The New Slavery System. 2010. (Illus.). 416p. pap. 17.99 *(978-1-4389-9133-7(9))* AuthorHouse.

Falola, Toyin & Brownell, Emily, eds. Africa, Empire & Globalization: Essays in Honor of A. G. Hopkins. 2011. 682p. 80.00 *(978-1-59460-915-2(2))* Carolina Academic Pr.

Falola, Toyin, et al. Emergent Themes & Methods in African Studies: Essays in Honor of Adiele E. Afigbo. 2008. *(978-1-59221-676-5(5))*; 708p. pap. *(978-1-59221-677-2(3))* Africa World Pr.

Faught, C. Brad. Into Africa: The Imperial Life of Margery Perham. 2012. (ENG., Illus.). 288p. 75.00 ***(978-1-84885-490-1(0))*** I. B. Tauris & Co., Ltd. GBR. Dist: Macmillan.

Feyissa, Dereje & Hoehne, Markus Virgil, eds. Borders & Borderlands as Resources in the Horn of Africa. 2010. (Eastern Africa Ser.). (Illus.). 224p. 70.00 *(978-1-84701-018-6(0))*, Currey, James) Boydell & Brewer, Ltd. GBR. Dist: Boydell & Brewer, Inc.

Finaldi, Giuseppe Maria. Italian National Identity in the Scramble for Africa: Italy's African Wars in the Era of Nation-Building, 1870-1900. 2009. (Illus.). 348p. pap. *(978-3-03911-803-8(X))* Lang, Peter.

Fitzgerald, Desmond. Many Parts: The Life & Travels of a Soldier Engineer & Arbitr. 2007. (ENG., Illus.). 288p. 51.00 *(978-1-84511-306-3(3)*, Radcliffe Pr., The) I. B. Tauris & Co., Ltd. GBR. Dist: Macmillan.

Francis, David J., ed. When War Ends: Building Peace in Divided Communities. 2012. 209p. 99.95 ***(978-1-4094-2294-5(1))*** Ashgate Publishing Co.

Freeman, Frederick. Africa's Redemption, the Salvation of Our Country. 2010. (ENG.). 392p. pap. 33.75 *(978-1-175-45327-3(7))* BiblioBazaar.

—Africa's Redemption, the Salvation of Our Country. 2009. 244p. pap. *(978-1-151-13296-3(9))* Books LLC.

—Africa's Redemption, the Salvation of Our Country. 2010. (Illus.). 220p. pap. 30.24 *(978-1-154-62187-7(1))* General Bks. LLC.

French Sheldon, May. Sultan to Sultan - Adventures of a Woman among the Masai & Other Tribes of East Afric. 2008. 492p. pap. *(978-1-906393-13-7(3))* Trotamundas Pr., Ltd.

Fujii, Lee Ann. Killing Neighbors: Webs of Violence in Rwanda. 2011. (Illus.). 224p. pap. 21.95 *(978-0-8014-7713-3(1))* Cornell Univ. Pr.

Furley, Oliver & May, Roy. Ending Africa's Wars: Progressing to Peace. 2006. 258p. 124.95 *(978-0-7546-3932-9(0))* Ashgate Publishing Co.

Games, Ambush. Bush Wars: Africa 1967-2010. 2012. (Force on Force Ser.). (ENG., Illus.). 96p. pap. 24.95 ***(978-1-84908-769-8(5))*** Osprey Publishing, Ltd. GBR. Dist: Random Hse., Inc.

Gates, Henry Louis, Jr. & Appiah, Kwame Anthony, eds. Encyclopedia of Africa, 2 vols., Set. 2010. (ENG., Illus.). 1392p. 315.00 *(978-0-19-533770-9(0))* Oxford Univ. Pr., Inc.

Genova, Ann & Falola, Toyin, eds. Yorùbá Identity & Power Politics. 2006. (Rochester Studies in African History & the Diaspora Ser.: Volume 22). (Illus.). 380p. 80.00 *(978-1-58046-219-8(7))* Univ. of Rochester Pr.

Getz, Trevor & Brizuela-Garcia, Esperanza. African Histories: New Sources & New Techniques for Studying African Pasts. rev. ed. 2011. (ENG., Illus.). 312p. (C). pap. 51.00 ***(978-0-13-615558-4(8)***, Prentice Hall) Prentice Hall PTR.

Giesing, Cornelia & Vydrine, Valentin. Ta: Rikh Mandinka de Bijini (Guinie-Bissau) La Mimoire des Mandinka et Sooninkee du Kaab. 2006. (African Sources for African History Ser.: Vol. 9). (FRE, MAN & ARA., Illus.). 398p. pap. *(978-90-04-14724-9(1))* BRILL.

Gilbert, Elizabeth L. Tribes of the Great Rift Valley. 2007. (ENG., Illus.). 272p. 75.00 *(978-0-8109-9411-9(9))* Abrams.

Gilbert, Erik & Reynolds, Jonathan T. Africa in World History: From Prehistory to the Present. 3rd rev. ed. 2011. (ENG., Illus.). 480p. (C). pap. 66.20 *(978-0-205-05399-5(8)*, Prentice Hall) Prentice Hall PTR.

Gilliam, Tanji & Zuberi, Tukufu, eds. A Perspective on Africa & the World. 2011. (ANNALS of the American Academy of Political & Social Science Ser.: 632). 132p. (C). 47.00 *(978-1-4129-9395-1(4)*, 295632C); pap. 34.00 *(978-1-4129-9394-4(6)*, 295632P) SAGE Pubns., Inc.

Goodwin, Stefan. Africa in Europe Vol. 1: Antiquity into the Age of Global Exploration, 2 vols. 2008. (ENG.). 260p. 73.50 *(978-0-7391-1725-5(4))*; pap. 31.50 *(978-0-7391-1726-2(2))* Lexington Bks.

—Africa in Europe Vol. 2: Interdependencies, Relocations, & Globalization, 2 vols. 2008. (ENG.). 430p. 83.99 *(978-0-7391-2765-0(9))*; pap. 40.99 *(978-0-7391-2766-7(7))* Lexington Bks.

Gordon, April A. & Gordon, Donald L., eds. Understanding Contemporary Africa, 4th Edition. 4th ed. 2006. (Illus.). 475p. (C). pap. 27.50 *(978-1-58826-466-4(1))* Rienner, Lynne Pubs.

Gordon, Charles Alexander. Through Three Victorian Campaigns: Experiences of a Regimental Surgeon During the Gwalior War, Campaigns in West Africa & the Indian Mutiny. 2009. 208p. *(978-1-84677-768-4(2))*; pap. *(978-1-84677-767-7(4))* Leonaur Ltd.

Griffo, Kedar & Berkley, Michael. African Origin found in Religion & Freemasonry. 2010. 160p. pap. 19.99 *(978-0-557-44543-1(4))* Lulu Enterprises Inc.

Gurney, David H. U. S. European Command (USECOM) Reprint of a Special Feature from the Journal, ¿Joint Forces Quarterly¿. 2007. (Illus.). 29p. (C). pap. 20.00 *(978-1-4223-1521-7(5))* DIANE Publishing Co.

Harries, Patrick. Butterflies & Barbarians: Swiss Missionaries & Systems of Knowledge in South-East Africa. 2007. (Illus.). 312p. pap. 34.95 *(978-0-85255-983-3(6)*, Currey, James) Boydell & Brewer, Ltd. GBR. Dist: Boydell & Brewer, Inc.

Hatzfeld, Jean. Life Laid Bare: The Survivors in Rwanda Speak. Coverdale, Linda, tr. from FRE. 2007. (ENG., Illus.). 256p. pap. 14.95 *(978-1-59051-273-9(1))* Other Pr., LLC.

Heneghan Communications Consulting. Makeda(r), the Queen of Sheba. 2006. (Illus.). 26p. pap. 25.00 *(978-0-9828879-0-5(6))* Ghenet Enterprises Ltd dba EthiDolls.

—When You See Water, Call It Water: The Story of Queen Mother Yaa Asantewaa. 2008. (Illus.). 27p. pap. 25.00 *(978-0-9828879-1-2(4))* Ghenet Enterprises Ltd dba EthiDolls.

Herbert, Edwin. Risings & Rebellions 1919-39: Organisation, Warfare, Dress & Weapons. Interwar Colonial Campaigns in Africa, Asia, & the Americas. 2007. (Armies of the Twentieth Century Ser.). (Illus.). 192p. 63.00 *(978-1-901543-12-4(9))* Foundry Bks. GBR. Dist: Casemate Pubs. & Bk. Distributors, LLC.

Hublin, Jean-Jacques & McPherron, Shannon P., eds. Modern Origins: A North African Perspective. 2012. (Vertebrate Paleobiology & Paleoanthropology Ser.). (ENG., Illus.). xxi, 244p. 139.00 ***(978-94-007-2928-5(6)***, 9400729286) Springer.

Hughes, Arnold. Historical Dictionary of the Gambia. 4th ed. 2008. (Historical Dictionaries of Africa Ser.). (ENG., Illus.). 376p. 99.00 *(978-0-8108-5825-1(8))* Scarecrow Pr., Inc.

Hunwick, John O. & Boye, Alida Jay. The Hidden Treasures of Timbuktu: Rediscovering Africa's Literary Culture. 2008. (ENG., Illus.). 176p. 50.00 *(978-0-500-51421-4(6)*, 551421) Thames & Hudson.

Igbani, B. Maduabuchi A. Motherland Afrika: The Footprint of a Generation. rev. ed. 2008. (ENG.). 116p. pap. 31.99 *(978-1-4389-3472-3(6))* AuthorHouse.

Ikime, Obaro & Osoba, Segun, eds. Tarikh. Incl. Vol. 4, No. 3-4. European Conquest & African Resistance, Pts. 1-2. 1974. Set pap. o.p. *(978-0-582-60870-2(8))* BRILL.

Iliffe, John. Africans: The History of a Continent. 2nd rev. ed. 2007. (African Studies). (ENG.). 384p. 92.00 *(978-0-521-86438-1(0))*; per. 28.99 *(978-0-521-68297-8(5))* Cambridge Univ. Pr.

Imperato, Pascal James & Imperato, Gavin H. Historical Dictionary of Mali. 4th ed. 2008. (Historical Dictionaries of Africa Ser.). (ENG.). 560p. 145.00 *(978-0-8108-5603-5(4))* Scarecrow Pr., Inc.

Irivuzumugabe, Eric & Lawrence, Tracey D. My Father, Maker of the Trees: How I Survived the Rwandan Genocide. 2009. 208p. 17.99 *(978-0-8010-1320-1(8))* Baker Bks.

Ittmann, Karl, et al, eds. The Demographics of Empire: The Colonial Order & the Creation of Knowledge. 2010. (ENG., Illus.). 352p. 64.95 *(978-0-8214-1932-8(3))*; pap. 28.95 *(978-0-8214-1933-5(1))* Ohio Univ. Pr.

Jeater, Diana. African History. 2013. (ENG.). 288p. (C). pap. 28.95 *(978-1-4039-1706-5(X))*; 85.00 *(978-1-4039-1705-8(1))* Palgrave Macmillan.

Jeppie, Shamil & Diagne, Souleymane Bachir, eds. The Meanings of Timbuktu. 2008. (ENG., Illus.). 376p. 60.00 *(978-0-7969-2204-5(7))* Human Sciences Research Council ZAF. Dist: Independent Pubs. Group.

Jinadu, L. Adele. Fanon: In Search of the African Revolution. 270p. (Orig.). 110.00 *(978-0-7103-0958-7(9))* Kegan Paul International, Ltd. GBR. Dist: Columbia Univ. Pr.

Johnston, Harry Hamilton. A History of the Colonization of Africa by Alien Races. 2nd ed. 2011. (ENG., Illus.). 538p. pap. 39.99 ***(978-0-521-23128-2(0))*** Cambridge Univ. Pr.

A Journey Through Africa, Asia, & the Pacific Realm Program Kit: All program components for A Journey Through Africa, 1 vol. 2009. 149.95 *(978-1-4236-0729-8(5))* Gibbs Smith, Publisher.

Kale Ewusi, Ebenezer Akwanga Jr. Bsc. Burundi's Negative Peace: The Shadow of a Broken Continent in the Era of NEPAD. 2010. 408p. pap. 21.96 *(978-1-4269-2355-5(4))* Trafford Publishing.

Kalinga, Owen J. Historical Dictionary of Malawi. 4th rev. ed. 2011. (Historical Dictionaries of Africa Ser.). (ENG.). 598p. 125.00 ***(978-0-8108-5961-6(0))*** Scarecrow Pr., Inc.

Kanya-Forstner, A. S. The Conquest of Western Sudan: A Study in French Military Imperialism. 2008. (ENG.). 308p. pap. 42.00 *(978-0-521-10372-5(X))* Cambridge Univ. Pr.

Kapteijns, Lidwien & Richters, J. M. Mediations of Violence in Africa: Fashioning new futures from contested Pasts. 2010. (Africa-Europe Group for Interdisciplinary Studies). (Illus.). 280p. pap. *(978-90-04-18536-4(4))* BRILL.

Kelly, Sean. Chasing Chaos: A Foreign Correspondent's Memoir. 2010. (Illus.). 385p. pap. 22.95 *(978-1-4327-4552-3(2))* Outskirts Pr., Inc.

Kerr, Gordon. A Short History of Africa: From the Origins of the Human Race to the Arab Revolts of 2011. 2012. (Pocket Essential Ser.). (ENG., Illus.). 160p. pap. 14.95 ***(978-1-84243-442-0(X))*** Pocket Essentials GBR. Dist: Independent Pubs. Group.

Khapoya, Vincent B. The African Experience: An Introduction. (ENG., (C). 3rd ed. 2009. Illus.). 320p. pap. 72.00 *(978-0-13-091843-7(1))* 4th rev. ed. 2012. 304p. pap. 70.00 ***(978-0-205-85171-3(1))*** Prentice Hall PTR. (Prentice Hall).

Kibreab, Gaim. Eritrea: A Dream Deferred. 2009. (Eastern Africa Ser.). (Illus.). 446p. 90.00 *(978-1-84701-008-7(3)*, Currey, James) Boydell & Brewer, Ltd. GBR. Dist: Boydell & Brewer, Inc.

King, Nathaniel. Conflict as Integration: Youth Aspiration to Personhood/Sierra Leone. 2007. (NAI Current African Issues Ser.). 40p. pap. 12.95 *(978-91-7106-604-6(7))* Nordiska Afrikainstitutet SWE. Dist: Stylus Publishing, LLC.

Klip, André & Sluiter, Göran. The International Criminal Tribunal for Rwanda 2003. 2007. 1036p. pap. 259.00 *(978-90-5095-651-2(3))* Intersentia Uitgevers N.V. BEL. Dist: International Specialized Bk. Services.

Klip, André & Sluiter, Göran, eds. Annotated Leading Cases of International Criminal Tribunals: The International Criminal Tribunal for Rwanda 1 December 2003 - 22 January 2004, Vol. 17. 2008. 716p. pap. 259.00 *(978-90-5095-798-4(6))* Intersentia Uitgevers N.V. BEL. Dist: International Specialized Bk. Services.

—Annotated Leading Cases of International Criminal Tribunals - Volume 18: The International Criminal Tribunal for Rwanda 2004. 2008. 898p. pap. 259.00 *(978-90-5095-799-1(4))* Intersentia Uitgevers N.V. BEL. Dist: International Specialized Bk. Services.

Knoll, Arthur J. German Colonial Experience: Select Documents on German Rule in Africa, China, & the Pacific, 1884-1914. 2010. (ENG.). 564p. pap. 61.99 *(978-0-7618-3900-2(3))* Univ. Pr. of America, Inc.

Koko, Jacques L. National Conference As a Strategy for Conflict Transformation & Peacemaking: The Legacy of the Republic of Benin Model (HB) 2008. 220p. *(978-1-905068-87-6(5))* Adonis & Abbey Publishers Ltd.

—National Conference As a Strategy for Conflict Transformation & Peacemaking: The Legacy of the Republic of Benin Model (PB) 2008. 220p. per. *(978-1-905068-52-4(2))* Adonis & Abbey Publishers Ltd.

Krabacher, Thomas, et al. Africa. 13th ed. 2010. (Global Studies). (ENG., Illus.). 320p. (C). pap. 50.00 *(978-0-07-352776-5(9)*, 0073527769, McGraw-Hill/Dushkin) McGraw-Hill Higher Education.

Krabacher, Thomas, et al. Global Studies: Africa. 14th ed. 2012. (Global Studies). (ENG., Illus.). 448p. (C). pap. 50.00 ***(978-0-07-802623-2(7)***, 0078026237, McGraw-Hill/Dushkin) McGraw-Hill Higher Education.

Kuhn, Alvin B. The Shadow of the Third Century. (African Studies). 525p. reprint ed. 40.00 *(978-0-938818-75-5(9))* ECA Assocs.

Laband, John. Daily Lives of Civilians in Wartime Africa: From Slavery Days to Rwandan Genocide, 1 vol. 2006. (Daily Life Through History Ser.). (Illus.). 312p. 65.00 *(978-0-313-33540-2(0)*, GR3540, Greenwood Pr.) Greenwood Publishing Group, Inc.

Laband, John, ed. Daily Lives of Civilians in Wartime Africa: From Slavery Days to Rwandan Genocide. 302p. pap. *(978-1-86914-109-7(1))* University of Kwazulu-Natal Press ZAF. Dist: International Specialized Bk. Services.

Lamphear, John. African Military History. 2007. (International Library of Essays on Military History Ser.). 548p. 325.00 *(978-0-7546-2521-6(4))* Ashgate Publishing Co.

Law, Robin, ed. Journals & Correspondence of Louis Fraser: British Vice-Consul to the Kingdom of Dahomey, West Africa, 1851-1852. 2012. (ENG., Illus.). 280p. 99.00 ***(978-0-19-726521-5(9))*** Oxford Univ. Pr., Inc.

Lawley, Jonathan. Beyond the Malachite Hills: A Life of Colonial Service & Business in the New Africa. 2009. (ENG., Illus.). 256p. 55.00 *(978-1-84885-049-1(2))* I. B. Tauris & Co., Ltd. GBR. Dist: Macmillan.

Lawrance, Benjamin N., et al, eds. Intermediaries, Interpreters, & Clerks: African Employees in the Making of Colonial Africa. 2006. (Africa & the Diaspora Ser.). (Illus.). 342p. 45.00 *(978-0-299-21950-5(X))* Univ. of Wisconsin Pr.

Lifshitz, Fima. An African Journey Through Its Art. 2009. 236p. pap. 75.99 *(978-1-4389-3450-1(5))* AuthorHouse.

Likaka, Osumaka. Naming Colonialism: History & Collective Memory in the Congo, 1870-1960. 2009. (Africa & the Diaspora Ser.). (ENG., Illus.). 216p. pap. 26.95 *(978-0-299-23364-8(2))* Univ. of Wisconsin Pr.

Longman, Timothy. Christianity & Genocide in Rwanda. 2009. (African Studies). (ENG., Illus.). 372p. 102.00 *(978-0-521-19139-5(4))* Cambridge Univ. Pr.

Magyar, Karl P. Prolonged Wars: A Post-Nuclear Challenge. Danopo, Constantine P., ed. 475p. pap. 27.00 *(978-1-58566-056-8(6))* Air University Pr.

Maiga, Hassimi. Balancing Written History with Oral Traditions: The Legacy of the Songhoy People. 2009. (African Studies). (ENG., Illus.). 230p. 125.00 *(978-0-415-96351-0(6))* Routledge.

Maimouni, F., ed. The Sierra Leone Special Court: Basic Documents. 2011. 318p. 90.00 *(978-90-5887-153-4(3))* International Courts Assn. NLD. Dist: International Specialized Bk. Services.

Mangala, Jack. Africa & the New World Era: From Humanitarianism to a Strategic View. Mangala, Jack, ed. 2010. (ENG.). 304p. 89.00 *(978-0-230-10286-6(7))* Palgrave Macmillan.

Mann, Gregory. Native Sons: West African Veterans & France in the Twentieth Century. 2006. (Politics, History, & Culture Ser.). (ENG., Illus.). 344p. (C). 94.95 *(978-0-8223-3755-3(X))* Duke Univ. Pr.

—Native Sons: West African Veterans & France in the Twentieth Century. annot. ed. 2006. (Politics, History, & Culture Ser.). (ENG., Illus.). 344p. per. 25.95 *(978-0-8223-3768-3(1))* Duke Univ. Pr.

Mann, Simon. Cry Havoc. 2011. (ENG., Illus.). 352p. 24.95 ***(978-1-84358-403-2(4))*** Blake, John Publishing, Ltd. GBR. Dist: Independent Pubs. Group.

Manson, Andrew & Mbenga, Bernard, eds. People of the Dew: A History of the Bafokeng of Rustenburg District, South Africa, from Early Times to 2000. 2011. (ENG.). 256p. pap. 39.00 *(978-1-77009-825-1(9))* Jacana Media ZAF. Dist: Independent Pubs. Group.

Massey, Gerald. Book of the Beginnings. (African Heritage Classical Research Studies). 654p. reprint ed. 75.00 *(978-0-938818-58-8(9))* ECA Assocs.

—Gerald Massey's Lectures. (African Studies). reprint ed. 40.00 *(978-0-938818-46-5(5))* ECA Assocs.

Mazrui, Ali A., et al, eds. Africa's Islamic Experience: History, Culture & Politics. 2008. 278p. 29.95 *(978-1-932705-78-2(3))* New Dawn Pr., Inc.

McGregor, JoAnn. Crossing the Zambezi: The Politics of Landscape on a Central African Frontier. 2009. (Illus.). 247p. 90.00 *(978-1-84701-402-3(X)*, Currey, James) Boydell & Brewer, Ltd. GBR. Dist: Boydell & Brewer, Inc.

McNeill, William H., et al, eds. Africa in World History. 2011. (Illus.). pap. 22.95 *(978-0-9770159-9-3(8))* Berkshire Publishing Group.

Melvern, Linda & MELVERN, Linda. A People Betrayed: The Role of the West in Rwanda's Genocide. 2nd ed. 2009. (ENG.). 384p. 99.95 *(978-1-84813-244-3(1))* Zed Bks., Ltd. GBR. Dist: Macmillan.

—A People Betrayed: The Role of the West in Rwanda's Genocide, Second. 2nd ed. 2009. (ENG., Illus.). 384p. pap. 29.95 *(978-1-84813-245-0(X))* Zed Bks., Ltd. GBR. Dist: Macmillan.

Mentan, Tatah. Democratizing or Reconfiguring Predatory Autocracy? Myths & Realities in Africa Today. 2009. 90p. pap. *(978-9956-558-57-5(5))* Langaa Research & Publishing Common Initiative Group CMR. Dist: Michigan State Univ. Pr.

Middleton, John & Miller, Joseph Calder. New Encyclopedia of Africa, 5 vols. 2007. (Illus.). *(978-0-684-31456-3(8))*; *(978-0-684-31459-4(2))*; *(978-0-684-31457-0(6))*; *(978-0-684-31458-7(4))*; *(978-0-684-31455-6(X))*;Set. 2nd rev. ed. 3000p. 753.00 *(978-0-684-31454-9(1))* Cengage Gale. (Charles Scribner's Sons).

Miller, S. M., ed. Soldiers & Settlers in Africa, 1850-1918. 2009. (History of Warfare Ser.). *(978-90-04-17751-2(5))* BRILL.

Miran, Jonathan. Red Sea Citizens: Cosmopolitan Society & Cultural Change in Massawa. 2009. (ENG., Illus.). 400p. 75.00 *(978-0-253-35312-2(2)*, 0253353122); pap. 27.95 *(978-0-253-22079-0(3)*, 0253220793) Indiana Univ. Pr.

Montgomery, Georgene Bess. The Spirit & the Word: A Theory of Spirituality in Africana Literary Criticism. 2008. *(978-1-59221-566-9(1))*; 252p. pap. *(978-1-59221-567-6(X))* Africa World Pr.

Muehlenbeck, Philip E. Betting on the Africans: John F. Kennedy's Courting of African Nationalist Leaders, 1 vol. 2012. (ENG., Illus.). 352p. 55.00 ***(978-0-19-539609-6(X))*** Oxford Univ. Pr., Inc.

Muhoozi, Francis Xavier Ndagabanye. A Deficit of Logic in the Great Lakes of Africa: The Floods of Innocent Human Blood that Could Have Been Spared. 2011. (Illus.). 340p. pap. 20.47 *(978-1-4567-7425-7(5))* AuthorHouse.

Murithi, Timothy & Murithi, Tim. The Ethics of Peacebuilding. Dower, Nigel, ed. 2009. (Edinburgh Studies in World Ethics Ser.). (ENG.). 208p. (gr. 17). 95.00 *(978-0-7486-2447-8(3))*; pap. 32.50 *(978-0-7486-2448-5(1))* Edinburgh Univ. Pr. GBR. Dist: Columbia Univ. Pr.

Musabyimana, Jean De Dieu. Love above All: Forgiveness of a Young Rwandan Genocide Survivor. 2011. (Illus.). 128p. pap. 14.89 *(978-1-4567-0044-7(8))* AuthorHouse.

Mutwol, Julius. Peace Agreements & Civil Wars in Africa: Insurgent Motivations, State Responses, & Third Party Peacemaking in Liberia, Rwanda, & Sierra Leone. 2008. 124.99 *(978-1-60497-555-0(5))* Cambria Pr.

Newbury, David. The Land beyond the Mists: Essays in Identity & Authority in Precolonial Congo & Rwanda. 2009. (ENG.). 512p. 69.95 *(978-0-8214-1874-1(2))*; pap. 32.95 *(978-0-8214-1875-8(0))* Ohio Univ. Pr.

Newman, James L. Paths Without Glory: Richard Francis Burton in Africa. 2009. (Illus.). 316p. 29.95 *(978-1-59797-287-1(8))* Potomac Bks., Inc.

Niane, D. T. Sundiata: An Epic of Old Mali. Pickett, G. D., tr. 2nd ed. 2006. (Longman African Writers Ser.). (ENG.). 120p. (C). pap. 16.00 *(978-1-4058-4942-5(8))* Longman Publishing.

Nicolaisen, Ida. Elusive Hunters: The Haddad of Kanem & the Bahr el Ghazal. 2010. (ENG., Illus.). 522p. (C). 80.00 *(978-87-7934-394-8(5))* Aarhus Universitetsforlag DNK. Dist: ISD.

Njoh, Ambe J. Tradition, Culture & Development in Africa: Historical Lessons for Modern Development Planning. 2006. (Heritage, Culture, & Identity Ser.). (Illus.). 240p. 130.00 *(978-0-7546-4884-0(2))* Ashgate Publishing Co.

Nugent, Paul. Africa since Independence. 2nd rev. ed. 2012. (ENG., Illus.). 680p. (C). pap. 39.00 ***(978-0-230-27288-0(6))*** Palgrave Macmillan.

Obiagwu, Chukwuma. Adventures of Ojemba: The Chronicle of Igbo People. 2008. (ENG.). 118p. pap. 26.50 *(978-0-7618-3945-3(3))* Hamilton Bks.

Olweiler, David B. Cowboy Boots in Africa. pap. *(978-1-882204-21-2(2))* Wilde Publishing.

Osborn, Emily Lynn & Roberts, Richard L. Intermediaries, Interpreters, & Clerks: African Employees in the Making of Colonial Africa. Lawrance, Benjamin N., ed. 2006. (Africa & the Diaspora Ser.). (Illus.). viii, 332p. pap. *(978-0-299-21954-3(2))* Univ. of Wisconsin Pr.

Osborn, Robert Durie. Islam under the Arabs. 2009. 454p. 42.99 *(978-1-117-32446-3(X))*; (ENG.). 453p. pap. 35.75 *(978-1-117-32447-0(8))* BiblioBazaar.

—Islam under the Arabs. 2009. 216p. pap. *(978-0-217-22679-0(5))* Books LLC.

Parker, John & Rathbone, Richard. African History. 2007. (Very Short Introductions Ser.: Vol. 160). (ENG., Illus.). 144p. per. 11.95 *(978-0-19-280248-4(8))* Oxford Univ. Pr., Inc.

Peavy, Daryl. Kings, Magic, & Medicine. 2010. 232p. pap. 35.00 *(978-0-557-18370-8(7))* Lulu Enterprises Inc.

Pecastaing, Camille. Jihad in the Arabian Sea. 2011. (Hoover Inst press Publication). (Illus.). (ENG.). 174p. 19.95 ***(978-0-8179-1374-8(2))***; xv, 186p. E-Book 14.95 ***(978-0-8179-1376-2(9))*** Hoover Institution Pr.

Peers, Chris. The African Wars: Warriors & Soldiers of the Colonial Campaigns. 2011. (Illus.). 240p. 39.95 *(978-1-84884-121-5(3))* Pen & Sword Bks. Ltd. GBR. Dist: Casemate Pubs. & Bk. Distributors, LLC.

Perxon, Macha. The African Promise: The Genesis of the African Conflicts & Their Remedies. 2011. 80p. pap. ***(978-3-639-34185-0(6))*** VDM Verlag Dr. Mueller e.K.

Peters, Krijn. War & the Crisis of Youth in Sierra Leone. 2011. (International African Library). (ENG., Illus.). 296p. 90.00 *(978-1-107-00419-1(5))* Cambridge Univ. Pr.

Peterson, Derek & Macola, Giacomo, eds. Recasting the Past: History Writing & Political Work in Modern Africa. 2009. (New African Histories Ser.). (ENG.). 280p. pap. 26.95 *(978-0-8214-1879-6(3))*; (Illus.). 49.95 *(978-0-8214-1878-9(5))* Ohio Univ. Pr.

Philips, John Edward, ed. Writing African History. 2007. (Rochester Studies in African History & the Diaspora Ser.: Volume 20). (Illus.). 546p. per. 34.95 *(978-1-58046-256-3(1))* Univ. of Rochester Pr.

Phillipson, David W. Foundations of an African Civilisation: Aksum & the northern Horn, 1000 BC - AD 1300. 2012. (Eastern Africa Ser.). (Illus.). 312p. 70.00 ***(978-1-84701-041-4(5)***, Currey, James) Boydell & Brewer, Ltd. GBR. Dist: Boydell & Brewer, Inc.

Pinel, Elsa. Secrets of the House of Dahomy: Guarded Secrets of the Caribbean Elders. 2007. 192p. (ENG.). 26.95 ***(978-0-595-69189-0(7))***; per. 16.95 *(978-0-595-44980-4(8))* iUniverse, Inc.

Quinn, Frederick. In Search of Salt: Changes in Beti (Cameroon) Society, 1880-1960. 2006. (Cameroon Studies: Vol. 6). (Illus.). 186p. 90.00 *(978-1-84545-006-9(X))* Berghahn Bks., Inc.

Ray, Bryan. Dangerous Frontiers. 2008. (Illus.). 224p. 39.95 *(978-1-84415-723-5(7))* Pen & Sword Bks. Ltd. GBR. Dist: Casemate Pubs. & Bk. Distributors, LLC.

Reid, Richard. War in Pre-Colonial Eastern Africa: The Patterns & Meanings of State-Level Conflict in the 19th Century. 2007. (Eastern African Studies). 256p. 59.95 *(978-0-8214-1794-2(0))* Ohio Univ. Pr.

—War in Pre-Colonial Eastern Africa: The Patterns & Meanings of State-Level Conflict in the Ninteenth Century. 2007. (Eastern African Studies). (ENG., Illus.). 256p. per. 26.95 *(978-0-8214-1795-9(9))* Ohio Univ. Pr.

Reid, Richard & Reid, Richard J. War in Pre-Colonial Eastern Africa: The Patterns & Meanings of State-Level Conflict in the Nineteenth Century. 2007. (Illus.). 272p. 95.00 *(978-1-84701-605-8(7))*; pap. 29.95 *(978-1-84701-604-1(9))* Boydell & Brewer, Ltd. GBR. (Currey, James). Dist: Boydell & Brewer, Inc.

Reid, Richard J. Frontiers of Violence in North-East Africa: Genealogies of Conflict since C. 1800. 2011. (ENG., Illus.). 338p. 99.00 *(978-0-19-921188-3(4))* Oxford Univ. Pr., Inc.

Reid, Richard J. A History of Modern Africa: 1800 to the Present. 2nd ed. 2012. (Blackwell Concise History of the Modern World Ser.). (ENG., Illus.). 408p. pap. 39.95 ***(978-0-470-65898-7(3)***, Wiley-Blackwell) Wiley, John & Sons, Inc.

Reno, William. Warfare in Independent Africa. 2011. (New Approaches to African History Ser.). (ENG., Illus.). 294p. (C). 85.00 ***(978-0-521-85045-2(2))***; pap. 27.99 ***(978-0-521-61552-5(6))*** Cambridge Univ. Pr.

Rich, Jeremy & Macpherson, Anne S. A Workman Is Worthy of His Meat: Food & Colonialism in the Gabon Estuary. 2007. (France Overseas). (ENG., Illus.). 352p. 45.00 *(978-0-8032-1091-2(4))* Univ. of Nebraska Pr.

Roberts, Allen F. A Dance of Assassins: Performing Early Colonial Hegemony in the Congo. 2012. (African Expressive Cultures Ser.). (ENG.). 280p. pap. 30.00 ***(978-0-253-00750-6(X)***, 025300750X); (Illus.). 85.00 ***(978-0-253-00743-8(7)***, 0253007437) Indiana Univ. Pr.

Robottom, John & Freeman, Anthony. Israel, Africa & Mideast. Date not set. (Making Modern World Ser.). (Illus.). 32p. pap. 48.00 *(978-0-582-22211-3(7))* Addison-Wesley Longman, Ltd. GBR. Dist: Trans-Atlantic Pubns., Inc.

Room, Adrian. African Placenames: Origins & Meanings of the Names for Natural Features, Towns Cities, Provinces, & Counties. 2nd rev. ed. 2008. (ENG.). 224p. 55.00 *(978-0-7864-3546-3(1))* McFarland & Co., Inc. Pubs.

Roome, William J. W. A Traveller in Uganda - a Historical Article on a Traveller's Experience in Afric. 2011. 38p. pap. 6.95 ***(978-1-4474-0987-8(6))*** Research Pr.

Ross, Eric S. Sufi City: Urban Design & Archetypes in Touba. 2006. (Rochester Studies in African History & the Diaspora Ser.: Volume 24). (Illus.). 308p. 80.00 *(978-1-58046-217-4(0))* Univ. of Rochester Pr.

Rudman, Jack. African & Afro-American History. (C). (ACT Proficiency Examination Program Ser.: Vol. 1). 49.95 *(978-0-8373-5551-1(6))*; (Regents College Proficiency Examination Ser.: Vol. 36). 49.95 *(978-0-8373-5486-6(2))* National Learning Corp. (Passbooks).

Rusesabagina, Paul & Zoellner, Tom. An Ordinary Man: An Autobiography. 2007. (ENG., Illus.). 224p. (gr. 12-18). 15.00 *(978-0-14-303860-3(5)*, Penguin (Non-Classics)) Penguin Group (USA) Inc.

Saavedra Casco, José Arturo. Utenzi, War Poems, & the German Conquest of East Africa: Swahili Poetry As a Historical Source. 2007. *(978-1-59221-377-1(4))*; pap. *(978-1-59221-378-8(2))* Africa World Pr.

Sanders, Peter. Throwing down White Man: Cape Rule & Misrule in Colonial Lesotho, 1871-1884. Huws, Ursula, ed. 2011. 306p. pap. 37.95 ***(978-0-85036-654-9(2))*** Merlin Pr. Ltd. GBR. Dist: Independent Pubs. Group.

Sanderson, Edgar. Africa in the Nineteenth Century. 2009. 238p. pap. *(978-1-4590-2877-7(5))* Books LLC.

Savigny, J. B. Henry. Narrative of a Voyage to Senegal in 1816. 2008. pap. *(978-1-4068-2629-6(4))* Echo Library.

Savigny, J. B. Henry & Corréard, Alexander. Narrative of a Voyage to Senegal in 1816. 2007. (ENG.). 190p. pap. 19.99 *(978-1-4346-2287-7(8))* BiblioBazaar.

Savigny, J. B. Henry & Correard, Alexander. Narrative of a Voyage to Senegal in 1816. 2008. 216p. 27.99 *(978-0-554-26991-7(0))*; 24.99 *(978-0-554-36294-6(5))* BiblioBazaar.

—Narrative of a Voyage to Senegal in 1816. 2007. 184p. per. *(978-1-4065-3879-3(5))* Dodo Pr.

Savigny, J. B. Henry & Corréard, Alexander. Narrative of a Voyage to Senegal in 1816. l.t. ed. 2007. (ENG.). 212p. pap. 22.99 *(978-1-4346-2345-4(9))* BiblioBazaar.

Schmidt, Peter. Historical Archaeology in Africa: Representation, Social Memory, & Oral Traditions. 2006. (African Archaeology Ser.). (ENG., Illus.). 240p. 93.00 *(978-0-7591-0964-3(8))*; per. 37.95 *(978-0-7591-0965-0(6))* AltaMira Pr.

Sears, Gareth. Late Roman African Urbanism: Continuity & Transformation in the City. 2007. (Bar S Ser.). (ENG., Illus.). 171p. (C). pap. 87.50 *(978-1-4073-0131-0(4))* British Archaeological Reports Ltd. GBR. Dist: Brown, David Bk. Co., The.

Sefa Dei, George J. Teaching Africa: Towards a Transgressive Pedagogy. 2011. (Explorations of Educational Purpose Ser.). (ENG.). xxvii, 130p. pap. 29.95 ***(978-94-007-2861-5(1)***, 9400728611) Springer.

Shillington, Kevin. A History of Africa. 3rd rev. ed. 2012. (ENG., Illus.). 528p. (C). pap. 39.00 ***(978-0-230-30847-3(3))*** Palgrave Macmillan.

Shireff, David. Bare Feet & Bandoliers: Wingate, Sandford, the Patriots & the Liberation of Ethiopia. 2009. (Illus.). 368p. 39.99 *(978-1-84884-029-4(2))* Pen & Sword Bks. Ltd. GBR. Dist: Casemate Pubs. & Bk. Distributors, LLC.

Sibanda, Thabani. Conflict Issues Across Disciplines. 2011. 198p. 29.99 ***(978-1-4568-1760-2(4))***; pap. 19.99 ***(978-1-4568-1759-6(0))*** Xlibris Corp.

Sims, Sedrick. Ancient AFRICAN History A Journey Highlighting Africa's Past. 2009. 117p. pap. 10.00 *(978-0-557-09694-7(4))* Lulu Enterprises Inc.

Sommers, Marc. Stuck: Rwandan Youth & the Struggle for Adulthood. 2012. (Studies in Security & International Affairs Ser.). (ENG., Illus.). 288p. 59.95 ***(978-0-8203-3890-3(7))***; pap. 22.95 ***(978-0-8203-3891-0(5))*** Univ. of Georgia Pr.

Steinglass, Matt. Making up Africa: Stories from an Invented Continent. Date not set. *(978-0-374-19926-5(4))* Farrar, Straus & Giroux.

Stokes, Jamie. Encyclopedia of the Peoples of Africa & the Middle East, 2-Volume Set, 2 vols. 2009. (Illus.). 880p. (C). (gr. 9). 175.00 *(978-0-8160-7158-6(6))* Facts On File, Inc.

Stuart, Andrew. Of Cargos Colonies & Kings. 2009. (ENG., Illus.). 256p. pap. 27.50 *(978-1-85043-978-3(8)*, Radcliffe Pr., The) I. B. Tauris & Co., Ltd. GBR. Dist: Macmillan.

Stuart, John. British Missionaries & the End of Empire: East, Central, & Southern Africa, 1939-1964. 2011. 240p. pap. 40.00 *(978-0-8028-6633-2(6))* Eerdmans, William B. Publishing Co.

Taha, Hagar. The Failure to Protect, Again. 2011. 124p. pap. ***(978-3-8443-3332-9(0))*** Lambert Academic Publishing.

Theron, Daniel J. O! South Afric. 2011. 204p. pap. 52.99 ***(978-1-4567-4765-7(7))*** AuthorHouse.

Thomas Nelson Publishing Staff. The Bishop of Rwanda, 0 vols. 2008. 256p. pap. 14.99 *(978-1-59555-237-2(5))* Nelson, Thomas Inc.

Tilley, Helen & Gordon, Robert J., eds. Ordering Africa: Anthropology, European Imperialism, & the Politics of Knowledge. 2007. (Studies in Imperialism Ser.). (ENG.). 416p. 89.00 *(978-0-7190-6239-1(X))* Manchester Univ. Pr. GBR. Dist: Macmillan.

Totten, Samuel & Ubaldo, Rafiki, eds. We Cannot Forget: Interviews with Survivors of the 1994 Genocide in Rwanda. 2011. (Genocide, Political Violence, Human Rights Ser.). (ENG., Illus.). 220p. (C). 72.00 *(978-0-8135-4969-9(8))* Rutgers Univ. Pr.

Totten, Samuel & Ubalco, Rafiki, eds. We Cannot Forget: Interviews with Survivors of the 1994 Genocide in Rwanda. 2011. (Genocide, Political Violence, Human Rights Ser.). (ENG., Illus.). 220p. (C). pap. 26.95 *(978-0-8135-4970-5(1))* Rutgers Univ. Pr.

Travels, Tj. Visit the African Continent: Know the facts & figures of the african Countries. 2011. 88p. pap. 34.48 ***(978-1-4567-8712-7(8))*** AuthorHouse.

Tshibengabo, Kamana. The, Rulers of Congo-Kinshasa: Felons at the Helm. 2011. (ENG.). 380p. pap. 20.95 ***(978-1-4327-8084-5(0))*** Outskirts Pr., Inc.

Tvedt, Terje. The River Nile in the Post-Colonial Age: Conflict & Cooperation among the Nile Basin Countries. 2009. (ENG., Illus.). 320p. 95.00 *(978-1-84511-970-6(3))* I. B. Tauris & Co., Ltd. GBR. Dist: Macmillan.

Utietiang, Bekeh Ukelina. Afridentity: Essays on Africa. 2nd rev. ed. 2007. per. *(978-0-9792386-0-4(9))* Arbi Pr.

Venter, Al. War Dog: Fighting Other People's Wars -the Modern Mercenary in Combat. 2008. (Illus.). 664p. pap. 22.95 *(978-1-932033-90-8(4))* Casemate Pubs. & Bk. Distributors, LLC.

Volney, C. F. Ruins of Empires. (African Heritage Classical Research Studies). 225p. reprint ed. 15.00 *(978-0-938818-62-5(7))* ECA Assocs.

Wabuke, Mel. Eye on Africa. 2010. (Illus.). 544p. 29.95 *(978-0-9820795-2-2(4))* Coltan Bks.

Wane, Njoki N. A Glance at Afric. 2009. 92p. pap. 27.49 *(978-1-4389-7469-7(2))* AuthorHouse.

Warshaw, Steven. Discovering History Vol. 4: Traditional African Religions & History. Date not set. (Illus.). pap. 24.95 *(978-0-87297-064-9(7))* Diablo Pr., Inc.

Watt, Nigel. Burundi: The Biography of a Small African Country. 2008. (Columbia/Hurst Ser.). (ENG.). 224p. (gr. 17). 55.00 *(978-0-231-70090-0(3))* Columbia Univ. Pr.

Wessels, Michael. Bushman Letters: Interpreting the /Xam Narratives of the Bleek & Lloyd Collection. 2010. (ENG.). 256p. pap. 29.95 *(978-1-86814-506-5(9))* Witwatersrand Univ. Pr. Pubns. ZAF. Dist: Transaction Pubs.

Wood, J. R. T. Operation Dingo: Rhodesian Raid on Chimoio & Tembué 1977. 2011. (Africa@war Ser.). (Illus.). 80p. pap. 29.95 ***(978-1-907677-36-6(4))*** Helion & Co., Ltd. GBR. Dist: Casemate Pubs. & Bk. Distributors, LLC.

Woolley, Nicholas. Rescue in Rwanda. 2007. (Timeline Ser.). (Illus.). 48p. pap. 8.99 *(978-1-4190-4395-6(1))* Houghton Mifflin Harcourt Supplemental Pubs.

Wright, Henry Tutwiler. Early State Formation in Central Madagascar: An Archaeological Survey of Western Avaradrano. 2007. (Illus.). 311p. 38.00 *(978-0-915703-63-0(7))* Univ. of Michigan, Museum of Anthropology, Pubns. Dept.

Young, Tom. Africa. 2010. (Beginners Guide (Oneworld) Ser.). (ENG., Illus.). 224p. pap. 14.95 *(978-1-85168-753-4(X))* Oneworld Pubns. GBR. Dist: National Bk. Network.

Zack-Williams, Tunde, ed. When the State Fails: Studies on Intervention in the Sierra Leone Civil War, 1 vol. 2012. (ENG., Illus.). 288p. pap. 32.00 ***(978-0-7453-3220-8(X))*** Pluto Pr. GBR. Dist: Macmillan.

Zeilig, Leo, ed. Class Struggle & Resistance in Africa. 2009. (ENG.). 224p. pap. 17.00 *(978-1-931859-68-4(X))* Haymarket Bks.

AFRICA—HISTORY—AUTONOMY AND INDEPENDENCE MOVEMENTS

Biesele, Megan & Hitchcock, Robert K. The Ju/'Hoan San of Nyae Nyae & Namibian Independence: Development, Democracy, & Indigenous Voices in Southern Africa. 2010. (Illus.). 302p. 95.00 *(978-1-84545-754-9(4))* Berghahn Bks., Inc.

Kibreab, Gaim. Critical Reflections on the Eritrean War of Independence: Social Capital, Associational Life, Religion, Ethnicity & Sowing Seeds of Dictatorship. 2007. *(978-1-56902-261-8(X))* Red Sea Pr.

Melady, Thomas Patrick & Melady, Margaret Badum. Ten African Heroes: The Sweep of Independence in Black Africa. 2011. (Illus.). 240p. *(978-1-57075-929-1(4)*, Orbis Bks.

AFRICA—HISTORY—STUDY AND TEACHING

Robertson, Clyde C. Africa Rising: Multidisciplinary Discussions on Africana Studies & History: From Ancient Times Through Modernity. 2009. *(978-1-59221-716-8(8))*; pap. *(978-1-59221-717-5(6))* Africa World Pr.

AFRICA—IN LITERATURE

Akínyemí, Akíntúndé & Falola, Toyin. Emerging Perspectives on Akinwumi Isola. 2007. *(978-1-59221-608-6(0))*; pap. *(978-1-59221-609-3(9))* Africa World Pr.

Amoko, Apollo Obonyo. Postcolonialism in the Wake of the Nairobi Revolution: Ngugi Wa Thiong'O & the Idea of African Literature. 2010. (ENG., Illus.). 216p. 84.00 *(978-0-230-10546-1(7))* Palgrave Macmillan.

Andrade, Susan Z. The Nation Writ Small: African Fictions & Feminisms, 1958-1988. 2011. (ENG., Illus.). 272p. 89.95 *(978-0-8223-4897-9(7))*; pap. 24.95 *(978-0-8223-4921-1(3))* Duke Univ. Pr.

Archer, Jermaine O. Antebellum Slave Narratives: Cultural & Political Expressions of Africa. 2008. (Studies in American Popular History & Culture Ser.). (ENG.). 142p. 125.00 *(978-0-415-99027-1(0))* Routledge.

Asanbe, Joseph. Selected Essays. 2008. xiv, 113p. pap. *(978-0-9786127-3-3(6))* Zone Three Pr./Ctr. for the Creative Arts.

Barnard, Rita. Apartheid & Beyond: South African Writers & the Politics of Place, 1 vol. (ENG.). 234p. 2012. pap. 24.95 ***(978-0-19-979116-3(3))*** 2006. (Illus.). 85.00 *(978-0-19-511286-3(5))* Oxford Univ. Pr., Inc.

Best, Curwen. Kamau Brathwaite & Christopher Okigbo: Art, Politics, & the Music of Ritual. 2009. 228p. pap. *(978-3-03911-716-1(5))* Lang, Peter.

Blake, Cecil. The African Origins of Rhetoric. 2009. (African Studies). (ENG.). 156p. 125.00 *(978-0-415-99771-3(2))* Routledge.

Bloom, Harold. Cry, the Beloved Country - Alan Paton. 2010. (Bloom's Modern Critical Interpretations Ser.). 194p. (C). (gr. 9-18). 45.00 *(978-1-60413-583-1(2)*, Chelsea Hse.) Facts On File, Inc.

Bloom, Harold, ed. Heart of Darkness. 2009. (Bloom's Guides). 128p. (C). (gr. 9-18). 30.00 *(978-1-60413-200-7(0)*, Chelsea Hse.) Facts On File, Inc.

Bloom, Harold, ed. & intro. Things Fall Apart. 2nd rev. ed. 2009. (Bloom's Modern Critical Interpretations Ser.). 232p. (C). (gr. 9-18). 45.00 *(978-1-60413-581-7(6)*, Chelsea Hse.) Facts On File, Inc.

Caminero-Santangelo, Byron & Myers, Garth, eds. Environment at the Margins: Literary & Environmental Studies in Africa. 2011. (ENG.). 304p. pap. 34.95 ***(978-0-8214-1978-6(1))*** Ohio Univ. Pr.

Caulker, Tcho Mbaimba. The African-British Long Eighteenth Century: An Analysis of African-British Treaties, Colonial Economics, & Anthropological Discourse. 2009. (ENG., Illus.). 216p. 68.50 *(978-0-7391-2743-8(8))* Lexington Bks.

Chaulet-Achour, Christiane. Albert Camus, Alger: L'étranger et Autres Récits. (FRE.). 217p. *(978-2-84394-089-7(3))* Atlantica editions.

Chiwengo, Ngwarsungu. Understanding Cry, the Beloved Country: A Student Casebook to Issues, Sources, & Historical Documents, 1 vol. 2007. (Greenwood Press "Literature in Context" Ser.). (Illus.). 248p. 45.00 *(978-0-313-33508-2(7)*, GR3508, Greenwood Pr.) Greenwood Publishing Group, Inc.

Clare, John. Captured in Time. 2011. 528p. pap. 38.00 *(978-1-86842-378-1(6))* Ball, Jonathan Pubs. ZAF. Dist: International Publishers Marketing.

Cousins, Helen & Dodgson-Katiyo, Pauline. Emerging Perspectives on Yvonne Vera. 2012. ***(978-1-59221-865-3(2))***; (Illus.). 280p. pap. ***(978-1-59221-866-0(0))*** Africa World Pr.

Deckard, Sharae. Paradise Discourse, Imperialism, & Globalization: Exploiting Eden. 2009. (Routledge Research in Postcolonial Literatures Ser.). (ENG.). 264p. (C). 125.00 *(978-0-415-99739-3(9))* Routledge.

Desai, Gaurav, ed. Teaching the African Novel. 2009. (ENG.). 40.00 *(978-1-60329-037-1(0))* Modern Language Assn. of America.

Desai, Gaurav Gajanan, ed. Teaching the African Novel. 2009. (ENG.). pap. 25.00 *(978-1-60329-038-8(9))* Modern Language Assn. of America.

Dovey, Lindiwe. African Film & Literature: Adapting Violence to the Screen. 2009. (Film & Culture Ser.). (ENG., Illus.). 360p. (gr. 17). 89.50 *(978-0-231-14754-5(6))*; pap. 32.50 *(978-0-231-14755-2(4))* Columbia Univ. Pr.

Elder, Arlene A. Narrative Shape-Shifting: Myth, Humor & History in the Fiction of Ben Okri, B. Kojo Laing & Yvonne Vera. 2009. 174p. 80.00 *(978-1-84701-012-4(1)*, Currey, James) Boydell & Brewer, Ltd. GBR. Dist: Boydell & Brewer, Inc.

Fenton, Robert W. Edgar Rice Burroughs & Tarzan: A Biography of the Author & His Creation. alt. ed. 2010. (ENG., Illus.). 254p. pap. 38.00 *(978-0-7864-4908-8(X))* McFarland & Co., Inc. Pubs.

François, Anne M. Rewriting the Return of Africa: Voices of Francophone Caribbean Women Writers. 2011. (ENG.). 146p. 60.00 *(978-0-7391-4826-6(5))* Lexington Bks.

François, Anne M. Rewriting the Return to Africa: Voices of Francophone Caribbean Women Writers. 2011. xxxiii, 111p. E-Book ***(978-0-7391-4828-0(1))*** Lexington Bks.

Glasgow, Jacqueline & Rice, Linda J. Exploring African Life & Literature: Novel Guides to Promote Socially Responsive Learning. 2007. 376p. 34.95 *(978-0-87207-609-9(1))* International Reading Assn.

Graham, James. Land & Nationalism in Fictions from Southern Africa. 2009. (Routledge Research in Postcolonial Literatures Ser.: Vol. 24). (ENG.). 214p. (C). 126.00 *(978-0-415-99581-8(7))* Routledge.

Hammond, Dorothy & Jablow, Alta. The Myth of Africa. 2012. 45.95 *(978-0-915042-03-6(7))* Library of Social Science.

Hewitt. Voices Out of Africa in Twentieth Century. 2009. (Illus.). 402p. 80.00 *(978-0-8387-5729-1(4))* Bucknell Univ. Pr.

Irele, Abiola & Jeyifo, Biodun. Africa in the World the World in Africa: Essays in Honor of Abiola Irele. 2011. ***(978-1-59221-827-1(X))***; (Illus.). 346p. pap. ***(978-1-59221-828-8(8))*** Africa World Pr.

Lewis, Desiree. Living on a Horizon: Bessie Head & the Politics of Imagining. 2007. 317p. *(978-1-59221-458-7(4))*; 313p. pap. *(978-1-59221-459-4(2))* Africa World Pr.

Lindfors, Bernth. Early East African Writers & Publishers. 2011. (Illus.). 272p. pap. *(978-1-59221-794-6(X))* Africa World Pr.

—Early Soyinka. 2008. *(978-1-59221-652-9(8))*; 296p. pap. *(978-1-59221-653-6(6))* Africa World Pr.

MacCann, Donnarae & Maddy, Yulisa Amadu. Neo-Imperialism in Children's Literature about Africa: A Study of Contemporary Fiction. 2008. (Children's Literature & Culture Ser.). (ENG.). 190p. (C). 125.00 *(978-0-415-99390-6(3))* Routledge.

Margerrison, Christine. ¿Ces forces obscures de L¿âme¿. Women, race & origins in the writings of Albert Camus. 2008. 360p. pap. 72.00 *(978-90-420-2379-6(1))* Rodopi.

Mathuray, Mark. On the Sacred in African Literature: Old Gods & New Worlds. 2009. (ENG., Illus.). 240p. 84.00 *(978-0-230-57755-8(5))* Palgrave Macmillan.

Moran, Shane. Representing Bushmen: South Africa & the Origin of Language. 2009. (Rochester Studies in African History & the Diaspora Ser.: Volume 38). (Illus.). 222p. 80.00 *(978-1-58046-294-5(4))* Univ. of Rochester Pr.

Nangia, Shonu. Male-Female Relations in the Literary Maghreb: Poetics & Politics of Violence & Liberation in Francophone North Africa by Tahar Ben Jelloun. 2011. 184p. 109.95 *(978-0-7734-1486-4(6))* Mellen, Edwin Pr., The.

Nassir, Ghazi Q. Samuel Johnson's Attitude Toward Islam: A Study of His Oriental Readings & Writings. 2011. (ENG.). 232p. 119.95 ***(978-0-7734-3917-7(X))*** Mellen, Edwin Pr., The.

Newell, Stephanie. West African Literatures: Ways of Reading. 2006. (Oxford Studies in Postcolonial Literatures). (ENG., Illus.). 288p. pap. 39.95 *(978-0-19-927397-3(9))* Oxford Univ. Pr., Inc.

Ogude, James & Nyairo, Joyce. Urban Legends, Colonial Myths: Popular Culture & Literature in East Africa. 2006. 434p. *(978-1-59221-498-3(3))*; pap. *(978-1-59221-499-0(1))* Africa World Pr.

Ogunyemi, Chikwenye Okonjo. Juju Fission: Women's Alternative Fictions from the Sahara, the Kalahari, & the Oases In-Between. 2007. (Society & Politics in Africa Ser.). 336p. (C). 38.95 *(978-1-4331-0089-5(4))* Lang, Peter Publishing, Inc.

Opoku-Agyemang, Naana Jane, et al. Africa & Trans-Atlantic Memories: Literary & Aesthetic Manifestations of Diaspora & History. 2008. 496p. *(978-1-59221-633-8(1))*; pap. *(978-1-59221-632-1(3))* Africa World Pr.

Owomoyela, Oyekan. The Columbia Guide to West African Literature in English since 1945. 2008. (Columbia Guides to Literature Since 1945 Ser.). (ENG.). 216p. (gr. 17). 85.00 *(978-0-231-12686-1(7))* Columbia Univ. Pr.

Oxfeldt, Elisabeth. Journeys from Scandinavia: Travelogues of Africa, Asia, & South America, 1840-2000. 2010. (Illus.). 328p. 75.00 *(978-0-8166-5634-9(7))*; pap. 25.00 *(978-0-8166-5635-6(5))* Univ. of Minnesota Pr.

Palmer, Eustace. Of War & Women, Oppression & Optimism: New Essays on the African Novel. 2008. 367p. *(978-1-59221-610-9(2))*; 390p. pap. *(978-1-59221-611-6(0))* Africa World Pr.

Palmer, Eustace & Porter, Abioseh Michael. Knowledge Is More Than Mere Words: Wey Dehn Sey? Dehn Sey Kapu Sehns nor Kapu Word: A Critical Introduction to Sierra Leonean Literature. 2008. *(978-1-59221-644-4(7))*; 366p. pap. *(978-1-59221-645-1(5))* Africa World Pr.

Richardson, Krystylle. A Touch of Africa... down in My Soul: A Collection of Poetry & a True Story of Afrili Dance, Drums, Father God & Mother Earth. 2007. per. 10.00 (978-0-9741657-5-2(1)) Galaxia Publishing Group, LLC.

Springstub, Lisa. En Égypte Avec Vigny: Le Roman Inachevé L'Almeh: Scènes du Désert. (FRE.). 221p. pap. 46.95 (978-3-631-56855-2(X)) Lang, Peter GmbH, Europaischer Verlag der Wissenschaften DEU. Dist: Lang, Peter Publishing, Inc.

Struck, Wolfgang. Die Eroberung der Phantasie: Kolonialismus, Literatur und Film zwischen deutschem Kaiserreich und Weimarer Republik. 2010. (Palaestra Ser.). (GER & ENG.). 345p. (C). 68.00 (978-3-89971-769-3(4)) Vandenhoeck & Ruprecht GmbH & Co. KG DEU. Dist: ISD.

Tautz, Birgit. Reading & Seeing Ethnic Differences in the Enlightenment: From China to Africa. annot. ed. 2007. (ENG.). 248p. 89.00 (978-1-4039-7641-3(4)) Palgrave Macmillan.

Thurman, Chris. Guy Butler: Reassessing a South African Literary Life. 2010. 382p. pap. 48.95 (978-1-86914-183-7(0)) University of Kwazulu-Natal Press ZAF. Dist: International Specialized Bk. Services.

Wilkin, Binnie Tate. African & African American Images in Newbery Award Winning Titles: Progress in Portrayals. 2009. (ENG.). 210p. pap. 45.00 (978-0-8108-6959-2(4)) Scarecrow Pr., Inc.

Woods, Tim. African Pasts: Memory & History in African Literatures. (ENG.). 304p. 2012. pap. 29.95 **(978-0-7190-6494-4(5))** 2007. (Illus.). 84.00 (978-0-7190-6493-7(7)) Manchester Univ. Pr. GBR. Dist: Macmillan.

Wright, Laura. Wilderness into Civilized Shapes: Reading the Postcolonial Environment. 2010. (ENG.). 178p. 69.95 (978-0-8203-3396-0(4)); pap. 24.95 (978-0-8203-3568-1(1)) Univ. of Georgia Pr.

Yenika-Agbaw, Vivian. Representing Africa in Children's Literature. 2011. (ENG.). 168p. pap. 34.95 **(978-0-415-69956-3(8))** Routledge.

Yenika-Agbaw, Vivian S. Representing Africa in Children's Literature: Old & New Ways of Seeing. 2007. (Children's Literature & Culture Ser.). (ENG.). 168p. 125.00 (978-0-415-97468-4(2)) Routledge.

Zauditu-Selassie, K. African Spiritual Traditions in the Novels of Toni Morrison. 2009. (ENG., Illus.). 224p. 69.95 (978-0-8130-3328-0(4)) Univ. Pr. of Florida.

AFRICA—INTELLECTUAL LIFE

Ambirish, Mahdi. Hadith Al-Ithnayn, 2 vols. 2008. (ARA.). (978-9959-866-03-5(3)) World Ctr. for the Studies & Researches of The Green Bk., The.

—Min Qadaya Al-Fikr. 2009. (ARA.). 432p. (978-9959-866-15-8(7)) World Ctr. for the Studies & Researches of The Green Bk., The.

Arenas, Fernando. Lusophone Africa: Beyond Independence. 2011. (ENG., Illus.). 368p. 75.00 (978-0-8166-6983-7(X)); pap. 25.00 (978-0-8166-6984-4(8)) Univ. of Minnesota Pr.

Bala, Salisu, et al. Nigeria's Intellectual Heritage. 2010. 248p. pap. (978-3-639-21831-2(0)) VDM Verlag Dr. Mueller e.K.

Blommaert, Jan. Grassroots Literacy: Writing, Identity & Voice in Central Africa. 2008. (Literacies Ser.). (Illus.). (ENG.). 240p. pap. 45.95 (978-0-415-42630-5(8)); XVI, 224p. 145.00 (978-0-415-42631-2(6)) Routledge.

Ce, Chin & Chin, Ce. Bards & Tyrants. 2008. 244p. 29.95 (978-978-35035-3-3(7)) Michigan State Univ. Pr.

Choukri, Mohamed. In Tangier: Paul Bowles, Jean Genet, Tennessee Williams. Bowles, Paul et al, trs. from ARA. 2010. (ENG.). 320p. pap. 15.95 (978-1-84659-061-0(2)) Telegram Bks. GBR. Dist: Consortium Bk. Sales & Distribution.

Corrado, Jacopo. The Creole Elite & the Rise of Angolan Proto-Nationalism (1870-1920) 2008. 109.95 (978-1-60497-529-1(6)) Cambria Pr.

Creary, Nicholas M., ed. African Intellectuals & Decolonization. 2012. (Ohio RIS Africa Ser.). (ENG.). 160p. pap. 19.95 **(978-0-89680-283-4(3))** Ohio Univ. Pr.

Currey. Africa Writes Back the African Writers Series & the Launch of African Literature. (Illus.). 2009. 350p. pap. 34.95 (978-1-84701-502-0(6)) 2008. 288p. 105.00 (978-1-84701-503-7(4)) Boydell & Brewer, Ltd. GBR. (Currey, James). Dist: Boydell & Brewer, Inc.

Currey, James. Africa Writes Back: The African Writers Series & the Launch of African Literature. 2008. (Illus.). 320p. 55.00 (978-0-8214-1842-0(4)); (ENG., pap. 26.95 (978-0-8214-1843-7(2)) Ohio Univ. Pr.

Dikeni, Leslie & Gumende, William, eds. The Poverty of Ideas: South African Democracy & the Retreat of the Intellectuals. 2010. (ENG.). 256p. pap. 23.00 (978-1-77009-775-9(9)) Jacana Media ZAF. Dist: Independent Pubs. Group.

El Shakry, Omnia. The Great Social Laboratory: Subjects of Knowledge in Colonial & Postcolonial Egypt. 2007. (ENG.). 344p. 30.00 (978-0-8047-5567-2(1)) Stanford Univ. Pr.

Eze, Chielozona. Moral Imaginations in Postcolonial African Literature & Culture. 2012. E-Book **(978-0-7391-4508-1(8))** Lexington Bks.

—Postcolonial Imaginations & Moral Representations in African Literature & Culture. 2011. (ENG.). 156p. 60.00 **(978-0-7391-4506-7(1))** Lexington Bks.

Holou, Roland A. A. Y. A Continent in Tears: The Origin of Africa's Collapse & How to Reverse It. 2010. 206p. pap. 18.95 (978-1-4327-1734-6(0)) Outskirts Pr., Inc.

Irele, Abiola & Jeyifo, Biodun. Africa in the World the World in Africa: Essays in Honor of Abiola Irele. 2011. **(978-1-59221-827-1(X))**; (Illus.). 346p. pap. **(978-1-59221-828-8(8))** Africa World Pr.

Irele, F. Abiola & Jeyifo, Biodun, eds. The Oxford Encyclopedia of African Thought, 2 vols., Set. 2010. (ENG., Illus.). 992p. 315.00 (978-0-19-533473-9(6)) Oxford Univ. Pr., Inc.

Kaluya, Professor M. D. The Audacity to Change: Breaking the Berlin Wall in Africa. 2011. 148p. pap. 14.95 (978-1-4502-8577-3(5)) iUniverse, Inc.

Kizza, Immaculate N. The Oral Tradition of the Baganda of Uganda: A Study & Anthology of Legends, Myths, Epigrams & Folktales. 2010. (ENG., Illus.). 216p. pap. 38.00 (978-0-7864-4015-3(5)) McFarland & Co., Inc. Pubs.

Kresse, Kai. Philosophising in Mombasa: Knowledge, Islam & Intellectual Practice on the Swahili Coast. 2007. (International African Library). (ENG., Illus.). 256p. (gr. 17). 120.00 (978-0-7486-2786-8(3)) Edinburgh Univ. Pr. GBR. Dist: Columbia Univ. Pr.

Lindfors, Bernth. Early Black South African Writing in English. 2011. **(978-1-59221-840-0(7))**; (Illus.). 236p. pap. **(978-1-59221-841-7(5))** Africa World Pr.

Lindfors, Bernth. Early East African Writers & Publishers. 2011. (978-1-59221-793-9(1)); (Illus.). 272p. pap. (978-1-59221-794-6(X)) Africa World Pr.

Mahmoud, Mahgoub El-Tigani. Linkages among African & African-American Thinkers: The Emergence of a Transgeographical Intellectual Community. 468p. 129.95 (978-0-7734-5207-7(9)) Mellen, Edwin Pr., The.

Manganyi, N. & Attwell, David, eds. Bury Me at the Marketplace: Es¿kia Mphahlele & Company. Letters 1943¿2006. 2010. (ENG.). 496p. pap. 39.95 (978-1-86814-489-1(5)) Witwatersrand Univ. Pr. Pubns. ZAF. Dist: Transaction Pubs.

Masilela, Ntongela. An Outline of the New African Movement in South Africa. 2012. **(978-1-59221-875-2(X))**; pap. **(978-1-59221-876-9(8))** Africa World Pr.

Mirmotahari, Emad. Islam in the Eastern African Novel. 2011. (Literatures & Cultures of the Islamic World Ser.). (ENG.). 222p. 85.00 (978-0-230-10843-1(1)) Palgrave Macmillan.

Mukhtar, Hassani. Tarikh Al-Dawlah Al-Ziyaniyah, 3 vols. 2007. (ARA.). (978-9961-76-758-0(6)) El Hadhara.

Newell, Stephanie. West African Literatures: Ways of Reading. 2006. (Oxford Studies in Postcolonial Literatures). (ENG., Illus.). 288p. pap. 39.95 (978-0-19-927397-3(9)) Oxford Univ. Pr., Inc.

Niehoff, Maren R. Jewish Exegesis & Homeric Scholarship in Alexandria. 2011. (ENG.). 236p. 85.00 (978-1-107-00072-8(6)) Cambridge Univ. Pr.

Ogude, James & Nyairo, Joyce. Urban Legends, Colonial Myths: Popular Culture & Literature in East Africa. 2006. 434p. (978-1-59221-498-3(3)); pap. (978-1-59221-499-0(1)) Africa World Pr.

Ogude, James, et al. Rethinking Eastern African Literary & Intellectual Landscapes. 2011. xxvi, 424p. **(978-1-59221-885-1(7))**; **(978-1-59221-886-8(5))** Africa World Pr.

Orlando, Valerie K. Francophone Voices of the New Morocco in Film & Print: (Re)presenting a Society in Transition. 2009. (ENG., Illus.). 284p. 100.00 (978-0-230-61631-8(3)) Palgrave Macmillan.

Owomoyela, Oyekan. The Columbia Guide to West African Literature in English since 1945. 2008. (Columbia Guides to Literature Since 1945 Ser.). (ENG.). 216p. (gr. 17). 85.00 (978-0-231-12686-1(7)) Columbia Univ. Pr.

Peterson, Derek & Macola, Giacomo, eds. Recasting the Past: History Writing & Political Work in Modern Africa. 2009. (New African Histories Ser.). (ENG.). 280p. pap. 26.95 (978-0-8214-1879-6(3)); (Illus.). 49.95 (978-0-8214-1878-9(5)) Ohio Univ. Pr.

Roscoe, Adrian A. & Roscoe, Adrian. The Columbia Guide to Central African Literature in English since 1945. 2007. (Columbia Guides to Literature Since 1945 Ser.). (ENG.). 220p. (gr. 17). 80.00 (978-0-231-13042-4(2)) Columbia Univ. Pr.

Ross, Eric S. Culture & Customs of Senegal, 1 vol. 2008. (Culture & Customs of Africa Ser.). (Illus.). 160p. 49.95 (978-0-313-34036-9(6), GR4036, Greenwood Pr.) Greenwood Publishing Group, Inc.

Saad, Elias N. Social History of Timbuktu: The Role of Muslim Scholars & Notables, 1400-1900. 2010. (Cambridge Studies in Islamic Civilization Ser.). (ENG., Illus.). 336p. pap. 29.99 (978-0-521-13630-3(X)) Cambridge Univ. Pr.

Tendi, Blessing-Miles. Making History in Mugabe's Zimbabwe: Politics, Intellectuals, & the Media. 2010. (Illus.). xviii, 286p. 63.95 (978-3-03911-989-9(3)) Lang, Peter Publishing, Inc.

Umar-Buratai, Mohammed Inuwa. Performance As Art & Power. 2010. 380p. pap. (978-3-639-19451-7(9)) VDM Verlag Dr. Mueller e.K.

AFRICA—JUVENILE LITERATURE

Zephaniah, Benjamin. J Is for Jamaica. 2011. (World Alphabets Ser.). (ENG., Illus.). 32p. (J). (gr. -1-2). pap. 8.95 (978-1-84507-609-2(5)) Lincoln, Frances Ltd. GBR. Dist: Perseus-PGW.

AFRICA—KINGS AND RULERS

Amani, Athar. History of Ancient Afric. 2010. 64p. pap. (978-3-8383-5706-5(X)) Lambert Academic Publishing.

Angwafo, Fo. Royalty & Politics the Story of My Life. 2009. 148p. pap. (978-9956-558-31-5(1)) Langaa Research & Publishing Common Initiative Group CMR. Dist: Michigan State Univ. Pr.

Chem-Langhee, Bongfen & Fanso, Verkijika. Royal Susseccion in the African Kingdom of Nso' A Study in Oral Historiography. 2008. (Illus.). 156p. (978-0-7734-5041-7(6)) Mellen, Edwin Pr., The.

Coughlan, Michael. Sundiata: The African King. 2007. (Timeline Ser.). (Illus.). 48p. pap. 8.99 (978-1-4190-4409-0(5)) Steck-Vaughn.

Ephirim-Donkor, Anthony. Making of an African King: Patrilineal & Matrilineal Struggle among the Effutu of Ghana. 2nd ed. 2009. (ENG.). 238p. pap. 35.99 (978-0-7618-4778-6(2)) Univ. Pr. of America, Inc.

Jenkins Earnestine. A Kingly Craft: Art & Leadership in Ethiopia: A Social History of Art & Visual Cutlure in Pre-Modern Africa. 2008. (ENG., Illus.). 126p. per. 26.50 (978-0-7618-3889-0(9)) Univ. Pr. of America, Inc.

Levine, Roger S. A Living Man from Africa: Jan Tzatzoe, Xhosa Chief & Missionary, & the Making of Nineteenth-Century South Africa. 2010. (New Directions in Narrative History Ser.). (ENG., Illus.). 328p. 30.00 (978-0-300-12521-4(6)) Yale Univ. Pr.

Mainga, Mutumba. Bulozi under the Luyana Kings: Political Evolution & State Formation in Pre-Colonial Zambia. 2nd ed. 2010. (Illus.). 292p. pap. (978-9982-24-052-9(8)) BookWorld Pubs. ZMB. Dist: Michigan State Univ. Pr.

Mansa Musa: African King of Gold, Grade 4 & Up. tchr. ed. 12.00 (978-0-382-40946-2(9)) Cobblestone Publishing Co.

Manson, Andrew & Mbenga, Bernard, eds. People of the Dew: A History of the Bafokeng of Rustenburg District, South Africa, from Early Times to 2000. 2011. (ENG.). 256p. pap. 39.00 (978-1-77009-825-1(9)) Jacana Media ZAF. Dist: Independent Pubs. Group.

Warnier, Jean-Pierre. The Pot-King: The Body & Technologies of Power. 2007. (African Social Studies). (Illus.). 325p. pap. (978-90-04-15217-5(2)) BRILL.

Wojcikiewicz, Andrew. Awakening the Pharaoh: How to Avoid World Cataclysm In 2012. 2009. 256p. 31.99 (978-1-4490-3922-6(7)) AuthorHouse.

Wylie, Dan. Myth of Iron: Shaka in History. 2008. (ENG., Illus.). 640p. pap. 29.95 (978-0-8214-1848-2(3)) Ohio Univ. Pr.

—Myth of Iron Shaka in History. 2008. (Illus.). 635p. pap. 34.95 (978-0-85255-441-8(9), Currey, James) Boydell & Brewer, Ltd. GBR. Dist: Boydell & Brewer, Inc.

Wylie, Dan. Shaka. 2011. (Pocket History Guides). (ENG., Illus.). 144p. pap. 15.99 **(978-1-77009-962-3(X))** Jacana Media ZAF. Dist: Independent Pubs. Group.

AFRICA—LANGUAGES

Ahabwe, Venansio. Globalisation & the Mother Tongue in Ugand. 2011. 120p. pap. **(978-3-8443-3409-8(2))** Lambert Academic Publishing.

Amoako, Joe. Ghanaian Pidgin English: Diachronic, Synchronic & Sociolinguistic Perspectives. 2011. (Languages & Linguistics Ser.). 135p. pap. 43.00 (978-1-61209-642-1(5)) Nova Science Pubs., Inc.

Antwi-Danso, Joana Portia. Some Morphological Processes in Akan-Twi. 2010. 176p. pap. (978-3-639-26477-7(0)) VDM Verlag Dr. Mueller e.K.

Atanga, Mufor. The Anglophone Cameroon Predicament. 2011. 266p. pap. **(978-9956-717-11-8(8))** Langaa Research & Publishing Common Initiative Group.

Bailey, Joseph A., 2nd. Afrocentric English & Critical Thinking. 2006. xi, 319p. per. 19.95 (978-1-59594-073-5(1)) WingSpan Publishing.

Bemile, Sebastian K. Dagara Proverbs Vol. 25: Language in Africa. 2010. (ENG.). 340p. 128.00 (978-3-496-02834-5(3)) Reimer, Dietrich DEU. Dist: Independent Pubs. Group.

Botha, Rudolf & Knight, Chris, eds. The Cradle of Language. 2009. (Studies in the Evolution of Language Ser.). (ENG., Illus.). 408p. pap. 45.00 (978-0-19-954586-5(3)) Oxford Univ. Pr., Inc.

Brenzinger, Matthias, ed. Language Death: Factual & Theoretical Explorations with Special Reference to East Africa. (Contributions to the Sociology of Language [CSL] Ser.). (ENG.). VIII, 445p. 105.00 **(978-3-11-179261-3(7))** De Gruyter, Mouton DEU. Dist: de Gruyter, Walter GmbH & Co. KG.

Bukari, James. Language Policy in West Afrc. 2009. 116p. pap. (978-3-639-11774-5(3)) VDM Verlag Dr. Mueller e.K.

Cahill, Michael C. Aspects of the Morphology & Phonology of Konni. 2007. 535p. pap. 50.00 (978-1-55671-184-8(0)) SIL International.

Caron, B. & Zima, P., eds. Sprachbund in the West African Sahel: Ael11. 2006. (Societe d'Etudes Linguistiques et Anthropologiques de France Ser.). (ENG.). 328p. (C). pap. 37.00 (978-90-429-1745-3(8)) Peeters Pubs. & Booksellers BEL. Dist: Brown, David Bk. Co., The.

Chia, Emmanuel N., et al, eds. Perspectives on Translation & Interpretation in Cameroon. 2009. 180p. pap. (978-9956-558-44-5(3)) Langaa Research & Publishing Common Initiative Group CMR. Dist: Michigan State Univ. Pr.

Eyrice Tepecikliogl u, Elem. Colonial Language Policy of the British Empire. 2011. 136p. pap. **(978-3-8443-0326-1(X))** Lambert Academic Publishing.

Farenkia, Bernard Mulo, ed. Linguistic Politeness in Cameroon: Approches Pragmatiques, Comparatives Et Interculturelles. 2007. (FRE & ENG.). 194p. pap. 46.95 (978-3-631-57158-3(5)) Lang, Peter Publishing, Inc.

Frajzyngier, Zygmunt. A Grammar of Wandala. 2012. (Mouton Grammar Library [MGL] Ser.: 47). (ENG.). XVI, 720p. (gr. 17-17). 210.00 (978-3-11-021840-4(2)); E-Book 321.00 **(978-3-11-173634-1(2))** De Gruyter, Mouton DEU. Dist: de Gruyter, Walter GmbH & Co. KG.

Hashim, Nadra & Hashim, Nadra O. Language & Collective Mobilization: The Story of Zanzibar. 2009. (ENG.). 222p. 73.50 (978-0-7391-2211-2(8)) Lexington Bks.

Hieda, Osamu, et al. A Geographical Typology of African Languages. 2011. (Illus.). 320p. (978-90-272-0769-2(0)) Benjamins, John Publishing Co.

Higgins, Christina. English as a Local Language: Post-colonial Identities & Multilingual Practices. 2009. (Critical Language & Literacy Studies). (ENG., Illus.). 176p. 39.95 (978-1-84769-180-4(3)); 149.95 (978-1-84769-181-1(1)) Multilingual Matters GBR. Dist: Univ. of Toronto Pr.

Iribemwangi, P. I. The Structure of Kiswahili. 2010. 240p. pap. (978-3-639-27066-2(5)) VDM Verlag Dr. Mueller e.K.

Kaye, Alan S. Morphologies of Asia & Africa. 2007. (C). 175.00 (978-1-57506-109-2(0)); (978-1-57506-111-5(2)); (978-1-57506-110-8(4)) Eisenbrauns, Inc.

Kebede, Solomon Niguse. Language Change in Tigrinya: A Historical Study Based on Early Tigrinya Texts. 2011. 76p. pap. **(978-3-639-32159-3(6))** VDM Verlag Dr. Mueller e.K.

Kisoro District Language Board Staff, contrib. by. Inyandika Y'Urufumbira: Rufumbira Orthography. (ENG.). xii, 36p. (978-9970-02-802-3(2)) Fountain Pubs. Ltd.

Koffi, Ettien. Paradigm Shift in Language Planning & Language Policy. 2011. (Contributions to the Sociology of Language [CSL] Ser.). (ENG.). 245p. 100.00 (978-1-934078-10-5(7)) De Gruyter, Walter Inc.

Kouega, Jean-Paul. A Dictionary of Cameroon English Usage. 2007. (Contemporary Studies in Descriptive Linguistics Ser.: Vol. 10). 202p. pap. (978-0-8204-9316-9(3)) Lang, Peter AG.

Laitin, David D. Language Repertoires & State Construction in Africa. 2007. (Cambridge Studies in Comparative Politics). (ENG.). 220p. pap. 50.00 (978-0-521-03327-5(6)) Cambridge Univ. Pr.

Lomotey, Charlotte Fofo. Vowels of Akan. 2010. 232p. pap. (978-3-639-24947-7(X)) VDM Verlag Dr. Mueller e.K.

Makerere University Staff, contrib. by. Dictionary: Kashoboorozi Y'Orunyankore-Rukiga. 2007. (Illus.). 624p. pap. (978-9970-02-622-7(4)) Fountain Pubs. Ltd. UGA. Dist: Michigan State Univ. Pr.

Mc Laughlin, Fiona, ed. The Languages of Urban Africa. 2011. (ENG.). 252p. pap. 44.95 **(978-1-4411-1785-4(7))** Continuum International Publishing Group, Ltd. GBR. Dist: National Bk. Network.

Mesfin, Gidena. Makedda & Solomon in the Eye of Ethiopian Traditional Accounts. 2010. 80p. pap. (978-3-639-26314-5(6)) VDM Verlag Dr. Mueller e.K.

Munderi, Juliana, compiled by. Ingingo Z'Urufumbira: Rufumbira Grammar. (ENG.). viii, 39p. (978-9970-02-781-1(6)) Fountain Pubs. Ltd.

Owusu, Sefa. Some Phonological Processes in Akan. 2010. 100p. pap. (978-3-639-27030-3(4)) VDM Verlag Dr. Mueller e.K.

Pugach, Sara Elizabeth Berg. Africa in Translation: A History of Colonial Linguistics in Germany & Beyond, 1814-1945. (Social History, Popular Culture, & Politics in Germany Ser.). 2012. (ENG.). 318p. 80.00 **(978-0-472-11782-6(3))** 2011. E-Book **(978-0-472-02777-4(8))** Univ. of Michigan Pr.

Sekyi-Baidoo, Yaw. Ghanaian Pidgin English, Sentence Type & Structure. 2011. 132p. pap. **(978-3-8443-8614-1(9))** Lambert Academic Publishing.

Shepherd, Nick & Robins, Steven L. New South African Keywords. Shepherd, Nick & Robins, Steven, eds. 2008. (ENG., Illus.). 278p. pap. 26.95 (978-0-8214-1868-0(8)) Ohio Univ. Pr.

Simpson, Andrew, ed. Language & National Identity in Africa. 2008. (ENG., Illus.). 448p. 165.00 (978-0-19-928674-4(4)) Oxford Univ. Pr., Inc.

Smith, Tony & Gravina, Richard. The Phonology of Two Central Chadic Languages. 2009. 267p. pap. 32.00 (978-1-55671-231-9(6)) SIL International.

Storch, Anne. Secret Manipulations: Language & Context in Africa, 1 vol. 2011. (ENG.). 262p. 99.00 (978-0-19-976897-4(8)); pap. 45.00 (978-0-19-976902-5(8)) Oxford Univ. Pr., Inc.

Taiwo, Rotimi & Chiluwa, Innocent. Computer-Mediated Discourse in Africa. 2012. **(978-1-62100-497-4(X))** Nova Science Pubs., Inc.

van der Vliet, J. Nubian Voices: Studies in Nubian Christian Civilization. Lajtar, Adam et al, eds. 2012. (Jjp Supplements Ser.: 15). (ENG., Illus.). 262p. (C). 75.00 **(978-83-925919-4-8(1))** Fundacja im. Rafa Taubenschlaga POL. Dist: Brown, David Bk. Co., The.

Wolf, Hans-Georg & Polzenhagen, Frank. World Englishes: A Cognitive Sociolinguistic Approach. 2009. (Applications of Cognitive Linguistics [ACL] Ser.). (ENG.). XIV, 278p. 137.00 (978-3-11-019633-7(6)); 210.00 **(978-3-11-173399-9(8))** De Gruyter, Mouton DEU. Dist: de Gruyter, Walter GmbH & Co. KG.

AFRICA—LIBRARY RESOURCES

McIlwaine, John. Africa: A Guide to Reference Material. 2nd ed. 2007. 666p. (978-0-9541029-3-7(2)) Hans Zell Publishing.

AFRICA—MAPS

Angola. rev. ed. (Cartographia International Road Map Ser.). (978-963-352-953-9(0), 6953) Cartographia Kft.

Betz, Richard L. The Mapping of Africa: A Cartobibliography of Printed Maps of the African Continent to 1700. 2007. (Illus.). 540p. 235.00 (978-90-6194-489-8(9)) HES & DE GRAAF Pubs. BV NLD. Dist: Oak Knoll Pr.

Campbell, Rusty & Porter, Malcolm. Atlas of Africa. 2010. (Illus.). 48p. (YA). pap. 11.75 (978-1-4358-9111-1(2), Rosen Central) Rosen Publishing Group, Inc., The.

Globetrotter. Westfalen, Ruhrgebiet. 8th ed. 2011. (Globetrotter Travel Atlas Ser.). (ENG., Illus.). 72p. pap. 14.95 (978-1-84773-833-2(8), Globetrotter) New Holland Pubs., Ltd. GBR. Dist: Globe Pequot Pr., The.

Kenya, Tanzania. (Cartographia International Road Map Ser.). (Illus.). (978-963-352-951-5(4), 6951) Cartographia Kft.

Mapping Africa: Grades 5-9. (Illus.). 72p. tchr. ed., spiral bd. 19.95 incl. trans. (978-0-382-40817-5(9)) Cobblestone Publishing Co.

Mendelsohn, John, compiled by. Atlas of Namibia: A Portrait of the Land & its People. 2010. 200p. 38.00 (978-1-920289-16-4(X)) Ball, Jonathan Pubs. ZAF. Dist: International Publishers Marketing.

Schluter, Thomas. Geological Atlas of Africa: With Notes on Stratigraphy, Tectonics, Economic Geology, Geohazards, Geosites & Geoscientific Education of Each Country. 2nd ed. 2008. (Illus.). 307p. 299.00 incl. cd-rom (978-3-540-76324-6(4)) Springer.

United Nations Environment Programme. Africa Water Atlas. 2011. (Illus.). 314p. 150.00 (978-92-807-3110-1(6)) United Nations Environment Programme KEN. Dist: National Bk. Network.

AFRICA—PICTORIAL WORKS

Bailey, Adrian, photos by. Safari: Journeys Through Wild Africa. 2007. (Illus.). 223p. 43.00 *(978-1-77007-394-4(9))* Struik Pubs. ZAF. Dist: International Publishers Marketing.

Bárkányi Csávás, Maria. The Magic of Africa. 2008. 160p. per. *(978-1-84747-463-6(2))* Chipmunkapublishing.

Bellani, Giovanni Giuseppe. Vanishing Wilderness of Africa. 2010. (ENG., Illus.). 272p. 39.95 *(978-88-544-0426-7(8))* White Star ITA. Dist: Sterling Publishing Co., Inc.

Bernasconi, Alex. Wild Africa. 2010. (ENG., Illus.). 270p. 49.95 *(978-1-55407-772-4(9))* Firefly Bks., Ltd.

Besey, Emilio Fontan. The Island of Corisco. 2007. (Illus.). 119p. 48.99 *(978-1-4257-4552-3(0))* Xlibris Corp.

Bialobrzeski, Peter, photos by. Peter Bialobrzeski: Informal Arrangements. 2010. (ENG & GER., Illus.). 96p. 45.00 *(978-3-7757-2660-3(8))* Hatje Cantz Verlag GmbH & Co KG DEU. Dist: D.A.P./Distributed Art Pubs.

Bickford, Barbara, et al, photos by. Ghana: An African Portrait Revisited. 2007. (ENG., Illus.). 168p. 40.00 *(978-1-931807-57-9(4))* Randall, Peter E. Pub.

Bloom, Steve. Living Africa. 2008. (ENG., Illus.). 336p. 75.00 *(978-0-500-51427-6(5))* Thames & Hudson.

Bonn, Guillaume. Le Mal D'Afrique: A Journey into Old & New Africa. 2006. (Illus.). 149p. 45.00 *(978-0-9779008-3-1(5))* Empire Editions.

Brandt, Nick, photos by. On This Earth, A Shadow Falls. 2010. (Illus.). 192p. 120.00 *(978-0-615-38574-7(5))* Meridian Printing.

Briggs, Philip. Africa: Continent of Contrasts. 2007. (Illus.). 296p. 43.95 *(978-1-77007-087-5(7))* Struik Pubs. ZAF. Dist: International Publishers Marketing.

Burton, Jean-Dominique. Jean-Dominique Burton. Porto-Novo: Cite rouge, esprit du lagon Red City, Spirit of the Lagoon, 1 vol. 2011. (ENG & FRE.). 120p. 68.00 ***(978-90-5779-124-6(2))*** Exhibitions International BEL. Dist: Innovative Logistics.

Burton, Jean-Dominique. Vaudou/Voodoo/Vudu. 2008. (ENG., Illus.). 256p. 75.00 *(978-88-7439-443-2(8))* 5 Continents ITA. Dist: Hachette Bk. Group.

Cassidy, Shelley-Maree. Great Escapes Africa. Taschen, Angelika, ed. 25th ed. 2009. (FRE, GER & ENG., Illus.). 360p. pap. 19.99 *(978-3-8365-1499-6(0))* TASCHEN DEU. Dist: Ingram Pub. Services.

Comaroff, John L., et al, eds. Picturing a Colonial Past: The African Photographs of Isaac Schapera. 2007. (Illus.). 234p. 65.00 *(978-0-226-11411-8(2))*; per. 30.00 *(978-0-226-11412-5(0))* Univ. of Chicago Pr.

Des Fontaines, Caroline Halley. Times & Silence. 2008. (Illus.). 96p. 45.00 *(978-3-8327-9242-8(2))* teNeues Publishing Co.

Diserens, Corrine, ed. Appropriated Landscapes: Contemporary African Photography from the Walther Collection, 1 vol. 2011. (ENG., Illus.). 448p. 72.00 ***(978-3-86930-387-1(5))*** Steidl, Gerhard Druckerei und Verlag DEU. Dist: Innovative Logistics.

Dover Publications Inc. Staff, creator. African Design. 2007. (Dover Pictura Electronic Clip Art Ser.). (ENG., Illus.). 128p. pap. 39.95 *(978-0-486-99845-6(0))* Dover Pubns., Inc.

Eloff, Fritz C. Giants of the Desert: The Elephants of the Namib & the World They Live In. 2012. (Illus.). 150p. 31.95 ***(978-1-86919-390-4(3))*** International Publishers Marketing.

Fisher, Angela & Beckwith, Carol. Faces of Africa: Thirty Years of Photography. 2009. (NG Collectors Ser.). (ENG., Illus.). 360p. 16.95 *(978-1-4262-0424-1(8),* National Geographic) National Geographic Society.

Follmi, Olivier. Africa. Williams, Gerald, tr. from FRE. 2006. (ENG., Illus.). 336p. 60.00 *(978-0-8109-4832-7(X))* Abrams.

Foster, Damon & Foster, Craig. Africa: Speaking with Earth & Sky. 2011. (Illus.). 256p. 57.95 *(978-0-86486-664-6(X))* International Publishers Marketing.

Fox, Justin, ed. Africa Lens: 20 Years of Getaway Photography. 2010. (ENG.). 144p. pap. 31.00 *(978-1-77009-760-5(0))* Jacana Media ZAF. Dist: Independent Pubs. Group.

Galembo, Phyllis, photos by. Maske. 2010. (ENG., Illus.). 208p. 45.00 *(978-1-905712-17-5(0))* Boot, Chris GBR. Dist: D.A.P./Distributed Art Pubs.

Gerard, Alain. Denis Felix: Au fil de L'Homme. 2012. (ENG & FRE., Illus.). 168p. 51.95 ***(978-2-7572-0497-9(1))*** Somogy Editions d'Art FRA. Dist: Independent Pubs. Group.

Haas, Robert. Through the Eyes of the Vikings: An Aerial Vision of Arctic Lands. 2010. (Illus.). 224p. 50.00 *(978-1-4262-0638-2(0),* National Geographic) National Geographic Society.

Haney, Erin. Photography & Africa. 2010. (Reaktion Books - Exposures Ser.). (ENG., Illus.). 144p. pap. 29.95 *(978-1-86189-382-6(5))* Reaktion Bks., Ltd. GBR. Dist: Chicago Distribution Ctr.

Hetherington, Tim, photos by. Long Story Bit by Bit: Liberia Retold. 2009. (ENG., Illus.). 140p. 45.00 *(978-1-884167-73-7(X))* Umbrage Editions.

Hinde, Gerald. Big Five of Africa. 2009. (Illus.). 144p. pap. 20.00 *(978-1-77007-157-5(1))* Struik Pubs. ZAF. Dist: International Publishers Marketing.

Hoeffgen, Thomas, photos by. Thomas Hoeffgen: African Arenas. 2010. (ENG., Illus.). 144p. 45.00 *(978-3-7757-2668-9(3))* Hatje Cantz Verlag GmbH & Co KG DEU. Dist: D.A.P./Distributed Art Pubs.

Hugo, Pieter. Permanent Error. 2011. (Illus.). 128p. 49.95 *(978-3-7913-4520-8(6))* Prestel Publishing.

Janssen, Volker, ed. Black: Volume 4: the African Male Nude in Art & Photography. 2007. (Black Ser.). (ENG., Illus.). 80p. pap. 34.95 *(978-1-919901-31-2(0))* Janssen Pubs. ZAF. Dist: Independent Pubs. Group.

Johnson, David. Voice of Beauty: A Photographic Celebration of African Women. 2009. 108p. pap. 19.99 *(978-1-59932-150-9(5))* Advantage Media Group.

Keene-Young, Robyn. Okavango: A Journey. 2006. (Illus.). 141p. pap. 22.00 *(978-1-77007-271-8(3))* Struik Pubs. ZAF. Dist: International Publishers Marketing.

Knape, Gunilla. David Goldblatt: Photographs: Hasselblad Award 2006, 1 vol. 2007. (ENG., Illus.). 84p. 50.00 *(978-3-7757-1917-9(2))* Hatje Cantz Verlag GmbH & Co KG DEU. Dist: D.A.P./Distributed Art Pubs.

Kompel, Schutz Kristina. Views of Africa. 2009. 320p. 59.99 *(978-0-8416-1646-2(9))* American Map Corp.

Lester, Rhoda Namwalizi. Cassava Is the Root. 2007. 115p. pap. 27.48 *(978-1-4116-7113-3(9))* Lulu Enterprises Inc.

Liebenberg, John, photos by. Bush of Ghosts. 2011. 304p. pap. 33.00 *(978-1-4152-0100-8(5))* Random Hse. Struik (Pty.), Ltd. ZAF. Dist: International Publishers Marketing.

Marais, Chris & Du Toit, Julienne. Namibia Space. 2007. (Illus.). 192p. pap. 23.95 *(978-1-77007-332-6(9))* Struik Pubs. ZAF. Dist: International Publishers Marketing.

McDonald, Christie. Images of Congo. 2008. (ENG., Illus.). 162p. 39.00 *(978-88-7439-220-9(6))* 5 Continents ITA. Dist: Hachette Bk. Group.

Mertz, Donald W. Youth2Youth. 30 Years after Soweto. Hallett, George, ed. 2007. (ENG., Illus.). 144p. (gr. 11). pap. 24.95 *(978-1-86814-438-9(0))* Witwatersrand Univ. Pr. Pubns. ZAF. Dist: Transaction Pubs.

Neerman, Marnix & Brussens, Herman. African Faces: A Homage to the African Mask. 2010. (ENG., Illus.). 336p. *(978-90-209-8348-7(2),* Lannoo Pubs. (Acc)) Antique Collectors' Club.

Nelson, John A. Going Back to Africa. 2009. pap. 17.99 *(978-1-60696-636-5(7))* Tate Publishing & Enterprises, LLC.

Njami, Simon, ed. & intro. A Useful Dream: African Photography 1960-2010, 1 vol. 2010. (ENG., Illus.). 192p. pap. 45.00 *(978-88-366-1659-6(3))* Silvana ITA. Dist: D.A.P./Distributed Art Pubs.

O'Connell, Caitlin. An Elephant's Life: An Intimate Portrait from Africa. 2011. (ENG., Illus.). 208p. 29.95 *(978-0-7627-6374-0(4),* Lyons Pr.) Globe Pequot Pr., The.

Overton, Cleve & Andreasen, Jude. The Doors of Senegal: Les Portes du Senegal. 2007. per. 16.95 *(978-0-9772393-1-3(4))* Diaspora Voices Pr.

Pickford, Peter & Pickford, Beverly. African Safari: Into the Great Game Reserves. 2011th ed. 2011. 300p. 49.95 ***(978-1-906780-44-9(7))*** Beaufoy, John Publishing GBR. Dist: Midpoint Trade Bks., Inc.

Poliza, Michael. The Essential Africa. 2007. (Illus.). 183p. 35.00 *(978-3-8327-9197-1(3))* teNeues Publishing Co.

—Eyes over Africa. 2007. 2000.00 *(978-3-8327-9221-3(X))* teNeues Publishing Co.

Poliza, Michael, photos by. Animals of Africa. 2008. 288p. 85.00 *(978-3-8327-9260-2(0))* teNeues Publishing Co.

—Classic Africa. 2010. (Illus.). 320p. 125.00 *(978-3-8327-9374-6(7))* teNeues Publishing Co.

—Classic Africa Collector's Edition. 2010. (ENG., Illus.). 320p. 3000.00 *(978-3-8327-9444-3(1))*; 3000.00 *(978-3-8327-9445-3(X))* teNeues Publishing Co.

—Eyes over Africa. collector's ed. 2007. 5000.00 *(978-3-8327-9223-7(6))* teNeues Publishing Co.

Reader, John. Africa. 2007. *(978-1-4262-0203-2(2))*; *(978-1-4262-0202-5(4))* National Geographic Society.

Riefenstahl, Leni & Taschen, Angelika. Leni Riefenstahl - Africa. 2010. (25 Ser.). (JPN, FRE, GER & ENG., Illus.). 320p. 39.99 *(978-3-8365-2317-2(5))* TASCHEN DEU. Dist: Ingram Pub. Services.

Robbins, Martha M. & Boesch, Christophe, eds. Among African Apes: Stories & Photos from the Field. 2011. (ENG., Illus.). 196p. 29.95 *(978-0-520-26710-7(9))* Univ. of California Pr.

Ross, Mark & Reesor, David. Predator: Life & Death in the African Bush. 2007. (ENG., Illus.). 208p. 35.00 *(978-0-8109-9301-3(5))* Abrams.

Salgado, Lelia, ed. Sebastiao Salgado, Africa. 2010. (Go Ser.). (ENG, FRE & GER., Illus.). 336p. 39.99 *(978-3-8365-2343-1(4))* TASCHEN DEU. Dist: Ingram Pub. Services.

Sassen, Viviane, photos by. Flamboya. 2009. (ENG., Illus.). 96p. 45.00 *(978-88-6965-139-7(8))* Contrasto DUE ITA. Dist: Consortium Bk. Sales & Distribution.

Schutyser, Sebastian. Flowers of the Moon: Afroalpine Vegetation of the Rwenzori Mountains. 2008. (ENG., Illus.). 120p. 45.00 *(978-88-7439-423-4(3))* 5 Continents ITA. Dist: Hachette Bk. Group.

Serani, Laura & Zannier, Sabrina. Malik Sidibé: The Portrait of Mali. Incarcona, Laura, ed. 2012. (ENG., Illus.). 140p. pap. 35.00 ***(978-88-572-1125-1(8))*** Skira Editore ITA. Dist: Random Hse., Inc.

Sevette, Jean-Baptiste. Bilad Al-Sudan: The Herders of the White Nile. 2008. (ENG., Illus.). 144p. 60.00 *(978-88-7439-329-9(6))* 5 Continents ITA. Dist: Hachette Bk. Group.

Shah, Anup & Shah, Manoj. Great Rift Valley. 2008. (Illus.). 144p. 21.95 *(978-1-77007-450-7(3))* Struik Pubs. ZAF. Dist: International Publishers Marketing.

Shay, Don. Endangered Liaisons. 2008. (Illus.). 320p. 60.00 *(978-0-615-21345-3(6))* Alarus Pr.

Sidibe, Malick, photos by. Malick Sidibe: la Vie en Rose, 1 vol. 2010. (FRE & ENG., Illus.). 160p. 60.00 *(978-88-366-1716-6(6))* Silvana ITA. Dist: D.A.P./Distributed Art Pubs.

Silvester, Hans. Ethiopia: Peoples of the Omo Valley. 2007. (ENG., Illus.). 464p. 125.00 *(978-0-8109-9326-6(0))* Abrams.

—Natural Fashion: Tribal Decoration from Africa. 2009. (ENG., Illus.). 168p. pap. 29.95 *(978-0-500-28805-4(4),* 528805) Thames & Hudson.

—A Window on Africa: Ethiopian Portraits. 2011. (ENG., Illus.). 160p. 40.00 *(978-0-500-51562-4(X),* 551562) Thames & Hudson.

Steines, Mark. See the Light: A Passage to Sierra Leone. 2009. *(978-1-61623-285-6(4))*; pap. *(978-1-61623-286-3(2))* Independent Pub.

Streissguth, Thomas. Mozambique in Pictures. 2009. (Visual Geography Series, Second Ser.). (gr. 5-12). 30.60 *(978-1-57505-954-9(1))* Lerner Publishing Group.

Strudsholm, Jasper, et al. Reality Bites: An African Decade. 2010. (Illus.). 144p. pap. 33.95 *(978-1-919930-22-0(1))* Double Storey Bks. ZAF. Dist: International Publishers Marketing.

Sutton, Sean, photos by. Angola: A Journey Through Change. 2008. (ENG., Illus.). 144p. 35.00 *(978-1-904587-43-9(7))* Lewis, Dewi Publishing GBR. Dist: Consortium Bk. Sales & Distribution.

Sondergaard, Trine, photos by. Trine Sondergaard: Monochrome Portraits. 2010. (ENG., Illus.). 64p. 40.00 *(978-3-7757-2614-6(4))* Hatje Cantz Verlag GmbH & Co KG DEU. Dist: D.A.P./Distributed Art Pubs.

Tillim, Guy. Avenue Patrice Lumumba: Guy Tillim. 2009. (POR, FRE & ENG., Illus.). 128p. 65.00 *(978-3-7913-4066-1(2))* Prestel Publishing.

van der Spuy, Una. Old Nectar: A Garden for All Seasons. 2010. (ENG., Illus.). 176p. pap. 35.00 *(978-1-77009-756-8(2))* Jacana Media ZAF. Dist: Independent Pubs. Group.

Van Oosten, Marsel & Sibbing, Daniëlla. Wild Romance. 2010. (Illus.). 296p. 36.00 *(978-1-77007-726-3(X),* Random Hse. Struik (Pty.), Ltd. ZAF. Dist: International Publishers Marketing.

AFRICA—POETRY

Amina, Akili & Chapin-Pinott, Elizabeth. Poetic Hearts for Peace in Africa, 1 vol. 2009. 74p. pap. 16.95 *(978-1-4489-2097-6(3))* PublishAmerica, Inc.

Barasa, Daniel. The Myra Tree. 2011. 48p. pap. 15.99 ***(978-1-4628-9259-4(0))*** Xlibris Corp.

Bestelink, Nina. Day Dreaming in Africa. 2006. pap. 10.00 *(978-1-4257-0701-9(7))* Xlibris Corp.

Brownlee, Daryl. Journey into My Dreams, 1 vol. 2009. 77p. pap. 16.95 *(978-1-60836-789-4(4))* PublishAmerica, Inc.

Diggle, James & Goodyear, F. R. D., eds. Flavii Cresconii Corippi Iohannidos. 2010. (ENG.). 212p. pap. 27.99 *(978-0-521-13000-4(X))* Cambridge Univ. Pr.

Dixon, Isobel. A Fold in the Map. 2008. (ENG.). 80p. pap. *(978-1-84471-501-5(9))* Salt Publishing.

Ebhodaghe, Omohan. Hightower: Ibhayu Poetry. 2007. 72p. pap. *(978-1-59221-513-3(0))* Africa World Pr.

Falola, Toyin & Adesanya, Aderonke A. Etches on Fresh Waters. 2009. 386p. 90.00 *(978-1-59460-587-1(4))* Carolina Academic Pr.

Le Bas, Jessica. Walking to Africa. 2009. (ENG.). 88p. pap. 14.95 *(978-1-86940-446-8(7))* Auckland Univ. Pr. NZL. Dist: Independent Pubs. Group.

Lyons, Theodore. Africa Poems. 2011. 58p. pap. 15.99 ***(978-1-4568-3990-1(X))*** Xlibris Corp.

Maboyi, Arun. My Freedom Is My Right. 2007. 64p. per. *(978-1-84401-852-9(0))* Athena Pr.

Moore, Gerald & Beier, Ulli, eds. Modern African Poetry. Moore, Gerald & Beier, Ulli, trs. 5th rev. ed. 2007. (ENG.). 448p. (gr. 12-18). 18.00 *(978-0-14-042472-0(5),* Penguin Classics) Penguin Group (USA) Inc.

Munachim, Samuel. The African Verses. 2008. 180p. pap. 15.99 *(978-1-4389-1550-0(0))* AuthorHouse.

Nwakanma, Obi. The Horsemen & Other Poems. 2006. *(978-1-59221-518-8(1))*; 99p. pap. *(978-1-59221-519-5(X))* Africa World Pr.

Ojaide, Tanure. The Tale of the Harmattan. 2010. (ENG.). 64p. pap. 23.95 *(978-0-7957-0255-6(8))* NB Pubs. Ltd. ZAF. Dist: International Publishers Marketing.

Parkinson, R. B. The Tale of Sinuhe: And Other Ancient Egyptian Poems, 1940-1640 B. C. Oxford Dictionaries Staff, ed. 2009. (Oxford World's Classics Ser.). (ENG., Illus.). 336p. pap. 15.95 *(978-0-19-955562-8(1))* Oxford Univ. Pr., Inc.

Stone, Nomi. Stranger's Notebook: Poems. 2008. (ENG.). 88p. 42.95 *(978-0-8101-2509-4(9))*; pap. 14.95 *(978-0-8101-2510-0(2))* Northwestern Univ. Pr. (TriQuarterly Bks.).

Tande, Dibussi. No Turning Back: Poems of Freedom 1990-1993. 2007. *(978-9956-558-05-6(2))* Langaa Research & Publishing Common Initiative Group CMR. Dist: Michigan State Univ. Pr.

AFRICA—POLITICS AND GOVERNMENT

see also Afro-Asian Politics; Pan-Africanism

Abass, Ademola. Protecting Human Security in Africa. 2010. (ENG.). 400p. 98.50 *(978-0-19-957898-6(2))* Oxford Univ. Pr., Inc.

Abebe, Lulsegged. Christian Councils As Agents of Reconciliation & Change. 2009. 228p. pap. *(978-3-639-07748-3(2))* VDM Verlag Dr. Mueller e.K.

Abegunrin, Olayiwola. Africa in Global Politics in the Twenty-First Century: Challenges & Opportunities. 2007. *(978-1-60021-625-1(0))* Nova Science Pubs., Inc.

Abel, Martin. Doubling Aid to Africa. 2008. 96p. pap. *(978-3-639-01708-3(0))* VDM Verlag Dr. Mueller e.K.

Abubakar, Jamila J., et al, eds. Conflict of Securities: Reflections on State & Human Security in Africa. 2010. 252p. pap. *(978-1-906704-34-6(1))* Adonis & Abbey Publishers Ltd.

—Conflict of Securities: Reflections on State & Human Security in Africa (HB) 2010. 252p. *(978-1-906704-33-9(3))* Adonis & Abbey Publishers Ltd.

Adam, Rahma. What Needs to Be Done to Develop Local Food Markets in Tanzania? 2010. 72p. pap. *(978-3-8383-4982-4(2))* Lambert Academic Publishing.

Adar, Korwa G. & Check, Nicasius A., eds. Cooperative Diplomacy, Regional Stability & National Interests the Nile River & the Riparian States. 2011. 284p. pap. ***(978-0-7983-0287-6(9))*** Africa Institute of South Africa.

Adibe, Jideofor. African Renaissance JuneJuly 2004. 2006. 208p. per. *(978-1-905068-35-7(2))* Adonis & Abbey Publishers Ltd.

—African Renaissance, Sept/Oct 2006. 2006. 168p. per. *(978-1-905068-50-0(6))* Adonis & Abbey Publishers Ltd.

Africa Business & Political Handbook: Companies-Products-Services. (Illus.). 600p. (Orig.). pap. 2400.00 *(978-0-7605-1336-1(8))* Rector Pr., Ltd.

African Renaissance NovemberDecember 200. 2006. 124p. per. *(978-1-905068-66-1(2))* Adonis & Abbey Publishers Ltd.

Afriki, Seiko. Constitution of the United States of Africa. 2009. 52p. pap. 8.43 *(978-0-557-07235-4(2))* Lulu Enterprises Inc.

Aga, Deribe Assefa. African Peer Review Mechanism in Ethiopi. 2011. 112p. pap. ***(978-3-8443-0237-0(9))*** Lambert Academic Publishing.

Agbahowe, Nathaniel U. Wake up Africa! 2009. 460p. pap. 20.49 *(978-1-4389-1466-4(0))* AuthorHouse.

Agwuele, Augustine, ed. Development, Modernism & Modernity in Africa. 2011. (Routledge African Studies). (ENG., Illus.). 340p. (C). 125.00 ***(978-0-415-89924-6(9))*** Routledge.

Akindele, Akin O. Geo-Political Road Kill Book #8: Revisiting Africa's Failing Quest for Liberty, Justice & Progress. 2009. 244p. 29.99 *(978-1-4363-9983-8(1))*; pap. 19.99 *(978-1-4363-9982-1(3))* Xlibris Corp.

Akokpari, John, et al, eds. The African Union & Its Institutions. 2009. (ENG.). 416p. pap. 22.00 *(978-1-920196-03-5(X))* Jacana Media ZAF. Dist: Independent Pubs. Group.

Akukwe, Chinua. African Renaissance JulyAugust 2006. 2006. 200p. per. *(978-1-905068-41-8(7))* Adonis & Abbey Publishers Ltd.

Allen, Christopher & Johnson, R. W., eds. African Perspectives: Papers in the History, Politics & Economics of Africa Presented to Thomas Hodgkin. 2008. (ENG.). 464p. pap. 58.00 *(978-0-521-10199-8(9))* Cambridge Univ. Pr.

and Peoples' Rights, African Commission on Hum & for Indigenous Affairs, International Work Group. Visit to Gabon: Report of the African Commission's Working: Group on Indigenous Populations. 2011. 150p. pap. 24.95 *(978-87-91563-74-4(7))* IWGIA DNK. Dist: Transaction Pubs.

Anderson, David & Cheeseman, Nic. Routledge Handbook of African Politics. 2013. (ENG., Illus.). 480p. (C). 220.00 *(978-0-415-57378-8(5))* Routledge.

Angwafo, Fo. Royalty & Politics the Story of My Life. 2009. 148p. pap. *(978-9956-558-31-5(1))* Langaa Research & Publishing Common Initiative Group CMR. Dist: Michigan State Univ. Pr.

Antwi-Boasiako, Kwame Badu & Bonna, Okyere. Traditional Institutions & Public Administration in Democratic Afric. 2009. 208p. 31.99 *(978-1-4415-2013-5(9))*; pap. 21.99 *(978-1-4415-2012-8(0))* Xlibris Corp.

Anyangwe, Carlson. Betrayal of Too Trusting a People the un, the Uk & the Trust Territory of the Southern Cameroons. 2009. 260p. pap. *(978-9956-558-81-0(8))* Langaa Research & Publishing Common Initiative Group CMR. Dist: Michigan State Univ. Pr.

Apter, Andrew. Beyond Words: Discourse & Critical Agency in Africa. 2007. (Illus.). 192p. 42.50 *(978-0-226-02351-9(6))*; per. 17.50 *(978-0-226-02352-6(4))* Univ. of Chicago Pr.

Archer, Jermaine O. Antebellum Slave Narratives: Cultural & Political Expressions of Africa. 2008. (Studies in American Popular History & Culture Ser.). (ENG.). 142p. 125.00 *(978-0-415-99027-1(0))* Routledge.

Arenas, Fernando. Lusophone Africa: Beyond Independence. 2011. (ENG., Illus.). 368p. 75.00 *(978-0-8166-6983-7(X))*; pap. 25.00 *(978-0-8166-6984-4(8))* Univ. of Minnesota Pr.

Arowosegbe, Jeremiah O. Democracy & Development in Afric. 2011. 644p. pap. ***(978-3-8443-9234-0(3))*** Lambert Academic Publishing.

—The State & the Challenges of Nationhood in Afric. 2011. 92p. pap. ***(978-3-8443-0063-5(5))*** Lambert Academic Publishing.

Arrous, Michel Ben & Ki-Zerbo, Lazare, eds. African Studies in Geography from Below. 2009. (FRE & ENG.). 360p. pap. *(978-2-86978-231-0(4))* Council for the Development of Social Science Research in Africa SEN. Dist: Michigan State Univ. Pr.

Artley, Oluwole &. Africation. 2007. 154p. pap. 11.95 *(978-0-7414-3932-1(8))* Infinity Publishing.

Asong, Linus & Chi, Ndeh, eds. Ndeh Ntumazah: A Conversational Auto Biography. 2011. 442p. pap. ***(978-9956-579-32-7(7))*** Langaa Research & Publishing Common Initiative Group.

Asres, Wondem. The State, the Crisis of State Institutions, & Refugee Migration in the Horn of Africa. 2006. 304p. 99.95 *(978-1-56902-236-8(4))*; 29.95 *(978-1-56902-237-5(2))* Red Sea Pr.

Atanga, Lilian Lem. Gender, Discourse & Power in the Cameroonian Parliament. 2009. 278p. pap. *(978-9956-615-46-9(3))* Langaa Research & Publishing Common Initiative Group CMR. Dist: Michigan State Univ. Pr.

Atanga, Mufor. The Anglophone Cameroon Predicament. 2011. 266p. pap. ***(978-9956-717-11-8(8))*** Langaa Research & Publishing Common Initiative Group.

Atangana, Martin. The End of French Rule in Cameroon. 2010. (ENG.). 160p. pap. 25.50 *(978-0-7618-5278-0(6))* Univ. Pr. of America, Inc.

Ayittey, George B. N. Defeating Dictators: Fighting Tyranny in Africa & Around the World. 2011. (ENG., Illus.). 288p. 28.00 *(978-0-230-10859-2(8))* Palgrave Macmillan.

Bach, Daniel C. & Gazibo, Mamoudou, eds. Neopatrimonialism in Africa & Beyond. 2012. (Routledge Studies on African Politics & International Relations Ser.). (ENG.). 272p. (C). 135.00 ***(978-0-415-68793-5(4))*** Routledge.

Baker, Bruce. Security in Post-Conflict Africa: The Role of Nonstate Policing. 2009. (Advances in Police Theory & Practice Ser.). (ENG., Illus.). 215p. 133.95 *(978-1-4200-9193-9(X)*, CRC Press) Taylor & Francis Group GBR. Dist: Taylor & Francis Group.

Bangura, Abdul Karim. African Peace Paradigms. rev. ed. 2007. (ENG.). 330p. pap. 83.08 *(978-0-7575-4859-8(8))* Kendall Hunt Publishing Co.

Banque Mondiale Staff & World Bank Staff. L' Education Au Mali: Diagnostic Pour le Renouvellement de la Politique Educative en Vue D'Atteindre les Objectifs du Millenaire. 2007. (Africa Human Development Ser.). (FRE., Illus.). 280p. per. 35.00 *(978-0-8213-7064-3(2)*, 9780821370643) World Bank Pubns.

Barkely, Russell L., ed. Africom: Security, Development, & Humanitarian Functions. 2009. 69.00 *(978-1-60692-443-3(5))* Nova Science Pubs., Inc.

Barrett, Christopher B. Understanding & Reducing Persistent Poverty in Africa. Carter, Michael & Little, Peter, eds. 2008. 256p. pap. 39.95 *(978-0-415-46389-8(0))* Routledge.

Basu, Partha, et al, eds. State, Nation & Democracy: Alternative Global Futures. 2007. 370p. *(978-81-8069-420-2(8))* Concept Publishing Co.

Bates, Robert H. When Things Fell Apart: State Failure in Late-Century Africa. 2008. (Cambridge Studies in Comparative Politics). (ENG., Illus.). 218p. pap. 22.99 *(978-0-521-71525-6(3))*; 216p. 65.00 *(978-0-521-88735-9(6))* Cambridge Univ. Pr.

Bayart, Jean-Francois. The State in Africa: The Politics of the Belly. 2nd ed. 2009. (ENG.). 420p. pap. 29.95 *(978-0-7456-4437-0(6))* Polity Pr. GBR. Dist: Wiley, John & Sons, Inc.

Beard, Virginia. Democratic Political Orientations in Emerging African Democracies. 2008. 236p. pap. *(978-3-639-08064-3(5))* VDM Verlag Dr. Mueller e.K.

Beck, Linda J. Brokering Democracy in Africa: The Rise of Clientelist Democracy in Senegal. 2008. (ENG., Illus.). 296p. 95.00 *(978-0-230-60283-0(5))* Palgrave Macmillan.

Beckman, Bjorn, et al, eds. Trade Unions & Party Politics: Labour Movements in Africa. 2010. (ENG.). 224p. pap. 25.95 *(978-0-7969-2306-6(X))* Human Sciences Research Council ZAF. Dist: Independent Pubs. Group.

Beckman, Bjorn & Adeoti, Gbemisola Remi, eds. Intellectuals & African Development: Pretension & Resistance in African Politics. 2006. (Africa in the New Millennium Ser.). (ENG.). 192p. 123.95 *(978-1-84277-764-0(5))*; per. 36.95 *(978-1-84277-765-7(3))* Zed Bks., Ltd. GBR. Dist: Macmillan.

Bekoe, Dorina A. Implementing Peace Agreements: Lessons from Mozambique, Angola, & Liberia. 2008. (ENG.). 240p. 89.00 *(978-0-230-60259-5(2))* Palgrave Macmillan.

Benjamin, Isaac. Great Giants of Wicked Purities. 2009. 236p. pap. 15.99 *(978-1-4343-9714-0(9))* AuthorHouse.

Bereket H. Selassie. Wounded Nation: How a Once Promising Eritrea Was Betrayed & Its Future Compromised. 2011. (Illus.). xiii, 311p. *(978-1-56902-339-6(5))* Red Sea Pr.

Better Homes and Gardens Books Staff & Kinzer, Stephen. A Thousand Hills: Rwanda's Rebirth & the Man Who Dreamed It. 2008. (ENG., Illus.). 400p. 25.95 *(978-0-470-12015-6(0)*, Wiley) Wiley, John & Sons, Inc.

Bijlsma, Sanne. The Burden of History. 2011. 124p. pap. ***(978-3-8443-0852-5(0))*** Lambert Academic Publishing.

Boås, Morten & Dunn, Kevin C. African Guerrillas: Raging Against the Machine. 2007. (Illus.). 250p. (C). pap. 23.50 *(978-1-58826-471-8(8))*; lib. bdg. 58.00 *(978-1-58826-495-4(5))* Rienner, Lynne Pubs.

Bogaards, Matthijs, et al, eds. Ethnic Party Bans in Africa. 2012. (ENG.). 224p. 140.00 ***(978-0-415-62363-6(4))*** Routledge.

Bompani, Barbara & Frahm-Arp, Maria, eds. Development & Politics from Below: Exploring Religious Spaces in the African State. 2010. (Non-Governmental Public Action Ser.). (ENG., Illus.). 272p. 89.00 *(978-0-230-23775-9(4))* Palgrave Macmillan.

Bond, Patrick. Looting Africa: The Economics of Exploitation. (Illus.). xix, 172p. *(978-1-86914-095-3(8))* University of Kwazulu-Natal Press ZAF. Dist: International Specialized Bk. Services.

—Looting Africa: The Economics of Exploitation. 2006. (ENG., Illus.). 224p. 79.95 *(978-1-84277-812-8(9))*; per. 25.95 *(978-1-84277-811-1(0))* Zed Bks., Ltd. GBR. Dist: Macmillan.

Boone, Catherine. Merchant Capital & the Roots of State Power in Senegal: 1930-1985. 2006. (Cambridge Studies in Comparative Politics). (ENG., Illus.). 320p. pap. 61.00 *(978-0-521-03039-7(0))* Cambridge Univ. Pr.

Booysen, Susan. The African National Congress & the Regeneration of Political Power: People, Party, Policy. 2012. (ENG., Illus.). 528p. pap. 34.95 ***(978-1-86814-542-3(5))*** Witwatersrand Univ. Pr. Pubns. ZAF. Dist: Transaction Pubs.

Bownik, Gregory J. Leadership & Nation Building in Africa: Challenges & Opportunities. 2010. 168p. pap. 18.95 *(978-1-4327-5948-3(5))* Outskirts Pr., Inc.

Brautigam, Deborah. The Dragon's Gift: The Real Story of China in Africa. 2010. (ENG., Illus.). 224p. 29.95 *(978-0-19-955022-7(0))* Oxford Univ. Pr., Inc.

Burns, Emile. Abyssinia & Italy. 2007. 224p. per. *(978-1-4067-8971-3(2)*, Pierides Pr.) Read Bks.

Cabral, Amilcar. Unity & Struggle: Selected Speeches & Writings (Second Edition) 2008. 358p. pap. 42.00 *(978-1-86888-450-6(3))* Unisa Press / Uitgewers GBR. Dist: International Specialized Bk. Services.

Calderisi, Robert. The Trouble with Africa: Why Foreign Aid Isn't Working. 2007. (ENG.). 256p. pap. 18.95 *(978-1-4039-7651-2(1))* Palgrave Macmillan.

Callahan, Michael D. Mandates & Empire: The League of Nations & Africa, 1914-1931. 2008. (ENG.). 304p. pap. 37.50 *(978-1-84519-297-6(4))* Sussex Academic Pr. GBR. Dist: International Specialized Bk. Services.

Cameron, Hazel. Complicity: The Hidden Role of Britain & France in Rwanda's Genocide. 2012. (ENG., Illus.). 176p. 125.00 *(978-0-415-61960-8(2))* Routledge.

Caplan, Gerald. The Betrayal of Africa. 2008. (Groundwork Guides). (ENG., Illus.). 144p. (gr. 9-12). 18.95 *(978-0-88899-824-8(4))* Groundwood Bks. CAN. Dist: Perseus-PGW.

—Betrayal of Africa. 2008. (Groundwork Guides). (ENG., Illus.). 144p. (gr. 9-18). pap. 10.00 *(978-0-88899-825-5(2))* Groundwood Bks. CAN. Dist: Perseus-PGW.

Carey. Protest, Repression & Political Regimes. 2009. (Security & Governance Ser.). (ENG., Illus.). 160p. (C). 140.00 *(978-0-415-42484-4(4))* Routledge.

Cargill, Tom. Our Common Strategic Interests: Africa's Role in the Post-G8 World. 2010. (ENG., Illus.). 56p. pap. 15.00 *(978-1-86203-224-8(6))* Royal Institute of International Affairs GBR. Dist: Brookings Institution Pr.

Carmody, Padraig Risteard & Carmody, Padraig. Neoliberalism, Civil Society & Security in Africa. 2007. (ENG., Illus.). 224p. 105.00 *(978-0-230-52159-9(2))* Palgrave Macmillan.

Carton, Benedict, et al, eds. Zulu Identities: Being Zulu, Past & Present. 2009. (Columbia/Hurst Ser.). (ENG.). 688p. (gr. 17). pap. 34.50 *(978-0-231-70059-7(8))* Columbia Univ. Pr.

Ceesay, Alhasan Sisawo. Country for President, Tribe & Party. 2011. 182p. pap. 24.95 ***(978-1-4560-7263-6(3))*** PublishAmerica, Inc.

Century of Change: Symposium on African Unity. 2011. (Illus.). 199p. pap. ***(978-1-61209-023-8(0))*** Nova Science Pubs., Inc.

Chabal, Patrick. Africa: The Politics of Suffering & Smiling. 2009. (Global Political Theories Ser.). (ENG.). 208p. 117.95 *(978-1-84277-908-8(7))*; pap. 29.95 *(978-1-84277-909-5(5))* Zed Bks., Ltd. GBR. Dist: Macmillan.

Chachage, Chambi & Cassam, Annar. Africa's Liberation: The Legacy of Nyerere. 2010. (Illus.). 216p. pap. 20.95 ***(978-1-906387-71-6(0))*** Pambazuka Pr. GBR. Dist: Independent Pubs. Group.

Chan, Stephen. Grasping Africa: A Tale of Achievement & Tragedy. 2007. (ENG.). 224p. pap. 36.00 *(978-1-84511-285-1(7))* I. B. Tauris & Co., Ltd. GBR. Dist: Macmillan.

Chiwandamira, Lindyn & Makaula, Monica, eds. Perspectives on African Governance. 2006. 112p. pap. *(978-1-920118-14-3(4))* IDASA Pubs. ZAF. Dist: Michigan State Univ. Pr.

Chuhan-Pole, Punam & Angwafo, Manka, eds. Yes, Africa Can: Success Stories from a Dynamic Continent. 2011. (ENG., Illus.). 496p. pap. 49.95 *(978-0-8213-8745-0(6)*, 9780821387450) World Bank Pubns.

Clapham, Christopher. Liberia & Sierra Leone: An Essay in Comparative Politics. 2009. (African Studies). (ENG.). 172p. pap. 31.99 *(978-0-521-09980-6(3))* Cambridge Univ. Pr.

Clark, Philip & Kaufman, Zachary, eds. After Genocide: Transitional Justice, Post-Conflict Reconstruction, & Reconciliation in Rwanda & Beyond. 2009. (Columbia/Hurst Ser.). (ENG.). 428p. (gr. 17). 50.00 *(978-0-231-70082-5(2))* Columbia Univ. Pr.

Columbus, Alexandra M., ed. Politics & Economics of Africa: Volume 9. 2011. (Politics & Economics of Africa Ser.). (Illus.). 171p. pap. 112.00 ***(978-1-61324-231-5(X))*** Nova Science Pubs., Inc.

Columbus, Frank. Politics & Economics of Africa. Volume 8. 2011. (Series: Politics & Economics of Africa Ser.). (Illus.). 326p. 165.00 *(978-1-61122-554-9(X))* Nova Science Pubs., Inc.

Columbus, Frank, ed. Politics & Economics of Africa. Volume 7. 2010. (Politics & Economics of Africa Ser.). 115.00 *(978-1-61668-013-8(X))* Nova Science Pubs., Inc.

Comaroff, Jean & Comaroff, John L. Theory from the South: Or, How Euro-America Is Evolving Toward Africa. 1 vol. 2011. (Radical Imagination Ser.). 272p. pap. 24.95 ***(978-1-59451-765-5(7))*** Paradigm Pubs.

Council on Foreign Relations Staff. Beyond Humanitarianism: What You Need to Know about Africa & Why it Matters. 2007. 240p. pap. 17.95 *(978-0-87609-375-7(6))* Council on Foreign Relations.

Cox, Dan G., et al. Terrorism, Instability, & Democracy in Asia & Africa. 2009. (Northeastern Series on Democratization & Political Development Ser.). (ENG., Illus.). 244p. (C). lib. bdg. 60.00 *(978-1-55553-705-0(7)*, Northeastern University Pr.) Univ. Pr. of New England.

Cram101 Textbook Reviews & Cram101 Textbook Reviews. Outlines & Highlights for Africa in the Century: Toward a New Future by Ama Mazama, ISBN. 2011. 114p. pap. 28.95 ***(978-1-61812-033-5(6))*** Cram101 Inc.

Crawford, Gordan & Hartmann, Christof, eds. Decentralisation in Africa: A Pathway out of Poverty & Conflict? 2008. (Eadi Ser.). 260p. pap. *(978-90-5356-934-4(0)*, Leiden Univ. Pr.) Amsterdam Univ. Pr.

Crawford, Gordon & Lynch, Gabrielle, eds. Democratization in Africa: Challenges & Propects. 2012. (ENG.). 304p. (C). 125.00 ***(978-0-415-50832-2(0))*** Routledge.

Daley, Patricia O. Gender & Genocide in Burundi: The Search for Spaces of Peace in the Great Lakes Region. 2008. (African Issues Ser.). (ENG., Illus.). 280p. 65.00 *(978-0-253-35171-5(5)*, 0253351715); pap. 24.95 *(978-0-253-21925-1(6)*, 0253219256) Indiana Univ. Pr.

Darch, Colin & Underwood, Peter. Freedom of Information & the Developing World: The citizen, the state & models of Openness. 2009. (Illus.). 336p. pap. *(978-1-84334-147-5(6)*, Chandos Publishing) Woodhead Publishing Ltd. GBR. Dist: Neal-Schuman Pubs., Inc.

Daubler-Gmelin, Herta, et al, eds. Afrika. Europas verkannter Nachbar: Ansichten und Einsuichten aus Theorie und Praxis. (GER & ENG., Illus.). 207p. pap. 23.95 *(978-3-631-55543-9(1))* Lang, Peter GmbH, Europaischer Verlag der Wissenschaften DEU. Dist: Lang, Peter Publishing, Inc.

Däubler-Gmelin, Herta & Helfrich, Ann Kathrin, eds. Afrika. Europas verkannter Nachbar: Band 2. 2008. 256p. pap. 43.95 *(978-3-631-56571-1(2))* Lang, Peter GmbH, Europaischer Verlag der Wissenschaften DEU. Dist: Lang, Peter.

De La Gorgendière, Louise, et al. Ethnicity in Africa: Roots, Meanings & Implications. vi, 360p. *(978-0-9527917-0-6(6))* University of Edinburgh Centre of African Studies.

Deegan, Heather. Africa Today: Culture, Economics, Religion, Security. (Illus.). 2009. XVI, 240p. 170.00 *(978-0-415-41883-6(6))* 2008. (ENG., 256p. (C). pap. 42.95 *(978-0-415-41884-3(4))* Routledge.

Deng, Francis Mading, et al. Identity, Diversity, & Constitutionalism in Africa. 2008. 308p. 50.00 *(978-1-60127-035-1(6))*; pap. 19.95 *(978-1-60127-034-4(8))* U. S. Institute of Peace Pr. (USIP Pr.).

Derrick, Jonathan. Africa's 'Agitators' Militant Anti-Colonialism in Africa & the West, 1918-1939. 2008. (Columbia/Hurst Ser.). (ENG.). 320p. (gr. 17). 50.00 *(978-0-231-70056-6(3))* Columbia Univ. Pr.

Diamond, Larry Jay & Plattner, Marc F., eds. Democratization in Africa: Progress & Retreat. 2nd ed. 2010. (Journal of Democracy Book Ser.). (ENG., Illus.). 392p. (C). (gr. 13-17). pap. 30.00 *(978-0-8018-9484-8(0))*; 60.00 *(978-0-8018-9483-1(2))* Johns Hopkins Univ. Pr.

Dickovick, J. Tyler. Africa. 46th ed. 2011. (World Today Series: Africa Ser.). (ENG., Illus.). 344p. pap. 18.50 ***(978-1-935264-18-7(4))*** Stryker-Post Pubns.

Dietz, Ton, et al, eds. African Engagements: Africa Negotiating an Emerging Multipolar World. 2011. (Africa-Europe Group for Interdisciplinary Studies). (Illus.). VIII, 392p. pap. ***(978-90-04-20988-6(3))*** BRILL.

Dokken, Karin. African Security Politics Redefined. 2008. (ENG., Illus.). 272p. 100.00 *(978-1-4039-7761-8(5))* Palgrave Macmillan.

Doyle, Arthur Conan. The Crime of the Congo. 2007. (ENG.). 132p. per. 10.95 *(978-1-60312-166-8(8))*; 24.95 *(978-1-60312-848-3(4))* Aegypan.

—The Crime of the Congo. reprint ed. lib. bdg. 98.00 *(978-0-7426-2721-5(7))* Classic Bks.

Drope, Jeffrey, ed. Tobacco Control in Africa: People, Politics & Policies. 2011. (Anthem Studies in Development & Globalization Ser.). (Illus.). 332p. 99.00 *(978-0-85728-783-0(4))* Anthem Pr. GBR. Dist: Books International, Inc.

Dundas, Carl W. The Lag of 21st Century Democratic Elections: In the African Union Member States. 2011. 484p. pap. 29.70 ***(978-1-4567-9706-5(9))*** AuthorHouse.

Edozie, Rita Kiki. Reconstructing the Third Wave of Democracy: Comparative African Democratic Politics. 2008. (ENG.). 220p. pap. 38.99 *(978-0-7618-4142-5(3))*; (Illus.). 70.50 *(978-0-7618-4141-8(5))* Univ. Pr. of America, Inc.

Elechi, O. Oko. Doing Justice Without the Stat: The Afikpo (Ehugbo) Nigeria Model. 2006. (African Studies). (Illus.). 256p. 128.00 *(978-0-415-97729-6(0))* Routledge.

Ellis, Frank, et al. Social Protection in Africa. 2009. (Illus.). 304p. 155.00 *(978-1-84844-258-0(0))*; pap. 50.00 *(978-1-84844-364-8(1))* Elgar, Edward Publishing, Inc.

Endeley, null & Endeley, Isaac N. Bloc Politics at the United Nations: The African Group. 2009. (ENG., Illus.). 60p. pap. 15.99 *(978-0-7618-4558-4(5))* Univ. Pr. of America, Inc.

Enoke, Ewa. Africa in a World of Mendacity: Understanding the African Condition & Why Political Paranoids can be Prosecuted. 2007. 262p. per. 35.00 *(978-0-9786517-3-2(1))* Synthesis Group, Inc.

Ensign, Margee & Bertrand, William E. Rwanda: History & Hope. 2009. (ENG.). 174p. 59.99 *(978-0-7618-4942-1(4))* Univ. Pr. of America, Inc.

Ensign/Bertrand. Rwanda: History & Hope. 2009. (ENG.). 174p. pap. 28.50 *(978-0-7618-4943-8(2))* Univ. Pr. of America, Inc.

Epprecht, Marc. Heterosexual Africa: The History of an Idea from the Age of Exploration to the Age of AIDS. 2008. xiii, 231p. pap. *(978-1-86914-157-8(1))* Univ. of Natal Pr. ZAF. Dist: International Specialized Bk. Services.

Erasmus, P. F. Terminal Africa: The curse of the ancestral Cord. 2007. 128p. per. *(978-0-7552-1069-5(7))* Authors OnLine, Ltd.

Evans, Malcolm & Murray, Rachel, eds. The African Charter on Human & Peoples' Rights: The System in Practice 1986-2006. 2nd rev. ed. 2008. (ENG.). 534p. 130.00 *(978-0-521-88399-3(7))* Cambridge Univ. Pr.

Ewumbue-Monono, Churchill. Youth & Nation-Building in Cameroon: A Study of National Youth Day Messages & Leadership Discourse (1949-2009) A Study of National Youth Day Messages & Leadership Discourse (1949-2009) 2009. 210p. pap. *(978-9956-558-32-2(X))* Langaa Research & Publishing Common Initiative Group CMR. Dist: Michigan State Univ. Pr.

Exploring the U.S. Africa Command & a New Strategic Relationship with Africa: Hearing Before the Subcommittee on African Affairs of the Committee on Foreign Relations, United States Senate, One Hundred Tenth Congress, First Session, August 1, 2007. 2008. iii, 48p. *(978-0-16-081675-8(0)*, 552-070-37906-1) United States Government Printing Office.

Faber, Paul. Long Live the President! Portrait-Cloths from Africa. 2010. (Illus.). 96p. pap. 29.95 *(978-94-6022-100-2(9))* Royal Tropical Institute Pr. (KIT (Koninklijk Instituut voor de Tropen) NLD. Dist: Stylus Publishing, LLC.

Falola, Toyin & Agwuele, Augustine, eds. Africans & the Politics of Popular Culture. 2009. (Rochester Studies in African History & the Diaspora Ser.: Volume 42). (Illus.). 347p. 80.00 *(978-1-58046-331-7(2))* Univ. of Rochester Pr.

Fardon, Richard, et al. African Socialisms & Postsocialisms. 2007. (ENG., Illus.). 128p. (gr. 17). pap. 36.00 *(978-0-7486-2483-6(X))* Edinburgh Univ. Pr. GBR. Dist: Columbia Univ. Pr.

Farrar, Elizabeth. African Leaders for Peace & Justice. 2007. (Illus.). 156p. pap. *(978-1-888105-76-6(3))* Avisson Pr., Inc.

FOMBAD, Zein, Charles Manga KEBONANG, et al. AU, NEPAD & the APRM: Democratisation Efforts Explored. 2006. (NAI Current African Issues Ser.). 56p. pap. 10.95 *(978-91-7106-569-8(5))* Nordiska Afrikainstitutet SWE. Dist: Stylus Publishing, LLC.

Forje, John W. Century of Change Symposium on African Unity. 2011. *(978-1-61122-034-6(3))* Nova Science Pubs., Inc.

—The Challenges of Administrative Political & Developmental Renewal in Africa: Emerging Issues. 2009. 69.00 *(978-1-60741-265-6(9))* Nova Science Pubs., Inc.

—The Challenges of Administrative Political & Developmental Renewal in Africa: Essays on Rethinking Government & Reorganization. 2009. 69.00 *(978-1-60741-266-3(7))* Nova Science Pubs., Inc.

—Here the People Rule: Political Transition & Challenges for Democratic Consolidation in Africa. (African Political, Economic, & Security Issues Ser.). 2011. 274p. pap. 43.00 *(978-1-61209-024-5(9))* 2009. xxxvi, 274p. 79.00 *(978-1-60692-706-9(X))* Nova Science Pubs., Inc.

—Perspectives on Democracy & Governance in Africa. 2011. *(978-1-61209-250-8(0))*; pap. *(978-1-61209-320-8(5))* Nova Science Pubs., Inc.

—State Building & Democracy in Africa: A Comparative & Developmental Approach. (African Political, Economic, & Security Issues Ser.). 2011. pap. 43.00 *(978-1-61209-025-2(7))* 2009. (Illus.). xvi, 260p. 79.00 *(978-1-60741-371-4(X))* Nova Science Pubs., Inc.

Forje, John Wilson. Century of Change: Symposium on African Unity. 2011. (Series: African Political, Economic, & Security Issues Ser.). 129.00 *(978-1-61222-034-5(7))* Nova Science Pubs., Inc.

Foster, Noel. Mauritania: The Struggle for Democracy. 2010. 280p. 72.50 *(978-1-935049-30-2(5))* FirstForumPress.

Francis, David J. Peace & Conflict in Africa. Francis, David J., ed. 2008. (ENG., Illus.). 224p. pap. 34.00 *(978-1-84277-954-5(0))* Zed Bks., Ltd. GBR. Dist: Macmillan.

Francis, David J., ed. Peace & Conflict in Africa. 2008. (ENG., Illus.). 224p. 117.00 *(978-1-84277-953-8(2))* Zed Bks., Ltd. GBR. Dist: Macmillan.

Francisco, Albertino & Agostinho, Nujoma. Exorcising Devils from the Throne: São Tomé & Príncipe in the Chaos of Democratization. 2011. pap. 23.95 ***(978-0-87586-846-2(0))***; pap. 33.95 ***(978-0-87586-847-9(9))*** Algora Publishing.

Franke, Benedikt. Security Cooperation in Africa: A Reappraisal. 2009. (Illus.). 230p. 75.00 *(978-1-935049-09-8(7))* FirstForumPress.

Frazer, Jendayi E. & Gyimah-Boadi, E., eds. Preventing Electoral Violence in Africa. 2011. (Carnegie Mellon Political Science Ser.). (ENG.). 112p. pap. 16.95 ***(978-0-88748-553-4(7))*** Carnegie-Mellon Univ. Pr.

Frere, Marie-Soleil. Elections & the Media in Post-Conflict Africa: Votes & Voices for Peace? 2011. (ENG.). 352p. pap. 39.95 *(978-1-78032-018-2(3))* Zed Bks., Ltd. GBR. Dist: Macmillan.

—The Media & Conflicts in Central Africa. 2006. 250p. (C). pap. 23.50 *(978-1-58826-465-7(3))*; lib. bdg. 55.00 *(978-1-58826-489-3(0))* Rienner, Lynne Pubs.

Fuller, Linda K. African Women's Unique Vulnerabilities to HIV/AIDS: Communication Perspectives & Promises. 2008. (ENG.). 328p. 105.00 *(978-1-4039-8405-0(0))* Palgrave Macmillan.

Gabriel, Akwen & BONIFACE, Ortindi. The African Union & the Challenges of Regional Integration in Afric. 2011. 144p. pap. ***(978-3-8443-1502-8(0))*** Lambert Academic Publishing.

Gandois, Hélène. From Ploughshare to Sword: Regionalism in Africa. 2010. 272p. pap. *(978-3-8383-2226-1(6))* Lambert Academic Publishing.

Gardner, Leigh A. Taxing Colonial Africa: The Political Economy of British Imperialism. 2012. (ENG., Illus.). 272p. 110.00 ***(978-0-19-966152-7(9))*** Oxford Univ. Pr., Inc.

Garuka Nsabimana, Christian. The Concept of Power Sharing. 2010. 60p. pap. *(978-3-639-25186-9(5))* VDM Verlag Dr. Mueller e.K.

Gaynor, Niamh. Transforming Participation? The Politics of Development in Malawi & Ireland. 2010. (Rethinking International Development Ser.). (ENG., Illus.). 256p. 89.00 *(978-0-230-23894-7(7))* Palgrave Macmillan.

Gebrewold, Belachew. Anatomy of Violence: Understanding the Systems of Conflict & Violence in Africa. 2009. 274p. 114.95 *(978-0-7546-7528-0(9))* Ashgate Publishing Co.

George, Thomas Boytee. Sierra Leone: Democracy & Reform. 2009. 288p. pap. 21.95 *(978-1-4327-3505-0(5))* Outskirts Pr., Inc.

Getachew Sertse, Wegene & Wegene, Getachew Sertse. Inter-Ethnic Conflict Management under the Ethiopian Federalism: The Case of Guji & Burji. 2011. 160p. pap. ***(978-3-639-32245-3(2))*** VDM Verlag Dr. Mueller e.K.

Gilliam, Tanji & Zuberi, Tukufu, eds. A Perspective on Africa & the World. 2011. (ANNALS of the American Academy of Political & Social Science Ser.: 632). 132p. (C). 47.00 *(978-1-4129-9395-1(4)*, 295632C); pap. 34.00 *(978-1-4129-9394-4(6)*, 295632P) SAGE Pubns., Inc.

Gilman, Lisa. The Dance of Politics: Gender, Performance, & Democratization in Malawi. (African Soundscapes Ser.). (ENG.). 268p. 2011. pap. 27.95

(978-1-59213-986-6(8)) 2009. (Illus.). 66.50 (978-1-59213-985-9(X)) Temple Univ. Pr.

Gitari, Joseph B. The Politics of Stability & Domination in Afric. 2008. 196p. pap. (978-3-639-08763-5(1)) VDM Verlag Dr. Mueller e.K.

Glennie, Jonathan. The Trouble with Aid: Why Less Could Mean More for Africa. 2008. (African Arguments Ser.). (ENG.). 192p. 69.95 (978-1-84813-039-5(2)); pap. 20.95 (978-1-84813-040-1(6)) Zed Bks., Ltd. GBR. Dist: Macmillan.

Gordon, April A. & Gordon, Donald L., eds. Understanding Contemporary Africa, 4th Edition. 4th ed. 2006. (Illus.). 475p. (C). pap. 27.50 (978-1-58826-466-4(1)) Rienner, Lynne Pubs.

Gray, Tim S. & Stewart, Amy. The Governance of Water & Sanitation in Africa: Achieving Sustainable Development through Partnerships. 2009. (International Library of African Studies). (ENG.). 304p. 92.50 (978-1-84885-027-9(1), Tauris Academic Studies) I. B. Tauris & Co., Ltd. GBR. Dist: Macmillan.

The Great Lakes Region: Current Conditions & U.S. Policy: Hearing Before the Subcommittee on Africa & Global Health of the Committee on Foreign Affairs, House of Representatives, One Hundred Eleventh Congress, Second Session, May 25, 2010. 2010. iii, 68p. (978-0-16-086452-0(6), 552-070-41509-2) United States Government Printing Office.

Guest, Robert. The Shackled Continent: Power, Corruption, & African Lives. 2010. (ENG.). 288p. pap. 21.95 (978-1-58834-297-3(2)) Smithsonian Institution Pr.

Gulbrandsen, Ørnulf. The State & the Social: State Formation in Botswana & Its Precolonial & Colonial Genealogies. 2012. (ENG.). 362p. 120.00 (978-0-85745-297-9(5)) Berghahn Bks., Inc.

Gumede, William Mervin. The Democracy Gap: Africa's Wasted Years. 2012. (African Arguments Ser.). (ENG.). 192p. pap. 23.95 (978-1-84813-042-5(2)) Zed Bks., Ltd. GBR. Dist: Macmillan.

Gumede, William Mervin & Gumede, William. The Democracy Gap: Africa's Wasted Years. 2012. (African Arguments Ser.). (ENG.). 192p. 72.95 (978-1-84813-041-8(4)) Zed Bks., Ltd. GBR. Dist: Macmillan.

Guo, Rongxing. The Land & Maritime Boundary Disputes of Africa. 2009. (African Political, Economic, & Security Issues Ser.). pap. 89.00 (978-1-60741-637-1(9)) Nova Science Pubs., Inc.

Guseh, James S. & Oritsejafor, Emmanuel O. Governance, Democracy & Development in sub-Saharan Africa. 2011. (ENG., Illus.). 256p. 50.00 (978-0-9770904-3-3(4)) Africana Homestead Legacy Pubs., Inc.

Haan, Leo de & Engel, Ulf, eds. African Alternatives. 2007. (African-Europe Group for Interdisciplinary Studies). pap. (978-90-04-16113-9(9)) BRILL.

Haddis Weldeghebrael, Ezana. Responsibility of the Ethiopian Floriculture Industry to Its Workers. 2010. 128p. pap. (978-3-639-26146-2(1)) VDM Verlag Dr. Mueller e.K.

Hagmann, Tobias & Péclard, Didier, eds. Negotiating Statehood: Dynamics of Power & Domination in Africa. 2011. (Development & Change Special Issues Ser.: 2). (ENG., Illus.). 240p. pap. 34.95 (978-1-4443-3868-3(4), Wiley-Blackwell) Wiley, John & Sons, Inc.

Hanson, Kobena, et al, eds. Rethinking Development Challenges for Public Policy: Insights from Contemporary Africa. 2012. (International Political Economy Ser.). (ENG., Illus.). 320p. 95.00 (978-0-230-39328-8(4)) Palgrave Macmillan.

Harrison. The World Bank & Africa. 2007. pap. 41.95 (978-0-415-45983-9(4)) Routledge.

Hashim, Nadra & Hashim, Nadra O. Language & Collective Mobilization: The Story of Zanzibar. 2009. (ENG.). 222p. 73.50 (978-0-7391-2211-2(8)) Lexington Bks.

Haugen, David M., ed. Africa. 2011. (Opposing Viewpoints Ser.). (Illus.). 240p. (ENG.). pap. 27.50 (978-0-7377-5704-0(3), Greenhaven Pr., Inc.); (YA). (gr. 9-12). 39.70 (978-0-7377-5703-3(5)) Cengage Gale.

Hentz, James J., ed. Routledge Handbook of African Security. 2013. (ENG.). 392p. (C). 200.00 (978-0-415-68214-5(2)) Routledge.

Hepner, Tricia Redeker. Soldiers, Martyrs, Traitors, & Exiles: Political Conflict in Eritrea & the Diaspora. 2009. (Ethnography of Political Violence Ser.). (Illus.). 272p. (C). 55.00 (978-0-8122-4171-6(1)) Univ. of Pennsylvania Pr.

Hepner, Tricia Redeker & O'Kane, David, eds. Biopolitics, Militarism, & Development: Eritrea in the Twenty-First Century. 2009. 236p. 80.00 (978-1-84545-567-5(3)) Berghahn Bks., Inc.

Hewlett, Barry S. & Hewlett, Bonnie L. Ebola, Culture, & Politics: The Anthropology of an Emerging Disease. 2007. (ENG., Illus.). 192p. (C). per. 44.95 (978-0-495-00918-4(0)) Wadsworth.

Heyen, Erk, ed. Yearbook of European Administrative History, Vol. 18: Colonial Administration in Africa between Central Policy & Local Reality. 2007. 419p. 89.00 (978-3-8329-2333-4(0)) Nomos Verlagsgesellschaft DEU. Dist: International Specialized Bk. Services.

Holden, Paul. The Arms Trade in Your Pocket. 2009. 376p. pap. 18.95 (978-1-86842-313-2(1), Ball, Jonathan Pubs. ZAF. Dist: International Publishers Marketing.

Hope, Kempe Ronald. Poverty, Livelihoods, & Governance in Africa: Fulfilling the Development Promise. 2008. (ENG.). 224p. 89.00 (978-0-230-60834-4(5)) Palgrave Macmillan.

Horn of Africa: Current Conditions & U.S. Policy: Hearing Before the Subcommittee on Africa & Global Health of the Committee on Foreign Affairs, House of Representatives, One Hundred Eleventh Congress, Second Session, June 17, 2010. 2010. iii, 79p. (978-0-16-086453-7(4), 552-070-41510-6) United States Government Printing Office.

Hülle, Anna Kathrin. Assessment of the United Nations' Intervention in Rwand. 2011. 124p. pap. (978-3-8433-7891-8(6)) Lambert Academic Publishing.

Hyden, Goran. African Politics in Comparative Perspective African Edition. 2008. (C). pap. 24.99 (978-0-521-68532-0(X)) Cambridge Univ. Pr.

Ibelema, Minabere. The African Press, Civic Cynicism, & Democracy. 2007. (Palgrave Macmillan Series in Internatioal Political Communication Ser.). (ENG.). 296p. 100.00 (978-1-4039-8201-8(5)) Palgrave Macmillan.

Igbani, B. Maduabuchi A. Motherland Afrika: The Footprint of a Generation. rev. ed. 2008. (ENG.). 116p. pap. 31.99 (978-1-4389-3472-3(6)) AuthorHouse.

Jiménez, Alfredo. Three Essays on the Proactive Use of Political Risk. 2011. 244p. pap. (978-3-8443-2779-3(7)) Lambert Academic Publishing.

Jinadu, L. Adele. Fanon: In Search of the African Revolution. 270p. (Orig.). 110.00 (978-0-7103-0958-7(9)) Kegan Paul International, Ltd. GBR. Dist: Columbia Univ. Pr.

Joy, Charlotte L. The Politics of Heritage Management in Mali: From UNESCO to Djenne. 2012. (Critical Cultural Heritage Ser.). (ENG., Illus.). 235p. 89.00 (978-1-61132-094-7(1)) Left Coast Pr., Inc.

Kaarsholm, Preben. Violence, Political Culture & Development in Africa. xi, 208p. (978-1-86914-116-5(4)) University of Kwazulu-Natal Press ZAF. Dist: International Specialized Bk. Services.

Kaarsholm, Preben, ed. Violence, Political Culture & Development in Africa. 2006. (Ohio RIS Global Ser.). 224p. per. 24.00 (978-0-89680-251-3(5)) Ohio Univ. Pr.

Kale Ewusi, Ebenezer Akwanga Jr. Bsc. Burundi's Negative Peace: The Shadow of a Broken Continent in the Era of NEPAD. 2010. 408p. 31.96 (978-1-4269-2354-6(6)) Trafford Publishing.

Kalla, Britt. Utopia or Reality? - the Implementation of a Human Rights-Based Approach to the New Partnership for Africa's Development. 2008. 104p. pap. (978-3-639-03238-3(1)) VDM Verlag Dr. Mueller e.K.

Kalu, Kelechi Amihe & Soyinka-Airewele, Peyi. Socio-Political Scaffolding & the Construction of Change: Constitutionalism & Democratic Governance in Africa. 2008. (978-1-59221-634-5(X)); 416p. pap. (978-1-59221-635-2(8)) Africa World Pr.

Kannemeyer, Anton. Pappa in Africa. 2011. (ENG.). 96p. pap. 35.95 (978-1-77009-871-8(2)) Jacana Media ZAF. Dist: Independent Pubs. Group.

Kaplan, Robert B. & Baldauf, Richard B., Jr., eds. Language Planning & Policy in Africa Vol. 2: Algeria, Cote d'Ivoire, Nigeria & Tunisia. 2007. (Language Planning & Policy Ser.: 7). (ENG.). 324p. 99.95 (978-1-84769-011-1(4)) Multilingual Matters GBR. Dist: Univ. of Toronto Pr.

Karbo, Tony. Variations in Violent Conflicts in Africa: The Relative Influence of Political & Environmental Factors. 2008. 300p. pap. (978-3-8364-9068-9(4)) VDM Verlag Dr. Mueller e.K.

Kasahun Woldemariam. The Rise of Elective Dictatorship & the Erosion of Social Capital: Peace, Development, & Democracy in Africa. 2009. (978-1-59221-668-0(4)); 338p. pap. (978-1-59221-669-7(2)) Africa World Pr.

Kassaye, Amare. Federalism & Conflict Management in Ethiopia: Implications on the Countries of the Horn of Africa. 2011. 124p. pap. (978-3-639-32562-1(1)) VDM Verlag Dr. Mueller e.K.

Kenday Samuel Kamara. Sierra Leone Policy Papers: Perspectives on Social Innovation & Change in Sierra Leone. 2009. 272p. pap. 28.95 (978-1-4401-8073-6(3)) iUniverse, Inc.

Kerekou, Monse Tchando. The Process of Integration in Afric. 2009. 96p. pap. (978-3-639-15558-7(0)) VDM Verlag Dr. Mueller e.K.

Ketumile, Quett. Masire: Memoirs of an African Democrat. Lewis, Stephen R., Jr., ed. 2007. (ENG., Illus.). 368p. pap. 41.00 (978-99912-404-8-0(9)) Palgrave Macmillan.

Khamis, Kassim. Promoting the African Union. 2008. 450p. 34.95 (978-0-936508-33-7(7)) Barber, Lilian Pr.

Kibreab, Gaim. Critical Reflections on the Eritrean War of Independence: Social Capital, Associational Life, Religion, Ethnicity & Sowing Seeds of Dictatorship. 2007. (978-1-56902-281-8(X)) Red Sea Pr.

Kieh, George Klay. Africa & the Third Millennium. 2007. (978-1-59221-604-8(8)); 326p. pap. (978-1-59221-605-5(6)) Africa World Pr.

Kieh, George Klay, Jr. Beyond State Failure & Collapse: Making the State Relevant in Africa. 2007. (ENG., Illus.). 304p. 73.50 (978-0-7391-0892-5(1)) Lexington Bks.

—Globalization & its Implications for Africa. Wonkeryor, Edward Lama, ed. 2011. (ENG.). 80.00 (978-0-9770904-2-6(6)) Africana Homestead Legacy Pubs., Inc.

Kieh, George Klay. Reconstituting the State in Africa. Agbese, Pita Ogaba, ed. 2007. (ENG.). 320p. 89.00 (978-1-4039-7313-9(X)) Palgrave Macmillan.

Kielland, Anne. Child Labor Migration in Benin: Incentive, Constraint, or Agency? 2008. 120p. pap. (978-3-639-06802-3(5)) VDM Verlag Dr. Mueller e.K.

King, Lamont DeHaven. Africa & the Nation-State: State Formation & Identity in Ancient Egypt, Hausaland, & Southern Africa. 2006. (Illus.). 252p. 109.95 (978-0-7734-5743-0(7)) Mellen, Edwin Pr., The.

King, Nathaniel. Conflict as Integration: Youth Aspiration to Personhood/Sierra Leone. 2007. (NAI Current African Issues Ser.). 40p. pap. 12.95 (978-91-7106-604-6(7)) Nordiska Afrikainstitutet SWE. Dist: Stylus Publishing, LLC.

Kiribedda, Mica. Africa'sturmoil, Miseries & Poverty: The Sour Sown Seeds of Political Hate & Destruction of Colnial Imperialism. 2011. 180p. pap. 18.79 (978-1-4567-7608-4(8)) AuthorHouse.

Kiwuwa, David. Ethnic Politics & Democratic Transition in Rwanda. 2012. E-Book (978-0-203-11987-7(8)) Routledge.

Koko, Jacques L. National Conference As a Strategy for Conflict Transformation & Peacemaking: The Legacy of the Republic of Benin Model (HB) 2008. 220p. (978-1-905068-87-6(5)) Adonis & Abbey Publishers Ltd.

—National Conference As a Strategy for Conflict Transformation & Peacemaking: The Legacy of the Republic of Benin Model (PB) 2008. 220p. per. (978-1-905068-52-4(2)) Adonis & Abbey Publishers Ltd.

Konare, Adame Ba. History, Democracy, Values: New Lines of Reflection. 2008. 56p. pap. (978-2-86978-258-7(6)) Council for the Development of Social Science Research in Africa SEN. Dist: Michigan State Univ. Pr.

Kondlo, Kwandiwe & Ejiogu, Chinenyengozi, eds. Africa in Focus: Governance in the 21st Century. 2011. (Africa in Focus Ser.). (ENG.). 400p. pap. 48.95 (978-0-7969-2344-8(2)) Human Sciences Research Council ZAF. Dist: Independent Pubs. Group.

Konings, Piet. Neoliberal Bandwagonism: Civil society & the politics of belonging in Anglophone Cameroon. 2009. 274p. pap. (978-9956-558-23-0(0)) Langaa Research & Publishing Common Initiative Group CMR. Dist: Michigan State Univ. Pr.

Konings, Piet. The Politics of Neoliberal Reforms in Africa State & Civil Society in Cameroon. 2011. 346p. pap. (978-9956-717-41-5(X)) Langaa Research & Publishing Common Initiative Group.

Kotele, Mothepane. Identities of News-Workers in a State-Owned Newspaper. 2011. 124p. pap. (978-3-8443-2880-6(7)) Lambert Academic Publishing.

Krabacher, Thomas, et al. Africa. (Global Studies). (ENG., Illus.). 320p. (C). 12th ed. 2008. pap. 50.00 (978-0-07-337977-7(8), 0073379778) 13th ed. 2010. pap. 50.00 (978-0-07-352776-5(9), 0073527769) McGraw-Hill Higher Education. (McGraw-Hill/Dushkin).

Krabacher, Thomas, et al. Global Studies: Africa. 14th ed. 2012. (Global Studies). (ENG., Illus.). 448p. (C). pap. 50.00 (978-0-07-802623-2(7), 0078026237, McGraw-Hill/Dushkin) McGraw-Hill Higher Education.

Kuwali, Dan. Persuasive Prevention: Towards a Mechanism for Implementing Article 4(h) & R2P by the African Union. 2009. (NAI Discussion Papers). 60p. pap. 12.95 (978-91-7106-650-3(0)) Nordiska Afrikainstitutet SWE. Dist: Stylus Publishing, LLC.

Larmer, Miles, et al. Social Movements & Anti-Globalization in Africa. 2012. (ENG.). 260p. pap. 17.00 (978-1-60846-120-2(3)) Haymarket Bks.

Lata, Leenco. Peacekeeping As State Building: Current Challenges in the Horn of Africa. 2011. (Illus.). x, 206p. (978-1-56902-352-5(2)); pap. (978-1-56902-353-2(0)) Red Sea Pr.

Latigo, Alfred A. R. The Best Options for Afric: 11 Political, Economic & Divine Principles. 2009. 236p. 35.00 (978-1-4269-1918-3(2)) Trafford Publishing.

—The Best Options for Africa: 11 Political, Economic & Divine Principles. 2009. 236p. 35.00 (978-1-4269-0767-8(2)) Trafford Publishing.

Laucci, Cyril. Digest of Jurisprudence of the Special Court for Sierra Leone: 2003-2005. 2006. 820p. (978-90-04-15234-2(2)) BRILL.

Lawson, Kay, et al, eds. Political Parties & Democracy Vol. 4: Africa & Oceania. 2010. (Political Parties in Context Ser.). (Illus.). 283p. 44.95 (978-0-313-35302-4(6), C35302, Praeger Pubs.) Greenwood Publishing Group, Inc.

Lee, Margaret C. & Nzongola-Ntalaja, Georges, eds. The State & Democracy in Africa. (FRE & ENG., Illus.). 232p. (978-0-7974-1745-8(1)) Southern African Research & Documentation Centre.

Lemarchand, Rene. The Dynamics of Violence in Central Africa. 2009. (National & Ethnic Conflict in the 21st Century Ser.). (Illus.). 344p. (C). pap. 27.50 (978-0-8122-2090-2(0)) Univ. of Pennsylvania Pr.

Levitt, Jeremy I. Illegal Peace in Africa: An Inquiry into the Legality of Power-Sharing with African Warlords, Rebels, & Junta. 2012. (ENG.). 314p. 99.00 (978-0-521-88868-4(9)) Cambridge Univ. Pr.

Lifshitz, Fima. An African Journey Through Its Art. 2009. 236p. pap. 75.99 (978-1-4389-3450-1(5)) AuthorHouse.

Lindberg, Staffan I. Democracy & Elections in Africa. 2006. (ENG., Illus.). 248p. (gr. 17). per. 27.95 (978-0-8018-8333-0(4)) Johns Hopkins Univ. Pr.

Lopes, Carlos, ed. Africa's Contemporary Challenges: The Legacy of Amilcar Cabral. 2009. (Illus.). VIII, 144p. 125.00 (978-0-415-56048-1(9)) Routledge.

Lukong, V. The Cameroon Nigeria Border Dispute. Management & Resolution, 1981-2011: Management & Resolution, 1981-2011. 2011. 236p. pap. (978-9956-717-59-0(2)) Langaa Research & Publishing Common Initiative Group.

Lund, Christian, ed. Twilight Institutions: Public Authority & Local Politics in Africa. 2007. (Development & Change Special Issues Ser.). (ENG., Illus.). 288p. per. 39.95 (978-1-4051-5528-1(0), Wiley-Blackwell) Wiley, John & Sons, Inc.

Lushaba, Lwazi. Development As Modernity, Modernity As Development. 2009. (Illus.). 78p. pap. (978-2-86978-252-5(7)) Council for the Development of Social Science Research in Africa SEN. Dist: Michigan State Univ. Pr.

Lust, Ellen M. & Ndegwa, Stephen N., eds. Governing Africa¿s Changing Societies: Dynamics of Reform. 2012. 180p. 55.00 (978-1-58826-834-1(9)) Rienner, Lynne Pubs.

Lyman, Princeton N. & Dorff, Patricia, eds. Beyond Humanitarianism: What You Need to Know about Africa & Why It Matters. 2007. (ENG.). 252p. per. 19.95 (978-0-87609-371-9(3)) Council on Foreign Relations.

Lyons & Lyons, Terrence. Conflict Management & African Politics: Ripeness, Bargaining, & Mediation. Lyons & Lyons, Terrence, eds. 2008. (Routledge Studies in Security & Conflict Management Ser.). (Illus.). XIII, 163p. 150.00 (978-0-415-44301-2(6)) Routledge.

Maathai, Wangari. The Challenge for Africa. 2010. (ENG.). 336p. pap. 15.95 (978-0-307-39028-8(4), Anchor) Knopf Doubleday Publishing Group.

Madut, Akok. Clash of the Major Powers in Afric. 2011. 80p. pap. (978-3-8443-2041-1(5)) Lambert Academic Publishing.

Makinda, Samuel M. & Okumu, F. Wafula. The African Union: Challenges of Globalization, Security, & Governance. 2007. (Global Institutions Ser.). (ENG., Illus.). 232p. (C). 140.00 (978-0-415-40350-4(2)) Routledge.

Mandova, Evans. National Patriotic Culture. 2011. 76p. pap. (978-3-8443-3249-0(9)) Lambert Academic Publishing.

Mangala, Jack. New Security Threats & Crises in Africa: Regional & International Perspectives. Mangala, Jack, ed. 2010. (ENG., Illus.). 296p. 89.00 (978-0-230-10796-0(6)) Palgrave Macmillan.

Mangu, André, et al. Obama's Election: Lessons for the Word, Africa, & US Foreign Policy. 2011. 216p. pap. (978-3-8443-1292-8(7)) Lambert Academic Publishing.

Marobela, Motsomi Ndala. Political Economy of Botswana Public Sector Management. 2010. 620p. pap. (978-3-639-22841-0(3)) VDM Verlag Dr. Mueller e.K.

Maundi, Mohammed O., et al. Getting In: Mediators' Entry into the Settlement of African Conflicts. 2006. (Illus.). 256p. pap. 19.95 (978-1-929223-62-6(5)) U. S. Institute of Peace Pr. (USIP Pr.).

Mazama, Ama. Africa in the 21st Century: Toward a New Future. 2007. (African Studies: History, Politics, Economics & Culture Ser.). 286p. 138.00 (978-0-415-95773-1(7)) Routledge.

Mazrui, Ali A., et al, eds. Africa's Islamic Experience: History, Culture & Politics. 2008. 278p. 29.95 (978-1-932705-78-2(3)) New Dawn Pr., Inc.

Mbaku, John. Corruption in Africa: Causes Consequences, & Cleanups. 2010. (ENG.). 402p. pap. 38.95 (978-0-7391-1317-2(8)) Lexington Bks.

Mbaku, John Mukum. Corruption in Africa: Causes Consequences, & Cleanups. 2007. (ENG.). 402p. 81.99 (978-0-7391-1316-5(X)) Lexington Bks.

Mbanaso, Michael U. & Korieh, Chima J. Minorities & the State in Africa. 2010. 370p. (978-1-60497-669-4(1)) Cambria Pr.

Mbile, Nerius Namaso. Cameroon Political Story Memories of an Authentic Eye Witness. 2011. 310p. pap. (978-9956-717-77-4(0)) Langaa Research & Publishing Common Initiative Group.

McCracken, John. Politics & Christianity in Malawi 1875-1940 3rd Edition: The Impact of the Livingstonia Mission in the Northern Province. 3rd ed. 2008. 380p. pap. (978-99908-87-50-1(0)) Kachere Series, Bks. on Religion, Theology & Society in Malawi MWI. Dist: Michigan State Univ. Pr.

McDonald, David A. Electric Capitalism: Recolonising Africa on the Power Grid. McDonald, David A. & McDonald David, eds. 2008. (ENG., Illus.). 536p. 136.50 (978-1-84407-714-4(4)) Routledge.

McGowan, Patrick J., et al, eds. Power, Wealth & Global Equity: An International Relations Textbook for Africa. 3rd ed. 2007. (ENG., Illus.). 441p. pap. 67.95 (978-1-919713-93-9(X)) Juta Academic ZAF. Dist: Independent Pubs. Group.

McGrath, Conor. Interest Groups & Lobbying in Latin America, Africa, the Middle East, & Asia: Essays on Drug Trafficking, Chemical Manufacture, Exchange Rates, & Women's Interests. McGrath, Conor, ed. 2009.Tr. of Essays on Drug Trafficking, Chemical Manufacture, Exchange Rates, & Women's Interests. (Illus.). 432p. 129.95 (978-0-7734-4694-6(X)) Mellen, Edwin Pr., The.

McQueen, Jeremy S. Economic, Political, & Social Issues of Africa. 2012. (Series: African Political, Economic, & Security Issues Ser.). 262p. 129.00 (978-1-61209-957-6(2)) Nova Science Pubs., Inc.

Mekonnen, Teferi & Teferi, Mekonnen. The Blue Nile Issue: A History of Hydropolitics,1884-1974. 2011. 144p. pap. (978-3-639-32450-1(1)) VDM Verlag Dr. Mueller e.K.

Mensah, Joseph A., ed. Neoliberalism & Globalization in Africa: Contestations on the Embattled Continent. 2008. (ENG., Illus.). 288p. 100.00 (978-0-230-60781-1(0)) Palgrave Macmillan.

Mentan, Tatah. Democratizing or Reconfiguring Predatory Autocracy? Myths & Realities in Africa Today. 2009. 90p. pap. (978-9956-558-57-5(5)) Langaa Research & Publishing Common Initiative Group CMR. Dist: Michigan State Univ. Pr.

—Held Together by Pins: Liberal Democracy under Siege in Africa. 2007. (978-1-59221-520-1(3)); 322p. pap. (978-1-59221-521-8(1)) Africa World Pr.

—The Recolonization of Africa: Revised Edition. 2nd ed. 2011. (Illus.). 264p. lib. bdg. (978-1-936320-17-2(7)) Academica Pr., LLC.

Mercer, Claire, et al. Development & the African Diaspora: Place & the Politics of Home. 2008. (ENG., Illus.). 272p. 108.95 (978-1-84277-900-2(1)); pap. 34.95 (978-1-84277-901-9(X)) Zed Bks., Ltd. GBR. Dist: Macmillan.

Meredith, Martin. The Fate of Africa: A History of the Continent since Independence. 2011. (ENG., Illus.). 816p. pap. 21.99 (978-1-61039-071-2(7)) PublicAffairs.

Miles, William F. S., ed. Political Islam in West Africa: State-Society Relations Transformed. 2007. (Illus.). 200p. lib. bdg. 52.50 (978-1-58826-527-2(7)) Rienner, Lynne Pubs.

Milner, James H. S. Refugees, the State & the Politics of Asylum in Africa. 2009. (St. Antony's Ser.). (ENG., Illus.). 288p. 95.00 (978-0-230-21504-7(1)) Palgrave Macmillan.

Minteh, Binneh. Democratization & Political Instability in West Afric: 1960-2010. 2010. 120p. pap. (978-3-8383-8022-3(3)) Lambert Academic Publishing.

Mlambo, Norman, ed. Violent Conflicts, Fragile Peace: Perspectives on Africa's Security Problems (PB) 2008. 304p. pap. (978-1-905068-98-2(0)) Adonis & Abbey Publishers Ltd.

—Violent Conflicts, Fragile Peace: Perspectives on Africa's Security Problems(HB) 2008. 304p. (978-1-905068-99-9(9)) Adonis & Abbey Publishers Ltd.

Moatlhaping, Segametsi Oreeditse. Indigenous Governance Systems. 2011. 144p. pap. (978-3-8443-9922-6(4)) Lambert Academic Publishing.

Mohamoud, Abdullah, ed. Shaping a New Africa. 2007. 208p. per. 35.00 (978-90-6832-583-6(3)) Royal Tropical Institute Pr. (KIT (Koninklijk Instituut voor de Tropen) NLD. Dist: Stylus Publishing, LLC.

Mohan, Giles & Zack-Williams, Tunde, eds. The Politics of Transition: State, Democracy, & Economic Development in Africa. 288p. 99.95 *(978-1-59221-152-4(6))* Africa World Pr.

Mokoena, Benjamin. The Political Economy of Burundi. 2010. 180p. pap. *(978-3-8383-6930-3(0))* Lambert Academic Publishing.

Morris-Evans, Janet. Into Africa, a Vision of Hope & a Sanctuary Born. 2009. 80p. pap. 9.95 *(978-1-60693-630-6(1)*, Eloquent Bks.) AEG Literary Publishing Services, Inc.

Moseley, William. Clashing Views on African Issues. 4th ed. 2011. (Taking Sides Ser.). (ENG., Illus.). 464p. (C). pap. 48.00 *(978-0-07-805008-4(1)*, 0078050081, McGraw-Hill/Dushkin) McGraw-Hill Higher Education.

Moseley, William G. Clashing Views on African Issues. 3rd ed. 2008. (Taking Sides Ser.). (ENG.). 416p. (C). pap. 48.00 *(978-0-07-351518-2(3)*, 0073515183, McGraw-Hill/Dushkin) McGraw-Hill Higher Education.

Moshi, Lioba. Democracy & Culture. 2008. (Illus.). 276p. *(978-1-905068-20-3(4))* Adonis & Abbey Publishers Ltd.

Moshi, Lioba & Osman, Abdulahi A. Democracy & Culture: An African Perspective(PB) 2008. (Illus.). 264p. pap. *(978-1-905068-92-0(1))* Adonis & Abbey Publishers Ltd.

Moto, Francis. Language, Power & Society. 2009. 242p. pap. 39.00 *(978-1-86888-434-6(1))* Unisa Press / Uitgewers GBR. Dist: International Specialized Bk. Services.

Moyo, Bhekinkosi, ed. Africa in Global Power Play: Debates, Challenges & Potential Reforms. 2007. 364p. per. *(978-1-905068-62-3(X))* Adonis & Abbey Publishers Ltd.

—Africa in Global Power Play: Debates, Challenges & Potential Reforms (HB) 2007. 364p. *(978-1-905068-61-6(1))* Adonis & Abbey Publishers Ltd.

Moyo, Sam & Yeros, Paris, eds. Reclaiming the Nation: The Return of the National Question in Africa, Asia & Latin America, 1 vol. 2011. (ENG., Illus.). 288p. 38.00 *(978-0-7453-3082-2(7))*; lib. bdg. 115.00 *(978-0-7453-3083-9(5))* Pluto Pr. GBR. Dist: Macmillan.

Muiu, Mueni wa & Martin, Guy. A New Paradigm of the African State: Fundi Wa Afrika. 2008. (ENG., Illus.). 288p. 100.00 *(978-0-230-60780-4(2))* Palgrave Macmillan.

Mukong, Albert. Prisoner Without a Crime Disciplining Dissent in Ahidjo's Cameroon. 2009. 158p. pap. *(978-9956-558-34-6(6))* Langaa Research & Publishing Common Initiative Group CMR. Dist: Michigan State Univ. Pr.

Muluneh, Yitages. Supervision by the Centre to Regions in South Africa & Ethiopi. 2011. 80p. pap. ***(978-3-8443-3107-3(7))*** Lambert Academic Publishing.

Munene, Ishmael. An Interdisciplinary Primer in African Studies. 2011. (ENG., Illus.). 330p. 85.00 *(978-0-7391-6597-3(6))* Lexington Bks.

Munene, Ishmael & Munene, Ishmael I. An Interdisciplinary Primer in African Studies. 2011. (ENG., Illus.). 330p. pap. 34.95 *(978-0-7391-6598-0(4))* Lexington Bks.

Munene, Ishmael I. An Interdisciplinary Primer in African Studies. 2011. (Illus.). xiii, 308p. ***(978-0-7391-6887-5(8))*** Lexington Bks.

Mungai, Rose & World Bank. Africa Development Indicators 2011. 2011. (ENG.). cd-rom 50.00 *(978-0-8213-8782-5(0)*, 9780821387825) World Bank Pubns.

Murangira, Emmanuel. Economics of Ethnic Identities. 2011. 96p. pap. ***(978-3-8433-9257-0(9))*** Lambert Academic Publishing.

Murindwa-Rutanga. Politics, Religion & Power in the Great Lakes Region. 2011. (Illus.). 270p. pap. ***(978-2-86978-492-5(9))*** Council for the Development of Social Science Research in Africa.

Murithi, Timothy & Murithi, Tim. The Ethics of Peacebuilding. Dower, Nigel, ed. 2009. (Edinburgh Studies in World Ethics Ser.). (ENG.). 208p. (gr. 17). 95.00 *(978-0-7486-2447-8(3))*; pap. 32.50 *(978-0-7486-2448-5(1))* Edinburgh Univ. Pr. GBR. Dist: Columbia Univ. Pr.

Musingafi, Maxwell, et al. Managing Conflict in Afric. 2011. 216p. pap. ***(978-3-8443-8234-1(8))*** Lambert Academic Publishing.

—Post-Conflict Reconstruction. 2011. 200p. pap. ***(978-3-8454-1440-9(5))*** Lambert Academic Publishing.

Mwakikagile, Godfrey. Africa Is in A Mess What Went Wrong and. 2006. pap. *(978-0-9802534-7-4(0))* New Africa Pr.

—Tanzania under Mwalimu Nyerere Reflectio. 2006. pap. *(978-0-9802534-9-8(7))* New Africa Pr.

Nasong'o, Shadrack Wanjala, ed. The African Search for Stable Forms of Statehood: Essays in Political Criticism. 438p. 129.95 *(978-0-7734-5237-4(0))* Mellen, Edwin Pr., The.

Ndulo, Muna, ed. Democartic Reform in Africa: The Impact on Governance & Poverty Alleviation. 2006. (Illus.). 320p. pap. 34.95 *(978-0-85255-946-8(1)*, Currey, James) Boydell & Brewer, Ltd. GBR. Dist: Boydell & Brewer, Inc.

—Democratic Reform in Africa: Its Impact on Governance & Poverty Alleviation. 2006. (Illus.). 304p. *(978-0-8214-1721-8(5))*; per. *(978-0-8214-1722-5(3))* Boydell & Brewer, Ltd. (Currey, James).

—Democratic Reform in Africa: The Impact on Governance & Poverty Alleviation. 2006. (Illus.). 320p. 90.00 *(978-0-85255-945-1(3)*, Currey, James) Boydell & Brewer, Ltd. GBR. Dist: Boydell & Brewer, Inc.

Ndulu, Benno, et al. Challenges of African Growth: Opportunities, Constraints, & Strategic Directions. 2007. (Stand Alones Ser.). (ENG., Illus.). 276p. per. 29.95 *(978-0-8213-6882-4(6)*, 9780821368824) World Bank Pubns.

Ndulu, Benno J., et al, eds. The Political Economy of Economic Growth in Africa, 1960-2000, 2 vols. 2007. (ENG., Illus.). 760p. 180.00 *(978-0-521-87849-4(7))* Cambridge Univ. Pr.

Ndulu, Benno J., et al. The Political Economy of Economic Growth in Africa, 1960-2000, 2 vols., Vol. 1. 2009. (ENG., Illus.). 470p. pap. 52.00 *(978-0-521-12775-2(0))* Cambridge Univ. Pr.

Ndura-Ouédraogo, Elavie, et al. Seeds Bearing Fruit: Pan African Peace Action for the 21st Century. 2011. xxxi, 475p. *(978-1-59221-781-6(8))*; (ENG., Illus.). 476p. pap. *(978-1-59221-782-3(6))* Africa World Pr.

Ngunjiri, Faith Wambura. Women's Spiritual Leadership in Africa: Tempered Radicals & Critical Servant Leaders. 2010. (Illus.). 224p. 60.00 *(978-1-4384-2977-9(0))* State Univ. of New York Pr.

Ngwane, Mwakimu George. The Power in the Writer: Collected Essays on Culture, Democracy & Development in Africa. 2008. 196p. *(978-9956-558-37-7(0))* Langaa Research & Publishing Common Initiative Group CMR. Dist: Michigan State Univ. Pr.

Nhema, Alfred & Zeleza, Paul Tiyambe, eds. The Resolution of African Conflicts: The Management of Conflict Resolution & Post-Conflict Reconstruction. 2008. (Illus.). 207p. pap. 24.95 *(978-0-8214-1808-6(4))* Ohio Univ. Pr.

—The Roots of African Conflicts: The Causes & Costs. 2008. (ENG., Illus.). 288p. pap. 24.95 *(978-0-8214-1809-3(2))* Ohio Univ. Pr.

Nhema, Alfred G. & Zeleza, Paul Tiyambe, eds. The Roots of African Conflicts: The Causes & Costs. 2008. 256p. pap. 29.95 *(978-1-84701-300-2(7)*, Currey, James) Boydell & Brewer, Ltd. GBR. Dist: Boydell & Brewer, Inc.

Niang, Abdoulaye. Globalization Key Peace Prosperity Africa. 2008. 144p. pap. 12.95 *(978-1-57197-846-2(1))* Pentland Pr., Inc.

Nicolini, Beatrice. Studies in Witchcraft, Magic, War & Peace in Africa: 19th & 20th Centuries. 2006. 400p. 119.95 *(978-0-7734-5727-0(5))* Mellen, Edwin Pr., The.

Nkuubi, James. When 'Messiahs' Turn 'Persecutors' 2010. 68p. pap. *(978-3-8383-1752-6(1))* Lambert Academic Publishing.

Ntsou, Bakwowi Jeshma. The Role of Agriculture to Reduce Poverty in Sub Sahara Afric. 2011. 88p. pap. ***(978-3-8454-0352-6(7))*** Lambert Academic Publishing.

Nugent, Paul. Africa since Independence. 2nd rev. ed. 2012. (ENG., Illus.). 680p. (C). 95.00 ***(978-0-230-27287-3(8))*** Palgrave Macmillan.

Nyamnjoh, Francis B. Mass Media & Democratisation in Cameroon in the Early 1990s. 2011. 208p. pap. ***(978-9956-717-18-7(5))*** Langaa Research & Publishing Common Initiative Group.

Obadan, Mike I. The Economic & Social Impact of Privatisation of State-Owned Enterprises in Afric. 2008. 92p. pap. *(978-2-86978-228-0(4))* Council for the Development of Social Science Research in Africa SEN. Dist: Michigan State Univ. Pr.

Odetola, Olatunde. Military Regimes & Development: A Comparative Analysis in African Societies. 2011. (ENG.). 216p. 95.00 *(978-0-415-60184-9(3))* Routledge.

Odjo, A. Lassissi. Between the Lines. 2007. (African Studies). (ENG.). 344p. 125.00 *(978-0-415-97456-1(9)*, RT19958) Routledge.

Okafor, Victor Oguejiofor, ed. Nigeria's Stumbling Democracy & Its Implications for Africa's Democratic Movement, 1 vol. 2008. (PSI Reports). (Illus.). 208p. 75.00 *(978-0-313-35586-8(X)*, C35586, Praeger Security International) Greenwood Publishing Group, Inc.

Okereke, Chukwumerije & Agupusi, Patricia. Socio-Economic Development in Africa. 2012. (Routledge Studies in African Politics & International Relations Ser.). (ENG.). 240p. (C). 135.00 ***(978-0-415-52574-9(8))*** Routledge.

Olusegun, Abejide. Ibb - Smart but Foolish: Reasons He Can't Be the Next President. 2010. 208p. 25.04 *(978-1-4269-4509-0(4))*; pap. 15.04 *(978-1-4269-4508-3(6))* Trafford Publishing.

Ondeng, Pete. Africa's Moment. 2010. 108p. pap., pap. 12.00 *(978-0-615-22190-8(4))* Asset Capital, Ltd.

Onitiri-Abiola, Modupe. Farewell to Poverty: Let There Be Light in Africa. 2007. pap. 9.00 *(978-0-8059-7377-8(X))* Dorrance Publishing Co., Inc.

Orji, Madukar. Lust for Corruption. 2009. 258p. 29.99 *(978-1-4415-4940-2(4))*; pap. 19.99 *(978-1-4415-4939-6(0))* Xlibris Corp.

Orosz, Kenneth J. Religious Conflict & the Evolution of Language Policy in German & French Cameroon, 1885-1939. 2007. (American University Studies IX: History Ser.). (C). 82.95 *(978-0-8204-7909-5(8))* Lang, Peter Publishing, Inc.

Oshionebo, Evaristus. Regulating Transnational Corporations in Domestic & International Regimes: An African Case Study. 2009. (ENG.). 384p. *(978-0-8020-9940-2(8))* Univ. of Toronto Pr.

Ostergard, Robert L., Jr., et al, eds. Power, Politics, & the African Condition: Collected Essays of Ali A. Mazrui. 310p. 99.95 *(978-1-59221-170-8(4))* Africa World Pr.

An Overview of U.S. Policy in Africa: Hearing Before the Subcommittee on Africa & Global Health of the Committee on Foreign Affairs, House of Representatives, One Hundred Eleventh Congress, Second Session, March 24, 2010. 2010. (Illus.). iii, 122p. *(978-0-16-086457-5(7)*, 552-070-41514-9) United States Government Printing Office.

Oxfam International. The African Women's Protocol: A Tool to Mobilise Resources for Financing Gender Equality & Women's Empowerment. 2010. (Programme Insights Ser.). 10.95 *(978-0-85598-641-4(7))* Oxfam Publishing GBR. Dist: Stylus Publishing, LLC.

Oyeniyi, Bukola Adeyemi. The Ife-Modakeke Conflict, 1800-2000. 2010. 100p. pap. *(978-3-639-28690-8(1))* VDM Verlag Dr. Mueller e.K.

Oyoo Yaye, Christopher. Towards a Meaningful Democracy in Keny. 2011. 120p. pap. ***(978-3-8443-0539-5(4))*** Lambert Academic Publishing.

Panikkar, K. M. The Afro-Asian States & their Problems. 2011. (ENG.). 128p. 90.00 *(978-0-415-60141-2(X))* Routledge.

Péan, Pierre. Carnages: Les Guerres Secrètes des Grandes Puissances en Afrique. 2010. (FRE., Illus.). 570p. pap. *(978-2-213-63806-5(3))* Fayard, Artheme, Librairie.

Peterside, Chamberlain S. WEALTH EFFECT Focus on Economic Reform & Sustainable Development in Nigeria. 2008. 288p. pap. 15.50 *(978-1-4357-1201-0(3))* Lulu Enterprises Inc.

Pinkney, Robert. NGOs, Africa & the Global Order. 2009. (ENG., Illus.). 288p. 100.00 *(978-0-230-54716-2(8))* Palgrave Macmillan.

Pitcher, M. Anne. Party Politics & Economic Reform in Africa's Democracies. 2012. (African Studies). (ENG., Illus.). 328p. pap. 29.99 ***(978-0-521-73826-2(1))*** Cambridge Univ. Pr.

Poku, Nana, et al. Politics in Africa. 2011. (ENG., Illus.). 240p. pap. 26.95 *(978-1-84277-982-8(6))* Zed Bks., Ltd. GBR. Dist: Macmillan.

Pretorius, Joelien. African Politics: Beyond the Third Wave of Democratisation. 2009. 240p. pap. 35.95 *(978-0-7021-7736-1(9))* Double Storey Bks. ZAF. Dist: International Publishers Marketing.

Pribenska, Eliska. Managed Liberalization in Southern & Eastern Afric. 2010. 140p. pap. *(978-3-8383-6447-6(3))* Lambert Academic Publishing.

Ramuhala, Mashudu Godfrey. Military Intervention in Africa after the Cold War. 2011. 124p. pap. ***(978-3-8383-9654-5(5))*** Lambert Academic Publishing.

Rasheed. Development, Participation & Democracy in Africa: Four Essays. xii, 148p. *(978-0-7983-0127-5(9))* Africa Institute of South Africa.

Reid, Richard, ed. Eritrea's External Relations: Understanding Its Regional Role & Foreign Policy. 2009. (ENG., Illus.). 208p. pap. 26.95 *(978-1-86203-201-9(7))* Royal Institute of International Affairs GBR. Dist: Brookings Institution Pr.

—Eritrea's External Relations: Understanding Its Regional Role & Foreign Policy. 2009. (ENG., Illus.). 208p. 52.95 *(978-1-86203-200-2(9))* Royal Institute of International Affairs GBR. Dist: Brookings Institution Pr.

Renders, Marleen. Consider Somaliland: State-Building with Traditional Leaders & Institutions. 2012. (African Social Studies Ser.). (ENG., Illus.). 304p. pap. ***(978-90-04-21848-2(3))*** BRILL.

Richards, Audrey & Kuper, Adam, eds. Councils in Action. 2009. (Cambridge Papers in Social Anthropology Ser.). (ENG.). 224p. pap. 33.99 *(978-0-521-11341-0(5))* Cambridge Univ. Pr.

Richey, Lisa Ann & Richey, Lisa Ann A. Population Politics & Development: From the Policies to the Clinics. 2007. (ENG., Illus.). 288p. 95.00 *(978-0-230-60292-2(4))* Palgrave Macmillan.

Rohleder, Poul, et al, eds. HIV/AIDs in South Africa 25 Years On: A Psychosocial Perspective. 2009. (ENG., Illus.). xix, 393p. 159.00 *(978-1-4419-0305-1(4)*, 1441903054) Springer.

Rothchild, Donald & Harbeson, John W. Africa in World Politics: Reforming Political Order. 4th ed. 2008. (ENG., Illus.). 424p. pap. 44.00 *(978-0-8133-4364-8(X))* Perseus Bks. Group.

Rowan, Christopher. Politics of Water in Africa: The European Union's Role in Development Aid Partnership. 2009. (International Library of African Studies). (ENG.). 320p. 89.00 *(978-1-84511-685-9(2)*, Tauris Academic Studies) I. B. Tauris & Co., Ltd. GBR. Dist: Macmillan.

Rukaranghira, Eugene. Picking up the Pieces in the Land of Multiple Boundaries. 2011. 76p. pap. ***(978-3-8443-0511-1(4))*** Lambert Academic Publishing.

Runge, Jargen, ed. Geological Resources & Good Governance in Central Africa. 2011. (ENG., Illus.). 292p. 99.95 *(978-0-415-58267-4(9)*, CRC Press) Taylor & Francis Group GBR. Dist: Taylor & Francis Group.

Rwengabo, Sabastiano. Beyond the Spiritual. 2011. 188p. pap. ***(978-3-8433-8896-2(2))*** Lambert Academic Publishing.

Sage, Andre Le. African Counterterrorism Cooperation: Assessing Regional & Subregional Initiatives. 2007. 240p. (C). 50.00 *(978-1-59797-176-8(6))*; pap. 25.00 *(978-1-59797-177-5(4))* Potomac Bks., Inc.

Saine, Abdoulaye. The Paradox of Third-Wave Democratization in Africa: The Gambia under AFPRC-APRC Rule, 1994-2008. 2010. (ENG.). 198p. pap. 29.50 *(978-0-7391-2922-7(8))* Lexington Bks.

Salih, M. A. Environmental Politics & Liberation in Contemporary Africa. 2010. (Environment & Policy Ser.). (Illus.). 200p. pap. 139.00 *(978-90-481-5196-7(1)*, 9048151961) Springer.

Samual Makinda Staff & Okumu, F. Wafula. The African Union: Challenges of Globalization, Security, & Governance. 2007. (Global Institutions Ser.). (Illus.). XVIII, 214p. pap. 29.95 *(978-0-415-40349-8(9))* Routledge.

Sanders, Peter. Throwing down White Man: Cape Rule & Misrule in Colonial Lesotho, 1871-1884. Huws, Ursula, ed. 2011. 306p. pap. 37.95 ***(978-0-85036-654-9(2))*** Merlin Pr. Ltd. GBR. Dist: Independent Pubs. Group.

Sany Nzima, Joseph. Reintegration of Ex-Combatants: A balancing Act. 2010. 132p. pap. *(978-3-8383-8273-9(0))* Lambert Academic Publishing.

Sarsar, Saliba & Adekunle, Julius O. Democracy in Africa: Political Changes & Challenges. 2012. 346p. pap. 42.00 ***(978-1-61163-002-2(9))*** Carolina Academic Pr.

Schilder. Quest for Self-Esteem: State, Islam, & Mundang Ethnicity in Northern Cameroon. (Illus.). xiv, 283p. *(978-90-5448-021-1(1))* Afrika-Studiecentrum.

Sebarenzi, Joseph. God Sleeps in Rwanda: A Journey of Transformation. 2009. (ENG., Illus.). 272p. 25.00 *(978-1-4165-7573-3(1)*, Beyond Words/Atria Bks.) Atria Bks.

Seely, Jennifer C. The Legacies of Transition Governments in Africa: The Cases of Benin & Togo. 2009. (ENG.). 224p. 84.00 *(978-0-230-61390-4(X))* Palgrave Macmillan.

Seidman, Ann Willcox, et al. Africa's Challenge: Using Law for Good Governance & Development. 2006. (Illus.). viii, 228p. *(978-1-59221-470-9(3))*; 360p. pap. *(978-1-59221-471-6(1))* Africa World Pr.

Selassie, Bereket Habte. Wounded Nation: How a Once Promising Eritrea Was Betrayed & Its Future Compromised. 2011. (ENG., Illus.). 314p. pap. *(978-1-56902-340-2(9))* Red Sea Pr.

Senghor, Jeggan Colley. The Politics of Senegambian Integration, 1958-1994. 2008. (Illus.). 335p. pap. 79.95 *(978-3-03911-132-9(9))* Lang, Peter Publishing, Inc.

Sesay, Amadu & Ukeje, Charles. Post-War Regimes & State Reconstruction in Liberia & Sierra Leone. 2009. 120p. pap. *(978-2-86978-256-3(X))* Council for the Development of Social Science Research in Africa SEN. Dist: Michigan State Univ. Pr.

Sethi, Rumina. The Politics of Postcolonialism: Globalisation & the Nation-State, 1 vol. 2011. (ENG.). 216p. lib. bdg. 90.00 *(978-0-7453-2364-0(2))* Pluto Pr. GBR. Dist: Macmillan.

Shivji, Issa G. Where Is Uhuru? Reflections on the Struggle for Democracy in Africa. 2009. (ENG.). 258p. pap. 27.95 ***(978-1-906387-46-4(X))*** Pambuzuka Pr. GBR. Dist: Independent Pubs. Group.

Simms, Rupe. A Gramscian Analysis of the Role of Religion in Politics: Case Studies in Domination, Accommodation, & Resistance in Africa & Europe. 2010. 316p. 119.95 *(978-0-7734-3754-8(1))* Mellen, Edwin Pr., The.

Sitoe, Eduardo J. Post-Colonial Political Transformations in Angola & Mozambique. 2011. 456p. pap. ***(978-3-8443-0078-9(3))*** Lambert Academic Publishing.

Skaine, Rosemarie. Women Political Leaders in Africa. 2007. (ENG., Illus.). 216p. per. 49.95 *(978-0-7864-3299-8(3))* McFarland & Co., Inc. Pubs.

Smith, James Howard & Hackett, Rosalind I. J., eds. Displacing the State: Religion & Conflict in Neoliberal Africa. 2011. (Kroc Inst Religion Conflict & Peacebldg Ser.). (ENG.). 288p. pap. 30.00 ***(978-0-268-03095-7(2))*** Univ. of Notre Dame Pr.

Soderbaum, Taylor. Afro-Regions: the Dynamics of Cross-Border Micro-Regionalism: In Africa. 2008. (Illus.). 210p. pap. 39.95 *(978-91-7106-618-3(7))* Nordiska Afrikainstitutet SWE. Dist: Stylus Publishing, LLC.

Sokoine Martine, Jackson. International Children's Rights Law Versus Maasai Traditional Culture: A Case of Loitokitok District, Kenya. 2011. 136p. pap. ***(978-3-639-33260-5(1))*** VDM Verlag Dr. Mueller e.K.

Soyinka-Airewele, Peyi & Edozie, Rita Kiki, eds. Reframing Contemporary Africa: Politics, Economics, & Culture in the Global Era. rev. ed. 2010. 412p. (C). pap. 44.00 *(978-0-87289-407-5(X))* CQ Pr.

Ssemambo, Joseph. Decentralization & Local Governance in Services Provision. 2010. 188p. pap. *(978-3-8383-5923-6(2))* Lambert Academic Publishing.

Stapenhurst, Frederick, et al, eds. African Parliamentary Reform. 2011. (Routledge Research in Comparative Politics Ser.). (ENG., Illus.). 192p. (C). 130.00 *(978-0-415-67723-3(8))* Routledge.

Strauss, Julia C. & O'Brien, Donal Cruise, eds. Staging Politics: Power & Performance in Asia & Africa. 2007. (International Library of Political Studies). (ENG., Illus.). 288p. 89.00 *(978-1-84511-367-4(5))* I. B. Tauris & Co., Ltd. GBR. Dist: Macmillan.

Stuart, Andrew. Of Cargos Colonies & Kings. 2009. (ENG., Illus.). 256p. pap. 27.50 *(978-1-85043-978-3(8)*, Radcliffe Pr., The) I. B. Tauris & Co., Ltd. GBR. Dist: Macmillan.

Swart, Gerrie, ed. Leadership in Afric: Trends, Triumphs & Challenges. 2008. 108p. pap. *(978-1-906704-02-5(3))* Adonis & Abbey Publishers Ltd.

Taku, Michael Fontem. Fontem Defang: Reminiscences of Leadership in a Post Colonial African Kingdom. 2008. (Illus.). 387p. pap. *(978-0-9755261-5-6(4))* Nkemnji Global Tech.

Tande, Dibussi. Scribbles from the Den Essays on Politics & Collective Memory in Cameroon. 2009. 232p. pap. *(978-9956-558-91-9(5))* Langaa Research & Publishing Common Initiative Group CMR. Dist: Michigan State Univ. Pr.

Tangwa, B. No Trifling Matter: Contributions of an Uncompromising Critic to the Democratic Process in Cameroon. 2011. 244p. pap. ***(978-9956-717-47-7(9))*** Langaa Research & Publishing Common Initiative Group.

Tangwa, Godfrey B. I Spit on Their Graves: Testimony Relevant to the Democratization Struggle in Cameroon. 2010. 222p. pap. *(978-9956-616-26-8(5))* Langaa Research & Publishing Common Initiative Group CMR. Dist: Michigan State Univ. Pr.

Thiam, Thierno. Political Leadership & the Quest for Unity & Development in Afric. 2009. 88p. pap. *(978-3-639-14692-9(1))* VDM Verlag Dr. Mueller e.K.

Thiessen, Inga. A History Forgotten, a Revolution Misunderstood. 2011. 60p. pap. ***(978-3-8433-9420-8(2))*** Lambert Academic Publishing.

Thompson, Vincent B. Africa & Unity. Date not set. (Illus.). xxv, 412p. pap. 24.40 *(978-0-582-64522-6(0))* Addison-Wesley Longman, Ltd. GBR. Dist: Trans-Atlantic Pubns., Inc.

Thomson, Alex. An Introduction to African Politics. 3rd rev. ed. 2010. (ENG., Illus.). 312p. (C). 44.95 *(978-0-415-48287-5(9))*; 138.00 *(978-0-415-47956-1(8))* Routledge.

Tony, Barnett, et al. Politics in Africa: A New Introduction. 2011. (ENG., Illus.). 240p. 107.95 *(978-1-84277-981-1(8))* Zed Bks., Ltd. GBR. Dist: Macmillan.

Tshibengabo, Kamana. The, Rulers of Congo-Kinshasa: Felons at the Helm. 2011. (ENG.). 380p. pap. 20.95 ***(978-1-4327-8084-5(0))*** Outskirts Pr., Inc.

Tucker, Peter. The Mission Boy from Shebar: An Autobiography. 2011. (Illus.). 308p. pap. 18.81 ***(978-1-4567-8154-5(5))*** AuthorHouse.

Ubink, Janine. Traditional Authorities in Africa: Resurgence in an Era of Democratisation. 2008. (Law, Governance, & Development Ser.). 39p. pap. *(978-90-8728-052-9(1)*, Leiden Univ. Pr.) Amsterdam Univ. Pr.

Udogu, Ike E. African Renaissance in the Millennium: The Political, Social, & Economic Discourses on the Way Forward. 2007. (ENG., Illus.). 216p. 78.99 *(978-0-7391-2251-8(7))*; per. 30.50 *(978-0-7391-2252-5(5))* Lexington Bks.

United Nations (UN) Staff. Accountable Government in Africa: Perspectives from Public Law & Political Studies. Chirwa, Danwood M. & Nijzink, Lia, eds. 2012.

(ENG.). 460p. pap. 42.00 ***(978-92-808-1205-3(X))*** United Nations Univ. Pr. JPN. Dist: Brookings Institution Pr.

United Nations Development Programme. Assessment of Development Results: Burkina Faso. 2010. 88p. pap. 15.00 *(978-92-1-126274-2(7))* United Nations Pubns.

United Nations Economic Commission for Africa. African Governance Report 2011. 2012. (ENG.). 280p. pap. 29.95 ***(978-0-19-964505-3(1))*** Oxford Univ. Pr., Inc.

United Nations, Economic Commission for Africa Staff. African Governance Report 2009. 2009. (ENG., Illus.). 288p. 35.00 *(978-0-19-957429-2(4))* Oxford Univ. Pr., Inc.

United Nations University Staff. African Security Governance: Emerging Issues. Cawthra, Gavin, ed. 2010. (ENG.). 218p. pap. 32.00 *(978-92-808-1177-3(0))* United Nations Univ. Pr. JPN. Dist: Brookings Institution Pr.

Utas, Mats. African Conflicts & Informal Power: Big Men & Network. Utas, Matt, ed. 2012. (Africa Now Ser.). (ENG.). 288p. pap. 26.95 *(978-1-84813-882-7(2))* Zed Bks., Ltd. GBR. Dist: Macmillan.

Utas, Mats, ed. African Conflicts & Informal Power: Big Men Null. 2012. (Africa Now Ser.). (ENG.). 288p. 125.95 *(978-1-84813-883-4(0))* Zed Bks., Ltd. GBR. Dist: Macmillan

Villa-Vicencio, Charles. Walk with Us & Listen: Political Reconciliation in Africa. 2009. (ENG.). 248p. pap. 29.95 *(978-1-58901-572-2(X))* Georgetown Univ. Pr.

Villalón, Leonardo A. Islamic Society & State Power in Senegal: Disciples & Citizens in Fatick. 2006. (African Studies). (ENG., Illus.). 360p. pap. 48.00 *(978-0-521-03232-2(6))* Cambridge Univ. Pr.

Vinck, Patrick & Pham, Phuong. Building Peace, Seeking Justice: A Population-Based Survey on Attitudes about Accountability & Social Reconstruction in the Central African Republic. 2010. (ENG., Illus.). 41p. pap. 19.95 *(978-0-9826323-0-7(4))* Human Rights Ctr., Univ. of California, Berkeley, The.

Wabgou, Maguemati. Sistemas Políticos Africanos: Debates Contemporáneos en Colombia Desde la Ciencia Política. 2007. (SPA., Illus.). 320p. pap. *(978-958-44-1468-7(2))* Universidad Nacional de Colombia, Unibiblos.

Waema, T. M. & Adera, Edith Ofwona. Local Governance & ICTs in Africa: Case Studies & Guidelines for Implementation & Evaluation. 2011. (ENG., Illus.). 384p. pap. ***(978-0-85749-032-2(X))*** Pambuzuka Pr.

Walker, John Frederick. Ivory's Ghosts: The White Gold of History & the Fate of Elephants. 2010. (ENG.). 320p. pap. 15.00 *(978-0-8021-4452-2(7)*, Grove Pr.) Grove/Atlantic, Inc.

Walton, Hanes, Jr., et al. The African Foreign Policy of Secretary of State Henry Kissinger: A Documentary Analysis. 2007. (ENG., Illus.). 298p. 104.99 *(978-0-7391-1786-6(6))* Lexington Bks.

Watt, Nigel. Burundi: The Biography of a Small African Country. 2008. (Columbia/Hurst Ser.). (ENG.). 224p. (gr. 17). 55.00 *(978-0-231-70090-0(3))* Columbia Univ. Pr.

Welz, Martin. Decolonization Sovereignty & the African Union. 2012. (Global Institutions Ser.). (ENG., Illus.). 208p. (C). 130.00 ***(978-0-415-52201-4(3))*** Routledge.

Williams, Paul D. War & Conflict in Africa. 2011. (ENG., Illus.). 320p. 69.95 *(978-0-7456-4544-5(5))*; pap. 24.95 *(978-0-7456-4545-2(3))* Polity Pr. GBR. Dist: Wiley, John & Sons, Inc.

Williams, Susan. The Colour Bar: The Triumph of Seretse Kama & His Nation. 2008. (ENG., Illus.). 432p. (gr. 12-18). 16.00 *(978-0-14-102613-8(8)*, Penguin Global) Penguin Group (USA) Inc.

Wilson, Zoë. The United Nations & Democracy in Africa: Labyrinths of Legitimacy. 2009. 256p. 39.95 *(978-0-415-80579-7(1))* 2006. 252p. 138.00 *(978-0-415-97987-0(0))* Routledge.

Wing, Susanna D. Constructing Democracy in Africa: Mali in Transition. 2010. (ENG.). 260p. pap. 31.00 *(978-0-230-10915-5(2))* Palgrave Macmillan.

World Bank. Africa Development Indicators 2011. 2011. (Africa Development Indicators Ser.). (ENG.). 194p. pap. 100.00 incl. cd-rom *(978-0-8213-8731-3(6)*, 9780821387313) World Bank Pubns.

—Engaging the Private Sector to Improve Health in Africa: Healthy Partnerships. 2011. (ENG., Illus.). 180p. pap. 30.00 *(978-0-8213-8472-5(4)*, 9780821384725) World Bank Pubns.

Yassin, Hussen. Institutionalizing the Right to Self Determination: The Case of the Oromo of Amhara State of Ethiopia: Legal Regimes & Political Dynamics. 2011. 124p. pap. ***(978-3-639-32619-2(9))*** VDM Verlag Dr. Mueller e.K.

Young, Tom. Africa. 2010. (Beginners Guide (Oneworld) Ser.). (ENG., Illus.). 224p. pap. 14.95 *(978-1-85168-753-4(X))* Oneworld Pubns. GBR. Dist: National Bk. Network.

Zeleza, Paul Tiyambe. Barack Obama & African Diasporas: Dialogues & Dissensions. 2009. (ENG.). 240p. pap. 28.00 *(978-0-8214-1896-3(3))* Ohio Univ. Pr.

Zenebe, Abdi. The African Unification Agend. 2010. 144p. pap. *(978-3-639-26330-5(8))* VDM Verlag Dr. Mueller e.K.

Zhang, Charles. Redrawing World Map: Exploration of Unification Between Countries. 2010. (Illus.). 224p. ***(978-1-4512-9489-7(1))***; pap. ***(978-1-4489-5805-4(9))*** PublishAmerica, Inc.

Zimba, Chris Zumani. Democracy under Attack. 2011. 332p. pap. 14.99 ***(978-1-61667-276-8(5))*** Raider Publishing International.

—Redemocratization of the Continent: Understanding 50 Golden Rules of How Africa's Democracy can be Revived, Made to Work, Consolidated & Sustained. 2011. 340p. pap. 15.95 ***(978-1-4327-6811-9(5))*** Outskirts Pr., Inc.

Zorbas, Eugenia. Reconciliation in Post-Genocide Rwand. 2011. 288p. pap. ***(978-3-8433-5736-4(6))*** Lambert Academic Publishing.

AFRICA—POPULATION

Clarke, John I. Population & Development Projects in Africa. 2009. (ENG.). 348p. pap. 36.99 *(978-0-521-12561-1(8))* Cambridge Univ. Pr.

Hill, Allan G., ed. Population Health & Nutrition in the Sahel: Issues in the Welfare of Selected West African Communities. 2011. (ENG.). 440p. 130.00 *(978-0-415-59285-7(2))* Routledge.

Singh, Jyoti Shankar. Creating a New Consensus on Population: The Politics of Reproductive Health, Reproductive Rights, & Women's Empowerment. 2nd rev. ed. 2009. (ENG., Illus.). 288p. 136.00 *(978-1-84407-905-6(8))*; pap. 39.95 *(978-1-84407-906-3(6))* Routledge.

Teller, Charles H. & Assefa Hailemariam. The Demographic Transition & Development in Africa: The Unique Case of Ethiopia. 2011. (ENG., Illus.). xxix, 359p. 189.00 *(978-90-481-8917-5(9)*, 9048189179) Springer.

AFRICA—RACE RELATIONS

Aubert, Guillaume. Constructing Race in the French Atlantic World, 1534-1789: The Blood of France. 2012. (Americas in the Early Modern Atlantic World Ser.). (ENG., Illus.). 256p. 85.00 *(978-0-230-61982-1(7))* Palgrave Macmillan.

Botha, Barry. The Afrikaner's Emancipation: Freeing South Africans from their Apartheid Mindset. 2008. 252p. pap. 19.95 *(978-0-595-52415-0(X))* iUniverse, Inc.

Brennan, James R. Taifa: Making Nation & Race in Urban Tanzania. 2012. (New African Histories Ser.). (ENG.). 264p. (C). pap. 32.95 ***(978-0-8214-2001-0(1))*** Ohio Univ. Pr.

Burroughs. Travel Writing & Atrocities: Eyewitness Accounts of Slavery in the Congo, Angola & the Putumayo. 2010. (Routledge Research in Travel Writing Ser.). (ENG., Illus.). 230p. (C). 125.00 *(978-0-415-99238-1(9))* Routledge.

Burroughs, Robert M. Travel Writing & Atrocities: Eyewitness Accounts of Colonialism in the Congo, Angola, & the Putumayo. 2010. (Illus.). xiv, 215p. 95.00 *(978-0-203-84916-3(7))* Routledge.

Chaza, Tororiro Isaac. Confessions of a Racist. 2011. 140p. pap. 23.51 ***(978-1-4567-7693-0(2))*** AuthorHouse.

Conyers, James, Jr., ed. Racial Structure & Radical Politics in the African Diaspora. 2009. (ENG., Illus.). 223p. pap. 29.95 *(978-1-4128-1045-6(0))* Transaction Pubs.

Davis, Garrick, ed. Praising It New: The Best of the New Criticism. 2008. (ENG.). 288p. pap. 19.95 *(978-0-8040-1109-9(5))* Swallow Pr.

Dennis, Benjamin G. & Dennis, Anita K. Slaves to Racism: An Unbroken Chain from America to Liberia. 2008. 264p. 33.95 *(978-0-87586-658-1(1))*; pap. 23.95 *(978-0-87586-657-4(3))* Algora Publishing.

Farris, Ron. Africans & African Americans Divided: The Male-Female African & African American Digital Divide. 2008. 228p. 34.95 *(978-1-4357-0009-3(0))* Lulu Enterprises Inc.

—Africans & African Americans Divided:the Male-Female African & African American Digital Divide. 2008. 228p. pap. 19.95 *(978-1-4357-0272-1(7))* Lulu Enterprises Inc.

Garvey, Marcus. The Marcus Garvey & Universal Negro Improvement Association Papers, Volume XI Vol. XI: The Caribbean Diaspora, 1910-1920. Yuen, Anthony et al, eds. 2011. (ENG., Illus.). 1128p. 120.00 *(978-0-8223-4690-6(7))* Duke Univ. Pr.

Glassman, Jonathon. War of Words, War of Stones: Racial Thought & Violence in Colonial Zanzibar. 2011. (ENG., Illus.). 414p. 80.00 *(978-0-253-35585-0(0)*, 0253355850); pap. 27.95 *(978-0-253-22280-0(X)*, 025322280X) Indiana Univ. Pr.

Natsios, Andrew S. Sudan & Darfur: What Everyone Needs to Know, 1 vol. 2012. (What Everyone Needs to Know Ser.). (ENG.). 280p. 74.00 ***(978-0-19-976420-4(4))*** Oxford Univ. Pr., Inc.

—Sudan & Darfur, & Darfur: What Everyone Needs to Know, 1 vol. 2012. (What Everyone Needs to Know Ser.). (ENG., Illus.). 208p. pap. 16.95 ***(978-0-19-976419-8(0))*** Oxford Univ. Pr., Inc.

Onianwah, Chinazor. It takes a village to name a Child: Celebrating the bestowment of ancestry, faith, family, heritage, identity & Legacy. 2008.Tr. of English. (ENG., Illus.). 120p. 51.95 *(978-0-615-21612-6(9))* Scripts, Graphics N Things.

Pierre, Jemima. The Predicament of Blackness: Postcolonial Ghana & the Politics of Race. 2012. 280p. pap. 30.00 ***(978-0-226-92303-1(7))***; (Illus.). 90.00 ***(978-0-226-92302-4(9))*** Univ. of Chicago Pr.

Russell, Margo & Russell, Martin. Afrikaners of the Kalahari: White Minority in a Black State. 2009. (African Studies). (ENG.). 184p. pap. 31.99 *(978-0-521-10140-0(9))* Cambridge Univ. Pr.

Schroeder, Richard A. Africa after Apartheid: South Africa, Race, & Nation in Tanzania. 2012. (ENG.). 240p. pap. 25.00 ***(978-0-253-00600-4(7)***, 0253006007); (Illus.). 75.00 ***(978-0-253-00599-1(X)***, 025300599X) Indiana Univ. Pr.

Smith, Barbara Robinson. Breaking the Curse of Racism from the Root. 2007. 344p. per. 17.99 *(978-1-60266-831-7(0))* Xulon Pr., Inc.

Taithe, Bertrand. The Killer Trail: A Colonial Scandal in the Heart of Africa. 2009. (ENG., Illus.). 304p. 34.95 *(978-0-19-923121-8(4))* Oxford Univ. Pr., Inc.

Tarikh, Asiwaju. White Society in Africa. Date not set. pap. 24.40 *(978-0-582-60960-0(7))* Addison-Wesley Longman, Ltd. GBR. Dist: Trans-Atlantic Pubns., Inc.

AFRICA—RELATIONS—FOREIGN COUNTRIES

Bangura, Abdul K. Pan-Africanism Caribbean Connections. 2007. 176p. per. 15.95 *(978-0-595-45193-7(4))* iUniverse, Inc.

Baxter, Joan. Dust from Our Eyes: An Unblinkered Look at Africa. 2nd ed. 2010. (ENG.). 425p. pap. 25.00 *(978-1-894987-47-9(0))* Wolsak & Wynn Pubs., Ltd. CAN. Dist: Univ. of Toronto Pr.

Benjamin, Thomas. The Atlantic World: Europeans, Africans, Indians & Their Shared History, 1400-1900. 2009. (ENG., Illus.). (C). 752p. 99.00 *(978-0-521-85099-5(1))*; 750p. pap. 46.99 *(978-0-521-61649-2(2))* Cambridge Univ. Pr.

Bodomo, Adams. Africans in China: A Sociocultural Study & Its Implications on Africa-China Relations. 2012. 14.99 ***(978-1-60497-790-5(6))*** Cambria Pr.

Des Forges, Alison Liebhafsky. Defeat Is the Only Bad News: Rwanda under Musinga 1896-1931. Newbury, David, ed. 2011. (Africa & the Diaspora Ser.). (ENG., Illus.). 256p. pap. 26.95 *(978-0-299-28144-1(2))* Univ. of Wisconsin Pr.

Goodwin, Stefan. Africa in Europe Vol. 1: Antiquity into the Age of Global Exploration, 2 vols. 2008. (ENG.). 260p. 73.50 *(978-0-7391-1725-5(4))*; pap. 31.50 *(978-0-7391-1726-2(2))* Lexington Bks.

Grubbs, Larry. Secular Missionaries: Americans & African Development in The 1960s. 2010. 256p. 34.95 net. *(978-1-55849-734-4(X))* Univ. of Massachusetts Pr.

Gupta, Pamila, et al, eds. Eyes Across the Water: Navigating the Indian Ocean. 2010. 408p. pap. 36.50 *(978-1-86888-572-5(0))* Unisa Press / Uitgewers GBR. Dist: International Specialized Bk. Services.

Hess, Andrew C. The Forgotten Frontier: A History of Sixteenth-Century Ibero-African Frontier. 2010. (Publications of the Center for Middle Eastern Studies). (Illus.). 290p. pap. 30.00 *(978-0-226-33031-0(1))* Univ. of Chicago Pr.

Jones, Jeannette Eileen. In Search of Brightest Africa: Reimagining the Dark Continent in American Culture, 1884-1936. 2010. (Race in the Atlantic World, 1700-1900 Ser.). (ENG., Illus.). 260p. 44.95 *(978-0-8203-3320-5(4))* Univ. of Georgia Pr.

Juang, Richard M. & Morrissette, Noelle, eds. Africa & the Americas: Culture, Politics, & History, 3 vols. 2008. (Transatlantic Relations Ser.). (Illus.). 1215p. 270.00 *(978-1-85109-441-7(5)*, AFATRLC) ABC-CLIO, LLC.

K'Orinda-Yimbo, Akinyi von. Darkest Europe & Africa's Nightmare: A Critical Observation of the Neighbouring Continents. 2007. 34.95 *(978-0-87586-519-5(4))*; pap. 22.95 *(978-0-87586-518-8(6))* Algora Publishing.

Manger, Leif & Assal, Munzoul. Diasporas Within & Without Africa: Dynamism, Heterogeneity, Variation. 2006. 200p. pap. 35.00 *(978-91-7106-563-6(6))* Nordiska Afrikainstitutet SWE. Dist: Stylus Publishing, LLC.

McDougall, James & Scheele, Judith. Saharan Frontiers: Space & Mobility in Northwest Africa. 2012. E-Book ***(978-0-253-00131-3(5))*** Indiana Univ. Pr.

McDougall, James & Scheele, Judith, eds. Saharan Frontiers: Space & Mobility in Northwest Africa. 2012. (Public Cultures of the Middle East & North Africa Ser.). (ENG., Illus.). 306p. 80.00 ***(978-0-253-00124-5(2)***, 0253001242); pap. 30.00 ***(978-0-253-00126-9(9)***, 0253001269) Indiana Univ. Pr.

Minter, William, et al. No Easy Victories: African Liberation & American Activists over a Half Century, 1950-2000. 2007. pap. *(978-1-59221-575-1(0))*; (Illus.). 240p. *(978-1-59221-574-4(2))* Africa World Pr.

Ogunsanwo, Alaba. China's Policy in Africa, 1958-71. 2010. (LSE Monographs in International Studies). (ENG.). 328p. pap. 25.99 *(978-0-521-13440-8(4))* Cambridge Univ. Pr.

Phaf-Rheinberger, Ineke & Pinto, Tiago de Oliveira. AfricAmericas: Itineraries, Dialogues, & Sounds. 2008. (Illus.). 224p. pap. 29.80 *(978-84-8489-380-6(4))* Iberoamericana Vervuert Publishing Corp.

Pratt, Mary Louise. Imperial Eyes: Travel Writing & Transculturation. 2nd rev. ed. 2007. (ENG., Illus.). 296p. pap. 37.95 *(978-0-415-43817-9(9))* Routledge.

Reid, Andrew & O'Connor, David, eds. Ancient Egypt in Africa. 2007. (Encounters with Ancient Egypt series, University College London Institute of Archaeology Publications). (ENG., Illus.). 233p. pap. 34.95 *(978-1-59874-205-3(1))* Left Coast Pr., Inc.

Soares de Oliveira, Ricardo, et al. China Returns to Africa: A Rising Power & a Continent Embrace. 2008. (Columbia/Hurst Ser.). (ENG., Illus.). 400p. (gr. 17). 75.00 *(978-0-231-70098-6(9))* Columbia Univ. Pr.

Stephens, Michelle Ann. Reconceptualization of the African Diaspora. Ball, Erica & Pappademos, Melina, eds. 2008. (ENG., Illus.). 240p. pap. 14.00 *(978-0-8223-6696-6(7))* Duke Univ. Pr.

Taylor, Ian. China¿s New Role in Africa. 2010. 227p. (C). pap. 25.00 *(978-1-58826-736-8(9))* Rienner, Lynne Pubs.

—China's New Role in Africa. 2008. (Illus.). 240p. 55.00 *(978-1-58826-636-1(2))* Rienner, Lynne Pubs.

Taylor, Ian. The Forum on China- Africa Cooperation (FOCAC) (ENG., Illus.). (C). 2012. 126p. pap. 42.95 ***(978-0-415-62851-8(2))*** 2011. 144p. 118.00 *(978-0-415-54860-1(8))* Routledge.

Waters, Mary-Alice & Koppel, Martin. Capitalism & the Transformation of Africa: Reports from Equatorial Guinea. 2009. (Illus.). 150p. pap. 10.00 *(978-1-60488-016-8(3))* Pathfinder Pr.

AFRICA—RELIGION

Adeola, Moses. Cultural & Religious Dilemma of Africans: In the Diaspora. 2006. per. 16.95 *(978-0-9787788-0-4(4))* LUMEN-US Pubns.

Adesogan, E. Faith, Politics & Challenges a Christian's First-Hand Account. 2007. 244p. pap. *(978-978-129-830-1(8))* Heinemann Educational Bks. (Nigeria), Ltd. NGA. Dist: Michigan State Univ. Pr.

Adogame, Afe, et al. African Traditions in the Study of Religion in Africa Emerging Trends Indigenous Spirituality & the Interface with Other World Religions. 2012. (Vitality of Indigenous Religions Ser.). (Illus.). 240p. 99.95 ***(978-1-4094-1970-9(3))*** Ashgate Publishing Co.

Adogame, Afeosemime U. Christianity in Africa & the African Diaspora: The Appropriation of a Scattered Heritage. Gerloff, Roswith & Hock, Klaus, eds. 2009. (ENG.). 368p. 150.00 *(978-1-84706-317-5(9))* Continuum International Publishing Group, Ltd. GBR. Dist: National Bk. Network.

Adogbo, Michael P. Comparative Historical & Interpretative Study of Religions. 2010. 130p. pap. *(978-978-8422-23-5(3))* Malthouse Press, Stoke on Trent.

African Gifts of the Spirit: Pentecostalism & the Rise of a Zimbabwean Transnational Religious Movement. 2006. (Illus.). 320p. 90.00 *(978-0-85255-965-9(8))*; pap. 34.95 *(978-0-85255-966-6(6))* Boydell & Brewer, Ltd. GBR. (Currey, James). Dist: Boydell & Brewer, Inc.

Agorsah, E. Kofi. Religion, Ritual & African Tradition: African Foundations. 2010. 156p. pap. 11.99 *(978-1-4490-0552-8(7))* AuthorHouse.

Aguilar, Mario. Theology, Liberation & Genocide: A Theology of the Periphery. 2011. x, 143p. pap. ***(978-0-334-04190-0(2)***, SCM Pr.) Hymns Ancient & Modern Ltd.

Alonso, Carlos & Eyles, Maureen. A History of the Augustinians & the Martyrs of Mombasa (1598-1698) 2007. (Illus.). 112p. *(978-9966-08-268-8(9))* Paulines Pubns., Africa.

An-Na'im, Abdullahi Ahmed, ed. Proselytization & Communal Self-Determination in Africa. 2009. 328p. pap. 38.00 *(978-1-60608-671-1(5)*, Wipf and Stock) Wipf & Stock Pubs.

Apocalypse, John. The End of Man: A Defense of the Orthodox Church Against Protestantism. 2011. 136p. pap. 12.00 ***(978-0-557-80864-9(2))*** Lulu Enterprises Inc.

Asante, Molefi Kete & Mazama, Ama, eds. Encyclopedia of African Religion, 2 vols. 2008. (Illus.). 920p. 345.00 *(978-1-4129-3636-1(5)*, B36365C) SAGE Pubns., Inc.

Asante, Molefi Kete & Nwadiora, Emeka. Spear Masters: An Introduction to African Religion. 2007. (ENG.). 128p. per. 33.99 *(978-0-7618-3574-5(1))* Univ. Pr. of America, Inc.

Austnaberg, Hans. Improving Preaching by Listening to Listeners: Sunday Service Preaching in the Malagasy Lutheran Church. 2012. ***(978-1-4331-1779-4(7))*** Lang, Peter Publishing, Inc.

Bae, Choon-Sup. Ancestor Worship. 2008. 248p. pap. *(978-3-639-08714-7(3))* VDM Verlag Dr. Mueller e.K.

Bakhita. 2011. 24.95 *(978-1-58617-642-6(0))* Ignatius Pr.

Bamidele, Emmanuel. Common Voice: Together for change in Africa. 2009. 64p. pap. 10.49 *(978-1-4490-2022-4(4))* AuthorHouse.

Barasa, Janet. Influence of Islam on Bukusu Culture. 2010. 240p. pap. *(978-3-8383-8263-0(3))* Lambert Academic Publishing.

Baraza, Patrick Wanakuta. Rival Claims for the Soul of Africa. 2007. (Illus.). 88p. pap. 10.95 *(978-1-934454-02-2(8))* Hillcrest Publishing Group, Inc.

Battle, Michael. Ubuntu: I in You & You in Me. 2009. 176p. 25.00 *(978-1-59627-113-5(2)*, Seabury Bks.) Church Publishing, Inc.

Battle Michael. Ubuntu: I in You & You in Me. 2009. 176p. pap. 18.00 *(978-1-59627-111-1(6)*, Seabury Bks.) Church Publishing, Inc.

Bediako, Kwame. Theology & Identity: The Impact of Culture upon Christian Thought in the Second Century & in Modern Africa. 2011. (Regnum Studies in Mission Ser.). 526p. pap. 63.00 ***(978-1-61097-440-0(9)***, Wipf and Stock) Wipf & Stock Pubs.

Bekele, Serawit. Hybridized Religious Practices. 2010. 72p. pap. *(978-3-639-23294-3(1))* VDM Verlag Dr. Mueller e.K.

Bezie, Tigab. Ethiopia's Claim on Deir Es-Sultan Monastery in Jerusalem, 1850s-1994. 2011. 148p. pap. ***(978-3-8443-0623-1(4))*** Lambert Academic Publishing.

Biri, Kudzai. African Tradition Religion & Pentecostalism in Zimbabwe. 2011. 60p. pap. ***(978-3-8443-9888-5(0))*** Lambert Academic Publishing.

Bompani, Barbara & Frahm-Arp, Maria, eds. Development & Politics from Below: Exploring Religious Spaces in the African State. 2010. (Non-Governmental Public Action Ser.). (ENG., Illus.). 272p. 89.00 *(978-0-230-23775-9(4))* Palgrave Macmillan.

Bongmba, Elias Kifon, ed. Blackwell Companion to African Religions. 2012. (Wiley-Blackwell Companions to Religion Ser.: 58). (ENG.). 632p. 195.00 ***(978-1-4051-9690-1(4)***, Wiley-Blackwell) Wiley, John & Sons, Inc.

Botha, Barry. The Afrikaner's Emancipation: Freeing South Africans from their Apartheid Mindset. 2008. 252p. pap. 19.95 *(978-0-595-52415-0(X))* iUniverse, Inc.

Breen, Marit. Contextual Bible Study among Poor & Marginalized Women, South Afric. 2010. 124p. pap. *(978-3-639-22890-8(1))* VDM Verlag Dr. Mueller e.K.

Briand-Ponsart, C. & Moderan, Yves, eds. Province et identite provinciales dans l'Afrique Romaine. 2011. (Tables Rondes du Crahm Ser.). (FRE.). 295p. (C). pap. 51.00 *(978-2-902685-68-4(8))* Brepols Pubs. BEL. Dist: Brown, David Bk. Co., The.

Bridgeman, Valerie & Page, Hugh. The Africana Bible: Reading Israel's Scriptures from Africa & the African Diaspora. 2009. 512p. 39.00 *(978-0-8006-2125-4(5)*, Fortress Pr.) Augsburg Fortress, Pubs.

Buor, Sei. No More War: Rebuilding Liberia through Faith, Determination & Education. 2009. 184p. pap. 16.95 *(978-1-4401-5655-7(7))* iUniverse, Inc.

Butler, Carolyn. Under African Skies: Reflections for Advent & Christmas. 2011. 96p. pap. 9.95 *(978-0-7963-0850-4(0))* NB Pubs. Ltd. ZAF. Dist: International Publishers Marketing.

Campbell, Gwyn. David Griffiths & the Missionary 'History of Madagascar' 2012. (ENG.). 1066p. ***(978-90-04-20980-0(8))*** BRILL.

Chege Kamau, Washington. Harambee: Evaluation of its historical & theological Contribution. 2011. 128p. pap. ***(978-3-8443-8406-2(5))*** Lambert Academic Publishing.

Clark, Dora Jane Armstrong. Congo Trails. 2011. 142p. 40.95 ***(978-1-258-07611-5(X))*** Literary Licensing, LLC.

Clark, Mary Ann. Then We'll Sing a New Song: African Influences on America's Religious Landscape. 2012. (ENG.). 216p. 35.00 ***(978-1-4422-0879-7(1))*** Rowman & Littlefield Publishers, Inc.

Colleyn, Jean-Paul. Bamana. 2008. (ENG., Illus.). 144p. pap. 34.95 *(978-88-7439-348-0(2))* 5 Continents ITA. Dist: Hachette Bk. Group.

Colleyn, Jean-Paul, et al. Boli. 2010. (FRE & ENG., Illus.). 176p. 50.00 *(978-2-35340-075-1(2))* Gourcuff Gradenigo FRA. Dist: National Bk. Network.

Colson, Elizabeth. Tonga Religious Life in the Twentieth Century. 2007. 316p. pap. *(978-9982-24-045-1(5))* BookWorld Pubs. ZMB. Dist: Michigan State Univ. Pr.

Conteh, Prince Sorie. Inter-Religious Encounters & Dialogue in Sierra Leone: Historical & Contemporary Endeavours. 2011. 138p. pap. 19.99 ***(978-1-4568-9787-1(X))*** Xlibris Corp.

Conteh, Prince Sorie. An Introduction to the Religion of the Limba of Sierra Leone. 2007. 186p. pap. 19.20 *(978-1-86888-432-2(5))* Unisa Press / Uitgewers GBR. Dist: International Specialized Bk. Services.

Corker, John. ISLAM in Africa: An African Perspective. 2008. per. 14.95 *(978-0-9787212-1-3(7))* Big Ben Pubns.

Creary, Nicholas M. Domesticating a Religious Import: The Jesuits & the Inculturation of the Catholic Church in Zimbabwe, 1879-1980. 2nd ed. 2011. (ENG., Illus.). 280p. 48.00 *(978-0-8232-3334-2(0))* Fordham Univ. Pr.

Daneel, M. L. The god of the Matopo Hills: An essay on the Mwari Cult in Rhodesia. (Communications / Afrika Studiecentrum, Leiden Ser.). (ENG.). 95p. 210.00 ***(978-3-11-211765-1(4))***; 135.00 ***(978-3-11-105216-8(8))*** De Gruyter, Mouton DEU. Dist: de Gruyter, Walter GmbH & Co. KG.

Dodge, Ralph E. The Revolutionary Bishop: Who Saw God at Work in Africa. 2008. pap. 17.95 *(978-1-60494-215-6(0))* Wheatmark.

Domnwachukwu, Chinaka Samuel. Incessant Warfare: A Critical History of Spiritual Warfare Through the Ages. 2011. 288p. 35.95 ***(978-1-4627-0569-6(3))***; pap. 19.95 ***(978-1-4627-0568-9(5))*** Cross Bks. Publishing.

Donnelly, John. A Twist of Faith: An American Christian's Quest to Help Orphans in Africa. 2012. (ENG.). 200p. 25.95 ***(978-0-8070-0132-5(5))*** Beacon Pr.

Dube, Lilian, et al. African Initiatives in Healing Ministry. 2011. 224p. pap. 32.00 *(978-1-86888-566-4(6))* Unisa Press / Uitgewers GBR. Dist: International Specialized Bk. Services.

Duvoix, Marcel. Holy Legacy. 2009. 810p. pap. 23.99 *(978-1-4415-5345-4(2))* Xlibris Corp.

Edward, Inyanwachi. The Practice of Inculturation in the Nigerian Church: The Role of Catholic Schools & Universities. 2011. 172p. pap. ***(978-3-639-31747-3(5))*** VDM Verlag Dr. Mueller e.K.

Ellis, Stephen. The Mask of Anarchy: The Destruction of Liberia & the Religious Dimension of an African Civil War. 2nd ed. 2006. (ENG., Illus.). 366p. pap. 25.00 *(978-0-8147-2238-1(5))* New York Univ. Pr.

Ephirim-Donkor, Anthony. African Religion Defined: A Systematic Study of Ancestor Worship among the Akan. 2010. (Illus.). 160p. pap. 25.50 *(978-0-7618-5328-2(6))* Univ. Pr. of America, Inc.

Essamuah, Casely B. Genuinely Ghanaian: A Postcolonial History of the Methodist Church, Ghana, 1961-2000. 2010. *(978-1-59221-747-2(8))* Africa World Pr.

Etuk, Emma Samuel. Listen Africans! A Revolution Is Coming: Why It Must Come & How We Should Deal with It. 2011. 212p. 27.95 *(978-1-4502-7736-5(5))*; pap. 17.95 *(978-1-4502-7734-1(9))* iUniverse, Inc.

Farelius, Birgitta. Origin of Kingship Traditions & Symbolism in the Great Lakes Region of Africa. 2008. (Acta Universitatis Upsaliensia Historia Religionum Ser.). (Illus.). 373p. pap. 87.50 *(978-91-554-7295-5(8))* Uppsala Universitet/Acta Universitatis Uppsaliensis SWE. Dist: Coronet Bks.

Fiedler, Klaus. The Story of Faith Missions: From Hudson Taylor to Present Day Africa. 2011. 428p. pap. 49.00 ***(978-1-61097-478-3(6)***, Wipf and Stock) Wipf & Stock Pubs.

Fischer, Moritz. Pfingstbewegung zwischen Fragilität und Empowerment: Beobachtungen zur Pfingstkirche »Nzambe Malamu« mit ihren transnationalen Verpflechtungen. 2011. (Kirche, Konfession, Religion Ser.). (GER., Illus.). 349p. (C). 68.00 ***(978-3-89971-843-0(7))*** Vandenhoeck & Ruprecht GmbH & Co. KG DEU. Dist: ISD.

Gathogo, Julius. African Hospitality from a Missiological Perspective. 2011. 184p. pap. ***(978-3-8443-0006-2(6))*** Lambert Academic Publishing.

—Christ's Hospitality from an African Theological Perspective. 2011. 212p. pap. ***(978-3-8443-0323-0(5))*** Lambert Academic Publishing.

—Liberation & Reconstruction in Afric. 2011. 476p. pap. ***(978-3-8433-9087-3(8))*** Lambert Academic Publishing.

—The Pangs of Birth in African Christianity. 2011. 476p. pap. ***(978-3-8443-0606-4(4))*** Lambert Academic Publishing.

—Responsible Church Leaders in Afric. 2011. 132p. pap. ***(978-3-8443-9155-8(X))*** Lambert Academic Publishing.

Gatwa, Tharcisse. The Churches & Ethnic Ideology in the Rwandan Crises, 1900-1994. 2008. (Regnum Studies in Mission Ser.). 312p. pap. 36.00 *(978-1-59752-823-8(4))* Wipf & Stock Pubs.

Gaunt, Bonnie. The Great Prophetic Design: Found in Africa. 2009. (Bible Code Ser.). (Illus.). 146p. pap. 12.95 *(978-1-931862-97-2(X))* Adventures Unlimited Pr.

Gebissa, Fekadu. Evangelical Faith Movement in Ethiopia: Origins & Establishment of the Ethiopian Evangelical Church Mekane Yesus. Gurmessa, Ezekiel, tr. from AMH. 2009. (Illus.). 196p. pap. 21.00 *(978-1-932688-39-9(0)*, Lutheran Univ. Pr.) Kirk Hse. Pubs.

Gehman, Richard J. Who Are the Living-Dead? A Theology of Death, Life after Death, & the Living-Dead. 2009. (Illus.). xviii, 350p. 24.99 *(978-9966-20-088-4(6))* Evangel Publishing Hse.

Gerloff, Roswith & Hock, Klaus. Christianity in Africa & the African Diaspora: The Appropriation of a Scattered Heritage. Gerloff, Roswith & Hock, Klaus, eds. Adogame, Afe, ed. 2011. (ENG.). 368p. pap. 49.95 *(978-1-4411-2330-5(X))* Continuum International Publishing Group, Ltd. GBR. Dist: National Bk. Network.

Gezehage, Teklemariam. Acts of God in Ethiopi. 2007. 168p. pap. 12.99 *(978-0-9790551-2-6(1))* Apostolic Experience Publishing.

Gibbs De Peza, Hazel Ann. My Faith - Spiritual Baptist Christian. 2007. 96p. per. 9.99 *(978-1-60266-509-5(5))* Xulon Pr., Inc.

Gifford, Paul. African Christianity: Its Public Role in Uganda & Other African Countries. viii, 368p. *(978-9970-02-170-3(2))* Fountain Pubs. Ltd. UGA. Dist: Michigan State Univ. Pr.

Gisege Omare, Simon. Religion & Environment Conservation. 2010. 192p. pap. *(978-3-8383-8314-9(1))* Lambert Academic Publishing.

Gitome, Josephine. Pastoral Care in African Context. 2011. 100p. pap. ***(978-3-8443-9467-2(2))*** Lambert Academic Publishing.

Gottlieb, Alma & Graham, Philip. Braided Worlds. 2012. 176p. 60.00 ***(978-0-226-30527-1(9))***; pap. 20.00 ***(978-0-226-30528-8(7))*** Univ. of Chicago Pr. (Orbit Books).

Haar, Gerrie ter. How God Became African: African Spirituality & Western Secular Thought. 2009. 136p. (C). 34.95 *(978-0-8122-4173-0(8))* Univ. of Pennsylvania Pr.

Halka. A Degree of Illumination (Section B) 2009. 684p. pap. 40.36 *(978-0-557-04810-6(9))* Lulu Enterprises Inc.

Harper, Dianne R. True Beginnings: Biblical African Perspective. 2011. 52p. pap. 11.99 ***(978-1-4567-4913-2(7))*** AuthorHouse.

Herford, James. Africa? What are we Doing ? 2007. 73p. pap. 15.95 *(978-0-615-16897-5(3))* Herford, James R.

Höschele, Stefan. Christian Remnant, African Folk Church: Seventh-Day Adventism in Tanzania, 1903-1980. 2007. (Studies in Christian Mission: Vol. 34). (Illus.). 700p. (C). *(978-90-04-16233-4(X))* BRILL.

Houle, Robert. Making African Christianity: Africans Reimagining Their Faith in Colonial South Africa. 2011. (ENG.). 332p. 80.00 ***(978-1-61146-081-0(6))*** Lehigh Univ. Pr.

Hunwick, John O. West Africa, Islam, & the Arab World: Studies in Honor of Basil Davidson. 2006. (Illus.). 147p. 88.95 *(978-1-55876-398-2(8))* Wiener, Markus Pubs., Inc.

Ike, Jude Chikodi. The Church as Locus of Man's Encounter with God: A Study of the Theology of Otto Semmelroth & its Implication for the Church in Africa. 2011. (Europäische Hochschulschriften. Reihe 23: Theologie Ser.). 388p. pap. 90.95 *(978-3-631-61709-0(7))* Lang, Peter GmbH, Europaischer Verlag der Wissenschaften DEU. Dist: Lang, Peter.

Ilibagiza, Immaculée. Nuestra Señora de Kibeho: Un Mensaje de María Desde el Corazón de África. 2009. (SPA & ENG.). 240p. pap. 12.95 *(978-1-4019-2379-2(8))* Hay Hse., Inc.

Iruoma, Iheanyi Hycenth. Church Politics: Church Crises: Will the Church Survive in Africa? 2010. 148p. 30.99 *(978-1-4520-6072-9(X))*; pap. 20.99 *(978-1-4520-6071-2(1))* AuthorHouse.

Jam, John Hawkins. Divine Prophecy & Blackman. 2009. 204p. pap. 15.99 *(978-1-4389-3442-6(4))* AuthorHouse.

James, Gary. Epiphany: Three Wise Kings of the Magi. 2008. 241p. pap. 24.95 *(978-1-60563-624-5(X))* PublishAmerica, Inc.

Jell-Bahlsen, Sabine. The Water Goddess in Igbo Cosmology: Ogbuide of Oguta Lake. 2007. *(978-1-59221-482-2(7))*; 320p. pap. *(978-1-59221-483-9(5))* Africa World Pr.

Jeske, Christine. Into the Mud: Inspiration for Everday Activists: True Stories of South Africa, 1 vol. 2010. (ENG.). 208p. pap. 13.99 *(978-0-8024-5879-7(3))* Moody Pubs.

Jestice, Phyllis & Sherry, Matthew, trs. from FRE. A Life Poured Out: Pierre Claverie of Algeria. 2007. Orig. Title: Pierre claverie: un Algerien par Alliance. (FRE., Illus.). 286p. per. 30.00 *(978-1-57075-706-8(2))* Orbis Bks.

Jindra, Michael & Noret, Joël, eds. Funerals in Africa: Explorations of a Social Phenomenon. 2011. (ENG., Illus.). 264p. 85.00 *(978-0-85745-205-4(3))* Berghahn Bks., Inc.

Jones, Damon R. Reshaping the Consciousness. 2010. 72p. pap. *(978-3-8383-3919-1(3))* Lambert Academic Publishing.

Kalu, Ogbu. African Christianity: An African Story. 2007. *(978-1-59221-580-5(7))*; 480p. pap. *(978-1-59221-581-2(5))* Africa World Pr.

—Clio in a Sacred Garb: Essays on Christian Presence & African Responses, 1900-2000. 2008. *(978-1-59221-630-7(7))*; 320p. pap. *(978-1-59221-631-4(5))* Africa World Pr.

Kalu, Ogbu, et al. African Christianity: Mission, Ferment, & Trauma. 2010. *(978-1-59221-776-2(1))*; 694p. pap. *(978-1-59221-777-9(X))* Africa World Pr.

—African Pentecostalism: Global Discourses, Migrations, Exchanges & Connections: The Collected Essays of Ogbu Uke Kalu. 2010. 506p. pap. *(978-1-59221-768-7(0))* Africa World Pr.

Kalu, Wilhelmina, et al. Religions in Africa: Conflicts, Politics & Social Ethics. 2010. *(978-1-59221-778-6(8))*; 492p. pap. *(978-1-59221-779-3(6))* Africa World Pr.

Karani, Ruri. Culture Versus Gospel in Afric. 2011. 120p. pap. ***(978-3-8443-3378-7(9))*** Lambert Academic Publishing.

Kasomo, Daniel. African Theology. 2010. 116p. pap. *(978-3-8383-8903-5(4))* Lambert Academic Publishing.

—The Essence of African Culture & Religion. 2010. 144p. pap. *(978-3-8383-8857-1(7))* Lambert Academic Publishing.

—The Traditional Oath in African Culture & Religion. 2010. 276p. pap. *(978-3-8383-8456-6(3))* Lambert Academic Publishing.

Kasomo, Daniel W. African Spirituality: An Introduction. 2011. 256p. pap. ***(978-3-8443-3071-7(2))*** Lambert Academic Publishing.

—Ethics & Morality from an African Perspective. 2011. 312p. pap. ***(978-3-8433-6891-9(0))*** Lambert Academic Publishing.

Kasomo, Daniel W. An Introduction to African Culture & Religion. 2010. 96p. pap. *(978-3-8383-9308-7(2))* Lambert Academic Publishing.

Kasomo, Rt. Rev. Daniel W. History of Christianity in Africa Made Simple. 2011. 332p. pap. ***(978-3-8454-0626-8(7))*** Lambert Academic Publishing.

Keeney, Bradford. The Bushman Way of Tracking God: The Original Spirituality of the Kalahari People. 2010. (ENG.). 304p. 24.00 *(978-1-58270-257-5(8)*, Beyond Words/Atria Bks.) Atria Bks.

Kiiru, MacMillan. Mobilizing & Managing Resources. 2009. 264p. pap. 24.99 *(978-9966-20-181-2(5))* Evangel Publishing Hse.

Kinyua, Johnson Kiriaku. Introducing Ordinary African Readers to Hermeneutics: A Case Study of the Agikuyu Encounter with the Bible. 2011. 400p. pap. ***(978-3-0343-0289-0(4))*** Lang, Peter Publishing, Inc.

Kirsch, Thomas G. Spirits & Letters: Reading, Writing & Charisma in African Christianity. 2011. (Illus.). 288p. 34.95 *(978-0-85745-142-2(1))* Berghahn Bks., Inc.

Kolini, Emmanuel M. & Holmes, Peter R. Christ Walks Where Evil Reigned: Responding to the Rwandan Genocide. 2008. (ENG.). 218p. per. 16.99 *(978-1-934068-41-0(1))* Authentic Media.

Koloss, Hans-Joachim. World-View & Society in Oku (Cameroon) 2009. (ENG.). 484p. pap. 128.00 *(978-3-496-02682-2(0)*, Art Stock Bks. Ltd/Csi) Continental Sales, Inc.

Kombo, James Henry Owino. The Doctrine of God in African Christian Thought: The Holy Trinity, Theological Hermeneutics & the African Intellectual Culture. 2007. (Studies in Reformed Theology Ser.). 298p. *(978-90-04-15804-7(9))* BRILL.

Kondolo, Kapembwa. The Spread of the African Independent Churches. 2011. 96p. pap. ***(978-3-8433-8818-4(0))*** Lambert Academic Publishing.

Koschorke, Klaus, et al, eds. A History of Christianity in Asia, Africa, & Latin America, 1450-1990: A Documentary Sourcebook. 2007. 426p. pap. 35.00 *(978-0-8028-2889-7(2))* Eerdmans, William B. Publishing Co.

Kuhn, Alvin B. Who Is This King of Glory? A Critical Study of the Christos - Messiah Tradition. (African Studies). 493p. reprint ed. 50.00 *(978-0-938818-83-0(X))* ECA Assocs.

Kusema, Wellingtone Garati. The Believers' Companion: A Concise Topical Handbook on Doctrine in the African Apostolic Church. 2011. 410p. pap. 14.99 ***(978-0-9557546-1-6(5))*** Heritage Pr.

Lado, Ludovic. Catholic Pentecostalism & the Paradoxes of Africanization: Processes of Localization in a Catholic Charismatic Movement in Cameroon. 2009. (Studies of Religion in Africa Ser.). (Illus.). 250p. *(978-90-04-16898-5(3))* BRILL.

Larsen, Kjersti, ed. Knowledge, Renewal & Religion. 2009. 310p. pap. 22.95 *(978-91-7106-635-0(7))* Nordiska Afrikainstitutet SWE. Dist: Stylus Publishing, LLC.

Lebaka, Morakeng Edward Kenneth. Old Testament Psalms & Pedi Psalm-Like Songs. 2010. 236p. pap. *(978-3-639-25445-7(7))* VDM Verlag Dr. Mueller e.K.

Lee, Anthony A. The Baha'i Faith in Africa: Establishing a New Religious Movement, 1952-1962. 2011. (Illus.). xii, 279p. ***(978-90-04-20684-7(1))*** BRILL.

Letsosa, Rantoa. Relevant Liturgy. 2010. 464p. pap. *(978-3-639-23062-8(0))* VDM Verlag Dr. Mueller e.K.

Levtzion, Nehemia & Pouwels, Randall L., eds. The History of Islam in Africa. 2010. (Illus.). 608p. pap. 34.95 *(978-0-85255-781-5(7)*, Currey, James) Boydell & Brewer, Ltd. GBR. Dist: Boydell & Brewer, Inc.

Lindsay, Ross. Out of Afric: The Breakaway Anglican Churches. 2011. 176p. 29.99 ***(978-1-61379-606-1(4))*** Xulon Pr., Inc.

Longman, Timothy. Christianity & Genocide in Rwanda. 2009. (African Studies). (ENG., Illus.). 372p. 102.00 *(978-0-521-19139-5(4))* Cambridge Univ. Pr.

Lotegeluaki, Stanley O. Africa: Intergalactic Federation of African Tribes: The Christian Kingdom of Jesus Christ. Kush the Land of 10,000 Tribes Swarming Through Space in a Quintillion Universes- the Promised Land. 2011. 784p. pap. 36.14 ***(978-1-4634-1177-0(4))*** AuthorHouse.

Lubawa, Richard. Shoulder to Shoulder (Bega Kwa Bega) A Lutheran Partnership Between Minnesota & Tanzania. 2007. (ENG.). 112p. pap. 12.00 *(978-1-932688-25-2(0)*, Lutheran Univ. Pr.) Kirk Hse. Pubs.

Lundström, Karl-Johan & Gebremedhin, Ezra. Kenisha: The Roots & Development of the Evangelical Church of Eritrea (ECE), 1866-1935. 2011. (Illus.). 520p. pap. *(978-1-56902-350-1(6))* Red Sea Pr.

MacKenzie, Geoffrey Shisumu. Homiletics Out of Afric. 2011. 56p. pap. ***(978-3-8443-9344-6(7))*** Lambert Academic Publishing.

Magaracha, Tendai Joseph & Masengwe, Gift. Power Struggles & Cultural Identity Crises in Aics. 2011. 88p. pap. ***(978-3-8383-3994-8(0))*** Lambert Academic Publishing.

Magesa, Laurenti. African Religion in the Dialogue Debate: From Intolerance to Coexistence. 2011. (ENG.). 208p. pap. 27.95 *(978-3-643-90018-0(X))* Lit Verlag DEU. Dist: Transaction Pubs.

Maina, Grace. Nun's Daughter. 2010. 262p. pap. 19.99 *(978-1-4535-1444-3(9))* Xlibris Corp.

Maina, Wilson Muoha. Historical & Social Dimensions in African Christian Theology: A Contemporary Approach. 2008. 132p. pap. 16.00 *(978-1-60608-124-2(1)*, Wipf and Stock) Wipf & Stock Pubs.

Maposa, Richard S. 'de-Colonization Extended to African Theology' 2011. 64p. pap. ***(978-3-8443-9709-3(4))*** Lambert Academic Publishing.

Mareng, Chuei. The Sudan's Dimensions. 2011. 68p. pap. ***(978-3-8443-2657-4(X))*** Lambert Academic Publishing.

Marsé Hazan Walda Qirqos. Tezetayé Selarasé Yamastawsaw, 1891-1923 A.Me. 2009. (AMH., Illus.). 289p. ***(978-0-578-02223-9(0))*** Magyar ISBN Iroda, Orszagos Szechenyi Konyvtar.

Martey, Emmanuel. African Theology: Inculturation & Liberation. 2009. 190p. pap. 22.00 *(978-1-60899-125-9(3)*, Wipf and Stock) Wipf & Stock Pubs.

Masengwe, Gift. The Church's Role in Social Healing & Reconciliation in Zimbabwe. 2010. 124p. pap. *(978-3-8383-6148-2(2))* Lambert Academic Publishing.

Mbiti, John S. Afrikanische Religion und Weltanschauung. Feuser, W. F., tr. (De Gruyter Studienbuch Ser.). (GER.). XVI, 375p. (C). 210.00 ***(978-3-11-177189-2(X))*** De Gruyter, Walter Inc.

Melekin, Embaye. The African Bible: The Record of the Abyssinian Prophets. 2011. 612p. 33.83 *(978-1-4567-4773-2(8))*; pap. 23.28 *(978-1-4567-4774-9(6))* AuthorHouse.

Michon, Jean-Louis. Ibn Ajiba: Two Treatises on the Oneness of Existence. Streight, David, tr. 2010. 96p. pap. 16.95 *(978-1-901383-15-7(6))* Archetype GBR. Dist: Midpoint Trade Bks., Inc.

Michon, Jean-Louis & Streight, David. Ibn Ajiba: Two Treatises on the Oneness of Existence. 2010. 96p. 29.95 *(978-1-901383-39-3(3))* Archetype GBR. Dist: Midpoint Trade Bks., Inc.

Mildred, A. J. Ndeda. Nomiya Luo Church (NLC) A Gender Analysis of the Dynamics of an African Independent Church among the Luo of Kenya. 2011. 320p. pap. ***(978-3-639-23292-9(5))*** VDM Verlag Dr. Mueller e.K.

Moodley, Edley J. Shembe, Ancestors, & Christ: A Christological Inquiry with Missiological Implications. 2008. (American Society of Missiology Monograph Ser.). 272p. pap. 30.00 *(978-1-55635-880-7(6)*, Pickwick Pubns.) Wipf & Stock Pubs.

Morojele, Pholoho Justice. Gender & Schooling in Lesotho Rural Communities. 2011. 332p. pap. ***(978-3-8443-3343-5(6))*** Lambert Academic Publishing.

Mucherera, Tapiwa N. Meet Me at the Palaver: Narrative Pastoral Counselling in Postcolonial Contexts. 2010. (ENG., Illus.). 151p. pap. 39.00 *(978-0-7188-9219-7(4))* Lutterworth Pr., The GBR. Dist: Brown, David Bk. Co., The.

Muchimba, Felix. Liberating the African Soul: Comparing African & Western Christian Music & Worship Styles. 2008. (ENG.). 156p. per. 14.99 *(978-1-934068-42-7(X))* Authentic Media.

Murindwa-Rutanga. Politics, Religion & Power in the Great Lakes Region. 2011. (Illus.). 270p. pap. ***(978-2-86978-492-5(9))*** Council for the Development of Social Science Research in Africa.

Murray, Muz. Sharing the Quest: Secrets of Self-Understanding. 2010. (Illus.). 384p. pap. 17.99 *(978-1-4490-9834-6(7))* AuthorHouse.

Myambo, Timothy. A Biblical Evaluation of the Avenging Spirits. 2010. 96p. pap. *(978-3-8383-4645-8(9))* Lambert Academic Publishing.

Naipaul, V. S. The Masque of Africa: Glimpses of African Belief. (Vintage International Ser.). (ENG.). 256p. 2011. pap. 16.00 *(978-0-307-45499-7(1)*, Vintage) 2010. 26.95 *(978-0-307-27073-3(4)*, Knopf) Knopf Doubleday Publishing Group.

Ncozana, Silas S. The Spirit Dimension in African Christianity: A Pastoral Study among the Tumbuka People of Northern Malawi. 2006. (Illus.). 207p. pap. 29.95 *(978-99908-81-03-5(0))* Kachere Series, Bks. on Religion, Theology & Society in Malawi MWI. Dist: Michigan State Univ. Pr.

Ndzigou, Brice Parfait. Sacred Light of the Blacks. 2009. 21.40 *(978-1-61623-244-3(7))* Independent Pub.

Ng'etich, Elias. Ethics in a Christian Perspective. 2011. 84p. pap. ***(978-3-8443-0517-3(3))*** Lambert Academic Publishing.

Nielssen, Hilde. Ritual Imagination: A Study of Tromba Possession among the Betsimisaraka in Eastern Madagascar. 2011. (Studies of Religion in Africa Ser.). (Illus.). 334p. ***(978-90-04-21524-5(7))*** BRILL.

Nkansah-Obrempong, James. Visual Theology. 2010. 296p. pap. *(978-3-639-23087-1(6))* VDM Verlag Dr. Mueller e.K.

Noel, James A. Black Religion & the Imagination of Matter in the Atlantic World. 2009. (Black Religion/Womanist Thought/Social Justice Ser.). (ENG., Illus.). 256p. 95.00 *(978-0-230-61506-9(6))* Palgrave Macmillan.

Noll, Mark A. & Nystrom, Carolyn. Clouds of Witnesses: Christian Voices from Africa & Asia. 2011. (ENG.). 286p. 25.00 *(978-0-8308-3834-9(1)*, IVP Bks.) InterVarsity Pr.

Ntamushobora, Faustin. From Trials to Triumphs. 2009. 96p. pap. 13.00 *(978-1-60608-631-5(6)*, Wipf and Stock) Wipf & Stock Pubs.

Ntarangwi, Mwenda. Jesus & Ubuntu: Exploring the Social Impact of Christianity in Africa. 2011. ***(978-1-59221-842-4(3))***; pap. ***(978-1-59221-843-1(1))*** Africa World Pr.

Ó Murchú, Diarmuid. Ancestral Grace: Meeting God in Our Human Story. 2008. xv, 270p. pap. 22.00 *(978-1-57075-794-5(1))* Orbis Bks.

Obafemi, Oluwo Ifakolade. Ile Ifa International. 2011. 80p. pap. 15.99 ***(978-1-4568-6224-4(3))*** Xlibris Corp.

obwoge, hezekiah & Obwoge, Hezekiah. Phenomenology. 2010. 136p. pap. (978-3-8383-7453-6(3)) Lambert Academic Publishing.

Oden, Thomas C. How Africa Shaped the Christian Mind: Rediscovering the African Seedbed of Western Christianity. (Early African Christianity Set Ser.). (ENG.). 204p. 2010. pap. 17.00 (978-0-8308-3705-2(1), IVP Acad.) 2007. (Illus.). 22.00 (978-0-8308-2875-3(3), IVP Bks.) InterVarsity Pr.

Oduyoye, Mercy A. Hearing & Knowing. 2009. 176p. pap. 20.00 (978-1-60608-361-6(0), Wipf and Stock) Wipf & Stock Pubs.

Ohadike, Don C. Sacred Drums of Liberation: Religions & Music of Resistance in Africa & the Diaspora. 2007. xlv, 259p. (978-1-59221-516-4(5)); 304p. pap. (978-1-59221-517-1(3)) Africa World Pr.

Okpalike, Chika J. B. G. +Ch+Aja in Igbo Traditional Religion: A Comparative Study with SACRIFICE in Judaism, Hinduism & Christianity. 2008. 248p. pap. 19.95 (978-0-595-53211-7(X)) iUniverse, Inc.

Ol'Leka, Shitandi Wilson. Meaning in Music, Culture & Theology: An Analysis of Legio Maria Church Hymnody in Kenya. 2011. 216p. pap. (978-3-639-33094-6(3)) VDM Verlag Dr. Mueller e.K.

Onunwa, Udobata R. Contempory Themes in African Religion & Culture. 2008. pap. 19.00 (978-0-8059-8555-9(7)) Dorrance Publishing Co., Inc.

—A Critical Review of Methodologies of African Religion & Culture. 2006. 18.00 (978-0-8059-8309-8(0)) Dorrance Publishing Co., Inc.

Orji, Cyril U. Ethnic & Religious Conflict in Africa: An Analysis of Bias, Decline, & Conversion Based on the Works of Bernard Lonergan. 2008. pap. (978-0-87462-736-7(2)) Marquette Univ. Pr.

P'Bitek, Okot. African Religions in European Scholarship. (African Heritage Classical Research Studies). 140p. reprint ed. 15.00 (978-0-938818-29-8(5)) ECA Assocs.

p'Bitek, Okot. Decolonizing African Religion: A Short History of African Religions in Western Scholarship. 2011. (Illus.). 111p. pap. 15.00 (978-0-9660201-5-1(4)) Diasporic Africa Pr.

Peters, Jamie & Peters, Lea. No Retreat - No Regrets. 2010. 370p. pap. 21.95 (978-1-934749-88-3(5), CrossHouse Publishing) Hannibal Bks.

Peterson, Brian James. Islamization from Below: The Making of Muslim Communities in Rural French Sudan, 1880-1960. 2011. (ENG., Illus.). 336p. pap. 45.00 (978-0-300-15270-8(1)) Yale Univ. Pr.

Phiri, Isabel Apawo. Women, Presbyterianism & Patriarchy: Religious Experience of Chewa Women in Central Malawi. Updated Edition. 2nd ed. 2007. 180p. pap. (978-99908-87-28-0(4)) Kachere Series, Bks. on Religion, Theology & Society in Malawi MWI. Dist: Michigan State Univ. Pr.

Pinches, Theophilus G. The Religion of Babylonia & Assyria. 2009. (ENG.). 132p. pap. 18.99 (978-1-117-06651-6(7), BiblioLife) BiblioBazaar.

—The Religion of Babylonia & Assyria. 2009. 76p. pap. (978-1-4099-4853-7(6)) Dodo Pr.

—The Religion of Babylonia & Assyria. 2007. (ENG.). 84p. per. (978-1-4068-3108-5(5)) Echo Library.

Pinches, Theophilus Goldridge. The Religion of Babylonia & Assyria. 2010. (Illus.). 50p. pap. 14.14 (978-1-154-07026-2(3)) General Bks. LLC.

Pinn, Anthony B. Black Religion & Aesthetics: Religious Thought & Life in Africa & the African Diaspora. Pinn, Anthony B., ed. 2009. (ENG., Illus.). 232p. 95.00 (978-0-230-60550-3(8)) Palgrave Macmillan.

Price, Charles. Becoming Rasta: Origins of Rastafari Identity in Jamaica. 2009. (ENG., Illus.). 288p. pap. 22.00 (978-0-8147-6747-4(8)) New York Univ. Pr.

Pype, Katrien. The Making of the Pentecostal Melodrama: Religion, Media & Gender in Kinshasa. 2012. (ENG.). 348p. 95.00 (978-0-85745-494-2(3)) Berghahn Bks., Inc.

Randall, Philip, et al. Fire in Their Bones: The True Story of a Missionary Couple's Forty Years in Africa. 2008. (Illus.). 274p. pap. 30.00 (978-1-60608-185-3(3)) Wipf & Stock Pubs.

Reuben, Kweingoti & Wangari Mwai Dorcus, Rev. Prof. Ritualization among the Abanyole. 2011. 152p. pap. (978-3-8443-3211-7(1)) Lambert Academic Publishing.

Rizk, Mohamed El-Mohammady. Women in Taarab: The Performing Art in East Africa. 198p. pap. 43.95 (978-3-631-53208-9(3)) Lang, Peter Publishing, Inc.

Rogers, Robert. The Holy Piby - the Blackman's Bible. 2007. 72p. per. 10.99 (978-1-59547-822-1(1)) NuVision Pubns., LLC.

Rouse, Ciona D. Like Breath & Water: Praying with Africa. 2010. (Illus.). 92p. (978-0-8358-1012-8(7)) Upper Room Bks.

Ruele, Moji. How Can We Sing the Lord's Song in a Strange Land? 2010. 316p. pap. (978-3-8383-7442-0(8)) Lambert Academic Publishing.

Semenya, Dr David Kwena & Semenya, David Kwena. Biblical Counselling of Sotho Christians Believing in Witchcraft. 2011. 112p. pap. (978-3-8454-1653-3(X)) Lambert Academic Publishing.

Simms, Rupe. A Gramscian Analysis of the Role of Religion in Politics: Case Studies in Domination, Accommodation, & Resistance in Africa & Europe. 2010. 316p. 119.95 (978-0-7734-3754-8(1)) Mellen, Edwin Pr., The.

Smiley, D. M. Africa - The Womb of God. 10.00 (978-0-9724025-0-7(0)) New Covenant Fellowship International.

Smith, James. Black Saints, Mystics & Holy Folk: The Ancient African Liturgical Church - Volume 1. 2007. 456p. per. 20.95 (978-1-60145-088-3(5)) Booklocker.com, Inc.

Smith, James Howard & Hackett, Rosalind I. J., eds. Displacing the State: Religion & Conflict in Neoliberal Africa. 2011. (Kroc Inst Religion Conflict & Peacebldg Ser.). (ENG.). 288p. pap. 30.00 (978-0-268-03095-7(2)) Univ. of Notre Dame Pr.

Spickard, Jim. Religion Crossing Boundaries: Transnational Religious & Social Dynamics in Africa & the New African Diaspora. Adogame, Afe, ed. 2010. (Religion & the Social Order Ser.). 274p. (978-90-04-18730-6(8)) BRILL.

Starcher, Richard. Africans in Pursuit of a Theological Doctorate. 2010. 244p. pap. (978-3-8383-8087-2(8)) Lambert Academic Publishing.

Strang, Fred Foy. Maasai Life & Christian Practice: A Photographic Portfolio. 2010. 96p. pap. 16.97 (978-0-578-05245-8(8)) Eden Green, LLC.

Teresa Okuru Staff. Concilium 2005/5: African Christianities. 2010. 141p. pap. (978-0-334-03086-7(2), SCM Pr.) Hymns Ancient & Modern Ltd.

Tesfai, Yacob. Holy Warriors, Infidels, & Peacemakers in Africa. 2010. (ENG., Illus.). 200p. 84.00 (978-0-230-10427-3(4)) Palgrave Macmillan.

Thomas, D. L. Defending Christ: The Latin Apologists before Augustine. 2011. (Studia Traditionis Theologiae Ser.). (ENG.). 230p. (C). pap. 94.00 (978-2-503-53669-9(7)) Brepols Pubs. BEL. Dist: ISD.

Tillyrides, Makarios. Adventures in the Unseen: My Adventures in Africa. 2007. 620p. pap. 29.95 (978-1-933275-13-0(8), Orthodox Research Institute) Cocheco Falls Publishing.

Tishken, Joel E., et al, eds. Sàngó in Africa & the African Diaspora. 2009. (African Expressive Cultures Ser.). (ENG & MUL., Illus.). 376p. 75.00 (978-0-253-35336-8(X), 025335336X); pap. 27.95 (978-0-253-22094-3(7), 0253220947) Indiana Univ. Pr.

Trost, Theodore Louis. The African Diaspora & the Study of Religion. Trost, Theodore Louis, ed. 2007. (Religion/Culture/Critique Ser.). (ENG., Illus.). 288p. 100.00 (978-1-4039-7786-1(0)) Palgrave Macmillan.

Turaki, Yusufu. The Trinity of Sin, 1 vol. 2012. (Hippo Ser.). (ENG.). 208p. pap. 19.99 (978-9966-00-318-8(5)) Zondervan.

van Beek, Walter E.A. The Dancing Dead: Ritual & Religion among the Kapsiki/Higi of North Cameroon & Northeastern Nigeria, 1 vol. 2012. (Oxford Ritual Studies Ser.). (ENG.). 384p. 99.00 (978-0-19-985814-9(4)); pap. 45.00 (978-0-19-985816-3(0)) Oxford Univ. Pr., Inc.

van Rensburg, Ewald. God Bless Africa: Nkosi Sikelel IAfrika. 2011. 288p. pap. 17.95 (978-0-7963-1081-1(5)) NB Pubs. Ltd. ZAF. Dist: International Publishers Marketing.

Volz, Stephen. African Teachers on the Colonial Frontier: Tswana Evangelists & Their Communities During the Nineteenth Century. 2011. (Bible & Theology in Africa Ser.). (C). 75.00 (978-1-4331-0949-2(2)) Lang, Peter Publishing, Inc.

Vose, Robin. Dominicans, Muslims & Jews in the Medieval Crown of Aragon. 2009. (Cambridge Studies in Medieval Life & Thought: Fourth Ser.). (ENG., Illus.). 310p. 102.00 (978-0-521-88643-7(0)) Cambridge Univ. Pr.

Wariboko, Nimi. The Depth & Destiny of Work: An African Theological Interpretation. 2008. (978-1-59221-618-5(8)); 284p. pap. (978-1-59221-619-2(6)) Africa World Pr.

Welch, P., ed. Church & Settler in Colonial Zimbabwe: A Study in the History of the Anglican Diocese of Mashonaland/Southern Rhodesia, 1890-1925. 2008. (Studies of Religion in Africa Ser.). (Illus.). 250p. (C). (978-90-04-16746-9(3)) BRILL.

Wesonga, Martin. Bride Wealth from an African Theological Perspective. 2011. 52p. pap. (978-3-8443-1466-3(0)) Lambert Academic Publishing.

West, G. & de Wit, H., eds. African & European Readers of the Bible in Dialogue: In Quest of a Shared Meaning. 2008. 430p. (978-90-04-16656-1(4)) BRILL.

Westmoreland-El, Jahne Jahmal. Lessons in Lyric. 2010. 156p. pap. 17.00 (978-1-4490-7015-1(9)); 24.00 (978-1-4490-7016-8(7)) AuthorHouse.

Whitehouse, Bruce. Migrants & Strangers in an African City. 2012. (Illus.). x, 274p. (978-0-253-00075-0(0)) Indiana Univ. Pr.

Whitehouse, Bruce. Migrants & Strangers in an African City: Exile, Dignity, Belonging. 2012. (ENG., Illus.). 288p. 70.00 (978-0-253-00081-1(5), 0253000815) Indiana Univ. Pr.

WIJSEN, Frans. Seeds of Conflict in a Haven of Peace: From Religious Studies to Interreligious Studies in Africa. 2007. 284p. per. (978-90-420-2188-4(8)) Rodopi.

Williams, Marcia D. Africa... God's Divine Vessel for the Nations. 2007. 197p. pap. 16.95 (978-1-4303-2171-2(7)) Lulu Enterprises Inc.

Wilson, Monica. Religion & the Transformation of Society: A Study in Social Change in Africa. 2009. (ENG.). 176p. pap. 31.99 (978-0-521-10411-1(4)) Cambridge Univ. Pr.

Yamekeh Ackah, James. The Significance of the Eucharistic Theology in Africa Today. 2009. 256p. pap. (978-3-639-13422-3(2)) VDM Verlag Dr. Mueller e.K.

Zaytun, Omary-Sijaona. There Is Only One Place on Earth: 126 Tribes with Different Religions United by One Language & Share Common Grounds of Peace, Freedom of Mind, Love & Unity. 2011. 84p. pap. (978-3-639-34365-6(4)) VDM Verlag Dr. Mueller e.K.

Zogbe, Mama. Mami Wata: Africa's Ancient God/dess Unveiled Vol. I. 2007. (Illus.). 565p. per. 53.33 (978-0-9716245-7-3(7)) Mami Wata Healers Society of North America, Inc.

—Mami Wata: Africa's Ancient God/dess Unveiled Vol. II. 2007. (Illus.). 368p. per. 30.64 (978-0-9716245-8-0(5)) Mami Wata Healers Society of North America, Inc.

—The Sibyls: Demystifying the Absence of the African Ancestress: The First Prophetess of Mami (Wata) 2007. (Illus.). 154p. per. 20.00 (978-0-9716245-6-6(9)) Mami Wata Healers Society of North America, Inc.

—Vodoun: An Illustrated History of Racism & Religious Persecution in America. 2007. (Illus.). 42p. per. 17.87 (978-0-9716245-9-7(3)) Mami Wata Healers Society of North America, Inc.

Zulu, Victor. Local Church Digital Justice. 2010. 64p. pap. (978-3-8383-8540-9(X)) Lambert Academic Publishing.

AFRICA—RURAL CONDITIONS

Cunguara, Benedito. Pathways Out of Poverty in Rural Mozambique. 2010. 96p. pap. (978-3-8383-2090-8(5)) Lambert Academic Publishing.

Hill, Polly. Studies in Rural Capitalism in West Africa. 2009. (African Studies). (ENG.). 192p. pap. 31.99 (978-0-521-10921-5(3)) Cambridge Univ. Pr.

Kaldi, Leita. Roller Skating in the Desert. 2010. 226p. (978-1-4512-8056-2(4)); 228p. pap. 24.95 (978-1-60749-180-4(X)) PublishAmerica, Inc.

Matondi, Prosper, et al, eds. Biofuels,Land Grabbng & Food Security in Africa. 2011. (Africa Now Ser.). (ENG., Illus.). 256p. pap. 39.95 (978-1-84813-878-0(4)) Zed Bks., Ltd. GBR. Dist: Macmillan.

—Biofuels,Land Grbbng & Fd Sec Africa. 2011. (Africa Now Ser.). (ENG., Illus.). 256p. 125.95 (978-1-84813-879-7(2)) Zed Bks., Ltd. GBR. Dist: Macmillan.

Michelo, Lawrence Maumbi. Analysis of Nongovernmental Organisation in Rural Development. 2010. 96p. pap. (978-3-8383-6915-0(7)) Lambert Academic Publishing.

Mortimore, Michael. Adapting to Drought: Farmers, Famines & Desertification in West Africa. 2009. (ENG., Illus.). 324p. pap. 42.00 (978-0-521-10427-2(0)) Cambridge Univ. Pr.

Ndenecho, Emmanuel Neba. Decentralisation & Spatial Rural Development Planning in Cameroon. 2011. 314p. pap. (978-9956-717-66-8(5)) Langaa Research & Publishing Common Initiative Group.

Valensi, Lucette. Tunisian Peasants in the Eighteenth & Nineteenth Centuries. 2009. (Studies in Modern Capitalism Ser.). (ENG.). 308p. pap. 42.00 (978-0-521-10901-7(9)) Cambridge Univ. Pr.

Vuza, Xolisa. Social & Technical Issues of Technology in Developing Countries. 2009. (Illus.). 128p. pap. (978-3-8383-0413-7(6)) Lambert Academic Publishing.

Wooten, Stephen R. The Art of Livelihood: Creating Expressive Agri-Culture in Rural Mali. 2009. 206p. pap. 30.00 (978-1-59460-731-8(1)) Carolina Academic Pr.

World Bank Institute Staff. Agricultural Land Redistribution: Towards Greater Consensus on the How. Binswanger-Mkhize, Hans P. & Bourguignon, Camille, eds. 2009. (Agriculture & Rural Development Ser.). (ENG., Illus.). 464p. pap. 40.00 (978-0-8213-7627-0(6), 9780821376270) World Bank Pubns.

AFRICA—SOCIAL CONDITIONS

Abass, Ademola. Protecting Human Security in Africa. 2010. (ENG.). 400p. 98.50 (978-0-19-957898-6(2)) Oxford Univ. Pr., Inc.

Abbas, Hakima. Africa's Long Road to Rights: Reflections on the 20th Anniversary of the African Commission on Human & Peoples' Rights. 2nd ed. 2007. (FRE.). 188p. per. 19.95 (978-1-906387-25-9(7)) Pambuzuka Pr. GBR. Dist: Independent Pubs. Group.

Abraham, Kinfe. African Quest. the Transition from the Oau to Au. 2010. 714p. pap. 25.75 (978-1-145-12003-7(2)) BiblioBazaar.

Adebajo, Adekeye. Un Peacekeeping in Africa: From the Suez Crisis to the Sudan Conflicts. 2011. 240p. (C). 58.50 (978-1-58826-757-3(1)); pap. 22.00 (978-1-58826-782-5(2)) Rienner, Lynne Pubs.

Adebambo, Olufunmilayo. Fundamentals of Animal Breeding & Genetics. 2010. 428p. pap. (978-3-639-11038-8(2)) VDM Verlag Dr. Mueller e.K.

Adeuyan, Jacob Oluwatayo. The Return of the Tidal Flow of the Middle Passage. 2011. 232p. 24.99 (978-1-4634-2409-1(4)); pap. 16.99 (978-1-4634-2410-7(8)) AuthorHouse.

Adogame, Afe, et al, eds. Unpacking the New: Critical Perspectives on Cultural Syncretization in Africa & Beyond. 2011. (ENG.). 384p. pap. 44.95 (978-3-8258-0719-1(3)) Lit Verlag DEU. Dist: Transaction Pubs.

Africa Contemporary Record: 2003-2004, Vol. XXVIIII. 2008. 495.00 (978-0-8419-1250-2(5)) Holmes & Meier Pubs., Inc.

African commission on Human and Peoples Rights. Reports of the African Commission's Working Group on Indigenous Populations: Research & Information Visit to the Republic of Congo, 5-19 September 2005. 2007. 70p. (gr. 11). pap. 18.95 (978-87-91563-31-7(3)) IWGIA DNK. Dist: Transaction Pubs.

—Reports of the African Commission's Working Group on Indigenous Populations/Communities in Africa: Mission to the Republic of Botswana, 15-23 June 2005. 2008. 120p. (gr. 11). pap. 18.95 (978-87-91563-29-4(1)) IWGIA DNK. Dist: Transaction Pubs.

—Reports of the African Commission's Working Group on Indigenous Populations/Communities in Africa: Research & Information Visit to Burundi, 27 March-9 April 2005. 2007. 50p. (gr. 11). pap. 18.95 (978-87-91563-30-0(5)) IWGIA DNK. Dist: Transaction Pubs.

Africa's Orphaned & Vulnerable Generations: Children Affected by AIDS. 2006. (Illus.). 12p. (978-92-806-4034-2(8)) United Nations Children's Fund, The (UNICEF).

Agergaard, Jytte. Rural-Urban Dynamics: Livelihoods, Mobility & Markets in African & Asian Frontiers. 2009. (Routledge Studies in Human Geography Ser.). (ENG., Illus.). 212p. 150.00 (978-0-415-47562-4(7)) Routledge.

Agergaard, Jytte, et al. Rural-Urban Dynamics: Livelihoods, Mobility & Markets in African & Asian Frontiers. 2009. (Illus.). xx, 212p. (C). 140.00 (978-0-203-87394-6(7)) Routledge.

Aguilar, Mario I. Rethinking Age in Africa: Colonial, Post-Colonial, & Contemporary Interpretations of Cultural Representations. 2006. x, 322p. pap. (978-1-59221-495-2(9)) Africa World Pr.

Agwuele, Augustine, ed. Development, Modernism & Modernity in Africa. 2011. (Routledge African Studies). (ENG., Illus.). 340p. (C). 125.00 (978-0-415-89924-6(9)) Routledge.

Akonor, Kwame. African Economic Institutions. 2009. (Global Institutions Ser.). (ENG., Illus.). 160p. (C). 126.00 (978-0-415-77637-0(6)) Routledge.

Ali, Kamran Asdar. Gendering Urban Space in the Middle East, South Asia, & Africa. Rieker, Martina & Ali, Kamran Asdar, eds. 2008. (ENG.). 248p. 95.00 (978-1-4039-7523-2(X)) Palgrave Macmillan.

April, Kurt. Diversity in Africa: The Coming of Age of a Continent. April, Kurt & Shockley, Marylou, eds. 2007. (ENG., Illus.). 320p. 126.00 (978-0-230-00684-3(1)) Palgrave Macmillan.

Apter, Andrew. Beyond Words: Discourse & Critical Agency in Africa. 2007. (Illus.). 192p. 42.50 (978-0-226-02351-9(6)); per. 17.50 (978-0-226-02352-6(4)) Univ. of Chicago Pr.

Arbache, Jorge Saba, et al. Gender Disparities in Africa's Labor Market. 2010. (Illus.). xxviii, 420p. E-Book 14.99 (978-0-8213-8070-3(2)) World Bank Pubns.

Armah, Collins. Intercountry Child Adoption. 2011. 108p. pap. (978-3-8454-0733-3(6)) Lambert Academic Publishing.

Artley, Oluwole &. Africation. 2007. 154p. pap. 11.95 (978-0-7414-3932-1(8)) Infinity Publishing.

Asah, Alexander Goodness. Transitional Justice Approaches in Post Conflict Sub-Saharan Afric. 2011. 136p. pap. (978-3-8443-2022-0(9)) Lambert Academic Publishing.

Atayi, Jane. Gender Discrimination under the Upe Program - a Ugandan Experience. 2011. 80p. pap. (978-3-8433-8460-5(6)) Lambert Academic Publishing.

Baechler, Ganther. Violence Through Environmental Discrimination: Causes, Rwanda Arena, & Conflict Model. 2010. (Social Indicators Research Ser.). 236p. pap. 219.00 (978-90-481-5144-8(9), 9048151449) Springer.

Bamidele, Emmanuel. Common Voice: Together for change in Africa. 2009. 64p. pap. 10.49 (978-1-4490-2022-4(4)) AuthorHouse.

Bangwanubusa, Theogene. Leadership & Genocidal Violence in Rwand. 2011. 288p. pap. (978-3-8443-1260-7(9)) Lambert Academic Publishing.

Bárkányi Csávás, Maria. The Magic of Africa. 2008. 160p. per. (978-1-84747-463-6(2)) Chipmunkapublishing.

Barlow, Aaron, ed. One Hand Does Not Catch a Buffalo Vol. 1: 50 Years of Amazing Peace Corps Stories - Africa. 2011. (Peace Corps @ 50 Ser.). (ENG.). 400p. pap. 18.95 (978-1-60952-000-7(9)) Travelers' Tales, Inc.

Barrett, Christopher B. Understanding & Reducing Persistent Poverty in Africa. Carter, Michael & Little, Peter, eds. 2008. 256p. pap. 39.95 (978-0-415-46389-8(0)) Routledge.

Baxter, Joan. Dust from Our Eyes: An Unblinkered Look at Africa. 2nd ed. 2010. (ENG.). 425p. pap. 25.00 (978-1-894987-47-9(0)) Wolsak & Wynn Pubs., Ltd. CAN. Dist: Univ. of Toronto Pr.

Bay, Edna G. & Donham, Donald L., eds. States of Violence: Politics, Youth, & Memory in Contemporary Africa. annot. ed. 2006. (ENG.). 320p. (gr. 17). 49.50 (978-0-8139-2569-1(X)) Univ. Pr. of Virginia.

Bayart, Jean-Francois. The State in Africa: The Politics of the Belly. 2nd ed. 2009. (ENG.). 420p. pap. 29.95 (978-0-7456-4437-0(6)) Polity Pr. GBR. Dist: Wiley, John & Sons, Inc.

Beasley, Thomas W. Poverty in Africa. 2009. (Poverty in Africa Ser.). 98.00 (978-1-60741-737-8(5)) Nova Science Pubs., Inc.

Beckman, Bjorn & Adeoti, Gbemisola Remi, eds. Intellectuals & African Development: Pretension & Resistance in African Politics. 2006. (Africa in the New Millennium Ser.). (ENG.). 192p. 123.95 (978-1-84277-764-0(5)); per. 36.95 (978-1-84277-765-7(3)) Zed Bks., Ltd. GBR. Dist: Macmillan.

Bekoe, Dorina A. Implementing Peace Agreements: Lessons from Mozambique, Angola, & Liberia. 2008. (ENG.). 240p. 89.00 (978-0-230-60259-5(2)) Palgrave Macmillan.

Benjamin, Isaac. Great Giants of Wicked Purities. 2009. 236p. pap. 15.99 (978-1-4343-9714-0(9)) AuthorHouse.

Berschinski, Robert G. AFRICOM's Dilemma: The Global War on Terrorism, Capacity Building, Humanitarianism, & the Future of U. S. Security Policy in Africa. 2007. (978-1-58487-328-0(0)) Strategic Studies Institute, U.S. Army War College Commandant (AWCC-DSI/Pubns.).

Bigman, David. Poverty, Hunger & Democracy in Africa: Potential & Limitations of Democracy in Cementing Multi-Ethnic Societies. 2011. (ENG., Illus.). 272p. 105.00 (978-0-230-20528-4(3)) Palgrave Macmillan.

Bikokoa, Ngoa. Anger of Tears: La Colère des Larmes. 2009. 112p. pap. 10.99 (978-1-4389-7581-8(3)) AuthorHouse.

Binns, Tony. Africa Binns. 2012. (ENG., Illus.). 432p. (C). 160.00 (978-0-415-41367-1(2)) Routledge.

Binns, Tony, et al. Africa: Diversity & Development. 2012. (ENG., Illus.). 432p. (C). pap. 59.95 (978-0-415-41368-8(0)) Routledge.

Boon, Mike. The African Way: The Power of Interactive Leadership. 2008. (Illus.). 208p. pap. 15.00 (978-1-77007-310-4(8)) Struik Pubs. ZAF. Dist: International Publishers Marketing.

Bouchat, Clarence J. Security & Stability in Africa: A Development Approach. 2010. (Letort Papers). viii, 155p. pap. (978-1-58487-421-8(X)) Strategic Studies Institute, U.S. Army War College Commandant (AWCC-DSI/Pubns.).

Bownik, Gregory J. Leadership & Nation Building in Africa: Challenges & Opportunities. 2010. 168p. pap. 18.95 (978-1-4327-5948-3(5)) Outskirts Pr., Inc.

Brown, Molly E. Famine Early Warning Systems & Remote Sensing Data. 2010. (ENG., Illus.). xviii, 313p. pap. 199.00 (978-3-642-09458-3(9), 3642094589) Springer.

Buckler, Michael L. From Microsoft to Malawi: Learning on the Front Lines as a Peace Corps Volunteer. 2010. (ENG.). 228p. pap. 19.95 (978-0-7618-5401-2(0)) Hamilton Bks.

Burnett, Patrick, et al, eds. Grace, Tenacity & Eloquence: The Struggle for Women's Rights in Africa. 2007. 232p. pap. 24.95 (978-0-9545637-2-1(7)) Pambuzuka Pr. GBR. Dist: Independent Pubs. Group.

Cargill, Tom. Our Common Strategic Interests: Africa's Role in the Post-G8 World. 2010. (ENG., Illus.). 56p. pap. 15.00 *(978-1-86203-224-8(6))* Royal Institute of International Affairs GBR. Dist: Brookings Institution Pr.

Ceesay, Alhasan Sisawo. Country for President, Tribe & Party. 2011. 182p. pap. 24.95 ***(978-1-4560-7263-6(3))*** PublishAmerica, Inc.

Chaza, Tororiro Isaac. Confessions of a Racist. 2011. 140p. pap. 23.51 ***(978-1-4567-7693-0(2))*** AuthorHouse.

Chervenyashka, Valya & Yordanov, Nikolay. Notes from Hell: A Bulgarian Nurse in Libya. 2011. (Illus.). 160p. pap. 14.95 *(978-1-920143-47-3(5))* 30° South Pubs. ZAF. Dist: International Publishers Marketing.

Christiansen, Catrine, et al. Navigating Youth, Generating Adulthood: Social Becoming in an African Context. Christiansen, Catrine et al, eds. 2006. 272p. pap. 37.50 *(978-91-7106-578-0(4))* Nordiska Afrikainstitutet SWE. Dist: Stylus Publishing, LLC.

Christine, Cubitt. Global Myths & Local Realities of Peacebuilding. 2011. (Conflict, Development & Peacebuilding Ser.). (ENG., Illus.). 256p. (C). 135.00 *(978-0-415-66491-2(8))* Routledge.

Chuhan-Pole, Punam & Angwafo, Manka, eds. Yes, Africa Can: Success Stories from a Dynamic Continent. 2011. (ENG., Illus.). 496p. pap. 49.95 *(978-0-8213-8745-0(6),* 9780821387450) World Bank Pubns.

Clark, Philip & Kaufman, Zachary, eds. After Genocide: Transitional Justice, Post-Conflict Reconstruction, & Reconciliation in Rwanda & Beyond. 2009. (Columbia/Hurst Ser.). (ENG.). 428p. (gr. 17). 50.00 *(978-0-231-70082-5(2))* Columbia Univ. Pr.

Clarke, Duncan. Africa's Future - Darkness to Destiny: How the Past Is Shaping Africa's Economic Evolution. 2012. (ENG., Illus.). 320p. 32.95 ***(978-1-84668-569-9(9))*** Profile Bks. Ltd. GBR. Dist: Consortium Bk. Sales & Distribution.

Cole, Jennifer. Sex & Salvation: Imagining the Future in Madagascar. 2010. (ENG., Illus.). 248p. 80.00 *(978-0-226-11330-2(2))*; pap. 27.50 *(978-0-226-11331-9(0))* Univ. of Chicago Pr.

Cole, Jennifer & Thomas, Lynn M., eds. Love in Africa. 2009. (ENG., Illus.). 280p. 63.00 *(978-0-226-11352-4(3))*; pap. 23.00 *(978-0-226-11353-1(1))* Univ. of Chicago Pr.

Colince, Nguelo. Biofuel Impacts on Food Crisis. 2010. 116p. pap. *(978-3-8383-6247-2(0))* Lambert Academic Publishing.

Columbus, Frank. Politics & Economics of Africa. Volume 8. 2011. (Series: Politics & Economics of Africa Ser.). (Illus.). 326p. 165.00 *(978-1-61122-554-9(X))* Nova Science Pubs., Inc.

Comaroff, Jean & Comaroff, John L. Theory from the South: Or, How Euro-America Is Evolving Toward Africa. 2011. (Radical Imagination Ser.). 272p. 106.00 *(978-1-59451-764-8(9))* Paradigm Pubs.

Conroy, Anne C., ed. Poverty, AIDS & Hunger: Breaking the Poverty Trap in Malawi. 2007. (ENG., Illus.). 280p. 95.00 *(978-1-4039-9833-0(7))* Palgrave Macmillan.

Conyers, James, Jr., ed. Racial Structure & Radical Politics in the African Diaspora. 2009. (ENG., Illus.). 223p. pap. 29.95 *(978-1-4128-1045-6(0))* Transaction Pubs.

Cooper, Ross Gordon. African Giant Rats - an Essay. 2010. 32p. pap. 28.50 *(978-0-557-41884-8(4))* Lulu Enterprises Inc.

Cordell. The Human Tradition In Modern Africa. 2011. (Human Tradition around the World Ser.). (ENG.). 316p. pap. 29.95 ***(978-0-7425-3733-0(1))*** Rowman & Littlefield Publishers, Inc.

Cordell, Dennis D. The Human Tradition In Modern Africa. 2011. (Human Tradition around the World Ser.). (ENG.). 288p. 84.00 ***(978-0-7425-3732-3(3))*** Rowman & Littlefield Publishers, Inc.

Cox, Dan G., et al. Terrorism, Instability, & Democracy in Asia & Africa. 2009. (Northeastern Series on Democratization & Political Development Ser.). (Illus.). 240p. (C). lib. bdg. 65.00 *(978-1-58465-753-8(7))*; (ENG., pap. 21.95 *(978-1-58465-754-5(5))* Univ. Pr. of New England. (Northeastern University Pr.).

Cram101 Textbook Reviews & Cram101 Textbook Reviews. Outlines & Highlights for Africa in the Century: Toward a New Future by Ama Mazama, ISBN. 2011. 114p. pap. 28.95 ***(978-1-61812-033-5(6))*** Cram101 Inc.

Dallaire, Roméo A. They Fight Like Soldiers, They Die Like Children: The Global Quest to Eradicate the Use of Child Soldiers. 2011. (ENG.). 320p. 26.00 *(978-0-8027-7956-4(5))* Walker & Co.

Daniels, Peyton E., ed. Africa's Connection to the Drug Trade. 2010. (African Political, Economic, & Security Issues Ser.). 89.00 *(978-1-61668-668-0(5))* Nova Science Pubs., Inc.

Daubler-Gmelin, Herta, et al, eds. Afrika. Europas verkannter Nachbar: Ansichten und Einsuichten aus Theorie und Praxis. (GER & ENG., Illus.). 207p. pap. 23.95 *(978-3-631-55543-9(1))* Lang, Peter GmbH, Europaischer Verlag der Wissenschaften DEU. Dist: Lang, Peter Publishing, Inc.

Däubler-Gmelin, Herta & Helfrich, Ann Kathrin, eds. Afrika. Europas verkannter Nachbar: Band 2. 2008. 256p. pap. 43.95 *(978-3-631-56571-1(2))* Lang, Peter GmbH, Europaischer Verlag der Wissenschaften DEU. Dist: Lang, Peter.

Davis, John. Africa & the War on Terrorism. 2007. 200p. 114.95 *(978-0-7546-7083-4(X))* Ashgate Publishing Co.

—Terrorism in Africa: The Evolving Front in the War on Terror. 2010. (ENG.). 324p. 78.99 *(978-0-7391-3575-4(9))* Lexington Bks.

Davis, Peter. Corporations, Global Governance & Post-Conflict Reconstruction. 2012. (Routledge Studies in International Business & the World Economy Ser.: 53). (ENG., Illus.). 256p. (C). 125.00 *(978-0-415-61724-6(3))* Routledge.

De Maio, Jennifer. Confronting Ethnic Conflict: The Role of Third Parties in Managing Africa's Civil Wars. 2009. (ENG., Illus.). 244p. 73.50 *(978-0-7391-2845-9(0))* Lexington Bks.

Deane, Phyllis. Colonial Social Accounting. 2011. (ENG.). 388p. pap. 31.99 *(978-1-107-60128-4(2))* Cambridge Univ. Pr.

Deegan, Heather. Africa Today: Culture, Economics, Religion, Security. (Illus.). 2009. XVI, 240p. 170.00 *(978-0-415-41883-6(6))* 2008. (ENG., 256p. (C). pap. 42.95 *(978-0-415-41884-3(4))* Routledge.

Dicks, Ian & Dollar, Shawn. A Practical Guide to Understanding Ciyawo. 2010. (YAO., Illus.). 176p. pap. *(978-99908-87-85-3(3))* Kachere Series, Bks. on Religion, Theology & Society in Malawi MWI. Dist: Michigan State Univ. Pr.

Disney, Jennifer Leigh. Women's Activism & Feminist Agency in Mozambique & Nicaragua. (ENG.). 2009. 306p. pap. 29.95 *(978-1-59213-829-6(2))* 2008. (Illus.). 304p. 71.50 *(978-1-59213-828-9(4))* Temple Univ. Pr.

Dokken, Karin. African Security Politics Redefined. 2008. (ENG., Illus.). 272p. 100.00 *(978-1-4039-7761-8(5))* Palgrave Macmillan.

Doris, David T. Vigilant Things: On Thieves, Yoruba Anti-Aesthetics, & the Strange Fates of Ordinary Objects in Nigeria. 2011. (ENG., Illus.). 416p. 60.00 *(978-0-295-99073-6(2))* Univ. of Washington Pr.

Ekine, Sokari & Manji, Firoze, eds. African Awakening: The Emerging Revolutions. 2011. 312p. pap. 29.95 ***(978-0-85749-021-6(4))*** Pambuzuka Pr. GBR. Dist: Independent Pubs. Group.

Ekonde, Cathy. Tourism Destination Marketing. 2011. (Illus.). 52p. pap. ***(978-3-639-34752-4(8))*** VDM Verlag Dr. Mueller e.K.

Elim, Lokapel David. The Growth & Development of the Turkana People of Kenya, East Africa: A Historical Perspective. 2011. 60p. pap. ***(978-3-639-23514-2(2))*** VDM Verlag Dr. Mueller e.K.

Ellis, Frank, et al. Social Protection in Africa. 2009. (Illus.). 304p. 155.00 *(978-1-84844-258-0(0))*; pap. 50.00 *(978-1-84844-364-8(1))* Elgar, Edward Publishing, Inc.

Ellis, Stephen. Season of Rains: Africa in the World. 2012. 224p. 25.00 ***(978-0-226-20559-5(2))*** Univ. of Chicago Pr.

Englund, Harri. Human Rights & African Airwaves: Mediating Equality on the Chichewa Radio. 2011. (ENG., Illus.). 308p. 70.00 *(978-0-253-35677-2(6),* 0253356776); pap. 24.95 *(978-0-253-22347-0(4),* 0253223474) Indiana Univ. Pr.

Ennaji, Moha & Sadiqi, Fatima. Migration & Gender in Morocco: The Impact of Migration on the Women Left Behind. 2008. *(978-1-56902-291-7(7))*; (Illus.). xi, 206p. pap. *(978-1-56902-292-4(5))* Red Sea Pr.

Ensign/Bertrand. Rwanda: History & Hope. 2009. (ENG.). 174p. pap. 28.50 *(978-0-7618-4943-8(2))* Univ. Pr. of America, Inc.

Epprecht, Marc. Heterosexual Africa: The History of an Idea from the Age of Exploration to the Age of AIDS. 2008. xiii, 231p. pap. *(978-1-86914-157-8(1))* Univ. of Natal Pr. ZAF. Dist: International Specialized Bk. Services.

Erasmus, P. F. Terminal Africa: The curse of the ancestral Cord. 2007. 128p. per. *(978-0-7552-1069-5(7))* Authors OnLine, Ltd.

Erin, Hartzell. Living in Africa: The Convergence of Poverty & the Hiv/Aids Epidemic. 2011. 76p. pap. ***(978-3-639-32788-5(8))*** VDM Verlag Dr. Mueller e.K.

Etuk, Emma Samuel. Listen Africans! A Revolution Is Coming: Why It Must Come & How We Should Deal with It. 2011. 212p. 27.95 *(978-1-4502-7736-5(5))*; pap. 17.95 *(978-1-4502-7734-1(9))* iUniverse, Inc.

Evers, Sandra, et al. Not Just a Victim: The Child As Catalyst & Witness of Contemporary Africa. 2011. (Illus.). 272p. pap. ***(978-90-04-20400-3(8))*** BRILL.

Falola, Toyin & House-Soremekun, Bessie. Gender, Sexuality & Mothering in Africa. 2011. ***(978-1-59221-861-5(X))***; 360p. pap. ***(978-1-59221-862-2(8))*** Africa World Pr.

Farris, Ron. Africans & African Americans Divided: The Male-Female African & African American Digital Divide. 2008. 228p. 34.95 *(978-1-4357-0009-3(0))* Lulu Enterprises Inc.

—Africans & African Americans Divided:the Male-Female African & African American Digital Divide. 2008. 228p. pap. 19.95 *(978-1-4357-0272-1(7))* Lulu Enterprises Inc.

Feldman-Savelsberg, Pamela. Collective Memory, Reproduction & Generation in Africa. 2007. (ENG., Illus.). 128p. (gr. 17). pap. 40.00 *(978-0-7486-2397-6(3))* Edinburgh Univ. Pr. GBR. Dist: Columbia Univ. Pr.

Fokwang, Jude & Langmia, Kehbuma, eds. Society & Change in Bali Nyonga: Critical Perspectives. 2011. 196p. pap. ***(978-9956-579-39-6(4))*** Langaa Research & Publishing Common Initiative Group.

Fosu, Augustin Kwasi & Mwabu, Germano, eds. Malaria & Poverty in Africa. 2007. 200p. (C). pap. *(978-9966-846-63-1(8))* Nairobi University Pr. KEN. Dist: Michigan State Univ. Pr.

Fox, M. Louise. Beating the Odds: Sustaining Inclusion in Mozambique's Growing Economy. 2008. (Directions in Development Ser.). (ENG., Illus.). 304p. pap. 35.00 incl. cd-rom *(978-0-8213-7565-5(2),* 9780821375655) World Bank Pubns.

Frere, Marie-Soleil. The Media & Conflicts in Central Africa. 2006. 250p. (C). pap. 23.50 *(978-1-58826-465-7(3))*; lib. bdg. 55.00 *(978-1-58826-489-3(0))* Rienner, Lynne Pubs.

Fuller, Linda K. African Women's Unique Vulnerabilities to HIV/AIDS: Communication Perspectives & Promises. 2008. (ENG.). 328p. 105.00 *(978-1-4039-8405-0(0))* Palgrave Macmillan.

Fullwiley, Duana. The Enculturated Gene: Sickle Cell Health Politics & Biological Difference in West Africa. 2011. (ENG., Illus.). 368p. (C). pap. 35.00 ***(978-0-691-12317-2(9))*** Princeton Univ. Pr.

—Mix of Life: Living Science & Disease in Modern Africa. 2011. (ENG., Illus.). 368p. (C). 90.00 ***(978-0-691-12316-5(0))*** Princeton Univ. Pr.

Galz. Unspoken Facts. 2008. 272p. pap. 29.95 *(978-0-7974-3407-3(0))* GALZ ZWE. Dist: Michigan State Univ. Pr.

Gam Nkwi, Walter. Voicing the Voiceless: Contributions to Closing Gaps in Cameroon History, 1958-2009. 2010. 200p. pap. *(978-9956-616-40-4(0))* Langaa Research & Publishing Common Initiative Group CMR. Dist: Michigan State Univ. Pr.

Gewald, J. -b. The Speed of Change: Motor Vehicles & People in Africa, 1890-2000. Gewald, J. -B. & Luning, S. W. J., eds. 2009. 304p. pap. *(978-90-04-17735-2(3))* BRILL.

Glover, John. Sufism & Jihad in Modern Senegal: The Murid Order. 2007. (Rochester Studies in African History & the Diaspora Ser.: Volume 32). (Illus.). 250p. 75.00 *(978-1-58046-268-6(5))* Univ. of Rochester Pr.

González, Ana Marta, et al. Frontiers of Globalization: Kinship & Family Structures in Africa. 2010. *(978-1-59221-771-7(0))* Africa World Pr.

Gordon, April A. & Gordon, Donald L., eds. Understanding Contemporary Africa, 4th Edition. 4th ed. 2006. (Illus.). 475p. (C). pap. 27.50 *(978-1-58826-466-4(1))* Rienner, Lynne Pubs.

Grosspietsch, Michael. Tourism & Poverty Reduction in Rwand. 2008. 448p. pap. *(978-3-639-07579-3(X))* VDM Verlag Dr. Mueller e.K.

Gruzd, Steven, ed. Grappling with Governance: Perspectives on the African Peer Review Mechanism. 2011. (ENG.). 232p. pap. 31.95 ***(978-1-920196-30-1(7))*** Jacana Media ZAF. Dist: Independent Pubs. Group.

Guest, Robert. The Shackled Continent: Power, Corruption, & African Lives. 2010. (ENG.). 288p. pap. 21.95 *(978-1-58834-297-3(2))* Smithsonian Institution Pr.

Guillebaud, Simon. For What It's Worth: A Call to No Holds Barred Discipleship, 1 vol. 2007. 224p. pap. 12.99 *(978-0-8254-6123-1(5),* Monarch Bks.) Lion Hudson PLC GBR. Dist: Kregel Pubns.

Haan, Leo de & Engel, Ulf, eds. African Alternatives. 2007. (African-Europe Group for Interdisciplinary Studies). pap. *(978-90-04-16113-9(9))* BRILL.

Haba, Joseph. Education, Democracy & Leadership: Changing Old African Cultures & Timing Innovative & Strategic Policies. 2009. 274p. pap. 16.95 *(978-1-4327-4062-7(8))* Outskirts Pr., Inc.

Hahn, Hans. Consumption in Africa: Anthropological Approaches. 2009. (ENG., Illus.). 208p. pap. 44.95 *(978-3-8258-0725-2(8))* Lit Verlag DEU. Dist: Transaction Pubs.

Hahn, Hans Peter, et al. Cultures of Migration: African Perspectives. Hahn, Hans Peter & Klute, Georg, eds. 2008. (ENG.). 296p. pap. 49.95 *(978-3-8258-0668-2(5))* Lit Verlag DEU. Dist: Transaction Pubs.

Haram, Liv & Yamba, Bawa, eds. Dealing with Uncertainty in Contemporary African Lives. 2009. 300p. pap. 22.95 *(978-91-7106-649-7(7))* Nordiska Afrikainstitutet SWE. Dist: Stylus Publishing, LLC.

Harrison, Graham. Neoliberal Africa: The Impact of Global Social Engineering. 2010. (ENG.). 192p. 116.95 *(978-1-84813-319-8(7))*; pap. 32.95 *(978-1-84813-320-4(0))* Zed Bks., Ltd. GBR. Dist: Macmillan.

Harriss-White, Barbara & Heyer, Judith, eds. The Comparative Political Economy of Development. 2012. (ENG., Illus.). 358p. (C). pap. 44.95 ***(978-0-415-80995-5(9))*** Routledge.

Harriss-white, Barbara & Heyer, Judith, eds. The Comparative Political Economy of Development: Africa & South Asia. 2010. (Routledge Studies in Development Economics Ser.). (ENG., Illus.). 384p. (C). 145.00 *(978-0-415-55288-2(5))* Routledge.

Haugen, David M., ed. Africa. 2011. (Opposing Viewpoints Ser.). (Illus.). 240p. (ENG.). pap. 27.50 *(978-0-7377-5704-0(3),* Greenhaven Pr., Inc.); (YA). (gr. 9-12). 39.70 *(978-0-7377-5703-3(5))* Cengage Gale.

Hecht, Gabrielle. Being Nuclear: Africans & the Global Uranium Trade. 2012. (ENG., Illus.). 440p. (gr. 17). 29.95 ***(978-0-262-01726-8(1))*** MIT Pr.

Helliker, Kirk & Murisa, Tendai. Land Struggles & Civil Society in Southern Africa. 2011. *(978-1-59221-815-8(6))*; 240p. pap. *(978-1-59221-816-5(4))* Africa World Pr.

Henderson, Callum. Beauty from Ashes: Journeys of Recovery from the Rwandan Genocide. 2007. (ENG.). 240p. per. 14.99 *(978-1-85078-722-8(0))* Authentic Media.

Hentz, James J., ed. Routledge Handbook of African Security. 2013. (ENG.). 392p. (C). 200.00 *(978-0-415-68214-5(2))* Routledge.

Hepburn, H. Randall & Radloff, Sarah E. Honeybees of Africa. 2010. (ENG., Illus.). xvi, 370p. pap. 171.00 *(978-3-642-08389-1(7),* 3642083897) Springer.

Holou, Roland A. A. Y. A Continent in Tears: The Origin of Africa's Collapse & How to Reverse It. 2010. 206p. pap. 18.95 *(978-1-4327-1734-6(0))* Outskirts Pr., Inc.

Honwana, Alcinda Manuel. The Time of Youth: Work, Social Change, & Politics in Africa. 2012. 75.00 ***(978-1-56549-471-8(7))***; pap. 27.95 ***(978-1-56549-472-5(5))*** Stylus Publishing, LLC. (Kumarian Pr).

Hope, Kempe Ronald. Poverty, Livelihoods, & Governance in Africa: Fulfilling the Development Promise. 2008. (ENG.). 224p. 89.00 *(978-0-230-60834-4(5))* Palgrave Macmillan.

Howard-Hassmann, Rhoda E. Reparations to Africa. 2008. (Pennsylvania Studies in Human Rights). 272p. (C). 59.95 *(978-0-8122-4101-3(0))* Univ. of Pennsylvania Pr.

Igbani, B. Maduabuchi A. Motherland Afrika: The Footprint of a Generation. rev. ed. 2008. (ENG.). 116p. pap. 31.99 *(978-1-4389-3472-3(6))* AuthorHouse.

Ige, Busayo. Impoliteness in Context. 2011. 264p. pap. ***(978-3-8443-9357-6(9))*** Lambert Academic Publishing.

Igwilo, Malachy. A Philosophical Analysis of Claude Ake's Idea of Development. 2011. 96p. pap. ***(978-3-8433-8467-4(3))*** Lambert Academic Publishing.

Imahküs, Seestah. Returning Home Ain't Easy but It Sure Is a Blessing. 2011. 312p. pap. ***(978-1-4251-4763-1(1))*** Trafford Publishing (UK) Ltd.

Imobighe, T.A. & Eguavoen, A. N. T. Terrorism & Counter-Terrorism an Africa Perspective. 2007. 220p. pap. *(978-978-129-999-5(1))* Heinemann Educational Bks. (Nigeria), Ltd. NGA. Dist: Michigan State Univ. Pr.

Izugbara, Chimaraoke O. Old Wineskins, New Wine: Readings in Sexuality in Sub-Saharan Africa. Ezeh, Alex C., ed. 2010. (Human Sexuality Ser.). 267p. 135.00 *(978-1-60876-954-4(2))* Nova Science Pubs., Inc.

Jackson, Bertha. Africa-A Pre-Trip Must! 2007. 64p. per. 9.99 *(978-1-60266-920-8(1))* Xulon Pr., Inc.

Janeske, Botes. The Hopeless Continent? 2007/2008 Local & International Media Representations of Africa. 2011. 116p. pap. ***(978-3-639-33148-6(6))*** VDM Verlag Dr. Mueller e.K.

Kaarsholm, Preben, ed. Violence, Political Culture & Development in Africa. 2006. (Ohio RIS Global Ser.). 224p. per. 24.00 *(978-0-89680-251-3(5))* Ohio Univ. Pr.

Kabbar, Reem, et al. Poverty in Khartoum State, Sudan. 2011. 84p. pap. ***(978-3-8443-9164-0(9))*** Lambert Academic Publishing.

Kale Ewusi, Ebenezer Akwanga Jr. Bsc. Burundi's Negative Peace: The Shadow of a Broken Continent in the Era of NEPAD. 2010. 408p. 31.96 *(978-1-4269-2354-8(6))* Trafford Publishing.

Kalla, Britt. Utopia or Reality? - the Implementation of a Human Rights-Based Approach to the New Partnership for Africa's Development. 2008. 104p. pap. *(978-3-639-03238-3(1))* VDM Verlag Dr. Mueller e.K.

Kalu, Ogbu, et al. African Pentecostalism: Global Discourses, Migrations, Exchanges, & Connections. 2010. *(978-1-59221-767-0(2))* Africa World Pr.

Kapere, Muzeyi. Sexual Concepts & Sexual Stories: The African Man's Perspective. 2009. (ENG.). 260p. pap. 22.00 *(978-1-58982-512-3(8),* Millennial Mind Publishing) American Bk. Publishing Group.

Kasomo, Daniel W. An Introduction to African Culture & Religion. 2010. 96p. pap. *(978-3-8383-9308-7(2))* Lambert Academic Publishing.

Keyanti, Federick Kanjo. The Plights of Internally Displaced Persons During Armed Conflict. 2011. 68p. pap. ***(978-3-8383-9165-6(9))*** Lambert Academic Publishing.

Khoza, Reuel J. Attuned Leadership: African Humanism as Compass. 2012. (ENG.). 544p. (gr. 12). 39.95 ***(978-0-14-352819-7(X)***, Penguin Global) Penguin Group (USA) Inc.

Kieh, George Klay, ed. Africa & the new Globalization. 2008. 206p. 114.95 *(978-0-7546-7138-1(0))* Ashgate Publishing Co.

King, Nathaniel. Conflict as Integration: Youth Aspiration to Personhood/Sierra Leone. 2007. (NAI Current African Issues Ser.). 40p. pap. 12.95 *(978-91-7106-604-6(7))* Nordiska Afrikainstitutet SWE. Dist: Stylus Publishing, LLC.

Kochalumchuvattil, Thomas. Kierkegaardian Subjectivity & African Philosophy. 2010. 368p. pap. *(978-3-8383-8276-0(5))* Lambert Academic Publishing.

Koko, Jacques L. National Conference As a Strategy for Conflict Transformation & Peacemaking: The Legacy of the Republic of Benin Model (HB) 2008. 220p. *(978-1-905068-87-6(5))* Adonis & Abbey Publishers Ltd.

—National Conference As a Strategy for Conflict Transformation & Peacemaking: The Legacy of the Republic of Benin Model (PB) 2008. 220p. per. *(978-1-905068-52-4(2))* Adonis & Abbey Publishers Ltd.

K'Orinda-Yimbo, Akinyi von. Darkest Europe & Africa's Nightmare: A Critical Observation of the Neighbouring Continents. 2007. 34.95 *(978-0-87586-519-5(4))*; pap. 22.95 *(978-0-87586-518-8(6))* Algora Publishing.

Krotz, Larry. The Uncertain Business of Doing Good: Outsiders in Africa. 2009. (ENG., Illus.). 220p. pap. 24.95 *(978-0-87013-852-2(9))* Michigan State Univ. Pr.

Kumase, Wokia-azi Ndangle. Aspects of Poverty & Inequality in Cameroon. 2009. (Göttinger Studien zur Entwicklungsökonomik. Göttingen Studies in Development Economics Ser.). (Illus.). 172p. 57.95 *(978-3-631-59535-0(2))* Lang, Peter GmbH, Europaischer Verlag der Wissenschaften DEU. Dist: Lang, Peter.

Kusow, Abdi & Bjork, Stephanie R. From Mogadishu to Dixon: The Somali Diaspora in a Global Context. 2007. *(978-1-56902-285-6(2))*; 342p. pap. *(978-1-56902-286-3(0))* Red Sea Pr.

Kuwali, Dan. Persuasive Prevention: Towards a Mechanism for Implementing Article 4(h) & R2P by the African Union. 2009. (NAI Discussion Papers). 60p. pap. 12.95 *(978-91-7106-650-3(0))* Nordiska Afrikainstitutet SWE. Dist: Stylus Publishing, LLC.

Lahire, Nathalie. Youth Employment & Skills Development in The Gambia. 2011. ***(978-0-8213-8813-6(4))*** World Bank Pubns.

Lamle, Elias Nankap. Laughter & Conflicts in Africa: Peace Studies & Conflict Resolution in Africa: A Case Study of the Middle Belt of Nigeria. 2011. 296p. pap. ***(978-3-639-32172-2(3))*** VDM Verlag Dr. Mueller e.K.

Langmia, Kehbuma. The Internet & the Construction of the Immigrant Public Sphere: The Case of the Cameroonian Diaspora. 2007. (ENG., Illus.). 100p. per. 26.50 *(978-0-7618-3792-3(2))* Univ. Pr. of America, Inc.

Larsen, Kjersti, ed. Knowledge, Renewal & Religion. 2009. 310p. pap. 22.95 *(978-91-7106-635-0(7))* Nordiska Afrikainstitutet SWE. Dist: Stylus Publishing, LLC.

Latigo, Alfred A. R. The Best Options for Afric: 11 Political, Economic & Divine Principles. 2009. 236p. 35.00 *(978-1-4269-1918-3(2))* Trafford Publishing.

—The Best Options for Africa: 11 Political, Economic & Divine Principles. 2009. 236p. 35.00 *(978-1-4269-0767-8(2))* Trafford Publishing.

Lawley, Jonathan. Beyond the Malachite Hills: A Life of Colonial Service & Business in the New Africa. 2009. (ENG., Illus.). 256p. 55.00 (978-1-84885-049-1(2)) I. B. Tauris & Co., Ltd. GBR. Dist: Macmillan.

Lebbady, Hasna. Feminist Traditions in Andalusi-Moroccan Oral Narratives. 2009. (ENG., Illus.). 256p. 84.00 (978-0-230-61940-1(1)) Palgrave Macmillan.

Lekogo, Rodolf Estimé & Lekogo, Rodolf Estimé. The Migration of Francophone Africans to Cape Town. 2011. 340p. pap. (978-3-8443-0995-9(0)) Lambert Academic Publishing.

Leslie, Agnes Ngoma. Social Movements & Democracy in Africa: The Impact of Women's Struggle for Equal Rights in Botswana. 2006. (African Studies: History, Politics, Economics & Culture Ser.). (ENG., Illus.). 192p. 138.00 (978-0-415-97847-7(5)) Routledge.

Light, David. Kick 4 Malawi. 2010. 249p. pap. 27.50 (978-1-4452-1426-9(1)) Lulu Enterprises Inc

Little, John & Hamlin, Catherine. Catherine's Gift: Stories of Hope from the Hospital by the River, 1 vol. 2010. (ENG., Illus.). 280p. pap. 14.99 (978-1-85424-955-5(X), Monarch Bks.) Lion Hudson PLC GBR. Dist: Kregel Pubns.

Lloyd, Harvey. Through My Eyes: The Remarkable Children of Senegal. 2010. (ENG.). 256p. 45.00 incl. DVD (978-1-932646-42-9(6)) Ruder-Finn Pr.

Lockwood, Matthew. The State They're In: An Agenda for International Action on Poverty in Africa. 2nd rev. ed. 2006. (Viewpoints Ser.). (ENG.). 208p. pap. 24.95 (978-1-85339-640-3(0)) Practical Action Publishing GBR. Dist: Stylus Publishing, LLC.

Lushaba, Lwazi. Development As Modernity, Modernity As Development. 2009. (Illus.). 78p. pap. (978-2-86978-252-5(7)) Council for the Development of Social Science Research in Africa SEN. Dist: Michigan State Univ. Pr.

Lust, Ellen M. & Ndegwa, Stephen N., eds. Governing Africa¿s Changing Societies: Dynamics of Reform. 2012. 180p. 55.00 (978-1-58826-834-1(9)) Rienner, Lynne Pubs.

Lwemamu, Helen. Gender & Work Challenges in the Informal Sector of Ugand. 2011. 168p. pap. (978-3-8443-0093-2(7)) Lambert Academic Publishing.

Lyons & Lyons, Terrence. Conflict Management & African Politics: Ripeness, Bargaining, & Mediation. Lyons & Lyons, Terrence, eds. 2008. (Routledge Studies in Security & Conflict Management Ser.). (Illus.). XIII, 163p. 150.00 (978-0-415-44301-2(6)) Routledge.

Maathai, Wangari. The Challenge for Africa. 2010. (ENG.). 336p. pap. 15.95 (978-0-307-39028-8(4), Anchor) Knopf Doubleday Publishing Group.

Maiga, Hassimi. Balancing Written History with Oral Traditions: The Legacy of the Songhoy People. 2009. (African Studies). (ENG., Illus.). 230p. 125.00 (978-0-415-96351-0(6)) Routledge.

Makhulu, A. M. Hard Work, Hard Times - Global Volatility & African Subjectives. 2010. (Global, Area, & International Archive Ser.). 256p. pap. 29.95 (978-0-520-09874-9(9)) Univ. of California Pr.

Mandova, Evans. National Patriotic Culture. 2011. 76p. pap. (978-3-8443-3249-0(9)) Lambert Academic Publishing.

Maticka-Tyndale, Eleanor, et al. Human Sexuality in Africa: Beyond Reproduction. 2008. (ENG.). 244p. pap. 17.00 (978-1-920196-02-8(1)) Jacana Media ZAF. Dist: Independent Pubs. Group.

Matimura, Masango. Building Peace in the Horn of Afric. 2010. 88p. pap. (978-3-639-28199-6(3)) VDM Verlag Dr. Mueller e.K.

Mazama, Ama. Africa in the 21st Century: Toward a New Future. 2007. (African Studies: History, Politics, Economics & Culture Ser.). 286p. 138.00 (978-0-415-95773-1(7)) Routledge.

Mazrui, Ali Al'Amin, et al. The Politics of War & the Culture of Violence: North-South Essays. 2007. (978-1-59221-584-3(X)); pap. (978-1-59221-585-0(8)) Africa World Pr.

Mbah, Emmanuel M. & Salm, Steven J. Globalization & the African Experience. 2012. pap. (978-1-61163-158-6(0)) Carolina Academic Pr.

Mbeseha, Timothy & Nkemnji, John. Bellah Ngeh Development Insight. 2008. (Illus.). 144p. (978-0-9755261-6-3(2)) Nkemnji Global Tech.

McCann, Gerard & McCloskey, Stephen. From the Local to the Global: Key Issues in Development Studies. 2nd ed. 2009. (ENG.). 320p. 95.00 (978-0-7453-2843-0(1)) Pluto Pr. GBR. Dist: Macmillan.

Mcclosky, Mccann, et al. From the Local to the Global: Key Issues in Development Studies. 2nd ed. 2009. (ENG.). 320p. pap. 29.00 (978-0-7453-2842-3(3)) Pluto Pr. GBR. Dist: Macmillan.

McGovern, Mike. Unmasking the State in Guinea. 2012. 320p. pap. 32.50 (978-0-226-92510-3(2)); (Illus.). 90.00 (978-0-226-92509-7(9)) Univ. of Chicago Pr.

McPeak, John G., et al. Risk & Social Change in an African Rural Economy: Livelihoods in Pastoralist Communities. 2011. (Routledge ISS Studies in Rural Livelihoods Ser.). (ENG., Illus.). 224p. (C). 125.00 (978-0-415-61598-3(4)) Routledge.

McQueen, Jeremy S. Economic, Political, & Social Issues of Africa. 2012. (Series: African Political, Economic, & Security Issues Ser.). 262p. 129.00 (978-1-61209-957-6(2)) Nova Science Pubs., Inc.

Mehlomakulu, Vuyelwa. Construction of Masculine Sexuality: A Psychological Discourse Analysis. 2010. 84p. pap. (978-3-8383-8252-4(8)) Lambert Academic Publishing.

Mekonnen, Daniel Rezene. TRANSITIONAL JUSTICE: Framing a Model for Eritrea. 2009. 340p. pap. (978-3-639-15372-9(3)) VDM Verlag Dr. Mueller e.K.

Melber, Henning, et al. Africa, Regional Cooperation & the World Market: Socio-Economic Strategies in Times of Global Trade Regimes. 2006. (NAI Discussion Papers). 72p. pap. 13.95 (978-91-7106-559-9(8)) Nordiska Afrikainstitutet SWE. Dist: Stylus Publishing, LLC.

Meredith, Martin. The Fate of Africa: A History of the Continent since Independence. 2011. (ENG., Illus.). 816p. pap. 21.99 (978-1-61039-071-2(7)) PublicAffairs.

Migration en Mauritanie: Profil national 2009. 2009. 121p. pap. (978-92-9068-558-6(1)) International Organization for Migration (IOM).

Miheso, Henry. Planning Issues in Multicultural Urban Communities. 2011. 96p. pap. (978-3-8443-0516-6(5)) Lambert Academic Publishing.

Morris, Brian. Wildlife & Landscapes in Malawi: Selected Essays on Natural History. 2009. 326p. pap. 21.79 (978-1-4251-7183-4(4)) Trafford Publishing.

Moseley, William. Clashing Views on African Issues. 4th ed. 2011. (Taking Sides Ser.). (ENG., Illus.). 464p. (C). pap. 48.00 (978-0-07-805008-4(1), 0078050081, McGraw-Hill/Dushkin) McGraw-Hill Higher Education.

Moseley, William G. Clashing Views on African Issues. 3rd ed. 2008. (Taking Sides Ser.). (ENG.). 416p. (C). pap. 48.00 (978-0-07-351518-2(3), 0073515183, McGraw-Hill/Dushkin) McGraw-Hill Higher Education.

Mudhal, Okoth Fred & Banda, Fackson. African Media & the Digital Public Sphere. Mudhal, Okoth Fred & Banda, Fackson, eds. Tettey, Wisdom J., ed. 2009. (Palgrave Macmillan Series in Internatioal Political Communication Ser.). (ENG.). 276p. 105.00 (978-0-230-61486-4(8)) Palgrave Macmillan.

Muecke, Stephen & Pam, Max. Contingency in Madagascar. Cramerotti, Alfredo, ed. 2012. (Intellect Books - Critical Photography Ser.). (ENG., Illus.). 128p. pap. 45.00 (978-1-84150-474-2(2)) Intellect, Ltd. GBR. Dist: Chicago Distribution Ctr.

Mungai, Rose & World Bank. Africa Development Indicators 2011. 2011. (ENG.). cd-rom 50.00 (978-0-8213-8782-5(0), 9780821387825) World Bank Pubns.

Mungwini, Pascah. Indigenous African Values, Ambivalence & Postcolonial Education. 2010. 208p. pap. (978-3-639-25320-7(5)) VDM Verlag Dr. Mueller e.K.

Musa, Bala. Framing Genocide: Media, Diplomacy & Conflict Transformation. 2007. 224p. lib. bdg. 74.95 (978-1-933146-16-4(8)) Academica Pr., LLC.

Musingafi, Maxwell, et al. Post-Conflict Reconstruction. 2011. 200p. pap. (978-3-8454-1440-9(5)) Lambert Academic Publishing.

Mustafa Elmulthum, Nagat. Poverty & Food Security in the Sudan. 2011. 84p. pap. (978-3-8443-2682-6(0)) Lambert Academic Publishing.

Muthuki, Janet. Renegotiation of Gender Identities in Transnational Spaces. 2010. 248p. pap. (978-3-8383-7433-8(9)) Lambert Academic Publishing.

Mwakikagile, Godfrey. Africa Is in A Mess What Went Wrong and. 2006. pap. (978-0-9802534-7-4(0)) New Africa Pr.

Myers, Andrea. God Loves Africa the Most. 2009. 78p. pap. 15.99 (978-1-4415-1206-2(3)) Xlibris Corp.

Nadeau, Carla. The Efficacy of Pre-Departure Cultural Orientation in Acculturation: An examination of employment as an element of acculturation success. 2008. 92p. pap. (978-3-639-09637-8(1)) VDM Verlag Dr. Mueller e.K.

Ndulo, Muna, ed. Democartic Reform in Africa: The Impact on Governance & Poverty Alleviation. 2006. (Illus.). 320p. pap. 34.95 (978-0-85255-946-8(1), Currey, James) Boydell & Brewer, Ltd. GBR. Dist: Boydell & Brewer, Inc.

—Democratic Reform in Africa: The Impact on Governance & Poverty Alleviation. 2006. (Illus.). 320p. 90.00 (978-0-85255-945-1(3), Currey, James) Boydell & Brewer, Ltd. GBR. Dist: Boydell & Brewer, Inc.

Neckebrouck, V. Entre le global et le Local: Inculturation et changement Social. 2007. (Annua Nuntia Lovaniensia Ser.). (ENG.). 198p. (C). pap. 65.00 (978-90-429-1960-0(4)) Peeters Pubs. & Booksellers BEL. Dist: Brown, David Bk. Co., The.

Nederlof, Suzanne & Heemskerk, Willem, eds. Access of the Poor to Agricultural Services: The Role of Farmers' Organizations in Social Inclusion. 2007. (Bulletins of the Royal Tropical Institute Ser.). (Illus.). 160p. per. 35.00 (978-90-6832-642-0(2)) Royal Tropical Institute Pr. (KIT (Koninklijk Instituut voor de Tropen) NLD. Dist: Stylus Publishing, LLC.

Newell, Sasha. The Modernity Bluff: Crime, Consumption, & Citizenship in Cote D'Ivoire. 2012. (ENG., Illus.). 296p. 85.00 (978-0-226-57519-3(5)); pap. 27.50 (978-0-226-57520-9(9)) Univ. of Chicago Pr.

Ngwane, Mwakimu George. The Power in the Writer: Collected Essays on Culture, Democracy & Development in Africa. 2008. 196p. (978-9956-558-37-7(0)) Langaa Research & Publishing Common Initiative Group CMR. Dist: Michigan State Univ. Pr.

Nhema, Alfred & Zeleza, Paul T. The Resolution of African Conflicts: The Management of Conflict Resolution & Post-Conflict Reconstruction. 2008. (Illus.). xv, 207p. (978-1-86888-493-3(7)) Ohio Univ. Pr.

Nhema, Alfred & Zeleza, Paul Tiyambe, eds. The Roots of African Conflicts: The Causes & Costs. 2008. (ENG., Illus.). 288p. pap. 24.95 (978-0-8214-1809-3(2)) Ohio Univ. Pr.

Nimeta, Mezgebu. Fertility Levels Trends & Determinants in Oromia Region, Ethiopi. 2010. 84p. pap. (978-3-639-19907-9(3)) VDM Verlag Dr. Mueller e.K.

Njoku, Raphael Chijoke, ed. Missions, States, & European Expansion in Africa. 2007. (African Studies). 302p. 128.00 (978-0-415-95559-1(9)) Routledge.

Ntagengwa, Jean Baptiste. Overcoming Cycles of Violence in Rwanda: Ethical Leadership & Ethnic Justice. 2010. 568p. 139.95 (978-0-7734-1411-2(8)) Mellen, Edwin Pr., The.

Ntlhakana, Teboho. Perceptions of Resilience to Social Environmental Risk Factors. 2011. 124p. pap. (978-3-8454-0317-5(9)) Lambert Academic Publishing.

Nugent, Paul, et al, eds. Making Nations, Creating Strangers: States & Citizenship in Africa. 2007. (African Social Studies). 277p. per. (978-90-04-15790-3(5)) BRILL.

Obono, Oka, ed. A Tapestry of Human Sexuality in Africa. 2010. (ENG.). 1500p. pap. 21.95 (978-1-920196-26-4(9)) Jacana Media ZAF. Dist: Independent Pubs. Group.

Ofosu-Donkoh, Kobina. Human Rights in African Religions & Philosophy. 2010. 204p. pap. (978-3-8383-4186-6(4)) Lambert Academic Publishing.

Omwa, Samuel Samson. Community-Based Initiatives in Enhancing Ovc Service Delivery. 2011. 172p. pap. (978-3-8443-2575-1(1)) Lambert Academic Publishing.

Ondeng, Pete. Africa's Moment. 2010. 108p. pap., pap. 12.00 (978-0-615-22190-8(4)) Asset Capital, Ltd.

Onitiri-Abiola, Modupe. Farewell to Poverty: Let There Be Light in Africa. 2007. pap. 9.00 (978-0-8059-7377-8(X)) Dorrance Publishing Co., Inc.

Oversight of the Feed the Future Initiative: Joint Hearing Before the Subcommittee on International Organizations, Human Rights, & Oversight & the Subcommittee on Africa & Global Health of the Committee on Foreign Affairs, House of Representatives, One Hundred Eleventh Congress, Second Session, July 20, 2010. 2010. (Illus.). v, 109p. (978-0-16-087068-2(2), 552-070-41925-0) United States Government Printing Office.

Oyewumi, Oyeronke. Gender Epistemologies in Africa: The Gendering of African Traditions, Spaces, Social Identities, & Institutions. 2010. (ENG.). 256p. 89.00 (978-0-230-62345-3(X)) Palgrave Macmillan.

Palmié, Stephan. Africas of the Americas: Beyond the Search for Origins in the Study of Afro-Atlantic Religions. Palmié, Stephan, ed. 2008. (Studies of Religion in Africa Ser.). 355p. (978-90-04-16472-7(3)) BRILL.

Patnaik, Utsa & Moyo, Sam. The Agrarian Question in the Neoliberal Era: Primitive Accumulation & the Peasantry. 2011. (Illus.). 96p. pap. 14.95 (978-0-85749-038-4(9)) Pambuzuka Pr. GBR. Dist: Independent Pubs. Group.

Patterson, Rubin, ed. African Brain Circulation: Beyond the Drain-Gain Debate. 2007. (International Studies in Sociology & Social Anthropology Ser.). 200p. pap. (978-90-04-15885-6(5)) BRILL.

Peters, Krijn. War & the Crisis of Youth in Sierra Leone. 2011. (International African Library). (ENG., Illus.). 296p. 90.00 (978-1-107-00419-1(5)) Cambridge Univ. Pr.

Phuka, John. Efficacy of Complementary Food Supplementation with Lipid-Based Nutrient Supplements on Growth of Malawian Children. 2009. (Acta Universitatis Tamperensis Ser.). 176p. pap. 82.50 (978-951-44-7832-1(0)) Tampere Univ. Pr. FIN. Dist: Coronet Bks.

Piipariner, Touko. The Transformation of un Conflict Management: Producing Images of Genocide from Rwanda to Darfur & Beyond. 2009. (Routledge Research on International Organisations Ser.). (ENG., Illus.). 240p. 130.00 (978-0-415-54408-5(4)) Routledge.

Poku, Nana K. & Senghor, Jeggan C., eds. Toward Africa's Renewal. 2007. (Illus.). 352p. 124.95 (978-0-7546-4670-9(X)) Ashgate Publishing Co.

Primorac, Ranka. African City Textualities. 2009. (ENG., Illus.). 128p. 140.00 (978-0-415-48155-7(4)) Routledge.

Pusatieri, Matheux & Cannamela, Jihed. Tunisia: Economic, Political & Social Issues. 2012. (978-1-61942-157-8(7)) Nova Science Pubs., Inc.

Quinn, Frederick. In Search of Salt: Changes in Beti (Cameroon) Society, 1880-1960. 2006. (Cameroon Studies: Vol. 6). (Illus.). 186p. 90.00 (978-1-84545-006-9(X)) Berghahn Bks., Inc.

Rakiya Omaar & Ashamu, Elizabeth. A Second Chance: What Economic Opportunities Mean for Impoverished Women in Rwanda. 2008. (Illus.). 152p. pap. (978-1-60643-261-7(3)) Independent Pub.

Reddy, Dr. D. Raja & Reddy, D. Raja. Endemic Skeletal Fluorosis. 2011. 180p. pap. (978-3-8454-1303-7(4)) Lambert Academic Publishing.

Rhazaoui, Ahmed, et al. The Millennium Development Goals in Africa. 2008. (ENG., Illus.). 300p. pap. 28.95 (978-2-7178-4853-3(3)) Economica, Editions FRA. Dist: Brookings Institution Pr.

Russell, Margo & Russell, Martin. Afrikaners of the Kalahari: White Minority in a Black State. 2009. (African Studies). (ENG.). 184p. pap. 31.99 (978-0-521-10140-0(9)) Cambridge Univ. Pr.

Sackey, Brigid M. New Directions In Gender And Religion. 2007. (ENG.). 228p. pap. 29.50 (978-0-7391-2400-0(5)) Lexington Bks.

Sage, Andre Le. African Counterterrorism Cooperation: Assessing Regional & Subregional Initiatives. 2007. 240p. (C). 50.00 (978-1-59797-176-8(6)); pap. 25.00 (978-1-59797-177-5(4)) Potomac Bks., Inc.

Salih, M. A. Environmental Politics & Liberation in Contemporary Africa. 2010. (Environment & Policy Ser.). (Illus.). 200p. pap. 139.00 (978-90-481-5196-7(1), 9048151961) Springer.

Saucier, Paul Khalil. Native Tongues: An African Hip-Hop Reader. 2011. 200p. pap. (978-1-59221-837-0(7)) Africa World Pr.

Schlee, Gunther & Watson, Elizabeth, eds. Changing Identifications & Alliances in Northeast Africa Vol. 2: Sudan, Uganda, & the Ethiopia-Sudan Borderlands, 2 vols. 2009. (Illus.). 268p. 95.00 (978-1-84545-604-7(1)) Berghahn Bks., Inc.

Shivji, Issa. Silences in NGO Discourse: The role & future of NGOs in Africa. 2007. 82p. pap. 12.95 (978-0-9545637-5-2(1)) Pambuzuka Pr. GBR. Dist: Independent Pubs. Group.

Sibanda, Thabani. Conflict Issues Across Disciplines. 2011. 198p. 29.99 (978-1-4568-1760-2(4)); pap. 19.99 (978-1-4568-1759-6(0)) Xlibris Corp.

Sirleaf, Amos. African Liberation. 2010. 168p. 33.49 (978-1-4490-9344-0(2)) AuthorHouse.

Sirleaf, Amos M. "Deluxe". African Liberation. 2010. 168p. pap. 17.99 (978-1-4490-9343-3(4)) AuthorHouse.

Sithole, George Nduma. Self-Reliance from an African Perspective. 2011. 166p. pap. (978-0-7552-0672-8(X)) Authors OnLine, Ltd.

Sitoe, Eduardo J. Post-Colonial Political Transformations in Angola & Mozambique. 2011. 456p. pap. (978-3-8443-0078-9(3)) Lambert Academic Publishing.

Slyomovics, Susan, ed. Clifford Geertz in Morocco. 2012. (ENG., Illus.). 248p. (C). pap. 45.95 (978-0-415-51816-1(4)) Routledge.

Smith, Malinda S., ed. Beyond the 'African Tragedy' Discourses on Development & the Global Economy. 2006. (Illus.). 330p. 120.00 (978-0-7546-4824-6(9)) Ashgate Publishing Co.

Sneyd, Adam. Governing Cotton: Globalization & Poverty in Africa. 2011. (International Political Economy Ser.). (ENG., Illus.). 256p. 85.00 (978-0-230-25278-3(8)) Palgrave Macmillan.

Sommers, Marc. Stuck: Rwandan Youth & the Struggle for Adulthood. 2012. (Studies in Security & International Affairs Ser.). (ENG., Illus.). 288p. 59.95 (978-0-8203-3890-3(7)); pap. 22.95 (978-0-8203-3891-0(5)) Univ. of Georgia Pr.

Spencer, Joshua. Contemporary Issues. 2008. 108p. per. 19.99 (978-1-4257-8512-3(3)) Xlibris Corp.

Stephens, Michelle Ann. Reconceptualization of the African Diaspora. Ball, Erica & Pappademos, Melina, eds. 2008. (ENG., Illus.). 240p. pap. 14.00 (978-0-8223-6696-6(7)) Duke Univ. Pr.

Strudsholm, Jasper, et al. Reality Bites: An African Decade. 2010. (Illus.). 144p. pap. 33.95 (978-1-919930-22-0(1)) Double Storey Bks. ZAF. Dist: International Publishers Marketing.

Sulayman, Hamdun Ibrahim. Building Values: Fight Corruption & Moral Degeneration. 2011. 240p. pap. (978-3-639-31962-0(1)) VDM Verlag Dr. Mueller e.K.

Sultan, Carolyn Chebet Sambai. Memory & Violence: A Study of John Ruganda's Plays: the Floods & the Burdens. 2011. 84p. pap. (978-3-639-34130-0(9)) VDM Verlag Dr. Mueller e.K.

Tamale & Tamale, Sylvia. African Sexualities: A Reader. 2011. (Illus.). 672p. pap. 40.95 (978-0-85749-016-2(8)) Pambuzuka Pr. GBR. Dist: Independent Pubs. Group.

Tapang, Paul. The Story Behind the Story in Africa: Visiting the Sins of the Fathers upon the Children unto the Second & Third Generations. 2006. 472p. pap. 29.95 (978-1-4241-5315-2(8)) PublishAmerica, Inc.

Tarikh, Asiwaju. White Society in Africa. Date not set. pap. 24.40 (978-0-582-60960-0(7)) Addison-Wesley Longman, Ltd. GBR. Dist: Trans-Atlantic Pubns., Inc.

Tasew, Yilma Tafere. Outcast: The Plight of Black African Refugees. 2011. (Illus.). 235p. pap. (978-1-56902-349-5(2)) Red Sea Pr.

Temilola, Olusegun, et al. Poverty & Wellbeing among the Elderly in Southwestern Nigeri. 2011. 172p. pap. (978-3-8443-1082-5(7)) Lambert Academic Publishing.

Thunde, Dziko. Impact of Used Car Imports on Brand New Car Dealerships. 2011. 68p. pap. (978-3-8443-9009-4(X)) Lambert Academic Publishing.

Tiepoh, M. Geepu Nah. Land Privatization & Cash Crop Production. 2008. 124p. per. (978-3-8364-3544-4(6)) VDM Verlag Dr. Mueller e.K.

Tilley, Gordon & Gordon, Robert J. Ordering Africa: Anthropology, European Imperialism & the Politics of Knowledge. Tilley, Helen L., ed. 2011. (Studies in Imperialism Ser.). (ENG.). 404p. pap. 50.00 (978-0-7190-8212-2(9)) Manchester Univ. Pr. GBR. Dist: Macmillan.

Tillyrides, Makarios. Adventures in the Unseen: The Mission Continues. 2011. 374p. pap. 29.95 (978-1-933275-57-4(X), Orthodox Research Institute) Cocheco Falls Publishing.

Touré, Maguèye. De L'imparfait Au Subjectif. 2009. (FRE.). 98p. (978-2-911673-46-7(8)) Feu De Brousse, Editions.

Tumasang, Emmanuel Nchangbah. The Impacts of Development Induced Displacements. 2010. 144p. pap. (978-3-8383-8308-8(7)) Lambert Academic Publishing.

Turner, Bryan S. & Yangwen, Zheng, eds. The Body in Asia. 2009. (Illus.). 240p. 90.00 (978-1-84545-550-7(9)) Berghahn Bks., Inc.

Uchendu, Egodi, ed. Masculinities in Contemporary Afric. 2008. 280p. pap. (978-2-86978-227-3(6)) Council for the Development of Social Science Research in Africa SEN. Dist: Michigan State Univ. Pr.

Uko, Nung. Africa in the Ancient World & Today: The Wealth of a Nation Is the Excellent Education & Skills of Its Honestly Hardworking Citizens. 2009. 704p. pap. 25.99 (978-1-4490-0127-8(0)) AuthorHouse.

Uncha, Abera. Gis Based Analysis of Tstse Fly Distribution in Afric. 2011. 92p. pap. (978-3-8433-8677-7(3)) Lambert Academic Publishing.

UNICEF Staff. Africa's Orphaned & Vulnerable Generations: Children Affected by AIDS. 2006. (Illus.). 48p. pap. 15.00 (978-92-806-4035-9(6)) United Nations Children's Fund, The (UNICEF).

United Nations Development Programme. Assessment of Development Results: Benin. 2009. 84p. pap. 23.00 (978-92-1-126239-1(9)) United Nations Pubns.

—Assessment of Development Results: Burkina Faso. 2010. 88p. pap. 15.00 (978-92-1-126274-2(7)) United Nations Pubns.

United Nations: Economic Commission for Africa & African Union. Economic report on Africa 2009: Developing African agriculture through regional value Chains. 2009. (ENG., Illus.). 210p. pap. 40.00 (978-92-1-125111-1(7)) United Nations Pubns.

United Nations: Economic Commission for Europe. Assessing Regional Integration in Africa Iv: Enhancing Intra-African Trade. 2010. (ENG.). 524p. pap. 55.00 (978-92-1-125114-2(1)) United Nations Pubns.

Utas, Mats. Traditional Healing of Young Sexual Abuse Survivors: Global Prospects in the Aftermath of an African War. 2009. (Nordic Africa Institute Policy Dialogues Ser.). 60p. pap. 12.95 (978-91-7106-648-0(9)) Nordiska Afrikainstitutet SWE. Dist: Stylus Publishing, LLC.

Uwazie-Ridley. Contemporary Issues to African Studies Reader. rev. ed. 2011. (ENG.). 344p. pap. 75.00 (978-0-7575-9569-1(3)) Kendall Hunt Publishing Co.

Uzoaru, Charles Onyegbule. Born in Africa. 2011. 112p. 21.23 (978-1-4567-9454-5(X)); pap. 10.68 (978-1-4567-9455-2(8)) AuthorHouse.

Viterbo, Paula & Ngalamulume, Kalala J. Medicine & Health in Africa: Multidisciplinary Perspectives. 2011. 240p. pap. (978-3-8258-9226-5(3)) Michigan State Univ. Pr.

Wabuke, Mel. Eye on Africa. 2010. (Illus.). 544p. 29.95 (978-0-9820795-2-2(4)) Coltan Bks.

Walker, Alice. Overcoming Speechlessness: A Poet Encounters the Horror in Rwanda, Eastern Congo, & Palestine/Israel. 2010. (ENG.). 64p. pap. 9.95 (978-1-58322-917-0(5)) Seven Stories Pr.

Walker, Jerald. Street Shadows: A Memoir of Race, Rebellion, & Redemption. 2012. (ENG.). 256p. pap. 17.95 (978-0-8032-4095-7(3), Bison Bks.) Univ. of Nebraska Pr.

Wassajja, Emmy. War, Displaced Communities, Livelihoods & Sustainable Development. 2011. 128p. pap. (978-3-8383-5515-3(6)) Lambert Academic Publishing.

Watanabe, Seiko. Hiv/Aids in Rural Botswana - Poverty, Gender Inequality, Marginalization, & Stigm. 2008. 100p. pap. (978-3-639-00077-1(3)) VDM Verlag Dr. Mueller e.K.

Wewe, Boniface. African Sex Education:Chronicles & Manual: Miyidima-the African's Erotic Convocation:Liberation of the Long Suffering Birds & Bees of Africa. 2010. 192p. pap. 16.95 (978-1-4502-4493-0(9)) iUniverse, Inc.

Wilson, Monica. Religion & the Transformation of Society: A Study in Social Change in Africa. 2009. (ENG.). 176p. pap. 31.99 (978-0-521-10411-1(4)) Cambridge Univ. Pr.

Wilson, Sigismond. The Spatial & Social Impacts of Sierra Leone's Civil War 1991-2001. 2011. 120p. pap. (978-3-8443-1741-1(4)) Lambert Academic Publishing.

Wodon, Quentin & Moreno-Dodson, Blanca, eds. Public Finance for Poverty Reduction: Concepts & Case Studies from Africa & Latin America. 2007. (Directions in Development Ser.). (ENG., Illus.). 504p. per. 35.00 (978-0-8213-6826-8(5), 9780821368268) World Bank Pubns.

Workman, James G. Heart of Dryness: How the Last Bushmen Can Help Us Endure the Coming Age of Permanent Drought. 2009. (ENG.). 336p. 26.00 (978-0-8027-1558-6(3)) Walker & Co.

World Bank. Africa Development Indicators 2011. 2011. (Africa Development Indicators Ser.). (ENG.). 194p. pap. 100.00 incl. cd-rom (978-0-8213-8731-3(6), 9780821387313) World Bank Pubns.

—Intensifying the Fight Against Malaria: Programme Renforcé de la Banque Mondiale pour la Lutte Contre le Paludisme en Afrique. 2008. (Document of the World Bank Ser.). (ENG.). 148p. pap. 25.00 (978-0-8213-7758-1(2), 9780821377581) World Bank Pubns.

—The Little Data Book on Africa 2010. 2010. (Africa Development Indicators Ser.). (ENG.). 128p. pap. 15.00 (978-0-8213-8255-4(1), 9780821382554) World Bank Pubns.

—Youth & Employment in Africa - The Potential, the Problem, the Promise 2008/2009. 2009. (Africa Development Indicators Ser.). (ENG.). 216p. pap. 100.00 incl. cd-rom (978-0-8213-7787-1(6), 9780821377871) World Bank Pubns.

World Bank Center Staff. Africa's Future, Africa's Challenge: Early Childhood Care & Development in Sub-Saharan Africa. Garcia, Marito et al, eds. 2008. (Directions in Development Ser.). (ENG., Illus.). 556p. per. 25.00 (978-0-8213-6886-2(9), 9780821368862) World Bank Pubns.

World Bank Staff. Africa Development Indicators 2007: Spreading & Sustaining Growth in Africa. 2008. (Africa Development Indicators Ser.). (ENG.). 176p. pap. 100.00 (978-0-8213-7283-8(1), 9780821372838) World Bank Pubns.

—The Little Data Book on Africa 2007. rev. ed. 2007. (Africa Development Indicators Ser.). (ENG.). 120p. per. 15.00 (978-0-8213-6971-5(7), 9780821369715) World Bank Pubns.

World Bank Staff, contrib. by. Little Data Book on Africa 2008-09. 2008. (ENG.). 128p. pap. 15.00 (978-0-8213-7788-8(4), 9780821377888) World Bank Pubns.

World Bank Staff & Timofeev, Andrey. World Bank Africa Database 2006. 2006th rev. ed. 2006. (African Development Indicators Ser.). 220p. cd-rom 200.00 (978-0-8213-6563-2(0)) World Bank Pubns.

Wright, Donald R. The World & a Very Small Place in Africa: A History of Globalization in Niumi, the Gambia. 3rd rev. ed. 2010. (Sources & Studies in World History Ser.). 336p. pap. 32.95 (978-0-7656-2484-0(2)); (Illus.). 89.95 (978-0-7656-2483-3(4)) Sharpe, M.E. Inc.

Zawati, Hilmi M. The Triumph of Ethnic Hatred & the Failure of International Political Will: Gendered Violence & Genocide in the Former Yugoslavia & Rwanda. 2010. xxiii, 456p. (978-0-7734-3698-5(7)) Mellen, Edwin Pr., The.

Zeilig, Leo, ed. Class Struggle & Resistance in Africa. 2009. (ENG.). 224p. pap. 17.00 (978-1-931859-68-4(X)) Haymarket Bks.

Zeleza, Paul Tiyambe. Barack Obama & African Diasporas: Dialogues & Dissensions. 2009. (ENG.). 240p. pap. 28.00 (978-0-8214-1896-3(3)) Ohio Univ. Pr.

AFRICA—SOCIAL LIFE AND CUSTOMS

Abingdon. Under the Baobab Tree Starter Kit, Vol. 2. 45.00 (978-0-687-00746-2(1)) Abingdon Pr.

Aborampah, Osei-Mensah & Sudarkasa, Niara. Extended Families in Africa & the African Diaspora. 2011. (Illus.). vi, 398p. (978-1-59221-812-7(1)); pap. (978-1-59221-811-0(3)) Africa World Pr.

Achebe, G-S Ifeanyi. Betrothed. 2011. 536p. pap. 39.95 (978-1-4567-3173-1(4)) AuthorHouse.

Adekunle, Julius O. Culture & Customs of Rwanda, 1 vol. 2007. (Culture & Customs of Africa Ser.). (Illus.). 192p. 49.95 (978-0-313-33177-0(4), GR3177, Greenwood Pr.) Greenwood Publishing Group, Inc.

Adésànyà, Adérónké Adésolá. Carving Wood, Making History: The Fákéye Family, Modernity & Yoruba Woodcarving. 2011. (Illus.). xv, 392p. (978-1-59221-879-0(2)); pap. (978-1-59221-880-6(6)) Africa World Pr.

Agbahowe, Nathaniel U. Wake up Africa! 2009. 460p. pap. 20.49 (978-1-4389-1466-4(0)) AuthorHouse.

Agorsah, E. Kofi. Religion, Ritual & African Tradition: African Foundations. 2010. 156p. pap. 11.99 (978-1-4490-0552-8(7)) AuthorHouse.

Akou, Heather M. The Politics of Dress in Somali Culture. 2011. (African Expressive Cultures Ser.). (ENG., Illus.). 200p. 70.00 (978-0-253-35629-1(6), 0253356296); pap. 24.95 (978-0-253-22313-5(X), 025322313X) Indiana Univ. Pr.

Amadou Nouhou Diallo. Male Circumcision & Initiation in Rural Afric: Autobiography, Culture & Traditions. 2009. 176p. pap. 12.99 (978-1-4389-9633-2(0)) AuthorHouse.

Amegago, Modesto. An African Music & Dance Curriculum Model: Performing Arts in Education. 2011. 360p. pap. 45.00 (978-1-61163-004-6(5)) Carolina Academic Pr.

Archer, Jermaine O. Antebellum Slave Narratives: Cultural & Political Expressions of Africa. 2008. (Studies in American Popular History & Culture Ser.). (ENG.). 142p. 125.00 (978-0-415-99027-1(0)) Routledge.

Atanga, Lilian Lem. Gender, Discourse & Power in the Cameroonian Parliament. 2009. 278p. pap. (978-9956-615-46-9(3)) Langaa Research & Publishing Common Initiative Group CMR. Dist: Michigan State Univ. Pr.

Ates, Orkun. Easy Swahili for Everybody. 2007. 220p. per. 19.95 (978-1-4327-1381-2(7)) Outskirts Pr., Inc.

Baraza, Patrick Wanakuta. Drumming up Dialogue: The Dialogic Philosophies of Martin Buber, Fred Iklé, & William Ury Compared & Applied to the Babukusu Community of Kenya. 2011. 420p. pap. 26.95 (978-1-4620-1620-4(0)) iUniverse, Inc.

Bargna, Ivan. Africa. 2009. (Dictionaries of Civilization Ser.). (ENG., Illus.). 388p. pap. 26.95 (978-0-520-25974-4(2)) Univ. of California Pr.

Bárkányi Csávás, Maria. The Magic of Africa. 2008. 160p. per. (978-1-84747-463-6(2)) Chipmunkapublishing.

Barnard, Alan. Anthropology & the Bushman. 2007. (ENG.). 224p. 99.95 (978-1-84520-428-0(X)); pap. 30.95 (978-1-84520-429-7(8)) Berg Pubs. GBR. Dist: Macmillan.

Barwani, Naila. Gone Is Yesterday - Imepita Jan. 2011. 256p. pap. (978-0-7552-1327-6(0)) Authors OnLine, Ltd.

Bassi, Marco. Decisions in the Shade: The Borana of Ethiopia. 560p. 109.95 (978-1-59221-148-7(8)) Africa World Pr.

Blakely, Sandra. Myth, Ritual & Metallurgy in Ancient Greece & Recent Africa. 2006. (ENG., Illus.). 342p. (C). 106.00 (978-0-521-85500-6(4)) Cambridge Univ. Pr.

Bompani, Barbara & Frahm-Arp, Maria, eds. Development & Politics from Below: Exploring Religious Spaces in the African State. 2010. (Non-Governmental Public Action Ser.). (ENG., Illus.). 272p. 89.00 (978-0-230-23775-9(4)) Palgrave Macmillan.

Bortolot, Alexander Ives. Revolutions: A Century of Makonde Masquerade in Mozambique. 2007. (Illus.). 72p. (978-1-884919-20-6(0)) Columbia Univ., The Miriam & Ira D. Wallach Art Gallery.

Botne, Robert Dale Olson & Schafer, Loveness. The Chindali Language of Malawi. 2008. (978-1-60618-909-2(3)); viii, 323p. (978-1-60618-911-5(5)); viii, 323p. (978-1-60618-910-8(7)) American Philosophical Society.

Bouttiaux, Anne-Marie. Persona: Masks of Africa - Identities Hidden & Revealed. 2009. (ENG., Illus.). 304p. 50.00 (978-88-7439-513-2(2)) 5 Continents ITA. Dist: Hachette Bk. Group.

Buthelezi, Vusi. Wailing Dunes. 2011. 24p. pap. 4.99 (978-1-61667-195-2(5)) Raider Publishing International.

Campbell, William H. Anthropology for the People: A Refutation of the Theory of the Adamic Origin of All Races. 2010. 346p. pap. 32.75 (978-1-147-59563-5(1)) BiblioBazaar.

Carton, Benedict, et al, eds. Zulu Identities: Being Zulu, Past & Present. 2009. (Columbia/Hurst Ser.). (ENG.). 688p. (gr. 17). 135.00 (978-0-231-70058-0(X)) Columbia Univ. Pr.

Carton, Benedict & Laband, John, eds. Zulu Identities: Being Zulu, Past & Present. 2008. 500p. pap. (978-1-86914-046-5(X)) University of Kwazulu-Natal Press ZAF. Dist: International Specialized Bk. Services.

Castiglioni, Angelo and Alfredo. Once upon a Time in Africa: 50 Years of Explorations & Adventures. 2010. (ENG., Illus.). 428p. 50.00 (978-88-544-0485-4(3)) White Star ITA. Dist: Random Hse., Inc.

Clack, Timothy A. R. Memory & the Mountain: Environmental Relations of the Wachagga of Kilimanjaro & Implications for Landscape Archaeology. 2007. (Bar S Ser.). (Illus.). 108p. (C). 72.50 (978-1-4073-0117-4(9)) British Archaeological Reports Ltd. GBR. Dist: Brown, David Bk. Co., The.

Cleary, Tim. Mauritius - Culture Smart! The Essential Guide to Customs & Culture. 2011. (Culture Smart! Ser.). (ENG., Illus.). 168p. pap. 9.95 (978-1-85733-542-2(2)) Kuperard Pubs. GBR. Dist: Random Hse., Inc.

Cole, Catherine M., et al, eds. Africa after Gender? 2007. (ENG.). 344p. 65.00 (978-0-253-34816-6(1), 0253348161); pap. 24.95 (978-0-253-21877-3(2), 0253218772) Indiana Univ. Pr.

Coleman, Angela D. A Journey Toward Womanhood Curriculum Guide. 5th ed. 2006. per. 55.00 (978-0-9786906-0-1(5)) Sisterhood Agenda Enterprises, LLC.

—A Journey Toward Womanhood Student Manual. 2006. spiral bd. 55.00 (978-0-9786906-1-8(3)) Sisterhood Agenda Enterprises, LLC.

Comaroff, John L., et al, eds. Picturing a Colonial Past: The African Photographs of Isaac Schapera. 2007. (Illus.). 234p. 65.00 (978-0-226-11411-8(2)); per. 30.00 (978-0-226-11412-5(0)) Univ. of Chicago Pr.

Conru, Kevin, et al. Bernatzik: Africa. 2006. (Imago Mundi Ser.). (Illus.). 288p. (978-88-7439-023-6(8)) 5 Continents.

Conyers, James L., Jr., ed. Law, Culture, & Africana Studies. 2007. (Africana Studies). (ENG.). 142p. (gr. 11). pap. 29.95 (978-1-4128-0660-2(7)) Transaction Pubs.

Critchley, William. More People, More Trees. 2011. (ENG., Illus.). 200p. pap. 29.95 incl. DVD (978-1-85339-717-2(2)) Practical Action Publishing GBR. Dist: Stylus Publishing, LLC.

Crossland, Cyril. Desert & Water Gardens of the Red Sea: Being an Account of the Natives & the Shore Formations of the Coast. 2010. (Cambridge Library Collection - Anthropology Ser.). (Illus.). 250p. pap. 22.99 (978-1-108-01601-8(4)) Cambridge Univ. Pr.

Davis, Pam. Mesi's Season of Change: A Friendship Story. 2008. (Girls 'n Grace Collection). (ENG.). 80p. pap. 7.99 (978-1-934068-79-3(9)) Authentic Media.

Dawson, Allan C., ed. Shrines in Africa: History, Politics, & Society. 2008. (Africa: Missing Voices: Ser.). (Illus.). 240p. pap. 39.95 (978-1-55238-246-2(X)) Univ. of Calgary Pr. CAN. Dist: Michigan State Univ. Pr.

De La Gorgendière, Louise, et al. Ethnicity in Africa: Roots, Meanings & Implications. vi, 360p. (978-0-9527917-0-6(6)) University of Edinburgh Centre of African Studies.

Debra Liebenow Daly. The Kingdom of Roses & Thorns. 2009. 276p. pap. 15.49 (978-1-4389-5488-2(3)) AuthorHouse.

Doris, David T. Vigilant Things: On Thieves, Yoruba Anti-Aesthetics, & the Strange Fates of Ordinary Objects in Nigeria. 2011. (ENG., Illus.). 416p. 60.00 (978-0-295-99073-6(2)) Univ. of Washington Pr.

Dow, Unity & Essex, Max. Saturday Is for Funerals. 2010. 240p. 19.95 (978-0-674-05077-8(0)) Harvard Univ. Pr.

Dowden, Richard. Africa: Altered States, Ordinary Miracles. 2010. (ENG., Illus.). 592p. pap. 19.95 (978-1-58648-816-1(3)) PublicAffairs.

Duncan, Nancy. The Nail That Sticks Up: An American Woman in Asia & Africa. 2007. 436p. per. 29.95 (978-1-4241-7539-0(9)) PublishAmerica, Inc.

Egesah, Omar. Male Circumcision in Africa. 2009. 184p. pap. (978-3-639-15435-1(5)) VDM Verlag Dr. Mueller e.K.

Epprecht, Marc. Heterosexual Africa? The History of an Idea from the Age of Exploration to the Age of AIDS. 2008. (New African Histories Ser.). (ENG.). 240p. 39.95 (978-0-8214-1798-0(3)); pap. 24.95 (978-0-8214-1799-7(1)) Ohio Univ. Pr.

Etkin, Nina L. Foods of Association: Biocultural Perspectives on Foods & Beverages That Mediate Sociability. 2009. (ENG., Illus.). 264p. 50.00 (978-0-8165-2777-9(6)) Univ. of Arizona Pr.

Fardon, Lela in Bali: History Through a Ceremony in Cameroon. 2006. (Cameroon Studies: Vol. 7). (Illus.). 176p. (C). 90.00 (978-1-84545-215-5(1)) Berghahn Bks., Inc.

Feldman, Douglas A., ed. AIDS, Culture, & Africa. 2008. (ENG., Illus.). 336p. 75.00 (978-0-8130-3253-5(9)) Univ. Pr. of Florida.

Fischer, Eberhard. Guro: Masks, Performances & Master Carvers in Ivory Coast. 2008. (Illus.). 518p. 90.00 (978-3-7913-3941-2(9)) Prestel Publishing.

Fisher, Angela & Beckwith, Carol. Faces of Africa: Thirty Years of Photography. 2009. (NG Collectors Ser.). (ENG., Illus.). 360p. 16.95 (978-1-4262-0424-1(8), National Geographic) National Geographic Society.

Friedson, Steven M. & Friedson, S. M. Remains of Ritual: Northern Gods in a Southern Land. 2009. (Chicago Studies in Ethnomusicology Ser.). (ENG., Illus.). 272p. 55.00 (978-0-226-26504-9(8)); pap. 22.00 (978-0-226-26505-6(6)) Univ. of Chicago Pr.

Fundisi. The Monkey's Wedding. 2009. 254p. pap. 21.50 (978-1-4092-8740-7(8)) Lulu Enterprises Inc.

Gamache Thomas, Kodji. Traditional Beliefs in Modern Society. 2009. 92p. pap. (978-3-639-19305-3(9)) VDM Verlag Dr. Mueller e.K.

Garcea, Elena A. A., ed. South-Eastern Mediterranean Peoples Between 130,000 & 10,000 Years Ago. 2010. (ENG., Illus.). 200p. (C). 96.00 (978-1-84217-403-6(7)) Oxbow Bks., Ltd. GBR. Dist: Brown, David Bk. Co., The.

Geuka, Amefika. Reflections on My Pilgrimage: A Conscious Black Son of Africa returns to his Motherland. 2006. per. 9.95 (978-0-9787394-2-3(6)) Protective Hands Communications.

Geurts & Cram101 Textbook Reviews Staff. Culture & the Senses. 2007. 60p. per. 9.95 (978-1-4288-2644-1(0)) Cram101 Inc.

Giansanti, Gianni, text. Last African Warriors. 2011. (ENG., Illus.). 216p. 60.00 (978-88-544-0472-4(1)) White Star ITA. Dist: Sterling Publishing Co., Inc.

Giesing, Cornelia & Vydrine, Valentin. Ta: Rikh Mandinka de Bijini (Guinie-Bissau) La Mimoire des Mandinka et Sooninkee du Kaab. 2006. (African Sources for African History Ser.: Vol. 9). (FRE, MAN & ARA., Illus.). 398p. pap. (978-90-04-14724-9(1)) BRILL.

Gilbert, Elizabeth L. Tribes of the Great Rift Valley. 2007. (ENG., Illus.). 272p. 75.00 (978-0-8109-9411-9(9)) Abrams.

Glave, E. J. Fetishism in Congo Land. 2006. (ENG.). 48p. per. 15.95 (978-1-4286-3640-8(4)) Kessinger Publishing, LLC.

Golan, Tamar & Ron, Tamar. Angolan Rendezvous: Man & Nature in the Shadow of War. 2010. (Illus.). 304p. pap. 29.95 (978-1-920143-42-8(4)) 30° South Pubs. ZAF. Dist: International Publishers Marketing.

Gottlieb, Alma & Graham, Philip. Braided Worlds. 2012. 176p. 60.00 (978-0-226-30527-1(9)); pap. 20.00 (978-0-226-30528-8(7)) Univ. of Chicago Pr. (Orbit Books).

Grinker, Roy Richard, et al, eds. Perspectives on Africa: A Reader in Culture, History & Representation. 2nd ed. 2010. (Global Perspectives Ser.: 3). (ENG., Illus.). 713p. pap. 66.95 (978-1-4051-9060-2(4)); 712p. 110.95 (978-1-4443-3522-4(7)) Wiley, John & Sons, Inc. (Wiley-Blackwell).

Gudhlanga, Enna Sukutai. Shona Culture & Its Various Aspects: A Case of the Novel in a Zimbabwean Indigenous Language. 2011. 60p. pap. (978-3-639-32752-6(7)) VDM Verlag Dr. Mueller e.K.

Hagaba, Jane Catherine. Principles for Developing Inculturated Theology in the African Context. 2011. 336p. pap. (978-3-8443-8422-2(7)) Lambert Academic Publishing.

Heneis, Julia. Inkulturation und ihre Relevanz für die Sozialarbeit mit AfrikanerInnen in Wien: Am Beispiel der afrikanischen katholischen Gemeinde. 2010. (Europäische Hochschulschriften. Reihe 22: Soziologie Ser.). (GER.). 120p. pap. 21.95 (978-3-631-59961-7(7)) Lang, Peter GmbH, Europaischer Verlag der Wissenschaften DEU. Dist: Lang, Peter.

Hoad, Neville Wallace. African Intimacies: Race, Homosexuality, & Globalization. 2007. 232p. 60.00 (978-0-8166-4915-0(4)); per. 22.50 (978-0-8166-4916-7(2)) Univ. of Minnesota Pr.

Imperato, Gavin H. & Imperato, Pascal James. Bundu, Sowei Headpieces of the Sande Society of West Africa: The Imperato Family Collection. 2012. (978-1-936658-10-7(0)) Kilima Hse. Pubs.

Jennings, Helen. New African Fashion. 2011. (ENG., Illus.). 256p. pap. 35.00 (978-3-7913-4579-6(6)) Prestel Publishing.

Jeske, Christine. Into the Mud: Inspiration for Everday Activists: True Stories of South Africa, 1 vol. 2010. (ENG.). 208p. pap. 13.99 (978-0-8024-5879-7(3)) Moody Pubs.

Jindra, Michael & Noret, Joël, eds. Funerals in Africa: Explorations of a Social Phenomenon. 2011. (ENG., Illus.). 264p. 85.00 (978-0-85745-205-4(3)) Berghahn Bks., Inc.

Jokwang, John Koyela & Fokwang, John Koyela. A Dictionary of Popular Bali Names. 2010. 134p. pap. (978-9956-616-47-3(8)) Langaa Research & Publishing Common Initiative Group CMR. Dist: Michigan State Univ. Pr.

Jones, Roger. Libya: A Quick Guide to Customs & Etiquette. 2008. (Culture Smart! Ser.). (ENG., Illus.). 168p. pap. 9.95 (978-1-85733-453-1(1)) Kuperard Pubs. GBR. Dist: Random Hse., Inc.

Kaminski, Joseph S. Asante Ivory Trumpet Music in Ghana: Culture Tradition & Sound Barrage. 2012. (Illus.). 220p. (978-1-4094-2684-4(X)) Ashgate Publishing, Ltd.

Kashaga, Frateline. The Commoditization of Culture for Rural Tourism in Tanzani. 2011. 92p. pap. (978-3-8383-3352-6(7)) Lambert Academic Publishing.

Kasomo, Daniel. The Belief in Mystical Powers in African Traditional Religion. 2010. 208p. pap. (978-3-8383-8350-7(8)) Lambert Academic Publishing.

—The Essence of African Culture & Religion. 2010. 144p. pap. (978-3-8383-8857-1(7)) Lambert Academic Publishing.

Kasomo, Daniel W. Philosophy of Religion from an Africa Perspective. 2011. 436p. pap. (978-3-8433-6051-7(0)) Lambert Academic Publishing.

Kath, Roxana & Rieger, Anna-Katharina, eds. Raum - Landschaft - Territorium: Zur Konstruktion physischer Raume als nomadischer und sesshafter Lebensraum. 2009. (Nomaden und Sesshafte Ser.). (GER & ENG., Illus.). 316p. (C). 134.00 (978-3-89500-656-2(4)) Reichert, Ludwig Dr. DEU. Dist: Brown, David Bk. Co., The.

Kibreab, Gaim. Critical Reflections on the Eritrean War of Independence: Social Capital, Associational Life, Religion, Ethnicity & Sowing Seeds of Dictatorship. 2007. (978-1-56902-281-8(X)) Red Sea Pr.

Kilbride, Philip & Farley, Noel J. J. Faith, Morality & Being Irish: A Caring Tradition in Africa. 2007. (ENG.). 146p. per. 29.50 (978-0-7618-3759-6(0)) Univ. Pr. of America, Inc.

Kilbride, Philip L. & Farley, Noel J. J. Faith, Morality & Being Irish: A Caring Tradition in Africa. 2007. (ENG.). 146p. 56.99 (978-0-7618-3760-2(4)) Univ. Pr. of America, Inc.

King, Roberta R. Pathways in Christian Music Communication: The Case of the Senufo of Cote D'Ivoire. 2008. (American Society of Missiology Monograph Ser.). 308p. pap. 34.00 (978-1-55635-927-9(6), Pickwick Pubns.) Wipf & Stock Pubs.

Koloss, Hans-Joachim. Traditional Institutions in Kembong (Cameroon) 2009. (GER & ENG., Illus.). 240p. pap. 99.00 (978-3-496-02811-6(4), Art Stock Bks. Ltd/Csi) Continental Sales, Inc.

—World-View & Society in Oku (Cameroon) 2009. (ENG.). 484p. pap. 128.00 (978-3-496-02682-2(0), Art Stock Bks. Ltd/Csi) Continental Sales, Inc.

Korn, Fadumo & Eichhorst, Sabine. Born in the Big Rains: A Memoir of Somalia & Survival. Levin, Tobe, tr. 2008. (Women Writing Africa Ser.). (ENG.). 196p. per. 15.95 (978-1-55861-578-6(4)) Feminist Pr. at The City Univ. of New York.

Krabacher, Thomas, et al. Africa. 13th ed. 2010. (Global Studies). (ENG., Illus.). 320p. (C). pap. 50.00 (978-0-07-352776-5(9), 0073527769, McGraw-Hill/Dushkin) McGraw-Hill Higher Education.

Krabacher, Thomas, et al. Global Studies: Africa. 14th ed. 2012. (Global Studies). (ENG., Illus.). 448p. (C). pap. 50.00 (978-0-07-802623-2(7), 0078026237, McGraw-Hill/Dushkin) McGraw-Hill Higher Education.

Larsen, Kjersti, ed. Knowledge, Renewal & Religion. 2009. 310p. pap. 22.95 (978-91-7106-635-0(7)) Nordiska Afrikainstitutet SWE. Dist: Stylus Publishing, LLC.

Lave, Jean. Apprenticeship in Critical Ethnographic Practice. 2011. (Lewis Henry Morgan Lecture Ser.). (ENG., Illus.). 216p. 85.00 *(978-0-226-47071-9(7))*; pap. 27.50 *(978-0-226-47072-6(5))* Univ. of Chicago Pr.

Lester, Rhoda Namwalizi. Cassava Is the Root. 2007. 115p. pap. 27.48 *(978-1-4116-7113-3(9))* Lulu Enterprises Inc.

Lewis-Coker, Eyamidé Ella. African Proverbs, Parables & Wise Sayings. 2011. 96p. pap. 9.99 ***(978-1-4520-1292-6(X))*** AuthorHouse.

Main, Michael. Botswana: A Quick Guide to Customs & Etiquette. 2007. (Culture Smart Ser.). (ENG., Illus.). 168p. pap. 9.95 *(978-1-85733-340-4(3))* Kuperard Pubs. GBR. Dist: Random Hse., Inc.

Marie, Deborah. Reparations Now!, Restoring Truth, Balance, & Harmony to the World. 2009. 124p. 22.50 *(978-1-60693-910-9(6)*, Eloquent Bks.) AEG Literary Publishing Services, Inc.

Marlowe, Frank. The Hadza: Hunter-Gatherers of Tanzania. 2010. (Origins of Human Behavior & Culture Ser.). (ENG., Illus.). 384p. 65.00 *(978-0-520-25341-4(8))*; 336p. pap. 28.95 *(978-0-520-25342-1(6))* Univ. of California Pr.

Mazrui, Ali A., et al. Swahili State & Society: The Political Economy of an African Language. 2011. (Illus.). 184p. pap. 24.95 *(978-0-85255-729-7(9)*, Currey, James) Boydell & Brewer, Ltd. GBR. Dist: Boydell & Brewer, Inc.

McCann, James C. Stirring the Pot: A History of African Cuisine. 2009. (Ohio Africa in World History Ser.). (ENG., Illus.). 240p. pap. 26.95 *(978-0-89680-272-8(8))* Ohio Univ. Pr.

McIntosh, Jane Banks. On a Mission: Mamadou's Wedding & My Naming Ceremony. 2007. 176p. per. 15.95 *(978-0-595-42257-9(8))* iUniverse, Inc.

Mensah, Opanin Kwabena. Frem. 2011. 156p. pap. 24.95 ***(978-1-4626-3417-0(6))*** PublishAmerica, Inc.

Miller, Susan Gilson & Hoffman, Katherine E., eds. Berbers & Others: Beyond Tribe & Nation in the Maghrib. 2010. (Public Cultures of the Middle East & North Africa Ser.). (ENG., Illus.). 240p. 65.00 *(978-0-253-35480-8(3)*, 0253354803); pap. 24.95 *(978-0-253-22200-8(1)*, 0253222001) Indiana Univ. Pr.

Morlandst°, Ingvill. Íqut Cubanfa! 2008. 176p. pap. *(978-3-639-07357-7(6))* VDM Verlag Dr. Mueller e.K.

Moshi, Lioba & Osman, Abdulahi A. Democracy & Culture: An African Perspective(PB) 2008. (Illus.). 264p. pap. *(978-1-905068-92-0(1))* Adonis & Abbey Publishers Ltd.

Mowlem, Debrah. I Wonder. 2010. 364p. pap. 17.99 *(978-1-4490-9457-7(0))* AuthorHouse.

Muhumuza, Moses. The People of Mountains of the Moon. 2009. 88p. pap. *(978-3-639-21127-6(8))* VDM Verlag Dr. Mueller e.K.

Mukonyora, Isabel. Wandering a Gendered Wilderness: Suffering & Healing in an African Initiated Church. 2007. (Illus.). xix, 154p. (C). 62.95 *(978-0-8204-5883-7(6))* Lang, Peter Publishing, Inc.

Munene, Ishmael. An Interdisciplinary Primer in African Studies. 2011. (ENG., Illus.). 330p. 85.00 *(978-0-7391-6597-3(6))* Lexington Bks.

Munene, Ishmael & Munene, Ishmael I. An Interdisciplinary Primer in African Studies. 2011. (ENG., Illus.). 330p. pap. 34.95 *(978-0-7391-6598-0(4))* Lexington Bks.

Munene, Ishmael I. An Interdisciplinary Primer in African Studies. 2011. (Illus.). xiii, 308p. ***(978-0-7391-6887-5(8))*** Lexington Bks.

Ndege, George O. Culture & Customs of Mozambique, 1 vol. 2006. (Culture & Customs of Africa Ser.). (Illus.). 168p. 49.95 *(978-0-313-33163-3(4)*, GR3163, Greenwood Pr.) Greenwood Publishing Group, Inc.

Nielssen, Hilde. Ritual Imagination: A Study of Tromba Possession among the Betsimisaraka in Eastern Madagascar. 2011. (Studies of Religion in Africa Ser.). (Illus.). 334p. ***(978-90-04-21524-5(7))*** BRILL.

Nkurunziza, Claver. Black Challenge. 2009. 88p. pap. 13.50 *(978-1-4490-3893-9(X))* AuthorHouse.

Nna, Daniel. Evening Chats: Reflections on Traditions of the Bulus of Southern Cameroon. Ze, Frederick, tr. 2007. 412p. per. 21.95 *(978-1-59594-211-1(4))* WingSpan Publishing.

Nnam, Nkuzi. Colonial Mentality in Africa. 2007. (ENG.). 152p. per. 31.50 *(978-0-7618-3291-1(2))* Hamilton Bks.

North, Peter. Cambodia, 1 vol. 2008. (CultureShock! Ser.). (ENG., Illus.). 280p. pap. 15.95 *(978-0-7614-5477-9(2))* Marshall Cavendish Corp.

Nyirenda, Nkhosikazi-Princess Zindaba. Talakata - the Tears of Afric. 2009. 236p. 30.00 *(978-1-934925-51-5(9)*, Strategic Bk. Publishing) AEG Literary Publishing Services, Inc.

Nyombe, George Bureng. Some Aspects of Bari Culture. 2006. 184p. (C). pap. *(978-9966-846-97-6(2))* Kachere Series, Bks. on Religion, Theology & Society in Malawi MWI. Dist: Michigan State Univ. Pr.

Onianwah, Chinazor. It takes a village to name a Child: Celebrating the bestowment of ancestry, faith, family, heritage, identity & Legacy. 2008.Tr. of English. (ENG., Illus.). 120p. 51.95 *(978-0-615-21612-6(9))* Scripts, Graphics N Things.

Onunwa, Udobata R. Contempory Themes in African Religion & Culture. 2008. pap. 19.00 *(978-0-8059-8555-9(7))* Dorrance Publishing Co., Inc.

Oppong, Christine. Marriage among a Matrilineal Elite: A Family Study of Ghanaian Senior Civil Servants. 2009. (Cambridge Studies in Social & Cultural Anthropology Ser.). (ENG.). 224p. pap. 31.99 *(978-0-521-09318-7(X))* Cambridge Univ. Pr.

Peek, Philip M. African Folklore: An Encyclopedia. 2009. (ENG., Illus.). 640p. pap. 59.95 *(978-0-415-80372-4(1))* Routledge.

Pemberton, John, 3rd. African Beaded Art: Power & Adornment. 2008. (Illus.). 224p. pap. *(978-0-87391-058-3(3))* Smith College Pubns.

Perry, Alex. Lifeblood: How to Change the World, One Dead Mosquito at a Time. 2011. (Illus.). xi, 242p. E-Book ***(978-1-61039-087-3(3))*** PublicAffairs.

Phiri, George Allan. Social-Cultural Anthropology: Communication with the African Society. 2009. 208p. pap. 23.00 *(978-1-60608-736-7(3)*, Resource Pubns.) Wipf & Stock Pubs.

Poussin, Alexandre & Poussin, Sonia. Africa Trek I: From the Cape of Good Hope to Mount Kilimanjaro. 2008. (Illus.). 496p. pap. 27.95 *(978-1-59299-357-4(5))* Inkwater Pr.

—Africa Trek II: From Mount Kilimanjaro to the Sea of Galilee. 2008. 672p. pap. 29.95 *(978-1-59299-358-1(3))* Inkwater Pr.

Ravelec, Vincent. Iboga. 2007. (ENG.). 1p. pap. 18.95 *(978-1-59477-176-7(6)*, Park Street Pr.) Inner Traditions International, Ltd.

Richmond, Yale & Gestrin, Phyllis. Into Africa: A Guide to Sub-Saharan Culture & Diversity. 2nd ed. 2010. (ENG.). 288p. pap. 24.95 *(978-1-931930-91-8(0))* Ebsco Publishing.

Robbins, Pat. Red-Spoted Ox: A Pokot Life. 2010. 396p. pap. 39.95 *(978-87-91563-70-6(4))* IWGIA DNK. Dist: Transaction Pubs.

Roschenthaler, Ute. Purchasing Culture: The Dissemination of Associations in the Cross River Region of Cameroon & Nigeria. 2011. (Illus.). 440p. pap. ***(978-1-59221-830-1(X))*** Africa World Pr.

Röschenthaler, Ute. Purchasing Culture: The Dissemination of Associations in the Cross River Region of Cameroon & Nigeria. 2011. ***(978-1-59221-829-5(6))*** Africa World Pr.

Ross, Eric S. Culture & Customs of Senegal, 1 vol. 2008. (Culture & Customs of Africa Ser.). (Illus.). 160p. 49.95 *(978-0-313-34036-9(6)*, GR4036, Greenwood Pr.) Greenwood Publishing Group, Inc.

Schramm, Katharina. African Homecoming: Pan-African Ideology & Contested Heritage. 2010. (Critical Cultural Heritage Ser.). (ENG., Illus.). 320p. 89.00 *(978-1-59874-513-9(1))*; pap. 36.95 *(978-1-59874-514-6(X))* Left Coast Pr., Inc.

Schulz, Dorothea E. Culture & Customs of Mali, 1 vol. 2012. (Culture & Customs of Africa Ser.). (Illus.). 204p. 50.00 ***(978-0-313-35912-5(1)***, GR5912) Greenwood Publishing Group, Inc.

Schulz, Dorothea Elisabeth. Culture & Customs of Mali. 2012. (Illus.). xvi, 201p. E-Book ***(978-0-313-35913-2(X)***, Greenwood Pr.) Greenwood Publishing Group, Inc.

Sheldon, Margaret. Life Changing Experiences in Africa. 2010. (Illus.). 116p. pap. 33.49 *(978-1-4490-5434-2(X))* AuthorHouse.

Shipton, Parker. The Nature of Entrustment: Intimacy, Exchange, & the Sacred in Africa. 2007. (Yale Agrarian Studies). (ENG., Illus.). 312p. 60.00 *(978-0-300-11601-4(2))* Yale Univ. Pr.

Silva, Sonia. Along an African Border: Angolan Refugees & Their Divination Baskets. 2011. (Contemporary Ethnography Ser.). (Illus.). 188p. (C). 39.95 *(978-0-8122-4293-5(9))* Univ. of Pennsylvania Pr.

Silvester, Hans. Natural Fashion: Tribal Decoration from Africa. 2009. (ENG., Illus.). 168p. pap. 29.95 *(978-0-500-28805-4(4)*, 528805) Thames & Hudson.

—A Window on Africa: Ethiopian Portraits. 2011. (ENG., Illus.). 160p. 40.00 *(978-0-500-51562-4(X)*, 551562) Thames & Hudson.

Sitole, Dorah. Cooking from Cape to Cairo. 2010. (Illus.). 160p. pap. 37.95 *(978-0-624-04746-9(6))* NB Pubs. Ltd. ZAF. Dist: International Publishers Marketing.

Skotnes. Unconquerable Spirit: G Stow's Paintings of the San. 2008. (Illus.). 218p. *(978-1-77009-599-1(3))* Ohio Univ. Pr.

Sonye, David. Stewardship: Transforming Africa Through Excellence in Stewardship. 2010. 164p. pap. 14.95 *(978-0-557-29607-1(2))* Lulu Enterprises Inc.

Spencer, Joshua. Let's Talk Africa & More. 2006. (ENG.). 76p. per. 16.95 *(978-1-4241-6048-8(0))* PublishAmerica, Inc.

St Aubin De Teran, Lisa. Mozambique Mysteries. 2009. (ENG., Illus.). 384p. *(978-1-84408-300-8(4)*, Virago Press) Little, Brown Bk. Group Ltd. GBR. Dist: Independent Pubs. Group.

Stokes, Jamie. Encyclopedia of the Peoples of Africa & the Middle East, 2-Volume Set, 2 vols. 2009. (Illus.). 880p. (C). (gr. 9). 175.00 *(978-0-8160-7158-6(6))* Facts On File, Inc.

Taieb. Chroniques Abidjanes. (FRE.). 128p. *(978-2-907888-60-8(9))* Sepia, Editions.

Tesfagiorgis G., Mussie. Eritrea. 2010. E-Book *(978-1-59884-232-6(3))*; (Illus.). 424p. 85.00 *(978-1-59884-231-9(5)*, ERITC) ABC-CLIO, LLC.

The World Bank, et al. Private Health Sector Assessment in Mali: The Post-Bamako Reality. 2011. (World Bank Working Papers: 212). (ENG., Illus.). 128p. pap. 20.00 *(978-0-8213-8535-7(6)*, 9780821385357) World Bank Pubns.

Tiony, Genevieve. Wounded Afric: The Cultural Differences Between Africa & America. 2009. 212p. 29.95 *(978-1-4389-4470-8(5))*; pap. 21.95 *(978-1-4389-4471-5(3))* AuthorHouse.

Tomaselli, Keyan G. Writing in the San/D: Autoethnography among Indigenous Southern Africans. 2007. (Crossroads in Qualitative Inquiry Ser.: Vol. 7). (AFR & ENG., Illus.). 190p. 80.00 *(978-0-7591-0950-6(8))* AltaMira Pr.

—Writing in the San/d: Autoethnography among Indigenous Southern Africans. 2007. (Crossroads in Qualitative Inquiry Ser.: Vol. 7). (AFR & ENG., Illus.). 190p. per. 32.95 *(978-0-7591-0951-3(6))* AltaMira Pr.

Ugwueze, Uche Lynn-Teresa. African Culture, Identity & Aesthetics: The Igbo Example. 2011. 128p. pap. 19.95 *(978-1-4567-2976-9(4))* AuthorHouse.

Under the Baobab Tree: Claiming Roots, Kindling Hope, Spreading God's Love. 20.00 *(978-0-687-08801-0(1))* Abingdon Pr.

van Beek, Walter E.A. The Dancing Dead: Ritual & Religion among the Kapsiki/Higi of North Cameroon & Northeastern Nigeria, 1 vol. 2012. (Oxford Ritual Studies Ser.). (ENG.). 384p. 99.00 ***(978-0-19-985814-9(4))***; pap. 45.00 ***(978-0-19-985816-3(0))*** Oxford Univ. Pr., Inc.

Ward, Herbert. Five Years with the Congo Cannibals. 2006. (Illus.). pap. 30.95 *(978-1-4286-4743-5(0))* Kessinger Publishing, LLC.

Wariboko, Nimi. Ethics & Time: Ethos of Temporal Orientation in Politics & Religion of the Niger Delta. 2010. xiv, 178p. *(978-0-7391-5030-6(8))* Lexington Bks.

Warnier, Jean-Pierre. The Pot-King: The Body & Technologies of Power. 2007. (African Social Studies). (Illus.). 325p. pap. *(978-90-04-15217-5(2))* BRILL.

Wesonga, Martin. Bride Wealth from an African Theological Perspective. 2011. 52p. pap. ***(978-3-8443-1466-3(0))*** Lambert Academic Publishing.

Wessels, Michael. Bushman Letters: Interpreting the /Xam Narratives of the Bleek & Lloyd Collection. 2010. (ENG.). 256p. pap. 29.95 *(978-1-86814-506-5(9))* Witwatersrand Univ. Pr. Pubns. ZAF. Dist: Transaction Pubs.

Westmoreland-El, Jahne Jahmal. Lessons in Lyric. 2010. 156p. pap. 17.00 *(978-1-4490-7015-1(9))*; 24.00 *(978-1-4490-7016-8(7))* AuthorHouse.

Whelan, Alan. African Brew Ha Ha. 2010. (ENG., Illus.). 352p. pap. 14.95 ***(978-1-84953-044-6(0))*** Summerdale Pubs. GBR. Dist: Independent Pubs. Group.

Whiting, Sharri. Namibia: The Essential Guide to Customs & Culture. 2008. (Culture Smart! Ser.). (ENG., Illus.). 168p. pap. 9.95 *(978-1-85733-473-9(6))* Kuperard Pubs. GBR. Dist: Random Hse., Inc.

Wilkens, Emily Star. African Rice Heart: A Young Woman's Journal of Radical Service. 2011. pap. 11.99 *(978-0-8163-2402-6(6))* Pacific Pr. Publishing Assn.

Willemse, Hein, et al. The Afrikaans of the Cape Muslims. 2012. (Illus.). 318p. pap. 33.00 ***(978-1-86919-236-5(2))*** International Publishers Marketing.

Wingfield, Chris. Patterns of Connection. 2009. 156p. pap. *(978-3-639-21564-9(8))* VDM Verlag Dr. Mueller e.K.

Woodfork, Jacqueline. Culture & Customs of the Central African Republic, 1 vol. 2006. (Culture & Customs of Africa Ser.). (Illus.). 232p. 49.95 *(978-0-313-33203-6(7)*, GR3203, Greenwood Pr.) Greenwood Publishing Group, Inc.

World Bank. Africa Development Indicators 2011. 2011. (Africa Development Indicators Ser.). (ENG.). 194p. pap. 100.00 incl. cd-rom *(978-0-8213-8731-3(6)*, 9780821387313) World Bank Pubns.

AFRICA—STATISTICS

Africa South of the Sahara 2011. 40th rev. ed. 2010. (ENG.). 1604p. 835.00 *(978-1-85743-564-1(8))* Routledge.

Chepete, Poloko. Molding Timss Dat: Botswana Data as an Example. 2010. 204p. pap. *(978-3-8383-4004-3(3))* Lambert Academic Publishing.

Euromonitor International. African Marketing Data & Statistics. 3rd ed. 2011. (ENG.). 274p. (C). ***(978-1-84264-548-2(X))*** Euromonitor International PLC.

Europa Publications, ed. Africa South of the Sahara 2012. 41st rev. ed. 2011. (ENG.). 1604p. 880.00 ***(978-1-85743-623-5(7))*** Routledge.

—The Middle East & North Africa 2012. 58th rev. ed. 2012. (ENG.). 1468p. 880.00 ***(978-1-85743-626-6(1))*** Routledge.

Europa Publications Staff, ed. Africa South of the Sahara 2009. 6th rev. ed. 2008. 1528p. 760.00 *(978-1-85743-469-9(2))* Europa Pubns.

—Africa South of the Sahara 2010. 39th rev. ed. 2009. (ENG.). 1588p. 810.00 *(978-1-85743-527-6(3))* Routledge.

—Middle East & North Africa 2010. 56th rev. ed. 2009. (ENG.). 1484p. 810.00 *(978-1-85743-530-6(3))* Routledge.

Migration in Ghana: A Country Profile 2009. 2009. 115p. pap. *(978-92-9068-557-9(3))* International Organization for Migration (IOM).

Mitchell, Brian. Africa, Asia & Oceania, 1750-2005, 3 vols. 6th rev. ed. 2007. (ENG.). 1152p. 400.00 *(978-0-230-00515-0(2))* Palgrave Macmillan.

Organisation for Economic Co-operation and Development. African Central Government Debt Statistical Yearbook 2003-2007. 2010. (Illus.). 136p. pap. 54.00 *(978-92-64-08443-8(6))* Organization for Economic Cooperation & Development.

Organisation for Economic Co-operation and Development. African Central Government Debt Statistical Yearbook 2003-2009. 2011. (Illus.). 180p. pap. 70.00 ***(978-92-64-11650-4(8))*** Organization for Economic Cooperation & Development.

Organisation for Economic Co-operation and Development Staff. African Economic Outlook 2008. 2008. (ENG.). 620p. pap. 124.00 *(978-92-64-04585-9(6))* Organization for Economic Cooperation & Development.

Picazo, Oscar F. & Zhao, Feng. The Zambia Health Sector Public Expenditure Review: Accounting for Resources to Improve Effective Service Coverage. 2009. (Country Studies). (ENG., Ilus.). 116p. pap. 25.00 *(978-0-8213-7804-5(X)*, 9780821378045) World Bank Pubns.

Rajkumar, Andrew Sunil, et al. Malnutrition in Ethiopia: Current Interventions, Cost-Benefit Analysis, & the Way Forward. 2011. ***(978-0-8213-8766-5(9))*** World Bank Pubns.

United Nations. African Statistical Yearbook 2009. 2011. (MUL & ENG., Illus.). 390p. pap. 55.00 ***(978-92-1-025164-8(4))*** United Nations Pubns.

United Nations. Asia-Pacific Development Journal, June 2007. 2008. (ENG.). 162p. pap. 29.00 *(978-92-1-120524-4(7))* United Nations Pubns.

United Nations & United Nations: Economic Commission For Africa. African Statistical Yearbook 2010. 2011. (MUL., Illus.). 400p. pap. 55.00 ***(978-92-1-025165-5(2))*** United Nations Pubns.

World Bank. Africa Development Indicators 2010: Silent & Lethal: How Quiet Corruption Undermines Africa's Development. 2010. (Africa Development Indicators Ser.). (ENG.). 214p. pap. 100.00 incl. cd-rom *(978-0-8213-8202-8(0)*, 9780821382028) World Bank Pubns.

World Bank & Arbache, Jorge Saba. Africa Development Indicators 2010: Silent & Lethal - How Quiet Corruption Undermines Africa's Development. 2010. (Africa Development Indicators Ser.). (ENG.). NaNp. cd-rom 50.00 *(978-0-8213-8204-2(7)*, 9780821382042) World Bank Pubns.

World Bank Staff. Africa Development Indicators 2007: Spreading & Sustaining Growth in Africa. 2008. (Africa Development Indicators Ser.). (ENG.). 176p. pap. 100.00 *(978-0-8213-7283-8(1)*, 9780821372838) World Bank Pubns.

AFRICA—STUDY AND TEACHING

Conyers, James L., Jr., ed. Law, Culture, & Africana Studies. 2007. (Africana Studies). (ENG.). 142p. (gr. 11). pap. 29.95 *(978-1-4128-0660-2(7))* Transaction Pubs.

Higgins, Godfrey. Anacalypsis. (African Studies). reprint ed. 75.00 *(978-0-938818-87-8(2))* ECA Assocs.

—Anacalypsis (Volume 1 of 2, Part 1 Of 2) 2007. (ENG.). 480p. per. 32.99 *(978-1-4209-2991-1(7))* Digireads.com.

—Anacalypsis (Volume 1 of 2, Part 2 Of 2) 2007. (ENG.). 432p. per. 32.99 *(978-1-4209-2992-8(5))* Digireads.com.

—Anacalypsis (Volume 2 Of 2) 2007. (ENG.). 536p. per. 32.99 *(978-1-4209-2993-5(3))* Digireads.com.

Hudson-Weems, Clenora, ed. Contemporary Africana Theory & Thought: A Guide to Africana Studies. 2007. 420p. 99.95 *(978-1-59221-309-2(X))* Africa World Pr.

Okafor, Victor O. Towards an Understanding of Africology. 3rd rev. ed. 2011. (ENG.). 298p. pap. 94.95 *(978-0-7575-7065-0(8))* Kendall Hunt Publishing Co.

Tomaselli, Keyan & Wright, Handel Kashope, eds. Africa Cultural Studies & Difference. 2011. (ENG.). 200p. (C). 125.00 *(978-0-415-61742-0(1))* Routledge.

AFRICA, CENTRAL

Here are entered works on the region of Africa that includes what are now the Central African Republic, Gabon, Congo (Democratic Republic), and Congo (Brazzaville).

Blanken, Leo J. Rational Empires: Institutional Incentives & Imperial Expansion. 2012. (ENG., Illus.). 208p. pap. 27.50 ***(978-0-226-05674-6(0))***; 218p. 85.00 ***(978-0-226-05673-9(2))*** Univ. of Chicago Pr.

Europa Publications Staff. Africa South of the Sahara 2008. 37th rev. ed. 2007. 1536p. 700.00 *(978-1-85743-421-7(8))* Routledge.

AFRICA, CENTRAL—DESCRIPTION AND TRAVEL

Baker, Samuel W. Ismailia: A Narrative of the Expedition to Central Africa for the Suppression of the Slave Trade, 2 Vols. reprint ed. 250.00 *(978-0-7222-9807-7(2))* Library Reprints, Inc.

Barth, Heinrich. Travels & Discoveries in North & Central Afric. 2009. 482p. pap. *(978-1-4589-8839-3(2))* Books LLC.

—Travels & Discoveries in North & Central Afric: Being a Journal of an Expedition Undertaken under the Auspices of H. B. M. 's Government, in the Y. 2010. 840p. pap. 56.75 *(978-1-149-78905-6(0))*; 728p. pap. 50.75 *(978-1-143-38882-8(8))*; 802p. pap. 54.75 *(978-1-143-55637-1(2))*; 812p. pap. 55.75 *(978-1-144-67970-3(2))*; 674p. pap. 47.75 *(978-1-143-96685-9(6))*; 738p. pap. 51.75 *(978-1-143-70590-8(4))*; 656p. pap. 46.75 *(978-1-143-82860-7(7))*; 696p. pap. 48.75 *(978-1-143-59948-4(9))*; 666p. pap. 47.75 *(978-1-143-36425-9(2))*; 706p. pap. 49.75 *(978-1-143-92011-0(2))* BiblioBazaar.

—Travels & Discoveries in North & Central Afric: Being a Journal of an Expedition Undertaken under the Auspices of H. B. M. 's Government, in the Yea. 2010. 760p. pap. 52.75 *(978-1-149-02286-3(8))*; 720p. pap. 49.75 *(978-1-149-01195-9(5))*; 696p. pap. 48.75 *(978-1-143-32541-0(9))* BiblioBazaar.

—Travels & Discoveries in North & Central Afric: Being a Journal of an Expedition Undertaken under the Auspices of H. B. M. 's Government in the Year. 2010. 724p. pap. 49.75 *(978-1-146-54293-7(3))* BiblioBazaar.

—Travels & Discoveries in North & Central Afric: Being a Journal of an Expedition Undertaken under the Auspices of H. B. Majesty's Government, Vol. 2010. 672p. pap. 47.75 *(978-1-149-03397-5(5))* BiblioBazaar.

—Travels & Discoveries in North & Central Afric: Timbúktu, Sókoto, & the Basins of the Niger & Bénuwé. 2010. 618p. pap. 45.75 *(978-1-143-39774-5(6))* BiblioBazaar.

—Travels & Discoveries in North & Central Africa. 2009. 482p. pap. *(978-0-217-41083-0(9))*; 442p. pap. *(978-0-217-30182-4(7))*; 498p. pap. *(978-0-217-30170-1(3))*; 442p. pap. *(978-0-217-64757-1(X))*; 428p. pap. *(978-0-217-64760-1(X))*; 450p. pap. *(978-0-217-41084-7(7))*; 616p. pap. *(978-0-217-64763-2(4))* Books LLC.

—Travels & Discoveries in North & Central Africa: Being a Journal of an Expedition Undertaken under the Auspices of H. B. M. 's Government, in the Years 1849-1855. 2011. (Cambridge Library Collection - Travel & Exploration Ser.). (ENG.). 706p. pap. 48.00 *(978-1-108-02945-2(0))*; 736p. pap. 48.00 *(978-1-108-02944-5(2))*; 742p. pap. 50.00 *(978-1-108-02947-6(7))*; 708p. pap. 48.00 *(978-1-108-02946-9(9))*; (Illus.). 688p. pap. 48.00 *(978-1-108-02943-8(4))* Cambridge Univ. Pr.

—Travels & Discoveries in North & Central Africa; Being a Journal of an Expedition Undertaken under the Auspices of H B M 's. 2010. 306p. pap. 30.05 *(978-1-154-11118-7(0))* General Bks. LLC.

—Travels & Discoveries in North & Central Africa: being a journal of an expedition undertaken under the auspices of H. B. M. 's Government, in the Years

1849-55. 2011. 711p. pap. 49.75 *(978-1-240-91753-2(8)*, British Library, Historical Print Editions) BiblioBazaar.

Barth, Henry. Travels & Discoveries in North & Central Africa, 1849-1855. 2010. 816p. pap. 55.75 *(978-1-149-05856-5(0))* BiblioBazaar.

—Travels & Discoveries in North & Central Africa, 1849-1855. 2009. 492p. pap. *(978-0-217-30173-2(8))* Books LLC.

Burton, Richard. The Lake Regions of Central Africa. 2008. (Adventure Classics Ser.). (ENG., Illus.). 612p. 18.95 *(978-88-544-0359-8(8))* White Star ITA. Dist: Random Hse., Inc.

Burton, Richard F. The Lake Regions of Central Africa: A Picture of Exploration. 2011. (Cambridge Library Collection - Travel & Exploration Ser.). (ENG.). 500p. pap. 35.99 *(978-1-108-03129-5(3))*; (Illus.). 446p. pap. 32.99 *(978-1-108-03128-8(5))* Cambridge Univ. Pr.

Caramaschi, Fabio, photos by. Zambia: Un Racconto/A Story, 1 vol. 2007. (ENG & ITA., Illus.). 144p. pap. 39.95 *(978-88-8158-613-4(4))* Charta ITA. Dist: D.A.P./Distributed Art Pubs.

Casati, Gaetano. Ten Years in Equatoria & the Return with Emin Pasha. 2010. 422p. pap. 34.75 *(978-1-146-62164-9(7))*; 472p. pap. 37.75 *(978-1-142-40474-1(9))*; 436p. pap. 35.75 *(978-1-142-61218-4(X))* BiblioBazaar.

—Ten Years in Equatoria & the Return with Emin Pasha. 2009. 196p. pap. *(978-1-150-29113-5(3))* Books LLC.

—Ten Years in Equatoria & the Return with Emin Pasha. 2010. 190p. pap. 27.55 *(978-1-153-98282-5(X))* 2009. 204p. pap. 19.99 *(978-1-151-12997-0(6))* General Bks. LLC.

Casati, Gaetano & Clay, J. Randolph. Ten Years in Equatoria & the Return with Emin Pasha. 2010. 476p. pap. 37.75 *(978-1-148-81190-1(7))* BiblioBazaar.

Denham, Dixon & Clapperton, Hugh. Narrative of Travels & Discoveries in Northern & Central Africa, in the Years 1822, 1823, And 1824. 2011. (Cambridge Library Collection - Travel & Exploration Ser.). (ENG., Illus.). 762p. pap. 50.00 *(978-1-108-03120-2(X))* Cambridge Univ. Pr.

Geary, Christraud M., ed. In & Out of Focus: Images from Central Africa, 1885-1960. (Illus.). 128p. pap. 30.00 *(978-0-85667-551-5(2))* Wilson, Philip Pubs., Ltd. GBR. Dist: Palgrave Macmillan.

Lampen, C. Dudley. Mirango the Man Eater: A Tale of Central Africa. 2007. (ENG.). 256p. 42.95 *(978-0-548-04537-4(2))* Kessinger Publishing, LLC.

Livingstone, David. The Last Journals of David Livingstone in Central Africa from 1865 to His Death. 2008. 356p. 31.99 *(978-0-554-26021-1(2))*; 340p. 29.99 *(978-0-554-26022-8(0))*; 356p. 29.99 *(978-0-554-35324-1(5))*; 340p. 28.99 *(978-0-554-35325-8(3))* BiblioBazaar.

—The Last Journals of David Livingstone in Central Africa from 1865 to His Death: Continued by a narrative of his last Moments... 2007. 1. 318p. pap. 23.99 *(978-1-4346-0227-5(3))*1. (ENG.). 354p. pap. 26.99 *(978-1-4346-0301-2(6))*2. (ENG.). 304p. pap. 23.99 *(978-1-4346-0228-2(1))*2. (ENG.). 338p. pap. 24.99 *(978-1-4346-0302-9(4))* BiblioBazaar.

Livingstone, David & Livingstone, Charles. Narrative of an Expedition to the Zambesi & its Tributaries: And of the Discovery of the Lakes Shirwa & Nyassa: 1858-64. 2011. (Cambridge Library Collection - Travel & Exploration Ser.). (ENG., Illus.). 666p. pap. 45.00 *(978-1-108-03121-9(8))* Cambridge Univ. Pr.

Locken, E. Travel Journal Central African Republic. 2009. 192p. pap. 20.95 *(978-0-557-07991-9(8))* Lulu Enterprises Inc.

—Travel Journal Chad. 2009. 192p. pap. 20.95 *(978-0-557-07979-7(9))* Lulu Enterprises Inc.

—Travel Journal Equatorial Guinea. 2010. 192p. pap. 19.99 *(978-0-557-43473-2(4))* Lulu Enterprises Inc.

Macqueen, Peter & MacQueen, Peter. In Wildest Africa - the Record of a Hunting & Exploration Trip Through Uganda, Victoria Nyansa, the Kilimanjaro Region & British East Africa, With. 2009. 524p. pap. 33.45 *(978-1-4446-2541-7(1))* Research Pr.

Oswell, William Edward. William Cotton Oswell, Hunter & Explorer: The Story of his Life with Certain Correspondence & Extracts from the Private Journal of David Livingstone, Hitherto Unpublished. 2011. (Cambridge Library Collection - Travel & Exploration Ser.). (ENG.). 310p. pap. 24.99 ***(978-1-108-03212-4(5))***; (Illus.). 326p. pap. 29.99 ***(978-1-108-03211-7(7))*** Cambridge Univ. Pr.

Park, Mungo. Life & Travels of Mungo Park in Central Africa. 2008. 428p. 32.99 *(978-0-554-22797-9(5))* 2007. (ENG.). 382p. pap. 25.99 *(978-1-4264-3061-9(2))* 2007. (ENG.). 424p. pap. 28.99 *(978-1-4264-3126-5(0))* BiblioBazaar.

Richardson, James. Narrative of a Mission to Central Africa Performed in the Years 1850-51. 2008. 276p. 28.99 *(978-0-554-25619-1(3))*; 272p. 28.99 *(978-0-554-26252-9(5))*; 272p. 25.99 *(978-0-554-35555-9(8))*; 276p. 25.99 *(978-0-554-34922-0(1))* BiblioBazaar.

—Narrative of a Mission to Central Africa Performed in the Years 1850-51. 2007. pap. *(978-1-84830-007-1(7)*, Wildhern Pr.) Echo Library.

—Narrative of a Mission to Central Africa Performed in the Years 1850-51: Under the Orders & at the Expense of Her Majesty. 2007. (ENG.). 242p. pap. 20.99 *(978-1-4346-0727-0(5))*; Vol. 1. 268p. pap. 23.99 *(978-1-4346-0787-4(9))* BiblioBazaar.

Schweinfurth, George. Heart of Africa V1 Three Years Travels A. 2006. pap. 44.95 *(978-1-4286-4872-2(0))* Kessinger Publishing, LLC.

—Heart of Africa V2 Three Years Travels A. 2006. pap. 43.95 *(978-1-4286-4873-9(9))* Kessinger Publishing, LLC.

Stanley, Henry M. How I Found Livingstone. 2008. (ENG.). 380p. pap. 23.45 *(978-1-4385-0092-8(0))*; pap. 17.45 *(978-1-4385-0927-3(8))* Standard Pubns., Inc. (Book Jungle).

—How I Found Livingstone; travels, adventures, & discoveres in Central Africa, including an account of four months' residence with Dr. Livingston: Abridged. 2006. (ENG.). 424p. pap. 26.99 *(978-1-4264-1190-8(1))* BiblioBazaar.

Stanley, Henry Morton. How I Found Livingstone. 2009. 330p. pap. *(978-0-217-93316-2(5))* Books LLC.

—How I Found Livingstone. 2006. (Adventure Classics Ser.). (ENG., Illus.). 384p. 14.95 *(978-88-544-0120-4(X)*, White Star) Rizzoli International Pubns., Inc.

Stead, Mike & Rorison, Sean. Angola. 2010. (Bradt Travel Guide Ser.). (ENG., Illus.). 240p. pap. 27.99 *(978-1-84162-304-7(0))* Bradt Travel Guides GBR. Dist: Globe Pequot Pr., The.

Swann, Alfred J. Fighting the Slave-Hunters in Central Africa: A Record of Twenty-Six Years of Travel & Adventure Round the Great Lakes & of the Overthrow of Tip-Pu-Tib, Rumaliza & Other Great Slave-Traders. 358p. reprint ed. 98.00 *(978-0-7222-9829-9(3))* Library Reprints, Inc.

Waller, Horace. The Last Journals of David Livingstone in Central Africa from 1865 to His Death. 600p. 2007. 59.95 *(978-0-548-13994-3(6))* 2006. (ENG.). per. 44.95 *(978-1-4286-5181-4(0))* Kessinger Publishing, LLC.

Ward, Herbert. Five Years with the Congo Cannibals. 2006. (Illus.). pap. 30.95 *(978-1-4286-4743-5(0))* Kessinger Publishing, LLC.

AFRICA, CENTRAL—HISTORY

Chretien, Jéan-Pierre. The Great Lakes of Africa: Two Thousand Years of History. Straus, Scott, tr. from FRE. 2006. (ENG., Illus.). 503p. (gr. 17). pap. 25.95 *(978-1-890951-35-1(8))* Zone Bks.

de Cherisey, Erwan. France in Centrafrique: From Bokassa & Operation Barracude to the Days of EUFOR. 2011. (Africa@war Ser.). (Illus.). 80p. pap. 29.95 ***(978-1-907677-37-3(2))*** Helion & Co., Ltd. GBR. Dist: Casemate Pubs. & Bk. Distributors, LLC.

Gatwa, Tharcisse. The Churches & Ethnic Ideology in the Rwandan Crises, 1900-1994. 2008. (Regnum Studies in Mission Ser.). 312p. pap. 36.00 *(978-1-59752-823-8(4))* Wipf & Stock Pubs.

Habamenshi, Um'Khonde Patrick. Rwanda, Where Souls Turn to Dust: My Journey from Exile to Legacy. 2009. 336p. 32.95 *(978-1-4401-6081-3(3))* iUniverse, Inc.

Liebowitz, Daniel & Pearson, Charles. The Last Expedition: Stanley's Mad Journey Through the Congo. 2007. (Illus.). 355p. 26.00 *(978-1-4223-6718-6(5))* DIANE Publishing Co.

—The Last Expedition: Stanley's Mad Journey Through the Congo. 2006. (ENG., Illus.). 400p. pap. 15.95 *(978-0-393-32873-8(2)*, 32873) Norton, W. W. & Co., Inc.

McKenna, Amy, ed. The History of Central & Eastern Africa. 2011. (Britannica Guide to Africa Ser.). (Illus.). 224p. (YA). 106.00 *(978-1-61530-441-7(X))*; (gr. 9-18). 53.00 *(978-1-61530-322-9(7))* Rosen Publishing Group, Inc., The.

Mujawiyera, Eugenie. The Rwandan Tutsis: A Tutsi Woman's Acco. 2006. 120p. per. *(978-1-905068-38-8(7))* Adonis & Abbey Publishers Ltd.

Nna, Daniel. Evening Chats: Reflections on Traditions of the Bulus of Southern Cameroon. Ze, Frederick, tr. 2007. 412p. per. 21.95 *(978-1-59594-211-1(4))* WingSpan Publishing.

Pennacini, Cecilia & Wittenberg, Hermann. Rwenzori: Histories & Cultures of an African Mountain. (Illus.). 388p. pap. *(978-9970-02-755-2(7))* Fountain Pubs. Ltd.

Rich, Jeremy. Missing Links: The African & American Worlds of R. L. Garner, Primate Collector. 2012. (Race in the Atlantic World, 1700-1900 Ser.). (ENG., Illus.). 200p. 59.95 ***(978-0-8203-4059-3(6))***; pap. 24.95 ***(978-0-8203-4060-9(X))*** Univ. of Georgia Pr.

Rurangwa, Révérien. My Stolen Rwanda. 2009. (Illus.). 176p. pap. *(978-1-906702-02-1(0))* Reportage Pr.

Stone, Lacey. Rwandan Genocide Economic Decline & Increased Willingness to Murder. 2008. 80p. pap. *(978-3-8364-9781-7(6))* VDM Verlag Dr. Mueller e.K.

Straus, Scott. The Order of Genocide: Race, Power, & War in Rwanda. 2008. (Illus.). 288p. pap. 19.95 *(978-0-8014-7492-7(2))* Cornell Univ. Pr.

Twagilimana, Aimable. Historical Dictionary of Rwanda. 2007. (Historical Dictionaries of Africa Ser.). (ENG., Illus.). 288p. 93.00 *(978-0-8108-5313-3(2))* Scarecrow Pr., Inc.

Um'Khonde Patrick Habamenshi. Rwanda, Where Souls Turn to Dust: My Journey from Exile to Legacy. 2009. 336p. pap. 22.95 *(978-1-4401-6083-7(X))* iUniverse, Inc.

Uvin, Peter. Life after Violence: A People's Story of Burundi. 2009. (African Arguments Ser.). (ENG.). 224p. 70.95 *(978-1-84813-179-8(8))* Zed Bks., Ltd. GBR. Dist: Macmillan.

Whitehouse, Bruce. Migrants & Strangers in an African City. 2012. (ENG., Illus.). 288p. pap. 25.00 *(978-0-253-00082-8(3)*, 0253000823) Indiana Univ. Pr.

Whitford, John. Trading Life in Western & Central Africa. 2009. 344p. 46.95 *(978-1-104-57256-3(7))*; pap. 31.95 *(978-1-104-51107-4(X))* Kessinger Publishing, LLC.

AFRICA, CENTRAL—JUVENILE LITERATURE

Haskins, Jim. Count Your Way Through Zimbabwe. 2007. (J). pap. 5.95 *(978-0-8225-6044-9(5))* Lerner Publishing Group.

AFRICA, CENTRAL—SOCIAL CONDITIONS

Ensign, Margee & Bertrand, William E. Rwanda: History & Hope. 2009. (ENG.). 174p. 59.99 *(978-0-7618-4942-1(4))* Univ. Pr. of America, Inc.

Ewusi, Kale. Heads Without Hearts: Akwanga & the Battle for the Soul of the Southern Cameroons Cause, 1 vol. 2010. 158p. pap. 24.95 *(978-1-4512-9325-8(9))* PublishAmerica, Inc.

Farelius, Birgitta. Origin of Kingship Traditions & Symbolism in the Great Lakes Region of Africa. 2008. (Acta Universitatis Upsaliensia Historia Religionum Ser.). (Illus.). 373p. pap. 87.50 *(978-91-554-7295-5(8))* Uppsala Universitet/Acta Universitatis Uppsaliensis SWE. Dist: Coronet Bks.

Gatwa, Tharcisse. The Churches & Ethnic Ideology in the Rwandan Crises, 1900-1994. 2008. (Regnum Studies in Mission Ser.). 312p. pap. 36.00 *(978-1-59752-823-8(4))* Wipf & Stock Pubs.

Minton, Carol. The Social Construction of Gender Inequality in Central Malawi: Women's Ritualized Barriers to Resources. 2008. 120p. pap. *(978-3-639-06644-9(8))* VDM Verlag Dr. Mueller e.K.

Nicolaisen, Ida. Elusive Hunters: The Haddad of Kanem & the Bahr el Ghazal. 2010. (ENG., Illus.). 522p. (C). 80.00 *(978-87-7934-394-8(5))* Aarhus Universitetsforlag DNK. Dist: ISD.

Oruonye, Emeka Daniel & S. Sanusi, S. Socio-Economic & Ecological Impact of Resettlement Scheme. 2011. 264p. pap. ***(978-3-8433-8541-1(6))*** Lambert Academic Publishing.

Tande, Dibussi. Scribbles from the Den Essays on Politics & Collective Memory in Cameroon. 2009. 232p. pap. *(978-9956-558-91-9(5))* Langaa Research & Publishing Common Initiative Group CMR. Dist: Michigan State Univ. Pr.

Uvin, Peter. Life after Violence: A People's Story of Burundi. 2009. (African Arguments Ser.). (ENG.). 224p. 70.95 *(978-1-84813-179-8(8))* Zed Bks., Ltd. GBR. Dist: Macmillan.

Vaughan, Megan. The Story of an African Famine: Gender & Famine in Twentieth-Century Malawi. 2007. (ENG.). 192p. pap. 46.00 *(978-0-521-03551-4(1))* Cambridge Univ. Pr.

Vudo, Emmanuel Yenshu, ed. Civil Society & the Search for Development Alternatives in Cameroon. 2008. 236p. pap. *(978-2-86978-220-4(9))* Council for the Development of Social Science Research in Africa SEN. Dist: Michigan State Univ. Pr.

Whitehouse, Bruce. Migrants & Strangers in an African City. 2012. (Illus.). x, 274p. ***(978-0-253-00075-0(0))***; (ENG., 288p. pap. 25.00 *(978-0-253-00082-8(3)*, 0253000823) Indiana Univ. Pr.

Whitehouse, Bruce. Migrants & Strangers in an African City: Exile, Dignity, Belonging. 2012. (ENG., Illus.). 288p. 70.00 *(978-0-253-00081-1(5)*, 0253000815) Indiana Univ. Pr.

Wilkens, Emily Star. African Rice Heart: A Young Woman's Journal of Radical Service. 2011. pap. 11.99 *(978-0-8163-2402-6(6))* Pacific Pr. Publishing Assn.

2006 UNICEF Botswana Annual Report. 2007. (Illus.). 44p. *(978-92-806-4173-8(5))* United Nations Children's Fund, The (UNICEF).

AFRICA, EAST

Here are entered works dealing collectively with Sudan, Eritrea, Ethiopia, Somalia, Djibouti, Kenya, Uganda, and Tanzania.

Patterson, John Henry. In the Grip of the Nyika: Further Adventures in British East Africa. 2009. (ENG.). 408p. reprint ed. 41.99 *(978-1-117-49793-8(3))* BiblioBazaar.

AFRICA, EAST—DESCRIPTION AND TRAVEL

Ames, Evelyn. A Glimpse of Eden. 2007. pap. 17.00 *(978-0-87797-356-0(3))* Cherokee Publishing Co.

Atwood, Melinda. Jambo, Mama: Memories of Africa. 2nd ed. 2009. 336p. pap. 16.95 *(978-1-879384-78-1(7))* Cypress Hse.

Barbosa, Duarte. A Description of the Coasts of East Africa & Malabar in the Beginning of the Sixteenth Century. Stanley, Henry E. J., tr. 2007. 260p. 42.95 *(978-0-548-33543-7(5))*; 264p. per. 27.95 *(978-1-4326-9452-4(9))* Kessinger Publishing, LLC.

Beard, Peter, ed. The End of the Game: The Last Word from Paradise. 2008. 39.99 *(978-3-8365-0531-4(2))*; 39.99 *(978-3-8365-0533-8(9))* TASCHEN DEU. Dist: Ingram Pub. Services.

Brandt, Nick. A Shadow Falls. 2009. (ENG., Illus.). 132p. 50.00 *(978-0-8109-5415-1(X))* Abrams.

Briggs, Philip. East African Wildlife: A Visitor's Guide. 2008. (Bradt Travel Guide Ser.). (ENG., Illus.). 288p. pap. 28.99 *(978-1-84162-208-8(7))* Bradt Travel Guides GBR. Dist: Globe Pequot Pr., The.

—Malawi. 5th ed. 2010. (ENG., Illus.). 352p. pap. 25.99 *(978-1-84162-313-9(X))* Bradt Travel Guides GBR. Dist: Globe Pequot Pr., The.

Burns, Cameron M. & Mountaineers Books Staff. Kilimanjaro & East Africa: A Climbing & Trekking Guide - Includes Mount Kenya, Mount Meru, & the Rwenzoris. 2nd rev. ed. 2006. (ENG., Illus.). 239p. pap. 19.95 *(978-0-89886-604-9(9))* Mountaineers Bks., The.

Burton, Richard F. Zanzibar: City, Island, & Coast. 2011. (Cambridge Library Collection - Travel & Exploration Ser.). (ENG.). 546p. pap. 39.99 ***(978-1-108-03147-9(1))***; (Illus.). 542p. pap. 39.99 ***(978-1-108-03146-2(3))*** Cambridge Univ. Pr.

Donley, Brady & Strand, Gary, photos by. Journey of Dreams: Safari Images & Bush Recipes from East Africa. 2007. per. 30.00 *(978-0-9799387-3-3(2))* Safi Publishing.

Grant, Richard. Crazy River: Exploration & Folly in East Africa. 2011. (ENG.). 352p. pap. 15.00 *(978-1-4391-5414-4(7)*, Free Pr.) Free Pr.

Greenfield, Joseph. A Quail Hunter's Odyssey. 2009. (ENG.). 200p. 34.95 *(978-1-57157-336-0(4))* Safari Pr., Inc.

Guadalupi, Gianni. The Nile: History, Adventure & Discovery. Bertinetti, Marcello & Accomazzo, Laura, eds. Davenport, Neil Frazer, tr. from ITA. 2008. (ENG., Illus.). 352p. 45.00 *(978-88-544-0339-0(3))* White Star ITA. Dist: Random Hse., Inc.

Lonely Planet Staff & Firestone, Matthew. Watching Wildlife East Africa. 2nd ed. 2009. (Watching Wildlife Ser.). (ENG., Illus.). 344p. pap. 22.99 *(978-1-74104-208-5(9))* Lonely Planet Pubns.

Lonely Planet Staff & Fitzpatrick, Mary. East Africa. 8th rev. ed. 2009. (Multi Country Guide Ser.). (ENG., Illus.). 664p. pap. 31.99 *(978-1-74104-769-1(2))* Lonely Planet Pubns.

Matthiessen, Peter. The Tree Where Man Was Born. rev. ed. 2010. (ENG.). 304p. (gr. 12). 17.00 *(978-0-14-310624-1(4)*, Penguin Classics) Penguin Group (USA) Inc.

McLeod, Lyons. Travels in Eastern Africa. 2009. 148p. pap. *(978-0-217-30212-8(2))* Books LLC.

Moloney, Joseph. With Captain Stairs to Katanga: Slavery & subjugation in the Congo 1891-92. Saffery, David, ed. 2007. (Illus.). 196p. per. *(978-0-9553936-5-5(5))* Jeppestown Pr.

Morrison, Dan. The Black Nile: One Man's Amazing Journey Through Peace & War on the World's Longest River. (ENG.). (gr. 12). 2011. 352p. 16.00 *(978-0-14-311937-1(0)*, Penguin (Non-Classics)) 2010. 320p. 26.95 *(978-0-670-02198-7(9)*, Viking Adult) Penguin Group (USA) Inc.

Patterson, J. H. The Man-Eaters of Tsavo & Other East African Adventures. 2009. 184p. pap. *(978-1-4099-6833-7(2))* Dodo Pr.

—The Man-Eaters of Tsavo & Other East African Adventures. 2006. (ENG.). pap. *(978-1-4068-3000-2(3))* Echo Library.

Patterson, John. The Man-Eaters of Tsavo & Other East African Adventures. 2007. 212p. 19.99 *(978-1-59986-705-2(2))* Filiquarian Publishing, LLC.

—The Man Eaters of Tsavo & Other East African Adventures. 2007. 148p. per. 9.95 *(978-1-60206-000-5(2))* Cosimo, Inc.

Patterson, John Henry. The Man-Eaters of Tsavo. 2009. 152p. pap. 7.75 *(978-1-60459-745-5(3))* Wilder Pubns., Ltd.

—The Man-Eaters of Tsavo & Other East African Adventures. 2009. 122p. pap. *(978-1-4589-2476-6(9))* Books LLC.

—The Man-Eaters of Tsavo & Other East African Adventures. 2007. pap. 7.99 *(978-1-59986-907-0(1)*, FQ Classics) Filiquarian Publishing, LLC.

Rainsford, William Stephen. The Land of the Lion. 2010. (ENG.). 556p. pap. 42.75 *(978-1-177-64597-3(1))* 2009. 552p. 36.99 *(978-1-115-85973-8(0))* 2009. 552p. pap. 41.75 *(978-1-115-85974-5(9))* 2009. 552p. pap. 40.75 *(978-1-115-85975-2(7))* 2009. (ENG.). 550p. pap. 31.99 *(978-1-115-85976-9(5)*, BiblioLife) 2009. (ENG.). 550p. pap. 30.99 *(978-1-115-85977-6(3)*, BiblioLife) 2009. 548p. 29.99 *(978-1-103-20507-3(2))* 2009. 548p. pap. 23.99 *(978-1-103-20506-6(4))* 2009. 548p. 29.99 *(978-0-559-98880-6(X))* 2009. 548p. pap. 23.99 *(978-0-559-98877-6(X))* BiblioBazaar.

—The Land of the Lion. 2009. 320p. pap. 23.19 *(978-0-217-59408-0(5))* General Bks. LLC.

—The Land of the Lion. 2008. 548p. pap. *(978-1-4437-0637-7(X))* Read Bks.

Smith, Arthur Donaldson. Through Unknown African Countries: The First Expedition from Somaliland to Lake Rudolf. 2009. (ENG., Illus.). 471p. 95.00 *(978-1-57898-687-3(7))* Martino Publishing.

Speke, John Hanning. Journal of the Discovery of the Source of the Nile. 2011. (Cambridge Library Collection - Travel & Exploration Ser.). (ENG., Illus.). 758p. pap. 50.00 *(978-1-108-03123-3(4))* Cambridge Univ. Pr.

Vermeulen, Jean-Paul. Gone Diving Mozambique. 2006. 88p. pap. 22.95 *(978-1-59800-499-1(9))* Outskirts Pr., Inc.

Williams, Lizzie. Zanzibar & Pemba Footprint Focus. 2011. (Footprint Focus Ser.). (ENG., Illus.). 128p. pap. 11.95 *(978-1-908206-18-3(7))* Footprint Handbooks GBR. Dist: Globe Pequot Pr., The.

AFRICA, EAST—ECONOMIC CONDITIONS

Alpers, Edward A. Ivory & Slaves: Changing Pattern of International Trade in East Central Africa to the Later Nineteenth Century. 2008. 320p. pap. 32.00 *(978-1-59740-610-9(4))* ACLS Humanities E-Book.

Icon Group International, Inc. Staff, compiled by. The 2006 Economic & Product Market Databook for Ali-Sabiah, Djibouti. 2006. 618p. ring bd. 95.00 *(978-0-497-80031-4(4))* Icon Group International, Inc.

—The 2006 Economic & Product Market Databook for Bujumbura, Burundi. 2006. 618p. ring bd. 95.00 *(978-0-497-80259-2(7))* Icon Group International, Inc.

—The 2006 Economic & Product Market Databook for Bururi, Burundi. 2006. 618p. ring bd. 95.00 *(978-0-497-80274-5(0))* Icon Group International, Inc.

—The 2006 Economic & Product Market Databook for Butare, Rwanda. 2006. 618p. ring bd. 95.00 *(978-0-497-80275-2(9))* Icon Group International, Inc.

—The 2006 Economic & Product Market Databook for Gisenyi, Rwanda. 2006. 618p. ring bd. 95.00 *(978-0-497-80600-2(2))* Icon Group International, Inc.

—The 2006 Economic & Product Market Databook for Mandie, Mozambique. 2006. 618p. ring bd. 95.00 *(978-0-497-80941-6(9))* Icon Group International, Inc.

—The 2006 Economic & Product Market Databook for Maputo, Mozambique. 2006. 618p. ring bd. 95.00 *(978-0-497-80008-6(X))* Icon Group International, Inc.

—The 2006 Economic & Product Market Databook for Ngozi, Burundi. 2006. 618p. ring bd. 95.00 *(978-0-497-81120-4(0))* Icon Group International, Inc.

—The 2006 Economic & Product Market Databook for Nhlangano, Swaziland. 2006. 618p. ring bd. 95.00 *(978-0-497-81121-1(9))* Icon Group International, Inc.

—The 2006 Economic & Product Market Databook for Nyabisindu, Rwanda. 2006. 618p. ring bd. 95.00 *(978-0-497-82044-2(7))* Icon Group International, Inc.

—The 2006 Economic & Product Market Databook for Obock, Djibouti. 2006. 618p. ring bd. 95.00 *(978-0-497-81152-5(9))* Icon Group International, Inc.

—The 2006 Economic & Product Market Databook for Pigg's Peak, Swaziland. 2006. 618p. ring bd. 95.00 *(978-0-497-81222-5(3))* Icon Group International, Inc.

—The 2006 Economic & Product Market Databook for Ruhengeri, Rwanda. 2006. 618p. ring bd. 95.00 *(978-0-497-81375-8(0))* Icon Group International, Inc.

—The 2006 Economic & Product Market Databook for Rumonge, Burundi. 2006. 618p. ring bd. 95.00 *(978-0-497-81376-5(9))* Icon Group International, Inc.

Kasule, Ssebunya. Regionalism in Afric. 2009. 144p. pap. *(978-3-639-12407-1(3))* VDM Verlag Dr. Mueller e.K.

Kimbugwe, Kato, et al. Economic Development Through Regional Trade: A Role for the New East African Community? 2012. (ENG., Illus.). 288p. 100.00 *(978-0-230-31421-4(X))* Palgrave Macmillan.

Mushongi, Cypridion. Traders As Drivers of Common Bean Marketing in Karagwe, Tanzani. 2010. 68p. pap. *(978-3-639-26882-9(2))* VDM Verlag Dr. Mueller e.K.

Rockel, Stephen J. Carriers of Culture: Labor on the Road in Nineteenth-Century East Africa, 1 vol. 2006. (Social History of Africa Ser.). (Illus.). 368p. per. 41.25 *(978-0-325-07133-6(0),* E07133) Heinemann.

Rockel, Stephen J., ed. Carriers of Culture: Labor on the Road in Nineteenth-Century East Africa, 1 vol. 2006. (Social History of Africa Ser.). (Illus.). 368p. 124.95 *(978-0-325-07116-9(0),* E07116, Praeger Pubs.) Greenwood Publishing Group, Inc.

AFRICA, EAST—HISTORY

Alpers, Edward A. East Africa & the Indian Ocean. 2008. 240p. (ENG.). pap. 28.95 *(978-1-55876-453-8(4));* (Illus.). 86.95 *(978-1-55876-452-1(6))* Wiener, Markus Pubs., Inc.

—Ivory & Slaves: Changing Pattern of International Trade in East Central Africa to the Later Nineteenth Century. 2008. 320p. pap. 32.00 *(978-1-59740-610-9(4))* ACLS Humanities E-Book.

Bizimana, John. Escape from Rwanda: A True Story of Faith, Hope, & Survival. 2010. (Illus.). 144p. 18.99 *(978-1-60641-830-7(0))* Deseret Bk. Co.

Blizzard, Sarah. Women's Roles in the 1994 Rwanda Genocide & the Empowerment of Women in the Aftermath. 2008. 100p. pap. *(978-3-8364-6293-8(1))* VDM Verlag Dr. Mueller e.K.

Capell, A. E. 2nd Rhodesia Regiment in East Africa. 2009. pap. *(978-1-84574-329-1(6))* Naval & Military Pr., The.

Chretien, Jéan-Pierre. The Great Lakes of Africa: Two Thousand Years of History. Straus, Scott, tr. from FRE. 2006. (ENG., Illus.). 503p. (gr. 17). pap. 25.95 *(978-1-890951-35-1(8))* Zone Bks.

Cruvellier, Thierry. Court of Remorse: Inside the International Criminal Tribunal for Rwanda. Voss, Chari, tr. from FRE. 2010. (Critical Human Rights Ser.). (ENG., Illus.). 204p. pap. 24.95 *(978-0-299-23674-8(9))* Univ. of Wisconsin Pr.

Curtis, Christian. Letters from the Horn of Africa 1923 - 1945: Sandy Curle, Soldier & Diplomat Extraordinary. 2009. (Illus.). 276p. 50.00 *(978-1-84415-845-4(4))* Pen & Sword Bks. Ltd. GBR. Dist: Casemate Pubs. & Bk. Distributors, LLC.

Des Forges, Alison Liebhafsky. Defeat Is the Only Bad News: Rwanda under Musinga, 1896-1931. Newbury, David, ed. 2011. (Africa & the Diaspora Ser.). (ENG., Illus.). 256p. pap. 26.95 *(978-0-299-28144-1(2))* Univ. of Wisconsin Pr.

Eno, Mohamed A. The Bantu - Jareer Somali: Unearthing Apartheid in the Horn of Africa. 2008. 320p. pap. *(978-1-905068-95-1(6))* Adonis & Abbey Publishers Ltd.

—The Bantu - Jareer Somalis: The bantu - jareer Somalis. 2008. 320p. *(978-1-905068-94-4(8))* Adonis & Abbey Publishers Ltd.

Galbraith, John S. Mackinnon & East Africa, 1878-1895: A Study in the 'New Imperialism' 2008. (Cambridge Commonwealth Ser.). (ENG.). 264p. pap. 37.99 *(978-0-521-10171-4(9))* Cambridge Univ. Pr.

Ilibagiza, Immaculée & Erwin, Steve. Led by Faith: Rising from the Ashes of the Rwandan Genocide. 2008. (ENG., Illus.). 264p. 24.95 *(978-1-4019-1887-3(5))* Hay Hse., Inc.

Katongole, Emmanuel & Wilson-Hartgrove, Jonathan. Mirror to the Church: Resurrecting Faith after Genocide in Rwanda, 1 vol. 2009. (ENG.). 176p. pap. 15.99 *(978-0-310-28489-5(9))* Zondervan.

Laurence, Tony. The Dar Mutiny Of 1964. 2010. 268p. 26.49 *(978-1-4490-9876-6(2));* pap. 17.49 *(978-1-4490-9875-9(4))* AuthorHouse.

Maxon, Robert M. East Africa: An Introductory History. 3rd ed. 2009. (ENG.). pap. 29.95 *(978-1-933202-46-4(7))* West Virginia Univ. Pr.

McKenna, Amy, ed. The History of Central & Eastern Africa. 2011. (Britannica Guide to Africa Ser.). (Illus.). 224p. (YA). 106.00 *(978-1-61530-441-7(X));* (gr. 9-18). 53.00 *(978-1-61530-322-9(7))* Rosen Publishing Group, Inc., The.

Medard, et al. Slavery in the Great Lakes Region of East Africa. 2007. (Illus.). 288p. 95.00 *(978-1-84701-602-7(2));* pap. 34.95 *(978-1-84701-603-4(0))* Boydell & Brewer, Ltd. GBR. (Currey, James). Dist: Boydell & Brewer, Inc.

Montgomery, Denis. A Beautiful Ivory Bangle. 2008. 300p. pap. 27.50 *(978-1-4357-5953-4(2))* Lulu Enterprises Inc.

Moorehead, Alan. The White Nile. lib. bdg. 27.95 *(978-0-8488-2006-0(1))* Amereon LTD.

Nicolini, Beatrice & Nicoline, Beatrice. Markran, Oman, & Zanzibar: Three-Terminal Cultural Corridor in the Western Indian Ocean (1799-1856) Watson, Penelope-Jane, tr. from ITA. 2011.Tr. of Sultanatodi Zanzibar nel XIX Secolo. (Illus.). 200p. pap. 26.95 *(978-1-55876-544-3(1))* Wiener, Markus Pubs., Inc.

Page, Malcolm. King's African Rifles: A History. 2011. (Illus.). 298p. pap. 24.95 *(978-1-84884-438-4(7))* Pen & Sword Bks. Ltd. GBR. Dist: Casemate Pubs. & Bk. Distributors, LLC.

Pizzo, David. To Devour the Land of Mkwawa. 2010. 264p. pap. *(978-3-8383-4542-0(6))* Lambert Academic Publishing.

Sebarenzi, Joseph. God Sleeps in Rwanda: A Journey of Transformation. 2011. (ENG., Illus.). 272p. pap. 15.00 *(978-1-4165-7577-1(4),* Beyond Words/Atria Bks.) Atria Bks.

Straus, Scott & Waldorf, Lars. Remaking Rwanda: State Building & Human Rights after Mass Violence. 2011. 320p. E-Book *(978-0-299-28263-9(5))* Univ. of Wisconsin Pr.

Straus, Scott & Waldorf, Lars, eds. Remaking Rwanda: State Building & Human Rights after Mass Violence. 2011. (Critical Human Rights Ser.). (ENG., Illus.). 320p. pap. 26.95 *(978-0-299-28264-6(3))* Univ. of Wisconsin Pr.

Uvin, Peter. Life after Violence: A People's Story of Burundi. 2009. (African Arguments Ser.). (ENG.). 224p. pap. 20.95 *(978-1-84813-180-4(1))* Zed Bks., Ltd. GBR. Dist: Macmillan.

Wheeler, Sara. Too Close to the Sun: The Audacious Life & Times of Denys Finch Hatton. 2009. (ENG., Illus.). 336p. pap. 18.00 *(978-0-8129-6892-7(1),* Random Hse. Trade Paperbacks) Random House Publishing Group.

AFRICA, EAST—POLITICS AND GOVERNMENT

Bradbury, Becoming Somaliland. 2008. (Illus.). 288p. 80.00 *(978-1-84701-311-8(2));* pap. 24.95 *(978-1-84701-310-1(4))* Boydell & Brewer, Ltd. GBR. (Currey, James). Dist: Boydell & Brewer, Inc.

Chalk, Frank, et al. Mobilizing the Will to Intervene: Leadership to Prevent Mass Atrocities. 2010. (ENG.). 200p. (C). pap. *(978-0-7735-3804-7(6))* McGill-Queen's Univ. Pr.

Des Forges, Alison Liebhafsky. Defeat Is the Only Bad News: Rwanda under Musinga, 1896-1931. Newbury, David, ed. 2011. (Africa & the Diaspora Ser.). (ENG., Illus.). 256p. pap. 26.95 *(978-0-299-28144-1(2))* Univ. of Wisconsin Pr.

Des Forges, Alison Liebhafsky & Newbury, David S. Defeat Is the Only Bad News: Rwanda under Musinga, 1897-1931. 2011. E-Book *(978-0-299-28143-4(4))* Univ. of Wisconsin Pr.

Fallers, Lloyd A. The Social Anthropology of the Nation-State. 2011. (ENG., Illus.). 184p. pap. 29.95 *(978-1-4128-1866-7(4))* Transaction Pubs.

Gossaye, Ashenafi. Inner-City Renewal in Addis Abab. 2008. 332p. pap. *(978-3-639-08806-9(9))* VDM Verlag Dr. Mueller e.K.

Hatchard, John, et al. Comparative Constitutionalism & Good Governance in the Commonwealth: An Eastern & Southern African Perspective. 2009. (ENG., Illus.). 388p. pap. 56.00 *(978-0-521-11829-3(8))* Cambridge Univ. Pr.

Hulterstrom, Karolina, et al. Political Opposition in African Countries: The Cases of Kenya, Namibia, Zambia & Zimbabwe. 2007. (NAI Discussion Papers). 85p. pap. 15.95 *(978-91-7106-587-2(3))* Nordiska Afrikainstitutet SWE. Dist: Stylus Publishing, LLC.

Joalahliae, Randolph M. K. The Indian as an Enemy: An Analysis of the Indian Question in East Africa. 2010. 92p. pap. 11.75 *(978-1-4520-1692-4(5))* AuthorHouse.

Khadiagala, Gilbert M. Meddlers or Mediators? African Interveners in Civil Conflicts in Eastern Africa. 2007. (International Negotiation Ser.). 274p. *(978-90-04-16331-7(X))* BRILL.

Laurence, Tony. The Dar Mutiny Of 1964. 2010. 268p. 26.49 *(978-1-4490-9876-6(2));* pap. 17.49 *(978-1-4490-9875-9(4))* AuthorHouse.

Lee, Jessica N. & Reyes, Dominick P., eds. East African Country Tensions & Relations. 2011. (African Political, Economic, & Security Issues Ser.). 172p. 89.00 *(978-1-61209-707-7(3))* Nova Science Pubs., Inc.

Maiyo, Josh. Political Parties & Democratic Consolidation in East Afric. 2010. 96p. pap. *(978-3-8383-6500-8(3))* Lambert Academic Publishing.

Mutua, Makau. Human Rights NGOs in East Africa: Political & Normative Tensions. Mutua, Makau, ed. 2008. (Pennsylvania Studies in Human Rights Ser.). (Illus.). 400p. (C). 79.95 *(978-0-8122-4112-9(6))* Univ. of Pennsylvania Pr.

Nabulyato, Robinson, ed. Good Governance & Civil Society Participation in Africa. 2008. 252p. pap. 29.95 *(978-99944-55-32-4(X))* African Bks. Collective, Ltd. GBR. Dist: Lightning Source, Inc.

Njogu, Kimani & Maupeu, HervT, eds. Songs & Politics in Eastern Afric. 2007. 420p. (C). pap. *(978-9987-449-42-2(5))* Mkuki na Nyoka Pubs. TZA. Dist: Michigan State Univ. Pr.

Nyamndi, G. D. Whether Losing, Whether Winning Essays in Political Realism. 2008. 120p. pap. *(978-9956-558-52-0(4))* Langaa Research & Publishing Common Initiative Group CMR. Dist: Michigan State Univ. Pr.

Ogalo, Dan. Good Governance & Constitutionalism in East Africa: Questioning the Contemporary Relevance of the Commonwealth. viii, 131p. *(978-9970-02-883-2(9))* Fountain Pubs. Ltd.

Pizzo, David. To Devour the Land of Mkwawa. 2010. 264p. pap. *(978-3-8383-4542-0(6))* Lambert Academic Publishing.

Rabasa, Angel & Rabasa. Radical Islam in East Africa. 2009. 110p. pap. 31.50 *(978-0-8330-4519-5(9),* mg782) RAND Corp., The.

Sebarenzi, Joseph. God Sleeps in Rwanda: A Journey of Transformation. 2011. (ENG., Illus.). 272p. pap. 15.00 *(978-1-4165-7577-1(4),* Beyond Words/Atria Bks.) Atria Bks.

Straus, Scott & Waldorf, Lars. Remaking Rwanda: State Building & Human Rights after Mass Violence. 2011. 320p. E-Book *(978-0-299-28263-9(5))* Univ. of Wisconsin Pr.

Straus, Scott & Waldorf, Lars, eds. Remaking Rwanda: State Building & Human Rights after Mass Violence. 2011. (Critical Human Rights Ser.). (ENG., Illus.). 320p. pap. 26.95 *(978-0-299-28264-6(3))* Univ. of Wisconsin Pr.

AFRICA, EAST—RELATIONS—FOREIGN COUNTRIES

Alpers, Edward A. East Africa & the Indian Ocean. 2008. 240p. (ENG.). pap. 28.95 *(978-1-55876-453-8(4));* (Illus.). 86.95 *(978-1-55876-452-1(6))* Wiener, Markus Pubs., Inc.

Chau, Donovan C. Kenya. 2010. (Global Security Watch Ser.). (Illus.). 194p. 49.95 *(978-0-313-37880-5(0),* C37880, Praeger Pubs.) Greenwood Publishing Group, Inc.

D'Souza, Blanche. Harnessing the Trade Winds: The Story of the Centuries-Old Indian Trade with East Africa, using the Monsoon Winds. 2008. (Illus.). 208p. pap. 29.95 *(978-9966-7123-2-5(1))* African Bks. Collective, Ltd. GBR. Dist: Lightning Source, Inc.

Rabasa, Angel & Rabasa. Radical Islam in East Africa. 2009. 110p. pap. 31.50 *(978-0-8330-4519-5(9),* mg782) RAND Corp., The.

AFRICA, EAST—RELIGION

Balisky, E. Paul. Wolaitta Evangelists. 2009. (American Society of Missiology Monograph Ser.). 410p. pap. 45.00 *(978-1-60608-157-0(8),* Pickwick Pubns.) Wipf & Stock Pubs.

Becker, Felicitas. Becoming Muslim in Mainland Tanzania, 1890-2000: The Spread of Islam Beyond the Indian Ocean Coast,1880-2000. 2008. (British Academy Ser.). (ENG., Illus.). 300p. 125.00 *(978-0-19-726427-0(1))* Oxford Univ. Pr., Inc.

Davis, Rebecca. With Two Hands: Stories of God at work in Ethiopia. 2010. (ENG., Illus.). 176p. 8.99 *(978-1-84550-539-4(5))* Christian Focus Pubns. GBR. Dist: STL Distribution North America.

Green, Maia. Priests, Witches & Power: Popular Christianity after Mission in Southern Tanzania. 2007. (Cambridge Studies in Social & Cultural Anthropology Ser.). (ENG., Illus.). 200p. (C). pap. 38.99 *(978-0-521-04027-3(2))* Cambridge Univ. Pr.

Harris, Grace Gredys. Casting out Anger: Religion among the Taita of Kenya. 2007. (Cambridge Studies in Social & Cultural Anthropology Ser.). (ENG., Illus.). 216p. pap. 48.00 *(978-0-521-04084-6(1))* Cambridge Univ. Pr.

Ilibagiza, Immaculée & Erwin, Steve. Our Lady of Kibeho: Mary Speaks to the World from the Heart of Africa. 2010. (ENG.). 240p. pap. 13.95 *(978-1-4019-2743-1(2))* Hay Hse., Inc.

Kariuki, David Mureithi. The Challenges Facing the East African Revival Movement. 2011. 72p. pap. **(978-3-8443-1846-3(1))** Lambert Academic Publishing.

Savage, Job K. Life in Ethiopia: Historical & Religious Highlights of A 2,000 Year Old African Dynasty. 2010. 156p. pap. 13.99 *(978-1-4520-5269-4(7))* AuthorHouse.

Settimba, Henry. Testing Times: Globalisation & Investing Theology in East Africa. 2009. 312p. pap. 15.49 *(978-1-4389-4798-3(4))* AuthorHouse.

Stambach, Amy. Faith in Schools: Religion, Education, & American Evangelicals in East Africa. 2009. (ENG.). 248p. 65.00 *(978-0-8047-6850-4(1));* pap. 24.95 *(978-0-8047-6851-1(X))* Stanford Univ. Pr.

Straight, Bilinda. Miracles & Extraordinary Experience in Northern Kenya. 2009. (Contemporary Ethnography Ser.). (Illus.). 296p. (C). pap. 24.95 *(978-0-8122-2092-6(7))* Univ. of Pennsylvania Pr.

AFRICA, EAST—SOCIAL CONDITIONS

Apoo Oitamong, Maria. The Revived East African Community. 2010. 64p. pap. *(978-3-8383-4467-6(7))* Lambert Academic Publishing.

Blum, Stefan. Elites, Coercion & Collective Goods: A Rational Choice Explanation of Variations in Violence in East Africa (Uganda, Tanzania & Zanzibar) 2011. 246p. pap. 55.00 *(978-3-8329-6014-8(7))* Nomos Verlagsgesellschaft DEU. Dist: International Specialized Bk. Services.

Grant, Richard. Crazy River: Exploration & Folly in East Africa. 2011. (ENG.). 352p. pap. 15.00 *(978-1-4391-5414-4(7),* Free Pr.) Free Pr.

Kaggwa. Organic Manure & Artificial Substrate Use in Fingerponds in Eas. 2007. (DUT & ENG., Illus.). 150p. (C). 83.95 *(978-0-415-41697-9(3),* Taylor & Francis) Taylor & Francis Group GBR. Dist: Taylor & Francis Group.

Mwela, Frank. Protection of Women Refugee Against Sexual Offences. 2011. 56p. pap. **(978-3-8433-9350-8(8))** Lambert Academic Publishing.

Uvin, Peter. Life after Violence: A People's Story of Burundi. 2009. (African Arguments Ser.). (ENG.). 224p. pap. 20.95 *(978-1-84813-180-4(1))* Zed Bks., Ltd. GBR. Dist: Macmillan.

AFRICA, EAST—SOCIAL LIFE AND CUSTOMS

Bergh, Leonard John VanDen. On the Trail of the Pigmies. 2009. 120p. pap. *(978-0-217-73534-6(7))* Books LLC.

Brennan, James, et al, eds. Dar Es Salaam Histories from an Emerging African Metropolis. 2007. 288p. (C). pap. *(978-9987-449-70-5(0))* Mkuki na Nyoka Pubs. TZA. Dist: Michigan State Univ. Pr.

Green, Maia. Priests, Witches & Power: Popular Christianity after Mission in Southern Tanzania. 2007. (Cambridge Studies in Social & Cultural Anthropology Ser.). (ENG., Illus.). 200p. (C). pap. 38.99 *(978-0-521-04027-3(2))* Cambridge Univ. Pr.

Hussen, Seid Ebrie. Gender Role Perception. 2010. 84p. pap. *(978-3-639-26743-3(5))* VDM Verlag Dr. Mueller e.K.

Nkonya, Leticia K. Rural Water Management in Africa: The Impact of Customary Institutions in Tanzania. 2008. 114.95 *(978-1-60497-537-6(7))* Cambria Pr.

Rabasa, Angel & Rabasa. Radical Islam in East Africa. 2009. 110p. pap. 31.50 *(978-0-8330-4519-5(9),* mg782) RAND Corp., The.

Sanders, Todd. Beyond Bodies: Rainmaking & Sense Making in Tanzania. 2008. (ENG., Illus.). 288p. pap. *(978-0-8020-9582-4(8))* Univ. of Toronto Pr.

Wheeler, Sara. Too Close to the Sun: The Audacious Life & Times of Denys Finch Hatton. 2009. (ENG., Illus.). 336p. pap. 18.00 *(978-0-8129-6892-7(1),* Random Hse. Trade Paperbacks) Random House Publishing Group.

AFRICA, FRENCH-SPEAKING EQUATORIAL

Here are entered works dealing collectively with Central African Republic, Chad, Congo (Brazzaville), and Gabon.

Ginio, Ruth. French Colonialism Unmasked: The Vichy Years in French West Africa. 2008. (France Overseas: Studies in Empire & D Ser.). (ENG., Illus.). 264p. pap. 24.95 *(978-0-8032-1746-1(3))* Univ. of Nebraska Pr.

Guide, Anne-Marie & Tsangarides, Charalambos G. The CFA Franc Zone: Common Currency, Uncommon Challenges. 2008. (Illus.). xi, 397p. *(978-1-58906-675-5(8))* International Monetary Fund.

Irele, Abiola. The Négritude Moment: Explorations in Francophone African & Caribbean Literature & Thought. 2010. xv, 259p. *(978-1-59221-797-7(4))* Africa World Pr.

Kanya-Forstner, A. S. The Conquest of Western Sudan: A Study in French Military Imperialism. 2008. (ENG.). 308p. pap. 42.00 *(978-0-521-10372-5(X))* Cambridge Univ. Pr.

Le Vine, Victor T. Politics in Francophone Africa. 2007. 425p. (C). pap. 28.50 *(978-1-58826-551-7(X))* Rienner, Lynne Pubs.

Thomas, Martin, ed. & intro. The French Colonial Mind Vol. 1: Mental Maps of Empire & Colonial Encounters, 2 vols., Vol. 1. 2012. (France Overseas: Studies in Empire & D Ser.). (ENG.). 424p. pap. 45.00 *(978-0-8032-2093-5(6))* Univ. of Nebraska Pr.

—The French Colonial Mind Vol. 2: Violence, Military Encounters, & Colonialism, 2 vols. 2012. (France Overseas: Studies in Empire & D Ser.). (ENG., Illus.). 440p. pap. 45.00 *(978-0-8032-2094-2(4))* Univ. of Nebraska Pr.

—The French Colonial Mind, 2-volume Set, 2 vols. 2012. (France Overseas: Studies in Empire & D Ser.). (ENG.). 864p. pap. 75.00 *(978-0-8032-3815-2(0))* Univ. of Nebraska Pr.

AFRICA, GERMAN SOUTHWEST

see Namibia

AFRICA, GERMAN WEST

see Cameroon

AFRICA, NORTH

Here are entered works dealing collectively with Morocco, Algeria, Tunisia, and Libya.

Europa Publications Staff, ed. Middle East & North Africa 2009. 55th rev. ed. 2008. (ENG.). 1436p. 760.00 *(978-1-85743-472-9(2))* Routledge.

Marouf, Nadir, ed. Les Identitts Rtgionales et la Dialectique Sud-Sud en Question. 2007. (FRE.). 192p. pap. *(978-2-86978-195-5(4))* Council for the Development of Social Science Research in Africa SEN. Dist: Michigan State Univ. Pr.

Routledge Staff, creator. The Middle East & North Africa 2007. 53rd rev. ed. 2006. (Middle East & North Africa Ser.). 1395p. 620.00 *(978-1-85743-390-6(4))* Routledge.

Schwedler, Jillian & Gerner, Deborah J., eds. Understanding the Contemporary Middle East, 3rd Edition. 3rd ed. 2008. 477p. (C). pap. 27.50 *(978-1-58826-565-4(X))* Rienner, Lynne Pubs.

AFRICA, NORTH—ANTIQUITIES

Carucci, Margherita. The Romano-African Domus: Studies in Space, Decoration, & Function. 2008. (Bar S Ser.). (Illus.). xii, 289p. (C). 100.00 *(978-1-4073-0175-4(6))* British Archaeological Reports Ltd. GBR. Dist: Brown, David Bk. Co., The.

Conant, Jonathan. Staying Roman: Conquest & Identity in Africa & the Mediterranean, 439-700. 2012. (Cambridge Studies in Medieval Life & Thought: Fourth Ser.). (ENG., Illus.) 456p. 99.00 **(978-0-521-19697-0(3))** Cambridge Univ. Pr.

De Haan, Nathalie. Römische Privatbäder: Entwicklung, Verbreitung, Struktur und Sozialer Status. 2011. (GER., Illus.). 556p. 141.95 *(978-3-631-60069-6(0))* Lang, Peter GmbH, Europaischer Verlag der Wissenschaften DEU. Dist: Lang, Peter.

Moser, Johannes & Nami, Mustapha. La Grotte d'Ifri N'Ammar: Tome 2. le Paleolithique Moyen. 2010. (Forschungen zur Archaologie Aussereuropaischer Kulturen Ser.). (FRE., Illus.). 338p. (C). 168.00 *(978-3-89500-684-5(X))* Reichert, Ludwig Dr. DEU. Dist: Brown, David Bk. Co., The.

Rind, Mareike. Romische Villen in Nordafrika: Nordafrika Untersuchungen zu Architektur und Wirtschaftsweise. 2009. (GER & ENG., Illus.). 133p. (C). pap. 82.50 *(978-1-4073-0588-2(3))* British Archaeological Reports Ltd. GBR. Dist: Brown, David Bk. Co., The.

Sears, Gareth. The Cities of Roman Africa. 2011. (ENG., Illus.). 176p. pap. 29.95 **(978-0-7524-4843-5(9))** History Pr. Ltd.,The GBR. Dist: Independent Pubs. Group.

Stern, Karen B. Inscribing Devotion & Death: Archaeological Evidence for Jewish Populations of North Africa. 2007. (Religions in the Graeco-Roman World Ser.). (Illus.). 342p. *(978-90-04-16370-6(0))* BRILL.

AFRICA, NORTH—BIBLIOGRAPHY

Ashbee, Henry Spencer. A Bibliography of Tunisia: from the Earliest Times to the End Of. 2007. pap. 20.95 *(978-1-4304-6939-1(0))* Kessinger Publishing, LLC.

Bleaney, C. H., ed. Index Islamicus: A Bibliography of Publications on Islam & the Muslim World Since 1906. 9th ed. 2007. cd-rom *(978-90-04-16638-7(6))* BRILL.

AFRICA, NORTH—DESCRIPTION AND TRAVEL

Al-Dihan, Salah, et al. The Travels of Ibn Al-Tayyib: The Forgotten Journey of an Eighteenth Century Traveller to the Hijaz. 2010. (Library of Middle East History Ser.). (ENG.). 288p. 92.50 *(978-1-84885-006-4(9),* Tauris Academic Studies) I. B. Tauris & Co., Ltd. GBR. Dist: Macmillan.

Barth, Heinrich. Travels & Discoveries in North & Central Afric. 2009. 482p. pap. *(978-1-4589-8839-3(2))* Books LLC.

—Travels & Discoveries in North & Central Afric: Being a Journal of an Expedition Undertaken under the Auspices of H. B. M. 's Government, in the Y. 2010. 840p. pap. 56.75 *(978-1-149-78905-6(0))*; 706p. pap. 49.75 *(978-1-143-92011-0(2))*; 656p. pap. 46.75 *(978-1-143-82860-7(7))*; 738p. pap. 51.75 *(978-1-143-70590-8(4))*; 674p. pap. 47.75 *(978-1-143-96685-9(6))*; 812p. pap. 55.75 *(978-1-144-67970-3(2))*; 802p. pap. 54.75 *(978-1-143-55637-1(2))*; 696p. pap. 48.75 *(978-1-143-59948-4(9))*; 728p. pap. 50.75 *(978-1-143-38882-8(8))*; 666p. pap. 47.75 *(978-1-143-36425-9(2))* BiblioBazaar.

—Travels & Discoveries in North & Central Afric: Being a Journal of an Expedition Undertaken under the Auspices of H. B. M. 's Government, in the Yea. 2010. 760p. pap. 52.75 *(978-1-149-02286-3(8))*; 720p. pap. 49.75 *(978-1-149-01195-9(5))*; 696p. pap. 48.75 *(978-1-143-32541-0(9))* BiblioBazaar.

—Travels & Discoveries in North & Central Afric: Being a Journal of an Expedition Undertaken under the Auspices of H. B. M. 's Government in the Year. 2010. 724p. pap. 49.75 *(978-1-146-54293-7(3))* BiblioBazaar.

—Travels & Discoveries in North & Central Afric: Being a Journal of an Expedition Undertaken under the Auspices of H. B. Majesty's Government, Vol. 2010. 672p. pap. 47.75 *(978-1-149-03397-5(5))* BiblioBazaar.

—Travels & Discoveries in North & Central Afric: Timbúktu, Sókoto, & the Basins of the Niger & Bénuwé. 2010. 618p. pap. 45.75 *(978-1-143-39774-5(6))* BiblioBazaar.

—Travels & Discoveries in North & Central Africa. 2009. 498p. pap. *(978-0-217-30170-1(3))*; 428p. pap. *(978-0-217-64760-1(X))*; 442p. pap. *(978-0-217-64757-1(X))*; 450p. pap. *(978-0-217-41084-7(7))*; 616p. pap. *(978-0-217-64763-2(4))*; 482p. pap. *(978-0-217-41083-0(9))*; 442p. pap. *(978-0-217-30182-4(7))* Books LLC.

—Travels & Discoveries in North & Central Africa: Being a Journal of an Expedition Undertaken under the Auspices of H. B. M. 's Government, in the Years 1849-1855. 2011. (Cambridge Library Collection - Travel & Exploration Ser.). (ENG.). 742p. pap. 50.00 *(978-1-108-02947-6(7))*; 736p. pap. 48.00 *(978-1-108-02944-5(2))*; 706p. pap. 48.00 *(978-1-108-02945-2(0))*; 708p. pap. 48.00 *(978-1-108-02946-9(9))*; (Illus.). 688p. pap. 48.00 *(978-1-108-02943-8(4))* Cambridge Univ. Pr.

—Travels & Discoveries in North & Central Africa; Being a Journal of an Expedition Undertaken under the Auspices of H B M 's. 2010. 306p. pap. 30.05 *(978-1-154-11118-7(0))* General Bks. LLC.

—Travels & Discoveries in North & Central Africa: being a journal of an expedition undertaken under the auspices of H. B. M. 's Government, in the Years 1849-55. 2011. 711p. pap. 49.75 *(978-1-240-91753-2(8)*, British Library, Historical Print Editions) BiblioBazaar.

Barth, Henry. Travels & Discoveries in North & Central Africa, 1849-1855. 2010. 816p. pap. 55.75 *(978-1-149-05856-5(0))* BiblioBazaar.

—Travels & Discoveries in North & Central Africa, 1849-1855. 2009. 492p. pap. *(978-0-217-30173-2(8))* Books LLC.

Brown, Hamish. The Mountains Look on Marrakech. 2007. (Illus.). 256p. *(978-1-870325-29-5(X))* Whittles Publishing.

Davies, Ethel. North Africa: The Roman Coast. 2009. (ENG., Illus.). 336p. pap. 25.99 *(978-1-84162-287-3(7))* Bradt Travel Guides GBR. Dist: Globe Pequot Pr., The.

Denham, Dixon & Clapperton, Hugh. Narrative of Travels & Discoveries in Northern & Central Africa, in the Years 1822, 1823, And 1824. 2011. (Cambridge Library Collection - Travel & Exploration Ser.). (ENG., Illus.). 762p. pap. 50.00 *(978-1-108-03120-2(X))* Cambridge Univ. Pr.

Hawes, Annie. A Handful of Honey: Away to the Palm Groves of Morocco & Algeria. 2008. (ENG.). 416p. 19.95 *(978-0-330-45722-4(5)*, Macmillan) Pan Macmillan GBR. Dist: Trans-Atlantic Pubns., Inc.

KayPublishing LLC, photos by. Mali: A Land of Diversity. 2007. (Illus.). pap. 45.00 *(978-0-9797214-0-3(7))* Kay Publishing LLC.

LeClercq, Anne Sinkler Whaley, ed. Elizabeth Sinkler Coxe's Tales from the Grand Tour, 1890-1910. (Women's Diaries & Letters of the South Ser.). 2010. pap. 21.95 *(978-1-57003-957-7(7))* 2006. (ENG., Illus.). 200p. 34.95 *(978-1-57003-633-0(0))* Univ. of South Carolina Pr.

Locken, E. Travel Journal Mauritania. 2010. 192p. pap. 19.99 *(978-0-557-43668-2(0))* Lulu Enterprises Inc.

Marshall Cavendish Corporation Staff, contrib. by. World & Its Peoples. 2006. *(978-0-7614-7575-0(3))*; *(978-0-7614-7626-9(1))*; *(978-0-7614-7578-1(8))*; *(978-0-7614-7579-8(6))*; *(978-0-7614-7628-3(8))*; *(978-0-7614-7581-1(8))*; *(978-0-7614-7573-6(7))*; *(978-0-7614-7625-2(3))*; *(978-0-7614-7582-8(6))*; *(978-0-7614-7574-3(5))*; *(978-0-7614-7572-9(9))* Marshall Cavendish Corp.

Mewshaw, Michael. Between Terror & Tourism: An Overland Journey Across North Africa. 2010. (ENG.). 384p. pap. 16.95 *(978-1-58243-434-6(4)*, Counterpoint Pr.) Basic Bks. GBR. Dist: Perseus-PGW.

Milet, Eric. Orientalist Photographs, 1870-1940. 2009. (ENG., Illus.). 204p. 60.00 *(978-2-08-030089-8(X))* Flammarion et Cie FRA. Dist: Random Hse., Inc.

Muller, Julius W. Ever Thine: A Selection of Excerpts from the Travel Letters of J. W. Muller. 2011. 130p. 40.95 ***(978-1-258-02250-1(8))*** Literary Licensing, LLC.

Nemec, Vilém & Nemec-Jirak, Jana R. Twenty-Five Years in Africa: The Beginning. 2011. pap. 20.99 ***(978-1-61777-324-2(7))*** Tate Publishing & Enterprises, LLC.

Pirajno, Alberto di. A Cure for Serpents. Naylor, Kathleen, tr. from ITA. 2006. (ENG., Illus.). 272p. pap. 33.95 *(978-0-907871-44-6(5))* Eland Bks. GBR. Dist: Dufour Editions, Inc.

Rae, Edward. The Country of the Moors: A Journey from Tripoli in Barbary to the City of Kairwân. 2010. (Folios Archive Library). 334p. pap., instr.'s gde. ed. 39.95 *(978-1-85964-230-6(6))* Garnet Publishing, Ltd. GBR. Dist: International Publishers Marketing.

Richardson, James. Narrative of a Mission to Central Africa Performed in the Years 1850-51. 2008. 272p. 28.99 *(978-0-554-26252-9(5))*; 276p. 25.99 *(978-0-554-34922-0(1))*; 272p. 25.99 *(978-0-554-35555-9(8))*; 276p. 28.99 *(978-0-554-25619-1(3))* BiblioBazaar.

—Narrative of a Mission to Central Africa Performed in the Years 1850-51. 2007. pap. *(978-1-84830-007-1(7)*, Wildhern Pr.) Echo Library.

—Narrative of a Mission to Central Africa Performed in the Years 1850-51: Under the Orders & at the Expense of Her Majesty. 2007. (ENG.). 242p. pap. 20.99 *(978-1-4346-0727-0(5))*; Vol. 1. 268p. pap. 23.99 *(978-1-4346-0787-4(9))* BiblioBazaar.

Riley, James & Robbins, Archibald. Accounts of the Wreck of the Commerce: Two Narratives of Shipwreck, Capture & Slavery by Arabs of American Seamen 1815. 2011. 568p. pap. ***(978-0-85706-720-3(6))*** Leonaur Ltd.

Shaw, Thomas. Travels, or Observations Relating to Several Parts of Barbary & the Levant. 2010. (ENG.). 728p. pap. 50.75 *(978-1-175-40334-6(2))*; 494p. pap. 38.75 *(978-1-142-20723-6(4))* BiblioBazaar.

Thompson, Carl, et al, eds. Women's Travel Writings in North Africa & the Middle East, 3 vols., Pt. 2. 2015. (Chawton House Library: Women's Travel Writings). (ENG.). 1200p. 495.00 *(978-1-84893-022-3(4))* Pickering & Chatto Pubs., Ltd. GBR. Dist: Ashgate Publishing Co.

Trent, Newmeyer. Travel Literatures & the Making Of 'orientalisms' Representations of Gender & Sexuality. 2011. 156p. pap. ***(978-3-639-32632-1(6))*** VDM Verlag Dr. Mueller e.K.

Weir, James. In Search of Eden: The Course of an Obsession. 2007. (Armchair Traveller Ser.). (ENG., Illus.). 174p. 19.95 *(978-1-905791-07-1(0))* Haus Publishing GBR. Dist: Consortium Bk. Sales & Distribution.

Wells, Billy. Snapshots of the Hippy Trail. 2008. 219p. pap. 25.50 *(978-1-4092-2160-9(1))* Lulu Enterprises Inc.

AFRICA, NORTH—ECONOMIC CONDITIONS

Abed, George T. & Davoodi, Hamid R. Challenges of Growth & Globalization in the Middle East & North Africa. (ARA.). pap. *(978-1-58906-237-5(X)*, CGGMAA) International Monetary Fund.

Binder, Leonard, ed. Rebuilding Devastated Economies in the Middle East. 2007. (ENG.). 296p. 95.00 *(978-0-230-60017-1(4))* Palgrave Macmillan.

Cobham, David & Boughzala, Mongi, eds. Inflation Targeting in MENA Countries: An Unfinished Journey. 2011. (ENG., Illus.). 256p. 105.00 *(978-0-230-29021-1(3))* Palgrave Macmillan.

Devlin. Challenges of Economic Development in. . 2010. (Illus.). viii, 557p. 135.00 *(978-981-279-344-7(5))* World Scientific Publishing Co., Inc.

Esfahani, Hadi S. & Tuna, Gulcay, eds. Economic Development in the Middle East & North African Countries: Contemporary Issues. 2011. (Politics & Economics of the Middle East Ser.). 140.00 *(978-1-61324-847-8(4))* Nova Science Pubs., Inc.

Europa Publications, ed. The Middle East & North Africa 2012. 58th rev. ed. 2012. (ENG.). 1468p. 880.00 ***(978-1-85743-626-6(1))*** Routledge.

Europa Publications Staff, ed. Middle East & North Africa 2010. 56th rev. ed. 2009. (ENG.). 1484p. 810.00 *(978-1-85743-530-6(3))* Routledge.

Icon Group International, Inc. Staff, compiled by. The 2006 Economic & Product Market Databook for Constantine, Algeria. 2006. 618p. ring bd. 95.00 *(978-0-497-80405-3(0))* Icon Group International, Inc.

—The 2006 Economic & Product Market Databook for Dakhla, Western Sahara. 2006. 618p. ring bd. 95.00 *(978-0-497-80436-7(0))* Icon Group International, Inc.

—The 2006 Economic & Product Market Databook for Kaedi, Mauritania. 2006. 618p. ring bd. 95.00 *(978-0-497-81964-4(3))* Icon Group International, Inc.

—The 2006 Economic & Product Market Databook for Kelo, Chad. 2006. 618p. ring bd. 95.00 *(978-0-497-81986-6(4))* Icon Group International, Inc.

—The 2006 Economic & Product Market Databook for Laayoune, Western Sahara. 2006. 618p. ring bd. 95.00 *(978-0-497-80809-9(9))* Icon Group International, Inc.

Ismail, Lubna. Doing Business in the Middle East & North Africa. Date not set. (Doing Business in Regions & Countries Around the World Ser.). *(978-1-882390-83-0(0))* Training Management Corp.

López-Cálix, José R. & Walkenhorst, Peter, eds. Trade Competitiveness of the Middle East & North Africa: Policies for Export Diversification. 2010. (Directions in Development Ser.). (ENG., Illus.). 364p. pap. 30.00 *(978-0-8213-8074-1(5)*, 9780821380741) World Bank Pubns.

Luciano, Vincent G., ed. Countries of North Africa: Background & Issues. 2010. (Illus.). x, 190p. 99.00 ***(978-1-61761-437-8(8))*** Nova Science Pubs., Inc.

Marouf, Nadir, ed. Les Identitts Rtgionales et la Dialectique Sud-Sud en Question. 2007. (FRE.). 192p. pap. *(978-2-86978-195-5(4))* Council for the Development of Social Science Research in Africa SEN. Dist: Michigan State Univ. Pr.

McKee, Chris, ed. International Country Risk Guide Annual - 2006 Vol. 4: Middle East & North Africa. 2006. (C). per. *(978-1-933539-23-2(2))* PRS Group Inc., The.

The Middle East & North Africa 2011. 57th rev. ed. 2010. 1464p. 835.00 *(978-1-85743-568-9(0))* Routledge.

Mukhtar, Hassani. Tarikh Al-Dawlah Al-Ziyaniyah, 3 vols. 2007. (ARA.). *(978-9961-76-758-0(6))* El Hadhara.

Nabli, Mustapha K. Breaking the Barriers to Higher Economic Growth: Better Governance & Deeper Reforms in the Middle East & North Africa. 2008. (ENG.). 476p. pap. 38.00 *(978-0-8213-7415-3(X)*, 9780821374153) World Bank Pubns.

Romagnoli, Alessandro & Mengoni, Luisa. The Economic Development Process in Mena. 2011. (Routledge Studies in Middle Eastern Economies Ser.). 240p. (C). 125.00 ***(978-0-415-59405-9(7))*** Routledge.

Sayan, Serdar, ed. Economic Performance in the Middle East & North Africa. 2011. (ENG., Illus.). 220p. pap. 42.95 ***(978-0-415-67337-2(2))*** Routledge.

Sayan, Serdar, ed. Economic Performance in the Middle East & North Africa: Institutions, Corruption & Reform. 2009. (Routledge Political Economy of the Middle East & North Africa Ser.). (Illus.). 288p. 170.00 *(978-0-415-43804-9(7))* Routledge.

Stevenson, Lois. Private Sector & Enterprise Development: Fostering Growth in the Middle East & North America. 2011. (Illus.). 384p. 150.00 *(978-1-84980-295-6(5))* Elgar, Edward Publishing, Inc.

World Bank. Poor Places, Thriving People: How the Middle East & North Africa Can Rise above Spatial Disparities. 2011. (MENA Development Report). (ENG., Illus.). 388p. pap. 35.00 *(978-0-8213-8321-6(3)*, 9780821383216) World Bank Pubns.

World Bank Group. From Privilege to Competition: Unlocking Private-Led Growth in the Middle East & North Africa. 2009. (MENA Development Report). (ENG., Illus.). 274p. pap. 38.00 *(978-0-8213-7877-9(5)*, 9780821378779) World Bank Pubns.

World Bank Staff, contrib. by. Poor Places, Thriving People: How the Middle East & North Africa Can Rise above Spatial Disparities. 2010. (Illus.). xxiii, 363p. *(978-0-8213-8423-7(6))* World Bank Pubns.

Zoubir, Yahia H. & Amirah-Fernández, Haizam, eds. North Africa: Politics, Region & the Limits of Transformation. 2008. (Illus.). XXIV, 400p. 45.95 *(978-0-415-42921-4(8))* Routledge.

Zoubir, Yahia H. & Amirah-Fernández, Haizam, eds. North Africa: Politics, Region & the Limits of Transformation. 2007. (Illus.). XXIV, 400p. 160.00 *(978-0-415-42920-7(X))* Routledge.

AFRICA, NORTH—FOREIGN RELATIONS

Dawson, Carl. EU Integration with North Africa: Trade Negotiations & Democracy Deficits in Morocco. 2009. (ENG.). 224p. 89.00 *(978-1-84511-784-9(0)*, Tauris Academic Studies) I. B. Tauris & Co., Ltd. GBR. Dist: Macmillan.

Lambert, Franklin. The Barbary Wars: American Independence in the Atlantic World. 2007. (ENG., Illus.). 240p. per. 16.00 *(978-0-8090-2811-5(5)*, Hill & Wang) Farrar, Straus & Giroux.

Luciano, Vincent G., ed. Countries of North Africa: Background & Issues. 2010. (Illus.). x, 190p. 99.00 ***(978-1-61761-437-8(8))*** Nova Science Pubs., Inc.

Nejjar, Bassam. Cultural Cooperation Between Morocco & Sub-Saharan Afric. 2010. 92p. pap. *(978-3-8383-5055-4(3))* Lambert Academic Publishing.

Parker, Richard B. Uncle Sam in Barbary: A Diplomatic History. 2008. (ENG., Illus.). 320p. pap. 29.95 *(978-0-8130-3344-0(6))* Univ. Pr. of Florida.

Sajed, Alina. Postcolonial Encounters with International Relations: The Politics of Transgression. 2013. (Interventions Ser.). (ENG.). 192p. (C). 130.00 *(978-0-415-78172-5(8))* Routledge.

Sayan, Serdar, ed. Economic Performance in the Middle East & North Africa: Institutions, Corruption & Reform. 2009. (Routledge Political Economy of the Middle East & North Africa Ser.). (Illus.). 288p. 170.00 *(978-0-415-43804-9(7))* Routledge.

World Bank Staff & Pigato, Miria. Strengthening China's & India's Trade & Investment Ties to the Middle East & North Africa. 2009. (ENG., Illus.). 216p. pap. 22.95 *(978-0-8213-7776-5(0)*, 9780821377765) World Bank Pubns.

Zoubir, Yahia H. & Amirah-Fernández, Haizam, eds. North Africa: Politics, Region & the Limits of Transformation. 2008. (Illus.). XXIV, 400p. 45.95 *(978-0-415-42921-4(8))* Routledge.

Zoubir, Yahia H. & Amirah-Fernández, Haizam, eds. North Africa: Politics, Region & the Limits of Transformation. 2007. (Illus.). XXIV, 400p. 160.00 *(978-0-415-42920-7(X))* Routledge.

AFRICA, NORTH—HISTORY

see also Almohades

Ahmida, Ali Abdullatif, ed. Beyond Colonialism & Nationalism in the Maghrib: History, Culture, & Politics. 2009. (ENG.). 272p. pap. 32.00 *(978-0-230-61363-8(2))* Palgrave Macmillan.

Aissaoui, Rabah. Immigration & National Identity: North African Political Movements in Colonial & Postcolonial France. 2009. (ENG.). 320p. 97.00 *(978-1-84511-835-8(9)*, Tauris Academic Studies) I. B. Tauris & Co., Ltd. GBR. Dist: Macmillan.

Al-Sharif, William. The Dearest Quest: A Biography of Ibn Tumart. 2010. 175p. pap. 24.95 *(978-1-4452-7825-4(1))* Lulu Enterprises Inc.

Alcidi, Edgar. Fallschirmjäger Brigade Ramcke in North Africa 1942-1943. 2009. (Illus.). 192p. bds. 79.99 *(978-0-7643-3353-8(4))* Schiffer Publishing, Ltd.

Allen, Gardner W. Our Navy & the Barbary Corsairs. 2007. (ENG.). 404p. 49.95 *(978-0-548-08592-9(7))* Kessinger Publishing, LLC.

Allen, Gardner Weld. Our Navy & the Barbary Corsairs. 2009. 282p. pap. *(978-1-4588-3807-0(2))* Books LLC.

—Our Navy & the Barbary Corsairs. 354p. reprint ed. 98.00 *(978-0-7222-7827-7(6))* Library Reprints, Inc.

Atkinson, Rick. An Army at Dawn Vol. 1: The War in North Africa, 1942-1943. rev. ed. 2007. (ENG., Illus.). 768p. pap. 17.00 *(978-0-8050-8724-6(9)*, Holt Paperback) Holt, Henry & Co.

Cohen, Getzel M. The Hellenistic Settlements in Syria, the Red Sea Basin, & North Africa. 2006. (Hellenistic Culture & Society Ser.: Vol. 46). (Illus.). 477p. 90.00 *(978-0-520-24148-0(7))* Univ. of California Pr.

Cronin, Stephanie, ed. Subalterns & Social Protest. 2007. (SOAS/Routledge Studies on the Middle East Ser.). XIV, 322p. 160.00 *(978-0-415-42355-7(4))* Routledge.

Cronin, Stephanie, ed. Subalterns & Social Protest. 2012. (ENG.). 336p. (C). pap. 44.95 ***(978-0-415-66582-7(5))*** Routledge.

Currey, E. Hamilton. Sea-Wolves of the Mediterranean: Moslem Corsairs of the Sixteenth Century 1492-1580. 2011. 280p. ***(978-0-85706-469-1(X))***; pap. ***(978-0-85706-470-7(3))*** Leonaur Ltd.

Davis, Diana K. Resurrecting the Granary of Rome: Environmental History & French Colonial Expansion in North Africa. 2007. (Ecology & History Ser.). (Illus.). 312p. 59.95 *(978-0-8214-1751-5(7))*; pap. 29.95 *(978-0-8214-1752-2(5))* Ohio Univ. Pr.

Davis, Diana K. & Burke, Edmund, III, eds. Environmental Imaginaries of the Middle East & North Africa. 2011. (Ecology & History Ser.). (ENG., Illus.). 280p. 59.95 ***(978-0-8214-1974-8(9))*** Ohio Univ. Pr.

Dowler, Amelia & Galvin, Elizabeth R., eds. Money, Trade & Trade Routes in Pre-Islamic North Africa. 2011. (British Museum Research Publication). (ENG., Illus.). 86p. (C). pap. 40.00 *(978-0-86159-176-3(3))* British Museum Pr. GBR. Dist: Brown, David Bk. Co., The.

Encyclopedie Berbere. Fasc. XXX. Maaziz - Matmata. 2010. (Encyclopedie Berbere Ser.). (FRE.). 261p. (C). pap. 44.00 ***(978-90-429-2367-6(9))*** Peeters Pubs. & Booksellers BEL. Dist: Brown, David Bk. Co., The.

Encyclopedie Berbere. Fasc. XXXI. Matmora-Mezrag. 2010. (Encyclopedie Berbere Ser.). (FRE.). 279p. (C). pap. 44.00 ***(978-90-429-2368-3(7))*** Peeters Pubs. & Booksellers BEL. Dist: Brown, David Bk. Co., The.

Encyclopedie Berbere. Fasc. XXXII. Mgild - Mzab. 2011. (Encyclopedie Berbere Ser.). (FRE., Illus.). 235p. (C). pap. 44.00 *(978-90-429-2369-0(5))* Peeters Pubs. & Booksellers BEL. Dist: Brown, David Bk. Co., The.

Farid Alatas, Syed. Applying Ibn Khaldn. 2011. 224p. (C). 130.00 *(978-0-415-67878-0(1))* Routledge.

Fields, Nic. Roman Conquests: North Africa. 2010. (Illus.). 176p. 39.95 *(978-1-84415-970-3(1))* Pen & Sword Bks. Ltd. GBR. Dist: Casemate Pubs. & Bk. Distributors, LLC.

Gearon, Eamonn. The Sahara: A Cultural History. 2011. (Landscapes of the Imagination Ser.). (ENG.). 288p. 74.00 ***(978-0-19-986196-5(X))***; pap. 16.95 ***(978-0-19-986195-8(1))*** Oxford Univ. Pr., Inc.

Haji, Hamid. Founding the Fatimid State: The Rise of an Early Islamic Empire. 2006. (Ismaili Texts & Translations Ser.). (ENG., Illus.). 350p. 68.00 *(978-1-85043-885-4(4)*, I. B. Tauris in Assn. with the Ins) I. B. Tauris & Co., Ltd. GBR. Dist: Macmillan.

Hess, Andrew C. The Forgotten Frontier: A History of Sixteenth-Century Ibero-African Frontier. 2010. (Publications of the Center for Middle Eastern Studies). (Illus.). 290p. pap. 30.00 *(978-0-226-33031-0(1))* Univ. of Chicago Pr.

Howe, Tankred. Vandalen, Barbaren und Arianer Bei Victor Von Vita. 2007. (Studien zur Alten Geschichte Ser.). (GER.). 411p. (C). 87.00 ***(978-3-938032-17-6(0))*** Antike, Verlag, e.K. DEU. Dist: ISD.

Ibn'Abd, Al-Hakam. The History of the Conquest of Egypt, North Africa & Spain Known As the Futuh Misr of Ibn'abd Al-Hakan. Torrey, Charles C., ed. (Yale Oriental Ser.: No. 3). reprint ed. 67.50 *(978-0-404-60273-4(8))* AMS Pr., Inc.

Jamieson, Alan. Lords of the Sea: A History of the Barbary Corsairs. 2012. (Illus.). 304p. 39.00 ***(978-1-86189-907-1(6))*** Reaktion Bks., Ltd. GBR. Dist: Chicago Distribution Ctr.

Jensen, Erik. Western Sahara: Anatomy of a Stalemate? 2nd ed. 2011. (Illus.). 160p. (C). 42.00 ***(978-1-58826-829-7(2))***; pap. 16.95 ***(978-1-58826-807-5(1))*** Rienner, Lynne Pubs.

Kaegi, Walter E. Muslim Expansion & Byzantine Collapse in North Africa. 2010. (ENG., Illus.). 366p. 104.00 *(978-0-521-19677-2(9))* Cambridge Univ. Pr.

Keller, Richard C. Colonial Madness: Psychiatry in French North Africa. 2007. (ENG., Illus.). 320p. 75.00 *(978-0-226-42972-4(5))*; per. 30.00 *(978-0-226-42973-1(3))* Univ. of Chicago Pr.

Kreikenbom, Detlev, et al, eds. Krise und Kult: Vorderer Orient und Nordafrika von Aurelian bis Justinian. 2010. (Millennium-Studien / Millennium Studies).Tr. of Crisis & Cult. (GER., Illus.). 378p. 140.00 *(978-3-11-022050-6(4))* De Gruyter, Walter Inc.

Lambert, Franklin. The Barbary Wars: American Independence in the Atlantic World. 2007. (ENG., Illus.). 240p. per. 16.00 *(978-0-8090-2811-5(5)*, Hill & Wang) Farrar, Straus & Giroux.

Lane-Poole, Stanley. The Barbary Corsairs. 2010. 336p. pap. 31.75 *(978-1-146-78431-3(7))* BiblioBazaar.

—The Barbary Corsairs. 2009. 168p. pap. *(978-1-4588-6079-8(5))* Books LLC.

—The Barbary Corsairs. 2010. 334p. 36.76 *(978-1-163-20249-4(5))*; pap. 24.76 *(978-1-162-73118-6(4))* Kessinger Publishing, LLC.

Lane-Poole, Stanley & Kelley, James Douglas Jerrold. The Barbary Corsairs. 2010. 344p. pap. 31.75 *(978-1-146-45728-6(6))* BiblioBazaar.

Laroui, Abdallah. The History of the Maghrib: An Interpretive Essay. 2008. 448p. pap. 44.00 *(978-1-59740-469-3(1))* ACLS Humanities E-Book.

Martin, Florence. Screens & Veils: Maghrebi Women's Cinema. 2011. (New Directions in National Cinemas Ser.). (ENG., Illus.). 288p. 70.00 *(978-0-253-35668-0(7)*, 0253356687); pap. 24.95 *(978-0-253-22341-8(5)*, 0253223415) Indiana Univ. Pr.

McKenna, Amy, ed. The History of Northern Africa. 2011. (Britannica Guide to Africa Ser.). (Illus.). 200p. (YA). 106.00 *(978-1-61530-442-4(8))* Rosen Publishing Group, Inc., The.

Merrills, Andrew & Miles, Richard. The Vandals. 2010. (Peoples of Europe Ser.: 15). (ENG., Illus.). 368p. 128.95 *(978-1-4051-6068-1(3)*, Wiley-Blackwell) Wiley, John & Sons, Inc.

Messier, Ronald A. The Almoravids & the Meanings of Jihad. 2010. E-Book *(978-0-313-38590-2(4))*; (Illus.). 248p. 44.95 *(978-0-313-38589-6(0)*, A3030C) Greenwood Publishing Group, Inc. (Praeger Pubs.).

Naylor, Phillip C. North Africa: A History from Antiquity to the Present. (ENG., Illus.). 373p. 2010. pap. 30.00 *(978-0-292-72291-0(5))* 2009. 45.00 *(978-0-292-71922-4(1))* Univ. of Texas Pr.

Pazzanita, Anthony G. Historical Dictionary of Mauritania. 3rd ed. 2008. (Historical Dictionaries of Africa Ser.). (ENG., Illus.). 648p. 151.00 *(978-0-8108-5596-0(8))* Scarecrow Pr., Inc.

Powers, David S. Law, Society & Culture in the Maghrib, 1300-1500. 2009. (Cambridge Studies in Islamic Civilization Ser.). (ENG., Illus.). 280p. (C). pap. 42.00 *(978-0-521-12059-3(4))* Cambridge Univ. Pr.

Rouighi, Ramzi. The Making of a Mediterranean Emirate: Ifriqiya & Its Andalusis, 1200-1400. 2011. (Middle Ages Ser.). (Illus.). 248p. (C). 55.00 *(978-0-8122-4310-9(2))* Univ. of Pennsylvania Pr.

Russell, Michael. History & Present Condition of the Barbary States. 2009. 258p. pap. *(978-0-217-22363-8(X))* Books LLC.

Sears, Gareth. The Cities of Roman Africa. 2011. (ENG., Illus.). 176p. pap. 29.95 ***(978-0-7524-4843-5(9))*** History Pr. Ltd.,The GBR. Dist: Independent Pubs. Group.

Tijani, Hakeem Ibikunle, et al. Africa & the Wider World. 2010. (ENG.). 464p. (C). pap. 83.80 *(978-0-558-85002-9(2))* Pearson Learning Solutions.

Tinniswood, Adrian. Pirates of Barbary: Corsairs, Conquests & Captivity in the Seventeenth-Century Mediterranean. (ENG.). 368p. (gr. 12). 2011. 16.00 *(978-1-59448-544-2(5)*, Riverhead Trade (Paperbacks)) 2010. 26.95 *(978-1-59448-774-3(X)*, Riverhead Bks. (Hardcover)) Penguin Group (USA) Inc.

Windrow, Martin. Our Friends Beneath the Sands: The Foreign Legion in France's Colonial Conquests, 1870-1935. 2012. (ENG., Illus.). 784p. pap. 19.95 ***(978-0-7538-2856-4(1)***, Phoenix) Orion Publishing Group, Ltd. GBR. Dist: Sterling Publishing Co., Inc.

AFRICA, NORTH—POLITICS AND GOVERNMENT

Aissaoui, Rabah. Immigration & National Identity: North African Political Movements in Colonial & Postcolonial France. 2009. (ENG.). 320p. 97.00 *(978-1-84511-835-8(9)*, Tauris Academic Studies) I. B. Tauris & Co., Ltd. GBR. Dist: Macmillan.

Beinin, Joel & Vairel, Frederic, eds. Social Movements, Mobilization, & Contestation in the Middle East & North Africa. 2011. (Stanford Studies in Middle Eastern & Islamic Societies & Cultures). (ENG.). 328p. 80.00 *(978-0-8047-7524-3(9))*; pap. 24.95 *(978-0-8047-7525-0(7))* Stanford Univ. Pr.

Beschel, Jr., Robert P., Robert P, et al, eds. Governance Reform in the Middle East & North Africa: The Lessons from Experience. 2012. (MENA Development Report). (ENG.). 320p. pap. 35.00 *(978-0-8213-8609-5(3)*, 9780821386095) World Bank Pubns.

Binder, Leonard, ed. Rebuilding Devastated Economies in the Middle East. 2007. (ENG.). 296p. 95.00 *(978-0-230-60017-1(4))* Palgrave Macmillan.

Cammett, Melani Claire. Globalization & Business Politics in Arab North Africa: A Comparative Perspective. 2010. (ENG., Illus.). 286p. pap. 29.99 *(978-0-521-15626-4(2))* Cambridge Univ. Pr.

Ehteshami, Anoushiravan. Globalization & Geopolitics in the Middle East: Old Games, New Rules. 2008. 272p. pap. 42.95 *(978-0-415-47712-3(3))* 2007. (Illus.). 258p. 150.00 *(978-0-415-42632-9(4))* Routledge.

Haynes, Jeffrey. Religion & Politics in Europe, the Middle East & North Africa. 2009. (Routledge/ECPR Studies in European Political Science Ser.). (Illus.). 240p. 140.00 *(978-0-415-47713-0(1))* Routledge.

Jensen, Erik. Western Sahara: Anatomy of a Stalemate? 2nd ed. 2011. (Illus.). 160p. (C). 42.00 ***(978-1-58826-829-7(2))***; pap. 16.95 ***(978-1-58826-807-5(1))*** Rienner, Lynne Pubs.

Joffé, George. Islamist Radicalisation in North Africa. 2011. (History & Society in the Islamic World Ser.). (ENG., Illus.). 232p. (C). 125.00 *(978-0-415-58806-5(5))* Routledge.

Joffé, George, ed. North Africa's Arab Spring. 2012. (ENG.). 240p. 140.00 ***(978-0-415-62319-3(7))*** Routledge.

King, Stephen J. & Cammett, Melani. The New Authoritarianism in the Middle East & North Africa. 2009. (Indiana Series in Middle East Studies). (ENG.). 288p. 65.00 *(978-0-253-35397-9(1)*, 0253353971); pap. 24.95 *(978-0-253-22146-9(3)*, 0253221463) Indiana Univ. Pr.

Lahnait, F., ed. The role of binational entrepreneurs as social & economic bridge builders between Europe & North Africa: Volume 53 NATO Science for Peace & Security Series - E: Human & Societal Dynamics. 2009. (Illus.). 120p. pap. 99.00 *(978-1-58603-996-7(2))* IOS Pr., Inc.

Long, David E., et al, eds. The Government & Politics of the Middle East & North Africa. 6th ed. 2010. (ENG., Illus.). 576p. (C). pap. 50.00 *(978-0-8133-4449-2(2))* Westview Pr.

Luciano, Vincent G., ed. Countries of North Africa: Background & Issues. 2010. (Illus.). x, 190p. 99.00 ***(978-1-61761-437-8(8))*** Nova Science Pubs., Inc.

Martín, Pablo San. Western Sahara: The Refugee Nation. 2011. (University of Wales - Iberian & Latin American Studies). (Illus.). 224p. pap. 35.00 *(978-0-7083-2380-9(4))* Univ. of Wales Pr. GBR. Dist: Chicago Distribution Ctr.

Mewshaw, Michael. Between Terror & Tourism: An Overland Journey Across North Africa. 2010. (ENG.). 384p. pap. 16.95 *(978-1-58243-434-6(4)*, Counterpoint Pr.) Basic Bks. GBR. Dist: Perseus-PGW.

Mezran, Karim. Negotiation & Construction of National Identities. 2007. (International Negotiation Ser.: Vol. 3). 222p. *(978-90-04-15808-5(1))* BRILL.

O'Brien, Donal B. Cruise. Saints & Politicians. 2009. (African Studies). (ENG., Illus.). 224p. pap. 31.99 *(978-0-521-10109-7(3))* Cambridge Univ. Pr.

Phares, Walid. The Coming Revolution: Struggle for Freedom in the Middle East. 2015. (ENG.). 400p. pap. 16.00 *(978-1-4391-7638-6(0)*, Threshold Editions) Threshold Editions.

Phares, Walid & Threshold Editions Staff. Coming Revolution: Struggle for Freedom in the Middle East. 2010. (ENG.). 400p. 26.00 *(978-1-4391-7637-9(2)*, Threshold Editions) Threshold Editions.

Sater, James N. Civil Society & Political Change in Morocco. 2011. (Illus.). 240p. pap. 39.95 ***(978-0-415-58948-2(7))*** Routledge.

World Bank Staff. Making the Most of Scarcity: Accountability for Better Water Management in the Middle East & North Africa. 2007. (MENA Development Report). (ENG., Illus.). 235p. per. 29.95 *(978-0-8213-6925-8(3)*, 9780821369258) World Bank Pubns.

Zoubir, Yahia H. & Amirah-Fernández, Haizam, eds. North Africa: Politics, Region & the Limits of Transformation. 2007. (Illus.). XXIV, 400p. 160.00 *(978-0-415-42920-7(X))* Routledge.

Zoubir, Yahia H. & Amirah-Fernández, Haizam, eds. North Africa: Politics, Region & the Limits of Transformation. 2008. (Illus.). XXIV, 400p. 45.95 *(978-0-415-42921-4(8))* Routledge.

Zunes, Stephen & Mundy, Jacob. Western Sahara: War, Nationalism, & Conflict Irresolution. 2010. (Illus.). 424p. *(978-0-8156-3219-1(3))* Syracuse Univ. Pr.

AFRICA, NORTH—RELIGION

Abrous, D. La Societe des Missionnaires d'Afrique a l'epreuve du mythe Berbere: Kabylie - Aures - Mzab. 2007. (Societe d'Etudes Linguistiques et Anthropologiques de France Ser.). (FRE.). 151p. (C). pap. 58.00 *(978-90-429-1959-4(0))* Peeters Pubs. & Booksellers BEL. Dist: Brown, David Bk. Co., The.

Cadotte, Alain. La romanisation des Dieux: L'interpretatio romana en Afrique du Nord sous le Haut-Empire. 2006. (FRE., Illus.). 408p. *(978-90-04-15258-8(X))* BRILL.

Evers, A. Church, Cities, & People: A Study of the Plebs in the Church & Cities of Roman Africa in Late Antiquity. 2010. (Interdisciplinary Studies in Ancient Culture & Religion Ser.). (ENG.). 367p. (C). pap. 85.00 *(978-90-429-2206-8(0))* Peeters Pubs. & Booksellers BEL. Dist: Brown, David Bk. Co., The.

Hardman, Ben. Islam & the Métropole: A Case Study of Religion & Rhetoric in Algeria. 2009. (American University Studies VII: Theology & Religion Ser.). (ENG.). 286p. (C). 77.95 *(978-1-4331-0271-4(4))* Lang, Peter Publishing, Inc.

Howe, Quincy. Tertullian of Africa: The origin of Christian thought in the West. 2010. 108p. pap. 12.95 *(978-1-4502-5843-2(3))* iUniverse, Inc.

Jenkins, John Philip. The Lost History of Christianity: The Thousand-Year Golden Age of the Church in the Middle East, Africa, & Asia — And How It Died. 2009. (ENG.). 304p. pap. 15.99 *(978-0-06-147281-7(6)*, HarperOne) HarperCollins Pubs.

Oden, Thomas C. Early Libyan Christianity: Uncovering a North African Tradition. 2011. (Early African Christianity Set Ser.). (ENG.). 334p. pap. 22.00 ***(978-0-8308-3943-8(7)***, IVP Acad.) InterVarsity Pr.

Paterno, Steve A. The Rev Fr Saturnino Lohure: A Roman Catholic Priest Turned Rebel, the South Sudan Experience. 2007. 328p. per. 29.95 *(978-1-4241-9483-4(0))* PublishAmerica, Inc.

Robertson, Noel. Religion & Reconciliation in Greek Cities: The Sacred Laws of Selinus & Cyrene. 2009. (American Philological Association Book Ser.). (ENG.). 432p. 99.00 *(978-0-19-539400-9(3))* Oxford Univ. Pr., Inc.

Taleb-Carlen, Sarah. The Jews of North Africa: From Dido to de Gaulle. 2010. (ENG.). 196p. pap. 30.50 *(978-0-7618-5043-4(0))* Univ. Pr. of America, Inc.

AFRICA, NORTH—SOCIAL CONDITIONS

Al-Werfalli, Mabroka. Political Alienation in Libya: Assessing Citizens' Political Attitude & Behaviour. 2011. 240p. 74.95 ***(978-0-86372-372-8(1)***, Ithaca Pr.) Garnet Publishing, Ltd. GBR. Dist: International Specialized Bk. Services.

Alvarado, David. La Yihad a Nuestras Puertas. 2010. (Foca Investigación Ser.: Vol. 109). (SPA., Illus.). 238p. *(978-84-96797-36-9(8))* Foca, Ediciones y Distribuciones Generales S.L., Grupo Akal.

Europa Publications, ed. The Middle East & North Africa 2012. 58th rev. ed. 2012. (ENG.). 1468p. 880.00 ***(978-1-85743-626-6(1))*** Routledge.

Europa Publications Staff, ed. Middle East & North Africa 2010. 56th rev. ed. 2009. (ENG.). 1484p. 810.00 *(978-1-85743-530-6(3))* Routledge.

Fischer, Anja & Kohl, Ines, eds. Tuareg Society Within a Globalized World: Saharan Life in Transition. 2010. (Library of Modern Middle East Studies). (ENG., Illus.). 320p. 99.00 *(978-1-84885-370-6(X)*, Tauris Academic Studies) I. B. Tauris & Co., Ltd. GBR. Dist: Macmillan.

Hafez, Sherine & Slyomovics, Susan, eds. Anthropology of the Middle East & North Africa: Into the New Millennium. 2012. (Public Cultures of the Middle East & North Africa Ser.). (ENG.). 368p. 85.00 ***(978-0-253-00746-9(1)***, 0253007461); pap. 30.00 ***(978-0-253-00753-7(4)***, 0253007534) Indiana Univ. Pr.

Linares, Olga F. Power, Prayer & Production: The Jola of Casamance, Senegal. 2007. (Cambridge Studies in Social & Cultural Anthropology Ser.). (ENG.). 284p. pap. 60.00 *(978-0-521-04035-8(3))* Cambridge Univ. Pr.

Maher, Vanessa. Women & Property in Morocco: Their Changing Relation to the Process of Social Stratification in the Middle Atlas. 2007. (Cambridge Studies in Social & Cultural Anthropology Ser.). (ENG.). 252p. pap. 51.00 *(978-0-521-04041-9(3))* Cambridge Univ. Pr.

Martín, Pablo San. Western Sahara: The Refugee Nation. 2011. (University of Wales - Iberian & Latin American Studies). (Illus.). 224p. pap. 35.00 *(978-0-7083-2380-9(4))* Univ. of Wales Pr. GBR. Dist: Chicago Distribution Ctr.

Mewshaw, Michael. Between Terror & Tourism: An Overland Journey Across North Africa. 2010. (ENG.). 384p. pap. 16.95 *(978-1-58243-434-6(4)*, Counterpoint Pr.) Basic Bks. GBR. Dist: Perseus-PGW.

The Middle East & North Africa 2011. 57th rev. ed. 2010. 1464p. 835.00 *(978-1-85743-568-9(0))* Routledge.

Mohamed, Mohamed Hassan. Between Caravan & Sultan: the Bayrouk of Southern Morocco: Study in History & Identity. 2011. (Studies in the History & Society of the Maghrib Ser.). 380p. *(978-90-04-18379-7(5))* BRILL.

Roumani, Maurice M. The Jews of Libya: Coexistence, Persecution, Resettlement. 2009. (ENG.). 310p. pap. 39.95 *(978-1-84519-367-6(9))* Sussex Academic Pr. GBR. Dist: International Specialized Bk. Services.

Thomson, Madia J. A. The Demise of Slavery in Southwestern Morocco, 1860 - 2000: Economic Modernization & the Transformation of Social Hierarchy. 2011. (ENG., Illus.). xxvii, 349p. 119.95 *(978-0-7734-1460-0(6))* Mellen, Edwin Pr., The.

Vazquez-Figueroa, Alberto. Tuareg. 2009. (ENG.). 240p. pap. 19.95 *(978-1-84694-192-4(X))* Hunt, John Publishing Ltd. GBR. Dist: National Bk. Network.

Wooten, Stephen R. The Art of Livelihood: Creating Expressive Agri-Culture in Rural Mali. 2009. 206p. pap. 30.00 *(978-1-59460-731-8(1))* Carolina Academic Pr.

Zereini, Fathi & Hötzl, Heinz, eds. Climatic Changes & Water Resources in the Middle East & North Africa. 2010. (Environmental Science & Engineering / Environmental Science Ser.). (Illus.). xx, 552p. pap. 239.00 *(978-3-642-09871-0(1)*, 3642098711) Springer.

AFRICA, NORTH—SOCIAL LIFE AND CUSTOMS

Abdel-Jaouad, Hedi. Rimbaud et l'Algerie. 174p. pap. 29.95 *(978-0-9665360-2-7(9))* Editions "Les Mains Secretes".

Beckwith, Carol & Fisher, Angela. Dinka: Legendary Cattle Keepers of Sudan. 2010. (ENG., Illus.). 224p. 75.00 *(978-0-8478-3497-6(2))* Rizzoli International Pubns., Inc.

Bernasek, Lisa. Artistry of the Everyday: Beauty & Craftsmanship in Berber Art. 2008. (Peabody Museum Collections Ser.). (Illus.). 128p. pap. 21.95 *(978-0-87365-405-0(6))* Peabody Museum of Archaeology & Ethnology, Harvard Univ., Pubns. Dept.

Kreikenbom, Detlev, et al, eds. Krise und Kult: Vorderer Orient und Nordafrika von Aurelian bis Justinian. 2010. (Millennium-Studien / Millennium Studies).Tr. of Crisis & Cult. (GER., Illus.). 378p. 140.00 *(978-3-11-022050-6(4))* De Gruyter, Walter Inc.

Linares, Olga F. Power, Prayer & Production: The Jola of Casamance, Senegal. 2007. (Cambridge Studies in Social & Cultural Anthropology Ser.). (ENG.). 284p. pap. 60.00 *(978-0-521-04035-8(3))* Cambridge Univ. Pr.

Robertson, Noel. Religion & Reconciliation in Greek Cities: The Sacred Laws of Selinus & Cyrene. 2009. (American Philological Association Book Ser.). (ENG.). 432p. 99.00 *(978-0-19-539400-9(3))* Oxford Univ. Pr., Inc.

Stone, David L. & Stirling, Lea M., eds. Mortuary Landscapes of North Africa. 2007. (Phoenix Supplementary Volumes Ser.). (ENG., Illus.). 270p. *(978-0-8020-9083-6(4))* Univ. of Toronto Pr.

von Hesse-Wartegg, Ernst. Tunis: The Land & the People. 2010. (Illus.). 304p. pap. 39.95 *(978-1-85964-231-3(4))* Garnet Publishing, Ltd. GBR. Dist: International Publishers Marketing.

Wheeler, Simon, photos by. The North African Kitchen: Regional Recipes & Stories. 2008. (Illus.). 192p. 29.95 *(978-1-56656-712-1(2))* Interlink Publishing Group, Inc.

Zarr, Gerald. Tunisia: The Essential Guide to Customs & Culture. 2009. (Culture Smart! Ser.). (ENG., Illus.). 168p. pap. 9.95 *(978-1-85733-477-7(9))* Kuperard Pubs. GBR. Dist: Random Hse., Inc.

AFRICA, SOUTH

see South Africa

AFRICA, SOUTHERN

Here are entered works on the area south of Congo (Democratic Republic) and Tanzania. Works on the Republic of South Africa are entered under South Africa.

Hilton, John & Gosling, Anne, eds. Alma Parens Originalis? The Receptions of Classical Literature & Thought in Africa, Europe, the United States, & Cuba. 359p. (C). pap. 66.95 *(978-3-03910-929-6(4))* Lang, Peter Publishing, Inc.

AFRICA, SOUTHERN—ANTIQUITIES

Calabrese, John Anthony. The Emergence of Social & Political Complexity in the Shashi-Limpopo Valley of Southern Africa, AD 900 to 1300: Ethnicity, Class, & Polity. 2007. (Bar S Ser.). (Illus.). xv, 384p. (C). pap. 120.00 *(978-1-4073-0029-0(6))* British Archaeological Reports Ltd. GBR. Dist: Brown, David Bk. Co., The.

Campbell, Alec C. Tsodilo Hills: Copper Bracelet of the Kalahari. 2010. (ENG.). 179p. pap. 39.95 *(978-0-87013-858-4(8))* Michigan State Univ. Pr.

Huffman, Thomas N. Handbook to the Iron Age: The Archaeology of Pre-Colonial Farming Societies in Southern Africa. 2007. (Illus.). 518p. (C). 84.95 *(978-1-86914-108-0(3))* University of Kwazulu-Natal Press ZAF. Dist: International Specialized Bk. Services.

Swanepoel, Natalie, et al, eds. Five Hundred Years Rediscovered: Southern African Precedents & Prospects. 2009. (ENG., Illus.). 296p. pap. 39.95 *(978-1-86814-474-7(7))* Witwatersrand Univ. Pr. Pubns. ZAF. Dist: Transaction Pubs.

AFRICA, SOUTHERN—DESCRIPTION AND TRAVEL

Anderson, Andrew A. TwentyFive Years in A Waggon Sport & T. 2006. pap. 37.95 *(978-1-4286-5084-8(9))* Kessinger Publishing, LLC.

Brenner, Joni, et al. Life of Bone: Art Meets Science. 2011. (ENG., Illus.). 160p. 50.00 ***(978-1-86814-539-3(5))*** Witwatersrand Univ. Pr. Pubns. ZAF. Dist: Transaction Pubs.

Cillie, Burger. Pocket Guide to Southern African Birds: Revised Third Edition. 2009. (Illus.). 160p. pap. 11.95 *(978-1-919938-65-3(6))* International Publishers Marketing.

Cohen, Callan, et al. Southern African Birdfinder: Where to Find 1,400 Bird Species in Southern Africa & Madagascar. 2007. (Illus.). 448p. pap. 29.95 *(978-1-86872-725-4(4))* Struik Pubs. ZAF. Dist: International Publishers Marketing.

Fleminger, David. Swaziland: A Southbound Pocket Guide. 2009. 176p. pap. 10.95 *(978-1-920143-27-5(0))* 30° South Pubs. ZAF. Dist: International Publishers Marketing.

Globetrotter. Westfalen, Ruhrgebiet. 8th ed. 2011. (Globetrotter Travel Atlas Ser.). (ENG., Illus.). 72p. pap. 14.95 *(978-1-84773-833-2(8)*, Globetrotter) New Holland Pubs., Ltd. GBR. Dist: Globe Pequot Pr., The.

Godwin, Peter. When a Crocodile Eats the Sun: A Memoir of Africa. 2008. (ENG., Illus.). 368p. pap. 14.99 *(978-0-316-01871-5(6)*, Back Bay Bks.) Little Brown & Co.

Hubbard, Douglass H. Bound for Africa: Cold War Fight along the Zambezi. 2008. (Illus.). 304p. *(978-1-59114-394-9(2))* Naval Institute Pr.

Lonely Planet Staff & Firestone, Matthew. Watching Wildlife Southern Africa. 2nd ed. 2009. (Watching Wildlife Ser.). (ENG., Illus.). 352p. pap. 22.99 *(978-1-74104-210-8(0))* Lonely Planet Pubns.

Lonely Planet Staff & Murphy, Alan. Southern Africa. 5th rev. ed. 2010. (Multi Country Guide Ser.). (ENG., Illus.). 808p. pap. 32.99 *(978-1-74059-545-2(9))* Lonely Planet Pubns.

—Zambia & Malawi. 2010. (Multi Country Guide Ser.). (ENG., Illus.). 332p. pap. 26.99 *(978-1-74179-433-5(1))* Lonely Planet Pubns.

Michler, Ian. Victoria Falls & Surrounds. 2009. (Illus.). 160p. pap. 25.95 *(978-1-77007-361-6(2))* Struik Pubs. ZAF. Dist: International Publishers Marketing.

Oates, Frank & Oates, C. G. Matabeleland & the Victoria Falls: The Letters & Journals of Frank Oates, 1873-1875. 2007. (Illus.). 216p. per. *(978-0-9553936-4-8(7))* Jeppestown Pr.

Rogers, David. Southern Africa. 2007. (Living Landscapes Ser.). (Illus.). 172p. 33.95 *(978-1-77007-356-2(6))* Struik Pubs. ZAF. Dist: International Publishers Marketing.

Saarinen, Jarkko. Sustainable Tourism in Southern Africa: Local Communities & Natural Resources in Transition. Saarinen, Jarkko et al, eds. 2009. (Aspects of Tourism Ser.). (ENG., Illus.). 256p. 49.95 *(978-1-84541-108-4(0))*; 109.95 *(978-1-84541-109-1(9))* Channel View Pubns., Ltd. GBR. Dist: Univ. of Toronto Pr.

Selous, Frederick. Travel & Adventure in South-East Africa. 2007. 524p. per. 20.95 *(978-1-60206-131-6(9))* Cosimo, Inc.

Selous, Frederick Courteney. Travel & Adventure in South-East Africa. 2011. (Cambridge Library Collection - History Ser.). (ENG., Illus.). 532p. pap. 39.99 *(978-1-108-03116-5(1))* Cambridge Univ. Pr.

Smith, Gideon F. & Van Wyk, Braam. Aloes in Southern Africa. 2011. (Illus.). 136p. pap. 22.00 *(978-1-77007-462-0(7))* Struik Pubs. ZAF. Dist: International Publishers Marketing.

Spenceley, Anna. Responsible Tourism: Critical Issues for Conservation & Development. Spenceley, Anna, ed. 2008. (ENG., Illus.). 416p. (C). 135.00 *(978-1-84407-639-0(3))* Routledge.

Torrissen, Bjo Christian. One for the Road. 2008. 400p. pap. 19.00 *(978-1-84799-453-0(9))* Lulu Enterprises Inc.

Unwin, Mike. Southern African Wildlife. 2nd rev. ed. 2011. (ENG., Illus.). 288p. pap. 26.99 *(978-1-84162-347-4(4))* Bradt Travel Guides GBR. Dist: Globe Pequot Pr., The.

AFRICA, SOUTHERN—ECONOMIC CONDITIONS

Andreasson, Stefan. Africa's Development Impasse: Towards a Political Economy of Transformation. 2010. (ENG.). 256p. 125.95 *(978-1-84277-971-2(0))*; pap. 34.95 *(978-1-84277-972-9(9))* Zed Bks., Ltd. GBR. Dist: Macmillan.

Buur, et al. The Security-Development Nexus: Expressions of Sovereignty & Securitization in Southern Africa. Buur, Lars et al, eds. 2007. 300p. pap. 44.95 *(978-91-7106-583-4(0))* Nordiska Afrikainstitutet SWE. Dist: Stylus Publishing, LLC.

Frayne, Bruce, et al, eds. Climate Change Assets & Food Security in Southern African Cities. 2012. (ENG., Illus.). 224p. 99.95 ***(978-1-84971-418-1(5))*** Routledge.

Icon Group International, Inc. Staff, compiled by. The 2006 Economic & Product Market Databook for Beira, Mozambique. 2006. 618p. ring bd. 95.00 *(978-0-497-80171-7(X))* Icon Group International, Inc.

—The 2006 Economic & Product Market Databook for Francistown, Botswana. 2006. 618p. ring bd. 95.00 *(978-0-497-80552-4(9))* Icon Group International, Inc.

—The 2006 Economic & Product Market Databook for Gaborone, Botswana. 2006. 618p. ring bd. 95.00 *(978-0-497-80570-8(7))* Icon Group International, Inc.

—The 2006 Economic & Product Market Databook for Kanye, Botswana. 2006. 618p. ring bd. 95.00 *(978-0-497-81970-5(8))* Icon Group International, Inc.

—The 2006 Economic & Product Market Databook for Karonga, Malawi. 2006. 618p. ring bd. 95.00 *(978-0-497-81973-6(2))* Icon Group International, Inc.

—The 2006 Economic & Product Market Databook for Leribe, Lesotho. 2006. 618p. ring bd. 95.00 *(978-0-497-80844-0(7))* Icon Group International, Inc.

—The 2006 Economic & Product Market Databook for Lilongwe, Malawi. 2006. 618p. ring bd. 95.00 *(978-0-497-80856-3(0))* Icon Group International, Inc.

—The 2006 Economic & Product Market Databook for Lobatse, Botswana. 2006. 618p. ring bd. 95.00 *(978-0-497-80873-0(0))* Icon Group International, Inc.

—The 2006 Economic & Product Market Databook for Mahalapye, Botswana. 2006. 618p. ring bd. 95.00 *(978-0-497-80917-1(6))* Icon Group International, Inc.

—The 2006 Economic & Product Market Databook for Maseru, Lesotho. 2006. 618p. ring bd. 95.00 *(978-0-497-80967-6(2))* Icon Group International, Inc.

—The 2006 Economic & Product Market Databook for Maun, Botswana. 2006. 618p. ring bd. 95.00 *(978-0-497-80982-9(6))* Icon Group International, Inc.

—The 2006 Economic & Product Market Databook for Mbabane, Swaziland. 2006. 618p. ring bd. 95.00 *(978-0-497-80990-4(7))* Icon Group International, Inc.

—The 2006 Economic & Product Market Databook for Mhlume, Swaziland. 2006. 618p. ring bd. 95.00 *(978-0-497-81018-4(2))* Icon Group International, Inc.

—The 2006 Economic & Product Market Databook for Ramotswa, Botswana. 2006. 618p. ring bd. 95.00 *(978-0-497-81329-1(7))* Icon Group International, Inc.

—The 2006 Economic & Product Market Databook for Siteki, Swaziland. 2006. 618p. ring bd. 95.00 *(978-0-497-81544-8(3))* Icon Group International, Inc.

—The 2006 Economic & Product Market Databook for Teyateyaneng, Lesotho. 2006. 618p. ring bd. 95.00 *(978-0-497-81665-0(2))* Icon Group International, Inc.

Jarrett, Alfred A. The Under-Development of Africa: Colonialism, Neo-Colonialism & Socialism. Date not set. 192p. (C). pap. 29.50 *(978-0-7618-0106-1(5))* Univ. Pr. of America, Inc.

Lule, Elizabeth & Haacker, Markus. The Fiscal Dimensions of HIV/AIDS in Botswana, South Africa, Swaziland, & Uganda. 2011. (ENG.). 308p. pap. 40.00 ***(978-0-8213-8807-5(X)***, 9780821388075) World Bank Pubns.

Meyn, Mareike. The Impact of EU Free Trade Agreements on Economic Development & Regional Integration in Southern Africa: The Example of EU-SACU Trade Relations, Vol. 55. 2006. (Development Economics & Policy Ser.). (Illus.). 453p. pap. *(978-0-8204-9921-5(8))* Lang, Peter AG.

Parsons, Raymond, ed. Zumanomics: Which Way to Shared Prosperity in South America? - Challenges for a New Government. 2010. (ENG.). 208p. pap. 22.95 *(978-1-77009-647-9(7))* Jacana Media ZAF. Dist: Independent Pubs. Group.

Shackleton, Charlie M., ed. Livelihoods & Vulnerability in the Arid & Semi-Arid Lands of Southern Africa. 2010. (Hunger & Poverty: Causes, Impacts & Eradication Ser.). (Illus.). 267p. 89.00 *(978-1-60876-940-7(2))* Nova Science Pubs., Inc.

Siwale, Mengo. Scenario Planning 2020 for Southern African Economic Empowerment. 2011. (Illus.). 100p. pap. ***(978-3-8443-2852-3(1))*** Lambert Academic Publishing.

Waldorff, Pttur. Conceptions of Poverty & Development. 2008. 108p. pap. *(978-3-639-02930-7(5))* VDM Verlag Dr. Mueller e.K.

AFRICA, SOUTHERN—FOREIGN RELATIONS

Adar, Korwa G. & Schraeder, Peter J., eds. Globalization & Emerging Trends in African Foreign Policy, Volume II: A Comparative Perspective of Eastern Africa, Vol. 2. 2nd ed. 2007. (ENG., Illus.). 320p. per. 41.99 *(978-0-7618-3287-4(4))* Univ. Pr. of America, Inc.

Khadiagala, Gilbert M. Allies in Adversity: The Frontline States in Southern African Security 1975-1993. 2007. (ENG.). 336p. per. 50.50 *(978-0-7618-3832-6(5))* Univ. Pr. of America, Inc.

Onslow, Sue. Cold War in Southern Africa: White Power, Black Liberation. 2009. (Cold War History Ser.). (ENG.). 272p. (C). 130.00 *(978-0-415-47420-7(5))* Routledge.

Onslow, Sue, ed. Cold War in Southern Africa: White Power, Black Liberation. 2012. (ENG.). 262p. (C). pap. 39.95 ***(978-0-415-62228-8(X))*** Routledge.

Roberts, Anthony E. African Cauldron. 2010. 168p. pap. *(978-1-84748-771-1(8))* Athena Pr.

AFRICA, SOUTHERN—HISTORY

Baines, Gary & Vale, Peter, eds. Beyond the Border War: New Perspectives on Southern Africa's Late-Cold War Conflicts. 2008. (Illus.). 362p. pap. 43.00 *(978-1-86888-456-8(2))* Unisa Press / Uitgewers GBR. Dist: International Specialized Bk. Services.

Bank, Andrew. Bushmen in a Victorian World: The Remarkable Story of the Bleek-Lloyd Collection of Bushman Folklore. 2008. (Illus.). 361p. pap. 36.00 *(978-1-77013-091-3(8))* Double Storey Bks. ZAF. Dist: International Publishers Marketing.

Boxer, C. R., ed. The Tragic History of the Sea, 1589-1622: Narratives of the shipwrecks of the Portuguese East Indiamen São Thomé (1589), Santo Alberto (1593), São João Baptista (1622) & the journeys of the survivors in South East Africa. 2010. (Hakluyt Society, Second Ser.). 312p. 69.95 *(978-1-4094-1478-0(7))* Hakluyt Society GBR. Dist: Ashgate Publishing Co.

Eldredge, Elizabeth A. Power in Colonial Africa: Conflict & Discourse in Lesotho, 1870-1960. 2007. (Africa & the Diaspora Ser.). (ENG., Illus.). 264p. 65.00 *(978-0-299-22370-0(1))* Univ. of Wisconsin Pr.

Farley, Jonathan. Southern Africa. 2008. (Making of the Contemporary World Ser.). (Illus.). (ENG.). 176p. 99.95 *(978-0-415-31034-5(2))*; 155p. pap. 29.95 *(978-0-415-31035-2(0))* Routledge.

Freemantle, D. M. A Hole in Our Lives Forever. 2011. 348p. 29.99 ***(978-1-4653-0007-2(4))***; pap. 19.99 ***(978-1-4653-0006-5(6))*** Xlibris Corp.

The Hot Cold War: The USSR in Southern Africa. 2008. pap. *(978-1-86914-155-4(5))* Univ. of Natal Pr. ZAF. Dist: International Specialized Bk. Services.

Hubbard, Douglass H. Bound for Africa: Cold War Fight along the Zambezi. 2008. (Illus.). 304p. *(978-1-59114-394-9(2))* Naval Institute Pr.

Hulterstrm, Karolina, et al. Political Opposition in African Countries: The Cases of Kenya, Namibia, Zambia & Zimbabwe. 2007. (NAI Discussion Papers). 85p. pap. 15.95 *(978-91-7106-587-2(3))* Nordiska Afrikainstitutet SWE. Dist: Stylus Publishing, LLC.

Kongo, Grades 6-9: A Kingdom Divided (NCHS) tchr. ed., spiral bd. 12.00 *(978-0-382-44618-4(6))* Cobblestone Publishing Co.

McKenna, Amy, ed. The History of Southern Africa. 2011. (Britannica Guide to Africa Ser.). (Illus.). 240p. (YA). 106.00 *(978-1-61530-443-1(6))* Rosen Publishing Group, Inc., The.

Schreuder, D. M. The Scramble for Southern Africa, 1877-1895: The politics of partition Reappraised. 2009. (Cambridge Commonwealth Ser.). (ENG.). 400p. pap. 39.99 *(978-0-521-10959-8(0))* Cambridge Univ. Pr.

Shubin, Vladimir Gennadyevich. The Hot 'Cold War' The USSR in Southern Africa. 2008. (ENG., Illus.). 320p. 100.00 *(978-0-7453-2473-9(8))*; pap. 30.00 *(978-0-7453-2472-2(X))* Pluto Pr. GBR. Dist: Macmillan.

Swanepoel, Natalie, et al, eds. Five Hundred Years Rediscovered: Southern African Precedents & Prospects. 2009. (ENG., Illus.). 296p. pap. 39.95 *(978-1-86814-474-7(7))* Witwatersrand Univ. Pr. Pubns. ZAF. Dist: Transaction Pubs.

Swart, Sandra, ed. Canis Africanis: A Dog History of Southern Africa. 2008. (Human-Animal Studies). (Illus.). 295p. pap. *(978-90-04-15419-3(1))* BRILL.

AFRICA, SOUTHERN—POLITICS AND GOVERNMENT

Bauer, Gretchen & Taylor, Scott D. Politics in Southern Africa: Transition & Transformation. 2nd ed. 2011. (Illus.). 400p. (C). pap. 26.50 *(978-1-58826-794-8(6))* Rienner, Lynne Pubs.

Buur, et al. The Security-Development Nexus: Expressions of Sovereignty & Securitization in Southern Africa. Buur, Lars et al, eds. 2007. 300p. pap. 44.95 *(978-91-7106-583-4(0))* Nordiska Afrikainstitutet SWE. Dist: Stylus Publishing, LLC.

Dagada, Rabelani, et al. Telecommunication Revolution in a Developmental State. 2011. 386p. pap. 16.99 ***(978-1-61667-282-9(X))*** Raider Publishing International.

Eldredge, Elizabeth A. Power in Colonial Africa: Conflict & Discourse in Lesotho, 1870-1960. 2007. (Africa & the Diaspora Ser.). (ENG., Illus.). 264p. 65.00 *(978-0-299-22370-0(1))* Univ. of Wisconsin Pr.

Hatchard, John, et al. Comparative Constitutionalism & Good Governance in the Commonwealth: An Eastern & Southern African Perspective. 2009. (ENG., Illus.). 388p. pap. 56.00 *(978-0-521-11829-3(8))* Cambridge Univ. Pr.

Hulterstrm, Karolina, et al. Political Opposition in African Countries: The Cases of Kenya, Namibia, Zambia & Zimbabwe. 2007. (NAI Discussion Papers). 85p. pap. 15.95 *(978-91-7106-587-2(3))* Nordiska Afrikainstitutet SWE. Dist: Stylus Publishing, LLC.

Jimu, Ignasio Malizani. Urban Appropriation & Transformation: Bicycle Taxi & Handcart Operators. 2008. 160p. pap. *(978-9956-558-75-9(3))* Langaa Research & Publishing Common Initiative Group CMR. Dist: Michigan State Univ. Pr.

Khadiagala, Gilbert M. Allies in Adversity: The Frontline States in Southern African Security 1975-1993. 2007. (ENG.). 336p. per. 50.50 *(978-0-7618-3832-6(5))* Univ. Pr. of America, Inc.

Melber. Governance & State Delivery in Southern Africa: Examples from Botswana, Namibia & Zimbabwe. Melber, Henning, ed. 2007. (NAI Discussion Papers). 68p. pap. 15.95 *(978-91-7106-588-9(1))* Nordiska Afrikainstitutet SWE. Dist: Stylus Publishing, LLC.

Mothusi, Bashi. Public Sector Reforms & Change Management in Botswan. 2009. 160p. pap. *(978-3-639-18018-3(6))* VDM Verlag Dr. Mueller e.K.

Nabulyato, Robinson, ed. Good Governance & Civil Society Participation in Africa. 2008. 252p. pap. 29.95 *(978-99944-55-32-4(X))* African Bks. Collective, Ltd. GBR. Dist: Lightning Source, Inc.

Nathan, Laurie. Community of Insecurity: Sadc's Struggle for Peace & Security in Southern Africa. 2012. (International Political Economy of New Regionalisms Ser.). (Illus.). 200p. 99.95 ***(978-1-4094-3044-5(8))*** Ashgate Publishing Co.

Onslow, Sue. Cold War in Southern Africa: White Power, Black Liberation. 2009. (Cold War History Ser.). (ENG.). 272p. (C). 130.00 *(978-0-415-47420-7(5))* Routledge.

Onslow, Sue, ed. Cold War in Southern Africa: White Power, Black Liberation. 2012. (ENG.). 262p. (C). pap. 39.95 ***(978-0-415-62228-8(X))*** Routledge.

Parsons, Raymond, ed. Zumanomics: Which Way to Shared Prosperity in South America? - Challenges for a New Government. 2010. (ENG.). 208p. pap. 22.95 *(978-1-77009-647-9(7))* Jacana Media ZAF. Dist: Independent Pubs. Group.

Power, Joey. Political Culture & Nationalism in Malawi: Building Kwacha. 2010. (Rochester Studies in African History & the Diaspora Ser.: Volume 43). (Illus.). 350p. 85.00 *(978-1-58046-310-2(X))* Univ. of Rochester Pr.

Ramutsindela, Maano. Transfrontier Conservation in Africa: At the Confluence of Capital, Politics, & Nature. 2007. (Illus.). 192p. 105.00 *(978-1-84593-221-3(8))* CABI GBR. Dist: Stylus Publishing, LLC.

Roberts, Anthony E. African Cauldron. 2010. 168p. pap. *(978-1-84748-771-1(8))* Athena Pr.

Saul, John S. The Next Liberation Struggle: Capitalism, Socialism, & Democracy in Southern Africa. xi, 354p. *(978-1-86914-076-2(1))* University of Kwazulu-Natal Press ZAF. Dist: International Specialized Bk. Services.

Sperfeld, Robert. Decentralisation in Lesotho. 2008. 108p. pap. *(978-3-8364-3103-3(3))* VDM Verlag Dr. Mueller e.K.

Spurlin, William J. Imperialism Within the Margins: Queer Representation & the Politics of Culture in Southern Africa. 2006. (ENG.). 192p. 84.00 *(978-1-4039-7413-6(6))* Palgrave Macmillan.

AFRICA, SOUTHERN—RACE RELATIONS

Adhikari, Mohamed. Burdened by Race - Coloured Identities in Southern Africa. 2010. 272p. pap. 42.95 *(978-1-919895-14-7(0))* Double Storey Bks. ZAF. Dist: International Publishers Marketing.

AFRICA, SOUTHERN—SOCIAL CONDITIONS

Allen, Kevin. Banana Man. 2007. 228p. per. *(978-1-905823-17-8(7))* Ecademy Pr. Ltd.

Debra Liebenow Daly. The Kingdom of Roses & Thorns. 2009. 276p. pap. 15.49 *(978-1-4389-5488-2(3))* AuthorHouse.

Draper, Peter & Mbirimi, Ivan, eds. Climate Change & Trade: The Challenges for Southern Africa. 2011. (ENG.). 290p. pap. 28.95 *(978-1-920196-28-8(5))* Jacana Media ZAF. Dist: Independent Pubs. Group.

Edkins, Don & Vehkalahti, Iikka. Steps by Steps. 2009. (ENG., Illus.). 240p. pap. 26.00 *(978-1-920196-09-7(9))* Jacana Media ZAF. Dist: Independent Pubs. Group.

Frayne, Bruce, et al, eds. Climate Change Assets & Food Security in Southern African Cities. 2012. (ENG., Illus.). 224p. 99.95 ***(978-1-84971-418-1(5))*** Routledge.

Moletsane, Lebo, et al, eds. Methodologies for Mapping a Southern African Girlhood in the Age of Aids. 2008. 160p. pap. *(978-90-8790-441-8(X))* Sense Pubs.

Moletsane, Lebo, et al. Methodologies for Mapping a Southern African Girlhood in the Age of Aids. 2008. 160p. *(978-90-8790-442-5(8))* Sense Pubs.

Moodley, Edley J. Shembe, Ancestors, & Christ: A Christological Inquiry with Missiological Implications. 2008. (American Society of Missiology Monograph Ser.). 272p. pap. 30.00 *(978-1-55635-880-7(6)*, Pickwick Pubns.) Wipf & Stock Pubs.

Murray, Colin. Families Divided: The Impact of Migrant Labour in Lesotho. 2009. (African Studies). (ENG., Illus.). 236p. pap. 34.99 *(978-0-521-10709-9(1))* Cambridge Univ. Pr.

Ramutsindela, M. Parks & People in Postcolonial Societies: Experiences in Southern Africa. 2010. (GeoJournal Library). vii, 191p. pap. 129.00 *(978-90-481-6731-9(0)*, 9048167310) Springer.

Saul, John S. Liberation Lite: The Roots of Recolonization in Southern Africa. 2011. ***(978-1-59221-834-9(2))***; 144p. pap. ***(978-1-59221-835-6(0))*** Africa World Pr.

Timberlake, Jonathan. Flora Zambesiaca. 2012. (Illus.). 54p. pap. 55.00 ***(978-1-84246-374-1(8))*** Kew Publishing GBR. Dist: Chicago Distribution Ctr.

AFRICA, SUB-SAHARAN

Aryeetey-Attoh, Samuel, et al. Geography of Sub-Saharan Africa. 3rd ed. 2009. (ENG.). 480p. (C). pap. 110.87 *(978-0-13-605631-7(8)*, Prentice Hall) Prentice Hall PTR.

Chau, Donovan C. Political Warfare in Sub-Saharan Africa: U. S. Capabilities & Chinese Operations in Ethiopia, Kenya, Nigeria, & South Africa. 2007. vii, 75p. pap. *(978-1-58487-285-6(3))* Strategic Studies Institute, U.S. Army War College Commandant (AWCC-DSI/Pubns.).

Chirambo, Kondwani, ed. The Political Cost of Aids in Africa Evidence from Six Countries. 2008. 408p. (C). pap. *(978-1-920118-65-5(9))* IDASA Pubs. ZAF. Dist: Michigan State Univ. Pr.

Cram101 Textbook Reviews Staff. Outlines & Highlights for Africa South of the Sahar: A Geographical Interpretation by Robert Stock, ISBN. 2009. 70p. pap. 27.95 *(978-1-4288-8742-8(3))* Cram101 Inc.

Cross, Catherine, et al, eds. Views on Migration in Sub-Saharan Africa: Proceedings of an African Migration Alliance Workshop. 2007. (ENG., Illus.). 304p. per. 29.95 *(978-0-7969-2165-9(2))* Human Sciences Research Council ZAF. Dist: Independent Pubs. Group.

Europa Publications Staff. Africa South of the Sahara 2008. 37th rev. ed. 2007. 1536p. 700.00 *(978-1-85743-421-7(8))* Routledge.

Frame, Iain, ed. Africa South of the Sahara. 36th rev. ed. 2006. (Africa South of the Sahara Ser.). (Illus.). 1513p. 620.00 *(978-1-85743-369-2(6))* Routledge.

Marouf, Nadir, ed. Les Identitts Rtgionales et la Dialectique Sud-Sud en Question. 2007. (FRE.). 192p. pap. *(978-2-86978-195-5(4))* Council for the Development of Social Science Research in Africa SEN. Dist: Michigan State Univ. Pr.

AFRICA, SUB-SAHARAN—DESCRIPTION AND TRAVEL

Balz-Cochois, Helgard. FUFU und Vergißmeinnicht: Die Afrika-Rundbriefe der Frau des Feldforschers. 2006. (GER., Illus.). 398p. pap. 34.90 *(978-3-8334-4754-9(0))* Bks. on Demand.

Geddes, Gary. Drink the Bitter Root: A Search for Justice & Healing in Africa. 2011. (ENG.). 304p. 26.00 ***(978-1-58243-788-0(2)***, Counterpoint) Counterpoint LLC.

Kennedy, Peter. The Fatal Sleep: Africa's Killer Disease That Went Undiscovered for Centuries. 2007. (ENG., Illus.). 264p. 30.00 *(978-1-905222-67-4(X))* Luath Pr. Ltd. GBR. Dist: Ingram Pub. Services.

Ternet, M. Bryce. Diplomatic Weekends in Africa, 1 vol. 2010. 188p. pap. 24.95 *(978-1-4489-4382-1(5))* PublishAmerica, Inc.

Tucker, Shelby. The Last Banana. 2010. (Illus.). 288p. 25.00 *(978-1-906768-21-8(8)*, Stacey International) Stacey Publishing GBR. Dist: Midpoint Trade Bks., Inc.

Uttley, David. Thirst. 2007. (Illus.). 96p. per. *(978-0-9793164-1-8(3))* DesignWorks Group, The.

AFRICA, SUB-SAHARAN—ECONOMIC CONDITIONS

Africa South of the Sahara 2011. 40th rev. ed. 2010. (ENG.). 1604p. 835.00 *(978-1-85743-564-1(8))* Routledge.

Ango, Tola Gemechu. Livelihood Issues & Sustainable Nautural Resource Managment. 2009. 84p. pap. *(978-3-639-16799-3(6))* VDM Verlag Dr. Mueller e.K.

Azam, Jean-Paul. Trade, Exchange Rate, & Growth in Sub-Saharan Africa. 2006. (ENG., Illus.). 280p. pap. 45.99 *(978-0-521-68407-1(2))*; 92.00 *(978-0-521-86536-4(0))* Cambridge Univ. Pr.

Banik, Dan. The Legal Empowerment Agenda: Poverty Labour & the Informal Economy in Africa. 2011. (Illus.). 242p. 124.95 *(978-1-4094-1118-5(4))*; pap. 49.95 *(978-1-4094-1119-2(2))* Ashgate Publishing Co.

Beyond Oil & Gas: African Growth & Opportunity Act's Benefits to Africa: Hearing Before the Subcommittee on Africa & Global Health of the Committee on Foreign Affairs, House of Representatives, One Hundred Tenth Congress, First Session, July 12, 2007. 2007. iii, 62p. *(978-0-16-079300-4(9)*, 552-070-36378-5) United States Government Printing Office.

Boas, Morten. The Political Economy of the Conflict Trade. 2011. (Routledge Advances in International Relations & Global Politics Ser.). (ENG.). 192p. (C). 120.00 *(978-0-415-58084-7(6)*, Routledge) Taylor & Francis Group GBR. Dist: Taylor & Francis Group.

Carey, Kevin, et al. Sub-Saharan Africa: Forging New Trade Links with Asia. 2007. (Illus.). vii, 55p. *(978-1-58906-667-0(7))* International Monetary Fund.

Chabal, Patrick & Daloz, Jean-Pascal. Africa Works: Disorder As Political Instrument. 2010. (African Issues Ser.). (Illus.). 192p. pap. 24.95 *(978-0-85255-814-0(7)*, Currey, James) Boydell & Brewer, Ltd. GBR. Dist: Boydell & Brewer, Inc.

Chinedu, Chinedu. The Debt - Growth Link in Sub-Saharan Afric. 2011. 92p. pap. ***(978-3-8443-0303-2(0))*** Lambert Academic Publishing.

Dibie, Robert A., et al, contrib. by. Non-Governmental Organizations (NGOs) & Sustainable Development in Sub-Saharan Africa. 2007. (ENG., Illus.). 302p. 78.99 *(978-0-7391-1653-1(3))* Lexington Bks.

Dinh, Hinh, et al, eds. Light Manufacturing in Africa: Focused Policies to Enhance Private Investment & Create Productive Jobs. 2012. (Africa Development Forum Ser.). (ENG.). 180p. pap. 30.00 ***(978-0-8213-8961-4(0)***, 9780821389614) World Bank Pubns.

Dinh, Hinh T. Light Manufacturing in Africa: Focused Policies to Enhance Private Investment & Create Productive Jobs. 2012. ***(978-0-8213-8974-4(2))*** World Bank Pubns.

Djurfeldt, Göran, et al, eds. African Smallholders: Food Crops, Markets & Policy. 2011. (Illus.). 304p. 160.00 *(978-1-84593-716-4(3))* CABI GBR. Dist: Stylus Publishing, LLC.

Donaldson, Ronnie & Marais, Lochner. Small Town Geographies in Africa: Experiences from South Africa & Elsewhere. 2011. (African Political, Economic, & Security Issues Ser.). 215.00 ***(978-1-62100-001-3(X))*** Nova Science Pubs., Inc.

Ecker, Olivier. Economics of Micronutrient Malnutrition: The Demand for Nutrients in Sub-Saharan Africa. 2009. (Illus.). xxiv, 169p. 64.95 *(978-3-631-59505-3(0))* Lang, Peter GmbH, Europaischer Verlag der Wissenschaften DEU. Dist: Lang, Peter.

Estache, Antonio & Wodon, Quentin. Infrastructure & Poverty in Sub-Saharan Africa. 2006. *(978-0-8213-6903-6(2))* World Bank Pubns.

Europa Publications, ed. Africa South of the Sahara 2012. 41st rev. ed. 2011. (ENG.). 1604p. 880.00 ***(978-1-85743-623-5(7))*** Routledge.

Europa Publications Staff, ed. Africa South of the Sahara 2009. 6th rev. ed. 2008. 1528p. 760.00 *(978-1-85743-469-9(2))* Europa Pubns.

—Africa South of the Sahara 2010. 39th rev. ed. 2009. (ENG.). 1588p. 810.00 *(978-1-85743-527-6(3))* Routledge.

Fieldhouse, D. K. Black Africa, 1945-1980: Economic Decolonization & Arrested Development. 2011. (ENG.). 288p. 105.00 *(978-0-415-59361-8(1))* Routledge.

Foster, Vivien, et al. Batir des Ponts: Le Rôle Croissan Tde la Chine Dans le Financement des Infrastructures en Afrique Subsaharienne. 2009. (Trends & Policy Options (PPIAF) Ser.: 5). (FRE., Illus.). 120p. pap. 22.00 *(978-0-8213-7938-7(0)*, 9780821379387) World Bank Pubns.

—Building Bridges: China's Growing Role as Infrastructure Financier for Africa. 2008. (Trends & Policy Options (PPIAF) Ser.: 5). (ENG., Illus.). 168p. pap. 22.00 *(978-0-8213-7554-9(7)*, 9780821375549) World Bank Pubns.

Gillies, Alexandra & Joseph, Richard A. Smart Aid for African Development. Joseph, Richard & Gillies, Alexandra, eds. 2008. (Illus.). 300p. (C). 59.95 *(978-1-58826-606-4(0))* Rienner, Lynne Pubs.

Go, Delfin S. & Page, John, eds. Africa at a Turning Point? Growth, Aid, & External Shocks. 2008. (World Bank Development Essays Ser.). (ENG., Illus.). 520p. pap. 49.95 *(978-0-8213-7277-7(7)*, 9780821372777) World Bank Pubns.

Grinker, Roy Richard, et al, eds. Perspectives on Africa: A Reader in Culture, History & Representation. 2nd ed. 2010. (Global Perspectives Ser.: 3). (ENG., Illus.). 713p. pap. 66.95 *(978-1-4051-9060-2(4))*; 712p. 110.95 *(978-1-4443-3522-4(7))* Wiley, John & Sons, Inc. (Wiley-Blackwell).

Hagos, Atakilt. External Debt & Economic Growth in Sub-Saharan Afric. 2011. 80p. pap. **(978-3-8443-1982-8(4))** Lambert Academic Publishing.

Hugon, Philippe. African Geopolitics. Rendall, Steven, tr. from FRE. 2008. 174p. pap. 26.95 *(978-1-55876-461-3(5))* Wiener, Markus Pubs., Inc.

International Monetary Fund Staff. Regional Economic Outlook: Sub-Saharan Africa. 2008. 135p. pap. 31.00 *(978-1-58906-711-0(8))* International Monetary Fund.

James, Christian. Africa, 1998-2006. 2007. *(978-0-88692-869-8(9))* ProQuest LLC.

Jarrett, Alfred A. The Under-Development of Africa: Colonialism, Neo-Colonialism & Socialism. Date not set. 192p. (C). 57.00 *(978-0-7618-0105-4(7))* Univ. Pr. of America, Inc.

Jarso, Jianmario. Structural Adjustment of Wb & Imf in Sub-Saharan Afric. 2011. 72p. pap. **(978-3-8443-0021-5(X))** Lambert Academic Publishing.

John O. Ogbor. Entrepreneurship in Sub-Saharan Afric: A Strategic Management Perspective. 2009. 712p. pap. 98.49 *(978-1-4389-3392-4(4))* AuthorHouse.

Joseph, Richard & Gillies, Alexandra, eds. Smart Aid for African Development. 2008. (Illus.). 300p. (C). pap. 24.50 *(978-1-58826-632-3(X))* Rienner, Lynne Pubs.

Kalu, Kenneth. Review of Financial Liberalization in Sub-Saharan Afric. 2009. 200p. pap. *(978-3-639-20994-5(X))* VDM Verlag Dr. Mueller e.K.

Keese, Alexander, ed. Ethnicity & the Long-Term Perspective: The African Experience. 2010. (CEAUP Studies on Africa Ser.). (Illus.). 216p. pap. *(978-3-0343-0337-8(8))* Lang, Peter.

Kimanuka, Oscar. Sub-Saharan Africa's Development Challenges: A Case Study of Rwanda's Post-Genocide Experience. 2008. (ENG., Illus.). 192p. 89.00 *(978-0-230-60656-2(3))* Palgrave Macmillan.

Labaste, Patrick, ed. Le Marche Europeen des Produits Horticoles: Opportunites Pour les Expotrateurs d'Afrique Subsaharienne. 2006. (World Bank Working Papers: 64). (FRE., Illus.). 148p. per. 20.00 *(978-0-8213-6352-2(2)*, 9780821363522) World Bank Pubns.

Lindell, Ilda, ed. Africa's Informal Workers: Collective Agency, Alliances & Transnational Organizing in Urban Africa. 2010. (Africa Now Ser.). (ENG., Illus.). 240p. 126.95 *(978-1-84813-451-5(7))*; pap. 39.95 *(978-1-84813-452-2(5))* Zed Bks., Ltd. GBR. Dist: Macmillan.

Major Companies of Africa South of the Sahara. 2011th ed. 2010. 840.00 *(978-1-86099-649-8(3))* Graham & Whiteside, Ltd. GBR. Dist: Cengage Gale.

Malmberg, Bo. Demography & the Development Potential of Sub-Saharan: Africa. 2008. (NAI Current African Issues Ser.). 56p. pap. 12.95 *(978-91-7106-621-3(7))* Nordiska Afrikainstitutet SWE. Dist: Stylus Publishing, LLC.

McKee, Chris, ed. International Country Risk Guide Annual - 2006 Vol. 5: Sub-Saharan Africa. 2006. (C). per. *(978-1-933539-24-9(0))* PRS Group Inc., The.

Mehler, Andreas, et al, eds. Africa Yearbook Volume 3: Politics, Economy & Society South of the Sahara In 2006. 2007. (Africa Yearbook: Politics, Economy, & Society South of the Sahara Ser.). (Illus.). 516p. pap. *(978-90-04-16263-1(1))* BRILL.

Mehler, Andres, et al, eds. Africa Yearbook: Politics, Economy & Society South of the Sahara In 2005. 2006. (Africa Yearbook: Politics, Economy, & Society South of the Sahara Ser.). (Illus.). 511p. pap. *(978-90-04-15486-5(8))* BRILL.

Miguel, Edward. Africa's Turn? 2009. (Boston Review Bks.). (ENG., Illus.). 176p. (gr. 17). 14.95 *(978-0-262-01289-8(8))* MIT Pr.

Mobolaji, Hakeem. Recent Issues on Financial Development in Sub-Saharan Afric. 2010. 156p. pap. *(978-3-639-13408-7(7))* VDM Verlag Dr. Mueller e.K.

Morrissey, Oliver & Zgovu, Evious. The Impact of China & India on Sub-Saharan Africa: Opportunities, Challenges & Policies. 2011. (ENG., Illus.). 90p. pap. 24.95 *(978-1-84929-055-5(5))* Commonwealth Secretariat GBR. Dist: Stylus Publishing, LLC.

Mukudi, Edith & Commins, Stephen K. HIV/AIDS in Africa: Challenges & Impact. 2008. pap. *(978-1-59221-625-3(0))* Africa World Pr.

Noman, Akbar, et al, eds. Good Growth & Governance in Africa: Rethinking Development Strategies. 2012. (ENG., Illus.). 576p. pap. 50.00 **(978-0-19-969857-8(0))** Oxford Univ. Pr., Inc.

Noman, Akbar, et al. Good Growth & Governance in Africa: Rethinking Development Strategies. Stiglitz, Joseph E., ed. 2012. (Illus.). 576p. 125.00 **(978-0-19-969856-1(2))** Oxford Univ. Pr., Inc.

Okpara, John. Management & Economic Development in Sub-Saharan Africa. 2007. 260p. *(978-1-905068-51-7(4))* Adonis & Abbey Publishers Ltd.

OSSREA, Ossrea. Assessment of Poverty Reduction Strategies in Sub-Saharan Africa: The Cases of Ethiopia, Kenya, Malawi, Rwanda, Uganda, & Zambia. 2008. 70p. pap. 19.95 *(978-99944-55-28-7(1))* African Bks. Collective, Ltd. GBR. Dist: Lightning Source, Inc.

Overbeeke, Marlies. Undernourishment in Sub-Saharan Afric. 2008. 132p. pap. *(978-3-8364-6724-7(0))* VDM Verlag Dr. Mueller e.K.

Pettit, Jenny. Teaching Africa Today for Middle School. 2006. pap. *(978-0-943804-53-8(1))* Univ. of Denver, Ctr. for Teaching International Relations Pubns.

Pickett, James & Singer, Hans, eds. Towards Economic Recovery in Sub-Saharan Africa. 2011. (ENG.). 296p. 115.00 *(978-0-415-59375-5(1))* Routledge.

Radelet, Steven. Emerging Africa: How 17 Countries Are Leading the Way. 2010. (ENG.). 169p. pap. 18.95 *(978-1-933286-51-8(2))* Ctr. for Global Development.

Razafimahefa, Ivohasina Fizara & Hamori, Shigeyuki. International Competitiveness in Africa: Policy Implications in the Sub-Saharan Region. 2010. (Advanced Studies in Theoretical & Applied Econometrics Ser.). (Illus.). xii, 170p. pap. 109.00 *(978-3-642-08845-2(7)*, 3642088457) Springer.

Rotberg, Robert. Africa's Successes: Evaluating Accomplishment, 43. 2007. (Belfer/WPF Report Ser.). pap. 19.95 *(978-0-9742651-9-3(5))* World Peace Foundation.

Salop, Joanne & Kaufman, Martin Daniel. The IMF & aid to Sub-Saharan Africa 1999-2005. 2007. pap. *(978-1-58906-635-9(9))* International Monetary Fund.

Sivini, Giordano. Resistance to Modernization in Africa: Journey among Peasants & Nomads. Hall, Joan, tr. 2007. (ENG., Illus.). 238p. (gr. 11). 49.95 *(978-0-7658-0361-0(5))* Transaction Pubs.

Tandrayen-Ragoobur, Verena. Foreign Direct Investment, Exports & Economic Growth. 2011. 136p. pap. **(978-3-8433-8553-4(X))** Lambert Academic Publishing.

United Nations: Department of Economic and Social Affairs: Division for Sustainable Development. Trends in sustainable Development: Africa Report. 2008. (ENG., Illus.). 572p. pap. 20.00 *(978-92-1-104576-5(2))* United Nations Pubns.

Walraven, Klaas van. Africa Yearbook Vol. 7: Politics, Economy & Society South of the Sahara 2010. Mehler, Andreas & Melber, Henning, eds. 2011. (Illus.). xvi, 550p. pap. **(978-90-04-20556-7(X))** BRILL.

Walraven, Klaas van & Melber, Henning, eds. Africa Yearbook 4: Politics, Economy & Society South of the Sahara 2007. 2008. (Africa Yearbook Ser.). 576p. pap. *(978-90-04-15805-3(2))* BRILL.

Wilson, Joseph M. African Economic & Political Developments. 2011. *(978-1-61122-067-4(X))* Nova Science Pubs., Inc.

World Bank Staff. At the Crossroads: Choices for Secondary Education & Training in Sub-Saharan Africa. 2008. (Africa Human Development Ser.). (ENG.). 410p. pap. 35.00 *(978-0-8213-7113-8(4)*, 9780821371138) World Bank Pubns.

Yago, Milton. Investment & Growth in Sub-Saharan Afric. 2010. 304p. pap. *(978-3-639-23551-7(7))* VDM Verlag Dr. Mueller e.K.

AFRICA, SUB-SAHARAN—FOREIGN RELATIONS

Abegunrin, Olayiwola. Africa in Global Politics in the Twenty-First Century: A Pan-African Perspective. 2009. (ENG.). 288p. 89.00 *(978-0-230-61890-9(1))* Palgrave Macmillan.

Bangui, Thierry. China: A New Partner for Africa's Development - Are We Heading for the End of European Privileges on the Black Continent? 2012. (Asian Political, Economic & Security Issues Ser.). 210p. 95.00 **(978-1-61324-923-9(3))** Nova Science Pubs., Inc.

Carey, Kevin, et al. Sub-Saharan Africa: Forging New Trade Links with Asia. 2007. (Illus.). vii, 55p. *(978-1-58906-667-0(7))* International Monetary Fund.

Copson, Raymond W. The United States in Africa: Bush Policy & Beyond. 2007. (African Arguments Ser.). (ENG.). 176p. 73.95 *(978-1-84277-914-9(1))*; per. 23.95 *(978-1-84277-915-6(X))* Zed Bks., Ltd. GBR. Dist: Macmillan.

Faber, Gerrit. Beyond Market Access for Economic Development: EU-Africa relations in Transition. Faber, Gerrit & Orbie, Jan, eds. 2009. (Routledge Studies in the European Economy Ser.). (Illus.). 416p. 150.00 *(978-0-415-48260-8(7))* Routledge.

Fiala, Natalie L. Sub-Saharan Africa: Economic Issues. 2011. pap. *(978-1-61761-891-8(8))* Nova Science Pubs., Inc.

Foster, Vivien, et al. Building Bridges: China's Growing Role as Infrastructure Financier for Africa. 2008. (Trends & Policy Options (PPIAF) Ser.: 5). (ENG., Illus.). 168p. pap. 22.00 *(978-0-8213-7554-9(7)*, 9780821375549) World Bank Pubns.

Haseeb, Khair el-Din, ed. The Arabs & Africa (RLE: the Arab Nation), Volume 3. 2012. (Routledge Library Editions: the Arab Nation Ser.). (ENG.). 736p. 200.00 **(978-0-415-62395-7(2))** Routledge.

Hugon, Philippe. African Geopolitics. Rendall, Steven, tr. from FRE. 2008. 174p. pap. 26.95 *(978-1-55876-461-3(5))* Wiener, Markus Pubs., Inc.

James, Christian. Africa, 1998-2006. 2007. *(978-0-88692-869-8(9))* ProQuest LLC.

Morrissey, Oliver & Zgovu, Evious. The Impact of China & India on Sub-Saharan Africa: Opportunities, Challenges & Policies. 2011. (ENG., Illus.). 90p. pap. 24.95 *(978-1-84929-055-5(5))* Commonwealth Secretariat GBR. Dist: Stylus Publishing, LLC.

Nejjar, Bassam. Cultural Cooperation Between Morocco & Sub-Saharan Afric. 2010. 92p. pap. *(978-3-8383-5055-4(3))* Lambert Academic Publishing.

Northrup, David. Africa's Discovery of Europe 1450-1850. 2nd ed. 2008. (ENG., Illus.). 224p. (C). pap. 34.95 *(978-0-19-534053-2(1))* Oxford Univ. Pr., Inc.

Pettit, Jenny. Teaching Africa Today for Middle School. 2006. pap. *(978-0-943804-53-8(1))* Univ. of Denver, Ctr. for Teaching International Relations Pubns.

Razafimahefa, Ivohasina Fizara & Hamori, Shigeyuki. International Competitiveness in Africa: Policy Implications in the Sub-Saharan Region. 2007. (Advanced Studies in Theoretical & Applied Econometrics Ser.). (Illus.). xii, 170p. 109.00 *(978-3-540-68920-1(6))* Springer.

Tandrayen-Ragoobur, Verena. Foreign Ownership, Exports & Labour Market. 2011. 128p. pap. **(978-3-8443-0850-1(4))** Lambert Academic Publishing.

Taylor, Ian. The International Relations of Sub-Saharan Africa. 2010. (ENG., Illus.). 192p. 110.00 *(978-0-8264-3490-6(8))*; pap. 32.95 *(978-0-8264-3401-2(0))* Continuum International Publishing Group, Ltd. GBR. Dist: National Bk. Network.

Vahsen, Urban. Eurafrikanische Entwicklungskooperation: Die Assoziierungspolitik der EWG gegenüber dem subsaharischen Afrika in den 1960er Jahren. 2010. (Studien zur Geschichte der Europäischen Integration Ser.). (GER.). 424p. (C). pap. 79.00 *(978-3-515-09667-6(1))* Steiner, Franz Verlag Wiesbaden GmbH DEU. Dist: Brown, David Bk. Co., The.

Walraven, Klaas van. Africa Yearbook Vol. 7: Politics, Economy & Society South of the Sahara 2010. Mehler, Andreas & Melber, Henning, eds. 2011. (Illus.). xvi, 550p. pap. **(978-90-04-20556-7(X))** BRILL.

AFRICA, SUB-SAHARAN—HISTORY

Aarde, Rudi van. World & Its Peoples. 2010. *(978-0-7614-7914-7(7))*; *(978-0-7614-7925-3(2))*; *(978-0-7614-7923-9(6))*; *(978-0-7614-7922-2(8))*; *(978-0-7614-7921-5(X))*; *(978-0-7614-7920-8(1))*; *(978-0-7614-7919-2(8))*; *(978-0-7614-7918-5(X))*; *(978-0-7614-7917-8(1))*; *(978-0-7614-7915-4(5))*; *(978-0-7614-7916-1(3))* Marshall Cavendish Corp. (Marshall Cavendish Reference Bks.).

Collins, Robert O. & Burns, James M. A History of Sub-Saharan Africa. 2007. (ENG., Illus.). 418p. 100.00 *(978-0-521-86746-7(0))*; per. 29.99 *(978-0-521-68708-9(X))* Cambridge Univ. Pr.

Cram101 Textbook Reviews. Outlines & Highlights for Africa South of the Sahar: A Geographical Interpretation by Robert Stock, ISBN. 2010. 148p. pap. 29.95 *(978-1-61698-162-4(8))* Cram101 Inc.

Englund, Harri, ed. Christianity & Public Culture in Africa. 2011. (Cambridge Centre of African Studies). (ENG.). 240p. 49.95 *(978-0-8214-1945-8(5))* Ohio Univ. Pr.

Falola, Toyin & Oyebade, Adebayo. Hot Spot: Sub-Saharan Africa. 2010. (Hot Spot Histories Ser.). (Illus.). 200p. 65.00 *(978-0-313-35971-2(7)*, GR5971) Greenwood Publishing Group, Inc.

Fasua, Tope. Crushed! Navigating Africa's Tortuous Quest for Development - Myths & Realities. 2011. 436p. pap. 20.47 *(978-1-4567-7021-1(7))* AuthorHouse.

Hansen, Thorkild. Ships of Slaves. Dako, Kari, tr. 2nd ed. 2007. 220p. pap. *(978-9988-647-53-7(0))* Sub-Saharan Pubs. & Traders GHA. Dist: Michigan State Univ. Pr.

Jarrett, Alfred A. The Under-Development of Africa: Colonialism, Neo-Colonialism & Socialism. Date not set. 192p. (C). 57.00 *(978-0-7618-0105-4(7))*; pap. 29.50 *(978-0-7618-0106-1(5))* Univ. Pr. of America, Inc.

Northrup, David. Africa's Discovery of Europe 1450-1850. 2nd ed. 2008. (ENG., Illus.). 224p. (C). pap. 34.95 *(978-0-19-534053-2(1))* Oxford Univ. Pr., Inc.

Snyder, C. Arnold & Lapp, John A., eds. Anabaptist Songs in African Hearts, 1 vol. 3rd ed. 2006. (Global Mennonite History Ser.). (ENG., Illus.). 300p. pap. 11.95 *(978-1-56148-549-9(7))* Good Bks.

Thompson, T. Jack. Light on Darkness: Missionary Photography of Africa in the Nineteenth & Early Twentieth Centuries. 2012. pap. **(978-0-8028-6524-3(0))** Eerdmans, William B. Publishing Co.

Waites, Bernard. South Asia & Africa after Independence: Post-Colonialism in Historical Perspective. 2012. (ENG., Illus.). 472p. (C). 95.00 **(978-0-230-23983-8(8))**; pap. 33.95 **(978-0-230-23984-5(6))** Palgrave Macmillan.

AFRICA, SUB-SAHARAN—POLITICS AND GOVERNMENT

Abegunrin, Olayiwola. Africa in Global Politics in the Twenty-First Century: A Pan-African Perspective. 2009. (ENG.). 288p. 89.00 *(978-0-230-61890-9(1))* Palgrave Macmillan.

Adisini, Jimi. Social Policy in Sub-Saharan African Context: In Search of Inclusive Development. Adésínà, Jìmí & United Nations Research Institute for Social Development, eds. 2007. (Social Policy in a Development Context Ser.). (ENG.). 258p. 126.00 *(978-0-230-52083-7(9))* Palgrave Macmillan.

Azam, Jean-Paul. Trade, Exchange Rate, & Growth in Sub-Saharan Africa. 2006. (ENG., Illus.). 280p. pap. 45.99 *(978-0-521-68407-1(2))*; 92.00 *(978-0-521-86536-4(0))* Cambridge Univ. Pr.

Barkan, Joel D., ed. Legislative Power in Emerging African Democracies. 2009. 270p. 59.95 *(978-1-58826-688-0(5))* Rienner, Lynne Pubs.

Basedau, Matthias, et al, eds. Votes, Money & Violence: Political Parties & Elections in Sub-Saharan Africa. 2007. 301p. pap. *(978-1-86914-119-6(9))* University of Kwazulu-Natal Press ZAF. Dist: International Specialized Bk. Services.

Basedau, Matthias, et al. Votes, Money & Violence: Political Parties & Elections in Sub-Saharan Africa. 2007. (Illus.). 300p. pap. 37.50 *(978-91-7106-579-7(2))* Nordiska Afrikainstitutet SWE. Dist: Stylus Publishing, LLC.

Buur, Lars & Kyed, Helene Maria. State Recognition & Democratization in Sub-Saharan Africa: A New Dawn for Traditional Authorities? 2007. (Governance, Security & Development Ser.). (ENG.). 256p. 95.00 *(978-0-230-60033-1(6))* Palgrave Macmillan.

Chabal, Patrick & Daloz, Jean-Pascal. Africa Works: Disorder As Political Instrument. 2010. (African Issues Ser.). (Illus.). 192p. pap. 24.95 *(978-0-85255-814-0(7)*, Currey, James) Boydell & Brewer, Ltd. GBR. Dist: Boydell & Brewer, Inc.

da Sousa, Cesar, et al. Rapid Appraisal of Social Inclusion Policies in Selected Sub-Saharan African Countries. 2009. (ENG., Illus.). 64p. pap. 14.95 *(978-0-7969-2225-0(X))* Human Sciences Research Council ZAF. Dist: Independent Pubs. Group.

Democratic Developments in Sub-Saharan Africa: Moving Forwards or Backwards?: Hearing Before the Subcommittee on African Affairs of the Committee on Foreign Relations, United States Senate, One Hundred Tenth Congress, First Session, July 17, 2007. 2007. (Illus.). iii, 71p. *(978-0-16-079839-9(6)*, 552-070-36733-1) United States Government Printing Office.

Eberhard, Anton, et al. Africa's Power Infrastructure: Investment, Integration, Efficiency. 2011. (Directions in Development Ser.). (ENG., Illus.). 336p. pap. 30.00 *(978-0-8213-8455-8(4)*, 9780821384558) World Bank Pubns.

Eberhard, Anton A. Africa's Power Infrastructure: Investment, Integration, Efficiency. 2011. *(978-0-8213-8652-1(2))* World Bank Pubns.

Egeru, Anthony. Subsistence Holders & Fuel Wood Demand. 2011. 112p. pap. **(978-3-8443-1808-1(9))** Lambert Academic Publishing.

Englebert, Pierre. Africa: Unity, Sovereignty, & Sorrow. 2009. 360p. (C). pap. 26.50 *(978-1-58826-623-1(0))* Rienner, Lynne Pubs.

Estache, Antonio & Wodon, Quentin. Infrastructure & Poverty in Sub-Saharan Africa. 2006. *(978-0-8213-6903-6(2))* World Bank Pubns.

Fall, Abdou. Cereal Banks at Your Service. (ENG., Illus.). 52p. (C). pap. 11.95 *(978-0-85598-157-0(1))* Oxfam Publishing GBR. Dist: Stylus Publishing, LLC.

Falola, Toyin & Oyebade, Adebayo. Hot Spot: Sub-Saharan Africa. 2010. (Illus.). xxiii, 200p. E-Book *(978-0-313-35972-9(5)*, Greenwood Pr.) Greenwood Publishing Group, Inc.

Gillies, Alexandra & Joseph, Richard A. Smart Aid for African Development. Joseph, Richard & Gillies, Alexandra, eds. 2008. (Illus.). 300p. (C). 59.95 *(978-1-58826-606-4(0))* Rienner, Lynne Pubs.

Go, Delfin S. & Page, John, eds. Africa at a Turning Point? Growth, Aid, & External Shocks. 2008. (World Bank Development Essays Ser.). (ENG., Illus.). 520p. pap. 49.95 *(978-0-8213-7277-7(7)*, 9780821372777) World Bank Pubns.

Grinker, Roy Richard, et al, eds. Perspectives on Africa: A Reader in Culture, History & Representation. 2nd ed. 2010. (Global Perspectives Ser.: 3). (ENG., Illus.). 713p. pap. 66.95 *(978-1-4051-9060-2(4))*; 712p. 110.95 *(978-1-4443-3522-4(7))* Wiley, John & Sons, Inc. (Wiley-Blackwell).

Hammond, Felix & Antwi, Yaw Adarkwah. Economic Analysis of Sub-Saharan Africa Real Estate Policies. 2010. (ENG., Illus.). 304p. 110.00 *(978-0-230-23231-0(0))* Palgrave Macmillan.

Herman, Fanie. Us-Sino Oil Diplomacy in Sub Saharan Afric. 2011. 100p. pap. **(978-3-8443-1913-2(1))** Lambert Academic Publishing.

Hodder-Williams, Richard. An Introduction to the Politics of Tropical Africa. 2011. (ENG.). 288p. 105.00 *(978-0-415-60131-3(2))* Routledge.

Hugon, Philippe. African Geopolitics. Rendall, Steven, tr. from FRE. 2nd ed. 2008. (Illus.). 174p. 69.95 *(978-1-55876-460-6(7))* Wiener, Markus Pubs., Inc.

Hunter-Gault, Charlayne. New News Out of Africa: Uncovering Africa's Renaissance. 2007. (ENG., Illus.). 192p. per. 14.95 *(978-0-19-533128-8(1))* Oxford Univ. Pr., Inc.

James, Christian. Africa, 1998-2006. 2007. *(978-0-88692-869-8(9))* ProQuest LLC.

Joseph, Richard & Gillies, Alexandra, eds. Smart Aid for African Development. 2008. (Illus.). 300p. (C). pap. 24.50 *(978-1-58826-632-3(X))* Rienner, Lynne Pubs.

Kathyola, Janet & Job, Oluwatoyin, eds. Decentralisation in Commonwealth Africa: Experiences from Botswana, Cameroon, Ghana, Mozambique & Tanzania. 2011. (ENG., Illus.). 310p. pap. 42.00 *(978-1-84929-044-9(X))* Commonwealth Secretariat GBR. Dist: Stylus Publishing, LLC.

Kimanuka, Oscar. Sub-Saharan Africa's Development Challenges: A Case Study of Rwanda's Post-Genocide Experience. 2008. (ENG., Illus.). 192p. 89.00 *(978-0-230-60656-2(3))* Palgrave Macmillan.

Madison, D. Soyini. Acts of Activism: Human Rights as Radical Performance. (Theatre & Performance Theory Ser.). (ENG.). 2012. 336p. pap. 36.00 **(978-1-107-40438-0(X))** 2010. (Illus.). 334p. 104.00 *(978-0-521-51922-9(5))* Cambridge Univ. Pr.

McTernan, Benedict, ed. Political Risk Yearbook - 2007 Vol. 4: Sub-Saharan Africa. 2007. per. *(978-1-933539-32-4(1))* PRS Group Inc., The.

Mehler, Andreas, et al, eds. Africa Yearbook Volume 3: Politics, Economy & Society South of the Sahara In 2006. 2007. (Africa Yearbook: Politics, Economy, & Society South of the Sahara Ser.). (Illus.). 516p. pap. *(978-90-04-16263-1(1))* BRILL.

Mehler, Andres, et al, eds. Africa Yearbook: Politics, Economy & Society South of the Sahara In 2005. 2006. (Africa Yearbook: Politics, Economy, & Society South of the Sahara Ser.). (Illus.). 511p. pap. *(978-90-04-15486-5(8))* BRILL.

Meyer, Matt & Ndura-Ouédraogo, Elavie. Seeds of New Hope: Pan-African Peace Studies for the Twenty-First Century. 2008. xii, 376p. *(978-1-59221-662-8(5))*; 412p. *(978-1-59221-663-5(3))* Africa World Pr.

Michael George, Kizito. Ethics & International Development. 2011. 468p. pap. **(978-3-8454-1154-5(6))** Lambert Academic Publishing.

Miguel, Edward. Africa's Turn? 2009. (Boston Review Bks.). (ENG., Illus.). 176p. (gr. 17). 14.95 *(978-0-262-01289-8(8))* MIT Pr.

Ndulu, Benno J., et al, eds. The Political Economy of Economic Growth in Africa, 1960-2000, 2 vols. 2007. (ENG., Illus.). 760p. 180.00 *(978-0-521-87849-4(7))* Cambridge Univ. Pr.

Osman, Abdulahi. Governance & Internal Wars in Sub-Saharan Africa. 2007. 208p. per. *(978-1-905068-53-1(0))* Adonis & Abbey Publishers Ltd.

Porko, Eero. Corruption & Development in Afric. 2010. 60p. pap. *(978-3-8383-8472-6(5))* Lambert Academic Publishing.

Razafimahefa, Ivohasina Fizara & Hamori, Shigeyuki. International Competitiveness in Africa: Policy Implications in the Sub-Saharan Region. 2010. (Advanced Studies in Theoretical & Applied Econometrics Ser.). (Illus.). xii, 170p. pap. 109.00 *(978-3-642-08845-2(7)*, 3642088457) Springer.

Rotberg, Robert. Africa's Successes: Evaluating Accomplishment, 43. 2007. (Belfer/WPF Report Ser.). pap. 19.95 *(978-0-9742651-9-3(5))* World Peace Foundation.

Spears, Ian S. Civil War in African States: The Search for Security. 2010. 260p. 65.00 *(978-1-935049-20-3(8))* FirstForumPress.

Tucker, Shelby. The Last Banana. 2010. (Illus.). 288p. 25.00 *(978-1-906768-21-8(8)*, Stacey International) Stacey Publishing GBR. Dist: Midpoint Trade Bks., Inc.

Tymowski, Michal. The Origins & Structures of Political Institutions in Pre-Colonial Black Africa: Dynastic Monarchy, Taxes & Tributes, War & Slavery, Kinship & Territory. 2009. (Illus.). 240p. 109.95 *(978-0-7734-4718-9(0))* Mellen, Edwin Pr., The.

Waites, Bernard. South Asia & Africa after Independence: Post-Colonialism in Historical Perspective. 2012. (ENG., Illus.). 472p. (C). 95.00 ***(978-0-230-23983-8(8))***; pap. 33.95 ***(978-0-230-23984-5(6))*** Palgrave Macmillan.

Walraven, Klaas van. Africa Yearbook Vol. 7: Politics, Economy & Society South of the Sahara 2010. Mehler, Andreas & Melber, Henning, eds. 2011. (Illus.). xvi, 550p. pap. ***(978-90-04-20556-7(X))*** BRILL.

Walraven, Klaas van & Melber, Henning, eds. Africa Yearbook 4: Politics, Economy & Society South of the Sahara 2007. 2008. (Africa Yearbook Ser.). 576p. pap. *(978-90-04-16805-3(2))* BRILL.

Whitfield, Lindsay. Turning Points in African Democracy. Mustapha, Abdul Raufu, ed. 2009. (Illus.). 255p. 95.00 *(978-1-84701-317-0(1)*, Currey, James) Boydell & Brewer, Ltd. GBR. Dist: Boydell & Brewer, Inc.

Zeilig, Leo. Revolt & Protest: Student Politics & Activism in Sub-Saharan Africa. 2007. (International Library of African Studies). (ENG., Illus.). 360p. 100.00 *(978-1-84511-476-3(0)*, Tauris Academic Studies) I. B. Tauris & Co., Ltd. GBR. Dist: Macmillan.

AFRICA, SUB-SAHARAN—POPULATION

Achura, Bob Marley. Counting the Dead & the Living- an Account of Data Quality in Ugand. 2011. 64p. pap. ***(978-3-8443-2070-1(9))*** Lambert Academic Publishing.

Caraël, Michel & Glynn, Judith, eds. HIV, resurgent infections & population change in Africa. 2007. (International Studies in Population Ser.). 284p. 139.00 *(978-1-4020-6172-1(2))* Springer.

Malmberg, Bo. Demography & the Development Potential of Sub-Saharan: Africa. 2008. (NAI Current African Issues Ser.). 56p. pap. 12.95 *(978-91-7106-621-3(7))* Nordiska Afrikainstitutet SWE. Dist: Stylus Publishing, LLC.

AFRICA, SUB-SAHARAN—RELIGIOUS LIFE AND CUSTOMS

Ranger, Shelagh. The Word of Wisdom & the Creation of Animals in Africa. 2007. (ENG., Illus.). 264p. per. 58.00 *(978-0-227-67986-9(5))* Clarke, James Co., Ltd. GBR. Dist: Brown, David Bk. Co., The.

Sheridan, et al. African Sacred Groves: Ecological Dynamics & Social Change. 2008. (Illus.). 240p. pap. 29.95 *(978-1-84701-400-9(3)*, Currey, James) Boydell & Brewer, Ltd. GBR. Dist: Boydell & Brewer, Inc.

Sheridan Nyamweru Staff, et al. African Sacred Groves: Ecological Dynamics & Social Change. 2008. (Illus.). 240p. 80.00 *(978-1-84701-401-6(1)*, Currey, James) Boydell & Brewer, Ltd. GBR. Dist: Boydell & Brewer, Inc.

Tovey, Phillip. Inculturation: The Eucharist in Africa. 2009. 88.00 *(978-1-60724-362-5(8))* Gorgias Pr., LLC.

AFRICA, SUB-SAHARAN—RELIGION

Adogame, Afeosemime U. Who Is Afraid of the Holy Ghost? Pentecostalism & Globalization in Africa & Beyond. 2011. *(978-1-59221-803-5(2))*; 258p. pap. *(978-1-59221-804-2(0))* Africa World Pr.

Allan, Tony, et al. African Myths & Beliefs. 2011. (World Mythologies Ser.). (ENG., Illus.). 144p. (YA). (gr. 9-12). lib. bdg. 39.95 ***(978-1-4488-5989-4(1))*** Rosen Publishing Group, Inc., The.

Éla, Jean-Marc. My Faith as an African. Brown, John Pairman & Perry, Susan, trs. 2009. 208p. pap. 23.00 *(978-1-60608-623-0(5)*, Wipf and Stock) Wipf & Stock Pubs.

Ephirim-Donkor, Anthony. African Spirituality: On Becoming Ancestors. 2011. (ENG.). 200p. pap. 29.50 *(978-0-7618-5467-8(3))* Univ. Pr. of America, Inc.

Ezigbo, Victor I. Re-Imagining African Christologies: Conversing with the Interpretations & Appropriations of Jesus in Contemporary African Christianity. 2010. (Princeton Theological Monographs). 356p. pap. 39.00 *(978-1-60608-822-7(X)*, Pickwick Pubns.) Wipf & Stock Pubs.

Flower, Marilyn O. The Woman Clothed by the Sun with the Moon under Her Feet. 2010. 208p. pap. *(978-3-8383-8270-8(6))* Lambert Academic Publishing.

Holland, Heidi. African Magic: Traditional Ideas That Heal a Continent. 2011. (ENG.). 265p. pap. 22.00 *(978-0-14-352735-0(5)*, Penguin Global) Penguin Group (USA) Inc.

Katongole, Emmanuel. The Sacrifice of Africa: A Political Theology for Africa. 2010. 200p. pap. 16.00 *(978-0-8028-6268-6(3))* Eerdmans, William B. Publishing Co.

Nwaogwugwu, Cletus Chukwuemeka. Ancestor Christology: A Christian Evaluation of the Ancestral Cult in the Traditional Religion of the Sub-Saharan Africa. 2011. 596p. 43.95 *(978-1-4502-6228-6(7))*; pap. 33.95 *(978-1-4502-6227-9(9))* iUniverse, Inc.

Ranger, T. O. Evangelical Christianity & Democracy in Africa. 2008. (ENG.). 288p. pap. 29.95 *(978-0-19-530802-0(6))* Oxford Univ. Pr., Inc.

Ranger, Terence O., ed. Evangelical Christianity & Democracy in Africa. 2008. (ENG.). 288p. 99.00 *(978-0-19-517477-9(1))* Oxford Univ. Pr., Inc.

Sekindi, Abdunur M. The Role of Religion in Shaping Saudi Arabia's Foreign Policy. 2011. 116p. pap. ***(978-3-8454-0227-7(X))*** Lambert Academic Publishing.

Trinitapoli, Jenny Ann & Weinreb, Alexander. Religion & AIDS in Africa. 2012. (ENG.). 272p. 29.95 ***(978-0-19-533594-1(5))*** Oxford Univ. Pr., Inc.

Westerlund, David. African Indigenous Religions & Disease Causation: From Spiritual Beings to Living Humans. 2006. (Studies of Religion in Africa Ser.). 237p. pap. *(978-90-04-14433-0(1))* BRILL.

AFRICA, SUB-SAHARAN—SOCIAL CONDITIONS

Abegunrin, Olayiwola. Africa in Global Politics in the Twenty-First Century: A Pan-African Perspective. 2009. (ENG.). 288p. 89.00 *(978-0-230-61890-9(1))* Palgrave Macmillan.

Adisini, Jimi. Social Policy in Sub-Saharan African Context: In Search of Inclusive Development. Adésínà, Jìmí & United Nations Research Institute for Social Development, eds. 2007. (Social Policy in a Development Context Ser.). (ENG.). 258p. 126.00 *(978-0-230-52083-7(9))* Palgrave Macmillan.

Africa South of the Sahara 2011. 40th rev. ed. 2010. (ENG.). 1604p. 835.00 *(978-1-85743-564-1(8))* Routledge.

Anejionu, Obinna. Application of Gis & Remote Sensing Techniques in Epidemiology. 2010. 204p. pap. *(978-3-639-25709-0(X))* VDM Verlag Dr. Mueller e.K.

Bay, Edna G. & Donham, Donald L., eds. States of Violence: Politics, Youth, & Memory in Contemporary Africa. 2007. (ENG.). 320p. (gr. 17). pap. 24.50 *(978-0-8139-2577-6(0))* Univ. Pr. of Virginia.

Brewer, Vernon & Yeatts, Noel. Children of Hope: Be touched. Be inspired. Be Changed. 2007. per. 14.99 *(978-0-9788041-2-1(0))* World Help Inc.

Bundy, Donald A. P., et al. Courage & Hope: Stories from Teachers Living with HIV in Sub-Saharan Africa. 2009. (ENG., Illus.). 100p. pap. 15.00 incl. cd-rom *(978-0-8213-7933-2(X)*, 9780821379332) World Bank Pubns.

Caraël, Michel & Glynn, Judith R. HIV, resurgent infections & population change in Africa. 2008. (International Studies in Population Ser.). (Illus.). 268p. pap. 59.95 *(978-1-4020-6173-8(0))* Springer.

Chau, Donovan C. U. S. Counterterrorism in Sub-Saharan Africa: Understanding Costs, Cultures, & Conflicts. 2008. (Letort Papers). *(978-1-58487-363-1(9))* Strategic Studies Institute, U.S. Army War College Commandant (AWCC-DSI/Pubns.).

Chinedu, Chinedu. The Debt - Growth Link in Sub-Saharan Afric. 2011. 92p. pap. ***(978-3-8443-0303-2(0))*** Lambert Academic Publishing.

Demery, Lionel & Christiaensen, Luc. Down to Earth: Agriculture & Poverty Reduction in Africa. 2007. (Directions in Development Ser.). (ENG., Illus.). 118p. per. 15.00 *(978-0-8213-6854-1(0)*, 9780821368541) World Bank Pubns.

Desta, Dereje, et al. Acriflavin Inhibits the Proliferation of Trypanosomamusculi: by Inducing Apoptosis with Specific BindingAffinity to KDNA of the Parasite. 2008. 128p. pap. *(978-3-639-09467-1(0))* VDM Verlag Dr. Mueller e.K.

Diao, Xinshen. The Role of Agriculture in Development: Implications for Sub-Saharan Africa. 2007. *(978-0-89629-161-4(8))* International Food Policy Research Institute.

Dibie, Robert A., et al, contrib. by. Non-Governmental Organizations (NGOs) & Sustainable Development in Sub-Saharan Africa. 2007. (ENG., Illus.). 302p. 78.99 *(978-0-7391-1653-1(3))* Lexington Bks.

Dunne, MßIrtad. Gender, Sexuality & Development. 2008. 268p. *(978-90-8790-471-5(1))* Sense Pubs.

Dunne, MßIrtad, ed. Gender, Sexuality & Development. 2008. 268p. pap. *(978-90-8790-470-8(3))* Sense Pubs.

Europa Publications, ed. Africa South of the Sahara 2012. 41st rev. ed. 2011. (ENG.). 1604p. 880.00 ***(978-1-85743-623-5(7))*** Routledge.

Europa Publications Staff, ed. Africa South of the Sahara 2009. 6th rev. ed. 2008. 1528p. 760.00 *(978-1-85743-469-9(2))* Europa Pubns.

—Africa South of the Sahara 2010. 39th rev. ed. 2009. (ENG.). 1588p. 810.00 *(978-1-85743-527-6(3))* Routledge.

Feldman, Douglas A., ed. AIDS, Culture, & Africa. 2011. (ENG., Illus.). 312p. pap. 32.95 *(978-0-8130-3721-9(2))* Univ. Pr. of Florida.

Geddes, Gary. Drink the Bitter Root: A Search for Justice & Healing in Africa. 2011. (ENG.). 304p. 26.00 ***(978-1-58243-788-0(2)***, Counterpoint) Counterpoint LLC.

Gillies, Alexandra & Joseph, Richard A. Smart Aid for African Development. Joseph, Richard & Gillies, Alexandra, eds. 2008. (Illus.). 300p. (C). 59.95 *(978-1-58826-606-4(0))* Rienner, Lynne Pubs.

Go, Delfin S. & Page, John, eds. Africa at a Turning Point? Growth, Aid, & External Shocks. 2008. (World Bank Development Essays Ser.). (ENG., Illus.). 520p. pap. 49.95 *(978-0-8213-7277-7(7)*, 9780821372777) World Bank Pubns.

Hugon, Philippe. African Geopolitics. Rendall, Steven, tr. from FRE. 2008. 174p. pap. 26.95 *(978-1-55876-461-3(5))* Wiener, Markus Pubs., Inc.

James, Christian. Africa, 1998-2006. 2007. *(978-0-88692-869-8(9))* ProQuest LLC.

Kedia, Satish. Annals of Anthropological Practice: Hiv/Aids & Food Insecurity in Sub-Saharan Africa - Challenges & Solutions. 2011. (NAPA Bulletin Ser.). (ENG.). 244p. pap. 25.00 ***(978-1-4443-6155-1(4)***, Wiley-Blackwell) Wiley, John & Sons, Inc.

Keese, Alexander, ed. Ethnicity & the Long-Term Perspective: The African Experience. 2010. (CEAUP Studies on Africa Ser.). (Illus.). 216p. pap. *(978-3-0343-0337-8(8))* Lang, Peter.

Kübler, Ulrike. The Route to Europe-African Migrant Experience in the Maltese Context. 2010. 112p. pap. *(978-3-639-27728-9(7))* VDM Verlag Dr. Mueller e.K.

Lindell, Ilda, ed. Africa's Informal Workers: Collective Agency, Alliances & Transnational Organizing in Urban Africa. 2010. (Africa Now Ser.). (ENG., Illus.). 240p. 126.95 *(978-1-84813-451-5(7))*; pap. 39.95 *(978-1-84813-452-2(5))* Zed Bks., Ltd. GBR. Dist: Macmillan.

Mehler, Andreas, et al, eds. Africa Yearbook Volume 3: Politics, Economy & Society South of the Sahara In 2006. 2007. (Africa Yearbook: Politics, Economy, & Society South of the Sahara Ser.). (Illus.). 516p. pap. *(978-90-04-16263-1(1))* BRILL.

Mehler, Andres, et al, eds. Africa Yearbook: Politics, Economy & Society South of the Sahara In 2005. 2006. (Africa Yearbook: Politics, Economy, & Society South of the Sahara Ser.). (Illus.). 511p. pap. *(978-90-04-15486-5(8))* BRILL.

Msoka, Gabriel Andrew. Basic Human Rights & the Humanitarian Crises in Sub-Saharan Africa: Ethical Reflections. 2007. (Princeton Theological Monographs). 200p. pap. 23.00 *(978-1-55635-100-6(3)*, Pickwick Pubns.) Wipf & Stock Pubs.

Mukudi, Edith & Commins, Stephen K. HIV/AIDS in Africa: Challenges & Impact. 2008. pap. *(978-1-59221-625-3(0))* Africa World Pr.

Nyanzi, Jassey. How to Be a 'Proper' Woman in the Times of HIV & AIDS. 2007. (NAI Current African Issues Ser.). 36p. pap. 10.95 *(978-91-7106-574-2(1))* Nordiska Afrikainstitutet SWE. Dist: Stylus Publishing, LLC.

Overbeeke, Marlies. Undernourishment in Sub-Saharan Afric. 2008. 132p. pap. *(978-3-8364-6724-7(0))* VDM Verlag Dr. Mueller e.K.

Pickett, James & Singer, Hans, eds. Towards Economic Recovery in Sub-Saharan Africa. 2011. (ENG.). 296p. 115.00 *(978-0-415-59375-5(1))* Routledge.

Sheridan, Michael J. & Nyamweru, Celia, eds. African Sacred Groves: Ecological Dynamics & Social Change. (Illus.). 240p. 2008. (ENG.). per. 26.95 *(978-0-8214-1789-8(4))* 2007. 59.95 *(978-0-8214-1788-1(6))* Ohio Univ. Pr.

van Eijk, Toon. Development & Work Ethic in sub-Saharan Africa. 2009. 267p. pap. 23.50 *(978-1-4092-8868-8(4))* Lulu Enterprises Inc.

Walraven, Klaas van. Africa Yearbook Vol. 7: Politics, Economy & Society South of the Sahara 2010. Mehler, Andreas & Melber, Henning, eds. 2011. (Illus.). xvi, 550p. pap. ***(978-90-04-20556-7(X))*** BRILL.

Walraven, Klaas van & Melber, Henning, eds. Africa Yearbook 4: Politics, Economy & Society South of the Sahara 2007. 2008. (Africa Yearbook Ser.). 576p. pap. *(978-90-04-16805-3(2))* BRILL.

AFRICA, WEST

Kamali, Hossein. Encounters in West Africa. 2007. (ENG.). 172p. 29.00 *(978-1-4251-6710-3(1))* Trafford Publishing.

AFRICA, WEST—ANTIQUITIES

Carey, Neil. Masks of the Koranko Poro: Form, Function & Comparison to the Toma. 2008. (Illus.). 65p. 34.95 *(978-0-9793290-1-2(9))* Ethnos Pubns.

De Jong, Ferdinand. Reclaiming Heritage: Alternative Imaginaries of Memory in West Africa. De Jong, Ferdinand & Rowlands, Michael, eds. 2008. (University College London Institute of Archaeology Publications, Critical Cultural Heritage Ser.). (ENG., Illus.). 270p. 94.00 *(978-1-59874-307-4(4))* Left Coast Pr., Inc.

de Jong, Ferdinand & Rowlands, Michael, eds. Reclaiming Heritage: Alternative Imaginaries of Memory in West Africa. 2009. (University College London Institute of Archaeology Publications). (ENG.). 270p. pap. 34.95 *(978-1-59874-308-1(2))* Left Coast Pr., Inc.

Dueppen, Stephen A. Egalitarian Revolution in the Savanna: The Origins of a West African Political System. 2012. (Approaches to Anthropological Archaeology Ser.). (ENG., Illus.). 364p. (C). 120.00 ***(978-1-908049-20-9(0))*** Equinox Publishing Ltd. GBR. Dist: ISD.

Lewicki, Tadeusz. West African Food in the Middle Ages: According to Arabic Sources. 2009. (ENG.). 280p. pap. 38.99 *(978-0-521-10202-5(2))* Cambridge Univ. Pr.

Linseele, Veerle. Archaeofaunal Remains from the Past 4000 Years in Sahelian West Africa: Domestic Livestock, Subsistence Strategies & Environmental Changes. 2007. (Bar S Ser.). (ENG., Illus.). 340p. (C). pap. 105.00 *(978-1-4073-0094-8(6))* British Archaeological Reports Ltd. GBR. Dist: Brown, David Bk. Co., The.

Ogundiran, Akinwumi & Falola, Toyin, eds. Archaeology of Atlantic Africa & the African Diaspora. 2010. (Blacks in the Diaspora Ser.). (ENG., Illus.). 528p. pap. 29.95 *(978-0-253-22175-9(7)*, 0253221757) Indiana Univ. Pr.

Togola, Téréba. Archaeological Investigations of Iron Age Sites in the Mema Region, Mali (West Africa) 2008. (Bar S Ser.). (Illus.). vi, 105p. (C). 65.00 *(978-1-4073-0178-5(0))* British Archaeological Reports Ltd. GBR. Dist: Brown, David Bk. Co., The.

AFRICA, WEST—DESCRIPTION AND TRAVEL

Anonymous & Anonymous. Two Trips to Gorilla Land & the Cataracts of the Congo. 2010. 328p. pap. 31.75 *(978-1-146-75999-1(1))* BiblioBazaar.

Atkins, John. A Voyage to Guinea, Brazil & the West Indies. 2010. (ENG.). 232p. pap. 17.95 *(978-1-897959-67-1(2))* Serif GBR. Dist: Interlink Publishing Group, Inc.

Benezet, Anthony. Some Historical Account of Guinea. 2007. 124p. per. *(978-1-4065-4772-6(7))* Dodo Pr.

Berggren, Chris. Somewhere in the Sand: In Search of Timbuktu. 2009. 224p. 28.95 *(978-1-4401-6363-0(4))*; 224p. pap. 18.95 *(978-1-4401-6364-7(2))*; viii, 212p. E-Book ***(978-1-4401-6365-4(0))*** iUniverse, Inc.

Bourque, Peter. Tarnished Ivory: Reflections on Peace Corps & Beyond. 2011. 224p. 29.99 ***(978-1-4628-7760-7(5))***; pap. 19.99 ***(978-1-4628-7759-1(1))*** Xlibris Corp.

Burton, Richard. Two Trips to Gorilla Land & the Cataracts of the Congo, Vol 1 (Webster's French Thesaurus Edition) 2008. 202p. (C). pap. 28.95 *(978-0-497-98805-0(4))* Icon Group International, Inc.

Burton, Richard F. A Mission to Gelele, King of Dahome. 2011. (Cambridge Library Collection - Travel & Exploration Ser.). (ENG.). 424p. pap. 31.99 *(978-1-108-03032-8(7))*; (Illus.). 406p. pap. 31.99 *(978-1-108-03031-1(9))* Cambridge Univ. Pr.

—Two Trips to Gorilla Land & the Cataracts of the Congo. 2010. 388p. pap. 33.75 *(978-1-149-57904-6(8))* 2010. 386p. pap. 33.75 *(978-1-142-82440-2(3))* 2010. 324p. pap. 30.75 *(978-1-142-32471-1(0))* 2010. 380p. pap. 33.75 *(978-1-142-73144-1(8))* 2010. 292p. pap. 28.75 *(978-1-141-77372-5(4))* 2008. 164p. 22.99 *(978-0-554-31615-4(3))* 2008. 216p. 24.99 *(978-0-554-31616-1(1))* 2008. 164p. 25.99 *(978-0-554-22312-4(0))* 2008. 216p. 27.99 *(978-0-554-22313-1(9))* Vol. 1. 2007. 160p. pap. 21.99 *(978-1-4264-2104-4(4))* Vol. 2. 2007. (ENG.). 212p. pap. 22.99 *(978-1-4264-2105-1(2))* BiblioBazaar.

—Two Trips to Gorilla Land & the Cataracts of the Congo. 2009. 174p. pap. *(978-1-150-52699-2(8))*; 150p. pap. *(978-0-217-41282-7(3))* Books LLC.

—Two Trips to Gorilla Land & the Cataracts of the Congo. 2011. (Cambridge Library Collection - Travel & Exploration Ser.). (ENG.). 288p. pap. 23.99 ***(978-1-108-03134-9(X))***; 382p. pap. 23.99 ***(978-1-108-03135-6(8))*** Cambridge Univ. Pr.

—Two Trips to Gorilla Land & the Cataracts of the Congo. 2008. 148p. pap. *(978-1-4099-0009-2(6))* Dodo Pr.

—Two Trips to Gorilla Land & the Cataracts of the Congo. 2010. 138p. pap. 22.72 *(978-1-153-72972-7(5))* 2010. (Illus.). 102p. pap. 20.00 *(978-1-153-72971-0(7))* 2009. 110p. pap. 20.00 *(978-1-151-25515-0(7))* General Bks. LLC.

—Two Trips to Gorilla Land & the Cataracts of the Congo. 2010. 154p. pap. *(978-1-4076-3399-2(6))*; 124p. pap. *(978-1-4076-3398-5(8))* HardPr.

—Two Trips to Gorilla Land & the Cataracts of the Congo, Vol. 1. 2010. 132p. 35.95 *(978-1-161-48372-7(1))* Kessinger Publishing, LLC.

—Two Trips to Gorilla Land & the Cataracts of the Congo. 2009. 156p. pap. 11.95 *(978-1-4385-2027-8(1)*, Book Jungle) Standard Pubns., Inc.

—Two Trips to Gorilla Land & the Cataracts of the Congo V1. 2010. 132p. 28.76 *(978-1-169-25582-1(5))*; pap. 16.76 ***(978-1-162-71508-7(1))*** Kessinger Publishing, LLC.

—Two Trips to Gorilla Land & the Cataracts of the Congo, Volume 1. 2007. 168p. pap. 19.99 *(978-1-4264-1993-5(7))* BiblioBazaar.

—Two Trips to Gorilla Land & the Cataracts of the Congo, Volume 2. 2006. 218p. pap. 20.99 *(978-1-4264-1994-2(5))* BiblioBazaar.

—Two Trips to Gorilla Land & the Cataracts of the Congo. [with illustrations & a Map.]. 2011. 387p. pap. 33.75 *(978-1-240-92455-4(0)*, British Library, Historical Print Editions) BiblioBazaar.

—Wanderings in West Africa. 2006. pap. 45.95 *(978-1-4286-4913-2(1))* Kessinger Publishing, LLC.

—Wanderings in West Africa from Liverpool to Fernando Po: By a F. R. G. S. 2011. (Cambridge Library Collection - Travel & Exploration Ser.). (ENG.). 306p. pap. 24.99 *(978-1-108-03052-6(1))*; (Illus.). 322p. pap. 24.99 *(978-1-108-03051-9(3))* Cambridge Univ. Pr.

Cohee, Jared. Calm of the Niger: A Peaceful River Winding Through the Storm of Africa. 2009. pap. *(978-1-61623-434-8(2))* Independent Pub.

Coombes, Anne. West Africa: Adventures in Ghana, 1 vol. 2010. 196p. pap. 24.95 *(978-1-61546-190-5(6))* PublishAmerica, Inc.

Corry, Joseph. Observations upon the Windward Coast of Africa. 2008. 160p. 25.99 *(978-0-554-24304-7(0))* 2007. 144p. pap. 18.99 *(978-1-4264-6169-9(0))* 2006. (ENG.). 158p. pap. 21.99 *(978-1-4264-6224-5(7))* BiblioBazaar.

Crowther, Samuel & Taylor, John Christopher. Gospel on the Banks of the Niger: Journals & Notices of the Native Missionaries Accompanying the Niger Expedition of, 1857-1859. 2010. (Cambridge Library Collection - Religion Ser.). (ENG., Illus.). 472p. pap. 35.99 *(978-1-108-01184-6(5))* Cambridge Univ. Pr.

Du Chaillu, Paul. Stories of the Gorilla Country. 2009. (Illus.). 312p. pap. 12.95 *(978-1-59915-234-9(7))* Yesterday's Classics.

Du Chaillu, Paul Belloni. My Apingi Kingdom: With Life in the Great Sahara, & Sketches of the Chase of the Ostrich, Hyena, andc. by Paul du Chaillu ... 2006. 264p. per. 23.99 *(978-1-4255-2321-3(8))* MPublishing.

Fagnola, Ferdinando. Voyage to Bandiagara: The Desplagnes Mission, 1904-1905. the First Exploration of Dogon. 2010. (ENG., Illus.). 384p. pap. *(978-88-89854-43-3(X)*, Officina Libraria (Acc)) Antique Collectors' Club.

Freeman, Thomas Birch & Beecham, John. Journal of Various Visits to the Kingdoms of Ashanti, Aku, & Dahomi, in Western Africa. 2010. (Cambridge Library Collection - Religion Ser.). (Illus.). 326p. pap. 24.99 *(978-1-108-02330-6(4))* Cambridge Univ. Pr.

Garner, R. Gorillas & Chimpanzees. 2007. 192p. per. *(978-1-4068-2337-0(6))* Echo Library.

Garrard, Timothy. African Gold. 2011. (ENG., Illus.). 248p. 45.00 *(978-3-7913-4119-4(7))* Prestel Publishing.

Goble, John. Palm Oil & Small Chop. 2011. (Illus.). 224p. pap. *(978-1-84995-011-4(3))* Whittles Publishing.

Isegawa, Moses. Viviane Sassen: Parasomnia. 2011. (Illus.). 104p. 49.95 ***(978-3-7913-4521-5(4))*** Prestel Publishing.

Joy, Emily. Green Oranges on Lion Mountain. 2010. (Eye Classics Ser.). (ENG., Illus.). 270p. pap. 12.95 *(978-1-903070-73-4(2))* Eye Bks. GBR. Dist: Independent Pubs. Group.

Kaldi, Leita. Roller Skating in the Desert. 2010. 226p. ***(978-1-4512-8056-2(4))***; 228p. pap. 24.95 ***(978-1-60749-180-4(X))*** PublishAmerica, Inc.

Katakis, Michael. Despatches: Sierra Leone, 3, Vol. 1. 185th ed. 2008. (Illus.). 25p. pap. 264.00 *(978-0-9644672-8-6(3))* Foolscap Pr.

Kingsley, Mary. Travels in West Africa, Congo FranYais, Corisco & Cameroons. 2010. (Cambridge Library Collection - Women's Writing Ser.). (Illus.). 798p. pap. 53.00 *(978-1-108-02200-2(6))* Cambridge Univ. Pr.

—West African Studies. 2010. (Cambridge Library Collection - Women's Writing Ser.). (ENG., Illus.). 722p. pap. 48.00 *(978-1-108-02201-9(4))* Cambridge Univ. Pr.

Kingsley, Mary H. Travels in West Africa. 2008. 492p. 33.99 *(978-0-554-22634-7(0))* 2007. (ENG.). 488p. pap. 30.99 *(978-1-4264-2806-7(5))* 2006. 458p. pap. 28.99 *(978-1-4264-2768-8(9))* BiblioBazaar.

—Travels in West Africa. 2007. (ENG.). 428p. per. *(978-1-4065-2891-6(9))* Dodo Pr.

Laister, Richard. Looking for Mr. Legba: A Voodoo Quest. 2010. (ENG., Illus.). 179p. pap. 23.99 ***(978-1-906791-44-5(9))*** Arena Bks. GBR. Dist: Lightning Source UK, Ltd.

Locken, E. Travel Journal Benin. 2010. 192p. pap. 19.99 *(978-0-557-43271-4(5))* Lulu Enterprises Inc.

—Travel Journal Burkina Faso. 2010. 192p. pap. 19.99 *(978-0-557-43279-0(0))* Lulu Enterprises Inc.

—Travel Journal Gambia. 2010. 192p. pap. 19.99 *(978-0-557-43590-6(0))* Lulu Enterprises Inc.

—Travel Journal Guinea. 2010. 192p. pap. 19.99 *(978-0-557-43594-4(3))* Lulu Enterprises Inc.

—Travel Journal Guinea-Bissau. 2010. 192p. pap. 19.99 *(978-0-557-43595-1(1))* Lulu Enterprises Inc.

—Travel Journal Ivory Coast. 2010. 192p. pap. 19.99 *(978-0-557-43452-7(1))* Lulu Enterprises Inc.

—Travel Journal Mali. 2010. 192p. pap. 19.99 *(978-0-557-43661-3(3))* Lulu Enterprises Inc.

—Travel Journal Senegal. 2010. 192p. pap. 19.99 *(978-0-557-43919-5(1))* Lulu Enterprises Inc.

—Travel Journal Togo. 2010. 192p. pap. 19.99 *(978-0-557-44070-2(X))* Lulu Enterprises Inc.

Lonely Planet Staff & Ham, Anthony. West Africa. 7th rev. ed. 2009. (Multi Country Guide Ser.). (ENG., Illus.). 904p. pap. 33.99 *(978-1-74104-821-6(4))* Lonely Planet Pubns.

Madigan, M. Kathleen. Senegal Sojourn: Selections from One Teacher's Journal. 2010. (ENG.). 252p. 73.50 *(978-0-7391-3462-7(0))* Lexington Bks.

Moore, Ian C. D. Return to My Native Land. 2006. 186p. per. 16.95 *(978-1-60002-259-3(6)*, 4392) Mountain Valley Publishing, LLC.

O'Connor, Derek. The King's Stranger: A Biography of John. 2006. (Illus.). 389p. pap. 30.00 *(978-1-59048-241-4(7))* Long Riders' Guild Pr., The.

Park, Mungo. Travels in the Interior of Africa. 2011. (ENG.). 320p. pap. 12.95 *(978-0-486-47913-2(7))* Dover Pubns., Inc.

—Travels in the Interior of Africa. 2009. (Stanfords Travel Classics Ser.). 232p. pap. 12.95 *(978-1-905780-00-5(5))* Beaufoy, John Publishing GBR. Dist: Midpoint Trade Bks., Inc.

Perlinot-Rataud, Nicole. Mali. 2010. 42p. pap. 33.95 *(978-1-4457-5083-5(X))* Lulu Enterprises Inc.

Sidibe, Malick, photos by. Malick Sidibé: Chemises, 1 vol. 2008. (ENG., Illus.). 168p. pap. 30.00 *(978-3-86521-523-9(8))* Steidl, Gerhard Druckerei und Verlag DEU. Dist: Innovative Logistics.

Snelgrave, William. A New Account of Some Parts of Guinea & the Slave Trade. 2010. (ENG.). 192p. pap. 17.95 *(978-1-897959-66-4(4))* Serif GBR. Dist: Interlink Publishing Group, Inc.

Thomas, Charles W. Adventures & Observations on the West Coast of Africa, & Its Islands. 2009. 286p. pap. *(978-1-4590-2783-1(3))* Books LLC.

—Adventures & Observations on the West Coast of Africa, & Its Islands Historical & Descriptive Sketches of Madeira, Canary, Biafra, & Cape Ver. 2006. 492p. per. 29.99 *(978-1-4255-5497-2(0))* MPublishing.

Thomas Cook Publishing. Traveller Guides the Gambia 3rd. 3rd ed. 2011. (Travellers - Thomas Cook Ser.). (ENG., Illus.). 160p. pap. 16.95 *(978-1-84848-426-3(3))* Cook, Thomas Publishing GBR. Dist: Globe Pequot Pr., The.

Trillo, Richard & Rough Guides Staff. West Africa. 5th ed. 2008. (Rough Guide Travel Guides). (ENG., Illus.). 1312p. (gr. 12). 34.99 *(978-1-84353-850-9(4))* Rough Guides, Ltd. GBR. Dist: Dorling Kindersley Publishing, Inc.

Van Bergeijk, Jeroen. My Mercedes Is Not for Sale: From Amsterdam to Ouagadougou... an Auto-Misadventure Across the Sahara. Antonides, John, tr. from DUT. 2008. (ENG., Illus.). 224p. pap. 12.95 *(978-0-7679-2869-4(5))* Broadway Bks.

Velton, Ross. Mali. 3rd rev. ed. 2009. (Bradt Travel Guide Ser.). (ENG., Illus.). 320p. pap. 25.99 *(978-1-84162-218-7(4))* Bradt Travel Guides GBR. Dist: Globe Pequot Pr., The.

Winsnes, Selena, ed. Letters on West Africa & the Slave Trade Paul Erdmann Isert's Journey to Guinea & the Carribean Islands in Columbia. 2007. 360p. (C). pap. *(978-9988-647-01-8(8))* Sub-Saharan Pubs. & Traders GHA. Dist: Michigan State Univ. Pr.

Zumo. An Awesome Run: Selected Works, 1978-2008. 2008. 284p. pap. 19.95 *(978-1-4389-2393-2(7))* AuthorHouse.

AFRICA, WEST—ECONOMIC CONDITIONS

Aderemi, Helen, et al. Electrical Energy Use Efficiency. 2010. 96p. pap. *(978-3-8383-9172-4(1))* Lambert Academic Publishing.

Agyeman-Duah, Ivor, ed. An Economic History of Ghana: Reflections on a Half-Century of Challenges & Progress. 2008. 290p. 58.00 *(978-0-9555079-8-4(7))* Clarke, Ayebia Publishing, Ltd. GBR. Dist: Rienner, Lynne Pubs.

Amin, Aloysius Ajab, ed. Developing a Sustainable Economy in Cameroon. 2008. 440p. pap. *(978-2-86978-209-9(8))* Council for the Development of Social Science Research in Africa SEN. Dist: Michigan State Univ. Pr.

Besada, Hany, ed. From Civil Strife to Peace Building: Examining Private Sector Involvement in West African Reconstruction. 2009. (Studies in International Governance Ser.). (ENG.). 312p. pap. 42.95 *(978-1-55458-052-1(8))* Wilfrid Laurier Univ. Pr. CAN. Dist: Univ. of Toronto Pr.

Biao, Idowu. Promoting Ecowas Vision 2020 Through Higher Education. 2010. 72p. pap. *(978-3-8383-9395-7(3))* Lambert Academic Publishing.

Cham. Currency Union for West Afric. 2011. 200p. pap. ***(978-3-8433-5577-3(0))*** Lambert Academic Publishing.

Icon Group International, Inc. Staff, compiled by. The 2006 Economic & Product Market Databook for Abidjan, Cote D'Ivoire. 2006. 605p. ring bd. 95.00 *(978-0-497-79944-1(8))* Icon Group International, Inc.

—The 2006 Economic & Product Market Databook for anécho, Togo. 2006. 618p. ring bd. 95.00 *(978-0-497-80069-7(1))* Icon Group International, Inc.

—The 2006 Economic & Product Market Databook for Bafata, Guinea-Bissau. 2006. 618p. ring bd. 95.00 *(978-0-497-80113-7(2))* Icon Group International, Inc.

—The 2006 Economic & Product Market Databook for Bafilo, Togo. 2006. 618p. ring bd. 95.00 *(978-0-497-80114-4(0))* Icon Group International, Inc.

—The 2006 Economic & Product Market Databook for Bafoussam, Cameroon. 2006. 618p. ring bd. 95.00 *(978-0-497-80115-1(9))* Icon Group International, Inc.

—The 2006 Economic & Product Market Databook for Bakau, the Gambia. 2006. 618p. ring bd. 95.00 *(978-0-497-80122-9(1))* Icon Group International, Inc.

—The 2006 Economic & Product Market Databook for Bamako, Mali. 2006. 618p. ring bd. 95.00 *(978-0-497-80128-1(0))* Icon Group International, Inc.

—The 2006 Economic & Product Market Databook for Bamenda, Cameroon. 2006. 618p. ring bd. 95.00 *(978-0-497-80130-4(2))* Icon Group International, Inc.

—The 2006 Economic & Product Market Databook for Banfora, Burkina Faso. 2006. 618p. ring bd. 95.00 *(978-0-497-80133-5(7))* Icon Group International, Inc.

—The 2006 Economic & Product Market Databook for Bangassou, Central African Republic. 2006. 618p. ring bd. 95.00 *(978-0-497-80134-2(5))* Icon Group International, Inc.

—The 2006 Economic & Product Market Databook for Bangui, Central African Republic. 2006. 618p. ring bd. 95.00 *(978-0-497-80136-6(1))* Icon Group International, Inc.

—The 2006 Economic & Product Market Databook for Banjul, the Gambia. 2006. 618p. ring bd. 95.00 *(978-0-497-80138-0(8))* Icon Group International, Inc.

—The 2006 Economic & Product Market Databook for Bassari, Togo. 2006. 618p. ring bd. 95.00 *(978-0-497-80155-7(8))* Icon Group International, Inc.

—The 2006 Economic & Product Market Databook for Basse Santa Su, the Gambia. 2006. 618p. ring bd. 95.00 *(978-0-497-80156-4(6))* Icon Group International, Inc.

—The 2006 Economic & Product Market Databook for Bo, Sierra Leone. 2006. 618p. ring bd. 95.00 *(978-0-497-80232-5(5))* Icon Group International, Inc.

—The 2006 Economic & Product Market Databook for Bobo-Dioulasso, Burkina Faso. 2006. 618p. ring bd. 95.00 *(978-0-497-80212-7(0))* Icon Group International, Inc.

—The 2006 Economic & Product Market Databook for Bonthe, Sierra Leone. 2006. 618p. ring bd. 95.00 *(978-0-497-80223-3(6))* Icon Group International, Inc.

—The 2006 Economic & Product Market Databook for Bouake, Cote D'Ivoire. 2006. 618p. ring bd. 95.00 *(978-0-497-80229-5(5))* Icon Group International, Inc.

—The 2006 Economic & Product Market Databook for Brikama, the Gambia. 2006. 618p. ring bd. 95.00 *(978-0-497-80248-6(1))* Icon Group International, Inc.

—The 2006 Economic & Product Market Databook for Cantchungo, Guinea-Bissau. 2006. 618p. ring bd. 95.00 *(978-0-497-80303-2(8))* Icon Group International, Inc.

—The 2006 Economic & Product Market Databook for Catio, Guinea-Bissau. 2006. 618p. ring bd. 95.00 *(978-0-497-80323-0(2))* Icon Group International, Inc.

—The 2006 Economic & Product Market Databook for Cotonou, Benin. 2006. 618p. ring bd. 95.00 *(978-0-497-80417-6(4))* Icon Group International, Inc.

—The 2006 Economic & Product Market Databook for Daloa, Cote D'Ivoire. 2006. 618p. ring bd. 95.00 *(978-0-497-80439-8(5))* Icon Group International, Inc.

—The 2006 Economic & Product Market Databook for Farefenni, the Gambia. 2006 618p. ring bd. 95.00 *(978-0-497-80528-9(6))* Icon Group International, Inc.

—The 2006 Economic & Product Market Databook for Farim, Guinea-Bissau. 2006. 618p. ring bd. 95.00 *(978-0-497-80529-6(4))* Icon Group International, Inc.

—The 2006 Economic & Product Market Databook for Foumban, Cameroon. 2006. 618p. ring bd. 95.00 *(978-0-497-80549-4(9))* Icon Group International, Inc.

—The 2006 Economic & Product Market Databook for Freetown, Sierra Leone. 2006. 618p. ring bd. 95.00 *(978-0-497-80557-9(X))* Icon Group International, Inc.

—The 2006 Economic & Product Market Databook for Gabu, Guinea-Bissau. 2006. 618p. ring bd. 95.00 *(978-0-497-80571-5(5))* Icon Group International, Inc.

—The 2006 Economic & Product Market Databook for Gagnoa, Cote D'Ivoire. 2006. 618p. ring bd. 95.00 *(978-0-497-80573-9(1))* Icon Group International, Inc.

—The 2006 Economic & Product Market Databook for Gao, Mali. 2006. 618p. ring bd. 95.00 *(978-0-497-80577-7(4))* Icon Group International, Inc.

—The 2006 Economic & Product Market Databook for Georgetown, the Gambia. 2006. 618p. ring bd. 95.00 *(978-0-497-80592-0(8))* Icon Group International, Inc.

—The 2006 Economic & Product Market Databook for Gunjur, the Gambia. 2006. 618p. ring bd. 95.00 *(978-0-497-81873-9(6))* Icon Group International, Inc.

—The 2006 Economic & Product Market Databook for Kankan, Guinea. 2006. 618p. ring bd. 95.00 *(978-0-497-80718-4(1))* Icon Group International, Inc.

—The 2006 Economic & Product Market Databook for Kaya, Burkina Faso. 2006. 618p. ring bd. 95.00 *(978-0-497-81981-1(3))* Icon Group International, Inc.

—The 2006 Economic & Product Market Databook for Kayes, Mali. 2006. 618p. ring bd. 95.00 *(978-0-497-81982-8(1))* Icon Group International, Inc.

—The 2006 Economic & Product Market Databook for Kenema, Sierra Leone. 2006. 618p. ring bd. 95.00 *(978-0-497-81987-3(2))* Icon Group International, Inc.

—The 2006 Economic & Product Market Databook for Korhogo, Cote D'Ivoire. 2006. 618p. ring bd. 95.00 *(978-0-497-82011-4(0))* Icon Group International, Inc.

—The 2006 Economic & Product Market Databook for Koudougou, Burkina Faso. 2006. 618p. ring bd. 95.00 *(978-0-497-80768-9(8))* Icon Group International, Inc.

—The 2006 Economic & Product Market Databook for Labe, Guinea. 2006. 618p. ring bd. 95.00 *(978-0-497-80810-5(2))* Icon Group International, Inc.

—The 2006 Economic & Product Market Databook for Lambarene, Gabon. 2006. 618p. ring bd. 95.00 *(978-0-497-80819-8(6))* Icon Group International, Inc.

—The 2006 Economic & Product Market Databook for Libreville, Gabon. 2006. 618p. ring bd. 95.00 *(978-0-497-80851-8(X))* Icon Group International, Inc.

—The 2006 Economic & Product Market Databook for Limbe, Cameroon. 2006. 618p. ring bd. 95.00 *(978-0-497-80859-4(5))* Icon Group International, Inc.

—The 2006 Economic & Product Market Databook for Lome, Togo. 2006. 618p. ring bd. 95.00 *(978-0-497-80876-1(5))* Icon Group International, Inc.

—The 2006 Economic & Product Market Databook for Makeni, Sierra Leone. 2006. 618p. ring bd. 95.00 *(978-0-497-80923-2(0))* Icon Group International, Inc.

—The 2006 Economic & Product Market Databook for Man, Cote D'Ivoire. 2006. 618p. ring bd. 95.00 *(978-0-497-80007-9(1))* Icon Group International, Inc.

—The 2006 Economic & Product Market Databook for Mango, Togo. 2006. 618p. ring bd. 95.00 *(978-0-497-80942-3(7))* Icon Group International, Inc.

—The 2006 Economic & Product Market Databook for Maroua, Cameroon. 2006. 618p. ring bd. 95.00 *(978-0-497-80960-7(5))* Icon Group International, Inc.

—The 2006 Economic & Product Market Databook for Mouila, Gabon. 2006. 618p. ring bd. 95.00 *(978-0-497-81063-4(8))* Icon Group International, Inc.

—The 2006 Economic & Product Market Databook for Natitingou, Benin. 2006. 618p. ring bd. 95.00 *(978-0-497-81107-5(3))* Icon Group International, Inc.

—The 2006 Economic & Product Market Databook for Nkongsamba, Cameroon. 2006. 618p. ring bd. 95.00 *(978-0-497-81133-4(2))* Icon Group International, Inc.

—The 2006 Economic & Product Market Databook for Nouadhibou, Mauritania. 2006. 618p. ring bd. 95.00 *(978-0-497-82041-1(2))* Icon Group International, Inc.

—The 2006 Economic & Product Market Databook for Nouakchott, Mauritania. 2006. 618p. ring bd. 95.00 *(978-0-497-82042-8(0))* Icon Group International, Inc.

—The 2006 Economic & Product Market Databook for Nzerekore, Guinea. 2006. 618p. ring bd. 95.00 *(978-0-497-81150-1(2))* Icon Group International, Inc.

—The 2006 Economic & Product Market Databook for Ouagadougou, Burkina Faso. 2006. 618p. ring bd. 95.00 *(978-0-497-81178-5(2))* Icon Group International, Inc.

—The 2006 Economic & Product Market Databook for Ouahigouya, Burkina Faso. 2006. 618p. ring bd. 95.00 *(978-0-497-81179-2(0))* Icon Group International, Inc.

—The 2006 Economic & Product Market Databook for Oyem, Gabon. 2006. 618p. ring bd. 95.00 *(978-0-497-81181-5(2))* Icon Group International, Inc.

—The 2006 Economic & Product Market Databook for Palimé, Togo. 2006. 618p. ring bd. 95.00 *(978-0-497-81185-3(5))* Icon Group International, Inc.

—The 2006 Economic & Product Market Databook for Parakou, Benin. 2006. 618p. ring bd. 95.00 *(978-0-497-81190-7(1))* Icon Group International, Inc.

—The 2006 Economic & Product Market Databook for Port Loko, Sierra Leone. 2006. 618p. ring bd. 95.00 *(978-0-497-82078-7(1))* Icon Group International, Inc.

—The 2006 Economic & Product Market Databook for Porto-Novo, Benin. 2006. 618p. ring bd. 95.00 *(978-0-497-81281-2(9))* Icon Group International, Inc.

—The 2006 Economic & Product Market Databook for Ribeira Grande, Cape Verde. 2006. 618p. ring bd. 95.00 *(978-0-497-81348-2(3))* Icon Group International, Inc.

—The 2006 Economic & Product Market Databook for Rosso, Mauritania. 2006. 618p. ring bd. 95.00 *(978-0-497-81369-7(6))* Icon Group International, Inc.

—The 2006 Economic & Product Market Databook for Sal Rei, Cape Verde. 2006. 618p. ring bd. 95.00 *(978-0-497-81400-7(5))* Icon Group International, Inc.

—The 2006 Economic & Product Market Databook for Santa Maria, Cape Verde. 2006. 618p. ring bd. 95.00 *(978-0-497-81450-2(1))* Icon Group International, Inc.

—The 2006 Economic & Product Market Databook for Santo Antonio, Sao Tome E Principe. 2006. 618p. ring bd. 95.00 *(978-0-497-81461-8(7))* Icon Group International, Inc.

—The 2006 Economic & Product Market Databook for Sao Tome, Sao Tome E Principe. 2006. 618p. ring bd. 95.00 *(978-0-497-81470-0(6))* Icon Group International, Inc.

—The 2006 Economic & Product Market Databook for Segou, Mali. 2006. 618p. ring bd. 95.00 *(978-0-497-81491-5(9))* Icon Group International, Inc.

—The 2006 Economic & Product Market Databook for Serrekunda, the Gambia. 2006. 618p. ring bd. 95.00 *(978-0-497-81507-3(9))* Icon Group International, Inc.

—The 2006 Economic & Product Market Databook for Sikasso, Mali. 2006. 618p. ring bd. 95.00 *(978-0-497-81537-0(0))* Icon Group International, Inc.

—The 2006 Economic & Product Market Databook for Sokodé, Togo. 2006. 618p. ring bd. 95.00 *(978-0-497-81554-7(0))* Icon Group International, Inc.

—The 2006 Economic & Product Market Databook for Sukuta, the Gambia. 2006. 618p. ring bd. 95.00 *(978-0-497-81578-3(8))* Icon Group International, Inc.

—The 2006 Economic & Product Market Databook for Timbuktu, Mali. 2006. 618p. ring bd. 95.00 *(978-0-497-81681-0(4))* Icon Group International, Inc.

—The 2006 Economic & Product Market Databook for Tsévié, Togo. 2006. 618p. ring bd. 95.00 *(978-0-497-81728-2(4))* Icon Group International, Inc.

—The 2006 Economic & Product Market Databook for Yamoussoukro, Cote D'Ivoire. 2006. 618p. ring bd. 95.00 *(978-0-497-81836-4(1))* Icon Group International, Inc.

—The 2006 Economic & Product Market Databook for Yaounde, Cameroon. 2006. 618p. ring bd. 95.00 *(978-0-497-81838-8(8))* Icon Group International, Inc.

Kargbo, Joseph M. Political Instability & Economic Recovery in Sierra Leone: Lessons in Applied Econometrics, Modeling, & Policy Making, Book 1, Book 2, 2 vols. 2011. (Illus.). 960p. ***(978-0-7734-1597-3(1))*** Mellen, Edwin Pr., The.

Life Within Limits: Well-Being in a World of Want. 2011. (ENG., Illus.). 248p. 79.95 *(978-0-8223-4892-4(6))*; pap. 22.95 *(978-0-8223-4915-0(9))* Duke Univ. Pr.

Neiland, Arthur E. & Béné, Christophe, eds. Poverty & Small-scale Fisheries in West Africa. 2010. 272p. pap. 75.00 *(978-90-481-6535-3(0)*, 9048165350) Springer.

Obi. Perspectives on Cote D'Ivoire: Bewteen Political Breakdown & Post-Colonial Peace. 2007. (NAI Discussion Papers). 70p. pap. 12.95 *(978-91-7106-606-0(3))* Nordiska Afrikainstitutet SWE. Dist: Stylus Publishing, LLC.

Organisation for Economic Co-operation and Development Staff & Michel Colin, de Verdiáre. West African Perspectives: Resources for Development. 2009. (West African Studies). (Illus.). 112p. pap. 63.00 *(978-92-64-05975-7(X))* Organization for Economic Cooperation & Development.

Ryan, Órla. Chocolate Nations: Living & Dying for Cocoa in West Africa. 2011. (African Arguments Ser.). (ENG.). 176p. 107.95 *(978-1-84813-004-3(X))*; 192p. pap. 14.95 *(978-1-84813-005-0(8))* Zed Bks., Ltd. GBR. Dist: Macmillan.

Sankara, Thomas. We Are the Heirs of the World's Revolutions: Speeches from the Burkina Faso Revolution 1983-87. 2nd ed. 2007. (Illus.). 108p. pap. 10.00 *(978-0-87348-989-8(6))* Pathfinder Pr.

Soderbaum, Taylor. Micro-Regionalism in West Africa: Evidence from Two Case Studies. Soderbaum, Fredrik & Taylor, Ian, eds. 2006. (Nordiska Afrikainstitutet Discussion Paper Ser.). (Illus.). 40p. pap. 12.95 *(978-91-7106-584-1(9))* Nordiska Afrikainstitutet SWE. Dist: Stylus Publishing, LLC.

Wodon, Quentin. Migration, Remittances, & Poverty: Case Studies from West Africa. Wodon, Quentin, ed. 2007. (World Bank Working Papers). 125p. pap. 20.00 *(978-0-8213-6627-1(0))* World Bank Pubns.

Wodon, Quentin, ed. Growth & Poverty Reduction: Case Studies from West Africa. 2007. (World Bank Working Papers: 79). (ENG., Illus.). 150p. per. 20.00 *(978-0-8213-6629-5(7)*, 9780821366295) World Bank Pubns.

AFRICA, WEST—HISTORY

Ajayi, Jacob Festus Ade. History of West Africa, Vol. 2. Date not set. (Illus.). xiv, 764p. pap. 24.40 *(978-0-582-64552-3(2))* Addison-Wesley Longman, Ltd. GBR. Dist: Trans-Atlantic Pubns., Inc.

Alpern, Stanley B. Amazons of Black Sparta: The Women Warriors of Dahomey: With a New Preface. 2011. 288p. pap. 22.00 *(978-0-8147-0772-2(6))* New York Univ. Pr.

Araoye, Lasisi Ademola. Cote D'Ivoire: The Conundrum of a Still Wretched of the Earth. 2012. ***(978-1-59221-863-9(6))***; (ENG., Illus.). 504p. pap. ***(978-1-59221-864-6(4))*** Africa World Pr.

Beah, Ishmael. A Long Way Gone: Memoirs of a Boy Soldier. 240p. 2008. (ENG., Illus.). pap. 12.00 *(978-0-374-53126-3(9))* 2007. 22.00 *(978-0-374-95191-7(8))* 2007. (ENG., Illus.). 24.00 *(978-0-374-10523-5(5))* Farrar, Straus & Giroux.

—A Long Way Gone: Memoirs of a Boy Soldier. 2008. (Illus.). 229p. (J). 19.65 *(978-1-60686-094-6(1))* Perfection Learning Corp.

—A Long Way Gone: Memoirs of A Boy Soldier. 2008. 229p. lib. bdg. 23.30 ***(978-1-4178-2845-6(5)***, Turtleback) Turtleback Bks.

Beah, Ishmael. A Long Way Gone: Memoirs of a Boy Soldier. 2009. 11.21 *(978-0-7848-2632-4(3)*, Everbind) Marco Bk. Co.

—A Long Way Gone: Memoirs of a Boy Soldier. lt. ed. 2008. 400p. (YA). pap. 13.95 *(978-1-59413-267-4(4)*, Large Print Pr.) Thorndike Pr.

Buxton, Thomas Fowell. The African Slave Trade. 2011. (Cambridge Library Collection - Slavery & Abolition Ser.). 262p. pap. 23.99 *(978-1-108-02768-7(7))* Cambridge Univ. Pr.

A

—The African Slave Trade & Its Remedy. 2009. 254p. pap. 22.07 (978-1-150-48852-8(2)) General Bks. LLC.

—The African Slave Trade & Its Remedy. 582p. reprint ed. 98.00 (978-0-7222-9707-0(6)) Library Reprints, Inc.

—The Remedy: Being a Sequel to the African Slave Trade. 2010. (Cambridge Library Collection - Slavery & Abolition Ser.). (Illus.). 306p. pap. 24.99 (978-1-108-02432-7(7)) Cambridge Univ. Pr.

Costa, Manuel E. The Making of the Cape Verdean. 2011. 336p. 28.28 (978-1-4634-0135-1(3)); pap. 17.72 (978-1-4634-0134-4(5)) AuthorHouse.

Coulter, Chris. Bush Wives & Girl Soldiers: Women's Lives Through War & Peace in Sierra Leone. 2009. (Illus.). 296p. 73.50 (978-0-8014-4782-2(8)); pap. 24.95 (978-0-8014-7512-2(0)) Cornell Univ. Pr.

De Jong, Ferdinand. Reclaiming Heritage: Alternative Imaginaries of Memory in West Africa. De Jong, Ferdinand & Rowlands, Michael, eds. 2008. (University College London Institute of Archaeology Publications, Critical Cultural Heritage Ser.). (ENG., Illus.). 270p. 94.00 (978-1-59874-307-4(4)) Left Coast Pr., Inc.

de Jong, Ferdinand & Rowlands, Michael, eds. Reclaiming Heritage: Alternative Imaginaries of Memory in West Africa. 2009. (University College London Institute of Archaeology Publications). (ENG.). 270p. pap. 34.95 (978-1-59874-308-1(2)) Left Coast Pr., Inc.

Denov, Myriam. Child Soldiers: Sierra Leone's Revolutionary United Front. 2010. (ENG., Illus.). 246p. 85.00 (978-0-521-87224-9(3)); pap. 30.00 (978-0-521-69321-9(7)) Cambridge Univ. Pr.

Doortmont, Michel R. & Smit, Jinna. Sources for the Mutual History of Ghana & the Netherlands: An annotated guide to the Dutch archives relating to Ghana & West Africa in the Nationaal Archief 1593-1960. 2007. pap. (978-90-04-15850-4(2)) BRILL.

Enworom, Sylvanus A. The Paragon of Civilization. 2011. 210p. pap. 24.95 (978-1-4626-1320-5(9)) PublishAmerica, Inc.

Falola, Toyin & Childs, Matt D. The Changing Worlds of Atlantic Africa: Essays in Honor of Robin Law. 2009. 536p. pap. 55.00 (978-1-59460-594-9(7)) Carolina Academic Pr.

Fowler, Will. Certain Death in Sierra Leone - the SAS & Operation Barras 2000. 2010. (Raid Ser.). (ENG., Illus.). 64p. pap. 18.95 (978-1-84603-850-1(2)) Osprey Publishing, Ltd. GBR. Dist: Random Hse., Inc.

Ginio, Ruth. French Colonialism Unmasked: The Vichy Years in French West Africa. 2008. (France Overseas: Studies in Empire & D Ser.). (ENG., Illus.). 264p. pap. 24.95 (978-0-8032-1746-1(3)) Univ. of Nebraska Pr.

Gottschalk, Pearl. 'How are We in this World Now?' Examining the Experiences of Persons Disabled by War in Sierra Leone. 2008. 96p. pap. (978-3-8364-8170-0(7)) VDM Verlag Dr. Mueller e.K.

Hall, Bruce S. A History of Race in Muslim West Africa, 1600-1960. 2011. (African Studies). (ENG., Illus.). 358p. 90.00 (978-1-107-00287-6(7)) Cambridge Univ. Pr.

Jones, Hilary. The Métis of Senegal: Urban Life & Politics in French West Africa. 2012. (ENG.). 256p. pap. 28.00 (978-0-253-00674-5(0), 0253006740); (Illus.). 80.00 (978-0-253-00673-8(2), 0253006732) Indiana Univ. Pr.

Knörr, Jacqueline & Trajano Filho, Wilson, eds. The Powerful Presence of the Past: Integration & Conflict along the Upper Guinea Coast. 2010. (African Social Studies). (Illus.). 384p. pap. (978-90-04-19000-9(7)) BRILL.

Law, Robin, ed. The English in West Africa, 1691-1699: The Local Correspondence of the Royal African Company of England, 1681-1699, 3 vols. 2007. (Fontes Historiae Africanae, New Series: Sources of African History Ser.: Pt. 3). (Illus.). 719p. 165.00 (978-0-19-726392-1(5)) Oxford Univ. Pr., Inc.

LeCoq, Baz. Disputed Desert: Decolonisation, Competing Nationalisms & Tuareg Rebellions in Northern Mali. 2010. (Afrika-Studiecentrum Ser.). (Illus.). xxxii, 433p. pap. (978-90-04-13983-1(4)) BRILL.

Levtzion, Nehemia, ed. & tr. from ARA. Medieval West Africa Before 1400: Ghana, Takrur, Gao (Songhay) & Mali as Described by Arab Scholars & Merchants. Hopkins, J. F., tr. from ARA. rev. ed. Date not set. Orig. Title: Corpus of Early Arab Sources for West African History. (Illus.). 320p. (C). 44.95 (978-1-55876-164-3(0)); pap. 28.95 (978-1-55876-165-0(9)) Wiener, Markus Pubs., Inc.

Lingna Nafafé, José. Colonial Encounters: Issues of Culture, Hybridity & Creolisation: Portuguese Mercantile Settlers in West Africa. (Illus.). x, 215p. pap. 51.95 (978-3-631-52779-5(9)) Lang, Peter GmbH, Europaischer Verlag der Wissenschaften DEU. Dist: Lang, Peter Publishing, Inc.

Lydon, Ghislaine. On Trans-Saharan Trails: Islamic Law, Trade Networks, & Cross-Cultural Exchange in Nineteenth-Century Western Africa. 2009. (ENG., Illus.). 496p. 95.00 (978-0-521-88724-3(0)) Cambridge Univ. Pr.

Mansa Musa: African King of Gold (NCHS) tchr. ed. 21.00 (978-0-382-40947-9(7)) Cobblestone Publishing Co.

McKenna, Amy, ed. The History of Western Africa. 2011. (Britannica Guide to Africa Ser.). (Illus.). 240p. (YA). 106.00 (978-1-61530-444-8(4)) Rosen Publishing Group, Inc., The.

Monroe, J. Cameron & Ogundiran, Akinwumi, eds. Power & Landscape in Atlantic West Africa: Archaeological Perspectives. 2012. (ENG., Illus.). 400p. 99.00 (978-1-107-00939-4(1)) Cambridge Univ. Pr.

Mwakikagile, Godfrey. Ethnic Diversity & Integration in the Gambi: The Land, the People & the Culture. 2010. 278p. pap. 19.95 (978-9987-9322-2-1(3)) Continental Pr.

Newitt, Malyn, ed. The Portuguese in West Africa, 1415-1670. 2010. (ENG., Illus.). 264p. (C). 90.00 (978-0-521-76894-8(2)); pap. 27.99 (978-0-521-15914-2(8)) Cambridge Univ. Pr.

Piot, Charles. Nostalgia for the Future: West Africa after the Cold War. 2010. (ENG., Illus.). 216p. 60.00 (978-0-226-66964-9(5)); pap. 20.00 (978-0-226-66965-6(3)) Univ. of Chicago Pr.

Robinson, Phyllis Jean. Grace & Mercy Brought Us Through. 2010. 232p. pap. 17.00 (978-1-4490-4121-2(3)) AuthorHouse.

Saad, Elias N. Social History of Timbuktu: The Role of Muslim Scholars & Notables, 1400-1900. 2010. (Cambridge Studies in Islamic Civilization Ser.). (ENG., Illus.). 336p. pap. 29.99 (978-0-521-13630-3(X)) Cambridge Univ. Pr.

Sankara, Thomas. Thomas Sankara Speaks: The Burkina Faso Revolution 1983-1987. 2nd exp. ed. 2007. (Illus.). 448p. pap. 24.00 (978-0-87348-986-7(1)) Pathfinder Pr.

Sesay, Amadu & Sesay. Does One Size Fit All? The Sierra Leone Truth & Reconciliation Commission Revisited. 2007. (NAI Discussion Papers). (Illus.). 58p. pap. 15.95 (978-91-7106-586-5(5)) Nordiska Afrikainstitutet SWE. Dist: Stylus Publishing, LLC.

Stewart, Gary & Amman, John. Black Man's Grave: Letters from Sierra Leone. 2007. (Illus.). 223p. pap. 14.95 (978-0-9790808-2-1(7)) Cold Run Bks.

Thomas, Graham A. Pirate Killers. 2011. (Illus.). 224p. 39.95 (978-1-84884-240-3(6)) Pen & Sword Bks. Ltd. GBR. Dist: Casemate Pubs. & Bk. Distributors, LLC.

Tijani, Hakeem Ibikunle, et al. Africa & the Wider World. 2010. (ENG.). 464p. (C). pap. 83.80 (978-0-558-85002-9(2)) Pearson Learning Solutions.

Valsecchi, Pierluigi. Powers & State Formation in West Africa: Appolonia from the Sixteenth to the Eighteenth Century. Cameron, Allan, tr. 2011. (ENG., Illus.). 304p. 95.00 (978-0-230-11776-1(7)) Palgrave Macmillan.

Whitford, John. Trading Life in Western & Central Africa. 2009. 344p. 46.95 (978-1-104-57256-3(7)); pap. 31.95 (978-1-104-51107-4(X)) Kessinger Publishing, LLC.

AFRICA, WEST—JUVENILE LITERATURE

Garten, Ethan Y. Foods of West Africa. 2011. (Culture in the Kitchen Ser.). 24p. (J). (gr. 2-5). pap. 8.15 (978-1-4339-5724-6(8)); (Illus.). lib. bdg. 22.60 (978-1-4339-5722-2(1)) Stevens, Gareth Publishing LLLP. (Stevens, Gareth Learning Library).

AFRICA, WEST—LITERATURES

Allan, Tuzyline Jita, et al, eds. Women Writing Africa: West Africa & the Sahel. 2008. (Women Writing Africa Ser.: Vol. 2). (ENG.). 560p. 75.00 (978-1-55861-501-4(6)) Feminist Pr. at The City Univ. of New York.

AFRICA, WEST—POLITICS AND GOVERNMENT

Abbascia, Davide & Poggi, Giusto, eds. Cote D'Ivoire (Ivory Coast) Election Crisis & Aftermath. 2011. (African Political, Economic, & Security Issues Ser.). 95.00 (978-1-61470-457-7(0)) Nova Science Pubs., Inc.

Agbu, Osita. West Africa's Trouble Spots & the Imperative for Peace-Building. 2006. 116p. pap. (978-2-86978-193-1(8)) Council for the Development of Social Science Research in Africa SEN. Dist: Michigan State Univ. Pr.

Amin, Aloysius Ajab, ed. Developing a Sustainable Economy in Cameroon. 2008. 440p. pap. (978-2-86978-209-9(8)) Council for the Development of Social Science Research in Africa SEN. Dist: Michigan State Univ. Pr.

Anyangwe, Carlson. Imperialistic Politics in Cameroun: Resistance & the Inception of the Restoration of the Statehood of Southern Cameroons. 2008. 172p. pap. (978-9956-558-50-6(8)) Langaa Research & Publishing Common Initiative Group CMR. Dist: Michigan State Univ. Pr.

Araoye, Lasisi Ademola. Cote D'Ivoire: The Conundrum of a Still Wretched of the Earth. 2012. (978-1-59221-863-9(6)); (ENG., Illus.). 504p. pap. (978-1-59221-864-6(4)) Africa World Pr.

Camara, Mohamed Saliou. The Development of a Trans-National Region in West Africa: Transcending the Politics of Sovereign Nation States. 2010. xii, 459p. (978-0-7734-3700-5(2)) Mellen, Edwin Pr., The.

Ceesay, Ebrima Jogomai. The Military & Democratisation in the Gambia, 1994-2003. 2011. (Illus.). 374p. pap. 34.70 (978-1-4251-0103-9(8)) Trafford Publishing.

Chalachew, Tadesse. Regional Security in West Africa: Building Regional Security Architecture under Ecowas in the Post-Cold War Era. 2011. 220p. pap. (978-3-639-33208-7(3)) VDM Verlag Dr. Mueller e.K.

Chalfin, Brenda. Neoliberal Frontiers: An Ethnography of Sovereignty in West Africa. 2010. (Chicago Studies in Practices of Meaning Ser.). (ENG., Illus.). 320p. 70.00 (978-0-226-10059-3(6)); pap. 23.00 (978-0-226-10061-6(8)) Univ. of Chicago Pr.

Doh, Emmanuel Fru. Africa's Political Wastelands: The Bastardization of Cameroon. 2008. 200p. pap. (978-9956-558-62-9(1)) Langaa Research & Publishing Common Initiative Group CMR. Dist: Michigan State Univ. Pr.

Drugs and Crime Prevention Committee Staff. Transnational Trafficking & the Rule of Law in West Africa: A Threat Assessment. 2012. (ENG.). 100p. pap. 25.00 (978-92-1-130284-4(6)) United Nations Pubns.

Edi, Eric M. Globalization & Politics in the Economic Community of West African States. 2007. (Carolina Academic Press Studies on Globalization & Society). 45.00 (978-1-59460-283-2(2)) Carolina Academic Pr.

Fonchingong, Tangie Nsoh & Gemandze, John Bobuin, eds. Cameroon: The Stakes & Challenges of Governance & Development. 2009. 232p. pap. (978-9956-558-45-2(1)) Langaa Research & Publishing Common Initiative Group CMR. Dist: Michigan State Univ. Pr.

Garrett, James L. & Natalicchio, Marcela. Working Multisectorally in Nutrition: Principles & Practices from Senegal & Colombia. 2010. (978-0-89629-181-2(2)) International Food Policy Research Institute.

Harris, David. Civil War & Democracy in West Africa: Conflict Resolution, Elections & Justice in Sierra Leone & Liberia. 2012. (International Library of African Studies). (ENG., Illus.). 320p. 95.00 (978-1-84885-687-5(3), Tauris Academic Studies) I. B. Tauris & Co., Ltd. GBR. Dist: Macmillan.

Horton, James Africanus Beale. West African Countries & Peoples, British & Native: And a Vindication of the African Race. 2011. (Cambridge Library Collection - Slavery & Abolition Ser.). (ENG., Illus.). 312p. pap. 24.99 (978-1-108-02859-2(4)) Cambridge Univ. Pr.

Ismail, Olawale. The Dynamics of Post-Conflict Reconstruction & Peace Building in West Africa: Between Change & Stability. 2009. (NAI Discussion Papers). 50p. pap. 12.95 (978-91-7106-637-4(3)) Nordiska Afrikainstitutet SWE. Dist: Stylus Publishing, LLC.

Jones, Hilary. The Métis of Senegal: Urban Life & Politics in French West Africa. 2012. (ENG.). 256p. pap. 28.00 (978-0-253-00674-5(0), 0253006740); (Illus.). 80.00 (978-0-253-00673-8(2), 0253006732) Indiana Univ. Pr.

Kargbo, Joseph M. Political Instability & Economic Recovery in Sierra Leone: Lessons in Applied Econometrics, Modeling, & Policy Making, Book 1, Book 2, 2 vols. 2011. (Illus.). 960p. (978-0-7734-1597-3(1)) Mellen, Edwin Pr., The.

Mansaray, Peter Sorie. Combating Corruption in Sierra Leone: A review & an assessment of strategies undertaken by past governments to curb corruption in Sierra Leone. 2008. 104p. pap. (978-3-8364-9737-4(9)) VDM Verlag Dr. Mueller e.K.

Manyong, Peterkins. God the Politician. 2008. 200p. (978-9956-558-96-4(6)) Langaa Research & Publishing Common Initiative Group CMR. Dist: Michigan State Univ. Pr.

Minteh, Binneh. Perils of Drugs in West Afric. 2010. 64p. pap. (978-3-8383-6113-0(X)) Lambert Academic Publishing.

—Rethinking the Military & Democratization. 2010. 64p. pap. (978-3-8383-6155-0(5)) Lambert Academic Publishing.

Mustapha, Marda & Bangura, Joseph J., eds. Sierra Leone beyond the Lome Peace Accord. 2010. (ENG.). 192p. 84.00 (978-0-230-10285-9(9)) Palgrave Macmillan.

Obi. Perspectives on Cote D'Ivoire: Bewteen Political Breakdown & Post-Colonial Peace. 2007. (NAI Discussion Papers). 70p. pap. 12.95 (978-91-7106-606-0(3)) Nordiska Afrikainstitutet SWE. Dist: Stylus Publishing, LLC.

Olukoshi, Adebayo. Governance Trends in West Africa 2006: A Synthesis Report. 2008. 68p. pap. (978-2-86978-212-9(8)) Council for the Development of Social Science Research in Africa SEN. Dist: Michigan State Univ. Pr.

Organisation for Economic Co-operation and Development Staff. The Development Dimension Fishing for Coherence in West Africa: Policy Coherence for Development in the Fisheries Sector in the Seven Csrp Countries. 2008. pap. 33.00 (978-92-64-04058-8(7)) Organization for Economic Cooperation & Development.

Organisation for Economic Co-operation and Development Staff & Michel Colin, de Verdiáre. West African Perspectives: Resources for Development. 2009. (West African Studies). (Illus.). 112p. pap. 63.00 (978-92-64-05975-7(X)) Organization for Economic Cooperation & Development.

Otti, Mazi Ngozi. Reflections of a Glorious Life: Patrick Nwakamma Otti. 2008. (Illus.). 51p. pap. 15.99 (978-1-4363-5762-3(4)) Xlibris Corp.

Percival, John. The 1961 Cameroon Plebiscite: Choice or Betrayal. 2008. 160p. (978-9956-558-49-0(4)) Langaa Research & Publishing Common Initiative Group CMR. Dist: Michigan State Univ. Pr.

Prairie, Michel, ed. & intro. Thomas Sankara Parle: La révolution au Burkina Faso 1983-1987. 2nd rev. exp. ed. 2007.Tr. of Thomas Sankara Speaks: the Burkina Faso Revolution 1983-1987. (FRE., Illus.). 480p. pap. 24.00 (978-0-87348-987-4(X)) Pathfinder Pr.

Reno, William. Corruption & State Politics in Sierra Leone. 2008. (African Studies). (ENG., Illus.). 244p. (C). pap. 31.99 (978-0-521-10347-3(9)) Cambridge Univ. Pr.

Saine, Abdoulaye S. The Paradox of Third-World Democratization in Africa: The Gambia under AFPRC-APRC Rule, 1994-2008. 2009. (ENG.). 198p. 68.50 (978-0-7391-2921-0(X)) Lexington Bks.

Saine, Abdoulaye S., et al. Elections & Democratization in West Africa, 1990-2009. 2011. (978-1-59221-773-1(7)); 320p. pap. (978-1-59221-774-8(5)) Africa World Pr.

Sankara, Thomas. Thomas Sankara Speaks: The Burkina Faso Revolution 1983-1987. 2nd exp. ed. 2007. (Illus.). 448p. pap. 24.00 (978-0-87348-986-7(1)) Pathfinder Pr.

—We Are the Heirs of the World's Revolutions: Speeches from the Burkina Faso Revolution 1983-87. 2nd ed. 2007. (Illus.). 108p. pap. 10.00 (978-0-87348-989-8(6)) Pathfinder Pr.

Smith-Höhn, Judy. Rebuilding the Security Sector in Post-Conflict Societies: Perceptions from Urban Liberia & Sierra Leone. 2011. (ENG., Illus.). 256p. pap. 49.95 (978-3-643-80074-9(6)) Lit Verlag DEU. Dist: Transaction Pubs.

Valsecchi, Pierluigi. Powers & State Formation in West Africa: Appolonia from the Sixteenth to the Eighteenth Century. Cameron, Allan, tr. 2011. (ENG., Illus.). 304p. 95.00 (978-0-230-11776-1(7)) Palgrave Macmillan.

World Bank. Decentralization, Democracy, & Development: Recent Experience from Sierra Leone. 2009. (Country Studies). (ENG., Illus.). 192p. pap. 20.00 (978-0-8213-7999-8(2), 9780821379998) World Bank Pubns.

Wundah, Michael Nicolas. Sierra Leone's Corridors of Power. 2009. 224p. 26.50 (978-1-60860-052-6(1), Strategic Bk. Publishing) AEG Literary Publishing Services, Inc.

AFRICA, WEST—RELIGION

Adefila, Johnson Ajibade. Was Christianity a Means of the Deafricanization & Social Control of Slaves? A Comparison of the Response of Free West Africans to Christianity with the Response of African Slaves in the United States. 2011. (ENG.). 184p. 109.95 (978-0-7734-3955-9(2)) Mellen, Edwin Pr., The.

Ba, Amadou Hampate. A Spirit of Tolerance: The Inspiring Life of Tierno Bokar. Gaetani, Roger, ed. 2007. (Library of Perennial Philosophy Ser.). (ENG., Illus.). 260p. per. 19.95 (978-1-933316-47-5(0)) World Wisdom, Inc.

Bay, Edna. Asen, Ancestors, & Vodun: Tracing Change in African Art. 2008. (Illus.). 208p. 42.00 (978-0-252-03255-4(1)) Univ. of Illinois Pr.

Conteh, Prince Sorie. Traditionalists, Muslims, & Christians in Africa: Interreligious Encounters & Dialogue. 2009. 248p. 104.99 (978-1-60497-596-3(2)) Cambria Pr.

De Jong, Ferdinand & de Jong, Ferdinand. Masquerades of Modernity: Power & Secrecy in Casamance, Senegal. 2007. (ENG., Illus.). 256p. 39.95 (978-0-253-35172-2(3), 0253351723) Indiana Univ. Pr.

Hanretta, Sean. Islam & Social Change in French West Africa: History of an Emancipatory Community. 2010. (African Studies). (ENG., Illus.). 110p. pap. 29.99 (978-0-521-15629-5(7)) Cambridge Univ. Pr.

Hunwick, John. West Africa,Islam & the Arab World. 2006. per. 24.95 (978-1-55876-399-9(6)) Wiener, Markus Pubs., Inc.

Jean, Yanick. Ahobobo: On the Sacramental Imagination in West Africa, Bénin, 2006-2008. 2010. (ENG.). 132p. pap. 22.00 (978-0-7618-5365-7(0)) Univ. Pr. of America, Inc.

Jennings, Brian K. Leading Virtue: A Model for the Contextualisation of Christian Ethics. 2009. (IC - Studien zur interkulturellen Geschichte des Christentums. Etudes d'histoire interculturelle de christianisme. Studies in the Intercultural History of Christianity Ser.). 154p. 47.95 (978-3-631-59300-4(7)) Lang, Peter GmbH, Europaischer Verlag der Wissenschaften DEU. Dist: Lang, Peter.

Laister, Richard. Looking for Mr. Legba: A Voodoo Quest. 2010. (ENG., Illus.). 179p. pap. 23.99 (978-1-906791-44-5(9)) Arena Bks. GBR. Dist: Lightning Source UK, Ltd.

Macon, Larry. The Black Church at Its Best: A Man, his Story & the Black Church. 2009. (ENG.). 200p. pap. 12.99 (978-0-9825303-6-8(6)) St. Paul Pr.

Pemberton, John, III, et al. Ibeji: The Cult of Yoruba Twins. 2008. (Hic Sunt Leones Ser.). (Illus.). 336p. (978-88-7439-060-1(2)) 5 Continents.

Sarro, Ramon. The Politics of Religious Change on the Upper Guinea Coast: Iconoclasm Done & Undone. 2009. (International African Library). (ENG., Illus.). 264p. (gr. 17). 75.00 (978-0-7486-3515-3(7)) Edinburgh Univ. Pr. GBR. Dist: Columbia Univ. Pr.

Seesemann, Rudiger. The Divine Flood: Ibrahim Niasse & the Roots of a Twentieth-Century Sufi Revival, 1 vol. 2011. (ENG., Illus.). 352p. 65.00 (978-0-19-538432-1(6)) Oxford Univ. Pr., Inc.

Smith, Jeremy. The staircase of a Patron: Sierra leone & the united brethren in Christ. 2011. 321p. pap. 42.50 (978-1-60947-016-6(8)) Emeth Pr.

Walker, Sheila S. The Religious Revolution in the Ivory Coast: The Prophet Harris & the Harrist Church. 2011. (ENG.). 223p. pap. 40.00 (978-0-8078-9805-5(8)) Univ. of North Carolina Pr.

AFRICA, WEST—SOCIAL CONDITIONS

Ademola, Joji. Ft-Venturing West Africa vs Northern Europe. 2010. 88p. pap. (978-3-8383-5353-1(6)) Lambert Academic Publishing.

Agyeman-Duah, Ivor, ed. An Economic History of Ghana: Reflections on a Half-Century of Challenges & Progress. 2008. 290p. 58.00 (978-0-9555079-8-4(7)) Clarke, Ayebia Publishing, Ltd. GBR. Dist: Rienner, Lynne Pubs.

Bangura, Umaru & Mohamed Koroma, Bashiru. Morbidity & Mortality among Children under Five Years in Freetown. 2010. 164p. pap. (978-3-8383-8683-6(3)) Lambert Academic Publishing.

Cakir, Metin. The Effiency Effects of Technical Change in Malian Rice Production. 2008. 80p. pap. (978-3-639-08855-7(7)) VDM Verlag Dr. Mueller e.K.

Denov, Myriam. Child Soldiers: Sierra Leone's Revolutionary United Front. 2010. (ENG., Illus.). 246p. 85.00 (978-0-521-87224-9(3)); pap. 30.00 (978-0-521-69321-9(7)) Cambridge Univ. Pr.

Goody, Esther N. Parenthood & Social Reproduction: Fostering & Occupational Roles in West Africa. 2007. (Cambridge Studies in Social & Cultural Anthropology Ser.). (ENG., Illus.). 368p. pap. 74.00 (978-0-521-04017-4(5)) Cambridge Univ. Pr.

Gottschalk, Pearl. 'How are We in this World Now?' Examining the Experiences of Persons Disabled by War in Sierra Leone. 2008. 96p. pap. (978-3-8364-8170-0(7)) VDM Verlag Dr. Mueller e.K.

Hill, Polly. Studies in Rural Capitalism in West Africa. 2009. (African Studies). (ENG.). 192p. pap. 31.99 (978-0-521-10921-5(3)) Cambridge Univ. Pr.

Ismail, Olawale. The Dynamics of Post-Conflict Reconstruction & Peace Building in West Africa: Between Change & Stability. 2009. (NAI Discussion Papers). 50p. pap. 12.95 (978-91-7106-637-4(3)) Nordiska Afrikainstitutet SWE. Dist: Stylus Publishing, LLC.

Jones, Hilary. The Métis of Senegal: Urban Life & Politics in French West Africa. 2012. (ENG.). 256p. pap. 28.00 (978-0-253-00674-5(0), 0253006740); (Illus.). 80.00 (978-0-253-00673-8(2), 0253006732) Indiana Univ. Pr.

Kea, Pamela. Land, Labour & Entrustment: West African Female Farmers & the Politics of Difference. 2010. 220p. pap. (978-90-04-18232-5(2)) BRILL.

Kelsall, Tim. Culture under Cross-Examination: International Justice & the Special Court for Sierra Leone. 2009. (Cambridge Studies in Law & Society Ser.). (ENG., Illus.). 312p. 113.00 (978-0-521-76778-1(4)) Cambridge Univ. Pr.

Martin, Kathleen. Kamakwie: Finding Peace, Love & Injustice in Sierra Leone, 1 vol. 2012. (ENG., Illus.). 176p. (J). pap. 19.95 **(978-0-88995-472-4(0))** Red Deer Pr. CAN. Dist: Ingram Pub. Services.

Massaquoi, Victor A. Perspectives on Communicating Critical Social Change in Sierra Leone, 1 vol. 2009. 192p. pap. 24.95 (978-1-60813-158-7(0)) PublishAmerica, Inc.

Minteh, Binneh. Perils of Drugs in West Afric. 2010. 64p. pap. (978-3-8383-6113-0(X)) Lambert Academic Publishing.

Olonisakin, Funmi. Peacekeeping in Sierra Leone: The Story of UNAMSIL. 2007. (Histories of un Peace Operations Ser.). 200p. (C). pap. 18.95 (978-1-58826-521-0(8)); lib. bdg. 45.00 (978-1-58826-520-3(X)) Rienner, Lynne Pubs.

Organisation for Economic Co-operation and Development Staff & Michel Colin, de Verdiáre. West African Perspectives: Resources for Development. 2009. (West African Studies). (Illus.). 112p. pap. 63.00 (978-92-64-05975-7(X)) Organization for Economic Cooperation & Development.

Ovadiya, Mirey & Zampaglione, Giuseppe. Escaping Stigma & Neglect: People with Disabilities in Sierra Leone. 2009. (World Bank Working Papers: 164). (ENG., Illus.). 52p. pap. 15.00 (978-0-8213-7918-9(6), 9780821379189) World Bank Pubns.

Owomoyela, Oyekan. The Columbia Guide to West African Literature in English since 1945. 2008. (Columbia Guides to Literature Since 1945 Ser.). (ENG.). 216p. (gr. 17). 85.00 (978-0-231-12686-1(7)) Columbia Univ. Pr.

Peters, Mark. Everyday Literacies in Semi-Rural Gambi. 2010. 108p. pap. (978-3-8383-9539-5(5)) Lambert Academic Publishing.

Rossi, Benedetta, ed. Reconfiguring Slavery: West African Trajectories. 2nd ed. 2009. (Liverpool University Press - Studies in European Regional Cultures Ser.). (ENG., Illus.). 256p. 95.00 (978-1-84631-199-4(3)) Liverpool Univ. Pr. GBR. Dist: Chicago Distribution Ctr.

Sankara, Thomas. We Are the Heirs of the World's Revolutions: Speeches from the Burkina Faso Revolution 1983-87. 2nd ed. 2007. (Illus.). 108p. pap. 10.00 (978-0-87348-989-8(6)) Pathfinder Pr.

Schroven, Anita. Women after War: Gender Mainstreaming & the Social Construction of Identity in Contemporary Sierra Leone. 2007. (ENG., Illus.). 152p. pap. 34.95 (978-3-8258-9627-0(7)) Lit Verlag DEU. Dist: Transaction Pubs.

Schumer, Tanja & Schimer, Tanja. New Humanitarianism: Britain & Sierra Leone, 1997-2003. 2007. (Palgrave Studies in Development Ser.). (ENG., Illus.). 256p. 100.00 (978-0-230-54517-5(3)) Palgrave Macmillan.

Solleh, Kumba Femusu. The Damby Tradition of the Kono People of Sierra Leone West Africa: Volume Ii. 2011. 224p. pap. 15.00 **(978-1-4490-7466-1(9))** AuthorHouse.

Taiwo, Damola. Art, Tribes, & Cultures Identify Us. 2011. 104p. pap. 13.95 **(978-1-4620-4336-1(4))** iUniverse, Inc.

Vaughan, Olufemi & Okome, Mojúbàolú Olúfúnké, eds. West African Migrations: Transnational & Global Pathways in a New Century. 2012. (ENG., Illus.). 294p. 90.00 **(978-0-230-33867-8(4))** Palgrave Macmillan.

Wodon, Quentin. Migration, Remittances, & Poverty: Case Studies from West Africa. Wodon, Quentin, ed. 2007. (World Bank Working Papers). 125p. pap. 20.00 (978-0-8213-6627-1(0)) World Bank Pubns.

AFRICA, WEST—SOCIAL LIFE AND CUSTOMS

Bourque, Peter. Tarnished Ivory: Reflections on Peace Corps & Beyond. 2011. 224p. pap. 19.99 **(978-1-4628-7759-1(1))** Xlibris Corp.

Burton, Jean-Dominique. Vaudou/Voodoo/Vudu. 2008. (ENG., Illus.). 256p. 75.00 (978-88-7439-443-2(8)) 5 Continents ITA. Dist: Hachette Bk. Group.

Calame-Griaule, Genevieve & Pataux, Agnes. Dogon: People of the Cliffs. 2006. (Imago Mundi Ser.). (Illus.). (978-88-7439-055-7(6)) 5 Continents.

Cohee, Jared. Calm of the Niger: A Peaceful River Winding Through the Storm of Africa. 2009. pap. (978-1-61623-434-8(2)) Independent Pub.

Daise, Ronald. Gullah Branches, West African Roots. 2007. (Illus.). 198p. per. (978-0-87844-182-2(4)) Sandlapper Publishing Co., Inc.

De Jong, Ferdinand & de Jong, Ferdinand. Masquerades of Modernity: Power & Secrecy in Casamance, Senegal. 2007. (ENG., Illus.). 256p. 39.95 (978-0-253-35172-2(3), 0253351723) Indiana Univ. Pr.

Ekunsanmi, Toye. What Africans Eat: Traditional Foods & Food Traditions of West Africa. 2010. (Illus.). 220p. pap. 13.95 **(978-1-4327-6192-9(7))** Outskirts Pr., Inc.

Gausset, Quentin. Constructing the Kwanja of Adamwa (Cameroon) Essay in Fractal Anthropology. 2011. (ENG.). 312p. pap. 41.95 (978-3-8258-1898-2(5)) Lit Verlag DEU. Dist: Transaction Pubs.

Holloway, Kris. Monique & the Mango Rains: Two Years with a Midwife in Mali. Bidwell, John, ed. 2006. (Illus.). 214p. pap. 19.95 (978-1-57766-435-2(3)) Waveland Pr., Inc.

Kumba Femusu Solleh. Kono Gold or Koine Gold: Onomastics. 2009. 328p. pap. 17.99 (978-1-4343-7341-0(X)) AuthorHouse.

Ladefoged, P. Phonetic Study of West African Languages. 2nd ed. 2009. (ENG., Illus.). 112p. pap. 28.99 (978-0-521-11623-7(6)) Cambridge Univ. Pr.

Laister, Richard. Looking for Mr. Legba: A Voodoo Quest. 2010. (ENG., Illus.). 179p. pap. 23.99 **(978-1-906791-44-5(9))** Arena Bks. GBR. Dist: Lightning Source UK, Ltd.

McNaughton, Patrick. A Bird Dance near Saturday City: Sidi Ballo & the Art of West African Masquerade. 2008. (African Expressive Cultures Ser.). (ENG., Illus.). 328p. 65.00 (978-0-253-35148-7(0), 0253351480); pap. 24.95 (978-0-253-21984-3(1), 0253219841) Indiana Univ. Pr.

Mommersteeg, Geert. In the City of the Marabouts: Islamic Culture in West Africa. Webb, Diane, tr. 2011. 156p. (C). pap. 16.95 **(978-1-57766-723-0(9))** Waveland Pr., Inc.

Montgomery, Michael, ed. The Crucible of Carolina: Essays in the Development of Gullah Language & Culture. 2008. (ENG., Illus.). 252p. pap. 24.95 (978-0-8203-3115-7(5)) Univ. of Georgia Pr.

Schulz, Dorothea E. Muslims & New Media in West Africa: Pathways to God. 2011. (ENG., Illus.). 328p. 80.00 (978-0-253-35715-1(2), 0253357152); pap. 27.95 (978-0-253-22362-3(8), 0253223628) Indiana Univ. Pr.

Solleh, Kumba Femusu. The Damby Tradition of the Kono People of Sierra Leone West Africa: With a Tribute to the Late Paramount Chief Fasuluku I of Kono District 1895-1978. 2010. 288p. pap. 20.00 (978-1-4389-9451-2(6)) AuthorHouse.

Starace, Chris. To Benin & Back: Short Stories, Essays, & Reflections about Life in Benin as A Peace Corps Volunteer & the Subsequent Readjustment Process. 2011. 324p. 29.95 **(978-1-4620-4622-5(3))**; pap. 19.95 **(978-1-4620-4621-8(5))** iUniverse, Inc.

Suso, Saiba K. Globalisation & Singing Culture. 2011. 104p. pap. **(978-3-8454-1486-7(3))** Lambert Academic Publishing.

Taiwo, Damola. Art, Tribes, & Cultures Identify Us. 2011. 104p. pap. 13.95 **(978-1-4620-4336-1(4))** iUniverse, Inc.

Van Den Bersselaar, Dmitri. The King of Drinks: Schnapps Gin from Modernity to Tradition. 2007. (African Social Studies). (Illus.). 268p. pap. (978-90-04-16091-0(4)) BRILL.

AFRICA IN LITERATURE

see Africa—In Literature

AFRICAANDERS

see Afrikaners

AFRICAN AMERICAN ACTORS

see also African American Motion Picture Actors and Actresses

Copeland, Brian. Not a Genuine Black Man: Or, How I Claimed My Piece of Ground in the Lily-White Suburbs. 2006. 272p. 22.95 (978-1-4013-0233-7(5)) Hyperion Pr.

Deane, Pamala S. James Edwards: African American Hollywood Icon. 2009. (ENG., Illus.). 236p. pap. 45.00 (978-0-7864-4415-1(0)) McFarland & Co., Inc. Pubs.

Gossett, Louis, Jr. & Karas, Phyllis. An Actor & a Gentleman. 2010. (ENG., Illus.). 320p. 26.95 (978-0-470-57471-3(2), Wiley) Wiley, John & Sons, Inc.

Grier, Pam. Foxy: My Life in Three Acts. 2011. (ENG., Illus.). 288p. pap. 14.99 (978-0-446-54848-9(0)) Grand Central Publishing.

Iannucci, Lisa. Will Smith: A Biography, 1 vol. 2009. (Greenwood Biographies Ser.). 133p. 35.00 (978-0-313-37610-8(7), GR7610) Greenwood Publishing Group, Inc.

Jacobs, Carole. Tyra Banks: A Biography. 2010. (Illus.). xl, 180p. E-Book (978-0-313-38275-8(1), Greenwood Electronic Media (GEM)) Greenwood Publishing Group, Inc.

Kujawinska Courtney, Krystyna & Lukowska, Maria, eds. Ira Aldridge (1807-1867) The Great Shakespearean Tragedian on the Bicentennial Anniversary of his Birth. 2009. 168p. pap. 50.95 (978-3-631-57734-9(6)) Lang, Peter GmbH, Europaischer Verlag der Wissenschaften DEU. Dist: Lang, Peter.

Lindfors, Bernth. Ira Aldridge: The Early Years, 1807-1833, 2 vols. 2011. (Rochester Studies in African History & the Diaspora Ser.: Volume 48). (Illus.). 402p. 55.00 (978-1-58046-381-2(9)) Univ. of Rochester Pr.

—Ira Aldridge: The Early Years, 1807-1833 & the Vagabond Years, 1833-1852. 2011. (Rochester Studies in African History & the Diaspora Ser.). 660p. 99.00 (978-1-58046-401-7(7)) Univ. of Rochester Pr.

—Ira Aldridge: The Vagabond Years, 1833-1852, 2 vols. 2011. (Rochester Studies in African History & the Diaspora Ser.: Volume 49). (Illus.). 258p. 55.00 (978-1-58046-394-2(0)) Univ. of Rochester Pr.

Nollen, Scott Allen. Paul Robeson: Film Pioneer. 2010. (ENG., Illus.). 215p. pap. 45.00 (978-0-7864-3520-3(8)) McFarland & Co., Inc. Pubs.

Ogelsby, Greta. Mama 'n Nem: Handprints on My Life. 2012. **(978-1-933794-48-8(8))** Kirk Hse. Pubs.

Regester, Charlene B. African American Actresses: The Struggle for Visibility, 1900-1960. 2010. (ENG., Illus.). 440p. pap. 27.95 (978-0-253-22192-6(7), 0253221927) Indiana Univ. Pr.

Stern, Bert. Marilyn Monroe: The Last Sitting. 2007. (ENG., Illus.). 128p. pap. 39.95 (978-0-307-39164-3(7)) Random House Mondadori ESP. Dist: Random Hse., Inc.

Tracy, Kathleen. Morgan Freeman: A Biography. 2006. (ENG., Illus.). 288p. 24.95 (978-1-56980-307-3(2)) Barricade Bks., Inc.

Walker, David, et al. Reflections on Blaxploitation: Actors & Directors Speak. 2009. (ENG., Illus.). 248p. 45.00 (978-0-8108-6706-2(0)) Scarecrow Pr., Inc.

Washington, Isaiah. A Man from Another Land: How Finding My Roots Changed My Life. 2011. (ENG., Illus.). 304p. 24.99 (978-1-59995-318-2(8)) Center St.

AFRICAN AMERICAN AGED

see Older African Americans

AFRICAN AMERICAN ART

see also African American Artists; African Americans in Art

Anderson, Iain. This Is Our Music: Free Jazz, the Sixties, & American Culture. 2007. (Arts & Intellectual Life in Modern America Ser.). (Illus.). 264p. (C). per. 24.95 (978-0-8122-2003-2(X)) Univ. of Pennsylvania Pr.

Bendolph, Mary Lee, et al. Gee's Bend: The Architecture of the Quilt. 2006. (ENG., Illus.). 224p. 50.00 (978-0-9719104-5-4(6)) Tinwood Bks.

Bernier, Celeste-Marie. African American Visual Arts: From Slavery to the Present. 2008. (ENG.). 296p. 59.95 (978-0-8078-3256-1(1)); pap. 26.95 (978-0-8078-5933-9(8)) Univ. of North Carolina Pr.

Calo, Mary Ann. Distinction & Denial: Race, Nation, & the Critical Construction of the African American Artist, 1920-40. 2007. (ENG.). 280p. 84.50 (978-0-472-11468-9(9)); per. 37.50 (978-0-472-03230-3(5)) Univ. of Michigan Pr.

Childs, Adrienne L., et al. Evolution: Five Decades of Printmaking. 2007. (Illus.). 128p. 30.00 (978-0-7649-4204-4(2), A141) Pomegranate Communications, Inc.

Collins, Thom & Fitzpatrick, Tracy, eds. American People, Black Light: Faith Ringgold's Paintings of The 1960s. 2011. (ENG., Illus.). 136p. pap. 30.00 (978-0-9795629-3-8(7)) Neuberger Museum of Art.

Cooks, Bridget R. Exhibiting Blackness: African Americans & the American Art Museum. 2011. (Illus.). 240p. pap. 29.95 (978-1-55849-875-4(3)) Univ. of Massachusetts Pr.

Douglas, Robert L. Resistance, Insurgence, & Identity: The Art of Mari Evans, Nelson Stevens, & the Black Arts Movement. 2008. (978-1-59221-564-5(5)); 376p. pap. (978-1-59221-565-2(3)) Africa World Pr.

Dunkley, Tina Maria & Cullum, Jerry. In the Eye of the Muses: Selections from the Clark Atlanta University Art Collection. 2012. **(978-0-615-59005-9(5))** Massachusetts College of Art.

Ebony Stitchers Quilt Guild Belinda Pedroso. Artistic Expressions of Quilters of Color, vol. 2010. 58p. 22.71 (978-0-615-38616-4(4)) Ebony Stitchers Quilt Guild.

English, Darby. How to See a Work of Art in Total Darkness. (ENG., Illus.). 376p. (gr. 17). 2010. pap. 19.95 (978-0-262-51493-4(1)) 2007. 32.00 (978-0-262-05083-8(8), MIT Pr.

Enns, Catherine M. The Journey of the Highwaymen. 2009. (ENG., Illus.). 336p. 42.00 (978-0-8109-7331-2(6)) Abrams.

Farrington, Lisa E. Creating Their Own Image: The History of African-American Women Artists, 1 vol. 2011. (ENG., Illus.). 368p. pap. 39.95 (978-0-19-976760-1(2)) Oxford Univ. Pr., Inc.

Finley, Cheryl, et al. Teenie Harris, Photographer: Image, Memory, History. 2011. (ENG.). 208p. pap. 24.95 **(978-0-8229-6174-1(1))**; (Illus.). 55.00 **(978-0-8229-4414-0(6))** Univ. of Pittsburgh Pr.

Fleming, Peggy & Fleming, Jennifer. Crown Me! Capital Pool Checkers Club. 2010. (Illus.). 111p. (978-0-9676322-2-3(6)) Three Sisters Pr.

Franklin, John Hope & Wardlaw, Alivia J. Collecting African American Art: The Museum of Fine Arts, Houston. 2009. (ENG., Illus.). 152p. pap. 35.00 (978-0-300-15291-3(4)) Museum of Fine Arts, Houston.

Franks, Pamela & Steele, Robert E. Embodied: Black Identities in American Art from the Yale University Art Gallery. 2010. (978-0-89467-977-3(5)) Yale Univ. Art Gallery.

Fredericq, Suzanne. Artist Eugene J. Martin's 2002 Acrylic Paintings on Canvas, Part 1. 2010. 97p. pap. 43.10 (978-0-9825704-9-4(X)) Estate of Eugene James Martin.

—Artist Eugene J. Martin's 2003 Acrylic Paintings on Canvas, Part 1. 2010. 99p. pap. 41.20 (978-0-9826351-0-0(9)) Estate of Eugene James Martin.

—Catalogue of the Inaugural Art Exhibit Eugene J. Martin: Spice of Life. 2009. 38p. 19.70 (978-0-9825704-0-1(6)) Estate of Eugene James Martin.

—Transformations: Works on Paper by Artist Eugene J. Martin, Part I. 2010. 103p. pap. 44.90 (978-0-9825704-6-3(5)) Estate of Eugene James Martin.

Glasrud, Bruce A. & Wintz, Cary D. The Harlem Renaissance in the American West: The New Negro's Western Experience. 2011. E-Book **(978-0-203-80558-9(5))** Routledge.

Golden, Thelma, et al. Kori Newkirk: 1997-2007. 2007. (Illus.). pap. (978-0-911291-33-9(4)) Fellows of Contemporary Art.

Gorschlüter, Peter. Afro Modern: Journeys Through the Black Atlantic. Barson, Tanya, ed. 2010. (ENG., Illus.). 208p. 32.50 (978-1-85437-923-8(2)) Tate Publishing, Ltd. GBR. Dist: Hachette Bk. Group.

Grove, Jeffrey. After 1968: Contemporary Artists & the Civil Rights Legacy. 2008. pap. 25.00 (978-1-932543-22-3(8)) High Museum of Art.

Hearne III, Archie & Hearne, Garbo Watson. Collaborations: Two Decades of African American Art¿Hearne Fine Art, 1988¿2008. 2009. (ENG., Illus.). 130p. 49.95 (978-1-60725-130-9(2)) Independent Pub.

Heffley, Scott. Bold Improvisation: Searching for African-American Quilts - the Heffley Collection. 2007. 124p. mass mkt. 29.95 (978-1-933466-25-5(1)) Kansas City Star Bks.

jegede, dele. Encyclopedia of African American Artists, 1 vol. 2009. (Artists of the American Mosaic Ser.). (Illus.). 293p. 85.00 (978-0-313-33761-1(6), GR3761, Greenwood Pr.) Greenwood Publishing Group, Inc.

Jones, Ben. Ben Jones: A Retrospective: The Art of the Journey. 2007. per. 39.95 (978-0-9791130-0-0(8)) Jones, Ben.

Jones, Kellie. Now Dig This! Art & Black Los Angeles, 1960-1980. 2011. (ENG., Illus.). 352p. 60.00 **(978-3-7913-5136-0(2))** Prestel Publishing.

Jones, Lisa, et al. EyeMinded: Living & Writing Contemporary Art. 2011. (ENG., Illus.). 528p. 99.95 (978-0-8223-4861-0(6)); pap. 27.95 (978-0-8223-4873-3(X)) Duke Univ. Pr.

Kibuuka, David. Modern Batik Art. 2009. 108p. pap. 61.99 (978-1-4363-5178-2(2)) Xlibris Corp.

Kim, Christine Y. Flow. 2008. pap. (978-0-942949-34-6(X)) Studio Museum in Harlem, The.

Kim, Christine Y., et al. The World Stage: Africa, Lagos - Dakar. 2008. (978-0-942949-35-3(8)) Studio Museum in Harlem, The.

Kinsey, Bernard W. & Kinsey, Shirley Pooler. The Kinsey Collection, Collectors Edition: Shared Treasures of Bernard & Shirley Kinsey: Where Art & History Intersect. 2010. (Illus.). 160p. 99.95 (978-0-9826225-1-3(1)) Allen, Charles Imaging Experts.

Ligon, Glenn, et al, texts. 30 Americans. 2009. (ENG., Illus.). 232p. 60.00 (978-0-9821195-1-8(8)) Rubell Family Collection.

Lock, Graham & Murray, David. The Hearing Eye: Jazz & Blues Influences in African American Visual Art. Lock, Graham & Murray, David, eds. 2009. (ENG., Illus.). 288p. 99.00 (978-0-19-534050-1(7)) Oxford Univ. Pr., Inc.

Lock, Graham & Murray, David, eds. The Hearing Eye: Jazz & Blues Influences in African American Visual Art. 2009. (ENG., Illus.). 288p. pap. 24.95 (978-0-19-534051-8(5)) Oxford Univ. Pr., Inc.

Mazloomi, Carolyn L. Textural Rhythms: Quilting the Jazz Tradition. 2007. (Illus.). 40.00 (978-0-9792675-0-5(1)) Paper Moon Pubns.

Mercer, Kobena & O'Meally, Robert, texts. Romare Bearden in the Modernist Tradition. 2010. (ENG., Illus.). 134p. pap. 30.00 (978-0-615-20291-4(8)) Bearden, Romare Foundation.

Online, Blackshear. Thomas Blackshear Collector Handbook & Secondary Market. 2010. pap. 24.95 (978-0-578-00520-1(4)) Blackshear Online.

Otfinoski, Steven. The Visual Arts. 2nd rev. ed. 2011. (A to Z of African Americans Ser.). (Illus.). 280p. (C). (gr. 9-18). 49.50 (978-0-8160-7840-0(8)) Facts On File, Inc.

Peress, Maurice. Dvorak to Duke Ellington: A Conductor Explores America's Music & Its African American Roots. 2008. (ENG., Illus.). 272p. pap. 24.95 (978-0-19-537447-6(9)) Oxford Univ. Pr., Inc.

Pinkney, Jerry. Jerry Pinkney: Aesop's Fables & Other Tails. 2007. (Illus.). 17p. pap. (978-0-9795872-1-4(2)) Brandywine River Museum.

Powell, Richard J., et al. African American Art: Harlem Renaissance, the Civil Rights Movement, & Beyond. 2012. (ENG., Illus.). 256p. 60.00 **(978-0-8478-3890-5(0)**, Skira) Rizzoli International Pubns., Inc.

Rosengarten, Dale, et al. Grass Roots: African Origins of an American Art. 2008. (Illus.). 269p. 60.00 (978-0-945802-50-1(1)); pap. 35.00 (978-0-945802-51-8(X)) Museum for African Art.

Ruffin, Sonie. The Soulful Art of African-American Quilts: Nineteen Bold, Improvisational Projects. 2007. 124p. pap. 24.95 (978-1-933466-33-0(2)) Kansas City Star Bks.

Russell, Charles, ed. Self-Taught Art: The Culture & Aesthetics of American Vernacular Art. 2006. (ENG., Illus.). 240p. 50.00 (978-1-57806-380-2(9)) Univ. Pr. of Mississippi.

Schulman, Daniel, ed. A Force for Change: African American Art & the Julius Rosenwald Fund. 2009. (ENG., Illus.). 176p. pap. 39.95 (978-0-8101-2588-9(9)) Northwestern Univ. Pr.

Talley, Clarence, et al. African-American Art Supplement. rev. ed. 2010. (ENG.). 146p. pap. 37.57 (978-0-7575-4995-3(0)) Kendall Hunt Publishing Co.

Thaggert, Miriam. Images of Black Modernism: Verbal & Visual Strategies of the Harlem Renaissance. 2010. (Illus.). 256p. (ENG.). pap. 28.95 (978-1-55849-831-0(1)); lib. bdg. 80.00 (978-1-55849-830-3(3)) Univ. of Massachusetts Pr.

Theisen, Olive Jensen. Walls That Speak: The Murals of John Thomas Biggers. 2010. (Illus.). 160p. 29.95 (978-1-57441-289-5(2)) Univ. of North Texas Pr.

Thurmer, Robert, frwd. Each in Their Own Voice: African American Artists in Cleveland, 1970 - 2005. 2009. (Illus.). 56p. pap. 10.00 (978-0-615-26752-4(1)) Cleveland State University Art Gallery.

Virginia Museum of Fine Arts Staff, contrib. by. Making History: 20th-Century African American Art. 2012. **(978-1-934351-00-0(8))** Virginia Museum of Fine Arts.

Wiley, Kehinde. Kehinde Wiley: the World Stage, India, Sri Lanka. 2012. (ENG., Illus.). 40p. 40.00 **(978-0-615-44459-8(8))** Hoffman, Rhona Gallery.

AFRICAN AMERICAN ARTISTS

see also African American Art

Arnett, Matt, et al. Mary Lee Bendolph, Gee's Bend Quilts, & Beyond. Metcalf, Eugene W., ed. 2006. (ENG., Illus.). 72p. 26.95 (978-0-9719104-8-5(0)) Tinwood Bks.

Auping, Michael, et al, texts. Martin Puryear, 1 vol. 2007. (ENG., Illus.). 192p. 60.00 (978-0-87070-714-8(0)) Museum of Modern Art.

Bearden, Romare. Romare Bearden: A Black Odyssey, 1 vol. 2008. (ENG., Illus.). 116p. 45.00 (978-0-9774965-9-4(7)) DC Moore Gallery.

Bedford, Christopher & Walker, Hamza. Mark Bradford. 2010. (Illus.). 256p. 65.00 (978-0-300-16358-2(4)) Yale Univ. Pr.

Bey, Sharif. Aaron Douglas & Hale Woodruff: The Social Responsiblity & Expanded Pedagogy of the Black Artist. 2008. 236p. pap. (978-3-639-10274-1(6)) VDM Verlag Dr. Mueller e.K.

Cain, Lisa. Art of the Spirit: The Culture of the Rural South, Self-Taught Artist Lisa Cain. 2011. 52p. pap. 28.50 (978-1-4567-3905-8(0)) AuthorHouse.

Childs, Adrienne L. & Humphrey, Margo. Margo Humphrey. 2009. (David C. Driskell Ser. of African American Art Ser.). 112p. 35.00 (978-0-7649-5069-8(X)) Pomegranate Communications, Inc.

Collins, Thom & Fitzpatrick, Tracy, eds. American People, Black Light: Faith Ringgold's Paintings of The 1960s. 2011. (ENG., Illus.). 136p. pap. 30.00 (978-0-9795629-3-8(7)) Neuberger Museum of Art.

Crampton, Luke. Michael Jackson: Music ICON. Crampton, Luke, ed. 2009. (FRE, GER & ENG., Illus.). 192p. pap. 9.99 (978-3-8365-2081-2(8)) TASCHEN DEU. Dist: Ingram Pub. Services.

Du Bois, W. E. B. The Negro American Artisan. 192p. (Orig.). reprint ed. 88.00 (978-0-7222-9720-9(3)) Library Reprints, Inc.

Earle, Susan, ed. Aaron Douglas: African American Modernist. 2007. (ENG., Illus.). 272p. 60.00 (978-0-300-12180-3(6)) Yale Univ. Pr.

Farrington, Lisa E. Creating Their Own Image: The History of African-American Women Artists, 1 vol. 2011. (ENG., Illus.). 368p. pap. 39.95 *(978-0-19-976760-1(2))* Oxford Univ. Pr., Inc.

Fredericq, Suzanne. Artist Eugene J. Martin's 2000 Acrylic Paintings on Canvas. 2009. 75p. pap., pap. 31.50 *(978-0-9825704-7-0(3))* Estate of Eugene James Martin.

—Artist Eugene J. Martin's 2001 Acrylic Paintings on Canvas, Part 1. 2009. 93p. pap. 41.90 *(978-0-9825704-8-7(1))* Estate of Eugene James Martin.

—Artist Eugene J. Martin's 2003-04 Acrylic Paintings on Canvas. 2010. 104p. pap. 42.70 *(978-0-9826351-2-4(5))* Estate of Eugene James Martin.

—Artist Eugene J. Martin's Secret Hieroglyphs. 2009. 62p. pap., pap. 29.00 *(978-0-9825704-5-6(7))* Estate of Eugene James Martin.

—Circle Drawings by Eugene J. Martin: 1969-1971. 2009. 93p. pap. 34.40 *(978-0-9825704-2-5(2))* Estate of Eugene James Martin.

—Eugene J. Martin's 1975 Sculptural Drawings. 2009. 100p. pap. 19.50 *(978-0-578-03371-6(2))* Estate of Eugene James Martin.

Gates, Henry Louis, Jr. Harlem Renaissance Lives: From the African American National Biography. Higginbotham, Evelyn Brooks, ed. 2009. (Illus.). 608p. 50.00 *(978-0-19-538795-7(3))* Oxford Univ. Pr., Inc.

Gellner, Uwe, ed. Rashid Johnson: Sharpening My Oyster Knife. 2009. (ENG., Illus.). 64p. pap. 22.50 *(978-3-86678-251-8(9))* Kerber Verlag DEU. Dist: D.A.P./Distributed Art Pubs.

Golden, Thelma, et al. Kori Newkirk: 1997-2007. 2007. (Illus.). pap. *(978-0-911291-33-9(4))* Fellows of Contemporary Art.

Goldstein, Nancy. Jackie Ormes: The First African American Woman Cartoonist. 2008. (ENG., Illus.). 240p. 40.00 *(978-0-472-11624-9(X))* Univ. of Michigan Pr.

Hills, Patricia & Hills, P. Painting Harlem Modern: The Art of Jacob Lawrence. 2010. (ENG., Illus.). 400p. 55.00 *(978-0-520-25241-7(1))* Univ. of California Pr.

jegede, dele. Encyclopedia of African American Artists, 1 vol. 2009. (Artists of the American Mosaic Ser.). (Illus.). 293p. 85.00 *(978-0-313-33761-1(6)*, GR3761, Greenwood Pr.) Greenwood Publishing Group, Inc.

Jones, Lisa, et al. EyeMinded: Living & Writing Contemporary Art. 2011. (ENG., Illus.). 528p. 99.95 *(978-0-8223-4861-0(6))*; pap. 27.95 *(978-0-8223-4873-3(X))* Duke Univ. Pr.

Jones, Lois Mailou & Hanzal, Carla M. Lois Mailou Jones: A Life in Vibrant Color. 2009. *(978-0-9762300-8-3(9))* Mint Museum, The.

Ligon, Glenn, et al, texts. 30 Americans. 2009. (ENG., Illus.). 232p. 60.00 *(978-0-9821195-1-8(8))* Rubell Family Collection.

Magee, David. The Education of Mr. Mayfield: An Unusual Story of Social Change at Ole Miss. 2009. (Illus.). 256p. 21.95 *(978-0-89587-366-8(4))* Blair, John F. Pub.

Marley, Anna O., ed. Henry Ossawa Tanner: Modern Spirit. 2012. (ENG., Illus.). 304p. 75.00 ***(978-0-520-27074-9(6))***; pap. 39.95 ***(978-0-520-27075-6(4))*** Univ. of California Pr.

McGee, Julie L. Artist & Scholar. 2006. (Illus.). 216p. 45.00 *(978-0-7649-3747-7(2)*, A127) Pomegranate Communications, Inc.

Monroe, Gary & Newton, Harold. Harold Newton: The Original Highwayman. 2007. (ENG., Illus.). 160p. 34.95 *(978-0-8130-3042-5(0))* Univ. Pr. of Florida.

Mooney, Paul. Black Is the New White. 2010. (ENG., Illus.). 272p. pap. 15.99 *(978-1-4165-8796-5(9))* Gallery Pr., The IRL. Dist: Simon & Schuster, Inc.

Myers, Julia R. Energy: Charles Mcgee at Eighty-Five. 2010. (Illus.). 100p. pap. 24.95 *(978-0-912042-99-2(0))* Eastern Michigan Univ. Pr.

Otfinoski, Steven. The Visual Arts. 2nd rev. ed. 2011. (A to Z of African Americans Ser.). (Illus.). 280p. (C). (gr. 9-18). 49.50 *(978-0-8160-7840-0(8))* Facts On File, Inc.

Painter, Nell Irvin. Creating Black Americans: African-American History & Its Meanings, 1619 to the Present. 2006. (ENG., Illus.). 496p. (C). pap. 44.95 *(978-0-19-513756-9(6))* Oxford Univ. Pr., Inc.

Price, Sally & Price, Richard. Romare Bearden: The Caribbean Dimension. 2006. (Illus.). 192p. (C). 49.95 *(978-0-8122-3948-5(2))* Univ. of Pennsylvania Pr.

Ridley Jackson, Kate & Ridley Smith, Constance. Greg Ridley, Master of Copper Tooling. 2009. 136p. pap. 55.00 *(978-1-4343-8040-1(8))* AuthorHouse.

Rudolph, William Keyse, et al. In Search of Julien Hudson: Free Artist of Color in Pre-Civil War New Orleans. 2011. *(978-0-917860-57-7(8))* Univ. Pr. of Florida.

Schoonmaker, Trevor, ed. Barkley L. Hendricks: Birth of the Cool. 2008. (ENG., Illus.). 140p. 39.95 *(978-0-938989-31-8(6))* Duke Univ. Pr.

Skelly, Julia. No Strangers to Beauty - Black Women Artists & the Hottentot Venus. 2008. 88p. pap. *(978-3-639-04476-8(2))* VDM Verlag Dr. Mueller e.K.

Smith, Charisa A. & Malloy, Tom. Blending Colors from Life: Trenton's Own Watercolorist, Tom Malloy. 2007. *(978-1-59221-433-4(9))*; pap. *(978-1-59221-434-1(7))* Africa World Pr.

Theisen, Olive Jensen. A Life on Paper: The Drawings & Lithographs of John Thomas Biggers. 2006. (ENG., Illus.). 160p. 29.95 *(978-1-57441-220-8(5))* Univ. of North Texas Pr.

—Walls That Speak: The Murals of John Thomas Biggers. 2010. (Illus.). 160p. 29.95 *(978-1-57441-289-5(2))* Univ. of North Texas Pr.

Thompson, Jerry & Deterville, Duane. Black Artists in Oakland. 2007. (Images of America Ser.). (ENG., Illus.). 128p. per. 19.99 *(978-0-7385-4725-1(5))* Arcadia Publishing.

Thurmer, Robert, frwd. Each in Their Own Voice: African American Artists in Cleveland, 1970 - 2005. 2009. (Illus.). 56p. pap. 10.00 *(978-0-615-26752-4(1))* Cleveland State University Art Gallery.

Tillman, Gregory. Hoopla in Harlem! The Renaissance of African American Art & Culture. 2009. (ENG.). 84p. pap. 17.99 *(978-0-7618-4570-6(4))* Univ. Pr. of America, Inc.

Todd, Leonard. Carolina Clay: The Life & Legend of the Slave Potter Dave. 2008. (ENG., Illus.). 320p. 25.95 *(978-0-393-05856-7(5)*, 5856) Norton, W. W. & Co., Inc.

Wallace, Michele. Invisibility Blues: From Pop to Theory. 2008. (Haymarket Ser.). (ENG., Illus.). 320p. pap. 21.95 *(978-1-85984-487-8(1)*, 859487) Verso Bks. GBR. Dist: Norton, W. W. & Co., Inc.

Wardlaw, Alvia J. & Hess, Aimee. Margaret Mead. 2007. (David C. Driskell Series of African American Art Ser.: 6). (Illus.). 64p. 12.95 *(978-0-7649-3766-8(9))* Pomegranate Communications, Inc.

Widener, Daniel. Black Arts West: Culture & Struggle in Postwar Los Angeles. 2010. (ENG., Illus.). 384p. 94.95 *(978-0-8223-4667-8(2))*; pap. 26.95 *(978-0-8223-4679-1(6))* Duke Univ. Pr.

AFRICAN AMERICAN ARTS

see also Harlem Renaissance; Hip-Hop

Batiste, Stephanie Leigh. Darkening Mirrors: Imperial Representation in Depression-Era African American Performance. 2012. (ENG., Illus.). 352p. 94.95 ***(978-0-8223-4898-6(5))***; pap. 25.95 ***(978-0-8223-4923-5(X))*** Duke Univ. Pr.

Gayle, Addison, Jr. The Addison Gayle Jr. Reader. Norment, Nathaniel, Jr., ed. 2009. (ENG., Illus.). 504p. pap. 37.00 *(978-0-252-07610-7(9))* Univ. of Illinois Pr.

Gayle, Addison, Jr. & Gayle, Addison. The Addison Gayle Jr. Reader. Norment, Nathaniel, Jr. & Norment, Nathaniel, eds. 2009. (ENG., Illus.). 504p. 78.00 *(978-0-252-03408-4(2))* Univ. of Illinois Pr.

Hillstrom, Kevin. Defining Moments: The Harlem Renaissance. 2011. (KWS Publishers - Defining Moments Ser.). (ENG., Illus.). 222p. (gr. 6). pap. 19.95 *(978-0-7808-1234-5(4))* KWS Pubs.

Hine, Darlene Clark & McCluskey, John, Jr., eds. The Black Chicago Renaissance. 2012. (New Black Studies Ser.). (ENG., Illus.). 272p. 80.00 ***(978-0-252-03702-3(2))***; pap. 27.95 ***(978-0-252-07858-3(6))*** Univ. of Illinois Pr.

Hooper, Lita. The Art of Work: The Art & Life of Haki R. Madhubuti. 2007. (Illus.). 109p. per. 14.95 *(978-0-88378-255-2(3))* Third World Press.

Huggins, Nathan I. Harlem Renaissance. 2007. (ENG., Illus.). 390p. (C). per. 19.95 *(978-0-19-506336-3(8))* Oxford Univ. Pr., Inc.

Jackson, Lawrence Patrick. The Indignant Generation: A Narrative History of African American Writers & Critics, 1934-1960. 2010. (ENG., Illus.). 608p. (C). 35.00 *(978-0-691-14135-0(5))* Princeton Univ. Pr.

Kramer, Hilton, ed. Counterpoints: 25 Years of the New Criterion on Culture & the Arts. 2007. (ENG.). 512p. 35.00 *(978-1-56663-706-0(6))* Dee, Ivan R. Pub.

Locke, Alain LeRoy. The Works of Alain Locke, 1 vol. Molesworth, Charles, ed. 2012. (Collected Black Writings). 624p. 45.00 ***(978-0-19-979504-8(5))*** Oxford Univ. Pr., Inc.

Munby, Jonathan. Under a Bad Sign: Criminal Self-Representation in African American Popular Culture. 2011. (ENG.). 224p. 65.00 *(978-0-226-55035-0(4))*; pap. 22.50 *(978-0-226-55036-7(2))* Univ. of Chicago Pr.

Ogbar, Jeffrey O. G., ed. The Harlem Renaissance Revisited: Politics, Arts, & Letters. 2010. (ENG.). 272p. (C). (gr. 13-17). pap. 30.00 *(978-0-8018-9461-9(1))* Johns Hopkins Univ. Pr.

Ongiri, Amy Abugo. Spectacular Blackness: The Cultural Politics of the Black Power Movement & the Search for a Black Aesthetic. 2009. (ENG.). 240p. (C). (gr. 13-17). pap. 22.50 *(978-0-8139-2860-9(5))*; (gr. 17). 55.00 *(978-0-8139-2859-3(1))* Univ. Pr. of Virginia.

Painter, Nell Irvin. Creating Black Americans: African-American History & Its Meanings, 1619 to the Present. 2006. (ENG., Illus.). 496p. (C). pap. 44.95 *(978-0-19-513756-9(6))* Oxford Univ. Pr., Inc.

Schoener, Allon, ed. Harlem on My Mind: Cultural Capital of Black America, 1900-1968. 2007. (ENG., Illus.). 258p. per. 24.95 *(978-1-59558-158-7(8))* New Pr., The.

Smith, R. J. The Great Black Way: L. A. in the 1940s & the Lost African-American Renaissance. 2007. (ENG., Illus.). 400p. per. 16.95 *(978-1-58648-521-4(0))* PublicAffairs.

Sosnoski, James J., et al. Teaching History & Configuring Virtual Worlds: Virtual Harlem & the VERITAS Studies. 2006. (Digital Formations Ser.: Vol. 18). (Illus.). 224p. (C). pap. 32.95 *(978-0-8204-6784-9(7))* Lang, Peter Publishing, Inc.

Watanabe, Yasushi & McConnell, David L., eds. Soft Power Superpowers: Cultural & National Assets of Japan & the United States. 2008. (ENG.). 328p. pap. 44.95 *(978-0-7656-2249-5(1))* Sharpe, M.E. Inc.

Widener, Daniel. Black Arts West: Culture & Struggle in Postwar Los Angeles. 2010. (ENG., Illus.). 384p. 94.95 *(978-0-8223-4667-8(2))*; pap. 26.95 *(978-0-8223-4679-1(6))* Duke Univ. Pr.

Young, Kevin. The Grey Album: On the Blackness of Blackness, 1 vol. 2012. (ENG.). 476p. pap. 25.00 ***(978-1-55597-607-1(7))*** Graywolf Pr.

AFRICAN AMERICAN ATHLETES

see also African Americans in Sports; Negro Leagues

Aaseng, Nathan. Athletes. 2nd rev. ed. 2011. (A to Z of African Americans Ser.). (Illus.). 288p. (C). (gr. 9-18). 49.50 *(978-0-8160-7869-1(6))* Facts On File, Inc.

Aiello, Thomas. The Kings of Casino Park: Black Baseball in the Lost Season of 1932. 2011. (ENG., Illus.). 264p. 39.95 *(978-0-8173-1742-3(2))* Univ. of Alabama Pr.

Allen, Marcus. Marcus. 2009. (ENG.). 410p. pap. 24.95 *(978-1-4128-1279-5(8))* Transaction Pubs.

Bowden, Tripp. Freddie & Me: Life Lessons from Freddie Bennett, Augusta National's Legendary Caddie Master. 2009. (ENG.). 224p. 19.95 *(978-1-60239-682-1(5)*, 239682) Skyhorse Publishing Co., Inc.

Boyce, Lucas Daniel. Living Proof: From Foster Care to the White House & the NBA. 2011. (ENG.). 228p. pap. 16.99 *(978-1-59932-257-5(9))* Advantage Media Group.

Brunson, James Edward. The Early Image of Black Baseball: Race & Representation in the Popular Press, 1871-1890. 2009. (ENG., Illus.). 232p. pap. 39.95 *(978-0-7864-4206-5(9))* McFarland & Co., Inc. Pubs.

Carroll, Brian. When to Stop the Cheering? The Black Press, the Black Community, & the Integration of Professional Baseball. 2006. (Studies in African American History & Culture). (Illus.). 271p. 126.00 *(978-0-415-97938-2(2))* Routledge.

Demas, Lane. Integrating the Gridiron: Black Civil Rights & American College Football. 2011. (ENG., Illus.). 194p. pap. 25.95 *(978-0-8135-4997-2(3))* Rutgers Univ. Pr.

Diversity & Social Justice in College Sports: Sport Management & the College Athlete. 2007. 448p. 69.00 *(978-1-885693-77-8(X))* Fitness Information Technology, Inc.

Early, Gerald L. A Level Playing Field: African American Athletes & the Republic of Sports. 2011. (Alain Locke Lecture Ser.). 288p. 25.95 *(978-0-674-05098-3(3))* Harvard Univ. Pr.

Eig, Jonathan. Opening Day: The Story of Jackie Robinson's First Season. 2008. (ENG., Illus.). 336p. pap. 15.00 *(978-0-7432-9461-4(0))* Simon & Schuster.

Freedman, Lew. African American Pioneers of Baseball: A Biographical Encyclopedia, 1 vol. 2007. (Illus.). 320p. 75.00 *(978-0-313-33851-9(5)*, GR3851, Greenwood Pr.) Greenwood Publishing Group, Inc.

Godfrey, Buck. The Team Nobody Would Play. 2008. 84p. pap. 12.99 *(978-0-8059-7764-6(3))* Dorrance Publishing Co., Inc.

Grant, Jim "Mudcat", et al. The Black Aces: Baseball's only african-american twenty-game Winners. 2007. (ENG.). 492p. 34.95 *(978-1-59330-488-1(9))*; 496p. per. 23.95 *(978-1-59330-487-4(0))* Aventine Pr.

Harris, Cecil & Kyle-Debose, Larryette. Charging the Net: A History of Blacks in Tennis from Althea Gibson & Arthur Ashe to the Williams Sisters. 2007. (Illus.). 288p. 26.95 *(978-1-56663-714-5(7))* Dee, Ivan R. Pub.

Harris, Francis C. Amistad Pictorial History of the African-American Athlete, Vol. 1. Date not set. 74.95 *(978-0-06-019893-0(1)*, Amistad) HarperCollins Pubs.

—Amistad Pictorial History of the African-American Athlete, 1886 to Present: Professional Volume. Date not set. 74.95 *(978-0-06-019895-4(8)*, Amistad) HarperCollins Pubs.

Harris, Francis C. & Harris, Charles F. Amistad Pictorial History of the African-American Athlete: 1946 to Present, Vol. 2. Date not set. 74.95 *(978-0-06-019894-7(X)*, Amistad) HarperCollins Pubs.

Hawkins, Billy. The New Plantation: Black Athletes, College Sports, & Predominantly White NCAA Institutions. 2010. (ENG.). 256p. 95.00 *(978-0-230-61517-5(1))* Palgrave Macmillan.

Hoffer, Richard. Something in the Air: American Passion & Defiance in the 1968 Mexico City Olympics. 2011. (ENG., Illus.). 272p. pap. 16.00 *(978-1-4165-8895-5(7)*, Free Pr.) Free Pr.

Hogan, Lawrence D., et al. Shades of Glory: The Negro Leagues & the Story of African-American Baseball. 2007. (ENG., Illus.). 448p. per. 15.95 *(978-1-4262-0033-5(1)*, National Geographic) National Geographic Society.

Jackson, Donald Maurice. Fourth down & Twenty Five Years to Go: The African American Athlete & the Justice System. 2007. 224p. (ENG.). 27.95 *(978-0-595-89619-6(7))*; per. 17.95 *(978-0-595-44108-2(4))* iUniverse, Inc.

Jacobs, Barry. Across the Line: Profiles in Basketball Courage - Tales of the First Black Players in the ACC & Southeastern Conferences. 2007. (ENG., Illus.). 384p. 24.95 *(978-1-59921-042-1(8)*, Lyons Pr.) Globe Pequot Pr., The.

Kaliss, Gregory J. Men's College Athletics & the Politics of Racial Equality: Five Pioneer Stories of Black Manliness, White Citizenship, & American Democracy. 2012. (ENG.). 248p. 49.50 ***(978-1-4399-0856-3(7))*** Temple Univ. Pr.

Kelley, Brent. The Negro Leagues Revisited: Conversations with 66 More Baseball Heroes. alt. ed. 2010. (ENG., Illus.). 399p. pap. 45.00 *(978-0-7864-4695-7(1))* McFarland & Co., Inc. Pubs.

Klein, Greg. The King of New Orleans: How the Junkyard Dog Became Professional Wrestling's First Black Superstar. 2012. (ENG., Illus.). 280p. pap. 19.95 ***(978-1-77041-030-5(9))*** ECW Pr. CAN. Dist: Independent Pubs. Group.

Knight, Dawn. Taliaferro: Breaking Barriers from the NFL Draft to the Ivory Tower. 2010. (ENG., Illus.). 200p. pap. 14.95 *(978-0-253-22224-4(9)*, 0253222249) Indiana Univ. Pr.

Lapchick, Richard. 100 Pioneers: African-Americans Who Broke Color Barriers in Sport. 2008. (Leaders in Sprort (Fit) Ser.). (Illus.). 488p. pap. 24.95 *(978-1-885693-81-5(8))* Fitness Information Technology, Inc.

Lattin, David. Slam Dunk to Glory: The Amazing True Story of the 1966 NCAA Season & the Championship Game That Changed America Forever. 2007. (Illus.). 235p. per. 14.99 *(978-1-59379-117-9(8))* White Stone Bks.

Laucella, Pamela & Laucella, Pamela C. Jesse Owens, the Press, & the 1936 Berlin Olympic Games. 2013. (Studies in African American History & Culture Ser.). (ENG.). 224p. 125.00 *(978-0-415-99614-3(7))* Routledge.

Lee, George L. Interesting Athletes: A Newspaper Artist's Look at Blacks in Sports. alt. ed. 2012. (ENG.). 176p. pap. 19.99 ***(978-0-7864-6766-2(5))*** McFarland & Co., Inc. Pubs.

Leonard, David J. Commodified & Criminalized: New Racism & African Americans in Contemporary Sports. 2011. (Perspectives on a Multiracial America Ser.). (ENG.). 272p. (gr. 17). 80.00 *(978-1-4422-0677-9(2))* Rowman & Littlefield Publishers, Inc.

Leonard, David J. & King, C. Richard. Commodified & Criminalized: New Racism & African Americans in Contemporary Sports. 2010. *(978-1-4422-0679-3(9))* Rowman & Littlefield Publishers, Inc.

Lomax, Michael E., ed. Sports & the Racial Divide: African American & Latino Experience in an Era of Change. 2011. 262p. pap. 30.00 ***(978-1-61703-045-1(7))*** 2008. (ENG.). 288p. 50.00 *(978-1-60473-014-2(5))* Univ. Pr. of Mississippi.

Lopez, Katherine. Cougars of Any Color: The Integration of University of Houston Athletics,1964-1968. 2008. (ENG., Illus.). 220p. pap. 35.00 *(978-0-7864-3721-4(9))* McFarland & Co., Inc. Pubs.

Luke, Bob. Willie Wells. 2007. (ENG., Illus.). 208p. pap. 19.95 *(978-0-292-71751-0(2))* Univ. of Texas Pr.

Luke, Robert A. The Baltimore Elite Giants: Sport & Society in the Age of Negro League Baseball. 2009. (ENG., Illus.). 208p. 30.95 *(978-0-8018-9116-8(7))* Johns Hopkins Univ. Pr.

Marantz, Steve. The Rhythm Boys of Central Omaha: High School Basketball at the '68 Racial Divide. 2011. (ENG., Illus.). 264p. pap. 17.95 *(978-0-8032-3434-5(1)*, Bison Bks.) Univ. of Nebraska Pr.

Markusen, Bruce. The Team That Changed Baseball: Roberte Clemente & the 1971 Pittsburgh Pirates. 2009. (ENG., Illus.). 240p. pap. 14.95 *(978-1-59416-089-9(9))* Westholme Publishing.

McCormack, Shaun. Cool Papa Bell. 2009. (Baseball Hall of Famers of the Negro Leagues Ser.). 112p. (gr. 5-8). 63.90 *(978-1-61511-522-8(6)*, Rosen Central) Rosen Publishing Group, Inc., The.

Mee, Bob. Liston & Ali: The Ugly Bear & the Boy Who Would Be King. 2011. (ENG., Illus.). 336p. 24.95 *(978-1-61608-369-4(7)*, 608369) Skyhorse Publishing Co., Inc.

Naomi Bryson, Ed. D. The Day Snow Turned Black. 2009. 192p. pap. 14.49 *(978-1-4389-6133-0(2))* AuthorHouse.

Posnanski, Joe. The Soul of Baseball: A Road Trip Through Buck O'Neil's America. (ENG.). 2008. 304p. pap. 13.99 *(978-0-06-085404-1(9)*, William Morrow Paperbacks) 2007. 256p. 24.95 *(978-0-06-085403-4(0)*, Morrow, William & Co.) HarperCollins Pubs.

Powell, Shaun. Souled Out? How Blacks Are Winning & Losing in Sports. 2007. (ENG., Illus.). 312p. 22.95 *(978-0-7360-6750-8(7))* Human Kinetics Pubs.

Provost, P. Paul. Ebony Legends in Sports. 2009. 236p. 24.99 *(978-1-4389-7958-8(4))*; pap. 18.70 *(978-1-4389-7957-1(6))* AuthorHouse.

Rhoden, William C. Forty Million Dollar Slaves: The Rise, Fall, & Redemption of the Black Athlete. 2007. (ENG., Illus.). 304p. per. 14.99 *(978-0-307-35314-6(1)*, Three Rivers Pr.) Crown Publishing Group.

Riley, Keith. The Case for Student Athletes Who Achieve - Time Use Patterns Influence on Academic Achievement among African American & Hispanic Male High School S. 2008. 124p. pap. *(978-3-639-11071-5(4))* VDM Verlag Dr. Mueller e.K.

Robert E. Wells. Sport & the Talented: African American Athletes at the Colleges & Universities of the Northeast, 1879-1920. 2010. 648p. pap. 49.95 *(978-1-4401-7551-0(9))* iUniverse, Inc.

Robinson, Jackie. Baseball Has Done It. 2007. (Illus.). 220p. pap. 13.00 *(978-1-4223-6622-6(7))* DIANE Publishing Co.

Rogosin, Donn. Invisible Men: Life in Baseball's Negro Leagues. 2007. (ENG., Illus.). 302p. pap. 24.95 *(978-0-8032-5969-0(7)*, Bison Bks.) Univ. of Nebraska Pr.

Runstedtler, Theresa. Jack Johnson, Rebel Sojourner: Boxing in the Shadow of the Global Color Line. 2012. (American Crossroads Ser.). (ENG., Illus.). 376p. 34.95 ***(978-0-520-27160-9(2))*** Univ. of California Pr.

Sailes, Gary. Modern Sport & the African American Experience. 2009. 376p. (C). pap. 98.95 *(978-1-935551-30-0(2))* Univ. Readers.

Smith, Earl. Race, Sport & the American Dream. 2007. pap. 28.00 *(978-1-59460-289-4(1))* 2nd ed. 2009. 320p. pap. 32.00 *(978-1-59460-723-3(0))* Carolina Academic Pr.

Smith, Tommie. Silent Gesture: The Autobiography of Tommie Smith. 2007. (Sporting Ser.). (Illus.). 288p. 65.00 *(978-1-59213-639-1(7))* Temple Univ. Pr.

Smith, Tommie, et al. Silent Gesture: The Autobiography of Tommie Smith. 2008. (Sporting Ser.). (ENG., Illus.). 288p. pap. 23.95 *(978-1-59213-640-7(0))* Temple Univ. Pr.

Snyder, Brad. A Well-Paid Slave: Curt Flood's Fight for Free Agency in Professional Sports. 2007. (ENG.). 480p. (gr. 12-18). 16.00 *(978-0-452-28891-1(6)*, Plume) Penguin Group (USA) Inc.

Sutherland, Adam. Athletes. 2012. (Black History Makers Ser.). (ENG.). 24p. (J). (gr. 3-8). pap. 8.25 ***(978-1-4488-7058-5(5))***; lib. bdg. 21.25 ***(978-1-4488-6640-3(5))*** Rosen Publishing Group, Inc., The. (PowerKids Pr.).

Tolen, Pamilla S. Mike Minter: Driven by Purpose... the Power of a Dream. Warder, James, ed. 2008. 210p. 21.99 *(978-0-9802051-0-7(7))* Comfort Publishing Services, LLC.

Tygiel, Jules. Baseball's Great Experiment: Jackie Robinson & His Legacy. 25th ed. 2008. (ENG., Illus.). 448p. per. 19.95 *(978-0-19-533928-4(2))* Oxford Univ. Pr., Inc.

Virtue, John. South of the Color Barrier: How Jorge Pasquel & the Mexican League Pushed Baseball Toward Racial Integration. 2007. (ENG., Illus.). 239p. per. 29.95 *(978-0-7864-3293-6(4))* McFarland & Co., Inc. Pubs.

Walter, John C. & Iida, Malina, eds. Better Than the Best: Black Athletes Speak, 1920-2007. 2010. (V Ethel Willis White Bks.). (ENG., Illus.). 288p. pap. 24.95 *(978-0-295-99053-8(8))* Univ. of Washington Pr.

Whitaker, Matthew C., ed. African American Icons of Sport: Triumph, Courage, & Excellence, 1 vol. 2008. (Greenwood Icons Ser.). (Illus.). 336p. 75.00 (978-0-313-34028-4(5), GR4028, Greenwood Pr.) Greenwood Publishing Group, Inc.

Wiggins, David K., ed. Out of the Shadows: A Biographical History of African American Athletes. 2006. (Illus.). 459p. 34.95 (978-1-55728-826-4(7)) Univ. of Arkansas Pr.

—Out of the Shadows: A Biogrpahical History of African American Athletes. 2008. (Illus.). 459p. per. 24.95 (978-1-55728-876-9(3)) Univ. of Arkansas Pr.

Williams, Billy & Mitchell, Fred. Billy Williams: My Sweet-Swinging Lifetime with the Cubs. 2008. (ENG., Illus.). 256p. 24.95 (978-1-60078-050-9(4)) Triumph Bks.

Zirin, Dave & Carlos, John Wesley. John Carlos Story: The Sports Moment That Changed the World. 2011. (ENG., Illus.). 220p. 22.95 **(978-1-60846-127-1(0))** Haymarket Bks.

AFRICAN AMERICAN AUTHORS

see also African American Historians; American Literature—African American Authors

Acampora, Christa Davis & Cotten, Angela L. Cultural Sites of Critical Insight: Philosophy, Aesthetics, & African American & Native American Women's Writings. Acampora, Christa Davis & Cotten, Angela L., eds. 2007. 216p. per. 29.95 (978-0-7914-6980-4(8)) State Univ. of New York Pr.

Adams, Grace. Black Authors & Published Writers Directory (2007/2008) 2007. E-Book 89.95 (978-1-877807-29-9(X)) Grace Publishing Co.

—2007/2008 Black Authors & Published Writers Directory: Industry Reference. 2007. (Illus.). 410p. pap. 119.95 (978-1-877807-28-2(1)) Grace Publishing Co.

—2008/2009 Black Authors & Published Writers Directory. 2008. (Illus.). 348p. pap. 119.95 (978-1-877807-30-5(3), Black Authors & Published Writers Directory) Grace Publishing Co.

Adams, Grace, ed. 2006/2007 Black Authors & Published Writers Directory: Black Literary Market Place. 2006. (Illus.). 358p. pap. 89.95 (978-1-877807-27-5(3)) Grace Publishing Co.

—2010-11 Black Authors & Published Writers Directory: A Writers Guide for Students & Teachers. 2010. 142p. pap. 24.95 (978-1-877807-36-7(2), Black Authors & Published Writers Directory) Grace Publishing Co.

—2010-2011 Black Authors & Published Writers Directory. 5th ed. 2010. (Illus.). 332p. pap. 89.95 (978-1-877807-32-9(X), Black Authors & Published Writers Directory) Grace Publishing Co.

Allen, Eddie B., Jr. & Allen, Eddie B. Low Road: The Life & Legacy of Donald Goines. 2008. (ENG., Illus.). 224p. pap. 16.99 (978-0-312-38351-0(7), St. Martin's Griffin) St. Martin's Pr.

Ardis, Angela. Inside a Thug's Heart. 2009. (ENG.). 256p. 14.00 (978-0-7582-0790-6(5), Dafina) Kensington Publishing Corp.

Bader, Philip. African-American Writers. 2nd rev. ed. 2010. (A to Z of African Americans Ser.) (Illus.). 352p. (C). (gr. 9-18). 49.50 (978-0-8160-8141-7(7)) Facts On File, Inc.

Baker, Barbara A. Albert Murray & the Aesthetic Imagination of a Nation. 2010. (ENG., Illus.). 264p. pap. 25.00 (978-0-8173-5593-7(6)) Univ. of Alabama Pr.

Baker, Barbara A., et al. Albert Murray & the Aesthetic Imagination of a Nation. 2010. (ENG., Illus.). 264p. 45.75 (978-0-8173-1697-6(3)) Univ. of Alabama Pr.

Bassard, Katherine Clay. Transforming Scriptures: African American Women Writers & the Bible. 2011. (ENG., Illus.). 180p. pap. 22.95 (978-0-8203-3880-4(X)) Univ. of Georgia Pr.

Bieze, Michael Scott & Gasman, Marybeth, eds. Booker T. Washington Rediscovered. 2012. (ENG., Illus.). 224p. (C). (gr. 13-17). pap. 34.95 **(978-1-4214-0471-4(0))** Johns Hopkins Univ. Pr.

Bishop, Rudine Sims. Free Within Ourselves: The Development of African American Children's Literature. 2007. (Illus.). 320p. 65.00 (978-0-313-34093-2(5), GR4093, Greenwood Pr.) Greenwood Publishing Group, Inc.

—Free Within Ourselves: The Development of African American Children's Literature. 2007. 352p. pap. 31.25 (978-0-325-07135-0(7), E07135) Heinemann.

Bloom, Harold, ed. Invisible Man - Ralph Ellison, New Edition. 2nd rev. ed. 2009. (Bloom's Modern Critical Interpretations Ser.). 216p. (C). (gr. 9-18). 45.00 (978-1-60413-584-8(0), Chelsea Hse.) Facts On File, Inc.

Boggis, JerriAnne, et al, eds. Harriet Wilson's New England: Race, Writing, & Region. 2007. (Revisiting New England Ser.). (Illus.). 272p. lib. bdg. 65.00 (978-1-58465-641-8(7), University of New Hampshire Press) Univ. Pr. of New England.

Bone. Richard Wright, Vol. 74. 2009. (ENG.). 48p. pap. 25.00 (978-0-8166-0524-8(6)) Univ. of Minnesota Pr.

Boyd, Herb. Baldwin's Harlem: A Biography of James Baldwin. 2008. (ENG.). 272p. pap. 17.99 (978-0-7432-9308-2(8), Beyond Words/Atria Bks.) Atria Bks.

Brown, William Wells & Greenspan, Ezra. William Wells Brown: A Reader. Greenspan, Ezra, ed. 2008. (ENG., Illus.). 488p. pap. 24.95 (978-0-8203-3224-6(0)); lib. bdg. 64.95 (978-0-8203-3223-9(2)) Univ. of Georgia Pr.

Bryant, Jacqueline Imani, ed. Gwendolyn Brooks & Working Writers. 2007. (Illus.). 95p. per. 12.95 (978-0-88378-279-8(0)) Third World Press.

Clampitt, Amy. Love, Amy: The Selected Letters of Amy Clampitt. Spiegelman, Willard, ed. 2007. (ENG., Illus.). 336p. (gr. 17). pap. 29.00 (978-0-231-13287-9(5)) Columbia Univ. Pr.

Cohen, William S. Love in Black & White: A Memoir of Race, Religion, & Romance. 2006. (ENG., Illus.). 304p. 26.95 (978-0-7425-5821-2(5)) Rowman & Littlefield Publishers, Inc.

Coleman, Finnie D. Sutton E. Griggs & the Struggle Against White Supremacy. 2007. 232p. 35.00 (978-1-57233-480-9(0)) Univ. of Tennessee Pr.

Collins, Michael. Understanding Etheridge Knight. 2012. (Understanding Contemporary American Literature Ser.). (ENG.). 168p. 39.95 **(978-1-61117-066-5(4))** Univ. of South Carolina Pr.

Delany, Samuel R. Conversations with Samuel R. Delany. Freedman, Carl, ed. 2009. (Literary Conversations Ser.). (ENG.). 256p. 50.00 (978-1-60473-277-1(6)); pap. 22.00 (978-1-60473-278-8(4)) Univ. Pr. of Mississippi.

Denard, Carolyn C., ed. Toni Morrison: Conversations. 2008. (ENG.). 224p. 50.00 (978-1-60473-018-0(8)); pap. 22.00 (978-1-60473-019-7(6)) Univ. Pr. of Mississippi.

Drew, Bernard A. 100 Most Popular African American Authors: Biographical Sketches & Bibliographies, 1 vol. 2006. (Popular Authors Ser.). (Illus.). 372p. 55.00 (978-1-59158-322-6(5), LU3225) Libraries Unlimited, Inc.

Dyja, Thomas. Walter White: The Dilemma of Black Identity in America. 2010. (ENG.). 224p. pap. 15.95 (978-1-56663-865-4(8)) Dee, Ivan R. Pub.

Elliott, Mark Emory. Color-Blind Justice: Albion Tourgee & the Quest for Racial Equality - From the Civil War to Plessy V. Ferguson. 2006. (ENG., Illus.). 400p. 30.00 (978-0-19-518139-5(5)) Oxford Univ. Pr., Inc.

Fitzgerald, Stephanie. Alice Walker: Author & Social Activist. 2008. (Signature Lives Ser.). (ENG., Illus.). 112p. (gr. 6-7). lib. bdg. 35.32 (978-0-7565-3474-5(7), Signature Lives) Compass Point Bks.

Foreman, P. Gabrielle. Activist Sentiments: Reading Black Women in the Nineteenth Century. 2009. (New Black Studies Ser.). (ENG., Illus.). 280p. 75.00 (978-0-252-03474-9(0)); pap. 25.00 (978-0-252-07664-0(8)) Univ. of Illinois Pr.

Forrest, Leon. Conversations with Leon Forrest. Williams, Dana A., ed. 2007. (ENG., Illus.). 141p. per. 22.00 (978-1-57806-990-3(4)) Univ. Pr. of Mississippi.

—Conversations with Leon Forrest. Williams, Dana A., ed. 2007. (ENG., Illus.). 141p. 50.00 (978-1-57806-989-7(0)) Univ. Pr. of Mississippi.

Fosberg, Michael A. Incognito: An American Odyssey of Race & Self-Discovery. 2011. 317p. pap. **(978-0-615-41396-9(X))** Incognito, Inc.

Francis, Conseula, ed. Conversations with Octavia Butler. (Literary Conversations Ser.). (ENG.). 288p. 2010. 50.00 (978-1-60473-275-7(X)) 2009. pap. 22.00 (978-1-60473-276-4(8)) Univ. Pr. of Mississippi.

Fullwood, Steven G. & Moore, Lisa C., eds. Carry the Word: A Bibliography of Black LGBTQ Books. 2007. 212p. per. 16.95 (978-0-9786251-4-6(5)) RedBone Pr.

Gasman, Marybeth & Bieze, Michael Scott, eds. Booker T. Washington Rediscovered. 2012. (ENG., Illus.). 224p. (C). (gr. 13-17). 70.00 **(978-1-4214-0470-7(2))** Johns Hopkins Univ. Pr.

Gates, Henry Louis, Jr. Harlem Renaissance Lives: From the African American National Biography. Higginbotham, Evelyn Brooks, ed. 2009. (Illus.). 608p. 50.00 (978-0-19-538795-7(3)) Oxford Univ. Pr., Inc.

George, Nelson. City Kid: A Writer's Memoir of Ghetto Life & Post-Soul Success. 2010. (ENG.). 288p. (gr. 12-18). 14.00 (978-0-452-29604-6(8), Plume) Penguin Group (USA) Inc.

Gilyard, Keith. John Oliver Killens: A Life of Black Literary Activism. (ENG., Illus.). 456p. 2011. pap. 26.95 **(978-0-8203-4031-9(6))** 2010. 39.95 (978-0-8203-3513-1(4)) Univ. of Georgia Pr.

Golden, Marita. The Word: Black Writers Talk about the Transformative Power of Reading & Writing. 2011. 224p. pap. 14.99 (978-0-7679-2991-2(8), Broadway Bks.

Green, Tara T. A Fatherless Child: Autobiographical Perspectives of African American Men. 2009. (ENG.). 184p. (C). 34.95 (978-0-8262-1821-6(0)) Univ. of Missouri Pr.

Greene, Brenda M. & Beauford, Fred, eds. Meditations & Ascensions: Black Writers on Writing. 2008. 204p. pap. 18.95 (978-0-88378-296-5(0)) Third World Press.

Greer, Bonnie. Langston Hughes: The Value of Contradiction. 2011. (BlackAmber Inspirations Ser.). (ENG., Illus.). 190p. pap. 14.95 (978-1-906413-76-7(2), Black Amber) Arcadia Bks. Ltd. GBR. Dist: Dufour Editions, Inc.

Grimes, Nikki. Out of the Dark. 2009. (ENG., Illus.). 56p. (J). pap. 8.00 (978-1-57274-977-1(6), Author at Work) Owen, Richard C. Pubs., Inc.

Hall, Calvin L. & Hall, Clavin L. African American Journalists: Autobiography as Memoir & Manifesto. 2009. (ENG.). 146p. pap. 40.00 (978-0-8108-6930-1(6)) Scarecrow Pr., Inc.

Harrison-Kahan, Lori. The White Negress: Literature, Minstrelsy, & the Black-Jewish Imaginary. 2011. (American Literatures Initiative Ser.). (ENG., Illus.). 240p. 65.00 (978-0-8135-4782-4(2)); pap. 24.95 (978-0-8135-4783-1(0)) Rutgers Univ. Pr.

Hinton, KaaVonia. Sharon M. Draper: Embracing Literacy. 2008. (Scarecrow Studies in Young Adult Literature Ser.). (ENG.). 148p. 45.00 (978-0-8108-5985-2(8)) Scarecrow Pr., Inc.

Jackson, Lawrence. Ralph Ellison: Emergence of Genius. 2007. (ENG.). 520p. pap. 24.95 (978-0-8203-2993-2(2)) Univ. of Georgia Pr.

James, C. L. R. You Don't Play with Revolution: The Montréal Lectures of C. L. R. James. Austin, David, ed. 2009. (ENG.). 256p. pap. 18.95 (978-1-904859-93-2(3)) AK Pr. GBR. Dist: Consortium Bk. Sales & Distribution.

Johnson, James Weldon. Along This Way: The Autobiography of James Weldon Johnson. rev. ed. 2008. (ENG.). 448p. (gr. 12-18). 16.00 (978-0-14-310517-6(5), Penguin Classics) Penguin Group (USA) Inc.

Junker, Carsten. Frames of Friction: Black Genealogies, White Hegemony, & the Essay as Critical Intervention. 2010. 294p. pap. 49.00 (978-3-593-39099-4(X)) Campus Verlag GmbH DEU. Dist: Chicago Distribution Ctr.

Kenan, Randall. The Fire This Time. 2007. (ENG.). 149p. 20.00 (978-1-933633-24-4(7)) Melville Hse. Publishing.

Komunyakaa, Yusef. Conversations with Yusef Komunyakaa. Hanshaw, Shirley A. James, ed. 2010. (Literary Conversations Ser.). (ENG.). 224p. 65.00 (978-1-60473-421-8(3)); pap. 22.00 (978-1-60473-422-5(1)) Univ. Pr. of Mississippi.

Lackey, Michael. African American Atheists & Political Liberation: A Study of the Sociocultural Dynamics of Faith. 2008. (History of African-American Religions Ser.). (ENG., Illus.). 192p. pap. 29.95 (978-0-8130-3318-1(7)) Univ. Pr. of Florida.

Luczak, Ewa / Barbara. How Their Living Outside America Affected Five African American Authors: Toward a Theory of Expatriate Literature. 2010. ix, 250p. (978-0-7734-3748-7(7)) Mellen, Edwin Pr., The.

Mars-Proietti, Laura & Hatcher, Sherry L., eds. Encyclopedia of African American Writing. 2nd rev. ed. 2009. 856p. (gr. 4-6). 135.00 (978-1-59237-291-1(0)) Grey Hse. Publishing.

Marshall, Paule. Triangular Road: A Memoir. (ENG., 2010. Illus.). 176p. (gr. 9). pap. 14.00 (978-0-465-01922-9(6)) 2009. 192p. 23.00 (978-0-465-01359-3(7), Basic Civitas Bks.) Basic Bks.

Martin, Lena C. Desperate for Love: Overcoming with Prayer. 2007. 436p. per. 18.95 (978-1-4327-0209-0(2)) Outskirts Pr., Inc.

Masters, Jarvis Jay. That Bird Has My Wings: The Autobiography of an Innocent Man on Death Row. 2010. (ENG.). 304p. pap. 14.99 (978-0-06-173048-1(3), HarperOne) HarperCollins Pubs.

McClane, Kenneth A. Color: Essays on Race, Family, & History. 2009. (ND Afro/Amer Intellectual Heritage Ser.). (ENG.). 120p. pap. 19.00 (978-0-268-03515-0(6)) Univ. of Notre Dame Pr.

—Walls: Essays, 1985-1990. 2010. (ND Afro/Amer Intellectual Heritage Ser.). (ENG.). 128p. pap. 20.00 (978-0-268-03520-4(2)) Univ. of Notre Dame Pr.

McKay, Claude. A Long Way from Home. Jarrett, Gene Andrew, ed. 2007. (Multi-Ethnic Literatures of the Americas Ser.). (ENG.). 312p. per. 23.95 (978-0-8135-3968-3(4)) Rutgers Univ. Pr.

McKay, Claude, ed. A Long Way from Home. 2007. (Multi-Ethnic Literatures of the Americas (MELA) Ser.). (ENG.). 302p. 68.00 (978-0-8135-3967-6(6)) Rutgers Univ. Pr.

Miller, Karen E. Quinones. Angry Ass Black Woman. 2012. (ENG.). 288p. pap. 15.00 (978-1-4516-0782-6(2), Gallery Books/Karen Hunter Publishing) Gallery Books/Karen Hunter Publishing.

Mitchell, Verner D. Western Echoes of the Harlem Renaissance: The Life & Writings of Anita Scott Coleman. Davis, Cynthia J., ed. 2008. (ENG., Illus.) 240p. (C). 45.00 (978-0-8061-3956-2(0)); pap. 19.95 (978-0-8061-3975-3(7)) Univ. of Oklahoma Pr.

Molesworth, Charles. And Bid Him Sing: A Biography of Countée Cullen. 2012. 304p. 30.00 **(978-0-226-53364-3(6))** Univ. of Chicago Pr.

Murphy, Barbara Thrash & Murphy, Deborah. Black Authors & Illustrators of Books for Children & Young Adults: A Biographical Dictionary. Murphy, Barbara T. & Murphy, Deborah L., eds. 4th rev. ed. 2006. (Illus.). 568p. 110.00 (978-0-415-97219-2(1)) Routledge.

Pereira, Malin, ed. Into a Light Both Brilliant & Unseen: Conversations with Contemporary Black Poets. 2010. (ENG.). 260p. 59.95 (978-0-8203-3107-2(4)); pap. 19.95 (978-0-8203-3713-5(7)) Univ. of Georgia Pr.

Petry, Elisabeth. At Home Inside: A Daughter's Tribute to Ann Petry. 2008. (ENG., Illus.). 208p. 30.00 (978-1-60473-100-2(1)) Univ. Pr. of Mississippi.

Plant, Deborah G. Zora Neale Hurston: A Biography of the Spirit, 1 vol. 2007. (Women Writers of Color Ser.). (Illus.). 264p. 49.95 (978-0-275-98751-0(5), C8751, Praeger Pubs.) Greenwood Publishing Group, Inc.

Pochmara, Anna. The Making of the New Negro: Black Authorship, Masculinity, & Sexuality in the Harlem Renaissance. 2011. (American Studies). (ENG., Illus.). 280p. pap. (978-90-8964-319-3(2)) Amsterdam Univ. Pr.

Raimon, Eve Allegra, et al, eds. Harriet Wilson's New England: Race, Writing, & Region. 2007. (Revisiting New England Ser.). (Illus.). 272p. per. 26.00 (978-1-58465-642-5(5), University of New Hampshire Press) Univ. Pr. of New England.

Ramesh, Kotti Sree & Kandula, Nirupa Rani. Claude Mckay: The Literary Identity from Jamaica to Harlem & Beyond. 2006. (ENG., Illus.). 216p. per. 35.00 (978-0-7864-2582-2(2)) McFarland & Co., Inc. Pubs.

Reisler, Jim. Black Writers/Black Baseball: An Anthology of Articles from Black Sportswriters Who Covered the Negro Leagues. rev. ed. 2007. (ENG., Illus.). 212p. per. 35.00 (978-0-7864-2907-3(0)) McFarland & Co., Inc. Pubs.

Robotham, Rosemarie, ed. Mending the World: Stories of Family by Contemporary Black Writers. 2008. (ENG.). 290p. 25.00 (978-1-4379-5230-8(5)) DIANE Publishing Co.

Rowley, Hazel. Richard Wright: The Life & Times. 2008. (Illus.). 638p. pap. 22.50 (978-0-226-73038-7(7)) Univ. of Chicago Pr.

Rutland, Eva. When We Were Colored: A Mother's Story. 2007. (ENG., Illus.). 164p. per. 12.95 (978-1-934178-00-3(4)) IWP, Bk. Pubs.

Sherrard-Johnson, Cherene. Dorothy West's Paradise: A Biography of Class & Color. 2012. (ENG., Illus.). 256p. (C). pap. 24.95 (978-0-8135-5167-8(6)); 264p. 72.00 (978-0-8135-5166-1(8)) Rutgers Univ. Pr.

Slim, Iceberg. The Naked Soul of Iceberg Slim. 160p. pap. (978-0-86241-633-1(7), Payback Press) Canongate Bks.

—The Naked Soul of Iceberg Slim. 2013. (ENG.). 336p. pap. 14.99 (978-1-936399-13-0(X), Cash Money Content) Cash Money Content LLC.

Stancliff, Michael. Frances Ellen Watkins Harper: African American Reform Rhetoric & the Rise of a Modern Nation State. 2010. (Studies in American Popular History & Culture Ser.). (ENG., Illus.). 220p. 125.00 (978-0-415-99763-8(1)) Routledge.

Thompson, Mark Christian. Black Fascisms: African American Literature & Culture Between the Wars. 2007. (ENG.). 240p. (gr. 17). 57.50 (978-0-8139-2670-4(X)); per. 19.50 (978-0-8139-2671-1(8)) Univ. Pr. of Virginia.

Tolson, Nancy. Black Children's Literature Got de Blues: The Creativity of Black Writers & Illustrators. 2008. (Illus.). xi, 116p. pap. 24.95 (978-0-8204-6332-2(9)) Lang, Peter Publishing, Inc.

Walker, Alice. The Chicken Chronicles: Sitting with the Angels Who Have Returned with My Memories - Glorious, Rufus, Gertrude Stein, Splendor, Hortensia, Agnes of God, the Gladyses, & Babe - A Memoir. 2011. (ENG.). 208p. 21.95 (978-1-59558-645-2(8)) New Pr., The.

Wallach, Jennifer Jensen. Richard Wright: From Black Boy to World Citizen. 2010. (ENG.). 224p. 26.00 (978-1-56663-824-1(0)) Dee, Ivan R. Pub.

Wallinger, Hanna. Pauline E. Hopkins: A Literary Biography. 2012. (ENG.). 384p. pap. 24.95 **(978-0-8203-4345-7(5))** Univ. of Georgia Pr.

West, Elizabeth J. African Spirituality in Black Women's Fiction: Threaded Visions of Memory, Community, Nature, & Being. 2012. E-Book **(978-0-7391-6886-8(X))** Lexington Bks.

Williams, John, ed. Dear Chester, Dear John: Letters Between Chester Hines & John A. Williams. 2008. 256p. 24.95 (978-0-8143-3359-4(1)) Wayne State Univ. Pr.

Williams, John A., ed. Dear Chester, Dear John: Letters Between Chester Hines & John A. Williams. 2008. (African American Life Ser.). (Illus.). 241p. 24.95 (978-0-8143-3355-6(9)) Wayne State Univ. Pr.

Williams, Oscar. George S. Schuyler: Portrait of a Black Conservative. 2007. (Illus.). 224p. 33.00 (978-1-57233-581-3(5)) Univ. of Tennessee Pr.

Wilson, Ivy G. Specters of Democracy: Blackness & the Aesthetics of Politics in the Antebellum U. S., 1 vol. 2011. (ENG., Illus.). 256p. pap. 29.95 (978-0-19-534035-8(3)) Oxford Univ. Pr., Inc.

Woodberry, George Edward. Nathaniel Hawthorne. 2008. 240p. 24.99 (978-0-554-34851-3(9)) 2008. 240p. 27.99 (978-0-554-25548-4(0)) 2007. (ENG.). 238p. pap. 22.99 (978-1-4264-9293-8(6)) BiblioBazaar.

—Nathaniel Hawthorne. 2009. 112p. pap. (978-0-217-51662-4(9)) Books LLC.

—Nathaniel Hawthorne. 2008. 172p. pap. (978-1-4099-3690-9(2)) Dodo Pr.

Young, Reggie Scott, et al. This Louisiana Thing That Drives Me: The Legacy of Ernest J. Gaines. 2009. (Illus.). 96p. 40.00 (978-1-887366-83-0(0)) Univ. of Louisiana at Lafayette Pr.

Zaborowska, Magdalena J. James Baldwin's Turkish Decade: Erotics of Exile. 2009. (ENG., Illus.). 416p. 94.95 (978-0-8223-4144-4(1)) Duke Univ. Pr.

Zaborowska, Magdalena J. & Zaborowska, Magdalena. James Baldwin's Turkish Decade: Erotics of Exile. 2009. (ENG., Illus.). 416p. pap. 26.95 (978-0-8223-4167-3(0)) Duke Univ. Pr.

AFRICAN AMERICAN BAPTISTS

Adelman, Bob. Remembering Martin Luther King. Life Magazine Editors, ed. 2008. (ENG., Illus.). 160p. (YA). (gr. 7-17). 24.95 (978-1-60320-044-8(4)) Time Home Entertainment, Inc.

Biographiq. Jesse Jackson - Civil Rights Activist & Minister. 2008. 52p. pap. 9.99 (978-1-59986-069-5(4), Biographiq) Filiquarian Publishing, LLC.

Davis, France A. & Atiya, Nayra. France Davis: An American Story Told. 2006. (ENG., Illus.). 288p. (gr. 9). 24.95 (978-0-87480-873-5(1)) Univ. of Utah Pr.

Earl, Thomas. A History of the NBC. 2007. (National Baptist Great Personalities Ser.: Vol. 2). 9.95 (978-0-910683-20-3(4)) Townsend Pr. - Sunday Schl. Publishing Board.

Fallin, Wilson & Fallin, Wilson, Jr. Uplifting the People: Three Centuries of Black Baptists in Alabama. 2007. (Religion & American Culture Ser.). (ENG., Illus.). 352p. 39.95 (978-0-8173-1569-6(1)) Univ. of Alabama Pr.

James, Isaac. The Sun Do Move: The Story of the Life of John Jasper. 2011. 56p. 36.95 **(978-1-258-09212-2(3))** Literary Licensing, LLC.

Jasper, John. De Sun Do Move: The Sermon of John J. Jasper. Bryan, John, tr. 2008. pap. 14.95 (978-0-9656314-4-0(3)) Charles Creek Publishing.

McMickle, Marvin A. Deacons in Today's Black Baptist Church. 2010. 160p. pap. 16.00 (978-0-8170-1640-1(6)) Judson Pr

Miller, Tyagan. Covenant: Scenes from an African American Church. 2007. (Polis Center Series on Religion & Urban Culture Ser.). (ENG., Illus.). 176p. 29.95 (978-0-253-34835-7(8), 0253348358) Indiana Univ. Pr.

National Baptist educational convention. Proceedings. 2006. 276p. per. 23.99 (978-1-4255-2447-0(8)) MPublishing.

Smith, Paris Lee. From Plantation to the Pulpit: The Transforming Message of the Black Baptist Church. 2007. 172p. 21.99 (978-1-60477-107-7(0)); per. 13.99 (978-1-60477-106-0(2)) Xulon Pr., Inc.

AFRICAN AMERICAN BUSINESSPEOPLE

see African Americans in Business

AFRICAN AMERICAN CHILDREN

Brice Heath, Shirley. Words at Work & Play: Three Decades in Family & Community Life. 2012. (ENG., Illus.). 240p. (C). pap. 27.99 **(978-0-521-60303-4(X))** Cambridge Univ. Pr.

Brooks, Wanda M. Embracing, Evaluating, & Examining African American Children's & Young Adult Literature. McNair, Jonda C., ed. 2007. (ENG., Illus.). 262p. per. 55.00 *(978-0-8108-6027-8(9))* Scarecrow Pr., Inc.

Campbell, Bebe Moore. Sweet Summer. 2009. (ENG.). 272p. (gr. 12-18). 15.00 *(978-0-425-22927-9(0)*, Berkley Trade) Penguin Group (USA) Inc.

Clair-Hull, Judith. Strategies for Educating African American Children. 2010. (Teaching for Spiritual Growth Ser.). 137p. per. 14.95 *(978-1-932715-79-8(7))* UMI (Urban Ministries, Inc.).

Clark, Tina. How to Home School your African American Child. 2009. 107p. pap. 19.36 *(978-0-557-10038-5(0))* Lulu Enterprises Inc.

Clincy, Sekou. The Socialization of the African American Child: In Contemporary America. 2010. 192p. 24.99 *(978-1-4490-8788-3(4))*; pap. 14.49 *(978-1-4490-8787-6(6))* AuthorHouse.

Cooper, Jr. Why? African american children can not Read. 2009. 76p. pap. 10.95 *(978-0-595-45735-9(5))* iUniverse, Inc.

Graham-Morgan, Ivet. Come, See Where We Work. 2009. 32p. pap. 14.50 *(978-1-4389-2732-9(0))* AuthorHouse.

Green, Lisa J. Language & the African American Child. 2010. (ENG., Illus.). 284p. 99.00 *(978-0-521-85309-5(5))*; 288p. pap. 32.99 *(978-0-521-61817-5(7))* Cambridge Univ. Pr.

Harris, Yvette R. & Bergen, Doris. Children & Families of African Origin: A Guide for Educators & Service Providers. 2008. pap. *(978-0-87173-173-9(8))* Assn. for Childhood Education International.

Harris, Yvette R. & Graham, James A. The African American Child: Development & Challenges. 2007. (C). 50.00 *(978-0-8261-2756-3(8))* Springer Publishing Co., Inc.

Hearing on Racial Disproportionality in Foster Care: Hearing Before the Subcommittee on Income Security & Family Support of the Committee on Ways & Means, U.S. House of Representatives, One Hundred Tenth Congress, Second Session, July 31, 2008. 2009. (Illus.). iii, 126p. *(978-0-16-083866-8(5)*, 552-070-39561-0) United States Government Printing Office.

Hill, Nancy E., et al, eds. African American Children & Mental Health Vols. 1 & 2: Development & Context. 2011. (Child Psychology & Mental Health Ser.). (Illus.). 498p. 104.95 *(978-0-313-38302-1(2)*, A2699C, Praeger Pubs.) Greenwood Publishing Group, Inc.

Holmes-Olenja, Dorothy. Great Grandma Gladys & Her Great Grandsons. 2010. 32p. pap. 18.99 *(978-1-4520-1373-2(X))* AuthorHouse.

Kaczmarek, Joanna, ed. Foster Care & African-american Youth. 2010. (Children's Issues, Laws & Programs Ser.). 153p. 69.00 *(978-1-60741-541-1(0))* Nova Science Pubs., Inc.

Kunjufu, Jawanza. 200+ Educational Strategies to Teach Children of Color. 2009. (ENG.). 200p. pap. 14.95 *(978-1-934155-19-6(5))* African American Images.

Lester, Neal A. Once upon a Time in a Different World: Issues & Ideas in African American Children's Literature. 2007. (Children's Literature & Culture Ser.). 304p. 131.00 *(978-0-415-98019-7(4))* Routledge.

Manning, M. Lee & Baruth, Leroy G. Multicultural Education of Children & Adolescents. 5th ed. 2008. (ENG., Illus.). 384p. (C). pap. 110.40 *(978-0-205-59256-2(2))* Allyn & Bacon, Inc.

Meier, Terry. Black Communications & Learning to Read: Building on Children's Linguistic & Cultural Strengths. 2007. (Illus.). 335p. 110.00 *(978-0-8058-5759-7(1))*; per. 45.95 *(978-0-8058-5760-3(5))* Erlbaum, Lawrence Assocs., Inc.

Mitchell, Mary. Raising Freedom's Child: Black Children & Visions of the Future after Slavery. 2010. (ENG., Illus.). 336p. pap. 24.00 *(978-0-8147-9633-7(8))* New York Univ. Pr.

Morris, Jerome. Troubling the Waters: Fulfilling the Promise of Quality Public Schooling for Black Children. 2010. (ENG.). 216p. 64.00 *(978-0-8077-5016-2(6))*; pap. 27.95 *(978-0-8077-5015-5(8))* Teachers College Pr., Teachers College, Columbia Univ.

Munin, Art. Color by Number: Understanding Racism through Facts & Stats on Children. 2012. 132p. 60.00 ***(978-1-57922-635-0(3))***; pap. 22.50 ***(978-1-57922-636-7(1))*** Stylus Publishing, LLC.

Robinson, Ethel. African American Middle-Income Parents: How Are They Involved in Their Children's Literacy Development? (HC) 2007. 108p. (C). 73.99 *(978-1-59311-830-3(9))* Information Age Publishing, Inc.

—African American Middle-Income Parents: How Are They Involved in Their Children's Literacy Development? (PB) 2007. 104p. (C). per. 39.99 *(978-1-59311-829-7(5))* Information Age Publishing, Inc.

Robinson, Sharon P. & Brown II, M. Christopher, eds. The Children Hurricane Katrina Left Behind: Schooling Context, Professional Preparation, & Community Politics. 2007. 226p. (C). 79.95 *(978-0-8204-9728-0(2))*; pap. 32.95 *(978-0-8204-8822-6(4))* Lang, Peter Publishing, Inc.

Saunders, Daveta. Shades of Identity. 2008. 148p. pap. *(978-3-639-03101-0(6))* VDM Verlag Dr. Mueller e.K.

Smith, Darron T., et al. White Parents, Black Children: Experiencing Transracial Adoption. 2011. (ENG., Illus.). 176p. 39.95 ***(978-1-4422-0762-2(0))*** Rowman & Littlefield Publishers, Inc.

Tough, Paul. Whatever It Takes: Geoffrey Canada's Quest to Change Harlem & America. 2009. (ENG.). 336p. pap. 14.95 *(978-0-547-24796-0(6)*, Mariner Bks.) Houghton Mifflin Harcourt Trade & Reference Pubs.

Truitt, Thomas E. Brick Walls: Reflections on Race in a Southern School District. 2006. 164p. 34.95 *(978-1-57003-638-5(1))* Univ. of South Carolina Pr.

Wallace, Charlton. Parenting the Black Male: An African American Male's Opinionated View of How It Should Be Done, 1 vol. 2010. 122p. pap. 19.95 *(978-1-4489-4620-4(4))* PublishAmerica, Inc.

Ward, Geoff K. The Black Child-Savers: Racial Democracy & Juvenile Justice. 2012. (ENG., Illus.). 344p. 90.00 ***(978-0-226-87316-9(1))***; pap. 30.00 ***(978-0-226-87318-3(8))*** Univ. of Chicago Pr.

White, Steve A. Helping Black Children Reach Their Full Potential. 2007. 40p. per. 9.00 *(978-0-9787394-4-7(2))* Protective Hands Communications.

Wiggan, Greg, ed. Education for the New Frontier: Race, Education & Triumph in Jim Crow America (1867-1945) 2011. (Illus.). xxiii, 100p. pap. *(978-1-61209-673-5(5))* Nova Science Pubs., Inc.

Wilson, Rowena Grice & Crewe, Sandra Edmonds. Tradition & Policy Perspectives in Kinship Care. 2007. (ENG., Illus.). 268p. 125.00 *(978-0-7890-3551-6(0))*; per. 54.50 *(978-0-7890-3552-3(9))* Routledge.

Woodhouse, Barbara Bennett. Hidden in Plain Sight: The Tragedy of Children's Rights from Ben Franklin to Lionel Tate. (Public Square Ser.). (ENG., Illus.). 384p. (C). 2010. pap. 19.95 *(978-0-691-14621-8(7))* 2008. 27.95 *(978-0-691-12690-6(9))* Princeton Univ. Pr.

Wynn, Mychal. Teaching, Parenting, & Mentoring Successful Black Males: A Quick Guide. Bascome, Glenn, ed. 2007. 128p. per. 5.95 *(978-1-880463-03-1(2))* Rising Sun Publishing, Inc.

AFRICAN AMERICAN CHURCHES

Barber, Barbara Beadle. By Faith: A Century of Progress. 2009. 340p. 32.95 *(978-0-595-50669-9(0))*; pap. 22.95 *(978-0-595-50491-6(4))* iUniverse, Inc.

Black Biblical Studies. 2010. pap. 17.00 *(978-0-687-33164-2(1))* Abingdon Pr.

Black Church Scholars Series, 7 vols. Incl. Black Christian Worship Experience. Hoyt, Thomas, Jr. 264p. 1992. pap. 13.00 *(978-1-884805-14-1(0))*; From Prison Cell to Church Pew: The Strategy of the African American Church. Smith, J. Alfred, Jr. & Umar, Warithu-Deen. Askew, Glorya & Wilmore, Gayraud, eds. 1993. pap. 8.95 *(978-1-884805-15-8(9))*; Rainbows & Reality: Selected Writings. Rooks, Charles S. Diamond, John C., ed. 158p. 1985. pap. 10.95 *(978-1-884805-05-9(1))*; Reclamation of Black Prisoners: A Challenge to the African American Church. Lincoln, C. Eric & Ducksworth, John. Askew, Glorya & Wilmore, Gayraud, eds. 134p. 1992. pap. 8.95 *(978-1-884805-13-4(2))*; Struggle for a Black Theology of Education: Pioneering Efforts of Post Civil War Clergy. Griffin, Paul R. Wilmore, Gayraud S., ed. 153p. (C). 1993. pap. 15.00 *(978-1-884805-06-6(X))*; *(978-1-884805-20-2(5))* Journal of the Interdenominational Theological Ctr.

Bridgeman, Valerie & Fosua, Safiyah, eds. Companion to the Africana Worship Book. 2008. 159p. 22.00 *(978-0-88177-533-4(9))* Discipleship Resources.

Bridges, Leander. Building the Black Church: 7 Curses Facing the Black Church. 2010. pap. 9.99 *(978-1-61663-310-3(7))* Tate Publishing & Enterprises, LLC.

Buchanan-Featherstone, Fannie. Outside of Eden: Part One. 2006. 20.99 *(978-1-60034-425-1(9))* Xulon Pr., Inc.

Crouch, William H., Jr. & Gregory, Joel C. What We Love about the Black Church: Can We Get a Witness? 2010. 160p. pap. 16.00 *(978-0-8170-1644-9(9))* Judson Pr.

Davis, Reginald F. The Black Church: Relevant or Irrelevant in the 21st Century? 2010. pap. *(978-1-57312-557-4(1))* Smyth & Helwys Publishing, Inc.

Douglas, Kelly Brown. Black Bodies & the Black Church: A Blues Slant. 2012. (Black Religion/Womanist Thought/Social Justice Ser.). (ENG., Illus.). 224p. 85.00 ***(978-0-230-11681-8(7))*** Palgrave Macmillan.

Ellis, Carl, Jr. Go Global: Beyond the Boundaries. 2010. 98p. stu. ed. 9.95 *(978-0-940955-95-0(4))* UMI (Urban Ministries, Inc.).

Ernest, John. A Nation Within a Nation: Organizing African-American Communities Before the Civil War. 2011. (ENG.). 232p. 35.00 *(978-1-56663-807-4(0))*; *(978-1-56663-917-0(4))* Dee, Ivan R. Pub.

Floyd, James E. An Ethnography of an African American Holy Ghost Church: The Role of Saints, Shouters, & Street People in the Organizatonal Environment of St. Paul Baptist Church in Omaha, Nebraska. 2011. 372p. 119.95 *(978-0-7734-1446-4(0))* Mellen, Edwin Pr., The.

Franklin, Robert M. Crisis in the Village: Restoring Hope in African American Communities. 2007. 280p. per. 16.00 *(978-0-8006-3887-0(5)*, Fortress Pr.) Augsburg Fortress, Pubs.

Hare, L. Nathan. The Role of the Church in the African American Rise to Freedom. 2007. (Illus.). 192p. 20.00 *(978-0-9798045-0-2(7))* Return to Promise Ministries.

Harris, Angelique. AIDS, Sexuality, & the Black Church: Making the Wounded Whole. 2010. (Martin Luther King, Jr. Memorial Studies in Religion, Culture, & Social Development Ser.). 198p. (C). 72.95 *(978-1-4331-0943-0(3))* Lang, Peter Publishing, Inc.

Hill, Kenneth H. Religious Education in the African American Church: A Comprehensive Introduction. 2007. (C). 24.99 *(978-0-8272-0820-9(0))* Chalice Pr.

Hinton, Mary. Commercial Church: Black Churches & the New Religious Marketplace in America. 2011. (ENG.). 170p. 60.00 *(978-0-7391-3772-7(7))* Lexington Bks.

J. Johnson, Rev. Lamont. Autonomous: 21st Century Look at the African-American Baptist Church. 2011. 226p. pap. 14.95 ***(978-0-9840955-6-8(X))*** Godzchild Inc.

Knox, Andrew. Blazing an African-American Trail. 2008. (ENG.). 108p. pap. 11.95 *(978-1-934937-04-4(5))* Mill City Pr., Inc.

Kunjufu, Jawanza. Developing Strong Black Male Ministries. 2006. (ENG., Illus.). 180p. pap. 14.95 *(978-0-9749000-9-4(5))* African American Images.

Lanzano, Stanley F. True Places: A Lowcountry Preacher, His Church, & His People. 2009. (ENG.). 124p. 19.95 *(978-1-57003-851-8(1))* Univ. of South Carolina Pr.

Latimer, Frances Bibbins. Landmarks: Historic Sites on the E. S. of Virginia. 2007. (Illus.). 168p. per. 18.00 *(978-1-886706-72-9(7))* Hickory Hse.

Levy, Michael Stephen, photos by. Revelations: Photographs of Cleveland's African American Churches. 2008. (Illus.). 39.00 *(978-0-87338-937-2(9))* Kent State Univ. Pr.

Lewis, Candace. New Day a New Way. 2009. 128p. pap. 14.00 *(978-0-88177-574-7(6))* Discipleship Resources.

Materson, Lisa G. For the Freedom of Her Race: Black Women & Electoral Politics in Illinois, 1877-1932. 2009. (ENG., Illus.). 352p. 44.00 *(978-0-8078-3271-4(5))* Univ. of North Carolina Pr.

McMickle, Marvin Andrew. A Time to Speak: How Black Pastors Can Respond to the HIV/AIDS Pandemic. 2008. 176p. 20.00 *(978-0-8298-1803-1(0))* Pilgrim Pr., The/United Church Pr.

Miller, James F. Go Grow Your Church! Spiritual Leadership for African American Congregations. 2008. (Illus.). 176p. *(978-0-8298-1801-7(4))* Pilgrim Pr., The/United Church Pr.

Miller, Tyagan. Covenant: Scenes from an African American Church. 2007. (Polis Center Series on Religion & Urban Culture Ser.). (ENG., Illus.). 176p. 29.95 *(978-0-253-34835-7(8)*, 0253348358) Indiana Univ. Pr.

Moore, Forrest. A History of the Black Church in Tuscaloos. 2009. 184p. 24.99 *(978-1-4389-2263-8(9))*; pap. 14.49 *(978-1-4389-2260-7(4))* AuthorHouse.

Owens, Michael Leo. God & Government in the Ghetto: The Politics of Church-State Collaboration in Black America. 2007. (Morality & Society Ser.). (Illus.). 304p. 60.00 *(978-0-226-64206-2(2))*; per. 25.00 *(978-0-226-64207-9(0))* Univ. of Chicago Pr.

Pinn, Anthony B. Understanding & Transforming the Black Church. 2009. 166p. pap. 19.00 *(978-1-55635-301-7(4)*, Cascade Bks.) Wipf & Stock Pubs.

Pollard, Deborah Smith. When the Church Becomes Your Party: Contemporary Gospel Music. 2008. (African American Life Ser.). (Illus.). 225p. pap. 24.95 *(978-0-8143-3218-4(8))* Wayne State Univ. Pr.

Price, Emmett G., III, ed. The Black Church & Hip Hop Culture: Toward Bridging the Generational Divide. 2011. (African American Cultural Theory & Heritage Ser.). (ENG.). 228p. (gr. 17). 65.00 ***(978-0-8108-8236-2(1))*** Scarecrow Pr., Inc.

Price, Emmett George. The Black Church & Hip-Hop Culture: Toward Bridging the Generational Divide. 2012. E-Book ***(978-0-8108-8237-9(X))*** Scarecrow Pr., Inc.

Riggs, Marcia Y. Plenty Good Room: Women Versus Male Power in the Black Church. 2008. 160p. pap. 18.00 *(978-1-60608-213-3(2)*, Wipf and Stock) Wipf & Stock Pubs.

Savage, Barbara Dianne. Your Spirits Walk Beside Us: The Politics of Black Religion. 2008. 368p. 27.95 *(978-0-674-03177-7(6)*, Belknap Pr.) Harvard Univ. Pr.

Smith, Norman R. Footprints of Black Louisian. 2011. 158p. 29.99 ***(978-1-4568-2631-4(X))***; pap. 19.99 ***(978-1-4568-2630-7(1))*** Xlibris Corp.

Smith, Robert London. From Strength to Strength: Shaping a Black Practical Theology for the 21st Century. 2007. (Illus.). 256p. (C). 71.95 *(978-0-8204-9518-7(2))* Lang, Peter Publishing, Inc.

Stepick, Alex, et al, eds. Churches & Charity in the Immigrant City: Religion, Immigration, & Civic Engagement in Miami. 2009. (ENG.). 336p. 70.00 *(978-0-8135-4459-5(9))*; pap. 25.95 *(978-0-8135-4460-1(2))* Rutgers Univ. Pr.

Stewart, Alexander C. & Bonner, W. L. A Partial Annotative Bibliography of Literature on the Pentecostal Movement: Presented in Honor of the Centennial Anniversary of the Azusa Street Revival & the 85th Birthday Celebration of Apostle William Lee Bonner. 2008. (Illus.). viii, 55p. *(978-1-932667-42-4(3))* Bookends Pr.

Stewart, Carlyle Fielding, III, ed. Growing the African American Church. 2006. 177p. per. 21.00 *(978-0-687-49839-0(2))* Abingdon Pr.

Strain, Christopher B. Burning Faith: Church Arson in the American South. 2008. (Southern Dissent Ser.). (ENG., Illus.). 224p. 34.95 *(978-0-8130-3239-9(3))* Univ. Pr. of Florida.

Tate, Kenneth J. The Importance of Mobilizing the Christian Church As a Family Preparation Center for Daily Christian Living. 2009. 156p. pap. 11.99 *(978-1-4490-0563-4(2))* AuthorHouse.

Tucker-Worgs, Tamelyn N. The Black Megachurch: Theology, Gender, & the Politics of Public Engagement. 2011. (ENG., Illus.). 275p. 39.95 *(978-1-932792-74-4(0))* Baylor Univ. Pr.

Walston, Vaughn J. & Stevens, Robert J. African-American Experience in World Mission: A Call Beyond Community. 2009. *(978-0-87808-461-6(4))* Carey, William Library Pubs.

Watkins, Ralph C. Leading Your African American Church through Pastoral Transition. 2010. 160p. pap. 16.00 *(978-0-8170-1641-8(4))* Judson Pr.

Weissinger, Sandra Ellen. A Sociology of Black Clergy in the State of Illinois: Activism & Acquiescence in the Post-Civil Rights Generation. 2011. 216p. 119.95 ***(978-0-7734-1499-0(1))*** Mellen, Edwin Pr., The.

Wesley, Michael W. When God Changes A Church. 2010. 274p. pap. 16.99 *(978-1-60957-337-9(4))* Xulon Pr., Inc.

Whelchel, L. H., Jr. The History & Heritage of African-American Churches: A Way Out of No Way. 2011. (ENG., Illus.). 366p. pap. 24.95 *(978-1-55778-893-1(6))* Paragon Hse. Pubs.

Williams, Audri Scott. Embers of Glory. 2010. 84p. pap. 12.95 *(978-0-557-43372-8(X))* Lulu Enterprises Inc.

=Williams, Carla, ed. Articles of Faith: African-American Community Churches in Chicago. 2009. (Center for American Places - Center Books on American Places Ser.). (ENG., Illus.). 96p. 50.00 *(978-1-930066-97-7(X))* Ctr. for American Places, Inc.

Williams, Johnny E. African American Religion & the Civil Rights Movement in Arkansas. 2008. (ENG.). 177p. pap. 25.00 *(978-1-60473-186-6(9))* Univ. Pr. of Mississippi.

AFRICAN AMERICAN CLERGY

Anyabwile, Thabiti, ed. & intro. May We Meet in the Heavenly World: The Piety of Lemuel Haynes. 2009. (Illus.). pap. 10.00 *(978-1-60178-065-2(6))* Reformation Heritage Bks.

Anyabwile, Thabiti M. The Faithful Preacher: Recapturing the Vision of Three Pioneering African-American Pastors. 2007. (Illus.). 192p. pap. 15.99 *(978-1-58134-827-9(4))* Crossway.

Bean, Carl. I Was Born This Way: A Gay Preacher's Journey Through Gospel Music, Disco Stardom, & a Ministry in Christ. 2010. (ENG., Illus.). 272p. 24.00 *(978-1-4165-9282-2(2))* Simon & Schuster.

Bell, Christopher. The Black Clergy's Misguided Worship Leadership: No More Idol Gods for Black People. 2010. 136p. pap. 19.00 *(978-1-4251-7806-2(5))* Trafford Publishing.

Black Church Scholars Series, 7 vols. Incl. Black Christian Worship Experience. Hoyt, Thomas, Jr. 264p. 1992. pap. 13.00 *(978-1-884805-14-1(0))*; From Prison Cell to Church Pew: The Strategy of the African American Church. Smith, J. Alfred, Jr. & Umar, Warithu-Deen. Askew, Glorya & Wilmore, Gayraud, eds. 1993. pap. 8.95 *(978-1-884805-15-8(9))*; Rainbows & Reality: Selected Writings. Rooks, Charles S. Diamond, John C., ed. 158p. 1985. pap. 10.95 *(978-1-884805-05-9(1))*; Reclamation of Black Prisoners: A Challenge to the African American Church. Lincoln, C. Eric & Ducksworth, John. Askew, Glorya & Wilmore, Gayraud, eds. 134p. 1992. pap. 8.95 *(978-1-884805-13-4(2))*; Struggle for a Black Theology of Education: Pioneering Efforts of Post Civil War Clergy. Griffin, Paul R. Wilmore, Gayraud S., ed. 153p. (C). 1993. pap. 15.00 *(978-1-884805-06-6(X))*; *(978-1-884805-20-2(5))* Journal of the Interdenominational Theological Ctr.

Dickerson, Dennis C. African American Preachers & Politics: The Careys of Chicago. (Margaret Walker Alexander Series in African American Studies). (ENG., Illus.). 2011. 304p. pap. 30.00 ***(978-1-61703-193-9(3))*** 2010. 236p. 65.00 *(978-1-60473-427-0(2))* Univ. Pr. of Mississippi.

Gona, Ophelia De Laine. Dawn of Desegregation: J.A. de Laine & Briggs V. Elliott. 2011. 216p. 29.95 *(978-1-57003-980-5(1))* Univ. of South Carolina Pr.

Hemesath, Sister Caroline. From Slave to Priest: The Inspirational Story of Fr. Augustine Tolton. 2010. 255p. pap. 16.95 *(978-1-58617-524-5(6))* Ignatius Pr.

Hill, Kenneth H. Religious Education in the African American Church: A Comprehensive Introduction. 2007. (C). 24.99 *(978-0-8272-0820-9(0))* Chalice Pr.

Hurdle-Toomey, Hannah. More Than a Slave: The Biography of Rev. A.J. Hurdle. 2010. (Illus.). 130p. pap. ***(978-0-615-36502-2(7))*** Culter, Robert Bks.

James, Isaac. The Sun Do Move: The Story of the Life of John Jasper. 2011. 56p. 36.95 ***(978-1-258-09212-2(3))*** Literary Licensing, LLC.

King, Martin Luther, Jr. Daddy King: My Life. 2007. (Illus.). 224p. pap. 16.95 *(978-1-58818-150-3(2))* Gibbs Smith, Publisher.

Lee, Shayne. T. D. Jakes: America's New Preacher. 2007. (ENG., Illus.). 216p. pap. 21.00 *(978-0-8147-5224-1(1))* New York Univ. Pr.

Mabee, Carleton. Promised Land: Father Divine's Interracial Communities in Ulster County, New York. 2008. (Illus.). 248p. pap. 22.50 *(978-1-930098-93-0(6))* Purple Mountain Pr., Ltd.

McMickle, Marvin Andrew. A Time to Speak: How Black Pastors Can Respond to the HIV/AIDS Pandemic. 2008. 176p. 20.00 *(978-0-8298-1803-1(0))* Pilgrim Pr., The/United Church Pr.

McRipley, Bernadine Grant. Sacred Memories: Then & Now. 2007. 11.00 *(978-0-8059-8839-0(4))* Dorrance Publishing Co., Inc.

Penn, Sabrina A. A Place for My Children, First Edition. 2007. 248p. pap. 20.00 *(978-0-9797359-0-5(4))* Penn Ink.

Pitt, Richard. Divine Callings: Understanding the Call to Ministry in Black Pentecostalism. 2012. (ENG.). 288p. 80.00 ***(978-0-8147-6823-5(7))***; pap. 25.00 ***(978-0-8147-6824-2(5))*** New York Univ. Pr.

Pitt, Richard N. Divine Callings: Understanding the Call to Ministry in Black Pentecostalism. 2012. E-Book ***(978-0-8147-6876-1(8))***; E-Book ***(978-0-8147-6825-9(3))*** New York Univ. Pr.

Porter, A. Toomer. Led on! Step by Step. 2010. (Distributed for Home House Press Ser.). pap. 29.95 *(978-0-9845580-0-1(4))* Univ. of South Carolina Pr.

Reddie, Richard S. Martin Luther King. 2011. (ENG., Illus.). 192p. pap. 16.95 ***(978-0-7459-5282-6(8))*** Lion Hudson PLC GBR. Dist: Independent Pubs. Group.

Smith, Paris Lee. From Plantation to the Pulpit: The Transforming Message of the Black Baptist Church. 2007. 172p. 21.99 *(978-1-60477-107-7(0))*; per. 13.99 *(978-1-60477-106-0(2))* Xulon Pr., Inc.

van Bavel, T. J. The Longing of the Heart: Augustine's Doctrine on Prayer. 2009. (ENG.). 175p. (C). pap. 44.00 *(978-90-429-1975-4(2))* Peeters Pubs. & Booksellers BEL. Dist: Brown, David Bk. Co., The.

Walker, Clarence Earl & Smithers, Gregory D. The Preacher & the Politician: Jeremiah Wright, Barack Obama, & Race in America. 2009. (ENG., Illus.). 168p. 22.95 *(978-0-8139-2886-9(9))* Univ. Pr. of Virginia.

Webber, Christopher. American to the Backbone: The Life of James W. C. Pennington, the Fugitive Slave Who Became One of the First Black Abolitionists. 2011. (ENG.). 432p. 29.95 *(978-1-60598-175-8(3)*, 605175) Pegasus Bks.

Zackodnik, Teresa C. Press, Platform, Pulpit: Black Feminist Publics in the ERA of Reform. 2011. (ENG., Illus.). xxxv, 339p. 45.00 ***(978-1-57233-826-5(1))*** Univ. of Tennessee Pr.

AFRICAN AMERICAN COLLEGES
see African American Universities and Colleges

AFRICAN AMERICAN COMPOSERS

Banfield, William. Representing Culture: Black Music Then, Now, & When Again? 2011. (African American Cultural Theory & Heritage Ser.). (ENG., Illus.). 312p. pap. 35.00 *(978-0-8108-7786-3(4))* Scarecrow Pr., Inc.

Banfield, William C. Representing Black Music Culture: Then, Now, & When Again? 2011. E-Book ***(978-0-8108-7787-0(2))*** Scarecrow Pr., Inc.

Barnett, Anthony. Listening for Henry Crowder: A Monograph on His Almost Lost Music: With the Poems & Music of Henry-Music, 1 bk + CD insert. 2007. (Illus.). 128p. pap. 89.50 *(978-0-907954-36-1(7))* Allardyce, Barnett, Pubs. GBR. Dist: SPD-Small Pr. Distribution.

Carter, Marva Griffin. Swing Along: The Musical Life of Will Marion Cook. 2008. (ENG., Illus.). 240p. 27.95 *(978-0-19-510891-0(4))* Oxford Univ. Pr., Inc.

Earl, Thomas. A History of the NBC. 2007. (National Baptist Great Personalities Ser.: Vol. 2). 9.95 *(978-0-910683-20-3(4))* Townsend Pr. - Sunday Schl. Publishing Board.

Jones, Charles K. Francis Johnson (1792-1844) Chronicle of a Black Musician in Early Nineteenth-Century Philadelphia. 2006. (Illus.). 330p. 57.50 *(978-0-934223-86-7(6))* Lehigh Univ. Pr.

Simpson, Eugene Thamon. Hall Johnson: His Life, His Spirit, & His Music. 2008. (ENG., Illus.). 404p. 87.00 *(978-0-8108-6038-4(4))* Scarecrow Pr., Inc.

Smith, Catherine Parsons. William Grant Still. 2008. (American Composers Ser.). (ENG., Illus.). 136p. 39.00 *(978-0-252-03322-3(1))* Univ. of Illinois Pr.

Still, Judith Anne & Headlee, Lisa M., eds. Just Tell the Story: Troubled Island. 2006. (ENG., Illus.). 603p. lib. bdg. 39.95 *(978-1-877873-02-7(0))* Master-Player Library, The.

Still, William Grant & Still, Judith Anne. My Life, My Words: The Autobiography of William Grant Still. 2011. (ENG., Illus.). 312p. 19.95 ***(978-1-877873-27-0(6))*** Master-Player Library, The.

Walker-Hill, Helen. From Spirituals to Symphonies: African-American Women Composers & Their Music. 2007. (Illus.). 428p. per. 26.00 *(978-0-252-07454-7(8))* Univ. of Illinois Pr.

AFRICAN AMERICAN CONSUMERS

Capparell, Stephanie. The Real Pepsi Challenge: How One Pioneering Company Broke Color Barriers in 1940s American Business. 2008. (ENG., Illus.). 384p. pap. 23.99 *(978-0-7432-6572-0(6),* Free Pr.) Free Pr.

Chambers, Jason. Madison Avenue & the Color Line: African Americans in the Advertising Industry. 2009. (Illus.). 328p. (C). pap. 24.95 *(978-0-8122-2060-5(9))* Univ. of Pennsylvania Pr.

Davis, James C. Commerce in Color: Race, Consumer Culture, & American Literature, 1893-1933. 2007. (Class: Culture Ser.). (ENG., Illus.). 312p. 75.00 *(978-0-472-09967-0(6));* per. 27.95 *(978-0-472-06987-3(X))* Univ. of Michigan Pr.

Hoffman, Andrea & Burnett, Leonard E. Black Is the New Green: Marketing to Affluent African Americans. 2010. (ENG., Illus.). 224p. 35.00 *(978-0-230-61684-4(4))* Palgrave Macmillan.

New Strategist Publications, Incorporated Staff. Who's Buying by Race & Hispanic Origin. 3rd ed. 2007. (The Who's Buying Ser.). 123p. pap. 59.95 *(978-1-933588-53-7(5))* New Strategist Pubns., Inc.

Richard, Levi. Opinion Leadership for Ethnic Products. 2010. 224p. pap. *(978-3-639-23173-1(2))* VDM Verlag Dr. Mueller e.K.

Who's Buying by Race & Hispanic Origin. 2nd ed. 2006. (Who's Buying Ser.). 127p. pap. 59.95 *(978-1-933588-18-6(7))* New Strategist Pubns., Inc.

AFRICAN AMERICAN COOKING

Allen, Lincoln. Caribbean/Soul Food Cookbook: A Collection of Favorite Recipes Including Jerk. 2010. 160p. pap. 14.75 *(978-1-4520-0629-5(9))* AuthorHouse.

Bower, Anne. African American Foodways: Explorations of History & Culture. Bower, Anne, ed. 2008. (Food Ser.). (ENG., Illus.). 200p. pap. 21.00 *(978-0-252-07630-5(3))* Univ. of Illinois Pr.

Davis-Gibson, Katonya. Plantation Sweetness: The True History of African-American Home Cooking. 2008. 140p. pap. 24.95 *(978-1-60610-150-6(1))* PublishAmerica, Inc.

Ganeshram, Ramin. America I Am Pass It down Cookbook: Over 130 Soul-Filled Recipes. Henderson, Jeff, ed. 2011. (ENG.). 320p. pap. 16.95 *(978-1-4019-3135-3(9))* Hay Hse., Inc.

The Get'Em Girl's Guide to Unlocking the Power of Cuisine. 2nd ed. 2007. per. 19.99 *(978-0-9791832-0-1(0))* Subira Publishing.

Harris, Jessica B. High on the Hog: A Culinary Journey from Africa to America. 2011. (ENG., Illus.). 304p. 26.00 *(978-1-59691-395-0(9))* Bloomsbury Publishing.

Holmes, Buster. The Buster Holmes Restaurant Cookbook: New Orleans Handmade Cookin', 1 vol. 2010. (ENG., Illus.). 128p. spiral bd. 16.95 *(978-1-58980-849-2(5))* Pelican Publishing Co., Inc.

Jones, Charita. Momma Cherri's Soul in a Bowl Cookbook. 2007. (ENG., Illus.). 160p. 29.95 *(978-1-904573-59-3(2))* Absolute Pr. GBR. Dist: Independent Pubs. Group.

Lawrence, Sandra. Harlem Really Cooks: The Nouvelle Soul Food of Harlem. 2006. (ENG., Illus.). 192p. per. 16.95 *(978-1-891105-18-0(3))* Lake Isle Pr., Inc.

Locker, Kimberly. Esther's Glow Cookbook: Healthy Living for Women of Color. 2007. 24p. 12.00 *(978-0-9711021-1-8(2))* Shepherd's Shield, Inc., The.

Medearis, Angela Shelf. The Kitchen Diva! The New African-American Kitchen. 2008. (ENG.). 256p. 21.95 *(978-1-891105-39-5(6))* Lake Isle Pr., Inc.

Mitchell, Willa. Black American Cookbook. 400p. 1. lib. bdg. 5.95 *(978-0-9603014-0-9(2))*2. lib. bdg. 6.95 *(978-0-9603014-1-6(0))* Evangelist Assn.

National Cancer Institute. Down Home Healthy Cooking Cookbook. 2009. (Food & Beverage Consumption & Health Ser.). pap. 43.00 *(978-1-60692-849-3(X))* Nova Science Pubs., Inc.

Opie, Frederick Douglass. Hog & Hominy: Soul Food from Africa to America. 2010. (Arts & Traditions of the Table: Perspectives on Culinary History Ser.). (ENG., Illus.). 256p. (gr. 17). pap. 17.95 *(978-0-231-14639-5(6))* Columbia Univ. Pr.

Opie, Fredrick Douglass & Opie, Frederick Douglass. Hog & Hominy: Soul Food from Africa to America. 2008. (Arts & Traditions of the Table: Perspectives on Culinary History Ser.). (ENG., Illus.). 256p. (gr. 17). 24.95 *(978-0-231-14638-8(8))* Columbia Univ. Pr.

Robinson, Sallie Ann & Harris, Jessica B. Cooking the Gullah Way, Morning, Noon, & Night. 2007. (ENG., Illus.). 176p. 24.95 *(978-0-8078-3150-2(6));* per. 18.00 *(978-0-8078-5843-1(9))* Univ. of North Carolina Pr.

Russell, Malinda. A Domestic Cook Book: Containing a Careful Selection of Useful Receipts for the Kitchen. fac. ed. 2007. pap. 25.00 *(978-1-4255-8881-6(6),* Clements, William L. Library) MPublishing.

Smart-Grosvenor, Vertamae. Vibration Cooking: Or, the Travel Notes of a Geechee Girl. 2011. (ENG.). 256p. pap. 19.95 *(978-0-8203-3739-5(0))* Univ. of Georgia Pr.

Terry, Bryant. Vegan Soul Kitchen: Fresh, Healthy, & Creative African-American Cuisine. 2009. (ENG., Illus.). 256p. pap. 18.95 *(978-0-7382-1228-9(8))* Da Capo Pr., Inc.

Tillery, Carolyn. Southern Homecoming Traditions: Recipes & Remembrances. 2010. (ENG.). 320p. pap. 16.95 *(978-0-8065-3204-2(1),* Citadel Pr.) Kensington Publishing Corp.

Tillman, Katherine, frwd. Federation Cook Book. 2007. (Cooking in America Ser.). (ENG.). 100p. per. 9.95 *(978-1-4290-1017-7(7))* Applewood Bks.

AFRICAN AMERICAN CRIMINALS

Allen, Eddie B., Jr. & Allen, Eddie B. Low Road: The Life & Legacy of Donald Goines. 2008. (ENG., Illus.). 224p. pap. 16.99 *(978-0-312-38351-0(7),* St. Martin's Griffin) St. Martin's Pr.

Chepesiuk, Ron. Black Gangsters of Chicago. 2007. (ENG., Illus.). 288p. 22.00 *(978-1-56980-331-8(5))* Barricade Bks., Inc.

Ferranti, Seth. Street Legends, 2. 2nd ed. 2008. 260p. reprint ed. per. 15.00 *(978-0-9800687-0-2(3))* Gorilla Convict Pubns.

Frazier, Harriet C. Slavery & Crime in Missouri, 1773-1865. alt. ed. 2011. (ENG., Illus.). 336p. pap. 45.00 *(978-0-7864-4331-4(6))* McFarland & Co., Inc. Pubs.

Free, Marvin D., Jr. & Ruesink, Mitch. Race & Justice: Wrongful Convictions of African American Men. 2012. 330p. 68.00 ***(978-1-58826-810-5(1))*** Rienner, Lynne Pubs.

Gorvin, Ian. Targeting Blacks: Drug Law Enforcement & Race in the United States. 2008. (Illus.). 64p. *(978-1-56432-315-6(3))* Human Rights Watch.

Gross, Kali N. Colored Amazons: Crime, Violence, & Black Women in the City of Brotherly Love, 1880-1910. 2006. (Politics, History, & Culture Ser.). (ENG., Illus.). 280p. per. 23.95 *(978-0-8223-3799-7(1))* Duke Univ. Pr.

Jacobson, Mark. American Gangster: And Other Tales of New York. 2007. (ENG.). 288p. (Orig.). per. 14.00 *(978-0-8021-4336-5(9),* Grove Pr.) Grove/Atlantic, Inc.

James M Stone. The Murder of Mingo Jack: New Jersey's only nineteenth century Lynching. 2010. 104p. pap. 11.95 *(978-1-4502-1320-2(0))* iUniverse, Inc.

Levi, Steven. Telling It All: My Life As A con Man. 2007. 148p. per. 16.99 *(978-0-9790878-6-8(4))* Community Pr.

Lucas, Frank & King, Aliya S. Original Gangster: The Real Life Story of One of America's Most Notorious Drug Lords. 2011. (ENG., Illus.). 320p. pap. 15.99 *(978-0-312-57164-1(X),* St. Martin's Griffin) St. Martin's Pr.

Marable, Manning, et al, eds. Racializing Justice, Disenfranchising Lives: The Racism, Criminal Justice, & Law Reader. 2007. (Critical Black Studies). (ENG.). 400p. 95.00 *(978-1-4039-7766-3(6));* pap. 30.00 *(978-1-4039-7767-0(4))* Palgrave Macmillan.

Miller, Jerome G. Search & Destroy: African-American Males in the Criminal Justice System. 2nd ed. 2010. (ENG., Illus.). 212p. 85.00 *(978-0-521-76779-8(2));* pap. 29.99 *(978-0-521-74381-5(8))* Cambridge Univ. Pr.

Raper, Arthur F. The Tragedy of Lynching. 2011. (ENG.). 508p. pap. 50.00 ***(978-0-8078-9758-4(2))*** Univ. of North Carolina Pr.

Russell-Brown, Katheryn. The Color of Crime: Racial Hoaxes, White Fear, Black Protectionism, Police Harassment, & Other Macroaggressions. 2nd ed. 2008. (ENG., Illus.). 224p. (C). pap. 22.00 *(978-0-8147-7616-6(3))* New York Univ. Pr.

Street Legends Vol. 2 Orginial Gangsters. 2010. 304p. pap. 15.00 *(978-0-9800687-1-9(1))* Gorilla Convict Pubns.

Unnever, James D. & Gabbidon, Shaun L. Race, Racism, & Crime: A Theory of African American Offending. 2011. (Criminology & Justice Studies). (ENG., Illus.). 288p. 149.00 *(978-0-415-88357-3(1))* Routledge.

—Race, Racism & Crime: A Theory of African American Offending. 2011. (Criminology & Justice Studies). (ENG., Illus.). 288p. pap. 35.95 *(978-0-415-88358-0(X))* Routledge.

Waldrep, Christopher & Nieman, Donald G., eds. Local Matters: Race, Crime, & Justice in the Nineteenth-Century South. 2011. (Studies in the Legal History of the South Ser.). (ENG.). 264p. pap. 24.95 ***(978-0-8203-4081-4(2))*** Univ. of Georgia Pr.

Williams, Dawayne. Reputations Fade Away: The memoir of dawayne Williams. 2006. 253p. per. 16.95 *(978-0-9786547-2-6(2))* Kojack Enterprise.

Wilson, Ed. D. Disposable Youth: Education or Incarceration? 2010. 266p. pap. 15.50 *(978-1-60911-412-1(4),* Eloquent Bks.) AEG Literary Publishing Services, Inc.

AFRICAN AMERICAN DANCE

Aduonum, Ma-Abena. West African Dance in the United States University Curriculum. 2011. 84p. pap. ***(978-3-8443-3214-8(6))*** Lambert Academic Publishing.

Dixon Gottschild, Brenda. Joan Myers Brown & the Audacious Hope of the Black Ballerina: A Biohistory of American Performance. 2011. (ENG., Illus.). 370p. pap. 27.00 ***(978-0-230-11409-8(1))*** Palgrave Macmillan.

Dixon, Melanye Young. Marion D. Cuyjet & Her Judimar School of Dance: Training Ballerinas in Black Philadelphia 1948-1971. 2011. (Illus.). 232p. 119.95 ***(978-0-7734-1592-8(0))*** Mellen, Edwin Pr., The.

George-Graves, Nadine. Urban Bush Women: Twenty Years of African American Dance Theater, Community Engagement, & Working It Out. 2010. (Studies in Dance History Ser.). (ENG., Illus.). 296p. pap. 29.95 *(978-0-299-23554-3(8))* Univ. of Wisconsin Pr.

Glass, Barbara S. African American Dance: An Illustrated History. 2006. (ENG., Illus.). 319p. 55.00 *(978-0-7864-2816-8(3))* McFarland & Co., Inc. Pubs.

Gottschild, Brenda Dixon. Joan Myers Brown & the Audacious Hope of the Black Ballerina: A Biohistory of American Performance. 2011. (ENG., Illus.). 370p. 90.00 ***(978-0-230-11408-1(3))*** Palgrave Macmillan.

Huntington, Carla Stalling. Black Social Dance in Television Advertising: An Analytical History. 2011. (ENG., Illus.). 200p. pap. 40.00 *(978-0-7864-5944-5(1))* McFarland & Co., Inc. Pubs.

Kraut, Anthea. Choreographing the Folk: The Dance Stagings of Zora Neale Hurston. 2008. (Illus.). 312p. pap. 25.00 *(978-0-8166-4712-5(7));* 75.00 *(978-0-8166-4711-8(9))* Univ. of Minnesota Pr.

Manning, Susan. Modern Dance, Negro Dance: Race in Motion. 2006. (Illus.). 320p. per. 26.50 *(978-0-8166-3737-9(7))* Univ. of Minnesota Pr.

Roberts, John W., ed. From Hucklebuck to Hip Hop: Social Dance in the African American Community in Philadelphia. (Illus.). 134p. (Orig.). pap. *(978-1-885066-11-4(2))* Four-G Pubs., Inc.

Schwartz, Peggy & Schwartz, Murray. The Dance Claimed Me: A Biography of Pearl Primus. 2011. (ENG., Illus.). 352p. 35.00 *(978-0-300-15534-1(4))* Yale Univ. Pr.

AFRICAN AMERICAN DRAMA (ENGLISH)
see American Drama—African American Authors

AFRICAN AMERICAN ENGLISH
see Black English

AFRICAN AMERICAN ENTERTAINERS
see also African American Actors; African American Musicians

Birkbeck, Matt. Deconstructing Sammy: Music, Money, & Madness. 2009. (ENG., Illus.). 304p. pap. 15.99 *(978-0-06-145067-9(7),* Harper Paperbacks) HarperCollins Pubs.

Bogle, Donald & Bogle. Brown Sugar: Over One Hundred Years of America's Black Female Superstars. 2007. (ENG., Illus.). 376p. pap. 44.95 *(978-0-8264-1675-9(6))* Continuum International Publishing Group, Ltd. GBR. Dist: National Bk. Network.

Brown, Jayna. Babylon Girls: Black Women Performers & the Shaping of the Modern. 2008. (ENG., Illus.). 360p. 94.95 *(978-0-8223-4133-8(6));* pap. 25.95 *(978-0-8223-4157-4(3))* Duke Univ. Pr.

Forbes, Camille F. Introducing Bert Williams: Burnt Cork, Broadway, & the Story of America's First Black Star. 2008. (ENG., Illus.). 416p. (gr. 9). 27.50 *(978-0-465-02479-7(3),* Basic Civitas Bks.) Basic Bks.

—Introducing Bert Williams: Burnt Cork, Broadway, & the Story of America's First Black Star. 2010. (ENG., Illus.). 416p. (gr. 9). pap. 18.95 *(978-0-465-01811-6(4))* Basic Bks.

Hale, Thomas A. Griots & Griottes: Masters of Words & Music. 2007. (ENG., Illus.). 432p. pap. 28.00 *(978-0-253-21961-9(2),* 0253219612) Indiana Univ. Pr.

Jules-Rosette, Bennetta. Josephine Baker in Art & Life: The Icon & the Image. 2007. (Illus.). 392p. pap. 26.00 *(978-0-252-07412-7(2));* 368p. 60.00 *(978-0-252-03157-1(1))* Univ. of Illinois Pr.

Regester, Charlene B. Black Entertainers in African American Newspaper Articles: An Annotated Bibliography of the Pittsburgh Courier & the California Eagle, 1912-1950. 2010. (Black Entertainers in African American Newspapers). (ENG.). 837p. pap. 195.00 *(978-0-7864-2495-5(8))* McFarland & Co., Inc. Pubs.

Vogel, Shane. The Scene of Harlem Cabaret: Race, Sexuality, Performance. 2009. (ENG., Illus.). 264p. 60.00 *(978-0-226-86251-4(8))* Univ. of Chicago Pr.

Vogel, Shane & Vogel, S. The Scene of Harlem Cabaret: Race, Sexuality, Performance. 2009. (ENG., Illus.) 272p. pap. 22.00 *(978-0-226-86252-1(6))* Univ. of Chicago Pr.

AFRICAN AMERICAN FAMILIES

Abatso, George & Abatso, Yvonne. How to Equip the African American Family: Issues & Guidelines for Building Strong Families. Birchett, Collen, ed. 183p. (Orig.). pap., tchr. ed. 6.95 *(978-0-940955-18-9(0),* 9-2410) UMI (Urban Ministries, Inc.).

Aborampah, Osei-Mensah & Sudarkasa, Niara. Extended Families in Africa & the African Diaspora. 2011. (Illus.). vi, 398p. *(978-1-59221-812-7(1));* pap. *(978-1-59221-811-0(3))* Africa World Pr.

Allen, John E. The Content of Their Character: The Story Behind This Antique Quilt & the History of the African American Family That Made It. 2009. 164p. pap. 44.48 *(978-1-4251-8812-2(5),* Trafford Publishing.

Bailey, John. America in Color. 2006. pap. 22.99 *(978-1-4257-2113-8(3))* Xlibris Corp.

Baker, Houston A. I Don't Hate the South: Reflections on Faulkner, Family, & the South. 2007. (ENG.). 224p. 125.00 *(978-0-19-508429-0(2))* Oxford Univ. Pr., Inc.

Baker, John F., Jr. The Washingtons of Wessyngton Plantation: Stories of My Family's Journey to Freedom. 2010. (ENG., Illus.). 432p. pap. 16.00 *(978-1-4165-6741-7(0),* Beyond Words/Atria Bks.) Atria Bks.

Banks, Ralph Richard. Is Marriage for White People? How the African American Marriage Decline Affects Everyone. (ENG.). 304p. (gr. 12). 2012. pap. 16.00 ***(978-0-452-29753-1(2),*** Plume) 2011. 25.95 *(978-0-525-95201-5(2),* Dutton Adult) Penguin Group (USA) Inc.

Bernard, Kimble. The Decay of the African American Family: The Biblical Perspective. 2006. lib. bdg. *(978-0-9717242-3-5(7))* ShaCoo Publishing.

Bloom, Harold, ed. Song of Solomon - Toni Morrison, New Edition. 2nd rev. ed. 2009. (Bloom's Modern Critical Interpretations Ser.). 224p. (C). (gr. 9-18). 45.00 *(978-1-60413-392-9(9),* Chelsea Hse.) Facts On File, Inc.

Casper, Scott E. Sarah Johnson's Mount Vernon: The Forgotten History of an American Shrine. 2010. 286p. (C). 25.00 *(978-1-4379-7307-5(8))* DIANE Publishing Co.

—Sarah Johnson's Mount Vernon: The Forgotten History of an American Shrine. 2009. (ENG., Illus.). 320p. pap. 24.00 *(978-0-8090-8415-9(5),* Hill & Wang) Farrar, Straus & Giroux.

Coles, Roberta. Best Kept Secret: Single Black. 2010. (ENG.). 180p. pap. 24.95 *(978-0-7425-6426-8(6))* Rowman & Littlefield Publishers, Inc.

Coles, Roberta & Green, Charles, eds. The Myth of the Missing Black Father. 2009. (ENG., Illus.). 400p. (gr. 17). 89.50 *(978-0-231-14352-3(4));* pap. 29.50 *(978-0-231-14353-0(2))* Columbia Univ. Pr.

Coles, Roberta L. The Best Kept Secret: Single Black Fathers. 2009. (ENG.). 180p. 37.50 *(978-0-7425-6425-1(8))* Rowman & Littlefield Publishers, Inc.

Collier, Melvin J. Mississippi to Africa: A Journey of Discovery. 2008. (Illus.). xviii, 279p. pap. 28.00 *(978-0-7884-4761-7(0))* Heritage Bks.

Curwood, Anastasia. Stormy Weather: Middle-Class African American Marriages between the Two World Wars. 2010. (Gender & American Culture Ser.). (ENG., Illus.). 240p. 35.00 *(978-0-8078-3434-3(3))* Univ. of North Carolina Pr.

Davis, Thulani. My Confederate Kinfolk: A Twenty-First Century Freedwoman Discovers Her Roots. 2007. (ENG., Illus.). 352p. per. 15.00 *(978-0-465-01574-0(3),* Basic Civitas Bks.) Basic Bks.

Eddings, L. H. Family Where Are We Going. 2011. 80p. 24.99 ***(978-1-4568-4889-7(5));*** pap. 15.99 ***(978-1-4568-4890-3(9))*** Xlibris Corp.

Golden, Marita. It's All Love: Black Writers on Soul Mates, Family & Friends. 2009. (ENG.). 432p. pap. 16.95 *(978-0-7679-1686-8(7))* Broadway Bks.

Gordon-Reed, Annette. The Hemingses of Monticello: An American Family. (ENG., Illus.). 2009. 816p. pap. 18.95 *(978-0-393-33776-1(6),* 33776) 2008. 800p. 35.00 *(978-0-393-06477-3(8),* 6477) Norton, W. W. & Co., Inc.

Grant, Gail Milissa. At the Elbows of My Elders: One Family's Journey Toward Civil Rights. 2008. (ENG.). 272p. (gr. 9). 24.95 *(978-1-883982-66-9(9))* Missouri Historical Society Pr.

Greason, Walter. The Path to Freedom: Black Families in New Jersey. 2010. (ENG., Illus.). 128p. pap. 19.99 *(978-1-59629-992-4(4))* History Pr., The.

Haley, Alex. Alex Haley: The Man Who Traced America's Roots. 2007. *(978-0-7621-0885-5(1))* Reader's Digest Assn., Inc., The.

—Roots: The Saga of an American Family. 30th ed. 2007. (ENG.). 899p. 23.60 *(978-0-7569-8232-4(4))* Perfection Learning Corp.

—Roots: The Saga of an American Family. 30th anniv. ed. 2007. (ENG.). 912p. per. 17.95 *(978-1-59315-449-3(6))* Vanguard Pr.

Harris, Larry C. 100 Ways to Put Families First: It all Starts at Home. 2007. per. 15.95 *(978-0-9767735-8-0(9))* Amber Bks.

Harris, Yvette R. & Bergen, Doris. Children & Families of African Origin: A Guide for Educators & Service Providers. 2008. pap. *(978-0-87173-173-9(8))* Assn. for Childhood Education International.

Hattery, Angela J. & Smith, Earl. African American Families. 2007. (Illus.). 408p. (C). per. 53.00 *(978-1-4129-2466-5(9),* B24669P) SAGE Pubns., Inc.

Hill, Robert B. Strengths of African American Families. 17.50 *(978-0-7618-1764-2(6))* Univ. Pr. of America, Inc.

Johnston, James H. From Slave Ship to Harvard: Yarrow Mamout & the History of an African American Family. 2012. (ENG., Illus.). 288p. 29.95 ***(978-0-8232-3950-4(0))*** Fordham Univ. Pr.

Jones, Jacqueline. Labor of Love, Labor of Sorrow: Black Women, Work, & the Family, from Slavery to the Present. 2nd ed. 2009. (ENG., Illus.). 480p. (gr. 9). pap. 18.95 *(978-0-465-01881-9(5))* Basic Bks.

King, Wilma. Stolen Childhood: Slave Youth in Nineteenth-Century America. 2nd exp. ed. 2011. (Blacks in the Diaspora Ser.). (ENG., Illus.). 544p. 70.00 *(978-0-253-35562-1(1),* 0253355621); pap. 24.95 *(978-0-253-22264-0(8),* 0253222648) Indiana Univ. Pr.

Kunjufu, Jawanza. Raising Black Boys. 2007. (ENG., Illus.). 200p. pap. 19.95 *(978-1-934155-07-3(1))* African American Images.

—State of Emergency. 2009. (ENG.). 200p. pap. 15.95 *(978-1-934155-09-7(8))* African American Images.

Marsh, Kris. Black Non-Family Households: Their Socioeconomic Position & Spatial Buffering. 2008. 128p. pap. *(978-3-639-03574-2(7))* VDM Verlag Dr. Mueller e.K.

Massey, Douglas & Sampson, Robert, eds. Moynihan Report Revisited: Lessons & Reflections after Four Decades. 2009. (ANNALS of the American Academy of Political & Social Science Ser.: 621). 328p. (C). pap. 37.95 (978-1-4129-7401-1(1), 295621P) SAGE Pubns., Inc.

Massey, Douglas S. & Sampson, Robert, eds. Moynihan Report Revisited: Lessons & Reflections after Four Decades. 2009. (ANNALS of the American Academy of Political & Social Science Ser.: 621). 328p. (C). 48.95 (978-1-4129-7402-8(X), 295621C) SAGE Pubns., Inc.

Masters, Henry L. Makin' Room in the Inn: Christmas Hospitality Through an African American Experience. 2010. 64p. 7.00 (978-1-4267-0371-3(6)) Abingdon Pr.

McAdoo, Harriette Pipes, ed. Black Families. 4th rev. ed. 2006. 384p. (C). 124.00 (978-1-4129-3637-8(3), B36373C); (Illus.). per. 63.00 (978-1-4129-3638-5(1), B36373P) SAGE Pubns., Inc.

McLoyd, Vonnie C., et al, eds. African American Family Life: Ecological & Cultural Diversity. 2007. (Duke Series in Child Develpment & Public Policy Ser.). (ENG.). 348p. pap. 35.00 (978-1-59385-467-6(6)) Guilford Pubns., Inc.

Miller, Karen E. Quinones. Angry Ass Black Woman. 2012. (ENG.). 288p. pap. 15.00 (978-1-4516-0782-6(2), Gallery Books/Karen Hunter Publishing) Gallery Books/Karen Hunter Publishing.

Mitchell, Erin Goseer. Born Colored: Life Before Bloody Sunday. 2006. 220p. (978-0-9761235-2-1(5)) Ampersand Publishing.

Muwwakkil, Tauheedah S. 360 Degrees: Obsession to Return to the Motherland: Have You Completed the Circle? 2007. (ENG.). 264p. per. 19.95 (978-0-7414-3213-1(7)) Infinity Publishing.

Pargas, Damian Alan. The Quarters & the Fields: Slave Families in the Non-Cotton South. 2011. (New Perspectives on the History of the South Ser.). (ENG., Illus.). 274p. pap. 27.95 (978-0-8130-3804-9(9)) Univ. Pr. of Florida.

Parker, Star. White Ghetto: How Middle Class America Reflects Inner City Decay, 0 vols. 2009. 256p. pap. 14.99 (978-1-59555-339-3(8)) Nelson, Thomas Inc.

Paschal, Angelia M. Voices of African-American Teen Fathers: I'm Doing What I Got to Do. 2006. (ENG.). 246p. per. 54.95 (978-0-7890-2738-2(0)); (Illus.). 128.00 (978-0-7890-2737-5(2)) Routledge.

Patterson, James T. Freedom Is Not Enough: The Moynihan Report & America's Struggle over Black Family Life- From LBJ to Obama. 2010. (ENG.). 288p. (gr. 9). 26.95 (978-0-465-01357-9(0)) Basic Bks.

Patterson, James T. Freedom Is Not Enough: The Moynihan Report & America's Struggle over Black Family Life — from LBJ to Obama. 2012. (ENG.). 288p. (gr. 9). pap. 18.00 (978-0-465-02853-5(5)) Basic Bks.

Raet, Iya. Holistic Parenting: From the pan-Afrikan Perspective. 2007. pap. 15.00 (978-1-56411-500-3(3), YBBG#490, United Sisters Bks.) UBUS Communications Systems.

Rice, Condoleezza. Extraordinary, Ordinary People: A Memoir of Family. (ENG.). 2011. 368p. pap. 15.00 (978-0-307-88847-1(9), Three Rivers Pr.) 2010. (Illus.). 352p. 27.00 (978-0-307-58787-9(8), Crown) Crown Publishing Group.

Ricketts, Percy. Fathers of African Descent: Their Relationships, Challenges & Why They Seldom Seek Help. 2007. 412p. per. 19.95 (978-1-4327-0194-9(0)) Outskirts Pr., Inc.

Robotham, Rosemarie, ed. Mending the World: Stories of Family by Contemporary Black Writers. 2008. (ENG.). 290p. 25.00 (978-1-4379-5230-8(5)) DIANE Publishing Co.

Schermerhorn, Jack L. & Schermerhorn, Calvin. Money over Mastery, Family over Freedom: Slavery in the Antebellum Upper South. 2011. (Studies in Early American Economy & Society from the Library Company of Philadelphia Ser.). (ENG., Illus.). 296p. (gr. 17). 60.00 (978-1-4214-0035-8(9)); pap. 30.00 (978-1-4214-0036-5(7)) Johns Hopkins Univ. Pr.

Shaw-Hunter, Bobbie. Speaking Life: A Research-Based Cultural Response to Connecting & Strengthening Families & Communities. 2011. 76p. pap. 15.49 (978-1-4520-9478-6(0)) AuthorHouse.

Sheppard, Eva Wolf. Almost Free: A Story about Family & Race in Antebellum Virginia. 2012. (Race in the Atlantic World, 1700-1900 Ser.). (ENG., Illus.). 192p. 59.95 (978-0-8203-3229-1(1)); pap. 19.95 (978-0-8203-3230-7(5)) Univ. of Georgia Pr.

Smith, Aaron/Anwar. Living on the up High, Not the down Low: The Movement to Uplift Good Black Men & the Empowerment of the African American Family. 2007. 160p. per. 12.99 (978-0-9795065-0-5(6)) Up High Assoc., The.

Spencer, Raymond. Thoughts of a Man Reflections of Love & Society. 2011. 192p. 29.99 (978-1-4568-4835-4(6)); pap. 19.99 (978-1-4568-4834-7(8)) Xlibris Corp.

St Hill, Ida V. RAAP: Responsibilitating African American Parents. 110p. pap. 5.95 (978-0-9640736-0-9(9)) Simountainhill Publishing Co.

Stanton, Lucia C. Those Who Labor for My Happiness: Slavery at Thomas Jefferson's Monticello. 2012. (Jeffersonian America Ser.). (ENG., Illus.). 384p. pap. 24.95 (978-0-8139-3223-1(8)) Univ. Pr. of Virginia.

—"Those Who Labor for My Happiness" Slavery at Thomas Jefferson's Monticello. 2012. E-Book (978-0-8139-3222-4(X)) Univ. Pr. of Virginia.

Taylor, Kea. I Still Do: A Celebration of African American Weddings. 2010. 128p. 29.99 (978-0-615-31320-7(5)) Imagine Photography.

The Kamoinge Workshop. The Sweet Breath of Life: A Poetic Narrative of the African-American Family. Stewart, Frank, ed. 2010. (ENG., Illus.). 192p. pap. 13.99 (978-0-7434-7898-4(3), Beyond Words/Atria Bks.) Atria Bks.

Vassel, Rachel. Daughters of Men: Portraits of African-American Women & Their Fathers. 2009. 192p. pap. 15.99 (978-0-06-135036-8(2), Harper Paperbacks) HarperCollins Pubs.

Washington, Kevin & Washington, Deleso. The Resurrection of Black Love. 14.95 (978-0-9749779-5-9(0)) Amber Bks.

Whyte, Daniel, III. God Has Smiled on Me: A Tribute to a Black Father Who Stayed & A Tribute to All Black Fathers Who Stay. 2009. (ENG.). 142p. pap. 11.99 (978-0-615-30191-4(6)) Torch Legacy Pubns.

Wilkins, Carolyn Marie. Damn near White: An African American Family's Rise from Slavery to Bittersweet Success. 3rd ed. 2010. (ENG., Illus.). 192p. 24.95 (978-0-8262-1899-5(7)) Univ. of Missouri Pr.

Williams, Charles. From Freedom to Slavery. 2007. (Illus.). (YA). per. 15.00 (978-0-9772579-1-1(6)) Parenting Institute of America Inc.

Williams, Heather Andrea. Help Me to Find My People: The African American Search for Family Lost in Slavery. 2012. (John Hope Franklin Series in African American History & Culture Ser.). (ENG., Illus.). 272p. 30.00 (978-0-8078-3554-8(4)) Univ. of North Carolina Pr.

Willie, Charles Vert & Reddick, Richard. A New Look at Black Families. 6th ed. 2010. (ENG.). 302p. 79.00 (978-0-7425-7006-1(1)); pap. 29.95 (978-0-7425-7007-8(X)) Rowman & Littlefield Publishers, Inc.

AFRICAN AMERICAN FARMERS

African-American Farmers Benefit Relief ACT of 2007 & the Pigford Claims Remedy ACT of 2007: Hearing Before the Subcommittee on the Constitution, Civil Rights, & Civil Liberties of the Committee on the Judiciary, House of Representatives, One Hundred Tenth Congress, First Session, on H.R. 558 & H.R. 899, June 21, 2007. 2007. (Illus.). iv, 153p. (978-0-16-079622-7(9), 552-070-36579-6) United States Government Printing Office.

Bond, Scott. From Slavery to Wealth: The Life of Scott Bond. Gatewood, Willard B., ed. 2008. (Illus.). 284p. per. 19.95 (978-0-9768007-6-7(4)) Phoenix International, Inc.

Guyette, Elise A. Discovering Black Vermont: African American Farmers in Hinesburgh, 1790-1890. 2010. (Illus.). 232p. pap. 26.95 (978-1-58465-760-6(X), University of Vermont Press) Univ. Pr. of New England.

Hersey, Mark D. My Work Is That of Conservation: An Environmental Biography of George Washington Carver. 2011. (Environmental History & the American South Ser.). (ENG., Illus.). 312p. 69.95 (978-0-8203-3088-4(4)); pap. 24.95 (978-0-8203-3870-5(2)) Univ. of Georgia Pr.

Kelsey, Carl. The Negro Farmer. 2007. (ENG.). 108p. per. 19.95 (978-0-548-67872-5(3)) Kessinger Publishing, LLC.

Reid, Debra A. & Bennett, Evan P., eds. Beyond Forty Acres & a Mule: African American Landowning Families since Reconstruction. 2012. (ENG., Illus.). 352p. 69.95 (978-0-8130-3986-2(X)) Univ. Pr. of Florida.

Roll, Jarod. Spirit of Rebellion: Labor & Religion in the New Cotton South. 2010. (Working Class in American History Ser.). (ENG., Illus.). 288p. 80.00 (978-0-252-03519-7(4)); pap. 30.00 (978-0-252-07703-6(2)) Univ. of Illinois Pr.

Sherrod, Shirley. The Courage to Hope: How I Stood up to the Politics of Fear. 2012. (ENG., Illus.). 256p. 24.99 (978-1-4516-5094-5(9), Beyond Words/Atria Bks.) Atria Bks.

Sherrod, Shirley & Whitney, Catherine. The Courage to Hope: How I Stood up to the Right Wing Media, the Obama Administration, & the Forces of Fear. 2012. pap. (978-1-4516-5101-0(5), Beyond Words/Atria Bks.) Atria Bks.

AFRICAN AMERICAN FICTION (ENGLISH)

see American Fiction—African American Authors

AFRICAN AMERICAN FOLKLORE

see African Americans—Folklore

AFRICAN AMERICAN HISTORIANS

Adams, Barbara Eleanor. John Henrik Clarke Master Teacher. 2011. (Illus.). 185p. pap. 15.95 (978-1-61759-012-2(6)) EWorld, Inc.

Dagbovie, Pero. African American History Reconsidered. 2010. (New Black Studies Ser.). (ENG.). 280p. pap. 25.00 (978-0-252-07701-2(6)) Univ. of Illinois Pr.

—The Early Black History Movement, Carter G. Woodson, & Lorenzo Johnston Greene. 2007. (New Black Studies Ser.). 280p. 67.00 (978-0-252-03190-8(3)) Univ. of Illinois Pr.

—The Early Black History Movement, Carter G. Woodson, & Lorenzo Johnston Greene. Hine, Darlene Clark & McBride, Dwight A., eds. 2007. (New Black Studies Ser.). 280p. per. 26.00 (978-0-252-07435-6(1)) Univ. of Illinois Pr.

Floyd-Thomas, Juan M. Origins of Black Humanism in America: Reverend Ethelred Brown & the Unitarian Church. 2008. (Black Religion/Womanist Thought/Social Justice Ser.). (ENG.). 288p. 100.00 (978-0-230-60677-7(6)) Palgrave Macmillan.

Franklin, John Hope. Mirror to America: The Autobiography of John Hope Franklin. 2006. (ENG., Illus.). 416p. pap. 15.00 (978-0-374-53047-1(5)) Farrar, Straus & Giroux.

Toure, Ahati N. N. John Henrik Clarke & the Power of Africana History: Africalogical Quest for Decolonization & Sovereignty. 2008. xi, 356p. (978-1-59221-626-0(9)); 256p. pap. (978-1-59221-627-7(7)) Africa World Pr.

AFRICAN AMERICAN INVENTORS

Baker, Henry E. American Black Inventors Pictorials Drawings & Illustrations Volume I. 2007. (Illus.). 369p. lib. bdg. (978-1-892824-30-1(2), afchron.com) AFCHRON.

Holmes, Keith C. Black Inventors, Crafting over 200 Years of Success. Holmes, Keith C. et al, eds. 2008. (ENG., Illus.). 179p. (YA). pap. 15.00 (978-0-9799573-0-7(3)) Global Black Inventor Research Projects, Inc.

Sluby, Patricia Carter. The Entrepreneurial Spirit of African American Inventors, 1 vol. 2011. (Illus.). 250p. 44.95 (978-0-313-36335-1(8), C36335); E-Book (978-0-313-36336-8(6)) Greenwood Publishing Group, Inc. (Praeger Pubs.).

—The Inventive Spirit of African Americans: Patented Ingenuity, 1 vol. 2008. (Illus.). 352p. pap. 22.95 (978-0-313-35156-3(2), B35156, Praeger Trade) Greenwood Publishing Group, Inc.

Williams, James Henry. African American Inventors & Pioneers. 2011. 54p. pap. 15.99 (978-1-4568-4000-6(2)) Xlibris Corp.

AFRICAN AMERICAN-JEWISH RELATIONS

see African Americans—Relations With Jews

AFRICAN AMERICAN JOURNALISM

see African American Press

AFRICAN AMERICAN JOURNALISTS

Agee, Gary B. A Cry for Justice: Daniel Rudd & His Life in Black Catholicism, Journalism, & Activism, 1854 -1933. 2011. 256p. 39.95 (978-1-55728-975-9(1)) Univ. of Arkansas Pr.

Andrews, Gregg. Thyra J. Edwards: Black Activist in the Global Freedom Struggle. 2011. (ENG., Illus.). 256p. (C). (gr. 12). 40.00 (978-0-8262-1912-1(8)) Univ. of Missouri Pr.

Andrews, Helena. Bitch Is the New Black: A Memoir. 2011. 256p. pap. 14.99 (978-0-06-177884-1(2), Harper Paperbacks) HarperCollins Pubs.

Boyd, Gerald M. My Times in Black & White: Race & Power at The New York Times. 2010. (ENG., Illus.). 432p. 26.95 (978-1-55652-952-8(X), Hill, Lawrence Bks.) Chicago Review Pr., Inc.

Brown, Lois. Pauline Elizabeth Hopkins: Black Daughter of the Revolution. 2008. (ENG., Illus.). 704p. 49.95 (978-0-8078-3166-3(2)) Univ. of North Carolina Pr.

Curtis, Susan. Colored Memories: A Biographer's Quest for the Elusive Lester A. Walton. 2008. (ENG., Illus.). 304p. (C). 39.95 (978-0-8262-1786-8(9)) Univ. of Missouri Pr.

Davis, Belva. Never in My Wildest Dreams: A Black Woman's Life in Journalism. 2012. (ENG.). 272p. pap. 15.95 (978-1-60994-466-7(6)) Berrett-Koehler Pubs., Inc.

Davis, Frank Marshall. Writings of Frank Marshall Davis: A Voice of the Black Press. Tidwell, John Edgar, ed. 2009. (ENG.). 256p. pap. 25.00 (978-1-60473-384-6(5)) Univ. Pr. of Mississippi.

Dawkins, Wayne. City Son: Andrew W. Cooper's Impact on Modern-Day Brooklyn. 2012. (Margaret Walker Alexander Series in African American Studies). (ENG.). 304p. 35.00 (978-1-61703-258-5(1)) Univ. Pr. of Mississippi.

Dickerson, Debra J. An American Story. pap. (978-0-385-72862-1(X)) Knopf Doubleday Publishing Group.

Gardner, Eric, ed. Jennie Carter: A Black Journalist of the Early West. 2007. (ENG.). 208p. 50.00 (978-1-934110-10-2(8)) Univ. Pr. of Mississippi.

Hall, Calvin L. & Hall, Clavin L. African American Journalists: Autobiography as Memoir & Manifesto. 2009. (ENG.). 146p. pap. 40.00 (978-0-8108-6930-1(6)) Scarecrow Pr., Inc.

Hunter-Gault, Charlayne. In My Place. tchr.'s training gde. ed. (978-0-394-26458-5(4), Vintage) Knopf Doubleday Publishing Group.

Lyles, Charlise. Do I Dare Disturb the Universe? From the Projects to Prep School. 2nd ed. 2008. (Illus.). 272p. pap. 14.95 (978-1-59851-041-6(X)) Gray and Company, Publishers.

Millner, Caille. The Golden Road: Notes on My Gentrification. 2008. (ENG.). 256p. (gr. 12-18). 14.00 (978-0-14-311297-6(X), Penguin (Non-Classics)) Penguin Group (USA) Inc.

Mitchell, Joe Henry. Ida B. Wells Versus Judge Lynch: the Anti-Lynching Trilogy. 2010. 235p. pap. 24.95 (978-0-557-35717-8(9)) Lulu Enterprises Inc.

Norris, Michele. The Grace of Silence: A Family Memoir. (Vintage Ser.). 2011. (ENG.). 240p. pap. 14.95 (978-0-307-47527-5(1), Vintage) 2010. (Illus.). 208p. 24.95 (978-0-307-37876-7(4), Pantheon) Knopf Doubleday Publishing Group.

O'Brien, Soledad & Arce, Rose Marie. The Next Big Story: My Journey Through the Land of Possibilities. (ENG.). 336p. (gr. 12). 2011. 15.00 (978-0-451-23284-7(4), Celebra) 2010. 24.95 (978-0-451-23137-6(6)) Penguin Group (USA) Inc.

Ottley, Roi. Roi Ottley's World War II: The Lost Diary of an African American Journalist. Huddle, Mark, ed. 2011. (Illus.). 200p. 29.95 (978-0-7006-1769-2(8)) Univ. Pr. of Kansas.

Rideau, Wilbert. In the Place of Justice: A Story of Punishment & Redemption. 2011. (Vintage Ser.). (ENG., Illus.). 416p. pap. 16.00 (978-0-307-27730-5(5), Vintage) Knopf Doubleday Publishing Group.

Sachsman, David. Seeking a Voice: Images of Race & Gender in the 19th Century. Rushing, S. Kitrell et al, eds. 2009. (ENG.). 347p. 64.95 (978-1-55753-505-4(1)); 330p. pap. 32.95 (978-1-55753-508-5(6)) Purdue Univ. Pr.

Tassy, Elaine. How the Sun Lost Its Shine: A Newsroom Memoir. 2009. (ENG.). 184p. pap. 29.99 (978-0-7618-5001-4(5)) Hamilton Bks.

Terry, Wallace. Missing Pages: Black Journalists of Modern America: an Oral History. 2007. (ENG.). 384p. per. 16.95 (978-0-7867-1993-8(1)) Basic Bks.

Whitaker, Mark. My Long Trip Home: A Family Memoir. 2011. (ENG., Illus.). 368p. 25.99 (978-1-4516-2754-1(8)) Simon & Schuster.

Wickham, DeWayne. Black Voices in Commentary. 2006. xiii, 129p. pap. 15.95 (978-0-9635720-9-7(1)) August Pr.

Williams, Oscar. George S. Schuyler: Portrait of a Black Conservative. 2007. (Illus.). 224p. 33.00 (978-1-57233-581-3(5)) Univ. of Tennessee Pr.

AFRICAN AMERICAN JUDGES

Gibson, Larry S. Young Thurgood: The Making of a Supreme Court Justice. 2012. (ENG., Illus.). 390p. 28.00 (978-1-61614-571-2(4)) Prometheus Bks., Pubs.

James, Rawn, Jr. Root & Branch: Charles Hamilton Houston, Thurgood Marshall, & the Struggle to End Segregation. 2010. (ENG., Illus.). 288p. 28.00 (978-1-59691-606-7(0)) Bloomsbury Publishing.

McGrane, Bill. All Rise: The Remarkable Journey of Alan Page. 2010. (ENG.). 256p. 24.95 (978-1-60078-504-7(2)) Triumph Bks.

McLeod, Jacqueline A. Daughter of the Empire State: The Life of Judge Jane Bolin. 2011. (ENG., Illus.). 168p. 30.00 (978-0-252-03657-6(3)) Univ. of Illinois Pr.

Merida, Kevin & Fletcher, Michael. Supreme Discomfort: The Divided Soul of Clarence Thomas. 2008. (ENG., Illus.). 448p. pap. 15.95 (978-0-7679-1636-3(0)) Broadway Bks.

Payne, Darwin. Quest for Justice: The Struggle for Equal Rights in Texas. 2009. (ENG.). 296p. 22.50 (978-0-87074-552-2(2)) Southern Methodist Univ. Pr.

Ramsey, Henry. The Life Story of Henry Ramsey Jr: An Autobiography. 2008. (Illus.). 653p. (978-0-9789979-2-2(1)) Hardscratch Pr.

Thomas, Clarence. My Grandfather's Son: A Memoir. 2008. 320p. pap. 15.95 (978-0-06-056556-5(X), HarperPerennial) HarperCollins Pubs.

Washington, Linn. Black Judges on Justice: Perspectives from the Bench. 2008. (ENG.). 265p. pap. 25.00 (978-1-4223-9452-6(2)) DIANE Publishing Co.

AFRICAN AMERICAN LAWYERS

Blakely, Gloria. Johnnie Cochran: Attorney. 2nd rev. ed. 2006. (Black Americans of Achievement Ser.). (Illus.). 152p. (YA). (gr. 7-12). lib. bdg. 35.00 (978-0-7910-9112-8(0)) Facts On File, Inc.

Canton, David A. Raymond Pace Alexander: A New Negro Lawyer Fights for Civil Rights in Philadelphia. 2010. (Margaret Walker Alexander Series in African American Studies). (ENG., Illus.). 272p. 50.00 (978-1-60473-425-6(6)) Univ. Pr. of Mississippi.

Chambliss, Prince. Prince of Peace: A Memoir of an African-American Attorney, Who Came of Age in Birmingham During the Civil Rights Movement. 2010. 152p. 29.00 (978-0-557-10943-2(4)) Lulu Enterprises Inc.

Chestnut, J. L., Jr. & Cass, Julia. Black in Selma: The Uncommon Life of J. L. Chestnut Jr. Cass, Julia, ed. 2007. (ENG., Illus.). 448p. per. 29.95 (978-0-8173-5461-9(1)) Univ. of Alabama Pr.

Elliott, Mark Emory. Color-Blind Justice: Albion Tourgee & the Quest for Racial Equality - From the Civil War to Plessy V. Ferguson. 2006. (ENG., Illus.). 400p. 30.00 (978-0-19-518139-5(5)) Oxford Univ. Pr., Inc.

Epner, Janet E. Gans. Visible Invisibility: Women of Color in Law Firms. 2007. (ENG., Illus.). 88p. per. 49.95 (978-1-59031-745-7(9)) American Bar Assn.

Evensen, Dorothy H. & Pratt, Carla D., eds. The End of the Pipeline: A Journey of Recognition for African Americans Entering the Legal Profession. 2011. 344p. 40.00 (978-1-59460-981-7(0)) Carolina Academic Pr.

Holmes, Robert A. Maynard Jackson: A Biography. 2009. (Illus.). 368p. 27.99 (978-0-9801744-0-3(6)) Barnhardt & Ashe Publishing, Inc.

Jordan, Vernon E., Jr. Make It Plain: Standing up & Speaking Out. 2009. (ENG.). 272p. pap. 13.95 (978-1-58648-775-1(2)) PublicAffairs.

—Vernon Can Read! A Memoir. 2008. (ENG., Illus.). 352p. pap. 16.00 (978-1-58648-670-9(5)) PublicAffairs.

Kershner, Jim. Carl Maxey: A Fighting Life. (ENG., Illus.). 288p. 2012. pap. 19.95 (978-0-295-99231-0(X)) 2008. 26.95 (978-0-295-98846-7(0)) Univ. of Washington Pr.

Kilpatrick, Judith. There When We Needed Him: Wiley Austin Branton, Civil Rights Warrior. 2007. (Illus.). 221p. 32.50 (978-1-55728-848-6(8)) Univ. of Arkansas Pr.

Long, Michael G. Marshalling Justice: The Early Civil Rights Letters of Thurgood Marshall. 2011. 448p. 27.99 (978-0-06-198518-8(X), Amistad) HarperCollins Pubs.

Mack, Kenneth W. Representing the Race: The Creation of the Civil Rights Lawyer. 2012. (ENG., Illus.). 352p. 35.00 (978-0-674-04687-0(0)) Harvard Univ. Pr.

McCabe, Katie & Roundtree, Dovey Johnson. Justice Older Than the Law: The Life of Dovey Johnson Roundtree. 2011. (Margaret Walker Alexander Series in African American Studies). (ENG., Illus.). 280p. pap. 22.00 (978-1-61703-121-2(6)) Univ. Pr. of Mississippi.

McClelland, Edward. Young Mr. Obama: Chicago & the Making of a Black President. 2010. (ENG., Illus.). 288p. 24.00 (978-1-60819-060-7(9)) Bloomsbury Publishing.

Payne, Darwin. Quest for Justice: The Struggle for Equal Rights in Texas. 2009. (ENG.). 296p. 22.50 (978-0-87074-552-2(2)) Southern Methodist Univ. Pr.

Ramsey, Henry. The Life Story of Henry Ramsey Jr: An Autobiography. 2008. (Illus.). 653p. (978-0-9789979-2-2(1)) Hardscratch Pr.

Regis, Jacqueline. The Daughter of L¿Arsenal. 2009. pap. 18.95 (978-1-58501-153-7(3), SterlingHouse Books) SterlingHouse Pubs., Inc.

Seay, Solomon S. & Boyd, Delores R. Jim Crow & Me. 2009. 176p. 25.00 (978-1-58838-175-0(7)) NewSouth, Inc.

Watson, Elwood D. Outsiders Within: Black Women in the Legal Academy after Brown v. Board. 2008. (ENG.). 160p. 70.00 (978-0-7425-4073-6(1)) Rowman & Littlefield Publishers, Inc.

AFRICAN AMERICAN LEGISLATORS

Amer, Mildred L., ed. Black Members of the United States Congress: With Bibliographies, 1789-2004. 2007. (Illus.). 76p. pap. 73.00 (978-1-59454-745-4(9)) Nova Science Pubs., Inc.

Brooke, Edward W. Bridging the Divide: My Life. 2006. (ENG., Illus.). 352p. 29.95 (978-0-8135-3905-8(6)) Rutgers Univ. Pr.

Brown, Willie L., Jr. Basic Brown: My Life & Our Times. 2011. (ENG., Illus.). 368p. pap. 22.99 (978-0-7432-9082-1(8)) Simon & Schuster.

Clemons, Michael L., ed. African Americans & Global Affairs: Contemporary Perspectives. 2010. (Illus.). 408p. pap. 35.00 (978-1-55553-722-7(7)) Univ. Pr. of New England.

—African Americans in Global Affairs: Contemporary Perspectives. 2010. (Illus.). 408p. (C). 65.00 *(978-1-55553-719-7(7))* Univ. Pr. of New England.

Dray, Philip. Capitol Men: The Epic Story of Reconstruction Through the Lives of the First Black Congressmen. 2010. (ENG., Illus.). 480p. pap. 15.95 *(978-0-547-24797-7(4),* Mariner Bks.) Houghton Mifflin Harcourt Trade & Reference Pubs.

Essence Magazine Staff, contrib. by. The Obamas: Portrait of America's New First Family. 2009. (ENG.). 112p. (YA). (gr. 7-17). 19.95 *(978-1-60320-073-8(8))* Time Home Entertainment, Inc.

Freedman, Eric & Jones, Stephen A. African Americans in Congress: A Documentary History. 00 vols. rev. ed. 2007. (Illus.). 543p. 142.00 *(978-0-87289-385-6(5))* CQ Pr.

Graham, Lawrence Otis. The Senator & the Socialite: The True Story of America's First Black Dynasty. (Illus.). 2007. 512p. per. 15.99 *(978-0-06-098513-4(5),* HarperPerennial) 2006. 816p. per. 27.95 *(978-0-06-112079-4(0))* HarperCollins Pubs.

Grose, Christian R. Congress in Black & White: Race & Representation in Washington & at Home. 2011. (ENG., Illus.). 256p. 80.00 *(978-1-107-00351-4(2))*; pap. 24.99 *(978-0-521-17701-6(4))* Cambridge Univ. Pr.

Hendon, Rickey. Backstabbers: The Reality of Politics. 2010. (ENG., Illus.). 200p. pap. 16.95 *(978-0-89733-602-4(X))* Academy Chicago Pubs., Ltd.

Hendon, Rickey & Smallwood, David. Black Enough/White Enough: The Obama Dilemma. 2009. (ENG.). pap. 19.95 *(978-0-88378-309-2(6))* Third World Press.

Jeansonne, Glen & Luhrssen, David. Changing Times: The Life of Barack Obama. 2009. (Illus.). 268p. pap. 18.95 *(978-1-59598-082-3(2))* HenschelHAUS Publishing.

Joens, David A. From Slave to State Legislator: John W. E. Thomas, Illinois' First African American Lawmaker. 2012. (Illus.). 288p. 34.95 *(978-0-8093-3058-4(X))* Southern Illinois Univ. Pr.

King-Meadows, Tyson & Schaller, Thomas F. Devolution & Black State Legislators: Challenges & Choices in the Twenty-First Century. 2007. (SUNY Series in African American Studies). (Illus.). 302p. per. 31.95 *(978-0-7914-6730-5(9))* State Univ. of New York Pr.

Lee, Barbara. Renegade for Peace & Justice: Congresswoman Barbara Lee Speaks for Me. 2008. (ENG., Illus.). 256p. 24.95 *(978-0-7425-5843-4(6))* Rowman & Littlefield Publishers, Inc.

Lee, Howard. The Courage to Lead: One Man's Journey in Public Service. 2008. (Illus.). 224p. 24.95 *(978-0-9816921-0-4(9))* Cotton Patch Pr., Inc.

Little Boy Blue. The African American Church: A Sociological History. 2009. 144p. pap. 11.99 *(978-1-4389-5526-1(X))* AuthorHouse.

Manning, Christopher. William L. Dawson & the Limits of Black Electoral Leadership. 2009. (Illus.). 251p. 37.00 *(978-0-87580-395-1(4))* Northern Illinois Univ. Pr.

Marsh, Michael. The Niba Guide to Barack Obama: The Political History, the Record, the Facts. 2007. per. *(978-0-9794242-0-5(8),* Niba Guides) Niba Media Group, LLC.

Marszalek, John F. A Black Congressman in the Age of Jim Crow: South Carolina's George Washington Murray. 2008. (New Perspectives on the History of the South Ser.). (ENG.). 232p. pap. 29.95 *(978-0-8130-3340-2(3))* Univ. Pr. of Florida

Mendell, David. Obama: From Promise to Power. 2008. (ENG., Illus.). 432p. pap. 14.95 *(978-0-06-085821-6(4))* 2007. 416p. 25.95 *(978-0-06-085820-9(6))* HarperCollins Pubs. (Amistad).

Middleton, Earl M. Knowing Who I Am: A Black Entrepreneur's Struggle & Success in the American South. 2008. (Illus.). 183p. 29.95 *(978-1-57003-715-3(9))* Univ. of South Carolina Pr.

Milner, Thirman L. Up from Slavery: A History from Slavery to City Hall in New England. 2009. 116p. 29.99 *(978-1-4141-1527-6(X))* Pleasant Word.

Minta, Michael D. Oversight - Representing the Interests of Black & Latinos in Congress. 2011. (ENG., Illus.). 192p. (C). pap. 24.95 *(978-0-691-14926-4(7))* Princeton Univ. Pr.

—Oversight - Representing the Interests of Black & Latinos in Congress. 2011. (ENG., Illus.). 192p. (C). 65.00 *(978-0-691-14925-7(9))* Princeton Univ. Pr.

Neer, Bob. Barack Obama for Beginners, Updated Edition: An Essential Guide. 2009. (For Beginners Ser.). (ENG., Illus.). 128p. pap. 12.95 *(978-1-934389-44-7(7),* For Beginners) Steerforth Pr.

Obama, Barack. La Audacia de la Esperanza: Reflexiones Sobre Cómo Restaurar el Sueño Americano. 2007. (Vintage Espanol Ser.). (SPA.). 400p. pap. 17.00 *(978-0-307-38711-0(9),* Vintage) Knopf Doubleday Publishing Group.

—The Audacity of Hope: Thoughts on Reclaiming the American Dream. 2008. *(978-1-84767-350-3(3))*; 384p. *(978-1-84767-083-0(0))* Canongate Bks.

—The Audacity of Hope: Thoughts on Reclaiming the American Dream. (ENG.). 384p. 2007. pap. 14.95 *(978-0-307-23770-5(2),* Three Rivers Pr.) 2006. 25.00 *(978-0-307-23769-9(5),* Crown) Crown Publishing Group.

—The Audacity of Hope: Thoughts on Reclaiming the American Dream. 2008. (Vintage Ser.). (ENG.). 464p. mass mkt. 7.99 *(978-0-307-45587-1(4))* Knopf Doubleday Publishing Group.

—The Audacity of Hope: Thoughts on Reclaiming the American Dream. 2011. 9.84 *(978-0-7848-3568-5(3),* Everbind) Marco Bk. Co.

—Barack Obama in His Own Words. Rogak, Lisa, ed. 2009. (ENG.). 112p. 4.95 *(978-0-7624-3789-4(8))* Running Pr. Bk. Pubs.

Price, Joann F. Barack Obama: A Biography, 1 vol. 2008. (Greenwood Biographies Ser.). (Illus.). 168p. 35.00 *(978-0-313-34488-6(4),* GR4488, Greenwood Pr.) Greenwood Publishing Group, Inc.

Rangel, Charles B. And I Haven't Had a Bad Day Since: From the Streets of Harlem to the Halls of Congress. 2008. (ENG., Illus.). 336p. pap. 16.99 *(978-0-312-38213-1(8),* St. Martin's Griffin) St. Martin's Pr.

Souza, Pete. The Rise of Barack Obama. (ENG., 2009. Illus.). 176p. pap. 14.95 *(978-1-60078-313-5(9))* 2008. 160p. 27.95 *(978-1-60078-163-6(2))* Triumph Bks.

Spritzer, Lorraine Nelson & Bergmark, Jean B. Grace Towns Hamilton & the Politics of Southern Change. 2009. (ENG.). 296p. pap. 24.95 *(978-0-8203-3387-8(5))* Univ. of Georgia Pr.

Sullivan, Jas M. & Winburn, Jonathan, eds. The Louisiana Legislative Black Caucus: Race & Representation in the Pelican State. 2011. (Illus.). 216p. 39.95 ***(978-0-8071-4036-9(8))*** Louisiana State Univ. Pr.

Vincent, Charles. Black Legislators in Louisiana During Reconstruction. 2011. (Illus.). 294p. E-Book *(978-0-8093-8581-2(3))*; 296p. pap. 28.95 *(978-0-8093-2969-4(7))* Southern Illinois Univ. Pr.

Wasniewski, Matthew, ed. Black Americans in Congress, 1870-2007. 3rd ed. 2008. (ENG., Illus.). 803p. 54.00 *(978-0-16-080194-5(X))* United States Government Printing Office.

Zimmerman, W. Frederick. Should Barack Obama Be President? 2007. 104p. per. 15.94 *(978-0-9788138-0-2(4))* Nimble Bks. LLC.

AFRICAN AMERICAN LIBRARIANS

Jackson, Andrew P., et al, eds. The 21st-Century Black Librarian in America. 2012. (ENG., Illus.). 300p. (gr. 17). 80.00 ***(978-0-8108-8245-4(0))*** Scarecrow Pr., Inc.

AFRICAN AMERICAN LITERATURE (ENGLISH)

see American Literature—African American Authors

AFRICAN AMERICAN MEN

Alexander, Bryant Ke. Performing Black Masculinity: Race, Culture, & Queer Identity. 2006. (Crossroads in Qualitative Inquiry Ser.). (ENG., Illus.). 282p. 93.00 *(978-0-7591-0928-5(1))* AltaMira Pr.

Anderson, Elijah, ed. Against the Wall: Poor, Young, Black, & Male. 2009. (City in the Twenty-First Century Ser.). (Illus.). 320p. (C). pap. 26.50 *(978-0-8122-2017-9(X))* Univ. of Pennsylvania Pr.

Baldwin, James A. One Day, When I Was Lost: A Scenario Based on Alex Haley's the Autobiography of Malcolm X. 2007. (Vintage International Ser.). (ENG., Illus.). 288p. pap. 13.00 *(978-0-307-27594-3(9),* Vintage) Knopf Doubleday Publishing Group.

Bazile, Ronald P., Sr., et al. You Have Cancer: A Death Sentence That Four African-American Men Turned into an Affirmation to Remain in the Land of the Living. 2007. (Illus.). 165p. per. 12.00 *(978-0-9639245-2-0(4))* Milligan Bks.

Berlinger, Cain. Black Men in Leather. 2nd ed. 2006. 278p. pap. 19.95 *(978-1-932657-70-8(3))* Third Millennium Pubns.

Big Boom & Big Boom. If You Want Closure in Your Relationship, Start with Your Legs: A Guide to Understanding Men. 2007. (ENG.). 224p. pap. 15.99 *(978-1-4165-4646-7(4),* Touchstone) Touchstone.

Binford, Virgie. The Pursuit of Victory: Empowering African American Males. 2009. (ENG.). 54p. pap. 8.95 *(978-1-57736-411-5(2))* Providence Hse Pubs.

Black, Helen, et al. From Zero to Eighty: Two African American Men's Narrative of Racism, Suffering, Survival, & Transformation. 2011. 308p. 31.95 ***(973-1-4620-0509-3(8))***; pap. 21.95 ***(978-1-4620-0507-9(1))*** iUniverse, Inc.

Bonner, Fred A. Academically Gifted African American Male College Students, 1 vol. 2010. 217p. 44.95 *(978-0-89789-857-7(5),* H857, Praeger Pubs.) Greenwood Publishing Group, Inc.

Boothe, Demico. Getting Out & Staying Out: A Black Man's Guide to Success after Prison. 2008. 72p. per. 9.00 *(978-0-9792953-1-7(9))* Full Surface Publishing, LLC.

—Why Are So Many Black Men in Prison? A Comprehensive Account of How & Why the Prison Industry Has Become A Predatory Entity in the Lives of African-American Men, & How Mass Targeting, Criminalization, & Incarceration of Black Male Youth Has Gone Toward Creating the Largest Prison System in the World. 2nd ed. 2007. 160p. pap. 14.00 *(978-0-9792953-0-0(0),* 076) Full Surface Publishing, LLC.

Boyd, Stacy. Black Men Worshipping: Intersecting Anxieties of Race, Gender, & Christian Embodiment. 2011. (Black Religion/Womanist Thought/Social Justice Ser.). (ENG., Illus.). 192p. 85.00 *(978-0-230-11371-8(0))* Palgrave Macmillan.

Bradley, Scott A. Breaking the Spirit of the American Black Male. Divers, Consuelo, ed. 150p. (Orig.). (C). pap. 9.95 *(978-0-9636928-1-8(X))* Rivers of Life Ministry.

Brown, Anthony L. & Donnor, Jamel K., eds. The Education of Black Males in a 'Post-Racial' World. 2011. (ENG., Illus.). 152p. (C). 125.00 *(978-0-415-67302-0(X))* Routledge.

Brown, Jerome. From Stone to Bread. 2012. ***(978-1-58982-666-3(3),*** Millennial Mind Publishing) American Bk. Publishing Group.

Brown, Kenneth. The System Versus the Law. 2008. (ENG.). pap. 20.00 *(978-0-9818939-1-4(0),* AHLP Bks.) Africana Homestead Legacy Pubs., Inc.

Butler-Derge, Shirley R. Rites of Passage: A Program for High School African American Males. 2009. (ENG., Illus.). 70p. pap. 15.99 *(978-0-7618-4320-7(5))* Univ. Pr. of America, Inc.

Carrillo, Ricardo & Tello, Jerry. Family Violence & Men of Color: Healing the Wounded Male Spirit. 2008. 224p. 45.00 *(978-0-8261-1178-4(5))* Springer Publishing Co., Inc.

Carson, Janice E. Life Histories of Successful Black Males Reared in Absent Father Families. 2008. 176p. pap. *(978-3-639-03951-1(3))* VDM Verlag Dr. Mueller e.K.

Cooper, William Fredrick. One Season (in Pinstripes) A Memoir. 2011. (ENG.). 448p. pap. 15.00 *(978-1-59309-354-9(3),* Strebor Bks.) Strebor Bks.

Covington, S. R. Sensual Astrology for the African-American Man: Everything You Need to Know about Your Woman Through Her Sun Sign. 2008. (ENG., Illus.). 283p. 14.95 *(978-1-60162-116-0(7))* Urban Bks.

—Sensual Astrology for the African American Woman. 2011. (ENG., Illus.). 304p. 6.99 *(978-1-60162-321-8(6))* Urban Bks.

Cram101 Textbook Reviews & Cram101 Textbook Reviews. Outlines & Highlights for Family Violence & Men of Color: Healing the Wounded Male Spirit by Carrillo, ISBN. 2011. 58p. pap. 26.95 ***(978-1-61461-625-2(6))*** Cram101 Inc.

Cram101 Textbook Reviews Staff. Outlines & Highlights for Black Sexual Politics: African Americans, Gender, & the New Racism by Patricia H Collins, ISBN. 2009. 90p. pap. 27.95 *(978-1-4288-9770-0(4))* Cram101 Inc.

Crawford, Carl J. The Truth. 2009. pap. 18.95 *(978-1-58501-151-3(7),* SterlingHouse Books) SterlingHouse Pubs., Inc.

Cuffee, Sallie M. Manchild Dying in the Promised Land: Strategies to Save Black Males. 2009. (ENG.). 150p. pap. 15.95 *(978-1-934155-13-4(6))* African American Images.

Davis, Lois M., et al. Reparable Harm: Assessing & Addressing Disparities Faced by Boys & Men of Color in California. 2009. (Illus.). 146p. pap. 55.00 *(978-0-8330-4561-4(X))*; 24p. pap. 29.00 *(978-0-8330-4563-8(6))* RAND Corp., The.

Dean, Terrance. Hiding in Hip Hop: On the down Low in the Entertainment Industry — from Music to Hollywood. 2009. (ENG.). 320p. pap. 15.00 *(978-1-4165-5340-3(1),* Beyond Words/Atria Bks.) Atria Bks.

Direda, James. Examining Barriers to Drug Treatment Entry. 2008. 136p. pap. *(978-3-639-08095-7(5))* VDM Verlag Dr. Mueller e.K.

Dybska, Aneta. Black Masculinities in American Social Science & Self-Narratives of the 1960s and 1970s. 2010. (American Studies & Media Ser.). 194p. 61.95 *(978-3-631-61330-6(X))* Lang, Peter GmbH, Europaischer Verlag der Wissenschaften DEU. Dist: Lang, Peter.

Eaves, John H. The Morehouse Mystique: Lessons to Develop Black Men. 2009. (ENG.). 250p. pap. 16.95 *(978-1-934155-14-1(4))* African American Images.

Ellis, Aimé J. If We Must Die: From Bigger Thomas to Biggie Smalls. 2014. (Illus.). 240p. pap. 24.95 *(978-0-8143-3413-3(X))* Wayne State Univ. Pr.

Ellis, Cyrus Marcellus & CARLSON, J. O. N., eds. Resiliency Achievement & Manhood. 2013. (Routledge Series on Counseling & Psychotherapy with Boys & Men Ser.). (ENG.). 224p. 90.00 *(978-0-415-88412-9(6))*; pap. 34.95 *(978-0-415-88413-6(6))* Routledge.

Emerson, Granville. Girls, Lies, & a Player. 2008. (ENG.). 288p. pap. 19.95 *(978-1-58982-465-2(2),* Millennial Mind Publishing) American Bk. Publishing Group.

Ernest H. Johnson Ph. D. & Champions. The Secrets for Motivating, Educating, & Lifting the Spirit of African American Males. 2011. 496p. 39.95 ***(978-1-4620-4544-7(4))***; pap. 29.95 ***(978-1-4620-4642-3(8))*** iUniverse, Inc.

Eye See Me: A True Life Story. Date not set. 64p. 10.95 *(978-0-9701562-0-4(0))* Enoch, Carlton.

Fleming, Peggy & Fleming, Jennifer. Crown Me! Capital Pool Checkers Club. 2010. (Illus.). 111p. *(978-0-9676322-2-3(6))* Three Sisters Pr.

Freightman, G. D. RIPPED & READY. 2010. 269p. pap. 22.00 *(978-0-557-23210-9(4))* Lulu Enterprises Inc.

—RIPPED & READY (SEASON 2) 2010. 249p. pap. 22.00 *(978-0-557-28430-6(9))* Lulu Enterprises Inc.

Gajda, Stanley. Persistence: A Phenomenology of African American Men Who Make A Difference. 2008. 180p. pap. *(978-3-639-09461-9(1))* VDM Verlag Dr. Mueller e.K.

Gale Editors, ed. Notable Black American Men. 2nd ed. 2006. (ENG., Illus.). 856p. 233.00 *(978-0-7876-6493-0(6))* Cengage Gale.

Garfield, Gail. Through Our Eyes: African American Men's Experiences of Race, Gender, & Violence. 2010. (ENG.). 256p. pap. 24.95 *(978-0-8135-4743-5(1))* Rutgers Univ. Pr.

Gause, C. P. Integration Matters: Navigating Identity, Culture, & Resistance. 2008. (Counterpoints: Studies in the Postmodern Theory of Education Ser.). 232p. (C). 32.95 *(978-1-4331-0202-8(1))* Lang, Peter Publishing, Inc.

Giltner, Scott E. Hunting & Fishing in the New South: Black Labor & White Leisure after the Civil War. 2008. (Johns Hopkins University Studies in Historical & Political Science Ser.: 126). (ENG., Illus.). 240p. (gr. 17). 55.00 *(978-0-8018-9023-9(3))* Johns Hopkins Univ. Pr.

Glave, Thomas. Words to Our Now: Imagination & Dissent. annot. ed. 2007. (Illus.). 216p. per. 17.95 *(978-0-8166-4680-7(5))* Univ. of Minnesota Pr.

Green, Tara T. A Fatherless Child: Autobiographical Perspectives of African American Men. 2009. (ENG.). 184p. (C). 34.95 *(978-0-8262-1821-6(0))* Univ. of Missouri Pr.

Griffin, Drs. James P. Jr. & Karen E. African American Manhood Development: Contemporary Life Lessons for Leaders — Student Guide. 2010. 96p. pap. 15.00 *(978-0-557-25503-0(1))* Lulu Enterprises Inc.

Harper, Hill. The Conversation: How Black Men & Women Can Build Loving, Trusting Relationships. 2010. (ENG.). 288p. (gr. 12). 15.00 *(978-1-59240-578-7(9),* Gotham) Penguin Group (USA) Inc.

—The Conversation: How Black Men & Women Can Build Loving, Trusting Relationships. lt. ed. 2010. 390p. 31.95 *(978-1-4104-2422-6(7))* Thorndike Pr.

Harris, Theresa & Taylor, George. Raising African American Males: Strategies & Interventions for Successful Outcomes. 2012. ***(978-1-60709-300-8(6))*** Rowman & Littlefield Education.

Harris, Theresa & Taylor, George, eds. Raising African-American Males: Strategies & Interventions for Successful Outcomes. 2012. (ENG.). 116p. 40.00 ***(978-1-60709-298-8(0))*** Rowman & Littlefield Education.

Harris, Whitney S. & Ferguson, Ronald T. What's up with the Brothers? Essays & Studies on African-American Masculinities. 2010. 172p. (YA). 45.00 *(978-1-931342-23-0(7))*; pap. 20.00 *(978-1-931342-22-3(9))* Men's Studies Pr.

Harris, Whitney Stewart & Ferguson, Ronald T. What's up with the Brothers? Essays & Studies on African-American Masculinities. 2010. (Illus.). 168p. E-Book *(978-1-931342-24-7(5))* Men's Studies Pr.

Harris/Taylor, ed. Raising African-American Males: Strategies & Interventions for Successful Outcomes. 2012. (ENG.). 116p. pap. 18.95 ***(978-1-60709-299-5(9))*** Rowman & Littlefield Education.

Hatton, Norman. Man-Ipulation. 2008. (Illus.). 80p. 34.95 *(978-1-919901-37-4(X))* Janssen Pubs. ZAF. Dist: Independent Pubs. Group.

Hornsby-Gutting, Angela. Black Manhood & Community Building in North Carolina, 1900-1930. 2011. (New Perspectives on the History of the South Ser.). (ENG., Illus.). 264p. pap. 27.95 *(978-0-8130-3679-3(8))* Univ. Pr. of Florida.

Howard, Stanley W. The Men We All Know. 2011. 84p. pap. 15.00 ***(978-1-4389-4745-7(3))*** AuthorHouse.

Jackson, Cassandra. Violence Visual Culture & the Black Male Body. 2010. (Routledge Research in Cultural & Media Studies). (ENG., Illus.). 152p. (C). 125.00 *(978-0-415-88042-8(4))* Routledge.

Jackson, Robert. No More Excuses: Black Men Stand up!: Black Men Stand Up! 2008. pap. 15.00 *(978-0-9659254-1-9(2))* Lavelle Publishing.

Jackson, Ronald L. Masculinity in the Black Imagination: Politics of communicating race & Manhood. 2011. (C). pap. 34.95 ***(978-1-4331-1247-8(7))*** Lang, Peter Publishing, Inc.

—Masculinity in the Black Imagination: Politics of Communicating Race & Manhood. 2011. (C). 139.95 ***(978-1-4331-1248-5(5))*** Lang, Peter Publishing Inc.

Jae', Jas. Say Goodbye to the Blackman Who Drains the Blackwoman. 2008. 104p. per. 9.99 *(978-1-60266-628-3(8))* Xulon Pr., Inc.

Janssen Publishers, creator. Black: Volume 6. 2007. (Black Ser.). (Illus.). 80p. pap. 34.95 *(978-1-919901-36-7(1))* Janssen Pubs. ZAF. Dist: Independent Pubs. Group.

Janssen, Volker, ed. Black: Volume 4: the African Male Nude in Art & Photography. 2007. (Black Ser.). (ENG., Illus.). 80p. pap. 34.95 *(978-1-919901-31-2(0))* Janssen Pubs. ZAF. Dist: Independent Pubs. Group.

—Black Volume 5: The African Male Nude in Art & Photography. 2007. (Black Ser.). (Illus.). 80p. per. 29.95 *(978-1-919901-32-9(9))* Janssen Pubs. ZAF. Dist: Independent Pubs. Group.

Johnson, Mayme Hatcher, et al. Harlem Godfather: The Rap on my Husband, Ellsworth Bumpy Johnson. 2010. 248p. pap. 15.00 *(978-0-9676028-3-7(1))* Oshun Publishing Co., Inc.

Johnson, Waldo Emerson, ed. Social Work with African American Males: Health, Mental Health, & Social Policy, 1 vol. 2010. (ENG., Illus.). 360p. 47.95 *(978-0-19-531436-6(0))* Oxford Univ. Pr., Inc.

Joseph, Jamal. Panther Baby. 2012. (ENG.). 272p. 23.95 *(978-1-56512-950-4(4),* 1565129504) Algonquin Bks. of Chapel Hill.

Kafele, Baruti. Motivating Black Males to Achieve in School & in Life. 2009. pap. 16.95 *(978-1-4166-0857-8(5))* Assn. for Supervision & Curriculum Development.

Kane, Julius. Ten Things Every Black Man Must Do Before He Dies. 2006. (ENG.). 137p. per. 12.95 *(978-0-9785056-1-5(1))* Maverick Publishing.

Kelly, Travis. And We Call Ourselves Men! Becoming the Men We Need to Be. 2009. 116p. pap. 11.95 *(978-1-4327-1160-3(1))* Outskirts Pr., Inc.

King, Rodney & Spagnola, Lawrence J. The Riot Within: My Journey from Rebellion to Redemption - Learning How We Can All Get Along. 2012. (ENG.). 272p. 25.99 ***(978-0-06-219443-5(7),*** HarperOne) HarperCollins Pubs.

Knowles, Gilbert A. Help Them Pull Their Pants Up: How Mentors & Communities Can Empower Young African American Men. 2008. 132p. 23.95 *(978-0-595-49903-8(1))*; 128p. pap. 13.95 *(978-0-595-50216-5(4))* iUniverse, Inc.

Kunjufu, Jawanza. State of Emergency. 2009. (ENG.). 200p. pap. 15.95 *(978-1-934155-09-7(8))* African American Images.

—Understanding Black Male Learning Styles. 2011. (ENG., Illus.). 160p. pap. 15.95 *(978-1-934155-38-7(1))* African American Images.

Leiter, Andrew B. In the Shadow of the Black Beast: African American Masculinity in the Harlem & Southern Renaissances. 2010. (Southern Literary Studies). 296p. 39.95 *(978-0-8071-3587-7(9))* Louisiana State Univ. Pr.

Lemelle, Anthony J., Jr. Black Masculinity & Sexual Politics. 2009. (Routledge Research in Race & Ethnicity Ser.). (ENG., Illus.). 302p. 103.00 *(978-0-415-87277-5(4))* Routledge.

LeVert, Eddie, Sr., et al. I Got Your Back: A Father & Son Keep It Real about Love, Fatherhood, Family, & Friendship. 2008. (ENG., Illus.). 224p. pap. 12.95 *(978-0-7679-2760-4(5))* Broadway Bks.

Lindquist, Malinda Alaine. Black Social Science & the Crisis of Manhood, 1890-1970. 2012. (Routledge Studies in African American History & Culture Ser.). (ENG.). 254p. (C). 125.00 ***(978-0-415-51743-0(5))*** Routledge.

Lowe, Tim. Unsupervised Cows. 2011. 230p. 29.99 ***(978-1-4568-2895-0(9))*** Xlibris Corp.

Lowther, Hastie. Willie E. Lowther: The Journey of My Life. 2007. (Illus.). 328p. per. 24.95 net. *(978-0-974773-6-3(3))* Soleil Pr.

Madhubuti, Haki R. Tough Notes: A Healing Call for Creating Exceptional Black Men. 2010. 150p. pap. 15.95 (978-0-88378-319-1(3)) Third World Press.
McCullum, Mdiv. The Plight of the African-American Male: An Informative Guide to Healing & Restoration. 2009. 128p. 21.99 (978-1-4490-0657-0(4)); pap. 16.99 (978-1-4490-0656-3(6)) AuthorHouse.
Miller, James A. Remembering Scottsboro: The Legacy of an Infamous Trial. 2009. (ENG., Illus.). 296p. (C). pap. 29.95 (978-0-691-14047-6(2)) Princeton Univ. Pr.
Miller, Monica L. Slaves to Fashion: Black Dandyism & the Styling of Black Diasporic Identity. 2009. (ENG., Illus.). 408p. 94.95 (978-0-8223-4585-5(4)); pap. 26.95 (978-0-8223-4603-6(6)) Duke Univ. Pr.
Mocombe, Paul. The Liberal Black Protestant Heterosexual Bourgeois Male: From W.E.B. du Bois to Barack Obama. 2010. (Illus.). v, 130p. E-Book (978-0-7618-4803-5(7)) Univ. Pr. of America, Inc.
Moore, Dante Sr. The Re-Education of the Female. 2008. (ENG.). 176p. pap. 13.00 (978-1-59309-170-5(2), Strebor Bks.) Strebor Bks.
Moore, Wes. Discovering Wes Moore. 2012. (ENG.). 160p. (YA). (gr. 7). 15.99 (978-0-385-74167-5(7), Delacorte Bks. for Young Readers) Random Hse. Children's Bks.
—Discovering Wes Moore: Chances, Choices, Changes. 2012. E-Book (978-0-375-98670-3(7), Delacorte Pr) Random House Publishing Group.
—Discovering Wes Moore: Chances, Choices, Changes. 2012. (ENG.). 160p. (YA). (gr. 7). lib. bdg. 18.99 (978-0-375-99018-2(6), Delacorte Bks. for Young Readers) Random Hse. Children's Bks.
Murray, Rolland. Our Living Manhood: Literature, Black Power, & Masculine Ideology. 2006. 160p. (C). 49.95 (978-0-8122-3972-0(5)) Univ. of Pennsylvania Pr.
Neal, Mark Anthony. New Black Man. 2006. (ENG.). 208p. per. 32.95 (978-0-415-97991-7(9)) Routledge.
Ntozake, Shange. The Black Book. 2010. (GER & ENG., Illus.). 108p. pap. 39.95 (978-3-8296-0460-4(2)) Schirmer/Mosel Verlag GmbH DEU. Dist: Prestel Publishing.
Orelus, Pierre W. The Agony of Masculinity: Race, Gender, & Education in the Age of New Racism & Patriarchy. 2009. (Counterpoints: Studies in the Postmodern Theory of Education Ser.). 240p. (C). 32.95 (978-1-4331-0417-6(2)) Lang, Peter Publishing, Inc.
Page, Thomas L. When Love Is Not Enough: Bringing Spirituality & Coping Back to Families & Homes. 2011. 124p. 23.95 (978-1-4620-1355-5(4)); pap. 13.95 (978-1-4620-1354-8(6)) iUniverse, Inc.
Palmer, Robert T. Black Men in College: Implications for Diversity, Recruitment, Support, & Retention. 2011. (ENG., Illus.). 224p. 140.00 (978-0-415-89383-1(6)); pap. 42.95 (978-0-415-89384-8(4)) Routledge.
Parks, Gregory S. & Hughey, Matthew W., eds. 12 Angry Men: True Stories of Being a Black Man in America Today. 2012. (ENG., Illus.). 224p. pap. 16.95 (978-1-59558-771-8(3)) New Pr., The.
Persaud, Rajen. Why Black Men Love White Women: Going Beyond Sexual Politics to the Heart of the Matter. 2009. (ENG.). 288p. pap. 15.00 (978-1-4165-9542-7(2), Gallery Books/Karen Hunter Publishing) Gallery Books/Karen Hunter Publishing.
Pete, Agbo. Loving the African Male: What Every Woman MUST Know. 2006. pap. 19.95 (978-0-9788068-0-4(8)) Coal City Entertainment Publishing.
Powell, Kevin. The Black Male Handbook: A Blueprint for Life. 2008. (ENG.). 272p. pap. 15.00 (978-1-4165-9224-2(5), Beyond Words/Atria Bks.) Atria Bks.
Presley, Greyling, II. No Disrespect Sista, but I Want to Be Happy! 2007. 149p. per. 14.99 (978-0-615-15118-2(3)) Presley, Greyling.
Redmond, Eric C., et al. Where Are All the Brothers? Straight Answers to Men's Questions about the Church. 2008. 112p. pap. 9.99 (978-1-4335-0178-4(3)) Crossway.
Reed, James W. & Shulman, Neil. Black Man's Guide to Good Health: Essential Advice for African-American Men & Their Families. 3rd rev. ed. 2011. (ENG., Illus.). 320p. pap. 17.95 (978-0-9743144-7-1(1)) Hilton Publishing Co.
Ricketts, Percy. Fathers of African Descent: Their Relationships, Challenges & Why They Seldom Seek Help. 2007. 412p. per. 19.95 (978-1-4327-0194-9(0)) Outskirts Pr., Inc.
Robinson, Tyrone H. Show Yourself & Be Not Ashamed - a Call to the African American Male for Visibility. 2008. 72p. pap. (978-3-639-00445-8(0)) VDM Verlag Dr. Mueller e.K.
Silver, April R., ed. Be a Father to Your Child: Real Talk from Black Men on Family, Love, & Fatherhood. 2008. (ENG., Illus.). 272p. pap. 17.95 (978-1-59376-192-9(9), Soft Skull Pr.) Counterpoint LLC.
Smith, Aaron/Anwar. Is There Really a Shortage of Good Black Men? 2010. 214p. 24.95 (978-1-60911-014-7(5), Strategic Bk. Publishing) AEG Literary Publishing Services, Inc.
Stevenson, Michael A. No More Excuses: Creating a Culture in the Church That Reaches African-American Men. 2008. (ENG.). 128p. pap. 9.99 (978-1-59979-391-7(1), Creation Hse.) Charisma Media.
Strength Within Surviving by the Grace of God. 2nd rev. ed. 2008. 288p. pap. 15.00 (978-0-615-21031-5(7)) Tyler, Roland Vincent.
Taylor, Shawn. Big Black Penis: Misadventures in Race & Masculinity. 2008. (ENG.). 208p. pap. 14.95 (978-1-55652-734-0(9), Hill, Lawrence Bks.) Chicago Review Pr., Inc.
Thomas, A. C. The Color of Success: Growing up black never stopped one man from Winning. 2007. pap. (978-0-9797103-0-8(8)) Algus Publishing.
Thompson, Gordon E. The Assimilationist Impulse in Four African American Narratives: Frederic Douglas, James Weldon Johnson, Richard Wright, & Leroi Jones. 2011. 248p. 119.95 (978-0-7734-1555-3(6)) Mellen, Edwin Pr., The.
Tucker, Linda G. Lockstep & Dance: Images of Black Men in Popular Culture. (ENG.). 2010. 204p. pap. 25.00 (978-1-60473-859-9(6)) 2007. 191p. 50.00 (978-1-57806-906-4(8)) Univ. Pr. of Mississippi.
Tukufu, Darryl S. A Guide Toward the Successful Development of African-American Males: The Remix. 2nd ed. 2009. 91p. pap. 12.95 (978-0-9662152-2-9(2)) Tukufu Group, The.
Washington Post Staff, et al. Being a Black Man: At the Corner of Progress & Peril. 2007. (ENG., Illus.). 384p. per. 13.95 (978-1-58648-522-1(9)) PublicAffairs.
White, Aaronette M. Ain't I a Feminist? African American Men Speak Out on Fatherhood, Friendship, Forgiveness, & Freedom. 2008. 272p. 86.50 (978-0-7914-7567-6(0)); pap. 29.95 (978-0-7914-7568-3(9)) State Univ. of New York Pr.
White, Miles. From Jim Crow to Jay-Z: Race, Rap, & the Performance of Masculinity. 2011. (African Amer Music in Global Perspective Ser.). (ENG.). 176p. 60.00 (978-0-252-03662-0(X)); pap. 22.00 (978-0-252-07832-3(2)) Univ. of Illinois Pr.
Why We Can't Wait: A Case for Philanthropic Action: Opportunities for Improving the Life Outcomes for African American Males. 2007. 81p. spiral bd. (978-0-916584-24-5(0)) Ford Foundation.
Wilkins, Rhonda. Swimming Upstream. 2008. 248p. pap. (978-3-8364-7843-4(9)) VDM Verlag Dr. Mueller e.K.
Willie E. Lowther: From Locust Grove to Harlem: the Journey of My Life. 2008. (Illus.). 328p. 36.95 (978-0-9742773-8-7(X)) Soleil Pr.
Willis Thomas, Hank, photos by. Pitch Blackness. 2008. (ENG., Illus.). 112p. 35.00 (978-1-59711-072-3(8)) Aperture Foundation, Inc.
Wynn, Mychal. Teaching, Parenting, & Mentoring Successful Black Boys: A Quick Guide. Bascome, Glenn, ed. 2nd ed. 2007. 128p. pap. 5.95 (978-1-880463-01-7(6)) Rising Sun Publishing, Inc.
Young, Vershawn Ashanti. Your Average Nigga: Performing Race, Literacy, & Masculinity. 2007. pap. 19.95 (978-0-8143-3248-1(X)) Wayne State Univ. Pr.
Zamani-Gallaher, Eboni M. & Polite, Vernon C. The State of the African American Male. Campbell, Alec, ed. 2010. (CourageousConversations series Ser.). (ENG.). 303p. pap. 29.95 (978-0-87013-870-6(7)) Michigan State Univ. Pr.

AFRICAN AMERICAN MILITARY PERSONNEL

see African American Soldiers; United States—Armed Forces—African Americans

AFRICAN AMERICAN MOTION PICTURE ACTORS AND ACTRESSES

Hendry, Gloria. Gloria. 2008. (Illus.). 99p. pap. (978-1-4257-9344-9(4)) Xlibris Corp.
Hill, Z. B. Halle Berry: From Beauty Queen to Oscar Winner. 2012. (978-1-4222-2295-9(0)); pap. (978-1-4222-2306-2(X)) Mason Crest Pubs.
Indovino, Shaina Carmel. Tyra Banks: From the Runway to the Television Screen. 2012. (978-1-4222-2294-2(2)); pap. (978-1-4222-2305-5(1)) Mason Crest Pubs.
Johnson, Melissa E. Halle Berry: A Biography. 2009. (Greenwood Biographies Ser.). 138p. 35.00 (978-0-313-35834-0(6), GR5834) Greenwood Publishing Group, Inc.
Mapp, Edward. African Americans & the Oscar: Decades of Struggle & Achievement. 2nd ed. 2008. (ENG., Illus.). 218p. 50.00 (978-0-8108-6105-3(4)); per. 25.00 (978-0-8108-6106-0(2)) Scarecrow Pr., Inc.
Mask, Mia. Divas on Screen: Black Women in American Film. 2009. (ENG., Illus.). 320p. 75.00 (978-0-252-03422-0(8)); pap. 26.00 (978-0-252-07619-0(2)) Univ. of Illinois Pr.
McCann, Bob. Encyclopedia of African American Actresses in Film & Television. 2009. (ENG., Illus.). 461p. 75.00 (978-0-7864-3790-0(1)) McFarland & Co., Inc. Pubs.
Poitier, Sidney. The Measure of a Man: A Spiritual Autobiography. 2007. (ENG.). 272p. pap. 14.99 (978-0-06-135790-9(1), HarperOne); (Illus.). 272p. 25.95 (978-0-06-135791-6(X), HarperOne); (ENG., Illus.). 320p. per. 16.95 (978-0-06-135792-3(8), HarperLuxe) HarperCollins Pubs.
Watkins, Mel. Stepin Fetchit: The Life & Times of Lincoln Perry. 2006. (Vintage Ser.). (ENG., Illus.). 368p. pap. 15.95 (978-1-4000-9676-3(6), Vintage) Knopf Doubleday Publishing Group.
Wolfe, David. Marsha Hunt Paper Dolls & Costumes of the 30s And 40s. 2008. (Illus.). 8p. pap. 12.00 (978-0-9795053-8-6(0)) Paper Studio Pr.

AFRICAN AMERICAN MOTION PICTURE PRODUCERS AND DIRECTORS

Diawara, Manthia & Mask, Mia, eds. Black American Cinema 2. 2008. (ENG.). 320p. 125.00 (978-0-415-97454-7(2)); pap. 34.95 (978-0-415-97455-4(0)) Routledge.
Flory, Dan. Philosophy, Black Film, Film Noir. (ENG., Illus.). 408p. pap. 35.00 (978-0-271-03345-7(2)); 2008. (C). 65.00 (978-0-271-03344-0(4)) Pennsylvania State Univ. Pr.
Green, Michelle Y. Oscar Invincible: The Life of Film Pioneer Oscar Micheaux. 2007. (978-0-8037-3003-8(9), Dial) Penguin Group (USA) Inc.
hooks, bell. Reel to Real: Race, Class & Sex at the Movies. 2008. (Routledge Classics Ser.). (ENG.). 320p. 25.95 (978-0-415-96480-7(6)) Routledge.
Mapp, Edward. African Americans & the Oscar: Decades of Struggle & Achievement. 2nd ed. 2008. (ENG., Illus.). 218p. 50.00 (978-0-8108-6105-3(4)); per. 25.00 (978-0-8108-6106-0(2)) Scarecrow Pr., Inc.
Mcgilligan, Patrick. The Great & Only The Life of America's First Black Filmmaker. 2008. (Illus.). 432p. pap. 16.95 (978-0-06-073140-3(0), HarperPerennial) HarperCollins Pubs.
Shell, Ray. Spike Lee: The Eternal Maverick. 2012. (ENG., Illus.). 200p. pap. 14.95 (978-1-906413-84-2(3), Black Amber) Arcadia Bks. Ltd. GBR. Dist: Dufour Editions, Inc.
Walker, David, et al. Reflections on Blaxploitation: Actors & Directors Speak. 2009. (ENG., Illus.). 248p. 45.00 (978-0-8108-6706-2(0)) Scarecrow Pr., Inc.

AFRICAN AMERICAN MUSIC

see African Americans—Music

AFRICAN AMERICAN MUSICIANS

Ames, Jeffery. A Pioneering Twentieth Century African-American Musician. 2009. 196p. pap. (978-3-639-15351-4(0)) VDM Verlag Dr. Mueller e.K.
Anderson, Iain. This Is Our Music: Free Jazz & the Transformation of American Culture. 2006. (Arts & Intellectual Life in Modern America Ser.). (Illus.). 254p. 39.95 (978-0-8122-3980-5(6)) Univ. of Pennsylvania Pr.
—This Is Our Music: Free Jazz, the Sixties, & American Culture. 2007. (Arts & Intellectual Life in Modern America Ser.). (Illus.). 264p. (C). per. 24.95 (978-0-8122-2003-2(X)) Univ. of Pennsylvania Pr.
Baraka, Amiri, pseud. Digging: The Afro-American Soul of American Classical Music. (Music of the African Diaspora Ser.). (Illus.). 2010. (ENG.). 426p. pap. 19.95 (978-0-520-26582-0(3)) 2009. 352p. 50.00 (978-0-520-25715-3(4)) Univ. of California Pr.
Bastfield, Darrin Keith. Back in the Day: My Life & Times with Tupac Shakur. 2008. (ENG.). 182p. pap. 15.00 (978-1-4379-5095-3(7)) DIANE Publishing Co.
Belafonte, Harry. My Song. 2012. (Vintage Ser.). (ENG., Illus.). 480p. pap. 16.00 (978-0-307-47342-4(2), Vintage) Knopf Doubleday Publishing Group.
Berresford, Mark. That's Got 'Em! The Life & Music of Wilbur C. Sweatman. 2010. (American Made Music Ser.). (ENG., Illus.). 240p. 50.00 (978-1-60473-099-9(4)) Univ. Pr. of Mississippi.
Berry, Lemuel, Jr. Great African American Musicians: From Marian Anderson to Stevie Wonder. 2011. (ENG., Illus.). 376p. (978-0-7734-3831-6(9)) Mellen, Edwin Pr., The.
Blakey, D. N. Revelation Blind Willie Johnson the Biography. 2007. 332p. pap. 36.95 (978-1-4303-2899-5(1)) Lulu Enterprises Inc.
Cadman, Chris & Halstead, Craig. Michael Jackson: For the Record. 2007. (Illus.). 412p. (978-0-7552-0267-6(8)) Authors OnLine, Ltd.
Clemons, Clarence & Reo, Don. Big Man: Real Life & Tall Tales. 2010. (ENG., Illus.). 384p. pap. 14.99 (978-0-446-54625-6(9)) Grand Central Publishing.
Cohen, Harvey G. Duke Ellington's America. (Illus.). 2011. (ENG.). 704p. pap. 22.50 (978-0-226-11264-0(0)) 2010. 720p. 40.00 (978-0-226-11263-3(2)) Univ. of Chicago Pr.
Cohn, Nik. Triksta: Life & Death & New Orleans Rap. 2007. (Vintage Ser.). (ENG.). 256p. pap. 13.95 (978-1-4000-7706-9(0), Vintage) Knopf Doubleday Publishing Group.
Davis, Sharon. Chinwaggin' 2008. 364p. pap. (978-1-904408-08-6(7)) Bank House Bks.
Donna J. Bosn & Arthur Lee Crume Sr. The Perfect Song. 2010. 408p. 34.99 (978-1-4535-3609-4(4)); pap. 23.99 (978-1-4535-3608-7(6)) Xlibris Corp.
Gluck, Bob. You'll Know When You Get There: Herbie Hancock & the Mwandishi Band. 2012. 272p. 37.50 (978-0-226-30004-7(8)) Univ. of Chicago Pr.
Green, Doris. No Longer an Oral Tradition: My Journey Through Percussion Notation. 2010. 232p. pap. 60.00 (978-1-60911-458-9(2), Eloquent Bks.) AEG Literary Publishing Services, Inc.
Guralnick, Peter. Dream Boogie: The Triumph of Sam Cooke. 2006. (ENG., Illus.). 768p. per. 16.99 (978-0-316-01329-1(3), Back Bay Bks.) Little Brown & Co.
Hayes, Eileen M. & Williams, Linda F., eds. Black Women & Music: More Than the Blues. 2007. (African American Music in Culture Ser.). (Illus.). 280p. per. 26.00 (978-0-252-07426-4(2)) Univ. of Illinois Pr.
Hennessey, Mike. The Little Giant: The Story of Johnny Griffin. 2008. (Illus.). 246p. 48.00 (978-0-9550908-5-1(7)) Northway Pubns. GBR. Dist: Parkwest Pubns., Inc.
Heron, Gil Scott. The Last Holiday: A Memoir. 2012. (ENG.). 384p. 25.00 (978-0-8021-2901-7(3), Grove Pr.) Grove/Atlantic, Inc.
James, Rick. The Confessions of Rick James: Memoirs of a Super Freak. 2007. (ENG., Illus.). 450p. per. 18.95 (978-0-9790976-3-8(0)) Amber Bks.
Kirby, David. Little Richard: The Birth of Rock 'n' Roll. 2009. (ENG.). 224p. 19.95 (978-0-8264-2965-0(3)) Continuum International Publishing Group, Ltd. GBR. Dist: National Bk. Network.
Lauterbach, Preston. The Chitlin' Circuit: And the Road to Rock 'N' Roll. 2012. (ENG., Illus.). 368p. pap. 16.95 (978-0-393-34294-9(8), 34294) Norton, W. W. & Co., Inc.
LeVert, Eddie, Sr., et al. I Got Your Back: A Father & Son Keep It Real about Love, Fatherhood, Family, & Friendship. 2008. (ENG., Illus.). 224p. pap. 12.95 (978-0-7679-2760-4(5)) Broadway Bks.
Marsh, J. B. The Story of the Jubilee Singers. 311p. reprint ed. lib. bdg. 98.00 (978-0-7222-4851-5(2)) Library Reprints, Inc.
Michael, Jason A. Strength of A Woman: The Phyllis Hyman Story. 2007. 236p. per. 16.95 (978-0-9794890-0-6(8)) JAM Bks., LLC.
Miller, Chuck. A Bridge to Success. 2011. 254p. 39.95 (978-0-557-92665-7(3)) Lulu Enterprises Inc.
Myers, Sam & Horton, Jeff. Sam Myers: The Blues Is My Story. 2006. (ENG.). 172p. 50.00 (978-1-57806-895-1(9)); per. 25.00 (978-1-57806-896-8(7)) Univ. Pr. of Mississippi.
O'Connell, Deirdre & Deirdre, O'Connell. The Ballad of Blind Tom, Slave Pianist: America's Lost Musical Genius. 2009. (ENG., Illus.). 272p. (gr. 12). 24.95 (978-1-59020-143-5(4)) Overlook Pr., The.
Pike, Gustavus D. The Singing Campaign for Ten Thousand Pounds. 2009. 92p. pap. (978-1-151-46711-9(1)) Books LLC.
Ratliff, Stanley. A Dream, A Goal, Never a Reality. 2008. 120p. pap. 12.99 (978-1-4343-6622-1(7)) AuthorHouse.
Reed, Bill. Hot from Harlem: Twelve African American Entertainers, 1890-1960. 2009. (ENG., Illus.). 271p. pap. 39.95 (978-0-7864-4467-0(3)) McFarland & Co., Inc. Pubs.
Reynolds, John & Robinson, Tiny. Lead Belly: A Life in Pictures, 1 vol. Reynolds, John & Robinson, Tiny, eds. 2008. (ENG., Illus.). 224p. 50.00 (978-3-86521-459-1(2)) Steidl, Gerhard Druckerei und Verlag DEU. Dist: Innovative Logistics.
Riesman. I Feel So Good. 2007. (Illus.). 306p. (978-0-415-97276-5(0), 0415972760, Routledge) Taylor & Francis Group.
Riesman, Robert & Riesman, Bob. I Feel So Good: The Life & Times of Big Bill Broonzy. 2011. (ENG., Illus.). 366p. 27.50 (978-0-226-71745-6(3)) Univ. of Chicago Pr.
Rowden, Terry. The Songs of Blind Folk: African American Musicians & the Cultures of Blindness. 2009. (Corporealities: Discourses of Disability Ser.). (ENG., Illus.). 184p. pap. 23.95 (978-0-472-05064-2(8)); 70.00 (978-0-472-07064-0(9)) Univ. of Michigan Pr.
Spencer, Jon M. Self-Made & Blues-Rich. Date not set. (Illus.). 130p. 11.95 (978-0-86543-503-2(0)) Africa World Pr.
Stone, Robert. Sacred Steel: Inside an African American Steel Guitar Tradition. 2010. (ENG., Illus.). 320p. 80.00 (978-0-252-03554-8(2)); pap. 25.00 (978-0-252-07743-2(1)) Univ. of Illinois Pr.
Stubbs, David. Jimi Hendrix: The Story Behind Every Song. 2nd ed. 2010. (Stories Behind the Songs Ser.). (ENG., Illus.). 192p. 14.95 (978-1-84732-587-7(4)) Carlton Bks., Ltd. GBR. Dist: Sterling Publishing Co., Inc.
Ware, David N. & Ware, David. Interviews with Sixteen Band Directors at Historically Black Colleges: Their Attitudes, Opinions, & Methods. 2008. 176p. 99.95 (978-0-7734-5005-9(X)) Mellen, Edwin Pr., The.
Weeks, Todd Bryant. Luck's in My Corner: The Life & Music of Hot Lips Page. 2008. (Illus.). 320p. pap. 39.95 (978-0-415-99077-6(7)) Routledge.

AFRICAN AMERICAN NURSES

Jones, Diane. The Story of Me a Black Nurse. 2011. 192p. pap. 19.99 (978-1-4567-2717-8(6)) AuthorHouse.
Nissim, Sara. Culturally Diverse Nurse's & the Meaning of Cultural Competence. 2010. 328p. pap. (978-3-639-26876-8(8)) VDM Verlag Dr. Mueller e.K.

AFRICAN AMERICAN ORATORS

Ellis, Catherine & Smith, Stephen Drury, eds. Say It Loud: Great Speeches on Civil Rights & African American Identity. 2010. (ENG.). 304p. 35.00 (978-1-59558-113-6(8)) New Pr., The.
Grant, Colin. Negro with a Hat: The Rise & Fall of Marcus Garvey. 2010. (ENG., Illus.). 544p. pap. 17.95 (978-0-19-539309-5(0)) Oxford Univ. Pr., Inc.
Jordan, Vernon E., Jr. Make It Plain: Standing up & Speaking Out. 2009. (ENG.). 272p. pap. 13.95 (978-1-58648-775-1(2)) PublicAffairs.
Leeman, Richard W. & Duffy, Bernard K., eds. The Will of a People: A Critical Anthology of Great African American Speeches. 2012. 474p. pap. 49.95 (978-0-8093-3057-7(1)) Southern Illinois Univ. Pr.
Smith, Stephen Drury & Ellis, Catherine J., eds. Say It Plain: A Century of Great African American Speeches. 2007. (ENG.). 254p. per. 17.95 (978-1-59558-126-6(X)) New Pr., The.
Woodson, Carter Godwin. Negro Orators & Their Orations. 2010. 726p. pap. 35.00 (978-1-57898-963-8(9)) Martino Publishing.

AFRICAN AMERICAN PERIODICALS

Lewis, Miles Marshall, ed. Bronx Biannual No. 2. 2007. (ENG.). 225p. per. 13.95 (978-1-933354-09-5(7)) Akashic Bks.
Wimberly, Edward P. African American History Month 2009: Daily Devotions. 2008. (African American History Month Daily Devotions Annual Ser.). 32p. pap. 2.00 (978-0-687-65392-8(4)) Abingdon Pr.

AFRICAN AMERICAN PHILOSOPHY

Asante, Molefi Kete. Maulana Karenga: An Intellectual Portrait. 2009. (ENG.). 224p. 69.95 (978-0-7456-4827-9(4)) Polity Pr. GBR. Dist: Wiley, John & Sons, Inc.
Conaway, Carol B. & Waters, Kristin B., eds. Black Women's Intellectual Traditions: Speaking Their Minds. 2007. (Illus.). 480p. per. 35.00 (978-1-58465-634-0(4)) Univ. Pr. of New England.
Gilyard, Keith. Composition & Cornel West: Notes Toward a Deep Democracy. 2008. (ENG.). 176p. pap. 35.00 (978-0-8093-2854-3(2)) Southern Illinois Univ. Pr.
Karenga. Kawaida & Questions of Life & Struggle: African American, Pan-African, & Global Issues. 2007. (978-0-943412-29-0(3)) Univ. of Sankore Pr., The.
Marshall, Stephen. The City on the Hill from Below: The Crisis of Prophetic Black Politics. 2011. (ENG.). 256p. 64.50 (978-1-4399-0655-2(6)) Temple Univ. Pr.
May, Vivian M. Anna Julia Cooper, Visionary Black Feminist: A Critical Introduction. 2007. (ENG., Illus.). 232p. 145.00 (978-0-415-95642-0(0)); pap. 36.95 (978-0-415-95643-7(9)) Routledge.
Pellegrino, Edmund D. & Prograis, Lawrence J., eds. African American Bioethics: Culture, Race, & Identity. 2007. (ENG.). 192p. per. 26.95 (978-1-58901-164-9(3)) Georgetown Univ. Pr.
Prograis, Lawrence J., Jr. & Pellegrino, Edmund D., eds. African American Bioethics: Culture, Race, & Identity. 2007. (ENG.). 192p. 44.95 (978-1-58901-163-2(5)) Georgetown Univ. Pr.

Rabaka, Reiland. Africana Critical Theory: Reconstructing the Black Radical Tradition, from W.E.B. du Bois & C.L.R. James to Frantz Fanon & Amilcar Cabral. 2009. (ENG.). 452p. 120.99 *(978-0-7391-2885-5(X))* Lexington Bks.
—Africana Critical Theory: Reconstructing The Black Radical Tradition, From W. E. B. Du Bois & C. L. R. James to Frantz Fanon & Amilcar Cabral. 2010. (ENG.). 452p. pap. 49.95 *(978-0-7391-2886-2(8))* Lexington Bks.
—W. E. B. du Bois & the Problems of the Twenty-First Century: An Essay on Africana Critical Theory. 2007. (ENG.). 296p. 83.99 *(978-0-7391-1682-1(7))* Lexington Bks.
—W.E.B. Du Bois & the Problems of the Twenty-First Century: An Essay on Africana Critical Theory. 2008. (ENG.). 296p. pap. 31.50 *(978-0-7391-1683-8(5))* Lexington Bks.
Reed, Adolph, Jr., et al. Renewing Black Intellectual History: The Ideological & Material Foundations of African American Thought, 1 vol. 2010. 336p. pap. 39.95 *(978-1-59451-666-5(9))* Paradigm Pubs.
Ruffin, Kimberly N. Black on Earth: African American Ecoliterary Traditions. 2010. (ENG., Illus.). 192p. 59.95 *(978-0-8203-2856-0(1))*; pap. 22.95 *(978-0-8203-3720-3(X))* Univ. of Georgia Pr.
Scriven, Darryl. A Dealer of Old Clothes: Philosophical Conversations with David Walker. 2007. (ENG.). 204p. 62.99 *(978-0-7391-2066-8(2))* Lexington Bks.

AFRICAN AMERICAN PHOTOGRAPHERS

Burke, J. T. Beautiful Again. 2010. 125.00 *(978-0-578-05703-3(4))*; pap. 30.00 *(978-0-578-05702-6(6))* Burke Triolo Studio Editions.
Duganne, Erina. The Self in Black & White: Race & Subjectivity in Postwar American Photography. 2010. (Interfaces: Studies in Visual Culture Ser.). (ENG., Illus.). 248p. pap. 35.00 *(978-1-58465-802-3(9)*, Dartmouth College Press) Univ. Pr. of New England.
Finley, Cheryl, et al. Teenie Harris, Photographer: Image, Memory, History. 2011. (ENG.). 208p. pap. 24.95 ***(978-0-8229-6174-1(1))***; (Illus.). 55.00 ***(978-0-8229-4414-0(6))*** Univ. of Pittsburgh Pr.
Mitchell, John Hanson. Looking for Mr. Gilbert: The Reimagined Life of an African American. 2006. (ENG., Illus.). 288p. per. 16.00 *(978-1-59376-142-4(2))* Counterpoint LLC.
Parks, Gordon & Huie, Wing Young. A Choice of Weapons. 2010. (ENG.). 192p. pap. 17.95 *(978-0-87351-769-0(5))* Minnesota Historical Society Pr.
Parks, Gordon & Parks, Gordon, Jr. A Hungry Heart: A Memoir. 2007. (ENG.). 352p. pap. 15.00 *(978-0-7432-6903-2(9)*, Washington Square Pr.) Washington Square Pr.
Parks, Gordon & W. W. Norton and Company Staff. To Smile in Autumn: A Memoir. 2009. (ENG., Illus.). 248p. pap. 18.95 *(978-0-8166-6555-6(9))* Univ. of Minnesota Pr.
Shames, Stephen, photos by. The Black Panthers, 1 vol. 2006. (ENG., Illus.). 152p. 35.00 *(978-1-59711-024-2(8))* Aperture Foundation, Inc.
Willis, Deborah. History of African American Photographers. Date not set. *(978-0-312-28639-2(2))* St. Martin's Pr.

AFRICAN AMERICAN PHYSICIANS

Beckford, Geraldine, compiled by. Biographical Dictionary of American Physicians of African Ancestry, 1800-1920. 2011. 125.00 *(978-0-9831151-4-4(1))*; pap. 90.00 *(978-0-9831151-5-1(X))* Africana Homestead Legacy Pubs., Inc.
Conner, Douglas L. A Black Physician's Story: Bringing Hope in Mississippi. 2009. (ENG.). 183p. pap. 25.00 *(978-1-60473-173-6(7))* Univ. Pr. of Mississippi.
Davis, Sampson, et al. The Bond. 2011. 14.45 *(978-0-7848-3370-4(2)*, Everbind) Marco Bk. Co.
—The Bond. 2008. (ENG.). 304p. (gr. 12-18). 15.00 *(978-1-59448-330-1(2)*, Riverhead Trade (Paperbacks)) Penguin Group (USA) Inc.
Dittmer, John. The Good Doctors: The Medical Committee for Human Rights & the Struggle for Social Justice in Health Care. (ENG., Illus.). 336p. 2010. pap. 18.00 *(978-1-60819-093-5(5))* 2009. 30.00 *(978-1-59691-567-1(6))* Bloomsbury Publishing.
Edelin, Kenneth C. Broken Justice: A True Story of Race, Sex & Revenge in a Boston Courtroom. 2007. (Illus.). 362p. per. 17.95 *(978-0-9792060-0-9(6))* PondView Pr.
Ellis, Jack D. Beside the Troubled Waters: A Black Doctor Remembers Life, Medicine, & Civil Rights in an Alabama Town. 2nd ed. 2011. (ENG., Illus.). 192p. 24.00 *(978-0-8173-1721-8(X))* Univ. of Alabama Pr.
Mason, Gilbert R. & Smith, James Patterson. Beaches, Blood, & Ballots: A Black Doctor's Civil Rights Struggle. 2007. (ENG., Illus.). 227p. per. 22.00 *(978-1-934110-28-7(0))* Univ. Pr. of Mississippi.
Norris, James E. C. Fight on, My Soul. 2009. (Illus.). 328p. pap. 14.95 *(978-0-9800084-6-3(8))* Write Place, The.
Oluseyi, Hakeem M., ed. Proceedings of the 2009 Joint Annual Conference of the National Society of Black Physicists & the National Society of Hispanic Physicists. 2010. (AIP Conference Proceedings Ser.). 198p. 197.00 *(978-0-7354-0830-2(0)*, 0735408300, AIP Pr.) Springer.
Renton, David. C L R James: Cricket's Philosopher King. 2007. (ENG., Illus.). 202p. 24.95 *(978-1-905791-01-9(1))* Haus Publishing GBR. Dist: Consortium Bk. Sales & Distribution.
Tallman, Jamie Q. The Notorious Dr. Flippin: Abortion & Consequence in the Early Twentieth Century. 2011. (Plains Histories Ser.). (ENG., Illus.). 228p. 34.95 *(978-0-89672-675-8(4))* Texas Tech Univ. Pr.
Ward, Thomas J. Black Physicians in the Jim Crow South. 2010. (Illus.). 385p. pap. 19.95 *(978-1-55728-936-0(0))* Univ. of Arkansas Pr.

AFRICAN AMERICAN POETRY (ENGLISH)

see American Poetry—African American Authors

AFRICAN AMERICAN POLICE

Bolden, Abraham. The Echo from Dealey Plaza: The True Story of the First African American on the White House Secret Service Detail & His Quest for Justice after the Assassination of JFK. 2009. (ENG.). 320p. pap. 13.95 *(978-0-307-38202-3(8)*, Three Rivers Pr.) Crown Publishing Group.
Bolton & Feagin. Black in Blue: African-American Police Officers & Racism. 2009. 288p. pap. 23.95 *(978-0-415-94519-6(4))* Routledge.
Burton, Art T. Black Gun, Silver Star: The Life & Legend of Frontier Marshal Bass Reeves. 2008. (Race & Ethnicity in the American West Ser.). (ENG., Illus.). 392p. pap. 18.95 *(978-0-8032-1747-8(1)*, Bison Bks.) Univ. of Nebraska Pr.
Holdaway, Simon. Black Police Associations: An Analysis of Race & Ethnicity Within Constabularies. 2010. (Clarendon Studies in Criminology Ser.). (ENG.). 184p. 120.00 *(978-0-19-957344-8(1))* Oxford Univ. Pr., Inc.
I'Tudai, "Ike" Ondue. Detroit Cop Tales: Volume 1 True Confessions. 2007. 132p. per. 14.99 *(978-0-9797928-4-7(3))* Hub Bks.
Lehr, Dick. The Fence: A Police Cover-Up along Boston's Racial Divide. 2010. 416p. pap. 14.99 *(978-0-06-078099-9(1)*, HarperPerennial) HarperCollins Pubs.
Rhodes, Richard S. Gun, Badge & Cuffs. 2011. 160p. 22.95 *(978-1-4490-9772-1(3))*; pap. 18.95 *(978-1-4490-9771-4(5))* AuthorHouse.
Royster, Brian. A Qualitative Study of the New Jersey State Police Promotion Policy. 2010. 260p. pap. *(978-3-8383-6684-5(0))* Lambert Academic Publishing.
Worthy, Arthur G. The Worthy Way: Memoirs of a Pioneer Black Law Enforcement Officer. 2007. 104p. pap. 15.00 *(978-1-60306-034-9(0))* NewSouth, Inc.

AFRICAN AMERICAN POLITICIANS

see also African American Legislators

Abu-Jamal, Mumia. We Want Freedom: A Life in the Black Panther Party. 2008. (ENG., Illus.). 176p. pap. 20.00 *(978-0-89608-718-7(2))* South End Pr.
Atkins, Carla. The White House-First African-American Couple. 2009. 128p. pap. 12.49 *(978-1-4389-4761-7(5))* AuthorHouse.
Benson Sr., Carl A. What Your Black Friends Don't Tell You: A Must Read Book for Whites & Their Black Friends. 2010. 144p. pap. 11.99 *(978-1-4343-5403-7(2))* AuthorHouse.
Berry, Mary Frances. My Face Is Black Is True: Callie House & the Struggle for Ex-Slave Reparations. 2006. (Vintage Ser.). (ENG., Illus.). 336p. pap. 15.95 *(978-0-307-27705-3(4)*, Vintage) Knopf Doubleday Publishing Group.
Carey, Charles W. Political Leaders. 2nd rev. ed. 2011. (A to Z of African Americans Ser.). (Illus.). 392p. (C). (gr. 9-18). 49.50 *(978-0-8160-8120-2(4))* Facts On File, Inc.
Clemons, Michael L., ed. African Americans & Global Affairs: Contemporary Perspectives. 2010. (Illus.). 408p. pap. 35.00 *(978-1-55553-722-7(7))* Univ. Pr. of New England.
—African Americans in Global Affairs: Contemporary Perspectives. 2010. (Illus.). 408p. (C). 85.00 *(978-1-55553-719-7(7))* Univ. Pr. of New England.
Danielson, Chris. After Freedom Summer: How Race Realigned Mississippi Politics, 1965-1986. 2011. (New Perspectives on the History of the South Ser.). (ENG., Illus.). 328p. 69.95 *(978-0-8130-3738-7(7))* Univ. Pr. of Florida.
Dossett, Kate. Bridging Race Divides: Black Nationalism, Feminism, & Integration in the United States, 1896-1935. 2009. (ENG., Illus.). 280p. pap. 29.95 *(978-0-8130-3495-9(7))* Univ. Pr. of Florida.
Dougherty, Steve. Hopes & Dreams: The Story of Barack Obama. rev. ed. 2009. (ENG., Illus.). 192p. pap. 12.95 *(978-1-57912-810-4(6)*, 1579128106) Black Dog & Leventhal Pubs., Inc.
Gillespie, Andra. Whose Black Politics? Cases in Post-Racial Black Leadership. 2009. (ENG., Illus.). 338p. 138.00 *(978-0-415-99215-2(X))* Routledge.
Glasrud, Bruce, ed. African Americans & the Presidency: The Road to the White House. 2009. (ENG., Illus.). 272p. (C). 130.00 *(978-0-415-80391-5(8))* Routledge.
Glasrud, Bruce & Wintz, Cary D., eds. African Americans & the Presidency: The Road to the White House. 2009. (ENG., Illus.). 256p. pap. 26.95 *(978-0-415-80392-2(6))* Routledge.
Glauberman, Stu & Burris, Jerry. The Dream Begins: How Hawai'i Shaped Barack Obama. 2009. 180p. pap. 17.95 *(978-0-9821698-2-7(5))* Watermark Publishing, LLC.
Gordly, Avel Louise. Remembering the Power of Words: The Life of an Oregon Activist, Legislator, & Community Leader. 2011. 176p. pap. 18.95 *(978-0-87071-604-1(2))* Oregon State Univ. Pr.
Gray, Kevin Alexander. The Decline of Black Politics: From Malcolm X to Barack Obama. 2008. 192p. pap. 16.95 *(978-1-84467-284-4(0))* Verso Bks. GBR. Dist: Norton, W. W. & Co., Inc.
Harris, Fredrick. The Price of the Ticket: Barack Obama & Rise & Decline of Black Politics. 2012. (ENG.). 232p. 24.95 ***(978-0-19-973967-7(6))*** Oxford Univ. Pr., Inc.
Hemphill, Amani Franklin. The Black Female Crisis & the Politics of Love in Black America. 2008. 121p. pap. 19.95 *(978-1-60474-555-9(X))* PublishAmerica, Inc.
Ifill, Gwen. The Breakthrough: Politics & Race in the Age of Obama. 2009. (ENG.). 320p. pap. 15.00 *(978-0-7679-2890-8(3)*, Knopf) Knopf Doubleday Publishing Group.
Jackson, David H., Jr. & Jackson, David H. A Chief Lieutenant of the Tuskegee Machine: Charles Banks of Mississippi. 2008. (ENG., Illus.). 304p. pap. 24.95 *(978-0-8130-3271-9(7))* Univ. Pr. of Florida.
Jones, Angela, ed. The History of Modern African American Political Thought: From Frederick Douglass to Barack Obama. 2012. (ENG., Illus.). 448p. (C). 160.00 *(978-0-415-89570-5(7))* Routledge.
Jones, Angela, ed. The Modern African American Thought Reader: From David Walker to Barack Obama. 2012. (ENG., Illus.). 448p. (C). pap. 54.95 ***(978-0-415-89573-6(1))*** Routledge.
Jones, Stephen A. & Freedman, Eric. Presidents & Black America, 00 vols. rev. ed. 2011. (Illus.). 584p. 145.00 *(978-1-60871-008-9(4))* CQ Pr.
Kennedy, Randall. Sellout: The Politics of Racial Betrayal. 2009. (Vintage Ser.). (ENG.). 240p. pap. 13.95 *(978-0-307-38842-1(5)*, Vintage) Knopf Doubleday Publishing Group.
Levy, Mitchell. Are We Ready for a Female or African-American President? 2008. 80p. per. 16.95 *(978-1-60005-085-5(9))* Happy About.
McClelland, Edward. Young Mr. Obama: Chicago & the Making of a Black President. 2010. (ENG., Illus.). 288p. 24.00 *(978-1-60819-060-7(9))* Bloomsbury Publishing.
Mitchell, Michael & Covin, David. Black Politics in a Time of Transition. 2011. (Illus.). 239p. pap. 29.95 ***(978-1-4128-4268-6(9))*** Transaction Pubs.
Monderson, Frederick. Barack Obam: Ready, Fit to Lead. 2008. 96p. pap. 10.49 *(978-1-4389-4125-7(0))* AuthorHouse.
Mouser, Bruce L. For Labor, Race, & Liberty: George Edwin Taylor, His Historic Run for the White House, & the Making of Independent Black Politics. 2011. (ENG., Illus.). 278p. pap. 24.95 *(978-0-299-24914-4(X))* Univ. of Wisconsin Pr.
Musgrove, George Derek. Rumor, Repression, & Racial Politics: How the Harassment of Black Elected Officials Shaped Post-Civil Rights America. 2012. (Since 1970: Histories of Contemporary America Ser.). (ENG., Illus.). 312p. 69.95 ***(978-0-8203-3459-2(6))***; pap. 24.95 ***(978-0-8203-4121-7(5))*** Univ. of Georgia Pr.
Olsson, Göran, ed. The Black Power Mixtape 1967-1975. 2012. (ENG., Illus.). 192p. 27.95 ***(978-1-60846-173-8(4))*** Haymarket Bks.
Parvis, Sarah. Barack Obama. 2009. (ENG.). 80p. 5.99 *(978-0-7407-8557-3(5))* Andrews McMeel Publishing.
Patrick, Deval. A Reason to Believe: Lessons from an Improbable Life. 2011. (Illus.). 240p. 21.99 *(978-0-7679-3112-0(2))* Broadway Bks.
Persons, Georgia Anne. Beyond the Boundaries: A New Structure of Ambition in African American Politics. Persons, Georgia, ed. 2009. (ENG., Illus.). 284p. pap. 29.95 *(978-1-4128-1048-7(5))* Transaction Pubs.
Remnick, David. The Bridge: The Life & Rise of Barack Obama. (Vintage Ser.). (ENG., Illus.). 2011. 704p. pap. 16.00 *(978-0-375-70230-3(X)*, Vintage) 2010. 672p. 29.95 *(978-1-4000-4360-6(3)*, Knopf) Knopf Doubleday Publishing Group.
Teal, Christopher. Hero of Hispaniola: America's First Black Diplomat, Ebenezer D. Bassett, 1 vol. 2008. (Illus.). 232p. 39.95 *(978-0-313-35195-2(3)*, C35195, Praeger Pubs.) Greenwood Publishing Group, Inc.

AFRICAN AMERICAN PRESS

see also African American Journalists

Burns, Ben. Nitty Gritty: A White Editor in Black Journalism. 2007. (ENG.). 248p. per. 25.00 *(978-1-934110-02-7(7))* Univ. Pr. of Mississippi.
Carroll, Brian. When to Stop the Cheering? The Black Press, the Black Community, & the Integration of Professional Baseball. 2009. 276p. 39.95 *(978-0-415-80602-2(X))* 2006. (Illus.). 271p. 126.00 *(978-0-415-97938-2(2))* Routledge.
Detweiler, Frederick German. The Negro Press in the United States. 2009. 288p. 24.99 *(978-1-103-18253-4(6))*; pap. 18.99 *(978-1-103-18251-0(X))* BiblioBazaar.
—The Negro Press in the United States. 2009. 194p. pap. *(978-0-217-35866-8(7))*; 192p. pap. *(978-0-217-09460-3(0))* Books LLC.
—The Negro Press in the United States. 2009. 284p. 43.95 *(978-1-104-34545-7(5))*; pap. 28.95 *(978-1-104-31678-5(1))* Kessinger Publishing, LLC.
Duncan, Mae Najiyyah. A Survey of Cincinnati's Black Press & Its Editors 1844-2010. 2011. 138p. 29.99 ***(978-1-4568-8417-8(4))***; pap. 19.99 ***(978-1-4568-8416-1(6))*** Xlibris Corp.
Eldridge, Lawrence Allen. Chronicles of a Two-Front War: Civil Rights & Vietnam in the African American Press. 2nd ed. 2012. (ENG., Illus.). 304p. (C). (gr. 11). 45.00 *(978-0-8262-1939-8(X))* Univ. of Missouri Pr.
Ernest, John. A Nation Within a Nation: Organizing African-American Communities Before the Civil War. 2011. (ENG.). 232p. 35.00 *(978-1-56663-807-4(0))*; *(978-1-56663-917-0(4))* Dee, Ivan R. Pub.
Gantt, Lucius. Beast Too: Dead Man Writing. 2009. 292p. pap. 19.99 *(978-1-4389-4915-4(4))* AuthorHouse.
Hutton, Frankie. The Early Black Press in America, 1827 To 1860, 1 vol. 2007. (Contributions in Afro-American & African Studies). 208p. pap. 50.00 *(978-0-275-99940-7(8)*, B9940) Greenwood Publishing Group, Inc.
Kinshasa, Kwando M. Emigration vs. Assimilation: The Debate in the African American Press, 1827-1861. alt. ed. 2011. (ENG.). 248p. pap. 25.00 ***(978-0-7864-6730-3(4))*** McFarland & Co., Inc. Pubs.
Pinnick, Timothy N. Finding & Using African American Newspapers. 2008. (ENG., Illus.). 73p. per. 12.00 *(978-0-944619-85-8(1)*, AD2186SB); 74p. 25.00 *(978-0-944619-89-6(4)*, AD2186HB) Gregath Publishing Co.

AFRICAN AMERICAN SAILORS

see also United States—Navy—African Americans

Freeman, Gregory. Troubled Water: Race, Mutiny, & Bravery on the USS Kitty Hawk. (ENG., Illus.). 272p. 2010. pap. 16.00 *(978-0-230-10339-9(1))* 2009. 27.00 *(978-0-230-61361-4(6))* Palgrave Macmillan.
Knoblock, Glenn A. African American World War II Casualties & Decorations in the Navy, Coast Guard & Merchant Marine: A Comprehensive Record. 2009. (ENG., Illus.). 592p. pap. 65.00 *(978-0-7864-3473-2(2))* McFarland & Co., Inc. Pubs.
Noble, Dennis L. & Strobridge, Truman R. Captain Hell Roaring Mike Healy: From American Slave to Arctic Hero. 2009. (New Perspectives on Maritime History & Nautical Archaeology Ser.). (ENG., Illus.). 352p. 34.95 *(978-0-8130-3368-6(3))* Univ. Pr. of Florida.
Schneller, Robert John, Jr. Breaking the Color Barrier: The U. S. Naval Academy's First Black Midshipmen & the Struggle for Racial Equality. 2007. (ENG., Illus.). 344p. pap. 24.00 *(978-0-8147-4055-2(3))* New York Univ. Pr.
Sherwood, John Darrell. Black Sailor, White Navy: Racial Unrest in the Fleet During the Vietnam War Era. 2007. (ENG., Illus.). 360p. 47.00 *(978-0-8147-4036-1(7))* New York Univ. Pr.
Stillwell, Paul, ed. The Golden Thirteen: Recollections of the First Black Naval Officers. (Illus.). 336p. pap. 19.95 *(978-1-59114-840-1(5))* Naval Institute Pr.
Tomblin, Barbara Brooks. Bluejackets & Contrabands: African Americans & the Union Navy. 2009. (ENG., Illus.). 400p. 39.95 *(978-0-8131-2554-1(5))* Univ. Pr. of Kentucky.

AFRICAN AMERICAN SCIENTISTS

Barber, John T. The Black Digital Elite: African American Leaders of the Information Revolution, 1 vol. 2006. (Illus.). 216p. 39.95 *(978-0-275-98504-2(0)*, C8504, Praeger Pubs.) Greenwood Publishing Group, Inc.
Carew, Joy G. & Carew, Joy Gleason. Blacks, Reds, & Russians: Sojourners in Search of the Soviet Promise. 2008. (ENG.). 296p. (C). 49.95 *(978-0-8135-4306-2(1))* Rutgers Univ. Pr.
Carey, Charles W., Jr. African Americans in Science: An Encyclopedia of People & Progress, 2 vols. 2008. (Illus.). 608p. 195.00 *(978-1-85109-998-6(0)*, AFAMSC1C) ABC-CLIO, LLC.
Clark, Glenn. The Man Who Talks with the Flowers: The Intimate Life Story of Dr. George Washington Carver. 2010. 68p. pap. 10.95 *(978-1-57898-877-8(2))* Martino Publishing.
Dodson, Howard & Palmer, Colin, eds. Ideology, Identity, & Assumptions. 2007. (Schomburg Studies on the Black Experience). (ENG., Illus.). 205p. per. 19.95 *(978-0-87013-795-2(6))* Michigan State Univ. Pr.
Holmes, Keith C. Black Inventors, Crafting over 200 Years of Success. Holmes, Keith C. et al, eds. 2008. (ENG., Illus.). 179p. (YA). pap. 15.00 *(978-0-9799573-0-7(3))* Global Black Inventor Research Projects, Inc.
Jordan, Diann. Sisters in Science: Conversations with Black Women Scientists about Race, Gender, & Their Passion for Science. 2006. (Illus.). 232p. per. 19.95 *(978-1-55753-445-3(4))* Purdue Univ. Pr.
Kremer, Gary R. George Washington Carver: A Biography, 1 vol. 2011. (Greenwood Biographies Ser.). (Illus.). 202p. 35.00 *(978-0-313-34796-2(4)*, GR4796); E-Book *(978-0-313-34797-9(2)*, Greenwood Pr.) Greenwood Publishing Group, Inc.
Sanders, Robert B. Contributions of African American Scientists to the Fields of Science, Medicine, & Inventions. 2009. 79.00 *(978-1-60741-319-6(1))* Nova Science Pubs., Inc.
Washington, Warren. Odyssey in Climate Modeling, Global Warming, & Advising Five Presidents. 2007. 304p. per. 23.75 *(978-1-4303-1696-1(9))* Lulu Enterprises Inc.
Williams, James Henry. African American Inventors & Pioneers. 2011. 54p. pap. 15.99 ***(978-1-4568-4000-6(2))*** Xlibris Corp.
Young, Lee D. & Young, LeParis. L. D. Rocketry, Race, & a Colorful Journey. 2010. 372p. 24.95 *(978-0-533-16246-8(7))* Vantage Pr., Inc.

AFRICAN AMERICAN SEAMEN

see African American Sailors

AFRICAN AMERICAN SLAVERY

see Slavery—United States

AFRICAN AMERICAN SLAVES

see Slaves—United States

AFRICAN AMERICAN SOLDIERS

Here are entered works on African American military personnel in the United States Army. Works on the organization, administration, and history of African American units within the United States Army are entered under United States—Army—African American Troops.

see also United States—Army—African American Troops; United States—History—Revolution, 1775-1783—African Americans; United States—History—War of 1812—Participation, African American; United States—History—Civil War, 1861-1865—Participation, African American

Addeman, Joshua M. & Higginson, Thomas Wentworth. They Fought for Liberty: Two Accounts of Coloured Troops in the American Civil War. 2009. 240p. pap. *(978-1-84677-855-1(7))* Leonaur Ltd.
Ash, Stephen V. Firebrand of Liberty: The Story of Two Black Regiments That Changed the Course of the Civil War. 2008. (ENG., Illus.). 304p. 25.95 *(978-0-393-06586-2(3)*, 6586) Norton, W. W. & Co., Inc.
Becton, Julius W., Jr. Becton: Autobiography of a Soldier & Public Servant. 2008. (Illus.). 318p. 32.95 *(978-1-59114-021-4(8))* Naval Institute Pr.
Brown, Joseph E. Black Soldier of Mercy. Lockhart, Lona, ed. 2010. (Illus.). 134p. pap. 15.00 *(978-1-934936-42-9(1))* Righter Publishing Co., Inc.
Brown, William Wells. The Negro in the American Rebellion: His Heroism & His Fidelity. 2010. 394p. pap. 33.75 *(978-1-145-72653-6(4))* BiblioBazaar.
—The Negro in the American Rebellion: His Heroism & His Fidelity. 2010. 402p. pap. 27.96 *(978-1-163-29397-3(0))* 2010. 402p. 39.96 ***(978-1-163-56358-8(7))*** 2007. (ENG.). 400p. 49.95 *(978-0-548-26264-1(0))* 2007. (ENG.). 404p. per. 34.95 *(978-1-4326-6669-9(X))* Kessinger Publishing, LLC.

—The Negro in the American Rebellion: His heroism & his Fidelity. 2010. (ENG.). 402p. pap. 34.75 *(978-1-171-71825-3(X))* BiblioBazaar.

—The Negro in the American Rebellion; His Heroism & His Fidelity. 2006. 400p. per. 26.99 *(978-1-4255-4224-5(7))* MPublishing.

Brummell, George E. Shades of Darkness: A Black Soldier's Journey through Vietnam, Blindness, & Back. 2006. xvii, 347p. pap. 17.50 *(978-0-9788917-0-1(8))* Brummel, George.

Coddington, Ronald S. African American Faces of the Civil War: An Album. 2012. ***(978-1-4214-0625-1(X))***; E-Book ***(978-1-4214-0723-4(X))*** Johns Hopkins Univ. Pr.

Controvich, James T. African-Americans in Defense of the Nation: A Bibliography. 2011. (ENG.). 430p. 85.00 *(978-0-8108-7234-9(X))* Scarecrow Pr., Inc.

Copeland, Jeffrey Scott & Copeland, Jeffrey. Inman's War: A Soldier's Story of Life in a Colored Battalion in WWII. 2006. (ENG., Illus.). 384p. pap. 17.95 *(978-1-55778-860-3(X))* Paragon Hse. Pubs.

Costa, Dora & Kahn, Matthew. Heroes & Cowards: The Social Face of War. 2008. (ENG., Illus.). 336p. (C). 27.95 *(978-0-691-13704-9(8))* Princeton Univ. Pr.

Cusic, Don. The Trials of Henry Flipper, First Black Graduate of West Point. 2008. (ENG., Illus.). 218p. pap. 35.00 *(978-0-7864-3969-0(6))* McFarland & Co., Inc. Pubs.

Dobak, William A. Freedom by the Sword: the U. S. Colored Troops, 1862-1867: The U. S. Colored Troops, 1862-1867. Center of Military History (U.S. Army), ed. 2011. (ENG., Illus.). 572p. 58.00 ***(978-0-16-086696-8(0))***; pap. 58.00 ***(978-0-16-086695-1(2))*** United States Government Printing Office. (Dept. of the Army).

Dorsey, Christopher. A Call to Arms: The Realities of Military Service for African Americans During the Civil War. 2007. (Illus.). 160p. per. 17.95 *(978-0-939479-29-0(X)*, Backintyme) Boxes & Arrows, Inc.

Durham, Carroll. The Forgotten Soldier. 2010. 240p. 29.99 *(978-1-4535-2794-8(X))*; pap. 19.99 *(978-1-4535-2793-1(1))* Xlibris Corp.

Fehrenbach, Heide. Race after Hitler: Black Occupation Children in Postwar Germany & America. 2007. (ENG., Illus.). 288p. (C). per. 28.95 *(978-0-691-13379-9(4))* Princeton Univ. Pr.

Gero, Anthony F. Black Soldiers of New York State: A Proud Legacy. 2009. (Excelsior Editions Ser.). (Illus.). 128p. 45.00 *(978-1-4384-2615-0(1))*; pap. 16.95 *(978-1-4384-2616-7(X))* State Univ. of New York Pr.

Gilbert, Alan. Black Patriots & Loyalists: Fighting for Emancipation in the War for Independence. 2012. (ENG.). 392p. 30.00 ***(978-0-226-29307-3(6))*** Univ. of Chicago Pr.

Glasrud, Bruce A. & Searles, Michael N. Buffalo Soldiers in the West: A Black Soldiers Anthology. 2007. 40.00 *(978-1-58544-612-4(2))* Texas A&M Univ. Pr.

Glasrud, Bruce A. & Searles, Michael N., eds. Buffalo Soldiers in the West: A Black Soldiers Anthology. 2007. (ENG.). 328p. (C). pap. 19.95 *(978-1-58544-620-9(3))* Texas A&M Univ. Pr.

Green, Michael Cullen. Black Yanks in the Pacific: Race in the Making of American Military Empire after World War II. 2010. (United States in the World Ser.). (Illus.). 224p. 35.00 *(978-0-8014-4896-6(4))* Cornell Univ. Pr.

Hanna, Charles W. African American Recipients of the Medal of Honor: A Biographical Dictionary, Civil War through Vietnam War. alt. ed. 2010. (ENG., Illus.). 199p. pap. 38.00 *(978-0-7864-4911-8(X))* McFarland & Co., Inc. Pubs.

Hawkins, Walter L. Black American Military Leaders: A Biographical Dictionary. alt. ed. 2009. (ENG., Illus.). 559p. pap. 49.95 *(978-0-7864-4462-5(2))* McFarland & Co., Inc. Pubs.

Higginson, Thomas W. Army Life in a Black Regiment. Date not set. 320p. 24.95 *(978-0-8488-2587-4(X))* Amereon LTD.

—Army Life in a Black Regiment. 296p. reprint ed. 98.00 *(978-0-7222-8017-1(3))* Library Reprints, Inc.

Houston, Ivan J. & Cohn, Gordon. Black Warriors: the Buffalo Soldiers of World War II: Memories of the Only Negro Infantry Division to Fight in Europe during World War II. 2011. 244p. pap. 14.95 *(978-1-936236-40-4(0))* iUniverse, Inc.

Humphreys, Margaret. Intensely Human: The Health of the Black Soldier in the American Civil War. 2008. (ENG., Illus.). 224p. (gr. 17). 42.00 *(978-0-8018-8696-6(1))* Johns Hopkins Univ. Pr.

Jefferson, Robert F. Fighting for Hope: African American Troops of the 93rd Infantry Division in World War II & Postwar America. 2008. (War/Society/Culture Ser.). (ENG., Illus.). 352p. (gr. 17). 55.00 *(978-0-8018-8828-1(X))* Johns Hopkins Univ. Pr.

Johnson, Shoshana. I'M Still Standing: From Captive U. S. Soldier to Free Citizen - My Journey Home. 2010. (ENG., Illus.). 288p. 23.99 *(978-1-4165-6748-6(8)*, Touchstone) Touchstone.

—I'm Still Standing: From Captive U. S. Soldier to Free Citizen — My Journey Home. 2011. (ENG., Illus.). 288p. pap. 15.00 *(978-1-4165-6749-3(6)*, Touchstone) Touchstone.

Kelly, Samuel E. Dr. Sam, Soldier, Educator, Advocate, Friend: An Autobiography. 2010. (ENG., Illus.). 240p. 30.00 *(978-0-295-99061-3(9))* Univ. of Washington Pr.

Koerner, Brendan I. Now the Hell Will Start: One Soldier's Flight from the Greatest Manhunt of World War II. 2009. (ENG.). 400p. (gr. 12-18). 16.00 *(978-0-14-311533-5(2)*, Penguin (Non-Classics)) Penguin Group (USA) Inc.

Laws, Anthony. Honoring Our Fathers: Celebrating a Man's Role in His Family & Community. 2009. 200p. pap. 16.95 *(978-1-934812-47-1(1))* Brown Bks. Publishing Group.

Leiker, James N. Racial Borders: Black Soldiers along the Rio Grande. 2010. (ENG.). 264p. pap. 19.95 *(978-1-60344-159-9(X))* Texas A&M Univ. Pr.

Lentz-Smith, Adriane. Freedom Struggles: African Americans & World War I. (Illus.). 336p. 2011. (ENG.). pap. 22.50 *(978-0-674-06205-4(1))* 2009. 37.00 *(978-0-674-03592-8(5))* Harvard Univ. Pr.

Livermore, George. A Historical Research Respecting the Opinions of the Founders of the Republic on Negroes As Slaves, As Citizens & As Soldiers. 2007. (ENG.). 202p. 39.95 *(978-0-548-05293-8(X))* Kessinger Publishing, LLC.

Longacre, Edward G. A Regiment of Slaves: The 4th United States Colored Infantry, 1863-1866. 2011. (ENG., Illus.). 242p. pap. 19.95 *(978-0-8032-3794-0(4)*, Bison Bks.) Univ. of Nebraska Pr.

Malcolm, Joyce Lee. Peter's War: A New England Slave Boy & the American Revolution. (ENG., Illus.). 272p. 2010. pap. 20.00 *(978-0-300-16806-8(3))* 2009. 28.00 *(978-0-300-11930-5(5))* Yale Univ. Pr.

McQueen, Clyde. The Black Army Officer. 2008. 268p. pap. 22.99 *(978-1-4343-1249-5(6))* AuthorHouse.

Mjagkij, Nina. Loyalty in Time of Trial: The African American Experience During World War I. 2011. (African American History Ser.). (ENG., Illus.). 224p. 40.00 *(978-0-7425-7043-6(6))* Rowman & Littlefield Publishers, Inc.

Morris, Robert V. Black Faces of War: A Legacy of Honor from the American Revolution to Today. 2011. (ENG., Illus.). 160p. 30.00 *(978-0-7603-3917-6(1)*, 0760339171, Zenith Pr.) MBI Publishing Co. LLC.

Moss, Juanita Patience. Forgotten Black Soldiers Who Served in White Regiments During the Civil War. 2008. (Illus.). 188p. pap. 21.00 *(978-0-7884-4647-4(9))* Heritage Bks.

Olafsen, Jake. Wearing the Green Beret: A Canadian with the Royal Marine Commandos. 2011. (ENG., Illus.). 320p. 29.99 *(978-0-7710-6852-2(2)*, McClelland & Stewart) McClelland & Stewart CAN. Dist: Random Hse., Inc.

Owens, Emiel W. Blood on German Snow: An African American Artilleryman in World War II & Beyond. 2006. (Texas A & M University Military History Ser.: 105). (ENG., Illus.). 160p. 24.95 *(978-1-58544-537-0(1))* Texas A&M Univ. Pr.

Phillips, Kimberley L. War! What Is It Good For? Black Freedom Struggles & the U. S. Military from World War II to Iraq. 2012. (John Hope Franklin Series in African American History & Culture Ser.). (ENG., Illus.). 352p. 34.95 *(978-0-8078-3502-9(1))* Univ. of North Carolina Pr.

Reef, Catherine. African Americans in the Military. 2nd rev. ed. 2010. (A to Z of African Americans Ser.). (Illus.). 304p. (C). (gr. 9-18). 49.50 *(978-0-8160-7839-4(4))* Facts On File, Inc.

Reid, Richard M. Freedom for Themselves: North Carolina's Black Soldiers in the Civil War Era. 2008. (ENG., Illus.). 440p. 44.00 *(978-0-8078-3174-8(3))* Univ. of North Carolina Pr.

Reis, Ronald A. African Americans & the Civil War. 2009. (Civil War: A Nation Divided Ser.). (Illus.). 136p. (gr. 6-12). 35.00 *(978-1-60413-038-6(5)*, Chelsea Hse.) Facts On File, Inc.

Samito, Christian G. Becoming American under Fire: Irish Americans, African Americans, & the Politics of Citizenship during the Civil War Era. 2011. (Illus.). 320p. pap. 24.95 ***(978-0-8014-7755-3(7))*** Cornell Univ. Pr.

Schneller, Robert John, Jr. Blue & Gold & Black: Racial Integration of the U. S. Naval Academy. 2007. (Texas AandM University Military History Ser.: Vol. 115). (ENG., Illus.). 456p. 45.00 *(978-1-60344-000-4(3))* Texas A&M Univ. Pr.

Schubert, Frank. Black Valor: Buffalo Soldiers & the Medal of Honor, 1870 - 1898. 2009. (ENG.). 244p. pap. 19.95 *(978-1-4422-0193-4(2))* Rowman & Littlefield Publishers, Inc.

Segars, J. H. & Barrow, Charles K., eds. Black Southereners in Confederate Armies. (Illus.). 230p. (C). pap. 16.00 *(978-0-9662454-1-7(5))* Southern Lion Bks.

Shellum, Brian. Black Officer in a Buffalo Soldier Regiment: The Military Career of Charles Young. 2010. (ENG., Illus.). 412p. pap. 19.95 *(978-0-8032-1385-2(9)*, Bison Bks.) Univ. of Nebraska Pr.

Small, Clara & Briddell, David. Men of Color, to Arms! Manumitted Slaves & Freed Blacks from the Lower Eastern Shore of Maryland Who Served in the Civil War. 2010. pap. 25.00 *(978-0-9703802-6-5(7))* Maryland History Pr.

Stevens, Michael E., ed. As If It Were Glory: Robert Beecham's Civil War from the Iron Brigade to the Black Regiments. 2007. (ENG., Illus.). 264p. per. 18.95 *(978-0-7425-5944-8(0))* Rowman & Littlefield Publishers, Inc.

Steward, T. G. Colored Regulars in the United States A. 2006. pap. *(978-1-4068-3052-1(6))* Echo Library.

Swartley, Ron. Buffalo Soldiers in the Southwest: Trials, Tribulations — & Triumphs. 2006. (Illus.). 52p. pap. 7.95 *(978-1-888571-13-4(6))* Frontier Image Pr.

Taylor, Jon E. Freedom to Serve: Equality of Treatment & Opportunity in the Armed Services. 2012. (Critical Moments in American History Ser.). (ENG., Illus.). 224p. 140.00 *(978-0-415-89449-4(2))*; pap. 27.95 *(978-0-415-89446-7(4))* Routledge.

Tucker, Phillip Thomas. Cathy Williams: From Slave to Buffalo Soldier. 2008. (ENG., Illus.). 258p. pap. 19.95 *(978-0-8117-3569-8(9))* Stackpole Bks.

Williams, Chad Louis. Torchbearers of Democracy: African American Soldiers in the World War I Era. 2010. (John Hope Franklin Series in African American History & Culture Ser.). (ENG., Illus.). 464p. 34.95 *(978-0-8078-3394-0(0))* Univ. of North Carolina Pr.

Wilson, Joseph T. The Black Phalanx: A History of the Negro Soldiers of the United States in the Wars of 1775-1812. 528p. reprint ed. 98.00 *(978-0-7222-9784-1(X))* Library Reprints, Inc.

Wilson, Keith P., ed. Honor in Command: Lt. Freeman S. Bowley's Civil War Service in the 30th United States Colored Infantry. 2006. (New Perspectives on the History of the South Ser.). (ENG., Illus.). 320p. 39.95 *(978-0-8130-2998-6(8))* Univ. Pr. of Florida.

Wynn, Neil. The African American Experience During World War II. 2011. (African American History Ser.). (ENG.). 200p. pap. 22.95 ***(978-1-4422-1031-8(1))*** Rowman & Littlefield Publishers, Inc.

Wynn, Neil A. The African American Experience During World War II. 2010. (African American History Ser.). (ENG.). 200p. 49.95 *(978-1-4422-0016-6(2))* Rowman & Littlefield Publishers, Inc.

AFRICAN AMERICAN SONGS

see African Americans—Music

AFRICAN AMERICAN SPIRITUALS

see Spirituals (Songs)

AFRICAN AMERICAN STUDENTS

Akassi, Monique Leslie. Neo Hybrid Pedagogy in Post Colonialism Composition. 2011. 160p. pap. ***(978-3-8443-3122-6(0))*** Lambert Academic Publishing.

Bartee, RoSusan D. School Matters: Why African American Students Need Multiple Forms of Capital. (Counterpoints: Studies in the Postmodern Theory of Education Ser.). 192p. (C). 89.95 *(978-1-4331-0039-0(8))* Lang, Peter Publishing, Inc.

Beals, Melba Patitllo. Warriors Don't Cry: A Searing Memoir of the Battle to Integrate Little Rock's Central High. 2007. (ENG., Illus.). 240p. (YA). (gr. 7-12). mass mkt. 6.99 *(978-1-4169-4882-7(1)*, Simon Pulse) Simon Pulse.

—Warriors Don't Cry: A Searing Memoir of the Battle to Integrate Little Rock's Central High. abr. ed. 2007. (ENG., Illus.). 226p. 17.20 *(978-1-4178-1397-1(0))* Turtleback Bks.

Bonner, Wilma F., et al. The Sumner Story: Capturing Our History Preserving Our Legacy. 2011. (ENG.). 214p. pap. 19.95 ***(978-1-60037-780-8(7))*** Morgan James Publishing.

Boykin, A. Wade & Noguera, Pedro. Creating the Opportunity to Learn: Moving from Research to Practice to Close the Achievement Gap. 2011. 231p. pap. 27.95 ***(978-1-4166-1306-0(4))*** Assn. for Supervision & Curriculum Development.

Bradley, Stefan M. Harlem vs. Columbia University: Black Student Power in the Late 1960s. 2009. (ENG., Illus.). 272p. 40.00 *(978-0-252-03452-7(X))* Univ. of Illinois Pr.

Brown, M. Christopher & Bartee, RoSusan D. School Matters: Why African American Students Need Multiple Forms of Capital. 2007. (Counterpoints: Studies in the Postmodern Theory of Education Ser.). (Illus.). 192p. (C). pap. 32.95 *(978-0-8204-8688-8(4))* Lang, Peter Publishing, Inc.

Buck, Stuart. Acting White: The Ironic Legacy of Desegregation. 2011. (ENG., Illus.). 272p. pap. 18.00 *(978-0-300-17120-4(X))* Yale Univ. Pr.

Byfield, Cheron. Black Boys Can Make It: How They Overcome the Obstacles to University in the UK & USA. 2008. (Illus.). 168p. (C). pap. 32.95 *(978-1-85856-431-9(X))* Trentham Bks. Ltd. GBR. Dist: Stylus Publishing, LLC.

Carter, Prudence L. Keepin' It Real: School Success Beyond Black & White. 2007. (Transgressing Boundaries: Studies in Black Politics & Black Communities Ser.). (ENG., Illus.). 240p. per. 19.95 *(978-0-19-532523-2(0))* Oxford Univ. Pr., Inc.

Chambers, Crystal Renée & Sharpe, Rhonda V., eds. Black Female Undergraduates on Campus: Successes & Challenges, Vol. 12. 2012. (Diversity in Higher Education Ser.). (Illus.). 240p. 114.95 ***(978-1-78052-502-0(8))*** Emerald Group Publishing Ltd. GBR. Dist: Turpin Distribution Services Ltd.

Coleman, Sheila. Social Justice. 2011. 224p. pap. ***(978-3-8443-0898-3(9))*** Lambert Academic Publishing.

Dahlk, Bill. Against the Wind: African Americans & the Schools in Milwaukee, 1963-2002. 2010. pap. *(978-0-87462-078-8(3))* Marquette Univ. Pr.

Dancy, T. Elon. The Brother Code: Manhood & Masculinity among African American Men in College. 2012. ***(978-1-61735-761-9(8))***; pap. ***(978-1-61735-760-2(X))*** Information Age Publishing, Inc.

Davis, Joy Lawson. Bright, Talented, & Black: A Guide for Families of African American Gifted Learners. 2010. pap. 18.95 *(978-1-935067-02-3(8))* Great Potential Pr., Inc.

Diversity & Social Justice in College Sports: Sport Management & the College Athlete. 2007. 448p. 69.00 *(978-1-885693-77-8(X))* Fitness Information Technology, Inc.

Eaves, John H. The Morehouse Mystique: Lessons to Develop Black Men. 2009. (ENG.). 250p. pap. 16.95 *(978-1-934155-14-1(4))* African American Images.

Ellington, Roni M. & Frederick, Rona M. Capitalizing on Culture: Successful Patterns of Parental Participation for African American Students. 2010. (Education in a Competitive & Globalizing World Ser.). xii, 42p. pap. 43.00 *(978-1-61728-763-3(6)*, Nova Novinka) Nova Science Pubs., Inc.

Fiore & Hill. Creating Personal Success on the HBCU Campus. 2011. (ENG.). 96p. (C). pap. 20.95 ***(978-1-111-83771-6(6))*** Wadsworth.

Fitzgerald, Terence D. White Prescriptions? The Dangerous Social Potential for Ritalin & Other Psychotropic Drugs to Harm Black Males. 2010. 210p. pap. 31.95 *(978-1-59451-690-0(1))* Paradigm Pubs.

Ford, Donna & Granthan, Tarek. Gifted & Advanced Black Students in School: An Anthology of Critical Works. 2011. (ENG.). 300p. pap. 45.00 *(978-1-59363-700-2(4))* Prufrock Pr.

Ford, Donna Y. Reversing Underachievement among Gifted Black Students, 2nd Ed. 2nd ed. 2010. (ENG.). 200p. pap. 39.95 *(978-1-59363-487-2(0))* Prufrock Pr.

Gordy, Sondra Hercher. Finding the Lost Year: What Happened When Little Rock Closed Its Public Schools? 2009. (Illus.). 248p. 29.95 *(978-1-55728-900-1(X))* Univ. of Arkansas Pr.

Greene, Cheryll Y. & Smiley Books Staff, eds. America I Am Legends: Rare Moments & Inspiring Words. 2009. (ENG.). 192p. 34.95 *(978-1-4019-2410-2(7))*; 150p. pap. 24.95 *(978-1-4019-2405-8(0))* Hay Hse., Inc.

Hawkins, Billy. The New Plantation: Black Athletes, College Sports, & Predominantly White NCAA Institutions. 2010. (ENG.). 256p. 95.00 *(978-0-230-61517-5(1))* Palgrave Macmillan.

Henderson, George. Race & the University: A Memoir. 2010. (ENG., Illus.). 272p. (C). 24.95 *(978-0-8061-4129-9(8))* Univ. of Oklahoma Pr.

Hill, Teresa. Every Closed Eye Ain't Sleep: African American Perspectives on the Achievement Gap. 2011. (ENG., Illus.). 126p. 40.00 *(978-1-61048-104-5(6))*; pap. 19.95 *(978-1-61048-105-2(4))* Rowman & Littlefield Education.

Hill, Teresa D. Every Closed Eye Ain't Sleep: African American Perspectives on the Achievement Gap. 2011. E-Book ***(978-1-61048-106-9(2))*** Rowman & Littlefield Publishers, Inc.

Hughey, Matthew W. & Parks, Gregory S., eds. Black Greek-Letter Organizations 2.0: New Directions in the Study of African American Fraternities & Sororities. 2011. (ENG.). 320p. 50.00 *(978-1-60473-921-3(5))* Univ. Pr. of Mississippi.

Hunter, Janis A. Factors Influencing African-American Students Enrollment. 2008. 548p. pap. *(978-3-8364-8193-9(6))* VDM Verlag Dr. Mueller e.K.

Jones, Christopher Michael. What to Expect When You're Accepted: An African American Christian's Guide to College. 2007. 114p. per. 10.00 *(978-0-8170-1517-6(5))* Judson Pr.

Jones, Johnny D. & Hornbeak, Jerrick L. How to Recruit African-American Students at Traditional White Colleges & Universities. 2010. (ENG.). 84p. pap. 13.95 *(978-1-58909-707-0(6))* Bookstand Publishing.

Kirk, John A., ed. An Epitaph for Little Rock: A Fiftieth Anniversary Retrospective on the Central High Crisis. 2008. 190p. pap. 19.95 *(978-1-55728-874-5(7))* Univ. of Arkansas Pr.

Kunjufu, Jawanza. There Is Nothing Wrong with Black Students. 2012. (ENG., Illus.). 128p. pap. 15.95 ***(978-1-934155-60-8(8))*** African American Images.

Lanier, Carlotta Walls & Page, Lisa Frazier. A Mighty Long Way: My Journey to Justice at Little Rock Central High School. 2010. (ENG., Illus.). 336p. pap. 16.00 *(978-0-345-51101-0(8)*, One World/Ballantine) Random House Publishing Group.

LaVeist, Thomas & LaVeist, William. Tom Joyner Presents How to Prepare for College. 2009. (ENG.). 144p. pap. 15.00 *(978-0-615-27097-5(2))* Amber Bks.

Lavergne, Gary M. Before Brown: Heman Marion Sweatt, Thurgood Marshall, & the Long Road to Justice. 2011. (ENG., Illus.). 384p. pap. 25.00 ***(978-0-292-74295-6(9))*** Univ. of Texas Pr.

Lee Jr, John Michael. American Higher Education Without Public Hbcus. 2011. 224p. pap. ***(978-3-8454-0546-9(5))*** Lambert Academic Publishing.

Lewis, Catherine & Richard. Race, Politics & Memory. 2007. (Illus.). 270p. (C). pap. 22.95 *(978-1-55728-857-8(7))* Univ. of Arkansas Pr.

Lewis, Catherine M. & Lewis, J. Richard, eds. Race, Politics, & Memory: A Documentary History of the Little Rock School Crisis. 2007. (Illus.). 242p. 65.00 *(978-1-55728-856-1(9))* Univ. of Arkansas Pr.

Lifted, Get. For Impoverished Students of Color Who Considered Dropping Out of College When the Refund Check Wasn't Enough. 2011. 78p. pap. 19.95 ***(978-1-4560-7467-8(9))*** PublishAmerica, Inc.

Long, Mark & Demonakos, Jim. The Silence of Our Friends. 2012. (ENG., Illus.). 208p. pap. 16.99 *(978-1-59643-618-3(2)*, First Second Bks.) Roaring Brook Pr.

Martin, Danny. Mathematics Teaching, Learning, & Liberation in the Lives of Black Children. Martin, Danny, ed. 2009. (Studies in Mathematical Thinking & Learning Ser.). (ENG., Illus.). 376p. 160.00 *(978-0-8058-6463-2(6))* Routledge.

Melius, Janella. Student Engagement as a Factor in Academic Achievement: The Case Study of Undergraduates at Norfolk State University, Virginia. 2010. (Illus.). v, 189p. *(978-0-7734-1347-4(2))* Mellen, Edwin Pr., The.

Moore, Wendy Leo. Reproducing Racism: White Space, Elite Law Schools, & Racial Inequality. 2007. (ENG.). 216p. 80.00 *(978-0-7425-6005-5(8))*; per. 29.95 *(978-0-7425-6006-2(6))* Rowman & Littlefield Publishers, Inc.

Muhammad, Shahid. How to Teach Math to Black Students: Student Workbook. 2009. (ENG.). 48p. (J). pap. 7.95 *(978-1-934155-17-2(9))* African American Images.

Mullins, Victor. African American Students in College. 2009. 144p. pap. *(978-3-639-17694-0(4))* VDM Verlag Dr. Mueller e.K.

Nasir, Na'ilah Suad. Racialized Identities: Race & Achievement among African American Youth. 2011. (ENG.). 216p. 70.00 *(978-0-8047-6018-8(7))*; pap. 22.95 *(978-0-8047-6019-5(5))* Stanford Univ. Pr.

Ogden, Dunbar H. My Father Said Yes: A White Pastor in Little Rock School Integration, 1 vol. 2008. (0915608162 Ser.). (ENG., Illus.). 200p. 24.95 *(978-0-8265-1592-6(4))* Vanderbilt Univ. Pr.

Palmer, Robert T. Black Men in College: Implications for Diversity, Recruitment, Support, & Retention. 2011. (ENG., Illus.). 224p. 140.00 *(978-0-415-89383-1(6))*; pap. 42.95 ***(978-0-415-89384-8(4))*** Routledge.

Petty, L. Jalik. Black Campus Ministry. 2nd ed. pap. 4.95 *(978-0-942428-01-8(3))* Universal Ministries, Inc., Publishing Hse.

Pitre, Abdul. Educating African American Students: Foundations, Curriculum, & Experiences. 2009. (Critical Black Pedagogy in Education Ser.). (ENG., Illus.). 176p. pap. 27.95 *(978-1-60709-233-9(6))* Rowman & Littlefield Education.

Pitre, Esrom, et al. Educating African American Students: Foundations, Curriculum, & Experiences. 2009. (Critical Black Pedagogy in Education Ser.). (ENG., Illus.). 176p. 55.00 *(978-1-60709-232-2(8))* Rowman & Littlefield Education.

Roberts, Terrence. Lessons from Little Rock. 2009. (ENG.). 200p. 24.95 *(978-1-935106-11-1(2))* Butler Ctr. for Arkansas Studies.

Robinson II, Charles F. & Williams, Lonnie R. Remembrances in Black: Personal Perspectives of the African American Experience at the University of Arkansas. 2010. (ENG.). 360p. (C). 45.00 *(978-1-55728-953-7(0))* Univ. of Arkansas Pr.

Rogers, Ibram H. The Black Campus Movement: Black Students & the Racial Reconstitution of Higher Education, 1965-1972. 2012. (Contemporary Black History Ser.). (ENG., Illus.). 256p. 90.00 ***(978-0-230-11780-8(5))***; pap. 27.00 ***(978-0-230-11781-5(3))*** Palgrave Macmillan.

Sadeh, Shamu. From 'Sit & Listen' to 'Shake it out yourself': HELPING URBAN MIDDLE SCHOOL STUDENTS TO BRIDGEPERSONAL KNOWLEDGE TO SCIENTIFIC KNOWLEDGE THROUGH ACOLLABORATIVE ENVIRONMENTAL JUSTICE CURRICULUM. 2008. 232p. pap. *(978-3-639-05008-0(8))* VDM Verlag Dr. Mueller e.K.

Schlachter, Gail Ann & Weber, R. David. Financial Aid for African Americans. 2009. (Financial Aid for African Americans Ser.). (ENG.). 500p. 42.50 *(978-1-58841-177-8(X))* Reference Service Pr.

Seltzer, Richard & Johnson. Experiencing Racism: Exploring Discrimination through the Eyes of College Students. 2009. (ENG.). 390p. pap. 34.99 *(978-0-7391-3432-0(9))* Lexington Bks.

Seltzer, Richard & Johnson, Nicole E. Experiencing Racism: Exploring Discrimination through the Eyes of College Students. 2009. (ENG.). 326p. 83.99 *(978-0-7391-3431-3(0))* Lexington Bks.

Smiley Group Staff, compiled by. America I AM Journal. 2010. (ENG.). 240p. pap. 11.95 *(978-1-4019-2407-2(7))* Hay Hse., Inc.

Smith, Willie J. The Euclid High School Scholars Program: Young Men Changing the Academic Culture in Their School & Community. 2010. 92p. pap. 11.99 *(978-1-4269-3907-5(8))* Trafford Publishing.

Spears-Bunton, L., et al. Toward a Literacy of Promise: Joining the African American Struggle. 2008. (Language, Culture, & Teaching Ser.). 224p. 150.00 *(978-0-415-99518-4(3))* Routledge.

Stokes, John A. & Viola, Herman J. Students on Strike: Jim Crow, Civil Rights, Brown, & Me. 2007. (ENG., Illus.). 128p. (J). (gr. 5-9). 23.90 *(978-1-4263-0154-4(5),* National Geographic Children's Bks.) National Geographic Society.

Suranyi, Szilvia. Oral Folk Traditions in Toni Morrison's Song of Solomon - African American History, Geneology & Cultural Identity. 2008. 52p. pap. *(978-3-639-01190-6(2))* VDM Verlag Dr. Mueller e.K.

Tharps, Lori & Tharps, Lori L. Kinky Gazpacho: Life, Love & Spain. 2009. (ENG.). 240p. pap. 13.00 *(978-0-7432-9648-9(6),* Washington Square Pr.) Washington Square Pr.

Thayer, Scott. Where You from? - the Impact of a Trio Upward Bound Program on the Academic Achievement of African-American Male Students. 2008. 184p. pap. *(978-3-639-02625-2(X))* VDM Verlag Dr. Mueller e.K.

Thompson, Gail L. Through Ebony Eyes: What Teachers Need to Know but Are Afraid to Ask about African American Students. 2007. (ENG.). 352p. per. 19.95 *(978-0-7879-8769-5(7),* Jossey-Bass) Wiley, John & Sons, Inc.

—Up Where We Belong: Helping African American & Latino Students Rise in School & in Life. 2007. (ENG.). 352p. 24.95 *(978-0-7879-9597-3(5),* Jossey-Bass) Wiley, John & Sons, Inc.

Thompson, Gail L., ed. The Power of One: How You Can Help or Harm African American Students. 2009. 200p. pap. 31.95 *(978-1-4129-7676-3(6),* B76763P) Corwin Pr.

Titus, Jill. Brown's Battleground: Students, Segregationists, & the Struggle for Justice in Prince Edward County, Virginia. 2011. (ENG., Illus.). 320p. 34.95 *(978-0-8078-3507-4(2))* Univ. of North Carolina Pr.

Tyson, Karolyn, ed. Integration Interrupted: Tracking, Black Students, & Acting White after Brown. 2011. (ENG., Illus.). 256p. pap. 24.95 *(978-0-19-973645-4(6))* Oxford Univ. Pr., Inc.

Vaught, Sabina Elena. Racism, Public Schooling, & the Entrenchment of White Supremacy: A Critical Race Ethnography. 2011. 256p. 75.00 *(978-1-4384-3467-4(7))*; (ENG.). pap. 29.95 *(978-1-4384-3468-1(5))* State Univ. of New York Pr. (Suny Pr.).

Whaley, Deborah Elizabeth. Disciplining Women: Alpha Kappa Alpha, Black Counterpublics, & the Cultural Politics of Black Sororities. 2010. (Illus.). 176p. 75.00 *(978-1-4384-3273-1(9))*; pap. 24.95 *(978-1-4384-3272-4(0))* State Univ. of New York Pr.

White, Barbara A. A Line in the Sand: The Battle to Integrate Nantucket Public Schools 1824-1847. 2009. (Illus.). 128p. pap. 20.00 *(978-0-932027-43-6(1))* Spinner Pubns., Inc.

Williams, Angela. Christian Spirituality Manifested in African American Students: Christian Spirituality Impacts the Academic Attitudes & Behaviors of African American Students. 2008. 108p. pap. *(978-3-639-09078-9(0))* VDM Verlag Dr. Mueller e.K.

Williams, Twyla J. Save Our Children: The Struggle Between Black Parents & Schools. 2009. (ENG.). 200p. pap. 15.95 *(978-1-934155-16-5(0))* African American Images.

Young, Ethel E. & Wilson, Jerome. African American Children & Missionary Nuns & Priests in Mississippi: Achievement against Jim Crow Odds. 2010. 132p. 22.95 *(978-1-4520-2278-9(X))*; (ENG.). pap. 12.99 *(978-1-4520-2279-6(8))* AuthorHouse.

AFRICAN AMERICAN STUDIES

see African Americans—Study and Teaching

AFRICAN AMERICAN TEACHERS

Baker, Houston A. I Don't Hate the South: Reflections on Faulkner, Family, & the South. 2007. (ENG.). 224p. 125.00 *(978-0-19-508429-0(2))* Oxford Univ. Pr., Inc.

Biddle, Daniel R. & Dubin, Murray. Tasting Freedom: Octavius Catto & the Battle for Equality in Civil War America. 2010. (ENG., Illus.). 656p. 35.00 *(978-1-59213-465-6(3))* Temple Univ. Pr.

Butchart, Ronald. Schooling the Freed People: Teaching, Learning, & the Struggle for Black Freedom, 1861-1876. 2010. (ENG., Illus.). 336p. 39.95 *(978-0-8078-3420-6(3))* Univ. of North Carolina Pr.

Charron, Katherine. Freedom's Teacher: The Life of Septima Clark. 2012. (ENG., Illus.). 480p. pap. 26.95 ***(978-0-8078-7222-2(9))*** Univ. of North Carolina Pr.

Charron, Katherine Mellen. Freedom's Teacher: The Life of Septima Clark. 2009. (ENG., Illus.). 480p. 36.95 *(978-0-8078-3332-2(0))* Univ. of North Carolina Pr.

Christian, Mark. Integrated but Unequal: Black Faculty in Predominately White Space. 2011. ***(978-1-59221-867-7(9))***; pap. ***(978-1-59221-868-4(7))*** Africa World Pr.

Codling, Jim. Forgotten Foundations of Education. rev. ed. 2006. (ENG.). 100p. pap. 83.08 *(978-0-7575-3272-6(1))* Kendall Hunt Publishing Co.

Dillihunt, Monica L. & Tyler, Kenneth Maurice. Connecting the Legacies: African American Scholars in Education. 2007. *(978-1-4331-0030-7(4))*; pap. *(978-0-8204-8174-6(2))* Lang, Peter Publishing, Inc.

Fairclough, Adam. A Class of Their Own: Black Teachers in the Segregated South. 2007. (Illus.). 552p. 29.95 *(978-0-674-02307-9(2),* Belknap Pr.) Harvard Univ. Pr.

Gilchrist, Eletra S. Experiences of Single African-American Women Professors. 2011. (ENG., Illus.). 250p. 70.00 ***(978-0-7391-7087-8(2))*** Lexington Bks.

Jackson, Sandra & Johnson, Richard Greggory. The Black Professoriat: Negotiating a Habitable Space in the Academy. 2011. vi, 254p. *(978-1-4331-1028-3(8))*; pap. *(978-1-4331-1027-6(X))* Lang, Peter GmbH, Europaischer Verlag der Wissenschaften.

James, Rawn, Jr. Root & Branch: Charles Hamilton Houston, Thurgood Marshall, & the Struggle to End Segregation. 2010. (ENG., Illus.). 288p. 28.00 *(978-1-59691-606-7(0))* Bloomsbury Publishing.

Johnson, Beverly Black. Gumbo for the Soul: Here's Our Child-Where's the Village? 2008. 128p. pap. 11.95 *(978-1-4401-0126-7(4))* iUniverse, Inc.

Kelly, Hilton. Race, Remembering, & Jim Crow's Teachers. 2010. (Studies in African American History & Culture Ser.). (ENG., Illus.). 154p. 125.00 *(978-0-415-80478-3(7))* Routledge.

Mayers, Jr. Ph. D. Chalmers & Mayers, Jr. Segregation, Integration, & Resegregation in a Deep-Southern Town. 2010. 124p. pap. *(978-3-8383-9553-1(0))* Lambert Academic Publishing.

McCray, James. Ebb Tide: Nancy Astor's Greatest Challenge. 2008. 24.95 *(978-0-9814650-9-8(9))* G Publishing LLC.

Miller, A. T. & Kaplan, Matthew, eds. Scholarship of Multicultural Teaching & Learning: New Directions for Teaching & Learning. 2007. (J-B TL Single Issue Teaching & Learning Ser.: 98). (ENG.). 128p. pap. 29.00 *(978-0-470-22382-6(0),* Jossey-Bass) Wiley, John & Sons, Inc.

Myers, Lena Wright. A Broken Silence. 2007. pap. 45.99 *(978-1-59311-385-8(4))* Information Age Publishing, Inc.

Obiakor, Festus E., ed. Voices of Foreign-Born African American Teacher Educators in the United States. 2010. (Education in a Competitive & Globalizing World Ser.). 204p. 89.00 *(978-1-60876-322-1(6))* Nova Science Pubs., Inc.

Ramsey, Sonya Yvette. Reading, Writing, & Segregation: A Century of Black Women Teachers in Nashville. 2008. (Women in American History Ser.). (Illus.). 208p. 37.00 *(978-0-252-03229-5(2))* Univ. of Illinois Pr.

Reflections of a Native Son in the New South. 2009. (Illus.). 152p. pap. 14.95 *(978-0-9794420-7-0(9))* Red Letter Pr.

Richards, Phillip M. An Integrated Boyhood: Coming of Age in White Cleveland. 2011. (Voices of Diversity Ser.). 160p. 29.95 *(978-1-60635-100-0(1))* Kent State Univ. Pr.

Richardson, Myra K. The Innocent Molester. 2007. (Illus.). 296p. per. 23.50 *(978-1-4251-1084-0(3))* Trafford Publishing.

Shircliffe, Barbara J. Just Schools/Just Teachers: The Politics of Race in the History of Desegregation of Public School Educators in the South. 2012. ***(978-1-4331-1238-6(8))***; pap. ***(978-1-4331-1237-9(X))***; E-Book ***(978-1-4539-0238-7(4))*** Lang, Peter Publishing, Inc.

Tate, William F., ed. Beyond Stock Stories & Folktales: African Americans' Paths to Stem Fields. 2011. (Diversity in Higher Education Ser.). (Illus.). 350p. ***(978-1-78052-168-8(5))*** Emerald Group Publishing Ltd.

Tillman, Linda C. The Sage Handbook of African American Education. 2008. (Illus.). 584p. 108.00 *(978-1-4129-3743-6(4),* B37434C) SAGE Pubns., Inc.

Twyman, Charles R. Daddy, There's a Light in the Sky: An Illumination of Life Stories. 2009. 224p. 24.99 *(978-1-4389-8581-7(9))*; pap. 14.49 *(978-1-4389-8582-4(7))* AuthorHouse.

West, Cornel & Ritz, David. Brother West: Living & Loving Out Loud, A Memoir. 2009. (ENG.). 288p. 25.95 *(978-1-4019-2189-7(2),* Smiley Bks.) Hay Hse., Inc.

Wright, Quentin. Factors Affecting African American Faculty Job Satisfaction. 2010. 96p. pap. *(978-3-8383-6751-4(0))* Lambert Academic Publishing.

AFRICAN AMERICAN UNIVERSITIES AND COLLEGES

AEHE Staff et al. Unearthing Promise & Potential: Our Nation's Historically Black Colleges & Universities. 2010. (J-B ASHE Higher Education Report Series (AEHE) Ser.: 135). (ENG.). 152p. pap. 29.00 *(978-0-470-63510-0(X),* Jossey-Bass) Wiley, John & Sons, Inc.

America's Black Colleges & Universities: Models of Excellence & Challenges for the Future: Hearing Before the Committee on Education & Labor, U.S. House of Representatives, One Hundred Tenth Congress, Second Session, Hearing Held in Washington, DC, March 13, 2008. 2008. iii, 57p. *(978-0-16-081512-6(6),* 552-070-37868-5) United States Government Printing Office.

Augusta-Dupar, Cora M. The Mission & Vision Statements of Ten Historically Black Colleges & Universities - a Content Analysis Study. 2008. 184p. pap. *(978-3-639-04374-7(X))* VDM Verlag Dr. Mueller e.K.

Betsey, Charles L., ed. Historically Black Colleges & Universities. 2008. (ENG.). 165p. pap. 24.95 *(978-1-4128-0782-1(4))* Transaction Pubs.

Brooks, F. Erik & Starks, Glenn L. Historically Black Colleges & Universities: An Encyclopedia. 2011. E-Book ***(978-0-313-39416-4(4),*** Greenwood Pr.) Greenwood Publishing Group, Inc.

Brown, Tamara L., et al, eds. African American Fraternities & Sororities: The Legacy & the Vision. 2010. (ENG., Illus.). 512p. pap. 29.95 *(978-0-8131-2965-5(6))* Univ. Pr. of Kentucky.

Dowdy, Joanne Kilgour. PhD Stories: Conversations with My Sisters. 2008. (Understanding Education & Policy Ser.). 176p. *(978-1-57273-796-9(4))*; *(978-1-57273-797-6(2))* Hampton Pr., Inc.

Evans, Stephanie Y. African Americans & Community Engagement in Higher Education: Community Service, Service-Learning, & Community-Based Research. Taylor, Colette M., tr. 2009. 288p. 75.00 *(978-1-4384-2873-4(1))*; pap. 24.95 *(978-1-4384-2874-1(X))* State Univ. of New York Pr. (Suny Pr.).

Gasman, Marybeth. Historically Black Colleges & Universities: Triumphs, Troubles, & Taboos. Gasman, Marybeth & Tudico, Christopher L., eds. 2008. (ENG.). 272p. 100.00 *(978-0-230-60273-1(8))* Palgrave Macmillan.

Gasman, Marybeth & Bowman III, Nelson. A Guide to Fundraising at Historically Black Colleges & Universities: An All Campus Approach. 2011. (ENG., Illus.). 200p. 145.00 *(978-0-415-89272-8(4))*; pap. 35.95 *(978-0-415-89273-5(2))* Routledge.

Glasgow Communications. Why She Stayed: At an African-American School, Solomon Coles, During Desegregation. 2nd ed. 2009. (Illus.). 117p. pap. 19.95 *(978-0-615-29648-7(3))* Glasgow Communications.

Hair, Beverly Ann. Examining the Experiences of Nontraditional Undergraduate Women. 2011. 292p. pap. ***(978-3-8433-8159-8(3))*** Lambert Academic Publishing.

HBCUs Models for Success: Supporting Achievement & Retention of Black Males. 2006. (FAR & ENG.). per. *(978-1-889732-49-7(4))* Word For Word Publishing Co.

Higher Education ACT: Institutional Support for Colleges & Universities under Title III & Title V: Hearing Before the Subcommittee on Higher Education, Lifelong Learning, & Competitiveness, Committee on Education & Labor, U.S. House of Representatives, One Hundred Tenth Congress, First Session, Hearing Held in Austin, TX, June 4, 2007. 2008. iii, 54p. *(978-0-16-080156-3(7),* 552-070-36893-1) United States Government Printing Office.

Irvine, Russell W. The African American Quest for Institutions of Higher Education Before the Civil War: The Forgotten Histories of the Ashmun Institute, Liberia College, & Avery College. 2010. (Illus.). 752p. 159.95 *(978-0-7734-1309-2(X))* Mellen, Edwin Pr., The.

Jones, Lee, et al. Who Shall Tell Our Story? The Storied Past & Relevance of Historically Black Colleges & Universities. 2009. 288p. 59.95 *(978-1-57922-092-1(4))*; pap. 24.95 *(978-1-57922-093-8(2))* Stylus Publishing, LLC.

Lakeland Community Heritage Project Inc. Lakeland: African Americans in College Park. 2009. (Images of America Ser.). (ENG., Illus.). 128p. pap. 21.99 *(978-0-7385-6759-4(0))* Arcadia Publishing.

Lovett, Bobby L. America's Historically Black Colleges: A Narrative History, 1837-2009. 2011. (America's Historically Black Colleges & Universities Ser.). 350p. 35.00 *(978-0-88146-215-9(2))* Mercer Univ. Pr.

Lucisano, Giovani. America's Historically Black Colleges & Universities. 2010. (Education in a Competitive & Globalizing World Ser.). 199p. 79.00 *(978-1-60741-510-7(0))* Nova Science Pubs., Inc.

Mbajekwe, Carolyn O. Wilson, ed. The Future of Historically Black Colleges & Universities: Ten Presidents Speak Out. 2006. (ENG., Illus.). 220p. per. 39.95 *(978-0-7864-2565-5(2))* McFarland & Co., Inc. Pubs.

Mishra, Jyotsna. Becoming President: Patterns of Professional Mobility of African American University Presidents. 2006. (ENG., Illus.). 96p. per. 26.50 *(978-0-7618-3628-5(4))* Univ. Pr. of America, Inc.

Mitchell, Keva. Perceptions from the Principals Desks. 2008. 96p. pap. *(978-3-639-03704-3(9))* VDM Verlag Dr. Mueller e.K.

Nafeo. The State of America's Black Colleges 2008. 2008. 156p. per. 14.95 *(978-0-9802380-4-4(8))* Beckham Pubns. Group, Inc.

Palmer, Robert T. Black Men in College: Implications for Diversity, Recruitment, Support, & Retention. 2011. (ENG., Illus.). 224p. 140.00 *(978-0-415-89383-1(6))*; pap. 42.95 ***(978-0-415-89384-8(4))*** Routledge.

Parks, Arnold G. Lincoln University: 1920-1970. 2007. (Campus History Ser.). (ENG., Illus.). 128p. per. 19.99 *(978-0-7385-5132-6(5))* Arcadia Publishing.

Parks, Gregory S., ed. Black Greek-Letter Organizations in the Twenty-First Century: Our Fight Has Just Begun. 2008. (ENG., Illus.). 508p. 39.95 *(978-0-8131-2491-9(3))* Univ. Pr. of Kentucky.

Range, Willard. The Rise & Progress of Negro Colleges in Georgia, 1865-1949. 2009. (ENG.). 268p. pap. 24.95 *(978-0-8203-3452-3(9))* Univ. of Georgia Pr.

Ricard, Ronyelle Bertrand & Brown, M. Christopher, II. Ebony Towers in Higher Education: The Evolution, Mission, & Presidency of Historically Black Colleges & Universities. 2008. 176p. 75.00 *(978-1-57922-273-4(0))*; pap. 29.95 *(978-1-57922-274-1(9))* Stylus Publishing, LLC.

Rockefeller Jr, John D., et al. To Men of Vision & High Purpose. 2011. 20p. 35.95 ***(978-1-258-00886-4(6))*** Literary Licensing, LLC.

Ross, Marilyn J. & Greenwood. Success Factors of Young African American Women at a Historically Black College. 2009. 152p. pap. 45.99 *(978-1-60752-074-0(5))* Information Age Publishing, Inc.

Smith, Norman R. Footprints of Black Louisian. 2011. 158p. 29.99 ***(978-1-4568-2631-4(X))***; pap. 19.99 ***(978-1-4568-2630-7(1))*** Xlibris Corp.

Starks, Glenn L. & Brooks, F. Erik. Historically Black Colleges & Universities: An Encyclopedia, 1 vol. 2011. (Illus.). 338p. 89.00 *(978-0-313-39415-7(6),* A3425C) Greenwood Publishing Group, Inc.

Ware, David N. & Ware, David. Interviews with Sixteen Band Directors at Historically Black Colleges: Their Attitudes, Opinions, & Methods. 2008. 176p. 99.95 *(978-0-7734-5005-9(X))* Mellen, Edwin Pr., The.

Westhauser, Karl E., et al, eds. Creating Community: Life & Learning at Montgomery's Black University. 2008. (ENG., Illus.). 192p. pap. 19.95 *(978-0-8173-5499-2(9))* Univ. of Alabama Pr.

Williams, Juan, et al. I'll Find a Way or Make One: A Tribute to Historically Black Colleges & Universities. 2007. (Illus.). 480p. per. 20.95 *(978-0-06-009456-0(7),* Amistad) HarperCollins Pubs.

Williamson, Joy Ann. Radicalizing the Ebony Tower: Black Colleges & the Black Freedom Struggle in Mississippi. 2008. (Reflective History Ser.). (ENG.). 224p. (C). *(978-0-8077-4864-0(1))*; pap. 30.95 *(978-0-8077-4863-3(3))* Teachers College Pr., Teachers College, Columbia Univ.

Wright, Quentin. Factors Affecting African American Faculty Job Satisfaction. 2010. 96p. pap. *(978-3-8383-6751-4(0))* Lambert Academic Publishing.

AFRICAN AMERICAN WIT AND HUMOR

Corrothers, James D. The Black Cat Club: Negro Humor & Folklore. 2007. (ENG.). 268p. 42.95 *(978-0-548-10500-9(6))* Kessinger Publishing, LLC.

Hall, Lauren, ed. I Live Real Close to Where You Used to Live: Kids' Letters to Michelle Obama (and to Sasha, Malia & Bo) 2010. (ENG., Illus.). 144p. (gr. k). pap. 12.00 *(978-1-936365-20-3(0))* McSweeney's Publishing.

Jingqiong, Zhou. Raymond Carver's Short Fiction in the History of Black Humor. 2006. 158p. (C). 60.95 *(978-0-8204-8620-8(5))* Lang, Peter Publishing, Inc.

Littleton, Darryl. Black Comedians on Black Comedy: How African-Americans Taught Us to Laugh. 2008. (ENG., Illus.). 348p. per. 17.95 *(978-1-55783-730-1(9),* 1557837309, Applause Theatre & Cinema) Leonard, Hal Corp.

Newman, Richard. African American Quotations. 504p. pap. *(978-0-681-28941-3(4),* Checkmark Bks.) Facts On File, Inc.

Pickens, William. American Aesop: Negro & Other Humor. reprint ed. 34.00 *(978-0-404-00206-0(4))* AMS Pr., Inc.

Robert C. Benchley. Love Conquers All. 2009. (CAM., Illus.). 204p. pap. 14.45 *(978-1-4385-3629-3(1),* Book Jungle) Standard Pubns., Inc.

Tafoya, Eddie M. Icons of African American Comedy, 1 vol. 2011. (Greenwood Icons Ser.). (Illus.). 283p. 95.00 *(978-0-313-38084-6(8),* A2231C) Greenwood Publishing Group, Inc.

Thurston, Baratunde. How to Be Black. 2012. (ENG.). 256p. 24.99 *(978-0-06-200321-8(6))* HarperCollins Pubs.

AFRICAN AMERICAN WOMEN

Abrahamse, Andrina D. Through the Eyes of a South African Woman & Other Children. 2010. 218p. pap. 13.95 *(978-1-60911-219-6(9),* Eloquent Bks.) AEG Literary Publishing Services, Inc.

Abrums, Mary E. Moving the Rock: Poverty & Faith in a Black Storefront Church. (ENG.). 252p. 2011. pap. 19.95 ***(978-0-7591-1320-6(3))*** 2009. 35.00 *(978-0-7591-1319-0(X))* AltaMira Pr.

Adams, Catherine & Pleck, Elizabeth Hafkin. Love of Freedom: Black Women in Colonial & Revolutionary New England, 1 vol. 2010. (ENG., Illus.). 320p. pap. 21.95 *(978-0-19-538908-1(5))* Oxford Univ. Pr., Inc.

Alexander, Adele Logan. Parallel Worlds: The Remarkable Gibbs-Hunts & the Enduring (In)Significance of Melanin. (ENG., Illus.). 416p. 2012. pap. 19.95 ***(978-0-8139-3245-3(9))*** 2010. (gr. 17). 29.95 *(978-0-8139-2887-6(7))* Univ. Pr. of Virginia.

Alston, Judy A. & McClellan, Patricia A. Herstories: Leading with the Lessons of the Lives of Black Women Activists. 2011. (C). pap. 33.95 *(978-1-4331-1193-8(4))*; 129.95 *(978-1-4331-1192-1(6))* Lang, Peter Publishing, Inc.

Alva, Rodrigo & Aparecida Andrade Salgueiro, Maria. Zora Neale Hurston & Their Eyes Were Watching God. 2010. 100p. pap. *(978-3-8383-9208-0(6))* Lambert Academic Publishing.

Anderson, Walter. Ivy: An Unauthorized History of Alpha Kappa Alpha. 2006. 132p. pap. 18.95 *(978-0-9647596-4-0(0))* Black Adonis Collectibles.

Andrews, Gregg. Thyra J. Edwards: Black Activist in the Global Freedom Struggle. 2011. (ENG., Illus.). 256p. (C). (gr. 12). 40.00 *(978-0-8262-1912-1(8))* Univ. of Missouri Pr.

Angelou, Maya. Letter to My Daughter. (ENG.). 192p. 2009. pap. 15.00 *(978-0-8129-8003-5(4),* Random Hse. Trade Paperbacks) 2008. 25.00 *(978-1-4000-6612-4(3),* Random House) Random House Publishing Group.

—Yo Se Por Que Canta el Pajaro Enjaulado.Tr. of I Know Why the Caged Bird Sings. (SPA.). 292p. 20.95 *(978-84-264-4911-5(5))* Editorial Lumen ESP. Dist: Lectorum Pubns., Inc.

Anita P. Jackson & Marlene R. Dorsey. Achieving Against the Odds: African American Professional Women in Higher Education. 2009. 148p. pap. 11.99 *(978-1-4343-7706-7(7))* AuthorHouse.

Anthony, Kim Hamilton. Unfavorable Odds: The Story of Ucla's First African-American Female Gymnastics Champion. 2010. pap. 15.99 *(978-1-61566-495-5(5))* Tate Publishing & Enterprises, LLC.

Antoinette Shar'Ron Johnson. No More Hair Dram. 2010. 156p. pap. 10.00 *(978-1-4269-0717-3(6))* Trafford Publishing.

Arlether, Wilson/Ann. Rewriting the Script. 2007. 399p. pap. 15.95 *(978-0-9797627-0-3(7))* Jerant Publishing.

Arnett, Matt, et al. Mary Lee Bendolph, Gee's Bend Quilts, & Beyond. Metcalf, Eugene W., ed. 2006. (ENG., Illus.). 72p. 26.95 *(978-0-9719104-8-5(0))* Tinwood Bks.

Arnett, Paul, et al. Gee's Bend: The Architecture of the Quilt. 2006. (ENG., Illus.). 224p. pap. 40.00 *(978-0-9719104-7-8(2))* Tinwood Bks.

Ashbaugh, Carolyn. Lucy Parsons: An American Revolutionary. 2012. (ENG., Illus.). 282p. pap. 16.00 ***(978-1-60846-213-1(7))*** Haymarket Bks.

Asher, Brad. Cecelia & Fanny: The Remarkable Friendship Between an Escaped Slave & Her Former Mistress. 2011. (ENG., Illus.). 240p. 30.00 *(978-0-8131-3414-7(5))* Univ. Pr. of Kentucky.

Ashun, Elizabeth. America the Land of More Than Enough. 2009. 96p. pap. 10.99 *(978-1-61579-050-0(0))* Xulon Pr., Inc.

Atwater, Deborah F. African American Women's Rhetoric: The Search for Dignity, Personhood, & Honor. (Race, Rites, & Rhetoric: Colors, Cultures, & Communication Ser.). (ENG.). 186p. 2010. pap. 28.50 *(978-0-7391-2177-1(4))* 2009. 62.99 *(978-0-7391-2176-4(6))* Lexington Bks.

Auset, Akua. SUPERWOMEN & GODDESSES: Workin' Your Power & Magic Book One. 2006. per. 9.95 *(978-0-9792161-0-7(9))* a-point-of-light Publishing.

Autumn, Christine. All That I Am. 2006. 31.49 *(978-1-4259-6683-6(7))*; pap. 22.49 *(978-1-4259-6682-9(9))* AuthorHouse.

Ayers, Lisa. Monah Lisa's Testimonial Tears. 2011. 180p. 29.99 ***(978-1-4568-5607-6(3))***; pap. 19.99 ***(978-1-4568-5606-9(5))*** Xlibris Corp.

Ballard, Maxine. The True Story of Florence Ballard. 2007. 249p. 49.95 *(978-0-9800574-0-9(X))* PRECIOUS4MAX, Inc.

Bandele, Asha. Something Like Beautiful: One Single Mother's Story. 2010. 208p. pap. 14.99 *(978-0-06-171039-1(3)*, Harper Paperbacks) HarperCollins Pubs.

Barnes, Adilah. On My Own Terms. 2008. 304p. 29.99 *(978-1-4257-9033-2(X))*; pap. 19.99 *(978-1-4257-9008-0(9))* Xlibris Corp.

Barnett, Amy Dubois. Get Yours! How to Have Everything You Ever Dreamed of & More. 2008. (ENG.). 288p. pap. 13.99 *(978-0-7679-2509-9(2)*, Harlem Moon) Broadway Bks.

Barrow-Pryor, Erany. Motherin' the BluesLinda Hopkins: The Continuing Legacy of The Blues Woman. 2008. 196p. pap. *(978-3-639-09649-1(5))* VDM Verlag Dr. Mueller e.K.

Bassard, Katherine Clay. Transforming Scriptures: African American Women Writers & the Bible. 2011. (ENG., Illus.). 180p. pap. 22.95 *(978-0-8203-3880-4(X))* Univ. of Georgia Pr.

Baszile, Jennifer Lynn. The Black Girl Next Door: A Memoir. 2009. (ENG., Illus.). 320p. pap. 15.00 *(978-1-4165-4328-2(7)*, Touchstone) Touchstone.

Battle-Baptiste, Whitney. Black Feminist Archaeology. 2011. (ENG., Illus.). 200p. 89.00 *(978-1-59874-378-4(3))*; pap. 29.95 *(978-1-59874-379-1(1))* Left Coast Pr., Inc.

Baum, Dale, ed. Counterfeit Justice: The Judicial Odyssey of Texas Freedwoman Azeline Hearne. 2009. (Conflicting Worlds: New Dimensions of the American Civil War Ser.). (Illus.). 320p. 45.00 *(978-0-8071-3405-4(8))* Louisiana State Univ. Pr.

Beamon, Nika C. & DePaulo, Bella. I Didn't Work This Hard Just to Get Married: Successful Single Black Women Speak Out. 2009. (ENG.). 224p. pap. 14.95 *(978-1-55652-819-4(1)*, Hill, Lawrence Bks.) Chicago Review Pr., Inc.

Bell, Monita K. Getting Hair Fixed. 2010. 60p. pap. *(978-3-8383-5036-3(7))* Lambert Academic Publishing.

Bernard, Regina Andrea. Black & Brown Waves: The Cultural Politics of Young Women of Color & Feminism. 2009. 170p. *(978-90-8790-809-6(1))*; pap. *(978-90-8790-808-9(3))* Sense Pubs.

Big Boom & Big Boom. If You Want Closure in Your Relationship, Start with Your Legs: A Guide to Understanding Men. 2007. (ENG.). 224p. pap. 15.99 *(978-1-4165-4646-7(4)*, Touchstone) Touchstone.

The Black Hair Care Revolution: A Simple Pocket Guide to Growing & Maintaining Healthy Natural & Permed Hair. 2009. (Illus.). 68p. pap. 11.99 *(978-1-4276-3760-4(1))* Aardvark Global Publishing.

Black, Mona Lisa. You Can't Fall off the Floor. 2011. 140p. pap. 11.95 *(978-1-4620-0811-7(9))* iUniverse, Inc.

Blair, Cynthia. I've Got to Make My Livin' Black Women's Sex Work in Turn-of-the-Century Chicago. 2010. (Historical Studies of Urban America Ser.). (ENG., Illus.). 344p. 40.00 *(978-0-226-05598-5(1))* Univ. of Chicago Pr.

Blair-Reed, Wilma. Portrait of A Sista' Gone Mad. 2011. (ENG.). 314p. pap. 19.95 ***(978-1-4327-7632-9(0))*** Outskirts Pr., Inc.

Blitz, Lisa. Sanctuary from Oppression. 2009. 364p. pap. *(978-3-639-11222-1(9))* VDM Verlag Dr. Mueller e.K.

Boehm, Lisa Krissoff. Making a Way Out of No Way: African American Women & the Second Great Migration. (Margaret Walker Alexander Series in African American Studies). (ENG., 304p. 2010. Illus.). pap. 25.00 *(978-1-60473-802-5(2))* 2009. 50.00 *(978-1-60473-216-0(4))* Univ. Pr. of Mississippi.

Boggis, JerriAnne, et al, eds. Harriet Wilson's New England: Race, Writing, & Region. 2007. (Revisiting New England Ser.). (Illus.). 272p. lib. bdg. 65.00 *(978-1-58465-641-8(7)*, University of New Hampshire Press) Univ. Pr. of New England.

Bohrnstedt, Jennifer Cain. Snapshots of A Century in African American Lives. 2010. 120p. pap. 39.95 *(978-1-4520-0511-9(7))* AuthorHouse.

Bolofo, Koto. Venus Williams. 2008. (ENG., Illus.). 100p. 60.00 *(978-3-86521-602-1(1))* Steidl, Gerhard Druckerei und Verlag DEU. Dist: D.A.P./Distributed Art Pubs.

Bond, Alma Halbert. Michelle Obama: A Biography, 1 vol. 2011. (Greenwood Biographies Ser.). (Illus.). 167p. 37.00 *(978-0-313-38104-1(6)*, A2245C) Greenwood Publishing Group, Inc.

Bond, Alma Halbert. Michelle Obama, a Biography. 2012. (Illus.). xvi, 167p. E-Book ***(978-0-313-38105-8(4)***, Greenwood Pr.) Greenwood Publishing Group, Inc.

Booker, Pamela. Dust: murmurs & a Play. 2009. 148p. pap. 15.00 *(978-0-615-19023-5(5))* Evolutionary Girls.

Bower, Beverly L. & Wolverton, Mimi. Answering the Call: African American Women in Higher Education Leadership. 2009. (Journeys to Leadership Ser.). 176p. 65.00 *(978-1-57922-253-6(6))*; pap. 22.50 *(978-1-57922-254-3(4))* Stylus Publishing, LLC.

Bracey, Earnest N. Fannie Lou Hamer: The Life of a Civil Rights Icon. 2011. (ENG., Illus.). 209p. pap. 38.00 *(978-0-7864-6030-4(X))* McFarland & Co., Inc. Pubs.

Bradley, Linda. Teen Sisters' Health: An African American Girls' Wellness Guide for Body, Mind, & Spirit. 2008. (ENG.). 250p. (YA). pap. 14.95 *(978-1-59624-067-4(9))* Cleveland Clinic Pr.

Branch, Enobong Hannah. Opportunity Denied: Limiting Black Women to Devalued Work. 2011. (ENG., Illus.). 208p. (C). pap. 23.95 *(978-0-8135-5123-4(4))*; 192p. 69.00 *(978-0-8135-5122-7(6))* Rutgers Univ. Pr.

Bridgforth, Glinda. Girl, Get Your Credit Straight! A Sister's Guide to Ditching Your Debt, Mending Your Credit, & Building a Strong Financial Future. 2007. (ENG.). 352p. pap. 13.99 *(978-0-7679-2674-4(9))* Broadway Bks.

Britt, Donna. Brothers (and Me) A Memoir of Loving & Giving. 2011. (ENG., Illus.). 320p. 25.99 ***(978-0-316-02184-5(9))*** Little Brown & Co.

Brock, Rovenia M. Dr. Ro's Ten Secrets to Livin' Healthy. 2007. (ENG., Illus.). 464p. mass mkt. 7.99 *(978-0-553-58558-2(4)*, Bantam) Random House Publishing Group.

Brode, Douglas & Orsak, Joe. Yellow Rose of Texas: The Myth of Emily Morgan. 2010. (ENG., Illus.). 135p. pap. 24.95 *(978-0-7864-4520-2(3))* McFarland & Co., Inc. Pubs.

Brooks-Bertram, Peggy, et al. Uncrowned Queens: African American Women Community Builders of Western New York, 2 vols. 2009. (Uncrowned Queens Institute Ser.). (Illus.). pap. 11.95 *(978-0-9722977-0-7(7))* Uncrowned Queens Institute for Research & Education On Women, Inc.

—Uncrowned Queens: The Legacy Continues, 1905-2005. 2009. (Uncrowned Queens Institute Ser.). (Illus.). xxvi, 205p. pap. 17.95 *(978-0-9722977-2-1(3))* Uncrowned Queens Institute for Research & Education On Women, Inc.

—Uncrowned Queens Vol. 2: African American Women Community Builders of Western New York, 2 vols. 2009. (Uncrowned Queens Institute Ser.). (Illus.). 13.95 *(978-0-9722977-1-4(5))* Uncrowned Queens Institute for Research & Education On Women, Inc.

Brooks, Pamela E. Boycotts, Buses, & Passes: Black Women's Resistance in the U. S. South & South Africa. 2008. (ENG., Illus.). 320p. pap. 29.95 *(978-1-55849-678-1(5))* Univ. of Massachusetts Pr.

—Boycotts, Buses, & Passes: Black Women's Resistance in the U.S. South & South Africa. 2008. (Illus.). 320p. lib. bdg. 98.00 net. *(978-1-55849-676-7(9))* Univ. of Massachusetts Pr.

Brown-Avery, Cheryl. Where It All Began. 2008. 84p. pap. 16.95 *(978-1-60672-982-3(9))* PublishAmerica, Inc.

Brown, Caroline. The Black Female Body in American Literature & Art. 2011. (Routledge Interdisciplinary Perspectives on Literature Ser.). (ENG., Illus.). 308p. (C). 125.00 *(978-0-415-89550-7(2))* Routledge.

Brown, Jayna. Babylon Girls: Black Women Performers & the Shaping of the Modern. 2008. (ENG., Illus.). 360p. 94.95 *(978-0-8223-4133-8(6))*; pap. 25.95 *(978-0-8223-4157-4(3))* Duke Univ. Pr.

Brown, Jeannette. African American Women Chemists, 1 vol. 2011. (ENG., Illus.). 264p. 35.00 *(978-0-19-974288-2(X))* Oxford Univ. Pr., Inc.

Brown, Kimberly Nichele. Writing the Black Revolutionary Diva: Women's Subjectivity & the Decolonizing Text. 2010. (Blacks in the Diaspora Ser.). (ENG.). 294p. 70.00 *(978-0-253-35525-6(7)*, 0253355257); pap. 24.95 *(978-0-253-22246-6(X)*, 025322246X) Indiana Univ. Pr.

Brown, Leslie. Upbuilding Black Durham: Gender, Class, & Black Community Development in the Jim Crow South. 2008. (ENG., Illus.). 424p. 73.95 *(978-0-8078-3138-0(7))*; 472p. pap. 27.95 *(978-0-8078-5835-6(8))* Univ. of North Carolina Pr.

Brown, Lois. Pauline Elizabeth Hopkins: Black Daughter of the Revolution. 2008. (ENG., Illus.). 704p. 49.95 *(978-0-8078-3166-3(2))* Univ. of North Carolina Pr.

Brown, Nikki. Private Politics & Public Voices: Black Women's Activism from World War I to the New Deal. 2006. (Blacks in the Diaspora Ser.). (ENG., Illus.). 208p. 29.95 *(978-0-253-34804-3(8)*, 0253348048) Indiana Univ. Pr.

Brown, Teresa L. Fry. Can a Sistah Get a Little Help? Encouragement for Black Women in Ministry. 2008. 176p. pap. 18.00 *(978-0-8298-1743-0(3))* Pilgrim Pr., The/United Church Pr.

Bryan, Carmen. It's No Secret: From Nas to Jay-Z, from Seduction to Scandal- A Hip-Hop Helen of Troy Tells All. 2007. (ENG., Illus.). 272p. pap. 14.00 *(978-1-4165-3720-5(1))* Gallery Bks./G-Unit.

Bukhari, Safiya. The War Before: The True Life Story of Becoming a Black Panther, Keeping the Faith in Prison, & Fighting for Those Left Behind. Whitehorn, Laura, ed. 2010. (ENG.). 320p. pap. 15.95 *(978-1-55861-610-3(1))* Feminist Pr. at The City Univ. of New York.

Bullard, Hank, et al. Why Black Women Are Alone: The Truth Revealed. 2008. 80p. pap. 10.95 *(978-0-595-51653-7(X))* iUniverse, Inc.

Bundles, Alelia. Madame C. J. Walker. 2008. (Black Americans of Achievement Legacy Edition Ser.). 112p. (gr. 6-12). 35.00 *(978-1-60413-072-0(5)*, Chelsea Hse.) Facts On File, Inc.

Burwell, Robyn. I Was under a Heavy Burden: The Life of Annie C. Tuggle. 2011. 160p. pap. 15.99 ***(978-0-89112-548-8(5))*** Abilene Christian Univ. Pr.

Bush-Baskette, Stephanie. Misguided Justice: The War on Drugs & the Incarceration of Black Women. 2010. 204p. 26.95 *(978-1-4502-1740-8(0))*; (ENG.). pap. 16.95 *(978-1-4502-1738-5(9))* iUniverse, Inc.

Cahn, Susan K. Sexual Reckonings: Southern Girls in a Troubling Age. 2012. (ENG., Illus.). 384p. pap. 19.95 ***(978-0-674-06393-8(7))*** Harvard Univ. Pr.

Calloway-Miller, Brenda "Saw Jesus+". If You Want Your Life, You Have to Fight!!! The brenda saw jesus Story. 2009. 148p. pap. 14.95 *(978-1-4401-2292-7(X))* iUniverse, Inc.

Cameron & Cameron, Theresa. Learning to Live: A Black Woman's Journey Beyond Foster Care. 2009. x, 278p. pap. *(978-1-59194-108-8(3))* Townsend Pr.

Canfield, Jack L., et al. Chicken Soup for the African American Woman's Soul. 2006. (Chicken Soup for the Soul Ser.). (ENG., Illus.). 384p. pap. 14.95 *(978-0-7573-0520-7(2))* Health Communications, Inc.

Carretta, Vincent. Phillis Wheatley: Biography of a Genius in Bondage. 2011. (ENG., Illus.). 304p. 29.95 ***(978-0-8203-3338-0(7))*** Univ. of Georgia Pr.

carter-Shabazz, Aginah. Choicez: How they impact our Lives. 2008. 176p. pap. 18.99 *(978-0-615-23027-6(X))* Sulemar-Aginah & Co., LLC.

Cary, Lorene. Black Ice. tchr.'s training gde. ed. *(978-0-394-27226-9(9)*, Vintage) Knopf Doubleday Publishing Group.

Casey, Trina. How to Date an Italian Man? It's a Question Not a Guide!, 1 vol. 2010. 176p. pap. 24.95 *(978-1-60749-053-1(6))* PublishAmerica, Inc.

Chambers, Crystal Renée & Sharpe, Rhonda V., eds. Black Female Undergraduates on Campus: Successes & Challenges, Vol. 12. 2012. (Diversity in Higher Education Ser.). (Illus.). 240p. 114.95 ***(978-1-78052-502-0(8))*** Emerald Group Publishing Ltd. GBR. Dist: Turpin Distribution Services Ltd.

Chambers, Jaysie Nyshia. The Slave Mind & the Mind of God: Rebuilding Our Relationships Within the African American Home, 1 vol. 2010. 78p. pap. 19.95 *(978-1-61582-640-7(8))* PublishAmerica, Inc.

Chapman, Erin D. Prove It on Me: New Negroes, Sex, & Popular Culture in the 1920s, 1 vol. 2012. (ENG., Illus.). 208p. pap. 21.95 ***(978-0-19-975832-6(8))*** Oxford Univ. Pr., Inc.

Charles, Patricia. They Want My Soul. 2011. 104p. pap. 12.99 ***(978-1-4567-6913-0(8))*** AuthorHouse.

Charron, Katherine. Freedom's Teacher: The Life of Septima Clark. 2012. (ENG., Illus.). 480p. pap. 26.95 ***(978-0-8078-7222-2(9))*** Univ. of North Carolina Pr.

Charron, Katherine Mellen. Freedom's Teacher: The Life of Septima Clark. 2009. (ENG., Illus.). 480p. 36.95 *(978-0-8078-3332-2(0))* Univ. of North Carolina Pr.

Cheatham, Gwendolyn Jevita. Big Mama: The World Is a Playground — Enjoy It! 2011. 187p. pap. 18.95 *(978-1-4327-1192-4(X))* Outskirts Pr., Inc.

Child, Brenda's. The Right Amount of Sunshine... Cultivating Little Girls into Young Ladies. 2010. 136p. pap. 19.00 *(978-0-557-37996-5(2))* Lulu Enterprises Inc.

Chilton, Karen. Hazel Scott: The Pioneering Journey of a Jazz Pianist, from Cafe Society to Hollywood to HUAC. 2010. (ENG., Illus.). 312p. pap. 22.95 *(978-0-472-03447-5(2))* Univ. of Michigan Pr.

Christian, Barbara. New Black Feminist Criticism, 1985-2000. Bowles, Gloria et al, eds. 2007. 272p. 35.00 *(978-0-252-03180-9(6))* Univ. of Illinois Pr.

Christie, Jackie. Proud to Be A Colored Girl. 2009. (ENG.). 76p. pap. 14.95 *(978-0-9794827-6-2(3))* Infinite Love Publishing.

Clark-Lewis, Elizabeth. Living In, Living Out: African American Domestics in Washington, D. C. , 1910-1940. 2010. (ENG., Illus.). 256p. pap. 29.95 *(978-1-58834-286-7(7))* Smithsonian Institution Pr.

Clarke, Averil Y. Inequalities of Love: College-Educated Black Women & the Barriers to Romance & Family. 2011. (Politics, History, & Culture Ser.). (ENG., Illus.). 432p. 94.95 *(978-0-8223-4995-2(7))*; pap. 26.95 *(978-0-8223-5008-8(4))* Duke Univ. Pr.

Clay, Augustella. Sojourners of Truth & Justice: Voices in Black & White... 2009. 74p. pap. 15.99 *(978-1-4415-5729-2(6))* Xlibris Corp.

Clinton, Catherine. Harriet Tubman: The Road to Freedom. 2006. (Illus.). 272p. reprint ed. 28.00 *(978-1-4223-5761-3(9))* DIANE Publishing Co.

Cobb, Regina M. About My Father's Business. 2008. 356p. pap. 19.99 *(978-1-60477-832-8(6))* Xulon Pr., Inc.

Cole, Stephanie & Ring, Natalie J., eds. The Folly of Jim Crow: Rethinking the Segregated South. 2012. (Walter Prescott Webb Memorial Lectures, published for the University of Texas At Ser.). (Illus.). 256p. 30.00 ***(978-1-60344-582-5(X))*** Texas A&M Univ. Pr.

Cole, Stephanie, et al. The Folly of Jim Crow: Rethinking the Segregated South. 2012. E-Book ***(978-1-60344-661-7(3))*** Texas A&M Univ. Pr.

Coleman, Angela D. Beautiful. Sisterhood Agenda, ed. 2007. (YA). per. *(978-0-9786906-2-5(1))* Sisterhood Agenda Enterprises, LLC.

Collier-Thomas, Bettye. Jesus, Jobs, & Justice: African American Women & Religion. 2010. (ENG., Illus.). 736p. 37.50 *(978-1-4000-4420-7(0)*, Knopf) Knopf Doubleday Publishing Group.

Collins, Catherine Fisher. The Imprisonment of African American Women: Causes, Experiences & Effects. 2nd rev. ed. 2010. (ENG., Illus.). 210p. pap. 39.95 *(978-0-7864-3384-1(1))* McFarland & Co., Inc. Pubs.

Collins, Catherine Fisher, ed. African American Women's Health & Social Issues, 1 vol. 2nd rev. ed. 2006. (Illus.). 232p. 59.95 *(978-0-275-98082-5(0)*, C8082, Praeger Pubs.) Greenwood Publishing Group, Inc.

Collins, Patricia Hill. Black Feminist Thought: Knowledge, Consciousness, & the Politics of Empowerment. 2nd ed. 2008. (Routledge Classics Ser.). (ENG.). 384p. 29.95 *(978-0-415-96472-2(5))* Routledge.

Collins, Thom & Fitzpatrick, Tracy, eds. American People, Black Light: Faith Ringgold's Paintings of The 1960s. 2011. (ENG., Illus.). 136p. pap. 30.00 *(978-0-9795629-3-8(7))* Neuberger Museum of Art.

Conaway, Carol B. & Waters, Kristin B., eds. Black Women's Intellectual Traditions: Speaking Their Minds. 2007. (Illus.). 480p. per. 35.00 *(978-1-58465-634-0(4))* Univ. Pr. of New England.

Cooper, Ann Nixon. A Century & Some Change: My Life Before the President Called My Name. 2010. (ENG., Illus.). 224p. 19.99 *(978-1-4391-5887-6(8)*, Beyond Words/Atria Bks.) Atria Bks.

Cooper, Ann Nixon & Bates, Karen Grigsby. A Century & Some Change: My Life Before the President Called My Name. 2010. pap. *(978-1-4391-5888-3(6)*, Beyond Words/Atria Bks.) Atria Bks.

Cooper, C. T. M. God Sent Us Angels in the Form of Good White Folks: Mama's Good White Folks Angels. 2011. 244p. pap. 19.95 ***(978-1-4497-2144-2(3)***, WestBow Pr.) Author Solutions, Inc.

—God Sent Us Angels in the Form of Good White Folks: Mama's Good White Folks Angels. 2011. 244p. 35.95 ***(978-1-4497-2146-6(X)***, WestBow Pr.) Author Solutions, Inc.

Cooper, Valerie C. Word, Like Fire: Maria Stewart, the Bible, & the Rights of African Americans. (Carter G. Woodson Institute Ser.). 2012. (ENG., Illus.). 224p. (gr. 17). 39.50 *(978-0-8139-3188-3(6))* 2011. E-Book ***(978-0-8139-3207-1(6))*** Univ. Pr. of Virginia.

Cotton, Dorothy. If Your Back's Not Bent: The Role of the Citizenship Education Program in the Civil Rights Movement. 2012. pap. ***(978-0-7432-9684-7(2))***; (ENG., Illus.). 352p. 25.00 ***(978-0-7432-9683-0(4))*** Atria Bks. (Beyond Words/Atria Bks.).

Covington, Jeanette. Crime & Racial Constructions: Cultural Misinformation about African Americans in Media & Academia. 2010. (ENG.). 344p. 83.99 *(978-0-7391-2591-5(5))* Lexington Bks.

Covington, S. R. Sensual Astrology for the African American Man. 2011. (ENG., Illus.). 304p. 6.99 *(978-1-60162-320-1(8))* Urban Bks.

Cram101 Textbook Reviews Staff. Outlines & Highlights for Black Sexual Politics: African Americans, Gender, & the New Racism by Patricia H Collins, ISBN. 2009. 90p. pap. 27.95 *(978-1-4288-9770-0(4))* Cram101 Inc.

Cross, Dolores. Beyond the Wall: A Memoir. 2010. 268p. (ENG.). 35.95 *(978-1-4497-0096-6(9))*; pap. 19.95 *(978-1-4497-0094-2(2))* Author Solutions, Inc. (WestBow Pr.).

Cross-White, Agnes. Possum Got Big Ears: Anatomy of a Child's Journey to Womanhood. 2008. 216p. pap. 15.99 *(978-1-60477-543-3(2))* Xulon Pr., Inc.

Dabel, Jane. A Respectable Woman: The Public Roles of African American Women in 19th-Century New York. 2008. (ENG., Illus.). 240p. 55.00 *(978-0-8147-2011-0(0))* New York Univ. Pr.

Danquah, Meri Nana-Ama, ed. The Black Body. 2009. (ENG.). 304p. pap. 18.95 *(978-1-58322-889-0(6))* Seven Stories Pr.

Davidson, James West. They Say: Ida B. Wells & the Reconstruction of Race. 2008. (New Narratives in American History Ser.). (ENG., Illus.). 256p. (C). pap. 19.95 *(978-0-19-516021-5(5))* Oxford Univ. Pr., Inc.

Davis, Belva. Never in My Wildest Dreams: A Black Woman's Life in Journalism. 2011. (ENG., Illus.). 272p. 24.95 *(978-1-936227-06-8(1))* Berrett-Koehler Pubs., Inc.

Davis, Dana-Ain. Battered Black Women & Welfare Reform: Between a Rock & a Hard Place. 2006. (SUNY Series in African American Studies). 215p. per. 29.95 *(978-0-7914-6844-9(5))* State Univ. of New York Pr.

Davis, Russella L. And We Fell Out Laughin' 2009. 64p. pap. 10.95 *(978-1-4259-0345-9(2))* AuthorHouse.

Davis-Sivasothy, Audrey. The Science of Black Hair: A Comprehensive Guide to Textured Hair Care. 2011. (Illus.). 256p. ***(978-0-9845184-3-2(6))***; ***(978-0-9845184-0-1(1))***; pap. ***(978-0-9845184-2-5(8))***; pap. ***(978-0-9845184-1-8(X))*** Saja Publishing Co., LLC.

Davis, Wonda Lee. Real Time with Miss Bipolar Bitch: Around & Around I Go! an African American Woman Admits to Being Manic-Depressive. 2011. 233p. pap. 14.95 ***(978-1-4327-6037-3(8))*** Outskirts Pr., Inc.

Dene, Debe. Now hair This! The Destruction of Black Hair. 2008. (Illus.). 141p. pap. 12.95 *(978-0-9801242-0-0(4))* Tell Pubns.

Dickerson, Debra J. An American Story. pap. *(978-0-385-72862-1(X))* Knopf Doubleday Publishing Group.

Dillard, Cynthia B. Learning to (Re)member the Things We've Learned to Forget: Endarkened Feminisms, Spirituality, & the Sacred Nature of (Re)search & Teaching. 2012. ***(978-1-4331-1282-9(5))***; pap. ***(978-1-4331-1281-2(7))***; E-Book ***(978-1-4539-0243-1(0))*** Lang, Peter Publishing, Inc.

Dillard, Cynthia B. On Spiritual Strivings: Transforming an African American Woman's Academic Life. 2007. (Suny Series, Women in Education). 136p. per. 24.95 *(978-0-7914-6812-8(7))* State Univ. of New York Pr.

Donaldson, Annie. Growing African American Hair Longer, Stronger & Healthier. 2009. (ENG.). 124p. 24.95 *(978-0-9744935-9-6(7))* AllWrite Advertising & Publishing.

Dossett, Kate. Bridging Race Divides: Black Nationalism, Feminism, & Integration in the United States, 1896-1935. 2009. (ENG., Illus.). 280p. pap. 29.95 *(978-0-8130-3495-9(7))* Univ. Pr. of Florida.

Dowdy, Joanne Kilgour. PhD Stories: Conversations with My Sisters. 2008. (Understanding Education & Policy Ser.). 176p. *(978-1-57273-796-9(4))*; *(978-1-57273-797-6(2))* Hampton Pr., Inc.

Dowdy, Joanne Kilgour & Golden, Sandra. Connecting the Literacy Puzzle: Linking the Professional, Personal, & Social Perspectives. 2011. ***(978-1-61289-061-6(X)); (978-1-61289-060-9(1))*** Hampton Pr., Inc.

Dreher, Kwakiutl L. Dancing on the White Page: Black Women Entertainers Writing Autobiography. 2008. 225p. per. 29.95 *(978-0-7914-7284-2(1))* State Univ. of New York Pr.

—Dancing on the White Page: Black Women Entertainers Writing Autobiography, 1950-1990. 2008. 74.50 *(978-0-7914-7283-5(3))* State Univ. of New York Pr.

Drumgoold, Kate. A Slave Girl's Story. 2009. 56p. pap. *(978-1-4099-6306-6(3))* Dodo Pr.

Drummond, Darlene K. A Diary of Gastric Bypass Surgery: When the Benefits Outweigh the Costs. 2008. 146p. 44.50 *(978-0-7914-7439-6(9))*; pap. 19.95 *(978-0-7914-7440-2(2))* State Univ. of New York Pr.

Dugan, Mary C. Spirituality in African American Women. 2008. 124p. per. *(978-3-8364-5869-6(1))* VDM Verlag Dr. Mueller e.K.

Dunbar, Erica Armstrong. A Fragile Freedom. 2011. (Society & the Sexes in the Modern Worl Ser.). (ENG., Illus.). 216p. pap. 24.00 ***(978-0-300-17702-2(X))*** Yale Univ. Pr.

Duneier, Mitchell. Poor Black Women. 2008. *(978-0-374-23582-6(1))* Farrar, Straus & Giroux.

Duvall, John. Identifying Fictions of Toni Morrison: Modernist Authenticity & Postmodern Blackness. 2009. (ENG.). 192p. pap. 27.00 *(978-0-230-62308-8(5))* Palgrave Macmillan.

Easlea, Daryl. Crazy in Love: The Beyonce Knowles Biography. 2011. (ENG., Illus.). 256p. pap. 19.95 *(978-1-84938-874-0(1))* Omnibus Pr.

Eaton, Kalenda C. Womanism, Literature, & the Transformation of the Black Community, 1965ndash;1980. 2012. (Studies in African American History & Culture Ser.). (ENG.). 122p. pap. 42.95 ***(978-0-415-54080-3(1))*** Routledge.

Edwards, Joyce P. Artelia: Portrait of an American Matriarch. 2012. pap. 19.95 ***(978-0-7414-7010-2(1))*** Infinity Publishing.

Ellis Eastman, Linda, ed. Survival Skills for the African American Woman. 2007. 19.95 *(978-0-9791153-5-6(3))* Professional Woman Publishing.

Eubanks, W. Ralph. The House at the End of the Road: The Story of Three Generations of an Interracial Family in the American South. 2011. (ENG.). 224p. pap. 25.00 ***(978-1-61703-081-9(3))*** Univ. Pr. of Mississippi.

Evans, Gina. Predicting Fat Consumption among African American Women. 2008. 136p. per. *(978-3-8364-2877-4(6))* VDM Verlag Dr. Mueller e.K.

Evans, Stephanie Y. Black Women in the Ivory Tower, 1850-1954: An Intellectual History. 2008. (ENG., Illus.). 288p. pap. 24.95 *(978-0-8130-3268-9(7))* Univ. Pr. of Florida.

Evans, Tammy. The Silencing of Ruby Mccollum: Race, Class, & Gender in the South. 2006. (ENG., Illus.). 208p. 34.95 *(978-0-8130-2973-3(2))* Univ. Pr. of Florida.

Farmer-Kaiser, Mary. Freedwomen & the Freedmen's Bureau: Race, Gender, & Public Policy in the Age of Emancipation. 4th ed. 2010. (Reconstructing America Ser.). (ENG.). 256p. 80.00 *(978-0-8232-3211-6(5))*; pap. 28.00 *(978-0-8232-3212-3(3))* Fordham Univ. Pr.

Farris, Christine King. Through It All: Reflections on My Life, My Family, & My Faith. 2010. (ENG., Illus.). 272p. pap. 15.00 *(978-1-4165-4882-9(3))*, Beyond Words/Atria Bks.) Atria Bks.

Feldman, Roberta M. & Stall, Susan. The Dignity of Resistance: Women Residents' Activism in Chicago Public Housing. 2006. (Cambridge Series in Environment & Behavior). (ENG., Illus.). 408p. per. 35.00 *(978-0-521-59686-2(6))* Cambridge Univ. Pr.

Ferguson, SallyAnn H. Nineteenth-Century Black Women's Literary Emergence: Evolutionary Spirituality, Sexuality, & Identity: An Anthology. 2008. (African American Literature & Culture: Expanding & Exploding the Boundaries Ser.: Vol. 17). 352p. (C). 119.95 *(978-1-4331-0158-8(0))*; pap. 34.95 *(978-1-4331-0157-1(2))* Lang, Peter Publishing, Inc.

Flake, Elaine M. God in Her Midst: Preaching Healing to Wounded Women. Stanley, Kathryn V., ed. 2007. 93p. per. 12.99 *(978-0-8170-1506-0(X))* Judson Pr.

Fletcher, Kami. The Niagara Movement - the Black Protest Reborn. 2008. 60p. pap. *(978-3-639-01922-3(9))* VDM Verlag Dr. Mueller e.K.

Folan, Karyn Langhorne. Don't Bring Home a White Boy: And Other Notions That Keep Black Women from Dating Out. 2010. (ENG.). 256p. 24.99 *(978-1-4391-5475-5(9)*, Gallery Books/Karen Hunter Publishing) Gallery Books/Karen Hunter Publishing.

Foreman, P. Gabrielle. Activist Sentiments: Reading Black Women in the Nineteenth Century. 2009. (New Black Studies Ser.). (ENG., Illus.). 280p. 75.00 *(978-0-252-03474-9(0))*; pap. 25.00 *(978-0-252-07654-0(8))* Univ. of Illinois Pr.

Forten, Charlotte L. The Journal of Charlotte L Forten: A Young Black Woman's Reaction to the White World of the Civil War Era. Billington, Ray Allen, ed. 2011. 254p. 46.95 ***(978-1-258-00700-3(2))*** Literary Licensing, LLC.

Foster, Frances Smith, et al, eds. Still Brave: The Evolution of Black Women's Studies. 2009. (ENG.). 400p. pap. 22.95 *(978-1-55861-611-0(X))* Feminist Pr. at The City Univ. of New York.

Franklin, Jamela. I'm Not Crazy-Just Menopausal. 2007. mass mkt. 19.95 *(978-0-615-14599-0(X))* Oyinde Enterprises Publishing Co.

Freeman, Clarence E. The Light-Skin Trigger. 2009. 228p. 29.99 *(978-1-4363-8820-7(1))*; pap. 19.99 *(978-1-4363-8819-1(8))* Xlibris Corp.

Frystak, Shannon. Our Minds on Freedom: Women & the Struggle for Black Equality in Louisiana, 1924-1967. 2009. 288p. 42.50 *(978-0-8071-3493-1(7))* Louisiana State Univ. Pr.

Gabbin, Joanne Veal, ed. Shaping Memories: Reflections of African American Women Writers. 2009. (ENG.). 240p. 30.00 *(978-1-60473-274-0(1))* Univ. Pr. of Mississippi.

Gallagher, Julie A. Black Women & Politics in New York City. 2012. E-Book ***(978-0-252-09410-1(7))***; (ENG., Illus.). 276p. 55.00 ***(978-0-252-03696-5(4))*** Univ. of Illinois Pr.

Gavin, James. Stormy Weather: The Life of Lena Horne. 2010. (ENG., Illus.). 608p. pap. 16.00 *(978-0-7432-7144-8(0)*, Beyond Words/Atria Bks.) Atria Bks.

Gentry & Gentry, Quinn M. Black Women's Risk for HIV: Rough Living. 2008. (ENG.). 282p. (C). 158.00 *(978-0-7890-3169-3(8))* Routledge.

Gentry, Quinn M. Black Women's Risk for HIV: Rough Living. 2007. (ENG.). 282p. per. 65.95 *(978-0-7890-3170-9(1))* Routledge.

Giddings, Paula J. IDA-A Sword among Lions: Ida B. Wells & the Campaign Against Lynching. 2009. 832p. pap. 19.99 *(978-0-06-079736-2(3)*, Harper Paperbacks) HarperCollins Pubs.

Gilchrist, Eletra S. Experiences of Single African-American Women Professors. 2011. (ENG., Illus.). 250p. 70.00 ***(978-0-7391-7087-8(2))*** Lexington Bks.

—Experiences of Single African-American Women Professors: With This Ph.D., I Thee Wed. 2011. ***(978-0-7391-7088-5(0))*** Lexington Bks.

Glasrud, Bruce A. & Pitre, Merline, eds. Black Women in Texas History. 2008. (Centennial Series of the Association of Former Students, Texas AandM University: No. 108). (ENG.). 256p. 40.00 *(978-1-60344-007-3(0))* Texas A&M Univ. Pr.

—Black Women in Texas History. 2008. (Centennial Series of the Association of Former Students, Texas AandM University). (ENG.). 256p. pap. 19.95 *(978-1-60344-031-8(3))* Texas A&M Univ. Pr.

Glymph, Thavolia. Out of the House of Bondage: The Transformation of the Plantation Household. 2008. (ENG.). 296p. 70.00 *(978-0-521-87901-9(9))*; pap. 27.00 *(978-0-521-70398-7(0))* Cambridge Univ. Pr.

Goldstein, Nancy. Jackie Ormes: The First African American Woman Cartoonist. 2008. (ENG., Illus.). 240p. 40.00 *(978-0-472-11624-9(X))* Univ. of Michigan Pr.

Gordly, Avel Louise. Remembering the Power of Words: The Life of an Oregon Activist, Legislator, & Community Leader. 2011. 173p. pap. 18.95 *(978-0-87071-604-1(2))* Oregon State Univ. Pr.

Gore, Dayo. Radicalism at the Crossroads: African American Women Activists in the Cold War. 2011. (ENG., Illus.). 240p. 39.00 *(978-0-8147-3236-6(4))* New York Univ. Pr.

Goza, Rogenia. Motivational Factors That Influence Career Choice - African American Women Legislators. 2008. 148p. pap. *(978-3-639-00728-2(X))* VDM Verlag Dr. Mueller e.K.

Greenhaven. Women's Issues in Zora Neale Hurston's Their Eyes Were Watching God. 2012. (Social Issues in Literature Ser.). (ENG., Illus.). 224p. (gr. 10-12). pap. 39.60 ***(978-0-7377-5822-1(8)***, Greenhaven Pr. Inc.); (YA). (gr. 9-12). lib. bdg. 27.30 ***(978-0-7377-5821-4(X))*** Cengage Gale.

Gresham, Sylvia L. Destined for Greater Things. 2007. *(978-0-9794861-1-1(4))* Truth Pubs.

Griffith, Marilynn, compiled by. SistahFaith: Real Stories of Pain, Truth, & Triumph. 2010. (ENG.). 240p. pap. 14.99 *(978-1-4391-5277-5(2)*, Howard Bks.) Howard Books.

Grimes, Nikki. Out of the Dark. 2009. (ENG., Illus.). 56p. (J). pap. 8.00 *(978-1-57274-977-1(6)*, Author at Work) Owen, Richard C. Pubs., Inc.

Gross, Kali N. Colored Amazons: Crime, Violence, & Black Women in the City of Brotherly Love, 1880-1910. 2006. (Politics, History, & Culture Ser.). (ENG., Illus.). 280p. per. 23.95 *(978-0-8223-3799-7(1))* Duke Univ. Pr.

Gunn, Carroll. The Life of Mary Shepard-Queen of the Legendary Club Ebony. 2007. 172p. pap. 20.00 *(978-0-615-21824-3(5))* Gunn, Jennie.

Haizlip, Shirlee. Finding Grace: Two Sisters & the Search for Meaning Beyond the Color Line. 2007. (ENG.). 296p. pap. 19.95 *(978-0-7432-0054-7(3)*, Free Pr.) Free Pr.

Hale, Cynthia. I'm a Piece of Work! Sisters Shaped by God. 2010. 144p. pap. 16.00 *(978-0-8170-1571-8(X))* Judson Pr.

Hall, James C. & Hathaway, Heather, eds. Conversations with Paule Marshall. 2010. (Literary Conversations Ser.). (ENG.). 240p. 40.00 *(978-1-60473-743-1(3))* Univ. Pr. of Mississippi.

Hancock, Fumi Stephanie Ogunleye. Beyond Idol Worship! 2007. 316p. per. 17.99 *(978-1-60266-476-0(5))* Xulon Pr., Inc.

Harper, A. Breeze. Sistah Vegan: Food, Identity, Health, & Society: Black Female Vegans Speak. 2009. *(978-1-59056-145-4(7))* Lantern Bks.

Harper, Hill. The Conversation: How Black Men & Women Can Build Loving, Trusting Relationships. 2010. (ENG.). 288p. (gr. 12). 15.00 *(978-1-59240-578-7(9)*, Gotham) Penguin Group (USA) Inc.

—The Conversation: How Black Men & Women Can Build Loving, Trusting Relationships. Lt. ed. 2010. 390p. 31.95 *(978-1-4104-2422-8(7))* Thorndike Pr.

Harris, Duchess. Black Feminist Politics from Kennedy to Obama. 2011. (Contemporary Black History Ser.). (ENG.). 240p. pap. 26.00 *(978-0-230-11255-1(2))* Palgrave Macmillan.

Harris, Gail & McLaughlin, Pam. A Woman's War: The Professional & Personal Journey of the Navy's First African American Female Intelligence Officer. 2009. (Scarecrow Professional Intelligence Education Ser.). (ENG.). 284p. pap. 37.00 *(978-0-8108-6793-2(1))* Scarecrow Pr., Inc.

Harris-Perry, Melissa V. Sister Citizen: Shame, Stereotypes, & Black Women in America. 2011. (Illus.). 392p. 28.00 *(978-0-300-16541-8(2))* Yale Univ. Pr.

Harris, Trudier. Summer Snow: Reflections from a Black Daughter of the South. 2007. (ENG.). 200p. pap. 16.00 *(978-0-8070-7255-4(9))* Beacon Pr.

Harrison, Renee K. Enslaved Women & the Art of Resistance in Antebellum America. 2009. (Black Religion/Womanist Thought/Social Justice Ser.). (ENG.). 304p. 89.00 *(978-0-230-61846-6(4))* Palgrave Macmillan.

Hawks, Joanne V. & Skemp, Sheila L., eds. Sex, Race, & the Role of Women in the South. 2011. 158p. pap. 30.00 ***(978-1-61703-057-4(0))*** Univ. Pr. of Mississippi.

Hayes, Eileen M. Songs in Black & Lavender: Race, Sexual Politics, & Women's Music. 2010. (African Amer Music in Global Perspective Ser.). (ENG.). 248p. 75.00 *(978-0-252-03514-2(3))*; pap. 25.00 *(978-0-252-07698-5(2))* Univ. of Illinois Pr.

Hayes, Eileen M. & Williams, Linda F., eds. Black Women & Music: More Than the Blues. 2007. (African American Music in Culture Ser.). (Illus.). 280p. per. 26.00 *(978-0-252-07426-4(2))* Univ. of Illinois Pr.

Haynes, Rosetta R. Radical Spiritual Motherhood: Autobiography & Empowerment in Nineteenth-Century African American Women. 2011. 264p. 39.95 *(978-0-8071-3694-2(8))* Louisiana State Univ. Pr.

Haywood, Della W. Years of a Lotus: Memoir of a Lust Baby. 2010. pap. 15.95 *(978-0-7414-5868-1(3))* Infinity Publishing.

Hebbar, Reshmi J. Modeling Minority Women. 2010. 288p. pap. 39.95 *(978-0-415-88243-9(5))* Routledge.

Hemphill, Amani Franklin. The Black Female Crisis & the Politics of Love in Black America. 2008. 121p. pap. 19.95 *(978-1-60474-555-9(X))* PublishAmerica, Inc.

Henderson, Carol E. Imagining the Black Female Body: Reconciling Image in Print & Visual Culture. Henderson, Carol E., ed. 2010. (ENG., Illus.). 232p. 84.00 *(978-0-230-10705-2(2))* Palgrave Macmillan.

Hicks, Cheryl D. Talk with You Like a Woman: African American Women, Justice, & Reform in New York, 1890-1935. 2010. (Gender & American Culture Ser.). (ENG., Illus.). 552p. 65.00 *(978-0-8078-3424-4(6))*; pap. 24.95 *(978-0-8078-7162-1(1))* Univ. of North Carolina Pr.

Hicks, Wanda. Baltimore's #1 Madam, Wanda Hicks from Po-Ho to Rich Bitch: You & Your Mamma & Daddy Taught Me How to Get It. 2007. 140p. pap. 20.99 *(978-1-4259-6596-9(2))* AuthorHouse.

Higashida, Cheryl. Black Internationalist Feminism: Women Writers of the Black Left, 1955-1995. 2011. (ENG.). 264p. 50.00 ***(978-0-252-03650-7(6))*** Univ. of Illinois Pr.

Hill, Anita F. Reimagining Equality: Stories of Gender, Race, & Finding Home. (ENG.). 224p. 2012. pap. 16.00 ***(978-0-8070-1443-1(5))*** 2011. 25.95 *(978-0-8070-1437-0(0))* Beacon Pr.

Hill, MarKeva. Womanism Against Socially-Constructed Matriarcha Images: A Theoretical Model Towards a Therapeutic Goal. 2012. (Black Religion/Womanist Thought/Social Justice Ser.). (ENG., Illus.). 184p. 80.00 ***(978-0-230-34065-7(2))*** Palgrave Macmillan.

Hilliard Mims, Barbara Tone. Don't Blame Me If I Got the Name Wrong. 2008. 324p. pap. 14.95 *(978-1-4327-2123-7(2))* Outskirts Pr., Inc.

Hinton, KaaVonia. Sharon M. Draper: Embracing Literacy. 2008. (Scarecrow Studies in Young Adult Literature Ser.). (ENG.). 148p. 45.00 *(978-0-8108-5585-2(8))* Scarecrow Pr., Inc.

Hollies, Linda H. Jesus & Those Bodacious Women: Life Lessons from One Sister to Another. 10th anniv. ed. 2007. 268p. (Orig.). per. 14.00 *(978-0-8298-1776-8(X))* Pilgrim Pr., The/United Church Pr.

hooks, bell. Ain't I a Woman: Black Women & Feminism. 2007. (South End Press Classics Ser.). 220p. pap. 16.00 *(978-0-89608-769-9(7))* South End Pr.

—Black Looks: Race & Representation. 2006. pap. 8.95 *(978-1-4288-1629-9(1))* Cram101 Inc.

—Sisters of the Yam: Black Women & Self-Recovery. 2nd ed. 2008. (ENG.). 220p. 40.00 *(978-0-89608-734-7(4))* South End Pr.

Hooks, JoAnne. I Don't Take It Lightly. 2006. per. 12.99 *(978-0-9789751-1-1(1))* CREE Publishing Hse.

Hoppe, Sherry L. & Speck, Bruce W. Maxinmaxine Smith's Unwilling Pupils: Lessons Learned in Memphis's Civil Rights Classroom. 2007. (Illus.). 200p. 39.95 *(978-1-57233-587-5(4))* Univ. of Tennessee Pr.

Horton-Stallings, LaMonda. Mutha Is Half a Word: Intersections of Folklore, Vernacular, Myth, & Queerness in Black Female Literature. 2007. (Black Performance & Cultural Criticism Ser.). cd-rom 9.95 *(978-0-8142-9135-1(X))* Ohio State Univ. Pr.

Howard-Oglesby, Pamela & Roberts, Brenda L. Savannah's Black First Ladies, Vol. I: The Past, Present, & Future. 2010. (Illus.). 120p. pap. 13.95 *(978-1-4327-3112-0(2))* Outskirts Pr., Inc.

Howell, Shevonica M. Girl, They Ain't Ready! 2011. 134p. 29.99 ***(978-1-4568-2594-2(1))***; pap. 19.99 ***(978-1-4568-2593-5(3))*** Xlibris Corp.

Hudson, Lynn M. The Making of Mammy Pleasant: A Black Entrepreneur in Nineteenth-Century San Francisco. 2008. (Women in American History Ser.). (ENG., Illus.). 224p. per. 21.00 *(978-0-252-07527-8(7))* Univ. of Illinois Pr.

Hughes, Melinda. Illness Perception & Coping among African American Women with Lupus - Alternative Medicine & Cultural Competence. 2007. pap. *(978-3-8364-2840-8(7))* VDM Verlag Dr. Mueller e.K.

Hunt, Marsha. Undefeated. 2006. (ENG., Illus.). 272p. pap. 16.95 *(978-1-55365-218-2(5)*, Greystone Bks.) D&M Pubs. Inc. CAN. Dist: Perseus-PGW.

Hunter, Jane Edna. A Nickel & a Prayer. Thomas, Rhondda Robinson, ed. 2011. (Regenerations Ser.). (ENG.). pap. 22.95 *(978-1-933202-64-8(5))* West Virginia Univ. Pr.

Hunter, Jane Edna & Thomas, Rhondda Robinson. A Nickel & a Prayer. 2011. (ENG.). 68.95 *(978-1-933202-65-5(3))* West Virginia Univ. Pr.

Hurston, Zora Neale. Dust Tracks on a Road: An Autobiography. 2010. (P. S. Ser.). (ENG.). 336p. pap. 16.99 *(978-0-06-200483-3(2)*, HarperPerennial) HarperCollins Pubs.

Ileweng, Nana T. & Parsons, Ellen B. Female African Americans & Health Research. Ileweng, Nana T. & Parsons, Ellen B., eds. 2008. (Illus.). xi, 181p. 185.00 *(978-1-60456-442-6(3))* Nova Science Pubs., Inc.

Ingram, Berneta L. Living Life on Life's Terms: The Spiritual Journey of an Addict, 1 vol. 2009. 75p. pap. 16.95 *(978-1-4489-9130-3(7))* PublishAmerica, Inc.

Jackson, Richie Jean Sherrod. The House by the Side of the Road: The Selma Civil Rights Movement. 2011. (ENG., Illus.). 176p. 24.95 *(978-0-8173-1694-5(9))* Univ. of Alabama Pr.

Jae', Jas. Say Goodbye to the Blackman Who Drains the Blackwoman. 2008. 104p. per. 9.99 *(978-1-60266-628-3(8))* Xulon Pr., Inc.

Johnson, Amanda. Our Voices: Issues Facing Black Women in America. Johnson, Amanda, ed. 2009. (ENG.). 240p. pap. 14.99 *(978-0-8024-7847-4(6)*, Lift Every Voice) Moody Pubs.

Johnson, Ella Mae Cheeks & Mulcahy, Patricia. It Is Well with My Soul: The Extraordinary Life of a 106-Year-Old Woman. 2010. (ENG.). 224p. (gr. 12). 14.00 *(978-0-14-311744-5(0)*, Penguin (Non-Classics)) Penguin Group (USA) Inc.

Johnson-Fisher, Angela. Afristocracy. 2008. 72p. pap. *(978-3-639-01270-5(4))* VDM Verlag Dr. Mueller e.K.

Johnson, Kalimah. Locs for Life: The Root to Well Being for African-American Women. 2008. 132p. pap. 12.00 *(978-1-4343-5721-2(X))* AuthorHouse.

Johnson, M. Mikell. The African American Woman Golfer: Her Legacy, 1 vol. 2007. (Illus.). 216p. 49.95 *(978-0-313-34904-1(5)*, C34904, Praeger Pubs.) Greenwood Publishing Group, Inc.

—Heroines of African American Golf: The Past, the Present, & the Future. 2010. 264p. 27.08 *(978-1-4269-3420-9(3))*; pap. 17.08 *(978-1-4269-3419-3(X))* Trafford Publishing.

Johnson, Nadine. Examination of the Concrete Ceiling Pers. 2006. 132p. per. 19.95 *(978-1-58112-343-2(4)*, Dissertation.com) Universal Pubs.

Jones, Angela. African American Civil Rights: Early Activism & the Niagara Movement, 1 vol. 2011. (Illus.). 281p. 44.95 *(978-0-313-39360-0(5)*, A3364C); E-Book ***(978-0-313-39361-7(3)***, Praeger Pubs.) Greenwood Publishing Group, Inc.

Jones, Jacqueline. Labor of Love, Labor of Sorrow: Black Women , Work, & the Family, from Slavery to the Present. 2nd ed. 2009. (ENG., Illus.). 480p. (gr. 9). pap. 18.95 *(978-0-465-01881-9(5))* Basic Bks.

Jones, Lois Mailou & Hanzal, Carla M. Lois Mailou Jones: A Life in Vibrant Color. 2009. *(978-0-9762300-8-3(9))* Mint Museum, The.

Jones, Martha S. All Bound up Together: The Woman Question in African American Public Culture, 1830-1900. 2007. (ENG., Illus.). 328p. pap. 22.00 *(978-0-8078-5845-5(5))* Univ. of North Carolina Pr.

Jones, Nicole & Jones, Nicole Roberts. Define Your Own Way: Empowering Young African American Women. 2010. 138p. pap. 18.00 *(978-0-8298-1870-3(7))* Pilgrim Pr., The/United Church Pr.

Jones, Tamara Bertrand, et al, eds. Pathways to Higher Education Administration for African American Women. 2012. 144p. 75.00 ***(978-1-57922-249-9(8))***; pap. 22.50 ***(978-1-57922-250-5(1))*** Stylus Publishing, LLC.

Jordan-Zachery, Julia & Jordan-Zachery, Julia Sheron. Black Women, Cultural Images, & Social Policy. 2008. (Routledge Studies in North American Politics Ser.). (ENG., Illus.). 230p. 125.00 *(978-0-415-99678-5(3))* Routledge.

Judice, Cheryl. Interracial Marriages Between Black Women & White Men. 2008. 212p. 99.95 *(978-1-60497-577-2(6))* Cambria Pr.

Karim, Jamillah. American Muslim Women: Negotiating Race, Class, & Gender within the Ummah. 2008. (ENG.). 224p. pap. 23.00 *(978-0-8147-4810-7(4))* New York Univ. Pr.

Keckley, Elizabeth. Behind the Scenes by Elizabeth Keckley or, Thirty Years a Slave, & Four Years in the White House. 2006. 380p. per. 26.99 *(978-1-4255-3971-9(8))* MPublishing.

—Behind the Scenes in the Lincoln White House: Memoirs of an African-American Seamstress. 2006. (Civil War Ser.). (ENG., Illus.). 160p. per. 7.95 *(978-0-486-45122-0(4))* Dover Pubns., Inc.

Keeling, Kara. The Witch's Flight: The Cinematic, the Black Femme, & the Image of Common Sense. 2007. (Perverse Modernities Ser.). (ENG.). 224p. (C). 79.95 *(978-0-8223-4013-3(5))*; (Illus.). per. 22.95 *(978-0-8223-4025-6(9))* Duke Univ. Pr.

Kennedy, Bernice Roberts. Depression & African American Women. 2009. 108p. pap. 12.95 *(978-1-4401-3437-1(5))* iUniverse, Inc.

King, Barbara Blake, frwd. Sage Sisters: Essential Lessons for African American Women in Ministry. 2007. 149p. per. *(978-0-8298-1764-5(6))* Pilgrim Pr., The/United Church Pr.

King, Toni C. & Ferguson, S. Alease. Black Womanist Leadership: Tracing the Motherline. King, Toni C. & Ferguson, S. Alease, eds. 2011. (ENG.). 256p. pap. 29.95 *(978-1-4384-3602-9(5))* State Univ. of New York Pr.

King, Toni C. & Ferguson, S. Alease, eds. Black Womanist Leadership: Tracing the Motherline. 2011. 256p. 80.00 *(978-1-4384-3601-2(7))* State Univ. of New York Pr.

King, Wilma & Reed, Linda. African American Women. 2006. 304p. (C). pap. 29.95 *(978-0-631-20741-2(4))*; 74.95 *(978-0-631-20740-5(6))* Wiley, John & Sons, Inc. (Wiley-Blackwell).

Kolin, Philip C., ed. Contemporary African American Women Playwrights: A Casebook. 2007. (Casebooks on Modern Dramatists Ser.). X, 214p. 120.00 *(978-0-415-97826-2(2))* Routledge.

LaBennett, Oneka. She's Mad Real: Popular Culture & West Indian Girls in Brooklyn. 2011. (ENG.). 253p. 75.00 *(978-0-8147-5247-0(0))*; pap. 22.00 *(978-0-8147-5248-7(9))* New York Univ. Pr.

—She's Mad Real: Popular Culture & West Indian Girls in Brooklyn. 2011. 240p. E-Book (978-0-8147-5312-5(4)) New York Univ. Pr.

Lambert, Lillian Lincoln & Brutico, Rosemary. The Road to Someplace Better: From the Segregated South to Harvard Business School & Beyond. 2010. (ENG., Illus.). 256p. 25.95 (978-0-470-40166-8(4), Wiley) Wiley, John & Sons, Inc.

Lau, Kimberly J. Body Language: Sisters in Shape, Black Women's Fitness, & Feminist Identity Politics. 2011. (ENG.). 208p. 79.50 (978-1-4399-0308-7(5)); pap. 25.95 (978-1-4399-0309-4(3)) Temple Univ. Pr.

Lauret, Maria. Alice Walker. 2nd rev. ed. 2011. (ENG.). 304p. 80.00 (978-0-230-57588-2(9)) Palgrave Macmillan.

Lee, Barbara. Renegade for Peace & Justice: A Memoir of Political & Personal Courage. 2011. (ENG.). 245p. pap. 16.95 (978-0-7425-5844-1(4)) Rowman & Littlefield Publishers, Inc.

—Renegade for Peace & Justice: Congresswoman Barbara Lee Speaks for Me. 2008. (ENG., Illus.). 256p. 24.95 (978-0-7425-5843-4(6)) Rowman & Littlefield Publishers, Inc.

Lee, Shayne. Erotic Revolutionaries: Black Women, Sexuality, & Popular Culture. 2010. (ENG.). 176p. pap. 27.00 (978-0-7618-5228-5(X)) Hamilton Bks.

Levenstein, Lisa. A Movement Without Marches: African American Women & the Politics of Poverty in Postwar Philadelphia. (John Hope Franklin Series in African American History & Culture Ser.). 2010. (ENG., Illus.). 320p. pap. 22.95 (978-0-8078-7164-5(8)) 2009. pap. (978-0-8078-5942-1(7)) 2009. (ENG., Illus.). 352p. 47.50 (978-0-8078-3272-1(3)) Univ. of North Carolina Pr.

Lewis, Catherine M. & Lewis, J. Richard. Women & Slavery in America: A Documentary History. 2011. (ENG., Illus.). 330p. 59.95 (978-1-55728-957-5(3)); pap. 22.50 (978-1-55728-958-2(1)) Univ. of Arkansas Pr.

Lightfoot, Elizabeth. Michelle Obama: First Lady of Hope. 2008. (ENG., Illus.). 240p. pap. 14.95 (978-1-59921-521-1(7), Lyons Pr.) Globe Pequot Pr., The.

Long, Carolyn Morrow. A New Orleans Voudou Priestess: The Legend & Reality of Marie Laveau. 2007. (ENG., Illus.). 336p. per. 26.00 (978-0-8130-3214-6(8)) Univ. Pr. of Florida.

Long, Nancy Ann Zrinyi. The Life & Legacy of Mary Mcleod Bethune. 3rd ed. 2008. (ENG.). (C). pap. 19.20 (978-0-558-05267-6(3)) Pearson Learning Solutions.

Lorde, Audre. Sister Outsider: Essays & Speeches. 2007. (ENG.). 192p. pap. 16.99 (978-1-58091-186-3(2), Crossing Pr.) Ten Speed Pr.

Love, Dennis & Brown, Stacy. Blind Faith: The Miraculous Journey of Lula Hardaway, Stevie Wonder's Mother. 2007. (ENG.). 288p. pap. 19.95 (978-1-4165-7785-0(8)) Simon & Schuster.

Lovell, Whitfield. Mercy, Patience & Destiny: the Women of Whitfield Lovell's Tableaux. 2010. (ENG., Illus.). 58p. pap. 20.00 (978-0-615-22202-8(1)) Savannah College of Art & Design Exhibitions.

Lowry, Beverly. Harriet Tubman: Imagining a Life. 2008. (ENG., Illus.). 432p. pap. 15.95 (978-0-385-72177-6(3), Anchor) Knopf Doubleday Publishing Group.

—Harriet Tubman: Imagining a Life:A Biography. 2007. (ENG., Illus.). 432p. 26.00 (978-0-385-50291-7(5), Doubleday) Doubleday Religious Publishing Group, The.

Lyons, Nick & Ward, Chris. Female Force: Condoleezza Rice: Condoleezza Rice. 2009. 32p. pap. 3.99 (978-1-4276-3932-5(9)) Bluewater Productions, Inc.

Mack, Cassandra. Her Rite of Passage: How to Design & Deliver a Rites of Passage Program for African-American Girls & Young Women. 2007. 160p. per. 20.95 (978-0-595-47036-5(X), Authors Choice Pr.) iUniverse, Inc.

Mack-Williams, Kibibi. Ahead of Her Time in Yesteryear: Geraldine Pierce Zimmerman Comes of Age in a Southern African American Family. 2010. (ENG., Illus.). 216p. 31.95 (978-1-57233-720-6(6)) Univ. of Tennessee Pr.

Mance, Ajuan Maria. Inventing Black Women: African American Women Poets & Self-Representation, 1877-2000. 2008. (ENG.). 216p. pap. 24.95 (978-1-57233-651-3(X)) 2007. 248p. 36.00 (978-1-57233-492-2(4)) Univ. of Tennessee Pr.

Marrow, Collis Duhart. Queens: The Evolution of the Black Woman. 2011. 108p. 21.23 (978-1-4634-4215-6(7)); pap. 10.68 (978-1-4634-4216-3(5)) AuthorHouse.

Martin, Lena C. Desperate for Love: Overcoming with Prayer. 2007. 436p. per. 18.95 (978-1-4327-0209-0(2)) Outskirts Pr., Inc.

Materson, Lisa G. For the Freedom of Her Race: Black Women & Electoral Politics in Illinois, 1877-1932. 2009. (ENG., Illus.). 352p. 44.00 (978-0-8078-3271-4(5)) Univ. of North Carolina Pr.

Mathis, Deborah. Sole Sisters: The Joys & Pains of Single Black Women. 2007. (ENG.). 230p. per. 14.00 (978-1-932841-27-5(X)) Agate Publishing, Inc.

Matthews Rander-Bryant, Mary Elizabeth. Steps: Going the Distance- 2008. 108p. 32.99 (978-1-4389-3008-4(9)); pap. 23.99 (978-1-4389-3009-1(7)) AuthorHouse.

May, Vivian M. Anna Julia Cooper, Visionary Black Feminist: A Critical Introduction. 2007. (ENG., Illus.). 232p. 145.00 (978-0-415-95642-0(0)); pap. 36.95 (978-0-415-95643-7(9)) Routledge.

McBride, Judith. The Enemy Within: Living with Sickle Cell Disease. 2011. 52p. 24.99 (978-1-4628-7481-1(9)); pap. 15.99 (978-1-4628-7480-4(0)) Xlibris Corp.

McCrary, Crystal & Williams, Nathan Hale. Inspiration: Profiles of Black Women Changing Our World. 2012. (ENG., Illus.). 256p. 40.00 (978-1-58479-959-7(5)) Stewart, Tabori & Chang.

McDaniel, Cyndar. A Page from Every Girl's Diary. 2008. 127p. pap. 19.95 (978-1-60610-532-0(9)) PublishAmerica, Inc.

McDonald, Katrina Bell. Embracing Sisterhood: Class, Identity, & Contemporary Black Women. 2006. (ENG.). 228p. 92.00 (978-0-7425-4574-8(1)); per. 30.95 (978-0-7425-4575-5(X)) Rowman & Littlefield Publishers, Inc.

McDuffie, Erik S. Sojourning for Freedom: Black Women, American Communism, & the Making of Black Left Feminism. 2011. (ENG., Illus.). 328p. 84.95 (978-0-8223-5033-0(5)); pap. 23.95 (978-0-8223-5050-7(5)) Duke Univ. Pr.

McElya, Micki. Clinging to Mammy: The Faithful Slave in Twentieth-Century America. 2007. (Illus.). 336p. 27.95 (978-0-674-02433-5(8)) Harvard Univ. Pr.

McGee, Robyn. California Nightmares. 2009. 68p. pap. (978-3-639-20220-5(1)) VDM Verlag Dr. Mueller e.K.

McGowan, James A. & Kashatus, William. Harriet Tubman: A Biography, 1 vol. 2011. (Greenwood Biographies Ser.). (Illus.). 167p. 35.00 (978-0-313-34881-5(2), GR4881) Greenwood Publishing Group, Inc.

McGowan, James A. & Kashatus, William C. Harriet Tubman: A Biography. 2011. E-Book (978-0-313-34882-2(0), Greenwood Pr.) Greenwood Publishing Group, Inc.

McGuire, Danielle L. At the Dark End of the Street: Black Women, Rape, & Resistance — A New History of the Civil Rights Movement from Rosa Parks to the Rise of Black Power. 2010. (ENG., Illus.). 352p. 27.95 (978-0-307-26906-5(X), Knopf) Knopf Doubleday Publishing Group.

—At the Dark End of the Street: Black Women, Rape, & Resistance — A New History of the Civil Rights Movement from Rosa Parks to the Rise of Black Power. 2011. (Vintage Ser.). (ENG., Illus.). 416p. pap. 16.95 (978-0-307-38924-4(3), Vintage) Knopf Doubleday Publishing Group.

Means, Myrtle C. The Recipe for Ecstasy: What Women Want: Sexual & Relationship Satisfaction. 2011. pap. 24.99 (978-0-615-49004-5(2)) Myrtle C. Means, Ph.D., P.C.

Meeks, Catherine. Through It All. 2007. (Illus.). 80p. per. (978-1-934144-19-0(3)) Indigo.

Meyer, Armin. Alternative Werbung mit Mixed-Reality-Technologie: Konzepte mit Mehrwert für die Kommunikationspolitikdurch den Einsatz von Mixed-Reality-Technologie. 2008. 96p. pap. (978-3-639-02123-3(1)) VDM Verlag Dr. Mueller e.K.

Miles, Steen. Teenie: Newslady in Training. 2007. 192p. per. 19.95 (978-1-891773-84-6(4)) Orman Pr.

Miller, Carroll L. L. & Pruitt-Logan, Anne S. Faithful to the Task at Hand: The Life of Lucy Diggs Slowe. 2012. (ENG.). 480p. 90.00 (978-1-4384-4259-4(9)) State Univ. of New York Pr.

—Faithful to the Task at Hand: The Life of Lucy Diggs Slowe. 2012. (ENG.). 480p. pap. 29.95 (978-1-4384-4258-7(0)) State Univ. of New York Pr.

Miller, Eva D. The Mysteries of Eva Miller Revealed. 2010. 148p. pap. 14.95 (978-1-4502-3522-8(0)) iUniverse, Inc.

Miller, Jody. Getting Played: African American Girls, Urban Inequality, & Gendered Violence. 2008. (ENG., Illus.). 312p. per. 23.00 (978-0-8147-5698-0(0)) New York Univ. Pr.

Mitchell, Finesse. Your Girlfriends Only Know So Much: The Surprising Truth about What Men Are Really Thinking. 2011. (ENG.). 208p. pap. 14.99 (978-1-4165-8994-5(5)) Gallery Pr., The IRL. Dist: Simon & Schuster, Inc.

Mitchell, Stacy Ann & Mitchell, Teri. Livin' Large. 2nd ed. 2008. (ENG.). 216p. pap. 16.95 (978-0-9800649-1-9(0)) Hilton Publishing Co.

Mitchell, Verner D., ed. This Waiting for Love: Helene Johnson, Poet of the Harlem Renaissance. 2006. (Illus.). 134p. per. 18.95 (978-1-55849-572-2(X)) Univ. of Massachusetts Pr.

Mitchell, Verner D. & Davis, Cynthia. Literary Sisters: Dorothy West & Her Circle, a Biography of the Harlem Renaissance. 2011. (ENG.). 216p. (C). pap. 24.95 (978-0-8135-5146-3(3)); (Illus.). 208p. 72.00 (978-0-8135-5145-6(5)) Rutgers Univ. Pr.

Mitchem, Stephanie Y. African American Women Tapping Power & Spiritual Wellness. 2010. 192p. pap. 22.00 (978-1-60899-179-2(2), Wipf and Stock) Wipf & Stock Pubs.

Montana-Leblanc, Phyllis. Not Just the Levees Broke: My Story During & after Hurricane Katrina. 2009. (ENG.). 240p. pap. 14.00 (978-1-4165-6347-1(4), Beyond Words/Atria Bks.) Atria Bks.

Montgomery, Leslie. The Faith of Condoleezza Rice. 2007. (Illus.). 224p. 19.99 (978-1-58134-799-9(5)) Crossway.

Moore, Dante Sr. The Re-Education of the Female. 2008. (ENG.). 176p. pap. 13.00 (978-1-59309-170-5(2), Strebor Bks.) Strebor Bks.

Moore, Shirley Ann Wilson. African American Women Confront the West, 1600-2000. Taylor, Quintard, ed. 2008. (ENG.). 400p. (C). pap. 24.95 (978-0-8061-3979-1(X)) Univ. of Oklahoma Pr.

Morrison, Toni. What Moves at the Margin: Selected Nonfiction. Denard, Carolyn C., ed. & intro. by. 2008. (ENG., Illus.). 212p. 30.00 (978-1-60473-017-3(X)) Univ. Pr. of Mississippi.

Moylan, Virginia Lynn. Zora Neale Hurston's Final Decade. 2011. (ENG., Illus.). 144p. 24.95 (978-0-8130-3578-9(3)) Univ. Pr. of Florida.

MPEROR. Tribute to the Black Woman. 2007. 112p. pap. 15.00 (978-0-615-16332-1(7)) BePublished.Org.

Muhammad, Mildred. Scared Silent. 2010. (ENG.). 304p. pap. 19.99 (978-1-59309-242-9(3), Strebor Bks.) Strebor Bks.

Mundy, Liza. Michelle: A Biography. 2009. (ENG.). 352p. mass mkt. 7.99 (978-1-4391-5932-3(7), Pocket Star) Pocket Star.

—Michelle: A Biography. 2009. (ENG., Illus.). 256p. pap. 15.00 (978-1-4165-9944-9(4)) Simon & Schuster.

Murphy, Larry G. Sojourner Truth: A Biography, 1 vol. 2011. (Greenwood Biographies Ser.). (Illus.). 176p. 35.00 (978-0-313-35728-2(5), GR5728); E-Book (978-0-313-35729-9(3), Greenwood Pr.) Greenwood Publishing Group, Inc.

Murray, Artie O. A Lingo of Our Own. 2011. 600p. pap. 25.00 (978-1-4567-5069-5(0)) AuthorHouse.

Muwwakkil, Edward H. Sistah Sistah Sistah: I Understand. 2010. 218p. (YA). 14.95 (978-0-615-39290-5(3)) Muwwakkil, Edward T.

Myers, Amrita Chakrabarti. Forging Freedom: Black Women & the Pursuit of Liberty in Antebellum Charleston. 2011. (Gender & American Culture Ser.). (ENG., Illus.). 288p. 39.95 (978-0-8078-3505-0(6)) Univ. of North Carolina Pr.

Myers, Lena Wright. A Broken Silence. 2007. pap. 45.99 (978-1-59311-385-8(4)) Information Age Publishing, Inc.

Myles, Lynette. Female Subjectivity in African American Women's Narratives of Enslavement: Beyond Borders. 2009. (ENG.). 208p. 84.00 (978-0-230-61593-9(7)) Palgrave Macmillan.

Nathans, Sydney. To Free a Family: The Journey of Mary Walker. 2012. (ENG., Illus.). 360p. 29.95 (978-0-674-06212-2(4)) Harvard Univ. Pr.

Neffe. My Happiness Is My Sanity. 2009. 152p. 22.49 (978-1-4389-3982-7(5)); pap. 14.99 (978-1-4389-3981-0(7)) AuthorHouse.

Nelson, Sophia. Black Woman Redefined: Dispelling Myths & Discovering Fulfillment in the Age of Michelle Obama. 2011. (ENG.). 260p. 24.95 (978-1-935618-94-2(6)) BenBella Bks.

Nevergold, Barbara A. Seals. Go, Tell Michelle: African American Women Write to the First Lady, Audiobook, Unabridged & Expanded. Brooks-Bertram, Peggy, ed. 2009. (Excelsior Editions Ser.). 29.95 (978-1-4384-3056-0(6), Suny Pr.) State Univ. of New York Pr.

—Go, Tell Michelle: African American Women Write to the New First Lady. Brooks-Bertram, Peggy, ed. 2009. (Excelsior Editions Ser.). xxii, 268p. pap. 19.95 (978-1-4384-2918-2(5), Suny Pr.) State Univ. of New York Pr.

Newman, Brooke. Jenniemae & James: A Memoir in Black & White. 2011. 320p. pap. 15.00 (978-0-307-46300-5(1), Three Rivers Pr.) Crown Publishing Group.

Nicholas, Carolyn Dungee. Hilda. 2010. (Illus.). xiv, 391p. E-Book (978-1-4490-9182-8(2)) AuthorHouse.

Nielsen, Natalie. My Mom Said She Wanted Me to Grow up Better Than Her. 2008. 320p. pap. (978-3-639-07666-0(4)) VDM Verlag Dr. Mueller e.K.

Norris, Michele. The Grace of Silence: A Family Memoir. (Vintage Ser.). 2011. (ENG.). 240p. pap. 14.95 (978-0-307-47527-5(1), Vintage) 2010. (Illus.). 208p. 24.95 (978-0-307-37876-7(4), Pantheon) Knopf Doubleday Publishing Group.

Nova. Finally Unrestricted. 2011. 240p. 28.95 (978-1-4502-7943-7(0)); pap. 18.95 (978-1-4502-7942-0(2)) iUniverse, Inc.

Office of the Secretary of State. Lillian Walker: Washington State's Civil Rights Pioneer. 2010. (Illus.). 198p. pap. 20.00 (978-1-889320-22-9(6)) Washington State Legacy Project.

Okagbue-Reaves, Janet. Crack Cocaine & the Experience of African American Women: A Statistical Study of Positive Treatment Outcomes. 2007. (ENG.). 124p. (978-0-7734-5402-6(0)) Mellen, Edwin Pr., The.

Orr, Emily Juana Burke. A Tale of Two Worlds: My Life as a Proud Black Woman with White Skin. 2008. pap. 19.99 (978-0-9795697-0-8(2)) Phenomenal Pr.

Osaigbovo, Rebecca Florence. Spiritual Sisterhood: Mentoring for Women of Color. 2011. (ENG.). 151p. pap. 15.00 (978-0-8308-3830-1(9), IVP Bks.) InterVarsity Pr.

Osayande, Ewuare. Misogyny & the Emcee: Sex, Race & Hip Hop. 2008. 112p. pap. 15.00 (978-0-9801635-7-5(9)) Talking Drum Communications.

Owens, Valerie. America Huh! I'm Going Home. 2009. pap. 15.00 (978-1-61658-166-4(2)) Independent Pub.

Page, Yolanda Williams, ed. Encyclopedia of African American Women Writers, 2 vols., Set. 2007. (Illus.). 728p. 175.00 (978-0-313-33429-0(3), GR3429, Greenwood Pr.) Greenwood Publishing Group, Inc.

Parker, Lonnae O'Neal. I'm Every Woman: Remixed Stories of Marriage, Motherhood, & Work. 2006. 272p. per. 13.95 (978-0-06-059293-6(1), Amistad) HarperCollins Pubs.

Parker, Monica. What It Takes: How Women of Color Can Thrive Within the Practice of Law. 2011. (ENG.). 160p. pap. 59.95 (978-1-59031-992-5(3)) American Bar Assn.

Pates, Carolyn Taylor. Life Line Dispatcher: May the Works I've Done Speak for Me. 2010. pap. 10.99 (978-1-61579-765-3(3)) Xulon Pr., Inc.

Pemberton, Jennifer. Who is Sayin' She's a Gold Digger? African American Femininities in Rap Music Lyrics. 2008. 220p. pap. (978-3-639-08574-7(4)) VDM Verlag Dr. Mueller e.K.

Pengra, Lilah. Sarah Campbell: The first white woman in the Black Hills was African American. 2009. (Illus.). 136p. pap. 18.95 (978-0-615-28873-4(1)) Lune Hse. Publishing.

Perkins, Kathy A., intro. African Women Playwrights. 2008. (Illus.). 280p. 65.00 (978-0-252-03387-2(6)) Univ. of Illinois Pr.

Persadsingh, Neil. The Hair in Black Women. 2008. 108p. pap. 11.99 (978-1-60647-382-5(4)) Xulon Pr., Inc.

Petry, Elisabeth. At Home Inside: A Daughter's Tribute to Ann Petry. 2008. (ENG., Illus.). 208p. 30.00 (978-1-60473-100-2(1)) Univ. Pr. of Mississippi.

Phillips, Layli. The Womanist Reader. 2006. (ENG., Illus.). 352p. (C). 140.00 (978-0-415-95410-5(X)); per. 39.95 (978-0-415-95411-2(8)) Routledge.

Pinnock, Pam. The Father Fracture. 2nd ed. 2007. 246p. 18.00 net. (978-0-9777449-0-9(6)) Healeth Publishing.

Pitre, Merline. In Struggle against Jim Crow: Lulu B. White & the NAACP, 1900-1957. 2010. (Centennial Series of the Association of Former Students, Texas A&M University Ser.). (ENG., Illus.). 200p. pap. 22.50 (978-1-60344-199-5(9)) Texas A&M Univ. Pr.

Plant, Deborah G. Zora Neale Hurston: A Biography of the Spirit, 1 vol. 2007. (Women Writers of Color Ser.). (Illus.). 264p. 49.95 (978-0-275-98751-0(5), C8751, Praeger Pubs.) Greenwood Publishing Group, Inc.

—Zora Neale Hurston: A Biography of the Spirit. 2011. (ENG.). 264p. pap. 15.95 (978-1-4422-0612-0(8)) Rowman & Littlefield Publishers, Inc.

Pool, Jeannie G. American Composer Zenobia Powell Perry: Race & Gender in the 20th Century. 2008. (ENG.). 300p. pap. 53.00 (978-0-8108-6376-7(6)) Scarecrow Pr., Inc.

Potter, Hillary. Battle Cries: Black Women & Intimate Partner Abuse. 2008. (ENG.). 295p. (C). pap. 24.00 (978-0-8147-6730-6(3)) New York Univ. Pr.

Powers & Powers, Georgia Davis. I Shared the Dream: The Pride, Passion & Politics of the First Black Woman Senator from Kentucky. 2010. (ENG.). 338p. pap. 21.95 (978-0-88282-354-6(X)) New Horizon Pr. Pubs., Inc.

Presley, Greyling, II. No Disrespect Sista, but I Want to Be Happy! 2007. 149p. per. 14.99 (978-0-615-15118-2(3)) Presley, Greyling.

Ra, Abuna Hetep. Vision for Regenerative Harmonious Society of Woman & the Law of Maat. 2009. 116p. pap. 19.99 (978-1-4415-3637-2(X)) Xlibris Corp.

Raimon, Eve Allegra, et al, eds. Harriet Wilson's New England: Race, Writing, & Region. 2007. (Revisiting New England Ser.). (Illus.). 272p. per. 26.95 (978-1-58465-642-5(5), University of New Hampshire Press) Univ. Pr. of New England.

Ramsey, Sonya Yvette. Reading, Writing, & Segregation: A Century of Black Women Teachers in Nashville. 2008. (Women in American History Ser.). (Illus.). 208p. 37.00 (978-0-252-03229-5(2)) Univ. of Illinois Pr.

Rice, Condoleezza. No Higher Honor: A Memoir of My Years in Washington. 2012. (ENG.). 784p. pap. 18.00 (978-0-307-98678-8(0)) Broadway Bks.

—No Higher Honor: A Memoir of My Years in Washington. 2011. (ENG., Illus.). 784p. 35.00 (978-0-307-58786-2(X), Crown) Crown Publishing Group.

Richardson, Wytress. Stress & Leadership: Voices of the Unheard. 2009. 132p. pap. (978-3-639-22114-5(1)) VDM Verlag Dr. Mueller e.K.

Richie, Beth. Arrested Justice: Black Women, Violence, & America's Prison Nation. 2012. E-Book (978-0-8147-0822-4(6)); E-Book (978-0-8147-2391-3(8)) New York Univ. Pr.

Ridley, Jo Ann. Zoë Dusanne: An Art Dealer Who Made a Difference. 2011. (ENG.). 176p. pap. 15.95 (978-1-56474-505-7(8), Fithian Pr) Daniel & Daniel, Pubs., Inc.

Robinson, Charles F. Forsaking All Others: A True Story of Interracial Sex & Revenge in the 1880s South. 2010. (ENG.). 160p. 30.95 (978-1-57233-724-4(9)) Univ. of Tennessee Pr.

Robinson, Cynthia P. No Longer the Victim. 2007. per. (978-0-9793095-0-2(6)) VisionWorks.

Robinson, Sandra. Specializing in the Wholly Impossible. 2008. 176p. pap. (978-3-639-01640-6(8)) VDM Verlag Dr. Mueller e.K.

Rooks, Veronda L. His Grace Is Sufficient! 2010. (ENG.). 77p. pap. 12.00 (978-0-557-45156-2(6)) Lulu Enterprises Inc.

Ross, Marilyn J. & Greenwood. Success Factors of Young African American Women at a Historically Black College. 2009. 152p. pap. 45.99 (978-1-60752-074-0(5)) Information Age Publishing, Inc.

Ross-Stroud, Catherine. Janet McDonald: The Original Project Girl. 2008. (Scarecrow Studies in Young Adult Literature Ser.). (ENG., Illus.). 160p. 45.00 (978-0-8108-5802-2(9)) Scarecrow Pr., Inc.

Rosser-Mims, Dionne. How & Why Black WOmen Are Elected to Political Office: A Narrative Analysis of Nine Cases in the State of Georgia. 2011. (ENG.). 228p. 119.95 (978-0-7734-3954-2(4)) Mellen, Edwin Pr., The.

Rousseau, Nicole. Black Woman's Burden: Commodifying Black Reproduction. 2011. (ENG.). 240p. pap. 28.00 (978-0-230-11316-9(8)) Palgrave Macmillan.

Ruiz, Vicki. Unequal Sisters: An Inclusive Reader in U.S. Women's History. 4th rev. ed. 2007. (Illus.). 656p. 47.95 (978-0-415-95841-7(5), 0415958415); 130.00 (978-0-415-95840-0(7), 0415958407) Routledge.

Russell, Heather & Bassard, Katherine Clay. Transforming Scriptures: African American Women Writers & the Bible. 2010. (ENG.). 180p. pap. 44.95 (978-0-8203-3090-7(6)) Univ. of Georgia Pr.

Rutledge, Lawanda S. Motivation & the Professional African American Woman. 2008. 116p. 25.95 (978-1-4389-0822-9(9)); pap. 19.95 (978-1-4389-0823-6(7)) AuthorHouse.

Ryan, Jennifer D. Post-Jazz Poetics: A Social History. 2010. (ENG., Illus.). 240p. 84.00 (978-0-230-62315-6(8)) Palgrave Macmillan.

Sadlier, Rosemary. Harriet Tubman: Freedom Seeker, Freedom Leader. 2012. (Quest Biography Ser.). (ENG., Illus.). 192p. pap. 19.99 (978-1-4597-0150-2(X)) Dundurn CAN. Dist: Ingram Pub. Services.

Sanchez, Sonia. I'm Black When I'm Singing, I'm Blue When I Ain't & Other Plays. Wood, Jacqueline, ed. 2010. (ENG.). 196p. 69.95 (978-0-8223-4757-6(1)); pap. 19.95 (978-0-8223-4778-1(4)) Duke Univ. Pr.

Sartain, Lee. Invisible Activists: Women of the Louisiana NAACP & the Struggle for Civil Rights, 1915-1945. 2007. 212p. 36.50 (978-0-8071-3221-0(7)) Louisiana State Univ. Pr.

Schafer, Daniel L. Anna Madgigine Jai Kingsley: African Princess, Florida Slave, Plantation Slaveowner. 2010. (ENG., Illus.). 192p. pap. 19.95 (978-0-8130-3554-3(6)) Univ. Pr. of Florida.

Scholder, Amy, ed. Dr. Rice in the House. 2007. (ENG., Illus.). 128p. per. 13.95 (978-1-58322-761-9(X)) Seven Stories Pr.

Schweik, Susan. Arrested Justice: Black Women, Violence, & Americarsquo;s Prison Nation. 2012. (ENG.). 240p. 74.00 (978-0-8147-7622-3(1)) New York Univ. Pr.

Scott, Anne Firor. Pauli Murray & Caroline Ware: Forty Years of Letters in Black & White. 2008. (Gender & American Culture Ser.). (ENG., Illus.). 210p. pap. 24.95 (978-0-8078-5928-5(1)) Univ. of North Carolina Pr.

Segrave, Kerry. Lynchings of Women in the United States: The Recorded Cases, 1851-1946. 2010. (ENG., Illus.). 195p. pap. 39.95 (978-0-7864-5898-1(4)) McFarland & Co., Inc. Pubs.

Sensbach, Jon F. Rebecca's Revival: Creating Black Christianity in the Atlantic World. 2006. (Illus.). 320p. per. 21.00 (978-0-674-02257-7(2)) Harvard Univ. Pr.

Sernett, Milton C. Harriet Tubman: Myth, Memory, & History. 2007. (ENG., Illus.). 424p. lib. bdg. 94.95 (978-0-8223-4052-2(6)); per. 26.95 (978-0-8223-4073-7(9)) Duke Univ. Pr.

Seven. A Black Woman's Worth. 2009. 284p. pap. 16.99 (978-1-4389-6608-3(3)) AuthorHouse.

Shabazz, Rsheed Ali. And God Made Man: The Creation of African America. 2008. pap. 10.00 (978-0-8059-7918-3(2)) Dorrance Publishing Co., Inc.

Shakir, Imam Zaid. Dear Self: A Year in the Life of a Welfare Mother. 2007. (ENG., Illus.). 448p. pap. 19.95 (978-0-9792281-0-0(7)) NID Pubs.

Sharpless, Rebecca. Cooking in Other Women's Kitchens: Domestic Workers in the South, 1865-1960. 2010. (John Hope Franklin Series in African American History & Culture Ser.). (ENG., Illus.). 304p. 35.00 (978-0-8078-3432-9(7)) Univ. of North Carolina Pr.

Sharpley-Whiting, T. & Sharpley-Whiting, T. Denean. Pimps up, Ho's Down: Hip Hop's Hold on Young Black Women. 2008. (ENG., Illus.). 200p. pap. 19.00 (978-0-8147-4064-4(2)) New York Univ. Pr.

Sharpley-Whiting, T. Denean. Pimps up, Ho's Down: Hip Hop's Hold on Young Black Women. 2007. (ENG.). 200p. 65.00 (978-0-8147-4014-9(6)) New York Univ. Pr.

Shaw, Andrea Elizabeth. The Embodiment of Disobedience: Fat Black Women's Unruly Political Bodies. 2006. (ENG.). 162p. 78.99 (978-0-7391-1486-5(7)); per. 24.50 (978-0-7391-1487-2(5)) Lexington Bks.

Shepherd, Sherri. Permission Slips: Every Woman's Guide to Giving Herself a Break. l.t. ed. 2010. (ENG.). 391p. 31.50 (978-1-4104-2242-2(9)) Thorndike Pr.

Sheryl The Pearl. Not Easily Broken. 2011. 90p. pap. 19.95 **(978-1-4512-7623-7(0))** PublishAmerica, Inc.

Simien, Evelyn M. Black Feminist Voices in Politics. 2006. 196p. 71.50 (978-0-7914-6789-3(9)); per. 29.95 (978-0-7914-6790-9(2)) State Univ. of New York Pr.

Simien, Evelyn M., ed. Gender & Lynching: The Politics of Memory. 2011. (ENG., Illus.). 208p. 80.00 (978-0-230-11270-4(6)) Palgrave Macmillan.

Singleton, Angie. Diamond's Fate. 2011. 220p. 29.99 **(978-1-4568-8878-7(1))**; pap. 19.99 **(978-1-4568-8877-0(3))** Xlibris Corp.

Skiffer, La Tanya. How Black Female Offenders Explain Their Crime & Describe Their Hopes: A Case Study of Inmates in a California Prison. 2008. iii, 144p. (978-0-7734-4916-9(7)) Mellen, Edwin Pr., The.

Skloot, Rebeca. Immortal Life of Henrietta. 2011. 15.45 **(978-0-7848-3620-0(5)**, Everbind) Marco Bk. Co.

Skloot, Rebecca. The Immortal Life of Henrietta Lacks. (ENG., Illus.). 2011. 400p. pap. 16.00 (978-1-4000-5218-9(1), Three Rivers Pr.) 2010. 384p. 26.00 (978-1-4000-5217-2(3), Crown) Crown Publishing Group.

—The Immortal Life of Henrietta Lacks. l.t. ed. 604p. 2011. (ENG.). pap. 16.99 (978-1-59413-432-6(4), Large Print Pr.) 2010. 31.99 (978-1-4104-2792-2(7)) Thorndike Pr.

Slipac, Melisa. Black Female Sexuality & Nature of Womanhood. 2009. 188p. pap. (978-3-639-22085-8(4)) VDM Verlag Dr. Mueller e.K.

Smith, Aaron/Anwar. Is There Really a Shortage of Good Black Men? 2010. 214p. 24.95 (978-1-60911-014-7(5), Strategic Bk. Publishing) AEG Literary Publishing Services, Inc.

Smith, Minister Regina. Bewitched! Yet Chosen for a Greater Destiny. 2009. 152p. 22.99 (978-1-60791-945-2(1)); pap. 14.99 (978-1-60791-944-5(3)) Xulon Pr., Inc.

Smith, Yolanda Y. Women's Spirituality & Education in the Black Church. 2012. (Black Religion/Womanist Thought/Social Justice Ser.). (ENG., Illus.). 256p. 85.00 (978-0-230-61833-6(2)) Palgrave Macmillan.

Sproule, Acquanetta M. Musings of an Odd Little Black Woman. 2010. 80p. pap. 10.00 (978-0-557-37744-2(7)) Lulu Enterprises Inc.

Stallings, L. H. Mutha Is Half a Word: Intersections of Folklore, Vernacular, Myth, & Queerness in Black Female Culture. 2007. (Black Performance & Cultural Criticism Ser.). (ENG.). 334p. 49.95 (978-0-8142-1056-7(2)) Ohio State Univ. Pr.

Steele, Bobbie L. Woman of Steele: A Personal & Political Journal. 2011. 184p. 24.99 **(978-1-4389-5333-5(X))**; pap. 15.99 **(978-1-4389-5332-8(1))** AuthorHouse.

Stith, Marva Woods. Black Star Girl: A Charter Beneficiary of the Civil Rights Movement Celebrates the Insightful Parenting of Her Father. It's His Story Too. 2010. 252p. 29.95 (978-1-4401-9579-2(X)); pap. 19.95 (978-1-4401-9581-5(1)) iUniverse, Inc.

Stone, Robin D. The Black Woman's Guide to Healthy Living: The Best Advice for Body, Mind + Spirit in Your 20s, 30s, 40s, 50s + Beyond. Essence Magazine Editors, ed. 2009. (ENG., Illus.). 176p. pap., instr.'s gde. ed. 17.95 (978-1-60320-043-1(6)) Time Home Entertainment, Inc.

The Struggle. 2007. 167p. (YA). per. 21.95 (978-0-9791781-0-8(X)) Parker & Sons Publishing, Inc.

Summer-Edmond, Janice L. The Secret Trust of Aspasia Cruvellier Mirault: The Life & Trials of a Free Woman of Color in Antebellum Georgia. 2008. (Illus.). 180p. 29.95 (978-1-55728-580-8(1)) Univ. of Arkansas Pr.

Sweeney, Megan. Reading Is My Window: Books & the Art of Reading in Women's Prisons. 2010. (ENG., Illus.). 360p. 65.00 (978-0-8078-3352-0(5)); pap. 22.95 (978-0-8078-7103-3(1)) Univ. of North Carolina Pr.

Swimmer, Susan. First Lady of Fashion & Style. 2009. (ENG., Illus.). 128p. pap. 9.95 (978-1-57912-826-5(2), 1579128262) Black Dog & Leventhal Pubs., Inc.

Taylor, Kristin Clark. The Forever Box. (ENG.). (gr. 1). 2012. 272p. 15.00 **(978-0-425-24561-3(6)**, Berkley Trade) 2011. 240p. 22.95 (978-0-425-24196-7(3), Berkley Hardcover) Penguin Group (USA) Inc.

Theoharis, Jeanne & Woodard, Komozi. Want to Start a Revolution? Radical Women in the Black Freedom Struggle. Gore, Dayo, ed. 2009. (ENG., Illus.). 368p. pap. 25.00 (978-0-8147-8314-6(7)) New York Univ. Pr.

Thomas, Chéree L. See Me for Who I Am. 2011. 108p. 21.99 (978-1-4520-9031-3(9)); pap. 10.99 (978-1-4520-9032-0(7)) AuthorHouse.

Thomas, Claudian Lynn. God Spare Life: An Autobiography. 2007. 360p. per. 26.95 (978-0-9777297-8-4(8), WME Bks.) Windsor Media Enterprises, Inc.

Thomas, Naturi. How to Die in Paris: A Memoir. 2011. (ENG.). 272p. pap. 17.00 (978-1-58005-364-6(5)) Seal Pr.

Thompson, Lisa B. Beyond the Black Lady: Sexuality & the New African American Middle Class. 2009. (New Black Studies Ser.). (ENG.). 200p. 40.00 (978-0-252-03426-8(0)) Univ. of Illinois Pr.

Timeless Visual Works Llc & Jefferson, Ollie. Time will tell Stage 1. 2010. 234p. 16.95 (978-0-615-37640-0(1)) Timeless Visual Works LLC.

Toler, Lynn. My Mother's Rules: A Practical Guide to Becoming an Emotional Genius. 2007. (ENG.). 300p. per. 15.00 (978-1-932841-22-0(9)) Agate Publishing, Inc.

Vakalahi, Halaevalu F. Ofahengaue, et al. Women of Color As Social Work Educators: Strengths & Survival. 2007. (978-0-87293-125-1(0)) Council on Social Work Education.

Vanzant, Iyanla. Tapping the Power Within: A Path to Self-Empowerment for Women. 20th anniv. ed. 2009. (ENG., Illus.). 312p. pap. 15.95 (978-1-4019-2305-1(4)) Hay Hse., Inc.

Vassel, Rachel. Daughters of Men: Portraits of African-American Women & Their Fathers. 2009. 192p. pap. 15.99 (978-0-06-135036-8(2), Harper Paperbacks) HarperCollins Pubs.

Vigen, Aana Marie. Women, Ethics, & Inequality in U. S. Healthcare: To Count among the Living. (Black Religion/Womanist Thought/Social Justice Ser.). (ENG.). 2011. 336p. pap. 30.00 (978-0-230-11363-3(X)) 2006. 304p. 100.00 (978-1-4039-7306-1(7)) Palgrave Macmillan.

Vizinau, D. Dexter. Shine on Me: The Story of Margaret Vizinau, A Determined African-American Woman & Her Faith in God. 2009. 460p. 38.95 (978-0-595-89696-7(0), iUniverse Star) iUniverse, Inc.

Voices: African American & Latina Women Share Their Stories of Success. 2006. (Illus.). 106p. 29.95 (978-0-915180-39-4(1), 0962) Harrowood Bks.

Wagner, Tricia Martineau. African American Women of the Old West. 2007. (ENG., Illus.). 168p. per. 12.95 (978-0-7627-3900-4(2), TwoDot) Globe Pequot Pr., The.

Walters, Cheryl. Blood, Sweat, & High Heels. 2011. 188p. 26.95 **(978-1-4620-5495-4(1))**; pap. 16.95 **(978-1-4620-5496-1(X))** iUniverse, Inc.

Walker-Hill, Helen. From Spirituals to Symphonies: African-American Women Composers & Their Music. 2007. (Illus.). 428p. per. 26.00 (978-0-252-07454-7(8)) Univ. of Illinois Pr.

Walker, Minda. The Day I Was Arrested. 2011. 50p. 24.99 **(978-1-4628-7858-1(X))**; pap. 15.99 **(978-1-4628-7857-4(1))** Xlibris Corp.

Walker, Susannah. Style & Status: Selling Beauty to African American Women, 1920-1975. 2007. (ENG., Illus.). 264p. 40.00 (978-0-8131-2433-9(6)) Univ. Pr. of Kentucky.

Wallace, Michele. Invisibility Blues: From Pop to Theory. 2008. (Haymarket Ser.). (ENG., Illus.). 320p. pap. 21.95 (978-1-85984-487-8(1), 859487) Verso Bks. GBR. Dist: Norton, W. W. & Co., Inc.

Wanzo, Rebecca Ann. The Suffering Will Not Be Televised: African American Women & Sentimental Political Storytelling. 2009. (Illus.). 240p. 70.00 (978-1-4384-2883-3(9)); pap. 24.95 (978-1-4384-2882-6(0)) State Univ. of New York Pr.

Ware, Flossie. A Costly Pearl. 1 vol. 2010. 74p. pap. 19.95 (978-1-4489-6012-5(6)) PublishAmerica, Inc.

Warren, Christiane. Anna Julia Cooper - Feminist & Scholar. 2010. 232p. pap. (978-3-8383-1952-0(4)) Lambert Academic Publishing.

Washington, Margaret. Sojourner Truth's America. 2011. (ENG., Illus.). 520p. pap. 25.00 (978-0-252-07801-9(2)) Univ. of Illinois Pr.

Washington Post Staff. Michelle: Her First Year as First Lady. 2010. (ENG.). 128p. pap. 14.95 (978-1-60078-311-1(2)) Triumph Bks.

Watkins, Audrey P. Sisters of Hope, Looking Back, Stepping Forward: The Educational Experiences of African-American Women. 2009. (Counterpoints: Studies in the Postmodern Theory of Education Ser.). 200p. (C). 32.95 (978-1-4331-0292-9(7)) Lang, Peter Publishing, Inc.

Watson, Elwood D. Outsiders Within: Black Women in the Legal Academy after Brown v. Board. 2008. (ENG.). 160p. 70.00 (978-0-7425-4073-6(1)) Rowman & Littlefield Publishers, Inc.

—Outsiders Within: Black Women in the Legal Academy After Brown v. Board. 2009. (ENG.). 164p. pap. 27.50 (978-0-7425-4074-3(X)) Rowman & Littlefield Publishers, Inc.

West, Elizabeth J. African Spirituality in Black Women's Fiction: Threaded Visions of Memory, Community, Nature, & Being. 2012. E-Book **(978-0-7391-6886-8(X))** Lexington Bks.

—African Spirituality in Black Women's Fiction: Threaded Visions of Memory, Community, Nature & Being. 2011. (ENG.). 192p. (gr. 17). 60.00 **(978-0-7391-6885-1(1))** Lexington Bks.

Wheeler, Jill C. Michelle Obama. 2009. (First Ladies Set 2 Ser.). (Illus.). 32p. (YA). (gr. 1-4). 25.65 (978-1-60453-633-1(0)) ABDO Publishing Co.

White, Aaronette M. African Americans Doing Feminism: Putting Theory into Everyday Practice. 2010. 304p. 75.00 (978-1-4384-3141-3(4)); pap. 24.95 (978-1-4384-3142-0(2)) State Univ. of New York Pr.

White, Deborah Gray, ed. Telling Histories: Black Women Historians in the Ivory Tower. 2008. (ENG., Illus.). 304p. 66.50 (978-0-8078-3201-1(4)); pap. 23.95 (978-0-8078-5881-3(1)) Univ. of North Carolina Pr.

White, Evelyn C., ed. The Black Women's Health Book. 2006. (978-1-58005-124-6(3)) Seal Pr.

Williams, Andrew, et al. Out of the Box: Building Robots, Transforming Lives. 1 vol. 2009. (ENG., Illus.). 176p. pap. 14.99 (978-0-8024-6760-7(1), Lift Every Voice) Moody Pubs.

Williams, Rita. If the Creek Don't Rise. 2007. (ENG., Illus.). 336p. pap. 18.95 (978-0-15-603285-8(6), Mariner Bks.) Houghton Mifflin Harcourt Trade & Reference Pubs.

Williams, Serena & Paisner, Daniel. On the Line. l.t. ed. 2010. (ENG.). 404p. 31.95 (978-1-4104-2243-9(7)) Thorndike Pr.

Williams, Vicki. The Leadership Traits of Head Basketball Coach C Vivian Stringer. 2010. 228p. pap. (978-3-8383-5074-5(X)) Lambert Academic Publishing.

Wills, Leslie P. Which Way Is Up? 2011. 116p. pap. **(978-3-8433-8709-5(5))** Lambert Academic Publishing.

Wilson, Meg. Health Behaviors of Homeless Women- Using a Cross-Sectional, Descriptive, & Non Experimental Design. 2007. 148p. per. (978-3-8364-2944-3(6)) VDM Verlag Dr. Mueller e.K.

Winans, CeCe. Always Sisters: Becoming the Princess You Were Created to Be. 2007. (ENG.). 160p. (J). (gr. 8-12). pap. 11.99 (978-1-4165-4339-8(2), Howard Bks.) Howard Books.

Women & Gender in the New South, 1865-1945. 2009. (Illus.). 271p. (C). pap. 18.95 (978-0-88295-265-9(X)) Davidson, Harlan Inc.

Wood, Peggy & Brown, Parker. Something Must Be Done: One Black. 2006. (Illus.). 153p. 9.95 (978-0-8156-0877-6(2)) Syracuse Univ. Pr.

Young, S. A. I Don't Want to Look Like a Man: Challenging Women's Misconceptions about Weight, Fitness & Body Image. 2011. 176p. pap. 14.95 **(978-1-4327-6842-3(5))** Outskirts Pr., Inc.

Yvonne, Wesley, ed. Black Women's Health: Challenges & Opportunities. 2010. (Public Health in the 21st Century Ser.). 89.00 (978-1-60876-453-2(2)) Nova Science Pubs., Inc.

Zackodnik. African American Feminisms 1828-1923, 6 vols., Vol. 3. 2007. (Illus.). 432p. (978-0-415-39540-3(2)) Routledge.

—African American Feminisms 1828-1923: We must be up & Doing, 6 vols. 2007. (Illus.). 608p. (978-0-415-39538-0(0)) Routledge.

—African American Feminisms 1828-1923 Vol. 2: We Must be up & Doing, 6 vols. 2007. (Illus.). 432p. (978-0-415-39539-7(9)) Routledge.

—African American Feminisms 1828-1923, Volume 4, 6 vols. 2007. (Illus.). 368p. (978-0-415-39541-0(0)) Routledge.

—African American Feminisms 1828-1923, Volume 5, 6 vols. 2007. (Illus.). 384p. (978-0-415-39542-7(9)) Routledge.

—African American Feminisms 1828-1923, Volume 6, 6 vols. 2007. (Illus.). 528p. (978-0-415-39543-4(7)) Routledge.

Zackodnik, Teresa C. African American Feminisms 1828-1923, 6 vols. 2007. (History of Feminism Ser.). (Illus.). 2736p. (C). 1600.00 (978-0-415-39537-3(2)) Routledge.

Zora Hurston & the Strange Case of Ruby Mccollum. 2009. (ENG., Illus.). 488p. 34.95 (978-0-9820940-6-0(0)) Gadfly Publishing, LLC.

AFRICAN AMERICAN YOUTH

Ahearn, Charlie. Wild Style: The Sampler. 2007. (ENG., Illus.). 200p. 35.00 (978-1-57687-364-9(1)) powerHouse Cultural Entertainment, Inc.

Anjejo, Dixon. Risk Behaviors of African Born Adolescents in United States of Americ. 2010. 148p. pap. (978-3-8383-4959-6(8)) Lambert Academic Publishing.

Bailey, Deryl F. & Bradbury-Bailey, Mary. Project Gentlemen on the Move: Nurturing Excellence in African American Youth. 2012. (Routledge Series on Counseling & Psychotherapy with Boys & Men Ser.). (ENG.). 192p. 90.00 **(978-0-415-88414-3(4))**; pap. 29.95 **(978-0-415-88415-0(2))** Routledge.

Belgrave, Faye Z. African American Girls: Reframing Perceptions & Changing Experiences. 2009. (Advancing Responsible Adolescent Development Ser.). (ENG.). xiii, 178p. 79.95 (978-1-4419-0089-0(6), 1441900896) Springer.

Bernadowski, Carianne. Teaching Literacy Skills to Adolescents Using Coretta Scott King Award Winners. 1 vol. 2009. 136p. pap. 35.00 (978-1-58683-337-4(5), A2655P) Libraries Unlimited, Inc.

Byfield, Cheron. Black Boys Can Make It: How They Overcome the Obstacles to University in the UK & USA. 2008. (Illus.). 168p. (C). pap. 32.95 (978-1-85856-431-9(X)) Trentham Bks. Ltd. GBR. Dist: Stylus Publishing, LLC.

Cohen, Cathy J. Democracy Remixed: Black Youth & the Future of American Politics. 1 vol. 2010. (Transgressing Boundaries: Studies in Black Politics & Black Communities Ser.). (ENG., Illus.). 304p. 27.95 (978-0-19-537800-9(8)) Oxford Univ. Pr., Inc.

Cohen, Cathy J. Democracy Remixed: Black Youth & the Future of American Politics. 1 vol. 2012. (Transgressing Boundaries: Studies in Black Politics & Black Communities Ser.). (ENG., Illus.). 304p. pap. 19.95 **(978-0-19-989626-4(7))** Oxford Univ. Pr., Inc.

Corpening, Denise. Learning & Enriching Who I Am: An African American Teen Mother to Be. 2008. 56p. pap. 12.95 (978-1-4343-9545-0(6)) AuthorHouse.

Curtis, Brian E. Wake up Young Brother. 2008. 160p. per. 13.99 (978-1-60477-502-0(5)) Xulon Pr., Inc.

Davis, Anthony & Jackson, Jeffrey. Yo, Little Brother ... Volume II: Basic Rules of Survival for Young African American Males. 2007. (ENG.). 140p. (YA). pap. 14.95 (978-1-934155-01-1(2)) African American Images.

DeVitis, Joseph L. & Irwin-DeVitis, Linda. Adolescent Education: A Reader. 2010. (Adolescent Cultures, School & Society Ser.). 520p. (C). 169.95 (978-1-4331-0505-0(5)); pap. 54.95 (978-1-4331-0504-3(7)) Lang, Peter Publishing, Inc.

Dimitriadis, Greg. Performing Identity/Performing Culture: Hip Hop As Text, Pedagogy, & Lived Practice. 2009. (Intersections in Communications & Culture: Global Approaches & Transdisciplinary Perspectives Ser.). 216p. (C). 29.95 (978-1-4331-0538-8(1)) Lang, Peter Publishing, Inc.

Fishman, Darwin. Political Activities of African American Teenagers: A Case Study of High School Students in the Washington DC Metropolitan Area. 2011. 164p. 109.95 (978-0-7734-1453-2(3)) Mellen, Edwin Pr., The.

Ginwright, Shawn A. Black Youth Rising: Activism & Radical Healing in Urban America. 2010. (ENG., Illus.). 192p. 62.00 (978-0-8077-5022-3(0)); pap. 25.95 (978-0-8077-5021-6(2)) Teachers College Pr., Teachers College, Columbia Univ.

Harris, Theresa & Taylor, George. Raising African American Males: Strategies & Interventions for Successful Outcomes. 2012. **(978-1-60709-300-8(6))** Rowman & Littlefield Education.

Harris, Theresa & Taylor, George, eds. Raising African-American Males: Strategies & Interventions for Successful Outcomes. 2012. (ENG.). 116p. 40.00 **(978-1-60709-298-8(0))** Rowman & Littlefield Education.

Harris/Taylor, ed. Raising African-American Males: Strategies & Interventions for Successful Outcomes. 2012. (ENG.). 116p. pap. 18.95 **(978-1-60709-299-5(9))** Rowman & Littlefield Education.

Hicks, Reginald E. Hidden in the Shadow of Truth: Why Our Black Boys Choose Criminality, Prison, & Enslavement. 2010. 206p. 27.95 (978-1-4502-1669-2(2)); (ENG.). pap. 17.95 (978-1-4502-1667-8(6)) iUniverse, Inc.

Horn, Aaron Lamont. The Role of Father-Like Care in the Education of Young Black Males. 2010. v, 133p. 99.95 (978-0-7734-3771-5(1)) Mellen, Edwin Pr., The.

Jones, Allen & Naison, Mark. The Rat That Got Away: A Bronx Memoir. 2011. (ENG., Illus.). 224p. pap. 16.95 **(978-0-8232-3103-4(8))** Fordham Univ. Pr.

Kafele, Baruti. Motivating Black Males to Achieve in School & in Life. 2009. pap. 16.95 (978-1-4166-0857-8(5)) Assn. for Supervision & Curriculum Development.

Kearse, Randy. Street Talk: Da Official Guide to Hip-Hop & Urban Slanguage. 2006. 686p. per. 19.95 (978-1-56980-320-2(X)) Barricade Bks., Inc.

Kinloch, Valerie. Harlem on Our Minds: Place, Race, & the Literacies of Urban Youth. 2010. (Language & Literacy Ser.). (ENG.). 224p. 64.00 (978-0-8077-5024-7(7)); pap. 25.95 (978-0-8077-5023-0(9)) Teachers College Pr., Teachers College, Columbia Univ.

KRS-One. The Gospel of Hip Hop: First Instrument. 2009. (ENG.). 832p. 24.95 (978-1-57687-497-4(4), powerHouse Bks.) powerHouse Cultural Entertainment, Inc.

Kunjufu, Jawanza. Understanding Black Male Learning Styles. 2011. (ENG., Illus.). 160p. pap. 15.95 (978-1-934155-38-7(1)) African American Images.

Mack, Cassandra. Her Rite of Passage: How to Design & Deliver a Rites of Passage Program for African-American Girls & Young Women. 2007. 160p. per. 20.95 (978-0-595-47036-5(X), Authors Choice Pr.) iUniverse, Inc.

Majithia, Pronoti. Exploring a Moral World. 2010. 68p. pap. (978-3-639-23992-8(X)) VDM Verlag Dr. Mueller e.K.

Mission, King. The Official Globalization of the ALKQN. 2008. 238p. pap. 19.95 (978-1-4357-1831-9(3)) Lulu Enterprises Inc.

Myers, William R. Black & White Styles of Youth Ministry. 2009. 232p. pap. 26.00 (978-1-60899-063-4(X), Wipf and Stock) Wipf & Stock Pubs.

Naison, Mark & Jones, Allen. The Rat That Got Away: A Bronx Memoir. 3rd ed. 2009. (ENG., Illus.). 224p. 70.00 (978-0-8232-3102-7(X)) Fordham Univ. Pr.

Nasir, Na'ilah Suad. Racialized Identities: Race & Achievement among African American Youth. 2011. (ENG.). 216p. 70.00 (978-0-8047-6018-8(7)); pap. 22.95 (978-0-8047-6019-5(5)) Stanford Univ. Pr.

Neri, Greg. Yummy: The Last Days of a Southside Shorty. 2007. (Illus.). (YA). (gr. 6-18). 18.95 (978-1-58430-266-7(6)) Lee & Low Bks., Inc.

Paikoff, Roberta L., ed. Community Collaborative Partnerships: The Foundation for HIV Prevention Research Efforts. 2007. (ENG., Illus.). 410p. 175.00 (978-0-7890-3253-9(8)); per. 56.95 (978-0-7890-3254-6(6)) Routledge.

Rice, David Wall. Balance: Advancing Identity Theory by Engaging the Black Male Adolescent. 2008. (ENG.). 148p. pap. 29.50 (978-0-7391-1889-4(7)); (Illus.). 57.99 (978-0-7391-1888-7(9)) Lexington Bks.

Rich, John A. Wrong Place, Wrong Time: Trauma & Violence in the Lives of Young Black Men. (ENG.). 232p. 2011. pap. 20.00 **(978-1-4214-0398-4(6))** 2009. 30.00 (978-0-8018-9363-6(1)) Johns Hopkins Univ. Pr.

Rios, Victor. Punished: Policing the Lives of Black & Latino Boys. 2011. (ENG.). 237p. 70.00 (978-0-8147-7637-7(X)); pap. 20.00 (978-0-8147-7638-4(8)) New York Univ. Pr.

Roberts, Tara, ed. What Your Mama Never Told You: True Stories about Sex & Love. 2007. (ENG.). 160p. (YA). (gr. 10-18). pap. 7.99 (978-0-618-64636-4(1)) Houghton Mifflin Harcourt Publishing Co.

Robinson-Easley, Christopher Anne. Our Children — Our Responsibilities: Saving the Youth We Are Losing to Gangs. 2012. xi, 225p. (C). pap. 139.95 **(978-1-4331-1200-3(0))** Lang, Peter Publishing, Inc.

Robinson-Easley, Christopher Anne. Our Children — Our Responsibilities: Saving the Youth We Are Losing to Gangs. 2012. xi, 225p. (C). pap. 34.95 ***(978-1-4331-1199-0(3))*** Lang, Peter Publishing, Inc.

—Our Children, Our Responsibilities: Saving the Youth We Are Losing to Gangs. 2012. xi, 225p. E-Book ***(978-1-4539-0265-3(1))*** Lang, Peter GmbH, Europaischer Verlag der Wissenschaften.

Samad, Anthony Asadullah. Saving the Race: Daily Affirmations for Young Black Males: Empowerment Through Wisdom. 2007. 400p. (YA). per. 15.00 *(978-0-9723880-3-0(6))* Kabili Pr.

Shabazz, Jamel, photos by. Back in the Days Remix. 10th anniv. ed. 2011. (ENG., Illus.). 132p. 35.00 *(978-1-57687-567-4(9))* powerHouse Cultural Entertainment, Inc.

Shepard, Raynel M. Cultural Adaptation of Somali Refugee Youth. 2008. (New Americans). 278p. 70.00 *(978-1-59332-233-5(X))* LFB Scholarly Publishing LLC.

Thompson, Gail. A Brighter Day: How Parents Can Help African American Youth. 2010. (ENG.). 225p. pap. 15.95 *(978-1-935521-74-7(8))* African American Images.

Tilton, Jennifer. Dangerous or Endangered? Race & the Politics of Youth in Urban America. 2010. (ENG., Illus.). 304p. 75.00 *(978-0-8147-8311-5(2))*; pap. 25.00 *(978-0-8147-8312-2(0))* New York Univ. Pr.

Tukufu, Darryl S. A Guide Toward the Successful Development of African-American Males: The Remix. 2nd ed. 2009. 91p. pap. 12.95 *(978-0-9662152-2-9(2))* Tukufu Group, The.

Turner, Richard. The Rise & Fall of the Crips. 2011. 126p. pap. 19.99 ***(978-1-4568-1832-6(5))*** Xlibris Corp.

Watkins, Ralph & Stephens, Benjamin. From Jay-Z to Jesus: Reaching & Teaching Young Adults in the Black Church. 2009. 128p. pap. 15.99 *(978-0-8170-1545-9(0))* Judson Pr.

W.C. Chandler. His Blood Cries Out for Justice. 2010. 108p. 22.95 *(978-1-4401-8743-8(6))*; pap. 12.95 *(978-1-4401-8741-4(X))* iUniverse, Inc.

Whalum, Kenneth T. Hip Hop Is Not Our Enemy: From A Preacher Who Keeps It Real. 2010. 184p. 24.99 *(978-1-4490-7425-8(1))*; pap. 14.49 *(978-1-4490-7424-1(3))* AuthorHouse.

Williams, Fay. Antecedents & Situated Factors of Juvenile Homicide. 2011. 144p. pap. ***(978-3-8443-8891-6(5))*** Lambert Academic Publishing.

Williams, Thomas Chatterton. Losing My Cool: Love, Literature, & a Black Man's Escape from the Crowd. 2011. (ENG.). 240p. (gr. 12). 15.00 *(978-0-14-311962-3(1)*, Penguin (Non-Classics)) Penguin Group (USA) Inc.

Womack, Ytasha. Beats Rhymes & Life: What We Love & Hate about Hip-Hop. Jasper, Kenji, ed. 2007. (ENG., Illus.). 320p. pap. 19.00 *(978-0-7679-1977-7(7)*, Harlem Moon) Broadway Bks.

Wylie, Arlet & Wylie, Same. Between Piety & Desire. 2010. 112p. pap. 15.00 *(978-1-60801-040-0(6))* Univ Of New Orleans Pr.

AFRICAN AMERICANS

Here are entered works on citizens of the United States of black African descent. Works on blacks who temporarily reside in the United States, such as aliens, students from abroad, etc., are entered under Blacks—United States. Works on blacks outside the United States are entered under Blacks—(Place).

see also Older African Americans

also subdivision African Americans under individual wars, e.g. World War, 1939-1945—African Americans; and headings beginning with African American

Adams, Grace, ed. 2010-2011 Black Authors & Published Writers Directory. 5th ed. 2010. (Illus.). 332p. pap. 89.95 *(978-1-877807-32-9(X)*, Black Authors & Published Writers Directory) Grace Publishing Co.

Aguirre Watts, A. Authentic Voices of Other Children's Parents: African American Parents' Experiences in, Perceptions of, & Understandings about Public Schools. 2007. 156p. per. 14.95 *(978-0-595-47575-9(2))* iUniverse, Inc.

American Friends Service Committee. Race & Conscience in Americ: A Review. 2011. 64p. 36.95 ***(978-1-258-03505-1(7))*** Literary Licensing, LLC.

Armstrong, Julie Buckner. Mary Turner & the Memory of Lynching. 2011. (ENG., Illus.). 264p. 59.95 *(978-0-8203-3765-4(X))*; pap. 24.95 *(978-0-8203-3766-1(8))* Univ. of Georgia Pr.

Baker, H. A. & Baker, Houston A. Betrayal: How Black Intellectuals Have Abandoned the Ideals of the Civil Rights Era. 2008. (ENG.). 272p. (gr. 17). 26.95 *(978-0-231-13964-9(0))* Columbia Univ. Pr.

Bani, Arno. Michael Jackson. 2010. (ENG.). 220p. 60.00 *(978-2-8123-0368-5(9)*, Hachette Livre (Acc)) Antique Collectors' Club GBR. Dist: National Bk. Network.

Banks, Ralph Richard. Is Marriage for White People? How the African American Marriage Decline Affects Everyone. 2012. (ENG.). 304p. (gr. 12). pap. 16.00 ***(978-0-452-29753-1(2)***, Plume) Penguin Group (USA) Inc.

Battle, Stafford. AFROCyberspace: 1000+ African American Websites That Will Change Your World. 2007. spiral bd. 14.95 net. *(978-1-60402-248-3(5))* Independent Pub.

Beemyn, Brett. Queer Capital. 2010. 320p. 95.00 *(978-0-415-92172-5(4))* Routledge.

Berry, Pamela. The Art of African American Hair Design. 2011. (ENG.). 250p. (C). pap. 46.50 *(978-0-615-18991-8(1)*, Milady Publishing Co.) Delmar Cengage Learning.

Bieze, Michael. Booker T. Washington & the Art of Self-Representation. 2008. (History of Schools & Schooling Ser.). (Illus.). 304p. (C). pap. 32.95 *(978-1-4331-0010-9(X))* Lang, Peter Publishing, Inc.

Bilberry, Charles. There's More Leaves on the Tree. 2011. 340p. pap. 24.99 ***(978-1-4634-0465-9(4))*** AuthorHouse.

Bordas. Salsa, Soul, & Spirit: Leadership for A Multicultural Age. 2nd rev. ed. 2012. (ENG.). 248p. pap. 22.95 ***(978-1-60994-117-8(9))*** Berrett-Koehler Pubs., Inc.

Bowser, Benjamin P. & Quimby, Ernest, eds. When Communities Assess their AIDS Epidemics: Results of Rapid Assessment of HIV/AIDS in Eleven U. S. Cities. 2008. (ENG.). 264p. pap. 31.50 *(978-0-7391-2949-4(X))* Lexington Bks.

Bowser, Benjamin P., et al. When Communities Assess Their AIDS Epidemics: Results of Rapid Assessment of HIV/AIDS in Eleven U. S. Cities. 2007. (ENG., Illus.). 264p. 68.50 *(978-0-7391-0752-2(6))* Lexington Bks.

Brooks, Jeffrey S. Black School White School: Racism & Educational (MIS) Leadership. 2012. (ENG.). 176p. pap. 26.95 ***(978-0-8077-5312-5(2))*** Teachers College Pr., Teachers College, Columbia Univ.

Brown, Joseph A. To Stand on the Rock: Meditations on Black Catholic Identity. 2011. 222p. pap. 24.00 ***(978-1-61097-568-1(5)***, Wipf and Stock) Wipf & Stock Pubs.

Brown, William W. My Southern Home: The South & Its People. (Muckrakers Ser.). (Illus.). 260p. reprint ed. lib. bdg. 32.95 *(978-0-8398-0177-1(7))* Irvington Pubs.

Carter, Edward R. The Black Side. 2009. 232p. pap. *(978-0-217-29186-6(4))* Books LLC.

Chesnutt, Charles Waddell. The Negro Problem. 2006. (Illus.). pap. *(978-1-4065-0983-0(3))* Dodo Pr.

Chesnutt, Charles Waddell, et al. The Portable Charles W. Chesnutt. Gates, Henry Louis, Jr. & Andrews, William L., eds. 2008. (ENG.). 544p. (gr. 12-18). 18.00 *(978-0-14-310534-3(5)*, Penguin Classics) Penguin Group (USA) Inc.

Clowes, William Laird. Black America: A Study of the Ex-Slave & His Late Master. 240p. reprint ed. 98.00 *(978-0-7222-9714-8(9))* Library Reprints, Inc.

Cole, Diedra. Three Strikes: A Soldier's Story. 2010. 132p. 23.95 *(978-1-4502-4624-8(9))* iUniverse, Inc.

Coleman, Mrs. Octavia, Mhsa & Charity, For the Cause, Inc. The Role of Community Leaders: Finding Solutions to the HIV/AIDS Epidemic. 2010. 140p. pap. 15.00 *(978-0-557-24464-5(1))* Lulu Enterprises Inc.

Connor, Michael E. & White, Joseph, eds. Black Fathers: An Invisible Presence in America. 2nd rev. ed. 2011. (ENG.). 302p. 110.00 *(978-0-415-88366-5(0))*; pap. 41.95 *(978-0-415-88367-2(9))* Taylor & Francis Group GBR. (Routledge). Dist: Taylor & Francis Group.

Corlett, J. Angelo. Heirs of Oppression. 2010. xv, 371p. *(978-1-4422-0816-2(3))* Rowman & Littlefield Publishers, Inc.

—Heirs of Oppression: Racism & Reparations. 2010. (Studies in Social, Political, & Legal Philosophy Ser.). (ENG.). 388p. pap. 34.95 *(978-1-4422-0815-5(5))* Rowman & Littlefield Publishers, Inc.

Cram101 Textbook Reviews & Cram101 Textbook Reviews. Outlines & Highlights for Family Violence & Men of Color: Healing the Wounded Male Spirit by Carrillo, ISBN. 2011. 58p. pap. 26.95 ***(978-1-61461-625-2(6))*** Cram101 Inc.

Crow, Jeffrey J., et al. A History of African Americans in North Carolina. 2nd ed. 2011. (Illus.). xii, 292p. pap. ***(978-0-86526-351-2(5))*** North Carolina Office of Archives & History.

Daniel, William R. Shootout at Miracle Valley. 2008. 224p. pap. 19.95 *(978-1-60494-152-4(9))* Wheatmark.

Davis, Charlie. Diary of a Madman. 2009. 58p. pap. 15.99 *(978-1-4415-4264-9(7))* Xlibris Corp.

Davis, Ossie. Life Lit by Some Large Vision: Selected Speeches & Writings. 2010. (ENG.). 272p. pap. 17.99 *(978-0-7432-8989-4(7)*, Washington Square Pr.) Washington Square Pr.

Davis, Sampson. The Pact: Three Young Men Make a Promise & Fulfill a Dream. 2006. (ENG.). 272p. (C). pap. 6.53 *(978-0-13-239349-2(2)*, Prentice Hall) Prentice Hall PTR.

Davis, Valerie Bridgeman & Fosua, Safiyah, eds. The Africana Worship Book, Year B. 2007. 256p. 32.00 incl. cd-rom *(978-0-88177-514-3(2))* Discipleship Resources.

Dawson, Michael C. Not in Our Lifetimes: The Future of Black Politics. 2011. (Illus.). 232p. 26.00 *(978-0-226-13862-6(3))* Univ. of Chicago Pr.

Du Bois, W. E. B. Darkwater. 2008. 224p. 24.99 *(978-0-554-34535-2(8))*; 27.99 *(978-0-554-25232-2(5))* BiblioBazaar.

—Darkwater: Voices from Within the Veil. 2007. (ENG.). 200p. pap. 19.99 *(978-1-4264-8470-4(4))* BiblioBazaar.

—Darkwater: Voices from Within the Veil. 2007. (ENG.). 172p. per. 16.95 *(978-1-60206-812-4(7))* Cosimo, Inc.

—Darkwater: Voices from Within the Veil. 2007. *(978-0-19-532577-5(X))* Oxford Univ. Pr., Inc.

—Darkwater: Voices from Within the Veil (2006. pap. *(978-1-4065-1120-8(X))* Dodo Pr.

—Darkwater: Voices from Within the Veil. reprint ed. 37.50 *(978-0-404-00151-3(3))* AMS Pr., Inc.

—Darkwater: Voices from Within the Veil. l.t. ed. 2007. (ENG.). 222p. pap. 22.99 *(978-1-4264-8528-2(X))* BiblioBazaar.

—The Negro. 2009. 168p. 25.00 *(978-1-59740-364-1(4))*; 166p. pap. 17.00 *(978-1-59740-365-8(2))* ACLS Humanities E-Book.

—The Negro. 2008. 188p. 25.99 *(978-0-554-29609-8(8))* 2008. 184p. 22.99 *(978-0-554-34581-9(1))* 2008. 184p. 25.99 *(978-0-554-25278-0(3))* 2008. 188p. 22.99 *(978-0-554-38912-7(6))* 2007. (ENG.). 186p. pap. 21.99 *(978-1-4346-8015-0(0))* 2007. (ENG.). 170p. pap. 19.99 *(978-1-4346-8014-3(2))* 2007. (ENG.). 162p. pap. 19.99 *(978-1-4264-8576-3(X))* 2007. (ENG.). 182p. pap. 21.99 *(978-1-4264-8633-3(2))* BiblioBazaar.

—The Negro. 2007. (ENG.). 156p. per. 11.95 *(978-1-60206-814-8(3))* Cosimo, Inc.

—The Negro. 2007. *(978-0-19-532576-8(1))* Oxford Univ. Pr., Inc.

—The Negro. 2009. 160p. pap. 11.95 *(978-1-4385-1906-7(0))*; (ENG.). pap. 14.45 *(978-1-4385-1287-7(2))* Standard Pubns., Inc. (Book Jungle).

—The Negro. 2008. 120p. pap. 7.99 *(978-1-60459-371-6(7))* Wilder Pubns., Ltd.

—The Sociological Souls of Black Folk. 2011. (ENG.). 260p. 70.00 *(978-0-7391-5073-3(1))* Lexington Bks.

—The Souls of Black Folk. 2008. 172p. pap. 5.99 *(978-1-60450-206-0(1))* Arc Manor.

—The Souls of Black Folk. 2008. 216p. 24.99 *(978-0-554-34557-4(9))*; 27.99 *(978-0-554-25254-4(6))* BiblioBazaar.

—The Souls of Black Folk. 2007. 176p. 21.95 *(978-1-60206-721-9(X))*; (ENG.). per. 7.95 *(978-1-60206-720-2(1))* Cosimo, Inc.

—The Souls of Black Folk. 2006. (ENG.). pap. *(978-1-4065-1119-2(6))* Dodo Pr.

—The Souls of Black Folk. 2008. 208p. pap. 13.95 *(978-1-60096-840-2(6))*; 232p. pap. 13.95 *(978-1-4341-0133-4(9))* Editorium, The.

—The Souls of Black Folk. 2007. (ENG.). 232p. 34.75 *(978-0-9793363-9-3(2))* Ellis, Frederick.

—The Souls of Black Folk. 2007. 248p. pap. 6.99 *(978-1-59986-759-5(1)*, FQ Classics) Filiquarian Publishing, LLC.

—The Souls of Black Folk. 2010. (Illus.). 120p. pap. 20.96 *(978-1-153-72129-5(5))* General Bks. LLC.

—The Souls of Black Folk. HarperCollins Pubs.

—The Souls of Black Folk. 2011. 182p. pap. 19.95 *(978-1-60444-264-9(6))* IndoEuropeanPublishing.com.

—The Souls of Black Folk. 2010. 154p. pap. 17.56 *(978-1-162-70874-4(3))*; 36.95 *(978-1-161-47738-2(1))* Kessinger Publishing, LLC.

—The Souls of Black Folk. 2009. (ENG.). 256p. (gr. 12-18). pap. 10.95 *(978-1-59853-054-4(2))* Library of America, The.

—The Souls of Black Folk. 2007. (ENG.). 152p. per. 12.99 *(978-1-59547-898-6(1))* NuVision Pubns., LLC.

—The Souls of Black Folk. 2012. (ENG.). 256p. (gr. 12). 5.95 *(978-0-451-53205-3(8)*, Signet Classics) Penguin Group (USA) Inc.

—The Souls of Black Folk. 2009. (ENG.). 330p. pap. 24.95 *(978-1-4128-1302-0(6))* Transaction Pubs.

Du Bois, W. e. b. The Souls of Black Folk. 2010. (ENG.). 149p. pap. 4.95 *(978-1-61600-221-3(2))* Mizzou Media - Univ. BookStores.

Du Bois, W. E. B. The Souls of Black Folk. l.t. ed. 2007. (ENG.). 212p. pap. 22.99 *(978-1-4264-8608-1(1))*; 226p. pap. 19.99 *(978-1-4264-8551-0(4))* BiblioBazaar.

—The Souls of Black Folk. 264p. reprint ed. 98.00 *(978-0-7222-9721-6(1))* Library Reprints, Inc.

—The Souls of Black Folk (Catawba Classic) 2007. per. 5.95 *(978-1-59712-087-6(1))* Catawba Publishing Co.

Duncan, Mary Grey Lundie. America As I Found It by the Mother of Mary Lundie Duncan. 2006. 456p. per. 29.99 *(978-1-4255-4985-5(3))* MPublishing.

Eastman, H. P. The Negro. reprint ed. 150.00 *(978-0-7222-9724-7(6))* Library Reprints, Inc.

Elk, Ronit & Landrine, Hope. Cancer Disparities: Causes & Evidence-Based Solutions. 2011. 480p. pap. ***(978-0-8261-0882-1(2))***; E-Book ***(978-0-8261-0883-8(0))*** Springer Publishing Co., Inc.

Epps, Kevin. Black Rock: The Dark Side of Alcatraz. 2009. (Illus.). pap. 18.95 *(978-0-935419-26-9(8)*, Mastamind) eAccess Corp.

Farr, Stacie. Black Girl in America: A Memoir. 2010. 84p. pap. 12.99 *(978-1-4269-2871-0(8))* Trafford Publishing.

Fields, Uriah J. The Fields School: An African American School Without Failures Located in Rural Alabama 1933-1949. 2009. 84p. pap. 12.00 *(978-1-4490-0438-5(5))* AuthorHouse.

Fisher, Sidney. The Laws of Race. 2008. (Civil War Ser.). (ENG.). 76p. pap. 9.95 *(978-1-4290-1585-1(3))* Applewood Bks.

Fogel, Robert William. The Slavery Debates, 1952-1990: A Retrospective. 2006. (Walter Lynwood Fleming Lectures in Southern History Ser.). 106p. per. 16.95 *(978-0-8071-3199-2(7))* Louisiana State Univ. Pr.

Fortune, Timothy Thomas. Black & White. 2009. 316p. 25.99 *(978-1-103-84243-8(9))* 2009. 316p. pap. 19.99 *(978-1-103-84235-3(8))* 2008. (ENG.). 224p. per. 24.75 *(978-1-4375-2389-8(7))* 2008. (ENG.). 250p. per. 26.75 *(978-1-4375-2525-0(3))* BiblioBazaar.

—Black & White. 2009. 164p. pap. *(978-1-4588-2489-9(6))* Books LLC.

—Black & White. 310p. reprint ed. 98.00 *(978-0-7222-9726-1(2))* Library Reprints, Inc.

Fulwood, Valaida. Giving Back: A Tribute to Generations of African American Philanthropists. 2011. (Illus.). 392p. 36.50 *(978-0-89587-564-8(0))* Blair, John F. Pub.

Gaines, Kevin K. American Africans in Ghana: Black Expatriates & the Civil Rights Era. 2008. (ENG., Illus.). 360p. per. 27.95 *(978-0-8078-5893-6(5))* Univ. of North Carolina Pr.

Gaines, Wesley John. The Negro & the White Man. 2010. 230p. pap. 25.75 *(978-1-141-67165-6(4))* BiblioBazaar.

—The Negro & the White Man. 2009. 118p. pap. 14.14 *(978-1-150-79000-3(8))* General Bks. LLC.

Garrett, Nathan. A Palette, Not a Portrait: Stories from the life of Nathan Garrett. 2010. 240p. 28.95 *(978-1-4502-4876-1(4))*; pap. 18.95 *(978-1-4502-4875-4(6))* iUniverse, Inc.

Gasman, Marybeth, et al. Race, Gender, & Leadership in Nonprofit Organizations. 2011. (ENG., Illus.). 208p. 85.00 *(978-0-230-12039-6(3))* Palgrave Macmillan.

Gaston-Thornton, Parichart. Teaching Oral Reading Fluency in the Classroom. 2010. 80p. pap. *(978-3-639-24251-5(3))* VDM Verlag Dr. Mueller e.K.

Gates, Henry Louis, Jr., ed. The Oxford W. E. B. du Bois, 19 vols., Set. 2007. (ENG.). 5360p. 895.00 *(978-0-19-531180-8(9))* Oxford Univ. Pr., Inc.

Goldberg, David & Griffey, Trevor. Black Power at Work: Community Control, Affirmative Action, & the Construction Industry. 2010. 280p. pap. 24.95 *(978-0-8014-7431-6(0)*, ILR Pr.) Cornell Univ. Pr.

Goldberg, David & Griffey, Trevor, eds. Black Power at Work: Community Control, Affirmative Action, & the Construction Industry. 2010. 280p. 65.00 *(978-0-8014-4658-0(9)*, ILR Pr.) Cornell Univ. Pr.

Graham, Stephen. Children of the Slaves. 2010. 338p. pap. 31.75 *(978-1-177-83069-0(8))* 2010. 328p. 36.99 *(978-1-140-20267-7(7))* 2010. 328p. 36.99 *(978-1-140-20273-8(1))* 2010. 328p. pap. 30.75 *(978-1-140-20274-5(X))* 2010. 328p. pap. 30.75 *(978-1-140-20268-4(5))* 2009. 328p. 32.99 *(978-1-110-03651-6(5))* 2009. 328p. pap. 30.75 *(978-1-110-03649-3(3))* 2009. (ENG.). 326p. pap. 23.99 *(978-1-110-03646-2(9)*, BiblioLife) 2009. (ENG.). 326p. pap. 24.99 *(978-1-110-03647-9(7)*, BiblioLife) BiblioBazaar.

—Children of the Slaves. 2009. 190p. pap. *(978-1-4590-4096-0(1))* Books LLC.

—Children of the Slaves. 2010. 328p. pap. 24.76 *(978-1-163-94731-9(8))* 2008. 326p. 45.95 *(978-0-548-96039-4(9))* 2007. (ENG.). 328p. per. 30.95 *(978-0-548-63575-9(7))* Kessinger Publishing, LLC.

—Children of the Slaves. 2008. 332p. pap. *(978-1-4086-7920-3(5))*; pap. *(978-1-4097-9829-3(1))* Read Bks.

Grayson, Sandra M., ed. A Literary Revolution: In the Spirit of the Harlem Renaissance. 2007. (ENG.). 172p. per. 32.99 *(978-0-7618-3924-8(0))* Univ. Pr. of America, Inc.

Greene, Larry A. & Ortlepp, Anke, eds. Germans & African Americans: Two Centuries of Exchange. 2010. (ENG.). 304p. 55.00 *(978-1-60473-784-4(0))* Univ. Pr. of Mississippi.

Hair, Beverly Ann. Examining the Experiences of Nontraditional Undergraduate Women. 2011. 292p. pap. ***(978-3-8433-8159-8(3))*** Lambert Academic Publishing.

Hamer, Jennifer. Abandoned in the Heartland: Work, Family, & Living in East St. Louis. 2011. (ENG., Illus.). 280p. 60.00 *(978-0-520-26931-6(4))*; pap. 24.95 *(978-0-520-26932-3(2))* Univ. of California Pr.

Harvey, Jennifer. Whiteness & Morality: Pursuing Racial Justice Through Reparations & Sovereignty. annot. ed. 2007. (Black Religion/Womanist Thought/Social Justice Ser.). (ENG.). 276p. 89.00 *(978-1-4039-7739-7(9))* Palgrave Macmillan.

Hassler, Thomasina F. Where the Rocks Are in the Pond. 2011. 164p. pap. ***(978-3-8443-8036-1(1))*** Lambert Academic Publishing.

Herskovits, Melville Jean. Anthropometry of the American Negro. (Columbia University, Contributions to Anthropology Ser.: No. 11). reprint ed. 32.50 *(978-0-404-50561-5(9))* AMS Pr., Inc.

Hill, Anthony & Barnett, Douglas E. Historical Dictionary of African American Theater. 2008. (Historical Dictionaries of Literature & the Arts Ser.). (ENG.). 624p. 121.00 *(978-0-8108-5534-2(8))* Scarecrow Pr., Inc.

Hoffman, Frederick L. Race Traits & Tendencies of the American Negro. 329p. reprint ed. 98.00 *(978-0-7222-9728-5(9))* Library Reprints, Inc.

Horne, Gerald. Red Seas: Ferdinand Smith & Radical Black Sailors in the United States & Jamaica. 2009. (ENG.). 384p. pap. 25.00 *(978-0-8147-3740-8(4))* New York Univ. Pr.

Hunt, B. P. Why Colored People in Philadelphia Are Excluded from the Street Cars. 2011. 30p. pap. 11.99 ***(978-1-4181-9340-9(2))*** MPublishing.

Information Publications, creator. Black Americans: A Statistical Sourcebook. 2007. (Black Americans: A Statistical Sourcebook Ser.). 360p. 116.00 *(978-0-929960-44-9(0))* Information Pubns., Inc.

Information Publications, ed. Black Americans 2008: A Statistical Sourcebook & Guide to Government Data. 2008. 390p. per. 77.00 *(978-0-929960-49-4(1))* Information Pubns., Inc.

Isham, Dell. Isom Dart & an Assortment of Scoundrels. 2010. 368p. pap. 19.95 *(978-1-4327-4427-4(5))* Outskirts Pr., Inc.

Jeter, Jon & Pierre, Robert. A Day Late & a Dollar Short: High Hopes & Deferred Dreams in Obama's Post Racial America. 2009. (ENG.). 256p. 25.95 *(978-0-470-52066-6(3)*, Wiley) Wiley, John & Sons, Inc.

Johnson, M. Dujon. Race & Racism in the Chinas: Chinese Racial attitudes toward Africans & African-Americans. 2007. 168p. per. 15.95 *(978-1-4259-8175-4(5))* AuthorHouse.

Jones, Lee. Black in America: Where a Ph. D. is Still Not Enough. 2007. 240p. pap. 24.95 *(978-1-57922-044-0(4))* Stylus Publishing, LLC.

Jones, LeRoi. Home: Social Essays. 2009. (Renegade Reprint Ser.). (ENG.). 250p. pap. 15.95 *(978-1-933354-67-5(4))* Akashic Bks.

Jones, R. Clifford. James K. Humphrey & the Sabbath-Day Adventists. 2010. (ENG.). 258p. pap. 25.00 *(978-1-60473-522-2(8))* Univ. Pr. of Mississippi.

June, Lee N. Counseling for Seemingly Impossible Problems: A Biblical Perspective, 1 vol. Black, Sabrina & Richardson, Willie, eds. 2007. (ENG.). 272p. (gr. 13). pap. 14.99 *(978-0-310-27843-6(0))* Zondervan.

Kerlin, Robert T. The Voice of the Negro. 2010. 204p. pap. 24.95 *(978-0-557-36546-3(5))* Lulu Enterprises Inc.

Khan, Lurey. William Still & the Underground Railroad: Fugitive Slaves & Family Ties. 2010. 352p. 33.95 *(978-1-4401-8628-8(6))*; pap. 23.95 *(978-1-4401-8626-4(X))* iUniverse, Inc.

Knecht, Sharon C. Oblate Sisters of Providence: A Pictorial History. 2007. *(978-1-57864-437-7(2))* Donning Co. Pubs.

LaRue, Cleophus J. I Believe I'll Testify: The Art of African American Preaching. 2011. (ENG.). 144p. pap. 17.00 *(978-0-664-23677-9(4))* Westminster John Knox Pr.

Lee, Dante. Black Business Secrets: 500 Tips, Strategies, & Resources for the African American Entrepreneurs. 2010. (ENG.). 336p. pap. 15.95 *(978-1-4019-2954-1(0))* Hay Hse., Inc.

Lewter, Justin. Why Scouting Works for Black Boys. 2008. (ENG., Illus.). 100p. pap. 12.95 *(978-1-934155-10-3(1))* African American Images.

Lieberman, Robert C. Shaping Race Policy: The United States in Comparative Perspective. 2007. (Princeton Studies in American Politics). (ENG., Illus.). 336p. (C). per. 27.95 *(978-0-691-13046-0(9))* Princeton Univ. Pr.

Liggins-Hill, Patricia. Anthology African-American Literature, Vol. 2. Date not set. (C). pap. 32.76 *(978-0-395-80964-8(9))* CENGAGE Learning.

Lowther, Kevin G. The African American Odyssey of John Kizell: The Life & Times of a South Carolina Slave Who Returned to Fight the Slave Trade in His African Homeland. 2011. 336p. 39.95 *(978-1-57003-960-7(7))* Univ. of South Carolina Pr.

Ludwig, Frieder & Asamoah-Gyadu, J. Kwabena. African Christian Presence in the West: New Immigrant Congregations & Transnational Networks in North America & Europe. 2011. *(978-1-59221-807-3(5))*; 238p. pap. *(978-1-59221-808-0(3))* Africa World Pr.

Marcus, Grania B. Discovering the African-American Experience in Suffolk County, 1620-1860. Date not set. lib. bdg. 14.95 *(978-0-8488-1720-6(6))* Amereon LTD.

Martin, Vernon. Master the Culture: The Way to Unleash Your Ultimate Potential. 2010. 124p. pap. 12.50 *(978-1-60844-484-7(8))* Dog Ear Publishing, LLC.

McCaskill, Carolyn. The Hidden Treasure of Black ASL: Its History & Structure. 2011. E-Book *(978-1-56368-490-6(X))* Gallaudet Univ. Pr.

McCaskill, Carolyn, et al. The Hidden Treasure of Black ASL: Its History & Structure. 2011. (ENG., Illus.). 240p. (C). 75.00 *(978-1-56368-489-0(6))* Gallaudet Univ. Pr.

McCree, Donna H., et al. African Americans & HIV/AIDS: Understanding & Addressing the Epidemic. 2010. (Illus.). xx, 323p. E-Book ***(978-0-387-78321-5(0))*** Springer.

Mendelsohn, Adam. Jews & the Civil War: A Reader. Sarna, Jonathan, ed. 2011. (ENG., Illus.). 445p. pap. 24.00 ***(978-0-8147-7113-6(0))*** New York Univ. Pr.

Merriam, George S. The Negro & the Nation. 436p. reprint ed. 98.00 *(978-0-7222-9733-9(5))* Library Reprints, Inc.

Miles, Tiya & Holland, Sharon Patricia, eds. Crossing Waters, Crossing Worlds: The African Diaspora in Indian Country. 2006. (ENG., Illus.). 392p. 94.95 *(978-0-8223-3812-3(2))*; pap. 26.95 *(978-0-8223-3865-9(3))* Duke Univ. Pr.

Miller, Kelly. Race Adjustment. 2009. 176p. pap. *(978-0-217-97988-7(2))* Books LLC.

—Race Adjustment. 2009. 166p. pap. 19.99 *(978-0-217-53958-6(0))* General Bks. LLC.

Mitchell, William Frank. African American Food Culture, 1 vol. 2009. (Food Cultures in America Ser.). (Illus.). 118p. 49.95 *(978-0-313-34620-0(8))*, GR4620, Greenwood Pr.) Greenwood Publishing Group, Inc.

Moore, Joseph Thomas. Larry Doby: The Struggle of the American League's First Black Player. 2012. (Dover Baseball Ser.). (ENG., Illus.). 256p. pap. 12.95 ***(978-0-486-48337-5(1))*** Dover Pubns., Inc.

Muhammad, Salahudcin M. Bridging the Divide Between Immigrant & African American Muslims by Utilizing the Concept of Tawheed As the Catalyst: Between Immigrant & African. 2011. 108p. 24.99 ***(978-1-4568-9155-8(3))***; pap. 15.99 ***(978-1-4568-9154-1(5))*** Xlibris Corp.

Mulroy, Kevin. The Seminole Freedmen: A History. 2007. (Race & Culture in the American West Ser.). (ENG., Illus.). 480p. (C). 36.95 *(978-0-8061-3865-7(3))* Univ. of Oklahoma Pr.

Murphy, Edgar G. The Basis of Ascendancy: A Discussion of Certain Principles of Public Policy Involved in the Development of the Southern States. 250p. reprint ed. 98.00 *(978-0-7222-9735-3(1))* Library Reprints, Inc.

Mwakikagile, Godfrey. Relations Between Africans African Ameri. 2007. pap. *(978-0-9802587-4-5(X))* New Africa Pr.

—Relations Between Africans & African A. 2007. pap. *(978-0-9802534-5-0(4))* New Africa Pr.

Nell, William Cooper. The Colored Patriots of the American Revolution. 2010. 382p. pap. *(978-1-60796-272-4(1))* Editorial Benei Noaj.

Nelson, Dana K. Mission & Migration: Fifty-Two African & Asian Congregations in Minnesota. 2007. (ENG., Illus.). 204p. per. 14.00 *(978-1-932688-21-4(8))*, Lutheran Univ. Pr.) Kirk Hse. Pubs.

Nevergold, Barbara & Brooks-Bertram, Peggy. Uncrowned Queens Vol. 4: African American Women Community Builders of Oklahoma. Nevergold, Barbara & Brooks-Bertram, Peggy, eds. 2009. (Uncrowned Queens Institute Ser.). (Illus.). 273p. (C). pap. 24.95 *(978-0-9722977-4-5(X))* Uncrowned Queens Institute for Research & Education On Women, Inc.

Norment, Nathaniel. The African American Studies Reader. 2nd ed. 2007. (ENG.). per. 60.00 *(978-1-59460-155-2(0))* Carolina Academic Pr.

Odum, Howard W. Race & Rumors of Race. 2011. (ENG.). 256p. pap. 40.00 *(978-0-8078-9742-3(6))* Univ. of North Carolina Pr.

Ogundiran, Akinwumi & Falola, Toyin, eds. Archaeology of Atlantic Africa & the African Diaspora. 2010. (Blacks in the Diaspora Ser.). (ENG., Illus.). 528p. pap. 29.95 *(978-0-253-22175-9(7)*, 0253221757) Indiana Univ. Pr.

Olivier, Sydney H. O. White Capital & Coloured Labour. 175p. reprint ed. 88.00 *(978-0-7222-9805-3(6))* Library Reprints, Inc.

Onkey, Lauren. Blackness & Transatlantic Irish Identity: Celtic Soul Brothers. 2009. (Routledge Research in Race & Ethnicity Ser.). (ENG.). 244p. 125.00 *(978-0-415-80189-8(3))* Routledge.

Page, Thomas Nelson. The Negro: The Southerner's Problem. 2009. 332p. 25.99 *(978-0-559-94329-4(6))*; pap. 19.99 *(978-0-559-94326-3(1))* BiblioBazaar.

—The Negro: The Southerner's Problem. 2007. (ENG.). 332p. 45.95 *(978-0-548-36057-6(X))*; per. 30.95 *(978-0-548-30334-4(7))* Kessinger Publishing, LLC.

Patterson, Raymond. The Negro & His Needs. 2008. 210p. 39.95 *(978-0-548-95249-8(3))* 2007. (ENG.). 212p. per. 24.95 *(978-0-548-62751-8(7))* Kessinger Publishing, LLC.

Pickett, William P. The Negro Problem. reprint ed. 98.00 *(978-0-7222-9740-7(8))* Library Reprints, Inc.

—The Negro Problem: Abraham Lincoln's Solution. 2007. 596p. 59.95 *(978-0-548-56160-7(5))*; (ENG.). per. 44.95 *(978-0-548-50269-3(2))* Kessinger Publishing, LLC.

—The Negro Problem: Abraham Lincoln's Solution. 580p. reprint ed. 98.00 *(978-0-7222-8799-6(2))* Library Reprints, Inc.

Pigeon, Gerard G. Etched in Black. 74.95 *(978-1-84014-467-3(X))* Ashgate Publishing, Ltd. GBR. Dist: Ashgate Publishing, Ltd.

Pine, Joslyn, ed. Book of African-American Quotations. 2011. (Dover Thrift Editions Ser.). (ENG.). 224p. pap. 3.50 *(978-0-486-47589-9(1))* Dover Pubns., Inc.

Pollard, Edward Alfred. The Lost Cause Regained by Edward a Pollard. 2006. 216p. per. 20.99 *(978-1-4255-1819-6(2))* MPublishing.

Rael, Patrick, ed. African-American Activism Before the Civil War: The Freedom Struggle in the Antebellum North. 2008. (ENG.). 320p. 135.00 *(978-0-415-95726-7(5))*; pap. 36.95 *(978-0-415-95727-4(3))* Routledge.

Record, C. Wilson. The Negro & the Communist Party. 2011. (ENG.). 352p. pap. 50.00 *(978-0-8078-9759-1(0))* Univ. of North Carolina Pr.

Reference Library of Black America, 5 vols. 1765p. 199.50 *(978-0-7876-1535-2(8))* Cengage Gale.

Rich, Wilbur C., ed. African American Perspectives on Political Science. 2007. (Illus.). 456p. 93.50 *(978-1-59213-108-2(5))*; per. 35.95 *(978-1-59213-109-9(3))* Temple Univ. Pr.

Richings, G. F. Evidences of Progress among Colored People. 2009. 168p. pap. *(978-1-150-55156-7(9))* Books LLC.

—Evidences of Progress among Colored People. 2007. (ENG.). 584p. 58.95 *(978-0-548-37532-7(1))*; per. 43.95 *(978-0-548-31859-1(X))* Kessinger Publishing, LLC.

Riggs, Marlon, prod. Black Is... Black Ain't. pap., stu. ed. 195.00 incl. VHS *(978-1-57254-001-9(X))* California Newsreel.

Román, Miriam Jiménez & Flores, Juan, eds. The Afro-Latin@ Reader: History & Culture in the United States. 2010. (John Hope Franklin Center Book Ser.). (ENG., Illus.). 584p. pap. 32.95 *(978-0-8223-4572-5(2))*; 104.95 *(978-0-8223-4558-9(7))* Duke Univ. Pr.

Roman, Meredith L. Opposing Jim Crow: African Americans & the Soviet Indictment of U. S. Racism, 1928-1937. 2012. (Justice & Social Inquiry Ser.). (ENG., Illus.). 320p. 55.00 ***(978-0-8032-1552-8(5))*** Univ. of Nebraska Pr.

Rose, Peter I., ed. Old Memories, New Moods Vol. 2: Americans from Africa. 2007. (ENG.). 479p. (gr. 11). pap. 39.95 *(978-0-202-36161-1(6))* Aldine Transaction.

—Slavery & Its Aftermath. 2007. (ENG., Illus.). 486p. pap. 44.95 *(978-0-202-30941-5(X))* Aldine Transaction.

Rousseve, Ronald J. Discord in Brown & White: Nine Essays on Intergroup Relations in the United States by A Negro American. 2011. 90p. 38.95 ***(978-1-258-07209-4(2))*** Literary Licensing, LLC.

Ruble, Blair A. Washington's U Street: A Biography. 2010. (ENG., Illus.). 432p. (gr. 17). 29.95 *(978-0-8018-9800-6(5))* Johns Hopkins Univ. Pr.

Salvatore, Nick. We All Got History: The Memory Books of Amos Webber. 2006. (Illus.). 464p. pap. 26.00 *(978-0-252-07440-0(8))* Univ. of Illinois Pr.

Shufeldt, R. W. America's Greatest Problem: the Negro. 2010. 463p. pap. 33.95 *(978-0-557-36234-9(2))* Lulu Enterprises Inc.

Shufeldt, Robert W. The Negro: A Menace to American Civilization. reprint ed. 98.00 *(978-0-7222-9742-1(4))* Library Reprints, Inc.

Shufeldt, Robert Wilson. America's Greatest Problem: the Negro. 2010. 465p. pap. 33.95 *(978-0-557-36375-9(6))* Lulu Enterprises Inc.

Smith, Charles N. The Last Shall Be The. 2008. 156p. pap. 12.95 *(978-1-4327-2791-8(5))* Outskirts Pr., Inc.

Smith, James Mccune. The Works of James Mccune Smith: Black Intellectual & Abolitionist. Stauffer, John, ed. 2007. (Collected Black Writings). (ENG., Illus.). 384p. 115.00 *(978-0-19-530961-4(8))* Oxford Univ. Pr., Inc.

Speight, Willie. Messy Black Women. 2010. 172p. pap. 11.99 *(978-1-4520-3902-2(X))* AuthorHouse.

Taulbert, Clifton L. & Decker, Douglas E. Facilitator's Guide Eight Habits of the Heart for Educators: Building Strong School Communites Through Timeless Values. 2006. (Illus.). 54p. pap. 16.95 *(978-1-4129-5045-6(5)*, B26300F) Corwin Pr.

Taylor, Teresa. Dear African American Brother. 2010. 16p. pap. *(978-1-55452-529-4(2)*, Epic Pr.) Essence Publishing.

Teal, Prince. Are You Raising One of the Next Generation of Hoodlums? 2007. 92p. per. 16.95 *(978-1-4241-7289-4(6))* PublishAmerica, Inc.

The Kamoinge Workshop. The Sweet Breath of Life: A Poetic Narrative of the African-American Family. Stewart, Frank, ed. 2010. (ENG., Illus.). 192p. pap. 13.99 *(978-0-7434-7898-4(3)*, Beyond Words/Atria Bks.) Atria Bks.

Tiony, Genevieve. Wounded Afric: The Cultural Differences Between Africa & America. 2009. 212p. 29.95 *(978-1-4389-4470-8(5))*; pap. 21.95 *(978-1-4389-4471-5(3))* AuthorHouse.

Unnever, James D. & Gabbidon, Shaun L. Race, Racism, & Crime: A Theory of African American Offending. 2011. (Criminology & Justice Studies). (ENG., Illus.). 288p. 149.00 *(978-0-415-88357-3(1))* Routledge.

Upton, William H. Negro Masonry Being A Critical Examinati. 2006. pap. 15.95 *(978-1-4286-4728-2(7))* Kessinger Publishing, LLC.

Villarosa, Clara. The Words of African-American Heroes. 2011. (Newmarket Words of Ser.). (ENG.). 160p. pap. 12.95 *(978-1-55704-645-2(9)*, William Morrow Paperbacks) HarperCollins Pubs.

Violent Islamist Extremism, 2009: Hearings Before the Committee on Homeland Security & Governmental Affairs, United States Senate of the One Hundred Eleventh Congress, First Session. 2010. iv, 199p. *(978-0-16-087080-4(1)*, 552-070-41937-3) United States Government Printing Office.

Wailoo, Keith. How Cancer Crossed the Color Line, 1 vol. 2011. (ENG., Illus.). 240p. 27.95 *(978-0-19-517017-7(2))* Oxford Univ. Pr., Inc.

Walters, Ronald. The Price of Racial Reconciliation. 2009. (Politics of Race & Ethnicity Ser.). (ENG., Illus.). 264p. pap. 25.95 *(978-0-472-03380-5(8))* Univ. of Michigan Pr.

Washington, Booker T. The Future of the American Negro. 2009. 76p. pap. *(978-1-151-67820-1(1))* Books LLC.

—The Future of the American Negro. 2009. 112p. pap. *(978-1-4099-4060-9(8))* Dodo Pr.

—The Future of the American Negro. 2007. (ENG.). 256p. 42.95 *(978-0-548-11646-3(6))* Kessinger Publishing, LLC.

—The Future of the American Negro. 244p. reprint ed. 98.00 *(978-0-7222-9749-0(1))* Library Reprints, Inc.

—The Future of the American Negro. 2009. (ENG.). 102p. pap. 8.95 *(978-1-4385-2736-9(5)*, Book Jungle) Standard Pubns., Inc.

Washington, Michael. Introduction to Black Studies 100: Readings in African American Cultural Pluralism. rev. ed. 2010. (ENG.). 328p. pap. 123.90 *(978-0-7575-7945-5(0))* Kendall Hunt Publishing Co.

West-Olatunji, Cirecie, et al. Counseling & Diversity: Counseling African American. 2010. (ENG., Illus.). 96p. (C). pap. 15.95 *(978-0-618-47043-3(3))* Wadsworth.

Wiggan, Greg, ed. Education for the New Frontier: Race, Education & Triumph in Jim Crow America (1867-1945) 2011. (Illus.). xxiii, 100p. pap. *(978-1-61209-673-5(5))* Nova Science Pubs., Inc.

Willis, Deborah. Posing Beauty: African American Images from the 1890s to the Present. 2009. (ENG., Illus.). 288p. 49.95 *(978-0-393-06696-6(7)*, 6696) Norton, W. W. & Co., Inc.

Willis, Jay Thomas. Things I Never Said: Emails to My African-American Son in College. 2010. pap. 12.95 *(978-0-7414-5994-7(9))* Infinity Publishing.

Woodson, Carter Godwin. Negro Orators & Their Orations. 2010. 726p. pap. 35.00 *(978-1-57898-963-8(9))* Martino Publishing.

Work, John W. Song of the American Negro. 131p. reprint ed. lib. bdg. 88.00 *(978-0-7222-4862-1(8))* Library Reprints, Inc.

Yancy, George. Black Bodies, White Gazes: The Continuing Significance of Race. 2008. (ENG.). 290p. 80.00 *(978-0-7425-5297-5(7))*; pap. 29.95 *(978-0-7425-5298-2(5))* Rowman & Littlefield Publishers, Inc.

Yarbrough, Fay A. Race & the Cherokee Nation: Sovereignty in the Nineteenth Century. 2007. (Illus.). 200p. (C). 59.95 *(978-0-8122-4056-6(1))* Univ. of Pennsylvania Pr.

Zuberi, Tukufu, pseud & Bonilla-Silva, Eduardo, eds. White Logic, White Methods: Racism & Methodology. 2008. (ENG., Illus.). 424p. 95.00 *(978-0-7425-4280-8(7))*; pap. 42.95 *(978-0-7425-4281-5(5))* Rowman & Littlefield Publishers, Inc.

AFRICAN AMERICANS—BIBLIOGRAPHY

Guthrie, Dorothy Littlejohn. Integrating African American Literature in the Library & Classroom, 1 vol. 2011. 294p. pap. 40.00 *(978-1-59884-751-2(1)*, A3360P) Pearson Education GBR. Dist: ABC-CLIO, LLC.

Hicks, Kyra E. This I Accomplish Harriet Powers' Bible Quilt & Other Pieces: Quilt Histories, Exhibition Lists, Annotated Bibliography & Timeline of a Great African American Quilter. 2009. (Illus.). 180p. pap. 19.95 *(978-0-9824796-5-0(4))* Black Threads Pr.

Hodge, Ruth E. Guide to African American Resources at the Pennsylvania State Archives. 2008. (ENG.). 598p. pap. 45.00 *(978-1-4223-9354-3(2))* DIANE Publishing Co.

Library Company of Philadelphia Staff & Historical Society of Pennsylvania Staff, contrib. by. Afro-Americana, 1553-1906: A Catalog of the Holdings of the Library Company of Philadelphia & the Historical Society of Pennsylvania. 2nd ed. 2008. 175.00 *(978-1-58456-236-8(6))* Oak Knoll Pr.

Martin, Tony. Amy Ashwood Garvey: Pan-Africanist, Feminist & Mrs. Marcus Garvey No. 1 or a Tale of Two Amies. 2007. (New Marcus Garvey Library: No. 4). (Illus.). 450p. 40.00 *(978-0-912469-06-5(4))* Majority Pr., The.

Neumann, Caryn E. Term Paper Resource Guide to African American History, 1 vol. 2009. (Term Paper Resource Guides). 304p. 65.00 *(978-0-313-35501-1(0)*, GR5501, Greenwood Pr.) Greenwood Publishing Group, Inc.

AFRICAN AMERICANS—BIOGRAPHY

Aaron, Darian. When Love Takes Over: A Celebration of SGL Couples of Color. 2011. 104p. pap. 11.95 ***(978-1-4620-1393-7(7))*** iUniverse, Inc.

Aaseng, Nathan. Athletes. 2nd rev. ed. 2011. (A to Z of African Americans Ser.). (Illus.). 288p. (C). (gr. 9-18). 49.50 *(978-0-8160-7869-1(6))* Facts On File, Inc.

—Religious Leaders. 2nd rev. ed. 2010. (A to Z of African Americans Ser.). (Illus.). 296p. (C). (gr. 9-18). 49.50 *(978-0-8160-7868-4(8))* Facts On File, Inc.

Abdurahman, Bilal. In the Key of Me: From Bedford-Stuy to Africa. Abdurahman, Bilal, ed. (Illus.). 110p. pap. 12.00 *(978-0-9619070-2-0(9))* Ethno Modes Folkloric Workshop, Inc.

Abernathy, Ralph David. And the Walls Came Tumbling Down: An Autobiography. 2010. (ENG., Illus.). 672p. pap. 19.95 *(978-1-56976-279-0(1)*, Hill, Lawrence Bks.) Chicago Review Pr., Inc.

Ackmann, Martha. Curveball: The Remarkable Story of Toni Stone the First Woman to Play Professional Baseball in the Negro League. 2010. (ENG., Illus.). 288p. 24.95 *(978-1-55652-796-8(9)*, Hill, Lawrence Bks.) Chicago Review Pr., Inc.

Adams, Barbara Eleanor. John Henrik Clarke Master Teacher. 2011. (Illus.). 185p. pap. 15.95 *(978-1-61759-012-2(6))* EWorld, Inc.

Adams, Ernest H. From Ghetto to Ghetto: An African American Journey to Judaism. 2009. 284p. pap. 20.95 *(978-1-4401-2085-5(4))* iUniverse, Inc.

Adams, Frank & Mathews, Burgin. Doc: The Story of a Birmingham Jazz Man. 2012. ***(978-0-8173-1780-5(5))*** Univ. of Alabama Pr.

Adebayo, Bob. Barack Obama by the Numbers: Uncovering the Life Path Numbers of A President. 2009. 168p. pap. 15.95 *(978-1-4327-4799-2(1))* Outskirts Pr., Inc.

Adeleke, Tunde. Without Regard to Race: The Other Martin Robison Delany. 2009. (ENG.). 274p. pap. 25.00 *(978-1-60473-250-4(4))* Univ. Pr. of Mississippi.

Adelman, Bob. Remembering Martin Luther King. Life Magazine Editors, ed. 2008. (ENG., Illus.). 160p. (YA). (gr. 7-17). 24.95 *(978-1-60320-044-8(4))* Time Home Entertainment, Inc.

Agee, Gary B. A Cry for Justice: Daniel Rudd & His Life in Black Catholicism, Journalism, & Activism, 1854-1933. 2011. 256p. 39.95 ***(978-1-55728-975-9(1))*** Univ. of Arkansas Pr.

Ahearne, Brian. My Greenhill & After. 2008. 376p. per. 22.00 *(978-1-84426-483-4(1))* Upfront Publishing Ltd. GBR. Dist: Printondemand-worldwide.com.

Aka Dms Mba Aviation, Jubril Olab. The New Rising Dawn - Barack Obam: The Messianic President. 2009. 296p. 33.40 *(978-1-4269-1828-5(3))*; pap. 23.40 *(978-1-4269-1827-8(5))* Trafford Publishing.

Alexander, Adele Logan. Parallel Worlds: The Remarkable Gibbs-Hunts & the Enduring (In)Significance of Melanin. (ENG., Illus.). 416p. 2012. pap. 19.95 ***(978-0-8139-3245-3(9))*** 2010. (gr. 17). 29.95 *(978-0-8139-2887-6(7))* Univ. Pr. of Virginia.

Alexander, Leslie & Rucker, Walter C., Jr., eds. Encyclopedia of African American History, 3 vols. 2010. (American Ethnic Experience Ser.). (Illus.). 1136p. 295.00 *(978-1-85109-769-2(4)*, AFRCAM1C) ABC-CLIO, LLC.

Allen, Caron Barton. From Whence They Came: The Genealogical History of an African-American Family, 1 vol. 2009. 207p. pap. 24.95 *(978-1-60703-130-7(2))* PublishAmerica, Inc.

Allen, John E. The Content of Their Character: The Story Behind This Antique Quilt & the History of the African American Family That Made It. 2009. 164p. pap. 44.48 *(978-1-4251-8812-2(5))* Trafford Publishing.

Allen, Marcus. Marcus. 2009. (ENG.). 410p. pap. 24.95 *(978-1-4128-1279-5(8))* Transaction Pubs.

Alston, Judy A. & McClellan, Patricia A. Herstories: Leading with the Lessons of the Lives of Black Women Activists. 2011. (C). pap. 33.95 *(978-1-4331-1193-8(4))*; 129.95 *(978-1-4331-1192-1(6))* Lang, Peter Publishing, Inc.

Amash, Jim & Nolen-Weathington, Eric. Matt Baker: the Art of Glamour: The Art of Glamour. 2012. (Illus.). 192p. 39.95 *(978-1-60549-032-8(6))* TwoMorrows Publishing.

Andersen, Margaret & Thomas, Neil F. Living Art: The Life of Paul R. Jones, African American Art Collector. 2009. (Illus.). 144p. 32.50 *(978-0-87413-073-7(5))* Univ. of Delaware Pr.

Anderson, M. T. Presbyterianism: Its Relation to the Negro. 2007. (Illus.). pap. 27.95 *(978-1-4304-6951-3(X))* Kessinger Publishing, LLC.

Andrews, Gregg. Thyra J. Edwards: Black Activist in the Global Freedom Struggle. 2011. (ENG., Illus.). 256p. (C). (gr. 12). 40.00 *(978-0-8262-1912-1(8))* Univ. of Missouri Pr.

Andrews, William L., ed. Slave Narratives after Slavery. 2011. (ENG., Illus.). 400p. pap. 34.95 ***(978-0-19-517943-9(9))*** Oxford Univ. Pr., Inc.

Angelou, Maya. The Heart of a Woman. 2009. (ENG.). 352p. pap. 15.00 *(978-0-8129-8032-5(8)*, Random Hse. Trade Paperbacks) Random House Publishing Group.

—Letter to My Daughter. (ENG.). 192p. 2009. pap. 15.00 *(978-0-8129-8003-5(4)*, Random Hse. Trade Paperbacks) 2008. 25.00 *(978-1-4000-6612-4(3)*, Random House) Random House Publishing Group.

—Yo Se Por Que Canta el Pajaro Enjaulado.Tr. of I Know Why the Caged Bird Sings. (SPA.). 292p. 20.95 *(978-84-264-4911-5(5))* Editorial Lumen ESP. Dist: Lectorum Pubns., Inc.

Anthony, Kim Hamilton. Unfavorable Odds: The Story of Ucla's First African-American Female Gymnastics Champion. 2010. pap. 15.99 *(978-1-61566-495-5(5))* Tate Publishing & Enterprises, LLC.

Anyabwile, Thabiti, ed. & intro. May We Meet in the Heavenly World: The Piety of Lemuel Haynes. 2009. (Illus.). pap. 10.00 *(978-1-60178-065-2(6))* Reformation Heritage Bks.

Ardizzone, Heidi. An Illuminated Life: Belle Da Costa Greene's Journey from Prejudice to Privilege. 2007. (ENG., Illus.). 592p. 35.00 *(978-0-393-05104-9(8)*, 5104) Norton, W. W. & Co., Inc.

Armstrong, Thomas M. & Bell, Natalie R. Autobiography of a Freedom Rider: My Life as a Foot Soldier for Civil Rights. 2011. (ENG.). 216p. pap. 14.95 (978-0-7573-1603-6(4)) Health Communications, Inc.

Arnold, Charlotte S. Over These Prison Walls. 2006. 136p. per. 24.95 (978-1-4241-0958-6(2)) PublishAmerica, Inc.

Arrington, Richard. There's Hope for the World: The Memoir of Birmingham, Alabama's First African American Mayor. 2008. (ENG., Illus.). 320p. 29.95 (978-0-8173-1623-5(X)) Univ. of Alabama Pr.

Asante, Molefi Kete. As I Run Toward Africa: A Memoir. 2011. 336p. 99.00 (978-1-61205-075-1(1)); pap. 26.95 (978-1-61205-076-8(X)) Paradigm Pubs.

Ashbaugh, Carolyn. Lucy Parsons: An American Revolutionary. 2012. (ENG., Illus.). 282p. pap. 16.00 (978-1-60846-213-1(7)) Haymarket Bks.

Ashun, Elizabeth. America the Land of More Than Enough. 2009. 96p. pap. 10.99 (978-1-61579-050-0(0)) Xulon Pr., Inc.

Atkins, Carla. Michael Jackson King of Pop an American Legend: Activity Book. 2010. 152p. pap. 11.99 (978-1-4490-5405-2(6)) AuthorHouse.

Aycock, Colleen & Scott, Mark. Joe Gans: A Biography of the First African American World Boxing Champion. 2008. (ENG., Illus.). 294p. pap. 35.00 (978-0-7864-3994-2(7)) McFarland & Co., Inc. Pubs.

Aycock, Colleen & Scott, Mark, eds. The First Black Boxing Champions: Essays on Fighters of the 1800s to The 1920s. 2011. (ENG., Illus.). 302p. 45.00 (978-0-7864-4991-0(8)) McFarland & Co., Inc. Pubs.

Azaransky, Sarah. The Dream Is Freedom: Pauli Murray & American Democratic Faith, 1 vol. 2011. 176p. 55.00 (978-0-19-974481-7(5)) Oxford Univ. Pr., Inc.

Bacon, Margaret Hope. But One Race: The Life of Robert Purvis. (Excelsior Editions Ser.). (Illus.). 2010. 293p. pap. 24.95 (978-0-7914-7008-4(3), Suny Pr.) 2007. 279p. 36.00 (978-0-7914-7007-7(5)) State Univ. of New York Pr.

Bader, Philip. African-American Writers. 2nd rev. ed. 2010. (A to Z of African Americans Ser.). (Illus.). 352p. (C). (gr. 9-18). 49.50 (978-0-8160-8141-7(7)) Facts On File, Inc.

Bailey, D'Army. The Education of a Black Radical: A Southern Civil Rights Activist's Journey, 1959-1964. 2009. 264p. 28.00 (978-0-8071-3476-4(7)) Louisiana State Univ. Pr.

Bailey, Samme. Samme: Breaking the Cycle. 2008. 88p. 12.95 (978-1-59713-059-2(1)) Goose River Pr.

Bailey, Tom. Satchel Paige: Baseball's Greatest Pitcher. 2009. (Illus.). 100p. (978-1-59421-046-4(2)) Seacoast Publishing, Inc.

Bailey, William H. Looking Up: Finding My Voice in Las Vegas. 2009. 240p. pap. 19.95 (978-1-935043-04-1(8)) Stephens Pr. LLC.

Baker, Barbara A. Albert Murray & the Aesthetic Imagination of a Nation. 2010. (ENG., Illus.). 264p. pap. 25.00 (978-0-8173-5593-7(6)) Univ. of Alabama Pr.

Baker, Barbara A., et al. Albert Murray & the Aesthetic Imagination of a Nation. 2010. (ENG., Illus.). 264p. 45.75 (978-0-8173-1697-6(3)) Univ. of Alabama Pr.

Baker, John F., Jr. The Washingtons of Wessyngton Plantation: Stories of My Family's Journey to Freedom. 2010. (ENG., Illus.). 432p. pap. 16.00 (978-1-4165-6741-7(0), Beyond Words/Atria Bks.) Atria Bks.

Baker, Kyle. Nat Turner. 2008. (ENG., Illus.). 208p. pap. 14.95 (978-0-8109-7227-8(1)) Abrams.

Balf, Todd. Major: A Black Athlete, a White Era, & the Fight to Be the World's Fastest Human Being. 2009. (ENG., Illus.). 320p. pap. 14.00 (978-0-307-23659-3(5), Three Rivers Pr.) Crown Publishing Group.

Ball, Charles. Fifty Years in Chains. 2009. 188p. pap. (978-1-150-34490-9(3)) Books LLC.

Ballard, Allen B. & Ballard, Allen B. Breaching Jericho's Walls: A Twentieth-Century African American Life. Ballard, Allen B., ed. 2011. (Excelsior Editions Ser.). (Illus.). 224p. 24.95 (978-1-4384-3623-4(8)) State Univ. of New York Pr.

Ballard, Maxine. The True Story of Florence Ballard. 2007. 249p. 49.95 (978-0-9800574-0-9(X)) PRECIOUS4MAX, Inc.

Bankston, Carl L. III & Bankston, Carl L. Great Lives from History. 2011. (978-1-58765-747-4(3)); (Illus.). xxviii, 1789p. (978-1-58765-751-1(1)); (Illus.). xxviii, 1789p. (978-1-58765-750-4(3)); (Illus.). xxviii, 1789p. (978-1-58765-752-8(X)); (Illus.). xxviii, 1789p. (978-1-58765-749-8(X)); (Illus.). xxviii, 1789p. (978-1-58765-748-1(1)) Salem Pr., Inc.

Barber, Barbara Beadle. By Faith: A Century of Progress. 2009. 340p. 32.95 (978-0-595-50669-9(0)); pap. 22.95 (978-0-595-50491-6(4)) iUniverse, Inc.

Barber, John T. The Black Digital Elite: African American Leaders of the Information Revolution, 1 vol. 2006. (Illus.). 216p. 39.95 (978-0-275-98504-2(0), C8504, Praeger Pubs.) Greenwood Publishing Group, Inc.

Barlow, Lena A. From the Pitts of Hell to the Road to Heaven: He Kept Me. 2008. 68p. pap. 12.50 (978-1-4343-9816-1(1)) AuthorHouse.

Barnes, Adilah. On My Own Terms. 2008. 304p. 29.99 (978-1-4257-9033-2(X)); pap. 19.99 (978-1-4257-9008-0(9)) Xlibris Corp.

Barnett, Anthony. Listening for Henry Crowder: A Monograph on His Almost Lost Music: With the Poems & Music of Henry-Music, 1 bk + CD insert. 2007. (Illus.). 128p. pap. 89.50 (978-0-907954-36-1(7)) Allardyce, Barnett, Pubs. GBR. Dist: SPD-Small Pr. Distribution.

Barr, Alwyn. Blacks in East Texas History: Selections from the East Texas Historical Journal. Glasrud, Bruce A. & McDonald, Archie P., eds. 2008. (ENG.). 208p. 29.95 (978-1-60344-041-7(0)) Texas A&M Univ. Pr.

Barr, Burton, Jr. & Barr, Burton. The Hoodlum Preacher: I Was Lost, Now I Am Found. 2006. 200p. per. 14.95 (978-0-9769117-1-5(X)) Kobalt Bks.

Barwick, Debbie B. Mott's Sketches: 1839 Biographical Sketches & Interesting Anecdotes of Persons of Color. 2007. 240p. per. 16.95 (978-1-4327-1778-0(2)) Outskirts Pr., Inc.

Bass, Amy. Those about Him Remained Silent: The Battle over W.E.B. du Bois. 2012. (Illus.). 224p. pap. 20.00 (978-0-8166-4496-4(9)) Univ. of Minnesota Pr.

Baszile, Jennifer Lynn. The Black Girl Next Door: A Memoir. 2009. (ENG., Illus.). 320p. pap. 15.00 (978-1-4165-4328-2(7), Touchstone) Touchstone.

Bates, Daisy. The Long Shadow of Little Rock. 2007. (ENG., Illus.). 260p. per. 18.95 (978-1-55728-863-9(1)) Univ. of Arkansas Pr.

Bates, Daisy. The Long Shadow of Little Rock: A Memoir. 2011. 268p. 47.95 (978-1-258-09783-7(4)) Literary Licensing, LLC.

Baum, Dale, ed. Counterfeit Justice: The Judicial Odyssey of Texas Freedwoman Azeline Hearne. 2009. (Conflicting Worlds: New Dimensions of the American Civil War Ser.). (Illus.). 320p. 45.00 (978-0-8071-3405-4(8)) Louisiana State Univ. Pr.

Baylor, Helen. No Greater Love: The Helen Baylor Story. 2007. (ENG., Illus.). 148p. per. 14.99 (978-0-9762730-0-4(4)) Vision Publishing.

Beckford, Geraldine, compiled by. Biographical Dictionary of American Physicians of African Ancestry, 1800-1920. 2011. 125.00 (978-0-9831151-4-4(1)); pap. 90.00 (978-0-9831151-5-1(X)) Africana Homestead Legacy Pubs., Inc.

Beineke, John A. Going over All the Hurdles: A Life of Oatess Archey. 2008. (978-0-87195-260-8(2)) Indiana Historical Society.

BelMonte, Kathryn I. African-American Heroes & Heroines of America: 150 True Stories of African-American Heroism. 2007. 300p. pap. (978-0-8119-0002-7(9)) Lifetime Bks.

Belton, Brian. East End Heroes, Stateside Kings: The Amazing True Story of Three Football Players Who Changed the World. 2008. (ENG., Illus.). 288p. 29.95 (978-1-84454-501-8(6)) Blake, John, Publishing, Ltd. GBR. Dist: Independent Pubs. Group.

Bennett, Tracey Gold. Washington, D. C. 1963-2006. 2007. (Black America Ser.). (ENG., Illus.). 128p. per. 21.99 (978-0-7385-4383-3(7)) Arcadia Publishing.

Berry, Lemuel, Jr. Great African American Musicians: From Marian Anderson to Stevie Wonder. 2011. (ENG., Illus.). 376p. (978-0-7734-3831-6(9)) Mellen, Edwin Pr., The.

Berry, S. Torriano & Berry, Venise T. The A to Z of African American Cinema. 84th ed. 2009. (A to Z Guide Ser.: No. 84). (ENG.). 450p. pap. 34.45 (978-0-8108-6871-7(7)) Scarecrow Pr., Inc.

—Historical Dictionary of African American Cinema. 2007. (Historical Dictionaries of Literature & the Arts Ser.: Vol. 12). (ENG., Illus.). 448p. 99.00 (978-0-8108-5545-8(3)) Scarecrow Pr., Inc.

Bial, Raymond. Champaign. 2008. (Images of America Ser.). (ENG., Illus.). 128p. pap. 21.99 (978-0-7385-5188-3(0)) Arcadia Publishing.

Biddle, Daniel R. & Dubin, Murray. Tasting Freedom: Octavius Catto & the Battle for Equality in Civil War America. 2010. (ENG., Illus.). 656p. 35.00 (978-1-59213-465-6(3)) Temple Univ. Pr.

Bieze, Michael Scott & Gasman, Marybeth, eds. Booker T. Washington Rediscovered. 2012. (ENG., Illus.). 224p. (C). (gr. 13-17). pap. 34.95 (978-1-4214-0471-4(0)) Johns Hopkins Univ. Pr.

Billingsley, Andrew. Yearning to Breathe Free: Robert Smalls of South Carolina & His Families. 2010. pap. 21.95 (978-1-57003-970-6(4)); (ENG., Illus.). 304p. 19.95 (978-1-57003-686-6(1)) Univ. of South Carolina Pr.

Billman, Rev. Robert " Bob". From Preacher to Porn Star. 2011. 468p. pap. 23.99 (978-1-4568-7507-7(8)) Xlibris Corp.

Biographiq. Harriet Tubman - African American Abolitionist. 2008. 76p. pap. 9.99 (978-1-59986-369-6(3), Biographiq) Filiquarian Publishing, LLC.

—Jesse Jackson - Civil Rights Activist & Minister. 2008. 52p. pap. 9.99 (978-1-59986-069-5(4), Biographiq) Filiquarian Publishing, LLC.

Birkbeck, Matt. Deconstructing Sammy: Music, Money, & Madness. 2009. (ENG., Illus.). 304p. pap. 15.99 (978-0-06-145067-9(7), Harper Paperbacks) HarperCollins Pubs.

Black Americans of Achievement. 2011. (Black Americans of Achievement Legacy Edition Ser.). (gr. 6-12). 1400.00 (978-0-7910-9960-5(1)) Facts On File, Inc.

Black, Helen, et al. From Zero to Eighty: Two African American Men's Narrative of Racism, Suffering, Survival, & Transformation. 2011. 308p. 31.95 (978-1-4620-0509-3(8)); pap. 21.95 (978-1-4620-0507-9(1)) iUniverse, Inc.

Black, Samuel W. & Williams, Regennia N. Through the Lens of Allen E. Cole: A History of African Americans in Cleveland, Ohio. 2012. (978-1-60635-090-4(0)) Kent State Univ. Pr.

Blair-Reed, Wilma. Portrait of A Sista' Gone Mad. 2011. (ENG.). 314p. pap. 19.95 (978-1-4327-7632-9(0)) Outskirts Pr., Inc.

Blake, J. Herman & Newton, Huey P. Revolutionary Suicide. 2009. (Penguin Classics Deluxe Edition Ser.). (ENG.). 384p. (gr. 12). 16.00 (978-0-14-310532-9(9), Penguin Classics) Penguin Group (USA) Inc.

Blake, John. Children of the Movement: The Sons & Daughters of Martin Luther King Jr. , Malcolm X, Elijah Muhammad, George Wallace, Andrew Young, Julian Bond, Stokely Carmichael, Bob Moses, James Chaney, Elaine Brown, & Others Reveal How the Civil Rights Movement Tested & Transformed Thei. 2007. (ENG., Illus.). 272p. per. 14.95 (978-1-55652-678-7(4), Hill, Lawrence Bks.) Chicago Review Pr., Inc.

Blight, David W. A Slave No More: Two Men Who Escaped to Freedom, Including Their Own Narratives of Emancipation. (Ser.). (ENG., Illus.). 320p. 2009. pap. 14.95 (978-0-15-603451-7(4), Mariner Bks.) 2007. 25.00 (978-0-15-101232-9(6)) Houghton Mifflin Harcourt Trade & Reference Pubs.

Blum, Edward J. W. E. B. du Bois: American Prophet. 2007. (Politics & Culture in Modern America Ser.). 288p. 42.50 (978-0-8122-4010-8(3)) Univ. of Pennsylvania Pr.

—W. E. B. du Bois, American Prophet. 2009. (Politics & Culture in Modern America Ser.). 288p. pap. 22.50 (978-0-8122-2086-5(2)) Univ. of Pennsylvania Pr.

Boehm, Lisa Krissoff. Making a Way Out of No Way: African American Women & the Second Great Migration. 2010. (Margaret Walker Alexander Series in African American Studies). (ENG., Illus.). 304p. pap. 25.00 (978-1-60473-802-5(2)) Univ. Pr. of Mississippi.

Bolden, Abraham. The Echo from Dealey Plaza: The True Story of the First African American on the White House Secret Service Detail & His Quest for Justice after the Assissination of JFK. 2009. (ENG.). 320p. pap. 13.95 (978-0-307-38202-3(8), Three Rivers Pr.) Crown Publishing Group.

Bond, Scott. From Slavery to Wealth: The Life of Scott Bond. Gatewood, Willard B., ed. 2008. (Illus.). 284p. per. 19.95 (978-0-9768007-6-7(4)) Phoenix International, Inc.

Boone, Beverly & Lowe, Nate. To Be Somebody. 2007. (ENG.). 196p. per. 16.95 (978-1-58736-722-9(X)) Wheatmark.

Boston, Michael B. The Business Strategy of Booker T. Washington: Its Development & Implementation. 2010. (ENG., Illus.). 308p. 69.95 (978-0-8130-3473-7(6)) Univ. Pr. of Florida.

Bowden, Tripp. Freddie & Me: Life Lessons from Freddie Bennett, Augusta National's Legendary Caddy Master. 2011. (ENG.). 224p. pap. 14.95 (978-1-61608-249-9(6), 608249) Skyhorse Publishing Co., Inc.

Bowman, Bertie. Step by Step: A Memoir of Living the American Dream. 2009. (ENG., Illus.). 224p. pap. 15.00 (978-0-345-50433-3(X), One World/Ballantine) Random House Publishing Group.

Boyce, Lucas Daniel. Living Proof: From Foster Care to the White House & the NBA. 2011. (ENG.). 228p. pap. 16.99 (978-1-59932-257-5(9)) Advantage Media Group.

Boyd, Gerald M. My Times in Black & White: Race & Power at The New York Times. 2010. (ENG., Illus.). 432p. 26.95 (978-1-55652-952-8(X), Hill, Lawrence Bks.) Chicago Review Pr., Inc.

Boyd, Michael. Forever the Fat Kid: How I Survived Dysfunction, Depression & Life in the Theater. 2010. 228p. 27.00 (978-1-4269-4241-9(9)); pap. 17.00 (978-1-4269-4240-2(0)) Trafford Publishing.

Bracey, Earnest N. Fannie Lou Hamer: The Life of a Civil Rights Icon. 2011. (ENG., Illus.). 209p. pap. 38.00 (978-0-7864-6030-4(X)) McFarland & Co., Inc. Pubs.

Bracks, Lean'tin. The African American Almanac: 400 Years of Triumph, Courage & Excellence. 2011. (ENG., Illus.). 512p. pap. 22.95 (978-1-57859-323-1(9)) Visible Ink Pr.

Bradford, Sarah. Harriet Tubman - the Moses of Her People. (gr. 4-7). 2008. 156p. (978-1-4437-3548-3(5)) 2006. 152p. per. (978-1-4067-9640-7(9)) Read Bks. (Hesperides Pr.).

Brewster-Walker, Sandi. The Colored Girl from Long Island: The Story of My Early Life. 2007. (Illus.). 178p. per. 19.95 (978-0-6151-3330-0579-8(7)) Lulu Enterprises Inc.

Bridge, Horatio. Journal of an African Cruiser. 2008. 259p. 22.99 (978-0-554-79903-2(0)); 230p. 25.99 (978-0-554-79894-3(8)); 196p. 22.99 (978-0-554-31899-8(7)); 196p. 25.99 (978-0-554-22596-8(4)); 165p. pap. 23.75 (978-0-554-79897-4(2)); 165p. pap. 22.75 (978-0-554-79902-5(2)) BiblioBazaar.

—Journal of an African Cruiser. Hawthorne, Nathaniel, ed. I.t. ed. 2007. (ENG.). 194p. pap. 21.99 (978-1-4264-2729-9(8)); 184p. pap. 19.99 (978-1-4264-2672-8(0)) BiblioBazaar.

—Journal of an African Cruiser. 2009. 176p. pap. (978-1-150-26641-6(4)) Books LLC.

Broadnax, Samuel L. Blue Skies, Black Wings: African American Pioneers of Aviation, 1 vol. 2007. (Illus.). 208p. 44.95 (978-0-275-99195-1(4), C9195, Praeger Pubs.) Greenwood Publishing Group, Inc.

—Blue Skies, Black Wings: African American Pioneers of Aviation. 2008. (ENG., Illus.). 208p. pap. 17.95 (978-0-8032-1774-4(9), Bison Bks.) Univ. of Nebraska Pr.

Brooks, Daphne A. Bodies in Dissent: Spectacular Performances of Race & Freedom, 1850-1910. 2006. (ENG., Illus.). 488p. 99.95 (978-0-8223-3710-2(X)); per. 27.95 (978-0-8223-3722-5(3)) Duke Univ. Pr.

Broughton, Virginia W. & Carter, Tomeiko Ashford. Virginia Broughton: The Life & Writings of a National Baptist Missionary. 2010. (978-1-57233-696-4(X)) Univ. of Tennessee Pr.

Broussard, Albert S. Expectations of Equality: A History of Black Westerners. 2012. pap. (978-0-88295-284-0(6)) Davidson, Harlan Inc.

Brown, Claude. Manchild in the Promised Land. 2012. (ENG.). 416p. 30.00 (978-1-4516-2667-4(3), Scribner) Scribner.

—Manchild in the Promised Land. 2011. (ENG.). 416p. pap. 16.00 (978-1-4516-3157-9(X), Touchstone) Touchstone.

Brown, Cornelia. Black & White Makes Brown. 2009. pap. 12.99 (978-1-60696-642-6(1)) Tate Publishing & Enterprises, LLC.

Brown, Cupcake. A Piece of Cake: A Memoir. 2007. (ENG.). 480p. pap. 15.00 (978-1-4000-5229-5(7), Three Rivers Pr.) Crown Publishing Group.

Brown, Henry Box. Narrative of the Life of Henry Box Brown. 2008. 84p. pap. 18.75 (978-0-559-33903-5(8)) BiblioBazaar.

—Narrative of the Life of Henry Box Brown. 2009. 84p. pap. 17.95 (978-1-104-29915-6(1)) Kessinger Publishing, LLC.

—Narrative of the Life of Henry Box Brown. Ernest, John, ed. 2008. (ENG., Illus.). 224p. 55.95 (978-0-8078-3196-0(4)) Univ. of North Carolina Pr.

—Narrative of the Life of Henry Box Brown, Written by Himself. Ernest, John, ed. 2008. (ENG., Illus.). 224p. pap. 19.95 (978-0-8078-5890-5(0)) Univ. of North Carolina Pr.

Brown, Jayna. Babylon Girls: Black Women Performers & the Shaping of the Modern. 2008. (ENG., Illus.). 360p. 94.95 (978-0-8223-4133-8(6)); pap. 25.95 (978-0-8223-4157-4(3)) Duke Univ. Pr.

Brown, Joseph E. Black Soldier of Mercy. Lockhart, Lona, ed. 2010. (Illus.). 134p. pap. 15.00 (978-1-934936-42-9(1)) Righter Publishing Co., Inc.

Brown, Lee Frances. Calvin J. Spann: Tuskegee "Red Tail" Fighter Pilot. 2009. (Illus.). xix, 210p. (978-1-4401-1790-9(X)) iUniverse, Inc.

Brown, Leslie & Valk, Anne. Living with Jim Crow: African American Women & Memories of the Segregated South. 2010. (Palgrave Studies in Oral History Ser.). (ENG., Illus.). 228p. 95.00 (978-0-230-61962-3(2)); pap. 29.00 (978-0-230-62152-7(X)) Palgrave Macmillan.

Brown, Mary Beth. Condi, 0 vols. 2009. 336p. pap. 16.99 (978-1-59555-326-3(6)) Nelson, Thomas Inc.

Brown, Nathaniel. A Gay Man in a Straight Man's Prison. 2009. 160p. pap. 16.99 (978-1-4389-6815-5(9)) AuthorHouse.

Brown, William. Narrative of William W Brown, a Fugitive Slave. 2007. 96p. per. 8.75 (978-1-60206-736-3(8)) Cosimo, Inc.

Brown, William Wells. The Black Man: His Antecedents, His Genius, & His Achievements. 2007. 312p. per. 26.95 (978-1-60206-676-2(0)) Cosimo, Inc.

—Narrative of William W Brown: A Fugitive Slave. 2008. 64p. pap. (978-1-4099-2556-9(0)) Dodo Pr.

—Narrative of William W. Brown, an American Slave: Written by Himself. 2011. (ENG.). 105p. pap. 25.00 (978-0-8078-6959-8(7)) Univ. of North Carolina Pr.

—Narrative of William W Brown, an American Slave, Written by Himself. 2010. 176p. pap. 22.75 (978-1-141-64969-3(1)) BiblioBazaar.

—Narrative of William W Brown, an American Slave, Written by Himself. 2009. 88p. pap. 14.14 (978-1-151-39956-4(6)) General Bks. LLC.

—The Negro in the American Revolution. 2007. 400p. reprint ed. pap. 26.95 (978-1-60206-630-4(2)) Cosimo, Inc.

—The Works of William Wells Brown: Using His Strong, Manly Voice. Robbins, Hollis & Garrett, Paula, eds. annot. ed. 2006. (ENG., Illus.). 519p. 115.00 (978-0-19-530963-8(4)) Oxford Univ. Pr., Inc.

Bryant, Howard. The Last Hero: A Life of Henry Aaron. (ENG.). 2011. 640p. pap. 16.95 (978-0-307-27992-7(8), Anchor) 2010. (Illus.). 624p. 29.95 (978-0-375-42485-4(7), Pantheon) Knopf Doubleday Publishing Group.

Bukhari, Safiya. The War Before: The True Life Story of Becoming a Black Panther, Keeping the Faith in Prison, & Fighting for Those Left Behind. Whitehorn, Laura, ed. 2010. (ENG.). 320p. pap. 15.95 (978-1-55861-610-3(1)) Feminist Pr. at The City Univ. of New York.

Bullock, Ralph W. In Spite of Handicaps: Brief Biographical Sketches with Discussion Outlines of Outstanding Negroes Now Living. 2011. 184p. 42.95 (978-1-258-08960-3(2)) Literary Licensing, LLC.

Bundles, Alelia. Madame C. J. Walker. 2008. (Black Americans of Achievement Legacy Edition Ser.). 112p. (gr. 6-12). 35.00 (978-1-60413-072-0(5), Chelsea Hse.) Facts On File, Inc.

Burbridge, Doris Auerille De Vonish, et al. African-Americans in the Military: World War I & World War II, Selected Biographies. 2008. (Illus.). 113p. (978-0-9727265-2-8(7)) Afro-American Historical & Genealogical Society, Inc., Jean Sampson Scott Greater New York Chapter.

Burch, Susan & Joyner, Hannah. Unspeakable: The Story of Junius Wilson. 2007. (ENG., Illus.). 312p. 31.95 (978-0-8078-3155-7(7)) Univ. of North Carolina Pr.

Burrow, Rufus, Jr. Martin Luther King Jr. for Armchair Theologians. 2009. (Armchair Theologians Ser.). (ENG.). 200p. pap. 17.00 (978-0-664-23284-9(1)) Westminster John Knox Pr.

Burton, Art T. Black Gun, Silver Star: The Life & Legend of Frontier Marshal Bass Reeves. 2008. (Race & Ethnicity in the American West Ser.). (ENG., Illus.). 392p. pap. 18.95 (978-0-8032-1747-8(1), Bison Bks.) Univ. of Nebraska Pr.

Butler, Paul. Let's Get Free: A Hip-Hop Theory of Justice. (ENG.). 2010. 224p. pap. 16.95 (978-1-59558-500-4(1)) 2009. 208p. 25.95 (978-1-59558-329-1(7), 955329) New Pr., The.

Butterfield, Fox. All God's Children: The Bosket Family & the American Tradition of Violence. 2008. (Vintage Ser.). (ENG., Illus.). 432p. pap. 16.00 (978-0-307-28033-6(0), Vintage) Knopf Doubleday Publishing Group.

Bynum, Cornelius L. A. Philip Randolph & the Struggle for Civil Rights. 2010. (ENG., Illus.). 272p. pap. 25.00 (978-0-252-07764-7(4)) Univ. of Illinois Pr.

Calarco, Tom. People of the Underground Railroad: A Biographical Dictionary, 1 vol. 2008. (Illus.). 408p. 75.00 (978-0-313-33924-0(4), GR3924) Greenwood Publishing Group, Inc.

Calloway, James. Black America, Not in This Americ. 2011. 152p. 29.99 (978-1-4628-6856-8(8)); pap. 19.99 (978-1-4628-6855-1(X)) Xlibris Corp.

Calloway-Miller, Brenda "Saw Jesus+". If You Want Your Life, You Have to Fight!!! The brenda saw jesus Story. 2009. 148p. pap. 14.95 (978-1-4401-2292-7(X)) iUniverse, Inc.

Campbell, Albert Alexander. Recalling the Fun of the Movement. 2007. (ENG.). 56p. per. 16.95 (978-1-4241-7243-6(8)) PublishAmerica, Inc.

Campbell, Bebe Moore. Sweet Summer. 2009. (ENG.). 272p. (gr. 12-18). 15.00 (978-0-425-22927-9(0), Berkley Trade) Penguin Group (USA) Inc.

Campbell, Curtis. Reflections of a Black Man. 2006. (ENG.). 116p. per. 13.95 (978-1-59800-830-2(7)) Outskirts Pr., Inc.

Canfield, Jack L., et al. Chicken Soup for the African American Woman's Soul. 2006. (Chicken Soup for the Soul Ser.). (ENG., Illus.). 384p. pap. 14.95 (978-0-7573-0520-7(2)) Health Communications, Inc.

Canton, David A. Raymond Pace Alexander: A New Negro Lawyer Fights for Civil Rights in Philadelphia. 2010. (Margaret Walker Alexander Series in African American Studies). (ENG., Illus.). 272p. 50.00 (978-1-60473-425-6(6)) Univ. Pr. of Mississippi.

Carew, Joy G. & Carew, Joy Gleason. Blacks, Reds, & Russians: Sojourners in Search of the Soviet Promise. 2008. (ENG.). 296p. (C). 49.95 (978-0-8135-4306-2(1)) Rutgers Univ. Pr.

Carey, Charles W. Political Leaders. 2nd rev. ed. 2011. (A to Z of African Americans Ser.). (Illus.). 392p. (C). (gr. 9-18). 49.50 (978-0-8160-8120-2(4)) Facts On File, Inc.

Carlisle, Evangelist Dee. I Learned Worship: Through the Things I've Suffered. 2009. 156p. 22.49 (978-1-4490-2177-1(8)); pap. 13.99 (978-1-4490-2176-4(X)) AuthorHouse.

Carretta, Vincent. Phillis Wheatley: Biography of a Genius in Bondage. 2011. (ENG., Illus.). 304p. 29.95 **(978-0-8203-3338-0(7))** Univ. of Georgia Pr.

Carroll, Diahann & Morris, Bob. The Legs Are the Last to Go: Aging, Acting, Marrying, & Other Things I Learned the Hard Way. 2008. 288p. 24.95 (978-0-06-076326-8(4), Amistad); 352p. pap. 24.95 (978-0-06-173485-4(3), HarperLuxe) HarperCollins Pubs.

Carson, Clayborne, et al. The Martin Luther King, Jr. Encyclopedia, 1 vol. 2008. (Illus.). 456p. 65.00 (978-0-313-29440-2(2), GR9440, Greenwood Pr.) Greenwood Publishing Group, Inc.

Carson, Harry. Captain for Life: My Story as a Hall of Fame Linebacker. 2011. (ENG., Illus.). 336p. 25.99 (978-0-312-55062-2(6)) St. Martin's Pr.

Carter, Antonia "Toya". Priceless Inspirations. 2011. (ENG.). 240p. pap. 14.95 (978-0-9827027-6-5(0)) Gray, Dr. Farrah Publishing LLC.

Carthran, Kaleda. Looking Through the Mirrors of Me. 2011. 64p. 24.99 **(978-1-4568-4109-6(2))** Xlibris Corp.

Cascadian, Courtney. The Nostridamus Document. 2007. pap. 15.95 (978-0-9778491-0-9(4)) Parker & Foster Publishing.

Casey, Trina. How to Date an Italian Man? It's a Question Not a Guide!, 1 vol. 2010. 176p. pap. 24.95 (978-1-60749-053-1(6)) PublishAmerica, Inc.

Cash Tate, Kimberly. More Christian Than African-American: And Other Ways Jesus Turned My Life Upside Down. 2008. (ENG.). 176p. pap. 13.99 (978-1-933204-84-0(2)) Deep River Bks.

Cashin, Sheryll. The Agitator's Daughter: A Memoir of Four Generations of One Extraordinary African-American Family. 2008. (ENG., Illus.). 288p. 26.00 (978-1-58648-422-4(2)) PublicAffairs.

Casper, Scott E. Sarah Johnson's Mount Vernon: The Forgotten History of an American Shrine. 2010. 286p. (C). 25.00 (978-1-4379-7307-5(8)) DIANE Publishing Co.

—Sarah Johnson's Mount Vernon: The Forgotten History of an American Shrine. 2009. (ENG., Illus.). 320p. pap. 24.00 (978-0-8090-8415-9(5), Hill & Wang) Farrar, Straus & Giroux.

Casteel, Clifton A. A Lady's Heart & Soul: My Life as a Colored - Negro - Black - African - American. 2009. 364p. pap. 17.99 (978-1-4343-4211-9(5)) AuthorHouse.

Cave, Alfred. Life Against All Odds. 2008. 240p. pap. 15.95 (978-1-4327-2912-7(8)) Outskirts Pr., Inc.

Cayton, Horace. Long Old Road: Back to Black Metropolis. 2010. (ENG.). 402p. pap. 39.95 (978-1-4128-1121-7(X)) Transaction Pubs.

Chambers, B. J. Prodigy Hustler. 2007. pap. 22.00 (978-0-9790152-0-5(0)) Billy Boy Enterprises.

Chambliss, Prince. Prince of Peace: A Memoir of an African-American Attorney, Who Came of Age in Birmingham During the Civil Rights Movement. 2010. 152p. 29.00 (978-0-557-10943-2(4)) Lulu Enterprises Inc.

Charron, Katherine. Freedom's Teacher: The Life of Septima Clark. 2012. (ENG., Illus.). 480p. pap. 26.95 **(978-0-8078-7222-2(9))** Univ. of North Carolina Pr.

Charron, Katherine Mellen. Freedom's Teacher: The Life of Septima Clark. 2009. (ENG., Illus.). 480p. 36.95 (978-0-8078-3332-2(0)) Univ. of North Carolina Pr.

Chesnutt, Charles Waddell. Frederick Douglass. (Beacon Biographies of Eminent Americans Ser.). 141p. reprint ed. 88.00 (978-0-7222-9054-4(0)) Library Reprints, Inc.

—Frederick Douglass. 141p. reprint ed. 48.00 (978-0-7950-1413-0(9)) New Library Press LLC.

Child, Brenda's. The Right Amount of Sunshine... Cultivating Little Girls into Young Ladies. 2010. 136p. pap. 19.00 (978-0-557-37996-5(2)) Lulu Enterprises Inc.

Chris Roberts. Michael Jackson: El Rey del Pop 1958-2009. 2010. (SPA., Illus.). 144p. (978-607-415-104-6(0)) Tomorrow's Guides, Ltd.

Christ, James, told to. Memories from Tuskegee: The Life Story of Lieutenant Colonel Clarence C. Jamison. 2006. (Illus.). 158p. per. 11.95 (978-0-9788604-0-0(3)) Tuskegee Leader LLC.

Christie, Doug & Christie, Jackie. No Ordinary Love: A True Story of Marriage & Basketball! 2007. 153p. 24.95 (978-0-9794827-0-0(4)) Infinite Love Publishing.

Christie, Ron. Black in the White House: Life Inside George W. Bush's West Wing, 0 vols. 2009. 328p. pap. 14.99 (978-1-59555-285-3(5)) Nelson, Thomas Inc.

Clark, Clinton, et al. Remember My Sacrifice: The Autobiography of Clinton Clark, Tenant Farm Organizer & Early Civil Rights Activist. 2007. (Illus.). 177p. 40.00 (978-0-8071-3277-7(2)) Louisiana State Univ. Pr.

Clark, Glenn. The Man Who Talks with the Flowers: The Intimate Life Story of Dr. George Washington Carver. 2011. 40p. pap. 6.49 **(978-1-61720-418-0(8))** Wilder Pubns., Ltd.

—The Man Who Talks with the Flowers-the Intimate Life Story of Dr George Washington Carver. 2011. 68p. pap. 6.95 **(978-1-61427-066-9(X))** Martino Publishing.

Clay, Roger, ed. The Legacy of Black Families in Jackson County, Florida. 2006. (Illus.). iv, 156p. lib. bdg. 30.00 (978-1-891647-98-7(9)) Heritage Publishing Consultants, Inc.

Clinton, Catherine. Harriet Tubman: The Road to Freedom. 2006. (Illus.). 272p. reprint ed. 28.00 (978-1-4223-5761-3(9)) DIANE Publishing Co.

Coates, Ta-Nehisi. The Beautiful Struggle: A Father, Two Sons, & an Unlikely Road to Manhood. 2009. (ENG.). 240p. pap. 15.00 (978-0-385-52746-0(2)) Spiegel & Grau.

Cobb, Regina M. About My Father's Business. 2008. 356p. pap. 19.99 (978-1-60477-832-6(6)) Xulon Pr., Inc.

Cobbs, Price. My American Life: From Rage to Entitlement. 2006. (ENG.). 272p. pap. 17.99 (978-0-7434-9622-3(1), Beyond Words/Atria Bks.) Atria Bks.

Coddington, Ronald S. African American Faces of the Civil War: An Album. 2012. **(978-1-4214-0625-1(X))**; E-Book **(978-1-4214-0723-4(X))** Johns Hopkins Univ. Pr.

Coggins, Patrick C. Tuskegee Airman Fighter Pilot: A Story of an Original Tuskegee Pilot Lt. Col. Hiram E. Mann. 2008. 272p. pap. 25.94 (978-1-4251-4732-7(1)) Trafford Publishing.

Cohen, Harvey G. Duke Ellington's America. 2010. (Illus.). 720p. 40.00 (978-0-226-11263-3(2)) Univ. of Chicago Pr.

Coleman-Adebayo, Marsha. No Fear: A Whistleblower's Triumph over Corruption & Retaliation at the EPA. 2011. (ENG., Illus.). 480p. 27.95 (978-1-55652-818-7(3), Hill, Lawrence Bks.) Chicago Review Pr., Inc.

Coleman, Rick. Blue Monday: Fats Domino & the Lost Dawn of Rock 'n' Roll. 2007. (ENG., Illus.). 416p. per. 15.95 (978-0-306-81531-7(1)) Da Capo Pr., Inc.

—Blue Monday: Fats Domino & the Lost Dawn of Rock 'n' Roll. Date not set. pap. 15.95 (978-0-06-051362-7(4)) HarperCollins Pubs.

Coleman, Terry Dwight. Don't Give up, Don't Give In. 2007. 328p. per. 17.99 (978-1-60477-465-6(7)) Xulon Pr., Inc.

Collier, Melvin J. Mississippi to Africa: A Journey of Discovery. 2008. (Illus.). xviii, 279p. pap. 28.00 (978-0-7884-4761-7(0)) Heritage Bks.

Condino, Meggin. African American Eras Library Set: Contemporary Times, 4 vols. 2010. (ENG., Illus.). 960p. (J). 292.00 (978-1-4144-3591-6(6), UXL) Cengage Gale.

Connerly, Ward. Lessons from My Uncle James. 2008. (ENG.). 350p. 19.95 (978-1-59403-221-9(1)) Encounter Bks.

Connor, Michal D. The Slave Letters. 2007. (ENG., Illus.). 48p. 29.95 (978-1-919901-12-1(4)) Janssen Pubs. ZAF. Dist: Independent Pubs. Group.

Contemporary Black Biography. (Contemporary Black Biography Ser.). (ENG.). 2008. 304p. 150.00 (978-1-4144-3276-2(3)) 2008. 304p. 150.00 (978-1-4144-3275-5(5)) 2008. 296p. 150.00 (978-0-7876-9544-6(0)) 2008. 288p. 150.00 (978-0-7876-9543-9(2)) 2008. 304p. 150.00 (978-0-7876-9541-5(6)) 2007. 288p. 150.00 (978-0-7876-7934-7(8)) 2007. 304p. 150.00 (978-0-7876-7933-0(X))70. 2008. 304p. 150.00 (978-1-4144-3277-9(1))71. 2009. 288p. 150.00 (978-1-4144-1929-2(7)) Vol. 77. 2010. 304p. 150.00 (978-1-4144-3970-9(9)) Vol. 78. 2010. 304p. 150.00 (978-1-4144-3971-6(7)) Vol. 79. 2010. 150.00 (978-1-4144-3972-3(5)) Vol. 80. 2010. 150.00 (978-1-4144-4601-1(2)) Cengage Gale.

Contemporary Black Biography: Profiles from the International Black Community. 2011. 150.00 (978-1-4144-5852-6(5)); 150.00 (978-1-4144-5851-9(7)) Cengage Gale.

Conyers, James L., Jr. & Smallwood, Andrew P. Malcolm X: An Historical Reader. 2008. (ENG.). 418p. pap. 40.00 (978-0-89089-228-2(8)) Carolina Academic Pr.

Cook, John I. Three Strikes, You're Out!!! The Cookbook, Part II. 2007. 200p. per. 16.95 (978-0-595-44830-2(5)) iUniverse, Inc.

Cooper, Ann Nixon. A Century & Some Change: My Life Before the President Called My Name. 2010. (ENG., Illus.). 224p. 19.99 (978-1-4391-5887-6(8), Beyond Words/Atria Bks.) Atria Bks.

Cooper, Ann Nixon & Bates, Karen Grigsby. A Century & Some Change: My Life Before the President Called My Name. 2010. pap. (978-1-4391-5888-3(6), Beyond Words/Atria Bks.) Atria Bks.

Cooper, Helene. The House at Sugar Beach: In Search of a Lost African Childhood. 2009. (ENG., Illus.). 384p. pap. 15.00 (978-0-7432-6625-3(0)) Simon & Schuster.

Cooper, Valerie C. Word, Like Fire: Maria Stewart, the Bible, & the Rights of African Americans. (Carter G. Woodson Institute Ser.). 2012. (ENG., Illus.). 224p. (gr. 17). 39.50 (978-0-8139-3188-3(6)) 2011. E-Book **(978-0-8139-3207-1(6))** Univ. Pr. of Virginia.

Copeland, Brian. Not a Genuine Black Man: My Life as an Outsider. 2008. 250p. pap. 14.00 (978-1-59692-311-9(3)) MacAdam/Cage Publishing, Inc.

—Not a Genuine Black Man: Or, How I Claimed My Piece of Ground in the Lily-White Suburbs. 2006. 272p. 22.95 (978-1-4013-0233-7(5)) Hyperion Pr.

Cotton, Dorothy. If Your Back's Not Bent: The Role of the Citizenship Education Program in the Civil Rights Movement. 2012. pap. **(978-0-7432-9684-7(2))**; (ENG., Illus.). 352p. 25.00 **(978-0-7432-9683-0(4))** Atria Bks. (Beyond Words/Atria Bks.).

Cottrell, Robert C. Two Pioneers: How Hank Greenberg & Jackie Robinson Transformed Baseball — and America. 2012. 280p. 27.50 **(978-1-59797-842-2(2))** Potomac Bks., Inc.

Craft, William & Ellen Craft. Running a Thousand Miles for Freedom: Or the Escape of William & Ellen Craft from Slavery. 2007. (ENG.). 72p. pap. 16.99 (978-1-4346-0479-8(9)); 78p. pap. 18.99 (978-1-4346-0512-2(4)) BiblioBazaar.

Crampton, Luke & Rees, Dafydd, eds. Music ICON Jimi Hendrix. 2009. (ENG.). 192p. pap. 9.99 (978-3-8365-1756-0(6)) TASCHEN DEU. Dist: Ingram Pub. Services.

Crane, Charlie. Image of a Black Father. 2007. 132p. (ENG.). 21.99 (978-1-60266-713-6(6)); per. 13.99 (978-1-60266-657-3(1)) Xulon Pr., Inc.

Crawford, Robert J. & Crawford, Robert J., Sr. Black Fire: Portrait of a Black Memphis Firefighter. 2007. (Illus.). 157p. pap., per. 19.99 (978-1-59629-328-1(4)) History Pr., The.

Cromwell, Adelaide M. Unveiled Voices, Unvarnished Memories: The Cromwell Family in Slavery & Segregation, 1692-1972. 2006. (ENG., Illus.). 368p. 39.95 (978-0-8262-1676-2(5)) Univ. of Missouri Pr.

Cross-White, Agnes. Possum Got Big Ears: Anatomy of a Child's Journey to Womanhood. 2008. 216p. pap. 15.99 (978-1-60477-543-3(2)) Xulon Pr., Inc.

Cunnigen, Donald, et al, eds. The Racial Politics of Booker T. Washington. 2006. 252p. 116.95 (978-0-7623-1011-1(1)) Emerald Group Publishing Ltd. GBR. Dist: Turpin Distribution Services Ltd.

Curtis, Susan. Colored Memories: A Biographer's Quest for the Elusive Lester A. Walton. 2008. (ENG., Illus.). 304p. (C). 39.95 (978-0-8262-1786-8(9)) Univ. of Missouri Pr.

Cusic, Don. The Trials of Henry Flipper, First Black Graduate of West Point. 2008. (ENG., Illus.). 218p. pap. 35.00 (978-0-7864-3969-0(6)) McFarland & Co., Inc. Pubs.

Dagbovie, Pero. The Early Black History Movement, Carter G. Woodson, & Lorenzo Johnston Greene. 2007. (New Black Studies Ser.). 280p. 67.00 (978-0-252-03190-8(3)) Univ. of Illinois Pr.

—The Early Black History Movement, Carter G. Woodson, & Lorenzo Johnston Greene. Hine, Darlene Clark & McBride, Dwight A., eds. 2007. (New Black Studies Ser.). 280p. per. 26.00 (978-0-252-07435-6(1)) Univ. of Illinois Pr.

Daniels, Dawn Marie & Sandy, Candace. How Long Will They Mourn Me? The Life & Legacy of Tupac Shakur. 2006. (ENG., Illus.). 176p. per. 6.99 (978-0-345-49483-2(0), One World/Ballantine) Random House Publishing Group.

Davis, Barbara B. Treasures of the Heart. 2007. (Illus.). 72p. pap. 15.00 (978-0-9795258-6-5(1)) Warwick Hse. Publishing.

Davis, Thulani. My Confederate Kinfolk: A Twenty-First Century Freedwoman Discovers Her Roots. 2007. (ENG., Illus.). 352p. per. 15.00 (978-0-465-01574-0(3), Basic Civitas Bks.) Basic Bks.

Davis, Wonda Lee. Real Time with Miss Bipolar Bitch: Around & Around I Go! an African American Woman Admits to Being Manic-Depressive. 2011. 233p. pap. 14.95 **(978-1-4327-6037-3(8))** Outskirts Pr., Inc.

Dawkins, Wayne. City Son: Andrew W. Cooper's Impact on Modern-Day Brooklyn. 2012. (Margaret Walker Alexander Series in African American Studies). (ENG.). 304p. 35.00 **(978-1-61703-258-5(1))** Univ. Pr. of Mississippi.

Day, Aaron L. & Kaletucker, Indira. The Heritage of African-Americans in Long Beach: Over 100 Years. 2007. 308p. pap. 24.95 (978-0-7414-3514-9(4)) Infinity Publishing.

Dean, Harry. Pedro Gorino: The Adventures of a Negro Sea-Captain in Africa & on the Seven Seas in His Attempts to Found an Ethiopian Empire. North, Sterling, ed. 2011. (ENG.). 304p. pap. 14.95 (978-1-59416-135-3(6)) Westholme Publishing.

Dean, Terrance. Hiding in Hip Hop: On the down Low in the Entertainment Industry — from Music to Hollywood. 2009. (ENG.). 320p. pap. 15.00 (978-1-4165-5340-3(1), Beyond Words/Atria Bks.) Atria Bks.

Deane, Pamala S. James Edwards: African American Hollywood Icon. 2009. (ENG., Illus.). 236p. pap. 45.00 (978-0-7864-4415-1(0)) McFarland & Co., Inc. Pubs.

Debardalo, Tom Johnson. Twenty End. 2009. 164p. pap. 14.95 (978-1-60844-213-3(6)) Dog Ear Publishing, LLC.

DeCosta-Willis, Miriam. Notable Black Memphians. 2008. 460p. 139.95 (978-1-60497-505-5(9)) Cambria Pr.

Dherbier, Yann-Brice & Bal, Candace, eds. Michael Jackson. 2009. (Life in Pictures Ser.). (ENG., Illus.). 192p. 40.00 (978-1-86205-880-4(6)) Chrysalis Children's Bks. GBR. Dist: Independent Pubs. Group.

Dickerson, Debra J. An American Story. pap. (978-0-385-72862-1(X)) Knopf Doubleday Publishing Group.

Dixon, Phil S. Wilber Bullet Rogan & the Kansas City Monarchs. 2010. (ENG., Illus.). 227p. pap. 39.95 (978-0-7864-4425-0(8)) McFarland & Co., Inc. Pubs.

Doctor, Bernard Aquina. Malcolm X for Beginners. 2007. (For Beginners Ser.). (ENG., Illus.). 192p. per. 14.95 (978-1-934389-04-1(8), For Beginners) Steerforth Pr.

Donna J. Bosn & Arthur Lee Crume Sr. The Perfect Song. 2010. 408p. 34.99 (978-1-4535-3609-4(4)); pap. 23.99 (978-1-4535-3608-7(6)) Xlibris Corp.

Donovan, Brian. Hard Driving: The Wendell Scott Story. 2009. (ENG.). 328p. 16.99 (978-1-58642-160-1(3)) Steerforth Pr.

Dorr, David F. A Colored Man Round the World. 2009. 192p. 22.99 (978-1-103-45853-0(1)); pap. 16.99 (978-1-103-45851-6(5)) BiblioBazaar.

—A Colored Man Round the World. 2008. 196p. 37.95 (978-1-4369-1788-9(3)); pap. 22.95 (978-1-4367-2157-8(1)) Kessinger Publishing, LLC.

Dossett, Kate. Bridging Race Divides: Black Nationalism, Feminism, & Integration in the United States, 1896-1935. 2009. (ENG., Illus.). 280p. pap. 29.95 (978-0-8130-3495-9(7)) Univ. Pr. of Florida.

Dougherty, Steve & Durkee, Cutler. People Tribute: Remembering Michael 1958-2009. 2009. (Illus.). 96p. pap. (978-1-60320-618-1(3)) Time Home Entertainment, Inc.

Douglass, Frederick. Narrative of the Life of Frederick Douglass. 2010. (Illus.). 70p. pap. 6.40 (978-1-4432-0125-4(1)) General Bks. LLC.

—Narrative of the Life of Frederick Douglass. 2010. 112p. pap. 12.95 (978-1-60444-238-0(7)) IndoEuropeanPublishing.com.

—Narrative of the Life of Frederick Douglass. 2006. (YA). 1.25 **(978-1-4193-8516-2(X))** Recorded Bks., LLC.

—Narrative of the Life of Frederick Douglass. 100p. 2011. pap. 6.99 **(978-1-61382-062-9(3))** 2010. pap. 6.75 **(978-1-936041-50-3(2))** 2010. pap. 4.94 (978-1-936041-20-6(0)) Simon & Brown.

—Narrative of the Life of Frederick Douglass. 2011. (ENG.). 114p. pap. 7.77 (978-1-936594-18-4(8)) Tribeca Bks.

—The Narrative of the Life of Frederick Douglass. 2008. (ENG.). 112p. pap. 10.45 (978-1-60597-228-2(2), Book Jungle) Standard Pubns., Inc.

—Narrative of the Life of Frederick Douglass. 2009. 7.62 (978-0-7848-0700-2(0)); 9.12 (978-0-7848-2758-1(3)) Marco Bk. Co. (Everbind).

—Narrative of the Life of Frederick Douglass: An American Slave. 2009. 102p. pap. 18.75 (978-1-110-36675-0(2)) BiblioBazaar.

—Narrative of the Life of Frederick Douglass: An American Slave & Incidents in the Life of a Slave Girl. 2007. pap. 6.99 (978-1-59986-871-4(7)) Filiquarian Publishing, LLC.

—Narrative of the Life of Frederick Douglass: An American Slave, Written by Himself. 2007. (ENG.). 128p. 19.99 (978-1-59986-703-8(6)) Filiquarian Publishing, LLC.

—Narrative of the Life of Frederick Douglass: An American Slave, Written by Himself. 2009. (John Harvard Library). (Illus.). 176p. pap. 8.50 (978-0-674-03401-3(5), Belknap Pr.) Harvard Univ. Pr.

Douglass, Frederick & Davis, Angela Y. Narrative of the Life of Frederick Douglass, an American Slave, Written by Himself: A New Critical Edition by Angela Y. Davis. 2009. (City Lights Open Media Ser.). (ENG., Illus.). 220p. pap. 12.95 (978-0-87286-527-3(4)) City Lights Bks.

Douglass, Frederick, et al. Three African-American Classics: Up from Slavery - The Souls of Black Folk - Narrative of the Life of Frederick Douglass. 2007. (African American Ser.). (ENG., Illus.). 448p. per. 7.95 (978-0-486-45757-4(5)) Dover Pubns., Inc.

Douglass II, Frederick. Facing America: The Arrival of a Black Man to His Native Land, 1 vol. 2010. 242p. pap. 24.95 (978-1-60610-383-8(0)) PublishAmerica, Inc.

Drape, Joe. Black Maestro: The Epic Life of an American Legend. 2007. 304p. mass mkt. 7.50 (978-0-06-053730-2(1)); per. 14.99 (978-0-06-125228-0(X), Harper Paperbacks) HarperCollins Pubs.

Dreher, W. Scott. The Tapestry Diary: One. 2007. 50p. pap. 16.95 (978-1-4241-9879-5(8)) PublishAmerica, Inc.

Dressman, Denny. Eddie Robinson: ... He Was the Martin Luther King of Football. 2010. 374p. pap. 24.95 (978-0-9774283-3-5(8)) ComServ LLC.

Drew, Mary E. C. Divine Will, Restless Heart: The Life & Works of Dr. John Jefferson Smallwood. 2010. 292p. 29.99 (978-1-4535-1197-8(0)); pap. 19.99 (978-1-4535-1196-1(2)) Xlibris Corp.

Drinkard, Dorothy. Indomitable: A Biography of James Farmer & the Civil Rights Movement. 2012. (ENG., Illus.). 368p. 27.99 (978-0-9801744-4-1(9)) Barnhardt & Ashe Publishing, Inc.

Drumgoold, Kate. A Slave Girl's Story. 2009. 56p. pap. (978-1-4099-6306-6(3)) Dodo Pr.

Drummond, Darlene K. A Diary of Gastric Bypass Surgery: When the Benefits Outweigh the Costs. 2008. 146p. 44.50 (978-0-7914-7439-6(9)); pap. 19.95 (978-0-7914-7440-2(2)) State Univ. of New York Pr.

Du Bois, W. E. B. The Autobiography of W.E.B. du Bois: A Soliloquy on Viewing My Life from the Last Decade of Its First Century. 2007. (978-0-19-532589-8(3)) Oxford Univ. Pr., Inc.

Dungy, Tony. Quiet Strength: The Principles, Practices, & Priorities of a Winning Life. (ENG., Illus.). 2008. 352p. pap. 14.99 (978-1-4143-1802-8(2)) 2007. 336p. 26.99 (978-1-4143-1801-1(4)) Tyndale Hse. Pubs.

Dunklin, Arthur L. African American Men & Opportunity in the Navy: Personal Histories of Eight Chiefs. 2008. (ENG.). 184p. pap. 35.00 (978-0-7864-3699-6(9)) McFarland & Co., Inc. Pubs.

Dunn, Dorsey Jerome. When the Power of Christ Compels You. 2010. 122p. pap. 11.99 (978-1-60957-483-3(4)) Xulon Pr., Inc.

Dunton-Downer, Leslie. The English Is Coming! How One Language Is Sweeping the World. 2010. (ENG., Illus.). 352p. 24.00 (978-1-4391-7665-8(5), Touchstone) Touchstone.

Durham, Carroll. The Forgotten Soldier. 2010. 240p. 29.99 (978-1-4535-2794-8(X)); pap. 19.99 (978-1-4535-2793-1(1)) Xlibris Corp.

Durough, Allen R. & Rayfield, Wallace A. The Architectural Legacy of Wallace A. Rayfield: Pioneer Black Architect of Birmingham, Alabama. 2nd ed. 2010. (ENG., Illus.). 176p. 32.95 (978-0-8173-1683-9(3)) Univ. of Alabama Pr.

Duster, Michelle. Ida in Her Own Words: The Timeless Writings of Ida B. Wells From 1893. 2008. 104p. pap. 12.95 (978-0-9802398-1-2(8)) Williams, Benjamin Publishing.

Dyja, Thomas. Walter White: The Dilemma of Black Identity in America. 2010. (ENG.). 224p. pap. 15.95 (978-1-56663-865-4(8)) Dee, Ivan R. Pub.

EBONY Magazine Staff. Martin Luther King Jr. 1929-1968: An Ebony Picture Biography. 2007. (ENG., Illus.). 80p. pap. 14.95 (978-0-87485-005-5(3)) Johnson Publishing Co., Inc.

Edds, Margaret. An Expendable Man: The near-Execution of Earl Washington, Jr. 2006. (ENG., Illus.). 288p. per. 23.00 (978-0-8147-2239-8(3)) New York Univ. Pr.

Edelin, Kenneth C. Broken Justice: A True Story of Race, Sex & Revenge in a Boston Courtroom. 2007. (Illus.). 362p. per. 17.95 (978-0-9792060-0-9(6)) PondView Pr.

Eeden, Trevor Von. The Original Johnson Volume 1, 2 vols. 2010. (Illus.). 128p. pap. 19.99 (978-1-60010-638-5(2)) Idea & Design Works, LLC.

Ellis, Jack D. Beside the Troubled Waters: A Black Doctor Remembers Life, Medicine, & Civil Rights in an Alabama Town. 2nd ed. 2011. (ENG., Illus.). 192p. 24.00 (978-0-8173-1721-8(X)) Univ. of Alabama Pr.

Emeka Wilie Obiozor. Back to Her Refuge: From the author of WHITE for BLACK. 2009. 148p. pap. 14.95 (978-1-4401-4428-8(1)) iUniverse, Inc.

Enriquez, Aniceto. My Journey, My Life. 2009. 164p. pap. 15.95 (978-0-595-45264-4(7)) iUniverse, Inc.

Evans, Bill. My Journey: The Life Story of William. 2006. (978-0-9753789-1-5(0)) Hines, C.W. & Assocs., Inc.

Evans, Cynthia. Voices of Cyn... Traces of A Backslider. 2012. (ENG.). pap. 15.00 **(978-0-9833461-4-2(3))** NCM Publishing.

Evers-Williams, Myrlie, ed. Autobiography of Medgar Evers: A Hero¿s Life & Legacy Revealed Through His Writings, Letters, & Speeches. 2008. (ENG.). 352p. 26.00 (978-1-4223-9197-6(3)) DIANE Publishing Co.

Evers-Williams, Myrlie & Marable, Manning. The Autobiography of Medgar Evers: A Hero's Life & Legacy Revealed Through His Writings, Letters, & Speeches. 2006. (ENG., Illus.). 400p. per. 18.99 (978-0-465-02178-9(6), Basic Civitas Bks.) Basic Bks.

Ezra, Michael, ed. Civil Rights Movement: People & Perspectives, 1 vol. 2009. (Perspectives in American Social History Ser.). (Illus.). 250p. 85.00 (978-1-59884-037-7(1), CIRIMO1C) ABC-CLIO, LLC.

Farmer, Vernon L. & Shepherd-Wynn, Evelyn, eds. Voices of Historical & Contemporary Black American Pioneers, 4 vols. 2012. (Illus.). 1408p. 257.00 (978-0-313-39224-5(2), A3243C, Praeger Pubs.) Greenwood Publishing Group, Inc.

Farris, Christine King. Through It All: Reflections on My Life, My Family, & My Faith. 2010. (ENG., Illus.). 272p. pap. 15.00 (978-1-4165-4882-9(3), Beyond Words/Atria Bks.) Atria Bks.

Federal Bureau Of Investigation & King, Martin Luther, Jr. Martin Luther King, Jr: The FBI Files. 2007. 228p. per. 22.99 (978-1-59986-253-8(0), Filibust) Filiquarian Publishing, LLC.

Flamming, Douglas. African Americans in the West, 1 vol. 2009. (Cultures in the American West Ser.). (Illus.). 353p. 65.00 (978-1-59884-002-5(9), AFAMWE1C) ABC-CLIO, LLC.

Forbes, Camille F. Introducing Bert Williams: Burnt Cork, Broadway, & the Story of America's First Black Star. 2010. (ENG., Illus.). 416p. (gr. 9). pap. 18.95 (978-0-465-01811-6(4)) Basic Bks.

Ford, Arthur Lee. When the Whippoorwill Sang: A Memoir of Rural Life During the Twilight of the Segregated South. 2008. (978-1-887366-84-7(9)) Univ. of Louisiana at Lafayette Pr.

Fordham, Damon L. True Stories of Black South Carolina. 2008. (Illus.). 166p. pap., per. 17.99 (978-1-59629-405-9(1)) History Pr., The.

—Voices of Black South Carolina: Legend & Legacy. 2008. (Regional Histories Ser.). 19.99 (978-1-59629-611-4(9)) History Pr., The.

Forten, Charlotte L. The Journal of Charlotte L Forten: A Young Black Woman's Reaction to the White World of the Civil War Era. Billington, Ray Allen, ed. 2011. 254p. 46.95 **(978-1-258-00700-3(2))** Literary Licensing, LLC.

Fradin, Judith Bloom & Frandin, Dennis Brindell. Stolen into Slavery: The True Story of Solomon Northup, Free Black Man. 2012. (ENG., Illus.). 128p. (J). (gr. 9-11). lib. bdg. 27.90 **(978-1-4263-0938-0(4))** National Geographic Society.

Francis, Aidan. Prince Fielder: Home-Run King. 2010. (Inspiring Lives Ser.). (ENG.). 32p. (gr. 5-8). pap. 10.50 (978-1-4339-3650-0(X)) Stevens, Gareth Publishing LLLP.

Frandin, Dennis Brindell & Fradin, Judith Bloom. Stolen into Slavery: The True Story of Solomon Northup, Free Black Man. 2012. (ENG., Illus.). 128p. (J). (gr. 5-9). 18.95 (978-1-4263-0937-3(6), National Geographic Children's Bks.) National Geographic Society.

Franklin, John Hope. Vintage Years. Date not set. 29.95 (978-0-06-019922-7(9), Amistad) HarperCollins Pubs.

Fredericq, Suzanne. Artist Eugene J. Martin's Secret Hieroglyphs. 2009. 62p. pap., pap. 29.00 (978-0-9825704-5-6(7)) Estate of Eugene James Martin.

Freeman, Mike. Jim Brown: The Fierce Life of an American Hero. 2007. (ENG.). 320p. pap. 14.99 (978-0-06-077683-1(8)) HarperCollins Pubs.

Friend, The Reverend Deacon Shelby M. Trouble Don't Last Always. 2008. 124p. 21.49 (978-1-4389-0075-9(9)) AuthorHouse.

Friends, text. A Woman's Journey: The Life & Work of Artis Lane. 2007. (Illus.). 96p. pap. 29.99 (978-0-9789818-1-5(2)) Friends, the Foundation of the CAAM.

Frost, Karolyn Smardz. I've Got a Home in Glory Land: A Lost Tale of the Underground Railroad. 2008. (ENG., Illus.). 480p. pap. 18.00 (978-0-374-53125-6(0)) Farrar, Straus & Giroux.

Fulwood-York, Pearline. Going to See Mama. 2007. pap. 17.00 (978-0-8059-8649-5(9)) Dorrance Publishing Co., Inc.

Funderburg, Lise. Pig Candy: Taking My Father South, Taking My Father Home - A Memoir. 2009. (ENG.). 320p. pap. 15.00 (978-1-4165-4767-9(3), Free Pr.) Free Pr.

Fusco, Gail C. Mama Nettie s Time to Love. 2010. 330p. pap. 18.99 (978-1-60957-379-9(X)) Xulon Pr., Inc.

Gale Cengage Publishing, creator. Contemporary Black Biography: Volume 65. 2008. (Contemporary Black Biography Ser.). (ENG., Illus.). 304p. 150.00 (978-0-7876-9542-2(4)) Cengage Gale.

Gale Editor, ed. Contemporary Black Biography: Profiles from the International Black Community. 2011. 264p. (ENG.). lib. bdg. 150.00 (978-1-4144-7173-0(4)); (ENG.). lib. bdg. 150.00 (978-1-4144-7172-3(6)); (ENG.). lib. bdg. 150.00 (978-1-4144-7171-6(8)); 150.00 (978-1-4144-7169-3(6)); (ENG.). 150.00 (978-1-4144-7168-6(8)); (ENG.). lib. bdg. 150.00 (978-1-4144-7170-9(X)) Cengage Gale.

Gardenhire, John Fouts. Life Lessons from My Father: Things Dad Used to Say. 2006. 81p. per. 9.95 (978-1-60002-242-5(1), 4173) Mountain Valley Publishing, LLC.

Gasman, Marybeth & Bieze, Michael Scott, eds. Booker T. Washington Rediscovered. 2012. (ENG., Illus.). 224p. (C). (gr. 13-17). 70.00 **(978-1-4214-0470-7(2))** Johns Hopkins Univ. Pr.

Gates, Henry Louis, Jr. In Search of Our Roots: How 19 Extraordinary African Americans Reclaimed Their Past. 2009. (ENG., Illus.). 448p. 27.50 (978-0-307-38240-5(0), Crown) Crown Publishing Group.

Gates, Henry Louis, Jr. & Higginbotham, Evelyn Brooks, eds. African American National Biography, 8 vols., Set. 2008. (ENG., Illus.). 5568p. 1115.00 (978-0-19-516019-2(3)) Oxford Univ. Pr., Inc.

Gavin, Camille. Biddy Mason A Place of Her Own. 2007. 53p. pap. 16.95 (978-1-4241-6041-9(3)) PublishAmerica, Inc.

Gavin, James. Stormy Weather: The Life of Lena Horne. 2010. (ENG., Illus.). 608p. pap. 16.00 (978-0-7432-7144-8(0), Beyond Words/Atria Bks.) Atria Bks.

Gelderman, Carol. A Free Man of Color & His Hotel: Race, Reconstruction, & the Role of the Federal Government. 2012. (Illus.). 184p. 27.50 **(978-1-59797-833-0(7))** Potomac Bks., Inc.

Gelderman, Carol W. A Free Man of Color & His Hotel: Race, Reconstruction, & the Role of the Federal Government. 2012. **(978-1-59797-834-7(5))** Potomac Bks., Inc., Pubs.

George Washington Carver National Monument (Mo.) Staff & George Washington Carver Birthplace Association Staff, contrib. by. George Washington Carver: His Life & Legacy. 2010. pap. (978-1-57864-628-9(6)) Donning Co. Pubs.

Gerzina, Gretchen Holbrook & Gerzina, Gretchen H. Mr. & Mrs. Prince: How an Extraordinary Eighteenth-Century Family Moved Out of Slavery & into Legend. 2009. (ENG.). 272p. pap. 14.99 (978-0-06-051074-9(9), Harper Paperbacks) HarperCollins Pubs.

Gibbs, Mifflin Wistar. Shadow & Light: an Autobiography with Reminiscences of the Last. 2007. pap. 33.95 (978-1-4304-6981-0(1)) Kessinger Publishing, LLC.

Gilbert, Olive. Narrative of Sojourner Truth. 2011. 122p. pap. 9.99 **(978-1-61203-035-7(1))** Bottom of the Hill Publishing.

Gilchrist, Eletra S. Experiences of Single African-American Women Professors: With This Ph.D., I Thee Wed. 2011. **(978-0-7391-7088-5(0))** Lexington Bks.

Gildea, William. The Longest Fight: In the Ring with Joe Gans, Boxing's First African-American Champion. 2012. (ENG., Illus.). 256p. 26.00 **(978-0-374-28097-0(5))** Farrar, Straus & Giroux.

Gillespie, Andra. The New Black Politician: Corey Booker, Newark, & Post-Racial America. 2012. (ENG.). 336p. 35.00 **(978-0-8147-3244-1(5))** New York Univ. Pr.

Gillespie, Marcia, et al. Maya Angelou: A Glorious Celebration. l.t. ed. 2008. 250p. 31.95 (978-1-4104-0983-6(X)) Thorndike Pr.

Gilyard, Keith. John Oliver Killens: A Life of Black Literary Activism. (ENG., Illus.). 456p. 2011. pap. 26.95 **(978-0-8203-4031-9(6))** 2010. 39.95 (978-0-8203-3513-1(4)) Univ. of Georgia Pr.

Gipson, Bernard F. You Can Make It If You Try: An African-American Surgeon's Inspiring Journey. 2008. (978-0-9800649-5-7(3)) Hilton Publishing Co.

Glasrud, Bruce A., et al, eds. Slavery to Integration: Black Americans in West Texas. 2008. (ENG., Illus.). 168p. pap. 21.95 (978-1-933337-26-5(5)) State Hse. Pr.

Glasrud, Bruce A. & Searles, Michael N. Buffalo Soldiers in the West: A Black Soldiers Anthology. 2007. 40.00 (978-1-58544-612-4(2)) Texas A&M Univ. Pr.

Glasrud, Bruce A. & Searles, Michael N., eds. Buffalo Soldiers in the West: A Black Soldiers Anthology. 2007. (ENG.). 328p. (C). pap. 19.95 (978-1-58544-620-9(3)) Texas A&M Univ. Pr.

Glauberman, Stu & Burris, Jerry. The Dream Begins: How Hawai'i Shaped Barack Obama. 2009. 180p. pap. 17.95 (978-0-9821698-2-7(5)) Watermark Publishing, LLC.

Glisson, Susan M. The Human Tradition in the Civil Rights Movement. 2006. (Human Tradition in America Ser.). (ENG., Illus.). 320p. 88.00 (978-0-7425-4408-6(7)) Rowman & Littlefield Publishers, Inc.

Goings, Henry. Rambles of a Runaway from Southern Slavery. Schermerhorn, Calvin et al, eds. 2012. (Carter G. Woodson Institute Ser.). (ENG., Illus.). 200p. (gr. 17). 45.00 **(978-0-8139-3238-5(6))** Univ. Pr. of Virginia.

Goings, Henry, et al. Rambles of a Runaway from Southern Slavery. 2012. E-Book **(978-0-8139-3240-8(8))** Univ. Pr. of Virginia.

Golden, Thelma, et al. Kori Newkirk: 1997-2007. 2007. (Illus.). pap. (978-0-911291-33-9(4)) Fellows of Contemporary Art.

Goldman, Robert M. One Man Out: Curt Flood Versus Baseball. 2008. 200p. (C). 35.00 (978-0-7006-1602-2(0)); pap. 16.95 (978-0-7006-1603-9(9)) Univ. Pr. of Kansas.

Goldstein, Nancy. Jackie Ormes: The First African American Woman Cartoonist. 2008. (ENG., Illus.). 240p. 40.00 (978-0-472-11624-9(X)) Univ. of Michigan Pr.

Gordly, Avel Louise. Remembering the Power of Words: The Life of an Oregon Activist, Legislator, & Community Leader. 2011. 176p. pap. 18.95 (978-0-87071-604-1(2)) Oregon State Univ. Pr.

Gordon-Reed, Annette. The Hemingses of Monticello: An American Family. (ENG., Illus.). 2009. 816p. pap. 18.95 (978-0-393-33776-1(6), 33776) 2008. 800p. 35.00 (978-0-393-06477-3(8), 6477) Norton, W. W. & Co., Inc.

Gossett, Louis, Jr. & Karas, Phyllis. An Actor & a Gentleman. 2010. (ENG., Illus.). 320p. 26.95 (978-0-470-57471-3(2), Wiley) Wiley, John & Sons, Inc.

Gould, Todd. For Gold & Glory: Charlie Wiggins & the African-American Racing Car Circuit. 2007. (ENG., Illus.). 240p. pap. 14.95 (978-0-253-21962-6(0), 0253219620) Indiana Univ. Pr.

Grant, Adrian. Michael Jackson: A Visual Documentary 1958 to 2009. 2009. (ENG., Illus.). 196p. pap. 29.95 (978-1-84938-261-8(1)) Omnibus Pr.

Grant, Gail Milissa. At the Elbows of My Elders: One Family's Journey Toward Civil Rights. 2008. (ENG.). 272p. (gr. 9). 24.95 (978-1-883982-66-9(9)) Missouri Historical Society Pr.

Greason, Walter. The Path to Freedom: Black Families in New Jersey. 2010. (ENG., Illus.). 128p. pap. 19.99 (978-1-59629-992-4(4)) History Pr., The.

Green, Michelle Y. Oscar Invincible: The Life of Film Pioneer Oscar Micheaux. 2007. (978-0-8037-3003-8(9), Dial) Penguin Group (USA) Inc.

Green, Tara T. A Fatherless Child: Autobiographical Perspectives of African American Men. 2009. (ENG.). 184p. (C). 34.95 (978-0-8262-1821-6(0)) Univ. of Missouri Pr.

Greene, Meg. Henry Louis Gates, Jr: A Biography, 1 vol. 2012. (Greenwood Biographies Ser.). (Illus.). 168p. 37.00 **(978-0-313-38046-4(5)**, A2208C) Greenwood Publishing Group, Inc.

Greer, Bonnie. Langston Hughes: The Value of Contradiction. 2011. (BlackAmber Inspirations Ser.). (ENG., Illus.). 190p. pap. 14.95 (978-1-906413-76-7(2), Black Amber) Arcadia Bks. Ltd. GBR. Dist: Dufour Editions, Inc.

Grenway, Bernard. Random Musings: Reflections of a Black Intellectual. 2011. (ENG.). 130p. pap. 22.00 (978-0-7618-5302-2(2)) Univ. Pr. of America, Inc.

Griffin, John Howard. Black Like Me. 50th anniv. ed. 2010. (ENG.). 208p. (gr. 12). 7.99 (978-0-451-23421-6(9), Signet) Penguin Group (USA) Inc.

Griffiths, Julia. Autographs for Freedom. 2010. (ENG.). 280p. pap. 28.75 (978-1-177-36342-6(9)) 2010. (ENG.). 376p. pap. 33.75 (978-1-176-48587-7(3)) 2010. 352p. pap. 32.75 (978-1-149-28739-2(X)) 2010. 328p. pap. 31.75 (978-1-143-01487-1(1)) 2009. (ENG.). 332p. 36.99 (978-1-117-30365-9(9)) 2009. (ENG.). 332p. pap. 30.75 (978-1-117-30366-6(7)) 2009. (ENG.). 332p. pap. 23.99 (978-1-117-30367-3(5), BiblioLife) 2008. 336p. 28.99 (978-0-559-45262-8(4)) 2008. 336p. pap. 30.75 (978-0-559-45259-8(4)) BiblioBazaar.

—Autographs for Freedom. 2009. 118p. pap. 19.99 (978-1-150-06097-7(2)) General Bks. LLC.

—Autographs for Freedom. 2010. 276p. pap. 22.36 (978-1-163-90205-9(5)) 2008. 274p. 42.95 (978-0-548-92511-9(9)) 2007. (ENG.). 276p. per. 27.95 (978-0-548-56568-1(6)) Kessinger Publishing, LLC.

Griffiths, Julia & DLC, Susan B. Anthony Collection. Autographs for Freedom. 2010. 356p. pap. 32.75 (978-1-149-28738-5(1)) BiblioBazaar.

Grigsby, Daryl. In Their Footsteps: Inspirational Reflections on Black History for Every Day of the Year. 2007. (Illus.). 384p. per. 14.95 (978-0-87946-336-6(8)) ACTA Pubns.

Grimes, Nikki. Out of the Dark. 2009. (ENG., Illus.). 56p. (J). pap. 8.00 (978-1-57274-977-1(6), Author at Work) Owen, Richard C. Pubs., Inc.

Grimes, William, et al. Life of William Grimes, the Runaway Slave. 2008. (ENG., Illus.). 192p. 74.00 (978-0-19-534331-1(X)); pap. 16.95 (978-0-19-534332-8(8)) Oxford Univ. Pr., Inc.

Gueye, Modou. Hell in Heaven. 2009. 108p. pap. 16.49 (978-1-4389-6637-3(7)) AuthorHouse.

Gunn, Carroll. The Life of Mary Shepard-Queen of the Legendary Club Ebony. 2007. 172p. pap. 20.00 (978-0-615-21824-3(5)) Gunn, Jennie.

Guyette, Elise A. Discovering Black Vermont: African American Farmers in Hinesburgh, 1790-1890. 2010. (Illus.). 232p. pap. 26.95 (978-1-58465-760-6(X), University of Vermont Press) Univ. Pr. of New England.

Hager, Ruth Ann Abels. Dred & Harriet Scott: Their Family Story. 2010. (Illus.). xvi, 173p. **(978-0-615-32762-4(1))** Well Fire Pubns.

Haggins, Bambi. Laughing Mad: The Black Comic Persona in Post-Soul America. 2007. (ENG., Illus.). 288p. 68.00 (978-0-8135-3984-3(6)); per. 23.95 (978-0-8135-3985-0(4)) Rutgers Univ. Pr.

Hairston, Otis L. Picturing Greensboro, North Carolina: Four Decades of African American Community. 2007. pap. 19.99 (978-1-59629-284-0(9)) History Pr., The.

Haizlip, Shirlee. Finding Grace: Two Sisters & the Search for Meaning Beyond the Color Line. 2007. (ENG.). 296p. pap. 19.95 (978-0-7432-0054-7(3), Free Pr.) Free Pr.

Haley, Alex. Alex Haley: The Man Who Traced America's Roots. 2007. (978-0-7621-0885-5(1)) Reader's Digest Assn., Inc., The.

—Roots: The Saga of an American Family. 30th ed. 2007. (ENG.). 899p. 23.60 (978-0-7569-8232-4(4)) Perfection Learning Corp.

—Roots: The Saga of an American Family. 30th anniv. ed. 2007. (ENG.). 912p. per. 17.95 (978-1-59315-449-3(6)) Vanguard Pr.

Hall, Ethel & Bivens, Carmelita James. My Journey: A Memoir of the First African American to Preside over the Alabama Board of Education. 2011. 24.95 (978-1-58838-257-3(5), NewSouth Bks.) NewSouth, Inc.

Hall, Ron. What Difference Do It Make? Stories of Hope & Healing. l.t. ed. 2010. (ENG.). 253p. 30.99 (978-1-4104-2778-6(1)) Thorndike Pr.

Hall, Ron & Moore, Denver. Same Kind of Different As Me: A Modern-Day Slave, an International Art Dealer, & the Unlikely Woman Who Bound Them Together. l.t. ed. 2010. (ENG.). 448p. pap. 17.99 (978-1-59415-318-1(3)) Cengage Gale.

—Same Kind of Different As Me: A Modern-Day Slave, an International Art Dealer, & the Unlikely Woman Who Bound Them Together, 0 vols. 2008. 256p. pap. 15.99 (978-0-8499-1910-7(X)) Nelson, Thomas Inc.

—Same Kind of Different As Me: A Modern-Day Slave, an International Art Dealer, & the Unlikely Woman Who Bound Them Together. l.t. ed. 2010. (ENG.). 440p. 30.95 (978-1-4104-2456-3(1)) Thorndike Pr.

Hall, Ron, et al. What Difference Do It Make? Stories of Hope & Healing, 0 vols. 2010. 224p. pap. 15.99 (978-0-8499-4619-6(0)) Nelson, Thomas Inc.

Hamilton, Ed. The Birth of an Artist: A journey of Discovery. 2006. 176p. per. 19.95 (978-1-58374-158-0(5)) Chicago Spectrum Pr.

Hancock, Fumi Stephanie Ogunleye. Beyond Idol Worship! 2007. 316p. per. 17.99 (978-1-60266-476-0(5)) Xulon Pr., Inc.

Hanna, Charles W. African American Recipients of the Medal of Honor: A Biographical Dictionary, Civil War through Vietnam War. alt. ed. 2010. (ENG., Illus.). 199p. pap. 38.00 (978-0-7864-4911-8(X)) McFarland & Co., Inc. Pubs.

Hardie, Mark Charles. The King of Israel. 2007. pap. 25.00 (978-0-9797327-0-6(0)) Hardie Bks. & Films.

Harmon, Byron. God Gave Me Some Bad Advice: Growing Up, Going to War, & Making It in America. 2008. (ENG.). 208p. pap. 15.00 (978-1-932841-34-3(2)) Agate Publishing, Inc.

HarperCollins Publishers Ltd. Staff. Oprah. (ENG.). 623p. pap. 14.00 (978-0-06-093364-7(X)) HarperCollins Pubs.

Harrington, Cliff. Just Tell the Truth: A Narrative History of Black Men Told from the Inside. 2011. 108p. 22.95 **(978-1-4620-0951-0(4))**; pap. 12.95 **(978-1-4620-0949-7(2))** iUniverse, Inc.

Harris, Dwight. American Nigger: Black Beyond King. 2007. 148p. per. 15.95 (978-0-9767575-3-5(2)) Topos Bks.

Harris, Eddie L. Ninety Degrees North: The Story of Matthew Henson, First Man to the North Pole. 2009. 160p. pap. 11.95 (978-0-06-058760-4(1), Amistad) HarperCollins Pubs.

Harris, Gail & McLaughlin, Pam. A Woman's War: The Professional & Personal Journey of the Navy's First African American Female Intelligence Officer. 2009. (Scarecrow Professional Intelligence Education Ser.). (ENG.). 284p. pap. 37.00 (978-0-8108-6793-2(1)) Scarecrow Pr., Inc.

Harris, Leonard & Molesworth, Charles. Alain L. Locke: The Biography of a Philosopher. 2010. (ENG., Illus.). 448p. pap. 25.00 (978-0-226-31777-9(3)) Univ. of Chicago Pr.

Harris, Trudier. Summer Snow: Reflections from a Black Daughter of the South. 2007. (ENG.). 200p. pap. 16.00 (978-0-8070-7255-4(9)) Beacon Pr.

Harvey, Alton, Sr. & Harvey, Alton. Freedom, an Optical Illusion. 2007. 190p. per. 12.99 (978-1-59886-735-0(0)) Tate Publishing & Enterprises, LLC.

Haskins, Jim. Diary of a Harlem School Teacher. 2008. 160p. 60.00 (978-1-59558-358-1(0)); (ENG.). 161p. pap. 18.95 (978-1-59558-339-0(4)) New Pr., The.

Hathorn, Ed. D. & Hathorn, Pauline Pearson. Escape from Paradise: How to Win Against All Odds. 2009. 204p. pap. 15.99 (978-1-60791-500-3(6)) Xulon Pr., Inc.

Hausround, Turnin A. Letters to the President. 2010. 92p. pap. 17.99 (978-0-557-26954-9(7)) Lulu Enterprises Inc.

Hawkins, Walter L. African American Biographies Vol. 3: Profiles of 909 Current Men & Women. 2009. (ENG., Illus.). 255p. pap. 55.00 (978-0-7864-4131-0(3)) McFarland & Co., Inc. Pubs.

—Black American Military Leaders: A Biographical Dictionary. alt. ed. 2009. (ENG., Illus.). 559p. pap. 49.95 (978-0-7864-4462-5(2)) McFarland & Co., Inc. Pubs.

Haynes, Rosetta R. Radical Spiritual Motherhood: Autobiography & Empowerment in Nineteenth-Century African American Women. 2011. 264p. 39.95 (978-0-8071-3694-2(8)) Louisiana State Univ. Pr.

Haywood, Della W. Years of a Lotus: Memoir of a Lust Baby. 2010. pap. 15.95 (978-0-7414-5868-1(3)) Infinity Publishing.

Haywood, Harry. Black Communist in the Freedom Struggle: The Life of Harry Haywood. Midlo Hall, Gwendolyn, ed. 2012. 336p. 75.00 **(978-0-8166-7905-8(3))**; pap. 24.95 **(978-0-8166-7906-5(1))** Univ. of Minnesota Pr.

Heaphy, Leslie A., ed. Satchel Paige & Company: Essays on the Kansas City Monarchs, Their Greatest Star & the Negro Leagues. 2007. (Jerry Malloy Conference Ser.). (ENG., Illus.). 308p. per. 35.00 (978-0-7864-3075-8(3)) McFarland & Co., Inc. Pubs.

Heatley, Michael. Michael Jackson: Life of a Legend, 1958-2009. 2009. (ENG., Illus.). 192p. 24.95 (978-0-7553-6053-6(2)) Headline Bk. Publishing GBR. Dist: Independent Pubs. Group.

Heisler, Mark. Kobe: And the New Lakers' Dynasty. 2009. (ENG.). 128p. pap. 14.95 (978-1-60078-350-0(3)) Triumph Bks.

Hemsath, Sister Caroline. From Slave to Priest: A Biography of the Reverend Augustine Tolton (1854-1897) First Black American Priest of the United States. 2006. (Illus.). 251p. 17.95 (978-1-58617-097-4(X)) Ignatius Pr.

Hendrick, George & Hendrick, Willene. Black Refugees in Canada: Accounts of Escape During the Era of Slavery. 2010. (ENG., Illus.). 192p. pap. 35.00 (978-0-7864-4733-6(8)) McFarland & Co., Inc. Pubs.

Hennessey, Mike. The Little Giant: The Story of Johnny Griffin. 2008. (Illus.). 246p. 48.00 (978-0-9550908-5-1(7)) Northway Pubns. GBR. Dist: Parkwest Pubns., Inc.

Henson & Henson, Josiah. Truth Stranger Than Fiction: Father Henson's Story of His Own Life. 2008. xiv, 105p. (978-1-4351-0838-7(8)) Barnes & Noble, Inc.

Henson, Josiah. Father Henson's Story of His Own Life. 2009. 100p. pap. 14.14 (978-1-151-53014-1(X)) General Bks. LLC.

—Father Henson's Story of His Own Life. 2008. 228p. 41.95 (978-1-4369-3132-8(0)) Kessinger Publishing, LLC.

Henson, Matthew A. Matthew A. Henson's Historic Arctic Journey: The Classic Account of One of the World's Greatest Black Explorers. 100th ed. 2009. (ENG., Illus.). 224p. 19.95 *(978-1-59921-308-8(7)*, Lyons Pr.) Globe Pequot Pr., The.

Henson, Matthew A. & Henson, Matthew Alexander. Henson at the North Pole. 2008. (Dover Books on Travel, Adventure Ser.). (ENG., Illus.). 128p. pap. 7.95 *(978-0-486-45472-6(X))* Dover Pubns., Inc.

Henwood, Simon, ed. & photos by. Rihanna: The Last Girl on Earth. 2010. (ENG., Illus.). 144p. 50.00 *(978-0-8478-3511-9(1))* Rizzoli International Pubns., Inc.

Herbert, Emily. Michael Jackson - King of Pop, 1958-2009. 2009. (ENG., Illus.). 268p. pap. 12.95 *(978-1-84454-897-2(X))* Blake, John Publishing, Ltd. GBR. Dist: Independent Pubs. Group.

Hersey, Mark D. My Work Is That of Conservation: An Environmental Biography of George Washington Carver. 2011. (Environmental History & the American South Ser.). (ENG., Illus.). 312p. 69.95 *(978-0-8203-3088-4(4))*; pap. 24.95 *(978-0-8203-3870-5(2))* Univ. of Georgia Pr.

Heyward, Gary. Corruption Officer. 2009. pap. 14.99 *(978-1-61658-344-6(4))* Independent Pub.

Hicks, Kyra E. This I Accomplish Harriet Powers' Bible Quilt & Other Pieces: Quilt Histories, Exhibition Lists, Annotated Bibliography & Timeline of a Great African American Quilter. 2009. (Illus.). 180p. pap. 19.95 *(978-0-9824796-5-0(4))* Black Threads Pr.

Hill, George M. How Far Is Forward? 2009. 224p. 29.99 *(978-1-4415-0029-8(4))*; pap. 19.99 *(978-1-4415-0028-1(6))* Xlibris Corp.

Hill, Leroy. From Selma to the Super Bowl: The Story of a Boy from the Bottoms. 2008. 176p. per. 18.95 *(978-0-9768677-1-5(0))* Joshua Tree Publishing.

Hilliard, David. Huey: Spirit of the Panther. 2006. (ENG., Illus.). 320p. per. 16.95 *(978-1-56025-897-1(7))* Basic Bks.

Hodges, Graham Russell. David Ruggles: A Radical Black Abolitionist & the Underground Railroad in New York City. 2010. (John Hope Franklin Series in African American History & Culture Ser.). (ENG., Illus.). 264p. 30.00 *(978-0-8078-3326-1(6))* Univ. of North Carolina Pr.

Hodgson, Godfrey. Martin Luther King. 2010. (Illus.). 249p. E-Book *(978-0-472-02572-5(4))*; (ENG., 264p. pap. 23.95 *(978-0-472-05128-1(8))* Univ. of Michigan Pr.

Hogan, Wesley C. Many Minds, One Heart: SNCC's Dream for a New America. 2009. (ENG., Illus.). 480p. pap. 23.95 *(978-0-8078-5959-9(1))* Univ. of North Carolina Pr.

Holland, Antonio F. Nathan B. Young: And the Struggle over Black Higher Education. 2006. (Missouri Biography Ser.). (ENG., Illus.). 248p. (C). 39.95 *(978-0-8262-1679-3(X))* Univ. of Missouri Pr.

Holland, Joseph H. From Harlem with Love: An Ivy Leaguer's Inner City Odyssey: A Memoir. 2012. ***(978-1-59056-322-9(0))***; E-Book ***(978-1-59056-323-6(9))*** Lantern Bks.

Holliday, Norma Jean. The Larry Holliday Story. 2008. 320p. per. 16.95 *(978-1-4327-1798-8(7))* Outskirts Pr., Inc.

Holloway, Jonathan Scott & Keppel, Ben, eds. Black Scholars on the Line: Race, Social Science, & American Thought in the Twentieth Century. 2007. (Afro/amer Intellectu Ser.). (Illus.). 600p. 85.00 *(978-0-268-03079-7(0))*; per. 40.00 *(978-0-268-03080-3(4))* Univ. of Notre Dame Pr.

Holmes, Kevin W. Daddy, I'm the Man You Could Have Been! 2011. 100p. pap. 15.99 ***(978-1-4568-5876-6(9))*** Xlibris Corp.

Holmes, Robert A. Maynard Jackson: A Biography. 2009. (Illus.). 368p. 27.99 *(978-0-9801744-0-3(6))* Barnhardt & Ashe Publishing, Inc.

Holway, John. Voices from the Great Black Baseball Leagues. rev. ed. 2010. (Dover Baseball Ser.). (ENG.). 448p. pap. 15.95 *(978-0-486-47541-7(7))* Dover Pubns., Inc.

Hooper, Lita. The Art of Work: The Art & Life of Haki R. Madhubuti. 2007. (Illus.). 109p. per. 14.95 *(978-0-88378-255-2(3))* Third World Press.

Hopkins, Pauline E. Daughter of the Revolution: The Major Nonfiction Works of Pauline E. Hopkins. 2007. (Multi-Ethnic Literatures of the Americas (MELA) Ser.). (ENG., Illus.). 456p. per. 34.95 *(978-0-8135-3952-1(5))* Rutgers Univ. Pr.

Hopkins, Pauline E. & Dworkin, Ira. Daughter of the Revolution: The Major Nonfiction Works of Pauline Hopkins. 2007. (Multi-Ethnic Literatures of the Americas Ser.). (ENG., Illus.). 456p. 70.00 *(978-0-8135-3961-4(7))* Rutgers Univ. Pr.

Horne, Gerald. The Color of Fascism: Lawrence Dennis, Racial Passing, & the Rise of Right-Wing Extremism in the United States. (ENG., Illus.). 256p. 2009. pap. 22.00 *(978-0-8147-3733-0(1))* 2006. 45.00 *(978-0-8147-3686-9(6))* New York Univ. Pr.

Horne, Gerald C. W. E. B. du Bois: A Biography, 1 vol. 2009. (Greenwood Biographies Ser.). (Illus.). 211p. 35.00 *(978-0-313-34979-9(7)*, GR4979) Greenwood Publishing Group, Inc.

Hornsby, Alton. Black America: A State-by-State Historical Encyclopedia. 2011. *(978-0-313-34113-7(3))*; *(978-0-313-34114-4(1))* ABC-CLIO, LLC.

Hornsby, Alton, Jr., ed. Black America: A State-by-State Historical Encyclopedia, 2 vols. 2011. (Illus.). 1010p. 180.00 *(978-0-313-34112-0(5)*, GR4112) Greenwood Publishing Group, Inc.

Houston, Ivan J. & Cohn, Gordon. Black Warriors: the Buffalo Soldiers of World War II: Memories of the Only Negro Infantry Division to Fight in Europe during World War II. 2011. 244p. pap. 14.95 *(978-1-936236-40-4(0))* iUniverse, Inc.

Howard-Oglesby, Pamela & Roberts, Brenda L. Savannah's Black First Ladies, Vol. I: The Past, Present, & Future. 2010. (Illus.). 120p. pap. 13.95 *(978-1-4327-3112-0(2))* Outskirts Pr., Inc.

Howard, Samuel H. The Flight of the Phoenix: Thoughts on Work & Life. 2007. (Illus.). 156p. 24.95 *(978-1-57736-379-8(5))* Providence Hse Pubs.

Howard, Stanley W. The Men We All Know. 2011. 84p. pap. 15.00 ***(978-1-4389-4745-7(3))*** AuthorHouse.

Howell, Shevonica M. Girl, They Ain't Ready! 2011. 134p. 29.99 ***(978-1-4568-2594-2(1))***; pap. 19.99 ***(978-1-4568-2593-5(3))*** Xlibris Corp.

Hubbard, Daniel R. Harlem Renaissance Resurrected: A Literary Biography of Four African American Masters. 2006. 143p. pap. 24.95 *(978-1-4241-1711-6(9))* PublishAmerica, Inc.

Hudson, Lynn M. The Making of Mammy Pleasant: A Black Entrepreneur in Nineteenth-Century San Francisco. 2008. (Women in American History Ser.). (ENG., Illus.). 224p. per. 21.00 *(978-0-252-07527-8(7))* Univ. of Illinois Pr.

Hughes, Brian & Hughes, Damian. Hit Man: The Thomas Hearns Story. 2010. (ENG., Illus.). 272p. pap. 17.95 *(978-1-903854-90-7(3))* Milo Bks. GBR. Dist: Consortium Bk. Sales & Distribution.

Hughes, Louis. Thirty Years a Slave. rev. ed. 2006. 140p. 25.95 *(978-1-4218-1798-9(5))*; pap. 10.95 *(978-1-4218-1898-6(1))* 1st World Publishing, Inc. (1st World Library - Literary Society).

—Thirty Years a Slave. 2010. (Illus.). 76p. pap. 20.00 *(978-1-153-74379-2(5))* General Bks. LLC.

—Thirty Years a Slave. 2010. 92p. pap. *(978-1-4076-0789-4(8))* HardPr.

—Thirty Years a Slave: From Bondage to Freedom. 2009. 232p. 23.99 *(978-1-103-70430-9(3))*; pap. 17.99 *(978-1-103-70425-5(7))* BiblioBazaar.

—Thirty Years a Slave: From Bondage to Freedom. 2009. 116p. pap. *(978-1-4099-6934-1(7))* Dodo Pr.

—Thirty Years a Slave from Bondage to Freedom the Institution of Slavery As Seen on the Plantation & in the Home of the Planter. 2010. (ENG.). 234p. pap. 26.75 *(978-1-177-99372-2(4))* BiblioBazaar.

—Thirty Years a Slave from Bondage to Freedom the Institution of Slavery As Seen on the Plantation & in the Home of the Planter. 2010. 76p. pap. *(978-1-153-17779-5(X))* Books LLC.

—Thirty Years a Slave; from Bondage to Freedom the Institution of Slavery As Seen on the Plantation & in the Home of the Planter. 2010. 80p. pap. 8.54 ***(978-0-217-73069-3(8))*** General Bks. LLC.

Hughes, Louis. Thirty Years a Slave from Bondage to Freedom the Institution of Slavery As Seen on the Plantation & in the Home of the Planter: Autobiography of Lou. 2010. 100p. 27.16 *(978-1-169-23979-1(X))*; 33.95 *(978-1-161-48226-3(1))* Kessinger Publishing, LLC.

Hull, Cadmus S. The Black History Bowl: Mini Biographies of African Americans. 2007. 352p. per. 19.95 *(978-1-59858-549-0(5))* Dog Ear Publishing, LLC.

Hunter, Jane Edna. A Nickel & a Prayer. Thomas, Rhondda Robinson, ed. 2011. (Regenerations Ser.). (ENG.). pap. 22.95 *(978-1-933202-64-8(5))* West Virginia Univ. Pr.

Hunter, Jane Edna & Thomas, Rhondda Robinson. A Nickel & a Prayer. 2011. (ENG.). 68.95 *(978-1-933202-65-5(3))* West Virginia Univ. Pr.

Hunter, Karen. Stop Being Niggardly: And Nine Other Things Black People Need to Stop Doing. 2010. (ENG.). 224p. 19.99 *(978-1-4165-6374-7(1)*, Gallery Books/Karen Hunter Publishing) Gallery Books/Karen Hunter Publishing.

Ijiti, Femi M. & Ugo, Millicent N. Ijiti: Reflections of A Soldier. 2011. 80p. 24.99 ***(978-1-4269-7222-5(9))*** Trafford Publishing.

—Ijiti: Reflections of a Soldier. 2011. 80p. pap. 14.99 ***(978-1-4269-7221-8(0))*** Trafford Publishing.

Ikedilo, Erasmus Uche. Questioning Relocation's Ideology. 2011. 58p. 24.99 ***(978-1-4568-6118-6(2))***; pap. 15.99 ***(978-1-4568-6117-9(4))*** Xlibris Corp.

Indovino, Shaina Carmel. Tyra Banks: From the Runway to the Television Screen. 2012. ***(978-1-4222-2294-2(2))***; pap. ***(978-1-4222-2305-5(1))*** Mason Crest Pubs.

Jackmon, Marvin. Somethin' Proper: The Life & Times of a North American African Poet. 278p. pap. 29.95 *(978-0-9649672-1-2(9))* Black Bird Pr.

Jackson, Andre J. Truth Holds No Secrets: The Son of A Beautiful Mind. 2011. 148p. pap. 13.14 ***(978-1-4269-6837-2(X))*** Trafford Publishing.

Jackson, David H., Jr. & Jackson, David H. A Chief Lieutenant of the Tuskegee Machine: Charles Banks of Mississippi. 2008. (ENG., Illus.). 304p. pap. 24.95 *(978-0-8130-3271-9(7))* Univ. Pr. of Florida.

Jackson, Madonna. Asbury Park: A West Side Story: A Pictorial Journey Through the Eyes of Joseph A. Carter, Sr. 2007. (Illus.). 244p. pap. 29.95 *(978-1-59800-963-7(X))* Outskirts Pr., Inc.

Jackson, Ruby West & McDonald, Walter T. Finding Freedom: The Untold Story of Joshua Glover, Runaway Slave. 2007. (ENG., Illus.). 176p. 18.95 *(978-0-87020-382-4(7))* Wisconsin Historical Society.

Jackson, Shirley Gordon. A Place to Be Someone: Growing up with Charles Gordone. 2008. (Illus.). 272p. 29.95 *(978-0-89672-635-2(5))* Texas Tech Univ. Pr.

Jackson, Troy. Becoming King: Martin Luther King Jr. & the Making of a National Leader. (Civil Rights & the Struggle for Black Equality in the Twentieth Century Ser.). (ENG.). 248p. 2011. pap. 21.95 *(978-0-8131-3390-4(4))* 2008. (Illus.). 50.00 *(978-0-8131-2520-6(0))* Univ. Pr. of Kentucky.

Jacobs, Carole. Tyra Banks: A Biography. 2010. (Illus.). x, 180p. E-Book *(978-0-313-38275-8(1)*, Greenwood Electronic Media (GEM)); 180p. 35.00 *(978-0-313-38274-1(3)*, A3155C) Greenwood Publishing Group, Inc.

Jacobs, Harriet & Douglass, Frederick. Incidents in the Life of a Slave Girl & Narrative of the Life of Frederick Douglass: Two Memoirs of Notable African-Americans During the Nineteenth Ce. 2011. 324p. ***(978-0-85706-695-4(1))***; pap. ***(978-0-85706-696-1(X))*** Leonaur Ltd.

Jacobson, Steve. Carrying Jackie's Torch: The Players Who Integrated Baseball-And America. 2009. (ENG., Illus.). 288p. pap. 14.95 *(978-1-55652-791-3(8)*, Hill, Lawrence Bks.) Chicago Review Pr., Inc.

Jacocks, William. Memoirs of Ratibu Shadidi: Incidents Struggles & Divine Interventions. 2007. (Illus.). 410p. per. 19.95 *(978-0-9767828-8-9(X))* Zoe Life Publications, Inc.

James, C. T. For My Father, 1 vol. 2010. 172p. pap. 24.95 *(978-1-61546-060-1(8))* PublishAmerica, Inc.

James, Rawn, Jr. Root & Branch: Charles Hamilton Houston, Thurgood Marshall, & the Struggle to End Segregation. 2010. (ENG., Illus.). 288p. 28.00 *(978-1-59691-606-7(0))* Bloomsbury Publishing.

James, Winston. The Struggles of John Brown Russwurm: The Life & Writings of a Pan-Africanist Pioneer, 1799-1851. 2010. (ENG., Illus.). 288p. pap. 22.00 *(978-0-8147-4290-7(4))* New York Univ. Pr.

—The Struggles of John Brown Russwurm: The Life & Writings of a Pan-Africanist Pioneer, 1799-1851. 2010. (ENG., Illus.). 305p. pap. *(978-976-640-249-5(3))* Univ. of the West Indies Pr.

Janken, Kenneth Robert. Walter White: Mr. NAACP. 2006. (ENG., Illus.). 512p. per. 27.95 *(978-0-8078-5780-9(7))* Univ. of North Carolina Pr.

Jarrett, Billy D. Pretty Much Dead. 2007. per. 16.95 *(978-0-9797616-3-8(8))* Lionhead Pr., The.

Jarvis, Malcolm Shorty & Nichols, Paul D. The Other Malcolm- Shorty Jarvis: His Memoir. West, Cornel, ed. alt. ed. 2008. (ENG., Illus.). 179p. pap. 35.00 *(978-0-7864-4057-3(0))* McFarland & Co., Inc. Pubs.

Jeffries, Judson L. Huey P. Newton: The Radical Theorist. 2006. 176p. 36.00 *(978-1-57806-432-8(5))* Univ. Pr. of Mississippi.

Jegede, dele. Encyclopedia of African American Artists, 1 vol. 2009. (Artists of the American Mosaic Ser.). (Illus.). 293p. 85.00 *(978-0-313-33761-1(6)*, GR3761, Greenwood Pr.) Greenwood Publishing Group, Inc.

Jelks, Randal Maurice. Benjamin Elijah Mays, Schoolmaster of the Movement: A Biography. 2012. (ENG., Illus.). 368p. 39.95 ***(978-0-8078-3536-4(6))*** Univ. of North Carolina Pr.

Jenkins, H.L. If You Can't Make It on Mark Avenue. 2008. 72p. pap. 10.00 *(978-1-4257-4676-6(4))* Xlibris Corp.

Jimeson, Bessie. Yesterday I Heard the Rain. 2008. pap. 10.00 *(978-0-8059-7910-7(7))* Dorrance Publishing Co., Inc.

Joens, David A. From Slave to State Legislator: John W.E. Thomas, Illinois' First African American Lawmaker. 2011. E-Book 34.95 ***(978-0-8093-3060-7(1))*** Southern Illinois Univ. Pr.

Johnella Wells. You Don't Look Like Someone Who. 2009. 116p. pap. 20.00 *(978-1-4269-0425-7(8))* Trafford Publishing.

Johnson, A. Mark. Basketball Slave: The Andy Johnson Harlem Globetrotter Story. 2010. 179p. pap. 19.95 *(978-0-615-17330-6(6))* Junior-Cam Publishing.

Johnson, Aaron & Rev. Aaron Johnson With Deb Cleveland. Man from Macedoni: My life of service, struggle, faith, & Hope. 2010. 272p. 35.95 *(978-1-4497-0030-0(6)*, WestBow Pr.) Author Solutions, Inc.

Johnson, Clifton H., ed. God Struck Me Dead: Voices of Ex-Slaves. 2011. 202p. pap. 22.00 *(978-1-61097-047-1(0)*, Wipf and Stock) Wipf & Stock Pubs.

Johnson, Ella Mae Cheeks & Mulcahy, Patricia. It Is Well with My Soul: The Extraordinary Life of a 106-Year-Old Woman. 2010. (ENG.). 224p. (gr. 12). 14.00 *(978-0-14-311744-5(0)*, Penguin (Non-Classics)) Penguin Group (USA) Inc.

Johnson, Jack. My Life & Battles. Rivers, Christopher, tr. from FRE. 2009. (Illus.). 152p. pap. 19.95 *(978-1-59797-267-3(3))* Potomac Bks., Inc.

Johnson, Melissa E. Halle Berry: A Biography. 2009. (Greenwood Biographies Ser.). 138p. 35.00 *(978-0-313-35834-0(6)*, GR5834) Greenwood Publishing Group, Inc.

Johnston, James H. From Slave Ship to Harvard: Yarrow Mamout & the History of an African American Family. 2012. (ENG., Illus.). 288p. 29.95 ***(978-0-8232-3950-4(0))*** Fordham Univ. Pr.

Jones, Allen & Naison, Mark. The Rat That Got Away: A Bronx Memoir. 2011. (ENG., Illus.). 224p. pap. 16.95 ***(978-0-8232-3103-4(8))*** Fordham Univ. Pr.

Jones, Angela, ed. The History of Modern African American Political Thought: From Frederick Douglass to Barack Obama. 2012. (ENG., Illus.). 443p. (C). 160.00 *(978-0-415-89570-5(7))* Routledge.

Jones, Angela, ed. The Modern African American Thought Reader: From David Walker to Barack Obama. 2012. (ENG., Illus.). 448p. (C). pap. 54.95 ***(978-0-415-89573-6(1))*** Routledge.

Jones, Col Lafayette. My Great, Great, Grandfather's Journey to an Island of Freedom in the Middle of Slavery. 2007. (Illus.). xvi, 119p. pap. *(978-0-615-22337-7(0))* Jenlaf.

Jordan, Vernon E., Jr. Make It Plain: Standing up & Speaking Out. 2009. (ENG.). 272p. pap. 13.95 *(978-1-58648-775-1(2))* PublicAffairs.

—Vernon Can Read! A Memoir. 2008. (ENG., Illus.). 352p. pap. 16.00 *(978-1-58648-670-9(5))* PublicAffairs.

Joseph, Jamal. Panther Baby. 2012. (ENG.). 272p. 23.95 *(978-1-56512-950-4(4)*, 1565129504) Algonquin Bks. of Chapel Hill.

Kamin, Ben. Room 306: The National Story of the Lorraine Motel. 2012. (ENG.). 200p. pap. 24.95 ***(978-1-61186-049-8(0))*** Michigan State Univ. Pr.

Karenga. Kawaida & Questions of Life & Struggle: African American, Pan-African, & Global Issues. 2007. *(978-0-943412-29-0(3))* Univ. of Sankore Pr., The.

Keckley, Elizabeth. Behind the Scenes, or, Thirty Years a Slave, & Four Years in the White House. 2011. (ENG., Illus.). 170p. pap. 25.00 ***(978-0-8078-6963-5(5))*** Univ. of North Carolina Pr.

Kelley, Brent. I Will Never Forget: Interviews with 39 Former Negro League Players. alt. ed. 2010. (ENG., Illus.). 199p. pap. 45.00 *(978-0-7864-4694-0(3))* McFarland & Co., Inc. Pubs.

Kelly, Samuel E. Dr. Sam, Soldier, Educator, Advocate, Friend: An Autobiography. 2010. (ENG., Illus.). 240p. 30.00 *(978-0-295-99061-3(9))* Univ. of Washington Pr.

Kendall, Mae A. Serving up Hope & Freedom: The Triumphant Story of James & Robert Paschal. 2007. 280p. 28.95 *(978-0-595-86329-7(9))*; (ENG.). per. 18.95 *(978-0-595-48348-294-0(6))* iUniverse, Inc. (iUniverse Star).

Kent, Herb & Smallwood, David. The Cool Gent: The Nine Lives of Radio Legend Herb Kent. 2009. (ENG., Illus.). 272p. 24.95 *(978-1-55652-774-6(8))*, Hill, Lawrence Bks.) Chicago Review Pr., Inc.

Kershner, Jim. Carl Maxey: A Fighting Life. 2008. (ENG., Illus.). 288p. 26.95 *(978-0-295-98846-7(0))* Univ. of Washington Pr.

Kersten, Andrew E. A Philip Randolph: A Life in the Vanguard. 2006. (African American History Ser.). (ENG., Illus.). 184p. 81.00 *(978-0-7425-4897-8(X))* Rowman & Littlefield Publishers, Inc.

Khan, Abraham Iqbal. Curt Flood in the Media: Baseball, Race, & the Demise of the Activist Athlete. 2012. (Race, Rhetoric, & Media Ser.). (ENG.). 224p. 55.00 ***(978-1-61703-138-0(0))*** Univ. Pr. of Mississippi.

King, Coretta Scott, compiled by. The Words of Martin Luther King, Jr. 2nd ed. 2008. (Words of Ser.). (ENG.). 128p. 15.95 *(978-1-55704-815-8(0)*, Morrow, William & Co.) HarperCollins Pubs.

King, Martin Luther. Mlk: A Celebration in Word & Image. Adelman, Bob, ed. 2011. (ENG., Illus.). 64p. 15.00 *(978-0-8070-0316-9(6))* Beacon Pr.

King, Robert Hillary. From the Bottom of the Heap: The Autobiography of Black Panther Robert Hillary King. 2008. (PM Press Ser.). (ENG., Illus.). 224p. 24.95 *(978-1-60486-039-9(1))* PM Pr.

King, Rodney & Spagnola, Lawrence J. The Riot Within: My Journey from Rebellion to Redemption - Learning How We Can All Get Along. 2012. (ENG.). 272p. 25.99 ***(978-0-06-219443-5(7)***, HarperOne) HarperCollins Pubs.

Kirk, John A. Beyond Little Rock: The Origins & Legacies of the Central High Crisis. 2007. 213p. per. 22.50 *(978-1-55728-851-6(8))* Univ. of Arkansas Pr.

Kirst, Sean. Moonfixer. 2009. 152p. 29.95 *(978-0-8156-0946-9(9))* Syracuse Univ. Pr.

Kiser, Brett. Baseball's War Roster: A Biographical Dictionary of Major & Negro League Players Who Served, 1861 to the Present. 2012. (ENG.). 284p. pap. 55.00 ***(978-0-7864-6679-5(0))*** McFarland & Co., Inc. Pubs.

Knight, Dawn. Taliaferro: Breaking Barriers from the NFL Draft to the Ivory Tower. 2010. (ENG., Illus.). 200p. pap. 14.95 *(978-0-253-22224-4(9)*, 0253222249) Indiana Univ. Pr.

Knight, Gladys. Icons of African American Protest: Trailblazing Activists of the Civil Rights Movement, 2 vols. 2008. (Greenwood Icons Ser.). (Illus.). 760p. 175.00 *(978-0-313-34062-8(5)*, GR4062, Greenwood Pr.) Greenwood Publishing Group, Inc.

Knoblock, Glenn A. African American World War II Casualties & Decorations in the Navy, Coast Guard & Merchant Marine: A Comprehensive Record. 2009. (ENG., Illus.). 592p. pap. 65.00 *(978-0-7864-3473-2(2))* McFarland & Co., Inc. Pubs.

—First Man Back. 2008. 112p. pap. 14.95 *(978-1-4357-5860-5(9))* Lulu Enterprises Inc.

Knott, Patricia A. The Search for Kum Ba Y. 2008. 304p. 27.99 *(978-1-60477-394-1(4))*; per. 17.99 *(978-1-60477-393-4(6))* Xulon Pr., Inc.

Kremer, Gary R. George Washington Carver: A Biography, 1 vol. 2011. (Greenwood Biographies Ser.). (Illus.). 202p. 35.00 *(978-0-313-34796-2(4)*, GR4796); E-Book *(978-0-313-34797-9(2)*, Greenwood Pr.) Greenwood Publishing Group, Inc.

Kuklick, Bruce. Black Philosopher, White Academy: The Career of William Fontaine. Fontaine, William, ed. 2008. (Illus.). 192p. (C). 59.95 *(978-0-8122-4098-6(7))* Univ. of Pennsylvania Pr.

Lanctot, Neil. Campy: The Two Lives of Roy Campanella. 2011. (ENG., Illus.). 528p. 28.00 *(978-1-4165-4704-4(5))* Simon & Schuster.

Lapchick, Richard. 100 Pioneers: African-Americans Who Broke Color Barriers in Sport. 2008. (Leaders in Sprort (Fit) Ser.). (Illus.). 488p. pap. 24.95 *(978-1-885693-81-5(8))* Fitness Information Technology, Inc.

Laws, Anthony. Honoring Our Fathers: Celebrating a Man's Role in His Family & Community. 2009. 200p. pap. 16.95 *(978-1-934812-47-1(1))* Brown Bks. Publishing Group.

Lee, Barbara. Renegade for Peace & Justice: A Memoir of Political & Personal Courage. 2011. (ENG.). 245p. pap. 16.95 *(978-0-7425-5844-1(4))* Rowman & Littlefield Publishers, Inc.

—Renegade for Peace & Justice: Congresswoman Barbara Lee Speaks for Me. 2008. (ENG., Illus.). 256p. 24.95 *(978-0-7425-5843-4(6))* Rowman & Littlefield Publishers, Inc.

Lee, George L. Inspiring African Americans: Black History Makers in the United States, 1750-1980. alt. ed. 2012. (ENG.). 144p. pap. 19.99 ***(978-0-7864-6765-5(7))*** McFarland & Co., Inc. Pubs.

—Interesting People: Black American History Makers. alt. ed. 2012. (ENG., Illus.). 224p. pap. 19.99 ***(978-0-7864-6767-9(3))*** McFarland & Co., Inc. Pubs.

Lee, Howard. The Courage to Lead: One Man's Journey in Public Service. 2008. (Illus.). 224p. 24.95 *(978-0-9816921-0-4(9))* Cotton Patch Pr., Inc.

Lee, Maureen Donnelly. Sissieretta Jones: The Greatest Singer of Her Race, 1868-1933. 2012. (ENG.). 320p. 39.95 ***(978-1-61117-072-6(9))*** Univ. of South Carolina Pr.

Lee, Nancy. This Is Their Story. 2010. 152p. pap. *(978-3-639-20418-6(2))* VDM Verlag Dr. Mueller e.K.

Lee, Shayne. T. D. Jakes: America's New Preacher. 2007. (ENG., Illus.). 216p. pap. 21.00 *(978-0-8147-5224-1(1))* New York Univ. Pr.

Leichtle, Kurt E. & Carveth, Bruce. Crusade Against Slavery: Edward Coles, Pioneer of Freedom. 2011. (Illus.). 280p. 34.95 *(978-0-8093-3042-3(3))* Southern Illinois Univ. Pr.

Leichtle, Kurt E. & Carveth, Bruce G. Crusade Against Slavery: Edward Coles, Pioneer of Freedom. 2011. (Illus.). 320p. E-Book 34.95 *(978-0-8093-8944-5(4))* Southern Illinois Univ. Pr.

Lemon, Don. Transparent. 2011. (ENG.). 244p. 24.95 *(978-0-9827027-8-9(7))* Gray, Dr. Farrah Publishing LLC.

Lemons, Gary L. Womanist Forefathers: Frederick Douglass & W.E.B. du Bois. 2009. 240p. 65.00 *(978-1-4384-2755-3(7))* State Univ. of New York Pr.

Levenstein, Lisa. A Movement Without Marches: African American Women & the Politics of Poverty in Postwar Philadelphia. 2010. (John Hope Franklin Series in African American History & Culture Ser.). (ENG., Illus.). 320p. pap. 22.95 *(978-0-8078-7164-5(8))* Univ. of North Carolina Pr.

LeVert, Eddie, Sr., et al. I Got Your Back: A Father & Son Keep It Real about Love, Fatherhood, Family, & Friendship. 2008. (ENG., Illus.). 224p. pap. 12.95 *(978-0-7679-2760-4(5))* Broadway Bks.

Levinsohn, Florence H. & Levinsohn, Florence. Looking for Farrakhan. 2009. (ENG.). 320p. pap. 26.00 *(978-1-56663-784-8(8))* Dee, Ivan R. Pub.

Levy, Alan Howard. Floyd Patterson: A Boxer & a Gentleman. 2008. (ENG., Illus.). 297p. pap. 35.00 *(978-0-7864-3950-8(5))* McFarland & Co., Inc. Pubs.

Lewin, Yael Tamar & Collins, Janet. Night's Dancer: The Life of Janet Collins. 2011. (ENG., Illus.). 404p. 37.00 *(978-0-8195-7114-4(8))* Wesleyan Univ. Pr.

Lewis, David Levering. W. E. B. du Bois: A Biography, 1868-1963. Field, Kendra Taira, ed. 2009. (ENG., Illus.). 912p. pap. 25.00 *(978-0-8050-8805-2(9)*, Holt Paperback) Holt, Henry & Co.

Lightfoot, Elizabeth. Michelle Obama: First Lady of Hope. 2008. (ENG., Illus.). 240p. pap. 14.95 *(978-1-59921-521-1(7)*, Lyons Pr.) Globe Pequot Pr., The.

Lillian, McEwen. D. C. Unmasked & Undressed: A Memoir. 2011. 256p. 25.95 *(978-0-9820009-9-1(5))* Titletown Publishing, LLC.

Lindfors, Bernth. Ira Aldridge: The Early Years, 1807-1833, 2 vols. 2011. (Rochester Studies in African History & the Diaspora Ser.: Volume 48). (Illus.). 402p. 55.00 *(978-1-58046-381-2(9))* Univ. of Rochester Pr.

—Ira Aldridge: The Vagabond Years, 1833-1852, 2 vols. 2011. (Rochester Studies in African History & the Diaspora Ser.: Volume 49). (Illus.). 258p. 55.00 *(978-1-58046-394-2(0))* Univ. of Rochester Pr.

Littlefield, Anthony. Bittersweet Journey: The Story of the Wounding, Healing & Triumph of a Family. 2008. 315p. pap. 29.95 *(978-1-60672-398-2(7))* PublishAmerica, Inc.

Lobb, Nancy. 16 Extraordinary African Americans. 2nd ed. 2007. (Illus.). 117p. (YA). (gr. 6-12). tchr. ed., per. 25.00 *(978-0-8251-6276-3(9))* Walch Education.

Long, Nancy Ann Zrinyi. The Life & Legacy of Mary Mcleod Bethune. 3rd ed. 2008. (ENG.). (C). pap. 19.20 *(978-0-558-05267-6(3))* Pearson Learning Solutions.

Love, Dennis & Brown, Stacy. Blind Faith: The Miraculous Journey of Lula Hardaway, Stevie Wonder's Mother. 2007. (ENG.). 288p. pap. 19.95 *(978-1-4165-7785-0(8))* Simon & Schuster.

Love, Shandra. Diversity Uncrowned, First & Thirty-four: The Linda Aldridge-Robertson Story. 2006. 53p. per. 8.95 *(978-1-59824-409-0(4))* E-BookTime LLC.

Lovejoy, Paul & Law, Robin, eds. Biography of Baquaqua: His Passage from Slavery to Freedom in Africa & America. 2nd exp. ed. 2006. (Illus.). 298p. per. 24.95 *(978-1-55876-430-9(5))* Wiener, Markus Pubs., Inc.

Lowry, Tiger. Gods in My Corner A Portrait of an Ameri. 2007. (Illus.). 202p. pap. 24.95 *(978-1-4241-5105-9(8))* PublishAmerica, Inc.

Lowther, Hastie. Willie E. Lowther: The Journey of My Life. 2007. (Illus.). 328p. per. 24.95 net. *(978-0-9742773-6-3(3))* Soleil Pr.

Lucas, William. Hard Times Don't Last Always. 2010. pap. 16.95 *(978-0-7414-6122-3(6))* Infinity Publishing.

Lyles, Charlise. Do I Dare Disturb the Universe? From the Projects to Prep School. 2nd ed. 2008. (Illus.). 272p. pap. 14.95 *(978-1-59851-041-6(X))* Gray and Company, Publishers.

Mabee, Carleton. Promised Land: Father Divine's Interracial Communities in Ulster County, New York. 2008. (Illus.). 248p. pap. 22.50 *(978-1-930098-93-0(6))* Purple Mountain Pr., Ltd.

Mack, Kenneth W. Representing the Race: The Creation of the Civil Rights Lawyer. 2012. (ENG., Illus.). 352p. 35.00 ***(978-0-674-04687-0(0))*** Harvard Univ. Pr.

Mack-Williams, Kibibi. Ahead of Her Time in Yesteryear: Geraldine Pierce Zimmerman Comes of Age in a Southern African American Family. 2010. (ENG., Illus.). 216p. 31.95 *(978-1-57233-720-6(6))* Univ. of Tennessee Pr.

Majok, Anthony Anei. Journey of Faith. 2011. 140p. 23.99 ***(978-1-4269-8178-4(3))***; pap. 13.99 ***(978-1-4269-8177-7(5))*** Trafford Publishing.

Malcolm, Joyce Lee. Peter's War: A New England Slave Boy & the American Revolution. (ENG., Illus.). 272p. 2010. pap. 20.00 *(978-0-300-16806-8(3))* 2009. 28.00 *(978-0-300-11930-5(5))* Yale Univ. Pr.

Mangun, Kimberley. A Force for Change: Beatrice Morrow Cannady & the Struggle for Civil Rights in Oregon, 1912-1936. 2010. (Illus.). 384p. pap. 24.95 *(978-0-87071-580-8(1))* Oregon State Univ. Pr.

Marable, Grace. Joys, Sorrows, & Hopes: The Life of an African American Family in the Depression-Era South. 2011. 140p. pap. 11.95 ***(978-1-4620-2314-1(2))*** iUniverse, Inc.

Marable, Manning. Malcolm X: A Life of Reinvention. 2011. (ENG.). 608p. (gr. 12). 18.00 ***(978-0-14-312032-2(8)***, Penguin (Non-Classics)); (Illus.). 30.00 *(978-0-670-02220-5(9)*, Viking Adult) Penguin Group (USA) Inc.

Maris, George. TRAP MAKES ME WANT to HOLLER TOO!! Story by Reggie Washington. 2009. 97p. pap. 14.38 *(978-0-557-08116-5(5))* Lulu Enterprises Inc.

Mars-Proietti, Laura & Hatcher, Sherry L., eds. Encyclopedia of African American Writing. 2nd rev. ed. 2009. 856p. (gr. 4-6). 135.00 *(978-1-59237-291-1(0))* Grey Hse. Publishing.

Marshall, Sheree. Kissing Kibo: Trekking to the Summit of Mount Kilimanjaro Via the Lemosho Route. 2011. 112p. pap. 12.95 ***(978-1-4502-4024-6(0))*** iUniverse, Inc.

Martin, C. Sunny. Who's Who in Black Atlanta: The Ninth Edition. 2006. (ENG.). 496p. per. 34.95 *(978-1-933879-10-9(6))* Who's Who Publishing Co.

—Who's Who in Black Cincinnati: The Third Edition. 3rd ed. 2006. (ENG.). 252p. per. *(978-1-933879-04-8(1))* Who's Who Publishing Co.

—Who's Who in Black Cleveland: The Third Edition. 3rd ed. 2007. (ENG.). 288p. per. *(978-1-933879-12-3(2))* Who's Who Publishing Co.

—Who's Who in Black Detroit: The Inaugural Edition. 2006. 392p. per. *(978-1-933879-06-2(8))* Who's Who Publishing Co.

—Who's Who in Black Houston: The Inaugural Edition. 2007. (ENG.). 320p. per. 34.95 net. *(978-1-933879-18-5(1))* Who's Who Publishing Co.

—Who's Who in Black Louisville: The Inaugural Edition. 2007. (ENG.). 288p. per. 24.95 net. *(978-1-933879-16-1(5))* Who's Who Publishing Co.

—Who's Who in Black South Florida: The Inaugural Edition. 2007. (ENG.). 320p. per. 24.95 net. *(978-1-933879-20-8(3))* Who's Who Publishing Co.

—Who's Who in Black St. Louis: The Third Edition. 3rd ed. 2006. (ENG.). 272p. per. 24.95 *(978-1-933879-08-6(4))* Who's Who Publishing Co.

Martin, Lena C. Desperate for Love: Overcoming with Prayer. 2007. 436p. per. 18.95 *(978-1-4327-0209-0(2))* Outskirts Pr., Inc.

Martin, S. Rudolph. On the Move: A Black Family's Western Saga. 2009. (Elma Dill Russell Spencer Series in the West & Southwest: No. 32). (ENG., Illus.). 216p. 24.95 *(978-1-60344-104-9(2))* Texas A&M Univ. Pr.

Mathis, Carrie A. Overcoming Shattered Dreams: Ouch! That Hurt! 2009. 276p. pap. 25.00 *(978-1-4251-9072-9(3))* Trafford Publishing.

Mathis, Nathaniel. Portrait of a Professional. 2011. 216p. pap. 19.99 ***(978-1-4628-9454-3(2))*** Xlibris Corp.

Matthews Rander-Bryant, Mary Elizabeth. Steps: Going the Distance- 2008. 108p. 32.99 *(978-1-4389-3008-4(9))*; pap. 23.99 *(978-1-4389-3009-1(7))* AuthorHouse.

Mayberry, B. D., ed. A George Washington Carver Handbook. 2007. 92p. pap. 15.95 *(978-1-60306-016-5(2))* NewSouth, Inc.

McBride, Judith. The Enemy Within: Living with Sickle Cell Disease. 2011. 52p. 24.99 ***(978-1-4628-7481-1(9))***; pap. 15.99 ***(978-1-4628-7480-4(0))*** Xlibris Corp.

Mccall, Erika R. Go for Yours: A Compilation of Young, African Americans Who Were Brave Enough to Reach for the Stars. 2011. 248p. pap. 16.99 ***(978-1-4670-4364-9(8))*** AuthorHouse.

McCann, Bob. Encyclopedia of African American Actresses in Film & Television. 2009. (ENG., Illus.). 461p. 75.00 *(978-0-7864-3790-0(1))* McFarland & Co., Inc. Pubs.

McCarthy, B. Eugene & Doughton, Thomas L., eds. From Bondage to Belonging: The Worcester Slave Narratives. 2007. 320p. pap. 22.95 net. *(978-1-55849-622-4(X))*; (Illus.). 325p. per. 80.00 net. *(978-1-55849-623-1(8))* Univ. of Massachusetts Pr.

McClane, Kenneth A. Walls: Essays, 1985-1990. 2010. (ND Afro/Amer Intellectual Heritage Ser.). (ENG.). 128p. pap. 20.00 *(978-0-268-03520-4(2))* Univ. of Notre Dame Pr.

McCray, James. Ebb Tide: Nancy Astor's Greatest Challenge. 2008. 24.95 *(978-0-9814650-9-8(9))* G Publishing LLC.

McDaniel, Cyndar. A Page from Every Girl's Diary. 2008. 127p. pap. 19.95 *(978-1-60610-532-0(9))* PublishAmerica, Inc.

McElroy, Njoki. 1012 Natchez: A Memoir of Joy, Harship, & Love. 2010. 216p. pap. 14.95 *(978-1-934812-55-6(2))* Brown Bks. Publishing Group.

McFarland, Bernard C. The Hill & the Bottoms: The Story from the Thousand Yard Stare. 2009. (Illus.). 112p. *(978-1-57864-538-1(7))* Donning Co. Pubs.

McGee, Nora Jefferson. The Family Reunion. 2007. pap. 9.00 *(978-0-8059-7381-5(8))* Dorrance Publishing Co., Inc.

McGrane, Bill. All Rise: The Remarkable Journey of Alan Page. 2010. (ENG.). 256p. 24.95 *(978-1-60078-504-7(2))* Triumph Bks.

McKee, Catherine. I Remember Your Smile: The hope of a little girl, the courage of her Mother. 2010. (Illus.). 96p. pap. 13.95 *(978-1-4327-5233-0(2))* Outskirts Pr., Inc.

McLean, Alan & Bassett, Jennifer. Martin Luther King. 2008. (ENG., Illus.). 80p. 9.38 *(978-0-19-423393-4(6))* Oxford Univ. Pr., Inc.

Meaders, Daniel E., compiled by & pref. Kidnappers in Philadelphia: Isaac Hopper's Tales of Oppression 1780-1843. 2nd ed. 2009. (Studies in African American & African Canadian History & Culture). 432p. reprint ed. 80.00 *(978-0-9818939-5-2(3))*; (ENG.). pap. 40.00 *(978-0-9818939-6-9(1))* Africana Homestead Legacy Pubs., Inc.

Meeks, Catherine. Through It All. 2007. (Illus.). 80p. per. *(978-1-934144-19-0(3))* Indigo.

Mends, Steven. An African Living with Depression in America. 2010. 168p. pap. 15.95 *(978-1-4502-2016-3(9))* iUniverse, Inc.

Merida, Kevin & Fletcher, Michael. Supreme Discomfort: The Divided Soul of Clarence Thomas. 2008. (ENG., Illus.). 448p. pap. 15.95 *(978-0-7679-1636-3(0))* Broadway Bks.

Michaels, Chidera. Coming Inside the Dream, 1 vol. 2009. 224p. pap. 24.95 *(978-1-60672-545-0(9))* PublishAmerica, Inc.

Miles, Steen. Teenie: Newslady in Training. 2007. 192p. per. 19.95 *(978-1-891773-84-6(4))* Orman Pr.

Miller, Carroll L. L. & Pruitt-Logan, Anne S. Faithful to the Task at Hand: The Life of Lucy Diggs Slowe. 2012. (ENG.). 480p. 90.00 ***(978-1-4384-4259-4(9))*** State Univ. of New York Pr.

—Faithful to the Task at Hand: The Life of Lucy Diggs Slowe. 2012. (ENG.). 480p. pap. 29.95 ***(978-1-4384-4258-7(0))*** State Univ. of New York Pr.

Miller, E. Ethelbert. The 5th Inning. 2009. (Busboys & Poets Ser.). (ENG.). 176p. 18.95 *(978-1-60486-062-7(6))* PM Pr.

Miller, Karen E. Quinones. Angry Ass Black Woman. 2012. (ENG.). 288p. pap. 15.00 *(978-1-4516-0782-6(2)*, Gallery Books/Karen Hunter Publishing) Gallery Books/Karen Hunter Publishing.

Miller, Leonard T. Racing While Black: How an African-American Stock Car Team Made Its Mark on NASCAR. 2010. (ENG.). 336p. 24.95 *(978-1-58322-896-8(9))* Seven Stories Pr.

Miller, Reginald. One Man s Thoughts. 2010. 112p. pap. 11.99 *(978-1-60957-237-2(8))* Xulon Pr., Inc.

Miller, Ron. Sellout. 2010. 266p. pap. 16.99 *(978-1-60957-365-2(X))* Xulon Pr., Inc.

Millner, Caille. The Golden Road: Notes on My Gentrification. 2008. (ENG.). 256p. (gr. 12-18). 14.00 *(978-0-14-311297-6(X)*, Penguin (Non-Classics)) Penguin Group (USA) Inc.

Minutaglio, Bill. In Search of the Blues: A Journey to the Soul of Black Texas. 2010. (ENG., Illus.). 183p. 50.00 *(978-0-292-72247-7(8))*; pap. 24.95 *(978-0-292-72289-7(3))* Univ. of Texas Pr.

Mitchell, Erin Goseer. Born Colored: Life Before Bloody Sunday. 2006. 220p. *(978-0-9761235-2-1(5))* Ampersand Publishing.

Mitchell, Verner D. Western Echoes of the Harlem Renaissance: The Life & Writings of Anita Scott Coleman. Davis, Cynthia J., ed. 2008. (ENG., Illus.). 240p. (C). 45.00 *(978-0-8061-3956-2(0))*; pap. 19.95 *(978-0-8061-3975-3(7))* Univ. of Oklahoma Pr.

Moffi, Larry & Kronstadt, Jonathan. Crossing the Line: Black Major Leaguers, 1947-1959. 2006. (ENG.). 1p. pap. 15.95 *(978-0-8032-8316-9(4)*, Bison Bks.) Univ. of Nebraska Pr.

Molentia Guttman, D. & Golden, Ernest. African Americans in Hawai'i. 2011. (Images of America Ser.). (Illus.). 128p. pap. 21.99 *(978-0-7385-8116-3(X))* Arcadia Publishing.

Molesworth, Charles. And Bid Him Sing: A Biography of Countée Cullen. 2012. 304p. 30.00 ***(978-0-226-53364-3(6))*** Univ. of Chicago Pr.

Montague, Magnificent & Baker, Bob. Burn, Baby! BURN! The Autobiography of Magnificent Montague. 2009. (Music in American Life Ser.). (ENG., Illus.). 216p. pap. 19.95 *(978-0-252-07684-8(2))* Univ. of Illinois Pr.

Montgomery, Leslie. The Faith of Condoleezza Rice. 2007. (Illus.). 224p. 19.99 *(978-1-58134-799-9(5))* Crossway.

Moon, Warren. Never Give up on Your Dream: My Journey. 2013. (ENG.). 288p. pap. 15.00 *(978-0-306-81875-2(2))* Da Capo Pr., Inc.

Mooney, Paul. Black Is the New White. 2010. (ENG., Illus.). 272p. pap. 15.99 *(978-1-4165-8796-5(9))* Gallery Pr., The IRL. Dist: Simon & Schuster, Inc.

Moore, Bill. My Quest for Success, the Hard Way: Searching for My Niche in Life. 2008. 204p. pap. 16.99 *(978-1-4343-8051-7(3))* AuthorHouse.

Moore, Kenneth Nathan. Saving the African American Community from Violence: Growing up tough in Chicago. 2011. 180p. pap. 19.99 ***(978-1-4568-1226-3(2))*** Xlibris Corp.

Moore, Wes. Discovering Wes Moore. 2012. (ENG.). 160p. (YA). (gr. 7). 15.99 ***(978-0-385-74167-5(7)***, Delacorte Bks. for Young Readers) Random Hse. Children's Bks.

—Discovering Wes Moore: Chances, Choices, Changes. 2012. E-Book ***(978-0-375-98670-3(7)***, Delacorte Pr) Random House Publishing Group.

—Discovering Wes Moore: Chances, Choices, Changes. 2012. (ENG.). 160p. (YA). (gr. 7). lib. bdg. 18.99 ***(978-0-375-99018-2(6)***, Delacorte Bks. for Young Readers) Random Hse. Children's Bks.

Moore, Wes. The Other Wes Moore: One Name, Two Fates. (ENG., Illus.). 2011. 272p. pap. 15.00 *(978-0-385-52820-7(5))* 2010. 256p. 25.00 *(978-0-385-52819-1(1))* Spiegel & Grau.

Moragne, Printz. Fade to Black. 2009. 194p. pap. 20.98 *(978-0-557-00299-3(0))* Lulu Enterprises Inc.

Morgan, Corrine. Dr. Corrine Morgan Presents the Light Within You. 2011. 75p. pap. 14.95 ***(978-0-9826841-6-0(9))*** September Summer.

Morris, Alfreida. Reuben Daniel Morris, III: A Biography, Life Here on Earth Well Done, an Amazing Presence. 2008. (Illus.). 167p. 19.95 *(978-0-9799702-1-4(0))* Morris, Alfreida.

—Reuben Daniel Morris, III: Life Here on Earth Well Done, an Amazing Presence: A Biography. 2008. (Illus.). 165p. pap. 12.95 *(978-0-9799702-0-7(2))* Morris, Alfreida.

Morris, Richard. A Life Unburdened: Getting over Weight & Getting on with My Life. 2007. (ENG., Illus.). 240p. per. 18.00 *(978-0-9792095-1-2(X))* New Trends Publishing, Inc.

Morris, Robert V. Black Faces of War: A Legacy of Honor from the American Revolution to Today. 2011. (ENG., Illus.). 160p. 30.00 *(978-0-7603-3917-6(1)*, 0760339171, Zenith Pr.) MBI Publishing Co. LLC.

Morrison-Reed, Mark D. In Between: Memoir of an Integration Baby. 2009. (ENG.). 1p. pap. 18.00 *(978-1-55896-541-6(6)*, Skinner Hse. Bks.) Unitarian Universalist Assn.

Morse, Stan. But for the Grace of God: One Man's Spiritual Walk from Self Destruction to Salvation. 2010. 332p. pap. 17.99 *(978-1-4490-6509-6(0))*; (ENG.). 28.49 *(978-1-4490-6510-2(4))* AuthorHouse.

Mourning, Alonzo & Wetzel, Dan. Resilience. 2009. (ENG., Illus.). 272p. pap. 15.00 *(978-0-345-50750-1(9)*, Ballantine Bks.) Random House Publishing Group.

Mouser, Bruce L. For Labor, Race, & Liberty: George Edwin Taylor, His Historic Run for the White House, & the Making of Independent Black Politics. 2011. (ENG., Illus.). 278p. pap. 24.95 *(978-0-299-24914-4(X))* Univ. of Wisconsin Pr.

Mullins, Lisa. Diane Nash: A Biography: the Fire of the Civil Rights Movement. 2007. (Illus.). 100p. per. *(978-0-9715402-8-6(4))* Barnhardt & Ashe Publishing, Inc.

Mundy, Liza. Michelle: A Biography. 2009. (ENG., Illus.). 256p. pap. 15.00 *(978-1-4165-9944-9(4))* Simon & Schuster.

Murphy, Larry G. Sojourner Truth: A Biography, 1 vol. 2011. (Greenwood Biographies Ser.). (Illus.). 176p. 35.00 *(978-0-313-35728-2(5)*, GR5728) Greenwood Publishing Group, Inc.

Murray, Samuel M., ed. Samuel: In Search of the American Dream. 2011. 244p. pap. 19.95 ***(978-1-4620-1554-2(9))*** iUniverse, Inc.

Myers, Melvin. Pomp & Sacrifice: Reflections on A Lifetime of Service. 2007. 132p. per. 12.00 *(978-0-9767828-9-6(8))* Zoe Life Publications, Inc.

Neer, Bob. Barack Obama for Beginners, Updated Edition: An Essential Guide. 2009. (For Beginners Ser.). (ENG., Illus.). 128p. pap. 12.95 *(978-1-934389-44-7(7)*, For Beginners) Steerforth Pr.

Nelson, Scott Reynolds. Steel Drivin' Man -John Henry- The Untold Story of an American Legend. 2008. (ENG., Illus.). 224p. pap. 14.95 *(978-0-19-534119-5(8))* Oxford Univ. Pr., Inc.

Nelson, Sophia. Black Woman Redefined: Dispelling Myths & Discovering Fulfillment in the Age of Michelle Obama. 2011. (ENG.). 260p. 24.95 *(978-1-935618-94-2(6))* BenBella Bks.

Nelson, Velvet D. Above the Storm. 2010. 92p. pap. 15.49 *(978-1-4520-7121-3(7))* AuthorHouse.

Neri, Greg. Yummy: The Last Days of a Southside Shorty. 2007. (Illus.). (YA). (gr. 6-18). 18.95 *(978-1-58430-266-7(6))* Lee & Low Bks., Inc.

Newkey-Burden, Chas. Michael Jackson: Legend, 1958-2009. 2009. (ENG., Illus.). 224p. 21.95 *(978-1-84317-440-0(5))*; pap. 14.95 *(978-1-84317-441-7(3))* O'Mara, Michael Bks., Ltd. GBR. Dist: Independent Pubs. Group.

Newsham, Gavin. The Official Treasures of Muhammad Ali. 2010. (ENG., Illus.). 64p. 34.95 *(978-1-84732-671-3(4))* Carlton Bks., Ltd. GBR. Dist: Sterling Publishing Co., Inc.

Nicholas, Carolyn Dungee. Hild. 2010. 408p. pap. 26.99 *(978-1-4389-9217-4(3))* AuthorHouse.

Nnoromele, Salome & Day-Lindsay, Lisa. Journeys Home: An Anthology of Contemporary African Diasporic Experience (Poems & Personal Narratives) 2009. *(978-1-59221-712-0(5))*; 182p. pap. *(978-1-59221-713-7(3))* Africa World Pr.

Noble, Dennis L. & Strobridge, Truman R. Captain Hell Roaring Mike Healy: From American Slave to Arctic Hero. 2009. (New Perspectives on Maritime History & Nautical Archaeology Ser.). (ENG., Illus.). 352p. 34.95 *(978-0-8130-3368-6(3))* Univ. Pr. of Florida.

Nolen, Rose M. African Americans in Mid-Missouri: From Pioneers to Ragtimers. 2010. *(978-1-59629-609-1(7))* History Pr., The.

Nollen, Scott Allen. Paul Robeson: Film Pioneer. 2010. (ENG., Illus.). 215p. pap. 45.00 *(978-0-7864-3520-3(8))* McFarland & Co., Inc. Pubs.

Normajean. The Larry Holliday Story: Someone You Should Know. 2009. 236p. 28.95 *(978-1-4327-4267-6(1))* Outskirts Pr., Inc.

Norrell, Robert J. Up from History: The Life of Booker T. Washington. 2011. (ENG., Illus.). 528p. pap. 19.95 *(978-0-674-06037-1(7)*, Belknap Pr.) Harvard Univ. Pr.

Norris, Michele. The Grace of Silence: A Family Memoir. (Vintage Ser.). 2011. (ENG.). 240p. pap. 14.95 *(978-0-307-47527-5(1)*, Vintage) 2010. (Illus.). 208p. 24.95 *(978-0-307-37876-7(4)*, Pantheon) Knopf Doubleday Publishing Group.

Northup, Solomon. Twelve Years a Slave. Gates, Henry Louis, Jr., ed. 2012. (ENG.). 288p. (gr. 12). pap. 16.00 ***(978-0-14-310670-8(8)***, Penguin Classics) Penguin Group (USA) Inc.

Northup, Solomon & Eakin, Sue L. Solomon Northup's Twelve Years a Slave: And Plantation Life in the Antebellum South. 2007. (Illus.). xviii, 543p. *(978-1-887366-75-5(X))* Univ. of Louisiana at Lafayette Pr.

Obama, Barack. The Audacity of Hope: Thoughts on Reclaiming the American Dream. l.t. ed. 2008. (ENG.). 608p. pap. 25.00 *(978-0-7393-2818-7(2))* Random Hse. Large Print.

—Dreams from My Father: A Story of Race & Inheritance. 2008. xvii, 442p. pap. *(978-1-84767-351-0(1))*; 464p. pap. *(978-1-84767-094-6(6))* Canongate Bks.

—Dreams from My Father: A Story of Race & Inheritance. 2007. (ENG.). 464p. 25.95 *(978-0-307-38341-9(5)*, Crown) Crown Publishing Group.

—Dreams from My Father: A Story of Race & Inheritance. 2011. 14.72 *(978-0-7848-3402-2(4)*, Everbind) Marco Bk. Co.

—Los Sueños de Mi Padre: Una Historia de Raza y Herencia. 2009. (Vintage Espanol Ser.). (SPA.). 432p. pap. 17.00 *(978-0-307-47387-5(2))* Knopf Doubleday Publishing Group.

O'Brien, Soledad & Arce, Rose Marie. The Next Big Story: My Journey Through the Land of Possibilities. 2010. (ENG.). 336p. (gr. 12). 24.95 *(978-0-451-23137-6(6))* Penguin Group (USA) Inc.

Odhoji, Benjamin M. O. Restorying the Margins. 2011. 252p. pap. ***(978-3-8443-8212-9(7))*** Lambert Academic Publishing.

Office of the Secretary of State. Lillian Walker: Washington State's Civil Rights Pioneer. 2010. (Illus.). 198p. pap. 20.00 *(978-1-889320-22-9(6))* Washington State Legacy Project.

Ogedegbe, Henry O. I wolk my Path alone with my Head Held way up High. 2009. 45.00 *(978-1-61584-883-6(5))* Independent Pub.

Ohiri, Aloysius U. Daring to Succeed: An Unbelievable Thriller. 2008. 272p. pap. 27.95 *(978-1-60672-538-2(6))* PublishAmerica, Inc.

Olakanmi, Bode. The Cradle & the Bed. 2009. 188p. 24.25 *(978-1-60860-176-9(5)*, Strategic Bk. Publishing) AEG Literary Publishing Services, Inc.

Omosa Julius Morara. African Americanized: An African Man's Life & Expedient Americanization. 2010. 428p. pap. 26.95 *(978-1-4401-7849-8(6))* iUniverse, Inc.

Orr, Charles Henry. A Night Watchman. 2009. 64p. pap. 15.99 *(978-1-4415-4449-0(6))* Xlibris Corp.

Orr, Emily Juana Burke. A Tale of Two Worlds: My Life as a Proud Black Woman with White Skin. 2008. pap. 19.99 *(978-0-9795697-0-8(2))* Phenomenal Pr.

Oshodi, John Egbeazien. A Glance at American Presidents in Black Lifea: George Washington to George W. Bush, a to Z. 2009. vii, 96p. E-Book *(978-0-7618-4464-8(3))* Univ. Pr. of America, Inc.

O'Sullivan, Christopher D. Colin Powell: A Political Biography. 2010. (Biographies American Foreign Policy Ser.). (ENG.). 236p. pap. 17.95 *(978-0-7425-5187-9(3))* Rowman & Littlefield Publishers, Inc.

—Colin Powell: American Power & Intervention from Vietnam to Iraq. 2009. (Biographies in American Foreign Policy Ser.). (ENG.). 240p. 37.50 *(978-0-7425-5186-2(5))* Rowman & Littlefield Publishers, Inc.

Otfinoski, Steven. The Performing Arts. 2nd rev. ed. 2010. (A to Z of African Americans Ser.). (Illus.). 288p. (C). (gr. 9-18). 49.50 *(978-0-8160-7838-7(6))* Facts On File, Inc.

—The Visual Arts. 2nd rev. ed. 2011. (A to Z of African Americans Ser.). (Illus.). 280p. (C). (gr. 9-18). 49.50 *(978-0-8160-7840-0(8))* Facts On File, Inc.

Otis, George. Hielo y Fuego: Eldridge Cleaver: Ice & Fire. (SPA.). 192p. *(978-84-7228-446-3(8)*, 220346) Clie, Editorial.

Owens, Charlie, et al. I Hate to Lose: How a Little-Known, Handicapped Black Man Beat the Best of the Best on the PGA Tour. Charlie Owens. 2008. 236p. pap. 18.95 *(978-1-4401-0662-0(2))* iUniverse, Inc.

Owens, Donald R. The Life & Times of Henry James. 2007. per. *(978-1-59916-283-6(0))* Printing Systems.

Owens, Hilton. Three of the First. 2011. 212p. 24.95 ***(978-1-4502-3364-4(3))***; pap. 14.95 ***(978-1-4502-3363-7(5))*** iUniverse, Inc.

Oxford University Press Staff, ed. Martin Luther King. 2009. (ENG., Illus.). 67p. 15.44 *(978-0-19-423597-6(1))* Oxford Univ. Pr., Inc.

Parker, John Stephen. A Compartmentalized Life. 2011. 324p. 29.99 ***(978-1-4568-4581-0(0))***; pap. 19.99 ***(978-1-4568-4580-3(2))*** Xlibris Corp.

Parker, Robert L. To Ride the Tiger: With Audio CD Inside. 2007. pap. 23.95 *(978-0-7414-4103-4(9))* Infinity Publishing.

Parker-Weaver, Stephanie. Rebirth: A Breast Cancer Journey of Many; Survival of Few. 2011. 316p. 29.99 ***(978-1-4653-4061-0(0))***; pap. 19.99 ***(978-1-4653-4060-3(2))*** Xlibris Corp.

Parks, Gordon & Hule, Wing Young. A Choice of Weapons. 2010. (ENG.). 192p. pap. 17.95 *(978-0-87351-769-0(5))* Minnesota Historical Society Pr.

Parks, Gordon & Parks, Gordon, Jr. A Hungry Heart: A Memoir. 2007. (ENG.). 352p. pap. 15.00 *(978-0-7432-6903-2(9)*, Washington Square Pr.) Washington Square Pr.

Parsons, Neil. Clicko: The Wild Dancing Bushman. 2010. (Illus.). 272p. 55.00 *(978-0-226-64741-8(2))*; pap. 18.00 *(978-0-226-64742-5(0))* Univ. of Chicago Pr.

Parvis, Sarah. Barack Obama. 2009. (ENG.). 80p. 5.99 *(978-0-7407-8557-3(5))* Andrews McMeel Publishing.

Patrick, Deval. A Reason to Believe: Lessons from an Improbable Life. 2011. (Illus.). 240p. 21.99 *(978-0-7679-3112-0(2))* Broadway Bks.

Patterson, Horace, Sr. Unbroken & Unbound: A Life Dedicated to God, Justice, & the South. 2007. 208p. pap. 19.95 *(978-1-60306-030-1(8))* NewSouth, Inc.

Patton, George. Black Jack. 2009. 372p. 30.95 *(978-1-4401-6878-9(4))*; pap. 20.95 *(978-1-4401-3666-5(1))* iUniverse, Inc.

Peery, Nelson. Black Radical: The Education of an American Revolutionary. 2007. (ENG.). 242p. 24.95 *(978-1-59558-145-7(6))* New Pr., The.

Pender, Jesse. From a Cat House to the White House: The Story of an African-American Chef. 2007. (ENG.). 172p. per. 24.95 *(978-1-4241-6401-1(X))* PublishAmerica, Inc.

Pendergast, Sara & Pendergast, Tom. Contemporary Black Biography: Profiles from the International Black Community. Vol. 59. 2007. (Contemporary Black Biography Ser.). (ENG., Illus.). 300p. 150.00 *(978-0-7876-7931-6(3))* Cengage Gale.

Pendergast, Tom, ed. Contemporary Black Biography: Profiles from the International Black Community. 2007. (Contemporary Black Biography Ser.: Vol. 63). (ENG., Illus.). 288p. 150.00 *(978-0-7876-7935-4(6))* Cengage Gale.

Penn, Sabrina A. A Place for My Children, First Edition. 2007. 248p. pap. 20.00 *(978-0-9797359-0-5(4))* Penn Ink.

Perry, Jeffrey B. Hubert Harrison Vol. 1: The Voice of Harlem Radicalism, 1883-1918, vol. 1. 2010. (ENG.). 624p. (gr. 17). pap. 26.50 *(978-0-231-13911-3(X))* Columbia Univ. Pr.

Perry, Jeffrey B. & Perry, Jeffrey Babcock. Hubert Harrison: The Voice of Harlem Radicalism, 1883-1918, vol. 1. 2008. (ENG., Illus.). 624p. (gr. 17). 37.50 *(978-0-231-13910-6(1))* Columbia Univ. Pr.

Person-Lynn, Kwaku. First Word: Black Scholars — Thinkers — Warriors. 2nd ed. 2011. (ENG.). 320p. pap. 21.95 *(978-0-88378-307-8(X))* Third World Press.

Peters, Leila. In Spite of Everything.... For the Woman She Loved. 2010. 268p. 26.95 *(978-1-4520-2411-0(1))* AuthorHouse.

—In Spite of Everything.... For the Woman she Loved. 2010. 268p. pap. 17.95 *(978-1-4520-2410-3(3))* AuthorHouse.

Peterson, Carla L. Black Gotham: A Family History of African Americans in Nineteenth-Century New York City. (Illus.). 446p. 2012. (ENG.). pap. 20.00 ***(978-0-300-18174-6(4))*** 2011. 32.00 *(978-0-300-16255-4(3))* Yale Univ. Pr.

Phillips. Exodus from the Door of No Return: Journey of an American Family. 2008. 200p. 24.99 *(978-1-4389-0348-4(0))* AuthorHouse.

Phillips, Ian. Dian: Queen of Motown. 2011. 328p. pap. ***(978-1-904408-86-4(9))*** Bank House Bks.

Phillips, Roy G. Exodus from the Door of No Return: Journey of an American Family. 2008. 200p. pap. 14.49 *(978-1-4389-0349-1(9))* AuthorHouse.

Piascik, Andy. Gridiron Gauntlet: The Story of the Men Who Integrated Pro Football, in Their Own Words. 2009. (ENG.). 272p. 24.95 *(978-1-58979-442-9(7))* Taylor Trade Publishing.

—Gridiron Gauntlet: The Story of the Men Who Integrated Pro Football in Their Own Words. 2011. (ENG.). 272p. pap. 16.95 *(978-1-58979-652-2(7))* Taylor Trade Publishing.

Pieratt, Marty Ford. First Black Red: The Story of Chuck Harmon, the First African American to Play for the Cincinnati Reds. 2010. 208p. (ENG.). 24.99 *(978-1-4520-1995-6(9))*; pap. 18.00 *(978-1-4520-1994-9(0))* AuthorHouse.

Pinn, Anthony B. Becoming ÒAmericaÓs Problem ChildÓ: An Outline of Pauli MurrayÕs Religious Life & Theology. 2008. 128p. pap. 16.00 *(978-1-55635-302-4(2)*, Pickwick Pubns.) Wipf & Stock Pubs.

Podair, Jerald & Podair, Jerald E. Bayard Rustin: American Dreamer. 2008. (African American History Ser.). (ENG., Illus.). 128p. 35.95 *(978-0-7425-4513-7(X))* Rowman & Littlefield Publishers, Inc.

Poitier, Sidney. The Measure of a Man: A Spiritual Autobiography. 2007. (ENG.). 272p. pap. 14.99 *(978-0-06-135790-9(1)*, HarperOne); (Illus.). 272p. 25.95 *(978-0-06-135791-6(X)*, HarperOne); (ENG., Illus.). 320p. per. 16.95 *(978-0-06-135792-3(8)*, HarperLuxe) HarperCollins Pubs.

Pone, Darrell. We've Come This Far by Faith. 2008. 121p. pap. 20.00 *(978-0-9787650-0-2(1))* Pone Inspirations.

Potter, Joan. African American Firsts: Famous Little-Known & Unsung Triumphs of Blacks in America (Updated) 2009. (ENG., Illus.). 424p. pap. 16.00 *(978-0-7582-4166-5(6))* Kensington Publishing Corp.

Poval, Allie & Calderone, Gary. The Time of Eddie Noel. 2010. 195p. pap. 13.99 *(978-1-935361-04-6(X))* Comfort Publishing Services, LLC.

Powell, Colin L & Koltz, Tony. It Worked for Me: In Life & Leadership. l.t. ed. 2012. (ENG.). 320p. pap. 27.99 ***(978-0-06-218406-1(7)***, HarperLuxe) HarperCollins Pubs.

Pritchett, Wendell E. Robert Clifton Weaver & the American City: The Life & Times of an Urban Reformer. 2008. (ENG., Illus.). 444p. 30.00 *(978-0-226-68448-2(2))* Univ. of Chicago Pr.

Qualls, Josephine S. Incredible Journey. 2009. 80p. pap. 9.99 *(978-0-9824931-1-3(8))* Faithful Life Pubs.

Ra, Abuna Hetep. Vision for Regenerative Harmonious Society of Woman & the Law of Maat. 2009. 116p. pap. 19.99 *(978-1-4415-3637-2(X))* Xlibris Corp.

Ramsey, Henry. The Life Story of Henry Ramsey Jr: An Autobiography. 2008. (Illus.). 653p. *(978-0-9789979-2-2(1))* Hardscratch Pr.

Randle, Raymond. Life Is Not Just Black or White. 2009. 112p. pap. 12.95 *(978-1-4327-1210-5(1))* Outskirts Pr., Inc.

Randolph, Ryan P. W. E. B. Dubois: The Fight for Civil Rights. 2009. (Library of American Lives & Times Ser.). 112p. (gr. 5-5). 69.20 *(978-1-60853-510-1(X))* Rosen Publishing Group, Inc., The.

Ratliff, Stanley. A Dream, A Goal, Never a Reality. 2008. 120p. pap. 12.99 *(978-1-4343-6622-1(7))* AuthorHouse.

Reddie, Richard S. Martin Luther King. 2011. (ENG., Illus.). 192p. pap. 16.95 ***(978-0-7459-5282-6(8))*** Lion Hudson PLC GBR. Dist: Independent Pubs. Group.

Reef, Catherine. African Americans in the Military. 2nd rev. ed. 2010. (A to Z of African Americans Ser.). (Illus.). 304p. (C). (gr. 9-18). 49.50 *(978-0-8160-7839-4(4))* Facts On File, Inc.

Reeves, Derek. Still Waters Run Deep: The Story of My Journey from East Harlem to Harvard. 2008. 300p. 31.95 *(978-0-595-51333-8(6))*; pap. 21.95 *(978-0-595-51807-4(9))* iUniverse, Inc.

Reflections of a Native Son in the New South. 2009. (Illus.). 152p. pap. 14.95 *(978-0-9794420-7-0(9))* Red Letter Pr.

Reid-Pharr, Robert. Once You Go Black: Choice, Desire, & the Black American Intellectual. 2007. (ENG., Illus.). 208p. 75.00 *(978-0-8147-7583-7(7))*; pap. 23.00 *(978-0-8147-7584-4(5))* New York Univ. Pr.

Rhodes-Pitts, Sharifa. Harlem Is Nowhere: A Journey to the Mecca of Black America. 2011. (ENG., Illus.). 304p. 24.99 *(978-0-316-01723-7(X))* Little Brown & Co.

Rice, Condoleezza. Extraordinary, Ordinary People: A Memoir of Family. (ENG.). 2011. 368p. pap. 15.00 *(978-0-307-88847-1(9)*, Three Rivers Pr.) 2010. (Illus.). 352p. 27.00 *(978-0-307-58787-9(8)*, Crown) Crown Publishing Group.

Rice, Sederick C. Four Tubas, a Guitar, & a Gallery of Cheerleaders: Transition in the Life of a Black Ph. D. 2010. 376p. 28.49 *(978-1-4520-5983-9(7))*; pap. 17.99 *(978-1-4520-5982-2(9))* AuthorHouse.

Richardson, Myra K. The Innocent Molester. 2007. (Illus.). 296p. per. 23.50 *(978-1-4251-1084-0(3))* Trafford Publishing.

Ridley, Jo Ann. Zoë Dusanne: An Art Dealer Who Made a Difference. 2011. (ENG.). 176p. pap. 15.95 *(978-1-56474-505-7(8)*, Fithian Pr) Daniel & Daniel, Pubs., Inc.

Riesman. I Feel So Good. 2007. (Illus.). 306p. *(978-0-415-97276-5(0)*, 0415972760, Routledge) Taylor & Francis Group.

Ritchie, Andrew. Major Taylor: The Fastest Bicycle Rider in the World. 2nd ed. 2009. (Illus.). 240p. 39.95 *(978-1-892495-65-5(1))* Cycle Publishing/Van Der Plas Pubns.

Roberts, Randy. Joe Louis: Hard Times Man. 2012. (ENG., Illus.). 328p. pap. 17.50 *(978-0-300-17763-3(1))* Yale Univ. Pr.

Roberts, Tara, ed. What Your Mama Never Told You: True Stories about Sex & Love. 2007. (ENG.). 160p. (YA). (gr. 10-18). pap. 7.99 *(978-0-618-64636-4(1))* Houghton Mifflin Harcourt Publishing Co.

Roberts, Terrence. Lessons from Little Rock. 2009. (ENG.). 200p. 24.95 *(978-1-935106-11-1(2))* Butler Ctr. for Arkansas Studies.

Robeson, Paul. The Undiscovered Paul Robeson Vol. 2: Quest for Freedom, 1939-1976. 2010. (ENG., Illus.). 432p. 35.00 *(978-0-471-40973-1(1)*, Wiley) Wiley, John & Sons, Inc.

Robinson, Edward J. To Save My Race from Abuse: The Life of Samuel Robert Cassius. 2nd ed. 2007. (Religion & American Culture Ser.). (ENG., Illus.). 224p. 39.95 *(978-0-8173-1555-9(1))* Univ. of Alabama Pr.

Robotham, Rosemarie, ed. Mending the World: Stories of Family by Contemporary Black Writers. 2008. (ENG.). 290p. 25.00 *(978-1-4379-5230-8(5))* DIANE Publishing Co.

Rodgers Sr, Kenneth W. Not My Shadow: A True African American Story. 2008. 120p. pap. 11.95 *(978-1-4327-2942-4(X))* Outskirts Pr., Inc.

Rogers, Phil. Ernie Banks: Mr. Cub & the Summer Of '69. 2011. (ENG.). 272p. 24.95 *(978-1-60078-519-1(0))* Triumph Bks.

Rooks, Veronda L. His Grace Is Sufficient! 2010. (ENG.). 77p. pap. 12.00 *(978-0-557-45156-2(6))* Lulu Enterprises Inc.

Roper, Moses. A Narrative of the Adventures & Escape of Moses Roper, from American Slavery. 2011. (ENG., Illus.). 55p. pap. 15.00 ***(978-0-8078-6965-9(1))*** Univ. of North Carolina Pr.

—Narrative of the Adventures & Escape of Moses Roper from American Slavery. 2010. 98p. pap. 15.16 *(978-1-163-96124-7(8))* 2007. (ENG.). 100p. per. 18.95 *(978-0-548-67938-8(X))* Kessinger Publishing, LLC.

—A Narrative of the Adventures & Escape of Moses Roper from American Slavery. 2009. 52p. pap. *(978-1-4099-8560-0(1))* Dodo Pr.

—A Narrative of the Adventures & Escape of Moses Roper from American Slavery. 2010. (Illus.). 40p. pap. 14.14 *(978-1-154-53502-0(9))* General Bks. LLC.

—Narrative of the Adventures & Escape of Moses Roper, from American Slavery. 2010. (ENG.). 102p. pap. 18.75 *(978-1-177-53882-4(2))* BiblioBazaar.

Roper, Moses & Price, Thomas. A Narrative of the Adventures & Escape of Moses Roper from American Slavery. 2011. 126p. pap. 19.75 ***(978-1-173-61369-3(2))*** BiblioBazaar.

Rose, Yvonne. Senior Stories - Straight from the Heart. 2011. pap. 12.99 ***(978-0-9824922-1-5(9))*** Amber Bks.

Ross-Stroud, Catherine. Janet McDonald: The Original Project Girl. 2008. (Scarecrow Studies in Young Adult Literature Ser.). (ENG., Illus.). 160p. 45.00 *(978-0-8108-5802-2(9))* Scarecrow Pr., Inc.

Royal, Alice C & Ellinger, Mickey. Allensworth, the Freedom Colony: A California African American Township. 2008. pap. *(978-1-59714-091-1(0))* Heyday.

Rummel, Jack. African-American Social Leaders & Activists. 2011. 262p. 49.50 ***(978-1-4381-3388-1(X))*** Facts On File, Inc.

Rummel, Jack. Social Leaders & Activists. 2nd rev. ed. 2011. (A to Z of African Americans Ser.). (Illus.). 272p. (C). (gr. 9-18). 49.50 *(978-0-8160-8092-2(5))* Facts On File, Inc.

Russell, Bill & Steinberg, Alan. Red & Me: A Great Coach, a Life-Long Friend. 2009. (Illus.). 208p. 24.99 *(978-0-06-176614-5(3))*; (ENG.). 224p. pap. 24.99 *(978-0-06-177499-7(5)*, HarperLuxe) HarperCollins Pubs.

Russell, Dick. Black Genius: Inspirational Portraits of African-American Leaders. 2009. (ENG.). 512p. pap. 16.95 *(978-1-60239-369-1(9)*, 239369) Skyhorse Publishing Co., Inc.

Rutland, Eva. When We Were Colored: A Mother's Story. 2007. (ENG., Illus.). 164p. per. 12.95 *(978-1-934178-00-3(4))* IWP, Bk. Pubs.

Rutledge, Archibald Hamilton. God's Children. 2009. 19.99 *(978-1-59629-642-8(9))* History Pr., The.

Ryan, William R. The World of Thomas Jeremiah: Charles Town on the Eve of the American Revolution, 1 vol. 2012. (ENG., Illus.). 282p. pap. 24.95 ***(978-0-19-992287-1(X))*** Oxford Univ. Pr., Inc.

Ryan, William Randolph. The World of Thomas Jeremiah: Charles Town on the Eve of the American Revolution, 1 vol. 2010. (ENG., Illus.). 280p. 49.95 *(978-0-19-538728-5(7))* Oxford Univ. Pr., Inc.

Saint-Arnaud, Pierre & Feldstein, Peter. African American Pioneers of Sociology: A Critical History. Feldstein, Peter, tr. from FRE. 2009. (ENG.). 416p. *(978-0-8020-9122-2(9))*; pap. *(978-0-8020-9405-6(8))* Univ. of Toronto Pr.

Saint, Chandler B. & Krimsky, George A. Making Freedom: The Extraordinary Life of Venture Smith. 2009. (Garnet Bks.). (ENG., Illus.). 204p. 19.95 *(978-0-8195-6854-0(6))* Wesleyan Univ. Pr.

Samuel, A. My Longest Journey. 2007. (ENG.). 124p. per. *(978-1-84747-115-4(3))* Chipmunkapublishing.

Samuelsson, Marcus. Yes, Chef: A Memoir. 2012. (ENG., Illus.). 336p. 27.00 *(978-0-385-34260-5(8)*, Dial Pr.) Random House Publishing Group.

Saunders, Hollie Ann. Through My Eyes: A History of Lancaster from A Black Perspective. 2007. 216p. pap. 19.99 *(978-0-9787850-1-7(0))* Ambassador Pr.

Schraff, Anne E. Jackie Robinson: An American Hero. 2008. (Townsend Library). 138p. (J). *(978-1-59194-102-6(4))* Townsend Pr. - Sunday Schl. Publishing Board.

Schroff, Laura L. & Tresniowski, Alex. An Invisible Thread: The True Story of an 11-Year-Old Panhandler, a Busy Sales Executive, & an Unlikely Meeting with Destiny. (ENG., Illus.). 272p. 2012. pap. 14.99 ***(978-1-4516-4897-3(9))*** 2011. 25.00 *(978-1-4516-4251-3(2))* Howard Books. (Howard Bks.).

Schwartz, Peggy & Schwartz, Murray. The Dance Claimed Me: A Biography of Pearl Primus. 2011. (ENG., Illus.). 352p. 35.00 *(978-0-300-15534-1(4))* Yale Univ. Pr.

Scott, Michelle R. Blues Empress in Black Chattanooga: Bessie Smith & the Emerging Urban South. 2008. (ENG., Illus.). 216p. 60.00 *(978-0-252-03338-4(8))*; pap. 26.00 *(978-0-252-07545-2(5))* Univ. of Illinois Pr.

The ScreamBed Chronicles: The last days of playas & other insecure Men. 2007. 186p. per. 19.95 *(978-0-615-17643-2(8))* KaChiza Bks.

Seagrave, Ronald Roy. Jefferson?ÇÖs Isaac: From Monticello to Petersburg. 2011. 170p. pap. 24.95 *(978-1-4327-7062-4(4))* Outskirts Pr., Inc.

Seagraves, David. Uncommon Hero: The John Seagraves Story. 2012. (ENG.). pap. 22.95 ***(978-0-9850555-0-9(2)***, Prana Pr.

Sensbach, Jon F. Rebecca's Revival: Creating Black Christianity in the Atlantic World. 2006. (Illus.). 320p. per. 21.00 *(978-0-674-02257-7(2))* Harvard Univ. Pr.

Shaw, Arnold. Belafonte: An Unauthorized Biography. 2011. 368p. 53.95 ***(978-1-258-06661-1(0))*** Literary Licensing, LLC.

Shaw, Charles E. The Untold Stories of Excellence: From a Life of Despair & Uncertainty to One that Offers Hope & a New Beginning. 2011. 510p. pap. 23.99 ***(978-1-4628-8836-8(4))*** Xlibris Corp.

Shellum, Brian. Black Officer in a Buffalo Soldier Regiment: The Military Career of Charles Young. 2010. (ENG., Illus.). 412p. pap. 19.95 *(978-0-8032-1385-2(9)*, Bison Bks.) Univ. of Nebraska Pr.

Shepherd, Sherri. Permission Slips: Every Woman's Guide to Giving Herself a Break. l.t. ed. 2010. (ENG.). 391p. 31.50 *(978-1-4104-2242-2(9))* Thorndike Pr.

Sherbia, Pam J., ed. Living at Home: A Memoir. 2010. 197p. pap. 19.95 *(978-0-615-33733-3(3))* U N I Publishing Co.

Sherwood, Marika. Malcolm X: Visits Abroad. 2011. 256p. pap. 24.95 ***(978-1-59907-050-6(2))*** Tsehai Pubs. & Distributors.

Sheryl The Pearl. Not Easily Broken. 2011. 90p. pap. 19.95 ***(978-1-4512-7623-7(0))*** PublishAmerica, Inc.

Shropshire, Kenneth. Being Sugar Ray: The Life of Sugar Ray Robinson, America's Greatest Boxer & the First Celebrity Athlete. 2008. (ENG., Illus.). 272p. per. 16.95 *(978-0-465-07804-2(4)*, Basic Civitas Bks.) Basic Bks.

Siller, Robert Jr. A Country Called Nigeri. 2008. (Illus.). 148p. 29.99 *(978-1-4257-9895-6(0))*; pap. 19.99 *(978-1-4257-9864-2(0))* Xlibris Corp.

Simmons, Roy & DiMarco, Damon. Out of Bounds: Coming Out of Sexual Abuse, Addiction, & My Life of Lies in the NFL Closet. 2006. (ENG.). 256p. per. 15.95 *(978-0-7867-1909-9(5))* Da Capo Pr., Inc.

Singletary, Wes. The Right Time: John Henry "Pop" Lloyd & Black Baseball. 2011. (ENG., Illus.). 234p. pap. 29.95 *(978-0-7864-3572-2(0))* McFarland & Co., Inc. Pubs.

Sitkoff, Harvard. King: Pilgrimage to the Mountaintop. 2009. (ENG., Illus.). 288p. pap. 15.00 *(978-0-8090-6349-9(2)*, Hill & Wang) Farrar, Straus & Giroux.

Slim, Iceberg. Pimp: The Story of My Life. 2011. (ENG.). 320p. pap. 14.99 *(978-1-4516-1713-9(5)*, Cash Money Content) Cash Money Content LLC.

Smith, Alvin D. & Edmunds, Henry E. George Washington Carver: Man of God. 2011. 76p. 36.95 ***(978-1-258-06113-5(9))*** Literary Licensing, LLC.

Smith, Charlene & Feister, John. Thea's Song: The Life of Thea Bowman. 2010 (Illus.). 352p. 28.00 *(978-1-57075-868-3(9))* Orbis Bks.

Smith-Forrest, Mary. Mary: Then & Now, an Autobiography in Her Own Words. 2010. 92p. pap. 15.49 *(978-1-4520-0314-6(9))* AuthorHouse.

Smith, Grace. He Threatened to Throw Me off the Bridge - With. 2011. pap. 15.95 ***(978-0-7414-6501-6(9))*** Infinity Publishing.

Smith, Jessie Carney, ed. Encyclopedia of African American Popular Culture, 4 vols. 2010. (Illus.). 1733p. 380.00 *(978-0-313-35796-1(X)*, GR5796) Greenwood Publishing Group, Inc.

Smith, Minister Regina. Bewitched! Yet Chosen for a Greater Destiny. 2009. 152p. 22.99 *(978-1-60791-945-2(1))*; pap. 14.99 *(978-1-60791-944-5(3))* Xulon Pr., Inc.

Smith, Norman R. Footprints of Black Louisian. 2011. 158p. 29.99 ***(978-1-4568-2631-4(X))***; pap. 19.99 ***(978-1-4568-2630-7(1))*** Xlibris Corp.

Smith, Ramone. African American Healthy Self-Esteem: Understanding Why Low Self Esteem in African Americans Occur & How to Elevate Self-Esteem. 2011. 152p. pap. 14.95 ***(978-1-4620-4996-7(6))*** iUniverse, Inc.

Smock, Raymond W. Booker T. Washington: Black Leadership in the Age of Jim Crow. (ENG.). 240p. 2010. pap. 15.95 *(978-1-56663-866-1(6))* 2009. (Illus.). 26.00 *(978-1-56663-725-1(2))* Dee, Ivan R. Pub.

Southgate, Joan E. 'Bout Time. 2007. (Illus.). 175p. pap. *(978-0-9759366-5-8(4))* Eagle Creek Pr.

Spearman, Joah & Harrison, Louis. Real Role Models: Successful African Americans Beyond Pop Culture. 2010. (ENG., Illus.). 182p. pap. 19.95 *(978-0-292-71832-6(2))* Univ. of Texas Pr.

Spearman, Joah & Harrison, Louis, Jr. Real Role Models: Successful African Americans Beyond Pop Culture. 2010. (ENG., Illus.). 182p. 45.00 *(978-0-292-72301-6(6))* Univ. of Texas Pr.

Spencer, Jon M. Self-Made & Blues-Rich. Date not set. (Illus.). 130p. 11.95 *(978-0-86543-503-2(0))* Africa World Pr.

Spruill, Harrell. The Harvesting the American Dream: from Farm to Classroom: 2007. (ENG.). 124p. 33.50 *(978-1-4122-0224-4(8))* Trafford Publishing.

Stamz, Richard & Roberts, Patrick A. Give 'Em Soul, Richard! Race, Radio, & Rhythm & Blues in Chicago. 2010. (ENG., Illus.). 160p. 60.00 *(978-0-252-03498-5(8))*; pap. 20.00 *(978-0-252-07686-2(9))* Univ. of Illinois Pr.

Stancliff, Michael. Frances Ellen Watkins Harper: African American Reform Rhetoric & the Rise of a Modern Nation State. 2010. (Studies in American Popular History & Culture Ser.). (ENG., Illus.). 220p. 125.00 *(978-0-415-99763-8(1))* Routledge.

Stanford, Karin L. & Institute for Arts and Media, Northridge, California State University Staff. African Americans in Los Angeles. 2010. (Images of America Ser.). (Illus.). 128p. pap. 21.99 *(978-0-7385-8094-4(5))* Arcadia Publishing.

Stauffer, John. Giants: The Parallel Lives of Frederick Douglass & Abraham Lincoln. 2009. (ENG.). 448p. pap. 14.99 *(978-0-446-69898-6(9)*, Twelve) Grand Central Publishing.

Stephenson, Frank. Chowan Beach: Remembering an African American Resort. 2006. (Illus.). 124p. pap., per. 14.99 *(978-1-59629-164-5(8))* History Pr., The.

Steverson, Bryan. Amazing Baseball Heroes: Inspirational Negro League Stories. 2011. (Illus.). xxii, 248p. ***(978-1-932604-81-8(2))*** Tennessee Valley Publishing.

Stone, Jennifer Arlene. Dear Roman, Dear Jacques: The Inefficacy of Brilliance. 2008. (Illus.). 170p. pap. 30.00 *(978-0-9679161-7-0(8))* javariBook.

The Story of Nannie Helen Burroughs. 2006. pap. 10.99 *(978-1-56309-848-2(2))* Woman's Missionary Union.

Strength Within Surviving by the Grace of God. 2nd rev. ed. 2008. 288p. pap. 15.00 *(978-0-615-21031-5(7))* Tyler, Roland Vincent.

Stricklin, David. Louis Armstrong. 2010. (ENG.). 200p. 26.00 *(978-1-56663-836-4(4))* Dee, Ivan R. Pub.

Strider, Herb. Bass, U. S. Deputy Marshal. 2009. 52p. pap. 10.00 *(978-1-4257-5200-2(4))* Xlibris Corp.

Stuart, David A. Limited Skies. 2008. 268p. pap. 15.95 *(978-1-4343-8310-5(5))* AuthorHouse.

Students of College Bound, contrib. by. Studio STL Anthology, No. 1. 2007. 106p. pap. 18.95 *(978-0-9795112-0-2(8))* StudioSTL.

Sugrue, Thomas J. Not Even Past: Barack Obama & the Burden of Race. 2010. (Lawrence Stone Lectures). (ENG.). 178p. 24.95 *(978-0-691-13730-8(7))* Princeton Univ. Pr.

Sullivan, Patrick. Brick by Brick: The Story of Auto Racing Pioneer Joie Ray. 2008. (Illus.). 208p. pap. 22.50 *(978-0-9719639-5-5(9))* American Scene Pr., LLC.

Summer-Edmond, Janice L. The Secret Trust of Aspasia Cruvellier Mirault: The Life & Trials of a Free Woman of Color in Antebellum Georgia. 2008. (Illus.). 180p. 29.95 *(978-1-55728-880-6(1))* Univ. of Arkansas Pr.

Sundquist, Eric J. King's Dream: The Legacy of Martin Luther King's I Have a Dream Speech. 2009. (Icons of America Ser.). (ENG., Illus.). 320p. pap. 14.00 *(978-0-300-15859-5(9))* Yale Univ. Pr.

Swanton, Barry & Mah, Jay-Dell. Black Baseball Players in Canada: A Biographical Dictionary, 1881-1960. 2009. (ENG., Illus.). 212p. pap. 39.95 *(978-0-7864-4468-7(1))* McFarland & Co., Inc. Pubs.

Swindall, Lindsey R. The Politics of Paul Robeson's Othello. (Margaret Walker Alexander Series in African American Studies). (ENG.). 224p. 2011. pap. 30.00 ***(978-1-61703-203-5(4))*** 2010. 50.00 *(978-1-60473-824-7(3))* Univ. Pr. of Mississippi.

Tafoya, Eddie M. Icons of African American Comedy, 1 vol. 2011. (Greenwood Icons Ser.). (Illus.). 283p. 95.00 *(978-0-313-38084-6(8)*, A2231C) Greenwood Publishing Group, Inc.

Talbot, Gerald E. & Price, H. H. Maine's Visible Black History: The First Chronicle of Its People. 2010. (Illus.). 429p. pap. 35.00 *(978-0-88448-275-8(8))* Tilbury Hse. Pubs.

Tallman, Jamie Q. The Notorious Dr. Flippin: Abortion & Consequence in the Early Twentieth Century. 2011. (Plains Histories Ser.). (ENG., Illus.). 228p. 34.95 *(978-0-89672-675-8(4))* Texas Tech Univ. Pr.

Tamini, Dofini. Coming to USA, 1 vol. 2010. 128p. pap. 19.95 *(978-1-4489-5221-2(2))* PublishAmerica, Inc.

Taylor, Theodore. The Flight of Jesse Leroy Brown. 2007. (Bluejacket Bks.). (Illus.). 300p. per. 18.95 *(978-1-59114-852-4(9))* Naval Institute Pr.

Telander, Rick. Heaven Is a Playground. 3rd ed. 2009. (ENG., Illus.). 256p. pap. 18.95 *(978-0-8032-2678-4(0)*, Bison Bks.) Univ. of Nebraska Pr.

Terrill, Robert E. Malcolm X: Inventing Radical Judgment. 2007. (Rhetoric & Public Affairs Ser.). (ENG.). 256p. per. 19.95 *(978-0-87013-803-4(0))* East African Educational Pubs., Ltd. KEN. Dist: Michigan State Univ. Pr.

Terrill, Robert E., ed. The Cambridge Companion to Malcolm X. 2010. (Cambridge Companions to American Studies). (ENG.). 208p. (C). pap. 24.99 *(978-0-521-73157-7(7))* Cambridge Univ. Pr.

Tesfamichael, Alazar. Trials & Tribulations. 2011. 310p. pap. 19.95 *(978-0-9818859-2-6(6))* Beatitude Pr.

The Kresge Foundation, creator. Marcus Belgrave Master of the Music: The Kresge Foundation. 2009. pap. 1.00 *(978-0-615-33397-7(4))* Kresge Foundation, The.

Theisen, Olive Jensen. Walls That Speak: The Murals of John Thomas Biggers. 2010. (Illus.). 160p. 29.95 *(978-1-57441-289-5(2))* Univ. of North Texas Pr.

Thomas, A. C. The Color of Success: Growing up black never stopped one man from Winning. 2007. pap. *(978-0-9797103-0-8(8))* Algus Publishing.

Thomas, Clarence. My Grandfather's Son: A Memoir. 2007. (Illus.). 304p. 26.95 *(978-0-06-056555-8(1))* HarperCollins Pubs.

Thompson, John. The Life of John Thompson, a Fugitive Slave. Andrews, William & Gates, Henry Louis, Jr., eds. 2011. (ENG.). 144p. (gr. 12). 14.00 *(978-0-14-310642-5(2)*, Penguin Classics) Penguin Group (USA) Inc.

Thomson Gale, creator. Contemporary Black Biography: Profiles from the International Black Community. (Contemporary Black Biography Ser.). (ENG., Illus.). Vol. 56. 2006. 288p. 150.00 *(978-0-7876-7928-6(3))* Vol. 60. 2007. 300p. 150.00 *(978-0-7876-7932-3(1))* Cengage Gale.

—Contemporary Black Biography, Volume 57, Vol. 57. 2006. (Contemporary Black Biography Ser.). (ENG., Illus.). 288p. 150.00 *(978-0-7876-7929-3(1))* Cengage Gale.

—Contemporary Black Biography, Volume 58: Profiles from the International Black Community, Vol. 58. 2007. (Contemporary Black Biography Ser.). (ENG., Illus.). 288p. 150.00 *(978-0-7876-7930-9(5))* Cengage Gale.

Thornton, Claude Edward. Ambition in the Eyes of a Child. 2008. 128p. pap. 12.00 *(978-1-4343-8544-4(2))* AuthorHouse.

Thurston, Baratunde. How to Be Black. 2012. (ENG.). 256p. 24.99 *(978-0-06-200321-8(6))* HarperCollins Pubs.

Tidwell, John Edgar & Ragar, Cheryl R., eds. Montage of a Dream: The Art & Life of Langston Hughes. 2007. (ENG.). 376p. (C). 44.95 *(978-0-8262-1716-5(8))* Univ. of Missouri Pr.

A to Z of African Americans. 2011. (A to Z of African Americans Ser.). (C). (gr. 9). 445.50 ***(978-0-8160-8491-3(2))*** Facts On File, Inc.

Toback, James. Jim: The Author's Self-Centered Memoir on the Great Jim Brown. 2009. (ENG.). 154p. pap. 25.00 *(978-0-9818056-3-4(9))* Rat Pr.

Todd, Leonard. Carolina Clay: The Life & Legend of the Slave Potter Dave. 2008. (ENG., Illus.). 320p. 25.95 *(978-0-393-05856-7(5)*, 5856) Norton, W. W. & Co., Inc.

Toler, Lynn. My Mother's Rules: A Practical Guide to Becoming an Emotional Genius. 2007. (ENG.). 300p. per. 15.00 *(978-1-932841-22-0(9))* Agate Publishing, Inc.

Townes, Gregory. The Tribe. 318p. pap. 14.95 *(978-0-9748051-3-9(0))* Black Print Publishing.

Trotman, C. James. Frederick Douglass: A Biography, 1 vol. 2011. (Greenwood Biographies Ser.). (Illus.). 158p. 35.00 *(978-0-313-35036-8(1)*, GR5036) Greenwood Publishing Group, Inc.

Truth, Myjourn'ees B. My Name Ain't Toby, 1 vol. 2009. 244p. pap. 24.95 *(978-1-60813-025-2(8))* PublishAmerica, Inc.

Truth, Sojourner & Gilbert, Olive. Narrative of Sojourner Truth: Literary Touchstone Classic. 2007. 144p. pap. 3.99 *(978-1-58049-733-6(0))* Prestwick Hse., Inc.

Truth, Sojourner, et al. Three Narratives of Slavery. 2008. (African American Ser.). (ENG.). 320p. pap. 8.95 *(978-0-486-46834-1(8))* Dover Pubns., Inc.

Tucker, Phillip Thomas. Cathy Williams: From Slave to Buffalo Soldier. 2008. (ENG., Illus.). 258p. pap. 19.95 *(978-0-8117-3569-8(9))* Stackpole Bks.

—Father of the Tuskegee Airmen, John C. Robinson. 2012. (Illus.). 400p. 29.95 *(978-1-59797-487-5(0))* Potomac Bks., Inc.

Turnipseed, Alfred Douglas. Triumph of an American Black Man: My Own Story. 2008. 140p. 21.95 *(978-0-595-49623-5(7))*; pap. 11.95 *(978-0-595-48920-6(6))* iUniverse, Inc.

Tutton, Thomas. A Friend Thru Terror: The Liberian Civil War, 1989 — 1996. 2008. 164p. pap. 15.99 *(978-1-4141-1107-0(X))* Pleasant Word.

Urban, Wayne J. Black Scholar: Horace Mann Bond, 1904-1972. 2008. (ENG.). 284p. pap. 24.95 *(978-0-8203-3255-0(0))* Univ. of Georgia Pr.

Vendryes, Margaret Rose. Barthé: A Life in Sculpture. 2008. (ENG., Illus.). 256p. 40.00 *(978-1-60473-092-0(7))* Univ. Pr. of Mississippi.

Villarosa, Clara. The Words of African-American Heroes. 2011. (Newmarket Words of Ser.). (ENG.). 160p. 18.95 *(978-1-55704-946-9(7)*, Morrow, William & Co.) HarperCollins Pubs.

Vizinau, D. Dexter. Shine on Me: The Story of Margaret Vizinau, A Determined African-American Woman & Her Faith in God. 2009. 460p. 38.95 *(978-0-595-89696-7(0)*, iUniverse Star) iUniverse, Inc.

Wainstock, Dennis. Malcolm X, African American Revolutionary. 2008. (ENG., Illus.). 229p. pap. 35.00 *(978-0-7864-3934-8(3))* McFarland & Co., Inc. Pubs.

Wakefield, Charles C. Black Choices: A Young Black Man's Guide to Prison Survival, 1 vol. 2009. 83p. pap. 16.95 *(978-1-60813-727-5(9))* PublishAmerica, Inc.

Waldschmidt-Nelson, Britta. Dreams & Nightmares: Martin Luther King Jr., Malcolm X, & the Struggle for Black Equality in America. 2012. (New Perspectives on the History of the South Ser.). (ENG., Illus.). 208p. 22.00 *(978-0-8130-3723-3(9))* Univ. Pr. of Florida.

Walker, Clarence Earl & Smithers, Gregory D. The Preacher & the Politician: Jeremiah Wright, Barack Obama, & Race in America. 2009. (ENG., Illus.). 168p. 22.95 *(978-0-8139-2886-9(9))* Univ. Pr. of Virginia.

Walker Jr., Robert A. C. Where's the Brothas? 2008. 138p. pap. 24.95 *(978-1-60610-927-4(8))* PublishAmerica, Inc.

Wallach, Jennifer Jensen. Closer to the Truth Than Any Fact: Memoir, Memory, & Jim Crow. (ENG.). 192p. 2010. pap. 22.95 *(978-0-8203-3502-5(9))* 2008. 34.95 *(978-0-8203-3069-3(8))* Univ. of Georgia Pr.

Wallenfeldt, Jeff, ed. Africa to America: From the Middle Passage Through The 1930S. 2010. (African American History & Culture Ser.). (Illus.). 272p. (YA). 90.00 *(978-1-61530-180-5(1))* Rosen Publishing Group, Inc., The.

Ward, Andrew. The Slaves' War: The Civil War in the Words of Former Slaves. (ENG.). 2009. 416p. pap. 14.95 *(978-0-547-23792-3(8)*, Mariner Bks.) 2008. (Illus.). 400p. 28.00 *(978-0-618-63400-2(2))* Houghton Mifflin Harcourt Trade & Reference Pubs.

Ward, Chris, et al. Black History Leaders. 2010. (ENG., Illus.). 96p. (YA). pap. 15.99 *(978-1-61623-923-7(9))* Bluewater Productions, Inc.

Ward, Samuel Ringgold. Autobiography of a Fugitive Negro; His Anti-Slavery Labours in the United States, Canad. 2010. 152p. pap. 23.85 *(978-1-153-29480-5(X))* General Bks. LLC.

Warner, Donald D. Resurrection. 2007. 436p. per. 19.95 *(978-1-4327-1449-9(X))* Outskirts Pr., Inc.

Warren, Nagueyalti. An Intellectual Biography of W.E.B. du Bois: Initiator of Black Studies in the University. 2010. iii, 198p. 109.95 *(978-0-7734-3715-9(0))* Mellen, Edwin Pr., The.

Washington, Booker T. The Booker T. Washington Reader (an African American Heritage Book) 2008. 420p. (ENG.). 34.95 *(978-1-60459-202-3(8))*; per. 24.95 *(978-1-60459-200-9(1))* Wilder Pubns., Ltd.

—My Larger Education. 2008. (Illus.). 212p. pap. *(978-1-4099-0266-9(8))* Dodo Pr.

—My Larger Education: Being Chapters from My Experience [1911]. 2010. 349p. pap. 26.96 *(978-0-557-35380-4(7))* Lulu Enterprises Inc.

—The Story of My Life & Work. 2008. (Illus.). xxi, 309p. *(978-1-4351-0839-4(6))* Barnes & Noble, Inc.

—Up from Slavery. 2007. (Illus.). 192p. reprint ed. 20.95 *(978-0-89190-799-2(8)*, American Reprint Co.) Amereon LTD.

—Up from Slavery. 2009. 172p. pap. *(978-0-217-14174-1(9))* Books LLC.

—Up from Slavery. 2007. 168p. per. 12.95 *(978-1-60206-801-8(1))* Cosimo, Inc.

—Up from Slavery. 2010. (ENG.). 272p. (gr. 12-18). 4.95 *(978-0-451-53147-6(7)*, Signet Classics) Penguin Group (USA) Inc.

—Up from Slavery. 2008. (ENG.). 148p. 24.95 *(978-1-60459-195-8(1))*; per. 9.99 *(978-1-60459-193-4(5))* Wilder Pubns., Ltd.

—Up from Slavery: An Authoritative Text, Contexts & Composition History, Criticism. reprint ed. 125.00 *(978-0-7222-9750-6(5))* Library Reprints, Inc.

—Up from Slavery: An Autobiography. 2008. 224p. 24.99 *(978-0-554-36116-1(7))* 2008. 224p. 27.99 *(978-0-554-26813-2(2))* 2007. (ENG.). 200p. pap. 19.99 *(978-1-4346-1769-9(6))* BiblioBazaar.

—Up from Slavery: An Autobiography. 2010. 232p. pap. 19.95 *(978-1-60444-084-3(8))* IndoEuropeanPublishing.com.

—Up from Slavery: An Autobiography, 1 vol. 2010. (ENG., Illus.). 336p. pap. 8.99 *(978-1-58980-789-1(8))* Pelican Publishing Co., Inc.

—Up from Slavery: An Autobiography. 2009. (ENG.). 425p. pap. 24.95 *(978-1-4128-1311-2(5))* Transaction Pubs.

—Up from Slavery: An Autobiography. 2007. (ENG.). 344p. 32.95 *(978-1-4344-9640-9(6))*; per. 22.95 *(978-1-4344-9639-3(2))* Wildside Pr., LLC.

—Up from Slavery: An autobiography. l.t. ed. 2007. (ENG.). 222p. pap. 22.99 *(978-1-4346-1938-9(9))* BiblioBazaar.

—Up from Slavery: An Autobiography (Dodo. 2006. pap. *(978-1-4065-0984-7(1))* Dodo Pr.

—Up from Slavery - an Autobiography. 2009. 184p. 32.99 *(978-1-59547-528-2(1))* 2007. 176p. per. 13.99 *(978-1-59547-896-2(5))* NuVision Pubns., LLC.

—Up from Slavery - an Autobiography. 2007. (ENG.). 228p. per. *(978-1-4086-3301-4(9))* Read Bks.

—Up from Slavery (an AUTOBIOGRAPHY) 2007. 264p. per. 12.95 *(978-1-60424-174-7(8)*, Book Jungle) Standard Pubns., Inc.

Washington, John. John Washington's Civil War: A Slave Narrative. Shifflett, Crandall, ed. 2008. (Illus.). 106p. pap. 16.95 *(978-0-8071-3302-6(7))* Louisiana State Univ. Pr.

Washington Post Staff, et al. Being a Black Man: At the Corner of Progress & Peril. 2007. (ENG., Illus.). 384p. per. 13.95 *(978-1-58648-522-1(9))* PublicAffairs.

Wasniewski, Matthew, ed. Black Americans in Congress, 1870-2007. 3rd ed. 2008. (ENG., Illus.). 803p. 54.00 *(978-0-16-080194-5(X))* United States Government Printing Office.

Watson, Tommy. A Face of Courage: The Tommy Watson Story-How did he Survive? 2008. 156p. pap. 14.95 *(978-0-595-53056-4(7))* iUniverse, Inc.

Weaver, Harold D., Jr. Black Fire: African American Quakers on Spirituality & Human Rights. Weaver, Harold D., Jr., ed. 2011. (Illus.). 249p. (C). pap. 23.95 *(978-1-888305-88-3(6))* Quaker Pr. of Friends General Conference.

Webber, Christopher. American to the Backbone: The Life of James W. C. Pennington, the Fugitive Slave Who Became One of the First Black Abolitionists. 2011. (ENG.). 432p. 29.95 *(978-1-60598-175-8(3)*, 605175) Pegasus Bks.

Weiss, Ellen. Robert R. Taylor & Tuskegee: An African American Architect Designs for Booker T. Washington. 2011. (ENG.). 400p. 39.95 *(978-1-58838-248-1(6)*, NewSouth Bks.) NewSouth, Inc.

Weiss, Stuart L. The Curt Flood Story: The Man Behind the Myth. 2007. (Sports & American Culture Ser.). (ENG., Illus.). 272p. (gr. 9). 34.95 *(978-0-8262-1740-0(0))* Univ. of Missouri Pr.

Welch, Bruce. They Made Me an Addict: An American Tale. 2011. 316p. 25.74 ***(978-1-4634-1996-7(1))*** AuthorHouse.

Welch, Sidney Eugene. Soldiers of Martin Luther King: A Memoir from the Trenches of the Civil Rights Movement. 2007. 14.00 *(978-0-8059-8953-3(6))* Dorrance Publishing Co., Inc.

Wells, Tony. Black Man under the Deep Blue Se: Memoirs of a Black Commercial Diver in Southeast Asia. 2007. 224p. per. 24.95 *(978-1-4241-7422-5(8))* PublishAmerica, Inc.

West, Cornel. Brother West: Living & Loving Out Loud, A Memoir. 2010. (ENG.). 288p. pap. 15.95 *(978-1-4019-2190-3(6)*, Smiley Bks.) Hay Hse., Inc.

West, John. There Are Always Blue Skies... over the Dark Clouds. (ENG.). rev. ed. 2006. 210p. pap. 45.67 *(978-0-7575-2557-5(1))* 2nd rev. ed. 2011. 252p. pap. 45.67 *(978-0-7575-6197-9(7))* Kendall Hunt Publishing Co.

Wheeler, Jill C. Michelle Obama. 2009. (First Ladies Set 2 Ser.). (Illus.). 32p. (YA). (gr. 1-4). 25.65 *(978-1-60453-633-1(0))* ABDO Publishing Co.

Whitaker, Matthew C. Icons of Black America: Breaking Barriers & Crossing Boundaries, 3 vols. 2011. (Greenwood Icons Ser.). (Illus.). 1122p. 265.00 *(978-0-313-37642-9(5)*, GR7642) Greenwood Publishing Group, Inc.

Whitaker, Matthew C., ed. African American Icons of Sport: Triumph, Courage, & Excellence, 1 vol. 2008. (Greenwood Icons Ser.). (Illus.). 336p. 75.00 *(978-0-313-34028-4(5)*, GR4028, Greenwood Pr.) Greenwood Publishing Group, Inc.

Whitall, Susan. Fever: Little Willie John's Fast Life, Mysterious Death & the Birth of Soul - The Authorized Biography. 2011. (ENG., Illus.). 352p. reprint ed. 25.99 *(978-0-85768-137-9(0)*, Titan Bks.) Titan Bks. Ltd. GBR. Dist: Random Hse., Inc.

White, Alvin G. Education Is Not a Four-Letter Word. 2010. 118p. 24.95 *(978-1-59594-397-2(8)*, Wingspan Pr.) WingSpan Publishing.

White, Augustus A. & Chanoff, David. Seeing Patients: Unconscious Bias in Health Care. 2011. (Illus.). 352p. 27.95 *(978-0-674-04905-5(5))* Harvard Univ. Pr.

White, Bill. Uppity: My Untold Story about the Games People Play. (ENG., Illus.). 320p. 2012. pap. 15.99 ***(978-0-446-55526-5(6))*** 2011. 26.99 *(978-0-446-55525-8(8))* Grand Central Publishing.

White, Deborah Gray, ed. Telling Histories: Black Women Historians in the Ivory Tower. 2008. (ENG., Illus.). 304p. 66.50 *(978-0-8078-3201-1(4))*; pap. 23.95 *(978-0-8078-5881-3(1))* Univ. of North Carolina Pr.

The Whiteman Made Me Do It. Date not set. pap. 10.95 *(978-1-930329-02-7(4))* Khalilullah, Dr. Riza M.

Whitlock, Flint. Turbulence Before Takeoff: The Life & Times of Aviation Pioneer Marlon Dewitt Green. 2009. (Illus.). 420p. 24.95 *(978-1-934980-66-8(8))*; pap. 17.95 *(978-1-934980-67-5(6))* Cable Publishing.

Who's Who among African Americans. 26th ed. 2011. 324.00 *(978-1-4144-8126-5(8))* Cengage Gale.

Who's Who among African Americans 25th Ed. 25th rev. ed. 2010. (ENG.). 324.00 *(978-1-4144-6708-5(7))* Cengage Gale.

Who's Who in Black Cincinnati. 3rd ed. 2006. *(978-1-933879-05-5(X))* Who's Who Publishing Co.

Who's Who in Black Detroit: The Inaugural Edition. 2006. *(978-1-933879-07-9(6))* Who's Who Publishing Co.

Wiggins, David K., ed. Out of the Shadows: A Biographical History of African American Athletes. 2006. (Illus.). 459p. 34.95 *(978-1-55728-826-4(7))* Univ. of Arkansas Pr.

—Out of the Shadows: A Biogrpahical History of African American Athletes. 2008. (Illus.). 459p. per. 24.95 *(978-1-55728-876-9(3))* Univ. of Arkansas Pr.

Wild, Patricia. Way Opens: A Spiritual Journey. 2008. 212p. pap. 15.00 net. *(978-0-9801315-2-9(9))* Warwick Hse. Publishing.

Wilderson, Frank B., III. Incognegro: A Memoir of Exile & Apartheid. 2008. (ENG.). 500p. pap. 18.00 *(978-0-89608-783-5(2))* South End Pr.

—Incognegro: From Black Power to Apartheid & Back. 2007. 272p. 24.95 *(978-0-8070-7268-4(0))* Beacon Pr.

Williams, Niama Leslie. The Journey. 2007. 371p. 35.24 *(978-1-4303-1545-2(8))* Lulu Enterprises Inc.

Williams, Alton Allen & Williams, Bonita Byrd. O. D. Out of Darkness: God Is Real ... for Real. 2010. 196p. 29.99 *(978-1-4490-9496-6(1))*; (ENG.). pap. 15.99 *(978-1-4490-9497-3(X))* AuthorHouse.

Williams, Camilla & Shonekan, Stephanie. The Life of Camilla Williams, African American Classical Singer & Opera Diva. 2011. (Illus.). 219p. 119.95 *(978-0-7734-1483-9(5))* Mellen, Edwin Pr., The.

Williams, Carl Gregory. From Playing to Praying. 2008. 208p. pap. 25.00 *(978-1-4389-0004-9(X))* AuthorHouse.

Williams, Lea E. & Williams, Lea Esther. Servants of the People: The 1960s Legacy of African American Leadership. 2nd rev. ed. 2008. (ENG.). 320p. pap. 37.00 *(978-0-230-60633-3(4))* Palgrave Macmillan.

Williams, Neil. Surfing the Color Line. 2006. 161p. pap. 24.95 *(978-1-4241-1908-0(1))* PublishAmerica, Inc.

Williams, Randall. Johnnie: The Life of Johnnie Rebecca Carr. 2007. (Illus.). 60p. (J). pap. 9.95 *(978-1-60306-033-2(2))* NewSouth, Inc.

Williams, Rita. If the Creek Don't Rise. 2007. (ENG., Illus.). 336p. pap. 18.95 *(978-0-15-603285-8(6)*, Mariner Bks.) Houghton Mifflin Harcourt Trade & Reference Pubs.

Williams, Serena. On the Line. 2009. (ENG., Illus.). 272p. 26.99 *(978-0-446-55366-7(2))* Grand Central Publishing.

Williams, Ted & Witter, Bret. A Golden Voice: How Faith, Hard Work, & Humility Brought Me from the Streets to Salvation. 2012. (ENG., Illus.). 304p. (gr. 12). 26.00 ***(978-1-59240-714-9(5)***, Gotham) Penguin Group (USA) Inc.

Williams, Walter E. Up from the Projects: An Autobiography. 2010. (Hoover inst press Publication). (ENG.). 150p. 24.95 *(978-0-8179-1254-3(1))*; pap. 14.95 *(978-0-8179-1255-0(X))* Hoover Institution Pr.

Williamson, Maurice. Mixed Message. 2006. pap. 12.75 *(978-0-9786296-7-0(1))* Hudson Bks.

Williamson, Vet. Purposes A Real Love Story. 2007. 73p. pap. 16.95 *(978-1-4241-5312-1(3))* PublishAmerica, Inc.

Willie E. Lowther: From Locust Grove to Harlem: the Journey of My Life. 2008. (Illus.). 328p. 36.95 *(978-0-9742773-8-7(X))* Soleil Pr.

Willis, Deborah, ed. Let Your Motto Be Resistance: African American Portraits. 2008. (ENG.). 176p. pap. 19.95 *(978-1-58834-246-1(8))* Smithsonian Institution Pr.

Willis, Jan. Dreaming Me: Black, Baptist, & Buddhist - One Woman's Spiritual Journey. 2008. (ENG.). 330p. pap. 16.95 *(978-0-86171-548-0(9))* Wisdom Pubns.

Wilson, John. Jackie Robinson & the American Dilemma. 2009. (ENG.). 224p. (C). pap. 25.20 *(978-0-205-59848-9(X)*, Prentice Hall) Prentice Hall PTR.

Wilson, Jon & Peck, Rosalie. St. Petersburg's Historic African American Neighborhoods: Community, Culture, & Connection. 2008. pap. 19.99 *(978-1-59629-279-6(2))* History Pr., The.

Wilson, Jr. The 4th Marking Period: A Memoir of an African American Male Guidance Counselor. 2008. 88p. pap. 10.50 *(978-1-4389-1918-8(2))* AuthorHouse.

Winfrey, Thomas. My Life: An Extraordinary Journey. 2006. 16.00 *(978-0-8059-7178-1(5))* Dorrance Publishing Co., Inc.

Winkey, Travis. The Prince of Fashion: A Look into the World of Travis Winkey. 2008. 293p. pap. 27.95 *(978-1-60610-646-4(5))* PublishAmerica, Inc.

Wolff, Mishna. I'm Down: A Memoir. (ENG., Illus.). 288p. 2010. pap. 13.99 *(978-0-312-37909-4(9)*, St. Martin's Griffin) 2009. 23.95 *(978-0-312-37855-4(6))* St. Martin's Pr.

Wood, Peggy & Brown, Parker. Something Must Be Done: One Black. 2006. (Illus.). 153p. 9.95 *(978-0-8156-0877-6(2))* Syracuse Univ. Pr.

Work Projects Administration. Slave Narratives. 2008. 132p. 24.99 *(978-0-554-24057-2(2))*; 288p. 28.99 *(978-0-554-25764-8(5))*; 132p. 21.99 *(978-0-554-33360-1(0))*; 288p. 25.99 *(978-0-554-35067-7(X))*; 372p. 29.99 *(978-0-554-38381-1(0))*; 148p. 24.99 *(978-0-554-24114-2(5))*; 148p. 21.99 *(978-0-554-33417-2(8))*; 372p. 31.99 *(978-0-554-29078-2(2))* BiblioBazaar.

—Slave Narratives: A Folk History of Slavery in the United States from Interviews with Former Slaves Arkansas Narratives, Part 6. 2007. (ENG.). 254p. pap. 21.99 *(978-1-4264-5587-2(9))* 2006. 292p. pap. 23.99 *(978-1-4264-5635-0(2))* BiblioBazaar.

—Slave Narratives: A Folk History of Slavery in the United States from Interviews with Former Slaves Florida Narratives. Lt. ed. 2007. (ENG.). 258p. pap. 23.99 *(978-1-4264-5999-3(8))* BiblioBazaar.

—Slave Narratives, Volume 3: A Folk History of Slavery in the United States from Interviews with Former Slaves Florida Narratives. 2007. (ENG.). 230p. pap. 20.99 *(978-1-4264-5931-3(9))* BiblioBazaar.

—Slave Narratives, Volume VII: A Folk History of Slavery in the United States from Interviews with Former Slaves. 2006. 114p. pap. 18.99 *(978-1-4264-5671-8(9))* 2007. (ENG.). 128p. pap. 19.99 *(978-1-4264-5716-6(2))* BiblioBazaar.

Wormser, Richard. Worse Than Slavery. Date not set. mass mkt. *(978-0-312-93915-6(6)*, St. Martin's Paperbacks) St. Martin's Pr.

Wright, Richard & Wright, Richard. Black Boy. 2008. (P. S. Ser.). (ENG.). 464p. pap. 16.99 *(978-0-06-144308-4(5)*, HarperPerennial) HarperCollins Pubs.

Wynn, Jimmy & McCurdy, Bill. Toy Cannon: The Autobiography of Baseball's Jimmy Wynn. 2010. (ENG., Illus.). 236p. pap. 29.95 *(978-0-7864-5856-1(9))* McFarland & Co., Inc. Pubs.

Xu, Dejin. Race & Form: Towards a Contextualized Narratology of African American Autobiography. 226p. pap. 47.95 *(978-3-03911-003-2(9))* Lang, Peter Publishing, Inc.

Yaeger, Don. Tarnished Heisman: Did Reggie Bush Turn His Final College Season into a Six-Figure Job? 2008. (ENG., Illus.). 256p. pap. 15.00 *(978-1-4165-7819-2(6))* Gallery Pr., The IRL. Dist: Simon & Schuster, Inc.

Yakima, Cheyenne Valentino. The Iceman Speaks. 2010. 196p. 29.99 *(978-1-4535-3264-5(1))* Xlibris Corp.

Young, Vershawn Ashanti. Your Average Nigga: Performing Race, Literacy, & Masculinity. 2007. pap. 19.95 *(978-0-8143-3248-1(X))* Wayne State Univ. Pr.

Youree, Barbara, et al. Courageous Journey: Walking the Lost Boys' Path from the Sudan to America. 2008. (ENG., Illus.). 330p. 24.95 *(978-0-88282-334-8(5))* New Horizon Pr. Pubs., Inc.

Zang, David W. Fleetwood Walker's Divided Heart. Zang, David W., ed. 2006. cd-rom 39.95 *(978-0-9779883-4-1(1))* Legacy Audio Bks.

AFRICAN AMERICANS—BIOGRAPHY—JUVENILE LITERATURE

Condino, Meggin, ed. African American Eras Library Set: Segregation to Civil Rights Times, 4 vols. 2010. 960p. 292.00 *(978-1-4144-3596-1(7))* Cengage Gale.

Hoose, Phillip. Claudette Colvin: Twice Toward Justice. 2010. lib. bdg. 20.85 ***(978-0-606-23188-6(9)**,* Turtleback) Turtleback Bks.

Macceca, Stephanie & Doak, Robin S. George Washington Carver: Agriculture Pioneer. 2010. (Mission: Science Biographies Ser.). (ENG.). 40p. (gr. 5-6). lib. bdg. 27.99 *(978-0-7565-4305-1(3)*, Exploring Science) Compass Point Bks.

Martin, Michael. Harriet Tubman & the Underground Railroad. 2008. (Graphic History Ser.). (ENG.). (gr. 3-4). 34.65 *(978-1-4296-2134-2(6))* Capstone Digital.

Whiting, Jim. W. E. B. du Bois: Civil Rights Activist, Author, Historian. 2010. (Transcending Race in America Ser.). (Illus.). 64p. (YA). (gr. 4-8). lib. bdg. 22.95 *(978-1-4222-1618-7(7))* Mason Crest Pubs.

AFRICAN AMERICANS—CIVIL RIGHTS

see also African Americans—Suffrage; March on Washington for Jobs and Freedom, 1963; Poor People's Campaign

Adams, Luther. Way up North in Louisville: African American Migration in the Urban South, 1930-1970. 2010. (John Hope Franklin Series in African American History & Culture Ser.). (ENG., Illus.). 320p. 49.95 *(978-0-8078-3422-0(X))* Univ. of North Carolina Pr.

Adamson, John, ed. The English Civil War: Conflict & Contexts, 1640-49. 2008. (Problems in Focus Ser.). (ENG.). 256p. pap. 43.00 *(978-0-333-98656-1(3))* Palgrave Macmillan.

Adamson, John & Adamson, J. S. A. The English Civil War: Conflict & Contexts, 1640-49. 2008. (Problems in Focus Ser.). (ENG.). 336p. 115.00 *(978-0-333-98655-4(5))* Palgrave Macmillan.

African-American Farmers Benefit Relief ACT of 2007 & the Pigford Claims Remedy ACT of 2007: Hearing Before the Subcommittee on the Constitution, Civil Rights, & Civil Liberties of the Committee on the Judiciary, House of Representatives, One Hundred Tenth Congress, First Session, on H.R. 558 & H.R. 899, June 21, 2007. 2007. (Illus.). iv, 153p. *(978-0-16-079622-7(9)*, 552-070-36579-6) United States Government Printing Office.

Agee, Gary B. A Cry for Justice: Daniel Rudd & His Life in Black Catholicism, Journalism, & Activism, 1854-1933. 2011. 256p. 39.95 ***(978-1-55728-975-9(1))*** Univ. of Arkansas Pr.

Alderman, Derek H. & Dwyer, Owen J. Civil Rights Memorials & the Geography of Memory. 2008. (Center Books on the American South Ser.). (ENG., Illus.). 224p. pap. 27.50 *(978-1-930066-83-0(X))*; 152p. lib. bdg. 49.50 *(978-1-930066-71-7(6))* Univ. of Georgia Pr.

Aldridge, Daniel W. Becoming American: The African American Quest for Civil Rights, 1861-1976. 2011. (C). 24.95 *(978-0-88295-260-2(3))* Davidson, Harlan Inc.

Alexander, Adele Logan. Parallel Worlds: The Remarkable Gibbs-Hunts & the Enduring (In)Significance of Melanin. (ENG., Illus.). 416p. 2012. pap. 19.95 ***(978-0-8139-3245-3(9))*** 2010. (gr. 17). 29.95 *(978-0-8139-2887-6(7))* Univ. Pr. of Virginia.

Alexander, Shawn Leigh. An Army of Lions: The Civil Rights Struggle Before the NAACP. 2011. (Politics & Culture in Modern America Ser.). (Illus.). 408p. (C). 49.95 ***(978-0-8122-4375-8(7))*** Univ. of Pennsylvania Pr.

Alexander, Shawn Leigh, ed. T. Thomas Fortune, the Afro-American Agitator: A Collection of Writings, 1880-1928. 2010. (New Perspectives on the History of the South Ser.). (ENG., Illus.). 342p. pap. 29.95 *(978-0-8130-3548-2(1))* Univ. Pr. of Florida.

Ali, Omar H. In the Balance of Power: Independent Black Politics & Third-Party Movements in the United States. 2008. (ENG.). 216p. 39.95 *(978-0-8214-1806-2(8))*; pap. 19.95 *(978-0-8214-1807-9(6))* Ohio Univ. Pr.

Alkebulan, Paul. Survival Pending Revolution: The History of the Black Panther Party. 2nd ed. 2007. (ENG.). 200p. 29.95 *(978-0-8173-1549-8(7))* Univ. of Alabama Pr.

Alston, Judy A. & McClellan, Patricia A. Herstories: Leading with the Lessons of the Lives of Black Women Activists. 2011. (C). pap. 33.95 *(978-1-4331-1193-8(4))*; 129.95 *(978-1-4331-1192-1(6))* Lang, Peter Publishing, Inc.

Anderson, Jennifer Joline. The Civil Rights Movement. 2011. (Essential Events Set 7 Ser.). (Illus.). 112p. (YA). (gr. 7-12). 34.22 *(978-1-61783-098-3(4))* ABDO Publishing Co.

Anderson, Kevin R. Agitations: Ideologies & Strategies in African American Politics. 2010. (ENG.). 263p. 34.95 *(978-1-55728-926-1(3))* Univ. of Arkansas Pr.

Arend, Orissa. Showdown in Desire: The Black Panthers Take a Stand in New Orleans. 2010. (ENG., Illus.). 294p. pap. 19.95 *(978-1-55728-896-7(6))* Univ. of Arkansas Pr.

Aretha, David. The Montgomery Bus Boycott. 2008. (Civil Rights Movement Ser.). 128p. (J). (gr. 4-7). 28.95 *(978-1-59935-020-2(3))* Reynolds, Morgan Inc.

Armstrong, Thomas M. & Bell, Natalie R. Autobiography of a Freedom Rider: My Life as a Foot Soldier for Civil Rights. 2011. (ENG.). 216p. pap. 14.95 *(978-0-7573-1603-6(4))* Health Communications, Inc.

Arsenault, Raymond. Freedom Riders: 1961 & the Struggle for Racial Justice, 1 vol. 2nd abr. ed. 2011. (ENG., Illus.). 352p. pap. 15.95 *(978-0-19-975431-1(4))* Oxford Univ. Pr., Inc.

—The Sound of Freedom: Marian Anderson, the Lincoln Memorial, & the Concert That Awakened America. (ENG., Illus.). 320p. 2010. pap. 18.00 *(978-1-60819-056-0(0))* 2009. 25.00 *(978-1-59691-578-7(1))* Bloomsbury Publishing.

Arthur, John. Race, Equality, & the Burdens of History. 2007. (ENG.). 340p. (C). 83.99 *(978-0-521-87937-8(X))*; per. 27.99 *(978-0-521-70495-3(2))* Cambridge Univ. Pr.

Asante, Molefi Kete. Erasing Racism: The Survival of the American Nation. 2nd rev. ed. 2009. (ENG., Illus.). 325p. pap. 19.00 *(978-1-59102-765-2(9))* Prometheus Bks., Pubs.

Asch, Chris Myers. The Senator & the Sharecropper: The Freedom Struggles of James O. Eastland & Fannie Lou Hamer. 2011. (ENG., Illus.). 392p. pap. 24.95 *(978-0-8078-7202-4(4))* Univ. of North Carolina Pr.

Asch, Christopher Myers. The Senator & the Sharecropper: The Freedom Struggles of James O. Eastland & Fannie Lou Hamer. 2008. (ENG., Illus.). 368p. 27.95 *(978-1-59558-332-1(7))* New Pr., The.

Ashmore, Susan Youngblood. Carry It On: The War on Poverty & the Civil Rights Movement in Alabama, 1964-1972. 2008. (ENG., Illus.). 416p. 69.95 *(978-0-8203-3007-5(8))*; pap. 24.95 *(978-0-8203-3051-8(5))* Univ. of Georgia Pr.

Aucoin, Brent J. A Rift in the Clouds: Race & the Southern Federal Judiciary, 1900-1910. 2007. (Illus.). 169p. 37.50 *(978-1-55728-849-3(6))* Univ. of Arkansas Pr.

Bacon, Jacqueline. Freedom's Journal: The First African-American Newspaper. 2007. (ENG.). 336p. per. 31.50 *(978-0-7391-1894-8(3))*; 83.99 *(978-0-7391-1893-1(5))* Lexington Bks.

Bacon, Margaret Hope. But One Race: The Life of Robert Purvis. (Excelsior Editions Ser.). (Illus.). 2010. 293p. pap. 24.95 *(978-0-7914-7008-4(3)*, Suny Pr.) 2007. 279p. 36.00 *(978-0-7914-7007-7(5))* State Univ. of New York Pr.

Badger, Anthony J. New Deal/New South: An Anthony J. Badger Reader. 2007. 270p. pr. 19.95 *(978-1-55728-844-8(5))* Univ. of Arkansas Pr.

Badger, Anthony J. & Badger, Tony. New Deal / New South: An Anthony J. Badger Reader. 2007. 320p. 64.95 *(978-1-55728-843-1(7))* Univ. of Arkansas Pr.

Bailey, D'Army. The Education of a Black Radical: A Southern Civil Rights Activist's Journey, 1959-1964. 2009. 264p. 28.00 *(978-0-8071-3476-4(7))* Louisiana State Univ. Pr.

Bailey, Eric J. The Cultural Rights Movement: Fulfilling the Promise of Civil Rights for African Americans. 2010. 216p. 44.95 *(978-0-313-36009-1(X)*, C36009, Praeger Pubs.) Greenwood Publishing Group, Inc.

Baker, Houston A. Betrayal: How Black Intellectuals Have Abandoned the Ideals of the Civil Rights Era. 2010. (ENG.). 272p. (gr. 17). pap. 18.95 *(978-0-231-13965-6(9))* Columbia Univ. Pr.

Baldwin, James. Notes of a Native Son. 2012. (ENG.). 192p. pap. 15.00 *(978-0-8070-0623-8(8))* Beacon Pr.

Balfour, Katharine Lawrence & Balfour, Lawrie. Democracy's Reconstruction: Thinking Politically with W. E. B. du Bois. 2011. (Transgressing Boundaries: Studies in Black Politics & Black Communities Ser.). (ENG.). 240p. 39.95 *(978-0-19-537729-3(X))* Oxford Univ. Pr., Inc.

Banner-Haley, Charles Pete T. From du Bois to Obama: African American Intellectuals in the Public Forum. 2010. (ENG.). 176p. 24.95 *(978-0-8093-2979-3(4))* Southern Illinois Univ. Pr.

Bass, Amy. Those about Him Remained Silent: The Battle over W. E. B. du Bois. 2009. (ENG., Illus.). 232p. 24.95 *(978-0-8166-4495-7(0))* Univ. of Minnesota Pr.

Battle, Randy, et al. The Great Pool Jump & Other Stories from the Civil Rights Movement in Southwest Georgia. de Lissovoy, Peter, ed. 2010. (ENG., Illus.). 280p. pap. 25.00 net. *(978-0-9844139-1-1(X))* YouArePerfectPress.

Behnken, Brian. Fighting Their Own Battles: Mexican Americans, African Americans, & the Struggle for Civil Rights in Texas. 2011. (ENG., Illus.). 352p. 45.00 *(978-0-8078-3478-7(5))* Univ. of North Carolina Pr.

Behnken, Brian D., ed. & intro. The Struggle in Black & Brown: African American & Mexican American Relations during the Civil Rights Era. 2012. (Justice & Social Inquiry Ser.). (ENG., Illus.). 312p. pap. 35.00 *(978-0-8032-6271-3(X))* Univ. of Nebraska Pr.

Berger, Martin A. Seeing through Race: A Reinterpretation of Civil Rights Photography. 2011. (ENG., Illus.). 208p. 60.00 *(978-0-520-26863-0(6))*; pap. 27.50 *(978-0-520-26864-7(4))* Univ. of California Pr.

Berry, Mary Frances. And Justice for All: The United States Commission on Civil Rights & the Continuing Struggle for Freedom in America. 2009. (ENG., Illus.). 448p. 30.00 *(978-0-307-26320-9(7)*, Knopf) Knopf Doubleday Publishing Group.

Biographiq. Jesse Jackson - Civil Rights Activist & Minister. 2008. 52p. pap. 9.99 *(978-1-59986-069-5(4)*, Biographiq) Filiquarian Publishing, LLC.

Black, Samuel W., ed. Soul Soldiers: African Americans & the Vietnam Era. ltd. ed. 2006. (Illus.). 224p. 29.95 *(978-0-936340-15-9(0))* Historical Society of Western Pennsylvania.

Blackmon, Douglas A. Slavery by Another Name: The Re-Enslavement of Black Americans from the Civil War to World War II. 2009. (ENG., Illus.). 496p. pap. 17.00 *(978-0-385-72270-4(2)*, Anchor) Knopf Doubleday Publishing Group.

Blair, Lewis H. Prosperity of the South Dependent upon the Elevation of the Negro. 147p. reprint ed. 88.00 *(978-0-7222-9704-9(1))* Library Reprints, Inc.

Blake, John. Children of the Movement: The Sons & Daughters of Martin Luther King Jr., Malcolm X, Elijah Muhammad, George Wallace, Andrew Young, Julian Bond, Stokely Carmichael, Bob Moses, James Chaney, Elaine Brown, & Others Reveal How the Civil Rights Movement Tested & Transformed Thei. 2007. (ENG., Illus.). 272p. per. 14.95 *(978-1-55652-678-7(4)*, Hill, Lawrence Bks.) Chicago Review Pr., Inc.

Boyce Davies, Carole, ed. Claudia Jones: Beyond Containment. 2011. (Illus.). 240p. pap. 24.95 *(978-0-9562401-6-3(X))* Clarke, Ayebia Publishing, Ltd. GBR. Dist: Rienner, Lynne Pubs.

Boyd, Tim S. R. Georgia Democrats, the Civil Rights Movement, & the Shaping of the New South. 2012. (ENG., Illus.). 288p. 74.95 *(978-0-8130-3765-3(4))* Univ. Pr. of Florida.

Bracey, Earnest N. Fannie Lou Hamer: The Life of a Civil Rights Icon. 2011. (ENG., Illus.). 209p. pap. 38.00 *(978-0-7864-6030-4(X))* McFarland & Co., Inc. Pubs.

Branch, Taylor. At Canaan's Edge: America in the King Years, 1965-68. 2007. (ENG., Illus.). 1056p. pap. 20.00 *(978-0-684-85713-8(8))* Simon & Schuster.

Brooks, Karl Boyd, ed. The Environmental Legacy of Harry S. Truman. 2009. (Truman Legacy Ser.). (ENG., Illus.). 184p. pap. 28.95 *(978-1-931112-93-2(2))* Truman State Univ. Pr.

Brooks, Maegan Parker & Houck, Davis W., eds. The Speeches of Fannie Lou Hamer: To Tell It Like It Is. 2010. (Margaret Walker Alexander Series in African American Studies). (ENG.). 288p. 38.00 *(978-1-60473-822-3(7))* Univ. Pr. of Mississippi.

Brooks, Pamela E. Boycotts, Buses, & Passes: Black Women's Resistance in the U. S. South & South Africa. 2008. (ENG., Illus.). 320p. pap. 29.95 *(978-1-55849-678-1(5))* Univ. of Massachusetts Pr.

—Boycotts, Buses, & Passes: Black Women's Resistance in the U.S. South & South Africa. 2008. (Illus.). 320p. lib. bdg. 98.00 net. *(978-1-55849-676-7(9))* Univ. of Massachusetts Pr.

Brooks, Roy L. Racial Justice in the Age of Obama. 2009. (ENG., Illus.). 262p. (C). 28.95 *(978-0-691-14198-5(3))* Princeton Univ. Pr.

Brown, David & Webb, Clive. Race in the American South: From Slavery to Civil Rights. 2007. (ENG.). 384p. per. 24.95 *(978-0-8130-3203-0(2))* Univ. Pr. of Florida.

Brown, Jacqueline Elaine. African American Responses to American Presidential Inaugural Addresses: A Counterpoint of Rhetorical Traditions. 2010. 208p. 109.95 *(978-0-7734-1317-7(0))* Mellen, Edwin Pr., The.

Brown, Nikki L. M. & Stentiford, Barry M. The Jim Crow Encyclopedia: Greenwood Milestones in African American History, 2 vols. Brown, Nikki L. M. & Stentiford, Barry M., eds. 2008. (Greenwood Milestones in African American History Ser.). (Illus.). 952p. 225.00 *(978-0-313-34181-6(8)*, GR4181) Greenwood Publishing Group, Inc.

Browne-Marshall, Gloria. Race, Law, & American Society 1607 to Present. 2007. (Criminology & Justice Studies). (Illus.). (ENG.). 416p. 145.00 *(978-0-415-95293-4(X))*; 432p. pap. 41.95 *(978-0-415-95294-1(8))* Routledge.

Bruce, Tap. The Fort Pillow Massacre: North, South, & the Status of African-Americans in the Civil War Era. 2012. (ENG.). 224p. 130.00 ***(978-0-415-80863-7(4))***; pap. 27.95 ***(978-0-415-80864-4(2))*** Routledge.

Bryant, Nick. The Bystander: John F. Kennedy & the Struggle for Black Equality. 2007. (ENG., Illus.). 576p. per. 16.95 *(978-0-465-00827-8(5))* Basic Bks.

Burns, Rebecca C. Rage in the Gate City: The Story of the 1906 Atlanta Race Riot. rev. ed. 2009. (ENG.). 232p. pap. 19.95 *(978-0-8203-3307-6(7))* Univ. of Georgia Pr.

Burrow, Rufus, Jr. Martin Luther King Jr. for Armchair Theologians. 2009. (Armchair Theologians Ser.). (ENG.). 200p. pap. 17.00 *(978-0-664-23284-9(1))* Westminster John Knox Pr.

Burton, Orville Vernon, et al, eds. The Struggle for Equality: Essays on Sectional Conflict, the Civil War, & the Long Reconstruction. 2011. (ENG., Illus.). 320p. (gr. 17). 45.00 *(978-0-8139-3173-9(8))* Univ. Pr. of Virginia.

Burton, Orville Vernon & O'Brien, David, eds. Remembering Brown at Fifty: The University of Illinois Commemorates Brown V. Board of Education. 2009. (ENG.). 456p. pap. 35.00 *(978-0-252-07665-7(6))* Univ. of Illinois Pr.

Burton, Orville Vernon, et al. The Struggle for Equality: Essays on Sectional Conflict, the Civil War, & the Long Reconstruction. 2011. E-Book *(978-0-8139-3177-7(0))* Univ. Pr. of Virginia.

Cabbil, Lila, et al, eds. Accountability & White Anti-racist Organizing: Stories from Our Work. 2010. 256p. pap. 17.95 *(978-1-934390-32-0(1))* Crandall, Dostie & Douglas Bks., Inc.

Carawan, Guy & Carawan, Candie, eds. Sing for Freedom: The Story of the Civil Rights Movement Through Its Songs. 2008. (ENG., Illus.). 266p. pap. 21.95 *(978-1-58838-193-4(5)*, NewSouth Bks.) NewSouth, Inc.

Carson, Clayborne, et al. The Martin Luther King, Jr. Encyclopedia, 1 vol. 2008. (Illus.). 456p. 65.00 *(978-0-313-29440-2(2)*, GR9440, Greenwood Pr.) Greenwood Publishing Group, Inc.

Cashin, Sheryll. The Agitator's Daughter: A Memoir of Four Generations of One Extraordinary African-American Family. 2008. (ENG., Illus.). 288p. 26.00 *(978-1-58648-422-4(2))* PublicAffairs.

Catsam, Derek Charles. Freedom's Main Line: The Journey of Reconciliation & the Freedom Rides. (Civil Rights & the Struggle for Black Equality in the Twentieth Century Ser.). (ENG.). 436p. 2011. pap. 25.00 *(978-0-8131-3377-5(7))* 2008. 50.00 *(978-0-8131-2511-4(1))* Univ. Pr. of Kentucky.

Chabot, Sean. Transnational Roots of the Civil Rights Movement: African American Explorations of the Gandhian Repertoire. 2012. E-Book ***(978-0-7391-4579-1(7))*** 2011. (ENG.). 220p. (gr. 17). 70.00 ***(978-0-7391-4577-7(0))*** Lexington Bks.

Chafe, William H., et al, eds. Remembering Jim Crow: African Americans Tell about Life in the Segregated South. 2008. (ENG.). 346p. pap. 19.95 *(978-1-59558-334-5(3))* New Pr., The.

Clarke, Roderick O. Manifest. 2010. 80p. pap. 15.49 *(978-1-4490-0070-7(3))* AuthorHouse.

Clawson, Rosalee A. & Waltenburg, Eric N. Legacy & Legitimacy: Black Americans & the Supreme Court. 2008. (ENG., Illus.). 232p. pap. 24.95 *(978-1-59213-903-3(5))* Temple Univ. Pr.

Clawson, Rosalee A., et al. Legacy & Legitimacy: Black Americans & the Supreme Court. 2008. (ENG., Illus.). 232p. 73.50 *(978-1-59213-902-6(7))* Temple Univ. Pr.

Cobb, William Jelani. The Substance of Hope: Barack Obama & the Paradox of Progress. 2010. (ENG., Illus.). 208p. 23.00 *(978-0-8027-1739-9(X))* Walker & Co.

Colaiaco, James A. Frederick Douglass & the Fourth of July. 2007. (ENG.). 256p. pap. 16.95 *(978-1-4039-8072-4(1))* Palgrave Macmillan.

Conyers, James L., Jr., ed. Engines of the Black Power Movement: Essays on the Influence of Civil Rights Actions, Arts, & Islam. 2006. (ENG., Illus.). 296p. per. 39.95 *(978-0-7864-2540-2(7))* McFarland & Co., Inc. Pubs.

Cook, Robert J. Troubled Commemoration: The American Civil War Centennial, 1961-1965. (Making the Modern South Ser.). 2011. 320p. pap. 22.50 ***(978-0-8071-4365-0(0))*** 2007. 300p. 45.00 *(978-0-8071-3227-2(6))* Louisiana State Univ. Pr.

Copeland, Jeffrey S. Olivia's Story: The Conspiracy of Heroes Behind Shelley V. Kraemer. 2010. (ENG.). 365p. 19.95 *(978-1-55778-884-9(7))* Paragon Hse. Pubs.

Cose, Ellis. The End of Anger: A New Generation's Take on Race & Rage. (ENG.). 2012. 224p. pap. 14.99 ***(978-0-06-199856-0(7))*** 2011. 320p. 24.99 *(978-0-06-199855-3(9))* HarperCollins Pubs. (Ecco).

Countryman, Matthew J. Up South: Civil Rights & Black Power in Philadelphia. 2007. (Politics & Culture in Modern America Ser.). (Illus.). 432p. (C). per. 24.95 *(978-0-8122-2002-5(1))* Univ. of Pennsylvania Pr.

Counts, Ira Wilmer. A Life Is More Than a Moment: The Desegregation of Little Rock's Central High. 50th anniv. ed. 2007. (ENG., Illus.). 104p. pap. 19.95 (978-0-253-21793-6(8), 0253217938) Indiana Univ. Pr.

Covin, David. Black Politics after the Civil Rights Movement: Activity & Beliefs in Sacramento, 1970-2000. 2009. (ENG., Illus.). 236p. pap. 49.95 (978-0-7864-4258-4(1)) McFarland & Co., Inc. Pubs.

Cox, Julian. Road to Freedom: Photographs from the Civil Rights Movement, 1956-1968. 2008. (Illus.). 152p. 35.00 (978-1-932543-23-0(6)) High Museum of Art.

—Road to Freedom: Photographs of the Civil Rights Movement, 1956-1968. 2008. pap. 25.00 (978-1-932543-21-6(X)) High Museum of Art.

Cox, LaWanda & Cox, John H. Politics, Principle, & Prejudice 1865-1866: Dilemma of Reconstruction America. 2008. 320p. pap. 31.00 (978-1-59740-408-2(X)) ACLS Humanities E-Book.

Crisis of Conscience: Arkansas Methodists & the Civil Rights Struggle. 2007. (Illus.). 203p. per. 18.50 (978-0-9708574-4-6(6)) Butler Ctr. for Arkansas Studies.

Crosby, Emilye, ed. Civil Rights History from the Ground Up: Local Struggles, a National Movement. 2011. (ENG., Illus.). 510p. 69.95 (978-0-8203-2963-5(0)); pap. 26.95 (978-0-8203-3865-1(6)) Univ. of Georgia Pr.

Daugherity, Brian J. & Bolton, Charles C., eds. With All Deliberate Speed: Implementing Brown V. Board of Education. 2008. 300p. (C). pap. 27.50 (978-1-55728-869-1(0)); 339p. 64.95 (978-1-55728-868-4(2)) Univ. of Arkansas Pr.

Davies, David R., ed. The Press & Race: Mississippi Journalists Confront the Movement. 2007. (ENG., Illus.). 312p. per. 25.00 (978-1-934110-52-2(3)) Univ. Pr. of Mississippi.

Davis, Hugh. We Will Be Satisfied with Nothing Less: The African American Struggle for Equal Rights in the North during Reconstruction. 2011. 232p. 45.00 **(978-0-8014-5009-9(8))** Cornell Univ. Pr.

de Jong, Greta. Invisible Enemy: The African American Freedom Struggle after 1965. 2010. (America's Recent Past Ser.). (ENG., Illus.). 256p. pap. 32.95 (978-1-4051-6718-5(1), Wiley-Blackwell) Wiley, John & Sons, Inc.

de Schweinitz, Rebecca. If We Could Change the World: Young People & America's Long Struggle for Racial Equality. 2011. (ENG., Illus.). 400p. pap. 24.95 (978-0-8078-7215-4(6)) Univ. of North Carolina Pr.

Debord, Guy. A Sick Planet. Nicholson-Smith, Donald, tr. from FRE. 2008. (SB-the French List Ser.). (Illus.). 104p. 60.00 (978-1-905422-68-5(7)) Seagull Bks. London Ltd. GBR. Dist: Chicago Distribution Ctr.

—A Sick Planet. Nicholson-Smith, Donald, tr. from FRE. 2008. (SB-the French List Ser.). (ENG., Illus.). 104p. pap. 16.95 (978-1-905422-69-2(5)) Seagull Bks. GBR. Dist: Chicago Distribution Ctr.

Delmont, Matthew F. The Nicest Kids in Town: American Bandstand, Rock 'n' Roll, & the Struggle for Civil Rights in 1950s Philadelphia. 2012. (American Crossroads Ser.). (ENG., Illus.). 312p. 65.00 **(978-0-520-27207-1(2))**; pap. 27.95 **(978-0-520-27208-8(0))** Univ. of California Pr.

Dierenfield, Bruce J. The Civil Rights Movement. rev. ed. 2008. (Seminar Studies in History Ser.). (ENG., Illus.). 220p. (C). pap. 28.20 (978-1-4058-7435-9(X)) Longman Publishing Group.

Dillard, Angela D. Faith in the City: Preaching Radical Social Change in Detroit. 2007. (ENG., Illus.). 416p. per. 26.95 (978-0-472-03207-5(0)) Univ. of Michigan Pr.

Dillard, Chet. The Final Curtain: Burning Mississippi by the Fbi. 2007. 224p. 24.95 (978-1-4327-0521-3(0)); per. 14.95 (978-1-4327-0443-8(5)) Outskirts Pr., Inc.

Dixie, Quinton & Eisenstadt, Peter. Visions of a Better World: Howard Thurman's Pilgrimage to India & the Origins of African American Nonviolence. 2011. (ENG.). 272p. 34.95 (978-0-8070-0045-8(0)) Beacon Pr.

Dixie, Quinton & Eisenstadt, Peter. Visions of a Better World: Howard Thurman's Pilgrimage to India & the Origins of African American Nonviolence. 2013. (ENG.). pap. 18.00 **(978-0-8070-0172-1(4))** Beacon Pr.

Dorsey, Mignette Y. Patrick. Speak Truth to Power: The Story of Charles Patrick, a Civil Rights Pioneer. 2nd ed. 2010. (Alabama Fire Ant Ser.). (ENG., Illus.). 152p. pap. 16.00 (978-0-8173-5556-2(1)) Univ. of Alabama Pr.

Douglas, Robert C. The Exercise of Informal Power within the Church of Christ: Black Civil Rights, Muted Justice, & Denominational Politics. 2008. 192p. 99.95 (978-0-7734-5012-7(2)) Mellen, Edwin Pr., The.

Douglass, Frederick. Collected Articles of Fredrick Douglass. 2007. 48p. per. 6.95 (978-1-60424-008-5(3), Book Jungle) Standard Pubns., Inc.

Douglass, Frederick. In the Words of Frederick Douglass: Quotations from Liberty's Champion. McKivigan, John R. & Kaufman, Heather L., eds. 2011. (Illus.). 288p. 22.95 **(978-0-8014-4790-7(9))** Cornell Univ. Pr.

Drinkard, Dorothy. Indomitable: A Biography of James Farmer & the Civil Rights Movement. 2012. (ENG., Illus.). 368p. 27.99 (978-0-9801744-4-1(9)) Barnhardt & Ashe Publishing, Inc.

Du Bois, W. E. B. John Brown. 406p. reprint ed. 98.00 (978-0-7222-9835-0(8)); 98.00 (978-0-7222-8437-7(3)) Library Reprints, Inc.

—John Brown. 2007. (978-0-19-532574-4(5)) Oxford Univ. Pr., Inc.

Dudziak, Mary L. Cold War Civil Rights - Race & the Image of American Democracy. 2011. (Politics & Society in Twentieth Century America Ser.). (ENG., Illus.). 352p. (C). pap. 24.95 **(978-0-691-15243-1(8))** Princeton Univ. Pr.

Durham, Michael S. & Moore, Charles. Powerful Days: The Civil Rights Photography of Charles Moore. 2nd ed. 2007. (ENG., Illus.). 208p. pap. 29.95 (978-0-8173-5481-7(6)) Univ. of Alabama Pr.

Dyja, Thomas. Walter White: The Dilemma of Black Identity in America. 2010. (ENG.). 224p. pap. 15.95 (978-1-56663-865-4(8)) Dee, Ivan R. Pub.

Dyson, Michael Eric. Come Hell or High Water: Hurricane Katrina & the Color of Disaster. 2007. cd-rom 49.95 (978-0-9779883-5-8(X)) Legacy Audio Bks.

Eagles, Charles W. The Price of Defiance: James Meredith & the Integration of Ole Miss. 2009. (ENG., Illus.). 584p. 36.95 (978-0-8078-3273-8(1)) Univ. of North Carolina Pr.

EBONY Magazine Staff. Martin Luther King Jr. 1929-1968: An Ebony Picture Biography. 2007. (ENG., Illus.). 80p. pap. 14.95 (978-0-87485-005-5(3)) Johnson Publishing Co., Inc.

Edelin, Kenneth C. Broken Justice: A True Story of Race, Sex & Revenge in a Boston Courtroom. 2007. (Illus.). 362p. per. 17.95 (978-0-9792060-0-9(6)) PondView Pr.

Ehle, John. The Free Men. 2007. 376p. per. 19.95 (978-0-9793049-1-0(1)) Press 53, LLC.

Eick, Gretchen Cassel. Dissent in Wichita: The Civil Rights Movement in the Midwest, 1954-72. 2007. (Illus.). 344p. per. 26.00 (978-0-252-07491-2(2)) Univ. of Illinois Pr.

Elliott, Mark & Elliot, Mark. Color Blind Justice: Albion Tourgee & the Quest for Racial Equality from the Civil War to Plessy V. Ferguson. 2008. (ENG., Illus.). 400p. pap. 17.95 (978-0-19-537021-8(X)) Oxford Univ. Pr., Inc.

Elliott, Mark & Smith, John David, eds. Undaunted Radical: The Selected Writings & Speeches of Albion W. Tourgée. 2010. (Conflicting Worlds: New Dimensions of the American Civil War Ser.). 448p. pap. 24.95 (978-0-8071-3593-8(3)) Louisiana State Univ. Pr.

Elliott, Mark Emory. Color-Blind Justice: Albion Tourgee & the Quest for Racial Equality - From the Civil War to Plessy V. Ferguson. 2006. (ENG., Illus.). 400p. 30.00 (978-0-19-518139-5(5)) Oxford Univ. Pr., Inc.

Ellis, Catherine & Smith, Stephen Drury, eds. Say It Loud: Great Speeches on Civil Rights & African American Identity. 2010. (ENG.). 304p. 35.00 (978-1-59558-113-6(8)) New Pr., The.

Ellis, William T. The Weak Link: How to Get Along with Negroes, a Layman's Approach to the Race Problem. Adams, Grace Ellis, ed. 2007. (Illus.). 116p. reprint ed. pap. 17.95 (978-1-877807-18-3(4)) Grace Publishing Co.

Emanuel, Rachel L. & Tureaud, Alexander P. A More Noble Cause: A. P. Tureaud & the Struggle for Civil Rights in Louisiana. 2011. (Illus.). 352p. 35.00 (978-0-8071-3793-2(6)) Louisiana State Univ. Pr.

Emmett Till Unsolved Civil Rights Crime ACT: Joint Hearing Before the Subcommittee on the Constitution, Civil Rights, & Civil Liberties & the Subcommittee on Crime, Terrorism, & Homeland Security of the Committee on the Judiciary, House of Representatives, One Hundred Tenth Congress, First Session, on H.R. 923, June 12, 2007. 2007. (Illus.). vi, 103p. (978-0-16-079490-2(0), 552-070-36483-8) United States Government Printing Office.

Epps, Garrett. Democracy Reborn: The Fourteenth Amendment & the Fight for Equal Rights in Post-Civil War America. 2007. (ENG., Illus.). 352p. pap. 17.00 (978-0-8050-8663-8(3), Holt Paperback) Holt, Henry & Co.

Escott, Paul D. What Shall We Do with the Negro? Lincoln, White Racism, & Civil War America. 2009. (ENG., Illus.). 328p. 29.95 (978-0-8139-2786-2(2)) Univ. Pr. of Virginia.

Etheridge, Eric. Breach of Peace: Portraits of the 1961 Mississippi Freedom Riders. 2009. (ENG., Illus.). 224p. 30.00 (978-0-9777433-9-1(X), 977749) Atlas & Co.

Euchner, Charles. Nobody Turn Me Around: A People's History of the 1963 March on Washington. 2011. (ENG.). 248p. pap. 17.00 (978-0-8070-0155-4(4)) Beacon Pr.

Evans, William McKee. Open Wound: The Long View of Race in America. 2009. (ENG.). 344p. 35.95 (978-0-252-03427-5(9)) Univ. of Illinois Pr.

Ezra, Michael, ed. Civil Rights Movement: People & Perspectives, 1 vol. 2009. (Perspectives in American Social History Ser.). (Illus.). 250p. 85.00 (978-1-59884-037-7(1), CIRIMO1C) ABC-CLIO, LLC.

Feagin, Joe R. Racist America: Roots, Current Realities & Future Reparations Remaking America with Anti-Racist Strategies. 2nd rev. ed. 2009. (ENG., Illus.). 256p. 150.00 (978-0-415-99206-0(0)) Routledge.

Feagin, Joe R., ed. & reader. Racist America: Roots, Current Realities & Future Reparations Remaking America with Anti-Racist Strategies. 2nd rev. ed. 2010. (ENG., Illus.). 376p. 31.95 (978-0-415-99207-7(9)) Routledge.

Federal Bureau Of Investigation & King, Martin Luther, Jr. Martin Luther King, Jr: The FBI Files. 2007. 228p. per. 22.99 (978-1-59986-253-8(0), Filibust) Filiquarian Publishing, LLC.

Finley, Keith M. Delaying the Dream: Southern Senators & the Fight Against Civil Rights, 1938-1965. 2008. (C). (978-0-8071-3345-3(0)) Louisiana State Univ. Pr.

—Delaying the Dream: Southern Senators & the Fight against Civil Rights, 1938-1965. 2010. (Making the Modern South Ser.). 352p. pap. 24.95 (978-0-8071-3711-6(1)) Louisiana State Univ. Pr.

Flack, Horace Edgar. The Adoption of the Fourteenth Amendment. 2009. 288p. 34.99 (978-1-116-27712-8(3)); pap. 27.75 (978-1-116-27715-9(8)); 30.99 (978-1-113-60065-3(9)); pap. 27.75 (978-1-113-60064-6(0)); pap. 28.75 (978-1-113-61082-9(4)); 30.99 (978-1-110-56677-8(8)); pap. 27.75 (978-1-110-56676-1(X)); 24.99 (978-1-103-79992-3(4)); pap. 18.99 (978-1-103-79986-2(X)) BiblioBazaar.

—The Adoption of the Fourteenth Amendment. 2009. 196p. pap. (978-1-4590-0353-8(5)) Books LLC.

—The Adoption of the Fourteenth Amendment. 2008. 288p. pap. (978-1-4086-6656-2(1)); pap. (978-1-4097-6717-6(5)) Read Bks.

Flamming, Douglas. Bound for Freedom: Black Los Angeles in Jim Crow America. 2006. (Illus.). 467p. per. 27.95 (978-0-520-24990-5(9)) Univ. of California Pr.

Fleming, Harold C. & Fleming, Victoria. The Potomac Chronicle: Public Policy & Civil Rights from Kennedy to Reagan. 2010. (ENG.). 314p. pap. 24.95 (978-0-8203-3623-7(8)) Univ. of Georgia Pr.

Fortune, T. Thomas. T. Thomas Fortune, the Afro-American Agitator: A Collection of Writings, 1880-1928. Alexander, Shawn Leigh, ed. 2008. (New Perspectives on the History of the South Ser.). (ENG.). 320p. 65.00 (978-0-8130-3232-0(6)) Univ. Pr. of Florida.

Fosl, Catherine & K'Meyer, Tracy E. Freedom on the Border: An Oral History of the Civil Rights Movement in Kentucky. 2010. (Kentucky Remembered: an Oral History Ser.). (ENG., Illus.). 344p. pap. 25.00 (978-0-8131-2606-7(1)) Univ. Pr. of Kentucky.

Fredrickson, George M. Big Enough to Be Inconsistent: Abraham Lincoln Confronts Slavery & Race. 2008. (W. E. B. du Bois Lectures). 168p. 19.95 (978-0-674-02774-9(4)) Harvard Univ. Pr.

Freyer, Tony A. Little Rock on Trial: Cooper V. Aaron & School Desegregation. 2007. (Landmark Law Cases & American Society Ser.). 276p. 35.00 (978-0-7006-1535-3(0)); per. 17.95 (978-0-7006-1536-0(9)) Univ. Pr. of Kansas.

Frymer, P. Uneasy Alliances (With New Afterword) Race & Party Competion. 2010. (Princeton Studies in American Politics: Historical, International, & Comparative Perspectives Ser.). (ENG., Illus.). 264p. (C). pap. 24.95 (978-0-691-14801-4(5)) Princeton Univ. Pr.

Frymer, Paul. Black & Blue: African Americans, the Labor Movement, & the Decline of the Democratic Party. 2007. (Princeton Studies in American Politics). (Illus.). 202p. 55.00 (978-0-691-13081-1(7)); (ENG., 224p. (C). per. 29.95 (978-0-691-13465-9(0)) Princeton Univ. Pr.

Frystak, Shannon. Our Minds on Freedom: Women & the Struggle for Black Equality in Louisiana, 1924-1967. 2009. 288p. 42.50 (978-0-8071-3493-1(7)) Louisiana State Univ. Pr.

Fujino, Diane C. Samurai among Panthers: Richard Aoki on Race, Resistance, & a Paradoxical Life. 2012. (Critical American Studies). 496p. 75.00 **(978-0-8166-7786-3(7))**; pap. 24.95 **(978-0-8166-7787-0(5))** Univ. of Minnesota Pr.

Gaillard, Frye, et al. Alabama's Civil Rights Trail: An Illustrated Guide to the Cradle of Freedom. 2nd ed. 2010. (Alabama the Forge of History Ser.). (ENG., Illus.). 328p. pap. 24.95 (978-0-8173-5581-4(2)) Univ. of Alabama Pr.

Garvey, Marcus. The Marcus Garvey & Universal Negro Improvement Association Papers: Africa for the Africans, 1923-1945. Hill, Robert A. et al, eds. 2006. (Marcus Garvey & Universal Negro Improvement Association Papers). (Illus.). 805p. 95.00 (978-0-520-24732-1(9)) Univ. of California Pr.

Gates, Henry Louis, Jr., et al, eds. The Oxford Handbook of African American Citizenship, 1865-Present, 1 vol. 2012. (Oxford Handbooks Ser.). (ENG., Illus.). 320p. 175.00 (978-0-19-518805-9(5)) Oxford Univ. Pr., Inc.

Gellman, Erik S. Death Blow to Jim Crow: The National Negro Congress & the Rise of Militant Civil Rights. 2012. (John Hope Franklin Series in African American History & Culture Ser.). (ENG., Illus.). 368p. 39.95 **(978-0-8078-3531-9(5))** Univ. of North Carolina Pr.

Gerber, Richard A. & Friedlander, Alan. The Civil Rights ACT of 1875: A Reexamination. 2008. (978-1-878508-28-7(8)) Connecticut Academy of Arts & Sciences.

Gill, Tiffany. Beauty Shop Politics: African American Women's Activism in the Beauty Industry. 2010. (Women in American History Ser.). (ENG., Illus.). 208p. pap. 25.00 (978-0-252-07696-1(6)) Univ. of Illinois Pr.

Gilmore, Glenda Elizabeth. Defying Dixie: The Radical Roots of Civil Rights, 1919-1950. 2008. (ENG., Illus.). 656p. 39.95 (978-0-393-06244-1(9), 6244) Norton, W. W. & Co., Inc.

Gilmore, Glenda Elizabeth, et al. Defying Dixie: The Radical Roots of Civil Rights, 1919-1950. 2009. (ENG., Illus.). 664p. pap. 21.95 (978-0-393-33532-3(1), 33532) Norton, W. W. & Co., Inc.

Gitlin, Marty. Brown V. the Board of Education. 2007. (Essential Events Ser.). (ENG., Illus.). 112p. (YA). (gr. 7-12). 34.22 (978-1-59928-850-5(8)) ABDO Publishing Co.

Glisson, Susan. The Human Tradition in the Civil Rights Movement. Glisson, Susan, ed. 2006. (Human Tradition in America Ser.). (ENG., Illus.). 320p. pap. 29.95 (978-0-7425-4409-3(5)) Rowman & Littlefield Publishers, Inc.

Glisson, Susan M. The Human Tradition in the Civil Rights Movement. 2006. (Human Tradition in America Ser.). (ENG., Illus.). 320p. 88.00 (978-0-7425-4408-6(7)) Rowman & Littlefield Publishers, Inc.

Gona, Ophelia De Laine. Dawn of Desegregation: J.A. de Laine & Briggs V. Elliott. 2011. 216p. 29.95 (978-1-57003-980-5(1)) Univ. of South Carolina Pr.

Gonzales, James Joullian. Gunny: Memoirs of Mobile's South Side Riding Alabama's Tide of White Supremacy. 2007. (Illus.). x, 446p. pap. (978-0-9794714-1-4(9)) Academy Bks.

Good, Timothy S. The Lincoln-Douglas Debates & the Making of a President. 2007. (ENG., Illus.). 215p. per. 49.95 (978-0-7864-3065-9(6)) McFarland & Co., Inc. Pubs.

Grady-Willis, Winston A. Challenging U. S. Apartheid: Atlanta & Black Struggles for Human Rights, 1960-1977. 2006. (ENG., Illus.). 312p. (C). 89.95 (978-0-8223-3778-2(9)) Duke Univ. Pr.

Graham, Patterson Toby. A Right to Read: Segregation & Civil Rights in Alabama's Public Libraries, 1900-1965. 2006. (ENG., Illus.). 208p. per. 22.00 (978-0-8173-5371-1(2)) Univ. of Alabama Pr.

Grant, Gail Milissa. At the Elbows of My Elders: One Family's Journey Toward Civil Rights. 2008. (ENG.). 272p. (gr. 9). 24.95 (978-1-883982-66-9(9)) Missouri Historical Society Pr.

Gray, Kevin Alexander. The Decline of Black Politics: From Malcolm X to Barack Obama. 2008. 192p. pap. 16.95 (978-1-84467-284-4(0)) Verso Bks. GBR. Dist: Norton, W. W. & Co., Inc.

Green, Laurie B. Battling the Plantation Mentality: Memphis & the Black Freedom Struggle. 2007. (John Hope Franklin Series in African American History & Culture Ser.). (ENG., Illus.). 400p. 73.95 (978-0-8078-3106-9(0)) Univ. of North Carolina Pr.

Greenhaw, Wayne. Fighting the Devil in Dixie: How Civil Rights Activists Took on the Ku Klux Klan in Alabama. 2011. (ENG., Illus.). 336p. 26.95 (978-1-56976-345-2(3), Hill, Lawrence Bks.) Chicago Review Pr., Inc.

Haines, Herbert H. Black Radicals & the Civil Rights Mainstream, 1954-1970. 224p. pap. 23.00 (978-1-57233-260-7(3)) Univ. of Tennessee Pr.

Hall, Simon. Peace & Freedom: The Civil Rights & Antiwar Movements in The 1960s. 2006. (Politics & Culture in Modern America Ser.). (Illus.). 280p. (C). per. 24.95 (978-0-8122-1975-3(9)) Univ. of Pennsylvania Pr.

Harding, Vincent. Hope & History: Why We Must Share the Story of the Moment. 2nd ed. 2009. 240p. pap. 16.00 (978-1-57075-857-7(3)) Orbis Bks.

Harris, Steve, narrated by. The Stories of Jimmy Lee Jackson, Reverend James Reeb, Viola Liuzzo & Vernon Dahmer, Grades 9-12. (Free at Last Ser.: Pt. 3). pap., tchr. ed. 24.95 incl. VHS (978-1-930545-31-1(2), 30006C) Choices, Inc.

Hartnell, Anna. Rewriting Exodus: American Futures from du Bois to Obama, 1 vol. 2011. (Decolonial Studies, Postcolonial Horizons Ser.). (ENG.). 240p. pap. 35.00 (978-0-7453-2955-0(1)) Pluto Pr. GBR. Dist: Macmillan.

Hatch, John B. Race & Reconciliation: Redressing Wounds of Injustice. (Race, Rites, & Rhetoric: Colors, Cultures, & Communication Ser.). (ENG.). 420p. 2009. pap. 40.99 (978-0-7391-2153-5(7)) 2008. 94.50 (978-0-7391-2152-8(9)) Lexington Bks.

Hay, Jeff, ed. The Montgomery Bus Boycott. 2011. (Perspectives on Modern World History Ser.). (Illus.). 224p. (YA). (gr. 9-12). 39.70 (978-0-7377-5795-8(7)) Cengage Gale.

Hays, Brooks. A Southern Moderate Speaks. 2011. (ENG.). 264p. pap. 40.00 **(978-0-8078-9680-8(2))** Univ. of North Carolina Pr.

Heard, Alexander. A Two-Party South? 2011. (ENG.). 352p. pap. 50.00 **(978-0-8078-9681-5(0))** Univ. of North Carolina Pr.

Hedblad, Alan, ed. African American Alamnac. 11th rev. ed. 2011. 1500p. 312.00 (978-1-4144-4547-2(4)) Cengage Gale.

Henry, Charles. Long Overdue: The Politics of Racial Reparations. 2009. (ENG.). 272p. pap. 22.00 (978-0-8147-3741-5(2)) New York Univ. Pr.

Henry, Charles P. Long Overdue: The Politics of Racial Reparations. 2007. (ENG.). 272p. 55.00 (978-0-8147-3692-0(0)) New York Univ. Pr.

Heron, Gil Scott. The Last Holiday: A Memoir. 2012. (ENG.). 384p. 25.00 **(978-0-8021-2901-7(3)**, Grove Pr.) Grove/Atlantic, Inc.

Higham, John, ed. Civil Rights & Social Wrongs: Black-White Relations since World War II. 2006. 223p. reprint ed. 25.00 (978-1-4223-5850-4(X)) DIANE Publishing Co.

Hilliard, David, ed. & selected by. The Black Panther: Intercommunal News Service, 1967-1980. 2007. (ENG., Illus.). 192p. pap. 25.00 (978-1-4165-3259-0(5), Beyond Words/Atria Bks.) Atria Bks.

Hogan, Wesley C. Many Minds, One Heart: SNCC's Dream for a New America. (ENG., Illus.). 480p. 2009. pap. 23.95 (978-0-8078-5959-9(1)) 2007. 38.95 (978-0-8078-3074-1(7)) Univ. of North Carolina Pr.

Höhn, Maria & Klimke, Martin A. Breath of Freedom: The Civil Rights Struggle, African American Gis, & Germany. 2010. (ENG., Illus.). 282p. 89.00 (978-0-230-10472-3(X)); pap. 26.00 (978-0-230-10473-0(8)) Palgrave Macmillan.

Holloway Bishop, Charlene & Holloway, Lucius, Sr. The Civil Rights Movement through the Eyes of Lucius Holloway Sr. By Charlene Holloway Bishop & Lucius Holloway Sr. 2008. 84p. pap. 15.00 (978-0-8059-7597-0(7)) Dorrance Publishing Co., Inc.

Holsaert, Faith S., et al, eds. Hands on the Freedom Plow: Personal Accounts by Women in SNCC. 2010. (ENG., Illus.). 656p. 34.95 (978-0-252-03557-9(7)) Univ. of Illinois Pr.

Honey, Michael K. Going down Jericho Road: The Memphis Strike, Martin Luther King's Last Campaign. 2007. (ENG., Illus.). 640p. 35.00 (978-0-393-04339-6(8), 4339) Norton, W. W. & Co., Inc.

Horwitz, Joshua & Anderson, Casey. Guns, Democracy, & the Insurrectionist Idea. 2009. (ENG.). 296p. pap. 27.95 (978-0-472-03370-6(0)) Univ. of Michigan Pr.

Houck, Davis W. & Dixon, David E., eds. Rhetoric, Religion & the Civil Rights Movement 1954-1965: Studies in Rhetoric & Religion 1. 2006. (Studies in Rhetoric & Religion: Vol. 1). 1050p. per. 49.95 (978-1-932792-54-6(6)) Baylor Univ. Pr.

—Women & the Civil Rights Movement, 1954-1965. (ENG.). 352p. 2011. pap. 30.00 (978-1-61703-050-5(3)) 2009. 65.00 (978-1-60473-107-1(9)) Univ. Pr. of Mississippi.

Houck, Davis W. & Grindy, Matthew A. Emmett till & the Mississippi Press. (ENG.). 2010. 230p. pap. 25.00 (978-1-60473-850-6(2)) 2008. 213p. 40.00 (978-1-934110-15-7(9)) Univ. Pr. of Mississippi.

Huntley, Horace & McKerley, John W., eds. Foot Soldiers for Democracy: The Men, Women, & Children of the Birmingham Civil Rights Movement. 2009. (ENG., Illus.). 264p. 75.00 (978-0-252-03478-7(3)); pap. 25.00 (978-0-252-07668-8(0)) Univ. of Illinois Pr.

Huntley, Horace & Montgomery, David, eds. Black Workers' Struggle for Equality in Birmingham. 2007. (Working Class in American History Ser.). 264p. per. 20.00 (978-0-252-07493-6(9)) Univ. of Illinois Pr.

Hurst, Rodney L. It Was Never about a Hotdog & a Coke. 2008. 204p. (ENG.). 28.95 *(978-1-59594-201-2(7))*; per. 14.95 *(978-1-59594-195-4(9))* WingSpan Publishing.

Jack, Bryan M. The St. Louis African American Community & the Exodusters. 2008. (ENG.). 192p. (C). 34.95 *(978-0-8262-1772-1(9))* Univ. of Missouri Pr.

Jackson, Harry R., Jr. The Truth in Black & White: A New Look at the Shifting Landscape of Race, Religion, & Politics in America Today. 2008. (ENG.). 256p. pap. 14.99 *(978-1-59979-268-2(0)*, Frontline) Charisma Media.

Jackson, Richie Jean Sherrod. The House by the Side of the Road: The Selma Civil Rights Movement. 2011. (ENG., Illus.). 176p. 24.95 *(978-0-8173-1694-5(9))* Univ. of Alabama Pr.

Jackson, Thomas F. From Civil Rights to Human Rights: Martin Luther King, Jr. , & the Struggle for Economic Justice. 2009. (Politics & Culture in Modern America Ser.). (Illus.). 472p. pap. 24.95 *(978-0-8122-2089-6(7))* Univ. of Pennsylvania Pr.

Jackson, Troy. Becoming King: Martin Luther King Jr. & the Making of a National Leader. 2011. (Civil Rights & the Struggle for Black Equality in the Twentieth Century Ser.). (ENG.). 248p. pap. 21.95 *(978-0-8131-3390-4(4))* Univ. Pr. of Kentucky.

Jalata, Asafa. Fighting Against the Injustice of the State & Globalization: Comparing the African American & Oromo Movements. 2012. (ENG., Illus.). 224p. pap. 32.00 ***(978-0-230-34003-9(2))*** Palgrave Macmillan.

James, Hunter. They Didn't Put That on the Huntley-Brinkley! A Vagabond Reporter Encounters the New South. 2008. (ENG.). 320p. pap. 24.95 *(978-0-8203-3192-8(9))* Univ. of Georgia Pr.

Jeanty, Richard. The Most Dangerous Gang in America: The Police. 2007. 300p. pap. 15.00 *(978-0-9769277-9-2(9))* RJ Pubns.

Jeffrey, Gary. Thurgood Marshall: The Supreme Court Rules on "Separate but Equal" 2012. (Graphic History of the Civil Rights Movement Ser.). (Illus.). 24p. (gr. 3-8). pap. 8.15 ***(978-1-4339-7504-2(1))***; lib. bdg. 23.95 ***(978-1-4339-7503-5(3))*** Stevens, Gareth Publishing LLLP.

Jeffries, Hasan. Bloody Lowndes: Civil Rights & Black Power in Alabama's Black Belt. (ENG., Illus.). 352p. 2010. pap. 22.00 *(978-0-8147-4331-7(5))* 2009. 60.00 *(978-0-8147-4305-8(6))* New York Univ. Pr.

Jeffries, Judson L., ed. Black Power in the Belly of the Beast. 2006. 336p. 67.00 *(978-0-252-03148-9(2))* Univ. of Illinois Pr.

—Comrades: A Local History of the Black Panther Party. 2007. (Blacks in the Diaspora Ser.). (ENG., Illus.). 336p. per. 24.95 *(978-0-253-21930-5(2)*, 0253219302) Indiana Univ. Pr.

Jeffries, Judson L., ed. On the Ground: The Black Panther Party in Communities Across America. (ENG.). 304p. 2011. pap. 30.00 ***(978-1-61703-200-4(X))*** 2010. 50.00 *(978-1-60473-492-8(2))* Univ. Pr. of Mississippi.

Jelks, Randal Maurice. Benjamin Elijah Mays, Schoolmaster of the Movement: A Biography. 2012. (ENG., Illus.). 368p. 39.95 ***(978-0-8078-3536-4(6))*** Univ. of North Carolina Pr.

Johnson, Arthur L. Race & Remembrance: A Memoir. 2008. (Illus.). 288p. 24.95 *(978-0-8143-3370-9(2))* Wayne State Univ. Pr.

Johnson, James Weldon. Along This Way: The Autobiography of James Weldon Johnson. rev. ed. 2008. (ENG.). 448p. (gr. 12-18). 16.00 *(978-0-14-310517-6(5)*, Penguin Classics) Penguin Group (USA) Inc.

Johnson, Kimberley S. Reforming Jim Crow: Southern Politics & State in the Age Before Brown, 1 vol. 2010. (ENG., Illus.). 336p. 35.00 *(978-0-19-538742-1(2))* Oxford Univ. Pr., Inc.

Johnson, Terrence L. Tragic Soul - Life: W. E. B. du Bois & the Moral Crisis Facing American Democracy, 1 vol. 2012. (Imagining the Americas Ser.). (ENG.). 192p. 65.00 *(978-0-19-538398-0(2))* Oxford Univ. Pr., Inc.

Jolly, Kenneth. Black Liberation in the Midwest: The Struggle in St. Louis, Missouri, 1964-1970. 2006. (Studies in African American History & Culture). 232p. 136.00 *(978-0-415-97969-6(2))* Routledge.

Jonas, Gilbert. Freedom's Sword: The NAACP & the Struggle Against Racism in America, 1909-1969. 2007. (Illus.). 520p. per. 29.95 *(978-0-415-95665-9(X))* Routledge.

Jones, Angela. African American Civil Rights: Early Activism & the Niagara Movement, 1 vol. 2011. (Illus.). 281p. 44.95 *(978-0-313-39360-0(5)*, A3364C); E-Book ***(978-0-313-39361-7(3)***, Praeger Pubs.) Greenwood Publishing Group, Inc.

Jones, Clarence B. & Connelly, Stuart. Behind the Dream: The Making of the Speech That Transformed a Nation. 2011. (ENG., Illus.). 224p. 22.00 *(978-0-230-10369-9(5))* Palgrave Macmillan.

Jones, Clarence B. & Connelly, Stuart. Behind the Dream: The Making of the Speech that Transformed a Nation. 2012. (ENG., Illus.). 224p. pap. 14.00 ***(978-0-230-33755-8(4))*** Palgrave Macmillan.

Jones, Patrick D. The Selma of the North: Civil Rights Insurgency in Milwaukee. 2010. (Illus.). 360p. pap. 22.95 *(978-0-674-05729-6(5))* Harvard Univ. Pr.

Jordan, Vernon E., Jr. Vernon Can Read! A Memoir. 2008. (ENG., Illus.). 352p. pap. 16.00 *(978-1-58648-670-9(5))* PublicAffairs.

Jordan, Vernon E., Jr., et al. Make It Plain: Standing up & Speaking Out. 2008. (ENG.). 272p. 24.95 *(978-1-58648-298-5(X))* PublicAffairs.

Joseph, Peniel E., ed. Neighborhood Rebels: Black Power at the Local Level. 2009. (Contemporary Black History Ser.). (ENG.). 264p. 100.00 *(978-0-230-62076-6(0))* Palgrave Macmillan.

Justesen, Benjamin R. Broken Brotherhood: The Rise & Fall of the National Afro-American Council. 2008. (ENG., Illus.). 276p. pap. 35.00 *(978-0-8093-2843-7(7))* Southern Illinois Univ. Pr.

Kalin, Berkley & Bauman, Mark K., eds. The Quiet Voices: Southern Rabbis & Black Civil Rights, 1880s to 1990s. 2007. (Judaic Studies Ser.). (ENG., Illus.). 448p. per. 44.50 *(978-0-8173-5429-9(8))* Univ. of Alabama Pr.

Kamin, Ben. Nothing Like Sunshine: A Story in the Aftermath of the MLK Assassination. 2010. (ENG.). 138p. pap. 19.95 *(978-0-87013-882-9(0))* Michigan State Univ. Pr.

Kamin, Ben. Room 306: The National Story of the Lorraine Motel. 2012. (ENG.). 200p. pap. 24.95 ***(978-1-61186-049-8(0))*** Michigan State Univ. Pr.

Kantrowitz, Stephen. More Than Freedom: Fighting for Black Citizenship in a White Republic, 1829-1889. 2012. (ENG.). 528p. (gr. 12). 36.00 ***(978-1-59420-342-8(3)***, Penguin Pr. HC, The) Penguin Group (USA) Inc.

Katagiri, Yasuhiro. The Mississippi State Sovereignty Commission: Civil Rights & States' Rights. (ENG.). 2007. 348p. per. 25.00 *(978-1-60473-008-1(0))* 2006. 312p. 50.00 *(978-1-57806-388-8(4))* Univ. Pr. of Mississippi.

Katznelson, Ira. When Affirmative Action Was White: An Untold History of Racial Inequality in Twentieth-Century America. 2006. (ENG.). 272p. pap. 16.95 *(978-0-393-32851-6(1)*, 32851) Norton, W. W. & Co., Inc.

Kelen, Leslie G., ed. This Light of Ours: Activist Photographers of the Civil Rights Movement. 2012. (ENG., Illus.). 256p. 45.00 ***(978-1-61703-171-7(2))*** Univ. Pr. of Mississippi.

Kelley, Blair L. M. Right to Ride: Streetcar Boycotts & African American Citizenship in the Era of Plessy V. Ferguson. 2010. (John Hope Franklin Series in African American History & Culture Ser.). (ENG., Illus.). 304p. 59.95 *(978-0-8078-3354-4(1))*; pap. 21.95 *(978-0-8078-7101-0(X))* Univ. of North Carolina Pr.

Kenan, Randall. The Fire This Time. 2007. (ENG.). 149p. 20.00 *(978-1-933633-24-4(7))* Melville Hse. Publishing.

Kimbrough, Natalie. Equality or Discrimination? African Americans in the U. S. Military during the Vietnam War. 2006. (ENG.). 196p. pap. 35.99 *(978-0-7618-3672-8(1))* Univ. Pr. of America, Inc.

King, Gilbert. Devil in the Grove: Thurgood Marshall, the Groveland Boys, & the Dawn of a New America. 2012. pap. ***(978-0-06-179226-7(8))***; E-Book ***(978-0-06-209771-2(7))***; (ENG.). 352p. 26.99 ***(978-0-06-179228-1(4))*** HarperCollins Pubs.

King-Livingston, S. Moving Forward on My Journey Sdrawkcab: An Uninterrupted Journey through the Passages of My Mind. 2009. 132p. 21.49 *(978-1-4389-4677-1(5))*; pap. 10.99 *(978-1-4389-4676-4(7))* AuthorHouse.

King, Martin Luther, Jr. Dream: The Words & Inspiration of Martin Luther King, Jr. 2007. (Illus.). 95p. 14.95 *(978-1-59842-240-5(5)*, Blue Mountain Pr.) Blue Mountain Arts Inc.

King, Martin Luther. Mlk: A Celebration in Word & Image. Adelman, Bob, ed. 2011. (ENG., Illus.). 64p. 15.00 *(978-0-8070-0316-9(6))* Beacon Pr.

King, Martin Luther, Jr. The Papers of Martin Luther King, Jr. Advocate of the Social Gospel: September 1948-March 1963. Carson, Clayborne, ed. 2007. (Papers of Martin Luther King, Jr.). (Illus.). 720p. 70.00 *(978-0-520-24874-8(0))* Univ. of California Pr.

—Stride Toward Freedom: The Montgomery Story, 1 vol. 2010. (King Legacy Ser.). (ENG.). 272p. 24.95 *(978-0-8070-0073-1(6))*; (Illus.). pap. 14.00 *(978-0-8070-0069-4(8))* Beacon Pr.

—Where Do We Go from Here: Chaos or Community? 2010. (King Legacy Ser.). (ENG.). 256p. 24.95 *(978-0-8070-0076-2(0))* Beacon Pr.

—Where Do We Go from Here: Chaos or Community? 2010. (King Legacy Ser.). (ENG.). 256p. pap. 14.00 *(978-0-8070-0067-0(1))* Beacon Pr.

King, Martin Luther. Why We Can't Wait. 2011. (King Legacy Ser.). 24.95 *(978-0-8070-0114-1(7))*; (ENG., Illus.). 256p. pap. 14.00 *(978-0-8070-0112-7(0))* Beacon Pr.

Kirk, John A. Beyond Little Rock: The Origins & Legacies of the Central High Crisis. 2007. 213p. 64.95 *(978-1-55728-850-9(X))*; per. 22.50 *(978-1-55728-851-6(8))* Univ. of Arkansas Pr.

Kirk, John A., ed. An Epitaph for Little Rock: A Fiftieth Anniversary Retrospective on the Central High Crisis. 2008. 190p. pap. 19.95 *(978-1-55728-874-5(7))* Univ. of Arkansas Pr.

Klarman, Michael J. Unfinished Business: Racial Equality in American History. 2007. (Inalienable Rights Ser.). (ENG., Illus.). 240p. 19.95 *(978-0-19-530428-2(4))* Oxford Univ. Pr., Inc.

K'Meyer, Tracy E. Civil Rights in the Gateway to the South: Louisville, Kentucky, 1945-1980. (Civil Rights & the Struggle for Black Equality in the Twentieth Century Ser.). (ENG., Illus.). 438p. 2010. pap. 25.00 *(978-0-8131-3006-4(9))* 2009. 50.00 *(978-0-8131-2539-8(1))* Univ. Pr. of Kentucky.

Knight, Gladys. Icons of African American Protest: Trailblazing Activists of the Civil Rights Movement, 2 vols. 2008. (Greenwood Icons Ser.). (Illus.). 760p. 175.00 *(978-0-313-34062-8(5)*, GR4062, Greenwood Pr.) Greenwood Publishing Group, Inc.

Kohl, Herbert & Brown, Cynthia. She Would Not Be Moved: How We Tell the Story of Rosa Parks & the Montgomery Bus Boycott. 2007. (Illus.). 126p. 23.00 *(978-1-4223-9036-8(5))* DIANE Publishing Co.

Kruse, Kevin M. & Tuck, Stephen. The Fog of War: The Second World War & the Civil Rights Movement, 1 vol. 2012. (ENG.). 256p. 99.00 ***(978-0-19-538241-9(2))*** Oxford Univ. Pr., Inc.

Kruse, Kevin Michael & Tuck, Stephen G. N. Fog of War: The Second World War & the Civil Rights Movement, 1 vol. 2012. (ENG.). 256p. pap. 21.95 ***(978-0-19-538240-2(4))*** Oxford Univ. Pr., Inc.

Kuettner, Al. March to a Promised Land: The Civil Rights Files of a White Reporter 1952-1968. 2007. (Capital Currents Ser.). (Illus.). 197p. per. 16.95 *(978-1-933102-49-8(7))* Capital Bks., Inc.

Kushner, David. Levittown: Two Families, One Tycoon, & the Fight for Civil Rights in America's Legendary Suburb. (ENG.). 256p. 2010. pap. 17.00 *(978-0-8027-1795-5(0))* 2009. (Illus.). 26.00 *(978-0-8027-1619-4(9))* Walker & Co.

Lambert, Frank. The Battle of Ole Miss: Civil Rights V. States' Rights. 2010. (Critical Historical Encounters Ser.). (ENG., Illus.). 208p. (C). pap. 19.95 *(978-0-19-538041-5(X))* Oxford Univ. Pr., Inc.

Lambert, Franklin. The Battle of Ole Miss: Civil Rights V. States' Rights. 2009. (Critical Historical Encounters Ser.). (ENG., Illus.). 224p. 22.95 *(978-0-19-538042-2(8))* Oxford Univ. Pr., Inc.

Lang, Clarence. Grassroots at the Gateway: Class Politics & Black Freedom Struggle in St. Louis, 1936-75. 2009. (Class: Culture Ser.). (ENG., Illus.). 344p. pap. 29.95 *(978-0-472-05065-9(6))* Univ. of Michigan Pr.

Lawson, Steven F. Running for Freedom: Civil Rights & Black Politics in America since 1941. 3rd ed. 2008. (ENG., Illus.). 408p. pap. 42.95 *(978-1-4051-7126-7(X)*, Wiley-Blackwell) Wiley, John & Sons, Inc.

Lazerow, Jama & Williams, Yohuru, eds. In Search of the Black Panther Party: New Perspectives on a Revolutionary Movement. 2006. (ENG., Illus.). 408p. 94.95 *(978-0-8223-3837-6(8))* Duke Univ. Pr.

Lemann, Nicholas. Redemption: The Last Battle of the Civil War. 2011. (ENG.). 257p. 24.00 *(978-1-4379-7643-4(3))* DIANE Publishing Co.

—Redemption: The Last Battle of the Civil War. 2007. (ENG., Illus.). 272p. pap. 16.00 *(978-0-374-53069-3(6))* Farrar, Straus & Giroux.

Levy, Alan Howard. Floyd Patterson: A Boxer & a Gentleman. 2008. (ENG., Illus.). 297p. pap. 35.00 *(978-0-7864-3950-8(5))* McFarland & Co., Inc. Pubs.

Lewis, Andrew B. The Shadows of Youth: The Remarkable Journey of the Civil Rights Generation. 2010. (ENG., Illus.). 368p. pap. 17.95 *(978-0-374-53240-6(0)*, Hill & Wang) Farrar, Straus & Giroux.

Lewis, Catherine & Richard. Race, Politics & Memory. 2007. (Illus.). 270p. (C). pap. 22.95 *(978-1-55728-857-8(7))* Univ. of Arkansas Pr.

Lewis, Catherine M. & Lewis, J. Richard, eds. Jim Crow America: A Documentary History. 2009. 245p. pap. 19.95 *(978-1-55728-895-0(X))*; (Illus.). 59.95 *(978-1-55728-894-3(1))* Univ. of Arkansas Pr.

—Race, Politics, & Memory: A Documentary History of the Little Rock School Crisis. 2007. (Illus.). 242p. 65.00 *(978-1-55728-856-1(9))* Univ. of Arkansas Pr.

Lewis, David Levering. W. E. B. du Bois: A Biography, 1868-1963. Field, Kendra Taira, ed. 2009. (ENG., Illus.). 912p. pap. 25.00 *(978-0-8050-8805-2(9)*, Holt Paperback) Holt, Henry & Co.

Lewis, George. Massive Resistance: The White Response to the Civil Rights Movement. 2006. (ENG., Illus.). 240p. pap. 45.00 *(978-0-340-90022-2(9))* Bloomsbury Publishing.

Lieberman, Robbie & Lang, Clarence. Anticommunism & the African American Freedom Movement: Another Side of the Story. Lieberman, Robbie & Lang, Clarence, eds. 2009. (Contemporary Black History Ser.). (ENG.). 272p. 95.00 *(978-0-230-60524-4(9))* Palgrave Macmillan.

Lieberman, Robbie & Lang, Clarence, eds. Anticommunism & the African American Freedom Movement: Another Side of the Story. 2011. (Contemporary Black History Ser.). (ENG.). 272p. pap. 32.00 *(978-0-230-11374-9(5))* Palgrave Macmillan.

Little, Kimberly K. You Must Be from the North: Southern White Women in the Memphis Civil Rights Movement. 2009. (ENG.). 208p. 40.00 *(978-1-60473-228-3(8))* Univ. Pr. of Mississippi.

Litwack, Leon F. How Free Is Free? The Long Death of Jim Crow. 2009. (Nathan I. Huggins Lectures). 208p. 21.00 *(978-0-674-03152-4(0))* Harvard Univ. Pr.

Lively, Donald E. The Constitution, Race, & Renewed Relevance of Original Intent. 2008. 99.95 *(978-1-60497-562-8(8))* Cambria Pr.

Locke, Alain LeRoy. The Works of Alain Locke, 1 vol. Molesworth, Charles, ed. 2012. (Collected Black Writings). 624p. 45.00 ***(978-0-19-979504-8(5))*** Oxford Univ. Pr., Inc.

Long, Michael G. Marshalling Justice: The Early Civil Rights Letters of Thurgood Marshall. 2011. 448p. 27.99 *(978-0-06-198518-8(X)*, Amistad) HarperCollins Pubs.

Luders, Joseph E. The Civil Rights Movement & the Logic of Social Change. 2010. (Cambridge Studies in Contentious Politics Ser.). (ENG., Illus.). 260p. 75.00 *(978-0-521-11651-0(1))*; pap. 25.99 *(978-0-521-13339-5(4))* Cambridge Univ. Pr.

Lusane, Clarence. The Black History of the White House. 2011. (City Lights Open Media Ser.). (ENG., Illus.). 544p. pap. 19.95 *(978-0-87286-532-7(0)*, 1311831) City Lights Bks.

Maclaury, Judson. To Advance Their Opportunities: Federal Policies Toward African American Workers from World War I to the Civil Rights Act Of 1964. 2008. (ENG.). 313p. pap. 24.95 *(978-0-9797292-3-2(8))* Univ. of Tennessee, Libraries of Newfound Pr.

Malbrew, Ricardo. No Niggers or Dogs Allowed- the Reexamination of the Brownsville Affair. 2007. 68p. per. *(978-3-8364-3416-4(4))* VDM Verlag Dr. Mueller e.K.

Malcolm X. End of White World Supremacy: Four Speeches. 2011. (ENG.). 160p. pap. 12.95 *(978-1-61145-016-3(0)*, 611016, Arcade Publishing) Skyhorse Publishing Co., Inc.

Mangun, Kimberley. A Force for Change: Beatrice Morrow Cannady & the Struggle for Civil Rights in Oregon, 1912-1936. 2010. (Illus.). 384p. pap. 24.95 *(978-0-87071-580-8(1))* Oregon State Univ. Pr.

Mann, Robert. When Freedom Would Triumph: The Civil Rights Struggle in Congress, 1954-1968. 2007. (Illus.). 318p. per. 19.95 *(978-0-8071-3250-0(0))* Louisiana State Univ. Pr.

Marable, Manning. Beyond Boundaries: The Manning Marable Reader, 1 vol. Rickford, Russell, ed. 2011. 336p. pap. 25.95 *(978-1-59451-862-1(9))* Paradigm Pubs.

—Let Nobody Turn Us Around: Voices of Resistance, Reform & Renewal: An African American Anthology. Mullings, Leith, ed. 2nd ed. 2009. (ENG.). 704p. 99.00 *(978-0-7425-6056-7(2))*; pap. 45.00 *(978-0-7425-6057-4(0))* Rowman & Littlefield Publishers, Inc.

—Living Black History: How Reimagining the African-American Past Can Remake America's Racial Future. 2011. (ENG.). 288p. (gr. 9). pap. 16.00 *(978-0-465-04395-8(X))* Basic Bks.

Marotti, Frank. The Cana Sanctuary: History, Diplomacy, & Black Catholic Marriage in Antebellum St. Augustine, Florida. 2012. (ENG.). 240p. 39.95 ***(978-0-8173-1747-8(3))*** Univ. of Alabama Pr.

Marsh, Charles. God's Long Summer: Stories of Faith & Civil Rights. 2008. (ENG., Illus.). 312p. (C). pap. 24.95 *(978-0-691-13067-5(1))* Princeton Univ. Pr.

Martinez, Elizabeth, ed. Letters from Mississippi: Reports from Civil Rights Volunteers & Freedom School Poetry of the 1964 Freedom Summer. 2007. (ENG.). 400p. pap. 16.95 *(978-0-939010-92-9(5))* Zephyr Pr.

Martinez, J. Michael. Coming for to Carry Me Home: Race in America from Abolitionism to Jim Crow. 2011. ***(978-1-4422-1500-9(3))*** Rowman & Littlefield Publishers, Inc.

Martinez, Michael J. Coming for to Carry Me Home: Race in America from Abolitionism to Jim Crow. 2011. (American Crisis Series: Books on the Civil War Era Ser.). (ENG.). 334p. 45.00 ***(978-1-4422-1498-9(8))*** Rowman & Littlefield Publishers, Inc.

Mason, Gilbert R. & Smith, James Patterson. Beaches, Blood, & Ballots: A Black Doctor's Civil Rights Struggle. 2007. (ENG., Illus.). 227p. per. 22.00 *(978-1-934110-28-7(0))* Univ. Pr. of Mississippi.

Masur, Kate. An Example for All the Land: Emancipation & the Struggle over Equality in Washington, D. C. 2010. (ENG., Illus.). 376p. 39.95 *(978-0-8078-3414-5(9))* Univ. of North Carolina Pr.

Materson, Lisa G. For the Freedom of Her Race: Black Women & Electoral Politics in Illinois, 1877-1932. 2009. (ENG., Illus.). 352p. 44.00 *(978-0-8078-3271-4(5))* Univ. of North Carolina Pr.

Matteson, Noelle. The Freedom Rides & Alabama: A Guide to Key Events & Places, Context, & Impact. 2011. 96p. pap. 9.95 ***(978-1-60306-106-3(1)***, NewSouth Bks.) NewSouth, Inc.

Matthews, H. K. Victory after the Fall: The Memories of Civil Rights Activist H. K. Matthews. 2007. 336p. 29.95 *(978-1-60306-000-4(6))* NewSouth, Inc.

Mayes, Keith. Civil Rights & Black Power: The Struggle for Black Equality in the United States, 1945-1975. 2009. (ENG., Illus.). 352p. 125.00 *(978-0-415-99128-5(5))* Routledge.

Mcadam & Cram101 Textbook Reviews Staff. Political Process & the Development of Black Insurgency 1930-1970. 2007. 60p. per. 9.95 *(978-1-4288-2326-6(3))* Cram101 Inc.

McCaul, Robert L. The Black Struggle for Public Schooling in Nineteenth-Century Illinois. 2nd ed. 2009. (ENG.). 208p. pap. 17.50 *(978-0-8093-2905-2(0))* Southern Illinois Univ. Pr.

McDougall, Harold. African American Civil Rights in the Age of Obama: A history & a Handbook. 2010. 234p. pap. 25.60 *(978-0-557-24832-2(9))* Lulu Enterprises Inc.

McGuire, Danielle L. At the Dark End of the Street: Black Women, Rape, & Resistance — A New History of the Civil Rights Movement from Rosa Parks to the Rise of Black Power. 2010. (ENG., Illus.). 352p. 27.95 *(978-0-307-26906-5(X)*, Knopf) Knopf Doubleday Publishing Group.

—At the Dark End of the Street: Black Women, Rape, & Resistance — A New History of the Civil Rights Movement from Rosa Parks to the Rise of Black Power. 2011. (Vintage Ser.). (ENG., Illus.). 416p. pap. 16.95 *(978-0-307-38924-4(3)*, Vintage) Knopf Doubleday Publishing Group.

McGuire, Danielle L. & Dittmer, John, eds. Freedom Rights: New Perspectives on the Civil Rights Movement. 2011. (Civil Rights & the Struggle for Black Equality in the Twentieth Century Ser.). (ENG., Illus.). 402p. 40.00 *(978-0-8131-3448-2(X))* Univ. Pr. of Kentucky.

McKinney, Charles W. Greater Freedom: The Evolution of the Civil Rights Struggle in Wilson, North Carolina. 2010. (ENG., Illus.). 314p. pap. 41.50 *(978-0-7618-5230-8(1))* Univ. Pr. of America, Inc.

McLean, Alan & Bassett, Jennifer. Martin Luther King. 2008. (ENG., Illus.). 80p. 9.38 *(978-0-19-423393-4(6))* Oxford Univ. Pr., Inc.

McWhorter, Ladelle. Racism & Sexual Oppression in Anglo-America: A Genealogy. 2009. (ENG.). 440p. 75.00 *(978-0-253-35296-5(7)*, 0253352967) Indiana Univ. Pr.

—Racism & Sexual Oppression in Anglo-America: A Genealogy. 2009. (ENG.). 440p. pap. 27.95 *(978-0-253-22063-9(7)*, 0253220637) Indiana Univ. Pr.

Miller, Eben. Born along the Color Line: The 1933 Amenia Conference & the Rise of a National Civil Rights Movement, 1 vol. 2012. (ENG., Illus.). 368p. 29.95 *(978-0-19-517455-7(0))* Oxford Univ. Pr., Inc.

Miller, James A. Remembering Scottsboro: The Legacy of an Infamous Trial. 2009. (ENG., Illus.). 296p. (C). pap. 29.95 *(978-0-691-14047-6(2))* Princeton Univ. Pr.

Miller, Paul T. The Postwar Struggle for Civil Rights: African Americans in San Francisco, 1945-1975. 2009. (Illus.). xv, 167p. E-Book 95.00 *(978-0-203-86612-2(6))*; (ENG., 184p. 125.00 *(978-0-415-80601-5(1))* Routledge.

Mills, Kay. This Little Light of Mine: The Life of Fannie Lou Hamer. 2007. (Civil Rights & the Struggle for Black Equality in the Twentieth Century Ser.). (ENG., Illus.). 426p. per. 24.95 *(978-0-8131-9182-9(3))* Univ. Pr. of Kentucky.

Minchin, Timothy J. From Rights to Economics: The Ongoing Struggle for Black Equality in the U. S. South. 2007. (New Perspectives on the History of the

South Ser.). (ENG., Illus.). 224p. 39.95 *(978-0-8130-3092-0(7))* Univ. Pr. of Florida.

Minchin, Timothy J. & Salmond, John A. After the Dream: Black & White Southerners Since 1965. 2011. (Civil Rights & the Struggle for Black Equality in the Twentieth Century Ser.). (ENG., Illus.). 424p. 40.00 *(978-0-8131-2978-5(8))* Univ. Pr. of Kentucky.

Mine Eyes Have Seen: Bearing Witness to the Civil Rights Struggle. 2008. (Time Inc. Ser.). (J). 33.27 *(978-1-57505-973-0(8)*, Twenty-First Century Bks.) Lerner Publishing Group.

Mitchell, Clarence, Jr. The Papers of Clarence Mitchell, 1946-1954, Vol. 3. Watson, Denton L., ed. 2010. (ENG., Illus.). 476p. 69.95 *(978-0-8214-1662-4(6))* Ohio Univ. Pr.

Mitchell Jr., Clarence. The Papers of Clarence Mitchell, V 4. Watson, Denton L., ed. 2010. (ENG., Illus.). 768p. 69.95 *(978-0-8214-1935-9(8))* Ohio Univ. Pr.

Monson, Ingrid. Freedom Sounds: Civil Rights Call out to Jazz & Africa, 1 vol. 2010. (ENG., Illus.). 416p. pap. 24.95 *(978-0-19-975709-1(7))* Oxford Univ. Pr., Inc.

Monson, Ingrid & Monson, Ingrid T. Freedom Sounds: Civil Rights Call Out to Jazz & Africa. 2007. (ENG., Illus.). 368p. 99.00 *(978-0-19-512825-3(7))* Oxford Univ. Pr., Inc.

Montgomery, Beverly. On the Shoulders of Greatness. 2009. 132p. 27.62 *(978-0-557-04014-8(0))* Lulu Enterprises Inc.

Moore, Winfred B., Jr. & Burton, Orville Vernon, eds. Toward the Meeting of the Waters: Currents in the Civil Rights Movement of South Carolina during the Twentieth Century. 416p. 2010. (ENG.). pap. 29.95 *(978-1-57003-971-3(2))* 2008. (Illus.). 49.95 *(978-1-57003-755-9(8))* Univ. of South Carolina Pr.

Morgan, Douglas. Lewis C. Sheafe: Apostle to Black America. 2010. 22.99 *(978-0-8280-2397-9(2))* Review & Herald Publishing Assn.

Muhammad, Dedrick. Understanding Racial Inequality in the Obama Era: A Primer. 2011. 208p. pap. 10.00 *(978-1-56656-823-4(4))* Interlink Publishing Group, Inc.

Mumford, Kevin. Newark: A History of Race, Rights, & Riots in America. 2008. (ENG.). 336p. pap. 24.00 *(978-0-8147-9563-7(3))* New York Univ. Pr.

Murphree, Vanessa. The Selling of Civil Rights: The Student Nonviolent Coordinating Committee & the Use of Public Relations. 2009. 206p. 39.95 *(978-0-415-80580-3(5))* 2006. (Illus.). 195p. 138.00 *(978-0-415-97889-7(0))* Routledge.

Murray, Gail S. Throwing off the Cloak of Privilege: White Southern Women Activists in the Civil Rights Era. 2008. (Southern Dissent Ser.). (ENG., Illus.). 272p. pap. 29.95 *(978-0-8130-3345-7(4))* Univ. Pr. of Florida.

Naftali, Timothy, et al. Lyndon B. Johnson: Mississippi Burning & the Passage of the Civil Rights Act: June 1, 1964-July 4 1964, 2 vols. McKee, Guian A. et al, eds. 2011. (Presidential Recordings Ser.: Vols. 7-8). (ENG., Illus.). 1120p. 150.00 *(978-0-393-08118-3(4)*, 8118) Norton, W. W. & Co., Inc.

Newman, Mark. The Civil Rights Movement. 2006. (BAAS Paperbacks Ser.). (ENG.). 200p. (gr. 17). pap. 34.00 *(978-0-7486-1593-3(8))* Edinburgh Univ. Pr. GBR. Dist: Columbia Univ. Pr.

Nichols, David A. A Matter of Justice: Eisenhower & the Beginning of the Civil Rights Revolution. 2008. (ENG., Illus.). 368p. pap. 22.99 *(978-1-4165-4151-6(9))* Simon & Schuster.

Nieves, Angel David & Alexander, Leslie M., eds. We Shall Independent Be: African American Place-Making & the Struggle to Claim Space in the United States. 2008. (ENG., Illus.). 544p. 50.00 *(978-0-87081-906-3(2))* Univ. Pr. of Colorado.

O'Dell, Jack. Climbin' Jacob's Ladder: The Black Freedom Movement Writings of Jack O'Dell. Singh, Nikhil, ed. 2010. (ENG.). 272p. 40.00 *(978-0-520-25958-4(0))* Univ. of California Pr.

Office of the Secretary of State. Lillian Walker: Washington State's Civil Rights Pioneer. 2010. (Illus.). 198p. pap. 20.00 *(978-1-889320-22-9(6))* Washington State Legacy Project.

Ogletree, Charles J., Jr., intro. After the Storm: Black Intellectuals Explore the Meaning of Hurricane Katrina. 2006. (ENG., Illus.). 164p. 22.95 *(978-1-59558-116-7(2))* New Pr., The.

Oguejiofor Okafor, Victor, ed. Studies in African American Leadership: Individuals, Movements, & Committees. 2006. 156p. 99.95 *(978-0-7734-5688-4(0))* Mellen, Edwin Pr., The.

Onyekwuluje, Anne B. Historical Influence: Reading Georgia Powers as a Grassroots Civil Rights Leader in the Rough Business of Kentucky Politics. 2011. (ENG., Illus.). 204p. 70.00 *(978-0-7391-5098-6(7))*; pap. 29.95 *(978-0-7391-5099-3(5))* Lexington Bks.

Ortiz, Paul. Emancipation Betrayed: The Hidden History of Black Organizing & White Violence in Florida from Reconstruction to the Bloody Election Of 1920. 2006. (American Crossroads Ser.). (Illus.). 382p. per. 24.95 *(978-0-520-25003-1(6))* Univ. of California Pr.

Oxford University Press Staff, ed. Martin Luther King. 2009. (ENG., Illus.). 67p. 15.44 *(978-0-19-423597-6(1))* Oxford Univ. Pr., Inc.

Paden, Catherine M. Civil Rights Advocacy on Behalf of the Poor. 2011. (American Governance: Politics, Policy, & Public Law Ser.). (Illus.). 240p. (C). 55.00 *(978-0-8122-4297-3(1))* Univ. of Pennsylvania Pr.

Parker, Alison M. Articulating Rights: Nineteenth-Century American Women on Race, Reform, & the State. 2010. (ENG., Illus.). 302p. 38.00 *(978-0-87580-416-3(0))* Northern Illinois Univ. Pr.

Parker, Christopher S. Fighting for Democracy: Black Veterans & the Struggle Against White Supremacy in the Postwar South. 2009. (Princeton Studies in American Politics: Historical, International, & Comparative Perspectives Ser.). (ENG., Illus.). 288p. (C). 62.95 *(978-0-691-14003-2(0))*; pap. 25.95 *(978-0-691-14004-9(9))* Princeton Univ. Pr.

Parks, Gregory S., et al, eds. Critical Race Realism: Intersections of Psychology, Race, & Law. (ENG.). 2010. 368p. pap. 39.95 *(978-1-59558-482-3(X))* 2008. (Illus.). 340p. 60.00 *(978-1-59558-146-4(4))* New Pr., The.

Parsons, Sara. From Southern Wrongs to Civil Rights: The Memoir of a White Civil Rights Activist. 2009. (ENG., Illus.). 216p. pap. 22.00 *(978-0-8173-5558-6(8))* Univ. of Alabama Pr.

Patterson, Collis D., ed. Dr Samuel Banks Speaks: Selected Writings. 2008. 124p. 21.49 *(978-1-4389-2488-5(7))*; pap. 10.99 *(978-1-4389-2489-2(5))* AuthorHouse.

Payne, Charles M. I've Got the Light of Freedom: The Organizing Tradition & the Mississippi Freedom Struggle. 2nd ed. 2007. (Illus.). 525p. per. 29.95 *(978-0-520-25176-2(8))* Univ. of California Pr.

Peery, Nelson. Black Radical: The Education of an American Revolutionary. 2007. (ENG.). 242p. 24.95 *(978-1-59558-145-7(6))* New Pr., The.

Peterson, Charles F. DuBois, Fanon, Cabral: The Margins of Elite Anti-Colonial Leadership. 2007. (ENG.). 170p. per. 31.50 *(978-0-7391-1159-8(0))* Lexington Bks.

Pfaff, Eugene, Jr. Keep on Walkin', Keep on Talkin' An Oral History of the Greensboro Civil Rights Movement. 2011. (ENG.). pap. 24.95 ***(978-0-9778026-2-3(0))*** Tudor Pubs., Inc.

Pfaff, Eugene E. Keep on Walkin', Keep on Talkin' An Oral History of the Greensboro Civil Rights Movement. 2011. ***(978-0-936389-36-3(2))*** Tudor Pubs., Inc.

Phibbs, Cheryl. The Montgomery Bus Boycott: A History & Reference Guide, 1 vol. 2009. (Illus.). 166p. 85.00 *(978-0-313-35887-6(7)*, GR5887) Greenwood Publishing Group, Inc.

Phillips, Kimberley L. War! What Is It Good For? Black Freedom Struggles & the U. S. Military from World War II to Iraq. 2012. (John Hope Franklin Series in African American History & Culture Ser.). (ENG., Illus.). 352p. 34.95 *(978-0-8078-3502-9(1))* Univ. of North Carolina Pr.

Pieratt, Marty Ford. First Black Red: The Story of Chuck Harmon, the First African American to Play for the Cincinnati Reds. 2010. 208p. (ENG.). 24.99 *(978-1-4520-1995-6(9))*; pap. 18.00 *(978-1-4520-1994-9(0))* AuthorHouse.

Pinderhughes, Dianne. Black Politics after the Civil Rights Revolution. 2012. (ENG.). 272p. 135.00 *(978-0-415-88155-5(2))*; pap. 33.95 *(978-0-415-88156-2(0))* Routledge.

Pitre, Merline. In Struggle against Jim Crow: Lulu B. White & the NAACP, 1900-1957. 2010. (Centennial Series of the Association of Former Students, Texas A&M University Ser.). (ENG., Illus.). 200p. pap. 22.50 *(978-1-60344-199-5(9))* Texas A&M Univ. Pr.

Podair, Jerald & Podair, Jerald E. Bayard Rustin: American Dreamer. 2008. (African American History Ser.). (ENG., Illus.). 128p. 35.95 *(978-0-7425-4513-7(X))* Rowman & Littlefield Publishers, Inc.

Proudfoot, Merrill. Diary of a Sit-in. 2011. (ENG.). 224p. pap. 40.00 ***(978-0-8078-6759-4(4))*** Univ. of North Carolina Pr.

Raiford, Leigh Renee. Imprisoned in a Luminous Glare: Photography & the African American Freedom Struggle. 2011. (ENG., Illus.). 328p. 45.00 *(978-0-8078-3430-5(0))* Univ. of North Carolina Pr.

Randolph, Ryan P. W. E. B. Dubois: The Fight for Civil Rights. 2009. (Library of American Lives & Times Ser.). 112p. (gr. 5-5). 69.20 *(978-1-60853-510-1(X))* Rosen Publishing Group, Inc., The.

Ranney, Joseph A. In the Wake of Slavery: Civil War, Civil Rights, & the Reconstruction of Southern Law, 1 vol. 2006. (Illus.). 212p. 49.95 *(978-0-275-98972-9(0)*, C8972, Praeger Pubs.) Greenwood Publishing Group, Inc.

Reed, Adolph, Jr., et al. Renewing Black Intellectual History: The Ideological & Material Foundations of African American Thought, 1 vol. 2010. 336p. pap. 39.95 *(978-1-59451-666-5(9))* Paradigm Pubs.

Reed, Christopher Robert. The Depression Comes to the South Side: Protest & Politics in the Black Metropolis, 1930-1933. 2011. (Blacks in the Diaspora Ser.). (ENG., Illus.). 204p. 29.95 *(978-0-253-35652-9(0)*, 0253356520) Indiana Univ. Pr.

Reed, Wornie & Dunn, Ronnie A. Racial Profiling: Causes & Consequences. rev. ed. 2011. (ENG.). 164p. pap. 40.00 *(978-0-7575-8686-6(4))* Kendall Hunt Publishing Co.

Reilly, Patrick. Politics & Protest. 2008. 96p. per. *(978-3-8364-3856-8(9))* VDM Verlag Dr. Mueller e.K.

Rhomberg, Chris. No There There: Race, Class, & Political Community in Oakland. 2007. (Illus.). 315p. per. 28.95 *(978-0-520-25166-3(0))* Univ. of California Pr.

Richardson, Henry J., 3rd. The Origins of African-American Interests in International Law. 2008. (ENG.). 544p. 65.00 *(978-1-59460-383-9(9))* Carolina Academic Pr.

Riches, William T. Martin. The Civil Rights Movement: Struggle & Resistance. 3rd rev. ed. 2010. (Studies in Contemporary History Ser.). (ENG.). 304p. 85.00 *(978-0-230-23705-6(3))*; pap. 19.00 *(978-0-230-23706-3(1))* Palgrave Macmillan.

Riser, R. Volney. Defying Disfranchisement: Black Voting Rights Activism in the Jim Crow South, 1890-1908. 2010. 344p. 40.00 *(978-0-8071-3638-6(7))* Louisiana State Univ. Pr.

Roberts, Gene & Klibanoff, Hank. The Race Beat: The Press, the Civil Rights Struggle, & the Awakening of a Nation. 2007. (Vintage Ser.). (ENG., Illus.). 544p. pap. 17.00 *(978-0-679-73565-6(8)*, Vintage) Knopf Doubleday Publishing Group.

Robinson, Devin A. & Roper, Vernon. Blacks: from the Plantation to the Prison: The Move, the Mockery, the Mental Slavery. 2008. (Illus.). 160p. pap. *(978-978-8174-51-6(5))* Loretta Davis.

Robinson, Sandra. Specializing in the Wholly Impossible. 2008. 176p. pap. *(978-3-639-01640-6(8))* VDM Verlag Dr. Mueller e.K.

Roman, Meredith L. Opposing Jim Crow: African Americans & the Soviet Indictment of U. S. Racism, 1928-1937. 2012. (Justice & Social Inquiry Ser.). (ENG., Illus.). 320p. 55.00 ***(978-0-8032-1552-8(5))*** Univ. of Nebraska Pr.

Rosenberg, Jonathan & Karabell, Zachary. Kennedy, Johnson, & the Quest for Justice: The Civil Rights Tapes. 2006. 368p. reprint ed. 28.00 *(978-1-4223-5887-0(9))* DIANE Publishing Co.

Roumain, Daniel. Dream of Heaven & Hell: Facts... Faith... or Fiction. 2008. (Illus.). 43p. 14.00 *(978-0-9799782-0-3(3))* Roumain, Daniel.

Salmond, John A. A Southern Rebel: The Life & Times of Aubrey Willis Williams, 1890-1965. 2011. (ENG.). 351p. pap. 50.00 ***(978-0-8078-9770-6(1))*** Univ. of North Carolina Pr.

Salter, John R. Jackson, Mississippi: An American Chronicle of Struggle & Schism. 2011. (ENG.). 272p. pap. 18.95 ***(978-0-8032-3808-4(8)***, Bison Bks.) Univ. of Nebraska Pr.

Samito, Christian G., ed. Changes in Law & Society During the Civil War & Reconstruction: A Legal History Documentary Reader. 2nd ed. 2009. (Legal History of the Civil War Era Ser.). (ENG., Illus.). 352p. (C). pap. 29.50 *(978-0-8093-2889-5(5))* Southern Illinois Univ. Pr.

Sanders, Vivienne. Civil Rights in the USA, 1945-68. 2008. (ENG., Illus.). 184p. pap. 17.95 *(978-0-340-96583-2(5))* Hodder Education GBR. Dist: Oxford Univ. Pr., Inc.

Sartain, Lee. Invisible Activists: Women of the Louisiana NAACP & the Struggle for Civil Rights, 1915-1945. 2007. 212p. 36.50 *(978-0-8071-3221-0(7))* Louisiana State Univ. Pr.

Scalmer, Sean. Gandhi in the West: The Mahatma & the Rise of Radical Protest. 2011. 254p. 90.00 *(978-0-521-76091-1(7))*; pap. 32.99 *(978-0-521-13958-8(9))* Cambridge Univ. Pr.

Schneider, Mark Robert. African Americans in the Jazz Age: A Decade of Struggle & Promise. 2006. (African American History Ser.). (ENG., Illus.). 176p. per. 24.95 *(978-0-7425-4417-8(6))* Rowman & Littlefield Publishers, Inc.

Schuyler, George S. Rac(e)Ing to the Right: Selected Essays George S. Schuyler. 2011. pap. 24.95 ***(978-1-57233-818-0(0))*** Univ. of Tennessee Pr.

Seay, Solomon S. & Boyd, Delores R. Jim Crow & Me. 2009. 176p. 25.00 *(978-1-58838-175-0(7))* NewSouth, Inc.

Selby, Gary S. Martin Luther King & the Rhetoric of Freedom: The Exodus Narrative in America's Struggle for Civil Rights. 2008. (Studies in Rhetoric & Religion Ser.). 225p. pap. 34.95 *(978-1-60258-016-9(2))* Baylor Univ. Pr.

Shaw, Todd Cameron. Now Is the Time! Detroit Black Politics & Grassroots Activism. 2009. (ENG., Illus.). 304p. 89.95 *(978-0-8223-4495-7(5))*; pap. 24.95 *(978-0-8223-4508-4(0))* Duke Univ. Pr.

Shuler, Jack. Blood & Bone: Truth & Reconciliation in a Southern Town. 2012. (ENG.). 248p. 29.95 ***(978-1-61117-048-1(6))*** Univ. of South Carolina Pr.

Shuler, Jack. Calling Out Liberty: The Stono Slave Rebellion & the Universal Struggle for Human Rights. (ENG., Illus.). 224p. 2011. pap. 30.00 ***(978-1-61703-196-0(8))*** 2009. 50.00 *(978-1-60473-273-3(3))* Univ. Pr. of Mississippi.

Sinclair, William A. & Alexander, Shawn Lee. The Aftermath of Slavery: A Study of the Condition & Environment of the American Negro. 2012. (Southern Classics Ser.). (ENG.). 424p. pap. 16.95 ***(978-1-61117-078-8(8))*** Univ. of South Carolina Pr.

Singler, Joan, et al. Seattle in Black & White: The Congress of Racial Equality & the Fight for Equal Opportunity. 2011. (ENG., Illus.). 288p. pap. 24.95 *(978-0-295-99084-2(8))* Univ. of Washington Pr.

Sitkoff, Harvard. King: Pilgrimage to the Mountaintop. 2009. (ENG., Illus.). 288p. pap. 15.00 *(978-0-8090-6349-9(2)*, Hill & Wang) Farrar, Straus & Giroux.

—A New Deal for Blacks: The Emergence of Civil Rights As a National Issue - The Depression Decade. 2008. (ENG.). 352p. (C). pap. 29.95 *(978-0-19-536753-9(7))* Oxford Univ. Pr., Inc.

—Struggle for Black Equality. 3rd rev. anniv. ed. 2008. (ENG., Illus.). 304p. pap. 16.00 *(978-0-8090-8924-6(6)*, Hill & Wang) Farrar, Straus & Giroux.

—Toward Freedom Land: The Long Struggle for Racial Equality in America. 2010. (ENG., Illus.). 232p. 50.00 *(978-0-8131-2583-1(9))* Univ. Pr. of Kentucky.

Skocpol, Theda, et al. What a Mighty Power We Can Be: African American Fraternal Groups & the Struggle for Racial Equality. (Princeton Studies in American Politics Ser.). (ENG., Illus.). 320p. (C). 2008. pap. 24.95 *(978-0-691-13836-7(2))* 2006. 32.95 *(978-0-691-12299-1(7))* Princeton Univ. Pr.

Slate, Nico. Colored Cosmopolitanism: The Shared Struggle for Freedom in the United States & India. 2012. (ENG., Illus.). 344p. 39.95 *(978-0-674-05967-2(0))* Harvard Univ. Pr.

Smallwood, James M. & Glasrud, Bruce A., eds. The African American Experience in Texas: An Anthology. 2007. (Illus.). 384p. per. 40.00 *(978-0-89672-609-3(6))* Texas Tech Univ. Pr.

Smith, C. Fraser. Here Lies Jim Crow: Civil Rights in Maryland. 2008. (ENG., Illus.). 344p. 31.95 *(978-0-8018-8807-6(7))* Johns Hopkins Univ. Pr.

Smith, Max. African America's 3rd Rail: SGL. 2009. 240p. pap. 19.95 *(978-0-615-28206-0(7))* Smith, Maxsonn.

Smith, Robert. Race, Labor & Civil Rights: Griggs Versus Duke Power & the Struggle for Equal Employment Opportunity. 2008. (Illus.). 264p. 37.50 *(978-0-8071-3363-7(9))* Louisiana State Univ. Pr.

Smith, Thomas. Showdown: JFK & the Integration of the Washington Redskins. 2012. (ENG.). 288p. pap. 18.00 ***(978-0-8070-0082-3(5))*** Beacon Pr.

Smith, Thomas G. Showdown: JFK & the Integration of the Washington Redskins. 2011. (ENG., Illus.). 256p. 26.95 *(978-0-8070-0074-8(4))* Beacon Pr.

Sokol, Jason. There Goes My Everything: White Southerners in the Age of Civil Rights, 1945-1975. 2007. (Vintage Ser.). (ENG., Illus.). 464p. pap. 17.00 *(978-0-307-27550-9(7)*, Vintage) Knopf Doubleday Publishing Group.

Sorenson, Lita. The Scottsboro Boys Trial: A Primary Source Account. 2009. (Great Trials of the Twentieth Century Ser.). 64p. (gr. 5-8). 58.50 *(978-1-61513-216-4(3))* Rosen Publishing Group, Inc., The.

Sowell, Thomas. A Man of Letters. 2007. (ENG., Illus.). 320p. 29.95 *(978-1-59403-196-0(7))* Encounter Bks.

Spagna, Ana Maria. Test Ride on the Sunnyland Bus: A Daughter's Civil Rights Journey. 2010. (River Teeth Literary Nonfiction Prize Ser.). (ENG., Illus.). 286p. pap. 19.95 *(978-0-8032-1712-6(9)*, Bison Bks.) Univ. of Nebraska Pr.

Spritzer, Lorraine Nelson & Bergmark, Jean B. Grace Towns Hamilton & the Politics of Southern Change. 2009. (ENG.). 296p. pap. 24.95 *(978-0-8203-3387-8(5))* Univ. of Georgia Pr.

Stanton, Mary. The Hand of Esau: Montgomery's Jewish Community & the Bus Boycott. 2007. (Illus.). 194p. per. 15.95 *(978-1-57966-041-3(X))* River City Publishing.

—Journey Toward Justice: Juliette Hampton Morgan & the Montgomery Bus Boycott. 2006. (ENG., Illus.). 296p. 29.95 *(978-0-8203-2857-7(X))* Univ. of Georgia Pr.

Steedman, Marek. Jim Crow Citizenship: How Southern Progressives Remade Race, Citizenship & Liberalism in America. 2011. (Routledge Series on Identity Politics Ser.). (ENG.). 216p. 125.00 *(978-0-415-89053-3(5))* Routledge.

Stockley, Grif. Race Relations in the Natural State. 2008. 212p. (C). 30.00 *(978-0-9708574-6-0(2))* Butler Ctr. for Arkansas Studies.

Stockley, Grif, Jr. & Stockley, Grif. Ruled by Race: Black/White Relations in Arkansas from Slavery to the Present. 2008. (Illus.). 400p. 34.95 *(978-1-55728-885-1(2))* Univ. of Arkansas Pr.

Street, Joe. Culture War in the Civil Rights Movement. 2007. (ENG.). 272p. 59.95 *(978-0-8130-3196-5(6))* Univ. Pr. of Florida.

Strickland, Carol Sills, et al, eds. Teach Freedom: Education for Liberation in the African-American Tradition. 2008. (Teaching for Social Justice Ser.). (ENG.). 288p. (C). *(978-0-8077-4873-2(0))* Teachers College Pr., Teachers College, Columbia Univ.

Strickland, Carol Sills & Payne, Charles M., eds. Teach Freedom: Education for Liberation in the African-American Tradition. 2008. (Teaching for Social Justice Ser.). (ENG.). 288p. pap. 30.95 *(978-0-8077-4872-5(2))* Teachers College Pr., Teachers College, Columbia Univ.

Sugarman, Tracy. We Had Sneakers, They Had Guns: The Kids Who Fought for Civil Rights in Mississippi. 2009. (Illus.). 320p. 34.95 *(978-0-8156-0938-4(8))* Syracuse Univ. Pr.

Sugrue, Thomas J. Not Even Past: Barack Obama & the Burden of Race. 2010. (Lawrence Stone Lectures). (ENG.). 178p. 24.95 *(978-0-691-13730-8(7))* Princeton Univ. Pr.

—Sweet Land of Liberty: The Forgotten Struggle for Civil Rights in the North. 2009. (ENG., Illus.). 736p. pap. 20.00 *(978-0-8129-7038-8(1)*, Random Hse. Trade Paperbacks) Random House Publishing Group.

Sullivan, Patricia. Lift Every Voice: The NAACP & the Making of the Civil Rights Movement. 2010. (ENG., Illus.). 560p. pap. 21.95 *(978-1-59558-544-8(3))* New Pr., The.

Sundquist, Eric J. King's Dream: The Legacy of Martin Luther King's I Have a Dream Speech. (Icons of America Ser.). 2009. (ENG., Illus.). 320p. pap. 14.00 *(978-0-300-15859-5(9))* 2008. 456p. pap. 35.00 *(978-0-300-15090-2(3))* Yale Univ. Pr.

Taylor, Jon E. Freedom to Serve: Equality of Treatment & Opportunity in the Armed Services. 2012. (Critical Moments in American History Ser.). (ENG., Illus.). 224p. 140.00 *(978-0-415-89449-4(2))*; pap. 27.95 *(978-0-415-89448-7(4))* Routledge.

Telfair Museum of Art. Freedom's March: Photographs of the Civil Rights Movement in Savannah by Frederick C. Baldwin. 2008. (ENG., Illus.). 112p. 34.95 *(978-0-933075-08-5(1))* Telfair Museum of Art.

Tennassee, Paul Nehru. History of the National Alliance of Postal & Federal Employees 1913-1945: Treat US Right not White. 2011. 220p. pap. 17.95 *(978-1-4502-7280-3(0))* iUniverse, Inc.

Theoharis, Jeanne & Woodard, Komozi. Want to Start a Revolution? Radical Women in the Black Freedom Struggle. Gore, Dayo, ed. 2009. (ENG., Illus.). 368p. pap. 25.00 *(978-0-8147-8314-6(7))* New York Univ. Pr.

Troutt, David Dante, ed. After the Storm: Black Intellectuals Explore the Meaning of Hurricane Katrina. 2007. (ENG.). 168p. per. 14.95 *(978-1-59558-203-4(7))* New Pr., The.

Tuck, Stephen. We Ain't What We Ought to Be: The Black Freedom Struggle from Emancipation to Obama. (Illus.). 528p. 2011. (ENG.). pap. 19.95 *(978-0-674-06229-0(9))* 2010. 29.95 *(978-0-674-03626-0(3))* Harvard Univ. Pr. (Belknap Pr.).

Turner, Jeffrey Alan. Sitting in & Speaking Out: Student Movements in the American South, 1960-1970. 2010. (ENG.). 380p. 69.95 *(978-0-8203-3593-3(2))*; (Illus.). pap. 24.95 *(978-0-8203-3599-5(1))* Univ. of Georgia Pr.

United States. Attorney-. Opinion of Attorney General Bates on Citizenship. 2011. 30p. pap. 11.99 ***(978-1-4181-9319-5(4))*** MPublishing.

Uschan, Michael V. Selma to Montgomery. 2011. (Lucent Library of Black History Ser.). (Illus.). 128p. lib. bdg. 33.45 *(978-1-4205-0571-9(8)*, Lucent Bks.) Cengage Gale.

Van Delinder, Jean. Struggles Before Brown: Early Civil Rights Protests & Their Significance Today. (Sociological Imagination Ser.). (Illus.). 208p. 2011. pap. 38.95 *(978-1-59451-459-3(3))* 2007. 125.00 *(978-1-59451-458-6(5))* Paradigm Pubs.

Verney, Kevern & Sartain, Lee, eds. Long Is the Way & Hard: One Hundred Years of the NAACP. 2009. (ENG.). 330p. 70.00 *(978-1-55728-908-7(5))*; pap. 29.95 *(978-1-55728-909-4(3))* Univ. of Arkansas Pr.

Vinson Williams, Michael. Medgar Evers: Mississippi Martyr. 2011. (ENG., Illus.). 453p. 34.95 ***(978-1-55728-973-5(5))*** Univ. of Arkansas Pr.

Wahrhaftig, Paul. Rev. James D. Mcmanus - the Civil Rights Years: The Movement in Microcosm. 2007. (Illus.). 192p. per. 19.95 net. *(978-0-9792463-0-2(X))* Fickle Pr.

Waite, Robert Montrose. Haunted by Africa. 2007. 192p. per. 16.95 *(978-0-595-44834-0(8))* iUniverse, Inc.

Waldrep, Christopher. Jury Discrimination: The Supreme Court, Public Opinion, & a Grassroots Fight for Racial Equality in Mississippi. (Studies in the Legal History of the South Ser.). (ENG., Illus.). 328p. 2011. pap. 24.95 ***(978-0-8203-4030-2(8))*** 2010. 44.95 *(978-0-8203-3002-0(7))* Univ. of Georgia Pr.

Waldrep, Christopher. Race & National Power. 2010. (ENG., Illus.). 336p. (C). 135.00 *(978-0-415-80280-2(6))*; pap. 34.95 *(978-0-415-80281-9(4))* Routledge.

Waldschmidt-Nelson, Britta. Dreams & Nightmares: Martin Luther King Jr., Malcolm X, & the Struggle for Black Equality in America. 2012. (New Perspectives on the History of the South Ser.). (ENG., Illus.). 208p. 22.00 *(978-0-8130-3723-3(9))* Univ. Pr. of Florida.

Wallgora-Davis, Nicole. Sanctuary: African Americans & Empire. 2011. (ENG., Illus.). 240p. 65.00 *(978-0-19-536991-5(2))* Oxford Univ. Pr., Inc.

Walker, Anders. The Ghost of Jim Crow: How Southern Moderates Used Brown V. Board of Education to Stall Civil Rights. 2009. (ENG.). 272p. 34.95 *(978-0-19-518174-6(3))* Oxford Univ. Pr., Inc.

Walker, Robert J. Let My People Go! The Miracle of the Montgomery Bus Boycott. 2007. (ENG.). 368p. per. 54.99 *(978-0-7618-3706-0(X))* Hamilton Bks.

Wallach, Jennifer Jensen & Kirk, John A. Arsnick: The Student Nonviolent Coordinating Committee in Arkansas. 2011. (ENG., Illus.). 225p. 65.00 *(978-1-55728-968-1(9))*; pap. 24.95 *(978-1-55728-966-7(2))* Univ. of Arkansas Pr.

Wallenfeldt, Jeff, ed. The Black Experience in America: From Civil Rights to the Present. 2010. (African American History & Culture Ser.). (Illus.). 232p. (YA). 90.00 *(978-1-61530-179-9(8))* Rosen Publishing Group, Inc., The.

Ward, Stephen, ed. Pages from a Black Radical's Notebook: A James Boggs Reader. 2010. 488p. pap. 27.95 *(978-0-8143-3256-6(0))* Wayne State Univ. Pr.

Washington, Booker T. The Negro Problem: A Series of Articles by Representative American Negroes of Today. 234p. reprint ed. 98.00 *(978-0-7222-9736-0(X))* Library Reprints, Inc.

Washington, Eliza. Tomorrow Is Another Day: Hope of a Better Future for Black Americans. 4.00 *(978-0-939354-00-9(4))* Washington, Eliza.

Watson, Bruce. Freedom Summer: The Savage Season of 1964 That Made Mississippi Burn & Made America a Democracy. 2011. (ENG., Illus.). 384p. (gr. 12). 17.00 *(978-0-14-311943-2(5)*, Penguin (Non-Classics)) Penguin Group (USA) Inc.

—Freedom Summer: The Savage Season That Made Mississippi Burn & Made America a Democracy. 2010. (ENG., Illus.). 384p. (gr. 12). 27.95 *(978-0-670-02170-3(9)*, Viking Adult) Penguin Group (USA) Inc.

Wax, Amy L. Race, Wrongs, & Remedies: Group Justice in the 21st Century. 2009. (Hoover Studies in Politics, Economics, & Society Ser.). (ENG.). 200p. 37.50 *(978-0-7425-6286-8(7))* Rowman & Littlefield Publishers, Inc.

Webb, Clive. Rabble Rousers: The American Far Right in the Civil Rights Era. 2010. (Politics & Culture in the Twentieth-Century South Ser.). (ENG., Illus.). 304p. 69.95 *(978-0-8203-2764-8(6))*; pap. 24.95 *(978-0-8203-3577-3(0))* Univ. of Georgia Pr.

Webber, Christopher. American to the Backbone: The Life of James W. C. Pennington, the Fugitive Slave Who Became One of the First Black Abolitionists. 2011. (ENG.). 432p. 29.95 *(978-1-60598-175-8(3)*, 605175) Pegasus Bks.

Welch, Sidney Eugene. Soldiers of Marin Luther King: A Memoir from the Trenches of the Civil Rights Movement. 2007. 14.00 *(978-0-8059-8953-3(6))* Dorrance Publishing Co., Inc.

Wendt, Simon. The Spirit & the Shotgun: Armed Resistance & the Struggle for Civil Rights. (New Perspectives on the History of the South Ser.). (ENG., Illus.). 304p. 2010. pap. 29.95 *(978-0-8130-3565-9(1))* 2007. 39.95 *(978-0-8130-3018-0(8))* Univ. Pr. of Florida.

West, Michael Rudolph. The Education of Booker T. Washington: American Democracy & the Idea of Race Relations. 2008. (ENG.). 296p. (gr. 17). pap. 27.00 *(978-0-231-13049-3(X))* Columbia Univ. Pr.

Williams, Chad Louis. Torchbearers of Democracy: African American Soldiers in the World War I Era. 2010. (John Hope Franklin Series in African American History & Culture Ser.). (ENG., Illus.). 464p. 34.95 *(978-0-8078-3394-0(0))* Univ. of North Carolina Pr.

Williams, Donnie & Greenhaw, Wayne. The Thunder of Angels: The Montgomery Bus Boycott & the People Who Broke the Back of Jim Crow. 2007. (ENG., Illus.). 320p. per. 14.95 *(978-1-55652-676-3(8)*, Hill, Lawrence Bks.) Chicago Review Pr., Inc.

Williams, Hettie V. We Shall Overcome to We Shall Overrun: The Collapse of the Civil Rights Movement & the Black Power Revolt (1962-1968) 2008. (ENG.). 124p. pap. 27.50 *(978-0-7618-4353-5(1))* Univ. Pr. of America, Inc.

Williams, Horace Randall, et al. This Day in Civil Rights History. 2009. 408p. 19.95 *(978-1-58838-241-2(9))* NewSouth, Inc.

Williams, Johnny E. African American Religion & the Civil Rights Movement in Arkansas. 2008. (ENG.). 177p. pap. 25.00 *(978-1-60473-186-6(9))* Univ. Pr. of Mississippi.

Williams, Karen G. & Queeley, Andrea. Study Guide for Let Nobody Turn Us Around. 2nd ed. 2009. (ENG.). 150p. pap. 15.00 *(978-1-4422-0013-5(8))* Rowman & Littlefield Publishers, Inc.

Williams, Randall. Johnnie: The Life of Johnnie Rebecca Carr. 2007. (Illus.). 60p. (J). pap. 9.95 *(978-1-60306-033-2(2))* NewSouth, Inc.

Williams, Randall & Beard, Ben. This Day in Civil Rights History. 2009. (Illus.). 405p. *(978-1-58835-241-5(2)*, NewSouth Bks.) NewSouth, Inc.

Wilson, Mabel O. Negro Building: Black Americans in the World of Fairs & Museums. 2012. (ENG., Illus.). 464p. 39.95 ***(978-0-520-26842-5(3))*** Univ. of California Pr.

Winsboro, Irvin D. S. Old South, New South, down South? Florida & the Modern Civil Rights Movement. 2009. (ENG.). 276p. pap. 24.95 *(978-1-933202-44-0(0))* West Virginia Univ. Pr.

—Old South, New South, or down South? Florida & the Modern Civil Rights Movement. 2009. (ENG.). 276p. 75.95 *(978-1-933202-45-7(9))* West Virginia Univ. Pr.

Wise, Tim. Colorblind: The Rise of Post-Racial Politics & the Retreat from Racial Equity. 2010. (City Lights Open Media Ser.). (ENG.). 160p. pap. 14.95 *(978-0-87286-508-2(8))* City Lights Bks.

Wolcott, Victoria W. Race, Riots, & Roller Coasters: The Struggle over Segregated Recreation in America. 2012. (Politics & Culture in Modern America Ser.). 328p. 34.95 ***(978-0-8122-4434-2(6))*** Univ. of Pennsylvania Pr.

Wood, Peggy & Brown, Parker. Something Must Be Done: One Black. 2006. (Illus.). 153p. 9.95 *(978-0-8156-0877-6(2))* Syracuse Univ. Pr.

Woodhouse, Barbara Bennett. Hidden in Plain Sight: The Tragedy of Children's Rights from Ben Franklin to Lionel Tate. 2010. (Public Square Ser.). (ENG., Illus.). 384p. (C). pap. 19.95 *(978-0-691-14621-8(7))* Princeton Univ. Pr.

Wynn, Daniel Webster. The Naacp Versus Negro Revolutionary Protest: A Comparative Study of the Effectiveness of Each Movement. 2011. 114p. 39.95 ***(978-1-258-08927-6(0))*** Literary Licensing, LLC.

Young, Andrew. An Easy Burden: The Civil Rights Movement & the Transformation of America. 2008. 550p. pap. 29.95 *(978-1-60258-073-2(1))* Baylor Univ. Pr.

Young, Andrew & Sehgal, Kabir. Walk in My Shoes: Conversations Between a Civil Rights Legend & His Godson on the Journey Ahead. 2010. (ENG., Illus.). 256p. 24.00 *(978-0-230-62360-6(3))* Palgrave Macmillan.

Young, Andrew J. & Sehgal, Kabir. Walk in My Shoes: Conversations between a Civil Rights Legend & his Godson on the Journey Ahead. 2011. (ENG., Illus.). 256p. pap. 16.00 *(978-0-230-11429-6(6))* Palgrave Macmillan.

Zellner, Bob & Curry, Constance. The Wrong Side of Murder Creek: A White Southerner in the Freedom Movement. 2008. 350p. 27.95 *(978-1-58838-222-1(2)*, NewSouth Bks.) NewSouth, Inc.

AFRICAN AMERICANS—CIVILIZATION

Bee, Tee. African American Puzzles. 2007. 72p. pap. 14.95 *(978-1-58909-371-3(2))* Bookstand Publishing.

Gundaker, Grey. Signs of Diaspora/Diaspora of Signs. Date not set. (Commonwealth Center Studies in American Culture). (Illus.). 288p. reprint ed. pap. 18.95 *(978-0-19-510770-8(5))* Oxford Univ. Pr., Inc.

Ra Un Nefer Amen I. The Ritual Systems of Ancient Black Civilizations Vol. 2: Auset, Mother of the Living. 42p. pap. 15.00 incl. audio *(978-1-877662-01-0(1))* Kamit Pubns.

Rosen, Hannah. Terror in the Heart of Freedom: Citizenship, Sexual Violence, & the Meaning of Race in the Postemancipation South. 2008. (Gender & American Culture Ser.). (ENG., Illus.). 424p. 69.95 *(978-0-8078-3202-8(2))* Univ. of North Carolina Pr.

Shropshire-West, Rosalynn. Black Vignettes: Essays in African American History & Culture. 2010. 599p. pap. 37.95 *(978-0-615-24436-5(X))* West, Rosalynn Shropshire.

Ugochukwu, Chukwunyere C. Urban Neighborhood Revitalization & Heritage Conservation: The Architecture of Urban Redesign. 2006. (Illus.). 240p. (C). 109.95 *(978-0-7734-5663-1(5))* Mellen, Edwin Pr., The.

AFRICAN AMERICANS—COLLECTIBLES

Ellis, Yvonne H. Collectible African American Dolls. 2008. (Identification & Value Guide Ser.). (ENG., Illus.). 192p. pap. 29.95 *(978-1-57432-574-4(4)*, 1574325744) Collector Bks.

Lindenberger, Jan. Black Memorabilia for the Kitchen. 4th rev. exp. ed. 2008. (Illus.). 144p. pap. 16.95 *(978-0-7643-2881-7(6))* Schiffer Publishing, Ltd.

Mauzy, Barbara. African-Americana. 2008. (Illus.). 192p. 39.99 *(978-0-7643-3144-2(2))* Schiffer Publishing, Ltd.

AFRICAN AMERICANS—COLONIZATION

Bacon, Margaret Hope & Lapsansky-Werner, Emma, eds. Back to Africa: Benjamin Coates & the Colonization Movement in America, 1848-1880. 2007. (ENG.). 368p. pap. 27.00 *(978-0-271-02763-6(0))* Pennsylvania State Univ. Pr.

Burin, Eric. Slavery & the Peculiar Solution: A History of the American Colonization Society. 2008. (Southern Dissent Ser.). (ENG., Illus.). 240p. pap. 24.95 *(978-0-8130-3273-3(3))* Univ. Pr. of Florida.

Delany, Martin Robison. The Condition Elevation Emigration & Destiny of the Colored People of the United States. 2008. 184p. 22.99 *(978-0-554-35552-8(3))* 2008. 184p. 25.99 *(978-0-554-26249-9(5))* 2007. (ENG.). 162p. pap. 19.99 *(978-1-4346-0724-9(0))* 2007. (ENG.). 182p. pap. 21.99 *(978-1-4346-0784-3(4))* BiblioBazaar.

Dewees, Jacob. The Great Future of America & Africa; an Essay Showing Our Whole Duty to the Black Man, Consistent with Our Own Safety & Glory by Jacob Dewees, M. 2006. 236p. per. 20.99 *(978-1-4255-1977-3(6))* MPublishing.

Durham, Frederick A. The Lone Star of Liberia: The Outcome of Reflections on Our Own People. 331p. reprint ed. 98.00 *(978-0-7222-9816-9(1))* Library Reprints, Inc.

Jackson, James S., et al, eds. Researching Black Communities: A Methodological Guide. 2011. (ENG., Illus.). 336p. 80.00 ***(978-0-472-11750-5(5))*** Univ. of Michigan Pr.

James, Winston. The Struggles of John Brown Russwurm: The Life & Writings of a Pan-Africanist Pioneer, 1799-1851. 2010. (ENG., Illus.). 288p. pap. 22.00 *(978-0-8147-4290-7(4))* New York Univ. Pr.

—The Struggles of John Brown Russwurm: The Life & Writings of a Pan-Africanist Pioneer, 1799-1851. 2010. (ENG., Illus.). 305p. pap. *(978-976-640-249-5(3))* Univ. of the West Indies Pr.

Kinshasa, Kwando M. Emigration vs. Assimilation: The Debate in the African American Press, 1827-1861. alt. ed. 2011. (ENG.). 248p. pap. 25.00 ***(978-0-7864-6730-3(4))*** McFarland & Co., Inc. Pubs.

Magness, Phillip W. & Page, Sebastian N. Colonization after Emancipation: Lincoln & the Movement for Black Resettlement. 2011. (ENG., Illus.). 178p. (C). 34.95 *(978-0-8262-1909-1(8))* Univ. of Missouri Pr.

Pelster, Mae. Abolitionists, Copperheads & Colonizers in Hudson & the Western Reserve. 2011. 128p. pap. 21.99 ***(978-1-60949-253-3(6))*** History Pr., The.

The Sixteenth Annual Report of the American Society for Colonizing the Free People of Colour from the United States. 2010. pap. 18.88 *(978-1-61143-183-4(2))* Gorgias Pr., LLC.

Tyler-McGraw, Marie. An African Republic: Black & White Virginians in the Making of Liberia. 2007. (ENG., Illus.). 264p. 39.95 *(978-0-8078-3167-0(0))* Univ. of North Carolina Pr.

AFRICAN AMERICANS—CRIMES AGAINST

Arend, Orissa. Showdown in Desire: The Black Panthers Take a Stand in New Orleans. 2010. (ENG., Illus.). 294p. pap. 19.95 *(978-1-55728-896-7(8))* Univ. of Arkansas Pr.

Arnold, Edwin T. What Virtue There Is in Fire: Cultural Memory & the Lynching of Sam Hose. (ENG., Illus.). 264p. 2012. pap. 24.95 ***(978-0-8203-4064-7(2))*** 2009. 28.95 *(978-0-8203-2891-1(X))* Univ. of Georgia Pr.

Barringer Wells, Susan. A Game Called Salisbury: The Spinning of a Southern Tragedy & the Myth of Race. 2007. 492p. per. 23.95 *(978-0-7414-4425-7(9))* Infinity Publishing.

Blackmon, Douglas A. Slavery by Another Name: The Re-Enslavement of Black Americans from the Civil War to World War II. 2009. (ENG., Illus.). 496p. pap. 17.00 *(978-0-385-72270-4(2)*, Anchor) Knopf Doubleday Publishing Group.

Emmett Till Unsolved Civil Rights Crime ACT: Joint Hearing Before the Subcommittee on the Constitution, Civil Rights, & Civil Liberties & the Subcommittee on Crime, Terrorism, & Homeland Security of the Committee on the Judiciary, House of Representatives, One Hundred Tenth Congress, First Session, on H.R. 923, June 12, 2007. 2007. (Illus.). vi, 103p. *(978-0-16-079490-2(0)*, 552-070-36483-8) United States Government Printing Office.

Houck, Davis W. & Grindy, Matthew A. Emmett till & the Mississippi Press. (ENG.). 2010. 230p. pap. 25.00 *(978-1-60473-850-6(2))* 2008. 213p. 40.00 *(978-1-934110-15-7(9))* Univ. Pr. of Mississippi.

Jaspin, Elliot. Buried in the Bitter Waters: The Hidden History of Racial Cleansing in America. 2008. (ENG.). 352p. pap. 15.95 *(978-0-465-03637-0(6))* Basic Bks.

Kinshasa, Kwando Mbiassi. Black Resistance to the Ku Klux Klan in the Wake of Civil War. alt. ed. 2008. (ENG., Illus.). 262p. pap. 39.95 *(978-0-7864-4100-6(3))* McFarland & Co., Inc. Pubs.

Lane, Charles. The Day Freedom Died: The Colfax Massacre, the Supreme Court, & the Betrayal of Reconstruction. 2009. (ENG.). 352p. pap. 17.99 *(978-0-8050-8922-6(5)*, Owl Bks.) Holt, Henry & Co.

Lehr, Dick. The Fence: A Police Cover-Up along Boston's Racial Divide. 2010. 416p. pap. 14.99 *(978-0-06-078099-9(1)*, HarperPerennial) HarperCollins Pubs.

McWhirter, Cameron. Red Summer: The Summer of 1919 & the Awakening of Black America. 2011. (ENG., Illus.). 368p. 32.50 *(978-0-8050-8906-6(3))* Holt, Henry & Co.

—Red Summer: The Summer of 1919 & the Awakening of Black America. 2012. (ENG.). 368p. pap. 16.99 ***(978-1-250-00906-7(5)***, St. Martin's Griffin) St. Martin's Pr.

Miller, Calvin Craig. Backlash: Race Riots in the Jim Crow ERA. 2012. (Civil Rights Movement Ser.). (Illus.). 128p. (YA). (gr. 7-12). 28.95 ***(978-1-59935-183-4(8))*** Reynolds, Morgan Inc.

Miller, Lisa L. The Perils of Federalism: Race, Poverty, & the Politics of Crime Control. 2010. (ENG., Illus.). 266p. pap. 24.95 *(978-0-19-975722-0(4))* Oxford Univ. Pr., Inc.

Nevels, Cynthia Skove. Lynching to Belong: Claiming Whiteness Through Racial Violence. 2007. (Centennial Series of the Association of Former Students, Texas AandM University). (ENG., Illus.). 208p. 24.95 *(978-1-58544-589-9(4))* Texas A&M Univ. Pr.

Petersen, Jennifer. Murder, the Media, & the Politics of Public Feelings: Remembering Matthew Shepard & James Byrd Jr. 2011. (ENG., Illus.). 222p. pap. 24.95 *(978-0-253-22339-5(3)*, 0253223393) Indiana Univ. Pr.

Robson, David. The Murder of Emmett Till. 2010. (Crime Scene Investigations Ser.). (Illus.). 128p. 32.45 *(978-1-4205-0213-8(1)*, Lucent Bks.) Cengage Gale.

Strain, Christopher B. Burning Faith: Church Arson in the American South. 2008. (Southern Dissent Ser.). (ENG., Illus.). 224p. 34.95 *(978-0-8130-3239-9(3))* Univ. Pr. of Florida.

Thompson, Carlyle Van. Eating the Black Body: Miscegenation As Sexual Consumption in African American Literature & Culture. 2006. (African-American Literature & Culture Ser.: Vol. 10). (C). pap. 29.95 *(978-0-8204-7931-6(4))* Lang, Peter Publishing, Inc.

Thurston, Robert W. Lynching: American Mob Murder in Global Perspective. 2011. (Illus.). 442p. 99.95 *(978-1-4094-0908-3(2))* Ashgate Publishing Co.

AFRICAN AMERICANS—DIRECTORIES

Adams, Grace. Black Authors & Published Writers Directory (2007/2008) 2007. E-Book 89.95 *(978-1-877807-29-9(X))* Grace Publishing Co.

—2007/2008 Black Authors & Published Writers Directory: Industry Reference. 2007. (Illus.). 410p. pap. 119.95 *(978-1-877807-28-2(1))* Grace Publishing Co.

—2008/2009 Black Authors & Published Writers Directory. 2008. (Illus.). 348p. pap. 119.95 *(978-1-877807-30-5(3)*, Black Authors & Published Writers Directory) Grace Publishing Co.

Carey, Charles W., Jr. African Americans in Science: An Encyclopedia of People & Progress, 2 vols. 2008. (Illus.). 608p. 195.00 *(978-1-85109-998-6(0)*, AFAMSC1C) ABC-CLIO, LLC.

Ibirogba, Babs. The National Black Community Resource Guide: A Key to Success. (Orig.). reprint ed. pap. 12.00 *(978-1-56411-142-5(3))* UBUS Communications Systems.

Lee, Dante. The 2007-2009 African American Scholarship Guide for Students & Parents: Presented by Dante Lee, CEO of Diversity City Media. 2007. (ENG.). 206p. pap. 16.95 *(978-0-9767735-7-3(0))* Amber Bks.

Martin, C. Sunny. Who's Who in Black Indianapolis. 4th ed. 2007. 344p. per. 24.95 net. *(978-1-933879-29-1(7))* Who's Who Publishing Co.

—Who's Who in Black Indianapolis: The Third Edition. 3rd ed. 2006. (ENG.). 312p. per. *(978-1-933879-02-4(5))* Who's Who Publishing Co.

Martin, C. Sunny, ed. Who's Who in Black Indianapolis. 3rd ed. 2006. *(978-1-933879-03-1(3))* Who's Who Publishing Co.

Reference Library of Black America, 5 vols. 1765p. 199.50 *(978-0-7876-1535-2(8))* Cengage Gale.

TIYM Publishing Company, Inc. Staff, ed. African American Yearbook: The Resource & Referral Guide for & about African Americans 2006/2007. 6th ed. 2007. 288p. 29.95 *(978-0-9777254-0-3(5))* TIYM Publishing Co., Inc.

AFRICAN AMERICANS—ECONOMIC CONDITIONS

see also African Americans—Employment

Addressing the Problem of African-American Male Unemployment: Hearing Before the Joint Economic Committee, Congress of the United States, One Hundred Tenth Congress, First Session, March 8, 2007. 2007. iii, 53p. *(978-0-16-079254-0(1)*, 552-070-36334-3) United States Government Printing Office.

Anderson, Maggie. Our Black Year: One Family's Quest to Buy Black in America's Racially Divided Economy. 2012. (ENG., Illus.). 320p. 25.99 *(978-1-61039-024-8(5))* PublicAffairs.

Anderson, Maggie & Gregory, Ted. Our Black Year: One Family's Quest to Buy Black in America's Racially Divided Economy. 2012. E-Book ***(978-1-61039-025-5(3))*** PublicAffairs.

Arthur, John. Race, Equality, & the Burdens of History. 2007. (ENG.). 340p. (C). 83.99 *(978-0-521-87937-8(X))*; per. 27.99 *(978-0-521-70495-3(2))* Cambridge Univ. Pr.

Benjamin Lois. Three Black Generations at the Crossroads: Community, Culture, & Consciousness. 2nd ed. 2007. (ENG., Illus.). 276p. 80.00 *(978-0-7425-6000-0(7))* Rowman & Littlefield Publishers, Inc.

Benjamin, Lois. Three Black Generations at the Crossroads: Community, Culture, & Consciousness. 2nd ed. 2007. (ENG.). 276p. per. 26.95 *(978-0-7425-6001-7(5))* Rowman & Littlefield Publishers, Inc.

Boston, Michael B. The Business Strategy of Booker T. Washington: Its Development & Implementation. 2010. (ENG., Illus.). 308p. 69.95 *(978-0-8130-3473-7(6))* Univ. Pr. of Florida.

Button, James W., et al. Blacks & the Quest for Economic Equality: The Political Economy of Employment in Southern Communities in the United States. 2009. (ENG.). 208p. 60.00 *(978-0-271-03555-0(2))* Pennsylvania State Univ. Pr.

Chambers, Samuel, 2nd. Let's See, Democrats, Republicans or the Issues... A guide in fulfilling our duty to grasp the issues affecting, All Americans Third Edition. 2007. 402p. per. *(978-0-9678464-3-9(9))* Stellar & Leigh.

Clingman, James. Black Empowerment with an Attitude! You Got a Problem with That? 2007. 318p. per. 17.95 *(978-0-9799308-4-3(7))* Milligan Bks.

Coleman, Larry E. The Black Man's Little Book of Success Secrets: 7 Spiritual Secrets for Breaking th Curse of Poverty. 2007. per. 14.95 *(978-0-9790644-2-5(2))* Crowner-Coleman Publishing.

Commission on Civil Rights (U.S.), ed. The Impact of Illegal Immigration on the Wages & Employment Opportunities of Black Workers, August 2010. 2010. (ENG.). 100p. pap. 15.00 *(978-0-16-086401-8(1))* United States Government Printing Office.

Conley, Dalton. Being Black, Living in the Red: Race, Wealth, & Social Policy in America. 10th anniv. ed. 2009. (ENG., Illus.). 234p. pap. 24.95 *(978-0-520-26130-3(5))* Univ. of California Pr.

Cox, Oliver Cromwell. Race Relations Raw & Uncensored: Elements & Social Dynamics. rev. ed. 2010. Orig. Title: Race Relations: Elements & Social Dynamics. (C). pap. 65.00 *(978-0-9761541-5-0(3))* Oliver Cromwell Cox Online Institute, The.

Darden, Joe T., et al. The State of Black Michigan, 1967-2007. Darden, Joe T. et al, eds. 2007. (ENG., Illus.). 364p. per. 39.95 *(978-0-87013-827-0(8))* Michigan State Univ. Pr.

Davidson, Wayne. Manufacturing African American Self-Employment. 2008. 292p. pap. *(978-3-639-08502-0(7))* VDM Verlag Dr. Mueller e.K.

Davis, Robert E. The American Negro's Dilemm: The Negro's Self-Imposed Predicament. 2011. 158p. 41.95 ***(978-1-258-04152-6(9))*** Literary Licensing, LLC.

Delton, Jennifer. Racial Integration in Corporate America, 1940-1990. 2009. (ENG.). 320p. 87.00 *(978-0-521-51509-2(2))*; pap. 24.99 *(978-0-521-73080-8(5))* Cambridge Univ. Pr.

Dodson, Howard & Palmer, Colin A. The Black Condition. Dodson, Howard, ed. 2008. (Schomburg Studies on the Black Experience: Ser.). (ENG., Illus.). 272p. pap. 24.95 *(978-0-87013-838-6(3))* Michigan State Univ. Pr.

Du Bois, W. E. B. Economic Co-operation among Negro Americans. 184p. reprint ed. 88.00 *(978-0-7222-9723-0(8))* Library Reprints, Inc.

Ellis, William. White Ethics & Black Power: The Emergence of the West Side Organization. 2009. (ENG.). 205p. pap. 24.95 *(978-0-202-36289-2(2))* Aldine Transaction.

Gill, Tiffany. Beauty Shop Politics: African American Women's Activism in the Beauty Industry. 2010. (Women in American History Ser.). (ENG., Illus.). 208p. pap. 25.00 *(978-0-252-07696-1(6))* Univ. of Illinois Pr.

Golden, Myron. The Ebony Treasure Map: The Roadmap to Riches for African Americans. 2006. per. 19.99 *(978-0-9788944-0-5(5))* Golden, Myron Enterprises.

Greene, Lorenzo J. & Woodson, Carter G. The Negro Wage Earner. 2008. 408p. 34.95 *(978-1-4344-7246-5(9))*; pap. 24.95 *(978-1-4344-7245-8(0))* Wildside Pr., LLC.

Harris, Laurie L. The Great Migration North, 1910-1970. 2011. (Defining Moments Ser.). (YA). lib. bdg. 55.00 *(978-0-7808-1186-7(0))* Omnigraphics, Inc.

Hattery, Angela J. & Smith, Earl. African American Families. 2007. (Illus.). 408p. (C). per. 53.00 *(978-1-4129-2466-5(9))*, B24669P) SAGE Pubns., Inc.

Hedblad, Alan, ed. African American Alamnac. 11th rev. ed. 2011. 1500p. 312.00 *(978-1-4144-4547-2(4))* Cengage Gale.

Hermann, Janet Sharp. The Pursuit of a Dream. 2006. (ENG., Illus.). 312p. reprint ed. per. 25.00 *(978-1-57806-129-7(6))* Univ. Pr. of Mississippi.

Higgs, Robert. Competition & Coercion: Blacks in the American Economy 1865-1914. 2008. (ENG., Illus.). 220p. (C). pap. 32.99 *(978-0-521-08840-4(2))* Cambridge Univ. Pr.

House-Soremekun, Bessie. Confronting the Odds: African American Entrepreneurship in Cleveland, Ohio. 2009. (Illus.). 250p. pap. *(978-1-60635-006-5(4))* Kent State Univ. Pr.

Jeffries, Judson L., ed. Comrades: A Local History of the Black Panther Party. 2007. (Blacks in the Diaspora Ser.). (ENG., Illus.). 336p. per. 24.95 *(978-0-253-21930-5(2)*, 0253219302) Indiana Univ. Pr.

Jewell, Joseph O. Race, Social Reform & the Making of a Black Middle Class: Atlanta, 1870-1900. 2007. (ENG.). 236p. 84.00 *(978-0-7425-3545-9(2))* Rowman & Littlefield Publishers, Inc.

Johnson, Hannibal B. Greenwood Cultural Center: Jewel in the Crown. 2008. *(978-1-57864-465-0(8))* Donning Co. Pubs.

Jones, Stephanie J. & Height, Dorothy. The State of Black America 2008: In the Black Woman's Voice. Jones, Stephanie J. et al, eds. Malveaux, Julianne, contrib. by. 2008. (State of Black America Ser.). (ENG., Illus.). 254p. pap. 19.95 *(978-0-914758-01-3(2))* National Urban League, National Headquarters.

Kirby, Edwena. Shifting the Paradigm: Through the Lens of the Disadvantaged. 2010. 144p. pap. *(978-3-8383-0094-8(7))* Lambert Academic Publishing.

Lamaute, Denise. The African-American Handbook & Guide to Rolling over into RetirementRich. 14.95 *(978-0-9749779-8-0(5))* Amber Bks.

Leiman, Melvin. The Political Economy of Racism. 2010. (ENG.). 432p. pap. 22.00 *(978-1-60846-066-3(5))* Haymarket Bks.

Levenstein, Lisa. A Movement Without Marches: African American Women & the Politics of Poverty in Postwar Philadelphia. (John Hope Franklin Series in African American History & Culture Ser.). (ENG., Illus.). 2010. 320p. pap. 22.95 *(978-0-8078-7164-5(8))* 2009. 352p. 47.50 *(978-0-8078-3272-1(3))* Univ. of North Carolina Pr.

Lipsitz, George. How Racism Takes Place. 2011. (ENG.). 312p. 76.50 *(978-1-4399-0255-4(0))*; 320p. pap. 26.95 *(978-1-4399-0256-1(9))* Temple Univ. Pr.

Malcolm, Nigel I. One More River to Cross: The Therapeutic Rhetoric of Race in the Post-Civil Rights Era. 2007. (ENG.). 116p. 45.50 *(978-0-7618-3959-0(3))*; per. 26.50 *(978-0-7618-3960-6(7))* Univ. Pr. of America, Inc.

Malveaux, Julianne. Surviving & Thriving: 365 Facts in Black Economic History, vol. 2010. (Illus.). 14.95 *(978-0-9827750-0-4(8))* Last Word Productions.

Marsh, Kris. Black Non-Family Households: Their Socioeconomic Position & Spatial Buffering. 2008. 128p. pap. *(978-3-639-03574-2(7))* VDM Verlag Dr. Mueller e.K.

Miller, Eben. Born along the Color Line: The 1933 Amenia Conference & the Rise of a National Civil Rights Movement, 1 vol. 2012. (ENG., Illus.). 368p. 29.95 *(978-0-19-517455-7(0))* Oxford Univ. Pr., Inc.

Muhammad, Dedrick. Understanding Racial Inequality in the Obama Era: A Primer. 2011. 208p. pap. 10.00 *(978-1-56656-823-4(4))* Interlink Publishing Group, Inc.

Newberry, Jay. Middle Class African Americans. 2010. 56p. pap. *(978-3-639-23477-0(4))* VDM Verlag Dr. Mueller e.K.

Okoye, Chiazam Ugo. President Reagans Conservative Fisal Policy: Unemployment among African Americans. 2006. (ENG.). 250p. 62.99 *(978-0-7618-3099-3(5))*; pap. 41.99 *(978-0-7618-3100-6(2))* Univ. Pr. of America, Inc.

O'Malley, Michael. Face Value: The Entwined History of Money & Race in America. 2012. (ENG., Illus.). 272p. 75.00 ***(978-0-226-62937-7(6))***; pap. 25.00 ***(978-0-226-62938-4(4))*** Univ. of Chicago Pr.

Ondaatje, Michael. Black Conservative Intellectuals in Modern America. 232p. (C). 2012. pap. 22.50 ***(978-0-8122-2204-3(0))*** 2009. 34.95 *(978-0-8122-4206-5(8))* Univ. of Pennsylvania Pr.

Parks-Yancy, Rochelle. Equal Work, Unequal Careers: African Americans in the Workforce. 2010. 150p. 55.00 *(978-1-935049-23-4(2))* FirstForumPress.

Reid, Debra A. & Bennett, Evan P., eds. Beyond Forty Acres & a Mule: African American Landowning Families since Reconstruction. 2012. (ENG., Illus.). 352p. 69.95 ***(978-0-8130-3986-2(X))*** Univ. Pr. of Florida.

Richardson, Gwen. Why African Americans Can't Get Ahead: And How We Can Change It with Group Economics. 2008. 186p. pap. 14.95 *(978-0-9800250-1-9(X))* Cushcity Communications.

Riles, Kevin. 40 Acres & a Mule: The African American Guide to Building Wealth Through Real Estate. 2008. 126p. pap. 15.95 *(978-0-615-18895-9(8))* Riles, Kevin.

Robinson, Eugene. Disintegration: The Splintering of Black America. (ENG.). 272p. 2011. pap. 15.95 *(978-0-7679-2996-7(9)*, Anchor) 2010. 24.95 *(978-0-385-52654-8(7)*, Doubleday) Knopf Doubleday Publishing Group.

Sacks, Marcy S. Before Harlem: The Black Experience in New York City Before World War I. 2006. (Politics & Culture in Modern America Ser.). (Illus.). 240p. (C). 59.95 *(978-0-8122-3961-4(X))* Univ. of Pennsylvania Pr.

Schutz, Mary Ellen, ed. The State of Black Madison 2008: Before the Tipping Point. 2008. 30p. pap. 5.00 *(978-0-615-20703-2(0))* Urban League of Greater Madison.

The Silent Depression: How Are Minorities Faring in the Economic Downturn?: Hearing Before the Committee on Oversight & Government Reform, House of Representatives, One Hundred Eleventh Congress, First Session, September 23, 2009. 2010. (Illus.). iii, 1658p. ***(978-0-16-088092-6(0)***, 552-070-42512-8) United States Government Printing Office.

Smith, J. Owens. The Politics of Ethnic & Racial Inequality: A Systematic Comparative Macro-Analysis from the Colonial Period to the Present. 3rd rev. ed. 2011. (ENG.). 428p. pap. 52.72 *(978-0-7575-0802-8(2)*, 0757508022) Kendall Hunt Publishing Co.

Solomon, Lewis D. Cycles of Poverty & Crime in America's Inner Cities. 2012. (ENG.). 171p. 39.95 ***(978-1-4128-4738-4(9))*** Transaction Pubs.

Sterner, Richard. The Negro's Share: A Study of Income, Consumption, Housing, & Public Assistance. 2008. 448p. pap. 45.00 *(978-1-59740-630-7(9))* ACLS Humanities E-Book.

Trotter, Joe W. & Day, Jared N. Race & Renaissance: African Americans in Pittsburgh since World War II. 2010. (ENG., Illus.). 304p. 29.95 *(978-0-8229-4391-4(3))* Univ. of Pittsburgh Pr.

Warren Hill, Laura & Rabig, Julia, eds. The Business of Black Power: Community Development, Capitalism, & Corporate Responsibility in Postwar America. 2012. (Illus.). 336p. 85.00 ***(978-1-58046-403-1(3))*** Univ. of Rochester Pr.

Weems, Robert. Business in Black & White: American Presidents & Black Entrepreneurs in the Twentieth Century. 2009. (ENG., Illus.). 352p. 55.00 *(978-0-8147-7517-2(9))* New York Univ. Pr.

Williams, Walter E. Race & Economics: How Much Can We Blame on Discrimination? 2011. (Hoover inst press Publication). (ENG.). 174p. 24.95 *(978-0-8179-1244-4(4))*; pap. 14.95 *(978-0-8179-1245-1(2))* Hoover Institution Pr.

Wilson, David. Cities & Race: America's New Black Ghetto. 2006. (Questioning Cities Ser.). (Illus.). 175p. per. 51.95 *(978-0-415-35806-4(X)*, RU5806X) Routledge.

Wilson, William Julius. The Declining Significance of Race: Blacks & Changing American Institutions. 3rd ed. 2012. (ENG.). 272p. pap. 20.00 ***(978-0-226-90141-1(6))*** Univ. of Chicago Pr.

—The Truly Disadvantaged: The Inner City, the Underclass, & Public Policy, Second Edition. 2nd ed. 2012. (ENG., Illus.). 320p. pap. 20.00 ***(978-0-226-90126-8(2))*** Univ. of Chicago Pr.

Woods, Clyde. Development Arrested: From the Plantation Era to the Katrina Crisis in the Mississippi Delta. rev. ed. 2012. 352p. pap. 26.95 *(978-1-84467-561-6(0)*, New Left Bks.) Verso Bks. GBR. Dist: Norton, W. W. & Co., Inc.

AFRICAN AMERICANS—EDUCATION

see also African American Students; African American Teachers; African American Universities and Colleges; African Americans—Study and Teaching

AEHE Staff, et al. Unearthing Promise & Potential: Our Nation's Historically Black Colleges & Universities. 2010. (J-B ASHE Higher Education Report Series (AEHE) Ser.: 135). (ENG.). 152p. pap. 29.00 *(978-0-470-63510-0(X)*, Jossey-Bass) Wiley, John & Sons, Inc.

Akassi, Monique Leslie. Neo Hybrid Pedagogy in Post Colonialism Composition. 2011. 160p. pap. ***(978-3-8443-3122-6(0))*** Lambert Academic Publishing.

Alliance Against the Odds: The Manual Training High School Story. 2008. 1000p. pap. 49.95 *(978-0-9815987-0-3(6))* D&J Educational Consulting & Publishing Services.

Alridge, Derrick P. The Educational Thought of W. E. B. du Bois: An Intellectual History. 2008. (ENG.). 208p. 58.00 *(978-0-8077-4837-4(4))* Teachers College Pr., Teachers College, Columbia Univ.

—The Educational Thought of W. E. B. Du Bois: An Intellectual History. 2008. (ENG.). 208p. pap. 26.95 *(978-0-8077-4836-7(6))* Teachers College Pr., Teachers College, Columbia Univ.

America's Black Colleges & Universities: Models of Excellence & Challenges for the Future: Hearing Before the Committee on Education & Labor, U.S. House of Representatives, One Hundred Tenth Congress, Second Session, Hearing Held in Washington, DC, March 13, 2008. 2008. iii, 57p. *(978-0-16-081512-6(6)*, 552-070-37868-5) United States Government Printing Office.

Anderson, James D. No Sacrifice Too Great: The History of African American Education from Slavery to Twenty-First Century. 2008. 224p. 23.95 *(978-0-8070-0028-1(0))* Beacon Pr.

Anderson/Kharem, ed. Education as Freedom: African American Educational Thought & Activism. (ENG.). 242p. 2010. pap. 29.95 *(978-0-7391-2069-9(7))* 2009. (Illus.). 73.50 *(978-0-7391-2068-2(9))* Lexington Bks.

Atkinson, Ann L. Education for the New Millennium. 2006. 50p. per. 8.95 *(978-1-59824-369-7(1))* E-BookTime LLC.

Augusta-Dupar, Cora M. The Mission & Vision Statements of Ten Historically Black Colleges & Universities - a Content Analysis Study. 2008. 184p. pap. *(978-3-639-04374-7(X))* VDM Verlag Dr. Mueller e.K.

Bartee, RoSusan D. School Matters: Why African American Students Need Multiple Forms of Capital. (Counterpoints: Studies in the Postmodern Theory of Education Ser.). 192p. (C). 89.95 *(978-1-4331-0039-0(8))* Lang, Peter Publishing, Inc.

Baumann, Roland M. Constructing Black Education at Oberlin College: A Documentary History. 2010. (ENG., Illus.). 472p. 65.00 *(978-0-8214-1887-1(4))* Ohio Univ. Pr.

Beachum, Floyd D. & McCray, Carlos R. Cultural Collision & Collusion: Reflections on Hip-Hop Culture, Values, & Schools. 2010. *(978-1-4331-0594-4(2))* Lang, Peter GmbH, Europaischer Verlag der Wissenschaften.

Beasley, Maya A. Opting Out: Losing the Potential of America's Young Black Elite. 2011. (ENG., Illus.). 240p. 70.00 *(978-0-226-04013-4(5))*; pap. 25.00 *(978-0-226-04014-1(3))* Univ. of Chicago Pr.

Belgrave, Faye Z., et al. Brothers of Ujima: A Cultural Enrichment Program to Empower Adolescent African American Males. 2011. pap. 26.95 ***(978-0-87822-652-8(4))*** Research Pr.

Belgrave, Faye Z., et al. Sisters of Nia: A Cultural Enrichment Program to Empower African American Girls. 2008. 174p. pap. 26.95 *(978-0-87822-606-1(0))* Research Pr.

Betsey, Charles L., ed. Historically Black Colleges & Universities. 2008. (ENG.). 165p. pap. 24.95 *(978-1-4128-0782-1(4))* Transaction Pubs.

Biondi, Martha. The Black Revolution on Campus. 2012. (ENG.). 366p. 34.95 ***(978-0-520-26922-4(5))*** Univ. of California Pr.

Blascoer, Frances. Colored School Children in New York. 2009. 188p. 26.99 *(978-1-110-11950-9(X))*; pap. 21.75 *(978-1-110-11947-9(X))* BiblioBazaar.

Boles, Ed D. James M., et al. Dr. Skinner's Remarkable School for "Colored Deaf, Dumb, & Blind Children," 1857-1860. 2010. (Illus.). 37p. pap. 9.95 ***(978-0-9845983-0-4(8))*** People Ink Pr.

Bolton, Charles C. The Hardest Deal of All: The Battle over School Integration in Mississippi, 1870-1980. 2007. (ENG., Illus.). 278p. pap. 25.00 *(978-1-934110-74-4(4))* Univ. Pr. of Mississippi.

Bonner, Fred A. Academically Gifted African American Male College Students, 1 vol. 2010. 217p. 44.95 *(978-0-89789-857-7(5)*, H857, Praeger Pubs.) Greenwood Publishing Group, Inc.

Boston (Mass.) Colored Citizens. Triumph of Equal School Rights in Boston Proceedings of the Presentation Meeting Held in Boston, Dec 17, 1855; Incl Addresses by John T Hilton, Wm. 2011. 26p. pap. 11.99 ***(978-1-4181-9195-5(7))*** MPublishing.

Brady, Diane. The Fraternity: In 1968, a Visionary Priest Recruited 20 Black Men to the College of the Holy Cross & Changed Their Lives & the Course of History. 2012. (ENG., Illus.). 256p. 25.00 *(978-0-385-52474-2(9))* Spiegel & Grau.

Brooks, F. Erik & Starks, Glenn L. Historically Black Colleges & Universities: An Encyclopedia. 2011. E-Book ***(978-0-313-39416-4(4)***, Greenwood Pr.) Greenwood Publishing Group, Inc.

Brown, Anthony L. & Donnor, Jamel K., eds. The Education of Black Males in a 'Post-Racial' World. 2011. (ENG., Illus.). 152p. (C). 125.00 *(978-0-415-67302-0(X))* Routledge.

Brown, M. Christopher. Broken Cisterns: African American Education Fifty Years after Brown. 2008. *(978-1-59311-043-7(X))*; pap. *(978-1-59311-042-0(1))* Information Age Publishing, Inc.

Brown, M. Christopher & Bartee, RoSusan D. School Matters: Why African American Students Need Multiple Forms of Capital. 2007. (Counterpoints: Studies in the Postmodern Theory of Education Ser.). (Illus.). 192p. (C). pap. 32.95 *(978-0-8204-8688-8(4))* Lang, Peter Publishing, Inc.

Burnley, Lawrence/A. Q. The Cost of Unity: African American Agency & Education & the Christian Church, 1865-1914. 2009. 320p. 45.00 *(978-0-88146-134-3(2))* Mercer Univ. Pr.

Burnside, Jacqueline Grisby. Berea & Madison County. 2007. (Black America Ser.). (ENG., Illus.). 128p. per. 19.99 *(978-0-7385-4432-8(9))* Arcadia Publishing.

Butler-Derge, Shirley R. Rites of Passage: A Program for High School African American Males. 2009. (ENG., Illus.). 70p. pap. 15.99 *(978-0-7618-4320-7(5))* Univ. Pr. of America, Inc.

Cary, Lorene. Black Ice. tchr.'s training gde. ed. *(978-0-394-27226-9(9)*, Vintage) Knopf Doubleday Publishing Group.

Chambers, Crystal Renée & Sharpe, Rhonda V., eds. Black Female Undergraduates on Campus: Successes & Challenges, Vol. 12. 2012. (Diversity in Higher Education Ser.). (Illus.). 240p. 114.95 ***(978-1-78052-502-0(8))*** Emerald Group Publishing Ltd. GBR. Dist: Turpin Distribution Services Ltd.

Charron, Katherine. Freedom's Teacher: The Life of Septima Clark. 2012. (ENG., Illus.). 480p. pap. 26.95 ***(978-0-8078-7222-2(9))*** Univ. of North Carolina Pr.

Charron, Katherine Mellen. Freedom's Teacher: The Life of Septima Clark. 2009. (ENG., Illus.). 480p. 36.95 *(978-0-8078-3332-2(0))* Univ. of North Carolina Pr.

Clair-Hull, Judith. Strategies for Educating African American Children. 2010. (Teaching for Spiritual Growth Ser.). 137p. per. 14.95 *(978-1-932715-79-8(7))* UMI (Urban Ministries, Inc.).

Clark, Tina. How to Home School your African American Child. 2009. 107p. pap. 19.36 *(978-0-557-10038-5(0))* Lulu Enterprises Inc.

Collins, Donald R. Conducting Multi-Generational Qualitative Research in Education: An Experiment in Grounded Theory. 2011. (Black Studies & Critical Thinking Ser.). 160p. (C). 129.95 ***(978-1-4331-1020-7(2))***; pap. 34.95 ***(978-1-4331-1019-1(9))*** Lang, Peter Publishing, Inc.

Comarcho, Carole. Minority Male Student Retention. 2010. 76p. pap. *(978-3-8383-4497-3(9))* Lambert Academic Publishing.

Cooper, Jr. Why? African american children can not Read. 2009. 76p. pap. 10.95 *(978-0-595-45735-9(5))* iUniverse, Inc.

Dabney, Charles W. Universal Education in the South Set, 2 vols. reprint ed. lib. bdg. 250.00 *(978-0-7222-0406-1(X))* Library Reprints, Inc.

Dabney, Charles Williams. Universal Education in the South: Vol. 1, from the Beginning To 1900. 2011. (ENG.). 584p. pap. 50.00 ***(978-0-8078-9644-0(6))*** Univ. of North Carolina Pr.

—Universal Education in the South: Vol. 2, the Southern Education Movement. 2011. (ENG.). 624p. pap. 50.00 ***(978-0-8078-9645-7(4))*** Univ. of North Carolina Pr.

Dahlk, Bill. Against the Wind: African Americans & the Schools in Milwaukee, 1963-2002. 2010. pap. *(978-0-87462-078-8(3))* Marquette Univ. Pr.

Dancy, T. Elon. The Brother Code: Manhood & Masculinity among African American Men in College. 2012. ***(978-1-61735-761-9(8))***; pap. ***(978-1-61735-760-2(X))*** Information Age Publishing, Inc.

Dartt, Rebecca H. Women Activists in the Fight for Georgia School Desegregation, 1958-1961. 2008. (ENG., Illus.). 229p. pap. 35.00 *(978-0-7864-3843-3(6))* McFarland & Co., Inc. Pubs.

Davis, Bernard. Portraits of the African-American Experience in Concord-Cabarrus, North Carolina 1860-2008. 2010. 562p. 34.99 *(978-1-4500-5238-2(X))*; pap. 23.99 *(978-1-4500-5237-5(1))* Xlibris Corp.

Deutsch, Stephanie. You Need a Schoolhouse. 2011. (ENG.). 244p. 24.95 *(978-0-8101-2790-6(3))* Northwestern Univ. Pr.

Diehl, Huston. Dream Not of Other Worlds: Teaching in a Segregated Elementary School,1970. 2007. (Sightline Bks.). (Illus.). 276p. 24.95 *(978-0-87745-996-5(7))* Univ. of Iowa Pr.

Diop, Mateen. Single-Gender Schools & the Inner-City; Can They Work? 2010. 140p. pap. *(978-3-639-23143-4(0))* VDM Verlag Dr. Mueller e.K.

Dodson, Howard & Palmer, Colin A. The Black Condition. Dodson, Howard, ed. 2008. (Schomburg Studies on the Black Experience: Ser.). (ENG., Illus.). 272p. pap. 24.95 *(978-0-87013-838-6(3))* Michigan State Univ. Pr.

Dowdy, Joanne Kilgour. PhD Stories: Conversations with My Sisters. 2008. (Understanding Education & Policy Ser.). *(978-1-57273-797-6(2))*; 176p. *(978-1-57273-796-9(4))* Hampton Pr., Inc.

Eaves, John H. The Morehouse Mystique: Lessons to Develop Black Men. 2009. (ENG.). 250p. pap. 16.95 *(978-1-934155-14-1(4))* African American Images.

Edwards, Patricia A., et al. Change Is Gonna Come: Transforming Literacy Education for African American Students. 2010. (Language & Literacy Ser.). (ENG., Illus.). 224p. pap. 24.95 *(978-0-8077-5084-1(0))*; 59.00 *(978-0-8077-5085-8(9))* Teachers College Pr., Teachers College, Columbia Univ.

Emdin, Chris. Urban Science Education for the Hip-Hop Generation. 2010. 142p. *(978-90-8790-987-1(X))* Sense Pubs.

Evans, Stephanie Y. African Americans & Community Engagement in Higher Education: Community Service, Service-Learning, & Community-Based Research. Taylor, Colette M., tr. 2009. 288p. 75.00 ***(978-1-4384-2873-4(1))***; pap. 24.95 *(978-1-4384-2874-1(X))* State Univ. of New York Pr. (Suny Pr.).

—Black Women in the Ivory Tower, 1850-1954: An Intellectual History. 2008. (ENG., Illus.). 288p. pap. 24.95 *(978-0-8130-3268-9(7))* Univ. Pr. of Florida.

Evans-Winters, Venus E. Teaching Black Girls: Resiliency in Urban — Revised Edition. 2011. (Counterpoints: Studies in the Postmodern Theory of Education Ser.). 200p. (C). pap. 29.95 *(978-1-4331-0593-7(4))* Lang, Peter Publishing, Inc.

Fallace, Thomas D. Dewey & the Dilemma of Race: An Intellectual History, 1895-1922. 2010. (ENG.). 224p. 31.95 *(978-0-8077-5164-0(2))*; pap. 68.00 *(978-0-8077-5165-7(0))* Teachers College Pr., Teachers College, Columbia Univ.

Fernandez, Paula B. Academic Orientations of African-American Adolescents. 2008. 120p. pap. (978-3-639-08195-4(1)) VDM Verlag Dr. Mueller e.K.

Fiore & Hill. Creating Personal Success on the HBCU Campus. 2011. (ENG.). 96p. (C). pap. 20.95 **(978-1-111-83771-6(6))** Wadsworth.

Fisher, Maisha. Black Literate Lives: Historical & Contemporary Perspectives. 2008. (Critical Social Thought Ser.). (Illus.). XXII, 178p. pap. 39.95 (978-0-415-95865-3(2)) Routledge.

Flowers, Lamont & Pascarella, Erne. African American Students College. 2011. 256p. pap. 24.95 (978-1-57922-128-7(9)) Stylus Publishing, LLC.

Flowers, Lamont A. & Pascarella, Ernest T. African Americans in College: The Impact of Institutional Racial Composition on Student Development & Educational Outcomes. 2011. 256p. 59.95 (978-1-57922-127-0(0)) Stylus Publishing, LLC.

Ford, Donna & Granthan, Tarek. Gifted & Advanced Black Students in School: An Anthology of Critical Works. 2011. (ENG.). 300p. pap. 45.00 (978-1-59363-700-2(4)) Prufrock Pr.

Foster, Lenoar & Tillman, Linda C. African American Perspectives on Leadership in Schools: Building a Culture of Empowerment. 2009. (ENG.). 264p. 74.95 (978-1-60709-488-3(6)); pap. 32.95 (978-1-60709-489-0(4)) Rowman & Littlefield Publishers, Inc.

From Servitude to Service. 232p. reprint ed. 98.00 (978-0-7222-9727-8(0)) Library Reprints, Inc.

Gandara, Patricia, et al, eds. Expanding Opportunity in Higher Education: Leveraging Promise. 2006. (SUNY Series, Frontiers in Education). (Illus.). 352p. (C). 94.50 (978-0-7914-6863-0(1)) State Univ. of New York Pr.

Gasman, Marybeth. Historically Black Colleges & Universities: Triumphs, Troubles, & Taboos. Gasman, Marybeth & Tudico, Christopher L., eds. 2008. (ENG.). 272p. 100.00 (978-0-230-60273-1(8)) Palgrave Macmillan.

Gasman, Marybeth & Bowman III, Nelson. A Guide to Fundraising at Historically Black Colleges & Universities: An All Campus Approach. 2011. (ENG., Illus.). 200p. 145.00 (978-0-415-89272-8(4)); pap. 35.95 (978-0-415-89273-5(2)) Routledge.

Gause, C. P. Integration Matters: Navigating Identity, Culture, & Resistance. 2008. (Counterpoints. Studies in the Postmodern Theory of Education Ser.). 232p. (C). 32.95 (978-1-4331-0202-8(1)) Lang, Peter Publishing, Inc.

Georges, Jean Ricardy. Don't Blame the Blacks Because Slavery Systems Still Exist. 2007. (978-1-59835-052-4(8)) Cambridge BrickHouse, Inc.

Gilyard, Keith. True to the Language Game: African American Discourse, Cultural Politics, & Pedagogy. 2011. (ENG., Illus.). 336p. 150.00 (978-0-415-88716-8(X)); pap. 39.95 (978-0-415-88717-5(8)) Routledge.

Glasgow Communications. Why She Stayed: At an African-American School, Solomon Coles, During Desegregation. 2nd ed. 2009. (Illus.). 117p. pap. 19.95 (978-0-615-29648-7(3)) Glasgow Communications.

Glenn, Charles. African-American/Afro-Canadian Schooling: From the Colonial Period to the Present. 2011. (ENG., Illus.). 216p. 85.00 (978-0-230-11416-6(4)) Palgrave Macmillan.

Goldstone, Dwonna. Integrating the 40 Acres: The Fifty-Year Struggle for Racial Equality at the University of Texas. (ENG.). 232p. 2012. pap. 24.95 **(978-0-8203-4085-2(5))** 2006. (Illus.). 29.95 (978-0-8203-2828-7(6)) Univ. of Georgia Pr.

Gordy, Sondra Hercher. Finding the Lost Year: What Happened When Little Rock Closed Its Public Schools? 2009. (Illus.). 248p. 29.95 (978-1-55728-900-1(X)) Univ. of Arkansas Pr.

Greenberg, Jack & Thomas, Kendall. 50 Years Later: The Legacy of Brown V. Board of Education: Reflections & Colloquy. 2009. x, 192p. pap. **(978-0-9747286-4-3(0))** Twelve Tables Pr.

Hanson, Sandra. Swimming Against the Tide: African American Girls & Science Education. 2009. (Illus.). 224p. pap. 24.95 (978-1-59213-622-3(2)) Temple Univ. Pr.

—Swimming Against the Tide: African American Girls & Science Education. 2008. (ENG., Illus.). 224p. 71.50 (978-1-59213-621-6(4)) Temple Univ. Pr.

Harlan, Louis R. Separate & Unequal: Public School Campaigns & Racism in the Southern Seaboard States, 1901-1915. 2011. (ENG.). 304p. pap. 40.00 (978-0-8078-6758-7(6)) Univ. of North Carolina Pr.

Harmon, Hugh J. Bridging the Achievement Gap. 2010. 118p. pap. 14.99 (978-0-557-05822-8(8)) Lulu Enterprises Inc.

Harris, Glen Anthony. The Ocean Hill-Brownsville Conflict: Intellectual Struggles Between Blacks & Jews at Midcentury. 2012. (ENG.). 204p. (gr. 17). 65.00 **(978-0-7391-6683-3(2))** Lexington Bks.

Harris, Theresa & Taylor, George. Raising African American Males: Strategies & Interventions for Successful Outcomes. 2012. **(978-1-60709-300-8(6))** Rowman & Littlefield Education.

Harris, Theresa & Taylor, George, eds. Raising African-American Males: Strategies & Interventions for Successful Outcomes. 2012. (ENG.). 116p. 40.00 **(978-1-60709-298-8(0))** Rowman & Littlefield Education.

Harris/Taylor, ed. Raising African-American Males: Strategies & Interventions for Successful Outcomes. 2012. (ENG.). 116p. pap. 18.95 **(978-1-60709-299-5(9))** Rowman & Littlefield Education.

HBCUs Models for Success: Supporting Achievement & Retention of Black Males. 2006. (FAR & ENG.). per. (978-1-889732-49-7(4)) Word For Word Publishing Co.

Hedblad, Alan, ed. African American Alamnac. 11th rev. ed. 2011. 1500p. 312.00 (978-1-4144-4547-2(4)) Cengage Gale.

Hicks, Terence. The Educational Lockout of African Americans in Prince Edward County, Virginia (1959-1964) Personal Accounts & Reflections. 2010. (Issues in Black Education Ser.). (ENG.). 118p. 41.99 (978-0-7618-5062-5(7)); pap. 20.99 (978-0-7618-5063-2(5)) Univ. Pr. of America, Inc.

Hill, Kenneth H. Religious Education in the African American Church: A Comprehensive Introduction. 2007. (C). 24.99 (978-0-8272-0820-9(0)) Chalice Pr.

Hill, Teresa. Every Closed Eye Ain't Sleep: African American Perspectives on the Achievement Gap. 2011. (ENG., Illus.). 126p. 40.00 (978-1-61048-104-5(6)); pap. 19.95 (978-1-61048-105-2(4)) Rowman & Littlefield Education.

Hill, Teresa D. Every Closed Eye Ain't Sleep: African American Perspectives on the Achievement Gap. 2011. E-Book **(978-1-61048-106-9(2))** Rowman & Littlefield Publishers, Inc.

Höggerl, Christiane. Problems of African American Education in Literature & Film. 2010. 112p. pap. (978-3-639-26933-8(0)) VDM Verlag Dr. Mueller e.K.

Holland, Antonio F. Nathan B. Young: And the Struggle over Black Higher Education. 2006. (Missouri Biography Ser.). (ENG., Illus.). 248p. (C). 39.95 (978-0-8262-1679-3(X)) Univ. of Missouri Pr.

Holmes, David G. Revisiting Racialized Voice: African American Ethos in Language & Literature. 2007. (ENG.). 144p. per. 30.00 (978-0-8093-2767-6(8)) Southern Illinois Univ. Pr.

Horn, Aaron Lamont. The Role of Father-Like Care in the Education of Young Black Males. 2010. v, 133p. 99.95 (978-0-7734-3771-5(1)) Mellen, Edwin Pr., The.

Horne, Odell, Jr. Voices of the Talented Tenth: Values of Young Black Males in Higher Education. 2007. (ENG., Illus.). 74p. per. 24.50 (978-0-7618-3637-7(3)) Univ. Pr. of America, Inc.

Ighodaro, Erhabor & Wiggan, Greg A. Curriculum Violence: America's New Civil Rights Issue. 2010. viii, 226p. pap. 98.00 (978-1-61728-683-4(4)) Nova Science Pubs., Inc.

Irvine, Russell W. The African American Quest for Institutions of Higher Education Before the Civil War: The Forgotten Histories of the Ashmun Institute, Liberia College, & Avery College. 2010. (Illus.). 752p. 159.95 (978-0-7734-1309-2(X)) Mellen, Edwin Pr., The.

Jackson, David H. Booker T. Washington & the Struggle Against White Supremacy: The Southern Educational Tours, 1908-1912. 2008. (ENG., Illus.). 288p. 89.00 (978-0-230-60652-4(0)) Palgrave Macmillan.

Jackson, David H., Jr. Booker T. Washington & the Struggle against White Supremacy: The Southern Educational Tours, 1908-1912. 2009. (ENG.). 272p. pap. 32.00 (978-0-230-62138-1(4)) Palgrave Macmillan.

Jackson, Jerlando F. L., ed. Strengthening the African American Educational Pipeline: Informing Research, Policy, & Practice. 2007. (Illus.). 220p. per. 29.95 (978-0-7914-6988-0(3)) State Univ. of New York Pr.

Jacoway, Elizabeth. Turn Away Thy Son: Little Rock, the Crisis That Shocked the Nation. 2008. 477p. pap. 19.95 (978-1-55728-878-3(X)) Univ. of Arkansas Pr.

Jairrels, Veda. African Americans & Standardized Tests: The Real Reason for Low Test Scores. 2009. (ENG.). 170p. pap. 15.95 (978-1-934155-15-8(2)) African American Images.

Jerke, Iris M. From Black & White to Ed. 2008. 140p. pap. (978-3-639-06737-8(1)) VDM Verlag Dr. Mueller e.K.

Johnson, Alexis. Marital Attitudes of African-Americans Obtaining Graduate Education. 2011. 116p. pap. **(978-3-8454-1992-3(X))** Lambert Academic Publishing.

Johnson, Beverly Black. Gumbo for the Soul: Here's Our Child-Where's the Village? 2008. 128p. pap. 11.95 (978-1-4401-0126-7(4)) iUniverse, Inc.

Johnson, Edward A. School History of the Negro Race in America, 2 vols. in 1. reprint ed. 26.50 (978-0-404-00176-6(9)) AMS Pr., Inc.

Jones, Charles Colcock. The Religious Instruction of Negroes. 38p. reprint ed. lib. bdg. 88.00 (978-0-7222-0859-5(6)) Library Reprints, Inc.

—The Religious Instruction of the Negroes. 2008. (Civil War Ser.). (ENG.). 56p. pap. 9.95 (978-1-4290-1179-2(3)) Applewood Bks.

Jones, Edd. Go & Come Again: Segregation, Tolerance, & Reflection. 2011. 168p. pap. 15.95 **(978-1-4575-0502-7(9))** Dog Ear Publishing, LLC.

Jones, Frank A. What Have We Done to Our Children? Success: Positioning Black Children For. 2007. per. 15.00 (978-0-9667248-3-7(6)) Gibbs Community Foundation.

Kafele, Baruti. Motivating Black Males to Achieve in School & in Life. 2009. pap. 16.95 (978-1-4166-0857-8(5)) Assn. for Supervision & Curriculum Development.

Karpinski, Carol F. A Visible Company of Professionals: African Americans & the National Education Association During the Civil Rights Movement. 2008. (History of Schools & Schooling Ser.). 256p. (C). 89.95 (978-1-4331-0025-3(8)); pap. 32.95 (978-0-8204-8848-6(8)) Lang, Peter Publishing, Inc.

Kelly, Hilton. Race, Remembering, & Jim Crow's Teachers. 2010. (Studies in African American History & Culture Ser.). (ENG., Illus.). 154p. 125.00 (978-0-415-80478-3(7)) Routledge.

Kirk, John A. Beyond Little Rock: The Origins & Legacies of the Central High Crisis. 2007. 213p. 64.95 (978-1-55728-850-9(X)) Univ. of Arkansas Pr.

Kunjufu, Jawanza. Reducing the Black Male Dropout Rate. 2010. (ENG., Illus.). 192p. pap. 15.95 (978-1-934155-22-6(5)) African American Images.

—200+ Educational Strategies to Teach Children of Color. 2009. (ENG.). 200p. pap. 14.95 (978-1-934155-19-6(5)) African American Images.

Ladson-Billings, Gloria, et al. The Dreamkeepers: Successful Teachers of African American Children. 2nd ed. 2009. (ENG., Illus.). 256p. pap. 22.95 (978-0-470-40815-5(4), Jossey-Bass) Wiley, John & Sons, Inc.

Lanney, Naomi E. The Spirit of My Children: Examining the American Educational System in the Urban Core Through a Belief in Student Capabilities. 2006. 97p. per. 16.95 (978-1-58597-395-8(5)) Leathers Publishing.

LaVeist, Thomas & LaVeist, William. Tom Joyner Presents How to Prepare for College. 2009. (ENG.). 144p. pap. 15.00 (978-0-615-27097-5(2)) Amber Bks.

Lee, Carol D. Culture, Literacy, & Learning: Taking Bloom in the Midst of the Whirlwind. 2007. (Multicultural Education Ser.). (ENG., Illus.). 256p. 67.00 (978-0-8077-4749-0(1)); pap. 34.50 (978-0-8077-4748-3(3)) Teachers College Pr., Teachers College, Columbia Univ.

Lewis, Alvin. Strategies for Educating African American Adults. 2010. (Teaching for Spiritual Growth Ser.). 160p. per. 14.95 (978-1-932715-80-4(0)) UMI (Urban Ministries, Inc.).

Littlejohn, Jeffrey L. & Ford, Charles H. Elusive Equality: Desegregation & Resegregation in Norfolk's Public Schools. 2012. (ENG., Illus.). 288p. (gr. 17). 45.00 **(978-0-8139-3288-0(2))** Univ. Pr. of Virginia.

Logan, Shirley W. Liberating Language: Sites of Rhetorical Education in Nineteenth-Century Black America. 2008. (ENG.). 224p. pap. 35.00 (978-0-8093-2872-7(0)) Southern Illinois Univ. Pr.

Lomotey, Kofi & Cohen, Robert S., eds. Encyclopedia of African American Education, 2 vols. 2009. 1152p. 345.00 (978-1-4129-4050-4(8), B40508C) SAGE Pubns., Inc.

Love, Derrick L. The Unfinished Journey. 2008. 86p. pap. 16.95 (978-1-60672-518-4(1)) PublishAmerica, Inc.

Lucisano, Giovani. America's Historically Black Colleges & Universities. 2010. (Education in a Competitive & Globalizing World Ser.). 199p. 79.00 (978-1-60741-510-7(0)) Nova Science Pubs., Inc.

Malveaux, Julianne. Tell Me Why Dear Bennett: Memoirs of Bennett College Belles Class of 1924-2012. 2010. (Illus.). 413p. **(978-0-7884-5160-7(X))** Heritage Bks.

Manson, Tony J., ed. Twenty Issues in Teaching African American Pupils: A Collective Experience of What Works. 2006. (Illus.). 332p. (978-0-7734-5685-3(6)) Mellen, Edwin Pr., The.

Martin, Danny. Mathematics Teaching, Learning & Liberation in the Lives of Black Children. 2009. (Studies in Mathematical Thinking & Learning Ser.). (ENG., Illus.). 376p. pap. 54.95 (978-0-8058-6464-9(4)) Routledge.

—Mathematics Teaching, Learning, & Liberation in the Lives of Black Children. Martin, Danny, ed. 2009. (Studies in Mathematical Thinking & Learning Ser.). (ENG., Illus.). 376p. 160.00 (978-0-8058-6463-2(6)) Routledge.

Mbaiekwe, Carolyn O. Wilson, ed. The Future of Historically Black Colleges & Universities: Ten Presidents Speak Out. 2006. (ENG., Illus.) 220p. per. 39.95 (978-0-7864-2565-5(2)) McFarland & Co., Inc. Pubs.

McAbee, Gary A. Wake Up! 42 Ways to Improve Black America Now! 2012. (ENG.). 158p. pap. 12.99 (978-1-4515-2475-8(7)) CreateSpace.

McCaul, Robert L. The Black Struggle for Public Schooling in Nineteenth-Century Illinois. 2nd ed. 2009. (ENG.). 208p. pap. 17.50 (978-0-8093-2905-2(0)) Southern Illinois Univ. Pr.

Mcchristian, Sarah. The 2 of Me. 2011. 56p. pap. 12.95 **(978-1-4634-6020-4(1))** AuthorHouse.

McCloskey, Patrick. The Street Stops Here: A Year at a Catholic High School in Harlem. 2010. (ENG., Illus.). 480p. pap. 18.95 (978-0-520-26797-8(4)) Univ. of California Pr.

McKinley, Johnnie. Raising Black Students' Achievement Through Culturally Responsive Teaching. 2010. 214p. pap. 28.95 (978-1-4166-1059-5(6)) Assn. for Supervision & Curriculum Development.

Means, Harriett. 19th Century African American Social Settlements. 2011. 140p. pap. **(978-3-8443-0951-5(9))** Lambert Academic Publishing.

Meier, Terry. Black Communications & Learning to Read: Building on Children's Linguistic & Cultural Strengths. 2007. (Illus.). 335p. 110.00 (978-0-8058-5759-7(1)); per. 45.95 (978-0-8058-5760-3(5)) Erlbaum, Lawrence Assocs., Inc.

Mitchell, Johnnie P. The Jig Is up: We Are One! Race Is a Hoax that Fails American Education. 2010. 220p. 27.95 (978-1-4502-1990-7(X)); (ENG.). pap. 17.95 (978-1-4502-1986-0(1)) iUniverse, Inc.

Morris, Jerome. Troubling the Waters: Fulfilling the Promise of Quality Public Schooling for Black Children. 2010. (ENG.). 216p. 64.00 (978-0-8077-5016-2(6)); pap. 27.95 (978-0-8077-5015-5(8)) Teachers College Pr., Teachers College, Columbia Univ.

Morris, Robert C. Reading, 'Riting, & Reconstruction: The Education of Freedmen in the South, 1861-1870. 2010. (ENG., Illus.). 358p. pap. 35.00 (978-0-226-53929-4(6)) Univ. of Chicago Pr.

Morris, Robert C., ed. Freedmen's Schools & Textbooks: Black Education in the South, 1861-1870, 6 vols., Set. Incl. Vol. 1. (Illus.). 506p. 1980. 62.50 (978-0-404-60761-6(6)); Vol. 2. (Illus.). 264p. 1980. 62.50 (978-0-404-60762-3(4)); Vol. 3. 62.50 (978-0-404-60763-0(2)); Vol. 4. (Illus.). 64p. 1980. 37.50 (978-0-404-60764-7(0)); Vol. 5. (Illus.). 96p. 1980. 42.50 (978-0-404-60765-4(9)); Vol. 6. vi, 277p. 1980. 37.50 (978-0-404-60766-1(7)); reprint ed. 305.00 (978-0-404-19519-9(9)) AMS Pr., Inc.

Moss, Hilary J. Schooling Citizens: The Struggle for African American Education in Antebellum America. 2009. (ENG., Illus.). 296p. 37.50 (978-0-226-54249-2(1)) Univ. of Chicago Pr.

Muhammad, Shahid. How to Teach Math to Black Students: Student Workbook. 2009. (ENG.). 48p. (J). pap. 7.95 (978-1-934155-17-2(9)) African American Images.

Nielsen, Natalie. My Mom Said She Wanted Me to Grow up Better Than Her. 2008. 320p. pap. (978-3-639-07666-0(4)) VDM Verlag Dr. Mueller e.K.

Ogbu, John U. Minority Status, Oppositional Culture & Schooling. 2008. (Sociocultural, Political, & Historical Studies in Education). (ENG., Illus.). 688p. 56.95 (978-0-8058-5104-5(6)) Routledge.

Ogbu, John U., ed. Minority Status, Oppositional Culture & Schooling. 2008. (Sociocultural, Political, & Historical Studies in Education). (ENG., Illus.). 688p. 170.00 (978-0-8058-5103-8(8)) Routledge.

Onwughalu, Obiefuna J. Parents' Involvement in Education: The Experience of an African Immigrant Community in Chicago. 2011. 344p. 29.95 **(978-1-4502-9611-3(4))**; pap. 19.95 **(978-1-4502-9612-0(2))** iUniverse, Inc.

Orfield, Gary, et al, eds. Expanding Opportunity in Higher Education: Leveraging Promise. 2006. (SUNY Series, Frontiers in Education). (Illus.). 302p. per. 33.95 (978-0-7914-6864-7(X)) State Univ. of New York Pr.

Palmer, Robert T. Black Men in College: Implications for Diversity, Recruitment, Support, & Retention. 2011. (ENG., Illus.). 224p. 140.00 (978-0-415-89383-1(6)); pap. 42.95 **(978-0-415-89384-8(4))** Routledge.

Parks, Gregory S. & Bradley, Stefan M., eds. Alpha Phi Alpha: A Legacy of Greatness, the Demands of Transcendence. 2011. (ENG., Illus.). 416p. 39.95 (978-0-8131-3421-5(8)) Univ. Pr. of Kentucky.

Patterson, Collis D., ed. Dr Samuel Banks Speaks: Selected Writings. 2008. 124p. 21.49 (978-1-4389-2488-5(7)); pap. 10.99 (978-1-4389-2489-2(5)) AuthorHouse.

Pedroni, Thomas. Market Movements: African American Involvement in School Voucher Reform. 2007. (Critical Social Thought Ser.). (ENG.). 192p. (C). 150.00 (978-0-415-95608-6(0)); per. 37.95 (978-0-415-95609-3(9)) Routledge.

Permetter Falato, Betty Katherine. Black Schools in Pottawatomie County, Oklahoma, 1891-1966, & School Censuses, 1930 - 1950. 2010. (Illus.). 200p. pap. 18.49 (978-0-615-31793-9(6)) Falato Living Trust.

Perrillo, Jonna. Uncivil Rights: Teachers, Unions, & Race in the Battle for School Equity. 2012. (ENG.). 264p. 85.00 **(978-0-226-66071-4(0))**; pap. 27.50 **(978-0-226-66072-1(9))** Univ. of Chicago Pr.

Pitre, Abdul. Educating African American Students: Foundations, Curriculum, & Experiences. 2009. (Critical Black Pedagogy in Education Ser.). (ENG., Illus.). 176p. pap. 27.95 (978-1-60709-233-9(6)) Rowman & Littlefield Education.

Pitre, Abul. The Educational Philosophy of Elijah Muhammad: Education for a New World. (ENG.). 2007. 92p. per. 26.50 (978-0-7618-3684-1(5)) 2nd ed. 2008. 132p. 57.99 (978-0-7618-4082-4(6)) Univ. Pr. of America, Inc.

—Elijah Muhammad Ideas for Black Education. 2007. pap. 15.00 (978-1-56411-544-7(5), YBBG#0509, UBUS Communications Systems) UBUS Communications Systems.

—An Introduction to Elijah Muhammad Studies: The New Educational Paradigm. 2010. (Elijah Muhammad Studies: Interdisciplinary, Educational, & Islamic Studies Ser.). (ENG.). 100p. 41.99 (978-0-7618-5080-9(5)) Univ. Pr. of America, Inc.

Pitre, Abul & Pahl, Ray. The Educational Philosophy of Elijah Muhammad: Education for a New World. 2nd ed. 2008. (ENG.). 132p. pap. 28.50 (978-0-7618-4083-1(4)) Univ. Pr. of America, Inc.

Pitre, Esrom, et al. Educating African American Students: Foundations, Curriculum, & Experiences. 2009. (Critical Black Pedagogy in Education Ser.). (ENG., Illus.). 176p. 55.00 (978-1-60709-232-2(8)) Rowman & Littlefield Education.

Pride, Richard A. The Political Use of Racial Narratives: School Desegregation in Mobile, Alabama, 1954-97. 2008. (ENG., Illus.). 328p. pap. 26.00 (978-0-252-07594-0(3)) Univ. of Illinois Pr.

Prier, Darius. Culturally Relevant Teaching: Hip-Hop Pedagogy in Urban Schools. 2012. E-Book **(978-1-4539-0535-7(9))** Lang, Peter Publishing, Inc.

Prier, Darius D. Culturally Relevant Teaching: Hip-Hop Pedagogy in Urban Schools. 2012. xiv, 238p. (C). pap. 36.95 **(978-1-4331-1058-0(X))**; pap. 139.95 **(978-1-4331-1057-3(1))** Lang, Peter Publishing, Inc.

Ricard, Ronyelle Bertrand & Brown, M. Christopher, II. Ebony Towers in Higher Education: The Evolution, Mission, & Presidency of Historically Black Colleges & Universities. 2008. 176p. 75.00 (978-1-57922-273-4(0)); pap. 29.95 (978-1-57922-274-1(9)) Stylus Publishing, LLC.

Richardson, Temeca L. Can the Black Church Save Young Black America? Closing the Educational Achievement Gap. 2007. pap. 19.95 (978-0-9789560-0-4(1)) Much Lov 2 Give LLC.

Rickford & Sweetland. African American English & Other Vernaculars in Education. 2012. (NCTE-Routledge Research Ser.). (ENG.). 336p. pap. 41.95 (978-0-415-88867-7(0)) Routledge.

Robinson II, Charles F. & Williams, Lonnie R. Remembrances in Black: Personal Perspectives of the African American Experience at the University of Arkansas. 2010. (ENG.). 360p. (C). 45.00 (978-1-55728-953-7(0)) Univ. of Arkansas Pr.

Robinson, Sharon P. & Brown II, M. Christopher, eds. The Children Hurricane Katrina Left Behind: Schooling Context, Professional Preparation, & Community Politics. 2007. 226p. (C). 79.95 (978-0-8204-9728-0(2)); pap. 32.95 (978-0-8204-8822-6(4)) Lang, Peter Publishing, Inc.

Rochell, Jacquelyn. Move Beyond the Colored Line. 2008. 260p. per. (978-0-9801297-5-5(3)) G Publishing LLC.

Rogers, Ibram H. The Black Campus Movement: Black Students & the Racial Reconstitution of Higher Education, 1965-1972. 2012. (Contemporary Black History Ser.). (ENG., Illus.). 256p. 90.00 **(978-0-230-11780-8(5))**; pap. 27.00 **(978-0-230-11781-5(3))** Palgrave Macmillan.

Rooks, Noliwe M. White Money/Black Power: The Surprising History of African American Studies & the Crisis of Race in Higher Education. 2007. (ENG.). 224p. per. 17.00 (978-0-8070-3271-8(9)) Beacon Pr.

Rose, Yvonne, ed. The African American Scholarship Guide. 2012. (ENG.). pap. 14.95 **(978-1-937269-20-3(5)**, Amber Books2) Amber Bks.

Rovai, Alfred P., et al, eds. Closing the African American Achievement Gap in Higher Education. 2007. (ENG., Illus.). 224p. 49.00 *(978-0-8077-4778-0(5))* Teachers College Pr., Teachers College, Columbia Univ.

Rury, John L. & Hill, Shirley A. The African American Struggle for Secondary Schooling, 1940-1980: Closing the Graduation Gap. 2011. (ENG., Illus.). 264p. 78.00 ***(978-0-8077-5278-4(9))***; pap. 36.95 ***(978-0-8077-5277-7(0))*** Teachers College Pr., Teachers College, Columbia Univ.

Ryden, Wendy & Marshall, Ian. Reading, Writing, & the Rhetorics of Whiteness. 2012. 190p. E-Book ***(978-0-203-80298-4(5))*** 2011. (ENG., Illus.). 200p. (C). 125.00 *(978-0-415-88865-3(4))* Routledge.

Sanon-Jules, Lisa. The Effects of Parental Level of Education: Social Capital among African-American College Students. 2008. 108p. pap. *(978-3-8364-8882-2(5))* VDM Verlag Dr. Mueller e.K.

Schlachter, Gail Ann & Weber, R. David. Financial Aid for African Americans. 2009. (Financial Aid for African Americans Ser.). (ENG.). 500p. 42.50 *(978-1-58841-177-8(X))* Reference Service Pr.

Scott, Daryl Michael, ed. The Negro Church. 2010. (ENG., Illus.). 350p. pap. 21.00 *(978-0-9768111-1-4(1))* ASALH Pr., The.

Scott, Lawrence L. African American Male Academic Success. 2011. 128p. pap. 25.95 ***(978-1-61233-762-3(7)***, Dissertation.com) Universal Pubs.

Seals, Latrice M., et al. Vocabulary Power Level 1: Lessons for Students Who Use African American Vernacular English, 4 vols. 2007. (Illus.). 304p. per. 49.95 *(978-1-55766-680-2(6))* Brookes, Paul H. Publishing Co.

—Vocabulary Power Level 2: Lessons for Students Who Use African American Vernacular English, 4 vols. 2007. (Illus.). 326p. per. 49.95 *(978-1-55766-681-9(4))* Brookes, Paul H. Publishing Co.

Shockley, Kmt G. The Miseducation of Black Children. 2008. (ENG.). 120p. pap. 12.95 *(978-1-934155-12-7(8))* African American Images.

Sizemore, Barbara A. Walking in Circles: The Black Struggle for School Reform. 2008. (ENG., Illus.). 400p. 34.95 *(978-0-88378-298-9(7))* Third World Press.

Slaughter-Defoe, Diana T. Black Educational Choice: Assessing the Private & Public Alternatives to Traditional K-12 Public Schools. 2011. E-Book ***(978-0-313-39384-6(2)***, Praeger Pubs.) Greenwood Publishing Group, Inc.

Slaughter-Defoe, Diana T., et al, eds. Black Educational Choice: Assessing the Private & Public Alternatives to Traditional K-12 Public Schools, 1 vol. 2011. 289p. 48.00 ***(978-0-313-39383-9(4)***, A3403C) Greenwood Publishing Group, Inc.

Smith, Jane Bowman. The Elephant in the Classroom: Race & Writing. 2010. 216p. *(978-1-57273-894-2(4))*; pap. *(978-1-57273-895-9(2))* Hampton Pr., Inc.

Smith, Robert G. Gaining on the Gap: Changing Hearts, Minds, & Practice. 2011. (Illus.). (ENG.). 204p. pap. 28.95 ***(978-1-61048-289-9(1))***; xii, 192p. ***(978-1-61048-290-5(5))*** Rowman & Littlefield Education.

Smith, Robert G., et al. Gaining on the Gap: Changing Hearts, Minds, & Practice. 2011. (ENG., Illus.). 204p. 65.00 ***(978-1-61048-288-2(3))*** Rowman & Littlefield Education.

Smith, Yolanda Y. Reclaiming the Spirituals: New Possibilities for African American Christian Education. 2010. 192p. pap. 22.00 *(978-1-60899-591-2(7)*, Wipf and Stock) Wipf & Stock Pubs.

Span, Christopher M. From Cotton Field to Schoolhouse: African American Education in Mississippi, 1862-1875. 2009. (ENG., Illus.). 264p. 36.95 *(978-0-8078-3290-5(1))* Univ. of North Carolina Pr.

Spears-Bunton, L., et al. Toward a Literacy of Promise: Joining the African American Struggle. 2008. (Language, Culture, & Teaching Ser.). 224p. 150.00 *(978-0-415-99518-4(3))* Routledge.

Spears-Bunton, Linda A. & Powell, Rebecca. Toward a Literacy of Promise: Joining the African American Struggle. Powell, Rebecca, ed. 2008. (Language, Culture, & Teaching Ser.). 224p. pap. 43.95 *(978-0-8058-4536-5(4))* Erlbaum, Lawrence Assocs., Inc.

Spencer, John Palmer. In the Crossfire: Marcus Foster & the Troubled History of American School Reform. 2012. (Politics & Culture in Modern America Ser.). 352p. 34.95 ***(978-0-8122-4435-9(4))*** Univ. of Pennsylvania Pr.

Spencer Maor, Faye. Lifting Word by Word. 2008. 84p. pap. *(978-3-639-06233-5(7))* VDM Verlag Dr. Mueller e.K.

Spivey, Donald. Schooling for the New Slavery: Black Industrial Education, 1868-1915. 2006. xvi, 161p. *(978-1-59221-506-5(8))*; 176p. pap. *(978-1-59221-507-2(6))* Africa World Pr.

Starks, Glenn L. & Brooks, F. Erik. Historically Black Colleges & Universities: An Encyclopedia, 1 vol. 2011. (Illus.). 338p. 89.00 *(978-0-313-39415-7(6)*, A3425C) Greenwood Publishing Group, Inc.

Strickland, Carol Sills, et al, eds. Teach Freedom: Education for Liberation in the African-American Tradition. 2008. (Teaching for Social Justice Ser.). (ENG.). 288p. (C). *(978-0-8077-4873-2(0))* Teachers College Pr., Teachers College, Columbia Univ.

Strickland, Carol Sills & Payne, Charles M., eds. Teach Freedom: Education for Liberation in the African-American Tradition. 2008. (Teaching for Social Justice Ser.). (ENG.). 288p. pap. 30.95 *(978-0-8077-4872-5(2))* Teachers College Pr., Teachers College, Columbia Univ.

Stulberg, Lisa M. Race, Schools, & Hope: African Americans & School Choice after Brown. 2008. (ENG.). 224p. (C). *(978-0-8077-4853-4(6))*; pap. 29.95 *(978-0-8077-4852-7(8))* Teachers College Pr., Teachers College, Columbia Univ.

Tatum, Alfred W. Reading for Their Life: (Re)building the Textual Lineages of African American Adolescent Males. 2009. 192p. pap. 26.25 *(978-0-325-02679-4(3)*, E02679) Heinemann.

Tatum, Beverly Daniel. Can We Talk about Race? And Other Conversations in an Era of School Resegregation. 2007. (Black Studies Ser.). (ENG.). 147p. *(978-0-8070-3284-8(0))* Beacon Pr.

Teichgraeber, Richard F., III. Building Culture: Studies in the Intellectual History of Industrializing America, 1867-1910. 2010. 44.95 *(978-1-57003-925-6(9))* Univ. of South Carolina Pr.

Tennant, Noah. Black Students, White Schools- Caught Between Two Worlds. 2007. 152p. per. *(978-3-8364-2867-5(9))* VDM Verlag Dr. Mueller e.K.

Terrell, Melvin Cleveland & Strayhorn, Terrell L., eds. The Evolving Challenges of Black College Students: New Insights for Practice & Research. 2010. (Illus.). 248p. 75.00 *(978-1-57922-245-1(5))*; pap. 29.95 *(978-1-57922-246-8(3))* Stylus Publishing, LLC.

Thomas, Dale A. A Band in Every School: Portraits of Historically Black School Bands in Florida. 2009. (Illus.). 168p. 30.00 *(978-0-9787299-0-5(0))* Harmonie Publishing, LLC.

Thompson, Gail. A Brighter Day: How Parents Can Help African American Youth. 2010. (ENG.). 225p. pap. 15.95 *(978-1-935521-74-7(8))* African American Images.

Thompson, Gail L. Up Where We Belong: Helping African American & Latino Students Rise in School & in Life. 2007. (ENG.). 352p. 24.95 *(978-0-7879-9597-3(5)*, Jossey-Bass) Wiley, John & Sons, Inc.

—What African American Parents Want Educators to Know. 2008. (ENG., Illus.). 232p. pap. 27.95 *(978-1-57886-743-1(6))* Rowman & Littlefield Education.

Thompson, Gail L. & Greenwood. African American Teens Discuss Their Schooling Experiences. 2009. 204p. pap. 45.99 *(978-1-60752-067-2(2))* Information Age Publishing, Inc.

Tillman, Linda C. The Sage Handbook of African American Education. 2008. (Illus.). 584p. 108.00 *(978-1-4129-3743-6(4)*, B37434C) SAGE Pubns., Inc.

Tough, Paul. Whatever It Takes: Geoffrey Canada's Quest to Change Harlem & America. 2009. (ENG.). 336p. pap. 14.95 *(978-0-547-24796-0(6)*, Mariner Bks.) Houghton Mifflin Harcourt Trade & Reference Pubs.

Tribble, Israel, Jr. Making Their Mark: Educating African-American Children. 124p. 12.95 *(978-0-931761-30-0(1))* Beckham Pubns. Group, Inc.

Truitt, Thomas E. Brick Walls: Reflections on Race in a Southern School District. 2006. 164p. 34.95 *(978-1-57003-638-5(1))* Univ. of South Carolina Pr.

Tyson, Karolyn, ed. Integration Interrupted: Tracking, Black Students, & Acting White after Brown. 2011. (ENG., Illus.). 256p. pap. 24.95 *(978-0-19-973645-4(6))* Oxford Univ. Pr., Inc.

Urban, Wayne J. Black Scholar: Horace Mann Bond, 1904-1972. 2008. (ENG.). 284p. pap. 24.95 *(978-0-8203-3255-0(0))* Univ. of Georgia Pr.

Walker, Lewis, et al. African Americans in Michigan. 2008. (Discovering the Peoples of Michigan Ser.). (ENG., Illus.). 63p. pap. 12.95 *(978-0-87013-583-5(X))* Michigan State Univ. Pr.

Walters, Ivan Hugh. Education in the Cultural Politics of the African Diaspora: Critical Redemptive Pedagogy for Social Justice. 2008. pap. *(978-1-4331-0320-9(6))* Lang, Peter Publishing, Inc.

Warren, Kim. The Quest for Citizenship: African American & Native American Education in Kansas, 1880-1935. 2010. (ENG., Illus.). 399p. 59.95 *(978-0-8078-3396-4(7))*; pap. 24.95 *(978-0-8078-7137-9(0))* Univ. of North Carolina Pr.

Warren, Nagueyalti. An Intellectual Biography of W.E.B. du Bois: Initiator of Black Studies in the University. 2010. iii, 198p. 109.95 *(978-0-7734-3715-9(0))* Mellen, Edwin Pr., The.

Washington, Booker T. Character Building. 2012. ***(978-1-4128-4732-2(X))*** Transaction Pubs.

Weiner, Melissa. Power, Protest, & the Public Schools: Jewish & African American Struggles in New York City. 2012. (ENG.). 272p. pap. 25.95 ***(978-0-8135-5351-1(2))*** Rutgers Univ. Pr.

Weiner, Melissa F. Power, Protest, & the Public Schools: Jewish & African American Struggles in New York City. 2010. (ENG., Illus.). 272p. 44.95 *(978-0-8135-4772-5(5))* Rutgers Univ. Pr.

Wesley, Charles H. History of Sigma Pi Phi: Black History. 462p. (C). reprint ed. lib. bdg. 5.00 *(978-0-9633346-0-2(3))* Sigma Pi Phi Fraternity.

White, Barbara A. A Line in the Sand: The Battle to Integrate Nantucket Public Schools 1824-1847. 2009. (Illus.). 128p. pap. 20.00 *(978-0-932027-43-6(1))* Spinner Pubns., Inc.

Wilkins, Rhonda. Swimming Upstream. 2008. 248p. pap. *(978-3-8364-7843-4(9))* VDM Verlag Dr. Mueller e.K.

Williams, Barbara Morrow. Battling Goliath. 2009. 284p. pap. *(978-3-639-00114-3(1))* VDM Verlag Dr. Mueller e.K.

Williams, Heather Andrea. Self-Taught: African American Education in Slavery & Freedom. 2007. (John Hope Franklin Series in African American History & Culture Ser.). (ENG., Illus.). 320p. per. 20.95 *(978-0-8078-5821-9(8))* Univ. of North Carolina Pr.

Williams, Ida J., compiled by. A History of Education for African Americans During the Segregation Period, 1886 through 1970 in Northampton County, Virginia. 2007. (Illus.). 100p. per. 18.00 *(978-1-60126-036-9(9))* Masthof Pr.

Williams, Juan, et al. I'll Find a Way or Make One: A Tribute to Historically Black Colleges & Universities. 2007. (Illus.). 480p. per. 20.95 *(978-0-06-009456-0(7)*, Amistad) HarperCollins Pubs.

Williams, Twyla J. Save Our Children: The Struggle Between Black Parents & Schools. 2009. (ENG.). 200p. pap. 15.95 *(978-1-934155-16-5(0))* African American Images.

Williamson, Carolyn E. Black Deaf Students: A Model for Educational Success. 2007. (Illus.). 224p. 39.95 *(978-1-56368-351-0(2))* Gallaudet Univ. Pr.

Williamson, Joy Ann. Radicalizing the Ebony Tower: Black Colleges & the Black Freedom Struggle in Mississippi. 2008. (Reflective History Ser.). (ENG.). 224p. (C). *(978-0-8077-4864-0(1))*; pap. 30.95 *(978-0-8077-4863-3(3))* Teachers College Pr., Teachers College, Columbia Univ.

Willis, William Shedrick & Zumwalt, Rosemary Levy. Franz Boas & W.E.B. Du Bois at Atlanta University, 1906. 2008. *(978-0-87169-982-4(6))* American Philosophical Society.

Wilpers, Birgit. The Topic of Education in Ernest J Gaines' Novel A Lesson Before Dying. 2011. 40p. pap. ***(978-3-640-80302-6(7))*** Hammer, Patrick, Tanja Hammer, Matthias Knoop, Julius Mittenzwei, Georg Steinbach u. Michael Teltscher. GRIN Verlag GbR.

Wilson, Maloyd Ben & Wilson Group Network Inc Staff. Black Chronicle: From the Slavery Era - 1778 to the Beginning of the Civil Rights Movement, 1956. 2008. (Illus.). 70p. pap. 20.00 *(978-0-9753210-0-3(5))* Wilson Group Network, Inc.

Woods-Buchanan, Yashica. African American College Students at Black Versus White Institutions. 2009. 52p. pap. *(978-3-639-03508-7(9))* VDM Verlag Dr. Mueller e.K.

Woodson, Carter. The Mis-Education of the Negro. 2007. 220p. per. 17.95 *(978-1-58509-320-5(3))* Book Tree, The.

Woodson, Carter G. The Mis-Education of the Negro. 2009. 100p. pap. 7.49 *(978-1-60459-816-2(6))* 2008. (ENG.). 108p. per. 9.99 *(978-1-60459-226-9(5))* Wilder Pubns., Ltd.

—The Mis-Education of the Negro (an African American Heritage Book) 2008. 108p. 19.99 *(978-1-60459-227-6(3))* Wilder Pubns., Ltd.

Woodson, Carter Godwin. The Mis-Education of the Negro. 2010. 116p. pap. 6.50 *(978-1-57898-918-8(3))* Martino Publishing.

—The Mis-Education of the Negro. 2011. (ENG.). 144p. pap. 7.77 *(978-1-936594-30-6(7))* Tribeca Bks.

—The Mis-Education of the Negro. 2008. 200p. pap. 14.99 *(978-1-60459-299-3(0))* Wilder Pubns., Ltd.

Woodson, Godwin Carter. The Education of the Negro Prior to 1861: A History of the Education of the Colored People of the United States from the Beginning of Slavery to the Civil War. 2007. 332p. pap. 23.99 *(978-1-4346-3022-3(6))*; (ENG.). 382p. pap. 26.99 *(978-1-4346-3023-0(4))* BiblioBazaar.

Woody, L. T. In Black in White. 2009. 424p. pap. 24.95 *(978-1-4401-3050-2(7))* iUniverse, Inc.

Zamani-Gallaher, Eboni M. & Polite, Vernon C. The State of the African American Male. Campbell, Alec, ed. 2010. (CourageousConversations series Ser.). (ENG.). 303p. pap. 29.95 *(978-0-87013-870-6(7))* Michigan State Univ. Pr.

AFRICAN AMERICANS—EMPLOYMENT

Addressing the Problem of African-American Male Unemployment: Hearing Before the Joint Economic Committee, Congress of the United States, One Hundred Tenth Congress, First Session, March 8, 2007. 2007. iii, 53p. *(978-0-16-079254-0(1)*, 552-070-36334-3) United States Government Printing Office.

Arnesen, Eric, ed. The Black Worker: Race, Labor, & Civil Rights since Emancipation. 2007. 328p. 62.00 *(978-0-252-03145-8(8))*; per. 22.00 *(978-0-252-07380-9(0))* Univ. of Illinois Pr.

Beasley, Maya A. Opting Out: Losing the Potential of America's Young Black Elite. 2011. (ENG., Illus.). 240p. 70.00 *(978-0-226-04013-4(5))*; pap. 25.00 *(978-0-226-04014-1(3))* Univ. of Chicago Pr.

Blackmon, Douglas A. Slavery by Another Name: The Re-Enslavement of Black Americans from the Civil War to World War II. 2009. (ENG., Illus.). 496p. pap. 17.00 *(978-0-385-72270-4(2)*, Anchor) Knopf Doubleday Publishing Group.

Brewer, James H. The Confederate Negro: Virginia's Craftsmen & Military Laborers, 1861-1865. 2007. (ENG., Illus.). 238p. pap. 29.95 *(978-0-8173-5486-2(7))* Univ. of Alabama Pr.

Button, James W., et al. Blacks & the Quest for Economic Equality: The Political Economy of Employment in Southern Communities in the United States. 2009. (ENG.). 208p. 60.00 *(978-0-271-03555-0(2))* Pennsylvania State Univ. Pr.

Cayton, Horace R. & Mitchell, George S. Black Workers & the New Unions. 19.95 *(978-0-405-18493-2(X))* Ayer Co. Pubs., Inc.

—Black Workers & the New Unions. 2010. (ENG.). 496p. pap. 53.00 *(978-0-8078-6763-1(2))* Univ. of North Carolina Pr.

Commission on Civil Rights (U.S.), ed. The Impact of Illegal Immigration on the Wages & Employment Opportunities of Black Workers, August 2010. 2010. (ENG.). 100p. pap. 15.00 *(978-0-16-086401-8(1))* United States Government Printing Office.

Davidson, Wayne. Manufacturing African American Self-Employment. 2008. 292p. pap. *(978-3-639-08502-0(7))* VDM Verlag Dr. Mueller e.K.

Du Bois, W. E. B. Black Reconstruction in America: An Essay Toward a History of the Part Which Black Folk Played in the Attempt to Reconstruct Democracy in America, 1860-1880. 2007. *(978-0-19-532581-2(8))* Oxford Univ. Pr., Inc.

Ford, Roderick O. J. D. Labor Matters. 2011. 464p. pap. 23.99 ***(978-1-4568-6373-9(8))*** Xlibris Corp.

Franklin, Charles L. Negro Labor Unionist of New York. (Columbia University, Studies in the Social Sciences: No. 420). reprint ed. 32.50 *(978-0-404-51420-4(0))* AMS Pr., Inc.

Frederickson, Mary E. Looking South: Race, Gender, & the Transformation of Labor from Reconstruction to Globalization. 2011. (Southern Dissent Ser.). (ENG., Illus.). 320p. 69.95 *(978-0-8130-3603-8(8))* Univ. Pr. of Florida.

Haynes, George E. Negro at Work in New York City. (Columbia University, Studies in the Social Sciences: No. 124). reprint ed. 27.50 *(978-0-404-51124-1(4))* AMS Pr., Inc.

Huntley, Horace & Montgomery, David, eds. Black Workers' Struggle for Equality in Birmingham. 2007. (Working Class in American History Ser.). 264p. per. 20.00 *(978-0-252-07493-6(9))* Univ. of Illinois Pr.

Johnson, Michelle T. Black Out: The Black Person's Guide to Redefining a Career Path Outside of Corporate America. 2007. (ENG.). 182p. per. 15.95 *(978-0-9767735-9-7(7))* Amber Bks.

—Working While Black: The Black Person's Guide to Success in the White Workplace. 2nd ed. 2011. (ENG.). 288p. pap. 14.95 *(978-1-56976-346-9(1)*, Hill, Lawrence Bks.) Chicago Review Pr., Inc.

Kennedy, Louise V. Negro Peasant Turns Cityward. (Columbia University, Studies in the Social Sciences: No. 329). reprint ed. 20.00 *(978-0-404-51329-0(8))* AMS Pr., Inc.

Koger, Larry. Black Slaveowners: Free Black Slave Masters in South Carolina, 1790-1860. alt. ed. 2011. (ENG.). 300p. pap. 25.00 ***(978-0-7864-6931-4(5))*** McFarland & Co., Inc. Pubs.

Kornweibel, Theodore, Jr. Railroads in the African American Experience: A Photographic Journey. 2010. (ENG., Illus.). 568p. 40.00 *(978-0-8018-9162-5(0))* Johns Hopkins Univ. Pr.

Kyser, Chaz. Embracing the Real World: The Black Woman's Guide to Life after College. 2007. per. 14.99 *(978-0-9788188-0-7(6))* Seshet Pr.

Lakes, Joyce M. Justice Delayed vs. Justice Denied. 2010. 84p. pap. 15.49 *(978-1-4208-6034-4(8))* AuthorHouse.

Lewis, Edward E. The Mobility of the Negro. (Columbia University, Studies in the Social Sciences: No. 342). reprint ed. 20.00 *(978-0-404-51342-9(5))* AMS Pr., Inc.

Maclaury, Judson. To Advance Their Opportunities: Federal Policies Toward African American Workers from World War I to the Civil Rights Act Of 1964. 2008. (ENG.). 313p. pap. 24.95 *(978-0-9797292-3-2(8))* Univ. of Tennessee, Libraries of Newfound Pr.

Massey, Douglas & Sampson, Robert, eds. Moynihan Report Revisited: Lessons & Reflections after Four Decades. 2009. (ANNALS of the American Academy of Political & Social Science Ser.: 621). 328p. (C). pap. 37.95 *(978-1-4129-7401-1(1)*, 295621P) SAGE Pubns., Inc.

Massey, Douglas S. & Sampson, Robert, eds. Moynihan Report Revisited: Lessons & Reflections after Four Decades. 2009. (ANNALS of the American Academy of Political & Social Science Ser.: 621). 328p. (C). 48.95 *(978-1-4129-7402-8(X)*, 295621C) SAGE Pubns., Inc.

Meier, August & Rudwick, Elliott. Black Detroit & the Rise of the UAW. 2007. (ENG., Illus.). 312p. (C). pap. 22.95 *(978-0-472-03219-8(4))* Univ. of Michigan Pr.

Pager, Devah. Marked: Race, Crime, & Finding Work in an ERA of Mass Incarceration. 2007. (Illus.). 256p. 25.00 *(978-0-226-64483-7(9))* Univ. of Chicago Pr.

Pager, Devah & Pager, D. Marked: Race, Crime, & Finding Work in an Era of Mass Incarceration. 2009. (Illus.). 264p. pap. 16.00 *(978-0-226-64484-4(7))* Univ. of Chicago Pr.

Pierce, Daniel Vincent. Diversity, Values, Professionalism,or Favoritism Racism: African Americans & Other Minorities in the Work Force. 2007. 60p. per. 9.95 *(978-0-595-47122-5(6))* iUniverse, Inc.

Rockman, Seth. Scraping By: Wage Labor, Slavery, & Survival in Early Baltimore. 2008. (Studies in Early American Economy & Society from the Library Company of Philadelphia Ser.). (ENG., Illus.). 392p. (gr. 17). pap. 27.00 *(978-0-8018-9007-9(1))* Johns Hopkins Univ. Pr.

Rose, Tony, ed. The African American Employment Guide: Finding & Keeping a Job. 2012. (ENG.). pap. 14.95 ***(978-1-937269-23-4(X)***, Amber Classics) Amber Bks.

Rose, Yvonne & Rose, Tony. Is Modeling for You? The Handbook & Guide for the Young Aspiring Black Model. 2009. 272p. pap. 14.95 *(978-0-9790976-9-0(X))* Amber Bks.

Rubio, Philip F. There's Always Work at the Post Office: African American Postal Workers & the Fight for Jobs, Justice, & Equality. 2010. (ENG., Illus.). 472p. 65.00 *(978-0-8078-3342-1(8))*; pap. 24.95 *(978-0-8078-5986-5(9))* Univ. of North Carolina Pr.

Scott, Daryl Michael, ed. The Negro Church. 2010. (ENG., Illus.). 350p. pap. 21.00 *(978-0-9768111-1-4(1))* ASALH Pr., The.

Smith, Sandra Susan. Lone Pursuit: Distrust & Defensive Individualism among the Black Poor. 2007. (Illus.). 246p. *(978-0-87154-773-6(2))* Russell Sage Foundation.

Trotter, Joe William, Jr. Black Milwaukee: The Making of an Industrial Proletariat, 1915-45. 2nd ed. 2006. (Illus.). 432p. per. 31.00 *(978-0-252-07410-3(6))* Univ. of Illinois Pr.

Voices: African American & Latina Women Share Their Stories of Success. 2006. (Illus.). 106p. 29.95 *(978-0-915180-39-4(1)*, 0962) Harrowood Bks.

Washington, Booker T. The Negro in Business. 2009. 196p. pap. *(978-1-150-24864-1(5))* Books LLC.

—The Negro in Business. 2007. (ENG.). 382p. 48.95 *(978-0-548-15156-3(3))*; 384p. per. 33.95 *(978-1-4304-4504-3(1))* Kessinger Publishing, LLC.

—The Negro in Business. 379p. reprint ed. 98.00 *(978-0-7222-9752-0(1))* Library Reprints, Inc.

Washington, Booker T. & Du Bois, W. E. B. The Negro in Business: Report of a Social Study Made under the Direction of Atlanta University. (Illus.). reprint ed. 29.50 *(978-0-404-00237-4(4))* AMS Pr., Inc.

Wilson, Francille Rusan. The Segregated Scholars: Black Social Scientists & the Creation of Black Labor Studies, 1890-1950. 2006. (Carter G. Woodson

Institute Ser.). (ENG.). 352p. (gr. 17). pap. 22.50 *(978-0-8139-2788-6(9))* Univ. Pr. of Virginia.
Woodson, Carter. The Mis-Education of the Negro. 2007. 220p. per. 17.95 *(978-1-58509-320-5(3))* Book Tree, The.
Woodson, Carter G. The Mis-Education of the Negro. 2009. 100p. pap. 7.49 *(978-1-60459-816-2(6))* 2008. (ENG.). 108p. per. 9.99 *(978-1-60459-226-9(5))* Wilder Pubns., Ltd.
—The Mis-Education of the Negro (an African American Heritage Book) 2008. 108p. 19.99 *(978-1-60459-227-6(3))* Wilder Pubns., Ltd.
Woodson, Carter Godwin. The Mis-Education of the Negro. 2010. 116p. pap. 6.50 *(978-1-57898-918-8(3))* Martino Publishing.
—The Mis-Education of the Negro. 2011. (ENG.). 144p. pap. 7.77 *(978-1-936594-30-6(7))* Tribeca Bks.
—The Mis-Education of the Negro. 2008. 200p. pap. 14.99 *(978-1-60459-299-3(0))* Wilder Pubns., Ltd.
Zieger, Robert H. For Jobs & Freedom: Race & Labor in America Since 1865. (Civil Rights & the Struggle for Black Equality in the Twentieth Century Ser.). (ENG., Illus.). 312p. 2010. pap. 22.95 *(978-0-8131-9259-8(5))* 2007. 40.00 *(978-0-8131-2460-5(3))* Univ. Pr. of Kentucky.

AFRICAN AMERICANS—FOLKLORE

see also John Henry (Legendary Character)

Abernethy, Francis Edward, et al, eds. Juneteenth Texas: Essays in African-American Folklore. 2010. (Publications of the Texas Folklore Society Ser.). (ENG.). 376p. pap. 29.95 *(978-1-57441-283-3(3))* Univ. of North Texas Pr.
Ballowe, Hewitt Leonard. The Lawd Sayin' the Same: Negro Folk Tales of the Creole Country. 2011. 270p. 47.95 ***(978-1-258-04812-9(4))*** Literary Licensing, LLC.
Brookes, Stella Brewer. Joel Chandler Harris, Folklorist. 2009. (ENG.). 200p. pap. 22.95 *(978-0-8203-3437-0(5))* Univ. of Georgia Pr.
Coggswell, Gladys Caines. Stories from the Heart: Missouri's African American Heritage. 2009. (Missouri Heritage Readers Ser.). (ENG., Illus.). 160p. (gr. 9). pap. 15.95 *(978-0-8262-1844-5(X))* Univ. of Missouri Pr.
Dobie, J. Frank, ed. Follow de Drinkin' Gou'd. 2007. 204p. per. 24.95 *(978-1-4325-7459-8(0))* Kessinger Publishing, LLC.
Ferry, Lee. Connection Point: A Different version of African American Folklore. 2009. 188p. pap. 21.49 *(978-1-4490-2707-0(5))* AuthorHouse.
Georgia Writer's Project & Joyner, Charles. Drums & Shadows. 2011. 226p. pap. 18.99 ***(978-1-61279-055-8(0))*** Publishing in Motion.
Green, Thomas A., ed. African American Folktales, 1 vol. 2009. (Stories from the American Mosaic Ser.). 184p. 49.95 *(978-0-313-36295-8(5)*, GR6295, Greenwood Pr.) Greenwood Publishing Group, Inc.
Harris, Joel Chandler. Nights with Uncle Remus: Myths & Legends of the Old Plantation. 2007. (ENG.). 496p. 53.95 *(978-0-548-37454-2(6))*; per. 38.95 *(978-0-548-31775-4(5))* Kessinger Publishing, LLC.
—Told by Uncle Remus: New Stories of the Old Plantation. 2007. (ENG.). 340p. 46.95 *(978-0-548-09384-9(9))* Kessinger Publishing, LLC.
—Told by Uncle Remus: New Stories of the Old Plantation. 295p. reprint ed. lib. bdg. 98.00 *(978-0-7222-0878-6(2))* Library Reprints, Inc.
—Uncle Remus: His Songs & His Sayings. 2007. (ENG.). 196p. pap. 19.99 *(978-1-4346-1752-1(1))* BiblioBazaar.
—Uncle Remus: His Songs & His Sayings. 2007. 156p. (gr. -1-3). per. *(978-1-4065-3271-5(1))* Dodo Pr.
—Uncle Remus: His Songs & His Sayings. 2010. 262p. pap. 26.75 *(978-1-145-61994-4(0))* BiblioBazaar.
—Uncle Remus: His Songs & His Sayings; 2010. 320p. pap. 30.75 *(978-1-146-39109-2(9))* BiblioBazaar.
—Uncle Remus: His Songs & His Sayings. I.t. ed. 2007. (ENG.). 214p. pap. 22.99 *(978-1-4346-1921-1(4))* BiblioBazaar.
—Uncle Remus & His Friends: Old Plantation Stories, Songs & Ballads with Sketches of Negro Character. 2007. (ENG.). 376p. 48.95 *(978-0-548-17157-8(2))* Kessinger Publishing, LLC.
—Uncle Remus & His Friends: Old Plantation Stories, Songs And. 2007. (Illus.). pap. 33.95 *(978-1-4304-6962-9(5))* Kessinger Publishing, LLC.
—Uncle Remus, His Songs & His Sayings. 2008. (ENG.). 336p. per. *(978-1-4086-5088-2(6))* Read Bks.
—Uncle Remus, His Songs & His Sayings. 2011. 292p. pap. 28.75 ***(978-1-245-54650-8(3))*** 2010. (ENG.). 312p. pap. 29.75 *(978-1-171-05158-9(1))* 2010. 322p. pap. 30.75 *(978-1-172-32007-3(1))* 2010. 316p. pap. 30.75 *(978-1-178-23146-5(1))* 2009. 314p. 36.99 *(978-1-117-58910-2(2))* 2009. (ENG.). 312p. pap. 28.75 *(978-1-117-58911-4(0))* 2009. (ENG.). 312p. pap. 23.99 *(978-1-117-58912-1(9)*, BiblioLife) BiblioBazaar.
—Uncle Remus, His Songs & His Sayings. 2010. 96p. pap. *(978-1-152-09161-0(1))* Books LLC.
—Uncle Remus, His Songs & His Sayings. 2010. (Illus.). 98p. pap. 20.00 ***(978-1-153-74327-3(2))*** General Bks. LLC.
Harris, Joel Chandler. Uncle Remus His Songs & His Sayings. 2010. 294p. 35.16 *(978-1-163-21012-3(9))*; pap. 23.16 *(978-1-162-77323-0(5))* Kessinger Publishing, LLC.
Harris, Joel Chandler, creator. Uncle Remus: His Songs & His Sayings. 2010. 266p. pap. 27.75 ***(978-1-171-93261-1(8))*** BiblioBazaar.
Harris, Joel Chandler & Frost, A. b. 1851-1928. Uncle Remus, His Songs & His Sayings. 2011. 342p. pap. 32.75 ***(978-1-245-53108-5(5))*** BiblioBazaar.
Harris, Joel Chandler & Frost, A. B. 1851-1928. Illus. Uncle Remus, His Songs & His Sayings. 2010. (ENG.). 320p. pap. 30.75 *(978-1-171-56905-3(X))* BiblioBazaar.
Harris, Joel Chandler & Frost, Arthur Burdett. Uncle Remus, His Songs & His Sayings. 2009. 318p. (gr. 4-7). 32.99 *(978-1-116-85169-4(5))*; 36.99 *(978-1-116-85168-7(7))*; pap. 29.75 *(978-1-116-85171-7(7))*; pap. 30.75 *(978-1-116-85170-0(9))* BiblioBazaar.
Hurston, Zora Neale. Mules & Men. 2008. (P. S. Ser.). (ENG., Illus.). 368p. per. 13.99 *(978-0-06-135017-7(6)*, HarperPerennial) HarperCollins Pubs.
Johnson, Guy B. John Henry: Tracking down a Negro Legend. reprint ed. 24.50 *(978-0-404-00177-3(7))* AMS Pr., Inc.
Jones, Christianne C. John Henry. 2011. (My First Classic Story Ser.).Tr. of John Henry. (ENG.). 32p. (gr. k-3). lib. bdg. 21.32 *(978-1-4048-6582-2(9)*, My First Classic Story) Picture Window Bks.
Kraut, Anthea. Choreographing the Folk: The Dance Stagings of Zora Neale Hurston. 2008. (Illus.). 312p. pap. 25.00 *(978-0-8166-4712-5(7))*; 75.00 *(978-0-8166-4711-8(9))* Univ. of Minnesota Pr.
Krensky, Stephen. John Henry. 2008. pap. 40.95 *(978-0-8225-9293-8(2))* Lerner Publishing Group.
Mitchem, Stephanie Y. African American Folk Healing. 2007. (ENG., Illus.). 208p. per. 23.00 *(978-0-8147-5732-1(4))* New York Univ. Pr.
Mullen, Patrick B. The Man Who Adores the Negro: Race & American Folklore. 2008. 224p. pap. 21.00 *(978-0-252-07486-8(6))* Univ. of Illinois Pr.
Owen, Mary Alicia. Old Rabbit, the Voodoo, & Other Sorcerers. 2007. 332p. per. 19.95 *(978-1-60206-667-0(1))* Cosimo, Inc.
Sale, John B. The Tree Named John. 2011. (ENG.). 168p. pap. 30.00 ***(978-0-8078-9769-0(8))*** Univ. of North Carolina Pr.
Waters, Donald J. Strange Ways & Sweet Dreams: Afro-American Folklore from the Hampton Institute. 460p. 2009. 69.00 *(978-1-59740-287-3(7))* 2008. pap. 46.00 *(978-1-59740-695-6(3))* ACLS Humanities E-Book.
Yeomans, Jessica, illus. John Henry, Steel-Driving Man. 2012. (J). *(978-1-60870-441-5(6))* Marshall Cavendish.

AFRICAN AMERICANS—GENEALOGY

Ailes, Jane, et al, contrib. by. Ancestors of Henry Louis Gates, Jr. In Maryland, Virginia, & West Virginia from Africa, West Africa, & Europe. 2010. (Illus.). xxvii, 65p. ***(978-0-88082-239-8(2))*** New England Historic Genealogical Society.
Allen, Caron Barton. From Whence They Came: The Genealogical History of an African-American Family, 1 vol. 2009. 207p. pap. 24.95 *(978-1-60703-130-7(2))* PublishAmerica, Inc.
Baker, John F., Jr. The Washingtons of Wessyngton Plantation: Stories of My Family's Journey to Freedom. 2010. (ENG., Illus.). 432p. pap. 16.00 *(978-1-4165-6741-7(0)*, Beyond Words/Atria Bks.) Atria Bks.
Beasley, Delilah L. The Negro Trail Blazers of California. 2007. (ENG.). 328p. per. 20.45 *(978-1-59462-592-3(1)*, 629, Book Jungle) Standard Pubns., Inc.
Blomquist, Ann K. & Walton-Raji, Angela Y. Black Indian Genealogy Research: African-American Ancestors among the Five Civilized Tribes, an Expanded Edition. 2007. pap. 24.50 *(978-0-7884-4474-6(3))* Heritage Bks.
Brown-Dean, Wanda F. The Roberts Family: A Biographical & Genealogical History of Two Slave Brothers. 103p. *(978-0-9654355-6-7(3))* Family History Pubs.
Clay, Roger, ed. The Legacy of Black Families in Jackson County, Florida. 2006. (Illus.). iv, 156p. lib. bdg. 30.00 *(978-1-891647-98-7(9))* Heritage Publishing Consultants, Inc.
Cochran, Anthony B. Kinship Ties: Bethea-McRae Family Heritage: The Union & History of an African American Family Beginning in the 18th Century Carolinas. 2nd ed. 2009. (Illus.). xvi, 127p. pap. *(978-0-615-28566-5(X))* Bereaved Parents Group.
Conner, Glen. Till Freedom Came: Slaves in Allen County, 1815-1866. 2010. *(978-1-935001-50-8(7))* Acclaim Pr., Inc.
Cruise, M. T. W. Guidelines for Ancestry Research with an Emphasis on African-American Genealogy. 2007. 43p. spiral bd. 10.00 *(978-0-9790433-2-1(8))* Cruise, M. T. W.
Davis, Thulani. My Confederate Kinfolk: A Twenty-First Century Freedwoman Discovers Her Roots. 2007. (ENG., Illus.). 352p. per. 15.00 *(978-0-465-01574-0(3)*, Basic Civitas Bks.) Basic Bks.
Duncan, Patricia B. Fairfax County, Virginia, Birth Register, 2 vols. 2010. ***(978-0-7884-8482-7(6))***; ***(978-0-7884-5239-0(8))***; pap. ***(978-0-7884-5240-6(1))*** Heritage Bks.
Duncan, Patricia B. Fauquier County, Virginia, Birth Register. 2008. pap. 32.50 *(978-0-7884-4185-1(X))* Heritage Bks.
Frazier, Eugene, Sr. A History of James Island Slave Descendants & Plantation Owners: The Blood Line. 2010. 192p. pap. 22.99 *(978-1-59629-976-4(2))* History Pr., The.
Frazier, Eugene, Sr. & Frazier, Eugene. James Island: Stories from Slave Descendants. 2006. (Illus.). 218p. pap., per. 24.99 *(978-1-59629-182-9(6))* History Pr., The.
Gates, Henry Louis, Jr. Finding Oprah's Roots: Finding Your Own. 2007. (ENG., Illus.). 192p. 19.95 *(978-0-307-38238-2(9)*, Crown) Crown Publishing Group.
—In Search of Our Roots: How 19 Extraordinary African Americans Reclaimed Their Past. 2009. (ENG., Illus.). 448p. 27.50 *(978-0-307-38240-5(0)*, Crown) Crown Publishing Group.
Gourdin, J. Raymond. Borrowed Identity: 128th United States Colored Troops. 2009. 288p. pap. 28.00 *(978-0-7884-5007-5(7))* Heritage Bks.
Harrison, Michael. Death of a Colored Man's Pedigree: A Chronicled Exposé of an Endangered Species, the Black American Family. 2010. 80p. 11.95 *(978-0-9842829-0-6(4))* Feride House Publishing.
Hughes, Lyn. An Anthology of Respect: The Pullman Porters National Historic Registry of African American Railroad Employees. 2007. pap. 39.95 *(978-0-9793941-1-9(2))* Hughes-Peterson Publishing.
—An Anthology of Respect: The Pullman Porters National Historic Registry of African American Railroad Employees. 2007. 44.95 *(978-0-9793941-2-6(0))* Hughes-Peterson Publishing.
Hynson, Jerry M. The African American Collection: Anne Arundel County, Maryland Marriage Licenses, 1865-1888. 2007. pap. 17.00 *(978-0-7884-3839-4(5))* Heritage Bks.
—The African American Collection , Indentures, Cecil County, Maryland 1777-1814. 2007. pap. 12.00 *(978-0-7884-4112-7(4))* Heritage Bks.
Johnson, Calvin. Who Came Before Me? A Story of the Search for My Tomes & Lightfoot Roots, & What I Found. 2009. (Illus.). xiii, 219p. *(978-0-615-27741-7(1))* Bereaved Parents Group.
Johnson, Turner H. The Family of America Reed Johnson: Of Rankin County, MS. 2010. 283p. pap. 29.95 *(978-0-615-34873-5(4))* T. J. Harrison Publishing Co.
Lawe, Gwendolyn McMillan. From Wolf to Wolfwood: A Genealogical & Historical Study of the Mcmillans & the African American Communities of Emory, Texas. 2011. 196p. 24.59 *(978-1-4567-2656-0(0))*; pap. 14.99 *(978-1-4567-2654-6(4))* AuthorHouse.
Lawson, Jacqueline A. An Index of African Americans Identified in Select Records of the Bureau of Refuges, Freedmen, & Abandoned Lands. 2008. 101p. (Orig.). pap. 14.00 *(978-0-7884-0291-3(9))* Heritage Bks.
Matthews, Harry Bradshaw. African American Journey to Freedom in New York & Related Sites, 1823-1870: Freedom Knows No Color. 2008. (Illus.). 480p. 45.00 *(978-0-9799537-4-3(X))*; per. 32.00 *(978-0-9799537-3-6(1))* Africana Homestead Legacy Pubs., Inc.
Morales, Leslie Anderson & Valaitis, Ada. Virginia Slave Births Index, 1853-1865. 2007. pap. 45.00 *(978-2-07-884445-8(4))* Heritage Bks.
Morales, Leslie Anderson, et al. Virginia Slave Births Index, 1853-1865. 2007. pap. 45.00 *(978-0-7884-4453-1(0))* Heritage Bks.
Oakdale / Union Hill Cemetery, Salisbury, North Carolina: A Study of A Twentieth Century African American Cemetery. 2007. 69.95 *(978-0-9777389-0-8(6))* Brown, Reginald.
Phillips. Exodus from the Door of No Return: Journey of an American Family. 2008. 200p. 24.99 *(978-1-4389-0348-4(0))* AuthorHouse.
Phillips, Roy G. Exodus from the Door of No Return: Journey of an American Family. 2008. 200p. pap. 14.49 *(978-1-4389-0349-1(9))* AuthorHouse.
Ruffin, Bernard. Norfolk, Virginia, Registry of Free Negroes, 1835-1861: Abstracts. 2010. 206p. ***(978-0-7884-8432-2(X))*** Heritage Bks.
Ruffin, C. Bernard. Norfolk, Virginia Registry of Free Negroes, 1835-1861, Abstracts. 2010. pap. 23.00 *(978-0-7884-5014-3(X))* Heritage Bks.
Smith, Colette Thomas. Secrets to African-American Roots: A Guide for Researching African American Records. 2006. (Illus.). 43p. per. 15.00 *(978-0-615-13423-9(8))* Thomas Smith, Colette.
Smith, Franklin Carter & Croom, Emily Anne. A Genealogist's Guide to Discovering Your African-American Ancestors. 2008. 250p. pap. 34.95 *(978-0-8063-1768-5(4))* Genealogical Publishing Co., Inc.
Smith, Leona W. St. Landry-up from Slavery Then Came the Fire!! 2011. 600p. 34.99 ***(978-1-4567-6034-2(3))***; pap. 25.99 ***(978-1-4567-6032-8(7))*** AuthorHouse.
Taylor, Frazine K. Researching African American Genealogy in Alabama: A Resource Guide. 2008. *(978-1-60306-044-8(8)*, NewSouth Bks.) NewSouth, Inc.
Thompson, Marilyn L. Grover C. Thompson Jr. Family Book: Good Stock. 2007. (Illus.). iii, 78p. pap. *(978-0-9792823-3-1(0))* Prioritybooks Pubns.
Walton-Raji, Angela Y. Black Indian Genealogy Research: African-American Ancestors among the Five Civilized Tribes, an Expanded Edition. 2007. pap. 24.50 *(978-0-7884-4473-9(5))* Heritage Bks.
Williams, Margo Lee. Miles Lassiter (circa 1777-1850) An Early African-American Quaker from Lassiter Mill, Randolph County, North Carolina: My Research Journey to Home. 2011. (ENG., Illus.). 156p. pap. 13.95 ***(978-0-939479-38-2(9))***, Backintyme) Boxes & Arrows, Inc.

AFRICAN AMERICANS—HEALTH AND HYGIENE

Allison-Francis, Emily. Correcting the Vitamin D Deficiency Dilemma: Strategies to Fight Diseases & Prolong Life for Black People. 2011. ***(978-0-912444-49-9(5))*** Dare Bks.
Belgrave, Faye Z., et al. Brothers of Ujima: A Cultural Enrichment Program to Empower Adolescent African American Males. 2011. pap. 26.95 ***(978-0-87822-652-8(4))*** Research Pr.
BeLue, Rhonda. Handbook of African American Health. Hampton, Robert L. et al, eds. 2010. (ENG.). 612p. 90.00 *(978-1-60623-716-8(0))* Guilford Pubns., Inc.
Braithwaite, Ronald L., et al, eds. Health Issues in the Black Community. 3rd ed. 2009. (ENG., Illus.). 656p. 85.00 *(978-0-470-43679-0(4)*, Jossey-Bass) Wiley, John & Sons, Inc.
Brock, Rovenia M. Dr. Ro's Ten Secrets to Livin' Healthy. 2007. (ENG., Illus.). 464p. mass mkt. 7.99 *(978-0-553-58558-2(4)*, Bantam) Random House Publishing Group.
Davis-Sivasothy, Audrey. The Science of Black Hair: A Comprehensive Guide to Textured Hair Care. 2011. (Illus.). 256p. ***(978-0-9845184-3-2(6))***; ***(978-0-9845184-0-1(1))***; pap. ***(978-0-9845184-1-8(X))***; pap. ***(978-0-9845184-2-5(8))*** Saja Publishing Co., LLC.
Du Bois, W. E. B. The Health & Physique of the Negro American. 112p. reprint ed. 88.00 *(978-0-7222-9722-3(X))* Library Reprints, Inc.
Ferdinand, Keith C., ed. Racial & Ethnic Minorities & Cardiovascular Disease. 2009. (Contemporary Cardiology Ser.). (Illus.). 400p. 179.00 *(978-1-58829-981-9(3))* Humana Pr.
Ferdinand, Keith C. & Armani, Annemarie. Cardiovascular Disease in Racial & Ethnic Minorities. 2009. (Illus.). xviii, 331p. *(978-1-60761-778-5(1))*; E-Book 129.00 *(978-1-59745-410-0(9))* Humana Pr.
Gourdine, Michelle A. Reclaiming Our Health: A Guide to African American Wellness. 2011. (Yale University Press Health & Wellness Ser.). (ENG., Illus.). 224p. pap. 19.95 *(978-0-300-13705-7(2))* Yale Univ. Pr.
Ileweng, Nana T. & Parsons, Ellen B. Female African Americans & Health Research. Ileweng, Nana T. & Parsons, Ellen B., eds. 2008. (Illus.). xi, 181p. 185.00 *(978-1-60456-442-6(3))* Nova Science Pubs., Inc.
Leach, Lesley. JUST MOVE: a Black Woman's Guide to Getting Fit. 2007. (ENG.). 88p. per. 16.95 *(978-1-4327-0159-8(2))* Outskirts Pr., Inc.
Lee, Nancy. This Is Their Story. 2010. 152p. pap. *(978-3-639-20418-6(2))* VDM Verlag Dr. Mueller e.K.
Lemelle, Anthony, et al, eds. Handbook of African American Health: Social & Behavioral Interventions. 2011. (ENG., Illus.). xviii, 289p. 189.00 *(978-1-4419-9615-2(X)*, 144199615X) Springer.
Liggan, Deborah Y. Taking Care of Our Folks: A Manual for Family Members Caring for the Black Elderly. 2009. 388p. 34.95 *(978-0-595-51502-8(9))*; pap. 24.95 *(978-0-595-52249-1(1))* iUniverse, Inc.
Mattingly, Cheryl. The Paradox of Hope: Journeys Through a Clinical Borderland. 2010. (ENG.). 291p. 60.00 *(978-0-520-26734-3(6))*; pap. 26.95 *(978-0-520-26735-0(4))* Univ. of California Pr.
McCree, Donna H., et al, eds. African Americans & HIV/AIDS: Understanding & Addressing the Epidemic. 2010. (ENG., Illus.). xx, 323p. 129.00 *(978-0-387-78320-8(2)*, 0387783202) Springer.
McQuirter, Tracye Lynn. By Any Greens Necessary: A Revolutionary Guide for Black Women Who Want to Eat Great, Get Healthy, Lose Weight, & Look Phat. 2010. (ENG., Illus.). 240p. pap. 14.95 *(978-1-55652-998-6(8)*, Hill, Lawrence Bks.) Chicago Review Pr., Inc.
Mohammed, Ovey N. Trials, Tribulations, & Celebrations: Past, Present, Future. Secundy, Marion Gray, ed. 2008. 150p. pap. 19.00 *(978-1-59244-917-0(4)*, Wipf and Stock) Wipf & Stock Pubs.
Molla, Michael T. & Madans, Jennifer H. Life Expectancy, Free of Chronic Condition-Induced Activity Limitations among White & Black Americans, 2000-2006. 2010. *(978-0-8406-0645-7(1))* National Ctr. for Health Statistics.
Payne Foster, Pamela. Is there a Balm in Black America?: Perspectives on HIV/AIDS in the African American Community. 2007. 312p. per. 19.99 *(978-1-4303-1670-1(5))* Lulu Enterprises Inc.
Perkins, Lottie. Eating to Die: Changing African American Attitudes about Health. 2007. (Illus.). 175p. per. 14.95 *(978-0-9799308-6-7(3))* Milligan Bks.
Persadsingh, Neil. The Hair in Black Women. 2008. 108p. pap. 11.99 *(978-1-60647-382-5(4))* Xulon Pr., Inc.
Pollock, Anne. Medicating Race: Heart Disease & Durable Preoccupations with Difference. 2012. (Experimental Futures Ser.). (ENG.). 280p. pap. 23.95 ***(978-0-8223-5344-7(X))***; (Illus.). 84.95 ***(978-0-8223-5329-4(6))*** Duke Univ. Pr.
Rawls, George, et al. Managing Cancer: The African American's Guide to Prevention, Diagnosis & Treatment. rev. ed. 2007. (ENG., Illus.). 362p. per. 16.95 *(978-0-9764443-2-9(1))* Hilton Publishing Co.
Reverby, Susan M. Examining Tuskegee: The Infamous Syphilis Study & Its Legacy. 2009. (John Hope Franklin Series in African American History & Culture Ser.). (ENG., Illus.). 424p. 32.00 *(978-0-8078-3310-0(X))* Univ. of North Carolina Pr.
Scott, Michael Thomas, , Michael Thomas. Shape Up: Strategies for Health Awareness through Preaching & Empowerment. 2010. 168p. pap. 11.99 *(978-1-4520-0697-0(0))* AuthorHouse.
Stern, Herbert, et al. The Heart of the Matter: Essential Advice for a Healthy Heart from Renowned Surgeons & Cardiologists. rev. ed. 2008. (ENG., Illus.). 195p. pap. 17.95 *(978-0-9743144-4-0(7))* Hilton Publishing Co.
Walker, Richard W., Jr. African-American Healthy: What You Need to Know to Protect Your Health. 2011. 160p. pap. 15.95 *(978-0-7570-0361-5(3))* Square One Pubs.
Wilson, Jamie Jaywann. Building a Healthy Black Harlem: Health Politics in Harlem, New York, from the Jazz Age to the Great Depression. 2009. 222p. 104.99 *(978-1-60497-624-3(1))* Cambria Pr.

AFRICAN AMERICANS—HISTORY

see also Freedmen—United States

Adefila, Johnson Ajibade. Was Christianity a Means of the Deafricanization & Social Control of Slaves? A Comparison of the Response of Free West Africans to Christianity with the Response of African Slaves in the United States. 2011. (ENG.). 184p. 109.95 ***(978-0-7734-3955-9(2))*** Mellen, Edwin Pr., The.
Adegbile, Isaiah. The African & African American History: An Introduction - The Political-Socio-Economic Context in Historical Perspective. 2008. (ENG.). 244p. per. 53.50 *(978-0-7618-3974-3(7))* Univ. Pr. of America, Inc.
African American History Month Poster. *(978-0-14-771976-8(3))* Penguin Group (USA) Inc.
Albert, Michele L. Reckoning with Our African Ancestors: Reclamation & Atonement by Their Descendants. 2007. 124p. per. 12.95 *(978-0-595-42279-1(9))* iUniverse, Inc.
Aldama, A. Enduring Legacies. 2010. 75.00 *(978-1-60732-049-4(5))*; pap. 29.95 *(978-1-60732-050-0(9))* Univ. Pr. of Colorado.
Aldama, Arturo J. Enduring Legacies: Ethnic Histories & Cultures of the Colorado Borderlands. 2011. E-Book *(978-1-60732-051-7(7))* Univ. Pr. of Colorado.

A

Alexander, Leslie & Rucker, Walter C., Jr., eds. Encyclopedia of African American History, 3 vols. 2010. (American Ethnic Experience Ser.). (Illus.). 1136p. 295.00 *(978-1-85109-769-2(4),* AFRCAM1C) ABC-CLIO, LLC.

Allen, John E. The Content of Their Character: The Story Behind This Antique Quilt & the History of the African American Family That Made It. 2009. 164p. pap. 44.48 *(978-1-4251-8812-2(5))* Trafford Publishing.

Allmendinger, Blake. Imagining the African American West. 2008. (Race & Ethnicity in the American West Ser.). (ENG.). 166p. pap. 19.95 *(978-0-8032-2082-9(0))* Univ. of Nebraska Pr.

Anderson, S. E. The Black Holocaust for Beginners. 2007. (For Beginners Ser.). (ENG., Illus.). 192p. per. 16.99 *(978-1-934389-03-4(X),* For Beginners) Steerforth Pr.

Aptheker, Herbert & Marable, Manning. Herbert Aptheker on Race & Democracy: A Reader. Foner, Eric, ed. 2010. (ENG.). 296p. pap. 25.00 *(978-0-252-07726-5(1))* Univ. of Illinois Pr.

Asante, Molefi K. The African American People: A Global History. 2011. E-Book ***(978-0-203-14508-1(9))*** Routledge.

Asante, Molefi Kete. The African American People. 2011. (ENG., Illus.). 416p. 125.00 ***(978-0-415-87254-6(5))***; pap. 39.95 ***(978-0-415-87255-3(3))*** Routledge.

—As I Run Toward Africa: A Memoir. 2011. 336p. 99.00 ***(978-1-61205-075-1(1))***; pap. 26.95 ***(978-1-61205-076-8(X))*** Paradigm Pubs.

Asante, Molefi Kete & Hall, Ronald E. Rooming in the Master's House: Power & Privilege in the Rise of Black Conservatism. 2010. 208p. pap. 24.95 *(978-1-59451-891-1(2))*; (ENG.). 100.00 *(978-1-59451-890-4(4))* Paradigm Pubs.

Ash, Stephen V. The Black Experience in the Civil War South, 1 vol. 2010. (Reflections on the Civil War Era Ser.). (Illus.). 127p. 44.95 *(978-0-275-98524-0(5),* C8524, Praeger Pubs.) Greenwood Publishing Group, Inc.

—Firebrand of Liberty: The Story of Two Black Regiments That Changed the Course of the Civil War. 2008. (ENG., Illus.). 304p. 25.95 *(978-0-393-06586-2(3),* 6586) Norton, W. W. & Co., Inc.

Bailey, Richard. Neither Carpetbaggers nor Scalawags. 5th ed. 2010. 400p. 29.95 *(978-1-58838-189-7(7))* NewSouth, Inc.

Bailey Sr., Joseph A. From Africa to Black Power. 2008. 376p. pap. 19.95 *(978-1-59594-263-0(7))* WingSpan Publishing.

Bakker, Daniel Z. Black Genocide. 2007. (ENG.). 277p. pap. 22.00 *(978-0-9779816-0-1(6))* K. B. Publishing.

Bankston, Carl L. III & Bankston, Carl L. Great Lives from History. 2011. ***(978-1-58765-747-4(3))***; (Illus.). xxviii, 1789p. ***(978-1-58765-752-8(X))***; (Illus.). xxviii, 1789p. ***(978-1-58765-750-4(3))***; (Illus.). xxviii, 1789p. ***(978-1-58765-751-1(1))***; (Illus.). xxviii, 1789p. ***(978-1-58765-749-8(X))***; (Illus.). xxviii, 1789p. ***(978-1-58765-748-1(1))*** Salem Pr., Inc.

BarCharts Inc., Staff. Black History: Civil War to Present. 2009. (ENG.). 6p. 5.95 *(978-1-4232-0851-8(X))* Barcharts, Inc.

Barksdale-Hall, Roland. African Americans in Mercer County. 2009. (Images of America Ser.). (ENG., Illus.). 128p. pap. 21.99 *(978-0-7385-6501-9(6))* Arcadia Publishing.

Barnes, Jodi A. The Materiality of Freedom: Archaeologies of Postemancipation Life. 2011. 256p. 49.95 ***(978-1-61117-034-4(6))*** Univ. of South Carolina Pr.

Bascom, Lionel C. Voices of the African American Experience, 3 vols. 2009. 717p. 275.00 *(978-0-313-34347-6(0),* GR4347, Greenwood Pr.) Greenwood Publishing Group, Inc.

Bee, Tee. African American Puzzles. 2007. 72p. pap. 14.95 *(978-1-58909-371-3(2))* Bookstand Publishing.

Bell, Janet Cheatham. Till Victory Is Won: Famous Black Quotations from the NAACP. 2006. 186p. reprint ed. pap. 14.00 *(978-1-4223-5531-2(4))* DIANE Publishing Co.

BelMonte, Kathryn I. African-American Heroes & Heroines of America: 150 True Stories of African-American Heroism. 2007. 300p. pap. *(978-0-8119-0002-7(9))* Lifetime Bks.

Benjamin, Orchester, Sr. Grandpa! Tell us a story/Drinking from Ancient Wells: Historical Authobiography trilogy/ book one, the Black Mind. 2007. 404p. pap. 24.95 *(978-0-9773421-1-2(5))* SoulViewWorld.

Bennett, Lerone, Jr. Before the Mayflower: A History of Black America. 8th ed. 2007. (ENG., Illus.). 804p. 44.95 *(978-0-87485-007-9(X))* Johnson Publishing Co., Inc.

—The Shaping of Black America. 2007. pap. 19.99 *(978-0-87485-001-7(0))* Johnson Publishing Co., Inc.

Berlin, Ira. The Making of African America: The Four Great Migrations. 2010. (ENG.). 320p. (gr. 12). 17.00 *(978-0-14-311879-4(X),* Penguin (Non-Classics)) Penguin Group (USA) Inc.

Bingham, Howard. Black Panthers 1968. Crist, Steve, ed. 2009. (ENG., Illus.). 192p. 100.00 *(978-1-934429-15-0(5))*; 44.95 *(978-1-934429-14-3(7))* AMMO Bks., LLC.

Black History I: Black History Month, Frederick Douglass, Harlem Renaissance, Jazz, Harriet Tubman, African American Inventors, Civil War, Reconstruction, Asante World, It's the Law. tchr. ed. 41.95 *(978-0-382-40659-1(1))* Cobblestone Publishing Co.

Blackmon, Douglas A. Slavery by Another Name: The Re-Enslavement of Black Americans from the Civil War to World War II. 2009. (ENG., Illus.). 496p. pap. 17.00 *(978-0-385-72270-4(2),* Anchor) Knopf Doubleday Publishing Group.

Blumrosen, Alfred W. & Blumrosen, Ruth G. Slave Nation. 2006. (ENG.). 304p. pap. 14.95 *(978-1-4022-0697-9(6))* Sourcebooks, Inc.

Boyle, David. African Americans. 2006. (Illus.). 128p. (J). (gr. 4-8). reprint ed. 15.00 *(978-1-4223-5294-6(3))* DIANE Publishing Co.

Bracks, Lean'tin. The African American Almanac: 400 Years of Triumph, Courage & Excellence. 2011. (ENG., Illus.). 512p. pap. 22.95 ***(978-1-57859-323-1(9))*** Visible Ink Pr.

Brawley, Benjamin. A Social History of the American Negro. 2008. 492p. 33.99 *(978-0-554-27000-5(5))*; 31.99 *(978-0-554-36303-5(8))* BiblioBazaar.

—A Social History of the American Negro. 2009. 456p. pap. *(978-1-4099-6265-6(2))* Dodo Pr.

—A Social History of the American Negro: Being a History of the Negro Problem in the United States; Including a History & Study of the Republic of Liberia. 2007. (ENG.). 430p. pap. 26.99 *(978-1-4346-2296-9(7))*; 488p. pap. 30.99 *(978-1-4346-2354-6(8))* BiblioBazaar.

Brawley, Benjamin G. A Social History of the American Negro. (Illus.). 420p. reprint ed. lib. bdg. 98.00 *(978-0-7222-4571-2(8))* Library Reprints, Inc.

Briggs-Dehorney, Jun &. Louise. Just the Typical American Negro. 2009. 232p. 24.99 *(978-1-4490-3065-0(3))* AuthorHouse.

Bristol, Douglas Walter, Jr. Knights of the Razor: Black Barbers in Slavery & Freedom. 2009. (ENG., Illus.). 232p. (gr. 17). 52.00 *(978-0-8018-9283-7(X))* Johns Hopkins Univ. Pr.

Broadnax, Samuel L. Blue Skies, Black Wings: African American Pioneers of Aviation. 2008. (ENG., Illus.). 208p. pap. 17.95 *(978-0-8032-1774-4(9),* Bison Bks.) Univ. of Nebraska Pr.

Broussard, Albert S. Expectations of Equality: A History of Black Westerners. 2012. pap. ***(978-0-88295-284-0(6))*** Davidson, Harlan Inc.

Browder, Glen. The South's New Racial Politics: Inside the Race Game of Southern History. 2009. 128p. pap. 14.95 *(978-1-60306-050-9(2),* NewSouth Bks.) NewSouth, Inc.

Brown, Jacqueline Elaine. African American Responses to American Presidential Inaugural Addresses: A Counterpoint of Rhetorical Traditions. 2010. 208p. 109.95 *(978-0-7734-1317-7(0))* Mellen, Edwin Pr., The.

Bunch, Lonnie G. Call the Lost Dream Back: Essays on History, Race & Museums. 2011. 218p. pap. 45.00 ***(978-0-8389-1124-2(2))*** American Library Assn.

Bunge, William. Fitzgerald: Geography of a Revolution. 2011. (Geographies of Justice & Social Transformation Ser.). (ENG., Illus.). 272p. pap. 26.95 *(978-0-8203-3874-3(5))* Univ. of Georgia Pr.

Butler, Brenda. Black History Trivia: 500 Questions & Answers. 2007. pap. 11.00 *(978-0-8059-8360-9(0))* Dorrance Publishing Co., Inc.

Butler, Sana. Sugar of the Crop: My Journey to Find the Children of Slaves. 2009. (ENG., Illus.). 256p. 24.95 *(978-1-59921-375-0(3),* Lyons Pr.) Globe Pequot Pr., The.

Bynum, Cornelius L. A. Philip Randolph & the Struggle for Civil Rights. 2010. (ENG., Illus.). 272p. pap. 25.00 *(978-0-252-07764-7(4))* Univ. of Illinois Pr.

Campbell, James T. Middle Passages: African American Journeys to Africa, 1787-2005. 2008. (ENG.). 513p. 30.00 *(978-1-4379-5107-3(4))* DIANE Publishing Co.

—Middle Passages: African American Journeys to Africa, 1787-2005. 2007. (ENG., Illus.). 544p. (gr. 12-18). 17.00 *(978-0-14-311198-6(1),* Penguin (Non-Classics)) Penguin Group (USA) Inc.

Campbell, Penelope. Africare: Black American Philanthropy in Africa. 2011. (ENG., Illus.). 245p. 39.95 *(978-1-4128-4243-3(3))* Transaction Pubs.

Capparell, Stephanie. The Real Pepsi Challenge: How One Pioneering Company Broke Color Barriers in 1940s American Business. 2008. (ENG., Illus.). 384p. pap. 23.99 *(978-0-7432-6572-0(6),* Free Pr.) Free Pr.

Carlisle, Edward E. & Carlisle, Josephine. Historical Sketches of the Ancient Negro. (African Studies). reprint ed. 20.00 *(978-0-938818-39-7(2))* ECA Assocs.

Carson, Clayborne, et al. The Struggle for Freedom: A History of African Americans, Concise Edition, Combined Volume (Penguin Academic Series) 2nd ed. 2010. (ENG., Illus.). 672p. (C). pap. 55.00 *(978-0-205-83240-8(7))* Pearson Education Canada CAN. Dist: Pearson Education.

—The Struggle for Freedom: A History of African Americans, Concise Edition, Volume 1 (Penguin Academic Series) 2nd ed. 2010. (ENG., Illus.). 360p. (C). pap. 38.67 *(978-0-205-83242-2(3),* Prentice Hall) Prentice Hall PTR.

—The Struggle for Freedom: A History of African Americans, Concise Edition, Volume 2 (Penguin Academic Series) 2nd ed. 2010. (ENG., Illus.). 408p. (C). pap. 38.67 *(978-0-205-83241-5(5),* Prentice Hall) Prentice Hall PTR.

Carter, Cynthia Jacobs, ed. Freedom in My Heart: Voices from the United States National Slavery Museum. 2009. (ENG., Illus.). 256p. 35.00 *(978-1-4262-0127-1(3),* National Geographic) National Geographic Society.

Chang, Derek. Citizens of a Christian Nation: Evangelical Missions & the Problem of Race in the Nineteenth Century. (Politics & Culture in Modern America Ser.). 248p. (C). 2012. pap. 24.95 ***(978-0-8122-2206-7(7))*** 2010. (Illus.). 39.95 *(978-0-8122-4218-8(1))* Univ. of Pennsylvania Pr.

Ciment, James. Atlas of African-American History. 2nd rev. ed. 2007. (Multicultural Atlas Ser.). (Illus.). 256p. per. 24.95 *(978-0-8160-6714-5(7),* Checkmark Bks.); (C). (gr. 9). 95.00 *(978-0-8160-6713-8(9))* Facts On File, Inc.

Cincere, N. Quamere. We Ain't No Niggas! Exposing the Deception of YOUR World History Education. 2007. (Illus.). 178p. per. 18.00 *(978-0-9787862-0-5(3),* 240-2984165) Knowledge of Self Publishing.

Cole, Bettie & Redcross, Autumn. African Americans in Sewickley Valley. 2008. (Images of America Ser.). (ENG., Illus.). 128p. pap. 19.99 *(978-0-7385-5687-1(4))* Arcadia Publishing.

Condino, Meggin. African American Eras Library Set: Contemporary Times, 4 vols. 2010. (ENG., Illus.). 960p. (J). 292.00 *(978-1-4144-3591-6(6),* UXL) Cengage Gale.

Cook, Robert J. Troubled Commemoration: The American Civil War Centennial, 1961-1965. 2007. (Making the Modern South Ser.). 300p. 45.00 *(978-0-8071-3227-2(6))* Louisiana State Univ. Pr.

Cooper, William A. A Portrayal of Negro Life. (Illus.). 110p. reprint ed. lib. bdg. 88.00 *(978-0-7222-0399-6(3))* Library Reprints, Inc.

Corbould, Clare. Becoming African Americans: Black Public Life in Harlem, 1919-1939. 2009. (Illus.). 304p. 42.00 *(978-0-674-03262-0(4))* Harvard Univ. Pr.

Countryman, Edward. Enjoy the Same Liberty: Black Americans & the Revolutionary Era. 2011. (African American History Ser.). (ENG.). 208p. 40.00 *(978-1-4422-0028-9(6))* Rowman & Littlefield Publishers, Inc.

Covey, Herbert C. African American Slave Medicine: Herbal & Non-Herbal Treatments. (ENG.). 216p. 2008. pap. 26.50 *(978-0-7391-1645-6(2))* 2007. 89.50 *(978-0-7391-1644-9(4))* Lexington Bks.

Cram101 Textbook Reviews. Outlines & Highlights for African American Odyssey by Hine & Harrold, Isbn: 9780136150121. 2010. 150p. pap. 29.95 *(978-1-61698-845-6(2))* Cram101 Inc.

Cram101 Textbook Reviews & Cram101 Textbook Reviews. Outlines & Highlights for African-American Odyssey, Volume 1-Special Edition by Darlene Clark Hine, Isbn: 9780205728763 0205728766. 2011. 324p. pap. 33.95 ***(978-1-61490-454-0(5))*** Cram101 Inc.

—Outlines & Highlights for African-American Odyssey, Volume 2-Special Edition by Darlene Clark Hine, Isbn: 9780205728770 0205728774. 2011. 316p. pap. 33.95 ***(978-1-61490-453-3(7))*** Cram101 Inc.

Cram101 Textbook Reviews Staff. Outlines & Highlights for African American Odyssey by Hine, Isbn: 9780136150121. 2009. 128p. pap. 28.95 *(978-1-4288-6790-1(2))* Cram101 Inc.

—Outlines & Highlights for African-American Odyssey, Volume 1 by Hine, Darlene Clark, Isbn: 9780136150138. 2009. 122p. pap. 28.95 *(978-1-4288-9386-3(5))* Cram101 Inc.

—Outlines & Highlights for African-American Odyssey Volume 2 by Darlene Clark Hine, Stanley Harrold, William C Hine, Isbn: 9780136149804. 2009. 180p. pap. 29.95 *(978-1-4288-9375-7(X))* Cram101 Inc.

—Outlines & Highlights for African Americans: Concise History, Combined by Darlene Clark Hine, Stanley Harrold, William C. Hine, ISBN. 2009. 128p. pap. 28.95 *(978-1-4288-9427-3(6))* Cram101 Inc.

Crouch, Barry. The Dance of Freedom: Texas African Americans During Reconstruction. Madaras, Larry, ed. 2007. (Jack & Doris Smothers Series in Texas History, Life, & Culture: No. 19). (ENG.). 286p. mass mkt. 25.00 *(978-0-292-71487-8(4))* Univ. of Texas Pr.

Culp, D. W., ed. Twentieth Century Negro Literature. 2011. 454p. pap. 24.99 ***(978-1-61203-065-4(3))*** Bottom of the Hill Publishing.

Curran, John J. Peekskill's African American History: A Hudson Valley Community's Untold Story. 2008. (Illus.). 155p. pap. 19.99 *(978-1-59629-484-4(1))* History Pr., The.

Curtis, Edward E., IV. Black Muslim Religion in the Nation of Islam, 1960-1975. 2006. (ENG., Illus.). 256p. per. 22.00 *(978-0-8078-5771-7(8))* Univ. of North Carolina Pr.

Curtis, Nancy C. Black Heritage Sites: The North. 2006. (Illus.). 234p. reprint ed. pap. 20.00 *(978-1-4223-5218-2(8))* DIANE Publishing Co.

—Black Heritage Sites: The South. 2006. (Illus.). 328p. reprint ed. pap. 20.00 *(978-1-4223-5219-9(6))* DIANE Publishing Co.

Dagbovie, Pero. African American History Reconsidered. 2010. (New Black Studies Ser.). (ENG.). 280p. pap. 25.00 *(978-0-252-07701-2(6))* Univ. of Illinois Pr.

Dale, Dianne. The Village That Shaped Us: Oen Woman's History of Anacostia. 2011. (Illus.). 328p. 29.95 ***(978-1-888018-41-7(0))*** KA Productions, LLC.

Dantas, Mariana L. R. & Dantas, Mariana. Black Townsmen: Urban Slavery & Freedom in Eighteenth-Century Americas. 2008. (Americas in the Early Modern Atlantic World Ser.). (ENG., Illus.). 296p. 95.00 *(978-1-4039-7576-8(0))* Palgrave Macmillan.

Davis, Hugh. We Will Be Satisfied with Nothing Less: The African American Struggle for Equal Rights in the North during Reconstruction. 2011. 232p. 45.00 ***(978-0-8014-5009-9(8))*** Cornell Univ. Pr.

de Jong, Greta. Invisible Enemy: The African American Freedom Struggle after 1965. 2010. (America's Recent Past Ser.: 3). (ENG., Illus.). 256p. 99.95 *(978-1-4051-6717-8(3),* Wiley-Blackwell) Wiley, John & Sons, Inc.

Delmont, Matthew F. The Nicest Kids in Town: American Bandstand, Rock 'n' Roll, & the Struggle for Civil Rights in 1950s Philadelphia. 2012. (American Crossroads Ser.). (ENG., Illus.). 312p. 65.00 ***(978-0-520-27207-1(2))***; pap. 27.95 ***(978-0-520-27208-8(0))*** Univ. of California Pr.

Denkler, Ann. Sustaining Identity, Recapturing Heritage: Exploring Issues of Public History, Tourism, & Race in a Southern Rural Town. 2007. (ENG.). 138p. 57.99 *(978-0-7391-1991-4(5))* Lexington Bks.

Dennis, Denise. Black History for Beginners. 2007. (For Beginners Ser.). (ENG., Illus.). 192p. per. 16.99 *(978-1-934389-19-5(6),* For Beginners) Steerforth Pr.

Dickerson, Vanessa D. Dark Victorians. 2008. 176p. 37.00 *(978-0-252-03256-1(X))* Univ. of Illinois Pr.

Diedrich, Maria & Heinrichs, Jürgen. From Black to Schwarz: Cultural Crossovers Between African America & Germany. 2011. (ENG.). 394p. pap. 49.95 *(978-0-87013-989-5(4))*; (Illus.). 344p. pap. *(978-3-643-10109-9(0))* Michigan State Univ. Pr.

Dodson, Howard & Palmer, Colin, eds. Origins. 2008. (ENG., Illus.). 225p. (C). pap. 19.95 *(978-0-87013-817-1(0))* Michigan State Univ. Pr.

Dowden, Priscilla A. Groping Toward Democracy: African American Social Welfare Reform in St. Louis, 1910-1949. 3rd ed. 2011. (ENG., Illus.). 320p. (C). 44.95 *(978-0-8262-1900-8(4))* Univ. of Missouri Pr.

Du Bois, W. E. B. Black Folk Then & Now: An Essay in the History & Sociology of the Negro Race. 2007. *(978-0-19-532582-9(6))* Oxford Univ. Pr., Inc.

—Black Reconstruction in America: An Essay Toward a History of the Part Which Black Folk Played in the Attempt to Reconstruct Democracy in America, 1860-1880. 2007. *(978-0-19-532581-2(8))* Oxford Univ. Pr., Inc.

—Black Reconstruction in America 1860-1880: An Essay Toward a History of the Part Which Black Folk Played in the Attempt to Reconstruct Democracy in America. 746p. reprint ed. lib. bdg. 148.00 *(978-0-7222-0414-6(0))* Library Reprints, Inc.

—Colonies & Democracy: Color & Race. (African Heritage Classical Research Studies). 143p. reprint ed. 20.00 *(978-0-938818-55-7(4))* ECA Assocs.

—The Gift of Black Folk: The Negroes in the Making of America. 2007. *(978-0-19-532578-2(8))* Oxford Univ. Pr., Inc.

—The Gift of Black Folk: The Negroes in the Making of America. 2009. (ENG.). 192p. pap. 14.95 *(978-0-7570-0319-6(2))* Square One Pubs.

Dudden, Faye E. Fighting Chance: The Struggle over Woman Suffrage & Black Suffrage in Reconstruction America, 1 vol. 2011. (ENG., Illus.). 296p. 34.95 *(978-0-19-977263-6(0))* Oxford Univ. Pr., Inc.

Dudziak, Mary L. Cold War Civil Rights - Race & the Image of American Democracy. 2011. (Politics & Society in Twentieth Century America Ser.). (ENG., Illus.). 352p. (C). pap. 24.95 ***(978-0-691-15243-1(8))*** Princeton Univ. Pr.

Duru, N. Jeremi. Advancing the Ball: Race, Reformation, & the Quest for Equal Coaching Opportunity in the NFL. 2012. (Law & Current Events Masters Ser.). (ENG.). 224p. pap. 19.95 ***(978-0-19-989625-7(9))*** Oxford Univ. Pr., Inc.

Duster, Michelle. Ida in Her Own Words: The Timeless Writings of Ida B. Wells From 1893. 2008. 104p. pap. 12.95 *(978-0-9802398-1-2(8))* Williams, Benjamin Publishing.

Egerton, Douglas R. Death or Liberty: African Americans & Revolutionary America, 1 vol. 2011. (ENG., Illus.). 352p. pap. 21.95 *(978-0-19-978225-3(3))* Oxford Univ. Pr., Inc.

Emilio, Luis Fenollosa. The History of the Fifty-Fourth Regiment of Massachusetts Volunteer Infantry 1863-1865. 410p. reprint ed. 98.00 *(978-0-7222-8151-2(X))* Library Reprints, Inc.

Ernest, John. A Nation Within a Nation: Organizing African-American Communities Before the Civil War. 2011. (ENG.). 232p. 35.00 *(978-1-56663-807-4(0))*; *(978-1-56663-917-0(4))* Dee, Ivan R. Pub.

Evans, William McKee. Open Wound: The Long View of Race in America. 2009. (ENG.). 344p. 35.95 *(978-0-252-03427-5(9))* Univ. of Illinois Pr.

Falola, Toyin. Encyclopedia of the Middle Passage. Warnock, Amanda, ed. 2007. (Greenwood Milestones in African American History Ser.). (Illus.). 464p. 75.00 *(978-0-313-33480-1(3),* GR3480, Greenwood Pr.) Greenwood Publishing Group, Inc.

Faulkner, Carol. Women's Radical Reconstruction: The Freedmen's Aid Movement. 2007. (Illus.). 208p. (C). per. 24.95 *(978-0-8122-1970-8(9))* Univ. of Pennsylvania Pr.

Finkelman, Paul, ed. Encyclopedia of African American History, 1896 to the Present Set: From the Age of Segregation to the Twenty-First Century, 5 vols. 2009. (ENG., Illus.). 2672p. 685.00 *(978-0-19-516779-5(1))* Oxford Univ. Pr., Inc.

Finkenbine & Cram101 Textbook Reviews Staff. Sources of the African American Past: Primary Sources in American History. 2007. 92p. per. 10.95 *(978-1-4288-2246-7(1))* Cram101 Inc.

Finley, Keith M. Delaying the Dream: Southern Senators & the Fight Against Civil Rights, 1938-1965. 2008. (C). *(978-0-8071-3345-3(0))* Louisiana State Univ. Pr.

Fleming, Harold C. & Fleming, Victoria. The Potomac Chronicle: Public Policy & Civil Rights from Kennedy to Reagan. 2010. (ENG.). 314p. pap. 24.95 *(978-0-8203-3623-7(8))* Univ. of Georgia Pr.

Ford, Arthur Lee. When the Whippoorwill Sang: A Memoir of Rural Life During the Twilight of the Segregated South. 2008. *(978-1-887366-84-7(9))* Univ. of Louisiana at Lafayette Pr.

Fordham, Damon L. True Stories of Black South Carolina. 2008. (Illus.). 166p. pap., per. 17.99 *(978-1-59629-405-9(1))* History Pr., The.

—Voices of Black South Carolina: Legend & Legacy. 2008. (Regional Histories Ser.). 19.99 *(978-1-59629-611-4(9))* History Pr., The.

Foster, Vonita White. Black Hanoverians: An Enlightened Past. Date not set. (Illus.). 185p. *(978-0-9646589-2-9(5))* ITS Pr.

Fowler, Charles H. Historical Romance of the American Negro. 2008. 332p. 45.95 *(978-0-548-98647-9(9))* 2007. (ENG.). 336p. per. 30.95 *(978-0-548-66073-7(5))* Kessinger Publishing, LLC.

Franklin, John Hope & Higginbotham, Evelyn Brooks. From Slavery to Freedom: A History of African Americans. 9th rev. ed. 2010. (ENG., Illus.). 736p. (C). pap. 119.00 *(978-0-07-296378-6(6),* 0072963786) McGraw-Hill Cos., The.

Franklin, John Hope, et al. From Slavery to Freedom. 2007. 288p. per. 15.95 *(978-1-4288-2760-8(9))* Cram101 Inc.

Frederickson, Mary E. Looking South: Race, Gender, & the Transformation of Labor from Reconstruction to Globalization. 2011. (Southern Dissent Ser.). (ENG., Illus.). 320p. 69.95 *(978-0-8130-3603-8(8))* Univ. Pr. of Florida.

Gant-Britton, Lisbeth. Holt African American History. 2008. (ENG., Illus.). 400p. (gr. 9-12). pap. 27.55 *(978-0-03-096954-6(9))* Houghton Mifflin Harcourt Publishing Co.

Gates, Henry Louis, Jr. Life upon These Shores: Looking at African American History, 1513-2008. 2011. (ENG., Illus.). 512p. 50.00 *(978-0-307-59342-9(8),* Knopf) Knopf Doubleday Publishing Group.

Gelderman, Carol. A Free Man of Color & His Hotel: Race, Reconstruction, & the Role of the Federal Government. 2012. (Illus.). 184p. 27.50 ***(978-1-59797-833-0(7))*** Potomac Bks., Inc.

Gillespie, Andra. Whose Black Politics? Cases in Post-Racial Black Leadership. 2009. (ENG., Illus.). 338p. 138.00 *(978-0-415-99215-2(X))* Routledge.

Glasgow Communications. Why She Stayed: At an African-American School, Solomon Coles, During Desegregation. 2nd ed. 2009. (Illus.). 117p. pap. 19.95 *(978-0-615-29648-7(3))* Glasgow Communications.

Glasrud, Bruce & Braithwaite, Charles A., eds. African Americans on the Great Plains: An Anthology. 2009. (ENG., Illus.). 404p. pap. 35.00 *(978-0-8032-2667-8(5))* Univ. of Nebraska Pr.

Glasrud, Bruce A., et al, eds. Slavery to Integration: Black Americans in West Texas. 2008. (ENG., Illus.). 168p. pap. 21.95 *(978-1-933337-26-5(5))* State Hse. Pr.

Glasrud, Bruce A. & Pitre, Merline, eds. Black Women in Texas History. 2008. (Centennial Series of the Association of Former Students, Texas AandM University). (ENG.). 256p. pap. 19.95 *(978-1-60344-031-8(3))* Texas A&M Univ. Pr.

Glave, Dianne D. Rooted in the Earth: Reclaiming the African American Environmental Heritage. 2010. (ENG., Illus.). 208p. pap. 18.95 *(978-1-55652-766-1(7),* Hill, Lawrence Bks.) Chicago Review Pr., Inc.

Goeser, Caroline. Picturing the New Negro: Harlem Renaissance Print Culture & Modern Black Identity. 2007. (Culture America Ser.). (Illus.). 360p. 34.95 *(978-0-7006-1466-0(4))* Univ. Pr. of Kansas.

Govenar, Alan. Untold Glory: African Americans in Pursuit of Freedom, Opportunity, & Achievement. 2007. (ENG., Illus.). 432p. pap. 15.95 *(978-0-7679-2117-6(8),* Harlem Moon) Broadway Bks.

Grady-Willis, Winston A. Challenging U. S. Apartheid: Atlanta & Black Struggles for Human Rights, 1960-1977. 2006. (ENG., Illus.). 312p. per. 24.95 *(978-0-8223-3791-1(6))* Duke Univ. Pr.

Green, Laurie B. Battling the Plantation Mentality: Memphis & the Black Freedom Struggle. 2007. (John Hope Franklin Series in African American History & Culture Ser.). (ENG., Illus.). 400p. 73.95 *(978-0-8078-3106-9(9))* Univ. of North Carolina Pr.

Greenberg, Cheryl. To Ask for an Equal Chance: African Americans in the Great Depression. (African American History Ser.). (ENG.). 200p. 2010. pap. 19.95 *(978-0-7425-5189-3(X))* 2009. (Illus.). 35.00 *(978-0-7425-5188-6(1))* Rowman & Littlefield Publishers, Inc.

Greene, Cheryll Y. & Smiley Books Staff, eds. America I Am Legends: Rare Moments & Inspiring Words. 2009. (ENG.). 192p. 34.95 *(978-1-4019-2410-2(7));* 150p. pap. 24.95 *(978-1-4019-2405-8(0))* Hay Hse., Inc.

Greene, S. Renee. The hearts of black Folk. 2008. 168p. pap. 19.97 *(978-0-557-02995-2(3))* Lulu Enterprises Inc.

Grégoire, Henri-Baptiste. An Enquiry Concerning the Intellectual & Moral Faculties & Literature of Negroes: Followed with an Account of the Life & Works of Fifteen Negroes & Mulattoes, Distinguished in Science, Literature, & the Arts. 2012. (AccessAble Bks.). (ENG.). 268p. pap. 19.95 *(978-1-57003-895-2(3))* Univ. of South Carolina Pr.

Grigsby, Daryl. In Their Footsteps: Inspirational Reflections on Black History for Every Day of the Year. 2007. (Illus.). 384p. per. 14.95 *(979-0-87946-336-6(8))* ACTA Pubns.

Grimshaw, Allen, ed. A Social History of Racial Violence. 2009. (ENG., Illus.). 571p. pap. 49.95 *(978-0-202-36263-2(9))* Aldine Transaction.

Grimshaw, William H. Freemasonry & Its Divisions & Gradations, Its Powers. 2006. pap. 9.95 *(978-1-4286-8911-4(7))* Kessinger Publishing, LLC.

Haggard, Dixie Ray, ed. African Americans in the Nineteenth Century: People & Perspectives, 1 vol. (Perspectives in American Social History Ser.). (Illus.). 258p. 85.00 *(978-1-59884-123-7(8),* AFAMN11C) ABC-CLIO, LLC.

Hahn, Steven, et al, eds. Land & Labor 1865 Vol. 1: A Documentary History of Emancipation, 1861-1867. 2008. (ENG., Illus.). 1112p. 95.00 *(978-0-8078-3147-2(6))* Univ. of North Carolina Pr.

Hahn, Steven, et al. Freedom Vol. 1: A Documentary History of Emancipation, 1861-1867, 2008. (Freedom, a Documentary History of Emancipation, 1861-1867 Ser.: Vol. 3). (Illus.). 992p. 89.95 *(978-0-521-22980-7(4))* Cambridge Univ. Pr.

Hairston, Otis L. Picturing Greensboro, North Carolina: Four Decades of African American Community. 2007. pap. 19.99 *(978-1-59629-284-0(9))* History Pr., The.

Haley, Alex. Alex Haley: The Man Who Traced America's Roots. 2007. *(978-0-7621-0885-5(1))* Reader's Digest Assn., Inc., The.

Hall, John H. Dancing & Crying to Be Free. 2009. 148p. 26.98 *(978-1-4269-1231-3(5))* Trafford Publishing.

Hare, L. Nathan. The Role of the Church in the African American Rise to Freedom. 2007. (Illus.). 192p. 20.00 *(978-0-9798045-0-2(7))* Return to Promise Ministries.

Harrington, Cliff. Just Tell the Truth: A Narrative History of Black Men Told from the Inside. 2011. 108p. 22.95 ***(978-1-4620-0951-0(4));*** pap. 12.95 ***(978-1-4620-0949-7(2))*** iUniverse, Inc.

Harrington, Lonnie. Both Sides of the Water: Essays on African-Native American Interactions. 2007. 16.00 *(978-0-8059-9132-1(8))* Dorrance Publishing Co., Inc.

Harris, Francis C. Amistad Pictorial History of the African-American Athlete, Vol. 1. Date not set. 74.95 *(978-0-06-019893-0(1),* Amistad) HarperCollins Pubs.

—Amistad Pictorial History of the African-American Athlete, 1886 to Present: Professional Volume. Date not set. 74.95 *(978-0-06-019895-4(8),* Amistad) HarperCollins Pubs.

Harris, Francis C. & Harris, Charles F. Amistad Pictorial History of the African-American Athlete: 1946 to Present, Vol. 2. Date not set. 74.95 *(978-0-06-019894-7(X),* Amistad) HarperCollins Pubs.

Harris, Jessica B. High on the Hog: A Culinary Journey from Africa to America. 2011. (ENG., Illus.). 304p. 26.00 *(978-1-59691-395-0(9))* Bloomsbury Publishing.

Harris, Middleton A., et al, eds. The Black Book. 35th anniv. ed. 2009. (Illus.). 224p. 35.00 *(978-1-4000-6848-7(7),* Random House) Random House Publishing Group.

Harris, Robert L., Jr. & Terborg-Penn, Rosalyn, eds. The Columbia Guide to African American History Since 1939. 2008. (Columbia Guides to American History & Cultures Ser.). (ENG.). 456p. (gr. 17). pap. 28.00 *(978-0-231-13811-6(3))* Columbia Univ. Pr.

Harris, Steve, narrated by. The Stories of Jimmy Lee Jackson, Reverend James Reeb, Viola Liuzzo & Vernon Dahmer, Grades 9-12. (Free at Last Ser.: Pt. 3). pap., tchr. ed. 24.95 incl. VHS *(978-1-930545-31-1(2),* 30006C) Choices, Inc.

Hay, Samuel. West Jupiter Quick Takes. 2011. 192p. pap. 14.95 *(978-0-533-16338-0(2))* Vantage Pr., Inc.

Haygood, Atticus G. Our Brother in Black: His Freedom & His Future. 2007. 256p. 41.95 *(978-0-548-53481-6(0));* (ENG.). per. 26.95 *(978-0-548-49441-7(X))* Kessinger Publishing, LLC.

Hedblad, Alan, ed. African American Alamnac. 11th rev. ed. 2011. 1500p. 312.00 *(978-1-4144-4547-2(4))* Cengage Gale.

Helm, Mary. From Darkness to Light: The Story of Negro Progress. 2007. (ENG.). 228p. 41.95 *(978-0-548-03709-6(4))* Kessinger Publishing, LLC.

Henderson, Francella. Hidden Secrets about Black History, Volume 1. 2008. (Illus.). 172p. per. 14.95 *(978-0-9799308-5-0(5))* Milligan Bks.

Heningburg, Keith. Readings in Us History: African-American Emphasis. rev. ed. 2010. (ENG.). 540p. pap. 153.36 *(978-0-7575-5703-3(1))* Kendall Hunt Publishing Co.

Hepburn, Sharon A. Roger. Crossing the Border: A Free Black Community in Canada. 2007. (Illus.). 272p. 42.00 *(978-0-252-03183-0(0))* Univ. of Illinois Pr.

Hermann, Janet Sharp. The Pursuit of a Dream. 2006. (ENG., Illus.). 312p. reprint ed. per. 25.00 *(978-1-57806-129-7(6))* Univ. Pr. of Mississippi.

Hilliard Mims, Barbara Tone. Don't Blame Me If I Got the Name Wrong. 2008. 324p. pap. 14.95 *(978-1-4327-2123-7(2))* Outskirts Pr., Inc.

Hine, Darlene Clark. African-American History. annot. ed. (YA). (gr. 9-12). tchr. ed. 59.97 *(978-0-13-194731-3(1))* Prentice Hall (Schl. Div.).

Hine, Darlene Clark, et al. African-Amaerican Odyssey, Vol. 2. 5th ed. 2011. (ENG.). 480p. (C). 49.33 *(978-0-205-18167-4(8),* Prentice Hall) Prentice Hall PTR.

—African-American History. 2nd ed. 2010. *(978-0-13-136637-4(8))* Prentice Hall PTR.

—African American Odyssey. 5th ed. 2011. (ENG.). (C). 46.67 *(978-0-205-18152-0(X),* Prentice Hall) Prentice Hall PTR.

—The African American Odyssey. 5th ed. 2011. (ENG.). 776p. (C). 82.67 *(978-0-205-18151-3(1),* Prentice Hall) Prentice Hall PTR.

—The African-American Odyssey, Vol. 1. 4th ed. 2007. (Illus.). 424p. pap. 80.00 incl. cd-rom *(978-0-13-615013-8(6))* Prentice Hall Higher Education.

—The African-American Odyssey, 2 vols. 5th ed. 2010. (ENG., Illus.). 480p. (C). pap. 93.00 *(978-0-205-73593-8(2),* Prentice Hall) Prentice Hall PTR.

—African American Odyssey, Vol. 1. 5th ed. 2011. (ENG.). 424p. (C). 49.33 *(978-0-205-18159-9(7),* Prentice Hall) Prentice Hall PTR.

—The African-American Odyssey, Vol. 2. 4th ed. 2007. (Illus.). 480p. per. 80.00 *(978-0-13-614980-4(4))* Prentice Hall Higher Education.

—African American Odyssey, Vols. 1 & 2. 5th ed. 2011. (ENG.). (C). 46.67 *(978-0-205-18161-2(9),* Prentice Hall) Prentice Hall PTR.

—The African-American Odyssey: Volume 2, Books a la Carte Plus MyHistoryLab. 5th ed. 2010. (ENG.). (C). ring bd. 67.33 *(978-0-205-19202-1(5),* Prentice Hall) Prentice Hall PTR.

—The African-American Odyssey: Volume 2, Books a la Carte Plus NEW MyHistoryLab. 5th ed. 2011. (ENG.). (C). ring bd. 67.33 ***(978-0-205-20388-8(4),*** Prentice Hall) Prentice Hall PTR.

—The African-American Odyssey since 1865, Vol. 2. 2007. 256p. per. 14.95 *(978-1-4288-2774-5(9))* Cram101 Inc.

—African-American Odyssey, the, Combined Volume. 5th ed. 2010. (ENG., Illus.). 776p. (C). 113.00 *(978-0-205-72881-7(2),* Prentice Hall) Prentice Hall PTR.

—African-American Odyssey, the, Combined Volume, Books a la Carte Edition. 5th ed. 2010. (ENG.). 776p. (C). ring bd. 74.00 *(978-0-205-19215-1(7),* Prentice Hall) Prentice Hall PTR.

—African-American Odyssey, the, Combined Volume, Books a la Carte Plus MyHistoryLab. 5th ed. 2011. (ENG.). (C). ring bd. 80.67 *(978-0-205-19200-7(9),* Prentice Hall) Prentice Hall PTR.

—African-American Odyssey, the, Combined Volume, Books a la Carte Plus NEW MyHistoryLab Pegasus. 5th ed. 2011. (ENG.). (C). ring bd. 80.67 ***(978-0-205-20386-4(8),*** Prentice Hall) Prentice Hall PTR.

—African-American Odyssey, the, Volume 1, 2 vols. 5th ed. 2010. (ENG., Illus.). 424p. (C). pap. 93.00 *(978-0-205-72886-2(3),* Prentice Hall) Prentice Hall PTR.

—African-American Odyssey, the, Volume 1, Books a la Carte Edition. 5th ed. 2010. (ENG.). 424p. (C). ring bd. 60.67 *(978-0-205-19216-8(5),* Prentice Hall) Prentice Hall PTR.

—African-American Odyssey, the, Volume 1, Books a la Carte Plus MyHistoryLab. 5th ed. 2010. (ENG.). (C). ring bd. 67.33 *(978-0-205-19201-4(7),* Prentice Hall) Prentice Hall PTR.

—African-American Odyssey, the, Volume 1, Books a la Carte Plus NEW MyHistoryLab. 5th ed. 2011. (ENG.). (C). ring bd. 67.33 ***(978-0-205-20387-1(6),*** Prentice Hall) Prentice Hall PTR.

—The African-American Odyssey to 1877, Vol. 1. 2007. 180p. per. 12.95 *(978-1-4288-2832-2(X))* Cram101 Inc.

—The African American Odyssey, Volume 2, Books a la Carte Edition. 5th ed. 2010. (ENG.). 480p. (C). ring bd. 60.67 *(978-0-205-19219-9(X),* Prentice Hall) Prentice Hall PTR.

—African Americans. 4th rev. ed. 2011. (ENG.). (C). 46.67 *(978-0-205-18131-5(7));* 720p. 49.33 *(978-0-205-18130-8(9));* Vol. 1. 46.67 *(978-0-205-18138-4(4));* Vol. 1. 368p. 49.33 *(978-0-205-18137-7(6));* Vol. 2. 432p. 49.33 *(978-0-205-18145-2(7))* Prentice Hall PTR. (Prentice Hall).

—African Americans: A Concise History. 3rd ed. 2008. (Illus.). 800p. pap. 70.00 incl. cd-rom *(978-0-13-600278-9(1))* Prentice Hall Higher Education.

—African Americans: A Concise History, 2 vols. 4th ed. 2011. (ENG., Illus.). 720p. (C). pap. 74.67 ***(978-0-205-80627-0(9),*** Prentice Hall) Prentice Hall PTR.

—African Americans Vol. 1: A Concise History, 2 vols. 4th ed. 2011. (ENG., Illus.). 368p. (C). pap. 53.33 ***(978-0-205-80936-3(7),*** Prentice Hall) Prentice Hall PTR.

—African Americans Vol. 1: A Concise History to 1877. 2007. 132p. per. 11.95 *(978-1-4288-2750-9(1))* Cram101 Inc.

Hine, Darlene Clark, et al. African Americans Vol. 2: A Concise History, 2 vols. 4th ed. 2011. (ENG., Illus.). 432p. (C). pap. 53.33 ***(978-0-205-80626-3(0),*** Prentice Hall) Prentice Hall PTR.

Hobbs, Antony O. Food for the Power of Thinking, Book II: The Roots of the Races. 2007. 58p. pap. 9.00 *(978-0-8059-7503-1(9))* Dorrance Publishing Co., Inc.

Hobbs, Barbara. Black America 1956-1966: The Break-Through Period. 2008. 84p. pap. 12.00 *(978-1-4343-7235-2(9))* AuthorHouse.

Hobson, Christopher Z. The Mount of Vision: African American Prophetic Tradition, 1800-1950. 2012. (ENG.). 304p. 65.00 ***(978-0-19-989586-1(4))*** Oxford Univ. Pr., Inc.

Hodge, Ruth E. Guide to African American Resources at the Pennsylvania State Archives. 2008. (ENG.). 598p. pap. 45.00 *(978-1-4223-9354-3(2))* DIANE Publishing Co.

Hogan, Lawrence. The Forgotten History of America's Negro Leagues, 1 vol. 2011. (Illus.). 204p. 48.00 *(978-0-313-37984-0(X),* A2038C, Praeger Pubs.) Greenwood Publishing Group, Inc.

Holt & Brown & Cram101 Textbook Reviews Staff. Major Problems in African-American History: Volume 2 - from Freedom to Freedom Now, 1865-1990s. 2007. 136p. per. 11.95 *(978-1-4288-2798-1(6))* Cram101 Inc.

Holt, Thomas C. Children of Fire: A History of African Americans. 2011. (ENG., Illus.). 464p. pap. 17.00 *(978-0-8090-3417-8(4),* Hill & Wang) Farrar, Straus & Giroux.

Hopkins, Pauline E. Daughter of the Revolution: The Major Nonfiction Works of Pauline E. Hopkins. 2007. (Multi-Ethnic Literatures of the Americas (MELA) Ser.). (ENG., Illus.). 456p. per. 34.95 *(978-0-8135-3962-1(5))* Rutgers Univ. Pr.

Hopkins, Pauline E. & Dworkin, Ira. Daughter of the Revolution: The Major Nonfiction Works of Pauline Hopkins. 2007. (Multi-Ethnic Literatures of the Americas Ser.). (ENG., Illus.). 456p. 70.00 *(978-0-8135-3961-4(7))* Rutgers Univ. Pr.

Horne, Gerald. Negro Comrades of the Crown: African Americans & the British Empire Fight the U.S. Before Emancipation. 2011. E-Book ***(978-0-8147-4463-5(X))*** New York Univ. Pr.

Hornsby, Alton. Black America: A State-by-State Historical Encyclopedia. 2011. *(978-0-313-34113-7(3)); (978-0-313-34114-4(1))* ABC-CLIO, LLC.

Hornsby, Alton, Jr., ed. Black America: A State-by-State Historical Encyclopedia, 2 vols. 2011. (Illus.). 1010p. 180.00 *(978-0-313-34112-0(5),* GR4112) Greenwood Publishing Group, Inc.

Hornsby, Alton, ed. A Companion to African American History. 2008. (Blackwell Companions to American History Ser.: 30). (ENG.). 584p. pap. 59.95 *(978-1-4051-7993-5(7),* Wiley-Blackwell) Wiley, John & Sons, Inc.

Horsford, Sonya Douglass. Learning in a Burning House: Educational Inequality, Ideology, & (Dis)Integration. 2011. (ENG.). 144p. 60.00 *(978-0-8077-5177-0(4));* pap. 26.95 *(978-0-8077-5176-3(6))* Teachers College Pr., Teachers College, Columbia Univ.

Horton, James O. & Kleintop, Amanda, eds. Race, Slavery & the Civil War: The Tough Stuff of American History & Memory. 2011. (ENG., Illus.). 160p. 23.95 *(978-0-9834012-0-9(9))* Virginia Sesquicentennial of the American Civil War Commission.

Houck, Davis W. & Dixon, David E., eds. Rhetoric, Religion & the Civil Rights Movement 1954-1965: Studies in Rhetoric & Religion 1. 2006. (Studies in Rhetoric & Religion: Vol. 1). 1050p. per. 49.95 *(978-1-932792-54-6(6))* Baylor Univ. Pr.

Howard, Walter T. Black Communists Speak on Scottsboro: A Documentary History. 2008. (ENG., Illus.). 200p. 51.00 *(978-1-59213-597-4(8))* Temple Univ. Pr.

Hull, Cadmus. The Black History Bowl. 2006. 116p. per. 12.95 *(978-1-59858-200-0(3))* Dog Ear Publishing, LLC.

Huntley, Horace & Montgomery, David, eds. Black Workers' Struggle for Equality in Birmingham. 2007. (Working Class in American History Ser.). 264p. per. 20.00 *(978-0-252-07493-6(9))* Univ. of Illinois Pr.

Hurt, R. Douglas, ed. & intro. African American Life in the Rural South, 1900-1950. 2011. (ENG., Illus.). 240p. (C). (gr. 13). pap. 30.00 *(978-0-8262-1960-2(8))* Univ. of Missouri Pr.

Hutton, Frankie. The Early Black Press in America, 1827 To 1860, 1 vol. 2007. (Contributions in Afro-American & African Studies). 208p. pap. 50.00 *(978-0-275-99940-7(8),* B9940) Greenwood Publishing Group, Inc.

Jacobs, Bruce A. Race Manners: Navigating the Minefield Between Black & White Americans. 2011. (ENG.). 288p. pap. 14.95 *(978-1-61145-031-6(4),* 611031, Arcade Publishing) Skyhorse Publishing Co., Inc.

James Charles Johnson. Evolution after Emancipation: America's Greatest Race. 2009. 380p. pap. 18.99 *(978-1-4389-6703-5(9))* AuthorHouse.

Jeffries, Judson L., ed. Black Power in the Belly of the Beast. 2006. 336p. 67.00 *(978-0-252-03148-9(2))* Univ. of Illinois Pr.

Jenkins, Everett. Pan-African Chronology II: A Comprehensive Reference to the Black Quest for Freedom in Africa, the Americas, Europe & Asia, 1865-1915, 2 vols. alt. ed. 2011. (Pan-African Chronologies Ser.). (ENG., Illus.). 582p. pap. 75.00 *(978-0-7864-4506-6(8))* McFarland & Co., Inc. Pubs.

—Pan-African Chronology III: A Comprehensive Reference to the Black Quest for Freedom in Africa, the Americas, Europe & Asia, 1914-1929, 2 vols. alt. ed. 2011. (Pan-African Chronologies Ser.). (ENG., Illus.). 640p. pap. 75.00 *(978-0-7864-4507-3(6))* McFarland & Co., Inc. Pubs.

Jennings, William. The African American King. 2008. 164p. pap. 19.95 *(978-1-4327-0216-8(5))* Outskirts Pr., Inc.

Johnson, Cedric. Revolutionaries to Race Leaders: Black Power & the Making of African American Politics. 2007. 320p. 60.00 *(978-0-8166-4477-3(2));* per. 20.00 *(978-0-8166-4478-0(0))* Univ. of Minnesota Pr.

Johnson-Fisher, Angela. Afristocracy. 2008. 72p. pap. *(978-3-639-01270-5(4))* VDM Verlag Dr. Mueller e.K.

Johnson, Robert A. & Riggins, Charlene. A Different Shade of Orange: Voices of Orange County, California, Black Pioneers. 2009. pap. *(978-0-930046-25-5(0))* California State Univ., San Bernardino, Robert V. Fullerton Art Museum.

Jonas, Gilbert. Freedom's Sword: The NAACP & the Struggle Against Racism in America, 1909-1969. 2007. (Illus.). 520p. per. 29.95 *(978-0-415-95665-9(X))* Routledge.

Jones, Angela. African American Civil Rights: Early Activism & the Niagara Movement. 2011. E-Book ***(978-0-313-39361-7(3),*** Praeger Pubs.) Greenwood Publishing Group, Inc.

Jones, Angela, ed. The History of Modern African American Political Thought: From Frederick Douglass to Barack Obama. 2012. (ENG., Illus.). 448p. (C). 160.00 *(978-0-415-89570-5(7))* Routledge.

Jones, Angela, ed. The Modern African American Thought Reader: From David Walker to Barack Obama. 2012. (ENG., Illus.). 448p. (C). pap. 54.95 ***(978-0-415-89573-6(1))*** Routledge.

Jones, Jacqueline. Labor of Love, Labor of Sorrow: Black Women, Work, & the Family, from Slavery to the Present. 2nd ed. 2009. (ENG., Illus.). 480p. (gr. 9). pap. 18.95 *(978-0-465-01881-9(5))* Basic Bks.

Jones, Martha S. All Bound up Together: The Woman Question in African American Public Culture, 1830-1900. 2007. (ENG., Illus.). 328p. pap. 22.00 *(978-0-8078-5845-5(5))* Univ. of North Carolina Pr.

Jordan, Winthrop D. White over Black: American Attitudes Toward the Negro, 1550-1812, 2nd Ed. 2nd ed. 2012. (Published for the Omohundro Institute of Early American History & Culture, Williamsburg, Virginia Ser.). (ENG., Illus.). 671p. 70.00 *(978-0-8078-3402-2(5));* pap. 29.95 *(978-0-8078-7141-6(9))* Univ. of North Carolina Pr.

Joseph, Peniel E. Dark Days, Bright Nights: From Black Power to Barack Obama. 2010. (ENG.). 288p. (gr. 13). 26.00 *(978-0-465-01366-1(X),* Basic Civitas Bks.) Basic Bks.

Justesen, Benjamin R. Broken Brotherhood: The Rise & Fall of the National Afro-American Council. 2008. (ENG., Illus.). 276p. pap. 35.00 *(978-0-8093-2843-7(7))* Southern Illinois Univ. Pr.

Kahrl, Andrew W. The Land Was Ours: African American Beaches from Jim Crow to the Sunbelt South. 2012. (ENG., Illus.). 376p. 39.95 ***(978-0-674-05047-1(9))*** Harvard Univ. Pr.

Karenga. Kawaida & Questions of Life & Struggle: African American, Pan-African, & Global Issues. 2007. *(978-0-943412-29-0(3))* Univ. of Sankore Pr., The.

Katz-Hyman, Martha B. & Rice, Kym S., eds. World of a Slave: Encyclopedia of the Material Life of Slaves in the United States, 2 vols. 2011. (Illus.). 581p. 180.00 *(978-0-313-34942-3(8),* GR4942) Greenwood Publishing Group, Inc.

Katz, Ralph & Warren, Rueben C. The Search for the Legacy of the USPHS Syphilis Study at Tuskegee. 2011. (ENG.). 208p. 60.00 *(978-0-7391-4725-2(0))* Lexington Bks.

Katznelson, Ira. When Affirmative Action Was White: An Untold History of Racial Inequality in Twentieth-Century America. 2006. (ENG.). 272p. pap. 16.95 *(978-0-393-32851-6(1),* 32851) Norton, W. W. & Co., Inc.

Kinchlow, Ben. Black Yellow Dogs: The Most Dangerous Citizen Is Not Armed, but Uninformed. 2008. (ENG.). 26.95 *(978-1-60037-285-8(6))* Morgan James Publishing.

King, Martin Luther, Jr. Where Do We Go from Here: Chaos or Community? 2010. (King Legacy Ser.). (ENG.). 256p. 24.95 *(978-0-8070-0076-2(0))* Beacon Pr.

—Where Do We Go from Here: Chaos or Community? 2010. (King Legacy Ser.). (ENG.). 256p. pap. 14.00 *(978-0-8070-0067-0(1))* Beacon Pr.

Kinshasa, Kwando M. African American Chronology: Chronologies of the American Mosaic, 1 vol. 2006. (Illus.). 208p. 45.00 *(978-0-313-33797-0(7),* GR3797, Greenwood Pr.) Greenwood Publishing Group, Inc.

A

Kinshasa, Kwando Mbiassi. Black Resistance to the Ku Klux Klan in the Wake of Civil War. alt. ed. 2008. (ENG., Illus.). 262p. pap. 39.95 *(978-0-7864-4100-6(3))* McFarland & Co., Inc. Pubs.

Kirk, John A. Beyond Little Rock: The Origins & Legacies of the Central High Crisis. 2007. 213p. per. 22.50 *(978-1-55728-851-6(8))* Univ. of Arkansas Pr.

Klarman, Michael J. Unfinished Business: Racial Equality in American History. 2007. (Inalienable Rights Ser.). (ENG., Illus.). 240p. 19.95 *(978-0-19-530428-2(4))* Oxford Univ. Pr., Inc.

Kly, Yussuf Naim. The Invisible War: The African-American War of Liberation, 1739-1858. 2006. (Illus.). 192p. per. 14.95 *(978-0-932863-50-8(7))* Clarity Pr., Inc.

Knecht, Sharon. Oblate Sisters of Providence: A Pictorial History. 2007. *(978-1-57864-411-7(9))* Donning Co. Pubs.

Knight, Michael Muhammad. The Five Percenters: Islam, Hip-Hop & the Gods of New York. (ENG., Illus.). 2008. 328p. pap. 19.95 *(978-1-85168-615-5(0))* 2007. 352p. 27.95 *(978-1-85168-513-4(8))* Oneworld Pubns. GBR. Dist: National Bk. Network.

Konadu, Kwasi. The Akan Diaspora in the Americas, 1 vol. 2012. (ENG.). 324p. pap. 24.95 ***(978-0-19-992285-7(3))*** Oxford Univ. Pr., Inc.

Kusmer, Kenneth L. & Trotter, Joe W., eds. African American Urban History since World War II. 2009. (Historical Studies of Urban America Ser.). (ENG., Illus.). 552p. 83.00 *(978-0-226-46509-8(8))*; pap. 30.00 *(978-0-226-46510-4(1))* Univ. of Chicago Pr.

Lane, Charles. The Day Freedom Died: The Colfax Massacre, the Supreme Court, & the Betrayal of Reconstruction. 2009. (ENG.). 352p. pap. 17.99 *(978-0-8050-8922-6(5),* Owl Bks.) Holt, Henry & Co.

Lawe, Gwendolyn McMillan. From Wolf to Wolfwood: A Genealogical & Historical Study of the Mcmillans & the African American Communities of Emory, Texas. 2011. 196p. 24.59 *(978-1-4567-2656-0(0))*; pap. 14.99 *(978-1-4567-2654-6(4))* AuthorHouse.

Lee, Lauranett. Making the American Dream Work: A Cultural History of African Americans in Hopewell, Virginia. 2008. (ENG., Illus.). 252p. 29.95 *(978-1-60037-466-1(2))* Morgan James Publishing.

Lee, Vera. The Black & White of American Popular Music: From Slavery to World War II. 2007. xii, 363p. *(978-0-87047-077-6(9))* Schenkman Bks., Inc.

Leeman, Richard W. & Duffy, Bernard K., eds. The Will of a People: A Critical Anthology of Great African American Speeches. 2012. 474p. pap. 49.95 ***(978-0-8093-3057-7(1))*** Southern Illinois Univ. Pr.

Leon Apolon Staff. Acknowledgement of Black History. 2009. 116p. pap. 30.00 *(978-1-4389-6496-6(X))* AuthorHouse.

Lepore, Jill. New York Burning: Liberty, Slavery, & Conspiracy in Eighteenth-Century Manhattan. 2006. (Vintage Ser.). (ENG., Illus.). 352p. pap. 16.95 *(978-1-4000-3226-6(1),* Vintage) Knopf Doubleday Publishing Group.

Lewis, David Levering. W. E. B. du Bois: A Biography, 1868-1963. Field, Kendra Taira, ed. 2009. (ENG., Illus.). 912p. pap. 25.00 *(978-0-8050-8805-2(9),* Holt Paperback) Holt, Henry & Co.

LiBrizzi, Marcus. Northeast Folklore: Lost Atusville: A Black Settlement from the American Revolution, Volume 42. 2009. (Illus.). 118p. pap. 19.95 *(978-0-943197-36-4(8))* Maine Folklife Center.

Lobb, Nancy. 16 Extraordinary African Americans. 2nd ed. 2007. (Illus.). 117p. (YA). (gr. 6-12). tchr. ed., per. 25.00 *(978-0-8251-6276-3(9))* Walch Education.

Lovelle Jenkins, Earnestine. African Americans in Memphis. 2009. (Images of America Ser.). (ENG., Illus.). 128p. pap. 21.99 *(978-0-7385-6750-1(7))* Arcadia Publishing.

Luczak, Ewa / Barbara. How Their Living Outside America Affected Five African American Authors: Toward a Theory of Expatriate Literature. 2010. ix, 250p. *(978-0-7734-3748-7(7))* Mellen, Edwin Pr., The.

Luqman, Amina, et al. African Americans of Petersburg. 2009. (Images of America Ser.). (ENG., Illus.). 128p. pap. 21.99 *(978-0-7385-5414-3(6))* Arcadia Publishing.

Lusane, Clarence. The Black History of the White House. 2011. (City Lights Open Media Ser.). (ENG., Illus.). 544p. pap. 19.95 *(978-0-87286-532-7(0),* 1311831) City Lights Bks.

Mackey, Stephen. Who Is Sambo? A Journey of Lessons. 2008. pap. 21.00 *(978-0-8059-8631-0(6))* Dorrance Publishing Co., Inc.

Malcolm X. End of White World Supremacy: Four Speeches. 2011. (ENG.). 160p. pap. 12.95 *(978-1-61145-016-3(0),* 611016, Arcade Publishing) Skyhorse Publishing Co., Inc.

Malveaux, Julianne. Surviving & Thriving: 365 Facts in Black Economic History, vol. 2010. (Illus.). 14.95 *(978-0-9827750-0-4(8))* Last Word Productions.

Marable, Manning. Let Nobody Turn Us Around: Voices of Resistance, Reform & Renewal: An African American Anthology. Mullings, Leith, ed. 2nd ed. 2009. (ENG.). 704p. 99.00 *(978-0-7425-6056-7(2))*; pap. 45.00 *(978-0-7425-6057-4(0))* Rowman & Littlefield Publishers, Inc.

—Living Black History: How Reimagining the African-American Past Can Remake America's Racial Future. 2011. (ENG.). 288p. (gr. 9). pap. 16.00 *(978-0-465-04395-8(X))* Basic Bks.

Marable, Manning & Aidi, Hishaam D., eds. Black Routes to Islam. 2009. (Critical Black Studies). (ENG.). 336p. 105.00 *(978-1-4039-8400-5(X))*; pap. 32.00 *(978-1-4039-7781-6(X))* Palgrave Macmillan.

Marsh, Charles. God's Long Summer: Stories of Faith & Civil Rights. 2008. (ENG., Illus.). 312p. (C). pap. 24.95 *(978-0-691-13067-5(1))* Princeton Univ. Pr.

Martin, Michael S., ed. Louisiana Beyond Black & White: New Interpretations of Twentieth-Century Race & Race Relations. 2011. 200p. pap. 20.00 *(978-1-935754-04-6(1))* Univ. of Louisiana at Lafayette Pr.

Martin, Michael T., et al, eds. Redress for Historical Injustices in the United States: On Reparations for Slavery, Jim Crow, & Their Legacies. 2007. (ENG., Illus.). 728p. per. 32.95 *(978-0-8223-4024-9(0))* Duke Univ. Pr.

Martin, Michael T. & Yaquinto, Marilyn, eds. Redress for Historical Injustices in the United States: On Reparations for Slavery, Jim Crow, & Their Legacies. 2007. (ENG., Illus.). 728p. 104.95 *(978-0-8223-4005-8(4))* Duke Univ. Pr.

Materson, Lisa G. For the Freedom of Her Race: Black Women & Electoral Politics in Illinois, 1877-1932. 2009. (ENG., Illus.). 352p. 44.00 *(978-0-8078-3271-4(5))* Univ. of North Carolina Pr.

Maye, Warren L. Soldiers of Uncommon Valor: The History of Salvationists of African Descent in the United States. 2007. *(978-0-89216-111-9(6))* Salvation Army.

Mazloomi, Carolyn L. Stitching a Culture Together: African American Quilters of Ohio. 2013. (Ohio Quilt Ser.). (ENG., Illus.). 128p. pap. 22.95 *(978-0-8214-1940-3(4))* Ohio Univ. Pr.

Mcadam & Cram101 Textbook Reviews Staff. Political Process & the Development of Black Insurgency 1930-1970. 2007. 60p. per. 9.95 *(978-1-4288-2326-6(3))* Cram101 Inc.

McFarland, Bernard C. The Hill & the Bottoms: The Story from the Thousand Yard Stare. 2009. (Illus.). 112p. *(978-1-57864-538-1(7))* Donning Co. Pubs.

McKibben, Carol. Racial Beachhead: Diversity & Democracy in a Military Town. 2011. (ENG.). 352p. 80.00 ***(978-0-8047-7698-1(9))***; pap. 24.95 ***(978-0-8047-7699-8(7))*** Stanford Univ. Pr.

McLaurin, Melton A. The Marines of Montford Point: America's First Black Marines. 2009. (ENG., Illus.). 216p. pap. 18.95 *(978-0-8078-6176-9(6))* Univ. of North Carolina Pr.

McLemee, Scott & Le Blanc, Paul, eds. C. L. R. James & Revolutionary Marxism: Selected Writings of C. L. R. James, 1939-1949. (Revolutionary Studies). (ENG.). 1p. pap. 28.98 *(978-1-57392-371-2(0),* Humanity Bks.) Prometheus Bks., Pubs.

McNeil, William F. Black Baseball Out of Season: Pay for Play Outside of the Negro Leagues. alt. ed. 2012. (ENG., Illus.). 244p. pap. 25.00 ***(978-0-7864-6924-6(2))*** McFarland & Co., Inc. Pubs.

Melton, J. Gordon. A Will to Choose: The Origins of African American Methodism. 2007. (ENG., Illus.). 330p. 89.00 *(978-0-7425-5264-7(0))*; per. 34.95 *(978-0-7425-5265-4(9))* Rowman & Littlefield Publishers, Inc.

Miller, Eben. Born along the Color Line: The 1933 Amenia Conference & the Rise of a National Civil Rights Movement, 1 vol. 2012. (ENG., Illus.). 368p. 29.95 *(978-0-19-517455-7(0))* Oxford Univ. Pr., Inc.

Miller, Paul T. The Postwar Struggle for Civil Rights: African Americans in San Francisco, 1945-1975. 2009. (Illus.). xvi, 167p. E-Book 95.00 *(978-0-203-86612-2(6))* Routledge.

Minchin, Timothy J. From Rights to Economics: The Ongoing Struggle for Black Equality in the U. S. South. 2007. (New Perspectives on the History of the South Ser.). (ENG., Illus.). 224p. 39.95 *(978-0-8130-3092-0(7))* Univ. Pr. of Florida.

Mintz, Steven, ed. African American Voices: A Documentary Reader, 1619-1877. 4th ed. 2009. (Uncovering the Past: Documentary Readers in American History Ser.: 1). (ENG., Illus.). 264p. pap. 34.95 *(978-1-4051-8267-6(9))*; 104.95 *(978-1-4051-8268-3(7))* Wiley, John & Sons, Inc. (Wiley-Blackwell).

Moore, Natalie Y. & Williams, Lance. The Almighty Black P Stone Nation: The Rise, Fall, & Resurgence of an American Gang. (ENG.). 2012. 304p. pap. 17.95 ***(978-1-61374-491-8(9))*** 2011. (Illus.). 272p. 26.95 *(978-1-55652-845-3(0))* Chicago Review Pr., Inc. (Hill, Lawrence Bks.).

Moore, Winfred B., Jr. & Burton, Orville Vernon, eds. Toward the Meeting of the Waters: Currents in the Civil Rights Movement of South Carolina during the Twentieth Century. 2010. (ENG.). 416p. pap. 29.95 *(978-1-57003-971-3(2))* Univ. of South Carolina Pr.

Morant, Mack Bernard. African Americans on Stamps. alt. ed. 2012. (ENG., Illus.). 254p. pap. 25.00 *(978-0-7864-6618-4(9))* McFarland & Co., Inc. Pubs.

Morgan, Philip, ed. African American Life in the Georgia Lowcountry: The Atlantic World & the Gullah Geechee. (Race in the Atlantic World, 1700-1900 Ser.). (ENG.). 2011. 376p. pap. 24.95 ***(978-0-8203-4307-5(2))*** 2010. (Illus.). 320p. 34.95 *(978-0-8203-3064-8(7))* Univ. of Georgia Pr.

Muhammad, Ashahed. The Black Principle: Prepare to Rule. 2008. per. *(978-0-9766066-1-1(5))* Truth Establishment Institute, The.

Mullins, Lisa. Diane Nash: A Biography: the Fire of the Civil Rights Movement. 2007. (Illus.). 100p. per. *(978-0-9715402-8-6(4))* Barnhardt & Ashe Publishing, Inc.

Myers, Andrew H. Black, White, & Olive Drab: Racial Integration at Fort Jackson, South Carolina, & the Civil Rights Movement. 2006. (American South Ser.). (ENG., Illus.). 320p. (gr. 17). 39.50 *(978-0-8139-2575-2(4))* Univ. Pr. of Virginia.

Myers-El, Noble Timothy. The Unknown Lore of Amexem's Indigenous People: An Aboriginal Treatise. 2008. 300p. pap. 18.00 *(978-1-4343-2767-3(1))* AuthorHouse.

NAACP Staff. The Crisis - a Record of the Darker Races 1910-60: Journal of the National Association for the Advancement of Colored People, 50 vols, Set. 1985.00 *(978-0-405-01001-9(X))* Ayer Co. Pubs., Inc.

Nash, Michael & Lewis, David Levering, eds. Red Activists & Black Freedom: James & Esther Jackson & the Long Civil Rights Revolution. 2009. (ENG., Illus.). 136p. (C). 125.00 *(978-0-415-47255-5(5))* Routledge.

National Society, Daughters of the American Revolution Staff & Grundset, Eric G. Forgotten Patriots: African Americans & American Indians in the Revolutionary War: A Guide to Service, Sources & Studies. 2009. 854p. 35.00 *(978-1-892237-10-1(5))* National Society, Daughters of the American Revolution.

Negro-Ology. 2006. 14.95 *(978-0-9790184-0-4(4))* MERL Pubs.

Nelson, Jack E., et al. Highland Beach on the Chesapeake Bay: Maryland's First African American Incorporated Town. 2008. *(978-1-57864-526-8(3))* Donning Co. Pubs.

Neumann, Caryn E. Term Paper Resource Guide to African American History, 1 vol. 2009. (Term Paper Resource Guides). 304p. 65.00 *(978-0-313-35501-1(0),* GR5501, Greenwood Pr.) Greenwood Publishing Group, Inc.

Newby-Alexander, Cassandra. An African American History of the Civil War in Hampton Roads. 2010. (ENG., Illus.). 128p. pap. 19.99 *(978-1-60949-077-5(0))* History Pr., The.

North Carolina African American History & Culture. 2007. (J). per. 32.96 *(978-1-888325-45-4(3))* Allosaurus Pubs.

Northrup, David. Crosscurrents in the Black Atlantic, 1770-1965: A Brief History with Documents. 2007. (Bedford Series in History & Culture). (ENG., Illus.). 208p. (C). per. 15.95 *(978-0-312-44244-6(0))* Bedford/Saint Martin's.

Nwachuku, Levi, ed. Exploring the African-American Experience, Fourth Edition. 2008. (C). pap. *(978-0-9798711-0-8(7))* Lincoln Univ. Pr.

Nyong'o, Tavia. The Amalgamation Waltz: Race, Performance, & the Ruses of Memory. 2009. (ENG., Illus.). 248p. 67.50 *(978-0-8166-5612-7(6))*; pap. 22.50 *(978-0-8166-5613-4(4))* Univ. of Minnesota Pr.

Nzeadibe, Richard E. The 2nd Migration: Being an Analysis of How & Why Africans are Migrating to the U. S. A. 2009. 92p. pap. 15.99 *(978-1-4363-9054-5(0))* Xlibris Corp.

Okafor, Victor O. Towards an Understanding of Africology. 3rd rev. ed. 2011. (ENG.). 298p. pap. 94.95 *(978-0-7575-7065-0(8))* Kendall Hunt Publishing Co.

O'Malley, Michael. Face Value: The Entwined History of Money & Race in America. 2012. (ENG., Illus.). 272p. 75.00 ***(978-0-226-62937-7(6))***; pap. 25.00 ***(978-0-226-62938-4(4))*** Univ. of Chicago Pr.

Opie, Frederick Douglass. Black Labor Migration in Caribbean Guatemala, 1882-1923. 2009. (Working in the Americas Ser.). (ENG., Illus.). 192p. 65.00 *(978-0-8130-3371-6(3))* Univ. Pr. of Florida.

Ortiz, Paul. Emancipation Betrayed: The Hidden History of Black Organizing & White Violence in Florida from Reconstruction to the Bloody Election Of 1920. 2006. (American Crossroads Ser.). (Illus.). 382p. per. 24.95 *(978-0-520-25003-1(6))* Univ. of California Pr.

Oshodi, John Egbeazien. A Glance at American Presidents in Black Lifea: George Washington to George W. Bush, a to Z. 2009. vii, 96p. E-Book *(978-0-7618-4464-8(3))* Univ. Pr. of America, Inc.

Painter, Nell Irvin. Creating Black Americans: African-American History & Its Meanings, 1619 to the Present. 2006. (ENG., Illus.). 496p. (C). pap. 44.95 *(978-0-19-513756-9(6))* Oxford Univ. Pr., Inc.

Palmié, Stephan. Africas of the Americas: Beyond the Search for Origins in the Study of Afro-Atlantic Religions. Palmié, Stephan, ed. 2008. (Studies of Religion in Africa Ser.). 355p. *(978-90-04-16472-7(3))* BRILL.

Parker, Honesty. African Americans of des Moines & Polk County. 2011. (Images of America Ser.). (ENG., Illus.). 128p. pap. 21.99 ***(978-0-7385-8296-2(4))*** Arcadia Publishing.

Patton, Carl A. Fallen Letters: Mis-education & Intellectual Confusion (Essays on the Black Experience) 2007. 202p. pap. 14.95 *(978-0-9656467-2-7(6))* FreedomJournal Pr.

Pennybacker, Susan D. From Scottsboro to Munich: Race & Political Culture in 1930s Britain. 2009. (ENG., Illus.). 400p. (C). pap. 28.95 *(978-0-691-14186-2(X))* Princeton Univ. Pr.

Penrice, Ronda Racha. African American History for Dummies. 2007. (ENG., Illus.). 432p. pap. 19.99 *(978-0-7645-5469-8(7),* For Dummies) Wiley, John & Sons, Inc.

Plastas, Melinda. A Band of Noble Women: Racial Politics in the Women's Peace Movement. 2011. (Illus.). 296p. ***(978-0-8156-3257-3(6))*** Syracuse Univ. Pr.

Potter, Joan. African American Firsts: Famous Little-Known & Unsung Triumphs of Blacks in America (Updated) 2009. (ENG., Illus.). 424p. pap. 16.00 *(978-0-7582-4166-5(6))* Kensington Publishing Corp.

Powell, Richard J. Cutting a Figure: Fashioning Black Portraiture. 2009. (ENG., Illus.). 296p. 55.00 *(978-0-226-67727-9(3))* Univ. of Chicago Pr.

Pursell, Carroll, ed. A Hammer in Their Hands: A Documentary History of Technology & the African-American Experience. 2006. (ENG., Illus.). 304p. (gr. 17). per. 20.00 *(978-0-262-66199-7(3))* MIT Pr.

Qualls, Josephine. Imani Trails. 2011. 64p. pap. 9.99 ***(978-1-937129-06-4(3))*** Faithful Life Pubs.

Ramsamy, et al. The Black Experience in America. 2nd rev. ed. 2011. (ENG.). 468p. pap. 70.00 ***(978-0-7575-9414-4(X))*** Kendall Hunt Publishing Co.

Randall, Stephen E. Calvin Didn't Know. 2007. (J). per. 13.00 *(978-0-9767189-3-2(6))* Better Day Publishing LLC.

Randolph, Ryan P. W. E. B. Dubois: The Fight for Civil Rights. 2009. (Library of American Lives & Times Ser.). 112p. (gr. 5-5). 69.20 *(978-1-60853-510-1(X))* Rosen Publishing Group, Inc., The.

Ray, Ruth, et al. The Struggle for Black History: Foundations for a Critical Black Pedagogy in Education. 2007. (ENG., Illus.). 110p. per. 26.50 *(978-0-7618-3836-4(8))* Univ. Pr. of America, Inc.

Reed, Christopher Robert. The Rise of Chicago's Black Metropolis, 1920-1929. 2011. (New Black Studies Ser.). (ENG., Illus.). 288p. 55.00 *(978-0-252-03623-1(9))* Univ. of Illinois Pr.

Regosin, Elizabeth A. & Shaffer, Donald R., eds. Voices of Emancipation: Understanding Slavery, the Civil War, & Reconstruction Through the U. S. Pension Bureau Files. 2008. (ENG., Illus.). 232p. pap. 23.00 *(978-0-8147-7587-5(X))* New York Univ. Pr.

Reid, Debra Ann. Reaping a Greater Harvest: African Americans, the Extension Service, & Rural Reform in Jim Crow Texas. 2007. (Sam Rayburn Series on Rural Life: No. 14). (ENG., Illus.). 328p. 39.95 *(978-1-58544-571-4(1))* Texas A&M Univ. Pr.

Richardson, Joe Martin. African Americans in the Reconstruction of Florida, 1865-1877. 2nd ed. 2008. (ENG.). 272p. pap. 27.95 *(978-0-8173-5524-1(3))* Univ. of Alabama Pr.

Richardson, Riche. Black Masculinity & the U. S. South: From Uncle Tom to Gangsta. 2007. (New Southern Studies Ser.). (ENG., Illus.). 304p. per. 24.95 *(978-0-8203-2890-4(1))* Univ. of Georgia Pr.

Rivers, Larry Eugene. Slavery in Florida: Territorial Days to Emancipation. 2009. (ENG., Illus.). 384p. pap. 19.95 *(978-0-8130-3381-5(0))* Univ. Pr. of Florida.

Roberts, Gene & Klibanoff, Hank. The Race Beat: The Press, the Civil Rights Struggle, & the Awakening of a Nation. 2007. (Vintage Ser.). (ENG., Illus.). 544p. pap. 17.00 *(978-0-679-73565-6(8),* Vintage) Knopf Doubleday Publishing Group.

Roberts, Samuel Kelton, Jr. Infectious Fear: Politics, Disease, & the Health Effects of Segregation. 2009. (Studies in Social Medicine Ser.). (ENG., Illus.). 336p. 62.95 *(978-0-8078-3259-2(6))*; pap. 26.95 *(978-0-8078-5934-6(6))* Univ. of North Carolina Pr.

Roberts, Sylvia Alden. Mining for Freedom: Black History Meets the California Gold Rush. 2008. 160p. pap. 14.95 *(978-0-595-52492-1(3))* iUniverse, Inc.

Robertson, Clyde C. Africa Rising: Multidisciplinary Discussions on Africana Studies & History: From Ancient Times Through Modernity. 2009. *(978-1-59221-716-8(8))*; pap. *(978-1-59221-717-5(6))* Africa World Pr.

Robertson, Gil L., IV, ed. Family Affair: What It Means to Be African-American Today. 2009. (ENG.). 432p. pap. 16.00 *(978-1-932841-35-0(0))* Agate Publishing, Inc.

Robinson, Devin A. & Roper, Vernon. Blacks: from the Plantation to the Prison: The Move, the Mockery, the Mental Slavery. 2008. (Illus.). 160p. pap. *(978-978-8174-51-6(5))* Loretta Davis.

Rogers, J. A. One Hundred Amazing Facts about the Negro with Complete Proof: A Short Cut to the World History of the Negro. 2011. 68p. 36.95 ***(978-1-258-03077-3(2))*** Literary Licensing, LLC.

Rogers, Joseph. The Struggle, the Pain but the Ultimate Victory. 2007. per. *(978-1-59581-387-9(X),* Brentwood Christian Pr.) Brentwood Communications Group.

Rojas, Fabio. From Black Power to Black Studies: How a Radical Social Movement Became an Academic Discipline. 2007. (ENG., Illus.). 304p. (gr. 17). 47.00 *(978-0-8018-8619-5(8))* Johns Hopkins Univ. Pr.

Rooks, Noliwe M. White Money/Black Power: The Surprising History of African American Studies & the Crisis of Race in Higher Education. 2007. (ENG.). pap. *(978-0-618-80239-5(8))* Beacon Pr.

Royal, Alice C. & Ellinger, Mickey. Allensworth, the Freedom Colony: A California African American Township. 2008. pap. *(978-1-59714-091-1(0))* Heyday.

Rudman, Jack. African & Afro-American History. (C). (ACT Proficiency Examination Program Ser.: Vol. 1). 49.95 *(978-0-8373-5551-1(6))*; (Regents College Proficiency Examination Ser.: Vol. 36). 49.95 *(978-0-8373-5486-6(2))* National Learning Corp. (Passbooks).

Rutkoff, Peter M. & Scott, William B. Fly Away: The Great African American Cultural Migrations. 2010. (ENG., Illus.). 432p. (gr. 17). 45.00 *(978-0-8018-9477-0(8))* Johns Hopkins Univ. Pr.

Saboe, Jon R. Snapshots in AMERICAN Black History: The Untold Stories of Courageous Americans in the Face of Unimaginable Obstacles. 2007. 68p. per. 12.95 *(978-1-4327-0627-2(6))* Outskirts Pr., Inc.

Salem, Dorothy. The Journey: A HISTORY of the AFRICAN AMERICAN EXPERIENCE, PART I: Africa to America In 1877 (CPSJ) 2007. (ENG.). 468p. (C). pap. 107.67 *(978-0-07-338760-4(6),* 0073387606) McGraw-Hill Cos., The.

Salem, Dorothy C. The Journey: A History of the African American Experience, Part II. 2007. (ENG., Illus.). 468p. (C). per. 105.00 *(978-0-07-338793-2(2),* 0073387932) McGraw-Hill Create (TM).

Sanders, Arthur L. From the Backs of Slaves to the Presidency. 2009. 76p. pap. 12.49 *(978-1-4490-1843-6(2))* AuthorHouse.

Sanders, Nancy. Black Abolitionists. 2011. (Perspectives on History Ser.). (ENG.). 120p. (gr. 9-14). pap. 7.95 *(978-1-932663-26-6(6))* History Compass, LLC.

Scarborough, William Sanders. The Works of William Sanders Scarborough: Black Classicist & Race Leader. Ronnick, Michele Valerie, ed. 2006. (Illus.). 560p. 115.00 *(978-0-19-530962-1(6))* Oxford Univ. Pr., Inc.

Schneider, Mark Robert. African Americans in the Jazz Age: A Decade of Struggle & Promise. 2006. (African American History Ser.). (ENG., Illus.). 176p. per. 24.95 *(978-0-7425-4417-8(6))* Rowman & Littlefield Publishers, Inc.

Schubert, Frank. Black Valor: Buffalo Soldiers & the Medal of Honor, 1870 - 1898. 2009. (ENG.). 244p. pap. 19.95 *(978-1-4422-0193-4(2))* Rowman & Littlefield Publishers, Inc.

Scott, Emmett J. Negro Migration During the War. 2009. 232p. pap. *(978-1-4099-9069-7(9))* Dodo Pr.

Seatts, Linda. The Truth about the Superior Lie: A book to resurrect the lives of African-Americans crucified by the Lie, 1. 2007. 76p. (YA). *(978-0-9793305-0-6(5))* Kittrell Publishing Hse.

Semmes, Clovis E. The Regal Theater & Black Culture. 2011. (ENG.). 304p. pap. 29.00 *(978-0-230-11315-2(X))* Palgrave Macmillan.

Shabazz, Rsheed Ali. And God Made Man: The Creation of African America. 2008. pap. 10.00 *(978-0-8059-7918-3(2))* Dorrance Publishing Co., Inc.
Shaw, Charles E. The Untold Stories of Excellence: From a Life of Despair & Uncertainty to One that Offers Hope & a New Beginning. 2011. 510p. 34.99 ***(978-1-4628-8835-1(6))*** Xlibris Corp.
Shropshire-West, Rosalynn. Black Vignettes: Essays in African American History & Culture. 2010. 599p. pap. 37.95 *(978-0-615-24436-5(X))* West, Rosalynn Shropshire.
Sidbury, James. Becoming African in America: Race & Nation in the Early Black Atlantic. 2009. (ENG., Illus.). 304p. pap. 19.95 *(978-0-19-538294-5(3))* Oxford Univ. Pr., Inc.
Simms, Patsy Ford. Famous African Americans: Eight People Who Made a Difference in Music, Inventions, Sports, & Science. 2011. (ENG.). 78p. pap. 49.99 *(978-1-4234-9620-5(5)*, 1423496205) Shawnee Pr., Inc.
Sinclair, Bruce, ed. Technology & the African-American Experience: Needs & Opportunities for Study. 2006. (ENG., Illus.). 288p. (gr. 17). per. 19.00 *(978-0-262-69344-8(5))* MIT Pr.
Sinclair, William A. The Aftermath of Slavery: A Study of the Condition & Environment of the American Negro. reprint ed. 98.00 *(978-0-7222-9744-5(0))* Library Reprints, Inc.
Sinclair, William A. & Alexander, Shawn Lee. The Aftermath of Slavery: A Study of the Condition & Environment of the American Negro. 2012. (Southern Classics Ser.). (ENG.). 424p. pap. 16.95 ***(978-1-61117-078-8(8))*** Univ. of South Carolina Pr.
Sitkoff, Harvard. A New Deal for Blacks: The Emergence of Civil Rights As a National Issue - The Depression Decade. 2008. (ENG.). 352p. (C). pap. 29.95 *(978-0-19-536753-9(7))* Oxford Univ. Pr., Inc.
Smart-Grosvenor, Vertamae. Vibration Cooking: Or, the Travel Notes of a Geechee Girl. 2011. (ENG.). 256p. pap. 19.95 *(978-0-8203-3739-5(0))* Univ. of Georgia Pr.
Smith, Alonzo Nelson. Empowering Communities — Changing Lives: 100 Years of the National Urban League & Black America, 1910-2010. 2011. ***(978-1-57864-683-8(9))*** Donning Co. Pubs.
Smith, Alonzo Nelson. Empowering Communities, Changing Lives: One Hundred Years of the National Urban League & Black America, 1910-2010. 2010. pap. *(978-1-57864-634-0(0))* Donning Co. Pubs.
Smith, David G. On the Edge of Freedom: The Fugitive Slave Issue in South Central Pennsylvania, 1820-1870. 2012. (ENG.). 260p. 45.00 ***(978-0-8232-4032-6(0))*** Fordham Univ. Pr.
Smith, Jessie Carney, ed. Encyclopedia of African American Popular Culture, 4 vols. 2010. (Illus.). 1733p. 380.00 *(978-0-313-35796-1(X)*, GR5796) Greenwood Publishing Group, Inc.
Smith, Mark M. How Race Is Made: Slavery, Segregation, & the Senses. 2008. (ENG., Illus.). 208p. pap. 22.00 *(978-0-8078-5925-4(7))* Univ. of North Carolina Pr.
Smith, Max. African America's 3rd Rail: SGL. 2009. 240p. pap. 19.95 *(978-0-615-28206-0(7))* Smith, Maxsonn.
Smith, Stephen Drury & Ellis, Catherine J., eds. Say It Plain: A Century of Great African American Speeches. 2007. (ENG.). 254p. per. 17.95 *(978-1-59558-126-6(X))* New Pr., The.
Sonnebom, Liz. The Great Black Migrations: From the Rural South to the Urban North. 2010. (Milestones in American History Ser.). (Illus.). 128p. (gr. 6-12). 35.00 *(978-1-60413-680-7(4)*, Chelsea Hse.) Facts On File, Inc.
Sosnoski, James J., et al. Teaching History & Configuring Virtual Worlds: Virtual Harlem & the VERITAS Studies. 2006. (Digital Formations Ser.: Vol. 18). (Illus.). 224p. (C). pap. 32.95 *(978-0-8204-6784-9(7))* Lang, Peter Publishing, Inc.
Span, Christopher M. From Cotton Field to Schoolhouse: African American Education in Mississippi, 1862-1875. 2009. (ENG., Illus.). 264p. 36.95 *(978-0-8078-3290-5(1))* Univ. of North Carolina Pr.
Stabile, Carol. White Victims, Black Villains: Gender, Race, & Crime News in US Culture. 2006. (Illus.). 235p. 140.00 *(978-0-415-37481-1(2))*; per. 39.95 *(978-0-415-37492-7(8))* Routledge.
Stanford, Karin. If We Must Die: African American Voices on War & Peace. 2009. (ENG.). 384p. pap. 37.50 *(978-0-7425-4114-6(2))* Rowman & Littlefield Publishers, Inc.
Stanford, Karin L., ed. If We Must Die: African American Voices on War & Peace. 2008. (ENG.). 384p. 63.95 *(978-0-7425-4113-9(4))* Rowman & Littlefield Publishers, Inc.
Stephens, Angela Sims. My Black History, My Character & Me. 2011. (Illus.). 32p. pap. 14.00 ***(978-1-4634-1754-3(3))*** AuthorHouse.
Stephens, Ronald J., et al. African Americans of Denver. 2008. (Images of America Ser.). (ENG., Illus.). 128p. pap. 21.99 *(978-0-7385-5625-3(4))* Arcadia Publishing.
Stephenson, Frank. Chowan Beach: Remembering an African American Resort. 2006. (Illus.). 124p. pap., per. 14.99 *(978-1-59629-164-5(8))* History Pr., The.
Stevens, Robert J & Johnson, Brian. Profiles of African American Missionaries. 2011. ***(978-0-87808-008-3(2))*** Carey, William Library Pubs.
Stockley, Grif, Jr. & Stockley, Grif. Ruled by Race: Black/White Relations in Arkansas from Slavery to the Present. 2008. (Illus.). 400p. 34.95 *(978-1-55728-885-1(2))* Univ. of Arkansas Pr.
Stuart, Claudia & Stuntz, Jean. African Americans in Amarillo. 2009. (Images of America Ser.). (ENG., Illus.). 128p. pap. 21.99 *(978-0-7385-7128-7(6))* Arcadia Publishing.
Sundquist, Eric J. King's Dream: The Legacy of Martin Luther King's I Have a Dream Speech. 2008. 456p. pap. 35.00 *(978-0-300-15090-2(3))* Yale Univ. Pr.
Suranyi, Szilvia. Oral Folk Traditions in Toni Morrison's Song of Solomon - African American History, Geneology & Cultural Identity. 2008. 52p. pap. *(978-3-639-01190-6(2))* VDM Verlag Dr. Mueller e.K.
Tayac, Gabrielle, ed. IndiVisible: African-Native American Lives in the Americas. 2009. (ENG.). 256p. pap. 19.95 *(978-1-58834-271-3(9))* Smithsonian Institution Pr.
Taylor, Jon E. Freedom to Serve: Equality of Treatment & Opportunity in the Armed Services. 2012. (Critical Moments in American History Ser.). (ENG., Illus.). 224p. 140.00 *(978-0-415-89449-4(2))*; pap. 27.95 *(978-0-415-89448-7(4))* Routledge.
Taylor, Quintard. America I Am Black Facts: The Timelines of African American History, 1601-2008. 2009. (ENG.). 200p. pap. 9.95 *(978-1-4019-2406-5(9))* Hay Hse., Inc.
—From Timbuktu to Katrina: Readings in African American History. 2007. (ENG., Illus.). 208p. (C). per. 43.95 *(978-0-495-09278-0(9))* Wadsworth.
—From Timbuktu to Katrina: Readings in African-American History. 2007. (ENG., Illus.). 192p. (C). per. 43.95 *(978-0-495-09277-3(0))* Wadsworth.
Thomas, William H. The American Negro, What He Was, What He Is, & What He May Become: A Critical & Practical Discussion. 440p. reprint ed. 98.00 *(978-0-7222-9747-6(5))* Library Reprints, Inc.
Thompson, Kenneth. The Early Sociology of Race & Ethnicity. 2007. 2400p. 1845.00 *(978-0-415-45702-6(5))* RoutledgeFalmer GBR. Dist: Taylor & Francis Group.
Thornton, John, et al. Central Africans, Atlantic Creoles, & the Foundation of the Americas, 1585-1660. 2007. (ENG., Illus.). 384p. (C). pap. 25.99 *(978-0-521-77922-7(7))*; 88.00 *(978-0-521-77065-1(3))* Cambridge Univ. Pr.
Tillery, Alvin B. Between Homeland & Motherland: Africa, U. S. Foreign Policy, & Black Leadership in America. 2011. (Illus.). 216p. pap. 22.95 *(978-0-8014-7734-8(4))* Cornell Univ. Pr.
Tillinghast, Joseph A. The Negro in Africa & America. 231p. reprint ed. 98.00 *(978-0-7222-9820-6(X))* Library Reprints, Inc.
Training the Best: Charles Herbert Flowers, Jr. Tuskegee Airman Flight Instructor. 2009. 120p. (YA). pap. 12.50 *(978-0-9776192-3-6(0))* Robnor Publishing.
Trotter, Joe W. & Day, Jared N. Race & Renaissance: African Americans in Pittsburgh since World War II. 2010. (ENG., Illus.). 304p. 29.95 *(978-0-8229-4391-4(3))* Univ. of Pittsburgh Pr.
Tuck, Stephen. We Ain't What We Ought to Be: The Black Freedom Struggle from Emancipation to Obama. (Illus.). 528p. 2011. (ENG.). pap. 19.95 *(978-0-674-06229-0(9))* 2010. 29.95 *(978-0-674-03626-0(3))* Harvard Univ. Pr. (Belknap Pr.).
Tyler Hollie, Donna, et al. African Americans of Fauquier County. 2009. (Images of America Ser.). (ENG., Illus.). 128p. pap. 21.99 *(978-0-7385-6757-0(4))* Arcadia Publishing.
Umfleet, LeRae Sikes. A Day of Blood: The 1898 Wilmington Race Riot. 2009. (Illus.). 288p. pap. 18.00 *(978-0-86526-344-4(2))* North Carolina Office of Archives & History.
UMI Editorial. Legends of Excellence Black History Collection. 2007. 39.99 *(978-1-60352-069-0(4))* UMI (Urban Ministries, Inc.).
Under the Baobab Tree: Claiming Roots, Kindling Hope, Spreading God's Love. 20.00 *(978-0-687-08801-0(1))* Abingdon Pr.
United States, National Archives and Records Administration Staff, contrib. by. Black Studies: A Select Catalog of National Archives Microfilm Publications. 2006. *(978-1-880875-27-8(6))* National Archives & Records Administration.
Vanepps-Taylor, Betti Carol. Forgotten Lives: African Americans in South Dakota. 2008. (Illus.). 287p. per. 17.95 *(978-0-9777955-5-0(1)*, South Dakota State Historical Society Pr.) South Dakota State Historical Society.
Villarosa, Clara. The Words of African-American Heroes. 2011. (Newmarket Words of Ser.). (ENG.). 160p. 18.95 *(978-1-55704-946-9(7)*, Morrow, William & Co.) HarperCollins Pubs.
Wade, Robert M. Surviving King Cotton: Cotton Pickin Po. 2007. 308p. per. 29.95 *(978-1-4241-8463-7(0))* PublishAmerica, Inc.
Wagner, Bryan. Disturbing the Peace: Black Culture & the Police Power after Slavery. 2009. (Illus.). 320p. 37.00 *(978-0-674-03508-9(9))* Harvard Univ. Pr.
Waligora-Davis, Nicole. Sanctuary: African Americans & Empire. 2011. (ENG., Illus.). 240p. 65.00 *(978-0-19-536991-5(2))* Oxford Univ. Pr., Inc.
Walker, Anders. The Ghost of Jim Crow: How Southern Moderates Used Brown V. Board of Education to Stall Civil Rights. 2009. (ENG.). 272p. 34.95 *(978-0-19-518174-6(3))* Oxford Univ. Pr., Inc.
Wallace, Maurice O. & Smith, Shawn Michelle, eds. Pictures & Progress: Early Photography & the Making of African American Identity. 2012. (ENG., Illus.). 408p. 99.95 ***(978-0-8223-5067-5(X))***; pap. 27.95 ***(978-0-8223-5085-9(8))*** Duke Univ. Pr.
Wallenfeldt, Jeff, ed. Africa to America: From the Middle Passage Through The 1930S. 2010. (African American History & Culture Ser.). (Illus.). 272p. (YA). 90.00 *(978-1-61530-180-5(1))* Rosen Publishing Group, Inc., The.
—The Black Experience in America: From Civil Rights to the Present. 2010. (African American History & Culture Ser.). (Illus.). 232p. (YA). 90.00 *(978-1-61530-179-9(8))* Rosen Publishing Group, Inc., The.
Walters, Ronald W. Freedom Is Not Enough: Black Voters, Black Candidates, & American Presidential Politics. 2007. (American Political Challenges Ser.). (ENG.). 256p. per. 28.95 *(978-0-7425-4806-0(6))* Rowman & Littlefield Publishers, Inc.
Warren, Kenneth W., et al. Renewing Black Intellectual History: The Ideological & Material Foundations of African American Thought. Reed, Adolph, Jr., ed. 2009. 336p. 125.00 *(978-1-59451-665-8(0))* Paradigm Pubs.
Washington, Booker T. The Negro in the South: His Economic Progress in Relation to His Moral & Religious Development. 222p. reprint ed. 98.00 *(978-0-7222-9755-1(6))* Library Reprints, Inc.
—The Story of the Negro: The Rise of the Race from Slavery. 2008. (ENG.). 480p. pap. 29.95 *(978-1-84588-604-2(6))* History Pr. Ltd., The GBR. Dist: Independent Pubs. Group.
—The Story of the Negro: The Rise of the Race from Slavery, 2 Vols. reprint ed. 250.00 *(978-0-7222-9753-7(X))* Library Reprints, Inc.
—The Story of the Negro: The Rise of the Race from Slavery V2. 2007. (ENG.). 444p. 51.95 *(978-0-548-08504-2(8))* Kessinger Publishing, LLC.
—The Story of the Negro: the Rise of the Race from Slavery (Vol. 1) 2010. 344p. pap. 26.97 *(978-0-557-35655-3(5))* Lulu Enterprises Inc.
Washington, Booker T. & Du Bois, W. E. B. The Negro in the South: His Economic Progress in Relation to His Moral & Religious Development. 2007. (ENG.). 224p. 39.95 *(978-0-548-15783-1(9))* Kessinger Publishing, LLC.
Washington, Jack. The Long Journey Home: A Bicentennial History of the Black Community of Princeton, New Jersey, 1776-1976. 320p. 84.95 *(978-1-59221-053-4(8))* Africa World Pr.
Wells, Donna & Battle, Thomas C., eds. Legacy: Treasures of Black History. 2006. (ENG., Illus.). 224p. 35.00 *(978-1-4262-0006-9(4)*, National Geographic) National Geographic Society.
Wheaton, Laura & Hartzold, Susan, eds. Presence, Pride & Passion: A History of African Americans in Mclean County. 2008. (Illus.). 40p. (YA). 10.00 *(978-0-943788-35-7(8))* McLean County Historical Society.
White, Barbara A. Visits with Lincoln: Abolitionists Meet the President at the White House. 2011. E-Book ***(978-0-7391-6418-1(X))*** Lexington Bks.
White, Derrick E. The Challenge of Blackness: The Institute of the Black World & Political Activism in The 1970s. 2011. (Southern Dissent Ser.). (ENG., Illus.). 288p. 69.95 *(978-0-8130-3735-6(2))* Univ. Pr. of Florida.
Wiener, Leo. Africa & the Discovery of America. 2009. 176p. pap. *(978-1-151-73256-9(7))*; 176p. pap. *(978-1-151-73252-1(4))*; 194p. pap. *(978-1-151-73254-5(0))* Books LLC.
—Africa & the Discovery of America, 3 vol., set. reprint ed. 375.00 *(978-0-7222-6426-3(7))* Library Reprints, Inc.
Wilkerson, Isabel. The Warmth of Other Suns: The Epic Story of America's Great Migration. 2010. (ENG.). 640p. 30.00 *(978-0-679-44432-9(7))* Random Hse., Inc.
William, George W. History of the Negro Race in America Fro. 2006. (ENG.). pap. 45.95 *(978-1-4286-4021-4(5))*; pap. 40.95 *(978-1-4286-4020-7(7))* Kessinger Publishing, LLC.
Williams, Charles. From Freedom to Slavery. 2007. (Illus.). (YA). per. 15.00 *(978-0-9772579-1-1(6))* Parenting Institute of America Inc.
Williams, George W. History of the Negro Race in America from 1619 to 1880, Vol. 1. l.t. ed. 2007. 696p. pap. 34.99 *(978-1-4264-8953-2(6))* BiblioBazaar.
—History of the Negro Race in America from 1619 to 1880, 2 Vols In 1. reprint ed. 125.00 *(978-0-7222-9780-3(7))* Library Reprints, Inc.
—History of the Negro Race in America from 1619 to 1880 Volume I. 2007. 618p. pap. 31.99 *(978-1-4264-8895-5(5))* BiblioBazaar.
Williams, Heather Andrea. Self-Taught: African American Education in Slavery & Freedom. 2007. (John Hope Franklin Series in African American History & Culture Ser.). (ENG., Illus.). 320p. per. 20.95 *(978-0-8078-5821-9(8))* Univ. of North Carolina Pr.
Williams, Horace Randall, et al. This Day in Civil Rights History. 2009. 408p. 19.95 *(978-1-58838-241-2(9))* NewSouth, Inc.
Williams, Karen G. & Queeley, Andrea. Study Guide for Let Nobody Turn Us Around. 2nd ed. 2009. (ENG.). 150p. pap. 15.00 *(978-1-4422-0013-5(8))* Rowman & Littlefield Publishers, Inc.
Williams, Kidada. They Left Great Marks on Me: African American Testimonies of Racial Violence from Emancipation to World War I. 2012. (ENG.). 288p. 75.00 ***(978-0-8147-9535-4(8))***; pap. 25.00 ***(978-0-8147-9536-1(6))*** New York Univ. Pr.
Williams, Kidada E. They Left Great Marks on Me: African American Testimonies of Racial Violence from Emancipation to World War I. 2012. xii, 281p. E-Book ***(978-0-8147-9537-8(4))***; E-Book ***(978-0-8147-8486-0(0))*** New York Univ. Pr.
Williams, Susan Millar & Hoffius, Stephen G. Upheaval in Charleston: Earthquake & Murder on the Eve of Jim Crow. 2011. (ENG., Illus.). 392p. 29.95 *(978-0-8203-3715-9(3))* Univ. of Georgia Pr.
Williams, Yohuru R. A Constant Struggle: African-American History 1865-Present. 2nd rev. ed. 2010. (ENG., Illus.). 706p. pap. 111.42 *(978-0-7575-1759-4(5)*, 0757517595) Kendall Hunt Publishing Co.
Williams, Yohuru R., et al. A Constant Struggle: African American History 1619-1865. rev. ed. 2008. (ENG.). 426p. pap. 104.99 *(978-0-7575-1675-7(0)*, 0757516750) Kendall Hunt Publishing Co.
Williams, Zachery. Africana Cultures & Policy Studies: Scholarship & the Transformation of Public Policy. Williams, Zachery, ed. 2009. (Contemporary Black History Ser.). (ENG.). 296p. 100.00 *(978-0-230-60280-9(0))* Palgrave Macmillan.
Wilson, Maloyd Ben & Wilson Group Network Inc Staff. Black Chronicle: From the Slavery Era - 1778 to the Beginning of the Civil Rights Movement, 1956. 2008. (Illus.). 70p. pap. 20.00 *(978-0-9753210-0-3(5))* Wilson Group Network, Inc.
Wintz, Cary D. & Glasrud, Bruce A., eds. The Harlem Renaissance in the American West: The New Negro's Western Experience. 2011. (New Directions in American History Ser.). (ENG., Illus.). 264p. (C). 150.00 *(978-0-415-88687-1(2))*; pap. 34.95 *(978-0-415-88688-8(0))* Routledge.
Wolcott, Victoria W. Race, Riots, & Roller Coasters: The Struggle over Segregated Recreation in America. 2012. (Politics & Culture in Modern America Ser.). 328p. 34.95 ***(978-0-8122-4434-2(6))*** Univ. of Pennsylvania Pr.
Wolf, Eva Sheppard. Race & Liberty in the New Nation: Emancipation in Virginia from the Revolution to Nat Turner's Rebellion. 2006. (Illus.). 284p. 45.00 *(978-0-8071-3194-7(6))* Louisiana State Univ. Pr.
Woodrum, Robert H. Everybody Was Black down There: Race & Industrial Change in the Alabama Coalfields. 2007. (Politics & Culture in the Twentieth-Century South Ser.). (ENG., Illus.). 328p. 69.95 *(978-0-8203-2739-6(5))*; per. 24.95 *(978-0-8203-2879-9(0))* Univ. of Georgia Pr.
Woodson, Carter G. A Century of Negro Migration. 2010. 240p. 32.99 *(978-1-140-18565-9(9))* BiblioBazaar.
—A Century of Negro Migration. 2008. 132p. pap. *(978-1-4065-7269-8(1))* Dodo Pr.
—A Century of Negro Migration. 2010. 132p. pap. *(978-1-4076-1087-0(2))* HardPr.
—A Century of Negro Migration. 2010. 168p. 29.56 *(978-1-169-27229-3(0))*; pap. 17.56 *(978-1-162-64777-7(9))*; 36.95 *(978-1-161-41642-8(0))* Kessinger Publishing, LLC.
Woodson, Carter G & Woodson, Carter G. A Century of Negro Migration. 2010. 240p. pap. 26.75 *(978-1-140-18566-6(7))* BiblioBazaar.
Woodson, Carter Godwin. A Century of Negro Migration. 2009. 244p. 23.99 *(978-1-103-56019-6(0))* 2009. 244p. pap. 17.99 *(978-1-103-56017-2(4))* 2009. 244p. 23.99 *(978-1-103-23591-9(5))*; 2009. 244p. pap. 17.99 *(978-1-103-23588-9(5))* 2008. 168p. 25.99 *(978-0-554-26952-8(X))* 2008. 168p. 22.99 *(978-0-554-36255-7(4))* 2007. (ENG.). 146p. pap. 18.99 *(978-1-4346-2188-7(X))* 2007. (ENG.). 166p. pap. 21.99 *(978-1-4346-2248-8(7))* BiblioBazaar.
—A Century of Negro Migration. 2009. 130p. pap. *(978-0-217-90627-2(3))*; 134p. pap. *(978-1-4432-5961-3(6))* Books LLC.
Wright, Kai. The African American Experience: Black History & Culture Through Speeches, Letters, Editorials, Poems, Songs, & Stories. Wright, Kai, ed. 2009. (ENG.). 720p. pap. 22.95 *(978-1-57912-773-2(8)*, 1579127738) Black Dog & Leventhal Pubs., Inc.
Wynn, Neil. The African American Experience During World War II. 2011. (African American History Ser.). (ENG.). 200p. pap. 22.95 ***(978-1-4422-1031-8(1))*** Rowman & Littlefield Publishers, Inc.
Wynn, Neil A. The African American Experience During World War II. 2010. (African American History Ser.). (ENG.). 200p. 49.95 *(978-1-4422-0016-6(2))* Rowman & Littlefield Publishers, Inc.
Yelvington, Kevin A. & Harrison, Faye Venetia. Afro-Atlantic Dialogues: Anthropology in the Diaspora. Yelvington, Kevin A., ed. (School of American Research Advanced Seminar Ser.). (Illus.). 528p. pap. 34.95 *(978-1-930618-46-6(8))* School for Advanced Research Pr./SAR Pr.
Zackodnik, Teresa C. Press, Platform, Pulpit: Black Feminist Publics in the ERA of Reform. 2011. (ENG., Illus.). xxxv, 339p. 45.00 ***(978-1-57233-826-5(1))*** Univ. of Tennessee Pr.

AFRICAN AMERICANS—HISTORY—TO 1863

see also Free African Americans

Berlin, Ira. Slaves Without Masters: The Free Negro in the Antebellum South. 2007. (ENG., Illus.). 428p. per. 18.95 *(978-1-59558-173-0(1))* New Pr., The.
Blakey, Michael L. & Rankin-Hill, Leslie M., eds. The New York African Burial Ground: Skeletal Biology of the New York African Burial Ground, Part I, 6 vols., Vol. 1. 2009. pap. *(978-0-88258-252-8(6))* Howard Univ. Pr.
—The New York African Burial Ground: Skeletal Biology of the New York African Burial Ground, Part II: Appendices, 6 vols., Vol. 1. 2009. pap. *(978-0-88258-253-5(4))* Howard Univ. Pr.
Burton, Orville Vernon. Slavery in America. 2007. *(978-1-4144-3014-0(0))*; *(978-1-4144-3015-7(9))* Cengage Gale.
Countryman, Edward. Enjoy the Same Liberty: Black Americans & the Revolutionary ERA. 2011. ***(978-1-4422-0029-6(4))*** Rowman & Littlefield Publishers, Inc.
Delany, Martin Robison. The Condition Elevation Emigration & Destiny of the Colored People of the United States. 2008. 184p. 22.99 *(978-0-554-35552-8(3))* 2008. 184p. 25.99 *(978-0-554-26249-9(5))* 2007. (ENG.). 162p. pap. 19.99 *(978-1-4346-0724-9(0))* 2007. (ENG.). 182p. pap. 21.99 *(978-1-4346-0784-3(4))* BiblioBazaar.
Dirck, Brian R. Abraham Lincoln & White America. 2012. 240p. 29.95 ***(978-0-7006-1827-9(9))*** Univ. Pr. of Kansas.
Follett, Richard J., et al. Slavery's Ghost: The Problem of Freedom in the Age of Emancipation. 2011. (Marcus Cunliffe Lecture Ser.). (ENG., 128p. (C). (gr. 13-17). Illus.). 45.00 *(978-1-4214-0235-2(1))*; pap. 19.95 *(978-1-4214-0236-9(X))* Johns Hopkins Univ. Pr.
Forten, Charlotte L. The Journal of Charlotte L Forten: A Young Black Woman's Reaction to the White World of the Civil War Era. Billington, Ray Allen, ed. 2011. 254p. 46.95 ***(978-1-258-00700-3(2))*** Literary Licensing, LLC.
Gates, Henry Louis, Jr., ed. & intro. The Classic Slave Narratives. 2012. (ENG.). 688p. (gr. 12). 7.95 ***(978-0-451-53213-8(9)**, Signet Classics)* Penguin Group (USA) Inc.
Harrell, Willie J. Origins of the African American Jeremiad: The Rhetorical Strategies of Social Protest & Activism, 1760-1861. 2011. (ENG.). 239p. pap. 55.00 ***(978-0-7864-6689-4(8))*** McFarland & Co., Inc. Pubs.

Jenkins, Everett Jr. & Jenkins, Everett. Pan-African Chronology I: A Comprehensive Reference to the Black Quest for Freedom in Africa, the Americas, Europe & Asia, 1400-1865. alt. ed. 2011. (Pan-African Chronologies Ser.). (ENG., Illus.). 448p. pap. 75.00 *(978-0-7864-4505-9(X))* McFarland & Co., Inc. Pubs.

Kinshasa, Kwando M. Emigration vs. Assimilation: The Debate in the African American Press, 1827-1861. alt. ed. 2011. (ENG.). 248p. pap. 25.00 *(978-0-7864-6730-3(4))* McFarland & Co., Inc. Pubs.

Livermore, George. A Historical Research Respecting the Opinions of the Founders of the Republic on Negroes As Slaves, As Citizens & As Soldiers. 2007. (ENG.). 202p. 39.95 *(978-0-548-05293-8(X))* Kessinger Publishing, LLC.

Malone, Christopher. Between Freedom & Bondage: Race, Party, & Voting Rights in the Antebellum North. 2007. (ENG.). 272p. 143.00 *(978-0-415-95696-3(X))*; per. 32.95 *(978-0-415-95697-0(8))* Routledge.

Medford, Edna Greene, ed. The New York African Burial Ground: Historical Perspectives of the Burial Ground: New York Blacks & the Diaspora, 6 vols., Vol. 3. 2009. 166p. pap. *(978-0-88258-257-3(7))* Howard Univ. Pr.

Perry, Warren R., et al, eds. The New York African Burial Ground: The Archaeology of the New York African Burial Ground, Part I, 6 vols., Vol. 2. 2009. pap. *(978-0-88258-254-2(2))* Howard Univ. Pr.

—The New York African Burial Ground: The Archaeology of the New York African Burial Ground, Part II: Descriptions of Burials, 6 vols., Vol. 2. 2009. pap. *(978-0-88258-255-9(0))* Howard Univ. Pr.

—The New York African Burial Ground: The Archaeology of the New York African Burial Ground, Part III: Appendices, 6 vols., Vol. 2. 2009. pap. *(978-0-88258-256-6(9))* Howard Univ. Pr.

Reiss, Oscar. Blacks in Colonial America. alt. ed. 2006. (ENG.). 301p. per. 39.95 *(978-0-7864-2957-8(7))* McFarland & Co., Inc. Pubs.

Rose, Tony, ed. & compiled by. African American History in the United States of America: An Anthology - from Africa to President Barack Obama. 2009. 432p. pap. 21.95 *(978-0-9824922-0-8(0))* Amber Bks.

Rosen, Hannah. Terror in the Heart of Freedom: Citizenship, Sexual Violence, & the Meaning of Race in the Postemancipation South. 2008. (Gender & American Culture Ser.). (ENG., Illus.). 424p. 69.95 *(978-0-8078-3202-8(2))* Univ. of North Carolina Pr.

Sidbury, James. Becoming African in America: Race & Nation in the Early Black Atlantic. 2007. (ENG., Illus.). 320p. 99.00 *(978-0-19-532010-7(7))* Oxford Univ. Pr., Inc.

Westwood, Howard. Black Troops, White Commanders, & Freedmen During the Civil War. 2008. (ENG.). 208p. (C). pap. 21.95 *(978-0-8093-2881-9(X))* Southern Illinois Univ. Pr.

Wilson, Carol. Freedom at Risk: The Kidnapping of Free Blacks in America, 1780-1865. 2009. (ENG.). 184p. pap. 30.00 *(978-0-8131-9297-0(8))* Univ. Pr. of Kentucky.

Woodson, Carter Godwin. The Mind of the Negro As Reflected in Letters Written During the Crisis 1800-1860. 2010. 714p. pap. 35.00 *(978-1-57898-960-7(4))* Martino Publishing.

Work Projects Administration. Slave Narratives. 2008. 372p. 31.99 *(978-0-554-29078-2(2))*; 132p. 21.99 *(978-0-554-33360-1(0))*; 148p. 21.99 *(978-0-554-33417-2(8))*; 288p. 25.99 *(978-0-554-35067-7(X))*; 372p. 29.99 *(978-0-554-38381-1(0))*; 148p. 24.99 *(978-0-554-24114-2(5))*; 132p. 24.99 *(978-0-554-24057-2(2))*; 288p. 28.99 *(978-0-554-25764-8(5))* BiblioBazaar.

Wright, Donald R. African Americans in the Colonial Era: From African Origins through the American Revolution. 3rd ed. 2010. (Illus.). 268p. (C). pap. 19.95 *(978-0-88295-274-1(9))* Davidson, Harlan Inc.

AFRICAN AMERICANS—HOUSING

Allen, Joe. People Wasn't Made to Burn: A True Story of Housing, Race, & Murder in Chicago. 2011. (Illus.). 22.95 ***(978-1-60846-132-5(7))*** Haymarket Bks.

Carr, James H., et al, eds. Segregation: The Rising Costs for America. 2008. (Illus.). 368p. 140.00 *(978-0-415-96534-7(9))* Routledge.

Carr, James H. & Kutty, Nandinee K., eds. Segregation: The Rising Costs for America. 2008. (ENG., Illus.). 368p. (C). 41.95 *(978-0-415-96533-0(0))* Routledge.

Deutsch, Morton & Collins, Mary Evans. Interracial Housing: A Psychological Evaluation of a Social Experiment. 2009. (ENG.). 189p. pap. 40.00 *(978-0-8166-5984-5(2))* Univ. of Minnesota Pr.

Freund, David M. P. Colored Property: State Policy & White Racial Politics in Suburban America. (Historical Studies of Urban America Ser.). (ENG., Illus.). 2010. 526p. pap. 24.00 *(978-0-226-26276-5(6))* 2007. 496p. 37.50 *(978-0-226-26275-8(8))* Univ. of Chicago Pr.

Galvin, Michael. Skyline Tower, 'Ghetto in the Sky' 2009. 88p. pap. *(978-3-639-16358-2(3))* VDM Verlag Dr. Mueller e.K.

Hill, Anita F. Reimagining Equality: Stories of Gender, Race, & Finding Home. (ENG.). 224p. 2012. pap. 16.00 ***(978-0-8070-1443-1(5))*** 2011. 25.95 *(978-0-8070-1437-0(0))* Beacon Pr.

Satter, Beryl. Family Properties: How the Struggle over Race & Real Estate Transformed Chicago & Urban America. 2010. (ENG., Illus.). 512p. pap. 18.00 *(978-0-8050-9142-7(4))* Picador.

Shaw, Todd Cameron. Now Is the Time! Detroit Black Politics & Grassroots Activism. 2009. (ENG., Illus.). 304p. 89.95 *(978-0-8223-4495-7(5))*; pap. 24.95 *(978-0-8223-4508-4(0))* Duke Univ. Pr.

Smith II, Preston H. Racial Democracy & the Black Metropolis: Housing Policy in Postwar Chicago. 2012. 456p. 82.50 ***(978-0-8166-3702-7(4))***; pap. 27.50 ***(978-0-8166-3703-4(2))*** Univ. of Minnesota Pr.

Taeuber, Karl & Taeuber, Alma. Residential Segregation & Neighborhood Change. 2009. (ENG., Illus.). 321p. pap. 34.95 *(978-0-202-36279-3(5))* Aldine Transaction.

AFRICAN AMERICANS—INTELLECTUAL LIFE

Adeleke, Tunde. Without Regard to Race: The Other Martin Robison Delany. 2009. (ENG.). 274p. pap. 25.00 *(978-1-60473-250-4(4))* Univ. Pr. of Mississippi.

Akolaema, Chiji. Folklore in New World Black Fiction: Writing & the Oral Traditional Aesthetics. 2007. x, 162p. cd-rom 9.95 *(978-0-8142-9148-1(1))* Ohio State Univ. Pr.

Akoma, Chiji. Folklore in New World Black Fiction: Writing & the Oral Traditional Aesthetics. 2007. (ENG.). 162p. 36.95 *(978-0-8142-1071-0(6))* Ohio State Univ. Pr.

Anadolu-Okur, Nilgun. Contemporary African American Theater: Afrocentricity in the Works of Larry Neal, Amiri Baraka, & Charles Fuller. 2010. (ENG.). 236p. pap. 39.95 *(978-0-415-88324-5(5))* Routledge.

Anderson, Kevin R. Agitations: Ideologies & Strategies in African American Politics. 2010. (ENG.). 263p. 34.95 *(978-1-55728-926-1(3))* Univ. of Arkansas Pr.

Asante, M. K., Jr. It's Bigger Than Hip Hop: The Rise of the Post-Hip-Hop Generation. 2009. (ENG., Illus.). 304p. pap. 15.99 *(978-0-312-59302-5(3))*, St. Martin's Griffin) St. Martin's Pr.

Asante, M. K., Jr. & Asante, M. K. It's Bigger Than Hip Hop: The Rise of the Post-Hip-Hop Generation. 2008. (ENG., Illus.). 304p. 25.95 *(978-0-312-37326-9(0))* St. Martin's Pr.

Asante, Molefi K. The African American People: A Global History. 2011. E-Book ***(978-0-203-14508-1(9))*** Routledge.

Asante, Molefi Kete. The African American People. 2011. (ENG., Illus.). 416p. 125.00 ***(978-0-415-87254-6(5))***; pap. 39.95 ***(978-0-415-87255-3(3))*** Routledge.

Azaransky, Sarah. The Dream Is Freedom: Pauli Murray & American Democratic Faith, 1 vol. 2011. 176p. 55.00 *(978-0-19-974481-7(5))* Oxford Univ. Pr., Inc.

Bader, Philip. African-American Writers. 2nd rev. ed. 2010. (A to Z of African Americans Ser.). (Illus.). 352p. (C). (gr. 9-18). 49.50 *(978-0-8160-8141-7(7))* Facts On File, Inc.

Bailey, Eric J. The Cultural Rights Movement: Fulfilling the Promise of Civil Rights for African Americans. 2010. 216p. 44.95 *(978-0-313-36009-1(X)*, C36009, Praeger Pubs.) Greenwood Publishing Group, Inc.

Bailey, Frankie Y. African American Mystery Writers: A Historical & Thematic Study. 2008. (ENG.). 277p. pap. 35.00 *(978-0-7864-3339-1(6))* McFarland & Co., Inc. Pubs.

Banks, Adam J. Digital Griots: African American Rhetoric in a Multimedia Age. 2011. 192p. E-Book *(978-0-8093-8619-2(4))*; 208p. pap. 32.00 *(978-0-8093-3020-1(2))* Southern Illinois Univ. Pr.

Banner-Haley, Charles Pete T. From du Bois to Obama: African American Intellectuals in the Public Forum. 2010. (ENG.). 176p. 24.95 *(978-0-8093-2979-3(4))* Southern Illinois Univ. Pr.

Bass, Amy. Those about Him Remained Silent: The Battle over W. E. B. du Bois. 2009. (ENG., Illus.). 232p. 24.95 *(978-0-8166-4495-7(0))* Univ. of Minnesota Pr.

—Those about Him Remained Silent: The Battle over W.E.B. du Bois. 2012. (Illus.). 224p. pap. 20.00 *(978-0-8166-4496-4(9))* Univ. of Minnesota Pr.

Bell, Bernard W. Bearing Witness to African American Literature: Validating & Valorizing Its Authority, Authenticity, & Agency. 2012. pap. 29.95 ***(978-0-8143-3714-1(7))***; E-Book ***(978-0-8143-3715-8(5))*** Wayne State Univ. Pr.

Black Church Scholars Series, 7 vols. Incl. Black Christian Worship Experience. Hoyt, Thomas, Jr. 264p. 1992. pap. 13.00 *(978-1-884805-14-1(0))*; From Prison Cell to Church Pew: The Strategy of the African American Church. Smith, J. Alfred, Jr. & Umar, Warithu-Deen. Askew, Glorya & Wilmore, Gayraud, eds. 1993. pap. 8.95 *(978-1-884805-15-8(9))*; Rainbows & Reality: Selected Writings. Rooks, Charles S. Diamond, John C., ed. 158p. 1985. pap. 10.95 *(978-1-884805-05-9(1))*; Reclamation of Black Prisoners: A Challenge to the African American Church. Lincoln, C. Eric & Ducksworth, John. Askew, Glorya & Wilmore, Gayraud, eds. 134p. 1992. pap. 8.95 *(978-1-884805-13-4(2))*; Struggle for a Black Theology of Education: Pioneering Efforts of Post Civil War Clergy. Griffin, Paul R. Wilmore, Gayraud S., ed. 153p. (C). 1993. pap. 15.00 *(978-1-884805-06-6(X))*; *(978-1-884805-20-2(5))* Journal of the Interdenominational Theological Ctr.

Blair, Sara. Harlem Crossroads: Black Writers & the Photograph in the Twentieth Century. 2007. (ENG., Illus.). 376p. (C). 42.00 *(978-0-691-13087-3(6))* Princeton Univ. Pr.

Bloom, Harold. African-American Poets, 2 vols., Vol. 2. 2nd rev. ed. 2010. (Bloom's Modern Critical Views Ser.). 202p. (C). (gr. 9-18). 45.00 *(978-1-60413-810-8(6)*, Chelsea Hse.) Facts On File, Inc.

Bloom, Harold, ed. African-American Poets: Volume 1, New Edition, 2 vols. 2nd rev. ed. 2009. (Bloom's Modern Critical Views Ser.). 272p. (C). (gr. 9-18). 45.00 *(978-1-60413-400-1(3)*, Chelsea Hse.) Facts On File, Inc.

Blum, Edward J. & Young, Jason R., eds. The Souls of W. E. B. du Bois: New Essays & Reflections. 2009. 288p. 45.00 *(978-0-88146-136-7(9))* Mercer Univ. Pr.

Bond, Frederick W. The Negro & the Drama: The Direct & Indirect Contribution Which the American Negro Has Made to Drama & the Legitimate Stage. 28.95 *(978-0-405-18492-5(1))* Ayer Co. Pubs., Inc.

Bone, Robert & Courage, Richard A. The Muse in Bronzeville: African American Creative Expression in Chicago, 1932-1950. 2011. (ENG., Illus.). 336p. (C). 75.00 *(978-0-8135-5043-5(2))*; pap. 29.95 *(978-0-8135-5044-2(0))* Rutgers Univ. Pr.

Boyle, David. African Americans. 2006. (Illus.). 128p. (J). (gr. 4-8). reprint ed. 15.00 *(978-1-4223-5294-6(3))* DIANE Publishing Co.

Bracey, Christopher Alan. Saviors or Sellouts: The Promise & Peril of Black Conservatism, from Booker T. Washington to Condoleezza Rice. 2009. (ENG.). 248p. pap. 20.00 *(978-0-8070-8376-5(3))* Beacon Pr.

Bracks, Lean'tin. The African American Almanac: 400 Years of Triumph, Courage & Excellence. 2011. (ENG., Illus.). 512p. pap. 22.95 ***(978-1-57859-323-1(9))*** Visible Ink Pr.

Burrell, Tom. Brainwashed: Challenging the Myth of Black Inferiority. 2010. (ENG.). 320p. pap. 15.95 *(978-1-4019-2592-5(8))* Hay Hse., Inc.

Byerman, Keith E. Fingering the Jagged Grain: Tradition & Form in Recent Black Fiction. 2010. (ENG.). 322p. pap. 24.95 *(978-0-8203-3776-0(5))* Univ. of Georgia Pr.

Caponi-Tabery, Gena. Jump for Joy: Jazz, Basketball, & Black Culture in 1930s America. 2008. (Illus.). 264p. pap. 26.95 *(978-1-55849-663-7(7))*; lib. bdg. 80.00 *(978-1-55849-662-0(9))* Univ. of Massachusetts Pr.

Cataliotti, Robert H. The Songs Became the Stories: The Music in African American Fiction, 1970-2005. (African American Literature & Culture: Expanding & Exploding the Boundaries Ser.). 280p. (C). pap. 32.95 *(978-0-8204-8850-9(X))* Lang, Peter Publishing, Inc.

Conaway, Carol B. & Waters, Kristin B., eds. Black Women's Intellectual Traditions: Speaking Their Minds. 2007. (Illus.). 480p. per. 35.00 *(978-1-58465-634-0(4))* Univ. Pr. of New England.

Curtis, Susan. Colored Memories: A Biographer's Quest for the Elusive Lester A. Walton. 2008. (ENG., Illus.). 304p. (C). 39.95 *(978-0-8262-1786-8(9))* Univ. of Missouri Pr.

Dickerson, Vanessa D. Dark Victorians. 2008. 176p. 37.00 *(978-0-252-03256-1(X))* Univ. of Illinois Pr.

Diedrich, Maria & Heinrichs, Jürgen. From Black to Schwarz: Cultural Crossovers Between African America & Germany. 2011. (ENG.). 394p. pap. 49.95 *(978-0-87013-989-5(4))* Michigan State Univ. Pr.

Dixon, Melvin. A Melvin Dixon Critical Reader. Joyce, Justin A. & McBride, Dwight A., eds. 2006. (ENG.). 159p. 45.00 *(978-1-57806-866-1(5))* Univ. Pr. of Mississippi.

Dockett, Kymo. The Post Hip-Hop Generation: 20 Principles for A Successful Generation. 2009. 188p. pap. 12.50 *(978-1-59330-610-6(5))* Aventine Pr.

Dodson, Howard & Palmer, Colin, eds. Cultural Life. 2007. (Schomburg Studies on the Black Experience). (ENG., Illus.). 395p. per. 19.95 *(978-0-87013-808-9(1))* Michigan State Univ. Pr.

Dolinar, Brian. The Black Cultural Front: Black Writers & Artists of the Depression Generation. 2012. (Margaret Walker Alexander Series in African American Studies). (ENG.). 288p. 60.00 ***(978-1-61703-269-1(7))*** Univ. Pr. of Mississippi.

Dossett, Kate. Bridging Race Divides: Black Nationalism, Feminism, & Integration in the United States, 1896-1935. 2009. (ENG., Illus.). 280p. pap. 29.95 *(978-0-8130-3495-9(7))* Univ. Pr. of Florida.

Dunning, Stefanie K. Queer in Black & White: Interraciality, Same Sex Desire, & Contemporary African American Culture. 2009. (ENG., Illus.). 152p. 49.95 *(978-0-253-35350-4(5)*, 0253353505); pap. 19.95 *(978-0-253-22109-4(9)*, 0253221099) Indiana Univ. Pr.

Falola, Toyin, et al. Migrations & Creative Expressions in Africa & the African Diaspora. 2008. 510p. pap. 55.00 *(978-1-59460-460-7(6))* Carolina Academic Pr.

Fisch, Audrey A., ed. The Cambridge Companion to the African American Slave Narrative. 2007. (Cambridge Companions to Literature Ser.). (ENG.). 290p. per. 28.99 *(978-0-521-61526-6(7))*; 91.00 *(978-0-521-85019-3(3))* Cambridge Univ. Pr.

Fisher, Maisha. Black Literate Lives: Historical & Contemporary Perspectives. 2008. (Critical Social Thought Ser.). (Illus.). XXII, 178p. 135.00 *(978-0-415-95864-6(4))* Routledge.

Foley, Barbara. Spectres Of 1919: Class & Nation in the Making of the New Negro. 2008. (ENG., Illus.). 328p. pap. 26.00 *(978-0-252-07585-8(4))* Univ. of Illinois Pr.

Franklin, A. Todd & Scott, Jacqueline, eds. Critical Affinities: Nietzsche & African American Thought. 2006. (SUNY Series, Philosophy & Race). 265p. per. 29.95 *(978-0-7914-6862-3(3))* State Univ. of New York Pr.

Friedel, Tania. Racial Discourse & Cosmopolitanism in Twentieth-Century African American Writing. 2007. (Studies in African American History & Culture Ser.). (ENG.). 214p. 133.00 *(978-0-415-96355-8(9)*, 0415963559) Routledge.

Garcia, Jay. Psychology Comes to Harlem: Rethinking the Race Question in Twentieth-Century America. 2012. (New Studies in American Intellectual & Cultural History Ser.). (ENG.). 232p. (gr. 17). 50.00 ***(978-1-4214-0519-3(9))*** Johns Hopkins Univ. Pr.

Gates, Henry Louis, Jr. Harlem Renaissance Lives: From the African American National Biography. Higginbotham, Evelyn Brooks, ed. 2009. (Illus.). 608p. 50.00 *(978-0-19-538795-7(3))* Oxford Univ. Pr., Inc.

—Signifying Monkey: A Theory of African American Literary Criticism. 2010. (ENG., Illus.). 336p. pap. 19.95 *(978-0-19-513647-0(0))* Oxford Univ. Pr., Inc.

Gates, Henry Louis, Jr. & Jarrett, Gene Andrew. The New Negro: Readings on Race, Representation, & African American Culture, 1892-1938. Gates, Henry Louis, Jr. & Jarrett, Gene Andrew, eds. 2007. (Illus.). 591p. 75.00 *(978-0-691-12651-7(8))*; (ENG.). 608p. (C). pap. 35.00 *(978-0-691-12652-4(6))* Princeton Univ. Pr.

Gayle, Addison, Jr. The Addison Gayle Jr. Reader. Norment, Nathaniel, Jr., ed. 2009. (ENG., Illus.). 504p. pap. 37.00 *(978-0-252-07610-7(9))* Univ. of Illinois Pr.

Gayle, Addison, Jr. & Gayle, Addison. The Addison Gayle Jr. Reader. Norment, Nathaniel, Jr. & Norment, Nathaniel, eds. 2009. (ENG., Illus.). 504p. 78.00 *(978-0-252-03408-4(2))* Univ. of Illinois Pr.

Gilroy, Paul. Darker Than Blue: On the Moral Economies of Black Atlantic Culture. 2011. (W. E. B. du Bois Lectures). 224p. pap. 18.95 *(978-0-674-06023-4(7)*, Belknap Pr.) Harvard Univ. Pr.

Gilyard, Keith. Composition & Cornel West: Notes Toward a Deep Democracy. 2008. (ENG.). 176p. pap. 35.00 *(978-0-8093-2854-3(2))* Southern Illinois Univ. Pr.

—John Oliver Killens: A Life of Black Literary Activism. (ENG., Illus.). 456p. 2011. pap. 26.95 ***(978-0-8203-4031-9(6))*** 2010. 39.95 *(978-0-8203-3513-1(4))* Univ. of Georgia Pr.

Glasrud, Bruce A. & Wintz, Cary D. The Harlem Renaissance in the American West: The New Negro's Western Experience. 2011. E-Book ***(978-0-203-80558-9(5))*** Routledge.

Golden, Marita. The Word: Black Writers Talk about the Transformative Power of Reading & Writing. 2011. 224p. pap. 14.99 *(978-0-7679-2991-2(8))* Broadway Bks.

Gooding-Williams, Robert. Critical Affinities: Reflections on the Connections Between Nietzsche & African American Thought. Franklin, A. Todd & Scott, Jacqueline, eds. 2006. (SUNY Series, Philosophy & Race). 256p. (C). 74.50 *(978-0-7914-6861-6(5))* State Univ. of New York Pr.

Green, Tara T., ed. From the Plantation to the Prison: African American Confinement Literature. 2008. (Voices of the African Diaspora Ser.). 176p. 35.00 *(978-0-88146-090-2(7))* Mercer Univ. Pr.

Gruesser, John Cullen. Confluences: Postcolonialism, African American Literary Studies, & the Black Atlantic. 2007. (ENG.). 192p. per. 22.95 *(978-0-8203-3026-6(4))* Univ. of Georgia Pr.

Gruesser, Wallinger. Loopholes & Retreats: African American Writers & the Nineteenth Century. Gruesser, John & Wallinger, Hanna, eds. 2009. (ENG.). 208p. pap. 44.95 *(978-3-8258-1892-0(6))* Lit Verlag DEU. Dist: Transaction Pubs.

Hakutani, Yoshinobu. Cross-Cultural Visions in African American Literature: West Meets East. Hakutani, Yoshinobu, ed. 2011. (ENG.). 242p. 85.00 *(978-0-230-11341-1(9))* Palgrave Macmillan.

—Cross-Cultural Visions in African American Modernism: From Spatial Narrative to Jazz Haiku. 2006. 251p. 69.95 *(978-0-8142-1030-7(9))*; ix, 251p. cd-rom 9.95 *(978-0-8142-9107-8(4))* Ohio State Univ. Pr.

Harris-Lacewell, Melissa Victoria. Barbershops, Bibles, & Bet: Everyday Talk & Black Political Thought. annot. ed. 2006. (ENG., Illus.). 368p. (C). per. 26.95 *(978-0-691-12609-8(7))* Princeton Univ. Pr.

Hawkins, Alfonso. Jazz Trope: A Theory of African American Literary & Vernacular Culture. 2008. (African American Cultural Theory Ser.). (ENG.). 270p. pap. 55.00 *(978-0-8108-6126-8(7))* Scarecrow Pr., Inc.

Haynes, Rosetta R. Radical Spiritual Motherhood: Autobiography & Empowerment in Nineteenth-Century African American Women. 2011. 264p. 39.95 *(978-0-8071-3694-2(8))* Louisiana State Univ. Pr.

Hebbar, Reshmi J. Modeling Minority Women. 2010. 288p. pap. 39.95 *(978-0-415-88243-9(5))* Routledge.

Hine, Darlene Clark & McCluskey, John, Jr., eds. The Black Chicago Renaissance. 2012. (New Black Studies Ser.). (ENG., Illus.). 272p. 80.00 ***(978-0-252-03702-3(2))***; pap. 27.95 ***(978-0-252-07858-3(6))*** Univ. of Illinois Pr.

Ho, Fred & Mullen, Bill V., eds. Afro Asia: Revolutionary Political & Cultural Connections Between African Americans & Asian Americans. 2008. (ENG., Illus.). 416p. 94.95 *(978-0-8223-4258-8(8))*; pap. 26.95 *(978-0-8223-4281-6(2))* Duke Univ. Pr.

Holcomb, Gary Edward. Claude Mckay, Code Name Sasha: Queer Black Marxism & the Harlem Renaissance. 2009. (ENG., Illus.). 288p. pap. 29.95 *(978-0-8130-3450-8(7))* Univ. Pr. of Florida.

Holloway, Karla F. C. Bookmarks: Reading in Black & White. 2008. (ENG.). 240p. pap. 19.95 *(978-0-8135-4351-2(7))* Rutgers Univ. Pr.

—BookMarks: Reading in Black & White. 2006. (ENG., Illus.). 240p. 24.95 *(978-0-8135-3907-2(2))* Rutgers Univ. Pr.

Holmes, David G. Revisiting Racialized Voice: African American Ethos in Language & Literature. 2007. (ENG.). 144p. per. 30.00 *(978-0-8093-2767-6(8))* Southern Illinois Univ. Pr.

Horne, Gerald C. The End of Empires: African Americans & India. 2009. (ENG.). 274p. pap. 27.95 *(978-1-59213-900-2(0))* Temple Univ. Pr.

—The End of Empires: African Americans & India. 2008. (ENG., Illus.). 272p. 56.50 *(978-1-59213-899-9(3))* Temple Univ. Pr.

Hudson-Weems, Clenora, ed. Contemporary Africana Theory & Thought: A Guide to Africana Studies. 2007. 420p. 99.95 *(978-1-59221-309-2(X))* Africa World Pr.

Irele, F. Abiola. The Cambridge Companion to the African Novel. 2009. (Cambridge Companions to Literature Ser.). (ENG.). 308p. (C). 99.00 *(978-0-521-85560-0(8))*; pap. 30.99 *(978-0-521-67168-2(X))* Cambridge Univ. Pr.

Iton, Richard. In Search of the Black Fantastic: Politics & Popular Culture in the Post-Civil Rights Era. 2010. (ENG.). 432p. pap. 21.95 *(978-0-19-973360-6(0))* Oxford Univ. Pr., Inc.

Jackson, Lawrence Patrick. The Indignant Generation: A Narrative History of African American Writers & Critics, 1934-1960. 2010. (ENG., Illus.). 608p. (C). 35.00 *(978-0-691-14135-0(5))* Princeton Univ. Pr.

Jackson, Maurice & Bacon, Jacqueline, eds. African Americans & the Haitian Revolution. 2009. (ENG., Illus.). 272p. (C). 150.00 *(978-0-415-80375-5(6))*; pap. 39.95 *(978-0-415-80376-2(4))* Routledge.

James, C. Boyd. Garvey, Garveyism, & the Problem of Black Redemption. 2008. *(978-1-59221-654-3(4))*; 416p. pap. *(978-1-59221-655-0(2))* Africa World Pr.

Jarrett, Gene. Representing the Race: A New Political History of African American Literature. 2011. (ENG.). 280p. 70.00 *(978-0-8147-4338-6(2))*; pap. 22.00 *(978-0-8147-4339-3(0))* New York Univ. Pr.

Jarrett, Gene Andrew. Deans & Truants: Race & Realism in African American Literature. 2006. (Illus.). 232p. (C). 55.00 *(978-0-8122-3973-7(3))* Univ. of Pennsylvania Pr.

—Representing the Race: A New Political History of African American Literature. 2011. 256p. E-Book *(978-0-8147-4340-9(4))* New York Univ. Pr.

Jarrett, Gene Andrew, ed. A Companion to African American Literature. 2010. (Blackwell Companions to Literature & Culture Ser.: 121). (ENG., Illus.). 488p. 159.95 *(978-1-4051-8862-3(6)*, Wiley-Blackwell) Wiley, John & Sons, Inc.

Jenkins, Candice M. Private Lives, Proper Relations: Regulating Black Intimacy. 2007. 240p. 67.50 *(978-0-8166-4787-3(9))*; per. 23.50 *(978-0-8166-4788-0(7))* Univ. of Minnesota Pr.

Johnson, Claudia D. Racism in Maya Angelou's I Know Why the Caged Bird Sings. 2007. (Social Issues in Literature Ser.). (ENG., Illus.). 150p. (YA). (gr. 10-12). 26.50 *(978-0-7377-3905-3(3)*, LML02109-238410); pap. 38.45 *(978-0-7377-3901-5(0)*, LML02109-238371) Cengage Gale. (Greenhaven Pr., Inc.).

Jones, Meta DuEwa. The Muse Is Music: Jazz Poetry from the Harlem Renaissance to Spoken Word. 2011. (New Black Studies Ser.). (ENG., Illus.). 304p. 55.00 *(978-0-252-03621-7(2))* Univ. of Illinois Pr.

Joseph, Peniel E. Waiting 'Til the Midnight Hour: A Narrative History of Black Power in America. 2007. (ENG., Illus.). 432p. pap. 17.99 *(978-0-8050-8335-4(9)*, Owl Bks.) Holt, Henry & Co.

Joyce, Justin A. & McBride, Dwight A., eds. A Melvin Dixon Critical Reader. 2010. (ENG.). 190p. pap. 25.00 *(978-1-60473-863-6(4))* Univ. Pr. of Mississippi.

Kaplan, Erin Aubry. Black Talk, Blue Thoughts, & Walking the Color Line: Dispatches from a Black Journalista. 2011. (Northeastern Library of Black Literature Ser.). 304p. pap. 19.95 *(978-1-55553-754-8(5)*, Northeastern University Pr.) Univ. Pr. of New England.

KRS-One. The Gospel of Hip Hop: First Instrument. 2009. (ENG.). 832p. 24.95 *(978-1-57687-497-4(4)*, powerHouse Bks.) powerHouse Cultural Entertainment, Inc.

Krstovic, Jelena O. Black Literature Criticism: Classic & Emerging Authors since 1950, 3 vols. 2008. (Illus.). *(978-1-4144-3173-4(2))*; *(978-1-4144-3171-0(6))*; *(978-1-4144-3172-7(4))* Cengage Gale.

Levecq, Christine. Slavery & Sentiment: The Politics of Feeling in Black Atlantic Antislavery Writing, 1770-1850. 2008. (Becoming Modern: New Nineteenth-Century Studies). (ENG.). 324p. lib. bdg. 35.00 *(978-1-58465-734-7(0)*, University of New Hampshire Press) Univ. Pr. of New England.

Lock, Graham & Murray, David, eds. Thriving on a Riff: Jazz & Blues Influences in African American Literature & Film. 2009. (ENG., Illus.). 288p. 99.00 *(978-0-19-533702-0(6))*; pap. 24.95 *(978-0-19-533709-9(3))* Oxford Univ. Pr., Inc.

Locke, Alain LeRoy. The Works of Alain Locke, 1 vol. Molesworth, Charles, ed. 2012. (Collected Black Writings). 624p. 45.00 ***(978-0-19-979504-8(5))*** Oxford Univ. Pr., Inc.

Looney, Dennis. Freedom Readers: The African American Reception of Dante Alighieri & the Divine Comedy. 2011. (ND Devers Series Dante & Med. Ital. Lit Ser.). (ENG., Illus.). 296p. pap. 30.00 *(978-0-268-03386-6(2))* Univ. of Notre Dame Pr.

Mahmoud, Mahgoub El-Tigani. Linkages among African & African-American Thinkers: The Emergence of a Transgeographical Intellectual Community. 468p. 129.95 *(978-0-7734-5207-7(9))* Mellen, Edwin Pr., The.

Major, Clarence. The Dark & the Feeling. 12.95 *(978-0-89388-119-1(8))* Okpaku Communications Corp.

Mance, Ajuan Maria. Inventing Black Women: African American Women Poets & Self-Representation, 1877-2000. 2008. (ENG.). 216p. pap. 24.95 *(978-1-57233-651-3(X))* 2007. 248p. 36.00 *(978-1-57233-492-2(4))* Univ. of Tennessee Pr.

Marable, Manning. Living Black History: How Reimagining the African-American Past Can Remake America's Racial Future. 2011. (ENG.). 288p. (gr. 9). pap. 16.00 *(978-0-465-04395-8(X))* Basic Bks.

Marable, Manning & Agard-Jones, Vanessa, eds. Transnational Blackness: Navigating the Global Color Line. 2008. (Critical Black Studies). (ENG.). 384p. 100.00 *(978-0-230-60267-0(3))*; pap. 31.00 *(978-0-230-60268-7(1))* Palgrave Macmillan.

Marcoux, Jean-Philippe. Jazz Griots: Music as History in the 1960s African American Poem. 2012. (ENG.). 240p. (gr. 17). 65.00 ***(978-0-7391-6673-4(5))*** Lexington Bks.

Mars-Proietti, Laura & Hatcher, Sherry L., eds. Encyclopedia of African American Writing. 2nd rev. ed. 2009. 856p. (gr. 4-6). 135.00 *(978-1-59237-291-1(0))* Grey Hse. Publishing.

Marshall, Paule. Triangular Road: A Memoir. (ENG., 2010. Illus.). 176p. (gr. 9). pap. 14.00 *(978-0-465-01922-9(6))* 2009. 192p. 23.00 *(978-0-465-01359-3(7)*, Basic Civitas Bks.) Basic Bks.

Mayes, Keith. Civil Rights & Black Power: The Struggle for Black Equality in the United States, 1945-1975. 2009. (ENG., Illus.). 352p. 125.00 *(978-0-415-99128-5(5))* Routledge.

Mays, Benjamin E. The Negro's God. 2010. 282p. pap. 31.00 *(978-1-60899-777-0(4)*, Wipf and Stock) Wipf & Stock Pubs.

Meehan, Kevin. People Get Ready: African American & Caribbean Cultural Exchange. (Caribbean Studies Ser.). (ENG.). 256p. 2011. pap. 30.00 ***(978-1-61703-201-1(8))*** 2009. 50.00 *(978-1-60473-281-8(4))* Univ. Pr. of Mississippi.

Miller, Henry D. Theorizing Black Theatre: Art Versus Protest in Critical Writings, 1898-1965. 2010. (ENG., Illus.). 284p. pap. 65.00 *(978-0-7864-5937-7(9))* McFarland & Co., Inc. Pubs.

Miller, R. Baxter. A Literary Criticism of Five Generations of African American Writing: The Artistry of Memory. 2008. 328p. 119.95 *(978-0-7734-4966-4(3))* Mellen, Edwin Pr., The.

Miller, R. Baxter. On the Ruins of Modernity: New Chicago Renaissance from Wright to Kent. 2011. pap. ***(978-1-86335-969-6(9))*** Common Ground Publishing Pty, Ltd.

Mitchell, Verner D. & Davis, Cynthia. Literary Sisters: Dorothy West & Her Circle, a Biography of the Harlem Renaissance. 2011. (ENG.). 216p. (C). pap. 24.95 *(978-0-8135-5146-3(3))*; (Illus.). 208p. 72.00 *(978-0-8135-5145-6(5))* Rutgers Univ. Pr.

Mocombe, Paul C. & Mocombe, Paul. The Soul-Less Souls of Black Folk: A Sociological Reconsideration of Black Consciousness as du Boisian Double Consciousness. 2008. (ENG.). 96p. pap. 26.50 *(978-0-7618-4295-8(0))* Univ. Pr. of America, Inc.

Murray, Rolland. Our Living Manhood: Literature, Black Power, & Masculine Ideology. 2006. 160p. (C). 49.95 *(978-0-8122-3972-0(5))* Univ. of Pennsylvania Pr.

Newkirk, Pamela, ed. Letters from Black America: Intimate Portraits of the African American Experience. 2011. (ENG.). 400p. pap. 18.00 *(978-0-8070-0115-8(5))* Beacon Pr.

Ogbar, Jeffrey O. G., ed. The Harlem Renaissance Revisited: Politics, Arts, & Letters. 2010. (ENG.). 272p. (C). (gr. 13-17). pap. 30.00 *(978-0-8018-9461-9(1))* Johns Hopkins Univ. Pr.

—The Harlem Renaissance Revisited: Politics, Arts, & Letters. 2010. (ENG.). 272p. (C). (gr. 13-17). 60.00 *(978-0-8018-9460-2(3))* Johns Hopkins Univ. Pr.

Okonkwo, Christopher N. A Spirit of Dialogue: Incarnations of Ogbanje, the Born-to-Die, in African American Literature. 2008. (ENG.). 266p. 48.00 *(978-1-57233-615-5(3))* Univ. of Tennessee Pr.

Ondaatje, Michael. Black Conservative Intellectuals in Modern America. 232p. (C). 2012. pap. 22.50 ***(978-0-8122-2204-3(0))*** 2009. 34.95 *(978-0-8122-4206-5(8))* Univ. of Pennsylvania Pr.

Ongiri, Amy Abugo. Spectacular Blackness: The Cultural Politics of the Black Power Movement & the Search for a Black Aesthetic. 2009. (ENG.). 240p. (C). (gr. 13-17). pap. 22.50 *(978-0-8139-2860-9(5))*,; (gr. 17). 55.00 *(978-0-8139-2859-3(1))* Univ. Pr. of Virginia.

Orrells, Daniel, et al, eds. African Athena: New Agendas. 2011. (Classical Presences Ser.). (ENG., Illus.). 496p. 160.00 ***(978-0-19-959500-6(3))*** Oxford Univ. Pr., Inc.

Page, Yolanda Williams. Icons of African American Literature: The Black Literary World. 2011. E-Book ***(978-0-313-35204-1(6)***, Greenwood Pr.) Greenwood Publishing Group, Inc.

Page, Yolanda Williams, ed. Icons of African American Literature: The Black Literary World, 1 vol. 2011. (Greenwood Icons Ser.). (Illus.). 519p. 100.00 *(978-0-313-35203-4(8)*, GR5203) Greenwood Publishing Group, Inc.

Pereira, Malin, ed. Into a Light Both Brilliant & Unseen: Conversations with Contemporary Black Poets. 2010. (ENG.). 260p. 59.95 *(978-0-8203-3107-2(4))*; pap. 19.95 *(978-0-8203-3713-5(7))* Univ. of Georgia Pr.

Perry, Jeffrey B. Hubert Harrison Vol. 1: The Voice of Harlem Radicalism, 1883-1918, vol. 1. 2010. (ENG.). 624p. (gr. 17). pap. 26.50 *(978-0-231-13911-3(X))* Columbia Univ. Pr.

Person-Lynn, Kwaku. First Word: Black Scholars — Thinkers — Warriors. 2nd ed. 2011. (ENG.). 320p. pap. 21.95 *(978-0-88378-307-8(X))* Third World Press.

Pickens, William. New Negro, His Political, Civil & Mental Status & Related Essays. reprint ed. 21.50 *(978-0-404-00271-8(4))* AMS Pr., Inc.

Quashie, Kevin Everod. The Sovereignty of Quiet: Beyond Resistance in Black Culture. 2012. (ENG.). 200p. (C). pap. 24.95 ***(978-0-8135-5310-8(5))***; E-Book ***(978-0-8135-5311-5(3))***; (ENG.). 200p. (C). 72.00 ***(978-0-8135-5309-2(1))*** Rutgers Univ. Pr.

Rabaka, Reiland. Against Epistemic Apartheid: W. E. B. du Bois & the Disciplinary Decadence of Sociology. 2010. (ENG.). 440p. 94.50 *(978-0-7391-4597-5(5))*; pap. 41.99 *(978-0-7391-4598-2(3))* Lexington Bks.

Rambsy, Howard. The Black Arts Enterprise & the Production of African American Poetry. 2011. (ENG., Illus.). 198p. 60.00 *(978-0-472-11733-8(5))* Univ. of Michigan Pr.

Ramey, Lauri. ed. The Heritage Series of Black Poetry, 1962-1975: A Research Compendium. 2008. (Illus.). 388p. 124.95 *(978-0-7546-5782-8(5))* Ashgate Publishing Co.

Reddy, Chandan. Freedom with Violence: Race, Sexuality, & the US State. 2011. (Perverse Modernities Ser.). (ENG.). 320p. 84.95 *(978-0-8223-5091-0(2))*; pap. 23.95 *(978-0-8223-5105-4(6))* Duke Univ. Pr.

Reed, Adolph, Jr., et al. Renewing Black Intellectual History: The Ideological & Material Foundations of African American Thought, 1 vol. 2010. 336p. pap. 39.95 *(978-1-59451-666-5(9))* Paradigm Pubs.

Reid-Pharr, Robert. Once You Go Black: Choice, Desire, & the Black American Intellectual. 2007. (ENG., Illus.). 208p. 75.00 *(978-0-8147-7583-7(7))*; pap. 23.00 *(978-0-8147-7584-4(5))* New York Univ. Pr.

Richardson, Elaine B. & Jackson, Ronald L. African Amer Rhetorics. 2007. (ENG.). 328p. pap. 30.00 *(978-0-8093-2745-4(7))* Southern Illinois Univ. Pr.

Schuyler, George S. Rac(e)ing to the Right: Selected Essays George S. Schuyler. 2011. pap. 24.95 ***(978-1-57233-818-0(0))*** Univ. of Tennessee Pr.

Smethurst, James. The African American Roots of Modernism: From Reconstruction to the Harlem Renaissance. 2011. (John Hope Franklin Series in African American History & Culture Ser.). (ENG.). 272p. 65.00 *(978-0-8078-3463-3(7))*; pap. 26.95 *(978-0-8078-7185-0(0))* Univ. of North Carolina Pr.

Smith, Henrietta M. The Coretta Scott King Awards, 1970-2009. 4th ed. 2009. (Illus.). xiii, 131p. *(978-0-8389-3584-2(2))* American Library Assn.

Smith, Jessie Carney, ed. Encyclopedia of African American Popular Culture, 4 vols. 2010. (Illus.). 1733p. 380.00 *(978-0-313-35796-1(X)*, GR5796) Greenwood Publishing Group, Inc.

Smith, Kimberly K. African American Environmental Thought: Foundations. 2007. (American Political Thought Ser.). 257p. 29.95 *(978-0-7006-1516-2(4))* Univ. Pr. of Kansas.

Sosnoski, James J., et al. Teaching History & Configuring Virtual Worlds: Virtual Harlem & the VERITAS Studies. 2006. (Digital Formations Ser.: Vol. 18). (Illus.). 224p. (C). pap. 32.95 *(978-0-8204-6784-9(7))* Lang, Peter Publishing, Inc.

Soto, Isabel & Showers Johnson, Violet, eds. Western Fictions, Black Realities: Meanings of Blackness & Modernities. 2012. (ENG.). 336p. pap. 39.95 ***(978-1-61186-044-3(X))*** Michigan State Univ. Pr.

Soto, Michael. Teaching the Harlem Renaissance: Course Design & Classroom Strategies. (African American Literature & Culture: Expanding & Exploding the Boundaries Ser.). 2008. 268p. (C). 99.95 *(978-1-4331-0391-9(5))* 2007. pap. 34.95 *(978-0-8204-9724-2(X))* Lang, Peter Publishing, Inc.

Sowell, Thomas. A Man of Letters. 2007. (ENG., Illus.). 320p. 29.95 *(978-1-59403-196-0(7))* Encounter Bks.

Stanley, Tarshia L., ed. Encyclopedia of Hip Hop Literature, 1 vol. 2008. 312p. 69.95 *(978-0-313-34389-6(6)*, GR4389, Greenwood Pr.) Greenwood Publishing Group, Inc.

Steen, Shannon, et al. AfroAsian Encounters: Culture, History, Politics. Raphael-Hernandez, Heike, ed. 2006. (ENG., Illus.). 336p. pap. 24.00 *(978-0-8147-7581-3(0))*; 75.00 *(978-0-8147-7580-6(2))* New York Univ. Pr.

Taylor, Eddie. Restoring the Mind of Black America. 2011. (ENG.). 120p. pap. 15.95 *(978-1-934155-61-5(6))* African American Images.

Taylor, James Lance. Black Nationalism in the United States: From Malcolm X to Barack Obama. 2011. (Illus.). 410p. 68.50 *(978-1-58826-778-8(4))* Rienner, Lynne Pubs.

Thaler, Ingrid. Black Atlantic Speculative Fictions: Octavia E. Butler, Jewelle Gomez, & Nalo Hopkinson. 2010. (ENG.). 204p. (C). 125.00 *(978-0-415-80441-7(8))* Routledge.

Thompson, Carlyle Van. Eating the Black Body: Miscegenation As Sexual Consumption in African American Literature & Culture. 2006. (African-American Literature & Culture Ser.: Vol. 10). (C). pap. 29.95 *(978-0-8204-7931-6(4))* Lang, Peter Publishing, Inc.

Thompson, Mark Christian. Black Fascisms: African American Literature & Culture Between the Wars. 2007. (ENG.). 240p. (gr. 17). 57.50 *(978-0-8139-2670-4(X))*; per. 19.50 *(978-0-8139-2671-1(8))* Univ. Pr. of Virginia.

Tidwell, John Edgar & Tracy, Steven C. After Winter: The Art & Life of Sterling A. Brown. Tidwell, John Edgar & Tracy, Steven C., eds. Tidwell, John Edgar, ed. 2009. (ENG., Illus.). 464p. pap. 39.95 *(978-0-19-536580-1(1))* Oxford Univ. Pr., Inc.

Tidwell, John Edgar & Tracy, Steven C., eds. After Winter: The Art & Life of Sterling A. Brown. 2009. (ENG., Illus.). 464p. 99.00 *(978-0-19-536579-5(8))* Oxford Univ. Pr., Inc.

Tracy, Steven C. Writers of the Black Chicago Renaissance. 2011. (ENG.). 536p. 50.00 ***(978-0-252-03639-2(5))*** Univ. of Illinois Pr.

Trotter, Joe W. & Day, Jared N. Race & Renaissance: African Americans in Pittsburgh since World War II. 2010. (ENG., Illus.). 304p. 29.95 *(978-0-8229-4391-4(3))* Univ. of Pittsburgh Pr.

Wallenfeldt, Jeff, ed. Africa to America: From the Middle Passage Through The 1930S. 2010. (African American History & Culture Ser.). (Illus.). 272p. (YA). 90.00 *(978-1-61530-180-5(1))* Rosen Publishing Group, Inc., The.

Ward, Jerry Washington. The Cambridge History of African American Literature. Graham, Maryemma, ed. 2011. 860p. 165.00 *(978-0-521-87217-1(0))* Cambridge Univ. Pr.

Watts, Eric King. Hearing the Hurt: Rhetoric, Aesthetics, & Politics of the New Negro Movement. 2012. (Albma Rhetoric Cult & Soc Crit Ser.). (ENG.). 253p. (C). 39.95 ***(978-0-8173-1766-9(X))*** Univ. of Alabama Pr.

West, Cornel. Hope on a Tightrope: Words & Wisdom. 2011. (ENG.). 140p. 14.95 *(978-1-4019-3076-9(X))* Hay Hse., Inc.

—Keeping Faith: Philosophy & Race in America. 2008. (Routledge Classics Ser.). XVIII, 286p. 25.95 *(978-0-415-96481-4(4))* Routledge.

West, Cornel & Ritz, David. Brother West: Living & Loving Out Loud, A Memoir. 2009. (ENG.). 288p. 25.95 *(978-1-4019-2189-7(2)*, Smiley Bks.) Hay Hse., Inc.

West, Elizabeth J. African Spirituality in Black Women's Fiction: Threaded Visions of Memory, Community, Nature, & Being. 2012. E-Book ***(978-0-7391-6886-8(X))*** Lexington Bks.

White, Derrick E. The Challenge of Blackness: The Institute of the Black World & Political Activism in The 1970s. 2011. (Southern Dissent Ser.). (ENG., Illus.). 288p. 69.95 *(978-0-8130-3735-6(2))* Univ. Pr. of Florida.

Whitfield, James Monroe. The Works of James M. Whitfield: America & Other Writings by a Nineteenth-Century African American Poet. Levine, Robert S. & Wilson, Ivy G., eds. 2011. (ENG.). 256p. 65.00 *(978-0-8078-3445-9(9))*; pap. 26.95 *(978-0-8078-7178-2(8))* Univ. of North Carolina Pr.

Williams, Oscar. George S. Schuyler: Portrait of a Black Conservative. 2007. (Illus.). 224p. 33.00 *(978-1-57233-581-3(5))* Univ. of Tennessee Pr.

Williams, Tyrone. African American Literature, 4 vols. 2008. (Masterplots Ser.). 1800p. lib. bdg. 404.00 *(978-1-58765-438-1(5))* Salem Pr., Inc.

—Masterplots II. 2008. 101.00 *(978-1-58765-442-8(3))*; 101.00 *(978-1-58765-439-8(3))*; 101.00 *(978-1-58765-440-4(7))*; 101.00 *(978-1-58765-441-1(5))* Salem Pr., Inc.

Wilson, Francille Rusan. The Segregated Scholars: Black Social Scientists & the Creation of Black Labor Studies, 1890-1950. 2006. (Carter G. Woodson Institute Ser.). (ENG.). 352p. (gr. 17). pap. 22.50 *(978-0-8139-2788-6(9))* Univ. Pr. of Virginia.

Womack, Ytasha. Beats Rhymes & Life: What We Love & Hate about Hip-Hop. Jasper, Kenji, ed. 2007. (ENG., Illus.). 320p. pap. 19.00 *(978-0-7679-1977-7(7)*, Harlem Moon) Broadway Bks.

Wright, W. D. Crisis of the Black Intellectual. 2007. (Illus.). 369p. 36.95 *(978-0-88378-283-5(9))*; per. 26.95 *(978-0-88378-251-4(0))* Third World Press.

Young, Cynthia. Soul Power: Culture, Radicalism & the Making of a U. S. Third World Left. 2006. (ENG., Illus.). 328p. (C). 89.95 *(978-0-8223-3679-2(0))* Duke Univ. Pr.

AFRICAN AMERICANS—JUVENILE LITERATURE

Anderson, Wayne. Fighting Racial Discrimination: Treating All Americans Fairly under the Law. 2006. (Primary Sources of the Progressive Movement Ser.). (ENG.). 32p. (gr. 4-8). pap. 10.00 *(978-1-4042-0847-6(X)*, Rosen Classroom Bks. & Materials) Rosen Publishing Group, Inc., The.

Condino, Meggin, ed. African American Eras Library Set: Segregation to Civil Rights Times, 4 vols. 2010. 960p. 292.00 *(978-1-4144-3596-1(7))* Cengage Gale.

Jeffrey, Gary. The Little Rock Nine & the Fight for Equal Education. 2012. (Graphic History of the Civil Rights Movement Ser.). 24p. (J). (gr. 3-8). pap. 8.15 ***(978-1-4339-7484-7(3))*** Stevens, Gareth Publishing LLLP.

Linde, Barbara M. Slavery in Early America. 2011. (Story of America Ser.). (Illus.). 32p. (J). (gr. 4-6). pap. 10.50 *(978-1-4339-4777-3(3)*, Stevens, Gareth Learning Library) Stevens, Gareth Publishing LLLP.

AFRICAN AMERICANS—LANGUAGE

see also Black English

Alim, H. Samy. Roc the MIC Right: The Language of Hip Hop Culture. 2006. (ENG., Illus.). 208p. 143.00 *(978-0-415-35877-4(9))* Routledge.

—Roc the Mic Right: The Language of Hip Hop Culture. 2006. (ENG., Illus.). 208p. per. 47.95 *(978-0-415-35878-1(7))* Routledge.

Alim, H. Samy & Baugh, John, eds. Talkin Black Talk: Language, Education, & Social Change. (Multicultural Education Ser.). (ENG., Illus.). 192p. 2007. pap. 26.95 *(978-0-8077-4746-9(7))* 2006. 60.00 *(978-0-8077-4747-6(5))* Teachers College Pr., Teachers College, Columbia Univ.

Anderson, Bridget L. Migration Accomodation & Language Change: Language at the Intersection of Regional & Ethnic Identity. 2008. (ENG., Illus.). 242p. 89.00 *(978-0-230-00886-1(0))* Palgrave Macmillan.

Atwater, Deborah F. African American Women's Rhetoric: The Search for Dignity, Personhood, & Honor. (Race, Rites, & Rhetoric: Colors, Cultures, & Communication Ser.). (ENG.). 186p. 2010. pap. 28.50 *(978-0-7391-2177-1(4))* 2009. 62.99 *(978-0-7391-2176-4(6))* Lexington Bks.

Burley, Dan. Dan Burley's Jive. Aiello, Thomas, ed. 2009. (ENG., Illus.). 220p. pap. 24.00 *(978-0-87580-623-5(6))* Northern Illinois Univ. Pr.

Egbokhare, Francis, ed. Globalization & the Future of African Languages. 2007. 496p. pap. *(978-978-066-800-6(4))* Ibadan Univ. Pr. NGA. Dist: Michigan State Univ. Pr.

Gundaker, Grey. Signs of Diaspora/Diaspora of Signs. Date not set. (Commonwealth Center Studies in American Culture). (Illus.). 288p. reprint ed. pap. 18.95 *(978-0-19-510770-8(5))* Oxford Univ. Pr., Inc.

Holmes, David G. Revisiting Racialized Voice: African American Ethos in Language & Literature. 2007. (ENG.). 144p. per. 30.00 *(978-0-8093-2767-6(8))* Southern Illinois Univ. Pr.

Kautzsch, Alexander. The Historical Evolution of Earlier African American English: An Empirical Comparison of Early Sources. (Topics in English Linguistics [TiEL] Ser.). (ENG.). XV, 335p. 180.00 ***(978-3-11-179679-6(5))*** De Gruyter, Mouton DEU. Dist: de Gruyter, Walter GmbH & Co. KG.

Minnick, Lisa Cohen. Dialect & Dichotomy: Literary Representations of African American Speech. 2nd ed. 2007. 216p. pap. 22.50 *(978-0-8173-5423-7(9))* Univ. of Alabama Pr.

Richardson, Elaine. Hiphop Literacies. 2006. (Literacies Ser.). (Illus.). 142p. 120.00 *(978-0-415-32928-6(0))*; (ENG., 160p. per. 39.95 *(978-0-415-32927-9(2))* Routledge.

Richardson, Elaine B. & Jackson, Ronald L. African Amer Rhetorics. 2007. (ENG.). 328p. pap. 30.00 *(978-0-8093-2745-4(7))* Southern Illinois Univ. Pr.

Rickford. African American English & Other Vernaculars in Education. pap. 150.00 *(978-0-8058-6051-1(7))* Erlbaum, Lawrence Assocs., Inc.

Rickford & Sweetland. African American English & Other Vernaculars in Education. 2012. (NCTE-Routledge Research Ser.). (ENG.). 336p. 135.00 *(978-0-8058-6050-4(9))* Routledge.

Simpson, Ritashona. Black Looks & Black Acts: The Language of Toni Morrison in the Bluest Eye & Beloved. 2007. (Illus.). 122p. (C). 55.95 (978-0-8204-9530-9(1)) Lang, Peter Publishing, Inc.

Smith, Jane Bowman. The Elephant in the Classroom: Race & Writing. 2010. 216p. (978-1-57273-894-2(4)); pap. (978-1-57273-895-9(2)) Hampton Pr., Inc.

Wade-Lewis, Margaret. Lorenzo Dow Turner: Father of Gullah Studies. 2008. (Illus.). 323p. 44.95 (978-1-57003-628-6(4)) Univ. of South Carolina Pr.

AFRICAN AMERICANS—LEGAL STATUS, LAWS, ETC.

African-American Farmers Benefit Relief ACT of 2007 & the Pigford Claims Remedy ACT of 2007: Hearing Before the Subcommittee on the Constitution, Civil Rights, & Civil Liberties of the Committee on the Judiciary, House of Representatives, One Hundred Tenth Congress, First Session, on H.R. 558 & H.R. 899, June 21, 2007. 2007. (Illus.). iv, 153p. (978-0-16-079622-7(9), 552-070-36579-6) United States Government Printing Office.

Anderson, S. E. The Black Holocaust for Beginners. 2007. (For Beginners Ser.). (ENG., Illus.). 192p. per. 16.99 (978-1-934389-03-4(X), For Beginners) Steerforth Pr.

Baum, Dale, ed. Counterfeit Justice: The Judicial Odyssey of Texas Freedwoman Azeline Hearne. 2009. (Conflicting Worlds: New Dimensions of the American Civil War Ser.). (Illus.). 320p. 45.00 (978-0-8071-3405-4(8)) Louisiana State Univ. Pr.

Browne-Marshall, Gloria. Race, Law, & American Society 1607 to Present. 2007. (Criminology & Justice Studies). (Illus.). (ENG.). 416p. 145.00 (978-0-415-95293-4(X)); 432p. pap. 41.95 (978-0-415-95294-1(8)) Routledge.

Butler, Paul. Let's Get Free: A Hip-Hop Theory of Justice. (ENG.). 2010. 224p. pap. 16.95 (978-1-59558-500-4(1)) 2009. 208p. 25.95 (978-1-59558-329-1(7), 955329) New Pr., The.

Campbell, Randolph B., ed. The Laws of Slavery in Texas: Historical Documents & Essays. 2011. (ENG.). 192p. pap. 19.95 (978-0-292-72899-8(9)) Univ. of Texas Pr.

Carnahan, Burrus M. Act of Justice: Lincoln's Emancipation Proclamation & the Law of War. (ENG.). 212p. 2011. pap. 24.95 (978-0-8131-3458-1(7)) 2007. 50.00 (978-0-8131-2463-6(8)) Univ. Pr. of Kentucky.

Cuba, Prince A. Lynch Law Through Due Process. (Illus.). 12p. (Orig.). reprint ed. pap. 3.00 (978-1-56411-145-6(8)) UBUS Communications Systems.

Dudziak, Mary L. Cold War Civil Rights - Race & the Image of American Democracy. 2011. (Politics & Society in Twentieth Century America Ser.). (ENG., Illus.). 352p. (C). pap. 24.95 (978-0-691-15243-1(8)) Princeton Univ. Pr.

Epner, Janet E. Gans. Visible Invisibility: Women of Color in Law Firms. 2007. (ENG., Illus.). 88p. per. 49.95 (978-1-59031-745-7(9)) American Bar Assn.

Escott, Paul D. What Shall We Do with the Negro? Lincoln, White Racism, & Civil War America. 2009. (ENG., Illus.). 328p. 29.95 (978-0-8139-2786-2(2)) Univ. Pr. of Virginia.

Fede, Andrew. People Without Rights. 2011. (Routledge Revivals Ser.). (ENG.). 282p. 115.00 (978-0-415-61679-3(7)) Routledge.

Finkelman, Paul. Race & the Constitution: From the Philadelphia Convention to the Age of Segregation. 2010. (978-0-87229-169-0(3)) American Historical Assn.

Finkelman, Paul, ed. Abolitionists in Northern Courts: The Pamphlet Literature. 2007. 25.00 (978-1-58477-739-7(7)) Lawbook Exchange, Ltd., The.

Finkelman, Paul, ed. & intro. Slave Rebels, Abolitionists, & Southern Courts: The Pamphlet Literature, 2 vols. 2007. 250.00 (978-1-58477-744-1(3)) Lawbook Exchange, Ltd., The.

Freyer, Tony & Campbell, Lyndsay, eds. Freedom's Conditions in the U. S. -Canadian Borderlands in the Age of Emancipation. 2011. 344p. 45.00 (978-1-59460-772-1(9)) Carolina Academic Pr.

Goldstone, Lawrence. Inherently Unequal: The Betrayal of Equal Rights by the Supreme Court, 1865-1903. 2011. (ENG., Illus.). 256p. 26.00 (978-0-8027-1792-4(6)) Walker & Co.

Green, William D. A Peculiar Imbalance: The Fall & Rise of Racial Equality in Early Minnesota. 2007. 232p. 32.95 (978-0-87351-586-3(2)) Minnesota Historical Society Pr.

Haws, Robert J., ed. The South's Role in the Creation of the Bill of Rights. 2009. (ENG.). 280p. pap. 25.00 (978-1-60473-262-7(8)) Univ. Pr. of Mississippi.

Henry, Charles. Long Overdue: The Politics of Racial Reparations. 2009. (ENG.). 272p. pap. 22.00 (978-0-8147-3741-5(2)) New York Univ. Pr.

Henry, Charles P. Long Overdue: The Politics of Racial Reparations. 2007. (ENG.). 272p. 55.00 (978-0-8147-3692-0(0)) New York Univ. Pr.

Jackson, Donald Maurice. Fourth down & Twenty Five Years to Go: The African American Athlete & the Justice System. 2007. 224p. per. 17.95 (978-0-595-44108-2(4)) iUniverse, Inc.

Johnson, Franklin. The Development of State Legislation Concerning the Free Negro. 2009. 218p. 32.99 (978-1-115-45903-7(1)) 2009. 218p. 28.99 (978-1-115-45904-4(X)) 2009. 218p. pap. 24.75 (978-1-115-45905-1(8)) 2009. 218p. pap. 23.75 (978-1-115-45906-8(6)) 2008. 220p. 24.99 (978-0-559-75856-0(1)) 2008. 220p. pap. 23.75 (978-0-559-75854-6(5)) BiblioBazaar.

—The Development of State Legislation Concerning the Free Negro. 2009. 190p. pap. 19.99 (978-1-151-10180-8(X)) General Bks. LLC.

—The Development of State Legislation Concerning the Free Negro. 2008. 216p. 39.95 (978-0-548-95287-0(6)) 2007. 220p. per. 24.95 (978-0-548-62790-7(8)) Kessinger Publishing, LLC.

—The Development of State Legislation Concerning the Free Negro. 2007. 27.95 (978-1-58477-751-9(6)) Lawbook Exchange, Ltd., The.

Katznelson, Ira. When Affirmative Action Was White: An Untold History of Racial Inequality in Twentieth-Century America. 2006. (ENG.). 272p. 16.95 (978-0-393-32851-6(1), 32851) Norton, W. W. & Co., Inc.

King, Lovalerie & Schur, Richard, eds. African American Culture & Legal Discourse. 2009. (ENG.). 272p. 95.00 (978-0-230-61988-3(6)) Palgrave Macmillan.

Lane, Sr. For Whites Only? How & Why America Became a Racist Nation: Second Edition. 2008. 452p. pap. 34.95 (978-1-4343-8480-5(2)) AuthorHouse.

Lapp, Rudolph M. Archy Lee: A California Fugitive Slave Case. 2008. (Illus.). 69p. pap. 12.95 (978-1-59714-080-5(5)) Heyday.

Lavergne, Gary M. Before Brown: Heman Marion Sweatt, Thurgood Marshall, & the Long Road to Justice. 2011. (ENG., Illus.). 384p. pap. 25.00 (978-0-292-74295-6(9)) Univ. of Texas Pr.

Martin, Michael T., et al, eds. Redress for Historical Injustices in the United States: On Reparations for Slavery, Jim Crow, & Their Legacies. 2007. (ENG., Illus.). 728p. per. 32.95 (978-0-8223-4024-9(0)) Duke Univ. Pr.

Martin, Michael T. & Yaquinto, Marilyn, eds. Redress for Historical Injustices in the United States: On Reparations for Slavery, Jim Crow, & Their Legacies. 2007. (ENG., Illus.). 728p. 104.95 (978-0-8223-4005-8(4)) Duke Univ. Pr.

McNair, Glenn. Criminal Injustice: Slaves & Free Blacks in Georgia's Criminal Justice System. 2009. (Carter G. Woodson Institute Ser.). (ENG.). 240p. (gr. 17). 45.00 (978-0-8139-2793-0(5)) Univ. Pr. of Virginia.

Mitchell, Clarence, Jr. The Papers of Clarence Mitchell, 1946-1954, Vol. 3. Watson, Denton L., ed. 2010. (ENG., Illus.). 476p. 69.95 (978-0-8214-1662-4(6)) Ohio Univ. Pr.

Mitchell Jr., Clarence. The Papers of Clarence Mitchell, V 4. Watson, Denton L., ed. 2010. (ENG., Illus.). 768p. 69.95 (978-0-8214-1935-9(8)) Ohio Univ. Pr.

Myers, Peter C. Frederick Douglass: Race & the Rebirth of American Liberalism. 2008. (American Political Thought Ser.). 265p. 34.95 (978-0-7006-1572-8(5)) Univ. Pr. of Kansas.

Nichols, David A. A Matter of Justice: Eisenhower & the Beginning of the Civil Rights Revolution. 2008. (ENG., Illus.). 368p. pap. 22.99 (978-1-4165-4151-6(9)) Simon & Schuster.

Parker, Monica. What It Takes: How Women of Color Can Thrive Within the Practice of Law. 2011. (ENG.). 160p. pap. 59.95 (978-1-59031-992-5(3)) American Bar Assn.

Richardson, Henry J., 3rd. The Origins of African-American Interests in International Law. 2008. (ENG.). 544p. 65.00 (978-1-59460-383-9(9)) Carolina Academic Pr.

Robinson, Charles Frank, II. Dangerous Liaisons: Sex & Love in the Segregated South. 2006. 196p. per. 19.95 (978-1-55728-833-2(X)) Univ. of Arkansas Pr.

Rosen, Hannah. Terror in the Heart of Freedom: Citizenship, Sexual Violence, & the Meaning of Race in the Postemancipation South. 2008. (Gender & American Culture Ser.). (ENG., Illus.). 424p. pap. 26.95 (978-0-8078-5882-0(X)) Univ. of North Carolina Pr.

Samito, Christian G. Becoming American under Fire: Irish Americans, African Americans, & the Politics of Citizenship During the Civil War Era. 2009. (Illus.). 312p. 39.95 (978-0-8014-4846-1(8)) Cornell Univ. Pr.

Samito, Christian G. Becoming American under Fire: Irish Americans, African Americans, & the Politics of Citizenship during the Civil War Era. 2011. (Illus.). 320p. pap. 24.95 (978-0-8014-7755-3(7)) Cornell Univ. Pr.

Samito, Christian G., ed. Changes in Law & Society During the Civil War & Reconstruction: A Legal History Documentary Reader. 2nd ed. 2009. (Legal History of the Civil War Era Ser.). (ENG., Illus.). 352p. (C). pap. 29.50 (978-0-8093-2889-5(5)) Southern Illinois Univ. Pr.

Schur, Richard L. Parodies of Ownership: Hip-Hop Aesthetics & Intellectual Property Law. 2009. (ENG.). 256p. pap. 27.95 (978-0-472-05060-4(5)) Univ. of Michigan Pr.

Schweninger, Loren, et al, eds. The Southern Debate over Slavery, Volume 2: Petitions to Southern County Courts, 1775-1867. 2008. (Illus.). 424p. 60.00 (978-0-252-03260-8(8)) Univ. of Illinois Pr.

Seay, Solomon S. & Boyd, Delores R. Jim Crow & Me. 2009. 176p. 25.00 (978-1-58838-175-0(7)) NewSouth, Inc.

Sheppard, Eva Wolf. Almost Free: A Story about Family & Race in Antebellum Virginia. 2012. (Race in the Atlantic World, 1700-1900 Ser.). (ENG., Illus.). 192p. 59.95 (978-0-8203-3229-1(1)); pap. 19.95 (978-0-8203-3230-7(5)) Univ. of Georgia Pr.

Shirley, Bill. The Search for Racial Justice Through Law. 3rd rev. ed. 2009. (ENG.). 314p. spiral bd. 55.71 (978-0-7575-6993-7(5)) Kendall Hunt Publishing Co.

Shirley, William. The Search for Racial Justice Through Law. 4th rev. ed. 2011. (ENG.). 380p. spiral bd. 56.95 (978-0-7575-9133-4(7)) Kendall Hunt Publishing Co.

Singley, Carl E., et al. Call to Order: African Americans & the Law. Date not set. (Illus.). 52p. 12.00 (978-0-9675021-0-6(1)) African American Museum in Philadelphia, The.

Stephenson, Gilbert T. Race Distinctions in American Law. reprint ed. 31.50 (978-0-404-00215-2(3)) AMS Pr., Inc.

Waldrep, Christopher & Nieman, Donald G., eds. Local Matters: Race, Crime, & Justice in the Nineteenth-Century South. 2011. (Studies in the Legal History of the South Ser.). (ENG.). 264p. pap. 24.95 (978-0-8203-4081-4(2)) Univ. of Georgia Pr.

Waligora-Davis, Nicole. Sanctuary: African Americans & Empire. 2011. (ENG., Illus.). 240p. 65.00 (978-0-19-536991-5(2)) Oxford Univ. Pr., Inc.

Washington, Booker T. The Negro Problem: A Series of Articles by Representative American Negroes of Today. 234p. reprint ed. 98.00 (978-0-7222-9736-0(X)) Library Reprints, Inc.

Watson, Elwood D. Outsiders Within: Black Women in the Legal Academy after Brown v. Board. 2008. (ENG.). 160p. 70.00 (978-0-7425-4073-6(1)) Rowman & Littlefield Publishers, Inc.

—Outsiders Within: Black Women in the Legal Academy After Brown v. Board. 2009. (ENG.). 164p. pap. 27.50 (978-0-7425-4074-3(X)) Rowman & Littlefield Publishers, Inc.

Wertheimer, John W. Law & Society in the South: A History of North Carolina Court Cases. 2010. (New Directions in Southern History Ser.). (ENG., Illus.). 292p. pap. 35.00 (978-0-8131-2615-9(0)) Univ. Pr. of Kentucky.

Wilson, Carol. Freedom at Risk: The Kidnapping of Free Blacks in America, 1780-1865. 2009. (ENG.). 184p. pap. 30.00 (978-0-8131-9297-0(8)) Univ. Pr. of Kentucky.

AFRICAN AMERICANS—MEDICAL CARE

BeLue, Rhonda. Handbook of African American Health. Hampton, Robert L. et al, eds. 2010. (ENG.). 612p. 90.00 (978-1-60623-716-8(0)) Guilford Pubns., Inc.

Covey, Herbert C. African American Slave Medicine: Herbal & Non-Herbal Treatments. (ENG.). 216p. 2008. pap. 26.50 (978-0-7391-1645-6(2)) 2007. 89.50 (978-0-7391-1644-9(4)) Lexington Bks.

Hoberman, John. Black & Blue: The Origins & Consequences of Medical Racism. 2012. (ENG.). 288p. 65.00 (978-0-520-24890-8(2)); 304p. pap. 26.95 (978-0-520-27401-3(6)) Univ. of California Pr.

Holloway, Karla F. C. Private Bodies, Public Texts: Race, Gender, & a Cultural Bioethics. 2011. (ENG.). 256p. 79.95 (978-0-8223-4894-8(2)); pap. 22.95 (978-0-8223-4917-4(5)) Duke Univ. Pr.

Humphrey, A. W. A History of Labour Representation. 2009. 229p. pap. 24.75 (978-1-117-57042-6(8)) BiblioBazaar.

Joubert, Cassandra, et al. Losing Control: Loving a Black Child with Bipolar Disorder. 2008. (ENG.). 206p. per. 14.99 (978-1-59932-060-1(6)) Advantage Media Group.

Lemelle, Anthony, et al, eds. Handbook of African American Health: Social & Behavioral Interventions. 2011. (ENG., Illus.). xviii, 289p. 189.00 (978-1-4419-9615-2(X), 144199615X) Springer.

Myles, Lessie. African-Americans & Aids: Why are Black People still dying of (AIDS) while other Races are Not? 2009. 156p. 22.99 (978-1-4490-3313-2(X)); pap. 17.99 (978-1-4490-3312-5(1)) AuthorHouse.

Nelson, Alondra. Body & Soul: The Black Panther Party & the Fight against Medical Discrimination. 2011. (ENG., Illus.). 288p. 24.95 (978-0-8166-7648-4(8)) Univ. of Minnesota Pr.

Parker, Lillian. African American Spousal Caregivers. 2010. 104p. pap. (978-3-8383-5915-1(1)) Lambert Academic Publishing.

Pollock, Anne. Medicating Race: Heart Disease & Durable Preoccupations with Difference. 2012. (Experimental Futures Ser.). (ENG.). 280p. pap. 23.95 (978-0-8223-5344-7(X)); (Illus.). 84.95 (978-0-8223-5329-4(6)) Duke Univ. Pr.

Washington, Harriet A. Medical Apartheid: The Dark History of Medical Experimentation on Black Americans from Colonial Times to the Present. 2008. (ENG., Illus.). 528p. pap. 17.00 (978-0-7679-1547-2(X), Harlem Moon) Broadway Bks.

AFRICAN AMERICANS—MENTAL HEALTH

American Psychiatric Association. Let's Talk Facts about Mental Health in African Americans: Package Of 50. 2009. 37.95 (978-0-89042-432-2(2)) American Psychiatric Publishing, Inc.

Jack, Leonard Jr. Diabetes in Black America: Public Health & Clinical Solutions to a National Crisis. Jack, Leonard Jr., ed. 2010. (ENG.). 456p. pap. 49.95 (978-0-9815381-9-8(3)) Hilton Publishing Co.

Logan, Sadye M. L., ed. Mental Health Care in the African-American Community. 2007. (ENG., Illus.). 426p. 132.95 (978-0-7890-2611-8(2)); per. 62.95 (978-0-7890-2612-5(0)) Routledge.

Metzl, Jonathan. The Protest Psychosis: How Schizophrenia Became a Black Disease. 2011. (Illus.). 272p. pap. 22.00 (978-0-8070-0127-1(9)) Beacon Pr.

Pierce-Baker, Charlotte. This Fragile Life: A Mother's Story of a Bipolar Son. 2012. (ENG.). 256p. 24.95 (978-1-61374-108-5(1), Hill, Lawrence Bks.) Chicago Review Pr., Inc.

Williams, Terrie. Black Pain: It Just Looks Like We're Not Hurting. 2009. (ENG.). 368p. pap. 15.00 (978-0-7432-9883-4(7), Scribner) Scribner.

AFRICAN AMERICANS—MISCELLANEA

Rogers, J. A. One Hundred Amazing Facts about the Negro with Complete Proof: A Short Cut to the World History of the Negro. 2011. 68p. 36.95 (978-1-258-03077-3(2)) Literary Licensing, LLC.

AFRICAN AMERICANS—MUSIC

see also African American Musicians; Blues (Music); Gospel Music; Jazz; Rhythm and Blues Music; Rock Music; Soul Music; Spirituals (Songs)

Abbington, James. Readings in African American Church Music & Worship. 2009. (ENG.). 602p. pap. 36.95 (978-1-57999-767-0(8)) G I A Pubns., Inc.

Abbott, Lynn & Seroff, Doug. Out of Sight: The Rise of African American Popular Music, 1889-1895. 2009. (American Made Music Ser.). (ENG., Illus.). 528p. pap. 40.00 (978-1-60473-244-3(X)) Univ. Pr. of Mississippi.

Alfred Publishing Staff. Hit the Keys! Funk, Soul, & R&B: Piano/Vocal/Guitar. 2011. (Hit the Keys! Ser.). 272p. pap., pap. 19.99 (978-0-7390-7961-4(1)) Alfred Publishing Co., Inc.

Allen, William. Slave Songs of the United States. 2008. 172p. (978-1-4437-3522-3(1)) 2006. 168p. per. (978-1-4067-9588-2(7)) Read Bks. (Hesperides Pr.).

Allen, William Francis, et al, eds. Slave Songs of the United States. 2011. (ENG., Illus.). 189p. pap. 25.00 (978-0-8078-6949-9(X)) Univ. of North Carolina Pr.

Allen, William Francis & Ware, Charles Pickard. Slave Songs of the United States. 2010. 176p. pap. 22.75 (978-1-141-05116-8(8)) BiblioBazaar.

Allen, William Francis, et al. Slave Songs of the United States. 2010. 172p. pap. 21.75 (978-1-148-72766-0(3)) BiblioBazaar.

—Slave Songs of the United States. 170p. 2010. 30.36 (978-1-164-97882-4(9)) 2010. pap. 18.36 (978-1-164-86309-0(6)) 2008. 37.95 (978-1-4371-9469-2(9)) 2008. pap. 22.95 (978-1-4370-6423-0(X)) Kessinger Publishing, LLC.

Armstrong, M. F. & Ludlow, Helen W. Hampton & Its Students. 2007. (ENG.). 264p. 42.95 (978-0-548-11785-9(3)) Kessinger Publishing, LLC.

Barnwell, Ysaye M. Singing in the African American Tradition: Building a Vocal Community. 2009. (ENG.). 49p. pap. 39.95 incl. audio compact disk (978-1-59773-276-5(1), 1597732761) Leonard, Hal Corp.

Blue Ii, Al W. African Americans on Album Covers: A Pictoral Essay. 2011. 52p. pap. 23.88 (978-1-4567-6197-4(8)) AuthorHouse.

Books, Hephaestus. Articles on African American Rock Singers, Including: Jimi Hendrix, Little Richard, Jada Pinkett Smith, Howard Jones (American Musician), Ronald Isley. 2011. 104p. pap. 18.75 (978-1-242-49753-7(6), Hephaestus Bks.) BiblioBazaar.

Bradley, Celeste. Devil in My Bed: The Runaway Brides. 2009. (ENG.). 352p. 7.99 (978-0-312-94308-0(3), St. Martin's Paperbacks) St. Martin's Pr.

Brown, Leonard, ed. John Coltrane & Black America's Quest for Freedom: Spirituality & the Music, 1 vol. 2010. (ENG.). 272p. pap. 27.95 (978-0-19-532892-9(2)) Oxford Univ. Pr., Inc.

Burleigh, Harry T. Album of Negro Spirituals: High Voice. 2007. (ENG.). 48p. pap. 22.95 (978-0-7390-4530-5(X)) Alfred Publishing Co., Inc.

—Album of Negro Spirituals: Low Voice. 2007. (ENG.). 48p. pap. 22.95 (978-0-7390-4532-9(6)) Alfred Publishing Co., Inc.

Cataliotti, Robert H. The Songs Became the Stories: The Music in African American Fiction, 1970-2005. (African American Literature & Culture: Expanding & Exploding the Boundaries Ser.). 280p. (C). pap. 32.95 (978-0-8204-8850-9(X)) Lang, Peter Publishing, Inc.

Clark, Edgar Rogie, ed. Copper Sun: A Collection of Negro Folk Songs for Voice & Piano. 2011. 48p. 35.95 (978-1-258-01592-3(7)) Literary Licensing, LLC.

Coleman, Victor. Driven to Our Knees. 2008. pap. 12.95 (978-0-615-18883-6(4)) Coleman, Victor D.

—Driven to Our Knees - Volume 2. 2009. 136p. pap. 12.95 (978-0-578-00430-3(5)) Coleman, Victor D.

Curtis-Burlin, Natalie. Negro FolkSongs the Hampton Series Books. 2006. pap. 22.95 (978-1-4286-4536-3(5)) Kessinger Publishing, LLC.

Dett, R. Nathaniel. Religious FolkSongs of the Negro As Sung. 2006. pap. 28.95 (978-1-4286-3466-4(5)) Kessinger Publishing, LLC.

Dobie, J. Frank, ed. Follow de Drinkin' Gou'd. 2007. 204p. per. 24.95 (978-1-4325-7459-8(0)) Kessinger Publishing, LLC.

Hedblad, Alan, ed. African American Alamnac. 11th rev. ed. 2011. 1500p. 312.00 (978-1-4144-4547-2(4)) Cengage Gale.

Hopkinson, Natalie. Go-Go Live: The Musical Life & Death of a Chocolate City. 2012. (ENG., Illus.). 232p. 79.95 (978-0-8223-5200-6(1)); pap. 22.95 (978-0-8223-5211-2(7)) Duke Univ. Pr.

Johnson, Hall. Hall Johnson: Thirty Spirituals: For Low Voice & Piano. 2007. (ENG.). 104p. pap. 19.95 incl. audio compact disk (978-1-4234-1592-3(2), 1423415922, G Schirmer, Inc.) Leonard, Hal Corp.

Johnson, James Weldon. The Book of American Negro Poetry. 2008. 220p. 27.99 (978-0-554-24089-3(0)); 24.99 (978-0-554-33392-2(9)) BiblioBazaar.

—The Book of American Negro Poetry. 2008. (ENG.). 200p. pap. 14.45 (978-1-60597-530-6(3), Book Jungle) Standard Pubns., Inc.

—Book of American Negro Spirituals. 2006. pap. 22.95 (978-1-4286-3429-9(0)) Kessinger Publishing, LLC.

—Lift Every Voice & Sing. 2007. (Illus.). 32p. (J). (gr. -1-3). 17.89 (978-0-06-145897-2(X), Amistad) HarperCollins Pubs.

Johnson, James Weldon, ed. The Book of American Negro Poetry. 2008. 208p. pap. (978-1-4065-5932-3(6)) Dodo Pr.

Kennedy, R. Emmet. Black Cameos. 2007. 238p. 41.95 (978-0-548-04501-5(1)) Kessinger Publishing, LLC.

Kimberling, Clark. Solos for Flute, Collection 1: African-American & Jamaican Melodies, 1 vol. 2008. (ENG.). 48p. pap. 9.95 (978-0-7866-7005-5(3)) Mel Bay Pubns., Inc.

—Solos for Soprano Recorder, Collection 1: African-American & Jamaican Melodies, 1 vol. 2008. (ENG.). 48p. pap. 9.95 (978-0-7866-6204-3(2)) Mel Bay Pubns., Inc.

Koonce, Richard. The Symbolic Rape of Representation- a Critical Analysis of Black Musical Expression. 2007. 184p. per. (978-3-8364-1902-4(5)) VDM Verlag Dr. Mueller e.K.

Lee-Thompson, Ann. Harbinger: Negro Spirituals, a Musical Miracle. 2008. 184p. pap. 18.00 (978-0-8059-7647-2(7)) Dorrance Publishing Co., Inc.

Living Colour. Living Colour - the Paris Concert: New Morning. 2009. (ENG.). 19.95 (978-1-4234-7406-7(6), 1423474066) Leonard, Hal Corp.

Marsh, J. B. The Story of the Jubilee Singers. 311p. reprint ed. lib. bdg. 98.00 (978-0-7222-4851-5(2)) Library Reprints, Inc.

McDonald, Anthony. A Catalog of Music Written in Honor of Martin Luther King Jr. 2012. E-Book (978-0-8108-8219-5(1)) 2011. (ENG.). 198p. 65.00 (978-0-8108-8198-3(5)) Scarecrow Pr., Inc.

Niles, John J. Singing Soldiers. 2010. 190p. pap. 18.36 (978-1-162-99419-2(3)) 2007. (ENG.). 188p. 37.95 (978-0-548-14074-1(X)) 2006. (ENG., Illus.). pap. 22.95 (978-1-4286-5273-6(6)) Kessinger Publishing, LLC.

Odhiambo, James. Secular Undertones in Selected Antebellum Negro Spirituals. 2010. 224p. pap. (978-3-639-23006-2(X)) VDM Verlag Dr. Mueller e.K.

Paulo, Joaquim. Funk & Soul Covers. Wiedemann, Julius, ed. 2010. (FRE, GER & ENG., Illus.). 432p. pap. 39.99 (978-3-8365-1986-1(0)) TASCHEN DEU. Dist: Ingram Pub. Services.

Pike, Gustavus D. The Singing Campaign for Ten Thousand Pounds. 2009. 92p. pap. (978-1-151-46717-9(1)) Books LLC.

Pinckney, Warren. The African American Musical Legacy: A Study Guide. rev. ed. 2009. (ENG.). 128p. pap. 75.62 (978-0-7575-4886-4(5)) Kendall Hunt Publishing Co.

Price, Emmett G., III, et al, eds. Encyclopedia of African American Music, 3 vols. 2010. (Illus.). 1116p. 280.00 (978-0-313-34199-1(0), GR4199) Greenwood Publishing Group, Inc.

Price, Emmett G., et al, eds. Encyclopedia of African American Music, Vol. 1. 2011. (978-0-313-34201-1(6)) ABC-CLIO, LLC.

—Encyclopedia of African American Music, Vol. 3. 2011. (978-0-313-34205-9(9)) ABC-CLIO, LLC.

Price, Emmett George. Encyclopedia of African American Music, Vol. 2. Maxille, Horace, ed. 2011. (978-0-313-34203-5(2)) ABC-CLIO, LLC.

Ramey, Lauri. Slave Songs & the Birth of African American Poetry. 2008. (ENG.). 216p. 84.00 (978-1-4039-7569-0(8)) Palgrave Macmillan.

Rijn, Guido Van. Kennedy's Blues: African-American Blues & Gospel Songs on JFK. (ENG.). 2010. 248p. pap. 25.00 (978-1-60473-858-2(8)) 2007. (Illus.). 220p. 50.00 (978-1-57806-957-6(2)) Univ. Pr. of Mississippi.

Saminsky, Lazare. Music of the Ghetto & the Bible. 2007. (ENG.). 272p. per. (978-1-4067-3938-1(3)) Read Bks.

Samuels, Dave. Afro-Cuban Big Band Play-Along for Mallets. 2008. (ENG.). 24p. pap. 19.95 (978-0-7390-5723-0(5)) Alfred Publishing Co., Inc.

Schlein, I. R. ving. Slave Songs of the United States. 2007. (ENG.). 184p. pap. 15.95 (978-1-4234-2262-4(7), 1423422627) Leonard, Hal Corp.

Simms, Patsy Ford. Famous African Americans: Eight People Who Made a Difference in Music, Inventions, Sports, & Science. 2011. (ENG.). 78p. pap. 49.99 (978-1-4234-9620-5(5), 1423496205) Shawnee Pr., Inc.

Thiam, Pascal Bokar. From Timbuktu to the Mississippi Delta. 2010. (C). pap. 0.00 (978-1-60927-861-8(5)) Univ. Readers.

Thomas, Lorenzo. Don't Deny My Name: Words & Music & the Black Intellectual Tradition. Nielsen, Aldon Lynn, ed. 2008. (ENG.). 232p. 80.00 (978-0-472-09892-7(6)); pap. 23.95 (978-0-472-06892-0(X)) Univ. of Michigan Pr.

Turner, Diane D., ed. Feeding the Soul: Black Music, Black Thought. 2010. (ENG., Illus.). 400p. pap. 25.95 (978-0-88378-226-2(X)) Third World Press.

Wagner, Bryan. Disturbing the Peace: Black Culture & the Police Power after Slavery. 2009. (Illus.). 320p. 37.00 (978-0-674-03508-9(9)) Harvard Univ. Pr.

Wynn, Neil A., ed. Cross the Water Blues: African American Music in Europe. 2010. (ENG.). 302p. pap. 25.00 (978-1-60473-546-8(5)) Univ. Pr. of Mississippi.

AFRICAN AMERICANS—MUSIC—HISTORY AND CRITICISM

Abbott, Lynn & Seroff, Doug. Ragged but Right: Black Traveling Shows, "Coon Songs", & the Dark Pathway to Blues & Jazz. 2007. (ENG., Illus.). 461p. 75.00 (978-1-57806-901-9(7)) Univ. Pr. of Mississippi.

Banfield, William. Representing Culture: Black Music Then, Now, & When Again? 2011. (African American Cultural Theory & Heritage Ser.). (ENG., Illus.). 312p. pap. 35.00 (978-0-8108-7786-3(4)) Scarecrow Pr., Inc.

Banfield, William C. Cultural Codes: Makings of a Black Music Philosophy - An Interpretive History from Spirituals to Hip Hop. 2009. (African American Cultural Theory & Heritage Ser.). (ENG.). 254p. pap. 42.00 (978-0-8108-7286-8(2)) Scarecrow Pr., Inc.

Banfield, William C. Representing Black Music Culture: Then, Now, & When Again? 2011. E-Book (978-0-8108-7787-0(2)) Scarecrow Pr., Inc.

Baraka, Amiri, pseud. Digging: The Afro-American Soul of American Classical Music. (Music of the African Diaspora Ser.). (Illus.). 2010. (ENG.). 426p. pap. 19.95 (978-0-520-26582-0(3)) 2009. 352p. 50.00 (978-0-520-25715-3(4)) Univ. of California Pr.

Barnwell, Ysaye M. Singing in the African American Tradition: Building a Vocal Community. 2009. (ENG.). 49p. pap. 39.95 incl. audio compact disk (978-1-59773-276-5(1), 1597732761) Leonard, Hal Corp.

Béthune, Christian. Le Jazz et L'Occident: Culture Afro-Américaine et Philosophie. 2008. (FRE.). 340p. (C). pap. 41.00 (978-2-252-03674-7(5)) Klincksieck, Editions FRA. Dist: ISD.

Bratcher, Melanie E. Words & Songs of Bessie Smith, Billie Holiday, & Nina Simone: Sound Motion, Blues Spirit, & African Memory. 2007. (Studies in African American History & Culture Ser.). (ENG., Illus.). 278p. 128.00 (978-0-415-98029-6(1)) Routledge.

Burnim, Mellonee V. & Maultsby, Portia K., eds. African American Music. 2nd rev. ed. 2012. (ENG., Illus.). 544p. pap. 62.95 (978-0-415-88181-4(1)); 140.00 (978-0-415-88180-7(3)) Routledge.

Carawan, Guy & Carawan, Candie, eds. Sing for Freedom: The Story of the Civil Rights Movement Through Its Songs. 2008. (ENG., Illus.). 266p. pap. 21.95 (978-1-58838-193-4(5), NewSouth Bks.) NewSouth, Inc.

Cram101 Textbook Reviews. Outlines & Highlights for African American Music: Introduction by Mellonee V. Burnim. 2011. 100p. pap. 27.95 (978-1-61906-048-7(5)) Cram101 Inc.

Evans, Freddi Williams. Congo Square: African Roots in New Orleans. 2011. 224p. pap. 20.00 (978-1-935754-03-9(3)) Univ. of Louisiana at Lafayette Pr.

Ferris, William. Give My Poor Heart Ease: Voices of the Mississippi Blues. 2009. (ENG., Illus.). 312p. 36.95 (978-0-8078-3325-4(8)) Univ. of North Carolina Pr.

Gulla, Bob, ed. Icons of R&B & Soul: An Encyclopedia of the Artists Who Revolutionized Rhythm, 2 vols. 2007. (Greenwood Icons Ser.). 552p. 175.00 (978-0-313-34044-4(7), GR4044, Greenwood Pr.) Greenwood Publishing Group, Inc.

Johnson, Guy B. John Henry: Tracking down a Negro Legend. reprint ed. 24.50 (978-0-404-00177-3(7)) AMS Pr., Inc.

Jones (Amiri Baraka), LeRoi. Black Music. 2010. (AkashiClassics: Renegade Reprint Ser.). (ENG.). 240p. pap. 15.95 (978-1-933354-93-4(3)) Akashic Bks.

Lankford, Ronnie D. Jazz. 2011. (Lucent Library of Black History Ser.). 128p. lib. bdg. 33.45 (978-1-4205-0570-2(X), Lucent Bks.) Cengage Gale.

Lee, Vera. The Black & White of American Popular Music: From Slavery to World War II. 2007. xii, 363p. (978-0-87047-077-6(9)) Schenkman Bks., Inc.

McGregory, Jerrilyn. Downhome Gospel: African American Spiritual Activism in Wiregrass Country. 2010. (ENG.). 224p. 65.00 (978-1-60473-782-0(4)) Univ. Pr. of Mississippi.

Munro, Martin. Different Drummers: Rhythm & Race in the Americas. 2010. (Music of the African Diaspora Ser.). (ENG.). 296p. 65.00 (978-0-520-26282-9(4)); pap. 27.50 (978-0-520-26283-6(2)) Univ. of California Pr.

Patterson, Michelle Wick. Natalie Curtis Burlin: A Life in Native & African American Music. 2010. (ENG., Illus.). 430p. 45.00 (978-0-8032-3757-5(X)) Univ. of Nebraska Pr.

Peretti, Burton W. Lift Every Voice: The History of African American Music. 2008. (African American History Ser.). (ENG., Illus.). 240p. 50.00 (978-0-7425-5811-3(8)) Rowman & Littlefield Publishers, Inc.

Pollard, Deborah Smith. When the Church Becomes Your Party: Contemporary Gospel Music. 2008. (African American Life Ser.). (Illus.). 225p. pap. 24.95 (978-0-8143-3218-4(8)) Wayne State Univ. Pr.

Ramey, Lauri. Slave Songs & the Birth of African American Poetry. 2010. (ENG.). 216p. pap. 28.00 (978-0-230-10034-3(1)) Palgrave Macmillan.

Reed, Bill. Hot from Harlem: Twelve African American Entertainers, 1890-1960. 2009. (ENG., Illus.). 271p. pap. 39.95 (978-0-7864-4467-0(3)) McFarland & Co., Inc. Pubs.

Rowden, Terry. The Songs of Blind Folk: African American Musicians & the Cultures of Blindness. 2009. (Corporealities: Discourses of Disability Ser.). (ENG., Illus.). 184p. pap. 23.95 (978-0-472-05064-2(8)); 70.00 (978-0-472-07064-0(9)) Univ. of Michigan Pr.

Rudinow, Joel. Soul Music: Tracking the Spiritual Roots of Pop from Plato to Motown. 2010. xiii, 250p. E-Book 28.95 (978-0-472-02279-3(2)); (ENG.). 264p. pap. 28.95 (978-0-472-05108-3(3)) Univ. of Michigan Pr.

Schenbeck, Lawrence. Racial Uplift & American Music, 1878-1943. 2012. (American Made Music Ser.). (ENG.). 304p. 60.00 (978-1-61703-229-5(8)) Univ. Pr. of Mississippi.

Seniors, Paula Marie. Beyond Lift Every Voice & Sing: The Culture of Uplift, Identity, & Politics in Black Musical Theater. 2009. (Black Performance & Cultural Criticism Ser.). (ENG.). 368p. cd-rom 14.95 (978-0-8142-9198-6(8)) Ohio State Univ. Pr.

Stolle, Roger. HH Mississippi Blues. 2011. pap. 19.99 (978-1-60949-219-9(6)) History Pr., The.

Sullivan, Denise. Keep on Pushing: Black Power Music from Blues to Hip-hop. 2011. (ENG., Illus.). 224p. pap. 16.95 (978-1-55652-817-0(5), Hill, Lawrence Bks.) Chicago Review Pr., Inc.

Turner, Richard Brent & Bellegarde-Smith, Patrick. Jazz Religion, the Second Line, & Black New Orleans. 2009. (ENG., Illus.). 200p. pap. 21.95 (978-0-253-22120-9(X), 025322120X) Indiana Univ. Pr.

White, Newman Ivey. American Negro Folk Songs. 2011. 512p. 60.95 (978-1-258-01314-1(2)) Literary Licensing, LLC.

Wild, David. Jazzpaths: An American Photomemento. 2012. (ENG., Illus.). 112p. 35.00 (978-0-907259-45-9(6)) Hyphen Pr. GBR. Dist: Hachette Bk. Group.

Wynn, Neil A., ed. Cross the Water Blues: African American Music in Europe. 2007. (ENG., Illus.). 289p. 50.00 (978-1-57806-960-6(2)) Univ. Pr. of Mississippi.

Young, Kevin. The Grey Album: On the Blackness of Blackness. 1 vol. 2012. (ENG.). 476p. pap. 25.00 (978-1-55597-607-1(7)) Graywolf Pr.

AFRICAN AMERICANS—POLITICS AND GOVERNMENT

see also African American Politicians; Black Power

Afary, Kamran. Performance & Activism: Grassroots Discourse after the Los Angeles Rebellion Of 1992. 2009. (Raya Dunayevskaya Series in Marxism & Humanism Ser.). (ENG.). 262p. 73.50 (978-0-7391-3356-9(X)) Lexington Bks.

—Performance & Activism: Grassroots Discourse after the Los Angeles Rebellion of 1992. 2009. (Raya Dunayevskaya Series in Marxism & Humanism Ser.). (ENG.). 262p. pap. 31.50 (978-0-7391-3357-6(8)) Lexington Bks.

Aharone, Ezrah. Sovereign Evolution: Manifest Destiny from Civil Rights to Sovereign Rights. 2008. 320p. pap. 21.00 (978-1-4389-3858-5(6)) AuthorHouse.

Aikins, Lenton. While African Americans Slept: Leadership by Parasites. 2008. per. 14.95 (978-0-9801594-0-0(7)) Zit Pubs., Inc.

Alexander, Shawn Leigh, ed. T. Thomas Fortune, the Afro-American Agitator: A Collection of Writings, 1880-1928. 2010. (New Perspectives on the History of the South Ser.). (ENG., Illus.). 342p. pap. 29.95 (978-0-8130-3548-2(1)) Univ. Pr. of Florida.

Ali, Omar H. In the Balance of Power: Independent Black Politics & Third-Party Movements in the United States. 2008. (ENG.). 216p. 39.95 (978-0-8214-1806-2(8)); pap. 19.95 (978-0-8214-1807-9(6)) Ohio Univ. Pr.

—In the Lion's Mouth: Black Populism in the New South, 1886-1900. 2010. (Margaret Walker Alexander Series in African American Studies). (ENG.). 288p. 55.00 (978-1-60473-778-3(6)) Univ. Pr. of Mississippi.

Alkebulan, Paul. Survival Pending Revolution: The History of the Black Panther Party. 2nd ed. 2007. (ENG.). 200p. 29.95 (978-0-8173-1549-8(7), Univ. of Alabama Pr.

Anderson, Kevin R. Agitations: Ideologies & Strategies in African American Politics. 2010. (ENG.). 263p. 34.95 (978-1-55728-926-1(3)) Univ. of Arkansas Pr.

Aptheker, Herbert & Marable, Manning. Herbert Aptheker on Race & Democracy: A Reader. Foner, Eric, ed. 2010. (ENG.). 296p. pap. 25.00 (978-0-252-07726-5(1)) Univ. of Illinois Pr.

Asante, Molefi Kete & Hall, Ronald E. Rooming in the Master's House: Power & Privilege in the Rise of Black Conservatism. 2010. 208p. pap. 24.95 (978-1-59451-891-1(2)); (ENG.). 100.00 (978-1-59451-890-4(4)) Paradigm Pubs.

Atkinson, Val. Southern Racial Politics & North Carolina's Black Vote. 2007. (ENG., Illus.). 196p. 39.95 (978-1-4251-6705-9(5)); per. 29.95 (978-1-4120-9324-8(4)) Trafford Publishing.

Austin, Curtis J. Up Against the Wall: Violence in the Making & Unmaking of the Black Panther Party. 2008. (ENG., Illus.). 456p. per. 22.50 (978-1-55728-875-2(5)) Univ. of Arkansas Pr.

Ayittey, George B. N. Defeating Dictators: Fighting Tyranny in Africa & Around the World. 2012. (ENG.). 288p. pap. 17.00 (978-0-230-34162-3(4)) Palgrave Macmillan.

Balaji, Murali. The Professor & the Pupil: The Politics & Friendship of W. E. B. du Bois & Paul Robeson. 2007. (ENG.). 512p. per. 18.95 (978-1-56858-355-6(9), Nation Bks.) Basic Bks.

Balfour, Katharine Lawrence & Balfour, Lawrie. Democracy's Reconstruction: Thinking Politically with W. E. B. du Bois. 2011. (Transgressing Boundaries: Studies in Black Politics & Black Communities Ser.). (ENG.). 240p. 39.95 (978-0-19-537729-3(X)) Oxford Univ. Pr., Inc.

Bandele, Ramla M. Black Star: African American Activism in the International Political Economy. 2008. (ENG., Illus.). 248p. 42.00 (978-0-252-03339-1(6)) Univ. of Illinois Pr.

Beckel, Deborah. Radical Reform: Interracial Politics in Post-Emancipation North Carolina. 2010. (American South Ser.). (ENG., Illus.). 312p. (gr. 17). 45.00 (978-0-8139-3002-2(2)) Univ. Pr. of Virginia.

Benham, Liza Abram. From Winning Elections to Influencing Policy: The Electoral-Policy Link for Minority Voters. 2008. (Law & Society Ser.). (Illus.). 304p. 75.00 (978-1-59332-274-8(7)) LFB Scholarly Publishing LLC.

Berg, Manfred. The Ticket to Freedom: The NAACP & the Struggle for Black Political Integration. 2007. (New Perspectives on the History of the South Ser.). (ENG.). 376p. per. 27.00 (978-0-8130-3216-0(4)) Univ. Pr. of Florida.

Bingham, Howard. Black Panthers 1968. Crist, Steve, ed. 2009. (ENG., Illus.). 192p. 100.00 (978-1-934429-15-0(5)); 44.95 (978-1-934429-14-3(7)) AMMO Bks., LLC.

Black Power: Politics of Liberation in America. (978-0-394-42293-0(7)) Knopf, Alfred A. Inc.

Boone, Wellington. Black Genocide: Tragedy of the American Culture. 2007. 24.95 (978-0-9776892-5-6(5)) Signature Editions.

Boyd, Michelle R. Jim Crow Nostalgia: Reconstructing Race in Bronzeville. 2008. 208p. 57.00 (978-0-8166-4677-7(5)); pap. 18.95 (978-0-8166-4678-4(3)) Univ. of Minnesota Pr.

Bracey, Christopher Alan. Saviors or Sellouts: The Promise & Peril of Black Conservatism, from Booker T. Washingtonto Condoleezza Rice. 2009. (ENG.). 248p. pap. 20.00 (978-0-8070-8376-5(3)) Beacon Pr.

Browder, Glen. The South's New Racial Politics: Inside the Race Game of Southern History. 2009. 128p. pap. 14.95 (978-1-60306-050-9(2), NewSouth Bks.) NewSouth, Inc.

Bush, Rod. The End of White World Supremacy: Black Internationalism & the Problem of the Color Line. 2009. (ENG.). 264p. 81.50 (978-1-59213-572-1(2)); pap. 29.95 (978-1-59213-573-8(0)) Temple Univ. Pr.

Caponi-Tabery, Gena. Jump for Joy: Jazz, Basketball, & Black Culture in 1930s America. 2008. (Illus.). 264p. pap. 26.95 (978-1-55849-663-7(7)); lib. bdg. 80.00 (978-1-55849-662-0(9)) Univ. of Massachusetts Pr.

Cashin, Sheryll. The Agitator's Daughter: A Memoir of Four Generations of One Extraordinary African-American Family. 2008. (ENG., Illus.). 288p. 26.00 (978-1-58648-422-4(2)) PublicAffairs.

Clarke, Kristen & Mullings, Leith. Barack Obama & African-American Empowerment: The Rise of Black America's New Leadership. Marable, Manning, ed. 2009. (Critical Black Studies). (ENG., Illus.). 280p. 95.00 (978-0-230-62050-6(7)) Palgrave Macmillan.

Clawson, Rosalee A. & Waltenburg, Eric N. Legacy & Legitimacy: Black Americans & the Supreme Court. 2008. (ENG., Illus.). 232p. pap. 24.95 (978-1-59213-903-3(5)) Temple Univ. Pr.

Clawson, Rosalee A., et al. Legacy & Legitimacy: Black Americans & the Supreme Court. 2008. (ENG., Illus.). 232p. 73.50 (978-1-59213-902-6(7)) Temple Univ. Pr.

Clemons, Michael L., ed. African Americans & Global Affairs: Contemporary Perspectives. 2010. (Illus.). 408p. pap. 35.00 (978-1-55553-722-7(7)) Univ. Pr. of New England.

—African Americans in Global Affairs: Contemporary Perspectives. 2010. (Illus.). 408p. (C). 85.00 (978-1-55553-719-7(7)) Univ. Pr. of New England.

Conaway, Carol B. & Waters, Kristin B., eds. Black Women's Intellectual Traditions: Speaking Their Minds. 2007. (Illus.). 480p. per. 35.00 (978-1-58465-634-0(4)) Univ. Pr. of New England.

Conyers, James L. African American Consciousness: Past & Present. 2011. (ENG.). 190p. pap. 29.95 (978-1-4128-4307-2(3)) Transaction Pubs.

Covin, David. Black Politics after the Civil Rights Movement: Activity & Beliefs in Sacramento, 1970-2000. 2009. (ENG., Illus.). 236p. pap. 49.95 (978-0-7864-4258-4(1)) McFarland & Co., Inc. Pubs.

Cruse, Harold. Rebellion or Revolution? 2009. (ENG.). 280p. pap. 18.50 (978-0-8166-5901-2(X)) Univ. of Minnesota Pr.

Cruson, Daniel. The Slaves of Central Fairfield County: The Journey from Slave to Freeman in Nineteenth-Century Connecticut. 2007. (Illus.). 124p. pap., per. 19.99 (978-1-59629-151-5(6)) History Pr., The.

Daniels, Lee A. Last Chance: The Political Threat to Black America. 2008. (ENG.). 240p. 22.95 (978-1-58648-495-8(8)) PublicAffairs.

Danielson, Chris. After Freedom Summer: How Race Realigned Mississippi Politics, 1965-1986. 2011. (New Perspectives on the History of the South Ser.). (ENG., Illus.). 328p. 69.95 (978-0-8130-3738-7(7)) Univ. Pr. of Florida.

Darden, Joe T., et al. The State of Black Michigan, 1967-2007. Darden, Joe T. et al, eds. 2007. (ENG., Illus.). 364p. per. 39.95 (978-0-87013-827-0(8)) Michigan State Univ. Pr.

Davis, John. Perspectives in Black Politics & Black Leadership. 2007. (ENG., Illus.). 192p. per. 32.99 (978-0-7618-3716-9(7)) Univ. Pr. of America, Inc.

Davis Jr., Theodore J. Black Politics Today: The Era of Socioeconomic Transition. 2011. (Routledge Series on Identity Politics Ser.). (ENG., Illus.). 200p. 135.00 (978-0-415-87914-9(0)); pap. 39.95 (978-0-415-87915-6(9)) Routledge.

Dawkins, Wayne. City Son: Andrew W. Cooper's Impact on Modern-Day Brooklyn. 2012. (Margaret Walker Alexander Series in African American Studies). (ENG.). 304p. 35.00 (978-1-61703-258-5(1)) Univ. Pr. of Mississippi.

Dawson, Michael C. Not in Our Lifetimes: The Future of Black Politics. 2011. (Illus.). 232p. 26.00 (978-0-226-13862-6(3)) Univ. of Chicago Pr.

Dickerson, Dennis C. African American Preachers & Politics: The Careys of Chicago. (Margaret Walker Alexander Series in African American Studies). (ENG., Illus.). 2011. 304p. pap. 30.00 (978-1-61703-193-9(3)) 2010. 236p. 65.00 (978-1-60473-427-0(2)) Univ. Pr. of Mississippi.

Dodson, Howard & Palmer, Colin, eds. Ideology, Identity, & Assumptions. 2007. (Schomburg Studies on the Black Experience). (ENG., Illus.). 205p. per. 19.95 (978-0-87013-795-2(6)) Michigan State Univ. Pr.

Dodson, Howard & Palmer, Colin A. The Black Condition. Dodson, Howard, ed. 2008. (Schomburg Studies on the Black Experience: Ser.). (ENG., Illus.). 272p. pap. 24.95 (978-0-87013-838-6(3)) Michigan State Univ. Pr.

Dowdy, G. Wayne. Crusades for Freedom: Memphis & the Political Transformation of the American South. 2010. (ENG., Illus.). 176p. 45.00 (978-1-60473-423-2(X)) Univ. Pr. of Mississippi.

—Mayor Crump Don't Like It: Machine Politics in Memphis. 2008. (ENG.). 168p. per. 25.00 (978-1-60473-113-2(3)) Univ. Pr. of Mississippi.

Du Bois, W. E. B. Black Reconstruction in America: An Essay Toward a History of the Part Which Black Folk Played in the Attempt to Reconstruct Democracy in America, 1860-1880. 2007. (978-0-19-532581-2(8)) Oxford Univ. Pr., Inc.

Dyson, Michael Eric. April 4 1968: Martin Luther King, Jr.'s Death & How It Changed America. 2009. (ENG.). 304p. pap. 14.95 (978-0-465-01286-2(8)) Basic Bks.

Emmett Till Unsolved Civil Rights Crime ACT: Joint Hearing Before the Subcommittee on the Constitution, Civil Rights, & Civil Liberties & the Subcommittee on Crime, Terrorism, & Homeland Security of the Committee on the Judiciary, House of Representatives, One Hundred Tenth Congress, First Session, on H.R. 923, June 12, 2007. 2007. (Illus.). vi, 103p. (978-0-16-079490-2(0), 552-070-36483-8) United States Government Printing Office.

Fauntroy, Michael K. Republicans & the Black Vote. 2008. 181p. (C). pap. 22.00 (978-1-58826-572-2(2)) 2007. 190p. lib. bdg. 49.95 (978-1-58826-470-1(X)) Rienner, Lynne Pubs.

Fleming, Cynthia Griggs. Yes We Did? From King's Dream to Obama's Promise. 2009. (ENG., Illus.). 336p. 29.95 (978-0-8131-2560-2(X)) Univ. Pr. of Kentucky.

Fleming, William H. Slavery & the Race Problem in the South. 66p. reprint ed. 88.00 (978-0-7222-9725-4(4)) Library Reprints, Inc.

Foley, Barbara. Spectres Of 1919: Class & Nation in the Making of the New Negro. 2008. (ENG., Illus.). 328p. pap. 26.00 (978-0-252-07585-8(4)) Univ. of Illinois Pr.

Ford, Pearl, ed. African Americans in Georgia: A Reflection of Politics & Policy in the New South. 2010. 224p. 40.00 (978-0-88146-184-8(9)) Mercer Univ. Pr.

Fortune, T. Thomas. T. Thomas Fortune, the Afro-American Agitator: A Collection of Writings, 1880-1928. Alexander, Shawn Leigh, ed. 2008. (New Perspectives on the History of the South Ser.). (ENG.). 320p. 65.00 (978-0-8130-3232-0(6)) Univ. Pr. of Florida.

Freedman, Eric & Jones, Stephen A. African Americans in Congress: A Documentary History. 00 vols. rev. ed. 2007. (Illus.). 543p. 142.00 (978-0-87289-385-6(5)) CQ Pr.

Gantt, Lucius. Beast Too: Dead Man Writing. 2009. 292p. pap. 19.99 (978-1-4389-4915-4(4)) AuthorHouse.

Gill, Tiffany. Beauty Shop Politics: African American Women's Activism in the Beauty Industry. 2010. (Women in American History Ser.). (ENG., Illus.). 208p. pap. 25.00 *(978-0-252-07696-1(6))* Univ. of Illinois Pr.

Gillespie, Andra. The New Black Politician: Corey Booker, Newark, & Post-Racial America. 2012. (ENG.). 336p. 35.00 ***(978-0-8147-3244-1(5))*** New York Univ. Pr.

Gillespie, Andra. Whose Black Politics? Cases in Post-Racial Black Leadership. 2009. (Illus.). 338p. 38.95 *(978-0-415-99216-9(8))*; (ENG., 138.00 *(978-0-415-99215-2(X))* Routledge.

Gilroy, Paul. Darker Than Blue: On the Moral Economies of Black Atlantic Culture. 2011. (W. E. B. du Bois Lectures). 224p. pap. 18.95 *(978-0-674-06023-4(7)*, Belknap Pr.) Harvard Univ. Pr.

Glasrud, Bruce, ed. African Americans & the Presidency: The Road to the White House. 2009. (ENG., Illus.). 272p. (C). 130.00 *(978-0-415-80391-5(8))* Routledge.

Glasrud, Bruce & Wintz, Cary D., eds. African Americans & the Presidency: The Road to the White House. 2009. (ENG., Illus.). 256p. pap. 26.95 *(978-0-415-80392-2(6))* Routledge.

Glaude, Eddie S., Jr. In a Shade of Blue: Pragmatism & the Politics of Black America. 208p. 2008. pap. 19.00 *(978-0-226-29825-2(6))* 2007. 25.00 *(978-0-226-29824-5(8))* Univ. of Chicago Pr.

Goff, Keli. Party Crashing: How the Hip-Hop Generation Declared Political Independence. 2008. (ENG.). 244p. per. 16.95 *(978-0-465-00332-7(X)*, Basic Civitas Bks.) Basic Bks.

Gooding-Williams, Robert. In the Shadow of du Bois: Afro-Modern Political Thought in America. 2011. (ENG.). 368p. pap. 18.95 *(978-0-674-06024-1(5))* Harvard Univ. Pr.

Goza, Rogenia. Motivational Factors That Influence Career Choice - African American Women Legislators. 2008. 148p. pap. *(978-3-639-00728-2(X))* VDM Verlag Dr. Mueller e.K.

Grady-Willis, Winston A. Challenging U. S. Apartheid: Atlanta & Black Struggles for Human Rights, 1960-1977. 2006. (ENG., Illus.). 312p. per. 24.95 *(978-0-8223-3791-1(6))* Duke Univ. Pr.

—Challenging U. S. Apartheid: Atlanta & Black Struggles for Human Rights, 1960-1977. 2006. (ENG., Illus.). 312p. (C). 89.95 *(978-0-8223-3778-2(9))* Duke Univ. Pr.

Gray, Kevin Alexander. Waiting for Lightning to Strike: The Fundamentals of Black Politics. 2008. (ENG., Illus.). 250p. pap. 15.95 *(978-1-904859-91-8(7))* AK Pr. GBR. Dist: Consortium Bk. Sales & Distribution.

Green, William D. A Peculiar Imbalance: The Fall & Rise of Racial Equality in Early Minnesota. 2007. 232p. 32.95 *(978-0-87351-586-3(2))* Minnesota Historical Society Pr.

Greene, Cheryll Y. & Smiley Books Staff, eds. America I Am Legends: Rare Moments & Inspiring Words. 2009. (ENG.). 192p. 34.95 *(978-1-4019-2410-2(7))*; 150p. pap. 24.95 *(978-1-4019-2405-8(0))* Hay Hse., Inc.

Griffith, Joanne, ed. Redefining Black Power: Reflections on the State of Black America. 2012. (City Lights Open Media Ser.). (ENG.). 208p. pap. 16.95 ***(978-0-87286-546-4(0))*** City Lights Bks.

Hahn, Steven. The Political Worlds of Slavery & Freedom. 2009. (Nathan I. Huggins Lectures). (Illus.). 272p. 21.95 *(978-0-674-03296-5(9))* Harvard Univ. Pr.

Haines, Herbert H. Black Radicals & the Civil Rights Mainstream, 1954-1970. 224p. pap. 23.00 *(978-1-57233-260-7(3))* Univ. of Tennessee Pr.

Hajnal, Zoltan & Lee, Taeku. Why Americans Don′t Enjoy the Party - Race, Immigration, & the Failure (of Political Parties) to Engage the Electorate. 2011. (ENG., Illus.). 344p. (C). pap. 27.95 *(978-0-691-14879-3(1))* Princeton Univ. Pr.

Hajnal, Zoltan & Lee, Takeu. Why American Don′t Join the Party - Race, Immigration, & the Failure (of Political Parties) to Engage the Electorate. 2011. (ENG., Illus.). 344p. (C). 75.00 *(978-0-691-14878-6(3))* Princeton Univ. Pr.

Hajnal, Zoltan L. Changing White Attitudes Toward Black Political Leadership. 2006. (ENG., Illus.). 230p. per. 26.99 *(978-0-521-67415-7(8))* Cambridge Univ. Pr.

Hall, Simon. Peace & Freedom: The Civil Rights & Antiwar Movements in The 1960s. 2006. (Politics & Culture in Modern America Ser.). (Illus.). 280p. (C). per. 24.95 *(978-0-8122-1975-3(9))* Univ. of Pennsylvania Pr.

Hardie, Marcus. Black & Bulletproof: An African American Warrior in the Israeli Army. 2010. (ENG.). 320p. 24.95 *(978-0-88282-346-1(9))* New Horizon Pr. Pubs., Inc.

Harris, Fredrick. The Price of the Ticket: Barack Obama & Rise & Decline of Black Politics. 2012. (ENG.). 232p. 24.95 ***(978-0-19-973967-7(6))*** Oxford Univ. Pr., Inc.

Harris-Lacewell, Melissa Victoria. Barbershops, Bibles, & Bet: Everyday Talk & Black Political Thought. annot. ed. 2006. (ENG., Illus.). 368p. (C). per. 26.95 *(978-0-691-12609-8(7))* Princeton Univ. Pr.

Harris-Perry, Melissa V. Sister Citizen: Shame, Stereotypes, & Black Women in America. 2011. (Illus.). 392p. 28.00 *(978-0-300-16541-8(2))* Yale Univ. Pr.

Henry, Charles P., et al. The Obama Phenomenon: Toward a Multiracial Democracy. 2011. (ENG.). 344p. pap. 25.00 ***(978-0-252-07822-4(5))***; (Illus.). 75.00 ***(978-0-252-03645-3(X))*** Univ. of Illinois Pr.

Hill, Johnny Bernard. The First Black President: Barack Obama, Race, Politics, & the American Dream. 2009. (ENG.). 208p. pap. 30.00 *(978-0-230-62114-5(7))* Palgrave Macmillan.

Hill, Ronald B. America: Truth vs. Illusions of Grandeur. 2010. 452p. pap. 22.99 *(978-1-4490-6119-7(2))* AuthorHouse.

Hilliard, David, ed. & selected by. The Black Panther: Intercommunal News Service, 1967-1980. 2007. (ENG., Illus.). 192p. pap. 25.00 *(978-1-4165-3259-0(5)*, Beyond Words/Atria Bks.) Atria Bks.

Ho, Fred & Mullen, Bill V., eds. Afro Asia: Revolutionary Political & Cultural Connections Between African Americans & Asian Americans. 2008. (ENG., Illus.). 416p. 94.95 *(978-0-8223-4258-8(8))*; pap. 26.95 *(978-0-8223-4281-6(2))* Duke Univ. Pr.

Hood, M. V., et al. The Rational Southerner: Black Mobilization, Republican Growth, & the Partisan Transformation of the American South. 2012. (ENG., Illus.). 240p. 39.95 ***(978-0-19-987382-1(8))*** Oxford Univ. Pr., Inc.

Hornsby, Alton. Black Power in Dixie: A Political History of African Americans in Atlanta. 2009. (Southern Dissent Ser.). (ENG., Illus.). 320p. 39.95 *(978-0-8130-3282-5(2))* Univ. Pr. of Florida.

Hudson, Janet G. Entangled by White Supremacy: Reform in World War I-era South Carolina. 2009. (New Directions in Southern History Ser.). (ENG.). 400p. pap. 50.00 *(978-0-8131-9293-2(5))* Univ. Pr. of Kentucky.

Huey P. Newton Foundation Staff. The Black Panther Party: Service to the People Programs. Hilliard, David & The Huey P. Newton Foundation, eds. 2008. (ENG., Illus.). 170p. pap. 21.95 *(978-0-8263-4394-9(5))* Univ. of New Mexico Pr.

Ifill, Gwen. The Breakthrough: Politics & Race in the Age of Obama. 2009. (ENG.). 320p. pap. 15.00 *(978-0-7679-2890-8(3)*, Knopf) Knopf Doubleday Publishing Group.

Iton, Richard. In Search of the Black Fantastic: Politics & Popular Culture in the Post-Civil Rights Era. 2010. (ENG.). 432p. pap. 21.95 *(978-0-19-973360-6(0))* Oxford Univ. Pr., Inc.

Jeffries, Hasan. Bloody Lowndes: Civil Rights & Black Power in Alabama's Black Belt. (ENG., Illus.). 352p. 2010. pap. 22.00 *(978-0-8147-4331-7(5))* 2009. 60.00 *(978-0-8147-4305-8(6))* New York Univ. Pr.

Jeffries, Judson L., ed. Comrades: A Local History of the Black Panther Party. 2007. (Blacks in the Diaspora Ser.). (ENG., Illus.). 336p. per. 24.95 *(978-0-253-21930-5(2)*, 0253219302) Indiana Univ. Pr.

—On the Ground: The Black Panther Party in Communities Across America. (ENG.). 304p. 2011. pap. 30.00 ***(978-1-61703-200-4(X))*** 2010. 50.00 *(978-1-60473-492-8(2))* Univ. Pr. of Mississippi.

Johnson, Cedric. Revolutionaries to Race Leaders: Black Power & the Making of African American Politics. 2007. 320p. 60.00 *(978-0-8166-4477-3(2))*; per. 20.00 *(978-0-8166-4478-0(0))* Univ. of Minnesota Pr.

Johnson, Loch K. & Bullock III, Charles S. Runoff Elections in the United States. 2011. (ENG.). 228p. pap. 40.00 ***(978-0-8078-6515-6(X))*** Univ. of North Carolina Pr.

Jonas, Gilbert. Freedom's Sword: The NAACP & the Struggle Against Racism in America, 1909-1969. 2007. (Illus.). 520p. per. 29.95 *(978-0-415-95665-9(X))* Routledge.

Jones, Angela, ed. The Modern African American Thought Reader: From David Walker to Barack Obama. 2012. (ENG., Illus.). 448p. (C). pap. 54.95 ***(978-0-415-89573-6(1))*** Routledge.

Jones, Ricky L. What's Wrong with Obamamania? Black America, Black Leadership, & the Death of Political Imagination. 2008. (C). 44.50 *(978-0-7914-7579-9(4))*; 160p. pap. 19.95 *(978-0-7914-7580-5(8))* State Univ. of New York Pr.

Jones, Stephanie. The State of Black America 2009: Message to the President. 2009. (ENG.). 290p. pap. 19.95 *(978-0-914758-02-0(0))* National Urban League, National Headquarters.

Jordan-Zachery, Julia & Jordan-Zachery, Julia Sheron. Black Women, Cultural Images, & Social Policy. 2008. (Routledge Studies in North American Politics Ser.). (ENG., Illus.). 230p. 125.00 *(978-0-415-99678-5(3))* Routledge.

Joseph, Peniel E. Waiting 'Til the Midnight Hour: A Narrative History of Black Power in America. 2007. (ENG., Illus.). 432p. pap. 17.99 *(978-0-8050-8335-4(9)*, Owl Bks.) Holt, Henry & Co.

Joseph, Peniel E., ed. Neighborhood Rebels: Black Power at the Local Level. 2009. (Contemporary Black History Ser.). (ENG.). 264p. 100.00 *(978-0-230-62076-6(0))* Palgrave Macmillan.

Kennedy, Randall. The Persistence of the Color Line: Racial Politics & the Obama Presidency. (Vintage Ser.). (ENG.). 336p. 2012. pap. 15.95 ***(978-0-307-45555-0(6)***, Vintage) 2011. 26.95 *(978-0-307-37789-0(X)*, Pantheon) Knopf Doubleday Publishing Group.

Kennedy, Randall. Sellout: The Politics of Racial Betrayal. 2009. (Vintage Ser.). (ENG.). 240p. pap. 13.95 *(978-0-307-38842-1(5)*, Vintage) Knopf Doubleday Publishing Group.

Kinchlow, Ben. Black Yellow Dogs: The Most Dangerous Citizen Is Not Armed, but Uninformed. 2008. (ENG.). 157p. per. 14.00 *(978-1-60037-284-1(8))* Morgan James Publishing.

King, Debra Walker. African Americans & the Culture of Pain. 2008. (Cultural Frames, Framing Culture Ser.). (ENG., Illus.). 224p. (C). (gr. 13-17). per. 20.00 *(978-0-8139-2681-0(5))*; (gr. 17). 55.00 *(978-0-8139-2680-3(7))* Univ. Pr. of Virginia.

King, Desmond & Smith, Roger. Still a House Divided - Race & Politics in Obama's America. 2011. (Princeton Studies in American Politics: Historical, International, & Comparative Perspectives Ser.). (ENG., Illus.). 320p. (C). 35.00 ***(978-0-691-14263-0(7))*** Princeton Univ. Pr.

King, Kendra. African American Politics. rev. ed. 2010. (UMP - US Minority Politics Ser.: 5). (ENG., Illus.). 288p. 75.95 *(978-0-7456-3280-3(7))*; pap. 26.95 *(978-0-7456-3281-0(5))* Polity Pr. GBR. Dist: Wiley, John & Sons, Inc.

King-Meadows, Tyson & Schaller, Thomas F. Devolution & Black State Legislators: Challenges & Choices in the Twenty-First Century. 2007. (SUNY Series in African American Studies). (Illus.). 302p. per. 31.95 *(978-0-7914-6730-5(9))* State Univ. of New York Pr.

Knadler, Stephen & Knadler, Stephen P. Remapping Citizenship & the Nation in African-American Literature. 2009. (Routledge Transnational Perspectives on American Literature Ser.). (ENG.). 248p. (C). 125.00 *(978-0-415-99631-0(7))* Routledge.

Lawson, Ernest. Political Self Destruction of Most African Americans. 2010. 548p. (ENG.). 40.00 *(978-1-4269-3007-2(0))*; pap. 30.00 *(978-1-4269-3006-5(2))* Trafford Publishing.

Lawson, Steven F. Running for Freedom: Civil Rights & Black Politics in America since 1941. 3rd ed. 2008. (ENG., Illus.). 408p. pap. 42.95 *(978-1-4051-7126-7(X)*, Wiley-Blackwell) Wiley, John & Sons, Inc.

Lazerow, Jama & Williams, Yohuru, eds. In Search of the Black Panther Party: New Perspectives on a Revolutionary Movement. 2006. (ENG., Illus.). 408p. 94.95 *(978-0-8223-3837-6(8))* Duke Univ. Pr.

Liu, Baodong & Vanderleeuw, James M. Race Rules: Electoral Politics in New Orleans, 1965-2006. 2007. (ENG., Illus.). 180p. 62.99 *(978-0-7391-1967-9(2))* Lexington Bks.

Liu/Vanderleeuw. Race Rules: Electoral Politics in New Orleans, 1965-2006. 2007. (ENG.). 180p. pap. 26.50 *(978-0-7391-1968-6(0))* Lexington Bks.

Lumpkins, Charles. American Pogrom: The East St. Louis Race Riot & Black Politics. 2008. (Law Society & Politics in the Midwest Ser.). (Illus.). 360p. 55.00 *(978-0-8214-1802-4(5))*; (ENG., pap. 28.95 *(978-0-8214-1803-1(3))* Ohio Univ. Pr.

Lusane, Clarence. The Black History of the White House. 2011. (City Lights Open Media Ser.). (ENG., Illus.). 544p. pap. 19.95 *(978-0-87286-532-7(0)*, 1311831) City Lights Bks.

Makalani, Minkah. In the Cause of Freedom: Radical Black Internationalism from Harlem to London, 1917-1939. 2011. (ENG., Illus.). 384p. 39.95 *(978-0-8078-3504-3(8))* Univ. of North Carolina Pr.

Malone, Christopher. Between Freedom & Bondage: Race, Party, & Voting Rights in the Antebellum North. 2007. (ENG.). 272p. 143.00 *(978-0-415-95696-3(X))*; per. 32.95 *(978-0-415-95697-0(8))* Routledge.

Manning, Christopher. William L. Dawson & the Limits of Black Electoral Leadership. 2009. (Illus.). 251p. 37.00 *(978-0-87580-395-1(4))* Northern Illinois Univ. Pr.

Marable, Manning. Beyond Black & White: Transforming African-American Politics. 2nd ed. 2009. (ENG.). 256p. 100.00 *(978-1-84467-382-7(0)*, 844382); pap. 24.95 *(978-1-84467-383-4(9)*, 844383) Verso Bks. GBR. Dist: Norton, W. W. & Co., Inc.

Marotti, Frank. The Cana Sanctuary: History, Diplomacy, & Black Catholic Marriage in Antebellum St. Augustine, Florida. 2012. (ENG.). 240p. 39.95 ***(978-0-8173-1747-8(3))*** Univ. of Alabama Pr.

Marshall, Stephen. The City on the Hill from Below: The Crisis of Prophetic Black Politics. 2011. (ENG.). 256p. 64.50 *(978-1-4399-0655-2(6))* Temple Univ. Pr.

Masur, Kate. An Example for All the Land: Emancipation & the Struggle over Equality in Washington, D. C. 2010. (ENG., Illus.). 376p. 39.95 *(978-0-8078-3414-5(9))* Univ. of North Carolina Pr.

Mayes, Keith. Civil Rights & Black Power: The Struggle for Black Equality in the United States, 1945-1975. 2009. (ENG., Illus.). 352p. 125.00 *(978-0-415-99128-5(5))* Routledge.

Mcadam & Cram101 Textbook Reviews Staff. Political Process & the Development of Black Insurgency 1930-1970. 2007. 60p. per. 9.95 *(978-1-4288-2326-6(3))* Cram101 Inc.

McDaniel, Eric L. Politics in the Pews: The Political Mobilization of Black Churches. 2008. (Politics of Race & Ethnicity Ser.). (ENG., Illus.). 224p. (C). 80.00 *(978-0-472-07046-6(0))*; pap. 26.95 *(978-0-472-05046-8(X))* Univ. of Michigan Pr.

Minta, Michael D. Oversight - Representing the Interests of Black & Latinos in Congress. 2011. (ENG., Illus.). 192p. (C). pap. 24.95 *(978-0-691-14926-4(7))* Princeton Univ. Pr.

—Oversight - Representing the Interests of Black & Latinos in Congress. 2011. (ENG., Illus.). 192p. (C). 65.00 *(978-0-691-14925-7(9))* Princeton Univ. Pr.

Mitchell, Michael & Covin, David. Black Politics in a Time of Transition. 2011. (Illus.). 239p. pap. 29.95 ***(978-1-4128-4268-6(9))*** Transaction Pubs.

Muhammad, Ashahed. The Black Principle: Prepare to Rule. 2008. per. *(978-0-9766066-1-1(5))* Truth Establishment Institute, The.

Mullings, Leith. Barack Obama & African-American Empowerment: The Rise of Black America's New Leadership. Marable, Manning & Clarke, Kristen, eds. 2009. (Critical Black Studies). (ENG., Illus.). 280p. pap. 30.00 *(978-0-230-62052-0(3))* Palgrave Macmillan.

Murch, Donna. Living for the City: Migration, Education, & the Rise of the Black Panther Party in Oakland, California. 2010. (John Hope Franklin Series in African American History & Culture Ser.). (ENG., Illus.). 344p. 65.00 *(978-0-8078-3376-6(2))*; pap. 22.95 *(978-0-8078-7113-3(3))* Univ. of North Carolina Pr.

Mwakikagile, Godfrey. Black Conservatives in the United States. 2006. pap. *(978-0-9802587-0-7(7))* New Africa Pr.

Ogbar, Jeffrey O. G., ed. The Harlem Renaissance Revisited: Politics, Arts, & Letters. 2010. (ENG.). 272p. (C). (gr. 13-17). pap. 30.00 *(978-0-8018-9461-9(1))* Johns Hopkins Univ. Pr.

—The Harlem Renaissance Revisited: Politics, Arts, & Letters. 2010. (ENG.). 272p. (C). (gr. 13-17). 60.00 *(978-0-8018-9460-2(3))* Johns Hopkins Univ. Pr.

Oguejiofor Okafor, Victor, ed. Studies in African American Leadership: Individuals, Movements, & Committees. 2006. 156p. 99.95 *(978-0-7734-5688-4(0))* Mellen, Edwin Pr., The.

Ortiz, Paul. Emancipation Betrayed: The Hidden History of Black Organizing & White Violence in Florida from Reconstruction to the Bloody Election Of 1920. 2006. (American Crossroads Ser.). (Illus.). 382p. per. 24.95 *(978-0-520-25003-1(6))* Univ. of California Pr.

Parker, Christopher S. Fighting for Democracy: Black Veterans & the Struggle Against White Supremacy in the Postwar South. 2009. (Princeton Studies in American Politics: Historical, International, & Comparative Perspectives Ser.). (ENG., Illus.). 288p. (C). 62.95 *(978-0-691-14003-2(0))*; pap. 25.95 *(978-0-691-14004-9(9))* Princeton Univ. Pr.

Perryman, Wayne. Whites, Blacks & Racist Democrats: The Untold Story of Race & Politics Within the Democratic Party From 1792-2009. 2010. (Illus.). 182p. 16.95 *(978-1-935359-30-2(4))* Book Pubs. Network.

Persons, Georgia A., ed. The Expanding Boundaries of Black Politics. 2007. (National Political Science Review Ser.: Vol. 11). (ENG., Illus.). 404p. (gr. 11). pap. 29.95 *(978-0-7658-0375-7(5))* Transaction Pubs.

Persons, Georgia Anne. Beyond the Boundaries: A New Structure of Ambition in African American Politics. Persons, Georgia, ed. 2009. (ENG., Illus.). 284p. pap. 29.95 *(978-1-4128-1048-7(5))* Transaction Pubs.

Philpot, Tasha. Race, Republicans, & the Return of the Party of Lincoln. 2007. (Politics of Race & Ethnicity Ser.). (ENG.). 224p. (C). 80.00 *(978-0-472-09967-2(1))*; (Illus.). per. 25.95 *(978-0-472-06967-5(5))* Univ. of Michigan Pr.

Pickens, William. New Negro, His Political, Civil & Mental Status & Related Essays. reprint ed. 21.50 *(978-0-404-00271-8(4))* AMS Pr., Inc.

Pinderhughes, Dianne. Black Politics after the Civil Rights Revolution. 2012. (ENG.). 272p. 135.00 *(978-0-415-88155-5(2))*; pap. 33.95 *(978-0-415-88156-2(0))* Routledge.

Piven, Frances Fox, et al. Keeping down the Black Vote: The Politics of Election Administration in America. 2009. (ENG., Illus.). 281p. 26.95 *(978-1-59558-354-3(8)*, 955354) New Pr., The.

Pohlmann, Marcus D. Black Politics in Conservative America. 3rd ed. 2007. (Illus.). 380p. (C). pap. 33.00 net. *(978-1-59738-012-6(1))* Sloan Publishing.

Rabaka, Reiland. Du Bois's Dialectics: Black Radical Politics & the Reconstruction of Critical Social Theory. 2008. (ENG.). 354p. 83.99 *(978-0-7391-1957-0(5))* Lexington Bks.

—W. E. B. du Bois & the Problems of the Twenty-First Century: An Essay on Africana Critical Theory. 2007. (ENG.). 296p. 83.99 *(978-0-7391-1682-1(7))* Lexington Bks.

Rangel, Charles B. And I Haven't Had a Bad Day Since: From the Streets of Harlem to the Halls of Congress. 2008. (ENG., Illus.). 336p. pap. 16.99 *(978-0-312-38213-1(8)*, St. Martin's Griffin) St. Martin's Pr.

Reed, Adolph, Jr., et al. Renewing Black Intellectual History: The Ideological & Material Foundations of African American Thought, 1 vol. 2010. 336p. pap. 39.95 *(978-1-59451-666-5(9))* Paradigm Pubs.

Reed, Christopher Robert. The Depression Comes to the South Side: Protest & Politics in the Black Metropolis, 1930-1933. 2011. (Blacks in the Diaspora Ser.). (ENG., Illus.). 204p. 29.95 *(978-0-253-35652-9(0)*, 0253356520) Indiana Univ. Pr.

Reid, Debra A. & Bennett, Evan P., eds. Beyond Forty Acres & a Mule: African American Landowning Families since Reconstruction. 2012. (ENG., Illus.). 352p. 69.95 ***(978-0-8130-3986-2(X))*** Univ. Pr. of Florida.

Salit, Jacqueline & Kurlander, Gabrielle, eds. Independent Black Leadership in America. 128p. pap. 9.95 *(978-0-9628621-0-6(X))* All Stars Project, Inc.

Savage, Barbara Dianne. Your Spirits Walk Beside Us: The Politics of Black Religion. 2008. 368p. 27.95 *(978-0-674-03177-7(6)*, Belknap Pr.) Harvard Univ. Pr.

Schuyler, George S. Rac(e)ing to the Right: Selected Essays George S. Schuyler. 2011. pap. 24.95 ***(978-1-57233-818-0(0))*** Univ. of Tennessee Pr.

Scruggs-Leftwich, Yvonne. Soundbytes of Protest. 2007. 120p. pap. 15.95 *(978-0-88378-272-9(3))* Third World Press.

Shabazz, Rsheed Ali. And God Made Man: The Creation of African America. 2008. pap. 10.00 *(978-0-8059-7918-3(2))* Dorrance Publishing Co., Inc.

Sharpley-Whiting, T. Denean, ed. The Speech: Race & Barack Obama's a More Perfect Union. 2009. (ENG.). 272p. pap. 18.00 *(978-1-59691-667-8(2))* Bloomsbury Publishing.

Simien, Evelyn M. Black Feminist Voices in Politics. 2006. 196p. 71.50 *(978-0-7914-6789-3(9))*; per. 29.95 *(978-0-7914-6790-9(2))* State Univ. of New York Pr.

Simone, AbdouMaliq. City Life from Jakarta to Dakar: Movements at the Crossroads. 2009. (Global Realities Ser.). (ENG., Illus.). 18p. 31.95 *(978-0-415-99322-7(9))* Routledge.

—City Life from Jakarta to Dakar - Movements at the Crossroads. 2009. (Global Realities Ser.). (ENG., Illus.). 18p. 135.00 *(978-0-415-99321-0(0))* Routledge.

Sinclair, Abiola, ed. & text. The Harlem Cultural - Political Movements, 1960-1970: From Malcolm X to "Black Is Beautiful" (Illus.). 132p. (Orig.). pap. 18.95 *(978-0-936073-25-5(X))* Gumbs & Thomas Pubs., Inc.

Sinclair, William A. & Alexander, Shawn Lee. The Aftermath of Slavery: A Study of the Condition & Environment of the American Negro. 2012. (Southern Classics Ser.). (ENG.). 424p. pap. 16.95 ***(978-1-61117-078-8(8))*** Univ. of South Carolina Pr.

Skinner, Devon. Awakening: Rejecting the Politicization of the African American Dream. 2009. 152p. pap. 14.95 *(978-1-4401-0646-0(0))* iUniverse, Inc.

Smart, Ian. Willie Lynch to the World Trade Center: An African American Response to Nine-One-One. 2nd ed. 2008. xiv, 165p. *(978-0-939423-20-0(0))* Original World Pr.

Smiley, Tavis, frwd. The Covenant in Action. 2007. (ENG.). 160p. per. 10.00 *(978-1-4019-1852-1(2)*, Smiley Bks.) Hay Hse., Inc.

Smith, Norma LaVonne. Hope, Change & Obama: A Collection of Essays on an Historic Election. 2009. 256p. pap. 17.99 *(978-0-9824236-7-7(5))* NLS Publishing.

Smith, Terry. Barack Obama, Post-Racialism, & the New Politics of Triangulation. 2012. (ENG., Illus.). 234p. 85.00 ***(978-0-230-37199-6(X))*** Palgrave Macmillan.

Spence, Lester K. Stare in the Darkness: The Limits of Hip-Hop & Black Politics. 2011. (Illus.). 240p. 67.50 *(978-0-8166-6987-5(2))*; pap. 22.50 *(978-0-8166-6988-2(0))* Univ. of Minnesota Pr.

Steele, Shelby. White Guilt: How Blacks & Whites Together Destroyed the Promise of the Civil Rights Era. 2007. (P. S. Ser.). (ENG.). 208p. pap. 13.99 *(978-0-06-057863-3(7)*, HarperPerennial) HarperCollins Pubs.

Tate, Katherine. What's Going On? Political Incorporation & the Transformation of Black Public Opinion. 2010. (ENG.). 208p. pap. 29.95 *(978-1-58901-702-3(1))* Georgetown Univ. Pr.

Taylor, James Lance. Black Nationalism in the United States: From Malcolm X to Barack Obama. 2011. (Illus.). 410p. 68.50 *(978-1-58826-778-8(4))* Rienner, Lynne Pubs.

Thompson, Ernest & Thompson, Mindy. Homeboy Came to Orange: A Story of People's Power. 2008. 240p. pap. 17.95 *(978-0-595-53036-6(2))* iUniverse, Inc.

Topping, Simon. Lincoln's Lost Legacy: The Republican Party & the African American Vote, 1928-1952. 2008. (ENG.). 320p. 65.00 *(978-0-8130-3228-3(8))* Univ. Pr. of Florida.

Udogu, Ike E. & Udogu, Emmanuel Ike. African American Politics in Rural America: Theory, Practice, & Case Studies from Florence County, South Carolina. 2006. (ENG.). 204p. 68.50 *(978-0-7618-3540-0(7))*; per. 36.99 *(978-0-7618-3541-7(5))* Univ. Pr. of America, Inc.

Verney, Kevern & Sartain, Lee, eds. Long Is the Way & Hard: One Hundred Years of the NAACP. 2009. (ENG.). 330p. 70.00 *(978-1-55728-908-7(5))*; pap. 29.95 *(978-1-55728-909-4(3))* Univ. of Arkansas Pr.

Walsh, Kenneth T. Family of Freedom: Presidents & African Americans in the White House. 2011. (Illus.). 288p. 26.95 *(978-1-59451-833-1(5))* Paradigm Pubs.

—Family of Freedom: The Presidents & Blacks in the White House from Slavery to the Obama ERA. 2011. pap. *(978-1-59451-834-8(3))* Paradigm Pubs.

Walters, Ronald W. Freedom Is Not Enough: Black Voters, Black Candidates, & American Presidential Politics. 2007. (American Political Challenges Ser.). (ENG.). 256p. per. 28.95 *(978-0-7425-4806-0(6))* Rowman & Littlefield Publishers, Inc.

Walton, Hanes & Smith, Robert C. American Politics & the African American Quest for Universal Freedom. 5th ed. 2009. (ENG.). 336p. (C). pap. 100.20 *(978-0-205-63936-9(8))* Longman Publishing Group.

Walton, Hanes & Smith, Robert Charles. American Politics & the African American Quest for Universal Freedom. 6th ed. 2011. (ENG.). 368p. (C). pap. 71.40 *(978-0-205-07391-9(1))* Longman Publishing Group.

Walton, Hanes, et al. American Politics & the African American Quest for Universal Freedom. 4th ed. 2007. (ENG., Illus.). 336p. (C). per. 104.60 *(978-0-205-53639-9(5))* Longman Publishing Group.

Walton Jr, Hanes, et al. The African American Electorate, 02 vols. rev. ed. 2012. 350.00 *(978-0-87289-508-9(4))* CQ Pr.

Warren, Roland Leslie. Politics & African-American Ghettos. 2008. (ENG.). 244p. pap. 29.95 *(978-0-202-36212-0(4))* Aldine Transaction.

Washington, Booker T. The Negro Problem. 2009. 120p. 21.99 *(978-0-559-08959-6(7))*; 24.99 *(978-0-559-08944-2(9))*; pap. 19.75 *(978-0-559-08955-8(4))*; pap. 19.75 *(978-0-559-08948-0(1))* BiblioBazaar.

—The Negro Problem. 2007. (ENG.). 76p. per. *(978-1-4068-1972-4(7))* Echo Library.

—The Negro Problem. 2009. 104p. pap. 11.45 *(978-1-4385-1907-4(9)*, Book Jungle) Standard Pubns., Inc.

Watkins, Rychetta. Black Power, Yellow Power, & the Making of Revolutionary Identities. 2012. (ENG.). 176p. 55.00 ***(978-1-61703-161-8(5))*** Univ. Pr. of Mississippi.

Watts, Eric King. Hearing the Hurt: Rhetoric, Aesthetics, & Politics of the New Negro Movement. 2012. (Albma Rhetoric Cult & Soc Crit Ser.). (ENG.). 253p. (C). 39.95 ***(978-0-8173-1766-9(X))*** Univ. of Alabama Pr.

Weinbaum, Alys Eve, ed. Next to the Color Line: Gender, Sexuality, & W. E. B. du Bois. 2007. (Critical American Studies). (Illus.). 416p. 75.00 *(978-0-8166-4722-4(4))*; per. 26.00 *(978-0-8166-4723-1(2))* Univ. of Minnesota Pr.

West, Cornel. Hope on a Tightrope: Words & Wisdom. 2011. (ENG.). 140p. 14.95 *(978-1-4019-3076-9(X))* Hay Hse., Inc.

—Keeping Faith: Philosophy & Race in America. 2008. (Routledge Classics Ser.). XVIII, 286p. 25.95 *(978-0-415-96481-4(4))* Routledge.

White, Ismail K. African-American Political Psychology: Identity, Opinion, & Action in the Post-Civil Rights Era. Philpot, Tasha S., ed. 2010. (ENG., Illus.). 264p. 89.00 *(978-0-230-62355-2(7))* Palgrave Macmillan.

Wilderson, Frank B., III. Incognegro: A Memoir of Exile & Apartheid. 2008. (ENG.). 500p. pap. 18.00 *(978-0-89608-783-5(2))* South End Pr.

Williams, Juan. Enough: The Phony Leaders, Dead-End Movements, & Culture of Failure That Are Undermining Black America — and What We Can Do about It. 2007. (ENG.). 256p. per. 13.95 *(978-0-307-33824-2(X)*, Three Rivers Pr.) Crown Publishing Group.

Williams, Yohuru & Lazerow, Jama, eds. Liberated Territory: Untold Local Perspectives on the Black Panther Party. 2009. (ENG.). 312p. 89.95 *(978-0-8223-4343-1(6))*; pap. 24.95 *(978-0-8223-4326-4(6))* Duke Univ. Pr.

Winfree, Guru Eric & Brown, Julius. The Black Paradox. 2007. 163p. pap. 19.99 *(978-0-615-16028-3(X))* Brown & Winfree.

Witt, Andrew. The Black Panthers in the Midwest: The Community Programs & Services of the Black Panther Party in Milwaukee, 1966-1977. 2007. (Studies in African American History & Culture). 152p. 126.00 *(978-0-415-98148-4(4))* Routledge.

Wolfe, Tom. Radical Chic & Mau-Mauing the Flak Catchers. 2009. (ENG.). 144p. pap. 15.00 *(978-0-312-42913-3(4))* Picador.

Wolfinger, James. Philadelphia Divided: Race & Politics in the City of Brotherly Love. (ENG., Illus.). 336p. 2011. pap. 24.95 *(978-0-8078-7190-4(7))* 2007. 55.95 *(978-0-8078-3149-6(2))* Univ. of North Carolina Pr.

Woods, Clyde. Development Arrested: From the Plantation Era to the Katrina Crisis in the Mississippi Delta. rev. ed. 2012. 352p. pap. 26.95 *(978-1-84467-561-6(0)*, New Left Bks.) Verso Bks. GBR. Dist: Norton, W. W. & Co., Inc.

Wright, Richard & Wright, Richard. Black Power: The Color Curtain - And White Man, Listen! 2008. (P. S. Ser.). (ENG., Illus.). 864p. pap. 18.95 *(978-0-06-144945-1(8)*, HarperPerennial) HarperCollins Pubs.

Young, Cynthia. Soul Power: Culture, Radicalism & the Making of a U. S. Third World Left. 2006. (ENG., Illus.). 328p. (C). 89.95 *(978-0-8223-3679-2(0))* Duke Univ. Pr.

AFRICAN AMERICANS—POLITICS AND SUFFRAGE

see African Americans—Politics and Government; African Americans—Suffrage

AFRICAN AMERICANS—PROFESSIONAL EDUCATION

Hunter, Janis A. Factors Influencing African-American Students Enrollment. 2008. 548p. pap. *(978-3-8364-8193-9(6))* VDM Verlag Dr. Mueller e.K.

Mays, James A. See One, Do One, T: To motivate youth, especially underserved black & Hispanic youth, to pursue the medical Profession. 2011. 636p. 34.99 ***(978-1-4628-9305-8(8))***; pap. 23.99 ***(978-1-4628-9306-5(6))*** Xlibris Corp.

AFRICAN AMERICANS—PSYCHOLOGY

Anderson, Elijah, ed. Against the Wall: Poor, Young, Black, & Male. 2009. (City in the Twenty-First Century Ser.). (Illus.). 320p. (C). pap. 26.50 *(978-0-8122-2017-9(X))* Univ. of Pennsylvania Pr.

Bailey, Eric J. Black America, Body Beautiful: How the African American Image Is Changing Fashion, Fitness, & Other Industries, 1 vol. 2008. 176p. 44.95 *(978-0-275-99595-9(X)*, C9595, Praeger Pubs.) Greenwood Publishing Group, Inc.

Beamon, Nika C. & DePaulo, Bella. I Didn't Work This Hard Just to Get Married: Successful Single Black Women Speak Out. 2009. (ENG.). 224p. pap. 14.95 *(978-1-55652-819-4(1)*, Hill, Lawrence Bks.) Chicago Review Pr., Inc.

Belgrave, Allison. African American Psychology from Africa. 2006. pap. 10.95 *(978-1-4288-1325-0(X))* Cram101 Inc.

Belgrave, Faye Z. & Allison, Kevin W. African American Psychology: From Africa to America. Belgrave, Faye Z. & Allison, Kevin W., eds. 2nd ed. 2009. 568p. (C). pap. 87.00 *(978-1-4129-5555-2(1)*, B65552P) SAGE Pubns., Inc.

Carroll, Grace. Died with a Bow. 2012. (Accessories Mystery Ser.). (ENG.). 288p. (gr. 12). mass mkt. 7.99 ***(978-0-425-25156-0(X)***, Berkley) Penguin Group (USA) Inc.

Cheek, Don. Assertive Black... Puzzled White: A Black Perspective on Assertive Behavior. 2010. (Illus.). 168p. pap. 14.95 *(978-1-4327-5574-4(9))* Outskirts Pr., Inc.

Cosby, Bill & Poussaint, Alvin F. Come on People: On the Path from Victims to Victors, 0 vols. 2009. 288p. pap. 14.99 *(978-1-59555-186-3(7))* Nelson, Thomas Inc.

Craig-Henderson, Kellina M. Black Women in Interracial Relationships: In Search of Love & Solace. 2010. (ENG., Illus.). 197p. 34.95 *(978-1-4128-1128-6(7))* Transaction Pubs.

Davison, James, Jr. & Davison, James. Sweet Release: The Last Step to Black Freedom. 2008. (ENG.). 255p. 26.98 *(978-1-59102-558-0(3))* Prometheus Bks., Pubs.

Dixon, Patricia. African American Relationships, Marriages, & Families. 2006. (ENG., Illus.). 304p. per. 51.95 *(978-0-415-95533-1(5))* Routledge.

Donaldson, Jam. Conversate Is Not a Word: Getting Away from Ghetto. 2010. (ENG., Illus.). 208p. pap. 14.95 *(978-1-55652-780-7(2)*, Hill, Lawrence Bks.) Chicago Review Pr., Inc.

Dybska, Aneta. Black Masculinities in American Social Science & Self-Narratives of the 1960s And 1970s. 2010. (American Studies & Media Ser.). 194p. 61.95 *(978-3-631-61330-6(X))* Lang, Peter GmbH, Europaischer Verlag der Wissenschaften DEU. Dist: Lang, Peter.

Ellis, Aimé J. If We Must Die: From Bigger Thomas to Biggie Smalls. 2014. (Illus.). 240p. pap. 24.95 *(978-0-8143-3413-3(X))* Wayne State Univ. Pr.

Ellis, Cyrus Marcellus & CARLSON, J. O. N., eds. Resiliency Achievement & Manhood. 2013. (Routledge Series on Counseling & Psychotherapy with Boys & Men Ser.). (ENG.). 224p. 90.00 *(978-0-415-88412-9(8))*; pap. 34.95 *(978-0-415-88413-6(6))* Routledge.

Ellis, William T. The Weak Link: How to Get Along with Negroes, a Layman's Approach to the Race Problem. Adams, Grace Ellis, ed. 2007. (Illus.). 116p. reprint ed. pap. 17.95 *(978-1-877807-18-3(4))* Grace Publishing Co.

Green, Tara T. A Fatherless Child: Autobiographical Perspectives of African American Men. 2009. (ENG.). 184p. (C). 34.95 *(978-0-8262-1821-6(0))* Univ. of Missouri Pr.

Griffin, Drs. James P. Jr. & Karen E. African American Manhood Development: Contemporary Life Lessons for Leaders — Student Guide. 2010. 96p. pap. 15.00 *(978-0-557-25503-0(1))* Lulu Enterprises Inc.

Harris-Lopez, Trudier. The Scary Mason-Dixon Line: African American Writers & the South. 2009. (Southern Literary Studies). 256p. 37.50 *(978-0-8071-3395-8(7))*; *(978-0-8018-3395-3(7))* Louisiana State Univ. Pr.

Harris, Whitney S. & Ferguson, Ronald T. What's up with the Brothers? Essays & Studies on African-American Masculinities. 2010. 172p. (YA). 45.00 *(978-1-931342-23-0(7))*; pap. 20.00 *(978-1-931342-22-3(9))* Men's Studies Pr.

Hunter, William. Dream Greatness Be Unstoppable: Live Your Dream & Leave a Legacy. 2008. (ENG.). 184p. per. 14.95 *(978-0-9792263-1-1(7))* William, Hunter.

Kaplan, Erin Aubry. Black Talk, Blue Thoughts, & Walking the Color Line: Dispatches from a Black Journalista. 2011. (Northeastern Library of Black Literature Ser.). 304p. pap. 19.95 *(978-1-55553-754-8(5)*, Northeastern University Pr.) Univ. Pr. of New England.

Kunjufu, Jawanza. State of Emergency. 2009. (ENG.). 200p. pap. 15.95 *(978-1-934155-09-7(8))* African American Images.

Lewis, Michele & Marshall, Isiah. LGBT Psychology: Research Perspectives & People of African Descent. 2011. (ENG., Illus.). xi, 20Cp. 129.00 ***(978-1-4614-0564-1(5)***, 1461405645) Springer.

Logan, Sadye M. L., ed. Mental Health Care in the African-American Community. 2007. (ENG., Illus.). 426p. 132.95 *(978-0-7890-2611-5(2))*; per. 82.95 *(978-0-7890-2612-5(0))* Routledge.

Lovejoy, Paul E., ed. Identity in the Shadow of Slavery. 2nd ed. 2009. (Harriet Tubman Ser. on the African Diaspora, the Ser.). (ENG., Illus.). 256p. pap. 32.95 *(978-0-8264-0396-4(4))* Continuum International Publishing Group, Ltd. GBR. Dist: National Bk. Network.

Mandy, Lionel. The I Am Model of Afrikan/African/Black Male Identity Development. 2009. 248p. pap. 14.49 *(978-1-4389-1429-9(6))* AuthorHouse.

McKenzie-Mavinga, Isha. Black Issues in the Therapeutic Process. 2009. (ENG., Illus.). 208p. pap. 39.00 *(978-0-230-57572-8(9))* Palgrave Macmillan.

McWhorter, John. Winning the Race: Beyond the Crisis in Black America. annot. ed. 2006. (ENG.). 448p. (gr. 8-18). per. 28.00 *(978-1-59240-270-0(4)*, Gotham) Penguin Group (USA) Inc.

Menchan, Angelia Vernon. Ramblings: A Booked Blog. 2009. 80p. pap. 7.95 *(978-0-9787835-6-3(5))* Menchan, acVernon.

Metzl, Jonathan. The Protest Psychosis: How Schizophrenia Became a Black Disease. 2011. (Illus.). 272p. pap. 22.00 *(978-0-8070-0127-1(9))* Beacon Pr.

Miller, Percy Master P. Guaranteed Success: When You Never Give Up. 2007. (ENG., Illus.). 300p. 16.95 *(978-1-60162-112-2(4))* Urban Bks.

Moore, Kevin. Did you Ever Wonder Why Black People Do the Things They Do? 2007. (ENG.). 112p. per. 9.95 *(978-1-59526-738-2(7)*, Llumina Pr.) Aeon Publishing Inc.

Moore, Natalie Y. & Hopkinson, Natalie. Deconstructing Tyrone: A New Look at Black Masculinity in the Hip-Hop Generation. 2006. (ENG.). 264p. per. 14.95 *(978-1-57344-257-2(7))* Cleis Pr.

Nobles, Wade W. Seeking the Sakhu: Foundational Writings for an African Psychology. 2006. (ENG., Illus.). 470p. per. 27.95 *(978-0-88378-276-7(6))* Third World Press.

Nunnally, Shayla. Trust in Black America: Race, Discrimination, & Politics. 2012. (ENG., Illus.). 296p. 75.00 ***(978-0-8147-5865-6(7))***; pap. 26.00 ***(978-0-8147-5866-3(5))*** New York Univ. Pr.

Nunnally, Shayla C. Trust in Black America: Race, Discrimination, & Politics. 2011. E-Book ***(978-0-8147-5931-8(9))***; E-Book ***(978-0-8147-5930-1(0))*** New York Univ. Pr.

Nyborg, Vanessa. Exploring Racism in the Lives of African American Boys. 2009. 68p. pap. *(978-3-639-13405-6(2))* VDM Verlag Dr. Mueller e.K.

Pillow, Gloria Thomas. Motherlove in Shades of Black: The Maternal Psyche in the Novels of African American Women. 2010. (ENG., Illus.). 199p. pap. 38.00 *(978-0-7864-3533-3(X))* McFarland & Co., Inc. Pubs.

Rich, John A. Wrong Place, Wrong Time: Trauma & Violence in the Lives of Young Black Men. (ENG.). 232p. 2011. pap. 20.00 ***(978-1-4214-0398-4(6))*** 2009. 30.00 *(978-0-8018-9363-6(1))* Johns Hopkins Univ. Pr.

Rollins, James. The Curse of Willie Lynch: How Social Engineering in the Year 1712 Continues to Affect African Americans Today. 2006. v, 100p. 28.00 *(978-1-4122-0214-5(0))*; 112p. per. 14.00 *(978-1-4251-0835-9(0))* Trafford Publishing.

The ScreamBed Chronicles: The last days of playas & other insecure Men. 2007. 186p. per. 19.95 *(978-0-615-17648-2(8))* KaChiza Bks.

See, Letha A. Lee, ed. Human Behavior in the Social Environment from an African-American Perspective. 2nd ed. 2007. (Illus.). 782p. 175.00 *(978-0-7890-2831-0(X))*; per. 49.95 *(978-0-7890-2832-7(8))* Routledge.

Sneed, Roger A. Representations of Homosexuality: Black Liberation Theology & Cultural Criticism. 2010. (Black Religion/Womanist Thought/Social Justice Ser.). (ENG.). 236p. 89.00 *(978-0-230-60824-5(8))* Palgrave Macmillan.

Taylor, Shawn. Big Black Penis: Misadventures in Race & Masculinity. 2008. (ENG.). 208p. pap. 14.95 *(978-1-55652-734-0(9)*, Hill, Lawrence Bks.) Chicago Review Pr., Inc.

Thompson, Lisa B. Beyond the Black Lady: Sexuality & the New African American Middle Class. 2009. (New Black Studies Ser.). (ENG.). 200p. 40.00 *(978-0-252-03426-8(0))* Univ. of Illinois Pr.

Tillotson, Michael. Invisible Jim Crow: Contemporary Ideological Threats to the Internal Security of African Americans. 2011. xxiv, 217p. *(978-1-59221-801-1(6))*; 245p. pap. *(978-1-59221-802-8(4))* Africa World Pr.

Toback, James. Jim: The Author's Self-Centered Memoir on the Great Jim Brown. 2009. (ENG.). 154p. pap. 25.00 *(978-0-9818056-3-4(9))* Rat Pr.

Touré. Who's Afraid of Post-Blackness? What It Means to Be Black Now. (ENG., Illus.). 272p. 2012. pap. 15.00 *(978-1-4391-7756-3(2))* 2011. 25.00 *(978-1-4391-7755-6(4))* Free Pr. (Free Pr.).

Tukufu, Darryl S. A Guide Toward the Successful Development of African-American Males: The Remix. 2nd ed. 2009. 91p. pap. 12.95 *(978-0-9662152-2-9(2))* Tukufu Group, The.

Tynes, Brendesha M., et al, eds. Handbook of African American Psychology. 2008. 584p. pap. 100.00 *(978-1-4129-5688-8(9)*, B56871P) SAGE Pubns., Inc.

Tynes, Brendesha M., et al. Handbook of African American Psychology. Tynes, Brendesha M. et al, eds. 2008. 584p. 150.00 *(978-1-4129-5687-1(0)*, B56871C) SAGE Pubns., Inc.

Watson, Peter. Psychology & Race. 2007. (ENG.). 491p. pap. 34.95 *(978-0-202-30929-3(0))* Aldine Transaction.

White, Ismail K. African-American Political Psychology: Identity, Opinion, & Action in the Post-Civil Rights Era. Philpot, Tasha S., ed. 2010. (ENG., Illus.). 264p. 89.00 *(978-0-230-62355-2(7))* Palgrave Macmillan.

White, Joseph L., et al. Psychology of Blacks. 4th ed. 2010. (ENG.). 256p. (C). pap. 74.40 *(978-0-13-182773-8(1*, Prentice Hall) Prentice Hall PTR.

Willis, Jay Thomas. Why Black Americans Behave as They Do: The Conditioning Process from Generation to Generation. 2006. 212p. pap. 13.95 *(978-0-7414-3682-5(5))* Infinity Publishing.

Willis Thomas, Hank, photos by. Pitch Blackness. 2008. (ENG., Illus.). 112p. 35.00 *(978-1-59711-072-3(8))* Aperture Foundation, Inc.

Winfrey, Aida McClellan. H. Y. P. E. Healing Young People Thru Empowerment. 2009. (ENG., Illus.). 200p. pap. 14.95 *(978-1-934155-20-2(9))* African American Images.

Wyatt, Randall C. & Seid, Erika L. Psychological Residuals of Slavery (Instructor's Version) 2007. 89.00 *(978-1-60124-051-4(1))* Psychotherapy.net.

AFRICAN AMERICANS—RACE IDENTITY

Abdur-Rahman, Aliyyah. Against the Closet: Black Political Longing & the Erotics of Race. 2012. (ENG.). 224p. pap. 23.95 ***(978-0-8223-5241-9(9))***; (Illus.). 84.95 ***(978-0-8223-5224-2(9))*** Duke Univ. Pr.

Adams, Ayin, intro. African Americans in Hawai'i: A Search for Identity. 2010. (ENG., Illus.). 225p. pap. 29.99 *(978-0-9841228-1-3(8))* Pacific Raven Pr.

Adeleke, Tunde. The Case Against Afrocentrism. 2009. (ENG.). 224p. 50.00 *(978-1-60473-293-1(8))* Univ. Pr. of Mississippi.

Alexander, Bryant Ke. Performing Black Masculinity: Race, Culture, & Queer Identity. 2006. (Crossroads in Qualitative Inquiry Ser.). (ENG., Illus.). 282p. 93.00 *(978-0-7591-0928-5(1))* AltaMira Pr.

Alexander, Bryant Keith. Performing Black Masculinity: Race, Culture, & Queer Identity. 2006. (Crossroads in Qualitative Inquiry Ser.). (ENG., Illus.). 282p. per. 34.95 *(978-0-7591-0929-2(X))* AltaMira Pr.

Alexander, Leslie M. African or American? Black Identity & Political Activism in New York City, 1784-1861. (ENG., Illus.). 288p. 2011. pap. 28.00 ***(978-0-252-07853-8(5))*** 2008. 47.00 *(978-0-252-03336-0(1))* Univ. of Illinois Pr.

Amenu-EL, Rommanie M. & Myrick-Bey, Elaine. The Negro, the Black, the Moor. 2008. (Illus.). x, 205p. *(978-0-615-17332-0(2))* Bereaved Parents Group.

Anderson, Kami. Black Away from Home. 2009. 200p. pap. *(978-3-639-09902-7(8))* VDM Verlag Dr. Mueller e.K.

Asante, M. K., Jr. It's Bigger Than Hip Hop: The Rise of the Post-Hip-Hop Generation. 2009. (ENG., Illus.). 304p. pap. 15.99 *(978-0-312-59302-5(3)*, St. Martin's Griffin) St. Martin's Pr.

Ashimolowo, Matthew. What Is Wrong with Being Black? Celebrating Our Heritage, Confronting Our Challenges. 2008. (Illus.). 348p. pap. 16.99 *(978-0-7684-2638-0(3))* Destiny Image Pubs.

Bailey, Julius. Race Patriotism: Protest & Print Culture in the A.M.E. Church. 2012. (ENG., Illus.). 192p. 47.00 ***(978-1-57233-845-6(8))*** Univ. of Tennessee Pr.

Bakari, Sadiki. Butt Naked Raw & Uncensored. 2007. 172p. pap. 18.96 *(978-0-615-15261-5(9))* Sadiki Bakari Publishing.

Banner-Haley, Charles Pete T. From du Bois to Obama: African American Intellectuals in the Public Forum. 2010. (ENG.). 176p. 24.95 *(978-0-8093-2979-3(4))* Southern Illinois Univ. Pr.

Batiste, Stephanie Leigh. Darkening Mirrors: Imperial Representation in Depression-Era African American Performance. 2012. (ENG., Illus.). 352p. 94.95 ***(978-0-8223-4898-6(5))***; pap. 25.95 ***(978-0-8223-4923-5(X))*** Duke Univ. Pr.

Boone, Sherle. Meanings Beneath the Skin: The Evolution of African-Americans. 2011. (ENG.). 424p. 80.00 ***(978-1-4422-1310-4(8))*** Rowman & Littlefield Publishers, Inc.

Boyd, Michelle R. Jim Crow Nostalgia: Reconstructing Race in Bronzeville. 2008. 208p. 57.00 *(978-0-8166-4677-7(5))*; pap. 18.95 *(978-0-8166-4678-4(3))* Univ. of Minnesota Pr.

Brady, Owen E. & Maus, Derek C., eds. Finding a Way Home: A Critical Assessment of Walter Mosley's Fiction. (ENG.). 224p. 2011. pap. 30.00 *(978-1-61703-065-9(1))* 2008. 65.00 *(978-1-60473-088-3(9))* Univ. Pr. of Mississippi.

Brown, Kimberly Nichele. Writing the Black Revolutionary Diva: Women's Subjectivity & the Decolonizing Text. 2010. (Blacks in the Diaspora Ser.). (ENG.). 294p. 70.00 *(978-0-253-35525-6(7)*, 0253355257); pap. 24.95 *(978-0-253-22246-6(X)*, 025322246X) Indiana Univ. Pr.

Brundage, W. Fitzhugh, ed. Beyond Blackface: African Americans & the Creation of American Popular Culture, 1890-1930. 2011. (ENG., Illus.). 400p. 65.00 *(978-0-8078-3462-6(9))*; pap. 27.50 *(978-0-8078-7184-3(2))* Univ. of North Carolina Pr.

Burrell, Tom. Brainwashed: Challenging the Myth of Black Inferiority. 2010. (ENG.). 320p. pap. 15.95 *(978-1-4019-2592-5(6))* Hay Hse., Inc.

Bynum, Cornelius L. A. Philip Randolph & the Struggle for Civil Rights. 2010. (ENG., Illus.). 272p. pap. 25.00 *(978-0-252-07764-7(4))* Univ. of Illinois Pr.

Campbell, Woody. Fade to Black: Thoughts on Black Americans. 2008. 96p. 19.95 *(978-0-9645493-9-5(5)*, Against the Wind Pr.) Bluebonnets, Boots & Bks. Pr.

Carmichael (Kwame Ture), Stokely. Stokely Speaks: From Black Power to Pan-Africanism. 2007. (ENG.). 256p. pap. 14.95 *(978-1-55652-649-7(0)*, Hill, Lawrence Bks.) Chicago Review Pr., Inc.

Carroll, Anne Elizabeth. Word, Image, & the New Negro: Representation & Identity in the Harlem Renaissance. 2007. (Blacks in the Diaspora Ser.). (ENG., Illus.). 294p. pap. 24.95 *(978-0-253-21919-0(1)*, 0253219191) Indiana Univ. Pr.

Caster, Peter. Prisons, Race, & Masculinity in Twentieth-Century U. S. Literature & Film. 2008. (Black Performance & Cultural Criticism Ser.). (ENG.). 296p. 69.95 *(978-0-8142-1073-4(2))*; cd-rom 14.95 *(978-0-8142-9150-4(3))* Ohio State Univ. Pr.

Cataliotti, Robert H. The Songs Became the Stories: The Music in African American Fiction, 1970-2005. (African American Literature & Culture: Expanding & Exploding the Boundaries Ser.). 280p. (C). pap. 32.95 *(978-0-8204-8850-9(X))* Lang, Peter Publishing, Inc.

Catanese, Brandi Wilkins. The Problem of the Color[blind]: Racial Transgression & the Politics of Black Performance. 2011. (Theater: Theory/Text/Performance Ser.). (ENG.). 244p. 75.00 *(978-0-472-07126-5(2))*; pap. 28.95 *(978-0-472-05126-7(1))* Univ. of Michigan Pr.

Clavin, Matthew J. Toussaint Louverture & the American Civil War: The Promise & Peril of a Second Haitian Revolution. 2011. (Illus.). 248p. (C). pap. 22.50 ***(978-0-8122-2184-8(2))*** Univ. of Pennsylvania Pr.

Colby, Tanner. Some of My Best Friends Are Black: The Strange Story of Integration in America. 2012. (ENG.). 320p. (gr. 12). 27.95 ***(978-0-670-02371-4(X)***, Viking Adult) Penguin Group (USA) Inc.

Conyers, James L. African American Consciousness: Past & Present. 2011. (ENG.). 190p. pap. 29.95 ***(978-1-4128-4307-2(3))*** Transaction Pubs.

Corbould, Clare. Becoming African Americans: Black Public Life in Harlem, 1919-1939. 2009. (Illus.). 304p. 42.00 *(978-0-674-03262-0(4))* Harvard Univ. Pr.

Cram101 Textbook Reviews & Cram101 Textbook Reviews. Outlines & Highlights for Identity Before Identity Politics by Linda Nicholson, Isbn: 9780521862134. 2011. 98p. pap. 27.95 ***(978-1-61461-176-9(9))*** Cram101 Inc.

Cram101 Textbook Reviews Staff. Outlines & Highlights for Black Sexual Politics: African Americans, Gender, & the New Racism by Patricia H Collins, ISBN. 2009. 90p. pap. 27.95 *(978-1-4288-9770-0(4))* Cram101 Inc.

Curtis, Susan. Colored Memories: A Biographer's Quest for the Elusive Lester A. Walton. 2008. (ENG., Illus.). 304p. (C). 39.95 *(978-0-8262-1786-8(9))* Univ. of Missouri Pr.

Davis, Thadious. Southscapes: Geographies of Race, Region, & Literature. 2011. (New Directions in Southern Studies). (ENG., Illus.). 416p. 39.95 *(978-0-8078-3521-0(8))* Univ. of North Carolina Pr.

Davison, James, Jr. & Davison, James. Sweet Release: The Last Step to Black Freedom. 2008. (ENG.). 255p. 26.98 *(978-1-59102-558-0(3))* Prometheus Bks., Pubs.

Dene, Debe. Now hair This! The Destruction of Black Hair. 2008. (Illus.). 141p. pap. 12.95 *(978-0-9801242-0-0(4))* Tell Pubns.

Denkler, Ann. Sustaining Identity, Recapturing Heritage: Exploring Issues of Public History, Tourism, & Race in a Southern Rural Town. 2007. (ENG., Illus.). 138p. 57.99 *(978-0-7391-1991-4(5))* Lexington Bks.

Denton, Robert. Studies of Identity in the 2008 Presidential Campaign. 2010. (Lexington Studies in Political Communication Ser.). (ENG.). 252p. 78.99 *(978-0-7391-4102-1(3))*; pap. 31.50 *(978-0-7391-4103-8(1))* Lexington Bks.

Dockett, Kymo. The Post Hip-Hop Generation: 20 Principles for A Successful Generation. 2009. 188p. pap. 12.50 *(978-1-59330-610-6(5))* Aventine Pr.

Donaldson, Jam. Conversate Is Not a Word: Getting Away from Ghetto. 2010. (ENG., Illus.). 208p. pap. 14.95 *(978-1-55652-780-7(2)*, Hill, Lawrence Bks.) Chicago Review Pr., Inc.

Douglas, Robert L. Resistance, Insurgence, & Identity: The Art of Mari Evans, Nelson Stevens, & the Black Arts Movement. 2008. 376p. pap. *(978-1-59221-565-2(3))* Africa World Pr.

Dowden, Priscilla A. Groping Toward Democracy: African American Social Welfare Reform in St. Louis, 1910-1949. 3rd ed. 2011. (ENG., Illus.). 320p. (C). 44.95 *(978-0-8262-1900-8(4))* Univ. of Missouri Pr.

Duganne, Erina. The Self in Black & White: Race & Subjectivity in Postwar American Photography. 2010. (Interfaces: Studies in Visual Culture Ser.). (ENG., Illus.). 248p. pap. 35.00 *(978-1-58465-802-3(9)*, Dartmouth College Press) Univ. Pr. of New England.

Dunning, Stefanie K. Queer in Black & White: Interraciality, Same Sex Desire, & Contemporary African American Culture. 2009. (ENG., Illus.). 152p. 49.95 *(978-0-253-35350-4(5)*, 0253353505); pap. 19.95 *(978-0-253-22109-4(9)*, 0253221099) Indiana Univ. Pr.

Eaton, Kalenda C. Womanism, Literature, & the Transformation of the Black Community, 1965-1980. 2007. (Studies in African American History & Culture Ser.). (ENG.). 122p. 125.00 *(978-0-415-96129-5(7)*, 0415961297) Routledge.

Eaton, Kalenda C. Womanism, Literature, & the Transformation of the Black Community, 1965ndash;1980. 2012. (Studies in African American History & Culture Ser.). (ENG.). 122p. pap. 42.95 ***(978-0-415-54080-3(1))*** Routledge.

Ellis, Catherine & Smith, Stephen Drury, eds. Say It Loud: Great Speeches on Civil Rights & African American Identity. 2010. (ENG.). 304p. 35.00 *(978-1-59558-113-6(8))* New Pr., The.

Ernest, John. A Nation Within a Nation: Organizing African-American Communities Before the Civil War. 2011. (ENG.). 232p. 35.00 *(978-1-56663-807-4(0))*; *(978-1-56663-917-0(4))* Dee, Ivan R. Pub.

Farris, Ron. Africans & African Americans Divided: The Male-Female African & African American Digital Divide. 2008. 228p. 34.95 *(978-1-4357-0009-3(0))* Lulu Enterprises Inc.

—Africans & African Americans Divided:the Male-Female African & African American Digital Divide. 2008. 228p. pap. 19.95 *(978-1-4357-0272-1(7))* Lulu Enterprises Inc.

Ferguson, Rebecca Hope. Rewriting Black Identities: Transition & Exchange in the Novels of Toni Morrison. 2007. (New Comparative Poetics Ser.: Vol. 8). 321p. pap. 34.95 *(978-90-5201-167-7(2))* Lang, Peter Publishing, Inc.

Fernandez, Paula B. Academic Orientations of African-American Adolescents. 2008. 120p. pap. *(978-3-639-08195-4(1))* VDM Verlag Dr. Mueller e.K.

Fisher, Maisha. Black Literate Lives: Historical & Contemporary Perspectives. 2008. (Critical Social Thought Ser.). (Illus.). XXII, 178p. pap. 39.95 *(978-0-415-95865-3(2))* Routledge.

Fleetwood, Nicole R. Troubling Vision: Performance, Visuality, & Blackness. 2011. (ENG., Illus.). 296p. 75.00 *(978-0-226-25302-2(3))*; pap. 25.00 *(978-0-226-25303-9(1))* Univ. of Chicago Pr.

Follett, Richard J., et al. Slavery's Ghost: The Problem of Freedom in the Age of Emancipation. 2011. (Marcus Cunliffe Lecture Ser.). (ENG., 128p. (C). (gr. 13-17). Illus.). 45.00 *(978-1-4214-0235-2(1))*; pap. 19.95 *(978-1-4214-0236-9(X))* Johns Hopkins Univ. Pr.

Foster, Frances Smith, et al, eds. Still Brave: The Evolution of Black Women's Studies. 2009. (ENG.). 400p. pap. 22.95 *(978-1-55861-611-0(X))* Feminist Pr. at The City Univ. of New York.

Frazier, John W., et al, eds. The African Diaspora in the United State & Canada at the Dawn of the 21st Century. 2010. (Global Academic Publishing Ser.). (Illus.). 383p. pap. 49.00 *(978-1-4384-3684-5(X)*, Suny Pr.) State Univ. of New York Pr.

—The African Diaspora in the United States & Canada at the Dawn of the 21st Century. 2009. pap. *(978-1-58684-271-0(4))* Global Academic Publishing.

Galvin, Michael. Skyline Tower, 'Ghetto in the Sky' 2009. 88p. pap. *(978-3-639-16358-2(3))* VDM Verlag Dr. Mueller e.K.

Garvey, Marcus. The Marcus Garvey & Universal Negro Improvement Association Papers: Africa for the Africans, 1923-1945. Hill, Robert A. et al, eds. 2006. (Marcus Garvey & Universal Negro Improvement Association Papers). (Illus.). 805p. 95.00 *(978-0-520-24732-1(9))* Univ. of California Pr.

Gause, C. P. Integration Matters: Navigating Identity, Culture, & Resistance. 2008. (Counterpoints: Studies in the Postmodern Theory of Education Ser.). 232p. (C). 32.95 *(978-1-4331-0202-8(1))* Lang, Peter Publishing, Inc.

Gillespie, Andra. Whose Black Politics? Cases in Post-Racial Black Leadership. 2009. (ENG., Illus.). 338p. 138.00 *(978-0-415-99215-2(X))* Routledge.

Gracia, Jorge J. E., ed. Race or Ethnicity? On Black & Latino Identity. 2007. 288p. per. 24.95 *(978-0-8014-7359-3(4))* Cornell Univ. Pr.

Greene. Stirring Up the African American Spirit. 136p. pap. 14.95 *(978-1-881165-19-4(1))* People Skills International.

Grove, Jeffrey. After 1968: Contemporary Artists & the Civil Rights Legacy. 2008. pap. 25.00 *(978-1-932543-22-3(8))* High Museum of Art.

Guran, Letitia. Reconsidering Contemporary African-American Identity. 2010. 60p. pap. *(978-3-639-23690-3(4))* VDM Verlag Dr. Mueller e.K.

Guridy, Frank Andre. Forging Diaspora: Afro-Cubans & African Americans in a World of Empire & Jim Crow. 2010. (Envisioning Cuba Ser.). (ENG., Illus.). 288p. 59.95 *(978-0-8078-3361-2(4))*; pap. 22.95 *(978-0-8078-7103-4(6))* Univ. of North Carolina Pr.

Hall, Stephen G. A Faithful Account of the Race: African American Historical Writing in Nineteenth-Century America. 2009. (John Hope Franklin Series in African American History & Culture Ser.). (ENG.). 352p. 69.95 *(978-0-8078-3305-6(3))*; pap. 23.95 *(978-0-8078-5967-4(2))* Univ. of North Carolina Pr.

Harold, Claudrena N. The Rise & Fall of the Garvey Movement in the Urban South, 1918-1942. 2007. (Studies in African American History & Culture). (Illus.). 171p. 120.00 *(978-0-415-95619-2(6))* Routledge.

Harrell, Willie J. Origins of the African American Jeremiad: The Rhetorical Strategies of Social Protest & Activism, 1760-1861. 2011. (ENG.). 239p. pap. 55.00 ***(978-0-7864-6689-4(8))*** McFarland & Co., Inc. Pubs.

Harris-Lopez, Trudier. The Scary Mason-Dixon Line: African American Writers & the South. 2009. (Southern Literary Studies). 256p. 37.50 *(978-0-8071-3395-8(7))*; *(978-0-8018-3395-3(7))* Louisiana State Univ. Pr.

Haynes, Rosetta R. Radical Spiritual Motherhood: Autobiography & Empowerment in Nineteenth-Century African American Women. 2011. 264p. 39.95 *(978-0-8071-3694-2(8))* Louisiana State Univ. Pr.

Hill, Johnny Bernard. The First Black President: Barack Obama, Race, Politics, & the American Dream. 2009. (ENG.). 208p. 100.00 *(978-0-230-61861-9(8))*; pap. 30.00 *(978-0-230-62114-5(7))* Palgrave Macmillan.

Hobbs, Antony O. Food for the Power of Thinking, Book II: The Roots of the Races. 2007. 58p. pap. 9.00 *(978-0-8059-7503-1(9))* Dorrance Publishing Co., Inc.

Hodge, Michael. Voices from Beneath the Veil: Analysis of the Trials, Tribulations, & Triumphs of Middle Class African Americans. 2009. (ENG.). 100p. pap. 20.99 *(978-0-7618-4525-6(9))* Univ. Pr. of America, Inc.

Holcomb, Gary Edward. Claude Mckay, Code Name Sasha: Queer Black Marxism & the Harlem Renaissance. 2009. (ENG., Illus.). 288p. pap. 29.95 *(978-0-8130-3450-8(7))* Univ. Pr. of Florida.

Hopson, Mark C. Notes from the Talking Drum: Exploring Black Communication & Critical Memory in Intercultural Communication Contexts. 2011. 128p. *(978-1-61289-005-0(9))*; *(978-1-61289-004-3(0))* Hampton Pr., Inc.

Hornsby-Gutting, Angela. Black Manhood & Community Building in North Carolina, 1900-1930. 2011. (New Perspectives on the History of the South Ser.). (ENG., Illus.). 264p. pap. 27.95 *(978-0-8130-3679-3(8))* Univ. Pr. of Florida.

Hudson, James. The Rising of Black America with the Assistance of White Americ. 2009. 284p. 27.50 *(978-1-60860-142-4(0)*, Eloquent Bks.) AEG Literary Publishing Services, Inc.

Ikard, David. Breaking the Silence: Toward a Black Male Feminist Criticism. 2007. 191p. 35.00 *(978-0-8071-3213-5(6))* Louisiana State Univ. Pr.

Iton, Richard. In Search of the Black Fantastic: Politics & Popular Culture in the Post-Civil Rights Era. 2010. (ENG.). 432p. pap. 21.95 *(978-0-19-973360-6(0))* Oxford Univ. Pr., Inc.

Jackson, Lawrence Patrick. The Indignant Generation: A Narrative History of African American Writers & Critics, 1934-1960. 2010. (ENG., Illus.). 608p. (C). 35.00 *(978-0-691-14135-0(5))* Princeton Univ. Pr.

Jackson, Maurice & Bacon, Jacqueline, eds. African Americans & the Haitian Revolution. 2009. (ENG., Illus.). 272p. (C). 150.00 *(978-0-415-80375-5(6))*; pap. 39.95 *(978-0-415-80376-2(4))* Routledge.

Jackson, Ronald L. Masculinity in the Black Imagination: Politics of communicating race & Manhood. 2011. (C). pap. 34.95 ***(978-1-4331-1247-8(7))*** Lang, Peter Publishing, Inc.

—Masculinity in the Black Imagination: Politics of Communicating Race & Manhood. 2011. (C). 139.95 ***(978-1-4331-1248-5(5))*** Lang, Peter Publishing, Inc.

Jackson, Sherman A. Islam & the Blackamerican: Looking Toward the Third Resurrection, 1 vol. 2011. (ENG.). 246p. pap. 24.95 *(978-0-19-978238-3(5))* Oxford Univ. Pr., Inc.

James, Jennifer C. A Freedom Bought with Blood: African American War Literature from the Civil War to World War II. 2007. (ENG., Illus.). 384p. 73.95 *(978-0-8078-3116-8(6))*; per. 27.95 *(978-0-8078-5807-3(2))* Univ. of North Carolina Pr.

Jenkins, H.L. If You Can't Make It on Mark Avenue. 2008. 72p. pap. 10.00 *(978-1-4257-4676-6(4))* Xlibris Corp.

Jennison, Watson W. Cultivating Race: The Expansion of Slavery in Georgia, 1750-1860. 2012. (New Directions in Southern History Ser.). (ENG., Illus.). 440p. 50.00 *(978-0-8131-3426-0(9))* Univ. Pr. of Kentucky.

Jones, Stephanie. The State of Black America 2009: Message to the President. 2009. (ENG.). 290p. pap. 19.95 *(978-0-914758-02-0(0))* National Urban League, National Headquarters.

Kaplan, Erin Aubry. Black Talk, Blue Thoughts, & Walking the Color Line: Dispatches from a Black Journalista. 2011. (Northeastern Library of Black Literature Ser.). 304p. pap. 19.95 *(978-1-55553-754-8(5)*, Northeastern University Pr.) Univ. Pr. of New England.

King, Debra Walker. African Americans & the Culture of Pain. 2008. (Cultural Frames, Framing Culture Ser.). (ENG., Illus.). 224p. (C). (gr. 13-17). per. 20.00 *(978-0-8139-2681-0(5))*; (gr. 17). 55.00 *(978-0-8139-2680-3(7))* Univ. Pr. of Virginia.

Kinloch, Valerie. Harlem on Our Minds: Place, Race, & the Literacies of Urban Youth. 2010. (Language & Literacy Ser.). (ENG.). 224p. 64.00 *(978-0-8077-5024-7(7))*; pap. 25.95 *(978-0-8077-5023-0(9))* Teachers College Pr., Teachers College, Columbia Univ.

Knadler, Stephen & Knadler, Stephen P. Remapping Citizenship & the Nation in African-American Literature. 2009. (Routledge Transnational Perspectives on American Literature Ser.). (ENG.). 248p. (C). 125.00 *(978-0-415-99631-0(7))* Routledge.

Konadu, Kwasi B. A View from the East: Black Cultural Nationalism & Education in New York City. 2nd ed. 2009. (Illus.). 232p. 29.95 *(978-0-8156-3206-1(1))* Syracuse Univ. Pr.

Lacy, Karyn R. Blue-Chip Black: Race, Class, & Status in the New Black Middle Class. 2007. (Illus.). 281p. 60.00 *(978-0-520-25115-1(6))* Univ. of California Pr.

Lawrence, Novotny. Blaxploitation Films of The 1970's: Blackness & Genre. 2007. (Studies in African American History & Culture Ser.). (ENG.). 146p. 125.00 *(978-0-415-96097-7(5))* Routledge.

Lindquist, Malinda Alaine. Black Social Science & the Crisis of Manhood, 1890-1970. 2012. (Routledge Studies in African American History & Culture Ser.). (ENG.). 254p. (C). 125.00 ***(978-0-415-51743-0(5))*** Routledge.

Lloyd, David. The Black & Green Atlantic: Cross-Currents of the African & Irish Diasporas. O'Neill, Peter, ed. 2009. (ENG., Illus.). 296p. 100.00 *(978-0-230-22818-4(6))* Palgrave Macmillan.

Locke, Alain LeRoy. The Works of Alain Locke, 1 vol. Molesworth, Charles, ed. 2012. (Collected Black Writings). 624p. 45.00 ***(978-0-19-979504-8(5))*** Oxford Univ. Pr., Inc.

Lovejoy, Paul E., ed. Identity in the Shadow of Slavery. 2nd ed. 2009. (Harriet Tubman Ser. on the African Diaspora, the Ser.). (ENG., Illus.). 256p. pap. 32.95 *(978-0-8264-0396-4(4))* Continuum International Publishing Group, Ltd. GBR. Dist: National Bk. Network.

Lowe, James H. The Forces Working Against a Sitting President. 2011. 118p. 29.99 ***(978-1-4568-5021-0(0))***; pap. 19.99 ***(978-1-4568-5020-3(2))*** Xlibris Corp.

Maffly-Kipp, Laurie F. Setting down the Sacred Past: African-American Race Histories. 2010. 352p. 29.95 *(978-0-674-05079-2(7)*, Belknap Pr.) Harvard Univ. Pr.

Malcolm X. End of White World Supremacy: Four Speeches. 2011. (ENG.). 160p. pap. 12.95 *(978-1-61145-016-3(0)*, 611016, Arcade Publishing) Skyhorse Publishing Co., Inc.

Marable, Manning & Agard-Jones, Vanessa, eds. Transnational Blackness: Navigating the Global Color Line. 2008. (Critical Black Studies). (ENG.). 384p. 100.00 *(978-0-230-60267-0(3))*; pap. 31.00 *(978-0-230-60268-7(1))* Palgrave Macmillan.

Miller, Monica L. Slaves to Fashion: Black Dandyism & the Styling of Black Diasporic Identity. 2009. (ENG., Illus.). 408p. 94.95 *(978-0-8223-4585-5(4))*; pap. 26.95 *(978-0-8223-4603-6(6))* Duke Univ. Pr.

Millner, Caille. The Golden Road: Notes on My Gentrification. 2008. (ENG.). 256p. (gr. 12-18). 14.00 *(978-0-14-311297-6(X)*, Penguin (Non-Classics)) Penguin Group (USA) Inc.

Mocombe, Paul. The Liberal Black Protestant Heterosexual Bourgeois Male: From W.E.B. du Bois to Barack Obama. 2010. (Illus.). v, 130p. E-Book ***(978-0-7618-4803-5(7))*** Univ. Pr. of America, Inc.

Mocombe, Paul C. & Mocombe, Paul. The Soul-Less Souls of Black Folk: A Sociological Reconsideration of Black Consciousness as du Boisian Double Consciousness. 2008. (ENG.). 96p. pap. 26.50 *(978-0-7618-4295-8(0))* Univ. Pr. of America, Inc.

Mooney, Carla. The Black Press. 2010. (Lucent Library of Black History Ser.). (Illus.). 128p. 32.45 *(978-1-4205-0230-5(1)*, Lucent Bks.) Cengage Gale.

Mullen, Patrick B. The Man Who Adores the Negro: Race & American Folklore. 2008. 224p. pap. 21.00 *(978-0-252-07486-8(6))* Univ. of Illinois Pr.

Nasir, Na'ilah Suad. Racialized Identities: Race & Achievement among African American Youth. 2011. (ENG.). 216p. 70.00 *(978-0-8047-6018-8(7))*; pap. 22.95 *(978-0-8047-6019-5(5))* Stanford Univ. Pr.

Nelson, Charles A. Back to Africa? 2009. 168p. 29.99 *(978-1-4415-1210-9(1))*; pap. 19.99 *(978-1-4415-1209-3(8))* Xlibris Corp.

Newkirk, Pamela, ed. Letters from Black America: Intimate Portraits of the African American Experience. 2011. (ENG.). 400p. pap. 18.00 *(978-0-8070-0115-8(5))* Beacon Pr.

Ngwenya, Thinkwell. The African American Dilemm. 2011. 96p. pap. ***(978-3-8443-8243-3(7))*** Lambert Academic Publishing.

Nicholson, Linda. Identity Before Identity Politics. 2008. (Cambridge Cultural Social Studies). (ENG.). 202p. 81.00 *(978-0-521-86213-4(2))*; pap. 34.00 *(978-0-521-68048-6(4))* Cambridge Univ. Pr.

Nobles, Wade W. Seeking the Sakhu: Foundational Writings for an African Psychology. 2006. (ENG., Illus.). 470p. per. 27.95 *(978-0-88378-276-7(6))* Third World Press.

Nwachuku, Levi, ed. Exlporing the African-American Experience, Fourth Edition. 2008. (C). pap. *(978-0-9798711-0-8(7))* Lincoln Univ. Pr.

Orelus, Pierre W. The Agony of Masculinity: Race, Gender, & Education in the Age of New Racism & Patriarchy. 2009. (Counterpoints: Studies in the Postmodern Theory of Education Ser.). 240p. (C). 32.95 *(978-1-4331-0417-6(2))* Lang, Peter Publishing, Inc.

Owens, Michael Eric. A New Philosophy of Black Identity: Yes I Am Who I Am. 2009. 183p. pap. 16.99 *(978-0-88144-323-3(9))* Yorkshire Publishing Group.

Pinkett, Randal, et al. Black Faces in White Places: 10 Game-Changing Strategies to Achieve Success & Find Greatness, 1 vol. 2010. (ENG., Illus.). 288p. 24.95 *(978-0-8144-1680-8(2))* Amacom.

Porter, Al. More Like Barack, Less Like Tupac: Countering Three Decades of the Hip Hop Hoax & Reclaiming the Image of African American Men. 2009. pap. 24.95 *(978-1-61623-791-2(0))* Independent Pub.

Powell, Richard J. Cutting a Figure: Fashioning Black Portraiture. 2009. (ENG., Illus.). 296p. 55.00 *(978-0-226-67727-9(3))* Univ. of Chicago Pr.

Price, Melanye. Dreaming Blackness: Black Nationalism & African American Public Opinion. 2009. (ENG.). 240p. pap. 22.00 *(978-0-8147-6745-0(1))* New York Univ. Pr.

Quashie, Kevin Everod. The Sovereignty of Quiet: Beyond Resistance in Black Culture. 2012. (ENG.). 200p. (C). pap. 24.95 ***(978-0-8135-5310-8(5))***; E-Book ***(978-0-8135-5311-5(3))***; (ENG.). 200p. (C). 72.00 ***(978-0-8135-5309-2(1))*** Rutgers Univ. Pr.

Reddick, Albert R. Becoming One: The USA & Diversity, 1 vol. 2009. 158p. pap. 24.95 *(978-1-60563-795-2(5))* PublishAmerica, Inc.

Reid-Pharr, Robert. Once You Go Black: Choice, Desire, & the Black American Intellectual. 2007. (ENG., Illus.). 208p. 75.00 *(978-0-8147-7583-7(7))*; pap. 23.00 *(978-0-8147-7584-4(5))* New York Univ. Pr.

Reiter, Bernd & Eison Simmons, Kimberly, eds. Afro-Descendants, Identity, & the Struggle for Development in the Americas. 2012. (African Diaspora Research Project Ser.). (ENG.). 344p. pap. 34.95 ***(978-1-61186-040-5(7))*** Michigan State Univ. Pr.

Rice, David Wall. Balance: Advancing Identity Theory by Engaging the Black Male Adolescent. 2008. (ENG.). 148p. pap. 29.50 *(978-0-7391-1889-4(7))*; (Illus.). 57.99 *(978-0-7391-1888-7(9))* Lexington Bks.

Roberts, Rita. Evangelicalism & the Politics of Reform in Northern Black Thought, 1776-1863. 2011. (Antislavery, Abolition, & the Atlantic World Ser.). 272p. 39.95 *(978-0-8071-3708-6(1))* Louisiana State Univ. Pr.

Roberts, Terrence J. Simple Not Easy: Reflections on Community Social Responsibility & Tolerance. 2010. (ENG.). 192p. 24.95 *(978-1-935166-16-0(6))* Parkhurst Brothers, Inc., Pubs.

Robinson, Eugene. Disintegration: The Splintering of Black America. (ENG.). 272p. 2011. pap. 15.95 *(978-0-7679-2996-7(9)*, Anchor) 2010. 24.95 *(978-0-385-52654-8(7)*, Doubleday) Knopf Doubleday Publishing Group.

Rolling, James H. Cinderella Story: A Scholarly Sketchbook about Race, Identity, Barack Obama, the Human Spirit, & Other Stuff That Matters. 2010. (Crossroads in Qualitative Inquiry Ser.). (ENG., Illus.). 228p. 75.00 *(978-0-7591-1176-9(6))* AltaMira Pr.

Ross, Paula T. Finding Common Ground. 2008. 108p. pap. *(978-3-8364-9464-9(7))* VDM Verlag Dr. Mueller e.K.

Russell, Kathy, et al. The Color Complex (Revised) The Politics of Skin Color among African Americans. 2012. (ENG.). 256p. pap. 15.95 ***(978-0-307-74423-4(X)***, Anchor) Knopf Doubleday Publishing Group.

Sandweiss, Martha A. Passing Strange: A Gilded Age Tale of Love & Deception Across the Color Line. 2010. (ENG.). 384p. (gr. 12-18). 17.00 *(978-0-14-311686-8(X)*, Penguin (Non-Classics)) Penguin Group (USA) Inc.

Scholder, Amy, ed. Dr. Rice in the House. 2007. (ENG., Illus.). 128p. per. 13.95 *(978-1-58322-761-9(X))* Seven Stories Pr.

Shelton, Norris. American Slaves, Inc. Renaissance PLan: The Next Step Forward. 2009. 105p. 11.95 *(978-0-9765417-6-9(9))* American Slaves, Inc.

Sherrard-Johnson, Cherene. Portraits of the New Negro Woman: Visual & Literary Culture in the Harlem Renaissance. 2007. (ENG., Illus.). 236p. per. 25.95 *(978-0-8135-3977-5(3))* Rutgers Univ. Pr.

Sidbury, James. Becoming African in America: Race & Nation in the Early Black Atlantic. (ENG., Illus.). 2009. 304p. pap. 19.95 ***(978-0-19-538294-5(3))*** 2007. 320p. 99.00 *(978-0-19-532010-7(7))* Oxford Univ. Pr., Inc.

Simpson, Ritashona. Black Looks & Black Acts: The Language of Toni Morrison in the Bluest Eye & Beloved. 2007. (Illus.). 122p. (C). 55.95 *(978-0-8204-9530-9(1))* Lang, Peter Publishing, Inc.

Singley, Bernestine, ed. When Race Becomes Real: Black & White Writers Confront Their Personal Histories. 2008. (ENG., Illus.). 352p. pap. 19.95 *(978-0-8093-2885-7(2))* Southern Illinois Univ. Pr.

Sklaroff, Lauren Rebecca. Black Culture & the New Deal: The Quest for Civil Rights in the Roosevelt Era. 2009. (ENG., Illus.). 328p. 36.95 *(978-0-8078-3312-4(6))* Univ. of North Carolina Pr.

Smith, Darron T., et al. White Parents, Black Children: Experiencing Transracial Adoption. 2011. (ENG., Illus.). 176p. 39.95 ***(978-1-4422-0762-2(0))*** Rowman & Littlefield Publishers, Inc.

Smith, Jessie Carney, ed. Encyclopedia of African American Popular Culture, 4 vols. 2010. (Illus.). 1733p. 380.00 *(978-0-313-35796-1(X)*, GR5796) Greenwood Publishing Group, Inc.

Soto, Isabel & Showers Johnson, Violet, eds. Western Fictions, Black Realities: Meanings of Blackness & Modernities. 2012. (ENG.). 336p. pap. 39.95 ***(978-1-61186-044-3(X))*** Michigan State Univ. Pr.

Stephens, Angela Sims. My Black History, My Character & Me. 2011. (Illus.). 32p. pap. 14.00 ***(978-1-4634-1754-3(3))*** AuthorHouse.

Stokes, Julie. The Psychology of African American Race Socialization. 2nd rev. ed. 2007. (ENG.). 90p. pap. 38.11 *(978-0-7575-4257-2(3))* Kendall Hunt Publishing Co.

Sugrue, Thomas J. Not Even Past: Barack Obama & the Burden of Race. 2010. (Lawrence Stone Lectures). (ENG.). 178p. 24.95 *(978-0-691-13730-8(7))* Princeton Univ. Pr.

Sullivan, Jas M. & Esmail, Ashraf, eds. African American Identity: Racial & Cultural Dimensions of the Black Experience. 2012. (ENG.). 450p. (gr. 17). 90.00 ***(978-0-7391-7174-5(7))*** Lexington Bks.

Tatum, Alfred W. Reading for Their Life: (Re)building the Textual Lineages of African American Adolescent Males. 2009. 192p. pap. 26.25 *(978-0-325-02679-4(3)*, E02679) Heinemann.

Tatum, Beverly Daniel. Can We Talk about Race? And Other Conversations in an Era of School Resegregation. 2007. (Black Studies Ser.). (ENG.). 147p. *(978-0-8070-3284-8(0))* Beacon Pr.

Taylor, Gary. Time, Space, Race: Geography & History of Atlantic Racism. 2013. (Signs of Race Ser.). (ENG., Illus.). 256p. 85.00 *(978-1-4039-7996-4(0))* Palgrave Macmillan.

Taylor, Shawn. Big Black Penis: Misadventures in Race & Masculinity. 2008. (ENG.). 208p. pap. 14.95 *(978-1-55652-734-0(9)*, Hill, Lawrence Bks.) Chicago Review Pr., Inc.

The InFamous Solutionary White Shoes. My Philosophy on Black. 2006. 153p. pap. 11.95 *(978-0-7414-3338-1(9))* Infinity Publishing.

Thomas, Ebony Elizabeth & Brooks-Tatum, Shanesha R. F. Reading African American Experiences in the Obama ERA: Theory, Advocacy, Activism. 2012. xv, 276p. E-Book ***(978-1-4539-0210-3(4))***; 296p. (C). pap. 149.95 ***(978-1-4331-1128-0(4))***; 296p. (C). pap. 36.95 ***(978-1-4331-1125-9(X))*** Lang, Peter Publishing, Inc.

Thompson, Gail. A Brighter Day: How Parents Can Help African American Youth. 2010. (ENG.). 225p. pap. 15.95 *(978-1-935521-74-7(8))* African American Images.

Tillotson, Michael. Invisible Jim Crow: Contemporary Ideological Threats to the Internal Security of African Americans. 2011. xxiv, 217p. *(978-1-59221-801-1(6))*; 245p. pap. *(978-1-59221-802-8(4))* Africa World Pr.

Tolson, Nancy. Black Children's Literature Got de Blues: The Creativity of Black Writers & Illustrators. 2008. (Illus.). xi, 116p. pap. 24.95 *(978-0-8204-6332-2(9))* Lang, Peter Publishing, Inc.

Touré. Who's Afraid of Post-Blackness? What It Means to Be Black Now. (ENG., Illus.). 272p. 2012. pap. 15.00 *(978-1-4391-7756-3(2))* 2011. 25.00 *(978-1-4391-7755-6(4))* Free Pr. (Free Pr.).

Tucker, Linda G. Lockstep & Dance: Images of Black Men in Popular Culture. (ENG.). 2010. 204p. pap. 25.00 *(978-1-60473-859-9(6))* 2007. 191p. 50.00 *(978-1-57806-906-4(8))* Univ. Pr. of Mississippi.

Vinson, Robert Trent. The Americans Are Coming! Dreams of African American Liberation in Segregationist South Africa. 2012. (New African Histories Ser.). (ENG., Illus.). 236p. pap. 32.95 ***(978-0-8214-1986-1(2))*** Ohio Univ. Pr.

Walker, Clarence E. Mongrel Nation: The America Begotten by Thomas Jefferson & Sally Hemings. 2010. (Jeffersonian America Ser.). (ENG.). 144p. pap. 13.95 *(978-0-8139-2778-7(1))* Univ. Pr. of Virginia.

Walker, Clarence Earl. Mongrel Nation: The America Begotten by Thomas Jefferson & Sally Hemings. 2008. (Jeffersonian America Ser.). (ENG.). 144p. 22.95 *(978-0-8139-2777-0(3))* Univ. Pr. of Virginia.

Wallace, Maurice O. & Smith, Shawn Michelle, eds. Pictures & Progress: Early Photography & the Making of African American Identity. 2012. (ENG., Illus.). 408p. 99.95 ***(978-0-8223-5067-5(X))***; pap. 27.95 ***(978-0-8223-5085-9(8))*** Duke Univ. Pr.

Washington Post Staff, et al. Being a Black Man: At the Corner of Progress & Peril. 2007. (ENG., Illus.). 384p. per. 13.95 *(978-1-58648-522-1(9))* PublicAffairs.

Watts, Eric King. Hearing the Hurt: Rhetoric, Aesthetics, & Politics of the New Negro Movement. 2012. (Albma Rhetoric Cult & Soc Crit Ser.). (ENG.). 253p. (C). 39.95 ***(978-0-8173-1766-9(X))*** Univ. of Alabama Pr.

West, Lawrence. The PHALLIC FACTOR: Are all men created Equal? 2007. (ENG.). 165p. per. 19.99 *(978-0-9785916-7-0(4))* BGNBT PUBLISHING.

Wilkins, Carolyn Marie. Damn near White: An African American Family's Rise from Slavery to Bittersweet Success. 3rd ed. 2010. (ENG., Illus.). 192p. 24.95 *(978-0-8262-1899-5(7))* Univ. of Missouri Pr.

Williams, Drew. Center Mass: The Power of One. 2007. per. 10.95 *(978-0-939479-26-9(5)*, Backintyme) Boxes & Arrows, Inc.

Williams, Thomas Chatterton. Losing My Cool: Love, Literature, & a Black Man's Escape from the Crowd. 2011. (ENG.). 240p. (gr. 12). 15.00 *(978-0-14-311962-3(1)*, Penguin (Non-Classics)) Penguin Group (USA) Inc.

Williams, Zachery. Africana Cultures & Policy Studies: Scholarship & the Transformation of Public Policy. Williams, Zachery, ed. 2009. (Contemporary Black History Ser.). (ENG.). 296p. 100.00 *(978-0-230-60280-9(0))* Palgrave Macmillan.

Wilmore, Larry. I'd Rather We Got Casinos: And Other Black Thoughts. 2009. (ENG.). 288p. 23.99 *(978-1-4013-0955-8(0))* Hyperion Pr.

Womack, Ytasha L. Post Black: How a New Generation Is Redefining African American Identity. 2010. (ENG., Illus.). 224p. pap. 16.95 *(978-1-55652-805-7(1)*, Hill, Lawrence Bks.) Chicago Review Pr., Inc.

Young, Harvey. Embodying Black Experience: Stillness Critical Memory, & the Black Body. 2010. (Theater: Theory/Text/Performance Ser.). (ENG., Illus.). 272p. 80.00 *(978-0-472-07111-1(4))*; pap. 32.50 *(978-0-472-05111-3(3))* Univ. of Michigan Pr.

Young, Vershawn Ashanti. Your Average Nigga: Performing Race, Literacy, & Masculinity. 2007. pap. 19.95 *(978-0-8143-3248-1(X))* Wayne State Univ. Pr.

Young, Vershawn Ashanti & Tsemo, Bridget Harris, eds. From Bourgeois to Boojie: Black Middle-Class Performances. 2015. (Illus.). 416p. pap. 24.95 *(978-0-8143-3468-3(7))* Wayne State Univ. Pr.

AFRICAN AMERICANS—RELATIONS WITH JEWS

Alpert, Rebecca T. Out of Left Field: Jews & Black Baseball. 2011. (ENG., Illus.). 256p. 27.95 *(978-0-19-539900-4(5))* Oxford Univ. Pr., Inc.

Barnstone, Willis. We Jews & Blacks: Memoir with Poems. annot. ed. 2007. (ENG., Illus.). 256p. pap. 19.95 *(978-0-253-21921-3(3)*, 0253219213) Indiana Univ. Pr.

Friedman, Murray. What Went Wrong? The Creation & Collapse of the Black-Jewish Alliance. 2007. (ENG.). 424p. pap. 28.95 *(978-1-4165-7668-6(1)*, Free Pr.) Free Pr.

Greenberg, Cheryl Lynn. Troubling the Waters: Black-Jewish Relations in the American Century. 2010. (Politics & Society in Twentieth Century America Ser.). (ENG., Illus.). 368p. (C). pap. 30.95 *(978-0-691-14616-4(0))* Princeton Univ. Pr.

Harris, Glen Anthony. The Ocean Hill-Brownsville Conflict: Intellectual Struggles Between Blacks & Jews at Midcentury. 2012. (ENG.). 204p. (gr. 17). 65.00 ***(978-0-7391-6683-3(2))*** Lexington Bks.

Heinze, Andrew R. "Is It 'Cos I's Black" Jews & the Whiteness Problem. 2007. (David W. Belin Lecture in American Jewish Affairs Ser.). pap. 5.00 *(978-1-881759-13-3(X))* Frankel, Jean & Samuel Ctr. for Judaic Studies.

Horowitz, Irving. Daydreams & Nightmares: Reflections of a Harlem Childhood. 2009. (ENG.). 159p. pap. 24.95 *(978-1-4128-1255-9(0))* Transaction Pubs.

Kalin, Berkley & Bauman, Mark K., eds. The Quiet Voices: Southern Rabbis & Black Civil Rights, 1880s to 1990s. 2007. (Judaic Studies Ser.). (ENG., Illus.). 448p. per. 44.50 *(978-0-8173-5429-9(8))* Univ. of Alabama Pr.

Kamin, Ben. Nothing Like Sunshine: A Story in the Aftermath of the MLK Assassination. 2010. (ENG.). 138p. pap. 19.95 *(978-0-87013-882-9(0))* Michigan State Univ. Pr.

Mendelsohn, Adam. Jews & the Civil War: A Reader. Sarna, Jonathan, ed. 2010. (ENG., Illus.). 445p. 65.00 *(978-0-8147-4091-0(X))* New York Univ. Pr.

Satter, Beryl. Family Properties: How the Struggle over Race & Real Estate Transformed Chicago & Urban America. 2010. (ENG., Illus.). 512p. pap. 18.00 *(978-0-8050-9142-7(4))* Picador.

Schneier, Marc. Shared Dreams: Martin Luther King, Jr. & the Jewish Community. 2009. 240p. pap. 18.99 *(978-1-58023-273-9(6))* Jewish Lights Publishing.

Stanton, Mary. The Hand of Esau: Montgomery's Jewish Community & the Bus Boycott. 2007. (Illus.). 194p. per. 15.95 *(978-1-57966-041-3(X))* River City Publishing.

Sundquist, Eric J. Strangers in the Land: Blacks, Jews, Post-Holocaust America. 2009. (Illus.). 672p. pap. 25.50 *(978-0-674-03069-5(9)*, Belknap Pr.) Harvard Univ. Pr.

Walker, Rebecca. Black, White & Jewish: Autobiography of a Shifting Self. (YA). (gr. 9-12). pap. 15.00 *(978-0-13-184808-5(9))* Prentice Hall (Schl. Div.).

AFRICAN AMERICANS—RELATIONS WITH WHITES

see United States—Race Relations

AFRICAN AMERICANS—RELIGION

see also African American Baptists; African American Churches; African American Clergy; Black Muslims; Black Theology

Aaseng, Nathan. Religious Leaders. 2nd rev. ed. 2010. (A to Z of African Americans Ser.). (Illus.). 296p. (C). (gr. 9-18). 49.50 *(978-0-8160-7868-4(8))* Facts On File, Inc.

Adeola, Moses. Cultural & Religious Dilemma of Africans: In the Diaspora. 2006. per. 16.95 *(978-0-9787788-0-4(4))* LUMEN-US Pubns.

Andrews, Lee. Family Destiny: Get Faith to Take Your Family Places! 2007. (Illus.). 44p. 6.99 *(978-0-9797126-0-9(2))* Andrews, Lee.

Anyabwile, Thabiti M. The Decline of African American Theology: From Biblical Faith to Cultural Captivity. 2007. (ENG., Illus.). 255p. per. 20.00 *(978-0-8308-2827-2(3)*, IVP Acad.) InterVarsity Pr.

—The Faithful Preacher: Recapturing the Vision of Three Pioneering African-American Pastors. 2007. (Illus.). 192p. pap. 15.99 *(978-1-58134-827-9(4))* Crossway.

Approaches in African American Pastoral Care & Psychology: Making it Plain, Volume 5. 2011. pap. 17.00 ***(978-0-687-33285-4(0))*** Abingdon Pr.

Bacote, Vincent, ed. Precepts for Living Annual Commentary 2009-2010. 12th ed. 2009. (Precepts for Living Ser.). 504p. pap. 16.95 *(978-1-60352-587-6(0))* UMI (Urban Ministries, Inc.).

Bacote, Vincent, ed. Precepts for Living Annual Commentary 2009-2010. 12th l.t. ed. 2009. (Precepts for Living Ser.). 504p. pap. 19.95 *(978-1-60352-686-9(2))* UMI (Urban Ministries, Inc.).

Baker-Fletcher, Garth Kasimu & Baker-Fletcher, Garth. Bible Witness in Black Churches. 2009. (Black Religion/Womanist Thought/Social Justice Ser.). (ENG.). 208p. 84.00 *(978-0-230-61771-1(9))* Palgrave Macmillan.

Baker, Phyllis. African American Spirituality 2006. 2nd ed. 2006. 120p. (C). pap. 25.95 *(978-0-7593-9093-5(2))* CENGAGE Learning Custom Publishing.

—African-American Spirituality, Thought & Culture. 2007. 112p. per. 12.95 *(978-0-595-44231-7(5))* iUniverse, Inc.

Best, W. D. Passionately Human, No Less Divine. 2007. (ENG., Illus.). 272p. (C). pap. 29.95 *(978-0-691-13375-1(1))* Princeton Univ. Pr.

Black Biblical Studies. 2010. pap. 17.00 *(978-0-687-33164-2(1))* Abingdon Pr.

Blum, Edward J. W. E. B. du Bois: American Prophet. 2007. (Politics & Culture in Modern America Ser.). 288p. 42.50 *(978-0-8122-4010-8(3))* Univ. of Pennsylvania Pr.

—W. E. B. du Bois, American Prophet. 2009. (Politics & Culture in Modern America Ser.). 288p. pap. 22.50 *(978-0-8122-2086-5(2))* Univ. of Pennsylvania Pr.

Blum, Edward J. & Young, Jason R., eds. The Souls of W. E. B. du Bois: New Essays & Reflections. 2009. 288p. 45.00 *(978-0-88146-136-7(9))* Mercer Univ. Pr.

Bowman, Thea & Nutt, Maurice J. Thea Bowman: In My Own Words. 2009. 14.99 *(978-0-7648-1782-3(5))* Liguori Pubns.

Bradley, Anthony B. Liberating Black Theology: The Bible & the Black Experience in America. 2010. 208p. pap. 17.99 *(978-1-4335-1147-9(9))* Crossway.

Bradley, Anthony B., ed. Keep Your Head Up: America's New Black Christian Leaders, Social Consciousness, & the Cosby Conversation. 2012. 224p. pap. 15.99 *(978-1-4335-0673-4(4))* Crossway.

Bridgeman, Davis & Fosua, Safiyah, eds. Africana Worship BK. 2006. 240p. 32.00 *(978-0-88177-490-0(1))* Discipleship Resources.

Brown, Joseph A. Sweet, Sweet Spirit: Prayer Services from the Black Catholic Church. 2006. 100p. per. 9.95 *(978-0-86716-626-2(6))* Franciscan Media.

Brown, Teresa L. Fry. Can a Sistah Get a Little Help? Encouragement for Black Women in Ministry. 2008. 176p. pap. 18.00 *(978-0-8298-1743-0(3))* Pilgrim Pr., The/United Church Pr.

Buhring, Kurt. Conceptions of God, Freedom, & Ethics in African American & Jewish Theology. 2008. (Black Religion/Womanist Thought/Social Justice Ser.). (ENG.). 272p. 95.00 *(978-1-4039-8479-1(4))* Palgrave Macmillan.

Burnley, Lawrence/A. Q. The Cost of Unity: African American Agency & Education & the Christian Church, 1865-1914. 2009. 320p. 45.00 *(978-0-88146-134-3(2))* Mercer Univ. Pr.

Burton, Michael C. Deep Roots: The African/Black Contribution to Christianity. 2008. 124p. pap. 10.95 *(978-1-4401-0323-0(2))* iUniverse, Inc.

Burwell, Robyn. I Was under a Heavy Burden: The Life of Annie C. Tuggle. 2011. 160p. pap. 15.99 ***(978-0-89112-548-8(5))*** Abilene Christian Univ. Pr.

Callahan, Allen Dwight. The Talking Book: African Americans & the Bible. 2008. (ENG.). 304p. per. 18.00 *(978-0-300-13616-6(1))* Yale Univ. Pr.

Carter, Anthony. Experiencing the Truth: Bringing the Reformation to the African-American Church. Carter, Anthony & Carter, Anthony J., eds. 2008. 192p. pap. 12.99 *(978-1-58134-887-3(8))* Crossway.

Chapman, Christine D. & Rasor, Stephen C. Black Power from the Pew: Laity Connecting Congregations & Communities. 2007. (Illus.). 176p. per. *(978-0-8298-1751-5(4))* Pilgrim Pr., The/United Church Pr.

Chireau, Yvonne. Black Magic: Religion & the African American Conjuring Tradition. 2006. (Illus.). 222p. per. 26.95 *(978-0-520-24988-2(7))* Univ. of California Pr.

Clark, Mary Ann. Then We'll Sing a New Song: African Influences on America's Religious Landscape. 2012. (ENG.). 216p. 35.00 ***(978-1-4422-0879-7(1))*** Rowman & Littlefield Publishers, Inc.

Cone, James H. The Cross & the Lynching Tree. 2011. 224p. 28.00 *(978-1-57075-937-6(5))* Orbis Bks.

Copeland, M. Shawn. Enfleshing Freedom: Body, Race, & Being. 2009. (Intersections in African American Theology Ser.). 176p. (C). pap. 20.00 *(978-0-8006-6274-5(1)*, Fortress Pr.) Augsburg Fortress, Pubs.

Copeland, M. Shawn, et al, eds. Uncommon Faithfulness: The Black Catholic Experience. 2009. 240p. pap. 26.00 *(978-1-57075-819-5(0))* Orbis Bks.

Costen, Melva Wilson. African American Christian Worship. 2nd ed. 2007. 158p. pap. 18.00 *(978-0-687-64622-7(7))* Abingdon Pr.

Cram101 Textbook Reviews. Outlines & Highlights for Canaan Land: A Religious History of African Americans by Raboteau, ISBN. 2011. 58p. pap. 26.95 ***(978-1-61812-631-3(8))*** Cram101 Inc.

Crouch, William H., Jr. & Gregory, Joel C. What We Love about the Black Church: Can We Get a Witness? 2010. 160p. pap. 16.00 *(978-0-8170-1644-9(9))* Judson Pr.

Crumbley, Deidre Helen. Saved & Sanctified: The Rise of a Storefront Church in Great Migration Philadelphia. 2012. (History of African-American Religions Ser.). (ENG., Illus.). 208p. 74.95 ***(978-0-8130-3984-8(3))*** Univ. Pr. of Florida.

Currie, Stephen. The African American Religious Experience. 2007. (Lucent Library of Black History Ser.). (ENG., Illus.). 104p. (YA). (gr. 8-12). lib. bdg. 33.45 *(978-1-4205-0006-6(6)*, Lucent Bks.) Cengage Gale.

Curtis, Edward E., IV & Sigler, Danielle Brune, eds. The New Black Gods: Arthur Huff Fauset & the Study of African American Religions. 2009. (Religion in North America Ser.). (ENG.). 283p. 65.00 *(978-0-253-35282-8(7)*, 0253352827); pap. 24.95 *(978-0-253-22057-8(2)*, 0253220572) Indiana Univ. Pr.

Dallam, Marie W. Daddy Grace: A Celebrity Preacher & His House of Prayer. 2007. (ENG., Illus.). 276p. 65.00 *(978-0-8147-2010-3(2))* New York Univ. Pr.

Dash, Michael I. N. & Chapman, Christine D. The Shape of Zion: Leadership & Life in Black Churches. 2007. (Illus.). 208p. pap. 23.00 *(978-1-55635-631-5(5))* Wipf & Stock Pubs.

Davis, Barbara B. Treasures of the Heart. 2007. (Illus.). 72p. pap. 15.00 *(978-0-9795258-6-5(1))* Warwick Hse. Publishing.

Davis, Cyprian, et al. The Journal of the Black Catholic Theological Symposium, Volume 1. Flint-Hamilton, Kimberly, ed. 2007. 125p. per. 29.99 *(978-0-9789635-6-9(3))* Fortuity Pr., LLC.

Dixon, Terry D. Black Issues: Spiritual & Social Ills. 2008. 116p. per. 12.95 *(978-1-4327-2189-3(5))* Outskirts Pr., Inc.

Dodson, Howard & Palmer, Colin, eds. Origins. 2008. (ENG., Illus.). 225p. (C). pap. 19.95 *(978-0-87013-817-1(0))* Michigan State Univ. Pr.

Duberry, Ivor. The African American & Missions: Beyond Community Seminar Study Guide. 2010. *(978-0-87808-016-8(3))* Carey, William Library Pubs.

Evans, Curtis J. The Burden of Black Religion. 2008. (ENG.). 392p. pap. 24.95 *(978-0-19-532931-5(7))* Oxford Univ. Pr., Inc.

Fancher, Mark. I Ain't Got Tired Yet: The Spiritual Battles of Enslaved African Christians & their Descendants. 2010. pap. 15.00 *(978-0-615-37842-8(0))* Mark P. Fancher.

Faulkerson, Jeffery A. Raising My V. O. I. C. E. Verbalizing Orderly Impressions Through Creative Endeavors. 2007. 142p. pap. 14.95 *(978-0-7414-4156-0(X))* Infinity Publishing.

Financial Basics 101 for African American Congregations. 16.00 *(978-0-687-06640-7(9))* Abingdon Pr.

Fosua, Safiyah. The Africana Worship. Davis, Valerie Bridgeman, ed. 2008. 256p. 32.00 *(978-0-88177-545-7(2))* Upper Room Bks.

Fountain, Daniel L. Slavery, Civil War, & Salvation: African American Slaves & Christianity, 1830-1870. 2010. (Conflicting Worlds: New Dimensions of the American Civil War Ser.). 184p. 36.00 *(978-0-8071-3699-7(9))* Louisiana State Univ. Pr.

Friend, Shelby M. Trouble Don't Last Always. 2008. 124p. pap. 10.99 *(978-1-4389-0076-6(7))* AuthorHouse.

Gay, Kathlyn. African-American Holidays, Festivals, & Celebrations: The History, Customs, & Symbols Associated with Both Traditional & Contemporary Religious & Secular Events Observed by Americans of African Descent. 2006. (Illus.). 569p. 65.00 *(978-0-7808-0779-2(0))* Omnigraphics, Inc.

Gemignani, Regina. African Immigrant Religions in America. Olupona, Jacob K., ed. 2007. (ENG.). 368p. 75.00 *(978-0-8147-6211-0(5))*; per. 25.00 *(978-0-8147-6212-7(3))* New York Univ. Pr.

Giggie, John M. & Giggie, John Michael. After Redemption: Jim Crow & the Transformation of African American Religion in the Delta, 1875-1915. 2007. (ENG., Illus.). 336p. 99.00 *(978-0-19-530403-9(9))*; per. 21.95 *(978-0-19-530404-6(7))* Oxford Univ. Pr., Inc.

Glaude, Eddie S., Jr. In a Shade of Blue: Pragmatism & the Politics of Black America. 208p. 2008. pap. 19.00 *(978-0-226-29825-2(6))* 2007. 25.00 *(978-0-226-29824-5(8))* Univ. of Chicago Pr.

Goode, W. Wilson, Sr., et al. Ministry with Prisoners & Families: The Way Forward. 2011. 192p. pap. 17.99 *(978-0-8170-1664-7(3))* Judson Pr.

Griffin, Horace L. Their Own Receive Them Not. 2010. 256p. pap. 28.00 *(978-1-60899-595-0(X)*, Wipf and Stock) Wipf & Stock Pubs.

—Their Own Receive Them Not: African American Lesbians & Gays in Black Churches. 2006. 240p. 24.00 *(978-0-8298-1599-3(6))* Pilgrim Pr., The/United Church Pr.

Hairston, Kevin S. Why Men Hide Behind Trees: African-American Man's Journey to Spirituality. 2009. 164p. pap. 15.95 *(978-1-4327-4060-3(1))* Outskirts Pr., Inc.

Haney, Marsha Snulligan. Evangelism among African American Presbyterians: Making Plain the Sacred Journey. 2007. (ENG.). 272p. per. 42.99 *(978-0-7618-3773-2(6))* Univ. Pr. of America, Inc.

Harrison, Renee K. Enslaved Women & the Art of Resistance in Antebellum America. 2009. (Black Religion/Womanist Thought/Social Justice Ser.). (ENG.). 304p. 89.00 *(978-0-230-61846-6(4))* Palgrave Macmillan.

Hart, William David. Afro-Eccentricity: Beyond the Standard Narrative of Black Religion. 2011. (ENG.). 250p. 85.00 *(978-0-230-11157-8(2))* Palgrave Macmillan.

—Black Religion: Malcolm X, Julius Lester, & Jan Willis. (ENG.). 244p. 2010. pap. 29.00 *(978-0-230-10721-2(4))* 2008. 89.00 *(978-0-230-60537-4(0))* Palgrave Macmillan.

Harvey, Paul. Through the Storm, Through the Night: A History of African American Christianity. 2011. (African American History Ser.). (ENG.). 232p. 40.00 *(978-0-7425-6473-2(8))* Rowman & Littlefield Publishers, Inc.

Herukhuti. Conjuring Black Funk: Notes on Culture, Sexuality & Spirituality. 2007. 238p. per. 15.95 *(978-0-9752987-3-2(9))* Vintage Entity Pr.

High, Eddrick. The Idolatry of Black Americ. 2009. 72p. pap. 12.00 *(978-1-4389-7469-9(8))* AuthorHouse.

Hill, Johnny B. Multidimensional Ministry for Today's Black Family. 2007. 122p. per. 14.99 *(978-0-8170-1518-3(3))* Judson Pr.

Hobson, Christopher Z. The Mount of Vision: African American Prophetic Tradition, 1800-1950. 2012. (ENG.). 304p. 65.00 ***(978-0-19-989586-1(4))*** Oxford Univ. Pr., Inc.

Hopkins, Dwight N. & Pinn, Anthony B., eds. Loving the Body: Black Religious Studies & the Erotic. 2006. (Black Religion/Womanist Thought/Social Justice Ser.). (ENG.). 384p. pap. 34.00 *(978-1-4039-7638-3(4))* Palgrave Macmillan.

Hopkins, Dwight N. & Thomas, Linda E., eds. Walk Together Children. 2009. 444p. pap. 48.00 *(978-1-60608-987-3(0),* Cascade Bks.) Wipf & Stock Pubs.

Hucks, Tracey E. Yoruba Traditions & African American Religious Nationalism. 2012. ***(978-0-8263-5077-0(1))***; (ENG., Illus.). 456p. (C). 60.00 ***(978-0-8263-5075-6(5))*** Univ. of New Mexico Pr.

Hunt, John, compiled by. Essential Writings of Amer. 2007. (ENG.). 800p. (gr. 11). 24.99 *(978-0-89957-648-0(6))* AMG Pubs.

In Defense of Uncle Tom. 2006. pap. 8.99 *(978-1-60034-263-9(9))* Xulon Pr., Inc.

Irons, Charles F. The Origins of Proslavery Christianity: White & Black Evangelicals in Colonial & Antebellum Virginia. 2008. (ENG., Illus.). 352p. 66.50 *(978-0-8078-3194-6(8))*; 384p. pap. 27.95 *(978-0-8078-5877-6(3))* Univ. of North Carolina Pr.

Jackson, Gerald P. The Suicide of the Black-American Culture: A Spiritual Remedy for the Self-Destructive Elements in the Black-American Culture. 2009. 202p. pap. 13.99 *(978-1-60604-824-5(4))* Tate Publishing & Enterprises, LLC.

Jackson, Harry R., Jr. The Truth in Black & White: A New Look at the Shifting Landscape of Race, Religion, & Politics in America Today. 2008. (ENG.). 256p. pap. 14.99 *(978-1-59979-268-2(0),* Frontline) Charisma Media.

Jackson, Sherman A. Islam & the Blackamerican: Looking Toward the Third Resurrection, 1 vol. 2011. (ENG.). 246p. pap. 24.95 *(978-0-19-978238-3(5))* Oxford Univ. Pr., Inc.

—Islam & the Problem of Black Suffering. 2009. (ENG.). 232p. 29.95 *(978-0-19-538206-8(4))* Oxford Univ. Pr., Inc.

Jakes, T. D. Mama Made the Difference: Life Lessons My Mother Taught Me. l.t. ed. 2007. (Walker Large Print Ser.). (ENG.). 384p. per. 17.95 *(978-1-59415-163-7(6),* Walker Large Print) Cengage Gale.

—Mama Made the Difference: Life Lessons My Mother Taught Me. 2007. (ENG.). 304p. (gr. 12-18). 14.00 *(978-0-425-21388-9(9),* Berkley Trade) Penguin Group (USA) Inc.

Johnson, Brian L. & Johnson, Brian. W. E. B. du Bois: Toward Agnosticism, 1868-1934. 2008. 154p. 65.00 *(978-0-7425-6449-7(5))* Rowman & Littlefield Publishers, Inc.

Johnson, Matthew V. The Tragic Vision of African American Religion. 2010. (Black Religion/Womanist Thought/Social Justice Ser.). (ENG.). 208p. 79.00 *(978-0-230-61889-3(8))* Palgrave Macmillan.

Johnson, Terrence L. Tragic Soul - Life: W. E. B. du Bois & the Moral Crisis Facing American Democracy, 1 vol. 2012. (Imagining the Americas Ser.). (ENG.). 192p. 65.00 *(978-0-19-538398-0(2))* Oxford Univ. Pr., Inc.

Johnston, Ruby Funchess. The Development of Negro Religion. 2011. 224p. 44.95 ***(978-1-258-07742-6(6))*** Literary Licensing, LLC.

Jones, Lawrence Neale. African Americans & the Christian Churches: 1619-1860. 2007. 320p. *(978-0-8298-1752-2(2))* Pilgrim Pr., The/United Church Pr.

Jones, R. Clifford. James K. Humphrey & the Sabbath-Day Adventists. 2006. (ENG.). 250p. 50.00 *(978-1-57806-891-3(6))* Univ. Pr. of Mississippi.

June, Lee N. Yet with a Steady Beat: The Black Church Through a Psychological & Biblical Lens. 2008. (ENG., Illus.). 152p. per. 13.99 *(978-0-8024-8092-7(6),* Lift Every Voice) Moody Pubs.

Kahn, Jonathon S. Divine Discontent: The Religious Imagination of W. E. B. du Bois, 1 vol. 2011. (ENG.). 192p. pap. 24.95 ***(978-0-19-982986-6(1))*** Oxford Univ. Pr., Inc.

Kay, Roy. The Ethiopian Prophecy in Black American Letters. 2011. (History of African-American Religions Ser.). (ENG., Illus.). 240p. 74.95 *(978-0-8130-3732-5(8))* Univ. Pr. of Florida.

Keeble, Marshall & Robinson, Edward J. A Godsend to His People: The Essential Writings & Speeches of Marshall Keeble. 2008. (ENG., Illus.). 192p. 39.95 *(978-1-57233-619-3(6))* Univ. of Tennessee Pr.

Keller, Mary & Fontenot, Chester J., Jr., eds. Re-Cognizing W. E. B. Dubois in the 21st Century. 2007. 288p. 60.00 *(978-0-88146-077-3(X))*; pap. 30.00 *(978-0-88146-059-9(1))* Mercer Univ. Pr.

Kelly, Elsia. The Melting Pot. 2008. 76p. pap. 12.99 *(978-1-60647-700-7(5))* Xulon Pr., Inc.

Kimbrough, Marjorie L. African American History Month 2008: Daily Devotions. 2007. 32p. pap. 2.00 *(978-0-687-49196-4(7))* Abingdon Pr.

King, Barbara Blake, frwd. Sage Sisters: Essential Lessons for African American Women in Ministry. 2007. 149p. per. *(978-0-8298-1764-5(6))* Pilgrim Pr., The/United Church Pr.

King, Melvinia Turner. The African American Moral Tradition as a Resource for Leadership Education: Developing Ethical Leaders for America. 2009. (Illus.). 148p. 99.95 *(978-0-7734-4780-6(6))* Mellen, Edwin Pr., The.

Knox, Andrew. Blazing an African-American Trail. 2008. (ENG.). 108p. pap. 11.95 *(978-1-934937-04-4(5))* Mill City Pr., Inc.

Kunjufu, Jawanza. Developing Strong Black Male Ministries. 2006. (ENG., Illus.). 180p. pap. 14.95 *(978-0-9749000-9-4(5))* African American Images.

Lackey, Michael. African American Atheists & Political Liberation: A Study of the Sociocultural Dynamics of Faith. 2007. (History of African-American Religions Ser.). (ENG., Illus.). 192p. 59.95 *(978-0-8130-3035-7(8))* Univ. Pr. of Florida.

—African American Atheists & Political Liberation: A Study of the Sociocultural Dynamics of Faith. 2008. (History of African-American Religions Ser.). (ENG., Illus.). 192p. pap. 29.95 *(978-0-8130-3318-1(7))* Univ. Pr. of Florida.

Lanzano, Stanley F. True Places: A Lowcountry Preacher, His Church, & His People. 2009. (ENG.). 124p. 19.95 *(978-1-57003-851-8(1))* Univ. of South Carolina Pr.

Lee, Hak Joon. We Will Get to the Promised Land: Martin Luther King, JR. 's Communal-Political Spirituality. 2006. 224p. per. *(978-0-8298-1526-9(0))* Pilgrim Pr., The/United Church Pr.

Lowe, Tim. Unsupervised Cows. 2011. 230p. 29.99 ***(978-1-4568-2896-7(7))***; pap. 19.99 ***(978-1-4568-2895-0(9))*** Xlibris Corp.

Ludwig, Frieder & Asamoah-Gyadu, J. Kwabena. African Christian Presence in the West: New Immigrant Congregations & Transnational Networks in North America & Europe. 2011. *(978-1-59221-807-3(5))*; 238p. pap. *(978-1-59221-808-0(3))* Africa World Pr.

Marable, Manning & Aidi, Hishaam D., eds. Black Routes to Islam. 2009. (Critical Black Studies). (ENG.). 336p. 105.00 *(978-1-4039-8400-5(X))*; pap. 32.00 *(978-1-4039-7781-6(X))* Palgrave Macmillan.

Mathis, Brondon. The Coming FORERUNNER Ministry Out of AFRICA: Africa & African America's End-Time Calling bringing Gods house of Prayer to Fullness. 2011. (ENG.). 396p. pap. 19.99 ***(978-1-4609-5849-0(7))*** CreateSpace.

Mathis, Deborah. What God Can Do: How Faith Changes Lives for the Better. 2007. (ENG.). 240p. pap. 16.95 *(978-0-7434-7641-6(7),* Beyond Words/Atria Bks.) Atria Bks.

May, Cedrick. Evangelism & Resistance in the Black Atlantic, 1760-1835. 2008. (ENG.). 168p. 39.95 *(978-0-8203-2798-3(0))* Univ. of Georgia Pr.

McCloud, Aminah Beverly. Transnational Muslims in American Society. 2006. (ENG.). 176p. 39.95 *(978-0-8130-2971-9(6))* Univ. Pr. of Florida.

McDaniel, Eric L. Politics in the Pews: The Political Mobilization of Black Churches. 2008. (Politics of Race & Ethnicity Ser.). (ENG., Illus.). 224p. (C). 80.00 *(978-0-472-07046-6(0))*; pap. 26.95 *(978-0-472-05046-8(X))* Univ. of Michigan Pr.

Mitchem, Stephanie Y. Name It & Claim It? Prosperity Preaching in the Black Church. 2007. 147p. per. *(978-0-8298-1709-6(3))* Pilgrim Pr., The/United Church Pr.

Mitchem, Stephanie Y. & Townes, Emilie M., eds. Faith, Health, & Healing in African American Life, 1 vol. 2008. (Religion, Health, & Healing Ser.). (Illus.). 232p. 49.95 *(978-0-275-99375-7(2),* C9375, Praeger Pubs.) Greenwood Publishing Group, Inc.

Moore, Forrest. A History of the Black Church in Tuscaloos. 2009. 184p. 24.99 *(978-1-4389-2263-8(9))*; pap. 14.49 *(978-1-4389-2260-7(4))* AuthorHouse.

Morgan, Philip, ed. African American Life in the Georgia Lowcountry: The Atlantic World & the Gullah Geechee. (Race in the Atlantic World, 1700-1900 Ser.). (ENG.). 2011. 376p. pap. 24.95 ***(978-0-8203-4307-5(2))*** 2010. (Illus.). 320p. 34.95 *(978-0-8203-3064-8(7))* Univ. of Georgia Pr.

Muhammad, Ashahed. The Black Principle: Prepare to Rule. 2008. per. *(978-0-9766066-1-1(5))* Truth Establishment Institute, The.

Murray, David. Matter, Magic, & Spirit: Representing Indian & African American Belief. 2007. 224p. (C). 59.95 *(978-0-8122-3996-6(2))* Univ. of Pennsylvania Pr.

Nawls, Alexander. Praising God: The Way Home for So-Called African Americans. 2012. ***(978-1-58982-672-4(8))*** American Bk. Publishing Group.

Nisbett, J. Mastine. A Journey to the Promised Land: The Struggle of a Suburban Church to Build an Edifice. 2011. 184p. pap. 19.99 *(978-1-4520-9233-1(8))* AuthorHouse.

Noel, James A. Black Religion & the Imagination of Matter in the Atlantic World. 2009. (Black Religion/Womanist Thought/Social Justice Ser.). (ENG., Illus.). 256p. 95.00 *(978-0-230-61506-9(6))* Palgrave Macmillan.

Oltman, Adele. Sacred Mission, Worldly Ambition: Black Christian Nationalism in the Age of Jim Crow. (ENG.). 264p. 2012. pap. 24.95 ***(978-0-8203-4126-2(6))*** 2008. 44.95 *(978-0-8203-3036-5(1))* Univ. of Georgia Pr.

Palmer, Gerald. The Church Has AIDS: Essays on Sexuality, Sexual Orientation, Taboos, & the Black Church. 2010. 84p. pap. 18.20 *(978-0-557-12464-0(6))* Lulu Enterprises Inc.

Petty, L. Jalik. Black Campus Ministry. 2nd ed. pap. 4.95 *(978-0-942428-01-8(3))* Universal Ministries, Inc., Publishing Hse.

Pinn, Anthony & Valentin, Benjamin, eds. Creating Ourselves: African Americans & Hispanic Americans on Popular Culture & Religious Expression. 2009. (ENG.). 400p. 94.95 *(978-0-8223-4549-7(8))* Duke Univ. Pr.

Pinn, Anthony B. African AMER Religious Experience in America. 2007. (History of African-American Religions Ser.). (ENG.). 384p. pap. 25.00 *(978-0-8130-3197-2(4))* Univ. Pr. of Florida.

—Becoming ÒAmericaÕs Problem ChildÓ: An Outline of Pauli MurrayÕs Religious Life & Theology. 2008. 128p. pap. 16.00 *(978-1-55635-302-4(2),* Pickwick Pubns.) Wipf & Stock Pubs.

—Black Religion & Aesthetics: Religious Thought & Life in Africa & the African Diaspora. Pinn, Anthony B., ed. 2009. (ENG., Illus.). 232p. 95.00 *(978-0-230-60550-3(8))* Palgrave Macmillan.

—The End of God-Talk: An African American Humanist Theology, 1 vol. 2012. (ENG.). 224p. pap. 21.95 ***(978-0-19-534083-9(3))*** Oxford Univ. Pr., Inc.

—Understanding & Transforming the Black Church. 2009. 166p. pap. 19.00 *(978-1-55635-301-7(4),* Cascade Bks.) Wipf & Stock Pubs.

—What Is African American Religion? 2011. (Facet Ser.). 128p. (C). pap. 9.99 *(978-0-8006-9846-1(0),* Fortress Pr.) Augsburg Fortress, Pubs.

Pinn, Anthony B. & Valentin, Benjamin, eds. Creating Ourselves: African Americans & Hispanic Americans on Popular Culture & Religious Expression. 2009. (ENG.). 400p. pap. 26.95 *(978-0-8223-4566-4(8))* Duke Univ. Pr.

Powery, Luke. Spirit Speech. 2009. 184p. pap. 19.00 *(978-0-687-65974-6(4))* Abingdon Pr.

Price, Emmett G., III, ed. The Black Church & Hip Hop Culture: Toward Bridging the Generational Divide. 2011. (African American Cultural Theory & Heritage Ser.). (ENG.). 228p. (gr. 17). 65.00 ***(978-0-8108-8236-2(1))*** Scarecrow Pr., Inc.

Price, Emmett George. The Black Church & Hip-Hop Culture: Toward Bridging the Generational Divide. 2012. E-Book ***(978-0-8108-8237-9(X))*** Scarecrow Pr., Inc.

Rasor, Stephen C. & Dudley, I. N. The Mark of Zion: Congregational Life in Black Churches. 2010. 160p. pap. 18.00 *(978-1-60899-586-8(0),* Wipf and Stock) Wipf & Stock Pubs.

Redmond, Eric C., et al. Where Are All the Brothers? Straight Answers to Men's Questions about the Church. 2008. 112p. pap. 9.99 *(978-1-4335-0178-4(3))* Crossway.

Reid-Salmon, Delroy A. Home Away from Home: The Caribbean Diasporan Church in the Black Atlantic Tradition. 2008. (Cross Cultural Theologies Ser.). (ENG.). 256p. (C). 99.95 *(978-1-84553-383-0(6))* Equinox Publishing Ltd. GBR. Dist: ISD.

—Home Away from Home: The Caribeean Diasporan Church in the Black Atlantic Tradition. 2008. (Cross Cultural Theologies Ser.). (ENG.). 256p. (C). pap. 34.95 *(978-1-84553-384-7(4))* Equinox Publishing Ltd. GBR. Dist: ISD.

Rigell, William R. Negro Religious Leadership on the Southe. 2006. pap. 16.95 *(978-1-4286-6326-8(6))* Kessinger Publishing, LLC.

Roberts, Rita. Evangelicalism & the Politics of Reform in Northern Black Thought, 1776-1863. 2011. (Antislavery, Abolition, & the Atlantic World Ser.). 272p. 39.95 *(978-0-8071-3708-6(1))* Louisiana State Univ. Pr.

Roberts, Samuel K. African American Christian Ethics. 2008. 318p. pap. 35.00 *(978-1-60608-143-3(8))* Wipf & Stock Pubs.

Robinson, Edward J. The Fight Is on in Texas: A History of African American Churches of Christ in the Lone Star State, 1865-2000. 2009. 222p. 34.95 *(978-0-89112-532-7(9))* Abilene Christian Univ. Pr.

—The Fight Is on in Texas: A History of African American Churches of Christ in the Lone Star State1865-2000. 2008. 222p. pap. 19.95 *(978-0-89112-533-4(7))* Abilene Christian Univ. Pr.

—Show Us How You Do It: Marshall Keeble & the Rise of Black Churches of Christ in the United States, 1914-1968. 2nd ed. 2008. (Religion & American Culture Ser.). (ENG., Illus.). 256p. 39.95 *(978-0-8173-1612-9(4))* Univ. of Alabama Pr.

—To Save My Race from Abuse: The Life of Samuel Robert Cassius. 2nd ed. 2009. (Religion & American Culture Ser.). (ENG., Illus.). 224p. pap. 24.00 *(978-0-8173-5597-5(9))* Univ. of Alabama Pr.

Robinson, Edward J., ed. To Lift up My Race: The Essential Writings of Samuel Robert Cassius. 2008. (ENG., Illus.). 215p. 46.95 *(978-1-57233-618-6(8))* Univ. of Tennessee Pr.

Robinson, Tyrone H. Show Yourself & Be Not Ashamed - a Call to the African American Male for Visibility. 2008. 72p. pap. *(978-3-639-00445-8(0))* VDM Verlag Dr. Mueller e.K.

Rogers, Joseph. The Struggle, the Pain but the Ultimate Victory. 2007. per. *(978-1-59581-387-9(X),* Brentwood Christian Pr.) Brentwood Communications Group.

Rogers, Shepherd. The Holy Piby: The Blackman's Bible. 2007. 100p. per. 8.95 *(978-1-60206-075-3(4))* Cosimo, Inc.

Russell, Heather & Bassard, Katherine Clay. Transforming Scriptures: African American Women Writers & the Bible. 2010. (ENG.). 180p. 44.95 *(978-0-8203-3090-7(6))* Univ. of Georgia Pr.

Savage, Barbara Dianne. Your Spirits Walk Beside Us: The Politics of Black Religion. 2008. 368p. 27.95 *(978-0-674-03177-7(6),* Belknap Pr.) Harvard Univ. Pr.

Shabazz, Rsheed Ali. And God Made Man: The Creation of African America. 2008. pap. 10.00 *(978-0-8059-7918-3(2))* Dorrance Publishing Co., Inc.

Slaughter, Shirley Harris. Our Lady of Victory: The Saga of an African-American Catholic Community. 2007. 224p. (ENG.). 28.95 *(978-0-595-89668-4(5))*; per. 18.95 *(978-0-595-43482-4(7))* iUniverse, Inc.

Stone, Jon R. & Piar, Carlos R. Readings in American Religious Diversity. rev. ed. 2012. (ENG.). 588p. pap. 94.80 *(978-0-7575-4091-2(0))* Kendall Hunt Publishing Co.

Strength of a Black Man: Destined for Self Empowerment. 2006. *(978-0-9791406-0-0(9))* McCollum, Walter.

Talbot, Frederick Hilborn. African American Worship: New Eyes for Seeing. 2007. 168p. pap. 19.00 *(978-1-59752-490-2(5),* Wipf and Stock) Wipf & Stock Pubs.

Thorpe, Jacqulyln, ed. God Delivers Me: A Model from Strengthening the Black Church for the 21st Century. 2008. 250p. 16.00 *(978-0-687-64889-4(0))* Abingdon Pr.

Tillman-Clark, Meylon. If There Ever Was a Time to Pray, the Time Is Now! Praying to Change Your Community, 1 vol. 2009. (ENG.). 150p. pap. 24.95 *(978-1-60610-184-1(6))* PublishAmerica, Inc.

Turner, Lee W. The Turner E. A. G. L. E. Technique for Incarnation Centered Spirituality: A Five-Fold Path to Spiritual Wholeness. Dingle, Pat, ed. 2009. (ENG.). 200p. pap. 25.00 *(978-1-4251-2135-8(7))* Trafford Publishing.

Walston, Vaughn J. & Stevens, Robert J. African-American Experience in World Mission: A Call Beyond Community. 2009. *(978-0-87808-461-6(4))* Carey, William Library Pubs.

Walton, Jonathan. Watch This! The Ethics & Aesthetics of Black Televangelism. 2009. (ENG.). 320p. pap. 23.00 *(978-0-8147-9452-4(1))*; (Illus.). 75.00 *(978-0-8147-9417-3(3))* New York Univ. Pr.

Weaver, Harold D., Jr. Black Fire: African American Quakers on Spirituality & Human Rights. Weaver, Harold D., Jr., ed. 2011. (Illus.). 249p. (C). pap. 23.95 *(978-1-888305-88-3(6))* Quaker Pr. of Friends General Conference.

Weddington, Brian. Lifted: The Little Book of Monologues & Scenes from the African American Christian Experience. 2011. 60p. pap. 11.00 ***(978-1-4251-7542-9(2))*** Trafford Publishing.

Weissinger, Sandra Ellen. A Sociology of Black Clergy in the State of Illinois: Activism & Acquiescence in the Post-Civil Rights Generation. 2011. 216p. 119.95 ***(978-0-7734-1499-0(1))*** Mellen, Edwin Pr., The.

West, Cornel. Hope on a Tightrope: Words & Wisdom. 2011. (ENG.). 140p. 14.95 *(978-1-4019-3076-9(X))* Hay Hse., Inc.

Whyte, Daniel, III. God Has Smiled on Me: A Tribute to a Black Father Who Stayed & A Tribute to All Black Fathers Who Stay. 2009. (ENG.). 142p. pap. 11.99 *(978-0-615-30191-4(6))* Torch Legacy Pubns.

Williams, Johnny E. African American Religion & the Civil Rights Movement in Arkansas. 2008. (ENG.). 177p. pap. 25.00 *(978-1-60473-186-6(9))* Univ. Pr. of Mississippi.

Wilson, Jacqueline E. Charting New Paths: History/National Assn of Black Catholic Administrators. 2007. (Illus.). 119p. pap. 20.00 net. *(978-0-9747324-1-1(9))* Wilson, Jacqueline E.

Wimberly, Anne E. Streaty. Nurturing Faith & Hope: Black Worship as a Model for Christian Education. 2010. 236p. pap. 26.00 *(978-1-60899-234-8(9),* Wipf and Stock) Wipf & Stock Pubs.

Wimberly, Edward P. African American History Month 2009: Daily Devotions. 2008. (African American History Month Daily Devotions Annual Ser.). 32p. pap. 2.00 *(978-0-687-65392-8(4))* Abingdon Pr.

—African American Pastoral Care. 2008. 151p. pap. 18.00 *(978-0-687-64949-5(8))* Abingdon Pr.

Yisrael, Bethuel Mariael. Let My People Go: A Letter to the Captivity. 2007. pap. 23.00 *(978-0-8059-8454-5(2))* Dorrance Publishing Co., Inc.

Zogbé, Mama. Origins of the Vodoun Religion in America: Reclamation of a Suppressed Heritage. 2007. (Illus.). 92p. per. 18.87 *(978-0-9716245-1-1(8))* Mami Wata Healers Society of North America, Inc.

—Vodoun: An Illustrated History of Racism & Religious Persecution in America. 2007. (Illus.). 42p. per. 17.87 *(978-0-9716245-9-7(3))* Mami Wata Healers Society of North America, Inc.

AFRICAN AMERICANS—SEGREGATION

Abel, Elizabeth. Signs of the Times: The Visual Politics of Jim Crow. 2010. (ENG., Illus.). 416p. pap. 25.95 *(978-0-520-26183-9(6))* Univ. of California Pr.

Arsenault, Raymond. Freedom Riders: 1961 & the Struggle for Racial Justice. (Pivotal Moments in American History Ser.). (ENG., Illus.). 2007. 704p. per. 21.95 *(978-0-19-532714-4(4))* 2nd abr. ed. 2011. 352p. pap. 15.95 *(978-0-19-975431-1(4))* Oxford Univ. Pr., Inc.

Bowers, Rick. Spies of Mississippi: The True Story of the Spy Network That Tried to Destroy the Civil Rights Movement. 2010. (Illus.). 128p. (gr. 7-18). (ENG.). (J). 16.95 *(978-1-4263-0595-5(8))*; (YA). 26.90 *(978-1-4263-0596-2(6))* National Geographic Society. (National Geographic Children's Bks.).

Bowman, Bertie. Step by Step: A Memoir of Living the American Dream. 2009. (ENG., Illus.). 224p. pap. 15.00 *(978-0-345-50433-3(X),* One World/Ballantine) Random House Publishing Group.

Boyd, Michelle R. Jim Crow Nostalgia: Reconstructing Race in Bronzeville. 2008. 208p. 57.00 *(978-0-8166-4677-7(5))*; pap. 18.95 *(978-0-8166-4678-4(3))* Univ. of Minnesota Pr.

Brown, Leslie & Valk, Anne. Living with Jim Crow: African American Women & Memories of the Segregated South. 2010. (Palgrave Studies in Oral History Ser.). (ENG., Illus.). 228p. 95.00 *(978-0-230-61962-3(2))*; pap. 29.00 *(978-0-230-62152-7(X))* Palgrave Macmillan.

Brown, Nikki L. M. & Stentiford, Barry M. The Jim Crow Encyclopedia: Greenwood Milestones in African American History, 2 vols. Brown, Nikki L. M. & Stentiford, Barry M., eds. 2008. (Greenwood Milestones in African American History Ser.). (Illus.). 952p. 225.00 *(978-0-313-34181-6(8),* GR4181) Greenwood Publishing Group, Inc.

Cahn, Susan K. Sexual Reckonings: Southern Girls in a Troubling Age. 2012. (ENG., Illus.). 384p. pap. 19.95 ***(978-0-674-06393-8(7))*** Harvard Univ. Pr.

Catsam, Derek Charles. Freedom's Main Line: The Journey of Reconciliation & the Freedom Rides. 2011. (Civil Rights & the Struggle for Black Equality in the

Twentieth Century Ser.). (ENG.). 436p. pap. 25.00 *(978-0-8131-3377-5(7))* Univ. Pr. of Kentucky.

Chafe, William H., et al, eds. Remembering Jim Crow: African Americans Tell about Life in the Segregated South. 2008. (ENG.). 346p. pap. 19.95 *(978-1-59558-334-5(3))* New Pr., The.

Cole, Stephanie & Ring, Natalie J., eds. The Folly of Jim Crow: Rethinking the Segregated South. 2012. (Walter Prescott Webb Memorial Lectures, published for the University of Texas At Ser.). (Illus.). 256p. 30.00 ***(978-1-60344-582-5(X))*** Texas A&M Univ. Pr.

Cole, Stephanie, et al. The Folly of Jim Crow: Rethinking the Segregated South. 2012. E-Book ***(978-1-60344-661-7(3))*** Texas A&M Univ. Pr.

Crisis of Conscience: Arkansas Methodists & the Civil Rights Struggle. 2007. (Illus.). 203p. per. 18.50 *(978-0-9708574-4-6(6))* Butler Ctr. for Arkansas Studies.

Dailey, Jane. Jim Crow. 2008. (Norton Casebooks in History Ser.). (ENG.). 434p. (C). pap. 17.35 net. *(978-0-393-92758-0(X),* 92758) Norton, W. W. & Co., Inc.

Deutsch, Morton & Collins, Mary Evans. Interracial Housing: A Psychological Evaluation of a Social Experiment. 2009. (ENG.). 189p. pap. 40.00 *(978-0-8166-5984-5(2))* Univ. of Minnesota Pr.

Dowden, Priscilla A. Groping Toward Democracy: African American Social Welfare Reform in St. Louis, 1910-1949. 3rd ed. 2011. (ENG., Illus.). 320p. (C). 44.95 *(978-0-8262-1900-8(4))* Univ. of Missouri Pr.

DuRocher, Kristina. Raising Racists: The Socialization of White Children in the Jim Crow South. 2011. (New Directions in Southern History Ser.). (ENG., Illus.). 248p. 40.00 *(978-0-8131-3001-9(8))* Univ. Pr. of Kentucky.

East, P. D. The Magnolia Jungle: The Life, Times & Education of A Southern Editor. 2011. 254p. 47.95 ***(978-1-258-04977-5(5))*** Literary Licensing, LLC.

Etheridge, Eric. Breach of Peace: Portraits of the 1961 Mississippi Freedom Riders. 2009. (ENG., Illus.). 224p. 30.00 *(978-0-9777433-9-1(X),* 977749) Atlas & Co.

Ford, Arthur Lee. When the Whippoorwill Sang: A Memoir of Rural Life During the Twilight of the Segregated South. 2008. *(978-1-887366-84-7(9))* Univ. of Louisiana at Lafayette Pr.

Gelderman, Carol. A Free Man of Color & His Hotel: Race, Reconstruction, & the Role of the Federal Government. 2012. (Illus.). 184p. 27.50 ***(978-1-59797-833-0(7))*** Potomac Bks., Inc.

Gelderman, Carol W. A Free Man of Color & His Hotel: Race, Reconstruction, & the Role of the Federal Government. 2012. ***(978-1-59797-834-7(5))*** Potomac Bks., Inc., Pubs.

Gellman, Erik S. Death Blow to Jim Crow: The National Negro Congress & the Rise of Militant Civil Rights. 2012. (John Hope Franklin Series in African American History & Culture Ser.). (ENG., Illus.). 368p. 39.95 ***(978-0-8078-3531-9(5))*** Univ. of North Carolina Pr.

Grady-Willis, Winston A. Challenging U. S. Apartheid: Atlanta & Black Struggles for Human Rights, 1960-1977. 2006. (ENG., Illus.). 312p. per. 24.95 *(978-0-8223-3791-1(6))* Duke Univ. Pr.

—Challenging U. S. Apartheid: Atlanta & Black Struggles for Human Rights, 1960-1977. 2006. (ENG., Illus.). 312p. (C). 89.95 *(978-0-8223-3778-2(9))* Duke Univ. Pr.

Greason, Walter. The Path to Freedom: Black Families in New Jersey. 2010. (ENG., Illus.). 128p. pap. 19.99 *(978-1-59629-992-4(4))* History Pr., The.

Green, Laurie B. Battling the Plantation Mentality: Memphis & the Black Freedom Struggle. 2007. (John Hope Franklin Series in African American History & Culture Ser.). (ENG., Illus.). 400p. 73.95 *(978-0-8078-3106-9(9));* per. 27.95 *(978-0-8078-5802-8(1))* Univ. of North Carolina Pr.

Hamlin, Francoise Nicole. Crossroads at Clarksdale: The Black Freedom Struggle in the Mississippi Delta after World War II. 2012. (John Hope Franklin Series in African American History & Culture Ser.). (ENG., Illus.). 368p. 39.95 ***(978-0-8078-3549-4(8))*** Univ. of North Carolina Pr.

Jaspin, Elliot. Buried in the Bitter Waters: The Hidden History of Racial Cleansing in America. 2008. (ENG.). 352p. pap. 15.95 *(978-0-465-03637-0(6))* Basic Bks.

Johnson, Kimberley S. Reforming Jim Crow: Southern Politics & State in the Age Before Brown, 1 vol. 2010. (ENG., Illus.). 336p. 35.00 *(978-0-19-538742-1(2))* Oxford Univ. Pr., Inc.

Katagiri, Yasuhiro. The Mississippi State Sovereignty Commission: Civil Rights & States' Rights. (ENG.). 2007. 348p. per. 25.00 *(978-1-60473-008-1(0))* 2006. 312p. 50.00 *(978-1-57806-388-8(4))* Univ. Pr. of Mississippi.

Kennedy, Stetson. Jim Crow Guide to the U. S. A: The Laws, Customs & Etiquette Governing the Conduct of Nonwhites & Other Minorities As Second-Class Citizens. 2nd ed. 2011. (ENG.). 232p. pap. 32.50 *(978-0-8173-5671-2(1))* Univ. of Alabama Pr.

—Jim Crow Guide to the U.S.A: The Laws, Customs & Etiquette Governing the Conduct of Nonwhites & Other Minorities As Second-Class Citizens. 2011. *(978-0-8173-8564-4(9))* Univ. of Alabama Pr.

King, Desmond. Separate & Unequal: African Americans & the US Federal Government. rev. ed. 2007. (ENG.). 384p. pap. 24.99 *(978-0-19-533622-1(4))* Oxford Univ. Pr., Inc.

Kornweibel, Theodore, Jr. Railroads in the African American Experience: A Photographic Journey. 2010. (ENG., Illus.). 568p. 40.00 *(978-0-8018-9162-5(0))* Johns Hopkins Univ. Pr.

Kruse, Kevin Michael. White Flight: Atlanta & the Making of Modern Conservatism. 2007. (Politics & Society in Twentieth-Century America Ser.). (ENG., Illus.). 352p. (C). per. 22.95 *(978-0-691-13386-7(7))* Princeton Univ. Pr.

Lassiter, Matthew D. & Crespino, Joseph, eds. The Myth of Southern Exceptionalism, 1 vol. 2009. (ENG., Illus.). 360p. 99.00 *(978-0-19-538474-1(1));* pap. 24.95 *(978-0-19-538475-8(X))* Oxford Univ. Pr., Inc.

Lemann, Nicholas. Redemption: The Last Battle of the Civil War. 2011. (ENG.). 257p. 24.00 *(978-1-4379-7643-4(3))* DIANE Publishing Co.

—Redemption: The Last Battle of the Civil War. 2007. (ENG., Illus.). 272p. pap. 16.00 *(978-0-374-53069-3(6))* Farrar, Straus & Giroux.

Lewis, Catherine M. & Lewis, J. Richard, eds. Jim Crow America: A Documentary History. 2009. 245p. pap. 19.95 *(978-1-55728-895-0(X));* (Illus.). 59.95 *(978-1-55728-894-3(1))* Univ. of Arkansas Pr.

Litwack, Leon F. How Free Is Free? The Long Death of Jim Crow. 2009. (Nathan I. Huggins Lectures). 208p. 21.00 *(978-0-674-03152-4(0))* Harvard Univ. Pr.

Loewen, James W. Sundown Towns: A Hidden Dimension of American Racism. 2006. (ENG., Illus.). 576p. pap. 17.99 *(978-0-7432-9448-5(3),* Touchstone) Touchstone.

Miller, Adam David. Ticket to Exile. 2007. 237p. per. *(978-1-59714-065-2(1))* Heyday.

Miller, Karl Hagstrom. Segregating Sound: Inventing Folk & Pop Music in the Age of Jim Crow. 2010. (Refiguring American Music Ser.). (ENG., Illus.). 384p. 94.95 *(978-0-8223-4689-0(3));* pap. 25.95 *(978-0-8223-4700-2(8))* Duke Univ. Pr.

Minchin, Timothy J. & Salmond, John A. After the Dream: Black & White Southerners Since 1965. 2011. (Civil Rights & the Struggle for Black Equality in the Twentieth Century Ser.). (ENG., Illus.). 424p. 40.00 *(978-0-8131-2978-5(8))* Univ. Pr. of Kentucky.

Moore, Winfred B., Jr. & Burton, Orville Vernon, eds. Toward the Meeting of the Waters: Currents in the Civil Rights Movement of South Carolina during the Twentieth Century. 416p. 2010. (ENG.). pap. 29.95 *(978-1-57003-971-3(2))* 2008. (Illus.). 49.95 *(978-1-57003-755-9(8))* Univ. of South Carolina Pr.

Norman, Brian. Representing Segregation: Toward an Aesthetics of Living Jim Crow, & Other Forms of Racial Division. Williams, Piper Kendrix, ed. 2010. (Illus.). 320p. 80.00 *(978-1-4384-3033-1(7));* pap. 29.95 *(978-1-4384-3032-4(9))* State Univ. of New York Pr.

O'Hara, Mackie & Richardson, Alex, eds. Beyond Central, Toward Acceptance: A Collection of Oral Histories from Students of Little Rock Central High. 2010. (Illus.). 242p. pap. 19.95 *(978-1-935106-21-0(X))* Butler Ctr. for Arkansas Studies.

Patler, Nicholas. Jim Crow & the Wilson Administration: Protesting Federal Segregation in the Early Twentieth Century. 2007. (ENG., Illus.). 236p. per. 23.95 *(978-0-87081-864-6(3))* Univ. Pr. of Colorado.

Phelts, Marsha Dean. An American Beach for African Americans. 2010. (ENG., Illus.). 200p. pap. 19.95 *(978-0-8130-3508-6(2))* Univ. Pr. of Florida.

Pietila, Antero. Not in My Neighborhood. 2010. (ENG.). 336p. 28.95 *(978-1-56663-843-2(7))* Dee, Ivan R. Pub.

—Not in My Neighborhood: How Bigotry Shaped a Great American City. 2011. (ENG.). 336p. pap. 17.95 *(978-1-56663-899-9(2))* Dee, Ivan R. Pub.

Rabaka, Reiland. Against Epistemic Apartheid: W. E. B. du Bois & the Disciplinary Decadence of Sociology. 2010. (ENG.). 440p. 94.50 *(978-0-7391-4597-5(5))* Lexington Bks.

Sabourin, Clemonce. Let the Righteous Speak: Travel Memoirs. 2011. 94p. 38.95 ***(978-1-258-09040-1(6))*** Literary Licensing, LLC.

Seay, Solomon S. & Boyd, Delores R. Jim Crow & Me. 2009. 176p. 25.00 *(978-1-58838-175-0(7))* NewSouth, Inc.

Smethurst, James. The African American Roots of Modernism: From Reconstruction to the Harlem Renaissance. 2011. (John Hope Franklin Series in African American History & Culture Ser.). (ENG.). 272p. 65.00 *(978-0-8078-3463-3(7));* pap. 26.95 *(978-0-8078-7185-0(0))* Univ. of North Carolina Pr.

Smith, Mark M. How Race Is Made: Slavery, Segregation, & the Senses. 2008. (ENG., Illus.). 208p. pap. 22.00 *(978-0-8078-5925-4(7))* Univ. of North Carolina Pr.

Steedman, Marek. Jim Crow Citizenship: How Southern Progressives Remade Race, Citizenship & Liberalism in America. 2011. (Routledge Series on Identity Politics Ser.). (ENG.). 216p. 125.00 *(978-0-415-89053-3(5))* Routledge.

Stockley, Grif. Race Relations in the Natural State. 2008. 212p. (C). 30.00 *(978-0-9708574-6-0(2))* Butler Ctr. for Arkansas Studies.

Stowe, Gene. Inherit the Land: Jim Crow Meets Miss Maggie's Will. 2007. (ENG., Illus.). 309p. per. 22.00 *(978-1-934110-60-7(4))* Univ. Pr. of Mississippi.

Taylor, Jon E. Freedom to Serve: Equality of Treatment & Opportunity in the Armed Services. 2012. (Critical Moments in American History Ser.). (ENG., Illus.). 224p. 140.00 *(978-0-415-89449-4(2));* pap. 27.95 *(978-0-415-89448-7(4))* Routledge.

Wallach, Jennifer Jensen. Closer to the Truth Than Any Fact: Memoir, Memory, & Jim Crow. (ENG.). 192p. 2010. pap. 22.95 *(978-0-8203-3502-5(9))* 2008. 34.95 *(978-0-8203-3069-3(8))* Univ. of Georgia Pr.

Wallach, Jennifer Jensen & Kirk, John A. Arsnick: The Student Nonviolent Coordinating Committee in Arkansas. 2011. (ENG., Illus.). 225p. 65.00 *(978-1-55728-968-1(9));* pap. 24.95 *(978-1-55728-966-7(2))* Univ. of Arkansas Pr.

Ward, Jason Morgan. Defending White Democracy: The Making of a Segregationist Movement & the Remaking of Racial Politics, 1936-1965. 2011. (ENG., Illus.). 272p. 34.95 *(978-0-8078-3513-5(7))* Univ. of North Carolina Pr.

Warren, Roland Leslie. Politics & African-American Ghettos. 2008. (ENG.). 244p. pap. 29.95 *(978-0-202-36212-0(4))* Aldine Transaction.

Watkins, Norma. The Last Resort: Taking the Mississippi Cure. 2011. (Willie Morris Books in Memoir & Biography Ser.). (ENG., Illus.). 240p. 28.00 *(978-1-60473-977-0(0))* Univ. Pr. of Mississippi.

Wilson, Francille Rusan. The Segregated Scholars: Black Social Scientists & the Creation of Black Labor Studies, 1890-1950. 2006. (Carter G. Woodson Institute Ser.). (ENG.). 352p. (gr. 17). pap. 22.50 *(978-0-8139-2788-6(9))* Univ. Pr. of Virginia.

Wolcott, Victoria W. Race, Riots, & Roller Coasters: The Struggle over Segregated Recreation in America. 2012. (Politics & Culture in Modern America Ser.). 328p. 34.95 ***(978-0-8122-4434-2(6))*** Univ. of Pennsylvania Pr.

AFRICAN AMERICANS—SOCIAL CONDITIONS

see also African Americans—Segregation

Abu-Lughod, Janet L. Race, Space, & Riots in Chicago, New York, & Los Angeles, 1 vol. (ENG., Illus.). 2012. 360p. pap. 24.95 ***(978-0-19-993655-7(2))*** 2007. 384p. 35.00 *(978-0-19-532875-2(2))* Oxford Univ. Pr., Inc.

African American Behavior in the Social Environment: New Perspec. 2008. (ENG.). 460p. 95.00 *(978-0-7890-3324-6(0));* pap. 51.95 *(978-0-7890-3325-3(9))* Routledge.

Akusani, Haddassandajah C. Imprisoned for Life in the Land of the Unfree: The Plight of African Americans in the American System of Justus. 2006. 34.00 *(978-0-8059-7313-6(3))* Dorrance Publishing Co., Inc.

Aldridge, Delores P. Imagine a World: Pioneering Black Women Sociologists. 2008. (ENG.). 174p. pap. 32.99 *(978-0-7618-4004-6(4))* Univ. Pr. of America, Inc.

Alexander, Michelle. The New Jim Crow: Mass Incarceration in the Age of Colorblindness. (ENG., 2012. Illus.). 336p. pap. 19.95 *(978-1-59558-643-8(1))* 2010. 304p. 27.95 *(978-1-59558-103-7(0))* New Pr., The.

—The New Jim Crow: Mass Incarceration in the Age of Colorblindness. 2011. (ENG., Illus.). 69p. spiral bd., pupil's gde. ed. 10.00 ***(978-0-9765145-4-1(0))*** Samuel DeWitt Proctor Conference.

Alexander, Shawn Leigh, ed. T. Thomas Fortune, the Afro-American Agitator: A Collection of Writings, 1880-1928. 2010. (New Perspectives on the History of the South Ser.). (ENG., Illus.). 342p. pap. 29.95 *(978-0-8130-3548-2(1))* Univ. Pr. of Florida.

Allen, Joe. People Wasn't Made to Burn: A True Story of Housing, Race, & Murder in Chicago. 2011. (ENG., Illus.). 328p. ***(978-1-60846-126-4(2))*** Pluto Pr.

Anderson, Elijah. Code of the Street: Decency, Violence & the Moral Life of the Inner City. 2006. pap. 8.95 *(978-1-4288-1549-0(X))* Cram101 Inc.

—The Cosmopolitan Canopy: Race & Civility in Everyday Life. 2011. (ENG., Illus.). 318p. 25.95 *(978-0-393-07163-4(4),* 7163) Norton, W. W. & Co., Inc.

Anderson, Elijah, ed. Against the Wall: Poor, Young, Black, & Male. 2009. (City in the Twenty-First Century Ser.). (Illus.). 320p. (C). pap. 26.50 *(978-0-8122-2017-9(X))* Univ. of Pennsylvania Pr.

Appiah, Dorothy. Adult Learning & Space Making. 2009. 168p. pap. *(978-3-639-15055-1(4))* VDM Verlag Dr. Mueller e.K.

Arend, Orissa. Showdown in Desire: The Black Panthers Take a Stand in New Orleans. 2010. (ENG., Illus.). 294p. pap. 19.95 *(978-1-55728-896-7(8))* Univ. of Arkansas Pr.

Arlether, Wilson/Ann. Rewriting the Script. 2007. 399p. pap. 15.95 *(978-0-9797627-0-3(7))* Jerant Publishing.

Armstead, Myra Beth Young. Freedom's Gardener: James F. Brown, Horticulture, & the Hudson Valley in Antebellum America. 2011. E-Book ***(978-0-8147-0791-3(2));*** E-Book ***(978-0-8147-0792-0(0))*** New York Univ. Pr.

Asante, M. K., Jr. It's Bigger Than Hip Hop: The Rise of the Post-Hip-Hop Generation. 2009. (ENG., Illus.). 304p. pap. 15.99 *(978-0-312-59302-5(3),* St. Martin's Griffin) St. Martin's Pr.

Asante, M. K., Jr. & Asante, M. K. It's Bigger Than Hip Hop: The Rise of the Post-Hip-Hop Generation. 2008. (ENG., Illus.). 304p. 25.95 *(978-0-312-37326-9(0))* St. Martin's Pr.

Asante, Molefi K. The African American People: A Global History. 2011. E-Book ***(978-0-203-14508-1(9))*** Routledge.

Asante, Molefi Kete. The African American People. 2011. (ENG., Illus.). 416p. 125.00 ***(978-0-415-87254-6(5));*** pap. 39.95 ***(978-0-415-87255-3(3))*** Routledge.

—As I Run Toward Africa: A Memoir. 2011. 336p. 99.00 ***(978-1-61205-075-1(1));*** pap. 26.95 ***(978-1-61205-076-8(X))*** Paradigm Pubs.

Asante, Molefi Kete. Erasing Racism: The Survival of the American Nation. 2nd rev. ed. 2009. (ENG., Illus.). 325p. pap. 19.00 *(978-1-59102-765-2(9))* Prometheus Bks., Pubs.

Asante, Molefi Kete & Hall, Ronald E. Rooming in the Master's House: Power & Privilege in the Rise of Black Conservatism. 2010. 208p. pap. 24.95 *(978-1-59451-891-1(2));* (ENG.). 100.00 *(978-1-59451-890-4(4))* Paradigm Pubs.

Ashmore, Susan Youngblood. Carry It On: The War on Poverty & the Civil Rights Movement in Alabama, 1964-1972. 2008. (ENG., Illus.). 416p. 69.95 *(978-0-8203-3007-5(8));* pap. 24.95 *(978-0-8203-3051-8(5))* Univ. of Georgia Pr.

Aubespin, Mervin, et al. Two Centuries of Black Louisville: A Photographic History. 2011. 45.00 ***(978-1-935497-36-3(7))*** Butler Bks., Inc.

Aukofer, Frank. City with a Chance: A Case History of Civil Rights Revolution. 2007. *(978-0-87462-021-4(X))* Marquette Univ. Pr.

Azania, Zolo A. Money & Power: Hook or Crook. 56p. (Orig.). reprint ed. pap. *(978-1-56411-144-9(X))* UBUS Communications Systems.

Bailey, Eric J. The Cultural Rights Movement: Fulfilling the Promise of Civil Rights for African Americans. 2010. 213p. 44.95 *(978-0-313-36009-1(X),* C36009, Praeger Pubs.) Greenwood Publishing Group, Inc.

Bailey, Joseph. Rising above Poverty. 2007. (ENG.). 404p. per. 19.95 *(978-1-59594-152-7(5),* Wingspan Pr.) WingSpan Publishing.

—Selfhood Mastery Inside African Tradition. 2007. 452p. per. 22.95 *(978-1-59594-208-1(4))* WingSpan Publishing.

Bakker, Daniel Z. Black Genocide. 2007. (ENG.). 277p. pap. 22.00 *(978-0-9779816-0-1(6))* K. B. Publishing.

Baldwin, Davarian L. Chicago's New Negroes: Modernity, the Great Migration, & Black Urban Life. 2007. (ENG., Illus.). 384p. 69.95 *(978-0-8078-3099-4(2))* Univ. of North Carolina Pr.

Baldwin, James. No Name in the Street. 2007. (Vintage International Ser.). (ENG.). 208p. pap. 14.00 *(978-0-307-27592-9(2),* Vintage) Knopf Doubleday Publishing Group.

—Notes of a Native Son. 2012. (ENG.). 192p. pap. 15.00 *(978-0-8070-0623-8(8))* Beacon Pr.

Balfour, Katharine Lawrence & Balfour, Lawrie. Democracy's Reconstruction: Thinking Politically with W. E. B. du Bois. 2011. (Transgressing Boundaries: Studies in Black Politics & Black Communities Ser.). (ENG.). 240p. 39.95 *(978-0-19-537729-3(X))* Oxford Univ. Pr., Inc.

Barr, Alwyn. Blacks in East Texas History: Selections from the East Texas Historical Journal. Glasrud, Bruce A. & McDonald, Archie P., eds. 2008. (ENG.). 208p. 29.95 *(978-1-60344-041-7(0))* Texas A&M Univ. Pr.

Battle, Juan & Barnes, Sandra L., eds. Black Sexualities: Probing Powers, Passions, Practices, & Policies. 2009. (ENG., Illus.). 474p. (C). 79.00 *(978-0-8135-4601-8(X));* pap. 32.95 *(978-0-8135-4602-5(8))* Rutgers Univ. Pr.

Beckett, Joyce Octavia. Lifting Our Voices: The Journeys into Family Caregiving of Professional Social Workers. 2008. (Illus.). 286p. E-Book 23.99 *(978-0-231-51195-7(7))* Columbia Univ. Pr.

Belgrave, Allison. African American Psychology from Africa. 2006. pap. 10.95 *(978-1-4288-1325-0(X))* Cram101 Inc.

Belgrave, Faye Z. African American Girls: Reframing Perceptions & Changing Experiences. 2011. (Advancing Responsible Adolescent Development Ser.). (ENG.). xii, 178p. pap. 44.95 ***(978-1-4614-1517-6(9),*** 1461415179) Springer.

Benjamin Lois. Three Black Generations at the Crossroads: Community, Culture, & Consciousness. 2nd ed. 2007. (ENG., Illus.). 276p. 80.00 *(978-0-7425-6000-0(7))* Rowman & Littlefield Publishers, Inc.

Benjamin, Lois. Three Black Generations at the Crossroads: Community, Culture, & Consciousness. 2nd ed. 2007. (ENG.). 276p. per. 26.95 *(978-0-7425-6001-7(5))* Rowman & Littlefield Publishers, Inc.

Benson Sr., Carl A. What Your Black Friends Don't Tell You: A Must Read Book for Whites & Their Black Friends. 2010. 144p. pap. 11.99 *(978-1-4343-5403-7(2))* AuthorHouse.

Berger, Martin A. Seeing through Race: A Reinterpretation of Civil Rights Photography. 2011. (ENG., Illus.). 208p. 60.00 *(978-0-520-26863-0(6));* pap. 27.50 *(978-0-520-26864-7(4))* Univ. of California Pr.

Berlin, Ira, et al, eds. Remembering Slavery: African Americans Talk about Their Personal Experiences of Slavery & Emancipation. 2007. (ENG., Illus.). 359p. pap. 29.95 *(978-1-59558-228-7(2))* New Pr., The.

Bernard, Regina Andrea. Black & Brown Waves: The Cultural Politics of Young Women of Color & Feminism. 2009. 170p. *(978-90-8790-809-6(1));* pap. *(978-90-8790-808-9(3))* Sense Pubs.

Binford, Virgie. The Pursuit of Victory: Empowering African American Males. 2009. (ENG.). 54p. pap. 8.95 *(978-1-57736-411-5(2))* Providence Hse Pubs.

Bingham, Howard. Black Panthers 1968. Crist, Steve, ed. 2009. (ENG., Illus.). 192p. 100.00 *(978-1-934429-15-0(5));* 44.95 *(978-1-934429-14-3(7))* AMMO Bks., LLC.

Black Americans of Achievement. 2011. (Black Americans of Achievement Legacy Edition Ser.). (gr. 6-12). 1400.00 ***(978-0-7910-9960-5(1))*** Facts On File, Inc.

Blair, William A. & Younger, Karen Fisher, eds. Lincoln's Proclamation: Emancipation Reconsidered. 2009. (Steven & Janice Brose Lectures in the Civil War Era Ser.). (ENG., Illus.). 248p. 32.00 *(978-0-8078-3316-2(9))* Univ. of North Carolina Pr.

Bois, William Edward Burghardt Du & Eaton, Isabel. The Philadelphia Negro: A Social Study. 2010. 562p. pap. 42.75 *(978-1-142-22095-2(8));* 570p. pap. 43.75 *(978-1-142-76335-0(8))* BiblioBazaar.

Bond, Horace Mann & Bond, Julia W. The Star Creek Papers. Fairclough, Adam, ed. 2011. (ENG.). 200p. pap. 22.95 ***(978-0-8203-4083-8(9))*** Univ. of Georgia Pr.

Bontemps, Alex. The Punished Self: Surviving Slavery in the Colonial South. 2008. (Illus.). 240p. pap. 25.95 *(978-0-8014-7482-8(5))* Cornell Univ. Pr.

Booker, Bryan D. African Americans in the United States Army in World War II. (ENG., Illus.). 366p. 2008. 75.00 *(978-0-7864-3195-3(4))* 2012. pap. 25.00 ***(978-0-7864-6904-8(8))*** McFarland & Co., Inc. Pubs.

Boothe, Demico. Why Are So Many Black Men in Prison? A Comprehensive Account of How & Why the Prison Industry Has Become A Predatory Entity in the Lives of African-American Men, & How Mass Targeting, Criminalization, & Incarceration of Black Male Youth Has Gone Toward Creating the Largest Prison System in the World. 2nd ed. 2007. 160p. pap. 14.00 *(978-0-9792953-0-0(0),* 076) Full Surface Publishing, LLC.

Borelli, Deneen. Blacklash. 2012. pap. ***(978-1-4516-4364-0(0),*** Threshold Editions) Threshold Editions.

Borelli, Deneen. Blacklash: How Obama & the Left Are Driving Americans to the Government Plantation. 2012. (ENG.). 304p. 26.00 *(978-1-4516-4286-5(5),* Threshold Editions) Threshold Editions.

Bosman, M. Martin & Chakraborty, Jayajit. Balancing the Scales: Spatial & Environmental Justice in Tampa Bay. 2010. *(978-1-60497-684-7(5))* Cambria Pr.

Bowser, Benjamin P. The Black Middle Class: Social Mobility, & Vulnerability. 2006. (Illus.). 180p. lib. bdg. 49.95 *(978-1-58826-455-8(6))* Rienner, Lynne Pubs.

Bradley, Anthony B. Black & Tired: Essays on Race, Politics, Culture, & International Development. 2011. 162p. pap. 19.00 *(978-1-60899-596-7(8),* Wipf and Stock) Wipf & Stock Pubs.

Bradley, Anthony B., ed. Keep Your Head Up: America's New Black Christian Leaders, Social Consciousness, & the Cosby Conversation. 2012. 224p. pap. 15.99 *(978-1-4335-0673-4(4))* Crossway.

Brawley, Benjamin. A Social History of the American Negro. 2008. 492p. 33.99 *(978-0-554-27000-5(5))*; 31.99 *(978-0-554-36303-5(8))* BiblioBazaar.

—A Social History of the American Negro. 2009. 456p. pap. *(978-1-4099-6265-6(2))* Dodo Pr.

Brawley, Benjamin G. A Social History of the American Negro. (Illus.). 420p. reprint ed. lib. bdg. 98.00 *(978-0-7222-4571-2(8))* Library Reprints, Inc.

Brooks-Burton, Carolyn. A Formula for Reparation: A Workable Forgiveness for a Long Overdue Sin. 2007. 38p. pap. 8.00 *(978-0-8059-7450-8(4))* Dorrance Publishing Co., Inc.

Brooks, Roy L. Racial Justice in the Age of Obama. 2009. (ENG., Illus.). 262p. (C). 28.95 *(978-0-691-14198-5(3))* Princeton Univ. Pr.

Brown, Cecil. Dude, Where's My Black Studies Department? The Disappearance of Black Americans from U. S. Universities. 2007. (Terra Nova Ser.). (ENG.). 160p. pap. 15.95 *(978-1-55643-573-7(8))* North Atlantic Bks.

Brown, David & Webb, Clive. Race in the American South: From Slavery to Civil Rights. 2007. (ENG.). 384p. per. 24.95 *(978-0-8130-3203-0(2))* Univ. Pr. of Florida.

Brown-Riggs, Constance. The African American Guide to Living Well with Diabetes. 2010. (ENG., Illus.). 1p. pap. 15.99 *(978-1-60163-115-2(4),* New Page Bks.) Career Pr., Inc.

Brown, Sterling Allen. A Negro Looks at the South. Tidwell, John Edgar & Sanders, Mark A., eds. 2007. (ENG., Illus.). 400p. 40.00 *(978-0-19-531399-4(2))* Oxford Univ. Pr., Inc.

Brown, William Wells. The Negro in the American Rebellion: His Heroism & His Fidelity. 2010. 394p. pap. 33.75 *(978-1-145-72653-6(4))* BiblioBazaar.

—The Negro in the American Rebellion: His Heroism & His Fidelity. 2010. 402p. pap. 27.96 *(978-1-163-29397-3(0))* 2010. 402p. 39.96 ***(978-1-163-56358-8(7))*** 2007. (ENG.). 400p. 49.95 *(978-0-548-26264-1(0))* 2007. (ENG.). 404p. per. 34.95 *(978-1-4326-6669-9(X))* Kessinger Publishing, LLC.

—The Negro in the American Rebellion: His heroism & his Fidelity. 2010. (ENG.). 402p. pap. 34.75 *(978-1-171-71825-3(X))* BiblioBazaar.

—The Negro in the American Rebellion; His Heroism & His Fidelity. 2006. 400p. per. 26.99 *(978-1-4255-4224-5(7))* MPublishing.

Bullard, Robert D. The Black Metropolis in the Twenty-First Century: Race, Power, & Politics of Place. 2007. (ENG., Illus.). 294p. 89.00 *(978-0-7425-4328-7(5))* Rowman & Littlefield Publishers, Inc.

Bunge, William. Fitzgerald: Geography of a Revolution. 2011. (Geographies of Justice & Social Transformation Ser.). (ENG., Illus.). 272p. pap. 26.95 *(978-0-8203-3874-3(5))* Univ. of Georgia Pr.

Burnley, Lawrence/A. Q. The Cost of Unity: African American Agency & Education & the Christian Church, 1865-1914. 2009. 320p. 45.00 *(978-0-88146-134-3(2))* Mercer Univ. Pr.

Burrell, Tom. Brainwashed: Challenging the Myth of Black Inferiority. 2010. (ENG.). 320p. pap. 15.95 *(978-1-4019-2592-5(8))* Hay Hse., Inc.

Cabbil, Lila, et al, eds. Accountability & White Anti-racist Organizing: Stories from Our Work. 2010. 256p. pap. 17.95 *(978-1-934390-32-0(1))* Crandall, Dostie & Douglas Bks., Inc.

Campbell, James M. & Fraser, Rebecca J., eds. Reconstruction: People & Perspectives, 1 vol. 2008. (Perspectives in American Social History Ser.). (Illus.). 279p. (gr. 9-18). 85.00 *(978-1-59884-021-6(5),* RECONS1C) ABC-CLIO, LLC.

Canfield, Jack L., et al. Chicken Soup for the African American Woman's Soul. 2006. (Chicken Soup for the Soul Ser.). (ENG., Illus.). 384p. pap. 14.95 *(978-0-7573-0520-7(2))* Health Communications, Inc.

Carroll, Grace. Died with a Bow. 2012. (Accessories Mystery Ser.). (ENG.). 288p. (gr. 12). mass mkt. 7.99 ***(978-0-425-25156-0(X),*** Berkley) Penguin Group (USA) Inc.

Cashin, Sheryll. The Agitator's Daughter: A Memoir of Four Generations of One Extraordinary African-American Family. 2008. (ENG., Illus.). 288p. 26.00 *(978-1-58648-422-4(2))* PublicAffairs.

Chavis, Bernard A. The Games of Tennis: An African American Journey. 2007. 210p. pap. 19.95 *(978-0-7414-4290-1(6))* Infinity Publishing.

Christie, Jackie. Proud to Be A Colored Girl. 2009. (ENG.). 76p. pap. 14.95 *(978-0-9794827-6-2(3))* Infinite Love Publishing.

Clark, Tom, et al. The Age of Obama: The Changing Place of Minorities in British & American Society. 2010. (ENG., Illus.). 192p. 74.95 *(978-0-7190-8277-1(3))*; pap. 19.95 *(978-0-7190-8278-8(1))* Manchester Univ. Pr. GBR. Dist: Macmillan.

Cobbs, Price. My American Life: From Rage to Entitlement. 2006. (ENG.). 272p. pap. 17.99 *(978-0-7434-9622-3(1),* Beyond Words/Atria Bks.) Atria Bks.

Cohen, Cathy J. Democracy Remixed: Black Youth & the Future of American Politics, 1 vol. 2012. (Transgressing Boundaries: Studies in Black Politics & Black Communities Ser.). (ENG., Illus.). 304p. pap. 19.95 ***(978-0-19-989626-4(7))*** Oxford Univ. Pr., Inc.

Colby, Tanner. Some of My Best Friends Are Black: The Strange Story of Integration in America. 2012. (ENG.). 320p. (gr. 12). 27.95 ***(978-0-670-02371-4(X),*** Viking Adult) Penguin Group (USA) Inc.

Cole, Stephanie & Ring, Natalie J., eds. The Folly of Jim Crow: Rethinking the Segregated South. 2012. (Walter Prescott Webb Memorial Lectures, published for the University of Texas At Ser.). (Illus.). 256p. 30.00 ***(978-1-60344-582-5(X))*** Texas A&M Univ. Pr.

Cole, Stephanie, et al. The Folly of Jim Crow: Rethinking the Segregated South. 2012. E-Book ***(978-1-60344-661-7(3))*** Texas A&M Univ. Pr.

Coleman, L. E. (Larry E.). We the People of Colors: For Sale to the Lowest Bidder. 2008. 138p. per. 14.95 *(978-0-9790644-5-6(7))* Crowner-Coleman Publishing.

Coleman, Larry E. We the People of Color: For Sale to the Lowest Bidder. 2008. 126p. 19.95 *(978-0-9790644-4-9(9))* Crowner-Coleman Publishing.

Coles, Roberta. Best Kept Secret: Single Black. 2010. (ENG.). 180p. pap. 24.95 *(978-0-7425-6426-8(6))* Rowman & Littlefield Publishers, Inc.

Coles, Roberta L. The Best Kept Secret: Single Black Fathers. 2009. (ENG.). 180p. 37.50 *(978-0-7425-6425-1(8))* Rowman & Littlefield Publishers, Inc.

Conley, Dalton. Being Black, Living in the Red: Race, Wealth, & Social Policy in America. 10th anniv. ed. 2009. (ENG., Illus.). 234p. pap. 24.95 *(978-0-520-26130-3(5))* Univ. of California Pr.

Conyers, James L. African American Consciousness: Past & Present. 2011. (ENG.). 190p. pap. 29.95 ***(978-1-4128-4307-2(3))*** Transaction Pubs.

Corbould, Clare. Becoming African Americans: Black Public Life in Harlem, 1919-1939. 2009. (Illus.). 304p. 42.00 *(978-0-674-03262-0(4))* Harvard Univ. Pr.

Cosby, Bill & Poussaint, Alvin F. Come on People: On the Path from Victims to Victors, 0 vols. 2009. 288p. pap. 14.99 *(978-1-59555-186-3(7))* Nelson, Thomas Inc.

Covington, Jeanette. Drugs in Black & White: African Americans & Drug Policy. 2007. (ENG.). 456p. 35.95 *(978-0-415-95417-4(7))*; 135.00 *(978-0-415-95416-7(9))* Routledge.

Cowan, Paul. The Tribes of America: Journalistic Discoveries of Our People & Their Cultures. 2008. (ENG.). 311p. per. 16.95 *(978-1-59558-230-0(4))* New Pr., The.

Cox, Oliver Cromwell. Race Relations Raw & Uncensored: Elements & Social Dynamics. rev. ed. 2010. Orig. Title: Race Relations: Elements & Social Dynamics. (C). pap. 65.00 *(978-0-9761541-5-0(3))* Oliver Cromwell Cox Online Institute, The.

Cramer, Kyle Stanford. American Frankenstein: How the United States Created A Monster! 2010. 208p. 24.99 *(978-1-4500-8569-4(5))*; pap. 17.99 *(978-1-4500-8568-7(7))* Xlibris Corp.

Cram101 Textbook Reviews & Cram101 Textbook Reviews. Outlines & Highlights for the Black Metropolis in the Twenty-First Century: Race, Power, & Politics of Place by Robert Bullard, ISBN. 2011. 216p. pap. 30.95 ***(978-1-61461-858-4(5))*** Cram101 Inc.

Cram101 Textbook Reviews Staff. Outlines & Highlights for Black Sexual Politics: African Americans, Gender, & the New Racism by Patricia H Collins, ISBN. 2009. 90p. pap. 27.95 *(978-1-4288-9770-0(4))* Cram101 Inc.

Crist, Steve, ed. Howard L. Bingham's Black Panthers 1968: Popular Edition. 2010. (ENG.). 192p. 19.95 *(978-1-934429-66-2(X))* AMMO Bks., LLC.

Crouch, Barry. The Dance of Freedom: Texas African Americans During Reconstruction. Madaras, Larry, ed. 2007. (Jack & Doris Smothers Series in Texas History, Life, & Culture: No. 19). (ENG.). 286p. mass mkt. 25.00 *(978-0-292-71487-8(4))* Univ. of Texas Pr.

Dancy, T. Elon. The Brother Code: Manhood & Masculinity among African American Men in College. 2012. ***(978-1-61735-761-9(8))***; pap. ***(978-1-61735-760-2(X))*** Information Age Publishing, Inc.

Daniels, Cora. Ghettonation: Dispatches from America's Culture War. 2008. (ENG.). 224p. pap. 15.00 *(978-0-7679-2240-1(9),* Harlem Moon) Broadway Bks.

Darden, Joe T., et al. The State of Black Michigan, 1967-2007. Darden, Joe T. et al, eds. 2007. (ENG., Illus.). 364p. per. 39.95 *(978-0-87013-827-0(8))* Michigan State Univ. Pr.

Dattel, Gene. Cotton & Race in the Making of America: The Human Costs of Economic Power. 2011. (ENG., Illus.). 432p. pap. 18.95 ***(978-1-56663-968-2(9))*** Dee, Ivan R. Pub.

Davidson, Harry X., et al. Somebody's Trying to Kill You Vol. II: The Economics of Death. Lewis, R. H., ed. 158p. pap. 15.00 *(978-0-9644417-0-5(5))* Davidson, Harry R.

Davis, Robert E. The American Negro's Dilemm: The Negro's Self-Imposed Predicament. 2011. 158p. 41.95 ***(978-1-258-04152-6(9))*** Literary Licensing, LLC.

Davison, James, Jr. & Davison, James. Sweet Release: The Last Step to Black Freedom. 2008. (ENG.). 255p. 26.98 *(978-1-59102-558-0(3))* Prometheus Bks., Pubs.

Dawkins, Wayne. City Son: Andrew W. Cooper's Impact on Modern-Day Brooklyn. 2012. (Margaret Walker Alexander Series in African American Studies). (ENG.). 304p. 35.00 ***(978-1-61703-258-5(1))*** Univ. Pr. of Mississippi.

DeMott, Benj. Perspectives by Incogruity: First of the Year. 2012. (ENG.). 314p. pap. 29.95 ***(978-1-4128-4311-9(1))*** Transaction Pubs.

Dene, Debe. Now hair This! The Destruction of Black Hair. 2008. (Illus.). 141p. pap. 12.95 *(978-0-9801242-0-0(4))* Tell Pubns.

Dill, Augustus. Morals & Manners among Negro Americans. 2010. (ENG.). 210p. 68.50 *(978-0-7391-1669-2(X))*; pap. 29.50 *(978-0-7391-1670-8(3))* Lexington Bks.

Dilworth, Vernolda L. Race: Reducing African American Crime Effectively. 2011. 54p. 24.99 ***(978-1-4628-9752-0(5))***; pap. 15.99 ***(978-1-4628-9751-3(7))*** Xlibris Corp.

Dimitriadis, Greg. Performing Identity/Performing Culture: Hip Hop As Text, Pedagogy, & Lived Practice. 2009. (Intersections in Communications & Culture: Global Approaches & Transdisciplinary Perspectives Ser.). 216p. (C). 29.95 *(978-1-4331-0538-8(1))* Lang, Peter Publishing, Inc.

Dixon, Patricia. African American Relationships, Marriages, & Families. 2006. (ENG., Illus.). 304p. per. 51.95 *(978-0-415-95533-1(5))* Routledge.

Dixon, Terry D. Black Issues: Spiritual & Social Ills. 2008. 116p. per. 12.95 *(978-1-4327-2189-3(5))* Outskirts Pr., Inc.

Dockett, Kymo. The Post Hip-Hop Generation: 20 Principles for A Successful Generation. 2009. 188p. pap. 12.50 *(978-1-59330-610-6(5))* Aventine Pr.

Dodson, Howard & Palmer, Colin, eds. Ideology, Identity, & Assumptions. 2007. (Schomburg Studies on the Black Experience). (ENG., Illus.). 205p. per. 19.95 *(978-0-87013-795-2(6))* Michigan State Univ. Pr.

Dodson, Howard & Palmer, Colin A. The Black Condition. Dodson, Howard, ed. 2008. (Schomburg Studies on the Black Experience: Ser.). (ENG., Illus.). 272p. pap. 24.95 *(978-0-87013-838-6(3))* Michigan State Univ. Pr.

Donaldson, Jam. Conversate Is Not a Word: Getting Away from Ghetto. 2010. (ENG., Illus.). 208p. pap. 14.95 *(978-1-55652-780-7(2),* Hill, Lawrence Bks.) Chicago Review Pr., Inc.

Donoghue, Eddie. Black Breeding Machines. 2008. 448p. 32.90 *(978-1-4389-0237-1(9))*; pap. 22.90 *(978-1-4343-9802-4(1))* AuthorHouse.

Douglass, Frederick, et al. Frederick Douglass: A Documentary History of His Fight for Freedom & Equality. 2010. (Illus.). 181p. pap. ***(978-1-932821-12-3(0))*** Gilder Lehrman Institute of American History, The.

Du Bois, W. E. B. Of the Dawn of Freedom. 2010. (Penguin Great Ideas Ser.). (ENG.). 112p. (gr. 12). 10.00 *(978-0-14-139928-7(7),* Penguin (Non-Classics)) Penguin Group (USA) Inc.

—The Philadelphia Negro. 2007. 540p. per. 17.75 *(978-1-60206-942-8(5))* Cosimo, Inc.

—The Philadelphia Negro: A Social Study. 2007. 542p. 57.95 *(978-0-548-21951-5(6))*; 544p. per. 42.95 *(978-1-4325-4019-7(X))* Kessinger Publishing, LLC.

—The Philadelphia Negro: A Social Study. 520p. reprint ed. 98.00 *(978-0-7222-9791-9(2))* Library Reprints, Inc.

—The Philadelphia Negro: A Social Study (1899) 2007. 572p. per. 43.95 *(978-0-548-80502-2(4))* Kessinger Publishing, LLC.

—The Philadelphia Negro A Social Study. 2009. 572p. pap. 33.46 *(978-1-4385-2072-8(7),* Book Jungle) Standard Pubns., Inc.

—The Philadelphia Negro a Social Study. 2010. 298p. pap. *(978-1-153-09425-2(8))* Books LLC.

—The Philadelphia Negro: A Social Study. 2010. 571p. pap. 35.97 *(978-0-557-36228-8(8))* Lulu Enterprises Inc.

—A Study of the Negro Problems. 23p. reprint ed. 88.00 *(978-0-7222-9718-6(1))* Library Reprints, Inc.

Du Bois, W. E. Burghardt. The Philadelphia Negro: A Social Study. 2010. 544p. 46.36 ***(978-1-163-52117-5(5))***; pap. 34.36 ***(978-1-163-25083-9(X))*** Kessinger Publishing, LLC.

Dubois, Laurent. Origins of the Black Atlantic: Rewriting Histories. 2009. (Rewriting Histories Ser.). (Illus.). 414p. pap. 38.95 *(978-0-415-99446-0(2))* Routledge.

Dukes, Maudine. The Honorable & the Brave. 2009. 68p. pap. 15.00 *(978-1-4490-4629-3(0))* AuthorHouse.

Dybska, Aneta. Black Masculinities in American Social Science & Self-Narratives of the 1960s And 1970s. 2010. (American Studies & Media Ser.). 194p. 61.95 *(978-3-631-61330-6(X))* Lang, Peter GmbH, Europaischer Verlag der Wissenschaften DEU. Dist: Lang, Peter.

Dyson, Michael Eric. April 4 1968: Martin Luther King, Jr.'s Death & How It Changed America. 2009. (ENG.). 304p. pap. 14.95 *(978-0-465-01286-2(8))* Basic Bks.

—Can You Hear Me Now? The Inspiration, Wisdom, & Insight of Michael Eric Dyson. 2011. (ENG., Illus.). 316p. (gr. 9). pap. 14.99 *(978-0-465-01967-0(6))* Basic Bks.

—Come Hell or High Water: Hurricane Katrina & the Color of Disaster. 2007. cd-rom 49.95 *(978-0-9779883-5-8(X))* Legacy Audio Bks.

—Race Rules: Navigating the Color Line. 2012. (ENG.). 240p. (gr. 9). pap. 15.99 *(978-0-465-02079-9(8))* Basic Bks.

Early, Gerald L. A Level Playing Field: African American Athletes & the Republic of Sports. 2011. (Alain Locke Lecture Ser.). 288p. 25.95 *(978-0-674-05098-3(3))* Harvard Univ. Pr.

Elfenbein, Jessica, et al. Baltimore '68: Riots & Rebirth in an American City. 2011. (ENG., Illus.). 294p. pap. 29.95 *(978-1-4399-0662-0(9))* Temple Univ. Pr.

Ellis, Aimé J. If We Must Die: From Bigger Thomas to Biggie Smalls. 2014. (Illus.). 240p. pap. 24.95 *(978-0-8143-3413-3(X))* Wayne State Univ. Pr.

Ellis, William. White Ethics & Black Power: The Emergence of the West Side Organization. 2009. (ENG.). 205p. pap. 24.95 *(978-0-202-36289-2(2))* Aldine Transaction.

Escott, Paul D. North Carolinians in the Era of the Civil War & Reconstruction. 2008. (ENG., Illus.). 320p. 55.95 *(978-0-8078-3222-6(7))*; pap. 24.95 *(978-0-8078-5901-8(X))* Univ. of North Carolina Pr.

Everett, Anna. Digital Diaspora: A Race for Cyberspace. 2009. (Illus.). 272p. 89.50 *(978-0-7914-7673-4(1))*; pap. 29.95 *(978-0-7914-7674-1(X))* State Univ. of New York Pr.

Falola, Toyin & Afolabi, Niyi, eds. African Minorities in the New World. 2012. (African Studies). (ENG.). 290p. pap. 42.95 ***(978-0-415-54084-1(4))*** Routledge.

Farmer, John Edward. From the Psychoanalysis Mind of an Intelligent Black Man from the Project. 2010. 116p. pap. 12.50 *(978-1-4269-3273-1(1))* Trafford Publishing.

Farris, Ron. Africans & African Americans Divided: The Male-Female African & African American Digital Divide. 2008. 228p. 34.95 *(978-1-4357-0009-3(0))* Lulu Enterprises Inc.

—Africans & African Americans Divided:the Male-Female African & African American Digital Divide. 2008. 228p. pap. 19.95 *(978-1-4357-0272-1(7))* Lulu Enterprises Inc.

Feagin, Joe R. Racist America: Roots, Current Realities & Future Reparations Remaking America with Anti-Racist Strategies. 2nd rev. ed. 2009. (ENG., Illus.). 256p. 150.00 *(978-0-415-99206-0(0))* Routledge.

—The White Racial Frame: Centuries of Racial Framing & Counter-Framing. 2009. (ENG.). 264p. pap. 34.95 *(978-0-415-99439-2(X))*; (Illus.). 144.00 *(978-0-415-99438-5(1))* Routledge.

Feagin, Joe R., ed. & reader. Racist America: Roots, Current Realities & Future Reparations Remaking America with Anti-Racist Strategies. 2nd rev. ed. 2010. (ENG., Illus.). 376p. 31.95 *(978-0-415-99207-7(9))* Routledge.

Ferdinand, Keith C. & Penner, D'Ann R. Overcoming Katrina: African American Voices from the Crescent City & Beyond. 2009. (Palgrave Studies in Oral History Ser.). (ENG., Illus.). 288p. pap. 21.00 *(978-0-230-60871-9(X))* Palgrave Macmillan.

Ferrell, Tena. Why I Voted for Barack Obama: Our First African-American President. 2008. 40p. pap. 14.95 *(978-0-557-02515-2(X))* Lulu Enterprises Inc.

Flamming, Douglas. African Americans in the West, 1 vol. 2009. (Cultures in the American West Ser.). (Illus.). 353p. 65.00 *(978-1-59884-002-5(9),* AFAMWE1C) ABC-CLIO, LLC.

Ford, Arthur Lee. When the Whippoorwill Sang: A Memoir of Rural Life During the Twilight of the Segregated South. 2008. *(978-1-887366-84-7(9))* Univ. of Louisiana at Lafayette Pr.

Ford, Pearl, ed. African Americans in Georgia: A Reflection of Politics & Policy in the New South. 2010. 224p. 40.00 *(978-0-88146-184-8(9))* Mercer Univ. Pr.

Ford, Richard Thompson & Ford, Richard Thompson T. Race Card: How Bluffing about Bias Makes Race Relations Worse. 2009. (ENG., Illus.). 416p. pap. 16.00 *(978-0-312-42826-6(X))* Picador.

Fortune, T. Thomas. T. Thomas Fortune, the Afro-American Agitator: A Collection of Writings, 1880-1928. Alexander, Shawn Leigh, ed. 2008. (New Perspectives on the History of the South Ser.). (ENG.). 320p. 65.00 *(978-0-8130-3232-0(6))* Univ. Pr. of Florida.

Franklin, Robert M. Crisis in the Village: Restoring Hope in African American Communities. 2007. 280p. per. 16.00 *(978-0-8006-3887-0(5),* Fortress Pr.) Augsburg Fortress, Pubs.

Frazier, John W., et al, eds. The African Diaspora in the United State & Canada at the Dawn of the 21st Century. 2010. (Global Academic Publishing Ser.). (Illus.). 383p. pap. 49.00 *(978-1-4384-3684-5(X),* Suny Pr.) State Univ. of New York Pr.

—The African Diaspora in the United States & Canada at the Dawn of the 21st Century. 2009. pap. *(978-1-58684-271-0(4))* Global Academic Publishing.

Freeman, Clarence E. The Light-Skin Trigger. 2009. 228p. 29.99 *(978-1-4363-8820-7(1))*; pap. 19.99 *(978-1-4363-8819-1(8))* Xlibris Corp.

Fuller, Paul. From Africans to African Americans: A Sociological & Historical Analysis of the Black Experience, 1 vol. 2010. 190p. pap. 24.95 *(978-1-4512-9357-9(7))* PublishAmerica, Inc.

Gadzekpo & Gadzekpo, Leonard. The African American Experience in a Pluralistic Society. rev. ed. 2010. (ENG.). 324p. pap. 87.81 *(978-0-7575-7943-1(4))* Kendall Hunt Publishing Co.

Gardner, Eric, ed. Jennie Carter: A Black Journalist of the Early West. 2007. (ENG.). 208p. 50.00 *(978-1-934110-10-2(8))* Univ. Pr. of Mississippi.

Gentry, Quinn M. Black Women's Risk for HIV: Rough Living. 2007. (ENG.). 282p. per. 65.95 *(978-0-7890-3170-9(1))* Routledge.

Georges, Jean Ricardy. Don't Blame the Blacks Because Slavery Systems Still Exist. 2007. *(978-1-59835-052-4(8))* Cambridge BrickHouse, Inc.

Gilchrist, Eletra S. Experiences of Single African-American Women Professors. 2011. (ENG., Illus.). 250p. 70.00 ***(978-0-7391-7087-8(2))*** Lexington Bks.

Glasrud, Bruce A., et al, eds. Slavery to Integration: Black Americans in West Texas. 2008. (ENG., Illus.). 168p. pap. 21.95 *(978-1-933337-26-5(5))* State Hse. Pr.

Glasrud, Bruce A. & Pitre, Merline, eds. Black Women in Texas History. 2008. (Centennial Series of the Association of Former Students, Texas AandM University). (ENG.). 256p. pap. 19.95 *(978-1-60344-031-8(3))* Texas A&M Univ. Pr.

Glave, Dianne D. Rooted in the Earth: Reclaiming the African American Environmental Heritage. 2010. (ENG., Illus.). 208p. pap. 18.95 *(978-1-55652-766-1(7),* Hill, Lawrence Bks.) Chicago Review Pr., Inc.

God Bless America, Bless America & God Bless America. Opinions & Perspectives by a Black Man That Are Guaranteed to Fuel Controversy. 2009. 88p. pap. 14.99 *(978-1-4490-3018-6(1))* AuthorHouse.

Goings, Henry. Rambles of a Runaway from Southern Slavery. Schermerhorn, Calvin et al, eds. 2012. (Carter G. Woodson Institute Ser.). (ENG., Illus.). 200p. (gr. 17). 45.00 ***(978-0-8139-3238-5(6))*** Univ. Pr. of Virginia.

Goings, Henry, et al. Rambles of a Runaway from Southern Slavery. 2012. E-Book *(978-0-8139-3240-8(8))* Univ. Pr. of Virginia.

Goosman, Stuart L. Group Harmony: The Black Urban Roots of Rhythm & Blues. 2010. (Illus.). 304p. (C). pap. 24.95 *(978-0-8122-2108-4(7))* Univ. of Pennsylvania Pr.

Gordon, Colin. Mapping Decline: St. Louis & the Fate of the American City. 2009. (Politics & Culture in Modern America Ser.). (Illus.). 304p. (C). pap. 37.50 *(978-0-8122-2094-0(3))* Univ. of Pennsylvania Pr.

Green, Tara T. A Fatherless Child: Autobiographical Perspectives of African American Men. 2009. (ENG.). 184p. (C). 34.95 *(978-0-8262-1821-6(0))* Univ. of Missouri Pr.

Green, William D. A Peculiar Imbalance: The Fall & Rise of Racial Equality in Early Minnesota. 2007. 232p. 32.95 *(978-0-87351-586-3(2))* Minnesota Historical Society Pr.

Greene, Brenda M. The African Presence & Influence on the Cultures of the Americas. 2010. 195p. *(978-1-4438-2216-9(7))* Cambridge Scholars Pub.

Greenwood, Janette Thomas. First Fruits of Freedom: The Migration of Former Slaves & Their Search for Equality in Worcester, Massachusetts, 1862-1900. 2010. (John Hope Franklin Series in African American History & Culture Ser.). (ENG., Illus.). 256p. 55.00 *(978-0-8078-3362-9(2))*; pap. 22.95 *(978-0-8078-7104-1(4))* Univ. of North Carolina Pr.

Griffin, Drs. James P. Jr. & Karen E. African American Manhood Development: Contemporary Life Lessons for Leaders — Student Guide. 2010. 96p. pap. 15.00 *(978-0-557-25503-0(1))* Lulu Enterprises Inc.

Griffin, John Howard. Black Like Me. 50th anniv. ed. 2010. (ENG.). 208p. (gr. 12). 7.99 *(978-0-451-23421-6(9))*, Signet) Penguin Group (USA) Inc.

Griffith, Joanne, ed. Redefining Black Power: Reflections on the State of Black America. 2012. (City Lights Open Media Ser.). (ENG.). 208p. pap. 16.95 *(978-0-87286-546-4(0))* City Lights Bks.

Guridy, Frank Andre. Forging Diaspora: Afro-Cubans & African Americans in a World of Empire & Jim Crow. 2010. (Envisioning Cuba Ser.). (ENG., Illus.). 288p. 59.95 *(978-0-8078-3361-2(4))*; pap. 22.95 *(978-0-8078-7103-4(6))* Univ. of North Carolina Pr.

Haggard, Dixie Ray, ed. African Americans in the Nineteenth Century: People & Perspectives, 1 vol. (Perspectives in American Social History Ser.). (Illus.). 258p. 85.00 *(978-1-59884-123-7(8)*, AFAMNI1C) ABC-CLIO, LLC.

Haley, Alex. Alex Haley: The Man Who Traced America's Roots. 2007. *(978-0-7621-0885-5(1))* Reader's Digest Assn., Inc., The.

Hammond, Tarana. Media Use, Hiv/Aids Knowledge, & Sexual Beliefs. 2008. 72p. pap. *(978-3-639-00175-4(3))* VDM Verlag Dr. Mueller e.K.

Harper, Kimberly. White Man's Heaven: The Lynching & Expulsion of Blacks in the Southern Ozarks, 1894-1909. 2010. (ENG., Illus.). 302p. 34.95 *(978-1-55728-941-4(7))* Univ. of Arkansas Pr.

Harris, Glen Anthony. The Ocean Hill-Brownsville Conflict: Intellectual Struggles Between Blacks & Jews at Midcentury. 2012. (ENG.). 204p. (gr. 17). 65.00 *(978-0-7391-6683-3(2))* Lexington Bks.

Harris, Laurie L. The Great Migration North, 1910-1970. 2011. (Defining Moments Ser.). (YA). lib. bdg. 55.00 *(978-0-7808-1186-7(0))* Omnigraphics, Inc.

Harris, William M. African American Community Development (with Twelve Case Studies) A Plan for Self-Determination. 2012. (ENG., Illus.). 260p. 119.95 *(978-0-7734-2614-6(0))* Mellen, Edwin Pr., The.

Hart, Philip S. African Americans & the Future of New Orleans: Rebirth, Renewal & Rebuilding — An American Dilemma. 2007. (ENG., Illus.). 180p. pap. 15.95 *(978-0-9790976-1-4(4))* Amber Bks.

Hatch, John B. Race & Reconciliation: Redressing Wounds of Injustice. (Race, Rites, & Rhetoric: Colors, Cultures, & Communication Ser.). (ENG.). 420p. 2009. pap. 40.99 *(978-0-7391-2153-5(7))* 2008. 94.50 *(978-0-7391-2152-8(9))* Lexington Bks.

Hattery, Angela J. & Smith, Earl. African American Families. 2007. (Illus.). 408p. (C). per. 53.00 *(978-1-4129-2466-5(9)*, B24669P) SAGE Pubns., Inc.

Hicks, Reginald E. Hidden in the Shadow of Truth: Why Our Black Boys Choose Criminality, Prison, & Enslavement. 2010. 206p. 27.95 *(978-1-4502-1669-2(2))*; (ENG.). pap. 17.95 *(978-1-4502-1667-8(6))* iUniverse, Inc.

Hill, Anita F. Reimagining Equality: Stories of Gender, Race, & Finding Home. (ENG.). 224p. 2012. pap. 16.00 *(978-0-8070-1443-1(5))* 2011. 25.95 *(978-0-8070-1437-0(0))* Beacon Pr.

Hill, Johnny Bernard. The First Black President: Barack Obama, Race, Politics, & the American Dream. 2009. (ENG.). 208p. 100.00 *(978-0-230-61861-9(8))*; pap. 30.00 *(978-0-230-62114-5(7))* Palgrave Macmillan.

Hinton, Elizabeth Kai. The New Black History: Revisiting the Second Reconstruction. Marable, Manning & Joseph, Peniel E., eds. 2011. (Critical Black Studies). (ENG.). 336p. pap. 28.00 *(978-1-4039-7777-9(1))*; (Illus.). 90.00 *(978-1-4039-8397-8(6))* Palgrave Macmillan.

Holloway, Pippa. Sexuality, Politics, & Social Control in Virginia, 1920-1945. 2006. (ENG.). 272p. per. 22.00 *(978-0-8078-5764-9(5))* Univ. of North Carolina Pr.

hooks, bell. Black Looks: Race & Representation. 2006. pap. 8.95 *(978-1-4288-1629-9(1))* Cram101 Inc.

Hornsby, Alton. Black Power in Dixie: A Political History of African Americans in Atlanta. 2009. (Southern Dissent Ser.). (ENG., Illus.). 320p. 39.95 *(978-0-8130-3282-5(2))* Univ. Pr. of Florida.

Hubbard, Daryl K. Hiding the Signs. 2007. (ENG.). 59p. (YA). per. 10.00 *(978-0-9791154-8-6(5)*, MSP) Main St Publishing, Inc.

Hudson, James. The Rising of Black America with the Assistance of White Americ. 2009. 284p. 27.50 *(978-1-60860-142-4(0)*, Eloquent Bks.) AEG Literary Publishing Services, Inc.

Hughes, Melinda. Illness Perception & Coping among African American Women with Lupus - Alternative Medicine & Cultural Competence. 2007. pap. *(978-3-8364-2840-8(7))* VDM Verlag Dr. Mueller e.K.

Hurt, R. Douglas, ed. & intro. African American Life in the Rural South, 1900-1950. 2011. (ENG., Illus.). 240p. (C). (gr. 13). pap. 30.00 *(978-0-8262-1960-2(8))* Univ. of Missouri Pr.

Hutchinson, Earl Ofari. The Latino Challenge to Black America: Towards a Conversation Between African Americans & Hispanics. 2007. (ENG.). 224p. *(978-1-881032-22-9(1))* Middle Passage Pr.

Irele, F. Abiola & Shelby, Tommie, eds. Transition 98. 2008. (Illus.). 184p. pap. 18.50 *(978-0-253-11683-3(X))* Indiana Univ. Pr.

Jabbar, Malik H. The Plot, the Cause, the Solution. 3rd ed. 35p. reprint ed. pap. 4.95 *(978-1-57154-001-0(6))* Rare Bks. Distributors.

Jack, Bryan M. The St. Louis African American Community & the Exodusters. 2008. (ENG.). 192p. (C). 34.95 *(978-0-8262-1772-1(9))* Univ. of Missouri Pr.

Jackson, David H. Booker T. Washington & the Struggle Against White Supremacy: The Southern Educational Tours, 1908-1912. 2008. (ENG., Illus.). 288p. 89.00 *(978-0-230-60652-4(0))* Palgrave Macmillan.

Jackson, David H., Jr. Booker T. Washington & the Struggle against White Supremacy: The Southern Educational Tours, 1908-1912. 2009. (ENG.). 272p. pap. 32.00 *(978-0-230-62138-1(4))* Palgrave Macmillan.

Jackson, Donald Maurice. Fourth down & Twenty Five Years to Go: The African American Athlete & the Justice System. 2007. (ENG.). 224p. 27.95 *(978-0-595-89619-6(7))* iUniverse, Inc.

Jackson, Sandra & Johnson, Richard Greggory. The Black Professoriat: Negotiating a Habitable Space in the Academy. 2011. vi, 254p. *(978-1-4331-1028-3(8))*; pap. *(978-1-4331-1027-6(X))* Lang, Peter GmbH, Europaischer Verlag der Wissenschaften.

James Charles Johnson. Evolution after Emancipation: America's Greatest Race. 2009. 380p. pap. 18.99 *(978-1-4389-6703-5(9))* AuthorHouse.

Jaspin, Elliot. Buried in the Bitter Waters: The Hidden History of Racial Cleansing in America. 2008. (ENG.). 352p. pap. 15.95 *(978-0-465-03637-0(5))* Basic Bks.

Jefferson, Mary. Old Negro & the New Negro by T Leroy J. 2006. 20.00 *(978-1-4257-1718-6(7))*; pap. 10.00 *(978-1-4257-1670-7(9))* Xlibris Corp.

Jennings, William. The African American King. 2008. 164p. pap. 19.95 *(978-1-4327-0216-8(5))* Outskirts Pr., Inc.

Jewell, Joseph O. Race, Social Reform & the Making of a Black Middle Class: Atlanta, 1870-1900. 2007. (ENG.). 236p. 84.00 *(978-0-7425-3545-9(2))* Rowman & Littlefield Publishers, Inc.

—Race, Social Reform, & the Making of a Middle Class: The American Missionary Association & Black Atlanta, 1870-1900. 2007. (ENG.). 236p. per. 29.95 *(978-0-7425-3546-6(0))* Rowman & Littlefield Publishers, Inc.

Jimeson, Bessie. Yesterday I Heard the Rain. 2008. pap. 10.00 *(978-0-8059-7910-7(7))* Dorrance Publishing Co., Inc.

Johnson, Beverly Black. Gumbo for the Soul: Here's Our Child-Where's the Village? 2008. 128p. pap. 11.95 *(978-1-4401-0126-7(4))* iUniverse, Inc.

Johnson, Charles S. Growing up in the Black Belt: Negro Youth in the Rural South. 2008. 392p. pap. 38.00 *(978-1-59740-627-7(9))* ACLS Humanities E-Book.

Johnson, Robert A. & Riggins, Charlene. A Different Shade of Orange: Voices of Orange County, California, Black Pioneers. 2009. pap. *(978-0-930046-25-5(0))* California State Univ., San Bernardino, Robert V. Fullerton Art Museum.

Jolly, Kenneth. Black Liberation in the Midwest: The Struggle in St. Louis, Missouri, 1964-1970. 2006. (Studies in African American History & Culture). 232p. 136.00 *(978-0-415-97969-6(2))* Routledge.

Jones, Clarence B. & Engel, Joel. What Would Martin Say? 2008. (ENG.). 256p. pap. 13.99 *(978-0-06-167267-5(X)*, HarperPerennial) HarperCollins Pubs.

Jones, Martha S. All Bound up Together: The Woman Question in African American Public Culture, 1830-1900. 2007. (ENG., Illus.). 328p. pap. 22.00 *(978-0-8078-5845-5(5))* Univ. of North Carolina Pr.

Jones, Nikki. Between Good & Ghetto: African American Girls & Inner City Violence. 2009. (Rutgers Series in Childhood Studies). (ENG.). (C). 224p. 72.00 *(978-0-8135-4614-8(1))*; 228p. pap. 22.95 *(978-0-8135-4615-5(X))* Rutgers Univ. Pr.

Jones, Ricky L. What's Wrong with Obamamania? Black America, Black Leadership, & the Death of Political Imagination. 2008. (C). 44.50 *(978-0-7914-7579-9(4))*; 160p. pap. 19.95 *(978-0-7914-7580-5(8))* State Univ. of New York Pr.

Jones, Stephanie. The State of Black America 2009: Message to the President. 2009. (ENG.). 290p. pap. 19.95 *(978-0-914758-02-0(0))* National Urban League, National Headquarters.

Jones, Stephanie J. & Height, Dorothy. The State of Black America 2008: In the Black Woman's Voice. Jones, Stephanie J. et al, eds. Malveaux, Julianne, contrib. by. 2008. (State of Black America Ser.). (ENG., Illus.). 254p. pap. 19.95 *(978-0-914758-01-3(2))* National Urban League, National Headquarters.

Jun, Helen. Race for Citizenship: Black Orientalism & Asian Uplift from Pre-Emancipation to Neoliberal America. 2011. (ENG.). 208p. 70.00 *(978-0-8147-4297-6(1))*; pap. 22.00 *(978-0-8147-4298-3(X))* New York Univ. Pr.

Kafele, Baruti. Motivating Black Males to Achieve in School & in Life. 2009. pap. 16.95 *(978-1-4166-0857-8(5))* Assn. for Supervision & Curriculum Development.

Kaplan, Erin Aubry. Black Talk, Blue Thoughts, & Walking the Color Line: Dispatches from a Black Journalista. 2011. (Northeastern Library of Black Literature Ser.). 304p. pap. 19.95 *(978-1-55553-754-8(5)*, Northeastern University Pr.) Univ. Pr. of New England.

Karenga. Kawaida & Questions of Life & Struggle: African American, Pan-African, & Global Issues. 2007. *(978-0-943412-29-0(3))* Univ. of Sankore Pr., The.

Kenan, Randall. The Fire This Time. 2007. (ENG.). 149p. 20.00 *(978-1-933633-24-4(7))* Melville Hse. Publishing.

Kennedy, Louise V. Negro Peasant Turns Cityward. (Columbia University, Studies in the Social Sciences: No. 329). reprint ed. 20.00 *(978-0-404-51329-0(8))* AMS Pr., Inc.

Kennedy, Stetson. Jim Crow Guide to the U. S. A: The Laws, Customs & Etiquette Governing the Conduct of Nonwhites & Other Minorities As Second-Class Citizens. 2nd ed. 2011. (ENG.). 232p. pap. 32.50 *(978-0-8173-5671-2(1))* Univ. of Alabama Pr.

—Jim Crow Guide to the U.S.A: The Laws, Customs & Etiquette Governing the Conduct of Nonwhites & Other Minorities As Second-Class Citizens. 2011. *(978-0-8173-8564-4(9))* Univ. of Alabama Pr.

King, Debra Walker. African Americans & the Culture of Pain. 2008. (Cultural Frames, Framing Culture Ser.). (ENG., Illus.). 224p. (C). (gr. 13-17). per. 20.00 *(978-0-8139-2681-0(5))*; (gr. 17). 55.00 *(978-0-8139-2680-3(7))* Univ. Pr. of Virginia.

Kirby Edwena. Shifting the Paradigm: Through the Lens of the Disadvantaged. 2010. 144p. pap. *(978-3-8383-0094-8(7))* Lambert Academic Publishing.

K'Meyer, Tracy E. Civil Rights in the Gateway to the South: Louisville, Kentucky, 1945-1980. 2009. (Civil Rights & the Struggle for Black Equality in the Twentieth Century Ser.). (ENG., Illus.). 438p. 50.00 *(978-0-8131-2539-8(1))* Univ. Pr. of Kentucky.

Knowles, Gilbert A. Help Them Pull Their Pants Up: How Mentors & Communities Can Empower Young African American Men. 2008. 132p. 23.95 *(978-0-595-49903-8(1))*; 128p. pap. 13.95 *(978-0-595-50216-5(4))* iUniverse, Inc.

Konadu, Kwasi. The Akan Diaspora in the Americas, 1 vol. 2012. (ENG.). 324p. pap. 24.95 *(978-0-19-992285-7(3))* Oxford Univ. Pr., Inc.

KRS-One. The Gospel of Hip Hop: First Instrument. 2009. (ENG.). 832p. 24.95 *(978-1-57687-497-4(4)*, powerHouse Bks.) powerHouse Cultural Entertainment, Inc.

Kruse, Kevin M. & Tuck, Stephen. The Fog of War: The Second World War & the Civil Rights Movement, 1 vol. 2012. (ENG.). 256p. 99.00 *(978-0-19-538241-9(2))* Oxford Univ. Pr., Inc.

Kruse, Kevin Michael & Tuck, Stephen G. N. Fog of War: The Second World War & the Civil Rights Movement, 1 vol. 2012. (ENG.). 256p. pap. 21.95 *(978-0-19-538240-2(4))* Oxford Univ. Pr., Inc.

Kunjufu, Jawanza. State of Emergency. 2009. (ENG.). 200p. pap. 15.95 *(978-1-934155-09-7(8))* African American Images.

Lacy, Karyn. Blue-Chip Black: Race, Class, & Status in the New Black Middle Class. 2007. (Illus.). 281p. per. 26.95 *(978-0-520-25116-8(4))* Univ. of California Pr.

Lacy, Karyn R. Blue-Chip Black: Race, Class, & Status in the New Black Middle Class. 2007. (Illus.). 281p. 60.00 *(978-0-520-25115-1(6))* Univ. of California Pr.

Lafleur, Tammy. Sick of Being Single: I Guarantee I Can Get You Married in 6 Months, 1 vol. 2010. 48p. pap. 16.95 *(978-1-4489-7875-5(0))* PublishAmerica, Inc.

Lang, Clarence. Grassroots at the Gateway: Class Politics & Black Freedom Struggle in St. Louis, 1936-75. 2009. (Class: Culture Ser.). (ENG., Illus.). 344p. pap. 29.95 *(978-0-472-05065-9(6))* Univ. of Michigan Pr.

Lanier, Tonya A. African Americans of Davidson County. 2010. (Images of America Ser.). (Illus.). 128p. pap. 21.99 *(978-0-7385-8628-1(5))* Arcadia Publishing.

Lawson, R. A. Jim Crow's Counterculture: The Blues & Black Southerners, 1890-1945. 2010. (Making the Modern South Ser.). (Illus.). 328p. 45.00 *(978-0-8071-3680-5(8))* Louisiana State Univ. Pr.

Lentz-Smith, Adriane. Freedom Struggles: African Americans & World War I. (Illus.). 336p. 2011. (ENG.). pap. 22.50 *(978-0-674-06205-4(1))* 2009. 37.00 *(978-0-674-03592-8(5))* Harvard Univ. Pr.

Leonard, David J. After Artest: The NBA & the Assault on Blackness. 2012. (ENG.). 288p. 85.00 *(978-1-4384-4205-1(X))*; pap. 29.95 *(978-1-4384-4206-8(8))* State Univ. of New York Pr.

Leonard, Kevin Allen. The Battle for Los Angeles: Racial Ideology & World War II. 2006. (ENG., Illus.). 372p. 39.95 *(978-0-8263-4047-4(4))* Univ. of New Mexico Pr.

Levada, Julia. Black man, black man stay out of Jail: The revolution continues with Lyou. 2007. (Illus.). 98p. (YA). pap. 15.00 *(978-0-9758609-2-2(5))* Hampton House Publishing.

Levy, Alan Howard. Floyd Patterson: A Boxer & a Gentleman. 2008. (ENG., Illus.). 297p. pap. 35.00 *(978-0-7864-3950-8(5))* McFarland & Co., Inc. Pubs.

Lewis, Barrington. Black Insolvency. 2010. 109p. pap. 14.00 *(978-0-557-25154-4(0))* Lulu Enterprises Inc.

Lewis-Colman, David M. Race against Liberalism: Black Workers & the UAW in Detroit. 2008. (Working Class in American History Ser.). (ENG., Illus.). 176p. 52.00 *(978-0-252-03300-1(0))* Univ. of Illinois Pr.

—Race Against Liberalism: Black Workers & the UAW in Detroit. 2008. (Working Class in American History Ser.). (ENG.). 176p. pap. 26.00 *(978-0-252-07505-6(6))* Univ. of Illinois Pr.

Lindquist, Malinda Alaine. Black Social Science & the Crisis of Manhood, 1890-1970. 2012. (Routledge Studies in African American History & Culture Ser.). (ENG.). 254p. (C). 125.00 *(978-0-415-51743-0(5))* Routledge.

Lipsitz, George. How Racism Takes Place. 2011. (ENG.). 312p. 76.50 *(978-1-4399-0255-4(0))*; 320p. pap. 26.95 *(978-1-4399-0256-1(9))* Temple Univ. Pr.

Littlefield, Daniel F., Jr. Africans & Seminoles: From Removal to Emancipation. 2006. (ENG., Illus.). 280p. pap. 22.00 *(978-1-57806-360-4(4))* Univ. Pr. of Mississippi.

Litwack, Leon F. How Free Is Free? The Long Death of Jim Crow. 2009. (Nathan I. Huggins Lectures). 208p. 21.00 *(978-0-674-03152-4(0))* Harvard Univ. Pr.

Lomotey, Kofi & Cohen, Robert S., eds. Encyclopedia of African American Education, 2 vols. 2009. 1152p. 345.00 *(978-1-4129-4050-4(8)*, B40508C) SAGE Pubns., Inc.

Lopez, Katherine. Cougars of Any Color: The Integration of University of Houston Athletics,1964-1968. 2008. (ENG., Illus.). 220p. pap. 35.00 *(978-0-7864-3721-4(9))* McFarland & Co., Inc. Pubs.

Love, Derrick L. The Unfinished Journey. 2008. 86p. pap. 16.95 *(978-1-60672-518-4(1))* PublishAmerica, Inc.

Mack-Williams, Kibibi. Ahead of Her Time in Yesteryear: Geraldine Pierce Zimmerman Comes of Age in a Southern African American Family. 2010. (ENG., Illus.). 216p. 31.95 *(978-1-57233-720-6(6))* Univ. of Tennessee Pr.

Mackey, Stephen. Who Is Sambo? A Journey of Lessons. 2008. pap. 21.00 *(978-0-8059-8631-0(6))* Dorrance Publishing Co., Inc.

Madhubuti, Haki R. Tough Notes: A Healing Call for Creating Exceptional Black Men. 2010. 150p. pap. 15.95 *(978-0-88378-319-1(3))* Third World Press.

Malcolm, Nigel I. One More River to Cross: The Therapeutic Rhetoric of Race in the Post-Civil Rights Era. 2007. (ENG.). 116p. 45.50 *(978-0-7618-3959-0(3))*; per. 26.50 *(978-0-7618-3960-6(7))* Univ. Pr. of America, Inc.

Malone, Herman & Schwab, Robert. Lynched by Corporate America: The Gripping True Story of How One African American Survived Doing Business with a Fortune 500 Giant. 2006. 101p. per. 15.95 *(978-0-9785094-4-5(7))* HMRS Publishing.

Manley, Theodoric, Jr. The Way They Saw It: The Changing Face of Bronzeville. 2008. 200p. pap. 23.00 *(978-0-8059-7507-9(1))* Dorrance Publishing Co., Inc.

Manning, Gordon. Fear of a Black P***S: Race, Class & the 21st Century Slave. 2007. 176p. per. 15.95 *(978-0-595-44857-9(7))* iUniverse, Inc.

Marable, Manning. Beyond Boundaries: The Manning Marable Reader, 1 vol. Rickford, Russell, ed. 2011. 336p. pap. 25.95 *(978-1-59451-862-1(9))* Paradigm Pubs.

—Let Nobody Turn Us Around: Voices of Resistance, Reform & Renewal: An African American Anthology. Mullings, Leith, ed. 2nd ed. 2009. (ENG.). 704p. 99.00 *(978-0-7425-6056-7(2))*; pap. 45.00 *(978-0-7425-6057-4(0))* Rowman & Littlefield Publishers, Inc.

—Race, Reform, & Rebellion: The Second Reconstruction & Beyond in Black America, 1945-2006. 3rd rev. ed. 2007. (ENG.). 312p. (C). per. 25.00 *(978-1-57806-154-9(7))*; 55.00 *(978-1-57806-153-2(9))* Univ. Pr. of Mississippi.

Marable, Manning, et al, eds. Racializing Justice, Disenfranchising Lives: The Racism, Criminal Justice, & Law Reader. 2007. (Critical Black Studies). (ENG.). 400p. 95.00 *(978-1-4039-7766-3(6))*; pap. 30.00 *(978-1-4039-7767-0(4))* Palgrave Macmillan.

Marable, Manning & Agard-Jones, Vanessa, eds. Transnational Blackness: Navigating the Global Color Line. 2008. (Critical Black Studies). (ENG.). 384p. 100.00 *(978-0-230-60267-0(3))*; pap. 31.00 *(978-0-230-60268-7(1))* Palgrave Macmillan.

Marsh, Kris. Black Non-Family Households: Their Socioeconomic Position & Spatial Buffering. 2008. 128p. pap. *(978-3-639-03574-2(7))* VDM Verlag Dr. Mueller e.K.

Marshall, Stephen. The City on the Hill from Below: The Crisis of Prophetic Black Politics. 2011. (ENG.). 256p. 64.50 *(978-1-4399-0655-2(6))* Temple Univ. Pr.

Mathieu, Sarah-Jane. North of the Color Line: Migration & Black Resistance in Canada, 1870-1955. 2010. (John Hope Franklin Series in African American History & Culture Ser.). (ENG., Illus.). 320p. 65.00 *(978-0-8078-3429-9(7))*; pap. 22.95 *(978-0-8078-7166-9(4))* Univ. of North Carolina Pr.

Matthews, Gerald E. A Declaration of Independence for Black Americans: An Essay for Change & Growth. 123p. (Orig.). reprint ed. pap. 9.00 *(978-1-56411-132-6(6))* UBUS Communications Systems.

McAdoo, Harriette Pipes, ed. Black Families. 4th rev. ed. 2006. 384p. (C). 124.00 *(978-1-4129-3637-8(3)*, B36373C); (Illus.). per. 63.00 *(978-1-4129-3638-5(1)*, B36373P) SAGE Pubns., Inc.

McClane, Kenneth A. Color: Essays on Race, Family, & History. 2009. (ND Afro/Amer Intellectual Heritage Ser.). (ENG.). 120p. pap. 19.00 *(978-0-268-03515-0(6))* Univ. of Notre Dame Pr.

McCullum, Mdiv. The Plight of the African-American Male: An Informative Guide to Healing & Restoration. 2009. 128p. 21.99 *(978-1-4490-0657-0(4))*; pap. 16.99 *(978-1-4490-0656-3(6))* AuthorHouse.

McCurry, Stephanie. Confederate Reckoning: Power & Politics in the Civil War South. 456p. 2012. (ENG.). pap. 21.95 *(978-0-674-06421-8(6))* 2010. 35.00 *(978-0-674-04589-7(0))* Harvard Univ. Pr.

McDonald, Jason. Racial Dynamics in Early Twentieth-Century Austin, Texas. 2012. (ENG.). 408p. (gr. 17). 90.00 *(978-0-7391-7097-7(X))* Lexington Bks.

McFarland, Bernard C. The Hill & the Bottoms: The Story from the Thousand Yard Stare. 2009. (Illus.). 112p. *(978-1-57864-538-1(7))* Donning Co. Pubs.

McKinney, Cynthia. Ain't Nothin' Like Freedom. 2009. 150p. pap. *(978-0-88378-285-9(5))* Third World Press.

McLoyd, Vonnie C., et al, eds. African American Family Life: Ecological & Cultural Diversity. 2007. (Duke Series in Child Develpment & Public Policy Ser.). (ENG.). 348p. pap. 35.00 *(978-1-59385-467-6(6))* Guilford Pubns., Inc.

McWhirter, Cameron. Red Summer: The Summer of 1919 & the Awakening of Black America. 2011. (ENG., Illus.). 368p. 32.50 *(978-0-8050-8906-6(3))* Holt, Henry & Co.

—Red Summer: The Summer of 1919 & the Awakening of Black America. 2012. (ENG.). 368p. pap. 16.99 ***(978-1-250-00906-7(5)***, St. Martin's Griffin) St. Martin's Pr.

McWhorter, John. Winning the Race: Beyond the Crisis in Black America. annot. ed. 2006. (ENG.). 448p. (gr. 8-18). per. 28.00 *(978-1-59240-270-0(4)*, Gotham) Penguin Group (USA) Inc.

Means, Harriett. 19th Century African American Social Settlements. 2011. 140p. pap. ***(978-3-8443-0951-5(9))*** Lambert Academic Publishing.

Metzler, Christoper J. The construction & rearticulation of race in a post-racial America. 2008. 189p. pap. 49.96 *(978-0-615-21670-6(6))* Aberdeen Univ. Pr. Services.

Middleton, Earl M. Knowing Who I Am: A Black Entrepreneur's Struggle & Success in the American South. 2008. (Illus.). 183p. 29.95 *(978-1-57003-715-3(9))* Univ. of South Carolina Pr.

Mintz, Steven, ed. African American Voices: A Documentary Reader, 1619-1877. 4th ed. 2009. (Uncovering the Past: Documentary Readers in American History Ser.: 1). (ENG., Illus.). 264p. pap. 34.95 *(978-1-4051-8267-6(9))*; 104.95 *(978-1-4051-8268-3(7))* Wiley, John & Sons, Inc. (Wiley-Blackwell).

Mjagkij, Nina. Loyalty in Time of Trial: The African American Experience During World War I. 2011. (African American History Ser.). (ENG., Illus.). 224p. 40.00 *(978-0-7425-7043-6(6))* Rowman & Littlefield Publishers, Inc.

Mocombe, Paul. The Liberal Black Protestant Heterosexual Bourgeois Male: From W.E.B. du Bois to Barack Obama. 2010. (Illus.). v, 130p. E-Book ***(978-0-7618-4803-5(7))*** Univ. Pr. of America, Inc.

Moore, Leonard N. Black Rage in New Orleans: Police Brutality & African American Activism from World War II to Hurricane Katrina. 2010. (Illus.). 320p. 35.00 *(978-0-8071-3590-7(9))* Louisiana State Univ. Pr.

Moore, Sharon E., et al. Dilemmas of Black Faculty at Predominantly White Institutions in the United States: Issues in the Post-Multicultural ERA. 2010. (Illus.). xxv, 364p. 119.95 *(978-0-7734-3622-0(7))* Mellen, Edwin Pr., The.

Moore, Wes. Discovering Wes Moore. 2012. (ENG.). 160p. (YA). (gr. 7). 15.99 ***(978-0-385-74167-5(7)***, Delacorte Bks. for Young Readers) Random Hse. Children's Bks.

—Discovering Wes Moore: Chances, Choices, Changes. 2012. E-Book ***(978-0-375-98670-3(7)***, Delacorte Pr) Random House Publishing Group.

—Discovering Wes Moore: Chances, Choices, Changes. 2012. (ENG.). 160p. (YA). (gr. 7). lib. bdg. 18.99 ***(978-0-375-99018-2(6)***, Delacorte Bks. for Young Readers) Random Hse. Children's Bks.

Morgan, Douglas. Lewis C. Sheafe: Apostle to Black America. 2010. 22.99 *(978-0-8280-2397-9(2))* Review & Herald Publishing Assn.

Morgan, Philip, ed. African American Life in the Georgia Lowcountry: The Atlantic World & the Gullah Geechee. (Race in the Atlantic World, 1700-1900 Ser.). (ENG.). 2011. 376p. pap. 24.95 ***(978-0-8203-4307-5(2))*** 2010. (Illus.). 320p. 34.95 *(978-0-8203-3064-8(7))* Univ. of Georgia Pr.

Mosley, Walter. Workin' on the Chain Gang: Shaking off the Dead Hand of History. 2006. (Class: Culture Ser.). (ENG.). 136p. pap. 15.95 *(978-0-472-03198-6(8))* Univ. of Michigan Pr.

Muhammad, Dedrick. Understanding Racial Inequality in the Obama Era: A Primer. 2011. 208p. pap. 10.00 *(978-1-56656-823-4(4))* Interlink Publishing Group, Inc.

Muhammad, Khalil Gibran. The Condemnation of Blackness: Race, Crime, & the Making of Modern Urban America. (Illus.). 392p. 2011. (ENG.). pap. 18.95 *(978-0-674-06211-5(6))* 2010. 37.00 *(978-0-674-03597-3(6))* Harvard Univ. Pr.

Murch, Donna. Living for the City: Migration, Education, & the Rise of the Black Panther Party in Oakland, California. 2010. (John Hope Franklin Series in African American History & Culture Ser.). (ENG., Illus.). 344p. 65.00 *(978-0-8078-3376-6(2))*; pap. 22.95 *(978-0-8078-7113-3(3))* Univ. of North Carolina Pr.

Murty, Komanduri S. Criminal Justice Issues & the African-American Community. 2008. 292p. pap. 19.95 *(978-0-9802380-2-0(1))* Beckham Pubns. Group, Inc.

Mwakikagile, Godfrey. Black Conservatives in the United States. 2006. pap. *(978-0-9802587-0-7(7))* New Africa Pr.

Myles, Lynette. Female Subjectivity in African American Women's Narratives of Enslavement: Beyond Borders. 2009. (ENG.). 208p. 84.00 *(978-0-230-61593-9(7))* Palgrave Macmillan.

Nelson, Alondra. Body & Soul: The Black Panther Party & the Fight against Medical Discrimination. 2011. (ENG., Illus.). 288p. 24.95 ***(978-0-8166-7648-4(8))*** Univ. of Minnesota Pr.

Nelson, Peter N. A More Unbending Battle: The Harlem Hellfighter's Struggle for Freedom in WWI & Equality at Home. 2009. (ENG.). 304p. 27.50 *(978-0-465-00317-4(6))* Perseus Bks. Group.

Neri, Greg. Yummy: The Last Days of a Southside Shorty. 2007. (Illus.). (YA). (gr. 6-18). 18.95 *(978-1-58430-266-7(6))* Lee & Low Bks., Inc.

Newberry, Jay. Middle Class African Americans. 2010. 56p. pap. *(978-3-639-23477-0(4))* VDM Verlag Dr. Mueller e.K.

Newkirk, Pamela, ed. Letters from Black America: Intimate Portraits of the African American Experience. 2011. (ENG.). 400p. pap. 18.00 *(978-0-8070-0115-8(5))* Beacon Pr.

Nieves, Angel David & Alexander, Leslie M., eds. We Shall Independent Be: African American Place-Making & the Struggle to Claim Space in the United States. 2008. (ENG., Illus.). 544p. 50.00 *(978-0-87081-906-3(2))* Univ. Pr. of Colorado.

Nix, Elizabeth. Baltimore '68: Riots & Rebirth in an American City. Elfenbein, Jessica & Hollowak, Thomas, eds. 2011. (ENG., Illus.). 294p. 74.50 *(978-1-4399-0661-3(0))* Temple Univ. Pr.

Nyborg, Vanessa. Exploring Racism in the Lives of African American Boys. 2009. 68p. pap. *(978-3-639-13405-6(2))* VDM Verlag Dr. Mueller e.K.

Oboe, Annalisa & Scacchi, Anna, eds. Recharting the Black Atlantic: Modern Cultures, Local Communities, Global Connections. 2008. (ENG., Illus.). 438p. 125.00 *(978-0-415-96111-0(4))* Routledge.

O'Dell, Jack. Climbin' Jacob's Ladder: The Black Freedom Movement Writings of Jack O'Dell. Singh, Nikhil, ed. 2010. (ENG.). 272p. 40.00 *(978-0-520-25958-4(0))* Univ. of California Pr.

Oduwole, Peter S. Plague: A Perpetual Struggle in the Lives of Black People. 2009. 88p. pap. 10.49 *(978-1-4389-7823-9(5))* AuthorHouse.

Ogletree, Charles J., Jr., intro. After the Storm: Black Intellectuals Explore the Meaning of Hurricane Katrina. 2006. (ENG., Illus.). 164p. 22.95 *(978-1-59558-116-7(2))* New Pr., The.

Oliver Jr, Sylvester W. Hidden Chronicles: Published Ads on Buying, Selling & Recapturing Enslaved Africans in Marshall County, Mississippi. 2008. 63p. pap. 10.95 *(978-1-59800-967-5(2))* Outskirts Pr., Inc.

Ondaatje, Michael. Black Conservative Intellectuals in Modern America. 232p. (C). 2012. pap. 22.50 ***(978-0-8122-2204-3(0))*** 2009. 34.95 *(978-0-8122-4206-5(8))* Univ. of Pennsylvania Pr.

Opie, Fredrick Douglass & Opie, Frederick Douglass. Hog & Hominy: Soul Food from Africa to America. 2008. (Arts & Traditions of the Table: Perspectives on Culinary History Ser.). (ENG., Illus.). 256p. (gr. 17). 24.95 *(978-0-231-14638-8(8))* Columbia Univ. Pr.

Ortiz, Paul. Emancipation Betrayed: The Hidden History of Black Organizing & White Violence in Florida from Reconstruction to the Bloody Election Of 1920. 2006. (American Crossroads Ser.). (Illus.). 382p. per. 24.95 *(978-0-520-25003-1(6))* Univ. of California Pr.

Owens, Michael Eric. A New Philosophy of Black Identity: Yes I Am Who I Am. 2009. 183p. pap. 16.99 *(978-0-88144-323-3(9))* Yorkshire Publishing Group.

Palmer, Gerald. The Church Has AIDS: Essays on Sexuality, Sexual Orientation, Taboos, & the Black Church. 2010. 84p. pap. 18.20 *(978-0-557-12464-0(6))* Lulu Enterprises Inc.

Palmié, Stephan. Africas of the Americas: Beyond the Search for Origins in the Study of Afro-Atlantic Religions. Palmié, Stephan, ed. 2008. (Studies of Religion in Africa Ser.). 355p. *(978-90-04-16472-7(3))* BRILL.

Palomino, Mark J. Who Is African-American-What Does It Mean? Plus Let's Talk about Race Relations in America. 2006. 98p. pap. 16.95 *(978-1-4241-2384-1(4))* PublishAmerica, Inc.

Parker, Star. White Ghetto: How Middle Class America Reflects Inner City Decay, 0 vols. 2009. 256p. pap. 14.99 *(978-1-59555-339-3(8))* Nelson, Thomas Inc.

Parks, Gregory & Hughey, Matthew W. The Obamas & a (Post) Racial America?, 1 vol. 2011. (Series in Political Psychology Ser.). 336p. 39.95 *(978-0-19-973520-4(4))* Oxford Univ. Pr., Inc.

Parks, Gregory S. & Hughey, Matthew W., eds. 12 Angry Men: True Stories of Being a Black Man in America Today. 2012. (ENG., Illus.). 224p. pap. 16.95 ***(978-1-59558-771-8(3))*** New Pr., The.

Patterson, Collis D., ed. Dr Samuel Banks Speaks: Selected Writings. 2008. 124p. 21.49 *(978-1-4389-2488-5(7))*; pap. 10.99 *(978-1-4389-2489-2(5))* AuthorHouse.

Patterson, James T. Freedom Is Not Enough: The Moynihan Report & America's Struggle over Black Family Life- From LBJ to Obama. 2010. (ENG.). 288p. (gr. 9). 26.95 *(978-0-465-01357-9(0))* Basic Bks.

Pattillo, Mary. Black on the Block: The Politics of Race & Class in the City. 2007. (ENG., Illus.). 400p. 29.00 *(978-0-226-64931-3(8))* Univ. of Chicago Pr.

—Black on the Block: The Politics of Race & Class in the City. 2008. (ENG., Illus.). 400p. pap. 20.00 *(978-0-226-64932-0(6))* Univ. of Chicago Pr.

Peller, Gary. Critical Race Consciousness: Reconsidering American Ideologies of Racial Justice. 2011. 256p. 115.00 *(978-1-59451-904-8(8))* Paradigm Pubs.

Penner, D'Ann, et al. Overcoming Katrina: African American Voices from the Crescent City & Beyond. 2009. (Palgrave Studies in Oral History Ser.). (ENG., Illus.). 288p. 105.00 *(978-0-230-60870-2(1))* Palgrave Macmillan.

Perkins, Alfred. Edwin Rogers Embree: The Julius Rosenwald Fund, Foundation Philanthropy, & American Race Relations. 2011. (Philanthropic & Nonprofit Studies). (ENG., Illus.). 384p. 39.95 *(978-0-253-35604-8(0)*, 0253356040) Indiana Univ. Pr.

Persons, Georgia A., ed. The Expanding Boundaries of Black Politics. 2007. (National Political Science Review Ser.: Vol. 11). (ENG., Illus.). 404p. (gr. 11). pap. 29.95 *(978-0-7658-0375-7(5))* Transaction Pubs.

Peterson, Carla L. Black Gotham: A Family History of African Americans in Nineteenth-Century New York City. (Illus.). 446p. 2012. (ENG.). pap. 20.00 ***(978-0-300-18174-6(4))*** 2011. 32.00 *(978-0-300-16255-4(3))* Yale Univ. Pr.

Phillips, Joseph C. He Talk Like a White Boy: Reflections of a Conservative Black Man on Faith, Family, Politics, & Authenticity. 2009. (ENG.). 304p. pap. 14.95 *(978-0-7624-3556-2(9)*, Running Pr.) Running Pr. Bk. Pubs.

Phillips, Kimberley. Daily Life During African American Migrations, 1 vol. 2012. (Greenwood Press Daily Life Through History Series: Daily Life in the United States Ser.). (Illus.). 226p. 58.00 ***(978-0-313-34373-5(X)***, GR4373) Greenwood Publishing Group, Inc.

Pierce, Daniel Vincent. Diversity, Values, Professionalism,or Favoritism Racism: African Americans & Other Minorities in the Work Force. 2007. 60p. per. 9.95 *(978-0-595-47122-5(6))* iUniverse, Inc.

Pierce, Kristy. Black & White: Why Are the Piano Keys Weighted? Reflections from a Colored Girl's Perspective. 2007. 76p. per. 16.95 *(978-1-4241-6838-5(4))* PublishAmerica, Inc.

Polyßk, Mariann. Isolation. 2008. 56p. pap. *(978-3-639-02089-2(8))* VDM Verlag Dr. Mueller e.K.

Porter, Al. More Like Barack, Less Like Tupac: Countering Three Decades of the Hip Hop Hoax & Reclaiming the Image of African American Men. 2009. pap. 24.95 *(978-1-61623-791-2(0))* Independent Pub.

Powdermaker, Hortense. After Freedom: A Cultural Study in the Deep South. 2008. 432p. pap. 43.00 *(978-1-59740-629-1(5))* ACLS Humanities E-Book.

Powell, Kevin. The Black Male Handbook: A Blueprint for Life. 2008. (ENG.). 272p. pap. 15.00 *(978-1-4165-9224-2(5)*, Beyond Words/Atria Bks.) Atria Bks.

Preston, S. H., et al. The Demography of African Americans 1930-1990. 2010. (Springer Series on Demographic Methods & Population Analysis Ser.). 224p. pap. 179.00 *(978-90-481-6395-3(1)*, 9048163951) Springer.

Prier, Darius. Culturally Relevant Teaching: Hip-Hop Pedagogy in Urban Schools. 2012. E-Book ***(978-1-4539-0535-7(9))*** Lang, Peter Publishing, Inc.

Prier, Darius D. Culturally Relevant Teaching: Hip-Hop Pedagogy in Urban Schools. 2012. xlv, 238p. (C). pap. 139.95 ***(978-1-4331-1057-3(1))***; pap. 36.95 ***(978-1-4331-1058-0(X))*** Lang, Peter Publishing, Inc.

Provost, P. Paul. Ebony Legends in Sports. 2009. 236p. 24.99 *(978-1-4389-7958-8(4))*; pap. 18.70 *(978-1-4389-7957-1(6))* AuthorHouse.

Publications International Staff, ed. Yesterday & Today: Civil Rights. 2010. 192p. 24.98 *(978-1-4508-1030-2(6))* Publications International, Ltd.

Rabaka, Reiland. W. E. B. du Bois & the Problems of the Twenty-First Century: An Essay on Africana Critical Theory. 2007. (ENG.). 296p. 83.99 *(978-0-7391-1682-1(7))* Lexington Bks.

Rainwater, Lee. Behind Ghetto Walls: Black Families in a Federal Slum. 2006. (ENG.). 591p. (gr. 11). pap. 39.95 *(978-0-202-30907-1(X))* Aldine Transaction.

Reed, Adolph, Jr., et al. Renewing Black Intellectual History: The Ideological & Material Foundations of African American Thought, 1 vol. 2010. 336p. pap. 39.95 *(978-1-59451-666-5(9))* Paradigm Pubs.

Reed, Christopher Robert. The Depression Comes to the South Side: Protest & Politics in the Black Metropolis, 1930-1933. 2011. (Blacks in the Diaspora Ser.). (ENG., Illus.). 204p. 29.95 *(978-0-253-35652-9(0)*, 0253356520) Indiana Univ. Pr.

Reed, Touré F. Not Alms but Opportunity: The Urban League & the Politics of Racial Uplift, 1910-1950. 2008. (ENG., Illus.). 272p. pap. 23.95 *(978-0-8078-5902-5(8))* Univ. of North Carolina Pr.

Regosin, Elizabeth A. & Shaffer, Donald R., eds. Voices of Emancipation: Understanding Slavery, the Civil War, & Reconstruction Through the U. S. Pension Bureau Files. 2008. (ENG., Illus.). 232p. pap. 23.00 *(978-0-8147-7587-5(X))* New York Univ. Pr.

Rhodes, Jane. Framing the Black Panthers: The Spectacular Rise of a Black Power Icon. 2007. (ENG., Illus.). 404p. 35.00 *(978-1-56584-961-7(2))* New Pr., The.

Rhodes-Pitts, Sharifa. Harlem Is Nowhere: A Journey to the Mecca of Black America. 2011. (ENG., Illus.). 304p. 24.99 *(978-0-316-01723-7(X))* Little Brown & Co.

Rice, David Wall. Balance: Advancing Identity Theory by Engaging the Black Male Adolescent. 2008. (ENG.). 148p. pap. 29.50 *(978-0-7391-1889-4(7))* Lexington Bks.

Rich, John A. Wrong Place, Wrong Time: Trauma & Violence in the Lives of Young Black Men. (ENG.). 232p. 2011. pap. 20.00 ***(978-1-4214-0398-4(6))*** 2009. 30.00 *(978-0-8018-9363-6(1))* Johns Hopkins Univ. Pr.

Richardson, Henry J., 3rd. The Origins of African-American Interests in International Law. 2008. (ENG.). 544p. 65.00 *(978-1-59460-383-9(9))* Carolina Academic Pr.

Richardson, Joe Martin. African Americans in the Reconstruction of Florida, 1865-1877. 2nd ed. 2008. (ENG.). 272p. pap. 27.95 *(978-0-8173-5524-1(3))* Univ. of Alabama Pr.

Richardson, Selden. Built by Blacks: African American Architecture & Neighborhoods in Richmond. Duke, Maurice, ed. 2008. (Illus.). 192p. pap. 19.99 *(978-1-59629-459-2(0))* History Pr., The.

Risen, Clay. A Nation on Fire: America in the Wake of the King Assassination. 2009. (ENG., Illus.). 312p. 25.95 *(978-0-470-17710-5(1)*, Wiley) Wiley, John & Sons, Inc.

Robertson, Gil L., IV. Not in My Family: AIDS in the African-American Community. 2006. (ENG.). 300p. per. 16.00 *(978-1-932841-24-4(5))* Agate Publishing, Inc.

Robeson, Paul, Jr. A Black Way of Seeing: From Liberty to Freedom. 2007. (ENG., Illus.). 224p. per. 14.95 *(978-1-58322-767-1(9))* Seven Stories Pr.

Robinson, Charles Frank, II. Dangerous Liaisons: Sex & Love in the Segregated South. 2006. 196p. per. 19.95 *(978-1-55728-833-2(X))* Univ. of Arkansas Pr.

Robinson, Eugene. Disintegration: The Splintering of Black America. (ENG.). 272p. 2011. pap. 15.95 *(978-0-7679-2996-7(9)*, Anchor) 2010. 24.95 *(978-0-385-52654-8(7)*, Doubleday) Knopf Doubleday Publishing Group.

Rochell, Jacquelyn. Move Beyond the Colored Line. 2008. 260p. per. *(978-0-9801297-5-5(3))* G Publishing LLC.

Rose, Arnold M. The Negro's Morale: Group Identification & Protest. 2011. 162p. 41.95 ***(978-1-258-05291-1(1))*** Literary Licensing, LLC.

Rush, Erik. Negrophilia: From Slave Block to Pedestal - America's Racial Obsession. 2010. 228p. 25.95 *(978-1-935071-82-2(3))* WND Bks, Inc.

Sacks, Marcy S. Before Harlem: The Black Experience in New York City Before World War I. 2006. (Politics & Culture in Modern America Ser.). (Illus.). 240p. (C). 59.95 *(978-0-8122-3961-4(X))* Univ. of Pennsylvania Pr.

Sanders, Vivienne. Civil Rights in the USA, 1945-68. 2008. (ENG., Illus.). 184p. pap. 17.95 *(978-0-340-96583-2(5))* Hodder Education GBR. Dist: Oxford Univ. Pr., Inc.

Satter, Beryl. Family Properties: How the Struggle over Race & Real Estate Transformed Chicago & Urban America. 2010. (ENG., Illus.). 512p. pap. 18.00 *(978-0-8050-9142-7(4))* Picador.

Schenbeck, Lawrence. Racial Uplift & American Music, 1878-1943. 2012. (American Made Music Ser.). (ENG.). 304p. 60.00 ***(978-1-61703-229-5(8))*** Univ. Pr. of Mississippi.

Schneider, Ann Christin. Affirmative Action in Higher Education. 2009. 124p. pap. *(978-3-639-11839-1(1))* VDM Verlag Dr. Mueller e.K.

Schneider, Mark Robert. African Americans in the Jazz Age: A Decade of Struggle & Promise. 2006. (African American History Ser.). (ENG., Illus.). 176p. per. 24.95 *(978-0-7425-4417-8(6))* Rowman & Littlefield Publishers, Inc.

Schultz, Mark. The Rural Face of White Supremacy: Beyond Jim Crow. 2006. (Illus.). 336p. per. 26.00 *(978-0-252-07436-3(X))* Univ. of Illinois Pr.

Schutz, Mary Ellen, ed. The State of Black Madison 2008: Before the Tipping Point. 2008. 30p. pap. 5.00 *(978-0-615-20703-2(0))* Urban League of Greater Madison.

Scott, Daryl Michael, ed. The Negro Church. 2010. (ENG., Illus.). 350p. pap. 21.00 *(978-0-9768111-1-4(1))* ASALH Pr., The.

Scott, Michelle R. Blues Empress in Black Chattanooga: Bessie Smith & the Emerging Urban South. 2008. (ENG., Illus.). 216p. 60.00 *(978-0-252-03338-4(8))* Univ. of Illinois Pr.

Scruggs-Leftwich, Yvonne. Soundbytes of Protest. 2007. 120p. pap. 15.95 *(978-0-88378-272-9(3))* Third World Press.

Seatts, Linda. The Truth about the Superior Lie: A book to resurrect the lives of African-Americans crucified by the Lie, 1. 2007. 76p. (YA). *(978-0-9793305-0-6(5))* Kittrell Publishing Hse.

See, Letha A. Lee, ed. Human Behavior in the Social Environment from an African-American Perspective. 2nd ed. 2007. (Illus.). 782p. 175.00 *(978-0-7890-2831-0(X))*; per. 49.95 *(978-0-7890-2832-7(8))* Routledge.

Senechal de la Roche, Roberta. In Lincoln's Shadow: The 1908 Race Riot in Springfield, Illinois. 2008. (ENG., Illus.). 264p. pap. 19.95 *(978-0-8093-2909-0(3))* Southern Illinois Univ. Pr.

Shaw-Taylor, Yoku & Tuch, Steven A. The Other African Americans: Contemporary African & Caribbean Immigrants in the United States. 2007. (ENG.). 308p. 85.00 *(978-0-7425-4087-3(1))*; pap. 32.95 *(978-0-7425-4088-0(X))* Rowman & Littlefield Publishers, Inc.

Shell-Weiss, Melanie. Coming to Miami: A Social History. 2009. (Sunbelt Studies). (ENG., Illus.). 384p. 39.95 *(978-0-8130-3296-2(2))* Univ. Pr. of Florida.

Shelton, Norris. American Slaves, Inc. Renaissance PLan: The Next Step Forward. 2009. 105p. 11.95 *(978-0-9765417-6-9(9))* American Slaves, Inc.

Shorter III, Joseph William. Raaw: Rediscovering African American Wisdom. 2007. 88p. per. 10.95 *(978-0-595-40702-6(1))* iUniverse, Inc.

Sims, Curtis Lee. A Nation Divided: Black vs. Black & Its Leadership Void. 2006. 252p. pap. 14.95 *(978-0-7414-3179-0(3))* Infinity Publishing.

Sinclair, William A. & Alexander, Shawn Lee. The Aftermath of Slavery: A Study of the Condition & Environment of the American Negro. 2012. (Southern Classics Ser.). (ENG.). 424p. pap. 16.95 ***(978-1-61117-078-8(8))*** Univ. of South Carolina Pr.

Singley, Bernestine, ed. When Race Becomes Real: Black & White Writers Confront Their Personal Histories. 2008. (ENG., Illus.). 352p. pap. 19.95 *(978-0-8093-2885-7(2))* Southern Illinois Univ. Pr.

Sitkoff, Harvard. A New Deal for Blacks: The Emergence of Civil Rights As a National Issue - The Depression Decade. 2008. (ENG.). 352p. (C). pap. 29.95 *(978-0-19-536753-9(7))* Oxford Univ. Pr., Inc.

—Toward Freedom Land: The Long Struggle for Racial Equality in America. 2010. (ENG., Illus.). 232p. 50.00 *(978-0-8131-2583-1(9))* Univ. Pr. of Kentucky.

Skinner, Devon. Awakening: Rejecting the Politicization of the African American Dream. 2009. 152p. pap. 14.95 *(978-1-4401-0646-0(0))* iUniverse, Inc.

Smiley, Tavis, frwd. The Covenant in Action. 2007. (ENG.). 160p. per. 10.00 *(978-1-4019-1852-1(2)*, Smiley Bks.) Hay Hse., Inc.

Smith, Aaron W. & Richardson, Brenda Lane. In the Black: Live Faithfully, Prosper Financially - The Ultimate 9-Step Plan for Financial Fitness. 2009. 304p. pap. 15.99 *(978-0-06-145069-3(3)*, Harper Paperbacks) HarperCollins Pubs.

Smith, Aaron/Anwar. Living on the up High, Not the down Low: The Movement to Uplift Good Black Men & the Empowerment of the African American Family. 2007. 160p. per. 12.99 *(978-0-9795065-0-5(6))* Up High Assoc., The.

Smith, Max. African America's 3rd Rail: SGL. 2009. 240p. pap. 19.95 *(978-0-615-28206-0(7))* Smith, Maxsonn.

Solomon, Lewis D. Cycles of Poverty & Crime in America's Inner Cities. 2012. (ENG.). 171p. 39.95 ***(978-1-4128-4738-4(9))*** Transaction Pubs.

Spellers, Regina E. & Moffitt, Kimberly R. Blackberries & Redbones: Critical Articulations of Black Hair/Body Politics in Africana Communities. 2010. (Illus.). xii, 472p. *(978-1-57273-880-5(4))*; pap. *(978-1-57273-881-2(2))* Hampton Pr., Inc.

Springs, Oressa. Racism & Black on Black Crime from A Biblical Perspective. 2008. pap. 10.99 *(978-1-932307-94-8(X))* Emerald Hse. Group, Inc.

Stamps, S. David & Stamps, Miriam Burny. Salt City & Its Black Community: A Sociological Study of Syracuse, New York. 2008. (Illus.). 331p. 29.95 *(978-0-8156-3180-4(4))* Syracuse Univ. Pr.

Stanfield II, John H. Black Reflective Sociology: Epistemology, Theory, & Methodology. 2011. (ENG.). 384p. 89.00 *(978-1-59874-646-4(4))*; pap. 34.95 *(978-1-59874-647-1(2))* Left Coast Pr., Inc.

—Historical Foundations of Black Reflective Sociology. 2011. (ENG.). 304p. 89.00 *(978-1-59874-648-8(0))*; pap. 36.95 *(978-1-59874-649-5(9))* Left Coast Pr., Inc.

Stanford, Karin. If We Must Die: African American Voices on War & Peace. 2009. (ENG.). 384p. pap. 37.50 *(978-0-7425-4114-6(2))* Rowman & Littlefield Publishers, Inc.

Stanford, Karin L., ed. If We Must Die: African American Voices on War & Peace. 2008. (ENG.). 384p. 63.95 *(978-0-7425-4113-9(4))* Rowman & Littlefield Publishers, Inc.

Sterner, Richard. The Negro's Share: A Study of Income, Consumption, Housing, & Public Assistance. 2008. 448p. pap. 45.00 *(978-1-59740-630-7(9))* ACLS Humanities E-Book.

Stockley, Grif. Race Relations in the Natural State. 2008. 212p. (C). 30.00 *(978-0-9708574-6-0(2))* Butler Ctr. for Arkansas Studies.

Stockley, Grif, Jr. & Stockley, Grif. Ruled by Race: Black/White Relations in Arkansas from Slavery to the Present. 2008. (Illus.). 400p. 34.95 *(978-1-55728-885-1(2))* Univ. of Arkansas Pr.

Stokes, Julie. The Psychology of African American Race Socialization. 2nd rev. ed. 2007. (ENG.). 90p. pap. 38.11 *(978-0-7575-4257-2(3))* Kendall Hunt Publishing Co.

Strausbaugh, John. Black Like You: Blackface, Whiteface, Insult & Imitation in American Popular Culture. 2007. (ENG., Illus.). 384p. (gr. 12-18). 15.95 *(978-1-58542-593-8(1)*, Tarcher) Penguin Group (USA) Inc.

The Struggle. 2007. 167p. (YA). per. 21.95 *(978-0-9791781-0-8(X))* Parker & Sons Publishing, Inc.

Sullivan, Jas M. & Esmail, Ashraf, eds. African American Identity: Racial & Cultural Dimensions of the Black Experience. 2012. (ENG.). 450p. (gr. 17). 90.00 ***(978-0-7391-7174-5(7))*** Lexington Bks.

Taylor, Shawn. Big Black Penis: Misadventures in Race & Masculinity. 2008. (ENG.). 208p. pap. 14.95 *(978-1-55652-734-0(9)*, Hill, Lawrence Bks.) Chicago Review Pr., Inc.

Telles, Edward Eric, et al. Just Neighbors? Research on African American & Latino Relations in the US. 2011. ***(978-0-87154-828-3(3))*** Russell Sage Foundation.

Terrell, Melvin Cleveland & Strayhorn, Terrell L., eds. The Evolving Challenges of Black College Students: New Insights for Practice & Research. 2010. (Illus.). 248p. 75.00 *(978-1-57922-245-1(5))*; pap. 29.95 *(978-1-57922-246-8(3))* Stylus Publishing, LLC.

Thomas, A. C. The Color of Success: Growing up black never stopped one man from Winning. 2007. pap. *(978-0-9797103-0-8(8))* Algus Publishing.

Thomas, Ebony Elizabeth & Brooks-Tatum, Shanesha R. F. Reading African American Experiences in the Obama ERA: Theory, Advocacy, Activism. 2012. xv, 273p. E-Book ***(978-1-4539-0210-3(4))***; 296p. (C). pap. 149.95 ***(978-1-4331-1128-0(4))***; 296p. (C). pap. 36.95 ***(978-1-4331-1125-9(X))*** Lang, Peter Publishing, Inc.

Thomas, Greg. The Sexual Demon of Colonial Power: Pan-African Embodiment & Erotic Schemes of Empire. 2007. (ENG.). 224p. 50.00 *(978-0-253-34841-8(2)*, 0253348412); pap. 21.95 *(978-0-253-21894-0(2)*, 0253218942) Indiana Univ. Pr.

Thomas, Pat. Listen, Whitey! The Sounds of Black Power 1965-1975. 2012. (ENG., Illus.). 224p. 39.99 *(978-1-60699-507-5(3)*, 699507) Fantagraphics Bks.

Thompson, Gordon E. The Assimilationist Impulse in Four African American Narratives: Frederic Douglas, James Weldon Johnson, Richard Wright, & Leroi Jones. 2011. 248p. 119.95 *(978-0-7734-1555-3(6))* Mellen, Edwin Pr., The.

Tillotson, Michael. Invisible Jim Crow: Contemporary Ideological Threats to the Internal Security of African Americans. 2011. xxiv, 217p. *(978-1-59221-801-1(6))*; 245p. pap. *(978-1-59221-802-8(4))* Africa World Pr.

Tracy, Steven C. Writers of the Black Chicago Renaissance. 2011. (ENG.). 536p. 50.00 ***(978-0-252-03639-2(5))*** Univ. of Illinois Pr.

Trethewey, Natasha. Beyond Katrina: A Meditation on the Mississippi Gulf Coast. (ENG.). 144p. 2012. pap. 17.95 ***(978-0-8203-4311-2(0))*** 2010. (Illus.). 22.95 *(978-0-8203-3381-6(6))* Univ. of Georgia Pr.

Trotter, Joe W. & Day, Jared N. Race & Renaissance: African Americans in Pittsburgh since World War II. 2010. (ENG., Illus.). 304p. 29.95 *(978-0-8229-4391-4(3))* Univ. of Pittsburgh Pr.

Trotter, Joe William, Jr. Black Milwaukee: The Making of an Industrial Proletariat, 1915-45. 2nd ed. 2006. (Illus.). 432p. per. 31.00 *(978-0-252-07410-3(6))* Univ. of Illinois Pr.

Troutt, David Dante, ed. After the Storm: Black Intellectuals Explore the Meaning of Hurricane Katrina. 2007. (ENG.). 168p. per. 14.95 *(978-1-59558-203-4(7))* New Pr., The.

Truitt, Tom, prologue by. Forty Million & A Tool: No More Waitin' or Beggin' for Reparations. 2007. 225p. *(978-0-9790140-1-7(8))* Pliab Press.

Tucker, Linda G. Lockstep & Dance: Images of Black Men in Popular Culture. 2007. (ENG.). 191p. 50.00 *(978-1-57806-906-4(8))* Univ. Pr. of Mississippi.

Tukufu, Darryl S. A Guide Toward the Successful Development of African-American Males: The Remix. 2nd ed. 2009. 91p. pap. 12.95 *(978-0-9662152-2-9(2))* Tukufu Group, The.

Tulsa-Greenwood Race Riot Claims Accountability ACT of 2007: Hearing Before the Subcommittee on the Constitution, Civil Rights, & Civil Liberties of the Committee on the Judiciary, House of Representatives, One Hundred Tenth Congress, First Session, on H.R. 1995, April 24, 2007. 2007. (Illus.). iii, 144p. *(978-0-16-079147-5(2)*, 552-070-36243-6) United States Government Printing Office.

Turner, Henry McNeal. An African American Pastor Before & During the American Civil War. 2010. 109.95 *(978-0-7734-1429-7(0))* Mellen, Edwin Pr., The.

Turner, Richard. The Rise & Fall of the Crips. 2011. 126p. pap. 19.99 ***(978-1-4568-1832-6(5))*** Xlibris Corp.

Van Gorder, A. Christian & Tait, Lewis T. Red, White, Black, & Blue: Black Anger, White Ignorance, & Racism in Obama's America. 2011. ***(978-1-59221-844-8(X))***; 340p. pap. ***(978-1-59221-845-5(8))*** Africa World Pr.

Vargas, Joao H. Costa. Never Meant to Survive: Genocide & Utopias in Black Diaspora Communities. 2008. (Transformative Politics Ser.). (ENG.). 262p. 85.00 *(978-0-7425-4101-6(0))* Rowman & Littlefield Publishers, Inc.

Waites, Cheryl. Social Work Practice with African American Families: An Intergenerational Perspective. 2008. (ENG.). 224p. 175.00 *(978-0-7890-3391-8(7))* Routledge.

Waites, Cheryl, ed. Social Work Practice with African American Families: An Intergenerational Perspective. 2008. (ENG.). 224p. pap. 54.95 *(978-0-7890-3392-5(5))* Routledge.

Wallgora-Davis, Nicole. Sanctuary: African Americans & Empire. 2011. (ENG., Illus.). 240p. 65.00 *(978-0-19-536991-5(2))* Oxford Univ. Pr., Inc.

Walker, Lewis & Wilson, Benjamin C. Black Eden: The Idlewild Community. 2007. (ENG., Illus.). 269p. per. 19.95 *(978-0-87013-804-1(9))* Michigan State Univ. Pr.

Wallach, Jennifer Jensen. Closer to the Truth Than Any Fact: Memoir, Memory, & Jim Crow. (ENG.). 192p. 2010. pap. 22.95 *(978-0-8203-3502-5(9))* 2008. 34.95 *(978-0-8203-3069-3(8))* Univ. of Georgia Pr.

Ward, Edward R. Life in the Valley of Death: Some Aspects of Race in Men's Basketball in the Missouri Valley Conference: 1959-1960, 1963-1964. 2007. per. *(978-0-9749989-1-6(5))* Graphix Products, Inc.

Ward, Stephen, ed. Pages from a Black Radical's Notebook: A James Boggs Reader. 2010. 488p. pap. 27.95 *(978-0-8143-3256-6(0))* Wayne State Univ. Pr.

Warren, Roland Leslie. Politics & African-American Ghettos. 2008. (ENG.). 244p. pap. 29.95 *(978-0-202-36212-0(4))* Aldine Transaction.

Washington, Booker T. The Negro in the South: His Economic Progress in Relation to His Moral & Religious Development. 222p. reprint ed. 98.00 *(978-0-7222-9755-1(6))* Library Reprints, Inc.

—The Negro Problem. 2009. 120p. 24.99 *(978-0-559-08944-2(9))*; 21.99 *(978-0-559-08959-6(7))*; pap. 19.75 *(978-0-559-08955-8(4))*; pap. 19.75 *(978-0-559-08948-0(1))* BiblioBazaar.

—The Negro Problem. 2007. (ENG.). 76p. per. *(978-1-4068-1972-4(7))* Echo Library.

—The Negro Problem. 2009. 104p. pap. 11.45 *(978-1-4385-1907-4(9)*, Book Jungle) Standard Pubns., Inc.

Washington, Booker T. & Du Bois, W. E. B. The Negro in the South: His Economic Progress in Relation to His Moral & Religious Development. 2007. (ENG.). 224p. 39.95 *(978-0-548-15783-1(9))* Kessinger Publishing, LLC.

Washington Post Staff, et al. Being a Black Man: At the Corner of Progress & Peril. 2007. (ENG., Illus.). 384p. per. 13.95 *(978-1-58648-522-1(9))* PublicAffairs.

Weinbaum, Alys Eve, ed. Next to the Color Line: Gender, Sexuality, & W. E. B. du Bois. 2007. (Critical American Studies). (Illus.). 416p. 75.00 *(978-0-8166-4722-4(4))*; per. 26.00 *(978-0-8166-4723-1(2))* Univ. of Minnesota Pr.

Whalen, Mark. The Great War & the Culture of the New Negro. 2008. (ENG., Illus.). 336p. 65.00 *(978-0-8130-3206-1(7))* Univ. Pr. of Florida.

White, Derrick E. The Challenge of Blackness: The Institute of the Black World & Political Activism in The 1970s. 2011. (Southern Dissent Ser.). (ENG., Illus.). 288p. 69.95 *(978-0-8130-3735-6(2))* Univ. Pr. of Florida.

White, Elisa Joy. Modernity, Freedom, & the African Diaspora: Dublin, New Orleans, Paris. 2012. (Blacks in the Diaspora Ser.). (ENG.). 356p. pap. 30.00 ***(978-0-253-00125-2(0)***, 0253001250); (Illus.). 80.00 ***(978-0-253-00115-3(3)***, 0253001153) Indiana Univ. Pr.

Whitlock, Joyce Ann. Sacred Ground. 2008. 128p. 21.49 *(978-1-4389-1593-7(4))*; pap. 10.99 *(978-1-4389-1594-4(2))* AuthorHouse.

Why We Can't Wait: A Case for Philanthropic Action: Opportunities for Improving the Life Outcomes for African American Males. 2007. 81p. spiral bd. *(978-0-916584-24-5(0))* Ford Foundation.

Wickham, DeWayne. Black Voices in Commentary. 2006. xiii, 129p. pap. 15.95 *(978-0-9635720-9-7(1))* August Pr.

Wilkins, Rhonda. Swimming Upstream. 2008. 248p. pap. *(978-3-8364-7843-4(9))* VDM Verlag Dr. Mueller e.K.

Williams, Barbara Morrow. Battling Goliath. 2009. 284p. pap. *(978-3-639-00114-3(1))* VDM Verlag Dr. Mueller e.K.

Williams, Chad Louis. Torchbearers of Democracy: African American Soldiers in the World War I Era. 2010. (John Hope Franklin Series in African American History & Culture Ser.). (ENG., Illus.). 464p. 34.95 *(978-0-8078-3394-0(0))* Univ. of North Carolina Pr.

Williams, DeRay. Three Strikes You're Out: for Black Men in America until the First Black President. 2010. 100p. pap. 17.95 *(978-0-557-36660-6(7))* Lulu Enterprises Inc.

Williams, Juan. Enough: The Phony Leaders, Dead-End Movements, & Culture of Failure That Are Undermining Black America— and What We Can Do about It. 2007. (ENG.). 256p. per. 13.95 *(978-0-307-33824-2(X)*, Three Rivers Pr.) Crown Publishing Group.

Williams, Karen G. & Queeley, Andrea. Study Guide for Let Nobody Turn Us Around. 2nd ed. 2009. (ENG.). 150p. pap. 15.00 *(978-1-4422-0013-5(8))* Rowman & Littlefield Publishers, Inc.

Williams, Richard. Hierarchical Structures & Social Value: The Creation of Black & Irish Identities in the United States. 2010. (ENG.). 208p. pap. 31.99 *(978-0-521-14479-7(5))* Cambridge Univ. Pr.

Williams, Thomas Chatterton. Losing My Cool: Love, Literature, & a Black Man's Escape from the Crowd. 2011. (ENG.). 240p. (gr. 12). 15.00 *(978-0-14-311962-3(1)*, Penguin (Non-Classics)) Penguin Group (USA) Inc.

Williams, Twyla J. Save Our Children: The Struggle Between Black Parents & Schools. 2009. (ENG.). 200p. pap. 15.95 *(978-1-934155-16-5(0))* African American Images.

Williams, Vernon J., Jr. The Social Sciences & Theories of Race. 2006. 168p. 50.00 *(978-0-252-03086-4(9))*; per. 25.00 *(978-0-252-07320-5(7))* Univ. of Illinois Pr.

Williams, Zachery. Africana Cultures & Policy Studies: Scholarship & the Transformation of Public Policy. Williams, Zachery, ed. 2009. (Contemporary Black History Ser.). (ENG.). 296p. 100.00 *(978-0-230-60280-9(0))* Palgrave Macmillan.

Willis, William Shedrick & Zumwalt, Rosemary Levy. Franz Boas & W.E.B. Du Bois at Atlanta University, 1906. 2008. *(978-0-87169-982-4(6))* American Philosophical Society.

Wilson, David. Cities & Race: America's New Black Ghetto. 2006. (Questioning Cities Ser.). (Illus.). 175p. per. 51.95 *(978-0-415-35806-4(X)*, RU5806X) Routledge.

Wilson, Maloyd Ben & Wilson Group Network Inc Staff. Black Chronicle: From the Slavery Era - 1778 to the Beginning of the Civil Rights Movement, 1956. 2008. (Illus.). 70p. pap. 20.00 *(978-0-9753210-0-3(5))* Wilson Group Network, Inc.

Wilson, William Julius. The Declining Significance of Race: Blacks & Changing American Institutions. 3rd ed. 2012. (ENG.). 272p. pap. 20.00 ***(978-0-226-90141-1(6))*** Univ. of Chicago Pr.

—More Than Just Race: Being Black & Poor in the Inner City. 2009. (Issues of Our Time Ser.). (ENG., Illus.). 256p. 24.95 *(978-0-393-06705-7(X)*, 6705) Norton, W. W. & Co., Inc.

Wilson, William Julius. The Truly Disadvantaged: The Inner City, the Underclass, & Public Policy, Second Edition. 2nd ed. 2012. (ENG., Illus.). 320p. pap. 20.00 ***(978-0-226-90126-8(2))*** Univ. of Chicago Pr.

Wilson, William Julius & Wilson, William J. More Than Just Race: Being Black & Poor in the Inner City. 2010. (Issues of Our Time Ser.). (ENG., Illus.). 190p. pap. 15.95 *(978-0-393-33763-1(4)*, 33763) Norton, W. W. & Co., Inc.

Winfree, Guru Eric & Brown, Julius. The Black Paradox. 2007. 163p. pap. 19.99 *(978-0-615-16028-3(X))* Brown & Winfree.

Wolfe, Tom. Radical Chic & Mau-Mauing the Flak Catchers. 2009. (ENG.). 144p. pap. 15.00 *(978-0-312-42913-3(4))* Picador.

Womack, Ytasha. Beats Rhymes & Life: What We Love & Hate about Hip-Hop. Jasper, Kenji, ed. 2007. (ENG., Illus.). 320p. pap. 19.00 *(978-0-7679-1977-7(7)*, Harlem Moon) Broadway Bks.

Womack, Ytasha L. Post Black: How a New Generation Is Redefining African American Identity. 2010. (ENG., Illus.). 224p. pap. 16.95 *(978-1-55652-805-7(1)*, Hill, Lawrence Bks.) Chicago Review Pr., Inc.

Woods-Buchanan, Yashica. African American College Students at Black Versus White Institutions. 2009. 52p. pap. *(978-3-639-03508-7(9))* VDM Verlag Dr. Mueller e.K.

Woods, Clyde. Development Arrested: From the Plantation Era to the Katrina Crisis in the Mississippi Delta. rev. ed. 2012. 352p. pap. 26.95 *(978-1-84467-561-6(0)*, New Left Bks.) Verso Bks. GBR. Dist: Norton, W. W. & Co., Inc.

Woodson, Carter. The Mis-Education of the Negro. 2007. 220p. per. 17.95 *(978-1-58509-320-5(3))* Book Tree, The.

Woodson, Carter G. The Mis-Education of the Negro. 2009. 100p. pap. 7.49 *(978-1-60459-816-2(6))* 2008. (ENG.). 108p. per. 9.99 *(978-1-60459-226-9(5))* Wilder Pubns., Ltd.

—The Mis-Education of the Negro (an African American Heritage Book) 2008. 108p. 19.99 *(978-1-60459-227-6(3))* Wilder Pubns., Ltd.

Woodson, Carter Godwin. The Mind of the Negro As Reflected in Letters Written During the Crisis 1800-1860. 2010. 714p. pap. 35.00 *(978-1-57898-960-7(4))* Martino Publishing.

—The Mis-Education of the Negro. 2010. 116p. pap. 6.50 *(978-1-57898-918-8(3))* Martino Publishing.

—The Mis-Education of the Negro. 2011. (ENG.). 144p. pap. 7.77 *(978-1-936594-30-6(7))* Tribeca Bks.

—The Mis-Education of the Negro. 2008. 200p. pap. 14.99 *(978-1-60459-299-3(0))* Wilder Pubns., Ltd.

Wortham, Robert A., ed. W. E. B. du Bois & the Sociological Imagination: A Reader, 1897-1914. 2009. (ENG.). 436p. pap. 49.95 *(978-1-60258-200-2(9))* Baylor Univ. Pr.

Wright, Kai. Drifting Toward Love: Black, Brown, Gay, & Coming of Age on the Streets of New York, 1 vol. 2009. (ENG.). 240p. pap. 16.00 *(978-0-8070-7969-0(3))* Beacon Pr.

Wright, Richard & Wright, Richard. Black Power: The Color Curtain - And White Man, Listen! 2008. (P. S. Ser.). (ENG., Illus.). 864p. pap. 18.95 *(978-0-06-144945-1(8)*, HarperPerennial) HarperCollins Pubs.

Wylie, Arlet & Wylie, Sarne. Between Piety & Desire. 2010. 112p. pap. 15.00 *(978-1-60801-040-0(6))* Univ Of New Orleans Pr.

Yewah, Emmanuel & Togunde, 'Dimeji. Across the Atlantic: African Immigrants in the United States Diaspora. 2010. pap. *(978-1-86335-788-3(2))* Common Ground Publishing Pty, Ltd.

Young Armstead, Myra B. Freedom's Gardener: James F. Brown, Horticulture, & the Hudson Valley in Antebellum America. 2012. (ENG., Illus.). 256p. 35.00 ***(978-0-8147-0510-0(3))*** New York Univ. Pr.

Young, Mark. Hindered the Fall & Impending Rise of Black America. 2007. 252p. 19.95 *(978-0-9801007-0-9(4))*; pap. 14.95 *(978-0-9801007-1-6(2))* Ascension Publishing.

Zamani-Gallaher, Eboni M. & Polite, Vernon C. The State of the African American Male. Campbell, Alec, ed. 2010. (CourageousConversations series Ser.). (ENG.). 303p. pap. 29.95 *(978-0-87013-870-6(7))* Michigan State Univ. Pr.

AFRICAN AMERICANS—SOCIAL LIFE AND CUSTOMS

Abernethy, Francis Edward, et al, eds. Juneteenth Texas: Essays in African-American Folklore. 2010. (Publications of the Texas Folklore Society Ser.). (ENG.). 376p. pap. 29.95 *(978-1-57441-283-3(3))* Univ. of North Texas Pr.

Alner, Christine. The Black Redemptive: Division Is Destructive. 2009. 180p. pap. 17.95 *(978-1-4389-9215-0(7))* AuthorHouse.

Ali, Jamal. Black & Green: Black Insights for the Green Movement. 2009. (ENG.). 90p. pap. 19.99 *(978-0-7618-4722-9(7))* Hamilton Bks.

Allen, Peggy Vonsherie. The Pecan Orchard: Journey of a Sharecropper's Daughter. (ENG., Illus.). 272p. 2011. pap. 18.95 *(978-0-8173-5659-0(2))* 2009. 29.95 *(978-0-8173-1672-3(8))* Univ. of Alabama Pr.

Aman, Yasser. The Evolution of Jazz & Blues As Cultural Kernels. 2010. 68p. pap. *(978-3-8383-8233-3(1))* Lambert Academic Publishing.

Anderson, Elijah. Code of the Street: Decency, Violence & the Moral Life of the Inner City. 2006. pap. 8.95 *(978-1-4288-1549-0(X))* Cram101 Inc.

Anderson, Sheila. Kwanzaa. 2009. (Cultural Holidays Ser.). (Illus.). 32p. (gr. -1-4). 28.50 *(978-1-60270-604-0(2)*, Looking Glass Library- Nonfiction) Magic Wagon.

Appiah, Dorothy. Adult Learning & Space Making. 2009. 168p. pap. *(978-3-639-15055-1(4))* VDM Verlag Dr. Mueller e.K.

Arnold, Harold L., Jr. Marriage ROCKS for Christian Couples. 2009. 192p. pap. 16.00 *(978-0-8170-1566-4(3))* Judson Pr.

—Marriage ROCKS for Christian Couples: A Leader's Guide. 2009. 72p. pap. 10.00 *(978-0-8170-1567-1(1))* Judson Pr.

Asante, Molefi Kete. Maulana Karenga: An Intellectual Portrait. 2009. (ENG.). 224p. 69.95 *(978-0-7456-4827-9(4))*; pap. 19.95 *(978-0-7456-4828-6(2))* Polity Pr. GBR. Dist: Wiley, John & Sons, Inc.

Bailey, Joseph. Anger in Black Americans. 2006. (ENG.). 408p. per. 19.95 *(978-1-59594-113-8(4)*, Wingspan Pr.) WingSpan Publishing.

Baker, Phyllis. African American Spirituality 3e. 3rd ed. 2006. (ENG.). 170p. (C). pap. 50.95 *(978-0-7593-9584-8(5))* CENGAGE Learning Custom Publishing.

Baraka, Amiri, pseud. Razor. 2011. (ENG.). 300p. pap. 19.95 *(978-0-88378-300-9(2))* Third World Press.

Bastfield, Darrin Keith. Back in the Day: My Life & Times with Tupac Shakur. 2008. (ENG.). 182p. pap. 15.00 *(978-1-4379-5095-3(7))* DIANE Publishing Co.

Bennings, Threatha Price. Moving to Grahamtown. Garza, Amy Ammons & Rucker, Virginia, eds. 2007. 96p. per. 20.00 *(978-0-9753023-8-5(8)*, Catch the Spirit of Appalachia) Ammons Communications, Ltd.

Birchett, Colleen. Family Ties: Restoring Unity in the African American Family. 2010. 192p. per. 9.99 *(978-1-932715-69-9(X))* UMI (Urban Ministries, Inc.).

Bird, Stephanie Rose. Healing Grove: African Tree Remedies & Rituals for the Body & Spirit. 2009. (ENG., Illus.). 368p. pap. 18.95 *(978-1-55652-764-7(0)*, Hill, Lawrence Bks.) Chicago Review Pr., Inc.

Black, Helen, et al. From Zero to Eighty: Two African American Men's Narrative of Racism, Suffering, Survival, & Transformation. 2011. 308p. 31.95 ***(978-1-4620-0509-3(8))***; pap. 21.95 ***(978-1-4620-0507-9(1))*** iUniverse, Inc.

Black, Ivory Abena. Bronzeville a Milwaukee Lifestyle: A Historical Overview. Di Frances, Sally, ed. 2006. (Illus.). 51p. per. 14.95 *(978-0-9771065-0-9(0))* Publishers Group, The.

Blended Families. 12.00 *(978-0-687-08878-2(X))* Abingdon Pr.

Boyd, Todd. African Americans & Popular Culture, 3 vols. 2008. (Illus.). 836p. 300.00 *(978-0-275-98922-4(4)*, C8922, Praeger Pubs.) Greenwood Publishing Group, Inc.

—Young, Black, Rich, & Famous: The Rise of the NBA, the Hip Hop Invasion, & the Transformation of American Culture. 2008. (ENG., Illus.). 224p. pap. 16.95 *(978-0-8032-1675-4(0)*, Bison Bks.) Univ. of Nebraska Pr.

Bracks, Lean'tin. The African American Almanac: 400 Years of Triumph, Courage & Excellence. 2011. (ENG., Illus.). 512p. pap. 22.95 ***(978-1-57859-323-1(9))*** Visible Ink Pr.

Brown, Lisa M. Strong on the Outside, Dying on the Inside. 2011. 122p. 19.99 *(978-1-61215-592-0(8))* Xulon Pr., Inc.

Brown, Sterling Allen. A Negro Looks at the South. Tidwell, John Edgar & Sanders, Mark A., eds. 2007. (ENG., Illus.). 400p. 40.00 *(978-0-19-531399-4(2))* Oxford Univ. Pr., Inc.

Canfield, Jack L., et al. Chicken Soup for the African American Woman's Soul. 2006. (Chicken Soup for the Soul Ser.). (ENG., Illus.). 384p. pap. 14.95 *(978-0-7573-0520-7(2))* Health Communications, Inc.

Carroll, Brian. When to Stop the Cheering? The Black Press, the Black Community, & the Integration of Professional Baseball. 2006. (Studies in African American History & Culture). (Illus.). 271p. 126.00 *(978-0-415-97938-2(2))* Routledge.

Cohen, Cathy J. Democracy Remixed: Black Youth & the Future of American Politics, 1 vol. 2012. (Transgressing Boundaries: Studies in Black Politics &

Black Communities Ser.). (ENG., Illus.). 304p. pap. 19.95 (978-0-19-989626-4(7)) Oxford Univ. Pr., Inc.
Cole, Harriette. Jumping the Broom: The African-American Wedding Planner. 2nd rev. ed. 2006. (Illus.). 283p. reprint ed. pap. 20.00 (978-1-4223-5274-8(9)) DIANE Publishing Co.
Cooper, William A. A Portrayal of Negro Life. (Illus.). 110p. reprint ed. lib. bdg. 88.00 (978-0-7222-0399-6(3)) Library Reprints, Inc.
Cross, Wilbur. Gullah Culture in America. 2012. (Illus.). 288p. pap. 16.95 (978-0-89587-573-0(X)) Blair, John F. Pub.
Cruson, Daniel. The Slaves of Central Fairfield County: The Journey from Slave to Freeman in Nineteenth-Century Connecticut. 2007. (Illus.). 124p. pap., per. 19.99 (978-1-59629-151-5(6)) History Pr., The.
Daise, Ronald. Gullah Branches, West African Roots. 2007. (Illus.). 198p. per. (978-0-87844-182-2(4)) Sandlapper Publishing Co., Inc.
Dancy, T. Elon. The Brother Code: Manhood & Masculinity among African American Men in College. 2012. (978-1-61735-761-9(8)); pap. (978-1-61735-760-2(X)) Information Age Publishing, Inc.
Dimitriadis, Greg. Performing Identity/Performing Culture: Hip Hop As Text, Pedagogy, & Lived Practice. 2009. (Intersections in Communications & Culture: Global Approaches & Transdisciplinary Perspectives Ser.). 216p. (C). 29.95 (978-1-4331-0538-8(1)) Lang, Peter Publishing, Inc.
Donaldson, Jam. Conversate Is Not a Word: Getting Away from Ghetto. 2010. (ENG., Illus.). 208p. pap. 14.95 (978-1-55652-780-7(2), Hill, Lawrence Bks.) Chicago Review Pr., Inc.
Duster, Michelle. Ida in Her Own Words: The Timeless Writings of Ida B. Wells From 1893. 2008. 104p. pap. 12.95 (978-0-9802398-1-2(8)) Williams, Benjamin Publishing.
Easton-Brooks, Donald. African Americanæs Academic Outcomes. 2008. 152p. pap. (978-3-639-04586-4(6)) VDM Verlag Dr. Mueller e.K.
Family, Ujamaa. Harambee! Kwanzaa Family Guide. 2009. 208p. pap. 19.99 (978-0-557-12693-4(2)) Lulu Enterprises Inc.
Flemming-McCall, Felicia. African Americans of Chesterfield County. 2008. (Images of America Ser.). (ENG., Illus.). 128p. pap. 19.99 (978-0-7385-5434-1(0)) Arcadia Publishing.
Flono, Fannie. Thriving in the Shadows: The Black Experience in Charlotte & Mecklenburg County. 2007. (Illus.). 152p. (978-0-9760963-8-2(2)) Novello Festival Pr.
Foley, Neil. Quest for Equality: The Failed Promise of Black-Brown Solidarity. 2010. (Nathan I. Huggins Lectures). (Illus.). 240p. 24.95 (978-0-674-05023-5(1)) Harvard Univ. Pr.
Foner, Nancy & Holtzman, Jon D. Nuer Journeys, Nuer Lives: Sudanese Refugees in Minnesota. 2nd ed. 2007. (New Immigrants Ser.). (ENG., Illus.). 160p. (C). per. 37.40 (978-0-205-54332-8(4)) Allyn & Bacon, Inc.
Foster, Frances Smith. 'Til Death or Distance Do Us Part: Love & Marriage in African America. 2010. (ENG.). 224p. 21.95 (978-0-19-532852-3(3)) Oxford Univ. Pr., Inc.
Fraser, Rebecca J. Courtship & Love among the Enslaved in North Carolina. 2011. pap. 30.00 (978-1-61703-038-3(4)) Univ. Pr. of Mississippi.
Freed, Leonard. Black in White America. 2010. (Illus.). 216p. pap. 29.95 (978-1-60606-011-7(2)) Getty Pubns.
Gates, Henry Louis, Jr. Tradition & the Black Atlantic: Critical Theory in the African Diaspora. 2010. (ENG.). 224p. (gr. 9). 23.95 (978-0-465-01410-1(0), Basic Civitas Bks.) Basic Bks.
Gay, Kathlyn. African-American Holidays, Festivals, & Celebrations: The History, Customs, & Symbols Associated with Both Traditional & Contemporary Religious & Secular Events Observed by Americans of African Descent. 2006. (Illus.). 569p. 65.00 (978-0-7808-0779-2(0)) Omnigraphics, Inc.
Gershenhorn, Jerry. Melville J. Herskovits & the Racial Politics of Knowledge. 2007. (Critical Studies in the History of Anthropology). (ENG.). 347p. pap. 29.95 (978-0-8032-2247-2(5)) Univ. of Nebraska Pr.
Glasrud, Bruce A. & Wintz, Cary D. The Harlem Renaissance in the American West: The New Negro's Western Experience. 2011. E-Book (978-0-203-80558-9(5)) Routledge.
Glass, Barbara S. African American Dance: An Illustrated History. 2006. (ENG., Illus.). 319p. 55.00 (978-0-7864-2816-8(3)) McFarland & Co., Inc. Pubs.
Gonzales, Ambrose, ed. The Black Border. 2010. 352p. pap. 19.95 (978-1-4290-2044-2(X)) Applewood Bks.
Grayson, Ebonie T. African-American Days 28 Ways of Praise: An Inspirational & Educational Affirmations Book, 1 vol. 2009. 152p. pap. 24.95 (978-1-60836-939-3(0)) PublishAmerica, Inc.
Greason, Walter. The Path to Freedom: Black Families in New Jersey. 2010. (ENG., Illus.). 128p. pap. 19.99 (978-1-59629-992-4(4)) History Pr., The.
Greene. Stirring Up the African American Spirit. 136p. pap. 14.95 (978-1-881165-19-4(1)) People Skills International.
Hairston, Otis L. Picturing Greensboro, North Carolina: Four Decades of African American Community. 2007. pap. 19.99 (978-1-59629-284-0(9)) History Pr., The.
Harris, Jermaine M. Identity: Who We Were, Who We Are, Who We Shall Become. 2011. 116p. pap. 15.90 (978-1-4634-4162-3(2)) AuthorHouse.
Harris, Middleton A., et al, eds. The Black Book. 35th anniv. ed. 2009. (Illus.). 224p. 35.00 (978-1-4000-6848-7(7), Random House) Random House Publishing Group.
Harrison, Milmon. Seek First the Kingdom: Gospels of Prosperity in American Culture. 2007. (978-0-8147-3680-7(7)); pap. (978-0-8147-3681-4(5)) New York Univ. Pr.
Haskins, Ethelbert. Victim Psychosis in the Center City Ghettos. 2010. 272p. pap. 19.95 (978-1-4327-3724-5(4)) Outskirts Pr., Inc.
Hilliard Mims, Barbara Tone. Don't Blame Me If I Got the Name Wrong. 2008. 324p. pap. 14.95 (978-1-4327-2123-7(2)) Outskirts Pr., Inc.
Hodari, Askhari Johnson. The African Book of Names: 5,000+ Common & Uncommon Names from the African Continent. 2009. (ENG.). 343p. pap. 14.95 (978-0-7573-0779-9(5)) Health Communications, Inc.
Hopkinson, Natalie. Go-Go Live: The Musical Life & Death of a Chocolate City. 2012. (ENG., Illus.). 232p. 79.95 (978-0-8223-5200-6(1)); pap. 22.95 (978-0-8223-5211-2(7)) Duke Univ. Pr.
Hornsby, Alton. African Americans in the Post-Emancipation South: The Outsiders' View. 2010. (ENG.). 190p. pap. 29.00 (978-0-7618-5105-9(4)) Univ. Pr. of America, Inc.
Humphrey, Imani A. First Fruits: The Family Guide to Celebrating Kwanzaa. 42p. pap. 7.95 (978-0-88378-002-2(X)) Third World Press.
Huntington, Carla Stalling. Black Social Dance in Television Advertising: An Analytical History. 2011. (ENG., Illus.). 200p. pap. 40.00 (978-0-7864-5944-5(1)) McFarland & Co., Inc. Pubs.
Jackson, Gerald P. The Suicide of the Black-American Culture: A Spiritual Remedy for the Self-Destructive Elements in the Black-American Culture. 2009. 202p. pap. 13.99 (978-1-60604-824-5(4)) Tate Publishing & Enterprises, LLC.
Johnson, J. Terry. Racial Disparity in Social Spatiality. 2008. 100p. per. (978-3-8364-3600-7(0)) VDM Verlag Dr. Mueller e.K.
Jones, Carla J. & Hull, Tonya M. African Americans of Giles County. 2010. (Images of America Ser.). (ENG., Illus.). 128p. pap. 21.99 (978-0-7385-6689-4(6)) Arcadia Publishing.
Karenga. The Message & Meaning of Kwanzaa: Bringing Good into the World: The Founder's Annual Statements 1994-2006. 2007. (978-0-943412-27-6(7)) Univ. of Sankore Pr., The.
King, J. L. CP Time: Why Some People Are Always Late. 2011. (ENG.). 144p. pap. 11.95 (978-1-4391-6560-7(2), Strebor Bks.) Strebor Bks.
King, Lovalerie & Schur, Richard, eds. African American Culture & Legal Discourse. 2009. (ENG.). 272p. 95.00 (978-0-230-61988-3(6)) Palgrave Macmillan.
Knowles, Gilbert A. Help Them Pull Their Pants Up: How Mentors & Communities Can Empower Young African American Men. 2008. 132p. 23.95 (978-0-595-49903-8(1)); 128p. pap. 13.95 (978-0-595-50216-5(4)) iUniverse, Inc.
Konadu, Kwasi. The Akan Diaspora in the Americas, 1 vol. 2012. (ENG.). 324p. pap. 24.95 (978-0-19-992285-7(3)) Oxford Univ. Pr., Inc.
Kopano, Baruti N. & Brown, Tamara Lizette. Soul Thieves: White America's Appropriation of African American Culture. 2012. (Contemporary Black History Ser.). (ENG.). 224p. 85.00 (978-0-230-10891-2(1)); pap. 25.00 (978-0-230-10897-4(0)) Palgrave Macmillan.
Ledwidge, Asher. Saving the Black Culture: Revolution of Hope, Black Unity, Brotherly Love. 2008. (For the Black Man Ser.). 258p. per. 15.00 (978-0-9636109-5-9(3)) Nuf-Love Publishing.
Lloyd, David. The Black & Green Atlantic: Cross-Currents of the African & Irish Diasporas. O'Neill, Peter, ed. 2009. (ENG., Illus.). 296p. 100.00 (978-0-230-22818-4(6)) Palgrave Macmillan.
Lornell, Kip & Stephenson Jr., Charles C. The Beat! Go-Go Music from Washington, D. C. 2009. (American Made Music Ser.). (ENG., Illus.). 304p. pap. 25.00 (978-1-60473-241-2(5)) Univ. Pr. of Mississippi.
Maffly-Kipp, Laurie F. Setting down the Sacred Past: African-American Race Histories. 2010. 352p. 29.95 (978-0-674-05079-2(7), Belknap Pr.) Harvard Univ. Pr.
Marable, Manning. Race, Reform, & Rebellion: The Second Reconstruction & Beyond in Black America, 1945-2006. 3rd rev. ed. 2007. (ENG.). 312p. (C). per. 25.00 (978-1-57806-154-9(7)); 55.00 (978-1-57806-153-2(9)) Univ. Pr. of Mississippi.
Mayes, Keith & Mayes, Keith A. Kwanzaa: Black Power & the Making of the African-American Holiday Tradition. 2009. (ENG., Illus.). 312p. 27.95 (978-0-415-99855-0(7)); 130.00 (978-0-415-99854-3(9)) Routledge.
Mazloomi, Carolyn L. Stitching a Culture Together: African American Quilters of Ohio. 2013. (Ohio Quilt Ser.). (ENG., Illus.). 128p. pap. 22.95 (978-0-8214-1940-3(4)) Ohio Univ. Pr.
McCollum, Michael. The Way We Wore: Black Style Then. 2006. (ENG., Illus.). 176p. 40.00 (978-0-9777531-1-6(5)) Glitterati, Inc.
McElroy, Njoki. 1012 Natchez: A Memoir of Joy, Harship, & Love. 2010. 216p. pap. 14.95 (978-1-934812-55-6(2)) Brown Bks. Publishing Group.
Minutaglio, Bill. In Search of the Blues: A Journey to the Soul of Black Texas. 2010. (ENG., Illus.). 183p. 50.00 (978-0-292-72247-7(8)); pap. 24.95 (978-0-292-72289-7(3)) Univ. of Texas Pr.
Mitchell, Erin Goseer. Born Colored: Life Before Bloody Sunday. 2006. 220p. (978-0-9761235-2-1(5)) Ampersand Publishing.
Nolen, Rose M. African Americans in Mid-Missouri: From Pioneers to Ragtimers. 2010. (978-1-59629-609-1(7)) History Pr., The.
North Carolina African American History & Culture. 2007. (J). per. 32.96 (978-1-888325-45-4(3)) Allosaurus Pubs.
Nunley, Vorris. Keepin' It Hushed: The Barbershop & African American Hush Harbor Rhetoric. 2010. pap. 24.95 (978-0-8143-3348-8(6)) Wayne State Univ. Pr.
Ople, Frederick Douglass. Hog & Hominy: Soul Food from Africa to America. 2010. (Arts & Traditions of the Table: Perspectives on Culinary History Ser.). (ENG., Illus.). 256p. (gr. 17). pap. 17.95 (978-0-231-14639-5(6)) Columbia Univ. Pr.
Osayande, Ewuare. Misogyny & the Emcee: Sex, Race & Hip Hop. 2008. 112p. pap. 15.00 (978-0-9801635-7-5(9)) Talking Drum Communications.
Parham, Marisa. Haunting & Displacement in African American Literature & Culture. 2008. (Literary Criticism & Cultural Theory Ser.). (ENG., Illus.). 162p. (C). 125.00 (978-0-415-99094-3(7)) Routledge.
Pender, Charles E. The Religion of Greed & Its Impact on African Americans: Social Engineered Progressive Geocide. 2010. 192p. pap. 15.00 (978-1-4520-4524-5(0)) AuthorHouse.
Perryman, Wayne. Unfounded Loyalty: An in-Depth Look into the Love Affair between Blacks & Democrats. 23.95 (978-1-56229-073-3(8), Christian Living Bks., Inc.) Pneuma Life Publishing, Inc.
Phillips, Kimberley. Daily Life During African American Migrations, 1 vol. 2012. (Greenwood Press Daily Life Through History Series: Daily Life in the United States Ser.). (Illus.). 226p. 58.00 (978-0-313-34373-5(X), GR4373) Greenwood Publishing Group, Inc.
Pollard, Deborah Smith. When the Church Becomes Your Party: Contemporary Gospel Music. 2008. (African American Life Ser.). (Illus.). 225p. pap. 24.95 (978-0-8143-3218-4(8)) Wayne State Univ. Pr.
Rivers, Annie W. Celebrating African American Marriages: African American Couples Share Intimate Details of their Successful Marriage. 2009. 84p. pap. 14.95 (978-1-4269-1333-4(8)) Trafford Publishing.
Rivers, Voza W., ed. Forever Harlem: Celebrating America's Most Diverse Community. 2006. (Illus.). 279p. 29.95 (978-1-59670-206-6(0), Spotlight Pr) Sports Publishing, LLC.
Rose, Yvonne. Senior Stories - Straight from the Heart. 2011. pap. 12.99 (978-0-9824922-1-5(9)) Amber Bks.
Rosenfield, Richard. African American Core Values: A Guide for Everyone. 2009. 244p. 29.95 (978-0-595-51263-8(1)); pap. 19.95 (978-0-595-48635-9(5)) iUniverse, Inc.
Ross, Dax-Devlon. The Nightmare & the Dream: Nas, Jay-Z & the History of Conflict in African-American Culture. 2008. 364p. pap. 15.00 (978-0-9817398-1-6(4)) Outside the Box Publishing, LLC.
Rutkoff, Peter M. & Scott, William B. Fly Away: The Great African American Cultural Migrations. 2010. (ENG., Illus.). 432p. (gr. 17). 45.00 (978-0-8018-9477-0(8)) Johns Hopkins Univ. Pr.
Rutledge, Archibald Hamilton. God's Children. 2009. 19.99 (978-1-59629-642-8(9)) History Pr., The.
Smith, Don. What I See: A New Prescription for Thought. 2009. 108p. 22.50 (978-1-60860-016-8(5), Eloquent Bks.) AEG Literary Publishing Services, Inc.
Smith, Jessie Carney, ed. Encyclopedia of African American Popular Culture, 4 vols. 2010. (Illus.). 1733p. 380.00 (978-0-313-35796-1(X), GR5796) Greenwood Publishing Group, Inc.
Smith, Michael P., et al. In the Spirit: The Photography of Michael P. Smith from the Historic New Orleans Collection. 2009. pap. (978-0-917860-54-6(3)) Univ. Pr. of Florida.
Smith, Sharon. Strapped. 2009. 126p. pap. 15.00 (978-0-557-08339-8(7)) Lulu Enterprises Inc.
Smith, Suzanne E. To Serve the Living: Funeral Directors & the African American Way of Death. 2010. (Illus.). 288p. 31.50 (978-0-674-03621-5(2), Belknap Pr.) Harvard Univ. Pr.
Spence, Lester K. Stare in the Darkness: The Limits of Hip-Hop & Black Politics. 2011. (Illus.). 240p. 67.50 (978-0-8166-6987-5(2)); pap. 22.50 (978-0-8166-6988-2(0)) Univ. of Minnesota Pr.
Stanford, Karin L. & Institute for Arts and Media, Northridge, California State University Staff. African Americans in Los Angeles. 2010. (Images of America Ser.). (Illus.). 128p. pap. 21.99 (978-0-7385-8094-4(5)) Arcadia Publishing.
Steffen, Charles G. Mutilating Khalid: The Symbolic Politics of Female Genital Cutting. 2010. 248p. pap. (978-1-56902-332-7(8)) Red Sea Pr.
Stephenson, Frank. Chowan Beach: Remembering an African American Resort. 2006. (Illus.). 124p. pap., per. 14.99 (978-1-59629-164-5(8)) History Pr., The.
Stodghill, Ron. Redbone: The Millionaire & the Gold Digger. 2008. (Illus.). 256p. per. 13.95 (978-0-06-089722-2(8), Amistad) HarperCollins Pubs.
Stolle, Roger. HH Mississippi Blues. 2011. pap. 19.99 (978-1-60949-219-9(6)) History Pr., The.
Szwed, John F. Crossovers: Essays on Race, Music, & American Culture. 2006. 296p. (C). per. 26.50 (978-0-8122-1972-2(4)) Univ. of Pennsylvania Pr.
Tate, Gayle T. & Randolph, Lewis A. The Black Urban Community: From Dusk till Dawn. 2006. (ENG.). 496p. 116.00 (978-1-4039-7067-1(X)); pap. 35.00 (978-1-4039-7068-8(8)) Palgrave Macmillan.
Taylor, Kea. I Still Do: A Celebration of African American Weddings. 2010. 128p. 29.99 (978-0-615-31320-7(5)) Imagine Photography.
Temple, Clyde. Having God's Best Marriage. 2007. (ENG.). 150p. pap. 14.95 (978-1-934155-04-2(7)) African American Images.
Thomas, Pat. Listen, Whitey! The Sounds of Black Power 1965-1975. 2012. (ENG., Illus.). 224p. 39.99 (978-1-60699-507-5(3), 699507) Fantagraphics Bks.
Wagner, Bryan. Disturbing the Peace: Black Culture & the Police Power after Slavery. 2009. (Illus.). 320p. 37.00 (978-0-674-03508-9(9)) Harvard Univ. Pr.
Walker, Lewis & Wilson, Benjamin C. Black Eden: The Idlewild Community. 2007. (ENG., Illus.). 269p. per. 19.95 (978-0-87013-804-1(9)) Michigan State Univ. Pr.
Weston Woods Staff, creator. Seven Candles for Kwanzaa. 2011. 18.95 (978-1-55592-745-5(9)) Weston Woods Studios, Inc.
Whalum, Kenneth T. Hip Hop Is Not Our Enemy: From A Preacher Who Keeps It Real. 2010. 184p. pap. 14.49 (978-1-4490-7424-1(3)) AuthorHouse.
White, Shane, et al. Playing the Numbers: Gambling in Harlem Between the Wars. 2010. 320p. 26.95 (978-0-674-05107-2(6)) Harvard Univ. Pr.
Wiethaus, Ulrike & Parent, Anthony S. Trauma & Resilience in American Indian & African American Southern History. 2012. (978-1-4331-1186-0(1)); E-Book (978-1-4539-0267-7(8)) Lang, Peter Publishing, Inc.
Williamson, Jerrelene & Spokane Northwest Black Pioneers. African Americans in Spokane. 2010. (Images of America Ser.). (Illus.). 128p. pap. 21.99 (978-0-7385-7011-2(7)) Arcadia Publishing.
Wintz, Cary D. & Glasrud, Bruce A., eds. The Harlem Renaissance in the American West: The New Negro's Western Experience. 2011. (New Directions in American History Ser.). (ENG., Illus.). 264p. (C). 150.00 (978-0-415-88687-1(2)); pap. 34.95 (978-0-415-88688-8(0)) Routledge.
Wright, Kai. The African American Experience: Black History & Culture Through Speeches, Letters, Editorials, Poems, Songs, & Stories. Wright, Kai, ed. 2009. (ENG.). 720p. pap. 22.95 (978-1-57912-773-2(8), 1579127738) Black Dog & Leventhal Pubs., Inc.
Wylie, Arlet & Wylie, Same. Between Piety & Desire. 2010. 112p. pap. 15.00 (978-1-60801-040-0(6)) Univ Of New Orleans Pr.
Yewah, Emmanuel & Togunde, 'Dimeji. Across the Atlantic: African Immigrants in the United States Diaspora. 2010. pap. (978-1-86335-788-3(2)) Common Ground Publishing Pty, Ltd.
Young, Kevin. The Grey Album: On the Blackness of Blackness, 1 vol. 2012. (ENG.). 476p. pap. 25.00 (978-1-55597-607-1(7)) Graywolf Pr.

AFRICAN AMERICANS—SOCIETIES, ETC.

Ernest, John. A Nation Within a Nation: Organizing African-American Communities Before the Civil War. 2011. (ENG.). 232p. 35.00 (978-1-56663-807-4(0)); (978-1-56663-917-0(4)) Dee, Ivan R. Pub.
Huey P. Newton Foundation Staff. The Black Panther Party: Service to the People Programs. Hilliard, David & The Huey P. Newton Foundation, eds. 2008. (ENG., Illus.). 170p. pap. 21.95 (978-0-8263-4394-9(5)) Univ. of New Mexico Pr.
Konadu, Kwasi B. A View from the East: Black Cultural Nationalism & Education in New York City. 2nd ed. 2009. (Illus.). 232p. 29.95 (978-0-8156-3206-1(1)) Syracuse Univ. Pr.
Skocpol, Theda, et al. What a Mighty Power We Can Be: African American Fraternal Groups & the Struggle for Racial Equality. (Princeton Studies in American Politics Ser.). (ENG., Illus.). 320p. (C). 2008. pap. 24.95 (978-0-691-13836-7(2)) 2006. 32.95 (978-0-691-12299-1(7)) Princeton Univ. Pr.

AFRICAN AMERICANS—STATISTICS, VITAL

New Strategist Staff. Blacks, Who We Are. 2007. 253p. pap. 89.95 (978-1-933588-81-0(0)) New Strategist Pubns., Inc.
Schutz, Mary Ellen, ed. The State of Black Madison 2008: Before the Tipping Point. 2008. 30p. pap. 5.00 (978-0-615-20703-2(0)) Urban League of Greater Madison.

AFRICAN AMERICANS—STUDY AND TEACHING

Aldridge, Delores P. Imagine a World: Pioneering Black Women Sociologists. 2008. (ENG.). 174p. pap. 32.99 (978-0-7618-4004-6(4)) Univ. Pr. of America, Inc.
Aldridge, Delores P. & James, E. Lincoln. Africana Studies: Philosophical Perspectives & Theoretical Paradigms. 2008. (Illus.). 338p. per. 24.95 (978-0-87422-294-4(X)) Washington State Univ. Pr.
Anderson, Talmadge. Introduction to African American Studies. rev. ed. 2008. (ENG.). 304p. pap. 64.15 (978-0-7872-3268-9(8)) Kendall Hunt Publishing Co.
Arnold, Harold L., Jr. Marriage ROCKS for Christian Couples: A Leader's Guide. 2009. 72p. pap. 10.00 (978-0-8170-1567-1(1)) Judson Pr.
Becknell, Jr. Charles E. & Becknell, Jr. A Critical Race Analysis of Black Studies in the Post Civil Rights Er. 2011. 240p. pap. (978-3-8443-8029-3(9)) Lambert Academic Publishing.
Bernier, Celeste-Marie. Public Art, Memorials & Atlantic Slavery. Newman, Judie, ed. 2009. (Illus.). 178p. 125.00 (978-0-415-48315-5(8)) Routledge.
Bonner, Emily. Unearthing Culturally Responsive Mathematics Teaching: The Legacy of Gloria Jean Merriex. 2010. (ENG.). 94p. pap. 18.50 (978-0-7618-5399-2(5)) Hamilton Bks.
Churn, Arlene. Power of the 10: How to Embrace the Commandments, Handle Stress & Achieve Success. 2009. (ENG.). 240p. pap. 12.95 (978-0-7679-1016-3(8), Harlem Moon) Broadway Bks.
Conyers, James L. African American Consciousness: Past & Present. 2011. (ENG.). 190p. pap. 29.95 (978-1-4128-4307-2(3)) Transaction Pubs.
Davidson, Jeanette R., ed. African American Studies. 2010. (Introducing Ethnic Studies). (ENG.). 272p. (gr. 17). 100.00 (978-0-7486-3714-0(1)); pap. 35.00 (978-0-7486-3715-7(X)) Edinburgh Univ. Pr. GBR. Dist: Columbia Univ. Pr.
Dickerson, Debra J. An American Story. pap. (978-0-385-72862-1(X)) Knopf Doubleday Publishing Group.
Dillard, Joey L., ed. Black Names. (Contributions to the Sociology of Language [CSL] Ser.). (ENG.). 114p. 45.00 (978-3-11-175457-4(X)) De Gruyter, Mouton DEU. Dist: de Gruyter, Walter GmbH & Co. KG.
Dodson, Howard & Palmer, Colin, eds. Cultural Life. 2007. (Schomburg Studies on the Black Experience). (ENG., Illus.). 395p. per. 19.95 (978-0-87013-808-9(1)) Michigan State Univ. Pr.
—Ideology, Identity, & Assumptions. 2007. (Schomburg Studies on the Black Experience). (ENG., Illus.). 205p. per. 19.95 (978-0-87013-795-2(6)) Michigan State Univ. Pr.
Gates, Henry Louis, Jr. & Burton, Jennifer. Call & Response: Key Debates in African American Studies. 2010. (ENG.). 1p. (C). pap. 28.00 net. (978-0-393-97578-9(9), 97578) Norton, W. W. & Co., Inc.

Georges, Jean Ricardy. Don't Blame the Blacks Because Slavery Systems Still Exist. 2007. (978-1-59835-052-4(8)) Cambridge BrickHouse, Inc.

Goldsby, Jacqueline. A Spectacular Secret: Lynching in American Life & Literature. 2006. (Illus.). 384p. 72.50 (978-0-226-30137-2(0)); per. 30.00 (978-0-226-30138-9(9)) Univ. of Chicago Pr.

Griffin, Farah Jasmine, comment & intro. Inclusive Scholarship: Developing Black Studies in the United States. 2007. 263p. pap. (978-0-916584-57-3(7)) Ford Foundation.

Guthrie, Dorothy Littlejohn. Integrating African American Literature in the Library & Classroom. 2011. E-Book **(978-1-59884-752-9(X))** Libraries Unlimited, Inc.

—Integrating African American Literature in the Library & Classroom, 1 vol. 2011. 294p. pap. 40.00 (978-1-59884-751-2(1), A3360P) Pearson Education GBR. Dist: ABC-CLIO, LLC.

Harding, Vincent. Hope & History: Why We Must Share the Story of the Movement. 2nd ed. 2009. 240p. pap. 16.00 (978-1-57075-857-7(3)) Orbis Bks.

Harris, Angel L. Kids Don't Want to Fail: Oppositional Culture & the Black-White Achievement Gap. 2011. (ENG., Illus.). 336p. 35.00 (978-0-674-05772-2(4)) Harvard Univ. Pr.

Harris, Joel Chandler. A Little Union Scout. 2009. 116p. 21.99 (978-0-559-06304-6(0)); 24.99 (978-0-559-06289-6(3)); pap. 19.75 (978-0-559-06293-3(1)); pap. 19.75 (978-0-559-06301-5(6)) BiblioBazaar.

—A Little Union Scout. 2008. (Illus.). 116p. pap. (978-1-4099-2688-7(5)) Dodo Pr.

—A Little Union Scout. 2007. (ENG.). 200p. 39.95 (978-0-548-23669-7(0)); per. 24.95 (978-1-4326-3778-1(9)) Kessinger Publishing, LLC.

—A Little Union Scout. 2009. (ENG.). 204p. 32.99 (978-1-117-63355-8(1)); (ENG.). 204p. pap. 20.99 (978-1-117-63357-2(8), BiblioLife); (ENG.). 204p. pap. 23.75 (978-1-117-63356-5(X)); 204p. 28.99 (978-1-113-80575-1(7)); 204p. 27.99 (978-1-113-80576-8(5)); 204p. pap. 22.99 (978-1-113-80573-7(0)); 204p. pap. 17.99 (978-1-113-80571-3(4)); (ENG.). 202p. pap. 20.99 (978-1-113-80567-6(6), BiblioLife); 204p. 28.99 (978-1-110-68970-5(5)); 204p. pap. 23.75 (978-1-110-68969-9(1)); (ENG.). 202p. pap. 22.99 (978-1-110-68968-2(3), BiblioLife); (ENG.). 202p. pap. 20.99 (978-1-110-68967-5(5), BiblioLife) BiblioBazaar.

—A Little Union Scout. 2009. 80p. pap. (978-1-151-65653-7(4)) Books LLC.

—A Little Union Scout. 2010. (Illus.). 64p. pap. 20.00 (978-1-153-77907-4(2)) General Bks. LLC.

—A Little Union Scout. 2010. 202p. pap. 19.96 (978-1-163-26456-0(3)); 31.96 **(978-1-163-53809-8(4))** Kessinger Publishing, LLC.

Harris, Norman. Signposts: Reading African American Culture. 210p. pap. (978-1-878531-05-6(0)) Black Resource Ctr., Inc.

Healy, Jane Heitman. Jumpstarters for African-American History: Short Daily Warm-Ups for the Classroom. 2010. (Jumpstarters Ser.). (ENG., Illus.). 48p. (gr. 4-9). pap. 8.99 (978-1-58037-532-0(4)) Twain, Mark Media, Inc. Pubs.

Hill, Lisa. African American Reader. rev. ed. 2010. (ENG.). 202p. pap. 41.75 (978-0-7575-7595-2(1)) Kendall Hunt Publishing Co.

Hudson-Weems, Clenora, ed. Contemporary Africana Theory & Thought: A Guide to Africana Studies. 2007. 420p. 99.95 (978-1-59221-309-2(X)) Africa World Pr.

III, Gibbs. A Little Union Scout. 2010. 208p. pap. 24.75 **(978-1-172-08238-4(3))** BiblioBazaar.

Levine, Lawrence W. Black Culture & Black Consciousness: Afro-American Folk Thought from Slavery to Freedom. 30th ed. 2007. (ENG.). 560p. per. 18.95 (978-0-19-530568-5(X)) Oxford Univ. Pr., Inc.

Lobb, Nancy. 16 Extraordinary African Americans. 2nd ed. 2007. (Illus.). 117p. (YA). (gr. 6-12). tchr. ed., per. 25.00 (978-0-8251-6276-3(9)) Walch Education.

Neumann, Caryn E. Term Paper Resource Guide to African American History, 1 vol. 2009. (Term Paper Resource Guides). 304p. 65.00 (978-0-313-35501-1(0), GR5501, Greenwood Pr.) Greenwood Publishing Group, Inc.

Norment, Nathaniel, Jr., ed. An Introduction to African American Studies: The Discipline & Its Dimensions. 2007. pap. (978-0-89089-373-9(X)) Carolina Academic Pr.

Okafor, Victor O. Towards an Understanding of Africology. 3rd rev. ed. 2011. (ENG.). 298p. pap. 94.95 (978-0-7575-7065-0(8)) Kendall Hunt Publishing Co.

Pemberton, Caroline H. Stephen the Black. 2010. (ENG.). 290p. pap. 28.75 (978-1-172-40994-5(3)) BiblioBazaar.

—Stephen the Black. 2010. 84p. pap. (978-1-151-82660-2(X)) Books LLC.

—Stephen the Black. 2010. 282p. pap. 22.36 (978-1-163-77933-0(4)) 2007. 284p. 42.95 (978-0-548-53838-8(7)) 2007. (ENG.). 284p. per. 27.95 (978-0-548-46171-6(6)) Kessinger Publishing, LLC.

Pike, Louise. Southern Echoes. 2009. 136p. 24.99 (978-1-113-90126-2(8)); (ENG.). 134p. pap. 19.99 (978-1-113-90121-7(7), BiblioLife); (ENG.). 134p. pap. 18.99 (978-1-113-90119-4(5), BiblioLife) BiblioBazaar.

—Southern Echoes. 2010. 136p. pap. 16.76 (978-1-153-88890-2(7)) 2008. 134p. 35.95 (978-0-548-91198-3(3)) 2007. (ENG.). 136p. per. 20.95 (978-0-548-59373-8(6)) Kessinger Publishing, LLC.

Rabaka, Reiland. Africana Critical Theory: Reconstructing the Black Radical Tradition, from W.E.B. du Bois & C.L.R. James to Frantz Fanon & Amilcar Cabral. 2009. (ENG.). 452p. 120.99 (978-0-7391-2885-5(X)) Lexington Bks.

—Africana Critical Theory: Reconstructing The Black Radical Tradition, From W. E. B. Du Bois & C. L. R. James to Frantz Fanon & Amilcar Cabral. 2010. (ENG.). 452p. pap. 49.95 (978-0-7391-2886-2(8)) Lexington Bks.

—W. E. B. du Bois & the Problems of the Twenty-First Century: An Essay on Africana Critical Theory. 2007. (ENG.). 296p. 83.99 (978-0-7391-1682-1(7)) Lexington Bks.

—W.E.B. Du Bois & the Problems of the Twenty-First Century: An Essay on Africana Critical Theory. 2008. (ENG.). 296p. pap. 31.50 (978-0-7391-1683-8(5)) Lexington Bks.

Robertson, Gil L., IV, ed. Family Affair: What It Means to Be African-American Today. 2009. (ENG.). 432p. pap. 16.00 (978-1-932841-35-0(0)) Agate Publishing, Inc.

Rojas, Fabio. From Black Power to Black Studies: How a Radical Social Movement Became an Academic Discipline. (ENG., Illus.). 304p. (gr. 17). 2010. pap. 26.00 (978-0-8018-9825-9(0)) 2007. 47.00 (978-0-8018-8619-5(8)) Johns Hopkins Univ. Pr.

Rooks, Noliwe M. White Money/Black Power: The Surprising History of African American Studies & the Crisis of Race in Higher Education. 2007. (ENG.). pap. (978-0-618-80239-5(8)); 224p. per. 17.00 (978-0-8070-3271-8(9)) Beacon Pr.

Sargent, Epes. Peculiar: A Tale of the Great Transition. 2007. 508p. 55.95 (978-0-548-55970-3(8)); (ENG.). per. 40.95 (978-0-548-46995-8(4)) Kessinger Publishing, LLC.

Soto, Michael. Teaching the Harlem Renaissance: Course Design & Classroom Strategies. 2007. (African American Literature & Culture: Expanding & Exploding the Boundaries Ser.). pap. 34.95 (978-0-8204-9724-2(X)) Lang, Peter Publishing, Inc.

Stockton, Frank Richard. What Might Have Been Expected. 2008. 180p. 22.99 (978-0-554-36625-8(8)) 2008. 180p. 25.99 (978-0-554-27322-8(5)) 2007. (ENG.). 160p. per. 19.99 (978-1-4346-2974-6(0)) 2007. (ENG.). 178p. per. 21.99 (978-1-4346-2992-0(9)) BiblioBazaar.

—What Might Have Been Expected. 2007. (ENG., Illus.). 188p. per. (978-1-4065-7903-1(3)) Dodo Pr.

—What Might Have Been Expected. 2008. 292p. 43.95 (978-0-548-95803-2(3)) 2007. (ENG.). 296p. per. 28.95 (978-0-548-63329-8(0)) Kessinger Publishing, LLC.

Warren, Nagueyalti. An Intellectual Biography of W.E.B. du Bois: Initiator of Black Studies in the University. 2010. iii, 198p. 109.95 (978-0-7734-3715-9(0)) Mellen, Edwin Pr., The.

White, Derrick E. The Challenge of Blackness: The Institute of the Black World & Political Activism in The 1970s. 2011. (Southern Dissent Ser.). (ENG., Illus.). 288p. 69.95 (978-0-8130-3735-6(2)) Univ. Pr. of Florida.

Young, Martha. Behind the Dark Pines. 2010. 80p. pap. (978-1-151-91319-7(7)) Books LLC.

—Behind the Dark Pines. 304p. 2010. 35.16 (978-1-163-73800-9(X)) 2010. pap. 23.16 (978-1-163-71680-9(4)) 2007. (ENG.). 43.95 (978-0-548-42448-3(9)) 2007. (ENG.). per. 28.95 (978-0-548-40132-3(2)) Kessinger Publishing, LLC.

Young, Martha & Condé, J. M. Behind the Dark Pines. 2009. 304p. 29.99 (978-1-113-92348-6(2)); (ENG.). 303p. pap. 23.99 (978-1-113-92338-7(5), BiblioLife); (ENG.). 303p. pap. 24.99 (978-1-113-92341-7(5), BiblioLife); 304p. pap. 28.75 (978-1-113-92342-4(3)) BiblioBazaar.

AFRICAN AMERICANS—SUFFRAGE

Adegbile, Debo P. The Most Fundamental Right: Contrasting Perspectives on the Voting Rights Act. McCool, Daniel, ed. 2012. (ENG.). 360p. 85.00 **(978-0-253-00192-4(7)**, 0253001927); pap. 35.00 **(978-0-253-00194-8(3)**, 0253001943) Indiana Univ. Pr.

Anderson, S. E. The Black Holocaust for Beginners. 2007. (For Beginners Ser.). (ENG., Illus.). 192p. per. 16.99 (978-1-934389-03-4(X), For Beginners) Steerforth Pr.

Benham, Liza Abram. From Winning Elections to Influencing Policy: The Electoral-Policy Link for Minority Voters. 2008. (Law & Society Ser.). (Illus.). 304p. 75.00 (978-1-59332-274-8(7)) LFB Scholarly Publishing LLC.

Berg, Manfred. The Ticket to Freedom: The NAACP & the Struggle for Black Political Integration. 2007. (New Perspectives on the History of the South Ser.). (ENG.). 376p. per. 27.00 (978-0-8130-3216-0(4)) Univ. Pr. of Florida.

Blum, Edward. The Unintended Consequences of Section 5 of the Voting Rights Act. 2007. (ENG.). 88p. pap. 15.00 (978-0-8447-4257-1(0), AEI Pr.) American Enterprise Institute for Public Policy Research.

Dudden, Faye E. Fighting Chance: The Struggle over Woman Suffrage & Black Suffrage in Reconstruction America, 1 vol. 2011. (ENG., Illus.). 296p. 34.95 (978-0-19-977263-6(0)) Oxford Univ. Pr., Inc.

Fleming, William H. Treaty-Making Power: Slavery & the Race Problem in the South. 2007. pap. 19.95 (978-1-4304-6982-7(X)) Kessinger Publishing, LLC.

Heard, Alexander. A Two-Party South? 2011. (ENG.). 352p. pap. 50.00 **(978-0-8078-9681-5(0))** Univ. of North Carolina Pr.

Henderson, Ana. Voting Rights ACT Reauthorization of 2006: Perspectives on Democracy, Participation, & Power. 2007. (978-0-87772-423-0(7)) Univ. of California, Institute of Governmental Studies.

Johnson, Donald William. Black but Not My Brother: Why I cannot vote for Barack Huessin Obama. 2008. 96p. pap. 15.00 (978-1-4389-2878-4(5)) AuthorHouse.

King-Meadows, Tyson. When the Letter Betrays the Spirit: Voting Rights Enforcement & African American Participation from Lyndon Johnson to Barack Obama. 2011. (ENG., Illus.). 374p. 80.00 **(978-0-7391-4912-6(1))**; pap. 32.95 **(978-0-7391-4913-3(X))** Lexington Bks.

Light, Steven Andrew. The Law Is Good: The Voting Rights Act, Redistricting, & Black Regime Politics. 2010. (Illus.). 282p. pap. 35.00 (978-1-59460-286-3(7)) Carolina Academic Pr.

Malone, Christopher. Between Freedom & Bondage: Race, Party, & Voting Rights in the Antebellum North. 2007. (ENG.). 272p. 143.00 (978-0-415-95696-3(X)); per. 32.95 (978-0-415-95697-0(8)) Routledge.

Martin, Gordon A., Jr. Count Them One by One: Black Mississippians Fighting for the Right to Vote. 2010. (Margaret Walker Alexander Series in African American Studies). (ENG., Illus.). 272p. 40.00 (978-1-60473-789-9(1)) Univ. Pr. of Mississippi.

Masur, Kate. An Example for All the Land: Emancipation & the Struggle over Equality in Washington, D. C. 2010. (ENG., Illus.). 376p. 39.95 (978-0-8078-3414-5(9)) Univ. of North Carolina Pr.

Mathews, John Mabry. Legislative & Judicial History of the Fifteenth Amendment. 2009. 482p. pap. (978-0-217-23034-6(2)) Books LLC.

—Legislative & Judicial History of the Fifteenth Amendment. 2009. 88p. pap. 14.14 (978-1-151-70465-8(2)) General Bks. LLC.

Pauley, Garth E. LBJ's American Promise: The 1965 Voting Rights Address. 2006. (Library of Presidential Rhetoric). (ENG., Illus.). 192p. (C). pap. 16.95 (978-1-58544-581-3(9)); 29.95 (978-1-58544-574-5(6)) Texas A&M Univ. Pr.

Pildes, Richard H. & de La Garza, Rodolfo O., eds. The Future of the Voting Rights Act. 2006. (Illus.). 367p. per. 35.00 (978-0-87154-072-0(X)) Russell Sage Foundation.

Porter, Kirk Harold. A History of Suffrage in the United States. 2008. 276p. 25.99 (978-0-559-67042-8(7)); pap. 26.75 (978-0-559-67039-8(7)) BiblioBazaar.

—A History of Suffrage in the United States. 2009. 160p. pap. (978-0-217-77024-8(X)) Books LLC.

—A History of Suffrage in the United States. 2009. 152p. pap. 19.99 (978-1-150-64595-2(4)) General Bks. LLC.

—A History of Suffrage in the United States. 260p. reprint ed. 98.00 (978-0-7222-2838-8(4)) Library Reprints, Inc.

Riser, R. Volney. Defying Disfranchisement: Black Voting Rights Activism in the Jim Crow South, 1890-1908. 2010. 344p. 40.00 (978-0-8071-3638-6(7)) Louisiana State Univ. Pr.

Rivers, Christina. The Congressional Black Caucus, Minority Voting Rights, & the U. S. Supreme Court. 2012. (ENG., Illus.). 248p. (C). 75.00 **(978-0-472-11810-6(2))** Univ. of Michigan Pr.

Thompson, Ernest & Thompson, Mindy. Homeboy Came to Orange: A Story of People's Power. 2008. 240p. pap. 17.95 (978-0-595-53036-6(2)) iUniverse, Inc.

Uschan, Michael V. Selma to Montgomery. 2011. (Lucent Library of Black History Ser.). (Illus.). 128p. lib. bdg. 33.45 (978-1-4205-0571-9(8), Lucent Bks.) Cengage Gale.

Walters, Ronald W. Freedom Is Not Enough: Black Voters, Black Candidates, & American Presidential Politics. 2007. (American Political Challenges Ser.). (ENG.). 256p. per. 28.95 (978-0-7425-4806-0(6)) Rowman & Littlefield Publishers, Inc.

Wang, Xi. The Trial of Democracy: Black Suffrage & Northern Republicans, 1860-1910. 2012. (Studies in the Legal History of the South Ser.). (ENG.). 480p. pap. 26.95 **(978-0-8203-4084-5(7))** Univ. of Georgia Pr.

Watson, Bruce. Freedom Summer: The Savage Season of 1964 That Made Mississippi Burn & Made America a Democracy. 2011. (ENG., Illus.). 384p. (gr. 12). 17.00 (978-0-14-311943-2(5), Penguin (Non-Classics)) Penguin Group (USA) Inc.

—Freedom Summer: The Savage Season That Made Mississippi Burn & Made America a Democracy. 2010. (ENG., Illus.). 384p. (gr. 12). 27.95 (978-0-670-02170-3(9), Viking Adult) Penguin Group (USA) Inc.

AFRICAN AMERICANS—ALABAMA

Allen, Peggy Vonsherie. The Pecan Orchard: Journey of a Sharecropper's Daughter. (ENG., Illus.). 272p. 2011. pap. 18.95 (978-0-8173-5659-0(2)) 2009. 29.95 (978-0-8173-1672-3(8)) Univ. of Alabama Pr.

Bailey, Richard. Neither Carpetbaggers nor Scalawags. 5th ed. 2010. 400p. 29.95 (978-1-58838-189-7(7)) NewSouth, Inc.

Cashin, Sheryll. The Agitator's Daughter: A Memoir of Four Generations of One Extraordinary African-American Family. 2008. (ENG., Illus.). 288p. 26.00 (978-1-58648-422-4(2)) PublicAffairs.

Dorsey, Mignette Y. Patrick. Speak Truth to Power: The Story of Charles Patrick, a Civil Rights Pioneer. 2nd ed. 2010. (Alabama Fire Ant Ser.). (ENG., Illus.). 152p. pap. 16.00 (978-0-8173-5556-2(1)) Univ. of Alabama Pr.

Ellis, Jack D. Beside the Troubled Waters: A Black Doctor Remembers Life, Medicine, & Civil Rights in an Alabama Town. 2nd ed. 2011. (ENG., Illus.). 192p. 24.00 (978-0-8173-1721-8(X)) Univ. of Alabama Pr.

Graham, Patterson Toby. A Right to Read: Segregation & Civil Rights in Alabama's Public Libraries, 1900-1965. 2006. (ENG., Illus.). 208p. per. 22.00 (978-0-8173-5371-1(2)) Univ. of Alabama Pr.

Harris, Trudier. Summer Snow: Reflections from a Black Daughter of the South. 2007. (ENG.). 200p. pap. 16.00 (978-0-8070-7255-4(9)) Beacon Pr.

Hunter-Clayton, Victoria Virginia. White & Black under the Old Regime. 195p. reprint ed. 88.00 (978-0-7222-8233-5(8)) Library Reprints, Inc.

Huntley, Horace & McKerley, John W., eds. Foot Soldiers for Democracy: The Men, Women, & Children of the Birmingham Civil Rights Movement. 2009. (ENG., Illus.). 264p. 75.00 (978-0-252-03478-7(3)); pap. 25.00 (978-0-252-07668-8(0)) Univ. of Illinois Pr.

Huntley, Horace & Montgomery, David, eds. Black Workers' Struggle for Equality in Birmingham. 2007. (Working Class in American History Ser.). 264p. per. 20.00 (978-0-252-07493-6(9)) Univ. of Illinois Pr.

Jackson, Troy. Becoming King: Martin Luther King Jr. & the Making of a National Leader. 2011. (Civil Rights & the Struggle for Black Equality in the Twentieth Century Ser.). (ENG.). 248p. pap. 21.95 (978-0-8131-3390-4(4)) Univ. Pr. of Kentucky.

Jeffries, Hasan. Bloody Lowndes: Civil Rights & Black Power in Alabama's Black Belt. (ENG., Illus.). 352p. 2010. pap. 22.00 (978-0-8147-4331-7(5)) 2009. 60.00 (978-0-8147-4305-8(6)) New York Univ. Pr.

King, Martin Luther, Jr. Stride Toward Freedom: The Montgomery Story, 1 vol. 2010. (King Legacy Ser.). (ENG.). 272p. 24.95 (978-0-8070-0073-1(6)); (Illus.). pap. 14.00 (978-0-8070-0069-4(8)) Beacon Pr.

Kolchin, Peter. First Freedom: The Responses of Alabama's Blacks to Emancipation & Reconstruction. 2008. (Library Alabama Classics Ser.). (Illus.). 248p. pap. 24.95 (978-0-8173-5535-7(9)) Univ. of Alabama Pr.

Novkov, Julie Lavonne. Racial Union: Law, Intimacy, & the White State in Alabama, 1865-1954. 2008. (ENG.). 368p. pap. 29.95 (978-0-472-06885-2(7)) Univ. of Michigan Pr.

Rice, Condoleezza. Extraordinary, Ordinary People: A Memoir of Family. (ENG.). 2011. 368p. pap. 15.00 (978-0-307-88847-1(9), Three Rivers Pr.) 2010. (Illus.). 352p. 27.00 (978-0-307-58787-9(8), Crown) Crown Publishing Group.

Taylor, Frazine K. Researching African American Genealogy in Alabama: A Resource Guide. 2008. (978-1-60306-044-8(8), NewSouth Bks.) NewSouth, Inc.

Walker, Robert J. Let My People Go! The Miracle of the Montgomery Bus Boycott. 2007. (ENG.). 368p. per. 54.99 (978-0-7618-3706-0(X)) Hamilton Bks.

Zellner, Bob & Curry, Constance. The Wrong Side of Murder Creek: A White Southerner in the Freedom Movement. 2008. 350p. 27.95 (978-1-58838-222-1(2), NewSouth Bks.) NewSouth, Inc.

AFRICAN AMERICANS—ARKANSAS

Bates, Daisy. The Long Shadow of Little Rock. 2007. (ENG., Illus.). 260p. per. 18.95 (978-1-55728-863-9(1)) Univ. of Arkansas Pr.

Boykin, Kristina. An Analysis of Feature 33 at Van Winkle's Mill Site. 2011. 92p. pap. **(978-3-8443-9615-7(2))** Lambert Academic Publishing.

Gordon, Fon. Caste & Class: The Black Experience in Arkansas, 1880-1920. 2007. (ENG.). 200p. per. 22.95 (978-0-8203-3130-0(9)) Univ. of Georgia Pr.

Hays, Brooks. A Southern Moderate Speaks. 2011. (ENG.). 264p. pap. 40.00 **(978-0-8078-9680-8(2))** Univ. of North Carolina Pr.

Jacoway, Elizabeth. Turn Away Thy Son: Little Rock, the Crisis That Shocked the Nation. 2008. 477p. pap. 19.95 (978-1-55728-878-3(X)) Univ. of Arkansas Pr.

Kirk, John A., ed. An Epitaph for Little Rock: A Fiftieth Anniversary Retrospective on the Central High Crisis. 2008. 190p. pap. 19.95 (978-1-55728-874-5(7)) Univ. of Arkansas Pr.

Robinson II, Charles F. & Williams, Lonnie R. Remembrances in Black: Personal Perspectives of the African American Experience at the University of Arkansas. 2010. (ENG.). 360p. (C). 45.00 (978-1-55728-953-7(0)) Univ. of Arkansas Pr.

Stockley, Grif, Jr. & Stockley, Grif. Ruled by Race: Black/White Relations in Arkansas from Slavery to the Present. 2008. (Illus.). 400p. 34.95 (978-1-55728-885-1(2)) Univ. of Arkansas Pr.

Whitaker, Robert. On the Laps of Gods: The Red Summer of 1919 & the Struggle for Justice That Remade a Nation. 2009. (ENG., Illus.). 400p. pap. 16.00 (978-0-307-33983-6(1), Three Rivers Pr.) Crown Publishing Group.

Work Projects Administration. Slave Narratives: a Folk History of Slavery in the United States from Interviews with Former Slaves: Arkansas Narratives, Part 1. 2007. (ENG.). 242p. pap. 20.99 (978-1-4264-4829-4(5)) BiblioBazaar.

—Slave Narratives: a Folk History of Slavery in the United States from Interviews with Former Slaves: Arkansas Narratives, Part 2. l.t. ed. 2007. (ENG.). 274p. pap. 23.99 (978-1-4264-4872-0(4)) BiblioBazaar.

—Slave Narratives: A Folk History of Slavery in the United States from Interviews with Former Slaves: Arkansas Narratives, Part 5. 2007. (ENG.). 260p. pap. 21.99 (978-1-4264-4743-3(4)) BiblioBazaar.

—Slave Narratives: A Folk History of Slavery in the United States from Interviews with Former Slaves: Arkansas Narratives, Part 6. l.t. ed. 2007. (ENG.). 294p. pap. 23.99 (978-1-4264-4781-5(7)) BiblioBazaar.

—Slave Narratives: A Folk History of Slavery in the United States from Interviews with Former Slaves: Arkansas Narratives, Part 7. 2006. 180p. pap. 19.99 (978-1-4264-4692-4(6)) BiblioBazaar.

—Slave Narratives: A Folk History of Slavery in the United States from Interviews with Former Slaves: Arkansas Narratives, Part 8. l.t. ed. 2007. (ENG.). 204p. pap. 22.99 (978-1-4264-4723-5(X)) BiblioBazaar.

AFRICAN AMERICANS—CALIFORNIA

Adkins, Jan Batiste. African Americans of San Francisco. 2012. (Images of America Ser.). (ENG., Illus.). 128p. pap. 21.99 **(978-0-7385-7619-0(0))** Arcadia Publishing.

Afary, Kamran. Performance & Activism: Grassroots Discourse after the Los Angeles Rebellion Of 1992. 2009. (Raya Dunayevskaya Series in Marxism & Humanism Ser.). (ENG.). 262p. 73.50 (978-0-7391-3356-9(X)) Lexington Bks.

Baszile, Jennifer Lynn. The Black Girl Next Door: A Memoir. 2009. (ENG., Illus.). 320p. pap. 15.00 (978-1-4165-4328-2(7), Touchstone) Touchstone.

Covin, David. Black Politics after the Civil Rights Movement: Activity & Beliefs in Sacramento, 1970-2000. 2009. (ENG., Illus.). 236p. pap. 49.95 (978-0-7864-4258-4(1)) McFarland & Co., Inc. Pubs.

Davenport, Christian. Media Bias, Perspective, & State Repression: The Black Panther Party. 2009. (Cambridge Studies in Contentious Politics Ser.). (ENG., Illus.). 264p. 87.00 (978-0-521-76600-5(1)); pap. 26.99 (978-0-521-75970-0(6)) Cambridge Univ. Pr.

Day, Aaron L. & Kaletucker, Indira. The Heritage of African-Americans in Long Beach: Over 100 Years. 2007. 308p. pap. 24.95 (978-0-7414-3514-9(4)) Infinity Publishing.

A

Gardner, Eric, ed. Jennie Carter: A Black Journalist of the Early West. 2007. (ENG.). 208p. 50.00 *(978-1-934110-10-2(8))* Univ. Pr. of Mississippi.

Hilliard, David, ed. & selected by. The Black Panther: Intercommunal News Service, 1967-1980. 2007. (ENG., Illus.). 192p. pap. 25.00 *(978-1-4165-3259-0(5)*, Beyond Words/Atria Bks.) Atria Bks.

Johnson, Robert A. & Riggins, Charlene. A Different Shade of Orange: Voices of Orange County, California, Black Pioneers. 2009. pap. *(978-0-930046-25-5(0))* California State Univ., San Bernardino, Robert V. Fullerton Art Museum.

Kurashige, Scott. The Shifting Grounds of Race: Black & Japanese Americans in the Making of Multiethnic Los Angeles. 2007. (Politics & Society in Twentieth-Century America Ser.). (ENG., Illus.). 368p. (C). 52.50 *(978-0-691-12639-5(9))* Princeton Univ. Pr.

Lapp, Rudolph M. Archy Lee: A California Fugitive Slave Case. 2008. (Illus.). 69p. pap. 12.95 *(978-1-59714-080-5(5))* Heyday.

McKibben, Carol. Racial Beachhead: Diversity & Democracy in a Military Town. 2011. (ENG.). 352p. 80.00 ***(978-0-8047-7698-1(9))***; pap. 24.95 ***(978-0-8047-7699-8(7))*** Stanford Univ. Pr.

Miller, Paul T. The Postwar Struggle for Civil Rights: African Americans in San Francisco, 1945-1975. 2009. (Studies in African American History & Culture Ser.). (ENG., Illus.). 184p. 125.00 *(978-0-415-80601-5(1))* Routledge.

Millner, Caille. The Golden Road: Notes on My Gentrification. 2008. (ENG.). 256p. (gr. 12-18). 14.00 *(978-0-14-311297-6(X)*, Penguin (Non-Classics)) Penguin Group (USA) Inc.

Murch, Donna. Living for the City: Migration, Education, & the Rise of the Black Panther Party in Oakland, California. 2010. (John Hope Franklin Series in African American History & Culture Ser.). (ENG., Illus.). 344p. 65.00 *(978-0-8078-3376-6(2))*; pap. 22.95 *(978-0-8078-7113-3(3))* Univ. of North Carolina Pr.

Royal, Alice C. & Ellinger, Mickey. Allensworth, the Freedom Colony: A California African American Township. 2008. pap. *(978-1-59714-091-1(0))* Heyday.

Sharon McGriff-Payne. John Grider's Century: African Americans in Solano, Napa, & Sonoma Counties from 1845 To 1925. 2009. 184p. 26.95 *(978-1-4401-6093-6(7))*; pap. 16.95 *(978-1-4401-6091-2(0))* iUniverse, Inc.

AFRICAN AMERICANS—CALIFORNIA—LOS ANGELES

Afary, Kamran. Performance & Activism: Grassroots Discourse after the Los Angeles Rebellion of 1992. 2009. (Raya Dunayevskaya Series in Marxism & Humanism Ser.). (ENG.). 262p. pap. 31.50 *(978-0-7391-3357-6(8))* Lexington Bks.

Flamming, Douglas. Bound for Freedom: Black Los Angeles in Jim Crow America. 2006. (Illus.). 467p. per. 27.95 *(978-0-520-24990-5(9))* Univ. of California Pr.

Knox, Andrew. Blazing an African-American Trail. 2008. (ENG.). 108p. pap. 11.95 *(978-1-934937-04-4(5))* Mill City Pr., Inc.

Kurashige, Scott. The Shifting Grounds of Race: Black & Japanese Americans in the Making of Multiethnic Los Angeles. 2010. (Politics & Society in Twentieth Century America Ser.). (ENG., Illus.). 368p. (C). pap. 30.95 *(978-0-691-14618-8(7))* Princeton Univ. Pr.

Ramon, Ana-Christina. Black Los Angeles: American Dreams & Racial Realities. Hunt, Darnell, ed. 2010. (ENG., Illus.). 432p. pap. 26.00 *(978-0-8147-3735-4(8))* New York Univ. Pr.

Smith, R. J. The Great Black Way: L. A. in the 1940s & the Lost African-American Renaissance. 2007. (ENG., Illus.). 400p. per. 16.95 *(978-1-58648-521-4(0))* PublicAffairs.

Stanford, Karin L. & Institute for Arts and Media, Northridge, California State University Staff. African Americans in Los Angeles. 2010. (Images of America Ser.). (Illus.). 128p. pap. 21.99 *(978-0-7385-8094-4(5))* Arcadia Publishing.

Vargas, Joao H. Cost. Never Meant to Survive: Genocide & Utopias in Black Diaspora Communities. 2010. (Transformative Politics Series, ed. Joy James Ser.). (ENG.). 262p. pap. 27.50 *(978-0-7425-4102-3(9))* Rowman & Littlefield Publishers, Inc.

Vargas, Joao H. Costa. Catching Hell in the City of Angels: Life & Meanings of Blackness in South Central Los Angeles. 2006. (Critical American Studies). (Illus.). 304p. 60.00 *(978-0-8166-4168-0(4))* Univ. of Minnesota Pr.

AFRICAN AMERICANS—CONNECTICUT

Cruson, Daniel. The Slaves of Central Fairfield County: The Journey from Slave to Freeman in Nineteenth-Century Connecticut. 2007. (Illus.). 124p. pap., per. 19.99 *(978-1-59629-151-5(6))* History Pr., The.

AFRICAN AMERICANS—FLORIDA

see also Gullahs

Clay, Roger, ed. The Legacy of Black Families in Jackson County, Florida. 2006. (Illus.). iv, 156p. lib. bdg. 30.00 *(978-1-891647-98-7(9))* Heritage Publishing Consultants, Inc.

McCarthy, Kevin M. African American Sites in Florida. 2007. (ENG., Illus.). 336p. 29.95 *(978-1-56164-385-1(8))* Pineapple Pr., Inc.

McGee, Nora Jefferson. The Family Reunion. 2007. pap. 9.00 *(978-0-8059-7381-5(8))* Dorrance Publishing Co., Inc.

Ortiz, Paul. Emancipation Betrayed: The Hidden History of Black Organizing & White Violence in Florida from Reconstruction to the Bloody Election Of 1920. 2006. (American Crossroads Ser.). (Illus.). 382p. per. 24.95 *(978-0-520-25003-1(6))* Univ. of California Pr.

Phelts, Marsha Dean. The American Beach Cookbook. 2008. (ENG., Illus.). 192p. per. 19.95 *(978-0-8130-3210-8(5))* Univ. Pr. of Florida.

Richardson, Joe Martin. African Americans in the Reconstruction of Florida, 1865-1877. 2nd ed. 2008. (ENG.). 272p. pap. 27.95 *(978-0-8173-5524-1(3))* Univ. of Alabama Pr.

Rivers, Larry Eugene. Slavery in Florida: Territorial Days to Emancipation. 2009. (ENG., Illus.). 384p. pap. 19.95 *(978-0-8130-3381-5(0))* Univ. Pr. of Florida.

Shell-Weiss, Melanie. Coming to Miami: A Social History. 2009. (Sunbelt Studies). (ENG., Illus.). 384p. 39.95 *(978-0-8130-3296-2(2))* Univ. Pr. of Florida.

Spagna, Ana Maria. Test Ride on the Sunnyland Bus: A Daughter's Civil Rights Journey. 2010. (River Teeth Literary Nonfiction Prize Ser.). (ENG., Illus.). 286p. pap. 19.95 *(978-0-8032-1712-6(9)*, Bison Bks.) Univ. of Nebraska Pr.

Susie, Debra Anne. In the Way of Our Grandmothers: A Cultural View of Twentieth-Century Midwifery in Florida. 2009. (ENG.). 280p. pap. 22.95 *(978-0-8203-3388-5(3))* Univ. of Georgia Pr.

Warren, Dan R. If It Takes All Summer: Martin Luther King, the KKK, & States' Rights in St. Augustine 1964. 2nd ed. 2008. (ENG., Illus.). 224p. 29.95 *(978-0-8173-1599-3(3))* Univ. of Alabama Pr.

Wilson, Jon & Peck, Rosalie. St. Petersburg's Historic African American Neighborhoods: Community, Culture, & Connection. 2008. pap. 19.99 *(978-1-59629-279-6(2))* History Pr., The.

AFRICAN AMERICANS—GEORGIA

see also Gullahs

Asante, Molefi Kete. As I Run Toward Africa: A Memoir. 2011. 336p. 99.00 ***(978-1-61205-075-1(1))***; pap. 26.95 ***(978-1-61205-076-8(X))*** Paradigm Pubs.

Fleming, William H. Slavery & the Race Problem in the South. 66p. reprint ed. 88.00 *(978-0-7222-9725-4(4))* Library Reprints, Inc.

—Treaty-Making Power: Slavery & the Race Problem in the South. 2007. pap. 19.95 *(978-1-4304-6982-7(X))* Kessinger Publishing, LLC.

Ford, Pearl, ed. African Americans in Georgia: A Reflection of Politics & Policy in the New South. 2010. 224p. 40.00 *(978-0-88146-184-8(9))* Mercer Univ. Pr.

Funderburg, Lise. Pig Candy: Taking My Father South, Taking My Father Home - A Memoir. 2009. (ENG.). 320p. pap. 15.00 *(978-1-4165-4767-9(3)*, Free Pr.) Free Pr.

Georgia Writer's Project & Joyner, Charles. Drums & Shadows. 2011. 226p. pap. 18.99 ***(978-1-61279-055-8(0))*** Publishing in Motion.

Gordon, Asa H. The Georgia Negro: A History. (Illus.). 426p. reprint ed. lib. bdg. 98.00 *(978-0-7222-0426-9(4))* Library Reprints, Inc.

Hicks, Kyra E. This I Accomplish Harriet Powers' Bible Quilt & Other Pieces: Quilt Histories, Exhibition Lists, Annotated Bibliography & Timeline of a Great African American Quilter. 2009. (Illus.). 180p. pap. 19.95 *(978-0-9824796-5-0(4))* Black Threads Pr.

Inscoe, John C., ed. Georgia in Black & White: Explorations in Race Relations of a Southern State, 1865-1950. 2009. 312p. pap. 24.95 *(978-0-8203-3505-6(3))* Univ. of Georgia Pr.

Jones, Jacqueline. Saving Savannah: The City & the Civil War. 2009. (Vintage Civil War Library). (ENG., Illus.). 544p. pap. 17.00 *(978-1-4000-7816-5(4)*, Vintage) Knopf Doubleday Publishing Group.

Leigh, Frances B. Ten Years on a Georgia Plantation since the War. (Illus.). 347p. reprint ed. lib. bdg. 98.00 *(978-0-7222-0867-0(7))* Library Reprints, Inc.

Miles, Tiya. Ties That Bind: The Story of an Afro-Cherokee Family in Slavery & Freedom. 2006. (American Crossroads Ser.). (Illus.). 306p. per. 25.95 *(978-0-520-25002-4(8))* Univ. of California Pr.

Mitchell, Erin Goseer. Born Colored: Life Before Bloody Sunday. 2006. 220p. *(978-0-9761235-2-1(5))* Ampersand Publishing.

Schultz, Mark. The Rural Face of White Supremacy: Beyond Jim Crow. 2006. (Illus.). 336p. per. 26.00 *(978-0-252-07436-3(X))* Univ. of Illinois Pr.

Smart-Grosvenor, Vertamae. Vibration Cooking: Or, the Travel Notes of a Geechee Girl. 2011. (ENG.). 256p. pap. 19.95 *(978-0-8203-3739-5(0))* Univ. of Georgia Pr.

Wood, Betty. Slavery in Colonial Georgia, 1730-1775. 2007. (ENG.). 264p. per. 24.95 *(978-0-8203-3149-2(X))* Univ. of Georgia Pr.

AFRICAN AMERICANS—GEORGIA—ATLANTA

Cooper, Ann Nixon. A Century & Some Change: My Life Before the President Called My Name. 2010. (ENG., Illus.). 224p. 19.99 *(978-1-4391-5887-6(8)*, Beyond Words/Atria Bks.) Atria Bks.

Cooper, Ann Nixon & Bates, Karen Grigsby. A Century & Some Change: My Life Before the President Called My Name. 2010. pap. *(978-1-4391-5888-3(6)*, Beyond Words/Atria Bks.) Atria Bks.

Farris, Christine King. Through It All: Reflections on My Life, My Family, & My Faith. 2010. (ENG., Illus.). 272p. pap. 15.00 *(978-1-4165-4882-9(3)*, Beyond Words/Atria Bks.) Atria Bks.

Gentry & Gentry, Quinn M. Black Women's Risk for HIV: Rough Living. 2008. (ENG.). 282p. (C). 158.00 *(978-0-7890-3169-3(8))* Routledge.

Grady-Willis, Winston A. Challenging U. S. Apartheid: Atlanta & Black Struggles for Human Rights, 1960-1977. 2006. (ENG., Illus.). 312p. per. 24.95 *(978-0-8223-3791-1(6))* Duke Univ. Pr.

—Challenging U. S. Apartheid: Atlanta & Black Struggles for Human Rights, 1960-1977. 2006. (ENG., Illus.). 312p. (C). 89.95 *(978-0-8223-3778-2(9))* Duke Univ. Pr.

Jewell, Joseph O. Race, Social Reform & the Making of a Black Middle Class: Atlanta, 1870-1900. 2007. (ENG.). 236p. 84.00 *(978-0-7425-3545-9(2))* Rowman & Littlefield Publishers, Inc.

—Race, Social Reform, & the Making of a Middle Class: The American Missionary Association & Black Atlanta, 1870-1900. 2007. (ENG.). 236p. per. 29.95 *(978-0-7425-3546-6(0))* Rowman & Littlefield Publishers, Inc.

AFRICAN AMERICANS—HAWAII

Adams, Ayin, intro. African Americans in Hawai'i: A Search for Identity. 2010. (ENG., Illus.). 225p. pap. 29.99 *(978-0-9841228-1-3(8))* Pacific Raven Pr.

Molentia Guttman, D. & Golden, Ernest. African Americans in Hawai'i. 2011. (Images of America Ser.). (Illus.). 128p. pap. 21.99 *(978-0-7385-8116-3(X))* Arcadia Publishing.

AFRICAN AMERICANS—ILLINOIS

Senechal de la Roche, Roberta. In Lincoln's Shadow: The 1908 Race Riot in Springfield, Illinois. 2008. (ENG., Illus.). 264p. pap. 19.95 *(978-0-8093-2909-0(3))* Southern Illinois Univ. Pr.

Sideman, Robert A. African Americans in Glencoe: The Little Migration. 2009. 128p. pap. 19.99 *(978-1-59629-814-9(6))* History Pr., The.

Wheaton, Laura & Hartzold, Susan, eds. Presence, Pride & Passion: A History of African Americans in Mclean County Illinois. 2008. (Illus.). 40p. (YA). 10.00 *(978-0-943788-35-7(8))* McLean County Historical Society.

AFRICAN AMERICANS—ILLINOIS—CHICAGO

Baldwin, Davarian L. Chicago's New Negroes: Modernity, the Great Migration, & Black Urban Life. 2007. (ENG., Illus.). 384p. 69.95 *(978-0-8078-3099-4(2))* Univ. of North Carolina Pr.

Black, Timuel D., Jr. Bridges of Memory: Chicago's Second Generation of Black Migration. 2008. (ENG., Illus.). 392p. per. 22.95 *(978-0-8101-5194-9(4))*; 320p. 34.95 *(978-0-8101-2295-6(2))* Northwestern Univ. Pr.

Boyd, Michelle R. Jim Crow Nostalgia: Reconstructing Race in Bronzeville. 2008. 208p. 57.00 *(978-0-8166-4677-7(5))*; pap. 18.95 *(978-0-8166-4678-4(3))* Univ. of Minnesota Pr.

Green, Adam & Green, A. Selling the Race: Culture, Community, & Black Chicago, 1940-1955. 2009. (Historical Studies of Urban America Ser.). (ENG., Illus.). 328p. pap. 20.00 *(978-0-226-30640-7(2))* Univ. of Chicago Pr.

McElroy, Njoki. 1012 Natchez: A Memoir of Joy, Harship, & Love. 2010. 216p. pap. 14.95 *(978-1-934812-55-6(2))* Brown Bks. Publishing Group.

Miller, R. Baxter. On the Ruins of Modernity: New Chicago Renaissance from Wright to Kent. 2011. pap. ***(978-1-86335-969-6(9))*** Common Ground Publishing Pty, Ltd.

Pattillo, Mary. Black on the Block: The Politics of Race & Class in the City. 2007. (ENG., Illus.). 400p. 29.00 *(978-0-226-64931-3(8))* Univ. of Chicago Pr.

—Black on the Block: The Politics of Race & Class in the City. 2008. (ENG., Illus.). 400p. pap. 20.00 *(978-0-226-64932-0(6))* Univ. of Chicago Pr.

Polikoff, Alexander. Waiting for Gautreaux: A Story of Segregation, Housing, & the Black Ghetto. 2007. (ENG.). 444p. per. 19.95 *(978-0-8101-2420-2(3))* Northwestern Univ. Pr.

Reed, Christopher Robert. The Depression Comes to the South Side: Protest & Politics in the Black Metropolis, 1930-1933. 2011. (Blacks in the Diaspora Ser.). (ENG., Illus.). 204p. 29.95 *(978-0-253-35652-9(0)*, 0253356520) Indiana Univ. Pr.

—The Rise of Chicago's Black Metropolis, 1920-1929. 2011. (New Black Studies Ser.). (ENG., Illus.). 288p. 55.00 *(978-0-252-03623-1(9))* Univ. of Illinois Pr.

Reed, Touré F. Not Alms but Opportunity: The Urban League & the Politics of Racial Uplift, 1910-1950. 2008. (ENG., Illus.). 272p. pap. 23.95 *(978-0-8078-5902-5(8))* Univ. of North Carolina Pr.

Slim, Iceberg. Pimp: The Story of My Life. 2011. (ENG.). 320p. pap. 14.99 *(978-1-4516-1713-9(5)*, Cash Money Content) Cash Money Content LLC.

Thompson, Lowell. African Americans in Chicago. 2012. (Images of America Ser.). (ENG., Illus.). 128p. pap. 21.99 ***(978-0-7385-8853-7(9))*** Arcadia Publishing.

Tracy, Steven C. Writers of the Black Chicago Renaissance. 2011. (ENG.). 536p. 50.00 ***(978-0-252-03639-2(5))*** Univ. of Illinois Pr.

Venkatesh, Sudhir Alladi & Venkatesh, Sudhir. Gang Leader for a Day: A Rogue Sociologist Takes to the Streets. 2008. (ENG.). 320p. (gr. 12-18). 16.00 *(978-0-14-311493-2(X)*, Penguin (Non-Classics)); 25.95 *(978-1-59420-150-9(1)*, Penguin Pr. HC, The) Penguin Group (USA) Inc.

Walker, Jerald. Street Shadows: A Memoir of Race, Rebellion, & Redemption. 2012. (ENG.). 256p. pap. 17.95 ***(978-0-8032-4095-7(3)***, Bison Bks.) Univ. of Nebraska Pr.

AFRICAN AMERICANS—INDIANA

Carr, Cynthia. Our Town: A Heartland Lynching, a Haunted Town, & the Hidden History of White America. 2007. (ENG., Illus.). 512p. pap. 14.95 *(978-0-307-34188-4(7)*, Three Rivers Pr.) Crown Publishing Group.

McFarland, Bernard C. The Hill & the Bottoms: The Story from the Thousand Yard Stare. 2009. (Illus.). 112p. *(978-1-57864-538-1(7))* Donning Co. Pubs.

AFRICAN AMERICANS—KANSAS

Delso, Donald L. & Woodburn, Don A. The Trails to Coffeyville, Kansas: Our Multicultural Roots. 2009. ix, 48p. pap. *(978-0-692-00070-0(4))* Coffeyville Community College.

Eick, Gretchen Cassel. Dissent in Wichita: The Civil Rights Movement in the Midwest, 1954-72. 2007. (Illus.). 344p. per. 26.00 *(978-0-252-07491-2(2))* Univ. of Illinois Pr.

Gardenhire, John Fouts. Life Lessons from My Father: Things Dad Used to Say. 2006. 81p. per. 9.95 *(978-1-60002-242-5(1)*, 4173) Mountain Valley Publishing, LLC.

Ponce, Pearl T., ed. Kansas's War: The Civil War in Documents. 2011. (Civil War in the Great Interior Ser.). (ENG., Illus.). 296p. pap. 18.65 *(978-0-8214-1936-6(6))* Ohio Univ. Pr.

AFRICAN AMERICANS—KENTUCKY

Aubespin, Mervin, et al. Two Centuries of Black Louisville: A Photographic History. 2011. 45.00 ***(978-1-935497-36-3(7))*** Butler Bks., Inc.

Coe, Samuel & Adams, R. A. Chronicles of the Coe Colony: Pea Ridge, Kentucky. Guffey, Billy N., ed. 2007. 200p. pap. 15.00 *(978-0-9797713-1-6(5))* Xerxes Publishing.

Conner, Glen. Till Freedom Came: Slaves in Allen County, 1815-1866. 2010. *(978-1-935001-50-8(7))* Acclaim Pr., Inc.

Fosl, Catherine & K'Meyer, Tracy E. Freedom on the Border: An Oral History of the Civil Rights Movement in Kentucky. 2010. (Kentucky Remembered: an Oral History Ser.). (ENG., Illus.). 344p. pap. 25.00 *(978-0-8131-2606-7(1))* Univ. Pr. of Kentucky.

Frost, Karolyn Smardz. I've Got a Home in Glory Land: A Lost Tale of the Underground Railroad. 2008. (ENG., Illus.). 480p. pap. 18.00 *(978-0-374-53125-6(0))* Farrar, Straus & Giroux.

Howard, Victor B. Black Liberation in Kentucky: Emancipation & Freedom, 1862-1884. 2010. (ENG.). 232p. pap. 30.00 *(978-0-8131-3397-3(1))* Univ. Pr. of Kentucky.

K'Meyer, Tracy E. Civil Rights in the Gateway to the South: Louisville, Kentucky, 1945-1980. 2009. (Civil Rights & the Struggle for Black Equality in the Twentieth Century Ser.). (ENG., Illus.). 438p. 50.00 *(978-0-8131-2539-8(1))* Univ. Pr. of Kentucky.

Wright, George C. A History of Blacks in Kentucky: In Pursuit of Equality, 1890-1980. 2009. (ENG.). 288p. pap. 25.00 *(978-0-916968-37-3(5))* Kentucky Historical Society.

AFRICAN AMERICANS—LOUISIANA

Bond, Horace Mann & Bond, Julia W. The Star Creek Papers. Fairclough, Adam, ed. 2011. (ENG.). 200p. pap. 22.95 ***(978-0-8203-4083-8(9))*** Univ. of Georgia Pr.

Broussard, Sherry T. African Americans in Lafayette & Southwest Louisiana. 2012. (Images of America Ser.). (ENG., Illus.). 128p. pap. 21.99 ***(978-0-7385-9110-0(6))*** Arcadia Publishing.

Fairclough, Adam. Race & Democracy: The Civil Rights Struggle in Louisiana, 1915-1972. 2nd ed. 2008. (ENG., Illus.). 688p. pap. 29.95 *(978-0-8203-3114-0(7))* Univ. of Georgia Pr.

Ford, Arthur Lee. When the Whippoorwill Sang: A Memoir of Rural Life During the Twilight of the Segregated South. 2008. *(978-1-887366-84-7(9))* Univ. of Louisiana at Lafayette Pr.

Frystak, Shannon. Our Minds on Freedom: Women & the Struggle for Black Equality in Louisiana, 1924-1967. 2009. 288p. 42.50 *(978-0-8071-3493-1(7))* Louisiana State Univ. Pr.

Kennedy, R. Emmet. Black Cameos. 2007. 238p. 41.95 *(978-0-548-04501-5(1))* Kessinger Publishing, LLC.

Lane, Charles. The Day Freedom Died: The Colfax Massacre, the Supreme Court, & the Betrayal of Reconstruction. 2009. (ENG.). 352p. pap. 17.99 *(978-0-8050-8922-6(5)*, Owl Bks.) Holt, Henry & Co.

Sullivan, Jas M. & Winburn, Jonathan, eds. The Louisiana Legislative Black Caucus: Race & Representation in the Pelican State. 2011. (Illus.). 216p. 39.95 ***(978-0-8071-4036-9(8))*** Louisiana State Univ. Pr.

AFRICAN AMERICANS—LOUISIANA—NEW ORLEANS

Arend, Orissa. Showdown in Desire: The Black Panthers Take a Stand in New Orleans. 2010. (ENG., Illus.). 294p. pap. 19.95 *(978-1-55728-896-7(8))* Univ. of Arkansas Pr.

Clarke, Kristen & Marable, Manning, eds. Seeking Higher Ground: The Hurricane Katrina Crisis, Race, & Public Policy Reader. 2007. (Critical Black Studies). (ENG.). 336p. 110.00 *(978-1-4039-8396-1(8))*; (Illus.). pap. 33.00 *(978-1-4039-7779-3(8))* Palgrave Macmillan.

Evans, Freddi Williams. Congo Square: African Roots in New Orleans. 2011. 224p. pap. 20.00 *(978-1-935754-03-9(3))* Univ. of Louisiana at Lafayette Pr.

Ferdinand, Keith C. & Penner, D'Ann R. Overcoming Katrina: African American Voices from the Crescent City & Beyond. 2009. (Palgrave Studies in Oral History Ser.). (ENG., Illus.). 288p. pap. 21.00 *(978-0-230-60871-9(X))* Palgrave Macmillan.

Flucker, Turry & Savage, Phoenix. African Americans of New Orleans. 2010. (Images of America Ser.). (ENG., Illus.). 128p. pap. 21.99 *(978-0-7385-6645-0(4))* Arcadia Publishing.

Hart, Philip S. African Americans & the Future of New Orleans: Rebirth, Renewal & Rebuilding — An American Dilemma. 2007. (ENG., Illus.). 180p. pap. 15.95 *(978-0-9790976-1-4(4))* Amber Bks.

Kennedy, Al. Big Chief Harrison & the Mardi Gras Indians, 1 vol. 2010. (ENG., Illus.). 416p. 35.00 *(978-1-58980-696-2(4))* Pelican Publishing Co., Inc.

Levitt, Jeremy I. & Whitaker, Matthew C. Hurricane Katrina: America's Unnatural Disaster. Levitt, Jeremy I. & Whitaker, Matthew C., eds. 2009. (Justice & Social Inquiry Ser.). (ENG., Illus.). 336p. 45.00 *(978-0-8032-1760-7(9))* Univ. of Nebraska Pr.

Liu, Baodong & Vanderleeuw, James M. Race Rules: Electoral Politics in New Orleans, 1965-2006. 2007. (ENG., Illus.). 180p. 62.99 *(978-0-7391-1967-9(2))* Lexington Bks.

Liu/Vanderleeuw. Race Rules: Electoral Politics in New Orleans, 1965-2006. 2007. (ENG.). 180p. pap. 26.50 *(978-0-7391-1968-6(0))* Lexington Bks.

Moore, Leonard N. Black Rage in New Orleans: Police Brutality & African American Activism from World War II to Hurricane Katrina. 2010. (Illus.). 320p. 35.00 *(978-0-8071-3590-7(9))* Louisiana State Univ. Pr.

Penner, D'Ann, et al. Overcoming Katrina: African American Voices from the Crescent City & Beyond. 2009. (Palgrave Studies in Oral History Ser.). (ENG., Illus.). 288p. 105.00 *(978-0-230-60870-2(1))* Palgrave Macmillan.

Rasmussen, Daniel. American Uprising: The Untold Story of America's Largest Slave Revolt. 2012. (ENG.). 320p. pap. 15.99 ***(978-0-06-199522-4(3)***, HarperPerennial) 2011. (ENG.). 288p. 26.99 *(978-0-06-199521-7(5))* 2011. (Illus.). 324p. pap. 26.99 *(978-0-06-201788-8(6)*, HarperLuxe) HarperCollins Pubs.

Rodriguez, Joseph, photos by. Still Here: Stories after Katrina. 2008. (Illus.). 144p. 35.00 *(978-1-57687-460-8(5))* powerHouse Cultural Entertainment, Inc.

Turner, Richard Brent & Bellegarde-Smith, Patrick. Jazz Religion, the Second Line, & Black New Orleans. 2009. (ENG., Illus.). 200p. pap. 21.95 *(978-0-253-22120-9(X), 025322120X)* Indiana Univ. Pr.

White, Elisa Joy. Modernity, Freedom, & the African Diaspora: Dublin, New Orleans, Paris. 2012. (Blacks in the Diaspora Ser.). (ENG.). 356p. pap. 30.00 ***(978-0-253-00125-2(0)***, 0253001250); (Illus.). 80.00 ***(978-0-253-00115-3(3)***, 0253001153) Indiana Univ. Pr.

AFRICAN AMERICANS—MARYLAND

Brackett, Jeffrey R. The Negro in Maryland. 268p. reprint ed. 98.00 *(978-0-7222-9789-6(0))* Library Reprints, Inc.

—The Negro in Maryland: A Study of the Institution of Slavery. (Johns Hopkins University. Studies in the Social Sciences, Thirtieth Ser.: 6). reprint ed. 27.50 *(978-0-404-61354-9(3))* AMS Pr., Inc.

—Notes on the Progress of the Colored People in Maryland Since the War. 96p. reprint ed. 86.00 *(978-0-7222-9790-2(4))* Library Reprints, Inc.

David, Jonathan. Together Let Us Sweetly Live: The Singing & Praying Bands. 2007. (Music in American Life Ser.). (Illus.). 264p. 83.00 *(978-0-252-03170-0(9))*; pap. 28.00 *(978-0-252-07419-6(X))* Univ. of Illinois Pr.

Diggs, Louis S., as told by. Our Struggles. 2007. per. 39.95 *(978-0-9795705-3-7(0))* Uptown Pr., Inc.

Goosman, Stuart L. Group Harmony: The Black Urban Roots of Rhythm & Blues. 2010. (Illus.). 304p. (C). pap. 24.95 *(978-0-8122-2108-4(7))* Univ. of Pennsylvania Pr.

Pietila, Antero. Not in My Neighborhood. 2010. (ENG.). 336p. 28.95 *(978-1-56663-843-2(7))* Dee, Ivan R. Pub.

Poe, William A. African Americans of Calvert County. 2008. (Images of America Ser.). (ENG., Illus.). 128p. pap. 19.99 *(978-0-7385-5440-2(5))* Arcadia Publishing.

Rockman, Seth. Scraping By: Wage Labor, Slavery, & Survival in Early Baltimore. 2008. (Studies in Early American Economy & Society from the Library Company of Philadelphia Ser.). (ENG., Illus.). 392p. (gr. 17). pap. 27.00 *(978-0-8018-9007-9(1))* Johns Hopkins Univ. Pr.

AFRICAN AMERICANS—MASSACHUSETTS

Dresser, Thomas. African Americans on Martha's Vineyard: From Enslavement to Presidential Visit. 2010. (ENG., Illus.). 160p. pap. 19.99 *(978-1-59629-069-3(2))* History Pr., The.

Greenwood, Janette Thomas. First Fruits of Freedom: The Migration of Former Slaves & Their Search for Equality in Worcester, Massachusetts, 1862-1900. 2010. (John Hope Franklin Series in African American History & Culture Ser.). (ENG., Illus.). 256p. 55.00 *(978-0-8078-3362-9(2))*; pap. 22.95 *(978-0-8078-7104-1(4))* Univ. of North Carolina Pr.

Johnson, Robert. Nantucket's People of Color: Essays on History, Politics & Community. 2006. (ENG.). 260p. 73.50 *(978-0-7618-3494-6(X))* Univ. Pr. of America, Inc.

Johnson, Robert, Jr., ed. Nantucket's People of Color: Essays on History, Politics & Community. 2006. (ENG.). 260p. per. 41.99 *(978-0-7618-3495-3(8))* Univ. Pr. of America, Inc.

AFRICAN AMERICANS—MASSACHUSETTS—BOSTON

Kantrowitz, Stephen. More Than Freedom: Fighting for Black Citizenship in a White Republic, 1829-1889. 2012. (ENG.). 528p. (gr. 12). 36.00 ***(978-1-59420-342-8(3)***, Penguin Pr. HC, The) Penguin Group (USA) Inc.

Lehr, Dick. The Fence: A Police Cover-Up along Boston's Racial Divide. 2010. 416p. pap. 14.99 *(978-0-06-078099-9(1)*, HarperPerennial) HarperCollins Pubs.

Mitchell, John Hanson. Looking for Mr. Gilbert: The Reimagined Life of an African American. 2006. (ENG., Illus.). 288p. per. 16.00 *(978-1-59376-142-4(2))* Counterpoint LLC.

AFRICAN AMERICANS—MICHIGAN

Cox, Anna-Lisa. A Stronger Kinship: One Town's Extraordinary Story of Hope & Faith. 2007. (ENG., Illus.). 296p. per. 19.95 *(978-0-8032-6018-4(0)*, Bison Bks.) Univ. of Nebraska Pr.

Darden, Joe T., et al. The State of Black Michigan, 1967-2007. Darden, Joe T. et al, eds. 2007. (ENG., Illus.). 364p. per. 39.95 *(978-0-87013-827-0(8))* Michigan State Univ. Pr.

Mull, Carol E. The Underground Railroad in Michigan. 2010. (ENG., Illus.). 223p. 55.00 *(978-0-7864-4638-4(2))* McFarland & Co., Inc. Pubs.

Smith, Sandra Susan. Lone Pursuit: Distrust & Defensive Individualism among the Black Poor. 2007. (Illus.). 246p. *(978-0-87154-773-6(2))* Russell Sage Foundation.

Walker, Lewis & Wilson, Benjamin C. Black Eden: The Idlewild Community. 2007. (ENG., Illus.). 269p. per. 19.95 *(978-0-87013-804-1(9))* Michigan State Univ. Pr.

Walker, Lewis, et al. African Americans in Michigan. 2008. (Discovering the Peoples of Michigan Ser.). (ENG., Illus.). 63p. pap. 12.95 *(978-0-87013-583-5(X))* Michigan State Univ. Pr.

AFRICAN AMERICANS—MICHIGAN—DETROIT

Anderson, Bridget L. Migration Accomodation & Language Change: Language at the Intersection of Regional & Ethnic Identity. 2008. (ENG., Illus.). 242p. 89.00 *(978-0-230-00886-1(0))* Palgrave Macmillan.

Arnett, Marvin V. Pieces from Life's Crazy Quilt. 2008. (American Lives Ser.). (ENG.). 208p. pap. 12.95 *(978-0-8032-1638-9(6)*, Bison Bks.) Univ. of Nebraska Pr.

Bergmann, Luke. Getting Ghost: Two Young Lives & the Struggle for the Soul of an American City. 2009. (ENG., Illus.). 315p. 27.95 *(978-1-59558-139-6(1)*, 955139) New Pr., The.

—Getting Ghost: Two Young Lives & the Struggle for the Soul of an American City. 2010. (ENG., Illus.). 332p. pap. 22.95 *(978-0-472-03436-9(7))* Univ. of Michigan Pr.

Bunge, William. Fitzgerald: Geography of a Revolution. 2011. (Geographies of Justice & Social Transformation Ser.). (ENG., Illus.). 272p. pap. 26.95 *(978-0-8203-3874-3(5))* Univ. of Georgia Pr.

Dillard, Angela D. Faith in the City: Preaching Radical Social Change in Detroit. 2007. (ENG., Illus.). 416p. per. 26.95 *(978-0-472-03207-5(0))* Univ. of Michigan Pr.

Elrick, M. L. & Schaefer, Jim. The Kwame Sutra: Musings on lust, life & leadership, from Detroit Mayor Kwame Kilpatrick, Vol. 1. 2009. (Illus.). 80p. pap. 7.99 *(978-0-615-33255-0(2))* Watchmen Ink LLC.

Fine, Sidney. Violence in the Model City: The Cavanagh Administration, Race Relations, & the Detroit Riot Of 1967. 2007. (ENG., Illus.). 648p. per. 24.95 *(978-0-87013-815-7(4))* Michigan State Univ. Pr.

Martelle, Scott. Detroit: A Biography. 2012. (ENG.). 304p. 24.95 ***(978-1-56976-526-5(X))*** Chicago Review Pr., Inc.

Shaw, Todd Cameron. Now Is the Time! Detroit Black Politics & Grassroots Activism. 2009. (ENG., Illus.). 304p. 89.95 *(978-0-8223-4495-7(5))*; pap. 24.95 *(978-0-8223-4508-4(0))* Duke Univ. Pr.

The Near Eastsiders. Detroit's near Eastside: A Journey of Excellence Against the Odds. Cargle, Council, ed. 2008. (Illus.). 200p. 35.00 *(978-1-888754-07-0(9))* Detroit Black Writer's Guild.

AFRICAN AMERICANS—MIDDLE WEST

Blocker, Jack S. A Little More Freedom: African Americans Enter the Urban Midwest, 1860-1930. 2008. (URBAN LIFE & URBAN LANDSCAPE Ser.). (Illus.). (ENG.). 368p. 49.95 *(978-0-8142-1067-3(8))*; xvii, 330p. cd-rom 9.95 *(978-0-8142-9152-8(X))* Ohio State Univ. Pr.

AFRICAN AMERICANS—MINNESOTA

Galvin, Michael. Skyline Tower, 'Ghetto in the Sky' 2009. 88p. pap. *(978-3-639-16358-2(3))* VDM Verlag Dr. Mueller e.K.

Green, William D. A Peculiar Imbalance: The Fall & Rise of Racial Equality in Early Minnesota. 2007. 232p. 32.95 *(978-0-87351-586-3(2))* Minnesota Historical Society Pr.

AFRICAN AMERICANS—MISSISSIPPI

Collier, Melvin J. Mississippi to Africa: A Journey of Discovery. 2008. (Illus.). xviii, 279p. pap. 28.00 *(978-0-7884-4761-7(0))* Heritage Bks.

Danielson, Chris. After Freedom Summer: How Race Realigned Mississippi Politics, 1965-1986. 2011. (New Perspectives on the History of the South Ser.). (ENG., Illus.). 328p. 69.95 *(978-0-8130-3738-7(7))* Univ. Pr. of Florida.

Elwang, William Wilson. The Negroes of Columbia, Missouri: A Concrete Study of the Race Problem. 2008. 88p. pap. 18.75 *(978-0-559-44941-3(0))* BiblioBazaar.

Hamlin, Francoise Nicole. Crossroads at Clarksdale: The Black Freedom Struggle in the Mississippi Delta after World War II. 2012. (John Hope Franklin Series in African American History & Culture Ser.). (ENG., Illus.). 368p. 39.95 ***(978-0-8078-3549-4(8))*** Univ. of North Carolina Pr.

Katagiri, Yasuhiro. The Mississippi State Sovereignty Commission: Civil Rights & States' Rights. (ENG.). 2007. 348p. per. 25.00 *(978-1-60473-008-1(0))* 2006. 312p. 50.00 *(978-1-57806-388-8(4))* Univ. Pr. of Mississippi.

Marsh, Charles. God's Long Summer: Stories of Faith & Civil Rights. 2008. (ENG., Illus.). 312p. (C). pap. 24.95 *(978-0-691-13067-5(1))* Princeton Univ. Pr.

Martin, Gordon A., Jr. Count Them One by One: Black Mississippians Fighting for the Right to Vote. 2010. (Margaret Walker Alexander Series in African American Studies). (ENG., Illus.). 272p. 40.00 *(978-1-60473-789-9(1))* Univ. Pr. of Mississippi.

Powdermaker, Hortense. After Freedom: A Cultural Study in the Deep South. 2008. 432p. pap. 43.00 *(978-1-59740-629-1(5))* ACLS Humanities E-Book.

Robson, David. The Murder of Emmett Till. 2010. (Crime Scene Investigations Ser.). (Illus.). 128p. 32.45 *(978-1-4205-0213-8(1)*, Lucent Bks.) Cengage Gale.

Span, Christopher M. From Cotton Field to Schoolhouse: African American Education in Mississippi, 1862-1875. 2009. (ENG., Illus.). 264p. 36.95 *(978-0-8078-3290-5(1))* Univ. of North Carolina Pr.

Stolle, Roger. HH Mississippi Blues. 2011. pap. 19.99 *(978-1-60949-219-9(6))* History Pr., The.

Trethewey, Natasha. Beyond Katrina: A Meditation on the Mississippi Gulf Coast. (ENG.). 144p. 2012. pap. 17.95 ***(978-0-8203-4311-2(0))*** 2010. (Illus.). 22.95 *(978-0-8203-3381-6(X))* Univ. of Georgia Pr.

Waldrep, Christopher. Jury Discrimination: The Supreme Court, Public Opinion, & a Grassroots Fight for Racial Equality in Mississippi. 2010. (Studies in the Legal History of the South Ser.). (ENG., Illus.). 328p. 44.95 *(978-0-8203-3002-0(7))* Univ. of Georgia Pr.

Wright, Richard & Wright, Richard. Black Boy. 2008. (P.S. Ser.). (ENG.). 464p. pap. 16.99 *(978-0-06-144308-4(5)*, HarperPerennial) HarperCollins Pubs.

AFRICAN AMERICANS—MISSOURI

Coggswell, Gladys Caines. Stories from the Heart: Missouri's African American Heritage. 2009. (Missouri Heritage Readers Ser.). (ENG., Illus.). 160p. (gr. 9). pap. 15.95 *(978-0-8262-1844-5(X))* Univ. of Missouri Pr.

Frazier, Harriet C. Slavery & Crime in Missouri, 1773-1865. alt. ed. 2011. (ENG., Illus.). 336p. pap. 45.00 *(978-0-7864-4331-4(6))* McFarland & Co., Inc. Pubs.

Gordon, Colin. Mapping Decline: St. Louis & the Fate of the American City. 2009. (Politics & Culture in Modern America Ser.). (Illus.). 304p. (C). pap. 37.50 *(978-0-8122-2094-0(3))* Univ. of Pennsylvania Pr.

Grant, Gail Milissa. At the Elbows of My Elders: One Family's Journey Toward Civil Rights. 2008. (ENG.). 272p. (gr. 9). 24.95 *(978-1-883982-66-9(9))*; Missouri Historical Society Pr.

Nolen, Rose M. African Americans in Mid-Missouri: From Pioneers to Ragtimers. 2010. *(978-1-59629-609-1(7))* History Pr., The.

AFRICAN AMERICANS—MISSOURI—SAINT LOUIS

Jack, Bryan M. The St. Louis African American Community & the Exodusters. 2008. (ENG.). 192p. (C). 34.95 *(978-0-8262-1772-1(9))* Univ. of Missouri Pr.

Jolly, Kenneth. Black Liberation in the Midwest: The Struggle in St. Louis, Missouri, 1964-1970. 2006. (Studies in African American History & Culture). 232p. 136.00 *(978-0-415-97969-6(2))* Routledge.

Rainwater, Lee. Behind Ghetto Walls: Black Families in a Federal Slum. 2006. (ENG.). 591p. (gr. 11). pap. 39.95 *(978-0-202-30907-1(X))* Aldine Transaction.

AFRICAN AMERICANS—NEVADA

Geran, Trish. Beyond the Glimmering Lights: The Pride & Perseverance of African Americans in Las Vegas. 2010. (Illus.). 171p. 19.95 *(978-1-932173-47-5(1))* Stephens Pr. LLC.

AFRICAN AMERICANS—NEW ENGLAND

Talbot, Gerald E. & Price, H. H. Maine's Visible Black History: The First Chronicle of Its People. 2010. (Illus.). 429p. pap. 35.00 *(978-0-88448-275-8(8))* Tilbury Hse. Pubs.

AFRICAN AMERICANS—NEW HAMPSHIRE

Cary, Lorene. Black Ice. tchr.'s training gde. ed. *(978-0-394-27226-9(9)*, Vintage) Knopf Doubleday Publishing Group.

AFRICAN AMERICANS—NEW JERSEY

Greason, Walter. The Path to Freedom: Black Families in New Jersey. 2010. (ENG., Illus.). 128p. pap. 19.99 *(978-1-59629-992-4(4))* History Pr., The.

Jackson, Madonna. Asbury Park: A West Side Story: A Pictorial Journey Through the Eyes of Joseph A. Carter, Sr. 2007. (Illus.). 244p. pap. 29.95 *(978-1-59800-963-7(X))* Outskirts Pr., Inc.

Jackson, Madonna Carter. Asbury Park: A West Side Story: A Pictorial Journey Through the Eyes of Joseph A. Carter, Sr. 2nd rev. ed. 2011. 254p. pap. 29.95 ***(978-1-4327-7407-3(7))*** Outskirts Pr., Inc.

Johnson, Nelson. The Northside: African Americans & the Creation of Atlantic City. 2010. 352p. 24.95 *(978-0-937548-73-8(1))* Plexus Publishing, Inc.

Mumford, Kevin. Newark: A History of Race, Rights, & Riots in America. 2008. (ENG.). 336p. pap. 24.00 *(978-0-8147-9563-7(3))* New York Univ. Pr.

Porambo, Ronald. No Cause for Indictment: An Autopsy of Newark. 2007. (ENG.). 425p. per. 18.95 *(978-1-933633-21-3(2))* Melville Hse. Publishing.

Rizzo, Dennis C. Parallel Communities: The Underground Railroad in South Jersey. 2008. pap. 19.99 *(978-1-59629-542-1(2))* History Pr., The.

Thompson, Ernest & Thompson, Mindy. Homeboy Came to Orange: A Story of People's Power. 2008. 240p. pap. 17.95 *(978-0-595-53036-6(2))* iUniverse, Inc.

Thornton, Yvonne S. The Ditchdigger's Daughters. 2008. (ENG., Illus.). 272p. 15.00 *(978-0-7582-2588-7(1)*, Dafina) Kensington Publishing Corp.

Washington, Jack. The Long Journey Home: A Bicentennial History of the Black Community of Princeton, New Jersey, 1776-1976. 320p. 84.95 *(978-1-59221-053-4(8))* Africa World Pr.

AFRICAN AMERICANS—NEW YORK (STATE)

Curran, John J. Peekskill's African American History: A Hudson Valley Community's Untold Story. 2008. (Illus.). 155p. pap. 19.99 *(978-1-59629-484-4(1))* History Pr., The.

Field, Phyllis F. The Politics of Race in New York: The Struggle for Black Suffrage in the Civil War Era. 2009. (Illus.). 268p. pap. 25.95 *(978-0-8014-7553-4(5))* Cornell Univ. Pr.

Goldschmidt, Henry. Race & Religion among the Chosen Peoples of Crown Heights. 2006. (ENG., Illus.). 296p. 68.00 *(978-0-8135-3883-9(1))*; per. 23.95 *(978-0-8135-3897-6(1))* Rutgers Univ. Pr.

Haynes, Bruce D. Red Lines, Black Spaces: The Politics of Race & Space in a Black Middle-Class Suburb. 2006. (ENG.). 208p. pap. 27.00 *(978-0-300-12454-5(6))* Yale Univ. Pr.

Jones, R. Clifford. James K. Humphrey & the Sabbath-Day Adventists. 2006. (ENG.). 250p. 50.00 *(978-1-57806-891-3(6))* Univ. Pr. of Mississippi.

Lemak, Jennifer A. Southern Life, Northern City: The History of Albany's Rapp Road Community. 2008. (Illus.). 210p. 25.00 *(978-0-7914-7581-2(6))* State Univ. of New York Pr.

Matthews, Harry Bradshaw. African American Journey to Freedom in New York & Related Sites, 1823-1870: Freedom Knows No Color. 2008. (Illus.). 480p. 45.00 *(978-0-9799537-4-3(X))*; per. 32.00 *(978-0-9799537-3-6(1))* Africana Homestead Legacy Pubs., Inc.

A Report to the Governor on the Disturbances in Crown Heights. (Illus.). 200p. pap. *(978-0-934393-75-1(3))* Rector Pr., Ltd.

Stamps, S. David & Stamps, Miriam Burny. Salt City & Its Black Community: A Sociological Study of Syracuse, New York. 2008. (Illus.). 331p. 29.95 *(978-0-8156-3180-4(4))* Syracuse Univ. Pr.

AFRICAN AMERICANS—NEW YORK (STATE)—NEW YORK

Alexander, Leslie M. African or American? Black Identity & Political Activism in New York City, 1784-1861. 2011. (ENG., Illus.). 288p. pap. 28.00 ***(978-0-252-07853-8(5))*** Univ. of Illinois Pr.

Benhelima, Charif. Charif Benhelima - Harlem on my mind-I was, I am. 2011. (ENG.). ***(978-3-940953-70-4(9))*** Snoeck Verlagsgesellschaft mbH.

Bernard, Emily. Carl Van Vechten & the Harlem Renaissance: A Portrait in Black & White. 2012. (ENG., Illus.). 376p. 30.00 ***(978-0-300-12199-5(7))*** Yale Univ. Pr.

Curtis, Susan. Colored Memories: A Biographer's Quest for the Elusive Lester A. Walton. 2008. (ENG., Illus.). 304p. (C). 39.95 *(978-0-8262-1786-8(9))* Univ. of Missouri Pr.

Dawkins, Wayne. City Son: Andrew W. Cooper's Impact on Modern-Day Brooklyn. 2012. (Margaret Walker Alexander Series in African American Studies). (ENG.). 304p. 35.00 ***(978-1-61703-258-5(1))*** Univ. Pr. of Mississippi.

Harris, Glen Anthony. The Ocean Hill-Brownsville Conflict: Intellectual Struggles Between Blacks & Jews at Midcentury. 2012. (ENG.). 204p. (gr. 17). 65.00 ***(978-0-7391-6683-3(2))*** Lexington Bks.

Haynes, George E. Negro at Work in New York City. (Columbia University, Studies in the Social Sciences: No. 124) reprint ed. 27.50 *(978-0-404-51124-1(4))* AMS Pr., Inc.

Horowitz, Irving Louis. Daydreams & Nightmares: Expanded Edition. 2nd ed. 2011. (ENG.). 144p. pap. 26.95 ***(978-1-4128-4589-2(0))*** Transaction Pubs.

Kiser, Clyde V. Sea Island to City: A Study of St. Helena Islanders in Harlem & Other Urban Centers. (Columbia University, Studies in the Social Sciences: No. 368). reprint ed. 20.00 *(978-0-404-51368-9(9))* AMS Pr., Inc.

Kramer, Victor A., ed. Georgia State Literary Studies, 12 vols. *(978-0-404-63200-7(9))* AMS Pr., Inc.

Lepore, Jill. New York Burning: Liberty, Slavery, & Conspiracy in Eighteenth-Century Manhattan. 2006. (Vintage Ser.). (ENG., Illus.). 352p. pap. 16.95 *(978-1-4000-3226-6(1)*, Vintage) Knopf Doubleday Publishing Group.

Lowther, Hastie. Willie E. Lowther: The Journey of My Life. 2007. (Illus.). 328p. per. 24.95 net. *(978-0-9742773-5-3(3))* Soleil Pr.

National Museum of African American History and Culture (U.S.) Staff. Ain't Nothing Like the Real Thing: How the Apollo Theater Shaped American Entertainment. Conwill, Kinshasha Holman & Carlin, Richard, eds. 2010. (ENG., Illus.). 264p. 35.00 *(978-1-58834-269-0(7))* Smithsonian Institution Pr.

Ogbar, Jeffrey O. G., ed. The Harlem Renaissance Revisited: Politics, Arts, & Letters. 2010. (ENG.). 272p. (C). (gr. 13-17). pap. 30.00 *(978-0-8018-9461-9(1))* Johns Hopkins Univ. Pr.

—The Harlem Renaissance Revisited: Politics, Arts, & Letters. 2010. (ENG.). 272p. (C). (gr. 13-17). 60.00 *(978-0-8018-9460-2(3))* Johns Hopkins Univ. Pr.

Ottley, Roi. New World A-Coming: Inside Black America. 2009. 374p. 48.95 *(978-1-104-84343-4(9))* 2007. (ENG.). 372p. per. 33.95 *(978-0-548-38760-3(5))* Kessinger Publishing, LLC.

Ovington, Mary White. Half a Man: the Status of the Negro in New York. 2007. pap. 26.95 *(978-1-4304-6966-7(8))* Kessinger Publishing, LLC.

Peterson, Carla L. Black Gotham: A Family History of African Americans in Nineteenth-Century New York City. (Illus.). 446p. 2012. (ENG.). pap. 20.00 ***(978-0-300-18174-6(4))*** 2011. 32.00 *(978-0-300-16255-4(3))* Yale Univ. Pr.

Reed, Ruth. Negro Illegitimacy in New York City. (Columbia University, Studies in the Social Sciences: No. 277). reprint ed. 20.00 *(978-0-404-51277-4(1))* AMS Pr., Inc.

—Negro Illegitimacy in New York City / by Ruth Reed. 2006. 156p. per. 18.99 *(978-1-4255-1160-9(0))* MPublishing.

Reed, Touré F. Not Alms but Opportunity: The Urban League & the Politics of Racial Uplift, 1910-1950. 2008. (ENG., Illus.). 272p. pap. 23.95 *(978-0-8078-5902-5(8))* Univ. of North Carolina Pr.

Rhodes-Pitts, Sharifa. Harlem Is Nowhere: A Journey to the Mecca of Black America. 2011. (ENG., Illus.). 304p. 24.99 *(978-0-316-01723-7(X))* Little Brown & Co.

Rivers, Voza W., ed. Forever Harlem: Celebrating America's Most Diverse Community. 2006. (Illus.). 279p. 29.95 *(978-1-59670-206-6(0)*, Spotlight Pr) Sports Publishing, LLC.

Sacks, Marcy S. Before Harlem: The Black Experience in New York City Before World War I. 2006. (Politics & Culture in Modern America Ser.). (Illus.). 240p. (C). 59.95 *(978-0-8122-3961-4(X))* Univ. of Pennsylvania Pr.

Schoener, Allon, ed. Harlem on My Mind: Cultural Capital of Black America, 1900-1968. 2007. (ENG., Illus.). 258p. per. 24.95 *(978-1-59558-158-7(8))* New Pr., The.

Schroff, Laura & Tresniowski, Alex. An Invisible Thread: The True Story of an 11-Year-Old Panhandler, a Busy Sales Executive, & an Unlikely Meeting with Destiny. lt. ed. 2012. (ENG.). 335p. 31.99 ***(978-1-4104-4786-9(3)***, Wheeler Publishing, Inc.) Cengage Gale.

SenGupta, Gunja. From Slavery to Poverty: The Racial Origins of Welfare in New York, 1840-1918. 2010. (ENG.). 352p. pap. 25.00 *(978-0-8147-4107-8(X))* New York Univ. Pr.

Seraile, William. Angels of Mercy: White Women & the History of New York's Colored Orphan Asylum. 2011. (Empire State Editions Ser.). (ENG., Illus.). 220p. 29.00 *(978-0-8232-3419-6(3))* Fordham Univ. Pr.

Sinclair, Abiola, ed. & text. The Harlem Cultural - Political Movements, 1960-1970: From Malcolm X to "Black Is Beautiful" (Illus.). 132p. (Orig.). pap. 18.95 *(978-0-936073-25-5(X))* Gumbs & Thomas Pubs., Inc.

Weiner, Melissa. Power, Protest, & the Public Schools: Jewish & African American Struggles in New York City. 2012. (ENG.). 272p. pap. 25.95 ***(978-0-8135-5351-1(2))*** Rutgers Univ. Pr.

Weiner, Melissa F. Power, Protest, & the Public Schools: Jewish & African American Struggles in New York City. 2010. (ENG., Illus.). 272p. 44.95 (978-0-8135-4772-5(5)) Rutgers Univ. Pr.

Willie E. Lowther: From Locust Grove to Harlem: the Journey of My Life. 2008. (Illus.). 328p. 36.95 (978-0-9742773-8-7(X)) Soleil Pr.

Wilson, James F. Bulldaggers, Pansies, & Chocolate Babies: Performance, Race, & Sexuality in the Harlem Renaissance. 2011. (Triangulations: Lesbian/Gay/Queer Theater/Drama/Performance Ser.). (ENG., Illus.). 262p. pap. 27.95 **(978-0-472-03489-5(8))** Univ. of Michigan Pr.

Wilson, Jamie Jaywann. Building a Healthy Black Harlem: Health Politics in Harlem, New York, from the Jazz Age to the Great Depression. 2009. 222p. 104.99 (978-1-60497-624-3(1)) Cambria Pr.

Wright, Kai. Drifting Toward Love: Black, Brown, Gay, & Coming of Age on the Streets of New York, 1 vol. 2009. (ENG.). 240p. pap. 16.00 (978-0-8070-7969-0(3)) Beacon Pr.

AFRICAN AMERICANS—NORTH CAROLINA

Barringer Wells, Susan. A Game Called Salisbury: The Spinning of a Southern Tragedy & the Myth of Race. 2007. 492p. per. 23.95 (978-0-7414-4425-7(9)) Infinity Publishing.

Beckel, Deborah. Radical Reform: Interracial Politics in Post-Emancipation North Carolina. 2010. (American South Ser.). (ENG., Illus.). 312p. (gr. 17). 45.00 (978-0-8139-3002-2(2)) Univ. Pr. of Virginia.

Bellamy, Rhonda, ed. Moving Forward Together: A Community Remembers 1898. 2008. (Illus.). 128p. 25.00 (978-0-9792431-5-8(7)) SlapDash Publishing.

Brown, Leslie. Upbuilding Black Durham: Gender, Class, & Black Community Development in the Jim Crow South. 2008. (ENG., Illus.). 424p. 73.95 (978-0-8078-3138-0(7)); 472p. pap. 27.95 (978-0-8078-5835-6(8)) Univ. of North Carolina Pr.

Burch, Susan & Joyner, Hannah. Unspeakable: The Story of Junius Wilson. 2007. (ENG., Illus.). 312p. 31.95 (978-0-8078-3155-7(7)) Univ. of North Carolina Pr.

Escott, Paul D. North Carolinians in the Era of the Civil War & Reconstruction. 2008. (ENG., Illus.). 320p. 55.95 (978-0-8078-3222-6(7)); pap. 24.95 (978-0-8078-5901-8(X)) Univ. of North Carolina Pr.

Federal Writers' Project, Regional Staff. North Carolina: A Guide to the Old North State. 2011. (ENG.). 640p. pap. 50.00 **(978-0-8078-7149-2(4))** Univ. of North Carolina Pr.

Fergus, Devin. Liberalism, Black Power, & the Making of American Politics, 1965-1980. 2009. (Politics & Culture in the Twentieth-Century South Ser.). (ENG., Illus.). 376p. pap. 26.95 (978-0-8203-3324-3(7)); lib. bdg. 69.95 (978-0-8203-3323-6(9)) Univ. of Georgia Pr.

Ferguson, Leland. God's Fields: Landscape, Religion, & Race in Moravian Wachovia. 2011. (Cultural Heritage Studies). (ENG., Illus.). 256p. 74.95 (978-0-8130-3748-6(4)) Univ. Pr. of Florida.

Flono, Fannie. Thriving in the Shadows: The Black Experience in Charlotte & Mecklenburg County. 2007. (Illus.). 152p. (978-0-9760963-8-2(2)) Novello Festival Pr.

Flucker, Turry & Savage, Phoenix. African Americans of Jackson. 2008. (Images of America Ser.). (ENG., Illus.). 128p. per. 21.99 (978-0-7385-5328-3(X)) Arcadia Publishing.

Fraser, Rebecca J. Courtship & Love among the Enslaved in North Carolina. 2007. (ENG., Illus.). 137p. 65.00 (978-1-934110-07-2(8)) Univ. Pr. of Mississippi.

Hairston, Otis L. Picturing Greensboro, North Carolina: Four Decades of African American Community. 2007. pap. 19.99 (978-1-59629-284-0(9)) History Pr., The.

Hamel, Beverly. Bethania: The Village by the Black Walnut Bottom. 2009. (American Chronicles Ser.). 160p. pap. 21.99 (978-1-59629-637-4(2)) History Pr., The.

Holder, Rose Howell. McIver of North Carolina. 2011. (ENG.). 292p. pap. 40.00 **(978-0-8078-6874-4(4))** Univ. of North Carolina Pr.

Jones, Wilbur D. A Sentimental Journey: Memoirs of a Wartime Boomtown. 2007. (Illus.). 240p. pap. 24.95 (978-1-57249-318-6(6), White Mane Bks.) White Mane Publishing Co., Inc.

Lane, Lunsford. The Narrative of Lunsford Lane, Formerly of Raleigh, N C. 2007. 64p. per. (978-1-4065-2598-4(7)) Dodo Pr.

—The Narrative of Lunsford Lane, Formerly of Raleigh, N C. 2009. 48p. pap. (978-1-4068-5146-5(9)) Echo Library.

Logan, Frenise A. The Negro in North Carolina, 1876-1894. 2011. (ENG.). 256p. pap. 40.00 **(978-0-8078-9712-6(4))** Univ. of North Carolina Pr.

Lowther, Hastie. Willie E. Lowther: The Journey of My Life. 2007. (Illus.). 328p. per. 24.95 net. (978-0-9742773-6-3(3)) Soleil Pr.

McDonald, Victoria A. Casey. The African Americans of Jackson County: A Pictorial History... from Slavery to Integration. Garza, Amy Ammons, ed. 2006. (Illus.). 96p. per. 21.95 (978-0-9753023-6-1(1)) Ammons Communications, Ltd.

Mills, Kincaid, et al, eds. Coming Through: Voices of a South Carolina Gullah Community from WPA Oral Histories. 2008. (Illus.). 384p. 29.95 (978-1-57003-721-4(3)) Univ. of South Carolina Pr.

North Carolina African American History & Culture. 2007. (J). per. 32.96 (978-1-888325-45-4(3)) Allosaurus Pubs.

Oakdale / Union Hill Cemetery, Salisbury, North Carolina: A Study of A Twentieth Cenrury African American Cemetery. 2007. 69.95 (978-0-9777389-0-8(6)) Brown, Reginald.

Stephenson, Frank. Chowan Beach: Remembering an African American Resort. 2006. (Illus.). 124p. pap., per. 14.99 (978-1-59629-164-5(8)) History Pr., The.

Stowe, Gene. Inherit the Land: Jim Crow Meets Miss Maggie's Will. 2007. (ENG., Illus.). 309p. per. 22.00 (978-1-934110-60-7(4)) Univ. Pr. of Mississippi.

Wertheimer, John W. Law & Society in the South: A History of North Carolina Court Cases. 2010. (New Directions in Southern History Ser.). (ENG., Illus.). 292p. pap. 35.00 (978-0-8131-2615-9(0)) Univ. Pr. of Kentucky.

Willie E. Lowther: From Locust Grove to Harlem: the Journey of My Life. 2008. (Illus.). 328p. 36.95 (978-0-9742773-8-7(X)) Soleil Pr.

AFRICAN AMERICANS—OHIO

Black, Samuel W. & Williams, Regennia N. Through the Lens of Allen E. Cole: A History of African Americans in Cleveland, Ohio. 2012. **(978-1-60635-090-4(0))** Kent State Univ. Pr.

Mazloomi, Carolyn L. Stitching a Culture Together: African American Quilters of Ohio. 2013. (Ohio Quilt Ser.). (ENG., Illus.). 128p. pap. 22.95 (978-0-8214-1940-3(4)) Ohio Univ. Pr.

Saunders, Hollie Ann. Through My Eyes: A History of Lancaster from A Black Perspective. 2007. 216p. pap. 19.99 (978-0-9787850-1-7(0)) Ambassador Pr.

Wesley, Charles H. Ohio Negroes in the Civil War: Ohio Civil War Centennial Commission, No. 6. 2011. 48p. 35.95 **(978-1-258-08515-5(1))** Literary Licensing, LLC.

AFRICAN AMERICANS—OHIO—CINCINNATI

Duncan, Mae Najiyyah. A Survey of Cincinnati's Black Press & Its Editors 1844-2010. 2011. 138p. 29.99 **(978-1-4568-8417-8(4))**; pap. 19.99 **(978-1-4568-8416-1(6))** Xlibris Corp.

Martin, C. Sunny. Who's Who in Black Cincinnati: The Third Edition. 3rd ed. 2006. (ENG.). 252p. per. (978-1-933879-04-8(1)) Who's Who Publishing Co.

Who's Who in Black Cincinnati. 3rd ed. 2006. (978-1-933879-05-5(X)) Who's Who Publishing Co.

AFRICAN AMERICANS—OKLAHOMA

Alliance Against the Odds: The Manual Training High School Story. 2008. 1000p. pap. 49.95 (978-0-9815987-0-3(6)) D&J Educational Consulting & Publishing Services.

Blomquist, Ann K. & Walton-Raji, Angela Y. Black Indian Genealogy Research: African-American Ancestors among the Five Civilized Tribes, an Expanded Edition. 2007. pap. 24.50 (978-0-7884-4474-6(3)) Heritage Bks.

Burton, Art T. Black Gun, Silver Star: The Life & Legend of Frontier Marshal Bass Reeves. 2008. (Race & Ethnicity in the American West Ser.). (ENG., Illus.). 392p. pap. 18.95 (978-0-8032-1747-8(1), Bison Bks.) Univ. of Nebraska Pr.

Estes, Mary W. Bass Reeves: Deputy U. S. Marshal 1875-1902. Williamson, Mary, ed. Date not set. 224p. pap. 19.95 (978-0-89896-307-6(9), American History Bk. Publishing Co.) Larksdale.

Johnson, Hannibal B. Greenwood Cultural Center: Jewel in the Crown. 2008. (978-1-57864-465-0(8)) Donning Co. Pubs.

Naylor, Celia E. African Cherokees in Indian Territory: From Chattel to Citizens. (ENG., Illus.). 376p. 2009. pap. 49.95 (978-0-8078-5883-7(8)) 2008. 62.95 (978-0-8078-3203-5(0)) Univ. of North Carolina Pr.

Walton-Raji, Angela Y. Black Indian Genealogy Research: African-American Ancestors among the Five Civilized Tribes, an Expanded Edition. 2007. pap. 24.50 (978-0-7884-4473-9(5)) Heritage Bks.

AFRICAN AMERICANS—PENNSYLVANIA

Hodge, Ruth E. Guide to African American Resources at the Pennsylvania State Archives. 2008. (ENG.). 598p. pap. 45.00 (978-1-4223-9354-3(2)) DIANE Publishing Co.

Matthews, Harry Bradshaw. African American Journey to Freedom in New York & Related Sites, 1823-1870: Freedom Knows No Color. 2008. (Illus.). 480p. 45.00 (978-0-9799537-4-3(X)); per. 32.00 (978-0-9799537-3-6(1)) Africana Homestead Legacy Pubs., Inc.

Union County Historical Society (Pa.) Staff, contrib. by. African Americans in Union County: Slave & Free. 2011. pap. (978-0-917127-21-2(8)) Union County Historical Society.

AFRICAN AMERICANS—PENNSYLVANIA—PHILADELPHIA

Anderson, Elijah. Code of the Street: Decency, Violence & the Moral Life of the Inner City. 2006. pap. 8.95 (978-1-4288-1549-0(X)) Cram101 Inc.

Bacon, Margaret Hope. But One Race: The Life of Robert Purvis. 2007. (Illus.). 279p. 36.00 (978-0-7914-7007-7(5)) State Univ. of New York Pr.

Bois, William Edward Burghardt Du & Eaton, Isabel. The Philadelphia Negro: A Social Study. 2010. 570p. pap. 43.75 (978-1-142-76335-0(8)); 562p. pap. 42.75 (978-1-142-22095-2(8)) BiblioBazaar.

Canton, David A. Raymond Pace Alexander: A New Negro Lawyer Fights for Civil Rights in Philadelphia. 2010. (Margaret Walker Alexander Series in African American Studies). (ENG., Illus.). 272p. 50.00 (978-1-60473-425-6(6)) Univ. Pr. of Mississippi.

Countryman, Matthew J. Up South: Civil Rights & Black Power in Philadelphia. 2007. (Politics & Culture in Modern America Ser.). (Illus.). 432p. (C). per. 24.95 (978-0-8122-2002-5(1)) Univ. of Pennsylvania Pr.

Crumbley, Deidre Helen. Saved & Sanctified: The Rise of a Storefront Church in Great Migration Philadelphia. 2012. (History of African-American Religions Ser.). (ENG., Illus.). 208p. 74.95 **(978-0-8130-3984-8(3))** Univ. Pr. of Florida.

Delmont, Matthew F. The Nicest Kids in Town: American Bandstand, Rock 'n' Roll, & the Struggle for Civil Rights in 1950s Philadelphia. 2012. (American Crossroads Ser.). (ENG., Illus.). 312p. 65.00 **(978-0-520-27207-1(2))**; pap. 27.95 **(978-0-520-27208-8(0))** Univ. of California Pr.

Douglass, William. Annals of the First African Church, in the United States of America, Now Styled the African Episcopal Church of St Thomas, Philadelphia, in Its Conne. 2006. 176p. per. 18.99 (978-1-4255-1360-3(3)) MPublishing.

Du Bois, W. E. B. The Philadelphia Negro. 2007. 540p. per. 17.75 (978-1-60206-942-8(5)) Cosimo, Inc.

—The Philadelphia Negro: A Social Study. 2007. 542p. 57.95 (978-0-548-21951-5(6)); 544p. per. 42.95 (978-1-4325-4019-7(X)) Kessinger Publishing, LLC.

—The Philadelphia Negro: A Social Study. 520p. reprint ed. 98.00 (978-0-7222-9791-9(2)) Library Reprints, Inc.

—The Philadelphia Negro: A Social Study (1899) 2007. 572p. per. 43.95 (978-0-548-80502-2(4)) Kessinger Publishing, LLC.

—The Philadelphia Negro A Social Study. 2009. 572p. pap. 33.46 (978-1-4385-2072-8(7), Book Jungle) Standard Pubns., Inc.

—The Philadelphia Negro a Social Study. 2010. 298p. pap. (978-1-153-09425-2(8)) Books LLC.

—The Philadelphia Negro: A Social Study. 2010. 571p. pap. 35.97 (978-0-557-36228-8(8)) Lulu Enterprises Inc.

Du Bois, W. E. Burghardt. The Philadelphia Negro: A Social Study. 2010. 544p. 46.36 **(978-1-163-52117-5(5))**; pap. 34.36 **(978-1-163-25083-9(X))** Kessinger Publishing, LLC.

Gordon, Elizabeth K. Walk with Us: Triplet Boys, Their Teen Parents & Two White Women Who Tagged Along. 2007. (ENG.). 320p. per. 19.95 (978-1-934390-30-6(5)) Crandall, Dostie & Douglas Bks., Inc.

Levenstein, Lisa. A Movement Without Marches: African American Women & the Politics of Poverty in Postwar Philadelphia. 2009. pap. (978-0-8078-5942-1(7)) Univ. of North Carolina Pr.

Meaders, Daniel E., compiled by & pref. Kidnappers in Philadelphia: Isaac Hopper's Tales of Oppression 1780-1843. 2nd ed. 2009. (Studies in African American & African Canadian History & Culture). 432p. reprint ed. 80.00 (978-0-9818939-5-2(3)); (ENG.). pap. 40.00 (978-0-9818939-6-9(1)) Africana Homestead Legacy Pubs., Inc.

Roberts, John W., ed. From Hucklebuck to Hip Hop: Social Dance in the African American Community in Philadelphia. (Illus.). 134p. (Orig.). pap. (978-1-885066-11-4(2)) Four-G Pubs., Inc.

Wolfinger, James. Philadelphia Divided: Race & Politics in the City of Brotherly Love. 2011. (ENG., Illus.). 336p. pap. 24.95 (978-0-8078-7190-4(7)) Univ. of North Carolina Pr.

AFRICAN AMERICANS—PENNSYLVANIA—PITTSBURGH

Brown, Eliza Smith. African American Historic Sites Survey of Allegheny County (Pennsylvania) 2007. (Illus.). 242p. (C). pap. 25.00 (978-1-4223-1490-6(1)) DIANE Publishing Co.

AFRICAN AMERICANS—SOUTH CAROLINA

see also Gullahs

Barber Adams, Marie & Scott Brooks, Deborah. African Americans of Lower Richland County. 2010. (Images of America Ser.). (Illus.). 128p. pap. 21.99 (978-0-7385-8665-6(X)) Arcadia Publishing.

Billingsley, Andrew. Yearning to Breathe Free: Robert Smalls of South Carolina & His Families. 2010. pap. 21.95 (978-1-57003-970-6(4)); (ENG., Illus.). 304p. 19.95 (978-1-57003-686-6(1)) Univ. of South Carolina Pr.

Botume, Elizabeth H. First Days Amongst the Contrabands. 286p. reprint ed. 98.00 (978-0-7222-9758-2(0)) Library Reprints, Inc.

Brown, Alphonso. A Gullah Guide to Charleston: Walking Through Black History. 2008. (ENG., Illus.). 160p. pap. 12.99 (978-1-59629-392-2(6)) History Pr., The.

Collier, Melvin J. Mississippi to Africa: A Journey of Discovery. 2008. (Illus.). xviii, 279p. pap. 28.00 (978-0-7884-4761-7(0)) Heritage Bks.

Doyle, Barbara, et al. Beyond the Fields: Slavery at Middleton Place. 2008. 80p. pap. 19.95 (978-0-615-20723-0(5)) Univ. of South Carolina Pr.

Felzer, Lissa. The Charleston Freedman's Cottage: An Architectural Tradition. 2008. pap. 19.99 (978-1-59629-286-4(5)) History Pr., The.

Flemming-McCall, Felicia. African Americans of Chesterfield County. 2008. (Images of America Ser.). (ENG., Illus.). 128p. pap. 19.99 (978-0-7385-5434-1(0)) Arcadia Publishing.

Fordham, Damon L. True Stories of Black South Carolina. 2008. (Illus.). 166p. pap., per. 17.99 (978-1-59629-405-9(1)) History Pr., The.

—Voices of Black South Carolina: Legend & Legacy. 2008. (Regional Histories Ser.). 19.99 (978-1-59629-611-4(9)) History Pr., The.

Frazier, Eugene, Sr. A History of James Island Slave Descendants & Plantation Owners: The Blood Line. 2010. 192p. pap. 22.99 (978-1-59629-976-4(2)) History Pr., The.

Frazier, Eugene, Sr. & Frazier, Eugene. James Island: Stories from Slave Descendants. 2006. (Illus.). 218p. pap., per. 24.99 (978-1-59629-182-9(6)) History Pr., The.

Gonzales, Ambrose, ed. The Black Border. 2010. 352p. pap. 19.95 (978-1-4290-2044-2(X)) Applewood Bks.

Hudson, Janet G. Entangled by White Supremacy: Reform in World War I-era South Carolina. 2009. (New Directions in Southern History Ser.). (ENG.). 400p. pap. 50.00 (978-0-8131-9293-2(5)) Univ. Pr. of Kentucky.

Joyner, Charles. Down by the Riverside: A South Carolina Slave Community. 25th anniv. ed. 2009. (ENG.). 408p. pap. 25.00 (978-0-252-07683-1(4)) Univ. of Illinois Pr.

Kiser, Clyde V. Sea Island to City: A Study of St. Helena Islanders in Harlem & Other Urban Centers. (Columbia University, Studies in the Social Sciences: No. 368). reprint ed. 20.00 (978-0-404-51368-9(9)) AMS Pr., Inc.

Mack-Williams, Kibibi. Ahead of Her Time in Yesteryear: Geraldine Pierce Zimmerman Comes of Age in a Southern African American Family. 2010. (ENG., Illus.). 216p. 31.95 (978-1-57233-720-6(6)) Univ. of Tennessee Pr.

Matthews, Harry Bradshaw. African American Journey to Freedom in New York & Related Sites, 1823-1870: Freedom Knows No Color. 2008. (Illus.). 480p. 45.00 (978-0-9799537-4-3(X)); per. 32.00 (978-0-9799537-3-6(1)) Africana Homestead Legacy Pubs., Inc.

Middleton, Earl M. Knowing Who I Am: A Black Entrepreneur's Struggle & Success in the American South. 2008. (Illus.). 183p. 29.95 (978-1-57003-715-3(9)) Univ. of South Carolina Pr.

Mills, Kincaid, et al, eds. Coming Through: Voices of a South Carolina Gullah Community from WPA Oral Histories. 2008. (Illus.). 384p. 29.95 (978-1-57003-721-4(3)) Univ. of South Carolina Pr.

Moore, Winfred B., Jr. & Burton, Orville Vernon, eds. Toward the Meeting of the Waters: Currents in the Civil Rights Movement of South Carolina during the Twentieth Century. 2010. (ENG.). 416p. pap. 29.95 (978-1-57003-971-3(2)) Univ. of South Carolina Pr.

Ryan, William R. The World of Thomas Jeremiah: Charles Town on the Eve of the American Revolution, 1 vol. 2012. (ENG., Illus.). 282p. pap. 24.95 **(978-0-19-992287-1(X))** Oxford Univ. Pr., Inc.

Ryan, William Randolph. The World of Thomas Jeremiah: Charles Town on the Eve of the American Revolution, 1 vol. 2010. (ENG., Illus.). 280p. 49.95 (978-0-19-538728-5(7)) Oxford Univ. Pr., Inc.

Shuler, Jack. Blood & Bone: Truth & Reconciliation in a Southern Town. 2012. (ENG.). 248p. 29.95 **(978-1-61117-048-1(6))** Univ. of South Carolina Pr.

Smith, Daniel M., Jr., text. African-Americans & Charleston: Histories Intertwined. 2010. (Illus.). ix, 113p. **(978-0-615-36805-4(0))** Independent Pub.

Strother, T. Ella. A Pictorial History of African Americans in Aiken County. 2008. (978-1-57864-487-2(9)) Donning Co. Pubs.

Thompson, Marilyn L. Grover C. Thompson Jr. Family Book: Good Stock. 2007. (Illus.). iii, 78p. pap. (978-0-9792823-3-1(0)) Prioritybooks Pubns.

Trinkley, Michael & Hacker, Debi. Shoolbred's Old Settlement: Excavations at 38CH123, Kiawah Island, Charleston County, South Carolina. 2010. (978-1-58317-072-4(3)) Chicora Foundation, Inc.

—A Small Sample of Burials at Randolph Cemetery: What Their Stories Tell Us about the Cemetery & African American Life in Columbia. 2007. (Illus.). 70p. per. 25.00 (978-1-58317-069-4(3)) Chicora Foundation, Inc.

United States. Dept. Of The Treasury. The Negroes at Port Royal Teport of E L Pierce, Government Agent, to the Hon Salmon P Chase, Secretary of the Treasury. 2011. 38p. pap. 11.99 **(978-1-4181-9549-6(9))** MPublishing.

AFRICAN AMERICANS—SOUTHERN STATES

Adelson, Bruce & Baker, Peter. Brushing Back Jim Crow: The Integration of Minor-League Baseball in the American South. 2007. (ENG., Illus.). 275p. per. 14.95 (978-0-8139-2645-2(9)) Univ. Pr. of Virginia.

Alderman, Derek H. & Dwyer, Owen J. Civil Rights Memorials & the Geography of Memory. 2008. (Center Books on the American South Ser.). (ENG., Illus.). 224p. pap. 27.50 (978-1-930066-83-0(X)) Univ. of Georgia Pr.

Ali, Omar H. In the Lion's Mouth: Black Populism in the New South, 1886-1900. 2010. (Margaret Walker Alexander Series in African American Studies). (ENG.). 288p. 55.00 (978-1-60473-778-3(6)) Univ. Pr. of Mississippi.

Arsenault, Raymond. Freedom Riders: 1961 & the Struggle for Racial Justice, 1 vol. 2nd abr. ed. 2011. (ENG., Illus.). 352p. pap. 15.95 (978-0-19-975431-1(4)) Oxford Univ. Pr., Inc.

Battles, David M. The History of Public Library Access for African Americans in the South: Or, Leaving Behind the Plow. 2008. (ENG.). 182p. pap. 50.00 (978-0-8108-6247-0(6)) Scarecrow Pr., Inc.

Berlin, Ira. Slaves Without Masters: The Free Negro in the Antebellum South. 2007. (ENG., Illus.). 428p. per. 18.95 (978-1-59558-173-0(1)) New Pr., The.

Berlin, Ira, et al, eds. Remembering Slavery: African Americans Talk about Their Personal Experiences of Slavery & Emancipation. 2007. (ENG., Illus.). 359p. pap. 29.95 (978-1-59558-228-7(2)) New Pr., The.

Blair, Lewis H. Prosperity of the South Dependent upon the Elevation of the Negro. 147p. reprint ed. 88.00 (978-0-7222-9704-9(1)) Library Reprints, Inc.

Blomquist, Ann K. & Walton-Raji, Angela Y. Black Indian Genealogy Research: African-American Ancestors among the Five Civilized Tribes, an Expanded Edition. 2007. pap. 24.50 (978-0-7884-4474-6(3)) Heritage Bks.

Browder, Glen. The South's New Racial Politics: Inside the Race Game of Southern History. 2009. 128p. pap. 14.95 (978-1-60306-050-9(2), NewSouth Bks.) NewSouth, Inc.

Brown, David & Webb, Clive. Race in the American South: From Slavery to Civil Rights. 2007. (ENG.). 384p. per. 24.95 (978-0-8130-3203-0(2)) Univ. Pr. of Florida.

Brown, Leslie & Valk, Anne. Living with Jim Crow: African American Women & Memories of the Segregated South. 2010. (Palgrave Studies in Oral History Ser.). (ENG., Illus.). 228p. 95.00 (978-0-230-61962-3(2)); pap. 29.00 (978-0-230-62152-7(X)) Palgrave Macmillan.

Brown, Nikki L. M. & Stentiford, Barry M. The Jim Crow Encyclopedia: Greenwood Milestones in African American History, 2 vols. Brown, Nikki L. M. & Stentiford, Barry M., eds. 2008. (Greenwood Milestones in African American History Ser.). (Illus.). 952p. 225.00 (978-0-313-34181-6(8), GR4181) Greenwood Publishing Group, Inc.

Brown, Sterling Allen. A Negro Looks at the South. Tidwell, John Edgar & Sanders, Mark A., eds. 2007. (ENG., Illus.). 400p. 40.00 (978-0-19-531399-4(2)) Oxford Univ. Pr., Inc.

Brown, William Wells. The Negro in the American Rebellion: His Heroism & His Fidelity. 2010. 394p. pap. 33.75 (978-1-145-72653-6(4)) BiblioBazaar.

—The Negro in the American Rebellion: His Heroism & His Fidelity. 2010. 402p. pap. 27.96 (978-1-163-29397-3(0)) 2010. 402p. 39.96

(978-1-163-55358-8(7)) 2007. (ENG.). 400p. 49.95 (978-0-548-26264-1(0)) 2007. (ENG.). 404p. per. 34.95 (978-1-4326-6669-9(X)) Kessinger Publishing, LLC.

—The Negro in the American Rebellion: His heroism & his Fidelity. 2010. (ENG.). 402p. pap. 34.75 (978-1-171-71825-3(X)) BiblioBazaar.

—The Negro in the American Rebellion; His Heroism & His Fidelity. 2006. 400p. per. 26.99 (978-1-4255-4224-5(7)) MPublishing.

Bullock, Charles S. & Gaddie, Ronald Keith. The Triumph of Voting Rights in the South. 2009. (ENG.). 448p. (C). 55.00 (978-0-8061-4079-7(8)) Univ. of Oklahoma Pr.

Burgess, M. Elaine. Negro Leadership in a Southern City. 2011. 244p. 46.95 **(978-1-258-08912-2(2))** Literary Licensing, LLC.

—Negro Leadership in a Southern City. 2011. (ENG.). 246p. pap. 40.00 **(978-0-8078-9631-0(4))** Univ. of North Carolina Pr.

Chafe, William H., et al, eds. Remembering Jim Crow: African Americans Tell about Life in the Segregated South. 2008. (ENG.). 346p. pap. 19.95 (978-1-59558-334-5(3)) New Pr., The.

Cole, Stephanie & Ring, Natalie J., eds. The Folly of Jim Crow: Rethinking the Segregated South. 2012. (Walter Prescott Webb Memorial Lectures, published for the University of Texas At Ser.). (Illus.). 256p. 30.00 **(978-1-60344-582-5(X))** Texas A&M Univ. Pr.

Cole, Stephanie, et al. The Folly of Jim Crow: Rethinking the Segregated South. 2012. E-Book **(978-1-60344-661-7(3))** Texas A&M Univ. Pr.

Cook, Robert J. Troubled Commemoration: The American Civil War Centennial, 1961-1965. 2007. (Making the Modern South Ser.). 300p. 45.00 (978-0-8071-3227-2(6)) Louisiana State Univ. Pr.

Dattel, Gene. Cotton & Race in the Making of America: The Human Costs of Economic Power. 2011. (ENG., Illus.). 432p. pap. 18.95 **(978-1-56663-968-2(9))** Dee, Ivan R. Pub.

Deutsch, Stephanie. You Need a Schoolhouse. 2011. (ENG.). 244p. 24.95 (978-0-8101-2790-6(3)) Northwestern Univ. Pr.

Ernest, John, ed. My Southern Home: The South & Its People. 2011. (ENG., Illus.). 288p. 69.95 (978-0-8078-3511-1(0)); pap. 27.95 (978-0-8078-7208-6(3)) Univ. of North Carolina Pr.

Evans, William McKee. Open Wound: The Long View of Race in America. 2009. (ENG.). 344p. 35.95 (978-0-252-03427-5(9)) Univ. of Illinois Pr.

Farmer-Kaiser, Mary. Freedwomen & the Freedmen's Bureau: Race, Gender, & Public Policy in the Age of Emancipation. 4th ed. 2010. (Reconstructing America Ser.). (ENG.). 256p. pap. 28.00 (978-0-8232-3212-3(3)) Fordham Univ. Pr.

Feimster, Crystal N. Southern Horrors: Women & the Politics of Rape & Lynching. (Illus.). 336p. 2011. (ENG.). pap. 19.95 (978-0-674-06185-9(3)) 2009. 37.00 (978-0-674-03562-1(3)) Harvard Univ. Pr.

Feldman, Glenn. The Disfranchisement Myth: Poor Whites & Suffrage Restriction in Alabama. 2010. (ENG.). 328p. pap. 24.95 (978-0-8203-3510-0(X)) Univ. of Georgia Pr.

Fluker, Walter Earl. Black Leaders & Ideologies in the South: Resistance & Non-Violence. King, Preston, ed. 2007. 240p. 39.95 (978-0-415-46364-5(5)) Routledge.

Fortune, T. Thomas. Black & White: Land, Labor, & Politics in the South. 2007. (ENG.). 256p. pap. 16.99 (978-0-7432-9104-0(2), Washington Square Pr.) Washington Square Pr.

Fountain, Daniel L. Slavery, Civil War, & Salvation: African American Slaves & Christianity, 1830-1870. 2010. (Conflicting Worlds: New Dimensions of the American Civil War Ser.). 184p. 36.00 (978-0-8071-3699-7(9)) Louisiana State Univ. Pr.

Gilmore, James Roberts. My Southern Friends. 2009. 184p. pap. (978-0-217-51411-8(1)) Books LLC.

Griffin, John Howard. Black Like Me. 50th anniv. ed. 2010. (ENG.). 208p. (gr. 12). 7.99 (978-0-451-23421-6(9), Signet) Penguin Group (USA) Inc.

Griffin, John Howard. Black Like Me: 50th Anniversary Edition. 3rd ed. 2011. (ENG., Illus.). 224p. 24.95 **(978-0-916727-68-0(8))** Wings Pr.

Harlan, Louis R. Separate & Unequal: Public School Campaigns & Racism in the Southern Seaboard States, 1901-1915. 2011. (ENG.). 304p. pap. 40.00 (978-0-8078-6758-7(6)) Univ. of North Carolina Pr.

Harold, Claudrena N. The Rise & Fall of the Garvey Movement in the Urban South, 1918-1942. 2007. (Studies in African American History & Culture). (Illus.). 171p. 120.00 (978-0-415-95619-2(6)) Routledge.

Hood, M. V., et al. The Rational Southerner: Black Mobilization, Republican Growth, & the Partisan Transformation of the American South. 2012. (ENG., Illus.). 240p. 39.95 **(978-0-19-987382-1(8))** Oxford Univ. Pr., Inc.

Hume, Richard L. & Gough, Jerry B. Blacks, Carpetbaggers, & Scalawags: The Constitutional Conventions of Radical Reconstruction. 2009. (C). (978-0-8071-3324-8(8)) Louisiana State Univ. Pr.

Hurt, R. Douglas, ed. & intro. African American Life in the Rural South, 1900-1950. 2011. (ENG., Illus.). 240p. (C). (gr. 13). pap. 30.00 (978-0-8262-1960-2(8)) Univ. of Missouri Pr.

Irons, Charles F. The Origins of Proslavery Christianity: White & Black Evangelicals in Colonial & Antebellum Virginia. 2008. (ENG., Illus.). 352p. 66.50 (978-0-8078-3194-6(8)); 384p. pap. 27.95 (978-0-8078-5877-6(3)) Univ. of North Carolina Pr.

Jackson, Antoinette T. Speaking for the Enslaved: Heritage Interpretation at Antebellum Plantation Sites. 2012. **(978-1-59874-550-4(6))**; **(978-1-61132-618-5(4))** Left Coast Pr., Inc.

Jackson, Antoinette T. Speaking for the Enslaved: Heritage Interpretation at Antebellum Plantation Sites. 2012. (Heritage, Tourism & Community Ser.). (ENG.). 216p. pap. 32.95 **(978-1-59874-549-8(2))**; (Illus.). 94.00 **(978-1-59874-548-1(4))** Left Coast Pr., Inc.

Jackson, David H. Booker T. Washington & the Struggle Against White Supremacy: The Southern Educational Tours, 1908-1912. 2008. (ENG., Illus.). 288p. 89.00 (978-0-230-60652-4(0)) Palgrave Macmillan.

Jackson, David H., Jr. Booker T. Washington & the Struggle against White Supremacy: The Southern Educational Tours, 1908-1912. 2009. (ENG.). 272p. pap. 32.00 (978-0-230-62138-1(4)) Palgrave Macmillan.

James, Hunter. They Didn't Put That on the Huntley-Brinkley! A Vagabond Reporter Encounters the New South. 2008. (ENG.). 320p. pap. 24.95 (978-0-8203-3192-8(9)) Univ. of Georgia Pr.

Kinshasa, Kwando Mbiassi. Black Resistance to the Ku Klux Klan in the Wake of Civil War. alt. ed. 2008. (ENG., Illus.). 262p. pap. 39.95 (978-0-7864-4100-6(3)) McFarland & Co., Inc. Pubs.

Kly, Yussuf Naim. The Invisible War: The African-American War of Liberation, 1739-1858. 2006. (Illus.). 192p. per. 14.95 (978-0-932863-50-8(7)) Clarity Pr., Inc.

Lawson, R. A. Jim Crow's Counterculture: The Blues & Black Southerners, 1890-1945. 2010. (Making the Modern South Ser.). (Illus.). 328p. 45.00 (978-0-8071-3680-5(8)) Louisiana State Univ. Pr.

Lewis, Hylan. Blackways of Kent. 2008. (Southern Classics (Univ of South Carolina) Ser.). (ENG., Illus.). 336p. pap. 16.95 (978-1-57003-725-2(6)) Univ. of South Carolina Pr.

Litwack, Leon F. How Free Is Free? The Long Death of Jim Crow. 2009. (Nathan I. Huggins Lectures). 208p. 21.00 (978-0-674-03152-4(0)) Harvard Univ. Pr.

Minchin, Timothy J. From Rights to Economics: The Ongoing Struggle for Black Equality in the U. S. South. 2007. (New Perspectives on the History of the South Ser.). (ENG., Illus.). 224p. 39.95 (978-0-8130-3092-0(7)) Univ. Pr. of Florida.

Murch, Donna. Living for the City: Migration, Education, & the Rise of the Black Panther Party in Oakland, California. 2010. (John Hope Franklin Series in African American History & Culture Ser.). (ENG., Illus.). 344p. 65.00 (978-0-8078-3376-6(2)); pap. 22.95 (978-0-8078-7113-3(3)) Univ. of North Carolina Pr.

Murphy, Edgar G. Problems of the Present South. 335p. reprint ed. 98.00 (978-0-7222-9734-6(3)) Library Reprints, Inc.

Norris, Hoke. We Dissent. 2009. 146p. pap. (978-1-150-79263-2(9)) Books LLC.

Odum, Howard W. Social & Mental Traits of the Negro. (Columbia University, Studies in the Social Sciences: No. 99). reprint ed. 29.50 (978-0-404-51099-2(X)) AMS Pr., Inc.

—Social & Mental Traits of the Negro. 302p. reprint ed. 98.00 (978-0-7222-9738-4(6)) Library Reprints, Inc.

Perdue, Theda. Race & the Atlanta Cotton States Exposition Of 1895. (Georgia Southern University Jack N. & Addie D. Averitt Lecture Ser.). (ENG., Illus.). 2011. 220p. pap. 24.95 **(978-0-8203-4035-7(9))** 2010. 128p. lib. bdg. 26.95 (978-0-8203-3402-8(2)) Univ. of Georgia Pr.

Riser, R. Volney. Defying Disfranchisement: Black Voting Rights Activism in the Jim Crow South, 1890-1908. 2010. 344p. 40.00 (978-0-8071-3638-6(7)) Louisiana State Univ. Pr.

Robinson, Charles Frank, II. Dangerous Liaisons: Sex & Love in the Segregated South. 2006. 196p. per. 19.95 (978-1-55728-833-2(X)) Univ. of Arkansas Pr.

Salmond, John A. A Southern Rebel: The Life & Times of Aubrey Willis Williams, 1890-1965. 2011. (ENG.). 351p. pap. 50.00 **(978-0-8078-9770-6(1))** Univ. of North Carolina Pr.

Sharpless, Rebecca. Cooking in Other Women's Kitchens: Domestic Workers in the South, 1865-1960. 2010. (John Hope Franklin Series in African American History & Culture Ser.). (ENG., Illus.). 304p. 35.00 (978-0-8078-3432-9(7)) Univ. of North Carolina Pr.

Skerritt, Andrew J. Ashamed to Die: Silence, Denial, & the AIDS Epidemic in the South. 2011. (ENG., Illus.). 320p. 24.95 (978-1-56976-814-3(5), Hill, Lawrence Bks.) Chicago Review Pr., Inc.

Stetson, George Rochford. The Southern Negro As He Is by G R S , Boston. 2011. 34p. pap. 11.99 **(978-1-4181-9401-7(8))** MPublishing.

Thomas, A. C. The Color of Success: Growing up black never stopped one man from Winning. 2007. pap. (978-0-9797103-0-8(8)) Algus Publishing.

Thomas, Kenneth. The Religious Dancing of American Slaves, 1820-1865: Spiritual Ecstasy at Baptisms, Funerals, & Sunday Meetings. 2008. 148p. 99.95 (978-0-7734-4926-8(4)) Mellen, Edwin Pr., The.

Waldrep, Christopher & Nieman, Donald G., eds. Local Matters: Race, Crime, & Justice in the Nineteenth-Century South. 2011. (Studies in the Legal History of the South Ser.). (ENG.). 264p. pap. 24.95 **(978-0-8203-4081-4(2))** Univ. of Georgia Pr.

Walton-Raji, Angela Y. Black Indian Genealogy Research: African-American Ancestors among the Five Civilized Tribes, an Expanded Edition. 2007. pap. 24.50 (978-0-7884-4473-9(5)) Heritage Bks.

Washington, Booker T. & Du Bois, W. E. B. The Negro in the South: His Economic Progress in Relation to His. 2007. pap. 24.95 (978-1-4304-5276-8(5)) Kessinger Publishing, LLC.

Wendt, Simon. The Spirit & the Shotgun: Armed Resistance & the Struggle for Civil Rights. (New Perspectives on the History of the South Ser.). (ENG., Illus.). 304p. 2010. pap. 29.95 (978-0-8130-3565-9(1)) 2007. 39.95 (978-0-8130-3018-0(8)) Univ. Pr. of Florida.

Wiethaus, Ulrike & Parent, Anthony S. Trauma & Resilience in American Indian & African American Southern History. 2012. **(978-1-4331-1186-0(1))**; E-Book **(978-1-4539-0267-7(8))** Lang, Peter Publishing, Inc.

AFRICAN AMERICANS—TENNESSEE

Baker, John F., Jr. The Washingtons of Wessyngton Plantation: Stories of My Family's Journey to Freedom. 2010. (ENG., Illus.). 432p. pap. 16.00 (978-1-4165-6741-7(0), Beyond Words/Atria Bks.) Atria Bks.

Butler, Devora E. African AMER in Rutherford County. 2009. 128p. pap. 21.99 (978-0-7385-6636-8(5)) Arcadia Publishing.

DeCosta-Willis, Miriam. Notable Black Memphians. 2008. 460p. 139.95 (978-1-60497-505-5(9)) Cambria Pr.

Dowdy, G. Wayne. Crusades for Freedom: Memphis & the Political Transformation of the American South. 2010. (ENG., Illus.). 176p. 45.00 (978-1-60473-423-2(X)) Univ. Pr. of Mississippi.

Elkington, John. Beale Street: Resurrecting the Home of the Blues. 2008. 25.99 (978-1-59629-492-9(2)) History Pr., The.

Hubbard, Rita Lorraine. African Americans of Chattanooga: A History of Unsung Heroes. 2007. (Illus.). 155p. pap., per. 19.99 (978-1-59629-315-1(2)) History Pr., The.

Lee, George W. Beale Street: Where the Blues Began. (Illus.). 296p. reprint ed. lib. bdg. 98.00 (978-0-7222-0471-9(X)) Library Reprints, Inc.

Reed, Wornie. Blacks in Tennessee: Past & Present. rev. ed. 2008. (ENG., Illus.). 288p. pap. 58.52 (978-0-7575-5107-9(6)) Kendall Hunt Publishing Co.

AFRICAN AMERICANS—TEXAS

Abernethy, Francis Edward, et al, eds. Juneteenth Texas: Essays in African-American Folklore. 2010. (Publications of the Texas Folklore Society Ser.). (ENG.). 376p. pap. 29.95 (978-1-57441-283-3(3)) Univ. of North Texas Pr.

Andrews, Lee. Family Destiny: Get Faith to Take Your Family Places! 2007. (Illus.). 44p. 6.99 (978-0-9797126-0-9(2)) Andrews, Lee.

Barr, Alwyn. Blacks in East Texas History: Selections from the East Texas Historical Journal. Glasrud, Bruce A. & McDonald, Archie P., eds. 2008. (ENG.). 208p. 29.95 (978-1-60344-041-7(0)) Texas A&M Univ. Pr.

Campbell, Randolph B., ed. The Laws of Slavery in Texas: Historical Documents & Essays. 2011. (ENG.). 192p. pap. 19.95 (978-0-292-72899-8(9)) Univ. of Texas Pr.

Crouch, Barry. The Dance of Freedom: Texas African Americans During Reconstruction. Madaras, Larry, ed. 2007. (Jack & Doris Smothers Series in Texas History, Life, & Culture: No. 19). (ENG.). 286p. mass mkt. 25.00 (978-0-292-71487-8(4)) Univ. of Texas Pr.

Farrington, Clifford. Biracial Unions on Galveston's Waterfront, 1865-1925. 2007. (ENG., Illus.). 300p. 29.95 (978-0-87611-217-5(3)) Texas State Historical Assn.

Friends of the Pflugerville Library, compiled by. Pflugerville: A Heritage to Remember. 2006. per. 15.00 (978-0-9702646-6-4(6)) New Sweden Pr.

Glasrud, Bruce A., ed. African Americans in South Texas History. 2011. (Perspectives on South Texas, sponsored by Texas A&M University-Kingsville Ser.). (Illus.). 496p. (C). 45.00 (978-1-60344-228-2(6)); pap. 23.00 (978-1-60344-229-9(4)) Texas A&M Univ. Pr.

Glasrud, Bruce A., et al, eds. Slavery to Integration: Black Americans in West Texas. 2008. (ENG., Illus.). 168p. pap. 21.95 (978-1-933337-26-5(5)) State Hse. Pr.

Glasrud, Bruce A. & Pitre, Merline, eds. Black Women in Texas History. 2008. (Centennial Series of the Association of Former Students, Texas AandM University: No. 108). (ENG.). 256p. 40.00 (978-1-60344-007-3(0)) Texas A&M Univ. Pr.

—Black Women in Texas History. 2008. (Centennial Series of the Association of Former Students, Texas AandM University). (ENG.). 256p. 19.95 (978-1-60344-031-8(3)) Texas A&M Univ. Pr.

Glasrud, Bruce A., et al. African Americans in Corpus Christi. 2012. (Images of America Ser.). (ENG., Illus.). 128p. pap. 21.99 **(978-0-7385-8528-4(9))** Arcadia Publishing.

Goldstone, Dwonna. Integrating the 40 Acres: The Fifty-Year Struggle for Racial Equality at the University of Texas. (ENG.). 232p. 2012. pap. 24.95 **(978-0-8203-4085-2(5))** 2006. (Illus.). 29.95 (978-0-8203-2828-7(6)) Univ. of Georgia Pr.

Hall, Ron & Moore, Denver. Same Kind of Different As Me: A Modern-Day Slave, an International Art Dealer, & the Unlikely Woman Who Bound Them Together. l.t. ed. 2010. (ENG.). 448p. pap. 17.99 (978-1-59415-318-1(3)) Cengage Gale.

—Same Kind of Different As Me: A Modern-Day Slave, an International Art Dealer, & the Unlikely Woman Who Bound Them Together, 0 vols. 2008. 256p. pap. 15.99 (978-0-8499-1910-7(X)) Nelson, Thomas Inc.

—Same Kind of Different As Me: A Modern-Day Slave, an International Art Dealer, & the Unlikely Woman Who Bound Them Together. l.t. ed. 2010. (ENG.). 440p. 30.95 (978-1-4104-2456-3(1)) Thorndike Pr.

Hall, Ron, et al. What Difference Do It Make? Stories of Hope & Healing, 0 vols. 2010. 224p. pap. 15.99 (978-0-8499-4619-6(0)) Nelson, Thomas Inc.

House, James. Through My Eyes: An Explorative of the Northern Brother. 2011. 80p. pap. 10.95 **(978-1-4620-4495-5(6))** iUniverse, Inc.

Jordan, Alonzo. Jasper, Texas: The Community Photographs, 1 vol. 2011. (ENG., Illus.). 240p. 65.00 (978-3-86930-151-8(1)) Steidl, Gerhard Druckerei und Verlag DEU. Dist: Innovative Logistics.

Lavergne, Gary M. Before Brown: Heman Marion Sweatt, Thurgood Marshall, & the Long Road to Justice. 2011. (ENG., Illus.). 384p. pap. 25.00 **(978-0-292-74295-6(9))** Univ. of Texas Pr.

Lawe, Gwendolyn McMillan. From Wolf to Wolfwood: A Genealogical & Historical Study of the Mcmillans & the African American Communities of Emory, Texas. 2011. 196p. 24.59 (978-1-4567-2656-0(0)); pap. 14.99 (978-1-4567-2654-6(4), AuthorHouse.

Laws, Anthony. Honoring Our Fathers: Celebrating a Man's Role in His Family & Community. 2009. 200p. pap. 16.95 (978-1-934812-47-1(1)) Brown Bks. Publishing Group.

Littlejohn, Calvin & Sanders, Bob Ray. Calvin Littlejohn: Portrait of a Community in Black & White. 2009. (ENG., Illus.). 216p. 29.95 (978-0-87565-381-5(2)) Texas Christian Univ. Pr.

McDonald, Jason. Racial Dynamics in Early Twentieth-Century Austin, Texas. 2012. (ENG.). 408p. (gr. 17). 90.00 **(978-0-7391-7097-7(X))** Lexington Bks.

McElroy, Njoki. 1012 Natchez: A Memoir of Joy, Harship, & Love. 2010. 216p. pap. 14.95 (978-1-934812-55-6(2)) Brown Bks. Publishing Group.

Mears, Michelle M. And Grace Will Lead Me Home: African American Freedmen Communities of Austin, Texas, 1865-1928. 2009. (Illus.). 256p. 45.00 (978-0-89672-654-3(1)) Texas Tech Univ. Pr.

Minutaglio, Bill. In Search of the Blues: A Journey to the Soul of Black Texas. 2010. (ENG., Illus.). 183p. 50.00 (978-0-292-72247-7(8)); pap. 24.95 (978-0-292-72289-7(3)) Univ. of Texas Pr.

Reid, Debra Ann. Reaping a Greater Harvest: African Americans, the Extension Service, & Rural Reform in Jim Crow Texas. 2007. (Sam Rayburn Series on Rural Life: No. 14). (ENG., Illus.). 328p. 39.95 (978-1-58544-571-4(1)) Texas A&M Univ. Pr.

Smallwood, James M. & Glasrud, Bruce A., eds. The African American Experience in Texas: An Anthology. 2007. (Illus.). 384p. per. 40.00 (978-0-89672-609-3(6)) Texas Tech Univ. Pr.

Williams, Miriam F. From Black Codes to Recodification: Removing the Veil from Regulatory Writing. 2010. v, 161p. 39.95 (978-0-89503-376-5(3)) Baywood Publishing Co., Inc.

AFRICAN AMERICANS—UNITED STATES

see African Americans

AFRICAN AMERICANS—VIRGINIA

Alexandria Library. Virginia Slave Births Index, 1853-1865, Volume 2, D-G. 2007. pap. 39.00 (978-0-7884-4333-6(X)) Heritage Bks.

—Virginia Slave Births Index, 1853-1865, Volume 3, H-L. 2007. pap. 41.00 (978-0-7884-4334-3(8)) Heritage Bks.

—Virginia Slave Births Index, 1853-1865, Volume 5, S-Z. 2007. pap. 50.00 (978-0-7884-4496-8(4)) Heritage Bks.

Baker, Kyle. Nat Turner. 2008. (ENG., Illus.). 208p. pap. 14.95 (978-0-8109-7227-8(1)) Abrams.

Boyd-Rush, Dorothy A. Register of Free Blacks, Rockingham County, Virginia, 1807-1859. 2008. 252p. (Orig.). pap. 23.50 (978-1-55613-658-0(7)) Heritage Bks.

Brewer, James H. The Confederate Negro: Virginia's Craftsmen & Military Laborers, 1861-1865. 2007. (ENG., Illus.). 238p. pap. 29.95 (978-0-8173-5486-2(7)) Univ. of Alabama Pr.

Bruce, Philip A. The Plantation Negro As a Freeman: Observations on His Character, Condition, & Prospects in Virginia. 262p. reprint ed. 98.00 (978-0-7222-9706-3(8)) Library Reprints, Inc.

Casper, Scott E. Sarah Johnson's Mount Vernon: The Forgotten History of an American Shrine. 2010. 286p. (C). 25.00 (978-1-4379-7307-5(8)) DIANE Publishing Co.

—Sarah Johnson's Mount Vernon: The Forgotten History of an American Shrine. 2009. (ENG., Illus.). 320p. pap. 24.00 (978-0-8090-8415-9(5), Hill & Wang) Farrar, Straus & Giroux.

Cruise, M. T. W. The Truth Is the Light If It's Told in the Dark, 1. 2007. (Illus.). 171p. per. 24.95 (978-0-9790433-0-7(1), 200) Cruise, M. T. W.

Denkler, Ann. Sustaining Identity, Recapturing Heritage: Exploring Issues of Public History, Tourism, & Race in a Southern Rural Town. 2007. (ENG., Illus.). 138p. 57.99 (978-0-7391-1991-4(5)) Lexington Bks.

Diehl, Huston. Dream Not of Other Worlds: Teaching in a Segregated Elementary School,1970. 2007. (Sightline Bks.). (Illus.). 276p. 24.95 (978-0-87745-996-5(7)) Univ. of Iowa Pr.

Duncan, Patricia B. Fairfax County, Virginia, Birth Register. 2010. pap. **(978-0-7884-5240-6(1))** Heritage Bks.

Duncan, Patricia B. Fauquier County, Virginia, Birth Register, 2 vols. 2008. pap. (978-0-7884-4186-8(8)); pap. 32.50 (978-0-7884-4185-1(X)) Heritage Bks.

Dusinberre, William. Strategies for Survival: Recollections of Bondage in Antebellum Virginia. 2009. (Carter G. Woodson Institute Ser.). (ENG., Illus.). 264p. (gr. 17). 40.00 (978-0-8139-2822-7(2)) Univ. Pr. of Virginia.

Hizer, Trenton E. Guide to the Personal Papers Collections at the Library of Virginia. 2008. (978-0-88490-208-9(0)) Library of Virginia, The.

Holloway, Pippa. Sexuality, Politics, & Social Control in Virginia, 1920-1945. 2006. (ENG.). 272p. 69.95 (978-0-8078-3051-2(8)); per. 22.00 (978-0-8078-5764-9(5)) Univ. of North Carolina Pr.

Irons, Charles F. The Origins of Proslavery Christianity: White & Black Evangelicals in Colonial & Antebellum Virginia. 2008. (ENG., Illus.). 384p. pap. 27.95 (978-0-8078-5877-6(3)) Univ. of North Carolina Pr.

Jackson, Lawrence Patrick. My Father's Name: A Black Virginia Family after the Civil War. 2012. (ENG., Illus.). 272p. 25.00 **(978-0-226-38949-3(9))** Univ. of Chicago Pr.

Jones, Carla J. & Hull, Tonya M. African Americans of Giles County. 2010. (Images of America Ser.). (ENG., Illus.). 128p. pap. 21.99 (978-0-7385-6689-4(6)) Arcadia Publishing.

Jones, Col Lafayette. My Great, Great, Grandfather's Journey to an Island of Freedom in the Middle of Slavery. 2007. (Illus.). xvi, 119p. pap. *(978-0-615-22337-7(0))* Jenlaf.

Jones, Hugh. The Present State of Virginia. (Illus.). 151p. reprint ed. lib. bdg. 88.00 *(978-0-7222-0927-1(4))* Library Reprints, Inc.

Lane, Sr. For Whites Only? How & Why America Became a Racist Nation: Second Edition. 2008. 452p. pap. 34.95 *(978-1-4343-8480-5(2))* AuthorHouse.

McConnell, John P. Negroes & Their Treatment in Virginia from 1865-1867. (Illus.). 126p. reprint ed. lib. bdg. 88.00 *(978-0-7222-4635-1(8))* Library Reprints, Inc.

McLeRoy, Sherrie & McLeRoy, William. Strangers in Their Midst: The Free Black Population of Amherst County, Virginia. 2007. (Illus.). viii, 317p. pap. *(978-0-7884-4373-2(9))* Heritage Bks.

Miller, Terry & Braxton, Roger. African Americans of Spotsylvania County. 2008. (Images of America Ser.). (ENG., Illus.). 128p. pap. 21.99 *(978-0-7385-5353-5(0))* Arcadia Publishing.

Morales, Leslie Anderson & Valaitis, Ada. Virginia Slave Births Index, 1853-1865. 2007. pap. 45.00 *(978-2-07-884445-8(4))* Heritage Bks.

Morales, Leslie Anderson, et al. Virginia Slave Births Index, 1853-1865. 2007. pap. 45.00 *(978-0-7884-4453-1(0))* Heritage Bks.

Morton, Richard L. The Negro in Virginia Politics, 1865-1902. 199p. reprint ed. lib. bdg. 88.00 *(978-0-7222-4679-5(X))* Library Reprints, Inc.

Nichols, Brenda Dabney. African Americans of Henrico County. 2010. (Images of America Ser.). (ENG., Illus.). 128p. pap. 21.99 *(978-0-7385-6650-4(0))* Arcadia Publishing.

Norris, James E. C. Fight on, My Soul. 2009. (Illus.). 328p. pap. 14.95 *(978-0-9800084-6-3(8))* Write Place, The.

Richardson, Selden. Built by Blacks: African American Architecture & Neighborhoods in Richmond. Duke, Maurice, ed. 2008. (Illus.). 192p. pap. 19.99 *(978-1-59629-459-2(0))* History Pr., The.

Ruffin, Bernard. Norfolk, Virginia, Registry of Free Negroes, 1835-1861: Abstracts. 2010. 206p. ***(978-0-7884-8432-2(X))*** Heritage Bks.

Ruffin, C. Bernard. Norfolk, Virginia Registry of Free Negroes, 1835-1861, Abstracts. 2010. pap. 23.00 *(978-0-7884-5014-3(X))* Heritage Bks.

Russell, John H. The Free Negro in Virginia, Sixteen Nineteen to Eighteen Sixty-Five. (Johns Hopkins University. Studies in the Social Sciences, Thirtieth Ser.: 3). reprint ed. 32.50 *(978-0-404-61194-1(X))* AMS Pr., Inc.

Tillson, Albert H. Accommodating Revolutions: Virginia's Northern Neck in an Era of Transformations, 1760-1810. 2010. (ENG., Illus.). 432p. (gr. 17). 45.00 *(978-0-8139-2845-6(1))* Univ. Pr. of Virginia.

Tyler-McGraw, Marie. An African Republic: Black & White Virginians in the Making of Liberia. 2007. (ENG., Illus.). 264p. 39.95 *(978-0-8078-3167-0(0))* Univ. of North Carolina Pr.

Williams, Ida J., compiled by. A History of Education for African Americans During the Segregation Period, 1886 through 1970 in Northampton County, Virginia. 2007. (Illus.). 100p. per. 18.00 *(978-1-60126-036-9(9))* Masthof Pr.

Wolf, Eva Sheppard. Race & Liberty in the New Nation: Emancipation in Virginia from the Revolution to Nat Turner's Rebellion. 2006. (Illus.). 284p. 45.00 *(978-0-8071-3194-7(6))* Louisiana State Univ. Pr.

AFRICAN AMERICANS—WASHINGTON (D.C.)

Dale, Dianne. The Village That Shaped Us: Oen Woman's History of Anacostia. 2011. (Illus.). 328p. 29.95 ***(978-1-888018-41-7(0))*** KA Productions, LLC.

Goosman, Stuart L. Group Harmony: The Black Urban Roots of Rhythm & Blues. 2010. (Illus.). 304p. (C). pap. 24.95 *(978-0-8122-2108-4(7))* Univ. of Pennsylvania Pr.

Hopkinson, Natalie. Go-Go Live: The Musical Life & Death of a Chocolate City. 2012. (ENG., Illus.). 232p. 79.95 ***(978-0-8223-5200-6(1))***; pap. 22.95 ***(978-0-8223-5211-2(7))*** Duke Univ. Pr.

Hynson, Jerry M. The African American Collection: Anne Arundel County, Maryland Marriage Licenses, 1865-1888. 2007. pap. 17.00 *(978-0-7884-3839-4(5))* Heritage Bks.

—The African American Collection , Indentures, Cecil County, Maryland 1777-1814. 2007. pap. 12.00 *(978-0-7884-4112-7(4))* Heritage Bks.

Ingle, Edward. The Negro in the District of Columbia. (Johns Hopkins University. Studies in the Social Sciences, Thirtieth Ser.: 3-4). reprint ed. 27.50 *(978-0-404-61081-4(1))* AMS Pr., Inc.

Lacy, Karyn. Blue-Chip Black: Race, Class, & Status in the New Black Middle Class. 2007. (Illus.). 281p. per. 26.95 *(978-0-520-25116-8(4))* Univ. of California Pr.

Lacy, Karyn R. Blue-Chip Black: Race, Class, & Status in the New Black Middle Class. 2007. (Illus.). 281p. 60.00 *(978-0-520-25115-1(6))* Univ. of California Pr.

Lornell, Kip & Stephenson Jr., Charles C. The Beat! Go-Go Music from Washington, D. C. 2009. (American Made Music Ser.). (ENG., Illus.). 304p. pap. 25.00 *(978-1-60473-241-2(5))* Univ. Pr. of Mississippi.

Masur, Kate. An Example for All the Land: Emancipation & the Struggle over Equality in Washington, D. C. 2010. (ENG., Illus.). 376p. 39.95 *(978-0-8078-3414-5(9))* Univ. of North Carolina Pr.

National Museum of African American History and Culture (U.S.) Staff. The Scurlock Studio & Black Washington: Picturing the Promise. 2009. (ENG., Illus.). 224p. 35.00 *(978-1-58834-262-1(X))* Smithsonian Institution Pr.

Singler, Joan, et al. Seattle in Black & White: The Congress of Racial Equality & the Fight for Equal Opportunity. 2011. (ENG., Illus.). 288p. pap. 24.95 *(978-0-295-99084-2(8))* Univ. of Washington Pr.

Valk, Anne M. Radical Sisters: Second-Wave Feminism & Black Liberation in Washington, D. C. 2010. (Women in American History Ser.). (ENG., Illus.). 280p. pap. 25.00 *(978-0-252-07754-8(7))* Univ. of Illinois Pr.

AFRICAN AMERICANS—WEST (U.S.)

Broussard, Albert S. Expectations of Equality: A History of Black Westerners. 2012. pap. ***(978-0-88295-284-0(6))*** Davidson, Harlan Inc.

Flamming, Douglas. African Americans in the West, 1 vol. 2009. (Cultures in the American West Ser.). (Illus.). 353p. 65.00 *(978-1-59884-002-5(9), AFAMWE1C)* ABC-CLIO, LLC.

Gardner, Eric, ed. Jennie Carter: A Black Journalist of the Early West. 2007. (ENG.). 208p. 50.00 *(978-1-934110-10-2(8))* Univ. Pr. of Mississippi.

Glasrud, Bruce A. & Searles, Michael N. Buffalo Soldiers in the West: A Black Soldiers Anthology. 2007. 40.00 *(978-1-58544-612-4(2))* Texas A&M Univ. Pr.

Glasrud, Bruce A. & Searles, Michael N., eds. Buffalo Soldiers in the West: A Black Soldiers Anthology. 2007. (ENG.). 328p. (C). pap. 19.95 *(978-1-58544-620-9(3))* Texas A&M Univ. Pr.

Glasrud, Bruce A. & Wintz, Cary D. The Harlem Renaissance in the American West: The New Negro's Western Experience. 2011. E-Book ***(978-0-203-80558-9(5))*** Routledge.

Martin, S. Rudolph. On the Move: A Black Family's Western Saga. 2009. (Elma Dill Russell Spencer Series in the West & Southwest: No. 32). (ENG., Illus.). 216p. 24.95 *(978-1-60344-104-9(2))* Texas A&M Univ. Pr.

Schubert, Frank. Black Valor: Buffalo Soldiers & the Medal of Honor, 1870 - 1898. 2009. (ENG.). 244p. pap. 19.95 *(978-1-4422-0193-4(2))* Rowman & Littlefield Publishers, Inc.

Schubert, Frank N. Voices of the Buffalo Soldier: Records, Reports, & Recollections of Military Life & Service in the West. 2009. (ENG., Illus.). 296p. pap. 24.95 *(978-0-8263-2310-1(3))* Univ. of New Mexico Pr.

Tucker, Phillip Thomas. Cathy Williams: From Slave to Buffalo Soldier. 2008. (ENG., Illus.). 258p. pap. 19.95 *(978-0-8117-3569-8(9))* Stackpole Bks.

AFRICAN AMERICANS—WISCONSIN

Schutz, Mary Ellen, ed. The State of Black Madison 2008: Before the Tipping Point. 2008. 30p. pap. 5.00 *(978-0-615-20703-2(0))* Urban League of Greater Madison.

AFRICAN AMERICANS—WISCONSIN—MILWAUKEE

Aukofer, Frank. City with a Chance: A Case History of Civil Rights Revolution. 2007. *(978-0-87462-021-4(X))* Marquette Univ. Pr.

Jones, Patrick D. The Selma of the North: Civil Rights Insurgency in Milwaukee. 2010. (Illus.). 360p. pap. 22.95 *(978-0-674-05729-6(5))* Harvard Univ. Pr.

Trotter, Joe William, Jr. Black Milwaukee: The Making of an Industrial Proletariat, 1915-45. 2nd ed. 2006. (Illus.). 432p. per. 31.00 *(978-0-252-07410-3(6))* Univ. of Illinois Pr.

AFRICAN AMERICANS AND LIBRARIES

see also African American Librarians

Battles, David M. The History of Public Library Access for African Americans in the South: Or, Leaving Behind the Plow. 2008. (ENG.). 182p. pap. 50.00 *(978-0-8108-6247-0(6))* Scarecrow Pr., Inc.

Graham, Patterson Toby. A Right to Read: Segregation & Civil Rights in Alabama's Public Libraries, 1900-1965. 2006. (ENG., Illus.). 208p. per. 22.00 *(978-0-8173-5371-1(2))* Univ. of Alabama Pr.

Holloway, Karla F. C. Bookmarks: Reading in Black & White. 2008. (ENG.). 240p. pap. 19.95 *(978-0-8135-4351-2(7))* Rutgers Univ. Pr.

—BookMarks: Reading in Black & White. 2006. (ENG., Illus.). 240p. 24.95 *(978-0-8135-3907-2(2))* Rutgers Univ. Pr.

Jackson, Andrew P., et al, eds. The 21st-Century Black Librarian in America. 2012. (ENG., Illus.). 300p. (gr. 17). 80.00 ***(978-0-8108-8245-4(0))*** Scarecrow Pr., Inc.

AFRICAN AMERICANS IN AERONAUTICS

Broadnax, Samuel L. Blue Skies, Black Wings: African American Pioneers of Aviation, 1 vol. 2007. (Illus.). 208p. 44.95 *(978-0-275-99195-1(4), C9195, Praeger Pubs.)* Greenwood Publishing Group, Inc.

AFRICAN AMERICANS IN ART

see also African American Art

Beecroft, Vanessa. VB65 PAC Milano. 2010. (ENG & ITA., Illus.). 120p. pap. 45.00 *(978-88-370-7105-9(1), Mondadori Electa (Acc))* Antique Collectors' Club GBR. Dist: National Bk. Network.

Brown, Iona Rozeal. Iona Rozeal Brown. 2010. (ENG., Illus.). 96p. 45.00 *(978-3-7757-2601-6(2))* Hatje Cantz Verlag GmbH & Co KG DEU. Dist: D.A.P./Distributed Art Pubs.

Coleman, Angela D. Beautiful. Sisterhood Agenda, ed. 2007. (YA). per. *(978-0-9786906-2-5(1))* Sisterhood Agenda Enterprises, LLC.

Hobbs, Robert, et al, contrib. by. Kehinde Wiley. 2012. (ENG., Illus.). 248p. 65.00 ***(978-0-8478-3549-2(9))*** Rizzoli International Pubns., Inc.

Jennings, John & Duffy, Damian. Black Comix: African American Independent Comics, Art & Culture. 2010. (ENG., Illus.). 176p. 45.00 *(978-0-9841906-5-2(1))* Batty, Mark Pub., LLC.

Jones, Ben. Ben Jones: A Retrospective: The Art of the Journey. 2007. per. 39.95 *(978-0-9791130-0-0(8))* Jones, Ben.

Kirschke, Amy H. & Kirschke, Amy Helene. Art in Crisis: W. E. B. du Bois & the Struggle for African American Identity & Memory. 2007. (ENG., Illus.). 296p. pap. 24.95 *(978-0-253-21813-1(6), 0253218136)* Indiana Univ. Pr.

McEvilley, Thomas, et al, texts. Kara Walker: My Complement, My Enemy, My Oppressor, My Love, 1 vol. 2007. (ENG., Illus.). 432p. 49.95 *(978-0-935640-86-1(X))* Walker Art Ctr.

Morgan, Jo-Ann. Uncle Tom's Cabin as Visual Culture. 2007. (ENG., Illus.). 280p. (C). 39.95 *(978-0-8262-1715-8(X))* Univ. of Missouri Pr.

Nama, Adilifu. Super Black: American Pop Culture & Black Superheroes. 2011. (Illus.). 180p. E-Book ***(978-0-292-73545-3(6))***; (ENG.). 200p. 55.00 *(978-0-292-72654-3(6))*; (ENG., 200p. pap. 24.95 *(978-0-292-72674-1(0))* Univ. of Texas Pr.

Powell, Richard J. Cutting a Figure: Fashioning Black Portraiture. 2009. (ENG., Illus.). 296p. 55.00 *(978-0-226-67727-9(3))* Univ. of Chicago Pr.

Rothkopf, Scott. Glenn Ligon: America. 2011. (ENG., Illus.). 304p. 65.00 *(978-0-300-16847-1(0))* Yale Univ. Pr.

Shulman, Ken, ed. Parallel. 2008. *(978-84-96954-38-0(2))* Actar Birkhauser Distribution.

Stephanic, Barbara. Joseph Holston - Color in Freedom: Journey along the Underground Railroad. 2008. 96p. 24.95 *(978-0-7649-4646-2(3))* Pomegranate Communications, Inc.

Sutton, Elizabeth A. Early Modern Dutch Prints of Africa. 2012. (Illus.). 280p. ***(978-1-4094-3970-7(4))*** Ashgate Publishing, Ltd.

Vassel, Rachel. Daughters of Men: Portraits of African-American Women & Their Fathers. 2007. (ENG., Illus.). 192p. 27.95 *(978-0-06-135035-1(4), Amistad)* HarperCollins Pubs.

Walker, Kara. After the Deluge. 2007. (ENG., Illus.). 120p. 29.95 *(978-0-8478-2981-1(2))* Rizzoli International Pubns., Inc.

Walker, Kara, text. Bureau of Refugees. 2008. (ENG., Illus.). 120p. pap. 39.95 *(978-88-8158-686-8(X))* Charta ITA. Dist: D.A.P./Distributed Art Pubs.

Wood, Peter H. Near Andersonville: Winslow Homer's Civil War. 2010. (Nathan I. Huggins Lectures). (Illus.). 152p. 18.95 *(978-0-674-05320-5(6))* Harvard Univ. Pr.

Young, Harvey. Embodying Black Experience: Stillness, Critical Memory, & the Black Body. 2010. (Theater: Theory/Text/Performance Ser.). (ENG., Illus.). 272p. 80.00 *(978-0-472-07111-1(4))*; pap. 32.50 *(978-0-472-05111-3(3))* Univ. of Michigan Pr.

AFRICAN AMERICANS IN BUSINESS

Amenga-Etego, Rose Mary. Mending the Broken Pieces: Indigenous Religion & Sustainable Rural Development in Northern Ghana. 2011. *(978-1-59221-813-4(X))*; (Illus.). 348p. pap. *(978-1-59221-814-1(8))* Africa World Pr.

America, Richard F. & Anderson, Bernard E. Soul in Management: How African-American Managers Thrive in the Competitive Corporate Environment. 2006. 236p. reprint ed. 20.00 *(978-1-4223-5599-2(3))* DIANE Publishing Co.

Andersen, Margaret & Thomas, Neil F. Living Art: The Life of Paul R. Jones, African American Art Collector. 2009. (Illus.). 144p. 32.50 *(978-0-87413-073-7(5))* Univ. of Delaware Pr.

Bandele, Ramla M. Black Star: African American Activism in the International Political Economy. 2008. (ENG., Illus.). 248p. 42.00 *(978-0-252-03339-1(6))* Univ. of Illinois Pr.

Bernard, Michael Todd. How to Be: Success Strategies for the Young, Gifted, & Black. 2007. 97p. pap. 10.95 *(978-0-7414-4126-3(8))* Infinity Publishing.

Bond, Scott. From Slavery to Wealth: The Life of Scott Bond. Gatewood, Willard B., ed. 2008. (Illus.). 284p. per. 19.95 *(978-0-9768007-6-7(4))* Phoenix International, Inc.

Boston, Michael B. The Business Strategy of Booker T. Washington: Its Development & Implementation. 2010. (ENG., Illus.). 308p. 69.95 *(978-0-8130-3473-7(6))* Univ. Pr. of Florida.

Bowman, Bertie. Step by Step: A Memoir of Living the American Dream. 2009. (ENG., Illus.). 224p. pap. 15.00 *(978-0-345-50433-3(X), One World/Ballantine)* Random House Publishing Group.

Bundles, Alelia. Madame C. J. Walker. 2008. (Black Americans of Achievement Legacy Edition Ser.). 112p. (gr. 6-12). 35.00 *(978-1-60413-072-0(5),* Chelsea Hse.) Facts On File, Inc.

Davidson, Wayne. Manufacturing African American Self-Employment. 2008. 292p. pap. *(978-3-639-08502-0(7))* VDM Verlag Dr. Mueller e.K.

Fairlie, Robert W. & Robb, Alicia M. Race & Entrepreneurial Success: Black-, Asian-, & White-Owned Businesses in the United States. 2010. (ENG., Illus.). 256p. (gr. 17). pap. 18.00 *(978-0-262-51494-1(X))* MIT Pr.

Gravely, Melvin J. & Gravely, Melvin J., II. Getting to the Next Level: A Continuing Story of Entrepreneurship: Business, Race & Our Common Goal to Be Competitive. 2007. (Illus.). 111p. 19.95 *(978-0-9656194-9-3(4))* Impact Group Consultants.

Haynes, George E. Negro at Work in New York City. (Columbia University, Studies in the Social Sciences: No. 124). reprint ed. 27.50 *(978-0-404-51124-1(4))* AMS Pr., Inc.

Hightower, et al. School of Business & Industry Superstars: Florida A & M University. 2008. (ENG.). (C). pap. 36.60 *(978-0-555-03657-0(X))* Pearson Learning Solutions.

Holmes, Kevin W. Daddy, I'm the Man You Could Have Been! 2011. 100p. pap. 15.99 ***(978-1-4568-5876-6(9))*** Xlibris Corp.

House-Soremekun, Bessie. Confronting the Odds: African American Entrepreneurship in Cleveland, Ohio. 2009. (Illus.). 250p. pap. *(978-1-60635-006-5(4))* Kent State Univ. Pr.

Howard, Samuel H. The Flight of the Phoenix: Thoughts on Work & Life. 2007. (Illus.). 156p. 24.95 *(978-1-57736-379-8(5))* Providence Hse Pubs.

Hudson, Lynn M. The Making of Mammy Pleasant: A Black Entrepreneur in Nineteenth-Century San Francisco. 2008. (Women in American History Ser.). (ENG., Illus.). 224p. per. 21.00 *(978-0-252-07527-8(7))* Univ. of Illinois Pr.

King, Paul. Reflections on Affirmative Action in Construction. 2009. 292p. 25.99 *(978-1-4389-9565-6(2))*; pap. 15.99 *(978-1-4389-9564-9(4))* AuthorHouse.

Knowling, Bob. You Can Get There from Here: My Journey from Struggle to Success. 2011. (ENG.). 288p. (gr. 12). 26.95 ***(978-1-59184-422-8(3)***, Portfolio (Hardcover)) Penguin Group (USA) Inc.

Lee, Dante. Black Business Secrets: 500 Tips, Strategies, & Resources for the African American Entrepreneurs. 2010. (ENG.). 336p. pap. 15.95 *(978-1-4019-2954-1(0))* Hay Hse., Inc.

Malone, Herman & Schwab, Robert. Lynched by Corporate America: The Gripping True Story of How One African American Survived Doing Business with a Fortune 500 Giant. 2006. 101p. per. 15.95 *(978-0-9785094-4-6(7))*; 19.95 *(978-0-9785094-3-9(9))* HMRS Publishing.

Martin, C. Sunny. Who's Who in Black Atlanta: The Ninth Edition. 2006. (ENG.). 496p. per. 34.95 *(978-1-933879-10-9(6))* Who's Who Publishing Co.

—Who's Who in Black Cleveland: The Third Edition. 3rd ed. 2007. (ENG.). 288p. per. *(978-1-933879-12-3(2))* Who's Who Publishing Co.

—Who's Who in Black Detroit: The Inaugural Edition. 2006. 392p. per. *(978-1-933879-06-2(8))* Who's Who Publishing Co.

—Who's Who in Black Houston: The Inaugural Edition. 2007. (ENG.). 320p. per. 34.95 net. *(978-1-933879-18-5(1))* Who's Who Publishing Co.

—Who's Who in Black Louisville: The Inaugural Edition. 2007. (ENG.). 288p. per. 24.95 net. *(978-1-933879-16-1(5))* Who's Who Publishing Co.

—Who's Who in Black South Florida: The Inaugural Edition. 2007. (ENG.). 320p. per. 24.95 net. *(978-1-933879-20-8(3))* Who's Who Publishing Co.

—Who's Who in Black St. Louis: The Third Edition. 3rd ed. 2006. (ENG.). 272p. per. 24.95 *(978-1-933879-08-6(4))* Who's Who Publishing Co.

Middleton, Earl M. Knowing Who I Am: A Black Entrepreneur's Struggle & Success in the American South. 2008. (Illus.). 183p. 29.95 *(978-1-57003-715-3(9))* Univ. of South Carolina Pr.

Muhammad, Ernest J. 101 Business Ideas for the Blackman. 2006. per. *(978-1-59872-654-1(4))* Instant Pub.

Newbold-Coco, Rain L. Lighting the Way for Success: Mentoring Black Professional Women. 2007. 124p. per. 19.95 *(978-1-4241-7949-7(1))* PublishAmerica, Inc.

Pinkett, Randal, et al. Black Faces in White Places: 10 Game-Changing Strategies to Achieve Success & Find Greatness, 1 vol. 2010. (ENG., Illus.). 288p. 24.95 *(978-0-8144-1680-8(2))* Amacom.

Rogers, W. Sherman. The African American Entrepreneur: Then & Now. 2009. (Illus.). xx, 316p. *(978-0-313-35111-2(2), Praeger Pubs.)* Greenwood Publishing Group, Inc.

Steward, Austin. TwentyTwo Years A Slave & Forty Years. 2006. pap. *(978-1-4068-3051-4(8))* Echo Library.

Taylor, Dashawn. From POVERTY to POWER MOVES (Second Edition) 2007. 176p. per. 15.00 *(978-0-9800154-1-6(3))* Next Level Publishing.

Turner, Sherman L. Minorities Deceived: The Sherman Turner Story Part I. 2010. 108p. 29.49 *(978-1-4520-4388-3(4))*; pap. 19.99 *(978-1-4520-4389-0(2))* AuthorHouse.

Walker, Juliet E. K. The History of Black Business in America: Capitalism, Race, Entrepreneurship: Volume 1, To 1865, 2 vols. 2nd ed. 2009. (ENG., Illus.). 432p. 69.95 *(978-0-8078-3241-7(3))*; pap. 26.95 *(978-0-8078-5910-0(9))* Univ. of North Carolina Pr.

Walton. African-American Managers' Perceptions about Factors That Impact Their Career Development & Job Opportunities. 2008. 80p. pap. 13.49 *(978-1-4343-2281-4(5))* AuthorHouse.

Warren Hill, Laura & Rabig, Julia, eds. The Business of Black Power: Community Development, Capitalism, & Corporate Responsibility in Postwar America. 2012. (Illus.). 336p. 85.00 ***(978-1-58046-403-1(3))*** Univ. of Rochester Pr.

Washington, Booker T. & Du Bois, W. E. B. The Negro in Business: Report of a Social Study Made under the Direction of Atlanta University. (Illus.). reprint ed. 29.50 *(978-0-404-00237-4(4))* AMS Pr., Inc.

Weems, Robert. Business in Black & White: American Presidents & Black Entrepreneurs in the Twentieth Century. 2009. (ENG., Illus.). 352p. 55.00 *(978-0-8147-7517-2(9))* New York Univ. Pr.

Who's Who in Black Detroit: The Inaugural Edition. 2006. *(978-1-933879-07-9(6))* Who's Who Publishing Co.

AFRICAN AMERICANS IN LITERATURE

Acampora, Christa Davis & Cotten, Angela L. Cultural Sites of Critical Insight: Philosophy, Aesthetics, & African American & Native American Women's Writings. Acampora, Christa Davis & Cotten, Angela L., eds. 2007. 216p. per. 29.95 *(978-0-7914-6980-4(8))* State Univ. of New York Pr.

Ahad, Badia Sahar. Freud Upside Down: African American Literature & Psychoanalytic Culture. 2010. (New Black Studies Ser.). (ENG., Illus.). 216p. 40.00 *(978-0-252-03566-1(6))* Univ. of Illinois Pr.

Ahlin, Lena. "New Negro" in the Old World: Culture & Performance in James Weldon Johnson, Jessie Fauset, & Nella Larsen. 2006. (Lund Studies in English: Vol. 111). 111p. (C). pap. 79.50 *(978-91-975158-0-1(9))* Lund Univ. Pr., Sweden SWE. Dist: Coronet Bks.

Akolaema, Chiji. Folklore in New World Black Fiction: Writing & the Oral Traditional Aesthetics. 2007. x, 162p. cd-rom 9.95 *(978-0-8142-9148-1(1))* Ohio State Univ. Pr.

Akoma, Chiji. Folklore in New World Black Fiction: Writing & the Oral Traditional Aesthetics. 2007. (ENG.). 162p. 36.95 *(978-0-8142-1071-0(6))* Ohio State Univ. Pr.

Allen, Eddie B., Jr. & Allen, Eddie B. Low Road: The Life & Legacy of Donald Goines. 2008. (ENG., Illus.). 224p. pap. 16.99 *(978-0-312-38351-0(7),* St. Martin's Griffin) St. Martin's Pr.

Alva, Rodrigo & Aparecida Andrade Salgueiro, Maria. Zora Neale Hurston & Their Eyes Were Watching God. 2010. 100p. pap. *(978-3-8383-9208-0(6))* Lambert Academic Publishing.

Anadolu-Okur, Nilgun. Contemporary African American Theater: Afrocentricity in the Works of Larry Neal, Amiri Baraka, & Charles Fuller. 2010. (ENG.). 236p. pap. 39.95 *(978-0-415-88324-5(5))* Routledge.

Anderson, Lisa M. Black Feminism in Contemporary Drama. 2008. (Illus.). 152p. 37.00 *(978-0-252-03228-8(4))* Univ. of Illinois Pr.

Bader, Philip. African-American Writers. 2nd rev. ed. 2010. (A to Z of African Americans Ser.). (Illus.). 352p. (C). (gr. 9-18). 49.50 *(978-0-8160-8141-7(7))* Facts On File, Inc.

Bailey, Frankie Y. African American Mystery Writers: A Historical & Thematic Study. 2008. (ENG.). 277p. pap. 35.00 *(978-0-7864-3339-1(6))* McFarland & Co., Inc. Pubs.

Baraka, Amiri, pseud. Razor. 2011. (ENG.). 300p. pap. 19.95 *(978-0-88378-300-9(2))* Third World Press.

Bell, Bernard W. Bearing Witness to African American Literature: Validating & Valorizing Its Authority, Authenticity, & Agency. 2012. pap. 29.95 ***(978-0-8143-3714-1(7))***; E-Book ***(978-0-8143-3715-8(5))*** Wayne State Univ. Pr.

Bernadowski, Carianne. Teaching Literacy Skills to Adolescents Using Coretta Scott King Award Winners. 1 vol. 2009. 136p. pap. 35.00 *(978-1-58683-337-4(5),* A2655P) Libraries Unlimited, Inc.

Bernard, Emily. Carl Van Vechten & the Harlem Renaissance: A Portrait in Black & White. 2012. (ENG., Illus.). 376p. 30.00 ***(978-0-300-12199-5(7))*** Yale Univ. Pr.

Bibler, Michael P. Cotton's Queer Relations: Same-Sex Intimacy & the Literature of the Southern Plantation, 1936-1968. 2009. (ENG.). 312p. (C). (gr. 13-17). pap. 22.50 *(978-0-8139-2792-3(7))*; (gr. 17). 55.00 *(978-0-8139-2791-6(9))* Univ. Pr. of Virginia.

Bickley, R. Bruce, Jr. Joel Chandler Harris: A Biography & Critical Study. 2008. (ENG.). 184p. per. 22.95 *(978-0-8203-3185-0(6))* Univ. of Georgia Pr.

Bigsby, Christopher. The Cambridge Companion to August Wilson. 2007. (Cambridge Companions to Literature Ser.). (ENG.). 290p. per. 30.99 *(978-0-521-68506-1(0))*; 240p. (C). 95.00 *(978-0-521-86606-4(5))* Cambridge Univ. Pr.

Birnbaum, Michele. Race, Work, & Desire in American Literature, 1860-1930. 2009. (Cambridge Studies in American Literature & Culture Ser.). (ENG.). 208p. pap. 32.99 *(978-0-521-12019-7(5))* Cambridge Univ. Pr.

Black Literature Criticism: Classic & Emerging Authors since 1950, 3 vols., Set. 2nd rev. ed. 2008. (ENG.). 544p. 552.00 *(978-1-4144-3170-3(8))* Cengage Gale.

Bloom, Harold. African-American Poets, 2 vols., Vol. 2. 2nd rev. ed. 2010. (Bloom's Modern Critical Views Ser.). 202p. (C). (gr. 9-18). 45.00 *(978-1-60413-810-8(6),* Chelsea Hse.) Facts On File, Inc.

—I Know Why the Caged Bird Sings. 2nd rev. ed. 2010. (Bloom's Guides). 122p. (C). (gr. 9). 30.00 *(978-1-60413-876-4(9),* Chelsea Hse.) Facts On File, Inc.

—Richard Wright. 2nd rev. ed. 2008. (Modern Critical Views Ser.). 224p. (C). (gr. 9). 45.00 *(979-0-7910-9622-2(X),* Chelsea Hse.) Facts On File, Inc.

—Richard Wright's Native Son. annot. ed. 2007. (Bloom's Guides). 136p. (YA). (gr. 9-12). lib. bdg. 30.00 *(978-0-7910-9368-9(9))* Facts On File, Inc.

Bloom, Harold, ed. African-American Poets: Volume 1, New Edition, 2 vols. 2nd rev. ed. 2009. (Bloom's Modern Critical Views Ser.). 272p. (C). (gr. 9-18). 45.00 *(978-1-60413-400-1(3),* Chelsea Hse.) Facts On File, Inc.

—August Wilson. 2009. (Bloom's Modern Critical Views Ser.). 200p. (C). (gr. 9-18). 45.00 *(978-1-60413-393-6(7),* Chelsea Hse.) Facts On File, Inc.

—The Bluest Eye. 2009. (Bloom's Guides). 130p. (C). (gr. 9-18). 30.00 *(978-1-60413-573-2(5),* Chelsea Hse.) Facts On File, Inc.

—Ralph Ellison. 2nd rev. ed. 2009. (Bloom's Modern Critical Views Ser.). 246p. (C). (gr. 9-18). 45.00 *(978-1-60413-578-7(6),* Bloom's Literary Criticism) Facts On File, Inc.

—Song of Solomon - Toni Morrison, New Edition. 2nd rev. ed. 2009. (Bloom's Modern Critical Interpretations Ser.). 224p. (C). (gr. 9-18). 45.00 *(978-1-60413-392-9(9),* Chelsea Hse.) Facts On File, Inc.

—Their Eyes Were Watching God. 2009. (Bloom's Guides). 112p. (C). (gr. 9-18). 30.00 *(978-1-60413-571-8(9),* Chelsea Hse.) Facts On File, Inc.

—Toni Morrison's Beloved. 2nd rev. ed. 2009. (Bloom's Modern Critical Interpretations Ser.). 232p. (C). (gr. 9-18). 45.00 *(978-1-60413-184-0(5),* Chelsea Hse.) Facts On File, Inc.

Bogumil, Mary L. Understanding August Wilson. (Understanding Contemporary American Literature Ser.). (ENG.). 2009. 168p. pap. 21.95 *(978-1-57003-879-2(1))* 2011. 184p. pap. 24.95 *(978-1-57003-979-9(8))* Univ. of South Carolina Pr.

Bond, Frederick W. The Negro & the Drama: The Direct & Indirect Contribution Which the American Negro Has Made to Drama & the Legitimate Stage. 28.95 *(978-0-405-18492-5(1))* Ayer Co. Pubs., Inc.

Bone, Richard Wright, Vol. 74. 2009. (ENG.). 48p. pap. 25.00 *(978-0-8166-0524-8(6))* Univ. of Minnesota Pr.

Boyd, Stacy. Black Men Worshipping: Intersecting Anxieties of Race, Gender, & Christian Embodiment. 2011. (Black Religion/Womanist Thought/Social Justice Ser.). (ENG., Illus.). 192p. 85.00 *(978-0-230-11371-8(0))* Palgrave Macmillan.

Brady, Owen E. & Maus, Derek C., eds. Finding a Way Home: A Critical Assessment of Walter Mosley's Fiction. (ENG.). 224p. 2011. pap. 30.00 *(978-1-61703-065-9(1))* 2008. 65.00 *(978-1-60473-088-3(9))* Univ. Pr. of Mississippi.

Brooks, Wanda M. Embracing, Evaluating, & Examining African American Children's & Young Adult Literature. McNair, Jonda C., ed. 2007. (ENG., Illus.). 262p. per. 55.00 *(978-0-8108-6027-8(9))* Scarecrow Pr., Inc.

Brown-Guillory, Elizabeth. Alice Childress: The Writings of a Rebel Spirit. (Illus.). (C). *(978-0-472-10798-8(4))* Univ. of Michigan Pr.

Brown, Stephanie. The Postwar African American Novel: Protest & Discontent, 1945-1950. 2011. (Margaret Walker Alexander Series in African American Studies). (ENG.). 176p. 55.00 *(978-1-60473-973-2(8))* Univ. Pr. of Mississippi.

Byerman, Keith E. Fingering the Jagged Grain: Tradition & Form in Recent Black Fiction. 2010. (ENG.). 322p. pap. 24.95 *(978-0-8203-3776-0(5))* Univ. of Georgia Pr.

Byrd, Rudolph P. Jean Toomer's Years with Gurdjieff: Portrait of an Artist, 1923-1936. 2010. (ENG.). 232p. pap. 24.95 *(978-0-8203-3777-7(3))* Univ. of Georgia Pr.

Campbell, Kofi Omoniyi Sylvanus & Campbell, Kofi. Literature & Culture in the Black Atlantic: From Pre-To Postcolonial. 2006. (ENG.). 208p. 84.00 *(978-1-4039-7223-1(0))* Palgrave Macmillan.

Carlacio, Jami L., ed. The Fiction of Toni Morrison: Reading & Writing on Race, Culture, & Identity. 2007. pap. *(978-0-8141-1679-1(5))* National Council of Teachers of English.

Carlson, Julie. Uncle Tom's Cabin & the Abolitionist Movement. 2009. (Looking at Literature Through Primary Sources Ser.). 64p. (gr. 5-8). 58.50 *(978-1-61514-309-2(2))* Rosen Publishing Group, Inc., The.

Carroll, Anne Elizabeth. Word, Image, & the New Negro: Representation & Identity in the Harlem Renaissance. 2007. (Blacks in the Diaspora Ser.). (ENG., Illus.). 294p. pap. 24.95 *(978-0-253-21919-0(1),* 0253219191) Indiana Univ. Pr.

Casement, Rose. Black History in the Pages of Children's Literature. 2007. (ENG.). 336p. 70.00 *(978-0-8108-5843-5(6))* Scarecrow Pr., Inc.

Caster, Peter & Buckner, Timothy R., eds. Fathers, Preachers, Rebels, Men: Black Masculinity in U. S. History & Literature, 1820-1945. 2011. (Black Performance & Cultural Criticism Ser.). 304p. 44.95 *(978-0-8142-1156-4(9))*; cd-rom 14.95 *(978-0-8142-9255-6(0))* Ohio State Univ. Pr.

Chakkalakal, Tess. Novel Bondage: Slavery, Marriage, & Freedom in Nineteenth-Century America. 2011. (ENG.). 160p. 40.00 ***(978-0-252-03633-0(6))*** Univ. of Illinois Pr.

Christian, Barbara. New Black Feminist Criticism, 1985-2000. Bowles, Gloria et al, ecs. 2007. 272p. 35.00 *(978-0-252-03180-9(6))* Univ. of Illinois Pr.

Colbert, Soyica Diggs. The African American Theatrical Body: Reception, Performance, & the Stage. 2011. (ENG., Illus.). 344p. 99.00 ***(978-1-107-01438-1(7))*** Cambridge Univ. Pr.

Coleman, Finnie D. Sutton E. Griggs & the Struggle Against White Supremacy. 2007. 232p. 35.00 *(978-1-57233-480-9(0))* Univ. of Tennessee Pr.

Coleman, James W. Writing Blackness: John Edgar Wideman's Art & Experimentation. 2010. 216p. 37.50 *(978-0-8071-3644-7(1))* Louisiana State Univ. Pr.

Conner, Marc C. & Nash, William R., eds. Charles Johnson: The Novelist as Philosopher. (ENG.). 2010. 240p. pap. 25.00 *(978-1-60473-506-2(6))* 2007. 199p. 50.00 *(978-1-57806-973-6(4))* Univ. Pr. of Mississippi.

Crump, Micah. Black Entrepreneurship: Literature & Reality. 2010. 248p. pap. *(978-3-639-25425-9(2))* VDM Verlag Dr. Mueller e.K.

Dace, Letitia. Langston Hughes: The Contemporary Reviews. Dace, Letitia & Dace, Tish, eds. 2009. (American Critical Archives Ser.). (ENG.). 788p. pap. 74.00 *(978-0-521-11430-1(6))* Cambridge Univ. Pr.

Dickel, Simon. Black/Gay: The Harlem Renaissance, the Protest Era, & the Constructions of Black Gay Identity in the 1980s & 90s. 2012. (ENG.). 308p. pap. 34.95 *(978-1-61186-009-2(1))* Michigan State Univ. Pr.

Dickstein, Morris. James Baldwin. 2010. (Critical Insights Ser.). 455p. (C). 85.00 *(978-1-58765-701-6(5))* Salem Pr., Inc.

Dixon, Melvin. A Melvin Dixon Critical Reader. Joyce, Justin A. & McBride, Dwight A., eds. 2006. (ENG.). 159p. 45.00 *(978-1-57806-866-1(5))* Univ. Pr. of Mississippi.

Dow, William & Craven, Alice, eds. Richard Wright: New Readings in the 21st Century. 2011. (Signs of Race Ser.). (ENG., Illus.). 304p. 85.00 *(978-0-230-11281-0(1))* Palgrave Macmillan.

Eaton, Kalenda C. Womanism, Literature, & the Transformation of the Black Community, 1965-1980. 2007. (Studies in African American History & Culture Ser.). (ENG.). 122p. 125.00 *(978-0-415-96129-5(7),* 0415961297) Routledge.

Edwards, Gus. Black Heroes in Monologues. 2006. 160p. per. 13.95 *(978-0-325-00925-4(2),* E00925, Drama) Heinemann.

Elam, Michele. The Souls of Mixed Folk: Race, Politics, & Aesthetics in the New Millennium. 2011. (ENG., Illus.). 308p. 75.00 *(978-0-8047-5629-7(5))*; pap. 24.95 *(978-0-8047-5630-3(9))* Stanford Univ. Pr.

Elizabeth & Young, Elizabeth. Black Frankenstein: The Making of an American Metaphor. 2008. (ENG.). 336p. (C). pap. 24.00 *(978-0-8147-9716-7(4))* New York Univ. Pr.

Ferguson, Rebecca Hope. Rewriting Black Identities: Transition & Exchange in the Novels of Toni Morrison. 2007. (New Comparative Poetics Ser.: Vol. 8). 321p. pap. 34.95 *(978-90-5201-167-7(2))* Lang, Peter Publishing, Inc.

Field, Douglas. A Historical Guide to James Baldwin. 2009. (History Gds American Ser.). (ENG., Illus.). 304p. pap. 27.95 *(978-0-19-536654-9(9))* Oxford Univ. Pr., Inc.

Fisch, Audrey A., ed. The Cambridge Companion to the African American Slave Narrative. 2007. (Cambridge Companions to Literature Ser.). (ENG.). 290p. per. 28.99 *(978-0-521-61526-6(7))*; 91.00 *(978-0-521-85019-3(3))* Cambridge Univ. Pr.

Fisher, Maisha. Black Literate Lives: Historical & Contemporary Perspectives. 2008. (Critical Social Thought Ser.). (Illus.). XXII, 178p. 135.00 *(978-0-415-95864-6(4))* Routledge.

Friedel, Tania. Racial Discourse & Cosmopolitanism in Twentieth-Century African American Writing. 2007. (Studies in African American History & Culture Ser.). (ENG.). 214p. 133.00 *(978-0-415-96355-8(9),* 0415963559) Routledge.

Gardner, Eric. Unexpected Places: Relocating Nineteenth-Century African American Literature. (Margaret Walker Alexander Series in African American Studies). (ENG.). 272p. 2011. pap. 30.00 ***(978-1-61703-211-0(5))*** 2009. 50.00 *(978-1-60473-283-2(0))* Univ. Pr. of Mississippi.

Gates, Henry Louis, Jr. The Henry Louis Gates, Jr. Reader. Wolf, Abby De, ed. 2012. (ENG.). 656p. (gr. 9). 29.99 ***(978-0-465-02831-3(4))*** Basic Bks.

Gates, Henry Louis, Jr. Signifying Monkey: A Theory of African American Literary Criticism. 2010. (ENG., Illus.). 336p. pap. 19.95 *(978-0-19-513647-0(0))* Oxford Univ. Pr., Inc.

Gates, Henry Louis, Jr. & Jarrett, Gene Andrew. The New Negro: Readings on Race, Representation, & African American Culture, 1892-1938. Gates, Henry Louis, Jr. & Jarrett, Gene Andrew, eds. 2007. (Illus.). 591p. 75.00 *(978-0-691-12651-7(8))*; (ENG.). 608p. (C). pap. 35.00 *(978-0-691-12652-4(6))* Princeton Univ. Pr.

Gayle, Addison, Jr. The Addison Gayle Jr. Reader. Norment, Nathaniel, Jr., ed. 2009. (ENG., Illus.). 504p. pap. 37.00 *(978-0-252-07610-7(9))* Univ. of Illinois Pr.

Gerstner, David A. Queer Pollen: White Seduction, Black Male Homosexuality, & the Cinematic. 2011. (New Black Studies Ser.). (ENG., Illus.). 216p. 80.00 *(978-0-252-03590-6(9))*; pap. 25.00 *(978-0-252-07787-6(3))* Univ. of Illinois Pr.

Golden, Marita. The Word: Black Writers Talk about the Transformative Power of Reading & Writing. 2011. 224p. pap. 14.99 *(978-0-7679-2991-2(8))* Broadway Bks.

Gómez-Galisteo, M. Carmen. The Wind Is Never Gone: Sequels, Parodies & Rewritings of Gone with the Wind. 2011. (ENG., Illus.). 216p. pap. 35.00 *(978-0-7864-5927-8(1))* McFarland & Co., Inc. Pubs.

Goulimari, Pelagia & Pelagia. Toni Morrison. 2011. (Routledge Guides to Literature Ser.). (ENG.). 288p. (C). pap. 26.95 *(978-0-415-42074-7(1))* Routledge.

Green, Tara T., ed. From the Plantation to the Prison: African American Confinement Literature. 2008. (Voices of the African Diaspora Ser.). 176p. 35.00 *(978-0-88146-090-2(7))* Mercer Univ. Pr.

Greene, Brenda M. & Beauford, Fred, eds. Meditations & Ascensions: Black Writers on Writing. 2008. 204p. pap. 18.95 *(978-0-88378-296-5(0))* Third World Press.

Greene, J. Lee. The Diasporan Self: Unbreaking the Circle in Western Black Novels. 2008. (ENG.). 264p. (C). (gr. 13-17). pap. 19.50 *(978-0-8139-2740-4(4))*; (gr. 17). 55.00 *(978-0-8139-2739-8(0))* Univ. Pr. of Virginia.

Gruesser, John Cullen. Confluences: Postcolonialism, African American Literary Studies, & the Black Atlantic. 2007. (ENG.). 192p. per. 22.95 *(978-0-8203-3026-6(4))* Univ. of Georgia Pr.

Guzzio, Tracie Church. All Stories Are True: History, Myth, & Trauma in the Work of John Edgar Wideman. 2011. (Margaret Walker Alexander Series in African American Studies). (ENG.). 352p. 60.00 *(978-1-61703-004-8(X))* Univ. Pr. of Mississippi.

Harrell, Willie J., Jr. We Wear the Mask: Paul Laurence Dunbar & the Politics of Representative Reality. 2011. (Illus.). 256p. 45.00 *(978-1-60635-046-1(3))* Kent State Univ. Pr.

Harrie: Beecher Stowe. Uncle Tom's Cabin. l.t. ed. 2007. 162p. pap. 32.99 *(978-1-4264-6630-4(7))* BiblioBazaar.

Harris-Lopez, Trudier. The Scary Mason-Dixon Line: African American Writers & the South. 2009. (Southern Literary Studies). 256p. 37.50 *(978-0-8071-3395-8(7))*; *(978-0-8018-3395-3(7))* Louisiana State Univ. Pr.

Henderson, Carol E. James Baldwin's Go Tell It on the Mountain: Historical & Critical Essays. 2006. 180p. (C). 63.95 *(978-0-8204-8158-6(0))* Lang, Peter Publishing, Inc.

Hill, Michael D. & Hill, Lena M. Ralph Ellison's Invisible Man: A Reference Guide, 1 vol. 2008. (Greenwood Guides to Multicultural Literature). 208p. 55.00 *(978-0-313-33465-8(X),* GR3465, Greenwood Pr.) Greenwood Publishing Group, Inc.

Hochman, Barbara. Uncle Tom's Cabin & the Reading Revolution: Race, Literacy, Childhood & Fiction, 1851¿1911. 2011. (Illus.). 352p. (ENG.). pap. 28.95 *(978-1-55849-894-5(X))*; lib. bdg. 80.00 *(978-1-55849-893-8(1))* Univ. of Massachusetts Pr.

Höggerl, Christiane. Problems of African American Education in Literature & Film. 2010. 112p. pap. *(978-3-639-26333-8(0))* VDM Verlag Dr. Mueller e.K.

Holloway, Karla F. C. Bookmarks: Reading in Black & White. 2008. (ENG.). 240p. pap. 19.95 *(978-0-8135-4351-2(7))* Rutgers Univ. Pr.

—BookMarks: Reading in Black & White. 2006. (ENG., Illus.). 240p. 24.95 *(978-0-8135-3907-2(2))* Rutgers Univ. Pr.

Holmes, Linda Janet & Wall, Cheryl A., eds. Savoring the Salt: The Legacy of Toni Cade Bambara. 2007. (ENG., Illus.). 320p. 81.50 *(978-1-59213-624-7(9))*; per. 26.95 *(978-1-59213-625-4(7))* Temple Univ. Pr.

Hutchinson, George, ed. The Cambridge Companion to the Harlem Renaissance. 2007. (Cambridge Companions to Literature Ser.). (ENG.). 296p. 109.00 *(978-0-521-85699-7(X))*; per. 34.00 *(978-0-521-67368-6(2))* Cambridge Univ. Pr.

Ikard, David. Breaking the Silence: Toward a Black Male Feminist Criticism. 2007. 191p. 35.00 *(978-0-8071-3213-5(6))* Louisiana State Univ. Pr.

Ingram, Kristy. Bigger Thomas: A Rolling Stone. 2010. 60p. pap. *(978-3-8383-0271-3(0))* Lambert Academic Publishing.

Iochem Valente, Marcela. Lorraine Hansberry & a Raisin in the Sun. 2010. 120p. pap. *(978-3-8383-6287-8(X))* Lambert Academic Publishing.

Irele, F. Abiola. The Cambridge Companion to the African Novel. 2009. (Cambridge Companions to Literature Ser.). (ENG.). 308p. (C). 99.00 *(978-0-521-85560-0(8))*; pap. 30.99 *(978-0-521-67168-2(X))* Cambridge Univ. Pr.

Izzo, David Garrett & Orban, Maria. Charles Chesnutt Reappraised: Essays on the First Major African American Fiction Writer. 2009. (ENG.). 246p. pap. 39.95 *(978-0-7864-4111-2(9))* McFarland & Co., Inc. Pubs.

James, Jennifer C. A Freedom Bought with Blood: African American War Literature from the Civil War to World War II. 2007. (ENG., Illus.). 384p. 73.95 *(978-0-8078-3116-8(6))*; per. 27.95 *(978-0-8078-5807-3(2))* Univ. of North Carolina Pr.

Japtok, Martin. Authentic Blackness/ Real Blackness: Essays on the Meaning of Blackness in Culture & Literature (CB) 2011. (C). 129.95 *(978-1-4331-1509-7(3))* Lang, Peter Publishing, Inc.

—Authentic Blackness/ Real Blackness: Essays on the Meaning of Blackness in Literature & Culture. 2011. (C). pap. 34.95 *(978-1-4331-1508-0(5))* Lang, Peter Publishing, Inc.

Jarrett, Gene Andrew. Deans & Truants: Race & Realism in African American Literature. 2006. (Illus.). 232p. (C). 55.00 *(978-0-8122-3973-7(3))* Univ. of Pennsylvania Pr.

Jarrett, Gene Andrew, ed. A Companion to African American Literature. 2010. (Blackwell Companions to Literature & Culture Ser.: 121). (ENG., Illus.). 488p. 159.95 *(978-1-4051-8862-3(6),* Wiley-Blackwell) Wiley, John & Sons, Inc.

Jenkins, Candice M. Private Lives, Proper Relations: Regulating Black Intimacy. 2007. 240p. 67.50 *(978-0-8166-4787-3(9))*; per. 23.50 *(978-0-8166-4788-0(7))* Univ. of Minnesota Pr.

Johnson, Charles. Turning the Wheel: Essays on Buddhism & Writing. 2007. (ENG.). 208p. pap. 15.95 *(978-1-4165-7243-5(0),* Scribner) Scribner.

Jones, Meta DuEwa. The Muse Is Music: Jazz Poetry from the Harlem Renaissance to Spoken Word. 2011. (New Black Studies Ser.). (ENG., Illus.). 304p. 55.00 *(978-0-252-03621-7(2))* Univ. of Illinois Pr.

Joyce, Joyce A., ed. Conversations with Sonia Sanchez. 2007. (ENG.). 213p. 50.00 *(978-1-57806-951-4(3))*; (Illus.). per. 22.00 *(978-1-57806-952-1(1))* Univ. Pr. of Mississippi.

Joyce, Justin A. & McBride, Dwight A., eds. A Melvin Dixon Critical Reader. 2010. (ENG.). 190p. pap. 25.00 *(978-1-60473-863-6(4))* Univ. Pr. of Mississippi.

Kaplan, Cora & Schwarz, Bill. James Baldwin: America & Beyond. 2011. (Illus.). 288p. E-Book ***(978-0-472-02761-3(1))*** Univ. of Michigan Pr.

Katz, Stephen. Red, Black, & Jew: New Frontiers in Hebrew Literature. 2010. (ENG.). 363p. pap. 30.00 *(978-0-292-72356-6(3))* Univ. of Texas Pr.

King, Lovalerie. The Cambridge Introduction to Zora Neale Hurston. 2008. (Cambridge Introductions to Literature Ser.). (ENG.). 160p. (C). 63.00 *(978-0-521-85457-3(1))*; pap. 20.99 *(978-0-521-67095-1(0))* Cambridge Univ. Pr.

—James Baldwin & Toni Morrison: Comparative Critical & Theoretical Essays. King, Lovalerie & Scott, Lynn Orilla, eds. 2009. (ENG.). 352p. pap. 29.00 *(978-0-230-61972-2(X))* Palgrave Macmillan.

—Race, Theft, & Ethics: Property Matters in African American Literature. 2007. (Southern Literary Studies). (Illus.). 187p. 35.00 *(978-0-8071-3257-9(8))* Louisiana State Univ. Pr.

King, Lovalerie & Selzer, Linda F., eds. New Essays on the African American Novel: From Hurston & Ellison to Morrison & Whitehead. 2008. (ENG.). 292p. 95.00 *(978-0-230-60327-1(0))* Palgrave Macmillan.

Knadler, Stephen & Knadler, Stephen P. Remapping Citizenship & the Nation in African-American Literature. 2009. (Routledge Transnational Perspectives on American Literature Ser.). (ENG.). 248p. (C). 125.00 *(978-0-415-99631-0(7))* Routledge.

Kolin, Philip C., ed. Suzan-Lori Parks: Essays on the Plays & Other Works. 2010. (ENG., Illus.). 219p. pap. 39.95 *(978-0-7864-4167-9(4))* McFarland & Co., Inc. Pubs.

Kramer, Victor A., ed. Georgia State Literary Studies, 12 vols. *(978-0-404-63200-7(9))* AMS Pr., Inc.

Krauthammer, Anna. The Representation of the Savage in James Fenimore Cooper & Herman Melville. 2008. 130p. (C). 67.95 *(978-0-8204-6810-5(X))* Lang, Peter Publishing, Inc.

Krstovic, Jelena O. Black Literature Criticism: Classic & Emerging Authors since 1950, 3 vols. 2008. (Illus.). *(978-1-4144-3172-7(4))*; *(978-1-4144-3171-0(6))*; *(978-1-4144-3173-4(2))* Cengage Gale.

Lackey, Michael. African American Atheists & Political Liberation: A Study of the Sociocultural Dynamics of Faith. 2007. (History of African-American Religions Ser.). (ENG., Illus.). 192p. 59.95 *(978-0-8130-3035-7(8))* Univ. Pr. of Florida.

—African American Atheists & Political Liberation: A Study of the Sociocultural Dynamics of Faith. 2008. (History of African-American Religions Ser.). (ENG., Illus.). 192p. pap. 29.95 *(978-0-8130-3318-1(7))* Univ. Pr. of Florida.

LaGrone, Kheven, ed. Alice Walker's the Color Purple. 2009. (Illus.). 345p. pap. 97.00 *(978-90-420-2544-8(1))* Rodopi.

Lamothe, Daphne. Inventing the New Negro: Narrative, Culture, & Ethnography. 2008. 240p. (C). 59.95 *(978-0-8122-4093-1(6))* Univ. of Pennsylvania Pr.

Lauret, Maria. Alice Walker. 2nd rev. ed. 2011. (ENG.). 304p. 80.00 *(978-0-230-57588-2(9))*; pap. 28.00 *(978-0-230-57589-9(7))* Palgrave Macmillan.

Lee, A. Robert, ed. African American Writing, 5 vols. 2012. (ENG.). 1736p. (C). 1425.00 ***(978-0-415-68048-6(4))*** Routledge.

Lee, Julia. Interracial Encounters: Reciprocal Representations in African & Asian American Literatures, 1896-1937. 2011. (ENG.). 228p. 75.00 ***(978-0-8147-5255-5(1))***; pap. 23.00 ***(978-0-8147-5256-2(X))*** New York Univ. Pr.

Lee, Julia H. Interracial Encounters: Reciprocal Representations in African American & Asian American Literatures, 1896-1937. 2011. E-Book ***(978-0-8147-5257-9(8))***; E-Book ***(978-0-8147-5328-6(0))*** New York Univ. Pr.

Leiter, Andrew B. In the Shadow of the Black Beast: African American Masculinity in the Harlem & Southern Renaissances. 2010. (Southern Literary Studies). 296p. 39.95 *(978-0-8071-3587-7(9))* Louisiana State Univ. Pr.

Lester, Neal A. Once upon a Time in a Different World: Issues & Ideas in African American Children's Literature. 2007. (Children's Literature & Culture Ser.). 304p. 131.00 *(978-0-415-98019-7(4))* Routledge.

Lewis, Leslie W. Telling Narratives: Secrets in African American Literature. 2007. (Illus.). 232p. 42.00 *(978-0-252-03211-0(X))* Univ. of Illinois Pr.

Li, Stephanie. Something Akin to Freedom: The Choice of Bondage in Narratives by African American Women. 2010. 160p. 60.00 *(978-1-4384-2971-7(1))* State Univ. of New York Pr.

Lockridge, Aisha Damali. Tipping on a Tight Rope: Divas in African American Literature. 2012. (C). pap. 89.95 ***(978-1-4331-0575-3(6))*** Lang, Peter Publishing, Inc.

Lowe, John, ed. Approaches to Teaching Hurston's Their Eyes Were Watching God & Other Works. 2009. (ENG.). 37.50 *(978-1-60329-043-2(5))*; pap. 19.75 *(978-1-60329-044-9(3))* Modern Language Assn. of America.

Lubin, Alex, ed. Revising the Blueprint: Ann Petry & the Literary Left. (ENG.). 2011. pap. 30.00 *(978-1-61703-039-0(2))* 2007. (Illus.). 179p. 65.00 *(978-1-57806-971-2(8))* Univ. Pr. of Mississippi.

Luczak, Ewa / Barbara. How Their Living Outside America Affected Five African American Authors: Toward a Theory of Expatriate Literature. 2010. ix, 250p. *(978-0-7734-3748-7(7))* Mellen, Edwin Pr., The.

Major, Clarence. The Dark & the Feeling. 12.95 *(978-0-89388-119-1(8))* Okpaku Communications Corp.

Mance, Ajuan Maria. Inventing Black Women: African American Women Poets & Self-Representation, 1877-2000. 2007. 248p. 36.00 *(978-1-57233-492-2(4))* Univ. of Tennessee Pr.

Mayberry, Susan Neal. Can't I Love What I Criticize? The Masculine & Morrison. 2007. (ENG.). 352p. 44.95 *(978-0-8203-2945-1(2))* Univ. of Georgia Pr.

Mays, Benjamin E. The Negro's God. 2010. 282p. pap. 31.00 *(978-1-60899-777-0(4)*, Wipf and Stock) Wipf & Stock Pubs.

Mhandu, Edwin. Crime in Alice Walker's Works. 2011. 108p. pap. ***(978-3-8443-0154-0(2))*** Lambert Academic Publishing.

Miller, Henry D. Theorizing Black Theatre: Art Versus Protest in Critical Writings, 1898-1965. 2010. (ENG., Illus.). 284p. pap. 65.00 *(978-0-7864-5937-7(9))* McFarland & Co., Inc. Pubs.

Miller, R. Baxter. A Literary Criticism of Five Generations of African American Writing: The Artistry of Memory. 2008. 328p. 119.95 *(978-0-7734-4966-4(3))* Mellen, Edwin Pr., The.

Miller, W. Jason. Langston Hughes & American Lynching Culture. 2011. (ENG., Illus.). 160p. 44.95 *(978-0-8130-3533-8(3))* Univ. Pr. of Florida.

Minnick, Lisa Cohen. Dialect & Dichotomy: Literary Representations of African American Speech. 2nd ed. 2007. 216p. pap. 22.50 *(978-0-8173-5423-7(9))* Univ. of Alabama Pr.

Mitchell, Verner D. & Davis, Cynthia. Literary Sisters: Dorothy West & Her Circle, a Biography of the Harlem Renaissance. 2011. (ENG.). 216p. (C). pap. 24.95 *(978-0-8135-5146-3(3))*; (Illus.). 208p. 72.00 *(978-0-8135-5145-6(5))* Rutgers Univ. Pr.

Montgomery, Maxine Lavon. The Fiction of Gloria Naylor: Houses & Spaces of Resistance. 2010. (ENG.). 144p. 35.00 *(978-1-57233-722-0(2))* Univ. of Tennessee Pr.

Mosley, Walter. Conversations with Walter Mosley. Brady, Owen E., ed. 2011. (Literary Conversations Ser.). (ENG.). 256p. 55.00 *(978-1-60473-942-8(8))*; pap. 25.00 *(978-1-60473-943-5(6))* Univ. Pr. of Mississippi.

Mvuyekure, Pierre-Damien. The Dark Heathenism of the American Novelist Ishmael Reed: African Voodoo as American Literary Hoodoo. 2007. 312p. *(978-0-7734-5440-8(3))* Mellen, Edwin Pr., The.

Nama, Adilifu. Super Black: American Pop Culture & Black Superheroes. 2011. (Illus.). 180p. E-Book ***(978-0-292-73545-3(6))***; (ENG., 200p. 55.00 *(978-0-292-72654-3(6))*; (ENG., 200p. pap. 24.95 *(978-0-292-72674-1(0))* Univ. of Texas Pr.

Nanda, Aparajita. Black California: A Literary Anthology. 2011. pap. *(978-1-59714-146-8(1))* Santa Clara Univ., de Saisset Museum.

Ndogo, Samuel. Narrating Double Consciousness. 2010. 136p. pap. *(978-3-639-26187-5(9))* VDM Verlag Dr. Mueller e.K.

Nilon, Charles H. Faulkner & the Negro: University of Colorado Studies, Series in Language & Literature No. 8, September 1962. Hulley, Karl K., ed. 2011. 114p. 39.95 ***(978-1-258-06992-6(X))*** Literary Licensing, LLC.

Nnoromele, Salome & Day-Lindsay, Lisa. Journeys Home: An Anthology of Contemporary African Diasporic Experience (Poems & Personal Narratives) 2009. *(978-1-59221-712-0(5))*; 182p. pap. *(978-1-59221-713-7(3))* Africa World Pr.

Norman, Brian. Neo-Segregation Narratives: Jim Crow in Post-Civil Rights American Literature. 2010. (ENG., Illus.). 212p. 59.95 *(978-0-8203-3596-4(7))*; pap. 24.95 *(978-0-8203-3597-1(5))* Univ. of Georgia Pr.

—Representing Segregation: Toward an Aesthetics of Living Jim Crow, & Other Forms of Racial Division. Williams, Piper Kendrix, ed. 2010. (Illus.). 320p. 80.00 *(978-1-4384-3033-1(7))*; pap. 29.95 *(978-1-4384-3032-4(9))* State Univ. of New York Pr.

Nunes, Ana. African American Women Writers' Historical Fiction. 2011. (ENG.). 258p. 85.00 *(978-0-230-11253-7(6))* Palgrave Macmillan.

Page, Yolanda Williams. Icons of African American Literature: The Black Literary World. 2011. E-Book ***(978-0-313-35204-1(6)***, Greenwood Pr.) Greenwood Publishing Group, Inc.

Page, Yolanda Williams, ed. Icons of African American Literature: The Black Literary World, 1 vol. 2011. (Greenwood Icons Ser.). (Illus.). 519p. 100.00 *(978-0-313-35203-4(8)*, GR5203) Greenwood Publishing Group, Inc.

Peterson, Nancy J. Beloved. 2008. (Character Studies). (ENG.). 128p. 75.00 *(978-0-8264-9574-7(5))* Continuum International Publishing Group, Ltd. GBR. Dist: National Bk. Network.

Peterson, Nancy J. & Peterson. Beloved. 2008. (Character Studies). (ENG.). 128p. 19.95 *(978-0-8264-9575-4(3))* Continuum International Publishing Group, Ltd. GBR. Dist: National Bk. Network.

Pillow, Gloria Thomas. Motherlove in Shades of Black: The Maternal Psyche in the Novels of African American Women. 2010. (ENG., Illus.). 199p. pap. 38.00 *(978-0-7864-3533-3(X))* McFarland & Co., Inc. Pubs.

Qualls, Loren L. Dark Language: Post Rebellion Fiction. 2008. (ENG.). 60p. pap. 22.50 *(978-0-7618-4312-2(4))* Univ. Pr. of America, Inc.

Rambsy, Howard. The Black Arts Enterprise & the Production of African American Poetry. 2011. (ENG., Illus.). 198p. 60.00 *(978-0-472-11733-8(5))* Univ. of Michigan Pr.

Ramesh, Kotti Sree & Kandula, Nirupa Rani. Claude Mckay: The Literary Identity from Jamaica to Harlem & Beyond. 2006. (ENG., Illus.). 216p. per. 35.00 *(978-0-7864-2582-2(2))* McFarland & Co., Inc. Pubs.

Rice, Herbert William. Ralph Ellison & the Politics of the Novel. 2007. (ENG.). 162p. per. 26.50 *(978-0-7391-2323-2(8))* Lexington Bks.

Righelato, Pat. Understanding Rita Dove. 2006. (Understanding Contemporary American Literature Ser.). 249p. 39.95 *(978-1-57003-637-8(3))* Univ. of South Carolina Pr.

Riss, Arthur. Race, Slavery, & Liberalism in Nineteenth-Century American Literature. 2009. (Cambridge Studies in American Literature & Culture Ser.). (ENG.). 248p. pap. 38.00 *(978-0-521-12020-3(9))* Cambridge Univ. Pr.

Ruffin, Kimberly N. Black on Earth: African American Ecoliterary Traditions. 2010. (ENG., Illus.). 192p. 59.95 *(978-0-8203-2856-0(1))*; pap. 22.95 *(978-0-8203-3720-3(X))* Univ. of Georgia Pr.

Sathyaraj, Venkatesan. Mapping the Margins: Ethnic Feminist Consciousness in Toni Morrison's Novels. 2011. 140p. pap. ***(978-3-639-33748-8(4))*** VDM Verlag Dr. Mueller e.K.

Scally, Mary Anthony. Negro Catholic Writers 1900 - 1943: A Bio-Bibliography. 2006. pap. 21.95 *(978-1-4286-5451-8(8))* Kessinger Publishing, LLC.

Schmidt, Peter. Sitting in Darkness: New South Fiction, Education, & the Rise of Jim Crow Colonialism, 1865-1920. (ENG.). 2011. pap. 30.00 ***(978-1-61703-207-3(7))*** 2008. (Illus.). 259p. 50.00 *(978-1-934110-39-3(6))* Univ. Pr. of Mississippi.

Schwarz, Bill & Kaplan, Cora. James Baldwin: America & Beyond. 2011. (ENG., Illus.). 268p. (C). 80.00 *(978-0-472-07152-4(1))*; pap. 29.95 *(978-0-472-05152-6(0))* Univ. of Michigan Pr.

Selzer, Linda Furgerson. Charles Johnson in Context. 2009. (Illus.). 320p. 80.00 net. *(978-1-55849-698-9(X))*; (ENG., pap. 29.95 net. *(978-1-55849-723-8(4))* Univ. of Massachusetts Pr.

Shea, Renee H. & Wilchek, Deborah L. Zora Neale Hurston in the Classroom: With a harp & a sword in my Hands. 2009. pap. *(978-0-8141-5975-0(3))* National Council of Teachers of English.

Shockley, Evie. Renegade Poetics: Black Aesthetics & Formal Innovation in African American Poetry. 2011. (Contemporary North American Poetry Ser.). (ENG.). 264p. pap. 39.95 ***(978-1-60938-058-8(4))*** Univ. of Iowa Pr.

Simmons, Ryan. Chesnutt & Realism: A Study of the Novels. 2nd ed. 2006. (Studies in American Literary Realism & Naturalism). (Illus.). 208p. 39.95 *(978-0-8173-1520-7(9))* Univ. of Alabama Pr.

Simpson, Ritashona. Black Looks & Black Acts: The Language of Toni Morrison in the Bluest Eye & Beloved. 2007. (Illus.). 122p. (C). 55.95 *(978-0-8204-9530-9(1))* Lang, Peter Publishing, Inc.

Smith, Henrietta M. The Coretta Scott King Awards, 1970-2009. 4th ed. 2009. (Illus.). xiii, 131p. *(978-0-8389-3584-2(2))* American Library Assn.

Smith, Katharine Capshaw. Children's Literature of the Harlem Renaissance. 2006. (Blacks in the Diaspora Ser.). (ENG., Illus.). 368p. pap. 21.95 *(978-0-253-21888-9(8)*, 0253218888) Indiana Univ. Pr.

Stanley, Tarshia L., ed. Encyclopedia of Hip Hop Literature, 1 vol. 2008. 312p. 69.95 *(978-0-313-34389-6(6)*, GR4389, Greenwood Pr.) Greenwood Publishing Group, Inc.

Stockton, Kathryn Bond. Beautiful Bottom, Beautiful Shame: Where Black Meets Queer. 2006. (Series Q). (ENG., Illus.). 288p. per. 23.95 *(978-0-8223-3796-6(7))* Duke Univ. Pr.

Tally, Justine. Toni Morrison's Beloved: Origins. 2008. (Routledge Transnational Perspectives on American Literature Ser.). (ENG., Illus.). 194p. (C). 125.00 *(978-0-415-32045-0(3))* Routledge.

Thaggert, Miriam. Images of Black Modernism: Verbal & Visual Strategies of the Harlem Renaissance. 2010. (Illus.). 256p. (ENG.). pap. 28.95 *(978-1-55849-831-0(1))*; lib. bdg. 80.00 *(978-1-55849-830-3(3))* Univ. of Massachusetts Pr.

Thomas, P. L. Reading, Learning, Teaching Ralph Ellison. 2008. (Confronting the Text, Confronting the World Ser.). viii, 143p. (C). pap. 29.95 *(978-1-4331-0090-1(8))* Lang, Peter Publishing, Inc.

Thompson-Cager, Chezia. Teaching Jean Toomer's 1923 Cane. 2006. (Studies in African & African-American Culture: Vol. 9). (Illus.). 184p. (C). pap. 28.95 *(978-0-8204-2492-7(7))* Lang, Peter Publishing, Inc.

Thompson, Carlyle Van. Eating the Black Body: Miscegenation As Sexual Consumption in African American Literature & Culture. 2006. (African-American Literature & Culture Ser.: Vol. 10). (C). pap. 29.95 *(978-0-8204-7931-6(4))* Lang, Peter Publishing, Inc.

Thursby, Jacqueline S. Critical Companion to Maya Angelou. 2011. (Critical Companion to Ser.). (Illus.). 440p. (C). (gr. 9). 75.00 *(978-0-8160-8093-9(3))* Facts On File, Inc.

Tolson, Nancy. Black Children's Literature Got de Blues: The Creativity of Black Writers & Illustrators. 2008. (Illus.). xi, 116p. pap. 24.95 *(978-0-8204-6332-2(9))* Lang, Peter Publishing, Inc.

Walker, Jeffrey. Leather-Stocking Redux, or, Old Tales, New Essays. 2008. *(978-0-404-64473-4(2))* AMS Pr., Inc.

Walrond, Eric. In Search of Asylum: The Later Writings of Eric Walrond. Parascandola, Louis J. & Wade, Carl A., eds. 2011. (ENG., Illus.). 224p. 74.95 *(978-0-8130-3560-4(0))* Univ. Pr. of Florida.

Ward, Jerry Washington. The Cambridge History of African American Literature. Graham, Maryemma, ed. 2011. 860p. 165.00 *(978-0-521-87217-1(0))* Cambridge Univ. Pr.

Wardi, Anissa J. Water & African American Memory: An Ecocritical Perspective. 2011. (ENG., Illus.). 160p. 74.95 *(978-0-8130-3745-5(X))* Univ. Pr. of Florida.

Warhol, Andy. Andy Warhol: Ladies & Gentlemen. 2010. (ENG., Illus.). 80p. 30.00 *(978-1-61623-717-2(1))* Skarstedt Fine Art.

Warren, Kenneth W. What Was African American Literature? 2011. (W. E. B. du Bois Lectures). (ENG.). 192p. 22.95 *(978-0-674-04922-2(5))* Harvard Univ. Pr.

Whitfield, James Monroe. The Works of James M. Whitfield: America & Other Writings by a Nineteenth-Century African American Poet. Levine, Robert S. & Wilson, Ivy G., eds. 2011. (ENG.). 256p. 65.00 *(978-0-8078-3445-9(9))*; pap. 26.95 *(978-0-8078-7178-2(8))* Univ. of North Carolina Pr.

Wilkin, Binnie Tate. African & African American Images in Newbery Award Winning Titles: Progress in Portrayals. 2009. (ENG.). 210p. pap. 45.00 *(978-0-8108-6959-2(4))* Scarecrow Pr., Inc.

Williams, Dana. August Wilson & Black Aesthetics. Shannon, Sandra, ed. 2011. (ENG.). 240p. pap. 30.00 *(978-0-230-11301-5(X))* Palgrave Macmillan.

Williams, Tyrone. African American Literature, 4 vols. 2008. (Masterplots Ser.). 1800p. lib. bdg. 404.00 *(978-1-58765-438-1(5))* Salem Pr., Inc.

—Masterplots II. 2008. 101.00 *(978-1-58765-441-1(5))*; 101.00 *(978-1-58765-442-8(3))*; 101.00 *(978-1-58765-439-8(3))*; 101.00 *(978-1-58765-440-4(7))* Salem Pr., Inc.

Wilson, Ivy G. Specters of Democracy: Blackness & the Aesthetics of Politics in the Antebellum U. S., 1 vol. 2011. (ENG., Illus.). 256p. pap. 29.95 *(978-0-19-534035-8(3))* Oxford Univ. Pr., Inc.

Woodward, A. A Review of Uncle Tom's Cabin: Or- an Essay on Slavery. 2007. (ENG.). 154p. pap. 19.99 *(978-1-4346-4002-4(7))*; 168p. pap. 21.99 *(978-1-4346-4003-1(5))* BiblioBazaar.

Wright, John S. Shadowing Ralph Ellison. (ENG.). 2010. 294p. pap. 25.00 *(978-1-60473-545-1(7))* 2006. 269p. 50.00 *(978-1-57806-850-0(9))* Univ. Pr. of Mississippi.

Zamir, Shamoon, ed. The Cambridge Companion to W. E. B. du Bois. 2008. (Cambridge Companions to American Studies). (ENG.). 192p. (C). 81.00 *(978-0-521-87151-8(4))* Cambridge Univ. Pr.

—The Cambridge Companion to W.E.B. Du Bois. 2008. (Cambridge Companions to American Studies). (ENG.). 192p. (C). pap. 25.99 *(978-0-521-69205-2(9))* Cambridge Univ. Pr. GBR. Dist: Cambridge Univ. Pr.

Zauchner, Sabine, et al. African Diasporas: Afro-German Literature in the Context of the African American Experience. 2007. (ENG.). 144p. (gr. 11). pap. 39.95 *(978-3-8258-9612-6(9))* Lit Verlag DEU. Dist: Transaction Pubs.

Zauditu-Selassie, K. African Spiritual Traditions in the Novels of Toni Morrison. 2009. (ENG., Illus.). 224p. 69.95 *(978-0-8130-3328-0(4))* Univ. Pr. of Florida.

AFRICAN AMERICANS IN MASS MEDIA

Adams, Grace. 2007/2008 Black Authors & Published Writers Directory: Industry Reference. 2007. (Illus.). 410p. pap. 119.95 *(978-1-877807-28-2(1))* Grace Publishing Co.

Adams, Grace, ed. 2010-11 Black Authors & Published Writers Directory: A Writers Guide for Students & Teachers. 2010. 142p. pap. 24.95 *(978-1-877807-36-7(2)*, Black Authors & Published Writers Directory) Grace Publishing Co.

—2010-2011 Black Authors & Published Writers Directory. 5th ed. 2010. (Illus.). 332p. pap. 89.95 *(978-1-877807-32-9(X)*, Black Authors & Published Writers Directory) Grace Publishing Co.

Afandi, Jolie. Primitive Liberation. 2010. 148p. pap. *(978-3-639-26429-6(0))* VDM Verlag Dr. Mueller e.K.

Brunson, James Edward. The Early Image of Black Baseball: Race & Representation in the Popular Press, 1871-1890. 2009. (ENG., Illus.). 232p. pap. 39.95 *(978-0-7864-4206-5(9))* McFarland & Co., Inc. Pubs.

Chambers, Jason. Madison Avenue & the Color Line: African Americans in the Advertising Industry. 2007. (Illus.). 328p. (C). 39.95 *(978-0-8122-4047-4(2))* Univ. of Pennsylvania Pr.

Hopson, Mark C. Notes from the Talking Drum: Exploring Black Communication & Critical Memory in Intercultural Communication Contexts. 2011. 128p. *(978-1-61289-005-0(9))*; *(978-1-61289-004-3(0))* Hampton Pr., Inc.

Markovitz, Jonathan. Racial Spectacles: Explorations in Media, Race, & Justice. 2011. (ENG., Illus.). 240p. (C). 125.00 *(978-0-415-88345-0(8))*; pap. 39.95 *(978-0-415-88383-2(0))* Routledge.

Pecora, Norma, ed. African Media, African Children: Yearbook 2008. 2008. (International Clearinghouse on Children, Youth & Media Ser.). 243p. pap. 87.50 *(978-91-89471-68-9(7))* International Clearinghouse on Childrennordicom SWE. Dist: Coronet Bks.

Reed, Ishmael. Barack Obama & the Jim Crow Media: The Return of the Nigger Breakers. 2010. (ENG., Illus.). 190p. pap. 19.95 *(978-0-9812405-7-2(7))*; 256p. 39.95 *(978-0-9812405-9-6(3))* Baraka Bks. CAN. Dist: Independent Pubs. Group.

Riley, Sam G., ed. African Americans in the Media Today: An Encyclopedia, 2 vols. 2007. 632p. 175.00 *(978-0-313-33679-9(2)*, GR3679, Greenwood Pr.) Greenwood Publishing Group, Inc.

Smith, Valerie, ed. Representing Blackness: Issues in Film & Video. (Illus.). 250p. pap. *(978-0-485-30081-9(8))* Continuum International Publishing Group, Ltd.

Squires, Catherine R. African Americans & the Media. 2009. (MM - Media & Minorities Ser.: 3). (ENG., Illus.). 248p. 79.95 *(978-0-7456-4034-1(6))* Polity Pr. GBR. Dist: Wiley, John & Sons, Inc.

—African Americans & the Media. 2009. (MM - Media & Minorities Ser.: 4). (ENG., Illus.). 248p. pap. 26.95 *(978-0-7456-4036-5(2))* Polity Pr. GBR. Dist: Wiley, John & Sons, Inc.

Washburn, Patrick S. The African American Newspaper: Voices of Freedom. 2006. (Visions of the American Press Ser.). (ENG.). 304p. pap. 24.95 *(978-0-8101-2290-1(1))* Northwestern Univ. Pr.

Wickham, DeWayne. Black Voices in Commentary. 2006. xiii, 129p. pap. 15.95 *(978-0-9635720-9-7(1))* August Pr.

Willis Thomas, Hank, photos by. Pitch Blackness. 2008. (ENG., Illus.). 112p. 35.00 *(978-1-59711-072-3(8))* Aperture Foundation, Inc.

AFRICAN AMERICANS IN MEDICINE

see also African American Nurses; African American Physicians

Gracia, J. Nadine. Not Solely for Medicinal Purposes: African-American Females in Medicine. 2007. per. 29.95 *(978-0-9791026-6-0(9))* Otherside Pr.

Miller, Linda, compiled by. The Negro in Medicine Updated. 2008. 100p. pap. 39.95 *(978-0-9799802-4-4(0))* Harper Hse. Pubs.

AFRICAN AMERICANS IN MILITARY SERVICE

see United States—Armed Forces—African Americans

AFRICAN AMERICANS IN MOTION PICTURES

Here are entered works on the portrayal of African Americans in motion pictures. Works on all aspects of African American involvement in motion pictures are entered under African Americans in the Motion Picture Industry. Works on specific aspects of African American involvement are entered under the particular subject, e.g. African American Motion Picture Actors and Actresses.

Baldwin, James. The Devil Finds Work. 2011. (Vintage International Ser.). (ENG.). 144p. pap. 14.00 *(978-0-307-27595-0(7)*, Vintage) Knopf Doubleday Publishing Group.

Barker, Deborah & McKee, Kathryn, eds. American Cinema & the Southern Imaginary. 2011. (New Southern Studies). (ENG., Illus.). 384p. 69.95 *(978-0-8203-3380-9(8))*; pap. 24.95 *(978-0-8203-3710-4(2))* Univ. of Georgia Pr.

Batiste, Stephanie Leigh. Darkening Mirrors: Imperial Representation in Depression-Era African American Performance. 2012. (ENG., Illus.). 352p. 94.95 ***(978-0-8223-4898-6(5))***; pap. 25.95 ***(978-0-8223-4923-5(X))*** Duke Univ. Pr.

Berry, S. Torriano & Berry, Venise T. The A to Z of African American Cinema. 84th ed. 2009. (A to Z Guide Ser.: No. 84). (ENG.). 450p. pap. 34.45 *(978-0-8108-6871-7(7))* Scarecrow Pr., Inc.

—Historical Dictionary of African American Cinema. 2007. (Historical Dictionaries of Literature & the Arts Ser.: Vol. 12). (ENG., Illus.). 448p. 99.00 *(978-0-8108-5545-8(3))* Scarecrow Pr., Inc.

Bickford-Smith. Black & White in Colour African Histiry on Screen. 2007. 384p. pap. 29.95 *(978-1-84701-522-8(0)*, Currey, James) Boydell & Brewer, Ltd. GBR. Dist: Boydell & Brewer, Inc.

Boyd, Stacy. Black Men Worshipping: Intersecting Anxieties of Race, Gender, & Christian Embodiment. 2011. (Black Religion/Womanist Thought/Social Justice Ser.). (ENG., Illus.). 192p. 85.00 *(978-0-230-11371-8(0))* Palgrave Macmillan.

Catanese, Brandi Wilkins. The Problem of the Color[blind]: Racial Transgression & the Politics of Black Performance. 2011. (Theater: Theory/Text/Performance Ser.). (ENG.). 244p. 75.00 *(978-0-472-07126-5(2))*; pap. 28.95 *(978-0-472-05126-7(1))* Univ. of Michigan Pr.

Covington, Jeanette. Crime & Racial Constructions: Cultural Misinformation about African Americans in Media & Academia. (ENG.). 344p. 2011. pap. 38.95 ***(978-0-7391-2592-2(3))*** 2010. 83.99 *(978-0-7391-2591-5(5))* Lexington Bks.

Cram101 Textbook Reviews. Outlines & Highlights for the African American Image in Film: Framing Blackness by Guerrero, ISBN. 2011. 154p. pap. 29.95 ***(978-1-61812-972-7(4))*** Cram101 Inc.

Diawara, Manthia & Mask, Mia, eds. Black American Cinema 2. 2008. (ENG.). 320p. 125.00 *(978-0-415-97454-7(2))*; pap. 34.95 *(978-0-415-97455-4(0))* Routledge.

Dickel, Simon. Black/Gay: The Harlem Renaissance, the Protest Era, & the Constructions of Black Gay Identity in the 1980s & 90s. 2012. (ENG.). 308p. pap. 34.95 *(978-1-61186-009-2(1))* Michigan State Univ. Pr.

Dunn, Stephane. Baad Bitches & Sassy Supermamas: Black Power Action Films. 2008. (New Black Studies Ser.). (ENG.). 192p. 50.00 *(978-0-252-03340-7(X))*; pap. 21.00 *(978-0-252-07548-3(X))* Univ. of Illinois Pr.

Flory, Dan. Philosophy, Black Film, Film Noir. (ENG., Illus.). 408p. pap. 35.00 *(978-0-271-03345-7(2))*; 2008. (C). 65.00 *(978-0-271-03344-0(4))* Pennsylvania State Univ. Pr.
Friedman, Ryan Jay. Hollywood's African American Films: The Transition to Sound. 2011. (ENG., Illus.). 288p. (C). 72.00 *(978-0-8135-5048-0(3))*; pap. 24.95 *(978-0-8135-5049-7(1))* Rutgers Univ. Pr.
Howard, Josiah. Blaxploitation Cinema. 2007. (Illus.). 192p. pap. 27.95 *(978-1-903254-44-8(2))* FAB Pr. GBR. Dist: SCB Distributors.
Keeling, Kara. The Witch's Flight: The Cinematic, the Black Femme, & the Image of Common Sense. 2007. (Perverse Modernities Ser.). (ENG.). 224p. (C). 79.95 *(978-0-8223-4013-3(5))*; (Illus.). per. 22.95 *(978-0-8223-4025-6(9))* Duke Univ. Pr.
King, C. Richard & Leonard, David J. Visual Economies Of/In Motion: Sport & Film. 2006. (Cultural Critique Ser.: Vol. 6). 288p. (C). pap. 34.95 *(978-0-8204-7852-4(0))* Lang, Peter Publishing, Inc.
Koven, Mikel J. Blaxploitation Films. 2010. (ENG., Illus.). 160p. pap. 19.95 *(978-1-84243-334-8(2))* Oldcastle Bks., Ltd. GBR. Dist: Independent Pubs. Group.
Lawrence, Novotny. Blaxploitation Films of The 1970's: Blackness & Genre. 2007. (Studies in African American History & Culture Ser.). (ENG.). 146p. 125.00 *(978-0-415-96097-7(5))* Routledge.
Lawrence, Novotny. Blaxploitation Films of The 1970s: Blackness & Genre. 2012. (Studies in African American History & Culture Ser.). (ENG.). 146p. pap. 42.95 ***(978-0-415-54095-7(X))*** Routledge.
Mapp, Edward. African Americans & the Oscar: Decades of Struggle & Achievement. 2nd ed. 2008. (ENG., Illus.). 218p. 50.00 *(978-0-8108-6105-3(4))*; per. 25.00 *(978-0-8108-6106-0(2))* Scarecrow Pr., Inc.
Martin, Courtney J. I Wish It Were True: A Collaborative Project. 2006. (ENG., Illus.). 16p. (C). 10.00 *(978-0-9762853-3-5(9))* Jamaica Ctr. for Arts & Learning.
Mask, Mia. Contemporary Black American Cinema: Race, Gender & Sexuality at the Movies. 2012. 256p. E-Book ***(978-0-203-11814-6(6))*** Routledge.
Mask, Mia. Divas on Screen: Black Women in American Film. 2009. (ENG., Illus.). 320p. 75.00 *(978-0-252-03422-0(8))*; pap. 26.00 *(978-0-252-07619-0(2))* Univ. of Illinois Pr.
Mask, Mia, ed. Contemporary Black American Cinema. 2012. (ENG., Illus.). 272p. (C). 125.00 ***(978-0-415-52322-6(2))*** Routledge.
McCluskey, Audrey Thomas, ed. Frame by Frame III: A Filmography of the African Diasporan Image, 1994-2004. 2007. (ENG.). 1112p. 75.00 *(978-0-253-34829-6(3)*, 0253348293) Indiana Univ. Pr.
Means Coleman, Robin R. Horror Noire. 2011. (ENG., Illus.). 296p. (C). 150.00 *(978-0-415-88019-0(X))*; pap. 35.95 *(978-0-415-88020-6(3))* Routledge.
Nama, Adilifu. Black Space: Imagining Race in Science Fiction Film. 2008. (ENG., Illus.). 212p. pap. 24.95 *(978-0-292-71745-9(8))* Univ. of Texas Pr.
Petty, Sheila J. Contact Zones: Memory, Origin, & Discourse in Black Diasporic Cinema. 2008. (Contemporary Approaches to Film & Television Ser.). (Illus.). 295p. per. 29.95 *(978-0-8143-3099-9(1))* Wayne State Univ. Pr.
Pines, Jim. Doing the Right Thing: The Spike Lee Phenomenon. 2010. (Inspirations Ser.). (ENG.). 200p. pap. 9.95 *(978-1-906413-41-5(X))* Arcadia Bks. Ltd. GBR. Dist: Independent Pubs. Group.
Pramaggiore, Maria. Irish & African American Cinema: Identifying Others & Performing Identities, 1980-2000. 2008. (SUNY Series, Cultural Studies in Cinema/Video). (Illus.). 245p. per. 29.95 *(978-0-7914-7096-1(2))* State Univ. of New York Pr.
Robinson, Cedric J. Forgeries of Memory & Meaning: Blacks & the Regimes of Race in American Theater & Film Before World War II. 2007. (ENG., Illus.). 445p. 73.95 *(978-0-8078-3148-9(4))*; pap. 24.95 *(978-0-8078-5841-7(2))* Univ. of North Carolina Pr.
Ross, Lawrence C., Jr. Money Shot: The Wild Nights & Lonely Days Inside the Black Porn Industry. 2007. (ENG., Illus.). 304p. per. 15.99 *(978-1-56025-913-8(2))* Running Pr. Bk. Pubs.
Sieving, Christopher. Soul Searching: Black-Themed Cinema from the March on Washington to the Rise of Blaxploitation. 2011. (Wesleyan Film Ser.). (ENG., Illus.). 280p. (C). 75.00 *(978-0-8195-7132-8(6))*; pap. 27.95 *(978-0-8195-7133-5(4))* Wesleyan Univ. Pr.
Sims, Yvonne D. Women of Blaxploitation: How the Black Action Film Heroine Changed American Popular Culture. 2006. (ENG., Illus.). 232p. per. 35.00 *(978-0-7864-2744-4(2))* McFarland & Co., Inc. Pubs.
Smith, Valerie, ed. Representing Blackness: Issues in Film & Video. (Illus.). 250p. pap. *(978-0-485-30081-9(8))* Continuum International Publishing Group, Ltd.
Walker, David, et al. Reflections on Blaxploitation: Actors & Directors Speak. 2009. (ENG., Illus.). 248p. 45.00 *(978-0-8108-6706-2(0))* Scarecrow Pr., Inc.
Weisenfeld, Judith. Hollywood Be Thy Name: African American Religion in American Film, 1929-1949. 2007. (Illus.). 341p. 65.00 *(978-0-520-22774-3(3))*; pr. 26.95 *(978-0-520-25100-7(8))* Univ. of California Pr.
Wilderson, Frank B., III. Red, White, & Black: Cinema & the Structure of U. S. Antagonisms. 2010. (ENG., Illus.). 408p. 94.95 *(978-0-8223-4692-0(3))*; pap. 26.95 *(978-0-8223-4701-9(6))* Duke Univ. Pr.
Winn, J. Emmett. Documenting Racism: African Americans in US Department of Agriculture Documentaries, 1921-42. 2012. (ENG., Illus.). 168p. 110.00 *(978-0-8264-0555-5(X))* Continuum International Publishing Group, Ltd. GBR. Dist: National Bk. Network.

AFRICAN AMERICANS IN SPORTS
see also African American Athletes; Negro Leagues
Brooks, Scott N. Black Men Can't Shoot. 2009. (Illus.). 248p. 22.00 *(978-0-226-07603-4(2))* Univ. of Chicago Pr.
Djata, Sundiata. Blacks at the Net: Black Achievement in the History of Tennis, Volume 2. 2008. (Sports & Entertainment Ser.). (Illus.). 270p. 29.95 *(978-0-8156-0898-1(5))* Syracuse Univ. Pr.
Fussman, Cal. After Jackie: Pride, Prejudice, & Baseball's Forgotten Heroes: an Oral History. 2007. (ENG., Illus.). 256p. 24.95 *(978-1-933060-18-7(2)*, ESPN Bks.) ESPN Enterprises.
Holway, John. Voices from the Great Black Baseball Leagues. rev. ed. 2010. (Dover Baseball Ser.). (ENG.). 448p. pap. 15.95 *(978-0-486-47541-7(7))* Dover Pubns., Inc.
Katz, Milton S. Breaking Through: John B. McLendon, Basketball Legend & Civil Rights Pioneer. 2007. (Illus.). 256p. 32.50 *(978-1-55728-847-9(X))* Univ. of Arkansas Pr.
Kent, Graeme. The Great White Hopes: The Quest to Defeat Jack Johnson. 2007. (Illus.). 253p. per. 14.95 *(978-0-7509-4613-1(X))* History Pr. Ltd., The GBR. Dist: Independent Pubs. Group.
Linge, Mary Kay. Jackie Robinson: A Biography. 1 vol. 2007. (Greenwood Biographies Ser.). (Illus.). 192p. 35.00 *(978-0-313-33828-1(0)*, GR3828, Greenwood Pr.) Greenwood Publishing Group, Inc.
McNeil, William F. Black Baseball Out of Season: Pay for Play Outside of the Negro Leagues. 2007. (ENG., Illus.). 244p. 49.95 *(978-0-7864-2901-1(1))* McFarland & Co., Inc. Pubs.
Moon, Warren. Never Give up on Your Dream: My Journey. 2013. (ENG.). 288p. pap. 15.00 *(978-0-306-81875-2(2))* Da Capo Pr., Inc.
Mourning, Alonzo & Wetzel, Dan. Resilience. 2009. (ENG., Illus.). 272p. pap. 15.00 *(978-0-345-50750-1(9)*, Ballantine Bks.) Random House Publishing Group.
Naomi Bryson, Ed. D. The Day Snow Turned Black. 2009. 192p. pap. 14.49 *(978-1-4389-6133-0(2))* AuthorHouse.
Ritchie, Andrew. Major Taylor: The Fastest Bicycle Rider in the World. 2nd ed. 2009. (Illus.). 240p. 39.95 *(978-1-892495-65-5(1))* Cycle Publishing/Van Der Plas Pubns.
Shields, David. Black Planet: Facing Race During an NBA Season. 2006. (ENG.). 225p. pap. 15.95 *(978-0-8032-9354-0(2)*, Bison Bks.) Univ. of Nebraska Pr.
White, Bill. Uppity: My Untold Story about the Games People Play. 2012. (ENG., Illus.). 320p. pap. 15.99 ***(978-0-446-55526-5(6))*** Grand Central Publishing.

AFRICAN AMERICANS IN TELEVISION BROADCASTING
Adamc, Gregory. African Americans in Television: Behind the Scenes. 2010. (Illus.). 216p. (C). 119.95 *(978-1-4331-1040-5(7))*; pap. 32.95 *(978-1-4331-1039-9(3))* Lang, Peter Publishing, Inc.
Bodroghkozy, Aniko. Equal Time: Television & the Civil Rights Movement. 2012. (Illus.). x, 265p. E-Book ***(978-0-252-09378-4(X))***; (ENG., 280p. 50.00 ***(978-0-252-03668-2(9))*** Univ. of Illinois Pr.
Bryant, Natriece. African American Television Sitcom Stereotypes. 2009. 60p. pap. *(978-3-639-12962-5(8))* VDM Verlag Dr. Mueller e.K.
Fearn-Banks, Kathleen. The A to Z of African-American Television. 2009. (a to Z Guide Ser.: 49). (ENG.). 586p. pap. 34.45 *(978-0-8108-6832-8(6))* Scarecrow Pr., Inc.
Indovino, Shaina Carmel. Tyra Banks: From the Runway to the Television Screen. 2012. ***(978-1-4222-2294-2(2))***; pap. ***(978-1-4222-2305-5(1))*** Mason Crest Pubs.
Jacobs, Carole. Tyra Banks: A Biography. 2010. (Illus.). xl, 180p. E-Book *(978-0-313-38275-8(1)*, Greenwood Electronic Media (GEM)); 180p. 35.00 *(978-0-313-38274-1(3)*, A3155C) Greenwood Publishing Group, Inc.
Kiuchi, Yuya. Struggles for Equal Voice: The History of African American Media Democracy. 2012. (ENG.). 336p. 85.00 ***(978-1-4384-4479-6(6))*** State Univ. of New York Pr.
Smith-Shomade, Beretta E. Pimpin' Ain't Easy: Selling Black Entertainment Television. 2007. (Illus.). 210p. 125.00 *(978-0-415-97678-7(2))*; per. 32.95 *(978-0-415-97679-4(0))* Routledge.
Wright, Carl Jeffrey. God's Vision or Television: How Television Influences What We Believe. 2010. 92p. 9.95 *(978-0-940955-90-5(3))* UMI (Urban Ministries, Inc.).

AFRICAN AMERICANS IN THE ARMED FORCES
see United States—Armed Forces—African Americans

AFRICAN AMERICANS IN THE MOTION PICTURE INDUSTRY
Here are entered works on all aspects of African American involvement in motion pictures. Works on the portrayal of African Americans in motion pictures are entered under African Americans in motion pictures. Works on specific aspects of African American involvement are entered under the particular subject, e.g. African American Motion Picture Actors and Actresses.
see also African American Motion Picture Actors and Actresses; African Americans in Motion Pictures
Berry, S. Torriano & Berry, Venise T. Historical Dictionary of African American Cinema. 2007. (Historical Dictionaries of Literature & the Arts Ser.: Vol. 12). (ENG., Illus.). 448p. 99.00 *(978-0-8108-5545-8(3))* Scarecrow Pr., Inc.
Friedman, Ryan Jay. Hollywood's African American Films: The Transition to Sound. 2011. (ENG., Illus.). 288p. (C). 72.00 *(978-0-8135-5048-0(3))*; pap. 24.95 *(978-0-8135-5049-7(1))* Rutgers Univ. Pr.
HarperCollins Publishers Ltd. Staff. Oprah. (ENG.). 623p. pap. 14.00 *(978-0-06-093364-7(X))* HarperCollins Pubs.
Mask, Mia. Contemporary Black American Cinema: Race, Gender & Sexuality at the Movies. 2012. 256p. E-Book ***(978-0-203-11814-6(6))*** Routledge.
Mask, Mia, ed. Contemporary Black American Cinema. 2012. (ENG., Illus.). 272p. (C). 125.00 ***(978-0-415-52322-6(2))*** Routledge.
Pramaggiore, Maria. Irish & African American Cinema: Identifying Others & Performing Identities, 1980-2000. (SUNY Series, Cultural Studies in Cinema/Video). (Illus.). 245p. 2008. per. 29.95 *(978-0-7914-7096-1(2))* 2007. 66.00 *(978-0-7914-7095-4(4))* State Univ. of New York Pr.
Ross, Lawrence C., Jr. Money Shot: The Wild Nights & Lonely Days Inside the Black Porn Industry. 2007. (ENG., Illus.). 304p. per. 15.99 *(978-1-56025-913-8(2))* Running Pr. Bk. Pubs.
Sieving, Christopher. Soul Searching: Black-Themed Cinema from the March on Washington to the Rise of Blaxploitation. 2011. (Wesleyan Film Ser.). (ENG., Illus.). 280p. (C). 75.00 *(978-0-8195-7132-8(6))*; pap. 27.95 *(978-0-8195-7133-5(4))* Wesleyan Univ. Pr.

AFRICAN AMERICANS IN THE PERFORMING ARTS
see also African American Entertainers; Minstrel Shows
Brooks, Daphne A. Bodies in Dissent: Spectacular Performances of Race & Freedom, 1850-1910. 2006. (ENG., Illus.). 488p. 99.95 *(978-0-8223-3710-2(X))*; per. 27.95 *(978-0-8223-3722-5(3))* Duke Univ. Pr.
Catanese, Brandi Wilkins. The Problem of the Color[blind]: Racial Transgression & the Politics of Black Performance. 2011. (Theater: Theory/Text/Performance Ser.). (ENG.). 244p. 75.00 *(978-0-472-07126-5(2))*; pap. 28.95 *(978-0-472-05126-7(1))* Univ. of Michigan Pr.
Dickerson, Glenda. African American Theater: A Cultural Companion. 2008. (PCHL-Polity Cultural History of Literature Ser.: 2). (ENG., Illus.). 256p. pap. 24.95 *(978-0-7456-3443-2(5))*; 79.95 *(978-0-7456-3442-5(7))* Polity Pr. GBR. Dist: Wiley, John & Sons, Inc.
Dixon Gottschild, Brenda. Joan Myers Brown & the Audacious Hope of the Black Ballerina: A Biohistory of American Performance. 2011. (ENG., Illus.). 370p. pap. 27.00 ***(978-0-230-11409-8(1))*** Palgrave Macmillan.
Fine, Elizabeth C. Soulstepping: African American Step Shows. 2007. (ENG., Illus.). 216p. per. 22.00 *(978-0-252-07534-6(X))* Univ. of Illinois Pr.
Gottschild, Brenda Dixon. Joan Myers Brown & the Audacious Hope of the Black Ballerina: A Biohistory of American Performance. 2011. (ENG., Illus.). 370p. 90.00 ***(978-0-230-11408-1(3))*** Palgrave Macmillan.
Kraut, Anthea. Choreographing the Folk: The Dance Stagings of Zora Neale Hurston. 2008. (Illus.). 312p. pap. 25.00 *(978-0-8166-4712-5(7))*; 75.00 *(978-0-8166-4711-8(9))* Univ. of Minnesota Pr.
McAllister, Marvin. Whiting Up: Whiteface Minstrels & Stage Europeans in African American Performance. 2011. (ENG., Illus.). 336p. 39.95 *(978-0-8078-3508-1(0))* Univ. of North Carolina Pr.
Otfinoski, Steven. The Performing Arts. 2nd rev. ed. 2010. (A to Z of African Americans Ser.). (Illus.). 288p. (C). (gr. 9-18). 49.50 *(978-0-8160-7838-7(6))* Facts On File, Inc.
Reed, Bill. Hot from Harlem: Twelve African American Entertainers, 1890-1960. 2009. (ENG., Illus.). 271p. pap. 39.95 *(978-0-7864-4467-0(3))* McFarland & Co., Inc. Pubs.
Robinson, Cedric J. Forgeries of Memory & Meaning: Blacks & the Regimes of Race in American Theater & Film Before World War II. 2007. (ENG., Illus.). 445p. 73.95 *(978-0-8078-3148-9(4))*; pap. 24.95 *(978-0-8078-5841-7(2))* Univ. of North Carolina Pr.
Sotiropoulos, Karen. Staging Race: Black Performers in Turn of the Century America. 2008. (Illus.). 304p. per. 22.50 *(978-0-674-02760-2(4))* Harvard Univ. Pr.
Wilson, James F. Bulldaggers, Pansies, & Chocolate Babies: Performance, Race, & Sexuality in the Harlem Renaissance. (Triangulations: Lesbian/Gay/Queer Theater/Drama/Performance Ser.). (Illus.). 2011. (ENG.). 262p. pap. 27.95 ***(978-0-472-03489-5(8))*** 2010. ix, 260p. E-Book 29.95 *(978-0-472-02696-8(8))* Univ. of Michigan Pr.
Young, Vershawn Ashanti & Tsemo, Bridget Harris, eds. From Bourgeois to Boojie: Black Middle-Class Performances. 2015. (Illus.). 416p. pap. 24.95 *(978-0-8143-3468-3(7))* Wayne State Univ. Pr.

AFRICAN AMERICANS IN THE RADIO INDUSTRY
Johnson, Phylis. KJLH-FM & the Los Angeles Riots Of 1992: Compton's Neighborhood Station in the Aftermath of the Rodney King Verdict. 2009. (ENG.). 222p. pap. 35.00 *(978-0-7864-4386-4(3))* McFarland & Co., Inc. Pubs.
Will Arbitron's Personal People Meter Silence Minority Owned Radio Stations? Hearing Before the Committee on Oversight & Government Reform, House of Representatives, One Hundred Eleventh Congress, First Session, December 2, 2009. 2010. (Illus.). iii, 235p. *(978-0-16-086321-9(X)*, 552-070-41408-8) United States Government Printing Office.

AFRICAN AMERICANS IN THE TELEVISION INDUSTRY
see African Americans in Television Broadcasting

AFRICAN AND MALAGASY UNION
Akokpari, John, et al, eds. The African Union & Its Institutions. 2009. (ENG.). 416p. pap. 22.00 *(978-1-920196-03-5(X))* Jacana Media ZAF. Dist: Independent Pubs. Group.

AFRICAN ARCHITECTURE
see Architecture—Africa

AFRICAN ART
see Art, African

AFRO-ASIAN POLITICS
see Afro-Asian Politics

AFRICAN AUTHORS
see Authors, African

AFRICAN BALLADS AND SONGS
see Folk Songs, African; Songs, African

AFRICAN COOKING
see Cooking, African

AFRICAN CULTS
see Cults—Africa

AFRICAN DIASPORA
Here are entered works dealing with the dispersion of Black Africans to countries outside of the African Continent, together with a description of life, attitude and outlook in their new surroundings.
see also headings of the type Africans—(Place) or Blacks—(Place)
Aborampah, Osei-Mensah & Sudarkasa, Niara. Extended Families in Africa & the African Diaspora. 2011. (Illus.). vi, 398p. *(978-1-59221-812-7(1))*; pap. *(978-1-59221-811-0(3))* Africa World Pr.
Adderley, Rosanne Marion. New Negroes from Africa: Slave Trade Abolition & Free African Settlement in the Nineteenth-Century Caribbean. 2006. (Blacks in the Diaspora Ser.). (ENG.). 360p. pap. 24.95 *(978-0-253-21827-8(6)*, 0253218276); 337p. 65.00 *(978-0-253-34703-9(3))* Indiana Univ. Pr.
Adeleke, Tunde. The Case Against Afrocentrism. 2009. (ENG.). 224p. 50.00 *(978-1-60473-293-1(8))* Univ. Pr. of Mississippi.
Adepoju, Aderanti, ed. International Migration Within, to & from Africa in a Globalised World. 2009. (Illus.). 264p. pap. *(978-9988-647-42-1(5))* Sub-Saharan Pubs. & Traders GHA. Dist: Michigan State Univ. Pr.
Adepoju, Aderanti, et al, eds. International Migration & National Development in Sub-Saharan Africa: Viewpoints & Policy Initiatives in the Countries of Origin. 2007. (Afrika-Studiecentrum Ser.). (Illus.). 307p. per. *(978-90-04-16354-6(9))* BRILL.
Adogame, Afeosemime U. Christianity in Africa & the African Diaspora: The Appropriation of a Scattered Heritage. Gerloff, Roswith & Hock, Klaus, eds. 2009. (ENG.). 368p. 150.00 *(978-1-84706-317-5(9))* Continuum International Publishing Group, Ltd. GBR. Dist: National Bk. Network.
Afolabi, Niyi, ed. Toyin Falola: The Man, the Mask, the Muse. 2010. 1116p. 65.00 *(978-1-59460-754-7(0))* Carolina Academic Pr.
Afolabi, Niyi & Falola, Toyin, eds. African Minorities in the New World. 2007. (African Studies: History, Politics, Economics & Culture Ser.). (ENG.). 290p. 125.00 *(978-0-415-96092-2(4))* Routledge.
Alpers, Edward A. African Diasporas: A Global Perspective. 2009. 296p. 43.95 *(978-0-415-26815-8(X))*; 130.00 *(978-0-415-26814-1(1))* Routledge.
Araujo, Ana Lucia, et al. Crossing Memories: Slavery & African Diaspora. 2011. *(978-1-59221-819-6(9))*; 310p. pap. *(978-1-59221-820-2(2))* Africa World Pr.
Arthur, John A. African Diaspora Identities: Negotiating Culture in Transnational Migration. 2010. (ENG., Illus.). 318p. 80.00 *(978-0-7391-4637-8(8))* Lexington Bks.
Asante, Molefi K. The African American People: A Global History. 2011. E-Book ***(978-0-203-14508-1(9))*** Routledge.
Asante, Molefi Kete. The African American People. 2011. (ENG., Illus.). 416p. 125.00 ***(978-0-415-87254-6(5))***; pap. 39.95 ***(978-0-415-87255-3(3))*** Routledge.
—An Afrocentric Manifesto. 2007. (ENG.). 192p. 69.95 *(978-0-7456-4102-7(4))* Polity Pr. GBR. Dist: Wiley, John & Sons, Inc.
—An Afrocentric Manifesto: Toward an African Renaissance. 2007. (ENG.). 192p. pap. 19.95 *(978-0-7456-4103-4(2))* Polity Pr. GBR. Dist: Wiley, John & Sons, Inc.
At Al Staff, et al. African Theatre - Diasporas, No. 8. Banham, Martin, ed. 2009. (African Theatre Ser.: Volume 8). (Illus.). 190p. pap. 29.95 *(978-1-84701-501-3(8)*, Currey, James) Boydell & Brewer, Ltd. GBR. Dist: Boydell & Brewer, Inc.
Bakari, Sadiki. Butt Naked Raw & Uncensored. 2007. 172p. pap. 18.96 *(978-0-615-15261-5(9))* Sadiki Bakari Publishing.
Bandele, Ramla M. Black Star: African American Activism in the International Political Economy. 2008. (ENG., Illus.). 248p. 42.00 *(978-0-252-03339-1(6))* Univ. of Illinois Pr.
Banerjee, Sukanya, et al, eds. New Routes for Diaspora Studies. 2012. (21st Century Studies). (ENG., Illus.). 252p. 85.00 ***(978-0-253-00217-4(6)***, 0253002176); pap. 30.00 ***(978-0-253-00210-5(9)***, 0253002109) Indiana Univ. Pr.
Bankie, B. F. & Mchombu, K. J. Pan-Africanism/African Nationalism: Strengthening the Unity of Africa & Its Diaspora. 2nd ed. 2008. *(978-1-56902-297-9(6))*; 400p. pap. *(978-1-56902-298-6(4))* Red Sea Pr.
Barry, Boubacar, et al. Africa, Brazil, & the Construction of Trans-Atlantic Black Identities. 2007. *(978-1-59221-526-3(2))*; x, 346p. pap. *(978-1-59221-527-0(0))* Africa World Pr.
Batalha, Luis & Carling, Jorgen, eds. Transnational Archipelago: Perspectives on Cape Verdean Migration & Diaspora. 2008. 288p. pap. *(978-90-5356-994-8(4)*, Leiden Univ. Pr.) Amsterdam Univ. Pr.
Bodomo, Adams. Africans in China: A Sociocultural Study & Its Implications on Africa-China Relations. 2012. 14.99 ***(978-1-60497-790-5(6))*** Cambria Pr.
Bonnett, Aubrey W. & Holder, Calvin B. Continuing Perspectives on the Black Diaspora. 2009. xxi, 263p. *(978-0-7618-4663-5(8))* Univ. Pr. of America, Inc.
Bressey, Caroline, ed. Belonging in Europe - the African Diaspora & Work. 2009. 192p. 150.00 *(978-0-415-48870-9(2))* Routledge.
Bryant, Sherwin K., et al, eds. Africans to Spanish America: Expanding the Diaspora. 2012. (New Black Studies Ser.). (ENG., Illus.). 288p. 50.00 ***(978-0-252-03663-7(8))*** Univ. of Illinois Pr.

Cabdisalaam M. Ciisa-Salwe, et al. Orality & Computer-Mediated Communication: Mailing List Usage in Peace & Conflict. 2010. (Illus.). 118p. pap. *(978-3-8383-4600-7(9))* Lambert Academic Publishing.

Carter, Donald Martin. Navigating the African Diaspora: The Anthropology of Invisibility. 2010. (Illus.). 328p. 90.00 *(978-0-8166-4777-4(1))*; pap. 30.00 *(978-0-8166-4778-1(X))* Univ. of Minnesota Pr.

Clarke, Kamari Maxine & Thomas, Deborah A., eds. Globalization & Race: Transformations in the Cultural Production of Blackness. 2006. (ENG., Illus.). 424p. (C). 99.95 *(978-0-8223-3759-1(2))* Duke Univ. Pr.

Corbould, Clare. Becoming African Americans: Black Public Life in Harlem, 1919-1939. 2009. (Illus.). 304p. 42.00 *(978-0-674-03262-0(4))* Harvard Univ. Pr.

Covi, Giovanna. Modernist Women Race Nation: Networking Women 1890-1950 Circum-Atlantic Connections. 2006. (Illus.). 214p. pap. 29.99 *(978-1-902294-29-2(7))* Mango Publishing GBR. Dist: SPD-Small Pr. Distribution.

Cram101 Textbook Reviews. Outlines & Highlights for Africana Studies: A Survey of Africa & the African Diaspora by Azevedo, ISBN. 2011. 122p. pap. 28.95 ***(978-1-61812-813-3(2))*** Cram101 Inc.

—Outlines & Highlights for Africana Studies: Survey of Africa & the African Diaspora by Azevedo, Mario, ISBN. 2011. 254p. pap. 31.95 ***(978-1-61812-522-4(2))*** Cram101 Inc.

Crush, Jonathan & Tevera, Daniel, eds. Zimbabwe's Exodus: Crisis, Migration, Survival. 2006. 432p. pap. *(978-1-920409-22-7(X))* IDASA Pubs. ZAF. Dist: Michigan State Univ. Pr.

Curry, Dawne Y., et al, eds. Extending the Diaspora: New Histories of Black People. 2009. (New Black Studies Ser.). (ENG., Illus.). 312p. 75.00 *(978-0-252-03459-6(7))*; 328p. pap. 30.00 *(978-0-252-07652-7(4))* Univ. of Illinois Pr.

Daise, Ronald. Gullah Branches, West African Roots. 2007. (Illus.). 198p. per. *(978-0-87844-182-2(4))* Sandlapper Publishing Co., Inc.

Davies, Carole Boyce, ed. Encyclopedia of the African Diaspora: Origins, Experiences, & Culture, 3 vols., Set. 2008. (Illus.). 1110p. 295.00 *(978-1-85109-700-5(7)*, AFRDISC) ABC-CLIO, LLC.

Davis, Darien J. Beyond Slavery: The Multilayered Legacy of Africans in Latin America & the Caribbean. 2006. (Jaguar Books on Latin America Ser.). (ENG., Illus.). 298p. 92.00 *(978-0-7425-4130-6(4))*; per. 34.95 *(978-0-7425-4131-3(2))* Rowman & Littlefield Publishers, Inc.

Demissie, Fassil, ed. African Diaspora & the Metropolis: Reading the African, African American & Caribbean Experience. 2009. (ENG.). 118p. 125.00 *(978-0-415-56034-4(9))* Routledge.

Dieng, Babacar. Reclaiming History: A Study of the Emerging Postcolonial Consciousness in Mid-century Novels of the African Diaspora. 2008. 204p. pap. *(978-3-8364-8943-0(0))* VDM Verlag Dr. Mueller e.K.

Dodson, Howard & Palmer, Colin, eds. Origins. 2008. (ENG., Illus.). 225p. (C). pap. 19.95 *(978-0-87013-817-1(0))* Michigan State Univ. Pr.

Drewal, Henry John. Sacred Waters: Arts for Mami Wata & Other Divinities in Africa & the Diaspora. Drewal, Henry John, ed. 2008. (African Expressive Cultures Ser.). (ENG., Illus.). 708p. 75.00 *(978-0-253-35156-2(1)*, 0253351561) Indiana Univ. Pr.

Drewal, Henry John & Drewal et al., Henry John. Mami Wata: Arts for Water Spirits in Africa & Its Diasporas. 2008. (ENG., Illus.). 228p. pap. *(978-0-9748729-9-5(7))* Univ. of California, Los Angeles, Fowler Museum of Cultural History.

Everett, Anna. Digital Diaspora: A Race for Cyberspace. 2009. (Illus.). 272p. 89.50 *(978-0-7914-7673-4(1))*; pap. 29.95 *(978-0-7914-7674-1(X))* State Univ. of New York Pr.

Falola, Toyin & Afolabi, Niyi, eds. African Minorities in the New World. 2012. (African Studies). (ENG.). 290p. pap. 42.95 ***(978-0-415-54084-1(4))*** Routledge.

—Trans-Atlantic Migration: The Paradoxes of Exile. (African Studies). (ENG.). 314p. 2012. pap. 42.95 ***(978-0-415-54249-4(9))*** 2007. (Illus.). 128.00 *(978-0-415-96091-5(6))* Routledge.

Falola, Toyin & Childs, Matt D. The Changing Worlds of Atlantic Africa: Essays in Honor of Robin Law. 2009. 536p. pap. 55.00 *(978-1-59460-594-9(7))* Carolina Academic Pr.

Falola, Toyin, et al. Migrations & Creative Expressions in Africa & the African Diaspora. 2008. 510p. pap. 55.00 *(978-1-59460-460-7(6))* Carolina Academic Pr.

Farah, A. Somalia. 2007. 340p. per. *(978-1-905068-83-8(2))* Adonis & Abbey Publishers Ltd.

Farred, Grant & Bell, David A. Africana Thought. Farred, Grant, ed. 2009. (ENG.). 204p. pap. 14.00 *(978-0-8223-6707-9(6))* Duke Univ. Pr.

Fennell, Christopher C. Crossroads & Cosmologies: Diasporas & Ethnogenesis in the New World. 2010. (Cultural Heritage Studies). (ENG., Illus.). 192p. pap. 29.95 *(978-0-8130-3496-6(5))* Univ. Pr. of Florida.

Freeman, Kassie & Johnson, Ethan, eds. Education in the Black Diaspora. 2011. (Routledge Research in Education Ser.). (ENG., Illus.). 214p. (C). 125.00 *(978-0-415-89034-2(9))* Routledge.

Garofalo, Leo. Afro-Latino Voices: Narratives from the Early Modern Ibero-Atlantic World, 1550-1812. McKnight, Kathryn Joy, ed. 2009. 416p. 57.00 *(978-0-87220-994-7(6))* Hackett Publishing Co., Inc.

Gerloff, Roswith & Hock, Klaus. Christianity in Africa & the African Diaspora: The Appropriation of a Scattered Heritage. Gerloff, Roswith & Hock, Klaus, eds. Adogame, Afe, ed. 2011. (ENG.). 368p. pap. 49.95 *(978-1-4411-2330-5(X))* Continuum International Publishing Group, Ltd. GBR. Dist: National Bk. Network.

Gershenhorn, Jerry. Melville J. Herskovits & the Racial Politics of Knowledge. 2007. (Critical Studies in the History of Anthropology). (ENG.). 347p. pap. 29.95 *(978-0-8032-2247-2(5))* Univ. of Nebraska Pr.

Gordon, Jacob U. Winning the Future for Africa & the Diaspora. 2011. (African Political, Economic, & Security Issues Ser.). 200p. 69.00 *(978-1-61122-813-7(1)*, Nova Novinka) Nova Science Pubs., Inc.

Hamilton, Ruth Simms. Routes of Passage: Volume 1, Part 2: Rethinking the African Diaspora. 2007. (African Diaspora Research Project Ser.). (ENG., Illus.). 260p. per. 34.95 *(978-0-87013-692-4(5))* Michigan State Univ. Pr.

Hamilton, Ruth Simms, ed. Routes of Passage: Rethinking the African Diaspora, Part 1. 2006. (African Diaspora Research Project Ser.). (ENG., Illus.). 384p. per. 34.95 *(978-0-87013-632-0(1))* Michigan State Univ. Pr.

Hargreaves, Alec, et al. Frenchness & the African Diaspora: Identity & Uprising in Contemporary France. Tshimanga, Charles et al, eds. 2009. (ENG., Illus.). 352p. 65.00 *(978-0-253-35375-7(0)*, 0253353750); pap. 24.95 *(978-0-253-22131-5(X)*, 0253221315) Indiana Univ. Pr.

Hawthorne, Walter. From Africa to Brazil: Culture, Identity, & an Atlantic Slave Trade, 1600-1830. 2010. (African Studies). (ENG., Illus.). 280p. 85.00 *(978-0-521-76409-4(2))*; 113p. pap. 25.99 *(978-0-521-15238-9(0))* Cambridge Univ. Pr.

Hine, Darlene Clark, et al, eds. Black Europe & the African Diaspora. 2009. (New Black Studies Ser.). (ENG., Illus.). 376p. 75.00 *(978-0-252-03467-1(8))*; pap. 30.00 *(978-0-252-07657-2(5))* Univ. of Illinois Pr.

Howard-Hassmann, Rhoda E. Reparations to Africa. 2008. (Pennsylvania Studies in Human Rights). 272p. (C). 59.95 *(978-0-8122-4101-3(0))* Univ. of Pennsylvania Pr.

Irele, F. Abiola & Jeyifo, Biodun, eds. The Oxford Encyclopedia of African Thought, 2 vols., Set. 2010. (ENG., Illus.). 992p. 315.00 *(978-0-19-533473-9(6))* Oxford Univ. Pr., Inc.

Jayasuriya, Shihan de S. The African Diaspora in Asian Trade Routes & Cultural Memories. 2010. (Illus.). viii, 198p. 109.95 *(978-0-7734-3651-0(0))* Mellen, Edwin Pr., The.

Joseph-Bani, Lynette. The Biblical Journey of Slavery: From Egypt to the Americas. 2010. 360p. 28.49 *(978-1-4520-0906-3(6))*; pap. 17.99 *(978-1-4520-0905-6(8))* AuthorHouse.

Josiah, Barbara P. Migration, Mining, & the African Diaspora: Guyana in the 19th & 20th Centuries. 2011. (ENG., Illus.). 320p. 85.00 *(978-0-230-11589-7(6))* Palgrave Macmillan.

Kane, Abdoulaye & Leedy, Todd H., eds. African Migrations: Patterns & Perspectives. 2012. (ENG.). 280p. 85.00 *(978-0-253-00308-9(3)*, 0253003083); pap. 32.00 ***(978-0-253-00576-2(0)***, 0253005760) Indiana Univ. Pr.

Konadu, Kwasi. The Akan Diaspora in the Americas, 1 vol. 2012. (ENG.). 324p. pap. 24.95 ***(978-0-19-992285-7(3))*** Oxford Univ. Pr., Inc.

Könighofer, Martina. The New Ship of Zion: Dynamic Diaspora Dimensions of the African Hebrew Israelites of Jerusalem. 2011. (ENG.). 144p. pap. 29.50 *(978-3-8258-1055-9(0))* Lit Verlag DEU. Dist: Transaction Pubs.

Kusow, Abdi & Bjork, Stephanie R. From Mogadishu to Dixon: The Somali Diaspora in a Global Context. 2007. *(978-1-56902-285-6(2))*; 342p. pap. *(978-1-56902-286-3(0))* Red Sea Pr.

Langmia, Kehbuma. The Internet & the Construction of the Immigrant Public Sphere: The Case of the Cameroonian Diaspora. 2007. (ENG., Illus.). 100p. per. 26.50 *(978-0-7618-3792-3(2))* Univ. Pr. of America, Inc.

Larson, Pier M. Ocean of Letters: Language & Creolization in an Indian Ocean Diaspora. 2009. (Critical Perspectives on Empire Ser.). (ENG., Illus.). 398p. pap. 35.99 *(978-0-521-73957-3(8))* Cambridge Univ. Pr.

Larson, Pier M. & Larson, Pier Martin. Ocean of Letters: Language & Creolization in an Indian Ocean Diaspora. 2009. (Critical Perspectives on Empire Ser.). (ENG., Illus.). 398p. 108.00 *(978-0-521-51827-7(X))* Cambridge Univ. Pr.

Manger, Leif & Assal, Munzoul. Diasporas Within & Without Africa: Dynamism, Heterogeneity, Variation. 2006. 200p. pap. 35.00 *(978-91-7106-563-6(6))* Nordiska Afrikainstitutet SWE. Dist: Stylus Publishing, LLC.

Manning, Patrick. The African Diaspora: A History Through Culture. (Columbia Studies in International & Global History Ser.). (ENG., Illus.). 424p. (gr. 17). 2010. pap. 24.50 *(978-0-231-14471-1(7))* 2009. 29.95 *(978-0-231-14470-4(9))* Columbia Univ. Pr.

Marable, Manning, ed. Beyond Race: New Social Movements in the African Diaspora. 2010. (Critical Black Studies). (ENG.). 256p. 75.00 *(978-1-4039-8398-5(4))* Palgrave Macmillan.

Marable, Manning & Clarke, Kristen. New Social Movements in the African Diaspora: Challenging Global Apartheid. Mullings, Leith, ed. 2009. (Critical Black Studies). (ENG., Illus.). 340p. 105.00 *(978-0-230-62139-8(2))*; pap. 32.00 *(978-0-230-62149-7(X))* Palgrave Macmillan.

Martin, Michael T., et al, eds. Redress for Historical Injustices in the United States: On Reparations for Slavery, Jim Crow, & Their Legacies. 2007. (ENG., Illus.). 728p. per. 32.95 *(978-0-8223-4024-9(0))* Duke Univ. Pr.

Martin, Michael T. & Yaquinto, Marilyn, eds. Redress for Historical Injustices in the United States: On Reparations for Slavery, Jim Crow, & Their Legacies. 2007. (ENG., Illus.). 728p. 104.95 *(978-0-8223-4005-8(4))* Duke Univ. Pr.

Mathis, Brondon. The Coming FORERUNNER Ministry Out of AFRICA: Africa & African America's End-Time Calling bringing Gods house of Prayer to Fullness. 2011. (ENG.). 396p. pap. 19.99 ***(978-1-4609-5849-0(7))*** CreateSpace.

McCarthy, Lloyd D. In-Dependence from Bondage: Claude McKay & Michael Manley: Defying the Ideological Clash & Policy Gaps in African Diaspora Relations. 2006. (Illus.). xii, 192p. *(978-1-59221-464-8(9))* Africa World Pr.

McKittrick, Katherine & Woods, Clyde, eds. Black Geographies & the Politics of Place. 2007. (ENG., Illus.). 288p. per. 20.00 *(978-0-89608-773-6(5))* South End Pr.

McKnight, Kathryn Joy & Garofalo, Leo, eds. Afro-Latino Voices: Narratives from the Early Modern Ibero-Atlantic World, 1550-1812. 2009. 416p. pap. 19.95 *(978-0-87220-993-0(8))* Hackett Publishing Co., Inc.

Mercer, Claire, et al. Development & the African Diaspora: Place & the Politics of Home. 2008. (ENG., Illus.). 272p. 108.95 *(978-1-84277-900-2(1))*; pap. 34.95 *(978-1-84277-901-9(X))* Zed Bks., Ltd. GBR. Dist: Macmillan.

Miles, Tiya & Holland, Sharon Patricia, eds. Crossing Waters, Crossing Worlds: The African Diaspora in Indian Country. 2006. (ENG., Illus.). 392p. 94.95 *(978-0-8223-3812-3(2))*; pap. 26.95 *(978-0-8223-3865-9(3))* Duke Univ. Pr.

Mirzai, Behnaz A., et al. Slavery, Islam & Diaspora. 2009. *(978-1-59221-704-5(4))*; 336p. pap. *(978-1-59221-705-2(2))* Africa World Pr.

Montgomery, Georgene Bess. The Spirit & the Word: A Theory of Spirituality in Africana Literary Criticism. 2008. *(978-1-59221-566-9(1))*; 252p. pap. *(978-1-59221-567-6(X))* Africa World Pr.

Moore, Lois Merriweather, ed. The Dispersion of Africans & African Culture Throughout the World: Essays on the African Diaspora. 2007. 225p. *(978-0-7734-5309-8(1))* Mellen, Edwin Pr., The.

Neethling, Estelle. Of Loss, Hope & Healing: Finding Lost Family of the Displaced. 2011. 272p. pap. 22.00 *(978-1-4152-0084-1(X))* Random Hse. Struik (Pty.), Ltd. ZAF. Dist: International Publishers Marketing.

Ogundiran, Akinwumi & Falola, Toyin, eds. Archaeology of Atlantic Africa & the African Diaspora. (Blacks in the Diaspora Ser.). (ENG., Illus.). 528p. 2010. pap. 29.95 *(978-0-253-22175-9(7)*, 0253221757) 2007. 59.95 *(978-0-253-34919-4(2)*, 0253349192) Indiana Univ. Pr.

Ohadike, Don C. Sacred Drums of Liberation: Religions & Music of Resistance in Africa & the Diaspora. 2007. xlv, 259p. *(978-1-59221-516-4(5))*; 304p. pap. *(978-1-59221-517-1(3))* Africa World Pr.

Olaniyan, Tejumola & Sweet, James H., eds. The African Diaspora & the Disciplines. 2010. (ENG., Illus.). 376p. 75.00 *(978-0-253-35464-8(1)*, 0253354641); pap. 27.95 *(978-0-253-22191-9(9)*, 0253221919) Indiana Univ. Pr.

Otero, Solimar. Afro-Cuban Diasporas in the Atlantic World. 2010. (Rochester Studies in African History & the Diaspora Ser.: Volume 45). (Illus.). 260p. 75.00 *(978-1-58046-326-3(6))* Univ. of Rochester Pr.

Peek, Philip M., ed. Twins in African & Diaspora Cultures: Double Trouble, Twice Blessed. 2011. (ENG., Illus.). 376p. 80.00 *(978-0-253-35624-6(5)*, 0253356245); pap. 27.95 *(978-0-253-22307-4(5)*, 0253223075) Indiana Univ. Pr.

Peterson, Charles F. DuBois, Fanon, Cabral: The Margins of Elite Anti-Colonial Leadership. 2007. (ENG.). 170p. 68.50 *(978-0-7391-1158-1(2))* Lexington Bks.

Phillips, Kimberley. Daily Life During African American Migrations, 1 vol. 2012. (Greenwood Press Daily Life Through History Series: Daily Life in the United States Ser.). (Illus.). 226p. 58.00 ***(978-0-313-34373-5(X)***, GR4373) Greenwood Publishing Group, Inc.

Pierre, Jemima. The Predicament of Blackness: Postcolonial Ghana & the Politics of Race. 2012. 280p. pap. 30.00 ***(978-0-226-92303-1(7))***; (Illus.). 90.00 ***(978-0-226-92302-4(9))*** Univ. of Chicago Pr.

Plaza, Sonia & Ratha, Dilip. Diaspora for Development in Africa. 2011. ***(978-0-8213-8619-4(0))*** World Bank Pubns.

Polsgrove, Carol. Ending British Rule in Africa: Writers in a Common Cause. 2009. (Studies in Imperialism Ser.). (ENG.). 240p. 89.95 *(978-0-7190-7767-8(2))* Manchester Univ. Pr. GBR. Dist: Macmillan.

Prabhu, Anjali. Contemporary Cinema of Africa & the Diaspora. 2010. (ENG.). 272p. pap. *(978-1-4051-9303-0(4)*, Wiley-Blackwell) Wiley, John & Sons, Ltd.

Rahier, Jean. Global Circuits of Blackness: Interrogating the African Diaspora. Hintzen, Percy C. & Smith, Felipe, eds. 2010. (ENG., Illus.). 288p. pap. 30.00 *(978-0-252-07753-1(9))* Univ. of Illinois Pr.

Rahier, Jean Muteba, et al, eds. Global Circuits of Blackness: Interrogating the African Diaspora. 2010. (ENG., Illus.). 288p. 80.00 *(978-0-252-03562-3(3))* Univ. of Illinois Pr.

Ratha, Dilip. Leveraging Migration for Africa: Remittances, Skills, & Investments. 2011. ***(978-0-8213-8718-4(9))*** World Bank Pubns.

Reid-Salmon, Delroy A. Home Away from Home: The Caribbean Diasporan Church in the Black Atlantic Tradition. 2008. (Cross Cultural Theologies Ser.). (ENG., Illus.). 256p. (C). 99.95 *(978-1-84553-383-0(6))* Equinox Publishing Ltd. GBR. Dist: ISD.

—Home Away from Home: The Caribeean Diasporan Church in the Black Atlantic Tradition. 2008. (Cross Cultural Theologies Ser.). (ENG.). 256p. (C). pap. 34.95 *(978-1-84553-384-7(4))* Equinox Publishing Ltd. GBR. Dist: ISD.

Robertson, Clyde C. Africa Rising: Multidisciplinary Discussions on Africana Studies & History: From Ancient Times Through Modernity. 2009. *(978-1-59221-716-8(8))*; pap. *(978-1-59221-717-5(6))* Africa World Pr.

Robertson, Ray Von. A Unique Examination of the Black Diaspor. 2009. 196p. pap. *(978-3-639-14760-5(X))* VDM Verlag Dr. Mueller e.K.

Sajovitz, Mathias. The African Diaspora in the Austrian Political Economy: A Marxist Analysis. 2008. 71p. pap. 11.99 *(978-1-4357-3534-7(X))* Lulu Enterprises Inc.

Shaw, Andrea Elizabeth. The Embodiment of Disobedience: Fat Black Women's Unruly Political Bodies. 2006. (ENG.). 162p. 78.99 *(978-0-7391-1486-5(7))*; per. 24.50 *(978-0-7391-1487-2(5))* Lexington Bks.

Sherwood, Marika. Origins of Pan-Africanism: Henry Sylvester Williams, Africa, & the African Diaspora. 2012. (ENG., Illus.). 354p. (C). pap. 39.95 ***(978-0-415-63323-9(0))*** Routledge.

Sherwood, Marika. Origins of Pan-Africanism: Henry Sylvester Williams & the African Diaspora in Britain. 2010. (Routledge Studies in Modern British History Ser.). (ENG., Illus.). 372p. (C). 125.00 *(978-0-415-87959-0(0))* Routledge.

Silva Jayasuriya, Shihan de & Angenot, Jean-Pierre, eds. Uncovering the History of Africans in Asia. 2008. 200p. pap. *(978-90-04-16291-4(7))* BRILL.

Simon, Benjamin. From Migrants to Missionaries: Christians of African Origin in Germany. 2010. (IC - Studien zur interkulturellen Geschichte des Christentums. Etudes d'histoire interculturelle de christianisme. Studies in the Intercultural History of Christianity Ser.). 278p. 72.95 *(978-3-631-59842-9(4))* Lang, Peter GmbH, Europaischer Verlag der Wissenschaften DEU. Dist: Lang, Peter.

Smallwood, Stephanie E. Saltwater Slavery: A Middle Passage from Africa to American Diaspora. (Illus.). 288p. 2008. pap. 19.95 *(978-0-674-03068-8(0))* 2007. 29.95 *(978-0-674-02349-9(8))* Harvard Univ. Pr.

Smiley, D. M. Africa - The Womb of God. 10.00 *(978-0-9724025-0-7(0))* New Covenant Fellowship International.

Smith, Faith Lois, et al. Gendering the African Diaspora: Women, Culture, & Historical Change in the Caribbean & Nigerian Hinterland. Byfield, Judith A. et al, eds. 2010. (Blacks in the Diaspora Ser.). (ENG., Illus.). 344p. 65.00 *(978-0-253-35416-7(1)*, 0253354161); pap. 24.95 *(978-0-253-22153-7(6)*, 0253221536) Indiana Univ. Pr.

Stephens, Michelle Ann. Reconceptualization of the African Diaspora. Ball, Erica & Pappademos, Melina, eds. 2008. (ENG., Illus.). 240p. pap. 14.00 *(978-0-8223-6696-6(7))* Duke Univ. Pr.

Takyi, Baffour K. & Arthur, John, eds. The New African Diaspora in North America: Trends, Community Building, & Adaptation. 2006. (ENG., Illus.). 310p. 73.50 *(978-0-7391-1151-2(5))* Lexington Bks.

Talton, Benjamin. Black Subjects in the African Diaspora. Mills, Quincy, ed. 2011. (ENG.). 224p. 85.00 *(978-0-230-11587-3(X))* Palgrave Macmillan.

Thomas, Deborah A. & Clarke, Kamari Maxine, eds. Globalization & Race: Transformations in the Cultural Production of Blackness. 2006. (ENG.). 424p. per. 27.95 *(978-0-8223-3772-0(X))* Duke Univ. Pr.

Tillery, Alvin B. Between Homeland & Motherland: Africa, U. S. Foreign Policy, & Black Leadership in America. 2011. (Illus.). 216p. pap. 22.95 *(978-0-8014-7734-8(4))* Cornell Univ. Pr.

—Between Homeland & Motherland: Africa, U.S. Foreign Policy, & Black Leadership in America. 2011. (Illus.). 216p. 69.95 *(978-0-8014-4897-3(2))* Cornell Univ. Pr.

Tishken, Joel E., et al, eds. Sàngó in Africa & the African Diaspora. 2009. (African Expressive Cultures Ser.). (ENG & MUL., Illus.). 376p. 75.00 *(978-0-253-35336-8(X)*, 025335336X); pap. 27.95 *(978-0-253-22094-3(7)*, 0253220947) Indiana Univ. Pr.

Toka Diagana (Howard University), ed. African Diaspora Mathematics Research Progress. 2008. viii, 151p. (C). 69.00 *(978-1-60456-204-0(8))* Nova Science Pubs., Inc.

Toledano, Ehud R. African Communities in Asia & the Mediterranean: Identities Between Integration & Conflict. 2011. 310p. ***(978-1-59221-850-9(4))***; pap. ***(978-1-59221-851-6(2))*** Africa World Pr.

Trost, Theodore Louis. The African Diaspora & the Study of Religion. Trost, Theodore Louis, ed. 2007. (Religion/Culture/Critique Ser.). (ENG., Illus.). 288p. 100.00 *(978-1-4039-7786-1(0))* Palgrave Macmillan.

Valdés, Vanessa Kimberly. Let Spirit Speak! Cultural Journey Through the African Diaspora. 2012. (ENG.). 160p. 50.00 ***(978-1-4384-4217-4(3))***; pap. 19.95 ***(978-1-4384-4218-1(1))*** State Univ. of New York Pr.

Wariboko, Waibinte E. Ruined by "Race" Afro-Caribbean Missionaries & the Evangelization of Southern Nigeria, 1895-1925. 2006. (Illus.). xv, 261p. *(978-1-59221-439-6(8))*; 278p. pap. *(978-1-59221-440-2(1))* Africa World Pr.

West, Michael O., et al, eds. From Toussaint to Tupac: The Black International since the Age of Revolution. 2009. (ENG., Illus.). 336p. 62.95 *(978-0-8078-3309-4(6))*; pap. 23.95 *(978-0-8078-5972-8(9))* Univ. of North Carolina Pr.

White, Elisa Joy. Modernity, Freedom, & the African Diaspora: Dublin, New Orleans, Paris. 2012. (Blacks in the Diaspora Ser.). (ENG.). 356p. pap. 30.00 ***(978-0-253-00125-2(0)***, 0253001250); (Illus.). 80.00 ***(978-0-253-00115-3(3)***, 0253001153) Indiana Univ. Pr.

Yeboah, Ian E. a. Black African Neo-Diaspora: Ghanaian Immigrant Experiences in the Greater Cincinnati, Ohio, Area. 2008. (ENG., Illus.). 258p. 78.99 *(978-0-7391-1352-3(6))* Lexington Bks.

Yelvington, Kevin A. & Harrison, Faye Venetia. Afro-Atlantic Dialogues: Anthropology in the Diaspora. Yelvington, Kevin A., ed. (School of American Research Advanced Seminar Ser.). (Illus.). 528p. pap. 34.95 *(978-1-930618-46-6(8))* School for Advanced Research Pr./SAR Pr.

Yewah, Emmanuel & Togunde, 'Dimeji. Across the Atlantic: African Immigrants in the United States Diaspora. 2010. pap. *(978-1-86335-788-3(2))* Common Ground Publishing Pty. Ltd.

Young, Jason R. Rituals of Resistance: African Atlantic Religion in Kongo & the Lowcountry South in the Era of Slavery. 2007. 258p. *(978-0-8071-3279-1(9))* Louisiana State Univ. Pr.

—Rituals of Resistance (p) African Atlantic Religion in Kongo & the Lowcountry South in the Era of Slavery. 2011. (Illus.). 272p. pap. 21.50 *(978-0-8071-3719-2(7))* Louisiana State Univ. Pr.

The check digit for ISBN-10 appears in parentheses after the full ISBN-13

Zeleza, Paul Tiyambe. In Search of African Diasporas: Testimonies & Encounters. 2012. 592p. 65.00 **(978-1-61163-056-5(8))** Carolina Academic Pr.

AFRICAN DRAMA

Alloula, Abdelkar, et al. Four Plays from North Africa. Carlson, Marvin, ed. 2008. (ENG., Illus.). 362p. pap. 20.00 *(978-0-9790570-2-1(7))* Segal, Martin E. Theatre Ctr.

Homann, Greg, ed. At This Stage: Plays from Post-apartheid South Africa. 2009. (ENG., Illus.). 184p. pap. 24.95 *(978-1-86814-493-8(3))* Witwatersrand Univ. Pr. Pubns. ZAF. Dist: Transaction Pubs.

Marzette, DeLinda. Africana Women Writers: Performing Diaspora, Staging Healing. 2012. **(978-1-4331-1380-2(5))** Lang, Peter Publishing, Inc.

Peimer, David. Armed Response: Plays from South Africa. 2009. 314p. 99.95 *(978-1-906497-08-8(7))* Seagull Bks. GBR. Dist: Chicago Distribution Ctr.

Peimer, David, ed. Armed Response: Plays from South Africa. 2009. (Seagull Books - in Performance Ser.). (ENG.). 314p. pap. 24.95 *(978-1-906497-07-1(9))* Seagull Bks. GBR. Dist: Chicago Distribution Ctr.

AFRICAN DRAMA (ENGLISH)

Dunton, Chris. Make Man Talk True: Nigerian Drama in English Since 1970. (ENG.). 215p. **(978-3-11-188639-8(5))** Saur, K. G. Verlag GmbH & Co.

AFRICAN DRAMA—HISTORY AND CRITICISM

Abessolo, Honorine Bernadette. Nsing the Civet Cat - a Dramatic Adaptation of Justine Mintsa's Histoire D'Awu. 2008. 72p. pap. *(978-3-8364-8117-5(0))* VDM Verlag Dr. Mueller e.K.

Amkpa. Theatre & Postcolonial Desires. 2007. 224p. 36.00 *(978-0-415-43544-4(7))* Routledge.

Boscolo, Cristina. Ọdún: Discourses, Strategies, & Power in the Yorùbá Play of Transformation. 2009. (Illus.). 368p. 99.00 *(978-90-420-2680-3(4))* Rodopi.

Conteh-Morgan, John. Theatre & Drama in Francophone Africa: A Critical Introduction. 2006. (ENG.). 256p. pap. 53.00 *(978-0-521-03471-5(X))* Cambridge Univ. Pr.

Igili, Oluchi Joyce. Social Commitment in Ola Rotimi's Plays. 2011. 92p. pap. **(978-3-8443-9758-1(2))** Lambert Academic Publishing.

Kachua, Effumbe. Socio-Political Perspectives in Nwamuo's Drama. 2009. vi, 184p. *(978-978-2503-52-7(5))* Kan sasana Printer.

Migraine-George, Thérèse. African Women & Representation: From Performance to Politics. 2008. 316p. *(978-1-59221-551-5(3))*; pap. *(978-1-59221-550-8(5))* Africa World Pr.

Mule, Katwiwa. Women's Spaces, Women's Visions: Politics, Poetics, & Resistance in African Women's Drama. 2007. *(978-1-59221-560-7(2))*; 324p. pap. *(978-1-59221-561-4(0))* Africa World Pr.

Ndigirigi, Josphat Gichingiri. Ngugi Wa Thiongo's Drama & the Kamirithu Popular Theater Experiment. 2006. *(978-1-59221-341-2(3))*; 318p. pap. *(978-1-59221-342-9(1))* Africa World Pr.

Peyma, Nasser Dasht. Postcolonial Drama: A Comparative Study of Wole Soyinka, Derek Walcott & Girish Karnad. 2009. 258p. 45.00 *(978-81-316-0282-9(6))* Rawat Pubns. IND. Dist: International Specialized Bk. Services.

AFRICAN FICTION

see also Short Stories, African

Conrad, Joseph. Heart of Darkness & Other Tales. Watts, Cedric, ed. 2nd rev. ed. 2008. (Oxford World's Classics Ser.). (ENG., Illus.). 272p. pap. 8.95 *(978-0-19-953601-6(5))* Oxford Univ. Pr., Inc.

Farah, Nuruddin. Crossbones: A Novel. 2012. (ENG.). 400p. (gr. 12). pap. 16.00 **(978-0-14-312253-1(3)**, Penguin (Non-Classics)) Penguin Group (USA) Inc.

Haggard, H. Rider. Benita an African Romance. 2008. 236p. 27.99 *(978-0-554-27128-6(1))* 2008. 236p. 24.99 *(978-0-554-36431-5(X))* 2007. (ENG.). 210p. pap. 20.99 *(978-1-4346-2569-4(9))* BiblioBazaar.

—Benita an African Romance. 2008. (ENG.). 208p. pap. 14.45 *(978-1-4385-1120-7(5)*, Book Jungle) Standard Pubns., Inc.

—Finished. 260p. 2008. (ENG.). per. 14.95 *(978-1-60312-426-3(8))* 2007. 26.95 *(978-1-60312-604-5(X))* Aegypan.

—Finished. 2009. 414p. pap. 34.75 *(978-1-115-75972-4(8))* 2009. 414p. pap. 33.75 *(978-1-115-75973-1(6))* 2008. 344p. 28.99 *(978-0-554-35982-3(0))* 2008. 344p. 29.99 *(978-0-554-26679-4(2))* BiblioBazaar.

—Finished. 2009. 236p. pap. *(978-0-217-21107-9(0))* Books LLC.

—Finished. 2008. 312p. per. *(978-1-4065-6925-4(9))* Dodo Pr.

—Finished. 2008. 364p. pap. 18.95 *(978-1-60096-924-9(0))*; 332p. pap. 17.95 *(978-1-60096-142-7(8))*; 332p. pap. 17.95 *(978-1-60096-619-4(5))* Editorium, The.

—Finished. 2008. 324p. pap. *(978-1-4097-2366-0(6))* Read Bks.

AFRICAN FICTION—HISTORY AND CRITICISM

Aoudjit, Abdelkader. The Algerian Novel & Colonial Discourse: Witnessing to a Différend. 2010. (Francophone Cultures & Literatures Ser.). 228p. (C). 74.95 *(978-1-4331-1074-0(1))* Lang, Peter Publishing, Inc.

Azeyeh, Albert. Le Sembene Ousmane le Mandat. 2011. (FRE.). 98p. pap. **(978-9956-717-06-4(1))** Langaa Research & Publishing Common Initiative Group.

Bamidele, Ayodele. The African Novel in the Context of Combat Poetics. 2011. 204p. pap. **(978-3-8443-2843-1(2))** Lambert Academic Publishing.

Bittner, Petra. Writing the Story of Kenya: Construction of Identity in the Novels of Marjorie Oludhe Macgoye. 2009. 184p. 57.95 *(978-3-631-58916-8(6))* Lang, Peter GmbH. Europaischer Verlag der Wissenschaften DEU. Dist: Lang, Peter.

Cazenave, Odile. Afrique Sur Seine: A New Generation of African Writers in Paris. 2007. (After the Empire: The Francophone World & Postcolonial France Ser.). (ENG.). 194p. per. 26.50 *(978-0-7391-2063-7(8))* Lexington Bks.

Collins, Walter. Tracing Personal Expansion: Reading Selected Novels as Modern African Bildungsroman. 2006. (ENG.). 150p. per. 31.50 *(978-0-7618-3483-0(4))* Univ. Pr. of America, Inc.

Danta, Chris, et al, eds. Strong Opinions: J. M. Coetzee & the Authority of Contemporary Fiction. 2011. (ENG.). 192p. 110.00 *(978-1-4411-0530-1(1))* Continuum International Publishing Group, Ltd. GBR. Dist: National Bk. Network.

Durojaiye Kehinde, Owoeye. Intertextuality & the Novels of Amos Tutuola & Ben Okri. 2011. 84p. pap. **(978-3-8443-2550-8(6))** Lambert Academic Publishing.

Elder, Arlene A. Narrative Shape-Shifting: Myth, Humor & History in the Fiction of Ben Okri, B. Kojo Laing & Yvonne Vera. 2009. 174p. 80.00 *(978-1-84701-012-4(1)*, Currey, James) Boydell & Brewer, Ltd. GBR. Dist: Boydell & Brewer, Inc.

Emenyonu, Ernest N. New Novels in African Literature Today, Vol. 27. Emenyonu, Ernest N., ed. 2009. (African Literature Today Ser.: Volume 27). 185p. pap. 29.95 *(978-0-85255-572-9(5)*, Currey, James) Boydell & Brewer, Ltd. GBR. Dist: Boydell & Brewer, Inc.

Higginson, Francis & Higginson, Pim. The Noir Atlantic: Chester Himes & the Birth of the Francophone African Crime Novel. 2011. (Liverpool University Press - Contemporary French & Francophone Cultures Ser.). (ENG.). 216p. 95.00 *(978-1-84631-690-6(1))* Liverpool Univ. Pr. GBR. Dist: Chicago Distribution Ctr.

Huntington, Julie Anne. Sounding Off: Rhythm, Music, & Identity in West African & Caribbean Francophone Novels. 2009. (African Soundscapes Ser.). (ENG.). 256p. 47.00 *(978-1-4399-0031-4(0))* Temple Univ. Pr.

Irele, F. Abiola. The Cambridge Companion to the African Novel. 2009. (Cambridge Companions to Literature Ser.). (ENG.). 308p. (C). 99.00 *(978-0-521-85560-0(8))*; pap. 30.99 *(978-0-521-67168-2(X))* Cambridge Univ. Pr.

Jacob, Mapara. Historicity & the Shona Novel: The Shona Novel & History. 2011. 104p. pap. **(978-3-639-31645-2(2))** VDM Verlag Dr. Mueller e.K.

Kahari, Lesiel. Spiritual Challenges in Waiting for the Rain & Ancestors. 2011. 116p. pap. **(978-3-8433-5930-6(X))** Lambert Academic Publishing.

Kalisa, Chantal & Kalisa, Marie. Violence in Francophone African & Caribbean Women's Literature. 2009. (ENG.). 236p. 45.00 *(978-0-8032-1102-5(3))* Univ. of Nebraska Pr.

Molvaer, Reidulf Knut. Tradition & Change in Ethiopi: Social & Cultural Life as Reflected in Amharic Fictional Literature (1930-1974) 2008. 284p. pap. 19.95 *(978-1-59907-037-7(5))* Tsehai Pubs. & Distributors.

Mortimer, Mildred. Writing from the Hearth: Public, Domestic, & Imaginative Space in Francophone Women's Fiction of Africa & the Caribbean. 2007. (After the Empire: The Francophone World & Postcolonial France Ser.). (ENG.). 224p. per. 31.50 *(978-0-7391-1907-5(9))* Lexington Bks.

Mortimer, Mildred P. Writing from the Hearth: Public, Domestic, & Imaginative Space in Francophone Women's Fiction of Africa & the Caribbean. 2007. (After the Empire: The Francophone World & Postcolonial France Ser.). (ENG.). 224p. 78.99 *(978-0-7391-1906-8(0))* Lexington Bks.

Mwangi, Evan Maina. Africa Writes Back to Self: Metafiction, Gender, Sexuality. 2010. 360p. pap. 26.95 *(978-1-4384-2682-2(8))*, Suny Pr.) State Univ. of New York Pr.

Odamtten, Vincent O. Broadening the Horizon: Critical Introductions to Amma Darko. 2007. 160p. pap. 23.50 *(978-0-9547023-8-0(7))* Clarke, Ayebia Publishing, Ltd. GBR. Dist: Rienner, Lynne Pubs.

Ogunyemi, Chikwenye Okonjo. Juju Fission: Women's Alternative Fictions from the Sahara, the Kalahari, & the Oases In-Between. 2007. (Society & Politics in Africa Ser.). 336p. (C). 38.95 *(978-1-4331-0089-5(4))* Lang, Peter Publishing, Inc.

Ouzgane, Lahoucine, ed. Men in African Film & Fiction. 2011. (Illus.). 192p. 80.00 *(978-1-84701-521-1(2)*, Currey, James) Boydell & Brewer, Ltd. GBR. Dist: Boydell & Brewer, Inc.

Palmer, Eustace. Of War & Women, Oppression & Optimism: New Essays on the African Novel. 2008. 367p. *(978-1-59221-610-9(2))*; 390p. pap. *(978-1-59221-611-6(0))* Africa World Pr.

Qader, Nasrin. Narratives of Catastrophe: Boris Diop, Ben Jelloun, Khatibi. 2nd ed. 2009. (ENG.). 304p. 65.00 *(978-0-8232-3048-8(1))* Fordham Univ. Pr.

Quayson, Ato, ed. The Cambridge History of Postcolonial Literature 2 Volume Set, 2 vols. 2012. (ENG.). 1424p. 350.00 **(978-0-521-51749-2(4))** Cambridge Univ. Pr.

Rastogi, Pallavi. Afrindian Fictions: Diaspora, Race, & National Desire in South Africa. 2008. (ENG.). cd-rom 14.95 *(978-0-8142-9099-6(X))* Ohio State Univ. Pr.

Sue Kossew Staff. Writing Woman, Writing Place. 2006. (Routledge Research in Postcolonial Literatures Ser.). 256p. 34.00 *(978-0-415-41859-1(3))* Routledge.

Tatira, Liveson. The Portrayal of White Characters As Stereotypes in the Shona Novels. 2011. 68p. pap. **(978-3-8443-1578-3(0))** Lambert Academic Publishing.

ten Kortenaar, Neil. Postcolonial Literature & the Impact of Literacy: Reading & Writing in African & Caribbean Fiction. 2011. (ENG., Illus.). 232p. 90.00 *(978-1-107-00867-0(0))* Cambridge Univ. Pr.

Vakunta, Peter W. Indigenization of Language in the African Francophone Novel: A New Literary Canon. 2011. xii, 166p. 68.95 *(978-1-4331-1271-3(X))* Lang, Peter Publishing, Inc.

AFRICAN LANGUAGES

see also names of languages, e.g. Bantu Languages; Fula Language; also subdivision Languages under names of African countries, regions, etc., e.g. Nigeria—Languages

Aboh, Enoch Oladé, et al, eds. Focus Strategies in African Languages: The Interaction of Focus & Grammar in Niger-Congo & Afro-Asiatic. 2007. (Trends in Linguistics. Studies & Monographs [TiLSM] Ser.). (ENG.). VI, 324p. 238.00 **(978-3-11-916812-0(2))** De Gruyter, Mouton DEU. Dist: de Gruyter, Walter GmbH & Co. KG.

Aboh, Enoch Oladé, et al. Focus Strategies in African Languages: The Interaction of Focus & Grammar in Niger-Congo & Afro-Asiatic. 2007. (Trends in Linguistics. Studies & Monographs [TiLSM] Ser.). (ENG., Illus.). VI, 324p. 154.00 *(978-3-11-019593-4(3))* De Gruyter, Mouton DEU. Dist: de Gruyter, Walter GmbH & Co. KG.

Anyanwu, Rose-Juliet. Fundamentals of Phonetics, Phonology & Tonology: With Specific African Sound Patterns. 2008. (Schriften zur Afrikanistik - Research in African Studies). (Illus.). 330p. pap. 81.95 *(978-3-631-57746-2(X))* Lang, Peter GmbH, Europaischer Verlag der Wissenschaften DEU. Dist: Lang, Peter.

Bai-Sheka, Abou. Temne-English Dictionary. 2007. (TEM, FRE, GER & ENG.). viii, 398p. *(978-0-9780908-1-4(0))* Culter, Robert Bks.

Bechhaus-Gerst, Marianne. The (Hi)story of Nobiin - 1000 Years of Language Change. 2011. 252p. 69.95 **(978-3-631-61494-5(2))** Lang, Peter GmbH, Europaischer Verlag der Wissenschaften DEU. Dist: Lang, Peter.

Bennett, Tsoeu. Multilingual Illustrated Dictionary. 2010. 372p. pap. 24.95 *(978-0-7021-6712-8(6))* NB Pubs. Ltd. ZAF. Dist: International Publishers Marketing.

Bleek, D. F. Comparative Vocabularies of Bushman Languages. 2011. (ENG.). 102p. pap. 19.99 *(978-1-107-67240-6(6))* Cambridge Univ. Pr.

Botne, Robert Dale Olson & Schafer, Loveness. The Chindali Language of Malawi. 2008. *(978-1-60618-909-2(3))* American Philosophical Society.

Brown, Kate. Setswana-English, English-Setswana Dictionary. *(978-0-7859-7470-3(9))* French & European Pubns., Inc.

Caron, B., ed. Subordination, dependance et parataxe dans les langues Africaines. 2008. (Societe d'Etudes Linguistiques et Anthropologiques de France Ser.). (FRE.). 200p. (C). pap. 87.00 *(978-90-429-2166-5(8))* Peeters Pubs. & Booksellers BEL. Dist: Brown, David Bk. Co., The.

Childs, G. Tucker. A Grammar of Mani. 2012. (Mouton Grammar Library [MGL] Ser.: 54). (ENG., Illus.). XIX, 270p. (gr. 17-17). E-Book 321.00 **(978-3-11-026662-7(8))** De Gruyter, Mouton DEU. Dist: de Gruyter, Walter GmbH & Co. KG.

Childs, George Tucker. A Grammar of Mani. 2011. (Mouton Grammar Library [MGL] Ser.). (ENG., Illus.). XIX, 270p. 210.00 **(978-3-11-026497-5(8))** De Gruyter, Mouton DEU. Dist: de Gruyter, Walter GmbH & Co. KG.

Cloete, Aletta Elizabth. Basic Afrikaans: The top 1000 words & Phrases. 2011. (AFR & ENG.). 120p. pap. 17.95 *(978-1-86890-116-6(5))* NB Pubs. Ltd. ZAF. Dist: International Publishers Marketing.

De Klerk Staff. Corpus Linguistics & World Englishes: An Analysis of Xhosa English. 2007. (Corpus & Discourse Ser.). (ENG., Illus.). 272p. 150.00 *(978-0-8264-8841-1(2))* Continuum International Publishing Group, Ltd. GBR. Dist: National Bk. Network.

Deng, Makwei Mabioor. Pioocku Thuongjang: The Elementary Modern Standard Dinka. 2011. 560p. pap. 23.99 **(978-1-4628-6031-9(1))** Xlibris Corp.

Dieckmann, Anja. Afrikanismen in der Modernen Umgangssprache Kubas: Einfluss der Musica Popular. (Sprachen, Gesellschaften und Kulturen in Lateinamerika Ser.: Vol. 2). (GER., Illus.). 141 S.p. 21.95 *(978-3-631-50178-8(1))* Lang, Peter Publishing, Inc.

Dimmendaal, Gerrit J. The Turkana Language. (GER.). VIII, 469p. 225.00 **(978-3-11-180502-3(6))** De Gruyter, Mouton DEU. Dist: de Gruyter, Walter GmbH & Co. KG.

Dimmendaal, Gerrit Jan. Coding Participant Marking: Construction Types in Twelve African Languages. 2009. (Studies in Language Companion Ser.). (Illus.). xiv, 389p. *(978-90-272-0577-3(9))* Benjamins, John Publishing Co.

Dlamini, Betty Sibongile. Asikhulume SiSwati: Let's Speak SiSwati. 2010. pap. *(978-1-59703-018-2(X))* Univ. of Wisconsin Pr.

Ehret, Christopher. History & the Testimony of Language. 2010. (California World History Library). (ENG., Illus.). 304p. 65.00 *(978-0-520-26204-1(2))*; pap. 29.95 *(978-0-520-26205-8(0))* Univ. of California Pr.

Euro Talk. Talk Now! Afrikaans. 2008. 29.99 *(978-1-84352-337-6(X))* TOPICS Entertainment.

Fedden, Sebastian. A Grammar of Mian. 2011. (Mouton Grammar Library [MGL] Ser.). (ENG., Illus.). XXI, 604p. E-Book 321.00 **(978-3-11-026661-0(X))** De Gruyter, Mouton DEU. Dist: de Gruyter, Walter GmbH & Co. KG.

Fiedler, Ines & Schwarz, Anne. The Expression of Information Structure: A Documentation of Its Diversity Across Africa. 2010. (Illus.). xii, 383p. *(978-90-272-0672-5(4))* Benjamins, John Publishing Co.

Greenberg, Joseph H. The languages of Africa. 3rd ed. (ENG.). VI, 180p. 210.00 **(978-3-11-206344-6(9))**; 135.00 **(978-3-11-118666-5(0))** De Gruyter, Mouton DEU. Dist: de Gruyter, Walter GmbH & Co. KG.

Gudhlanga, Enna Sukutai. Shona Culture & Its Various Aspects: A Case of the Novel in a Zimbabwean Indigenous Language. 2011. 60p. pap. **(978-3-639-32752-6(7))** VDM Verlag Dr. Mueller e.K.

Heine, Bernd & Nurse, Derek, eds. A Linguistic Geography of Africa. (Cambridge Approaches to Language Contact Ser.). (ENG., Illus.). 2011. 390p. pap. 45.00 *(978-0-521-18269-0(7))* 2007. 408p. 141.00 *(978-0-521-87611-7(7))* Cambridge Univ. Pr.

Icon Group International, Inc. Staff, compiled by. Webster's Algerian Dardja - English Thesaurus Dictionary. 2008. 65p. ring bd. 28.95 incl. audio compact disk *(978-0-497-83423-4(5))* Icon Group International, Inc.

—Webster's Bena - English Thesaurus Dictionary. 2008. 86p. ring bd. 28.95 incl. audio compact disk *(978-0-497-83438-8(3))* Icon Group International, Inc.

—Webster's Bondei - English Thesaurus Dictionary. 2008. 148p. ring bd. 28.95 incl. audio compact disk *(978-0-497-83448-7(0))* Icon Group International, Inc.

—Webster's Bukusu - English Thesaurus Dictionary. 2008. 120p. ring bd. 28.95 incl. audio compact disk *(978-0-497-83453-1(7))* Icon Group International, Inc.

—Webster's Bungu - English Thesaurus Dictionary. 2008. 116p. ring bd. 28.95 incl. audio compact disk *(978-0-497-83455-5(3))* Icon Group International, Inc.

—Webster's Chuka - English Thesaurus Dictionary. 2008. 117p. ring bd. 28.95 incl. audio compact disk *(978-0-497-83471-5(5))* Icon Group International, Inc.

—Webster's Fipa - English Thesaurus Dictionary. 2008. 101p. ring bd. 28.95 incl. audio compact disk *(978-0-497-83493-7(6))* Icon Group International, Inc.

—Webster's Fon - English Thesaurus Dictionary. 2008. 27p. ring bd. 28.95 incl. audio compact disk *(978-0-497-83494-4(4))* Icon Group International, Inc.

—Webster's Gullah - English Thesaurus Dictionary. 2008. 159p. ring bd. 28.95 incl. audio compact disk *(978-0-497-83505-7(3))* Icon Group International, Inc.

—Webster's Gweno - English Thesaurus Dictionary. 2008. 96p. ring bd. 28.95 incl. audio compact disk *(978-0-497-83508-8(8))* Icon Group International, Inc.

—Webster's Gwere - English Thesaurus Dictionary. 2008. 99p. ring bd. 28.95 incl. audio compact disk *(978-0-497-83509-5(6))* Icon Group International, Inc.

—Webster's Hangaza - English Thesaurus Dictionary. 2008. 97p. ring bd. 28.95 incl. audio compact disk *(978-0-497-83511-8(8))* Icon Group International, Inc.

—Webster's Haya - English Thesaurus Dictionary. 2008. 73p. ring bd. 28.95 incl. audio compact disk *(978-0-497-83514-9(2))* Icon Group International, Inc.

—Webster's Ikizu - English Thesaurus Dictionary. 2008. 95p. ring bd. 28.95 incl. audio compact disk *(978-0-497-83519-4(3))* Icon Group International, Inc.

—Webster's Ikoma - English Thesaurus Dictionary. 2008. 97p. ring bd. 28.95 incl. audio compact disk *(978-0-497-83520-0(7))* Icon Group International, Inc.

—Webster's Jita - English Thesaurus Dictionary. 2008. 107p. ring bd. 28.95 incl. audio compact disk *(978-0-497-83532-3(0))* Icon Group International, Inc.

—Webster's Kahe - English Thesaurus Dictionary. 2008. 54p. ring bd. 28.95 incl. audio compact disk *(978-0-497-83534-7(7))* Icon Group International, Inc.

—Webster's Kati - English Thesaurus Dictionary. 2008. 44p. ring bd. 28.95 incl. audio compact disk *(978-0-497-83541-5(X))* Icon Group International, Inc.

—Webster's Kibosho - English Thesaurus Dictionary. 2008. 116p. ring bd. 28.95 incl. audio compact disk *(978-0-497-83547-7(9))* Icon Group International, Inc.

—Webster's Kibosho Unn - English Thesaurus Dictionary. 2008. 71p. ring bd. 28.95 incl. audio compact disk *(978-0-497-83546-0(0))* Icon Group International, Inc.

—Webster's Kilegi - English Thesaurus Dictionary. 2008. 120p. ring bd. 28.95 incl. audio compact disk *(978-0-497-83549-1(5))* Icon Group International, Inc.

—Webster's Kimbu - English Thesaurus Dictionary. 2008. 129p. ring bd. 28.95 incl. audio compact disk *(978-0-497-83550-7(9))* Icon Group International, Inc.

—Webster's Kinga - English Thesaurus Dictionary. 2008. 117p. ring bd. 28.95 incl. audio compact disk *(978-0-497-83552-1(5))* Icon Group International, Inc.

—Webster's Kivinza - English Thesaurus Dictionary. 2008. 127p. ring bd. 28.95 incl. audio compact disk *(978-0-497-83558-3(4))* Icon Group International, Inc.

—Webster's Kuria Mago - English Thesaurus Dictionary. 2008. 120p. ring bd. 28.95 incl. audio compact disk *(978-0-497-83560-6(6))* Icon Group International, Inc.

—Webster's Kuria Tari - English Thesaurus Dictionary. 2008. 138p. ring bd. 28.95 incl. audio compact disk *(978-0-497-83561-3(4))* Icon Group International, Inc.

—Webster's Kutu - English Thesaurus Dictionary. 2008. 119p. ring bd. 28.95 incl. audio compact disk *(978-0-497-83563-7(0))* Icon Group International, Inc.

—Webster's Kwere - English Thesaurus Dictionary. 2008. 126p. ring bd. 28.95 incl. audio compact disk *(978-0-497-83565-1(7))* Icon Group International, Inc.

—Webster's Lambya - English Thesaurus Dictionary. 2008. 115p. ring bd. 28.95 incl. audio compact disk *(978-0-497-83569-9(X))* Icon Group International, Inc.

—Webster's Lango - English Thesaurus Dictionary. 2008. 120p. ring bd. 28.95 incl. audio compact disk *(978-0-497-83570-5(3))* Icon Group International, Inc.

—Webster's Logooli - English Thesaurus Dictionary. 2008. 128p. ring bd. 28.95 incl. audio compact disk *(978-0-497-83581-1(9))* Icon Group International, Inc.

—Webster's Lozi - English Thesaurus Dictionary. 2008. 300p. ring bd. 28.95 incl. audio compact disk *(978-0-497-83584-2(3))* Icon Group International, Inc.

—Webster's Luhyia - English Thesaurus Dictionary. 2008. 83p. ring bd. 28.95 incl. audio compact disk *(978-0-497-83585-9(1))* Icon Group International, Inc.

—Webster's Lukimi - English Thesaurus Dictionary. 2008. 29p. ring bd. 28.95 incl. audio compact disk *(978-0-497-83586-6(X))* Icon Group International, Inc.

—Webster's Lumasaaba - English Thesaurus Dictionary. 2008. 88p. ring bd. 28.95 incl. audio compact disk *(978-0-497-83587-3(8))* Icon Group International, Inc.

—Webster's Mabia - English Thesaurus Dictionary. 2008. 88p. ring bd. 28.95 incl. audio compact disk *(978-0-497-83591-0(6))* Icon Group International, Inc.

—Webster's Machambe - English Thesaurus Dictionary. 2008. 111p. ring bd. 28.95 incl. audio compact disk *(978-0-497-83593-4(2))* Icon Group International, Inc.

—Webster's Machame Unn - English Thesaurus Dictionary. 2008. 75p. ring bd. 28.95 incl. audio compact disk *(978-0-497-83594-1(0))* Icon Group International, Inc.

—Webster's Makonde - English Thesaurus Dictionary. 2008. 128p. ring bd. 28.95 incl. audio compact disk *(978-0-497-83595-8(9))* Icon Group International, Inc.

—Webster's Malila - English Thesaurus Dictionary. 2008. 123p. ring bd. 28.95 incl. audio compact disk *(978-0-497-83598-9(3))* Icon Group International, Inc.

—Webster's Mambwe - English Thesaurus Dictionary. 2008. 127p. ring bd. 28.95 incl. audio compact disk *(978-0-497-83600-9(9))* Icon Group International, Inc.

—Webster's Matengo - English Thesaurus Dictionary. 2008. 89p. ring bd. 28.95 incl. audio compact disk *(978-0-497-83606-1(8))* Icon Group International, Inc.

—Webster's Matumbi - English Thesaurus Dictionary. 2008. 103p. ring bd. 28.95 incl. audio compact disk *(978-0-497-83607-8(6))* Icon Group International, Inc.

—Webster's Meru - English Thesaurus Dictionary. 2008. 117p. ring bd. 28.95 incl. audio compact disk *(978-0-497-83611-5(4))* Icon Group International, Inc.

—Webster's Mkuu - English Thesaurus Dictionary. 2008. 73p. ring bd. 28.95 incl. audio compact disk *(978-0-497-83617-7(3))* Icon Group International, Inc.

—Webster's Mòoré - English Thesaurus Dictionary. 2008. 35p. ring bd. 28.95 incl. audio compact disk *(978-0-497-83621-4(1))* Icon Group International, Inc.

—Webster's Mwanga - English Thesaurus Dictionary. 2008. 127p. ring bd. 28.95 incl. audio compact disk *(978-0-497-83626-9(2))* Icon Group International, Inc.

—Webster's Mwera - English Thesaurus Dictionary. 2008. 144p. ring bd. 28.95 incl. audio compact disk *(978-0-497-83627-6(0))* Icon Group International, Inc.

—Webster's Ndali - English Thesaurus Dictionary. 2008. 125p. ring bd. 28.95 incl. audio compact disk *(978-0-497-83631-3(9))* Icon Group International, Inc.

—Webster's Ndamba - English Thesaurus Dictionary. 2008. 116p. ring bd. 28.95 incl. audio compact disk *(978-0-497-83632-0(7))* Icon Group International, Inc.

—Webster's Ndengereko - English Thesaurus Dictionary. 2008. 87p. ring bd. 28.95 incl. audio compact disk *(978-0-497-83634-4(3))* Icon Group International, Inc.

—Webster's Ngindo - English Thesaurus Dictionary. 2008. 110p. ring bd. 28.95 incl. audio compact disk *(978-0-497-83637-5(8))* Icon Group International, Inc.

—Webster's Ngoni - English Thesaurus Dictionary. 2008. 86p. ring bd. 28.95 incl. audio compact disk *(978-0-497-83638-2(6))* Icon Group International, Inc.

—Webster's Ngurmi - English Thesaurus Dictionary. 2008. 91p. ring bd. 28.95 incl. audio compact disk *(978-0-497-83639-9(4))* Icon Group International, Inc.

—Webster's Nguungulu - English Thesaurus Dictionary. 2008. 97p. ring bd. 28.95 incl. audio compact disk *(978-0-497-83640-5(8))* Icon Group International, Inc.

—Webster's Nyakyusa-Ngonde - English Thesaurus Dictionary. 2008. 121p. ring bd. 28.95 incl. audio compact disk *(978-0-497-83643-6(2))* Icon Group International, Inc.

—Webster's Nyambo - English Thesaurus Dictionary. 2008. 168p. ring bd. 28.95 incl. audio compact disk *(978-0-497-83644-3(0))* Icon Group International, Inc.

—Webster's Nyiha - English Thesaurus Dictionary. 2008. 111p. ring bd. 28.95 incl. audio compact disk *(978-0-497-83649-8(1))* Icon Group International, Inc.

—Webster's Nyiramba - English Thesaurus Dictionary. 2008. 126p. ring bd. 28.95 incl. audio compact disk *(978-0-497-83650-4(5))* Icon Group International, Inc.

—Webster's Pangwa - English Thesaurus Dictionary. 2008. 109p. ring bd. 28.95 incl. audio compact disk *(978-0-497-83659-7(9))* Icon Group International, Inc.

—Webster's Pare - English Thesaurus Dictionary. 2008. 140p. ring bd. 28.95 incl. audio compact disk *(978-0-497-83662-7(9))* Icon Group International, Inc.

—Webster's Pimbwe - English Thesaurus Dictionary. 2008. 115p. ring bd. 28.95 incl. audio compact disk *(978-0-497-83667-2(X))* Icon Group International, Inc.

—Webster's Pogolo - English Thesaurus Dictionary. 2008. 94p. ring bd. 28.95 incl. audio compact disk *(978-0-497-83670-2(X))* Icon Group International, Inc.

—Webster's Rufiji - English Thesaurus Dictionary. 2008. 122p. ring bd. 28.95 incl. audio compact disk *(978-0-497-83686-3(6))* Icon Group International, Inc.

—Webster's Ruguru - English Thesaurus Dictionary. 2008. 115p. ring bd. 28.95 incl. audio compact disk *(978-0-497-83687-0(4))* Icon Group International, Inc.

—Webster's Shashi Siz - English Thesaurus Dictionary. 2008. 84p. ring bd. 28.95 incl. audio compact disk *(978-0-497-83704-4(8))* Icon Group International, Inc.

—Webster's Siha - English Thesaurus Dictionary. 2008. 106p. ring bd. 28.95 incl. audio compact disk *(978-0-497-83709-9(9))* Icon Group International, Inc.

—Webster's Siha Unn - English Thesaurus Dictionary. 2008. 72p. ring bd. 28.95 incl. audio compact disk *(978-0-497-83708-2(0))* Icon Group International, Inc.

—Webster's Suba - English Thesaurus Dictionary. 2008. 127p. ring bd. 28.95 incl. audio compact disk *(978-0-497-83720-4(X))* Icon Group International, Inc.

—Webster's Sumbwa - English Thesaurus Dictionary. 2008. 107p. ring bd. 28.95 incl. audio compact disk *(978-0-497-83722-8(6))* Icon Group International, Inc.

—Webster's Taita - English Thesaurus Dictionary. 2008. 88p. ring bd. 28.95 incl. audio compact disk *(978-0-497-83732-7(3))* Icon Group International, Inc.

—Webster's Tharaka - English Thesaurus Dictionary. 2008. 85p. ring bd. 28.95 incl. audio compact disk *(978-0-497-83739-6(0))* Icon Group International, Inc.

—Webster's Tooro - English Thesaurus Dictionary. 2008. 76p. ring bd. 28.95 incl. audio compact disk *(978-0-497-83741-9(2))* Icon Group International, Inc.

—Webster's Wolof - English Thesaurus Dictionary. 2008. 44p. ring bd. 28.95 incl. audio compact disk *(978-0-497-83764-8(1))* Icon Group International, Inc.

—Webster's Yao - English Thesaurus Dictionary. 2008. 213p. ring bd. 28.95 incl. audio compact disk *(978-0-497-83767-9(6))* Icon Group International, Inc.

—Webster's Zalamo - English Thesaurus Dictionary. 2008. 90p. ring bd. 28.95 incl. audio compact disk *(978-0-497-83770-9(6))* Icon Group International, Inc.

—Webster's Zarma - English Thesaurus Dictionary. 2008. 218p. ring bd. 28.95 incl. audio compact disk *(978-0-497-83772-3(2))* Icon Group International, Inc.

—Webster's Zigula - English Thesaurus Dictionary. 2008. 90p. ring bd. 28.95 incl. audio compact disk *(978-0-497-83774-7(9))* Icon Group International, Inc.

—The 2009-2014 World Outlook for Parts & Accessories for Non-Electric Lighting Equipment. 2008. 178p. ring bd. 28.95 incl. audio compact disk *(978-0-497-83544-6(4))* Icon Group International, Inc.

—The 2009-2014 World Outlook for Reproduction of Laser & Other Video Discs. 2008. 582p. ring bd. 28.95 incl. audio compact disk *(978-0-497-83469-2(3))* Icon Group International, Inc.

Ka, Omar. Nanu Dégg Wolof: Let's Speak Wolof: A First-Year Textbook. 2009. pap. *(978-1-59703-017-5(1))* National African Language Resource Ctr.

Kautzsch, Alexander. The Historical Evolution of Earlier African American English: An Empirical Comparison of Early Sources. (Topics in English Linguistics [TiEL] Ser.). (ENG.). XV, 335p. 180.00 ***(978-3-11-179679-6(5))*** De Gruyter, Mouton DEU. Dist: de Gruyter, Walter GmbH & Co. KG.

König, Christa. Case in Africa. 2008. (ENG., Illus.). 384p. 150.00 *(978-0-19-923282-6(2))* Oxford Univ. Pr., Inc.

Kouega, Jean-Paul. A Dictionary of Cameroon English Usage. Davis, Graeme & Bernhardt, Karl A., eds. 202p. pap. 54.95 *(978-3-03911-027-8(6))* Lang, Peter Publishing, Inc.

Kriel, T. J. & Prinsloo, D.J. Popular Northern Sotho Dictionary. 2011. 335p. pap. 12.95 *(978-1-86890-079-4(7))* NB Pubs. Ltd. ZAF. Dist: International Publishers Marketing.

Leroy, Jacqueline. Le Mankon: Langue Bantoue des Grassfields: Province Nord-Ouest du Cameroun. 2007. *(978-2-87723-958-5(6))* Peeters Pubs. & Booksellers.

Leroy, Jacqueline & Leroy, J. Le mankon. Langue bantoue des Grassfields (Province Nord-Ouest du Cameroun) 2007. (Société d'Études Linguistiques et Anthropologiques de France Ser.). (ENG.). 466p. (C). pap. 87.00 *(978-90-429-1861-0(6))* Peeters Pubs. & Booksellers BEL. Dist: Brown, David Bk. Co., The.

Linn, Stella, et al. Translation & Interculturality: Africa & the West. 2008. (FRE & ENG., Illus.). ix, 156p. pap. 49.95 *(978-3-631-57642-7(0))* Lang, Peter GmbH, Europaischer Verlag der Wissenschaften DEU. Dist: Lang, Peter.

Lipski, John M. Afro-Bolivian Spanish. 2008. (Illus.). 227p. pap. 44.00 *(978-84-8489-367-7(7))* Iberoamericana Vervuert Publishing Corp.

—A History of Afro-Hispanic Language: Five Centuries - Five Continents. 2009. (ENG.). 376p. pap. 38.99 *(978-0-521-11558-2(2))* Cambridge Univ. Pr.

Mafundikwa, Saki. Afrikan Alphabets: The Story of Writing in Africa. 2006. (ENG., Illus.). 192p. pap. 16.95 *(978-0-9772827-6-0(7))* Batty, Mark Pub., LLC.

Mawadza, Aquilina. A Basic Ndebele Grammar. 2009. 99p. ***(978-1-931546-73-7(8))*** Dunwoody Pr.

Mbeje, Audrey. Colloquial Zulu. 2011. 280p. pap. 28.95 *(978-0-415-49746-6(9))* Routledge.

Moran, Steven. A Grammatical Sketch of Isaalo. 2008. 164p. pap. *(978-3-639-06198-7(5))* VDM Verlag Dr. Mueller e.K.

Mpofu, Anita. Asikhulume Isindebele: Let's Speak Ndebele. 2010. pap. *(978-1-59703-020-5(1))* Univ. of Wisconsin Pr.

Mufwene, Salikoko S., ed. Globalization & Language Vitality: Perspectives from Africa. 2009. (ENG., Illus.). 272p. 150.00 *(978-0-8264-9514-3(1))* Continuum International Publishing Group, Ltd. GBR. Dist: National Bk. Network.

Na'Allah, Abdul-Rasheed & Na'allah, Abdul Rasheed. African Discourse in Islam, Oral Traditions, & Performance. 2009. (African Studies). (ENG., Illus.). 198p. 125.00 *(978-0-415-80592-6(9))* Routledge.

Ndhlovu, Finex. The Politics of Language & Nation Building in Zimbabwe. 2009. (Africa in Development Ser.). (Illus.). 49.95 *(978-3-03911-942-4(7))* Lang, Peter AG GBR. Dist: Lang, Peter.

Ndlovu, Lindiwe. Taboo Words, Euphemisms & Language Change. 2011. 64p. pap. ***(978-3-8443-0812-9(1))*** Lambert Academic Publishing.

Ngowi, Epaphra P. M. Travellers Highlights: Setswana - Swahili - English Translations. 2011. 92p. pap. 17.24 ***(978-1-4567-8050-0(6))*** AuthorHouse.

Nkomo, Dion. Specialised Lexicography in African Languages. 2011. 196p. pap. ***(978-3-8443-1016-0(9))*** Lambert Academic Publishing.

Odejobi, Odetunji Ajadi. Computer Text-to-Speech Synthesis of African Languages - Modern Tools, Techniques & Technologies. 2008. 372p. pap. *(978-3-639-02330-5(7))* VDM Verlag Dr. Mueller e.K.

Ojwang, Benson. The Pragmatics of Politeness Strategies in Nurse-Client Interactions. 2011. 188p. pap. ***(978-3-8433-9443-7(1))*** Lambert Academic Publishing.

Osborn, Don. African Languages in a Digital Age: Challenges & Opportunities for Indigenous Language Computing. 2010. (ENG.). 176p. pap. 20.95 *(978-0-7969-2249-6(7))* Human Sciences Research Council ZAF. Dist: Independent Pubs. Group.

Oyler, Dianne White. The History of the N'ko Alphabet & Its Role in Mande Transnational Identity: Word as Weapons. 2007. (Illus.). 256p. per. 32.00 *(978-0-9799537-5-0(8))* Africana Homestead Legacy Pubs., Inc.

Parker, Enid M. Afar-English Dictionary. 2009. viii, 224p. ***(978-1-931546-60-7(6))*** Dunwoody Pr.

Payne, Doris L. & Peña, Jaime, eds. Selected Proceedings of the 37th Annual Conference on African Linguistics. 2007. (Illus.). 203p. lib. bdg. 250.00 *(978-1-57473-420-1(2)*, Cascadilla Proceedings Project) Cascadilla Pr.

Phindane, Pule. Lexical Semantics & Deverbal Nominalisations in Sesotho. 2011. 440p. pap. ***(978-3-8433-9471-0(7))*** Lambert Academic Publishing.

Rilly, Claude & de Voogt, Alex. Meroitic: A Linguistic & Philological Introduction. 2012. (ENG., Illus.). 284p. 105.00 ***(978-1-107-00866-3(2))*** Cambridge Univ. Pr.

Sall, Adjaratou Oumar. La phrase complexe wolof: Une étude syntaxique et sémantique. 2008. 396p. pap. *(978-3-639-09436-7(0))* VDM Verlag Dr. Mueller e.K.

Simo Bobda, Augustin, ed. Explorations into Language Use in Africa. 2008. (Duisburger Arbeiten zur Sprach- und Kulturwissenschaft. Duisburg Papers on Research in Language & Culture Ser.). 252p. pap. 60.95 *(978-3-631-56239-0(X))* Lang, Peter GmbH, Europaischer Verlag der Wissenschaften DEU. Dist: Lang, Peter.

Van Otterloo, Karen & Van Otterloo, Roger. The Kifuliiru Language, Two Volume Set. 2011. 1132p. pap. 99.00 ***(978-1-55671-279-1(0))*** SIL International.

Velde, Mark van de. A Grammar of Eton. 2008. (Mouton Grammar Library [MGL] Ser.). (ENG., Illus.). XXII, 428p. 217.00 *(978-3-11-020440-7(1))* De Gruyter, Mouton DEU. Dist: de Gruyter, Walter GmbH & Co. KG.

Vigouroux, Cécile. Globalization & Language Vitality: Perspectives from Africa. Mufwene, Salikoko S. & Vigouroux, Cécile B., eds. 2009. (ENG., Illus.). 272p. 49.95 *(978-0-8264-9515-0(X))* Continuum International Publishing Group, Ltd. GBR. Dist: National Bk. Network.

Watters, David E. A Grammar of Kham. 2009. (Cambridge Grammatical Descriptions Ser.). (ENG & SIT.). 504p. pap. 53.00 *(978-0-521-12051-7(9))* Cambridge Univ. Pr.

Wilson, William A. A. Guinea Languages of the Atlantic Group: Description & Internal Classification. Storch, Anne, ed. 2007. (Research in African Studies Ser.: Vol. 12). (Illus.). 271p. (C). pap. 54.95 *(978-0-8204-9891-1(2))* Lang, Peter Publishing, Inc.

Zawawi, Sharifa. Jifunze Kiswahili Chetu, Vol. 2.Tr. of Learn Our Kiswahili. 300p. 24.95 *(978-0-86543-175-1(2))* Africa World Pr.

Zorc, R. David Paul & Nibagwire, Louise. Kinyarwanda & Kirundi Comparative Grammar. 2007. (RUN, KIN & ENG.). xii, 368p. *(978-1-931546-32-4(0))* Dunwoody Pr.

AFRICAN LANGUAGES—PHONOLOGY

Bickmore, Lee. Cilungu Phonology. 2007. 532p. pap. 49.00 *(978-1-57586-550-8(5))* CSLI Pubns.

Diagne, Anna Marie. Phonologie et Morphologie du Soninke. 2008. 328p. pap. *(978-3-639-03274-1(8))* VDM Verlag Dr. Mueller e.K.

Guldemann, T. Quotative indexes in African Languages. 2008. (Empirical Approaches to Language Typology [EALT] Ser.). (ENG.). XXI, 686p. 175.00 *(978-3-11-018590-4(3))* De Gruyter, Mouton DEU. Dist: de Gruyter, Walter GmbH & Co. KG.

Ladefoged, P. Phonetic Study of West African Languages. 2nd ed. 2009. (ENG., Illus.). 112p. pap. 28.99 *(978-0-521-11623-7(6))* Cambridge Univ. Pr.

Lonely Planet Staff. Africa: With 3500-Word Two-Way Dictionary. 2007. (Lonely Planet Phrasebook: Africa Ser.). (MUL & ENG., Illus.). 256p. pap. 10.99 *(978-1-74059-692-3(7))* Lonely Planet Pubns.

AFRICAN LITERATURE

see also African Drama; African Fiction; African Poetry

Couto, Mia & Wojciechowska, Danuta. A Chuva Pasmada. (POR., Illus.). 74p. *(978-972-21-1654-1(1))* Caminho, Editorial.

Falola, Toyin & Ngom, Fallou. Oral & Written Expressions of African Cultures. 2009. 264p. pap. 28.00 *(978-1-59460-647-2(1))* Carolina Academic Pr.

Giovannucci, Perri. Literature & Development in North Africa: The Modernizing Mission. 2008. (Literary Criticism & Cultural Theory Ser.). (ENG.). 254p. 125.00 *(978-0-415-95818-9(0))* Routledge.

Ihrie, Maureen & Oropesa, Salvador, eds. World Literature in Spanish: An Encyclopedia, 3 vols. 2011. 1294p. 350.00 *(978-0-313-33770-3(5)*, GR3770) ABC-CLIO, LLC.

Ihrie, Maureen & Oropesa, Salvador A. World Literature in Spanish: An Encyclopedia, 3 vols. 2011. lxxvi, 1294p. E-Book *(978-0-313-08083-8(6))* ABC-CLIO, LLC.

Ikonya, Philo. Kenya, Will You Marry Me? 2011. 252p. pap. ***(978-9956-579-79-2(3))*** Langaa Research & Publishing Common Initiative Group.

Latinus, Ioannes, et al. The First African Authors to Write in Latin, 3 wks. (B. E. Ser.: No. 1). 60.00 *(978-0-8115-2952-5(5))* Periodicals Service Co.

Maalu-Bungi. Littérature Orale Africaine: Nature, Genres, Caractéristiques et Fonctions. (FRE.). 255p. pap. 35.95 *(978-90-5201-319-0(5))* Lang, Peter Publishing, Inc.

Mumia, Osaaji. Style in Modern African Literature: Omondi Mak'Oloo. 2011. 80p. pap. ***(978-3-639-32084-8(0))*** VDM Verlag Dr. Mueller e.K.

Ngugi wa Thiongo. Globalectics: Theory & the Politics of Knowing. 2012. E-Book ***(978-0-231-53075-0(7))*** Columbia Univ. Pr.

Njoya, Wandia. In Search of El Dorado? Immigration, French Ideals & the African Experience In Contemporary African Novels. 2008. 300p. pap. *(978-3-8364-8413-8(7))* VDM Verlag Dr. Mueller e.K.

Nnomo, Marcelline, et al. Rupture et Transversalité de la Littérature Camerounaise. 2010. (FRE & ENG.). 443p. *(978-9956-0-9178-2(2))* Cle, Editions.

Oduwole, Ebunoluwa. The Concept of Truth in an African Language. 2011. 172p. pap. ***(978-3-8443-0273-8(5))*** Lambert Academic Publishing.

Thiong'o, Ngugi Wa. Globalectic: Theory & the Politics of Knowing. 2012. (Wellek Library Lectures). (ENG., Illus.). 120p. (gr. 17). 22.50 ***(978-0-231-15950-0(1))*** Columbia Univ. Pr.

Wisner, Geoff, ed. A Basket of Leaves: 99 Books that Capture the Spirit of Africa. 2008. (ENG.). 292p. pap. 25.95 *(978-1-77009-206-8(4))* Jacana Media ZAF. Dist: Independent Pubs. Group.

AFRICAN LITERATURE—BIBLIOGRAPHY

Ojaide, Tanure. Dictionary of Literary Biography: Twentieth-Century African Writers. 2011. (Illus.). 432p. 315.00 *(978-0-7876-8178-4(4))* Cengage Gale.

AFRICAN LITERATURE—HISTORY AND CRITICISM

Abrahams, Cecil, ed. The Romantic Vision of Alex la Guma & Other Critical Essays. 261p. 59.95 *(978-0-86543-578-0(2))* Africa World Pr.

Abrahams, Kunle. A Study Guide to Chinua Achebe's Anthills of the Savannah. 2007. 64p. per. *(978-1-84549-258-8(7))* arima publishing.

Accilien, Cecile. Rethinking Marriage in Francophone African & Caribbean Literatures. 2008. (After the Empire: the Francophone World & Postcolonial France Ser.). (ENG.). 206p. pap. 28.50 *(978-0-7391-1658-6(4))* Lexington Bks.

Adams, Anne V. & Mayes, Janis A., eds. African Literature & Africa's Development. 176p. pap. 14.00 *(978-0-89410-735-1(6))*; Vol. 13. 22.00 *(978-0-89410-734-4(8))* Cornell Univ., Africana Studies & Research Ctr.

Afolabi, Niyi. Emerging Perspectives on Ungulani Ba Ka Khosa: Prophet Trickster, & Provocateur. 2009. *(978-1-59221-616-1(1))*; 470p. pap. *(978-1-59221-617-8(X))* Africa World Pr.

Aguilar, Mario, ed. Rethinking Age in Africa. 2006. 264p. pap. *(978-1-59221-496-9(7))* Africa World Pr.

Amoko, Apollo Obonyo. Postcolonialism in the Wake of the Nairobi Revolution: Ngugi Wa Thiong'O & the Idea of African Literature. 2010. (ENG., Illus.). 216p. 84.00 *(978-0-230-10546-1(7))* Palgrave Macmillan.

Andrade, Susan Z. The Nation Writ Small: African Fictions & Feminisms, 1958-1988. 2011. (ENG., Illus.). 272p. 89.95 *(978-0-8223-4897-9(7))*; pap. 24.95 *(978-0-8223-4921-1(3))* Duke Univ. Pr.

Andrzejewski, B. W., et al, eds. Literatures in African Languages: Theoretical Issues & Sample Surveys. 2010. (ENG.). 676p. pap. 62.00 *(978-0-521-12625-0(8))* Cambridge Univ. Pr.

Azodo, Ada Uzoamaka. Emerging Perspectives on Aminata Sow Fall: The Real & the Imaginary in Her Novels. 2007. *(978-1-59221-556-0(4))* Africa World Pr.

Azodo, Ada Uzoamaka & Eke, Maureen N. Gender & Sexuality in African Literature & Film. 2006. (Illus.). xv, 333p. *(978-1-59221-468-6(1))* Africa World Pr.

Azodo, Ada Uzoamaka & Eke, Maureen Ngozi. Gender & Sexuality in African Literature & Film. 2006. (Illus.). 350p. pap. *(978-1-59221-469-3(X))* Africa World Pr.

Baker, Charlotte. Expressions of the Body: Representations in African Text & Image. 2009. (Illus.). 392p. 77.95 *(978-3-03911-546-4(4))* Lang, Peter AG GBR. Dist: Lang, Peter.

Bessa, Tesfaye Tolessa. A History of Written Oromo Literature To 1991. 2010. 176p. pap. *(978-3-639-27498-1(9))* VDM Verlag Dr. Mueller e.K.

Bishop, Stephen L. Legal Oppositional Narrative: A Case Study in Cameroon. 2008. (After the Empire Ser.). (ENG.). 188p. 68.50 *(978-0-7391-1318-9(6))* Lexington Bks.

Bourget, Carine. Star the Cross & the Crescent: Pb. 2011. (After the Empire: the Francophone World & Postcolonial France Ser.). (ENG.). 206p. pap. 31.95 ***(978-0-7391-2658-5(X))*** Lexington Bks.

Bourget, Carine. The Star, the Cross, & the Crescent: Religions & Conflicts in Francophone Literature from the Arab World. 2010. (After the Empire: the Francophone World & Postcolonial France Ser.). (ENG.). 206p. 62.99 *(978-0-7391-2657-8(1))* Lexington Bks.

Brahimi, Denise & Trevarthen, Anne. Les Femmes Dans la Littérature Africaine: Portraits. (FRE.). 238p. *(978-2-86537-838-8(1))* Editions-Diffusion Karthala.

Breitinger, Eckhard, et al. Words & Worlds: African Writing, Literature, & Society: A Commemorative Publication in Honour of Eckhard Breitinger. 2006. 414p. pap. *(978-1-59221-497-6(5))* Africa World Pr.

Briault, Manus & Briault, Vicki. Emerging Traditions: Toward a Postcolonial Stylistics of Black South African Fiction in English. 2011. (ENG.). 348p. 80.00 *(978-0-7391-4807-5(9))* Lexington Bks.

Briault Manus, Vicki. Emerging Traditions: Towards a Postcolonial Stylistics of Black South African Fiction in English. 2011. *(978-0-7391-6695-6(6))* Lexington Bks.

Cancel, Robert & Woodhull, Winifred. African Diasporas: Ancestors, Migrations & Borders. 2008. *(978-1-59221-648-2(X))*; pap. *(978-1-59221-649-9(8))* Africa World Pr.

Caplan, Marc. How Strange the Change: Language, Temporality, & Narrative Form in Peripheral Modernisms. 2011. (Stanford Studies in Jewish History & C Ser.). (ENG.). 360p. 60.00 *(978-0-8047-7476-5(5))* Stanford Univ. Pr.

Cazenave, Odile M. & Célérier, Patricia. Contemporary Francophone African Writers & the Burden of Commitment. 2011. (ENG.). 256p. (C). (gr. 13-17). pap. 24.50 *(978-0-8139-3096-1(0))*; (gr. 17). 55.00 *(978-0-8139-3095-4(2))* Univ. Pr. of Virginia.

Cheref, Abdelkader. Gender & Identity in North Africa: Postcolonialism & Feminism in Maghrebi Women's Literature. 2010. (Library of Modern Middle East Studies). (ENG.). 256p. 92.00 *(978-1-84885-449-9(8)*, Tauris Academic Studies) I. B. Tauris & Co., Ltd. GBR. Dist: Macmillan.

Coly, Ayo A. The Pull of Postcolonial Nationhood: Gender & Migration in Francophone African Literatures. 2010. (ENG.). 176p. 62.99 *(978-0-7391-4511-1(8))* Lexington Bks.

Conteh-Morgan, John & d'Almeida, Irène Assiba, eds. The Original Explosion That Created Worlds: Essays on Werewere Liking's Art & Writings. 2010. (FRE., Illus.). 363p. pap. 101.00 *(978-90-420-2971-2(4))* Rodopi.

Creary, Nicholas M., ed. African Intellectuals & Decolonization. 2012. (Ohio RIS Africa Ser.). (ENG.). 160p. pap. 19.95 ***(978-0-89680-283-4(3))*** Ohio Univ. Pr.

Currey. Africa Writes Back the African Writers Series & the Launch of African Literature. (Illus.). 2009. 350p. pap. 34.95 *(978-1-84701-502-0(6))* 2008. 288p. 105.00 *(978-1-84701-503-7(4))* Boydell & Brewer, Ltd. GBR. (Currey, James). Dist: Boydell & Brewer, Inc.

Currey, James. Africa Writes Back: The African Writers Series & the Launch of African Literature. 2008. (Illus.). 320p. 55.00 *(978-0-8214-1842-0(4))*; (ENG., pap. 26.95 *(978-0-8214-1843-7(2))* Ohio Univ. Pr.

Dathorne, O. R. The Black Mind: A History of African Literature. 2009. (ENG.). 544p. pap. 60.00 *(978-0-8166-5739-1(4))* Univ. of Minnesota Pr.

De Meyer, Bernard & ten Kortenaar, Neil, eds. The Changing Face of African Literature / les nouveaux visages de la littérature Africaine. 2009. (ENG & FRE., Illus.). 240p. 65.00 *(978-90-420-2580-6(8))* Rodopi.

Drayton, Arthur D., et al. Perspectives on African Literatures at the Millennium. 2006. 352p. *(978-1-59221-510-2(6))*; pap. *(978-1-59221-511-9(4))* Africa World Pr.

Elkin, Susan. Purple Hibiscus. 2011. (Philip Allan Literature Guide for A-Level Ser.). 84p. (gr. 10-12). 19.95 ***(978-1-4441-2145-2(6))*** Trans-Atlantic Pubns., Inc.

Emenyonu, Ernest, ed. New Women's Writing in African Literature 24: African Literature Today. 172p. 79.95 *(978-1-59221-134-0(8))* Africa World Pr.

Emenyonu, Ernest N., ed. ALT 29 Teaching African Literature Today. 2011. (African Literature Today Ser.: Volume 29). (Illus.). 173p. pap. 29.95 *(978-1-84701-511-2(5),* Currey, James) Boydell & Brewer, Ltd. GBR. Dist: Boydell & Brewer, Inc.

Evans, Jane E. Tactical Silence in the Novels of Malika Mokeddem. 2011. (ENG., Illus.). 230p. pap. 62.00 *(978-90-420-3176-0(X))* Rodopi.

Eze, Chielozona. Moral Imaginations in Postcolonial African Literature & Culture. 2012. E-Book ***(978-0-7391-4508-1(8))*** Lexington Bks.

—Postcolonial Imaginations & Moral Representations in African Literature & Culture. 2011. (ENG.). 156p. 60.00 ***(978-0-7391-4506-7(1))*** Lexington Bks.

Falola, Toyin & Akinyemi, Tunde. Emerging Perspectives on Femi Osofisan. 2009. *(978-1-59221-698-7(6))*; 468p. pap. *(978-1-59221-699-4(4))* Africa World Pr.

Frindéthié, K. Martial. The Black Renaissance in Francophone African & Caribbean Literatures. 2008. (ENG., Illus.). 215p. pap. 39.95 *(978-0-7864-3663-7(8))* McFarland & Co., Inc. Pubs.

Genet, Sintayehu. Political & Social Satire in Contemporary Amharic Stories. 2009. 84p. pap. *(978-3-639-19429-6(2))* VDM Verlag Dr. Mueller e.K.

Gikandi, Simon. Encyclopedia of African Literature. 2009. (ENG., Illus.). 648p. (C). 62.95 *(978-0-415-54962-2(0))* Routledge.

—Ngugi wa Thiong'o. 2009. (Cambridge Studies in African & Caribbean Literature Ser.). (ENG.). 344p. (C). pap. 50.00 *(978-0-521-11901-6(4))* Cambridge Univ. Pr.

Giovannucci, Perri. Literature & Development in North Africa: The Modernizing Mission. 2012. (Literary Criticism & Cultural Theory Ser.). (ENG.). 254p. pap. 42.95 ***(978-0-415-54164-0(6))*** Routledge.

Goff, Barbara & Simpson, Michael. Crossroads in the Black Aegean: Oedipus, Antigone, & Dramas of the African Diaspora. 2008. (Classical Presences Ser.). (ENG., Illus.). 420p. 150.00 *(978-0-19-921718-2(1))* Oxford Univ. Pr., Inc.

Graebner, Seth. History's Place: Nostalgia & the City in French Algerian Literature. 2007. (After the Empire: the Francophone World & Postcolonial France Ser.). (ENG., Illus.). 356p. 110.50 *(978-0-7391-1581-7(2))*; per. 38.99 *(978-0-7391-1582-4(0))* Lexington Bks.

Hamilton, Russell G. Voices from an Empire: A History of Afro-Portuguese Literature. 2009. (ENG.). 464p. pap. 60.00 *(978-0-8166-5781-0(5))* Univ. of Minnesota Pr.

Harries, Patrick. Butterflies & Barbarians: Swiss Missionaries & Systems of Knowledge in South-East Africa. 2007. (Illus.). 312p. pap. 34.95 *(978-0-85255-983-3(6),* Currey, James) Boydell & Brewer, Ltd. GBR. Dist: Boydell & Brewer, Inc.

Hiddleston, Jane. Assia Djebar: Out of Algeria. (ENG.). 192p. 2011. (Liverpool University Press - Contemporary French & Francophone Cultures Ser.). pap. 32.95 *(978-1-84631-685-2(5))* 2006. (Contemporary French & Francophone Cultures Ser.: 6). 70.00 *(978-1-84631-031-7(8))* Liverpool Univ. Pr. GBR. Dist: Chicago Distribution Ctr.

Irele, Abiola & Jeyifo, Biodun. Africa in the World the World in Africa: Essays in Honor of Abiola Irele. 2011. ***(978-1-59221-827-1(X))*** Africa World Pr.

Katulwende, Malama. The Fire at the Core Discourses on African Aesthetics, Music, Jurisprudence, Ethno-Politics & Good Governance. 2011. 218p. pap. 18.95 ***(978-1-59569-193-4(6))*** Mondial.

Kpoda, Daniella. Das Bild der afrikanischen Frau in der deutschen und der französischen Kolonialliteratur und sein Gegenentwurf in der frankophonen afrikanischen Literatur der Kolonialzeit. 2008. (Im Medium fremder Sprachen und Kulturen Ser.). (FRE, GER & ENG.). 304p. pap. 74.95 *(978-3-631-59496-5(2))* Lang, Peter GmbH, Europaischer Verlag der Wissenschaften DEU. Dist: Lang, Peter.

Kruger, Marie. Women's Literature in Kenya & Uganda: The Trouble with Modernity. 2010. (ENG.). 272p. 89.00 *(978-0-230-10887-5(3))* Palgrave Macmillan.

Larquie, Jeanne-Sarah de. Emerging Perspectives on Ken Bugul: From Alternative Choices to Oppositional Practices. Azodo, Ada Uzoamaka, ed. 2009. (Illus.). 388p. pap. *(978-1-59221-673-4(0))* Africa World Pr.

Lee, Benjamin Todd, et al, eds. Apuleius & Africa. 2012. (Routledge Monographs in Classical Studies). (ENG.). 272p. (C). 125.00 ***(978-0-415-53309-6(0))*** Routledge.

Levin, Tobe & Assah, Augustine H., eds. Empathy & Rage: Female Genital Mutilation in African Literature. 2009. (Illus.). 220p. (C). pap. 28.50 *(978-0-9555079-4-6(4))* Clarke, Ayebia Publishing, Ltd. GBR. Dist: Rienner, Lynne Pubs.

Lewis, Marvin. An Introduction to the Literature of Equatorial Guinea: Between Colonialism & Dictatorship. 2007. (ENG.). 232p. (C). per. 29.95 *(978-0-8262-1713-4(3))* Univ. of Missouri Pr.

Lewis, Shireen K. Race, Culture, & Identity: Francophone West African & Caribbean Literature & Theory from Negritude to Creolite. 2006. (Caribbean Studies (Lexington Books) Ser.). (ENG.). 188p. per. 27.50 *(978-0-7391-1473-5(5))* Lexington Bks.

Lindfors, Bernth. Early Achebe. 2009. *(978-1-59221-702-1(8))*; 224p. pap. *(978-1-59221-703-8(6))* Africa World Pr.

—Early East African Writers & Publishers. 2011. *(978-1-59221-793-9(1))*; (Illus.). 272p. pap. *(978-1-59221-794-6(X))* Africa World Pr.

—Early Soyinka. 2008. *(978-1-59221-652-9(8))*; 296p. pap. *(978-1-59221-653-6(6))* Africa World Pr.

—Popular Literatures in Africa. 136p. 12.95 *(978-0-86543-221-5(X))* Africa World Pr.

Loingsigh, Aedin Ní. Postcolonial Eyes: Intercontinental Travel in Francophone African Literature. 2009. (Liverpool University Press - Contemporary French & Francophone Cultures Ser.). (ENG., Illus.). 224p. 95.00 *(978-1-84631-049-2(0))* Liverpool Univ. Pr. GBR. Dist: Chicago Distribution Ctr.

Losambe, Lokangaka. An Introduction to the African Prose Narrative. 290p. 84.95 *(978-1-59221-136-4(4))* Africa World Pr.

Losambe, Lokangaka & Eke, Maureen N. Literature, the Visual Arts, & Globalization in Africa & Its Diaspora. 2011. (Illus.). xvii, 242p. *(978-1-59221-817-2(2))*; 340p. pap. *(978-1-59221-810-3(5))* Africa World Pr.

Makward, Edris, et al, eds. North-South Linkages & Connections in Continental & Diaspora African Literature 12: ALA Annual. 328p. 99.95 *(978-1-59221-156-2(9))* Africa World Pr.

Marais, Mike. Secretary of the Invisible: The Idea of Hospitality in the Fiction of J. M. Coetzee. 2009. (ENG., Illus.). 266p. 77.00 *(978-90-420-2712-1(6))* Rodopi.

Marques, Irene. Critical Approaches, Vol. 1. Irene, Marques, ed. 2008. 208p. *(978-978-35035-4-0(5))* Michigan State Univ. Pr.

Medin, Daniel. Three Sons: Franz Kafka & the Fiction of J. M. Coetzee, Philip Roth & W. G. Sebald. 2010. (Avant-Garde & Modernism Studies). (ENG.). 228p. pap. 29.95 *(978-0-8101-2568-1(4))* Northwestern Univ. Pr.

Milne, Lorna. Postcolonial Violence, Culture & Identity in Francophone Africa & the Antilles. Milne, Lorna, ed. 233p. pap. 62.95 *(978-3-03910-330-0(X))* Lang, Peter Publishing, Inc.

Mirmotahari, Emad. Islam in the Eastern African Novel. 2011. (Literatures & Cultures of the Islamic World Ser.). (ENG.). 222p. 85.00 *(978-0-230-10843-1(1))* Palgrave Macmillan.

Mlambo, Nelson. The Paradox of Modernisation in African Literature. 2010. 88p. pap. *(978-3-8383-7362-1(6))* Lambert Academic Publishing.

Muchemwa, Kizito Z. & Muponde, Robert, eds. Manning the Nation Father Figures in Zimbabwean Literature & Society. 2007. 224p. (C). pap. *(978-1-77922-069-1(3))* Weaver Pr. ZWE. Dist: Michigan State Univ. Pr.

Mugambi, Helen Nabasuta & Allan, Tuzyline Jita, eds. Masculinities in African Literary & Cultural Texts. 2009. 260p. pap. *(978-0-9555079-5-3(2))* Clarke, Ayebia Publishing, Ltd. GBR. Dist: Rienner, Lynne Pubs.

Mukundi, Paul M. Preventing Things from Falling Further Apart: The Preservation of Cultural Identities in Postcolonial African, Indian, & Caribbean Literatures. 2010. 204p. pap. *(978-1-906704-71-1(6))* Adonis & Abbey Publishers Ltd.

—Preventing Things from Falling Further Apart: The Preservation of Cultural Identities in Postcolonial African, Indian, & Caribbean Literatures (HB) 2010. 204p. *(978-1-906704-70-4(8))* Adonis & Abbey Publishers Ltd.

Mwangi, Meja. The Cockroach Dance. 2008. (ENG.). (YA). pap. *(978-0-9796476-2-8(2))* HM Bks.

Negash, Ghirmai. A History of Tigrinya Literature in Eritrea: The Oral & the Written 1890-1991. 2009. *(978-1-56902-312-9(3))*; pap. *(978-1-56902-313-6(1))* Red Sea Pr.

A New Generation of African Writers: Migration, Material Culture & Language. 2008. pap. *(978-1-86914-156-1(3))* Univ. of Natal Pr. ZAF. Dist: International Specialized Bk. Services.

Nicholls, Brendon. Ngugi Wa Thiong'O Gender & the Ethics of Postcolonial Reading. 2010. 222p. 99.95 *(978-0-7546-5825-2(2))* Ashgate Publishing Co.

Nyamndi, G. D. Babi Yar Symphony. 2008. 112p. pap. *(978-9956-558-51-3(6))* Langaa Research & Publishing Common Initiative Group CMR. Dist: Michigan State Univ. Pr.

Obiero, Ogone John & Orwenjo, Daniel Ochieng'. TEXT, LANGUAGE, AND LITERATURE: Empirical & Theoretical Perspectives from Kenya. 2008. 292p. pap. *(978-3-639-09748-1(3))* VDM Verlag Dr. Mueller e.K.

Ogede, Ode. Intertextuality in Contemporary African Literature: Looking Inward. 2011. xvii, 229p. E-Book ***(978-0-7391-6448-8(1))***; (ENG.). 248p. 65.00 ***(978-0-7391-6446-4(5))*** Lexington Bks.

Ogunyemi, Chikwene Okonjo & Allan, Tuzyline Jita, eds. The Twelve Best Books by African Women: Critical Readings. 2009. (Ohio RIS Africa Ser.). (ENG.). 304p. pap. 28.00 *(978-0-89680-266-7(3))* Ohio Univ. Pr.

Ojaide, Tanure. Contemporary African Literature: New Approaches. 2012. 208p. pap. 28.00 ***(978-1-61163-029-9(0))*** Carolina Academic Pr.

Ojaide, Tanure. Ordering the African Imagination. 2007. 184p. pap. *(978-978-023-204-7(4))* Malthouse Press Ltd, Nigeria NGA. Dist: Michigan State Univ. Pr.

Ojo-Ade, Femi. Configuring the African World: Continental & Diasporic Literatures & Cultures. 2006. *(978-1-59221-447-1(9))*; 312p. pap. *(978-1-59221-448-8(7))* Africa World Pr.

Olaniyan, Tejumola & Quayson, Ato, eds. African Literature: An Anthology of Criticism & Theory. 2007. (ENG., Illus.). 792p. pap. 61.95 *(978-1-4051-1201-7(8),* Wiley-Blackwell) Wiley, John & Sons, Inc.

Peterson, Derek & Macola, Giacomo, eds. Recasting the Past: History Writing & Political Work in Modern Africa. 2009. (New African Histories Ser.). (ENG., Illus.). 280p. 49.95 *(978-0-8214-1878-9(5))* Ohio Univ. Pr.

Primorac, Ranka. The Place of Tears: The Novel & Politics in Modern Zimbabwe. 2006. (ENG.). 224p. 100.00 *(978-1-84511-120-5(6),* Tauris Academic Studies) I. B. Tauris & Co., Ltd. GBR. Dist: Macmillan.

Quayson, Ato, et al, eds. African Literature: An Anthology of Criticism & Theory. 2007. (ENG., Illus.). 800p. 129.95 *(978-1-4051-1200-0(X),* Wiley-Blackwell) Wiley, John & Sons, Inc.

Quest, Matthew. In the Shadow of State Power: C. L. R. James, Direct Democracy, & National Liberation Struggles. 2012. (ENG., Illus.). 352p. pap. 21.00 ***(978-1-84935-084-6(1))*** AK Pr. GBR. Dist: Consortium Bk. Sales & Distribution.

Raji, Wumi. Long Dreams in Short Chapters: Essays in African Postcolonial Literary, Cultural & Political Criticisms. 2011. (ENG.). 224p. pap. 44.95 *(978-3-8258-1841-8(1))* Lit Verlag DEU. Dist: Transaction Pubs.

Rattray, R. Sutherland. Hausa Folk-Lore Customs, Proverbs, etc V1: Collected And. 2006. (ENG.). 356p. per. 31.95 *(978-1-4286-3949-2(7))* Kessinger Publishing, LLC.

—Hausa FolkLore Customs Proverbs etc V2 C. 2006. pap. 30.95 *(978-1-4286-3950-8(0))* Kessinger Publishing, LLC.

Rice, Laura. Of Irony & Empire: Islam, the West, & the Transcultural Invention of Africa. 2008. ix, 241p. pap. 29.95 *(978-0-7914-7216-3(7))* 2007. 241p. 70.00 *(978-0-7914-7215-6(9))* State Univ. of New York Pr.

Richter, Elke. Ich-Entwürfe im hybriden Raum - das Algerische Quartett von Assia Djebar. 2008. (Méditerranée: Littératures - Cultures. Mittelmeer: Literaturen - Kulturen Ser.). 306p. pap. 74.95 *(978-3-631-57195-8(X))* Lang, Peter GmbH, Europaischer Verlag der Wissenschaften DEU. Dist: Lang, Peter.

Rooney. African Literature, Animism & Politics. 2006. (Routledge Research in Postcolonial Literatures Ser.). 256p. 34.00 *(978-0-415-41855-3(0))* Routledge.

Samatar, Said S. Oral Poetry & Somali Nationalism: The Case of Sayid Mahammad 'Abdille Hasan. 2009. (African Studies). (ENG.). 248p. pap. 34.99 *(978-0-521-10457-9(2))* Cambridge Univ. Pr.

Sander, Reinhard W., et al, eds. Ngugi Wa Thiongo Speaks: Interviews with the Kenyan Writer. 2006. 376p. pap. 34.95 *(978-0-85255-580-4(6),* Currey, James) Boydell & Brewer, Ltd. GBR. Dist: Boydell & Brewer, Inc.

Sankara, Edgard. Postcolonial Francophone Autobiographies: From Africa to the Antilles. 2011. viii, 218p. E-Book ***(978-0-8139-3176-0(2))***; (ENG.). 232p. (C). (gr. 13-17). pap. 24.50 ***(978-0-8139-3172-2(X))***; (ENG., Illus.). 232p. (gr. 17). 55.00 ***(978-0-8139-3171-5(1))*** Univ. Pr. of Virginia.

Stansmore, William. The Natural Order: The Blueprint for the New Age. 2011. 112p. 29.99 ***(978-1-4628-7340-1(5))***; pap. 19.99 ***(978-1-4628-7339-5(1))*** Xlibris Corp.

Tajani, Larbi. L' Interculturalite Dans la Litterature Marocaine D'Expression Francaise. 2008. 96p. pap. *(978-3-8364-7821-2(8))* VDM Verlag Dr. Mueller e.K.

Thomas, M. Idle & Desperate: Africa's Common Errors. Lt. ed. 2012. (ENG.). 62p. pap. 15.00 *(978-1-4528-2265-5(4))* CreateSpace.

Vassallo, Helen. Body Besieged: The Embodiment of Historical Memory in Nina Bouraoui & Leïla Sebbar. 2012. (After the Empire: the Francophone World & Postcolonial France Ser.). (ENG.). 176p. (gr. 17). 60.00 ***(978-0-7391-7142-4(9))*** Lexington Bks.

Veit-Wild, Flora. Writing Madness: Borderlines of the Body in African Literature. 2006. (Illus.). 192p. pap. 29.95 *(978-0-85255-583-5(0),* Currey, James) Boydell & Brewer, Ltd. GBR. Dist: Boydell & Brewer, Inc.

Vladislavic, Ivan. The Loss Library & Other Unfinished Stories. 2012. (Seagull Books - the Africa List Ser.). (ENG., Illus.). 121p. 25.00 *(978-0-85742-012-1(7))* Seagull Bks. GBR. Dist: Chicago Distribution Ctr.

Wehrs, Donald R. Islam, Ethics, Revolt: Politics & Piety in Francophone West African & Maghreb Narrative. 2008. (ENG.). 290p. 78.99 *(978-0-7391-1649-4(5))* Rowman & Littlefield Publishers, Inc.

—Pre-Colonial Africa in Colonial African Narratives: From Ethiopia Unbound to Things Fall Apart, 1911-1958. 2008. 206p. 99.95 *(978-0-7546-6088-0(5))* Ashgate Publishing Co.

Zabus, Chantal. The African Palimpsest: Indigenization of Language in the West African Europhone Novel. (Second Enlarged Edition) 2007. (Illus.). 284p. per. 76.00 *(978-90-420-2224-9(8))* Rodopi.

—Between Rites & Rights: Excision in Women's Experiential Texts & Human Contexts. 2007. (ENG.). 344p. 65.00 *(978-0-8047-5687-7(2))* Stanford Univ. Pr.

Zegeye, Abebe & Vambe, Maurice. Close to the Sources: Essays on Contemporary African Culture, Politics & Academy. 2011. (Routledge African Studies). 182p. 125.00 *(978-0-415-89595-8(2))* Routledge.

AFRICAN LITERATURE—STUDY AND TEACHING

Desai, Gaurav, ed. Teaching the African Novel. 2009. (ENG.). 40.00 *(978-1-60329-037-1(0))* Modern Language Assn. of America.

Desai, Gaurav Gajanan, ed. Teaching the African Novel. 2009. (ENG.). pap. 25.00 *(978-1-60329-038-8(9))* Modern Language Assn. of America.

Jua, Roselyne M. & Besong, Bate. To the Budding Creative Writer: A Handbook. 2009. 140p. pap. *(978-9956-558-93-3(1))* Langaa Research & Publishing Common Initiative Group CMR. Dist: Michigan State Univ. Pr.

AFRICAN LITERATURE—TRANSLATIONS INTO ENGLISH

Ennaji, Moha. Women Writing Africa: The Northern Region, Vol. 4. Nowaira, Amira et al, eds. 2009. (Women Writing Africa Ser.). (ENG.). 696p. 75.00 *(978-1-55861-588-5(1))* Feminist Pr. at The City Univ. of New York.

Ennaji, Moha, et al. The Northern Region, Vol. 4. Nowaira, Amira et al, eds. 2009. (Women Writing Africa Ser.). (ENG.). 696p. pap. 29.95 *(978-1-55861-589-2(X))* Feminist Pr. at The City Univ. of New York.

Spillman, Rob. Gods & Soldiers: The Penguin Anthology of Contemporary African Writing. Spillman, Rob, ed. 2009. (ENG., Illus.). 368p. (gr. 12-18). 16.00 *(978-0-14-311473-4(5),* Penguin (Non-Classics)) Penguin Group (USA) Inc.

AFRICAN LITERATURE—WOMEN AUTHORS

Allan, Tuzyline Jita, et al, eds. Women Writing Africa: West Africa & the Sahel. 2008. (Women Writing Africa Ser.: Vol. 2). (ENG.). 560p. 75.00 *(978-1-55861-501-4(6))* Feminist Pr. at The City Univ. of New York.

Andrade, Susan Z. The Nation Writ Small: African Fictions & Feminisms, 1958-1988. 2011. (ENG., Illus.). 272p. 89.95 *(978-0-8223-4897-9(7))*; pap. 24.95 *(978-0-8223-4921-1(3))* Duke Univ. Pr.

Browdy de Hernandez, Jennifer, et al, eds. African Women Writing Resistance: An Anthology of Contemporary Voices. 2010. (Women in Africa & the Diaspora Ser.). (ENG.). 360p. pap. 26.95 *(978-0-299-23664-9(1))* Univ. of Wisconsin Pr.

Cheref, Abdelkader. Gender & Identity in North Africa: Postcolonialism & Feminism in Maghrebi Women's Literature. 2010. (Library of Modern Middle East Studies). (ENG.). 256p. 92.00 *(978-1-84885-449-9(8),* Tauris Academic Studies) I. B. Tauris & Co., Ltd. GBR. Dist: Macmillan.

Emenyonu, Ernest, ed. New Women's Writing in African Literature 24: African Literature Today. 172p. 79.95 *(978-1-59221-134-0(8))* Africa World Pr.

Ennaji, Moha. Women Writing Africa: The Northern Region, Vol. 4. Nowaira, Amira et al, eds. 2009. (Women Writing Africa Ser.). (ENG.). 696p. 75.00 *(978-1-55861-588-5(1))* Feminist Pr. at The City Univ. of New York.

Ennaji, Moha, et al. The Northern Region, Vol. 4. Nowaira, Amira et al, eds. 2009. (Women Writing Africa Ser.). (ENG.). 696p. pap. 29.95 *(978-1-55861-589-2(X))* Feminist Pr. at The City Univ. of New York.

Govinden, Devarashanam. Sister Outsiders: Identity & Difference in the Writings of South African Indian Women. 2008. (Imagined South Africa Ser.). (C). pap. *(978-1-86888-296-0(9))* BRILL.

Kaur Singh, Jaspal. Representation & Resistance: Indian & African Women's Texts at Home & in the Diasporas. 2008. (ENG.). 246p. pap. 34.95 *(978-1-55238-245-5(1))* Univ. of Calgary Pr. CAN. Dist: Chicago Distribution Ctr.

Mule, Katwiwa. Women's Spaces, Women's Visions: Politics, Poetics, & Resistance in African Women's Drama. 2007. *(978-1-59221-560-7(2))*; 324p. pap. *(978-1-59221-561-4(0))* Africa World Pr.

Ogunyemi, Chikwene Okonjo & Allan, Tuzyline Jita, eds. The Twelve Best Books by African Women: Critical Readings. 2009. (Ohio RIS Africa Ser.). (ENG.). 304p. pap. 28.00 *(978-0-89680-266-7(3))* Ohio Univ. Pr.

Rooney, Caroline & Thompson, Liz. Decolonising Gender: Literature & a Poetics of the Real. 2007. (Routledge Research in Postcolonial Literatures Ser.). (ENG., Illus.). 264p. (C). 120.00 *(978-0-415-42418-9(6))* Routledge.

Shigali, Hellen Roselyne. Alternative Conceptualization of Empowerment. 2010. 128p. pap. *(978-3-639-25340-5(X))* VDM Verlag Dr. Mueller e.K.

Strong-Leek, Linda. Excising the Spirit: A Literary Analysis of Female Circumcision. 2009. x, 245p. *(978-1-59221-674-1(9))*; 525p. pap. *(978-1-59221-675-8(7))* Africa World Pr.

Vassallo, Helen. Body Besieged: The Embodiment of Historical Memory in Nina Bouraoui & Leïla Sebbar. 2012. (After the Empire: the Francophone World & Postcolonial France Ser.). (ENG.). 176p. (gr. 17). 60.00 ***(978-0-7391-7142-4(9))*** Lexington Bks.

Zabus, Chantal. Between Rites & Rights: Excision in Women's Experiential Texts & Human Contexts. 2007. (ENG.). 344p. 65.00 *(978-0-8047-5687-7(2))* Stanford Univ. Pr.

AFRICAN LITERATURE (ENGLISH)

see also African Drama (English); African Poetry (English)

Glasgow, Jacqueline & Rice, Linda J. Exploring African Life & Literature: Novel Guides to Promote Socially Responsive Learning. 2007. 376p. 34.95 *(978-0-87207-609-9(1))* International Reading Assn.

Hardwick, Lorna & Gillespie, Carol. Classics in Post-Colonial Worlds. 2010. (Classical Presences Ser.). (ENG., Illus.). 448p. pap. 45.00 *(978-0-19-959132-9(6))* Oxford Univ. Pr., Inc.

AFRICAN LITERATURE (ENGLISH)—BIBLIOGRAPHY

Killam, Douglas & Kerfoot, Alicia L. Student Encyclopedia of African Literature, 1 vol. 2007. 368p. 85.00 *(978-0-313-33580-8(X),* GR3580, Greenwood Pr.) Greenwood Publishing Group, Inc.

Ojaide, Tanure. Dictionary of Literary Biography: Twentieth-Century African Writers. 2011. (Illus.). 432p. 315.00 *(978-0-7876-8178-4(4))* Cengage Gale.

AFRICAN LITERATURE (ENGLISH)—HISTORY AND CRITICISM

Adams, Anne V., ed. Essays in Honour of Ama Ata Aidoo At 70: A Reader in African Cultural Studies. 2012. 544p. pap. 30.00 ***(978-0-9569307-0-5(0))*** Clarke, Ayebia Publishing, Ltd. GBR. Dist: Rienner, Lynne Pubs.

Ambanasom, Shadrach A. The Cameroonian Novel of English Expression an Introduction. 2009. 232p. pap. *(978-9956-558-69-8(9))* Langaa Research & Publishing Common Initiative Group CMR. Dist: Michigan State Univ. Pr.

Asanbe, Joseph. Selected Essays. 2008. xiv, 113p. pap. *(978-0-9786127-3-3(6))* Zone Three Pr./Ctr. for the Creative Arts.

Barber, Karin. The Anthropology of Texts, Persons & Publics: Oral & Written Culture in Africa & Beyond. (New Departures in Anthropology Ser.). (ENG.). 286p. 2008. per. 35.00 *(978-0-521-54687-4(7))* 2007. 90.99 *(978-0-521-83787-3(1))* Cambridge Univ. Pr.

Bishop, Stephen L. Legal Oppositional Narrative: A Case Study in Cameroon. 2008. (After the Empire Ser.). (ENG.). 188p. 68.50 *(978-0-7391-1318-9(6))* Lexington Bks.

A

Black Literature Criticism: Classic & Emerging Authors since 1950, 3 vols., Set. 2nd rev. ed. 2008. (ENG.). 544p. 552.00 *(978-1-4144-3170-3(8))* Cengage Gale.

Brahimi, Denise & Trevarthen, Anne. Les Femmes Dans la Littérature Africaine: Portraits. (FRE.). 238p. *(978-2-86537-838-8(1))* Editions-Diffusion Karthala.

Caminero-Santangelo, Byron & Myers, Garth, eds. Environment at the Margins: Literary & Environmental Studies in Africa. 2011. (ENG.). 304p. pap. 34.95 ***(978-0-8214-1978-6(1))*** Ohio Univ. Pr.

Ce, Chin & Chin, Ce. Bards & Tyrants. 2008. 244p. 29.95 *(978-978-35035-3-3(7))* Michigan State Univ. Pr.

Collins, Walter P. Emerging African Voices: A Study of Contemporary African Literature. 2010. (Illus.). 356p. *(978-1-60497-664-9(0))* Cambria Pr.

Currey. Africa Writes Back the African Writers Series & the Launch of African Literature. (Illus.). 2009. 350p. pap. 34.95 *(978-1-84701-502-0(6))* 2008. 288p. 105.00 *(978-1-84701-503-7(4))* Boydell & Brewer, Ltd. GBR. (Currey, James). Dist: Boydell & Brewer, Inc.

Currey, James. Africa Writes Back: The African Writers Series & the Launch of African Literature. 2008. (Illus.). 320p. 55.00 *(978-0-8214-1842-0(4))*; (ENG., pap. 26.95 *(978-0-8214-1843-7(2))* Ohio Univ. Pr.

Emenyonu, Ernest N., ed. ALT 28 Film & African Literature Today. 2010. (African Literature Today Ser.: Volume 28). 172p. pap. 29.95 *(978-1-84701-510-5(7)*, Currey, James) Boydell & Brewer, Ltd. GBR. Dist: Boydell & Brewer, Inc.

Gikandi, Simon & Mwangi, Evan. The Columbia Guide to East African Literature in English Since 1945. 2007. (Columbia Guides to Literature Since 1945 Ser.). (ENG., Illus.). 224p. (gr. 17). 80.00 *(978-0-231-12520-8(8))* Columbia Univ. Pr.

Govinden, Devarashanam. Sister Outsiders: Identity & Difference in the Writings of South African Indian Women. 2008. (Imagined South Africa Ser.). (C). pap. *(978-1-86888-296-0(9))* BRILL.

Goyal, Yogita. Romance, Diaspora, & Black Atlantic Literature. 2010. (Cambridge Studies in American Literature & Culture Ser.). (ENG.). 288p. 89.00 *(978-0-521-76359-2(2))* Cambridge Univ. Pr.

Head, Dominic. The Cambridge Introduction to J. M. Coetzee. 2009. (Cambridge Introductions to Literature Ser.). (ENG.). 130p. (C). 65.99 *(978-0-521-86747-4(9))*; pap. 22.99 *(978-0-521-68709-6(8))* Cambridge Univ. Pr.

Irele, Abiola & Jeyifo, Biodun. Africa in the World the World in Africa: Essays in Honor of Abiola Irele. 2011. (Illus.). 346p. pap. ***(978-1-59221-828-8(8))*** Africa World Pr.

Kaur Singh, Jaspal. Representation & Resistance: Indian & African Women's Texts at Home & in the Diasporas. 2008. (ENG.). 246p. pap. 34.95 *(978-1-55238-245-5(1))* Univ. of Calgary Pr. CAN. Dist: Chicago Distribution Ctr.

Killam, Douglas & Kerfoot, Alicia L. Student Encyclopedia of African Literature, 1 vol. 2007. 368p. 85.00 *(978-0-313-33580-8(X)*, GR3580, Greenwood Pr.) Greenwood Publishing Group, Inc.

Lewis, Simon. British & African Literature in Transnational Context: Beyond Writing Back. 2011. (ENG., Illus.). 256p. 74.95 *(978-0-8130-3602-1(X))* Univ. Pr. of Florida.

Lindfors, Bernth. Early East African Writers & Publishers. 2011. *(978-1-59221-793-9(1))*; (Illus.). 272p. pap. *(978-1-59221-794-6(X))* Africa World Pr.

Makokha, J. K. S., et al, eds. East African Literature: Essays on Written & Oral Traditions. 2011. 510p. pap. ***(978-3-8325-2816-4(4))*** Logos Verlag Berlin.

Mathuray, Mark. On the Sacred in African Literature: Old Gods & New Worlds. 2009. (ENG., Illus.). 240p. 84.00 *(978-0-230-57755-8(5))* Palgrave Macmillan.

Mengistu, Melakneh. Post-Colonialism & Mainstream Anglophone African Novel. 2010. 252p. pap. *(978-3-639-23193-9(7))* VDM Verlag Dr. Mueller e.K.

Montgomery, Georgene Bess. The Spirit & the Word: A Theory of Spirituality in Africana Literary Criticism. 2008. *(978-1-59221-566-9(1))*; 252p. pap. *(978-1-59221-567-6(X))* Africa World Pr.

Newell, Stephanie. West African Literatures: Ways of Reading. 2006. (Oxford Studies in Postcolonial Literatures). (ENG., Illus.). 288p. pap. 39.95 *(978-0-19-927397-3(9))* Oxford Univ. Pr., Inc.

Nne Onyeoziri, Gloria. Shaken Wisdom: Irony & Meaning in Postcolonial African Fiction. 2011. E-Book ***(978-0-8139-3200-2(9))*** Univ. Pr. of Virginia.

Ogoke, Chinedu. African Writers in Exile. 2011. (ENG.). pap. 38.88 *(978-0-9831853-1-4(X))* Piraeus Bks., LLC.

Ogude, James, et al. Rethinking Eastern African Literary & Intellectual Landscapes. 2011. xxvi, 424p. ***(978-1-59221-886-8(5))***; ***(978-1-59221-885-1(7))*** Africa World Pr.

Okolo, M. S. C. African Literature As Political Philosophy. 2007. (Africa in the New Millennium Ser.). (ENG.). 218p. 123.95 *(978-1-84277-894-4(3))*; per. 36.95 *(978-1-84277-895-1(1))* Zed Bks., Ltd. GBR. Dist: Macmillan.

Onyeoziri, Gloria Nne. Shaken Wisdom: Irony & Meaning in Postcolonial African Fiction. 2011. (ENG., Illus.). 192p. (C). (gr. 13-17). pap. 21.50 *(978-0-8139-3187-6(8))* Univ. Pr. of Virginia.

Onyeoziri, Gloria Nne. Shaken Wisdom: Irony & Meaning in Postcolonial African Fiction. 2011. (ENG., Illus.). 192p. (gr. 17). 49.50 ***(978-0-8139-3186-9(X))*** Univ. Pr. of Virginia.

Opoku-Agyemang, Naana Jane, et al. Africa & Trans-Atlantic Memories: Literary & Aesthetic Manifestations of Diaspora & History. 2008. 496p. *(978-1-59221-633-8(1))*; pap. *(978-1-59221-632-1(3))* Africa World Pr.

Owomoyela, Oyekan. The Columbia Guide to West African Literature in English since 1945. 2008. (Columbia Guides to Literature Since 1945 Ser.). (ENG.). 216p. (gr. 17). 85.00 *(978-0-231-12686-1(7))* Columbia Univ. Pr.

Palmer, Eustace & Porter, Abioseh Michael. Knowledge Is More Than Mere Words: Wey Dehn Sey? Dehn Sey Kapu Sehns nor Kapu Word: A Critical Introduction to Sierra Leonean Literature. 2008. *(978-1-59221-644-4(7))*; 366p. pap. *(978-1-59221-645-1(5))* Africa World Pr.

Rooney, Caroline & Thompson, Liz. Decolonising Gender: Literature & a Poetics of the Real. 2007. (Routledge Research in Postcolonial Literatures Ser.). (ENG., Illus.). 264p. (C). 120.00 *(978-0-415-42418-9(6))* Routledge.

Roscoe, Adrian A. & Roscoe, Adrian. The Columbia Guide to Central African Literature in English since 1945. 2007. (Columbia Guides to Literature Since 1945 Ser.). (ENG.). 220p. (gr. 17). 80.00 *(978-0-231-13042-4(2))* Columbia Univ. Pr.

Rutere, Albert Mugambi. Women & Patriarchal Power in the Selected Novels of Ngugi Wa Thiong'o. 2010. *(978-0-87831-022-7(3))*; pap. *(978-0-87831-021-0(5))* Black Academy Pr., Inc.

Steiner, Tina. Translated People, Translated Texts: Language & Migration in Contemporary African Literature. 2009. 176p. pap. *(978-1-905763-18-4(2))* St. Jerome Publishing.

Strong-Leek, Linda. Excising the Spirit: A Literary Analysis of Female Circumcision. 2009. x, 245p. *(978-1-59221-674-1(9))*; 525p. pap. *(978-1-59221-675-8(7))* Africa World Pr.

Woods, Tim. African Pasts: Memory & History in African Literatures. (ENG.). 304p. 2012. pap. 29.95 ***(978-0-7190-6494-4(5))*** 2007. (Illus.). 84.00 *(978-0-7190-6493-7(7))* Manchester Univ. Pr. GBR. Dist: Macmillan.

AFRICAN LITERATURE (FRENCH)

Accilien, Cecile. Rethinking Marriage in Francophone African & Caribbean Literatures. 2008. (After the Empire Ser.). (ENG.). 202p. 68.50 *(978-0-7391-1657-9(6))* Lexington Bks.

Brahimi, Denise & Trevarthen, Anne. Les Femmes Dans la Littérature Africaine: Portraits. (FRE.). 238p. *(978-2-86537-838-8(1))* Editions-Diffusion Karthala.

Collins, Walter P. Emerging African Voices: A Study of Contemporary African Literature. 2010. (Illus.). 356p. *(978-1-60497-664-9(0))* Cambria Pr.

Gregoire, Henri. De la Litterature des Negres. 2009. 300p. 43.95 *(978-1-120-56482-5(4))*; pap. 28.95 *(978-1-120-47419-3(1))* Kessinger Publishing, LLC.

—De la Litterature des Negres. Warden, D. B., tr. from FRE. (B. E. Ser.: No. 70). 65.00 *(978-0-8115-3021-7(3))* Periodicals Service Co.

Gyasi, Kwaku Addae. The Francophone African Text: Translation & the Postcolonial Experience. 2006. (Francophone Cultures & Literatures Ser.: Vol. 48). 142p. (C). 59.95 *(978-0-8204-7830-2(X))* Lang, Peter Publishing, Inc.

Irele, Abiola. The Négritude Moment: Explorations in Francophone African & Caribbean Literature & Thought. 2010. xv, 259p. *(978-1-59221-797-7(4))*; 256p. pap. *(978-1-59221-798-4(2))* Africa World Pr.

Ngue, Julie Nack. Critical Conditions: Reading Illness & Disability in Francophone African & Caribbean Women's Writing. 2011. (ENG.). 208p. (gr. 17). 60.00 ***(978-0-7391-5114-3(2))*** Lexington Bks.

Nne Onyeoziri, Gloria. Shaken Wisdom: Irony & Meaning in Postcolonial African Fiction. 2011. E-Book ***(978-0-8139-3200-2(9))*** Univ. Pr. of Virginia.

Onyeoziri, Gloria Nne. Shaken Wisdom: Irony & Meaning in Postcolonial African Fiction. 2011. (ENG., Illus.). 192p. (C). (gr. 13-17). pap. 21.50 *(978-0-8139-3187-6(8))* Univ. Pr. of Virginia.

Onyeoziri, Gloria Nne. Shaken Wisdom: Irony & Meaning in Postcolonial African Fiction. 2011. (ENG., Illus.). 192p. (gr. 17). 49.50 ***(978-0-8139-3186-9(X))*** Univ. Pr. of Virginia.

Sankara, Edgard. Postcolonial Francophone Autobiographies: From Africa to the Antilles. 2011. viii, 218p. E-Book ***(978-0-8139-3176-0(2))***; (ENG.). 232p. (C). (gr. 13-17). pap. 24.50 ***(978-0-8139-3172-2(X))***; (ENG., Illus.). 232p. (gr. 17). 55.00 ***(978-0-8139-3171-5(1))*** Univ. Pr. of Virginia.

AFRICAN LYMPHOMA

see Burkitt's Lymphoma

AFRICAN MAGIC

see Magic, African

AFRICAN METHODIST EPISCOPAL CHURCH

Bailey, Julius. Race Patriotism: Protest & Print Culture in the A.M.E. Church. 2012. (ENG., Illus.). 192p. 47.00 ***(978-1-57233-845-6(8))*** Univ. of Tennessee Pr.

Bell, Michale. Constant Contact. 2009. pap. 12.95 *(978-1-61584-466-1(X))* Independent Pub.

Dickerson, Dennis C. African American Preachers & Politics: The Careys of Chicago. (Margaret Walker Alexander Series in African American Studies). (ENG., Illus.). 2011. 304p. pap. 30.00 ***(978-1-61703-193-9(3))*** 2010. 236p. 65.00 *(978-1-60473-427-0(2))* Univ. Pr. of Mississippi.

Ekechi, Felix. Pioneer, Patriot, & Nigerian Nationalist: A Biography of the Reverend M. D. Opara, 1915-1965. 2010. 464p. pap. 55.00 *(978-1-59460-805-6(9))* Carolina Academic Pr.

Jackie, Stanton. I Go to Reid Temple A. M. E. Church. 2007. (Illus.). 34p. (J). 7.99 *(978-0-9761322-1-9(4))* EoH Publishing.

Newman, Richard. Freedom's Prophet: Bishop Richard Allen, the AME Church, & the Black Founding Fathers. 2009. (ENG., Illus.). 368p. pap. 23.00 *(978-0-8147-5857-1(6))* New York Univ. Pr.

Ontario Genealogical Society, Oxford County Branch Staff, contrib. by. Cemetery Transcription of African Methodist Episcopal Cemetery: Concession VIII, Lot 12, South Norwich Township, Now Known As 732695 Pick Line, Norwich Township. 2008. (Illus.). 7p. pap. ***(978-0-7779-3520-0(1))*** Ontario Genealogical Society.

Russaw, Ethel H. Call the Roll: Laity in the African Methodist Episcopal Church. 2011. 112p. pap. 15.00 ***(978-1-4634-3188-4(0))*** AuthorHouse.

Turner, Henry McNeal. An African American Pastor Before & During the American Civil War. 2010. 109.95 *(978-0-7734-1429-7(0))* Mellen, Edwin Pr., The.

AFRICAN MUSIC

see Music, African

AFRICAN MYTHOLOGY

see Mythology, African

AFRICAN NATIONAL CONGRESS

Booysen, Susan. The African National Congress & the Regeneration of Political Power: People, Party, Policy. 2012. (ENG., Illus.). 528p. pap. 34.95 ***(978-1-86814-542-3(5))*** Witwatersrand Univ. Pr. Pubns. ZAF. Dist: Transaction Pubs.

Callinicos, Luli. Oliver Tambo: His Life & Legacy, 1917-1993. 2011. (ENG.). 36p. pap. 8.95 *(978-1-919855-85-1(8))* STE Pubs. ZAF. Dist: Independent Pubs. Group.

Cherry, Janet. Umkhonto Wesizwe. 2011. (Pocket History Guides). 150p. pap. 15.99 ***(978-1-77009-961-6(1))*** Jacana Media ZAF. Dist: Independent Pubs. Group.

du Preez, Max & Rossouw, Mandy. The World According to Julius Malema. 2010. 128p. pap. 17.95 *(978-0-7957-0292-1(2))* NB Pubs. Ltd. ZAF. Dist: International Publishers Marketing.

Feinstein, Andrew. After the Party: Corruption, the ANC & South Africa's Uncertain Future. 2010. (ENG.). 308p. pap. 19.95 *(978-1-84467-627-9(7)*, 844627) Verso Bks. GBR. Dist: Norton, W. W. & Co., Inc.

Forde, Fiona. Julius Malema & the Future of South Africa. 2011. 280p. pap. 27.00 *(978-1-86842-380-4(8))* Ball, Jonathan Pubs. ZAF. Dist: International Publishers Marketing.

Gordin, Jeremy. Zuma: A Biography. 2009. (Illus.). 324p. pap. 20.95 *(978-1-86842-263-0(1))* Ball, Jonathan Pubs. ZAF. Dist: International Publishers Marketing.

Hughes, Heather. The First President: A Life of John L. Dube, Founding President of the ANC. 2011. (ENG., Illus.). 288p. pap. 35.95 ***(978-1-77009-813-8(5))*** Jacana Media ZAF. Dist: Independent Pubs. Group.

Kasrils, Ronnie. The Unlikely Secret Agents. 2011. (ENG., Illus.). 192p. pap. 22.00 *(978-1-77009-890-9(9))* Jacana Media ZAF. Dist: Independent Pubs. Group.

Klammer, Martin & La Guma, Blanche. In the Dark with My Dress on Fire: My Life in Cape Town, London, Havana & Home Again. 2011. (ENG.). 256p. pap. 25.95 *(978-1-77009-888-6(7))* Jacana Media ZAF. Dist: Independent Pubs. Group.

Limb, Peter. The ANC's Early Years: Nation, Class & Place in South Africa Before 1940. 2010. 602p. pap. 48.95 *(978-1-86888-529-9(1))* Unisa Press / Uitgewers GBR. Dist: International Specialized Bk. Services.

Macola, Giacomo. Liberal Nationalism in Central Africa: A Biography of Harry Mwaanga Nkumbula. 2009. (ENG., Illus.). 240p. 100.00 *(978-0-230-62274-6(7))* Palgrave Macmillan.

Mandela, Nelson. Let Freedom Reign: The Words of Nelson Mandela. Russell, Henry, ed. 2010. (ENG.). 144p. 14.95 *(978-1-56656-800-5(5)*, Interlink Bks.) Interlink Publishing Group, Inc.

—Selected Speeches & Writings of Nelson Mandela: The End of Apartheid in South Africa. 2010. 290p. pap. *(978-1-934941-78-2(6))* Red & Black Pubs.

Manghezi, Nadja. The Maputo Connection: ANC Life in the World of Frelimo. 2010. (ENG., Illus.). 264p. pap. 25.00 *(978-1-77009-768-1(6))* Jacana Media ZAF. Dist: Independent Pubs. Group.

Masilela, Elias. Number 43 Trelawney Park KwaMagogo. 2011. (Illus.). 256p. pap. 30.95 *(978-0-86486-706-3(9))* International Publishers Marketing.

Meredith, Martin. Mandela. 2010. (ENG., Illus.). 688p. 29.95 *(978-1-58648-832-1(5))* PublicAffairs.

—Mandela: A Biography. 2011. (ENG., Illus.). 688p. pap. 21.99 *(978-1-58648-951-9(8))* PublicAffairs.

Ngculu, James. The Honour to Serve: Recollections of an Umkhonto Soldier. 2011. 272p. pap. 34.95 *(978-0-86486-733-9(6))* International Publishers Marketing.

O'Malley, Padraig. Shades of Difference: Mac Maharaj & the Struggle for South Africa. 2007. (Illus.). xix, 648p. *(978-0-670-08523-1(5)*, Viking Adult) Penguin Group (USA) Inc.

Russell, Alec. Bring Me My Machine Gun: The Battle for the Soul of South Africa from Mandela to Zuma. 2009. (ENG., Illus.). 336p. 26.95 *(978-1-58648-738-6(8))* PublicAffairs.

Sadet (South African Democracy Education Trust), ed. The Road to Democracy in South Africa: Volume 1 (1960-1970) (Revised Edition) 2010. 735p. 52.00 *(978-1-86888-563-3(1))* Unisa Press / Uitgewers GBR. Dist: International Specialized Bk. Services.

Shubin, Vladimir Gennadyevich. ANC: A View from Moscow. 2nd ed. 2009. (ENG.). 384p. pap. 19.95 *(978-1-77009-631-8(0))* Jacana Media ZAF. Dist: Independent Pubs. Group.

Sisulu, Elinor Batezat. Walter & Albertina Sisulu: In Our Lifetime. 2011. 688p. pap. 42.95 *(978-0-86486-639-4(9))* International Publishers Marketing.

Smith, David James. Young Mandela: The Revolutionary Years. 2010. (ENG., Illus.). 416p. 27.99 *(978-0-316-03548-4(3))* Little Brown & Co.

Suttner, Raymond. The ANC Underground in South Africa, 1950-1976. 2009. 199p. 55.00 *(978-1-935049-13-5(5))* FirstForumPress.

Trewhela, Paul. Inside Quatro: Uncovering the Exile History of the ANC & SWAPO. 2010. (ENG.). 256p. pap. 24.00 *(978-1-77009-776-6(7))* Jacana Media ZAF. Dist: Independent Pubs. Group.

Turok, Ben, ed. The ANC & the Turn to Armed Struggle. 2011. (Understanding the ANC Today Ser.). (ENG., Illus.). 144p. pap. 15.95 *(978-1-77009-968-5(9))* Jacana Media ZAF. Dist: Independent Pubs. Group.

—The Historical Roots of the ANC. 2011. (Understanding the ANC Today Ser.). (ENG., Illus.). 144p. pap. 15.95 *(978-1-77009-965-4(4))* Jacana Media ZAF. Dist: Independent Pubs. Group.

Turok, Ben, ed. Readings in the ANC Tradition: Volume I: Policy & Praxis, 2 vols. 2011. (Understanding the ANC Today Ser.). (ENG., Illus.). 264p. pap. 15.95 ***(978-1-77009-969-2(7))*** Jacana Media ZAF. Dist: Independent Pubs. Group.

Wilderson, Frank B., III. Incognegro: A Memoir of Exile & Apartheid. 2008. (ENG.). 500p. pap. 18.00 *(978-0-89608-783-5(2))* South End Pr.

—Incognegro: From Black Power to Apartheid & Back. 2007. 272p. 24.95 *(978-0-8070-7268-4(0))* Beacon Pr.

AFRICAN NEWSPAPERS

Nyarota, Geoffrey. Against the Grain: Memoirs of a Zimbabwean Newsman. 2006. (Illus.). 352p. pap. 29.95 *(978-1-77007-112-4(1))* Struik Pubs. ZAF. Dist: International Publishers Marketing.

AFRICAN OIL-PALM

see Oil Palm

AFRICAN PERIODICALS

Dickovick, J. Tyler. Africa. 46th ed. 2011. (World Today Series: Africa Ser.). (ENG., Illus.). 344p. pap. 18.50 ***(978-1-935264-18-7(4))*** Stryker-Post Pubns.

AFRICAN PHILOSOPHY

see Philosophy, African

AFRICAN POETRY

Ifowodo, Ogaga. Homeland & Other Poems. 2nd ed. 2007. *(978-1-59221-594-2(7))*; pap. *(978-1-59221-595-9(5))* Africa World Pr.

Peyron, Michael, ed. Berber Odes: Poetry from the Mountains of Morocco. 2011. (Poetry of Place Ser.). (ENG.). 128p. pap. 16.95 *(978-1-906011-28-4(1))* Eland Bks. GBR. Dist: Dufour Editions, Inc.

Rafael, Luis. Stained Glass: Poetry from the Land of Mozambique. 2011. 246p. 39.95 *(978-93-80905-15-0(7))* ROMAN Bks. IND. Dist: Lightning Source, Inc.

Sidikou, Aissata G. & Hale, Thomas A., eds. Women's Voices from West Africa: An Anthology of Songs from the Sahel. 2012. (ENG., Illus.). 128p. 34.95 *(978-0-253-35670-3(9)*, 0253356709) Indiana Univ. Pr.

AFRICAN POETRY (ENGLISH)

Emezue, Gloria Monica & Gloria, Emezue. Comparative Studies in African Dirge Poetry. 2008. 212p. *(978-978-36034-1-7(8))* Michigan State Univ. Pr.

AFRICAN POETRY—HISTORY AND CRITICISM

Cremeens & Kirunda, Christopher W. N. Hybridity & Christopher Okigbo's Poetry. xv, 223p. *(978-9970-02-983-9(5))* Fountain Pubs. Ltd.

Emezue, Gloria Monica & Gloria, Emezue. Comparative Studies in African Dirge Poetry. 2008. 212p. *(978-978-36034-1-7(8))* Michigan State Univ. Pr.

English, Parker. What We Say, Who We Are: Leopold Senghor, Zora Neale Hurston, & the Philosophy of Language. 2009. (ENG.). 134p. 57.99 *(978-0-7391-2651-6(2))* Lexington Bks.

Neser, Ashlee. Stranger at Home: The Praise Poet in Apartheid South Africa. 2011. (ENG.). 280p. pap. 34.95 ***(978-1-86814-537-9(9))*** Witwatersrand Univ. Pr. Pubns. ZAF. Dist: Transaction Pubs.

Olali, Tom. Performance of a Swahili Poem during the Lamu Maulidi Festival. 2008. 192p. (C). pap. 15.95 *(978-0-9795851-5-9(5))* Sahel Bks. Inc.

Opland, Jeff. Xhosa Oral Poetry: Aspects of a Black South African Tradition. 2009. (Cambridge Studies in Oral & Literate Culture Ser.). (ENG.). 316p. pap. 42.00 *(978-0-521-10478-4(5))* Cambridge Univ. Pr.

Owonibi, Sola & Virtanen, Beth L. The Mines of His Mind: Critical Reflections on the Works of Tayo Olafioye. 2007. 300p. pap. *(978-1-59221-549-2(1))* Africa World Pr.

Rafael, Luis. Stained Glass: Poetry from the Land of Mozambique. 2011. 246p. 39.95 *(978-93-80905-15-0(7))* ROMAN Bks. IND. Dist: Lightning Source, Inc.

Virtanen, Beth L. & Owonibi, Sola. The Mines of His Mind: Critical Reflections on the Works of Tayo Olafioye. 2007. *(978-1-59221-548-5(3))* Africa World Pr.

AFRICAN POETRY—TRANSLATIONS INTO ENGLISH

d'Almeida, Irène Assiba, ed. A Rain of Words: A Bilingual Anthology of Women's Poetry in Francophone Africa. Mayes, Janis A., tr. 2009. (CARAF Books: Caribbean & African Literature Translated from the French Ser.). (FRE & ENG.). 368p. (C). (gr. 13-17). pap. 24.50 *(978-0-8139-2766-4(8))*; (gr. 17). 69.50 *(978-0-8139-2765-7(X))* Univ. Pr. of Virginia.

AFRICAN RELATIONS

see Pan-Africanism

AFRICAN SCULPTURE

see Sculpture—Africa

AFRICAN SONGS

see Songs, African

AFRICAN STUDIES

see Africa—Study and Teaching

AFRICAN SWINE FEVER

Penrith, Mary-Louise, et al. Preparation of African Swine Fever Contingency Plans. 2010. (FAO Animal Production & Health Manual Ser.). (Illus.). 69p. pap. *(978-92-5-106426-9(1))* Food & Agriculture Organization of the United Nations.

AFRICAN VIOLETS

Wilson, Helen Van Pelt, ed. 1,001 African Violet Questions Answered by Twelve Experts. 2011. 384p. 53.95 ***(978-1-258-06102-9(3))*** Literary Licensing, LLC.

AFRICAN WIT AND HUMOR

Francis, Stephen. Mother Anderson's Secret Book of Wit & Wisdom. 2011. (ENG., Illus.). 96p. pap. 14.95 *(978-1-4314-0107-9(2))* Jacana Media ZAF. Dist: Independent Pubs. Group.

AFRICANIZED HONEYBEE

Waring, Rob. Killer Bees! 2008. (ENG.). 24p. (C). pap. 10.95 *(978-1-4240-4460-3(X))* Cengage Heinle.

AFRICANS

see also North Africans

Attias-Donfut, Claudine, et al, eds. Citizenship, Belonging & Intergenerational Relations in African Migration. 2012. (ENG., Illus.). 224p. 85.00 *(978-0-230-25274-5(5))* Palgrave Macmillan.

Barcia, Manuel. The Great African Slave Revolt of 1825: Cuba & the Fight for Freedom in Matanzas. 2012. (Illus.). 272p. 42.50 *(978-0-8071-4332-2(4))* Louisiana State Univ. Pr.

Barnes, Hugh. The Stolen Prince: Gannibal, Adopted Son of Peter the Great, Great-Grandfather of Alexander Pushkin, & Europe's First Black Intellectual. 320p. pap. 13.95 *(978-0-06-093688-4(6))* HarperCollins Pubs.

Bodomo, Adams. Africans in China: A Sociocultural Study & Its Implications on Africa-China Relations. 2012. 14.99 *(978-1-60497-790-5(6))* Cambria Pr.

Bohannan, Paul & Curtin, Philip D. Africa & Africans. 4th ed. 2006. pap. 8.95 *(978-1-4288-1516-2(3))* Cram101 Inc.

Boittin, Jennifer Anne. Colonial Metropolis: The Urban Grounds of Anti-Imperialism & Feminism in Interwar Paris. 2010. (France Overseas: Studies in Empire & D Ser.). (ENG., Illus.). 354p. 45.00 *(978-0-8032-2545-9(8))* Univ. of Nebraska Pr.

Chaudhuri, Shubh. Remembered Rhythms: Issues of Diaspora & Music in India. Seeger, Anthony, ed. 2007. (ENG., Illus.). 256p. 99.95 *(978-1-905422-49-4(0))* Seagull Bks. GBR. Dist: Chicago Distribution Ctr.

Chaudhuri, Shubha & Seeger, Anthony, eds. Remembered Rhythms: Issues of Music & Diaspora in India. 2011. (Illus.). 282p. 29.00 *(978-1-905422-50-0(4))* Seagull Bks. GBR. Dist: Chicago Distribution Ctr.

Crul, Maurice & Heering, Liesbeth, eds. The Position of the Turkish & Moroccan Second Generation in Amsterdam & Rotterdam: The TIES Study in the Netherlands. 2009. (Amsterdam University Press - IMISCOE Reports). 192p. pap. 34.50 *(978-90-8964-061-1(4),* Leiden Univ. Pr.) Amsterdam Univ. Pr. NLD. Dist: Chicago Distribution Ctr.

de Silva Jaysuriya, Shihan. African Identity in Asia: Cultural Effects of Forced Migration. 2009. (Illus.). xiv, 164p. 89.95 *(978-1-55876-471-2(2));* 260p. pap. 28.95 *(978-1-55876-472-9(0))* Wiener, Markus Pubs., Inc.

Demos, T. J. Pieter Hugo: Selected Works. 2012. (Illus.). 228p. 60.00 *(978-3-7913-4689-2(X))* Prestel Publishing.

Depelchin, Jacques. Reclaiming African History. 2011. 104p. pap. 20.95 *(978-1-906387-98-3(2))* Pambazuka Pr. GBR. Dist: Independent Pubs. Group.

Earle, T. F. & Lowe, K. J. P., eds. Black Africans in Renaissance Europe. 2010. (ENG., Illus.). 436p. pap. 34.99 *(978-0-521-17660-6(3))* Cambridge Univ. Pr.

Edward, Jane Kani. Sudanese Women Refugees: Transformations & Future Imaginings. 2007. (ENG.). 288p. 95.00 *(978-1-4039-8077-9(2))* Palgrave Macmillan.

Eze, Smart. My Four Worlds. 2010. 268p. pap. 14.49 *(978-1-4520-5077-5(5))* AuthorHouse.

Falola, Toyin & Afolabi, Niyi, eds. Trans-Atlantic Migration: The Paradoxes of Exile. (African Studies). (ENG.). 314p. 2012. pap. 42.95 *(978-0-415-54249-4(9))* 2007. (Illus.). 128.00 *(978-0-415-96091-5(6))* Routledge.

Garofalo, Leo. Afro-Latino Voices: Narratives from the Early Modern Ibero-Atlantic World, 1550-1812. McKnight, Kathryn Joy, ed. 2009. 416p. 57.00 *(978-0-87220-994-7(6))* Hackett Publishing Co., Inc.

Geurts & Cram101 Textbook Reviews Staff. Culture & the Senses. 2007. 60p. per. 9.95 *(978-1-4288-2644-1(0))* Cram101 Inc.

Goodwin, Stefan. Africa in Europe Vol. 1: Antiquity into the Age of Global Exploration, 2 vols. 2008. (ENG.). 260p. 73.50 *(978-0-7391-1725-5(4));* pap. 31.50 *(978-0-7391-1726-2(2))* Lexington Bks.

—Africa in Europe Vol. 2: Interdependencies, Relocations, & Globalization, 2 vols. 2008. (ENG.). 430p. 83.99 *(978-0-7391-2765-0(9));* pap. 40.99 *(978-0-7391-2766-7(7))* Lexington Bks.

Howard-Hassmann, Rhoda E. Reparations to Africa. 2011. (Pennsylvania Studies in Human Rights Ser.). 272p. (C). pap. 24.95 *(978-0-8122-2164-0(8))* Univ. of Pennsylvania Pr.

Ighodaro, MacDonald E. Living the Experience: Migration, Exclusion, & Anti-Racist Practice. 2007. (ENG.). 192p. pap. 24.95 *(978-1-55266-210-6(1))* Fernwood Publishing Co., Ltd. CAN. Dist: Independent Pubs. Group.

Janssen, Volker, ed. Black Volume 5: The African Male Nude in Art & Photography. 2007. (Black Ser.). (Illus.). 80p. per. 29.95 *(978-1-919901-32-9(9))* Janssen Pubs. ZAF. Dist: Independent Pubs. Group.

Jenkins, Jennifer. West Africans in Paris. 2008. 180p. pap. *(978-3-8364-9726-8(3))* VDM Verlag Dr. Mueller e.K.

Johnson, M. Dujon. Race & Racism in the Chinas: Chinese Racial attitudes toward Africans & African-Americans. 2007. 168p. per. 15.95 *(978-1-4259-8175-4(5))* AuthorHouse.

Kane, Abdoulaye & Leedy, Todd H., eds. African Migrations: Patterns & Perspectives. 2012. (ENG.). 280p. 85.00 *(978-0-253-00308-9(3),* 0253003083); pap. 32.00 *(978-0-253-00576-2(0),* 0253005760) Indiana Univ. Pr.

Khalique, Amna. The Peoples of African Descent in Pakistan. 2009. 64p. pap. *(978-3-639-18263-7(4))* VDM Verlag Dr. Mueller e.K.

Knight, Frederick. Working the Diaspora: The Impact of African Labor on the Anglo-American World, 1650-1850. 2010. (ENG., Illus.). 240p. 48.00 *(978-0-8147-4818-3(X))* New York Univ. Pr.

Macdonell, Bror Urme. Mzee Ali. 2008. (Illus.). 224p. pap. 14.95 *(978-0-9584890-5-8(X))* 30° South Pubs. ZAF. Dist: International Publishers Marketing.

Madibbo, Amal Ibrahim. Minority Within a Minority: Black Francophone Immigrants & the Dynamics of Power & Resistance. 2006. (New Approaches in Sociology Ser.). (Illus.). 256p. 138.00 *(978-0-415-97911-5(0))* Routledge.

Matsinhe, David M. Apartheid Vertigo: South African & African Outsiders. 2011. (Interdisciplinary Research Ser. in Ethnic, Gender & Class Relations Ser.). (Illus.). 230p. 99.95 *(978-1-4094-2619-6(X))* Ashgate Publishing Co.

McDougall, James & Scheele, Judith. Saharan Frontiers: Space & Mobility in Northwest Africa. 2012. E-Book *(978-0-253-00131-3(5))* Indiana Univ. Pr.

McDougall, James & Scheele, Judith, eds. Saharan Frontiers: Space & Mobility in Northwest Africa. 2012. (Public Cultures of the Middle East & North Africa Ser.). (ENG., Illus.). 306p. 80.00 *(978-0-253-00124-5(2),* 0253001242); pap. 30.00 *(978-0-253-00126-9(9),* 0253001269) Indiana Univ. Pr.

McEachrane, Michael, ed. Afro-Nordic Landscapes. 2012. (Routledge Studies on African & Black Diaspora Ser.). (ENG.). 240p. (C). 125.00 *(978-0-415-89743-3(2))* Routledge.

McKnight, Kathryn Joy & Garofalo, Leo, eds. Afro-Latino Voices: Narratives from the Early Modern Ibero-Atlantic World, 1550-1812. 2009. 416p. pap. 19.95 *(978-0-87220-993-0(8))* Hackett Publishing Co., Inc.

McLeod, John & Robbins, Kenneth X. African Elites in India: Habshi Amarat. 2006. (ENG., Illus.). 224p. 65.00 *(978-1-890206-97-0(0))* Mapin Publishing Pvt. Ltd IND. Dist: National Bk. Network.

Mohapatra, Sanket & Ratha, Dilip. Remittance Markets in Africa. 2011. *(978-0-8213-8553-1(4))* World Bank Pubns.

Mohapatra, Sanket & Ratha, Dilip, eds. Remittance Markets in Africa. 2011. (Directions in Development Ser.). (ENG., Illus.). 420p. pap. 39.95 *(978-0-8213-8475-6(9),* 9780821384756) World Bank Pubns.

Moore, Lois Merriweather, ed. The Dispersion of Africans & African Culture Throughout the World: Essays on the African Diaspora. 2007. 225p. *(978-0-7734-5309-8(1))* Mellen, Edwin Pr., The.

Northrup, David. Africa's Discovery of Europe 1450-1850. 2nd ed. 2008. (ENG., Illus.). 224p. (C). pap. 34.95 *(978-0-19-534053-2(1))* Oxford Univ. Pr., Inc.

Nzira, Viola. Social Care with African Families in the UK. 2010. (ENG.). 168p. (C). 42.95 *(978-0-415-48294-3(1));* 125.00 *(978-0-415-48293-6(3))* Routledge.

Ohadike, Don C. Sacred Drums of Liberation: Religions & Music of Resistance in Africa & the Diaspora. 2007. xiv, 259p. *(978-1-59221-516-4(5));* 304p. pap. *(978-1-59221-517-1(3))* Africa World Pr.

Okpewho, Isidore & Nzegwu, Nkiru, eds. The New African Diaspora: The New African Immigrant Experience. 2009. (ENG., Illus.). 544p. 75.00 *(978-0-253-35337-5(8),* 0253353378); pap. 29.95 *(978-0-253-22095-0(5),* 0253220955) Indiana Univ. Pr.

Olopade, Olufunmilayo I. & Falkson, Carla I., eds. Breast Cancer in Women of African Descent. 2010. xxii, 383p. pap. 179.00 *(978-90-481-6929-0(1),* 9048169291) Springer.

Orrells, Daniel, et al, eds. African Athena: New Agendas. 2011. (Classical Presences Ser.). (ENG., Illus.). 496p. 160.00 *(978-0-19-959500-6(3))* Oxford Univ. Pr., Inc.

O'Toole, Rachel Sarah. Bound Lives: Africans, Indians, & the Making of Race in Colonial Peru. 2012. (Pitt Latin American Studies). (ENG.). 280p. pap. 25.95 *(978-0-8229-6193-2(8))* Univ. of Pittsburgh Pr.

Plaza, Sonia & Ratha, Dilip. Diaspora for Development in Africa. 2011. *(978-0-8213-8619-4(0))* World Bank Pubns.

Reeves, William Kpaye Kamma & Davis, Alphonsus Gbenon Nyanet. Founder Yawah Toe & Paramount Chief Wrea Musu, Heroes of Gedebo or Kleo, A Subsection of Grebo Land in Liberia. 2008. (Illus.). 128p. 25.00 *(978-0-9818939-0-7(2))* Africana Homestead Legacy Pubs., Inc.

Renzaho, Andre M. N. Migrants Getting Fat in Australia: Acculturation & its Effects on the Nutrition & Physical Activity of African Migrants to Developed Countries. 2007. (Illus.). 163p. 150.00 *(978-1-60021-496-7(7),* Bibliotheca Pr.) Nova Science Pubs., Inc.

Restall, Matthew. The Black Middle: Africans, Mayas, & Spaniards in Colonial Yucatan. 2009. (ENG., Illus.). 456p. 65.00 *(978-0-8047-4983-1(3))* Stanford Univ. Pr.

Rich, Jeremy. Missing Links: The African & American Worlds of R. L. Garner, Primate Collector. 2012. (Race in the Atlantic World, 1700-1900 Ser.). (ENG., Illus.). 200p. 59.95 *(978-0-8203-4059-3(6));* pap. 24.95 *(978-0-8203-4060-9(X))* Univ. of Georgia Pr.

Sajovitz, Mathias. The African Diaspora in the Austrian Political Economy: A Marxist Analysis. 2008. 71p. pap. 11.99 *(978-1-4357-3534-7(X))* Lulu Enterprises Inc.

Salgado, Leila, ed. Sebastiao Salgado, Africa. 2010. (Go Ser.). (ENG, FRE & GER., Illus.). 336p. 39.99 *(978-3-8365-2343-1(4))* TASCHEN DEU. Dist: Ingram Pub. Services.

Schilder. Quest for Self-Esteem: State, Islam, & Mundang Ethnicity in Northern Cameroon. (Illus.). xiv, 283p. *(978-90-5448-021-1(1))* Afrika-Studiecentrum.

Sidibe, Malick, photos by. Malick Sidibe: la Vie en Rose, 1 vol. 2010. (FRE & ENG., Illus.). 160p. 60.00 *(978-88-366-1716-6(6))* Silvana ITA. Dist: D.A.P./Distributed Art Pubs.

Simon, Benjamin. From Migrants to Missionaries: Christians of African Origin in Germany. 2010. (IC - Studien zur interkulturellen Geschichte des Christentums. Etudes d'histoire interculturelle de christianisme. Studies in the Intercultural History of Christianity Ser.). 278p. 72.95 *(978-3-631-59842-9(4))* Lang, Peter GmbH, Europaischer Verlag der Wissenschaften DEU. Dist: Lang, Peter.

Smallwood, Stephanie E. Saltwater Slavery: A Middle Passage from Africa to American Diaspora. 2008. (Illus.). 288p. pap. 19.95 *(978-0-674-03068-8(0))* Harvard Univ. Pr.

Sofela, Babatunde. Emancipados: Slave Societies in Brazil & Cuba. 2009. *(978-1-59221-602-4(1));* 292p. pap. *(978-1-59221-603-1(X))* Africa World Pr.

Spickard, Jim. Religion Crossing Boundaries: Transnational Religious & Social Dynamics in Africa & the New African Diaspora. Adogame, Afe, ed. 2010. (Religion & the Social Order Ser.). 274p. *(978-90-04-18730-6(8))* BRILL.

Stewart, James Brewer, ed. Venture Smith & the Business of Slavery & Freedom. 2010. (Illus.). 256p. 34.95 net. *(978-1-55849-740-5(4))* Univ. of Massachusetts Pr.

van Wyk Smith, Malvern. The First Ethiopians: The Image of Africa & Africans in the Early Mediterranean World. 2010. (ENG.). 544p. pap. 39.95 *(978-1-86814-499-0(2))* Witwatersrand Univ. Pr. Pubns. ZAF. Dist: Transaction Pubs.

Whitehouse, Bruce. Migrants & Strangers in an African City. 2012. (Illus.). x, 274p. *(978-0-253-00075-0(0));* (ENG., 288p. pap. 25.00 *(978-0-253-00082-8(3),* 0253000823) Indiana Univ. Pr.

Whitehouse, Bruce. Migrants & Strangers in an African City: Exile, Dignity, Belonging. 2012. (ENG., Illus.). 288p. 70.00 *(978-0-253-00081-1(5),* 0253000815) Indiana Univ. Pr.

Winders, James A. Paris Africain: Rhythms of the African Diaspora. 2006. (ENG.). 248p. 82.00 *(978-1-4039-6004-7(6))* Palgrave Macmillan.

AFRICANS—ETHNIC IDENTITY

Amadou Nouhou Diallo. Male Circumcision & Initiation in Rural Afric: Autobiography, Culture & Traditions. 2009. 176p. pap. 12.99 *(978-1-4389-9633-2(0))* AuthorHouse.

Arthur, John A. The African Diaspora in the United States & Europe: The Ghanaian Experience. 2008. (Research in Migration & Ethnic Relations Ser.). 220p. 114.95 *(978-0-7546-4841-3(9))* Ashgate Publishing Co.

Bakari, Sadiki. Butt Naked Raw & Uncensored. 2007. 172p. pap. 18.96 *(978-0-615-15261-5(9))* Sadiki Bakari Publishing.

Bayissa, Gudetta Urgessa. Transformed Oromo Lives & Secularization. 2008. 192p. pap. *(978-3-639-05666-2(3))* VDM Verlag Dr. Mueller e.K.

Carton, Benedict, et al, eds. Zulu Identities: Being Zulu, Past & Present. 2009. (Columbia/Hurst Ser.). (ENG.). 688p. (gr. 17). pap. 34.50 *(978-0-231-70059-7(8))* Columbia Univ. Pr.

Fennell, Christopher C. Crossroads & Cosmologies: Diasporas & Ethnogenesis in the New World. 2010. (Cultural Heritage Studies). (ENG., Illus.). 192p. pap. 29.95 *(978-0-8130-3496-6(5))* Univ. Pr. of Florida.

Hall, Gwendolyn Midlo. Slavery & African Ethnicities in the Americas: Restoring the Links. 2007. (ENG., Illus.). 248p. pap. 22.00 *(978-0-8078-5862-2(5))* Univ. of North Carolina Pr.

Jayasuriya, Shihan de S. The African Diaspora in Asian Trade Routes & Cultural Memories. 2010. (Illus.). viii, 196p. 109.95 *(978-0-7734-3651-0(0))* Mellen, Edwin Pr., The.

Klinker, Sonja. Maghrebiner in Frankreich, Türken in Deutschland: Eine vergleichende Untersuchung zu Identität und Integration muslimischer Einwanderergruppen in europäische Mehrheitsgesellschaften. 2010. (Hildesheimer Schriften zur Interkulturellen Kommunikation Ser.). (GER.). 358p. 86.95 *(978-3-631-59940-2(4))* Lang, Peter GmbH, Europaischer Verlag der Wissenschaften DEU. Dist: Lang, Peter.

Nelson, Steven. From Cameroon to Paris: Mousgoum Architecture in & Out of Africa. 2007. (Illus.). 304p. 55.00 *(978-0-226-57183-6(1))* Univ. of Chicago Pr.

Palmié, Stephan. Africas of the Americas: Beyond the Search for Origins in the Study of Afro-Atlantic Religions. Palmié, Stephan, ed. 2008. (Studies of Religion in Africa Ser.). 355p. *(978-90-04-16472-7(3))* BRILL.

Reed, Ann, ed. Pilgrimage Tourism of Diaspora Africans to Ghana. 2012. (Routledge Studies on African & Black Diaspora Ser.). (ENG.). 240p. (C). 125.00 *(978-0-415-88502-7(7))* Routledge.

Schroven, Anita. Women after War: Gender Mainstreaming & the Social Construction of Identity in Contemporary Sierra Leone. 2007. (ENG., Illus.). 152p. pap. 34.95 *(978-3-8258-9627-0(7))* Lit Verlag DEU. Dist: Transaction Pubs.

Soares, Mariza de Carvalho. People of Faith: Slavery & African Catholics in Eighteenth-Century Rio de Janeiro. Metz, Jerry D., tr. from POR. 2011. (Latin America in Translation Ser.). (ENG., Illus.). 336p. 84.95 *(978-0-8223-5023-1(8));* pap. 23.95 *(978-0-8223-5040-8(8))* Duke Univ. Pr.

Toledano, Ehud R. African Communities in Asia & the Mediterranean: Identities Between Integration & Conflict. 2011. 310p. *(978-1-59221-850-9(4));* pap. *(978-1-59221-851-6(2))* Africa World Pr.

Vasu, Norman. How Diasporic Peoples Maintain Their Identity in Multicultural Societies: Chinese, Africans, & Jews. 2009. (Illus.). iii, 273p. *(978-0-7734-4896-4(9))* Mellen, Edwin Pr., The.

Waldman, Linda. The Griqua Conundrum: Political & Socio-Cultural Identity in the Northern Cape, South Africa. 254p. pap. 59.95 *(978-3-03910-562-5(0));* 2007. pap. 59.95 *(978-0-8204-7589-9(0))* Lang, Peter Publishing, Inc.

Yewah, Emmanuel & Togunde, 'Dimeji. Across the Atlantic: African Immigrants in the United States Diaspora. 2010. pap. *(978-1-86335-788-3(2))* Common Ground Publishing Pty, Ltd.

AFRICANS—UNITED STATES

see also African Americans

Abdullah, Zain. Black Mecca: The African Muslims of Harlem, 1 vol. 2010. (ENG., Illus.). 320p. 35.00 *(978-0-19-531425-0(5))* Oxford Univ. Pr., Inc.

Agbese, Ajeori. The Role of Intercultural Communication in Conflict Resolution. 2010. 84p. pap. *(978-3-8383-2159-2(6))* Lambert Academic Publishing.

Arthur, John A. The African Diaspora in the United States & Europe: The Ghanaian Experience. 2008. (Research in Migration & Ethnic Relations Ser.). 220p. 114.95 *(978-0-7546-4841-3(9))* Ashgate Publishing Co.

—African Women Immigrants in the United States: Crossing Transnational Borders. 2009. (ENG.). 244p. 89.00 *(978-0-230-61778-0(6))* Palgrave Macmillan.

DuVal, Kathleen & DuVal, John. Interpreting a Continent: Voices from Colonial America. 2009. (ENG., Illus.). 312p. 95.00 *(978-0-7425-5182-4(2));* pap. 35.00 *(978-0-7425-5183-1(0))* Rowman & Littlefield Publishers, Inc.

Fennell, Christopher C. Crossroads & Cosmologies: Diasporas & Ethnogenesis in the New World. 2010. (Cultural Heritage Studies). (ENG., Illus.). 192p. pap. 29.95 *(978-0-8130-3496-6(5))* Univ. Pr. of Florida.

Getahun, Solomon Addis. The History of Ethiopian Immigrants & Refugees in America, 1900-2000: Patterns of Migration, Survival, & Adjustment. 2006. (New Americans). (Illus.). 342p. 80.00 *(978-1-59332-151-2(1))* LFB Scholarly Publishing LLC.

Harris, Yvette R. & Bergen, Doris. Children & Families of African Origin: A Guide for Educators & Service Providers. 2008. pap. *(978-0-87173-173-9(8))* Assn. for Childhood Education International.

Herr, Ojoma E. Ojoma's Song: Becoming a Woman Nigerian Style. 2008. (ENG.). 96p. pap. 15.95 *(978-1-934668-01-6(X))* ACW Pr.

Horsham, Cyril. The Burning House: Joe Six-Pack Speaks of Integration, 1 vol. 2009. 230p. pap. 24.95 *(978-1-60836-165-6(9))* PublishAmerica, Inc.

Mott, Tamar. African Refugee Resettlement in the United States. 2009. (New Americans). 322p. 80.00 *(978-1-59332-333-2(6))* LFB Scholarly Publishing LLC.

Obiakor, Festus E., ed. Voices of Foreign-Born African American Teacher Educators in the United States. 2010. (Education in a Competitive & Globalizing World Ser.). 204p. 89.00 *(978-1-60876-322-1(6))* Nova Science Pubs., Inc.

Ocloo, Komla Happy. Understanding the Needs of Elderly African Immigrants: A Resource Guide for Service Providers in Central Minnesota. 2011. 64p. pap. 11.95 *(978-1-4620-1926-7(9))* iUniverse, Inc.

Okpewho, Isidore & Nzegwu, Nkiru, eds. The New African Diaspora: The New African Immigrant Experience. 2009. (ENG., Illus.). 544p. 75.00 *(978-0-253-35337-5(8),* 0253353378); pap. 29.95 *(978-0-253-22095-0(5),* 0253220955) Indiana Univ. Pr.

Oriola, Bukola. Imprisoned: The Travails of a Trafficked Victim. rev. ed. 2009. 155p. pap. 19.50 *(978-0-615-32880-5(6))* Bukola Braiding & Beauty Supply.

Shaw-Taylor, Yoku & Tuch, Steven A. The Other African Americans: Contemporary African & Caribbean Immigrants in the United States. 2007. (ENG.). 308p. 85.00 *(978-0-7425-4087-3(1));* pap. 32.95 *(978-0-7425-4088-0(X))* Rowman & Littlefield Publishers, Inc.

Smallwood, Stephanie E. Saltwater Slavery: A Middle Passage from Africa to American Diaspora. 2007. (Illus.). 288p. 29.95 *(978-0-674-02349-9(8))* Harvard Univ. Pr.

Steffen, Charles G. Mutilating Khalid: The Symbolic Politics of Female Genital Cutting. 2010. *(978-1-56902-331-0(X));* 248p. pap. *(978-1-56902-332-7(8))* Red Sea Pr.

Swigart, Leigh. Extended Lives: The African Immigrant Experience in Philadelphia: a Balch Institute Community Profile. Wilson, Kathryn, ed. 2006. (Illus.). 54p. reprint ed. pap. 20.00 *(978-1-4223-5824-5(0))* DIANE Publishing Co.

Vaughan, Olufemi & Okome, Mojúbàolú Olúfúnké, eds. West African Migrations: Transnational & Global Pathways in a New Century. 2012. (ENG., Illus.). 294p. 90.00 *(978-0-230-33867-8(4))* Palgrave Macmillan.

Voeks, Robert & Rashford, John, eds. African Ethnobotany in the Americas. 2012. (ENG., Illus.). 332p. pap. 49.95 *(978-1-4614-0835-2(0),* 1461408350) Springer.

Young, Jason R. Rituals of Resistance: African Atlantic Religion in Kongo & the Lowcountry South in the Era of Slavery. 2007. 258p. *(978-0-8071-3279-1(9))* Louisiana State Univ. Pr.

—Rituals of Resistance (p) African Atlantic Religion in Kongo & the Lowcountry South in the Era of Slavery. 2011. (Illus.). 272p. pap. 21.50 *(978-0-8071-3719-2(7))* Louisiana State Univ. Pr.

Zellar, Gary. African Creeks: Estelvste & the Creek Nation. 2007. (Race & Culture in the American West Ser.: Vol. 1). (ENG., Illus.). 368p. (C). 34.95 *(978-0-8061-3815-2(7))* Univ. of Oklahoma Pr.

AFRICANS IN LITERATURE

Blackmore, Josiah. Moorings: Portuguese Expansion & the Writing of Africa. 2008. (Illus.). 224p. pap. 25.00 *(978-0-8166-4833-7(6))* Univ. of Minnesota Pr.

Blackmore, Josiah & Blackmore. Moorings: Portuguese Expansion & the Writing of Africa. 2008. (Illus.). 224p. 75.00 *(978-0-8166-4832-0(8))* Univ. of Minnesota Pr.

Falola, Toyin & Ngom, Fallou. Facts, Fiction, & African Creative Imaginations. Falola, Toyin & Ngom, Fallou, eds. 2009. (Routledge African Studies). (ENG., Illus.). 348p. 125.00 *(978-0-415-80316-8(0))* Routledge.

MacCann, Donnarae & Maddy, Yulisa Amadu. Neo-Imperialism in Children's Literature about Africa: A Study of Contemporary Fiction. 2008. (Children's Literature & Culture Ser.). (ENG.). 190p. (C). 125.00 *(978-0-415-99390-6(3))* Routledge.

Ojo-Ade, Femi. Configuring the African World: Continental & Diasporic Literatures & Cultures. 2006. *(978-1-59221-447-1(9))*; 312p. pap. *(978-1-59221-448-8(7))* Africa World Pr.

Tomaselli, Keyan G. Writing in the San/d: Autoethnography among Indigenous Southern Africans. 2007. (Crossroads in Qualitative Inquiry Ser.: Vol. 7). (AFR & ENG., Illus.). 190p. per. 32.95 *(978-0-7591-0951-3(6))* AltaMira Pr.

van Wyk Smith, Malvern. The First Ethiopians: The Image of Africa & Africans in the Early Mediterranean World. 2010. (ENG.). 544p. pap. 39.95 *(978-1-86814-499-0(2))* Witwatersrand Univ. Pr. Pubns. ZAF. Dist: Transaction Pubs.

Wilkin, Binnie Tate. African & African American Images in Newbery Award Winning Titles: Progress in Portrayals. 2009. (ENG.). 210p. pap. 45.00 *(978-0-8108-6959-2(4))* Scarecrow Pr., Inc.

Yenika-Agbaw, Vivian. Representing Africa in Children's Literature. 2011. (ENG.). 168p. pap. 34.95 ***(978-0-415-69956-3(8))*** Routledge.

AFRIKAANDERS
see Afrikaners

AFRIKAANS LANGUAGE
Here are entered works on the language spoken and written by the descendents of the Dutch colonists in South Africa which gradually evolved and differentiated from the Dutch South African dialects of the earlier periods. Works on Dutch South African dialects not conforming to Dutch as spoken or written in the Netherlands are entered under Dutch Language—Dialects—South Africa.

Bennett, John & Tsoeu, Nthuseng. Multilingual Illustrated Dictionary. 2011. 372p. pap. 24.95 ***(978-1-86890-107-4(6))*** NB Pubs. Ltd. ZAF. Dist: International Publishers Marketing.

Botha, Rudolf P. The function of the lexicon in transformational generative Grammar. (Janua Linguarum. Series Maior Ser.). (ENG.). 272p. 210.00 ***(978-3-11-198045-4(6))***; 135.00 ***(978-3-11-099527-5(1))*** De Gruyter, Mouton DEU. Dist: de Gruyter, Walter GmbH & Co. KG.

Dictionaries, Pharos. English-Afrikaans Concise Dictionary. 2010. 1600p. pap. 61.95 *(978-1-86890-048-0(7))* NB Pubs. Ltd. ZAF. Dist: International Publishers Marketing.

—Pharos Afrikaans-English: English-Afrikaans Dictionary: Mini Woordeboek Dictionary. 2010. 641p. pap. 9.95 *(978-1-86890-064-0(9))* NB Pubs. Ltd. ZAF. Dist: International Publishers Marketing.

Euro Talk. Talk More Afrikaans. 2008. 29.99 *(978-1-60077-213-9(7))* TOPICS Entertainment.

—World Talk Afrikaans. 2008. 29.99 *(978-1-84352-537-0(2))* TOPICS Entertainment.

McDermott, Lydia. Complete Afrikaans. 3rd ed. 2011. (TY: Language Guides). (ENG.). 368p. pap. 32.00 *(978-0-07-175632-7(9), 0071756329)* McGraw-Hill Cos., The.

—Complete Afrikaans with Two Audio CDs: A Teach Yourself Guide. 3rd ed. 2011. (TY: Language Guides). (ENG.). 368p. pap. 46.00 incl. audio compact disk, audio compact disk *(978-0-07-175631-0(0), 0071756310)* McGraw-Hill Cos., The.

Pharos Staff. Pharos Tweetalige Woordeboek / Bilingual Dictionary. 2010. (AFR & ENG.). 1552p. 59.95 *(978-1-86890-044-2(4))* NB Pubs. Ltd. ZAF. Dist: International Publishers Marketing.

Uys, Isabel. English-Afrikaans-Northern Sotho-Tswana Aid. 2010. 280p. pap. 20.95 *(978-1-86890-084-8(3))* NB Pubs. Ltd. ZAF. Dist: International Publishers Marketing.

Van Os, Leonard. Afrikaans Self-Taught: By the Natural Method with Phonetic Pronunciation (Thimm's System) 2007. (AFR.). 260p. per. *(978-1-84356-022-7(4))* Wallenberg, Simon Pr.

Willemse, Hein, et al. The Afrikaans of the Cape Muslims. 2012. (Illus.). 318p. pap. 33.00 ***(978-1-86919-236-5(2))*** International Publishers Marketing.

AFRIKAANS LITERATURE

Van der Merwe, C. N. & Viljoen, Hein. Across the Threshold: Explorations of Liminality in Literature. 2007. (Illus.). 280p. (C). pap. 29.95 *(978-1-4331-0002-4(9))* Lang, Peter Publishing, Inc.

AFRIKANDER LANGUAGE
see Afrikaans Language

AFRIKANDERS
see Afrikaners

AFRIKANER BOND

Wilburn, Kenneth E. The Life of Statesman & Industrialist Sir James Sivewright of South Africa, 1848-1916: Builder of Railways, Telegraphs, & Waterworks. 2010. (Illus.). xxxii, 567p. 159.95 *(978-0-7734-3673-2(1))* Mellen, Edwin Pr., The.

AFRIKANERS

Chapman, William & Stassen, Nicol. William Chapman: Reminiscences Including an Account of the Trek Boers into Angola & of Their Sojourn During the Forty-Eight Years They Struggled in That Country under Portuguese Rule. 2012. (Illus.). 476p. 50.00 ***(978-1-86919-192-4(7))*** International Publishers Marketing.

Davies, Rebecca. Afrikaners in the New South Africa: Identity Politics in a Globalised Economy. 2009. (International Library of African Studies). (ENG.). 224p. 86.00 *(978-1-84511-785-6(9)*, Tauris Academic Studies) I. B. Tauris & Co., Ltd. GBR. Dist: Macmillan.

Duffy, Joanne L. The Politics of Ethnic Nationalism: Afrikaner Unity, the National Party, & the Radical Right in Stellenbosch, 1934-1948. 2006. (African Studies: History, Politics, Economics & Culture Ser.). (Illus.). 273p. 128.00 *(978-0-415-97986-3(2))* Routledge.

Giliomee, Hermann. The Afrikaners: Biography of a People, expanded & updated Edition. 2011. 752p. pap. 53.95 *(978-0-624-04823-7(3))* NB Pubs. Ltd. ZAF. Dist: International Publishers Marketing.

Hillegas, Howard C. With the Boers: A Journalist's Experiences of the Anglo-Boer War from the Boer Perspective. 2011. 204p. ***(978-0-85706-575-9(0))*** Leonaur Ltd.

Jackson, Murray Cosby. A Soldier's Diary: South Africa 1899-1901-the Experiences of a N. C. O. of the Hants. Regiment & 7th Mounted Infantry During the Boer War. 2010. 232p. *(978-1-84677-914-5(6))* Leonaur Ltd.

Jansen, Jonathan D. Knowledge in the Blood: Confronting Race & the Apartheid Past. 2009. (ENG.). 360p. 65.00 *(978-0-8047-6194-9(9))*; pap. 21.95 *(978-0-8047-6195-6(7))* Stanford Univ. Pr.

Knecht, Annette. Ein Geheimbund als Akteur des Wandels: Der Afrikaner Broederbond und seine Rolle im Transformationsprozess Sudafrikas. (GRE, AFR, GER & ENG., Illus.). 426p. pap. 89.95 *(978-3-631-56318-2(3))* Lang, Peter GmbH, Europaischer Verlag der Wissenschaften DEU. Dist: Lang, Peter Publishing, Inc.

Mouton, F. A. Prophet Without Honour: F.S. Malan: Afrikaner, South African & Cape Liberal. 2012. (Illus.). 156p. pap. 30.00 ***(978-1-86919-414-7(4))*** International Publishers Marketing.

O'Meara, Dan. Volkskapitalisme: Class, Capital & Ideology in the Development of Afrikaner Nationalism, 1934-1948. 2009. (African Studies). (ENG.). 300p. pap. 38.99 *(978-0-521-10467-8(X))* Cambridge Univ. Pr.

Rule, Stephen, et al, eds. South African Social Attitudes: Changing Times, Diverse Voices. 2007. (South African Social Attitudes Ser.). (ENG., Illus.). 400p. pap. 34.95 *(978-0-7969-2117-8(2))* Human Sciences Research Council ZAF. Dist: Independent Pubs. Group.

Russell, Margo & Russell, Martin. Afrikaners of the Kalahari: White Minority in a Black State. 2009. (African Studies). (ENG.). 184p. pap. 31.99 *(978-0-521-10140-0(9))* Cambridge Univ. Pr.

Thomas, C. H. Origin of the Anglo-Boer War Revealed (2. 2006. 2p. *(978-1-4068-1171-1(8))* Echo Library.

van Warmelo, Dietlof. On Commando. 2007. 104p. per. *(978-1-4065-4736-8(0))* Dodo Pr.

Wassermann, Johan. Caught Between the Empire & the Republics. 2009. 508p. pap. *(978-3-639-20525-1(1))* VDM Verlag Dr. Mueller e.K.

AFRO (HAIR STYLE)
see Hairdressing of Blacks

AFRO-AMERICAN ACTORS
see African American Actors

AFRO-AMERICAN AGED
see Older African Americans

AFRO-AMERICAN ART
see African American Art

AFRO-AMERICAN ARTISTS
see African American Artists

AFRO-AMERICAN ARTS
see African American Arts

AFRO-AMERICAN ATHLETES
see African American Athletes

AFRO-AMERICAN AUTHORS
see African American Authors

AFRO-AMERICAN BAPTISTS
see African American Baptists

AFRO-AMERICAN BUSINESSPEOPLE
see African Americans in Business

AFRO-AMERICAN CHILDREN
see African American Children

AFRO-AMERICAN CHURCHES
see African American Churches

AFRO-AMERICAN CLERGY
see African American Clergy

AFRO-AMERICAN COLLEGES
see African American Universities and Colleges

AFRO-AMERICAN COMPOSERS
see African American Composers

AFRO-AMERICAN CONSUMERS
see African American Consumers

AFRO-AMERICAN COOKING
see African American Cooking

AFRO-AMERICAN CRIMINALS
see African American Criminals

AFRO-AMERICAN DANCE
see African American Dance

AFRO-AMERICAN DRAMA (ENGLISH)
see American Drama—African American Authors

AFRO-AMERICAN ENGLISH
see Black English

AFRO-AMERICAN ENTERTAINERS
see African American Entertainers

AFRO-AMERICAN FAMILIES
see African American Families

AFRO-AMERICAN FARMERS
see African American Farmers

AFRO-AMERICAN FICTION (ENGLISH)
see American Fiction—African American Authors

AFRO-AMERICAN FOLKLORE
see African Americans—Folklore

AFRO-AMERICAN HISTORIANS
see African American Historians

AFRO-AMERICAN INVENTORS
see African American Inventors

AFRO-AMERICAN-JEWISH RELATIONS
see African Americans—Relations With Jews

AFRO-AMERICAN JOURNALISM
see African American Press

AFRO-AMERICAN JOURNALISTS
see African American Journalists

AFRO-AMERICAN JUDGES
see African American Judges

AFRO-AMERICAN LAWYERS
see African American Lawyers

AFRO-AMERICAN LEGISLATORS
see African American Legislators

AFRO-AMERICAN LIBRARIANS
see African American Librarians

AFRO-AMERICAN LITERATURE (ENGLISH)
see American Literature—African American Authors

AFRO-AMERICAN MEN
see African American Men

AFRO-AMERICAN MOTION PICTURE ACTORS AND ACTRESSES
see African American Motion Picture Actors and Actresses

AFRO-AMERICAN MOTION PICTURE PRODUCERS AND DIRECTORS
see African American Motion Picture Producers and Directors

AFRO-AMERICAN MUSIC
see African Americans—Music

AFRO-AMERICAN MUSICIANS
see African American Musicians

AFRO-AMERICAN NURSES
see African American Nurses

AFRO-AMERICAN ORATORS
see African American Orators

AFRO-AMERICAN PERIODICALS
see African American Periodicals

AFRO-AMERICAN PHILOSOPHY
see African American Philosophy

AFRO-AMERICAN PHOTOGRAPHERS
see African American Photographers

AFRO-AMERICAN PHYSICIANS
see African American Physicians

AFRO-AMERICAN POETRY (ENGLISH)
see American Poetry—African American Authors

AFRO-AMERICAN POLICE
see African American Police

AFRO-AMERICAN POLITICIANS
see African American Politicians

AFRO-AMERICAN PRESS
see African American Press

AFRO-AMERICAN SAILORS
see African American Sailors

AFRO-AMERICAN SCIENTISTS
see African American Scientists

AFRO-AMERICAN SEAMEN
see African American Sailors

AFRO-AMERICAN SLAVES
see Slaves—United States

AFRO-AMERICAN SOLDIERS
see African American Soldiers

AFRO-AMERICAN SONGS
see African Americans—Music

AFRO-AMERICAN SPIRITUALS
see Spirituals (Songs)

AFRO-AMERICAN STUDENTS
see African American Students

AFRO-AMERICAN STUDIES
see African Americans—Study and Teaching

AFRO-AMERICAN TEACHERS
see African American Teachers

AFRO-AMERICAN UNIVERSITIES AND COLLEGES
see African American Universities and Colleges

AFRO-AMERICAN WIT AND HUMOR
see African American Wit and Humor

AFRO-AMERICAN WOMEN
see African American Women

AFRO-AMERICAN YOUTH
see African American Youth

AFRO-AMERICANS
see African Americans

AFRO-AMERICANS AND LIBRARIES
see African Americans and Libraries

AFRO-AMERICANS AS CONSUMERS
see African American Consumers

AFRO-AMERICANS IN AERONAUTICS
see African Americans in Aeronautics

AFRO-AMERICANS IN ART
see African Americans in Art

AFRO-AMERICANS IN BUSINESS
see African Americans in Business

AFRO-AMERICANS IN LITERATURE
see African Americans in Literature

AFRO-AMERICANS IN MASS MEDIA
see African Americans in Mass Media

AFRO-AMERICANS IN MEDICINE
see African Americans in Medicine

AFRO-AMERICANS IN MOTION PICTURES
see African Americans in Motion Pictures

AFRO-AMERICANS IN SPORTS
see African Americans in Sports

AFRO-AMERICANS IN TELEVISION BROADCASTING
see African Americans in Television Broadcasting

AFRO-AMERICANS IN THE MOTION PICTURE INDUSTRY
see African Americans in the Motion Picture Industry

AFRO-AMERICANS IN THE PERFORMING ARTS
see African Americans in the Performing Arts

AFRO-AMERICANS IN THE RADIO INDUSTRY
see African Americans in the Radio Industry

AFRO-AMERICANS IN THE TELEVISION INDUSTRY
see African Americans in Television Broadcasting

AFRO-ASIAN POLITICS

Adem, Seifudein. Afrasia, a Tale of Two Continents: Allies, Rivals or Adversaries? 2012. (ENG.). 380p. pap. 43.00 ***(978-0-7618-4771-7(5))*** Univ. Pr. of America, Inc.

Ampiah, Kweku. The Political & Moral Imperatives of the Bandung Conference of 1955: The Reactions of the US, UK & Japan. 2007. 252p. *(978-1-905246-40-3(4))* BRILL.

Lee, Christopher, ed. Making a World after Empire: The Bandung Moment & Its Political Afterlives. 2010. (Ohio RIS Global Ser.). (ENG., Illus.). 280p. pap. 29.95 *(978-0-89680-277-3(9))* Ohio Univ. Pr.

Lee, Christopher J. Making a World after Empire: The Bandung Moment & Its Political Afterlives. 2010. 280p. *(978-0-89680-468-5(2))* Ohio Univ. Pr.

Patil, Vrushali. Negotiating Decolonization in the United Nations: Politics of Space, Identity, & International Community. 2007. (New Approaches in Sociology Ser.). (ENG., Illus.). 206p. 125.00 *(978-0-415-95856-1(3))* Routledge.

Shekhawat, Seema. Afro-Asian Conflicts: Changing Contours, Costs & Consequences. Mahapatra, Debidatta, ed. 2008. 300p. 44.75 *(978-81-7708-183-1(7))* New Century Publications IND. Dist: International Specialized Bk. Services.

AFRO-ASIATIC LANGUAGES
see Afroasiatic Languages

AFRO-BRAZILIAN CULTS
see also Candomble (Cult); Umbanda (Cult)

Capone, Stefania. Searching for Africa in Brazil: Power & Tradition in Candomblé. Grant, Lucy Lyall, tr. from FRE. 2010. (ENG., Illus.). 336p. pap. 23.95 *(978-0-8223-4636-4(2))* Duke Univ. Pr.

Cohen, Emma. The Mind Possessed: The Cognition of Spirit Possession in an Afro-Brazilian Religious Tradition, 1 vol. 2010. (Illus.). 256p. pap. 24.95 *(978-0-19-976744-1(0))* Oxford Univ. Pr., Inc.

Dantas, Beatriz Góis. Nago Grandma & White Papa: Candomble & the Creation of Afro-Brazilian Identity. Berg, Stephen, tr. from POR. 2009. (Latin America in Translation/en Traduccion/em Traducao Ser.). (ENG., Illus.). 208p. 62.95 *(978-0-8078-3177-9(8))*; pap. 26.95 *(978-0-8078-5975-9(3))* Univ. of North Carolina Pr.

Hayes, Kelly E. Holy Harlots: Femininity, Sexuality, & Black Magic in Brazil. 2011. (ENG., Illus.). 312p. 65.00 (978-0-520-26264-5(6)); pap. 27.95 (978-0-520-26265-2(4)) Univ. of California Pr.

AFROASIATIC LANGUAGES
see also Berber Languages; Coptic Language; Cushitic Languages; Egyptian Language; Semitic Languages

Aboh, Enoch Olacé, et al, eds. Focus Strategies in African Languages: The Interaction of Focus & Grammar in Niger-Congo & Afro-Asiatic. 2007. (Trends in Linguistics. Studies & Monographs [TiLSM] Ser.). (ENG.). VI, 324p. 238.00 **(978-3-11-916812-0(2))** De Gruyter, Mouton DEU. Dist: de Gruyter, Walter GmbH & Co. KG.

Aboh, Enoch Olacé, et al. Focus Strategies in African Languages: The Interaction of Focus & Grammar in Niger-Congo & Afro-Asiatic. 2007. (Trends in Linguistics. Studies & Monographs [TiLSM] Ser.). (ENG., Illus.). VI, 324p. 154.00 (978-3-11-019593-4(3)) De Gruyter, Mouton DEU. Dist: de Gruyter, Walter GmbH & Co. KG.

Akililu, Abera. Negation in Wolayta: Sentential, Constituent, & Interaction of Negation with Tenses & Aspects. 2011. 128p. pap. **(978-3-639-32316-0(5))** VDM Verlag Dr. Mueller e.K.

Dolgopolskii, A., et al. Semito-Hamitic Festschrift for A.B. Dolgopolsky & H. Jungraithmayr. 2009. (ENG., Illus.). 378p. 99.00 (978-3-496-02810-9(6), Art Stock Bks. Ltd/Csi) Continental Sales, Inc.

Frajzyngier, Zygmunt & Shay, Erin. Interaction of Morphology & Syntax: Case Studies in Afroasiatic. Frajzyngier, Zygmunt & Shay, Erin, eds. 2008. (Typological Studies in Languages Ser.: 75). (Illus.). 226p. 110.00 (978-90-272-2987-8(2)) Benjamins, John Publishing Co.

Frajzyngier, Zygmunt & Shay, Erin, eds. The Afroasiatic Languages. 2012. (Cambridge Language Surveys Ser.). (ENG., Illus.). 600p. 160.00 **(978-0-521-86533-3(6))** Cambridge Univ. Pr.

Takacs, Gabor. Studies in Afro-Asiatic Comparative Phonology: Consonants. 2011. (ENG.). 250p. 98.00 (978-3-496-02842-0(4)) Reimer, Dietrich DEU. Dist: Independent Pubs. Group.

AFROCENTRICITY
see Afrocentrism

AFROCENTRISM
Adeleke, Tunde. The Case Against Afrocentrism. 2009. (ENG.). 224p. 50.00 (978-1-60473-293-1(8)) Univ. Pr. of Mississippi.

Alexander, Willie J. Entering the Promised Land. 2007. (Illus.). 190p. spiral bd. 24.95 (978-0-9798779-0-2(3)) Entering The Promised Land.

Asante, Molefi Kete. Maulana Karenga: An Intellectual Portrait. 2009. (ENG.). 224p. 69.95 (978-0-7456-4827-9(4)); pap. 19.95 (978-0-7456-4828-6(2)) Polity Pr. GBR. Dist: Wiley, John & Sons, Inc.

Belgrave, Allison. African American Psychology from Africa. 2006. pap. 10.95 (978-1-4288-1325-0(X)) Cram101 Inc.

Bratcher, Melanie E. Words & Songs of Bessie Smith, Billie Holiday, & Nina Simone: Sound Motion, Blues Spirit, & African Memory. 2012. (Studies in African American History & Culture Ser.). (ENG.). 278p. pap. 42.95 **(978-0-415-54081-0(X))** Routledge.

Burton, Keith Augustus. The Blessing of Africa: The Bible & African Christianity. 2007. (ENG.). 294p. per. 22.00 (978-0-8308-2762-6(5), IVP Acad.) InterVarsity Pr.

Callahan, Allen Dwight. The Talking Book: African Americans & the Bible. 2008. (ENG.). 304p. per. 18.00 (978-0-300-13616-6(1)) Yale Univ. Pr.

Cannon-Brown, Willie. Nefer: The Aesthetic Ideal in Classical Egypt. 2006. (African Studies: History, Politics, Economics & Culture Ser.). (Illus.). 116p. 138.00 (978-0-415-97994-8(3)) Routledge.

Davison, James, Jr. & Davison, James. Sweet Release: The Last Step to Black Freedom. 2008. (ENG.). 255p. 26.98 (978-1-59102-558-0(3)) Prometheus Bks., Pubs.

Konadu, Kwasi B. A View from the East: Black Cultural Nationalism & Education in New York City. 2nd ed. 2009. (Illus.). 232p. 29.95 (978-0-8156-3206-1(1)) Syracuse Univ. Pr.

Ngwane, Mwakimu George. The Power in the Writer: Collected Essays on Culture, Democracy & Development in Africa. 2008. 196p. (978-9956-558-37-7(0)) Langaa Research & Publishing Common Initiative Group CMR. Dist: Michigan State Univ. Pr.

Nobles, Wade W. Seeking the Sakhu: Foundational Writings for an African Psychology. 2006. (ENG., Illus.). 470p. per. 27.95 (978-0-88378-276-7(6)) Third World Press.

Ukpong, Justin S. African Interpretation of the Bible: A Reader. 2006. (978-90-04-15114-7(1)) BRILL.

—African Interpretation of the Bible: A Reader. 2006. (978-1-58983-242-8(6)) Society of Biblical Literature.

Yamauchi, Edwin M. Africa & the Bible. 2006. (Illus.). 304p. (C). pap. 26.00 (978-0-8010-3119-9(2)) Baker Academic.

AFTER-DINNER SPEECHES
see Public Speaking

AFTER EFFECTS (COMPUTER PROGRAM)
see Adobe After Effects (Computer Program)

AFTERLIFE
see Future Life

AFTERNOON TEAS
AA Publishing, A. A. Publishing. Afternoon Tea: Perfect Places for Afternoon Tea. 3rd ed. 2012. (AA Lifestyle Guides). (ENG., Illus.). 352p. pap. 17.95 **(978-0-7495-6639-5(6))** Automobile Assn. GBR. Dist: Independent Pubs. Group.

AA Publishing Staff. Afternoon Tea: Perfect Places for Afternoon Tea. 2nd ed. 2009. (AA Lifestyle Guides). (ENG., Illus.). 352p. pap. 19.95 (978-0-7495-6060-7(6)) Automobile Assn. GBR. Dist: Independent Pubs. Group.

Amos, Sarah. Sarah's Tea Time, 1 vol. rev. ed. 2009. (ENG., Illus.). 48p. (978-1-894898-76-8(1)) TouchWood Editions.

Barnes, Emilie. An Invitation to Tea: Special Celebrations with Treasured Friends. 2009. 32p. 12.99 (978-0-7369-2237-1(7)) Harvest Hse. Pubs.

—The Twelve Teas of Inspiration: Celebrations to Nourish the Soul. 2007. 64p. 16.99 (978-0-7369-2016-2(1)) Harvest Hse. Pubs.

Bea Vo. Tea with Bea. 2011. (Illus.). 144p. (978-1-84975-143-8(9)) Ryland Peters & Small.

Blake, Susannah. Afternoon Tea. 2006. (ENG., Illus.). 64p. (978-1-84597-206-6(6)) Ryland Peters & Small.

—Afternoon Tea Parties. 2008. (ENG., Illus.). 144p. (978-1-84597-724-5(6)) Ryland Peters & Small.

Caldicott, Chris & Caldicott, Carolyn. Vintage Tea Party. 2012. (ENG., Illus.). 128p. 14.95 **(978-0-7112-3327-0(6))** Lincoln, Frances Ltd. GBR. Dist: Perseus-PGW.

Day, Martha. Traditional Afternoon Tea. 2012. (ENG., Illus.). 64p. 9.99 **(978-0-7548-2170-0(6))** Anness Publishing GBR. Dist: National Bk. Network.

Fox, Haley & Fox, Lauren. Alice's Tea Cup: Delectable Recipes for Scones, Cakes, Sandwiches, & More from New York's Most Whimsical Tea Spot. 2010. (ENG., Illus.). 256p. 24.00 (978-0-06-196492-3(1), Morrow, William Cookbooks) HarperCollins Pubs.

Hood, Karen Jean Matsko. Tea Time Delights Cookbook: A Collection of Tea Time Recipes. Whispering Pine Press International, ed. 2010. (ENG.). 320p. per. 19.95 (978-1-59434-494-7(9)) Whispering Pine Pr. International, Inc.

—Tea Time Delights Cookbook: A Collection of Tea Time Recipes. 2008. (ENG.). 22.95 (978-1-59434-496-1(5)); 29.95 (978-1-59434-493-0(0)); (ENG.). spiral bd. 22.95 (978-1-59434-495-4(7)); (ENG.). cd-rom 15.95 (978-1-59434-498-5(1)); (ENG.). pap. 29.95 (978-1-59434-497-8(3)) Whispering Pine Pr. International, Inc.

—Tea Time Delights Cookbook: A Collection of Tea Time Recipes Cookbook Series. l.t. ed. 2008. (Delights Ser.). ring bd. 29.95 (978-1-59649-939-3(7)) Whispering Pine Pr. International, Inc.

Hylton, Dawn, et al, texts. Taking Tea with Alice: Looking Glass Tea Parties. 2008. (ENG., Illus.). 85p. (J). 19.95 (978-0-9793431-4-8(3)) Benjamin Pr.

Johnson, Margaret M. & Chronicle Books Staff. Tea & Crumpets: Recipes & Rituals from Tea Rooms & Cafes. 2009. (ENG., Illus.). 168p. 19.95 (978-0-8118-6214-1(3)) Chronicle Bks. LLC.

Lanier, Pamela. Cinnamon Mornings & Savory Nights: Romantic Recipes from America's Inns. (ENG.). 2009. 160p. pap. 19.95 (978-0-9840850-0-2(9)) 2008. (Illus.). 1p. pap. 19.95 (978-1-58008-940-1(2)) Ten Speed Pr.

Oakwell, Mary. Tea Time in Alberta: 54 Great Tea Houses from Grande Prairie to Waterton Lakes. (Illus.). 128p. pap. (978-1-894739-01-6(9)) Blue Couch Bks.

Patten, Marguerite. Marguerite Patten's 100 Top Teatime Treats. 2008. (Illus.). 100p. (978-1-904943-29-7(2)) Grub Street.

Pettigrew, Jane. Good Old-Fashioned Teatime Treats. 2010. (ENG., Illus.). 112p. 12.95 (978-1-905400-90-4(X)) National Trust, Aylesbury GBR. Dist: Independent Pubs. Group.

Richardson, Bruce. The Great Tea Rooms of America. 2008. (ENG.). 137p. 24.95 (978-0-9793431-5-5(1)) Benjamin Pr.

Rodgers, Rick. Tea & Cookies: Enjoy the Perfect Cup of Tea-With Dozens of Delectable Recipes for Teatime Treats. 2010. (ENG., Illus.). 160p. 21.99 (978-0-06-193833-7(5), Morrow, William Cookbooks) HarperCollins Pubs.

Stern, Tracy & Matheson, Christie. Tea Party: 20 Themed Tea Parties with Recipes for Every Occasion, from Fabulous Showers to Intimate Gatherings. 2007. (ENG., Illus.). 208p. 28.99 (978-0-307-34643-8(9), Clarkson Potter) Crown Publishing Group.

Wild, Antony & Pastor, Carol. The Perfect Afternoon Tea Recipe Book: More Than 160 Classic Recipes for Sandwiches, Pretty Cakes & Bakes, Biscuits, Bars, Pastries, Cupcakes, Celebration Cakes & Glorious Gateaux. 2011. (ENG., Illus.). 256p. 35.00 (978-0-7548-2349-0(0)) Anness Publishing GBR. Dist: National Bk. Network.

Wolgemuth, Bobbie. Tea Parties with a Purpose: 10 Simple & Fun Party Ideas for Kids of All Ages. 2009. (ENG., Illus.). 128p. 14.99 (978-1-4165-7294-7(5), Howard Bks.) Howard Books.

AGA KHAN III, 1877-1957
Pendragon, A. U. Aga Khan's Billions & the Assassins: Ismailis-the Next Islamic Threat? (Sex, Money & Power: an Insider's Account of the Secret World of the Aga Khan) 2008. 185p. pap. 24.95 (978-1-60610-714-0(3)) PublishAmerica, Inc.

Ruthven, Malise & Wilkinson, Gerald. The Children of Time: The Aga Khan & the Ismailis. 2012. (ENG., Illus.). 408p. 45.00 (978-1-84511-722-1(0)) , B. Tauris & Co., Ltd. GBR. Dist: Macmillan.

AGA KHAN IV, 1936-
Jodidio, Philip. A Racing & Breeding Tradition: The Horses of the Aga Khan. 2011. (Illus.). 272p. 75.00 (978-3-7913-5072-1(2)) Prestel Publishing.

—Under the Eaves of Architecture: The Aga Khan: Builder & Patron. 2007. (Illus.). 208p. 75.00 (978-3-7913-3781-4(5)) Prestel Publishing.

AGAMEMNON (GREEK MYTHOLOGY)
Beck, Martha Catherine. Interpreting Aeschylus' Agamemnon Through the Categories of Aristotle: How Greek Tragedy Shaped Ethical Citizens. 2011. 272p. 119.95 (978-0-7734-1521-8(1)) Mellen, Edwin Pr., The.

Gere, Cathy. The Tomb of Agamemnon. 2012. (Wonders of the World Ser.). (Illus.). 208p. pap. 14.95 **(978-0-674-06388-4(0))** Harvard Univ. Pr.

Raeburn, David & Thomas, Oliver. The Agamemnon of Aeschylus: A Commentary for Students. 2012. (Illus.). (GEC & ENG.). 300p. 135.00 (978-0-19-959560-0(7)); (ENG & GEC.). 368p. pap. 55.00 (978-0-19-959561-7(5)) Oxford Univ. Pr., Inc.

AGAPE
Boyd, Craig A. Visions of Agapé: Problems & Possibilities in Human & Divine Love. 2008. 164p. 89.95 (978-0-7546-5818-4(X)) Ashgate Publishing Co.

Floyd, Lola Guice. A. G. A. P. e: A Gift, A People, Evolving. 2006. 33p. pap. 8.95 (978-0-7414-3675-7(2)) Infinity Publishing.

Gowdy, Rick. Agape-Love How Important Is It Anyhow? 2007. 168p. per. 13.99 (978-1-60266-329-9(7)) Xulon Pr., Inc.

Jackson, Timothy P. The Priority of Love: Christian Charity & Social Justice. 2009. (New Forum Bks.). (ENG., Illus.). 248p. (C). pap. 22.95 (978-0-691-14428-3(1)) Princeton Univ. Pr.

Smyth, Sandy. The Spirit-Led Organization. 2010. 156p. pap. 14.99 (978-1-60957-227-3(0)) Xulon Pr., Inc.

Spicq, Ceslaus. Agape in the New Testament Vol. 1: Agape in the Synoptic Gospels. 2006. 168p. pap. 20.00 (978-1-59752-855-6(0), Wipf and Stock) Wipf & Stock Pubs.

—Agape in the New Testament Vol. 2: Agape in the Epistles of St. Paul, the Acts of the Apostles & the Epistles of St. James, St. Peter, & St. Jude. 2006. (Agape in the New Testament Ser.). 460p. pap. 44.00 (978-1-59752-857-3(9), Wipf and Stock) Wipf & Stock Pubs.

—Agape in the New Testament Vol. 3: Agape in the Gospels, Epistles, & Apocalypse of St. John. 2006. (Agape in the New Testament Ser.). 272p. pap. 27.00 (978-1-59752-858-0(7), Wipf and Stock) Wipf & Stock Pubs.

—Agape in the New Testament, 3 Volumes. 2007. 900p. pap. 90.00 (978-1-55635-344-4(8), Wipf and Stock) Wipf & Stock Pubs.

Wolterstorff, Nicholas. Justice in Love. 2011. 35.00 (978-0-8028-6615-3(8)) Eerdmans, William B. Publishing Co.

AGARICALES
Bessette, Alan. North American Mushrooms: A Guide to the Genus Tricholoma. 2012. E-Book **(978-0-292-74234-5(7))** Univ. of Texas Pr.

Rogers, Robert. The Fungal Pharmacy: The Complete Guide to Medicinal Mushrooms & Lichens of North America. 2011. (ENG., Illus.). 608p. pap. 29.95 (978-1-55643-953-7(9)) North Atlantic Bks.

Trudell, Steven A., et al. North American Mushrooms: A Guide to the Genus Tricholoma. 2013. (ENG.). 224p. pap. 29.95 **(978-0-292-74233-8(3))** Univ. of Texas Pr.

AGASSIZ, ALEXANDER, 1835-1910
De Forest, John W. The Wetherel Affair. reprint ed. 69.00 (978-0-403-04567-9(3)) Somerset Pubs., Inc.

AGASSIZ, LOUIS, 1807-1873
Gould, Alice Bache. Louis Agassiz. 2009. 62p. pap. (978-1-151-35637-6(9)) Books LLC.

—Louis Agassiz. 2008. 176p. 37.95 (978-1-4366-2801-3(6)); pap. 22.95 (978-0-548-84379-6(1)) Kessinger Publishing, LLC.

—Louis Agassiz. (Beacon Biographies Ser.). 154p. reprint ed. 88.00 (978-0-7222-8529-9(9)) Library Reprints, Inc.

Marcou, Jules. Life, Letters, & Works of Louis Agassiz. 2011. (Cambridge Library Collection - Life Sciences Ser.). (ENG.). 340p. pap. 28.99 (978-1-108-07261-8(5)); (Illus.). 336p. pap. 28.99 (978-1-108-07260-1(7)) Cambridge Univ. Pr.

Robinson, Mabel L. Runner of the Mountain Tops: The Life of Louis Agassiz. 304p. 2008. 43.95 (978-1-4366-9873-3(1)) 2007. (ENG.). per. 28.95 (978-1-4325-5535-1(9)) Kessinger Publishing, LLC.

Rogers, Molly & Blight, David. Delia's Tears: Race, Science, & Photography in Nineteenth-Century America. 2010. (Illus.). 384p. 37.50 (978-0-300-11548-2(2)) Yale Univ. Pr.

AGATES
Pabian, Roger, et al. Agates: Treasures of the Earth. 2006. (ENG., Illus.). 184p. 35.00 (978-1-55407-098-5(8)) Firefly Bks., Ltd.

Petrovic, Richard L. Agates of the Oregon Coast: An Illustrated Guide of Information on agates, jasper, fossils & petrified wood commonly found on the Oregon Coast. 2008. pap. (978-1-60585-774-9(2)) Independent Pub.

Scott, Wolter. Lake Superior Agate 4th Ed. 2008. pap. 24.95 (978-1-60250-123-2(8)) Partners Bk. Distributing, Inc.

Wagner, Connie. Beads & Agate Jewelry to Create Yourself. 2008. (Illus.). 64p. pap. 14.99 (978-0-7643-2998-2(7)) Schiffer Publishing, Ltd.

Wolter, Scott. Amazing Agates. 2010. 48p. 9.95 (978-0-9792006-9-4(5)) PondView Pr.

AGATHA (INSECTS)
see Mayflies

AGATHOCLES, TYRANT OF SYRACUSE, 361-289 B.C.
Tillyard, Henry Julius Wetenhall. Agathocles. 2009. 248p. 41.95 (978-1-104-68805-9(0)); pap. 26.95 (978-1-104-60858-3(8)) Kessinger Publishing, LLC.

AGE
see Age Groups; Longevity; Middle Age; Old Age; Youth

AGE (LAW)
Cipriani, Don. Children's Rights & the Minimum Age of Criminal Responsibility: A Global Perspective. 2009. (Advances in Criminology Ser.). (Illus.). 252p. 124.95 (978-0-7546-7730-7(3)) Ashgate Publishing Co.

Freeman, Michael, ed. Law & Childhood Studies: Current Legal Issues Volume 14. 2012. (ENG., Illus.). 450p. 170.00 **(978-0-19-965250-1(3))** Oxford Univ. Pr., Inc.

Hynes, J. Dennis & Loewenstein, Mark J. Agency, Partnership, & the Llc in A Nutshell, 5th. 5th rev. ed. 2011. (Nutshell Ser.). pap. 38.00 **(978-0-314-27614-8(9)**, West Legalworks) West.

Marcovitz, Hal. Should the Drinking Age Be Lowered? 2011. (YA). (978-1-60152-144-6(8)) ReferencePoint Pr., Inc.

AGE (PSYCHOLOGY)
see also Adulthood; Age and Intelligence; Maturation (Psychology)

Huber, Bruno & Huber, Louise. Astrolog I: Life & Meaning. 2008. (Illus.). 328p. per. (978-0-9547680-7-2(8)) HopeWell.

Lavin, Maud, ed. The Oldest We've Ever Been: Seven True Stories of Midlife Transitions. 2008. (ENG.). 224p. pap. 15.95 (978-0-8165-2616-1(8)) Univ. of Arizona Pr.

Meslier, Jean. Superstition in All Ages. 2009. (ENG.). 348p. 36.99 (978-1-117-48905-6(1)) 2009. 348p. pap. 31.75 (978-1-117-48906-3(X)) 2009. (ENG.). 346p. pap. 23.99 (978-1-117-48907-0(8), BiblioLife) 2008. 284p. 25.99 (978-0-554-35767-6(4)) 2008. 284p. 28.99 (978-0-554-26464-6(1)) BiblioBazaar.

—Superstition in All Ages. 2010. 344p. 46.95 (978-1-161-35549-9(9)) Kessinger Publishing, LLC.

—Superstition in All Ages. 2007. (ENG.). 196p. per. 17.99 (978-1-59547-786-6(1)) NuVision Pubns., LLC.

Monteith, Erika G. Now You Are 60 or More. 2009. 288p. pap. 15.49 (978-1-4389-7700-3(X)) AuthorHouse.

Mosher, Ralph L., et al, eds. Human Development Across the Life Span: Educational & Psychological Applications. 2006. (ENG.). 296p. per. 39.99 (978-1-59311-302-5(1)) Information Age Publishing, Inc.

Murillo, Maria Concepcion Lucas. Dignity in Care for Older People. Nordenfelt, Lennart, ed. 2009. (ENG., Illus.). 232p. pap. 82.99 (978-1-4051-8342-0(X), Wiley-Blackwell) Wiley, John & Sons, Inc.

AGE, DRINKING
see Drinking Age

AGE AND CRIME
see Crime and Age

AGE AND EMPLOYMENT
see also Ability, Influence Of Age On; Career Changes; Child Labor; Life Span, Productive; Retirement Age

Armstrong, James. Now What? Discovering Your New Life & Career After 50. 2007. 196p. per. 13.99 (978-1-933656-06-9(9)) Lighthouse Pubns., Inc.

Axley, Leonard E., ed. Older Worker Trends. 2009. 69.00 (978-1-60692-839-4(2)) Nova Science Pubs., Inc.

Bogan, David & Davies, Keith. Avoid Retirement & Stay Alive: The New Retirement Revolution. 2007. (ENG.). 282p. per. 16.95 (978-0-07-154593-8(X), 007154593X) McGraw-Hill Cos., The.

Cappelli, Peter & Novelli, Bill. Managing the Older Worker: How to Prepare for the New Organizational Order. 2010. (ENG., Illus.). 240p. 29.95 (978-1-4221-3165-7(3)) Harvard Business Review Pr.

Chase, Benjamin V. Older Workers Navigating Employment & Retirement. 2011. (Aging Issues, Health & Financial Alternatives Ser.). (Illus.). viii, 108p. 95.00 **(978-1-61470-253-5(5))** Nova Science Pubs., Inc.

Colie, Courtney C. & Levine, Phillip B. Reconsidering Retirement: How Losses & Layoffs Affect Older Workers. 2010. (ENG., Illus.). 156p. 28.95 (978-0-8157-0499-7(2)) Brookings Institution Pr.

Czaja, Sara J. & Sharit, Joseph, eds. Aging & Work: Issues & Implications in a Changing Landscape. 2009. (ENG., Illus.). 456p. (gr. 17). 67.00 (978-0-8018-9273-8(2)) Johns Hopkins Univ. Pr.

Eberts, Randall W. & Hobbie, Richard. Older & Out of Work: Jobs & Social Insurance for a Changing Economy. 2008. (Illus.). 240p. (ENG.). 40.00 (978-0-88099-330-2(8)); pap. 18.00 (978-0-88099-329-6(4)) Upjohn, W.E. Institute for Employment Research.

Ennals, Richard & Salomon, Robert H., eds. Older Workers in A Sustainable Society. 2011. (Arbeit, Bildung & Gesellschaft. Labour, Education & Society Ser.). (Illus.). 294p. 64.95 (978-3-631-61480-8(2)) Lang, Peter GmbH, Europaischer Verlag der Wissenschaften DEU. Dist: Lang, Peter.

Fineman, Stephen. Organizing Age. 2011. (ENG., Illus.). 208p. 99.00 (978-0-19-957804-7(4)); pap. 35.00 (978-0-19-957805-4(2)) Oxford Univ. Pr., Inc.

Freedman, Marc. Encore: Finding Work that Matters in the Second Half of Life. 2008. (ENG., Illus.). 272p. pap. 14.95 (978-1-58648-634-1(9)) Perseus Bks. Group.

Hawley, Casey. Managing the Older Employee: Overcome the Generation Gap to Get the Most Out of Your Workplace. 2009. (ENG.). 224p. pap. 12.95 (978-1-59869-858-9(3)) Adams Media Corp.

Hedge, Jerry W. & Borman, Walter C., eds. The Oxford Handbook of Work & Aging, 1 vol. 2012. (Oxford Library of Psychology Ser.). (ENG.). 768p. 175.00 (978-0-19-538505-2(5)) Oxford Univ. Pr., Inc.

H.R. 3721: The Protecting Older Workers Against Discrimination ACT: Hearing Before the Subcommittee on Health, Employment, Labor, & Pensions,

Committee on Education & Labor, U.S. House of Representatives, One Hundred Eleventh Congress, Second Session, Hearing Held in Washington, DC, May 5, 2010. 2010. iii, 52p. ***(978-0-16-087684-4(2)***, 552-070-42236-6) United States Government Printing Office.

Imi, Sari. Ageing Apparatuses at Work: Transdisciplinary Negotiations of Sex, Age & Materiality. 2010. xi, 273p. *(978-951-765-536-1(3))* Abo Akademis forlag.

Kumashiro, Masaharu. Promotion of Work Ability Towards Productive Aging: Selected Papers of the 3rd International Symposium on Work Ability, Hanoi, Vietnam, 22-24 October 2007. 2008. (ENG., Illus.). 374p. 172.95 *(978-0-415-48590-6(8)*, CRC Press) Taylor & Francis Group GBR. Dist: Taylor & Francis Group.

Kunisch, Sven, et al, eds. From Grey to Silver: Managing the Demographic Change Successfully. 2010. (ENG., Illus.). xx, 228p. 69.95 *(978-3-642-15593-2(6)*, 3642155936) Springer.

Laser, Stephen. Out-of-Work & Over-40: Practical Advice for Surviving Unemployment & Finding a Job. 2011. 168p. 29.99 ***(978-1-4628-8095-9(9))***; pap. 19.99 ***(978-1-4628-8094-2(0))*** Xlibris Corp.

MacKay, Carleen, et al. Return of the Boomers: Crossing the Bridge to the Future with the Help of the Mature Workforce. 2008. 185p. pap. 19.95 *(978-0-9773408-2-8(1))* Cambridge Media, LLC.

Magnuson, Debra, et al. Work with Me: A New Lens of Leading the Multigenerational Workforce. 2008. 196p. pap. 19.95 *(978-0-938529-36-1(6))* Personnel Decisions International.

McMullin, Julie & Marshall, Victor W., eds. Aging & Working in the New Economy: Changing Career Structures in Small IT Firms. 2010. (Illus.). 256p. 112.00 *(978-1-84844-177-4(0))* Elgar, Edward Publishing, Inc.

McMullin, Julie Ann, ed. Age, Gender, & Work: Small Information Technology Firms in the New Economy. 2011. (ENG., Illus.). 200p. pap. 32.95 ***(978-0-7748-1972-5(3))*** Univ. of British Columbia Pr. CAN. Dist: Univ. of Washington Pr.

Munnell, Alicia H. & Sass, Steven A. Working Longer: The Solution to the Retirement Income Challenge. 2009. (ENG., Illus.). 207p. pap. 20.95 *(978-0-8157-0311-2(2))* Brookings Institution Pr.

Pang, Ha-Nam. Han'guk Peibibum Sedae Ui Kullo Saengae (Work Life) Yon'gu. 2010. (KOR., Illus.). iv, 179p. *(978-89-7356-810-9(8))* Korea Labor Institute.

Sargeant, Malcolm. The Law on Age Discrimination in the EU. 2008. (Illus.). *(978-90-411-2522-4(1))* Kluwer Law International.

Sass, Steven A. & Munnell, Alicia H. Working Longer: The Solution to the Retirement Income Challenge. 2008. (ENG., Illus.). 207p. 36.95 *(978-0-8157-5898-3(7))* Brookings Institution Pr.

Shultz, Kenneth S. & Adams, Gary A., eds. Aging & Work in the 21st Century. 2007. (Applied Psychology Ser.). (ENG., Illus.). 336p. 135.00 *(978-0-8058-5726-9(5))*; per. 44.95 *(978-0-8058-5727-6(3))* Taylor & Francis Group GBR. (Psychology Press). Dist: Taylor & Francis Group.

Weinstein, Deborah & Kaufman, David Micah. Putting Experience to Work: A Guide to Navigating Legal & Management Issues Relating to a Mature Workforce. 2007. (Illus.). 96p. *(978-0-8237-0897-0(7))* Conference Board, Inc., The.

Woodward, Jeannette. Finding a Job After 50: Reinvent Yourself for the 21st Century. 2007. (ENG., Illus.). 1p. per. 14.99 *(978-1-56414-894-0(7))* Career Pr., Inc.

Young, Mary B., et al. Gray Skies, Silver Linings: How Companies Are Forecasting, Managing, & Recruiting a Mature Workforce. 2007. (Illus.). 94p. *(978-0-8237-0903-8(5))* Conference Board, Inc., The.

Zhan, Yujie. Antecedents & Health Outcomes of Bridge Employment. 2010. 80p. pap. *(978-3-639-12611-2(4))* VDM Verlag Dr. Mueller e.K.

AGE AND INTELLIGENCE

Bolvary, Jeanette. Born Smart. 2009. 129p. pap. 24.95 *(978-1-4092-5238-2(8))* Lulu Enterprises Inc.

Lamont, Allison. Age-Related Memory Loss: 20 to 100 years - A Research Study of Healthy Adults. 2008. 348p. pap. *(978-3-639-03582-7(8))* VDM Verlag Dr. Mueller e.K.

Powell, Douglas H. The Aging Intellect. 2011. (ENG., Illus.). 319p. 36.95 *(978-0-415-99685-3(6))* Routledge.

Torres-Guzman, Maria E. Freedom at Work: Language, Professional, & Intellectual Development in Schools. 2009. (Series in Critical Narrative Ser.). 198p. 125.00 *(978-1-59451-699-3(5))* Paradigm Pubs.

AGE AND MENTAL ABILITY

see Age and Intelligence

AGE DISCRIMINATION

Here are entered works on discriminatory behavior toward people based on their age. Works on negative or prejudicial attitudes toward people based on their age are entered under Ageism.

Cattan, Mima & Forte, Denise. Mental Health & Well-Being in Later Life. 2009. (ENG., Illus.). 184p. (C). pap. 45.00 *(978-0-335-22892-8(5)*, 0335228925) McGraw-Hill Education GBR. Dist: McGraw-Hill Cos., The.

Greene, Roberta R. Narratives of Social & Economic Justice. 2009. 34.99 *(978-0-87101-388-0(6)*, NASW Pr.) National Assn. of Social Workers/NASW Pr.

Sargeant, Malcolm. Age Discrimination & Diversity: Multiple Discrimination from an Age Perspective. 2011. (ENG., Illus.). 222p. 99.00 *(978-1-107-00377-4(6))* Cambridge Univ. Pr.

United Nations: Department of Economic and Social Affairs: Population Division. World Population Ageing 2009. 2010. (ENG., Illus.). 128p. pap. 30.00 *(978-92-1-151468-1(1))* United Nations Pubns.

Young-Bruehl, Elisabeth. Childism: Confronting Prejudice Against Children. 2012. (ENG.). 368p. 28.00 *(978-0-300-17311-6(3))* Yale Univ. Pr.

AGE DISCRIMINATION—LAW AND LEGISLATION

Cheetham, S. Age Discrimination. 2006. (New Law Ser.). (ENG., Illus.). 272p. pap. *(978-1-84661-026-4(5))* Jordan Publishing, Ltd.

Cotter, Anne-Marie Mooney. Just a Number: An International Legal Analysis on Age Discrimination. 2008. 356p. 144.95 *(978-0-7546-7206-7(9))* Ashgate Publishing Co.

Cotter, Anne-Marie Mooney. Little Angels: An International Legal Perspective on Child Discrimination. 2012. 320p. 124.95 ***(978-1-4094-2980-7(6))*** Ashgate Publishing Co.

Examining the Federal Aviation Administration's Age 60 Rule: Hearing Before the Subcommittee on Aviation of the Committee on Commerce, Science, & Transportation, United States Senate, One Hundred Ninth Congress, First Session, July 19, 2005. 2011. (Illus.). iii, 61p. ***(978-0-16-088032-2(7)***, 552-070-42456-0) United States Government Printing Office.

H.R. 3721: The Protecting Older Workers Against Discrimination ACT: Hearing Before the Subcommittee on Health, Employment, Labor, & Pensions, Committee on Education & Labor, U.S. House of Representatives, One Hundred Eleventh Congress, Second Session, Hearing Held in Washington, DC, May 5, 2010. 2010. iii, 52p. ***(978-0-16-087684-4(2)***, 552-070-42236-6) United States Government Printing Office.

Wiener, Richard L. & Willborn, Steven, eds. Disability & Aging Discrimination: Perspectives in Law & Psychology. 2010. (ENG., Illus.). x, 270p. 129.00 *(978-1-4419-6292-8(1)*, 1441962921) Springer.

AGE DISCRIMINATION IN EMPLOYMENT

see also Older People—Employment

Beisheim, Margret & Maier, Florentine, eds. Constructions of Women's Age at the Workplace. 2008. (Frauen, Forschung und Wirtschaft Ser.). (Illus.). 144p. pap. 39.95 *(978-3-631-57836-0(9))* Lang, Peter GmbH, Europaischer Verlag der Wissenschaften DEU. Dist: Lang, Peter.

Chase, Benjamin V. Older Workers Navigating Employment & Retirement. 2011. (Aging Issues, Health & Financial Alternatives Ser.). (Illus.). viii, 108p. 95.00 ***(978-1-61470-253-5(5))*** Nova Science Pubs., Inc.

Leibold, Marius & Voelpel, Sven C. Managing the Aging Workforce: Challenges & Solutions. 2007. (ENG., Illus.). 240p. 50.00 *(978-3-89578-284-8(X)*, Wiley) Wiley, John & Sons, Inc.

Mujtaba, Bahaudin G. & Cavico, Frank J. The Aging Workforce: Challenges & Opportunities for Human Resource Professionals. 2010. 260p. 27.95 *(978-1-936237-01-2(6))* ILEAD Academy, LLC.

Sargeant, Malcolm. Age Discrimination: Age Employment & the Delivery of Facilities Goods & Services. 2011. 260p. 124.95 ***(978-0-566-08926-8(2)***, Gower Publishing Co., Ltd.) Ashgate Publishing, Ltd. GBR. Dist: Ashgate Publishing Co.

AGE DISCRIMINATION IN EMPLOYMENT—LAW AND LEGISLATION

Howard-Byrd, Sherlynn Teas'La'Rea. Gender & Age Discrimination among Women in the Broadcast News Industry: A Legal Pursuit of Justice. 2008. 160p. 99.95 *(978-0-7734-5144-5(7))* Mellen, Edwin Pr., The.

Hulett, John K. Age Discrimination: An Epidemic in America Affecting People of All Ages. 2011. 152p. 31.99 ***(978-1-4670-5451-5(8))***; pap. 16.49 ***(978-1-4670-5450-8(X))*** AuthorHouse.

Sargeant, Malcolm. Age Discrimination: Age Employment & the Delivery of Facilities Goods & Services. 2011. 260p. 124.95 ***(978-0-566-08926-8(2)***, Gower Publishing Co., Ltd.) Ashgate Publishing, Ltd. GBR. Dist: Ashgate Publishing Co.

—Age Discrimination in Employment. 2007. 242p. 134.95 *(978-0-566-08774-5(X)*, Gower Publishing Co., Ltd.) Ashgate Publishing, Ltd. GBR. Dist: Ashgate Publishing Co.

—The Law on Age Discrimination in the EU. 2008. (Illus.). *(978-90-411-2522-4(1))* Kluwer Law International.

Silken, Lewis. Age Discrimination. 2007. 608p. pap. 140.00 *(978-1-84592-459-1(2)*, Bloomsbury Professional) Bloomsbury Publishing Plc GBR. Dist: International Specialized Bk. Services.

Steinau. Age Discrimination: Law in EUrope. 2009. xlvi, 401p. 152.00 *(978-90-411-3131-7(0))* Wolters Kluwer Law & Business.

"Workplace Fairness: Has the Supreme Court Been Misinterpreting Laws Designed to Protect American Workers from Discrimination?": Hearing Before the Committee on the Judiciary, United States Senate, One Hundred Eleventh Congress, First Session, October 7, 2009. 2010. (Illus.). iii, 309p. *(978-0-16-086106-2(3)*, 552-070-51216-6) United States Government Printing Office.

AGE GROUPS

see also Adulthood; Children; Conflict of Generations; Older People

Aguilar, Mario I. Rethinking Age in Africa: Colonial, Post-Colonial, & Contemporary Interpretations of Cultural Representations. 2006. x, 322p. *(978-1-59221-494-5(0))* Africa World Pr.

Antonucci, Toni. Intergenerational Relations: Theory, Research & Policy. 2008. (Journal of Social Issues Ser.). (ENG., Illus.). 228p. pap. 33.95 *(978-1-4051-8584-4(8)*, Wiley-Blackwell) Wiley, John & Sons, Inc.

Burton, Andrew & Charton-Bigot, Helene. Generations Past: Youth in East African History. 2010. (Illus.). 432p. *(978-0-8214-4343-9(7))* Ohio Univ. Pr.

Cole, Jennifer, et al, eds. Generations & Globalization: Youth, Age, & Family in the New World Economy. 2006. (Tracking Globalization Ser.). (ENG., Illus.). 240p. 65.00 *(978-0-253-34803-6(X)*, 025334803X) Indiana Univ. Pr.

Durham, Deborah & Cole, Jennifer, eds. Generations & Globalization: Youth, Age, & Family in the New World Economy. 2006. (Tracking Globalization Ser.). (ENG., Illus.). 240p. pap. 24.95 *(978-0-253-21870-4(5)*, 0253218705) Indiana Univ. Pr.

Groth, Hans & Eberstadt, Nicholas. Europe's Coming Demographic Challenge: Unlocking the Value of Health. 2007. (ENG., Illus.). 84p. pap. 15.00 *(978-0-8447-7200-4(3)*, AEI Pr.) American Enterprise Institute for Public Policy Research.

Howe, Christine. Peer Groups & Children's Development. 2010. (Understanding Children's Worlds Ser.: 13). (ENG., Illus.). 248p. 104.95 *(978-1-4051-7945-4(7))*; pap. 44.95 *(978-1-4051-7944-7(9))* Wiley, John & Sons, Inc. (Wiley-Blackwell).

Kresl. The Aging Population & the Competitiveness of Cities Benefits to the Urban Economy. 2010. (Illus.). 208p. 112.00 *(978-1-84844-212-2(2))* Elgar, Edward Publishing, Inc.

Levin, Jack. The Changing Meanings of Age. 2012. (ENG.). 150p. 140.00 ***(978-0-415-50380-8(9))***; pap. 25.95 ***(978-0-415-50382-2(5))*** Routledge.

Lovell, Stephen. Generations in Twentieth-Century Europe. 2007. (ENG., Illus.). 272p. 100.00 *(978-0-230-00891-5(7))* Palgrave Macmillan.

Magnus, George. The Age of Aging: How Demographics Are Changing the Global Economy & Our World. 2008. (ENG., Illus.). 256p. 38.00 *(978-0-470-82291-3(0)*, Wiley) Wiley, John & Sons, Inc.

Magnuson, Debra, et al. Work with Me: A New Lens of Leading the Multigenerational Workforce. 2008. 196p. pap. 19.95 *(978-0-938529-36-1(6))* Personnel Decisions International.

Muenz, Rainer, et al. Overcrowded World: Global Population & International Migration. 2010. (Sustainability Project Ser.). (ENG., Illus.). 270p. pap. 14.95 *(978-1-906598-10-5(X))* Haus Publishing GBR. Dist: Consortium Bk. Sales & Distribution.

Palmer. Life Transitions & Generational C. 2010. (Essential Coaching Skills & Knowledge Ser.). (ENG., Illus.). 240p. (C). 84.95 *(978-0-415-47359-0(4))*; pap. 30.95 *(978-0-415-47360-6(8))* Routledge.

Rowland, Donald T. Population Aging: The Transformation of Societies. 2012. (International Perspectives on Aging Ser.). (ENG., Illus.). xix, 293p. 179.00 ***(978-94-007-4049-5(2)***, 9400740492) Springer.

Spencer, Paul. Time, Space & the Unknown: Maasai Configurations of Power & Providence. 2009. 290p. pap. 39.95 *(978-0-415-55516-6(7))* Routledge.

SunWolf. Peer Groups: Expanding Our Study of Small Group Communication. 2008. (Illus.). 240p. (C). pap. 47.00 *(978-1-4129-2686-7(6)*, B26866P) SAGE Pubns., Inc.

Taylor, Myra. Friendships, Peer Socialization & Social Identity among Adolescent Skateboarders & Graffiti Writers. Houghton, Stephen & Bednall, John, eds. 2010. (Social Issues, Justice & Status Ser.). 51p. pap. 43.00 *(978-1-61668-760-1(6)*, Nova Novinka) Nova Science Pubs., Inc.

Uhlenberg, Peter, ed. International Handbook of Population Aging. 2009. (International Handbooks of Population Ser.). (ENG., Illus.). xii, 772p. 389.00 *(978-1-4020-8355-6(6))* Springer.

Vos, Rob, et al. Ageing & Development. Vos, Rob et al, eds. 2008. (ENG., Illus.). 272p. pap. 33.95 *(978-1-84813-053-1(8))* United Nations Pubns.

AGE HARDENING

see Precipitation Hardening

AGE OF CONSENT

Waites, Matthew. The Age of Consent: Young People, Sexuality & Citizenship. 2009. (ENG.). 296p. pap. 31.00 *(978-0-230-23718-6(5))* Palgrave Macmillan.

AGE OF ROCKS

see Geological Time; Geology, Stratigraphic

AGED

see Older People

AGED, WRITINGS OF THE

see Older People's Writings

AGED MEN

see Older Men

AGED WOMEN

see Older Women

AGEE, JAMES, 1909-1955

Agee, James. The Letters of James Agee to Father Flye. 2011. 246p. 46.95 ***(978-1-258-05082-5(X))*** Literary Licensing, LLC.

Allred, Jeff. American Modernism & Depression Documentary. 2009. (ENG., Illus.). 288p. 65.00 *(978-0-19-533568-2(6))* Oxford Univ. Pr., Inc.

Blinder, Caroline, ed. New Critical Essays on James Agee & Walker Evans: Perspectives on Let Us Now Praise Famous Men. 2010. (ENG., Illus.). 204p. 79.00 *(978-0-230-10292-7(1))* Palgrave Macmillan.

Davis, Hugh. The Making of James Agee. 2008. (ENG.). 296p. 39.95 *(978-1-57233-607-0(2))* Univ. of Tennessee Pr.

Lofaro, Michael A., ed. Agee Agonistes: Essays on the Life, Legend, & Works of James Agee. 2007. (Illus.). 334p. 48.00 *(978-1-57233-574-5(2))* Univ. of Tennessee Pr.

Maharidge, Dale & Williamson, Michael. And Their Children after Them: The Legacy of Let Us Now Praise Famous Men. 2008. (ENG., Illus.). 264p. pap. 17.95 *(978-1-58322-657-5(5))* Seven Stories Pr.

Sun, Emily. Succeeding King Lear: Literature, Exposure, & the Possibility of Politics. 2nd ed. 2010. (ENG., Illus.). 176p. 55.00 *(978-0-8232-3280-2(8))* Fordham Univ. Pr.

Ward, Joseph. American Silences: The Realism of James Agee, Walker Evans, & Edward Hopper. 2010. (ENG., Illus.). 235p. pap. 29.95 *(978-1-4128-1097-5(3))* Transaction Pubs.

AGEISM

Here are entered works on negative or prejudicial attitudes toward people based on their age. Works on discriminatory behavior toward people based on their age are entered under Age Discrimination.

Beletic, Elizabeth. Deconstructing Ageism Through Educational Curriculum: An Implementation Evaluation. 2008. 88p. pap. *(978-3-639-11072-2(2))* VDM Verlag Dr. Mueller e.K.

Gullette, Margaret Morganroth. Agewise: Fighting the New Ageism in America. 2011. (Illus.). 304p. 29.00 *(978-0-226-31073-2(6))* Univ. of Chicago Pr.

Gutman, Gloria & Spencer, Charmaine, eds. Aging, Ageism & Abuse: Moving from Awareness to Action. 2010. (ENG., Illus.). 120p. 66.95 *(978-0-12-381508-8(8))* Elsevier Science & Technology Bks.

Kelly, Brent Robert. Who Will Care for Grandma? Critiquing Ageism in Medicine. 2008. 260p. pap. 29.00 *(978-1-55635-913-2(6)*, Wipf and Stock) Wipf & Stock Pubs.

Lachs, Mark, , Mark. What Your Doctor Won't Tell You about Getting Older: A Doctor's Guide to Getting the Best Care as You or a Loved One Gets Older. l.t. ed. 2011. 689p. 32.99 ***(978-1-4104-4109-6(1))*** Thorndike Pr.

Lachs, Mark. Treat Me, Not My Age: A Doctor's Guide to Getting the Best Care As You or a Loved One Gets Older. 2010. (ENG.). 400p. (gr. 12). 27.95 *(978-0-670-02210-6(1)*, Viking Adult) Penguin Group (USA) Inc.

Sanjek, Roger. Gray Panthers. 320p. (C). 2011. (Illus.). pap. 26.50 ***(978-0-8122-2191-6(5))*** 2009. 65.00 *(978-0-8122-4137-2(1))* Univ. of Pennsylvania Pr.

Sargeant, Malcolm. Age Discrimination & Diversity: Multiple Discrimination from an Age Perspective. 2011. (ENG., Illus.). 222p. 99.00 *(978-1-107-00377-4(6))* Cambridge Univ. Pr.

Sohm, Philip. The Artist Grows Old: The Aging of Art & Artists in Italy, 1500-1800. 2007. (ENG., Illus.). 224p. 50.00 *(978-0-300-12123-0(7))* Yale Univ. Pr.

Steinem, Gloria. Doing Sixty & Seventy. 2006. 96p. 19.95 *(978-0-9758744-2-4(X))* Elders Academy Pr.

Williams, John. Elder Law. 2013. (ENG.). 350p. 160.00 *(978-0-415-45421-6(2))* Routledge.

AGENCIES, EMPLOYMENT

see Employment Agencies

AGENCIES, MODEL

see Modeling Agencies

AGENCIES, THEATRICAL

see Theatrical Agencies

AGENCY (LAW)

see also Bailments; Brokers; Commercial Agents; Commission Merchants; Franchises (Retail Trade)—Law and Legislation; Power of Attorney; Proxy; Real Estate Business—Law and Legislation; Traveling Sales Personnel

Anderson, John. Spark Law Agency & Partnership. 2008. per. 17.95 *(978-0-9801482-0-6(0))* Mclaren Legal Pubs. LLC.

Anson, William Reynell. Principles of the English Law of Contract & of Agency in its Relation to Contract, 1. 11th ed. 2008. 406p. 85.00 *(978-1-56169-966-7(7))* Gaunt, Inc.

Bowstead, William. A Digest of the Law of Agency. 2006. 95.00 *(978-1-58477-700-7(1))* Lawbook Exchange, Ltd., The.

Carey, Bill & Carey, Chantal Howell. Make Money as a Buyer's Agent: Double Your Commissions by Working with Real Estate Buyers. 2007. (ENG.). 240p. 24.95 *(978-0-470-05125-2(6)*, Wiley) Wiley, John & Sons, Inc.

Casenotes Publishing Co., Inc. Staff. Agency & Partnership: Keyed to Course Using Hynes & Loewenstein's Agency, Partnership, & the Llc. 2007. (Casenote Legal Briefs Ser.). 243p. stu. ed., per. 38.95 *(978-0-7355-6984-3(3)*, Aspen Pubs.) Wolters Kluwer Law & Business.

Chopra, Samir & White, Laurence F. A Legal Theory for Autonomous Artificial Agents. 2011. (ENG., Illus.). 264p. (C). 85.00 *(978-0-472-07145-6(9))*; (ENG., Illus.). 264p. (C). pap. 35.00 *(978-0-472-05145-8(8))*; 256p. E-Book *(978-0-472-02676-0(3))* Univ. of Michigan Pr.

Gregory, William A. & Hurst, Thomas R. Unincorporated Business Associations, Including Agency, Partnership & Limited Liabilities Companies. 3rd rev. ed. 2006. 897p. 133.00 *(978-0-314-16056-0(6)*, West Legalworks) West.

Hynes, J. Dennis & Loewenstein, Mark J. Agency, Partnership, & the LLC: The Law of Unincorporated Business Enterprises. 7th ed. 2008. xxiv, 504p. pap. *(978-1-4224-1153-7(2))* LexisNexis Matthew Bender.

—Agency, Partnership, & the LLC: The Law of Unincorporated Business Enterprises: Cases, Materials, Problems. 7th ed. 2007. xxxvii, 986p. *(978-3-00-300007-9(1))* 7th ed. 2007. xxxvii, 986p. 118.00 *(978-1-4224-0787-5(X))* 8th ed. 2012. xxiii, 618p. ***(978-1-4224-9609-1(0))*** 8th ed. 2011. ***(978-1-4224-8531-6(5))*** LexisNexis Matthew Bender.

ICC. ICC Model Distributorship Contract. 2nd ed. 2009. 65p. pap. *(978-90-411-3185-0(X))* Kluwer Law International.

Jacobus, Charles J. & Stephens, George. Texas Real Estate Brokerage & Law of Agency. 5th ed. 2008. (ENG.). 366p. (C). pap. 33.95 *(978-0-324-59250-4(7))* Cengage South-Western.

Klein, et al. Agency, Partnerships, & Limited Liability Entities: Cases & Materials on Unincorporated Business Associations. 3rd ed. 2011. (University Casebook Ser.). 560p. 170.00 *(978-1-59941-497-3(X)*, Foundation Pr.) West.

Klein, William A. & Ramseyer, J. Mark. Business Associations-Agency, Partnerships, LLC's & Corporations, 2009 Statutes & Rules. 2009. (Academic

Statutes Ser.). 332p. pap. 32.00 *(978-1-59941-696-0(4)*, Foundation Pr.) West.

—Business Associations-Agency, Partnerships, LLCs & Corporations, 2011 Statutes & Rules. 2011. 375p. pap. 34.00 ***(978-1-59941-965-7(3)***, Foundation Pr.) West.

—Business Associations, Cases & Materials on Agency, Partnership & Corporations, 6th Edition, 2008 Supplement. 6th rev. ed. 2008. (University Casebook Ser.). 86p. pap. 17.00 *(978-1-59941-461-4(9)*, Foundation Pr.) West.

—Business Associations, Cases & Materials on Agency, Partnerships, & Corporations, 7th, 2010 Supplement. 7th rev. ed. 2010. (University Casebook Ser.). 66p. 21.00 *(978-1-59941-907-7(6)*, Foundation Pr.) West.

—Klein, Ramseyer & Bainbridge's Business Associations-Agency, Partnerships, LLC's & Corporations- 2008 Statutes & Rules. 2008. (Academic Statutes Ser.). 332p. pap. 30.00 *(978-1-59941-521-5(6)*, Foundation Pr.) West.

—Klein, Ramseyer & Bainbridge's Business Associations-Agency, Partnerships, LLC's & Corporations, Statutes & Rules 2010. 7th rev. ed. 2010. 328p. pap. 34.00 *(978-1-59941-835-3(5)*, Foundation Pr.) West.

Klein, William A., et al. Agency, Partnerships, & Limited Liability Entities: Unincorporated Business Associations: Cases & Materials. 3rd ed. 2012. xx, 533p. ***(978-1-60930-110-1(2))*** West.

Klein, William A., et al. Business Associations: Agency, Partnerships, & Corporations: Cases & Materials. 7th ed. 2009. xxix, 893p. *(978-1-59941-702-8(2)*, Foundation Pr.) West.

Kleinberger, Daniel S. Agency, Partnerships, & LLC's. 3rd ed. 2008. (Examples & Explanations Ser.). (Illus.). xxxiii, 615p. pap., stu. ed. 44.95 *(978-0-7355-5856-4(6)*, Aspen Pubs.) Wolters Kluwer Law & Business.

Kurm, Kairi. Negotiating with an Export Agent. 2010. 68p. pap. *(978-3-8383-5462-9(7))* Lambert Academic Publishing.

Leible. Principles of EUropean Contract Law & German Law. 2011. *(978-90-411-2588-0(4))* Kluwer Law International.

Livermore, Samuel. A Treatise on the Law: Relative to Principals, Agents, Factors, Auctioneers, & Brokers. 2007. 95.00 *(978-1-58477-729-8(X))* Lawbook Exchange, Ltd., The.

Melvin A.Eisenberg. An Introduction to Agency, Partnerships & LLC's. 5th rev. ed. 2006. 756p. 143.00 *(978-1-59941-208-5(X)*, Foundation Pr.) West.

Munday, R. J. C. Agency: Law & Principles. 2010. (ENG.). 400p. pap. 95.00 *(978-0-19-923037-2(4))* Oxford Univ. Pr., Inc.

Murdoch, John. Law of Estate Agency. 5th rev. ed. 2009. (ENG.). 360p. pap. 59.95 *(978-0-7282-0559-8(9))* Estates Gazette, Ltd. GBR. Dist: Taylor & Francis Group.

Peeples, Donna & Peeples, Minor. Texas Real Estate Agency, 6th Edition Update. Williams, A., ed. 6th ed. 2008. (ENG.). 376p. pap. 37.97 *(978-1-4277-7875-8(2))* Kaplan Publishing.

Ramseyer, J. Mark, compiled by. Business Associations: Agency, Partnerships, LLCs & Corporations 2006 Statutes & Rules. rev. ed. 2007. 307p. per. 29.00 *(978-1-59941-095-1(8))* West.

—Business Associations: Agency, Partnerships, LLCs & Corporations: 2007 Statutes & Rules. 2007. 324p. per. 29.00 *(978-1-59941-287-0(X))* West.

Rautenberg, Bjö Alexander. Der Fiskal am Reichskammergericht: Überblick und exemplarische Untersuchungen vorwiegend zum 16. Jahrhundert. 2008. (Rechtshistorische Reihe Ser.). (GER.). 238p. pap. 61.95 *(978-3-631-57145-3(3))* Lang, Peter GmbH, Europaischer Verlag der Wissenschaften DEU. Dist: Lang, Peter.

Saccuzzo, Dennis P. & Johnson, Nancy E. Bar Secrets: Agency & Partnership: Substantive Law. 2007. (Bar Secrets Ser.). xii, 52p. pap. *(978-1-933089-24-9(5))* Applications of Psychology of Law, Inc.

Singleton, Susan. Commercial Agency Agreements: Law & Practice (Third Edition) 3rd ed. 2010. (Illus.). 347p. 225.00 *(978-1-84766-572-0(1)*, Bloomsbury Professional) Bloomsbury Publishing Plc GBR. Dist: International Specialized Bk. Services.

Sitarz, Daniel. Powers of Attorney Simplified, 2nd Edition: Te Ultimate Guide to Powers of Attorney. 2nd ed. 2010. (ENG.). 320p. pap. 29.95 incl. cd-rom *(978-1-892949-56-1(3))* Nova Publishing Co.

Story, Joseph. Commentaries on the Law of Agency, As a Branch of Commercial & Maritime Jurisprudence, with Occasional Illustrations from the Civil & Foreign Law. 2006. *(978-1-57588-915-3(3))* Hein, William S. & Co., Inc.

Texas Agency & Partnership. 2007. (C). *(978-1-934563-06-9(4))* Flood Publishing.

Thomson West, creator. Business Associations: Keyed to Klein's Casebook on Business Associations. 6th rev. ed. 2007. (High Court Case Summaries Ser.). (Illus.). 340p. per. 34.00 *(978-0-314-17968-5(2)*, West Legalworks) West.

AGENCY (PHILOSOPHY)

see Agent (Philosophy)

AGENT (PHILOSOPHY)

see also Act (Philosophy)

Atkins, Kim & Mackenzie, Catriona, eds. Practical Identity & Narrative Agency. 2010. 312p. pap. 39.95 *(978-0-415-88391-7(1))* Routledge.

Atkinson, Kim, ed. Practical Identity & Narrative Agency. 2007. (Routledge Studies in Contemporary Philosophy Ser.). XII, 308p. 118.00 *(978-0-415-95847-9(4))* Routledge.

Balconi, Michela. Neuropsychology of the Sense of Agency. 2010. (Psychology Research Progress Ser.). 79.00 *(978-1-60876-358-0(7))* Nova Science Pubs., Inc.

Barnett, Bernard & Barnett, Bernard R. "You Ought To!" A Psychoanalytic Study of the Superego & Conscience. 2007. (Psychoanalytic Ideas Ser.). 190p. per. 32.95 *(978-1-85575-983-1(7))* Karnac Bks. GBR. Dist: Stylus Publishing, LLC.

Besley, Timothy. Principled Agents? The Political Economy of Good Government. (Lindahl Lectures on Monetary & Fiscal Policy Ser.). (ENG., Illus.). 2007. 288p. per. 29.95 *(978-0-19-928391-0(5))* 2006. 280p. 55.00 *(978-0-19-927150-4(X))* Oxford Univ. Pr., Inc.

Bishop, John. Natural Agency: An Essay on the Causal Theory of Action. 2008. (Cambridge Studies in Philosophy Ser.). (ENG.). 224p. pap. 46.00 *(978-0-521-06397-5(3))* Cambridge Univ. Pr.

Bratman, Michael. Structures of Agency: Essays. 2007. (ENG.). 336p. per. 30.00 *(978-0-19-518771-7(7))* Oxford Univ. Pr., Inc.

Carson, Siri Granum & Wyller, Truls, eds. Nature & Rational Agency. 2009. 160p. 51.95 *(978-3-631-59033-1(4))* Lang, Peter GmbH, Europaischer Verlag der Wissenschaften DEU. Dist: Lang, Peter.

Chodat, Robert. Worldly Acts & Sentient Things: The Persistence of Agency from Stein to Delillo. 2008. 254p. 41.95 *(978-0-8014-4678-8(3))* Cornell Univ. Pr.

Ciotti, Manuela. Political Agency & Gender in India. 2009. (Routledge/Edinburgh South Asian Studies Ser.). 224p. 130.00 *(978-0-415-48273-8(9))* Routledge.

Coole, Diana & Frost, Samantha, eds. New Materialisms: Ontology, Agency, & Politics. 2010. (ENG.). 352p. 89.95 *(978-0-8223-4753-8(9))*; pap. 24.95 *(978-0-8223-4772-9(5))* Duke Univ. Pr.

Coval, S. C. & Campbell, P. G. A Critique of the Liberal Idea of a Person: The Contradiction Within Equalitarian Ethical Theory. 2010. 140p. 99.95 *(978-0-7734-1394-8(4))* Mellen, Edwin Pr., The.

Cram101 Textbook Reviews & Cram101 Textbook Reviews. Outlines & Highlights for Agents, Structures & International Relations: Politics as Ontology by Colin Wight, ISBN. 2011. 122p. pap. 28.95 ***(978-1-61461-162-2(9))*** Cram101 Inc.

—Outlines & Highlights for Constructing Adulthood: Agency & Subjectivity in Adolescence & Adulthood, Vol. 11 by Ross Macmillan, ISBN. 2011. 108p. pap. 28.95 ***(978-1-61744-943-7(1))*** Cram101 Inc.

Davies, Paul Sheldon & Davies, P. S. Subjects of the World: Darwin's Rhetoric & the Study of Agency in Nature. 2009. (Illus.). 272p. 40.00 *(978-0-226-13762-9(7))* Univ. of Chicago Pr.

de Gaynesford, Maximilian. Agents & Their Actions. 2011. (Ratio Special Issues Ser.: 6). (ENG.). 152p. pap. 34.95 *(978-1-4443-3908-6(7)*, Wiley-Blackwell) Wiley, John & Sons, Inc.

Ferguson, Michaele L. Sharing Democracy. 2012. (ENG.). 224p. 99.00 ***(978-0-19-992158-4(X))***; pap. 27.95 ***(978-0-19-992160-7(1))*** Oxford Univ. Pr., Inc.

Forbes-Pitt, Kate. The Assumption of Agency Theory. 2011. (ENG., Illus.). 184p. 140.00 *(978-0-415-78211-1(2))* Routledge.

Frie, Roger, ed. Psychological Agency: Theory, Practice, & Culture. 2008. (ENG.). 272p. (gr. 17). 56.00 *(978-0-262-06267-1(4))*; pap. 28.00 *(978-0-262-56231-7(6))* MIT Pr.

Gardner, Andrew, ed. Agency Uncovered: Archaeological Perspectives on Social Agency, Power, & Being Human. 2007. (University College London Institute of Archaeology Publications). (ENG., Illus.). 268p. pap. 34.95 *(978-1-59874-211-4(6))* Left Coast Pr., Inc.

Green, Michael K. How Do We Create a Philosophical Cosmos for Acting Socially & Being Happy? Four Strategies for Living in an Uncertain World (Hume, Aquinas, Swedenborg, Kant) 2007. 408p. *(978-0-7734-5513-9(2)*, Mellen, Edwin Pr., The.

Horty, John F. Agency & Deontic Logic. 2009. (ENG., Illus.). 208p. pap. 29.95 *(978-0-19-539198-5(5))* Oxford Univ. Pr., Inc.

Jaeger Gary. Repression, Integrity & Practical Reasoning. 2012. (ENG., Illus.). 192p. 85.00 ***(978-0-230-36850-7(6))*** Palgrave Macmillan.

Jeffery, Liz. Understanding Agency: Social Welfare & Change. 2011. 136p. 85.00 *(978-1-84742-331-3(0))*; pap. 32.95 *(978-1-84742-330-6(2))* Policy Pr. GBR. Dist: Chicago Distribution Ctr.

Kim, David Kyuman. Melancholic Freedom: Agency & the Spirit of Politics. 2008. (AAR Reflection & Theory in the Study of Religion Ser.). (ENG.). 208p. pap. 22.95 *(978-0-19-537246-5(8))* Oxford Univ. Pr., Inc.

Knappett, Carl & Malafouris, Lambros, eds. Material Agency: Towards a Non-Anthropocentric Approach. (ENG., Illus.). xix, 256p. 2010. pap. 109.00 *(978-1-4419-4512-9(1)*, 1441945121) 2008. 109.00 *(978-0-387-74710-1(9)*, 0387747109) Springer.

Korsgaard, Christine M. Self-Constitution: Agency, Identity, & Integrity. 2009. (ENG.). 248p. pap. 35.00 *(978-0-19-955280-1(0))*; 105.00 *(978-0-19-955279-5(7))* Oxford Univ. Pr., Inc.

Le Grand, Julian. Motivation, Agency, & Public Policy: Of Knights & Knaves, Pawns & Queens. 2006. (ENG., Illus.). 256p. per. 40.00 *(978-0-19-929891-4(2))* Oxford Univ. Pr., Inc.

List, Christian & Pettit, Philip. Group Agency: The Possibility, Design, & Status of Corporate Agents. 2011. (ENG., Illus.). 240p. 45.00 *(978-0-19-959156-5(3))* Oxford Univ. Pr., Inc.

Lowe, E. J. Personal Agency: The Metaphysics of Mind & Action. (ENG.). 2010. 240p. pap. 35.00 *(978-0-19-959250-0(0))* 2008. (Illus.). 224p. 75.00 *(978-0-19-921714-4(9))* Oxford Univ. Pr., Inc.

—Subjects of Experience. 2006. (Cambridge Studies in Philosophy Ser.). (ENG.). 220p. pap. 48.00 *(978-0-521-03155-4(9))* Cambridge Univ. Pr.

Lumer, Christoph & Nannini, Sandro, eds. Intentionality Deliberation & Autonomy: The Action- Theoretic Basis of Practical Philosophy. 2007. 326p. 134.95 *(978-0-7546-6058-3(3))* Ashgate Publishing Co.

Macmillan, Ross, ed. Constructing Adulthood: Agency & Subjectivity in Adolescence & Adulthood. 2006. (ENG.). 346p. 105.00 *(978-0-7623-1201-6(7)*, JAI Pr.) Elsevier Science & Technology Bks.

Marcus, Eric. Rational Causation. 2012. (ENG., Illus.). 280p. 45.00 ***(978-0-674-05990-0(5))*** Harvard Univ. Pr.

Martin, Peter J. & Dennis, Alex, eds. Human Agents & Social Structures. 2010. (ENG.). 208p. pap. 29.95 *(978-0-7190-8172-9(6))*; 90.00 *(978-0-7190-7861-3(X))* Manchester Univ. Pr. GBR. Dist: Macmillan.

McCarty, Richard. Kant's Theory of Action. 2009. (ENG.). 256p. 85.00 *(978-0-19-956772-0(7))* Oxford Univ. Pr., Inc.

McLean, George F. Beyond Modernity: The Recovery of Person & Community in Global Times: Lectures in China & Vietnam. 2008. pap. *(978-1-56518-257-8(X))* Council for Research in Values & Philosophy.

McNay, Lois. Against Recognition. 2008. (ENG.). 240p. 69.95 *(978-0-7456-2931-5(8))*; pap. 26.95 *(978-0-7456-2932-2(6))* Polity Pr. GBR. Dist: Wiley, John & Sons, Inc.

Meynell, Letitia. Embodiment & Agency. Sherwin, Susan, ed. 2009. (ENG., Illus.). 272p. 65.00 *(978-0-271-03522-2(6))* Pennsylvania State Univ. Pr.

Nachtomy, Ohad. Possibility, Agency, & Individuality in Leibniz's Metaphysics. 2010. (New Synthese Historical Library). xii, 272p. pap. 169.00 *(978-90-481-7319-8(1)*, 9048173191) Springer.

O'Brien, Lucy. Self-Knowing Agents. (ENG.). 256p. 2010. pap. 35.00 *(978-0-19-959204-3(7))* 2007. 85.00 *(978-0-19-926148-2(2))* Oxford Univ. Pr., Inc.

O'Brien, Lucy & Soteriou, Matthew, eds. Mental Actions. 2009. (ENG.). 296p. 99.00 *(978-0-19-922598-9(2))* Oxford Univ. Pr., Inc.

Oshana, Marina. The Importance of How We See Ourselves: Self-Identity & Responsible Agency. 2010. (ENG.). 186p. pap. 27.95 *(978-0-7391-2626-4(1))*; ix, 173p. E-Book *(978-0-7391-4935-5(0))* Rowman & Littlefield Publishers, Inc.

Oshana, Marina A. L. The Importance of How We See Ourselves: Self-Identity & Responsible Agency. 2010. (ENG.). 184p. 65.00 *(978-0-7391-2625-7(3))* Rowman & Littlefield Publishers, Inc.

Pippin, Robert B. Hegel's Practical Philosophy: Rational Agency as Ethical Life. 2008. (ENG.). 320p. 100.00 *(978-0-521-42957-3(9))* Cambridge Univ. Pr.

—Hegel's Practical Philosophy: Rational Agency As Ethical Life. 2008. (ENG.). 320p. pap. 33.00 *(978-0-521-72872-0(X))* Cambridge Univ. Pr.

Political Agency & Gender in India. 2011. (C). 150.00 *(978-0-203-88381-5(0))* Routledge.

Prinz, Wolfgang. Open Minds: The Social Making of Agency & Intentionality. 2012. (ENG., Illus.). 352p. (gr. 17). 40.00 ***(978-0-262-01703-9(2))*** MIT Pr.

Rödl, Sebastian. Self-Consciousness. 2007. 222p. 46.00 *(978-0-674-02494-6(X))* Harvard Univ. Pr.

Rozmarin, Miri. Creating Oneself: Agency, Desire & Feminist Transformations. 2011. (ENG.). 184p. pap. 53.95 ***(978-3-0343-0707-9(1))*** Lang, Peter AG GBR. Dist: Lang, Peter.

Sandell, Richard, et al, eds. Re-Presenting Disability: Activism & Agency in the Museum. 2010. (ENG., Illus.). 304p. (C). pap. 42.95 *(978-0-415-49473-1(7))* Routledge.

Sandell, Richard & Jocelyn Dodd, eds. Re-Presenting Disability: Activism & Agency in the Museum. 2010. (ENG., Illus.). 304p. (C). 125.00 *(978-0-415-49471-7(0)*, Routledge) Taylor & Francis Group GBR. Dist: Taylor & Francis Group.

Segal Jerome M. Agency Illusion & Well Being: Essays in Moral Psychology & Philosophical Economics. 2009. (ENG.). 260p. 78.99 *(978-0-7391-2968-5(6))* Lexington Bks.

—Agency, Illusion, & Well-Being: Essays in Moral Psychology & Philosophical Economics. 2008. (ENG.). 260p. pap. 31.50 *(978-0-7391-2969-2(4))* Lexington Bks.

Steadman, Sharon R. & Ross, Jennifer C. Agency & Identity in the Ancient near East: New Paths Forward. 2010. (Approaches to Anthropological Archaeology Ser.). (ENG., Illus.). 215p. (C). 125.00 *(978-1-84553-443-1(3))* Equinox Publishing Ltd. GBR. Dist: ISD.

Steward, Helen. A Metaphysics for Freedom. 2012. (ENG.). 256p. 60.00 ***(978-0-19-955205-4(3)***, Oxford Univ. Pr., Inc.

Swindal, James. Action & Existence: A Case for Agent Causation. 2011. (ENG., Illus.). 216p. 85.00 ***(978-0-230-29667-1(X))*** Palgrave Macmillan.

Taylor, Gabriele. Deadly Vices. (ENG.). 176p. 2008. pap. 27.95 *(978-0-19-954868-2(4)*, 2006. 99.00 *(978-0-19-823580-4(1))* Oxford Univ. Pr., Inc.

Thomasma, David C., et al, eds. Personhood & Health Care. 2010. (International Library of Ethics, Law, & the New Medicine Ser.). 462p. pap. 249.00 *(978-90-481-5858-4(3)*, 9048158583) Springer.

Thompson, Michael. Life & Action: Elementary Structures of Practice & Practical Thought. (Illus.). 240p. 2012. (ENG.). pap. 22.95 ***(978-0-674-06398-3(8))*** 2008. 44.00 *(978-0-674-01670-5(X))* Harvard Univ. Pr.

van Nijnatten, Carolus. Children's agency, children's Welfare: A dialogical approach to child development, policy & Practice. 2010. 168p. 99.00 *(978-1-84742-489-1(9)*, Policy Pr. GBR. Dist: Chicago Distribution Ctr.

Varela, Charles R. Science for Humanism: The Recovery of Human Agency. 2009. 352p. pap. 40.00 *(978-0-415-48520-3(7))*; 150.00 *(978-0-415-48182-3(1))* Routledge.

Velleman, J. David. Practical Reflection. 2007. (Center for the Study of Language & Information - Lecture Notes Ser.). 332p. per. 32.50 *(978-1-57586-534-8(3))* CSLI Pubns.

Vollmer, F. Agent Causality. 2010. (Synthese Library). 176p. pap. 109.00 *(978-90-481-5272-8(0)*, 9048152720) Springer.

AGENT ORANGE

Agent Orange in Vietnam: Recent Developments in Remediation: Hearing Before the Subcommittee on Asia, the Pacific, & the Global Environment of the Committee on Foreign Affairs, House of Representatives, One Hundred Eleventh Congress, Second Session, July 15, 2010. 2010. iii, 67p. ***(978-0-16-087454-3(8)***, 552-070-42146-7) United States Government Printing Office.

Arsenault, Chris. Blowback: A Canadian History of Agent Orange & the War at Home. 2009. (ENG., Illus.). 96p. pap. 15.95 *(978-1-55266-296-0(9))* Fernwood Publishing Co., Ltd. CAN. Dist: Independent Pubs. Group.

Committee on Blue Water Navy Vietnam Veterans and Agent Orange Exposure & Institute of Medicine. Blue Water Navy Vietnam Veterans & Agent Orange Exposure. 2011. (ENG.). 158p. pap. 37.50 ***(978-0-309-16247-0(5))*** National Academies Pr.

Committee on Making Best Use of the Agent Orange Exposure Reconstruction Model. The Utility of Proximity-Based Herbicide Exposure Assessment in Epidemiologic Studies of Vietnam Veterans. 2008. (ENG.). 160p. pap. 38.00 *(978-0-309-11449-3(7))* National Academies Pr.

Committee to Review the Health Effects in Vietnam Veterans of Exposure to Herbicides (Eighth Biennial Update) & Institute of Medicine. Veterans & Agent Orange: Update 2010. 2012. (ENG.). 800p. 146.50 ***(978-0-309-21447-6(5))*** National Academies Pr.

Committee to Review the Health Effects in Vietnam Veterans of Exposure to Herbicides (Sixth Biennial Update) & Institute of Medicine. Veterans & Agent Orange: Update 2006. 2007. (ENG.). 896p. pap. 213.25 *(978-0-309-14552-7(X,)* National Academies Pr.

Gaudet, Bernard. Risk Assessments of Dioxins: A Comparative Literature Review. 2009. 108p. pap. *(978-3-639-21948-7(1))* VDM Verlag Dr. Mueller e.K.

Health Effects of the Vietnam War: The Aftermath: Hearing Before the Committee on Veterans' Affairs, U.S. House of Representatives, One Hundred Eleventh Congress, Second Session, May 5, 2010. 2010. (Illus.). iv, 114p. ***(978-0-16-087679-0(6)***, 552-070-42231-5) United States Government Printing Office.

Institute of Medicine Staff, creator. Veterans & Agent Orange. 2007. (Illus.). 871p. 129.00 *(978-0-309-10708-2(3))* National Academies Pr.

Our Forgotten Responsibility: What Can We Do to Help Victims of Agent Orange?: Hearing Before the Subcommittee on Asia, the Pacific, & the Global Environment of the Committee on Foreign Affairs, House of Representatives, One Hundred Tenth Congress, Second Session, May 15, 2008. 2008. (Illus.). iii, 102p. *(978-0-16-082617-7(9)*, 552-070-38635-1) United States Government Printing Office.

Review the Health Effects in Vietnam Veterans of Exposure to Herbicides (Seventh Biennial Update) Committee & Institute of Medicine Staff. Veterans & Agent Orange: Update 2008. 2009. (ENG.). 708p. 131.00 *(978-0-309-13884-0(1,)* National Academies Pr.

Waugh, Charles & Lien, Huy, eds. Family of Fallen Leaves: Stories of Agent Orange by Vietnamese Writers. 2010. (ENG.). 164p. 59.95 *(978-0-8203-3600-8(9,)*; pap. 19.95 *(978-0-8203-3714-2(5))* Univ. of Georgia Pr.

Young, Alvin Lee. The History, Use, Disposition & Environmental Fate of Agent Orange. 2009. (ENG., Illus.). xviii, 339p. 114.00 *(978-0-387-87485-2(2)*, 0387874852) Springer.

AGENTS, COMMERCIAL

see Commercial Agents

AGENTS, INDIAN

see Indian Agents

AGENTS, LITERARY

see Literary Agents

AGENTS, REAL ESTATE

see Real Estate Agents

AGENTS, SPORTS

see Sports Agents

AGFANS

see Pushtuns

AGGADA

Blau, Yitzchak. Fresh Fruit & Vintage Wine: The Ethics & Wisdom of the Aggada. 2009. *(978-1-60280-008-3(1))* Ktav Publishing Hse., Inc.

Caredio, Even. Haggadah Illuminated, 1 vol. 2007. (HEB & ENG., Illus.). 96p. 19.95 *(978-1-58980-495-1(3))* Pelican Publishing Co., Inc.

Durkin, Mary Greeley, et al. Virtues & Vices: Stories of the Moral Life. 2007. (ENG.). 148p. per. 20.00 *(978-0-664-23235-1(3))* Westminster John Knox Pr.

Edels, Samuel Eliezer ben Judah & Finkel, Avraham Yaakov. Maharsha on Aggados: [Agadot Maharsha]: Selected Portions. 2007. x, 102p. *(978-1-892692-20-7(1))* Yeshiva Beth Moshe.

Ginzberg, Louis. The Legends of the Jews, Volume 2. 2007. (ENG.). 272p. pap. 21.99 *(978-1-4346-0934-7(7))* BiblioBazaar.

Lehman, Marjorie. The en Yaaqov: Jacob ibn Habib's Search for Faith in the Talmudic Corpus. 2011. 49.95 *(978-0-8143-3480-5(6))* Wayne State Univ. Pr.

Licht, Chaim. In the Grip of Bereavement An. 2009. 272p. pap. 18.95 *(978-965-229-446-3(2))* Gefen Publishing Hse., Ltd ISR. Dist: Strauss Consultants.

Megilla. reprint ed. 68.00 *(978-0-7222-9931-9(1))* Library Reprints, Inc.

Neusner, Jacob. Theology in Action: How the Rabbis of the Talmud Present Theology (Aggadah) in the Medium of the Law (Halakhah): an Anthology.

2006. (Studies in Judaism Ser.). (ENG.). 170p. per. 32.99 *(978-0-7618-3488-5(5))* Univ. Pr. of America, Inc.

Polano, H. The Talmud Selections from the Contents of That Ancient Book Also Brief Sketches of the Men Who Made & Commented upon It Tr from the Original. 2006. 372p. per. 26.99 *(978-1-4255-3913-9(0))* MPublishing.

Robinson, Gershon, tr. Talelei Oros: The Haggadah Anthology. 420p. 25.99 *(978-1-58330-598-0(X))* Feldheim Pubs.

Rubenstein, Jeffrey L. Stories of the Babylonian Talmud. 2010. (ENG.). 336p. (gr. 17). 55.00 *(978-0-8018-9449-7(2))* Johns Hopkins Univ. Pr.

Rubin, Yissachar Dov. Talelei Oros, 5 vols. Robinson, Gershon, tr. 25.99 *(978-1-58330-622-2(6))* Feldheim Pubs.

—Talelei Oros: The Megillah Anthology, 5 vols. Robinson, Gershon, tr. 25.99 *(978-1-58330-597-3(1))* Feldheim Pubs.

—Talelei Oros: The Sukkos Anthology. 25.99 *(978-1-58330-637-6(4))* Feldheim Pubs.

Sherwin, Byron L. Studies in Jewish Theology. 2007. 384p. (C). 75.00 *(978-0-85303-692-0(6))*; pap. 35.00 *(978-0-85303-694-4(2))* Vallentine Mitchell Pubs. GBR. Dist: International Specialized Bk. Services.

Tabory, Joseph. Aggadah & Its Interpretation. 2011. (Touro College Ser.). (ENG.). 400p. 89.00 ***(978-1-936235-79-7(X))*** Academic Studies Pr.

AGGLUTINANTS

see Adhesives

AGGREGATES

see Set Theory

AGGREGATES (BUILDING MATERIALS)

see also Sand; Slag

Aci, ed. Aggregates for Concrete. 2007. per. *(978-0-87031-248-9(0))* American Concrete Institute.

Construction: Concrete & Aggregates, 04.02. 2007. (Annual Book of ASTM Standards Ser.). 928p. 193.00 *(978-0-8031-4108-7(4))* American Society for Testing & Materials.

Guide for Use of Normal Weight & Heavyweight Aggregates in Concrete. 2007. per. *(978-0-87031-229-8(4))* American Concrete Institute.

Highway Innovative Technology Evaluation Center (U.S.) Staff, contrib. by. Evaluation of Geopier Rammed Aggregate Piers by Geopier Foundation Company: Final Report. 2007. *(978-0-7844-0955-8(2))* American Society of Civil Engineers.

Lawler, John S. Guidelines for Concrete Mixtures Containing Supplementary Cementitious Materials to Enhance Durability of Bridge Decks. 2007. (Illus.). 119p. 47.00 *(978-0-309-09897-7(1))* Transportation Research Board.

Lucius, Jeffrey E., et al. An Introduction to Using Surface Geophysics to Characterize Sand & Gravel Deposits. 2007. (Illus.). iv, 33p. *(978-1-4113-1841-0(2))* United States Geological Survey.

Masad, E., et al. Test Methods for Characterizing Aggregate Shape, Texture, & Angularity. 2007. (Illus.). per. 43.00 *(978-0-309-09882-3(3))* Transportation Research Board.

Prowell, Brian D. & Brown, E. Ray. Superpave Mix Design: Verifying Gyration Levels in the Ndesign Table. 2007. (Illus.). 62p. per. 50.00 *(978-0-309-09877-9(7))* Transportation Research Board.

Saeed, Athar. Performance-Related Tests of Recycled Aggregates for Use in Unbound Pavement Layers. 2008. (Illus.). 61p. pap. 40.00 *(978-0-309-09920-2(X))* Transportation Research Board.

Taylor, Peter C. Specifications & protocols for Acceptance Tests on Processing Additions in Cement Manufacturing. 2008. (Illus.). 86p. pap. 50.00 *(978-0-309-09934-9(X))* Transportation Research Board.

AGGRESSION (INTERNATIONAL LAW)

Byers, Michael. War Law, 1 vol. (ENG.). 224p. 35.00 *(978-1-55365-151-2(0))* D&M Pubs. Inc. CAN. Dist: Perseus-PGW.

Centre of Excellence Defence Against Terrorism, Turkey, Ankara, ed. Legal Aspects of Combating Terrorism: Volume 47 NATO Science for Peace & Security Series - Human & Societal Dynamics. 2008. 80p. pap. 167.00 *(978-1-58603-930-1(X))* IOS Pr., Inc.

Dinstein, Yoram. The Conduct of Hostilities under the Law of International Armed Conflict. 2nd rev. ed. 2010. (ENG.). 348p. 128.00 *(978-0-521-19813-4(5))*; 328p. pap. 52.00 *(978-0-521-12131-6(0))* Cambridge Univ. Pr.

—War, Aggression & Self-Defence. 5th ed. 2011. (ENG.). 408p. pap. 70.00 ***(978-1-107-40145-7(3))*** Cambridge Univ. Pr.

—War, Aggression, & Self-Defence. 5th ed. 2011. (ENG.). 408p. 125.00 ***(978-1-107-00899-1(9))*** Cambridge Univ. Pr.

Gazzini, Tarcisio & Tsagourias, Nicholas. The Use of Force in International Law. 2012. (International Law of Peace & Security Ser.). 648p. 300.00 ***(978-0-7546-2948-1(1))*** Ashgate Publishing Co.

Glennon, Michael. Fog of Law: Pragmatism, Security, & International Law. 2010. (ENG.). 224p. 40.00 *(978-0-8047-7175-7(8))* Stanford Univ. Pr.

Gray, Christine D. International Law & the Use of Force. 3rd ed. 2008. (Foundations of Public International Law Ser.). (ENG.). 450p. 181.50 *(978-0-19-923914-6(2))*; pap. 65.00 *(978-0-19-923915-3(0))* Oxford Univ. Pr., Inc.

Kemp, Gerhard. Individual Criminal Liability for the International Crime of Aggression. 2010. 292p. pap. 96.75 *(978-94-000-0013-1(8))* Intersentia Uitgevers N.V. BEL. Dist: International Specialized Bk. Services.

Kre, Claus & Barriga, Stefan, eds. The Travaux Préparatoires of the Crime of Aggression. 2011. (ENG.). 876p. 150.00 ***(978-1-107-01527-2(8))***; pap. 80.00 ***(978-1-107-63920-1(4))*** Cambridge Univ. Pr.

Kühn, Michael. Unilaterale präventive Gewaltanwendung: Eine Untersuchung zur 'präventiven Selbstverteidigung' im Völkerrecht. 2009. (Öffentliches und Internationales Recht Ser.). (GER.). 31p. 122.95 *(978-3-631-59440-7(2))* Lang, Peter GmbH, Europaischer Verlag der Wissenschaften DEU. Dist: Lang, Peter.

Laursen, Andreas. Changing International Law to Meet New Challenges: Interpretation, Modification & the Use of Force. 2006. 331p. (C). pap. 60.00 *(978-87-574-1529-2(3))* Djof Publishing DNK. Dist: International Specialized Bk. Services.

Mahan, Alfred Thayer. Armaments & Arbitration. 2009. 162p. pap. *(978-1-4590-7998-4(1))* Books LLC.

—Armaments & Arbitration: Or the Place of Force in the International Relations of States (1912) 2009. 272p. 42.95 *(978-1-120-23759-0(9))*; pap. 27.95 *(978-1-120-15818-5(4))* Kessinger Publishing, LLC.

—Armaments & Arbitration, or, the Place of Force in the International Relations of States. 2010. 272p. 34.99 *(978-1-140-55868-2(4))* BiblioBazaar.

—Armaments & Arbitration, or, the Place of Force in the International Relations of States. reprint ed. pap. 125.00 *(978-1-4047-3931-4(9))* Classic Textbooks.

Matheson, M. Council Unbound: The Growth of un Decision Making on Conflict & Postconflict Issues after the Cold War. 2006. 336p. (C). 50.00 *(978-1-929223-79-4(X))* U. S. Institute of Peace Pr. (USIP Pr.).

Matheson, Michael J. Council Unbound: The Growth of un Decision Making on Conflict & Postconflict Issues after the Cold War. 2006. 336p. (C). pap. 19.95 *(978-1-929223-78-7(1))* U. S. Institute of Peace Pr. (USIP Pr.).

May, Larry. Aggression & Crimes Against Peace. 2008. (Philosophical & Legal Aspects of War & Conflict Ser.). (ENG.). 366p. 85.00 *(978-0-521-89431-9(X))*; 368p. pap. 28.99 *(978-0-521-71915-5(1))* Cambridge Univ. Pr.

Nugent, Walter. Habits of Empire: A History of American Expansionism. 2009. (Vintage Ser.). (ENG., Illus.). 432p. pap. 17.00 *(978-1-4000-7818-9(0), Vintage)* Knopf Doubleday Publishing Group.

O'Connell, Mary Ellen. International Law & the Use of Force: Cases & Materials. 2nd ed. 2009. (University Casebook Ser.). xxv, 758p. ***(978-1-60930-089-0(0),*** Foundation Pr.) West.

Olusanya, Olaoluwa. Identifying the Aggressor under International Law: A Principles Approach. 2006. 211p. pap. 45.95 *(978-0-8204-8003-9(7))* Lang, Peter Publishing, Inc.

Pedrozo, Raul A. "Pete". The War in Iraq: A Legal Analysis. 2010. (International Law Studies). (ENG.). 550p. 20.00 *(978-1-884733-75-8(1),* Dept. of the Navy) United States Government Printing Office.

Reisman, W. Michael & Baker, James E. Regulating Covert Action: Practices Contexts & Policies of Covert Coercion Abroad in International & American Law. 2011. (ENG.). 260p. pap. 26.00 ***(978-0-300-17694-0(5))*** Yale Univ. Pr.

Rodin, David & Shue, Henry, eds. Just & Unjust Warriors: The Moral & Legal Status of Soldiers. (ENG.). 2010. 272p. pap. 40.00 *(978-0-19-959323-1(X))* 2008. 320p. 110.00 *(978-0-19-923312-0(8))* Oxford Univ. Pr., Inc.

Ruys, Tom. 'Armed Attack' & Article 51 of the un Charter: Evolutions in Customary Law & Practice. 2010. (Cambridge Studies in International & Comparative Law Ser.). (ENG.). 616p. 120.00 *(978-0-521-76664-7(8))* Cambridge Univ. Pr.

Sharpe, J. Forrest & O'Huallachain, D. Liam, eds. Neo-Conned! Just War Principles: A Condemnation of War in Iraq. 2006. (ENG., Illus.). 447p. per. 19.95 *(978-1-932528-06-0(7))* IHS Pr.

Sturchler, Nikolas. The Threat of Force in International Law. 2007. (Cambridge Studies in International & Comparative Law). (ENG.). 384p. 125.00 *(978-0-521-87388-8(6))* Cambridge Univ. Pr.

Stürchler, Nikolas. The Threat of Force in International Law. 2009. (Cambridge Studies in International & Comparative Law Ser.). (ENG.). 384p. pap. 39.00 *(978-0-521-13361-6(0))* Cambridge Univ. Pr.

United Nations: Limitations in Leading Missions Requiring Force to Restore Peace. 56p. pap. 20.00 *(978-0-7881-7951-8(9))* DIANE Publishing Co.

Van Der Wolf, W., ed. Aggression & International Criminal Law. 2011. (International Criminal Law Ser.). 363p. 140.00 *(978-90-5887-079-7(0))*; pap. 100.00 *(978-90-5887-080-3(4))* International Courts Assn. NLD. Dist: International Specialized Bk. Services.

Westra, Joel. International Law & the Use of Armed Force: The un Charter & the Major Powers. 2008. 244p. pap. 37.95 *(978-0-415-49515-8(6))* Routledge.

Westra, Joel H. International Law & the Use of Armed Force: The un Charter & the Major Powers. 2007. (Contemporary Security Studies). (Illus.). 224p. 160.00 *(978-0-415-77098-9(X))* Routledge.

Wilson, Page. Aggression Crime & International Security. 2012. (Contemporary Security Studies). (ENG.). (C). pap. 44.95 ***(978-0-415-69156-7(7))*** Routledge.

Wilson, Page. Aggression, Crime & International Security: Moral, Political & Legal Dimensions of International Relations. 2009. 192p. 120.00 *(978-0-415-48524-1(X))* Routledge.

AGGRESSION (PSYCHOLOGY)

see Aggressiveness

AGGRESSIVE BEHAVIOR

see Aggressiveness

AGGRESSIVENESS

see also Assertiveness (Psychology); Bullying; Fighting (Psychology); Hostility (Psychology)

Adams, Sheila. Women & Relationship Violence. 2010. 152p. pap. *(978-3-8383-1782-3(3))* Lambert Academic Publishing.

Alvarez, Alex & Bachman, Ronet. Violence: The Enduring Problem. 2007. (Illus.). 360p. (C). per. 57.00 *(978-1-4129-1685-1(2),* B16852P) SAGE Pubns., Inc.

Amdur, Ellis. In the Eye of the Hurricane: Calming & de-escalation of Aggressive Family Members. 2008. pap. 20.00 *(978-0-9796206-9-0(4))* Stand & Live, Inc.

Apsche, Jack & DiMeo, Lucia R. Mode Deactivation Therapy for Aggression & Oppositional Behavior in Adolescents: An Integrative Methodology Using ACT, DBT, & CBT. 2012. (ENG.). 216p. pap. 59.95 ***(978-1-60882-107-5(2))*** New Harbinger Pubns.

Arsenio, William Frank & Lemerise, Elizabeth B. Emotions, Aggression, & Morality in Children: Bridging Development & Psychopathology. 2010. x, 270p. 59.95 *(978-1-4338-0764-0(5))* American Psychological Assn.

Avtgis, Theodore & Rancer, Andrew S., eds. Arguments Aggression & Conflict: New Directions in Theory & Research. 2010. (ENG., Illus.). 448p. (C). 125.00 *(978-0-415-99639-6(2))*; pap. 49.95 *(978-0-415-99641-9(4))* Taylor & Francis Group GBR. (Routledge). Dist: Taylor & Francis Group.

Barash, David P. & Lipton, Judith Eve. Payback: Why We Retaliate, Redirect Aggression, & Take Revenge, 1 vol. 2011. (ENG.). 272p. 24.95 *(978-0-19-539514-3(X))* Oxford Univ. Pr., Inc.

Barratt, Robin, ed. The Mammoth Book of Tough Guys. 2011. (ENG.). 448p. pap. 13.95 *(978-0-7624-4099-3(6))* Running Pr. Bk. Pubs.

Bergman, Daniel. Conditions Influencing Aggression. 2009. 152p. pap. *(978-3-639-00152-5(4))* VDM Verlag Dr. Mueller e.K.

Billias, Nancy & Praeg, Leonhard, eds. Creating Destruction: Constructing Images of Violence & Genocide. 2011. (Illus.). 224p. pap. 63.00 *(978-90-420-3338-2(X))* Rodopi.

Botha, Albertus Johannes. The experiences of SA secondary school male educators own aggression: Male educators' experiences of own aggression. 2008. 128p. pap. *(978-3-639-09200-4(7))* VDM Verlag Dr. Mueller e.K.

Budhal, Rishichand Sookai. Aggression. 2010. 164p. pap. *(978-3-8383-6159-8(8))* Lambert Academic Publishing.

Caspi, Jonathan. Sibling Aggression: Assessment & Treatment. 2011. 250p. pap. ***(978-0-8261-2415-9(1))***; E-Book ***(978-0-8261-2416-6(X))*** Springer.

Cavell, Timothy A. & Malcolm, Kenya T., eds. Anger, Aggression, & Interventions for Interpersonal Violence. 2006. (ENG.). 472p. 120.95 *(978-0-8058-5554-8(8))*; per. 47.95 *(978-0-8058-6152-5(1))* Routledge.

Coleman, Rhonda D. Mr. Nice Guy Hates Your Guts: Insights into Passive Aggressive Personality Disorder. 2006. pap. 14.95 *(978-0-615-13710-0(5))* Trophylicious Bks.

Contee, Roxanne. Designed to Decrease Aggressive Behavior on the Part of Students in the Classroom. 2011. 80p. pap. 15.99 ***(978-1-4628-5529-2(6))*** Xlibris Corp.

Cotto Guevara, Bernardo & Adorno Becerra, Noe, eds. Psychology of Aggression: New Research. 2012. ***(978-1-61942-452-4(5))*** Nova Science Pubs., Inc.

Cram101 Textbook Reviews & Cram101 Textbook Reviews. Outlines & Highlights for the Cambridge Handbook of Violent Behavior & Aggression by Daniel Flannery, Isbn: 9780521607858. 2011. 490p. pap. 37.95 ***(978-1-61461-038-0(X))*** Cram101 Inc.

Crenshaw, David A. & Mordock, John B. A Handbook of Play Therapy with Aggressive Children. 2007. (ENG., Illus.). 312p. per. 41.99 *(978-0-7657-0579-2(6),* Aronson, Jason) Rowman & Littlefield Publishers, Inc.

—Understanding & Treating the Aggression of Children: Fawns in Gorilla Suits. 2007. (ENG., Illus.). 312p. per. 36.99 *(978-0-7657-0561-7(3),* Aronson, Jason) Rowman & Littlefield Publishers, Inc.

Curwin, Richard L., et al. Strategies for Successful Classroom Management: Helping Students Succeed Without Losing Your Dignity or Sanity. 2007. (Illus.). 176p. 66.95 *(978-1-4129-3783-2(3),* B37833C); per. 27.95 *(978-1-4129-3784-9(1),* B37833P) Corwin Pr.

Dennison, Pamela S. Civilizing the City Dog: A Guide to Rehabilitating Aggressive Dogs in an Urban Environment: Supplement to How to Right a Dog Gone Wrong. 2007. (Illus.). 84p. pap. 14.95 *(978-1-57779-089-1(8))* Alpine Pubns., Inc.

Denzler, Markus. Catharsis Revisited: The Impact of Goals on Aggressive Thoughts & Aggressive Behavior. 2008. 160p. pap. *(978-3-8364-9487-8(6))* VDM Verlag Dr. Mueller e.K.

Dippel, John V. H. War & Sex: A Brief History of Men's Urge for Battle. 2010. (ENG.). 465p. 27.00 *(978-1-61614-188-2(3))* Prometheus Bks., Pubs.

Fisher-Blando, Judith. Workplace Bullying: Aggressive Behavior. 2010. 160p. pap. *(978-3-8383-6576-3(3))* Lambert Academic Publishing.

Flannery, Daniel, et al, eds. The Cambridge Handbook of Violent Behavior & Aggression. 2007. (Cambridge Handbooks in Psychology Ser.). (ENG., Illus.). 838p. 148.99 *(978-0-521-84567-0(X))* Cambridge Univ. Pr.

Flannery, Daniel J., et al, eds. The Cambridge Handbook of Violent Behavior & Aggression. 2007. (Cambridge Handbooks in Psychology Ser.). (ENG., Illus.). 840p. per. 68.99 *(978-0-521-60785-8(X))* Cambridge Univ. Pr.

Flerx, Vicki Crocker, et al. Class Meetings That Matter: A Year's Worth of Resources for Grades 6-8. 2009. (Illus.). vii, 181p. ***(978-1-59285-831-6(7))*** Hazelden Publishing & Educational Services.

Forgas, Joseph P., et al, eds. The Psychology of Social Conflict & Aggression. 2011. (Sydney Symposium in Social Psychology Ser.). (ENG., Illus.). 342p. 78.75 *(978-1-84872-932-2(4),* Psychology Press) Taylor & Francis Group GBR. Dist: Taylor & Francis Group.

Gentile, Douglas A., et al. Violent Video Game Effects on Children & Adolescents: Theory, Research, & Public Policy. 2007. (ENG., Illus.). 200p. 37.99 *(978-0-19-530983-6(9))* Oxford Univ. Pr., Inc.

Gordon, Mary. Roots of Empathy: Changing the World Child by Child. 2009. (ENG.). 312p. pap. 15.95 *(978-1-61519-007-2(4),* 1615190074) Experiment LLC, The.

Graves, Kelly. Aggression among Female Adolescents. 2009. 68p. pap. *(978-3-639-12870-3(2))* VDM Verlag Dr. Mueller e.K.

Hartup, Willard W. & Wit, Jan de, eds. Origins of Aggression. (Psychological Studies). (ENG.). X, 364p. 210.00 ***(978-3-11-176688-1(8))*** De Gruyter, Mouton DEU. Dist: de Gruyter, Walter GmbH & Co. KG.

Harvey, Pat & Penzo, Jeanine A. Parenting a Child Who Has Intense Emotions: Dialectical Behavior Therapy Skills to Help Your Child Regulate Emotional Outbursts & Aggressive Behaviors. 2009. (ENG.). 224p. pap. 18.95 *(978-1-57224-649-2(9))* New Harbinger Pubns.

Hawley, Patricia H., et al, eds. Aggression & Adaptation: The Bright Side to Bad Behavior. 2007. (ENG., Illus.). 304p. 135.00 *(978-0-8058-5245-5(X))*; per. 44.95 *(978-0-8058-6234-8(X))* Routledge.

Hogh, Annie. Aggression at Work. 2009. 88p. pap. *(978-3-639-17635-3(9))* VDM Verlag Dr. Mueller e.K.

Hoover, John H. & Oliver, Ronald L. The Bullying Prevention Handbook: A Guide for Principals, Teachers, & Counselors. 2nd ed. 2008. (Illus.). 232p. pap. 29.95 incl. audio compact disk *(978-1-934009-11-6(3))* Solution Tree.

Hudley, Cynthia. You Did That on Purpose: Understanding & Changing Children's Aggression. 2008. (ENG.). 192p. 35.00 *(978-0-300-11085-2(5))* Yale Univ. Pr.

Jewell, R. Todd, ed. Violence & Aggression in Sporting Contests: Economics, History & Policy. 2011. (Sports Economics, Management & Policy Ser.). (ENG., Illus.). xii, 275p. 139.00 *(978-1-4419-6629-2(3),* 1441966293) Springer.

Kaplan, R. M., ed. Aggression in Children & Youth. 2010. (NATO Science Series D: (closed) Ser.). 376p. pap. 409.00 *(978-90-481-8278-7(6),* 9048182786) Springer.

Karlekar, Hiranmay. Savage Humans & Stray Dogs: A study in Aggression. 2008. (Illus.). 296p. (C). pap. 29.95 *(978-81-7829-879-5(1),* B98795P) SAGE Pubns., Inc.

Kernberg, Otto F. The Inseparable Nature of Love & Aggression: Clinical & Theoretical Perspectives. 2011. 380p. pap. 59.00 ***(978-1-58562-428-7(4))*** American Psychiatric Publishing, Inc.

Kevorkian, Meline. Tackling Bullying in Athletics: Best Practices for Modeling Appropriate Behavior. 2010. (ENG.). 100p. 60.00 *(978-1-60709-379-4(0))*; pap. 17.95 *(978-1-60709-380-0(4))* Rowman & Littlefield Education.

Kevorkian, Meline M. & D'Antona, Robin. Tackling Bullying in Athletics: Guidelines for Modeling Appropriate Behavior. 2010. 17.95 *(978-1-60709-381-7(2))* Rowman & Littlefield Publishers, Inc.

Kloth-Zanard, Joan. Where Did I Go Wrong? How Did I Miss the Signs? Dealing with Hostile Parenting & Parental Alienation. 2010. 307p. pap. 27.99 *(978-0-557-44779-4(8))* Lulu Enterprises Inc.

Knutson, John F. & Knutson, John, eds. The Control of Aggression: Implications from Basic Research. 2007. (ENG., Illus.). 310p. pap. 34.95 *(978-0-202-30952-1(5))* Aldine Transaction.

Kornadt, Hans-Joachim. Aggression: Die Rolle der Erziehung in Europa und Ostasien. 2011. (GER., Illus.). 284p. pap. *(978-3-531-16550-9(X))* Westdeutscher Verlag GmbH.

Kotsko, Adam. Why We Love Sociopaths: A Guide to Late Capitalist Television. 2012. (ENG.). 107p. pap. 14.95 ***(978-1-78099-091-0(X))*** Hunt, John Publishing Ltd. GBR. Dist: National Bk. Network.

Landry, Nicole E. R. The Mean Girl Motive: Negotiating Power & Femininity. 2008. (ENG.). 110p. pap. 17.95 *(978-1-55266-266-3(7))* Fernwood Publishing Co., Ltd. CAN. Dist: Independent Pubs. Group.

Larson, Jim & Lochman, John E. Helping Schoolchildren Cope with Anger, Second Edition: A Cognitive-Behavioral Intervention. 2nd ed. 2010. (ENG., Illus.). 222p. (gr. 3-6). pap. 30.00 *(978-1-60623-973-5(2))* Guilford Pubns., Inc.

Leifer, Ron. Vinegar into Honey: Seven Steps to Understanding & Transforming Anger, Agression, & Violence. 2008. (ENG.). 144p. pap. 14.95 *(978-1-55939-293-8(2))* Snow Lion Pubns., Inc.

Lochman, John E., et al. Coping Power: Child Group Facilitator's Guide, 2 vols. 2008. (Treatments That Work Ser.). (ENG.). 288p. (C). pap. 57.95 *(978-0-19-532787-8(X))* Oxford Univ. Pr., Inc.

Long, Nicholas James, et al. The Angry Smile: The Psychology of Passive-Aggressive Behavior in Families, Schools, & Workplaces. 2nd ed. 2008. 26.00 *(978-1-4164-0423-1(6))* PRO-ED, Inc.

Martinez, Manuela, ed. Prevention & Control of Aggression & the Impact on its Victims. 2010. (ENG., Illus.). 450p. pap. 129.00 *(978-1-4419-3366-9(2),* 1441933662) Springer.

Mattson, Mark P., ed. Neurobiology of Aggression: Understanding & Preventing Violence. 2010. (Contemporary Neuroscience Ser.). (Illus.). 336p. pap. 179.00 *(978-1-61737-410-4(5),* 1617374105) Humana Pr.

McDonnell, Andrew A. & Sturmey, Peter. Managing Aggressive Behaviour in Care Settings: Understanding & Applying Low Arousal Approaches. 2010. (ENG., Illus.). 270p. pap. 55.95 *(978-0-470-51231-9(8),* Wiley) Wiley, John & Sons, Inc.

Muller, Martin N. Sexual Coercion in Primates & Humans: An Evolutionary Perspective on Male Aggression Against Females. Wrangham, Richard, ed. 2009. (Illus.). 504p. 58.00 *(978-0-674-03324-5(8))* Harvard Univ. Pr.

Noels, Rodri A. School Bullying & Aggression: Assessment Tools. 2012. (Psychology of Emotions, Motivations & Actions/Children's Issues Ser.). 186p. 95.00 ***(978-1-61470-883-4(5))*** Nova Science Pubs., Inc.

Novaco, Raymond W., et al. Anger Treatment for Offenders. (Wiley Series in Forensic Clinical Psychology Ser.). 350p. pap. 150.00 *(978-0-471-49153-8(5))* Wiley, John & Sons, Inc.

O'Leary, K. Daniel & Woodin, Erica M., eds. Psychological & Physical Aggression in Couples: Causes & Interventions. 2009. 280p. 49.95 *(978-1-4338-0453-3(0))* American Psychological Assn.

Österman, Karin, ed. Indirect & Direct Aggression. 2010. 432p. pap. 72.95 *(978-3-631-60028-3(3))* Lang, Peter GmbH, Europaischer Verlag der Wissenschaften DEU. Dist: Lang, Peter.

Parens, Henri. The Development of Aggression in Early Childhood. 2007. (ENG.). 436p. per. 57.99 *(978-0-7657-0510-5(9),* Aronson, Jason) Rowman & Littlefield Publishers, Inc.

—Handling Children's Aggression Constructively: Toward Taming Human Destructiveness. 2011. (ENG.). 300p. 65.00 *(978-0-7657-0687-4(3))* 2010. *(978-0-7657-0689-8(X))* Rowman & Littlefield Publishers, Inc. (Aronson, Jason).

Passley, Josef A. From Depression to Aggression. 2008. 120p. pap. *(978-3-639-05899-4(2))* VDM Verlag Dr. Mueller e.K.

Petermann, Franz & Petermann, Ulrike. Behavior Therapy with Aggressive Childre & Adolescents: Studies in Adolescence & Family Research, Vol. 2. 2006. 135p. pap. *(978-0-8204-9887-4(4))* Lang, Peter AG.

Pickhardt, Carl E. Why Good Kids Act Cruel: The Hidden Truth about the Pre-Teen Years. 2010. (ENG.). 320p. pap. 14.99 *(978-1-4022-1944-3(X))* Sourcebooks, Inc.

Portmann, Rosemarie. Dealing with Aggression. (Illus.). 208p. pap. *(978-0-86388-410-8(5),* 002-5124) Speechmark Publishing Ltd.

Quin, Caitriona & Tawse, Scott. Handbook of Aggressive Behavior Research. 2009. (Psychology of Emotions, Motivations & Actions Ser.). 195.00 *(978-1-60741-583-1(6))* Nova Science Pubs., Inc.

Redshaw, Nick & Bethan. 345 - PSYA3 Relationships, Aggression & Eating Behaviour. 2010. 128p. pap. 27.50 *(978-1-4457-7346-9(5))* Lulu Enterprises Inc.

—346 - PSYA3 Relationships, Aggression & Gender. 2010. 128p. pap. 27.50 *(978-1-4461-6650-5(3))* Lulu Enterprises Inc.

—456 - PSYA3 Aggression, Eating Behaviour & Gender. 2010. 118p. pap. 27.50 *(978-1-4461-3784-0(8))* Lulu Enterprises Inc.

—478 - PSYA 3 Aggression, Intelligence & Learning, Cognition & Development. 2010. 133p. pap. 27.50 *(978-1-4461-6986-5(3))* Lulu Enterprises Inc.

Ritter, Dominik. Raging Minds. 2009. 204p. pap. *(978-3-639-14569-4(0))* VDM Verlag Dr. Mueller e.K.

Roff, Hermione. Reflective Interpersonal Therapy for Children & Parents (RICAP) Mind That Child! A New Way of Helping Parents & Children with Extreme Conduct Disorder. 2008. (ENG., Illus.). 318p. 144.95 *(978-0-470-98648-6(4),* Wiley) Wiley, John & Sons, Inc.

Russell, Gordon W. Aggression in the Sports World: A Social Psychological Perspective. 2008. (ENG., Illus.). 336p. 45.00 *(978-0-19-518959-9(0))* Oxford Univ. Pr., Inc.

Schottmayer, Georg. Umgang mit Gewalt: Reformation statt Deformation des Sozialen. 2011. (Soziale Baustellen. ein Programm zur Aktivierung von Sozialkapital Ser.). (GER.). 340p. pap. 43.95 *(978-3-631-58214-5(5))* Lang, Peter GmbH, Europaischer Verlag der Wissenschaften DEU. Dist: Lang, Peter.

Sharp, Anne Wallace, ed. Sports Violence. 2011. (Hot Topics Ser.). (Illus.). 128p. (YA). (gr. 9-12). lib. bdg. 33.45 *(978-1-4205-0625-9(0))* Cengage Gale.

Shaver, Phillip R. & Mikulincer, Mario. Human Aggression & Violence: Causes, Manifestations, & Consequences. 2010. (Illus.). xvi, 419p. *(978-1-4338-0860-9(9));* 69.95 *(978-1-4338-0859-3(5))* American Psychological Assn.

Silver, Rawley. The Silver Drawing Test & Draw a Story: Assessing Depression, Aggression, & Cognitive Skills. 2nd rev. ed. 2007. (ENG., Illus.). 320p. per. 52.95 *(978-0-415-95534-8(3))* Routledge.

Simmons, Rachel. Odd Girl Out: The Hidden Culture of Aggression in Girls. rev. ed. 2011. (ENG.). 432p. (gr. 9-12). pap. 14.95 *(978-0-547-52019-3(0),* Mariner Bks.) Houghton Mifflin Harcourt Trade & Reference Pubs.

Simon, George K. In Sheep's Clothing: Understanding & Dealing with Manipulative People. 2010. (ENG.). 176p. pap. 16.95 *(978-1-935166-30-6(1))* Parkhurst Brothers, Inc., Pubs.

Steffgen, Georges & Gollwitzer, Mario, eds. Emotions & Aggressive Behavior. 2007. (Illus.). 230p. 44.00 *(978-0-88937-343-3(4))* Hogrefe Publishing.

Stoff, David M. & Susman, Elizabeth J., eds. Developmental Psychobiology of Aggression. 2009. (ENG.). 320p. pap. 42.00 *(978-0-521-12699-1(1))* Cambridge Univ. Pr.

Sturmey, Peter & McDonnell, Andrew A. Managing Aggressive Behaviour in Care Settings: Understanding & Applying Low Arousal Approaches. 2010. (ENG., Illus.). 270p. 110.95 *(978-0-470-51232-6(6),* Wiley) Wiley, John & Sons, Inc.

Sue, Derald Wing. Microaggressions in Everyday Life: Race, Gender, & Sexual Orientation. 2010. (ENG., Illus.). 352p. 48.00 *(978-0-470-49140-9(X),* Wiley) Wiley, John & Sons, Inc.

Sue, Derald Wing, ed. Microaggressions & Marginality: Manifestation, Dynamics, & Impact. 2010. (ENG., Illus.). 360p. 48.00 *(978-0-470-49139-3(6),* Wiley) Wiley, John & Sons, Inc.

Sukhodolsky, Denis G. & Scahill, Lawrence. Cognitive-Behavioral Therapy for Anger & Aggression in Children. 2012. (ENG.). 184p. pap. 30.00 *(978-1-4625-0632-3(1))* Guilford Pubns., Inc.

Taffe, Richard. Social Skills Training with Aggressive-Rejected Children. 2010. 180p. pap. *(978-3-8383-5108-7(8))* Lambert Academic Publishing.

Tlusty, B. Ann. The Martial Ethic in Early Modern Germany: Civic Duty & the Right of Arms. 2011. (ENG., Illus.). 384p. 95.00 *(978-0-230-57656-8(7))* Palgrave Macmillan.

Train, Alan. The Bullying Problem: How to Deal with Difficult Children. 2nd ed. 2009. (ENG.). 208p. pap. 19.95 *(978-0-285-63829-7(7))* Souvenir Pr. Ltd. GBR. Dist: Independent Pubs. Group.

Vernberg, Eric M. & Biggs, Bridget K. Preventing & Treating Bullying & Victimization. 2010. (ENG., Illus.). 424p. 59.95 *(978-0-19-533587-3(2))* Oxford Univ. Pr., Inc.

Verity, Patricia M. Violence & Aggression Around the Globe. 2008. (Illus.). 188p. (C). 89.00 *(978-1-60021-235-2(2))* Nova Science Pubs., Inc.

Waite, Pete. Aggressive Volleyball. 2009. (ENG., Illus.). 216p. pap. 21.95 *(978-0-7360-7441-4(4))* Human Kinetics Pubs.

Ward, Tony, et al, eds. Aggressive Offenders' Cognition: Theory, Research & Practice. 2007. (Wiley Series in Forensic Clinical Psychology Ser.: 34). (ENG., Illus.). 296p. 172.95 *(978-0-470-03402-6(5),* Wiley-Interscience) Wiley, John & Sons, Inc.

—Aggressive Offenders' Cognition: Theory, Research & Practice. 2007. (Wiley Series in Forensic Clinical Psychology Ser.: 35). (ENG., Illus.). 296p. per. 66.95 *(978-0-470-03401-9(7),* Wiley-Interscience) Wiley, John & Sons, Inc.

Wells, Karen, et al. Coping Power: Parent Group Facilitator's Guide, 2 vols. 2008. (Treatments That Work Ser.). (ENG.). 192p. (C). pap. 47.95 *(978-0-19-532788-5(8))* Oxford Univ. Pr., Inc.

—Coping Power Set: Parent Group. 2008. (Treatments That Work Ser.). (ENG.). 128p. (C). pap., wbk. ed. 98.50 *(978-0-19-532796-0(9))* Oxford Univ. Pr., Inc.

Williams. Aggression: From Fantasy to Action. 2011. (Psychoanalytic Ideas Ser.). 260p. pap. 34.95 ***(978-1-85575-891-9(1))*** Karnac Bks. GBR. Dist: Stylus Publishing, LLC.

Williams, Emma E. & Barlow, Rebecca. Anger Control Training, 3 vols. (Illus.). 186p. spiral bd. *(978-0-86388-334-7(6),* 002-309*) Speechmark Publishing Ltd.

Wolfe, David A. Acting Out: Understanding & Reducing Aggressive Behaviour in Children & Youth. 2007. ***(978-0-88868-532-2(7))*** Centre for Addiction & Mental Health.

Yokley, James. Social Responsibility Therapy for Adolescents & Young Adults: A Multicultural Treatment Manual for Harmful Behavior. 2008. (Illus.). (ENG.). 360p. 125.00 *(978-0-7890-3120-4(5));* 376p. pap. 54.50 *(978-0-7890-3121-1(3))* Routledge.

AGILE DEVELOPMENT (COMPUTER SCIENCE)
see Agile Software Development

AGILE METHODS (COMPUTER SCIENCE)
see Agile Software Development

AGILE PROCESSES (COMPUTER SCIENCE)
see Agile Software Development

AGGRESSIVENESS (PSYCHOLOGY)
see Aggressiveness

AGILE SOFTWARE DEVELOPMENT

Abrahamsson, Pekka, et al. Agile Processes in Software Engineering & Extreme Programming: 10th International Conference, XP 2009, Sardinia, Italy, May 25-29, 2009, Proceedings. 2009. (Lecture Notes in Business Information Processing Ser.). xvi, 278p. pap. 69.95 *(978-3-642-01852-7(1),* 3642018521) Springer.

—Extreme Programming & Agile Processes in Software Engineering: 7th International Conference, XP 2006, Oulu, Finland, June 17-22, 2006, Proceedings. 2006. (Lecture Notes in Computer Science Ser.: Vol. 4044). (Illus.). XII, 230p. pap. 58.00 *(978-3-540-35094-1(2),* 3540350942) Springer.

Abrahamsson, Pekka, et al, eds. Agile Processes in Software Engineering & Extreme Programming: 9th International Conference, XP 2008 - Limerick, Ireland, June 2008 - Proceedings. 2008. (Lecture Notes in Business Information Processing Ser.). (ENG., Illus.). xiv, 258p. pap. 69.95 *(978-3-540-68254-7(6),* 3540682546) Springer.

Abrahamsson, Pekka & Oza, Nilay, eds. Lean Enterprise Software & Systems: First International Conference, LESS 2010, Helsinki, finland, October 17-20, 2010, Proceedings. 2010. (Lecture Notes in Business Information Processing Ser.). xiii, 185p. pap. 72.00 *(978-3-642-16415-6(3),* 3642164153) Springer.

Agile Processes in Software Engineering & Extreme Programming: 8th International Conference, XP 2007, Como, Italy, June 18-22, 2007, Proceedings. 2007. (Lecture Notes in Computer Science Ser.). (Illus.). 276p. pap. 69.95 *(978-3-540-73100-9(8))* Springer.

Andriole, Stephen J., ed. Managing it People. 2011. (ENG., Illus.). 224p. 69.95 *(978-1-4398-7658-9(4))* Auerbach Pubs., Inc.

Appelo, Jurgen. Management 3. 0: Leading Agile Developers, Developing Agile Leaders. rev. ed. 2010. (Addison-Wesley Signature Series (Cohn) Ser.). (ENG.). 464p. pap. 47.99 *(978-0-321-71247-9(1))* Addison Wesley Professional.

Berridge, Eric & Kirven, Michael. Iterate or Die: Agile Consulting for 21st Century Business Success. 2008. 188p. 24.99 *(978-1-4389-1223-3(4))* AuthorHouse.

Beyer, Hugh. Contextual Design for Agile Teams. Carroll, John, ed. 2010. (Synthesis Lectures on Human-Centered Informatics Ser.). 71p. pap. 25.00 *(978-1-60845-372-6(3))* Morgan & Claypool Pubs.

Bhandarkar, Jagdish. Scrum Software Development. 2012. (Infosys Press Ser.). (ENG., Illus.). 275p. pap. 49.95 *(978-1-4398-2699-7(4),* CRC Press) Taylor & Francis Group GBR. Dist: Taylor & Francis Group.

Boyer, Jérôme & Mili, Hafedh. Agile Business Rule Development: Process, Architecture, & JRules Examples. 2011. xxvi, 567p. 59.95 *(978-3-642-19040-7(5),* 3642190405) Springer.

Buresh, Donald. Customer Satisfaction & Agile Methods: Assessing Customer Satisfaction & Agile Project Management Methods. 2008. 208p. pap. *(978-3-639-09476-3(X))* VDM Verlag Dr. Mueller e.K.

Butterworth, Kevin. Enhancing the Collection of Treatment Outcomes Data Through Canisc. 2010. 108p. pap. *(978-3-8383-8665-2(5))* Lambert Academic Publishing.

Carroll, John. Agile Project Management in Easy Steps. 2012. (In Easy Steps Ser.). (ENG., Illus.). 192p. pap. 14.99 ***(978-1-84078-447-3(4))*** Computer Step GBR. Dist: Perseus-PGW.

Cauldwell, Patrick. Code Leader: Using People, Tools, & Processes to Build Successful Software. 2008. (ENG., Illus.). 233p. pap. 39.99 *(978-0-470-25924-5(8),* Wrox) Wiley, John & Sons, Inc.

Cockburn, Alistair. Agile Software Development: The Cooperative Game. 2nd rev. ed. 2006. (Agile Software Development Ser.). (ENG., Illus.). 504p. per. 59.99 *(978-0-321-48275-4(1))* Addison-Wesley Longman, Inc.

Cohen, Greg. Agile Excellence for Product Managers: A Guide to Creating Winning Products with Agile Development Teams. 2010. 152p. pap. 24.95 *(978-1-60773-074-3(X),* Super Star Pr.) Happy About.

Crispin, Lisa & Gregory, Janet. Agile Testing: A Practical Guide for Testers & Agile Teams. 2008. (Addison-Wesley Signature Series (Cohn) Ser.). (ENG., Illus.). 576p. pap. 57.99 *(978-0-321-53446-0(8))* Addison Wesley Professional.

Davies, Rachel & Sedley, Liz. Agile Coaching. 2009. (ENG., Illus.). 250p. pap. 34.95 *(978-1-934356-43-2(3),* Pragmatic Bookshelf, The) Pragmatic Programmers, LLC, The.

Dingsoyr, Torgeir, et al. Agile Software Development: Current Research & Future Directions. 2010. (ENG., Illus.). xvii, 240p. 89.95 *(978-3-642-12574-4(3),* 3642125743) Springer.

Douglass, Bruce Powel. Real-Time Agility: The Harmony/ESW Method for Real-Time & Embedded Systems Development. 2009. (ENG., Illus.). 560p. pap. 54.99 *(978-0-321-54549-7(4))* Addison Wesley Professional.

Eckstein, Jutta. Agile Software Development with Distributed Teams: Staying Agile in a Global World. 2010. *(978-0-932633-71-2(4))* Dorset Hse. Publishing.

Elssamadisy, Amr. Agile Adoption Patterns: A Roadmap to Organizational Success. 2008. (Illus.). 408p. pap. 49.99 *(978-0-321-51452-3(1))* Addison Wesley Professional.

Farnham, Aaron, et al. Merb: What You Need to Know. 2009. 120p. pap. 19.99 *(978-1-4302-1865-4(7))* Apress L. P.

Gärtner, Markus. ATDD by Example: A Practical Guide to Acceptance Test-Driven Development. rev. ed. 2012. (Addison-Wesley Signature Series (Beck) Ser.). (ENG.). 224p. pap. 34.99 ***(978-0-321-78415-5(4))*** Addison Wesley Professional.

Gulati, Vinay & Das, Sudhendu. The CMMI for Agile Management of Projects, Programs, & Governance: An Adaptive Process Framework. 2010. 69.95 *(978-1-4200-8631-7(6))* Auerbach Pubs., Inc.

Hazzan, Orit & Dubinsky, Yael. Agile Software Engineering. 2008. (Undergraduate Topics in Computer Science Ser.). (Illus.). 305p. pap. 39.95 *(978-1-84800-198-5(3))* Springer.

Hibbs, Curt, et al. The Art of Lean Software Development: A Practical & Incremental Approach. 2009. (ENG., Illus.). 144p. pap. 34.99 *(978-0-596-51731-1(9))* O'Reilly Media, Inc.

Highsmith, Jim. Agile Project Management: Creating Innovative Products. 2nd ed. 2009. (Agile Software Development Ser.). (ENG., Illus.). 432p. pap. 49.99 *(978-0-321-65839-5(6))* Addison Wesley Professional.

Holcombe, Mike & Holcombe, W. M. L. Running an Agile Software Development Project. 2008. (ENG., Illus.). 312p. 94.95 *(978-0-470-13669-0(3),* Wiley) Wiley, John & Sons, Inc.

Holtsnider, Bill, et al. Agile Development & Business Goals: The Six Week Solution. 2010. (ENG., Illus.). 256p. pap. 41.95 *(978-0-12-381520-0(7),* Morgan Kaufmann) Elsevier Science & Technology Bks.

Huttermann, Michael. Agile Alm: Lightweight tools & Agile Strategies. 2011. (ENG.). 360p. pap. 54.99 *(978-1-935182-63-4(3))* Manning Pubns. Co.

Keith, Clinton. Agile Game Development with Scrum. rev. ed. 2010. (Addison-Wesley Signature Series (Cohn) Ser.). (ENG., Illus.). 384p. pap. 44.99 *(978-0-321-61852-8(1))* Addison Wesley Professional.

Kelly, Allan. Changing Software Development: Learning to Become Agile. 2008. (ENG., Illus.). 258p. pap. 60.00 *(978-0-470-51504-4(X),* Wiley) Wiley, John & Sons, Inc.

Kniberg, Henrik. Lean from the Trenches: Managing Large-Scale Projects with Kanban. 2011. (ENG.). 176p. pap. 30.00 ***(978-1-934356-85-2(9),*** Pragmatic Bookshelf, The) Pragmatic Programmers, LLC, The.

Kniberg, Henrik & Skarin, Mattias. Kanban & Scrum - making the most of Both. 2010. (Illus.). 120p. pap. 22.95 *(978-0-557-13832-6(9))* Lulu Enterprises Inc.

Lacey, Mitch. The Scrum Field Guide: Practical Advice for Your First Year. 2012. (Agile Software Development Ser.). (ENG.). 416p. pap. 42.99 ***(978-0-321-55415-4(9))*** Addison Wesley Professional.

Langr, Jeff & Ottinger, Tim. Agile in a Flash: Speed-Learning Agile Software Development. 2011. (ENG.). 110p. pap. 15.00 *(978-1-934356-71-5(9),* Pragmatic Bookshelf, The) Pragmatic Programmers, LLC, The.

Larman, Craig & Vodde, Bas. Practices for Scaling Lean & Agile Development: Large, Multisite, & Offshore Product Development with Large-Scale Scrum. 2010. (ENG., Illus.). 624p. pap. 54.99 *(978-0-321-63640-9(6))* Addison Wesley Professional.

—Scaling Lean & Agile Development: Thinking & Organizational Tools for Large-Scale Scrum. 2008. (Agile Software Development Ser.). (ENG., Illus.). 368p. pap. 54.99 *(978-0-321-48096-5(1))* Addison Wesley Professional.

Layton, Mark C. & Maurer, Rachele. Agile Project Management for Dummies. 2012. (ENG.). 360p. pap. 29.99 *(978-1-118-02624-3(1),* For Dummies) Wiley, John & Sons, Inc.

Leffingwell, Dean. Scaling Software Agility: Best Practices for Large Enterprises. 2007. (Agile Software Development Ser.). (ENG., Illus.). 384p. pap. 54.99 *(978-0-321-45819-3(2))* Addison Wesley Professional.

Levine, Michael K. A Tale of Two Transformations: Bringing Lean & Agile Software Development to Life. 2011. (ENG., Illus.). 323p. 59.95 ***(978-1-4398-7975-7(3))*** Productivity Pr.

Madeyski, Lech. Test-Driven Development: An Empirical Evaluation of Agile Practice. 2009. (ENG., Illus.). xx, 245p. 99.00 *(978-3-642-04287-4(2),* 3642042872) Springer.

McMahon, Paul E. Integrating CMMI & Agile Development: Case Studies & Proven Techniques for Faster Performance Improvement. 2010. (SEI Series in Software Engineering Ser.). (ENG., Illus.). 368p. pap. 49.99 *(978-0-321-71410-7(5))* Addison Wesley Professional.

Microsoft Press Staff & Krebs, Jochen. Agile Portfolio Management. 2008. (ENG.). 240p. pap. 34.99 *(978-0-7356-2567-9(0))* Microsoft Pr.

Muhammed, Idris Zehrudin. Lean & Agile Manufacturing Systems. 2009. 132p. pap. *(978-3-639-19115-8(3))* VDM Verlag Dr. Mueller e.K.

Patton, Jeff. User Story Mapping. 2012. (ENG.). 50p. pap. 29.99 *(978-1-4493-0455-3(9))* O'Reilly Media, Inc.

Pham, Andrew & Pham, Phuong-Van 'Kym'. Scrum in Action. 2011. (ENG.). 320p. pap. 39.99 *(978-1-4354-5913-7(X))* Course Technology.

Pichler, Roman. Agile Product Management with Scrum: Creating Products That Customers Love. 2010. (Addison-Wesley Signature Ser.). (ENG., Illus.). 160p. pap. 34.99 *(978-0-321-60578-8(0))* Addison Wesley Professional.

Pugh, Kenneth. Lean-Agile Acceptance Test-Driven Development: Better Software Through Collaboration. 4th rev. ed. 2010. (Net Objectives Lean-Agile Ser.). (ENG., Illus.). 368p. pap. 39.99 *(978-0-321-71408-4(3))* Addison Wesley Professional.

Ratcliffe, Lindsay & McNeill, Marc. Agile Experience Design: A Digital Designer's Guide to Agile, Lean, & Continuous. 2011. (ENG., Illus.). 320p. pap. 44.99 ***(978-0-321-80481-5(3))*** New Riders Publishing.

Resnick, Steve, et al. Professional Scrum with Team Foundation Server 2010. 2011. (ENG., Illus.). 336p. pap. 44.99 *(978-0-470-94333-5(5),* Wrox) Wiley, John & Sons, Inc.

Rico, David F., et al. The Business Value of Agile Software Methods: Maximizing ROI with Just-In-Time Processes & Documentation. 2009. 280p. *(978-1-60427-031-0(4))* Ross, J. Publishing, Inc.

Roebuck, Kevin. Agile Software Development: High-impact Strategies - What You Need to Know. 2011. 454p. pap. ***(978-1-74304-483-4(6),*** Tebbo) Emereo Pty Ltd.

Rubin, Kenneth S. Scrum: A Manager's Guide: A Non-technical Introduction to the Most Popular Agile Process. rev. ed. 2012. (Addison-Wesley Signature Series (Cohn) Ser.). (ENG.). 504p. pap. 44.99 ***(978-0-13-704329-3(5))*** Addison Wesley Professional.

Rumpe, Bernhard. Agile Modellierung mit UML: Codegenerierung, Testfälle, Refactoring. 2006. (Xpert. press Ser.). (Illus.). XIV, 334p. 69.95 *(978-3-540-20905-8(0),* 3540209050) Springer.

Russo, Barbara. Agile Technologies in Open Source Development. 2009. 388p. 180.00 *(978-1-59904-681-5(4))* IGI Global.

Schiel, James. Certified ScrumMaster: The CSM Study Guide. 2011. (Applied Software Engineering Ser.). (ENG., Illus.). 234p. 69.95 *(978-1-4398-5991-9(4))* Auerbach Pubs., Inc.

—Enterprise-Scale Agile Software Development. 2009. (Applied Software Engineering Ser.). (ENG., Illus.). 382p. 89.95 *(978-1-4398-0321-9(8),* CRC Press) Taylor & Francis Group GBR. Dist: Taylor & Francis Group.

Schwaber, Ken, et al. Software in 30 Days: How Agile Managers Beat the Odds, Delight Their Customers, & Leave Competitors in the Dust. 2012. (ENG.). 216p. pap. 29.95 ***(978-1-118-20666-9(5),*** Wiley) Wiley, John & Sons, Inc.

Seyam, Mohammed. Agile Methodologies in Information Systems Development. 2010. 144p. pap. *(978-3-8383-7192-4(5))* Lambert Academic Publishing.

Sfetsos, Panagiotis, ed. Agile Software Development Quality Assurance. 2007. (Illus.). 268p. 165.00 *(978-1-59904-216-9(9))* IGI Global.

Sillitti, Alberto, et al, eds. Agile Processes in Software Engineering & Extreme Programming: 11th International Conference, XP 2010, Trondheim, Norway, June 1-4, 2010, Proceedings. 2010. (Lecture Notes in Business Information Processing Ser.). xv, 418p. pap. 99.00 *(978-3-642-13053-3(4),* 3642130534) Springer.

Sliger, Michele & Broderick, Stacia. The Software Project Manager's Bridge to Agility. 2008. (Agile Software Development Ser.). (ENG., Illus.). 384p. pap. 49.99 *(978-0-321-50275-9(2))* Addison Wesley Professional.

So, Chaehan. Making Software Teams Effective: How Agile Practices Lead to Project Success Through Teamwork Mechanisms. 2010. 208p. 57.95 *(978-3-631-60337-6(1))* Lang, Peter GmbH, Europaischer Verlag der Wissenschaften DEU. Dist: Lang, Peter.

Sterling, Chris M. Managing Software Debt: Building for Inevitable Change. 2010. (Agile Software Development Ser.). (ENG., Illus.). 288p. 49.99 *(978-0-321-55413-0(2))* Addison Wesley Professional.

Stober, Thomas & Hansmann, Uwe. Agile Software Development: Best Practices for Large Software Development Projects. 2009. (ENG., Illus.). xxiii, 179p. 89.95 *(978-3-540-70830-8(8),* 3540708308) Springer.

Thimm, Rouven. Workflow Management Concepts for Agile Long-Term Workflows - Enabling Model Changes on Active Workflow Instances. 2008. 172p. per. *(978-3-8364-5038-6(0))* VDM Verlag Dr. Mueller e.K.

Tomi, Juhola. Customized Agile Development Process for Embedded Software Development: A Study of Special Characteristics of Embedded Software & Agile Development. 2011. 100p. pap. ***(978-3-639-28595-6(6))*** VDM Verlag Dr. Mueller e.K.

A

Vanbrabant, Robbie. Google Guice: Agile Lightweight Dependency Injection Framework. 2008. (FirstPress Ser.). (ENG., Illus.). 192p. pap. 19.99 *(978-1-59059-997-6(7))* Apress L. P.

Walther, Stephen, et al. Agile ASP. NET Unleashed. 2012. (Unleashed Ser.). (ENG.). 400p. pap. 44.99 ***(978-0-672-33582-2(4))*** Sams.

Watkins, John. Agile Testing: How to Succeed in an Extreme Testing Environment. 2009. (ENG., Illus.). 334p. 98.00 *(978-0-521-19181-4(5))*; pap. 49.99 *(978-0-521-72687-0(5))* Cambridge Univ. Pr.

Widrig, Don & Leffingwell, Dean. Agile Software Requirements: Lean Requirements Practices for Teams, Programs, & the Enterprise. 2010. (Agile Software Development Ser.). (ENG., Illus.). 560p. 49.99 *(978-0-321-63584-6(1))* Addison Wesley Professional.

Woodward, Elizabeth, et al. A Practical Guide to Distributed Scrum. 2010. (ENG., Illus.). 240p. pap., instr.'s gde. ed. 44.99 *(978-0-13-704113-8(6))* Pearson Education.

Younker, Jeff. Foundations of Agile Python Development. 2008. (Expert's Voice in Open Source Ser.). (ENG.). 416p. pap. 42.99 *(978-1-59059-981-5(0))* Apress L. P.

AGILITY

see Motor Ability

AGINCOURT, BATTLE OF, AGINCOURT, FRANCE, 1415

Curry, Anne. Agincourt: A New History. 2006. (ENG., Illus.). 336p. per. 27.50 *(978-0-7524-3813-9(1))* History Pr. Ltd.,The GBR. Dist: Independent Pubs. Group.

—Agincourt 1415: The Archers' Story. 2008. (ENG., Illus.). 176p. pap. 34.95 *(978-0-7524-4566-3(9))* History Pr. Ltd.,The GBR. Dist: Independent Pubs. Group.

Gillot, Christophe. Azincourt: Et la Vie Quotidienne En 1415. 2007. (FRE., Illus.). 80p. 29.95 *(978-2-84048-240-6(1))* Editions Heimdal FRA. Dist: Casemate Pubs. & Bk. Distributors, LLC.

Hawley Jarman, Rosemary. Crispin's Day - Agincourt 1415. 2011. (Illus.). 192p. 29.95 ***(978-1-4456-0233-2(4))*** Amberley Publishing GBR. Dist: Casemate Pubs. & Bk. Distributors, LLC.

AGING

see also Immortalism

Abbott, Pauline S. Re-Creating Neighborhoods for Successful Aging. Abbott, Pauline et al, eds. 2008. (Illus.). 304p. per. 38.95 *(978-1-932529-24-1(1))* Health Professions Pr.

Adams, Peter D. & Sedivy, John M., eds. Cellular Senescence & Tumor Suppression. 2009. (ENG., Illus.). xii, 272p. 159.00 *(978-1-4419-1074-5(3))*, 1441910743) Springer.

Address, Richard F. Seekers of Meaning: Baby Boomers, Judaism, & the Pursuit of Healthy Aging. 2011. ***(978-0-8074-1226-8(0))*** URJ Pr.

Agin, Brent & Perkins, Sharon. Healthy Aging for Dummies. l.t. ed. 2009. 662p. 32.95 *(978-1-4104-1454-0(X))* Thorndike Pr.

—Healthy Aging for Dummies. 2008. (ENG., Illus.). 384p. per. 21.99 *(978-0-470-14975-1(2)*, For Dummies) Wiley, John & Sons, Inc.

Agronin, Marc. How We Age: A Doctor's Journey into the Heart of Growing Old. 2012. (ENG.). 320p. pap. 15.00 ***(978-0-7382-1558-7(9))*** Da Capo Pr., Inc.

Aguilar, Mario I. Rethinking Age in Africa: Colonial, Post-Colonial, & Contemporary Interpretations of Cultural Representations. 2006. x, 322p. *(978-1-59221-494-5(0))*; pap. *(978-1-59221-495-2(9))* Africa World Pr.

Ajayi, Joel A. A. A Biblical Theology of Gerassapience. 2010. (Studies in Biblical Literature Ser.). 280p. (C). 79.95 *(978-1-4331-0785-6(6))* Lang, Peter Publishing, Inc.

Alexander, Lynn. Caregiver Tsunami, 1 vol. 2010. 54p. pap. 16.95 *(978-1-4512-0138-3(9))* PublishAmerica, Inc.

Alvarez, Julia Tavares. Speeches for the Ages. 2007. 152p. per. 20.99 *(978-1-4257-7814-9(3))* Xlibris Corp.

—Speeches for the Ages: An Ambassador Speaks out on Worldwide Aging. 2007. 152p. 30.99 *(978-1-4257-7816-3(X))* Xlibris Corp.

Amacher, Ryan C. A Baby Boomer's Guide to Their Second Sixties. 2012. pap. ***(978-0-86534-855-4(3))*** Sunstone Pr.

American Institute of Architects Design for Aging. Design for Aging. 2006. (ENG.). 240p. 65.00 *(978-1-86470-097-8(1))* Images Publishing Group AUS. Dist: National Bk. Network.

—Design for Aging, Vol. 2. 6th ed. 2006. (ENG., Illus.). 65.00 *(978-1-920744-17-5(7))* Images Publishing Group AUS. Dist: National Bk. Network.

Anderson, Nina, et al. The Secrets of Staying Young Revised. l.t. rev. ed. 2007. (ENG., Illus.). 176p. pap. 11.95 *(978-1-884820-43-4(3))* SAFE GOODS/ATN Publishing.

Angel, Jacqueline L. & Settersten, Richard A., Jr., eds. Handbook of Sociology of Aging. 2011. (Handbooks of Sociology & Social Research Ser.). (ENG.). xxv, 792p. 279.00 *(978-1-4419-7373-3(7))*, 1441973737) Springer.

Arenson, Christine & Reichel, William. Reichel's Care of the Elderly: Clinical Aspects of Aging. Arenson, Christine et al, eds. 6th rev. ed. 2009. (ENG., Illus.). 656p. 99.99 *(978-0-521-86929-4(3))* Cambridge Univ. Pr.

Arifin, Evi Nurvidya & Ananta, Aris. Older Persons in Southeast Asia: An Emerging Asset. 2009. (Illus.). xxxi, 425p. *(978-981-230-944-0(6))* Institute of Southeast Asian Studies.

Askanas, Valerie & Engel, W. King, eds. Muscle Aging, Inclusion-Body Myositis & Myopathies. 2012. (ENG., Illus.). 262p. 129.95 ***(978-1-4051-9646-8(7)***, Wiley-Blackwell) Wiley, John & Sons, Inc.

Aspinall, Richard, ed. Aging of the Organs & Systems. 2010. (Biology of Aging & its Modulation Ser.). x, 318p. pap. 189.00 *(978-90-481-6486-8(9)*, 9048164869) Springer.

Atchley, Robert C. Social Forces & Aging: An Introduction to Social Gerontology. 10th ed. 2006. (ENG.). pap. 10.95 *(978-1-4288-1749-4(2))* Cram101 Inc.

Athill, Diana. Somewhere Towards the End: A Memoir. 2009. (ENG.). 192p. 24.95 *(978-0-393-06770-5(X)*, 6770) Norton, W. W. & Co., Inc.

Atsalis, S., et al, eds. Primate Reproductive Aging: Cross-Taxon Perspectives. 2008. (Interdisciplinary Topics in Gerontology Ser.). (Illus.). 200p. *(978-3-8055-8522-4(5))* Karger, S. AG.

Austad, Steven N. & Masoro, Edward J., eds. Handbook of the Biology of Aging. 7th ed. 2010. (Handbooks of Aging Ser.). (ENG., Illus.). 520p. pap. 99.95 *(978-0-12-378638-8(X)*, Academic Pr.) Elsevier Science & Technology Bks.

Baars, Jan. Aging & the Art of Living. 2012. ***(978-1-4214-0646-6(2))***; E-Book ***(978-1-4214-0709-8(4))*** Johns Hopkins Univ. Pr.

Backman, Lars, et al. Memory, Aging & the Brain: A Festschrift in Honour of Lars-Goran Nilsson. Nyberg, Larseric, ed. 2009. (Psychology Press Festschrift Ser.). (ENG., Illus.). 368p. 90.00 *(978-1-84169-692-8(7)*, Psychology Press) Taylor & Francis Group GBR. Dist: Taylor & Francis Group.

Baker, Joseph J., et al. The Masters Athlete: Understanding the Role of Sport & Exercise in Optimizing Aging. Baker, Joseph (joe) et al, eds. 2009. (ENG., Illus.). 204p. pap. 51.95 *(978-0-415-47657-7(7))* Routledge.

Barja, Gustavo, ed. Longevity & Evolution. 2011. (Aging Issues, Health & Financial Alternatives Ser.). 208p. 89.00 *(978-1-61668-334-4(1))* Nova Science Pubs., Inc.

Barnett, Yvonne A. & Barnett, Christopher R., eds. Aging Methods & Protocols. 2010. (Methods in Molecular Medicine Ser.). (Illus.). 400p. pap. 149.00 *(978-1-61737-083-0(5)*, 1617370835) Humana Pr.

Baudisch, Annette. Inevitable Aging? Contributions to Evolutionary-Demographic Theory. (Demographic Research Monographs). (Illus.). 2010. xxii, 170p. pap. 139.00 *(978-3-642-09534-4(8)*, 3642095348) 2008. 170p. 139.00 *(978-3-540-76655-1(3))* Springer.

Bauer, M. E. & De la Fuente, M., eds. Neuroimmunomodulation & Aging. 2008. (Illus.). 180p. pap. *(978-3-8055-8979-6(4))* Karger, S. AG.

Baumgartner, Richard N., ed. Aging & Human Body Composition: Medical Measurement & Therapeutic Applications. 2009. (Aging Medicine Ser.). 300p. 125.00 *(978-1-934115-21-3(5))* Humana Pr.

Baumlin, James S. & Knickerbocker, Eric, eds. Jim W. Corder on Living & Dying in West Texas: A Postmodern Scrapbook. 2007. 15.00 *(978-0-913785-06-5(7)*, Moon City Pr.) Department of English.

Bean, Tim & Laing, Anne. Turn Back Your Age Clock: Look & Feel 20 Years Younger in Only 8 Weeks. 2009. (ENG., Illus.). 144p. pap. 14.99 *(978-0-600-61717-4(3)*, Hamlyn) Octopus Publishing Group GBR. Dist: Hachette Bk. Group.

Bengtson, Vern L. Handbook of Theories of Aging. 2nd ed. 2008. (Illus.). 800p. (C). 90.00 *(978-0-8261-6251-9(7))* Springer Publishing Co., Inc.

Bengtsson, Tommy, ed. Population Ageing - A Threat to the Welfare State? The Case of Sweden. 2010. (Demographic Research Monographs). (Illus.). xv, 123p. 139.00 *(978-3-642-12611-6(1)*, 3642126111) Springer.

Bennett, Robert F., ed. Getting Older, Staying Healthier: The Demographics of Health Care: Congressional Hearing. 2006. (Illus.). 82p. (C). reprint ed. pap. 25.00 *(978-1-4223-0600-0(3))* DIANE Publishing Co.

Benninghouse, Harriet T. & Rosset, Andria G., eds. Women & Aging: New Research. 2008. (Illus.). xxv, 691p. 315.00 *(978-1-60456-575-1(6))* Nova Science Pubs., Inc.

Bentely, Jennifer V. & Keller, Mary Ann. Handbook on Longevity: Genetics, Diet & Disease. 2009. (Illus.). xvii, 495p. 195.00 *(978-1-60741-075-1(3))* Nova Science Pubs., Inc.

Biddle, Sue. Memories. 2011. 24p. pap. 12.99 ***(978-0-557-38583-6(0))*** Lulu Enterprises Inc.

Biegert, John E. So We're Growing Older. 2009. 24p. pap. 4.00 *(978-1-60608-216-4(7))* Wipf & Stock Pubs.

Biggs, Simon & Lowenstein, Ariela. Generational Intelligence. 2011. (ENG.). 200p. (C). 130.00 *(978-0-415-54654-6(0))* Routledge.

—Generational Intelligence: A Critical Approach to Age Relations. 2011. (ENG.). 200p. (C). pap. 39.95 *(978-0-415-54655-3(9))* Routledge.

Binstock, Robert H. & George, Linda K., eds. Handbook of Aging & the Social Sciences. 7th ed. 2010. (Handbooks of Aging Ser.). (ENG., Illus.). 388p. pap. 99.95 *(978-0-12-380880-6(4)*, Academic Pr.) Elsevier Science & Technology Bks.

Biology of Aging. 2013. pap. 120.00 ***(978-0-8153-4213-7(6)***, Garland Science) Taylor & Francis Group.

Black, Kathy & Elkins, Heather Murray, eds. Wising Up: Ritual Resources for Women of Faith in Their Journey of Aging. 2010. 192p. pap. 22.00 *(978-1-60899-226-3(8)*, Wipf and Stock) Wipf & Stock Pubs.

Black, Sue, et al, eds. Age Estimation in the Living: The Practitioner's Guide. 2010. (ENG., Illus.). 318p. instr.'s gde. ed. 139.95 *(978-0-470-51967-7(3)*, Wiley) Wiley, John & Sons, Inc.

Blake, Quentin. You're Only Young Twice. 2010. (ENG., Illus.). 48p. (J). 14.99 *(978-1-84270-856-9(2))* Andersen GBR. Dist: Independent Pubs. Group.

Blanchard, Eliza. The Seasoned Soul: Reflections on Growing Older. 2012. (ENG.). 184p. pap. 14.00 ***(978-1-55896-662-8(5))***; E-Book ***(978-1-55896-663-5(3))*** Unitarian Universalist Assn. (Skinner Hse. Bks.).

Blanchette. Prevention of the Disease of Aging. 2007. 260p. (ENG.). 25.99 *(978-1-60266-557-6(5))*; per. 15.99 *(978-1-60266-079-3(4))* Xulon Pr., Inc.

Blando. Counseling Older Adults. 2010. (ENG., Illus.). 442p. pap. 39.95 *(978-0-415-99051-6(3))* Routledge.

Bludau, Juergen. Aging, but Never Old: The Realities, Myths, & Misrepresentations of the Anti-Aging Movement, 1 vol. 2010. (Praeger Series on Contemporary Health & Living Ser.). (Illus.). 179p. 44.95 *(978-0-313-38018-1(X)*, A2055C, Praeger Pubs.) Greenwood Publishing Group, Inc.

—Aging, but Never Old: The Realities, Myths, & Misrepresentations of the Anti-Aging Movement. 2010. (Illus.). xiv, 179p. E-Book *(978-0-313-38019-8(8)*, Praeger Pubs.) Greenwood Publishing Group, Inc.

Bond, John, et al, eds. Ageing in Society. 3rd ed. 2007. (Illus.). 384p. (C). 146.00 *(978-1-4129-0019-5(0)*, B00190C); per. 62.00 *(978-1-4129-0020-1(4)*, B00190P) SAGE Pubns., Ltd. GBR. Dist: SAGE Pubns., Inc.

Bondy, Stephen & Maiese, Kenneth, eds. Studies on Aging. 2010. (Oxidative Stress in Applied Basic Research & Clinical Practice Ser.). (ENG., Illus.). xvi, 472p. 239.00 *(978-1-60761-601-6(7)*, 1607616017) Humana Pr.

Bortz, Walter M. & Bortz, Walter M., II. We Live Too Short & Die Too Long: How to Achieve & Enjoy Your Natural 100-Year-Plus Life Span. 2007. 292p. per. 14.95 *(978-1-59079-116-5(9))* Select Bks.

Botelho, Lynn, et al, eds. The History of Old Age in England, 1600-1800, Part I, 4 vols., Vols. 1-4. 2008. (ENG.). 1232p. 625.00 *(978-1-85196-869-5(5))* Pickering & Chatto Pubs., Ltd. GBR. Dist: Ashgate Publishing Co.

Bottke, Allison. Setting Boundaries with Your Aging Parents: Finding Balance Between Burnout & Respect. 2010. 240p. pap. 12.99 *(978-0-7369-2674-4(7))* Harvest Hse. Pubs.

Bottomley, Jennifer. Geriatric Rehabilitation: A Textbook for the Physical Therapist Assistant. 2010. (ENG., Illus.). 368p. (C). 65.95 *(978-1-55642-816-6(2))* SLACK, Inc.

Bouwer, J., ed. Successful Aging, Spirituality & Meaning: Multidisciplinary Perspectives. 2010. (Studies in Spirituality Supplements Ser.). (ENG.). 284p. (C). pap. 70.00 *(978-90-429-2268-6(0))* Peeters Pubs. & Booksellers BEL. Dist: Brown, David Bk. Co., The.

Brancato, Fred. Ancient Wisdom & the Measure of Our Days: The Spiritual Dimensions of Retirement, Aging & Loss. 2009. 60p. pap. 12.95 *(978-1-60693-702-0(2)*, Strategic Bk. Publishing) AEG Literary Publishing Services, Inc.

Breitenbach, Michael, et al, eds. Aging Research in Yeast. 2011. (Subcellular Biochemistry Ser.). (ENG., Illus.). xii, 365p. 239.00 ***(978-94-007-2560-7(4)***, 9400725604) Springer.

Brewster, Joy. Diminishment: A Memoir. 2011. 19.95 ***(978-1-894667-88-3(3))*** Clements Publishing.

Brhel, Susan. The Bio-Psychosocial Approach to Therapeutic Activities & Successful Aging: A Guide for Professionals Working with the Geriatric Population. 2006. per. 49.95 *(978-0-9779214-0-9(9))* Goals Seminars and Consultants.

Brinkley, Shirley W. Help! Help! When Did This Happen? I Can't be 60-years-old, I just Graduated from High School. 2006. 150p. pap. 13.75 *(978-0-9676547-1-3(8))* Brinkley, Shirley W.

Brougham, Ruby R., ed. New Directions in Aging Research: Health & Cognition. 2009. (Aging Issues, Health & Financial Alternatives Ser.). (Illus.). xvii, 200p. 89.00 *(978-1-60741-976-1(9)*, Nova Biomedical Bks.) Nova Science Pubs., Inc.

Brown, Guy. The Living End: The Future of Death, Aging & Immortality. rev. ed. 2007. (MacSci Ser.). (ENG., Illus.). 240p. 24.95 *(978-0-230-51757-8(9))* Palgrave Macmillan.

Buchanan, Missy. Aging Faithfully: 28 Days of Prayer. 2011. 10.00 *(978-0-8358-1063-0(1))* Upper Room Bks.

Burda, Angela N. Communication & Swallowing Changes in Healthy Aging Adults. rev. ed. 2010. 194p. pap. 61.95 *(978-0-7637-7656-5(4))* Jones & Bartlett Learning, LLC.

Burdette, Carol Janice. Polish Your Golden Years. 2010. 130p. pap. 10.95 *(978-1-60860-805-8(0)*, Eloquent Bks.) AEG Literary Publishing Services, Inc.

Bustad, Leo K. Animals, Aging, & the Aged. 2009. (ENG.). 248p. pap. 50.00 *(978-0-8166-5716-2(5))* Univ. of Minnesota Pr.

Cambron, Jeff, et al, eds. Grant Funding for Elderly Health Services. 6th ed. 2008. (Illus.). 170p. pap. 189.00 *(978-1-882364-84-8(8))* Health Resources Publishing.

Carey, J. R., et al. Longevity & Frailty. 2010. (Research & Perspectives in Longevity Ser.). (Illus.). xii, 161p. pap. 169.00 *(978-3-642-06429-6(9)*, 3642064299) Springer.

Carlisle, Anthony. An Essay on the Disorders of Old Age, & on the Means for Prolonging Human Life. 2009. 76p. pap. 16.95 *(978-1-104-01369-1(X))* Kessinger Publishing, LLC.

Carmel, Sara, ed. Aging in Israel: Research, Policy & Practice. 2009. (ENG., Illus.). 503p. 79.95 *(978-1-4128-1164-4(3))*; pap. 34.95 *(978-1-4128-1165-1(1))* Transaction Pubs.

Carr, Dawn C. & Komp, Kathrin. Gerontology in the ERA of the Third Age: Implications & Next Steps. 2011. (Illus.). 296p. *(978-0-8261-0596-7(3))*; xv, 269p. E-Book *(978-0-8261-0597-4(1))* Springer Publishing Co., Inc.

Carstensen, Laura. A Long Bright Future. 2011. (ENG., Illus.). 352p. pap. 15.99 *(978-1-61039-057-6(1))* PublicAffairs.

Cavallotti, Carlo & Cerulli, Luciano, eds. Age-Related Changes of the Human Eye. 2010. (Aging Medicine Ser.). (Illus.). xiii, 410p. pap. 229.00 *(978-1-61737-936-9(0)*, 1617379360) Humana Pr.

Cavanaugh, John C. & Blanchard-Fields, Fredda. Adult Development & Aging. 6th ed. 2010. (ENG.). 640p. (C). 206.95 *(978-0-495-60174-6(8))* Wadsworth.

Center for Economic, Governance, and International Studies & National Research Council. Grand Challenges of Our Aging Society: Workshop Summary. 2010. (ENG.). 88p. pap. 21.00 *(978-0-309-15010-1(8))* National Academies Pr.

Chan, Y. S. & He, J., eds. Recent Advances in Vestibulo-Auditory Neurobiology. (Illus.). 96p. pap. *(978-3-8055-8227-8(7))* Karger, S. AG.

Chanson, P., et al, eds. Endocrine Aspects of Successful Aging: Genes, Hormones & Lifestyles: Genes, Hormones & Lifestyles. 2010. (Research & Perspectives in Endocrine Interactions Ser.). (Illus.). xii, 231p. pap. 169.00 *(978-3-642-07359-5(X)*, 364207359X) Springer.

Cheyne, George. An Essay of Health & Long Life. 2009. 108p. pap. *(978-0-217-16681-2(4))* Books LLC.

—An Essay of Health & Long Life. 2007. (ENG.). 280p. 42.95 *(978-0-548-33948-0(1))*; per. 27.95 *(978-1-4326-9887-4(7))* Kessinger Publishing, LLC.

Chinese Academy of Social Sciences, et al. Preparing for the Challenges of Population Aging in Asia: Strengthening the Scientific Basis of Policy Development. 2010. (ENG., Illus.). 28p. pap. 15.00 *(978-0-309-15937-1(7))* National Academies Pr.

Chodzko-Zajko, Wojtek, et al. Enhancing Cognitive Functioning & Brain Plasticity. 2009. (ENG., Illus.). 248p. 51.00 *(978-0-7360-5791-2(9))* Human Kinetics Pubs.

Chopra, Deepak. Cuerpos Sin Edad, Mentes Sin Tiempo. 2009.Tr. of Ageless Bodies, Timeless Minds. 430p. pap. 12.95 *(978-84-96778-81-8(9))* Ediciones B ESP. Dist: Ediciones Urano S. A.

Christner-Lile, Donna. Aging in Place: Safely Living in Your Home Sweet Home until You're 100+ 2011. pap. 11.99 ***(978-1-61777-603-8(3))*** Tate Publishing & Enterprises, LLC.

Cockerham, William C. This Aging Society. 2nd ed. 2009. (ENG.). (C). pap. 65.13 *(978-0-205-70385-2(2)*, Prentice Hall) Prentice Hall PTR.

Cohen, Barney & Menken, Jane A., eds. Aging in Sub-Saharan Africa: Recommendations for Furthering Research. 2006. (ENG., Illus.). 368p. pap. 73.25 *(978-0-309-10281-0(2))* National Academies Pr.

Cohen, Patricia. In Our Prime: The Invention of Middle Age. (ENG.). 2013. 304p. pap. 16.00 ***(978-1-4165-7290-9(2))*** 2012. (Illus.). 320p. 25.00 *(978-1-4165-7289-3(9))* Scribner. (Scribner).

Cole, Thomas R., et al, eds. A Guide to Humanistic Studies in Aging: What Does It Mean to Grow Old? 2010. (ENG., Illus.). 400p. (gr. 17). 60.00 *(978-0-8018-9433-6(6))* Johns Hopkins Univ. Pr.

Coleman, Peter. Belief & Ageing: Spiritual Pathways in Later Life. 2011. (Policy Press - Ageing & the Lifecourse Ser.). 192p. 99.00 *(978-1-84742-460-0(0))*; pap. 42.95 *(978-1-84742-459-4(7))* Policy Pr. GBR. Dist: Chicago Distribution Ctr.

Collins, Jan & Warner, Jan. Next Steps: A Practical Guide to Planning for the Best Half of Your Life. 2009. (Best Half of Life Ser.). (ENG.). 258p. pap. 14.95 *(978-1-884956-96-6(3))* Linden Publishing Co., Inc.

Cook, Ian Gillespie & Halsall, Jamie. Aging in Comparative Perspective: Processes & Policies. 2011. (International Perspectives on Aging Ser.). (ENG., Illus.). viii, 94p. 129.00 ***(978-1-4614-1977-8(8)***, 1461419778) Springer.

Copeland, Gloria. Live Long, Finish Strong: The Divine Secret to Living Healthy, Happy, & Healed. (ENG.). 272p. 2011. pap., pap. 13.99 *(978-0-446-55927-0(X))* 2010. 21.99 *(978-0-446-55928-7(8))* FaithWords.

Corte Franco, Georgina, et al. Environmental Actigraphy a New Concept to Evaluate Elderly People. 2011. 196p. pap. ***(978-3-8443-1059-7(2))*** Lambert Academic Publishing.

Coulmas, Florian. Population Decline & Ageing in Japan: The Social Consequences. 2007. (Routledge Contemporary Japan Ser.). (Illus.). 167p. 150.00 *(978-0-415-40125-8(9))* Routledge.

Cox, Harold. Annual Editions: Aging 11/12. 24th ed. 2011. (Annual Editions Ser.). (ENG., Illus.). 192p. (C). pap. 44.00 *(978-0-07-805086-2(3)*, 0078050863, McGraw-Hill/Dushkin) McGraw-Hill Higher Education.

Cox, Harold. Annual Editions: Aging 12/13. 25th ed. 2012. (Annual Editions Ser.). (ENG., Illus.). 176p. (C). pap. 44.00 ***(978-0-07-805120-3(7)***, 0078051207, McGraw-Hill/Dushkin) McGraw-Hill Higher Education.

Cox, Harold G. Later Life: The Realities of Aging. 6th ed. 2006. pap. 10.95 *(978-1-4288-1820-0(0))* Cram101 Inc.

Craik, Fergus I. M. & Salthouse, Timothy A. The Handbook of Aging & Cognition. Craik, Fergus I. M. & Salthouse, Timothy A., eds. 3rd ed. 2007. (ENG., Illus.). 672p. 136.95 *(978-0-8058-5990-4(X)*, Psychology Press) Taylor & Francis Group GBR. Dist: Taylor & Francis Group.

Cram101 Textbook Reviews. Outlines & Highlights for Adulthood & Aging by Marion G Mason, Isbn: 9780205433513. 2011. 160p. pap. 29.95 ***(978-1-61461-902-4(6))*** Cram101 Inc.

—Outlines & Highlights for Aging Well by May L Wykle. 2011. 78p. pap. 27.95 ***(978-1-4672-6702-1(3))*** Cram101 Inc.

—Outlines & Highlights for Basic Geriatric Nursing by Wold. 2011. 136p. pap. 28.95 ***(978-1-61906-189-7(9))*** Cram101 Inc.

—Outlines & Highlights for Geriatric Rehabilitation: A Clinical Approach by Carole B. Lewis. 2010. 306p. pap. 32.95 *(978-1-4288-5289-1(1))* Cram101 Inc.

Cram101 Textbook Reviews. Outlines & Highlights for Social Work with Older Adults by Kathleen Mcinnis-Dittrich, Isbn: 9780205593606 0205593607. 2011. 166p. pap. 29.95 ***(978-1-61812-460-9(9))*** Cram101 Inc.

Cram101 Textbook Reviews & Cram101 Textbook Reviews. Outlines & Highlights for Aging: Concepts & Controversies by Harry R. Moody, ISBN. 2011. 104p. pap. 28.95 ***(978-1-61744-980-2(6))*** Cram101 Inc.

—Outlines & Highlights for Hdev by Spencer a Rathus. 2011. 116p. pap. 28.95 ***(978-1-61830-318-9(X))*** Cram101 Inc.

—Outlines & Highlights for Hdev by Spencer a Rathus, Isbn: 9780495601524. 2011. 136p. pap. 28.95 (978-1-61744-872-0(9)) Cram101 Inc.
—Outlines & Highlights for Issues in Aging by Mark Novak, Isbn: 9780205578696. 2011. 152p. pap. 29.95 (978-1-61744-999-4(7)) Cram101 Inc.
—Outlines & Highlights for Toward Healthy Aging by Ann Schmidt Luggen. 2011. 416p. pap. 35.95 (978-1-61830-731-6(2)) Cram101 Inc.
Cram101 Textbook Reviews Staff. Outlines & Highlights for Human Aging by Foos, Isbn: 0205544010. 2008. 216p. pap. 13.95 (978-1-4288-5930-2(6)) Cram101 Inc.
—Outlines & Highlights for Issues in Aging by Novak, Isbn: 0205439187. 2008. 96p. pap. 10.95 (978-1-4288-6238-8(2)) Cram101 Inc.
—Outlines & Highlights for Social Gerontology: A Multidisciplinary Perspective by Hooyman, ISBN. 2008. 120p. pap. 11.95 (978-1-4288-6090-2(8)) Cram101 Inc.
Cravit, David. The New Old: How the Boomers Are Changing Everything... Again. 2008. (ENG., Illus.). 300p. pap. 19.95 (978-1-55022-843-4(9)) ECW Pr. CAN. Dist: Independent Pubs. Group.
Crews, Douglas E. Human Senescence: Evolutionary & Biocultural Perspectives. 2011. (Cambridge Studies in Biological & Evolutionary Anthropology Ser.). (ENG., Illus.). 302p. (C). pap. 39.99 (978-0-521-18231-7(X)) Cambridge Univ. Pr.
Cromack, George. Ageing Well: A Guide to Rejuvenation & Longevity. 2009. 148p. pap. 15.95 (978-1-4327-3365-0(6)) Outskirts Pr., Inc.
Crowe, Patty. Quotes on the Beauty of Aging. Wertz, Laura, ed. & tr. by. 2009. (ENG.). 50p. pap. 8.95 (978-0-9776269-3-9(8)) Richer Resources Pubns.
Csatari, Jeff. Your Best Body at 40+ The 4-Week Plan to Get Back in Shape-and Stay Fit Forever! 2009. (978-1-60529-455-1(1)) Rodale Pr., Inc.
Curing the Cause & Preventing Disease: A New Approach to the Diagnosis & Treatment of Illness & Aging with Functional Diagnostic Medicine. 2007. (978-0-9796135-0-0(7)) Curing the Cause Enterprise.
D'Adamo, Peter J. & Whitney, Catherine. Aging: Fight It with the Blood Type Diet - The Individualized Plan for Preventing & Treating Brain Impairment, Hormonal Deficiency, & the Loss of Vitality Associated with Advancing Years. 2007. (ENG.). 256p. (gr. 12-18). 6.99 (978-0-425-21341-4(2), Berkley) Penguin Group (USA) Inc.
Dannefer, Dale & Phillipson, Chris R., eds. The SAGE Handbook of Social Gerontology. 2010. (Illus.). 712p. 150.00 (978-1-4129-3464-0(8), B34648C) SAGE Pubns., Ltd. GBR. Dist: SAGE Pubns., Inc.
Davis, Mary-Ann. Alzheimer's Disease Mortality. 2008. 220p. pap. (978-3-639-06536-7(0)) VDM Verlag Dr. Mueller e.K.
de Grey, Aubrey, et al. Ending Aging: The Rejuvenation Breakthroughs That Could Reverse Human Aging in Our Lifetime. 2008. (ENG., Illus.). 448p. pap. 16.99 (978-0-312-36707-7(4), St. Martin's Griffin) St. Martin's Pr.
Diekemper, Lou Dunn. Let Us Share: A Conversation on Growing Older. 2007. (ENG.). 192p. 17.95 (978-1-933538-76-1(7)) Synergy Bks.
Dowling, John. The Great Brain Debate: Nature or Nurture? 2007. (Science Essentials Ser.). (ENG., Illus.). 200p. per. 20.95 (978-0-691-13310-2(7)) Princeton Univ. Pr.
Downs, Marion. Shut up & Live! 2007. (ENG.). 144p. (gr. 12-18). 12.95 (978-1-58333-292-4(8), Avery) Penguin Group (USA) Inc.
Drabble, Margaret. The Pattern in the Carpet: A Personal History with Jigsaws. 2009. (ENG., Illus.). 368p. 25.00 (978-0-547-24144-9(5)) Houghton Mifflin Harcourt Trade & Reference Pubs.
Dulmus, Catherine N. & Blackburn, James A., eds. Handbook of Gerontology: Evidence-Based Approaches to Theory, Practice, & Policy. 2007. (Wiley Desktop Editions Ser.). (ENG., Illus.). 600p. 110.00 (978-0-471-77170-8(8), Wiley) Wiley, John & Sons, Inc.
Durrett, Charles. Senior Cohousing: A Community Approach to Independent Living. 2nd ed. 2009. (ENG., Illus.). 320p. pap., instr.'s hndbk. ed. 34.95 (978-0-86571-611-7(0), 9780865716117) New Society Pubs., Ltd. CAN. Dist: Consortium Bk. Sales & Distribution.
Eggleston, Karen & Tuljapurkar, Shripad, eds. Aging Asia: The Economic & Social Implications of Rapid Demographic Change in China, Japan, & South Korea. 2011. (ENG., Illus.). 360p. pap. 28.95 (978-1-931368-20-9(1)) Shorenstein, Walter H. Asia-Pacific Research Ctr.
Ekeanyanwu, Chukwuma & ONUIGBO, Adaku. The Theories of Aging. 2011. 224p. pap. (978-3-8443-2160-9(8)) Lambert Academic Publishing.
Ellor, James W. Methods in Religion, Spirituality & Aging. 2009. (ENG.). 246p. instr.'s hndbk. ed. 130.00 (978-0-415-99509-2(4)) Routledge.
Elm, Dorothee. Alterstopoi: Das Wissen von den Lebensaltern in Literatur, Kunst und Theologie. Elm, Dorothee et al, eds. 2009.Tr. of Topoi of Man's Ages. the knowledge of Life Stages in Literature, Art & Theology. (GER., Illus.). VI, 346p. 126.00 (978-3-11-020845-0(8)) De Gruyter, Walter Inc.
Elsersawi. Biochemistry of Aging: Wellness & Longevity. 2010. 340p. pap. 27.95 (978-1-4490-7380-0(8)) AuthorHouse.
Emann, A. T. It Ain't Easy Getting Old. 2009. 48p. pap. 9.95 (978-1-60693-968-0(8), Eloquent Bks.) AEG Literary Publishing Services, Inc.
Ephron, Nora. I Feel Bad about My Neck: And Other Thoughts on Being a Woman. l.t. ed. 2008. (ENG.). 176p. (YA). pap. 13.95 (978-1-59413-275-9(5), Large Print Pr.) Thorndike Pr.
Erwin, Joseph M. & Hof, Patrick R., eds. Aging in Non-Human Primates, Vol. 31. (Interdisciplinary Topics in Gerontology Ser.: Vol. 31). (Illus.). (978-3-8055-7312-2(X)) Karger, S. AG.
Fahy, Gregory M., et al, eds. The Future of Aging: Pathways to Human Life Extension. 2010. (ENG.). 900p. 279.00 (978-90-481-3998-9(8), 9048139988) Springer.
Fairley, Josephine & Stacey, Sarah. Feel Fab Forever: The Anti-Ageing Health & Beauty Bible. rev. ed. 2008. (ENG., Illus.). 256p. pap. (978-1-85626-685-7(0)) Cathie, Kyle Ltd. GBR. Dist: Independent Pubs. Group.
Farley, Alistair, et al. The Physiological Effects of Ageing. 2011. (ENG., Illus.). 232p. pap. 45.99 (978-1-4051-8073-3(0), Wiley-Blackwell) Wiley, John & Sons, Inc.
Feller, Irwin. A Strategy for Assessing Science: Behavioral & Social Research on Aging. Stern, Paul C., ed. 2007. (ENG.). 176p. per. 35.00 (978-0-309-10397-8(5)) National Academies Pr.
Field, Anne. Blessed by Our Brokenness: Finding Peace in the Challenges of Aging & Illness. 2007. 9.95p. pap. 9.95 (978-1-59325-111-6(4)) Word Among Us Pr.
Fischer, Ed. Over-The-Hill & Lovin' It. 2008. (978-0-88166-536-9(3)) Meadowbrook Pr.
Fischer, Lucy Rose. I'm New at Being Old. 2010. 80p. pap. 19.95 (978-0-615-33519-3(5)) Temuna Pr.
Fisher, James C. & Simmons, Henry C. A Journey Called Aging: Challenges & Opportunities in Older Adulthood. (ENG.). 276p. 2008. 175.00 (978-0-7890-3383-3(6)) 2007. per. 54.95 (978-0-7890-3384-0(4)) Routledge.
Fleisher, A., ed. Alzheimer's Disease & Mild Cognitive Impairment: New Insights from Imaging - Book Edition of Behavioural Neurology. 2009. 140p. pap. 160.00 (978-1-60750-066-7(3)) IOS Pr., Inc.
Fong, Clinton. Secrets of How to Look & Feel Younger for the Infinite Being. 2010. (ENG.). 241p. pap. 30.00 (978-1-4092-1764-0(7)) Lulu Enterprises Inc.
Food Forum & Institute of Medicine. Providing Healthy & Safe Foods As We Age: Workshop Summary. 2010. (ENG.). 192p. pap. 40.00 (978-0-309-15883-1(4)) National Academies Pr.
Foos, Paul W. & Clark, M. Cherie. Human Aging. 2nd ed. 2007. (ENG., Illus.). 512p. (C). 136.40 (978-0-205-54401-1(0)) Allyn & Bacon, Inc.
Fotenos, Anthony. Structural Neuroimaging Across the Adult Life-Span. 2010. (Illus.). 140p. pap. (978-3-8383-4893-3(1)) Lambert Academic Publishing.
Francina, Suza. The New Yoga for Healthy Aging: Living Longer, Living Stronger & Loving Every Day. 2007. (ENG., Illus.). 365p. pap. 16.95 (978-0-7573-0532-0(6)) Health Communications, Inc.
Friedman, Dayle A. Jewish Visions for Aging: A Practical Professional Handbook. 2008. 300p. 40.00 (978-1-58023-348-4(1)) Jewish Lights Publishing.
Fu, Tsung-Hsi & Hughes, Rhidian, eds. Ageing in East Asia: Challenges & Policies for the Twenty-First Century. 2009. (Comparative Development & Policy in Asia Ser.). (ENG., Illus.). 208p. (C). 160.00 (978-0-415-45465-0(4)) Routledge.
Fülöp, Tamás. Handbook on Immunosenescence: Basic Understanding & Clinical Applications, 2 vols. 2009. (Illus.). xxxi, 1648p. (978-1-4020-9063-9(3)); 1200p. 539.00 (978-1-4020-9062-2(5)) Springer.
Gagnon, Ed. I Am Old. 2010. 122p. 19.95 (978-1-60911-253-0(9), Eloquent Bks.) AEG Literary Publishing Services, Inc.
Gambert, Steven R. Be Fit for Life: A Guide to Successful Aging - A Wellness, Weight Management, & Fitness Program You Can Live With. 2009. 290p. pap. 29.95 (978-981-4273-09-1(0)) World Scientific Publishing Co., Inc.
Gandotra, Veena & Patel, Sarjoo, eds. Ageing: An Interdisciplinary Approach. 2011. (Illus.). 284p. 50.00 (978-81-316-0389-5(X)) Rawat Pubns. IND. Dist: International Specialized Bk. Services.
Garcia-Segura, Luis Miguel. Hormones & Brain Plasticity. 2009. (Series in Behavioral Neuroendocrinology Ser.). (ENG., Illus.). 496p. (C). 65.00 (978-0-19-532661-1(X)) Oxford Univ. Pr., Inc.
Garrett, Ruth. Embracing Aging: Discovering Fulfillment Through Coping with Life's Changes. 2010. 236p. pap. (978-1-57736-425-2(2)) Providence Hse Pubs.
Gates, Donna & Schrecengost, Lyndi. The Baby Boomer Diet: Body Ecology's Guide to Growing Younger: Anti-Aging Wisdom for Every Generation. 2011. (ENG.). 27.95 (978-1-4019-3545-0(1)) Hay Hse., Inc.
Gembris, Heiner, ed. Musik im Alter: Soziokulturelle Rahmenbedingungen und individuelle Möglichkeiten. 2008. 310p. pap. 69.95 (978-3-631-57809-4(1)) Lang, Peter GmbH, Europaischer Verlag der Wissenschaften DEU. Dist: Lang, Peter.
Gentry, Judi Haven. Aging Outrageously Well: How to Save Your Own Life & Have Fun Doing It. 2008. (Illus.). 248p. per. 19.95 (978-0-9764302-1-6(5)) Silverhawk Pr.
—Aging Outrageously Well: How to Save Your Own Life & Have Fun Doing It. 2009. (Illus.). 244p. pap. 19.95 (978-0-9764302-0-9(7)) Silverhawk Pr.
Gerstenblith, Gary, ed. Cardiovascular Disease in the Elderly. 2010. (Contemporary Cardiology Ser.). (Illus.). 432p. pap. 119.00 (978-1-61737-470-8(9), 1617374709) Humana Pr.
Gibson, Heather J. & Singleton, Jerome F., eds. Leisure & Aging: Theory & Practice. 2011. (Illus.). 280p. (C). 59.00 (978-0-7360-9463-4(6)) Human Kinetics Pubs.
Gillick, M.D., Muriel R. The Denial of Aging: Perpetual Youth, Eternal Life, & Other Dangerous Fantasies. 2007. (Illus.). 352p. per. 20.00 (978-0-674-02543-1(1)) Harvard Univ. Pr.
Gragnolati, Michele. Growing Old in & Older Brazil: Implications of Population Aging on Growth, Poverty, Public Finance & Service Delivery. 2011. E-Book (978-0-8213-8803-7(7)) World Bank Pubns.
Gragnolati, Michele, et al. Growing Old in an Older Brazil: Implications of Population Aging on Growth, Poverty, Public Finance & Service Delivery. 2011. (Directions in Development Ser.). (ENG.). 304p. pap. 35.00 (978-0-8213-8802-0(9), 9780821388020) World Bank Pubns.
Graham, Billy. Nearing Home: Life, Faith, & Finishing Well. 2011. 192p. 19.99 (978-0-8499-4832-9(0)) Nelson, Thomas Inc.
—Nearing Home: Life, Faith, & Finishing Well. l.t. ed. 2012. (ENG.). 240p. 30.99 (978-1-4104-4287-1(X)) Thorndike Pr.
Graydon, Shari. I Feel Great about My Hands: And Other Unexpected Joys of Aging, 1 vol. 2011. (ENG., Illus.). 264p. pap. 17.95 (978-1-55365-786-5(1)) D&M Pubs. Inc. CAN. Dist: Perseus-PGW.
Greenwood, Pamela M. & Parasuraman, Raja. Nurturing the Older Brain & Mind. 2012. (ENG., Illus.). 352p. (gr. 17). 40.00 (978-0-262-01714-5(8)) MIT Pr.
Grenier Amanda. Transitions & the Lifecourse: Challenging the Constructions of 'Growing Old' 2012. (Ageing & the Lifecourse Ser.). 241p. 110.00 (978-1-84742-692-5(1)); 224p. pap. 45.95 (978-1-84742-691-8(3)) Policy Pr. GBR. Dist: Chicago Distribution Ctr.
Griffin, Emilie. Souls in Full Sail: A Christian Spirituality for the Later Years. 2010. (ENG.). 183p. pap. 15.00 (978-0-8308-3548-5(2), IVP Bks.) InterVarsity Pr.
Gross, Kim Johnson. What to Wear for the Rest of Your Life: Ageless Secrets of Style. 2010. (ENG., Illus.). 288p. 24.99 (978-0-446-53494-9(3), Springboard Pr.) Grand Central Publishing.
Growing Old in America. 2010. (Information Plus Reference Ser.). (ENG.). 160p. 58.00 (978-1-4144-4119-1(3)) Cengage Gale.
Guan, Lee Hock, ed. Ageing in Southeast & East Asi: Family, Social Protection, Policy Challenges. 2008. (Illus.). 264p. (978-981-230-766-8(4)) Institute of Southeast Asian Studies.
Guest, Andrew. Taking Sides: Clashing Views in Life-Span Development. 4th ed. 2012. (Taking Sides Ser.). (ENG.). 448p. (C). pap. 48.00 (978-0-07-805029-9(4), 0078050294, McGraw-Hill/Dushkin) McGraw-Hill Higher Education.
Gupta, Sanjay. Chasing Life: New Discoveries in the Search for Immortality to Help You Age Less Today. 2008. (ENG., Illus.). 272p. pap. 14.99 (978-0-446-69818-4(0), Wellness Central) Grand Central Publishing.
—Chasing Life: New Discoveries in the Search for Immortality to Help You Age Less Today. l.t. ed. 2007. (Thorndike Health, Home & Learning Ser.). 359p. 30.95 (978-0-7862-9819-8(7)) Thorndike Pr.
Gussin, Robert & Gussin, Patricia. What's Next ... for You? The Gussin Guide to Big Changes, Big Decisions, & Big Fun. 2010. 144p. pap. 13.50 (978-1-933515-73-1(2)) Oceanview Publishing.
Hamerman, David. Geriatric Bioscience: The Link Between Aging & Disease. 2007. (ENG., Illus.). 316p. (gr. 17). 47.00 (978-0-8018-8692-8(9)) Johns Hopkins Univ. Pr.
Hammond, Jeffrey. Small Comforts: Essays at Middle Age. 2008. pap. 18.95 (978-0-87338-946-4(8)) Kent State Univ. Pr.
Hansen, R. Jack & Haas, Jerry P. Shaping a Life of Significance for Retirement. 2010. 110p. (978-0-8358-1025-8(9)) Upper Room Bks.
Hareven, Tamara K., ed. Aging & Generational Relations over the Life Course: A Historical & Cross-Cultural Perspective. (ENG.). VI, 533p. 224.00 (978-3-11-178031-3(7)) De Gruyter, Walter Inc.
Harper, Christopher. Flyover Country: Baby Boomers & Their Stories. 2010. (ENG.). 150p. pap. 25.00 (978-0-7618-5332-9(4)) Hamilton Bks.
Hartung, Heike & Maierhofer, Roberta, eds. Narratives of Life: Mediating Age. 2011. (ENG.). 208p. pap. 34.95 (978-3-8258-1229-4(4)) Lit Verlag DEU. Dist: Transaction Pubs.
Harwood, Jake. Understanding Communication & Aging: Developing Knowledge & Awareness. 2007. (Illus.). 344p. (C). per. 59.00 (978-1-4129-2609-6(2), B26092P) SAGE Pubns., Inc.
Hay, Jack. Stay Fit & Fantastic over 50. (ENG., Illus.). 1p. 11.95 (978-0-572-02887-9(3)) Foulsham, W. Co., Ltd. GBR. Dist: APG Sales & Distribution Services.
Heckles, Jim P. & Bergin, Laura M. Aging: Mental Aspects, Social Welfare & Health. 2011. (Aging Issues, Health & Financial Alternatives Ser.). (Illus.). 196p. 95.00 (978-1-61324-579-3(3)) Nova Science Pubs., Inc.
Heitzman, Andrea. For Your Eyes Only: Caution: Warning Female Readers! This Book Is Only for Women Forty-Five Years or Older. 2011. 56p. 20.16 (978-1-4269-5182-4(5);); pap. 10.16 (978-1-4269-5181-7(7)) Trafford Publishing.
Henderson, Veronique & Henshaw, Pat. Color Me Younger: How to Look Younger & Feel Great! 2009. (ENG.). 160p. pap. 17.99 (978-0-600-61961-1(3), Hamlyn) Octopus Publishing Group GBR. Dist: Hachette Bk. Group.
Higgs, Paul & Jones, Ian Rees. Medical Sociology & Old Age: Towards a Sociology of Health in Later Life. 2008. (Critical Studies in Health & Society Ser.). (ENG., Illus.). 160p. (C). 140.00 (978-0-415-39855-8(X)); pap. 45.95 (978-0-415-39860-2(6)) Routledge.
Higgs, Paul, et al. Consumption & Generational Change: The Rise of Consumer Lifestyles. Jones, Ian & Higgs, Paul, eds. Ekerdt, David, ed. 2008. (ENG., Illus.). 218p. 49.95 (978-1-4128-0857-6(X)) Transaction Pubs.
Hodge, Gerald. The Geography of Aging: Preparing Communities for the Surge in Seniors. 2008. (ENG., Illus.). 336p. (C). (978-0-7735-3429-2(6)); pap. (978-0-7735-3430-8(X)) McGill-Queen's Univ. Pr.
Hodgman, Ann. 1,003 Ways to Stay Young. 2007. (ENG.). 320p. pap. 9.99 (978-0-7407-5668-9(0)) Andrews McMeel Publishing.
Hoff, Andreas, ed. Population Ageing in Central & Eastern Europe: Societal & Policy Implications. 2011. (New Perspectives on Ageing & Later Life Ser.). (Illus.). 290p. 114.95 (978-0-7546-7828-1(8)) Ashgate Publishing Co.
Holliday, Robin. Aging: the Paradox of Life: Why We Age. 2010. (ENG.). xiv, 134p. pap. 69.95 (978-90-481-7416-4(3), 9048174163) Springer.
—Aging: the Paradox of Life: Why We Age. 2007. (ENG., Illus.). xiv, 134p. 69.95 (978-1-4020-5640-6(0), 1402056400) Springer London, Ltd. GBR. Dist: Springer.
Hollvich, Matthias, ed. New Aging. 2012. (ENG.). 140p. pap. (978-84-92861-97-2(8)) Actar Birkhauser Distribution.
Holstein, Martha B., et al. Ethics, Aging, & Society: The Critical Turn. 2010. xxii, 298p. (978-0-8261-1634-5(5)); E-Book (978-0-8261-1635-2(3)) Springer Publishing Co., Inc.
Holt, Gary A., et al. Extend Your Lifespan: How You Can Live a Long & Healthy Life. Date not set. (Illus.). 846p. 34.50 (978-0-931541-52-0(2)) Mancorp Publishing, Inc.
Holzmann, Robert. Aging Populations, Pension Funds, & Financial Markets: Regional Perspectives & Global Challenges for Central, Eastern, & Southern Europe. 2008. (978-0-8213-7733-8(7)) World Bank Pubns.
Hooyman, Nancy & Kiyak, H. Asuman. Social Gerontology: A Multidisciplinary Perspective. 9th ed. 2010. (ENG.). 816p. (C). 154.20 (978-0-205-76313-9(8), Prentice Hall) Prentice Hall PTR.
Hoshi, Toshinori, et al, eds. Oxidative Stress & Aging: From Chemistry to Human Dietary Supplements. 2009. (Aging Medicine Ser.). (Illus.). 400p. 135.00 (978-1-60327-548-4(7), 1603275487) Humana Pr.
Howe, Michele. Still Going It Alone: Mothering with Faith & Finesse When the Children Have Grown. 2009. 130p. pap. 14.95 (978-1-59856-241-5(X)) Hendrickson Pubs. Marketing, LLC.
Hoyer, William J. & Roodin, Paul A. Adult Development & Aging. 6th rev. ed. 2008. (ENG., Illus.). 560p. (C). 181.00 (978-0-07-312854-2(6), 0073128546) McGraw-Hill Cos., The.
Hultsch, David F. & Tuokko, Holly, eds. Mild Cognitive Impairment: International Perspectives. 2006. (Studies on Neuropsychology, Neurology, & Cognition). (ENG., Illus.). 336p. 105.95 (978-1-84169-466-5(5), Psychology Press) Taylor & Francis Group GBR. Dist: Taylor & Francis Group.
Inman, Valerie N. All My Relations. 2008. 212p. pap. 17.95 (978-0-9814908-1-6(6)); 27.95 (978-0-9814908-0-9(8)) Pilamaye Pr.
Izuhara, Misa, ed. Ageing & Intergenerational Relations: Family reciprocity from a global Perspective. 176p. 2011. pap. 39.95 (978-1-84742-204-0(7)) 2010. 85.00 (978-1-84742-205-7(5)) Policy Pr. GBR. Dist: Chicago Distribution Ctr.
Jackowski, Edward J. Escape Your Age. Date not set. 24.95 (978-0-312-31201-5(6)); pap. (978-0-312-31202-2(4), St. Martin's Paperbacks); mass mkt. (978-0-312-98862-3(1), St. Martin's Paperbacks) St. Martin's Pr.
Jackson, Richard & Howe, Neil. The Graying of the Great Powers: Demography & Geopolitics in the 21st Century. 2008. (Illus.). 224p. pap. 21.95 (978-0-89206-532-5(X), CSIS Pr. The) Ctr. for Strategic & International Studies.
Jackson, Tracey. Between a Rock & a Hot Place: Why Fifty Is Not the New Thirty. 2011. (ENG.). 288p. 25.99 (978-0-06-166927-9(X)) HarperCollins Pubs.
—Between a Rock & a Hot Place: Why Fifty Is Not the New Thirty. l.t. ed. 2011. 348p. pap. 25.99 (978-0-06-201795-6(0), HarperLuxe) HarperCollins Pubs.
Jackson, Tracey. Between a Rock & a Hot Place: Why Fifty Is the New Fifty. 2012. (ENG.). 288p. pap. 14.99 (978-0-06-166928-6(8), Harper Paperbacks) HarperCollins Pubs.
Jacoby, Susan. Never Say Die: The Myth & Marketing of the New Old Age. 2011. (ENG.). 352p. 27.95 (978-0-307-37794-4(6), Pantheon) Knopf Doubleday Publishing Group.
Jacoby, Susan. Never Say Die: The Myth of the New Old Age. 2012. (Vintage Ser.). (ENG.). 352p. pap. 15.95 (978-0-307-45628-1(5), Vintage) Knopf Doubleday Publishing Group.
James, Jacquelyn Boone & Wink, Paul, eds. Annual Review of Gerontology & Geriatrics: The Crown of Life: Dynamics of the Early Postretirement Period. 2007. (Annual Review of Gerontology & Geriatrics Ser.). (Illus.). 336p. 58.00 (978-0-8261-0228-7(X)) Springer Publishing Co., Inc.
Jarski, Rosemarie, et al. The Big Book of Wrinklies Wit & Wisdom. 2008. (ENG.). 512p. pap. 28.95 (978-1-85375-670-2(9)) Prion GBR. Dist: Independent Pubs. Group.
Jeanne R Kraus. Wrinkles, Waistlines, & Wet Pants: Improbable Scenarios of the Not-So-Rich & the Not-So-Famous. 2010. 256p. 29.95 (978-1-4502-0087-5(7)) Universe Inc.
Jensen, Mark P. & Molten, Ivan. Aging with a Physical Disability, an Issue of Physical Medicine & Rehabilitation Clinics. 2010. (Clinics: Orthopedics Ser.: 21-2). (ENG., Illus.). xvi, 254p. 105.00 (978-1-4377-1860-7(4), Saunders) Elsevier - Health Sciences Div.
Johnson, Wingate M. The Years after Fifty. 18.95 (978-0-405-18502-1(2)) Ayer Co. Pubs., Inc.
Jones, Althea. Colorful Memories. 2007. (ENM.). 140p. per. 19.95 (978-1-58942-351-0(8)) R.H. Boyd Publishing Corp.
Jones, Sharon. Sixty... So What? A Handbook for Staying Young at Sixty. 2007. 51p. per. 7.99 (978-1-60247-465-9(6)) Tate Publishing & Enterprises, LLC.
Josefowitz, Natasha. Been There, Done That, Doing It Better: A Witty Look at Growing Older by a Formerly Young Person. Josefowitz, Natasha, ed. 2009. (ENG.). 96p. pap. 13.95 (978-1-59842-423-2(8)) Blue Mountain Arts Inc.
Kainz, Therese & Bye, Lynne. Use of Prescription Medicines among Older People. 2011. 64p. pap. (978-3-8433-9280-8(3)) Lambert Academic Publishing.
Kalb, John. Winning at Aging: Your Game Plan for Healthy Living. 2011. (ENG.). 288p. pap. 16.95 (978-1-935952-49-7(8), Confluence Bks.) White Cloud Pr.
Kanamoto, Itsuko. Aging among Japanese American Immigrants: Activating Ethnicity. 2006. (Studies in Asian Americans Ser.). (ENG.). 160p. 125.00 (978-0-415-97946-7(3)) Routledge.

A

Kathryn, Mary. Women: Fit at Fifty: A Guide for Living Long. 2011. 144p. 23.95 ***(978-1-4670-4042-6(8))*** AuthorHouse.

Katz, Jeanne, et al, eds. Adult Lives: A Life Course Perspective. 2012. (Illus.). 400p. 110.00 ***(978-1-4473-0044-1(0))***; pap. 45.95 ***(978-1-4473-0043-4(2))*** Policy Pr. GBR. Dist: Chicago Distribution Ctr.

Keding, Dan. Elder Tales: Stories of Wisdom & Courage from Around the World, 1 vol. 2007. 204p. per. 30.00 *(978-1-59158-594-7(5)*, LU8594) Libraries Unlimited, Inc.

Khavinson, V. Kh & Malinin, Vladimir V. Gerontological Aspects of Genome Peptide Regulation. (Illus.). *(978-3-8055-7895-0(4))* Karger, S. AG.

Kimura, Daiki. Cell Growth Processes: New Research. 2008. (C). 129.00 *(978-1-60456-132-6(7))* Nova Science Pubs., Inc.

Klie, Thomas, et al, eds. Praktische Theologie des Alterns. 2009. (Praktische Theologie Im Wissenschaftsdiskurs Ser.).Tr. of Practical Theology of Aging. (GER.). VII, 617p. 210.00 ***(978-3-11-173305-0(X))*** De Gruyter, Walter Inc.

Klie, Thomas, et al. Praktische Theologie des Alterns. 2009. (Praktische Theologie Im Wissenschaftsdiskurs Ser.).Tr. of Practical Theology of Aging. (GER., Illus.). VII, 617p. 137.00 *(978-3-11-020374-5(X))* De Gruyter, Walter Inc.

Kolb, Patricia. Understanding Aging & Diversity: Theories & Concepts. 2012. (Routledge Advances in Sociology Ser.). (ENG.). 224p. (C). 135.00 *(978-0-415-67881-0(1))* Routledge.

Krause, Neal M. Aging in the Church: How Social Relationships Affect Health. 2008. (ENG.). 320p. (C). pap. 36.95 *(978-1-59947-144-0(2))* Templeton Pr.

Kreamer, Anne. Going Gray: How to Embrace Your Authentic Self with Grace & Style. 2009. (ENG.). 240p. pap. 14.99 *(978-0-316-16662-1(6)*, Back Bay Bks.) Little Brown & Co.

Kristiansen, Magnus N., ed. Topics in Aging Research. 2008. (Illus.). xiii, 204p. (C). 98.00 *(978-1-60456-514-0(4))* Nova Science Pubs., Inc.

Kuchel, George A. & Hof, Patrick R., eds. Autonomic Nervous System in Old Age, Vol. 33. (Interdisciplinary Topics in Gerontology Ser.: Vol. 33). (Illus.). *(978-3-8055-7685-7(4))* Karger, S. AG.

Kunkel, Suzanne R., et al, eds. The International Handbook on Aging: Current Research & Developments. 3rd rev. ed. 2009. 705p. 54.95 *(978-0-313-35230-0(5)*, C35230, Praeger Pubs.) Greenwood Publishing Group, Inc.

Lachs, Mark, , Mark. What Your Doctor Won't Tell You about Getting Older: A Doctor's Guide to Getting the Best Care as You or a Loved One Gets Older. l.t. ed. 2011. 689p. 32.99 ***(978-1-4104-4109-6(1))*** Thorndike Pr.

Lachs, Mark. What Your Doctor Won't Tell You about Getting Older: An Insider's Survival Manual for Outsmarting the Health-Care System. 2011. (ENG.). 400p. (gr. 12). 17.00 *(978-0-14-312008-7(5)*, Penguin (Non-Classics)) Penguin Group (USA) Inc.

Lane, Cynthia Rose. Conscious Aging: An ABC Book for Seniors & the People Who Love Them. 2010. 63p. pap. 14.95 *(978-1-4327-5353-5(3))* Outskirts Pr., Inc.

Lane, John. The Art of Ageing: Inspiration for a Positive & Abundant Life. 2010. (ENG., Illus.). 128p. 18.00 *(978-1-900322-73-7(0))* Green Bks. GBR. Dist: Chelsea Green Publishing.

Langer, Ellen J. Counterclockwise: Mindful Health & the Power of Possibility. 2009. (ENG.). 240p. 25.00 *(978-0-345-50204-9(3)*, Ballantine Bks.) Random House Publishing Group.

Le Bourg, Éric. Retraites, Démographie, Santé- Vieillir en France Aujourd'hui et Demain. 2010. (Illus.). vi, 250p. *(978-2-311-00187-7(6))* Vuibert, Librairie.

Le Verrier, Renée. Yoga for Movement Disorders: Rebuilding Strength, Balance & Flexibility for Parkinson's Disease & Dystonia. 2008. (Illus.). 120p. spiral bd. 19.95 *(978-1-873413-53-1(X))* Merit Publishing International, Inc.

Leonard, Barry. Bound for Your Good Health: A Collection of Age Pages. 2007. (Illus.). 206p. (C). pap. 30.00 *(978-1-4223-1517-0(7))* DIANE Publishing Co.

Lesnoff-Caravaglia, Gari. Health aspects of Aging: The Experience of Growing Old. 2nd ed. 2007. 208p. 50.95 *(978-0-398-07695-5(2))*; pap. 32.95 *(978-0-398-07696-2(0))* Thomas, Charles C. Pub., Ltd.

Lettmann, Vicky & Roan, Carol, eds. When Last on the Mountain: The View from Writers Over 50. 2011. (ENG.). 392p. pap. 17.95 *(978-0-9823545-2-0(5))* Holy Cow! Pr.

Leung, Ping-Chung. Healthy Aging. 2010. 284p. 108.00 *(978-981-4317-71-9(3))* World Scientific Publishing Co., Inc.

Lewis, Steven. Fear & Loathing of Boca Raton: A Hippies' Guide to the Second Sixties. 2007. (Best Half of Life Ser.). (ENG.). 150p. pap. 14.95 *(978-1-884956-74-4(2))* Quill Driver Bks.

Lindbergh, Reeve. Forward from Here: Leaving Middle Age — and Other Unexpected Adventures. 2009. (ENG.). 240p. pap. 14.00 *(978-0-7432-7512-5(8))* Simon & Schuster.

—Forward from Here: Leaving Middle Age — and Other Unexpected Adventures. l.t. ed. 2008. 330p. (YA). 30.95 *(978-1-4104-0772-6(1))* Thorndike Pr.

Liponis, Mark. UltraLongevity: The Seven-Step Program for a Younger, Healthier You. 2008. (ENG.). 304p. pap. 14.99 *(978-0-316-01729-9(9))* Little Brown & Co.

—UltraLongevity: The Seven-Step Program for a Younger, Healthier You. l.t. ed. 2008. (Thorndike Health, Home & Learning Ser.). 495p. 31.95 *(978-1-4104-0356-8(4))* Thorndike Pr.

Living Better, Living Longer: The Secrets of Healthy Aging. 2008. 26.00 *(978-1-933812-43-4(5))* Harvard Medical Schl., Harvard Health Pubns.

Lloyd, Liz. Health & Care in Ageing Societies: A New International Approach. 2012. (Policy Press - Ageing & the Lifecourse Ser.). 176p. 110.00 ***(978-1-86134-919-4(X))***; pap. 39.95 ***(978-1-86134-918-7(1))*** Policy Pr. GBR. Dist: Chicago Distribution Ctr.

Lockhart, Charles & Giles-Sims, Jean. Aging Across the United States: Matching Needs to States' Differing Opportunities & Services. 2011. (ENG.). 226p. 58.95 *(978-0-271-03756-1(3))* Pennsylvania State Univ. Pr.

Loe, Meika. Aging Our Way: Lessons for Living from 85 & Beyond, 1 vol. 2011. (ENG., Illus.). 344p. 29.95 *(978-0-19-979790-5(0))* Oxford Univ. Pr., Inc.

Loue, Sana, et al, eds. Encyclopedia of Aging & Public Health. 2008. (Springer Reference Ser.). (Illus.). 843p. 299.00 *(978-0-387-33753-1(9)*, 0387337539) Springer.

Love, Helen Mendes. Reflections on the Upsides of Aging: Living with Joy & Purpose after Age 50. 2011. 316p. 37.95 *(978-1-4497-1133-7(2))*; pap. 22.95 *(978-1-4497-1132-0(4))* Author Solutions, Inc. (WestBow Pr.).

Mackinnon, A. J. The Well at the World's End: The Epic True Story of One Man's Search for the Secret to Eternal Youth. 2011. (ENG., Illus.). 320p. 24.95 *(978-1-61608-366-3(2)*, 608366) Skyhorse Publishing Co., Inc.

Macklin, Mary Kathryn. Women: Fit at Fifty: A Guide for Living Long. 2011. 144p. pap. 15.95 ***(978-1-4670-4043-3(6))*** AuthorHouse.

MacLaine, Shirley. Sage-ing While Age-ing. 2008. (ENG.). 272p. pap. 15.00 *(978-1-4165-5042-6(9)*, Beyond Words/Atria Bks.) Atria Bks.

Majonica, Ernst. The Cultural Context of Aging: Worldwide Perspectives. 3rd ed. 2008. (Illus.). 808p. 124.95 *(978-0-275-99288-0(8)*, C9288, Praeger Pubs.) Greenwood Publishing Group, Inc.

Mandell, Nancy, et al. Connection, Compromise, & Control: Canadian Women Discuss Midlife. 2008. (ENG.). 256p. pap. 39.95 *(978-0-19-541793-7(3))* Oxford Univ. Pr., Inc.

Manning, Diane. Are the Golden Years Tarnished? 2011. 100p. pap. 15.99 ***(978-1-4568-8066-8(7))*** Xlibris Corp.

Marcelo, Nunes & Suely, Santos. Frequency of Knowledge of Performance in Motor Learning in the Elderly: An Analysis of the Process Through Which an Elderly Individual Learns a Motor Skill. 2011. 80p. pap. ***(978-3-639-33324-4(1))*** VDM Verlag Dr. Mueller e.K.

Markides, Kyriakos S., ed. Encyclopedia of Health & Aging. 2007. 680p. 160.00 *(978-1-4129-0949-5(X)*, B0949XC) SAGE Pubns., Inc.

Markson, Elizabeth W. Social Gerontology Today: An Introduction. 2006. pap. 9.95 *(978-1-4288-1611-4(9))* Cram101 Inc.

Marohn, Stephanie, ed. Audacious Aging: Eldership as a Revolutionary Endeavor. 2009. 29.95 *(978-1-60070-061-3(6)*, Elite Bks.) Author's Publishing Cooperative.

Marshall, Leni & Lipscomb, Valerie. Staging Age: The Performance of Age in Theatre, Dance, & Film. 2010. (ENG., Illus.). 250p. 84.00 *(978-0-230-62365-1(4))* Palgrave Macmillan.

Martz, Sandra, ed. I Shall Wear Purple. 4th ed. 2007. (Illus.). 204p. pap. 14.95 *(978-1-57601-078-5(3)*, Papier-Mache Pr.) Moyer Bell.

Matsumoto, Yoshiko, ed. Faces of Aging: The Lived Experiences of the Elderly in Japan. 2011. (ENG., Illus.). 304p. 75.00 *(978-0-8047-7148-1(0))*; pap. 24.95 *(978-0-8047-7149-8(9))* Stanford Univ. Pr.

Mattlin, Everett. Last Laughs: A Pocketful of Wry for the Aging. 2011. (ENG.). 207p. pap. 14.95 ***(978-1-936401-34-5(7))*** Two Harbors Pr., Inc.

Matzkin, Alice. The Art of Aging: Celebrating the Authentic Aging Self. 2009. (ENG.). 160p. pap. 24.95 *(978-1-59181-081-0(7))* Sentient Pubns.

Mayer, Catherine. Amortality: The Pleasures & Perils of Living Agelessly. 2011. (ENG.). 304p. pap. 23.95 ***(978-0-09-193936-6(4))*** Random Hse. GBR. Dist: Independent Pubs. Group.

McDaniel, Susan A., ed. Ageing, 4 vols. 2008. (Key Issues for the 21st Century Ser.). (Illus.). 1624p. 995.00 *(978-1-4129-3558-6(X)*, B3558XC) SAGE Pubns., Ltd. GBR. Dist: SAGE Pubns., Inc.

McGovern, Rene J. & Korr, Irvin M. Living Long & Loving It: Achieving a Healthy & Active Lifestyle. 2008. (ENG., Illus.). 300p. pap. 19.98 *(978-1-59102-572-6(9))* Prometheus Bks., Pubs.

McPherson, Barry D. & Wister, Andrew. Aging as a Social Process: Canadian Perspectives. 5th ed. 2009. (ENG., Illus.). 448p. 59.95 *(978-0-19-542719-6(X))* Oxford Univ. Pr., Inc.

Mehta, Kalyani & Singh, Amarjit, eds. Indian Diaspor: Voices of the Diasporic Elders in Five Countries. 2008. 160p. *(978-90-8790-406-7(1))*; pap. *(978-90-8790-405-0(3))* Sense Pubs.

Meiser, Frances & Anderson, Nina. Overcoming Senior Moments Expanded Edition. exp. ed. 2006. (ENG., Illus.). 80p. pap. 9.95 *(978-0-9701110-9-8(6))* SAFE GOODS/ATN Publishing.

Meletis, Chris & Wood, Sara. The Male Menopause Controversy: Arguments, Affects, & Treatments of Andropause, 1 vol. 2009. (Complementary & Alternative Medicine Ser.). (Illus.). 149p. 42.95 *(978-0-313-36023-7(5)*, C36023, Praeger Pubs.) Greenwood Publishing Group, Inc.

Meyer, Gail. 7 Steps to Looking & Feeling 10 Years Younger in 30 Days. 2010. 104p. pap. 17.97 *(978-0-557-60633-7(0))* Lulu Enterprises Inc.

Miller, David Niven. Grow Youthful: A Practical Guide to Slowing Your Ageing. 2007. (ENG.). 384p. per. 19.95 *(978-1-84694-004-0(4))* Hunt, John Publishing Ltd. GBR. Dist: National Bk. Network.

Miller, William Ian. Losing It: In Which an Aging Professor Laments His Shrinking Brain. 2011. (ENG., Illus.). 336p. 27.00 *(978-0-300-17101-3(3))* Yale Univ. Pr.

Mirzayansfnof;x, Razmik & Murray, David. Cellular Senescence: Implications for Cancer Therapy. 2008. pap. 37.00 *(978-1-60692-676-5(4))* Nova Science Pubs., Inc.

Mobbs, C., et al, eds. Body Composition & Aging. 2010. (Interdisciplinary Topics in Gerontology Ser.). (ENG., Illus.). 198p. *(978-3-8055-9521-6(2))* Karger, S. AG.

Moody, Harry R. & Sasser, Jennifer S. Aging: Concepts & Controversies. 7th ed. 2011. (Illus.). 576p. (C). pap. 99.00 ***(978-1-4522-0309-6(1)***, B03096P) SAGE Pubns., Inc.

Moon, Susan. This Is Getting Old: Zen Thoughts on Aging with Humor & Dignity. 2010. (ENG., Illus.). 208p. pap. 14.95 *(978-1-59030-776-2(3))* Shambhala Pubns., Inc.

Moorstein, Mark. Super-Aging: The Moral Dangers of Seeking Immortality. 2010. 132p. pap. 13.95 *(978-1-4502-2346-1(X))* iUniverse, Inc.

Mordini, E. & Hert, P. De, eds. Ageing & Invisibility: Volume 7 Ambient Intelligence & Smart Environments. 2010. 138.00 *(978-1-60750-614-0(9))* IOS Pr., Inc.

Morgan, Leslie A. & Kunkel, Suzanne R. Aging, Society, & the Life Course. 3rd ed. 2007. (Illus.). 388p. 85.00 *(978-0-8261-0212-6(3))* Springer Publishing Co., Inc.

—Aging, Society & the Life Course. 4th ed. 2011. E-Book *(978-0-8261-1938-4(7))*; (Illus.). 384p. *(978-0-8261-1937-7(9))* Springer Publishing Co., Inc.

Morgan, Richard Lyon. Settling In: My First Year in a Retirement Community. 2007. 187p. 16.00 *(978-0-8358-9908-6(X))* Upper Room Bks.

Morley, John E. & van den Berg, Lucretia, eds. Endocrinology of Aging. 2010. (Contemporary Endocrinology Ser.). 280p. pap. 139.00 *(978-1-61737-171-4(8)*, 1617371718) Humana Pr.

Morris, Barbara. No More Little Old Ladies! 15 Essential & Specific Proven Anti-Aging Strategies for Gutsy Women in Their 40s And 50s. 2009. (ENG.). pap. 14.95 *(978-1-60037-521-7(9))* Morgan James Publishing.

Moss, Charles. Power of the Five Elements: The Chinese Medicine Path to Healthy Aging & Stress Resistance. 2010. (ENG., Illus.). 312p. pap. 18.95 *(978-1-55643-874-5(5))* North Atlantic Bks.

Mueller, Laurence D., et al. Does Aging Stop?, 1 vol. 2011. (ENG., Illus.). 224p. 49.95 *(978-0-19-975422-9(5))* Oxford Univ. Pr., Inc.

Naegele, Gerhard & Walker, Alan. Social Policy in Ageing Societies: Britain & Germany Compared. Walker, Alan, ed. 2009. (ENG., Illus.). 224p. 105.00 *(978-0-230-52098-1(7))* Palgrave Macmillan.

Narrett, Matt, et al. Old Is the New Young: Erickson's Secrets to Healthy Living. 2009. (ENG.). 256p. pap. 16.95 *(978-0-7627-5011-5(1))* Globe Pequot Pr., The.

Naveh-Benjamin, Moshe & Ohta, Nobuo, eds. Memory & Aging. 2011. (ENG.). 439p. 80.00 ***(978-1-84872-918-6(9)***, Psychology Press) Taylor & Francis Group GBR. Dist: Taylor & Francis Group.

Norman, Marty. Generation G: Advice for Savvy Grandmothers Who Will Never Go Gray, 0 vols. 2008. (Illus.). 208p. per. 14.99 *(978-0-7852-2812-7(8))* Nelson, Thomas Inc.

Novak, Mark. Issues in Aging. 3rd rev. ed. 2011. (ENG., Illus.). 576p. (C). pap. 101.00 ***(978-0-205-83195-1(8)***, Prentice Hall) Prentice Hall PTR.

Nuland, Sherwin B. The Art of Aging: A Doctor's Prescription for Well-Being. 2008. (ENG.). 320p. pap. 16.00 *(978-0-8129-7541-3(3)*, Random Hse. Trade Paperbacks) Random House Publishing Group.

O'Brien, Matt. The Magic Pill: Your Prescription for a Longer, Healthier, & Happier Life. 2011. 376p. 34.95 *(978-1-4502-8282-6(2))*; pap. 24.95 *(978-1-4502-8280-2(6))* iUniverse, Inc.

O'Connor, Karen. The Golden Years Ain't for Wimps: Humorous Stories for Your Senior Moments. 2008. 252p. per. 12.99 *(978-0-7369-2247-0(4))* Harvest Hse. Pubs.

—It's Taken Years to Get This Old. 2010. 240p. pap. 12.99 *(978-0-7369-2953-0(3))* Harvest Hse. Pubs.

O'Connor, Kathleen & Weinstein, Maxine, eds. The Biodemography of Reproductive Aging. 2010. (Annals of the New York Academy of Sciences Ser.: 58). (ENG., Illus.). 300p. pap. 130.00 *(978-1-57331-775-7(6)*, Wiley-Blackwell) Wiley, John & Sons, Inc.

Omoigui, Sota. The Inflammation Pathway from Cholesterol to Aging: Medications & Plants that prevent & treat Aging, Heart Disease, Osteoporosis, Arthritis, Type-2 Diabetes, Dementia & Alzheimer's Disease. 2007. mass mkt. 39.95 *(978-0-9650767-9-1(2))* State-of-the-Art Technologies, Inc.

Organisation for Economic Co-operation and Development Staff. Ageing & the Public Service: Human Resource Challenges. 2007. pap. 65.00 *(978-92-64-02970-5(2))* Organization for Economic Cooperation & Development.

Osiewacz, H. D., ed. Aging of Organisms. 2010. (Biology of Aging & its Modulation Ser.). 304p. pap. 189.00 *(978-90-481-6332-8(3)*, 9048163323) Springer.

Ottaway, Susannah R. The Decline of Life: Old Age in Eighteenth-Century England. 2007. (Cambridge Studies in Population, Economy & Society in Past Time Ser.). (ENG., Illus.). 340p. pap. 69.00 *(978-0-521-03792-1(1))* Cambridge Univ. Pr.

Padwa, Lynette. Quick, Answer Me Before I Forget the Question: 100 Answers You're Old Enough to Hear. 2007. (ENG., Illus.). 304p. (gr. 12-18). 13.00 *(978-0-14-311289-1(9)*, Penguin (Non-Classics)) Penguin Group (USA) Inc.

Pandya, Samta. Ageing & Spirituality. 2010. 180p. pap. *(978-3-8383-7863-3(6))* Lambert Academic Publishing.

Panno, Joseph. The New Biology. 2011. (New Biology Ser.). (gr. 6-12). 280.00 ***(978-0-8160-8487-6(4))*** Facts On File, Inc.

Parker, Sarah & Heller, Tamar. Disability Through the Life Course. 2011. (SAGE Reference Series on Disability: Key Issues & Future Directions Ser.). (Illus.). 320p. 75.00 *(978-1-4129-8767-7(9)*, B87677C) SAGE Pubns., Inc.

Parrish, Berta. Wise Woman's Way. 2007. 308p. pap. 19.95 *(978-0-9725000-1-2(4))* Morro Pr.

Partridge, Linda & Wallace, Douglas C., eds. Molecular Biology of Aging. 2007. (ENG., Illus.). 610p. 135.00 *(978-0-87969-824-9(1))* Cold Spring Harbor Laboratory Pr.

Pathseekers Staff. Aging in America, 3 vols. Cavanaugh, John C. & Cavanaugh, Christine K., eds. 2009. 867p. 184.95 *(978-0-313-35093-1(0)*, C35093) Greenwood Publishing Group, Inc.

Paul, Angela. The Beauty of Aging: A Woman's Guide to Joyful Living. 2009. 172p. pap. 21.95 *(978-0-595-44683-4(3))* iUniverse, Inc.

Pawelec, Graham, ed. Immunosenescence. (Medical Intelligence Unit Ser.). (Illus.). 2010. xviii, 194p. pap. 209.00 *(978-1-4419-2639-5(9)*, 1441926399) 2008. 194p. 209.00 *(978-0-387-76840-3(8))* Springer.

Peel, Nancye. The Risk of Fall-Related Hip Fracture Injury in Older People. 2010. 244p. pap. *(978-3-8383-3648-0(8))* Lambert Academic Publishing.

Peiper, Howard. Create a Miracle with Hexagonal Water: The Simple Solution for Vital Health & Longevity. 2008. (Illus.). 61p. pap. 9.95 *(978-1-884820-91-5(3))* ATN Group Publishing.

Percival, Steven L. Microbiology & Aging: Clinical Manifestations. Rose, Noel R. et al, eds. 2009. (ENG., Illus.). xii, 348p. 169.00 *(978-1-58829-640-5(7)*, 1588296407) Humana Pr.

Pescatore, Fred & Gazella, Karolyn A. Boost Your Health with Bacteria. 2009. 250p. pap. 15.95 *(978-1-935297-21-5(X))* Better Nutrition Magazine.

Phellas, Constantinos, ed. Aging in European Societies: Healthy Aging in Europe. 2012. (Springer Series on International Aging Ser.). (ENG.). 200p. 189.00 *(978-1-4419-8344-2(9)*, 1441983449) Springer.

Phillipson, Chris, ed. Social Issues of Aging, 4 vols., Set. 2011. 1295.00 *(978-0-415-40151-7(8))* Routledge.

Pickering, Samuel F. Autumn Spring. 2007. (ENG.). 152p. per. 19.95 *(978-1-57233-596-7(3))* Univ. of Tennessee Pr.

Pillemer, Karl. 30 Lessons for Living: Tried & True Advice from the Wisest Americans. (ENG.). 288p. (gr. 12). 2012. pap. 16.00 ***(978-0-452-29848-4(2)***, Plume) 2011. 25.95 *(978-1-59463-084-2(4)*, Hudson Street Pr.) Penguin Group (USA) Inc.

—30 Lessons for Living: Tried & True Advice from the Wisest Americans. l.t. ed. 2012. (ENG.). 395p. 31.99 ***(978-1-4104-4737-1(5))*** Thorndike Pr.

Pilotto, Alberto, et al, eds. Aging & the Gastrointestinal Tract, Vol. 32. (Interdisciplinary Topics in Gerontology Ser.: Vol. 32). (Illus.). *(978-3-8055-7555-3(6))* Karger, S. AG.

Poljsak, Borut, ed. Decreasing Oxidative Stress & Retarding the Aging Process. 2009. (Aging Issues, Health & Financial Alternatives Ser.). 89.00 *(978-1-61728-345-1(2)*, Nova Biomedical Bks.) Nova Science Pubs., Inc.

Poon, Leonard W. & Perls, Thomas T., eds. Biopsychosocial Approaches to Longevity. 2008. (Annual Review of Gerontology & Geriatrics Ser.). (Illus.). 273p. 58.00 *(978-0-8261-1537-9(3))* Springer Publishing Co., Inc.

Powell, Jason L. Aging & Social Policy: A Foucauldian Excursion. 2011. (Social Perspectives of Aging (Series Editor: Jason L. Powell, Dean of Faculty, University of Ser.). 190p. 69.00 *(978-1-61209-838-8(X))* Nova Science Pubs., Inc.

—Aging, Theory & Globalization. 2011. 67p. *(978-1-61761-947-2(7))*; 43.00 net. *(978-1-61762-947-1(2))* Nova Science Pubs., Inc.

Powell, Jason L. China, Aging, & Theory. 2012. pap. ***(978-1-62100-915-3(7))*** Nova Science Pubs., Inc.

Powell, Jason L. & Chen, Sheying. The Global Dynamics of Aging. 2012. ***(978-1-62100-936-8(X))*** Nova Science Pubs., Inc.

Powell, Jason L. & Cook, Ian G. Aging in Asia. 2009. (Aging Issues, Health & Financial Alternatives Ser.). (Illus.). 219p. 79.00 *(978-1-60741-649-4(2))* Nova Science Pubs., Inc.

Powell/Chamberlain. Social Theory, Aging, & Social Welfare. 2nd ed. 2012. (ENG.). 194p. 65.00 ***(978-0-7391-4777-1(3))*** Lexington Bks.

—Social Welfare, Aging, & Social Theory. 2nd ed. 2012. (ENG.). 194p. pap. 27.95 ***(978-0-7391-4778-8(1))*** Lexington Bks.

Prasad, Amiya. The Fine Art of Looking Younger: A Leading Cosmetic Surgeon's Guide to Long Lasting Beauty. 2009. (Illus.). 240p. pap. 19.95 *(978-0-9792240-2-7(0))* MDPublish.com.

Pratt, Steven & Kolberg, Sharyn. SuperHealth: 6 Simple Steps, 6 Easy Weeks, 1 Longer, Healthier Life. 2010. (ENG.). 384p. (gr. 12-18). 7.99 *(978-0-451-22762-1(X)*, Signet) Penguin Group (USA) Inc.

Prieto, Emily. Home Health Care Provider: A Guide to Essential Skills. 2008. (Illus.). 35.00 *(978-0-8261-2852-2(1))* Springer Publishing Co., Inc.

Prskawetz, Alexia, et al. Population Aging, Human Capital Accumulation, & Productivity Growth. 2008. pap. *(978-0-87834-116-0(1))* Population Council.

Pruchno, Rachel. Challenges of an Aging Society: Ethical Dilemmas, Political Issues. Pruchno, Rachel A. et al, eds. 2007. (ENG., Illus.). 464p. (gr. 17). 51.95 *(978-0-8018-8648-5(1))* Johns Hopkins Univ. Pr.

Pruit, Suzette. The Middle Ages: Navigating the Years from 40 To 60. 2009. 184p. pap. 13.95 *(978-0-9841468-0-2(6))* Anglin Ramsey Pr.

Putnam, Rita J. Our Positively Golden Years Vol. 1: Reflections on Aging. l.t. ed. Date not set. (Illus.). 200p. (Orig.). pap. *(978-1-886909-04-5(0))* Dynamic Communications, Inc.

Rai, Gurcharan & Mulley, Graham. Elderly Medicine: A Training Guide. 2nd rev. ed. 2007. (ENG., Illus.). 520p. (C). 145.00 *(978-0-443-10302-5(X)*, Churchill Livingstone) Elsevier - Health Sciences Div.

Ramsey, Janet L. & Blieszner, Rosemary. Spiritual Resiliency & Aging: Hope, Relationality, & the Creative Self. 2012. ***(978-0-89503-474-8(3))***; ***(978-0-89503-387-1(9))*** Baywood Publishing Co., Inc.

Ramsey, Valerie & Hummel, Heather. Gracefully: Looking & Being Your Best at Any Age. 2008. (ENG., Illus.). 304p. 24.95 *(978-0-07-154623-2(5)*, 0071546235) McGraw-Hill Cos., The.

Randall, William L. & McKim, Elizabeth. Reading Our Lives: The Poetics of Growing Old. 2008. (ENG.). 224p. 39.95 *(978-0-19-530687-3(2))* Oxford Univ. Pr., Inc.

RASMUSSEN, Susan. POETICS & POLITICS of TUAREG AGING: Life course & personal destiny in Niger. 2009. 208p. pap. 22.00 *(978-0-87580-624-2(4))* Northern Illinois Univ. Pr.

Rathus, Spencer A. HDEV. 2nd ed. 2011. (PSY 232 Developmental Psychology Ser.). (ENG.). 416p. pap. 69.95 *(978-1-111-51982-7(X))* Wadsworth.

Rattan, S. I., ed. Modulating Aging & Longevity. 2010. (Biology of Aging & its Modulation Ser.). 336p. pap. 239.00 *(978-90-481-5311-3(0),* 9048163110) Springer.

Rattan, Suresh & Kassem, Moustapha, eds. Prevention & Treatment of Age-related Diseases. 2006. (ENG., Illus.). vii, 364p. 189.00 *(978-1-4020-4884-5(X),* 140204884X) Springer.

Rattan, Suresh I. S., et al, eds. Understanding & Modulating Aging. 2006. (Annals of the New York Academy of Sciences Ser.: Vol. 1067). (ENG., Illus.). 352p. pap. 139.95 *(978-1-57331-599-9(0),* Wiley-Blackwell) Wiley, John & Sons, Inc.

Rattan, Suresh I. S. & Kassem, Moustapha, eds. Prevention & Treatment of Age-related Diseases. 2010. (ENG.). vii, 364p. pap. 189.00 *(978-90-481-7217-7(9),* 9048172179) Springer.

Reid, Bill. Senior Citizens Writing II. 2009. 360p. pap. 30.00 *(978-1-60235-107-3(4))* Parlor Pr.

Rhoades, Lillian. When Youth Fades: Reach a Ripe Old Age Without Rotting on the Vine - Aging from a Biblical Perspective. 2010. 160p. 24.98 *(978-1-4389-8511-4(8))*; pap. 15.98 *(978-1-4389-8510-7(X))* AuthorHouse.

Richmond, Lewis. Aging as a Spiritual Practice: A Contemplative Guide to Growing Older & Wiser. 2012. (ENG.). 256p. (gr. 12). 22.50 *(978-1-59240-690-6(4),* Gotham) Penguin Group (USA) Inc.

Robbins, John. Healthy At 100: The Scientifically Proven Secrets of the World's Healthiest & Longest-Lived Peoples. 2007. (ENG.). 384p. per. 17.00 *(978-0-345-49011-7(8),* Ballantine Bks.) Random House Publishing Group.

—Healthy At 100: The Scientifically Proven Secrets of the World's Healthiest & Longest-Lived Peoples. l.t. ed. 2007. (Thorndike Health, Home & Learning Ser.). 671p. 29.95 *(978-0-7862-9900-3(2))* Thorndike Pr.

Robinson, Mary, et al, eds. Global Health & Global Aging. 2007. (ENG., Illus.). 400p. 58.00 *(978-0-7879-8810-4(3),* Jossey-Bass) Wiley, John & Sons, Inc.

Rockwood, Kenneth, et al. Textbook of Geriatric Medicine & Gerontology. 7th ed. 2010. (ENG., Illus.). 1152p. (C). 285.00 *(978-1-4160-6231-8(9),* Saunders) Elsevier - Health Sciences Div.

Rodiek, Susan D. & Schwarz, Benyamin, eds. The Role of the Outdoors in Residential Environments for Aging. 2006. (ENG., Illus.). 294p. 175.00 *(978-0-7890-3243-0(0))*; pap. 54.95 *(978-0-7890-3244-7(9))* Routledge.

Rogers, Jim. Midlife Metamorphosis. 2009. 218p. pap. 14.95 *(978-1-60860-415-9(2),* Eloquent Bks.) AEG Literary Publishing Services, Inc.

Rohr, Richard. Falling Upward: A Spirituality for the Two Halves of Life. 2011. (ENG.). 240p. 19.95 *(978-0-470-90775-7(4),* Jossey-Bass) Wiley, John & Sons, Inc.

Roizen, Michael F. & Hafen, Tracy. The RealAge Workout: Maximum Health, Minimum Work. 2007. (Illus.). 240p. per. 16.95 *(978-0-06-000938-0(1),* William Morrow Paperbacks) HarperCollins Pubs.

Rolland, Yves. Sarcopenia, an Issue of Clinics in Geriatric Medicine. 2011. (Clinics: Internal Medicine Ser.: 27-3). (ENG., Illus.). 168p. 110.00 *(978-1-4557-0454-5(7),* Saunders) Elsevier - Health Sciences Div.

Rose, Jerry & Rose, Shirley. Significant Living: A Road Map for the Second Half of Your Life. 2009. 272p. 19.99 *(978-1-60374-085-2(6),* 770852) Whitaker Hse.

Roth, Norma. Aging Gracefully with Dignity, Integrity & Spunk Intact: Aging Defiantly. 2009. 252p. pap. 18.95 *(978-1-4389-6432-4(3))* AuthorHouse.

Rothstein, Pauline M. & Schull, Diantha Dow. Boomers & Beyond: Reconsidering the Role of Libraries. 2009. (Illus.). 144p. 55.00 *(978-0-8389-1014-6(9))* American Library Assn.

Rowan, Roy. Never Too Late: A 90-Year-Old's Pursuit of a Whirlwind Life. 2011. (ENG.). 240p. 19.95 *(978-0-7627-6376-4(0),* Lyons Pr.) Globe Pequot Pr., The.

Rubin, Lillian B. 60 on Up: The Truth about Aging in the Twenty-first Century. 2008. (ENG.). 192p. pap. 15.00 *(978-0-8070-2929-9(7))* Beacon Pr.

Rudolph, K. Lenhard. Molecular Mechanisms of Adult Stem Cell Aging. 2010. (Illus.). viii, 107p. *(978-3-8055-9244-4(2))* Karger, S. AG.

—Telomeres & Telomerase in Ageing, Disease, & Cancer: Molecular Mechanisms of Adult Stem Cell Ageing. Rudolph, K. Lenhard, ed. 2007. (ENG., Illus.). xiv, 330p. 239.00 *(978-3-540-73708-7(1),* 3540737081) Springer.

Rudolph, K. Lenhard, ed. Molecular Mechanisms of Adult Stem Cell Aging. 2010. (Else Kroener-Fresenius Symposia Ser.). (ENG., Illus.). 108p. *(978-3-8055-9243-7(4))* Karger, S. AG.

—Telomeres & Telomerase in Aging, Disease, & Cancer: Molecular Mechanisms of Adult Stem Cell Ageing. 2010. (ENG., Illus.). xiv, 330p. pap. 239.00 *(978-3-642-09288-6(8),* 3642092888) Springer.

Ryan, Patrick & Coughlan, Barry J., eds. Ageing & Older Adults. 2011. (ENG., Illus.). 296p. (C). 100.00 *(978-0-415-58289-6(X))*; pap. 34.95 *(978-0-415-58290-2(3))* Routledge.

Ryan, Thomas. Remember to Live! Embracing the Second Half of Life. 2012. (Illus.). xii, 238p. *(978-1-61643-134-1(2))*; 256p. pap. 19.95 *(978-0-8091-4758-8(0))* Paulist Pr.

Salnikov, Lev. A New Look at the Mechanisms & Theory of Aging. 2011. 64p. 24.99 *(978-1-4628-5625-1(X))*; pap. 15.99 *(978-1-4628-5624-4(1))* Xlibris Corp.

Sanders, Ruth. My Parent: My Child. 2007. 48p. per. 16.95 *(978-1-60441-110-2(4))* PublishAmerica, Inc.

Santin, Janaina Rigo, et al. Envelhecimento Humano: Saúde e Qualidade de Vida. 2009. (POR., Illus.). 282p. *(978-85-7515-712-1(4))* Fundacao Universidade de Passo Fundo-Upf Editora.

Schrijvers, Dirk, ed. ESMO Handbook of Cancer in the Senior Patient. 2010. 168p. pap. 99.00 *(978-1-84184-709-2(7),* Informa Healthcare) Taylor & Francis Group.

Schut, Holly. Midlife Momentum: Living with Purpose on Purpose in Midlife & Beyond. 2011. 167p. pap. 13.95 *(978-1-4327-6954-3(5))* Outskirts Pr., Inc.

Schwaiger, Elisabeth. Ageing, Gender, Embodiment & Dance: Finding a Balance. 2011. (ENG., Illus.). 232p. 85.00 *(978-0-230-27640-6(7))* Palgrave Macmillan.

Schwarz, Norbert & Park, Denise C., eds. Cognitive Aging: A Primer. 2nd rev. ed. 2008. 336p. 34.95 *(978-1-84169-432-0(0),* Psychology Press) Taylor & Francis Group GBR. Dist: Taylor & Francis Group.

Services for the Aging in America: Four Scenarios for the Next Decade. 130p. (Orig.). pap. *(978-1-930599-10-9(2))* American Assn. of Homes & Services for The Aging.

Severson, D. W. Natural Medicines for Deadly Diseases: Recommended Reading for All Senior Citizens, 1 vol. 2010. 78p. pap. 19.95 *(978-1-4512-0961-7(4))* PublishAmerica, Inc.

Shaffer, Joyce. Ideal Aging: 7 Steps to Keep Your Brain Fit. 2007. per. 29.97 *(978-0-9770411-1-4(5))* Ideal Pr.

Shammas, Nicolas W., et al. Live Longer, Live Healthier: The Secrets for Graceful Aging. 2007. (Illus.). xii, 410p. *(978-0-9755384-2-5(X))* Midwest Cardiovascular Research Foundation.

Shostak, Stanley. The Evolution of Death: Why We Are Living Longer. 2006. (SUNY Series in Philosophy & Biology). (Illus.). 256p. (C). pap. 29.95 *(978-0-7914-6946-0(8))*; 246p. 80.50 *(978-0-7914-6945-3(X))* State Univ. of New York Pr.

Shulman, Neil, et al. The Real Truth about Aging: A Survival Guide for Older Adults & Caregivers. 2009. (ENG., Illus.). 368p. pap. 21.98 *(978-1-59102-719-5(5))* Prometheus Bks., Pubs.

Sigloh, Jane. Like Trees Walking: In the Second Half of Life. 2007. (ENG.). 144p. per. 13.95 *(978-1-56101-290-9(4))* Cowley Pubns.

Signorile, Joseph F. Bending the Aging Curve: The Complete Exercise Guide for Older Adults. 2011. (ENG., Illus.). 328p. (C). pap. 46.00 *(978-0-7360-7445-2(7))* Human Kinetics Pubs.

Silva, David. More Senior Moments Getting the Most Ou. 2007. pap. 13.95 *(978-1-4327-0107-9(X))* Outskirts Pr., Inc.

Simon, George K. Character Disturbance: The phenomenon of our Age. 2011. (ENG., Illus.). 256p. (gr. 13). 29.95 *(978-1-935166-32-0(8))*; pap. 19.95 *(978-1-935166-33-7(6))* Parkhurst Brothers, Inc., Pubs.

Simopoulos, Artemis P., ed. Nutrition & Fitness: Mental Health, Aging & the Implementation of a Healthy Diet & Physical Activity Lifestyle, Vol. 95. (World Review of Nutrition & Dietetics Ser.: Vol. 95). (Illus.). *(978-3-8055-7945-2(4))* Karger, S. AG.

Sinclair, Donna. The Long View: An Elderwoman's Book of Wisdom, 1 vol. 2011. (ENG.). 336p. pap. 19.95 *(978-1-55145-595-2(1))* Northstone Publishing, Inc. CAN. Dist: Westminster John Knox Pr.

Singh, Yadawendra. Population Aging & Its Implications for Health Expenditure. 2010. 92p. pap. *(978-3-639-25519-5(4))* VDM Verlag Dr. Mueller e.K.

Small, Gary & Vorgan, Gigi. The Longevity Bible: 8 Essential Strategies for Keeping Your Mind Sharp & Your Body Young. 2007. (Illus.). 336p. pap. 14.00 *(978-1-4013-0898-8(8))* Hyperion Pr.

Soares, C. N. & Warren, Michelle P., eds. The Menopausal Transition: Interface Between Gynecology & Psychiatry. 2009. (Key Issues in Mental Health Ser.). (Illus.). 150p. *(978-3-8055-9101-0(2))* Karger, S. AG.

Social Structures: Demographic Changes & the Well-Being of Older Persons. 2007. (Societal Impact on Aging Ser.). (Illus.). 314p. 90.00 *(978-0-8261-2407-4(0))* Springer Publishing Co., Inc.

Sokolovsky, Jay. The Cultural Context of Aging: Worldwide Perspectives, 1 vol. Sokolovsky, Jay, ed. 3rd ed. 2008. (Illus.). 808p. pap. 44.95 *(978-0-275-99302-3(7),* B9302, Praeger Pubs.) Greenwood Publishing Group, Inc.

Soladay, James Richard. Aging Abcs Some Not-Quite-Posthumous Notes. 2007. 204p. per. 13.95 *(978-1-59330-486-7(2))* Aventine Pr.

Somer, Elizabeth. Age-Proof Your Body: Your Complete Guide to Looking & Feeling Younger. 2nd ed. 2006. (ENG., Illus.). 400p. per. 18.95 *(978-0-07-146264-8(3),* 0071462643) McGraw-Hill Cos., The.

Spencer, Olga Brom. New Frontiers in Aging: Spirit & Science to Maximize Peak Experience in Your 60s, 70s, & Beyond, 1 vol. 2008. 200p. 34.95 *(978-0-313-35933-0(4),* C35933, Praeger Pubs.) Greenwood Publishing Group, Inc.

Stafford, Philip B. Elderburbia: Aging with a Sense of Place in America, 1 vol. 2009. (Illus.). 187p. 44.95 *(978-0-313-36436-5(2),* C36436, Praeger Pubs.) Greenwood Publishing Group, Inc.

Stansbury, Apostle Raymond P. I Just Rose to Tell You What Nobody Told Me: How to age gracefully, & enjoy it! 2009. 156p. 22.49 *(978-1-4389-4230-8(3))*; pap. 11.99 *(978-1-4389-4231-5(1))* AuthorHouse.

Stathis, Gonos & Suresh, Rattan. Molecular Mechanisms & Models of Aging. Chondrogianni, Niki et al, eds. 2008. (Annals of the New York Academy of Sciences Ser.: 64). (ENG.). 300p. pap. 154.95 *(978-1-57331-686-6(5),* Wiley-Blackwell) Wiley, John & Sons, Inc.

Steinem, Gloria. Doing Sixty & Seventy. 2006. 96p. 19.95 *(978-0-9758744-2-4(X))* Elders Academy Pr.

Stern, Yaakov. Cognitive Reserve: Theory & Applications. 2006. (Studies on Neuropsychology, Neurology, & Cognition). (ENG., Illus.). 368p. 105.95 *(978-1-84169-474-0(6),* Psychology Press) Taylor & Francis Group GBR. Dist: Taylor & Francis Group.

Stone, Carol Leth. Geriatrics, 1 vol. 2011. (Health & Medical Issues Today Ser.). (Illus.). 199p. 35.00 *(978-0-313-37618-4(2),* GR7618) Greenwood Publishing Group, Inc.

—Geriatrics. 2011. *(978-0-313-37619-1(0),* Greenwood Pr.) Greenwood Publishing Group, Inc.

Sutherland, Caroline. The Body Knows... How to Stay Young: Healthy-Aging Secrets from a Medical Intuitive. 2008. (ENG.). 200p. pap. 15.95 *(978-1-4019-2024-1(1))* Hay Hse., Inc.

Sweeting, George. The Joys of Successful Aging: Living Your Days to the Fullest. 2008. (ENG.). 160p. pap. 14.99 *(978-0-8024-7290-3(7))* Moody Pubs.

Tavernarakis, Nektarios. Protein Metabolism & Homeostasis in Aging. 2010. (Advances in Experimental Medicine & Biology Ser.). (ENG., Illus.). xxii, 248p. 189.00 *(978-1-4419-7001-5(0),* 1441970010) Springer.

Teitell, Beth. Drinking Problems at the Fountain of Youth. l.t. ed. 2008. (ENG.). 288p. pap. 24.95 *(978-0-06-166818-0(4),* HarperLuxe) HarperCollins Pubs.

Teo, Peggy, et al. Ageing in Singapore: Service Needs & the State. 2006. (Routledge Contemporary Southeast Asia Ser.: Vol. 10). (Illus.). 180p. 160.00 *(978-0-415-37487-3(1))* Routledge.

Thomas, Allison E., ed. DNA Repair: Damage, Repair Mechanisms & Aging. 2010. (DNA: Properties & Modifications, Functions & Interactions, Recombination & Applications Ser.). 145.00 *(978-1-61668-914-8(5))* Nova Science Pubs., Inc.

Timiras, Paola S., ed. Physiological Basis of Aging & Geriatrics. 4th rev. ed. 2007. Orig. Title: Physiological Basis of Geriatrics. (ENG., Illus.). 536p. 250.00 *(978-0-8493-7305-3(0),* Informa Healthcare) Taylor & Francis Group GBR. Dist: Taylor & Francis Group.

Timonen, Virpi. Ageing Societies: A Comparative Introduction. 2008. (ENG., Illus.). 224p. (C). 154.00 *(978-0-335-22270-4(6),* 0335222706, Open University Pr.); pap. 47.00 *(978-0-335-22269-8(2),* 0335222692) McGraw-Hill Education GBR. Dist: McGraw-Hill Cos., The.

Tollefsbol, Trygve O., ed. Biological Aging: Methods & Protocols. 2007. (Methods in Molecular Biology Ser.: Vol. 371). (Illus.). XVI, 414p. 199.00 *(978-1-58829-658-0(X),* 158829658X) Humana Pr.

Touhy, Theris A. & Jett, Kathleen F. Ebersole & Hess' Gerontological Nursing & Healthy Aging. 3rd ed. 2009. (ENG., Illus.). 496p. (C). pap. 61.95 *(978-0-323-05701-1(2),* Mosby) Elsevier - Health Sciences Div.

—Ebersole & Hess' Toward Healthy Aging: Human Needs & Nursing Response. 8th ed. 2011. (ENG., Illus.). 520p. (C). pap. 69.95 *(978-0-323-07316-5(6),* Mosby) Elsevier - Health Sciences Div.

Trickett, Donna M. Caregiving 101: 101 Easy-to-Understand bits of Vital Information. 2011. 228p. 29.99 *(978-1-4568-8751-3(3))*; pap. 19.99 *(978-1-4568-8750-6(5))* Xlibris Corp.

Troyansky, David G. Aging in World History. 2012. (Themes in World History Ser.). (ENG.). 192p. 115.00 *(978-0-415-77906-7(5))* Routledge.

Tulle, Emmanuelle. Ageing, the Body & Social Change: Running in Later Life. 2008. (ENG., Illus.). 256p. 89.00 *(978-0-230-51759-2(5))* Palgrave Macmillan.

Turner, Bryan S. Can We Live Forever? A Sociological & Moral Inquiry. 2009. (Key Issues in Modern Sociology Ser.). (ENG., Illus.). 174p. 99.00 *(978-1-84331-780-7(X))*; pap. 32.95 *(978-1-84331-794-4(X))* Anthem Pr. GBR. Dist: Books International, Inc.

Upham, Emily W. & Gravenson, Linda. In the Fullness of Time: 32 Women on Life After 50. Guethe, Gravenson, ed. 2010. (ENG.). 304p. pap. 16.00 *(978-1-4391-0923-6(0),* Beyond Words/Atria Bks.) Atria Bks.

Urster, Johan P., ed. Research Trends in Nutrition for the Middle Aged & Elderly. 2008. (Illus.). 250p. 129.00 *(978-1-60456-147-0(5),* Nova Biomedical Bks.) Nova Science Pubs., Inc.

Vavra, Elisabeth. Alterskulturen des Mittelalters und der fruhen Neuzeit: Internationaler Kongress, Krems an der Donau, 16. bis 18. Oktober 2006. 2008. (Sitzungsberichte der Phil. -Hist. Klasse Ser.). (Illus.). 387p. (C). pap. 48.00 *(978-3-7001-6108-0(5))* Austrian Academy of Sciences Press AUT. Dist: Brown, David Bk. Co., The.

von Zglinicki, T., ed. Aging at the Molecular Level. 2012. (Biology of Aging & its Modulation Ser.). (ENG.). x, 248p. pap. 229.00 *(978-90-481-6482-0(6),* 9048164826) Springer.

Vukotic, Dragutin & Kovacevic, Z. Vremenska Nepodudarnost Bioloskog I Hronoloskog Starenja U Crnoj Gorii [sic]. 2009. (Illus.). 401p. *(978-86-7215-228-9(X))* Crnogorska akademija nauka i umjetnosti.

Wahidin, Azrini & Cain, Maureen, eds. Ageing, Crime & Society. 2006. (Illus.). (C). (ENG.). 296p. 89.95 *(978-1-84392-153-0(7))*; 276p. pap. 49.95 *(978-1-84392-152-3(9))* Willan Publishing GBR. Dist: Taylor & Francis Group.

Wahl, Hans-Werner, et al, eds. The Many Faces of Health, Competence & Well-Being in Old Age: Integrating Epidemiological, Psychological & Social Perspectives. 2010. (ENG.). x, 267p. pap. 169.00 *(978-90-481-7056-2(7),* 9048170567) Springer.

—New Dynamics in Old Age: Individual, Environmental & Societal Perspectives. 2007. (Society & Aging Ser.). (Illus.). 400p. (C). 74.50 *(978-0-89503-322-2(4))* Baywood Publishing Co., Inc.

Waldman, Christina. You Are Not Getting Older, You Are Getting Better. 2010. pap. 10.00 *(978-0-578-05607-4(0))* Torretilla, Christina D.

Walford, Roy. Maximum Life Span. 2006. 276p. per. 17.95 *(978-0-393-33085-4(0))* Norton, W. W. & Co., Inc.

Walker, Alan & Aspalter, Christian, eds. Active Aging in Asia. 2012. (Routledge Studies in Social Welfare in Asia Ser.). (ENG.). 240p. (C). 125.00 *(978-0-415-69735-4(2))* Routledge.

Walsh, Mel. Hot Granny: Fabulous at 50, 60 & Beyond! 2007. (ENG., Illus.). 136p. 12.95 *(978-0-8118-5628-7(3))* Chronicle Bks. LLC.

Weber, Pavel. Elderly Patients with Multi-Morbidity, Frailty, & Geriatric Syndromes: Therapeutic Problem of Contemporary & Incoming Medicine at Intensive Care Unit (ICU) from the Geriatrician's Viewpoint. 2010. pap. 49.00 *(978-1-61761-176-6(X))* Nova Science Pubs., Inc.

Weil, Andrew. Healthy Aging: A Lifelong Guide to Your Well-Being. (ENG.). 2007. 368p. pap. 15.95 *(978-0-307-27754-1(2))* 2006. 384p. mass mkt. 7.99 *(978-0-307-27949-1(9))* Knopf Doubleday Publishing Group. (Anchor).

Weiniger, Steven. Stand Taller Live Longer: An Anti-Aging Strategy. 2008. (Illus.). 240p. per. 22.95 *(978-0-9797136-0-6(9))* BodyZone.com Pr.

Weinstein, Barbara. Geriatric Audiology. 2011. (ENG., Illus.). 368p. 79.99 *(978-1-60406-174-1(X))* Thieme Medical Pubs., Inc.

Weiler, Noah J. & Rattan, Suresh I. S., eds. Healthy Aging & Longevity: Third International Conference. 2007. (Annals of the New York Academy of Sciences Ser.). (ENG.). 500p. pap. 159.95 *(978-1-57331-680-4(6),* Wiley-Blackwell) Wiley, John & Sons, Inc.

Wexler, Barbara. Growing Old in America. 2009. (Information Plus Ser.). (ENG., Illus.). 208p. pap. 53.00 *(978-1-4144-0757-9(2))* Cengage Gale.

Whyte, John. Is This Normal? The Essential Guide to Middle Age & Beyond. 2011. (ENG., Illus.). 272p. 25.99 *(978-1-60961-121-7(7))* Rodale Pr., Inc.

Wildman, Frank. Change Your Age: Using Your Body & Brain to Feel Younger, Stronger, & More Fit. 2010. (ENG.). 240p. pap. 18.95 *(978-0-7382-1363-7(2))* Da Capo Pr., Inc.

Williams, Richard, et al, eds. Process of Aging: Social & Psychological Perspectives (Two Volumes), 2 vols. 2008. (ENG., Illus.). 1157p. pap. 195.00 *(978-0-202-36303-5(1))* Aldine Transaction.

Witten, Tarynn M. & Eyler, A. Evan, eds. Gay, Lesbian, Bisexual, & Transgender Aging: Challenges in Research, Practice, & Policy. 2012. (ENG.). 360p. (C). (gr. 13-17). 60.00 *(978-1-4214-0319-9(6))*; pap. 30.00 *(978-1-4214-0320-5(X))* Johns Hopkins Univ. Pr.

Wold, Gloria Hoffman. Basic Geriatric Nursing. 5th ed. 2011. (ENG., Illus.). 408p. (C). pap. 41.95 *(978-0-323-07399-8(9),* Mosby) Elsevier - Health Sciences Div.

Wolf, Norman S., ed. Comparative Biology of Aging. 2010. (ENG., Illus.). viii, 388p. 199.00 *(978-90-481-3464-9(1),* 9048134641) Springer.

Wood, Ellen. The Secret Method for Growing Younger: A Step-by-Step Anti-Aging Process Using the Law of Attraction to Help You Stop Aging, Grow Younger & Enjoy Life. 2007. 142p. 14.95 *(978-0-9794045-0-4(9))* StarHouse Creations.

World Bank Institute Staff. Aging Populations, Pension Funds, & Financial Markets: Regional Perspectives & Global Challenges for Central, Eastern, & Southern Europe. Holzmann, Robert, ed. 2009. (Directions in Development Ser.). (ENG., Illus.). 184p. pap. 25.00 *(978-0-8213-7732-1(9),* 9780821377321) World Bank Pubns.

World Health Organization Staff & United Nations Population Fund Staff, contrib. by. Women, Ageing & Health: A Framework for Action: Focus on Gender. 2007. (Nonserial Publication Ser.). 55p. pap. 18.00 *(978-92-4-156352-9(4))* World Health Organization.

Ylänne, Virpi, ed. Representing Ageing: Images & Identities. 2012. (ENG., Illus.). 280p. 85.00 *(978-0-230-27259-0(2))* Palgrave Macmillan.

Youth Within. Date not set. 472p. pap. 39.95 *(978-1-884350-64-1(X))* Alpha Publishing, Inc.

Zavasta, Tonya. Quantum Eating: The Ultimate Elixir of Youth. 2007. 456p. pap. 30.00 *(978-0-9742434-5-0(0))* BR Publishing LLC.

Zeng, Yi, et al, eds. Healthy Longevity in China: Demographic, Socioeconomic, & Psychological Dimensions. 2009. (Springer Series on Demographic Methods & Population Analysis Ser.). xvi, 435p. pap. 79.95 *(978-1-4020-9478-1(7),* 1402094787) Springer.

—Longer Life & Healthy Aging. 2007. (International Studies in Population Ser.). (Illus.). x, 354p. pap. 69.95 *(978-1-4020-4791-6(6),* 1402047916) Springer.

Zoet Bankson, Marjory. Creative Aging: Rethinking Retirement & Non-Retirement in a Changing World. 2010. 160p. 16.99 *(978-1-59473-281-2(7))* SkyLight Paths Publishing.

AGING—ECONOMIC ASPECTS

Brandstätter, Jana. International divergierende demographische Entwicklungen und internationale Kapitalbewegungen. 2008. (Schriften zur Wirtschaftstheorie und Wirtschaftspolitik Ser.). 150p. pap. 49.95 *(978-3-631-57906-0(3))* Lang, Peter GmbH, Europaischer Verlag der Wissenschaften DEU. Dist: Lang, Peter.

Brown, David. Return Journey. 2011. 222p. pap. *(978-1-907652-42-4(6))* Grosvenor Hse. Publishing Ltd.

Chiocchi, Roger. Baby Boomer Bust? How the Generation of Promise Became the Generation of Panic. 2010. (ENG.). 212p. pap. 17.95 *(978-1-60037-751-8(3))* Morgan James Publishing.

Congressional Budget Office (U.S.), compiled by. The Long-Term Budget Outlook (June 2009) 2009. (ENG., Illus.). 80p. pap. 15.00 *(978-0-16-083497-4(X),* Congressional Budget Office) United States Government Printing Office.

Creedy, John & Guest, Ross. New Developments in the Economics of Ageing. 2007. (International Library of Critical Writings in Economics Ser.). (Illus.). 688p. (C). 330.00 *(978-1-84542-992-9(6))* Elgar, Edward Publishing, Inc.

Davies, Amanda & James, Amity. Geographies of Ageing. 2011. (International Population Studies Ser.). (Illus.). 224p. 99.95 *(978-1-4094-1776-7(X))* Ashgate Publishing Co.

Fishman, Ted C. Shock of Gray: The Aging of the World's Population & How it Pits Young Against Old, Child Against Parent, Worker Against Boss, Company Against Rival, & Nation Against Nation. 2010. (ENG.). 416p. 27.50 (978-1-4165-5102-7(6), Scribner) Scribner.

Gonnot, Jean-Pierre, et al. Social Security, Household, & Family Dynamics in Ageing Societies. 2010. (European Studies of Population Ser.). 248p. pap. 179.00 (978-90-481-4530-0(9), 9048145309) Springer.

Hamada. Ageing & the Labor Market in Japan: Problems & Policies. 2007. (ESRI Studies Series on Ageing). (Illus.). 224p. (C). 119.00 (978-1-84542-849-5(8)) Elgar, Edward Publishing, Inc.

Hegland, Kenney F. & Fleming, Robert. Alive & Kicking. 2007. (ENG.). 288p. pap. 24.95 (978-1-59460-322-8(7)) Carolina Academic Pr.

Kohlbacher, Florian. The Silver Market Phenomenon. 2008. (Illus.). 400p. 89.95 (978-3-540-75330-8(3)) Springer.

Kunisch, Sven, et al, eds. From Grey to Silver: Managing the Demographic Change Successfully. 2010. (ENG., Illus.). xx, 228p. 69.95 (978-3-642-15593-2(6), 3642155936) Springer.

Magnus, George. The Age of Aging: How Demographics Are Changing the Global Economy & Our World. 2008. (ENG., Illus.). 256p. 38.00 (978-0-470-82291-3(0), Wiley) Wiley, John & Sons, Inc.

McMorrow, Kieran & Röger, Werner. The Economic & Financial Market Consequences of Global Ageing. 2010. (European & Transatlantic Studies). (Illus.). xiv, 345p. pap. 149.00 (978-3-642-07355-7(7), 3642073557) Springer.

Mulino, Daniel. The Macroeconomic Impact of an Aging Society: The Impact of Age Structure on Capital Deepening & International Factor Flows. 2008. 136p. pap. (978-3-639-08449-8(7)) VDM Verlag Dr. Mueller e.K.

Ogawa, Naohiro & Mason, Andrew, eds. Population Aging, Intergenerational Transfers & the Macroeconomy. 2007. 320p. (C). 137.00 (978-1-84720-099-0(0)) Elgar, Edward Publishing, Inc.

Page, Ben. Long-Term Budget Outlook. (ENG.). 20p. (C). 2009. pap. 15.00 (978-1-4379-0327-0(4)) 2008. pap. 15.00 (978-1-4379-0131-3(X)) DIANE Publishing Co.

Reisman, David. Social Policy in an Ageing Society: Age & Health in Singapore. 2009. (Illus.). 320p. 137.00 (978-1-84844-094-4(4)) Elgar, Edward Publishing, Inc.

Securing Retirement Coverage for Future Generations: Hearing Before the Subcommittee on Health, Employment, Labor & Pensions, Committee on Education & Labor, U.S. House of Representatives, One Hundred Tenth Congress, First Session, Hearing Held in Washington, DC, November 8, 2007. 2008. (Illus.). iii, 79p. (978-0-16-081516-4(9), 552 — 070-37872-3) United States Government Printing Office.

United Nations Staff, creator. Development in an Ageing World. 60th ed. 2007. (World Economic & Social Survey Ser.). (ENG., Illus.). 212p. per. 60.00 (978-92-1-109154-0(3)) United Nations Pubns.

United Nations: Economic Commission for Europe. A society for all Ages: Challenges & opportunities; proceedings of the UNECE Ministerial Conference on Ageing, 6-8 November 2007, León, Spain. 2009. (ENG.). 116p. pap. 25.00 (978-92-1-116991-1(7)) United Nations Pubns.

Vettori, Stella. Ageing Populations & Changing Labour Markets: Social & Economic Impacts of the Demographic Time Bomb. 2010. (Corporate Social Responsibility Ser.). (Illus.). 284p. 124.95 (978-0-566-08910-7(6), Gower Publishing Co., Ltd.) Ashgate Publishing, Ltd. GBR. Dist: Ashgate Publishing Co.

Widjaja, Muliadi. Designing Pension Program toStrengthen Formal Labor Market in Developing Countries: The Case of Indonesia. 2008. 148p. pap. (978-3-8364-8353-7(X)) VDM Verlag Dr. Mueller e.K.

Wise, David. Explorations in the Economics of Aging. 2011. (National Bureau of Economic Research Conference Report). (ENG., Illus.). 400p. 110.00 (978-0-226-90337-8(0)) Univ. of Chicago Pr.

Wise, David A. Investigations in the Economics of Aging. 2012. E-Book (978-0-226-90316-3(8)) Univ. of Chicago Pr.

Wise, David A. Research Findings in the Economics of Aging. 2010. (National Bureau of Economic Research Conference Report). (Illus.). 504p. 115.00 (978-0-226-90306-4(0)) Univ. of Chicago Pr.

Wise, David A., ed. Developments in the Economics of Aging. 2009. (National Bureau of Economic Research Conference Report). (Illus.). 432p. 99.00 (978-0-226-90335-4(4)) Univ. of Chicago Pr.

Wise, David A., ed. Investigations in the Economics of Aging. 2012. (National Bureau of Economic Research Conference Report). (ENG., Illus.). 504p. 110.00 (978-0-226-90313-2(3)) Univ. of Chicago Pr.

AGING—GENETIC ASPECTS

David-Rus, Diana. Theoretical Studies of Aging. 2009. 224p. pap. (978-3-639-16487-9(3)) VDM Verlag Dr. Mueller e.K.

Doppeler, Jana & Prinzinger, Roland. Programmed Aging: Altersgene und ihre Funktion. 2009. (Wissenschaftliche Gesellschaft an der Johann Wolfgang Goethe-Universitat Frankfurt, Main u Sitzungsberichte Ser.). (GER & ENG., Illus.). 95p. (C). pap. 45.00 (978-3-515-09300-2(1)) Steiner, Franz Verlag Wiesbaden GmbH DEU. Dist: Brown, David Bk. Co., The.

Kimura, Honoka & Suzuki, Aoi. New Research on DNA Damage. 2008. (Illus.). xvi, 410p. 150.00 (978-1-60456-581-2(0)) Nova Science Pubs., Inc.

Klotz, Lars-Oliver, et al. Molecular Processes of Aging. 2012. (ENG.). 450p. pap. 115.00 (978-3-527-32284-8(1), Wiley-VCH) Wiley, John & Sons, Inc.

Lezhava, Teimuraz. Human Chromosomes & Aging. 2009. (Illus.). 177p. pap. 49.00 (978-1-60456-471-6(7), Nova Biomedical Bks.) Nova Science Pubs., Inc.

Read, Catherine Y., et al, eds. Aging, Biotechnology, & the Future. 2008. (ENG., Illus.). 296p. (gr. 17). 47.00 (978-0-8018-8788-8(7)) Johns Hopkins Univ. Pr.

Rose, Michael R. & Finch, Caleb E., eds. Genetics & Evolution of Aging. 2010. (Contemporary Issues in Genetics & Evolution Ser.). (Illus.). 312p. pap. 389.00 (978-90-481-4416-7(7), 9048144167) Springer.

Seplina, Pauline T., ed. New Topics in Aging. 2008. 69.00 (978-1-60692-009-1(X)) Nova Science Pubs., Inc.

Tollefsbol, Trygve O. Epigenetics of Aging. 2010. (Illus.). xiv, 469p. E-Book (978-1-4419-0639-7(8)) Springer.

Vijg, Jan. Aging of the Genome: The Dual Role of DNA in Life & Death. 2007. (ENG., Illus.). 384p. pap. 75.00 (978-0-19-856923-7(8)) Oxford Univ. Pr., Inc.

AGING—NUTRITIONAL ASPECTS

see also Older People—Nutrition

Alschuler, Lise. Healthy Aging: Discover the Japanese Secret. 2009. (Healthy Living Guide Ser.). (ENG.). 32p. pap. 4.95 (978-1-935297-17-8(1)) Better Nutrition Magazine.

Anderson, Nina, et al. The Secrets of Staying Young Revised. l.t. rev. ed. 2007. (ENG., Illus.). 176p. pap. 11.95 (978-1-884820-43-4(3)) SAFE GOODS/ATN Publishing.

Antonaccio, Helena. What's Your Secret? How One Centerfold Stays Alluring & Fit Past the Age of Fifty. 2007. 164p. per. 14.95 (978-0-595-41012-5(X)) iUniverse, Inc.

Bales & Ritchie, eds. Handbook of Clinical Nutrition & Aging. 2nd ed. 2008. (Nutrition & Health Ser.). (Illus.). 500p. 189.00 (978-1-60327-384-8(0)) Springer.

Bidlack, Wayne R. & Meskin, Mark S., eds. Phytochemicals: Aging & Health. 2008. (ENG., Illus.). 232p. 139.95 (978-1-4200-6137-6(2), CRC Press) Taylor & Francis Group GBR. Dist: Taylor & Francis Group.

Braverman, Eric R. Younger You: Unlock the Hidden Power of Your Brain to Look & Feel 15 Years Younger. 2007. 256p. 24.95 (978-0-07-146613-4(4), 9780071466134) McGraw-Hill Cos., The.

Cutter, Teresa. The Anti-Ageing. (ENG., Illus.). 160p. pap. 24.95 (978-1-55285-492-1(2)) Whitecap Bks., Ltd. CAN. Dist: Graphic Arts Ctr. Publishing Co.

Dangour, Alan, et al, eds. Ageing Well: Nutrition, Health, & Social Interventions. 2007. (Society for the Study of Human Biology Ser.: Vol. 47). (ENG., Illus.). 192p. 109.95 (978-0-8493-7474-6(X), CRC Press) Taylor & Francis Group GBR. Dist: Taylor & Francis Group.

Elmadfa, I. & Freisling, H., eds. Healthy Ageing: the Role of Food, Nutrition & Lifestyle: A European Symposium with Outcomes of the Nutri-Senex Project: Supplement Issue: Annals of Nutrition & Metabolism 2008, Vol. 52, Suppl. 1. 2008. (Illus.). 78p. pap. (978-3-8055-8528-6(4)) Karger, S. AG.

Everitt, Arthur V., et al, eds. Calorie Restriction, Aging & Longevity. 2010. (ENG., Illus.). xvi, 500p. 209.00 (978-90-481-8555-9(6), 9048185556) Springer.

FC&A Medical Publishing Staff, contrib. by. The Senior's Guide to Metabolism. 2011. (Illus.). ii, 380p. (978-1-935574-06-4(X)) FC&A Publishing.

Foyer, Christine, et al, eds. Redox Metabolism, Vol. 62. 2009. (Experimental Biology Reviews Ser.). (Illus.). 280p. pap. 223.00 (978-0-415-41954-3(9)) Taylor & Francis Group.

Gallo, Roe & Zocchi, Stephen. Overcoming the Myths of Aging: Lose Weight, Look Great & Live a Happier & Healthier Life. 2007. per. 19.95 (978-0-9642253-1-2(X)) Gallo Pubns.

Holford, Patrick, et al. The 10 Secrets of Healthy Ageing: How to Live Longer, Look Younger & Feel Great. 2012. (ENG., Illus.). 432p. pap. 23.95 (978-0-7499-5654-7(2)) Piatkus Bks. GBR. Dist: Independent Pubs. Group.

Kampf, Antje, et al, eds. Aging Men: Masculinities & Modern Medicine. 2012. (ENG.). 250p. (C). 125.00 (978-0-415-69938-9(X)) Routledge.

Koffman, Dan. Simple Pleasures for Special Seniors: Fruits. 2008. 48p. pap. 20.00 (978-1-59858-726-5(9)) Dog Ear Publishing, LLC.

—Simple Pleasures for Special Seniors: Fun Foods. 2008. 48p. pap. 20.00 (978-1-59858-727-2(7)) Dog Ear Publishing, LLC.

Krusinski, Anna, ed. Cooking Well: Anti-Aging: Over 100 Easy & Delicious Recipes for Longevity & Youthfulness. 2012. (Cooking Well Ser.). (ENG., Illus.). 112p. pap. 11.00 (978-1-57826-372-1(7)) Hatherleigh Co., Ltd., The.

Lindsay, David. Diet & Healthy Ageing. 2008. (Illus.). 352p. pap. (978-1-4051-3093-6(8), Wiley-Blackwell) Wiley, John & Sons, Ltd.

Logan, Alan C., et al. Your Skin, Younger: New Science Secrets to Reverse the Effects of AGE. 2010. (ENG., Illus.). 320p. 21.99 (978-1-58182-705-7(9), Cumberland Hse.) Sourcebooks, Inc.

Mathers, John & BNF Metals Technology Centre Staff. Healthy Ageing: The Role of Nutrition & Lifestyle. Buttriss, Judy, ed. 2009. (British Nutrition Foundation Ser.: 3). (ENG., Illus.). 448p. pap. 115.99 (978-1-4051-7877-8(9), Wiley-Blackwell) Wiley, John & Sons, Inc.

Mitchell, Deborah. Foods That Combat Aging: The Nutritional Way to Stay Healthy Longer. 2007. (Lynn Sonberg Bks.). (ENG., Illus.). 240p. per. 6.99 (978-0-06-134620-0(9)) HarperCollins Pubs.

Nicholas Perricone, M.D. Forever Young: The Science of Nutrigenomics for Glowing, Wrinkle-Free Skin & Radiant Health at Every Age. 2011. (ENG., Illus.). 368p. pap. 16.99 (978-1-4391-7736-5(8), Beyond Words/Atria Bks.) Atria Bks.

Piergeorge, MS, RD, RD, Susan M., Susan M. Boomer Be Well! Rebel Against Aging Through Food, Nutrition & Lifestyle. 2011. (ENG.). 301p. pap. 25.00 (978-0-9846006-0-1(4)) Asante Pubns., LLC.

Stutman, Fred A. Diet-Step 30 Grams/30 Minutes - For Seniors Only! 2008. (Illus.). 304p. 26.95 (978-0-934232-11-1(3)); pap. 16.95 (978-0-934232-12-8(1)) Medical Manor Bks.

Webb, Geoffrey P. & Copeman, June. The Nutrition of Older Adults. (ENG., Illus.). 240p. (Orig.). (978-0-340-60156-3(6), Hodder Arnold) Hodder Education.

Yarrow, Jesse J. Nutrition Neglect & Early Human Aging, Sickness & Disease with Index & Medical Analysis of New Research Information for All Nations. 2006. (Illus.). 160p. 69.95 (978-0-7883-4250-9(9), 07883-42509) ABBE Pubs. Assn. of Washington, D.C.

AGING—PREVENTION

Here are entered works on minimizing the ill effects of aging and maximizing the period of active, healthy life.

Amen, Daniel G. Use Your Brain to Change Your Age: Secrets to Look, Feel, & Think Younger Every Day. 2012. (ENG., Illus.). 384p. 26.00 (978-0-307-88854-9(1), Crown Archetype) Crown Publishing Group.

Barnard, Michael. What I Learned at Work Today: A Collection of Lessons on Life, 1 vol. 2009. 84p. pap. 16.95 (978-1-60813-919-4(0)) PublishAmerica, Inc.

Berns, J. B. Do It or Age Quickly - 60- Second Practices to Live Better, Stronger, & Longer: A Guide Full of the Wisdom My Friend Jb Berns Has Gathered from Chinese Medicineduring His Years of Martial Arts Training & Teaching. 2010. 214p. pap. 19.95 (978-0-578-05833-7(2)) Urban Productions, Inc.

Bohan, Suzanne. 50 Simple Ways to Live a Longer Life: Everyday Techniques from the Forefront of Science. 2007. 304p. pap. 6.99 (978-1-4022-1304-5(2)) Sourcebooks, Inc.

Bortz, Walter M., II & Stickrod, Randall. Roadmap to 100: The Breakthrough Science of Living a Long & Healthy Life. 2010. (ENG.). 256p. 25.00 (978-0-230-10068-8(6)) Palgrave Macmillan.

Bortz, Walter M. & Stickrod, Randall. The Roadmap To 100: The Breakthrough Science of Living a Long & Healthy Life. 2011. (ENG., Illus.). 256p. pap. 16.00 (978-0-230-11205-6(6)) Palgrave Macmillan.

Braverman, Eric R. The Younger (Thinner) You Diet: How Understanding Your Brain Chemistry Can Help You Lose Weight, Reverse Aging, & Fight Disease. 2009. (ENG.). 352p. pap. 15.99 (978-1-60529-477-3(2)) Rodale Pr., Inc.

Brumfield, Theresa L. Guide to Muscular Healing. 2010. 60p. pap. 12.99 (978-1-4520-2770-8(6)) AuthorHouse.

Butler, Robert N. The Longevity Prescription: The 8 Proven Keys to a Long, Healthy Life. 2011. (ENG.). 288p. (gr. 12). 16.00 (978-1-58333-430-0(0), Avery) Penguin Group (USA) Inc.

Butler, Robert Neil. The Longevity Prescription: The 8 Proven Keys to a Long, Healthy Life. 2010. (ENG.). 288p. (gr. 12). 26.00 (978-1-58333-388-4(6), Avery) Penguin Group (USA) Inc.

Challem, Jack. The Fountain: 25 Experts Reveal Their Secrets of Health & Longevity from the Fountain of Youth, 1 vol. 2009. (ENG.). 224p. 24.95 (978-1-59120-248-6(5)) Basic Health Pubns., Inc.

Chang, Joseph. The Aging Myth: Unlocking the Mysteries of Looking & Feeling Young. 2011. 208p. 21.95 (978-0-9776288-7-2(6)) Aylesbury Publishing, LLC.

Conley, Rosemary. The Secrets of Staying Young. 2011. (ENG., Illus.). 222p. 36.95 (978-1-84605-731-1(0)) Random Hse. GBR. Dist: Independent Pubs. Group.

Elwins, Dannie. The Most Well-Known Spas & Anti-Aging Treatments in America. 2009. 36p. pap. 16.99 (978-0-557-15420-3(0)) Lulu Enterprises Inc.

Epstein, Samuel S. & Fitzgerald, Randall. Healthy Beauty: Your Guide to Ingredients to Avoid & Products You Can Trust. 2010. (ENG.). 284p. pap. 16.95 (978-1-935251-72-9(4)) BenBella Bks.

Etoh, Toshihito. Ultimate Anti-Aging Ways: Exotic Wisdom from a Japanese Doctor. 2010. 88p. pap. 9.95 (978-1-4502-4233-2(2)) iUniverse, Inc.

Fonda, Jane. Prime Time: Love, Health, Sex, Fitness, Friendship, Spirit - Making the Most of All of Your Life. 2012. (ENG., Illus.). 448p. pap. 17.00 (978-0-8129-7858-2(7), Random Hse. Trade Paperbacks) Random House Publishing Group.

—Prime Time: Love, Health, Sex, Fitness, Friendship, Spirit - Making the Most of All of Your Life. l.t. ed. 2011. (ENG.). 608p. pap. 27.00 (978-0-7393-7842-7(2)) Random Hse. Large Print.

—Prime Time: Love, Health, Sex, Fitness, Friendship, Spirit- Making the Most of All of Your Life. 2011. (ENG., Illus.). 448p. 27.00 (978-1-4000-6697-1(2)); 27.00 (978-0-8129-9323-3(3)) Random House Publishing Group. (Random House).

Forsythe, James. Anti-Aging Cures: Life Changing Secrets to Reverse the Effects of Aging. 2012. (ENG.). 304p. 25.99 (978-0-9844307-3-4(3)) Red Rock Picture Holdings, Inc.

Godoy, Tadeu. Health & Happiness for a Longer Life: A Guide to Staying Young. 2011. 120p. 21.23 (978-1-4567-2420-7(7)); pap. 10.68 (978-1-4567-2419-1(3)) AuthorHouse.

Greene, Bob. 20 Years Younger: Look Younger, Feel Younger, Be Younger! 2011. 44.99 (978-1-61113-654-8(7), Sound Library) AudioGO.

—20 Years Younger: Look Younger, Feel Younger, Be Younger! (ENG., Illus.). 2012. 320p. pap. 15.99 (978-0-316-13379-1(5)) 2011. 320p. 27.99 (978-0-316-13378-4(7)) 2011. 464p. 29.99 (978-0-316-17796-2(2)) Little Brown & Co.

Guest, Andrew. Clashing Views in Life-Span Development. 3rd ed. 2010. (Taking Sides Ser.). (ENG.). 448p. (C). pap. 48.00 (978-0-07-804995-8(4), 0078049954, McGraw-Hill/Dushkin) McGraw-Hill Higher Education.

Harrold, Glenn. Look Young Live Longer: The 7-Step Programme That Will Slow the Ageing Process & Improve the Quality of Your Life. 2010. (ENG.). 208p. pap. 14.95 (978-0-7528-8610-7(X)) Orion Bks. Ltd. GBR. Dist: Sterling Publishing Co., Inc.

Hartford, Kathleen A. The Key to Vital Living: The Biological Rejuvenation Program. 2007. ring bd. incl. audio compact disk (978-0-9749070-3-1(0)) Grelin Pr.

Haycock, David Boyd. Mortal Coil: A Short History of Living Longer. 2009. (Illus.). 320p. pap. 22.00 (978-0-300-15825-0(4)) Yale Univ. Pr.

Holt, Stephen. The Anti-Aging Triad. 2011. 320p. pap. 89.95 (978-1-4567-5576-8(5)) AuthorHouse.

Klotz, Lars-Oliver, et al. Molecular Processes of Aging. 2012. (ENG.). 450p. pap. 115.00 (978-3-527-32284-8(1), Wiley-VCH) Wiley, John & Sons, Inc.

Krusinski, Anna, ed. Cooking Well: Anti-Aging: Over 100 Easy & Delicious Recipes for Longevity & Youthfulness. 2012. (Cooking Well Ser.). (ENG., Illus.). 112p. pap. 11.00 (978-1-57826-372-1(7)) Hatherleigh Co., Ltd., The.

Lippman, Richard. Stay 40: Without Diet or Exercise. 2008. 264p. 33.95 (978-1-4327-2927-1(6)) Outskirts Pr., Inc.

Maranan, Julia. The 100 Best Ways to Stop Aging & Stay Young: Scientifically Proven Strategies for Taking Years off Your Body. 2011. (ENG., Illus.). 240p. pap. 19.99 (978-1-59233-449-0(0), 1592334490) Quayside.

Meletis, Chris. The Hyaluronic Acid Miracle: Instant Facelift, Anti-Aging, Rejuvenation. 2010. (ENG.). 66p. pap. 8.95 (978-1-893910-69-0(5)) Freedom Pr., Inc., The.

Morelli, Vincent & Sidani, Mohamed. Successful Aging , an Issue of Clinics in Geriatric Medicine. 2011. (Clinics: Internal Medicine Ser.: 27-4). (ENG., Illus.). 240p. 110.00 (978-1-4557-0667-9(1), Saunders) Elsevier - Health Sciences Div.

Murad, Howard. The Water Secret: The Cellular Breakthrough to Look & Feel 10 Years Younger. 2010. (ENG., Illus.). 272p. pap. 18.95 (978-0-470-55470-8(3), Wiley) Wiley, John & Sons, Inc.

National Academies Keck Futures Initiative Healthspan Steering Committee. The National Academies Keck Futures Initiative: The Future of Human Healthspan - Demography, Evolution, Medicine, & Bioengineering, Task Group Summaries. 2008. (ENG.). 140p. pap. 34.50 (978-0-309-11559-9(0)) National Academies Pr.

Nirdosh, Neetu. Dr Nirdosh's Anti Ageing Secrets. 2010. (ENG., Illus.). 256p. pap. 13.95 (978-1-84454-948-1(8)) Blake, John Publishing, Ltd. GBR. Dist: Independent Pubs. Group.

Nyszik, Anita. Take My Wrinkled Hand, Lord: A Humorous Devotional for the Aging. 2011. 124p. pap. 10.68 (978-1-4634-5018-2(4)) AuthorHouse.

Pappas, Apostolos, ed. Nutrition & Skin: Lessons for Anti-Aging, Beauty & Healthy Skin. 2011. (ENG., Illus.). x, 228p. 189.00 (978-1-4419-7966-7(2), 1441979662) Springer.

Passport to Peak Performance: Unlock Your MindPower. 2008. (Illus.). 32p. (978-1-880011-04-1(2)) Dundas-Devonhills Assoc. Pubs.

Plasker, Eric. The 100-Year Lifestyle: Dr. Eric Plasker's Breakthrough Solution for Living Your Best Life — Every Day of Your Life! 2nd ed. 2007. (ENG., Illus.). 256p. 19.95 (978-1-59869-093-4(0)) Adams Media Corp.

Potter, Beverly A. Youth Extension A to Z. 2010. (ENG., Illus.). 192p. pap. 14.95 (978-1-57951-090-9(6)) Ronin Publishing.

Retzler, Kathryn, ND. HormoneSynergy — Optimal Aging & Hormone Balance. 2010. 169p. pap. 14.95 (978-0-557-37056-6(6)) Lulu Enterprises Inc.

Roizen, Michael F. & Oz, Mehmet C. Staying Young: The Owner's Manual for Extending Your Warranty. l.t. ed. 2008. (Illus.). 519p. 31.95 (978-1-4104-0444-2(7)) Thorndike Pr.

Roizen, Michael F., et al. You: Staying Young: The Owner's Manual for Extending Your Warranty. 2007. (ENG., Illus.). 432p. 26.00 (978-0-7432-9256-6(1), Free Pr.) Free Pr.

Russo, Mario L. Rejuvenating Skin Without Surgery. 2009. 58p. pap. 17.95 (978-1-873413-94-4(7)) Merit Publishing International, Inc.

Sears, William. Prime-Time Health: A Scientifically Proven Plan for Feeling Young & Living Longer. l.t. ed. 2010. (ENG.). 736p. pap. 25.99 (978-0-316-07401-8(2)) Little Brown & Co.

Sinclair, David. Just in Time: The Discovery of Sirtuin & How it Will Change Everything. 2011. (ENG., Illus.). 26.00 (978-1-4391-3576-1(2), Free Pr.) Free Pr.

Sixsmith, Andrew, ed. Technology for Active Aging. 2012. (Springer Series on International Aging Ser.). (ENG.). 250p. 189.00 (978-1-4419-8347-3(3), 1441983473) Springer.

Sobh, Rana. Approach & Avoidance Self-Regulation. 2010. 240p. pap. (978-3-639-26094-6(5)) VDM Verlag Dr. Mueller e.K.

Somers, Suzanne. Bombshell: Explosive Medical Secrets That Will Redefine Aging. 2012. (ENG.). 368p. 26.00 (978-0-307-58854-8(8), Crown Archetype) Crown Publishing Group.

Swayzee, Nancy Lister. Moment by Moment an Ageless Process. 2011. 146p. 29.99 (978-1-4568-6492-7(0)); pap. 19.99 (978-1-4568-6491-0(2)) Xlibris Corp.

Tao, Liang-Che. A Whole-Body Approach to Slowing down Aging: Helping You Live Healthier & Longer. 2011. 208p. 27.95 (978-1-4502-9950-3(4)); pap. 17.95 (978-1-4502-9949-7(0)) iUniverse, Inc.

Veurink, Gerald. A Radical Approach to Treating Degenerative Diseases. 2009. 304p. pap. (978-3-639-19736-5(4)) VDM Verlag Dr. Mueller e.K.

Weale, Robert A. Youth Prolonged: Old Age Postponed. 2009. (Illus.). 148p. pap. 24.95 (978-1-84816-507-6(2)) Imperial College Pr. GBR. Dist: World Scientific Publishing Co., Inc.

Weintraub, Arlene. Selling the Fountain of Youth: How the Anti-Aging Industry Made a Disease Out of Getting Old-And Made Billions. 2010. (ENG.). 256p. (gr. 9). 25.95 (978-0-465-01721-8(5)) Basic Bks.

Welch, Raquel. Raquel: Beyond the Cleavage. (ENG., Illus.). 2011. 304p. pap. 15.00 *(978-1-60286-136-7(6))* 2010. 288p. 26.95 *(978-1-60286-097-1(1))*, Weinstein Bks.) Perseus Bks. Group.

Yue, May, et al. May Yue's Tao of Youth: Let Nature Heal You. 2007. 196p. per. 25.00 *(978-0-9794923-0-3(0))* Tao of Youth Publishing.

AGING—PSYCHOLOGICAL ASPECTS

see also Ageism; Older People—Psychology

Agronin, Marc E. How We Age: A Doctor's Journey into the Heart of Growing Old. 2011. (ENG.). 320p. 25.00 *(978-0-306-81853-0(1))* Da Capo Pr., Inc.

Albert, Steven M. & Freedman, Vicki A. Public Health & Aging: Maximizing Function & Well-Being. 2nd ed. 2009. (Illus.). 408p. 65.00 *(978-0-8261-2151-6(9))* Springer Publishing Co., Inc.

Aldwin, Carolyn M., et al, eds. Handbook of Health Psychology & Aging. 2007. (ENG., Illus.). 450p. 65.00 *(978-1-59385-057-9(3))* Guilford Pubns., Inc.

Alexander, William. Hi, I'm Bill & I'm Old: Reinventing My Sobriety for the Long Haul. 2008. (ENG.). 200p. pap. 14.95 *(978-1-59285-663-3(2))* Hazelden Publishing & Educational Services.

Allen, K Eileen & Starbuck, Judith. I Like Being Old: A Guide to Making the Most of Aging. 2011. 172p. pap. 13.95 ***(978-1-936236-67-1(2))*** iUniverse, Inc.

Alwin, Duane F. & Hofer, Scott M., eds. Handbook of Cognitive Aging: Interdisciplinary Perspectives. 2008. (Illus.). 744p. pap. 116.00 *(978-1-4129-6028-1(2)*, B41059P) SAGE Pubns., Inc.

—Handbook of Cognitive Aging: Interdisciplinary Perspectives. 2008. (Illus.). 744p. 150.00 *(978-1-4129-4105-1(9)*, B41059C) SAGE Pubns., Inc.

Amen, Daniel G. Use Your Brain to Change Your Age: Secrets to Look, Feel, & Think Younger Every Day. 2012. (ENG., Illus.). 384p. 26.00 ***(978-0-307-88854-9(1)***, Crown Archetype) Crown Publishing Group.

American Institute of Architects Staff. Design for Aging Post-Occupancy Evaluations: Lessons Learned from Senior Living Environments Featured in the AIA's Design for Aging Review. Anderzhon, Jeffrey W. et al, eds. 2007. (Wiley Series in Healthcare & Senior Living Design Ser.: 8). (ENG., Illus.). 328p. 85.00 *(978-0-471-75714-6(4)*, Wiley) Wiley, John & Sons, Inc.

Anderson, Nina, et al. The Secrets of Staying Young Revised. l.t. rev. ed. 2007. (ENG., Illus.). 176p. pap. 11.95 *(978-1-884820-43-4(3))* SAFE GOODS/ATN Publishing.

Baby Boomer's Guide to Growing Old Gracefully. 2006. *(978-0-9774357-0-8(9))* Grayson, Kate.

Ballesteros, Soledad. Ageing, Cognition, & Neuroscience: A Special Issue of the European Journal of Cognitive Psychology. 2009. (Special Issues of the European Journal of Cognitive Psychology Ser.). (ENG., Illus.). 296p. 79.95 *(978-1-84872-707-6(0)*, Psychology Press) Taylor & Francis Group GBR. Dist: Taylor & Francis Group.

Bateson, Mary Catherine. Composing a Further Life: The Age of Active Wisdom. 2011. (Vintage Ser.). (ENG.). 272p. pap. 15.95 *(978-0-307-27963-7(4)*, Vintage) Knopf Doubleday Publishing Group.

Beaman, Ronda. You're Only Young Twice: 10 Do-Overs to Reawaken Your Spirit. 2006. (Illus.). 226p. per. 14.95 *(978-1-889242-25-5(X))* VanderWyk & Burnham.

Bee, Bjorklund. Journey of Adulthood. 2006. pap. 9.95 *(978-1-4288-1800-2(6))* Cram101 Inc.

Belsky, Janet K. The Psychology of Aging: Theory, Research & Interventions - Test Bank. *(978-0-534-35913-3(2))* Wadsworth.

Bittles, A. H. & Collins, K. J. The Biology of Human Ageing. 2009. (Society for the Study of Human Biology Symposium Ser.). (ENG., Illus.). 292p. pap. 42.00 *(978-0-521-11261-1(3))* Cambridge Univ. Pr.

Bizon, Jennifer L., et al. Animal Models of Human Cognitive Aging. 2009. (Aging Medicine Ser.). (Illus.). 312p. 139.00 *(978-1-58829-996-3(1))* Humana Pr.

Bjorklund, Barbara R. & Bee, Helen L. Journey of Adulthood. 7th ed. 2010. (ENG., Illus.). 456p. (C). 160.00 *(978-0-205-01805-5(X)*, Prentice Hall) Prentice Hall PTR.

Boyd, Malcolm. Wisdom for the Aging: Practical Advice for Living the Best Years of Your Life Right Now. 2009. 197p. pap. 15.00 *(978-0-9819435-4-1(3))* Arnold, Ken Bks.

Brokaw, Sarah. Fortytude: Making the Next Decades the Best Years of Your Life — Through the 40s, 50s, & Beyond. 2011. (ENG.). 288p. pap. 13.99 ***(978-1-4013-4182-4(9))*** Hyperion Pr.

Brokaw, Sarah. Fortytude: Making the Next Decades the Best Years of Your Life - Through the 40s, 50s, & Beyond. 2011. (ENG.). 288p. 23.99 *(978-1-4013-4119-0(5))* Hyperion Pr.

Browne-Miller, Angela. Will You Still Need Me? Feeling Wanted, Loved, & Meaningful as We Age, 1 vol. 2010. (Illus.). 247p. 44.95 *(978-0-313-35390-1(5)*, C35390, Praeger Pubs.) Greenwood Publishing Group, Inc.

Bugental, Elizabeth. Love Fills in the Blanks: Paradoxes of Our Final Years. 2008. *(978-0-9758744-7-9(0))* Elders Academy Pr.

Burr, Andrew. Values & Well-Being in the Retirement Transition. 2008. 108p. pap. *(978-3-8364-3694-6(9))* VDM Verlag Dr. Mueller e.K.

Caracciolo, Rick. Aging Grace: Advice for Pastors, Couselors, & Families of Aging Relatives. 2010. (ENG.). 192p. pap. 14.99 *(978-1-935245-08-7(2))* HigherLife Development Services, Inc.

Carlson, John. Second Thoughts While Aging. 2011. 28p. pap. 12.95 ***(978-1-4327-6723-5(2))*** Outskirts Pr., Inc.

Chancellor, Richard A. Wisdom for Aging Well. 2007. 120p. per. 12.95 *(978-0-595-43592-7(7))* iUniverse, Inc.

Charles, Susan T. & Association for Psychological Science Staff. Current Directions in Adulthood & Aging. 2008. (Association for Psychological Science Readers Ser.). (ENG., Illus.). 224p. (C). per. 53.60 *(978-0-205-59749-9(1))* Allyn & Bacon, Inc.

Chatterjee, Suhita Chopra, et al, eds. Discourses on Aging & Dying. 2008. (Illus.). 272p. (C). pap. 32.95 *(978-0-7619-3644-2(0)*, B36442P) SAGE Pubns., Inc.

Chittister, Joan. The Gift of Years: Growing Older Gracefully. (ENG.). 240p. 2010. pap. 13.95 *(978-1-933346-33-5(7))* 2008. 19.95 *(978-1-933346-10-6(8))* BlueBridge.

Clare, Linda, et al, eds. Handbook of the Clinical Psychology of Ageing. 2nd ed. 2008. (ENG., Illus.). 658p. 245.00 *(978-0-470-01230-7(7)*, Wiley-Interscience) Wiley, John & Sons, Inc.

Clarke, Laura Hurd. Facing Age: Women Growing Older in Anti-Aging Culture. 2010. ix, 165p. *(978-1-4422-0761-5(2))* Rowman & Littlefield Publishers, Inc.

Cochran Molcar, Carol. Place Attachment & Spiritual Well-Being Across the Lifespan. 2008. 96p. pap. *(978-3-639-06030-0(X))* VDM Verlag Dr. Mueller e.K.

Cohen, Gene D. The Mature Mind: The Positive Power of the Aging Brain. 2006. (ENG.). 256p. per. 16.99 *(978-0-465-01204-6(3))* Basic Bks.

—The Mature Mind: The Positive Power of the Aging Brain. rev. ed. 2007. (Thorndike Health, Home & Learning Ser.). (Illus.). 359p. 30.95 *(978-0-7862-9279-0(2))* Thorndike Pr.

Cooper, Stephanie. Body & Being: How we Age, 1. 2007. (Illus.). 67p. per. *(978-0-9779397-0-1(7))* odesign + publishing.

Cram101 Textbook Reviews. Outlines & Highlights for Gerontological Nursing: Competencies for Care by Mauk, Kristen L., ISBN. 2010. 58p. pap. 26.95 *(978-1-61698-398-7(1))* Cram101 Inc.

Cram101 Textbook Reviews. Outlines & Highlights for Human Aging: Biological Perspectives 2nd by Augustine Gaspar Digiovanna, ISBN. 2011. 556p. pap. 38.95 ***(978-1-61461-478-4(4))*** Cram101 Inc.

Cram101 Textbook Reviews & Cram101 Textbook Reviews. Outlines & Highlights for Adult Development & Aging by John C Cavanaugh, Isbn: 9780495601746. 2011. 116p. pap. 28.95 ***(978-1-4288-8825-8(X))*** Cram101 Inc.

—Outlines & Highlights for Handbook of Cognitive Aging: Interdisciplinary Perspectives by Scott Hofer, ISBN. 2011. 152p. pap. 29.95 ***(978-1-61812-015-1(8))*** Cram101 Inc.

—Outlines & Highlights for Handbook of the Psychology of Aging by K Schaie, Isbn: 9780123808820. 2011. 120p. pap. 28.95 ***(978-1-4288-0486-9(2))*** Cram101 Inc.

—Outlines & Highlights for Journey of Adulthood by Barbara R Bjorklund. 2011. 78p. pap. 27.95 ***(978-1-61830-465-0(8))*** Cram101 Inc.

—Outlines & Highlights for Learning to Be Old: Gender, Culture, & Aging by Margaret Cruikshank. 2011. 178p. pap. 29.95 ***(978-1-61830-571-8(9))*** Cram101 Inc.

—Outlines & Highlights for Valuing Older People: The Positive Psychology of Ageing by Elspeth Stirling, ISBN. 2011. 56p. pap. 26.95 ***(978-1-4288-6178-7(5))*** Cram101 Inc.

Cram101 Textbook Reviews Staff. Outlines & Highlights for Adult Development & Aging by Cavanaugh, Isbn: 0534520669. 2008. 140p. per. 11.95 *(978-1-4288-5766-7(4))* Cram101 Inc.

—Outlines & Highlights for Gerontological Nursing: Competencies for Care by Mauk, Kristen L., ISBN. 2009. 58p. pap. 26.95 *(978-1-4288-8416-8(5))* Cram101 Inc.

—Outlines & Highlights for Journey of Adulthood, the by Bjorklund, Isbn: 0131888323. 2008. 100p. pap. 10.95 *(978-1-4288-5927-2(6))* Cram101 Inc.

Cruikshank, Margaret & CRUIKSHANK, Margaret. Learning to Be Old: Gender, Culture, & Aging. 2nd ed. 2009. (ENG.). 266p. pap. 27.95 *(978-0-7425-6594-4(7))* Rowman & Littlefield Publishers, Inc.

Damon, William. The Handbook of Life-Span Development: Cognition, Biology, & Methods, 2 vols., Volume 1. Lerner, Richard M. & Overton, Willis F., eds. 2010. (ENG., Illus.). 1040p. 158.00 *(978-0-470-39011-5(5)*, Wiley) Wiley, John & Sons, Inc.

de Hennezel, Marie. The Art of Growing Old: Aging with Grace. 2012. (ENG.). 192p. (gr. 12). 24.95 ***(978-0-670-02345-5(0)***, Viking Adult) Penguin Group (USA) Inc.

Dolgoff, Stephanie. My Formerly Hot Life: Dispatches from Just the Other Side of Young. 2010. 224p. 25.00 *(978-0-345-52145-3(5)*, Ballantine Bks.) Random House Publishing Group.

Doppeler, Jana & Prinzinger, Roland. Programmed Aging: Altersgene und ihre Funktion. 2009. (Wissenschaftliche Gesellschaft an der Johann Wolfgang Goethe-Universitat Frankfurt, Main u Sitzungsberichte Ser.). (GER & ENG., Illus.). 95p. (C). pap. 45.00 *(978-3-515-09300-2(1))* Steiner, Franz Verlag Wiesbaden GmbH DEU. Dist: Brown, David Bk. Co., The.

Douty, Linda. How Did I Get to Be 70 When I'm 35 Inside? Spiritual Surprises of Later Life. 2011. 192p. pap. 16.99 *(978-1-59473-297-3(3))* SkyLight Paths Publishing.

Duara Ranjan Staff. Mild Cognitive Impairment Early Diagnosis & Treatment. 2010. (ENG., Illus.). 400p. 169.95 *(978-0-8493-3613-3(9)*, Informa Healthcare) Taylor & Francis Group GBR. Dist: Taylor & Francis Group.

Eby, David W., et al. Maintaining Safe Mobility in an Aging Society. 2008. (Human Factors in Transportation Ser.). (ENG., Illus.). 248p. 82.95 *(978-1-4200-6453-7(3)*, CRC Press) Taylor & Francis Group GBR. Dist: Taylor & Francis Group.

Egger, Katharina S. & Moser, Leonie H. Women & Addictions: New Research. 2008. 98.00 *(978-1-60456-971-1(9))* Nova Science Pubs., Inc.

Ellison, James E., et al, eds. Mood Disorders in Later Life. 2nd rev. ed. 2008. (ENG., Illus.). 368p. 200.00 *(978-1-4200-5329-6(9)*, Informa Healthcare) Taylor & Francis Group GBR. Dist: Taylor & Francis Group.

Elmadfa, I. & Freisling, H., eds. Healthy Ageing: the Role of Food, Nutrition & Lifestyle: A European Symposium with Outcomes of the Nutri-Senex Project: Supplement Issue: Annals of Nutrition & Metabolism 2008, Vol. 52, Suppl. 1. 2008. (Illus.). 78p. pap. *(978-3-8055-8528-6(4))* Karger, S. AG.

Erber, Joan T. Aging & Older Adulthood. 2nd ed. 2009. (Wiley Desktop Editions Ser.). (ENG., Illus.). 504p. pap. 82.95 *(978-1-4051-7005-5(0)*, Wiley-Blackwell) Wiley, John & Sons, Inc.

Fatio, Bonnie. Ageesteem: Growing a Positive Attitude Toward Aging. 2007. (ENG.). per. 14.95 *(978-1-60037-267-4(8))* Morgan James Publishing.

Fatio, Bonnie Lou. Ageesteem: Growing a Positive Attitude Toward Aging. 2007. (ENG.). 147p. 24.95 *(978-1-60037-268-1(6))* Morgan James Publishing.

Fernandez-Ballesteros, Rocio. Active Aging: The Contribution of Psychology. 2008. (Illus.). 194p. pap. 42.00 *(978-0-88937-360-0(4))* Hogrefe Publishing.

Fernández-Ballesteros, Rocío, ed. GeroPsychology: European Perspectives for an Aging World. 2007. (Illus.). 254p. 44.00 *(978-0-88937-340-2(X))* Hogrefe Publishing.

Finch, Caleb E. The Biology of Human Longevity: Inflammation, Nutrition, & Aging in the Evolution of Lifespans. 2007. (ENG., Illus.). 640p. 79.95 *(978-0-12-373657-4(9)*, Academic Pr.) Elsevier Science & Technology Bks.

Fishel, M.Ed, Ruth, Ruth. Wrinkles Don't Hurt: Daily Meditations on the Joy of Aging Mindfully. 2011. (ENG., Illus.). 408p. pap. 14.95 ***(978-0-7573-1590-9(9))*** Health Communications, Inc.

Fonda, Jane. Prime Time: Love, Health, Sex, Fitness, Friendship, Spirit - Making the Most of All of Your Life. 2012. (ENG., Illus.). 448p. pap. 17.00 ***(978-0-8129-7858-2(7)***, Random Hse. Trade Paperbacks) Random House Publishing Group.

—Prime Time: Love, Health, Sex, Fitness, Friendship, Spirit - Making the Most of All of Your Life. l.t. ed. 2011. (ENG.). 608p. pap. 27.00 *(978-0-7393-7842-7(2))* Random Hse. Large Print.

—Prime Time: Love, Health, Sex, Fitness, Friendship, Spirit- Making the Most of All of Your Life. 2011. (ENG., Illus.). 448p. 27.00 *(978-1-4000-6697-1(2))*; 27.00 ***(978-0-8129-9323-3(3))*** Random House Publishing Group. (Random House).

Forrest, Derek. Defy Your Age & Regain Your Youth. 2008. 132p. pap. *(978-1-906645-16-8(7))* Grosvenor Hse. Publishing Ltd.

Fry, Prem S. & Keyes, Corey L. M., eds. New Frontiers in Resilient Aging: Life-Strengths & Well-Being in Late Life. 2010. (ENG., Illus.). 388p. 110.00 *(978-0-521-50985-5(8))* Cambridge Univ. Pr.

Gallo, Roe & Zocchi, Stephen. Overcoming the Myths of Aging: Lose Weight, Look Great & Live a Happier & Healthier Life. 2007. per. 19.95 *(978-0-9642253-1-2(X))* Gallo Pubns.

Gariépy, Quentin & Ménard, Raphaël, eds. Handbook of Cognitive Aging: Causes, Processes & Effects. 2009. (Aging Issues, Health & Financial Alternatives Ser.). 195.00 *(978-1-60876-028-2(6)*, Nova Biomedical Bks.) Nova Science Pubs., Inc.

Glicken, Morley D. Evidence-Based Counseling & Psychotherapy for an Aging Population. 2009. (Practical Resources for the Mental Health Professional Ser.). (ENG.). 450p. 72.95 *(978-0-12-374937-6(9)*, Academic Pr.) Elsevier Science & Technology Bks.

Goldsmith, Theodore. The Evolution of Aging: How New Theories Will Change the Future of Medicine. 2nd rev. ed. 2006. (Illus.). 200p. pap. 14.95 *(978-0-9788709-0-4(5))* Azinet LLC.

Green, John H. Elder Cool Time. 2006. x, 126p. pap. 13.39 *(978-1-4120-9076-6(8))* Trafford Publishing.

Greenberg, Tamara McClintock. Psychodynamic Perspectives on Aging & Illness. 2009. (ENG.). x, 150p. 148.00 *(978-1-4419-0285-6(6)*, 1441902856) Springer.

—Psychodynamic Perspectives on Aging & Illness. 2010. (ENG.). x, 150p. pap. 34.95 *(978-1-4419-6972-9(1)*, 1441969721) Springer.

Grinning Idiot Press Staff. Look Like a Winner after 50. 2nd ed. Date not set. 15.95 *(978-0-88100-089-4(2))* National Writers Pr., The.

Grossman, Michael. Coming to Terms with Aging: The Secret to Meaningful Time. 2007. 144p. 14.95 *(978-1-57143-169-1(1))* RDR Bks.

Gullette, Margaret Morganroth. Agewise: Fighting the New Ageism in America. 2011. (Illus.). 304p. 29.00 *(978-0-226-31073-2(6))* Univ. of Chicago Pr.

Guttmann, David. Finding Meaning in Life, at Midlife & Beyond: Wisdom & Spirit from Logotherapy, 1 vol. 2008. (Social & Psychological Issues: Challenges & Solutions Ser.). 192p. 39.95 *(978-0-313-36017-6(0)*, C36017, Praeger Pubs.) Greenwood Publishing Group, Inc.

Hadler, Nortin M. Worried Sick: A Prescription for Health in an Overtreated America. (H. Eugene & Lillian Youngs Lehman Ser.). (ENG.). 392p. 2012. pap. 22.00 ***(978-0-8078-7233-8(4))*** 2008. (Illus.). 30.00 *(978-0-8078-3187-8(5))* Univ. of North Carolina Pr.

Hansen, Mark Victor & Linkletter, Art. How to Make the Rest of Your Life the Best of Your Life, 0 vols. 2006. (Illus.). 272p. 24.99 *(978-0-7852-1890-6(4))* Nelson, Thomas Inc.

Hayslip, Bert & Hicks-Patrick, Julie. Adult Development & Aging. 5th ed. 2011. ***(978-1-57524-308-5(3))*** Krieger Publishing Co.

Hayslip, Bert, et al. Adult Development & Aging. 4th ed. 2007. *(978-1-57524-245-3(1))* Krieger Publishing Co.

Helvie, R.N., Carl O. Healthy Holistic Aging: A Blueprint for Success. 2007. (Illus.). 305p. per. 18.00 *(978-0-929636-71-9(6))* Syren Bk. Co.

Herring, Richard. How Not to Grow Up! A Coming of Age Memoir - Sort Of. 2010. (ENG.). 320p. pap. 22.95 ***(978-0-09-193208-4(4))*** Ebury Publishing GBR. Dist: Independent Pubs. Group.

Hill, Robert D. Seven Strategies for Positive Aging. 2008. (ENG., Illus.). 288p. pap. 19.95 *(978-0-393-70523-2(4)*, 70523) Norton, W. W. & Co., Inc.

Hover-Kramer, Dorothea. Second Chance at Your Dream: Engaging Your Body's Energy Resources for Optimal Aging, Creativity & Health. 2009. 248p. pap. 17.95 *(978-1-60415-038-4(6))* Energy Psychology Pr.

Hoyer, William J. & Roodin, Paul A. Adult Development & Aging. 6th ed. 2007. (C). 118.75 *(978-0-07-319184-3(1)*, 9780073191843, McGraw-Hill Humanities, Social Sciences & World Languages) McGraw-Hill Higher Education.

Hughes, Julian C. Alzheimer's & other Dementias. 2011. (ENG., Illus.). 176p. pap. 21.95 ***(978-0-19-959655-3(7))*** Oxford Univ. Pr., Inc.

Hultsch, David F., et al. Memory Change in the Aged. 2010. (ENG.). 356p. pap. 36.99 *(978-0-521-15358-4(1))* Cambridge Univ. Pr.

Hurd Clarke, Laura. Facing Age: Women Growing Older in Anti-Aging Culture. 2010. (Diversity & Aging Ser.). (ENG.). 176p. (C). (gr. 13-17). 75.00 *(978-1-4422-0759-2(0))*; pap. 22.95 *(978-1-4422-0760-8(4))* Rowman & Littlefield Publishers, Inc.

Juan, Vicente Ali, ed. The Gift of Life. 2008. 191p. pap. *(978-84-96855-14-4(7))* Actar Birkhauser Distribution.

Judd, Naomi. Naomi's Guide to Aging Gratefully: Facts, Myths, & Good News for Boomers. 2008. (ENG.). 272p. pap. 17.99 *(978-0-7432-7516-3(0))* Simon & Schuster.

Kahn. Aging & Cognition. Date not set. pap. 40.00 net. *(978-1-56593-866-3(6))* CENGAGE Learning.

Kalmar, Jessica. Information Processing Speed in Clinical Applications. DeLuca, John, ed. 2007. (Studies on Neuropsychology, Neurology, & Cognition). (ENG., Illus.). 328p. 105.95 *(978-1-84169-476-4(2)*, Psychology Press) Taylor & Francis Group GBR. Dist: Taylor & Francis Group.

Kane, Robert L., et al. Essentials of Clinical Geriatrics. 6th ed. 2008. (ENG., Illus.). 598p. pap. 64.00 *(978-0-07-149822-7(2)*, 0071498222) McGraw-Hill Professional Publishing.

Kelly, Brent Robert. Who Will Care for Grandma? Critiquing Ageism in Medicine. 2008. 260p. pap. 29.00 *(978-1-55635-913-2(6)*, Wipf and Stock) Wipf & Stock Pubs.

Kenton, Leslie. Ageless Ageing. (Illus.). 384p. pap. 13.95 *(978-0-09-946690-1(2))* Random Hse. GBR. Dist: Trafalgar Square Publishing.

Key, Sheila & Spencer, Peggy. 50 Ways to Leave Your 40s: Living It up in Life's Second Half. 2008. (ENG.). 288p. per. 14.95 *(978-1-57731-545-2(6))* New World Library.

Kilpatrick, Bill. How to Be an Old Guy: Dispatches from the Retiree Front. 2009. 184p. pap. 19.95 *(978-1-933167-34-3(3))* Hatala Geroproducts.

Lachs, Mark. Treat Me, Not My Age: A Doctor's Guide to Getting the Best Care As You or a Loved One Gets Older. 2010. (ENG.). 400p. (gr. 12). 27.95 *(978-0-670-02210-6(1)*, Viking Adult) Penguin Group (USA) Inc.

Lamont, Allison. Age-Related Memory Loss: 20 to 100 years - A Research Study of Healthy Adults. 2008. 348p. pap. *(978-3-639-03582-7(8))* VDM Verlag Dr. Mueller e.K.

Lassiter, Sybil M. The Good Life: A Positive Approach to Growing Older. 2010. 128p. pap. 1999.00 *(978-0-9801744-1-0(4))* Barnhardt & Ashe Publishing, Inc.

Lawrence-Lightfoot, Sara. The Third Chapter: Passion, Risk, & Adventure in the 25 Years after 50. 2009. (ENG., Illus.). 304p. pap. 15.00 *(978-0-374-53221-5(4))*; 272p. 25.00 *(978-0-374-27549-5(1))* Farrar, Straus & Giroux.

—The Third Chapter: Passion, Risk, & Adventure in the 25 Years after 50. l.t. ed. 2009. 368p. 31.95 *(978-1-4104-1496-0(5))* Thorndike Pr.

Lee, Ilchi & Jones, Jessie. In Full Bloom: A Brain Education Guide for Successful Aging. 2008. (Illus.). 231p. pap. 18.95 *(978-0-9799388-4-9(8))* BEST Life Media.

Lee, Sharon Dian, ed. HIV & Aging. 2008. (Illus.). 160p. pap. 99.95 *(978-1-4200-8390-3(2)*, Informa Healthcare) Taylor & Francis Group GBR. Dist: Taylor & Francis Group.

Lemme, Barbara H. Development in Adulthood. 2006. 3rd ed. pap. 9.95 *(978-1-4288-1715-9(8))* 4th ed. pap. 11.95 *(978-1-4288-1322-9(5))* Cram101 Inc.

Lerner, Richard M., et al. The Handbook of Life-Span Development, 2 vols., Set. 2010. (ENG., Illus.). 1774p. 316.00 *(978-0-470-39013-9(1)*, Wiley) Wiley, John & Sons, Inc.

Levine, Kathy. We Should Be So Lucky. 2011. (ENG.). 240p. pap. 15.99 ***(978-1-4516-6190-3(8))*** Pocket Books.

Levine, Robert. Aging with Attitude: Growing Older with Dignity & Vitality, 1 vol. 2008. 240p. pap. 19.95 *(978-0-313-36318-4(8)*, B36318, Praeger Trade) Greenwood Publishing Group, Inc.

Linkletter, Art & Hansen, Mark Victor. How to Make the Rest of Your Life the Best of Your Life, 0 vols. 2007. 320p. per. 14.99 *(978-0-7852-8926-5(7))* Nelson, Thomas Inc.

Masley, Steven. Ten Years Younger: The Amazing Ten-Week Plan to Look Better, Feel Better, & Turn Back the Clock. 2007. (ENG.). 400p. pap. 15.99 *(978-0-7679-2171-8(2)*, Broadway) Broadway Bks.

Mason, Marion G. Adulthood & Aging. 2010. (ENG.). 480p. (C). 160.00 *(978-0-205-43351-3(0)*, Prentice Hall) Prentice Hall PTR.

Mauk, Kristen L. Gerontological Nursing: Competencies for Care. 2nd rev. ed. 2009. (Illus.). 869p. pap. 72.95 *(978-0-7637-5580-5(X))* Jones & Bartlett Learning, LLC.

Miwa, Satomi, et al, eds. Oxidative Stress in Aging: From Model Systems to Human Diseases. 2010. (Aging Medicine Ser.). (Illus.). viii, 320p. pap. 149.00 *(978-1-61737-870-6(4),* 1617378704) Humana Pr.

—Oxidative Stress in Aging: From Model Systems to Human Diseases. 2008. (Aging Medicine Ser.). (Illus.). 388p. (C). 149.00 *(978-1-58829-991-8(0),* 1588299910) Springer.

Molinari, Victor, ed. Specialty Competencies in Geropsychology. 2010. (Specialty Competencies in Professional Psychology Ser.). (ENG., Illus.). 240p. pap. 39.95 *(978-0-19-538567-0(5))* Oxford Univ. Pr., Inc.

Mould, Paul, ed. Finding Your Own Fountain of Youth. 2008. 214p. pap. *(978-1-904959-64-9(4))* Mould, Paul Publishing GBR. Dist: Empire Publishing Service.

Moulton, Peter. Brain Agility: Keeping a Healthy & Youthful Brain. 2007. (Illus.). 280p. per. 19.95 *(978-0-615-16166-2(9))* Northwest Border Pubns.

Nyström, Thomas & Osiewacz, Heinz D., eds. Model Systems in Aging. 2010. (Topics in Current Genetics Ser.). (Illus.). xiii, 301p. pap. 269.00 *(978-3-642-05698-7(9),* 3642056989) Springer.

Orrell, Martin & Spector, Aimee. Psychology of Aging. 2009. (International Library of Psychology Ser.). (Illus.). 440p. 225.00 *(978-0-7546-2789-0(6))* Ashgate Publishing Co.

Overton, Willis F. The Handbook of Life-Span Development: Social & Emotional Development, 2 vols. 2010. (ENG., Illus.). 749p. 158.00 *(978-0-470-39012-2(3),* Wiley) Wiley, John & Sons, Inc.

Palmer. Life Transitions & Generational C. 2010. (Essential Coaching Skills & Knowledge Ser.). (ENG., Illus.). 240p. (C). 84.95 *(978-0-415-47359-0(4));* pap. 30.95 *(978-0-415-47360-6(8))* Routledge.

Papalia, Stems & Cram101 Textbook Reviews Staff. Adult Development & Aging. 2007. 176p. per. 12.95 *(978-1-4288-2114-9(7))* Cram101 Inc.

Potter, Beverly A. Youth Extension A to Z. 2010. (ENG., Illus.). 192p. pap. 14.95 *(978-1-57951-090-9(6))* Ronin Publishing.

Provenzano, Roberta. Roberta's Papers on the Psychology of Aging. 2011. 64p. 19.95 ***(978-1-4620-0711-0(2));*** pap. 9.95 ***(978-1-4620-0712-7(0))*** iUniverse, Inc.

Quinodoz, Danielle. Growing Old: A Journey of Self-Discovery. 2009. (ENG.). 232p. (C). 95.00 *(978-0-415-54565-5(X));* pap. 27.50 *(978-0-415-54566-2(8))* Routledge.

Rabbitt, Patrick, ed. Psychology of Ageing, 4 vols. 2009. (Critical Concepts in Psychology Ser.). (ENG.). 1976p. (C). 1505.00 *(978-0-415-42989-4(7),* Psychology Press) Taylor & Francis Group GBR. Dist: Taylor & Francis Group.

—The Quarterly Journal of Experimental Psychology: Human Experimental Psychology. 2008. (Special Issues of the Quarterly Journal of Experimental Psychology: Section A Ser.). (ENG.). 192p. 79.95 *(978-1-84169-850-2(4),* Psychology Press) Taylor & Francis Group GBR. Dist: Taylor & Francis Group.

Rathus, Spencer A. CDEV. 2010. (Available Titles CourseMate Ser.). (ENG.). 352p. pap. 59.95 *(978-0-495-90553-0(4))* Wadsworth.

Rattan, Suresh I. S. & Akman, Serif, eds. Biogerontology: Mechanisms & Interventions. 2007. (Annals of the New York Academy of Sciences Ser.: Vol. 1099). (ENG., Illus.). 500p. per. 169.95 *(978-1-57331-679-8(2),* Wiley-Blackwell) Wiley, John & Sons, Inc.

Read, Catherine Y., et al, eds. Aging, Biotechnology, & the Future. 2008. (ENG., Illus.). 296p. (gr. 17). 47.00 *(978-0-8018-8788-8(7))* Johns Hopkins Univ. Pr.

Rimbach, Peter K. Retirement: Life's Mt. Everest. 2011. 220p. 29.99 ***(978-1-4628-8555-8(1));*** pap. 19.99 ***(978-1-4628-8554-1(3))*** Xlibris Corp.

Roth, Norma. Aging Gracefully with Dignity, Integrity & Spunk Intact: Aging Defiantly. 2009. 252p. 29.95 *(978-1-4490-2101-6(8))* AuthorHouse.

Rowe, Heidemarie. Boomers & Beyond, Prescription for the Golden Years. 2007. 204p. per. 16.95 *(978-1-934246-82-5(4))* Peppertree Pr., The.

Rubin, Harriet. The Mona Lisa Stratagem: The Art of Women, Age, & Power. 2008. (ENG.). 256p. pap. 20.99 *(978-0-446-69481-0(9))* Grand Central Publishing.

Schaie, K. Warner & Abeles, Ronald P. Social Structures & Aging Individuals: Continuing Challenges. 2008. 412p. 90.00 ***(978-0-8261-2408-1(9))*** Springer Publishing Co., Inc.

Schaie, K. Warner & Willis, Sherry L., eds. Handbook of the Psychology of Aging. 7th ed. 2010. (Handbooks of Aging Ser.). (ENG., Illus.). 434p. pap. 99.95 *(978-0-12-380882-0(0),* Academic Pr.) Elsevier Science & Technology Bks.

Schwalbe, Robert. Sixty, Sexy, & Successful: A Guide for Aging Male Baby Boomers, 1 vol. 2008. (Sex, Love, & Psychology Ser.). (Illus.). 320p. 49.95 *(978-0-275-99928-5(9),* C9928, Praeger Pubs.) Greenwood Publishing Group, Inc.

Seplina, Pauline T., ed. New Topics in Aging. 2008. 69.00 *(978-1-60692-009-1(X))* Nova Science Pubs., Inc.

Shapira, Eric Z. A New Wrinkle: What I Learned from Older People Who Never Acted Their Age. 2011. 324p. pap. 18.95 ***(978-1-936236-55-8(9))*** iUniverse, Inc.

Sherman, Edmund. Contemplative Aging: A Way of Being in Later Life. 2010. (Illus.). 198p. pap. 21.95 *(978-1-884092-99-2(3),* Gordian Knot Bks.) Altschuler, Richard & Assocs., Inc.

Sloan, Tina. Changing Shoes: Getting Older — Not Old — With Style, Humor, & Grace. 2010. (ENG.). 224p. (gr. 12). 22.50 *(978-1-59240-568-8(1),* Gotham) Penguin Group (USA) Inc.

—Changing Shoes: Staying in the Game with Style, Humor, & Grace. 2011. (ENG.). 224p. (gr. 12). 16.00 *(978-1-59240-664-7(5),* Gotham) Penguin Group (USA) Inc.

Smith, Anne Marie & Gamble-Risley, Michelle. Second Bloom: 10 Steps to Reinvent, Rejuvenate, & Realize a New Life. 2009. 136p. 19.95 *(978-0-9818322-0-3(2))* Kaabrah Publishing.

Sobh, Rana. Approach & Avoidance Self-Regulation. 2010. 240p. pap. *(978-3-639-26094-6(5))* VDM Verlag Dr. Mueller e.K.

Solimeo, Samantha. With Shaking Hands: Aging with Parkinson's Disease in America's Heartland. 2009. (Studies in Medical Anthropology). (ENG., Illus.). 232p. 72.00 *(978-0-8135-4543-1(9));* pap. 24.95 *(978-0-8135-4544-8(7))* Rutgers Univ. Pr.

Stirling, Elspeth. Valuing Older People: Positive Psychological Practice. 2010. (ENG., Illus.). 224p. 110.95 *(978-0-470-68335-4(X));* pap. 44.95 *(978-0-470-68334-7(1))* Wiley, John & Sons, Inc. (Wiley).

Stuart-Hamilton, Ian. The Psychology of Ageing: An Introduction. 5th rev. ed. 2012. (ENG.). 420p. pap. ***(978-1-84905-245-0(X))*** Kingsley, Jessica Ltd.

Stuart-Hamilton, Ian. The Psychology of Ageing: An Introduction. 4th ed. 2006. (ENG.). 4p. per. *(978-1-84310-426-1(1))* Kingsley, Jessica Ltd.

Tai, Paul Ling. 8 Powerful Secrets to Anti-Aging. 2007. 49.95 *(978-1-934216-90-3(9))* United Writers Pr.

Taylor, Albert W. & Johnson, Michel J. Physiology of Exercise & Healthy Aging. 2007. (ENG., Illus.). 304p. (C). 78.00 *(978-0-7360-5838-4(9))* Human Kinetics Pubs.

Textor-Black, Sharon. Elsa's Own Blue Zone: America's Centenarian Sweetheart's Insights for Positive Aging & Living. 2009. (ENG., Illus.). 162p. pap. 14.95 *(978-1-60037-579-8(0))* Morgan James Publishing.

Vaillant, George. Aging Well: Surprising Guideposts to a Happier Life. 2006. pap. 8.95 *(978-1-4288-1321-2(7))* Cram101 Inc.

—Aging Well: Surprising Guideposts to a Happier Life. 384p. pap. 35.00 *(978-0-908011-64-3(4))* Scribe Pubns. AUS. Dist: Independent Pubs. Group.

Wakan, Naomi Beth. A roller-coaster Ride: Thinking about Aging. 2011. (ENG.). 150p. pap. 19.00 ***(978-1-894987-64-6(0))*** Wolsak & Wynn Pubs., Ltd. CAN. Dist: Univ. of Toronto Pr.

Walsh, Gregory & Lavery, Michael. Whole Brain Power: the Fountain of Youth for the Mind & Body. 2008. 308p. pap. 19.95 *(978-0-557-00514-7(0))* Lulu Enterprises Inc.

Walston, Jeremy D. Frailty, an Issue of Clinics in Geriatric Medicine. 2010. (Clinics: Internal Medicine Ser.: 27-1). (ENG., Illus.). 128p. 105.00 *(978-1-4377-2452-3(3),* Saunders) Elsevier - Health Sciences Div.

Weisstub, D. N., et al, eds. Aging: Decisions at the End of Life: Decisions at the End of Life. 2010. (International Library of Ethics, Law, & the New Medicine Ser.). 284p. pap. 149.00 *(978-90-481-5898-0(2),* 9048158982) Springer.

Werman, Robert. Living with an Aging Brain: A Self-Help Guide for Your Senior Years. 199 + ixp. pap. *(978-965-294-141-1(7))* Freund Publishing Hse., Ltd.

Whitbourne, Susan Krauss. Adult Development & Aging: Biopsychosocial Perspectives. 3rd ed. 2007. (ENG., Illus.). 496p. (C). 172.95 *(978-0-470-11860-3(1),* Wiley) Wiley, John & Sons, Inc.

Whitbourne, Susan Krauss & Sliwinski, Martin J., eds. The Wiley-Blackwell Handbook of Adulthood & Aging. 2012. (Blackwell Handbooks of Developmental Psychology Ser.: 30). (ENG., Illus.). 584p. 199.95 ***(978-1-4443-3147-9(7),*** Wiley-Blackwell) Wiley, John & Sons, Inc.

Whitbourne, Susan Krauss & Whitbourne, Stacey B. Adult Development & Aging: Biopsychosocial Perspectives. 4th ed. 2010. (ENG., Illus.). 404p. (C). 172.95 *(978-0-470-64697-7(7),* Wiley) Wiley, John & Sons, Inc.

Williams, Richard, et al. Lives Through the Years: Styles of Life & Successful Aging. 2006. (ENG., Illus.). 298p. (gr. 11). pap. 29.95 *(978-0-202-30901-9(0))* Aldine Transaction.

AGING—RESEARCH

Alonso-Fernández, Patricia, et al, eds. Neutrophils in Biological Age & Longevity. 2009. (Cell Biology Research Progress Ser.). (Illus.). viii, 84p. pap. 43.00 *(978-1-61728-281-2(2),* Nova Biomedical Bks.) Nova Science Pubs., Inc.

Ashman, Ori. Aging in the Social-Cultural Context. 2008. 140p. pap. *(978-3-639-02147-9(9))* VDM Verlag Dr. Mueller e.K.

Baars, Jan & Visser, Henk, eds. Aging & Time: Multidisciplinary Perspectives. 2007. (Society & Aging Ser.). (Illus.). 216p. (C). 47.95 *(978-0-89503-367-3(4))* Baywood Publishing Co., Inc.

Cabrera, M. & Malanowski, N., eds. Information & Communication Technologies for Active Ageing: Opportunities & Challenges for the European Union - Volume 23 Assistive Technology Research Series. 2009. (Illus.). 284p. 167.00 *(978-1-58603-937-0(7))* IOS Pr., Inc.

Carmel, Sara, et al, eds. Lessons on Aging from Three Nations: The Art of Aging Well, 2 vols., Vol. 1. 2007. (Society & Aging Ser.). (Illus.). 242p. (C). 49.00 *(978-0-89503-369-7(0))* Baywood Publishing Co., Inc.

—Lessons on Aging from Three Nations Vol. 2: The Art of Caring for Older Adults, 2 vols. 2007. (Society & Aging Ser.). (Illus.). 254p. (C). 49.00 *(978-0-89503-370-3(4))* Baywood Publishing Co., Inc.

Cram101 Textbook Reviews Staff. Outlines & Highlights for Aging & Older Adulthood by Erber, Isbn. 2008. 124p. pap. 11.95 *(978-1-4288-5871-8(7))* Cram101 Inc.

Dröge, Wulf. Challenging the Limits of the Human Life Span: - Can We Live Longer Than 120 Years - New Guidelines. 2010. 188p. 26.95 *(978-1-4502-4005-5(4));* pap. 16.95 *(978-1-4502-4004-8(6))* iUniverse, Inc.

Massie, Harold. Aging Research: A Look at Some of the Scientific Evidence on Aging. 2007. 232p. per. 19.50 *(978-1-4251-0141-1(0))* Trafford Publishing.

Newsom, Jason, et al, eds. Best Practices for Data Analysis of Longitudinal Studies on Aging. 2011. (Multivariate Applications Ser.). (ENG., Illus.). 405p. 95.00 *(978-0-415-87414-4(9));* pap. 54.95 *(978-0-415-87415-1(7))* Taylor & Francis Group GBR. (Routledge). Dist: Taylor & Francis Group.

Sahar, Nadder D. Exercise, Aging & Bone Tissue Quality. 2010. 136p. pap. *(978-3-8383-6642-5(5))* Lambert Academic Publishing.

Tollefsbol, Trygve O., ed. Epigenetics of Aging. 2009. (ENG., Illus.). xii, 448p. 199.00 *(978-1-4419-0638-0(X),* 144190638X) Springer.

Vaillant, George. Aging Well: Surprising Guideposts to a Happier Life. 2006. pap. 8.95 *(978-1-4288-1321-2(7))* Cram101 Inc.

—Aging Well: Surprising Guideposts to a Happier Life. 384p. pap. 35.00 *(978-0-908011-64-3(4))* Scribe Pubns. AUS. Dist: Independent Pubs. Group.

Zeller, Mary Louise & Akagi, Michael. Secrets of the Fountain of Youth. 2007. 288p. per. 18.98 *(978-1-933973-04-3(8))* KiwE Publishing, Ltd.

AGING PARENTS

Here are entered works on parents who have grown old and whose children are middle aged or older. Works on persons who became parents after reaching middle age are entered under Older Parents.

Abrams, Hillary. Aging Parents & Options in Care: A Simple Handbook Making the Best Decisions for Loved Ones During Stressful Times. 2008. 76p. pap. 10.95 *(978-0-595-46686-3(9))* iUniverse, Inc.

Abramson, Alexis & Dunkin, Mary Anne. The Caregiver's Survival Handbook: How to Care for Your Aging Parent Without Losing Yourself. rev. ed. 2011. (ENG.). 288p. (gr. 12). 15.95 *(978-0-399-53642-7(6),* Perigee Trade) Penguin Group (USA) Inc.

AgeWiseLiving LLC. The Ultimate Caregiver's Survival Guide: The Step by Step Blueprint for Resolving Your Eldercare Issues by Choice, Not Crisis. 2008. 151p. spiral bd. 97.00 *(978-0-9796879-1-4(8))* AgeWiseLiving.

Altoonian, Linda J. Living Agelessly: Answers to Your Most Common Questions about Aging Gracefully. 2008. (DiaMedica Guide to Optimum Wellness Ser.). (ENG.). 256p. pap. 16.95 *(978-0-9793564-4-5(X))* DiaMed, LLC.

Asep, Mildred. Injustice to the Elder: Experiences in a Labyrinth for Aunt Lena. 2008. 300p. pap. 15.49 *(978-1-4343-8129-3(3))* AuthorHouse.

Auger, Sherri & Wickens, Barbara. Now What? A Practical Guide to Dealing with Aging, Illness, & Death. 2010. 160p. *(978-2-89646-217-9(1))* Novalis Publishing.

Barsamian, Gloria G. Sustenance & Hope for Caregivers of Elderly Parents: The Bread of Angels. 2009. (Praeger Series on Contemporary Health & Living Ser.). 34.95 *(978-0-313-36011-4(1));* E-Book *(978-0-313-36012-1(X))* Greenwood Publishing Group, Inc. (Praeger Pubs.).

Beerman, Susan. Eldercare 911: The Caregiver's Complete Handbook for Making Decisions. rev. ed. 2008. (ENG., Illus.). 640p. pap. 26.98 *(978-1-59102-616-7(4))* Prometheus Bks., Pubs.

Berit, Kari. The Unexpected Caregiver: How Boomers Can Keep Mom & Dad Active, Safe & Independent. 2007. 192p. pap. 19.00 *(978-1-57861-606-0(9))* Attainment Co., Inc.

Berman, Raeann & Shulman, Bernard H. Caring for Your Aging Parents. 2009. (ENG.). 256p. pap. 14.99 *(978-1-4022-1861-3(3))* Sourcebooks, Inc.

Brown Hartley, Bonnie & Gibson, John W. Health Care Issues of Aging Families: A Fire Drill for Building Strength & Flexibility in Families. 2006. 148p. per. 34.99 *(978-0-9727985-9-4(5))* Cambio Pr. LLC.

Bruneaux, Nanette. Choices for the Choiceless: the Lost Sheep. 2007. 231p. pap. 17.94 *(978-1-4116-3657-6(0))* Lulu Enterprises Inc.

Butler, Lynne. Estate Planning Through Family Meetings. 2010. (ENG.). 160p. pap. 23.95 *(978-1-77040-036-8(2))* Self-Counsel Pr., Inc. CAN. Dist: Midpoint Trade Bks., Inc.

Callaway, Phil. Family Squeeze: Tales of Hope & Hilarity for a Sandwiched Generation. 2008. (ENG., Illus.). 208p. per. 13.99 *(978-1-59052-916-4(2),* Multnomah) Doubleday Religious Publishing Group, The.

Calo-oy, Starr. Caregiving Tips A-Z: Everything you need to know to care for your loved one at Home! 2007. per. 29.95 *(978-0-9753195-2-9(3))* Orchard Pubns.

—Caregiving Tips A-Z Alzheimer's & Other Dementias: Everything you need to know to care for your loved one at Home. 2007. per. 29.95 *(978-0-9753195-3-6(1))* Orchard Pubns.

Caro, Francis G. Family & Aging Policy. 2007. (Illus.). 237p. 175.00 *(978-0-7890-3373-4(9));* per. 54.95 *(978-0-7890-3374-1(7))* Routledge.

Carol L. Russell Ed.D. Sandwiched! Tales, Tips, & Tools to Balance Life in the Sandwich Generation. 2009. 384p. pap. 24.95 *(978-1-4401-5482-9(1))* iUniverse, Inc.

Carter, Dale C. Transitioning Your Aging Parent: A 5 Step Guide Through Crisis & Change. 2010. 77p. pap. 14.95 *(978-0-557-44740-4(2))* Lulu Enterprises Inc.

Comer, Jim. When Roles Reverse: A Guide to Parenting Your Parents. 2006. (ENG., Illus.). 328p. per. 17.95 *(978-1-57174-500-2(9))* Hampton Roads Publishing Co., Inc.

Cummings-Lamnek, Earlene. My Parents' Passing: An Inspirational Story for Victims of Alzheimer's & Their Families. 2011. pap. 10.99 *(978-1-61739-294-8(4))* Tate Publishing & Enterprises, LLC.

Delehanty, Hugh & Ginzler, Elinor. Caring for Your Parents: The Complete Family Guide. 2008. (AARP Ser.). (ENG., Illus.). 256p. per. 12.95 *(978-1-4027-5857-7(X))* Sterling Publishing Co., Inc.

Dodds, Monica. A Catholic Guide to Caring for Your Aging Parent. 2006. (ENG.). 360p. per. 14.95 *(978-0-8294-1872-9(5))* Loyola Pr.

Ehlert, Mary Anne. The Gift I Was Given: The Journey of a Caregiver Through the Stages of What Now?, Why Me?, & Ah Ha! 2009. (ENG.). pap. 14.95 *(978-1-60037-504-0(9))* Morgan James Publishing.

Epstein, Lita. The 250 Eldercare Questions Everyone Should Ask. 2009. (ENG.). 192p. pap. 10.95 *(978-1-59869-890-9(7))* Adams Media Corp.

Ferguson, Frances. Mum. 2011. 72p. pap. 11.99 ***(978-1-4575-0356-6(5))*** Dog Ear Publishing, LLC.

Giroux, Philip & Lamb, Sally. Cash under the Mattress: The Ultimate Estate & Crisis Handbook. 2011. 192p. pap. 24.95 ***(978-1-4567-0110-9(X))*** AuthorHouse.

Gross, Jane. A Bittersweet Season: Caring for Our Aging Parents — and Ourselves. (ENG.). 2012. 448p. pap. 15.95 ***(978-0-307-47240-3(X),*** Vintage) 2011. 368p. 26.95 *(978-0-307-27182-2(X),* Knopf) Knopf Doubleday Publishing Group.

Grumbles, Sally & Stretcher, Virginia. Whoever Is There Decides. 2007. per. 14.99 *(978-1-59872-853-8(9))* Instant Pub.

Hall, Julie. The Boomer Burden: Dealing with Your Parents' Lifetime Accumulation of Stuff, 0 vols. 2008. 256p. pap. 14.99 *(978-0-7852-2825-7(X))* Nelson, Thomas Inc.

Hartmann, Christine W. So Far Away: A Daughter's Memoir of Life, Loss, & Love. 2011. (ENG., Illus.). 224p. 49.95 *(978-0-8265-1795-1(1));* pap. 21.95 *(978-0-8265-1796-8(X))* Vanderbilt Univ. Pr.

Hawkins, Liane. Stardust Memories. 2008. 128p. pap. 13.95 *(978-0-595-50541-8(4))* iUniverse, Inc.

Highe, Jackie. Now Where Did I Put My Glasses? Caring for Your Elder Parents - A Practical & Emotional Lifeline. 2007. (ENG.). 276p. pap. 23.95 *(978-0-7432-9531-4(5))* Simon & Schuster, Ltd. GBR. Dist: Independent Pubs. Group.

Horgan, David & Block, Shira. When Your Parent Moves In: Every Adult Child's Guide to Living with an Aging Parent. 2009. (ENG.). 256p. pap. 12.95 *(978-1-60550-012-6(7))* Adams Media Corp.

Hyams, Jacky. Time to Help Your Parents: A Practical Guide to Recognising Problems & Providing Support. (ENG.). 288p. 2011. pap. 14.95 *(978-0-7499-4065-2(4))* 2007. pap. 16.95 *(978-0-7499-2810-0(7))* Piatkus Bks. GBR. Dist: Independent Pubs. Group.

Ieron, Julie-Allyson. The Overwhelmed Woman's Guide To — Caring for Aging Parents. 2008. (ENG., Illus.). 208p. pap. 13.99 *(978-0-8024-5281-8(7))* Moody Pubs.

Kelly, Jo Anna. Dementia & Caregiving. 2008. 204p. pap. *(978-3-639-03270-3(5))* VDM Verlag Dr. Mueller e.K.

Kennedy, Laurel. The Daughter Trap: Taking Care of Mom & Dad... & You. 2010. (ENG., Illus.). 320p. 25.99 *(978-0-312-38510-1(2),* Dunne, Thomas Bks.) St. Martin's Pr.

Koslow, Sally. Slouching Toward Adulthood: Observations from the Not-So-Empty Nest. 2012. (ENG.). 272p. (gr. 12). 25.95 ***(978-0-670-02362-2(0),*** Viking Adult) Penguin Group (USA) Inc.

Loverde, Joy. The Complete Eldercare Planner, Revised & Updated Edition: Where to Start, Which Questions to Ask, & How to Find Help. 2009. (ENG.). 400p. pap. 19.95 *(978-0-307-40962-1(7),* Three Rivers Pr.) Crown Publishing Group.

Lynch, Terry. But I Don't Want Eldercare! Helping Your Parents Stay As Strong As They Can As Long As They Can. 2008. 328p. per. 17.95 *(978-0-9770179-6-6(6))* Legal Ctr. for People with Disabilities, The.

MacEnulty, Pat. Wait until Tomorrow: A Daughter's Memoir. 2011. (ENG.). 256p. pap. 16.95 *(978-1-55861-701-8(9))* Feminist Pr. at The City Univ. of New York.

MacEnulty, Pat & Titus, Tamara. This Is the Way We Say Goodbye. 2011. *(978-1-55861-772-8(8))* Feminist Pr. at The City Univ. of New York.

Mccullough, Dennis. My Mother, Your Mother: Embracing Slow Medicine, the Compassionate Approach to Caring for Your Aging Loved Ones. 2009. (ENG.). 288p. pap. 14.99 *(978-0-06-124303-5(5),* Harper Paperbacks) HarperCollins Pubs.

Mindszenthy, Bart J. & Gordon, Michael. Parenting Your Parents: Support Strategies for Meeting the Challenge of Aging in America. 2006. (ENG., Illus.). 275p. pap. 19.99 *(978-1-55002-664-1(X),* Dundurn Pr.) Dundurn CAN. Dist: Ingram Pub. Services.

Nicol, Colleen. Senior Days: Insightful Tales & No-Nonsense Help from the Frontlines of Eldercare. 2008. (ENG., Illus.). 134p. pap. 14.95 *(978-0-9794896-0-0(1))* Long Lake Pr.

Osis, Maureen & Worrell, Judy. Your Aging Parents: Arriving at Shared Solutions for Housing, Health & Relationships. 2007. (Illus.). 184p. per. 19.09 *(978-1-4251-0796-3(6))* Trafford Publishing.

Phillips, Kathy J. The Moon in the Water: Reflections on an Aging Parent. 2008. (Illus.). (ENG.). 160p. 19.95 *(978-0-8265-1586-5(X));* xiii, 139p. pap. *(978-0-8265-1587-2(8))* Vanderbilt Univ. Pr.

Piercy, Kathleen W. Working with Aging Families: Therapeutic Solutions for Caregivers, Spouses, & Adult Children. 2010. (ENG.). 288p. 27.95 *(978-0-393-73282-5(7),* 73282) Norton, W. W. & Co., Inc.

Praver, Frances Cohen. Crossroads at Midlife: Your Aging Parents, Your Emotions & Your Self. 2008. 184p. pap. 19.95 *(978-0-313-36316-0(1),* B36316, Praeger Trade) Greenwood Publishing Group, Inc.

Putnam, Ann. Full Moon at Noontide: A Daughter's Last Goodbye. 2009. (Medical humanities Ser.). (ENG.). 224p. 22.50 *(978-0-87074-555-3(7))* Southern Methodist Univ. Pr.

Qualls, Sara H. & Zarit, Steven H., eds. Aging Families & Caregiving. 2009. (Wiley Series in Clinical Geropsychology Ser.: 3). (ENG., Illus.). 338p. 64.00 *(978-0-470-00855-3(5),* Wiley) Wiley, John & Sons, Inc.

Quan, Kathy. Caring for Aging Parents: Reassuring Advice to Help You Support Your Loved Ones. 2009. (ENG.). 304p. pap. 15.95 *(978-1-59869-648-6(3))* Adams Media Corp.

Rava, Susan. Swimming Solo: A Daughter's Memoir of Her Parents, His Parents, & Alzheimer's Disease. 2011. (Illus.). 310p. pap. 14.95 *(978-0-9814795-0-7(2),* Plateau Bks.) Plateau Bks.

Rember, Julie, ed. & intro. Saying Goodbye: To the People, Places & Things in Our Lives. 2010. (ENG.). 230p. pap. 13.95 *(978-0-9825794-4-2(6))* Dream of Things.

Roberts, Shirley. Doris Inc: A Business Approach to Caring for Your Elderly Parents. 2012. (ENG.). 272p. pap. 26.95 ***(978-1-118-10022-6(0)***, Wiley) Wiley, John & Sons, Inc.

Russo, Francine. They're Your Parents, Too! How Siblings Can Survive Their Parents' Aging Without Driving Each Other Crazy. 2010. (ENG.). 304p. 26.00 *(978-0-553-80699-1(8))* Random House Publishing Group.

Sandell, Diane & Hudson, Lois. Ending Elder Abuse: A Family Guide. 2010. 160p. pap. 16.95 *(978-0-936609-43-0(5))* QED Pr.

Sander, Dorothy. Caring for Mom. 2010. 127p. pap. 13.95 *(978-0-557-32423-1(8))* Lulu Enterprises Inc.

Saxon, Ro & Anderson, Shirley. My Parents Are Getting Older. (Illus.). 246p. pap. *(978-0-7344-0265-3(1)*, Lothian Children's Bks.) Hachette Australia.

Schlenker, Linda L. Aging in America: A Wake-up Call & Call to Action for Seniors & Those Who Love & Serve Them. 2007. 60p. per. 15.95 *(978-0-9795777-4-1(8))* PCI Publishing Group, LLC.

Scott, Linda & Dunn, Barbara. Our Turn to Parent: Shared Experiences & Practical Advice on Caring for Aging Parents in Canada. 2009. (ENG.). 272p. pap. 20.95 *(978-0-307-35713-7(9)*, Random Hse CAN) Random Hse. of Canada, Ltd. CAN. Dist: Random Hse., Inc.

Silin, Jonathan G. My Father's Keeper: The Story of a Gay Son & His Aging Parents. 2007. (ENG.). 184p. per. 16.00 *(978-0-8070-7965-2(0))* Beacon Pr.

Snyder, CMC, Monique, MA. Before the Storm. 2009. 49p. pap. 10.99 *(978-0-557-08659-7(0))* Lulu Enterprises Inc.

Spring, Janis Abrahms, PhD & Spring, Michael. Life with Pop: Lessons on Caring for an Aging Parent. 2010. (ENG.). 240p. (gr. 12). 16.00 *(978-1-58333-395-2(9)*, Avery) Penguin Group (USA) Inc.

Stimpson, Turner. Love Spoken Here. 2007. 60p. 26.95 *(978-1-886057-78-4(8))* Warren Publishing, Inc.

Swan, W. A. & Swan, Bill. The Complete Guide to Managing Your Parents' Finances When They Cannot: A Step-by-Step Plan to Protect Their Assets, Limit Taxes, & Ensure Their Wishes Are Fulfilled. 2009. (ENG.). 288p. pap. 24.95 *(978-1-60138-313-6(4))* Atlantic Publishing Co.

Tales from the Doctor's Lounge. 3rd ed. Date not set. (Illus.). 239p. reprint ed. pap. 15.00 *(978-1-889249-04-9(1))* Concorde Publishing Co.

Taylor, Daniel & Taylor, Dan. The Parent Care Conversation: Six Strategies for Dealing with the Emotional & Financial Challenges of Aging Parents. 2006. (ENG.). 272p. (gr. 12-18). 14.00 *(978-0-14-303764-4(1)*, Penguin (Non-Classics)) Penguin Group (USA) Inc.

Tobin & Lindsey, Karen. That Silver-Haired Daddy of Mine: Family Caregiving with A Nurse Care-Manager Approach. 2008. 148p. pap. 11.99 *(978-1-4389-0439-9(8))* AuthorHouse.

Toledano, Phillip. Days with My Father. 2010. (ENG., Illus.). 92p. 19.95 *(978-0-473-15804-0(3))* Chronicle Bks. LLC.

Tucker, Michael. Family Meals: Coming Together to Care for an Aging Parent. 2010. (ENG.). 256p. pap. 14.00 *(978-0-8021-4508-6(6)*, Grove Pr.) Grove/Atlantic, Inc.

Walker, Lomie. Arcyle Park A Memoir of My Sisters Suici. 2006. iv, 146p. pap. 15.95 *(978-1-4120-8573-1(X))* Trafford Publishing.

Wesson, Nancy Daniel. Moving Our Aging Parents: Fulfilling Their Needs & Yours Before, During, & after the Move. 2008. pap. *(978-1-932690-54-5(9))* Loving Healing Pr., Inc.

Winakur, Jerald. Memory Lessons: A Doctor's Story. 2008. 304p. 24.95 *(978-1-4013-0302-0(1))* Hyperion Pr.

Windmill, Veronica. Aging Today. (Illus.). 96p. pap. *(978-0-7131-8534-8(1)*, Hodder Arnold) Hodder Education.

Woodson, Cheryl E. To Survive Caregiving: A Daughter's Experience, A Doctor's Advice on Finding Hope, Help & Health. 2007. (ENG.). 180p. per. 18.95 *(978-0-7414-3725-9(2))* Infinity Publishing.

Zebra Communications & Janis M. Whipple Editorial Services, eds. Mom Minus Dad: The Essential Resource Guide for Busy Adults with a Newly Widowed Parent. 2008. 320p. per. 14.95 *(978-1-934953-19-8(9))* Blooming Women Pr., LLC.

AGITATORS (MACHINERY)

see Mixing Machinery

AGNELLI, GIANNI, 1921-2003

Clark, Jennifer. Mondo Agnelli: Fiat, Chrysler, & the Power of a Dynasty. 2011. (ENG., Illus.). 368p. 29.95 ***(978-1-118-01852-1(4)***, Wiley) Wiley, John & Sons, Inc.

AGNES, PRINCESS OF BOHEMIA, 1205-1282

Mueller, Joan. The Privilege of Poverty: Clare of Assisi, Agnes of Prague, & the Struggle for a Franciscan Rule for Women. (ENG., Illus.). 176p. 2008. pap. 25.00 *(978-0-271-02769-2(X))* 2006. 40.00 *(978-0-271-02893-4(9))* Pennsylvania State Univ. Pr.

Seton, Walter W. Some New Sources for the Life of Blessed Agnes of Bohemia: Including a Fourteenth-Century Latin Version (Bamberg, Misc. Hist. 146, E. VII, 19): & a Fifteenth-Century German Version (Berlin, Germ. Oct. 484) 2010. (Cambridge Library Collection - History Ser.). (Illus.). 200p. pap. 21.00 *(978-1-108-01760-2(6))* Cambridge Univ. Pr.

AGNEW, SPIRO T., 1918-1996

Witcover, Jules. Very Strange Bedfellows: The Short & Unhappy Marriage of Richard Nixon & Spiro Agnew. 2008. (ENG.). 432p. pap. 15.95 *(978-1-58648-571-9(7))* PublicAffairs.

AGNON, SHMUEL YOSEF, 1888-1970

Hagbi, Yaniv. Language, Absence, Play. 2009. (Judaic Traditions in Literature, Music, & Art Ser.). Orig. Title: Lashon, he'ader, Mishak. 234p. 34.95 *(978-0-8156-3227-6(4))* Syracuse Univ. Pr.

Hasak-Lowy, Todd. Here & Now: History, Nationalism, & Realism in Modern Hebrew Fiction. 2008. (Judaic Traditions in Literature, Music & Art Ser.). 176p. 29.95 *(978-0-8156-3157-6(X))* Syracuse Univ. Pr.

Laor, Dan. Life of Agnon. 2009. *(978-0-8419-1446-9(X))* Holmes & Meier Pubs., Inc.

AGNOSIA

see also Apraxia

Humphreys, Glyn W. & Riddoch, Jane. To See but Not to See, 2nd Edition: A Case Study of Visual Agnosia. 2nd rev. ed. 2012. (ENG.). 224p. 80.00 *(978-1-84872-072-5(6))*; pap. 34.65 *(978-1-84872-073-2(4))* Taylor & Francis Group GBR. (Psychology Press). Dist: Taylor & Francis Group.

Mindick, Nancy L. Understanding Facial Recognition Difficulties in Children: Prosopagnosia Management Strategies for Parents & Professionals. 2010. (ENG.). 160p. pap. *(978-1-84905-802-5(4))* Kingsley, Jessica Ltd.

Prigatano, George P., ed. The Study of Anosognosia. 2010. (ENG., Illus.). 560p. 89.95 *(978-0-19-537909-9(8))* Oxford Univ. Pr. GBR. Dist: Rittenhouse Bk. Distributors.

Sellers, Heather. You Don't Look Like Anyone I Know. 2010. (ENG.). 368p. (gr. 12). 25.95 *(978-1-59448-773-6(1)*, Riverhead Bks. (Hardcover)) Penguin Group (USA) Inc.

AGNOSTICISM

see also Atheism; Belief and Doubt; Faith; God; Positivism; Skepticism

Abbot, Francis Ellingwood. The Way Out of Agnosticism: Or the Philosophy of Free Religion. 2007. (ENG.). 88p. per. 18.95 *(978-1-4304-4342-1(1))* Kessinger Publishing, LLC.

Abinitio, Samuel. The Agnostic's Guide to Prayer. 2008. 88p. per. 11.95 *(978-1-933482-50-7(8))* White Turtle Bks.

Alter, Torin Andrew & Howell, Robert J. The God Dialogues: A Philosophical Journey. 1 vol. 2010. (ENG.). 192p. (C). pap. 19.95 *(978-0-19-539559-4(X))* Oxford Univ. Pr., Inc.

Anderson, William A. How to Develop & Apply Your Confidence & Faith for Healing: Healing the Supernatural. 2011. 90p. pap. 13.95 *(978-1-4327-6976-5(6))* Outskirts Pr., Inc.

Blatchford, Robert. God & My Neighbour. 2007. (ENG.). 208p. per. *(978-1-4067-8992-8(5)*, Pierides Pr.) Read Bks.

Bugliosi, Vincent. Divinity of Doubt: The God Question. 2011. (ENG.). 352p. 26.99 *(978-1-59315-629-9(4))* Vanguard Pr.

Carus, Paul. Kant & Spencer: A Study of the Fallacies of Agnosticism. 2009. 116p. 21.99 *(978-1-103-91036-6(1))*; pap. 15.99 *(978-1-103-91028-1(0))* BiblioBazaar.

—Kant & Spencer: A Study of the Fallacies of Agnosticism. 2007. 112p. 34.95 *(978-0-548-51173-0(4))*; (ENG.). per. 19.95 *(978-0-548-51262-3(0))* Kessinger Publishing, LLC.

Corlett, J. Angelo. The Errors of Atheism. 2010. (ENG.). 272p. 110.00 *(978-1-4411-5187-2(7))*; pap. 29.95 *(978-1-4411-5893-2(6))* Continuum International Publishing Group, Ltd. GBR. Dist: National Bk. Network.

Flint, Robert. Agnosticism. 2009. 620p. 38.99 *(978-1-113-61200-7(2))*; pap. 45.75 *(978-1-113-61199-4(5))*; pap. 44.75 *(978-1-113-61198-7(7))* BiblioBazaar.

—Agnosticism. 2009. 360p. pap. *(978-0-217-16783-3(7))*; 398p. pap. *(978-1-4590-2274-4(2))* Books LLC.

—Agnosticism. 2007. (ENG.). 680p. 64.95 *(978-0-548-12228-0(8))* Kessinger Publishing, LLC.

Flynn, Tom, ed. The New Encyclopedia of Unbelief. 2007. (ENG.). 800p. 199.98 *(978-1-59102-391-3(2))* Prometheus Bks., Pubs.

Green Ingersoll, Robert. Lectures of Col R G Ingersoll. 2007. 216p. per. *(978-1-4068-1765-2(1))* Echo Library.

Hobbs, Delbert D. The Legend of Ole Three Toes. 2011. 27p. pap. 11.95 ***(978-1-4327-7090-7(X))*** Outskirts Pr., Inc.

Horwitz, Paul Ph. The Agnostic Age: Law, Religion, & the Constitution, 1 vol. 2011. (ENG.). 348p. 65.00 *(978-0-19-973772-7(X))* Oxford Univ. Pr., Inc.

Huhn, Wilson R. Telling Right from Wrong Without the Help of God. 2008. 198p. pap. 22.00 *(978-1-59460-536-9(X))* Carolina Academic Pr.

Hult, Raymond A. Agnosticity Volume 1: An Agnostic View O. 2006. pap. 15.99 *(978-1-4120-9030-8(X))* Trafford Publishing.

—Agnosticity Volume 2: an agnostic view of bothersome mormon Doctrine. 2006. (ENG.). 172p. per. 17.99 *(978-1-4120-9700-0(2))* Trafford Publishing.

Humphrys, John. In God We Doubt: Confessions of a Failed Atheist. 2008. (ENG.). 368p. pap. 15.95 *(978-0-340-97673-9(X)*, Hodder & Stoughton) Hodder General Publishing Div. GBR. Dist: Independent Pubs. Group.

—In God We Doubt: Confessions of a Failed Athiest. 2007. (ENG.). 336p. 36.95 *(978-0-340-95126-2(5)*, Hodder & Stoughton) Hodder General Publishing Div. GBR. Dist: Independent Pubs. Group.

Huxley, Thomas Henry. Christianity & Agnosticism: A Controversy. 2006. pap. 22.95 *(978-1-4286-4292-8(7))* Kessinger Publishing, LLC.

—Science & Christian Tradition. 2009. 194p. pap. *(978-0-217-04479-0(4))* Books LLC.

—Science & Christian Tradition. 2009. 206p. pap. 19.99 *(978-1-4589-9621-3(2))* General Bks. LLC.

Ingersoll, Robert Green. Lectures of Col. Robert Green Ingersoll. 2006. 334p. pap. 23.99 *(978-1-4264-2923-1(1))* 2007. (ENG.). 372p. pap. 26.99 *(978-1-4264-2976-7(2))* BiblioBazaar.

—Lectures of Col. Robert Green Ingersoll Vol. 1: Including His Answers to the Clergy His Oration at his Brother's Grave, Etc., Etc. 1st. ed. 2007. (ENG.). 314p. pap. 24.99 *(978-1-4264-2635-3(6))* BiblioBazaar.

—Lectures of Col. Robert Green Ingersoll, Volume I: Including His Answers to the Clergy His Oration at his Brother's Grave, etc., Etc. 2007. (ENG.). 290p. pap. 21.99 *(978-1-4264-2594-3(5))* BiblioBazaar.

James Kirk Wall. To Be an Agnostic: An Agnostic Approach to Life, Liberty, & the Pursuit of Happiness. 2009. 176p. 25.95 *(978-1-4401-6656-3(0))*; pap. 15.95 *(978-1-4401-6658-7(7))* iUniverse, Inc.

Jesus, A Likely Story: A non-theistic view of Christianity's central figure, gleaned from the Gospel of Matthew. 2006. per. 14.95 *(978-0-9788430-1-4(0))* Ultimate Bks.

Johnson, Brian L. & Johnson, Brian. W. E. B. du Bois: Toward Agnosticism, 1868-1934. 2008. 154p. 65.00 *(978-0-7425-6449-7(5))* Rowman & Littlefield Publishers, Inc.

Joshi, S. T. The Agnostic Reader. 2007. (ENG.). 1p. per. 21.98 *(978-1-59102-533-7(8))* Prometheus Bks., Pubs.

—Icons of Unbelief: Atheists, Agnostics, & Secularists, 1 vol. Joshi, S. T., ed. 2008. (Greenwood Icons Ser.). 476p. 75.00 *(978-0-313-34759-7(X)*, GR4759) Greenwood Publishing Group, Inc.

—The Unbelievers: The Evolution of Modern Atheism. 2011. (ENG.). 300p. pap. 19.00 *(978-1-61614-236-0(7))* Prometheus Bks., Pubs.

Kenny, Anthony & Kenny. What I Believe. 2007. (ENG.). 184p. 19.95 *(978-0-8264-9616-4(4))* Continuum International Publishing Group, Ltd. GBR. Dist: National Bk. Network.

King, Mike. Postsecularism: The Hidden Challenge to Extremism. 2009. (ENG.). 279p. pap. 53.00 *(978-0-227-17247-6(7))* Clarke, James Co., Ltd. GBR. Dist: Brown, David Bk. Co., The.

Krasny, Michael. Spiritual Envy: An Agnostic's Quest. (ENG.). 264p. 2012. pap. 14.95 ***(978-1-60868-069-6(X))*** 2010. 22.95 *(978-1-57731-912-2(5))* New World Library.

Le Poidevin, Robin. Agnosticism: A Very Short Introduction. 2010. (Very Short Introductions Ser.). (ENG., Illus.). 144p. pap. 11.95 *(978-0-19-957526-8(6))* Oxford Univ. Pr., Inc.

Lucas, George J. Agnosticism & Religion Being an Examin. 2006. pap. 21.95 *(978-1-4286-6203-2(0))* Kessinger Publishing, LLC.

Mabry, John R. The Monster God: Coming to Terms with the Dark Side of Divinity. 2008. (ENG., Illus.). 192p. pap. 19.95 *(978-1-84694-084-2(2))* Hunt, John Publishing Ltd. GBR. Dist: National Bk. Network.

Maeterlinck, Maurice. The Great Secret. 2010. 276p. pap. 24.95 *(978-0-557-34461-1(1))* Lulu Enterprises Inc.

Schaap, Andrew. Law & Agonistic Politics. 2009. (Edinburgh/Glasgow Law & Society Ser.). 242p. 124.95 *(978-0-7546-7314-9(6))* Ashgate Publishing Co.

Stephen, Leslie. A Defense of Philosophical Skepticism & Other Essays. 2011. 50p. 35.95 ***(978-1-258-00934-2(X))*** Literary Licensing, LLC.

Suk, John D. Not Sure: A Pastor's Journey from Faith to Doubt. 2011. 213p. pap. 18.00 ***(978-0-8028-6650-9(6))*** Eerdmans, William B. Publishing Co.

Swearingen, Rodger. Why Bad Things Happen to Good People. Swearingen, Rodger et al, eds. 2009. 150p. pap. 20.00 *(978-1-935444-18-3(2))* World Audience Pubs.

Uhl, Stephen Frederick. Imagine No Superstition: The Power to Enjoy Life with No Guilt. No Shame, No Blame. 2007. (ENG., Illus.). 190p. per. 18.95 *(978-0-9793169-0-6(1))* Golden Rule Pubs.

Vernon, Mark. After Atheism: Science, Religion & the Meaning of Life. 2008. (ENG., Illus.). 216p. pap. 19.00 *(978-0-230-01342-1(2))* Palgrave Macmillan.

—How to Be an Agnostic. 2011. (ENG., Illus.). 272p. pap. 15.00 *(978-0-230-29321-2(2))* Palgrave Macmillan.

Walker, Paul mm. I Still Haven't Found What I'm Looking For: God for Agnostics. 2006. (ENG.). 160p. per. 19.95 *(978-1-905047-76-5(2))* Hunt, John Publishing Ltd. GBR. Dist: National Bk. Network.

Wall, James Kirk. Agnosticism: The Battle Against Shameless Ignorance. 2011. 284p. 30.95 *(978-1-4502-8709-8(3))*; pap. 20.95 *(978-1-4502-8707-4(7))* iUniverse, Inc.

Wallace, Bill. Diabolical Wager. 2006. 96p. per. *(978-1-897312-15-5(6))* Adlibbed Ltd.

White, Stephen R. A Space for Unknowing: The Place of Agnosis in Faith. 2007. (ENG.). 160p. per. 27.95 *(978-1-85607-544-2(3))* Columba Pr. IRL. Dist: Dufour Editions, Inc.

AGORAPHOBIA

Auriana, Julie. Silently Suffering with Anxiety, Depression, & Agoraphobi. 2008. 164p. per. 11.95 *(978-1-4327-1836-7(3))* Outskirts Pr., Inc.

Bartlett, Manda M. Outside These Four Walls: The Life of an Agoraphobic. 2011. 32p. pap. 16.95 ***(978-1-4626-1349-6(7))*** PublishAmerica, Inc.

Benincasa, Sara. Agorafabulous! Dispatches from My Bedroom. 2012. (ENG.). 272p. 24.99 ***(978-0-06-202441-1(8)***, Morrow, William & Co.) HarperCollins Pubs.

Clark, Michael F. Life by Suicide: One mans journey to find happiness & Salvation. 2010. 192p. 24.99 *(978-1-4490-5547-9(8))* AuthorHouse.

Craske, Michelle G. & Barlow, David H. Mastery of Your Anxiety & Panic: Workbook for Primary Care Settings. 4th rev. ed. 2007. (Treatments That Work Ser.). (ENG.). 136p. pap. 27.95 *(978-0-19-531134-1(5))* Oxford Univ. Pr., Inc.

Gray, Elizabeth. I Relived My Nightmare from Hell: Overcoming Abuse & Agoraphobia. 2009. 100p. pap. 13.95 *(978-1-4389-5367-0(4))* AuthorHouse.

Grayson, Richard. Summer in Brooklyn. 2008. 187p. pap. 12.00 *(978-0-615-23794-7(0))* Superstition Mountain Pr.

Lemon, David John. Agoraphobia in Everyday Life. 2008. 240p. pap. *(978-3-639-01547-8(9))* VDM Verlag Dr. Mueller e.K.

Mendoza, Marilyn. From Agoraphobia to Zen: Uncovering the Core of My Anxiety & Reclaiming My Life. 2011. 238p. pap. ***(978-1-84991-523-6(7))*** Chipmunkapublishing.

Messias, Erick. Mental Health Needs in the United States: Epidemiological Estimates. 2008. 180p. pap. *(978-3-639-08850-2(6))* VDM Verlag Dr. Mueller e.K.

Milun, Kathryn. Pathologies of Modern Space: Empty Space, Urban Anxiety, & the Recovery of the Public Self. 2006. (ENG., Illus.). 240p. 140.00 *(978-0-415-95273-6(5))*; per. 39.95 *(978-0-415-95274-3(3))* Routledge.

O'Neill, J. Escape! The Complete AGORAPHOBIA Recovery Course. 2008. 312p. pap. *(978-1-84747-656-2(2))* Chipmunkapublishing.

Pincus, Donna, et al. Riding the Wave. 2008. (Treatments That Work Ser.). (ENG., Illus.). 64p. pap., wbk. ed. 21.99 *(978-0-19-533581-1(3))* Oxford Univ. Pr., Inc.

Reuter, Shelley Z. Narrating Social Order: Agoraphobia & the Politics of Classification. 2007. (ENG.). 176p. *(978-0-8020-9088-1(5))* Univ. of Toronto Pr.

Shawn, Allen. Wish I Could Be There: Notes from a Phobic Life. 2008. (ENG.). 288p. (gr. 12-18). 15.00 *(978-0-14-311307-2(0)*, Penguin (Non-Classics)) Penguin Group (USA) Inc.

Silove, Derrick & Manicavasagar, Vijaya, texts. Overcoming Panic: A Self-Help Guide Using Cognitive Behavioral Techniques. 2009. (Overcoming Ser.). (ENG., Illus.). 256p. pap. 14.95 *(978-0-465-01107-0(1))* Basic Bks.

Smith, Varrel. Phobia. 2006. 55p. pap. 16.95 *(978-1-4241-4303-0(9))* PublishAmerica, Inc.

Trujillo, Lida Alegria. Diary of an Agoraphobic: A Spiritual Journey of a Woman Suffering from Agoraphobia, 1 vol. 2009. 313p. pap. 24.95 *(978-1-60703-437-7(9))* PublishAmerica, Inc.

Tucker, Lisa. Looking for an Exit: From Panic to Empowerment. 2011. pap. 13.99 ***(978-1-61777-599-4(1))*** Tate Publishing & Enterprises, LLC.

Zulkowski, Michelle. Broken Inside! Breaking Free of Panic Disorder with Agoraphobia. 2007. 124p. pap. 12.95 *(978-1-4303-2401-0(5))* Lulu Enterprises Inc.

AGRA (INDIA)

Brown, Lindsay. Rajasthan, Delhi & Agra. 3rd rev. ed. 2011. (Regional Guide Ser.). (ENG., Illus.). 388p. pap. 24.99 *(978-1-74179-460-1(9))* Lonely Planet Pubns.

Jain, Poornima. Religious Sects & Social Development: A Comparative Study of Jains, Christians, & Sikhs. 2010. 216p. 45.00 *(978-81-316-0262-1(1))* Rawat Pubns. IND. Dist: International Specialized Bk. Services.

Kassabova, K. & Ghose, S. Delhi, Jaipur & Agra. 4th ed. 2010. (Globetrotter Travel Packs Ser.). (ENG., Illus.). 128p. 14.95 *(978-1-84773-675-8(0)*, Globetrotter) New Holland Pubs., Ltd. GBR. Dist: Globe Pequot Pr., The.

Thomas Cook Publishing. Traveller Guides Delhi, Agra & Rajasthan, 5th: Popular, compact guides for discovering the very best of country, regional & city Destinations. 5th ed. 2011. (Travellers - Thomas Cook Ser.). (ENG., Illus.). 192p. pap. 16.95 *(978-1-84848-445-0(3))* Cook, Thomas Publishing GBR. Dist: Globe Pequot Pr., The.

Thomas, Gavin & Rough Guides Staff. Rajasthan, Delhi & Agra. 2nd ed. 2010. (ENG., Illus.). 456p. 23.99 *(978-1-84836-555-1(1))* Rough Guides, Ltd. GBR. Dist: Dorling Kindersley Publishing, Inc.

AGRA (INDIA)—DESCRIPTION AND TRAVEL

COLOUR, LOCAL. Taj Mahal. (Our World in Colour Ser.). (Illus.). 80p. *(978-962-8711-23-9(7))* Local Colour, Ltd. HKG. Dist: 7 Hills Bk. Distributors.

Dorling Kindersley Publishing Staff. Delhi, Agra & Jaipur. 2010. (Eyewitness Travel Guides). (ENG.). 320p. pap. 25.00 *(978-0-7566-6182-3(X))* Dorling Kindersley Publishing, Inc.

Havell, E.B. A Handbook to Agra & the Taj. 2006. pap. *(978-1-4068-3384-3(3))* Echo Library.

AGRA (INDIA)—TAJ MAHAL

see Taj Mahal (Agra, India)

AGRAPHIA

Berninger, Virginia Wise & Wolf, Beverly. Teaching Students with Dyslexia & Dysgraphia: Lessons from Teaching & Science. 2009. (ENG.). 256p. pap. 39.95 *(978-1-55766-934-6(1))* Brookes, Paul H. Publishing Co.

Eli, the Boy Who Hated to Write: Understanding Dysgraphia, 2nd Edition. 2nd rev. ed. 2008. 144p. (J). pap. 20.00 *(978-0-9661353-6-7(9))* RET Center Pr.

AGRARIAN QUESTION

see Agriculture—Economic Aspects; Agriculture and State

AGRARIAN REFORM

see Land Reform

AGRARIAN TENURE

see Land Tenure

AGREEMENTS

see Contracts

AGREEMENTS, INTERSTATE

see Interstate Agreements

AGRIBUSINESS

see Agricultural Industries; Agriculture—Economic Aspects

AGRICOLA, GNAEUS JULIUS, 40-93

Charlesworth, Martin Percival. Five Men: Character Studies from the Roman Empire. 2011. 180p. 42.95 ***(978-1-258-02399-7(7))*** Literary Licensing, LLC.

Steele, R. B. Notes to the Dialogus de Oratoribus Based on Gudeman's Edition. 2009. pap. 19.12 *(978-1-60724-610-7(4))* Gorgias Pr., LLC.

Tacitus. Agricola & Germania. Rives, James, ed. Mattingly, Harold, tr. from LAT. rev. ed. 2010. (ENG., Illus.). 224p. (gr. 12-18). 15.00 *(978-0-14-045540-3(X),* Penguin Classics) Penguin Group (USA) Inc.

—Agricola & Germany. Birley, Anthony, tr. from LAT. 2009. (Oxford World's Classics Ser.). (ENG., Illus.). 224p. pap. 13.95 *(978-0-19-953926-0(X))* Oxford Univ. Pr., Inc.

Tacitus, Cornelius. The Agricola & the Germania. 2008. 100p. pap. 10.99 *(978-1-4209-3162-4(8))* Digireads.com.

—The Germania, Agricola, & Dialogus de Oratoribus of Tacitus with Notes by George Stuart. 2006. 244p. per. 20.99 *(978-1-4255-2092-2(8))* MPublishing.

—The Germania & Agricola with Notes by W S Tyler. 2006. 216p. per. 20.99 *(978-1-4255-1779-3(X))* MPublishing.

Wolfson, Stan. Tacitus, Thule & Caledonia: The Achievements of Agricola's Navy in Their True Perspective. 2008. (Bar Ser.). (ENG., Illus.). 118p. (C). pap. 67.50 *(978-1-4073-0274-4(4))* British Archaeological Reports Ltd. GBR. Dist: Brown, David Bk. Co., The.

AGRICOLA, RODOLPHUS, 1443?-1485

Agricola, Rodolphus. Letters. (LAT & ENG., Illus.). ix, 435 p. *(978-90-232-3808-9(7))* Bow Historical Bks.

Akkerman, Fokke, ed. Rudolph Agricola: Six Lives & Erasmus' Testimonies: Edited, translated & annotated by Fokke Akkerman. 2012. (Bibliotheca Latinitatis Novae Ser.). (ENG.). ***(978-90-8728-134-2(X),*** Leiden Univ. Pr.) Amsterdam Univ. Pr.

AGRICULTURAL ADMINISTRATION

see also Agricultural Extension Work

Baldwin, Sidney. Poverty & Politics: The Rise & Decline of the Farm Security Administration. 2011. (ENG.). 448p. pap. 50.00 *(978-0-8078-9612-9(8))* Univ. of North Carolina Pr.

Vorobeva, D. A. Selskii Sotsium: Obshchestvennye Ustoi I Vektory Transformatsii. 2009. (RUS.). 323p. *(978-5-9999-0210-8(X))* Nauka.

AGRICULTURAL ASSISTANCE

Here are entered works on international aid to agriculture given to underdeveloped areas in the form of technical assistance.

see also Agricultural Development Projects; Agriculture—International Cooperation

Agriculture Food & Development, 6 vols., Set A. 2011. 1865p. 600.00 *(978-0-415-59717-3(X))* Routledge.

Cullather, Nick, et al. The Hungry World: America's Cold War Battle Against Poverty in Asia. 2010. (ENG., Illus.). 368p. 35.00 *(978-0-674-05078-5(9))* Harvard Univ. Pr.

Haggblade, Steven & Hazell, Peter B. R., eds. Successes in African Agriculture: Lessons for the Future. 2010. (ENG., Illus.). 464p. (gr. 17). 90.00 *(978-0-8018-9502-9(2))*; pap. 45.00 *(978-0-8018-9503-6(0))* Johns Hopkins Univ. Pr.

Hearing to Review Efforts to Deliver International Food Aid & Provide Foreign Agricultural Development Assistance: Hearing Before the Subcommittee on Specialty Crops, Rural Development, & Foreign Agriculture of the Committee on Agriculture, House of Representatives, One Hundred Tenth Congress, Second Session, July 16, 2008. 2009. (Illus.). iii, 81p. *(978-0-16-083743-2(X),* 552-070-37445-1) United States Government Printing Office.

Mougeot, Luc J. A. Growing Better Cities: Urban Agriculture for Sustainable Development. 2006. (In Focus Ser.). (Illus.). 106p. pap. 20.00 *(978-1-55250-226-6(0))* IDRC/CRDI CAN. Dist: Stylus Publishing, LLC.

Oversight of the Feed the Future Initiative: Joint Hearing Before the Subcommittee on International Organizations, Human Rights, & Oversight & the Subcommittee on Africa & Global Health of the Committee on Foreign Affairs, House of Representatives, One Hundred Eleventh Congress, Second Session, July 20, 2010. 2010. (Illus.). v, 109p. ***(978-0-16-087068-2(2),*** 552-070-41925-0) United States Government Printing Office.

Promoting Global Food Security: Next Steps for Congress & the Administration: Hearing Before the Committee on Foreign Relations, United States Senate, One Hundred Eleventh Congress, Second Session, April 22, 2010. 2011. iii, 71p. ***(978-0-16-088017-9(3),*** 552-070-42441-5) United States Government Printing Office.

Rao, A. V. Nageswara, et al. Supply Chain Strategies for Agribusiness. 2011. 232p. pap. ***(978-3-639-14741-4(3))*** VDM Verlag Dr. Mueller e.K.

Reilly, Katherine V. Food Aid Policy & Challenges. 2009. (Illus.). x, 178p. E-Book 69.00 ***(978-1-61209-750-3(2))*** Nova Science Pubs., Inc.

Rivera, Angela N. Global Food Security. 2011. (Illus.). viii, 263p. *(978-1-61761-765-2(2))* Nova Science Pubs., Inc.

Shaw, D. John & Shaw, D. J. World Food Security: A History Since 1945. 2007. (ENG.). 472p. 231.00 *(978-0-230-55355-2(9))* Palgrave Macmillan.

The World Bank. Growth & Productivity in Agriculture & Agribusiness: Evaluative Lessons from World Bank Group Experience. 2011. (Independent Evaluation Group Studies). (ENG., Illus.). 200p. pap. 25.00 *(978-0-8213-8606-4(9),* 9780821386064) World Bank Pubns.

United States, Congress House Committee on Financial Services Subcommittee on Domestic and International Monetary Policy, Trade, and Technology Staff, contrib. by. The International Fund for Agricultural Development (IFAD) & the Importance of Agriculture Development in Sustainable Global Poverty Reduction: Hearing Before the Subcommittee on Domestic & International Monetary Policy, Trade, & Technology of the Committee on Financial Services, U.S. House of Representatives, One Hundred Ninth Congress, Second Session, September 12, 2006. 2007. v, 56p. *(978-0-16-078406-4(9),* 552-070-35701-7) United States Government Printing Office.

World Bank Staff. World Bank Assistance to Agriculture in Sub-Saharan Africa: An IEG Review. 2007. (Independent Evaluation Group Studies). (ENG., Illus.). 224p. per. 35.00 *(978-0-8213-7350-7(1),* 9780821373507) World Bank Pubns.

AGRICULTURAL ASSOCIATIONS

see Agricultural Societies

AGRICULTURAL BANKS

see Banks and Banking

AGRICULTURAL BIOTECHNOLOGY

Ahmad, Iqbal, et al, eds. Plant-Bacteria Interactions: Strategies & Techniques to Promote Plant Growth. 2008. (ENG., Illus.). 330p. 219.95 *(978-3-527-31901-5(8),* Wiley-VCH) Wiley, John & Sons, Inc.

Altman, Arie & Hasegawa, Paul Michael, eds. Plant Biotechnology & Agriculture: Prospects for the 21st Century. 2011. (ENG.). 624p. 199.95 ***(978-0-12-381466-1(9),*** Academic Pr.) Elsevier Science & Technology Bks.

Amat Llombart, Pablo & Llombart, Pablo Amat. Derecho de la Biotecnología y Los Transgénicos: (Especial Referencia Al Sector Agrario y Alimentario) 2008. (SPA.). 382p. *(978-84-9876-019-4(4))* Tirant lo Blanch.

Andrée, Peter. Genetically Modified Diplomacy: The Global Politics of Agricultural Biotechnology & the Environment. 2007. (ENG., Illus.). 336p. *(978-0-7748-1268-9(0))* Univ. of British Columbia Pr.

Andree, Peter. Genetically Modified Diplomacy: The Global Politics of Agricultural Biotechnology & the Environment. 2008. (ENG.). 336p. pap. 32.95 *(978-0-7748-1269-6(9))* Univ. of Washington Pr.

Ashihara, Hiroshi, et al, eds. Plant Metabolism & Biotechnology. 2011. (ENG., Illus.). 420p. 170.00 *(978-0-470-74703-2(X),* Wiley) Wiley, John & Sons, Inc.

Ashwani Kumar & Arya, H. C. Plant Tissue Culture & Moelcular [i.e. Molecular] Markers: Their Role in Improving Crop Productivity: Prof. K.C. Arya Commemoration Volume. 2009. (Illus.). xx, 686p. (C). *(978-81-89866-10-5(9))* I.K. International Publishing House Pvt. Ltd.

Bajaj, Y.P.S., ed. Maize. 2008. (Biotechnology in Agriculture & Forestry Ser.). (Illus.). xxvi, 632p. 599.00 *(978-3-540-56392-1(X))* Springer.

Benkeblia, Noureddine, ed. Sustainable Agriculture & New Biotechnologies. 2011. (Advances in Agroecology Ser.). (ENG., Illus.). 555p. 129.95 *(978-1-4398-2504-4(1),* CRC Press) Taylor & Francis Group GBR. Dist: Taylor & Francis Group.

Bernard, Alain, et al, eds. Animal Cell Technology: Products from Cells, Cells as Products: Products from Cells, Cells as Products. 2010. 634p. pap. 399.00 *(978-90-481-5363-3(8),* 9048153638) Springer.

Brown, Corrie. Foreign Animal Diseases, Seventh Edition: The United States Animal Health Association, the Gray Book. 2008. (ENG., Illus.). 470p. per. 20.00 *(978-0-9659583-4-9(5))* Boca Pubns. Group, Inc.

Chambers, W. Bradnee. Interlinkages & the Effectiveness of Multilateral Environmental Agreements. 2008. (ENG., Illus.). 252p. pap. 34.00 *(978-92-808-1149-0(5))* United Nations Univ. Pr. JPN. Dist: Brookings Institution Pr.

Committee on the Impact of Biotechnology on Farm-Level Economics and Sustainability & National Research Council. Impact of Genetically Engineered Crops on Farm Sustainability in the United States. 2010. (ENG.). 270p. pap. 49.00 *(978-0-309-14708-8(5))* National Academies Pr.

Cummings, Claire Hope. Uncertain Peril: Genetic Engineering & the Future of Seeds, 1 vol. 2009. (ENG.). 256p. pap. 16.00 *(978-0-8070-8581-3(2))* Beacon Pr.

Denison, R. F. Darwinian Agriculture: Where Does Nature's Wisdom Lie? 2012. (ENG., Illus.). 248p. (C). 39.50 ***(978-0-691-13950-0(4))*** Princeton Univ. Pr.

Ditta, Allah, et al. Use of Pgpr Biotechnology to Mitigate Salinity Stress in Wheat. 2011. 88p. pap. ***(978-3-8443-8930-2(X))*** Lambert Academic Publishing.

Doherty, Catherine. Apostolic Farming: Healing the Earth. 2nd exp. ed. 96p. pap. *(978-0-921440-03-1(0))* Madonna Hse. Pubns.

Dutta Gupta, S. & Ibaraki, Yasuomi, eds. Plant Tissue Culture Engineering. 2010. (Focus on Biotechnology Ser.). viii, 480p. pap. 289.00 *(978-90-481-6906-1(2),* 9048169062) Springer.

Edizioni Polistampa, ed. I Georgofili. Quaderni 2010-V. Frontiere della tracciabilita molecolare e sicurezza dei prodotti Alimentari: Firenze, 18 Marzo 2010. 2011. (I Georgofili Ser.). (ITA., Illus.). 96p. (C). pap. 17.00 ***(978-88-596-0895-0(3))*** Polistampa ITA. Dist: Brown, David Bk. Co., The.

Eggers, Sharon. Sub-Imbibed Storage. 2011. 184p. pap. ***(978-3-8443-8447-5(2))*** Lambert Academic Publishing.

El-Shemy, Hany. Protein Production in Terms of Plant Physiology & Molecular Biology. 2010. 152p. pap. *(978-3-8383-7311-9(1))* Lambert Academic Publishing.

Endress, Rudolf. Plant Cell Biotechnology, 1 vol. 2010. (ENG., Illus.). xiv, 353p. pap. 229.00 *(978-3-642-08165-1(7),* 3642081657) Springer.

Engdahl, F. William. Seeds of Destruction: The Hidden Agenda of Genetic Manipulation. 2007. 341p. pap. *(978-0-9737147-2-2(7))* Global Research, Ctr. for Research on Globalization (CRG).

Engelhard, Margret. Genetic Engineering in Livestock. 2008. (Ethics of Science & Technology Assessment Ser.). 79.95 *(978-3-540-85842-3(3),* 3540858423) Springer.

Erickson, L., et al, eds. Molecular Farming of Plants & Animals for Human & Veterinary Medicine. 2010. 400p. pap. 249.00 *(978-90-481-6110-2(X),* 904816110X) Springer.

Ferry, Natalie & Gatehouse, A. M. R., eds. Environmental Impact of Genetically Modified Crops. 2009. (Illus.). 440p. 180.00 *(978-1-84593-409-5(1))* CABI GBR. Dist: Stylus Publishing, LLC.

Fiechter, Armin & Sautter, Christof. Green Gene Technology: Research in an Area of Social Conflict. 2010. (Advances in Biochemical Engineering Biotechnology Ser.). (Illus.). xvi, 287p. pap. 339.00 *(978-3-642-09042-4(7),* 3642090427) Springer.

Fladung, Matthias & Ewald, Dietrich, eds. Tree Transgenesis: Recent Developments. 2010. (ENG., Illus.). xx, 360p. pap. 269.00 *(978-3-642-06881-2(2),* 3642068812) Springer.

Fletcher, Garth L. & Rise, Matthew L., eds. Aquaculture Biotechnology. 2012. (ENG., Illus.). 390p. 199.95 ***(978-0-8138-1028-7(0),*** Wiley-Blackwell) Wiley, John & Sons, Inc.

Gigliotti, Carol, ed. Leonardo's Choice: Genetic Technologies & Animals. 2009. (ENG., Illus.). xxviii, 256p. 139.00 *(978-90-481-2478-7(6),* 9048124786) Springer.

Gomase, Virendra & Murti, Madhur. Animal Biotechnology. 2010. 364p. pap. *(978-3-639-25031-2(1))* VDM Verlag Dr. Mueller e.K.

Gomase, Virendra & Sherkhane, Anant. Plant Biotechnology. 2010. 392p. pap. *(978-3-639-03208-6(X))* VDM Verlag Dr. Mueller e.K.

Gupta, Vijai Kumar, et al. Current Research Advancement on Wilt Disease of Psidium Guajava L. 2010. 260p. pap. *(978-3-8383-9000-0(8))* Lambert Academic Publishing.

Halford, N. G. Genetically Modified Crops. 2nd ed. 2011. (Illus.). 200p. 66.00 ***(978-1-84816-838-1(1))*** Imperial College Pr. GBR. Dist: World Scientific Publishing Co., Inc.

Harrison, Beth H. Shedding Light on Genetically Engineered Food. 2007. 172p. per. 15.95 *(978-0-595-45180-7(2))* iUniverse, Inc.

—Shedding Light on Genetically Engineered Food: What You Don't Know about the Food You're Eating & What You Can Do to Protect Yourself. 2007. 172p. 25.95 *(978-0-595-69326-9(1))* iUniverse, Inc.

Hearing to Review the Opportunities & Benefits of Agricultural Biotechnology: Hearing Before the Subcommittee on Rural Development, Research, Biotechnology, & Foreign Agriculture of the Committee on Agriculture, House of Representatives, One Hundred Twelfth Congress, First Session, June 23, 2011. 2011. iii, 153p. ***(978-0-16-089259-2(7),*** 552-070-43255-8) United States Government Printing Office.

Heldman, Dennis R., et al. Encyclopedia of Biotechnology in Agriculture & Food. 2010. (ENG., Illus.). 784p. 399.95 *(978-0-8493-5027-6(1),* CRC Press) Taylor & Francis Group GBR. Dist: Taylor & Francis Group.

Holdrege, Craig & Talbott, Steve. Beyond Biotechnology: The Barren Promise of Genetic Engineering. (Culture of the Land Ser.). (ENG., Illus.). 272p. 2010. pap. 30.00 *(978-0-8131-9256-7(0))* 2008. 70.00 *(978-0-8131-2484-1(0))* Univ. Pr. of Kentucky.

Hood, Elizabeth E. & Howard, J. A., eds. Plants as Factories for Protein Production. 2010. 224p. pap. 195.00 *(978-90-481-6113-3(4),* 9048161134) Springer.

Hou, Ching T. & Shaw, Jei-Fu. Biocatalysis & Agricultural Biotechnology. 2009. (ENG., Illus.). 442p. 185.95 *(978-1-4200-7703-2(1),* CRC Press) Taylor & Francis Group GBR. Dist: Taylor & Francis Group.

Howlett, Michael & Laycock, David, eds. Regulating Next Generation Agri-Food Bio-Technologies: Lessons from European & Asian Experiences. 2012. (Genetics & Society Ser.). (ENG., Illus.). 288p. (C). 135.00 ***(978-0-415-69361-5(6))*** Routledge.

Iijima, Shinji & Nishijima, Ken-ichi, eds. Animal Cell Technology: Basic & Applied Aspects: Proceedings of the Seventeenth Annual Meeting of the Japanese Association for Animal Cell Technology (JAACT), Nagoya, Japan, November 15-18 2004. 2010. (Animal Cell Technology: Basic & Applied Aspects Ser.). xi, 440p. pap. 359.00 *(978-90-481-7106-4(7),* 9048171067) Springer.

Ikura, Kouji, et al, eds. Animal Cell Technology: Challenges for the 21st Century: Challenges for the 21st Century. 2010. 452p. pap. 299.00 *(978-90-481-5259-9(3),* 9048152593) Springer.

International Assessment of Agricultural Knowledge, Science, and Technology. Agriculture at a Crossroads: International Assessment of Agricultural Science & Technology for Development - East & South Asia & the Pacific. 2009. (ENG., Illus.). 226p. 125.00 *(978-1-59726-544-7(6))* Island Pr.

—Agriculture at a Crossroads Vol. 1: Central & West Asia & North Africa. 2009. (ENG., Illus.). 192p. 125.00 *(978-1-59726-542-3(X))*; 2nd ed. pap. 75.00 *(978-1-59726-543-0(8))* Island Pr.

—Agriculture at a Crossroads Vol. 2: East & South Asia & the Pacific. 2009. (ENG.). 226p. pap. 75.00 *(978-1-59726-545-4(4))* Island Pr.

—Agriculture at a Crossroads Vol. 3: Latin America & the Caribbean. 2009. (ENG., Illus.). 248p. 125.00 *(978-1-59726-546-1(2))* Island Pr.

—Agriculture at a Crossroads Vol. 4: Latin America & the Caribbean. 2nd ed. 2009. (ENG.). 248p. pap. 75.00 *(978-1-59726-547-8(0))* Island Pr.

—Agriculture at a Crossroads Vol. 5: Sub-Saharan Africa. 2009. (ENG.). 160p. pap. 75.00 *(978-1-59726-541-6(1))* Island Pr.

—Agriculture at a Crossroads Vol. V: Sub-Saharan Africa. 2nd ed. 2009. (ENG., Illus.). 160p. 125.00 *(978-1-59726-540-9(3))* Island Pr.

—North America & Europe Vol. 5: International Assessment of Agricultural Knowledge, Science & Technology for Development. 2009. (ENG.). 312p. pap. 75.00 *(978-1-59726-549-2(7))*; (Illus.). 125.00 *(978-1-59726-548-5(9))* Island Pr.

Jenkins, Nigel, et al, eds. Proceedings of the 21st Annual Meeting of the European Society for Animal Cell Technology (ESACT), Dublin, Ireland, June 7-10 2009. 2011. (ESACT Proceedings Ser.). (ENG., Illus.). xliv, 753p. 349.00 *(978-94-007-0883-9(1),* 9400708831) Springer.

Just, Richard E., et al, eds. Regulating Agricultural Biotechnology: Economics & Policy. (Natural Resource Management & Policy Ser.). (Illus.). 2010. viii, 732p. pap. 229.00 *(978-1-4419-4239-5(4),* 1441942394) 2006. 732p. 229.00 *(978-0-387-36952-5(X),* 038736952X) Springer.

Kamihira, Masamichi, et al, eds. Animal Cell Technology: Basic & Applied Aspects: Proceedings of the 21st Annual & International Meeting of the Japanese Association for Animal Cell Technology (JAACT), Fukuoka, Japan, November 24-27 2008. 2010. (ENG.). 464p. 189.00 *(978-90-481-3582-0(6),* 9048135826) Springer.

—Basic & Applied Aspects: Proceedings of the 21st Annual & International Meeting of the Japanese Association for Animal Cell Technology (JAACT), Fukuoka, Japan, November 24-27 2008. 2010. (Animal Cell Technology: Basic & Applied Aspects Ser.). (ENG., Illus.). xxx, 464p. 269.00 *(978-90-481-3891-3(4),* 9048138914) Springer.

Kannaiyan, S. Soil Microbiology & Soil Biotechnology, 2 vols. 2010. (Illus.). *(978-81-85211-85-5(X),* Library of Congress — New Delhi Overseas Office); *(978-81-85211-83-1(3),* Library of Congress — New Delhi Overseas Office); *(978-81-85211-84-8(1),* Library of Congress — New Delhi Overseas Office) Associated Publishing Co.

Karasev, Alexander V. Plant-Produced Microbial Vaccines. 2009. (Current Topics in Microbiology & Immunology Ser.). (Illus.). x, 120p. 159.00 *(978-3-540-70857-5(X))* Springer.

Karplus, Valerie J. Agricultural Biotechnology in China: Origins & Prospects. 2007. (Illus.). 165p. 109.00 *(978-0-387-71138-6(4))* Springer.

Kefialew, Yonas & Ayalew (), Amare. Postharvest Biological Control of Anthracnose on Mango. 2011. 132p. pap. ***(978-3-8433-7564-1(X))*** Lambert Academic Publishing.

Kesan, Jay P. Agricultural Biotechnology & Intellectual Property Protection: Seeds of Change. 2007. 416p. 160.00 *(978-1-84593-201-5(3))* CABI GBR. Dist: Stylus Publishing, LLC.

Kortei, Julian Nii Korley. Growing Oyster Mushrooms on Composted Agrowastes. 2011. 120p. pap. ***(978-3-8454-2107-0(X))*** Lambert Academic Publishing.

Lin, Zhi-Qing & Banuelos, Gary Stephan. Development & Uses of Biofortified Agricultural Products. Banuelos, Gary S. & Lin, Zhi-Qing, eds. 2008. (ENG., Illus.). 320p. 129.95 *(978-1-4200-6005-8(8),* CRC Press) Taylor & Francis Group GBR. Dist: Taylor & Francis Group.

Liong, Min-Tze. Bioprocess Sciences & Technology. 2011. (Biochemistry Research Trends Ser.). (Illus.). 526p. 195.00 *(978-1-61122-950-9(2))* Nova Science Pubs., Inc.

Maheshwari, Dinesh K., ed. Bacteria in Agrobiology: Stress Management: Stress Management. 2012. (ENG., Illus.). xii, 333p. 209.00 ***(978-3-642-23464-4(X),*** 364223464X) Springer.

Mahmood, Sajid. Azeemi-Surge Irrigation Advance Rate Performance Model. 2010. 168p. pap. *(978-3-639-24779-4(5))* VDM Verlag Dr. Mueller e.K.

Malik, C. P. & et al., eds. Advanced Topics in Biotechnology & Plant Biology. 2008. (Illus.). 452p. 115.00 *(978-81-7533-144-0(5))* M. D. Pubns. Pvt. Ltd. IND. Dist: Coronet Bks.

Mansour, Ahmed & Ismail, Omayma M. Mahmoud. Biotechnology in Agriculture. 2008. 104p. pap. *(978-3-639-08108-4(0))* VDM Verlag Dr. Mueller e.K.

Mariani, Meredith T. The Intersection of International Law, Agricultural Biotechnology, & Infectious Disease. 2007. 250p. *(978-1-57105-373-2(5))* BRILL.

Mebrate, Adugna. The Role of Farmer to Farmer Knowledge Sharing in Innovation Process. 2010. (Illus.). 116p. pap. *(978-3-8383-6792-7(8))* Lambert Academic Publishing.

Morrissey, Kate L. Biological & chemical induction of systemic resistance in the barley powdery mildew Pathosystem. 2007. (Schriften des Forschungszentrums Jülich: 73). 138p. pap. *(978-3-89336-475-6(7))* Forschungszentrum Julich GmbH - Zentralbibliothek, Verlag.

Mudzwiri, Mashudu & Lalini Reddy. Traditional South African Leafy Plants. 2010. 132p. pap. *(978-3-8383-6218-2(7))* Lambert Academic Publishing.

Murhammer, David W., ed. Baculovirus & Insect Cell Expression Protocols. 2nd ed. 2010. (Methods in Molecular Biology Ser.). (Illus.). xiv, 470p. pap. 209.00 *(978-1-61737-629-0(9),* 1617376299) Humana Pr.

Murphy, Denis. Plants, Biotechnology & Agriculture. 2011. (Modular Texts). 312p. 145.00 ***(978-1-84593-913-7(1))*** CABI GBR. Dist: Stylus Publishing, LLC.

Murphy, Denis J. People, Plants & Genes: The Story of Crops & Humanity. 2007. (ENG., Illus.). 432p. per. 70.00 *(978-0-19-920714-5(3))* Oxford Univ. Pr., Inc.

—Plants, Biotechnology & Agriculture. 2011. *(978-1-84593-871-0(2))* CABI.

—Plants, Biotechnology & Agriculture. 2011. (Modular Texts). 312p. pap. 75.00 *(978-1-84593-688-4(4))* CABI GBR. Dist: Stylus Publishing, LLC.

Nedovic, Viktor & Willaert, Ronnie, eds. Applications of Cell Immobilisation Biotechnology. 2010. (Focus on Biotechnology Ser.). vi, 573p. pap. 279.00 *(978-90-481-6820-0(1),* 9048168201) Springer.

Neelwarne, Bhagyalakshmi, ed. Red Beet Biotechnology: Food & Pharmaceutical Applications. 2012. (ENG., Illus.). xii, 448p. 209.00 ***(978-1-4614-3457-3(2),*** 1461434572) Springer.

Neumann, K. H., et al. Recent Advances in Plant Biotechnology & Its Applications: Prof. Dr. Karl-Hermann Neumann Commemorative Volume. 2008. (Illus.). xiv, 694p. (C). *(978-81-89866-09-9(5))* I.K. International Publishing House Pvt. Ltd.

Nick, Peter. Plant Microtubules: Development & Flexibility. 2nd ed. 2008. (Plant Cell Monographs). (ENG., Illus.). xiv, 269p. 219.00 *(978-3-540-77175-3(1),* 3540777151) Springer.

Noll, Thomas, ed. Proceedings of the 20th ESACT Meeting, Dresden, Germany, June 17-20,2007. 2009. (ESACT Proceedings Ser.). (ENG., Illus.). 800p. 349.00 *(978-90-481-3418-2(8),* 9048134188) Springer.

Olmstead, Alan & Rhode, Paul. Creating Abundance: Biological Innovation & American Agricultural Development. 2008. (ENG., Illus.). 480p. 85.00 *(978-0-521-85711-6(2))* Cambridge Univ. Pr.

Olmstead, Alan, et al. Creating Abundance: Biological Innovation & American Agricultural Development. 2008. (ENG., Illus.). 480p. pap. 24.99 *(978-0-521-67387-7(9))* Cambridge Univ. Pr.

Otero, Gerardo, ed. Food for the Few: Neoliberal Globalism & Biotechnology in Latin America. 2010. (ENG., Illus.). 335p. pap. 30.00 *(978-0-292-72613-0(9))* Univ. of Texas Pr.

Paarlberg, Robert & Paarlberg, Robert L. Starved for Science: How Biotechnology Is Being Kept Out of Africa. 2009. (Illus.). 256p. pap. 17.95 *(978-0-674-03347-4(7))* Harvard Univ. Pr.

Pal, B. P. Search for New Genes. Bhat, S. R. et al, eds. 2007. (ENG., Illus.). 500p. 79.95 *(978-81-7188-632-6(9))* Academic Foundation IND. Dist: Independent Pubs. Group.

Pandit, M. W., et al. You Deserve, We Conserve: A Biotechnological Approach to Wildlife Conservation. 2007. (Illus.). xii, 142p. (C). *(978-81-89866-24-2(9))* I.K. International Publishing House Pvt. Ltd.

Paudel, Mina Nath. Ed Culture of Maize for Enhancing Productivity. 2011. 100p. pap. ***(978-3-8443-0296-7(4))*** Lambert Academic Publishing.

Pedraz, José Luis & Orive, Gorka, eds. Therapeutic Applications of Cell Microencapsulation. 2010. (Advances in Experimental Medicine & Biology Ser.). (ENG., Illus.). xxii, 125p. 209.00 *(978-1-4419-5785-6(5),* 1441957855) Springer.

Ponterio, Claude. Jatropha Curcas As a Premier Biofuel: Cost, Growing & Management. Ferra, Costanza, ed. 2010. (Energy Science, Engineering & Technology Ser.). (Illus.). 210p. 129.00 *(978-1-60876-003-9(0))* Nova Science Pubs., Inc.

Qaim, Matin, et al, eds. Agricultural Biotechnology in Developing Countries: Towards Optimizing the Benefits for the Poor: Towards Optimizing the Benefits for the Poor. 2010. (ENG.). 448p. pap. 210.00 *(978-1-4419-4864-9(3),* 1441948643) Springer.

Rees, Andy. Genetically Modified Food: A Short Guide for the Confused. 2006. (ENG.). 240p. 74.00 *(978-0-7453-2440-1(1));* per. 19.95 *(978-0-7453-2439-5(8))* Pluto Pr. GBR. Dist: Macmillan.

Renaville, R. & Burny, A., eds. Biotechnology in Animal Husbandry. 2010. (Focus on Biotechnology Ser.). (Illus.). 368p. pap. 189.00 *(978-90-481-5667-2(X),* 904815667X) Springer.

Shan, Guomin, ed. Immunoassays in Agricultural Biotechnology. 2011. (ENG., Illus.). 368p. 127.00 *(978-0-470-28952-5(X),* Wiley) Wiley, John & Sons, Inc.

Smyth, Stuart J., et al. Innovation & Liability in Biotechnology: Transnational & Comparative Perspectives. 2010. (Illus.). 224p. 112.00 *(978-1-84720-664-0(6))* Elgar, Edward Publishing, Inc.

Steering Committee on Global Challenges and Directions for Agricultural Biotechnology: Mapping the Course & National Research Council. Global Challenges & Directions for Agricultural Biotechnology: Workshop Report. 2008. (ENG.). 74p. pap. 21.00 *(978-0-309-12077-7(2))* National Academies Pr.

Stewart, C. Neal, ed. Plant Biotechnology & Genetics: Principles, Techniques & Applications. 2008. (ENG., Illus.). 416p. 117.00 *(978-0-470-04381-3(4),* Wiley-Interscience) Wiley, John & Sons, Inc.

Taylor, Iain E. P. Genetically Engineered Crops: Interim Policies, Uncertain Legislation. 2007. (ENG.). 393p. 104.95 *(978-1-56022-988-9(8));* (Illus.). per. 69.95 *(978-1-56022-989-6(6))* Taylor & Francis Group GBR. (CRC Press). Dist: Taylor & Francis Group.

Teng, P. S. Business Potential for Agricultural Biotechnology Products. 2007. (Illus.). 197p. *(978-92-833-2371-6(8))* Asian Productivity Organization.

Thenkabail, Prasad, et al, eds. Remote Sensing of Global Croplands for Food Security. 2009. (Remote Sensing Applications Ser.). (ENG., Illus.). 556p. 133.95 *(978-1-4200-9009-3(7),* CRC Press) Taylor & Francis Group GBR. Dist: Taylor & Francis Group.

Thompson, R. Paul. Agro-Technology: A Philosophical Introduction. 2011. (Cambridge Introductions to Philosophy & Biology Ser.). (ENG., Illus.). 258p. (C). 90.00 ***(978-0-521-11797-5(6))***; pap. 28.99 ***(978-0-521-13375-3(0))*** Cambridge Univ. Pr.

Thomson, Jennifer A. Seeds for the Future: The Impact of Genetically Modified Crops on the Environment. 2007. (Illus.). 158p. pap. 24.95 *(978-0-8014-7368-5(3),* Comstock Publishing Assocs.) Cornell Univ. Pr.

Tripp, Robert Burnet. Biotechnology & Agricultural Development: Transgenic Cotton, Rural Institutions & Resource-Poor Farmers. Tripp, Rob, ed. 2009. (Routledge Explorations in Environmental Economics Ser.: Vol. 19). (Illus.). 280p. pap. 45.95 *(978-0-415-54384-2(3))* Routledge.

—Biotechnology & Agricultural Development: Transgenic Cotton, Rural Institutions & Resource-poor Farmers. 2009. (Routledge Explorations in Environmental Economics Ser.: Vol. 19). (ENG., Illus.). 280p. 145.00 *(978-0-415-49963-7(1))* Routledge.

University of Toronto Press. Animal Biotechnology. 2010. *(978-1-4426-3997-3(0))* Univ. of Toronto Pr.

Upadhyay, Rajeev K., ed. Advances in Microbial Toxin Research & its Biotechnological Exploitation. 2010. (ENG.). 300p. pap. 189.00 *(978-1-4419-3384-3(0),* 1441933840) Springer.

Varshney, Rajeev & Tuberosa, Roberto, eds. Genomics-Assisted Crop Improvement, Volume 1: Genomics Approaches & Platforms. 2008. (Illus.). 386p. 229.00 *(978-1-4020-6294-0(X))* Springer.

—Genomics-Assisted Crop Improvement, Volume 2: Genomics Applications in Crops. 2008. (Illus.). 509p. 259.00 *(978-1-4020-6296-4(6))* Springer.

Vasil, Indra K., ed. Plant Biotechnology 2002 & Beyond. 2012. (ENG.). 625p. pap. 289.00 *(978-90-481-6220-8(3),* 9048162203) Springer.

Vilcinskas, Andreas, ed. Insect Biotechnology. 2010. (Biologically-Inspired Systems Ser.). (Illus.). xii, 250p. 189.00 *(978-90-481-9640-1(X),* 904819640X) Springer.

Vlak, Just M., et al, eds. Insect Cell Cultures: Fundamental & Applied Aspects. 2010. (Current Applications of Cell Culture Engineering Ser.). 324p. pap. 409.00 *(978-90-481-4531-7(7),* 9048145317) Springer.

Vollmann, Johann & Rajcan, Istvan. Oil Crop Breeding. 2009. (Handbook of Plant Breeding Ser.). (Illus.). 500p. 199.00 *(978-0-387-77593-7(5))* Springer.

Wang, Aiming & Ma, Shengwu, eds. Molecular Farming in Plants: Recent Advances & Future Prospects: Recent Advances & Future Prospects. 2011. (ENG., Illus.). xii, 279p. 189.00 ***(978-94-007-2216-3(8),*** 9400722168) Springer.

Wang, Kan. Agrobacterium Protocols: Volume II, 2 vols. 2nd ed. 2006. (Methods in Molecular Biology Ser.: Vol. 344). (Illus.). 485p. 209.00 *(978-1-58829-843-0(4),* 1588298434) Humana Pr.

Wang, Kan, ed. Agrobacterium Protocols: Volume I. 2nd ed. 2010. (Methods in Molecular Biology Ser.). (Illus.). 512p. pap. 209.00 *(978-1-61737-628-3(0),* 1617376280) Humana Pr.

—Agrobacterium Protocols: Volume II. 2nd ed. 2010. (Methods in Molecular Biology Ser.). (Illus.). 512p. pap. 209.00 *(978-1-61737-803-4(8),* 1617378038) Humana Pr.

Williamson, Meredith A. U. S. Biobased Products Market Potential & Projections Through 2025. 2009. (Agriculture Issues & Politics Ser.). 79.00 *(978-1-60741-033-1(8))* Nova Science Pubs., Inc.

World Health Organization. FAO/WHO Expert Meeting on the Application of Nanotechnologies in the Food & Agriculture Sectors: Potential Food Safety Implications: Meeting Report. 2010. (Nonserial Publication). (ENG., Illus.). 129p. pap. 36.00 *(978-92-4-156393-2(1))* World Health Organization.

Wozniak, Chris A. & McHughen, Alan, eds. Regulation of Agricultural Biotechnology: the United States & Canada: The United States & Canada. 2012. (ENG., Illus.). xx, 230p. 189.00 ***(978-94-007-2155-5(2),*** 9400721552) Springer.

Xu, Zhihong, et al, eds. Biotechnology & Sustainable Agriculture 2006 & Beyond: Proceedings of the 11th IAPTC&B Congress, August 13-18, 2006 Beijing, China. (ENG.). xxii, 498p. 2010. pap. 219.00 *(978-90-481-7685-4(9),* 9048176859) 2007. (Illus.). 219.00 *(978-1-4020-6634-4(1),* 1402066341) Springer.

Yagasaki, Kazumi, et al, eds. Animal Cell Technology: Basic & Applied Aspects: Volume 13. 2010. (Animal Cell Technology: Basic & Applied Aspects Ser.). 520p. pap. 299.00 *(978-90-481-6557-5(1),* 9048165571) Springer.

Zivin, Joshua S. Graff & Perloff, Jeffrey M., eds. The Intended & Unintended Effects of U. S. Agricultural & Biotechnology Policies. 2012. (National Bureau of Economic Research Conference Report). (ENG., Illus.). 312p. 99.00 ***(978-0-226-98803-0(1))*** Univ. of Chicago Pr.

AGRICULTURAL BOTANY

see Botany, Economic

AGRICULTURAL CHEMICALS

see also Fertilizers and Manures; Fungicides; Herbicides; Insecticides; Pesticides; Plant Regulators; Trace Elements

Cheremisinoff, Nicholas P. & Rosenfeld, Paul. Best Practices in the Agrochemical Industry, Vol. 3. 2010. (ENG., Illus.). 320p. 199.00 *(978-1-4377-7825-0(9))* William Andrew, Inc.

Greene, Stanley A. & Haber, Richard P. Sittig's Handbook of Pesticides & Agricultural Chemicals. Greene, Stanley A. et al, eds. 2007. (ENG.). 1213p. 435.00 *(978-0-8155-1516-6(2))* William Andrew, Inc.

Gupta, Umesh C., ed. Molybdenum in Agriculture. 2007. (ENG.). 292p. pap. 60.00 *(978-0-521-03722-8(0))* Cambridge Univ. Pr.

Kagima, David. Variable Rate Herbicide Application Gps Gis, & Vrt Technology. 2008. 64p. pap. *(978-3-639-07988-3(4))* VDM Verlag Dr. Mueller e.K.

Kennedy, Ivan R., et al, eds. Rational Environmental Management of Agrochemicals: Risk Assessment, Monitoring, & Remedial Action. 2007. (ACS Symposium Ser.). (ENG., Illus.). 428p. (C). 160.00 *(978-0-8412-7420-4(7))* American Chemical Society.

Meister Pro Crop Protection Handbook (2008), Vol. 94. 2008. (Illus.). 840p. pap. 139.00 *(978-1-892829-20-7(7))* Meister Publishing Co.

Meister Pro Crop Protection Handbook 2009: The Global Industry Standard, Vol. 95. 2009. (Illus.). 580p. pap. 99.00 *(978-1-892829-21-4(5))* Meister Publishing Co.

Meisterpro Crop Protection Handbook (2007) The Global Industry Standard. 2007. (Illus.). 864p. pap. 139.00 *(978-1-892829-18-4(5))* Meister Publishing Co.

Milne, G. W. A., ed. Pesticides: An International Guide to 1800 Pest Control Chemicals. 2nd ed. 2006. (ENG.). 632p. 249.00 *(978-0-471-72334-9(7),* Wiley-Interscience) Wiley, John & Sons, Inc.

Pang, Guo-Fang, et al. Determination of Pesticides & Related Chemicals in Grains & Cereals. 2008. pap. 39.00 *(978-1-60456-162-3(9))* Nova Science Pubs., Inc.

Rodale, Maria. Organic Manifesto: How Organic Farming Can Heal Our Planet, Feed the World, & Keep Us Safe. 2010. (ENG.). 224p. 23.99 *(978-1-60529-485-8(3))* Rodale Pr., Inc.

—Organic Manifesto: How Organic Food Can Heal Our Planet, Feed the World, & Keep Us Safe. 2011. (ENG.). 240p. pap. 14.99 *(978-1-60961-136-1(5))* Rodale Pr., Inc.

Wiley-VCH Staff. Ullmann's Agrochemicals, 2 vols. 2007. (ENG., Illus.). 932p. 570.00 *(978-3-527-31604-5(3),* Wiley-VCH) Wiley, John & Sons, Inc.

AGRICULTURAL CHEMISTRY

see also Agricultural Chemicals; Chemurgy; Dairy Products—Analysis and Examination; Fertilizers and Manures; Plants—Chemical Analysis; Soil Chemistry; Soils; Wood—Chemistry

Barker, Allen V. Science & Technology of Organic Farming. 2010. (ENG., Illus.). 240p. 72.95 *(978-1-4398-1612-7(3),* CRC Press) Taylor & Francis Group GBR. Dist: Taylor & Francis Group.

Boussingault, J. B. (Jean Baptiste). Rural Economy, in Its Relations with Chemistry, Physics, & Meteorology; or, Chemistry Applied to Agriculture by J B Boussingault, Translated, Wit. 2006. 532p. per. 29.99 *(978-1-4255-5874-1(7))* MPublishing.

Davy, Humphry. The Collected Works of Sir Humphry Davy. 2010. 390p. pap. 33.75 *(978-1-143-66957-6(6))* BiblioBazaar.

—The Collected Works of Sir Humphry Davy. 2009. 272p. pap. *(978-0-217-88944-5(1))* Books LLC.

—The Collected Works of Sir Humphry Davy: Elements of chemical Philosophy (1840) 2009. 216p. pap. *(978-0-217-88947-6(6))* Books LLC.

—The Collected Works of Sir Humphry Davy; Discourses Delivered Before the Royal Society, & Agricultural Lectures, Pt. 2009. 204p. pap. *(978-1-150-29295-8(4))* Books LLC.

—The Collected Works of Sir Humphry Davy; Discourses Delivered Before the Royal Society Elements of Agricultural Chemistry, Pt I. 2009. 214p. pap. 19.66 *(978-1-150-09233-6(5))* General Bks. LLC.

—The Collected Works of Sir Humphry Davy, Ed by J Davy. 2009. 202p. pap. 19.99 *(978-1-150-51030-4(7))* General Bks. LLC.

Elkhateeb, Ayman. Natural Compounds of Fruit Tree Leaves Extracts As. 2011. 176p. pap. ***(978-3-8454-1685-4(8))*** Lambert Academic Publishing.

He, Zhongqi. Environmental Chemistry of Animal Manure. 2011. (Environmental Science, Engineering & Technology Ser.). (Illus.). viii, 459p. 195.00 *(978-1-61209-222-5(5))* Nova Science Pubs., Inc.

Johnson, Samuel W. How Crops Grow. 2006. 400p. per. 26.99 *(978-1-4255-4234-4(4))* MPublishing.

Nash, John Adams. The Progressive Farmer: A Scientific Treatise on Agricultural Chemistry, the Geology of Agriculture; on Plants, Animals, Manures, & Soils. Applied T. 2006. 268p. per. 23.99 *(978-1-4255-2351-0(X))* MPublishing.

Norton, John Pitkin. Elements of Scientific Agriculture, or the Connection Between Science & the Art of Practical Farming Prize Essay of the New York State Agricultural. 2006. 240p. per. 20.99 *(978-1-4255-2017-5(0))* MPublishing.

Parker, Rick. Plant & Soil Science: Fundamentals & Applications. 2009. (Texas Science Ser.). (ENG.). 816p. (C). 131.95 *(978-1-4283-3480-9(7))* Delmar Cengage Learning.

Science & Technology of Organic Farming. 2011. 69.95 ***(978-1-4398-1613-4(1),*** CRC Press) Taylor & Francis Group GBR. Dist: Taylor & Francis Group.

AGRICULTURAL CLIMATOLOGY

see Crops and Climate

AGRICULTURAL CLUBS

see Agricultural Societies

AGRICULTURAL COLLEGES

see also Agricultural Education; Agricultural Extension Work

Reed, Lawrence E. A Garden of Paradise: A History of el Vergel. 2008. 568p. pap. 23.99 *(978-1-4389-1425-1(3))* AuthorHouse.

Sayre, Laura & Clark, Sean, eds. Fields of Learning: The Student Farm Movement in North America. 2011. (Culture of the Land Ser.). (ENG., Illus.). 378p. 40.00 *(978-0-8131-3374-4(2))* Univ. Pr. of Kentucky.

AGRICULTURAL COLONIES

Here are entered works on settlement of the land by organized groups of colonists. General works on occupation of the land are entered under the heading Land Settlement.

see also Jews—Colonization

Blaich, Horst. Exiled from the Holy Land. 2009. 238p. pap. 25.00 *(978-1-4251-3891-2(8))* Trafford Publishing.

Brandes, Joseph. Immigrants to Freedom. 2009. 400p. 29.99 *(978-1-4415-0598-9(9));* pap. 19.99 *(978-1-4415-0597-2(0))* Xlibris Corp.

Carter, Joseph Coleman & Prieto, Alberto, eds. The Chora of Metaponto 3: Archaeological Survey — Bradano to Basento. 2011. (ENG., Illus.). 1648p. 200.00 *(978-0-292-72678-9(3))* Univ. of Texas Pr.

Cottle, Ann S. The Roots of Penderlea: A Memory of a New Deal Homstead Community. 2008. (ENG., Illus.). 100p. pap. 19.95 *(978-0-9791403-3-4(1))* Publishing Laboratory at UNC Wilmington, The.

Dick, Lyle. Farmers "Making Good" The Development of Abernethy District, Saskatchewan, 1880-1920. 2nd ed. 2008. (Parks & Heritage Ser.). (ENG., Illus.). 336p. pap. 34.95 *(978-1-55238-241-7(9))* Univ. of Calgary Pr. CAN. Dist: Chicago Distribution Ctr.

Goldstein, Philip R. Social Aspects of the Jewish Colonies of South Jersey. (Illus.). 74p. reprint ed. lib. bdg. 88.00 *(978-0-7222-0258-6(X))* Library Reprints, Inc.

Harnack, Curtis. Gentlemen on the Prairie: Victorians in Pioneer Iowa. 2011. (Bur Oak Book Ser.). (ENG., Illus.). 262p. pap. 24.00 *(978-1-58729-967-4(4))* Univ. of Iowa Pr.

Kleinpenning, J. M. G. Rural Paraguay 1870-1963: A Geography of Progress, Plunder & Poverty, 2 vols. 2009. (Illus.). pap. *(978-84-8489-483-4(5))* Iberoamericana Vervuert Publishing Corp.

Lapadula, Erminia & Carter, Joseph Coleman. The Chora of Metaponto 4: The Late Roman Farmhouse at San Biagio. 2012. E-Book ***(978-0-292-73542-2(1))*** Univ. of Texas Pr.

Meline, Jules. The Return to the Land. 2008. 270p. 42.95 *(978-1-4366-3951-4(4));* 272p. pap. 27.95 *(978-0-548-84155-6(1))* Kessinger Publishing, LLC.

—The Return to the Land. 2009. 272p. pap. 28.95 *(978-1-4446-1681-1(1))* Thorndike Pr.

Pollack, Emmanu. Tradesmen & the Farmers of Yiddishland. 2006. 96p. 29.95 *(978-2-85056-862-6(7))* Somogy Editions d'Art FRA. Dist: Independent Pubs. Group.

Saugera, Eric. Reborn in America: French Exiles & Refugees in the United States & the Vine & Olive Adventure, 1815-1865. 2011. *(978-0-8173-8511-8(8))* Univ. of Alabama Pr.

—Reborn in America: French Exiles & Refugees in the United States & the Vine & Olive Adventure, 1815-1865. Velguth, Madeleine, tr. 3rd ed. 2011. (Atlantic Crossings Ser.). (ENG., Illus.). 584p. 30.00 *(978-0-8173-1723-2(6))* Univ. of Alabama Pr.

Troen, S. Ilan. Imagining Zion: Dreams, Designs, & Realities in a Century of Jewish Settlement. 2011. (ENG.). 360p. pap. 37.00 ***(978-0-300-17853-1(0))*** Yale Univ. Pr.

Urrutia Cobo Staff. Sustainable Management after Irrigation System Transfer. 2006. (ENG., Illus.). 289p. (C). 115.95 *(978-0-415-41693-1(0),* Taylor & Francis) Taylor & Francis Group GBR. Dist: Taylor & Francis Group.

Yaron, Hadas. Zionist Arabesques: Modern Landscapes, Non-Modern Texts. 2010. (Israel: Society, Culture, & History Ser.). (ENG.). 250p. 55.00 *(978-1-934843-78-9(4))* Academic Studies Pr.

AGRICULTURAL COMMODITIES

see Farm Produce

AGRICULTURAL CONTRACTS

see Contracts, Agricultural

AGRICULTURAL COOPERATION

see Agriculture, Cooperative

AGRICULTURAL COOPERATIVE CREDIT ASSOCIATIONS

Misra, Biswa Swarup. Credit Cooperatives in India. 2012. (ENG., Illus.). 192p. (C). pap. 42.95 ***(978-0-415-53363-8(5))*** Routledge.

Misra, Biswa Swarup. Credit Cooperatives in India: Past, Present & Future. 2010. (Routledge Studies in Development Economics Ser.). (ENG., Illus.). XXIV, 168p. (C). 130.00 *(978-0-415-56699-5(1),* Routledge) Taylor & Francis Group GBR. Dist: Taylor & Francis Group.

Rajkumar, K. Agricultural Finance in India: The Role of NABARD. 2008. 231p. 34.50 *(978-81-7708-180-0(2))* New Century Publications IND. Dist: International Specialized Bk. Services.

AGRICULTURAL CREDIT

African-American Farmers Benefit Relief ACT of 2007 & the Pigford Claims Remedy ACT of 2007: Hearing Before the Subcommittee on the Constitution, Civil Rights, & Civil Liberties of the Committee on the Judiciary, House of Representatives, One Hundred Tenth Congress, First Session, on H.R. 558 & H.R. 899, June 21, 2007. 2007. (Illus.). iv, 153p. *(978-0-16-079622-7(9),* 552-070-36579-6) United States Government Printing Office.

Bishoff, Jonathan M., ed. Agricultural Finance & Credit. 2008. (C). pap. 50.00 *(978-1-60456-072-5(X))* Nova Science Pubs., Inc.

Congressional Oversight Panel Special Report: Farm Loan Restructuring. 2009. (Illus.). iii, 97p. *(978-0-16-084207-8(7),* 552-070-39784-1) United States Government Printing Office.

Devi, Reena. Reforms in Credit Market, Performance of Crops & Capital Formation. 2010. 124p. pap. *(978-3-639-27950-4(6))* VDM Verlag Dr. Mueller e.K.

Ferrari, Aurora. Increasing Access to Rural Finance in Bangladesh: The Forgotten Missing Middle. 2007. (Directions in Development Ser.). (ENG., Illus.). 156p. per. 20.00 *(978-0-8213-7333-0(1),* 9780821373330) World Bank Pubns.

Firth, Raymond & Yamey, B. S. Capital, Saving & Credit in Peasant Societies. Firth, Raymond William, ed. 2007. (ENG.). 399p. pap. 37.95 *(978-0-202-30918-7(5))* Aldine Transaction.

Fitzgerald, Deborah. Every Farm a Factory: The Industrial Ideal in American Agriculture. 2010. (ENG.). 256p. pap. 26.00 *(978-0-300-11128-6(2))* Yale Univ. Pr.

Gómez Mont, María Teresa. Manuel Gómez Morin, 1915-1939: La Raíz y la Simiente de un Proyecto Nacional. 2009. (Vida y Pensamiento de México Ser.). (SPA., Illus.). 998p. 57.99 *(978-968-16-8600-0(4))* Fondo de Cultura Económica.

—Manuel Gomez Morin, 1915-1939: La Raiz y la Simiente de un Proyecto Nacional. 2009. (Vida y Pensamiento de Mexico Ser.). (SPA., Illus.). 998p. pap. 49.99 *(978-968-16-8336-8(6))* Fondo de Cultura Economica USA.

Hansen, Bradley A. Institutions, Entrepreneurs, & American Economic History: How the Farmers' Loan & Trust Company Shaped the Laws of Business from 1822-1929. 2009. (ENG.). 240p. 95.00 *(978-0-230-60392-9(0))* Palgrave Macmillan.

Hearing on Farm Credit: Congressional Oversight Panel, One Hundred Eleventh Congress, First Session, Hearing Held in Greeley, CO, June 7, 2009. 2009. (Illus.). iii, 73p. *(978-0-16-084202-3(6),* 552-070-39779-5) United States Government Printing Office.

A

Hearing to Review Credit Conditions in Rural America: Hearing Before the Subcommittee on Conservation, Credit, Energy, & Research of the Committee on Agriculture, House of Representatives, One Hundred Eleventh Congress, First Session, June 11, 2009. 2009. (Illus.). v, 82p. *(978-0-16-084858-2(X)*, 552-070-40259-4) United States Government Printing Office.

Hearing to Review Credit Conditions in Rural America: Hearing Before the Subcommittee on Department Operations, Oversight, & Credit of the Committee on Agriculture, House of Representatives, One Hundred Twelfth Congress, First Session, April 14, 2011. 2011. (Illus.). iii, 70p. ***(978-0-16-089026-0(8)***, 552-070-43058-0) United States Government Printing Office.

Hearing to Review Proposals to Amend the Program Crop Provisions of the Farm Security & Rural Investment ACT of 2002: Hearing Before the Subcommittee on General Farm Commodities & Risk Management of the Committee on Agriculture, House of Representatives, One Hundred Tenth Congress, First Session, April 26, 2007. 2009. (Illus.). iii, 178p. *(978-0-16-082965-9(8)*, 552-070-38876-1) United States Government Printing Office.

Joshi, Sharad P. Down to Earth. 2010. (ENG.). 388p. 79.95 *(978-81-7188-842-9(9))* Academic Foundation IND. Dist: Independent Pubs. Group.

Kohl, David. Weighing the Variables: A Guide to Ag Credit Management. Topping, Kathy, ed. 160p. (C). stu. ed. 60.00 *(978-0-89982-336-2(X))* American Bankers Assn.

Loucks, Henry Langford. The Great Conspiracy of the House of Morgan & How to Defeat It. 2007. (ENG.). 310p. 45.95 *(978-0-548-15601-8(8))*; 312p. per. 30.95 *(978-1-4304-5055-9(X))* Kessinger Publishing, LLC.

Low, Alaine. A Bibliographical Survey of Rotating Savings & Credit Associations. (Oxfam Research Discussion Papers). (ENG.). 75p. (C). pap. 23.95 *(978-0-85598-298-0(5))* Oxfam Publishing GBR. Dist: Stylus Publishing, LLC.

Management of Civil Rights at the USDA: Hearing Before the Subcommittee on Government Management, Organization, & Procurement of the Committee on Oversight & Government Reform, House of Representatives, One Hundred Tenth Congress, Second Session, May 14, 2008. 2009. (Illus.). iii, 166p. *(978-0-16-083107-2(5)*, 552-070-38990-3) United States Government Printing Office.

Mishra, Srijit & Narasimha Reddy, D. Agrarian Crisis in India. Reddy, D. Narasimha & Mishra, Srijit, eds. 2009. (ENG., Illus.). 272p. 49.95 *(978-0-19-569595-3(X))* Oxford Univ. Pr., Inc.

Misra, Biswa Swarup. Credit Cooperatives in India. 2012. (ENG., Illus.). 192p. (C). pap. 42.95 ***(978-0-415-53363-8(5))*** Routledge.

Misra, Biswa Swarup. Credit Cooperatives in India: Past, Present & Future. 2010. (Routledge Studies in Development Economics Ser.). (ENG., Illus.). XXIV, 168p. (C). 130.00 *(978-0-415-56699-5(1)*, Routledge) Taylor & Francis Group GBR. Dist: Taylor & Francis Group.

My Duyen, Trang Thi. Agricultural Credit in Vietnam. 2011. 92p. pap. ***(978-3-8443-0182-3(8))*** Lambert Academic Publishing.

Narzary, Devonath & Goyari, Phanindra. Institutional Agriculture Credit in Indi. 2011. 100p. pap. ***(978-3-8443-8661-5(0))*** Lambert Academic Publishing.

Review the Availability of Credit in Rural America: Hearing Before the Subcommittee on Conservation, Credit, Energy, & Research of the Committee on Agriculture, House of Representatives, One Hundred Tenth Congress, First Session, March 27, 2007. 2007. (Illus.). iii, 217p. *(978-0-16-079610-4(5)*, 552-070-36566-4) United States Government Printing Office.

Review the Financial Structure of Renewable Energy Sources: Hearing Before the Subcommittee on Conservation, Credit, Energy, & Research of the Committee on Agriculture, House of Representatives, One Hundred Tenth Congress, First Session, March 7, 2007. 2007. (Illus.). iii, 143p. *(978-0-16-079757-6(8)*, 552-070-36675-0) United States Government Printing Office.

Teklu, Hagos W/Gebriel. Smallholder Farmers Access to Agricultural Credit & Its Impact. 2011. 140p. pap. ***(978-3-8443-3404-3(1))*** Lambert Academic Publishing.

Tostlebe, Alvin S. Bank of North Dakota. (Columbia University, Studies in the Social Sciences: No. 254). reprint ed. 21.50 *(978-0-404-51254-5(2))* AMS Pr., Inc.

AGRICULTURAL CREDIT CORPORATIONS

see also Agricultural Cooperative Credit Associations

Rajkumar, K. Agricultural Finance in India: The Role of NABARD. 2008. 231p. 34.50 *(978-81-7708-180-0(2))* New Century Publications IND. Dist: International Specialized Bk. Services.

AGRICULTURAL CROPS

see Crops

AGRICULTURAL DEVELOPMENT PROJECTS

Alao, Abiodun. The Impact of Icts on Agricultural Development in the Rural Community. 2010. 176p. pap. *(978-3-639-26002-1(3))* VDM Verlag Dr. Mueller e.K.

Batte, Richard. Agricultural Information Systems Development. 2010. 116p. pap. *(978-3-8383-3455-4(8))* Lambert Academic Publishing.

Birke, Hailemariam. Meeting Sustainable Land Management Challenges to Curb Climate Change. 2010. 112p. pap. *(978-3-639-23305-6(0))* VDM Verlag Dr. Mueller e.K.

Catlink, David & Catling, David. An Elusive Harvest: Working with Smallholder Farmers in South Africa. 2009. (ENG.). 352p. pap. 24.95 *(978-1-920196-10-3(2))* Jacana Media ZAF. Dist: Independent Pubs. Group.

Chowdhury, Ataharul Huq. Having a System Does Not Make a Home of It. 2010. 176p. pap. *(978-3-639-27648-0(5))* VDM Verlag Dr. Mueller e.K.

Diao, Xinshen. Agricultural Growth & Investment Options for Poverty Reduction in Rwanda. 2010. *(978-0-89629-176-8(6))* International Food Policy Research Institute.

Food Security in Africa: The Impact of Agricultural Development: Hearing Before the Subcommittee on Africa & Global Health of the Committee on Foreign Affairs, House of Representatives, One Hundred Tenth Congress, First Session, on H.R. 2003, July 18, 2007. 2007. iii, 61p. *(978-0-16-079466-7(8)*, 552-070-36451-0) United States Government Printing Office.

Friederichsen, Jakob Rupert. Opening up Knowledge Production through Participatory Research? Agricultural Research for Vietnam's Northern Uplands. 2009. (Development Economics & Policy Ser.). (Illus.). 280p. pap. 74.95 *(978-3-631-58842-0(9))* Lang, Peter GmbH, Europaischer Verlag der Wissenschaften DEU. Dist: Lang, Peter.

Haggblade, Steven & Hazell, Peter B. R., eds. Successes in African Agriculture: Lessons for the Future. 2010. (ENG., Illus.). 464p. (gr. 17). 90.00 *(978-0-8018-9502-9(2))*; pap. 45.00 *(978-0-8018-9503-6(0))* Johns Hopkins Univ. Pr.

Hearing to Review Efforts to Deliver International Food Aid & Provide Foreign Agricultural Development Assistance: Hearing Before the Subcommittee on Specialty Crops, Rural Development, & Foreign Agriculture of the Committee on Agriculture, House of Representatives, One Hundred Tenth Congress, Second Session, July 16, 2008. 2009. (Illus.). iii, 81p. *(978-0-16-083743-2(X)*, 552-070-37445-1) United States Government Printing Office.

HIV / AIDS & Livelihoods: Experiences in Mainstreaming from Malawi. (FRE.). pap. 16.50 *(978-0-85598-544-8(5))* Oxfam Publishing GBR. Dist: Stylus Publishing, LLC.

Johnson, Michael & Flaherty, Kathleen. Strategic Analysis & Knowledge Support Systems (SAKSS) for Agriculture & Rural Development in Africa: Translating Evidence into Action: A Source Book. 2010. *(978-0-89629-784-5(5))* International Food Policy Research Institute.

Kägi, Wolfram. Economics of Climate Change: the Contribution of Forestry Projects: The Contribution of Forestry Projects. 2010. (Environment & Policy Ser.). 176p. pap. 159.00 *(978-90-481-5372-5(7)*, 9048153727) Springer.

Karienyeh, Margaret. Best Way to Empower Resource Poor Small-Scale Women Farmers. 2010. 100p. pap. *(978-3-639-23575-3(4))* VDM Verlag Dr. Mueller e.K.

Kirsten, Johann. Institutional Economics Perspectives on African Agricultural Development. 2009. *(978-0-89629-781-4(0))* International Food Policy Research Institute.

Laycock, Adrian. Irrigation Systems: Design, Planning & Construction. 2007. (Illus.). 300p. 125.00 *(978-1-84593-263-3(3))* CABI GBR. Dist: Stylus Publishing, LLC.

Maatman, Arno. Competitive Agricultural Systems & Enterprises (CASE) Volume 1: Reference framework & early experiences, 2 , 2011. pap. 10.00 ***(978-0-88090-168-0(3))*** IFDC.

Mgemezulu, Overtoun. The Social Impact of Community Based Targeting Mechanisms. 2010. 132p. pap. *(978-3-8383-5885-7(6))* Lambert Academic Publishing.

Molla, Adamu. Barley-Wheat ed Cropping. 2011. 172p. pap. ***(978-3-8454-1907-7(5))*** Lambert Academic Publishing.

Nasution, Muhammad Zarnal. Farm Development & Rural Poverty in Kulonprogo Regency, Indonesi. 2008. 92p. pap. *(978-3-639-07469-7(6))* VDM Verlag Dr. Mueller e.K.

Nilsen, Alf Gunvald. Dispossession & Resistance in India. 2012. (ENG., Illus.). 256p. (C). pap. 42.95 ***(978-0-415-53362-1(7))*** Routledge.

Nkonya, Ephraim. From the Ground Up: Impacts of a Pro-Poor Community-Driven Development Project in Nigeria. 2010. *(978-0-89629-179-9(0))* International Food Policy Research Institute.

Nyandoro, Mark. Development & Differentiation: The subtitle: The Case of TILCOR/ARDA IrrigationActivities in Sanyati (Zimbabwe), 1939 to 2000. 2008. 508p. pap. *(978-3-639-09069-7(1))* VDM Verlag Dr. Mueller e.K.

Omamo, Steven Were. Strategic Priorities for Agricultural Development in Eastern & Central Africa. 2006. *(978-0-89629-158-4(8))* International Food Policy Research Institute.

Pandya, Pravinaben & Maurvi Pandya. Development & Agriculture. 2010. 108p. pap. *(978-3-639-25242-2(X))* VDM Verlag Dr. Mueller e.K.

Pender, J., et al, eds. Sustainable Poverty Reduction in Less-Favoured Areas. 2007. (Illus.). 464p. 160.00 *(978-1-84593-277-0(3))* CABI GBR. Dist: Stylus Publishing, LLC.

Rivera, Angela N. Global Food Security. 2011. (Illus.). viii, 263p. *(978-1-61761-765-2(2))* Nova Science Pubs., Inc.

Roetter, R. P. Science for Agriculture & Rural Development in Low-Income Countries. Keulen, H. Van et al, eds. 2007. (ENG., Illus.). xxvi, 222p. 189.00 *(978-1-4020-6616-0(3)*, 1402066163) Springer.

Roetter, Reimund, et al, eds. Science for Agriculture & Rural Development in Low-Income Countries. 2008. (ENG., Illus.). xxvi, 222p. pap. 99.00 *(978-1-4020-9285-5(7)*, 1402092857) Springer.

Sharma, Rajeev. Agricultural Development & Crop Diversification in Jammu & Kashmir. 2010. 84p. pap. *(978-3-639-25032-9(X))* VDM Verlag Dr. Mueller e.K.

Sithole, Pinimidzai. Designing & Planning Dynamics: The Dande Irrigation Project, Zimbabwe. 2010. 72p. pap. *(978-3-8383-0105-1(6))* Lambert Academic Publishing.

Spielman, David J. & Pandya-Lorch, Rajul. Highlights from Millions Fed: Proven Successes in Agricultural Development. 2009. (Illus.). 24p. pap. ***(978-0-89629-659-6(8))*** International Food Policy Research Institute.

—Millions Fed: Proven Successes in Agricultural Development. 2009. *(978-0-89629-661-9(X))* International Food Policy Research Institute.

—Proven Successes in Agricultural Development: A Technical Compendium to Millions Fed 2010. 2010. *(978-0-89629-669-5(5))* International Food Policy Research Institute.

Teklu, Hagos W/Gebriel. Smallholder Farmers Access to Agricultural Credit & Its Impact. 2011. 140p. pap. ***(978-3-8443-3404-3(1))*** Lambert Academic Publishing.

Thurow, Roger. The Last Hunger Season: A Year on an African Farm Community on the Brink of Change. 2012. (ENG., Illus.). 304p. 26.99 ***(978-1-61039-067-5(9))*** PublicAffairs.

van der Fliert, Elske, et al. Integrated Assessment of Agricultural Sustainability: Exploring the Use of Models in Stakeholder Processes. 2013. (International Journal Agricultural Sustainability Ser.). (ENG.). 90p. 99.95 *(978-1-84971-406-8(1))* Routledge.

Waldorff, Pttur. Conceptions of Poverty & Development. 2008. 108p. pap. *(978-3-639-02930-7(5))* VDM Verlag Dr. Mueller e.K.

Wennink, Bertus, et al. Outsourcing Agricultural Advisory Services: Enhancing Rural Innovation in Sub-Saharan Africa. 2008. (Bulletins of the Royal Tropical Institute Ser.). 150p. (C). pap. 35.00 *(978-90-6832-646-8(5))* Royal Tropical Institute Pr. (KIT (Koninklijk Instituut voor de Tropen) NLD. Dist: Stylus Publishing, LLC.

World Bank Staff. World Bank Assistance to Agriculture in Sub-Saharan Africa: An IEG Review. 2007. (Independent Evaluation Group Studies). (ENG., Illus.). 224p. per. 35.00 *(978-0-8213-7350-7(1)*, 9780821373507) World Bank Pubns.

AGRICULTURAL ECOLOGY

see also Crops and Climate; Garden Ecology

Aghajanian, Alfred. Chinampas: Their Role in Aztec Empire - Building & Expansion, Second Edition. 2007. 128p. per. 19.95 *(978-1-60444-003-4(1))* IndoEuropeanPublishing.com.

Ashworth, William. Ogallala Blue: Water & Life on the High Plains. 2007. (ENG.). 330p. per. 16.95 *(978-0-88150-736-2(9)*, 150736) Countryman Pr.

Bohlen, Patrick J. & House, Garfield J., eds. Sustainable Agroecosystem Management: Integrating Ecology, Economics, & Society. 2009. (Advances in Agroecology Ser.: Vol. 14). (ENG., Illus.). 328p. 99.95 *(978-1-4200-5214-5(4)*, CRC Press) Taylor & Francis Group GBR. Dist: Taylor & Francis Group.

Buck, Louise E., et al. Understanding Ecoagriculture: Ecoagriculture Discussion Paper Number 2. 2006. 63p. spiral bd. 0.00 *(978-0-9793871-1-1(6))* Ecoagriculture Partners.

Burchett, Stephen & Burchett, Sarah. Introduction to Wildlife Conservation in Farming. 2011. (ENG., Illus.). 326p. 149.95 *(978-0-470-69935-5(3))*; pap. 62.95 *(978-0-470-69934-8(5))* Wiley, John & Sons, Inc. (Wiley).

Campbell, W. Bruce & Ortiz, Silvia López, eds. Integrating Agriculture, Conservation & Ecotourism: Examples from the Field: Examples from the Field. 2011. (Issues in Agroecology â€" Present Status & Future Prospectus Ser.). (ENG., Illus.). xix, 303p. 209.00 *(978-94-007-1308-6(8)*, 9400713088) Springer.

Chang. Rice Genetics & Cytogenetics (V6) 2008. pap. 73.00 *(978-981-281-869-0(3))* World Scientific Publishing Co., Inc.

Cheeke, Tanya, et al, eds. Microbial Ecology in Sustainable Agroecosystems. 2012. (Advances in Agroecology Ser.: 18). (ENG., Illus.). 312p. 99.95 ***(978-1-4398-5296-5(0)***, CRC Press) Taylor & Francis Group GBR. Dist: Taylor & Francis Group.

Cram101 Textbook Reviews. Outlines & Highlights for Ecological Management of Agricultural Weeds by Charles L Mohler Matt Liebman, Isbn: 9780521037877. 2011. 132p. pap. 28.95 ***(978-1-61461-475-3(X))*** Cram101 Inc.

Deguine. Crop Protection: from Agrochemistry: To Agroecology. 2009. 220p. pap. *(978-1-57808-652-8(3))* Science Pubs.

Estabrook, Barry. Tomatoland: How Modern Industrial Agriculture Destroyed Our Most Alluring Fruit. 2011. (ENG., Illus.). 240p. 19.99 *(978-1-4494-0109-2(0))* Andrews McMeel Publishing.

Garcia-Torres, L., et al, eds. Conservation Agriculture: Environment, Farmers Experiences, Innovations, Socio-Economy, Policy. 2010. 516p. pap. 259.00 *(978-90-481-6211-6(4)*, 9048162114) Springer.

Gitau, Thomas, et al. Integrated Assessment of Health & Sustainability of Agroecosystems. 2008. (Advances in Agroecology Ser.). (ENG., Illus.). 256p. 104.95 *(978-1-4200-7277-8(3)*, CRC Press) Taylor & Francis Group GBR. Dist: Taylor & Francis Group.

Gliessman, Stephen R. Agroecology: The Ecology of Sustainable Food Systems. 2nd rev. ed. 2006. (ENG., Illus.). 408p. (C). 73.95 *(978-0-8493-2845-9(4)*, 2845, CRC Press) Taylor & Francis Group GBR. Dist: Taylor & Francis Group.

—Field & Laboratory Investigations in Agroecology. 2nd rev. ed. 2006. (ENG., Illus.). 320p. (C). per. 41.95 *(978-0-8493-2846-6(2)*, 2846, CRC Press) Taylor & Francis Group GBR. Dist: Taylor & Francis Group.

—Package Price Agroecology, 2 vols. 2nd rev. ed. 2007. (ENG.). (C). 96.95 *(978-1-4200-5376-0(0)*, CRC Press) Taylor & Francis Group GBR. Dist: Taylor & Francis Group.

Gruber, Ina. The Impact of Socio-Economic Development & Climate Change on Livestock Management in Benin. 2009. (Europäische Hochschulschriften. Reihe 5: Volks- und Betriebswirtschaft Ser.). 250p. pap. 69.95 *(978-3-631-59049-2(0))* Lang, Peter GmbH, Europaischer Verlag der Wissenschaften DEU. Dist: Lang, Peter.

Hargis, Anthony G. Agricultural Conservation. 2009. (Agriculture Issues & Policies Ser.). pap. 69.00 *(978-1-60692-273-6(4))* Nova Science Pubs., Inc.

Hillel, Daniel & Rosenzweig, Cynthia. Handbook of Climate Change & Agroecosystems: Impacts, Adaptation, & Mitigation. 2010. (Illus.). 452p. 168.00 *(978-1-84816-655-4(9))* Imperial College Pr. GBR. Dist: World Scientific Publishing Co., Inc.

Homewood, Katherine. Ecology of African Pastoralist Societies. 2008. (Illus.). 312p. 90.00 *(978-0-85255-991-8(7))*; pap. 34.95 *(978-0-85255-990-1(9))* Boydell & Brewer, Ltd. GBR. (Currey, James). Dist: Boydell & Brewer, Inc.

—Ecology of African Pastoralist Societies. 2009. (Illus.). 320p. 55.00 *(978-0-8214-1840-6(8))*; (ENG., pap. 26.95 *(978-0-8214-1841-3(6))* Ohio Univ. Pr.

Horvath, Anna V. & Morel, Simon L. Agricultural Conservation. 2011. (Illus.). 157p. *(978-1-61209-928-6(9))* Nova Science Pubs., Inc.

Hoy, Marjorie. Agricultural Acarology: Introduction to Integrated Mite Management. 2011. (ENG., Illus.). 430p. 99.95 *(978-1-4398-1751-3(0)*, CRC Press) Taylor & Francis Group GBR. Dist: Taylor & Francis Group.

Jackson, Wes. Altars of Unhewn Stone: Science & the Earth. 2006. 176p. per. 15.95 *(978-1-59098-287-7(8))* Wooster Bk. Co., The.

—Consulting the Genius of the Place: An Ecological Approach to a New Agriculture. 2010. (ENG., Illus.). 224p. 26.00 *(978-1-58243-513-8(8)*, Counterpoint Pr.) Basic Bks. GBR. Dist: Perseus-PGW.

—Consulting the Genius of the Place: An Ecological Approach to a New Agriculture. 2011. (ENG.). 288p. pap. 16.95 *(978-1-58243-780-4(7)*, Counterpoint) Counterpoint LLC.

—Nature As Measure: The Selected Essays of Wes Jackson. 2011. (ENG.). 304p. pap. 16.95 *(978-1-58243-700-2(9)*, Counterpoint) Counterpoint LLC.

Jandl, Robert, et al, eds. Soil Carbon in Sensitive European Ecosystems: From Science to Land Management. 2012. (ENG., Illus.). 296p. 129.95 ***(978-1-119-97001-9(6)***, Wiley) Wiley, John & Sons, Inc.

Jarvis, Devra I., et al, eds. Managing Biodiversity in Agricultural Ecosystems. 2010. (ENG., Illus.). 512p. (gr. 17). pap. 34.50 *(978-0-231-13649-5(8))* Columbia Univ. Pr.

Kirch, Patrick Vinton. Roots of Conflict: Soils, Agriculture, & Sociopolitical Complexity in Ancient Hawaii. 2010. (Illus.). xix, 199p. *(978-1-934691-26-7(7))* School for Advanced Research Pr./SAR Pr.

Krishna, K. R. Agroecosystems of South India: Nutrient Dynamics, Ecology & Productivity. 2010. 552p. pap. 69.95 *(978-1-59942-533-7(5)*, Brown Walker Pr.) Universal Pubs.

Kristiansen, P., et al, eds. Organic Agriculture: A Global Perspective. 2006. (Illus.). 320p. 160.00 *(978-1-84593-169-8(6))* CABI GBR. Dist: Stylus Publishing, LLC.

Lauzon, Glenn P. Civic Learning Through Agricultural Improvement: Bringing the Loom & the Anvil into Proximity with the Plow. 2010. *(978-1-61735-148-8(2))*; pap. *(978-1-61735-147-1(4))*; E-Book *(978-1-61735-149-5(0))* Information Age Publishing, Inc.

Lefroy, E. C., et al, eds. Agriculture as a Mimic of Natural Ecosystems. 2010. (Current Plant Science & Biotechnology in Agriculture Ser.). 436p. pap. 419.00 *(978-90-481-5319-0(0)*, 9048153190) Springer.

Lichtfouse, Eric, ed. Agroecology & Strategies for Climate Change. 2011. (Sustainable Agriculture Reviews Ser.). (ENG., Illus.). vi, 335p. 209.00 ***(978-94-007-1904-0(3)***, 9400719043) Springer.

Liebman, Matt, et al. Ecological Management of Agricultural Weeds. 2007. (ENG., Illus.). 548p. pap. 105.00 *(978-0-521-03787-7(5))* Cambridge Univ. Pr.

Moss, Lynne H., et al. Evaluating the Risks & Benefits of Soil Amendments Used in Agriculture. (Illus.). *(978-1-893664-59-3(7))*; *(978-1-57278-207-5(2))* Water Environment Research Foundation.

Murphy, Steven N. Agricultural Conservation: Programs & Issues. 2010. pap. 49.00 *(978-1-61761-288-6(X))* Nova Science Pubs., Inc.

Nelson, Lynn A. Pharsalia: An Environmental Biography of a Southern Plantation, 1780-1880. (Environmental History & the American South Ser.). (ENG., Illus.). 320p. 2009. pap. 24.95 *(978-0-8203-3416-5(2))* 2007. lib. bdg. 39.95 *(978-0-8203-2627-6(5))* Univ. of Georgia Pr.

Ouma, Richard. Anatomy of Participatory Approach in Project Planning & Development. 2011. 84p. pap. ***(978-3-8443-2673-4(1))*** Lambert Academic Publishing.

Padoch, C., et al, eds. Managing Biodiversity in Agricultural Ecosystems. 2007. (ENG., Illus.). 512p. (gr. 17). 80.00 *(978-0-231-13648-8(X))* Columbia Univ. Pr.

Perfecto, Ivette, et al. Nature's Matrix: Linking Agriculture, Conservation & Food Sovereignty. 2009. (ENG., Illus.). 272p. 136.00 *(978-1-84407-781-6(0))*; pap. 34.95 *(978-1-84407-782-3(9))* Routledge.

Pimentel, David, ed. Global Economic & Environmental Aspects of Biofuels. 2012. (Advances in Agroecology Ser.). (ENG., Illus.). 453p. 99.95 ***(978-1-4398-3463-3(6)***, CRC Press) Taylor & Francis Group GBR. Dist: Taylor & Francis Group.

Postali Parra, José Roberto, et al, eds. Egg Parasitoids in Agroecosystems with emphasis on Trichogramma. 2010. (Progress in Biological Control Ser.). (ENG., Illus.). 450p. 199.00 *(978-1-4020-9109-4(5)*, 1402091095) Springer.

Schröder, Peter, et al. Perspectives for Agroecosystem Management: Balancing Environmental & Socio-Economic Demands. Schroder, Peter et al, eds. 2007. (ENG., Illus.). 456p. 86.95 *(978-0-444-51905-4(X)*, Elsevier Science) Elsevier Science & Technology Bks.

Snapp, Sieglinde & Pound, Barry, eds. Agricultural Systems: Agroecology & Rural Innovation for Development. 2008. (ENG., Illus.). 400p. (C). 77.95 *(978-0-12-372517-2(8)*, Academic Pr.) Elsevier Science & Technology Bks.

Taji, Acram & Reganold, John, eds. Organic Agriculture: A Global Perspective. 2006. (Comstock Bks.). (Illus.). 449p. 104.95 *(978-0-8014-4524-8(8)*, ILR Pr.) Cornell Univ. Pr.

Tanji, Kenneth K. & Wallender, Wesley W., eds. Agricultural Salinity Assessment & Management. 2nd ed. 2011. (ENG.). 1124p. 180.00 ***(978-0-7844-1169-8(7))*** American Society of Civil Engineers.

Tovey, Hilary & Bruckmeier, Karl. Rural Sustainable Development in the Knowledge Society. 2009. (Perspectives on Rural Policy & Planning Ser.). 316p. 134.95 *(978-0-7546-7425-2(8))* Ashgate Publishing Co.

U.S. Farms & Conservation Programs. 2011. 164p. *(978-1-61209-927-9(0))* Nova Science Pubs., Inc.

Vandermeer, John H. The Ecology of Agroecosystems. rev. ed. 2009. 392p. pap. 97.95 *(978-0-7637-7153-9(8))* Jones & Bartlett Learning, LLC.

Wall, Ellen, et al, eds. Farming in a Changing Climate: Agricultural Adaptation in Canada. 2008. (ENG., Illus.). 288p. pap. *(978-0-7748-1394-5(6))* Univ. of British Columbia Pr.

Warner, Keith Douglass. Agroecology in Action: Extending Alternative Agriculture Through Social Networks. 2006. (Food, Health, & the Environment Ser.). (ENG., Illus.). 296p. (gr. 17). 62.00 *(978-0-262-23252-4(9))*; per. 26.00 *(978-0-262-73180-5(0))* MIT Pr.

Wilson. Agroecology Laboratory Manual. rev. ed. 2011. (ENG.). 104p. spiral bd. 36.00 ***(978-0-7575-9454-0(9))*** Kendall Hunt Publishing Co.

Wilson, David W. Agroecology Laboratory Manual. rev. ed. 2010. (ENG.). 100p. spiral bd. 31.80 *(978-0-7575-7411-5(4))* Kendall Hunt Publishing Co.

Wittering, Shirley. Ecology of Enclosure: The Effect of Enclosure on Society, Farming & the Environment in South Cambridgeshire, 1798-1850. 2012. (ENG., Illus.). 192p. pap. 70.00 ***(978-1-905119-44-8(5))*** Windgather Pr. GBR. Dist: Brown, David Bk. Co., The.

Wojtkowski, Paul A. Agroecological Economics: Sustainability & Biodiversity. 2007. (ENG., Illus.). 320p. per. 80.95 *(978-0-12-374117-2(3)*, Academic Pr.) Elsevier Science & Technology Bks.

—Introduction to Agroecology: Principles & Practices. 2006. (ENG., Illus.). 404p. (C). 115.95 *(978-1-56022-316-0(2))*; per. 104.95 *(978-1-56022-317-7(0))* Taylor & Francis Group GBR. (CRC Press). Dist: Taylor & Francis Group.

AGRICULTURAL ECONOMICS

see Agriculture—Economic Aspects

AGRICULTURAL EDUCATION

Here are entered general works on education in agriculture. Works on methods of instruction in agriculture are entered under Agriculture—Study and Teaching.

see also Agricultural Colleges; Agricultural Extension Work; Agriculture—Study and Teaching; Forestry Schools and Education; Four-H Clubs

Committee on a Leadership Summit to Effect Change in Teaching and Learning & National Research Council Staff. Transforming Agricultural Education for a Changing World. 2009. (ENG.). 220p. pap. 45.00 *(978-0-309-13221-3(5))* National Academies Pr.

Deere, John. The Operation, Care, & Repair of Farm Machinery: Practical Hints for Handymen. 2nd ed. 2008. 248p. pap. 14.95 *(978-1-59921-461-0(X)*, Lyons Pr.) Globe Pequot Pr., The.

Hiler, Edward A. & Bosserman, Steven L. Together We Can: Pathways to Collective Leadership in Agriculture at Texas A&M. 2011. (AgriLife Research & Extension Service Ser.). (Illus.). 128p. 25.00 ***(978-1-60344-428-6(9))*** Texas A&M Univ. Pr.

Hilgard, Eugene W. Address on Progressive Agriculture, & Industrial Education, Delivered Before the Mississippi Agricultural & Mechanical Fair Association, at Jackso. 2011. 34p. pap. 11.99 ***(978-1-4181-9506-9(5))*** MPublishing.

International Assessment of Agricultural Knowledge, Science, and Technology. Agriculture at a Crossroads: International Assessment of Agricultural Science & Technology for Development - East & South Asia & the Pacific. 2009. (ENG., Illus.). 226p. 125.00 *(978-1-59726-544-7(6))* Island Pr.

—Agriculture at a Crossroads Vol. 1: Central & West Asia & North Africa. 2009. (ENG., Illus.). 192p. 125.00 *(978-1-59726-542-3(X))*; 2nd ed. pap. 75.00 *(978-1-59726-543-0(8))* Island Pr.

—Agriculture at a Crossroads Vol. 2: East & South Asia & the Pacific. 2009. (ENG.). 226p. pap. 75.00 *(978-1-59726-545-4(4))* Island Pr.

—Agriculture at a Crossroads Vol. 3: Latin America & the Caribbean. 2009. (ENG., Illus.). 248p. 125.00 *(978-1-59726-546-1(2))* Island Pr.

—Agriculture at a Crossroads Vol. 4: Latin America & the Caribbean. 2nd ed. 2009. (ENG.). 248p. pap. 75.00 *(978-1-59726-547-8(0))* Island Pr.

—Agriculture at a Crossroads Vol. 5: Sub-Saharan Africa. 2009. (ENG.). 160p. pap. 75.00 *(978-1-59726-541-6(1))* Island Pr.

—Agriculture at a Crossroads Vol. V: Sub-Saharan Africa. 2nd ed. 2009. (ENG., Illus.). 160p. 125.00 *(978-1-59726-540-9(3))* Island Pr.

—North America & Europe Vol. 5: International Assessment of Agricultural Knowledge, Science & Technology for Development. 2009. (ENG.). 312p. pap. 75.00 *(978-1-59726-549-2(7))*; (Illus.). 125.00 *(978-1-59726-548-5(9))* Island Pr.

Investing in Our Nation's Future Through Agricultural Research: Hearing Before the Committee on Agriculture, Nutrition, & Forestry, United States Senate, One Hundred Tenth Congress, First Session, March 7, 2007. 2007. (Illus.). iv, 192p. *(978-0-16-078869-7(2)*, 552-070-35998-2) United States Government Printing Office.

Johnstone, Robert F. Agricultural Education, an Individual, State & National Necessity; Suggestions for the Establishment & Endowment of an Agricultural College in Mic. 2011. 26p. pap. 11.99 ***(978-1-4181-9292-1(9))*** MPublishing.

Kagima, David. Training Programs in Sustainable Agriculture & Postharvest Technology. 2008. 172p. pap. *(978-3-639-07341-6(X))* VDM Verlag Dr. Mueller e.K.

Kibwika, Paul. Learning to make Change: Developing innovation competence for recreating the African university of the 21st Century. 2006. 208p. pap. 45.00 *(978-90-8686-017-3(6))* Wageningen Academic Publishers NLD. Dist: Enfield Publishing & Distribution Co., Inc.

Lee, Jasper S., et al. Agriscience. 5th ed. 2009. 752p. (C). pap. 93.33 *(978-0-13-509622-2(7)*, Prentice Hall) Prentice Hall PTR.

Lurio, Ansel. What the Farmers' Museum Can Learn from Farm-Based Education. 2010. 64p. pap. *(978-3-8383-5658-7(6))* Lambert Academic Publishing.

Massachusetts. Commissioners concerning. Report of Commissioners Concerning an Agricultural School January 1851. 2006. 108p. per. 16.99 *(978-1-4255-0691-9(7))* MPublishing.

Peterson's. Graduate Programs in the Physical Science, Mathematics, Agricultural Sciences, the Environment & Natural Resources 2011: More Than 2,700 Graduate Programs in 59 Disciplines. 45th ed. 2010. (ENG.). 476p. (YA). 54.95 *(978-0-7689-2855-6(9))* Peterson's.

Peterson's. Graduate Programs in the Physical Sciences, Mathematics, Agricultural Sciences, the Environment & Natural Resources 2012 (Grad 4) 46th ed. 2011. (ENG.). 480p. (YA). (gr. 7-17). 54.95 ***(978-0-7689-3283-6(1))*** Peterson's.

Peterson's Guides Staff, creator. Peterson's Graduate Programs in the Physical Sciences, Mathematics, Agricultural Sciences, the Environment & Natural Resources, Bk. 4. 41st ed. 2006. (ENG.). 768p. 54.00 *(978-0-7689-2155-7(4))* Peterson's.

Sayre, Laura & Clark, Sean, eds. Fields of Learning: The Student Farm Movement in North America. 2011. (Culture of the Land Ser.). (ENG., Illus.). 376p. 40.00 *(978-0-8131-3374-4(2))* Univ. Pr. of Kentucky.

Stewart, Jessica & Scheihing, Caitlin. Oklahoma 4-H: Generations of Clover. 2010. *(978-1-57864-614-2(6))* Donning Co. Pubs.

Vaughn, Rosco C., et al. Foundations of Agricultural Education. 2nd ed. 2007. (Illus.). 532p. pap. *(978-0-9761445-3-3(0))* Professional Educators Pubns., Inc.

AGRICULTURAL ENGINEERING

see also Agricultural Mechanics; Agricultural Processing; Drainage; Farm Equipment; Forestry Engineering; Irrigation

Akinbile, Christopher Oluwakunmi. Upland Rice Responses to Water Application under Sprinkler Irrigation. 2011. 224p. pap. ***(978-3-8383-8975-2(1))*** Lambert Academic Publishing.

Albiac, José. The Management of Water Quality & Irrigation Technologies. Dinar, Ariel, ed. 2008. (ENG., Illus.). 320p. 117.00 *(978-1-84407-670-3(9))* Routledge.

Ali, Usman. Simulation of Sediment Flushing at Intake Structure of Kohala Dam: By Using Ssiim Model. 2011. 96p. pap. ***(978-3-639-32465-5(X))*** VDM Verlag Dr. Mueller e.K.

American Society of Agricultural and Biological Engineers (ASABE) Staff, compiled by. Annual International Meeting of the American Society of Agricultural & Biological Engineers 2007. 2007. 7327p. pap. 1995.00 *(978-1-60423-961-4(1))* Curran Assocs., Inc.

Bakker-Arkema, F. & Maier, P. E. Handbook of Agricultural Crop Drying & Storage. Date not set. (Illus.). *(978-0-8247-9437-8(0))* Dekker, Marcel Inc.

Cram101 Textbook Reviews & Cram101 Textbook Reviews. Outlines & Highlights for Introduction to Agricultural Engineering Technology: A Problem Solving Approach by Harry L. Field. 2011. 74p. pap. 27.95 ***(978-1-61830-823-8(8))*** Cram101 Inc.

Erdogdu, Ferruh. Optimization in Food Engineering. Erdogdu, Ferruh, ed. 2008. (Contemporary Food Engineering Ser.). (ENG., Illus.). 758p. 195.95 *(978-1-4200-6141-3(0)*, CRC Press) Taylor & Francis Group GBR. Dist: Taylor & Francis Group.

Farm Equipment Electrical Systems. (Illus.). 48p. reprint ed. pap. 3.50 *(978-0-87288-445-8(7)*, IT-2) Penton Media, Inc.

Field, Harry L. & Solie, John. Introduction to Agricultural Engineering Technology: A Problem Solving Approach. 3rd rev. ed. 2007. (ENG., Illus.). vi, 394p. pap. 84.95 *(978-0-387-36913-6(9)*, 0387369139) Springer.

Gibbens, Gerald A. & Anderson, Susan S. SCADA & Related Technologies for Irrigation System Modernization, II: A USCID Water Management Conference. 2007. (Illus.). 241p. pap. *(978-1-887903-21-9(6))* U. S. Committee on Irrigation & Drainage.

Jian cha bu zhu shui li bu jian cha ju Staff, contrib. by. Shui Li Gong Cheng Jian She Xiang Mu Zhi Fa Jian Cha Shi Yong Shou Ce. 2009. (CHI.). 300p. *(978-7-5084-6982-9(8))* Zhongguo Shuili Shuidian Chubanshe.

Lal, Mohan & Kumar Jena, Subhendu. Ergonomic Evaluation of Manual Winnower. 2011. 64p. pap. ***(978-3-8443-0847-1(4))*** Lambert Academic Publishing.

Li, Daoliang, et al, eds. Computer & Computing Technologies in Agriculture IV: 4th IFIP TC 12 Conference, CCTA 2010, Nanchang, China, October 22-25, 2010, Part II, Selected Papers, 4 vols. 2011. (IFIP Advances in Information & Communication Technology Ser.). (Illus.). xiv, 745p. 209.00 *(978-3-642-18335-5(2)*, 3642183352) Springer.

—Computer & Computing Technologies in Agriculture IV: 4th IFIP TC 12 Conference, CCTA 2010, Nanchang, China, October 22-25, 2010, Selected Papers, Part I. 2011. (IFIP Advances in Information & Communication Technology Ser.). xxxviii, 754p. 209.00 *(978-3-642-18332-4(8)*, 3642183328) Springer.

—Computer & Computing Technologies in Agriculture IV: 4th IFIP TC 12 International Conference, CCTA 2010, Nanchang, China, October 22-25, 2010, Selected Papers, Part III, 4 vols. 2011. (IFIP Advances in Information & Communication Technology Ser.). (Illus.). xiv, 751p. 209.00 *(978-3-642-18353-9(0)*, 3642183530) Springer.

—Computer & Computing Technologies in Agriculture IV: 4th IFIP TC 12 International Conference, CCTA 2010, Nanchang, China, October 22-25, 2010, Selected Papers, Part IV, 4 vols. 2011. (IFIP Advances in Information & Communication Technology Ser.). (Illus.). xiv, 774p. 209.00 *(978-3-642-18368-3(9)*, 3642183689) Springer.

Liebig, Mark, et al, eds. Managing GRACEnet Greenhouse Gases: Coordinated Agricultural Research through GRACEnet to Address our Changing Climate. 2012. (ENG.). 572p. 129.95 ***(978-0-12-386897-8(1)***, Academic Pr.) Elsevier Science & Technology Bks.

Lorenzen, Margaret Brownell. A Life to Remember: The Life of Robert Theodore Lorenzen. 2008. 435p. per. 50.00 *(978-0-9786211-3-1(1)*, Ithaca Pr.) Authors & Artists Publishers of New York, Inc.

Marbs, Juan. Co2 Enrichment & Hot Water Heat in a Greenhouse. 2010. 148p. pap. *(978-3-8383-3145-4(1))* Lambert Academic Publishing.

Mollison, Bill. Permaculture: A Designers' Manual. 2009. (Illus.). 576p. reprint ed. *(978-0-908228-01-0(5))* Tagari Pubns.

Opara, Umezuruike Linus, ed. Agricultural & Biological Engineering Education. 2011. (Contemporary Food Engineering Ser.). (ENG., Illus.). 576p. 129.95 *(978-1-4398-0771-2(X)*, CRC Press) Taylor & Francis Group GBR. Dist: Taylor & Francis Group.

Recchia, Lucia, et al. Multicriteria Analysis & LCA Techniques: With Applications to Agro-Engineering Problems. 2011. (Green Energy & Technology Ser.). (ENG., Illus.). x, 155p. 179.00 *(978-0-85729-703-7(1)*, 0857297031) Springer.

Rovira-Má, et al. Stereoscopic Vision for Agriculture. 2011. 200p. pap. ***(978-3-8443-3172-1(7))*** Lambert Academic Publishing.

Sam-Amoah, Livingstone. Potential & Actual Performance of Rice Production Systems in Ghan. 2011. 176p. pap. ***(978-3-8454-0545-2(7))*** Lambert Academic Publishing.

Tan, Honghua. Piageng 2010: Photonics & Imaging for Agricultural Engineering. 2011. (Proceedings of SPIE Ser.). 404p. pap. 90.00 ***(978-0-8194-8245-7(5))*** SPIE.

Tan, Honghua & Luo, Qi. PIAGENG 2009: 11-12 July 2009, Zhangjiajie, China. 2009. (Proceedings of SPIE Ser.). (Illus.). 290p. pap. 80.00 *(978-0-8194-7802-3(4))*; 330p. pap. 80.00 *(978-0-8194-7800-9(8))* SPIE.

Various. Starting a Duck Farm - a Collection of Articles on Stock Selection, Rearing, Economics & Other Aspects of Duck Farming. 2011. 82p. pap. 26.45 ***(978-1-4465-3661-2(0)***, Kent Pr.) Kent Communications, Ltd.

AGRICULTURAL EXHIBITIONS

Here are entered works on competitive exhibitions of farm products, livestock, baked goods, etc., with prizes for excellence, often combined with carnival-like entertainment, and held annually by states, counties, etc. Works on public gatherings at a stated time and place at which goods are exhibited and sold are entered under Fairs. Works on areas within which or arrangements by which many buyers and sellers are brought into contact with one another in order to exchange goods or services are entered under Markets.

see also Livestock Exhibitions

also names of individual exhibitions

Ahearn, Molly. The Dutchess County Fair: Portrait of an American Tradition. 2007. (Illus.). 122p. per. 15.95 *(978-1-883789-55-8(9))* Black Dome Pr. Corp.

Awad, Jenny. The Aurora Farmers Fair: 100 Years. 2008. (Images of America Ser.). (ENG., Illus.). 128p. pap. 19.99 *(978-0-7385-5168-5(6))* Arcadia Publishing.

Board, Prudy Taylor. The Story of the South Florida Fair. 2007. *(978-1-57864-469-8(0))* Donning Co. Pubs.

Davies, Wynne. Sixty Years of Royal Welsh Champions: A Celebration of Welsh Pony & Cob Champions, 1947-2007. 2009. (ENG., Illus.). 400p. 95.00 *(978-0-85131-955-1(6))* Trafalgar Square Bks.

Heine, Steven Robert. The Oregon State Fair. 2007. (Images of America Ser.). (Illus.). 127p. per. 19.99 *(978-0-7385-4877-7(4))* Arcadia Publishing.

Hokanson, Drake & Kratz, Carol. Purebred & Homegrown: America's County Fairs. 2008. (ENG., Illus.). 200p. pap. 29.95 *(978-0-299-22824-8(X))* Univ. of Wisconsin Pr.

Miller, Harold Lee, photos by. Fair Culture: Images from Indiana Fairs. 2009. *(978-0-87195-278-3(5))* Indiana Historical Society.

Miller, Susan Lambert. State Fair: The Great Minnesota Get-Together. 2008. (ENG.). 128p. 24.95 *(978-0-87351-615-0(X))* Minnesota Historical Society Pr.

Miller, Susan Lambert, photos by. Minnesota County Fairs: Kids, Cows, Carnies, & Chow. 2009. (ENG., Illus.). 128p. 24.95 *(978-0-87351-719-5(9))* Minnesota Historical Society Pr.

Neely, Wayne C. Agricultural Fair. reprint ed. 27.50 *(978-0-404-04669-9(X))* AMS Pr., Inc.

Parker, J. O. & Tindle Parker, Debbie. Iowa's Tradition: An ABC Photo Album of the Iowa State Fair. 2006. (Illus.). per. 19.95 *(978-0-9786931-0-7(8))* Our Front Porch Bks.

Richardson, Fchs Debra J. Come to the Fair! 150 Years of the Fillmore County Fair. 2009. pap. *(978-1-61584-076-2(1))* Independent Pub.

Runnion, Dale F., et al. The Saddle & Sirloin Portrait Collection: A Directory & Biographical Catalog. Runnion, Dale F. & Runnion, June A., eds. 4th ed. 2009. (ENG., Illus.). 127p. (Orig.). pap. 10.00 *(978-0-9634756-3-3(0))* North American International Livestock Exposition.

Tilling, Brian J. The White Horse Show: A Village Charity. 2007. (Illus.). 304p. per. *(978-1-84748-007-1(1))* Athena Pr.

Walton, Cinda Lou. The History of the Hillsdale County Fair: In the Eyes of the Woman's Congress Ladies & Friends: The Pictures. 2009. (Illus.). 50p. pap. ***(978-1-4490-1304-2(X))*** AuthorHouse.

AGRICULTURAL EXTENSION WORK

see also Agricultural Education; Community Development

Ali, Jaffar, et al. Decentralization in Agriculture Extension. 2011. 92p. pap. ***(978-3-8454-0987-0(8))*** Lambert Academic Publishing.

Ashraf, Ijaz & Sher Muhammad. Decentralized Extension in Pakistan. 2011. 224p. pap. ***(978-3-8443-8124-5(4))*** Lambert Academic Publishing.

Butt, Tahir Munir. Agricultural Extension Approach. 2011. 108p. pap. ***(978-3-8443-2816-5(5))*** Lambert Academic Publishing.

Ghimire, Nav & Martin, Robert. A Model for Applying Educational Process Competencies. 2011. 148p. pap. ***(978-3-8443-8850-3(8))*** Lambert Academic Publishing.

Investing in Our Nation's Future Through Agricultural Research: Hearing Before the Committee on Agriculture, Nutrition, & Forestry, United States Senate, One Hundred Tenth Congress, First Session, March 7, 2007. 2007. (Illus.). iv, 192p. *(978-0-16-078869-7(2)*, 552-070-35998-2) United States Government Printing Office.

Ison, Ray, ed. Agricultural Extension & Rural Development: Breaking out of Traditions. 2007. (ENG., Illus.). 252p. pap. 56.00 *(978-0-521-03941-3(X))* Cambridge Univ. Pr.

Isubikalu, Prossy. Stepping-Stones to Improve Functioning of Agricultural Extension Programs. 2007. 220p. pap. 45.00 *(978-90-8686-021-0(4))* Wageningen Academic Publishers NLD. Dist: Enfield Publishing & Distribution Co., Inc.

Luqman, Muhammad, et al. Effectiveness of Decentralized Agriculture Extension System. 2011. 100p. pap. ***(978-3-8443-1317-8(6))*** Lambert Academic Publishing.

Mangheni, Margaret Najjingo. Experiences, Innovations & Issues in Agricultural Extension in Uganda: Lessons & Prospects. 2007. (Illus.). 192p. pap. *(978-9970-02-715-6(8))* Fountain Pubs. Ltd. UGA. Dist: Michigan State Univ. Pr.

Streatfeild, Jeremy & Lacey, Simon. New Reflections on International Trade: Essays on Agriculture, WTO Accession & Systemic Issues. 2008. (Illus.). 453p. 260.00 *(978-1-905017-46-1(4))* Cameron May, Ltd. GBR. Dist: Gaunt, Inc.

Wennink, Bertus, et al. Outsourcing Agricultural Advisory Services: Enhancing Rural Innovation in Sub-Saharan Africa. 2008. (Bulletins of the Royal Tropical Institute Ser.). 150p. (C). pap. 35.00 *(978-90-6832-646-8(5))* Royal Tropical Institute Pr. (KIT (Koninklijk Instituut voor de Tropen) NLD. Dist: Stylus Publishing, LLC.

AGRICULTURAL FAIRS

see Agricultural Exhibitions

AGRICULTURAL GEOGRAPHY

see also Agricultural Systems; Crop Zones

Chauhan, Dharmender Singh. Agricultural Geography. 2010. (Illus.). 194p. *(978-81-87445-50-0(5)*, Library of Congress — New Delhi Overseas Office) Ritu Pubns.

Cooper, Rosalind. The Wine Year. 2010. (ENG., Illus.). 224p. 39.95 *(978-1-85894-514-9(3))* Merrell Pubs. Ltd. GBR. Dist: Perseus Distribution.

Daniels, Jeffrey J., et al, eds. Handbook of Agricultural Geophysics. 2008. (Books in Soils, Plants, & the Environment). (ENG., Illus.). 432p. 162.95 *(978-0-8493-3728-4(3)*, CRC Press) Taylor & Francis Group GBR. Dist: Taylor & Francis Group.

Dougherty, Percy H., ed. The Geography of Wine: Regions, Terroir & Techniques. 2012. (ENG., Illus.). xii, 255p. 129.00 *(978-94-007-0463-3(1)*, 9400704631) Springer.

Ervin, Brenda. Country Faith: Rural America Stories of Faith from Forty of the Most Inspirational People of Our Time, Volume I, Bk. 1. Nesbit, Dennis E., ed. num. ed. 2010. (Illus.). 164p. 27.95 *(978-0-9674808-0-0(9))* Rural America Bks.

Harvey, Nigel. Fields, Hedges & Ditches. 2nd ed. 2011. (Shire Library). (ENG., Illus.). 32p. pap. 11.95 *(978-0-85263-868-2(X))* Shire Pubns., Ltd. GBR. Dist: Random Hse., Inc.

AGRICULTURAL IMPLEMENTS

see also Gardening—Equipment and Supplies

American Society of Mechanical Engineers Staff, ed. Double-Pitch Conveyor Roller Chains, Attachments & Sprockets. 40p. 32.00 *(978-0-7918-2269-2(9))* ASME Pr.

Ashgriz, Nasser. Handbook of Atomization & Sprays: Theory & Applications. Ashgriz, Nasser, ed. 2011. (Illus.). xvi, 935p. 349.00 *(978-1-4419-7263-7(3)*, 1441972633) Springer.

Bell, Jonathan & Watson, Mervyn. A History of Irish Farming, 1750-1950. 2008. (Illus.). 344p. (C). 60.00 *(978-1-84682-096-0(0))* Four Courts Pr. IRL. Dist: International Specialized Bk. Services.

Cobleigh, Rolfe. Handy Farm Devices: And How to Make Them. 2nd ed. 2008. 288p. pap. 14.95 *(978-1-59921-325-5(7)*, Lyons Pr.) Globe Pequot Pr., The.

—Handy Farm Devices & How to Make Them. 2010. 114p. pap. *(978-1-151-85163-5(9))* Books LLC.

—Handy Farm Devices & How to Make Them. 2009. 298p. 43.95 (978-1-104-80977-5(X)); pap. 28.95 (978-1-104-75866-0(0)) Kessinger Publishing, LLC.

—Handy Farm Devices & How to Make Them. 2007. (ENG., Illus.). 296p. pap. 9.95 (978-1-60239-103-1(3), 239103) Skyhorse Publishing Co., Inc.

—Handy Farm Devices & How to Make Them. (Illus.). 204p. 2011. pap. 15.99 (978-1-61720-225-4(8)) 2008. pap. 9.95 (978-1-60459-586-4(8)) Wilder Pubns., Ltd.

Moore, Sam. Implements for Farming with Horses & Mules: A Modern All-In-One Manual. 2006. (978-1-893707-10-8(5)) Rural Heritage.

Richman, Irwin & Emery, Michael. Yesterday's Farm Tools & Equipment. 2010. (Illus.). 208p. 39.99 (978-0-7643-3603-4(7)) Schiffer Publishing, Ltd.

Skyhorse Publishing, ed. Homemade Contrivances & How to Make Them: 1001 Labor-Saving Devices for Farm, Garden, Dairy, & Workshop. 2007. (ENG., Illus.). 640p. per. 14.95 (978-1-60239-018-8(5), 239018) Skyhorse Publishing Co., Inc.

Sloane, Eric. A Museum of Early American Tools. 2008. (ENG., Illus.). 128p. 19.95 (978-0-486-46303-2(6)) Dover Pubns., Inc.

White, K. D. Agricultural Implements of the Roman World. 2010. (ENG.). 266p. pap. 23.99 (978-0-521-14757-6(3)) Cambridge Univ. Pr.

AGRICULTURAL INDUSTRIES

see also Animal Industry

Aicpa. AICPA Audit & Accounting Guide Agricultural Producers & Agricultural Cooperatives. 2007. pap. 61.25 (978-0-87051-681-8(7)) American Institute of Certified Public Accountants.

Akridge, Jay T. Agribusiness Management. 4th ed. 2012. E-Book (978-0-203-12418-5(9)) Routledge.

Akridge, Jay T., et al. Agribusiness Management. 4th rev. ed. 2012. (Routledge Textbooks in Environmental & Agricultural Economics Ser.). (ENG., Illus.). 480p. (C). 180.00 (978-0-415-59695-4(5)); pap. 85.00 (978-0-415-59696-1(3)) Routledge.

Allen, Patricia. Together at the Table: Sustainability & Sustenance in the American Agrifood System. 2007. (Rural Studies). 260p. per. 27.00 (978-0-271-02977-1(3)) Pennsylvania State Univ. Pr.

Allen, Will. The War on Bugs. 2007. (ENG., Illus.). 336p. pap. 35.00 (978-1-933392-46-2(0)) Chelsea Green Publishing.

Anderson, Kym & Swinnen, Johan F. M. Distortions to Agricultural Incentives in Europe's Transition Economies. 2008. (Trade & Development Ser.). (ENG., Illus.). 408p. (C). pap. 39.95 (978-0-8213-7419-1(2), 9780821374191) World Bank Pubns.

Anderson, Kym & Valdés, Alberto. Distortions to Agricultural Incentives in Latin America. 2008. (Trade & Development Ser.). (ENG., Illus.). 440p. (C). pap. 39.95 (978-0-8213-7513-6(X), 9780821375136) World Bank Pubns.

Anderson, Leigh, et al, eds. Seed Trade in Rural Markets: Implications for Crop Diversity & Agricultural Development. 2009. (ENG., Illus.). 224p. 136.00 (978-1-84407-784-7(5)) Routledge.

Arzjani, Zahra. Role of Sugar Factory in the Transformation of the Rural Economy. 2010. 244p. pap. (978-3-8383-4824-7(9)) Lambert Academic Publishing.

Asian Development Bank, Board of Directors Staff. Agriculture, Food Security, & Rural Development. 2011. (ENG., Illus.). 384p. 49.95 (978-0-19-806466-4(7)) Oxford Univ. Pr., Inc.

Ávila Dorantes, José Antonio, et al. Presente y Futuro Del Sector Agrícola Mexicano en el Contexto Del TLCAN. 2008. (Estudios Económicos Ser.). (SPA., Illus.). 385p. pap. 39.99 (978-968-12-1346-6(7)) El Colegio de México, A.C., Biblioteca Miguel Cosio Villegas MEX. Dist: Fondo de Cultura Economica USA.

BIA. Key Livestock, Crop, & Service Companies of Russia, Volume 1: Far Eastern, Siberian, Urals, Volga Federal Districts. 6th rev. ed. 2006. 422p. (J). pap. 249.00 (978-1-4187-4521-9(9)) Business Information Agency.

—Key Livestock, Crop, & Service Companies of Russia, Volume 2: Southern, Central, Northwestern Federal Districts. 6th rev. ed. 2006. 452p. (J). pap. 249.00 (978-1-4187-4522-6(7)) Business Information Agency.

Bohnet, Iris. Exploring Landscape Character. 2011. 512p. pap. (978-3-8443-1166-2(1)) Lambert Academic Publishing.

Bonanno, Alessandro & Cavalcanti, Josefa Salete Barbosa. Globalization & the Time-Space Reorganization: Capital Mobility in Agriculture & Food in the Americas. Bonanno, Alessandro & Cavalcanti, Josefa Salete Barbosa, eds. 2011. (Research in Rural Sociology & Development Ser.: Vol. 17). (Illus.). 250p. 114.95 (978-0-85724-317-1(9)) Emerald Group Publishing Ltd. GBR. Dist: Turpin Distribution Services Ltd.

Bourlakis, Michael, et al, eds. Intelligent Agrifood Chains & Networks. 2011. (ENG., Illus.). 312p. 209.95 (978-1-4051-8299-7(7), Wiley-Blackwell) Wiley, John & Sons, Inc.

Brandow, Patrick M., ed. Agriculture & Agribusiness Developments in India. 2010. (Agriculture Issues & Policies Ser.). (Illus.). viii, 172p. 98.00 (978-1-61668-946-9(3)) Nova Science Pubs., Inc.

Bryceson, Kim P. E Issues in Agribusiness: The What, Why & How. 2006. (Illus.). 384p. 70.00 (978-1-84593-071-4(1)) CABI GBR. Dist: Stylus Publishing, LLC.

Bujak, Edward. England's Rural Realms: Landholding & the Agricultural Revolution. 2007. (ENG., Illus.). 272p. 89.00 (978-1-84511-472-5(8), Tauris Academic Studies) I. B. Tauris & Co., Ltd. GBR. Dist: Macmillan.

Christie, G., et al. Financial Management for Agribusiness. 2007. (Landlinks Press Ser.). (Illus.). 360p. pap. 57.50 (978-0-643-09295-2(1)) CSIRO Publishing AUS. Dist: Stylus Publishing, LLC.

Clapp, Jennifer & Fuchs, Doris, eds. Corporate Power in Global Agrifood Governance. 2009. (Food, Health, & the Environment Ser.). (ENG., Illus.). 328p. (gr. 17). 48.00 (978-0-262-01275-1(8)); pap. 25.00 (978-0-262-51237-4(8)) MIT Pr.

Concentration in Agriculture & an Examination of the JBS/Swift Acquisitions: Hearing Before the Subcommittee on Antitrust, Competition Policy, & Consumer Rights of the Committee on the Judiciary, United States Senate, One Hundred Tenth Congress, Second Session, May 7, 2008. 2008. (Illus.). iv, 228p. (978-0-16-082087-8(1), 552-070-38243-7) United States Government Printing Office.

Coupe, Stuart & Lewins, Roger. Negotiating the Seed Treaty. 2007. (ENG., Illus.). 64p. pap. 29.95 (978-1-85339-628-1(1)) Practical Action Publishing GBR. Dist: Stylus Publishing, LLC.

Cox, Andrew, et al. Strategies for Supply Chains & Markets: Optimising Business Performance in the Food & Farming Industry. 2013. (ENG.). 256p. 79.95 (978-0-230-54316-4(2)) Palgrave Macmillan.

Cramer, Gail L., ed. Agricultural Economics, 4 vols., Set. 2010. (Critical Concepts in Economics Ser.). (ENG.). 1712p. (C). 1360.00 (978-0-415-54745-1(8)) Routledge.

Cram101 Textbook Reviews & Cram101 Textbook Reviews. Outlines & Highlights for Agribusiness Fundamentals & Applications by Ricketts. 2011. 240p. pap. 31.95 (978-1-61830-966-2(8)) Cram101 Inc.

—Outlines & Highlights for Principles of Agribusiness Management by James Beierlein, Isbn: 9781577665403. 2011. 70p. pap. 27.95 (978-1-61461-236-0(6)) Cram101 Inc.

Custance, Paul. Market Orientation: Transforming Food & Agribusiness Around the Customer. Lindgreen, Adam et al, eds. 2010. (Food & Agricultural Marketing Ser.). (Illus.). 394p. 134.95 (978-0-566-09208-4(5), Gower Publishing Co., Ltd.) Ashgate Publishing, Ltd. GBR. Dist: Ashgate Publishing Co.

Da Silva, Carlos A., et al. Agro-Industries for Development. 2009. (Illus.). 304p. 125.00 (978-1-84593-576-4(4)); pap. 85.00 (978-1-84593-577-1(2)) CABI GBR. Dist: Stylus Publishing, LLC.

Dev, S. Mahendra & Rao, N. Chandrasekhara, eds. India: Perspectives on Equitable Development. 2009. (ENG., Illus.). 616p. 79.95 (978-81-7188-685-2(X)) Academic Foundation IND. Dist: Independent Pubs. Group.

Duzgun, Murat. The Image of Turkish Industrial Products for Export. 2011. 148p. pap. (978-3-8443-8509-0(6)) Lambert Academic Publishing.

Eubanks, Sharon Y. & Glantz, Stanton A. Continuing Bad Acts. 2012. (978-0-87553-017-8(6)) American Public Health Assn.

Fearne, Andrew, et al, eds. Regoverning Markets: A Place for Small Scale Producers in Modern Agrifood Chains. 2007. (Gower Sustainable Food Chains Ser.). 248p. 124.95 (978-0-566-08730-1(8), Gower Publishing Co., Ltd.) Ashgate Publishing, Ltd. GBR. Dist: Ashgate Publishing Co.

Federation of Societies for Coatings Technology (FSCT) Staff, compiled by. International Coatings Expo (ICE 2007) Clean-Lean-Green: Innovative Solutions for the Global Coatings Community. 2007. 2100p. pap. 245.00 (978-1-60423-929-4(8)) Curran Assocs., Inc.

Fetalvero, Eddie & Faminial, Tomas. Potentials of Tiger Grass Industry. 2011. 64p. pap. (978-3-8443-8699-8(8)) Lambert Academic Publishing.

Fischer, C. & Hartmann, M., eds. Agri-food Chain Relationships. 2010. (Illus.). 290p. 160.00 (978-1-84593-642-6(6)) CABI GBR. Dist: Stylus Publishing, LLC.

Fitting, Elizabeth M. The Struggle for Maize: Campesinos, Workers, & Transgenic Corn in the Mexican Countryside. 2010. (ENG., Illus.). 320p. 84.95 (978-0-8223-4938-9(8)) Duke Univ. Pr.

Frederick, Gus. Silverton. 2011. (Images of America Ser.). (ENG., Illus.). 128p. pap. 21.99 (978-0-7385-7533-9(X)) Arcadia Publishing.

Harper, Malcolm. Inclusive Value Chains Vol. 4: A Pathway Out of Poverty. 2010. (Illus.). 312p. 58.00 (978-981-4293-89-1(X)) World Scientific Publishing Co., Inc.

Hazell, P. B. R. & Reardon, Thomas Anthony. Transforming the Rural Nonfarm Economy: Opportunities & Threats in the Developing World. Hazell, Peter B. R. et al, eds. 2007. (ENG., Illus.). 512p. (gr. 17). 70.00 (978-0-8018-8663-8(5)) Johns Hopkins Univ. Pr.

Hazell, Peter B. R., et al, eds. Transforming the Rural Nonfarm Economy: Opportunities & Threats in the Developing World. 2007. (ENG., Illus.). 512p. (gr. 17). per. 30.00 (978-0-8018-8664-5(3)) Johns Hopkins Univ. Pr.

Hearing to Review Food Aid & Agriculture Trade Programs Operated by the U.S. Department of Agriculture & the U.S. Agency for International Development: Hearing Before the Subcommittee on Specialty Crops, Rural Development, & Foreign Agriculture of the Committee on Agriculture, House of Representatives, One Hundred Tenth Congress, First Session, May 10, 2007. 2009. (Illus.). iii, 143p. (978-0-16-083011-2(7), 552-070-38909-1) United States Government Printing Office.

Hearing to Review Structural Changes That Are Taking Place in the Agricultural Economy & Their Impacts: Hearing Before the Committee on Agriculture, House of Representatives, One Hundred Tenth Congress, First Session, October 18, 2007. 2009. (Illus.). iii, 50p. (978-0-16-083332-8(9), 552-070-39156-8) United States Government Printing Office.

Hearing to Review the Future of Our Nation's Forests: Hearing Before the Subcommittee on Department Operations, Oversight, Nutrition, & Forestry of the Committee on Agriculture, House of Representatives, One Hundred Eleventh Congress, First Session, June 3, 2009. 2009. (Illus.). iii, 140p. (978-0-16-084395-2(2), 552-070-39937-2) United States Government Printing Office.

Herzig, Christian. Environmental Management Accounting: Case Studies in South-East Asian Companies. 2012. (Illus.). 256p. pap. (978-0-415-50678-6(6)); E-Book (978-0-203-12536-6(3)) Routledge.

Herzig, Christian, et al, eds. Environmental Management Accounting: Case Studies in South-East Asian Companies. 2012. (ENG., Illus.). 352p. (C). 145.00 (978-0-415-69431-5(0)) Routledge.

Keating, Anjelina Michelle. The American Seed Trade Association: Celebrating 125 Years. 2008. (978-1-57864-493-3(3)) Donning Co. Pubs.

Korthals, M. Before Dinner: Philosophy & Ethics of Food. 2010. (International Library of Environmental, Agricultural & Food Ethics Ser.). xiii, 215p. pap. 189.00 (978-90-481-6763-0(9), 9048167639) Springer.

Kugelman, Michael, et al. Land Grab? The Race for the World's Farmland. 2009. (Illus.). x, 123p. (978-1-933549-55-2(6)) Woodrow Wilson International Ctr. fo Scholars.

Larsen, Kurt, et al, eds. Agribusiness & Innovation Systems in Africa. 2009. (Agriculture & Rural Development Ser.). (ENG., Illus.). 472p. pap. 35.00 (978-0-8213-7944-8(5), 9780821379448) World Bank Pubns.

Light, Melanie & Light, Ken, photos by. Valley of Shadows & Dreams. 2012. (978-1-59714-172-7(0)) Heyday.

Lindgreen, Adam & Hingley, Martin. Opportunities from Ethnic Diversity: Food & Agribusiness Marketing in an Age of Fusion & Fragmentation. 2009. (Food & Agricultural Marketing Ser.). (Illus.). 344p. 134.95 (978-0-566-08813-1(4), Gower Publishing Co., Ltd.) Ashgate Publishing, Ltd. GBR. Dist: Ashgate Publishing Co.

Lingohr-Wolf, Susanne. Industrialisation & Rural Livelihoods in China. 2010. (Routledge Contemporary China Ser.). (ENG., Illus.). 256p. (C). 130.00 (978-0-415-55937-9(5)) Routledge.

Linskens, Hans F. & Jackson, John F., eds. Analysis of Plant Waste Materials. 2010. (Molecular Methods of Plant Analysis Ser.). (Illus.). xvi, 214p. pap. 289.00 (978-3-642-08431-7(1), 3642084311) Springer.

Lipper, Leslie, et al, eds. Seed Trade in Rural Markets: Implications for Crop Diversity & Agricultural Development. 2009. (ENG., Illus.). 224p. pap. 47.95 (978-1-84407-785-4(3)) Routledge.

McCord, Lynn M. & Quinn, Barry J. Global Agricultural Imports. 2011. (Agriculture Issues & Policies Ser.). 115.00 (978-1-61209-110-5(5)) Nova Science Pubs., Inc.

McMahon, Joseph A., ed. Trade & Agriculture: Negotiating a New Agreement? 483p. 150.00 (978-1-874698-81-4(3)) Cameron May, Ltd. GBR. Dist: Gaunt, Inc.

Mfune Mubukwanu, Elizabeth. Effects of an Agribusiness Collapse on Contract Growers. 2010. 108p. pap. (978-3-8383-7522-9(X)) Lambert Academic Publishing.

Miljkovic, Dragan, ed. International Agricultural Trade & Development: New Research. 2012. (Series: Agriculture Issues & Policies Binding: Hardcover Ser.). 282p. 140.00 (978-1-61324-788-4(5)) Nova Science Pubs., Inc.

Munawar, Edi. Ghgs Emissions of Indonesia Agricultural Sector & Fertilizer Industry. 2010. 152p. pap. (978-3-8383-4884-1(2)) Lambert Academic Publishing.

Norton, James & Dilley, Becca. The Master Cheesemakers of Wisconsin. 2009. (ENG., Illus.). 204p. pap. 24.95 (978-0-299-23434-8(7)) Univ. of Wisconsin Pr.

Organisation for Economic Co-operation and Development Staff. Business for Development 2008. 2008. 124p. pap. 63.00 (978-92-64-04469-2(8)) Organization for Economic Cooperation & Development.

Pacheco Castro, Jorge A. Cambio y Continuidad Sociocultural en la Región Sur Del Campo Yucateco. 2009. (SPA., Illus.). 355p. 37.00 (978-970-722-682-1(X)) Plaza y Valdes, S.A. de C.V. MEX. Dist: Sony Electronics.

Pappadà, Gabriella & Antonazzo, Luca. Formazione e Lavoro Nel Settore Agroalimentare in Europa. 2010. (ITA., Illus.). 152p. (978-88-568-3290-7(9)) Angeli.

Puyana de Palacios, Alicia & Romero, José Antonio. El Sector Agropecuario y el Tratado de Libre Comercio de America Del Norte: Efectos Económicos y Sociales. 2008. (Estudios Económicos Ser.). (SPA., Illus.). 165p. pap. 21.99 (978-968-12-1324-4(6)) El Colegio de México, A.C., Biblioteca Miguel Cosio Villegas MEX. Dist: Fondo de Cultura Economica USA.

Rao, A. V. Nageswara, et al. Supply Chain Strategies for Agribusiness. 2011. 232p. pap. (978-3-639-14741-4(3)) VDM Verlag Dr. Mueller e.K.

Ricketts, Cliff & Ricketts, Kristina G. Agribusiness Fundamentals & Applications. 2nd rev. ed. 2008. (ENG., Illus.). 600p. (C). 144.95 (978-1-4180-3231-9(X)) Delmar Cengage Learning.

Ruben, Ruerd, et al, eds. Tropical food Chains: Governance regimes for quality Management. 2007. 310p. 77.00 (978-90-8686-027-2(3)) Wageningen Academic Publishers NLD. Dist: Enfield Publishing & Distribution Co., Inc.

Schurman, Rachel & Munro, William A. Fighting for the Future of Food: Activists versus Agribusiness in the Struggle over Biotechnology. 2010. (Social Movements, Protest & Contention Ser.). (ENG., Illus.). 280p. pap. 22.50 (978-0-8166-4762-0(3)) Univ. of Minnesota Pr.

Sidhu, Surjit S. & Mudahar, Mohinder S., eds. Privatization & Deregulation: Needed Policy Reforms for Agribusiness Development. 2010. 290p. pap. 149.00 (978-90-481-5221-6(6), 9048152216) Springer.

Simonetti, Luca. Mangi, chi puo. Meglio, meno e Piano: L'ideologia di Slow Food. 2010. (Arare Ser.). (ITA., Illus.). 120p. (C). pap. 15.00 (978-88-564-0092-2(8)) Brown, David Bk. Co., The.

Stringer, Christina & Heron, Richard Le. Agri-Food Commodity Chains & Globalising Networks. 2008. (Dynamics of Economic Space Ser.). (Illus.). 258p. 124.95 (978-0-7546-7336-1(7)) Ashgate Publishing Co.

Telg, Ricky & Irani, Tracy Anne. Agricultural Communications in Action: A Hands-on Approach. 2011. (ENG.). 368p. (C). 100.95 (978-1-111-31714-0(3)) Delmar Cengage Learning.

Thaiprasert, Nalitra. Rethinking the Role of Agriculture & Agro-Industry. 2010. 232p. pap. (978-3-639-22688-1(7)) VDM Verlag Dr. Mueller e.K.

The World Bank. Growth & Productivity in Agriculture & Agribusiness: Evaluative Lessons from World Bank Group Experience. 2011. (Independent Evaluation Group Studies). (ENG., Illus.). 200p. pap. 25.00 (978-0-8213-8606-4(9), 9780821386064) World Bank Pubns.

Tomlinson, Jim, et al. The Decline of Jute: Managing Industrial Change, 1 vol. 2011. (Perspectives in Economic & Social History Ser.). (ENG., Illus.). 240p. 99.00 (978-1-84893-124-4(7)) Pickering & Chatto Pubs., Ltd. GBR. Dist: Ashgate Publishing Co.

Vorobeva, D. A. Selskii Sotsium: Obshchestvennye Ustoi I Vektory Transformatsii. 2009. (RUS.). 323p. (978-5-9999-0210-8(X)) Nauka.

Walchuck, Marilyn C. Ethanol & Corn: Changes from Expanding Use. 2011. (Renewable Energy: Research, Development & Policies Ser.). 89.00 (978-1-61761-597-9(8)) Nova Science Pubs., Inc.

Webber, C. Martin & Labaste, Patrick. Building Competitiveness in Africa's Agriculture: A Guide to Value Chain Concepts & Applications. 2010. pap. 30.00 (978-0-8213-8284-4(5)) 2009. (ENG., Illus.). 182p. pap. 40.00 (978-0-8213-7952-3(6), 9780821379523) World Bank Pubns.

Weldeselassie, Berhane Ghebremichael. Cooperatives & Agribusiness in Developing Countries. 2010. 136p. pap. (978-3-639-24484-7(2)) VDM Verlag Dr. Mueller e.K.

Welter, Friederike. The Handbook of Research on Entrepreneurship in Agriculture & Rural Development. Alsos, Gry Agnete et al, eds. 2011. (Illus.). 336p. 195.00 (978-1-84844-625-0(X)) Elgar, Edward Publishing, Inc.

Young, Daniel J., ed. The Science Surrounding Food. 2009. (Agriculture Issues & Politics Ser.). (Illus.). viii, 170p. 80.10 (978-1-60876-033-6(2)) Nova Science Pubs., Inc.

AGRICULTURAL INNOVATIONS

see also Green Revolution

Aiking, Harry, et al, eds. Sustainable Protein Production & Consumption: Pigs or Peas? Pigs or Peas? 2010. (Environment & Policy Ser.). xvi, 226p. pap. 179.00 (978-90-481-7027-2(3), 9048170273) Springer.

Akram-Lodhi, A. Haroon & Kay, Cristobal. Peasants & Globalization: Political Economy, Rural Transformation & the Agrarian Question. Akram-Lodhi, A. Haroon & Kay, Cristóbal, eds. 2009. (Routledge ISS Studies in Rural Livelihoods Ser.). 336p. 150.00 (978-0-415-44629-7(5)) Routledge.

Amsel, Louis & Hirsch, Lena, eds. Food Science & Security. 2009. 98.00 (978-1-60692-977-3(1)) Nova Science Pubs., Inc.

Anderson, J. L. Industrializing the Corn Belt: Agriculture, Technology, & Environment, 1945-1972. 2008. (Illus.). 248p. 32.95 (978-0-87580-392-0(X)) Northern Illinois Univ. Pr.

Awasthi, Dushyant Kumar, et al. Pulse Production Technology: Knowledge & Adoption. 2011. 192p. pap. (978-3-639-21227-3(4)) VDM Verlag Dr. Mueller e.K.

Barker, Allen V. Science & Technology of Organic Farming. 2010. (ENG., Illus.). 240p. 72.95 (978-1-4398-1612-7(3), CRC Press) Taylor & Francis Group GBR. Dist: Taylor & Francis Group.

Chang. Rice Genetics & Cytogenetics (V6) 2008. pap. 73.00 (978-981-281-869-0(3)) World Scientific Publishing Co., Inc.

Chiarolla, Claudio. Intellectual Property, Agriculture & Global Food Security: The Privatisation of Crop Biodiversity. 2011. 256p. 115.00 (978-1-84980-733-3(7)) Elgar, Edward Publishing, Inc.

Committee on a Study of Technologies to Benefit Farmers in Africa and South Asia & National Research Council. Emerging Technologies to Benefit Farmers in Sub-Saharan Africa & South Asia. 2009. (ENG.). 292p. pap. 60.25 (978-0-309-12494-2(8)) National Academies Pr.

Conkin, Paul K. A Revolution down on the Farm: The Transformation of American Agriculture Since 1929. (ENG., Illus.). 240p. 2009. pap. 22.50 (978-0-8131-9242-0(0)) 2008. 50.00 (978-0-8131-2519-0(7)) Univ. Pr. of Kentucky.

Ekboir, Javier. Successful Organizational Learning in the Management of Agricultural Research & Innovation: The Mexican Produce Foundations. 2009. (978-0-89629-171-3(5)) International Food Policy Research Institute.

Ellenberg, George B. Mule South to Tractor South: Mules, Machines, & the Transformation of the Cotton South. 2008. (ENG., Illus.). 240p. 42.50 (978-0-8173-1597-9(7)) Univ. of Alabama Pr.

Faasse, Patricia E. In Splendid Isolation: A History of the Willie Commelin Scholten Phytopathology Laboratory, 1894-1992. 2010. (Edita - History of Science & Scholarship in the Netherlands Ser.). (ENG., Illus.). 304p. 60.00 (978-90-6984-541-8(5)) Koninklijke Nederlandse Academie van Wetenschappen NLD. Dist: Chicago Distribution Ctr.

Frewer, Lynn J., et al, eds. Nanotechnology in the Agri-Food Sector: Implications for the Future. 2011. (ENG., Illus.). 328p. 135.00 (978-3-527-33060-7(7), Wiley-VCH) Wiley, John & Sons, Inc.

Gangemi, Michael. Economic Impact of a Farming Innovation Organisation. 2010. 304p. pap. (978-3-639-23660-6(2)) VDM Verlag Dr. Mueller e.K.

Gebre-Mariam, Yohann. Holistic Analysis of Household Decision-Making: Adoption of Agricultural Technologies & Development in Ethiopia. 2011. (ENG.). 362p. pap. 36.95 (978-0-7618-5641-2(2)) Univ. Pr. of America, Inc.

Goodyear, Norman & Hope-Simpson, Maggie. Utilization of Circulating Fluidized Bed Ash - As an Agricultural Soil Amendment. 2009. 212p. pap. *(978-3-639-04153-8(4))* VDM Verlag Dr. Mueller e.K.

Hartwich, Frank. Building Public-Private Partnerships for Agricultural Innovation. 2008. *(978-0-89629-771-5(3))* International Food Policy Research Institute.

—Formando Alianzas Publico-Privadas para la Innovacion Agricola. 2008. *(978-0-89629-762-3(4))* International Food Policy Research Institute.

Heintzman, Andrew & Solomon, Evan. Feeding the Future: From Fat to Famine, How to Solve the World's Food Crises. 2006. (Ingenuity Project Ser.). (ENG., Illus.). 336p. pap. 18.95 *(978-0-88784-744-8(7))* House of Anansi Pr. CAN. Dist: Perseus-PGW.

—Food & Fuel: Solutions for the Future, 1 vol. 2009. (ENG.). 400p. pap. 15.95 *(978-0-88784-826-1(5))* House of Anansi Pr. CAN. Dist: Perseus-PGW.

Innovation Africa: Enriching Farmers' Livelihoods. 2008. (ENG., Illus.). 384p. 166.00 *(978-1-84407-671-0(7))* Routledge.

Innovation Africa: Enriching Farmers' Livelihoods. 2008. (ENG., Illus.). 384p. pap. 58.50 *(978-1-84407-672-7(5))* Routledge.

Juma, Calestous. The New Harvest: Agricultural Innovation in Africa, 1 vol. 2011. (ENG.). 288p. pap. 19.95 *(978-0-19-978319-9(5))* Oxford Univ. Pr., Inc.

Karplus, Valerie J. Agricultural Biotechnology in China: Origins & Prospects. 2007. (Illus.). 165p. 109.00 *(978-0-387-71138-6(4))* Springer.

Larsen, Kurt, et al, eds. Agribusiness & Innovation Systems in Africa. 2009. (Agriculture & Rural Development Ser.). (ENG., Illus.). 472p. pap. 35.00 *(978-0-8213-7944-8(5)*, 9780821379448) World Bank Pubns.

Latesteijn, Henk van. The TransForum Model: Transforming Agro Innovation Toward Sustainable Development: Transforming Agro Innovation Toward Sustainable Development. Andeweg, Karin & van Latesteijn, Henk, eds. 2010. (ENG., Illus.). xii, 162p. 189.00 *(978-90-481-9780-4(5)*, 9048197805) Springer.

Li, Daoliang, ed. Computer & Computing Technologies in Agriculture, Volume I: First IFIP TC 12 International Conference on Computer & Computing Technologies in Agriculture (CCTA 2007), Wuyishan, China, August 18-20 2007. 2008. (IFIP International Federation for Information Processing Ser.). xviii, 736p. 269.00 *(978-0-387-77250-9(2))* Springer.

—Computer & Computing Technologies in Agriculture, Volume II: First IFIP TC 12 International Conference on Computer & Computing Technologies in Agriculture (CCTA 2007), Wuyishan, China, August 18-20 2007. 2008. (IFIP International Federation for Information Processing Ser.). xx, 744p. 269.00 *(978-0-387-77252-3(9))* Springer.

Li, Daoliang & Zhao, Chunjiang, eds. Computer & Computing Technologies in Agriculture II, Volume 1: The Second IFIP International Conference on Computer & Computing Technologies in Agriculture (CCTA2008), October 18-20, 2008, Beijing, China. 2009. (IFIP International Federation for Information Processing Ser.). (ENG., Illus.). xxiv, 788p. 299.00 *(978-1-4419-0208-5(2))* Springer.

—Computer & Computing Technologies in Agriculture II, Volume 2: The Second IFIP International Conference on Computer & Computing Technologies in Agriculture (CCTA2008), October 18-20, 2008, Beijing, China. 2009. (IFIP International Federation for Information Processing Ser.). (ENG., Illus.). xxiv, 740p. 299.00 *(978-1-4419-0210-8(4))* Springer.

—Computer & Computing Technologies in Agriculture II, Volume 3: The Second IFIP International Conference on Computer & Computing Technologies in Agriculture (CCTA2008), October 18-20, 2008, Beijing, China. (IFIP Advances in Information & Communication Technology Ser.). (ENG., Illus.). xxiv, 776p. 2010. pap. 299.00 ***(978-1-4419-5495-4(3)***, 1441954953) 2009. 299.00 *(978-1-4419-0212-2(0))* Springer.

Li, Daoliang & Zhao, Chunjiang, eds. Computer & Computing Technologies in Agriculture III: Third IFIP TC 12 International Conference, CCTA 2009, Beijing, China, October 14-17, 2009, Revised Selected Papers. 2010. (IFIP Advances in Information & Communication Technology Ser.). xv, 561p. 169.00 *(978-3-642-12219-4(1)*, 3642122191) Springer.

Mangheni, Margaret Najjingo. Experiences, Innovations & Issues in Agricultural Extension in Uganda: Lessons & Prospects. 2007. (Illus.). 192p. pap. *(978-9970-02-715-6(8))* Fountain Pubs. Ltd. UGA. Dist: Michigan State Univ. Pr.

McBeath, Jennifer H. & McBeath, Jerry. Environmental Change & Food Security in China. 2009. (Advances in Global Change Research Ser.). (Illus.). xvii, 303p. 199.00 *(978-1-4020-9179-7(6))* Springer.

Millar, Kate, et al, eds. Ethical Futures: Bioscience & food Horizons. 2009. (Illus.). 448p. pap. 92.00 *(978-90-8686-115-6(6))* Wageningen Academic Publishers NLD. Dist: Enfield Publishing & Distribution Co., Inc.

Moore, John Hebron. Agriculture in Ante-Bellum Mississippi. 2010. (Southern Classics Ser.). 288p. pap. 14.95 *(978-1-57003-877-8(5))* Univ. of South Carolina Pr.

Moore, Keith M., ed. Innovating for Sustainable Agriculture & Natural Resource Management: The Science of Adaptive Management. 2009. pap. *(978-0-9769432-7-3(1))* Soil and Water Conservation Society.

Olmstead, Alan & Rhode, Paul. Creating Abundance: Biological Innovation & American Agricultural Development. 2008. (ENG., Illus.). 480p. 85.00 *(978-0-521-85711-6(2))* Cambridge Univ. Pr.

Olmstead, Alan, et al. Creating Abundance: Biological Innovation & American Agricultural Development. 2008. (ENG., Illus.). 480p. pap. 24.99 *(978-0-521-67387-7(9))* Cambridge Univ. Pr.

Otsuka, Keijiro & Kalirajan, Kaliappa, eds. Agriculture in Developing Countries: Technology Issues. 2008. (Illus.). 172p. (C). 39.95 *(978-0-7619-3662-6(9)*, B36626C) SAGE Pubns., Inc.

Ouch, Kosol, et al. The Rain Maker Device: A Path to Harness Mother Nature. 2006. 411p. per. 20.95 *(978-1-59824-374-1(8))* E-BookTime LLC.

Rogers, Everett M. & Asian Media Information and Communication Centre Staff, mems. The Fourteenth Paw: Growing up on an Iowa Farm in the 1930s. 2008. (Illus.). xii, 148p. *(978-981-4136-11-2(5))* 4a.

Sambodo, Leonardo. The Decision Making Processes of Semi-Commercial Farmers. 2009. 376p. pap. *(978-3-639-12530-6(4))* VDM Verlag Dr. Mueller e.K.

Sampson, Abigail N., ed. Horticulture in the 21st Century. 2010. (Botanical Research & Practices Ser.). 129.00 *(978-1-61668-582-9(4))* Nova Science Pubs., Inc.

Science & Technology of Organic Farming. 2011. 69.95 ***(978-1-4398-1613-4(1)***, CRC Press) Taylor & Francis Group GBR. Dist: Taylor & Francis Group.

Shanmugavelu, K. G. Production Technology of Vegetable Crops. (C). 24.00 *(978-81-204-0414-4(9))* Oxford IBH IND. Dist: South Asia Bks.

Snapp, Sieglinde & Pound, Barry, eds. Agricultural Systems: Agroecology & Rural Innovation for Development. 2008. (ENG., Illus.). 400p. (C). 77.95 *(978-0-12-372517-2(8)*, Academic Pr.) Elsevier Science & Technology Bks.

Strange, Marty. Family Farming: A New Economic Vision. 2008. (ENG., Illus.). 336p. pap. 16.95 *(978-0-8032-1748-5(X)*, Bison Bks.) Univ. of Nebraska Pr.

Suiatna, R. Utju. Bertani Dengan Akal & Nurani. 2011. (IND., Illus.). 250p. *(978-602-8349-21-5(6))*; *(978-979-24-5721-6(6))* Nuansa.

Swaminathan, M. S. Science & Sustainable Food Security. 2009. (Illus.). 436p. 111.00 *(978-981-4282-10-9(3))* World Scientific Publishing Co., Inc.

Tessema, Wengelawit. Technical Efficiency of Smallholder Farmers in Ethiopi. 2010. 72p. pap. *(978-3-8383-5285-5(8))* Lambert Academic Publishing.

The World Bank. Agriculture Innovation Systems: An Investment Sourcebook. 2012. (Agriculture & Rural Development Ser.). (ENG.). 680p. pap. 49.95 ***(978-0-8213-8684-2(0)***, 9780821386842) World Bank Pubns.

Tsakok, Isabelle & Gardner, Bruce L. Success in Agricultural Transformation. 2011. (ENG., Illus.). 424p. 110.00 ***(978-0-521-88894-3(8))*** Cambridge Univ. Pr.

Uekotter, Frank. Die Wahrheit ist auf dem Feld: Eine Wissensgeschichte der deutschen Landwirtschaft. 2011. (Umwelt und Gesellschaft Ser.). (GER.). 524p. (C). 68.00 *(978-3-525-31705-1(0))* Vandenhoeck & Ruprecht GmbH & Co. KG DEU. Dist: ISD.

Vaidyanathan, A. Agricultural Growth in India: The Role of Technology, Incentives, & Institutions. 2010. (ENG., Illus.). 300p. 55.00 *(978-0-19-806447-3(0))* Oxford Univ. Pr., Inc.

van der Ploeg, Jan Douwe. The New Peasantries: Struggles for Autonomy & Sustainability in an Era of Empire & Globalization. 2009. (ENG., Illus.). 352p. pap. 47.95 *(978-1-84407-882-0(5))* Routledge.

—The New Peasantries: Struggles for Autonomy & Sustainability in an ERA of Empire & Globalization. 2008. (ENG., Illus.). 352p. (C). 140.00 *(978-1-84407-558-4(3))* Routledge.

Warner, Keith Douglass. Agroecology in Action: Extending Alternative Agriculture Through Social Networks. 2006. (Food, Health, & the Environment Ser.). (ENG., Illus.). 296p. (gr. 17). 62.00 *(978-0-262-23252-4(9))*; per. 26.00 *(978-0-262-73180-5(0))* MIT Pr.

World Bank Staff. Enhancing Agricultural Innovation: How to Go Beyond the Strengthening of Research Systems. 2006. (Agriculture & Rural Development Ser.). (ENG., Illus.). 184p. per. 29.95 *(978-0-8213-6741-4(2)*, 9780821367414) World Bank Pubns.

World Book, Inc Staff, contrib. by. Agriculture. 2009. (Inventions & Discoveries Ser.). (J). *(978-0-7166-0385-6(3))* World Bk., Inc.

AGRICULTURAL INSURANCE

Babcock, B. A., et al, eds. Risk Management & the Environment: Agriculture in Perspective: Agriculture in Perspective. 2010. 220p. pap. 179.00 *(978-90-481-6158-4(4)*, 9048161584) Springer.

Chand, Ramesh & Raju, S. S. Agricultural Risk & Insurance in India: Problems & Prospects. 2010. (ENG.). 106p. 35.95 *(978-81-7188-765-1(1))* Academic Foundation IND. Dist: Independent Pubs. Group.

Gil, Angela M. Agriculture Disaster & Crop Insurance: Background & Issues. 2011. (Agriculture Issues & Policies Ser.). 115.00 *(978-1-61761-559-7(5))* Nova Science Pubs., Inc.

Hearing to Review Producers' Views on the Effectiveness of the Federal Crop Insurance Program: Hearing Before the Subcommittee on General Farm Commodities & Risk Management of the Committee on Agriculture, House of Representatives, One Hundred Eleventh Congress, First Session, April 22, 2009. 2009. (Illus.). iii, 81p. *(978-0-16-084357-0(X)*, 552-070-39900-3) United States Government Printing Office.

Hearing to Review the Federal Crop Insurance Program: Hearing Before the Subcommittee on General Farm Commodities & Risk Management of the Committee on Agriculture, House of Representatives, One Hundred Tenth Congress, First Session, May 14, 2007. 2009. (Illus.). iii, 64p. *(978-0-16-082956-7(9)*, 552-070-38867-2) United States Government Printing Office.

Hearing to Review the Integrity & Efficacy of the Federal Crop Insurance Program: Hearing Before the Subcommittee on General Farm Commodities & Risk Management of the Committee on Agriculture, House of Representatives, One Hundred Tenth Congress, First Session, Thursday, June 7, 2007. 2007. (Illus.). iii, 168p. *(978-0-16-080266-9(0)*, 552-070-36974-1) United States Government Printing Office.

Hearing to Review the State of the Crop Insurance Industry: Hearing Before the Subcommittee on General Farm Commodities & Risk Management of the Committee on Agriculture, House of Representatives, One Hundred Eleventh Congress, Second Session, July 22, 2010. 2010. (Illus.). iii, 104p. ***(978-0-16-086675-3(8)***, 552-070-41653-6) United States Government Printing Office.

Hearing to Review the State of the Crop Insurance Industry: Hearing Before the Subcommittee on General Farm Commodities & Risk Management of the Committee on Agriculture, House of Representatives, One Hundred Tenth Congress, First Session, Tuesday, May 1, 2007. 2008. (Illus.). iii, 118p. *(978-0-16-083039-6(7)*, 552-070-38934-2) United States Government Printing Office.

Mahul, Olivier & Stutley, Charles J. Government Support to Agricultural Insurance: Challenges & Options for Developing Countries. 2010. (ENG., Illus.). 224p. pap. 30.00 *(978-0-8213-8217-2(9)*, 9780821382172) World Bank Pubns.

Waste, Fraud, & Abuse in the Federal Crop Insurance Program: Hearing Before the Committee on Oversight & Government Reform, House of Representatives, One Hundred Tenth Congress, First Session, May 3, 2007. 2008. iii, 108p. *(978-0-16-081984-1(9)*, 552-070-38156-2) United States Government Printing Office.

Zivin, Joshua S. Graff & Perloff, Jeffrey M., eds. The Intended & Unintended Effects of U. S. Agricultural & Biotechnology Policies. 2012. (National Bureau of Economic Research Conference Report). (ENG., Illus.). 312p. 99.00 ***(978-0-226-98803-0(1))*** Univ. of Chicago Pr.

AGRICULTURAL JOURNALISM

see Journalism, Agricultural

AGRICULTURAL LABORERS

see also Migrant Agricultural Laborers; Peasants

American Specialty Agriculture ACT: Hearing Before the Subcommittee on Immigration Policy & Enforcement of the Committee on the Judiciary, House of Representatives, One Hundred Twelfth Congress, First Session, on H.R. 2847, September 8, 2011. 2011. (Illus.). iii, 165p. ***(978-0-16-090038-9(7)***, 552-070-43815-7) United States Government Printing Office.

Anonymous. China's Migrant Workers: Photographs 1990-2000. 2012. (ENG.). 225p. pap. 16.95 ***(978-1-59265-099-6(6))*** Long River Pr.

Arcury, Thomas A. & Quandt, Sara A. Latino Farmworkers in the Eastern United States: Health, Safety & Justice. 2009. (ENG., Illus.). x, 240p. 89.95 *(978-0-387-88346-5(0)*, 0387883460) Springer.

Artz, Georgeanne M., et al. Farm Machinery & Labor Sharing Manual: Tools to Help You Evaluate Sharing Machinery & Labor As an Option in Your Farming Operation. 2009. *(978-0-89373-106-9(4))* MidWest Plan Service.

Barndt, Deborah. Tangled Routes: Women, Work & Globalization on the Tomato Trail. 2006. pap. 8.95 *(978-1-4288-1524-7(4))* Cram101 Inc.

Barrientos, Stephanie, contrib. by. Women & Agribusiness: Working Miracles in the Chilean Fruit Export Sector. (Illus.). xvii, 231p. 13.95 *(978-0-333-68292-0(0))* Macmillan Pubs., Ltd. GBR. Dist: Trans-Atlantic Pubns., Inc.

Bender, Steven W. One Night in America: Robert Kennedy, César Chávez, & the Dream of Dignity. 2008. (Illus.). 264p. per. 33.95 *(978-1-59451-429-6(1))* Paradigm Pubs.

Berube, Rea S., ed. Hired Farmworkers: Profile & Labor Issues. 2009. 69.00 *(978-1-60741-232-8(2))* Nova Science Pubs., Inc.

Bruns, Roger A. Cesar Chavez & the United Farm Workers Movement. 2011. E-Book *(978-0-313-38651-0(X)*, Greenwood Pr.) Greenwood Publishing Group, Inc.

Bruns, Roger A. & Bruns, Roger. Cesar Chavez & the United Farm Workers Movement, 1 vol. 2011. (Landmarks of the American Mosaic Ser.). (Illus.). 186p. 35.00 *(978-0-313-38650-3(1)*, A3092C) Greenwood Publishing Group, Inc.

Coles, Robert, frwd. Growing Season: The Life of a Migrant Community. 2006. (Illus.). 160p. pap. 19.95 *(978-0-87338-892-4(5))* Kent State Univ. Pr.

Do Federal Programs Ensure U.S. Workers Are Recruited First Before Employees [i.e. Employers] Hire from Abroad? Hearing Before the Committee on Education & Labor, U.S. House of Representatives, One Hundred Tenth Congress, Second Session, Hearing Held in Washington, DC, May 6, 2008. 2009. iii, 112p. *(978-0-16-082551-4(2)*, 552-070-38580-1) United States Government Printing Office.

Dorsey, Jennifer Hull. Hirelings: African American Workers & Free Labor in Early Maryland. 2011. (Illus.). 224p. 45.00 *(978-0-8014-4778-5(X))* Cornell Univ. Pr.

Duncan, Kenneth & Rutledge, Ian, eds. Land & Labour in Latin America: Essays on the Development of Agrarian Capitalism in the nineteenth & twentieth Centuries. 2009. (Cambridge Latin American Studies). (ENG., Illus.). 552p. pap. 63.00 *(978-0-521-09320-0(1))* Cambridge Univ. Pr.

Eder, James F. Who Shall Succeed? Agricultural Development & Social Inequality on a Philippine Frontier. 2009. (ENG.). 284p. pap. 38.99 *(978-0-521-10497-5(1))* Cambridge Univ. Pr.

Espinoza, Yolanda. El Caracol - the Story of Alfonso: Labor Camp Child. 2010. (ENG.). 176p. pap. 14.95 *(978-1-936400-58-4(8))* Mill City Pr., Inc.

Frank, Matthew Gavin. Pot Farm. 2012. (ENG.). 232p. pap. 16.95 ***(978-0-8032-3784-1(7))*** Univ. of Nebraska Pr.

Franklin, Richard. Epidemiology of Farm Injuries in New South Wales, Australi. 2008. 396p. pap. *(978-3-639-06492-6(5))* VDM Verlag Dr. Mueller e.K.

Ganz, Marshall. Why David Sometimes Wins: Leadership, Organization, & Strategy in the California Farm Worker Movement, 1 vol. 2010. (ENG., Illus.). 368p. pap. 24.95 *(978-0-19-975785-5(2))* Oxford Univ. Pr., Inc.

Garcia, Mario T. & Garcia, Mario, eds. A Dolores Huerta Reader. 2008. (ENG., Illus.). 380p. pap. 29.95 *(978-0-8263-4513-4(1))* Univ. of New Mexico Pr.

Genovese, Eugene D. & Fox-Genovese, Elizabeth. Fatal Self-Deception: Slaveholding Paternalism in the Old South. 2011. (ENG.). 256p. 90.00 ***(978-1-107-01164-9(7))***; pap. 26.99 ***(978-1-107-60502-2(4))*** Cambridge Univ. Pr.

Grivno, Max L. Gleanings of Freedom: Free & Slave Labor along the Mason-Dixon Line, 1790-1860. 2011. E-Book ***(978-0-252-09356-2(9))*** Univ. of Illinois Pr.

Harwood, Gary, photos by. Growing Season: The Life of a Migrant Community. 2006. (Illus.). 159p. 24.95 *(978-0-87338-873-3(9))* Kent State Univ. Pr.

Heitland, William Emerton. Agricola: A Study of Agriculture & Rustic Life in the Greco-Roman World from the Point of View of Labour. 2011. (Cambridge Library Collection - Classics Ser.). (ENG.). 508p. pap. 37.99 *(978-1-108-02895-0(0))* Cambridge Univ. Pr.

Irigaray, Paulina M. An Analysis of the H-2a Agricultural Guest Worker Program & Recommendations for Future Policy. 2011. 94p. pap. 25.95 ***(978-1-59942-382-1(0)***, Dissertation.com) Universal Pubs.

Jung, Moon-Ho. Coolies & Cane: Race, Labor, & Sugar in the Age of Emancipation. 2008. (ENG., Illus.). 288p. (gr. 17). pap. 27.00 *(978-0-8018-9082-6(9))* Johns Hopkins Univ. Pr.

Knight, Frederick. Working the Diaspora: The Impact of African Labor on the Anglo-American World, 1650-1850. 2010. (ENG., Illus.). 240p. 48.00 *(978-0-8147-4818-3(X))* New York Univ. Pr.

Lessenger, James E., ed. Agricultural Medicine: A Practical Guide. 2010. (ENG., Illus.). xvii, 541p. pap. 69.95 *(978-1-4419-2058-4(7)*, 1441920587) Springer.

Light, Melanie & Light, Ken, photos by. Valley of Shadows & Dreams. 2012. ***(978-1-59714-172-7(0))*** Heyday.

Lope-Alzina, Diana G. Gender Relations As a Basis for Varietal Selection. 2010. 120p. pap. *(978-3-8383-6049-2(4))* Lambert Academic Publishing.

Mitchell, Don. They Saved the Crops: Labor, Landscape, & the Struggle over Industrial Farming in Bracero-Era California. 2012. (Geographies of Justice & Social Transformation Ser.). (ENG.). 576p. 79.95 ***(978-0-8203-4175-0(4))***; pap. 26.95 ***(978-0-8203-4176-7(2))*** Univ. of Georgia Pr.

Nolan-Ferrell, Catherine A. Constructing Citizenship: Transnational Workers & Revolution on the Mexico-Guatemala Border, 1880 — 1950. 2012. (ENG., Illus.). 192p. 50.00 ***(978-0-8165-2980-3(9))*** Univ. of Arizona Pr.

Okyere, W. Asenso. Interactions Between Health & Farm-Labor Productivity. 2011. (Illus.). viii, 24p. pap. ***(978-0-89629-542-1(7))*** International Food Policy Research Institute.

Patterson, Bruce. Turned Round in My Boots: A Memoir. 2010. pap. *(978-1-59714-144-4(5))* Heyday.

—Walking Tractor: And Other Country Tales. 2008. 218p. pap. 14.95 *(978-1-59714-082-9(1))* Heyday.

Pleysier, Albert & Vinogradov, Alexey. The Women of Izmaelovka: A Soviet Union Collective Farm in Siberia. 2007. (ENG., Illus.). 120p. 46.50 *(978-0-7618-3722-0(1))* Univ. Pr. of America, Inc.

Prosper, Doamekpor. Prevention of Respiratory Diseases in Agriculture & Related Industries: A Health Belief Approach to the Design, Implementation & Evaluation of Occupational Safety & Health Programs. 2011. 136p. pap. ***(978-3-639-33193-6(1))*** VDM Verlag Dr. Mueller e.K.

Protecting America's Harvest: Hearing Before the Subcommittee on Immigration, Citizenship, Refugees, Border Security, & International Law of the Committee on the Judiciary, House of Representatives, One Hundred Eleventh Congress, Second Session, Friday, September 24, 2010. 2010. iii, 58p. ***(978-0-16-087797-1(0)***, 552-070-42301-0) United States Government Printing Office.

Prügl, Elisabeth. Transforming Masculine Rule: Agriculture & Rural Development in the European Union. 2011. 200p. E-Book *(978-0-472-02735-4(2))* Univ. of Michigan Pr.

Prugl, Elisabeth M. Transforming Masculine Rule: Agriculture & Rural Development in the European Union. 2011. (ENG., Illus.). 192p. (C). 65.00 *(978-0-472-11773-4(4))* Univ. of Michigan Pr.

Rubio, Blanca. Explotados y Excluidos: Los Campesinos Latinamericanos en la Fase Agroexportadora Neoliberal. 2009. (SPA., Illus.). 239p. 10.00 *(978-968-856-966-5(6))* Plaza y Valdes, S.A. de C.V. MEX. Dist: Sony Electronics.

Schmidt, Ella. The Dream Fields of Florida: Mexican Farmworkers & the Myth of Belonging. 2009. (ENG.). 160p. 62.99 *(978-0-7391-3872-4(3))* Lexington Bks.

Schuman, Stanley H. Rainbows in Washtubs: Diagnostic Mysteries in Agromedicine. 2008. 152p. 36.00 *(978-0-7890-3276-8(7)*, Informa Healthcare) Taylor & Francis Group.

Shaw, Randy. Beyond the Fields: Cesar Chavez, the UFW, & the Struggle for Justice in the 21st Century. 2008. (Illus.). 368p. 45.00 *(978-0-520-25107-6(5))* Univ. of California Pr.

Shotwell, Louisa R. The Harvesters: The Story of the Migrant People. 2009. 242p. 41.95 *(978-1-104-84756-2(6))* 2007. (ENG.). 240p. per. 26.95 *(978-0-548-45135-9(4))* Kessinger Publishing, LLC.

Spirn, Anne Whiston. Daring to Look: Dorothea Lange's Photographs & Reports from the Field. (ENG., Illus.). 376p. 2009. pap. 30.00 *(978-0-226-76985-1(2))* 2008. 40.00 *(978-0-226-76984-4(4))* Univ. of Chicago Pr.

Street, Richard Steven. Everyone Had Cameras: Photography & Farmworkers in California, 1850-2000. 2008. (Illus.). 720p. 105.00 *(978-0-8166-4966-2(9))*; pap. 34.95 *(978-0-8166-4967-9(7))* Univ. of Minnesota Pr.

Telpov, Irwin B. Farm Labor: 21st Century Issues & Challenges. Burton, Alvin W., ed. 2008. (C). 69.00 *(978-1-60456-005-3(3))* Nova Science Pubs., Inc.

Thaiprasert, Nalitra. Rethinking the Role of Agriculture & Agro-Industry. 2010. 232p. pap. *(978-3-639-22688-1(7))* VDM Verlag Dr. Mueller e.K.

Thorp, Michael. Elephants, Tigers & Tappers. 2010. (Illus.). 221p. pap. *(978-981-261-746-0(9))* Marshall Cavendish.

Valdés, Dennis Nodín. Organized Agriculture & the Labor Movement Before the UFW: Puerto Rico, Hawaii, California. 2011. (Illus.). 328p. E-Book ***(978-0-292-73472-2(7))*** Univ. of Texas Pr.

Valdés, Dionicio Nodín. Organized Agriculture & the Labor Movement Before the UFW: Puerto Rico, Hawai'i, California. 2011. (ENG., Illus.). 323p. 55.00 *(978-0-292-72639-0(2))* Univ. of Texas Pr.

Valdés, Dionicio Nodín. Organized Agriculture & the Labor Movement before the UFW: Puerto Rico, Hawai'i, California. 2012. (ENG., Illus.). 323p. pap. 30.00 ***(978-0-292-74396-0(3))*** Univ. of Texas Pr.

Valledor, Sid. The Original Writings of Philip Vera Cruz. 2006. 220p. per. 14.95 *(978-1-59858-226-0(7))* Dog Ear Publishing, LLC.

Wadood, Syed Naimul. Crop Choices & Employment Uncertainty. 2009. 136p. pap. *(978-3-639-14321-8(3))* VDM Verlag Dr. Mueller e.K.

World Bank, et al. Gender in Agriculture Sourcebook. 2010. (ENG.). pap. 33.75 *(978-0-8213-8170-0(9))* World Bank Pubns.

World Bank Staff, et al, contrib. by. Gender in Agriculture Sourcebook. 2008. (Agriculture & Rural Development Ser.). (ENG., Illus.). 792p. pap. 45.00 *(978-0-8213-7587-7(3)*, 9780821375877) World Bank Pubns.

AGRICULTURAL LABORERS—HOUSING

see Housing, Rural

AGRICULTURAL LABORERS—POLITICAL ACTIVITY

Zumbrunnen, John. Silence & Democracy: Athenian Politics in Thucydides' History. 2008. (ENG.). 208p. (C). 45.00 *(978-0-271-03357-0(6))* Pennsylvania State Univ. Pr.

AGRICULTURAL LABORERS—AFRICA

Atkinson, Doreen. Going for Broke: The Fate of Farm Workers in Arid South Africa. 2007. (ENG., Illus.). 312p. pap. 34.95 *(978-0-7969-2176-5(8))* Human Sciences Research Council ZAF. Dist: Independent Pubs. Group.

Catley, Andy, et al, eds. Pastoralism & Development in Africa: Dynamic Change at the Margins. 2012. (Pathways to Sustainability Ser.). (ENG., Illus.). 320p. (C). 145.00 ***(978-0-415-54071-1(2))***; pap. 44.95 ***(978-0-415-54072-8(0))*** Routledge.

Hebinck, Paul & Lent, Peter C., eds. Livelihoods & Landscapes: The People of Guquka & Koloni & Their Resources. 2007. (Afrika-Studiecentrum Ser.). (Illus.). 394p. pap. *(978-90-04-16169-6(4))* BRILL.

Viall, Jeanne, et al. Grape: Stories of the Vineyards in South Africa. 2012. (Illus.). 272p. pap. 37.95 ***(978-0-624-04938-8(8))*** International Publishers Marketing.

Zimmerman, Andrew. Alabama in Africa: Booker T. Washington, the German Empire, & the Globalization of the New South. 2010. (America in the World Ser.). (ENG., Illus.). 416p. (C). 35.00 *(978-0-691-12362-2(4))* Princeton Univ. Pr.

AGRICULTURAL LABORERS—GERMANY

Schroeder, Hans Joachim. Max Landowski, Landarbeiter Band 15: Ein Leben zwischen Westpreussen & Schleswig-Holstein: Lebensformen. (GER.). 302p. *(978-3-496-02691-4(X))* Reimer, Dietrich.

AGRICULTURAL LABORERS—GREAT BRITAIN

Green, F. E. The Tyranny of the Countryside. 2011. (Cambridge Library Collection - History Ser.). (Illus.). 290p. pap. 23.99 *(978-1-108-02529-4(3))* Cambridge Univ. Pr.

Haggard, H. Rider. Rural England: Being an Account of Agricultural & Social Researches Carried Out in the Years 1901 And 1902. 2011. (Cambridge Library Collection - History Ser.). (ENG.). 684p. pap. 48.00 *(978-1-108-02549-2(8))*; (Illus.). 700p. pap. 48.00 *(978-1-108-02548-5(X))* Cambridge Univ. Pr.

Handford, Kay. The Agricultural Labourer in 19th Century England. 2011. (Illus.). 60p. pap. ***(978-1-908105-30-1(5))*** Grosvenor Hse. Publishing Ltd.

Heath, Francis George. The English Peasantry. 2009. 122p. pap. 16.98 *(978-1-151-09931-0(7))*; pap. 18.50 *(978-1-150-71780-2(7))* General Bks. LLC.

—The English Peasantry. 2007. (ENG.). 284p. 43.95 *(978-0-548-02128-6(7))* Kessinger Publishing, LLC.

Heath, Richard. The English Peasant: Studies: Historical, Local, & Biographic. 2011. (Cambridge Library Collection - History Ser.). 396p. pap. 31.99 *(978-1-108-02528-7(5))* Cambridge Univ. Pr.

Hutchinson, Cecil G. & Chapman, Frank, eds. Village Life & Labour: An Anthology. 2010. (ENG.). 180p. pap. 12.99 *(978-0-521-16633-1(0))* Cambridge Univ. Pr.

Jefferies, Richard. Hodge & His Masters. 2009. 320p. 28.99 *(978-1-116-35519-2(1))* 2009. 320p. pap. 29.75 *(978-1-116-35521-5(3))* 2009. 372p. 38.99 *(978-1-115-43153-8(6))* 2009. 320p. 36.99 *(978-1-116-35518-5(3))* 2009. 372p. 33.99 *(978-1-115-43151-4(X))* 2009. 372p. pap. 32.75 *(978-1-115-43150-7(1))* 2009. 372p. pap. 31.75 *(978-1-115-43148-4(X))* 2009. 320p. pap. 30.75 *(978-1-116-35520-8(5))* 2008. 319p. 28.99 *(978-0-554-99066-8(0))* 2008. 319p. 29.99 *(978-0-554-99062-0(8))* 2008. 364p. 29.99 *(978-0-554-33341-0(4))* 2008. 364p. 31.99 *(978-0-554-24038-1(6))* 2008. 319p. pap. 29.75 *(978-0-554-99065-1(2))* 2008. 319p. pap. 30.75 *(978-0-554-99063-7(6))* 2006. 324p. pap. 23.99 *(978-1-4264-5604-6(2))* BiblioBazaar.

—Hodge & His Masters. 2009. 140p. pap. *(978-0-217-92995-0(8))* Books LLC.

—Hodge & His Masters. 2007. (ENG.). 308p. per. *(978-1-4065-2714-8(9))* Dodo Pr.

—Hodge & his Masters. 2011. (Cambridge Library Collection - History Ser.). (ENG.). 374p. pap. 29.99 ***(978-1-108-03582-8(5))***; 324p. pap. 24.99 ***(978-1-108-03583-5(3))*** Cambridge Univ. Pr.

—Hodge & His Masters. l.t. ed. 2007. (ENG.). 360p. pap. 26.99 *(978-1-4264-5652-7(2))* BiblioBazaar.

—The Toilers of the Field. 2010. (Cambridge Library Collection - History Ser.). (Illus.). 342p. pap. 28.99 *(978-1-108-02532-4(3))* Cambridge Univ. Pr.

Jeffries, Richard. Hodge & His Masters. (Illus.). xxiv, 309p. pap. 4.95 *(978-0-7043-3259-1(0))* Quartet Bks., Ltd. GBR. Dist: Charles River Bks.

—Hodge & His Masters. 2008. 320p. *(978-1-4437-3616-9(3)*, Hesperides Pr.) Read Bks.

Kussmaul, Ann. Servants in Husbandry in Early Modern England. 2008. (Interdisciplinary Perspectives on Modern History Ser.). (ENG.). 248p. pap. 34.99 *(978-0-521-07159-8(3))* Cambridge Univ. Pr.

Moses, Gary. Rural Moral Reform in Nineteenth-Century England: The Crusade Against Adolescent Farm Servants & Hiring Fairs. 2007. (Illus.). 256p. 109.95 *(978-0-7734-5277-0(X))* Mellen, Edwin Pr., The.

Muldrew, Craig. Food, Energy & the Creation of Industriousness: Work & Material Culture in Agrarian England, 1550-1780. 2011. (Cambridge Studies in Economic History - Second Ser.). (ENG., Illus.). 376p. 99.00 *(978-0-521-88185-2(4))* Cambridge Univ. Pr.

Richardson, R. C. Household Servants in Early Modern England. 2010. (ENG., Illus.). 272p. 95.00 *(978-0-7190-6894-2(0))* Manchester Univ. Pr. GBR. Dist: Macmillan.

AGRICULTURAL LABORERS—INDIA

Mehta, Niti. Economic Wellbeing of Hired Workers in a Growing Regional Economy. 2010. 124p. pap. *(978-3-639-26846-1(6))* VDM Verlag Dr. Mueller e.K.

Raman, Ravi. Global Capital & Peripheral Labour: The History & Political Economy of Plantation Workers in India. 2012. (ENG., Illus.). (C). pap. 42.95 ***(978-0-415-62739-9(7))*** Routledge.

Raman, Ravi & Ravi Raman, K. Global Capital & Peripheral Labour: The History & Political Economy of Plantation Workers in India. 2010. (Routledge Contemporary South Asia Ser.). (ENG., Illus.). 288p. (C). 143.00 *(978-0-415-55103-8(X))* Routledge.

AGRICULTURAL LABORERS—SOVIET UNION

Vinogradov/Pleysier, et al. The Women of Izmaelovka: A Soviet Union Collective Farm in Siberia. 2007. (ENG., Illus.). 120p. pap. 26.50 *(978-0-7618-3661-2(6))* Univ. Pr. of America, Inc.

AGRICULTURAL LABORERS, MIGRANT

see Migrant Agricultural Laborers

AGRICULTURAL LAWS AND LEGISLATION

Here are entered general works on agricultural law and legislation. Works on farm law for the use of farmers are entered under Farm Law.

see also Animal Industry—Law and Legislation; Consolidation of Land Holdings; Contracts, Agricultural; Farm Law; Land Reform—Law and Legislation; Plant Quarantine

Amat Llombart, Pablo & Llombart, Pablo Amat. Derecho Agrario y Alimentario Español y de la Unión Europea. 2007. (SPA.). 702p. *(978-84-8456-899-5(7))* Tirant lo Blanch.

Brouwer, Floor, et al, eds. The Economics of Regulation in Agriculture: Compliance with Public & Private Standards. 2012. 272p. 145.00 *(978-1-84593-557-3(8))* CABI GBR. Dist: Stylus Publishing, LLC.

Brubaker, Elizabeth. Greener Pastures: Decentralizing the Regulation of Agricultural Pollution. 2007. (University of Toronto Centre for Public Management Monograph Ser.). (ENG.). 152p. *(978-0-7727-8621-0(6))*; pap. *(978-0-7727-8620-3(8))* Univ. of Toronto Pr.

Butler, Julie, ed. Tax Planning for Farm & Land Diversification. 3rd rev. ed. 2011. 576p. pap. *(978-1-84592-485-0(1)*, Bloomsbury Professional) Bloomsbury Publishing Plc.

Conner, Mary T. Farm Bill of 2008: Major Provisions & Legislative Action. 2010. (Agriculture Issues & Policies Ser.). 301p. 79.00 *(978-1-60741-750-7(2))* Nova Science Pubs., Inc.

Coupe, Stuart & Lewins, Roger. Negotiating the Seed Treaty. 2007. (ENG., Illus.). 64p. pap. 29.95 *(978-1-85339-628-1(1))* Practical Action Publishing GBR. Dist: Stylus Publishing, LLC.

Danielsen. Eu Agriculture Law. 2011. *(978-90-411-3280-2(5))* Kluwer Law International.

Davis, Nigel, et al. Agricultural Precedents Handbook. 2nd rev. ed. 2009. (ENG., Illus.). 564p. incl. cd-rom *(978-1-84661-061-5(3))* Jordan Publishing, Ltd.

Desta. Law of International Trade Agricultural Products Gatt 1947 2nd Ed. 2nd rev. ed. 2011. *(978-90-411-3127-0(2))* Wolters Kluwer Law & Business.

Ehlers, Ralf-Udo, ed. Regulation of Biological Control Agents in Europe. 2011. (ENG., Illus.). xii, 417p. 209.00 *(978-90-481-3663-6(6)*, 9048136636) Springer.

Hearing to Review Implementation of the Horticulture & Organic Agriculture Title of the Food, Conservation, & Energy ACT of 2008: Hearing Before the Subcommittee on Horticulture & Organic Agriculture of the Committee on Agriculture, House of Representatives, One Hundred Eleventh Congress, First Session, October 28, 2009. 2009. (Illus.). iii, 29p. *(978-0-16-084877-3(6)*, 552-070-40273-0) United States Government Printing Office.

Hearing to Review Pending Climate Legislation: Hearing Before the Committee on Agriculture, House of Representatives, One Hundred Eleventh Congress, First Session, June 11, 2009. 2009. (Illus.). iv, 263p. *(978-0-16-084941-1(1)*, 552-070-40332-9) United States Government Printing Office.

Hearing to Review the 2007 Farm Bill Proposals of the U.S. Department of Agriculture: Hearing Before the Committee on Agriculture, House of Representatives, One Hundred Tenth Congress, First Session, February 14, 2007. 2009. iii, 112p. *(978-0-16-084211-5(5)*, 552-070-39788-4) United States Government Printing Office.

Hearing to Review the Proposals of the United States Department of Agriculture for the 2007 Farm Bill with Respect to Specialty Crops & Organic Agriculture: Hearing Before the Subcommittee on Horticulture & Organic Agriculture of the Committee on Agriculture, House of Representatives, One Hundred Tenth Congress, First Session, February 28, 2007. 2009. iii, 38p. *(978-0-16-084879-7(2)*, 552-070-40275-6) United States Government Printing Office.

Hesperides. Agricultural Legislation in India - Agricultural Production & Development. 2007. 484p. per. *(978-1-4067-5056-0(5)*, Hesperides Pr.) Read Bks.

Jian cha bu zhu shui li bu jian cha ju Staff, contrib. by. Shui Li Gong Cheng Jian She Xiang Mu Zhi Fa Jian Cha Shi Yong Shou Ce. 2009. (CHI.). 300p. *(978-7-5084-6982-9(8))* Zhongguo Shuili Shuidian Chubanshe.

Kim, Sun-Jong. Se Reposer Pour la Terre, Se Reposer Pour Dieu: L'Année Sabbatique en Lv 25,1-7. 2012. (Beihefte zur Zeitschrift für die alttestamentliche Wissenschaft Ser.). (FRE.). 360p. (gr. 17). 140.00 ***(978-3-11-027557-5(0))*** De Gruyter, Walter Inc.

Lehrer, Nadine. U.S. Farm Bills & Policy Reforms: Ideological Conflicts over World Trade, Renewable Energy, & Sustainable Agriculture. 2010. *(978-1-60497-701-1(9))* Cambria Pr.

Lightbourne, Muriel. Food Security Biological Diversity & Intellectual Property Rights. 2009. (Intellectual Property, Theory, Culture Ser.). 328p. 124.95 *(978-0-7546-7611-9(0))* Ashgate Publishing Co.

Looseleaf Law Publications, suppl. Agriculture & Markets Law. 2010. 506p. ring bd. 38.95 *(978-1-889031-53-8(4))* Looseleaf Law Pubns., Inc.

Mcmahon. Research Handbook on the Wto Agriculture Agreement. 2012. (Research Handbooks on the WTO Ser.). 336p. 195.00 ***(978-1-84844-116-3(9))*** Elgar, Edward Publishing, Inc.

McMahon, Joseph. EU Agricultural Law. 2008. (ENG.). 520p. 363.00 *(978-1-904501-65-7(6))* Oxford Univ. Pr., Inc.

McMahon, Joseph A. The WTO Agreement on Agriculture: A Commentary. 2007. 358p. 192.50 *(978-0-19-927568-7(8))* Oxford Univ. Pr., Inc.

Moegele, Rudolf & Erlbacher, Friedrich, eds. Single Common Market Organisation: Article-by-Article Commentary of the Legal Framework for Agricultural Markets in the European Union. 2011. 1086p. 520.00 *(978-1-84113-994-4(7))* Hart Publishing Ltd. GBR. Dist: International Specialized Bk. Services.

National Archives and Records Administration, creator. Animals & Animal Products: Parts 1 To 199. 2011. (Code of Federal Regulations Ser.). 1067p. pap. 67.00 ***(978-1-60946-320-5(X))*** National Archives & Records Administration.

Office of the Federal Register (U.S.), compiled by. Code of Federal Regulations, Title 7, Agriculture, Pt. 1200-1599, Revised as of January 1 2011. rev. ed. 2011. (ENG.). 1042p. pap. 67.00 *(978-0-16-087535-9(8)*, Office of the Federal Register) United States Government Printing Office.

—Code of Federal Regulations, Title 7, Agriculture, Pt. 1200-1599, Revised as of January 1 2012. rev. ed. 2012. (ENG.). 1093p. pap. 67.00 ***(978-0-16-090069-3(7)***, Office of the Federal Register) United States Government Printing Office.

—Code of Federal Regulations, Title 7, Agriculture, Pt. 1600-1759, Revised as of January 1 2011. rev. ed. 2011. (ENG., Illus.). 827p. pap. 70.00 *(978-0-16-087536-6(6)*, Office of the Federal Register) United States Government Printing Office.

—Code of Federal Regulations, Title 7, Agriculture, Pt. 1600-1759, Revised as of January 1 2012. rev. ed. 2012. (ENG., Illus.). 838p. pap. 70.00 ***(978-0-16-090070-9(0)***, Office of the Federal Register) United States Government Printing Office.

—Code of Federal Regulations, Title 7, Agriculture, Pt. 1760-1939, Revised as of January 1 2011. rev. ed. 2011. (ENG.). 673p. pap. 36.00 *(978-0-16-087537-3(4)*, Office of the Federal Register) United States Government Printing Office.

—Code of Federal Regulations, Title 7, Agriculture, Pt. 1760-1939, Revised as of January 1 2012. rev. ed. 2012. (ENG.). 661p. pap. 36.00 ***(978-0-16-090071-6(9)***, Office of the Federal Register) United States Government Printing Office.

—Code of Federal Regulations, Title 7, Agriculture, Pt. 1940-1949, Revised as of January 1 2012. rev. ed. 2012. (ENG.). 395p. pap. 56.00 ***(978-0-16-090072-3(7)***, Office of the Federal Register) United States Government Printing Office.

—Code of Federal Regulations, Title 7, Agriculture, Pt. 1950-1999, Revised as of January 1 2011. rev. ed. 2011. (ENG.). 412p. pap. 70.00 *(978-0-16-087539-7(0)*, Office of the Federal Register) United States Government Printing Office.

—Code of Federal Regulations, Title 7, Agriculture, Pt. 1950-1999, Revised as of January 1 2012. rev. ed. 2012. (ENG.). 412p. pap. 52.00 ***(978-0-16-090073-0(5)***, Office of the Federal Register) United States Government Printing Office.

—Code of Federal Regulations, Title 7, Agriculture, Pt. 2000-End, Revised as of January 1 2011. rev. ed. 2011. (ENG.). 1016p. pap. 56.00 *(978-0-16-087540-3(4)*, Office of the Federal Register) United States Government Printing Office.

—Code of Federal Regulations, Title 7, Agriculture, Pt. 2000-End, Revised as of January 1 2012. rev. ed. 2012. (ENG.). 1147p. pap. 56.00 ***(978-0-16-090074-7(3)***, Office of the Federal Register) United States Government Printing Office.

—Code of Federal Regulations, Title 7, Agriculture, Pt. 210-299, Revised as of January 1 2011. rev. ed. 2011. (ENG.). 1107p. pap. 68.00 *(978-0-16-087529-8(3)*, Office of the Federal Register) United States Government Printing Office.

—Code of Federal Regulations, Title 7, Agriculture, Pt. 210-299, Revised as of January 1 2012. rev. ed. 2012. (ENG.). 1113p. pap. 68.00 ***(978-0-16-090062-4(X)***, Office of the Federal Register) United States Government Printing Office.

—Code of Federal Regulations, Title 7, Agriculture, Pt. 300-399, Revised as of January 1 2011. rev. ed. 2011. (ENG.). 580p. pap. 52.00 *(978-0-16-087530-4(7)*, Office of the Federal Register) United States Government Printing Office.

—Code of Federal Regulations, Title 7, Agriculture, Pt. 300-399, Revised as of January 1 2012. rev. ed. 2012. (ENG.). 589p. pap. 52.00 ***(978-0-16-090064-8(6)***, Office of the Federal Register) United States Government Printing Office.

—Code of Federal Regulations, Title 7, Agriculture, Pt. 400-699, Revised as of January 1 2011. rev. ed. 2011. (ENG.). 655p. pap. 47.00 *(978-0-16-087531-1(5)*, Office of the Federal Register) United States Government Printing Office.

—Code of Federal Regulations, Title 7, Agriculture, Pt. 400-699, Revised as of January 1 2012. rev. ed. 2012. (ENG.). 655p. pap. 47.00 ***(978-0-16-090065-5(4)***, Office of the Federal Register) United States Government Printing Office.

—Code of Federal Regulations, Title 7, Agriculture, Pt. 53-209, Revised as of January 1 2011. rev. ed. 2011. (ENG.). 487p. pap. 42.00 *(978-0-16-087528-1(5)*, Office of the Federal Register) United States Government Printing Office.

—Code of Federal Regulations, Title 7, Agriculture, Pt. 53-209, Revised as of January 1 2012. rev. ed. 2012. (ENG.). 483p. pap. 42.00 ***(978-0-16-090061-7(1)***, Office of the Federal Register) United States Government Printing Office.

—Code of Federal Regulations, Title 7, Agriculture, Pt. 700-899, Revised as of January 1 2011. rev. ed. 2011. (ENG.). 581p. pap. 49.00 *(978-0-16-087532-8(3)*, Office of the Federal Register) United States Government Printing Office.

—Code of Federal Regulations, Title 7, Agriculture, Pt. 900-999, Revised as of January 1 2011. rev. ed. 2011. (ENG.). 800p. pap. 66.00 *(978-0-16-087533-5(1)*, Office of the Federal Register) United States Government Printing Office.

Office of the Federal Register (U.S.), compiled by. Code of Federal Regulations, Title 7, Agriculture, Pt. 900-999, Revised as of January 1 2012. rev. ed. 2012. (ENG.). 800p. pap. 66.00 ***(978-0-16-090067-9(0)***, Office of the Federal Register) United States Government Printing Office.

Office of the Federal Register (U.S.), ed. Code of Federal Regulations, Title 7, Agriculture, Pt. 1-26, Revised as of January 1 2011. 2011. (ENG.). 590p. pap. 50.00 *(978-0-16-087526-7(9)*, Office of the Federal Register) United States Government Printing Office.

—Code of Federal Regulations, Title 7, Agriculture, Pt. 1000-1199, Revised as of January 1 2011. 2011. (ENG.). 269p. pap. 26.00 *(978-0-16-087534-2(X)*, Office of the Federal Register) United States Government Printing Office.

—Code of Federal Regulations, Title 7, Agriculture, Pt. 27-52, Revised as of January 1 2011. rev. ed. 2011. (ENG., Illus.). 635p. pap. 55.00 *(978-0-16-087527-4(7)*, Office of the Federal Register) United States Government Printing Office.

Office of the Federal Register (U.S.), ed. Code of Federal Regulations, Title 7, Agriculture, Pt. 27-52, Revised as of January 1 2012. rev. ed. 2012. (ENG., Illus.). 637p. pap. 55.00 ***(978-0-16-090060-0(3)***, Office of the Federal Register) United States Government Printing Office.

Orden, David, et al, eds. WTO Disciplines on Agricultural Support: Seeking a Fair Basis for Trade. 2011. (ENG., Illus.). 520p. 125.00 *(978-1-107-00544-0(2))* Cambridge Univ. Pr.

Owens, Jasper T. The Farm Bill & Its Far-Ranging Impact. 2008. (Illus.). xvi, 265p. 82.00 *(978-1-60456-631-4(0))* Nova Science Pubs., Inc.

Penrose, William. Agricultural Law in Ireland. 2006. pap. 142.50 *(978-1-904480-49-5(7))* First Law IRL. Dist: Gaunt, Inc.

Petrov, M. I. Kommentarii K Federalnomu Zakonu Ot 24 Iiulia 2002 G. No. 101-FZ "Ob Oborote Zemel Selskokhoziaistvennogo Naznacheniia" V Red. Federalnykh Zakonov Ot 7 Iiulia 2003 G. No. 113 FZ, Ot 29 Iiunia 2004 G. No. 58 FZ ...: Postateinyi: S Uchetom Noveishikh Podzakonnykh Aktov I Sudebnoi Praktiki. 2010. (RUS.). 237p. *(978-5-7205-1063-3(X))* Juridiceskij Dom Justicinform.

Rodgers, Christopher P. & Rodgers, C. P. Agricultural Law. 3rd rev. ed. 2008. (Illus.). 934p. pap. 195.00 *(978-1-84592-092-0(9)*, Bloomsbury Professional) Bloomsbury Publishing Plc GBR. Dist: International Specialized Bk. Services.

Romano Orlando, Pietro. Derecho Agrario Comunitario e Internacional. 2007. (SPA.). 341p. pap. 31.00 *(978-958-710-307-6(6))* Universidad Externado de Colombia COL. Dist: Siglo del Hombre.

Schneider, Susan A. Food, Farming, & Sustainability: Readings in Agricultural Law. 2010. 754p. pap. 70.00 *(978-1-59460-588-8(2))* Carolina Academic Pr.

Severini, Simone, et al. The Common Agricultural Policy after the Fischler Reform: National Implementations Impact Assessment & the Agenda for Future Reforms. 2011. (Illus.). 544p. 144.95 *(978-1-4094-2194-8(5))* Ashgate Publishing Co.

Spellman, Frank R. & Whiting, Nancy E. Environmental Management of Concentrated Animal Feeding Operations (CAFOS) 2007. (ENG., Illus.). 496p. 157.95 *(978-0-8493-7098-4(1),* CRC Press) Taylor & Francis Group GBR. Dist: Taylor & Francis Group.

State Trading Enterprises: Compliance with the General Agreement on Tariffs & Trade. 32p. pap. 30.00 *(978-0-7881-4177-5(5))* DIANE Publishing Co.

Stephenson, Andrew. Public Lands & Agrarian Laws of the Ro. 2006. pap. *(978-1-4068-3034-7(8))* Echo Library.

Tannenbaum, Frank. The Mexican Agrarian Revolution. 2008. 564p. pap. 56.00 *(978-1-59740-623-9(6))* ACLS Humanities E-Book.

United States, Congress Senate Committee on Agriculture, Nutrition, and Forestry Staff, contrib. by. Discussion of the U.S. Department of Agriculture Farm Bill Proposal: Hearing Before the Committee on Agriculture, Nutrition, & Forestry, United States Senate, One Hundred Tenth Congress, First Session, February 7, 2007. 2007. (Illus.). iv, 392p. *(978-0-16-078854-3(4),* 552-070-35989-3) United States Government Printing Office.

U.S. Department of Agriculture Fiscal Year 2008 Budget Priorities: Hearing Before the Committee on the Budget, House of Representatives, One Hundred Tenth Congress, First Session, Hearing Held in Washington, DC, February 15, 2007. 2007. (Illus.). iii, 80p. *(978-0-16-079741-5(1),* 552-070-36454-4) United States Government Printing Office.

Wilson, Richard & Southern, David. Law of the Common Agricultural Policy: The Single Payment, Cross-Compliance & Enforcement. 2009. 170.00 *(978-1-84661-019-6(2))* Jordan Publishing, Ltd. GBR. Dist: International Specialized Bk. Services.

Womach, Jasper, et al. The USDA 2007 Farm Bill Proposal. 2008. 102p. pap. 39.00 *(978-1-60456-813-4(5))* Nova Science Pubs., Inc.

AGRICULTURAL LAWS AND LEGISLATION—POPULAR WORKS

see Farm Law

AGRICULTURAL LENDING

see Agricultural Credit

AGRICULTURAL MACHINERY

see also Agricultural Implements; Farm Equipment; Farm Mechanization; Harvesting Machinery; Separators (Machines); Threshing Machines; Tillage; Traction-Engines

Alex, Adisa. Development & Operational Principle of Grain Stripping Harvester. 2010. 200p. pap. *(978-3-639-24580-6(6))* VDM Verlag Dr. Mueller e.K.

Artz, Georgeanne M., et al. Farm Machinery & Labor Sharing Manual: Tools to Help You Evaluate Sharing Machinery & Labor As an Option in Your Farming Operation. 2009. *(978-0-89373-106-9(4))* MidWest Plan Service.

Beck, William. Gehl Company, West Bend, Wisconsin: 150th Anniversary History. 2008. *(978-1-57864-524-4(7))* Donning Co. Pubs.

Bell, Brian. Fifty Years of Garden Machinery. (Illus.). 240p. 44.95 *(978-0-85236-301-0(X))* Farming Pr., Ltd. GBR. Dist: Diamond Farm Bk. Pubs.

Bezzant, John. Tools & Machinery for the Smallholder: An Essential Guide to Their Use & Maintenance, 1 vol. 2011. (ENG., Illus.). 192p. 34.95 ***(978-1-84797-236-1(5))*** Crowood Pr., Ltd. GBR. Dist: Independent Pubs. Group.

Brigden, Roy. Harvesting Machinery. 2008. (Shire Library). (ENG., Illus.). 32p. pap. 11.95 *(978-0-85263-979-5(1))* Shire Pubns., Ltd. GBR. Dist: Random Hse., Inc.

British Standards Institute Staff. Agricultural machinery. Guards for moving parts of power transmission. Guard opening without Tool. 12p. pap. 142.00 *(978-0-580-53014-2(0))* Artech Hse., Inc.

Brown, Jonathan. Steam on the Farm: A History of Agricultural Steam Engines 1800 To 1950. 2008. (ENG., Illus.). 192p. 50.00 *(978-1-84797-052-7(4))* Crowood Pr., Ltd. GBR. Dist: Independent Pubs. Group.

Carolina Biological Staff, compiled by. Determining Agricultural Resources. 2009. (Inquiries in Science Environmental Ser.). *(978-1-4350-0430-6(2))* Carolina Biological Supply Co.

Carroll, John. The World Encyclopedia of Tractors: An Illustrated History & Comprehensive Directory of Tractors Around the World with Full Coverage of All the Great Marques, Designers, & Manufacturers. 2007. (Illus.). 256p. pap. 19.99 *(978-1-84476-418-1(4),* Southwater) Anness Publishing GBR. Dist: National Bk. Network.

Deere, John. The Operation, Care, & Repair of Farm Machinery: Practical Hints for Handymen. 2nd ed. 2008. 248p. pap. 14.95 *(978-1-59921-461-0(X),* Lyons Pr.) Globe Pequot Pr., The.

Dewey, Peter. 'Iron Harvests of the Field' The Making of Farm Machinery in Britain Since 1800. 2012. (Illus.). 368p. 45.95 ***(978-1-85936-180-1(3))*** International Publishers Marketing.

Durr, Kenneth & Sullivan, Lee. International Harvester, Mccormick, Navistar: Milestones in the Company That Helped Build America. 2007. (Illus.). 247p. 60.00 *(978-0-88240-662-6(0))* Graphic Arts Ctr. Publishing Co.

Elsbree, Chuck. Antique Farm Equipment: The Elsbree Collection. 2011. (ENG., Illus.). 72p. 27.95 ***(978-1-877810-41-1(X))*** Rayve Productions, Inc.

Frost & Sullivan Staff, contrib. by. European Agrochemical Markets. Date not set. (Illus.). 364p. *(978-0-7889-0357-1(8))* Frost & Sullivan Market Intelligence.

Hunt, Donnell. Farm Power & Machinery Management. 10th ed. 2008. (Illus.). 368p. (C). pap. 53.95 *(978-1-57766-573-1(2))* Waveland Pr., Inc.

Johnston, Ian M. Tractors, Kalashnikovs & Green Tea: My Life of Tractors & Travels. 2011. (Illus.). 320p. 39.95 ***(978-1-921719-04-2(4))*** Rosenberg Publishing Pty, Ltd. AUS. Dist: International Specialized Bk. Services.

Lal, Mohan. Impact of Rotavator As a Conservation Tillage Implement. 2011. 52p. pap. ***(978-3-8443-0466-4(5))*** Lambert Academic Publishing.

Maggard, James H. Rough & Tumble Engineering. 2008. 140p. 24.99 *(978-0-554-28307-4(7))* 2008. 140p. 21.99 *(978-0-554-37610-3(5))* 2007. (ENG.). 130p. pap. 18.99 *(978-1-4346-5107-5(X))* 2007. (ENG.). 136p. pap. 19.99 *(978-1-4346-5108-2(8))* BiblioBazaar.

—Rough & Tumble Engineering. 2009. 100p. pap. 13.95 *(978-1-4385-1169-6(8),* Book Jungle) Standard Pubns., Inc.

Moore, Sam. Implements for Farming with Horses & Mules: A Modern All-In-One Manual. 2006. *(978-1-893707-10-8(5))* Rural Heritage.

Quick, Graeme R. International Harvester: Tractors & Equipment in Australia & New Zealand. 2009. (Illus.). 184p. 49.95 *(978-1-877058-75-2(0))* Rosenberg Publishing Pty, Ltd. AUS. Dist: International Specialized Bk. Services.

—Remarkable Australian Farm Machines. 2007. (Illus.). 160p. pap. 29.95 *(978-1-877058-58-5(0))* Rosenberg Publishing Pty, Ltd. AUS. Dist: International Specialized Bk. Services.

Rottensteiner, Christian. Evaluation of the Feller-Buncher Moipu 400 E. 2010. 64p. pap. *(978-3-639-23453-4(7))* VDM Verlag Dr. Mueller e.K.

Sharma, Ajay Kumar. Drawbar Performance Prediction of Agricultural Tractors. 2011. 240p. pap. ***(978-3-8433-5745-6(5))*** Lambert Academic Publishing.

Successful Farming Magazine Staff. Rust Book 2009. 2nd rev. ed. 2008. (Rust Book Bi-Annual Antique & Classic Price Guides). 416p. pap. 19.95 *(978-0-696-24233-5(8))* Meredith Bks.

—Sprayer & General Ag Reference Guide. 2008. (Successful Farming Reference Guides). 176p. pap. 9.95 *(978-0-696-24235-9(4))* Meredith Bks.

—Top Shops: The Best Shops in the Country. 2nd rev. ed. 2009. (Successful Farming Reference Guides). 128p. pap. 17.95 *(978-0-696-24303-5(2))* Meredith Bks.

Van Alen, James H. Steam Cultivation in England a Paper Read Before the Farmers' Club of the American Institute. 2011. 18p. pap. 11.99 ***(978-1-4181-9057-6(8))*** MPublishing.

AGRICULTURAL MACHINERY—JUVENILE LITERATURE

Ruck, Colleen. Tractors. 2011. (My Favorite Machines Ser.). 24p. (J). (gr. 1-4). 24.95 *(978-1-59920-679-0(X))* Black Rabbit Bks.

AGRICULTURAL MARKETING

see Farm Produce—Marketing; Produce Trade

AGRICULTURAL MECHANICS

Deere, John. The Operation, Care, & Repair of Farm Machinery: Practical Hints for Handymen. 2nd ed. 2008. 248p. pap. 14.95 *(978-1-59921-461-0(X),* Lyons Pr.) Globe Pequot Pr., The.

Herren, Ray V. Agricultural Mechanics: Fundamentals & Applications. 6th ed. 2009. (ENG.). 912p. (C). 128.95 *(978-1-4354-0097-9(6))* Delmar Cengage Learning.

—Lab Manual CD-ROM for Herren's Agricultural Mechanics: Fundamentals & Applications, 6th. 6th ed. 2009. (ENG.). (C). 457.95 *(978-1-4354-0101-3(8))* Delmar Cengage Learning.

—Lab Manual for Herren's Agricultural Mechanics: Fundamentals & Applications, 6th. 6th ed. 2009. (ENG.). 400p. (C). pap. 84.95 *(978-1-4354-0099-3(2))* Delmar Cengage Learning.

AGRICULTURAL MECHANIZATION

see Farm Mechanization

AGRICULTURAL METEOROLOGY

see Meteorology, Agricultural

AGRICULTURAL PESTS

see also Garden Pests; Insect Pests; Plant Diseases; Plant Quarantine; Spraying and Dusting in Agriculture; Weeds

also subdivision Diseases and Pests under names of crops, etc., Fruit—Diseases and Pests

Asma, Lodhi & Azam, Farooq E. Fate of Cyfluthrin in Soil-Plant System: Degradation, Translocation & Metabolism of 14 C- Cyfluthrin. 2011. 132p. pap. ***(978-3-639-32244-6(4))*** VDM Verlag Dr. Mueller e.K.

Burton, Earl N. & Williams, Peter V., eds. Crop Protection Research Advances. 2008. 185.00 *(978-1-60456-040-4(1))* Nova Science Pubs., Inc.

Caldwell, Brian. Growing Healthy Vegetable Crops: Working with Nature to Control Diseases & Pests Organically. 2011. (ENG.). 104p. pap. 12.95 *(978-1-60358-349-7(1))* Chelsea Green Publishing.

Copping, L. G., ed. The Manual of Biocontrol Agents: A World Compendium. 2011. 896p. 315.00 *(978-1-901396-17-1(7))* CABI GBR. Dist: Stylus Publishing, LLC.

Dept. Agriculture and Agri-Food Canada Staff. Atlas of Aphids Trapped in Agricultural Crops. (Illus.). 66p. pap. *(978-0-660-15551-7(6))* Canadian Government Publishing.

Dubey, N. K., ed. Natural Products in Plant Pest Management. 2011. (Illus.). 293p. 160.00 *(978-1-84593-671-6(X))* CABI GBR. Dist: Stylus Publishing, LLC.

Freshwater Community Responses to Mixtures of Agricultural Pesticides: Synergistic Effects of Atrazine & Bifenthrin. 29p. pap. 30.00 *(978-0-7881-1580-6(4))* DIANE Publishing Co.

Gillman, Jeff. The Truth about Organic Gardening: Benefits, Drawbacks, & the Bottom Line. 2008. (ENG.). 208p. pap. 12.95 *(978-0-88192-862-4(3),* 0881928623) Timber Pr., Inc.

Gurr, Geoff M., et al, eds. Biodiversity & Insect Pests: Key Issues for Sustainable Management. 2012. (ENG.). 360p. 129.95 ***(978-0-470-65686-0(7),*** Wiley-Blackwell) Wiley, John & Sons, Inc.

Hall, Franklin R. & Menn, Julius J., eds. Biopesticides: Use & Delivery. 2010. (Methods in Biotechnology Ser.). 640p. pap. 209.00 *(978-1-61737-058-8(4),* 1617370584) Humana Pr.

Hearing to Examine the Joint Performance of APHIS, U.S. Department of Agriculture, & CBP, U.S. Department of Homeland Security in Protecting U.S. Agriculture from Foreign Pests & Diseases: Hearing Before the Subcommittee on Horticulture & Organic Agriculture of the Committee on Agriculture, House of Representatives, One Hundred Tenth Congress, First Session, Wednesday, October 3, 2007. 2009. iii, 137p. *(978-0-16-083288-8(8),* 552-070-39116-9) United States Government Printing Office.

Hedimbi, Marius & Sarker, Rakha Hari. Pathogenicity of Entomopathogenic Fungi to Ticks. 2011. 80p. pap. ***(978-3-8383-7705-6(2))*** Lambert Academic Publishing.

Helyer, Neil, et al. Biological Control in Plant Protection. 2nd ed. 2012. (ENG., Illus.). 160p. pap. 49.95 *(978-1-84076-117-7(2))* Manson Publishing, Ltd. GBR. Dist: Thieme Medical Pubs., Inc.

Hill, Dennis S. Agricultural Entomology. 2009. (ENG.) 636p. pap. 69.95 *(978-1-60469-101-6(8),* 1604691018) Timber Pr., Inc.

—Pests of Crops in Warmer Climates & Their Control. (ENG.). xii, 708p. 2010. pap. 419.00 *(978-90-481-7707-3(3),* 9048177073) 2008. (Illus.). 419.00 *(978-1-4020-6737-2(2),* 1402067372) Springer.

Horne, Paul & Page, Jessica. Integrated Pest Management for Crops & Pastures. 2008. (Landlinks Press Ser.). 200p. pap. 49.95 *(978-0-643-09257-0(9))* CSIRO Publishing AUS. Dist: Stylus Publishing, LLC.

Imran, Ahmed, et al. Biopesticides & Cotton Insect Pest: Sustainable Management of Insect Pest Complex of Cotton. 2011. 112p. pap. ***(978-3-639-32707-6(1))*** VDM Verlag Dr. Mueller e.K.

Kaur Brar, Satinder, ed. Biocontrol: Management, Processes & Challenges. 2012. ***(978-1-61942-803-4(2))*** Nova Science Pubs., Inc.

Mekbib, Sissay Bekele. Citrus Sinensis Cultivation in Ethiopia & Postharvest Biocontrol. 2009. 200p. pap. *(978-3-639-17243-0(4))* VDM Verlag Dr. Mueller e.K.

Nganga, Joseph, et al. Biological Control of Flower Thrips. 2011. 68p. pap. ***(978-3-8443-9246-3(7))*** Lambert Academic Publishing.

Nukmal, Nismah. Bio-Ecology of Psyllyds on Eucalyptus. 2011. 176p. pap. ***(978-3-8443-3431-9(9))*** Lambert Academic Publishing.

Patil, Satilal. Development of Entomopathogenic Fungi Based Biopesticide Technology. 2011. 188p. pap. ***(978-3-8433-9282-2(X))*** Lambert Academic Publishing.

Radcliffe, Edward B., et al, eds. Integrated Pest Management: Concepts, Tactics, Strategies & Case Studies. 2008. (ENG., Illus.). 550p. 150.99 *(978-0-521-87595-0(1));* pap. 65.99 *(978-0-521-69931-0(2))* Cambridge Univ. Pr.

Rafiee Dastjerdi, Hooshang, et al. Effect of Insecticides on Helicoverpa Armigera & Habrobracon Hebetor. 2010. 56p. pap. *(978-3-639-27365-6(5))* VDM Verlag Dr. Mueller e.K.

Reddy, Vudem Dashavantha, et al, eds. Pests & Pathogens: Management Strategies. 2011. (ENG.). 590p. 169.95 *(978-0-415-66576-6(0),* CRC Press) Taylor & Francis Group GBR. Dist: Taylor & Francis Group.

Ueckermann, Edward A., ed. Eriophyoid Mites: Progress & Prognoses: Progress & Prognoses. 2010. (Illus.). vi, 310p. 209.00 *(978-90-481-9561-9(6),* 9048195616) Springer.

AGRICULTURAL PHYSICS

see also Crops and Climate; Soil Physics

Glinski, Jan, et al, eds. Encyclopedia of Agrophysics. 2011. (Encyclopedia of Earth Sciences Ser.). (ENG., Illus.). xlvi, 1028p. 549.00 *(978-90-481-3584-4(2),* 9048135842) Springer.

AGRICULTURAL POLICY

see Agriculture and State

AGRICULTURAL PRICE SUPPORTS

Anderson, Kym & Tyers, Rodney. Disarray in World Food Markets: A Quantitative Assessment. 2011. (Trade & Development Ser.). (ENG.). 470p. pap. 45.00 *(978-0-521-17231-8(4))* Cambridge Univ. Pr.

Expanding Our Food & Fiber Supply Through a Strong U.S. Farm Policy: Hearing Before the Committee on Agriculture, Nutrition, & Forestry, United States Senate, One Hundred Eleventh Congress, Second Session, June 30, 2010. 2011. (Illus.). iv, 191p. ***(978-0-16-089264-6(3),*** 552-070-43260-4) United States Government Printing Office.

Hearing to Review Dairy Policy: Hearing Before the Committee on Agriculture, House of Representatives, One Hundred Eleventh Congress, Second Session, April 20, 2010, Harrisburg, PA. 2010. (Illus.). iii, 84p. *(978-0-16-086246-5(9),* 552-070-41337-5) United States Government Printing Office.

Jordan, Cecilia M., ed. Sugar: Background, Policies & Issues. 2010. (Agriculture Issues & Policies Ser.). (Illus.). x, 200p. 115.00 *(978-1-61761-116-2(6),* Nova Science Pubs., Inc.

Rashid, Shahidur, et al, eds. From Parastatals to Private Trade: Lessons from Asian Agriculture. 2008. (ENG., Illus.). 280p. (gr. 17). 65.00 *(978-0-8018-8815-1(8))* Johns Hopkins Univ. Pr.

Responding to Low Dairy Prices: Exploring Avenues for Federal Action: Hearing Before the Subcommittee on Domestic & Foreign Marketing, Inspection, & Plant & Animal Health & the Subcommittee on Production, Income Protection & Price Support of the Committee on Agriculture, Nutrition, & Forestry, United States Senate, One Hundred Eleventh Congress, First Session, October 27, 2009. 2011. (Illus.). iv, 143p. ***(978-0-16-088060-5(2),*** 552-070-42482-2) United States Government Printing Office.

AGRICULTURAL PRICES

see also Agricultural Price Supports; Farm Income; Food Prices

Alagh, Munish. Agricultural Prices in a Changing Economy: An Empirical Study of Indian Agriculture. 2012. (Illus.). 174p. 49.95 ***(978-81-7188-810-8(0))*** Academic Foundation IND. Dist: Independent Pubs. Group.

Anderson, Kym, et al, eds. Agricultural Price Distortions, Inequality, & Poverty. 2010. (Trade & Development Ser.). (ENG., Illus.). 540p. pap. 39.95 *(978-0-8213-8184-7(9),* 9780821381847) World Bank Pubns.

Babcock, B. A., et al, eds. Risk Management & the Environment: Agriculture in Perspective: Agriculture in Perspective. 2010. 220p. pap. 179.00 *(978-90-481-6158-4(4,* 9048161584) Springer.

Castillo, Philip. In the Footsteps of the Orange. 2010. 280p. pap. *(978-3-639-23036-9(1))* VDM Verlag Dr. Mueller e.K.

Cochrane, Willard W. Farm Prices: Myth & Reality. 2009. (ENG.). 200p. pap. 50.00 *(978-0-8166-5732-2(7))* Univ. of Minnesota Pr.

Henson, Spencer & Jaffee, Steven, eds. Agri-Food Systems & Economic Development. 2013. (Routledge Studies in Development Economics Ser.). (ENG.). 256p. (C). 130.00 *(978-0-415-49695-7(0))* Routledge.

Hudson, Darren. Agricultural Markets & Prices. 2006. (ENG., Illus.). 256p. 82.95 *(978-1-4051-3667-9(7),* Wiley-Blackwell) Wiley, John & Sons, Inc.

Kennedy, Liam & Solar, Peter. Irish Agriculture: A Price History from the Mid-Eighteenth Century to the Eve of the First World War. 2007. (Illus.). 206p. 45.00 *(978-1-904890-41-6(5))* Royal Irish Academy IRL. Dist: International Specialized Bk. Services.

Lusk, Jayson L. & Norwood, F. Bailey. Agricultural Marketing & Price Analysis. 2007. (ENG., Illus.). 464p. (C). pap. 113.60 *(978-0-13-221121-5(1),* Prentice Hall) Prentice Hall PTR.

Minot, Nicholas. Trade Liberalization & Poverty in the Middle East & North Africa. 2009. *(978-0-89629-174-4(X))* International Food Policy Research Institute.

Piot-Lepetit, Isabelle & M'Barek, Robert, eds. Methods to Analyse Agricultural Commodity Price Volatility. 2011. (ENG., Illus.). xvi, 231p. 139.00 *(978-1-4419-7633-8(7),* 1441976337) Springer.

Rao, D. S. Prasado, ed. Declining Agricultural Commodity Prices: Productivity Gain or Immiserising Growth? 2006. (Economic Paper Ser.). (ENG., Illus.). 100p. per. 35.00 *(978-0-85092-834-1(6))* Commonwealth Secretariat GBR. Dist: Stylus Publishing, LLC.

Schnepf, Randy. High Agricultural Commodity Prices: What Are the Issues? 2008. pap. 39.00 *(978-1-60692-013-8(8))* Nova Science Pubs., Inc.

Takle, S. R. & Bhise, V. B. Behaviour of Market Prices of Agricultural Commodities. 2007. viii, 211p. *(978-81-8387-074-0(0))* Serials Publications.

Vercammen, James. Agricultural Marketing: Structural Models for Price Analysis. 2011. (Routledge Textbooks in Environmental & Agricultural Economics Ser.). (ENG., Illus.). 216p. 140.00 *(978-0-415-48043-7(4));* pap. 55.95 *(978-0-415-48044-4(2))* Routledge.

Woldie, Getachew Abebe. Agricultural Supply Response & Yield & Price Risk. 2010. 80p. pap. *(978-3-639-21877-0(9))* VDM Verlag Dr. Mueller e.K.

AGRICULTURAL PROCESSING

Here are entered general works on the processing of agricultural products. Works on the specific aspect or method of processing are entered under the heading for the specific process. Works on the processing of food in general and on the marketing of processed food products are entered under Food Industry and Trade. Works on the processing of specific kinds of food products are entered under the heading for the specific product, with or without the subdivision Processing, or under the heading for the industry.

Food Process Engineering Operations. 2011. (C). 84.95 ***(978-1-4200-8354-5(6),*** CRC Press) Taylor & Francis Group GBR. Dist: Taylor & Francis Group.

Griffiths, M., ed. Improving the Safety & Quality of Milk: Improving Quality in Milk Products, 2 vols., Vol. 2. 2010. (Illus.). 528p. 265.00 *(978-1-84569-806-5(1))* Woodhead Publishing Ltd. GBR. Dist: Taylor & Francis Group.

Griffiths, Michael, ed. Improving the Safety & Quality of Milk: Milk Production & Processing, 2 vols. 2010. (Illus.). 520p. *(978-1-84569-438-8(4))* Woodhead Publishing Ltd.

Hearing to Review Current Food Safety Systems: Hearing Before the Committee on Agriculture, House of Representatives, One Hundred Eleventh Congress, First Session, April 2, 2009. 2009. (Illus.). iii, 139p. *(978-0-16-084442-3(8),* 552-070-39969-1) United States Government Printing Office.

Hearing to Review Current Issues in Food Safety: Hearing Before the Committee on Agriculture, House of Representatives, One Hundred Eleventh Congress, First Session, July 16, 2009. 2009. (Illus.). iv, 137p. *(978-0-16-084396-9(0),* 552-070-39938-1) United States Government Printing Office.

Kagima, David. Training Programs in Sustainable Agriculture & Postharvest Technology. 2008. 172p. pap. *(978-3-639-07341-6(X))* VDM Verlag Dr. Mueller e.K.

Reese, Jennifer. Make the Bread, Buy the Butter: What You Should & Shouldn't Cook from Scratch — Over 120 Recipes for the Best Homemade Foods. 2011. (ENG., Illus.). 256p. 24.00 *(978-1-4516-0587-7(0),* Free Pr.) Free Pr.

AGRICULTURAL PRODUCTION ECONOMICS

see Agriculture—Economic Aspects

AGRICULTURAL PRODUCTION FUNCTIONS

see Agriculture—Economic Aspects—Mathematical Models; Farm Management—Mathematical Models

A

AGRICULTURAL PRODUCTS
see Farm Produce; Produce Trade

AGRICULTURAL PROGRAMS
see Agricultural Administration

AGRICULTURAL RESEARCH
see Agriculture—Research

AGRICULTURAL SAFETY
see Agriculture—Safety Measures

AGRICULTURAL SCHOOLS
see Agricultural Colleges

AGRICULTURAL SOCIETIES
see also Future Farmers of America; National Grange

Buck, Solon J. The Agrarian Crusade. (Chronicles of America Ser.). 215p. reprint ed. 98.00 *(978-0-7222-7097-4(6))* Library Reprints, Inc.

—The Agrarian Crusade: A Chronicle of the Farmer in Politics. 215p. reprint ed. lib. bdg. 98.00 *(978-0-7222-4775-4(3))* Library Reprints, Inc.

Buck, Solon Justus. The Agrarian Crusade: A Chronicle of the Farmer in Politics. 2008. 228p. 24.99 *(978-0-559-76545-2(2))* 2008. 228p. pap. 24.75 *(978-0-559-76542-1(8))* 2007. (ENG.). 124p. pap. 18.99 *(978-1-4346-4463-3(4))* 2007. (ENG.). 136p. pap. 19.99 *(978-1-4346-4464-0(2))* BiblioBazaar.

Kradin, Nikolay, et al. Nomadic Pathway in Social Evolution. 2011. 228p. pap. ***(978-3-8443-1681-0(7))*** Lambert Academic Publishing.

Walsh, Rhonda E. Who's Minding Our Future?, 1 vol. 2009. 93p. pap. 16.95 *(978-1-60836-611-8(1))* PublishAmerica, Inc.

AGRICULTURAL STATISTICS
see Agriculture—Statistics

AGRICULTURAL SUBSIDIES
see also Agricultural Price Supports

Anderson, Kym, ed. Distortions to Agricultural Incentives: A Global Perspective, 1955-2007. 2009. (Trade & Development Ser.). (ENG., Illus.). 680p. 80.00 *(978-0-8213-7973-8(9))*, 9780821379738) World Bank Pubns.

—Distortions to Agricultural Incentives: A Global Perspective 1955 to 2007. 2009. (Trade & Development Ser.). (ENG., Illus.). 680p. pap. 39.95 *(978-0-8213-7665-2(9))*, 9780821376652) World Bank Pubns.

Anderson, Kym & Martin, Will, eds. Distortions to Agricultural Incentives in Asia. 2009. (Trade & Development Ser.). (ENG., Illus.). 608p. pap. 39.95 *(978-0-8213-7662-1(4))*, 9780821376621) World Bank Pubns.

Anderson, Kym & Masters, William A., eds. Distortions to Agricultural Incentives in Africa. 2009. (Trade & Development Ser.). (ENG., Illus.). 656p. pap. 39.95 *(978-0-8213-7652-2(7))*, 9780821376522) World Bank Pubns.

Anderson, Kym & Swinnen, Johan F. M. Distortions to Agricultural Incentives in Europe's Transition Economies. 2008. (Trade & Development Ser.). (ENG., Illus.). 408p. (C). pap. 39.95 *(978-0-8213-7419-1(2))*, 9780821374191) World Bank Pubns.

Anderson, Kym & Valdés, Alberto. Distortions to Agricultural Incentives in Latin America. 2008. (Trade & Development Ser.). (ENG., Illus.). 440p. (C). pap. 39.95 *(978-0-8213-7513-6(X))*, 9780821375136) World Bank Pubns.

Babcock, B. A., et al, eds. Risk Management & the Environment: Agriculture in Perspective: Agriculture in Perspective. 2010. 220p. pap. 179.00 *(978-90-481-6158-4(4))*, 9048161584) Springer.

Birner, Regina, et al. The Political Economy of Agricultural Policy Reform in India: The Case of Fertilizer Supply & Electricity Supply for Groundwater Irrigation. 2009. *(978-0-89629-172-0(3))* International Food Policy Research Institute.

Colorado Views on Federal Agriculture & Rural Policies: The 2007 Farm Bill: Hearing Before the Committee on Agriculture, Nutrition, & Forestry, United States Senate, One Hundred Tenth Congress, First Session, March 12, 2007. 2007. (Illus.). iv, 166p. *(978-0-16-078891-8(9))*, 552-070-36023-9) United States Government Printing Office.

Cunha, Arlindo & Swinbank, Alan. An Inside View of the CAP Reform Process: Explaining the MacSharry, Agenda 2000, & Fischler Reforms. 2011. (ENG., Illus.). 256p. 99.00 *(978-0-19-959157-2(1))* Oxford Univ. Pr., Inc.

Expanding Our Food & Fiber Supply Through a Strong U.S. Farm Policy: Hearing Before the Committee on Agriculture, Nutrition, & Forestry, United States Senate, One Hundred Eleventh Congress, Second Session, June 30, 2010. 2011. (Illus.). iv, 191p. ***(978-0-16-089264-6(3))***, 552-070-43260-4) United States Government Printing Office.

Full Committee Hearing on Family Farmer & Rural Small Business Priorities for 2007 Farm Bill. 2007. (Illus.). v, 83p. *(978-0-16-079944-0(9))*, 552-070-36771-3) United States Government Printing Office.

Hamda, Yonas. Equity of Farm Subsidies: Analysis of Farm Program Payments in South Dakota: 1990-2001. 2008. 100p. pap. *(978-3-639-09422-0(0))* VDM Verlag Dr. Mueller e.K.

Hearing to Review Implementation of the Food, Conservation, & Energy ACT of 2008: Hearing Before the Subcommittee on General Farm Commodities & Risk Management of the Committee on Agriculture, House of Representatives, One Hundred Eleventh Congress, First Session, June 24, 25, 2009. 2009. iii, 101p. *(978-0-16-084273-3(5))*, 552-070-39838-4) United States Government Printing Office.

Hearing to Review Implementation of the Horticulture & Organic Agriculture Title of the Food, Conservation, & Energy ACT of 2008: Hearing Before the Subcommittee on Horticulture & Organic Agriculture of the Committee on Agriculture, House of Representatives, One Hundred Eleventh Congress, First Session, October 28, 2009. 2009. (Illus.). iii, 29p. *(978-0-16-084877-3(6))*, 552-070-40273-0) United States Government Printing Office.

Hearing to Review Proposals to Amend the Program Crop Provisions of the Farm Security & Rural Investment ACT of 2002: Hearing Before the Subcommittee on General Farm Commodities & Risk Management of the Committee on Agriculture, House of Representatives, One Hundred Ninth Congress, First Session, April 26, 2007. 2009. (Illus.). iii, 178p. *(978-0-16-082965-9(8))*, 552-070-38876-1) United States Government Printing Office.

Hearing to Review the 2007 Farm Bill Proposals of the U.S. Department of Agriculture: Hearing Before the Committee on Agriculture, House of Representatives, One Hundred Tenth Congress, First Session, February 14, 2007. 2009. iii, 112p. *(978-0-16-084211-5(5))*, 552-070-39788-4) United States Government Printing Office.

Hearing to Review the State of Agriculture in Kansas: Hearing Before the Subcommittee on General Farm Commodities & Risk Management of the Committee on Agriculture, House of Representatives, One Hundred Tenth Congress, First Session, June 5, 2007, Salina, KS. 2009. (Illus.). iv, 102p. *(978-0-16-082991-8(7))*, 552-070-38893-1) United States Government Printing Office.

Imhoff, Daniel. Food Fight - The Citizen's Guide to the Next Food & Farm Bill. rev. ed. 2012. (ENG., Illus.). 212p. pap. 19.95 *(978-0-9709500-7-9(1))* Watershed Media Pr.

Iowa & Nebraska Views on Federal Agriculture & Rural Policies: The 2007 Farm Bill: Field Hearing Before the Committee on Agriculture, Nutrition, & Forestry, United States Senate, One Hundred Tenth Congress, First Session, April 14, 2007. 2007. (Illus.). iv, 114p. *(978-0-16-079443-8(9))*, 552-070-36437-4) United States Government Printing Office.

Kostigen, Thomas M. The Big Handout: How Government Subsidies & Corporate Welfare Corrupt the World We Live In & Wreak Havoc on Our Food Bills. 2011. (ENG., Illus.). 304p. 24.99 *(978-1-60961-113-2(6))* Rodale Pr., Inc.

Lesjak, Heli Annika. Explaining Organic Farming Through Past Policies - Comparing Support Policies of Austria, Finland & the European Union. 2008. (Illus.). 236p. pap. *(978-3-639-03896-5(7))* VDM Verlag Dr. Mueller e.K.

Maliro, Dyton Duncan. Agricultural Input Subsidies Versus Social Cash Transfers in Malawi. 2011. 312p. pap. ***(978-3-8443-8860-2(5))*** Lambert Academic Publishing.

Management of Civil Rights at the USDA: Hearing Before the Subcommittee on Government Management, Organization, & Procurement of the Committee on Oversight & Government Reform, House of Representatives, One Hundred Tenth Congress, Second Session, May 14, 2008. 2009. (Illus.). iii, 166p. *(978-0-16-083107-2(5))*, 552-070-38990-3) United States Government Printing Office.

Merino, Noël. Agricultural Subsidies. 2009. (OPPOSING VIEWPOINTS Ser.). (ENG., Illus.). 240p. 27.50 *(978-0-7377-4501-6(0))*; pap. 39.70 *(978-0-7377-4500-9(2))* Cengage Gale. (Greenhaven Pr., Inc.).

Organisation for Economic Co-operation and Development Staff. Set: National Accounts of Oecd Countries: Volume IIIa - Financial Accounts - Flows & Volume IIIb - Financial Balance Sheets - Stocks - 1993-2005, 2006 Edition-Set: Comptes Nationaux des Pays de l'Ocde: Volume IIIa - Comptes Financiers - Flux et Volume IIIb - Comptes de Patrimoine Financier - Stock. 2008. (Illus.). 120p. pap. 32.00 *(978-92-64-03172-2(3))* Organization for Economic Cooperation & Development.

Peterson, E. Wesley F. Billion Dollars a Day: The Economics & Politics of Agricultural Subsidies. 2009. (ENG., Illus.). 320p. 89.95 *(978-1-4051-8587-5(2))*, Wiley-Blackwell) Wiley, John & Sons, Inc.

—A Billion Dollars a Day: The Economics & Politics of Agricultural Subsidies. 2009. (ENG., Illus.). 320p. pap. 36.95 *(978-1-4051-8586-8(4))*, Wiley-Blackwell) Wiley, John & Sons, Inc.

Pinstrup-Andersen, Per & Cheng, Fuzhi. Food Policy for Developing Countries, 3 vols. 2009. (Illus.). Vol. 1. 264p. pap. 24.95 *(978-0-8014-7555-9(4))* Vol. 1. 240p. pap. 24.95 *(978-0-8014-7554-2(6))* Vol. 3. 256p. pap. 24.95 *(978-0-8014-7556-6(2))* Cornell Univ. Pr.

Schnepf, Randy & Womach, Jasper. Potential Challenges to U. S. Farm Subsidies in the WTO. 2008. (C). 69.00 *(978-1-60456-420-4(2))* Nova Science Pubs., Inc.

United States, Congress Senate Committee on Agriculture, Nutrition, and Forestry Staff, contrib. by. Regional Farm Bill Field Hearing: Field Hearing Before the Committee on Agriculture, Nutrition, & Forestry, United States Senate, One Hundred Ninth Congress, Second Session, June 23, 2006. 2007. (Illus.). iv, 188p. *(978-0-16-078494-1(8))*, 552-070-35775-1) United States Government Printing Office.

United States, Congress Senate Committee on Agriculture, Nutrition, and Forestry Subcommittee on Forestry, Conservation, and Rural Revitalization Staff, contrib. by. Field Hearing on 2007 Farm Bill: Hearing Before the Subcommittee on Forestry, Conservation, & Rural Revitalization of the Committee on Agriculture, Nutrition, & Forestry, United States Senate, One Hundred Ninth Congress, Second Session, August 11, 2006. 2007. iv, 140p. *(978-0-16-078351-7(8))*, 552-070-35652-5) United States Government Printing Office.

Zhao, Yuepeng. China's Rural Financial System: Households' Demand for Credit & Recent Reforms. 2010. (Routledge Studies on the Chinese Economy Ser.). (ENG., Illus.). 192p. (C). 140.00 *(978-0-415-54793-2(8))* Routledge.

Zivin, Joshua S. Graff & Perloff, Jeffrey M., eds. The Intended & Unintended Effects of U. S. Agricultural & Biotechnology Policies. 2012. (National Bureau of Economic Research Conference Report). (ENG., Illus.). 312p. 99.00 ***(978-0-226-98803-0(1))*** Univ. of Chicago Pr.

2007 Farm Bill Opportunities for Vermont & the Northeast: Hearing Before the Committee on Agriculture, Nutrition, & Forestry, United States Senate, One Hundred Tenth Congress, First Session, March 12, 2007. 2007. (Illus.). iv, 254p. *(978-0-16-078876-5(5))*, 552-070-36005-1) United States Government Printing Office.

AGRICULTURAL SUPPLIES
see Farm Supplies

AGRICULTURAL SURPLUSES
see Surplus Agricultural Commodities

AGRICULTURAL SYSTEMS
see also Farm Management; Grazing; Tillage

Abaidoo, Samuel. The Role of Environmental Ethics in Human-Nature Interaction. 2010. 192p. pap. *(978-3-8383-1787-8(4))* Lambert Academic Publishing.

Aghajanian, Alfred. Chinampas: Their Role in Aztec Empire - Building & Expansion, Second Edition. 2007. 128p. per. 19.95 *(978-1-60444-003-4(1))* IndoEuropeanPublishing.com.

Alavalapati, Janaki R. R. & Mercer, D. Evan, eds. Valuing Agroforestry Systems: Methods & Applications. 2010. (Advances in Agroforestry Ser.). ix, 314p. pap. 199.00 *(978-90-481-6655-8(1))*, 9048166551) Springer.

Belay, Asfaw. Direct: Lessons from a 60-year-old RotationalExperiment in Pretoria, South Africa. 2008. 112p. pap. *(978-3-639-10170-6(7))* VDM Verlag Dr. Mueller e.K.

Benckiser, Gero, ed. Biodiversity in Agricultural Production Systems. 2006. (Books in Soils, Plants, & the Environment Ser.: Vol. 114). (ENG., Illus.). 429p. 165.95 *(978-1-57444-589-3(8))*, CRC Press) Taylor & Francis Group GBR. Dist: Taylor & Francis Group.

Campbell, Bruce M. S. & Campbell, B. M. S. Field Systems & Farming Systems in Late Medieval England. 2008. (Variorum Collected Studies). (Illus.). 332p. 154.95 *(978-0-7546-5946-4(1))* Ashgate Publishing Co.

Castalonge, Oliver W. Agricultural Systems: Economics, Technology, & Diversity. 2008. 79.00 *(978-1-60692-025-1(1))* Nova Science Pubs., Inc.

Chau Thi Minh, Long. Sustainability of Agricultural Systems in Vietnam. 2010. 136p. pap. *(978-3-8383-8076-6(2))* Lambert Academic Publishing.

Committee on Twenty-First Century Systems Agriculture & National Research Council. Toward Sustainable Agricultural Systems in the 21st Century. 2010. (ENG., Illus.). 598p. pap. 65.00 *(978-0-309-14896-2(0))* National Academies Pr.

Cram101 Textbook Reviews. Outlines & Highlights for Ecological Management of Agricultural Weeds by Charles L Mohler Matt Liebman, Isbn: 9780521037877. 2011. 132p. pap. 28.95 ***(978-1-61461-475-3(X))*** Cram101 Inc.

Flichman, Guillermo, ed. Bio-Economic Models applied to Agricultural Systems. 2011. (ENG., Illus.). xii, 220p. 189.00 ***(978-94-007-1901-9(9))***, 9400719019) Springer.

Goyari, Phanindra. Cropping Pattern Changes in the North-Eastern Region of Indi. 2010. 92p. pap. *(978-3-639-27632-9(9))* VDM Verlag Dr. Mueller e.K.

Kersebaum, K. Ch., et al, eds. Modelling Water & Nutrient Dynamics in Soil-Crop Systems: Applications of Different Models to Common Data Sets - Proceedings of a Workshop Held 2004 in Müncheberg, Germany. 2010. (ENG.). viii, 272p. pap. 179.00 *(978-90-481-7133-0(4))*, 9048171334) Springer.

Kirch, Patrick Vinton. Roots of Conflict: Soils, Agriculture, & Sociopolitical Complexity in Ancient Hawaii. 2010. (Illus.). xix, 199p. *(978-1-934691-26-7(7))* School for Advanced Research Pr./SAR Pr.

Kramar, Laura. Assessing the Sustainability of Agricultural Systems. 2008. 108p. pap. *(978-3-639-04857-5(1))* VDM Verlag Dr. Mueller e.K.

Kropff, M. J., et al, eds. Applications of Systems Approaches at the Field Level. 2010. (System Approaches for Sustainable Agricultural Development Ser.). 496p. pap. 439.00 *(978-90-481-4763-2(8))*, 9048147638) Springer.

Laheen, Mary. Drystone Walls of the Aran Islands: Exploring the Cultural Landscape. 2010. (ENG., Illus.). 192p. pap. 36.95 *(978-1-84889-025-1(7))* Collins Pr., The IRL. Dist: Dufour Editions, Inc.

Lefroy, E. C., et al, eds. Agriculture as a Mimic of Natural Ecosystems. 2010. (Current Plant Science & Biotechnology in Agriculture Ser.). 436p. pap. 419.00 *(978-90-481-5319-0(0))*, 9048153190) Springer.

Liebman, Matt, et al. Ecological Management of Agricultural Weeds. 2007. (ENG., Illus.). 548p. pap. 105.00 *(978-0-521-03787-7(5))* Cambridge Univ. Pr.

Lokhorst, C. & Groot Koerkamp, P. W. G., eds. Precision livestock Farming '09. 2009. (Illus.). 368p. 108.00 *(978-90-8686-112-5(1))* Wageningen Academic Publishers NLD. Dist: Enfield Publishing & Distribution Co., Inc.

Mahajan, Anil. Integrated Nutrient Management (INM) in a Sustainable Rice-Wheat Cropping System. 2009. (ENG., Illus.). xxxii, 268p. 179.00 *(978-1-4020-9874-1(X))*, 140209874X) Springer.

Mahmood, Sajid & Manzoor Ahmed, Saqib. Crop Water Allocation Model - Cwam. 2010. 80p. pap. *(978-3-639-25798-4(7))* VDM Verlag Dr. Mueller e.K.

Mazhar, Farhad, et al. Food Sovereignty & Uncultivated Biodiversity in South Asia: Essays on the Poverty of Food Policy & the Wealth of the Social Landscape. 2007. (Illus.). 75p. pap. 39.95 incl. cd-rom *(978-81-7188-614-2(0))* Academic Foundation IND. Dist: Independent Pubs. Group.

Mutsaers, H. J. W. Peasants, Farmers & Scientists: A Chronicle of Tropical Agricultural Science in the Twentieth Century. (ENG.). xxviii, 612p. 2010. pap. 139.00 *(978-90-481-7555-0(0))*, 9048175550) 2007. 139.00 *(978-1-4020-6165-3(X))*, 140206165X) Springer.

Nuthall, P. L. Farm Business Management: Analysis of Farming Systems. 2011. 464p. 220.00 ***(978-1-84593-839-0(9))*** CABI GBR. Dist: Stylus Publishing, LLC.

Oyewole, Charles. Yield & Economic Implication of Intercropping Millet with Groundnut. 2011. 108p. pap. ***(978-3-8443-0585-2(8))*** Lambert Academic Publishing.

Peluffo, Matias. Adopting New Zealand Dairy Farm Principles in Argentina. 2008. 256p. pap. *(978-3-639-02588-0(1))* VDM Verlag Dr. Mueller e.K.

Pinstrup-Andersen, Per, ed. The African Food System & Its Interactions with Human Health & Nutrition. 2010. (United Nations University Ser.). (Illus.). 384p. pap. 29.95 *(978-0-8014-7692-1(5))* Cornell Univ. Pr.

Postali Parra, José Roberto, et al, eds. Egg Parasitoids in Agroecosystems with emphasis on Trichogramma. 2010. (Progress in Biological Control Ser.). (ENG., Illus.). 450p. 199.00 *(978-1-4020-9109-4(5))*, 1402091095) Springer.

Prabhakar, Sivapuram V. R. K. & Yaduraju, N. T. Survival of Little Seed Canary Grass Seeds in Rice-Wheat Systems. 2011. 96p. pap. ***(978-3-8433-9233-4(1))*** Lambert Academic Publishing.

Rigueiro-Rodríguez, Antonio, et al, eds. Agroforestry in Europe: Current Status & Future Prospects. 2010. (Advances in Agroforestry Ser.). (Illus.). xxiv, 452p. pap. 239.00 *(978-90-481-7827-8(4))*, 9048178274) Springer.

Shams, Amr. Intercropping Maize with Peanut. 2011. 172p. pap. ***(978-3-8443-0369-8(3))*** Lambert Academic Publishing.

Snapp, Sieglinde & Pound, Barry, eds. Agricultural Systems: Agroecology & Rural Innovation for Development. 2008. (ENG., Illus.). 400p. (C). 77.95 *(978-0-12-372517-2(8))*, Academic Pr.) Elsevier Science & Technology Bks.

Ssekabembe, Charles. Unlocking Myths of Crop Yield. 2011. 220p. pap. ***(978-3-8443-1782-4(1))*** Lambert Academic Publishing.

Stehfest, Elke. Modelling of Global Crop Production & Resulting N2o Emissions. 2008. 168p. pap. *(978-3-639-02913-0(5))* VDM Verlag Dr. Mueller e.K.

Sundara, B. Ratoon Cropping. 2010. (Agriculture Issues & Policies Ser.). 195.00 *(978-1-61728-695-7(8))* Nova Science Pubs., Inc.

Tapio-Bistrom, Marja-Liisa. Climate Change Mitigation & Agriculture. Wollenberg, Eva et al, eds. 2012. (ENG., Illus.). 456p. 140.00 ***(978-1-84971-392-4(8))***; pap. 49.95 ***(978-1-84971-393-1(6))*** Routledge.

Tow, Philip, et al, eds. Rainfed Farming Systems. 2009. 239.00 *(978-1-4020-9131-5(1))* Springer.

Umeh, Simon. Partial Nutrient Balance Studies in an Intercropping System. 2011. 196p. pap. ***(978-3-8443-1592-9(6))*** Lambert Academic Publishing.

van der Zijpp, A. J., et al, eds. Fishponds in Farming Systems. 2007. (Illus.). 312p. 86.00 *(978-90-8686-013-5(3))* Wageningen Academic Publishers NLD. Dist: Enfield Publishing & Distribution Co., Inc.

van t'Hooft, Katrien, et al. Livestock Management for Poverty Alleviation & Food Security. 2012. 208p. 145.00 ***(978-1-84593-827-7(5))*** CABI GBR. Dist: Stylus Publishing, LLC.

AGRICULTURAL TOOLS
see Agricultural Implements

AGRICULTURAL WARRANTS
see Chattel Mortgages

AGRICULTURAL WASTES
see also Compost

Ashworth, Geoffrey S. & Azevedo, Pablo. Agricultural Wastes. 2009. (Agricultural Issues & Policies Ser.). (Illus.). xiii, 306p. 129.00 *(978-1-60741-305-9(1))* Nova Science Pubs., Inc.

Danielski, Leandro. Supercritical Processing of Plant Materials. 2008. 200p. pap. *(978-3-639-02458-6(3))* VDM Verlag Dr. Mueller e.K.

Ezeji, Thaddeus, et al. Biofuels from Agricultural Wastes & Byproducts. 2010. (ENG., Illus.). 276p. 209.95 *(978-0-8138-0252-7(0))*, Wiley-Blackwell) Wiley, John & Sons, Inc.

Garcha, Seema. Composting Agricultural Residues for Value Addition. 2010. 140p. pap. *(978-3-639-27605-3(1))* VDM Verlag Dr. Mueller e.K.

Gayen, Soumi & Ghosh, Uma. Ed Ssf for Production of Pme by Penicillium Notatum Ncim 923. 2011. 76p. pap. ***(978-3-8443-2648-2(0))*** Lambert Academic Publishing.

He, Zhongqi & Dou, Zhengxia, eds. Phosphorus Forms in Animal Manure & the Impact on Soil P Status. 2009. (Animal Science, Issues & Professions Ser.). (Illus.). 37p. pap. 43.00 *(978-1-61668-980-3(3))*, Nova Novinka) Nova Science Pubs., Inc.

Kai, Lea. Agricultural Residue Management in Developing Countries. 2009. (Illus.). 120p. pap. *(978-3-639-14566-3(6))* VDM Verlag Dr. Mueller e.K.

Liu, Sean X. Food & Agricultural Wastewater Utilization & Treatment. 2007. (ENG., Illus.). 296p. 229.95 *(978-0-8138-1423-0(5))*, Wiley-Blackwell) Wiley, John & Sons, Inc.

Morgan, Sally. Leftover Food. 2007. (Dealing with Waste/Watts Ser.). (Illus.). 30p. (J). (gr. 4-7). lib. bdg. 28.50 *(978-1-59920-009-5(0))* Black Rabbit Bks.

Rockland, Samuel D., ed. Anaerobic Digestion for Energy Generation & Greenhouse Gas Reduction. 2009. (Energy Science, Engineering & Technology Ser.). 115.00 *(978-1-61728-679-7(6))* Nova Science Pubs., Inc.

Someus, Edward. Food Crop Mineral Deficiency & Disturbance Stress Mitigation in Temperate Climatic Regions by Economical & Environmental Valorization of Agricultural By-Products. 2009. (Illus.). 132p. pap. 79.00 *(978-1-60692-243-9(2))* Nova Science Pubs., Inc.

AGRICULTURAL WATER SUPPLY
see Water-Supply, Agricultural

AGRICULTURAL WORKERS
see Agricultural Laborers; Collective Bargaining—Agriculture

AGRICULTURE

see also Acclimatization (Plants); Aeronautics in Agriculture; Agriculturists; Agroforestry; Agronomy; Animal Industry; Antibiotics in Agriculture; Aquaculture; Botany, Economic; Burning of Land; Chemurgy; Communism and Agriculture; Electricity in Agriculture; Farm Produce; Farmers; Farms; Forests and Forestry; Gardening; Green Revolution; Horticulture; Irrigation Farming; Land Use, Rural; Livestock; Organic Farming; Pastures; Plant Breeding; Plants, Cultivated; Plants, Protection of; Seeds; Shifting Cultivation; Soil Science; Sustainable Agriculture; Tillage; Traditional Farming; Urban Agriculture; Water in Agriculture; Women in Agriculture

also subdivision Agriculture under ethnic groups; and headings beginning with the word Agricultural and Farm

Agriculture, Vol. 14. *(978-0-8357-0652-0(4))* Univ. Microfilms, Inc.

Aicpa. AICPA Audit & Accounting Guide Agricultural Producers & Agricultural Cooperatives. 2007. pap. 61.25 *(978-0-87051-681-8(7))* American Institute of Certified Public Accountants.

Alam. Communication Exposure of Sub-Assistant Agriculture Officers. 2010. 64p. pap. *(978-3-639-27700-5(7))* VDM Verlag Dr. Mueller e.K.

Albajes, Ramon, et al, eds. Integrated Pest & Disease Management in Greenhouse Crops. 2010. (Developments in Plant Pathology Ser.). (Illus.). 568p. pap. 519.00 *(978-90-481-5188-2(0),* 9048151880) Springer.

Alexander, Christopher. De las matematicas Y. (SPA.). 144p. *(978-84-7223-405-5(3),* 6070) Tusquets Editores.

Ali, Qurban, et al. Pulses. 2011. 196p. pap. ***(978-3-8443-8027-9(2))*** Lambert Academic Publishing.

Allen-Taylor, Duffie J. Life in Fertile Soil: Growing up on the Farm During the 1930's, '40's And '50's. 2010. 237p. pap. 19.95 *(978-1-4327-3439-8(3))* Outskirts Pr., Inc.

American Farmer's New & Universal Handbook or, an Improved & Complete Guide to the Treatment of Soils; the Operations of Productive Field Husba. 2006. 604p. per. 32.99 *(978-1-4255-6438-4(0))* MPublishing.

Andreae, Bernd. Farming, Development & Space: A World Agricultural Geography. Gregor, Howard F., tr. (ENG.). 345p. 210.00 ***(978-3-11-178677-3(3))*** De Gruyter, Walter Inc.

Apps, Jerry. Horse-Drawn Days: A Century of Farming with Horses. 2010. (ENG., Illus.). 216p. pap. 24.95 *(978-0-87020-445-6(9))* Wisconsin Historical Society.

Ashraf, M., et al. Salinity & Water Stress: Improving Crop Efficiency. 2008. (Tasks for Vegetation Science Ser.). (ENG., Illus.). xiv, 246p. 199.00 *(978-1-4020-9064-6(1))* Springer.

Bailey, L. H. & Jack, Zachary Michael. Liberty Hyde Bailey: Essential Agrarian & Environmental Writings. Jack, Zachary Michael, ed. 2008. 288p. 29.95 *(978-0-8014-4709-9(7))* Cornell Univ. Pr.

Beecher, Henry Ward. Plain & Pleasant Talk about Fruits, Flowers & Farming / by Henry Ward Beecher. 2006. 424p. per. 26.99 *(978-1-4255-4556-7(4))* MPublishing.

Behnassi, Mohamed, et al, eds. Sustainable Agricultural Development: Recent Approaches in Resources Management & Environmentally -Balanced Production Enhancement. 2011. (ENG., Illus.). xl, 278p. 129.00 *(978-94-007-0518-0(2),* 9400705182) Springer.

Belanger, Jerome D. The Complete Idiot's Guide to Raising Chickens. 2010. (Complete Idiot's Guide Ser.). (ENG., Illus.). 208p. (gr. 12-18). 14.95 *(978-1-59257-986-0(8),* Alpha Bks.) Penguin Group (USA) Inc.

Berklian, Yaram J. Crop Rotation. 2008. 79.00 *(978-1-60692-100-5(2))* Nova Science Pubs., Inc.

Bernard, Raymond W. Super Foods from Super Soil. 2010. 32p. 30.95 *(978-1-162-55830-1(X));* pap. 15.95 *(978-1-162-55635-2(8))* Kessinger Publishing, LLC.

Bernstein, Sylvia. Aquaponic Gardening, A Step-by-Step Guide to Raising Vegetables. 2011. (ENG., Illus.). 288p. pap. 29.95 ***(978-0-86571-701-5(X),*** 9780865717015) New Society Pubs., Ltd. CAN. Dist: Consortium Bk. Sales & Distribution.

Bertrand, Dominique. Chemometrics in Food & Agricultural Sciences. 2007. (ENG., Illus.). 352p. 199.99 *(978-1-4051-0868-3(1),* Wiley-Blackwell) Wiley, John & Sons, Inc.

Blake, John Lauris. The Farm & the Fireside: Or, the Romance of Agriculture. Being Half Hour Sketches of Life in the Country. by the Rev. John L. Blake ... 2006. 484p. per. 29.99 *(978-1-4255-5337-1(0))* MPublishing.

Bonynge, Francis. The Future Wealth of America: Being A Glance at the Resources of the United States & the Commercial & Agricultural Advantages of Cultivating Tea. 2006. 244p. per. 20.99 *(978-1-4255-2117-2(7))* MPublishing.

Boussingault, J. B. (Jean Baptiste). Rural Economy, in Its Relations with Chemistry, Physics, & Meteorology; or, Chemistry Applied to Agriculture by J B Boussingault, Translated, Wit. 2006. 532p. per. 29.99 *(978-1-4255-5874-1(7))* MPublishing.

Boyd, Freeman. The Search for an Agricultural Ethic. 2008. 196p. pap. *(978-3-639-01527-0(4))* VDM Verlag Dr. Mueller e.K.

Brackett, George E. Farm Talk. 2006. 132p. per. 16.99 *(978-1-4255-0889-0(8))* MPublishing.

Bromfield, Louis. Out of the Earth. 305p. reprint ed. lib. bdg. 24.95 *(978-0-88411-541-0(0))* Amereon LTD.

Buck, Franklin A. A Yankee Trader in the Gold Rush: The Letters of Franklin A. Buck. White, Katherine A., ed. 2011. 320p. 50.95 ***(978-1-258-01595-4(1))*** Literary Licensing, LLC.

Burton, DeVere. Lab Manual for Burton's Agriscience Fundamentals & Applications, 5th. 5th ed. 2009. (ENG.). 232p. (C). pap. 85.95 *(978-1-4354-1968-1(5))* Delmar Cengage Learning.

Burton, L. DeVere. Agriscience Fundamentals & Applications. 5th ed. 2009. (ENG.). 848p. (C). 139.95 *(978-1-4354-1966-7(9))* Delmar Cengage Learning.

Bux, Hadi, et al. Utilization of Synthetic Hexaploids for Wheat Improvement: Part I. 2011. 248p. pap. ***(978-3-8443-9816-8(3))*** Lambert Academic Publishing.

Bytyqi, Hysen. Basic Principles of Livestock Management. 2011. 112p. pap. ***(978-3-8443-8302-7(6))*** Lambert Academic Publishing.

Callaway, Todd R. & Edrington, Tom S., eds. On-Farm Strategies to Control Foodborne Pathogens. 2012. ***(978-1-62100-411-0(2))*** Nova Science Pubs., Inc.

Chalmin, Philippe. Le Monde a Faim: Quelques Réflexions Sur L'avenir Agricole et Alimentaire de L'humanité Au XXIe Siècle. (FRE.). 136p. *(978-2-84941-111-7(6))* Bourin Editeur.

Chen, Y. R., et al. Optics for Natural Resources, Agriculture, & Foods II: 10-11 September 2007, Boston, Massachusetts, USA. 2007. (Proceedings of SPIE Ser.). (Illus.). 290p. pap. 90.00 *(978-0-8194-6921-2(1))* SPIE.

Cherrington, John. On the Smell of an Oily Rag. (Illus.). 256p. pap. 12.95 *(978-0-85236-256-3(0))* Farming Pr., Ltd. GBR. Dist: Diamond Farm Bk. Pubs.

Chiles, Frederic Caire. Justinian Caire & Santa Cruz Island: The Rise & Fall of a California Dynasty. 2011. (ENG., Illus.). 240p. 34.95 *(978-0-87062-400-1(8),* Clark, Arthur H. Co., The) Univ. of Oklahoma Pr.

Clay, David & Shanahan, John F., eds. GIS Applications in Agriculture: Nutrient Management for Energy Efficiency. 2011. (GIS Applications in Agriculture Ser.). (ENG., Illus.). 472p. 139.95 *(978-1-4200-9270-7(7),* CRC Press) Taylor & Francis Group GBR. Dist: Taylor & Francis Group.

Cohen, Mark N. & Crane-Kramer, Gillian M. M., eds. Ancient Health: Skeletal Indicators of Agricultural & Economic Intensification. 2012. (Bioarchaeological Interpretations of the Human Past: Local, Regional, & Global Ser.). (ENG.). 464p. pap. 35.95 ***(978-0-8130-4403-3(0))*** Univ. Pr. of Florida.

Cohen, Mark Nathan & Crane-Kramer, Gillian M. M., eds. Ancient Health: Skeletal Indicators of Agricultural & Economic Intensification. 2007. (Bioarchaeological Interpretations of the Human Past: Local, Ser.). (ENG., Illus.). 464p. 75.00 *(978-0-8130-3082-1(X))* Univ. Pr. of Florida.

Collinge, David B., et al, eds. Sustainable disease management in a European Context. 2010. (ENG.). vi, 198p. pap. 109.00 *(978-90-481-7985-5(8),* 9048179858) Springer.

Commercial Biotech Agriculture & Aquaculture. *(978-81-204-0827-2(6))* Science Pubs.

Conklin, Alfred R., et al. World Food: Production & Use. 2007. (ENG., Illus.). 445p. 111.00 *(978-0-470-04382-0(2),* Wiley-Interscience) Wiley, John & Sons, Inc.

Connolly, Bryan. Organic Seed Production & Saving: The Wisdom of Plant Heritage. 2011. (ENG.). 128p. pap. 12.95 *(978-1-60358-353-4(X))* Chelsea Green Publishing.

Cox, S., ed. Precision Livestock Farming '07. 2007. (Illus.). 312p. 102.00 *(978-90-8686-023-4(0))* Wageningen Academic Publishers NLD. Dist: Enfield Publishing & Distribution Co., Inc.

Cp, Jomit & Subhash, K. Agrarian Distress & Changing Rural Livelihoods in Kerala: A Case of Wayanad District. 2011. 164p. pap. ***(978-3-639-33812-6(X))*** VDM Verlag Dr. Mueller e.K.

Crapo, Henry Howland. Address Delivered by Hon Henry H Crapo, Governor of Michigan, Before the Central Michigan Agricultural Society, at Their Sheepshearing Exhibition, H. 2011. 22p. pap. 11.99 ***(978-1-4181-9128-3(0))*** MPublishing.

Dando, William A. Food & Famine in the 21st Century, 2 vols. 2012. (Illus.). 860p. 189.00 ***(978-1-59884-730-7(9),*** A3314C); E-Book ***(978-1-59884-731-4(7))*** ABC-CLIO, LLC.

DeClerck, Fabrice, et al, eds. Ecosystem Services from Agriculture & Agroforestry: Measurement & Payment. 2011. (ENG., Illus.). 448p. 99.95 *(978-1-84971-147-0(X))* Routledge.

Delgado, Jorge A. & Follett, Ronald F., eds. Advances in Nitrogen Management for Water Quality. 2010. 35.00 *(978-0-9769432-0-4(4))* Soil and Water Conservation Society.

DeMatta, Fabio. Fabio Dematta (Dept. of Plant Biology, Federal University of Vicosa, Brazil) 2010. (Agriculture Issues & Policies Ser.). (Illus.). xiv, 389p. 195.00 *(978-1-60876-392-4(7))* Nova Science Pubs., Inc.

Deming, Henry Champion. A Speech for the Useful Arts Delivered at New Haven, January 2d, 1856, Before the Agricultural Society of the State of Connecticut by Henry Champion. 2011. 34p. pap. 11.99 ***(978-1-4181-9461-1(1))*** MPublishing.

Denham, Timothy, et al. Rethinking Agriculture: Archaeological & Ethnoarchaeological Perspectives. 2009. (One World Archaeology, Vol. 51 Ser.). (ENG., Illus.). 476p. pap. 39.95 *(978-1-59874-261-9(2))* Left Coast Pr., Inc.

Dillehay, Tom D. From Foraging to Farming in the Andes: New Perspectives on Food Production & Social Organization. 2011. (ENG., Illus.). 350p. 90.00 *(978-1-107-00527-3(2))* Cambridge Univ. Pr.

Dix, John A. Address, Delivered October 2d, 1851, at the Tenth Annual Exhibition of the Queens County Agricultural Society, at Jamaica, L I, by the Hon John a D. 2011. 22p. pap. 11.99 ***(978-1-4181-9171-9(X))*** MPublishing.

Downing, Andrew Jackson. Andrew Jackson Downing: Essential Texts. Twombly, Robert, ed. 2012. (ENG., Illus.). 400p. pap. 35.00 ***(978-0-393-73359-4(9),*** 73359) Norton, W. W. & Co., Inc.

Dris, Ramdane & Jain, S. Mohan, eds. Production Practices & Quality Assessment of Food Crops: Volume 2: Plant Mineral Nutrition & Pesticide Management. 2010. 288p. pap. 209.00 *(978-90-481-6459-2(1),* 9048164591) Springer.

Dunlop, Tom. Morning Glory Farm & the Family That Feeds an Island: Including 70 Favorite Martha's Vineyard Recipes. 2nd ed. 2009. (Illus.). 156p. pap. 24.95 *(978-0-615-26606-0(1))* Vineyard Stories.

El Bassam, N. Bioenergy Crops: A Complete Reference to Species, Development & Applications. 2010. (ENG., Illus.). 544p. instr.'s hndbk. ed. 240.00 *(978-1-84407-854-7(X))* Routledge.

Emerson, George B. (George Barrell). Manual of Agriculture, for the School, the Farm, & the Fireside / by George B Emerson & Charles L Flint. 2006. 316p. per. 23.99 *(978-1-4255-3004-4(4))* MPublishing.

Fan, Shenggen & Pandya-Lorch, Rajul. Reshaping Agriculture for Nutrition & Health. 2012. ***(978-0-89629-673-2(3))*** International Food Policy Research Institute.

Feinberg, Margaret. Scouting the Divine: My Search for God in Wine, Wool, & Wild Honey, 1 vol. 2009. (ENG.). 224p. 16.99 *(978-0-310-29122-0(4))* Zondervan.

Fick, Gary W. Food, Farming, & Faith. 2008. (SUNY Series on Religion & the Environment). (Illus.). 223p. 49.50 *(978-0-7914-7383-2(X));* pap. 19.95 *(978-0-7914-7384-9(8))* State Univ. of New York Pr.

Finley, Amy. How to Eat a Small Country: A Family's Pursuit of Happiness, One Meal at a Time. 2011. 288p. 24.00 *(978-0-307-59138-8(7),* Clarkson Potter) Crown Publishing Group.

Fox, Charles. The American Text Book of Practical & Scientific Agriculture. 2006. 368p. per. 26.99 *(978-1-4255-3793-7(6))* MPublishing.

Garnett, Thomas. Essays in Natural History & Agriculture. 2008. 212p. 24.99 *(978-0-554-33226-0(4))* 2008. 212p. 27.99 *(978-0-554-23923-1(X))* 2007. (ENG.). 186p. pap. 19.99 *(978-1-4264-5158-4(X))* 2006. 210p. pap. 22.99 *(978-1-4264-5459-2(7))* BiblioBazaar.

—Essays in Natural History & Agriculture. 2007. 184p. per. *(978-1-4065-2787-2(4))* Dodo Pr.

Gashi, Ferim. Conditions for Development of Agriculture in the Municipality of Klinë. 2011. 120p. pap. ***(978-3-8443-9627-0(6))*** Lambert Academic Publishing.

George, Raymond A. T. Agricultural Seed Production. 2012. (Illus.). 248p. 125.00 ***(978-1-84593-819-2(4))*** CABI GBR. Dist: Stylus Publishing, LLC.

Gilk, Paul. Nature's Unruly Mob: Farming & the Crisis in Rural Culture. 2009. 200p. pap. 23.00 *(978-1-60608-737-4(1),* Wipf and Stock) Wipf & Stock Pubs.

Gilliland, Jennifer H. St. Paul's Parish. 2012. (Images of America Ser.). (ENG., Illus.). 128p. pap. 21.99 ***(978-0-7385-9119-3(X))*** Arcadia Publishing.

Gladders. Pest & Disease Management Handbook. 2nd ed. 2013. (ENG.). 684p. 299.99 *(978-1-4443-3326-8(7),* Wiley-Blackwell) Wiley, John & Sons, Inc.

Goodrich, Landon Charles. The First Book of Farming. 2007. (ENG.). 238p. pap. 20.99 *(978-1-4346-0583-2(3));* 260p. pap. 23.99 *(978-1-4346-0658-7(9))* BiblioBazaar.

Green, Greg. The Cannabis Grow Bible: The Definitive Guide to Growing Marijuana for Recreational & Medical Use. 2nd ed. 2009. (ENG., Illus.). 416p. pap. 28.00 *(978-1-931160-58-2(9))* Green Candy Pr.

Gregg, B. R. & Billups, Gary L. Seed Conditioning. 2009. (Illus.). *(978-1-57808-687-0(6)); (978-1-57808-688-7(4))* Science Pubs.

Gregg, Bill & Billups, Gary. Seed Conditioning. 2010. (ENG.). 1000p. 179.95 *(978-1-57808-608-5(6))* BIOS Scientific Publishers Ltd. GBR. Dist: Taylor & Francis Group.

Hall, Bolton. Three Acres & Liberty. l.t. ed. 2007. (ENG.). 222p. pap. 22.99 *(978-1-4264-1695-8(4))* BiblioBazaar.

Hamel, Chantal & Plenchette, Christian. Mycorrhizae in Crop Production. 2007. (ENG., Illus.). 319p. 83.95 *(978-1-56022-306-1(5));* per. 59.95 *(978-1-56022-307-8(3))* Taylor & Francis Group GBR. (CRC Press). Dist: Taylor & Francis Group.

Heidhus, Franz J., et al, eds. Sustainable Land Use in Mountainous Regions of Southeast Asia: Meeting the Challenges of Ecological, Socio-Economic & Cultural Diversity. 2010. (Environmental Science & Engineering / Environmental Science Ser.). (Illus.). xxx, 404p. pap. 239.00 *(978-3-642-09030-1(3),* 3642090303) Springer.

Herren, Ray V. Exploring Agriscience. 4th ed. 2010. (ENG.). (C). 224p. pap., lab manual ed. 84.95 *(978-1-4354-3968-9(6));* (Illus.). 576p. 127.95 *(978-1-4354-3966-5(X))* Delmar Cengage Learning.

Herren, Ray V(Ray V. Herren). The Science of Agriculture: A Biological Approach. 4th ed. 2011. (ENG.). (C). 320p. pap. 84.95 *(978-1-4390-5774-2(5));* 457.95 *(978-1-4390-5772-8(9));* 159.95 *(978-1-4390-5771-1(0));* 784p. 139.95 *(978-1-4390-5776-6(1))* Delmar Cengage Learning.

Hirai, Atsushi, et al. Rice Biology in the Genomics Era. 2008. (Biotechnology in Agriculture & Forestry Ser.). (Illus.). 380p. 359.00 *(978-3-540-74248-7(4),* 3540742484) Springer.

Hirano, Hiro-Yuki, et al. Rice Biology in the Genomics Era. 2010. (Biotechnology in Agriculture & Forestry Ser.). (Illus.). xxii, 382p. pap. 359.00 *(978-3-642-09358-6(2),* 3642093582) Springer.

Hobson, J. C. Jeremy & Rant, Phil. Successful Smallholding: Planning, Starting & Managing Your Enterprise. Hermon, E. W., ed. 2009. (ENG., Illus.). 160p. 45.00 *(978-1-84797-075-6(3))* Crowood Pr., Ltd. GBR. Dist: Independent Pubs. Group.

Hood, George W. Spray MacHinery & Spray Materials Used in Farm Cultivation. 2011. 22p. pap. 6.95 ***(978-1-4465-3085-6(X))*** Barclay Pr., Inc.

Hoyle, Richard W. Custom Improvement & Anti-Improvement in Early Modern Britain. 2011. (Illus.). 328p. 124.95 *(978-1-4094-0052-3(2))* Ashgate Publishing Co.

Huopalahti, Rainer, et al, eds. Bioactive Egg Compounds. 2010. (ENG., Illus.). xx, 298p. pap. 189.00 *(978-3-642-07238-3(0),* 3642072380) Springer.

Hutchinson, Joseph. Farming & Food Supply: The Interdependence of Countryside & Town. 2009. (ENG.). 160p. pap. 28.99 *(978-0-521-10716-7(4))* Cambridge Univ. Pr.

Irrigation Association Membership Directory & Buyers Guide, 95-96. 5th ed. 50.00 *(978-0-935030-06-8(9))* Irrigation Assn., The.

Jain, S. Mohan & Brar, D. S., eds. Molecular Techniques in Crop Improvement: 2nd Edition. 2nd ed. 2009. (Illus.). ix, 772p. 229.00 *(978-90-481-2966-9(4),* 9048129664) Springer.

James, A. Young & Cheryl G. Young. Collecting, Processing & Germinating Seeds of Wildland Plants. 2009. (ENG.). 236p. pap. 24.95 *(978-1-60469-073-6(9),* 1604690739) Timber Pr., Inc.

Jenks, Matthew A. & Wood, Andrew J., eds. Genes for Plant Abiotic Stress. 2009. (ENG., Illus.). 344p. 220.95 *(978-0-8138-1502-2(9),* Wiley-Blackwell) Wiley, John & Sons, Inc.

Jones, J. G. W., ed. The Biological Efficiency of Protein Production. 2011. (ENG., Illus.). 398p. pap. 50.00 *(978-0-521-27940-6(2))* Cambridge Univ. Pr.

Kaye, Frances W. Goodlands: A Meditation & History on the Great Plains. 2011. (ENG.). 388p. pap. 37.95 ***(978-1-897425-98-5(8))*** Univ. of British Columbia Pr. CAN. Dist: Univ. of Washington Pr.

Khalid, Halimahtun M., ed. Proceedings of Agriculture Ergonomics Development Conference. 2007. (Illus.). 328p. pap. 30.00 *(978-0-9768143-6-8(6))* IEA Pr.

Khan, Mohammad Saghir, et al, eds. Microbial Strategies for Crop Improvement. 2009. (ENG., Illus.). xviii, 358p. 199.00 *(978-3-642-01978-4(1),* 3642019781) Springer.

Khan, Mohammad Saghir & Zaidi, Almas, eds. Phosphate Solubilising Microbes for Crop Improvement. 2009. (Agriculture Issues & Policies Ser.). 89.00 *(978-1-60876-112-8(6))* Nova Science Pubs., Inc.

Kim, Moon, et al. Sensing for Agriculture & Food Quality & Safety III. 2011. (Proceedings of SPIE Ser.). 246p. pap. 90.00 ***(978-0-8194-8601-1(9))*** SPIE.

Kirschenmann, Frederick. Cultivating an Ecological Conscience: Essays from a Farmer Philosopher. Falk, Constance L., ed. 2011. (ENG.). 416p. pap. 18.95 *(978-1-58243-752-1(1),* Counterpoint) Counterpoint LLC.

Knö, et al. Designing, Modeling & Evaluation of Intercropping Systems in Chin. 2011. 216p. pap. ***(978-3-8381-2578-7(9))*** Südwestdeutscher Verlag für Hochschulschriften AG & Co. KG.

Kole, Chittaranjan, ed. Wild Crop Relatives - Genomic & Breeding Resources: Temperate Fruits. 2011. (ENG.). xxii, 247p. 189.00 *(978-3-642-16056-1(5),* 3642160565) Springer.

Krolski, Michael E. & Lunchick, Curt, eds. Non-Dietary Human Exposure & Risk Assessment, 1 vol. 2011. (ACS Symposium Ser.). (ENG., Illus.). 128p. 150.00 *(978-0-8412-2588-6(5))* American Chemical Society.

Krueger, W. C. Farm Structures & Equipment - with Information on the Farmhouse, Wells, Water Piping, Heating Systems & Livestock Houses. 2011. 86p. pap. 26.45 ***(978-1-4465-3071-9(X),*** Kent Pr.) Kent Communications, Ltd.

Kubota, Chieri & Changhoo Chun, eds. Transplant Production in the 21st Century. 2010. 304p. pap. 145.00 *(978-90-481-5570-5(3),* 9048155703) Springer.

Kuligowski, Robert J., et al. Agriculture & Hydrology Applications of Remote Sensing: 15-17 November, 2006, Goa, India. 2006. (Proceedings of SPIE Ser.). (Illus.). 382p. pap. 130.00 *(978-0-8194-6518-4(6))* SPIE.

Logsdon, Sally, et al, eds. Soil Science: Step-by-Step Field Analysis. 2008. spiral bd. 75.00 *(978-0-89118-849-0(5))* ASA-CSSA-SSSA.

Lokhorst, C. & Groot Koerkamp, P. W. G., eds. Precision livestock Farming '09. 2009. (Illus.). 368p. 108.00 *(978-90-8686-112-5(1))* Wageningen Academic Publishers NLD. Dist: Enfield Publishing & Distribution Co., Inc.

Markham, Brett L. Maximizing Your Mini Farm: Self-Sufficiency on 1/4 Acre. 2012. (ENG., Illus.). 240p. pap. 16.95 ***(978-1-61608-610-7(6),*** 608610) Skyhorse Publishing Co., Inc.

Marlitt, Wendy. Trust Instead of Dominance: Working toward a new form of ethical Horsemanship. 2011. (ENG.). 128p. pap. 29.95 *(978-0-85788-001-7(2))* Cadmos Verlag GmbH DEU. Dist: Independent Pubs. Group.

Mars, Ross & Mars, Jenny. Getting Started in Permaculture: Over 50 DIY Projects for House & Garden Using Recycled Materials. 2007. (ENG., Illus.). 96p. per. 14.95 *(978-1-85623-035-3(X))* Permanent Pubns. GBR. Dist: Chelsea Green Publishing.

Martin, Robert A. Presentation & Sales Strategies for an Agricultural Audience. rev. ed. 2010. (ENG.). 232p. pap. 46.47 *(978-0-7575-6870-1(X))* Kendall Hunt Publishing Co.

McNabb, OP, Fr. Vincent, Vincent. Nazareth or Social Chaos. 2010. (ENG., Illus.). 96p. pap. 19.95 *(978-1-932528-19-0(9))* IHS Pr.

Megersa, Birhanu & Hebo, Mamo. Exploring the Dynamic Linkages. 2010. 140p. pap. *(978-3-639-24957-6(7))* VDM Verlag Dr. Mueller e.K.

Mellor, David, et al. The Sciences of Animal Welfare. 2009. (UFAW Animal Welfare Ser.: 5). (ENG., Illus.). 224p. pap. 72.99 *(978-1-4051-3495-8(X),* Wiley-Blackwell) Wiley, John & Sons, Inc.

Messer, Kent D. & Kaiser, Harry M. Mathematical Programming for Agricultural, Environmental, & Resource Economics. 2012. (ENG., Illus.). 494p. (C). 115.95 *(978-0-470-59936-5(7),* Wiley) Wiley, John & Sons, Inc.

Mitchell, Donald Grant. My Farm of Edgewood: A Country Book. by the Author of Reveries of A Bachelor. 2006. 336p. per. 23.99 *(978-1-4255-3396-4(1))* MPublishing.

Mitchell, Donald Grant. My Farm of Edgewood: A country book. by the author of Reveries of a Bachelor. 2011. 338p. pap. 23.99 ***(978-1-4255-7634-9(6))*** MPublishing.

Momsen, Janet & Besson, Jean, eds. Caribbean Land & Development Revisited. 2007. (Studies of the Americas Ser.). (ENG., Illus.). 292p. 95.00 (978-1-4039-7392-4(X)) Palgrave Macmillan.

Moning, Elias Tana. Reinventing Indigenous Knowledge. 2008. 244p. pap. (978-3-639-03913-9(0)) VDM Verlag Dr. Mueller e.K.

Morris, Edmund. How to Get a Farm, & Where to Find. 2008. 352p. 28.99 (978-0-559-36691-8(4)); pap. 31.75 (978-0-559-36690-1(6)) BiblioBazaar.

—How to Get a Farm, & Where to Find. 2009. 180p. pap. 19.99 (978-0-217-84890-9(7)) General Bks. LLC.

—How to Get a Farm, & Where to Find. 2006. 356p. per. 26.99 (978-1-4255-3620-6(4)) MPublishing.

—Ten Acres Enough. 2009. (Gardening in America Ser.). (ENG.). 260p. pap. 17.95 (978-1-4290-1392-5(3)) Applewood Bks.

Mucherino, Antonio, et al. Data Mining in Agriculture. 2009. (Illus.). xviii, 272p. (978-0-387-88615-2(X)) Springer.

Muhammad, Saleem, et al. Plant Extracts & Red Flour Beetle: Effect of Different Plant Extracts & Oils Against Red Flour Beetle. 2011. 104p. pap. **(978-3-639-32089-3(1))** VDM Verlag Dr. Mueller e.K.

Murphy, Denis. Plants, Biotechnology & Agriculture. 2011. (Modular Texts). 312p. 145.00 **(978-1-84593-913-7(1))** CABI GBR. Dist: Stylus Publishing, LLC.

Murphy, Denis J. Plants, Biotechnology & Agriculture. 2011. (978-1-84593-871-0(2)) CABI.

—Plants, Biotechnology & Agriculture. 2011. (Modular Texts). 312p. pap. 75.00 (978-1-84593-688-4(4)) CABI GBR. Dist: Stylus Publishing, LLC.

Nash, John Adams. The Progressive Farmer: A Scientific Treatise on Agricultural Chemistry, the Geology of Agriculture; on Plants, Animals, Manures, & Soils. Applied T. 2006. 268p. per. 23.99 (978-1-4255-2351-0(X)) MPublishing.

National Research Council (U.S.), Committee on the Earth System Science for Decisions About Human Welfare: Contributions of Remote Sensing Staff, contrib. by. Contributions of Land Remote Sensing for Decisions about Food Security & Human Health: Workshop Report. 2006. (ENG., Illus.). 112p. pap. 29.75 (978-0-309-10295-7(2)) National Academies Pr.

Neale, Christopher M. U. & Maltese, Antonino. Remote Sensing for Agriculture, Ecosystems, & Hydrology XI: 1-3 September 2009, Berlin, Germany. 2009. (Proceedings of SPIE Ser.). (Illus.). 476p. pap. 160.00 (978-0-8194-7777-4(X)) SPIE.

Nelson, Gerald C. Agriculture & Climate Change: An Agenda for Negotiation in Copenhagen. 2009. pap. **(978-0-89629-658-9(X))** International Food Policy Research Institute.

—Climate Change: Impact on Agriculture & Costs of Adaptation. 2009. (Illus.). ix, 19p. pap. **(978-0-89629-535-3(4))** International Food Policy Research Institute.

Nevo, E., et al. Evolution of Wild Emmer & Wheat Improvement: Population Genetics, Genetic Resources, & Genome Organization of Wheat's Progenitor, Triticum Dicoccoides. 2010. (ENG., Illus.). xxii, 364p. pap. 339.00 (978-3-642-07512-4(6), 3642075126) Springer.

Nitrogen in Agricultural Systems. 2008. (Agronomy Ser.: 49). lib. bdg. 150.00 (978-0-89118-164-4(4)) ASA-CSSA-SSSA.

Nord, Chelsea, ed. The Beck's Experience: 75 Years of a Remarkable Way to do Business. 2012. (ENG.). 49.99 **(978-0-9850622-0-0(7))** Beck's Hybrids.

Norton, John Pitkin. Elements of Scientific Agriculture, or the Connection Between Science & the Art of Practical Farming Prize Essay of the New York State Agricultural. 2006. 240p. per. 20.99 (978-1-4255-2017-5(0)) MPublishing.

Oerke, Erich-Christian, et al, eds. Precision Crop Protection - the Challenge & Use of Heterogeneity. 2010. (ENG., Illus.). xxiv, 441p. 209.00 (978-90-481-9276-2(5), 9048192765) Springer.

Olcott, Henry Steel. Outlines of the First Course of Yale Agricultural Lectures by Henry S Olcott with an Introduction by John a Porter. 2006. 200p. per. 18.99 (978-1-4255-1614-7(9)) MPublishing.

Owe, Manfred. Remote Sensing for Agriculture, Ecosystems, & Hydrology VIII: 11-13 September, 2006, Stockholm, Sweden. 2006. (Proceedings of SPIE Ser.). (Illus.). 364p. pap. 120.00 (978-0-8194-6454-5(6)) SPIE.

Owe, Manfred, et al. Remote Sensing for Agriculture, Ecosystems, & Hydrology IX: 18-20 September 2007, Florence, Italy. 2007. (Proceedings of SPIE Ser.). (Illus.). 354p. pap. 120.00 **(978-0-8194-6900-7(9))** SPIE.

Owe, Manfred, et al. Remote Sensing for Agriculture, Ecosystems, & Hydrology X: 16-18 September 2008, Cardiff, Wales, United Kingdom. 2008. (Proceedings of SPIE Ser.). (Illus.). 390p. pap. 90.00 (978-0-8194-7335-6(9)) SPIE.

Patil, Manjunath S. & J. Dinakara Adiga. Strategies for in Vitro Conservation of Gladiolus. 2011. 84p. pap. **(978-3-8433-9339-3(7))** Lambert Academic Publishing.

Pearson, Haydn Sandborn. Successful Part Time Farming. 2011. 352p. 51.95 **(978-1-258-10161-9(0))** Literary Licensing, LLC.

Phoenix, Laurel & Walter, Lynn. Critical Food Issues: Problems & State-of-the-Art Solutions Worldwide, 2 vols. 2009. (Illus.). 556p. 195.00 (978-0-313-35444-1(8), C35444, Praeger Pubs.) Greenwood Publishing Group, Inc.

Pinhasi, Ron & Stock, Jay T., eds. Human Bioarchaeology of the Transition to Agriculture. 2011. (ENG., Illus.). 500p. 159.95 (978-0-470-74730-8(7), Wiley) Wiley, John & Sons, Inc.

Posudin. Practical Spectro Agricult Food Scien: Practical Spectroscopy in Agriculture & Food Science. 2007. (ENG.). 208p. (C). 69.95 (978-1-57808-505-7(5)) BIOS Scientific Publishers Ltd. GBR. Dist: Taylor & Francis Group.

Robards, Hugh J. Foxhunting: How to Watch & Listen. 2011. (Foxhunters Library). (ENG., Illus.). 160p. pap. 16.95 (978-1-58667-120-4(0)) Derrydale Pr., The.

Robinson, Solon. Guano. 2008. 148p. 21.99 (978-0-554-37334-8(3)); 24.99 (978-0-554-28031-8(0)) BiblioBazaar.

—Guano: A Treatise of Practical Information for Farmers. 2007. (ENG.). 132p. pap. 18.99 (978-1-4346-4551-7(7)) BiblioBazaar.

Robson, A. D. & Abbott, L. K., eds. Management of Mycorrhizas in Agriculture, Horticulture & Forestry. 2011. (Developments in Plant & Soil Sciences Ser.). 252p. pap. 229.00 (978-90-481-4364-1(0), 9048143640) Springer.

Rosmann, Michael. Excellent Joy: Fishing, Farming, Hunting, & Psychology. 2011. 184p. pap. 21.95 **(978-1-888160-55-0(1))** Ice Cube Pr.

Rosso Grossman, Margaret, ed. Agriculture & the Polluter Pays Principle. 2009. 392p. pap. 140.00 (978-1-905221-22-6(3)) British Institute of International & Comparative Law GBR. Dist: International Specialized Bk. Services.

Routledge Staff, contrib. by. Agriculture, 12 vols., Set. 2006. (Routledge Library Editions). 3600p. 2125.00 (978-0-415-37652-5(1)) Routledge.

Saint Maur, Kate. The Earth's Bounty. 2008. (Cooking in America Ser.). (ENG.). 548p. pap. 31.95 (978-1-4290-1135-8(1)) Applewood Bks.

Salander, Lawrence M. & Alwell, Dana N. Food Production: New Research. 2011. (Food Science & Technology Ser.). (Illus.). 191p. 129.00 (978-1-61209-631-5(X)) Nova Science Pubs., Inc.

Schmitt, Donald Peter & Schmitt, Julia Marie Pualeialii. Agriculture, Nematology & the Society of Nematologists. 2007. 19.59 net. (978-0-9753229-1-8(5)) Schmitt & Assocs. of Marceline.

Schuman, Stanley H. Rainbows in Washtubs: Diagnostic Mysteries in Agromedicine. 2008. 152p. 36.00 (978-0-7890-3276-8(7), Informa Healthcare) Taylor & Francis Group.

Shafi, Dr. Mohammad, et al. Enhancing Soil Fertility & Crop Yield by Crop Rotation & Crop Residues. 2011. 132p. pap. **(978-3-8443-9125-1(8))** Lambert Academic Publishing.

Simopoulos, A. P., ed. Healthy Agriculture, Healthy Nutrition, Healthy People. 2011. (World Review of Nutrition & Dietetics Ser.). (ENG., Illus.). 274p. **(978-3-8055-9779-1(7))** Karger, S. AG.

Singh, A. k. & Singh, A. K. Reclamation of Coal Mined Out Lands. 2011. 76p. pap. **(978-3-8454-1603-8(3))** Lambert Academic Publishing.

Souza, Ricardo M., ed. Plant-Parasitic Nematodes of Coffee. 2010. xvi, 340p. pap. 239.00 (978-90-481-7967-1(X), 904817967X) Springer.

Srinivasan, Ancha, ed. Handbook of Precision Agriculture: Principles & Applications. 2006. (ENG., Illus.). 833p. 149.95 (978-1-56022-954-4(3)); pap. 104.95 (978-1-56022-955-1(1)) Taylor & Francis Group GBR. (CRC Press). Dist: Taylor & Francis Group.

Stafford, J. V., ed. Precision Agriculture '07. 2007. 876p. 195.00 (978-90-8686-024-1(9)) Wageningen Academic Publishers NLD. Dist: Enfield Publishing & Distribution Co., Inc.

Steinmentz, Jasia. Eat Local: Simple Steps to Enjoy Locally-Grown, Healthy & Affordable Foods. 2011. (ENG.). 196p. pap. 12.95 (978-0-9632814-5-6(3)) New World Publishing.

Stephens, Henry. The Book of the Farm: Detailing the Labours of the Farmer, Farm-steward, Ploughman, Shepherd, Hedger, Cattle-man, Field-worker, & Dairy-maid. 2011. (Cambridge Library Collection - History Ser.). (ENG.). 738p. pap. 48.00 (978-1-108-02495-2(5)); (ENG.). 706p. pap. 48.00 (978-1-108-02496-9(3)); (Illus.). 710p. pap. 48.00 (978-1-108-02494-5(7)) Cambridge Univ. Pr.

Streeter, John Williams. The Fat of the Land: The Story of an American Farm. 2007. 274p. pap. 21.99 (978-1-4346-0172-8(2)); (ENG.). 306p. pap. 24.99 (978-1-4346-0246-6(X)) BiblioBazaar.

—The Fat of the Land: The Story of an American Farm. 2009. 276p. pap. (978-1-4099-7223-5(2)) Dodo Pr.

Successful Farming Magazine Staff. Ag Reference Guide: All the Measurements, Conversions & Formulas You'll Need for the Farm. 2008. (Successful Farming Reference Guides). 160p. pap. 9.95 (978-0-696-23614-3(1)) Meredith Bks.

Surjandari, Isti. Three Essays on Site Specific Management. 2009. 120p. pap. (978-3-639-19569-9(8)) VDM Verlag Dr. Mueller e.K.

Swapna, M. & Srivastava, Sangeeta. Molecular Marker Applications for Improving Sugar Content in Sugarcane. 2012. (SpringerBriefs in Plant Science Ser.). (ENG., Illus.). vii, 49p. pap. 49.95 **(978-1-4614-2256-3(6)**, 1461422566) Springer.

Taeb, M. & A. H. Zakri. Agriculture, Human Security, & Peace: A Crossroad in African Development. 2008. (Illus.). 187p. pap. 29.95 (978-1-55753-482-8(9)) Purdue Univ. Pr.

Thornley, J. H. M. & France, J. Mathematical Models in Agriculture: Quantitative Methods for the Plant, Animal & Ecological Sciences. 2nd rev. ed. 2006. 928p. (C). 315.00 (978-0-85199-010-1(X)) CABI GBR. Dist: Stylus Publishing, LLC.

Thun, Maria & Thun, Matthias. The North American Biodynamic Sowing & Planting Calendar 2009. 2008. (Illus.). 64p. pap. 13.95 (978-0-86315-655-7(X)) Floris Bks. GBR. Dist: SteinerBooks, Inc.

Titchmarsh, Alan. The Complete Countryman: A User's Guide to Traditional Skills & Lost Crafts. 2011. (ENG., Illus.). 312p. 45.00 **(978-1-84607-393-9(6))** BBC Worldwide GBR. Dist: Independent Pubs. Group.

Torres, Rebecca Maria & Momsen, Janet, eds. Tourism & Agriculture. 2011. (Contemporary Geographies of Leisure, Tourism & Mobility Ser.). (ENG., Illus.). 240p. (C). 148.00 (978-0-415-58429-6(9)) Routledge.

Turner, Suzanne & Wilson, Joanne Seale. Houston's Silent Garden: Glenwood Cemetery, 1871-2009. 2010. (Sara & John Lindsey Series in the Arts & Humanities Ser.). (ENG.). 304p. 60.00 (978-1-60344-163-6(8)) Texas A&M Univ. Pr.

Ucko, Peter & Dimbleby, G., eds. The Domestication & Exploitation of Plants & Animals. 2007. (ENG., Illus.). 607p. (gr. 11). pap. 44.95 (978-0-202-36169-7(1)) Aldine Transaction.

Ullah, Inam, et al. Inheritance of Important Traits in Bread Wheat Using Diallel Analysis. 2011. 144p. pap. **(978-3-8433-7330-2(2))** Lambert Academic Publishing.

Van Henten, E. J., et al, eds. Precision Agriculture '09. 2009. (Illus.). 992p. 203.00 (978-90-8686-113-2(X)) Wageningen Academic Publishers NLD. Dist: Enfield Publishing & Distribution Co., Inc.

Various. The Farming Year. 2010. 192p. 34.45 (978-1-4455-1601-1(2)); pap. 27.95 (978-1-4455-1217-4(3)) Research Pr.

Varshney, Rajeev K. & Tuberosa, Roberto, eds. Genomics-Assisted Crop Improvement: Vol 2: Genomics Applications in Crops. 2010. xx, 509p. pap. 259.00 (978-90-481-7600-7(X), 904817600X) Springer.

Waddell, Gene, ed. John Bachman: Selected Writings on Science, Race, & Religion. 2011. (Publications of the Southern Texts Society Ser.). (ENG., Illus.). 400p. 39.95 (978-0-8203-3818-7(4)) Univ. of Georgia Pr.

Waddington, Paul. 21st-Century Smallholder: From Window Boxes to Allotments - How to Go Back to the Land Without Leaving Home. 2008. (ENG., Illus.). 224p. pap. 15.95 (978-1-905811-16-8(0)) Transworld Publishers Ltd. GBR. Dist: Independent Pubs. Group.

Wajad, Nazeer. Inheritance Pattern of Some Yield Contributing Traits in Spring Wheat: Differential Gene Expression Patterns for Some Polygenically Controlled Yield Contributing Traits in Wheat (Triticum Aestivum L.) 2011. 84p. pap. **(978-3-639-33106-6(0))** VDM Verlag Dr. Mueller e.K.

Wallach, Daniel. Working with Dynamic Crop Models: Evaluation, Analysis, Parameterization, & Applications. Wallach, Daniel et al, eds. 2006. (ENG., Illus.). 462p. (C). 101.00 (978-0-444-52135-4(6), Elsevier Science) Elsevier Science & Technology Bks.

Wambaugh, Joseph. The Onion Field. 2007. (ENG.). 512p. pap. 15.00 (978-0-385-34159-2(8), Delta) Random House Publishing Group.

Wani, Suhas P., et al. Integrated Watershed Management in Rainfed Agriculture. 2011. (ENG., Illus.). 496p. (C). 119.95 (978-0-415-88277-4(X), CRC Press) Taylor & Francis Group GBR. Dist: Taylor & Francis Group.

Waring, George E. (George Edwin). The Elements of Agriculture. 2006. 308p. per. 23.99 (978-1-4255-2906-2(2)) MPublishing.

Weidenbörner, Martin. Mycotoxins in Feedstuffs. 2nd ed. 2011. (ENG., Illus.). xxv, 267p. 209.00 **(978-1-4614-0802-4(4)**, 1461408024) Springer.

White, Mason & Przybylski, Maya, eds. On Farming: Bracket 1. 2010. (ENG., Illus.). 252p. pap. (978-84-92861-21-7(5)) Actar Birkhauser Distribution.

Willis, J. C. Agriculture in the Tropics: An Elementary Treatise. 3rd rev. ed. 2011. (Illus.). 288p. pap. 23.99 (978-1-107-60020-1(0)) Cambridge Univ. Pr.

Winder, Gordon M. The American Reaper: Harvesting Networks & Technology, 1830-1910. 2012. (Modern Economic & Social History Ser.). (Illus.). 230p. E-Book 119.95 **(978-1-4094-2461-1(8))** Ashgate Publishing Co.

Xu, Fangsen, et al, eds. Advances in Plant & Animal Boron Nutrition: Proceedings of the 3rd International Symposium on all Aspects of Plant & Animal Boron Nutrition. 2010. xvi, 402p. pap. 259.00 (978-90-481-7356-3(6), 9048173566) Springer.

Yadav, Shyam S., et al, eds. Lentil: An Ancient Crop for Modern Times. 2010. xxiv, 462p. pap. 259.00 (978-90-481-7605-2(0), 9048176050) Springer.

Zimdahl, Robert L. Agriculture's Ethical Horizon. 2nd ed. 2012. (ENG.). 308p. 53.95 **(978-0-12-416043-9(3))** Elsevier Science & Technology Bks.

AGRICULTURE—ACCOUNTING

Aicpa. AICPA Audit & Accounting Guide Agricultural Producers & Agricultural Cooperatives. 2007. pap. 61.25 (978-0-87051-681-8(7)) American Institute of Certified Public Accountants.

Armbruster, David B. & Red Wing Business Systems Staff. Introduction to Agricultural Accounting. Date not set. (Orig.). pap. 19.95 (978-0-87265-011-4(1)) Red Wing Business Systems, Inc.

Elliot, Jack. Agribusiness: Decisions & Dollars. 2nd ed. 2008. (ENG.). (C). 112p. pap., wbk. ed. 37.95 (978-1-4283-1914-1(X)); (Illus.). 336p. 139.95 (978-1-4283-1912-7(3)) Delmar Cengage Learning.

Jack, Lisa. Sustainable Change Through Benchmarking in Food & Farming. 2009. (Gower Sustainable Food Chains Ser.). (Illus.). 148p. 114.95 (978-0-566-08835-3(5), Gower Publishing Co., Ltd.) Ashgate Publishing, Ltd. GBR. Dist: Ashgate Publishing Co.

Moore, Donna & Moore, Brent. Better Farm Accounting: A Practical Guide for Preparing Farm Income Tax Returns, Financial Statements, & Analysis Reports. 5th rev. ed. 2007. (ENG.). 48p. pap. 6.50 (978-0-8138-2156-6(8), Wiley-Blackwell) Wiley, John & Sons, Inc.

Wheeling, Barbara M. Introduction to Agricultural Accounting. 2007. (ENG., Illus.). 336p. (C). 87.95 (978-1-4180-3834-2(2)) Delmar Cengage Learning.

AGRICULTURE—ADMINISTRATION

see Agricultural Administration

AGRICULTURE—BIBLIOGRAPHY

Agriculture, Vol. 1. 746p. (978-0-8357-0832-6(2)) Univ. Microfilms, Inc.

Rogers, Elizabeth Barlow. Writing the Garden: A Literary Conversation across Two Centuries. 2011. (ENG., Illus.). 312p. 27.95 (978-1-56792-440-4(9)) Godine, David R. Pub.

Wilkinson, Anne. The Victorian Gardener. 2011. (ENG., Illus.). 256p. pap. 23.95 **(978-0-7524-6034-5(X))** History Pr. Ltd.,The GBR. Dist: Independent Pubs. Group.

AGRICULTURE—COLLECTIVE LABOR AGREEMENTS

see Collective Bargaining—Agriculture

AGRICULTURE—DATA PROCESSING

Agricultural, Farming, & Ranching Software Guide. 2009. 322p. 19.95 (978-0-912603-25-4(9)) Micro Information Publishing / NXTgen.

Banks, Aiden & Melves, Scott F. Horizons in Crop Production: Precision Agriculture & No-Till Farming. 2012. pap. **(978-1-61942-109-7(7))** Nova Science Pubs., Inc.

Clay, David & Shanahan, John F., eds. GIS Applications in Agriculture: Nutrient Management for Energy Efficiency. 2011. (GIS Applications in Agriculture Ser.). (ENG., Illus.). 472p. 139.95 (978-1-4200-9270-7(7), CRC Press) Taylor & Francis Group GBR. Dist: Taylor & Francis Group.

Clay, Sharon A. GIS Applications in Agriculture Vol. 2: Invasive Species. 2011. (GIS Applications in Agriculture Ser.). (ENG., Illus.). 448p. 129.95 (978-1-4200-7880-0(1), CRC Press) Taylor & Francis Group GBR. Dist: Taylor & Francis Group.

Course Technology. SAM 2007 Projects 4. 0 Printed Access Card. 2009. (ENG.). (C). 44.95 (978-1-4390-4434-6(1)) Course Technology.

Do Prado, Hércules Antonio, et al, eds. Computational Methods for Agricultural Research: Advances & Applications. 2010. (Illus.). 350p. 180.00 (978-1-61692-871-1(9), Information Science Reference) IGI Global.

Li, Daoliang, ed. Computer & Computing Technologies in Agriculture, Volume I: First IFIP TC 12 International Conference on Computer & Computing Technologies in Agriculture (CCTA 2007), Wuyishan, China, August 18-20 2007. (IFIP Advances in Information & Communication Technology Ser.). xviii, 736p. 2010. pap. 269.00 (978-1-4419-4583-9(0), 1441945830) 2008. 269.00 (978-0-387-77250-9(2)) Springer.

—Computer & Computing Technologies in Agriculture, Volume II: First IFIP TC 12 International Conference on Computer & Computing Technologies in Agriculture (CCTA 2007), Wuyishan, China, August 18-20 2007. (IFIP Advances in Information & Communication Technology Ser.). xx, 744p. 2010. pap. 269.00 (978-1-4419-4584-6(9), 1441945849) 2008. 269.00 (978-0-387-77252-3(9)) Springer.

Li, Daoliang, et al, eds. Computer & Computing Technologies in Agriculture IV: 4th IFIP TC 12 Conference, CCTA 2010, Nanchang, China, October 22-25, 2010, Part II, Selected Papers, 4 vols. 2011. (IFIP Advances in Information & Communication Technology Ser.). (Illus.). xiv, 745p. 209.00 (978-3-642-18335-5(2), 3642183352) Springer.

—Computer & Computing Technologies in Agriculture IV: 4th IFIP TC 12 Conference, CCTA 2010, Nanchang, China, October 22-25, 2010, Selected Papers, Part I. 2011. (IFIP Advances in Information & Communication Technology Ser.). xxxviii, 754p. 209.00 (978-3-642-18332-4(8), 3642183328) Springer.

—Computer & Computing Technologies in Agriculture IV: 4th IFIP TC 12 International Conference, CCTA 2010, Nanchang, China, October 22-25, 2010, Selected Papers, Part III, 4 vols. 2011. (IFIP Advances in Information & Communication Technology Ser.). (Illus.). xiv, 751p. 209.00 (978-3-642-18353-9(0), 3642183530) Springer.

—Computer & Computing Technologies in Agriculture IV: 4th IFIP TC 12 International Conference, CCTA 2010, Nanchang, China, October 22-25, 2010, Selected Papers, Part IV, 4 vols. 2011. (IFIP Advances in Information & Communication Technology Ser.). (Illus.). xiv, 774p. 209.00 (978-3-642-18368-3(9), 3642183689) Springer.

Li, Daoliang & Zhao, Chunjiang, eds. Computer & Computing Technologies in Agriculture II, Volume 1: The Second IFIP International Conference on Computer & Computing Technologies in Agriculture (CCTA2008), October 18-20, 2008, Beijing, China. 2009. (IFIP International Federation for Information Processing Ser.). (ENG., Illus.). xxiv, 788p. 299.00 (978-1-4419-0208-5(2)) Springer.

—Computer & Computing Technologies in Agriculture II, Volume 2: The Second IFIP International Conference on Computer & Computing Technologies in Agriculture (CCTA2008), October 18-20, 2008, Beijing, China. 2009. (IFIP International Federation for Information Processing Ser.). (ENG., Illus.). xxiv, 740p. 299.00 (978-1-4419-0210-8(4)) Springer.

—Computer & Computing Technologies in Agriculture II, Volume 3: The Second IFIP International Conference on Computer & Computing Technologies in Agriculture (CCTA2008), October 18-20, 2008, Beijing, China. (IFIP Advances in Information & Communication Technology Ser.). (ENG., Illus.). xxiv, 776p. 2010. pap. 299.00 **(978-1-4419-5495-4(3)**, 1441954953) 2009. 299.00 (978-1-4419-0212-2(0)) Springer.

Li, Daoliang & Zhao, Chunjiang, eds. Computer & Computing Technologies in Agriculture III: Third IFIP TC 12 International Conference, CCTA 2009, Beijing, China, October 14-17, 2009, Revised Selected Papers. 2010. (IFIP Advances in Information & Communication Technology Ser.). xv, 561p. 169.00 (978-3-642-12219-4(1), 3642122191) Springer.

Manos, Basil. Decision Support Systems in Agriculture, Food & the Environment: Trends, Applications & Advances. 2010. (Illus.). 350p. 180.00 (978-1-61520-881-4(X)) IGI Global.

Mucherino, Antonio, et al. Data Mining in Agriculture. 2009. (Springer Optimization & Its Applications Ser.). (ENG., Illus.). xviii, 274p. 59.95 (978-0-387-88614-5(1), 0387886141) Springer.

Papajorgji, Petraq J. & Pardalos, Panos M. Software Engineering Techniques Applied to Agricultural Systems: An Object-Oriented & UML Approach. 2010. (Applied Optimization Ser.). (Illus.). xiv, 247p. pap. 129.00 (978-1-4419-3926-5(1), 1441939261) Springer.

Papajorgji, Petraq J. & Pardalos, Panos M., eds. Advances in Modeling Agricultural Systems. 2008. (Springer Optimization & Its Applications Ser.). (Illus.). 304p. 139.00 (978-0-387-75180-1(7)) Springer.

Phongphom, Artittaya & PONGQUAN, Soparth. Farmer's Network Approach. 2011. 252p. pap. ***(978-3-8443-1150-1(5))*** Lambert Academic Publishing.

Pierce, Francis J. & Clay, David, eds. GIS Applications in Agriculture. 2007. (GIS Applications for Agriculture Ser.: Vol. 1). (ENG., Illus.). 224p. 125.95 *(978-0-8493-7526-2(6)*, CRC Press) Taylor & Francis Group GBR. Dist: Taylor & Francis Group.

Plant, Richard E. Spatial Statistics in Ecology & Agriculture Using R & Geoda. 2012. (ENG., Illus.). 648p. 89.95 ***(978-1-4398-1913-5(0)***, CRC Press) Taylor & Francis Group GBR. Dist: Taylor & Francis Group.

Tan, Honghua & Luo, Qi. PIAGENG 2009: 11-12 July 2009, Zhangjiajie, China. 2009. (Proceedings of SPIE Ser.). (Illus.). 690p. pap. 130.00 *(978-0-8194-7801-6(6))* SPIE.

AGRICULTURE—DICTIONARIES, INDEXES, ETC.

A. and C. Black Publishers Staff, et al. Dictionary of Agriculture: Over 6,000 Terms Clearly Defined. 3rd rev. ed. 2006. (ENG.). 288p. per. 16.95 *(978-0-7136-7778-2(3))* A & C Black GBR. Dist: Macmillan.

Considine, Glenn. Foods & Food Production Encyclopedia, 4 vols. 2nd ed. 2011. 3000p. 1350.00 *(978-0-387-75130-6(0)*, 0387751300) Springer.

Gehring, Abigail R. The Illustrated Encyclopedia of Country Living. 2011. (ENG., Illus.). 912p. pap. 29.95 *(978-1-61608-467-7(7)*, 608467) Skyhorse Publishing Co., Inc.

Larousse Staff. Larousse Dictionnaire Agricole. (FRE.). 195.00 *(978-0-320-00621-0(2))* French & European Pubns., Inc.

Metallie, G. Dictionnaire d'Agriculture: Science de l'Animal (Chinois-Francais-Anglais) - Animal Science (Chinese-French-English) Date not set.Tr. of Dictionary of Agriculture. 624p. pap. 195.00 *(978-0-7859-9184-7(0))* French & European Pubns., Inc.

AGRICULTURE—EARLY WORKS TO 1800

Cato, Marcus Porcius. Roman Farm Management: The Treatises of Cato & Varro. 2008. 380p. 29.99 *(978-0-559-22509-3(1))* 2008. 380p. pap. 32.75 *(978-0-559-22506-2(7))* 2007. (ENG.). 242p. pap. 20.99 *(978-1-4264-5811-8(8))* 2007. (ENG.). 282p. pap. 23.99 *(978-1-4264-5871-2(1))* BiblioBazaar.

—Roman Farm Management: The Treatises of Cato & Varro. 2007. (ENG.). 172p. per. *(978-1-4068-4446-7(2))* Echo Library.

Cato, Marcus Porcius & Varro, Marcus Terentius. Roman Farm Management: The Treatises of Cato & Varro. Belvoir, F. H., ed. 2009. 240p. pap. *(978-1-4099-5490-3(0))* Dodo Pr.

Dalby, Andrew. Geoponika: Farm Work - A Modern Translation of the Roman & Byzantine Farming Handbook. 2011. (ENG.). 368p. (C). 60.00 *(978-1-903018-69-9(2))* Prospect Bks. GBR. Dist: Brown, David Bk. Co., The.

Eliot, Jared. Essays upon Field Husbandry in New England & Other Papers, 1748-1762. Carman, Harry J. & Tugwell, Rexford G., eds. reprint ed. 24.50 *(978-0-404-02276-1(6))* AMS Pr., Inc.

Rodgers, R. H. L. Iuni Moderati Columellae Res Rustica: Incerti auctoris Liber de Arboribus. 2010. (ENG & LAT.). 600p. 99.00 *(978-0-19-927154-2(2))* Oxford Univ. Pr., Inc

Taegio, Bartolomeo. La Villa. 2011. (Penn Studies in Landscape Architecture Ser.). (ITA & ENG., Illus.). 312p. (C). 65.00 *(978-0-8122-4317-8(X))* Univ. of Pennsylvania Pr.

Tusser, Thomas. Five Hundred Points of Good Husbandry. 2007. (ENG.). 404p. 49.95 *(978-0-548-22797-8(7))*; 408p. per. 34.95 *(978-1-4325-5052-3(7))* Kessinger Publishing, LLC.

—A Hundreth Good Pointes of Husbandrie. 2010. (ENG.). 40p. pap. 36.95 *(978-1-4092-1230-0(0))* Lulu Enterprises Inc.

AGRICULTURE—ECOLOGY

see Agricultural Ecology

AGRICULTURE—ECONOMIC ASPECTS

see also Agricultural Development Projects; Agricultural Industries; Agricultural Prices; Farm Management; Farm Produce—Marketing; Produce Trade; Rent

Akinyemi, O.M. Agricultural Production: Organic & Conventional Systems. 2007. (ENG.). 240p. (C). 69.95 *(978-1-57808-512-5(8))* BIOS Scientific Publishers Ltd. GBR. Dist: Taylor & Francis Group.

Akram-Lodhi, A. Haroon & Kay, Cristobal. Peasants & Globalization: Political Economy, Rural Transformation & the Agrarian Question. Akram-Lodhi, A. Haroon & Kay, Cristòbal, eds. 2009. (Routledge ISS Studies in Rural Livelihoods Ser.). 336p. 150.00 *(978-0-415-44629-7(5))* Routledge.

Alao, Abiodun. The Impact of Icts on Agricultural Development in the Rural Community. 2010. 176p. pap. *(978-3-639-26002-1(3))* VDM Verlag Dr. Mueller e.K.

Albritton, Robert, told to. Let Them Eat Junk: How Capitalism Creates Hunger & Obesity. 2009. (ENG., Illus.). 259p. pap. 24.95 *(978-1-894037-38-9(3))* Arbeiter Ring Publishing CAN. Dist: AK Pr. Distribution.

Ali Meerza, Syed Imran. Role of Rural-Urban Migration in Increasing Rural Child Labor. 2010. 64p. pap. *(978-3-639-25809-7(6))* VDM Verlag Dr. Mueller e.K.

Amad, Mohammad. Agriculture Poverty & Reform in Iran (Rle Iran E) 2011. (Routledge Library Editions: Iran Ser.). (ENG.). 192p. 100.00 *(978-0-415-61438-2(4))* Routledge.

Anderson, Kym, ed. The Political Economy of Agricultural Price Distortions. 2010. (ENG., Illus.). 464p. 95.00 *(978-0-521-76323-3(1))* Cambridge Univ. Pr.

Angelsen, Arild, et al. Measuring Livelihoods & Environmental Dependence: Methods for Research & Fieldwork. Smith Olsen, Carsten, ed. 2011. (ENG., Illus.). 288p. pap. 49.95 *(978-1-84971-133-3(X))* Routledge.

Bachev, Hrabrin. Governing of Agro-Ecosystem Services. 2009. 88p. pap. *(978-3-639-20773-6(4))* VDM Verlag Dr. Mueller e.K.

Bagchi, Kanak, ed. Regional Disparities in India's Socio-Economic Development. 2011. (Illus.). 252p. 42.25 *(978-81-7708-258-6(2))* New Century Publications IND. Dist: International Specialized Bk. Services.

Ball, V. Eldon, et al, eds. The Economic Impact of Public Support to Agriculture: An International Perspective. 2010. (Studies in Productivity & Efficiency Ser.). (Illus.). xi, 348p. 219.00 *(978-1-4419-6384-0(7)*, 1441963847) Springer.

Ball, V. Eldon, et al. The Economic Impact of Public Support to Agriculture: An International Perspective. 2010. (Studies in Productivity & Efficiency: Vol. 7). (Illus.). xi, 348p. E-Book ***(978-1-4419-6385-7(5))*** Springer.

Barbier, Edward. Scarcity & Frontiers: How Economies Have Developed Through Natural Resource Exploitation. 2010. (ENG., Illus.). 768p. 105.00 *(978-0-521-87773-2(3))* Cambridge Univ. Pr.

Barrett, Christopher B., ed. Agricultural Development, 4 vols., Set. 2011. (Critical Concepts in Development Studies). (ENG., Illus.). 1760p. (C). 1095.00 ***(978-0-415-58187-5(7))*** Routledge.

Beierlein, James G., et al. Principles of Agribusiness Management. 4th ed. 2008. 354p. (C). 60.95 *(978-1-57766-540-3(6))* Waveland Pr., Inc.

Bello, Walden. The Food Wars. 2009. (ENG., Illus.). 160p. pap. 16.95 *(978-1-84467-331-5(6)*, 844331) Verso Bks. GBR. Dist: Norton, W. W. & Co., Inc.

Bhimani, Hirenkumar, et al. The Winning Innings of Management: A Case from Amlsad Multipurpose PACS. 2011. 100p. pap. ***(978-3-8443-9297-5(1))*** Lambert Academic Publishing.

Bohnet, Iris. Exploring Landscape Character. 2011. 512p. pap. ***(978-3-8443-1166-2(1))*** Lambert Academic Publishing.

Borras Jr., Saturnino M., et al, eds. The Politics of Biofuels, Land & Agrarian Change. 2011. (Critical Agrarian Studies). (ENG., Illus.). 408p. (C). 158.00 *(978-0-415-61320-0(5))* Routledge.

Boussard, Jean-Marc, et al. Should Global Agriculture Be Liberalized? Theories, Models & Realities. 2008. (ENG., Illus.). 175p. (C). pap. 39.95 *(978-1-57808-542-2(X))* BIOS Scientific Publishers Ltd. GBR. Dist: Taylor & Francis Group.

Brenner, Y. S. Agriculture & the Economic Development of Low Income Countries. (ENG.). 254p. 210.00 ***(978-3-11-177256-1(X))*** De Gruyter, Mouton DEU. Dist: de Gruyter, Walter GmbH & Co. KG.

Brouwer, Floor M. & Ittersum, Martin van, eds. Environmental & Agricultural Modelling: Integrated Approaches for Policy Impact Assessment. 2010. (ENG., Illus.). xx, 325p. 169.00 *(978-90-481-3618-6(0)*, 9048136180) Springer.

Bulliet, Richard W. Cotton, Climate, & Camels in Early Islamic Iran: A Moment in World History. 2011. (ENG.). 184p. (gr. 17). pap. 24.50 *(978-0-231-14837-5(2))* Columbia Univ. Pr.

Canavari, M. & Fritz, M., eds. Food Supply Networks: Trust & E-business. 2012. 272p. 110.00 *(978-1-84593-639-6(6))*; pap. 55.00 *(978-1-84593-638-9(8))* CABI GBR. Dist: Stylus Publishing, LLC.

Carey, Henry Charles. Letters to the Hon Schuyler Colfax by H C Carey. 2006. 120p. per. 16.99 *(978-1-4255-0819-7(7))* MPublishing.

Chala, Zelalem. Least Cost Solutions for Removing Poultry Litter from Eucha-Spavinaw Watershed - Optimum Allocation & Processing Into Electricity & Fertilizer Und. 2008. 76p. pap. *(978-3-639-03084-6(2))* VDM Verlag Dr. Mueller e.K.

Chameides, Bill & Willey, Zach, eds. Harnessing Farms & Forests in the Low-Carbon Economy: How to Create, Measure, & Verify Greenhouse Gas Offsets. 2007. (ENG., Illus.). 240p. per. 60.00 *(978-0-8223-4168-0(9))* Duke Univ. Pr.

Christie, G., et al. Financial Management for Agribusiness. 2007. (Landlinks Press Ser.). (Illus.). 360p. pap. 57.50 *(978-0-643-09295-2(1))* CSIRO Publishing AUS. Dist: Stylus Publishing, LLC.

Clunies-Ross, Tracey & Hildyard, Nicholas. The Politics of Industrial Agriculture. 2nd ed. 2009. (Natural Resource Management Set Ser.). (ENG.). 172p. 110.00 *(978-1-84971-022-0(8))* Routledge.

Cohen, R. L. The Economics of Agriculture. 2008. 216p. *(978-1-4437-4018-0(7)*, Obscure Pr.) Read Bks.

Cramer, Gail L. Agricultural Economics & Agribusiness 9th rev. ed. 2008. 544p. 102.95 *(978-0-471-71899-4(8))* Wiley, John & Sons, Inc.

Cramer, Gail L., ed. Agricultural Economics, 4 vols., Set. 2010. (Critical Concepts in Economics Ser.). (ENG.). 1712p. (C). 1360.00 *(978-0-415-54745-1(8))* Routledge.

Cram101 Textbook Reviews. Outlines & Highlights for Financial Management in Agriculture by Peter Barry, Isbn: 9780813431765. 2010. 112p. pap. 28.95 *(978-1-61654-138-5(5))* Cram101 Inc.

Cram101 Textbook Reviews Staff. Outlines & Highlights for Introduction to Agricultural Economics by C Parr Rosson, Isbn: 9780131592483. 2009. 84p. pap. 27.95 *(978-1-4288-2167-5(8))* Cram101 Inc.

De Noronha Vaz, Teresa, et al. Traditional Food Production & Rural Sustainable Development: A European Challenge. Rastoin, Jean-Louis, ed. 2009. (Ashgate Economic Geography Ser.). (Illus.). 300p. 124.95 *(978-0-7546-7462-7(2))* Ashgate Publishing Co.

Deininger, Klaus, et al. The Land Governance Assessment Framework: Identifying & Monitoring Good Practice in the Land Sector. 2011. (Agriculture & Rural Development Ser.). (ENG.). 164p. pap. 25.00 *(978-0-8213-8758-0(8)*, 9780821387580) World Bank Pubns.

Drummond, H. Evan & Goodwin, John W. Agricultural Economics. 3rd ed. 2010. (ENG., Illus.). 408p. (C). pap. 156.40 *(978-0-13-607192-1(9)*, Prentice Hall) Prentice Hall PTR.

Evenson, Robert E., et al, eds. Handbook of Agricultural Economics: Agricultural Development: Farm Policies & Regional Development. 2009. (Handbook of Agricultural Economics Ser.: 4). (ENG., Illus.). 912p. 150.00 *(978-0-444-51874-3(6)*, North Holland) Elsevier Science & Technology Bks.

Evenson, Robert E. & Pingali, Prabhu, eds. Handbook of Agricultural Economics Vol. 3: Agricultural Development - Farmers, Farm Production & Farm Markets. 2007. (Handbook of Agricultural Economics Ser.: 3). (ENG., Illus.). 846p. instr.'s hndbk. ed. 150.00 *(978-0-444-51873-6(8)*, North Holland) Elsevier Science & Technology Bks.

Federico, Giovanni. Feeding the World: An Economic History of Agriculture, 1800-2000. 2008. (Princeton Economic History of the Western World Ser.). (ENG., Illus.). 416p. (C). pap. 26.95 *(978-0-691-13853-4(2))* Princeton Univ. Pr.

Firth, Raymond & Yamey, B. S. Capital, Saving & Credit in Peasant Societies. Firth, Raymond William, ed. 2007. (ENG.). 399p. pap. 37.95 *(978-0-202-30918-7(5))* Aldine Transaction.

Goldin, Liliana R. & Goldin, Liliana R. Global Maya: Work & Ideology in Rural Guatemala. 2009. (ENG & SPA., Illus.). 264p. 50.00 *(978-0-8165-2688-8(5))* Univ. of Arizona Pr.

Government Printing Office Staff. World Agricultural Supply & Demand Estimates. pap. 53.00 *(978-0-16-009437-8(2)*, Agriculture Dept.) United States Government Printing Office.

Goyari, Phanindra. Cropping Pattern Changes in the North-Eastern Region of Indi. 2010. 92p. pap. *(978-3-639-27632-9(9))* VDM Verlag Dr. Mueller e.K.

Hansen, Henning Otte. Food Economics. 2012. (Routledge Textbooks in Environmental & Agricultural Economics Ser.). (ENG., Illus.). 256p. (C). 160.00 *(978-0-415-60459-8(1))*; pap. 60.00 *(978-0-415-60461-1(3))* Routledge.

Hansson, Helena, et al. Drivers & Restraints for Economically Efficient Farm Production. 2009. (Agriculture Issues & Policies Ser.). (Illus.). 100p. 43.00 *(978-1-60876-171-5(1))* Nova Science Pubs., Inc.

Harboe Knudsen, Ida. New Lithuania in Old Hands: Effects & Outcomes of EUropeanization in Rural Lithuania. 2012. (Anthem Studies in Development & Globalization Ser.). (Illus.). 204p. 99.00 ***(978-0-85728-453-2(3))*** Anthem Pr. GBR. Dist: Books International, Inc.

Harding, Susan Friend. Remaking Ibieca: Rural Life in Aragon under Franco. 2011. (ENG.). 348p. pap. 40.00 *(978-0-8078-9677-8(2))* Univ. of North Carolina Pr.

Hart, Rhonda Massingham. The Dirt-Cheap Green Thumb: 400 Thrifty Tips for Saving Money, Time, & Resources as You Garden. 2nd ed. 2009. (ENG., Illus.). 281p. pap. 10.95 *(978-1-60342-441-7(5)*, 1603424415) Workman Publishing Co., Inc.

Herm, Eric. Son of a Farmer, Child of the Earth: A Path to Agriculture's Higher Consciousness. 2010. 248p. pap. 16.95 *(978-0-9797908-9-8(1))* Dreamriver Pr.

Hicks, John D. Populist Revolt: A History of the Farmers' Alliance & the People's Party. 2009. (ENG.). 487p. pap. 60.00 *(978-0-8156-6008-7(5))* Univ. of Minnesota Pr.

Hobhouse, Henry. Seeds of Wealth: Four Plants That Made Men Rich. 2009. (ENG.). 255p. 25.00 *(978-1-4379-6703-6(5))* DIANE Publishing Co.

Hussain, Ijaz & Zakir Hussain, Prof. The Indus Basin. 2011. 196p. pap. ***(978-3-8443-8026-2(4))*** Lambert Academic Publishing.

Ivan, Garcia. Grain Receipts As Collateral for Agribusiness' Financing. 2009. 92p. pap. *(978-3-639-12273-2(9))* VDM Verlag Dr. Mueller e.K.

Jashimuddin, Mohammed. Drivers of Land Use Change & Policy Analysis in Bangladesh. 2011. 244p. pap. ***(978-3-8443-1245-4(5))*** Lambert Academic Publishing.

Jiménez, Jaime R. Pagán. De Antiquos Pueblos BAR S1687: El Archipiélago Borincano y la Llegada de los Primeros Pobladores Agroceramistas. 2007. (Bar S Ser.). (SPA., Illus.). 268p. (C). pap. 105.00 *(978-1-4073-0125-9(X))* British Archaeological Reports Ltd. GBR. Dist: Brown, David Bk. Co., The.

Kakooza, James. Cost-Benefit Evaluation of Ecological Sanitation. 2010. 56p. pap. *(978-3-639-23573-9(8))* VDM Verlag Dr. Mueller e.K.

Karantininis, Kostas & Nilsson, Jerker, eds. Vertical Markets & Cooperative Hierarchies: The Role of Cooperatives in the Agri-Food Industry. 2010. (ENG.). xiv, 285p. pap. 169.00 *(978-90-481-7031-9(1)*, 9048170311) Springer.

Kay, Ronald D., et al. Farm Management. 7th ed. 2011. (ENG., Illus.). 480p. (C). 178.00 *(978-0-07-354587-5(2)*, 0073545872, McGraw-Hill Science, Engineering & Mathematics) McGraw-Hill Higher Education.

Kimhi, Ayal & Finkelshtain, Israel, eds. The Economics of Natural & Human Resources in Agriculture. 2009. (Illus.). 353p. 79.00 *(978-1-60741-029-4(X))* Nova Science Pubs., Inc.

Kirsten, Johann, ed. The New Landscape of Global Agriculture. 2012. (Agricultural Economics Ser.: 2). (ENG.). 200p. pap. 39.95 *(978-1-4443-3956-7(7)*, Wiley-Blackwell) Wiley, John & Sons, Inc.

Kjeldsen-Kragh. The Role of Agriculture in Economic Development the Lessons of History. 2007. 412p. pap. 48.00 *(978-87-630-0194-6(2))* Copenhagen Business Schl. Pr. DNK. Dist: International Specialized Bk. Services.

Kloeppinger-Todd, Renate & Sharma, Manohar. Innovations in Rural & Agriculture Finance. 2010. (Illus.). 30p. pap. ***(978-0-89629-668-8(7))*** International Food Policy Research Institute.

Kontoleon, Andreas. Agrobiodiversity, Conservation & Economic Development. Smale, Melinda & Pascual, Unai, eds. 2008. (Routledge Explorations in Environmental Economics Ser.). (ENG., Illus.). 456p. (C). 185.00 *(978-0-415-46505-2(2))* Routledge.

Kontoleon, Andreas, et al, eds. Agrobiodiversity Conservation & Economic Development. 2011. (Illus.). 456p. pap. 42.95 ***(978-0-415-61976-9(9))*** Routledge.

Kopsidis, Michael. Agrarentwicklung: Historische Agrarrevolutionen und Entwicklungsökonomie. 2006. (Grundzuge der modernen Wirtschaftsgeschichte Ser.). (GER.). 391p. (C). 34.00 *(978-3-515-08341-6(3))* Steiner, Franz Verlag Wiesbaden GmbH DEU. Dist: Brown, David Bk. Co., The.

Kristiansen, P., et al, eds. Organic Agriculture: A Global Perspective. 2006. (Illus.). 320p. 160.00 *(978-1-84593-169-8(6))* CABI GBR. Dist: Stylus Publishing, LLC.

Lal, Rattan & Stewart, B. A., eds. World Soil Resources & Food Security. 2011. (Advances in Soil Science Ser.). (ENG., Illus.). 574p. 129.95 *(978-1-4398-4450-2(X)*, CRC Press) Taylor & Francis Group GBR. Dist: Taylor & Francis Group.

Langmaier, Thomas. Common Agricultural Policy & Eu Agriculture. 2010. 136p. pap. *(978-3-639-21465-9(X))* VDM Verlag Dr. Mueller e.K.

Lee, Tomas H., ed. Agricultural Economics: New Research. 2010. (Agriculture Issues & Policies Ser.). (Illus.). xi, 266p. 125.00 *(978-1-61668-077-0(6))* Nova Science Pubs., Inc.

Lerman, Zvi. Russia's Agriculture in Transition: Factor Markets & Constraints on Growth. 2007. (Rural Economies in Transition Ser.). (ENG., Illus.). 394p. 89.50 *(978-0-7391-2009-5(3))* Lexington Bks.

Lipper, Leslie. Payment for Environmental Services in Agricultural Landscapes: Economic Policies & Poverty Reduction in Developing Countries. Lipper, Leslie Marie et al, eds. 2008. (Natural Resource Management & Policy Ser.). (Illus.). 250p. 149.00 *(978-0-387-72969-5(0))* Springer.

Lund, Jens. Measuring Livelihoods & Environmental Dependence: Methods for Research & Fieldwork. Angelsen, Arild et al, eds. 2011. (ENG., Illus.). 288p. 140.00 *(978-1-84971-132-6(1))* Routledge.

Mahmood, Hafiz Zahid. Accounting for Land. 2010. 164p. pap. *(978-3-639-23754-2(4))* VDM Verlag Dr. Mueller e.K.

Maiti, Ratikanta, et al. Crop Plant Anatomy. 2012. (Illus.). 320p. 145.00 ***(978-1-78064-019-8(6))*** CABI GBR. Dist: Stylus Publishing, LLC.

Marsden, Terry & Murdoch, Jonathan, eds. Between the Local & the Global: Confronting Complexity in the Contemporary Agri-Food Sector. 2006. 374p. 111.95 *(978-0-7623-1317-4(X))* Emerald Group Publishing Ltd. GBR. Dist: Turpin Distribution Services Ltd.

Martiin, Carin. The world of agricultural Economics. (Routledge Textbooks in Environmental & Agricultural Economics Ser.). (ENG., Illus.). 256p. (C). 2013. 150.00 ***(978-0-415-59359-5(X))*** 2012. pap. 51.99 ***(978-0-415-59360-1(3))*** Routledge.

McManus, Curtis R. Happyland: A History of the Dirty Thirties in Saskatchewan, 1914-1937. 2011. (West Ser.). (ENG., Illus.). 275p. pap. 41.95 *(978-1-55238-524-1(8))* Univ. of Calgary Pr. CAN. Dist: Chicago Distribution Ctr.

Miljkovic, Dragan, ed. International Agricultural Trade & Development: New Research. 2012. (Series: Agriculture Issues & Policies Binding: Hardcover Ser.). 282p. 140.00 *(978-1-61324-788-4(5))* Nova Science Pubs., Inc.

Millar, Kate, et al, eds. Ethical Futures: Bioscience & food Horizons. 2009. (Illus.). 448p. pap. 92.00 *(978-90-8686-115-6(6))* Wageningen Academic Publishers NLD. Dist: Enfield Publishing & Distribution Co., Inc.

Miller. Agricultural Value Chain Finance: Approach, Instruments & Lessons. 2010. (ENG., Illus.). 192p. pap. 39.95 *(978-1-85339-702-8(4))* Practical Action Publishing GBR. Dist: Stylus Publishing, LLC.

Miller, Sally. Edible Action: Food Activism & Alternative Economics. 2009. (ENG.). 192p. pap. 22.95 *(978-1-55266-280-9(2))* Fernwood Publishing Co., Ltd. CAN. Dist: Independent Pubs. Group.

Minarik, Pavol. Good Rules, Good Farms? 2011. 68p. pap. ***(978-3-8443-0600-2(5))*** Lambert Academic Publishing.

Moore, Henry Ludwell. Economic Cycles: Their Law & Cause. 2008. 160p. 22.99 *(978-0-559-44836-2(8))*; pap. 20.75 *(978-0-559-44833-1(3))* BiblioBazaar.

Moreta, Angel. Capitalismo y Descampesinización en el Suroeste Dominicano. 2009. (SPA., Illus.). 369p. *(978-9945-02-065-6(X))* Archivo General de la Nacion.

Morgan, Ora S., ed. Agricultural Systems of Middle Europe: A Symposium. reprint ed. 31.50 *(978-0-404-04434-3(4))* AMS Pr., Inc.

Morgan, W. Scott. History of the Wheel & Alliance & the Impending Revolution. 2009. 426p. pap. 29.50 *(978-0-217-26091-6(8))* General Bks. LLC.

Moss, Charles B. & Gunderson, Michael A. Agricultural Finance. 2013. (Routledge Textbooks in Environmental & Agricultural Economics Ser.). (ENG., Illus.). 256p. 157.41 ***(978-0-415-59904-7(0))***; pap. 74.25 ***(978-0-415-59907-8(5))*** Routledge.

Moss, Joanne R. & Moss Joanne. Farm Business Tenancy Guide. 2009. 350p. pap., instr.'s gde. ed. 110.00 *(978-1-84661-108-7(3))* Jordan Publishing, Ltd. GBR. Dist: International Specialized Bk. Services.

Naidu, V. Nagarajan & K.K.John, . Crop Rotation & Economic Sustainability of Agriculture. 2011. 240p. pap. ***(978-3-8443-8080-4(9))*** Lambert Academic Publishing.

Nash, John & McCalla, Alex F., eds. Reforming Agricultural Trade for Developing Countries Vol. 1: Key Issues for a Pro-Development Outcome of the Doha Round, 2 vols. 2006. (Agriculture & Rural Development Ser.: 1). (ENG., Illus.). 362p. per. 45.00 *(978-0-8213-6496-3(0)*, 9780821364963) World Bank Pubns.

Norberg-Hodge, Helena, et al. Bringing the Food Economy Home: Local Alternatives to Global Agribusiness. (Illus.). 176p. (978-1-84277-232-4(5)); pap. (978-1-84277-233-1(3)) Zed Bks., Ltd. GBR. Dist: Palgrave Macmillan.

OECD, Organization for Economic Cooperation and Development. OECD Insights: Agriculture & Food: Feeding Nine Billion People. 2012. (ENG.). 150p. pap. 19.00 (978-92-64-08083-6(X)) Organization for Economic Cooperation & Development.

Oecd Publishing. Guidelines for Cost-Effective Agri-Environmental Policy Measures. 2010. 120p. pap. 42.00 (978-92-64-08665-4(X)) Organization for Economic Cooperation & Development.

Organisation for Economic Co-operation and Development. Agricultural Policies in OECD Countries: At a Glance 2010. 2010. (Illus.). 125p. pap. 39.00 (978-92-64-08379-0(0)) Organization for Economic Cooperation & Development.

Organisation for Economic Co-operation and Development & Food and Agriculture Organization. Oecd-Fao Agricultural Outlook 2010-2019. 2010. (Illus.). 247p. pap. 72.00 (978-92-64-08375-2(8)) Organization for Economic Cooperation & Development.

Organisation for Economic Co-operation and Development Staff. Agricultural Policies in Emerging Economies 2009: Monitoring & Evaluation. 2009. (Illus.). 191p. pap. 63.00 (978-92-64-05927-6(X)) Organization for Economic Cooperation & Development.

—Agricultural Policies in Oecd Countries: At a Glance 2008. 2008. (Illus.). 141p. pap. 63.00 (978-92-64-03213-2(4)) Organization for Economic Cooperation & Development.

—Managing Risk in Agriculture: A Holistic Approach. 2009. (Illus.). 170p. pap. 63.00 (978-92-64-07530-6(5)) Organization for Economic Cooperation & Development.

—Oecd-Fao Agricultural Outlook 2007-2016. 2007. pap. 78.00 (978-92-64-02509-7(X)) Organization for Economic Cooperation & Development.

—Perspectives Agricoles de l'Ocde et de la Fao: 2006-2015. 2006. 228p. per. 75.00 (978-92-64-02462-5(X)) Organization for Economic Cooperation & Development.

—Les Politiques Agricoles des Pays de l'Ocde: Panorama 2008. 2008. 148p. pap. 63.00 (978-92-64-04465-4(5)) Organization for Economic Cooperation & Development.

—Politiques Agricoles des Pays Non-Membres de l'Ocde: Suivi et éValuation 2007. 2007. (FRE.). 220p. per. 52.00 (978-92-64-03123-4(5)) Organization for Economic Cooperation & Development.

—Proceedings of the Workshop on Multifunctionality in Agriculture: Evaluating the Degree of Jointness, Policy Implications. 2008. pap. 63.00 (978-92-64-03361-0(0)) Organization for Economic Cooperation & Development.

—Set: National Accounts of Oecd Countries: Volume IIIa - Financial Accounts - Flows & Volume IIIb - Financial Balance Sheets - Stocks - 1993-2005, 2006 Edition-Set: Comptes Nationaux des Pays de l'Ocde: Volume IIIa - Comptes Financiers - Flux et Volume IIIb - Comptes de Patrimoine Financier - Stock. 2008. (Illus.). 120p. pap. 32.00 (978-92-64-03172-2(3)) Organization for Economic Cooperation & Development.

Organisation for Economic Co-operation and Development Staff & Food and Agriculture Organization. OECD-FAO agricultural Outlook 2006-2015. 2006. (Illus.). 208p. per. 75.00 (978-92-64-02460-1(3)) Organization for Economic Cooperation & Development.

Organisation for Economic Co-operation and Development: Development Assistance Committee. Creditor Reporting System 2009: Aid Activities in Support of Agriculture. 2010. (Illus.). 182p. pap. 63.00 (978-92-64-07702-7(2)) Organization for Economic Cooperation & Development.

Otsuka, Keijiro & Kalirajan, Kaliappa. Contributions of Agricultural Economics to Critical Policy Issues: Proceedings of the Twenty-Sixth Conference of the International Association of Agricultural Economists. 2007. (Agricultural Economics Ser.: 3). (ENG., Illus.). 300p. pap. 50.95 (978-1-4051-8100-6(1), Wiley-Blackwell) Wiley, John & Sons, Inc.

Otzen, Uwe & Brandt, Hartmut. Poverty Oriented Agricultural & Rural Development. 2007. (Routledge Studies in Development & Society Ser.). (Illus.). 342p. 158.00 (978-0-415-36853-7(7)) Routledge.

Patel, Raj. Stuffed & Starved: The Hidden Battle for the World Food System. 2008. (ENG., Illus.). 416p. pap. 19.95 (978-1-933633-49-7(2)) Melville Hse. Publishing.

Patton, F. Lester. Diminishing Returns in Agriculture. (Columbia University, Studies in the Social Sciences: No. 284). reprint ed. 20.00 (978-0-404-51284-2(4)) AMS Pr., Inc.

Penson, John B., Jr. Introduction to Agricultural Economics. 2006. (ENG.). pap. 14.95 (978-1-4288-1070-9(6)) Cram101 Inc.

Peterson, E. Wesley F. Billion Dollars a Day: The Economics & Politics of Agricultural Subsidies. 2009. (ENG., Illus.). 320p. 89.95 (978-1-4051-8587-5(2), Wiley-Blackwell) Wiley, John & Sons, Inc.

—A Billion Dollars a Day: The Economics & Politics of Agricultural Subsidies. 2009. (ENG., Illus.). 320p. pap. 36.95 (978-1-4051-8586-8(4), Wiley-Blackwell) Wiley, John & Sons, Inc.

Porter, John. The History & Economics of the New Hampshire Dairy Industry. 2007. (Illus.). 124p. per. 19.95 (978-0-9719675-7-1(1)) Univ. of New Hampshire, Cooperative Extension.

Postan, M. M. Essays on Medieval Agriculture & General Problems of the Medieval Economy. 2008. (ENG.). 320p. pap. 44.00 (978-0-521-08846-6(1)) Cambridge Univ. Pr.

Prasen, Daimari. Agricultural Transition among Tribes: A Study of Assam Plains in Northeast India. 2011. 208p. pap. **(978-3-639-33577-4(5))** VDM Verlag Dr. Mueller e.K.

Ricketts, Cliff & Ricketts, Kristina G. Agribusiness Fundamentals & Applications. 2nd rev. ed. 2008. (ENG., Illus.). 600p. (C). 144.95 (978-1-4180-3231-9(X)) Delmar Cengage Learning.

Robbins, Mike. Crops & Carbon: Paying Farmers to Combat Climate Change. 2011. (ENG., Illus.). 320p. 84.95 (978-1-84971-375-7(8)) Routledge.

Rosset, Peter M. Food Is Different: Why We Must Get the WTO Out of Agriculture. 2006. (Global Issues Ser.). (ENG., Illus.). 194p. 62.95 (978-1-84277-754-1(8)); per. 20.95 (978-1-84277-755-8(6)) Zed Bks., Ltd. GBR. Dist: Macmillan.

Rosson, C. Parr, et al. Introduction to Agricultural Economics. 5th ed. 2009. (ENG., Illus.). 432p. (C). pap. 137.20 (978-0-13-159248-3(3), Prentice Hall) Prentice Hall PTR.

Ruttan, Vernon W. & Hayami, Yujiro. Can Economic Growth Be Sustained? The Collected Papers of Vernon W. Ruttan & Yujiro Hayami, 1 vol. Otsuka, Keijiro & Runge, C. Ford, eds. 2011. (ENG., Illus.). 416p. 74.00 (978-0-19-975435-9(7)) Oxford Univ. Pr., Inc.

Salinger, James, et al, eds. Increasing Climate Variability & Change: Reducing the Vulnerability of Agriculture & Forestry. 2010. (ENG.). vi, 362p. pap. 159.00 (978-90-481-6842-2(2), 9048168422) Springer.

Samuel, Binuomote. Supply Response of Export & Food Crops in Some Ecowas Countries. 2011. 264p. pap. **(978-3-8443-1873-9(9))** Lambert Academic Publishing.

Sanchez, Gustavo. Endogenous Trade Protection under Regional Trade Agreements. 2008. 84p. pap. (978-3-639-08183-1(8)) VDM Verlag Dr. Mueller e.K.

Sapkota, Deepak. Response of Late-Sown Wheat to Nitrogen. 2011. 96p. pap. **(978-3-8443-0503-6(3))** Lambert Academic Publishing.

Seitz, Wesley D., et al. Economics of Resources, Agriculture, & Food. 2nd ed. 2009. 520p. (C). 69.95 (978-1-57766-624-0(0)) Waveland Pr., Inc.

Shiva, Vandana. Soil Not Oil: Environmental Justice in an Age of Climate Crisis. 2008. (ENG.). 200p. pap. 16.00 (978-0-89608-782-8(4)) South End Pr.

Smedshaug, Christian Anton. Feeding the World in the 21st Century: A Historical Analysis of Agriculture & Society. 2010. (Anthem Other Canon Ser.). (ENG., Illus.). 322p. pap. 40.00 (978-1-84331-867-5(9)) Anthem Pr. GBR. Dist: Books International, Inc.

Southgate, Douglas, et al. The World Food Economy. 2006. (ENG., Illus.). 416p. per. 55.95 (978-1-4051-0597-2(6), Wiley-Blackwell) Wiley, John & Sons, Inc.

Southgate, Douglas D., Jr., et al. The World Food Economy. 2nd ed. 2010. (ENG., Illus.). 464p. (C). pap. 73.95 (978-0-470-59362-2(8), Wiley) Wiley, John & Sons, Inc.

Strom, Claire. Profiting from the Plains: The Great Northern Railway & Corporate Development of the American West. 2007. (ENG., Illus.). 240p. per. 25.00 (978-0-295-98663-0(8)) Univ. of Washington Pr.

Taji, Acram & Reganold, John, eds. Organic Agriculture: A Global Perspective. 2006. (Comstock Bks.). (Illus.). 449p. 104.95 (978-0-8014-4524-8(8), ILR Pr.) Cornell Univ. Pr.

Timmer, C. Peter. A World Without Agriculture: The Structural Transformation in Historical Perspective. 2009. (ENG.). 93p. pap. 15.00 (978-0-8447-4279-3(1), AEI Pr.) American Enterprise Institute for Public Policy Research.

Tsakok, Isabelle & Gardner, Bruce L. Success in Agricultural Transformation. 2011. (ENG., Illus.). 424p. pap. 37.99 (978-0-521-71769-4(8)); 110.00 **(978-0-521-88894-3(8))** Cambridge Univ. Pr.

United Nations. Status of Agrifood Regulatory Coordination under the North American Free Trade Agreement. 2007. (Studies & Perspectives Ser.). (ENG.). 40p. pap. 10.00 (978-92-1-121657-8(5)) United Nations Pubns.

United Nations Conference on Trade and Development Staff. World investment Report 2009: Transnational corporations, agricultural production & Development. 2009. (ENG., Illus.). 312p. pap. 95.00 incl. lp (978-92-1-112775-1(0)) United Nations Pubns.

United Nations Staff, contrib. by. Rural Households' Livelihood & Well-Being: Statistics on Rural Development & Agriculture Household Income. 2007. (ENG., Illus.). 552p. pap. 115.00 (978-92-1-116967-6(4)) United Nations Pubns.

Van Steenbergen, F. Charging for Irrigation Services: Guidelines for Practitioners. 2006. 100p. (C). pap. (978-1-84339-141-8(4)) IWA Publishing.

Vanslembrouck, Isabel & Van Huylenbroeck, Guido. Landscape Amenities: Economic Assessment of Agricultural Landscapes. 2010. (Landscape Ser.). xv, 202p. pap. 159.00 (978-90-481-6804-0(X), 904816804X) Springer.

von Thünen, Johann. The Isolated State in Relation to Agriculture & Political Economy Pt. 3: Principles for the Determination of Rent, the Most Advantageous Rotation Period & the Value of Stands of Varying Age in Pinewoods. van Suntum, Ulrich, ed. 2009. (ENG., Illus.). 224p. 100.00 (978-0-230-22251-9(X)) Palgrave Macmillan.

Wager, Felix C., ed. Agricultural Production. 2010. (Agriculture Issues & Policies Ser.). 89.00 (978-1-61668-695-6(2)) Nova Science Pubs., Inc.

Wassmann, Reiner & Vlek, Paul L.G., eds. Tropical Agriculture in Transition - Opportunities for Mitigating Greenhouse Gas Emissions? 2010. 284p. pap. 88.00 (978-90-481-6341-0(2), 9048163412) Springer.

Waters, Tony. The Persistence of Subsistence Agriculture: Life Beneath the Level of the Marketplace. (ENG., Illus.). 272p. 2008. pap. 34.99 (978-0-7391-2836-7(1)) 2006. 89.50 (978-0-7391-0768-3(2)) Lexington Bks.

Weis, Tony. The Global Food Economy: The Battle for the Future of Farming. 2007. (ENG., Illus.). 256p. per. 31.95 (978-1-84277-795-4(5)) Zed Bks., Ltd. GBR. Dist: Macmillan.

—The Global Food Economy: The Battle for the Future of Farming. 2007. (ENG., Illus.). 256p. 94.95 (978-1-84277-794-7(7)) Zed Bks., Ltd. GBR. Dist: Macmillan.

Westhoff, Patrick. The Economics of Food: How Feeding & Fueling the Planet Affects Food Prices. 2010. (ENG., Illus.). 256p. 25.99 (978-0-13-700610-6(1)) FT Press.

Wilson. Small Farmers, Big Change. 2011. (ENG.). 176p. pap. 14.95 **(978-1-85339-712-7(1))** Practical Action Publishing GBR. Dist: Stylus Publishing, LLC.

Wilson, G. A. Multifunctional Agriculture: A Transition Theory Perspective. 2007. (Illus.). 368p. 145.00 (978-1-84593-256-5(0)) CABI GBR. Dist: Stylus Publishing, LLC.

Wiswall, Richard. The Organic Farmer's Business Handbook: A Complete Guide to Managing Finances, Crops, & Staff-And Making a Profit. 2009. (ENG., Illus.). 224p. 34.95 (978-1-60358-142-4(1)) Chelsea Green Publishing.

Wojtkowski, Paul A. Agroecological Economics: Sustainability & Biodiversity. 2007. (ENG., Illus.). 320p. per. 80.95 (978-0-12-374117-2(3), Academic Pr.) Elsevier Science & Technology Bks.

World Bank Staff. Agriculture for Development 2008. rev. ed. 2007. (World Development Report). (ENG., Illus.). 384p. 50.00 (978-0-8213-6808-4(7), 9780821368084); per. 26.00 (978-0-8213-6807-7(9), 9780821368077) World Bank Pubns.

World Bank Staff, et al. OECD-FAO Agricultural Outlook, 2009-2018. 2009. (Illus.). 274p. pap. 63.00 (978-92-64-01144-1(7)) Organization for Economic Cooperation & Development.

AGRICULTURE—ECONOMIC ASPECTS—MATHEMATICAL MODELS

Gruber, Ina. The Impact of Socio-Economic Development & Climate Change on Livestock Management in Benin. 2009. (Europäische Hochschulschriften. Reihe 5: Volks- und Betriebswirtschaft Ser.). 250p. pap. 69.95 (978-3-631-59049-2(0)) Lang, Peter GmbH, Europaischer Verlag der Wissenschaften DEU. Dist: Lang, Peter.

Hess, Sebastian. Meta-Analyse angewandter Gleichgewichtsmodelle des internationalen Agrarhandels. 2008. (Cege-Schriften Ser.). 192p. pap. 56.95 (978-3-631-57718-9(4)) Lang, Peter GmbH, Europaischer Verlag der Wissenschaften DEU. Dist: Lang, Peter.

Mitchell, Nina H. Mathematical Applications in Agriculture. 2nd ed. 2011. (ENG., Illus.). 297p. (C). pap. 93.95 **(978-1-111-31066-0(1))** Delmar Cengage Learning.

Waugh, Frederick V. Selected Writings on Agricultural Policy & Economic Analysis. Houck, James P. & Abel, Martin E., eds. 2009. (ENG.). 488p. pap. 60.00 (978-0-8166-6057-5(3)) Univ. of Minnesota Pr.

AGRICULTURE—ECONOMIC ASPECTS—AFRICA

Adeiza, Mahmood. Effects of Poor Banking Support for Agriculture in Northern Nigeri. 2011. 88p. pap. **(978-3-8454-1356-3(5))** Lambert Academic Publishing.

Anandajayasekeram, P. & Keswani, C. L. Impact of Science on African Agriculture & Food Security. Rukani, M. et al, eds. 2007. 310p. (C). 145.00 (978-1-84593-267-1(6)) CABI GBR. Dist: Stylus Publishing, LLC.

Anderson, Kym & Masters, William A., eds. Distortions to Agricultural Incentives in Africa. 2009. (Trade & Development Ser.). (ENG., Illus.). 656p. pap. 39.95 (978-0-8213-7652-2(7), 9780821376522) World Bank Pubns.

Bernard, Tanguy. Cooperatives for Staple Crop Marketing Evidence from Ethiopia. 2010. (978-0-89629-175-1(8)) International Food Policy Research Institute.

Birgegard, Lars-Erik, et al. African Agriculture & the World Bank: Development or Impoverishment? 2008. (Illus.). 75p. pap. 23.95 (978-91-7106-608-4(X)) Nordiska Afrikainstitutet SWE. Dist: Stylus Publishing, LLC.

Blakeney, Michael, et al, eds. Extending the Protection of Geographical Indications: Case Studies of Agricultural Products in Africa. 2012. (ENG., Illus.). 384p. 135.00 **(978-0-415-50102-6(4))** Routledge.

Breisinger, Clemens. A New ERA of Transformation in Ghana: Lessons from the Past & Scenarios for the Future. 2011. (978-0-89629-788-3(8)); (978-0-89629-186-7(3)) International Food Policy Research Institute.

Bukenya, Christopher. Meeting Farmer Demand? 2010. 400p. pap. (978-3-8383-6244-1(6)) Lambert Academic Publishing.

Bumb, Balu. Policy Workshop on Strengthening Regional Trade in Agricultural Inputs in Africa: Issues & Options; & Private Sector Roundtable Meeting on Expanding Fertilizer Markets in Africa: Issues & Options: Summary Reports. 2010. (978-0-88090-166-6(7)) IFDC.

Demery, Lionel & Christiaensen, Luc. Down to Earth: Agriculture & Poverty Reduction in Africa. 2007. (Directions in Development Ser.). (ENG., Illus.). 118p. per. 15.00 (978-0-8213-6854-1(0), 9780821368541) World Bank Pubns.

Deveze, Jean-Claude, ed. Challenges for African Agriculture. 2010. (ENG., Illus.). 292p. pap. 35.00 (978-0-8213-8481-7(3), 9780821384817) World Bank Pubns.

Diao, Xinshen. Agricultural Growth & Investment Options for Poverty Reduction in Rwanda. 2010. (978-0-89629-176-8(6)) International Food Policy Research Institute.

—The Role of Agriculture in Development: Implications for Sub-Saharan Africa. 2007. (978-0-89629-161-4(8)) International Food Policy Research Institute.

Diao, Xinshen. Strategies & Priorities for African Agriculture: Economywide Perspectives from Country Studies. 2012. **(978-0-89629-195-9(2))** International Food Policy Research Institute.

Djurfeldt, Göran, et al, eds. African Smallholders: Food Crops, Markets & Policy. 2011. (Illus.). 304p. 160.00 (978-1-84593-716-4(3)) CABI GBR. Dist: Stylus Publishing, LLC.

Duma, Moses. Contract Farming: Is it a win-win Relationship? 2010. 100p. pap. (978-3-8383-9466-4(6)) Lambert Academic Publishing.

Fava Neves, Marcos, et al, eds. The orange juice Business: A Brazilian Perspective. 2011. 176p. pap. 75.00 **(978-90-8686-181-1(4))** Wageningen Academic Publishers NLD. Dist: Enfield Publishing & Distribution Co., Inc.

Fold, Neils. Globalization & Restructuring of African Commodity Flows. Larsen, Marianne Nylandsted & Fold, Larsen, eds. 2008. 276p. pap. 45.95 (978-91-7106-616-9(0)) Nordiska Afrikainstitutet SWE. Dist: Stylus Publishing, LLC.

Gatere, Fiona. Market-Led Agricultural Transformation for Pro-Poor Growth? 2010. 80p. pap. (978-3-639-27737-1(6)) VDM Verlag Dr. Mueller e.K.

Gebissa, Ezekiel. Taking the Place of Food: Khat in Ethiopia. 2010. (978-1-56902-317-4(4)) Red Sea Pr.

Gertel, Jorg & Breuer, Ingo, eds. Pastoral Morocco: Globalizing Scapes of Mobility & Insecurity. 2007. (Nomaden und Sesshafte Ser.). (ENG., Illus.). 268p. (C). 92.00 (978-3-89500-552-7(5)) Reichert, Ludwig Dr. DEU. Dist: Brown, David Bk. Co., The.

Gottwald, Franz-Theo, et al, eds. Fostering Subsistence Agriculture, Food Supplies & Health in Sub-Saharan Africa. 2007. (Support Africa International Ser.: Vol. 2). 199p. pap. 46.95 (978-3-631-57380-8(4)) Lang, Peter GmbH, Europaischer Verlag der Wissenschaften DEU. Dist: Lang, Peter Publishing, Inc.

Gruber, Ina. The Impact of Socio-Economic Development & Climate Change on Livestock Management in Benin. 2009. (Europäische Hochschulschriften. Reihe 5: Volks- und Betriebswirtschaft Ser.). 250p. pap. 69.95 (978-3-631-59049-2(0)) Lang, Peter GmbH, Europaischer Verlag der Wissenschaften DEU. Dist: Lang, Peter.

Heyde, Maximilian. The Impact of the Common Agricultural Policy on Food Prices. 2009. 60p. pap. (978-3-639-17772-5(X)) VDM Verlag Dr. Mueller e.K.

Hill, Polly. Studies in Rural Capitalism in West Africa. 2009. (African Studies). (ENG.). 192p. pap. 31.99 (978-0-521-10921-5(3)) Cambridge Univ. Pr.

Howell, Paul, et al, eds. The Jonglei Canal: Impact & Opportunity. 2009. (Cambridge Studies in Applied Ecology & Resource Management Ser.). (ENG., Illus.). 572p. pap. 63.00 (978-0-521-10549-1(8)) Cambridge Univ. Pr.

Juma, Calestous. The New Harvest: Agricultural Innovation in Africa, 1 vol. 2011. (ENG.). 288p. pap. 19.95 (978-0-19-978319-9(5)) Oxford Univ. Pr., Inc.

Kabubo-Mariara, Jane. Agricultural Productivity & Environmental Conservation in Keny. 2010. 152p. pap. (978-3-8383-4877-3(X)) Lambert Academic Publishing.

Köhlin, Gunnar & Bluffstone, Randall, eds. Agricultural Investment & Productivity: Building Sustainability in East Africa. 2011. (Environment for Development Ser.). (ENG., Illus.). 224p. 99.95 (978-1-61726-091-9(6), RFF Pr.) Earthscan LLC.

Larsen, Kurt, et al, eds. Agribusiness & Innovation Systems in Africa. 2009. (Agriculture & Rural Development Ser.). (ENG., Illus.). 472p. pap. 35.00 (978-0-8213-7944-8(5), 9780821379448) World Bank Pubns.

Li, Xiaoyun, et al. Agricultural Development in China & Africa. 2012. (ENG., Illus.). 328p. 99.95 **(978-1-84971-388-7(X))** Routledge.

Maatman, Arno. Competitive Agricultural Systems & Enterprises (CASE) Volume 1: Reference framework & early experiences, 2 , 2011. pap. 10.00 **(978-0-88090-168-0(3))** IFDC.

Makana, Nicholas. Changing Patterns of Indigenous Economic Systems. 2008. 248p. pap. (978-3-639-07218-1(9)) VDM Verlag Dr. Mueller e.K.

Minot, Nicholas. Trade Liberalization & Poverty in the Middle East & North Africa. 2009. (978-0-89629-174-4(X)) International Food Policy Research Institute.

Mithöfer, Dagmar & Waibel, Hermann, eds. Vegetable Production & Marketing in Africa: Socio-Economic Research. 2011. (Illus.). 288p. 160.00 (978-1-84593-649-5(3)) CABI GBR. Dist: Stylus Publishing, LLC.

Morris, Michael L., et al. Awakening Africa's Sleeping Giant: Prospects for Commercial Agriculture in the Guinea Savannah Zone & Beyond. 2009. (Directions in Development Ser.). (ENG., Illus.). 232p. pap. 30.00 (978-0-8213-7941-7(0), 9780821379417) World Bank Pubns.

Nin-Pratt, Alejandro. Yield Gaps & Potential Agricultural Growth in West & Central Africa. 2010. (978-0-89629-182-9(0)) International Food Policy Research Institute.

Odularu, Gbadebo Olusegun. The Impact of Agricultural Trade Liberalization on National Food Security in Nigeria, 1970-2000. 2010. 62p. pap. 19.95 (978-1-59942-340-1(5), Dissertation.com) Universal Pubs.

Omamo, Steven Were. Strategic Priorities for Agricultural Development in Eastern & Central Africa. 2006. (978-0-89629-158-4(8)) International Food Policy Research Institute.

Organisation for Economic Co-operation and Development Staff. Business for Development 2008. 2008. 124p. pap. 63.00 (978-92-64-04469-2(8)) Organization for Economic Cooperation & Development.

Palchick, Michaela. Agricultural Transformation & Livelihood Struggles. 2009. 116p. pap. (978-3-639-17828-9(9)) VDM Verlag Dr. Mueller e.K.

Patnaik, Utsa & Moyo, Sam. The Agrarian Question in the Neoliberal Era: Primitive Accumulation & the Peasantry. 2011. (Illus.). 96p. pap. 14.95 **(978-0-85749-038-4(9))** Pambuzuka Pr. GBR. Dist: Independent Pubs. Group.

Pender, J., et al. Strategies for Sustainable Land Management in the East African Highlands. 2006. *(978-0-89629-757-9(8))* International Food Policy Research Institute.

Peppelenbos, Lucian, et al. Chain Empowerment: Supporting African Farmers to Develop Markets. 2010. 280p. pap. 39.95 *(978-94-6022-073-9(8))* Royal Tropical Institute Pr. (KIT (Koninklijk Instituut voor de Tropen) NLD. Dist: Stylus Publishing, LLC.

Pretty, Jules, et al, eds. Sustainable Intensification: Increasing Productivity in African Food & Agricultural Systems. 2011. (International Journal Agricultural Sustainability Ser.). (ENG., Illus.). 200p. 99.95 *(978-1-84971-332-0(4))* Routledge.

Smale, Melinda & Tushemereirwe, W. An Economic Assessment of Banana Genetic Improvement & Innovation in the Lake Victoria Region of Uganda & Tanzania. 2007. *(978-0-89629-164-5(2))* International Food Policy Research Institute.

Tache, Getachew Vergia. Challenges & Opportunities of Local Seed Business Sector in Ethiopia: Development in Endamekhoni & Atsbiwemberta Weredas/Districts/, Tigray, Ethiopia. 2011. 116p. pap. **(978-3-639-32507-2(9))** VDM Verlag Dr. Mueller e.K.

Taeb, M. & A. H. Zakri. Agriculture, Human Security, & Peace: A Crossroad in African Development. 2008. (Illus.). 187p. pap. 29.95 *(978-1-55753-482-8(9))* Purdue Univ. Pr.

Thebe, Vusilizwe. Cultivating Starvation. 2010. 76p. pap. *(978-3-8383-6480-3(5))* Lambert Academic Publishing.

United Nations: Economic Commission for Africa & African Union. Economic report on Africa 2009: Developing African agriculture through regional value Chains. 2009. (ENG., Illus.). 210p. pap. 40.00 **(978-92-1-125111-1(7))** United Nations Pubns.

Valensi, Lucette. Tunisian Peasants in the Eighteenth & Nineteenth Centuries. 2009. (Studies in Modern Capitalism Ser.). (ENG.). 308p. pap. 42.00 *(978-0-521-10901-7(9))* Cambridge Univ. Pr.

Wale, Edilegnaw, et al, eds. The Economics of Managing Crop Diversity On-farm: Case studies from the Genetic Resources Policy Initiative. 2010. (Issues in Agricultural Biodiversity Ser.). (ENG., Illus.). 160p. 140.00 *(978-1-84971-221-7(2))* Routledge.

—The Economics of Managing Crop Diversity On-Farm: Case Studies from the Genetic Resources Policy Initiative. 2010. (Issues in Agricultural Biodiversity Ser.). (ENG., Illus.). 160p. pap. 49.95 *(978-1-84971-222-4(0))* Routledge.

Webber, C. Martin & Labaste, Patrick. Building Competitiveness in Africa's Agriculture: A Guide to Value Chain Concepts & Applications. 2010. pap. 30.00 *(978-0-8213-8284-4(5))* 2009. (ENG., Illus.). 182p. pap. 40.00 *(978-0-8213-7952-3(6),* 9780821379523) World Bank Pubns.

World Bank Institute Staff. Agricultural Land Redistribution: Towards Greater Consensus on the How. Binswanger-Mkhize, Hans P. & Bourguignon, Camille, eds. 2009. (Agriculture & Rural Development Ser.). (ENG., Illus.). 464p. pap. 40.00 *(978-0-8213-7627-0(6),* 9780821376270) World Bank Pubns.

World Bank Staff. L' appui de la Banque à l'agriculture en Afrique Subsaharienne:Examen de L'IEG: Examen de l'ieg. 2008. (Independent Evaluation Group Studies). (FRE.). 148p. pap. 35.00 *(978-0-8213-7595-2(4),* 9780821375952) World Bank Pubns.

Yu, Bingxin. Agricultural Productivity Growth in Sub-Saharan Afric. 2008. 220p. pap. *(978-3-639-07548-9(X))* VDM Verlag Dr. Mueller e.K.

AGRICULTURE—ECONOMIC ASPECTS—ASIA

Adhikari, Dadhi. Technology Adoption Behavior under Credit Constraint. 2010. 100p. pap. *(978-3-8383-9382-7(1))* Lambert Academic Publishing.

Anderson, Kym & Martin, Will, eds. Distortions to Agricultural Incentives in Asia. 2009. (Trade & Development Ser.). (ENG., Illus.). 608p. pap. 39.95 *(978-0-8213-7662-1(4),* 9780821376621) World Bank Pubns.

Arifullah, Shahnaz. Pakistan's Crop Sector. 2010. 172p. pap. *(978-3-8383-4021-0(3))* Lambert Academic Publishing.

Balisacan, Arsenio & Fuwa, Nobuhiko, eds. Reasserting the Rural Development Agenda: Lessons Learned & Emerging Challenges in Asia. 2007. 436p. *(978-981-230-412-4(6))* Institute of Southeast Asian Studies.

Bayliss-Smith, Tim & Wanmali, Sudhir, eds. Understanding Green Revolutions: Agrarian Change & Development Planning in South Asia. 2009. (ENG.). 400p. pap. 39.99 *(978-0-521-10912-3(4))* Cambridge Univ. Pr.

Cho, Yong-Gwan & Yi, Si-Yong. Chungang Asia Kukkadul Ui Nongop Chongch'aek Kwa Han, Chungang Asia Nongop Hyomyok Hwaktae Pangan: K'ajahust'an, Ujubek'isut'an, K'irugijusut'an Ui Chungsim Uro. 2010. (KOR., Illus.). 90p. *(978-89-322-2174-8(X))* Korea Institute for International Economic Policy.

Djalalov, Sandjar & Babu, Suresh Chandra, eds. Policy Reforms & Agriculture Development in Central Asia. 2010. (Natural Resource Management & Policy Ser.). (Illus.). xiv, 494p. pap. 179.00 *(978-1-4419-4001-8(4),* 1441940014) Springer.

Eder, James F. Who Shall Succeed? Agricultural Development & Social Inequality on a Philippine Frontier. 2009. (ENG.). 284p. pap. 38.99 *(978-0-521-10497-5(1))* Cambridge Univ. Pr.

Gulati, Ashok, et al, eds. Agricultural Diversification & Smallholders in South Asia. 2007. (ENG., Illus.). 624p. 79.95 *(978-81-7188-551-0(9))* Academic Foundation IND. Dist: Independent Pubs. Group.

Gulati, Ashok & Dixon, John, eds. Maize in Asia: Changing Markets & Incentives. 2008. (ENG., Illus.). 488p. 69.95 *(978-81-7188-663-0(9))* Academic Foundation IND. Dist: Independent Pubs. Group.

Hinnebusch, Raymond, et al. Agriculture & Reform in Syria. 2010. (Illus.). 120p. (C). pap. 17.95 *(978-0-9559687-7-8(1))* Rienner, Lynne Pubs.

Hufbauer, Gary Clyde & Burki, Shahid Javed. Sustaining Reform W/A Us-Pakistan Free Trade Agreement. 2006. (Policy Analyses in International Economics Ser.: 80). 295p. per. 23.95 *(978-0-88132-395-5(0))* Peterson Institute for International Economics.

Koninck, Rodolphe de, et al. Borneo Transformed: Agricultural Expansion on the Southeast Asian Frontier. 2011. (Illus.). ix, 216p. 32.00 **(978-9971-69-544-6(8))** National Univ. of Singapore Pr. SGP. Dist: Univ. of Hawaii Pr.

Razzaque, Mohammad A. & Laurent, Edwin, eds. Global Rice & Agricultural Trade Liberalisation: Poverty & Welfare Implications for South Asia. 2008. (ENG., Illus.) 240p. pap. 38.95 *(978-0-85092-861-7(3))* Commonwealth Secretariat GBR. Dist: Stylus Publishing, LLC.

Teng, P. S. Business Potential for Agricultural Biotechnology Products. 2007. (Illus.). 197p. *(978-92-833-2371-6(8))* Asian Productivity Organization.

Wenzlhuemer, Roland. From Coffee to Tea Cultivation in Ceylon, 1880-1900: An Economic & Social History. 2008. (Brill's Indological Library Ser.). (Illus.). 336p. *(978-90-04-16361-4(1))* BRILL.

Wilson, Trevor, ed. Myanmar's Long Road to National Reconciliation. 2006. 310p. (C). pap. *(978-981-230-362-2(6),* PIC142) Asia Pacific Pr.

AGRICULTURE—ECONOMIC ASPECTS—AUSTRALIA

Gangemi, Michael. Economic Impact of a Farming Innovation Organisation. 2010. 304p. pap. *(978-3-639-23660-6(2))* VDM Verlag Dr. Mueller e.K.

AGRICULTURE—ECONOMIC ASPECTS—BANGLADESH

Hasan, Mohammad Rajib & Mandal, M. A. Sattar. Contract Farming for Production & Export of Vegetables in Bangladesh: An Economic Analysis of Contract Farming for Production & Export of High Value Vegetables in Bangladesh. 2011. 144p. pap. **(978-3-639-32273-6(8))** VDM Verlag Dr. Mueller e.K.

Sarwar, Golam. How Institutions Constraint the Livelihood of Farmers? 2009. 76p. pap. *(978-3-639-20974-7(5))* VDM Verlag Dr. Mueller e.K.

Yu, Winston, et al. Climate Change Risks & Food Security in Bangladesh. 2010. (ENG., Illus.). 176p. 110.00 *(978-1-84971-130-2(5))* Routledge.

AGRICULTURE—ECONOMIC ASPECTS—BRAZIL

Almeida Monteiro, Gabriela. The Biodiesel Program & Sustainable Livelihoods. 2010. 80p. pap. *(978-3-8383-8770-3(8))* Lambert Academic Publishing.

Carvalho, Gustavo. Efficiency in Sugar Cane Crop Production. 2010. 104p. pap. *(978-3-639-22865-6(0))* VDM Verlag Dr. Mueller e.K.

Neves, Erivaldo Fagundes. Uma Comunidade Sertaneja: Da Sesmaria Ao Minifúndio: Um Estudo de História Regional e Local. 2nd ed. 2008. (POR., Illus.). 384p. *(978-85-232-0549-2(7))* Universidade Federal da Bahia, Centro Editorial e Didatico.

AGRICULTURE—ECONOMIC ASPECTS—CANADA

Galbraith, John Kenneth. "Does It Pay?" John Kenneth Galbraith Interviews Topnotchers: Previously Published in the St. Thomas Times-Journal 1925-1932. 2010. (ENG., Illus.). 710p. pap. 49.95 *(978-0-9866410-0-8(6))* Village Crier CAN. Dist: Outskirts Pr., Inc.

Schmitz, Andrew, et al. Agricultural Policy, Agribusiness & Rent-Seeking Behaviour. 2nd ed. 2010. (Illus.). 512p. pap. *(978-0-8020-9547-3(X))* Univ. of Toronto Pr.

AGRICULTURE—ECONOMIC ASPECTS—CHILE

Organisation for Economic Co-operation and Development Staff. Oecd Review of Agricultural Policies Chile. 2008. (Illus.). 153p. pap. 63.00 *(978-92-64-04223-0(7))* Organization for Economic Cooperation & Development.

Zegarra, Eduardo. Water Markets & Coordination Failures. 2008. 140p. pap. *(978-3-639-07331-7(2))* VDM Verlag Dr. Mueller e.K.

AGRICULTURE—ECONOMIC ASPECTS—CHINA

Heerink, Nico, et al. Dragons with Clay Feet? Transition, Sustainable Land Use, & Rural Environment in China & Vietnam. 2010. (Rural Economies in Transition Ser.). (ENG.). 256p. pap. 42.95 *(978-0-7391-4656-9(4))* Lexington Bks.

Jeffries, Russell H., ed. China's Agricultural Modernization. 2009. (China in the 21st Century Ser.). pap. 69.00 *(978-1-60876-088-6(X))* Nova Science Pubs., Inc.

Lardy, Nicholas R. Agriculture in China's Modern Economic Development. 2008. (ENG., Illus.). 300p. pap. 42.00 *(978-0-521-07170-3(4))* Cambridge Univ. Pr.

Lee, Mabel P. Economic History of China. (Columbia University, Studies in the Social Sciences: No. 225). reprint ed. 39.50 *(978-0-404-51225-5(9))* AMS Pr., Inc.

Li, Xiaoyun, et al. Agricultural Development in China & Africa. 2012. (ENG., Illus.). 323p. 99.95 **(978-1-84971-388-7(X))** Routledge.

Spoor, Max, et al, eds. Dragons with Clay Feet? Transition, Sustainable Land Use, & Rural Environment in China & Vietnam. 2007. (Rural Economies in Transition Ser.). (ENG., Illus.). 356p. 99.99 *(978-0-7391-1369-1(0))* Lexington Bks.

Vermeer, Eduard B. & Vermeer, E. B. Economic Development in Provincial China: The Central Shaanxi since 1930. 2009. (Contemporary China Institute Publications). (ENG.). 552p. pap. 56.00 *(978-0-521-11543-8(4))* Cambridge Univ. Pr.

Wang, Wei. Zhongguo Nong Cun Jin Rong Fu Wu Ti Xi Xie Tiao Fa Zhan Yan Jiu: Zhongguo Nongcun Jinrong Fuwu Tixi Xietiao Fazhan Yanjiu. 2010. (CHI., Illus.). *(978-7-207-08527-6(3))* Heilongjiang People's Publishing Hse.

Zhang, Li. Incentives & Strategic Behavoirs of Governments. 2009. 180p. pap. *(978-3-639-19861-4(1))* VDM Verlag Dr. Mueller e.K.

Zhenglai, Deng. China's Economy Vol. 1: Rural Reform & Agricultural Development. 2009. 432p. 111.00 *(978-981-4291-35-9(4))* World Scientific Publishing Co., Inc.

AGRICULTURE—ECONOMIC ASPECTS—COLOMBIA

Aceituno, Francisco Javier & Loaiza, Nicolas. Domesticación del bosque en el Cauca medio colombiano entre el Pleistoceno final y el Holoceno medio. 2007. (Bar S Ser.). (SPA., Illus.). 138p. (C). pap. 72.50 *(978-1-4073-0090-0(3))* British Archaeological Reports Ltd. GBR. Dist: Brown, David Bk. Co., The.

Kalmanovitz, Salomón & López E, Enrique. La Agricultura Colombiana en el Siglo. 2006. (Economia Ser.). (SPA., Illus.). 433p. pap. *(978-958-38-0132-7(1))* Fondo de Cultura Economica.

AGRICULTURE—ECONOMIC ASPECTS—DEVELOPING COUNTRIES

Bigman, David. Globalization & the Least Developed Countries: Potentials & Pitfalls. 2007. (Illus.). 336p. 145.00 *(978-1-84593-308-1(7))* CABI GBR. Dist: Stylus Publishing, LLC.

Breger Bush, Sasha. Derivatives & Development: A Political Economy of Global Finance, Farming, & Poverty. 2012. (ENG., Illus.). 256p. 100.00 **(978-0-230-33892-0(5))** Palgrave Macmillan.

Bresciani. Beyond Food Production the Role of Agriculture in Poverty Reduction. 2007. (Illus.). 240p. (C). 119.00 *(978-1-84720-075-4(3))* Elgar, Edward Publishing, Inc.

Bresciani, Fabrizio & Valdés, Alberto. Beyond Food Production: The Role of Agriculture in Poverty Reduction. 2007. (Illus.). viii, 232p. *(978-92-5-105534-2(3))*; pap. *(978-92-5-105535-9(1))* Elgar, Edward Publishing, Inc.

Carletto, Calogero, et al. Migration, Transfers & Economic Decision Making among Agricultural Households. 2010. (Illus.). 192p. 125.00 *(978-0-415-49513-4(X))* Routledge.

Chang, Ha-Joon, ed. Public Policy & Agricultural Development. 2011. (Routledge ISS Studies in Rural Livelihoods Ser.). (ENG., Illus.). 320p. (C). 140.00 *(978-0-415-61930-1(0))* Routledge.

Contributing Factors & International Responses to the Global Food Crisis: Hearing Before the Committee on Financial Services, U.S. House of Representatives, One Hundred Tenth Congress, Second Session, May 14, 2008. 2008. (Illus.). iii, 92p. *(978-0-16-081473-0(1),* 552-070-37835-9) United States Government Printing Office.

Da Silva, Carlos A., et al. Agro-Industries for Development. 2009. (Illus.). 304p. 125.00 *(978-1-84593-576-4(4))*; pap. 85.00 *(978-1-84593-577-1(2))* CABI GBR. Dist: Stylus Publishing, LLC.

Food and Agriculture Organization of the United Nations. Commodities and Trade Division. Basic Foodstuffs Service & CIMMYT Economics Program Staff, contrib. by. White Maize: A Traditional Food Grain in Developing Countries: a Joint Study. (Illus.). 26p. *(978-92-5-103882-6(1))* Food & Agriculture Organization of the United Nations ITA. Dist: Balogh International, Inc.

Glaeser, Bernhard, ed. The Green Revolution Revisited. 2011. (ENG.). 224p. 105.00 *(978-0-415-59249-9(6))* Routledge.

Hazell, P. B. R. The Future of Small Farms for Poverty Reduction & Growth. 2007. (2020 Discussion Paper Ser.: Vol. 42). (Illus.). ix, 38p. *(978-0-89629-764-7(0))* International Food Policy Research Institute.

Hazell, P. B. R. & Reardon, Thomas Anthony. Transforming the Rural Nonfarm Economy: Opportunities & Threats in the Developing World. Hazell, Peter B. R et al, eds. 2007. (ENG., Illus.). 512p. (gr. 17). 70.00 *(978-0-8018-8663-8(5))* Johns Hopkins Univ. Pr.

Hazell, Peter B. R., et al, eds. Transforming the Rural Nonfarm Economy: Opportunities & Threats in the Developing World. 2007. (ENG., Illus.). 512p. (gr. 17). per. 30.00 *(978-0-8018-8664-5(3))* Johns Hopkins Univ. Pr.

Kibirige, Douglas, et al. Analysis of T E & a E of Apep on Maize Farmers; Masindi District. 2010. 68p. pap. *(978-3-8383-7163-4(1))* Lambert Academic Publishing.

Kugelman, Michael, et al. Land Grab? The Race for the World's Farmland. 2009. (Illus.). x, 123p. **(978-1-933549-55-2(6))** Woodrow Wilson Interantional Ctr. fo Scholars.

Lipton, Michael & Longhurst, Richard. New Seeds & Poor People. 2011. (ENG.). 496p. 130.00 *(978-0-415-59537-7(1))* Routledge.

Mendelsohn, R. M. & Dinar, André. Climate Change & Agriculture: An Economic Analysis of Global Impacts, Adaptation & Distributional Effects. 2009. (New Horizons in Environmental Economics Ser.). (Illus.). 256p. 119.00 *(978-1-84720-670-1(0))* Elgar, Edward Publishing, Inc.

Mendelsohn, Robert O. & Dinar, Ariel, eds. Handbook on Climate Change & Agriculture. 2012. (Elgar Original Reference Ser.). (Illus.). 544p. 245.00 **(978-1-84980-116-4(9))** Elgar, Edward Publishing, Inc.

Nair, K. P. Prabhakaran. The Agronomy & Economy of Important Tree Crops of the Developing World. 2010. (ENG., Illus.). 368p. 145.00 *(978-0-12-384677-8(3))* Elsevier Science & Technology Bks.

Norton, George W., et al. The Economics of Agricultural Development. 2nd ed. 2010. (Routledge Textbooks in Environmental & Agricultural Economics Ser.). (ENG., Illus.). 480p. 64.95 *(978-0-415-49424-3(9))*; 160.00 *(978-0-415-49264-5(5))* Routledge.

—The Economics of Agricultural Development: World Food Systems & Resource Use. 2006. (ENG., Illus.). 464p. (C). 180.00 *(978-0-415-77045-3(9))* Routledge.

The World Bank. Growth & Productivity in Agriculture & Agribusiness: Evaluative Lessons from World Bank Group Experience. 2011. (Independent Evaluation Group Studies). (ENG., Illus.). 200p. pap. 25.00 *(978-0-8213-8606-4(9),* 9780821386064) World Bank Pubns.

Watkins, Marilyn M. World Poverty Issues. Finn, Jerald D., ed. 2008. (Illus.). 168p. 120.00 *(978-1-60456-057-2(6))* Nova Science Pubs., Inc.

Weldeselassie, Berhane Ghebremichael. Cooperatives & Agribusiness in Developing Countries. 2010. 136p. pap. *(978-3-639-24484-7(2))* VDM Verlag Dr. Mueller e.K.

Wharton, Clifton R. Subsistence Agriculture & Economic Development. Wharton, Clifton, Jr., ed. 2008. (ENG.). 494p. pap. 39.95 *(978-0-202-36225-0(6))* Aldine Transaction.

World Bank. Gender & Governance in Rural Services: Insights from India, Ghana, & Ethiopia. 2010. (Agriculture & Rural Development Ser.). (ENG.). 376p. pap. 35.00 *(978-0-8213-7658-4(6),* 9780821376584) World Bank Pubns.

AGRICULTURE—ECONOMIC ASPECTS—ETHIOPIA

Abate Weldeyesus, Mengistu. Smallholder Irrigation & Household Food Security in Ethiopi. 2011. 100p. pap. **(978-3-8433-8519-0(X))** Lambert Academic Publishing.

Abdurezack, Hussein. Market Efficiency of the Ethiopia Commodity Exchange: The Case of Export Coffee Trading. 2011. 120p. pap. **(978-3-639-32209-5(6))** VDM Verlag Dr. Mueller e.K.

Aregawi, Tesfay Kidanemariam. Determinants of Rural Household Micro-Credit Utilization & Repayment: The Case of Eastern Zone of Tigray, Ethiopia. 2011. 96p. pap. **(978-3-639-32734-2(9))** VDM Verlag Dr. Mueller e.K.

Birhane, Emiru, et al. Woody Species Diversity in Enclosures. 2010. 76p. pap. *(978-3-639-28273-3(6))* VDM Verlag Dr. Mueller e.K.

Fisseha, Zelalem. Association of Traits & Stability of Haricot Bean in Ethiopi. 2011. 84p. pap. **(978-3-8433-9207-5(2))** Lambert Academic Publishing.

Gebissa, Ezekiel. Khat in Ethiopia: Taking the Place of Food. 2010. 348p. pap. *(978-1-56902-318-1(2))* Red Sea Pr.

Gebrehiwot, Nahusenay Teamer & Ghebremichael, Berhane. Cooperatives & Agricultural Production. 2010. 172p. pap. *(978-3-639-25896-7(7))* VDM Verlag Dr. Mueller e.K.

Gebreselassie, Arsiema Girmay. Problems & Prospectus of Agricultural Marketing Information. 2010. 116p. pap. *(978-3-639-23883-9(4))* VDM Verlag Dr. Mueller e.K.

Giziew, Almaz. Determinants of Adoption & Its Intensity on Agricultural Technologies. 2010. 160p. pap. *(978-3-639-25953-7(X))* VDM Verlag Dr. Mueller e.K.

Hailemichael Asgedom, Aklilu. Exploring Village Poultry Development in Ethiopi. 2010. 156p. pap. *(978-3-8383-4517-8(7))* Lambert Academic Publishing.

Karthikeyan, Muthumariappan & Bayisa, Befakadu. Determinants of Cooperative Leadership in Ethiopi. 2010. 156p. pap. *(978-3-639-27061-7(4))* VDM Verlag Dr. Mueller e.K.

Kaske, Deribe. Agricultural Information Networks of Farm Woman in Southern Ethiopi. 2011. 120p. pap. **(978-3-8454-0473-8(6))** Lambert Academic Publishing.

Kenea, Aster. Onion Production in the Rift Valley of Ethiopi. 2010. 96p. pap. *(978-3-639-25942-1(4))* VDM Verlag Dr. Mueller e.K.

Ketema, Dessalegn Molla. Social Networks & Diffusion of Agricultural Technology. 2010. 120p. pap. *(978-3-8383-4427-0(8))* Lambert Academic Publishing.

Mahmud, Jemal. Performances of Cooperatives in Agricultural Marketing, Eastern Tigray. 2010. 140p. pap. *(978-3-639-24959-0(3))* VDM Verlag Dr. Mueller e.K.

Reba, Yeneneh Bekele, et al. Response of Chickpea to Moisture Stress: Response of Chickpea Varieties to Terminal Moisture Stress at Midaltitude & Lowland Areas of Central Ethiopia. 2011. 100p. pap. **(978-3-639-33901-7(0))** VDM Verlag Dr. Mueller e.K.

Tadesse, Matebu. Agricultural Development Communication Practices in Central Ethiopi. 2010. 112p. pap. *(978-3-639-25003-9(6))* VDM Verlag Dr. Mueller e.K.

Tatek, Bekele. Economic Valuation of Land Use Options in Ethiopia: Economic Valuation of Alternative Land Use Options in Boswellia Papyrifera Dominated Woodland Area of Metema, Northwest Ethiopia. 2011. 112p. pap. **(978-3-639-34164-5(3))** VDM Verlag Dr. Mueller e.K.

Teklay, Fitsum. Socioeconomic Status of Farmers on Fertility of Organic Coffee Soils. 2010. 84p. pap. *(978-3-639-24804-3(X))* VDM Verlag Dr. Mueller e.K.

Tekle, Melete Gebregiorgis. Household Rainwater Harvesting Ponds in Ethiopia: An Assessment of Benefits & Challenges of Pond Adoption in Kilte Awlaelo Woreda, Tigray. 2011. 116p. pap. **(978-3-639-32704-5(7))** VDM Verlag Dr. Mueller e.K.

Temesgen Leye Staff. Conservation Tillage Systems & Water Productivity Implications. 2007. (ENG., Illus.). 130p. 57.95 *(978-0-415-43946-6(9),* Taylor & Francis) Taylor & Francis Group GBR. Dist: Taylor & Francis Group.

Wassie, Getachew Adugna. Determinants of Land Degradation in the Lake Tana Basin: Implications for Sustainable Land Management the Case of Angereb & Gish-Abbay Watersheds. 2011. 76p. pap. **(978-3-639-30893-8(X))** VDM Verlag Dr. Mueller e.K.

Woldie, Getachew Abebe. Agricultural Supply Response & Yield & Price Risk. 2010. 80p. pap. *(978-3-639-21677-0(9))* VDM Verlag Dr. Mueller e.K.

AGRICULTURE—ECONOMIC ASPECTS—EUROPE

Albayrak, Dilan. Enlargement Negotiations Between Poland & Eu. 2009. 124p. pap. *(978-3-639-12815-4(X))* VDM Verlag Dr. Mueller e.K.

Almås, Reidar & Rouhinen, Sauli. Om Landbruksforhold I Nordiske Land: Antologi. 2011. (NOR, DAN, SWE & ENG.). 280p. (C). pap. 32.00 **(978-87-87564-21-2(1))** Aarhus Universitetsforlag DNK. Dist: ISD.

Brassley, Paul, et al, eds. War Agriculture & Food. 2012. (Routledge Studies in Modern European History Ser.). (ENG., Illus.). 286p. (C). 125.00 **(978-0-415-52216-8(1))** Routledge.

A

Calamia, Diego & Esposito, Mekhi. U. S. & Eu Agriculture: Comparisons & Linkages. 2011. (Agriculture Issues & Policies Ser.). 66p. pap. 47.00 (978-1-61470-698-4(0)) Nova Science Pubs., Inc.

Daugbjerg, Carsten & Swinbank, Alan. Ideas, Institutions, & Trade: The WTO & the Curious Role of EU Farm Policy in Trade Liberalization. 2009. (ENG., Illus.). 256p. 95.00 (978-0-19-955775-2(6)) Oxford Univ. Pr., Inc.

Greenwood, Davydd J. Unrewarding Wealth: The Commercialization & Collapse of Agriculture in a Spanish Basque Town. 2009. (ENG.). 236p. pap. 34.99 (978-0-521-10707-5(5)) Cambridge Univ. Pr.

Harsche, Johannes. Regionale Inzidenz und ökonomische Bestimmungsgrößen der Gemeinsamen Europäischen Agrarpolitik. 2009. (Schriften zur internationalen Entwicklungs- und Umweltforschung Ser.). (GER.). 264p. pap. 65.95 (978-3-631-58096-7(7)) Lang, Peter GmbH, Europaischer Verlag der Wissenschaften DEU. Dist: Lang, Peter.

Kitsikopoulos, Harilaos, ed. Agrarian Change & Crisis in Europe 1200-1500. 2011. (Routledge Research in Medieval Studies). (ENG., Illus.). 376p. (C). 125.00 (978-0-415-89578-1(2)) Routledge.

Kleinpenning, J. M. G. Rural Paraguay 1870-1963: A Geography of Progress, Plunder & Poverty, 2 vols. 2009. (Illus.). pap. (978-84-8489-483-4(5)) Iberoamericana Vervuert Publishing Corp.

Lains, Pedro & Pinilla, Vicente. Agriculture & Economic Development in Europe since 1870. Lains, Pedro & Pinilla, Vicente, eds. 2009. (Routledge Explorations in Economic History Ser.). (Illus.). 400p. 170.00 (978-0-415-42487-5(9)) Routledge.

Lampietti, Julian A., et al. The Changing Face of Rural Space: Agriculture & Rural Development in the Western Balkans. 2009. (Directions in Development Ser.). (ENG., Illus.). 176p. pap. 35.00 (978-0-8213-7931-8(3), 9780821379318) World Bank Pubns.

Landsteiner, E., et al, eds. Agrosystems & Labour Relations in European Rural Societies. 2010. (Rural History in Europe Ser.). (EGY & ENG.). 218p. (C). pap. 88.00 (978-2-503-52954-7(2)) Brepols Pubs. BEL. Dist: ISD.

Malanima, P. Pre-Modern European Economy: One Thousand Years (10th-19th Centuries) 2009. (Global Economic History Ser.). (Illus.). 406p. (978-90-04-17822-9(8)) BRILL.

Marfany, Julie. Land Proto-Industry & Population in Catalonia C. 1680-1829: An Alternative Transition to Capitalism? 2012. (Modern Economic & Social History Ser.). (Illus.). 190p. 124.95 (978-1-4094-4465-7(1)) Ashgate Publishing Co.

Markou, Marinos. A Plan to Place Succesfully Organic Products in Cyprus. 2010. 120p. pap. (978-3-8383-8299-9(4)) Lambert Academic Publishing.

Meuwissen, Miranda P. M., et al, eds. Income stabilisation in European Agriculture: Design & economic impact of risk management Tools. 2008. (Illus.). 224p. 89.00 (978-90-8686-079-1(6)) Wageningen Academic Publishers NLD. Dist: Enfield Publishing & Distribution Co., Inc.

Olsson, M. & Svennson, Patrick, eds. Growth & Stagnation in European Historical Agriculture. 2011. (Rural History in Europe Ser.). (ENG.). 307p. (C). pap. 103.00 (978-2-503-54076-4(7)) Brepols Pubs. BEL. Dist: ISD.

Pagria, Ina. Partnerships Business in Rural Development of the Country. 2011. 116p. pap. (978-3-8443-2890-5(4)) Lambert Academic Publishing.

Piorr, Annette & Muller, Klaus. Rural Landscapes & Agricultural Policies in Europe. 2009. (Illus.). 380p. 169.00 (978-3-540-79469-1(7)) Springer.

Range, Willard. A Century of Georgia Agriculture, 1850-1950. 2010. (ENG.). 346p. pap. 24.95 (978-0-8203-3551-3(7)) Univ. of Georgia Pr.

Scrieciu, S. Serban. Socioeconomic & Environmental Impacts on Agriculture in the New Europe: Post-Communist Transition & Accession to the European Union. 2011. (Routledge Studies in Ecological Economics Ser.). (ENG., Illus.). 240p. (C). 125.00 (978-0-415-47588-4(0)) Routledge.

Segers, Yves & Van Molle, Leen, eds. The Rural Economy & Society in North-Western Europe, 500-2000: The Agro-Food Market - Production, Distribution, & Consumption. 2012. (Rural Economy & Society in North-Western Europe, 500-2000 Ser.). (ENG.). 450p. (C). 109.00 (978-2-503-53048-2(6)) Brepols Pubs. BEL. Dist: Brown, David Bk. Co., The.

Senior Nello, Susan Mary & Pierani, Pierpaolo, eds. International Trade, Consumer Interests & Reform of the Common Agricultural Policy. 2010. (Routledge Studies in the European Economy Ser.). (ENG., Illus.). 208p. (C). 150.00 (978-0-415-57019-0(0), Routledge) Taylor & Francis Group GBR. Dist: Taylor & Francis Group.

Stewart, Pamela J. & Strathern, Andrew, eds. Landscape, Heritage, & Conservation: Farming Issues in the European Union. 2010. 340p. pap. 42.00 (978-1-59460-774-5(5)) Carolina Academic Pr.

Thompson, I. A. A. & Casalilla, Bartolomi Yun, eds. The Castilian Crisis of the Seventeenth Century: New Perspectives on the Economic & Social History of Seventeenth-Century Spain. 2009. (Past & Present Publications). (ENG., Illus.). 348p. pap. 46.00 (978-0-521-10525-5(0)) Cambridge Univ. Pr.

Torre, André & Traversac, Jean Baptiste. Territorial Governance: Local Development, Rural Areas & Agrofood Systems. 2011. (ENG., Illus.). xxxiii, 207p. 139.00 (978-3-7908-2421-6(6), 3790824216) Physica-Verlag DEU. Dist: Springer.

AGRICULTURE—ECONOMIC ASPECTS—FRANCE

Golob, Eugene O. Meline Tariff: French Agriculture & Nationalist Economic Policy. (Columbia University, Studies in the Social Sciences: No. 506). reprint ed. 27.50 (978-0-404-51506-5(1)) AMS Pr., Inc.

AGRICULTURE—ECONOMIC ASPECTS—GERMANY

Gerhardt, Uta. Soziologie Im Zwanzigsten Jahrhundert: Studien Zu Ihrer Geschichte in Deutschland. 2009. (Studien zur geschichte der deutschen Forschungsgemeinschaft Ser.). 430p. (C). 75.00 (978-3-515-09255-5(2)) Steiner, Franz Verlag Wiesbaden GmbH DEU. Dist: Brown, David Bk. Co., The.

Kopsidis, Michael. Agrarentwicklung: Historische Agrarrevolutionen und Entwicklungsökonomie. 2006. (Grundzuge der modernen Wirtschaftsgeschichte Ser.). (GER.). 391p. (C). 34.00 (978-3-515-08341-6(3)) Steiner, Franz Verlag Wiesbaden GmbH DEU. Dist: Brown, David Bk. Co., The.

AGRICULTURE—ECONOMIC ASPECTS—GREAT BRITAIN

Bailey, Mark. A Marginal Economy? East Anglian Breckland in the Later Middle Ages. 2008. (Cambridge Studies in Medieval Life & Thought: Fourth Ser.). (ENG.). 368p. pap. 48.00 (978-0-521-07314-1(6)) Cambridge Univ. Pr.

Britnell, Richard & Mullan, John. Land & Family: Trends & Local Variations in the Peasant Land Market on the Winchester Bishopric Estates, 1263-1415. 2010. (Studies in Regional & Local History Ser.). (ENG., Illus.). 288p. 80.00 (978-1-902806-94-5(8)) Univ. of Hertfordshire Pr. GBR. Dist: Independent Pubs. Group.

Campbell, Bruce M. S. The Medieval Antecedents of English Agricultural Progress. 2007. (Variorum Collected Studies). (Illus.). 368p. 170.00 (978-0-7546-5919-8(4)) Ashgate Publishing Co.

Collins, E. J. T., ed. The Agrarian History of England & Wales, 1850-1914, 3 vols., Vol. 7. 2011. (Agrarian History of England & Wales Ser.). (ENG.). 2333p. pap. 200.00 (978-1-107-40110-5(0)) Cambridge Univ. Pr.

Collins, E. J. T. & Thirsk, Joan, eds. The Agrarian History of England & Wales - 2011. 782p. pap. 0.00 (978-1-107-40109-9(7)) Cambridge Univ. Pr.

Gardiner, Tim. Hopping Back to Happiness? 2009. (Illus.). 194p. pap. (978-3-639-17363-3(X)) VDM Verlag Dr. Mueller e.K.

Grigg, David. The Agricultural Revolution in South Lincolnshire. 2009. (Cambridge Studies in Economic History Ser.). (ENG.). 236p. pap. 34.99 (978-0-521-10615-3(X)) Cambridge Univ. Pr.

Hallam, H. E., ed. The Agrarian History of England & Wales, 1042-1350, Vol. 2. 2011. (Agrarian History of England & Wales Ser.). (ENG.). 1128p. pap. 100.00 (978-0-521-20011-0(3)) Cambridge Univ. Pr.

Kennedy, Geoff. Diggers, Levellers, & Agrarian Capitalism: Radical Political Thought in Seventeenth Century England. 2008. (ENG.). 276p. 73.50 (978-0-7391-2374-4(2)) Lexington Bks.

Kopsidis, Michael. Agrarentwicklung: Historische Agrarrevolutionen und Entwicklungsökonomie. 2006. (Grundzuge der modernen Wirtschaftsgeschichte Ser.). (GER.). 391p. (C). 34.00 (978-3-515-08341-6(3)) Steiner, Franz Verlag Wiesbaden GmbH DEU. Dist: Brown, David Bk. Co., The.

Leclercq, Eric. Diversification of Atlantic Salmon Grow-Out Technology. 2011. 92p. pap. (978-3-8443-2442-6(9)) Lambert Academic Publishing.

Miller, Edward, ed. The Agrarian History of England & Wales, 1348-1500, Vol. 3. 2011. (Agrarian History of England & Wales Ser.). (ENG.). 1022p. pap. 100.00 (978-0-521-20012-7(1)) Cambridge Univ. Pr.

Mingay, G. E., ed. The Agrarian History of England & Wales, 2 vols., Pt. 2, Vol. 6. 2011. (Agrarian History of England & Wales Ser.). 1237p. pap. 105.00 (978-1-107-40113-6(5)) Cambridge Univ. Pr.

Mullan, John & Britnell, Richard. Land & Family - Trends & Local Variations in the Peasant: Land Market on the Winchester Bishopric Estates, 1263-1415. 2010. (Studies in Regional & Local History Ser.). (ENG., Illus.). 192p. pap. 37.95 (978-1-902806-95-2(6)) Univ. of Hertfordshire Pr. GBR. Dist: Independent Pubs. Group.

Patriquin, Larry. Agrarian Capitalism & Poor Relief in England, 1500-1860: Rethinking the Origins of the Welfare State. 2007. (ENG.). 280p. 100.00 (978-0-230-51693-9(9)) Palgrave Macmillan.

Phillips, A. D. M. The Underdraining of Farmland in England During the Nineteenth Century. 2009. (Cambridge Studies in Historical Geography Ser.). (ENG.). 332p. pap. 36.99 (978-0-521-10580-4(3)) Cambridge Univ. Pr.

Ravensdale, J. R. Liable to Floods: Village Landscape on the Edge of the Fens A. D. 450-1850. 2008. (ENG.). 228p. pap. 32.99 (978-0-521-08284-6(6)) Cambridge Univ. Pr.

Scruton, Roger & Scruton. News from Somewhere: On Settling. 2006. (ENG.). 192p. 17.95 (978-0-8264-9091-9(3)) Continuum International Publishing Group, Ltd. GBR. Dist: National Bk. Network.

Stewart, Pamela J. & Strathern, Andrew, eds. Landscape, Heritage, & Conservation: Farming Issues in the European Union. 2010. 340p. pap. 42.00 (978-1-59460-774-5(5)) Carolina Academic Pr.

Thirsk, Joan. The Agrarian History of England & Wales, Vol. 1. Piggott, Stuart, ed. 2011. (Agrarian History of England & Wales Ser.). (ENG.). 1077p. pap. 100.00 (978-1-107-40114-3(3)) Cambridge Univ. Pr.

Thirsk, Joan, ed. The Agrarian History of England & Wales, 2 vols., Pt. 2, Vol. 5. 2011. (Agrarian History of England & Wales Ser.). (ENG.). 1526p. pap. 105.00 (978-1-107-40118-1(6)) Cambridge Univ. Pr.

—The Agrarian History of England & Wales, 1500-1640, Vol. 4. 2011. (Agrarian History of England & Wales Ser.). (ENG.). 984p. pap. 100.00 (978-0-521-20020-2(2)) Cambridge Univ. Pr.

Whetham, Edith H., ed. The Agrarian History of England & Wales, 1914-1939, Vol. 8. 2011. (Agrarian History of England & Wales Ser.). (ENG.). 378p. pap. 50.00 (978-0-521-20013-4(X)) Cambridge Univ. Pr.

Wyatt, Lee T. The Industrial Revolution, 1 vol. 2008. (Greenwood Guides to Historic Events 1500-1900 Ser.). (Illus.). 304p. 45.00 (978-0-313-33769-7(1), GR3769, Greenwood Pr.) Greenwood Publishing Group, Inc.

AGRICULTURE—ECONOMIC ASPECTS—GUATEMALA

Goldín, Liliana R. Global Maya: Work & Ideology in Rural Guatemala. 2011. (ENG & SPA., Illus.). 264p. pap. 24.95 (978-0-8165-2987-2(6)) Univ. of Arizona Pr.

AGRICULTURE—ECONOMIC ASPECTS—HUNGARY

Swain, Nigel. Collective Farms which Work? 2008. (Cambridge Russian, Soviet & Post-Soviet Studies). (ENG.). 248p. pap. 34.99 (978-0-521-05759-2(0)) Cambridge Univ. Pr.

AGRICULTURE—ECONOMIC ASPECTS—INDIA

Abdul Samad, Syed & P., Girija. International Development Enterprise India's (IDEI) Affordable Irrigation Technology: Making a Big Social Impact. 2010. (C). pap. 20.00 (978-1-61674-541-7(X)) Davidson, William Institute At The Univ. of Michigan, The.

Ali, Mohd & Bhaskar, G., eds. Wto, Globalization & Indian Agriculture. 2011. (Illus.). 196p. 34.50 (978-81-7708-264-7(7)) New Century Publications IND. Dist: International Specialized Bk. Services.

Ansari, Mahmood. Agency & Crop Marketing. 2011. 140p. pap. (978-3-8443-0502-9(5)) Lambert Academic Publishing.

Asian Development Bank Staff & International Food Policy Research Institute Staff, contrib. by. High-Value Crops & Marketing: Strategic Options for Development in Uttarakhand. 2010. (ENG., Illus.). 132p. pap. 49.95 (978-81-7188-758-3(9)) Academic Foundation IND. Dist: Independent Pubs. Group.

Bharamappanavara, Saikumar C. Farming Systems in the Tank Commands in North Eastern Karnataka. 2011. 184p. pap. (978-3-8433-8455-1(X)) Lambert Academic Publishing.

Bhaumik, Sankar Kumar, ed. Reforming Indian Agriculture: Towards Employment Generation & Poverty Reduction Essays in Honour of G K Chadha. 2008. (Illus.). 592p. (C). 49.95 (978-0-7619-3645-9(9), B36459C) SAGE Pubns., Inc.

Birner, Regina, et al. The Political Economy of Agricultural Policy Reform in India: The Case of Fertilizer Supply & Electricity Supply for Groundwater Irrigation. 2009. (978-0-89629-172-0(3)) International Food Policy Research Institute.

Brandow, Patrick M., ed. Agriculture & Agribusiness Developments in India. 2010. (Agriculture Issues & Policies Ser.). (Illus.). viii, 172p. 98.00 (978-1-61668-946-9(3)) Nova Science Pubs., Inc.

Charyulu, M. Yadagira & Reddy, A. Vinayak, eds. Indian Agriculture: Challenges of Globalisation. 2008. 346p. 42.50 (978-81-7708-171-8(3)) New Century Publications IND. Dist: International Specialized Bk. Services.

Chauhan, Dharmender Singh. Agricultural Geography. 2010. (Illus.). 194p. (978-81-87445-50-0(5), Library of Congress — New Delhi Overseas Office) Ritu Pubns.

Devi, Reena. Reforms in Credit Market, Performance of Crops & Capital Formation. 2010. 124p. pap. (978-3-639-27950-4(6)) VDM Verlag Dr. Mueller e.K.

Dhesi, Autar S. & Gurmail Singh. Rural Development in Punjab: A Success Story Going Astray. Dhesi, Autar S. & Singh, Gurmail, eds. 2008. (Illus.). 420p. 110.00 (978-0-415-45681-4(9), Routledge India) Taylor & Francis Group GBR. Dist: Taylor & Francis Group.

Diwakar, D. M. & Nayak, Sanatan. Development Challenges: Afflicting Uttar Pradesh. 2007. x, 388p. (978-81-7827-169-9(9)) Manak Pubns. Pvt., Ltd.

Gidwani, Vinay & Gidwani, Vinay K. Capital, Interrupted: Agrarian Development & the Politics of Work in India. 2008. (Illus.). 368p. 75.00 (978-0-8166-4958-7(8)); pap. 25.00 (978-0-8166-4959-4(6)) Univ. of Minnesota Pr.

Habib, Irfan. The Agrarian System of Mughal India: 1556-1707. 3rd ed. 2012. (ENG., Illus.). 584p. pap. 35.00 (978-0-19-807742-8(4)) Oxford Univ. Pr., Inc.

Harriss-White, Barbara. Rural Commercial Capital: Agricultural Markets in West Bengal. 2008. (ENG., Illus.). 400p. 58.95 (978-0-19-569159-7(8)) Oxford Univ. Pr., Inc.

Hatai, Dr. Lakshmi Dhar & Hatai, Lakshmi Dhar. Betelvine Production in Orissa - an Economic Analysis. 2011. 76p. pap. (978-3-8454-1913-8(X)) Lambert Academic Publishing.

Hatai, Lakshmi Dhar. Agricultural Sustainability. 2011. 132p. pap. (978-3-8443-3322-0(3)) Lambert Academic Publishing.

Islam, M. Mufakharul. Bengal Agriculture 1926-46: A Quantitative Study. 2007. (Cambridge South Asian Studies). (ENG.). 300p. pap. 36.99 (978-0-521-04985-6(7)) Cambridge Univ. Pr.

Joshi, Sharad P. Down to Earth. 2010. (ENG.). 388p. 79.95 (978-81-7188-842-9(9)) Academic Foundation IND. Dist: Independent Pubs. Group.

Kapila, Uma, ed. Indian Agriculture in the New Millennium: Changing Perceptions & Development Policy, 2 vols. 2006. (ENG., Illus.). 398p. 69.95 (978-81-7188-513-8(6)); 349p. 65.95 (978-81-7188-514-5(4)) Academic Foundation IND. Dist: Independent Pubs. Group.

Kapila, Uma & Krishna, K. L. Readings in Indian Agriculture & Industry. Kapila, Uma & Krishna, K. L., eds. 2009. (ENG., Illus.). 642p. 69.95 (978-81-7188-734-7(1)) Academic Foundation IND. Dist: Independent Pubs. Group.

Ludden, David. An Agrarian History of South Asia. 2011. (New Cambridge History of India Ser.). (ENG.). 276p. (C). pap. 36.99 (978-0-521-17967-6(X)) Cambridge Univ. Pr.

Ludden, David E. Peasant History in South Indi. 2009. 352p. 50.00 (978-1-59740-305-4(9)) ACLS Humanities E-Book.

Mehta, Niti. Economic Wellbeing of Hired Workers in a Growing Regional Economy. 2010. 124p. pap. (978-3-639-26846-1(6)) VDM Verlag Dr. Mueller e.K.

Pandian, Anand. Crooked Stalks: Cultivating Virtue in South India. 2009. (ENG., Illus.). 344p. 94.95 (978-0-8223-4514-5(5)); pap. 25.95 (978-0-8223-4531-2(5)) Duke Univ. Pr.

Prasad, Chandra. Agriculture & Rural Development in India Since 1947. 2009. 512p. 106.50 (978-81-7708-201-2(9)) New Century Publications IND. Dist: International Specialized Bk. Services.

Radhakrishna, R., et al, eds. India in a Globalising World: Some Aspects of Macroeconomy, Agriculture & Poverty: Essays in Honour of C. H. Hanumantha Rao. 2006. (ENG., Illus.). 528p. 79.95 (978-81-7188-516-9(0)) Academic Foundation IND. Dist: Independent Pubs. Group.

Singh, Narendra. Economics of Production & Marketing Profile for Cumin Seed. 2011. 124p. pap. (978-3-8433-9340-9(0)) Lambert Academic Publishing.

Singh, Narendra, et al. Marketing of Maize in Indi: Policies & Issues for Market Development. 2011. 100p. pap. (978-3-8443-0574-6(2)) Lambert Academic Publishing.

Suchandan, Bernal, et al. Climatic Variability & Rice Productivity: Seasonal Climatic Variability & Impact Analysis on Rice Productivity in Haryana, India. 2011. 120p. pap. (978-3-639-32284-2(3)) VDM Verlag Dr. Mueller e.K.

Swaminathan, M. S. From Green to Evergreen Revolution: Indian Agriculture - Performance & Emerging Challenges. 2010. 410p. 79.95 (978-81-7188-797-2(X)) Academic Foundation IND. Dist: Independent Pubs. Group.

Vaidyanathan, A. Agricultural Growth in India: The Role of Technology, Incentives, & Institutions. 2010. (ENG., Illus.). 300p. 55.00 (978-0-19-806447-3(0)) Oxford Univ. Pr., Inc.

Wolchuck, Natalie A., ed. India: Tariff Issues for U. S. Agricultural Exports. 2010. (Agriculture Issues & Policies Ser.). 137.00 (978-1-61668-948-3(X)) Nova Science Pubs., Inc.

World Bank Staff. From Competition at Home to Competing Abroad: The Case of Indian Horticulture. 2007. (ENG., Illus.). 114p. pap. 39.95 (978-0-19-568593-0(8)) Oxford Univ. Pr., Inc.

AGRICULTURE—ECONOMIC ASPECTS—INDONESIA

Henky, Widjaja. Contract Farming & Smallholders: Critical Perspective on Peanuts Contract Farming in Ntb Province of Indonesia. 2011. 68p. pap. (978-3-639-32406-8(4)) VDM Verlag Dr. Mueller e.K.

AGRICULTURE—ECONOMIC ASPECTS—IRELAND

Crotty, Raymond, Jr. Irish Agricultural Production. (Illus.). (978-0-902561-39-7(1)) Cork Univ. Pr.

Kennedy, Liam & Solar, Peter. Irish Agriculture: A Price History from the Mid-Eighteenth Century to the Eve of the First World War. 2007. (Illus.). 206p. 45.00 (978-1-904890-41-6(5)) Royal Irish Academy IRL. Dist: International Specialized Bk. Services.

Patterson, James G. In the Wake of the Great Rebellion: Republicanism, Agrarianism & Banditry in Ireland After 1798. (ENG.). 208p. 2011. pap. 26.95 (978-0-7190-8556-7(X)) 2008. 84.00 (978-0-7190-7693-0(5)) Manchester Univ. Pr. GBR. Dist: Macmillan.

AGRICULTURE—ECONOMIC ASPECTS—ISRAEL

Oecd Publishing. Oecd Review of Agricultural Policies Oecd Review of Agricultural Policies: Israel 2010. 2010. 208p. pap. 67.00 (978-92-64-07934-2(3)) Organization for Economic Cooperation & Development.

Rivlin, Paul. The Israeli Economy from the Foundation of the State Through the 21st Century. 2010. (ENG., Illus.). 312p. (C). 90.00 (978-0-521-19037-4(1)); pap. 31.99 (978-0-521-15020-0(5)) Cambridge Univ. Pr.

AGRICULTURE—ECONOMIC ASPECTS—ITALY

Erdkamp, Paul. The Grain Market in the Roman Empire: A Social, Political & Economic Study. 2009. (ENG., Illus.). 380p. pap. 44.00 (978-0-521-11783-8(6)) Cambridge Univ. Pr.

AGRICULTURE—ECONOMIC ASPECTS—JAMAICA

Mintz, Sidney Wilfred & Hall, Douglas. The Origins of the Jamaican Internal Marketing System: Yale University Publications in Anthropology, No. 57. Rouse, Irving, ed. 2011. 28p. 35.95 (978-1-258-09118-7(6)) Literary Licensing, LLC.

Plantation Jamaica, 1750-1850: Capital & Control in a Colonial Economy. 2008. (Illus.). 386p. per. (978-976-640-209-9(4)) Univ. of the West Indies Pr.

AGRICULTURE—ECONOMIC ASPECTS—LATIN AMERICA

Hartwich, Frank. Formando Alianzas Publico-Privadas para la Innovacion Agricola. 2008. (978-0-89629-762-3(4)) International Food Policy Research Institute.

Yudelman, Montague & Howard, Frederic. Agricultural Development & Economic Integration in Latin America. 2011. (ENG.). 336p. 115.00 (978-0-415-59436-3(7)) Routledge.

AGRICULTURE—ECONOMIC ASPECTS—MALAYSIA

Alam, Mahmudul, et al. Socioeconomic Study of Climate Change. 2010. 116p. pap. (978-3-8383-5210-7(6)) Lambert Academic Publishing.

AGRICULTURE—ECONOMIC ASPECTS—MEXICO

Appendini, Kirsten A. de & Torres-Mazuera, Gabriela. ¿Ruralidad Sin Agricultura? Perspectivas Multidisciplinarias de una Realidad Fragmentada. 2008. (Estudios Económicos Ser.). (Illus.). 257p. pap. 29.99 (978-968-12-1382-4(3)) El Colegio de México, A.C., Biblioteca Miguel Cosio Villegas MEX. Dist: Fondo de Cultura Economica USA.

Benavides, Guillermo. Commodity Prices, Options & Futures Behaviour. 2010. 308p. pap. (978-3-8383-6338-7(8)) Lambert Academic Publishing.

Brading, David. Haciendas & Ranchos in the Mexican Bajío: León, 1700-1860. 2009. (Cambridge Latin American Studies). (ENG.). 280p. pap. 38.99 *(978-0-521-10236-0(7))* Cambridge Univ. Pr.

César Dachary, Alfredo A. Produccion colectiva y desarrollo capitalista en el agro Mexicano: (1970 - 1980) (Latin America Studies). (GER.). XI, 350p. 135.00 ***(978-3-11-116705-3(4))*** De Gruyter, Mouton DEU. Dist: de Gruyter, Walter GmbH & Co. KG.

Chavez, Manuel, et al. NAFTA & the Campesinos: The Impact of NAFTA on Small-Scale Agricultural Producers in Mexico & the Prospects for Change. Rivera, Juan & Chavez, Manuel, eds. Whiteford, Scott, ed. 2009. (Illus.). 200p. pap. 25.00 *(978-1-58966-180-6(X))* Univ. of Scranton Pr.

Eakin, Hallie. Weathering Risk in Rural Mexico: Climatic, Institutional, & Economic Change. 2006. (ENG., Illus.). 288p. 50.00 *(978-0-8165-2500-3(5))* Univ. of Arizona Pr.

Frank, Andre Gunder. Mexican Agriculture 1521-1630: Transformation of the Mode of Production. 2008. (Studies in Modern Capitalism Ser.). (ENG.). 108p. pap. 31.99 *(978-0-521-08568-7(3))* Cambridge Univ. Pr.

Pacheco Castro, Jorge A. Cambio y Continuidad Sociocultural en la Región Sur Del Campo Yucateco. 2009. (SPA., Illus.). 355p. 37.00 *(978-970-722-682-1(X))* Plaza y Valdes, S.A. de C.V. MEX. Dist: Sony Electronics.

Puyana de Palacios, Alicia & Romero, José Antonio. Diez Años con el TLCAN: Las Experiencias Del Sector Agropecuario Mexicano. 2nd ed. 2008. (Estudios Económicos Ser.). (SPA., Illus.). 231p. pap. 44.99 *(978-968-12-1371-8(8))* El Colegio de México, A.C., Biblioteca Miguel Cosío Villegas MEX. Dist: Fondo de Cultura Economica USA.

West, Robert C. Sonora: Its Geographical Personality. 2009. (ENG., Illus.). 207p. pap. 19.95 *(978-0-292-72258-3(3))* Univ. of Texas Pr.

AGRICULTURE—ECONOMIC ASPECTS—MIDDLE EAST

Minot, Nicholas. Trade Liberalization & Poverty in the Middle East & North Africa. 2009. *(978-0-89629-174-4(X))* International Food Policy Research Institute.

Watson, Andrew M. Agricultural Innovation in the Early Islamic World. 2008. (Cambridge Studies in Islamic Civilization Ser.). (ENG., Illus.). 284p. pap. 36.99 *(978-0-521-06883-3(5))* Cambridge Univ. Pr.

AGRICULTURE—ECONOMIC ASPECTS—NEPAL

Chapagain, Prem Sagar. Agriculture & Environment in the Eastern Nepal Himalayas. 2009. 180p. pap. *(978-3-639-17232-4(9))* VDM Verlag Dr. Mueller e.K.

Dahal, Nirmal Mani & Upadhya, Madhukar. Changing Rainfall Pattern & Paddy Production in Mid-Hills of Nepal. 2011. 92p. pap. ***(978-3-8443-8244-0(5))*** Lambert Academic Publishing.

Dillon, Andrew, et al. Estimating the Impact of Access to Infrastructure & Extension Services in Rural Nepal. 2011. ***(978-0-89629-188-1(X))*** International Food Policy Research Institute.

Ghimire, Puspa Lal. Value Chain Analysis of Ginger Sector of Nepal. 2011. 84p. pap. ***(978-3-8443-9492-4(3))*** Lambert Academic Publishing.

Parajulee, Neeta. Economic Analysis of Dairy Co-Operatives & Their Impact. 2011. 84p. pap. ***(978-3-8443-1376-5(1))*** Lambert Academic Publishing.

Paudel, Indra. Economics of Agricultural Biodiversity. 2011. 128p. pap. ***(978-3-8443-2884-4(X))*** Lambert Academic Publishing.

Poudel, Dilli Prasad. Livelihood of Himalayan People. 2009. 136p. pap. *(978-3-639-21328-7(9))* VDM Verlag Dr. Mueller e.K.

Shrestha, Ram Krishna. Sustainable Soil Management Practices in the Mid Hills of Nepal. 2011. 92p. pap. ***(978-3-8443-1829-6(1))*** Lambert Academic Publishing.

AGRICULTURE—ECONOMIC ASPECTS—NIGERIA

Odoemenem, Innocent. Efficiency in Capital Resource Mobilization & Use. 2010. 84p. pap. *(978-3-8383-9059-8(8))* Lambert Academic Publishing.

Oyewole, Charles. The Man with the Hoe. 2011. 84p. pap. ***(978-3-8443-2145-6(4))*** Lambert Academic Publishing.

AGRICULTURE—ECONOMIC ASPECTS—PACIFIC AREA

Gerber, James & Guang, Lei. Agriculture & Rural Connections in the Pacific, 1500-1900. 2006. (Pacific World Ser.: Vol. 13). (Illus.). 424p. 170.00 *(978-0-7546-3978-7(9))* Ashgate Publishing Co.

Mortimore, Michael. Adapting to Drought: Farmers, Famines & Desertification in West Africa. 2009. (ENG., Illus.). 324p. pap. 42.00 *(978-0-521-10427-2(0))* Cambridge Univ. Pr.

Tonts, Matthew & Siddique, M.A.B., eds. Globalisation, Agriculture & Development: Perspectives from the Asia-Pacific. 2011. (Illus.). 264p. 110.00 *(978-1-84720-818-7(5))* Elgar, Edward Publishing, Inc.

AGRICULTURE—ECONOMIC ASPECTS—PHILIPPINES

Cororaton, Caesar B. & Corong, Erwin. Philippine Agricultural & Food Policies: Implications for Poverty & Income Distribution. 2009. *(978-0-89629-170-6(7))* International Food Policy Research Institute.

AGRICULTURE—ECONOMIC ASPECTS—SOUTH AFRICA

Bundy, Colin. The Rise & Fall of the South African Peasantry. 308p. 2009. 46.00 *(978-1-59740-296-5(6))* 2008. pap. 30.00 *(978-1-59740-611-6(2))* ACLS Humanities E-Book.

AGRICULTURE—ECONOMIC ASPECTS—SOVIET UNION

Ioffe, Grigory, et al. The End of Peasantry? The Disintegration of Rural Russia. 2006. (Pitt Series in Russian & East European Studies). (Illus.). 254p. (C). per. 27.95 *(978-0-8229-5941-0(0))* Univ. of Pittsburgh Pr.

Pallot, Judith & Nefedova, Tatyana. Russia's Unknown Agriculture: Household Production in Post-Socialist Rural Russia. 2007. (Oxford Geographical & Environmental Studies Ser.). (ENG., Illus.). 256p. 75.00 *(978-0-19-922741-9(1))* Oxford Univ. Pr., Inc.

Vorobeva, D. A. Selskii Sotsium: Obshchestvennye Ustoi I Vektory Transformatsii. 2009. (RUS.). 323p. *(978-5-9999-0210-8(X))* Nauka.

Wegren, Stephen. Agriculture & the State in Soviet & Post-Soviet Russia. 2009. (Pitt Russian East European Ser.). (ENG.). 312p. (C). pap. 27.95 *(978-0-8229-8585-3(3))* Univ. of Pittsburgh Pr.

AGRICULTURE—ECONOMIC ASPECTS—UNITED STATES

Alston, Julian M., et al. Persistence Pays: U. S. Agricultural Productivity Growth & the Benefits from Public R&D Spending. 2009. (Natural Resource Management & Policy Ser.). (ENG., Illus.). xxxii, 504p. 219.00 *(978-1-4419-0657-1(6))*, 1441906576) Springer.

Barry, Richard. Theme Song 1936: Give Us Back Our Independence. 2011. 160p. 41.95 ***(978-1-258-08285-7(3))*** Literary Licensing, LLC.

Blank, Steven C. The Economics of American Agriculture: Evolution & Global Development. 2008. (ENG., Illus.). 488p. 110.95 *(978-0-7656-2228-0(9))* Sharpe, M.E. Inc.

Bosworth, Samuel D., ed. Million Dollar Farms in the New Century. 2010. (Agriculture Issues & Policies Ser.). pap. 43.00 *(978-1-60741-755-2(3))* Nova Science Pubs., Inc.

Brooks, Robert P. The Agrarian Revolution to Georgia, 1865-1912. (Illus.). 129p. reprint ed. lib. bdg. 88.00 *(978-0-7222-0898-4(7))* Library Reprints, Inc.

Brooks, Tyler E. & Sanders, Emily M. United States Agricultural Trade. 2011. (Agriculture Issues & Policies Ser.). 89.00 *(978-1-61209-128-0(8))* Nova Science Pubs., Inc.

Buck, Salon Justus. The Granger Movement: A Study of Agricultural Organization & Its Political, Economic & Social Manifestations, 1870-1880. 384p. reprint ed. 98.00 *(978-0-7222-7279-4(0))* Library Reprints, Inc.

Calamia, Diego & Esposito, Mekhi. U. S. & Eu Agriculture: Comparisons & Linkages. 2011. (Agriculture Issues & Policies Ser.). 66p. pap. 47.00 ***(978-1-61470-698-4(0))*** Nova Science Pubs., Inc.

Capper, Arthur. The Agricultural Bloc. 2008. 184p. 22.99 *(978-0-559-88139-8(8))*; pap. 21.75 *(978-0-559-88138-1(X))* BiblioBazaar.

—The Agricultural Bloc. 171p. reprint ed. 88.00 *(978-0-7222-2713-8(2))* Library Reprints, Inc.

Cicero, Thomas A. Cicero Farm's Hometown Livonia. 2007. 100p. per. 9.95 *(978-1-4327-1559-5(3))* Outskirts Pr., Inc.

Cochrane, Willard W. The City Man's Guide to the Farm Problem. 2009. (ENG.). 256p. pap. 50.00 *(978-0-8166-5731-5(9))* Univ. of Minnesota Pr.

—Farm Prices: Myth & Reality. 2009. (ENG.). 200p. pap. 50.00 *(978-0-8166-5732-2(7))* Univ. of Minnesota Pr.

Conkin, Paul K. A Revolution down on the Farm: The Transformation of American Agriculture Since 1929. 2009. (ENG., Illus.). 240p. pap. 22.50 *(978-0-8131-9242-0(0))* Univ. Pr. of Kentucky.

Cram101 Textbook Reviews & Cram101 Textbook Reviews. Outlines & Highlights for Agribusiness Fundamentals & Applications by Ricketts. 2011. 240p. pap. 31.95 ***(978-1-61830-966-2(8))*** Cram101 Inc.

Cram101 Textbook Reviews Staff. Outlines & Highlights for Agricultural Economics by Drummond & Goodwin, Isbn: 0130474525. 2009. 80p. pap. 27.95 *(978-1-4288-3957-1(7))* Cram101 Inc.

Creating Jobs with Climate Solutions: How Agriculture & Forestry Can Help Lower Costs in a Low-Carbon Economy: Hearing Before the Subcommittee on Rural Revitalization, Conservation, Forestry, & Credit of the Committee on Agriculture, Nutrition, & Forestry, United States Senate, One Hundred Tenth Congress, Second Session, May 21, 2008. 2009. (Illus.). iii, 402p. *(978-0-16-082756-3(6))*, 552-070-38761-7) United States Government Printing Office.

Drummond and, Goodwin. Agricultural Economics. 2006. pap. 13.95 *(978-1-4288-0816-4(7))* Cram101 Inc.

Eggerman, Chris. Projecting Net Incomes for Texas Crop Producers - an Application of Probabilistic Forecasting. 2008. 104p. per. *(978-3-8364-3553-6(5))* VDM Verlag Dr. Mueller e.K.

Ellis, David Maldwyn. Landlords & Farmers in the Hudson-Mohawk Region, 1790-1850. 2010. 362p. pap. 29.95 *(978-0-8014-7614-3(3))*, Fall Creek Bks.) Cornell Univ. Pr.

Fitzgerald, Deborah. Every Farm a Factory: The Industrial Ideal in American Agriculture. 2010. (ENG.). 256p. pap. 26.00 *(978-0-300-11128-6(2))* Yale Univ. Pr.

Full Committee Hearing on Family Farmer & Rural Small Business Priorities for 2007 Farm Bill. 2007. (Illus.). v, 83p. *(978-0-16-079944-0(9))*, 552-070-36771-3) United States Government Printing Office.

George, Holly & Rilla, Ellen L. Agritourism & Nature Tourism in California. 2nd ed. 2011. (Illus.). vi, 151p. ***(978-1-60107-742-4(4))*** A N R Pubns.

Government Printing Office Staff. Agricultural Outlook. pap. 60.00 *(978-0-16-009189-6(6))*, Agriculture Dept.) United States Government Printing Office.

Hamilton, Lucas A., ed. Understanding U. S. Farm Exits, Farm Survival & the Role of Commodity Payments. 2010. (Agriculture Issues & Policies Ser.). 80.10 *(978-1-61668-995-7(1))* Nova Science Pubs., Inc.

Harvest over the Horizon: The Challenges of Aging in Agriculture: Hearing Before the Special Committee on Aging, United States Senate, One Hundred Tenth Congress, First Session, Washington, DC, June 21, 2007. 2008. (Illus.). iii, 52p. *(978-0-16-080152-5(4))*, 552-070-36889-2) United States Government Printing Office.

Hayes-Conroy, Allison. Reconnecting Lives to the Land: An Agenda for Critical Dialogue. 2007. 240p. (C). 49.50 *(978-0-8386-4130-9(X))* Fairleigh Dickinson Univ. Pr.

Haynes, Williams. Southern Horizons. 2010. 338p. pap. 31.75 *(978-1-171-84611-6(8))* BiblioBazaar.

—Southern Horizons. 2010. 138p. pap. 22.63 *(978-1-153-55313-1(9))* General Bks. LLC.

Hearing to Review Pending Climate Legislation: Hearing Before the Committee on Agriculture, House of Representatives, One Hundred Eleventh Congress, First Session, June 11, 2009. 2009. (Illus.). iv, 263p. *(978-0-16-084941-1(1))*, 552-070-40332-9) United States Government Printing Office.

Hearing to Review Structural Changes That Are Taking Place in the Agricultural Economy & Their Impacts: Hearing Before the Committee on Agriculture, House of Representatives, One Hundred Tenth Congress, First Session, October 18, 2007. 2009. (Illus.). iii, 50p. *(978-0-16-083332-8(9))*, 552-070-39156-8) United States Government Printing Office.

Hearing to Review the Costs & Benefits of Agriculture Offsets: Hearing Before the Subcommittee on Conservation, Credit, Energy, & Research of the Committee on Agriculture, House of Representatives, One Hundred Eleventh Congress, First Session, December 3, 2009. 2010. (Illus.). v, 119p. *(978-0-16-085295-4(1))*, 552-070-40634-4) United States Government Printing Office.

Hearing to Review the Potential Economic Impacts of Climate Change on the Farm Sector: Hearing Before the Subcommittee on Conservation, Credit, Energy, & Research of the Committee on Agriculture, House of Representatives, One Hundred Eleventh Congress, First Session, December 2, 2009. 2010. (Illus.). v, 266p. *(978-0-16-085491-0(1))*, 552-070-40742-1) United States Government Printing Office.

Hearing to Review the State of the Farm Economy: Hearing Before the Committee on Agriculture, House of Representatives, One Hundred Twelfth Congress, First Session, February 17, 2011. 2011. iii, 51p. ***(978-0-16-088535-8(3))***, 552-070-42712-1) United States Government Printing Office.

Hearing to Review the State of the Farm Economy: Hearing Before the Subcommittee on General Farm Commodities & Risk Management of the Committee on Agriculture, House of Representatives, One Hundred Eleventh Congress, First Session, April 1, 2009. 2009. (Illus.). iii, 118p. *(978-0-16-084251-1(4))*, 552-070-39821-0) United States Government Printing Office.

Hearing to Review U.S. Farm Safety Net Programs in Advance of the 2012 Farm Bill: Hearings Before the Subcommittee on General Farm Commodities & Risk Management of the Committee on Agriculture, House of Representatives, One Hundred Eleventh Congress, Second Session, June 17, 24, 2010. 2010. (Illus.). iv, 146p. ***(978-0-16-086969-3(2))***, 552-070-41835-1) United States Government Printing Office.

Henderson, Elizabeth, et al. Sharing the Harvest: A Citizen's Guide to Community Supported Agriculture. rev. ed. 2007. (ENG., Illus.). 320p. pap. 35.00 *(978-1-933392-10-3(X))* Chelsea Green Publishing.

Hoag, Dana L, ed. Applied Risk Management in Agriculture. 2009. (ENG., Illus.). 419p. 87.95 *(978-1-4398-0973-0(9))*, CRC Press) Taylor & Francis Group GBR. Dist: Taylor & Francis Group.

Hopkins, Cyril G. The Farm That Won't Wear Out. 2008. 48p. per. *(978-1-4065-6843-1(0))* Dodo Pr.

Johnson, C. S. & Embree, E. R. The Collapse of Cotton Tenancy. 81p. reprint ed. lib. bdg. 88.00 *(978-0-7222-0452-8(3))* Library Reprints, Inc.

Johnson, Glenn Leroy & Quance, Leroy. The Overproduction Trap in U. S. Agriculture: A Study of Resource Allocation from World War I to the Late 1960's. 6 vols. 2011. (RFF Agriculture & Fisheries Set Ser.). (ENG.). 211p. 99.95 *(978-1-61726-014-8(2))*, RFF Pr.) Earthscan LLC.

Jurenas, Remy. Agriculture in U.S. Free Trade Agreements: Trade with Current & Prospective Partners, Impact & Issues. 2008. (Illus.). (C). pap. 39.00 *(978-1-60456-418-1(0))* Nova Science Pubs., Inc.

Just, Richard E. & Pope, Rulon D., eds. A Comprehensive Assessment of the Role of Risk in U. S. Agriculture. 2010. (Natural Resource Management & Policy Ser.). 600p. pap. 199.00 *(978-1-4419-4924-0(0))*, 1441949240) Springer.

Kagochi, John. Evaluating the Competitiveness of Us Agricultural Market Commodities - the Role of Technology Adoption & Commodity Differentiation. 2008. 168p. per. *(978-3-8364-6721-6(6))* VDM Verlag Dr. Mueller e.K.

Larson, Henrietta M. Wheat Market & the Farmer in Minnesota, 1858-1900. (Columbia University, Studies in the Social Sciences: No. 269). reprint ed. 29.50 *(978-0-404-51269-9(0))* AMS Pr., Inc.

Lewandrowski, Jan. Economics of Sequestering Carbon in the US Agricultural Sector. 2006. (Illus.). 61p. (C). reprint ed. pap. 25.00 *(978-1-4223-0694-9(1))* DIANE Publishing Co.

Majewski, John & Majewski, John D. Modernizing a Slave Economy: The Economic Vision of the Confederate Nation. 2009. (Civil War America Ser.). (ENG., Illus.). 256p. 41.95 *(978-0-8078-3251-6(0))* Univ. of North Carolina Pr.

Mapes, Kathleen. Sweet Tyranny: Migrant Labor, Industrial Agriculture, & Imperial Politics. 2009. (Working Class in American History Ser.). (ENG., Illus.). 336p. 80.00 *(978-0-252-03436-7(8))*; pap. 31.00 *(978-0-252-07667-1(2))* Univ. of Illinois Pr.

McCabe, James Dabney. History of the Grange Movement; or, the Farmer's War Against Monopolies: Being A Full & Authentic Account of the Struggles of the American Farmers A. 2006. 560p. per. 32.99 *(978-1-4255-6144-4(6))* MPublishing.

Mearns, Linda O., ed. Issues in the Impacts of Climate Variability & Change on Agriculture: Applications to the southeastern United States. 2010. 224p. pap. 149.00 *(978-90-481-6420-2(6))*, 9048164206) Springer.

Nation, Allan. Land Livestock & Life: A grazier's guide to Finance. 2007. 224p. per. 25.00 *(978-0-9721597-2-2(X))* Green Park Pr.

Olmstead, Alan & Rhode, Paul. Creating Abundance: Biological Innovation & American Agricultural Development. 2008. (ENG., Illus.). 480p. 85.00 *(978-0-521-85711-6(2))* Cambridge Univ. Pr.

Olmstead, Alan, et al. Creating Abundance: Biological Innovation & American Agricultural Development. 2008. (ENG., Illus.). 480p. pap. 24.99 *(978-0-521-67387-7(9))* Cambridge Univ. Pr.

Olson, Albert L. Agricultural Economy & the Population in Eighteenth Century Connecticut. 932p. reprint ed. lib. bdg. 248.00 *(978-0-7222-0483-2(3))* Library Reprints, Inc.

Panel to Review USDA's Agricultural Resource Management Survey & National Research Council. Understanding American Agriculture: Challenges for the Agricultural Resource Management Survey. 2007. (ENG.). 214p. pap. 50.00 *(978-0-309-11092-1(0))* National Academies Pr.

Phillips, Sarah T. This Land, This Nation: Conservation, Rural America, & the New Deal. 2007. (ENG., Illus.). 302p. 81.00 *(978-0-521-85270-8(6))*; per. 25.99 *(978-0-521-61796-3(0))* Cambridge Univ. Pr.

Rhodes, V. James, et al. The Agricultural Marketing System. 6th ed. 2007. xii, 372p. *(978-1-890871-68-0(0))* Holcomb Hathaway, Inc.

Rozeff, Norman. Sugarcane & the Development of the Lower Rio Grande Valley, 1875-1922. 2007. (Illus.). 256p. pap. *(978-0-935071-20-7(2))* New Santander Pr.

Schmitz, Andrew, et al. Agricultural Policy, Agribusiness & Rent-Seeking Behaviour. 2nd ed. 2010. (Illus.). 512p. pap. *(978-0-8020-9547-3(X))* Univ. of Toronto Pr.

Schnepf, Randy & Womach, Jasper. Potential Challenges to U. S. Farm Subsidies in the WTO. 2008. (C). 69.00 *(978-1-60456-420-4(2))* Nova Science Pubs., Inc.

Smith, Ross. History of the Danville Grange: Patrons of Husbandry. 2008. (Illus.). 119p. 23.00 net. *(978-0-938260-03-5(0))* Ashford Pubns.

Stephens, A. Ray. The Taft Ranch: A Texas Principality. 2011. (ENG.). 312p. pap. 25.00 ***(978-0-292-73727-3(0))*** Univ. of Texas Pr.

Strange, Marty. Family Farming: A New Economic Vision. 2008. (ENG., Illus.). 336p. pap. 16.95 *(978-0-8032-1748-5(X))*, Bison Bks.) Univ. of Nebraska Pr.

United States, Congress Senate Committee on Agriculture, Nutrition, and Forestry Staff, contrib. by. Discussion of the U.S. Department of Agriculture Farm Bill Proposal: Hearing Before the Committee on Agriculture, Nutrition, & Forestry, United States Senate, One Hundred Tenth Congress, First Session, February 7, 2007. 2007. (Illus.). iv, 392p. *(978-0-16-078854-3(4))*, 552-070-35989-3) United States Government Printing Office.

—Working Land Conservation: Conservation Security Program & Environmental Quality Incentives Program: Hearing Before the Committee on Agriculture, Nutrition, & Forestry, United States Senate, One Hundred Tenth Congress, First Session, January 17, 2007. 2007. (Illus.). iii, 256p. *(978-0-16-078573-3(1))*, 552-070-35837-4) United States Government Printing Office.

Vaught, David. After the Gold Rush: Tarnished Dreams in the Sacramento Valley. 2007. (ENG., Illus.). 328p. (gr. 17). 60.00 *(978-0-8018-8497-9(7))* Johns Hopkins Univ. Pr.

Vaught, David & Vaught, D. After the Gold Rush: Tarnished Dreams in the Sacramento Valley. 2009. (ENG., Illus.). 328p. (gr. 17). pap. 32.00 *(978-0-8018-9257-8(0))* Johns Hopkins Univ. Pr.

Walker, Melissa & Cobb, James C., eds. The New Encyclopedia of Southern Culture: Volume 11: Agriculture & Industry. 2008. (ENG., Illus.). 376p. (C). 47.50 *(978-0-8078-3240-0(5))*; pap. 23.95 *(978-0-8078-5909-4(5))* Univ. of North Carolina Pr.

Waugh, Frederick V. Selected Writings on Agricultural Policy & Economic Analysis. Houck, James P. & Abel, Martin E., eds. 2009. (ENG.). 488p. pap. 60.00 *(978-0-8166-6057-5(3))* Univ. of Minnesota Pr.

Wellson, Alison J. Organic Agriculture in the U. S. 2006. 260p. (C). 69.00 *(978-1-60021-305-2(7))* Nova Science Pubs., Inc.

Wiebe, Keith Daniel & Gollehon, Noel R. Agricultural Resources & Environmental Indicators. 2006. 278p. (C). 69.00 *(978-1-60021-467-7(3))* Nova Science Pubs., Inc.

Wuthnow, Robert. Remaking the Heartland: Middle America since the 1950's. 2010. (ENG., Illus.). 376p. (C). 35.00 *(978-0-691-14611-9(X))* Princeton Univ. Pr.

Young, Austen W. Impact of Global Economic Crisis on Agriculture. 2010. pap. 47.00 *(978-1-61761-180-3(8))* Nova Science Pubs., Inc.

AGRICULTURE—ECONOMIC ASPECTS—VIETNAM

Heerink, Nico, et al. Dragons with Clay Feet? Transition, Sustainable Land Use, & Rural Environment in China & Vietnam. 2010. (Rural Economies in Transition Ser.). (ENG.). 256p. pap. 42.95 *(978-0-7391-4656-9(4))* Lexington Bks.

Spoor, Max, et al, eds. Dragons with Clay Feet? Transition, Sustainable Land Use, & Rural Environment in China & Vietnam. 2007. (Rural Economies in Transition Ser.). (ENG., Illus.). 356p. 99.99 *(978-0-7391-1369-1(0))* Lexington Bks.

AGRICULTURE—ECONOMIC ASPECTS—ZAMBIA

Mfune Mubukwanu, Elizabeth. Effects of an Agribusiness Collapse on Contract Growers. 2010. 108p. pap. *(978-3-8383-7522-9(X))* Lambert Academic Publishing.

Michelo, Kelly. Casting the Net on Land: Catching the Rural Farmer. 2010. 128p. pap. *(978-3-8383-7572-0(3))* Lambert Academic Publishing.

AGRICULTURE—ENVIRONMENTAL ASPECTS

see also Agricultural Ecology

Aiking, Harry, et al, eds. Sustainable Protein Production & Consumption: Pigs or Peas? Pigs or Peas? 2010. (Environment & Policy Ser.). xvi, 226p. pap. 179.00 *(978-90-481-7027-2(3)*, 9048170273) Springer.

Allen, Patricia. Together at the Table: Sustainability & Sustenance in the American Agrifood System. 2007. (Rural Studies). 260p. per. 27.00 *(978-0-271-02977-1(3))* Pennsylvania State Univ. Pr.

Araus, Jose Luis & Slafer, Gustavo A. Crop Stress Management & Global Climate Change. 2011. (CABI Climate Change Ser.). (Illus.). 224p. 145.00 *(978-1-84593-680-8(9))* CABI GBR. Dist: Stylus Publishing, LLC.

Arcand, Yves & Boye, Joyce I., eds. Green Technologies in Food Production & Processing. 2012. (Food Engineering Ser.). (ENG., Illus.). xviii, 681p. 279.00 ***(978-1-4614-1586-2(1)***, 1461415861) Springer.

Ashraf, Mohammad. Global Warming & Food Security: An Economic Inquiry. 2011. 68p. pap. ***(978-3-8443-1781-7(3))*** Lambert Academic Publishing.

Astyk, Sharon & Newton, Aaron. A Nation of Farmers: Defeating the Food Crisis on American Soil. 2009. (ENG., Illus.). 400p. pap. 19.95 *(978-0-86571-623-0(4)*, 9780865716230) New Society Pubs., Ltd. CAN. Dist: Consortium Bk. Sales & Distribution.

Beinart, William. The Rise of Conservation in South Africa: Settlers, Livestock, & the Environment 1770-1950. 2008. (ENG., Illus.). 456p. pap. 55.00 *(978-0-19-954122-5(1))* Oxford Univ. Pr., Inc.

Bennett, Jeff, et al, eds. Environmental Protection in China: Land-Use Management. 2008. (Illus.). 240p. (C). 119.00 *(978-1-84720-589-6(5))* Elgar, Edward Publishing, Inc.

Bert, Theresa M. Ecological & Genetic Implications of Aquaculture Activities. 2007. (Reviews: Methods & Technologies in Fish Biology & Fisheries Ser.). (Illus.). 560p. 209.00 *(978-1-4020-0884-9(8)*, 1402008848) Springer.

Bhusal, Tej Narayan. Cms-Ceres-Maize Model. 2011. 132p. pap. ***(978-3-8443-0272-1(7))*** Lambert Academic Publishing.

Blatt, Harvey. America's Food: What You Don't Know about What You Eat. (ENG., Illus.). 352p. (gr. 17). 2011. pap. 18.95 *(978-0-262-51595-5(4))* 2008. 29.95 *(978-0-262-02652-9(X))* MIT Pr.

Brenton, Paul. Carbon Footprints & Food Systems: Do Current Accounting Methodologies Disadvantage Developing Countries? 2010. (World Bank Studies). (ENG., Illus.). 84p. pap. 15.00 *(978-0-8213-8539-5(9)*, 9780821385395) World Bank Pubns.

Brouwer, F. M., et al, eds. Governance of Water-Related Conflicts in Agriculture: New Directions in Agri-Environmental & Water Policies in the EU. 2010. (Environment & Policy Ser.). 236p. pap. 169.00 *(978-90-481-6397-7(8)*, 9048163978) Springer.

Brouwer, Floor & McCarl, Bruce A., eds. Agriculture & Climate Beyond 2015: A New Perspective on Future Land Use Patterns. 2010. (Environment & Policy Ser.). xvii, 307p. pap. 159.00 *(978-90-481-7028-9(1)*, 9048170281) Springer.

Brouwer, Floor M. & Ittersum, Martin van, eds. Environmental & Agricultural Modelling: Integrated Approaches for Policy Impact Assessment. 2010. (ENG., Illus.). xx, 325p. 169.00 *(978-90-481-3618-6(0)*, 9048136180) Springer.

Brubaker, Elizabeth. Greener Pastures: Decentralizing the Regulation of Agricultural Pollution. 2007. (University of Toronto Centre for Public Management Monograph Ser.). (ENG.). 152p. *(978-0-7727-8621-0(6))*; pap. *(978-0-7727-8620-3(8))* Univ. of Toronto Pr.

Carolan, Michael. The Real Cost of Cheap Food. 2011. (ENG., Illus.). 288p. 125.00 *(978-1-84971-320-7(0))*; pap. 34.95 *(978-1-84971-321-4(9))* Routledge.

Carpenter, David. Agriculture, Biodiversity & Markets: Livelihoods & Agroecology in Comparative Perspective. Lockie, Stewart, ed. 2009. (ENG., Illus.). 336p. 96.00 *(978-1-84407-776-2(4))* Routledge.

Committee on the Mississippi River and the Clean Water Act: Scientific, Modeling and Technical Aspects of Nutrient Pollutant Load Allocation and Implementation & National Research Council. Nutrient Control Actions for Improving Water Quality in the Mississippi River Basin & Northern Gulf of Mexico. 2009. (ENG.). 94p. pap. 21.00 *(978-0-309-13000-4(X))* National Academies Pr.

Conway, Gordon R. & Pretty, Jules N. Unwelcome Harvest: Agriculture & Pollution. 2009. (Natural Resource Management Set Ser.). (ENG.). 676p. 110.00 *(978-1-84971-021-3(X))* Routledge.

Despommier, Dickson. The Vertical Farm: Feeding the World in the 21st Century. 2011. (ENG., Illus.). 336p. pap. 16.00 *(978-0-312-61069-2(6))* Picador.

Doherty, Catherine. Apostolic Farming: Healing the Earth. 2nd exp. ed. 96p. pap. *(978-0-921440-03-1(0))* Madonna Hse. Pubns.

El-Ramady, Hassan, et al. Glossary of Agricultural & Environmental Sciences Terms. 2010. 528p. pap. *(978-3-639-26157-8(7))*; 612p. pap. *(978-3-639-26332-9(4))*; 384p. pap. *(978-3-639-25880-6(0))*; 412p. pap. *(978-3-639-25885-1(1))*; 508p. pap. *(978-3-639-25912-4(2))*; 484p. pap. *(978-3-639-25758-8(8))* VDM Verlag Dr. Mueller e.K.

Estabrook, Barry. Tomatoland: How Modern Industrial Agriculture Destroyed Our Most Alluring Fruit. 2011. (ENG., Illus.). 240p. 19.99 *(978-1-4494-0109-2(0))* Andrews McMeel Publishing.

Faegri, Knut & Nilsson, L. Anders. Principles of Pollination Ecology. 4th ed. Date not set. 59.95 *(978-0-8493-9235-1(7))* CRC Pr. LLC.

Filson, Glen, et al, eds. Agriculture & Environmental Security in Southern Ontario's Watersheds. 2010. (Agriculture Issues & Policies Ser.). (Illus.). xiii, 209p. 43.00 *(978-1-61668-156-2(X))* Nova Science Pubs., Inc.

From the Corn Belt to the Gulf: Societal & Environmental Implications of Alternative Agricultural Futures. 2007. (ENG., Illus.). 272p. pap. 45.00 *(978-1-933115-48-1(3))*; 120.00 *(978-1-933115-47-4(5))* Routledge.

Full Committee Hearing on Climate Change Solutions for Small Businesses & Family Farmers: Hearing Before the Committee on Small Business, United States House of Representatives, One Hundred Eleventh Congress, First Session, Hearing Held April 29, 2009. 2009. v, 89p. *(978-0-16-083602-2(6)*, 552-070-39320-0) United States Government Printing Office.

Goetz, Stephan J. & Brouwer, Floor, eds. New Perspectives on Agri-Environmental Policies: A Multidisciplinary & Transatlantic Approach. 2009. (Routledge Explorations in Environmental Economics Ser.). (ENG., Illus.). 304p. 145.00 *(978-0-415-77702-5(X))* Routledge.

Goh, Kean S. Pesticide Mitigation Strategies for Surface Water Quality. 2012. (ACS Symposium Ser.: 1075). (ENG.). 400p. 150.00 ***(978-0-8412-2656-2(3))*** American Chemical Society.

Gottlieb, Robert & Joshi, Anupama. Food Justice. 2010. (Food, Health, & the Environment Ser.). (ENG., Illus.). 304p. (gr. 17). 28.95 *(978-0-262-07291-5(2))* MIT Pr.

Gujarathi, Ninad. Phytoremediation of Antibiotics from Wastes of Animal Feedlots. 2009. (Illus.). 152p. pap. *(978-3-639-13576-3(8))* VDM Verlag Dr. Mueller e.K.

Gullick, R., et al. Source Water Protection for Concentrated Animal Feeding Operations: A Guide for Drinking Water Utilities: AwwaRF Report 91159. 2007. 212p. (C). pap. *(978-1-84339-154-8(6))* IWA Publishing.

Guo, Lei, et al, eds. Understanding Greenhouse Gas Emissions from Agricultural Management. 2012. (ACS Symposium Ser.). (ENG.). 544p. 195.00 ***(978-0-8412-2654-8(7))*** American Chemical Society.

Haan, Leo de, et al, contrib. by. Looking at Maps in the Dark: Directions for Geographical Research in Land Management & Sustainable Development in Rural & Urban Environments of the Third World. (Illus.). 165p. *(978-90-6809-261-5(8))* Koninklijk Nederlands Aardrijkskundig Genootschap.

Hahlbrock, Klaus. Feeding the Planet: Environmental Protection through Sustainable Agriculture. 2010. (Sustainability Project Ser.). (ENG., Illus.). 270p. pap. 14.95 *(978-1-906598-11-2(8))* Haus Publishing GBR. Dist: Consortium Bk. Sales & Distribution.

Herm, Eric. Son of a Farmer, Child of the Earth: A Path to Agriculture's Higher Consciousness. 2010. 248p. pap. 16.95 *(978-0-9797908-9-8(1))* Dreamriver Pr.

Hudspeth, Christopher A. & Reeve, Timothy E. Agricultural Runoff, Coastal Engineering & Flooding. 2009. (Series: Environmental Science, Engineering & Technology Ser.). 129.00 *(978-1-60741-097-3(4))* Nova Science Pubs., Inc.

Ingram, John, et al, eds. Food Security & Global Environmental Change. 2010. (ENG., Illus.). 384p. 140.00 *(978-1-84971-127-2(5))*; pap. 39.95 *(978-1-84971-128-9(3))* Routledge.

Jose, Shibu, ed. Agroforestry for Ecosystem Services & Environmental Benefits. 2009. (Advances in Agroforestry Ser.). (ENG., Illus.). vi, 266p. 199.00 *(978-90-481-3322-2(X)*, 904813322X) Springer.

Just, Richard E. & Pope, Rulon D., eds. A Comprehensive Assessment of the Role of Risk in U. S. Agriculture. 2010. (Natural Resource Management & Policy Ser.). 600p. pap. 199.00 *(978-1-4419-4924-0(0)*, 1441949240) Springer.

Kang, Manjit S. Agricultural & Environmental Sustainability: Considerations for the Future. 2007. (ENG., Illus.). 224p. 94.95 *(978-1-56022-170-8(4))*; per. 79.95 *(978-1-56022-171-5(2))* Taylor & Francis Group GBR. (CRC Press). Dist: Taylor & Francis Group.

Kennedy, Ivan R., et al, eds. Rational Environmental Management of Agrochemicals: Risk Assessment, Monitoring, & Remedial Action. 2007. (ACS Symposium Ser.). (ENG., Illus.). 428p. (C). 160.00 *(978-0-8412-7420-4(7))* American Chemical Society.

Khan, Ayub, et al. Phytohormones Application in Groundnut under Drought. 2010. 116p. pap. *(978-3-639-27259-8(5))* VDM Verlag Dr. Mueller e.K.

Koirala, Madan, et al. Livelihood Linked Environmental Determinants in Himalaya Landscape. 2011. 156p. pap. ***(978-3-8433-8296-0(4))*** Lambert Academic Publishing.

Kontoleon, Andreas. Agrobiodiversity, Conservation & Economic Development. Smale, Melinda & Pascual, Unai, eds. 2008. (Routledge Explorations in Environmental Economics Ser.). (ENG., Illus.). 456p. (C). 185.00 *(978-0-415-46505-2(2))* Routledge.

Kontoleon, Andreas, et al, eds. Agrobiodiversity Conservation & Economic Development. 2011. (Illus.). 456p. pap. 42.95 ***(978-0-415-61976-9(9))*** Routledge.

Kristiansen, P., et al, eds. Organic Agriculture: A Global Perspective. 2006. (Illus.). 320p. 160.00 *(978-1-84593-169-8(6))* CABI GBR. Dist: Stylus Publishing, LLC.

Lewandrowski, Jan. Economics of Sequestering Carbon in the US Agricultural Sector. 2006. (Illus.). 61p. (C). reprint ed. pap. 25.00 *(978-1-4223-0694-9(1))* DIANE Publishing Co.

Lichtfouse, Eric. Biodiversity, Biofuels, Agroforestry & Conservation Agriculture. Lichtfouse, Eric, ed. 2010. (Sustainable Agriculture Reviews Ser.). (Illus.). x, 390p. 209.00 *(978-90-481-9512-1(8)*, 9048195128) Springer.

Lichtfouse, Eric, ed. Agroecology & Strategies for Climate Change. 2011. (Sustainable Agriculture Reviews Ser.). (ENG., Illus.). vi, 335p. 209.00 ***(978-94-007-1904-0(3)***, 9400719043) Springer.

Melillo, Edward/D. Green Revolutions: Agricultural Expansion & the Global Environment in Three Countries. 2010. 30p. *(978-0-9823382-5-4(2))* Publishing Laboratory at UNC Wilmington, The.

Mendelsohn, R. M. & Dinar, André. Climate Change & Agriculture: An Economic Analysis of Global Impacts, Adaptation & Distributional Effects. 2009. (New Horizons in Environmental Economics Ser.). (Illus.). 256p. 119.00 *(978-1-84720-670-1(0))* Elgar, Edward Publishing, Inc.

Mendelsohn, Robert O. & Dinar, Ariel, eds. Handbook on Climate Change & Agriculture. 2012. (Elgar Original Reference Ser.). (Illus.). 544p. 245.00 ***(978-1-84980-116-4(9))*** Elgar, Edward Publishing, Inc.

Mengistu, Dejene Kassahun. Physiology of Tef under Water Stress. 2010. 88p. pap. *(978-3-639-25188-3(1))* VDM Verlag Dr. Mueller e.K.

Mishra, Srijit & Narasimha Reddy, D. Agrarian Crisis in India. Reddy, D. Narasimha & Mishra, Srijit, eds. 2009. (ENG., Illus.). 272p. 49.95 *(978-0-19-569595-3(X))* Oxford Univ. Pr., Inc.

Mohamed Nor Azhari, Azman, et al. Non-Point Source Pollution Modelling with Gis. 2011. 156p. pap. ***(978-3-8443-1821-0(6))*** Lambert Academic Publishing.

Mulvaney, Dustin, ed. Green Food: An A-to-Z Guide. 2010. (SAGE Reference Series on Green Society: Toward a Sustainable Future-Series Editor: Paul Robbins Ser.: 3). (Illus.). 544p. 110.00 *(978-1-4129-9680-8(5)*, B96808C) SAGE Pubns., Inc.

Nowak, Pete & Schnepf, Max, eds. Managing Agricultural Landscapes for Environmental Quality II: Achieving More Effective Conservation. 2010. pap. 26.00 *(978-0-9769432-8-0(X))* Soil and Water Conservation Society.

O'Connor, George. The Agronomic & Environmental of Biosolids-P (Phase II) 2007. 108p. (C). pap. *(978-1-84339-782-3(X))* IWA Publishing.

Oecd Publishing. Oecd Review of Agricultural Policies Oecd Review of Agricultural Policies: Israel 2010. 2010. 208p. pap. 67.00 *(978-92-64-07934-2(3))* Organization for Economic Cooperation & Development.

Oecd Publishing, Publishing & Oecd Publishing. Climate Change & Agriculture: Impacts, Adaptation & Mitigation. 2010. 138p. pap. 46.00 *(978-92-64-08686-9(2))* Organization for Economic Cooperation & Development.

Organisation for Economic Co-operation and Development Staff. Environmental Performance of Oecd Agriculture since 1990: At a Glance. 2008. pap. 63.00 *(978-92-64-04589-7(9))* Organization for Economic Cooperation & Development.

—Environmental Performance of Oecd Agriculture since 1990: Environmental Indicators for Agriculture Volume 4. 2008. pap. 63.00 *(978-92-64-04092-2(7))* Organization for Economic Cooperation & Development.

—Proceedings of the Workshop on Multifunctionality in Agriculture: Evaluating the Degree of Jointness, Policy Implications. 2008. pap. 63.00 *(978-92-64-03361-0(0))* Organization for Economic Cooperation & Development.

Organisation for Economic Co-operation and Development Staff, creator. Environment, Water Resources & Agricultural Policies: Lessons from China & OECD Countries. 2007. (ENG., Illus.). 287p. per. 67.00 *(978-92-64-02846-3(3))* Organization for Economic Cooperation & Development.

Pearson, Craig & Pilgrim, Sarah, eds. Urban Agriculture: Diverse Activities & Benefits for City Society. 2010. (International Journal Agricultural Sustainability Ser.). (ENG., Illus.). 128p. 99.95 *(978-1-84971-124-1(0))* Routledge.

Poston, Karl T., ed. Environmental Services & Agriculture. 2009. (Illus.). 106p. pap. 43.00 *(978-1-60741-053-9(2))* Nova Science Pubs., Inc.

PSV & McDowell, Richard W. Environmental Impacts of Pasture-Based Farming. McDowell, R. W., ed. 2008. (Illus.). 304p. 145.00 *(978-1-84593-411-8(3))* CABI GBR. Dist: Stylus Publishing, LLC.

Robbins, Mike. Crops & Carbon: Paying Farmers to Combat Climate Change. 2011. (ENG., Illus.). 320p. 84.95 *(978-1-84971-375-7(8))* Routledge.

The Role of Agriculture & Forestry in Global Warming Legislation: Hearing Before the Committee on Agriculture, Nutrition, & Forestry, United States Senate, One Hundred Eleventh Congress, First Session, July 22, 2009. 2010. (Illus.). v, 294p. ***(978-0-16-087062-0(3)***, 552-070-4191905) United States Government Printing Office.

Sargsyan, Eric A. & Ochion, Adam J. Environmental Considerations in Agriculture. 2011. (Environmental Science, Engineering & Technology Ser.). 95.00 ***(978-1-61470-077-7(X))*** Nova Science Pubs., Inc.

Satapathy, Kunja & Chand, Pradeep. Azoll: A Biofertilizer. 2010. 200p. pap. *(978-3-639-19138-7(2))* VDM Verlag Dr. Mueller e.K.

Schnepf, Max & Cox, Craig A. Managing Agricultural Landscapes for Environmental Quality: Strengthening the Science Base. 2007. per. *(978-0-9769432-4-2(7))* Soil and Water Conservation Society.

Sheaffer, Craig C. & Moncada, Kristine M. Introduction to Agronomy: Food, Crops, & Environment. 2008. (ENG., Illus.). 576p. (C). 123.95 *(978-1-4180-5037-5(7))* Delmar Cengage Learning.

Sivakumar, Mannava V. K., et al, eds. Natural Disasters & Extreme Events in Agriculture: Impacts & Mitigation. 2010. (ENG., Illus.). xx, 368p. pap. 209.00 *(978-3-642-06133-2(8)*, 3642061338) Springer.

Sivakumar, Mannava V. K. & Hansen, James, eds. Climate Prediction & Agriculture: Advances & Challenges. 2010. (ENG., Illus.). xxvi, 306p. pap. 209.00 *(978-3-642-07946-7(6)*, 3642079466) Springer.

Sutter, Paul S. & Manganiello, Christopher J., eds. Environmental History & the American South: A Reader. 2009. (Environmental History & the American South Ser.). (ENG.). 504p. pap. 26.95 *(978-0-8203-3322-9(0))* Univ. of Georgia Pr.

—Environmental History & the American South: A Reader. 2009. (Environmental History & the American South Ser.). (ENG.). 504p. lib. bdg. 69.95 *(978-0-8203-3280-2(1))* Univ. of Georgia Pr.

Swaminathan, M. S. From Green to Evergreen Revolution: Indian Agriculture - Performance & Emerging Challenges. 2010. 410p. 79.95 *(978-81-7188-797-2(X))* Academic Foundation IND. Dist: Independent Pubs. Group.

Taji, Acram & Reganold, John, eds. Organic Agriculture: A Global Perspective. 2006. (Comstock Bks.). (Illus.). 449p. 104.95 *(978-0-8014-4524-8(8)*, ILR Pr.) Cornell Univ. Pr.

Van Tuat, N. & Hilbeck, A. Environmental Risk Assessment of Genetically Modified Organisms Vol. 4: Challenges & Opportunities with Bt Cotton in Vietnam. Andow, D. A., ed. 2008. (Illus.). 384p. 160.00 *(978-1-84593-390-6(7))* CABI GBR. Dist: Stylus Publishing, LLC.

Warren, John, et al. The Agri-Environment. 2007. (ENG., Illus.). 232p. (C). 126.00 *(978-0-521-84965-4(9))*; pap. 57.00 *(978-0-521-61488-7(0))* Cambridge Univ. Pr.

Wassmann, Reiner & Vlek, Paul L.G., eds. Tropical Agriculture in Transition - Opportunities for Mitigating Greenhouse Gas Emissions? 2010. 284p. pap. 88.00 *(978-90-481-6341-0(2)*, 9048163412) Springer.

Wells, Spencer. Pandora's Seed: The Unforeseen Cost of Civilization. 2010. (ENG., Illus.). 256p. 26.00 *(978-1-4000-6215-7(2)*, Random House) Random House Publishing Group.

—Pandora's Seed: Why the Hunter-Gatherer Holds the Key to Our Survival. 2011. (ENG., Illus.). 256p. pap. 16.00 *(978-0-8129-7191-0(4)*, Random Hse. Trade Paperbacks) Random House Publishing Group.

Wellson, Alison J. Organic Agriculture in the U. S. 2006. 260p. (C). 69.00 *(978-1-60021-305-2(7))* Nova Science Pubs., Inc.

Wiebe, Keith Daniel & Gollehon, Noel R. Agricultural Resources & Environmental Indicators. 2006. 278p. (C). 69.00 *(978-1-60021-467-7(3))* Nova Science Pubs., Inc.

Wilson, G. A. Multifunctional Agriculture: A Transition Theory Perspective. 2007. (Illus.). 368p. 145.00 *(978-1-84593-256-5(0))* CABI GBR. Dist: Stylus Publishing, LLC.

Wojtkowski, Paul A. Agroecological Economics: Sustainability & Biodiversity. 2007. (ENG., Illus.). 320p. per. 80.95 *(978-0-12-374117-2(3)*, Academic Pr.) Elsevier Science & Technology Bks.

AGRICULTURE—EQUIPMENT AND SUPPLIES

see Agricultural Implements; Agricultural Machinery; Farm Equipment; Farm Supplies

AGRICULTURE—EXHIBITIONS

see Agricultural Exhibitions

AGRICULTURE—EXPERIMENTATION

see also Field Experiments

Ireland, Clive. Statistics for Agriculture & Horticulture. 2010. (Modular Texts). (Illus.). 380p. pap. 75.00 *(978-1-84593-537-5(3))* CABI GBR. Dist: Stylus Publishing, LLC.

Schilthuis, Willy. Biodynamic Agriculture. 2nd rev. ed. (Illus.). 128p. (Orig.). pap. 14.95 *(978-0-86315-397-6(6))* Floris Bks. GBR. Dist: SteinerBooks, Inc.

Whitcher, Monlux & Carrier, L. Hands-on Hortscience Practical Investigations & Experimental Designs in Agriculture & Biology. rev. ed. 2010. (ENG., Illus.). ix, 153p. pap. 63.93 *(978-0-7575-5296-0(X))* Kendall Hunt Publishing Co.

AGRICULTURE—FIELD EXPERIMENTS

see Field Experiments

AGRICULTURE—FINANCE

see also Agricultural Credit; Agricultural Credit Corporations

Babcock, B. A., et al, eds. Risk Management & the Environment: Agriculture in Perspective: Agriculture in Perspective. 2010. 220p. pap. 179.00 *(978-90-481-6158-4(4)*, 9048161584) Springer.

Barry, Peter J., et al. Financial Management in Agriculture. 7th rev. ed. 2010. (ENG.). 408p. (C). 101.20 *(978-0-13-503759-1(X)*, Prentice Hall) Prentice Hall PTR.

Ellinger, Paul N., et al. Financial Management in Agriculture, Student Value Edition. 7th ed. 2010. (ENG.). 408p. (C). ring bd. 65.80 *(978-0-13-137758-5(2)*, Prentice Hall) Prentice Hall PTR.

Elliot, Jack. Agribusiness: Decisions & Dollars. 2nd ed. 2008. (ENG.). (C). 112p. pap., wbk. ed. 37.95 *(978-1-4283-1914-1(X))*; (Illus.). 336p. 139.95 *(978-1-4283-1912-7(3))* Delmar Cengage Learning.

Hearing to Review Agriculture Research Programs: Hearing Before the Subcommittee on Conservation, Credit, Energy, & Research of the Committee on Agriculture, House of Representatives, One Hundred Tenth Congress, First Session, May 10, 2007. 2008. (Illus.). iii, 172p. *(978-0-16-083236-9(5)*, 552-070-39064-2) United States Government Printing Office.

Hearing to Review Credit Conditions in Rural America: Hearing Before the Subcommittee on Conservation, Credit, Energy, & Research of the Committee on Agriculture, House of Representatives, One Hundred Eleventh Congress, First Session, June 11, 2009. 2009. (Illus.). v, 82p. *(978-0-16-084858-2(X)*, 552-070-40259-4) United States Government Printing Office.

Hearing to Review Credit Conditions in Rural America: Hearing Before the Subcommittee on Department Operations, Oversight, & Credit of the Committee on Agriculture, House of Representatives, One Hundred Twelfth Congress, First Session, April 14, 2011. 2011. (Illus.). iii, 70p. ***(978-0-16-089026-0(8)***, 552-070-43058-0) United States Government Printing Office.

Investing in Our Nation's Future Through Agricultural Research: Hearing Before the Committee on Agriculture, Nutrition, & Forestry, United States Senate, One Hundred Tenth Congress, First Session, March 7, 2007. 2007. (Illus.). iv,

192p. *(978-0-16-078869-7(2)*, 552-070-35998-2) United States Government Printing Office.

Just, Richard E. & Pope, Rulon D., eds. A Comprehensive Assessment of the Role of Risk in U. S. Agriculture. 2010. (Natural Resource Management & Policy Ser.). 600p. pap. 199.00 *(978-1-4419-4924-0(0)*, 1441949240) Springer.

Kloeppinger-Todd, Renate & Sharma, Manohar. Innovations in Rural & Agriculture Finance. 2010. (Illus.). 30p. pap. ***(978-0-89629-668-8(7))*** International Food Policy Research Institute.

Miller, Agricultural Value Chain Finance: Approach, Instruments & Lessons. 2010. (ENG., Illus.). 192p. pap. 39.95 *(978-1-85339-702-8(4))* Practical Action Publishing GBR. Dist: Stylus Publishing, LLC.

Moss, Charles B. & Gunderson, Michael A. Agricultural Finance. 2013. (Routledge Textbooks in Environmental & Agricultural Economics Ser.). (ENG., Illus.). 256p. 157.41 ***(978-0-415-59904-7(0))***; pap. 74.25 ***(978-0-415-59907-8(5))*** Routledge.

Organisation for Economic Co-operation and Development Staff. Managing Risk in Agriculture: A Holistic Approach. 2009. (Illus.). 170p. pap. 63.00 *(978-92-64-07530-6(5))* Organization for Economic Cooperation & Development.

Royal Tropical Institute & International Institute of Rural Reconstruction. Value Chain Finance: Beyond Microfinance for Rural Entrepreneurs. 2010. 280p. pap. 39.95 *(978-94-6022-055-5(X))* Royal Tropical Institute Pr. (KIT (Koninklijk Instituut voor de Tropen) NLD. Dist: Stylus Publishing, LLC.

Wang, Wei. Zhongguo Nong Cun Jin Rong Fu Wu Ti Xi Xie Tiao Fa Zhan Yan Jiu: Zhongguo Nongcun Jinrong Fuwu Tixi Xietiao Fazhan Yanjiu. 2010. (CHI., Illus.). *(978-7-207-08527-6(3))* Heilongjiang People's Publishing Hse.

Zhao, Yuepeng. China's Rural Financial System: Households' Demand for Credit & Recent Reforms. 2010. (Routledge Studies on the Chinese Economy Ser.). (ENG., Illus.). 192p. (C). 140.00 *(978-0-415-54793-2(8))* Routledge.

AGRICULTURE—FOLKLORE

Cauvin, Jacques. The Birth of the Gods & the Origins of Agriculture. Watkins, Trevor, tr. from FRE. 2007. (New Studies in Archaeology). (ENG.). 288p. pap. 60.00 *(978-0-521-03908-6(8))* Cambridge Univ. Pr.

AGRICULTURE—GOVERNMENT POLICY

see Agriculture and State

AGRICULTURE—HANDBOOKS, MANUALS, ETC.

Allen, Richard, et al. American Farm Book. 2008. (Gardening in America Ser.). (ENG.). 392p. pap. 23.95 *(978-1-4290-1418-2(0))* Applewood Bks.

Allen, Richard Lamb. The American Farm Book or, Compend of American Agriculture: Being A Practical Treatise on Soils, Manures, Draining Irrigation, Grassegrain Roots. 2006. 340p. per. 23.99 *(978-1-4255-3416-5(3))* MPublishing.

Blake, John Lauris. The Modern Farmer or, Home in the Country; Designed for Instruction & Amusement on Rainy Days & Winter Evenings, by Rev John L Blake. 2006. 520p. per. 29.99 *(978-1-4255-5756-0(2))* MPublishing.

Candlin, Alison. Country Skills: A Practical Guide to Self-Sufficiency. 2011. (ENG., Illus.). 256p. 24.95 *(978-1-61608-361-8(1)*, 608361) Skyhorse Publishing Co., Inc.

Cobleigh, Rolfe. Handy Farm Devices: And How to Make Them. 2nd ed. 2008. 288p. pap. 14.95 *(978-1-59921-325-5(7)*, Lyons Pr.) Globe Pequot Pr., The.

Farmer-Proven Integrated Agriculture: A Technology Information Kit. (Illus.). pap. 10.00 *(978-0-942717-33-4(3))* International Institute of Rural Reconstruction.

Gehring, Abigail R., ed. The Homesteading Handbook: A Back to Basics Guide to Growing Your Own Food, Canning, Keeping Chickens, Generating Your Own Energy, Crafting, Herbal Medicine, & More. 2011. (Back to Basics Guides). (ENG., Illus.). 272p. pap. 14.95 *(978-1-61608-265-9(8)*, 608265) Skyhorse Publishing Co., Inc.

Kains, Maurice. Five Acres & Independence. 2007. 408p. per. *(978-956-291-446-8(1))*; (SPA., Illus.). *(978-956-291-449-9(6))* Editorial Benei Noaj.

Markham, Brett L. Mini Farming: Self-Sufficiency on 1/4 Acre. 2010. (ENG., Illus.). 240p. pap. 16.95 *(978-1-60239-984-6(0)*, 239984) Skyhorse Publishing Co., Inc.

Morris Copeland, Robert. Country Life: A Handbook of Agriculture, Horticulture, & Landscape Gardening. 2009. (Illus.). 896p. reprint ed. 49.95 *(978-1-55849-694-1(7))* Univ. of Massachusetts Pr.

Ohmart, Clifford P. A View from the Vineyard: A Practical Guide to Sustainable Wine Grape Growing. 2011. (ENG., Illus.). 192p. pap. 34.95 ***(978-1-935879-90-9(1))*** Wine Appreciation Guild, Ltd.

Saint Maur, Kate. A Self-Supporting Home. 2008. (Cooking in America Ser.). (ENG.). 384p. pap. 23.95 *(978-1-4290-1128-0(9))* Applewood Bks.

Smith, Barry. The Farming Handbook. 2006. (Illus.). 432p. 59.95 *(978-1-86914-090-8(7))* University of Kwazulu-Natal Press ZAF. Dist: Internationa Specialized Bk. Services.

Todd, Sereno Edwards. The Young Farmers' Manual. 2006. 460p. per. 29.99 *(978-1-4255-5046-2(0))* MPublishing.

U. S. Department of Agriculture, Adjustment Administration Staff. Living on an Acre: A Practical Guide to the Self-Reliant Life. Woodside, Christine, ed. 2nd ed. 2010. (ENG.). 336p. pap. 16.95 *(978-1-59921-885-4(2)*, Lyons Pr.) Globe Pequot Pr., The.

Van Krevelen, Jean Ann. Growing Food: A Guide for Beginners. 2009. 139p. pap. 17.96 *(978-0-557-05874-7(0))* Lulu Enterprises Inc.

AGRICULTURE—HISTORY

Alonso De Herrera, Gabriel. Ancient Agriculture: Roots & Application of Sustainable Farming. 1 vol. Lopez-Gaston, Rosa, tr. from SPA. 2006. (ENG., Illus.). 168p. 24.95 *(978-1-4236-0120-3(3))* Gibbs Smith, Publisher.

Atwood, Bert L. My Father Was A Crop Duster: The Story of Atwood Crop Dusters. 2008. (Illus.). 192p. 39.95 *(978-0-9799287-2-7(9))* AAAA Publishing.

Barker, Graeme. The Agricultural Revolution in Prehistory: Why Did Foragers Become Farmers? 2006. (ENG., Illus.). 616p. 199.00 *(978-0-19-928109-1(2))* Oxford Univ. Pr., Inc.

Barker, Graeme & Janowski, Monica, eds. Why Cultivate? Anthropological & Archaeological Approaches to Foraging-Farming Transitions in Southeast Asia. 2011. (McDonald Institute Monographs). (ENG., Illus.). 142p. (C). 70.00 ***(978-1-902937-58-8(9))*** McDonald Institute for Archaeological Research.

Bellard, Carlos Gomez & Dommelen, Peter van. Rural Landscapes of the Punic World. 2008. (Monographs in Mediterranean Archaeology Ser.). (ENG., Illus.). 299p. (C). 100.00 *(978-1-84553-270-3(8))* Equinox Publishing Ltd. GBR. Dist: ISD.

Boomgaard, Peter. Smallholders & Stockbreeders: Histories of Foodcrop & Livestock Farming in Southeast Asia. Henley, David, ed. 2010. (Verhandelingen Van Het Koninklijk Instituut Voor Taal-, Land Ser.). (Illus.). 352p. pap. 38.00 *(978-90-6718-225-6(7))* KITLV Pr. NLD. Dist: Univ. of Hawaii Pr.

Carolan, Michael. The Sociology of Food & Agriculture. 2012. (Earthscan Food & Agriculture Ser.). (ENG., Illus.). 336p. (C). 145.00 ***(978-0-415-69851-1(0))***; pap. 39.95 ***(978-0-415-69858-0(8))*** Routledge.

Gupta, U. S. What's New about Crop Plants: Novel Discoveries of the 21st Century. 2011. (ENG.). 649p. 179.95 *(978-1-57808-699-3(X))* BIOS Scientific Publishers Ltd. GBR. Dist: Taylor & Francis Group.

Hamilton, David E. From New Day to New Deal: American Farm Policy from Hoover to Roosevelt, 1928-1933. 2011. (ENG.). 352p. pap. 50.00 ***(978-0-8078-6542-2(7))*** Univ. of North Carolina Pr.

Hopkins, David C. The Highlands of Canaan: Agricultural Life in the Early Iron Age. (Social World of Biblical Antiquity Ser.: Vol. 3). (Illus.). 315p. pap. *(978-0-907459-39-2(0)*, Burns & Oates) Continuum International Publishing Group, Ltd.

Ireland, Central Statistics Office Staff, contrib. by. Farming since the Famine: Irish Farm Statistics, 1847-1996. (Illus.). 408p. *(978-0-7076-1813-5(4))* Stationery Office Dublin IRL. Dist: Balogh International, Inc.

Maat, H. Science Cultivating Practice: A History of Agricultural Science in the Netherlands & its Colonies, 1863-1986. 2010. (International Library of Environmental, Agricultural & Food Ethics Ser.). 258p. pap. 149.00 *(978-90-481-5864-5(6)*, 9048158648) Springer.

Mann, Charles C. 1493: Uncovering the New World Columbus Created. (Vintage Ser.). (ENG.). 560p. 2012. pap. 16.95 ***(978-0-307-27824-1(7)**, Vintage)* 2011. (Illus.). 30.50 *(978-0-307-26572-2(2)*, Knopf) Knopf Doubleday Publishing Group.

Manning, Richard. Against the Grain: How Agriculture Has Hijacked Civilization. 2006. 232p. reprint ed. 24.00 *(978-1-4223-5653-1(1))* DIANE Publishing Co.

Marchildon, Gregory, ed. Agricultural History: History of the Prairie West. 2011. (Hpws Ser.). (ENG.). 432p. 59.95 ***(978-0-88977-237-3(1))*** Canadian Plains Research Ctr. CAN. Dist: Univ. of Toronto Pr.

McCreery, David. Frontier Goias, 1822-1889. 2006. (ENG., Illus.). 312p. 60.00 *(978-0-8047-5179-7(X))* Stanford Univ. Pr.

Myrda, Janken & Soderberg, Gabriel. Dovring Saga: A Story of Academic Immigration. 2010. (Historiska Serien Ser.). 255p. pap. 72.50 *(978-91-7402-395-4(0))* Kungl. Vitterhets Historie och Antikvitets Akademien, Sweden SWE. Dist: Coronet Bks.

Pearson, Craig & Nasby, Judith. The Cultivated Landscape: An Exploration of Art & Agriculture. 2008. (ENG., Illus.). 304p. (C). *(978-0-7735-3246-5(3))* McGill-Queen's Univ. Pr.

Price, T. Douglas & Gebauer, Anne B., eds. Last Hunters - First Farmers: New Perspectives on the Prehistory Transition to Agriculture. (Advanced Seminar Ser.). (Illus.). 354p. pap. 29.95 *(978-0-933452-91-5(8))* School for Advanced Research Pr./SAR Pr.

Rice, Harvey. Letters from the Pacific Slope. 2011. 143p. pap. 11.95 *(978-1-4290-4579-7(5))* Applewood Bks.

Rimas, Andrew & Fraser, Evan D. G. Empires of Food: Feast, Famine, & the Rise & Fall of Civilizations. 2010. (ENG., Illus.). 320p. 27.00 *(978-1-4391-0189-6(2)*, Free Pr.) Free Pr.

Salem Press Editors. Agriculture in History. 2009. (Magill's Choice Ser.). 73.00 *(978-1-58765-552-4(7))*; 73.00 *(978-1-58765-553-1(5))* Salem Pr., Inc.

Salem Press Editors & Rasmussen, R. Kent. Agriculture in History. 2009. (Magill's Choice Ser.). 73.00 *(978-1-58765-554-8(3))*; (Illus.). 960p. 217.00 *(978-1-58765-551-7(9))* Salem Pr., Inc.

Sanders, Ralph W. The Farm Tractor: 100 Years of North American Tractors. 2009. (ENG., Illus.). 384p. pap. 27.99 *(978-0-7603-3559-8(1)*, 0760335591, Voyageur Pr) MBI Publishing Co. LLC.

Selyem, Bruce & Krupp Selyem, Barbara. Old Time Grain Elevators: Stories & Photography of A Vanishing Way of Life. 2007. (Illus.). 180p. 25.00 *(978-0-9796869-0-0(3))* Headhouse Bks.

Sinclair, Thomas R. & Sinclair, Carol Janas. Bread, Beer & the Seeds of Change: Agriculture's Impact on World History. 2010. (Illus.). 208p. 65.00 *(978-1-84593-705-8(8))*; pap. 30.00 *(978-1-84593-704-1(X))* CABI GBR. Dist: Stylus Publishing, LLC.

Sprott, Gavin. Farming. Date not set. (Scotland's Past in Action Ser.). (Illus.). 96p. pap. 7.95 *(978-0-948636-69-1(6)*, 6696) NMS Enterprises Ltd. - Publishing GBR. Dist: Weatherhill, Inc.

Standage, Tom. An Edible History of Humanity. Lt. ed. 2009. 416p. 31.95 *(978-1-4104-1850-0(2))* Thorndike Pr.

—An Edible History of Humanity. 2010. (ENG.). 288p. pap. 16.00 *(978-0-8027-1991-1(0))* Walker & Co.

Tauger, Mark. Agriculture in World History. 2010. (Themes in World History Ser.). (ENG., Illus.). 208p. (C). 29.95 *(978-0-415-77387-4(3))*; 115.00 *(978-0-415-77386-7(5))* Routledge.

Timmer, C. Peter. A World Without Agriculture: The Structural Transformation in Historical Perspective. 2009. (ENG.). 93p. pap. 15.00 *(978-0-8447-4279-3(1)*, AEI Pr.) American Enterprise Institute for Public Policy Research.

Tsakok, Isabelle & Gardner, Bruce L. Success in Agricultural Transformation. 2011. (ENG., Illus.). 424p. 110.00 ***(978-0-521-88894-3(8))*** Cambridge Univ. Pr.

Watson, Andrew M. Agricultural Innovation in the Early Islamic World. 2008. (Cambridge Studies in Islamic Civilization Ser.). (ENG., Illus.). 284p. pap. 36.99 *(978-0-521-06883-3(5))* Cambridge Univ. Pr.

World Book, Inc Staff, contrib. by. Agriculture. 2009. (Inventions & Discoveries Ser.). (J). *(978-0-7166-0385-6(3))* World Bk., Inc.

Zvelebil, Marek. Hunters in Transition: Mesolithic Societies of Temperate Eurasia & their Transition to Farming. 2009. (New Directions in Archaeology Ser.). (ENG.). 204p. pap. 31.99 *(978-0-521-10957-4(4))*, Cambridge Univ. Pr.

AGRICULTURE—INFORMATION SERVICES

see also Agricultural Extension Work

Costa, Temra. Farmer Jane: Women Changing the Way We Eat. 1 vol. 2010. (ENG., Illus.). 224p. pap. 15.99 *(978-1-4236-0562-1(4))* Gibbs Smith, Publisher.

Eswara Reddy, Deva B. Agricultural Information Transfer Systems. 2011. (Agriculture Issues & Policies Ser.). pap. 43.00 *(978-1-61761-857-4(8)*, Nova Novinka) Nova Science Pubs., Inc.

Mancs, Basil. Decision Support Systems in Agriculture, Food & the Environment: Trends, Applications & Advances. 2010. (Illus.). 350p. 180.00 *(978-1-61520-881-4(X))* IGI Global.

Meerkerk, Andrt. Rainfed Orchards in Semi-Arid Environments. 2009. 200p. pap. *(978-3-639-12947-2(4))* VDM Verlag Dr. Mueller e.K.

Papajorgji, Petraq & Pinet, François, eds. New Technologies for Constructing Complex Agricultural & Environmental Systems. 2012. 435p. 180.00 ***(978-1-4666-0333-2(X)**,* Information Science Reference) IGI Global.

Papajorgji, Petraq J. & Pinet, François. New Technologies for Constructing Complex Agricultural & Environment Systems. 2012. ***(978-1-4666-0335-6(6))*** IGI Global.

AGRICULTURE—INTERNATIONAL COOPERATION

see also Agricultural Assistance

Bingen, Jim & Busch, Lawrence, eds. Agricultural Standards: The Shape of the Global Food & Fiber System. 2010. (International Library of Environmental, Agricultural & Food Ethics Ser.). xvii, 259p. pap. 219.00 *(978-90-481-7007-4(9)*, 9048170079) Springer.

Blight, Denis. CABI: A Century of Scientific Endeavour. 2011. *(978-1-84593-873-4(9))* CABI.

Jr., Amanullah. International Agricultural Research Organizations. 2011. 340p. pap. ***(978-3-8443-9220-3(3))*** Lambert Academic Publishing.

Raitzer, D. A. & Norton, G. W., eds. Prioritizing Agricultural Research for Development: Experiences & Lessons. 2009. (Illus.). 256p. 145.00 *(978-1-84593-566-5(7))* CABI GBR. Dist: Stylus Publishing, LLC.

Raitzer, David A., et al, contrib. by. Prioritizing Agricultural Research for Development: Experiences & Lessons. 2009. (Illus.). 256p. pap. 150.00 *(978-1-84593-568-9(3))* CABI GBR. Dist: Stylus Publishing, LLC.

United Nations Conference on Trade and Development Staff. World Investment Report 2009: Transnational corporations, agricultural production & Development. 2009. (ENG., Illus.). 312p. pap. 95.00 incl. lp *(978-92-1-112775-1(0))* United Nations Pubns.

United Nations: Department of Economic and Social Affairs. Achieving Sustainable Development & Promoting Development Cooperation: Dialogues at the Economic & Social Council. 2009. (ENG., Illus.). 312p. pap. 32.00 *(978-92-1-104587-1(8))* United Nations Pubns.

United States, Congress House Committee on Financial Services Subcommittee on Domestic and International Monetary Policy, Trade, and Technology Staff, contrib. by. The International Fund for Agricultural Development (IFAD) & the Importance of Agriculture Development in Sustainable Global Poverty Reduction: Hearing Before the Subcommittee on Domestic & International Monetary Policy, Trade, & Technology of the Committee on Financial Services, U.S. House of Representatives, One Hundred Ninth Congress, Second Session, September 12, 2006. 2007. v, 56p. *(978-0-16-078406-4(9)*, 552-070-35701-7) United States Government Printing Office.

AGRICULTURE—LABORATORY MANUALS

Herren, Ray V. Lab Manual for Herren's Agricultural Mechanics: Fundamentals & Applications, 6th. 6th ed. 2009. (ENG.). 400p. (C). pap. 84.95 *(978-1-4354-0099-3(2))* Delmar Cengage Learning.

Wilson, Agroecology Laboratory Manual. rev. ed. 2011. (ENG.). 104p. spiral bd. 36.00 ***(978-0-7575-9454-0(9))*** Kendall Hunt Publishing Co.

Wilson, David W. Agroecology Laboratory Manual. rev. ed. 2010. (ENG.). 100p. spiral bd. 31.80 *(978-0-7575-7411-5(4))* Kendall Hunt Publishing Co.

AGRICULTURE—LAW AND LEGISLATION

see Agricultural Laws and Legislation

AGRICULTURE—OUTLINES, SYLLABI, ETC.

Cram101 Textbook Reviews. Outlines & Highlights for Statistics for Life Sciences by Jeffrey a Witmer, Isbn: 9780130413161. 2010. 128p. pap. 28.95 *(978-1-61698-834-0(7))* Cram101 Inc.

Cram101 Textbook Reviews Staff. Outlines & Highlights for Agricultural Economics by Drummond & Goodwin, Isbn: 0130474525. 2009. 80p. pap. 27.95 *(978-1-4288-3957-1(7))* Cram101 Inc.

—Outlines & Highlights for Introduction to Agricultural Economics by C Parr Rosson, Isbn: 9780131592483. 2009. 84p. pap. 27.95 *(978-1-4288-2167-5(8))* Cram101 Inc.

AGRICULTURE—POLITICAL ASPECTS

see Agriculture and Politics

AGRICULTURE—PRICES

see Agricultural Prices

AGRICULTURE—RESEARCH

Abido, Waleed. Agronomic Studies on Potatoes. 2010. 180p. pap. *(978-3-8383-8258-6(7))* Lambert Academic Publishing.

Ahuja, Laj R. & Ma, Liwang, eds. Methods of Introducing System Models into Agricultural Research. 2011. 454p. lib. bdg. 120.00 ***(978-0-89118-180-4(6))*** ASA-CSSA-SSSA.

Anandajayasekeram, P. & Keswani, C. L. Impact of Science on African Agriculture & Food Security. Rukeni, M. et al, eds. 2007. 310p. (C). 145.00 *(978-1-84593-267-1(6))* CABI GBR. Dist: Stylus Publishing, LLC.

Angelsen, Arild, et al. Measuring Livelihoods & Environmental Dependence: Methods for Research & Fieldwork. Smith Olsen, Carsten, ed. 2011. (ENG., Illus.). 288p. pap. 49.95 *(978-1-84971-133-3(X))* Routledge.

Aredo, Mengistu Ketema. Impact of Technology on Wheat Production. 2009. 134p. pap. *(978-3-639-18389-4(4))* VDM Verlag Dr. Mueller e.K.

Bekele Gemechu, Dereje. Farmers Participation in Farmers' Participatory Research. 2010. 112p. pap. *(978-3-639-26115-8(1))* VDM Verlag Dr. Mueller e.K.

Bengtsson, M.I. Agricultural Research at the Crossroads: Revisited Resource-Poor Farmers & the Millennium Development Goals. 2007. (ENG.). 350p. 59.95 *(978-1-57808-514-9(4))* BIOS Scientific Publishers Ltd. GBR. Dist: Taylor & Francis Group.

Blight, Denis. CABI: A Century of Scientific Endeavour. 2011. *(978-1-84593-873-4(5))* CABI.

Bundgaard, Kristian & Isaksen, Luke. Agriculture Research & Technology. 2010. (Agriculture Issues & Policies Ser.). (Illus.). xvii, 478p. 195.00 *(978-1-60741-850-4(5))* Nova Science Pubs., Inc.

Committee to Review the NIOSH Agriculture, Forestry, and Fishing Research Program & National Research Council. Agriculture, Forestry, & Fishing Research at NIOSH. 2008. (ENG.). 354p. pap. 70.75 *(978-0-309-11579-7(5))* National Academies Pr.

Do Prado, Hércules Antonio, et al, eds. Computational Methods for Agricultural Research: Advances & Applications. 2010. (Illus.). 350p. 180.00 *(978-1-61692-871-1(9)*, Information Science Reference) IGI Global.

Ekboir, Javier. Successful Organizational Learning in the Management of Agricultural Research & Innovation: The Mexican Produce Foundations. 2009. *(978-0-89629-171-3(5))* International Food Policy Research Institute.

Escobedo, Héctor J. & Madrigal, Sergio M., eds. Agriculture & Food Science Research Biographical Sketches & Research Summaries. 2012. ***(978-1-62100-934-4(3))*** Nova Science Pubs., Inc.

Fan, Shenggen. Halving Hunger: Meeting the First Millennium Development Goal Through "Business As Unusual" 2010. (Illus.). viii, 16p. ***(978-0-89629-538-4(9))*** International Food Policy Research Institute.

Fernández Prieto, Lourenzo & Prieto, Lourenzo Fernández. El Apagón Tecnológico Del Franquismo: Estado e Innovación en la Agricultura Española Del Siglo XX. 2007. (SPA., Illus.). 389p. *(978-84-8456-965-7(9))* Tirant lo Blanch.

Friederichsen, Jakob Rupert. Opening up Knowledge Production through Participatory Research? Agricultural Research for Vietnam's Northern Uplands. 2009. (Development Economics & Policy Ser.). (Illus.). 260p. pap. 74.95 *(978-3-631-58842-0(9))* Lang, Peter GmbH, Europaischer Verlag der Wissenschaften DEU. Dist: Lang, Peter.

Gemechu, Dibaba & Aweke, Girma. Application of Spatial ed Model in Agricultural Field Experiment. 2011. 96p. pap. ***(978-3-8443-9315-6(3))*** Lambert Academic Publishing.

Gerhardt, Uta. Soziologie Im Zwanzigsten Jahrhundert: Studien Zu Ihrer Geschichte in Deutschland. 2009. (Studien zur geschichte der deutschen Forschungsgemeinschaft Ser.). 430p. (C). 75.00 *(978-3-515-09255-5(2))* Steiner, Franz Verlag Wiesbaden GmbH DEU. Dist: Brown, David Bk. Co., The.

Gogi, M. Dildar, et al. Integrated Management of Melon Fruit Fly in Bitter Gourd. 2011. 220p. pap. ***(978-3-639-32724-3(1))*** VDM Verlag Dr. Mueller e.K.

Government Printing Office Staff. Agricultural Research. pap. 50.00 *(978-0-16-009204-6(3)*, Agriculture Dept.) United States Government Printing Office.

Haider, Karar, et al. Integrated Pest Management of Mango: Bio-Ecology & Management of Mango Mealybug Drosicha Mangiferae (G.) in Pakistan. 2011. 216p. pap. ***(978-3-639-32857-8(4))*** VDM Verlag Dr. Mueller e.K.

Hartwich, Frank. Formando Alianzas Publico-Privadas para la Innovacion Agricola. 2008. *(978-0-89629-762-3(4))* International Food Policy Research Institute.

Harwood, Jonathan. Europe's Green Revolution. 2012. (Routledge Explorations in Economic History Ser.: 57). (ENG., Illus.). 288p. (C). 140.00 ***(978-0-415-59868-2(3))*** Routledge.

Hearing to Review Agriculture Research Programs: Hearing Before the Subcommittee on Conservation, Credit, Energy, & Research of the Committee on Agriculture, House of Representatives, One Hundred Tenth Congress, First Session, May 10, 2007. 2008. (Illus.). iii, 172p. (978-0-16-083236-9(5), 552-070-39064-2) United States Government Printing Office.

Hearing to Review the Implementation of the Research Title of the 2008 Farm Bill: Hearing Before the Subcommittee on Conservation, Credit, Energy, & Research of the Committee on Agriculture, House of Representatives, One Hundred Eleventh Congress, First Session, September 30, 2009. 2009. v, 60p. (978-0-16-084616-8(1), 552-070-40119-9) United States Government Printing Office.

Heim, Susanne. Calories, Caoutchouc, Careers: Plant Breeding & Agrarian Research in Kaiser-Wilhelm-Institutes 1933-1945. 2008. (Boston Studies in the Philosophy of Science Ser.). (Illus.). 300p. 179.00 (978-1-4020-6717-4(8)) Springer.

Hendriks, Barbara P. Agricultural Research Updates. 2011. (Agricultural Research Updates Ser.). 325.00 (978-1-61470-191-0(1)) Nova Science Pubs., Inc.

Hendriks, Barbara P., ed. Agricultural Research Updates. 2011. (Series: Agricultural Research Updates Ser.). 190p. 95.00 (978-1-61324-292-6(1)) Nova Science Pubs., Inc.

Henke, Christopher R. Cultivating Science, Harvesting Power: Science & Industrial Agriculture in California. 2008. (Inside Technology Ser.). (ENG., Illus.). 248p. (gr. 17). 32.00 (978-0-262-08373-7(6)) MIT Pr.

Hunt, Lesley. Compliance at Work. 2008. 304p. pap. (978-3-639-05751-5(1)) VDM Verlag Dr. Mueller e.K.

Investing in Our Nation's Future Through Agricultural Research: Hearing Before the Committee on Agriculture, Nutrition, & Forestry, United States Senate, One Hundred Tenth Congress, First Session, March 7, 2007. 2007. (Illus.). iv, 192p. (978-0-16-078869-7(2), 552-070-35998-2) United States Government Printing Office.

Ireland, Clive. Statistics for Agriculture & Horticulture. 2010. (Modular Texts). (Illus.). 380p. pap. 75.00 (978-1-84593-537-5(3)) CABI GBR. Dist: Stylus Publishing, LLC.

Jharwal, S. M., et al, eds. Glimpses of Indian Agriculture: Macro & Micro Aspects, 2 vols. & 3 pts. 2007. (ENG., Illus.). 1584p. 149.95 (978-81-7188-597-8(7)) Academic Foundation IND. Dist: Independent Pubs. Group.

Jr., Amanullah. International Agricultural Research Organizations. 2011. 340p. pap. (978-3-8443-9220-3(3)) Lambert Academic Publishing.

Kidane, Tsion Tesfaye. Effectiveness of Agricultural Training to Farmers. 2010. 172p. pap. (978-3-8383-8815-1(1)) Lambert Academic Publishing.

Lilja, Nina, et al, eds. Participatory Research & Gender Analysis. 2010. (Development in Practice Ser.). (ENG., Illus.). 232p. (C). 125.00 (978-0-415-57768-7(3), Routledge) Taylor & Francis Group GBR. Dist: Taylor & Francis Group.

Loebenstein, G. & Thottappilly, G., eds. Agricultural Research Management. (ENG.). xx, 388p. 2010. pap. 239.00 (978-90-481-7520-8(8), 9048175208) 2007. (Illus.). 239.00 (978-1-4020-6056-4(4), 1402060564) Springer.

Lund, Jens. Measuring Livelihoods & Environmental Dependence: Methods for Research & Fieldwork. Angelsen, Arild et al, eds. 2011. (ENG., Illus.). 288p. 140.00 (978-1-84971-132-6(1)) Routledge.

Maat, H. Science Cultivating Practice: A History of Agricultural Science in the Netherlands & its Colonies, 1863-1986. 2010. (International Library of Environmental, Agricultural & Food Ethics Ser.). 258p. pap. 149.00 (978-90-481-5864-5(8), 9048158648) Springer.

Meinzen-Dick, Ruth & Adato, Michelle, eds. Agricultural Research, Livelihoods, & Poverty: Studies of Economic & Social Impacts in Six Countries. 2007. (ENG., Illus.). 416p. (gr. 17). 60.00 (978-0-8018-8596-9(5)) Johns Hopkins Univ. Pr.

Meinzen-Dick, Ruth Suseela. Engendering Agricultural Research, Development & Extension. 2012. (978-0-89629-190-4(1)) International Food Policy Research Institute.

Oberkrome, Willi. Ordnung und Autarkie: Die Geschichte der deutschen Landbauforschung, Agrarokonomie und landlichen Sozialwissenschaft im Spiegel von Forschungsdienst und DFG (1920-1970) 2009. (Studien zur geschichte der deutschen Forschungsgemeinschaft Ser.). 371p. (C). pap. 80.00 (978-3-515-092555-7(1)) Steiner, Franz Verlag Wiesbaden GmbH DEU. Dist: Brown, David Bk. Co., The.

Otsuka, Keijiro & Kalirajan, Kaliappa, eds. Agriculture in Developing Countries: Technology Issues. 2008. (Illus.). 172p. (C). 39.95 (978-0-7619-3662-6(9), B36626C) SAGE Pubns., Inc.

Ouma, George & Gottwald, Franz-Theo, eds. Agrarian Science for Sustainable Resource Management in Sub-Saharan Africa. 2009. (Studies in sub-Saharan Africa Ser.). 130p. pap. 39.95 (978-3-631-58524-5(1)) Lang, Peter GmbH, Europaischer Verlag der Wissenschaften DEU. Dist: Lang, Peter.

Pal, B. P. Search for New Genes. Bhat, S. R. et al, eds. 2007. (ENG., Illus.). 500p. 79.95 (978-81-7188-632-6(9)) Academic Foundation IND. Dist: Independent Pubs. Group.

Raitzer, D. A. & Norton, G. W., eds. Prioritizing Agricultural Research for Development: Experiences & Lessons. 2009. (Illus.). 256p. 145.00 (978-1-84593-566-5(7)) CABI GBR. Dist: Stylus Publishing, LLC.

Raitzer, David A., et al, contrib. by. Prioritizing Agricultural Research for Development: Experiences & Lessons. 2009. (Illus.). 256p. pap. 150.00 (978-1-84593-568-9(3)) CABI GBR. Dist: Stylus Publishing, LLC.

Reiter, Gary C. & Schuster, Caleb J. Encyclopedia of Agriculture Research, 2 vols. 2012. (Agriculture Issues & Policies Ser.). 1002p. 295.00 (978-1-61209-955-2(6)) Nova Science Pubs., Inc.

Roy, Amit & Chakrabarty, Suhrita. Evolving Agriculture Research Plan in Hill Agriculture. 2011. 76p. pap. (978-3-8443-9362-0(5)) Lambert Academic Publishing.

Scoones, Ian & Thompson, John, eds. Farmer First Revisited: Farmer-Led Innovation for Agricultural Research & Development. 2009. (ENG., Illus.). 369p. pap. 25.95 (978-1-85339-682-3(6)) Practical Action Publishing GBR. Dist: Stylus Publishing, LLC.

Singh, Phool. Modelling Crop Production: Principles & Application. 2008. (ENG., Illus.). 510p. pap. 59.95 (978-1-57808-418-0(0)) BIOS Scientific Publishers Ltd. GBR. Dist: Taylor & Francis Group.

Sumberg, James & Thompson, John, eds. Contested Agronomy. 2012. (Pathways to Sustainability Ser.). (ENG., Illus.). 232p. (C). pap. 35.95 (978-0-415-50714-1(6)) Routledge.

—Contested Agronomy: Agricultural Research in a Changing World. 2012. (Pathways to Sustainability Ser.). (ENG., Illus.). 232p. (C). 155.00 (978-0-415-69806-1(5)) Routledge.

Young, Daniel J., ed. The Science Surrounding Food. 2009. (Agriculture Issues & Politics Ser.). (Illus.). 170p. 80.10 (978-1-60876-033-6(2)) Nova Science Pubs., Inc.

AGRICULTURE—SAFETY MEASURES

Bertoni, Daniel. Homeland Security: Management & Coordination Problems Increase the Vulnerability of U. S. Agriculture to Foreign Pests & Diseases. 2006. 69p. (C). pap. 20.00 (978-1-4223-0779-3(4)) DIANE Publishing Co.

Dales, Daniel. A Poultry All-Hazard Threat, Vulnerability, & Capability Assessment. 2011. 120p. pap. (978-3-8454-1495-9(2)) Lambert Academic Publishing.

Kim, Moon, et al. Sensing for Agriculture & Food Quality & Safety III. 2011. (Proceedings of SPIE Ser.). 246p. pap. 90.00 (978-0-8194-8601-1(9)) SPIE.

Kim, Moon S., et al. Sensing for Agriculture & Food Quality & Safety: 14-15 April 2009, Orlando, Florida, United States. 2009. (Proceedings of SPIE Ser.). (Illus.). 222p. pap. 90.00 (978-0-8194-7581-7(5)) SPIE.

Kubik, Rick. The Farm Safety Handbook. rev. ed. 2006. (Country Workshop Ser.). (ENG., Illus.). 128p. pap. 21.95 (978-0-7603-2385-4(2), 0760323852, Voyageur Pr) MBI Publishing Co. LLC.

Prosper, Doamekpor. Prevention of Respiratory Diseases in Agriculture & Related Industries: A Health Belief Approach to the Design, Implementation & Evaluation of Occupational Safety & Health Programs. 2011. 136p. pap. (978-3-639-33193-6(1)) VDM Verlag Dr. Mueller e.K.

AGRICULTURE—SOCIAL ASPECTS

Angelsen, Arild, et al. Measuring Livelihoods & Environmental Dependence: Methods for Research & Fieldwork. Smith Olsen, Carsten, ed. 2011. (ENG., Illus.). 288p. pap. 49.95 (978-1-84971-133-3(X)) Routledge.

Arcury, Thomas A. & Quandt, Sara A. Latino Farmworkers in the Eastern United States: Health, Safety & Justice. 2009. (ENG., Illus.). x, 240p. 89.95 (978-0-387-88346-5(0), 0387883460) Springer.

Berry, Wendell. The Gift of Good Land: Further Essays Cultural & Agricultural. 2009. (ENG.). 304p. pap. 15.95 (978-1-58243-484-1(0), Counterpoint Pr.) Basic Bks. GBR. Dist: Perseus-PGW.

Carolan, Michael. Embodied Food Politics. 2011. (Critical Food Studies). (Illus.). 190p. 89.95 (978-1-4094-2209-9(7)) Ashgate Publishing Co.

Carolan, Michael. The Sociology of Food & Agriculture. 2012. (Earthscan Food & Agriculture Ser.). (ENG., Illus.). 336p. (C). 145.00 (978-0-415-69851-1(0)); pap. 39.95 (978-0-415-69858-0(8)) Routledge.

Cohen, Benjamin R. Notes from the Ground: Science, Soil, & Society in the American Countryside. 2011. (Yale Agrarian Studies Ser.). (ENG., Illus.). 288p. pap. 27.50 (978-0-300-17770-1(4)) Yale Univ. Pr.

Deveze, Jean-Claude, ed. Challenges for African Agriculture. 2010. (ENG., Illus.). 292p. pap. 35.00 (978-0-8213-8481-7(3), 9780821384817) World Bank Pubns.

Dhesi, Autar S. & Gurmail Singh. Rural Development in Punjab: A Success Story Going Astray. Dhesi, Autar S. & Singh, Gurmail, eds. 2008. (Illus.). 420p. 110.00 (978-0-415-45681-4(9), Routledge India) Taylor & Francis Group GBR. Dist: Taylor & Francis Group.

Dougherty, Debbie. The Reluctant Farmer: An exploration of work, social class, & the production of Food. 2011. (ENG.). 244p. pap. (978-1-84876-384-5(0)) Troubadour Publishing Ltd.

Downs, William, Jr. Stories of Survival: Arkansas Farmers During the Great Depression. 2011. (ENG., Illus.). 304p. pap. 19.95 (978-0-9824295-5-6(X)) Phoenix International, Inc.

Du Bry, Travis. Immigrants, Settlers, & Laborers: The Socioeconomic Transformation of a Farming Community. 2006. (Illus.). (C). (978-1-59332-157-4(0)) LFB Scholarly Publishing LLC.

Gebissa, Ezekiel. Khat in Ethiopia: Taking the Place of Food. 2010. 348p. pap. (978-1-56902-318-1(2)) Red Sea Pr.

Gehlsen, Duane. Social Complexity & the Origins of Agriculture. 2009. 294p. pap. (978-3-639-12399-9(9)) VDM Verlag Dr. Mueller e.K.

Gitau, Thomas, et al. Integrated Assessment of Health & Sustainability of Agroecosystems. 2008. (Advances in Agroecology Ser.). (ENG., Illus.). 256p. 104.95 (978-1-4200-7277-8(3), CRC Press) Taylor & Francis Group GBR. Dist: Taylor & Francis Group.

Graham, Mark E. Sustainable Agriculture: A Christian Ethic of Gratitude. 2009. 256p. pap. 28.00 (978-1-60608-806-7(8), Wipf and Stock) Wipf & Stock Pubs.

Harvest over the Horizon: The Challenges of Aging in Agriculture: Hearing Before the Special Committee on Aging, United States Senate, One Hundred Tenth Congress, First Session, Washington, DC, June 21, 2007. 2008. (Illus.). iii, 52p. (978-0-16-080152-5(4), 552-070-36889-2) United States Government Printing Office.

Harwood, Jonathan. Europe's Green Revolution. 2012. (Routledge Explorations in Economic History Ser.: 57). (ENG., Illus.). 288p. (C). 140.00 (978-0-415-59868-2(0)) Routledge.

Hayes-Conroy, Allison. Reconnecting Lives to the Land: An Agenda for Critical Dialogue. 2007. 240p. (C). 49.50 (978-0-8386-4130-9(X)) Fairleigh Dickinson Univ. Pr.

Hovorka, Alice, et al, eds. Women Feeding Cities: Mainstreaming Gender in Urban Agriculture & Food Security. 2009. (ENG., Illus.). 399p. pap. 39.95 (978-1-85339-685-4(0)) Practical Action Publishing GBR. Dist: Stylus Publishing, LLC.

Kitsikopoulos, Harilaos, ed. Agrarian Change & Crisis in Europe 1200-1500. 2011. (Routledge Research in Medieval Studies). (ENG., Illus.). 376p. (C). 125.00 (978-0-415-89578-1(2)) Routledge.

Kneafsey, Moya, et al. Reconnecting Consumers, Producers & Food: Exploring Alternatives. 2008. (Cultures of Consumption Ser.). (ENG., Illus.). 224p. pap. 39.95 (978-1-84520-253-8(8)) Berg Pubs. GBR. Dist: Macmillan.

Knuttila, Murray & Stirling, Bob. The Prairie Agrarian Movement: The Centenary Symposium on the Foundation of the Territorial Grain Growers Association. rev. ed. 2007. (Canadian Plains Studies(CPS) Ser.). (ENG.). 293p. pap. 29.95 (978-0-88977-183-3(9)) Canadian Plains Research Ctr. CAN. Dist: Univ. of Toronto Pr.

Koninck, Rodolphe de, et al. Borneo Transformed: Agricultural Expansion on the Southeast Asian Frontier. 2011. (Illus.). ix, 216p. 32.00 (978-9971-69-544-6(8)) National Univ. of Singapore Pr. SGP. Dist: Univ. of Hawaii Pr.

Korieh, Chima J. & Matthews, S. The Land Has Changed: History, Society & Gender in Colonial Eastern Nigeria. 2010. (Africa: Missing Voices Ser.). (Illus.). 390p. pap. 39.95 (978-1-55238-268-4(0)) Univ. of Calgary Pr. CAN. Dist: Michigan State Univ. Pr.

Lund, Jens. Measuring Livelihoods & Environmental Dependence: Methods for Research & Fieldwork. Angelsen, Arild et al, eds. 2011. (ENG., Illus.). 288p. 140.00 (978-1-84971-132-6(1)) Routledge.

Major, William H. Grounded Vision: New Agrarianism & the Academy. 2011. 240p. (ENG.). 35.00 (978-0-8173-1734-8(1)); (978-0-8173-8544-6(4)) Univ. of Alabama Pr.

Manning, Richard. Against the Grain: How Agriculture Has Hijacked Civilization. 2006. 232p. reprint ed. 24.00 (978-1-4223-5653-1(1)) DIANE Publishing Co.

Meinzen-Dick, Ruth & Adato, Michelle, eds. Agricultural Research, Livelihoods, & Poverty: Studies of Economic & Social Impacts in Six Countries. 2007. (ENG., Illus.). 416p. (gr. 17). 60.00 (978-0-8018-8596-9(5)) Johns Hopkins Univ. Pr.

Meinzen-Dick, Ruth Suseela. Engendering Agricultural Research, Development & Extension. 2012. (978-0-89629-190-4(1)) International Food Policy Research Institute.

Middendorf, Gerad & Wright, Wynne, eds. The Fight over Food: Producers, Consumers, & Activists Challenge the Global Food System. 2008. (Rural Studies). (ENG., Illus.). 296p. 65.00 (978-0-271-03274-0(X)) Pennsylvania State Univ. Pr.

Miller, Sally. Edible Action: Food Activism & Alternative Economics. 2009. (ENG.). 192p. pap. 22.95 (978-1-55266-280-9(2)) Fernwood Publishing Co., Ltd. CAN. Dist: Independent Pubs. Group.

Moreta, Angel. Capitalismo y Descampesinización en el Suroeste Dominicano. 2009. (SPA., Illus.). 369p. (978-9945-02-065-6(X)) Archivo General de la Nacion.

Nation, Allan. The Moving Feast: A Cultural History of Heritage Foods in Southeast Mississippi. 2010. (978-0-9721597-5-3(4)) Green Park Pr.

Otero, Gerardo, ed. Food for the Few: Neoliberal Globalism & Biotechnology in Latin America. 2010. (ENG., Illus.). 335p. pap. 30.00 (978-0-292-72613-0(9)) Univ. of Texas Pr.

Pargas, Damian Alan. The Quarters & the Fields: Slave Families in the Non-Cotton South. 2011. (New Perspectives on the History of the South Ser.). (ENG., Illus.). 274p. pap. 27.95 (978-0-8130-3804-9(9)) Univ. Pr. of Florida.

Patel, Raj. Stuffed & Starved: The Hidden Battle for the World Food System. 2008. (ENG., Illus.). 416p. pap. 19.95 (978-1-933633-49-7(2)) Melville Hse. Publishing.

Pearson, Craig & Pilgrim, Sarah, eds. Urban Agriculture: Diverse Activities & Benefits for City Society. 2010. (International Journal Agricultural Sustainability Ser.). (ENG., Illus.). 128p. 99.95 (978-1-84971-124-1(0)) Routledge.

Phillips, Sarah T. This Land, This Nation: Conservation, Rural America, & the New Deal. 2007. (ENG., Illus.). 302p. 81.00 (978-0-521-85270-8(6)); per. 25.99 (978-0-521-61796-3(0)) Cambridge Univ. Pr.

Roy, Amit & Chakrabarty, Suhrita. Resource Appraisal for Identifying Livelihood Potentials. 2011. 68p. pap. (978-3-8443-2126-5(8)) Lambert Academic Publishing.

Scrieciu, S. Serban. Socioeconomic & Environmental Impacts on Agriculture in the New Europe: Post-Communist Transition & Accession to the European Union. 2011. (Routledge Studies in Ecological Economics Ser.). (ENG., Illus.). 240p. (C). 125.00 (978-0-415-47588-4(0)) Routledge.

Shil, Sandip, et al. A Suitable Methodology for Evaluation Web Portals. 2011. 120p. pap. (978-3-8443-8687-5(4)) Lambert Academic Publishing.

Smedshaug, Christian Anton. Feeding the World in the 21st Century: A Historical Analysis of Agriculture & Society. 2010. (Anthem Other Canon Ser.). (ENG., Illus.). 322p. pap. 40.00 (978-1-84331-867-5(9)) Anthem Pr. GBR. Dist: Books International, Inc.

Sumberg, James & Thompson, John, eds. Contested Agronomy. 2012. (Pathways to Sustainability Ser.). (ENG., Illus.). 232p. (C). pap. 35.95 (978-0-415-50714-1(6)) Routledge.

—Contested Agronomy: Agricultural Research in a Changing World. 2012. (Pathways to Sustainability Ser.). (ENG., Illus.). 232p. (C). 155.00 (978-0-415-69806-1(5)) Routledge.

Vorobeva, D. A. Selskii Sotsium: Obshchestvennye Ustoi I Vektory Transformatsii. 2009. (RUS.). 323p. (978-5-9999-0210-8(X)) Nauka.

Wood, Donald C. Ogata-Mura: Sowing Dissent & Reclaiming Identity in a Japanese Farming Village. 2012. (ENG.). 260p. 90.00 (978-0-85745-524-6(9)) Berghahn Bks., Inc.

Wright, Wynne & Middendorf, Gerad, eds. The Fight over Food: Producers, Consumers, & Activists Challenge the Global Food System. 2008. (Rural Studies). (ENG., Illus.). 296p. pap. 28.50 (978-0-271-03275-7(8)) Pennsylvania State Univ. Pr.

AGRICULTURE—STATISTICS

see also Crop Yields

Bansil, P. C. Agricultural Statistics in India. 3rd rev. ed. 14.00 (978-0-8364-1500-1(0)) Oxford IBH IND. Dist: South Asia Bks.

Benedetti, Roberto, et al, eds. Agricultural Survey Methods. 2010. (ENG., Illus.). 434p. 145.00 (978-0-470-74371-3(9), Wiley) Wiley, John & Sons, Inc.

Bitz, Robert. Four Hundred Years of Agricultural Change in the Empire State. 2009. (ENG.). pap. 19.95 (978-0-615-31865-3(7)) Bitz, Ward Publishing.

Cram101 Textbook Reviews. Outlines & Highlights for Statistics for Life Sciences by Jeffrey a Witmer, Isbn: 9780130413161. 2010. 128p. pap. 28.95 (978-1-61698-834-0(7)) Cram101 Inc.

Department of Agriculture and Cooperation ,Directorate of Economics and Statistics Staff. Agricultural Statistics at a Glance 2008. 2009. (ENG.). 378p. pap. 35.95 (978-81-7188-717-0(1)) Academic Foundation IND. Dist: Independent Pubs. Group.

Epeju, William Faustine. Productivity: Evidence from farmers & their advisers in Teso, Uganda. 2010. 344p. pap. (978-3-639-20514-5(6)) VDM Verlag Dr. Mueller e.K.

Food and Agriculture Organization. 2000 World Census of Agriculture: Main Results & Metadata by Country (1996-2005) 2010. 248p. pap. (978-92-5-106568-6(3)) Food & Agriculture Organization of the United Nations.

Food and Agriculture Organization of the United Nations Staff. FAO Trade Yearbook. (Statistics Ser.). (Illus.). 366p. Beman Assocs.

Green, Linda L. Alabama 1850 Agricultural & Manufacturing Census, Volume 3 for Autauga, Baldwin, Barbour, Benton, Bibb, Blount, Butler, Chambers, Cherokee, Choctaw, Clarke, Coffee, Conecuh, Coosa, Covington Counties. 2009. 264p. pap. 33.00 (978-0-7884-4907-9(9)) Heritage Bks.

—Alabama 1860 Agricultural & Manufacturing Census: Volume 4 for Perry, Pickens, Pike, Randolph, Russell, Shelby, St. Clair, Sumter, Tallapoosa, Talladega, Tuscaloosa, Walker, Washington, Wilcox, Winston. 2009. 376p. pap. 41.00 (978-0-7884-5021-1(2)) Heritage Bks.

—Missouri 1850 Agricultural Census: Volume 1. 2010. pap. 35.00 (978-0-7884-5196-6(0)) Heritage Bks.

—North Carolina 1850 Agricultural Census: Volume 2. 2008. pap. 30.00 (978-0-7884-4573-6(1)) Heritage Bks.

—North Carolina 1850 Agricultural Census: Volume 3. 2008. pap. 30.00 (978-0-7884-4579-8(0)) Heritage Bks.

—North Carolina 1850 Agricultural Census: Volume 4. 2008. pap. 29.50 (978-0-7884-4581-1(2)) Heritage Bks.

—Tennessee 1850 Agricultural Census. 2007. (978-0-7884-5170-6(7)); (978-0-7884-8355-4(2)) Heritage Bks. (Willow Bend Bks.).

—Tennessee 1850 Agricultural Census: Volume 5. 2010. pap. 34.00 (978-0-7884-5197-3(9)) Heritage Bks.

—Texas 1860 Agricultural Census. 2009. 200p. pap. 27.50 (978-0-7884-4774-7(2)) Heritage Bks.

—Texas 1860 Agricultural Census: Volume 1. 2009. 190p. pap. 27.50 (978-0-7884-4638-2(X)) Heritage Bks.

—Texas 1860 Agricultural Census: Volume 2. 2009. 262p. pap. 32.50 (978-0-7884-4796-9(3)) Heritage Bks.

—West Virginia 1860 Agricultural Census, Volume 1. 2008. pap. 26.00 (978-0-7884-4562-0(6)) Heritage Bks.

—West Virginia 1860 Agricultural Census, Volume 2. 2008. pap. (978-0-7884-4563-7(4)) Heritage Bks.

Green, Linda L., compiled by. Missouri 1850 Agricultural Census. 2011. (978-0-7884-5228-4(2)) 2011. (978-0-7884-8655-5(1)) 2011. (978-0-7884-5247-5(9)) 2011. (978-0-7884-8656-2(X)) 2011. (978-0-7884-5255-0(X)) 2011. (978-0-7884-8654-8(3)) 2010. (978-0-7884-8434-6(6)) Heritage Bks. (Willow Bend Bks.).

—North Carolina 1850 Agricultural Census. 2008. (978-0-7884-4629-0(0)); (978-0-7884-7158-2(9)); (978-0-7884-7667-9(X)); pap. 27.50 (978-0-7884-4628-3(2)); pap. 28.00 (978-0-7884-4571-2(5)) Heritage Bks. (Willow Bend Bks.).

—Texas 1860 Agricultural Census. 2008. (978-0-7884-7501-6(0)); (978-0-7884-7578-8(9)); (978-0-7884-7467-5(7)) Heritage Bks. (Willow Bend Bks.).

—West Virginia 1850 Agricultural Census, 2 vols. 2007. (978-0-7884-4311-4(9)); (978-0-7884-4253-7(8)) Heritage Bks. (Willow Bend Bks.).

—West Virginia 1860 Agricultural Census. 2007. pap. 26.00 (978-0-7884-4488-3(3), Willow Bend Bks.) Heritage Bks.

Holcomb, Richard, ed. Agricultural Statistics 2010. 2011. (ENG., Illus.). 508p. pap. 45.00 *(978-0-16-088287-6(7)*, Agricultural Research Service) United States Government Printing Office.

Ireland, Central Statistics Office Staff, contrib. by. Farming since the Famine: Irish Farm Statistics, 1847-1996. (Illus.). 408p. *(978-0-7076-1813-5(4))* Stationery Office Dublin IRL. Dist: Balogh International, Inc.

Islam, M. Mufakharul. Bengal Agriculture 1926-46: A Quantitative Study. 2007. (Cambridge South Asian Studies). (ENG.). 300p. pap. 36.99 *(978-0-521-04985-6(7))* Cambridge Univ. Pr.

Oliver, M. A., ed. Geostatistical Applications for Precision Agriculture. 2010. (ENG.). v, 295p. 189.00 *(978-90-481-9132-1(7)*, 9048191327) Springer.

Organisation for Economic Co-operation and Development Staff. Oecd-Fao Agricultural Outlook 2007-2016. 2007. pap. 78.00 *(978-92-64-02509-7(X))* Organization for Economic Cooperation & Development.

—Perspectives Agricoles de l'Ocde et de la Fao: 2006-2015. 2006. 228p. per. 75.00 *(978-92-64-02462-5(X))* Organization for Economic Cooperation & Development.

Organisation for Economic Co-operation and Development Staff & Food and Agriculture Organization. OECD-FAO agricultural Outlook 2006-2015. 2006. (Illus.). 208p. per. 75.00 *(978-92-64-02460-1(3))* Organization for Economic Cooperation & Development.

Organisation for Economic Co-operation and Development: Development Assistance Committee. Creditor Reporting System 2009: Aid Activities in Support of Agriculture. 2010. (Illus.). 182p. pap. 63.00 *(978-92-64-07702-7(2))* Organization for Economic Cooperation & Development.

Panel to Review USDA's Agricultural Resource Management Survey & National Research Council. Understanding American Agriculture: Challenges for the Agricultural Resource Management Survey. 2007. (ENG.). 214p. pap. 50.00 *(978-0-309-11092-1(0))* National Academies Pr.

Petrone, Rose M., ed. Agricultural Statistics, 2007. 2007. (ENG., Illus.). 544p. pap. 42.00 *(978-0-16-077207-8(9)*, National Agricultural Statistics Service) United States Government Printing Office.

Samuels, Myra L. & Witmer, Jeffrey A. Statistics for the Life Sciences. 3rd ed. 2006. pap. 9.95 *(978-1-4288-1445-5(0))* Cram101 Inc.

—Student Solutions Manual for Statistics for the Life Sciences. 4th ed. 2011. (ENG.). 96p. (C). pap. 36.67 *(978-0-321-69307-5(8))* Addison Wesley.

Samuels, Myra L., et al. Statistics for the Life Sciences. 4th rev. ed. 2010. (ENG.). 672p. (C). 146.67 *(978-0-321-65280-5(0))* Addison Wesley.

United Nations Staff. Statistical Abstract of the ESCWA Region: 28th Issue. 2010. (ENG, FRE & MUL.). 270p. pap. 45.00 *(978-92-1-128327-3(2))* United Nations Pubns.

Us Department of Agriculture. Agricultural Statistics. 2011. (Agricultural Statistics Ser.). (Illus.). pap. 46.00 ***(978-1-59804-598-7(9))*** Claitor's Publishing Div., Inc.

U.S. Dept. of Commerce, compiled by. United States Census of Agriculture, 1925. Reports for States, with Statistics for Counties & a Summary for the United States Part II: The Southern States. 2008. 1328p. lib. bdg. 500.00 net. *(978-0-88354-244-6(7))* Ross Publishing Incorporated.

U.S. Dept. of Commerce Staff, compiled by. United States Census of Agriculture, 1925. Reports for States, with Statistics for Counties & a Summary for the United States Pt. 1: The Northern States. 2008. 1328p. lib. bdg. 500.00 net. *(978-0-88354-243-9(9))* Ross Publishing Incorporated.

AGRICULTURE—STUDY AND TEACHING

Here are entered works on methods of instruction in agriculture. General works on education in agriculture are entered under Agricultural Education.

see also Agricultural Colleges; Forestry Schools and Education

BarCharts Inc., Staff. Spanish for Landscaping. 2009. (ENG.). 6p. 5.95 *(978-1-4232-0533-3(2))* Barcharts, Inc.

Carolina Biological Staff, compiled by. Determining Agricultural Resources. 2009. (Inquiries in Science Environmental Ser.). tchr. ed., spiral bd. *(978-1-4350-0429-0(9))* Carolina Biological Supply Co.

Elliot, Jack & Jepsen, Heather R. Communicating Knowledge in Agriculture & the Life Sciences. rev. ed. 2009. 442p. spiral bd. 67.00 *(978-0-7575-5272-4(2))* Kendall Hunt Publishing Co.

Koch, Pamela A., et al. Farm to Table & Beyond. 2008. (Illus.). 432p. *(978-0-915873-50-0(8))* National Gardening Assn., Inc., The.

Maat, H. Science Cultivating Practice: A History of Agricultural Science in the Netherlands & its Colonies, 1863-1986. 2010. (International Library of Environmental, Agricultural & Food Ethics Ser.). 258p. pap. 149.00 *(978-90-481-5864-5(8)*, 9048158648) Springer.

Namirembe, S. Design of Appropriate Agroforestry Interventions in Uganda: Agroforestry In-Service Training Manual. Agea, J. G., ed. 2007. (Illus.). 140p. pap. *(978-9970-02-677-7(1))* Fountain Pubs. Ltd. UGA. Dist: Michigan State Univ. Pr.

Parker, Rick. 2009 Annual NACTA Journal. 2010. 280p. pap. 30.50 *(978-0-557-28583-9(6))* Lulu Enterprises Inc.

Peterson's. Graduate Programs in the Physical Sciences, Mathematics, Agricultural Sciences, the Environment, & Natural Resources 2009. Oram, Fern, ed. 43rd ed. 2008. (ENG.). 792p. 54.95 *(978-0-7689-2565-4(7))* Peterson's.

Phipps, Lloyd J., et al. Handbook on Agricultural Education in Public Schools. 6th ed. 2007. (ENG.). 592p. (C). 117.95 *(978-1-4180-3993-6(4))* Delmar Cengage Learning.

AGRICULTURE—VOCATIONAL GUIDANCE

Ferguson. Careers in Focus - Agriculture. 2nd rev. ed. 2011. (Careers in Focus Ser.). 210p. (gr. 6-12). 32.95 *(978-0-8160-8036-6(4)*, Ferguson Publishing Co.) Facts On File, Inc.

AGRICULTURE—AFRICA

Abukutsa-Onyango, Mary. African Indigenous Vegetables in Urban Agriculture. Drescher, A. W. et al, eds. 2009. (ENG., Illus.). 344p. pap. 48.95 *(978-1-84407-715-1(2))* Routledge.

Amoah, Barbara Amoh. Efficacy of Some Pesticidal Plants on Two Insect Pests of Cowpe. 2011. 108p. pap. ***(978-3-8433-7400-2(7))*** Lambert Academic Publishing.

Ampadu, Richard . A. Supply Response of Food Crops in Rural Farming Communities. 2011. 92p. pap. ***(978-3-8443-9259-3(9))*** Lambert Academic Publishing.

Aredo, Mengistu Ketema. Impact of Technology on Wheat Production. 2009. 134p. pap. *(978-3-639-18389-4(4))* VDM Verlag Dr. Mueller e.K.

Ayalew, Asrat, et al. Growth & Yield of Garlic: Effects of Varieties, Inter Row & Intra Row Spacings at Dabat, North Ethiopia. 2011. 100p. pap. ***(978-3-639-31606-3(1))*** VDM Verlag Dr. Mueller e.K.

Azlabah, Samson A. Small Scale Irrigation Schemes. 2011. 88p. pap. ***(978-3-8443-1508-0(X))*** Lambert Academic Publishing.

Bekele Gemechu, Dereje. Farmers Participation in Farmers' Participatory Research. 2010. 112p. pap. *(978-3-639-26115-8(1))* VDM Verlag Dr. Mueller e.K.

Bilew, Amsalu. Effectiveness of Farmers-Research-Extension Linkage. 2011. 144p. pap. ***(978-3-8383-0455-7(1))*** Lambert Academic Publishing.

Birgegard, Lars-Erik, et al. African Agriculture & the World Bank: Development or Impoverishment? 2008. (Illus.). 75p. pap. 23.95 *(978-91-7106-608-4(X))* Nordiska Afrikainstitutet SWE. Dist: Stylus Publishing, LLC.

Boakye, Samuel. Emerging Trends in Urban Agriculture in Ghan: Security of Tenure. 2009. 228p. pap. *(978-3-639-14874-9(6))* VDM Verlag Dr. Mueller e.K.

Buchmann, Christine. Cuban Homegardens. 2010. 112p. pap. *(978-3-639-15156-5(9))* VDM Verlag Dr. Mueller e.K.

Committee on a Study of Technologies to Benefit Farmers in Africa and South Asia & National Research Council. Emerging Technologies to Benefit Farmers in Sub-Saharan Africa & South Asia. 2009. (ENG.). 292p. pap. 60.25 *(978-0-309-12494-2(8))* National Academies Pr.

Diao, Xinshen, et al. Market Opportunities for African Agriculture: A General Equilibrium Examination of Demand-Side Constraints on Agricultural Growth in East & Southern Africa. 2007 *(978-0-89629-163-8(4))* International Food Policy Research Institute.

Dinar, Ariel, et al. Climate Change & Agriculture in Africa: Impact Assessment & Adaptation Strategies. Benhin, James, ed. 2008. (ENG., Illus.). 224p. (C). 97.50 *(978-1-84407-547-8(8))* Routledge.

Diogo, Rodrigue Vivien Cao. Horizontal Nutrient Fluxes & Production Efficiencies. 2010. 128p. pap. *(978-3-639-25096-1(6))* VDM Verlag Dr. Mueller e.K.

Engels, J. M. M., et al, eds. Plant Genetic Resources of Ethiopia. 2008. (ENG.). 400p. pap. 69.00 *(978-0-521-06553-5(4))* Cambridge Univ. Pr.

Epeju, William Faustine. Productivity: Evidence from farmers & their advisers in Teso, Uganda. 2010. 344p. pap. *(978-3-639-20514-5(6))* VDM Verlag Dr. Mueller e.K.

Food Security in Africa: The Impact of Agricultural Development: Hearing Before the Subcommittee on Africa & Global Health of the Committee on Foreign Affairs, House of Representatives, One Hundred Tenth Congress, First Session, on H.R. 2003, July 18, 2007. 2007. iii, 61p. *(978-0-16-079466-7(8)*, 552-070-36451-0) United States Government Printing Office.

Fufa, Diriba & Diriba, Fufa. Quality Analysis of Farmers Chickpea Seed Sources in Ethiopia: Identification of Chickpea Seed Sources Physical,Physiological & Health Quality Analysis of Chickpea Seed in Ethiopia. 2011. 80p. pap. ***(978-3-639-31970-5(2))*** VDM Verlag Dr. Mueller e.K.

Gebre-Mariam, Yohann. Holistic Analysis of Household Decision-Making: Adoption of Agricultural Technologies & Development in Ethiopia. 2011. (ENG.). 362p. pap. 36.95 ***(978-0-7618-5641-2(2))*** Univ. Pr. of America, Inc.

Girma, Berhe & Desalegn, Chemeda. Spatio-Temporal Variability of Climate for Crop Production: Analysis & Mapping of Dry & Wet Spells for Crop Production in Some Selected Areas of Upper Awash Basin (UAB), Ethiopia. 2011. 160p. pap. ***(978-3-639-33977-2(0))*** VDM Verlag Dr. Mueller e.K.

Haggblade, Steven & Hazell, Peter B. R., eds. Successes in African Agriculture: Lessons for the Future. 2010. (ENG., Illus.). 464p. (gr. 17). 90.00 *(978-0-8018-9502-9(2))*; pap. 45.00 *(978-0-8018-9503-6(0))* Johns Hopkins Univ. Pr.

Hassan, Fekri A., ed. Droughts, Food & Culture: Ecological Change & Food Security in Africa's Later Prehistory. 2012. (ENG.). 372p. pap. 159.00 *(978-1-4419-3380-5(8)*, 1441933808) Springer.

Henson, Spencer & Jaffee, Steven, eds. Agri-Food Systems & Economic Development. 2013. (Routledge Studies in Development Economics Ser.). (ENG.). 256p. (C). 130.00 *(978-0-415-49695-7(0))* Routledge.

Homewood, Katherine. Ecology of African Pastoralist Societies. 2008. (Illus.). 312p. 90.00 *(978-0-85255-991-8(7))*; pap. 34.95 *(978-0-85255-990-1(9))* Boydell & Brewer, Ltd. GBR. (Currey, James). Dist: Boydell & Brewer, Inc.

—Ecology of African Pastoralist Societies. 2009. (Illus.). 320p. 55.00 *(978-0-8214-1840-6(8))*; (ENG., pap. 26.95 *(978-0-8214-1841-3(6))* Ohio Univ. Pr.

Huffman, Thomas N. Handbook to the Iron Age: The Archaeology of Pre-Colonial Farming Societies in Southern Africa. 2007. (Illus.). 518p. (C). 84.95 *(978-1-86914-108-0(3))* University of Kwazulu-Natal Press ZAF. Dist: International Specialized Bk. Services.

Imfeld, Al & Suter, Lotta. Elefanten in der Sahara: Agrar-Geschichten aus Afrika. 2009. (GER., Illus.). 255p. pap. *(978-3-85869-404-1(5))* Rotpunktverlag.

International Assessment of Agricultural Knowledge, Science, and Technology. Agriculture at a Crossroads: International Assessment of Agricultural Science & Technology for Development - East & South Asia & the Pacific. 2009. (ENG., Illus.). 226p. 125.00 *(978-1-59726-544-7(6))* Island Pr.

—Agriculture at a Crossroads Vol. 1: Central & West Asia & North Africa. 2009. (ENG., Illus.). 192p. 125.00 *(978-1-59726-542-3(X))*; 2nd ed. pap. 75.00 *(978-1-59726-543-0(8))* Island Pr.

—Agriculture at a Crossroads Vol. 2: East & South Asia & the Pacific. 2009. (ENG.). 226p. pap. 75.00 *(978-1-59726-545-4(4))* Island Pr.

—Agriculture at a Crossroads Vol. 5: Sub-Saharan Africa. 2009. (ENG.). 160p. pap. 75.00 *(978-1-59726-541-6(1))* Island Pr.

—Agriculture at a Crossroads Vol. V: Sub-Saharan Africa. 2nd ed. 2009. (ENG., Illus.). 160p. 125.00 *(978-1-59726-540-9(3))* Island Pr.

International Center for Soil Fertility and Agricultural Development Staff, contrib. by. Africa Fertilizer Summit Proceedings: June 9-13, 2006, Abuja, Nigeria. 2007. *(978-0-88090-159-8(4))* IFDC.

Kadyampakeni, Davie. Irrigation & Water Management Techniques for Bean Cultivation. 2011. 152p. pap. ***(978-3-8433-9146-7(7))*** Lambert Academic Publishing.

Kanyenyeh, Margaret. Best Way to Empower Resource Poor Small-Scale Women Farmers. 2010. 100p. pap. *(978-3-639-23575-3(4))* VDM Verlag Dr. Mueller e.K.

Kebede, Tadesse. Development of Wheat Stem Rust Epidemics in Ethiopia: Temporal Development of Stem Rust (Puccinia Graminis F. Sp. Tritici) & Its Effect on Grain Yield & Quality of Bread Wheat in Ethiopia. 2011. 104p. pap. ***(978-3-639-32487-7(0))*** VDM Verlag Dr. Mueller e.K.

Kinfe, Esayas, et al. Nutritional Composition of Some Capsicum Varieties Grown in Ethiopi. 2011. 76p. pap. ***(978-3-8443-0594-4(7))*** Lambert Academic Publishing.

Korsten, Lise, et al. Horticultural Chain Management for Eastern & Southern Africa: A Practical Manual, Vol. 2. 2008. (ENG.). 40p. spiral bd. 9.95 *(978-0-85092-859-4(1))* Commonwealth Secretariat GBR. Dist: Stylus Publishing, LLC.

—Horticultural Chain Management for Eastern & Southern Africa: A Theoretical Manual, Vol. 2. 2008. (ENG.). 224p. pap. 29.00 *(978-0-85092-858-7(3))* Commonwealth Secretariat GBR. Dist: Stylus Publishing, LLC.

Laven, Anna. The Risks of Inclusion: Shifts in Governance Processes & Upgrading Opportunities for Small-scale Cocoa Farmers in Ghana. 2010. 256p. pap. 39.95 *(978-94-6022-111-8(4))* Royal Tropical Institute Pr. (KIT (Koninklijk Instituut voor de Tropen) NLD. Dist: Stylus Publishing, LLC.

Lericollais, André. Sob: étude géographique d'un terroir Sérèr (Sénégal) (Atlas des structures agraires au sud du Sahara Ser.). (FRE.). 110p. 135.00 ***(978-3-11-125681-8(2))*** De Gruyter, Mouton DEU. Dist: de Gruyter, Walter GmbH & Co. KG.

Lwoga, Edda Tandi. Indigenous & Exogenous Knowledge. 2010. 636p. pap. *(978-3-639-25805-9(3))* VDM Verlag Dr. Mueller e.K.

Mangheni, Margaret Najjingo. Experiences, Innovations & Issues in Agricultural Extension in Uganda: Lessons & Prospects. 2007. (Illus.). 192p. pap. *(978-9970-02-715-6(8))* Fountain Pubs. Ltd. UGA. Dist: Michigan State Univ. Pr.

Mekbib, Sissay Bekele. Citrus Sinensis Cultivation in Ethiopia & Postharvest Biocontrol. 2009. 200p. pap. *(978-3-639-17243-0(4))* VDM Verlag Dr. Mueller e.K.

Mkandawire, Frackson L. & Mkpado, Mmaduabuchukwu, eds. Low-Input Agricultural Technologies for Sub-Saharan Africa. 2011. (Studies in sub-Saharan Africa Ser.). 120p. 35.95 *(978-3-631-60635-3(4))* Lang, Peter GmbH, Europaischer Verlag der Wissenschaften DEU. Dist: Lang, Peter.

Mogga, Lado, et al. Inheritance of Resistance to Rymv in Selected Rice Cultivars in Ugand. 2011. 104p. pap. ***(978-3-8433-8683-8(8))*** Lambert Academic Publishing.

Namirembe, S. Design of Appropriate Agroforestry Interventions in Uganda: Agroforestry In-Service Training Manual. Agea, J. G., ed. 2007. (Illus.). 140p. pap. *(978-9970-02-677-7(1))* Fountain Pubs. Ltd. UGA. Dist: Michigan State Univ. Pr.

Nederlof, Suzanne & Heemskerk, Willem, eds. Access of the Poor to Agricultural Services: The Role of Farmers' Organizations in Social Inclusion. 2007. (Bulletins of the Royal Tropical Institute Ser.). (Illus.). 160p. per. 35.00 *(978-90-6832-642-0(2))* Royal Tropical Institute Pr. (KIT (Koninklijk Instituut voor de Tropen) NLD. Dist: Stylus Publishing, LLC.

Niekerk, Alvin van, ed. Ethics in Agriculture - an African Perspective. 2010. (ENG.). viii, 167p. pap. 149.00 *(978-90-481-6761-6(2)*, 9048167612) Springer.

Nkamleu, Guy Blaise, ed. Root Causes of the Food Crisis: Technological Progress & Productivity Growth in African Agriculture. 2010. (African Political, Economic, & Security Issues Ser.). 174p. 89.00 *(978-1-60876-324-5(2))* Nova Science Pubs., Inc.

Nkansah, Andrews. Reuse of Organic Waste & Human Excreta in Kumasi, Ghan. 2011. 112p. pap. ***(978-3-8454-0547-7(2))*** Lambert Academic Publishing.

Ntsou, Bakwowi Jeshma. The Role of Agriculture to Reduce Poverty in Sub Sahara Afric. 2011. 88p. pap. ***(978-3-8454-0352-6(7))*** Lambert Academic Publishing.

Ouma, George & Gottwald, Franz-Theo, eds. Agrarian Science for Sustainable Resource Management in Sub-Saharan Africa. 2009. (Studies in sub-Saharan Africa Ser.). 130p. pap. 39.95 *(978-3-631-58524-5(1))* Lang, Peter GmbH, Europaischer Verlag der Wissenschaften DEU. Dist: Lang, Peter.

Oweis, T., et al, eds. Rainfed Agriculture: Unlocking the Potential. 2009. (Comprehensive Assessment of Water Management in Agriculture Ser.). (Illus.). 328p. 160.00 *(978-1-84593-389-0(3))* CABI GBR. Dist: Stylus Publishing, LLC.

Owusu-Sekyere, Joshua. Water Table Control for Rice Production in Ghan. 2011. 256p. pap. ***(978-3-8443-8595-3(9))*** Lambert Academic Publishing.

Pali, Pamela. The Profitability of Integrated Nutrient Management Practices. 2008. 68p. pap. *(978-3-639-09148-9(5))* VDM Verlag Dr. Mueller e.K.

Peppelenbos, Lucian, ed. Trading Up. 2008. 298p. (C). pap. 39.95 *(978-90-6832-699-4(6))* Royal Tropical Institute Pr. (KIT (Koninklijk Instituut voor de Tropen) NLD. Dist: Stylus Publishing, LLC.

Powell, Larkin. Farming with Wildlife. 2010. 50p. pap. 19.95 *(978-0-557-64898-6(X))* Lulu Enterprises Inc.

Prabhakar, Akhilesh Chandra. Agricultural Transformation & Rural Development. 2011. 368p. pap. ***(978-3-8443-9951-6(8))*** Lambert Academic Publishing.

Prain, Gordon, et al, eds. African Urban Harvest: Agriculture in the Cities of Cameroon, Kenya & Uganda. 2010. (ENG., Illus.). xvi, 300p. 139.00 *(978-1-4419-6249-2(2)*, 1441962492) Springer.

Prain, Gordon, et al. African Urban Harvest: Agriculture in the Cities of Cameroon, Kenya & Uganda. 2010. (Illus.). xx, 322p. E-Book ***(978-1-4419-6250-8(6))*** Springer.

—African Urban Harvest: Agriculture in the Cities of Cameroon, Kenya & Uganda. 2010. (Illus.). xx, 322p. pap. ***(978-1-4419-6571-4(8))*** Springer Singapore Pte. Ltd.

Remy, Gérard. Yobri: Étude Géographique du Terroir d'Un Village Gourmantché de Haute-Volta. (Atlas des structures agraires au sud du Sahara Ser.). (FRE., Illus.). 99p. 210.00 ***(978-3-11-193089-6(4))*** De Gruyter, Mouton DEU. Dist: de Gruyter, Walter GmbH & Co. KG.

Remy, Gerard. Yobri: étude géographique du terroir d'un village gourmantché de Haute-Volta. (Atlas des structures agraires au sud du Sahara Ser.). (FRE.). 99p. 135.00 ***(978-3-11-104902-1(7))*** De Gruyter, Mouton DEU. Dist: de Gruyter, Walter GmbH & Co. KG.

Saheb, Azad Ismail & Al-Ablani, Salem. Aquaculture in the Middle East & North Africa: Status & Research Needs. 2011. *(978-1-61209-834-0(7))* Nova Science Pubs., Inc.

Sarris, Alexander & Morrison, Jamie, eds. Food Security in Africa: Market & Trade Policy for Staple Foods in Eastern & Southern Africa. 2010. (Illus.). 448p. 155.00 *(978-1-84844-851-3(1))* Elgar, Edward Publishing, Inc.

Srivastava, Amit Kumar. Management of Yam Production. 2010. 104p. pap. *(978-3-639-13878-8(3))* VDM Verlag Dr. Mueller e.K.

Sunderland, David, ed. Economic Development of Africa, 1880-1939. 5 vols. 2011. (Britain & Africa Ser.). (ENG.). 2272p. 795.00 *(978-1-84893-063-6(1))* Pickering & Chatto Pubs., Ltd. GBR. Dist: Ashgate Publishing Co.

Swindell, Kenneth & Jeng, Alieu. Migrants, Credit & Climate: The Gambian Groundnut Trade, 1834-1934. 2006. (African Social Studies Ser.: Vol. 12). (Illus.). 250p. (C). *(978-90-04-14059-2(X))* BRILL.

Tenywa, Moses & Kimoone, George. A Training Module. 2011. 60p. pap. ***(978-3-8443-1738-1(4))*** Lambert Academic Publishing.

Tessema Zewdu Kelkay. Improved Pasture Production in Developing Countries: The Case of Ethiopia, Eastern Africa. 2010. 235.00 *(978-1-61761-009-7(7))* Nova Science Pubs., Inc.

Teye, Ernest. Post-Harvest of Sweet Potatoes. 2011. 112p. pap. ***(978-3-8454-1974-9(1))*** Lambert Academic Publishing.

United Nations University Staff. Land Policy & Agriculture in Eastern & Southern Africa: Selected Papers Presented at a Workshop Held in Gaborone, Botswana, 14-19 February 1982. (Illus.). 150p. 20.00 *(978-92-808-0604-5(1)*, E.86.III.A.6) United Nations Univ. Pr. JPN. Dist: United Nations Pubns.

van der Veen, Marijke, ed. The Exploitation of Plant Resources in Ancient Africa. 2010. (ENG.). 284p. pap. 189.00 *(978-1-4419-3316-4(6)*, 1441933166) Springer.

Wanjekeche Katiambo, Sellah. Impact of Improved Climbing Beans. 2011. 92p. pap. ***(978-3-8443-9783-3(3))*** Lambert Academic Publishing.

Watson, Elizabeth E. Living Terraces in Ethiopia: Konso Landscape, Culture & Development. 2009. (Eastern Africa Ser.). (Illus.). 256p. 80.00 *(978-1-84701-005-6(9)*, Currey, James) Boydell & Brewer, Ltd. GBR. Dist: Boydell & Brewer, Inc.

Wood, Adrian, et al. Wetland Management & Sustainable Livelihoods in Africa. 2012. (ENG.). 224p. 140.00 ***(978-1-84971-411-2(8))***; pap. 49.95 ***(978-1-84971-412-9(6))*** Earthscan LLC.

World Bank. Organization & Performance of Cotton Sectors in Africa: Learning from Reform Experience. Tschirley, David et al, eds. 2009. (Agriculture & Rural Development Ser.). (ENG., Illus.). 268p. pap. 24.95 *(978-0-8213-7770-3(1)*, 9780821377703) World Bank Pubns.

Yamano, Takashi, et al, eds. Emerging Development of Agriculture in East Africa: Markets, Soil, & Innovations. 2011. (ENG., Illus.). xviii, 214p. 179.00 *(978-94-007-1200-3(6)*, 9400712006) Springer.

Yamoah, Charles, et al. Effects of Climate Change on Cropping Systems. 2011. 60p. pap. ***(978-3-8443-9104-6(3))*** Lambert Academic Publishing.

Yao, Wei. Agricultural Commodity Prices & Household Welfare in Ghan. 2008. 56p. pap. *(978-3-639-08446-7(2))* VDM Verlag Dr. Mueller e.K.

Yimam Ahmed, Mulat. Effects of Sowing Date, Seeding Rate & Varieties on Yield of Rice. 2011. 84p. pap. ***(978-3-8433-8925-9(X))*** Lambert Academic Publishing.

Zimmerman, Andrew. Alabama in Africa: Booker T. Washington, the German Empire, & the Globalization of the New South. 2012. (America in the World

Ser.). (ENG., Illus.). 416p. (C). pap. 24.95 (978-0-691-15586-9(0)) Princeton Univ. Pr.

AGRICULTURE—ALASKA

Grant, Dona. Today's Homestead: Volume I. 2008. 256p. pap. 14.95 (978-1-60264-224-9(9)) Virtualbookworm.com Publishing, Inc.

—Today's Homestead Volume II. 2008. 376p. pap. 15.95 (978-1-60264-273-7(7)) Virtualbookworm.com Publishing, Inc.

Stimple, Bert. Fun on the Farm in Alask. 2011. 174p. 42.95 (978-1-258-06274-3(7)) Literary Licensing, LLC.

AGRICULTURE—AMERICA

Jansen, Hans G. P. Rural Development Policies & Sustainable Land Use in the Hillside Areas of Honduras: A Quantitative Livelihoods Approach. 2006. (Illus.). xi, 103p. (978-0-89629-156-0(1)) International Food Policy Research Institute.

Knight, Frederick. Working the Diaspora: The Impact of African Labor on the Anglo-American World, 1650-1850. 2010. (ENG., Illus.). 240p. 48.00 (978-0-8147-4818-3(X)) New York Univ. Pr.

Tueth, Matthew. Sustainability Factors in Pre-Columbian Societies of the Americas. 2009. 56p. pap. (978-3-639-16017-8(7)) VDM Verlag Dr. Mueller e.K.

AGRICULTURE—ARGENTINA

Hang, Susana, et al. Integral Study of Atrazine & N Leaching in Argentinean Soils. 2011. 68p. pap. (978-3-8443-3047-2(X)) Lambert Academic Publishing.

Peluffo, Matias. Adopting New Zealand Dairy Farm Principles in Argentina. 2008. 256p. pap. (978-3-639-02588-0(1)) VDM Verlag Dr. Mueller e.K.

Rodrí, et al. The Constitution of the Field of Rural Development. 2010. 352p. pap. (978-3-8383-4474-4(X)) Lambert Academic Publishing.

AGRICULTURE—ASIA

Alexander, Kim. Agricultural Change in Lao Pdr. 2009. 288p. pap. (978-3-639-14253-2(5)) VDM Verlag Dr. Mueller e.K.

Aung, Lwin Lwin. The Farmer Field School Approach to Legume Production in Myanmar. 2011. 244p. pap. (978-3-8383-7007-1(4)) Lambert Academic Publishing.

Barker, Graeme & Janowski, Monica, eds. Why Cultivate? Anthropological & Archaeological Approaches to Foraging-Farming Transitions in Southeast Asia. 2011. (McDonald Institute Monographs). (ENG., Illus.). 142p. (C). 70.00 (978-1-902937-58-8(9)) McDonald Institute for Archaeolgoical Research.

Bichsel, Christine. Conflict Transformation in Central Asia: Irrigation Disputes in the Ferghana Valley. 2009. (Central Asian Studies). (Illus.). 192p. 150.00 (978-0-415-46725-4(X)) Routledge.

Boomgaard, Peter. Smallholders & Stockbreeders: Histories of Foodcrop & Livestock Farming in Southeast Asia. Henley, David, ed. 2010. (Verhandelingen Van Het Koninklijk Instituut Voor Taal-, Land Ser.). (Illus.). 352p. pap. 38.00 (978-90-6718-225-6(7)) KITLV Pr. NLD. Dist: Univ. of Hawaii Pr.

Bretan, Andreea. Die Syrische Steppe: Mobile Viehzucht, internationale Entwicklungshilfe und globale Markte. 2010. (Nomaden und Sesshafte Ser.). (GER., Illus.). 208p. (C). 115.00 (978-3-89500-642-5(4)) Reichert, Ludwig Dr. DEU. Dist: Brown, David Bk. Co., The.

Committee on a Study of Technologies to Benefit Farmers in Africa and South Asia & National Research Council. Emerging Technologies to Benefit Farmers in Sub-Saharan Africa & South Asia. 2009. (ENG.). 292p. pap. 60.25 (978-0-309-12494-2(8)) National Academies Pr.

Cunningham, Sally. Asian Vegetables. 2010. (ENG., Illus.). 132p. pap. 24.95 (978-1-899233-16-8(4)) Eco-Logic Bks. GBR. Dist: Chelsea Green Publishing.

De Silva, Sena S. & Davy, F. Brian, eds. Success Stories in Asian Aquaculture. 2009. (ENG., Illus.). xiv, 214p. 129.00 (978-90-481-3085-6(9), 9048130859) Springer.

Dumas-Johansen, Marc Kristof. Effect of the Sri. 2011. 96p. pap. (978-3-8443-9175-6(4)) Lambert Academic Publishing.

Guchgeldiev, Oleg. Cotton Production in Turkmenistan. 2011. 96p. pap. (978-3-8443-8957-9(1)) Lambert Academic Publishing.

Hargrove, Tom. A Dragon Lives Forever: War & Rice in Vietnam's Mekong Delta. 2008. (Williams-Ford Texas A&M University Military History Ser.). (ENG.). 488p. pap. 23.95 (978-1-60344-060-8(7)) Texas A&M Univ. Pr.

Harris, David R. Origins of Agriculture in Western Central Asia: An Environmental-Archaeological Study. 2010. (Illus.). 328p. (C). 65.00 (978-1-934536-16-2(4), Univ. of Pennsylvania Museum of Archaeology & Anthropology) Univ. Museum Pubns.

Khanpara, A. V. Eco-Friendly Management of H Armigera Infesting Pigeonpe. 2011. 104p. pap. (978-3-8443-2198-2(5)) Lambert Academic Publishing.

Koirala, Madan, et al. Livelihood Linked Environmental Determinants in Himalaya Landscape. 2011. 156p. pap. (978-3-8433-8296-0(4)) Lambert Academic Publishing.

Mirza, M. Monirul Qader, et al, eds. Flood Problem & Management in South Asia. 2010. 224p. pap. 108.00 (978-90-481-6197-3(5), 9048161975) Springer.

Mukherji, Aditi. Groundwater Governance in the Indo-Gangetic & Yellow River Basins: Realities & Challenges. Sharma, Bharat R. et al, eds. 2009. (IAH - Selected Papers on Hydrogeology Ser.). (ENG., Illus.). 328p. 113.95 (978-0-415-46580-9(X), CRC Press) Taylor & Francis Group GBR. Dist: Taylor & Francis Group.

Nath, Susanta. Ecology of a Pest Grasshopper. 2011. 68p. pap. (978-3-8383-6042-3(7)) Lambert Academic Publishing.

Oweis, T., et al, eds. Rainfed Agriculture: Unlocking the Potential. 2009. (Comprehensive Assessment of Water Management in Agriculture Ser.). (Illus.). 328p. 160.00 (978-1-84593-389-0(3)) CABI GBR. Dist: Stylus Publishing, LLC.

Rajeswari, Kanniah. Breeders vs Farmers: The Contest for Rights over Plant Varieties in Selected Asian Countries. 2011. 340p. pap. (978-3-639-33425-8(6)) VDM Verlag Dr. Mueller e.K.

Ray, Ramesh C. & R. Swain, Manas. Agricultural & Biotechnological Potential of Bacillus Subtilis. 2011. 212p. pap. (978-3-8443-1189-1(0)) Lambert Academic Publishing.

Subedi, Sushil & Rosyara, Umesh. Participatory Varietal Selection in Upland Rice in Nepal. 2011. 68p. pap. (978-3-8454-0389-2(6)) Lambert Academic Publishing.

Thompson, Thomas P. The Social Performance of an Innovative Method of Rice Fertilization in Southern Asia. 2007. (978-0-88090-160-4(8)) IFDC.

United Nations Staff. Sustainable Agriculture & Food Security in Asia & the Pacific. 2009. (ENG.). 132p. pap. 56.00 (978-92-1-120578-7(6)) United Nations Pubns.

Volodya, Sodgerel. Mongolian Agriculture. 2011. 84p. pap. (978-3-8433-7817-8(7)) Lambert Academic Publishing.

AGRICULTURE—AUSTRALIA

Dawborn, Kerry & Smith, Caroline, eds. Permaculture Pioneers: Stories from the New Frontier. 2011. (ENG.). 384p. pap. 34.95 (978-0-9750786-2-4(3)) Holmgren Design Services AUS. Dist: Chelsea Green Publishing.

Franklin, Richard. Epidemiology of Farm Injuries in New South Wales, Australi. 2008. 396p. pap. (978-3-639-06492-6(5)) VDM Verlag Dr. Mueller e.K.

Gerritsen, Rupert. Australia & the Origins of Agriculture. 2008. (Bar S Ser.). (Illus.). 205p. (C). 92.50 (978-1-4073-0354-3(6)) British Archaeological Reports Ltd. GBR. Dist: Brown, David Bk. Co., The.

Henzell, Ted. Australian Agriculture: Its History & Challenges. 2007. 320p. pap. 70.00 (978-0-643-99342-6(8)) CSIRO Publishing AUS. Dist: Stylus Publishing, LLC.

Hitchcock, Maria. Correas: Australian Plants for Waterwise Gardens. 2010. (Illus.). 176p. pap. 35.00 (978-1-877058-92-9(0)) Rosenberg Publishing Pty, Ltd. AUS. Dist: International Specialized Bk. Services.

Horne, Paul & Page, Jessica. Integrated Pest Management for Crops & Pastures. 2008. (Landlinks Press Ser.). 200p. pap. 49.95 (978-0-643-09257-0(9)) CSIRO Publishing AUS. Dist: Stylus Publishing, LLC.

Lefroy, Ted, et al, eds. Biodiversity: Integrating Conservation & Production. 2009. (Illus.). 270p. pap. 70.00 (978-0-643-09458-1(X)) CSIRO Publishing AUS. Dist: Stylus Publishing, LLC.

Nukmal, Nismah. Bio-Ecology of Psyllyds on Eucalyptus. 2011. 176p. pap. (978-3-8443-3431-9(9)) Lambert Academic Publishing.

Quick, Graeme R. International Harvester: Tractors & Equipment in Australia & New Zealand. 2009. (Illus.). 184p. 49.95 (978-1-877058-75-2(0)) Rosenberg Publishing Pty, Ltd. AUS. Dist: International Specialized Bk. Services.

—Remarkable Australian Farm Machines. 2007. (Illus.). 160p. pap. 29.95 (978-1-877058-58-5(0)) Rosenberg Publishing Pty, Ltd. AUS. Dist: International Specialized Bk. Services.

Rencken, Ingrid. Uncultivated Vegetation: A source of insect Predators? 2010. 160p. pap. (978-3-8383-0208-9(7)) Lambert Academic Publishing.

AGRICULTURE—BANGLADESH

Amina, Pervin, et al. Situation of Primary Education in Tea Garden: A Study Conducted in Malnicherra Tea Estate of Sylhet, Bangladesh. 2011. 64p. pap. (978-3-639-33314-5(4)) VDM Verlag Dr. Mueller e.K.

Bhuyan, M. H. M. Borhannuddin. Low Cost Oyster Mushroom Production. 2011. 136p. pap. (978-3-8454-0057-0(9)) Lambert Academic Publishing.

Ishtiaque, Asif. Agricultural Land Utilization. 2011. 56p. pap. (978-3-8454-1858-2(3)) Lambert Academic Publishing.

Kabir, Dewan Muhammad Humayun. Agrobiodiversity & Farmers' Rights. 2011. 444p. pap. (978-3-8443-3262-9(6)) Lambert Academic Publishing.

Mostofa, Mohammad. Climate Change & Cost-Benefit of T Aman Rice in Bangladesh. 2011. 72p. pap. (978-3-8454-0087-7(0)) Lambert Academic Publishing.

Rahman, Syed. Cost Benefit & Livelihood Impacts of Agroforestry in Bangladesh. 2011. 172p. pap. (978-3-8433-5484-4(7)) Lambert Academic Publishing.

Salles, J. F. & Bovagne, M., eds. Pundranagara, cite antique du Bengale. Fouilles de Mahasthan: Rapport Preliminaire 1993-1999. 2007. (Indicopleustoi Ser.). (Illus.). 436p. (C). 136.00 (978-2-503-99108-5(4)) Brepols Pubs. BEL. Dist: Brown, David Bk. Co., The.

Sarder, Jalal Uddin. Current Fertility Status in Cattle of Mini-Dairy Farms: Reproductive & Productive Performance in Cows Due to Some Factors at Private Mini-Dairy Farms of Natore District in Bangladesh. 2011. 72p. pap. (978-3-639-32198-2(7)) VDM Verlag Dr. Mueller e.K.

Sultana, Naz Afrin. Gdp of Bangladesh: Inter dependency with relevant Variables. 2011. 64p. pap. (978-3-8454-0086-0(2)) Lambert Academic Publishing.

Sumon, Abu. Flash Flood & Adaptive Crop Agriculture in North-Eastern Bangladesh. 2010. 172p. pap. (978-3-639-27183-6(1)) VDM Verlag Dr. Mueller e.K.

Than, Popo. Survey of Plant Parasitic Nematodes on Some Economic Crops in Myanmar. 2010. 92p. pap. (978-3-639-24012-2(X)) VDM Verlag Dr. Mueller e.K.

Zaman, Mohammad Ashraf Uz, et al. Pesticides in Bangladesh. 2011. 92p. pap. (978-3-8454-1498-0(7)) Lambert Academic Publishing.

AGRICULTURE—BRAZIL

Agra FNP Research. Agriculture in Brazil Yearbook 2010: Brazil Agrianual. 16th ed. 2011. 237p. (C). cd-rom 715.00 (978-0-415-66767-8(4), CRC Press) Taylor & Francis Group GBR. Dist: Taylor & Francis Group.

—Agriculture in Brazil Yearbook 2011: Brazil Agrianual. 17th ed. 2011. (ENG.). 237p. (C). cd-rom 715.00 (978-0-415-66768-5(2), CRC Press) Taylor & Francis Group GBR. Dist: Taylor & Francis Group.

McCreery, David. Frontier Goias, 1822-1889. 2006. (ENG., Illus.). 312p. 60.00 (978-0-8047-5179-7(X)) Stanford Univ. Pr.

Rosalino, Luís M. & Gheler-Costa, Carla. Middle-Sized Carnivores in Agricultural Landscapes. 2011. (978-1-61122-033-9(5)) Nova Science Pubs., Inc.

Sara, Brune. The Brazilian Biodiesel Program (PNPB) & Social Inclusion: A Multi-Level Study of Family Farmers' Participation in the Brazilian Biodiesel Program in the State of Piaui, Brazil. 2011. 112p. pap. (978-3-639-32545-4(1)) VDM Verlag Dr. Mueller e.K.

AGRICULTURE—CANADA

Bennett, John W. & Bennett, John. Northern Plainsmen: Adaptive Strategy & Agrarian Life. 2007. (ENG., Illus.). 368p. pap. 34.95 (978-0-202-30964-4(9)) Transaction Pubs.

Caird, James. Prairie Farming in America. 2009. 94p. pap. (978-0-217-74051-7(0)) Books LLC.

—Prairie Farming in America. 2006. 136p. per. 16.99 (978-1-4255-0955-2(X)) MPublishing.

Clarke, John. The Ordinary People of Essex: Environment, Culture, & Economy on the Frontier of Upper Canada. (Carleton Library Ser.). (ENG.). 776p. (C). 2011. pap. (978-0-7735-3777-4(5)) 2010. (978-0-7735-3674-6(4)) McGill-Queen's Univ. Pr.

Culver, Keith & Castle, David, eds. Aquaculture, Innovation & Social Transformation. 2010. (International Library of Environmental, Agricultural & Food Ethics Ser.). xii, 348p. pap. 229.00 (978-90-481-8002-8(3), 9048180023) Springer.

Dale-Burnett, Lisa Lynne. Saskatchewan Agriculture: Lives Past & Present. 2006. (Trade Books based in Scholorship(TBS) Ser.). (ENG., Illus.). 205p. pap. 19.95 (978-0-88977-169-7(3)) Canadian Plains Research Ctr. CAN. Dist: Univ. of Toronto Pr.

Filson, Glen, et al, eds. Agriculture & Environmental Security in Southern Ontario's Watersheds. 2010. (Agriculture Issues & Policies Ser.). (Illus.). xiii, 209p. 43.00 (978-1-61668-156-2(X)) Nova Science Pubs., Inc.

Francis, Charles, ed. Organic Farming: The Ecological System. 2009. (Agronomy Ser.: 54). lib. bdg. 70.00 (978-0-89118-173-6(3)) ASA-CSSA-SSSA.

Gardner, Frank D. Traditional American Farming Techniques. 2nd rev. ed. 2007. (Traditional Ser.). (ENG., Illus.). 1088p. per. 29.95 (978-1-59921-079-7(7), Lyons Pr.) Globe Pequot Pr., The.

Hurt, R. Douglas. The Big Empty: The Great Plains in the Twentieth Century. 2011. (Modern American West Ser.). (ENG., Illus.). 344p. 65.00 (978-0-8165-2970-4(1)); pap. 29.95 (978-0-8165-2972-8(8)) Univ. of Arizona Pr.

Johnston, Jas. F. W. (James Finlay Weir). Notes on North America, Agricultural, Economical, & Social. 2006. 436p. pap. 26.99 (978-1-4255-4719-6(2)); 528p. per. 29.99 (978-1-4255-5806-2(2)) MPublishing.

Marchildon, Gregory, ed. Agricultural History: History of the Prairie West. 2011. (Hpws Ser.). (ENG.). 432p. 59.95 (978-0-88977-237-3(1)) Canadian Plains Research Ctr. CAN. Dist: Univ. of Toronto Pr.

Samson, Daniel. The Spirit of Industry & Improvement: Liberal Government & Rural-Industrial Society, Nova Scotia, 1790-1862. 2008. (ENG., Illus.). 448p. (C). (978-0-7735-3353-0(2)) McGill-Queen's Univ. Pr.

Samson, Daniel & Samson, Danny. The Spirit of Industry & Improvement: Liberal Government & Rural-Industrial Society, Nova Scotia, 1790-1862. 2008. (ENG., Illus.). 448p. (C). pap. (978-0-7735-3354-7(0)) McGill-Queen's Univ. Pr.

Schryer, Frans. Farming in a Global Economy: A Case Study of Dutch Immigrant Farmers in Canada. 2006. (International Studies in Sociology & Social Anthropology Ser.: Vol. 101). (Illus.). 310p. pap. (978-90-04-15170-3(2)) BRILL.

Shirreff, Patrick. Shirreff's Tour Through North America. 2007. (Travel in America Ser.). (ENG.). 492p. 49.95 (978-1-4290-0174-8(7)) Applewood Bks.

—Shirreff's Tour Through North America: Together with a Comprehensive View of the Canadas & United States, as Adapted for Agricultural Emigration. 2007. (Travel in America Ser.). 492p. per. 24.95 (978-1-4290-0175-5(5)) Applewood Bks.

Spahr, David L. Edible & Medicinal Mushrooms of New England & Eastern Canada. 2009. (ENG., Illus.). 248p. pap. 19.95 (978-1-55643-795-3(1)) North Atlantic Bks.

Wilson, Catharine Anne. Tenants in Time: Family Strategies, Land, & Liberalism in Upper Canada, 1799-1871. 2009. (ENG.). 384p. (C). pap. (978-0-7735-3523-7(3)) McGill-Queen's Univ. Pr.

Wood, J. David. Places of Last Resort: The Expansion of the Farm Frontier into the Boreal Forest in Canada, C. 1910-1940. 2006. (ENG., Illus.). 264p. (C). per. (978-0-7735-3097-3(5)) McGill-Queen's Univ. Pr.

AGRICULTURE—CHINA

Benedict, Carol. Golden-Silk Smoke: A History of Tobacco in China, 1550-2010. 2011. (ENG., Illus.). 309p. 49.95 (978-0-520-26277-5(8)) Univ. of California Pr.

Bennett, Jeff, et al, eds. Environmental Protection in China: Land-Use Management. 2008. (Illus.). 240p. (C). 119.00 (978-1-84720-589-6(5)) Elgar, Edward Publishing, Inc.

Chen, Chunlai & Duncan, Ron, eds. Agriculture & Food Security in China: What Effect WTO Accession & Regional Trade Agreements? 2008. 512p. pap. (978-0-7315-3817-1(X)) Asia Pacific Pr.

Devine, Mark T. Agricultural Trade in China. 2012. (978-1-62100-602-2(6)) Nova Science Pubs., Inc.

Fang, Jian. Nan Song Nong Ye Shi. 2010. (CHI.). 40p. (978-7-01-008450-3(5)) People's Publishing Hse., The.

Göbel, Christian. The Politics of Rural Reform in China: State Policy & Village Predicament in the Early 2000s. 2010. (Chinese Worlds Ser.). (ENG., Illus.). 240p. (C). 130.00 (978-0-415-55935-5(9), Routledge) Taylor & Francis Group GBR. Dist: Taylor & Francis Group.

Karplus, Valerie J. Agricultural Biotechnology in China: Origins & Prospects. 2007. (Illus.). 165p. 109.00 (978-0-387-71138-6(4)) Springer.

King, F. H. Farmers of Forty Centuries: Permanent Organic Farming in China, Korea, & Japan. 2011. 452p. (978-1-84902-406-8(5)) Benediction Classics.

King, Peter. Farmers of Forty Centuries. 2008. (Illus.). 380p. (C). 110.00 (978-1-905246-80-9(3)) Univ. of Hawaii Pr.

Lee, Mabel P. Economic History of China. (Columbia University, Studies in the Social Sciences: No. 225). reprint ed. 39.50 (978-0-404-51225-5(9)) AMS Pr., Inc.

Seefeld, Linda. Rural Women's Use & High Regard of Tsamp. 2008. 120p. pap. (978-3-639-04145-3(3)) VDM Verlag Dr. Mueller e.K.

Squires, Victor. Towards Sustainable Use of Rangelands in North-West China. Squires, Victor et al, eds. 2010. (ENG., Illus.). xxxi, 353p. 189.00 (978-90-481-9621-0(3), 9048196213) Springer.

Wang, Lihua. Zhongguo Nong Ye Tong Shi. 2009. (CHI., Illus.). 11p. (978-7-109-13995-4(6)) Agricultural Publishing Hse.

Wang, Wei. Zhongguo Nong Cun Jin Rong Fu Wu Ti Xi Xie Tiao Fa Zhan Yan Jiu: Zhongguo Nongcun Jinrong Fuwu Tixi Xietiao Fazhan Yanjiu. 2010. (CHI., Illus.). (978-7-207-08527-6(3)) Heilongjiang People's Publishing Hse.

Zhao, Qiguo & Huang, Jikun, eds. Agricultural Science & Technology in China: A Roadmap To 2050: A Roadmap To 2050. 2011. (ENG., Illus.). 180p. pap. 99.00 (978-3-642-19127-5(4), 3642191274) Springer.

Zhao, Yuepeng. China's Rural Financial System: Households' Demand for Credit & Recent Reforms. 2010. (Routledge Studies on the Chinese Economy Ser.). (ENG., Illus.). 192p. (C). 140.00 (978-0-415-54793-2(8)) Routledge.

AGRICULTURE—CONGO (DEMOCRATIC REPUBLIC)

Kavatsurwa, Muyisa. Organosulfur Pesticide Residues in Selected Vegetables of Bukavu, Drc. 2011. 100p. pap. (978-3-8443-9495-5(8)) Lambert Academic Publishing.

AGRICULTURE—COSTA RICA

Sick, Deborah. Farmers of the Golden Bean: Costa Rican Households, Global Coffee, & Fair Trade. 2007. (Illus.). 220p. per. 22.00 (978-0-87580-617-4(1)) Northern Illinois Univ. Pr.

AGRICULTURE—DENMARK

Bogetoft. Cooperatives & Payment Schemes Lessons from Theory & Examples from Danish Agriculture. 2007. (Illus.). 245p. pap. 48.00 (978-87-630-0195-3(0)) Copenhagen Business Schl. Pr. DNK. Dist: International Specialized Bk. Services.

Haggard, H. Rider. Rural Denmark & Its Lessons. 2009. 380p. 26.99 (978-1-103-04707-9(8)); pap. 20.99 (978-1-103-04704-8(3)) BiblioBazaar.

AGRICULTURE—DEVELOPING COUNTRIES

Amsel, Louis & Hirsch, Lena, eds. Food Science & Security. 2009. 98.00 (978-1-60692-977-3(1)) Nova Science Pubs., Inc.

Andersen, Regine. Governing Agrobiodiversity: Plant Genetics & Developing Countries. 2008. (Global Environmental Governance Ser.). (Illus.). 442p. 134.95 (978-0-7546-4741-6(2)) Ashgate Publishing Co.

Angelsen, Arild, et al. Measuring Livelihoods & Environmental Dependence: Methods for Research & Fieldwork. Smith Olsen, Carsten, ed. 2011. (ENG., Illus.). 288p. pap. 49.95 (978-1-84971-133-3(X)) Routledge.

Brenner, Y. S. Agriculture & the Economic Development of Low Income Countries. (ENG.). 254p. 210.00 (978-3-11-177256-1(X)) De Gruyter, Mouton DEU. Dist: de Gruyter, Walter GmbH & Co. KG.

Chandrashekar, Dr. H. M., et al. Quality Management. 2011. 208p. pap. (978-3-8433-8080-5(5)) Lambert Academic Publishing.

Coles, Christopher & Mitchell, Jonathan, eds. Markets & Rural Poverty: Upgrading in Value Chains. 2011. (ENG., Illus.). 292p. 84.95 (978-1-84971-313-9(8)) Routledge.

George, Raymond A. T. Tropical Vegetable Production. 2011. (Illus.). 236p. 125.00 (978-1-84593-753-9(8)) CABI GBR. Dist: Stylus Publishing, LLC.

Girma, Adugna. The Role of Faults & Fractures on Groundwater Occurrence & Flow. 2010. 140p. pap. (978-3-639-24339-0(0)) VDM Verlag Dr. Mueller e.K.

Gudrun, Kochendorfer-Lucius & Boris, Pleskovic, eds. Agriculture & Development. 2008. (Berlin Workshop Ser.). (ENG.). 244p. pap. 30.00 (978-0-8213-7127-5(4), 9780821371275) World Bank Pubns.

Haan, Leo de, et al, contrib. by. Looking at Maps in the Dark: Directions for Geographical Research in Land Management & Sustainable Development in Rural & Urban Environments of the Third World. (Illus.). 165p. (978-90-6809-261-5(8)) Koninklijk Nederlands Aardrijkskundig Genootschap.

International Trade Centre. Export Promotion & the WTO: A Brief Guide. 2010. (ENG.). 52p. pap. 50.00 (978-92-9137-372-7(9)) United Nations Pubns.

Kai, Lea. Agricultural Residue Management in Developing Countries. 2009. (Illus.). 120p. pap. (978-3-639-14566-3(6)) VDM Verlag Dr. Mueller e.K.

Kamal, Javed Ahmad & Siddiqui, Badar Naseem. Devolution in Agriculture Extension. 2011. 124p. pap. (978-3-8454-0990-0(8)) Lambert Academic Publishing.

Lund, Jens. Measuring Livelihoods & Environmental Dependence: Methods for Research & Fieldwork. Angelsen, Arild et al, eds. 2011. (ENG., Illus.). 288p. 140.00 *(978-1-84971-132-6(1))* Routledge.

Lutaladio, NeBambi, et al. Sustainable Potato Production: Guidelines for Developing Countries. 2010. (Illus.). 91p. pap. *(978-92-5-106409-2(1))* Food & Agriculture Organization of the United Nations.

Mahul, Olivier & Stutley, Charles J. Government Support to Agricultural Insurance: Challenges & Options for Developing Countries. 2010. (ENG., Illus.). 224p. pap. 30.00 *(978-0-8213-8217-2(9)*, 9780821382172) World Bank Pubns.

Mitchell, Jonathan & Coles, Christopher. Markets & Rural Poverty. 2011. (ENG., Illus.). 292p. pap. 84.95 ***(978-0-415-69412-4(4))*** Routledge.

Okyere, W. Asenso. Interactions Between Health & Farm-Labor Productivity. 2011. (Illus.). viii, 24p. pap. ***(978-0-89629-542-1(7))*** International Food Policy Research Institute.

Otsuka, Keijiro & Kalirajan, Kaliappa, eds. Agriculture in Developing Countries: Technology Issues. 2008. (Illus.). 172p. (C). 39.95 *(978-0-7619-3662-6(9)*, B36626C) SAGE Pubns., Inc.

Pandey, Santosh Raj. Sustainable Use of Reclaimed Water for Irrigation Purposes. 2011. 200p. pap. ***(978-3-8443-1050-4(9))*** Lambert Academic Publishing.

Promoting Global Food Security: Next Steps for Congress & the Administration: Hearing Before the Committee on Foreign Relations, United States Senate, One Hundred Eleventh Congress, Second Session, April 22, 2010. 2011. iii, 71p. ***(978-0-16-088017-9(3)***, 552-070-42441-5) United States Government Printing Office.

Redwood, Mark, ed. Agriculture in Urban Planning: Generating Livelihoods & Food Security. 2008. (ENG., Illus.). 272p. 127.00 *(978-1-84407-668-0(7))* Routledge.

Roetter, Reimund, et al, eds. Science for Agriculture & Rural Development in Low-Income Countries. 2008. (ENG., Illus.). xxvi, 222p. pap. 99.00 *(978-1-4020-9285-5(7)*, 1402092857) Springer.

Tauqir, Nasir. Silage; a Vital Solution to Fodder Scarcity in Developing Countries. 2009. 184p. pap. *(978-3-639-19877-5(8))* VDM Verlag Dr. Mueller e.K.

Tessema, Yemataye & Lema(), Tesfaye. Analysis of Livelihood Strategy & Food Security. 2010. 124p. pap. *(978-3-8383-4882-7(6))* Lambert Academic Publishing.

Tessema Zewdu Kelkay. Improved Pasture Production in Developing Countries: The Case of Ethiopia, Eastern Africa. 2010. 235.00 *(978-1-61761-009-7(7))* Nova Science Pubs., Inc.

van der Fliert, Elske, et al. Integrated Assessment of Agricultural Sustainability: Exploring the Use of Models in Stakeholder Processes. 2013. (International Journal Agricultural Sustainability Ser.). (ENG.). 90p. 99.95 *(978-1-84971-406-8(1))* Routledge.

van t'Hooft, Katrien, et al. Livestock Management for Poverty Alleviation & Food Security. 2012. 208p. 145.00 ***(978-1-84593-827-7(5))*** CABI GBR. Dist: Stylus Publishing, LLC.

Vasan, A. Reservoir Optimization & Performance Evaluation of Irrigation Systems. 2011. 348p. pap. ***(978-3-8443-3353-4(3))*** Lambert Academic Publishing.

Wadood, Syed Naimul. Crop Choices & Employment Uncertainty. 2009. 136p. pap. *(978-3-639-14321-8(3))* VDM Verlag Dr. Mueller e.K.

AGRICULTURE—ECUADOR

Cuellar, Andrea M. The Quijos Chiefdoms: Social Change & Agriculture in the Eastern Andes of Ecuador = Los Cacicazgos Quijos: Cambio Social y Agricultura en los Andes Orientales del Ecuador. 2009. (ENG & SPA., Illus.). 206p. pap. *(978-1-877812-87-3(0))* Univ. of Pittsburgh Ctr. for Comparative Archaeology.

AGRICULTURE—EGYPT

Thompson, Gunnar. Ancient Egyptian Maize I. 2010. 215p. pap. 21.95 *(978-0-557-30308-3(7))* Lulu Enterprises Inc.

AGRICULTURE—EUROPE

Akalpler, Ergin. The European Unions Cap on Free Trade Turkey. 2008. 252p. pap. *(978-3-639-04879-7(2))* VDM Verlag Dr. Mueller e.K.

Bachev, Hrabrin, ed. Governance of Agrarian Sustainability. 2010. (Agriculture Issues & Policies Ser.). pap. 43.00 *(978-1-60876-888-2(0))* Nova Science Pubs., Inc.

Bakels, Corrie C. The Western European Loess Belt: Agrarian History, 5300 BC - AD 1000. 2009. (ENG., Illus.). viii, 295p. 159.00 *(978-1-4020-9839-0(1)*, 1402098391) Springer.

Bazok, Renata & Barcic, Jasminka Igrc, eds. Pheromone Applications in Maize Pest Control. 2010. (Insects & Other Terrestrial Arthropods: Biology, Chemistry & Behavior Ser.). (Illus.). viii, 56p. pap. 43.00 *(978-1-61728-010-8(0))* Nova Science Pubs., Inc.

Brouwer, F. M., et al, eds. Governance of Water-Related Conflicts in Agriculture: New Directions in Agri-Environmental & Water Policies in the EU. 2010. (Environment & Policy Ser.). 236p. pap. 169.00 *(978-90-481-6397-7(8)*, 9048163978) Springer.

Chantreuil, Frédéric, et al, eds. The Future of EU Agricultural Markets by AGMEMOD 2011. (ENG., Illus.). xv, 128p. 129.00 ***(978-94-007-2290-3(7)***, 9400722907) Springer.

Civitaresi, Hector Martin. Governance Structures in Global Agro-Commodities Chains. 2010. 52p. pap. *(978-3-8383-8318-7(4))* Lambert Academic Publishing.

Colledge Conolly Staff. Early Neolithic Agriculture in Southwest Asia & Europe: Archaeo. 2006. 256p. *(978-1-84472-191-7(4)*, Routledge Cavendish) Taylor & Francis Group.

Commission of the European Communities. Directorate-General for Agriculture, contrib. by. Rural Developments: CAP 2000. (Illus.). ii, 75p. *(978-92-828-2053-7(X))* European Commission BEL. Dist: Balogh International, Inc.

Cunha, Arlindo & Swinbank, Alan. An Inside View of the CAP Reform Process: Explaining the MacSharry, Agenda 2000, & Fischler Reforms. 2011. (ENG., Illus.). 256p. 99.00 *(978-0-19-959157-2(1))* Oxford Univ. Pr., Inc.

Danielsen. Eu Agriculture Law. 2011. *(978-90-411-3280-2(5))* Kluwer Law International.

Dosi, Cesare, ed. Agricultural Use of Groundwater: Towards Integration between Agricultural Policy & Water Resources Management. 2010. (Economics, Energy & Environment Ser.). (Illus.). 320p. pap. 229.00 *(978-90-481-5650-4(5)*, 9048156505) Springer.

Fonte, Maria & Papadopoulos, Apostolos G. Naming Food after Places: Food Relocalization & Knowledge Dynamics in Rural Development. 2010. (Perspectives on Rural Policy & Planning Ser.). (Illus.). 306p. 99.95 *(978-0-7546-7718-5(4))* Ashgate Publishing Co.

Forbes, Bruce C., et al. Reindeer Management in Northernmost Europe: Linking Practical & Scientific Knowledge in Social-Ecological Systems. 2010. (Ecological Studies). (Illus.). xxil, 397p. pap. 219.00 *(978-3-642-06548-4(1)*, 364206548*) Springer.

Hadjikoumis, Angelos, et al, eds. Dynamics of Neolithisation: Studies in Honour of Andrew Sherratt. 2011. (ENG.). 389p. (C). 80.00 *(978-1-84217-999-4(3))* Oxbow Bks., Ltd. GBR. Dist: Brown, David Bk. Co., The.

Haverkort, Anton J. & Anisimov, Boris V., eds. Potato Production & Innovative Technologies. 2007. (Illus.). 424p. pap. 102.00 *(978-90-8686-042-5(7))* Wageningen Academic Publishers NLD. Dist: Enfield Publishing & Distribution Co., Inc.

International Assessment of Agricultural Knowledge, Science, and Technology. North America & Europe Vol. 5: International Assessment of Agricultural Knowledge, Science & Technology for Development. 2009. (ENG.). 312p. pap. 75.00 *(978-1-59726-549-2(7))*; (Illus.). 125.00 *(978-1-59726-548-5(9))* Island Pr.

Jack, Brian. Agriculture & Eu Environmental Law. 2009. 300p. 124.95 *(978-0-7546-4540-5(1))* Ashgate Publishing Co.

Jarman, M. R., et al. Early European Agriculture: Its Foundation & Development. 2009. (ENG., Illus.). 296p. pap. 38.99 *(978-0-521-10506-4(4))* Cambridge Univ. Pr.

Kavallari, Aikaterini. Agricultural Trade Policy Reforms & Trade Liberalisation in the Mediterranean Basin: A Partial Equilibrium Analysis of Regional Effects on the EU-27 & on the Mediterranean Partner Countries. 2009. (Schriften zur internationalen Entwicklungs- und Umweltforschung Ser.). 256p. 72.95 *(978-3-631-59203-8(5))* Lang, Peter GmbH, Europaischer Verlag der Wissenschaften DEU. Dist: Lang, Peter.

Kullaj, Endrit. Organic Farming Policies for a Sustainable Development of Rural Areas. 2010. 216p. pap. *(978-3-8383-6360-8(4))* Lambert Academic Publishing.

Ladurie, Emmanuel Le Roy & Goy, Joseph. Tithe & Agrarian History from the Fourteenth to the Nineteenth Century: An Essay in Comparative History. 2008. (ENG., Illus.). 220p. pap. 32.99 *(978-0-521-09078-0(4))* Cambridge Univ. Pr.

Massachusetts. Commissioners concerning. Report of Commissioners Concerning an Agricultural School January 1851. 2006. 108p. per. 16.99 *(978-1-4255-0691-9(7))* MPublishing.

McMahon, Joseph. EU Agricultural Law. 2008. (ENG.). 520p. 363.00 *(978-1-904501-65-7(6))* Oxford Univ. Pr., Inc.

Morgan, Ora S., ed. Agricultural Systems of Middle Europe: A Symposium. reprint ed. 31.50 *(978-0-404-04434-3(4))* AMS Pr., Inc.

Muller, Dietmar & Harre, Angela, eds. Transforming Rural Societies: Agrarian Property & Agrarianism in East Central Europe in the Nineteenth & Twentieth Centuries. 2011. (ENG.). 250p. pap. 44.95 *(978-3-7065-4950-9(6))* StudienVerlag GesmbH AUT. Dist: Transaction Pubs.

Organisation for Economic Co-Operation and Development & Czech Republic: Ministry of Agriculture. Challenges for Agricultural Research. 2011. (Illus.). 301p. pap. ***(978-92-64-09009-5(6))*** Organization for Economic Cooperation & Development.

Rigueiro-Rodriguez, Antonio, et al, eds. Agroforestry in Europe: Current Status & Future Prospects. 2010. (Advances in Agroforestry Ser.). (Illus.). xxiv, 452p. pap. 239.00 *(978-90-481-7827-8(4)*, 9048178274) Springer.

Spikins, Penny. Mesolithic Europe. Bailey, Geoff, ed. 2010. (ENG.). 498p. pap. 45.00 *(978-0-521-14797-2(2))* Cambridge Univ. Pr.

Successful Farming Magazine Staff. 2009 Dutch Farmer's Almanac: Charts, historical data, key events, trends, tips & Forecasts. 2008. (Successful Farming Reference Guides). 160p. pap. 15.00 *(978-0-696-24344-8(X))* Meredith Bks.

Tiltman, H. Hessell. Peasant Europe. 2006. (Illus.). 336p. 250.00 *(978-0-7103-1155-9(9))* Taylor & Francis Group.

United Nations: Economic Commission for Europe. UNECE Standard: Porcine meat carcases & Cuts. 2006th ed. 2009. (ENG., Illus.). 58p. pap. 10.00 *(978-92-1-116953-9(4))* United Nations Pubns.

Utset, Angel, ed. Climate Variability, Modeling Tools & Agricultural Decision-Making. 2009. 79.00 *(978-1-60692-703-3(5))* Nova Science Pubs., Inc.

Youssefic...Et. Environmental, Health & Humanity Issues in the down Danubian Region: Multidisciplinary Approach. Mihailovic, Dragutin T., ed. 2008. (Illus.). xviii, 371p. 150.00 *(978-981-283-439-3(7))* World Scientific Publishing Co., Inc.

AGRICULTURE—EUROPE—HISTORY

Ambrosoli, Mauro. The Wild & the Sown: Botany & Agriculture in Western Europe, 1350-1850. 2009. (Past & Present Publications). (ENG., Illus.). 504p. pap. 58.00 *(978-0-521-10881-2(0))* Cambridge Univ. Pr.

Antoine, Annie, ed. Agricultural Specialization & Rural Patterns of Development. 2011. (Rural History in Europe Ser.). (ENG., Illus.). 256p. (C). pap. 90.00 *(978-2-503-53228-8(4))* Brepols Pubs. BEL. Dist: Brown, David Bk. Co., The.

Bell, Jonathan & Watson, Mervyn, eds. A history of Irish Farming, 1750-1950. 2009. 344p. pap. 39.95 *(978-1-84682-208-7(4))* Four Courts Pr. IRL. Dist: International Specialized Bk. Services.

Bieleman, Jan. Five centuries of Farming: A short history of Dutch Agriculture 1500 - 2000. 2010. (Illus.). 350p. pap. 93.00 *(978-90-8686-133-0(4))* Wageningen Academic Publishers NLD. Dist: Enfield Publishing & Distribution Co., Inc.

Britnell, Richard & Dodds, Ben, eds. Agriculture & Rural Society after the Black Death: Common Themes & Regional Variations. 2009. (Studies in Regional & Local History Ser.). (ENG., Illus.). 288p. pap. 37.95 *(978-1-902806-79-2(4))* Univ. of Hertfordshire Pr. GBR. Dist: Independent Pubs. Group.

Colledge, Sue & Conolly, James, eds. The Origins & Spread of Domestic Plants in Southwest Asia & Europe. 2007. (University College London Institute of Archaeology Publications). (ENG., Illus.). 462p. 99.00 *(978-1-59874-988-5(9))* Left Coast Pr., Inc.

Finlayson, Bill & Warren, Graeme. Landscapes in Transition. 2010. (Levant Supplementary Ser.). (ENG., Illus.). 239p. (C). pap. 70.00 *(978-1-84217-416-6(9))* Oxbow Bks., Ltd. GBR. Dist: Brown, David Bk. Co., The.

Hägermann, Dieter & Kasten, Brigitte. Tätigkeitsfelder und Erfahrungshorizonte des Ländlichen Menschen in der Frühmittelalterlichen Grundherrschaft (Bis Ca. 1000) Festschrift Für Dieter Hägermann Zum 65. Geburtstag. 2006. (Vierteljahrschrift fur Sozial- und Wirtschaftsgeschichte - Beihefte (VSWG-B) Ser.). (FRE, GER & ENG., Illus.). 408p. (C). 119.00 *(978-3-515-08788-9(5))* Steiner, Franz Verlag Wiesbaden GmbH DEU. Dist: Brown, David Bk. Co., The.

Kennedy, Liam & Solar, Peter. Irish Agriculture: A Price History from the Mid-Eighteenth Century to the Eve of the First World War. 2007. (Illus.). 206p. 45.00 *(978-1-904890-41-6(5))* Royal Irish Academy IRL. Dist: International Specialized Bk. Services.

Pinilla, Vicente, ed. Markets & Agricultural Change in Europe from the 13th to the 20th Century. 2009. (Rural History in Europe Ser.). (ENG.). 247p. (C). pap. 90.00 *(978-2-503-52952-3(6))* Brepols Pubs. BEL. Dist: ISD.

Range, Willard. A Century of Georgia Agriculture, 1850-1950. 2010. (ENG.). 346p. pap. 24.95 *(978-0-8203-3551-3(7))* Univ. of Georgia Pr.

Segers, Y., et al, eds. Exploring the Food Chain: Food Production & Food Processing in Western Europe, 1850-1980. 2009. (Comparative Rural History of the North Sea Area Ser.: Vol. 7). (ENG., Illus.). 289p. (C). pap. 102.00 *(978-2-503-51779-7(X))* Brepols Pubs. BEL. Dist: ISD.

AGRICULTURE—FINLAND

Jantunen, Juha. Semi-natural Grasslands in Finnish & Russian Karelia: Quantity, vegetation, & management. 2008. 52p. pap. *(978-3-639-11049-4(8))* VDM Verlag Dr. Mueller e.K.

AGRICULTURE—FRANCE

Cleary, Mark C. Peasants, Politicians & Producers: The Organisation of Agriculture in France Since 1918. 2007. (Cambridge Studies in Historical Geography Ser.). (ENG., Illus.). 220p. pap. 48.00 *(978-0-521-03377-0(2))* Cambridge Univ. Pr.

Finley, Amy. How to Eat a Small Country: A Family's Pursuit of Happiness, One Meal at a Time. 2012. (ENG.). 288p. pap. 14.00 ***(978-0-307-98496-3(6))*** Broadway Bks.

AGRICULTURE—GERMANY

Regionalverband Ruhr Staff, contrib. by. Feldstudien / Field Studies: Zur neuen Ästhetik urbaner Landwirtschaft / The New Aesthetics of Urban Agriculture. 2010. (ENG., Illus.). 112p. 54.95 *(978-3-0346-0260-0(X))* Birkhauser Verlag AG CHE. Dist: Actar Birkhauser Distribution.

Uekotter, Frank. Die Wahrheit ist auf dem Feld: Eine Wissensgeschichte der deutschen Landwirtschaft. 2011. (Umwelt und Gesellschaft Ser.). (GER.). 524p. (C). 68.00 *(978-3-525-31705-1(0))* Vandenhoeck & Ruprecht GmbH & Co. KG DEU. Dist: ISD.

AGRICULTURE—GREAT BRITAIN

Bell, Brian. Fifty Years of Farm Machinery. (Illus.). 240p. 44.95 *(978-0-85236-263-1(3))* Farming Pr., Ltd. GBR. Dist: Diamond Farm Bk. Pubs.

Bell, G. D. H. Cultivated Plants of the Farm. 2011. (ENG.). 292p. pap. 23.99 *(978-1-107-66279-7(6))* Cambridge Univ. Pr.

Bradley, Edith. The Lighter Branches of Agriculture. 2010. 86p. pap. *(978-1-152-38835-2(5))* Books LLC.

—The Lighter Branches of Agriculture. 346p. reprint ed. 98.00 *(978-0-7222-1607-1(6))* Library Reprints, Inc.

Burritt, Elihu. A Walk from London to John O'Groat's. 2008. 284p. 28.99 *(978-0-554-26997-9(X))* 2008. 284p. 25.99 *(978-0-554-36300-4(3))* 2007. (ENG.). 252p. pap. 21.99 *(978-1-4346-2293-8(2))* BiblioBazaar.

—Walk from London to John OGroats. 2006. pap. *(978-1-4068-0096-8(1))* Echo Library.

—A Walk from London to John O'Groat's. lt. ed. 2007. (ENG.). 280p. pap. 23.99 *(978-1-4346-2351-5(3))* BiblioBazaar.

Caird, James. English Agriculture In 1850-51. 2011. (Cambridge Library Collection - History Ser.). (ENG., Illus.). 582p. pap. 43.00 *(978-1-108-02473-0(4))* Cambridge Univ. Pr.

Campbell, Bruce M. S. & Campbell, B. M. S. Field Systems & Farming Systems in Late Medieval England. 2008. (Variorum Collected Studies). (Illus.). 332p. 154.95 *(978-0-7546-5946-4(1))* Ashgate Publishing Co.

Clements, Hugh. The Fields of Great Britain - a Text-Book of Agriculture Adapted to the Syllabus of the Science & Art Department, South Kensington. 2010. 392p. pap. 32.45 *(978-1-4455-9009-7(3))* Palmer Pr., The.

Cobbett, William. Cottage Economy. 2009. (Cooking in America Ser.). (ENG.). 232p. pap. 15.95 *(978-1-4290-1277-5(3))* Applewood Bks.

—Cottage Economy. 2007. 204p. per. 19.95 *(978-1-60206-809-4(7))* Cosimo, Inc.

Cornock, Richard. A Year on a Dairy Farm. 2010. (ENG., Illus.). 120p. pap. 29.95 *(978-1-84868-984-8(5))* Amberley Publishing GBR. Dist: Casemate Pubs. & Bk. Distributors, LLC.

Curtler, W. H. R. The Enclosure & Redistribution of Our Land. 2009. 286p. pap. *(978-0-217-34771-6(1))* Books LLC.

Davenport, Frances Gardiner. The Economic Development of a Norfolk Manor, 1086-1565. 2010. (Cambridge Library Collection - History Ser.). (Illus.). 232p. pap. 22.99 *(978-1-108-01605-6(7))* Cambridge Univ. Pr.

Davis, Nigel, et al. Agricultural Precedents Handbook. 2nd rev. ed. 2009. (ENG., Illus.). 564p. incl. cd-rom *(978-1-84661-061-5(3))* Jordan Publishing, Ltd.

Dewey, Peter. 'Iron Harvests of the Field' The Making of Farm Machinery in Britain Since 1800. 2012. (Illus.). 368p. 45.95 ***(978-1-85936-180-1(3))*** International Publishers Marketing.

Evans, Roger. Over the Farmer's Gate. 2010. (ENG., Illus.). 224p. 18.00 ***(978-1-906122-25-6(3))*** Unwin, Merlin Bks. GBR. Dist: SCB Distributors.

Gray, Howard Levi. English Field Systems. 2009. 580p. 37.99 *(978-1-115-18425-0(3))*; 44.99 *(978-1-115-18427-4(X))*; pap. 43.75 *(978-1-115-18423-6(7))* BiblioBazaar.

—English Field Systems. 568p. reprint ed. 98.00 *(978-0-7222-2709-1(4))*; 98.00 *(978-0-7222-7287-9(1))* Library Reprints, Inc.

Haggard, H. Rider. Rural England: Being an Account of Agricultural & Social Researches Carried Out in the Years 1901 And 1902. 2011. (Cambridge Library Collection - History Ser.) (ENG.). 684p. pap. 48.00 *(978-1-108-02549-2(8))*; (Illus.). 700p. pap. 48.00 *(978-1-108-02548-5(X))* Cambridge Univ. Pr.

Hall, Alfred. Farm Life on Field & Fell. lt. ed. 2009. 224p. 23.99 *(978-1-84262-688-7(4))* Dales Large Print Bks. GBR. Dist: Ulverscroft Large Print Bks., Ltd.

Harris, Toby. Business & Agricultural Property Relief. 5th rev. ed. 2011. (Illus.). 670p. pap. 145.00 *(978-1-84592-344-0(8)*, Bloomsbury Professional) Bloomsbury Publishing Plc GBR. Dist: International Specialized Bk. Services.

Hibbard, Benjamin Horace. Effects of the Great War upon Agriculture in the United States And. 2007. (ENG.). 248p. per. 26.95 *(978-1-4304-4812-9(1))* Kessinger Publishing, LLC.

Jarman & Sutcliffe. Agriculture & Rural Issues. Date not set. (Illus.). 64p. pap. 36.00 *(978-0-582-02428-1(5))* Addison-Wesley Longman, Ltd. GBR. Dist: Trans-Atlantic Pubns., Inc.

Lainsbury, Martin A., ed. The UK Pesticide Guide 2011. 2011. 700p. pap. 85.00 *(978-1-84593-830-7(5))* CABI GBR. Dist: Stylus Publishing, LLC.

Lanham, Hugh. Garden Farming, 1 vol. 2010. (ENG., Illus.). 160p. 23.95 *(978-1-84797-166-1(0))* Crowood Pr., Ltd. GBR. Dist: Independent Pubs. Group.

Minter, Sue. A Well-Connected Gardener: A Biography of Alicia Amherst, Founder of Garden History. 2010. (Illus.). 124p. 34.95 *(978-1-84624-513-8(3))* Book Guild, Ltd. GBR. Dist: Trans-Atlantic Pubns., Inc.

Olmsted, Frederick Law. Walks & Talks of an American Farmer in England. 2010. 122p. pap. *(978-1-152-10761-8(5))* 2009. 312p. pap. *(978-1-4589-4859-5(5))* 2009. 296p. pap. *(978-0-217-41687-0(X))* 2009. 248p. pap. *(978-0-217-41685-6(3))* Books LLC.

—Walks & Talks of an American Farmer in England. 2010. 102p. pap. 20.00 *(978-1-152-10764-9(X))* General Bks. LLC.

—Walks & Talks of an American Farmer in England. 2008. 198p. 39.95 *(978-1-4365-1095-0(3))* 2007. (ENG.). 200p. per. 24.95 *(978-0-548-69281-3(5))* Kessinger Publishing, LLC.

—Walks & Talks of an American Farmer in England. 2006. (ENG.). 252p. per. 23.99 *(978-1-4255-2234-6(3))* MPublishing.

—Walks & Talks of an American Farmer in England by Frederick Law Olmsted. 2006. 380p. per. 26.99 *(978-1-4255-4015-9(5))* MPublishing.

Popoff, Mischa. Is it Organic. 2011. 574p. pap. 27.99 *(978-1-61215-462-6(X))* Xulon Pr., Inc.

Pressdee, Colin. Food Wales - Eating Out Guide 2011. 2nd ed. 2012. (ENG., Illus.). 128p. pap. 12.65 ***(978-1-905582-47-1(1))*** Graffeg GBR. Dist: National Bk. Network.

Prothero, Rowland Edmund. The Land & its People: Chapters in Rural Life & History. 2011. (Cambridge Library Collection - History Ser.). 274p. pap. 23.99 *(978-1-108-02530-0(7))* Cambridge Univ. Pr.

Reynolds, Peter J. Ancient Farming. 2011. (Shire Archaeology Ser.). (ENG., Illus.). 64p. pap. 13.95 *(978-0-85263-876-7(0))* Shire Pubns., Ltd. GBR. Dist: Random Hse., Inc.

Richards, J. M. The Bombed Buildings of Britain - a Record of Architectural Casualties: 1940-41. 2011. 144p. pap. 26.95 ***(978-1-4465-2787-0(5))***, Kent Pr.) Kent Communications, Ltd.

Shirreff, John. General View of the Agriculture of the Orkney Islands. reprint ed. 31.50 *(978-0-404-16480-5(3))* AMS Pr., Inc.

—General View of the Agriculture of the Orkney Islands. 2009. 342p. pap. 22.07 *(978-0-217-83775-0(1))* General Bks. LLC.

Stephens, Henry. Book of the Farm: Concise Edition. Langlands, Alex, ed. 2011. (ENG., Illus.). 304p. 29.95 *(978-1-906388-91-1(1)*, Batsford, B. T. Ltd.) Anova Bks. GBR. Dist: Sterling Publishing Co., Inc.

Wibberley, T. Continuous Cropping & Tillage Dairy Fa. 2006. 188p. per. *(978-1-4067-9695-7(6)*, Hesperides Pr.) Read Bks.

Williams, R. G. Agricultural Valuations: A Practical Guide. 4th rev. ed. 2008. (ENG.). 352p. pap. 59.95 *(978-0-7282-0551-2(3))* Estates Gazette, Ltd. GBR. Dist: Taylor & Francis Group.

Young, Arthur. The Farmer's Calendar: Containing the Business Necessary to be Performed on Various Kinds of Farms during Every Month of the Year. 2011. (Cambridge Library Collection - History Ser.). (ENG., Illus.). 626p. pap. 43.00 ***(978-1-108-03716-7(X))*** Cambridge Univ. Pr.

AGRICULTURE—GREAT BRITAIN—HISTORY

Alexander, William. Notes & Sketches Illustrative of Northern Rural Life in the Eighteenth Century. 2009. 156p. pap. *(978-1-151-18514-3(0))* Books LLC.

—Notes & Sketches Illustrative of Northern Rural Life in the Eighteenth Century. 2007. (ENG.). 228p. 41.95 *(978-0-548-22875-3(2))*; per. 26.95 *(978-1-4325-5161-2(2))* Kessinger Publishing, LLC.

Attack, R. S. John Clare: A Voice of Freedom. 2010. (ENG.). 96p. pap. 14.95 *(978-0-85683-270-3(7))* Shepheard-Walwyn Pubs., Ltd. GBR. Dist: Independent Pubs. Group.

Blaxter, Kenneth & Robertson, Noel R. From Dearth to Plenty: The Modern Revolution in Food Production. 2007. (ENG., Illus.). 316p. pap. 66.00 *(978-0-521-04195-9(3))* Cambridge Univ. Pr.

Britnell, Richard & Dodds, Ben, eds. Agriculture & Rural Society after the Black Death: Common Themes & Regional Variations. 2009. (Studies in Regional & Local History Ser.). (ENG., Illus.). 288p. pap. 37.95 *(978-1-902806-79-2(4))* Univ. of Hertfordshire Pr. GBR. Dist: Independent Pubs. Group.

BROWN, Jonathan. The Edwardian Farm. 2010. (Shire Library). (ENG., Illus.). 64p. pap. 12.95 *(978-0-7478-0807-7(4))* Shire Pubns., Ltd. GBR. Dist: Random Hse., Inc.

BROWN, Jonathan. Farming in the 1920s And 30s. 2012. (Shire Library). (ENG., Illus.). 64p. pap. 12.95 ***(978-0-7478-1094-0(X))*** Shire Pubns., Ltd. GBR. Dist: Random Hse., Inc.

Curtler, W. H. R. A Short History of English Agriculture. 2009. 404p. 31.99 *(978-0-559-12861-5(4))*; 29.99 *(978-0-559-12876-9(2))*; pap. 20.99 *(978-0-559-12873-8(8))*; pap. 34.75 *(978-0-559-12864-6(9))* BiblioBazaar.

—A Short History of English Agriculture. 2010. (Illus.). 256p. pap. 33.59 *(978-1-4432-1012-6(9))* General Bks. LLC.

Curtler, William Henry Ricketts. A Short History of English Agriculture. 2010. (ENG.). 400p. pap. 34.75 *(978-1-177-45849-8(7))* BiblioBazaar.

Davenport, Frances Gardiner. A Classified List of Printed Original Materials for English Manorial & Agrarian History During the Middle Ages. 2009. 68p. pap. 14.14 *(978-0-217-26354-2(2))* General Bks. LLC.

Elding, Fred. Ploughing Through Time. 2008. (Illus.). 96p. per. *(978-1-84748-233-4(3))* Athena Pr.

Garnier, Russell M. History of the English landed interest: its customs, laws & agriculture: modern Period. 2010. (ENG.). 588p. pap. 44.75 ***(978-1-240-17777-6(1))*** BiblioBazaar.

Hallam, H. E., ed. The Agrarian History of England & Wales, 1042-1350, Vol. 2. 2011. (Agrarian History of England & Wales Ser.). (ENG.). 1128p. pap. 100.00 *(978-0-521-20011-0(3))* Cambridge Univ. Pr.

Harvey, Nigel. Fields, Hedges & Ditches. 2nd ed. 2011. (Shire Library). (ENG., Illus.). 32p. pap. 11.95 *(978-0-85263-868-2(X))* Shire Pubns., Ltd. GBR. Dist: Random Hse., Inc.

Hennell, Thomas. Change in the Farm. 2nd rev. ed. 2012. (ENG., Illus.). 224p. pap. 34.99 ***(978-1-107-65140-1(9))*** Cambridge Univ. Pr.

Hughes, Anne. The Diary of a Farmer's Wife, 1796-1797. 2009. (ENG., Illus.). 168p. pap. 13.99 *(978-1-904871-59-0(3)*, 1904871593) Good Life Pr., The GBR. Dist: MBI Distribution Services/Quayside Distribution.

Miller, Edward, ed. The Agrarian History of England & Wales, 1348-1500, Vol. 3. 2011. (Agrarian History of England & Wales Ser.). (ENG.). 1022p. pap. 100.00 *(978-0-521-20012-7(1))* Cambridge Univ. Pr.

Mingay, G. E., ed. The Agrarian History of England & Wales, 2 vols., Pt. 2, Vol. 6. 2011. (Agrarian History of England & Wales Ser.). 1237p. pap. 105.00 *(978-1-107-40113-6(5))* Cambridge Univ. Pr.

Moses, Gary. Rural Moral Reform in Nineteenth-Century England: The Crusade Against Adolescent Farm Servants & Hiring Fairs. 2007. (Illus.). 256p. 109.95 *(978-0-7734-5277-0(X))* Mellen, Edwin Pr., The.

Orde, Anne, ed. Matthew & George Culley: Farming Letters, 1798-1804. 2006. (Publications of the Surtees Society Ser.: Volume 210). (Illus.). 670p. 90.00 *(978-0-85444-065-8(8))* Surtees Society GBR. Dist: Boydell & Brewer, Inc.

Overton, Mark & Griffiths, Elizabeth. Farming to Halves: The Hidden History of Sharefarming in England from Medieval to Modern Times. 2009. (ENG., Illus.). 288p. 84.00 *(978-0-230-20223-8(3))* Palgrave Macmillan.

Phelps, Humphrey. A Gloucestershire Notebook. 2008. (ENG.). 240p. pap. 23.95 *(978-1-84588-629-5(1))* History Pr. Ltd.,The GBR. Dist: Independent Pubs. Group.

Sly, Rex. Soil in Their Souls: A History of Fenland Farming. 2011. (ENG., Illus.). 160p. pap. 26.95 *(978-0-7524-5733-8(0))* History Pr. Ltd.,The GBR. Dist: Independent Pubs. Group.

Sutherland, Jon & Canwell, Diane. Farming Industry: Images of the Past. 2011. (Illus.). 112p. pap. 29.95 *(978-1-84468-113-6(0))* Pen & Sword Bks. Ltd. GBR. Dist: Casemate Pubs. & Bk. Distributors, LLC.

Thirsk, Joan. The Agrarian History of England & Wales, Vol. 1. Piggott, Stuart, ed. 2011. (Agrarian History of England & Wales Ser.). (ENG.). 1077p. pap. 100.00 *(978-1-107-40114-3(3))* Cambridge Univ. Pr.

Thirsk, Joan, ed. The Agrarian History of England & Wales, 2 vols., Pt. 2, Vol. 5. 2011. (Agrarian History of England & Wales Ser.). (ENG.). 1526p. pap. 105.00 *(978-1-107-40118-1(6))* Cambridge Univ. Pr.

—The Agrarian History of England & Wales, 1500-1640, Vol. 4. 2011. (Agrarian History of England & Wales Ser.). (ENG.). 984p. pap. 100.00 *(978-0-521-20020-2(2))* Cambridge Univ. Pr.

Tilling, Brian J. The White Horse Show: A Village Charity. 2007. (Illus.). 304p. per. *(978-1-84748-007-1(1))* Athena Pr.

Wade Martins, Susanna. Coke of Norfolk (1754-1842) A Biography. 2010. (Illus.). 240p. pap. 24.95 *(978-1-84383-531-8(2)*, Boydell Press) Boydell & Brewer, Ltd. GBR. Dist: Boydell & Brewer, Inc.

Whetham, Edith H., ed. The Agrarian History of England & Wales, 1914-1939, Vol. 8. 2011. (Agrarian History of England & Wales Ser.). (ENG.). 378p. pap. 50.00 *(978-0-521-20013-4(X))* Cambridge Univ. Pr.

Wickham-Jones, Caroline. Fear of Farming. 2010. (ENG., Illus.). 176p. pap. 33.95 *(978-1-905119-32-5(1))* Windgather Pr. GBR. Dist: Brown, David Bk. Co., The.

AGRICULTURE—GREECE

Foxhall, Lin. Olive Cultivation in Ancient Greece: Seeking the Ancient Economy. 2007. (ENG., Illus.). 320p. 165.00 *(978-0-19-815288-0(4))* Oxford Univ. Pr., Inc.

AGRICULTURE—INDIA

Ahmed, Quazi Nasim & Parimal Kanti Biswas. Different Cultivation Methods of Paddy: New scopes for Bangladesh. 2010. 116p. pap. *(978-3-639-27056-3(8))* VDM Verlag Dr. Mueller e.K.

Awasthi, Dushyant Kumar, et al. Pulse Production Technology: Knowledge & Adoption. 2011. 192p. pap. ***(978-3-639-21227-3(4))*** VDM Verlag Dr. Mueller e.K.

Balasubramanian, Saranya. Changing Scenario in Agriculture & Water Resources in Sithalapakkam. 2011. 80p. pap. ***(978-3-8443-9272-2(6))*** Lambert Academic Publishing.

Bansil, P. C. Agricultural Statistics in India. 3rd rev. ed. 14.00 *(978-0-8364-1500-1(0))* Oxford IBH IND. Dist: South Asia Bks.

Barad, Kishor & V.K. Sapovadia, Prof. Cooperative Sugar Industry of Indi. 2010. 376p. pap. *(978-3-639-27716-6(3))* VDM Verlag Dr. Mueller e.K.

Chauhan, Avinash & Raj K Thakur. Bumble Bees: A new pollinator in Indian Agriculture. 2011. 152p. pap. ***(978-3-8443-2035-0(0))*** Lambert Academic Publishing.

Chengappa, P. G., et al. International Conference on 21st Century Challenges to Sustainable Agri-Food Systems: Biotechnology, Environment, Nutrition, Trade & Policy, 15th-17th March, 2007. 2007. (Illus.). xvi, 830p. (C). *(978-81-89866-29-7(X))* I.K. International Publishing House Pvt. Ltd.

Davara, Paresh & C. Patel, N. Post Harvest Practices for Banana Followed in Gujarat. 2011. 124p. pap. ***(978-3-8443-0573-9(4))*** Lambert Academic Publishing.

Department of Agriculture and Cooperation ,Directorate of Economics and Statistics Staff. Agricultural Statistics at a Glance 2008. 2009. (ENG.). 378p. pap. 35.95 *(978-81-7188-717-0(1))* Academic Foundation IND. Dist: Independent Pubs. Group.

Dhesi, Autar S. & Gurmail Singh. Rural Development in Punjab: A Success Story Going Astray. Dhesi, Autar S. & Singh, Gurmail, eds. 2008. (Illus.). 420p. 110.00 *(978-0-415-45681-4(9)*, Routledge India) Taylor & Francis Group GBR. Dist: Taylor & Francis Group.

Gupta, Meenakshi & Vikas Sharma. Unveiling the Supply Network Structure of Milk. 2011. 112p. pap. ***(978-3-8443-3432-6(7))*** Lambert Academic Publishing.

Gupta, Vijaya. Dry Farming Technology in Rajasthan, Indi. 2010. 208p. pap. *(978-3-639-23788-7(9))* VDM Verlag Dr. Mueller e.K.

Hesperides. Agricultural Legislation in India - Agricultural Production & Development. 2007. 484p. per. *(978-1-4067-5056-0(5)*, Hesperides Pr.) Read Bks.

Hutchinson, Joseph. Evolutionary Studies in World Crops: Diversity & change in the Indian Subcontinent. 2009. (ENG.). 184p. pap. 29.99 *(978-0-521-11760-9(7))* Cambridge Univ. Pr.

Jharwal, S. M., et al, eds. Glimpses of Indian Agriculture: Macro & Micro Aspects, 2 vols. & 3 pts. 2007. (ENG., Illus.). 1584p. 149.95 *(978-81-7188-597-8(7))* Academic Foundation IND. Dist: Independent Pubs. Group.

John, Jacob. Allelopathic Effect of Trees in the Homesteads of Kerala, Indi. 2010. 76p. pap. *(978-3-8383-8988-2(3))* Lambert Academic Publishing.

Krishna, K. R. Agroecosystems of South India: Nutrient Dynamics, Ecology & Productivity. 2010. 552p. pap. 69.95 *(978-1-59942-533-7(5)*, Brown Walker Pr.) Universal Pubs.

Krishna, Sumi, ed. Agriculture & a Changing Environment: Perspectives on Northeastern India. 2012. (Transition in Northeastern India Ser.). (ENG.). (C). 95.00 ***(978-0-415-63289-8(7)***, Routledge India) Taylor & Francis Group GBR. Dist: Taylor & Francis Group.

Kumar, M. Dinesh, et al, eds. Water Management, Food Security & Sustainable Agriculture in India. 2012. (Earthscan Studies in Water Resource Management Ser.). (ENG., Illus.). 288p. (C). 140.00 ***(978-0-415-62407-7(X))*** Routledge.

Melillo, Edward/D. Green Revolutions: Agricultural Expansion & the Global Environment in Three Countries. 2010. 30p. *(978-0-9823382-5-4(2))* Publishing Laboratory at UNC Wilmington, The.

Mina, Usha. An Impact Assessment of Ozone Phtotoxicity on Indian Crops. 2011. 96p. pap. ***(978-3-8383-4708-0(0))*** Lambert Academic Publishing.

Misra, Biswa Swarup. Credit Cooperatives in India. 2012. (ENG., Illus.). 192p. (C). pap. 42.95 ***(978-0-415-53363-8(5))*** Routledge.

Misra, Biswa Swarup. Credit Cooperatives in India: Past, Present & Future. 2010. (Routledge Studies in Development Economics Ser.). (ENG., Illus.). XXIV, 168p. (C). 130.00 *(978-0-415-56699-5(1)*, Routledge) Taylor & Francis Group GBR. Dist: Taylor & Francis Group.

Mohanty, Biswajit. Agriculture-an Assured Livelihoods for the Blind People in Rural Areas. 2011. 96p. pap. ***(978-3-8443-3331-2(2))*** Lambert Academic Publishing.

Nair, K. P. Prabhakaran. Agronomy & Economy of Black Pepper & Cardamom: The King & Queen of Spices. 2011. (ENG.). 380p. 140.00 *(978-0-12-391865-9(0))* Elsevier Science & Technology Bks.

Pereira, Winin & Seabrook, Jeremy. Asking the Earth: Farms, Forestry & Survival in India. 2009. (Natural Resource Management Set Ser.). (ENG.). 244p. 110.00 *(978-1-84971-016-9(3))* Routledge.

Ponnusamy, Kuppusamy. Integrated Coastal Farming Systems. 2011. 188p. pap. ***(978-3-8443-1997-2(2))*** Lambert Academic Publishing.

Ray, Shovan. Handbook of Agriculture in India. (ENG.). 2009. 248p. pap. 24.95 *(978-0-19-806251-6(6))* 2007. (Illus.). 300p. 60.00 *(978-0-19-568673-9(X))* Oxford Univ. Pr., Inc.

Roy, Amit & Chakrabarty, Suhrita. Adoption of Improved Technology in Jute. 2011. 104p. pap. ***(978-3-8454-0122-5(2))*** Lambert Academic Publishing.

—Agriculture Livelihood in Disadvantaged Agriculture. 2011. 76p. pap. ***(978-3-8443-1027-6(4))*** Lambert Academic Publishing.

—Effectiveness of Voluntary Organisations in Hill Agriculture. 2011. 120p. pap. ***(978-3-8443-0131-1(3))*** Lambert Academic Publishing.

—Evolving Agriculture Research Plan in Hill Agriculture. 2011. 76p. pap. ***(978-3-8443-9362-0(5))*** Lambert Academic Publishing.

—Resource Appraisal for Identifying Livelihood Potentials. 2011. 68p. pap. ***(978-3-8443-2126-5(8))*** Lambert Academic Publishing.

Sanford, A. Whitney. Growing Stories from India: Religion & the Fate of Agriculture. 2011. (Culture of the Land Ser.). (ENG., Illus.). 288p. 40.00 *(978-0-8131-3412-3(9))* Univ. Pr. of Kentucky.

Shanmugavelu, K. G. Production Technology of Vegetable Crops. (C). 24.00 *(978-81-204-0414-4(9))* Oxford IBH IND. Dist: South Asia Bks.

Shareef, Mohammad, et al. Use of Genetically Modified Seeds in Indi. 2011. 372p. pap. ***(978-3-8443-0684-2(6))*** Lambert Academic Publishing.

Sharma, Rajeev. Agricultural Development & Crop Diversification in Jammu & Kashmir. 2010. 84p. pap. *(978-3-639-25032-9(X))* VDM Verlag Dr. Mueller e.K.

Soundari, M., ed. Indian Agriculture & Information & Communications Technology (Ict) 2011. (Illus.). 214p. 36.50 *(978-81-7708-254-8(X))* New Century Publications IND. Dist: International Specialized Bk. Services.

Sreekumar, K. M., et al. Indigenous Knowledge of Farming in North Malabar. 2006. (Illus.). xviii, 156p. *(978-81-7596-348-1(4))* Cambridge Univ. Pr. India Pvt. Ltd.

Srivastava, Sanjay. Alleviating Rural Poverty & Food Security in Changing Climate. 2011. 76p. pap. ***(978-3-8433-8737-8(0))*** Lambert Academic Publishing.

Sucharita, Sanhita & Narayan Sethi. Impact of Land Degradation on Sustainable Development of Agriculture. 2010. 92p. pap. *(978-3-639-25734-2(0))* VDM Verlag Dr. Mueller e.K.

Swaminathan, M. S., ed. Agriculture Cannot Wait: New Horizons in Indian Agriculture. 2007. (ENG., Illus.). 550p. 69.95 *(978-81-7188-625-8(6))* Academic Foundation IND. Dist: Independent Pubs. Group.

Swaminathan, Marimuthu. Conservation Priorities & Livelihood Functions of Cattle Resources. 2011. 92p. pap. ***(978-3-8443-0624-8(2))*** Lambert Academic Publishing.

Takle, S. R. & Bhise, V. B. Behaviour of Market Prices of Agricultural Commodities. 2007. viii, 211p. *(978-81-8387-074-0(0))* Serials Publications.

Thakur, Devendra, ed. Planning & Development of Key Sectors in India, 5 vols. 4700p. (C). 325.00 *(978-81-7100-329-7(X))* Anmol Pubns., Pubs. & Distributors IND. Dist: South Asia Bks.

Thakur, Nishant. Continuity & Change in Local Ecological Knowledge. 2010. 108p. pap. *(978-3-8383-9418-3(6))* Lambert Academic Publishing.

Upadhyay, Priti. Genetic Diversity in Popular Rice Varieties of Indi. 2011. 92p. pap. ***(978-3-8443-0881-5(4))*** Lambert Academic Publishing.

Vishwanath Gowdru, Nithya. Comparative Analysis of Bt & Non Bt Cotton-an Econometric Analysis. 2011. 92p. pap. ***(978-3-8443-0523-4(8))*** Lambert Academic Publishing.

Wojtilla, Gyula, ed. Kasyapiyakrsisukti. A Sanskrit Work on Agriculture. 2010. (Beiträge Zur Kenntnis Südasiatischer Sprachen und Literaturen Ser.). (ENG.). 144p. (C). pap. 57.00 *(978-3-447-06265-7(7))* Harrassowitz, Otto Verlag DEU. Dist: ISD.

Wolfreys, Julian. Thomas Hardy. 2009. (Critical Issues Ser.). (ENG., Illus.). 272p. 80.00 *(978-0-333-92249-1(2))* Palgrave Macmillan.

World Bank Staff. Overcoming Drought: Adaptation Strategies for Andhra Pradesh, India. 2006. (Directions in Development Ser.). (ENG., Illus.). 164p. per. 20.00 *(978-0-8213-6664-6(5)*, 9780821366646) World Bank Pubns.

Yadav, Chouth Mal & Chaudhary, Jagdish Lal. Feeding of Protected Protein on Lactating Crossbred Cows & Heifers. 2011. 156p. pap. ***(978-3-8443-8808-4(7))*** Lambert Academic Publishing.

AGRICULTURE—INDONESIA

Sambodo, Leonardo. The Decision Making Processes of Semi-Commercial Farmers. 2009. 376p. pap. *(978-3-639-12530-6(4))* VDM Verlag Dr. Mueller e.K.

Suiatna, R. Utju. Bertani Dengan Akal & Nurani. 2011. (IND., Illus.). 250p. *(978-602-8349-21-5(6))*; *(978-979-24-5721-6(6))* Nuansa.

AGRICULTURE—IRELAND

Bell, Jonathan & Watson, Mervyn. A History of Irish Farming, 1750-1950. 2008. (Illus.). 344p. (C). 60.00 *(978-1-84682-096-0(0))* Four Courts Pr. IRL. Dist: International Specialized Bk. Services.

Bell, Jonathan & Watson, Mervyn, eds. A history of Irish Farming, 1750-1950. 2009. 344p. pap. 39.95 *(978-1-84682-208-7(4))* Four Courts Pr. IRL. Dist: International Specialized Bk. Services.

Cox, Michael. Overlooking the River Mourne: Four Centuries of Family Farms in Edymore & Cavanalee in County Tyrone. 2006. (ENG., Illus.). 157p. pap. *(978-1-903688-44-1(2))* Ulster Historical Foundation GBR. Dist: Independent Pubs. Group.

Ireland, Central Statistics Office Staff, contrib. by. Farming since the Famine: Irish Farm Statistics, 1847-1996. (Illus.). 408p. *(978-0-7076-1813-5(4))* Stationery Office Dublin IRL. Dist: Balogh International, Inc.

Laheen, Mary. Drystone Walls of the Aran Islands: Exploring the Cultural Landscape. 2010. (ENG., Illus.). 192p. pap. 36.95 *(978-1-84889-025-1(7))* Collins Pr., The IRL. Dist: Dufour Editions, Inc.

Medcalf, David. Plough Music. 2010. (ENG.). 191p. 27.95 *(978-1-905483-78-5(3))* Liberties Pr. IRL. Dist: Dufour Editions, Inc.

Montauo, John Patrick. The Roots of English Colonialism in Ireland. 2011. (Critical Perspectives on Empire Ser.). (ENG., Illus.). 440p. 99.00 *(978-0-521-19828-8(3))* Cambridge Univ. Pr.

Nelson, Charles. The Wild Plants of the Burren & the Aran Islands: A Field Guide. 2nd rev. ed. 2008. (ENG., Illus.). 160p. pap. 29.95 *(978-1-905172-67-2(2))* Collins Pr., The IRL. Dist: Dufour Editions, Inc.

O'Brien, William. Local Worlds: Early Settlement Landscapes & Upland Farming in Southwest Ireland. 2010. (ENG., Illus.). 528p. 92.95 *(978-1-84889-021-3(4))* Collins Pr., The IRL. Dist: Dufour Editions, Inc.

Penrose, William. Agricultural Law in Ireland. 2006. pap. 142.50 *(978-1-904480-49-5(7))* First Law IRL. Dist: Gaunt, Inc.

AGRICULTURE—ISRAEL

Chet. Wolf Prize in Agriculture. 2009. 190.00 *(978-981-283-584-0(9))* World Scientific Publishing Co., Inc.

Yaron, Hadas. Zionist Arabesques: Modern Landscapes, Non-Modern Texts. 2010. (Israel: Society, Culture, & History Ser.). (ENG.). 250p. 55.00 *(978-1-934843-78-9(4))* Academic Studies Pr.

AGRICULTURE—ITALY

Ambrosoli, Mauro. The Wild & the Sown: Botany & Agriculture in Western Europe, 1350-1850. 2009. (Past & Present Publications). (ENG., Illus.). 504p. pap. 58.00 *(978-0-521-10881-2(0))* Cambridge Univ. Pr.

Costantini. Manual Methods for Soil & Land Eval. 2009. (ENG., Illus.). 564p. 119.95 *(978-1-57808-571-2(3))* BIOS Scientific Publishers Ltd. GBR. Dist: Taylor & Francis Group.

Taegio, Bartolomeo. La Villa. 2011. (Penn Studies in Landscape Architecture Ser.). (ITA & ENG., Illus.). 312p. (C). 65.00 *(978-0-8122-4317-8(X))* Univ. of Pennsylvania Pr.

Tirabassi Leonardo. La mia Terra: Intervista storico-politica a Federico Vecchioni. 2011. (ITA., Illus.). 112p. (C). pap. 18.00 ***(978-88-564-0156-1(8))*** Polistampa ITA. Dist: Brown, David Bk. Co., The.

AGRICULTURE—JAPAN

Fukuoka, Masanobu. The One-Straw Revolution: An Introduction to Natural Farming. Korn, Larry, tr. from JPN. 2009. (New York Review Books Classics). (ENG., Illus.). 200p. 15.95 *(978-1-59017-313-8(9)*, NYRB Classics) New York Review of Bks., Inc., The.

King, F. H. Farmers of Forty Centuries: Permanent Organic Farming in China, Korea, & Japan. 2011. 452p. ***(978-1-84902-406-8(5))*** Benediction Classics.

King, Peter. Farmers of Forty Centuries. 2008. (Illus.). 380p. (C). 110.00 *(978-1-905246-80-9(3))* Univ. of Hawaii Pr.

Kumar, Ann. Globalizing the Prehistory of Japan: Language, genes & Civilisation. 2012. (Routledge Studies in the Early History of Asia Ser.). (ENG., Illus.). 224p. (C). pap. 42.95 ***(978-0-415-54207-4(3))*** Routledge.

Mau Dung, Nguyen & PHUONG LE, Nguyen. Agricultural Cooperative Management. 2011. 76p. pap. ***(978-3-8443-1198-3(X))*** Lambert Academic Publishing.

Nasu, Shiroshi. Aspects of Japanese Agriculture: A Preliminary Survey. (Institute of Pacific Relations Ser.). reprint ed. 32.50 *(978-0-404-59575-3(8))* AMS Pr., Inc.

AGRICULTURE—KOREA

King, F. H. Farmers of Forty Centuries: Permanent Organic Farming in China, Korea, & Japan. 2011. 452p. ***(978-1-84902-406-8(5))*** Benediction Classics.

King, Peter. Farmers of Forty Centuries. 2008. (Illus.). 380p. (C). 110.00 *(978-1-905246-80-9(3))* Univ. of Hawaii Pr.

No, Chung-Guk. Han'guk Kodae Ui Sujon Nongop Kwa Suri Sisol. 2010. (KOR., Illus.). 544p. *(978-89-606-2055-1(6))* Seogyeong Munhwasa.

AGRICULTURE—KENYA

Bürgi, Jürg. Insect Resistant Maize: A Case Study of Fighting the African Stem Borer. 2009. (Illus.). 433p. 145.00 *(978-1-84593-569-6(1))* CABI GBR. Dist: Stylus Publishing, LLC.

Echoka, Jackson. Analysis of Determinants of Agricultural Credit Performance in Keny. 2011. 116p. pap. ***(978-3-8443-0817-4(2))*** Lambert Academic Publishing.

Egesa, John, et al. Food Production in the Face of Violence. 2011. 112p. pap. *(978-3-8383-5982-3(8))* Lambert Academic Publishing.

Foeken, Dick. To Subsidise My Income: Urban Farming in an East-African Town. 2006. (Afrika-Studiecentrum Ser.: Vol. 7). (Illus.). 223p. pap. *(978-90-04-15202-1(4))* BRILL.

Kipkembol. Fingerponds: Integrated Seasonal Aquaculture in East African Fres. 2007. (ENG., Illus.). 165p. (C). 79.95 *(978-0-415-41696-2(5)*, Taylor & Francis) Taylor & Francis Group GBR. Dist: Taylor & Francis Group.

Kirumba, Edith, et al. Gender Differentials in Adoption of Agricultural Innovations in Keny. 2010. 128p. pap. *(978-3-8383-9783-2(5))* Lambert Academic Publishing.

Mandere, Nicodemus. Sugar Beet Cultivation in Keny. 2011. 60p. pap. ***(978-3-8443-2298-9(1))***; 72p. pap. ***(978-3-8433-9253-2(6))*** Lambert Academic Publishing.

Marinda, Pamela. Effects of Gender Inequality in Resource Ownership & Access on Household Welfare & Food Security in Kenya: A Case Study of West Pokot District, Vol. 51. 2006. (Development Economics & Policy Ser.). (Illus.). xx,223p. pap. 47.95 *(978-0-8204-9878-2(5))* Lang, Peter Publishing, Inc.

Nzuma, Jonathan. Impacts of Trade Liberalization on Kenya's Maize Sector - a Partial Equilibrium Analysis. 2008. 168p. pap. *(978-3-639-00933-0(9))* VDM Verlag Dr. Mueller e.K.

Sorre, Benard. Cash Crop Production, Food Security & Nutrition in Rural Households. 2011. 88p. pap. ***(978-3-8433-6141-5(X))*** Lambert Academic Publishing.

Tanui, Prisca. Differential Gender Access to Agricultural Resources in Keny. 2010. 188p. pap. *(978-3-639-27743-2(0))* VDM Verlag Dr. Mueller e.K.

AGRICULTURE—LATIN AMERICA

Hartwich, Frank. Building Public-Private Partnerships for Agricultural Innovation. 2008. *(978-0-89629-771-5(3))* International Food Policy Research Institute.

International Assessment of Agricultural Knowledge, Science, and Technology. Agriculture at a Crossroads Vol. 3: Latin America & the Caribbean. 2009. (ENG., Illus.). 248p. 125.00 *(978-1-59726-546-1(2))* Island Pr.

—Agriculture at a Crossroads Vol. 4: Latin America & the Caribbean. 2nd ed. 2009. (ENG.). 248p. pap. 75.00 *(978-1-59726-547-8(0))* Island Pr.

Maletta, Hector & Maletta, Emiliano. Climate Change, Agriculture & Food Security in Latin America. 2011. 448p. pap. ***(978-1-907132-31-5(7))*** Multi Science Publishing Co., Ltd.

AGRICULTURE—MALAWI

Mgemezulu, Overtoun. The Social Impact of Community Based Targeting Mechanisms. 2010. 132p. pap. *(978-3-8383-5885-7(6))* Lambert Academic Publishing.

AGRICULTURE—MEDITERRANEAN REGION

Bellard, Carlos Gomez & Dommelen, Peter van. Rural Landscapes of the Punic World. 2008. (Monographs in Mediterranean Archaeology Ser.). (ENG., Illus.). 299p. (C). 100.00 *(978-1-84553-270-3(8))* Equinox Publishing Ltd. GBR. Dist: ISD.

Harfouche, Romana. Histoire des Paysages Méditerranéens Terrassés: Aménagements et Agriculture. 2007. (Bar S Ser.). (FRE., Illus.). 265p. (C). pap. 92.50 *(978-1-4073-0048-1(2))* British Archaeological Reports Ltd. GBR. Dist: Brown, David Bk. Co., The.

Kavallari, Aikaterini. Agricultural Trade Policy Reforms & Trade Liberalisation in the Mediterranean Basin: A Partial Equilibrium Analysis of Regional Effects on the EU-27 & on the Mediterranean Partner Countries. 2009. (Schriften zur internationalen Entwicklungs- und Umweltforschung Ser.). 256p. 72.95 *(978-3-631-59203-8(5))* Lang, Peter GmbH, Europaischer Verlag der Wissenschaften DEU. Dist: Lang, Peter.

Rosalino, Luis M. & Gheler-Costa, Carla. Middle-Sized Carnivores in Agricultural Landscapes. 2011. *(978-1-61122-033-9(5))* Nova Science Pubs., Inc.

AGRICULTURE—MEXICO

Barrett, Ward J. The Sugar Hacienda of the Marqueses Del Valle. 2009. (ENG.). 160p. pap. 40.00 *(978-0-8166-5703-2(3))* Univ. of Minnesota Pr.

Matson, Pamela A., ed. Seeds of Sustainability: Lessons from the Birthplace of the Green Revolution in Agriculture. 2011. (Illus.). 312p. pap. 45.00 ***(978-1-59726-525-6(X))*** Island Pr.

Matson, Pamlea, ed. Seeds of Sustainability: Lessons from the Birthplace of the Green Revolution in Agriculture. 2011. (ENG., Illus.). 332p. 90.00 *(978-1-59726-522-5(5))* Island Pr.

Mellilo, Edward/D. Green Revolutions: Agricultural Expansion & the Global Environment in Three Countries. 2010. 30p. *(978-0-9823382-5-4(2))* Publishing Laboratory at UNC Wilmington, The.

Perramond, Eric P. Political Ecologies of Cattle Ranching in Northern Mexico: Private Revolutions. 2010. (ENG., Illus.). 288p. 35.00 *(978-0-8165-2721-2(0))* Univ. of Arizona Pr.

Tannenbaum, Frank. Mexican Agrarian Revolution. (Brookings Institution Reprint Ser.). (Illus.). 543p. reprint ed. pap. 9.95 *(978-0-89197-845-9(3))*; lib. bdg. 35.00 *(978-0-697-00172-6(5))* Irvington Pubs.

Walsh, Casey. Building the Borderlands: A Transnational History of Irrigated Cotton along the Mexico-Texas Border. 2008. (Environmental History Ser.). (ENG., Illus.). 248p. 47.50 *(978-1-60344-013-4(5))* Texas A&M Univ. Pr.

AGRICULTURE—MIDDLE EAST

Bonzanigo, Laura & Borgia, Cecilia. Tracing Evolutions of Water Control in Wadi Siham, Yemen. 2010. 140p. pap. *(978-3-8383-5622-8(5))* Lambert Academic Publishing.

Colledge Conoly Staff. Early Neolithic Agriculture in Southwest Asia & Europe: Archaeo. 2006. 256p. *(978-1-84472-191-7(4)*, Routledge Cavendish) Taylor & Francis Group.

Colledge, Sue & Conolly, James, eds. The Origins & Spread of Domestic Plants in Southwest Asia & Europe. 2007. (University College London Institute of Archaeology Publications). (ENG., Illus.). 462p. 99.00 *(978-1-59874-988-5(9))* Left Coast Pr., Inc.

Finlayson, Bill & Warren, Graeme. Landscapes in Transition. 2010. (Levant Supplementary Ser.). (ENG., Illus.). 239p. (C). pap. 70.00 *(978-1-84217-416-6(9))* Oxbow Bks., Ltd. GBR. Dist: Brown, David Bk. Co., The.

Gehlsen, Duane. Social Complexity & the Origins of Agriculture. 2009. 294p. pap. *(978-3-639-12399-9(9))* VDM Verlag Dr. Mueller e.K.

Giuliani, Alessandro. Developing Markets for Agrobiodiversity: Securing Livelihoods in Dryland Areas. 2007. (Earthscan Research Editions Ser.). (ENG., Illus.). 144p. 117.00 *(978-1-84407-468-6(4))* Routledge.

Saheb, Azad Ismail & Al-Abiani, Salam. Agriculture in the Middle East & North Africa: Status & Research Needs. 2011. *(978-1-61209-834-0(7))* Nova Science Pubs., Inc.

Saidel, Benjamin A. On the Fringe of Society: Archaeological & Ethnoarchaeological Perspectives on Pastoral & Agricultural Societies. van der Steen, Eveline J., ed. 2007. (Bar S Ser.). (Illus.). 132p. (C). pap. 72.50 *(978-1-4073-0093-1(8))* British Archaeological Reports Ltd. GBR. Dist: Brown, David Bk. Co., The.

Smith, Daryl, et al. The Tallgrass Prairie Center Guide to Prairie Restoration in the Upper Midwest. 2010. (Bur Oak Guide Ser.). (Illus.). 338p. pap. 27.50 *(978-1-58729-916-2(X))* Univ. of Iowa Pr.

Sutton, Jacqueline. Reconstructing Agriculture in Afghan: Agriculture & Food Security. 2008. (ENG.). 370p. (C). pap. 35.95 *(978-1-85339-634-2(6))* Intermediate Technology Development Group of North America.

AGRICULTURE—NEPAL

Acharya, Govind. Interventions on Soil Erosion & Loss of Plant Nutrients. 2011. 172p. pap. ***(978-3-8443-2939-1(0))*** Lambert Academic Publishing.

Bajracharya, Jwala. On-Farm Rice Diversity in Nepal, the Himalayan Country. 2009. 284p. pap. *(978-3-639-14892-3(4))* VDM Verlag Dr. Mueller e.K.

Bhusal, Tej Narayan. Cms-Ceres-Maize Model. 2011. 132p. pap. ***(978-3-8443-0272-1(7))*** Lambert Academic Publishing.

Ghimire, Nav. Participatory Agricultural Development. 2011. 136p. pap. ***(978-3-8443-1530-1(6))*** Lambert Academic Publishing.

Khadka, Chhatra Bahadur. Climate Change & Cash Crops in Annapurna Conservation Are. 2011. 68p. pap. ***(978-3-8443-8263-1(1))*** Lambert Academic Publishing.

Khanal, Dipendra. Moisture Sorption Behavior of Te. 2011. 76p. pap. ***(978-3-8443-9318-7(8))*** Lambert Academic Publishing.

Marahatta, Santosh. Performance of Winter Maize. 2011. 96p. pap. ***(978-3-8443-8830-5(3))*** Lambert Academic Publishing.

—Response of Client Oriented Rice Genotypes. 2011. 160p. pap. ***(978-3-8443-1564-6(0))*** Lambert Academic Publishing.

Pokhrel, Min Raj. Opportunities & Threats of Using Microbial Pest Control Agents. 2011. 104p. pap. ***(978-3-8443-9159-6(2))*** Lambert Academic Publishing.

Ranabhat, Nar Bahadur. Bee-Keeping. 2010. 84p. pap. *(978-3-8383-8269-2(2))* Lambert Academic Publishing.

Shiwakoti, Suvash. Occurrence of Bovine Paratuberculosis in Chitwan District of Nepal. 2011. 64p. pap. ***(978-3-8454-0228-4(8))*** Lambert Academic Publishing.

Timilsina, Ram Hari. Local Innovations: A case from chitwan & dhading districts of Nepal. 2011. 104p. pap. ***(978-3-8383-6536-7(4))*** Lambert Academic Publishing.

AGRICULTURE—NEW ZEALAND

Hunt, Lesley. Compliance at Work. 2008. 304p. pap. *(978-3-639-05751-5(1))* VDM Verlag Dr. Mueller e.K.

Lambert, Simon. The Expansion of Sustainability through New Economic Space: Maori Potatoes & Cultural Resilience. 2008. 188p. pap. *(978-3-639-09118-2(3))* VDM Verlag Dr. Mueller e.K.

Muscat, Joanne. Understanding Organic As a Socially Contested Notion. 2010. 164p. pap. *(978-3-8383-8099-5(1))* Lambert Academic Publishing.

Peluffo, Matias. Adopting New Zealand Dairy Farm Principles in Argentina. 2008. 256p. pap. *(978-3-639-02588-0(1))* VDM Verlag Dr. Mueller e.K.

Peters, Monica. New Zealand Maori Farmers & Soil Health: Indicators, Understandings & Monitoring Methodology. 2010. (Illus.). vi, 108p. pap. *(978-3-8383-4192-7(9))* Lambert Academic Publishing.

Sully, Dean, ed. Decolonizing Conservation: Caring for Maori Meeting Houses Outside New Zealand. 2008. (Critical Cultural Heritage Ser.). (ENG., Illus.). 272p. 94.00 *(978-1-59874-309-8(0))* Left Coast Pr., Inc.

AGRICULTURE—NIGERIA

Akinbile, Christopher Oluwakunmi. Upland Rice Responses to Water Application under Sprinkler Irrigation. 2011. 224p. pap. ***(978-3-8383-8975-2(1))*** Lambert Academic Publishing.

Korieh, Chima J. & Matthews, S. The Land Has Changed: History, Society & Gender in Colonial Eastern Nigeria. 2010. (Africa: Missing Voices Ser.). (Illus.). 390p. pap. 39.95 *(978-1-55238-268-4(0))* Univ. of Calgary Pr. CAN. Dist: Michigan State Univ. Pr.

Nmadu, Job. Sorghum Production in Nigeri. 2010. 132p. pap. *(978-3-639-23806-8(0))* VDM Verlag Dr. Mueller e.K.

Nwonwu, Francis O. C. Indigenous Knowledge Systems in Igbo Traditional Agriculture. 2011. 412p. pap. 21.93 ***(978-1-4520-9718-3(6))*** AuthorHouse.

Odiaka, Ngozi Ifeoma. Production & Diversity of Indigenous Leaf Vegetable. 2011. 156p. pap. ***(978-3-8433-7333-3(7))*** Lambert Academic Publishing.

Oduwole, Olusoji. Adoption of Modern Agronomic Practices by Cocoa Farmers in Nigeri. 2011. 220p. pap. ***(978-3-8443-1320-8(6))*** Lambert Academic Publishing.

Oyewole, Charles. Yield & Economic Implication of Intercropping Millet with Groundnut. 2011. 108p. pap. ***(978-3-8443-0585-2(8))*** Lambert Academic Publishing.

Saliu, Jamiu. Fertilizer Use in Rice Production in North Central Zone of Nigeri. 2011. 148p. pap. ***(978-3-8443-8759-9(5))*** Lambert Academic Publishing.

AGRICULTURE—NORTH AMERICA

Bailey, Liberty Hyde. Cyclopedia of American Agriculture: A Popular Survey of Agricultural Conditions, Practices & Ideals in the United States & Canada, 4 vols., Set. (Illus.). reprint ed. lib. bdg. 500.00 *(978-0-7222-3094-7(X))* Library Reprints, Inc.

Hinrichs, C. Clare & Lyson, Thomas A., eds. Remaking the North American Food System: Strategies for Sustainability. 2008. (Our Sustainable Future Ser.). (ENG., Illus.). 384p. 45.00 *(978-0-8032-2438-4(9))* Univ. of Nebraska Pr.

International Assessment of Agricultural Knowledge, Science, and Technology. North America & Europe Vol. 5: International Assessment of Agricultural Knowledge, Science & Technology for Development. 2009. (ENG.). 312p. pap. 75.00 *(978-1-59726-549-2(7))*; (Illus.). 125.00 *(978-1-59726-548-5(9))* Island Pr.

Ray-Mukherjee, Jayanti. Evaluating Native Wheatgrasses for Restoration of Sagebrush Steppes. 2011. 180p. pap. ***(978-3-8443-9038-4(3))*** Lambert Academic Publishing.

Rosenberg, Norman J. A Biomass Future for the North American Great Plains: Toward Sustainable Land Use & Mitigation of Greenhouse Warming. 2010. (Advances in Global Change Research Ser.). xvii, 198p. pap. 169.00 *(978-90-481-7405-8(8))*, 9048174058) Springer.

Sanders, Ralph W. The Farm Tractor: 100 Years of North American Tractors. 2009. (ENG., Illus.). 384p. pap. 27.99 *(978-0-7603-3559-8(1)*, 0760335591, Voyageur Pr) MBI Publishing Co. LLC.

Smith, Bruce D. Rivers of Change: Essays on Early Agriculture in Eastern North America. 2nd rev. ed. 2007. (Illus.). 336p. per. 40.00 *(978-0-8173-5425-1(5))* Univ. of Alabama Pr.

AGRICULTURE—PACIFIC AREA

United Nations Staff. Sustainable Agriculture & Food Security in Asia & the Pacific. 2009. (ENG.). 132p. pap. 56.00 *(978-92-1-120578-7(6))* United Nations Pubns.

AGRICULTURE—PAKISTAN

Abbas, Saqi Kosar, et al. Citrus Botanicals & Lesser Grain Borer: Potential of Citrus Essential Oils Against Two Strains of Lesser Grain Borer (Coleoptera: Bostrichidae) of Southern Punjab, Pakistan. 2011. 96p. pap. ***(978-3-639-32809-7(4))*** VDM Verlag Dr. Mueller e.K.

Ali, Jaffar, et al. Decentralization in Agriculture Extension. 2011. 92p. pap. ***(978-3-8454-0987-0(8))*** Lambert Academic Publishing.

Anwar, Hussain Gill & Mirza Azhar Beg. Scarp Ponds of Cholistan Desert: Impacts on Vegetation & Birds. 2011. 188p. pap. ***(978-3-639-32683-3(0))*** VDM Verlag Dr. Mueller e.K.

Ashraf, Ijaz & Sher Muhammad. Decentralized Extension in Pakistan. 2011. 224p. pap. ***(978-3-8443-8124-5(4))*** Lambert Academic Publishing.

Asma, Lodhi & Azam, Farooq E. Fate of Cyfluthrin in Soil-Plant System: Degradation, Translocation & Metabolism of 14 C- Cyfluthrin. 2011. 132p. pap. ***(978-3-639-32244-6(4))*** VDM Verlag Dr. Mueller e.K.

Bakhsh, Khuda. Efficiency & Profitability Analysis in Vegetable Production. 2011. 176p. pap. ***(978-3-8454-0307-6(1))*** Lambert Academic Publishing.

Butt, Tahir Munir. Agricultural Extension Approach. 2011. 108p. pap. ***(978-3-8443-2816-5(5))*** Lambert Academic Publishing.

Hussain, Ijaz & Zakir Hussain, Prof. The Indus Basin. 2011. 196p. pap. ***(978-3-8443-8026-2(4))*** Lambert Academic Publishing.

Hussain, Izhar, et al. Genotype by Environment Interactions of Maize Hybrids Across Locations. 2010. 60p. pap. *(978-3-639-25044-2(3))* VDM Verlag Dr. Mueller e.K.

Khan, Muhammad Ishfaq. Studies on Biology, Ecology & Management of Wild Onion in Chickpe. 2009. 156p. pap. *(978-3-639-15873-1(3))* VDM Verlag Dr. Mueller e.K.

Khan, Sher Aslam, et al. Genetic Regulation of Yield & Oil Quality Attributes in Sunflower. 2010. 224p. pap. *(978-3-639-24430-4(3))* VDM Verlag Dr. Mueller e.K.

Luqman, Muhammad, et al. Effectiveness of Decentralized Agriculture Extension System. 2011. 100p. pap. ***(978-3-8443-1317-8(6))*** Lambert Academic Publishing.

Mahmood, Hafiz Zahid. Accounting for Land. 2010. 164p. pap. *(978-3-639-23754-2(4))* VDM Verlag Dr. Mueller e.K.

Mellilo, Edward/D. Green Revolutions: Agricultural Expansion & the Global Environment in Three Countries. 2010. 30p. *(978-0-9823382-5-4(2))* Publishing Laboratory at UNC Wilmington, The.

Sabir, A. M., et al. Bumblebees & Utilization of Food Resources in Northern Pakistan. 2011. 224p. pap. ***(978-3-8443-9049-0(9))*** Lambert Academic Publishing.

Sadiqi, Muhammad Hanif, et al. Combining Ability in Sunflower for Yield & Oil Quality: Sunflower(Helianthus Annuus L., General & Specific Combining Ability, Yield & Oil Quality. 2011. 72p. pap. ***(978-3-639-32203-3(7))*** VDM Verlag Dr. Mueller e.K.

Saeed, Muhammad & Khan Bahader Marwat, Prof. Interference of Horse Purslane. 2010. 104p. pap. *(978-3-639-27308-3(7))* VDM Verlag Dr. Mueller e.K.

Shabbir, Nauman. Response of Maize Hybrids to Exogenous Boron Supply. 2011. 96p. pap. ***(978-3-8443-2259-0(0))*** Lambert Academic Publishing.

Shahid, Sohaib & Sohaib, Shahid. Aphids & Their Parasitoids Trends: Aphids & Parasitoids Population. 2011. 88p. pap. ***(978-3-639-31855-5(2))*** VDM Verlag Dr. Mueller e.K.

Suhail, Anjum, et al. Insects' Biodiversity Associated with Rice Crop. 2010. 260p. pap. *(978-3-8383-8009-7(8))* Lambert Academic Publishing.

Tariq, Ata-Ur-Rehman, et al. Rainfall-Recharge Estimation by Different Methods. 2010. 80p. pap. *(978-3-639-24382-6(X))* VDM Verlag Dr. Mueller e.K.

Ullah, Naimat & S. Mumtaz, A. Durable Resistance Against Stripe Rust in Wheat. 2011. 60p. pap. ***(978-3-8443-2666-7(8))*** Lambert Academic Publishing.

AGRICULTURE—ROMANIA

Mitrany, David. The Land & the Peasant in Rumani: The War & Agrarian Reform, 1917-1921. 2008. 666p. pap. 66.00 *(978-1-59740-701-4(1))* ACLS Humanities E-Book.

AGRICULTURE—ROME

Rodgers, R. H. L. Iuni Moderati Columellae Res Rustica: Incerti auctoris Liber de Arboribus. 2010. (ENG & LAT.). 600p. 99.00 *(978-0-19-927154-2(2))* Oxford Univ. Pr., Inc.

Stephenson, Andrew. Public Lands & Agrarian Laws of the Ro. 2006. pap. *(978-1-4068-3034-7(8))* Echo Library.

White, K. D. Agricultural Implements of the Roman World. 2010. (ENG.). 286p. pap. 23.99 *(978-0-521-14757-6(3))* Cambridge Univ. Pr.

—Farm Equipment of the Roman World. 2010. (ENG.). 296p. pap. 24.99 *(978-0-521-13423-1(4))* Cambridge Univ. Pr.

AGRICULTURE—RUSSIA (FEDERATION)

Graziosi, Andrea & Shapoval, IU I. Lysty Z Kharkova: Holod V Ukraini Ta Na Pivnichnomu Kavkazi V Povidomlenniakh Italiiskykh Dyplomativ 1932-1933 Rokiv. 2007. (UKR.). 255p. *(978-966-03-4063-3(X))* Folio.

Jantunen, Juha. Semi-natural Grasslands in Finnish & Russian Karelia: Quantity, vegetation, & management. 2008. 52p. pap. *(978-3-639-11049-4(8))* VDM Verlag Dr. Mueller e.K.

Lerman, Zvi. Russia's Agriculture in Transition: Factor Markets & Constraints on Growth. 2007. (Rural Economies in Transition Ser.). (ENG., Illus.). 394p. 89.50 *(978-0-7391-2009-5(3))* Lexington Bks.

Sharashkin, Leonid. Family Gardens: Russia's primary Agriculture. 2008. (Illus.). 280p. 29.95 *(978-0-9801812-9-6(1))* Ringing Cedars Pr.

AGRICULTURE—SCOTLAND

Fenton, Alexander & Veitch, Kenneth. Farming the Land: A Compendium of Scottish Ethnology. 2012. (Illus.). 1232p. 95.95 ***(978-1-906566-05-0(4))*** Birlinn, Ltd. GBR. Dist: Independent Pubs. Group.

Gray, John N. At Home in the Hills: Sense of Place in the Scottish Borders. 2011. 282p. pap. 29.95 ***(978-0-85745-179-8(0))*** Berghahn Bks., Inc.

Leask, Nigel. Robert Burns & Pastoral: Poetry & Improvement in Late Eighteenth-Century Scotland. 2010. (ENG., Illus.). 336p. 99.00 *(978-0-19-957261-8(5))* Oxford Univ. Pr., Inc.

Sprott, Gavin. Farming. Date not set. (Scotland's Past in Action Ser.). (Illus.). 96p. pap. 7.95 *(978-0-948636-69-1(6)*, 6696) NMS Enterprises Ltd. - Publishing GBR. Dist: Weatherhill, Inc.

AGRICULTURE—SOUTH AFRICA

Atkinson, Doreen. Going for Broke: The Fate of Farm Workers in Arid South Africa. 2007. (ENG., Illus.). 312p. pap. 34.95 *(978-0-7969-2176-5(8))* Human Sciences Research Council ZAF. Dist: Independent Pubs. Group.

Buchan, Angus. A Farmer's Year: Daily Truth to Change Your Life, 1 vol. Waldeck, Val, ed. 2007. (Illus.). 384p. 14.99 *(978-0-8254-6183-5(9)*, Monarch Bks.) Lion Hudson PLC GBR. Dist: Kregel Pubns.

Johnston, Peter. The Uptake & Usefulness of Seasonal Forecasting Products. 2011. 208p. pap. ***(978-3-8443-9694-2(2))*** Lambert Academic Publishing.

Kabuya, Francois Ilunga. Monograph for Southern African Agricultural & Food Policy. 2011. 96p. pap. ***(978-3-8454-1158-3(9))*** Lambert Academic Publishing.

Nepolo, Emmanuel. Genetic Variations of Marama Bean in the Namibian Germplasm. 2011. 83p. pap. ***(978-3-8433-7001-1(X))*** Lambert Academic Publishing.

Smith, Barry. The Farming Handbook. 2006. (Illus.). 432p. 59.95 *(978-1-86914-090-8(7))* University of Kwazulu-Natal Press ZAF. Dist: International Specialized Bk. Services.

AGRICULTURE—SOVIET UNION

Gustafson, Thane. Reform in Soviet Politics: The Lessons of Recent Policies on Land & Water. 2009 (ENG.). 236p. pap. 34.99 *(978-0-521-10187-5(5))* Cambridge Univ. Pr.

Smith, Robert Ernest Frederick. Peasant Farming in Muscovy. 2008. (ENG.). 316p. pap. 42.00 *(978-0-521-08652-3(3))* Cambridge Univ. Pr.

AGRICULTURE—SPAIN

Amat Llombart, Pablo & Llombart, Pablo Amat. Derecho de la Biotecnología y Los Transgénicos: (Especial Referencia Al Sector Agrario y Alimentario) 2008. (SPA.). 382p. *(978-84-9876-019-4(4))* Tirant lo Blanch.

Fernández Prieto, Lourenzo & Prieto, Lourenzo Fernández. El Apagón Tecnológico Del Franquismo: Estado e Innovacion en la Agricultura Española Del Siglo XX. 2007. (SPA., Illus.). 389p. *(978-84-8456-965-7(9))* Tirant lo Blanch.

Harding, Susan Friend. Remaking Ibieca: Rural Life in Aragon under Franco. 2011. (ENG.). 348p. pap. 40.00 *(978-0-8078-9677-8(2))* Univ. of North Carolina Pr.

Kerr, Peter. Snowball Oranges. 10th ed. 2011. (ENG.). 320p. pap. 14.95 ***(978-1-84953-025-5(4))*** Summerdale Pubs. GBR. Dist: Independent Pubs. Group.

Kirchner, Helena, ed. Por una Arqueologia Agraria: Perspectivas de Investigacion Sobre Espacios de Cultivo en las Sociedades Medievales Hispanicas. 2010. (Bar S Ser.). (SPA & ENG., Illus.). 202p. (C). pap. 162.50 *(978-1-4073-0553-0(0))* British Archaeological Reports Ltd. GBR. Dist: Brown, David Bk. Co., The.

AGRICULTURE—SRI LANKA

Bonavia, Emanuel. The Cultivated Oranges & Lemons, Etc. of India & Ceylon. 2009. (Gardening in America Ser.). (ENG.). 408p. pap. 24.95 *(978-1-4290-1430-4(X))* Applewood Bks.

Theivendram, Vigneswaran. Fitting a Time Series Model. 2009. 96p. pap. *(978-3-639-17081-8(4))* VDM Verlag Dr. Mueller e.K.

AGRICULTURE—SUDAN

Khalid, Siddig. Market Linkages & Price Transmission in Sudan: Lessons from Sesame Markets. 2011. 64p. pap. ***(978-3-639-33354-1(3))*** VDM Verlag Dr. Mueller e.K.

M. Mubarak, Amel, et al. Economic Policies & the Irrigated Agriculture in Sudan. 2011. 108p. pap. ***(978-3-8443-9015-5(4))*** Lambert Academic Publishing.

Mohammed, Ismail & Abdel Gabbar Gumaa. Genetic Diversity of Some Cucurbits in Khartoum State, Sudan. 2011. 120p. pap. ***(978-3-8443-0189-2(5))*** Lambert Academic Publishing.

AGRICULTURE—SWEDEN

Lageras, Per. The Ecology of Expansion & Abandonment: Medieval & Post-Medieval Agriculture & Settlement in a Landscape Perspective. 2007. (ENG., Illus.). 256p. (C). pap. 24.00 *(978-91-7209-441-3(9))* Riksantikvarieambetet och Statens historiska museer SWE. Dist: Brown, David Bk. Co., The.

Myrdal, Janken & Morell, Mats, eds. Agrarian History of Sweden: From 4000 BC to AD 2000. 2011. (ENG., Illus.). 336p. 54.95 ***(978-91-85509-56-0(6))*** Nordic Academic Pr., Sweden SWE. Dist: Independent Pubs. Group.

AGRICULTURE—TAIWAN

Lee, C. Y. & Partners. Taipei 101: The Tallest of the Tall. 2009. (ENG., Illus.). 224p. 65.00 *(978-1-86470-248-4(6))* Images Publishing Group AUS. Dist: National Bk. Network.

AGRICULTURE—TANZANIA

Glaeser, Bernhard. Ecodevelopment in Tanzania: An Empirical Contribution on Needs, Self-sufficiency, & Environmentally-sound Agriculture on Peasant Farms. (ENG.). XX, 229p. 210.00 ***(978-3-11-177084-0(2))*** De Gruyter, Mouton DEU. Dist: de Gruyter, Walter GmbH & Co. KG.

Masuki, Kenneth F. G. Farm-Level Adoption of Water System Innovations in Semi-Arid Areas. 2011. 148p. pap. ***(978-3-8443-2970-4(6))*** Lambert Academic Publishing.

Mzirai, Omari. Modeling of MacRo-Catchment Rainwater Harvesting in Semi-Arid Areas. 2011. 148p. pap. ***(978-3-8443-2079-4(2))*** Lambert Academic Publishing.

AGRICULTURE—THAILAND

Chalation, Vijittra. Jatropha Oil for Diesel Engine Application. 2011. 124p. pap. ***(978-3-8443-0334-6(0))*** Lambert Academic Publishing.

Phongphom, Artittaya & PONGQUAN, Soparth. Farmer's Network Approach. 2011. 252p. pap. ***(978-3-8443-1150-1(5))*** Lambert Academic Publishing.

AGRICULTURE—TROPICS

see also Tropical Crops

Bonynge, Francis. The Future Wealth of America: Being A Glance at the Resources of the United States & the Commercial & Agricultural Advantages of Cultivating Tea. 2006. 244p. per. 20.99 *(978-1-4255-2117-2(7))* MPublishing.

Chu, Thai Hoanh. Environment & Livelihoods in Tropical Coastal Zones: Managing Agriculture-Fishery-Aquaculture Conflicts. Gowing, J. W. et al, eds. 2006. (Comprehensive Assessment of Water Management in Agriculture Ser.: Vol. 2). (Illus.). 336p. 145.00 *(978-1-84593-107-0(6))* CABI GBR. Dist: Stylus Publishing, LLC.

Dion, Patrice, ed. Soil Biology & Agriculture in the Tropics. 2010. (Soil Biology Ser.). (Illus.). xiii, 350p. 239.00 *(978-3-642-05075-6(1), 3642050751)* Springer.

Mutsaers, H. J. W. Peasants, Farmers & Scientists: A Chronicle of Tropical Agricultural Science in the Twentieth Century. (ENG.). xxviii, 612p. 2010. pap. 139.00 *(978-90-481-7555-0(0), 9048175550)* 2007. 139.00 *(978-1-4020-6165-3(X), 140206165X)* Springer.

AGRICULTURE—TURKEY

Akalpler, Ergin. The European Unions Cap on Free Trade Turkey. 2008. 252p. pap. *(978-3-639-04879-7(2))* VDM Verlag Dr. Mueller e.K.

Miller, Naomi F. Botanical Aspects of Environment & Economy at Gordion, Turkey. 2010. (Illus.). 288p. (C). 69.95 *(978-1-934536-15-5(6),* Univ. of Pennsylvania Museum of Archaeology & Anthropology) Univ. Museum Pubns.

AGRICULTURE—UKRAINE

Michlmayr-Gomenyuk, Julia. The Privatization Process in Ukraine. 2010. 116p. pap. *(978-3-639-25482-2(1))* VDM Verlag Dr. Mueller e.K.

AGRICULTURE—UNITED STATES

Here are entered works on agriculture in the United States as a whole, as well as specific areas of the United States.

Abrahamsen, Martin A. & Scroggs, Claud L., eds. Agricultural Cooperation: Selected Readings. 2009. (ENG.). 592p. pap. 60.00 *(978-0-8166-5691-2(6))* Univ. of Minnesota Pr.

Adeleke, Oluwole & Adeleke, Moromoke. Gender & Technical Efficiency in Cassava Production in Nigeri. 2011. 140p. pap. ***(978-3-8433-9024-8(X))*** Lambert Academic Publishing.

Allen, Patricia. Together at the Table: Sustainability & Sustenance in the American Agrifood System. 2007. (Rural Studies). 260p. per. 27.00 *(978-0-271-02977-1(3))* Pennsylvania State Univ. Pr.

Allen, Richard, et al. American Farm Book. 2008. (Gardening in America Ser.). (ENG.). 392p. pap. 23.95 *(978-1-4290-1418-2(0))* Applewood Bks.

Allen, Richard Lamb. The American Farm Book or, Compend of American Agriculture: Being A Practical Treatise on Soils, Manures, Draining Irrigation, Grassegrain, Roots. 2006. 340p. per. 23.99 *(978-1-4255-3416-5(3))* MPublishing.

Arens, Curt. Down to Earth: Celebrating the Blessed Life of the Farmer. 2008. (American Catholic Experience Ser.). 110p. per. 9.95 *(978-0-87946-347-2(3))* ACTA Pubns.

Astyk, Sharon & Newton, Aaron. A Nation of Farmers: Defeating the Food Crisis on American Soil. 2009. (ENG., Illus.). 400p. pap. 19.95 *(978-0-86571-623-0(4), 978086571623 0)* New Society Pubs., Ltd. CAN. Dist: Consortium Bk. Sales & Distribution.

Backlund, Peter, et al. The Effects of Climate Change on Agriculture, Land Resources, Water Resources, & Biodiversity in the United States. 2008. pap. 39.00 *(978-1-60456-989-6(1))* Nova Science Pubs., Inc.

Berry, Wendell. The Gift of Good Land: Further Essays Cultural & Agricultural. 2009. (ENG.). 304p. pap. 15.95 *(978-1-58243-484-1(0),* Counterpoint Pr.) Basic Bks. GBR. Dist: Perseus-PGW.

Bertoni, Daniel. Homeland Security: Management & Coordination Problems Increase the Vulnerability of U. S. Agriculture to Foreign Pests & Diseases. 2006. 69p. (C). pap. 20.00 *(978-1-4223-0779-3(4))* DIANE Publishing Co.

Bishoff, Jonathan M., ed. Agricultural Finance & Credit. 2008. (C). pap. 50.00 *(978-1-60456-072-5(X))* Nova Science Pubs., Inc.

Blatt, Harvey. America's Food: What You Don't Know about What You Eat. (ENG., Illus.). 352p. (gr. 17). 2011. pap. 18.95 *(978-0-262-51595-5(4))* 2008. 29.95 *(978-0-262-02652-9(X))* MIT Pr.

Board, Prudy Taylor. The Story of the South Florida Fair. 2007. *(978-1-57864-469-8(0))* Donning Co. Pubs.

Boning, Charles R. Florida's Best Herbs & Spices: Native & Exotic Plants Grown for Scent & Flavor. 2010. (ENG.). 200p. pap. 19.95 *(978-1-56164-453-7(6))* Pineapple Pr., Inc.

Bonner, Robert & Churchill, Beryl. Home in the Valley: Powell's First Century. 2008. (Illus.). 336p. pap. 27.50 *(978-0-9771286-7-9(9))* WordsWorth.

Brennan, Carol. American Social Reform Movements: Biographies. 2006. (UXL American Social Reform Movements Reference Library). (ENG., Illus.). 320p. (J). (gr. 3-7). 83.00 *(978-1-4144-0218-5(X),* UXL) Cengage Gale.

Brockman, Terra. The Seasons on Henry's Farm: A Year of Food & Life on a Sustainable Farm. 2010. (ENG.). 310p. pap. 17.00 *(978-1-57284-115-4(X))* Surrey Bks.

Brooks, Emily. Connecticut Farmer & Feast: Harvesting Local Bounty. 2011. (Farmer & Feast Ser.). (ENG., Illus.). 224p. pap. 19.95 *(978-0-7627-6145-6(8))* Globe Pequot Pr., The.

Buck, Solon J. The Agrarian Crusade; a Chronicle of the Farmer in Politics. 2010. (Illus.). 76p. pap. 20.00 *(978-1-153-69147-5(7))* General Bks. LLC.

Buck, Solon J. 1884 & Buck, Solon J. 1884-1962. The Agrarian Crusade; a Chronicle of the Farmer in Politics. 2010. 260p. pap. 26.75 *(978-1-149-26677-9(5))* BiblioBazaar.

Buck, Solon Justus. The Agrarian Crusade; a Chronicle of the Farmer in Politics. 2010. (Illus.). 76p. pap. 14.14 *(978-1-154-06553-4(7))* General Bks. LLC.

Capper, Arthur. The Agricultural Bloc. 2008. 184p. pap. 22.99 *(978-0-559-88139-8(8));* pap. 21.75 *(978-0-559-88138-1(X))* BiblioBazaar.

—The Agricultural Bloc. 171p. reprint ed. 88.00 *(978-0-7222-2713-8(2))* Library Reprints, Inc.

Carr, Robert S. & Harrington, Timothy A. The Everglades. 2012. (Images of America Ser.). (ENG., Illus.). 128p. pap. 21.99 ***(978-0-7385-9127-8(0))*** Arcadia Publishing.

Carriker, Robert M. Urban Farming in the West: A New Deal Experiment in Subsistence Homesteads. 2010. (ENG., Illus.). 304p. 50.00 *(978-0-8165-2820-2(9))* Univ. of Arizona Pr.

Castle, Emery N. Reflections of a Pragmatic Economist: My Intellectual Journey. 2010. 288p. pap. 24.95 *(978-0-87071-586-0(0))* Oregon State Univ. Pr.

Cleland, Robert Glass & Hardy, Osgood. March of Industry: California. 2007. (ENG.). 332p. 45.95 *(978-0-548-01535-3(X))* Kessinger Publishing, LLC.

Cobbett, William. A Year's Residence in the United States of America: Treating of the Face of the Country, the Climate, the Soil... of the Expenses of Housekeeping... of the Manners & Customs of the People; and, of the Institutions of the Country... 2011. (Cambridge Library Collection - History Ser.). (ENG., Illus.). 630p. pap. 43.00 ***(978-1-108-03270-4(2))*** Cambridge Univ. Pr.

Cobbett, William & Hulme, Thomas. A Year's Residence in the United States. 2007. (Travel in America Ser.). (ENG.). 392p. per. 24.95 *(978-1-4290-0119-9(4))* Applewood Bks.

Cochran, Trevor J. Emerging Issues in the U. S. Organic Food Industry. 2011. (Food Science & Technology Ser.). 115.00 *(978-1-61761-284-8(7))* Nova Science Pubs., Inc.

Committee on Twenty-First Century Systems Agriculture & National Research Council. Toward Sustainable Agricultural Systems in the 21st Century. 2010. (ENG., Illus.). 598p. pap. 65.00 *(978-0-309-14896-2(0))* National Academies Pr.

Committee to Review the NIOSH Agriculture, Forestry, and Fishing Research Program & National Research Council. Agriculture, Forestry, & Fishing Research at NIOSH. 2008. (ENG.). 354p. pap. 70.75 *(978-0-309-11579-7(5))* National Academies Pr.

Conner, Mary T. Farm Bill of 2008: Major Provisions & Legislative Action. 2010. (Agriculture Issues & Policies Ser.). 301p. 79.00 *(978-1-60741-750-7(2))* Nova Science Pubs., Inc.

Cook, George Hammell. Report on the Geology & Agricultural Resources of the Southern Division of the State [of New Jersey]. 2011. 36p. pap. 11.99 ***(978-1-4181-9538-0(3))*** MPublishing.

Cool Springs Press Publications Staff & Nardozzi, Charlie. Northeast Fruit & Vegetable Gardening: Plant, Grow, & Eat the Best Edibles for Northeast Gardens. 2012. (Guide to Fruit & Vegetable Gardening Ser.). (ENG., Illus.). 256p. pap. 22.99 *(978-1-59186-529-2(8),* 1591865298) Cool Springs Pr.

Daniel, Diane. Farm Fresh North Carolina: The Go-to Guide to Great Farmers' Markets, Farm Stands, Farms, Apple Orchards, U-Picks, Kids' Activities, Lodging, Dining, Choose-and-Cut Christmas Trees, Vineyards & Wineries, & More. 2011. (Southern Gateways Guides). (ENG., Illus.). 304p. pap. 18.95 *(978-0-8078-7182-9(6))* Univ. of North Carolina Pr.

Dennett, Daniel. Louisiana As It Is: Its topography & Material Resources; Its Cotton, Sugar Cane, Rice & tobacco Fields; Its Corn & Grain Lands ... Reliable Info. 2006. 292p. per. 23.99 *(978-1-4255-2604-7(7))* MPublishing.

Dowsett, C. A Start in Life, a Journey Across America. 2007. (Travel in America Ser.). (ENG.). 124p. per. 24.95 *(978-1-4290-0497-8(5))* Applewood Bks.

Dowsett, Charles. A Start in Life: A Journey Across America, Fruit Farming in California. 2007. (Travel in America Ser.). (ENG.). 124p. 49.95 *(978-1-4290-0496-1(7))* Applewood Bks.

Du Bry, Travis. Immigrants, Settlers, & Laborers: The Socioeconomic Transformation of a Farming Community. 2006. (Illus.). (C). *(978-1-59332-157-4(0))* LFB Scholarly Publishing LLC.

Duffin, Andrew P. Plowed Under: Agriculture & Environment in the Palouse. (Weyerhaeuser Environmental Bks.). (ENG., Illus.). 272p. 2010. pap. 24.95 *(978-0-295-99017-0(1))* 2007. 35.00 *(978-0-295-98743-9(X))* Univ. of Washington Pr.

Duram, Leslie A., ed. Encyclopedia of Organic, Sustainable, & Local Food. 2011. (ENG., Illus.). 504p. pap. 34.95 *(978-0-8032-3625-7(5),* Bison Bks.) Univ. of Nebraska Pr.

Egendorf, Laura K. Food. 2006. (Opposing Viewpoints Ser.). (ENG., Illus.). 227p. (gr. 10-12). 27.50 *(978-0-7377-3232-0(6),* Greenhaven Pr., Inc.); (YA). (gr. 9-12). pap. 39.70 *(978-0-7377-3231-3(8))* Cengage Gale.

Ferguson. Careers in Focus - Agriculture. 2nd rev. ed. 2011. (Careers in Focus Ser.). 210p. (gr. 6-12). 32.95 *(978-0-8160-8036-6(4),* Ferguson Publishing Co.) Facts On File, Inc.

Francis, Charles, ed. Organic Farming: The Ecological System. 2009. (Agronomy Ser.: 54). lib. bdg. 70.00 *(978-0-89118-173-6(3))* ASA-CSSA-SSSA.

Full Committee Hearing on Climate Change Solutions for Small Businesses & Family Farmers: Hearing Before the Committee on Small Business, United States House of Representatives, One Hundred Eleventh Congress, First Session, Hearing Held April 29, 2009. 2009. v, 89p. *(978-0-16-083602-2(6),* 552-070-39320-0) United States Government Printing Office.

Gardner, Frank D. Traditional American Farming Techniques. 2nd rev. ed. 2007. (Traditional Ser.). (ENG., Illus.). 1088p. per. 29.95 *(978-1-59921-079-7(7),* Lyons Pr.) Globe Pequot Pr., The.

Gehring, Abigail R., ed. The Homesteading Handbook: A Back to Basics Guide to Growing Your Own Food, Canning, Keeping Chickens, Generating Your Own Energy, Crafting, Herbal Medicine, & More. 2011. (Back to Basics Guides). (ENG., Illus.). 272p. pap. 14.95 *(978-1-61608-265-9(8),* 608265) Skyhorse Publishing Co., Inc.

Globe Program 1997. pap., tchr. ed. *(978-0-16-060915-2(1),* Commerce Dept.) United States Government Printing Office.

Government Printing Office Staff. Agricultural Research. pap. 50.00 *(978-0-16-009204-6(3),* Agriculture Dept.) United States Government Printing Office.

Greeley, Horace. What I Know of Farming. 2009. 294p. pap. 19.99 *(978-0-217-90408-7(4));* 296p. pap. 19.99 *(978-1-4589-5031-4(X))* General Bks. LLC.

—What I Know of Farming: A Series of Brief & Plain Expositions of Practical Agriculture As an Art Based upon Science. 2010. 344p. pap. 31.75 *(978-1-145-17595-2(3))* BiblioBazaar.

Green, Linda L. Alabama 1850 Agricultural & Manufacturing Census, Volume 3 for Autauga, Baldwin, Barbour, Benton, Bibb, Blount, Butler, Chambers, Cherokee, Choctaw, Clarke, Coffee, Conecuh, Coosa, Covington Counties. 2009. 264p. pap. 33.00 *(978-0-7884-4907-9(9))* Heritage Bks.

—Alabama 1860 Agricultural & Manufacturing Census: Volume 4 for Perry, Pickens, Pike, Randolph, Russell, Shelby, St. Clair, Sumter, Tallapoosa, Talladega, Tuscaloosa, Walker, Washington, Wilcox, Winston. 2009. 376p. pap. 41.00 *(978-0-7884-5021-1(2))* Heritage Bks.

—Mississippi 1850 Agricultural Census, 3 vols. 2008. *(978-0-7884-4773-0(4),* Willow Bend Bks.) Heritage Bks.

—Missouri 1850 Agricultural Census: Volume 1. 2010. pap. 35.00 *(978-0-7884-5196-6(0))* Heritage Bks.

—North Carolina 1850 Agricultural Census: Volume 2. 2008. pap. 30.00 *(978-0-7884-4573-6(1))* Heritage Bks.

—North Carolina 1850 Agricultural Census: Volume 3. 2008. pap. 30.00 *(978-0-7884-4579-8(0))* Heritage Bks.

—North Carolina 1850 Agricultural Census: Volume 4. 2008. pap. 29.50 *(978-0-7884-4581-1(2))* Heritage Bks.

—West Virginia 1860 Agricultural Census, Volume 1. 2008. pap. 26.00 *(978-0-7884-4562-0(6))* Heritage Bks.

—West Virginia 1860 Agricultural Census, Volume 2. 2008. pap. *(978-0-7884-4563-7(4))* Heritage Bks.

Green, Linda L., compiled by. Mississippi 1850 Agricultural Census, 2 vols. 2008. *(978-0-7884-4679-5(7)); (978-0-7884-4511-8(1))* Heritage Bks. (Willow Bend Bks.).

—Missouri 1850 Agricultural Census, 4 vols. 2010. ***(978-0-7884-8434-6(6),*** Willow Bend Bks.) Heritage Bks.

—North Carolina 1850 Agricultural Census. 2008. *(978-0-7884-7158-2(9)); (978-0-7884-7669-3(6)); (978-0-7884-7668-6(8)); (978-0-7884-4629-0(0))* Heritage Bks. (Willow Bend Bks.).

—West Virginia 1850 Agricultural Census, 2 vols. 2007. *(978-0-7884-4311-4(9)); (978-0-7884-4253-7(8))* Heritage Bks. (Willow Bend Bks.).

Hahnel, Eugene Stephens. Down to Earth: The Pleasures & Perils of Becoming A Farmer. 2011. 112p. 39.95 ***(978-1-258-08669-5(7))*** Literary Licensing, LLC.

Hall, Rita Hiltenbrand. Millington. 2012. (Images of America Ser.). (ENG., Illus.). 128p. pap. 21.99 ***(978-0-7385-9128-5(9))*** Arcadia Publishing.

Hamda, Yonas. Equity of Farm Program Payments in South Dakota: 1990-2001. 2008. 100p. pap. *(978-3-639-09422-0(0))* VDM Verlag Dr. Mueller e.K.

Hamilton, Lisa M. Deeply Rooted: Unconventional Farmers in the Age of Agribusiness. (ENG.). 2010. 320p. pap. 15.95 *(978-1-58243-586-2(3))* 2009. 304p. 25.00 *(978-1-59376-180-6(5))* Basic Bks. GBR. (Counterpoint Pr.). Dist: Perseus-PGW.

Harris, Evelyn. The Barter Lady: A Woman Farmer Sees It Through. 2009. (ENG.). 344p. pap. 14.95 *(978-1-59416-094-3(5))* Westholme Publishing.

Harrison, Jill Lindsay. Pesticide Drift & the Pursuit of Environmental Justice. 2011. (Food, Health, & the Environment Ser.). (ENG., Illus.). 296p. (gr. 17). 46.00 *(978-0-262-01598-1(6))* MIT Pr.

Harrison, Jill Lindsey. Pesticide Drift & the Pursuit of Environmental Justice. 2011. (Food, Health, & the Environment Ser.). (ENG., Illus.). 296p. (gr. 17). pap. 23.00 *(978-0-262-51628-0(4))* MIT Pr.

Hearing to Review Agriculture Research Programs: Hearing Before the Subcommittee on Conservation, Credit, Energy, & Research of the Committee on Agriculture, House of Representatives, One Hundred Tenth Congress, First Session, May 10, 2007. 2008. (Illus.). iii, 172p. *(978-0-16-083236-9(5),* 552-070-39064-2) United States Government Printing Office.

Hearing to Review Credit Conditions in Rural America: Hearing Before the Subcommittee on Conservation, Credit, Energy, & Research of the Committee on Agriculture, House of Representatives, One Hundred Eleventh Congress, First Session, June 11, 2009. 2009. (Illus.). v, 82p. *(978-0-16-084858-2(X),* 552-070-40259-4) United States Government Printing Office.

Hearing to Review Credit Conditions in Rural America: Hearing Before the Subcommittee on Department Operations, Oversight, & Credit of the Committee on Agriculture, House of Representatives, One Hundred Twelfth Congress, First Session, April 14, 2011. 2011. (Illus.). iii, 70p. ***(978-0-16-089026-0(8),*** 552-070-43058-0) United States Government Printing Office.

Hearing to Review Dairy Policy: Hearing Before the Committee on Agriculture, House of Representatives, One Hundred Eleventh Congress, Second Session, April 20, 2010, Harrisburg, PA. 2010. (Illus.). iii, 84p. *(978-0-16-086246-5(9),* 552-070-41337-5) United States Government Printing Office.

Hearing to Review the Administration & Delivery of Conservation Programs: Hearing Before the Subcommittee on Conservation, Credit, Energy, & Research of the Committee on Agriculture, House of Representatives, One Hundred Eleventh Congress, Second Session, July 1, 2010. 2010. (Illus.). v, 74p. *(978-0-16-086791-0(6),* 552-070-41707-9) United States Government Printing Office.

Hearing to Review the Impact of the Indirect Land Use & Renewable Biomass Provisions in the Renewable Fuel Standard: Hearing Before the Subcommittee on Conservation, Credit, Energy, & Research of the Committee on Agriculture, House of Representatives, One Hundred Eleventh Congress, First Session, May 6, 2009. 2009. (Illus.). v, 396p.

(978-0-16-084342-6(1), 552-070-39886-4) United States Government Printing Office.

Hearing to Review the State of Agriculture in Kansas: Hearing Before the Subcommittee on General Farm Commodities & Risk Management of the Committee on Agriculture, House of Representatives, One Hundred Tenth Congress, First Session, June 5, 2007, Salina, KS. 2009. (Illus.). iv, 102p. (978-0-16-082991-8(7), 552-070-38893-1) United States Government Printing Office.

Heigel, Ken, photos by. New Orleans Culinary Impressions. 2008. (Illus.). 15.00 (978-0-89730-248-7(6)) R. J. Berg Pub.

Hibbard, Benjamin Horace. Effects of the Great War upon Agriculture in the United States And. 2007. (ENG.). 248p. per. 26.95 (978-1-4304-4812-9(1)) Kessinger Publishing, LLC.

Hilgard, Eugene W. Address on Progressive Agriculture, & Industrial Education, Delivered Before the Mississippi Agricultural & Mechanical Fair Association, at Jackso. 2011. 34p. pap. 11.99 (978-1-4181-9506-9(5)) MPublishing.

Hittell, John Shertzer. The Resources of California, Comprising Agriculture, Mining, Geography, Climate, Commerce, etc etc & the Past & Future Development of the State. 2006. 484p. per. 29.99 (978-1-4255-5303-6(6)) MPublishing.

Hobbs, Samuel Huntington & Bond, Marjorie N. North Carolina Today. 2011. (ENG.). 434p. pap. 50.00 (978-0-8078-6872-0(8)) Univ. of North Carolina Pr.

Hokanson, Drake & Kratz, Carol. Purebred & Homegrown: America's County Fairs. 2008. (ENG., Illus.). 200p. pap. 29.95 (978-0-299-22824-8(X)) Univ. of Wisconsin Pr.

Holcomb, Richard, ed. Agricultural Statistics 2010. 2011. (ENG., Illus.). 508p. pap. 45.00 (978-0-16-088287-6(7), Agricultural Research Service) United States Government Printing Office.

Holthaus, Gary. From the Farm to the Table: What All Americans Need to Know about Agriculture. (Culture of the Land Ser.). (ENG., Illus.). 384p. 2009. pap. 27.95 (978-0-8131-9226-0(9)) 2007. 50.00 (978-0-8131-2419-3(0)) Univ. Pr. of Kentucky.

Hulme, Thomas & Cobbett, William. A Year's Residence in the United States. 2007. (Travel in America Ser.). (ENG.). 392p. 49.95 (978-1-4290-0118-2(6)) Applewood Bks.

Hurt, R. Douglas. The Big Empty: The Great Plains in the Twentieth Century. 2011. (Modern American West Ser.). (ENG., Illus.). 344p. 65.00 (978-0-8165-2970-4(1)); pap. 29.95 (978-0-8165-2972-8(8)) Univ. of Arizona Pr.

Ikerd, John E. Crisis & Opportunity: Sustainability in American Agriculture. 2008. (Our Sustainable Future Ser.). (ENG., Illus.). 342p. pap. 18.95 (978-0-8032-1142-1(2), Bison Bks.) Univ. of Nebraska Pr.

Investing in Our Nation's Future Through Agricultural Research: Hearing Before the Committee on Agriculture, Nutrition, & Forestry, United States Senate, One Hundred Tenth Congress, First Session, March 7, 2007. 2007. (Illus.). iv, 192p. (978-0-16-078869-7(2), 552-070-35998-2) United States Government Printing Office.

Iowa Department of Agriculture Staff. Iowa Year Book of Agriculture. (Illus.). reprint ed. lib. bdg. 98.00 (978-0-7222-4788-4(5)) Library Reprints, Inc.

Isto, Sarah Crawford. The Fur Farms of Alaska: Two Centuries of History & a Forgotten Stampede. 2012. (ENG., Illus.). 250p. pap. 29.95 (978-1-60223-171-9(0)) Univ. of Alaska Pr.

Jackson, Wes. Altars of Unhewn Stone: Science & the Earth. 2006. 176p. per. 15.95 (978-1-59098-287-7(8)) Wooster Bk. Co., The.

—Consulting the Genius of the Place: An Ecological Approach to a New Agriculture. 2010. (ENG., Illus.). 224p. 26.00 (978-1-58243-513-8(8), Counterpoint Pr.) Basic Bks. GBR. Dist: Perseus-PGW.

—Consulting the Genius of the Place: An Ecological Approach to a New Agriculture. 2011. (ENG.). 288p. pap. 16.95 (978-1-58243-780-4(7), Counterpoint) Counterpoint LLC.

Jefferson, Thomas. The Farm Book by Thomas Jefferson with light notes & annotations by Sam Sloan. Sloan, Sam, ed. 2006. 192p. per. 19.95 (978-0-923891-80-0(3)) Ishi Pr. International.

Jesness, Oscar B. & Nowell, Reynolds I. A Program for Land Use in Northern Minnesota: A Type Study in Land Utilization. 338p. reprint ed. lib. bdg. 98.00 (978-0-7222-0449-8(3)) Library Reprints, Inc.

Johnston, Jas. F. W. (James Finlay Weir). Notes on North America, Agricultural, Economical, & Social. 2006. 436p. pap. 26.99 (978-1-4255-4719-6(2)); 528p. per. 29.99 (978-1-4255-5806-2(2)) MPublishing.

Judge, Phyll Ann, afterword by. Chronicles of Life in the Midwest: A Decade of Transition. 2008. (Illus.). 132p. pap. 15.00 (978-0-9770573-2-0(1)) Salt Marsh Cottage Bks.

Kains, Maurice. Five Acres & Independence. 2007. 408p. per. (978-956-291-446-8(1)); (SPA., Illus.). (978-956-291-449-9(6)) Editorial Benei Noaj.

Kellar, Herbert A., ed. Solon Robinson Set: Pioneer & Agriculturist; Selected Writings, 2 vols. reprint ed. lib. bdg. 250.00 (978-0-7222-0458-0(2)) Library Reprints, Inc.

Kentucky Department of Agriculture Staff. Biennial Report. 273p. reprint ed. lib. bdg. 98.00 (978-0-7222-0605-8(4)) Library Reprints, Inc.

Killebrew, Joseph B. Tennessee: Its Agricultural & Mineral Wealth, Showing the Extent, Value & Accessibility of Its Ores, with Analyses of the Same. (Illus.). 196p. reprint ed. lib. bdg. 88.00 (978-0-7222-4831-7(8)) Library Reprints, Inc.

Kingsolver, Barbara. Animal, Vegetable, Miracle: A Year of Food Life. 2009. (Playaway Top Adult Picks B Ser.). 69.99 (978-1-4332-5584-7(7)) Findaway World, LLC.

Kingsolver, Barbara & Kingsolver, Camille. Animal, Vegetable, Miracle: A Year of Food Life. l.t. ed. 2007. pap. 26.95 (978-0-06-128529-5(3), HarperLuxe) HarperCollins Pubs.

Kingsolver, Barbara, et al. Animal, Vegetable, Miracle: A Year of Food Life. (P. S. Ser.). 2008. (ENG., Illus.). 400p. pap. 15.99 (978-0-06-085256-6(9), HarperPerennial) 2007. 384p. 26.95 (978-0-06-085255-9(0)) HarperCollins Pubs.

Kirch, Patrick Vinton. Roots of Conflict: Soils, Agriculture, & Sociopolitical Complexity in Ancient Hawaii. 2010. (Illus.). xix, 199p. (978-1-934691-26-7(7)) School for Advanced Research Pr./SAR Pr.

Koweek, Jim. Just Add Water. 2007. 192p. pap. 17.50 (978-0-615-17465-5(5)) Koweek, Jim.

Krist, John. Living Legacy. 2007. (Illus.). 128p. lib. bdg. 39.95 (978-0-9798780-0-8(4)) Farm Bureau of Ventura County.

Kroeck, Seth. Crop Rotation & Cover Cropping: Soil Resiliency & Health on the Organic Farm. 2011. (ENG.). 96p. pap. 12.95 (978-1-60358-345-9(9)) Chelsea Green Publishing.

Leverett, Frank. Surface Geology & Agricultural Conditions of Michigan. (Illus.). reprint ed. lib. bdg. 125.00 (978-0-7222-0077-3(3)) Library Reprints, Inc.

MacLachlan, Janine. Farmers' Markets of the Heartland. 2012. (Heartland Foodways Ser.). (ENG., Illus.). 256p. pap. 24.95 (978-0-252-07863-7(2)) Univ. of Illinois Pr.

Manalo, Paula, et al. Greenhorns: 50 Dispatches from the Young Farmers' Movement. Manalo, Paula et al, eds. 2012. (ENG., Illus.). 256p. pap. 14.95 (978-1-60342-772-2(4), 1603427724) Storey Publishing, LLC.

Maryland. Agricultural chemist. First[-Second] Report of Philip T Tyson, State Agricultural Chemist, to the House of Delegates of Maryland, January 1860[-January 1862]. 2006. 176p. per. 18.99 (978-1-4255-1415-0(4)) MPublishing.

Mason, David Hastings. How Western Farmers Are Benefited by Protection. 2006. 116p. per. 16.99 (978-1-4255-0746-6(8)) MPublishing.

Massachusetts. Commissioners concerning. Report of Commissioners Concerning an Agricultural School January 1851. 2006. 108p. per. 16.99 (978-1-4255-0691-9(7)) MPublishing.

Matuz, Roger. American Social Reform Movements: Primary Sources. Edgar, Kathleen J., ed. 2006. (UXL American Social Reform Movements Reference Library). (ENG., Illus.). 320p. 83.00 (978-1-4144-0219-2(8), UXL) Cengage Gale.

Michigan State Agricultural Society Staff. The Transactions of the State Agricultural Society of Michigan; with Reports of County Agricultural Societies, for the Year 1849-59 Pub by Order Of. 2006. (ENG.). 676p. per. 36.99 (978-1-4255-6806-1(8)); 508p. per. 29.99 (978-1-4255-5693-8(0)); 604p. per. 32.99 (978-1-4255-6437-7(2)); (ENG.). 628p. per. 34.99 (978-1-4255-6594-7(8)) MPublishing.

Michigan. State Dept. Of Agriculture. Annual Report of the Secretary of the State Board of Agriculture for the Year 1865. 2011. 336p. pap. 23.99 (978-1-4181-8797-2(6)) MPublishing.

—Annual Report of the Secretary of the State Board of Agriculture for the Year 1870. 2011. 486p. pap. 29.99 (978-1-4181-8861-0(1)) MPublishing.

Milk Comes from A Cow? 2007. (Illus.). 16p. (J). 8.00 (978-0-9797653-0-8(7)) Kansas Farm Bureau.

Miller, Susan Lambert, photos by. Minnesota County Fairs: Kids, Cows, Carnies, & Chow. 2009. (ENG., Illus.). 128p. 24.95 (978-0-87351-719-5(9)) Minnesota Historical Society Pr.

Minnis, John & Beaver, Lauren. Michigan State Fair. 2010. (Images of America Ser.). (ENG., Illus.). 128p. pap. 21.99 (978-0-7385-7789-0(8)) Arcadia Publishing.

Mississippi Geological, Economic. Report on the Geological & Agricultural Survey of the State of Mississippi by Eugene W Hilgard, State Geologist. 2011. 24p. pap. 11.99 (978-1-4181-9158-0(2)) MPublishing.

Missouri. State Geologist. Geological Report of the Country along the Line of the Southwestern Branch of the Pacific Railroad, State of Missouri. 2006. 120p. per. 16.99 (978-1-4255-0812-8(X)) MPublishing.

Mitchell, Shelley. Organic Agriculture in Oklahom. 2008. 96p. pap. (978-3-8364-9846-3(4)) VDM Verlag Dr. Mueller e.K.

Nahmias, Rick. The Migrant Project: Contemporary California Farm Workers. 2008. (ENG., Illus.). 168p. pap. 27.95 (978-0-8263-4407-6(0)) Univ. of New Mexico Pr.

Nakane, Kazuko. Nothing Left in My Hands: The Issei of a Rural California Town, 1900-1942. 2009. pap. (978-1-59714-109-3(7)) Heyday.

Nash, George & Waterman, Jane. Homesteading in the 21st Century: How One Family Created a More Sustainable, Self-Sufficient, & Satisfying Life. 2011. (ENG., Illus.). 416p. pap. 24.95 (978-1-60085-296-1(3)) Taunton Pr., Inc.

NC Department of Cultural Resources & NC Cooperative Extension. Homegrown Handmade: Art Roads & Farm Trails. 2008. (Illus.). 387p. pap. 19.95 (978-0-89587-355-2(9)) Blair, John F. Pub.

New Hampshire state agricultural society. Transactions of the New Hampshire State Agricultural Society, 1850/52-1860, with Condensed Reports of County Societies. 2006. 276p. per. 23.99 (978-1-4255-2468-5(0)) MPublishing.

Office of the Federal Register (U.S.), compiled by. Code of Federal Regulations, Title 7, Agriculture, Pt. 1200-1599, Revised as of January 1 2011. rev. ed. 2011. (ENG.). 1042p. pap. 67.00 (978-0-16-087535-9(8), Office of the Federal Register) United States Government Printing Office.

—Code of Federal Regulations, Title 7, Agriculture, Pt. 1200-1599, Revised as of January 1 2012. rev. ed. 2012. (ENG.). 1093p. pap. 67.00 (978-0-16-090069-3(7), Office of the Federal Register) United States Government Printing Office.

—Code of Federal Regulations, Title 7, Agriculture, Pt. 1600-1759, Revised as of January 1 2011. rev. ed. 2011. (ENG., Illus.). 827p. pap. 70.00 (978-0-16-087536-6(6), Office of the Federal Register) United States Government Printing Office.

—Code of Federal Regulations, Title 7, Agriculture, Pt. 1600-1759, Revised as of January 1 2012. rev. ed. 2012. (ENG., Illus.). 838p. pap. 70.00 (978-0-16-090070-9(0), Office of the Federal Register) United States Government Printing Office.

—Code of Federal Regulations, Title 7, Agriculture, Pt. 1760-1939, Revised as of January 1 2011. rev. ed. 2011. (ENG.). 673p. pap. 36.00 (978-0-16-087537-3(4), Office of the Federal Register) United States Government Printing Office.

—Code of Federal Regulations, Title 7, Agriculture, Pt. 1760-1939, Revised as of January 1 2012. rev. ed. 2012. (ENG.). 661p. pap. 36.00 (978-0-16-090071-6(9), Office of the Federal Register) United States Government Printing Office.

—Code of Federal Regulations, Title 7, Agriculture, Pt. 1940-1949, Revised as of January 1 2012. rev. ed. 2012. (ENG.). 395p. pap. 56.00 (978-0-16-090072-3(7), Office of the Federal Register) United States Government Printing Office.

—Code of Federal Regulations, Title 7, Agriculture, Pt. 1950-1999, Revised as of January 1 2011. rev. ed. 2011. (ENG.). 412p. pap. 70.00 (978-0-16-087539-7(0), Office of the Federal Register) United States Government Printing Office.

—Code of Federal Regulations, Title 7, Agriculture, Pt. 1950-1999, Revised as of January 1 2012. rev. ed. 2012. (ENG.). 412p. pap. 52.00 (978-0-16-090073-0(5), Office of the Federal Register) United States Government Printing Office.

—Code of Federal Regulations, Title 7, Agriculture, Pt. 2000-End, Revised as of January 1 2011. rev. ed. 2011. (ENG.). 1016p. pap. 56.00 (978-0-16-087540-3(4), Office of the Federal Register) United States Government Printing Office.

—Code of Federal Regulations, Title 7, Agriculture, Pt. 2000-End, Revised as of January 1 2012. rev. ed. 2012. (ENG.). 1147p. pap. 56.00 (978-0-16-090074-7(3), Office of the Federal Register) United States Government Printing Office.

—Code of Federal Regulations, Title 7, Agriculture, Pt. 210-299, Revised as of January 1 2011. rev. ed. 2011. (ENG.). 1107p. pap. 68.00 (978-0-16-087529-8(3), Office of the Federal Register) United States Government Printing Office.

—Code of Federal Regulations, Title 7, Agriculture, Pt. 210-299, Revised as of January 1 2012. rev. ed. 2012. (ENG.). 1113p. pap. 68.00 (978-0-16-090062-4(X), Office of the Federal Register) United States Government Printing Office.

—Code of Federal Regulations, Title 7, Agriculture, Pt. 300-399, Revised as of January 1 2011. rev. ed. 2011. (ENG.). 580p. pap. 52.00 (978-0-16-087530-4(7), Office of the Federal Register) United States Government Printing Office.

—Code of Federal Regulations, Title 7, Agriculture, Pt. 300-399, Revised as of January 1 2012. rev. ed. 2012. (ENG.). 589p. pap. 52.00 (978-0-16-090064-8(6), Office of the Federal Register) United States Government Printing Office.

—Code of Federal Regulations, Title 7, Agriculture, Pt. 400-699, Revised as of January 1 2011. rev. ed. 2011. (ENG.). 655p. pap. 47.00 (978-0-16-087531-1(5), Office of the Federal Register) United States Government Printing Office.

—Code of Federal Regulations, Title 7, Agriculture, Pt. 400-699, Revised as of January 1 2012. rev. ed. 2012. (ENG.). 655p. pap. 47.00 (978-0-16-090065-5(4), Office of the Federal Register) United States Government Printing Office.

—Code of Federal Regulations, Title 7, Agriculture, Pt. 53-209, Revised as of January 1 2011. rev. ed. 2011. (ENG.). 487p. pap. 42.00 (978-0-16-087528-1(5), Office of the Federal Register) United States Government Printing Office.

—Code of Federal Regulations, Title 7, Agriculture, Pt. 53-209, Revised as of January 1 2012. rev. ed. 2012. (ENG.). 483p. pap. 42.00 (978-0-16-090061-7(1), Office of the Federal Register) United States Government Printing Office.

—Code of Federal Regulations, Title 7, Agriculture, Pt. 700-899, Revised as of January 1 2011. rev. ed. 2011. (ENG.). 581p. pap. 49.00 (978-0-16-087532-8(3), Office of the Federal Register) United States Government Printing Office.

—Code of Federal Regulations, Title 7, Agriculture, Pt. 900-999, Revised as of January 1 2011. rev. ed. 2011. (ENG.). 800p. pap. 66.00 (978-0-16-087533-5(1), Office of the Federal Register) United States Government Printing Office.

Office of the Federal Register (U.S.), compiled by. Code of Federal Regulations, Title 7, Agriculture, Pt. 900-999, Revised as of January 1 2012. rev. ed. 2012. (ENG.). 800p. pap. 66.00 (978-0-16-090067-9(0), Office of the Federal Register) United States Government Printing Office.

Office of the Federal Register (U.S.), ed. Code of Federal Regulations, Title 7, Agriculture, Pt. 1-26, Revised as of January 1 2011. 2011. (ENG.). 590p. pap. 50.00 (978-0-16-087526-7(9), Office of the Federal Register) United States Government Printing Office.

—Code of Federal Regulations, Title 7, Agriculture, Pt. 1000-1199, Revised as of January 1 2011. 2011. (ENG.). 269p. pap. 26.00 (978-0-16-087534-2(X), Office of the Federal Register) United States Government Printing Office.

—Code of Federal Regulations, Title 7, Agriculture, Pt. 27-52, Revised as of January 1 2011. rev. ed. 2011. (ENG., Illus.). 635p. pap. 55.00 (978-0-16-087527-4(7), Office of the Federal Register) United States Government Printing Office.

Office of the Federal Register (U.S.), ed. Code of Federal Regulations, Title 7, Agriculture, Pt. 27-52, Revised as of January 1 2012. rev. ed. 2012. (ENG., Illus.). 637p. pap. 55.00 (978-0-16-090060-0(3), Office of the Federal Register) United States Government Printing Office.

Ohmart, Clifford P. A View from the Vineyard: A Practical Guide to Sustainable Wine Grape Growing. 2011. (ENG., Illus.). 192p. pap. 34.95 (978-1-935879-90-9(1)) Wine Appreciation Guild, Ltd.

Olin, Walter H. American Irrigation Farming. (Illus.). 364p. reprint ed. lib. bdg. 98.00 (978-0-7222-4713-6(3)) Library Reprints, Inc.

Owens, Jasper T. The Farm Bill & Its Far-Ranging Impact. 2008. (Illus.). xvi, 265p. 82.00 (978-1-60456-631-4(0)) Nova Science Pubs., Inc.

Paddock, Wendell & Whipple, Orville. Fruit-Growing in Arid Regions. 2008. (Gardening in America Ser.). (ENG.). 428p. pap. 25.95 (978-1-4290-1329-1(X)) Applewood Bks.

Parkinson, Richard & Washington, George. Tour in America in 1798, 1799, & 1800: Exhibiting Sketches of Society & Manners, & a Particular Account of the America System of Agriculture, with Its Recent Improvements. 2007. (Travel in America Ser.). (ENG.). 340p. 49.95 (978-1-4290-0026-0(0)); per. 24.95 (978-1-4290-0027-7(9)) Applewood Bks.

Petty, Dustin. Michigan FFA (Future Farmers of America) A Legacy of Great Lakes Leadership. 2008. (Illus.). 112p. lib. bdg. 39.50 (978-1-932439-63-2(3)) M.T. Publishing Co., Inc.

Popoff, Mischa. Is It Organic. 2011. 574p. pap. 27.99 (978-1-61215-462-6(X)) Xulon Pr., Inc.

Protecting America's Harvest: Hearing Before the Subcommittee on Immigration, Citizenship, Refugees, Border Security, & International Law of the Committee on the Judiciary, House of Representatives, One Hundred Eleventh Congress, Second Session, Friday, September 24, 2010. 2010. iii, 58p. (978-0-16-087797-1(0), 552-070-42301-0) United States Government Printing Office.

Pscheidt, Jay W. & Ocamb, Cynthia M., eds. Pacific Northwest Plant Disease Management Handbook. 2007th rev. ed. 2007. per. 40.00 (978-1-931979-15-3(4)) Oregon State Univ. Extension Service.

Reed, Dick. Letters from the Past: Revelations. 2010. 232p. 28.99 (978-1-4490-0814-7(3)); pap. 18.99 (978-1-4490-0813-0(5)) AuthorHouse.

Review Colony Collapse Disorder in Honey Bee Colonies Across the United States: Hearing Before the Subcommittee on Horticulture & Organic Agriculture of the Committee on Agriculture, House of Representatives, One Hundred Tenth Congress, First Session, March 29, 2007. 2007. (Illus.). iv, 184p. (978-0-16-079721-7(7), 552-070-36663-6) United States Government Printing Office.

Review the Availability of Credit in Rural America: Hearing Before the Subcommittee on Conservation, Credit, Energy, & Research of the Committee on Agriculture, House of Representatives, One Hundred Tenth Congress, First Session, March 27, 2007. 2007. (Illus.). iii, 217p. (978-0-16-079610-4(5), 552-070-35566-4) United States Government Printing Office.

Richardson, Jill. Recipe for America: Why Our Food System Is Broken & What We Can Do to Fix It. 2009. (ENG.). 224p. pap. 15.95 (978-0-9815040-3-2(5)) Ig Publishing, Inc.

Ridder, Mary. Roots of Change: Nebraska's New Agriculture. 2007. (Our Sustainable Future Ser.: Vol. 18). (ENG., Illus.). 152p. pap. 24.95 (978-0-8032-9013-6(6), Bison Bks.) Univ. of Nebraska Pr.

Robinson, Edward V. Early Economic Conditions & the Development of Agriculture in Minnesota. (Illus.). 306p. reprint ed. lib. bdg. 98.00 (978-0-7222-4762-4(1)) Library Reprints, Inc.

Rogers, Henry. The Greyson Letters: Selections from the Correspondence of R. E. H. Greyson, Esq. [Pseud.] Ed. by Henry Rogers. 2006. 532p. per. 29.99 (978-1-4255-5921-2(2)) MPublishing.

The Role of Agriculture & Forestry in Global Warming Legislation: Hearing Before the Committee on Agriculture, Nutrition, & Forestry, United States Senate, One Hundred Eleventh Congress, First Session, July 22, 2009. 2010. (Illus.). v, 294p. (978-0-16-087062-0(3), 552-070-4191905) United States Government Printing Office.

Salatin, Joel. Everything I Want to Do Is Illegal: War Stories from the Local Food Front. 2007. (ENG.). 352p. per. 23.95 (978-0-9638109-5-3(2)) Polyface, Inc.

—The Sheer Ecstasy of Being a Lunatic Farmer. 2010. (ENG.). 300p. pap. 25.00 (978-0-9638109-6-0(0)) Polyface, Inc.

Scoery, Edwin James. Transcendentalism: A Story of Brook Farm. 2011. 34p. 35.95 (978-1-258-10191-6(2)) Literary Licensing, LLC.

Scheuring, Ann Foley. Valley Empires: Hugh Glenn & Henry Miller in the Shaping of California. 2010. (Illus.). 320p. pap. 29.95 (978-0-615-34123-1(3)) Gold Oak Pr.

Schnepf, Randy. High Agricultural Commodity Prices: What Are the Issues? 2008. pap. 39.00 (978-1-60692-013-8(8)) Nova Science Pubs., Inc.

Shirreff, Patrick. Shirreff's Tour Through North America. 2007. (Travel in America Ser.). (ENG.). 492p. 49.95 (978-1-4290-0174-8(7)) Applewood Bks.

—Shirreff's Tour Through North America: Together with a Comprehensive View of the Canadas & United States, as Adapted for Agricultural Emigration. 2007.

(Travel in America Ser.). (ENG.). 492p. per. 24.95 *(978-1-4290-0175-5(5))* Applewood Bks.

Smith, Jeremy N. Growing a Garden City: How Farmers, First Graders, Counselors, Troubled Teens, Foodies, a Homeless Shelter Chef, Single Mothers, & More are Transforming Themselves & Their Neighborhoods Through the Intersection of Local Agriculture & Community. 2010. (ENG., Illus.). 240p. 24.95 *(978-1-61608-108-9(2)*, 608108) Skyhorse Publishing Co., Inc.

Spaulding, Ken & Spaulding, Janice. Goat School: A Master Class in Caprine Care & Cooking, 1 vol. 2011. (ENG.). 200p. pap. 19.95 *(978-0-89272-956-2(2))* Down East Bks.

Spellman, Frank R. & Whiting, Nancy E. Environmental Management of Concentrated Animal Feeding Operations (CAFOS) 2007. (ENG., Illus.). 496p. 157.95 *(978-0-8493-7098-4(1)*, CRC Press) Taylor & Francis Group GBR. Dist: Taylor & Francis Group.

Starr, Frederick. Farm Echoes. 2008. (Gardening in America Ser.). (ENG.). 116p. pap. 10.95 *(978-1-4290-1276-8(5))* Applewood Bks.

Starrs, Paul & Goin, Peter. Field Guide to California Agriculture. 2010. (California Natural History Guides). (ENG., Illus.). 504p. 60.00 *(978-0-520-24764-2(7))*; pap. 24.95 *(978-0-520-26543-1(2))* Univ. of California Pr.

Steelman, L. W. A Few Acres & Security: Your Complete Guide to Independence with Little Capital & Lots of Contentment. 2011. 334p. 50.95 ***(978-1-258-06456-3(1))*** Literary Licensing, LLC.

Stephenson, Garry Owen. Farmers' Markets: Success, Failure, & Management Ecology. 2008. (Illus.). 244p. (C). 99.95 *(978-1-60497-509-3(1))* Cambria Pr.

Tennessee Department of Agriculture Staff. Biennial Reports. reprint ed. lib. bdg. 1250.00 *(978-0-7222-4826-3(1))* Library Reprints, Inc.

Thomas, J. J. Rural Affairs: A Practical & Copiously Illustrated Register of Rural Economy & Rural Taste, including Country Dwellings, Improving & Planting G. 2006. (ENG.). 340p. per. 23.99 *(978-1-4255-3441-7(4))*; 328p. per. 23.99 *(978-1-4255-3215-4(2))*; (ENG.). 328p. per. 23.99 *(978-1-4255-3276-5(4))*; (ENG.). 340p. per. 23.99 *(978-1-4255-3410-3(4))* MPublishing.

Thomson Gale Staff. American Social Reform Movements Reference Library, 4.0. 2006. (American Social Reform Movements Reference Ser.). (ENG., Illus.). 800p. (J). 292.00 *(978-1-4144-0214-7(7)*, UXL) Cengage Gale.

—American Social Reform Movements Reference Library Almanac, 2.0. 2006. (American Social Reform Movements Reference Ser.). (ENG., Illus.). 150.00 *(978-1-4144-0215-4(5)*, UXL) Cengage Gale.

Thorness, Bill. Edible Heirlooms: Heritage Vegetables for the Maritme Garden. 2009. (ENG.). 160p. pap. 18.95 *(978-1-59485-142-1(5)*, Skipstone) Mountaineers Bks., The.

Turner, David G. Eugene. 2012. (Images of America Ser.). (ENG., Illus.). 128p. pap. 21.99 ***(978-0-7385-9323-4(0))*** Arcadia Publishing.

U. S. Department of Agriculture, Adjustment Administration Staff. Living on an Acre: A Practical Guide to the Self-Reliant Life. Woodside, Christine, ed. 2nd ed. 2010. (ENG.). 336p. pap. 16.95 *(978-1-59921-885-4(2)*, Lyons Pr.) Globe Pequot Pr., The.

U. S. Department of Agriculture Staff. Yearbook of Agriculture. (Illus.). reprint ed. lib. bdg. *(978-0-7222-3095-4(8))* Library Reprints, Inc.

Virginia Department of Agriculture Staff. Virginia. (Illus.). 264p. reprint ed. lib. bdg. 98.00 *(978-0-7222-0580-8(5))* Library Reprints, Inc.

Vossen, Paulus H. Organic Olive Production Manual. 2007. 112p. pap. 18.00 *(978-1-60107-440-9(9))* A N R Pubns.

Walsh, Casey. Building the Borderlands: A Transnational History of Irrigated Cotton along the Mexico-Texas Border. 2008. (Environmental History Ser.). (ENG., Illus.). 248p. 47.50 *(978-1-60344-013-4(5))* Texas A&M Univ. Pr.

Waltz, Christopher L. Local Food Systems: Background & Issues. 2011. (Agriculture Issues & Policies Ser.). (Illus.). 160p. 115.00 *(978-1-61761-594-8(3))* Nova Science Pubs., Inc.

Warner, Helen. Florida Fruits & How to Raise Them. 2008. (Gardening in America Ser.). (ENG.). 348p. pap. 22.95 *(978-1-4290-1424-3(5))* Applewood Bks.

Warner, Keith Douglass. Agroecology in Action: Extending Alternative Agriculture Through Social Networks. 2006. (Food, Health, & the Environment Ser.). (ENG., Illus.). 296p. (gr. 17). 62.00 *(978-0-262-23252-4(9))*; per. 26.00 *(978-0-262-73180-5(0))* MIT Pr.

Wedin, Walter F. & Fales, Steven L., eds. Grassland: Quietness & Strength for a New American Agriculture. 2009. lib. bdg. 80.00 *(978-0-89118-171-2(7))* ASA-CSSA-SSSA.

Wildfeuer, Sherry. Stella Natura 2008: Working with Cosmic Rhythms: Inspiration & Practical Advice for Home Gardeners & Professional Growers. 2007. (Illus.). 40p. pap. 14.95 *(978-0-9795530-0-4(8))* Growing Biodynamics, LLC.

Williamson, Cici. The Best of Virginia Farms Cookbook & Tour Book: Recipes, People, Places. 2008. (ENG., Illus.). 310p. pap. 19.95 *(978-0-89732-657-5(1))* Menasha Ridge Pr., Inc.

Winthrop, Robert C. American Agriculture; an Address Delivered Before the Bristol County Agricultural Society, on Occasion of Their Annual Cattle Show & Fair at Taunton. 2011. 36p. pap. 11.99 ***(978-1-4181-9555-7(3))*** MPublishing.

Wisconsin Department of Agriculture and Markets Staff. Wisconsin. (Illus.). 36p. reprint ed. lib. bdg. 88.00 *(978-0-7222-0297-5(0))* Library Reprints, Inc.

Woo, Rosten, et al. Above the Pavement, the Farm: Architectural Agriculture at Public Farm 1. Michaels, Adam, ed. 2010. (ENG., Illus.). 208p. pap. 19.95 *(978-1-56898-935-8(0))* Princeton Architectural Pr.

Woodward, Carl Raymond. Ploughs & Politicks. 2011. 516p. 60.95 ***(978-1-258-09936-7(5))*** Literary Licensing, LLC.

Wuthnow, Robert. Remaking the Heartland: Middle America since the 1950's. 2010. (ENG., Illus.). 376p. (C). 35.00 *(978-0-691-14611-9(X))* Princeton Univ. Pr.

Young, Daniel J., ed. The Science Surrounding Food. 2009. (Agriculture Issues & Politics Ser.). (Illus.). viii, 170p. 80.10 *(978-1-60876-033-6(2))* Nova Science Pubs., Inc.

AGRICULTURE—UNITED STATES—HISTORY

Anderson, J. L. Industrializing the Corn Belt: Agriculture, Technology, & Environment, 1945-1972. 2008. (Illus.). 248p. 32.95 *(978-0-87580-392-0(X))* Northern Illinois Univ. Pr.

Ashworth, William. Ogallala Blue: Water & Life on the High Plains. 2007. (ENG.). 330p. per. 16.95 *(978-0-88150-736-2(9)*, 150736) Countryman Pr.

Barn Raising: Stories of a Vanishing American Legacy. 2008. (Illus.). pap. 11.95 *(978-0-9792974-1-0(9))* Essential Communications.

Beene, Gary. The Seeds We Sow: Kindness That Fed a Hungry World. 2011. (ENG.). pap. 26.95 *(978-0-86534-788-5(3))* Sunstone Pr.

Benziger, Jeff. Ceres. 2010. (Images of America Ser.). (ENG., Illus.). 128p. pap. 21.99 *(978-0-7385-8101-9(1))* Arcadia Publishing.

Bitz, Robert. Four Hundred Years of Agricultural Change in the Empire State. 2009. (ENG.). pap. 19.95 *(978-0-615-31865-3(7))* Bitz, Ward Publishing.

Bonner, James C. History of Georgia Agriculture, 1732-1860. 2009. (ENG.). 256p. pap. 24.95 *(978-0-8203-3500-1(2))* Univ. of Georgia Pr.

Boswell, Marsha. Kansas Gold: Historical Notes & Heritage Recipes from the First Fifty Years of the Kansas Wheat Commission. Boswell, Marsha, ed. 2007. (Illus.). 144p. 30.00 *(978-1-56944-360-6(2))* Terrell Creative.

Bromfield, Louis. From My Experience. 355p. reprint ed. lib. bdg. 26.95 *(978-0-88411-540-3(2))* Amereon LTD.

Carrier, Lyman. Agriculture in Virginia, 1607-1699. 2010. (Illus.). 30p. pap. 14.14 *(978-1-153-81481-2(1))* General Bks. LLC.

Cohen, Benjamin R. Notes from the Ground: Science, Soil, & Society in the American Countryside. 2011. (Yale Agrarian Studies Ser.). (ENG., Illus.). 288p. pap. 27.50 *(978-0-300-17770-1(4))* Yale Univ. Pr.

Conkin, Paul K. A Revolution down on the Farm: The Transformation of American Agriculture Since 1929. (ENG., Illus.). 240p. 2009. pap. 22.50 *(978-0-8131-9242-0(0))* 2008. 50.00 *(978-0-8131-2519-0(7))* Univ. Pr. of Kentucky.

Craig, Tom Moore, ed. Upcountry South Carolina Goes to War: Letters of the Anderson, Brockman, & Moore Families, 1853-1865. 2011. 224p. pap. 22.50 *(978-1-61117-005-4(2))* Univ. of South Carolina Pr.

Craig, Tom Moore & Walker, Melissa, intros. Upcountry South Carolina Goes to War: Letters of the Anderson, Brockman, & Moore Families, 1853-1865. 2009. (Illus.). xxxii, 190p. *(978-1-57003-798-6(1))* Univ. of South Carolina Pr.

Craven, Avery Odelle. Soil Exhaustion as a Factor in the Agricultural History of Virginia & Maryland, 1606-1860. 2006. (Southern Classics Ser.). 184p. per. 16.95 *(978-1-57003-681-1(0))* Univ. of South Carolina Pr.

Danbom, David B. Born in the Country: A History of Rural America. 2nd ed. 2006. (Revisiting Rural America Ser.). (ENG., Illus.). 320p. (C). (gr. 13-17). per. 22.00 *(978-0-8018-8459-7(4))*; 51.95 *(978-0-8018-8458-0(6))* Johns Hopkins Univ. Pr.

Doepkens, Frederick H. Farming in Anne Arundel County. 2011. (Images of America Ser.). (Illus.). 128p. pap. 21.99 ***(978-0-7385-8756-1(7))*** Arcadia Publishing.

Donahue, Brian. The Great Meadow: Farmers & the Land in Colonial Concord. 2007. (Yale Agrarian Studies). (ENG., Illus.). 344p. per. 23.00 *(978-0-300-12369-2(8))* Yale Univ. Pr.

Durham, Suzanne K. & Dobbs, Emma Elaine. Carrollton. 2010. (Then & Now Ser.). (ENG., Illus.). 96p. pap. 21.99 *(978-0-7385-6646-7(2))* Arcadia Publishing.

Frazier, Michael. Rhinebeck. 2012. (Images of America Ser.). (ENG., Illus.). 128p. pap. 21.99 ***(978-0-7385-9251-0(X))*** Arcadia Publishing.

Gerber, Judith. Farming in Torrance & the South Bay. 2008. (Images of America Ser.). (ENG., Illus.). 128p. pap. 21.99 *(978-0-7385-5930-8(X))* Arcadia Publishing.

Green, Linda L. Tennessee 1850 Agricultural Census. 2007. ***(978-0-7884-8367-7(6))***; ***(978-0-7884-5170-6(7))***; ***(978-0-7884-8355-4(2))***; ***(978-0-7884-5175-1(8))*** Heritage Bks. (Willow Bend Bks.).

—Tennessee 1850 Agricultural Census: Volume 5. 2010. pap. 34.00 *(978-0-7884-5197-3(9))* Heritage Bks.

—Virginia 1850 Agricultural Census, Volume 3. 2007. pap. 28.50 *(978-0-7884-4280-3(5))* Heritage Bks.

—Virginia 1850 Agricultural Census, Volume 5. 2007. pap. 38.00 *(978-0-7884-4451-7(4))* Heritage Bks.

—West Virginia 1860 Agricultural Census, Volume 3. 2007. pap. 27.00 *(978-0-7884-4466-1(2))* Heritage Bks.

Hagenstein, Edwin C., et al, eds. American Georgics: Writings on Farming, Culture, & the Land. 2011. (Yale Agrarian Studies Ser.). (ENG., Illus.). 432p. 35.00 *(978-0-300-13709-5(5))* Yale Univ. Pr.

Hale, Jennifer. Historic Plantations of Alabama's Black Belt. 2009. (Landmarks Ser.). 160p. pap. 19.99 *(978-1-59629-669-5(0))* History Pr., The.

Harrison, Charles H. Tending the Garden State: Preserving Agriculture in New Jersey. 2006. (Rivergate Ser.). (ENG., Illus.). 188p. 29.95 *(978-0-8135-3906-5(4))* Rutgers Univ. Pr.

Hendricks, Carson. California State Fair. 2010. (Images of America Ser.). (ENG., Illus.). 128p. pap. 21.99 *(978-0-7385-8089-0(9))* Arcadia Publishing.

Hoover, Dwight W. A Good Day's Work: An Iowa Farm in the Great Depression. 2007. (ENG., Illus.). 256p. 26.00 *(978-1-56663-702-2(3))* Dee, Ivan R. Pub.

Jack, Zachary Michael. Love of the Land: Essential Farm & Conservation Readings from an American Golden Age, 1880-1920. 2006. (ENG., Illus.). 488p. 94.95 *(978-1-934043-33-2(8))* Cambria Pr.

Latta, W. C. Outline History of Indiana Agriculture. 372p. reprint ed. lib. bdg. 98.00 *(978-0-7222-0469-6(8))* Library Reprints, Inc.

Lauters, Amy Mattson. More Than a Farmer's Wife: Voices of American Farm Women, 1910-1960. 2009. (ENG., Illus.). 208p. (C). 39.95 *(978-0-8262-1852-0(0))* Univ. of Missouri Pr.

Logan, Linda H. Wythe County: Reflections of Farm Life Traditions. 2009. (American Chronicles (History Press) Ser.). (Illus.). 96p. pap. 19.99 *(978-1-59629-736-4(0))* History Pr., The.

McEwan, Barbara. Thomas Jefferson: Farmer. alt. ed. 2011. (ENG.). 231p. pap. 25.00 ***(978-0-7864-6732-7(0))*** McFarland & Co., Inc. Pubs.

McNulty, Lyndi. Farming in Carroll County. 2009. (Images of America Ser.). (ENG., Illus.). 128p. pap. 21.99 *(978-0-7385-6833-1(3))* Arcadia Publishing.

Moore, John Hebron. Agriculture in Ante-Bellum Mississippi. 2010. (Southern Classics Ser.). 288p. pap. 14.95 *(978-1-57003-877-8(5))* Univ. of South Carolina Pr.

Owens, David B. & Photographs by Conneaut Area Historical Society. Conneaut. 2010. (Images of America Ser.). (ENG., Illus.). 128p. pap. 21.99 *(978-0-7385-7731-9(6))* Arcadia Publishing.

Pfluger, Marsha. Across Time & Territory: A Walk Through the National Ranching Heritage Center. 2007. (Illus.). 116p. 39.00 *(978-0-9759360-0-9(X))* Ranching Heritage Assoc.

Phillips, Sarah T. This Land, This Nation: Conservation, Rural America, & the New Deal. 2007. (ENG., Illus.). 302p. 81.00 *(978-0-521-85270-8(6))*; per. 25.99 *(978-0-521-61796-3(0))* Cambridge Univ. Pr.

Player, W. Kirby. Barns, Barbecue, & Bales of Cotton: A Rural Retrospective of South Carolina Agriculture. 2009. *(978-1-57864-589-3(1))* Donning Co. Pubs.

Richman, Irwin & Emery, Michael. Yesterday's Farm Tools & Equipment. 2010. (Illus.). 208p. 39.99 *(978-0-7643-3603-4(7))* Schiffer Publishing, Ltd.

Rickard, J. A. Early Cattle Ranching on the Texas South Plains. ltd. ed. 2008. 148p. 42.95 *(978-0-9767799-9-5(4))* Copano Bay Pr.

Salstrom, Paul. From Pioneering to Persevering: Family Farming in Indiana to 1880. 2007. (Illus.). 208p. per. 23.95 *(978-1-55753-453-8(5))* Purdue Univ. Pr.

Smith, Ross. History of the Danville Grange: Patrons of Husbandry. 2008. (Illus.). 119p. 23.00 net. *(978-0-938260-03-5(0))* Ashford Pubns.

Stacy, Susan. Tom & Julia Davis Some Good Place Boise, Idaho. 2007. (Illus.). 137p. per. 19.95 net. *(978-0-9798767-1-4(0))* T&J Publishing.

U.S. Dept. of Commerce, compiled by. United States Census of Agriculture, 1925. Reports for States, with Statistics for Counties & a Summary for the United States Part II: The Southern States. 2008. 1328p. lib. bdg. 500.00 net. *(978-0-88354-244-6(7))* Ross Publishing Incorporated.

U.S. Dept. of Commerce Staff, compiled by. United States Census of Agriculture, 1925. Reports for States, with Statistics for Counties & a Summary for the United States Pt. 1: The Northern States. 2008. 1328p. lib. bdg. 500.00 net. *(978-0-88354-243-9(9))* Ross Publishing Incorporated.

Wagenen, Jared van & Austin, Erwin H. The Golden Age of Homespun. 2009. (Illus.). 300p. pap. 24.95 *(978-0-8014-7598-6(8)*, Fall Creek Bks.) Cornell Univ. Pr.

Walker, Melissa & Cobb, James C., eds. The New Encyclopedia of Southern Culture: Volume 11: Agriculture & Industry. 2008. (ENG., Illus.). 376p. (C). 47.50 *(978-0-8078-3240-0(5))*; pap. 23.95 *(978-0-8078-5909-4(5))* Univ. of North Carolina Pr.

Wall, James T. Wall Street & the Fruited Plain: Money, Expansion, & Politics in the Gilded Age. 2008. (ENG.). 394p. pap. 56.99 *(978-0-7618-4124-1(5))* Univ. Pr. of America, Inc.

Washington Government Printing Office, creator. Report of the Secretary of Agriculture. 2010. 710p. pap. 49.75 *(978-1-146-59125-6(X))* BiblioBazaar.

Whayne, Jeannie. Delta Empire: Lee Wilson & the Transformation of Agriculture in the New South. 2011. (Making the Modern South Ser.). (Illus.). 312p. 45.00 ***(978-0-8071-3855-7(X))*** Louisiana State Univ. Pr.

AGRICULTURE—VENEZUELA

Stålberg, Annie. Agrarian Reform in Venezuel. 2009. 52p. pap. *(978-3-639-20140-6(X))* VDM Verlag Dr. Mueller e.K.

AGRICULTURE—VIETNAM

Do_Thu, Nga, et al. Material Flow Analysis - Benefit Sustainable Management Tool. 2011. 148p. pap. ***(978-3-8433-8988-4(8))*** Lambert Academic Publishing.

Friederichsen, Jakob Rupert. Opening up Knowledge Production through Participatory Research? Agricultural Research for Vietnam's Northern Uplands. 2009. (Development Economics & Policy Ser.). (Illus.). 280p. pap. 74.95 *(978-3-631-58842-0(9))* Lang, Peter GmbH, Europaischer Verlag der Wissenschaften DEU. Dist: Lang, Peter.

Hargrove, Tom. A Dragon Lives Forever: War & Rice in Vietnam's Mekong Delta. 2008. (Williams-Ford Texas A&M University Military History Ser.). (ENG.). 488p. pap. 23.95 *(978-1-60344-060-8(7))* Texas A&M Univ. Pr.

Mau Dung, Nguyen & PHUONG LE, Nguyen. Agricultural Cooperative Management. 2011. 76p. pap. ***(978-3-8443-1198-3(X))*** Lambert Academic Publishing.

Mumtaz, Jalal Akbar. Gender in the Rural Agricultural Sector of Transitional Economies. 2009. 52p. pap. *(978-3-639-06844-3(0))* VDM Verlag Dr. Mueller e.K.

My Duyen, Trang Thi. Agricultural Credit in Vietnam. 2011. 92p. pap. ***(978-3-8443-0182-3(8))*** Lambert Academic Publishing.

Pham Trung, Tuan. Agricultural Cooperatives in Vietnam. 2009. 108p. pap. *(978-3-639-16392-6(3))* VDM Verlag Dr. Mueller e.K.

Thapa, Rajesh Bahadur. Land Assessment Framework for Peri-Urban Agriculture. 2010. 124p. pap. *(978-3-8383-0189-1(7))* Lambert Academic Publishing.

Van Tuat, N. & Hilbeck, A. Environmental Risk Assessment of Genetically Modified Organisms Vol. 4: Challenges & Opportunities with Bt Cotton in Vietnam. Andow, D. A., ed. 2008. (Illus.). 384p. 160.00 *(978-1-84593-390-6(7))* CABI GBR. Dist: Stylus Publishing, LLC.

AGRICULTURE—WALES

Davies, Wynne. Sixty Years of Royal Welsh Champions: A Celebration of Welsh Pony & Cob Champions, 1947-2007. 2009. (ENG., Illus.). 400p. 95.00 *(978-0-85131-955-1(6))* Trafalgar Square Bks.

Griffin, Chas. More Scenes from a Smallholding. 2006. (ENG., Illus.). 352p. per. 13.95 *(978-0-09-190588-0(5)*, Ebury Pr.) Ebury Publishing GBR. Dist: Independent Pubs. Group.

Stevens, D. P., et al. Grasslands of Wales: A Survey of Lowland Species-Rich Grasslands, 1987-2004. 2010. (ENG., Illus.). 336p. 85.00 *(978-0-7083-2255-0(7))* Univ. of Wales Pr. GBR. Dist: Chicago Distribution Ctr.

AGRICULTURE—WEST INDIES

Davy, John. The West Indies, Before & since Slave Emancipation: Comprising the Windward & Leeward Islands' Military Command. 2010. (Cambridge Library Collection - History Ser.). (Illus.). 580p. pap. 43.00 *(978-1-108-02073-2(9))* Cambridge Univ. Pr.

Roughley, Thomas. The Jamaica Planter's Guide: Or, a System for Planting & Managing a Sugar Estate or Other Plantations in that Island, & Throughout the British West Indies in General. 2010. (Cambridge Library Collection - Slavery & Abolition Ser.). 436p. pap. 32.99 *(978-1-108-02430-3(0))* Cambridge Univ. Pr.

AGRICULTURE—ZIMBABWE

Chaumba, Joseph Arrif. Opportunities for & Constraints on Crop Production. 2011. 112p. pap. ***(978-3-8443-9075-9(8))*** Lambert Academic Publishing.

Chidoko, Clainos & Mudzingiri, Calvin. Food Aid & Food Crop Production in Zimbabwe. 2011. 72p. pap. ***(978-3-8443-8492-5(8))*** Lambert Academic Publishing.

Gundu, Moira. An Information Appraoch to Household Food Security. 2011. 156p. pap. ***(978-3-8443-9089-6(8))*** Lambert Academic Publishing.

Kujinga, Kraspосy. The Dynamics of Stakeholder Participation. 2010. 120p. pap. *(978-3-639-23761-0(7))* VDM Verlag Dr. Mueller e.K.

Svubure, Oniward. Participation & Institutional Reform in the Water Sector in Zimbabwe. 2011. 96p. pap. ***(978-3-8443-0491-6(6))*** Lambert Academic Publishing.

Thebe, Vusilizwe. Cultivating Starvation. 2010. 76p. pap. *(978-3-8383-6480-3(5))* Lambert Academic Publishing.

AGRICULTURE, COOPERATIVE

Here are entered works which deal with cooperation in the production as well as in the disposal of agricultural products.

see also Agriculture—International Cooperation; Collective Farms

Abrahamsen, Martin A. & Scroggs, Claud L., eds. Agricultural Cooperation: Selected Readings. 2009. (ENG.). 592p. pap. 60.00 *(978-0-8166-5691-2(6))* Univ. of Minnesota Pr.

Aicpa. AICPA Audit & Accounting Guide Agricultural Producers & Agricultural Cooperatives. 2007. pap. 61.25 *(978-0-87051-681-8(7))* American Institute of Certified Public Accountants.

Almås, Reidar & Rouhinen, Sauli. Om Landbruksforhold I Nordiske Land: Antologi. 2011. (NOR, DAN, SWE & ENG.). 280p. (C). pap. 32.00 ***(978-87-87564-21-2(1))*** Aarhus Universitetsforlag DNK. Dist: ISD.

Basu, Pratyusha. Villages, Women, & the Success of Dairy Cooperatives in India: Making Place for Rural Development. 2009. 286p. 109.99 *(978-1-60497-625-0(X))* Cambria Pr.

Bernard, Tanguy. Cooperatives for Staple Crop Marketing Evidence from Ethiopia. 2010. *(978-0-89629-175-1(8))* International Food Policy Research Institute.

Bogetoft. Cooperatives & Payment Schemes Lessons from Theory & Examples from Danish Agriculture. 2007. (Illus.). 245p. pap. 48.00 *(978-87-630-0195-3(0))* Copenhagen Business Schl. Pr. DNK. Dist: International Specialized Bk. Services.

César Dachary, Alfredo A. Produccion colectiva y desarrollo capitalista en el agro Mexicano: (1970 - 1980) (Latin America Studies). (GER.). XI, 350p. 135.00 ***(978-3-11-116705-3(4))*** De Gruyter, Mouton DEU. Dist: de Gruyter, Walter GmbH & Co. KG.

Cleary, Mark C. Peasants, Politicians & Producers: The Organisation of Agriculture in France Since 1918. 2007. (Cambridge Studies in Historical Geography Ser.). (ENG., Illus.). 220p. pap. 48.00 *(978-0-521-03377-0(2))* Cambridge Univ. Pr.

Costa, Temra. Farmer Jane: Women Changing the Way We Eat, 1 vol. 2010. (ENG., Illus.). 224p. pap. 15.99 *(978-1-4236-0562-1(4))* Gibbs Smith, Publisher.

de Koning, Maurits & de Steenhuijsen Piters, Bart. Farmers as Shareholders: A Close Look at Recent Experience. 2009. (Bulletins of the Royal Tropical Institute Ser.). 70p. pap. 35.00 *(978-94-6022-039-5(8))* Royal Tropical Institute Pr. (KIT (Koninklijk Instituut voor de Tropen) NLD. Dist: Stylus Publishing, LLC.

Edson, Milan C. Solaris Farm: A Story of the Twentieth Century. 2010. 464p. pap. 37.75 *(978-1-146-92752-9(5))* BiblioBazaar.

Freitag, Carla Neeley. Taxation of Cooperatives & Their Patrons. 2nd ed. 2007. (Tax Management Portfolios Ser.: 744-2nd). spiral bd. 400.00 *(978-1-55871-568-4(1))* Tax Management, Inc.

Greaves, Thomas C., et al. Vicos & Beyond: A Half Century of Applying Anthropology in Peru. 2010. (Illus.). xiii, 359p. *(978-0-7591-1976-5(7))* AltaMira Pr.

Greaves/Bolton/Zapat. Vicos & Beyond: A Half Century of Applying Anthropology in Peru. 2010. (ENG., Illus.). 358p. 75.00 *(978-0-7591-1974-1(0))* AltaMira Pr.

Gudrun, Kochendorfer-Lucius & Boris, Pleskovic, eds. Agriculture & Development. 2008. (Berlin Workshop Ser.). (ENG.). 244p. pap. 30.00 *(978-0-8213-7127-5(4)*, 9780821371275) World Bank Pubns.

Haggard, H. Rider. Rural Denmark & Its Lessons. 2009. 380p. 26.99 *(978-1-103-04707-9(8))*; pap. 20.99 *(978-1-103-04704-8(3))* BiblioBazaar.

Henderson, Elizabeth, et al. Sharing the Harvest: A Citizen's Guide to Community Supported Agriculture. rev. ed. 2007. (ENG., Illus.). 320p. pap. 35.00 *(978-1-933392-10-3(X))* Chelsea Green Publishing.

Karantininis, Kostas & Nilsson, Jerker, eds. Vertical Markets & Cooperative Hierarchies: The Role of Cooperatives in the Agri-Food Industry. 2010. (ENG.). xiv, 265p. pap. 169.00 *(978-90-481-7031-9(1)*, 9048170311) Springer.

Karthikeyan, Muthumariappan & Bayisa, Befakadu. Determinants of Cooperative Leadership in Ethiopi. 2010. 156p. pap. *(978-3-639-27061-7(4))* VDM Verlag Dr. Mueller e.K.

Mau Dung, Nguyen & PHUONG LE, Nguyen. Agricultural Cooperative Management. 2011. 76p. pap. ***(978-3-8443-1198-3(X))*** Lambert Academic Publishing.

Mayer, Enrique. Ugly Stories of the Peruvian Agrarian Reform. 2009. (Latin America Otherwise Ser.). (ENG., Illus.). 328p. 89.95 *(978-0-8223-4453-7(X))*; pap. 24.95 *(978-0-8223-4469-8(6))* Duke Univ. Pr.

Pare, William. Co-Operative Agriculture. reprint ed. 29.00 *(978-0-404-60087-7(5))* AMS Pr., Inc.

Peppelenbos, Lucian, ed. Trading Up. 2008. 298p. (C). pap. 39.95 *(978-90-6832-699-4(6))* Royal Tropical Institute Pr. (KIT (Koninklijk Instituut voor de Tropen) NLD. Dist: Stylus Publishing, LLC.

Pham Trung, Tuan. Agricultural Cooperatives in Vietnam. 2009. 108p. pap. *(978-3-639-16392-6(3))* VDM Verlag Dr. Mueller e.K.

Ridder, Mary. Roots of Change: Nebraska's New Agriculture. 2007. (Our Sustainable Future Ser.: Vol. 18). (ENG., Illus.). 152p. pap. 24.95 *(978-0-8032-9013-6(6))*, Bison Bks.) Univ. of Nebraska Pr.

Smith, Jeremy N. Growing a Garden City: How Farmers, First Graders, Counselors, Troubled Teens, Foodies, a Homeless Shelter Chef, Single Mothers, & More are Transforming Themselves & Their Neighborhoods Through the Intersection of Local Agriculture & Community. 2010. (ENG., Illus.). 240p. 24.95 *(978-1-61608-108-9(2)*, 608108) Skyhorse Publishing Co., Inc.

Yang, C. K. A Chinese Village in Early Communist Transition. 2011. 296p. 48.95 ***(978-1-258-10308-8(7))*** Literary Licensing, LLC.

AGRICULTURE, FOLKLORE OF

see Agriculture—Folklore

AGRICULTURE, PERMANENT

see Permaculture

AGRICULTURE, PREHISTORIC

Aceituno, Francisco Javier & Loaiza, Nicolas. Domesticación del bosque en el Cauca medio colombiano entre el Pleistoceno final y el Holoceno medio. 2007. (Bar S Ser.). (SPA., Illus.). 138p. (C). pap. 72.50 *(978-1-4073-0090-0(3))* British Archaeological Reports Ltd. GBR. Dist: Brown, David Bk. Co., The.

Bakels, Corrie C. The Western European Loess Belt: Agrarian History, 5300 BC - AD 1000. 2009. (ENG., Illus.). viii, 295p. 159.00 *(978-1-4020-9839-0(1)*, 1402098391) Springer.

Barker, Graeme. The Agricultural Revolution in Prehistory: Why Did Foragers Become Farmers? 2006. (ENG., Illus.). 616p. 199.00 *(978-0-19-928109-1(2))* Oxford Univ. Pr., Inc.

Bohrer, Vorsila. Pre-Ceramic Subsistence in Two Rock Shelters. 2007. (Arizona State Museum Archaeological Ser.). (ENG.). 235p. pap. 24.95 *(978-1-889747-81-1(5))* Arizona State Museum.

Cappers, R. T. J., ed. Fields of Change: Progress in African Archaeobotany. 2007. (Groningen Archaeological Studies). (ENG., Illus.). 214p. (C). pap. 44.00 ***(978-90-77922-30-9(X))*** Barkhuis Publishing NLD. Dist: Brown, David Bk. Co., The.

Colledge Conolly Staff. Early Neolithic Agriculture in Southwest Asia & Europe: Archaeo. 2006. 256p. *(978-1-84472-191-7(4)*, Routledge Cavendish) Taylor & Francis Group.

Colledge, Sue & Conolly, James, eds. The Origins & Spread of Domestic Plants in Southwest Asia & Europe. 2007. (University College London Institute of Archaeology Publications). (ENG., Illus.). 462p. 99.00 *(978-1-59874-988-5(9))* Left Coast Pr., Inc.

Finlayson, Bill & Warren, Graeme M. Changing Natures: Hunter-gatherers, Farmers & the Modern World. 2011. (Illus.). 144p. pap. 24.95 *(978-0-7156-3813-2(0))* Duckworth Publishers GBR. Dist: International Publishers Marketing.

Geib, Phil. Foragers & Farmers of the Northern Kayenta Region: Excavations along the Navajo Mountain Road. 2011. (ENG., Illus.). 416p. 70.00 *(978-1-60781-003-2(4))* Univ. of Utah Pr.

Gerritsen, Rupert. Australia & the Origins of Agriculture. 2008. (Bar S Ser.). (Illus.). 205p. (C). 92.50 *(978-1-4073-0354-3(6))* British Archaeological Reports Ltd. GBR. Dist: Brown, David Bk. Co., The.

Gregory, David A. Excavations in the Santa Cruz River Floodplain: Further Investigations at Los Pozos. 2007. (Illus.). viii, 142p. *(978-1-886398-58-0(5))* Ctr. for Desert Archaeology.

Hadjikoumis, Angelos, et al, eds. Dynamics of Neolithisation: Studies in Honour of Andrew Sherratt. 2011. (ENG.). 389p. (C). 80.00 *(978-1-84217-999-4(3))* Oxbow Bks., Ltd. GBR. Dist: Brown, David Bk. Co., The.

Hald, Mette Marie. A Thousand Years of Farming: Late Chalcolithic Agricultural Practices at Tell Brak in Northern Mesopotamia. 2008. (Bar S Ser.). (Illus.). 175p. (C). 85.00 *(978-1-4073-0360-4(0))* British Archaeological Reports Ltd. GBR. Dist: Brown, David Bk. Co., The.

Harris, David R. Origins of Agriculture in Western Central Asia: An Environmental-Archaeological Study. 2010. (Illus.). 328p. (C). 65.00 *(978-1-934536-16-2(4))*, Univ. of Pennsylvania Museum of Archaeology & Anthropology) Univ. Museum Pubns.

Hassan, Fekri A., ed. Droughts, Food & Culture: Ecological Change & Food Security in Africa's Later Prehistory. 2012. (ENG.). 372p. pap. 159.00 *(978-1-4419-3380-5(8)*, 1441933808) Springer.

Ikeya, Kazunobu, et al. Interactions Between Hunter-Gatherers & Farmers: From Prehistory to Present. 2009. (Illus.). i, 277p. *(978-4-901906-65-4(8))* National Museum of Ethnology.

Jones, Richard, ed. Manure Matters: Historical, Archaeological & Ethnographic Perspectives. 2012. (Illus.). 203p. 124.95 ***(978-0-7546-6988-3(2))*** Ashgate Publishing Co.

Kent, Susan, ed. Farmers as Hunters: The Implications of Sedentism. 2008. (New Directions in Archaeology Ser.). (ENG.). 168p. pap. 31.99 *(978-0-521-10198-1(0))* Cambridge Univ. Pr.

Kuijt, Ian, ed. Life in Neolithic Farming Communities: Social Organization, Identity, & Differentiation. 2010. (Fundamental Issues in Archaeology Ser.). 348p. pap. 199.00 *(978-1-4419-3317-1(4)*, 1441933174) Springer.

Mason, Sarah L. R. Hunter-Gatherer Archaeobotany: Perspectives from the Northern Temperate Zone. Hather, Jon G., ed. 2009. (Univ Col London Inst Arch Pub Ser.). (ENG., Illus.). 208p. 74.95 *(978-0-905853-38-3(5))* Left Coast Pr., Inc.

Mateus, Jose Eduardo, et al, eds. Session C11: Ancient Cultural Landscapes in South Europe - Their Ecological Setting & Evolution. 2010. (Bar S Ser.). (ENG., Illus.). 188p. (C). pap. 95.00 *(978-1-4073-0665-0(0))* British Archaeological Reports Ltd. GBR. Dist: Brown, David Bk. Co., The.

Ming Jia, Wei. Transition from Foraging to Farming in Northeast China. 2007. (Bar S Ser.). (Illus.). 211p. (C). pap. 90.00 *(978-1-4073-0043-6(1))* Archaeopress GBR. Dist: Brown, David Bk. Co., The.

No, Chung-Guk. Han'guk Kodae Ui Sujon Nongop Kwa Suri Sisol. 2010. (KOR., Illus.). 544p. *(978-89-606-2055-1(6))* Seogyeong Munhwasa.

O'Brien, William. Local Worlds: Early Settlement Landscapes & Upland Farming in Southwest Ireland. 2010. (ENG., Illus.). 528p. 92.95 *(978-1-84889-021-3(4))* Collins Pr., The IRL. Dist: Dufour Editions, Inc.

Price, T. Douglas & Gebauer, Anne B., eds. Last Hunters - First Farmers: New Perspectives on the Prehistory Transition to Agriculture. (Advanced Seminar Ser.). (Illus.). 354p. pap. 29.95 *(978-0-933452-91-6(8))* School for Advanced Research Pr./SAR Pr.

Reynolds, Peter J. Ancient Farming. 2011. (Shire Archaeology Ser.). (ENG., Illus.). 64p. pap. 13.95 *(978-0-85263-876-7(0))* Shire Pubns., Ltd. GBR. Dist: Random Hse., Inc.

Saidel, Benjamin A. On the Fringe of Society: Archaeological & Ethnoarchaeological Perspectives on Pastoral & Agricultural Societies. van der Steen, Eveline J., ed. 2007. (Bar S Ser.). (Illus.). 132p. (C). pap. 72.50 *(978-1-4073-0093-1(8))* British Archaeological Reports Ltd. GBR. Dist: Brown, David Bk. Co., The.

Scarre, Chris. The Human Past: World Prehistory & the Development of Human Societies. 2nd ed. 2009. (ENG., Illus.). 784p. (C). pap. 60.00 net. *(978-0-500-28781-1(3)*, 528781) Thames & Hudson.

Sellet, Frédéric, et al, eds. Archaeology & the Ethnoarchaeology of Mobility. 2006. (ENG., Illus.). 320p. 65.00 *(978-0-8130-2956-6(2))* Univ. Pr. of Florida.

Simmons, Alan H. The Neolithic Revolution in the near East: Transforming the Human Landscape. (ENG., Illus.). 360p. 2011. pap. 30.00 *(978-0-8165-2966-7(3))* 2007. 55.00 *(978-0-8165-2442-6(4))* Univ. of Arizona Pr.

Smith, Bruce D. Rivers of Change: Essays on Early Agriculture in Eastern North America. 2nd rev. ed. 2007. (Illus.). 336p. per. 40.00 *(978-0-8173-5425-1(5))* Univ. of Alabama Pr.

Spikins, Penny. Mesolithic Europe. Bailey, Geoff, ed. 2010. (ENG.). 498p. pap. 45.00 *(978-0-521-14797-2(2))* Cambridge Univ. Pr.

Thurston, Tina & Fisher, Christopher T., eds. Seeking a Richer Harvest: The Archaeology of Subsistence Intensification, Innovation, & Change. 2010. (Studies in Human Ecology & Adaptation Ser.). (Illus.). x, 274p. pap. 149.00 *(978-1-4419-4102-2(9)*, 1441941029) Springer.

van der Veen, Marijke, ed. The Exploitation of Plant Resources in Ancient Africa. 2010. (ENG.). 284p. pap. 189.00 *(978-1-4419-3316-4(6)*, 1441933166) Springer.

Vrydaghs, Luc, et al, eds. Rethinking Agriculture: Archaeological & Ethnoarchaeological Perspectives. 2007. (One World Archaeology Ser.). (ENG., Illus.). 476p. 99.95 *(978-1-59874-260-2(4))* Left Coast Pr., Inc.

Watkins, Trevor. Origins of Agriculture in the near East. 2009. (Illus.). 328p. 33.95 *(978-0-415-22152-8(8))*; 110.00 *(978-0-415-22151-1(X))* Routledge.

Wellman, Kevin D., ed. The Valley Farms Sites: Prehistoric Floodplain Agriculture on the Santa Cruz River in Southern Arizona. 2008. (SWCA Anthropological Research Papers). (ENG., Illus.). 242p. pap. 30.00 *(978-1-931901-22-2(8))* SWCA, Inc.

White, Peter. The Emergence of Agriculture. Denham, Timothy, ed. 2006. (One World Archaeology Readers Ser.: Vol. 1). (ENG., Illus.). 288p. (C). 39.95 *(978-0-415-40445-7(2))* Routledge.

White, Peter & Denham, Timothy, eds. The Emergence of Agriculture: A Global View. 2006. (One World Archaeology Readers Ser.: Vol. 1). (ENG., Illus.). 288p. 130.00 *(978-0-415-40444-0(4))* Routledge.

Zohary, Daniel, et al. Domestication of Plants in the Old World: The origin & spread of domesticated plants in Southwest Asia, Europe, & the Mediterranean Basin. 4th ed. 2012. (ENG., Illus.). 280p. 99.99 ***(978-0-19-954906-1(0))*** Oxford Univ. Pr., Inc.

AGRICULTURE, PRIMITIVE

see Traditional Farming

AGRICULTURE, SOILLESS

see Hydroponics

AGRICULTURE AND COMMUNISM

see Communism and Agriculture

AGRICULTURE AND ENERGY

see also Biomass Energy; Renewable Energy Sources

Aguirre, Jessica, et al. Agrofuels in the Americas. Jonasse, Richard, ed. 2009. (ENG.). 194p. pap. 18.95 *(978-0-935028-36-2(6))* Institute for Food & Development Policy/Food First Bks.

America's Energy Future Panel on Alternative Liquid Transportation Fuels Staff, et al. Liquid Transportation Fuels from Coal & Biomass: Technological Status, Costs, & Environmental Impacts. National Academy of Engineering Staff, ed. 2009. (ENG.). 388p. pap. 49.95 *(978-0-309-13712-6(8))* National Academies Pr.

Committee on Water Implications of Biofuels Production in the United States & National Research Council. Water Implications of Biofuels Production in the United States. 2008. (ENG.). 88p. pap. 30.00 *(978-0-309-11361-8(X))* National Academies Pr.

Hearing to Review Low Carbon Fuel Standard Proposals: Hearing Before the Committee on Agriculture, House of Representatives, One Hundred Eleventh Congress, First Session, May 21, 2009. 2009. (Illus.). iii, 88p. *(978-0-16-084226-9(3)*, 552-070-39804-0) United States Government Printing Office.

Hearing to Review Pending Climate Legislation: Hearing Before the Committee on Agriculture, House of Representatives, One Hundred Eleventh Congress, First Session, June 11, 2009. 2009. (Illus.). iv, 263p. *(978-0-16-084941-1(1)*, 552-070-40332-9) United States Government Printing Office.

Hearing to Review the Costs & Benefits of Agriculture Offsets: Hearing Before the Subcommittee on Conservation, Credit, Energy, & Research of the Committee on Agriculture, House of Representatives, One Hundred Eleventh Congress, First Session, December 3, 2009. 2010. (Illus.). v, 119p. *(978-0-16-085295-4(1)* 552-070-40634-4) United States Government Printing Office.

Hearing to Review the Future of Next Generation Biofuels: Hearing Before the Subcommittee on Conservation, Credit, Energy, & Research of the Committee on Agriculture, House of Representatives, One Hundred Eleventh Congress, First Session, October 29, 2009. 2009. (Illus.). v, 75p. *(978-0-16-084838-4(5)*, 552-070-40239-0) United States Government Printing Office.

Laughton, Rebecca. Surviving & Thriving on the Land: How to Use Your Time & Energy to Run a Successful Smallholding. 2009. (ENG., Illus.). 328p. pap. 24.95 *(978-1-900322-28-7(5))* Green Bks. GBR. Dist: Chelsea Green Publishing.

Pfeiffer, Dale Allen. Eating Fossil Fuels: Oil, Food & the Coming Crisis in Agriculture. 2006. (ENG., Illus.). 125p. per. 11.95 *(978-0-86571-565-3(3)*, 0865715653) New Society Pubs., Ltd. CAN. Dist: Consortium Bk. Sales & Distribution.

Pimentel, David & Pimentel, Marcia. Food, Energy, & Society. 3rd rev. ed. 2007. (ENG., Illus.). 400p. 89.95 *(978-1-4200-4667-0(5)*, CRC Press) Taylor & Francis Group GBR. Dist: Taylor & Francis Group.

Review the Financial Structure of Renewable Energy Sources: Hearing Before the Subcommittee on Conservation, Credit, Energy, & Research of the Committee on Agriculture, House of Representatives, One Hundred Tenth Congress, First Session, March 7, 2007. 2007. (Illus.). iii, 143p. *(978-0-16-079757-6(8)*, 552-070-36675-0) United States Government Printing Office.

Royal Society of Chemistry Staff. Energy Crops. Halford, Nigel G. & Karp, Angela, eds. 2010. (RSC Energy & Environment Ser.). (ENG., Illus.). 442p. 224.00 ***(978-1-84973-032-7(6))*** Royal Society of Chemistry, The GBR. Dist: Ingram Pub. Services.

Subcommittee Hearing on Impacts of Outstanding Regulatory Policy on Small Biofuels Producers & Family Farmers: Hearing Before the Committee on Small Business, United States House of Representatives, One Hundred Eleventh Congress, First Session. Hearing Held May 20, 2009. 2009. v, 86p. *(978-0-16-083908-5(4)*, 552-070-39597-1) United States Government Printing Office.

van Ierland, Ekko C. & Oude Lansink, A. G., eds. Economics of Sustainable Energy in Agriculture. 2010. (Economy & Environment Ser.). (Illus.). 256p. pap. 189.00 *(978-90-481-6089-1(3)*, 9048160898) Springer.

Weissenbacher, Manfred. Sources of Power: How Energy Forges Human History. 2 vols. 2009. (Illus.). 890p. 124.95 *(978-0-313-35626-1(2)*, C35626) Greenwood Publishing Group, Inc.

Womach, Jasper, et al. The USDA 2007 Farm Bill Proposal. 2008. 102p. pap. 39.00 *(978-1-60456-813-4(5))* Nova Science Pubs., Inc.

Wright, Julia. Sustainable Agriculture & Food Security in an Era of Oil Scarcity. 2012. (ENG.). 280p. pap. 42.95 ***(978-0-415-50734-9(0))*** Routledge.

Wright, Julia. Sustainable Agriculture & Food Security in an Era of Oil Scarcity: Lessons from Cuba. 2008. (ENG., Illus.). 280p. 117.00 *(978-1-84407-572-0(9))* Routledge.

Zivin, Joshua S. Graff & Perloff, Jeffrey M., eds. The Intended & Unintended Effects of U. S. Agricultural & Biotechnology Policies. 2012. (National Bureau of Economic Research Conference Report). (ENG., Illus.). 312p. 99.00 ***(978-0-226-98803-0(1))*** Univ. of Chicago Pr.

AGRICULTURE AND POLITICS

Achura, Bob Marley. Implementation Challenges of Nusaf Intervention. 2011. 72p. pap. ***(978-3-8443-1623-0(X))*** Lambert Academic Publishing.

Anderson, Kym, ed. The Political Economy of Agricultural Price Distortions. 2010. (ENG., Illus.). 464p. 95.00 *(978-0-521-76323-3(1))* Cambridge Univ. Pr.

Brookfield, Harold & Parsons, Helen. Family Farms: Survival & Prospect: A World-Wide Analysis. 2007. (Routledge Studies in Human Geography Ser.). (ENG., Illus.). 272p. (C). 178.00 *(978-0-415-41441-8(5))* Routledge.

Gerasimov, Ilya V. Modernism & Public Reform in Late Imperial Russia: Rural Professionals & Self-Organization, 1905-30. 2009. (ENG., Illus.). 352p. 110.00 *(978-0-230-22947-1(6))* Palgrave Macmillan.

Gillman, Jeff & Heberlig, Eric. How the Government Got in Your Backyard: Superweeds, Frankenfoods, Lawn Wars, & the (Nonpartisan) Truth about Environmental Policies. 2011. (ENG.). 248p. 23.95 *(978-1-60469-001-9(1)*, 1604690011) Timber Pr., Inc.

Jenner, Robert E. FDR's Republicans: Domestic Political Realignment & American Foreign Policy. (ENG.). 2011. 232p. pap. 29.95 *(978-0-7391-3613-3(5))* 2009. 234p. 73.50 *(978-0-7391-3612-6(7))* Lexington Bks.

Mapes, Kathleen. Sweet Tyranny: Migrant Labor, Industrial Agriculture, & Imperial Politics. 2009. (Working Class in American History Ser.). (ENG., Illus.). 336p. 80.00 *(978-0-252-03436-7(8))*; pap. 31.00 *(978-0-252-07667-1(2))* Univ. of Illinois Pr.

Nielsen, Helle. Bounded Rationality in Decision-making: How Cognitive Shortcuts & Professional Value May Interfere with Market-based Regulation. 2010. (ENG., Illus.). 256p. 90.00 *(978-0-7190-7992-4(6))* Manchester Univ. Pr. GBR. Dist: Macmillan.

Ostrovsky, Max. Y Equals Arctg X: The Hyperbola of the World Order. 2006. (ENG., Illus.). 308p. per. 56.99 *(978-0-7618-3499-1(0))* Univ. Pr. of America, Inc.

Rosset, Peter M. Food Is Different: Why We Must Get the WTO Out of Agriculture. 2006. (Global Issues Ser.). (ENG., Illus.). 194p. 62.95 *(978-1-84277-754-1(8))*; per. 20.95 *(978-1-84277-755-8(6))* Zed Bks., Ltd. GBR. Dist: Macmillan.

Sevelius, Gunnar. The Nine Pillars of History: An Anthropological Review of History, Five Religions, Sexuality & Modern Economics, All as a Guide for Peace. 2010. 368p. (ENG.). 36.49 *(978-1-4520-2351-9(4))*; pap. 22.99 *(978-1-4520-0061-9(1))* AuthorHouse.

Summerhill, Thomas. Harvest of Dissent: Agrarianism in Nineteenth-Century New York. 2008. (ENG., Illus.). 304p. per. 26.00 *(978-0-252-07547-6(1))* Univ. of Illinois Pr.

von Thünen, Johann. The Isolated State in Relation to Agriculture & Political Economy Pt. 3: Principles for the Determination of Rent, the Most Advantageous Rotation Period & the Value of Stands of Varying Age in Pinewoods. van Suntum, Ulrich, ed. 2009. (ENG., Illus.). 224p. 100.00 *(978-0-230-22251-9(X))* Palgrave Macmillan.

Watkins, Kevin. Agricultural Trade & Food Security. (ENG.). 112p. pap. 20.75 *(978-971-91752-0-9(6))* Oxfam Publishing GBR. Dist: Stylus Publishing, LLC.

AGRICULTURE AND STATE

see also Agricultural Administration; Agricultural Laws and Legislation; Agricultural Subsidies; Green Revolution; Land Reform; Rural Development; Surplus Agricultural Commodities

Almås, Reider & Campbell, Hugh, eds. Rethinking Agricultural Policy Regimes: Food Security, Climate Change & the Future Resilience of Global Agriculture. 2012. (Research in Rural Sociology & Development Ser.). (Illus.). 250p. 114.95 ***(978-1-78052-348-4(3))*** Emerald Group Publishing Ltd. GBR. Dist: Turpin Distribution Services Ltd.

Amin, Samir. Food Movements Unite! Strategies to Transform Our Food Systems. Holt-Gimenez, Eric, ed. 2011. (ENG., Illus.). 372p. pap. 24.99 ***(978-0-935028-38-6(2))*** Institute for Food & Development Policy/Food First Bks.

Anderson, Kym, ed. Distortions to Agricultural Incentives: A Global Perspective, 1955-2007. 2009. (Trade & Development Ser.). (ENG., Illus.). 680p. 80.00 *(978-0-8213-7973-8(9)*, 9780821379738) World Bank Pubns.

—Distortions to Agricultural Incentives: A Global Perspective 1955 to 2007. 2009. (Trade & Development Ser.). (ENG., Illus.). 680p. pap. 39.95 *(978-0-8213-7665-2(9)*, 9780821376652) World Bank Pubns.

Anderson, Kym & Tyers, Rodney. Disarray in World Food Markets: A Quantitative Assessment. 2011. (Trade & Development Ser.). (ENG.). 470p. pap. 45.00 *(978-0-521-17231-8(4))* Cambridge Univ. Pr.

Andreopoulou, Zacharoula, et al, eds. Agricultural & Environmental Informatics, Governance & Management: Emerging Research Applications. 2011. 350p. 180.00 *(978-1-60960-621-3(3)*, Information Science Reference) IGI Global.

Ball, V. Eldon, et al, eds. The Economic Impact of Public Support to Agriculture: An International Perspective. 2010. (Studies in Productivity & Efficiency Ser.). (Illus.). xi, 348p. 219.00 *(978-1-4419-6384-0(7)*, 1441963847) Springer.

Ball, V. Eldon, et al. The Economic Impact of Public Support to Agriculture: An International Perspective. 2010. (Studies in Productivity & Efficiency: Vol. 7). (Illus.). xi, 348p. E-Book ***(978-1-4419-6385-7(5))*** Springer.

Bansouleh, Bahman Farhadi. Development of a Spatial Planning Support System for Agricultural Policy Formulation Related to Land & Water Resources in Borkhar & Meymeh District, Iran. 2009. (Illus.). vi, 267p. *(978-90-8585-381-7(8))* Wageningen Agricultural University.

Campbell, Fergus. Land & Revolution: Nationalist Politics in the West of Ireland 1891-1921. 2008. (ENG., Illus.). 376p. pap. 55.00 *(978-0-19-954150-8(7))* Oxford Univ. Pr., Inc.

Clunies-Ross, Tracey & Hildyard, Nicholas. The Politics of Industrial Agriculture. 2nd ed. 2009. (Natural Resource Management Set Ser.). (ENG.). 172p. 110.00 *(978-1-84971-022-0(8))* Routledge.

Commission of the European Communities. Directorate-General for Agriculture, contrib. by. Rural Developments: CAP 2000. (Illus.). ii, 75p. *(978-92-828-2053-7(X))* European Commission BEL. Dist: Balogh International, Inc.

Contreras, Laura M. Agricultural Policies: New Developments. 2011. (Agriculture Issues & Policies Ser.). (Illus.). 293p. 129.00 *(978-1-61209-630-8(1))* Nova Science Pubs., Inc.

Cram101 Textbook Reviews. Outlines & Highlights for Rural Geography: Processes, Responses & Experiences in Rural Restructuring by Michael Woods, ISBN. 2011. 136p. pap. 28.95 ***(978-1-4288-2962-6(8))*** Cram101 Inc.

Dudwick, Nora, et al. Land Reform & Farm Restructuring in Transition Countries: The Experience of Bulgaria, Moldova, Azerbaijan, & Kazakhstan. 2007. (World Bank Working Papers: 104). (Illus.). (ENG.). 106p. per. 19.95 *(978-0-8213-7088-9(X)*, 9780821370889); (RUS., 126p. per. 19.95 *(978-0-8213-7034-6(0)*, 9780821370346) World Bank Pubns.

Ehrstrom, Henrik J., ed. Effects of Liberalizing World Agricultural Trade. 2009. 188p. 69.00 *(978-1-60741-198-7(9))* Nova Science Pubs., Inc.

Eichert, Christian. Examples for Policy Evaluation & Stakeholder Integration in the European Organic Farming Sector. 2011. 160p. pap. ***(978-3-8325-2896-6(2))*** Logos Verlag Berlin.

Fernández Prieto, Lourenzo & Prieto, Lourenzo Fernández. El Apagón Tecnológico Del Franquismo: Estado e Innovacíon en la Agricultura Española Del Siglo XX. 2007. (SPA., Illus.). 389p. *(978-84-8456-965-7(9))* Tirant lo Blanch.

Hesperides. Agricultural Legislation in India - Agricultural Production & Development. 2007. 484p. per. *(978-1-4067-5056-0(5)*, Hesperides Pr.) Read Bks.

Hill, Berkeley & Davidova, Sophia. Understanding the Common Agricultural Policy. 2012. (Earthscan Food & Agriculture Ser.). (ENG., Illus.). 352p. 147.00 *(978-1-84407-777-9(2))*; pap. 58.95 *(978-1-84407-778-6(0))* Routledge.

Horvath, Anna V. & Morel, Simon L. Agricultural Conservation. 2011. (Illus.). 157p. *(978-1-61209-928-6(9))* Nova Science Pubs., Inc.

Howlett, Michael & Laycock, David, eds. Regulating Next Generation Agri-Food Bio-Technologies: Lessons from European & Asian Experiences. 2012. (Genetics & Society Ser.). (ENG., Illus.). 288p. (C). 135.00 ***(978-0-415-69361-5(6))*** Routledge.

Just, Richard E., et al, eds. Regulating Agricultural Biotechnology: Economics & Policy. 2010. (Natural Resource Management & Policy Ser.). (Illus.). viii, 732p. pap. 229.00 *(978-1-4419-4239-5(4)*, 1441942394) Springer.

Kimhi, Ayal & Finkelshtain, Israel, eds. The Economics of Natural & Human Resources in Agriculture. 2009. (Illus.). 353p. 79.00 *(978-1-60741-029-4(X))* Nova Science Pubs., Inc.

Langmaier, Thomas. Common Agricultural Policy & Eu Agriculture. 2010. 136p. pap. *(978-3-639-21465-9(X))* VDM Verlag Dr. Mueller e.K.

Larsen, Kurt, et al, eds. Agribusiness & Innovation Systems in Africa. 2009. (Agriculture & Rural Development Ser.). (ENG., Illus.). 472p. pap. 35.00 *(978-0-8213-7944-8(5)*, 9780821379448) World Bank Pubns.

Laven, Anna. Knowing More about Sustainable Cocoa: The Dutch Knowledge Base. 2011. 144p. pap. 39.95 *(978-94-6022-103-3(3))* Royal Tropical Institute Pr. (KIT (Koninklijk Instituut voor de Tropen) NLD. Dist: Stylus Publishing, LLC.

Lekakis, J., ed. Freer Trade, Sustainability, & the Primary Production Sector in the Southern EU: Unraveling the Evidence from Greece: Unraveling the Evidence from Greece. 2010. (Economy & Environment Ser.). 228p. pap. 169.00 *(978-90-481-5060-1(4)*, 9048150604) Springer.

Lerman, Zvi. Russia's Agriculture in Transition: Factor Markets & Constraints on Growth. 2007. (Rural Economies in Transition Ser.). (ENG., Illus.). 394p. 89.50 *(978-0-7391-2009-5(3))* Lexington Bks.

Major, William H. Grounded Vision: New Agrarianism & the Academy. 2011. 240p. (ENG.). 35.00 *(978-0-8173-1734-8(1))*; *(978-0-8173-8544-6(4))* Univ. of Alabama Pr.

Marlin-Bennett, Renée. Food Fights: International Regimes & the Politics of Agricultural Trade Disputes. 2009. (Routledge Revivals Ser.). 192p. 100.00 *(978-0-415-56713-8(0))* Routledge.

—Food Fights (Routledge Revivals) 2009. 192p. pap. 39.95 *(978-0-415-56820-3(X))* Routledge.

McMahon, Joseph A. The WTO Agreement on Agriculture: A Commentary. 2007. 358p. 192.50 *(978-0-19-927568-7(8))* Oxford Univ. Pr., Inc.

Merino, Noël. Agricultural Subsidies. 2009. (OPPOSING VIEWPOINTS Ser.). (ENG., Illus.). 240p. 27.50 *(978-0-7377-4501-6(0))*; pap. 39.70 *(978-0-7377-4500-9(2))* Cengage Gale. (Greenhaven Pr., Inc.).

Oecd Publishing. Guidelines for Cost-Effective Agri-Environmental Policy Measures. 2010. 120p. pap. 42.00 *(978-92-64-08665-4(X))* Organization for Economic Cooperation & Development.

Ollington, Jennifer T., ed. Agro-Terrorism. 2008. pap. 39.00 *(978-1-60692-088-6(X))* Nova Science Pubs., Inc.

Organisation for Economic Co-operation and Development. Agricultural Policies in OECD Countries: At a Glance 2010. 2010. (Illus.). 125p. pap. 39.00 *(978-92-64-08379-0(0))* Organization for Economic Cooperation & Development.

Organisation for Economic Co-operation and Development & Food and Agriculture Organization. Oecd-Fao Agricultural Outlook 2010-2019. 2010. (Illus.). 247p. pap. 72.00 *(978-92-64-08375-2(8))* Organization for Economic Cooperation & Development.

Organisation for Economic Co-Operation and Development & Moreddu, Catherine. Disaggregated Impacts of Cap Reforms: Proceedings of an Oecd Workshop. 2011. (Illus.). 313p. pap. ***(978-92-64-09653-0(1))*** Organization for Economic Cooperation & Development.

Organisation for Economic Co-operation and Development Staff. Agricultural Policies in Emerging Economies 2009: Monitoring & Evaluation. 2009. (Illus.). 191p. pap. 63.00 *(978-92-64-05927-6(X))* Organization for Economic Cooperation & Development.

—Agricultural Policies in Oecd Countries: At a Glance 2008. 2008. (Illus.). 141p. pap. 63.00 *(978-92-64-03213-2(4))* Organization for Economic Cooperation & Development.

—Agricultural Policies in OECD Countries: Monitoring & Evaluation. 2009. (Illus.). 277p. pap. 63.00 *(978-92-64-06172-9(X))* Organization for Economic Cooperation & Development.

—Agricultural Policy & Trade Reform: The Impact on World Commodity Markets. 2007. pap. 32.00 *(978-92-64-02787-9(4))* Organization for Economic Cooperation & Development.

—The Cost of Implementing Agricultural Policies. 2007. pap. 60.00 *(978-92-64-03091-6(3))* Organization for Economic Cooperation & Development.

—Effective Targeting of Agricultural Policies: Best Practices for Policy Design & Implementation. 2007. pap. 29.00 *(978-92-64-03827-1(2))* Organization for Economic Cooperation & Development.

—Managing Risk in Agriculture: A Holistic Approach. 2009. (Illus.). 170p. pap. 63.00 *(978-92-64-07530-6(5))* Organization for Economic Cooperation & Development.

—Oecd-Fao Agricultural Outlook 2007-2016. 2007. pap. 78.00 *(978-92-64-02509-7(X))* Organization for Economic Cooperation & Development.

—Perspectives Agricoles de l'Ocde et de la Fao: 2006-2015. 2006. 228p. per. 75.00 *(978-92-64-02462-5(X))* Organization for Economic Cooperation & Development.

—Les Politiques Agricoles des Pays de l'Ocde: Panorama 2008. 2008. 148p. pap. 63.00 *(978-92-64-04465-4(5))* Organization for Economic Cooperation & Development.

—Politiques Agricoles des Pays Non-Membres de l'Ocde: Suivi et éValuation 2007. 2007. (FRE.). 220p. per. 52.00 *(978-92-64-03123-4(5))* Organization for Economic Cooperation & Development.

—Proceedings of the Workshop on Multifunctionality in Agriculture: Evaluating the Degree of Jointness, Policy Implications. 2008. pap. 63.00 *(978-92-64-03361-0(0))* Organization for Economic Cooperation & Development.

Organisation for Economic Co-operation and Development Staff & Food and Agriculture Organization. OECD-FAO agricultural Outlook 2006-2015. 2006. (Illus.). 208p. per. 75.00 *(978-92-64-02460-1(3))* Organization for Economic Cooperation & Development.

Paarlberg, Robert. Food Politics: What Everyone Needs to Know, 1 vol. 2010. (What Everyone Needs to Know Ser.). (ENG.). 240p. pap. 16.95 *(978-0-19-538959-3(X))* Oxford Univ. Pr., Inc.

Rajeswari, Kanniah. Breeders vs Farmers: The Contest for Rights over Plant Varieties in Selected Asian Countries. 2011. 340p. pap. ***(978-3-639-33425-8(6))*** VDM Verlag Dr. Mueller e.K.

Ringler, Claudia, et al, eds. Global Change: Impacts on Water & food Security: Impacts on Water & food Security. 2010. (Water Resources Development & Management Ser.). (ENG., Illus.). xv, 265p. 129.00 *(978-3-642-04614-8(2)*, 3642046142) Springer.

Romeo Casabona, Carlos M., et al, eds. Global Food Security: Ethical & Legal Challenges. 2010. (Illus.). 532p. pap. 102.00 *(978-90-8686-154-5(7))* Wageningen Academic Publishers NLD. Dist: Enfield Publishing & Distribution Co., Inc.

Rupp, Helen. Agricultural Trade Liberalization & Gender: A Case Study on Small Farmers in El Salvador Facing CAFTA. 2008. 112p. pap. *(978-3-8364-6555-7(8))* VDM Verlag Dr. Mueller e.K.

Santilli, Juliana. Agrobiodiversity & the Law: Regulating Genetic Resources, Food Security & Cultural Diversity. 2011. xx, 348p. E-Book ***(978-0-203-15525-7(4))*** Earthscan LLC.

—Agrobiodiversity & the Law: Regulating Genetic Resources, Food Security & Cultural Diversity. 2011. (ENG., Illus.). 368p. 99.95 *(978-1-84971-372-6(3))* Routledge.

Scott, James C. Decoding Subaltern Politics: Ideology, Disguise, & Resistance in Agrarian Politics. 2012. (Asia's Transformations/Critical Asian Scholarship Ser.). (ENG., Illus.). 208p. pap. 45.95 ***(978-0-415-54010-0(0))***; 140.00 ***(978-0-415-53975-3(7))*** Routledge.

Skogstad, Grace & Verdun, Amy, eds. The Common Agricultural Policy: Policy Dynamics in a Changing Context. 2009. (ENG., Illus.). 176p. 125.00 *(978-0-415-55356-8(3))* Routledge.

Southgate, Douglas, et al. The World Food Economy. 2006. (ENG., Illus.). 416p. per. 55.95 *(978-1-4051-0597-2(6)*, Wiley-Blackwell) Wiley, John & Sons, Inc.

Sumberg, James & Thompson, John, eds. Contested Agronomy. 2012. (Pathways to Sustainability Ser.). (ENG., Illus.). 232p. (C). pap. 35.95 ***(978-0-415-50714-1(6))*** Routledge.

—Contested Agronomy: Agricultural Research in a Changing World. 2012. (Pathways to Sustainability Ser.). (ENG., Illus.). 232p. (C). 155.00 ***(978-0-415-69806-1(5))*** Routledge.

Tauger, Mark. The Struggle for Bread: Famine & Agricultural. 284p. *(978-0-312-23270-2(5))* Palgrave Macmillan.

Tsakok, Isabelle & Gardner, Bruce L. Success in Agricultural Transformation. 2011. (ENG., Illus.). 424p. pap. 37.99 *(978-0-521-71769-4(8))* Cambridge Univ. Pr.

Warren, John, et al. The Agri-Environment. 2007. (ENG., Illus.). 232p. (C). 126.00 *(978-0-521-84965-4(9))*; pap. 57.00 *(978-0-521-61488-7(0))* Cambridge Univ. Pr.

Wilson, G. A. Multifunctional Agriculture: A Transition Theory Perspective. 2007. (Illus.). 368p. 145.00 *(978-1-84593-256-5(0))* CABI GBR. Dist: Stylus Publishing, LLC.

Winne, Mark. Food Rebels, Guerilla Gardeners, & Smart-Cookin' Mamas: Fighting Back in an Age of Industrial Agriculture. 2010. (ENG.). 208p. 24.95 *(978-0-8070-4733-0(3))* Beacon Pr.

—Food Rebels, Guerrilla Gardeners, & Smart-Cookin' Mamas: Fighting Back in an Age of Industrial Agriculture. 2011. (ENG.). 208p. pap. 16.00 *(978-0-8070-4737-8(6))* Beacon Pr.

Woods, Michael. Rural. 2010. (Key Ideas in Geography Ser.). (ENG., Illus.). 352p. (C). pap. 46.95 *(978-0-415-44240-4(0))* Routledge.

World Bank Staff, et al. OECD-FAO Agricultural Outlook, 2009-2018. 2009. (Illus.). 274p. pap. 63.00 *(978-92-64-01144-1(7))* Organization for Economic Cooperation & Development.

Wright, Julia. Sustainable Agriculture & Food Security in an Era of Oil Scarcity. 2012. (ENG.). 280p. pap. 42.95 ***(978-0-415-50734-9(0))*** Routledge.

AGRICULTURE AND STATE—AFRICA

Anderson, Kym & Masters, William A., eds. Distortions to Agricultural Incentives in Africa. 2009. (Trade & Development Ser.). (ENG., Illus.). 656p. pap. 39.95 *(978-0-8213-7652-2(7)*, 9780821376522) World Bank Pubns.

Batungi, Nasani. Land Reform in Uganda: Towards a Harmonised Tenure System. (Illus.). xiv, 261p. *(978-9970-02-811-5(1))* Fountain Pubs. Ltd.

Benin, S. Impact of Uganda's National Agricultural Advisory Services Program. 2012. ***(978-0-89629-189-8(8))*** International Food Policy Research Institute.

Bumb, Balu. Policy Workshop on Strengthening Regional Trade in Agricultural Inputs in Africa: Issues & Options; & Private Sector Roundtable Meeting on Expanding Fertilizer Markets in Africa: Issues & Options: Summary Reports. 2010. *(978-0-88090-166-6(7))* IFDC.

Carswell, Grace. Cultivating Success in Uganda: Kigezi Farmers & Colonial Policies. 2007. (Illus.). 272p. 90.00 *(978-1-84701-600-3(6))*; pap. 29.95 *(978-1-84701-601-0(4))* Boydell & Brewer, Ltd. GBR. (Currey, James). Dist: Boydell & Brewer, Inc.

—Cultivating Success in Uganda: Kigezi Farmers & Colonial Policies. 2007. (Eastern African Studies). (Illus.). 272p. 59.95 *(978-0-8214-1779-9(7))*; 258p. per. 26.95 *(978-0-8214-1780-5(0))* Ohio Univ. Pr.

Deveze, Jean-Claude, ed. Challenges for African Agriculture. 2010. (ENG., Illus.). 292p. pap. 35.00 *(978-0-8213-8481-7(3)*, 9780821384817) World Bank Pubns.

Diao, Xinshen. The Role of Agriculture in Development: Implications for Sub-Saharan Africa. 2007. *(978-0-89629-161-4(8))* International Food Policy Research Institute.

Diao, Xinshen. Strategies & Priorities for African Agriculture: Economywide Perspectives from Country Studies. 2012. ***(978-0-89629-195-9(2))*** International Food Policy Research Institute.

Djurfeldt, Göran, et al, eds. African Smallholders: Food Crops, Markets & Policy. 2011. (Illus.). 304p. 160.00 *(978-1-84593-716-4(3))* CABI GBR. Dist: Stylus Publishing, LLC.

Firmin-Sellers, Kathryn. The Transformation of Property Rights in the Gold Coast: An Empirical Analysis Applying Rational Choice Theory. 2007. (Political Economy of Institutions & Decisions Ser.). (ENG., Illus.). 216p. per. 48.00 *(978-0-521-03935-2(5))* Cambridge Univ. Pr.

Innovation Africa: Enriching Farmers' Livelihoods. 2008. (ENG., Illus.). 384p. 166.00 *(978-1-84407-671-0(7))* Routledge.

Innovation Africa: Enriching Farmers' Livelihoods. 2008. (ENG., Illus.). 384p. pap. 58.50 *(978-1-84407-672-7(5))* Routledge.

Kebede, Gutema, et al. Female Headed Farmers' Participation in Agricultural Extension: Female Headed Farm Households' Participation in Agricultural Extension Packages, Lume, Oromia National Regional State, Ethiopia. 2011. 104p. pap. ***(978-3-639-33887-4(1))*** VDM Verlag Dr. Mueller e.K.

Kirsten, Johann. Institutional Economics Perspectives on African Agricultural Development. 2009. *(978-0-89629-781-4(0))* International Food Policy Research Institute.

Korieh, Chima J. & Matthews, S. The Land Has Changed: History, Society & Gender in Colonial Eastern Nigeria. 2010. (Africa: Missing Voices Ser.). (Illus.). 390p. pap. 39.95 *(978-1-55238-268-4(0))* Univ. of Calgary Pr. CAN. Dist: Michigan State Univ. Pr.

Li, Xiaoyun, et al. Agricultural Development in China & Africa. 2012. (ENG., Illus.). 328p. 99.95 ***(978-1-84971-388-7(X))*** Routledge.

Maatman, Arno. Competitive Agricultural Systems & Enterprises (CASE) Volume 1: Reference framework & early experiences, 2 , 2011. pap. 10.00 ***(978-0-88090-168-0(3))*** IFDC.

Melber, Henning, et al. Africa, Regional Cooperation & the World Market: Socio-Economic Strategies in Times of Global Trade Regimes. 2006. (NAI Discussion Papers). 72p. pap. 13.95 *(978-91-7106-559-9(8))* Nordiska Afrikainstitutet SWE. Dist: Stylus Publishing, LLC.

Morris, Michael L., et al. Fertilizer Use in African Agriculture: Lessons Learned & Good Practice Guidelines. 2007. (Directions in Development Ser.). (ENG., Illus.). 160p. pap. 20.00 incl. cd-rom *(978-0-8213-6880-0(X)*, 9780821368800) World Bank Pubns.

Mpuga, Paul. Characteristics of Demand for Rural Credit. 2008. 88p. pap. *(978-3-639-01794-6(3))* VDM Verlag Dr. Mueller e.K.

Murisa, Tendai. From Rhetoric to Policy Action: An Analysis of Agricultural Policy Reform in Six African Countries. 2011. ***(978-1-59221-891-2(1))***; ***(978-1-59221-892-9(X))*** Africa World Pr.

Mwangolela, Tafadzwa Fungayi. Re-Imagining Agrarian Transformation in South Afric. 2011. 96p. pap. ***(978-3-8454-2408-8(7))*** Lambert Academic Publishing.

Nhira, Calvin & Mapiki, Alfred, eds. Land & Water Management in Southern Africa: Towards sustainable Agriculture. 2008. 686p. pap. *(978-0-7983-0214-2(3))* Africa Institute of South Africa ZAF. Dist: Michigan State Univ. Pr.

Nzioka, Charles. Market Integration in Mozambican Maize Markets. 2008. 116p. pap. 19.95 *(978-99944-55-26-3(5))* African Bks. Collective, Ltd. GBR. Dist: Lightning Source, Inc.

Obi, Ajuruchukwu. Trends in South African Agricultural Land Prices. 2008. 328p. per. *(978-3-8364-6378-2(4))* VDM Verlag Dr. Mueller e.K.

Okpara, John, ed. Management & Economic Development in Sub-Saharan Afric: Theoretical & Applied Perspectives. 2007. 260p. per. *(978-1-905068-85-2(9))* Adonis & Abbey Publishers Ltd.

Organisation for Economic Co-operation and Development Staff. Business for Development 2008. 2008. 124p. pap. 63.00 *(978-92-64-04469-2(8))* Organization for Economic Cooperation & Development.

Paarlberg, Robert & Paarlberg, Robert L. Starved for Science: How Biotechnology Is Being Kept Out of Africa. 2009. (Illus.). 256p. pap. 17.95 *(978-0-674-03347-4(7))* Harvard Univ. Pr.

Palchick, Michaela. Agricultural Transformation & Livelihood Struggles. 2009. 116p. pap. *(978-3-639-17828-9(9))* VDM Verlag Dr. Mueller e.K.

Pender, J., et al. Strategies for Sustainable Land Management in the East African Highlands. 2006. *(978-0-89629-757-9(8))* International Food Policy Research Institute.

Taeb, M. & A. H. Zakri. Agriculture, Human Security, & Peace: A Crossroad in African Development. 2008. (Illus.). 187p. pap. 29.95 *(978-1-55753-482-8(9))* Purdue Univ. Pr.

Tchale, Hardwick. Agricultural Policy & Soil Fertility Management in the Maize-based Smallholder Farming System in Malawi, Vol. 53. 2006. (Development Economics & Policy Ser.). xix,164p. pap. 43.95 *(978-0-8204-9824-9(6))* Lang, Peter Publishing, Inc.

Workineh Kelbessa. Indigenous & Modern Environmental Ethics: A Study of the Indigenous Oromo Environmental Ethic & Modern Issues of Environment & Development. 2008. pap. *(978-1-56518-253-0(7))* Council for Research in Values & Philosophy.

World Bank Staff. L' appui de la Banque à l'agriculture en Afrique Subsaharienne:Examen de L'IEG: Examen de l'Ieg. 2008. (Independent Evaluation Group Studies). (FRE.). 148p. pap. 35.00 *(978-0-8213-7595-2(4)*, 9780821375952) World Bank Pubns.

AGRICULTURE AND STATE—ASIA

Anderson, Kym & Martin, Will, eds. Distortions to Agricultural Incentives in Asia. 2009. (Trade & Development Ser.). (ENG., Illus.). 608p. pap. 39.95 *(978-0-8213-7662-1(4)*, 9780821376621) World Bank Pubns.

Anderson, Kym & Swinnen, Johan F. M. Distortions to Agricultural Incentives in Europe's Transition Economies. 2008. (Trade & Development Ser.). (ENG., Illus.). 408p. (C). pap. 39.95 *(978-0-8213-7419-1(2)*, 9780821374191) World Bank Pubns.

Bayliss-Smith, Tim & Wanmali, Sudhir, eds. Understanding Green Revolutions: Agrarian Change & Development Planning in South Asia. 2009. (ENG.). 400p. pap. 39.99 *(978-0-521-10912-3(4))* Cambridge Univ. Pr.

Cho, Yong-Gwan & Yi, Si-Yong. Chungang Asia Kukkadul Ui Nongop Chongch'aek Kwa Han, Chungang Asia Nongop Hyomyok Hwaktae Pangan: K'ajahusut'an, Ujubek'isut'an, K'irugijusut'an Ui Chungsim Uro. 2010. (KOR., Illus.). 90p. *(978-89-322-2174-8(X))* Korea Institute for International Economic Policy.

Djalalov, Sandjar & Babu, Suresh Chandra, eds. Policy Reforms & Agriculture Development in Central Asia. 2010. (Natural Resource Management & Policy Ser.). (Illus.). xiv, 494p. pap. 179.00 *(978-1-4419-4001-8(4)*, 1441940014) Springer.

Hall, Derek, et al. Powers of Exclusion: Land Dilemmas in Southeast Asia. 2011. pap. 35.00 *(978-0-8248-3603-0(0))* Univ. of Hawaii Pr.

Heerink, Nico, et al. Dragons with Clay Feet? Transition, Sustainable Land Use, & Rural Environment in China & Vietnam. 2010. (Rural Economies in Transition Ser.). (ENG.). 256p. pap. 42.95 *(978-0-7391-4656-9(4))* Lexington Bks.

Hinnebusch, Raymond, et al. Agriculture & Reform in Syria. 2010. (Illus.). 120p. (C). pap. 17.95 *(978-0-9559687-7-8(1))* Rienner, Lynne Pubs.

Rigg, Jonathan & Vandergeest, Peter. Revisiting Rural Places: Pathways to Poverty & Prosperity in Southeast Asia. 2011. pap. 34.00 ***(978-0-8248-3620-7(0))*** Univ. of Hawaii Pr.

Silpakar, Sandesh, et al. Implications of Land Tenure on Food Sufficiency. 2011. 108p. pap. ***(978-3-8383-8573-0(X))*** Lambert Academic Publishing.

Sutton, William R. Integrating Environment into Agriculture & Forestry: Progress & Prospects in Eastern Europe & Central Asia. 2008. (ENG., Illus.). 92p. pap. 25.00 incl. cd-rom *(978-0-8213-7743-7(4)*, 9780821377437) World Bank Pubns.

AGRICULTURE AND STATE—AUSTRALIA

Meng, Erika C. H. & Brennan, John P. Economic Analysis of Diversity in Modern Wheat. 2009. (ENG., Illus.). 204p. 99.95 *(978-1-57808-575-0(6))* BIOS Scientific Publishers Ltd. GBR. Dist: Taylor & Francis Group.

Whitford, Troy. Australia's Rural Reconstruction Commission. 2010. 184p. pap. *(978-3-8383-6452-0(X))* Lambert Academic Publishing.

AGRICULTURE AND STATE—BRAZIL

Czinkota & Uczai, Pedro F. Matematicamente Incorreto. (POR., Illus.). 323p. *(978-0-00-293029-1(3)*, Wiley-Blackwell) Wiley, John & Sons, Inc.

AGRICULTURE AND STATE—CANADA

Brubaker, Elizabeth. Greener Pastures: Decentralizing the Regulation of Agricultural Pollution. 2007. (University of Toronto Centre for Public Management Monograph Ser.). (ENG.). 152p. *(978-0-7727-8621-0(6))*; pap. *(978-0-7727-8620-3(8))* Univ. of Toronto Pr.

Kirbyson, Anna Maria, ed. Recipes for Success: A Celebration of Food Security Work in Canada. 2006. (ENG.). 130p. pap. 17.95 *(978-1-895752-52-6(3))* Fernwood Publishing Co., Ltd. CAN. Dist: Independent Pubs. Group.

Knuttila, Murray & Stirling, Bob. The Prairie Agrarian Movement: The Centenary Symposium on the Foundation of the Teritorial Grain Growers Association. rev. ed. 2007. (Canadian Plains Studies(CPS) Ser.). (ENG.). 293p. pap. 29.95 *(978-0-88977-183-3(9))* Canadian Plains Research Ctr. CAN. Dist: Univ. of Toronto Pr.

Kuyek, Devlin. Good Crop/Bad Crop: Seed Politics & the Future of Food in Canada. 2007. 208p. pap. 22.95 *(978-1-897071-21-2(3))* Between the Lines CAN. Dist: Univ. of Toronto Pr.

Matsui, Kenichi. Native Peoples & Water Rights: Irrigation, Dams, & the Law in Western Canada. 2009. (McGill-Queen's Native & Northern Ser.). 176p. pap. *(978-0-7735-3534-3(9))*; (ENG.). (C). *(978-0-7735-3521-3(7))* McGill-Queen's Univ. Pr.

Schmitz, Andrew, et al. Agricultural Policy, Agribusiness & Rent-Seeking Behaviour. 2nd ed. 2010. (Illus.). 512p. pap. *(978-0-8020-9547-3(X))* Univ. of Toronto Pr.

Skogstad, Grace. Internationalization & Canadian Agriculture: Policy & Governing Paradigms. 2008. (Studies in Comparative Political Economy & Public Policy Ser.). (ENG., Illus.). 352p. *(978-0-8020-9880-1(0))* Univ. of Toronto Pr.

Wall, Ellen, et al, eds. Farming in a Changing Climate: Agricultural Adaptation in Canada. 2008. (ENG., Illus.). 288p. pap. *(978-0-7748-1394-5(6))* Univ. of British Columbia Pr.

Wozniak, Chris A. & McHughen, Alan, eds. Regulation of Agricultural Biotechnology: the United States & Canada: The United States & Canada. 2012. (ENG., Illus.). xx, 230p. 189.00 ***(978-94-007-2155-5(2)***, 9400721552) Springer.

AGRICULTURE AND STATE—CARIBBEAN AREA

International Assessment of Agricultural Knowledge, Science, and Technology. Agriculture at a Crossroads Vol. 3: Latin America & the Caribbean. 2009. (ENG., Illus.). 248p. 125.00 *(978-1-59726-546-1(2))* Island Pr.

—Agriculture at a Crossroads Vol. 4: Latin America & the Caribbean. 2nd ed. 2009. (ENG.). 248p. pap. 75.00 *(978-1-59726-547-8(0))* Island Pr.

Wright, Julia. Sustainable Agriculture & Food Security in an Era of Oil Scarcity: Lessons from Cuba. 2008. (ENG., Illus.). 280p. 117.00 *(978-1-84407-572-0(9))* Routledge.

AGRICULTURE AND STATE—CHILE

Organisation for Economic Co-operation and Development Staff. Oecd Review of Agricultural Policies Chile. 2008. (Illus.). 153p. pap. 63.00 *(978-92-64-04223-0(7))* Organization for Economic Cooperation & Development.

Silva, Patricio. Estado, neoliberalismo y politica agraria en Chile 1973 - 1981. (Latin America Studies). (GER.). 389p. 225.00 ***(978-3-11-209982-7(6))***; 146.00 ***(978-3-11-122900-3(9))*** De Gruyter, Mouton DEU. Dist: de Gruyter, Walter GmbH & Co. KG.

AGRICULTURE AND STATE—CHINA

Baumler, Alan. The Chinese & Opium under the Republic: Worse Than Floods & Wild Beasts. 2008. (Illus.). 298p. per. 29.95 *(978-0-7914-6954-5(9))* State Univ. of New York Pr.

Brown, Colin G., et al. Sustainable Development in Western China: Managing People, Livestock & Grasslands in Pastoral Areas. 2008. (Illus.). 320p. 137.00 *(978-1-84542-744-3(0))* Elgar, Edward Publishing, Inc.

Cheng, Shi. China's Rural Industrialization Policy: Growing under Orders Since 1949. 2006. (ENG., Illus.). 368p. 137.00 *(978-1-4039-9615-2(6))* Palgrave Macmillan.

Fan, Shenggen. The Dragon & the Elephant: Agricultural & Rural Reforms in China & India. Fan, Shenggen & Gulati, Ashok, eds. 2007. (ENG., Illus.). 576p. (gr. 17). per. 38.00 *(978-0-8018-8787-1(9))* Johns Hopkins Univ. Pr.

Fang, Jian. Nan Song Nong Ye Shi. 2010. (CHI.). 40p. *(978-7-01-008450-3(5))* People's Publishing Hse., The.

Gulati, Ashok & Fan, Shenggen, eds. The Dragon & the Elephant: A Comparative Study of Agricultural & Rural Reforms in China & India. 2008. (ENG.). 560p. 50.00 *(978-0-19-569350-8(7))* Oxford Univ. Pr., Inc.

—The Dragon & the Elephant: Agricultural & Rural Reforms in China & India. 2007. (ENG., Illus.). 576p. (gr. 17). 75.00 *(978-0-8018-8786-4(0))* Johns Hopkins Univ. Pr.

Guo, Ruiping. Wo Guo Nong Cun Gong Gong Chan Pin Gong Gei Zhi du Yan Jiu: Woguo Nongcun Gonggongchanpin Gongjizhide Yanjiu. 2008. (CHI., Illus.). *(978-7-5004-7234-6(X))* China Social Sciences Pr.

Jeffries, Russell H., ed. China's Agricultural Modernization. 2009. (China in the 21st Century Ser.). pap. 69.00 *(978-1-60876-088-6(X))* Nova Science Pubs., Inc.

Kuo-Chin, Chao. Agrarian Policies of Mainland Chin: A Documentary Study 1949-1956. 2011. 292p. 48.95 ***(978-1-258-10472-6(5))*** Literary Licensing, LLC.

Lardy, Nicholas R. Agriculture in China's Modern Economic Development. 2008. (ENG., Illus.). 300p. pap. 42.00 *(978-0-521-07170-3(4))* Cambridge Univ. Pr.

Li, Huaiyin. Village China under Socialism & Reform: A Micro History, 1948-2008. 2009. (ENG., Illus.). 424p. 65.00 *(978-0-8047-5974-8(X))* Stanford Univ. Pr.

—Village China under Socialism & Reform: A Micro-History, 1948-2008. 2010. (ENG., Illus.). 424p. pap. 27.95 *(978-0-8047-7657-8(1))* Stanford Univ. Pr.

Li, Xiaoyun, et al. Agricultural Development in China & Africa. 2012. (ENG., Illus.). 328p. 99.95 ***(978-1-84971-388-7(X))*** Routledge.

Lingohr-Wolf, Susanne. Industrialisation & Rural Livelihoods in China. 2010. (Routledge Contemporary China Ser.). (ENG., Illus.). 256p. (C). 130.00 *(978-0-415-55937-9(5))* Routledge.

McBeath, Jennifer H. & McBeath, Jerry. Environmental Change & Food Security in China. 2009. (Advances in Global Change Research Ser.). (Illus.). xvii, 303p. 199.00 *(978-1-4020-9179-7(6))* Springer.

Meng, Erika C. H. & Brennan, John P. Economic Analysis of Diversity in Modern Wheat. 2009. (ENG., Illus.). 204p. 99.95 *(978-1-57808-575-0(6))* BIOS Scientific Publishers Ltd. GBR. Dist: Taylor & Francis Group.

Orden, David. Agricultural Producer Support Estimates for Developing Countries: Measurement Issues & Evidence from India, Indonesia, China, & Vietnam. 2007. *(978-0-89629-160-7(X))* International Food Policy Research Institute.

Ou, Suying. Taiwan Sheng Can Yi Hui Shi Liao Hui Bian. 2009. (CHI.). ix, 32p. *(978-986-02-1054-5(3))* Academia Sinica.

Song, Shunfeng & Chen, Aimin. China's Rural Economy after WTO: Problems & Strategies. 2006. (Chinese Economy Ser.). (Illus.). 384p. 130.00 *(978-0-7546-4695-2(5))* Ashgate Publishing Co.

Spoor, Max, et al, eds. Dragons with Clay Feet? Transition, Sustainable Land Use, & Rural Environment in China & Vietnam. 2007. (Rural Economies in Transition Ser.). (ENG., Illus.). 356p. 99.99 *(978-0-7391-1369-1(0))* Lexington Bks.

Sun, Hongzhi. She Hui Zhu Yi Xin Nong Cun Jian She Shi Jian Yan Jiu. 2008. (CHI., Illus.). *(978-7-5035-3952-7(6))* Party Schl. Pr. of the Central Committee of CPC, The.

Wang, Wei. Zhongguo Nong Cun Jin Rong Fu Wu Ti Xi Xie Tiao Fa Zhan Yan Jiu: Zhongguo Nongcun Jinrong Fuwu Tixi Xietiao Fazhan Yanjiu. 2010. (CHI., Illus.). *(978-7-207-08527-6(3))* Heilongjiang People's Publishing Hse.

Zeng, Tao & Goodwin, Barry K. Chinese Agricultural Household. 2008. 176p. pap. *(978-3-639-05959-5(X))* VDM Verlag Dr. Mueller e.K.

Zhenglai, Deng. China's Economy Vol. 1: Rural Reform & Agricultural Development. 2009. 432p. 111.00 *(978-981-4291-85-9(4))* World Scientific Publishing Co., Inc.

AGRICULTURE AND STATE—DEVELOPING COUNTRIES

Bresciani. Beyond Food Production the Role of Agriculture in Poverty Reduction. 2007. (Illus.). 240p. (C). 119.00 *(978-1-84720-075-4(3))* Elgar, Edward Publishing, Inc.

Bresciani, Fabrizio & Valdés, Alberto. Beyond Food Production: The Role of Agriculture in Poverty Reduction. 2007. (Illus.). viii, 232p. *(978-92-5-105534-2(3))*; pap. *(978-92-5-105535-9(1))* Elgar, Edward Publishing, Inc.

Chang, Ha-Joon, ed. Public Policy & Agricultural Development. 2011. (Routledge ISS Studies in Rural Livelihoods Ser.). (ENG., Illus.). 320p. (C). 140.00 *(978-0-415-61930-1(0))* Routledge.

Glaeser, Bernhard, ed. The Green Revolution Revisited. 2011. (ENG.). 224p. 105.00 *(978-0-415-59249-9(6))* Routledge.

Hoda, Anwarul & Gulati, Ashok. WTO Negotiations on Agriculture & Developing Countries. 2008. (ENG., Illus.). 320p. (gr. 17). 60.00 *(978-0-8018-8698-0(8))*; per. 27.95 *(978-0-8018-8793-2(3))* Johns Hopkins Univ. Pr.

Joshi, Seema. Growth & Structure of Tertiary Sector in Developing Economies. 2007. (ENG.). 244p. 45.95 *(978-81-7188-631-9(0))* Academic Foundation IND. Dist: Independent Pubs. Group.

Koning, Niek & Pinstrup-Andersen, Per, eds. Agricultural Trade Liberalization & the Least Developed Countries. (Wageningen UR Frontis Ser.). 2008. viii, 252p. 129.00 *(978-1-4020-6079-3(3))* 2007. (Illus.). 249p. pap. 79.95 *(978-1-4020-6085-4(8))* Springer.

McCalla, Alex F. & Nash, John D., eds. Reforming Agricultural Trade for Developing Countries Vol. 2: Quantifying the Impact of Multilateral Trade Reform, 2 vols. 2006. (Agriculture & Rural Development Ser.: 2). (ENG., Illus.). 274p. per. 45.00 *(978-0-8213-6716-2(1)*, 9780821367162) World Bank Pubns.

Orden, David. Agricultural Producer Support Estimates for Developing Countries: Measurement Issues & Evidence from India, Indonesia, China, & Vietnam. 2007. *(978-0-89629-160-7(X))* International Food Policy Research Institute.

Organisation for Economic Co-operation and Development Staff. Agricultural Policies in Non-Oecd Countries: Monitoring & Evaluation 2007. 2007. pap. 52.00 *(978-92-64-03121-0(9))* Organization for Economic Cooperation & Development.

Sauber, Martin. The Agricultural Productivity Gap- Comparative Advantage Concerning Agriculture in Developing Countries. 2007. 68p. pap. *(978-3-8364-0588-1(1))* VDM Verlag Dr. Mueller e.K.

Scholten, Bruce A. India's White Revolution: Operation Flood, Food Aid & Development. 2010. (Library of Development Studies). (ENG., Illus.). 352p. 99.00 *(978-1-84885-176-4(6)*, Tauris Academic Studies) I. B. Tauris & Co., Ltd. GBR. Dist: Macmillan.

Spielman, David J. & Pandya-Lorch, Rajul. Highlights from Millions Fed: Proven Successes in Agricultural Development. 2009. (Illus.). 24p. pap. ***(978-0-89629-659-6(8))*** International Food Policy Research Institute.

—Millions Fed: Proven Successes in Agricultural Development. 2009. *(978-0-89629-661-9(X))* International Food Policy Research Institute.

—Proven Successes in Agricultural Development: A Technical Compendium to Millions Fed 2010. 2010. *(978-0-89629-669-5(5))* International Food Policy Research Institute.

Stockbridge, Michael. Agricultural Trade Policy in Developing Countries During Take-off. 2007. (Oxfam International Research Report). (ENG., Illus.). 60p. per. 29.95 *(978-0-85598-584-4(4))* Oxfam Publishing GBR. Dist: Stylus Publishing, LLC.

Tripp, Robert Burnet. Biotechnology & Agricultural Development: Transgenic Cotton, Rural Institutions & Resource-Poor Farmers. Tripp, Rob, ed. 2009. (Routledge Explorations in Environmental Economics Ser.: Vol. 19). (Illus.). 280p. pap. 45.95 *(978-0-415-54384-2(3))* Routledge.

—Biotechnology & Agricultural Development: Transgenic Cotton, Rural Institutions & Resource-poor Farmers. 2009. (Routledge Explorations in Environmental Economics Ser.: Vol. 19). (ENG., Illus.). 280p. 145.00 *(978-0-415-49963-7(1))* Routledge.

Zilberman, David, et al, eds. Health & Animal Agriculture in Developing Countries. 2011. (Natural Resource Management & Policy Ser.). (ENG., Illus.). vii, 424p. 139.00 *(978-1-4419-7076-3(2)*, 1441970762) Springer.

AGRICULTURE AND STATE—ETHIOPIA

Haile, Mekbib Gebretsadik. Technology Adoption & Commercialization of Chickpea in Ethiopia: Econometric Analysis Using the Augmented Double Hurdle Model. 2011. 72p. pap. ***(978-3-639-33133-2(8))*** VDM Verlag Dr. Mueller e.K.

Kagima, David. Training Programs in Sustainable Agriculture & Postharvest Technology. 2008. 172p. pap. *(978-3-639-07341-6(X))* VDM Verlag Dr. Mueller e.K.

Rahmato, Dessalegn. Agrarian Reform in Ethiopia. 105p. per. 7.95 *(978-0-932415-07-3(5))* Red Sea Pr.

AGRICULTURE AND STATE—EUROPE

Acosta, Francisco, et al. Socialismo y Democracia en el Campo (1880-1930) Los Origenes de la Federación Nacional de Trabajadores de la Tierra. 2009. (Illus.). 496p. *(978-84-491-0970-6(1)*, LearnVerbs.com) Ministerio de Agricultura, Pesca y Alimentación.

Amat Llombart, Pablo & Llombart, Pablo Amat. Derecho Agrario y Alimentario Español y de la Unión Europea. 2007. (SPA.). 702p. *(978-84-8456-899-5(7))* Tirant lo Blanch.

Anderson, Kym & Swinnen, Johan F. M. Distortions to Agricultural Incentives in Europe's Transition Economies. 2008. (Trade & Development Ser.). (ENG., Illus.). 408p. (C). pap. 39.95 *(978-0-8213-7419-1(2)*, 9780821374191) World Bank Pubns.

Churchill, Robin R. & Owen, Daniel. The EU Common Fisheries Policy: Law & Practice. 2009. (Oxford European Community Law Library). (ENG.). 400p. 275.00 *(978-0-19-927584-7(X))* Oxford Univ. Pr., Inc.

Daugbjerg, Carsten & Swinbank, Alan. Ideas, Institutions, & Trade: The WTO & the Curious Role of EU Farm Policy in Trade Liberalization. 2009. (ENG., Illus.). 256p. 95.00 *(978-0-19-955775-2(6))* Oxford Univ. Pr., Inc.

De Vries, Sybe & Gerbrandy, Anna. Agricultural Policy & Eu Competition Law: Possibilities & Limits for Self-Regulation in the Dairy Sector. 2011. 60p. pap. 24.00 ***(978-94-90947-11-8(3))*** Eleven International Publishing NLD. Dist: International Specialized Bk. Services.

Fuller, Frank. European Agriculture: Enlargement, Structural Change, CAP Reform, & Trade Liberalization. Beghin, John C., ed. 2008. (C). 98.00 *(978-1-60021-966-5(7))* Nova Science Pubs., Inc.

Garzon, Isabelle. Reforming the Common Agricultural Policy: History of a Paradigm Change. 2007. (Palgrave studies in European Union Politics Ser.). (ENG., Illus.). 224p. 105.00 *(978-0-230-00184-8(X))* Palgrave Macmillan.

Greenaway, David, ed. The World Economy: Global Trade Policy 2009. 2010. (World Economy Special Issues Ser.: 7). (ENG.). 176p. pap. 39.95 *(978-1-4051-9704-5(8)*, Wiley-Blackwell) Wiley, John & Sons, Inc.

Greer, Alan (Principal Research Scientist & Greer, Alan. Agricultural Policy in Europe. 2009. (European Policy Studies). (ENG.). 258p. pap. 34.00 *(978-0-7190-8061-6(4))* Manchester Univ. Pr. GBR. Dist: Macmillan.

Haas, Dieter. Agricultural Policies in the Eu & Us- a Comparison of Policy Objectives & Their Realization. 2007. 140p. per. *(978-3-8364-1126-4(1))* VDM Verlag Dr. Mueller e.K.

Harsche, Johannes. Regionale Inzidenz und ökonomische Bestimmungsgrößen der Gemeinsamen Europäischen Agrarpolitik. 2009. (Schriften zur internationalen Entwicklungs- und Umweltforschung Ser.). (GER.). 264p. pap. 65.95 *(978-3-631-58096-7(7))* Lang, Peter GmbH, Europaischer Verlag der Wissenschaften DEU. Dist: Lang, Peter.

Kaditi, Eleni & Swinnen, Johan, eds. Trade Agreements, Multifunctionality & Eu Agriculture. 2007. (ENG.). 324p. per. 28.00 *(978-92-9079-672-5(3))* Ctr. for European Policy Studies BEL. Dist: Brookings Institution Pr.

Kaljonen, Minna. Caught Between Standardisation & Complexity: Study on the Institutional Ambiguities of Agri-Environmental Policy Implementation in Finland. 2011. (Acta Universitatis Tamperensis Ser.). 122p. pap. 82.50 *(978-951-44-8375-2(8))* Tampere Univ. Pr. FIN. Dist: Coronet Bks.

Knudsen, Ann-Christina L. Farmers on Welfare: The Making of Europe's Common Agricultural Policy. 2009. (Illus.). 360p. 47.50 *(978-0-8014-4727-3(5))* Cornell Univ. Pr.

Lains, Pedro & Pinilla, Vicente. Agriculture & Economic Development in Europe since 1870. Lains, Pedro & Pinilla, Vicente, eds. 2009. (Routledge Explorations in Economic History Ser.). (Illus.). 400p. 170.00 *(978-0-415-42487-5(9))* Routledge.

Lampietti, Julian A., et al. The Changing Face of Rural Space: Agriculture & Rural Development in the Western Balkans. 2009. (Directions in Development Ser.). (ENG., Illus.). 176p. pap. 35.00 *(978-0-8213-7931-8(3)*, 9780821379318) World Bank Pubns.

Lynggaard, K. The Common Agricultural Policy & Organic Farming: An Institutional Perspective on Continuity & Change. 2006. (Illus.). 224p. 125.00 *(978-1-84593-114-8(9))* CABI GBR. Dist: Stylus Publishing, LLC.

Merriënboer, Johan van. Mansholt: A Biography. 2011. (Mémoires de l'Europe en devenir Ser.). (ENG.). 642p. pap. 59.95 ***(978-90-5201-757-0(3))*** PIE - Peter Lang BEL. Dist: Lang, Peter.

Oskam, Arie, et al, eds. EU policy for agriculture, food & rural Areas. (Illus.). 2011. 454p. pap. 66.00 ***(978-90-8686-180-4(6))*** 2010. 400p. pap. 60.00 *(978-90-8686-118-7(0))* Wageningen Academic Publishers NLD. Dist: Enfield Publishing & Distribution Co., Inc.

Patel, Kiran, ed. Fertile Ground for Europe? The History of European Integration & the Common Agricultural Policy Since 1945. 2009. 302p. pap. 49.00 *(978-3-8329-4494-0(X))* Nomos Verlagsgesellschaft DEU. Dist: International Specialized Bk. Services.

Piorr, Annette & Muller, Klaus. Rural Landscapes & Agricultural Policies in Europe. 2009. (Illus.). 380p. 169.00 *(978-3-540-79469-1(7))* Springer.

Schierholz, Friederike & J. Garcia, Roberto. Norwegian Dairy Policies & the Wto. 2010. 108p. pap. *(978-3-639-27435-6(0))* VDM Verlag Dr. Mueller e.K.

Senior Nello, Susan Mary & Pierani, Pierpaolo, eds. International Trade, Consumer Interests & Reform of the Common Agricultural Policy. 2010. (Routledge Studies in the European Economy Ser.). (ENG., Illus.). 208p. (C). 150.00 *(978-0-415-57019-0(0)*, Routledge) Taylor & Francis Group GBR. Dist: Taylor & Francis Group.

Severini, Simone, et al. The Common Agricultural Policy after the Fischler Reform: National Implementations Impact Assessment & the Agenda for Future Reforms. 2011. (Illus.). 544p. 144.95 *(978-1-4094-2194-8(5))* Ashgate Publishing Co.

Stewart, Pamela J. & Strathern, Andrew, eds. Landscape, Heritage, & Conservation: Farming Issues in the European Union. 2010. 340p. pap. 42.00 *(978-1-59460-774-5(5))* Carolina Academic Pr.

Sutton, William R. Integrating Environment into Agriculture & Forestry: Progress & Prospects in Eastern Europe & Central Asia. 2008. (ENG., Illus.). 92p. pap. 25.00 incl. cd-rom *(978-0-8213-7743-7(4)*, 9780821377437) World Bank Pubns.

TV. Labels of Origin for Food: Local Development, Global Recognition. Sylvander, B., ed. 2011. (Illus.). 240p. 145.00 *(978-1-84593-352-4(4))* CABI GBR. Dist: Stylus Publishing, LLC.

van Berkum, Siemen & Bogdanov, Natalija. Serbia on the Road to EU Accession: Consequences for Agricultural Policy & the Agri-food Chain. 2012. 240p. 145.00 ***(978-1-78064-145-4(1))*** CABI GBR. Dist: Stylus Publishing, LLC.

AGRICULTURE AND STATE—FRANCE

Cleary, Mark C. Peasants, Politicians & Producers: The Organisation of Agriculture in France Since 1918. 2007. (Cambridge Studies in Historical Geography Ser.). (ENG., Illus.). 220p. pap. 48.00 *(978-0-521-03377-0(2))* Cambridge Univ. Pr.

Rosenthal, Jean-Laurent. The Fruits of Revolution: Property Rights, Litigation & French Agriculture, 1700-1860. 2009. (Political Economy of Institutions & Decisions Ser.). (ENG.). 236p. pap. 34.99 *(978-0-521-10312-1(6))* Cambridge Univ. Pr.

AGRICULTURE AND STATE—GERMANY

Harwood, Jonathan. Europe's Green Revolution. 2012. (Routledge Explorations in Economic History Ser.: 57). (ENG., Illus.). 288p. (C). 140.00 ***(978-0-415-59868-2(0))*** Routledge.

Last, George. After the Socialist Spring: Collectivisation & Economic Transformation in the GDR. 2009. (Illus.). 288p. 90.00 *(978-1-84545-552-1(5))* Berghahn Bks., Inc.

AGRICULTURE AND STATE—GREAT BRITAIN

Hodge, Joseph Morgan. Triumph of the Expert: Agrarian Doctrines of Development & the Legacies of British Colonialism. 2007. (Ecology & History Ser.). (Illus.). 408p. 59.95 *(978-0-8214-1717-1(7))*; (ENG., per. 26.95 *(978-0-8214-1718-8(5))* Ohio Univ. Pr.

Northern Ireland, Dept. of Agriculture and Rural Development Staff, contrib. by. 2007 Set-Aside Handbook & Guidance for Northern Ireland. 2007. 48p. *(978-1-85527-861-5(8))* Department of Agriculture & Rural Development.

Stewart, Pamela J. & Strathern, Andrew, eds. Landscape, Heritage, & Conservation: Farming Issues in the European Union. 2010. 340p. pap. 42.00 (978-1-59460-774-5(5)) Carolina Academic Pr.

AGRICULTURE AND STATE—INDIA

Ali, Mohd & Bhaskar, G., eds. Wto, Globalization & Indian Agriculture. 2011. (Illus.). 196p. 34.50 (978-81-7708-264-7(7)) New Century Publications IND. Dist: International Specialized Bk. Services.

Asian Development Bank, Board of Directors Staff. Agriculture, Food Security, & Rural Development. 2011. (ENG., Illus.). 384p. 49.95 (978-0-19-806466-4(7)) Oxford Univ. Pr., Inc.

Ballabh, Vishwa. Institutional Alternatives & Governance of Agriculture. Ballabh, Vishwa, ed. 2007. (ENG., Illus.). 328p. 49.95 (978-81-7188-601-2(9)) Academic Foundation IND. Dist: Independent Pubs. Group.

Bhaumik, Sankar Kumar, ed. Reforming Indian Agriculture: Towards Employment Generation & Poverty Reduction Essays in Honour of G K Chadha. 2008. (Illus.). 592p. (C). 49.95 (978-0-7619-3645-9(9), B36459C) SAGE Pubns., Inc.

Bhide, Shashanka, et al. Strategies for Achieving Sustained High Economic Growth: The Case of Indian States. 2010. (Illus.). 256p. (C). 39.95 (978-81-321-0448-3(X), B04483C) SAGE Pubns., Inc.

Birner, Regina, et al. The Political Economy of Agricultural Policy Reform in India: The Case of Fertilizer Supply & Electricity Supply for Groundwater Irrigation. 2009. (978-0-89629-172-0(3)) International Food Policy Research Institute.

Brandow, Patrick M., ed. Agriculture & Agribusiness Developments in India. 2010. (Agriculture Issues & Policies Ser.). (Illus.). viii, 172p. 98.00 (978-1-61668-946-9(3)) Nova Science Pubs., Inc.

Deshpande, R. S. & Arora, Saroj, eds. Agrarian Crisis & Farmers Suicides. 2010. (Land Reforms in India Ser.). (Illus.). 464p. (C). 42.95 (978-81-321-0512-1(5), B05121C) SAGE Pubns., Inc.

Dhesi, Autar S. & Gurmail Singh. Rural Development in Punjab: A Success Story Going Astray. Dhesi, Autar S. & Singh, Gurmail, eds. 2008. (Illus.). 420p. 110.00 (978-0-415-45681-4(9), Routledge India) Taylor & Francis Group GBR. Dist: Taylor & Francis Group.

Fan, Shenggen. The Dragon & the Elephant: Agricultural & Rural Reforms in China & India. Fan, Shenggen & Gulati, Ashok, eds. 2007. (ENG., Illus.). 576p. (gr. 17). per. 38.00 (978-0-8018-8787-1(9)) Johns Hopkins Univ. Pr.

Gulati, Ashok & Fan, Shenggen, eds. The Dragon & the Elephant: A Comparative Study of Agricultural & Rural Reforms in China & India. 2008. (ENG.). 560p. 50.00 (978-0-19-569350-8(7)) Oxford Univ. Pr., Inc.

—The Dragon & the Elephant: Agricultural & Rural Reforms in China & India. 2007. (ENG., Illus.). 576p. (gr. 17). 75.00 (978-0-8018-8786-4(0)) Johns Hopkins Univ. Pr.

Habib, Irfan. The Agrarian System of Mughal India: 1556-1707. 3rd ed. 2012. (ENG., Illus.). 584p. pap. 35.00 **(978-0-19-807742-8(4))** Oxford Univ. Pr., Inc.

Jharwal, S. M., et al, eds. Glimpses of Indian Agriculture: Macro & Micro Aspects, 2 vols. & 3 pts. 2007. (ENG., Illus.). 1584p. 149.95 (978-81-7188-597-8(7)) Academic Foundation IND. Dist: Independent Pubs. Group.

Joshi, Sharad P. Down to Earth. 2010. (ENG.). 388p. 79.95 (978-81-7188-842-9(9)) Academic Foundation IND. Dist: Independent Pubs. Group.

Kapila, Uma & Krishna, K. L. Readings in Indian Agriculture & Industry. Kapila, Uma & Krishna, K. L., eds. 2009. (ENG., Illus.). 642p. 69.95 (978-81-7188-734-7(1)) Academic Foundation IND. Dist: Independent Pubs. Group.

Mishra, Srijit & Narasimha Reddy, D. Agrarian Crisis in India. Reddy, D. Narasimha & Mishra, Srijit, eds. 2009. (ENG., Illus.). 272p. 49.95 (978-0-19-569595-3(X)) Oxford Univ. Pr., Inc.

Mittal, Surabhi & Mukherjee, Arpita, eds. Food for Policy: Reforming Agriculture. 2008. (ENG., Illus.). 274p. (978-81-7596-621-5(1)) Cambridge Univ. Pr. India Pvt. Ltd.

Narzary, Devonath & Goyari, Phanindra. Institutional Agriculture Credit in Indi. 2011. 100p. pap. **(978-3-8443-8661-5(0))** Lambert Academic Publishing.

Orden, David. Agricultural Producer Support Estimates for Developing Countries: Measurement Issues & Evidence from India, Indonesia, China, & Vietnam. 2007. (978-0-89629-160-7(X)) International Food Policy Research Institute.

Prasad, Chandra. Agriculture & Rural Development in India Since 1947. 2009. 512p. 106.50 (978-81-7708-201-2(9)) New Century Publications IND. Dist: International Specialized Bk. Services.

Reddy, V. Ratna, et al. Changing Contours of Asian Agriculture: Policies, Performance, & Challenges: Essays in Honour of Professor V.S. Vyas. Reddy, V. Ratna & Singh, Surjit, eds. 2009. (ENG., Illus.). 598p. 79.95 (978-81-7188-726-2(0)) Academic Foundation IND. Dist: Independent Pubs. Group.

Sidhu, Aman & Jaijee, Inderjit Singh. Debt & Death in Rural India: The Punjab Story. 2011. (Illus.). 348p. (C). 50.00 **(978-81-321-0653-1(9)**, B06531C) SAGE Pubns., Inc.

Sivaramakrishnan, Arvind. Public Policy & Citizenship: Battling Managerialism in India. 2011. 304p. (C). 40.00 (978-81-321-0633-3(4), B06334C) SAGE Pubns., Inc.

Swaminathan, M. S., ed. Agriculture Cannot Wait: New Horizons in Indian Agriculture. 2007. (ENG., Illus.). 550p. 69.95 (978-81-7188-625-8(6)) Academic Foundation IND. Dist: Independent Pubs. Group.

Vaidyanathan, A. Agricultural Growth in India: The Role of Technology, Incentives, & Institutions. 2010. (ENG., Illus.). 300p. 55.00 (978-0-19-806447-3(0)) Oxford Univ. Pr., Inc.

Wolchuck, Natalie A., ed. India: Tariff Issues for U. S. Agricultural Exports. 2010. (Agriculture Issues & Policies Ser.). 137.00 (978-1-61668-948-3(X)) Nova Science Pubs., Inc.

AGRICULTURE AND STATE—IRELAND

Crotty, Raymond, Jr. Irish Agricultural Production. (Illus.). (978-0-902561-39-7(1)) Cork Univ. Pr.

AGRICULTURE AND STATE—ISRAEL

Oecd Publishing. Oecd Review of Agricultural Policies Oecd Review of Agricultural Policies: Israel 2010. 2010. 208p. pap. 67.00 (978-92-64-07934-2(3)) Organization for Economic Cooperation & Development.

AGRICULTURE AND STATE—ITALY

Tirabassi Leonardo. La mia Terra: Intervista storico-politica a Federico Vecchioni. 2011. (ITA., Illus.). 112p. (C). pap. 18.00 **(978-88-564-0156-1(8))** Polistampa ITA. Dist: Brown, David Bk. Co., The.

AGRICULTURE AND STATE—JAPAN

Francks. Rural Economic Development in Japan. 2007. (Illus.). 320p. 39.95 (978-0-415-44406-4(3)) Routledge.

AGRICULTURE AND STATE—KENYA

Little, Peter D. The Elusive Granary: Herder, Farmer, & State in Northern Kenya. 2009. (African Studies). (ENG., Illus.). 228p. pap. 34.99 (978-0-521-10536-1(6)) Cambridge Univ. Pr.

AGRICULTURE AND STATE—LATIN AMERICA

Anderson, Kym & Valdés, Alberto. Distortions to Agricultural Incentives in Latin America. 2008. (Trade & Development Ser.). (ENG., Illus.). 440p. (C). pap. 39.95 (978-0-8213-7513-6(X), 9780821375136) World Bank Pubns.

Otero, Gerardo, ed. Food for the Few: Neoliberal Globalism & Biotechnology in Latin America. 2010. (ENG., Illus.). 335p. pap. 30.00 (978-0-292-72613-0(9)) Univ. of Texas Pr.

AGRICULTURE AND STATE—MEXICO

César Dachary, Alfredo A. Produccion colectiva y desarrollo capitalista en el agro Mexicano: (1970 - 1980) (Latin America Studies). (GER.). XI, 350p. 135.00 **(978-3-11-116705-3(4))** De Gruyter, Mouton DEU. Dist: de Gruyter, Walter GmbH & Co. KG.

Chavez, Manuel, et al. NAFTA & the Campesinos: The Impact of NAFTA on Small-Scale Agricultural Producers in Mexico & the Prospects for Change. Rivera, Juan & Chavez, Manuel, eds. Whiteford, Scott, ed. 2009. (Illus.). 200p. pap. 25.00 (978-1-58966-180-6(X)) Univ. of Scranton Pr.

Puyana de Palacios, Alicia & Romero, José Antonio. Diez Años con el TLCAN: Las Experiencias Del Sector Agropecuario Mexicano. 2nd ed. 2008. (Estudios Económicos Ser.). (SPA., Illus.). 231p. pap. 44.99 (978-968-12-1371-8(8)) El Colegio de México, A.C., Biblioteca Miguel Cosio Villegas MEX. Dist: Fondo de Cultura Economica USA.

Sanchez, Maria Consuelo. Gender & Natural Resources: Maya Women & Land Property Rights. 2008. 128p. pap. (978-3-639-09273-8(2)) VDM Verlag Dr. Mueller e.K.

AGRICULTURE AND STATE—MIDDLE EAST

Karapinar, Baris, et al, eds. Rethinking Structural Reform in Turkish Agriculture: Beyond the World Bank's Strategy. 2010. (Agriculture Issues & Policies Ser.). 125.00 (978-1-60876-718-2(3)) Nova Science Pubs., Inc.

AGRICULTURE AND STATE—PHILIPPINES

Borras, Saturnino M. Competing Views & Strategies on Agrarian Reform. 38.00 (978-971-550-559-8(7)); 40.00 (978-971-550-558-1(9)) Ateneo de Manila Univ. Pr. PHL. Dist: Univ. of Hawaii Pr.

Cororaton, Caesar B. & Corong, Erwin. Philippine Agricultural & Food Policies: Implications for Poverty & Income Distribution. 2009. (978-0-89629-170-6(7)) International Food Policy Research Institute.

Costales, Achilles. Scale & Access Issues Affecting Smallholder Hog Producers in an Expanding Peri-Urban Market: Southern Luzon, Philippines. 2006. (978-0-89629-159-1(6)) International Food Policy Research Institute.

Falvo, Daniel. An Illustration of Signaling Biogeography. 2008. 140p. pap. (978-3-8364-9952-1(5)) VDM Verlag Dr. Mueller e.K.

AGRICULTURE AND STATE—ROMANIA

Iordachi, Constantin & Dobrincu, Dorin, eds. Transforming Peasants, Property & Power: The Collectivization of Agriculture in Romania, 1949-1962. 2009. 500p. 59.95 (978-963-9776-25-8(4)) Central European Univ. Pr.

Kligman, Gail & Verdery, Katherine. Peasants under Siege - Collectivization in Romania 1949-1962. 2011. (ENG., Illus.). 520p. (C). 95.00 (978-0-691-14972-1(0)); pap. 39.50 (978-0-691-14973-8(9)) Princeton Univ. Pr.

AGRICULTURE AND STATE—SOVIET UNION

Hudson, Hugh D., Jr. Peasants, Political Police, & the Early Soviet State: Surveillance & Accommodation under the New Economic Policy. 2011. (ENG., Illus.). 208p. 80.00 **(978-0-230-33886-9(0))** Palgrave Macmillan.

Ioffe, Grigory, et al. The End of Peasantry? The Disintegration of Rural Russia. 2006. (Pitt Series in Russian & East European Studies). (Illus.). 254p. (C). per. 27.95 (978-0-8229-5941-0(0)) Univ. of Pittsburgh Pr.

Leonard, Carol. Agrarian Reform in Russia: The Road from Serfdom. 2010. (ENG., Illus.). 416p. 90.00 (978-0-521-85849-6(6)) Cambridge Univ. Pr.

Perrie, Maureen. The Agrarian Policy of the Russian Socialist-Revolutionary Party: From Its Origins Through the Revolution of 1905-1907. 2008. (Cambridge Russian, Soviet & Post-Soviet Studies). (ENG., Illus.). 236p. pap. 33.99 (978-0-521-08115-3(7)) Cambridge Univ. Pr.

Rogalina, N. L. Vlast I Agrarnye Reformy V Rossii XX Veka: Uchebnoe Posobie. 2010. (RUS., Illus.). 230p. (978-5-88367-053-3(9)) Enciklopedija rossijskih dereven.

Stanchevici, Dmitri. Stalinist Genetics: The Constitutional Rhetoric of T. D. Lysenko. 2011. 200p. 47.95 (978-0-89503-402-1(6)) Baywood Publishing Co., Inc.

Stanchevici, Dmitri. Stalinist Genetics: The Constitutional Rhetoric of T.D. Lysenko. 2012. v, 194p. **(978-0-89503-455-7(7))** Baywood Publishing Co., Inc.

Wegren, Stephen. Agriculture & the State in Soviet & Post-Soviet Russia. 2009. (Pitt Russian East European Ser.). (ENG.). 312p. (C). pap. 27.95 (978-0-8229-8585-3(3)) Univ. of Pittsburgh Pr.

AGRICULTURE AND STATE—TROPICS

Wassmann, Reiner & Vlek, Paul L.G., eds. Tropical Agriculture in Transition - Opportunities for Mitigating Greenhouse Gas Emissions? 2010. 284p. pap. 88.00 (978-90-481-6341-0(2), 9048163412) Springer.

AGRICULTURE AND STATE—UNITED STATES

Barry, Richard. Theme Song 1936: Give Us Back Our Independence. 2011. 160p. 41.95 **(978-1-258-08285-7(3))** Literary Licensing, LLC.

Bello, Walden. The Food Wars. 2009. (ENG., Illus.). 160p. pap. 16.95 (978-1-84467-331-5(6), 844331) Verso Bks. GBR. Dist: Norton, W. W. & Co., Inc.

Benson, Ezra Taft. Cross Fire: The Eight Years with Eisenhower. 2011. 664p. 68.95 **(978-1-258-00274-9(4))** Literary Licensing, LLC.

Coburn, Foster D. Kansas & Her Resources. (Illus.). 69p. reprint ed. lib. bdg. 88.00 (978-0-7222-4893-5(8)) Library Reprints, Inc.

Colorado Views on Federal Agriculture & Rural Policies: The 2007 Farm Bill: Hearing Before the Committee on Agriculture, Nutrition, & Forestry, United States Senate, One Hundred Tenth Congress, First Session, March 12, 2007. 2007. (Illus.). iv, 166p. (978-0-16-078891-8(9), 552-070-36023-9) United States Government Printing Office.

Conkin, Paul K. A Revolution down on the Farm: The Transformation of American Agriculture Since 1929. (ENG., Illus.). 240p. 2009. pap. 22.50 (978-0-8131-9242-0(0)) 2008. 50.00 (978-0-8131-2519-0(7)) Univ. Pr. of Kentucky.

Conserving Data in the Conservation Reserve: How a Regulatory Program Runs on Imperfect Information. 2010. (ENG.). 168p. 75.00 (978-1-933115-82-5(3)); pap. 24.95 (978-1-933115-81-8(5)) Earthscan LLC. (RFF Pr.).

Crosson, Pierre R. The Cropland Crisis: Myth or Reality?, 6 vols. 2011. (RFF Agriculture & Fisheries Set Ser.). (ENG.). 250p. 99.95 (978-1-61726-013-1(4), RFF Pr.) Earthscan LLC.

Diakosavvas, Dimitris & Organisation for Economic Co-Operation and Development. Evaluation of Agricultural Policy Reforms in the United States. 2011. (Illus.). 211p. pap. **(978-92-64-09671-4(X))** Organization for Economic Cooperation & Development.

Expanding Our Food & Fiber Supply Through a Strong U.S. Farm Policy: Hearing Before the Committee on Agriculture, Nutrition, & Forestry, United States Senate, One Hundred Eleventh Congress, Second Session, June 30, 2010. 2011. (Illus.). iv, 191p. **(978-0-16-089264-6(3)**, 552-070-43260-4) United States Government Printing Office.

From the Corn Belt to the Gulf: Societal & Environmental Implications of Alternative Agricultural Futures. 2007. (ENG., Illus.). 272p. pap. 45.00 (978-1-933115-48-1(3)); 120.00 (978-1-933115-47-4(5)) Routledge.

Gillman, Jeff & Heberlig, Eric. How the Government Got in Your Backyard: Superweeds, Frankenfoods, Lawn Wars, & the (Nonpartisan) Truth about Environmental Policies. 2011. (ENG.). 248p. 23.95 (978-1-60469-001-9(1), 1604690011) Timber Pr., Inc.

Haas, Dieter. Agricultural Policies in the Eu & Us- a Comparison of Policy Objectives & Their Realization. 2007. 140p. per. (978-3-8364-1126-4(1)) VDM Verlag Dr. Mueller e.K.

Hamilton, David E. From New Day to New Deal: American Farm Policy from Hoover to Roosevelt, 1928-1933. 2011. (ENG.). 352p. pap. 50.00 **(978-0-8078-6542-2(7))** Univ. of North Carolina Pr.

Hearing to Review Implementation of the Food, Conservation, & Energy ACT of 2008: Hearing Before the Subcommittee on General Farm Commodities & Risk Management of the Committee on Agriculture, House of Representatives, One Hundred Eleventh Congress, First Session, June 24, 25, 2009. 2009. iii, 101p. (978-0-16-084273-3(5), 552-070-39838-4) United States Government Printing Office.

Hearing to Review Recent Investigations & Audits Conducted by the USDA Inspector General: Hearing Before the Subcommittee on Department Operations, Oversight, & Credit of the Committee on Agriculture, House of Representatives, One Hundred Twelfth Congress, First Session, June 2, 2011. 2011. iii, 32p. **(978-0-16-089120-5(5)**, 552-070-43132-2) United States Government Printing Office.

Hearing to Review the Implementation of the Conservation Title of the 2008 Farm Bill: Hearing Before the Subcommittee on Conservation, Credit, Energy, & Research of the Committee on Agriculture, House of Representatives, One Hundred Eleventh Congress, First Session, October 7, 2009. 2009. (Illus.). v, 82p. (978-0-16-084620-5(X), 552-070-40123-7) United States Government Printing Office.

Hearing to Review the Implementation of the Research Title of the 2008 Farm Bill: Hearing Before the Subcommittee on Conservation, Credit, Energy, & Research of the Committee on Agriculture, House of Representatives, One Hundred Eleventh Congress, First Session, September 30, 2009. 2009. v, 60p. (978-0-16-084616-8(1), 552-070-40119-9) United States Government Printing Office.

Hearing to Review the State of the Farm Economy: Hearing Before the Committee on Agriculture, House of Representatives, One Hundred Twelfth Congress, First Session, February 17, 2011. 2011. iii, 51p. **(978-0-16-088535-8(3)**, 552-070-42712-1) United States Government Printing Office.

Hearing to Review U.S. Agriculture Policy in Advance of the 2012 Farm Bill: Hearing Before the Committee on Agriculture, House of Representatives, One Hundred Eleventh Congress, Second Session, 2 vols. 2010. (Illus.). (978-0-16-086889-4(0), 552-070-41505-0 (pt.1)) United States Government Printing Office.

Hearing to Review U.S. Agriculture Policy in Advance of the 2012 Farm Bill: Hearing Before the Committee on Agriculture, House of Representatives, One Hundred Eleventh Congress, Second Session, April 21, 2010: May 13, 2010. 2010. (Illus.). (978-0-16-086446-9(1), 552-070-41505-0 (pt.1)) United States Government Printing Office.

Hearing to Review U.S. Farm Safety Net Programs in Advance of the 2012 Farm Bill: Hearings Before the Subcommittee on General Farm Commodities & Risk Management of the Committee on Agriculture, House of Representatives, One Hundred Eleventh Congress, Second Session, June 17, 24, 2010. 2010. (Illus.). iv, 146p. **(978-0-16-086969-3(2)**, 552-070-41835-1) United States Government Printing Office.

Iowa & Nebraska Views on Federal Agriculture & Rural Policies: The 2007 Farm Bill: Field Hearing Before the Committee on Agriculture, Nutrition, & Forestry, United States Senate, One Hundred Tenth Congress, First Session, April 14, 2007. 2007. (Illus.). iv, 114p. (978-0-16-079443-8(9), 552-070-36437-4) United States Government Printing Office.

Johnson, D. Patrick. Cornucopia: Understanding Health through Understanding Agriculture. 2011. 84p. pap. 22.95 **(978-0-7618-5596-5(3))** Hamilton Bks.

Johnson, Glenn Leroy & Quance, Leroy. The Overproduction Trap in U. S. Agriculture: A Study of Resource Allocation from World War I to the Late 1960's, 6 vols. 2011. (RFF Agriculture & Fisheries Set Ser.). (ENG.). 211p. 99.95 (978-1-61726-014-8(2), RFF Pr.) Earthscan LLC.

Kastner, Justin. Food & Agriculture Security: An Historical, Multidisciplinary Approach. 2010. E-Book (978-0-313-38323-6(5), Praeger Pubs.) Greenwood Publishing Group, Inc.

Kastner, Justin J., ed. Food & Agriculture Security: An Historical, Multidisciplinary Approach, 1 vol. 2010. (Praeger Security International Ser.). (Illus.). 162p. 34.95 (978-0-313-38322-9(7), A2714C, Praeger Pubs.) Greenwood Publishing Group, Inc.

Lehrer, Nadine. U.S. Farm Bills & Policy Reforms: Ideological Conflicts over World Trade, Renewable Energy, & Sustainable Agriculture. 2010. (978-1-60497-701-1(9)) Cambria Pr.

Morgan, Robert J. Governing Soil Conservation: Thirty Years of the New Decentralization, 6 vols. 2011. (RFF Agriculture & Fisheries Set Ser.). (ENG.). 399p. 99.95 (978-1-61726-011-7(8), RFF Pr.) Earthscan LLC.

Oecd Publishing. Évaluation des Réformes de la Politique Agricole Aux États-Unis. 2011. 252p. pap. 78.00 **(978-92-64-09674-5(4))** Organization for Economic Cooperation & Development.

Promoting Agricultural Exports: Reviewing U.S. Agricultural Trade Policy & the Farm Bill's Trade Title: Hearing Before the Committee on Agriculture, Nutrition, & Forestry, United States Senate, One Hundred Eleventh Congress, Second Session, August 4, 2010. 2011. iv, 120p. **(978-0-16-089337-7(2)**, 552-070-43329-5) United States Government Printing Office.

Reed, Ananya Mukherjee. International Trade in Agricultural Prod. 2006. pap. 11.95 (978-1-4288-0910-9(4)) Cram101 Inc.

Reid, Debra Ann. Reaping a Greater Harvest: African Americans, the Extension Service, & Rural Reform in Jim Crow Texas. 2007. (Sam Rayburn Series on Rural Life: No. 14). (ENG., Illus.). 328p. 39.95 (978-1-58544-571-4(1)) Texas A&M Univ. Pr.

Review of USDA Farm Bill Conservation Programs: Hearing Before the Subcommittee on Conservation, Credit, Energy, & Research of the Committee on Agriculture, House of Representatives, One Hundred Tenth Congress, First Session, April 19, 2007. 2009. (Illus.). iv, 269p. (978-0-16-082682-5(9), 552-070-38699-8) United States Government Printing Office.

Sargsyan, Eric A. & Ochion, Adam J. Environmental Considerations in Agriculture. 2011. (Environmental Science, Engineering & Technology Ser.). 95.00 **(978-1-61470-077-7(X))** Nova Science Pubs., Inc.

Schäfer, Claus, ed. Agriculture & Food. 2010. (Agriculture Issues & Policies Ser.). (Illus.). x, 186p. 79.00 (978-1-60692-038-1(3)) Nova Science Pubs., Inc.

Schmitz, Andrew, et al. Agricultural Policy, Agribusiness & Rent-Seeking Behaviour. 2nd ed. 2010. (Illus.). 512p. pap. (978-0-8020-9547-3(X)) Univ. of Toronto Pr.

Schnepf, Max & Cox, Craig A. Environmental Benefits of Conservation Practices on Cropland: The Status of Our Knowledge. 2007. (978-0-9769432-3-5(9)) Soil & Water Conservation Society.

Strange, Marty. Family Farming: A New Economic Vision. 2008. (ENG., Illus.). 336p. pap. 16.95 (978-0-8032-1748-5(X), Bison Bks.) Univ. of Nebraska Pr.

Thompson, Paul B. The Agrarian Vision: Sustainability & Environmental Ethics. 2010. (Culture of the Land Ser.). (ENG., Illus.). 336p. 40.00 (978-0-8131-2587-9(1)) Univ. Pr. of Kentucky.

United States, Congress Senate Committee on Agriculture, Nutrition, and Forestry Staff, contrib. by. Discussion of the U.S. Department of Agriculture Farm Bill Proposal: Hearing Before the Committee on Agriculture, Nutrition, & Forestry, United States Senate, One Hundred Tenth Congress, First Session, February 7, 2007. 2007. (Illus.). iv, 392p. (978-0-16-078854-3(4), 552-070-35989-3) United States Government Printing Office.

—Regional Farm Bill Field Hearing: Field Hearing Before the Committee on Agriculture, Nutrition, & Forestry, United States Senate, One Hundred Ninth Congress, Second Session, June 23, 2006. 2007. (Illus.). iv, 188p. *(978-0-16-078494-1(8)*, 552-070-35775-1) United States Government Printing Office.

United States, Congress Senate Committee on Agriculture, Nutrition, and Forestry Subcommittee on Forestry, Conservation, and Rural Revitalization Staff, contrib. by. Field Hearing on 2007 Farm Bill: Hearing Before the Subcommittee on Forestry, Conservation, & Rural Revitalization of the Committee on Agriculture, Nutrition, & Forestry, United States Senate, One Hundred Ninth Congress, Second Session, August 11, 2006. 2007. iv, 140p. *(978-0-16-078351-7(8)*, 552-070-35652-5) United States Government Printing Office.

United States, Congress Senate Committee on Energy and Natural Resources Staff, contrib. by. St. Mary Diversion & Conveyance Works & Milk River Project: Hearing Before the Committee on Energy & Natural Resources, United States Senate, One Hundred Ninth Congress, Second Session, on S. 3563 ... Havre, MT, September 1, 2006. 2007. iii, 74p. *(978-0-16-078063-9(2)*, 552-070-35476-0) United States Government Printing Office.

U.S. Department of Agriculture Fiscal Year 2008 Budget Priorities: Hearing Before the Committee on the Budget, House of Representatives, One Hundred Tenth Congress, First Session, Hearing Held in Washington, DC, February 15, 2007. 2007. (Illus.). iii, 80p. *(978-0-16-079741-5(1)*, 552-070-36454-4) United States Government Printing Office.

Waugh, Frederick V. Selected Writings on Agricultural Policy & Economic Analysis. Houck, James P. & Abel, Martin E., eds. 2009. (ENG.). 488p. pap. 60.00 *(978-0-8166-6057-5(3))* Univ. of Minnesota Pr.

Winders, Bill & Scott, James. The Politics of Food Supply: U. S. Agricultural Policy in the World Economy. 2012. (Yale Agrarian Studies Ser.). (ENG., Illus.). 302p. pap. 22.00 ***(978-0-300-18186-9(8))*** Yale Univ. Pr.

Winders, Bill & Winders, B. The Politics of Food Supply: U. S. Agricultural Policy in the World Economy. 2009. (Yale Agrarian Studies Ser.). (ENG., Illus.). 304p. 55.00 *(978-0-300-13924-2(1))* Yale Univ. Pr.

Womach, Jasper, et al. The USDA 2007 Farm Bill Proposal. 2008. 102p. pap. 39.00 *(978-1-60456-813-4(5))* Nova Science Pubs., Inc.

Wozniak, Chris A. & McHughen, Alan, eds. Regulation of Agricultural Biotechnology: the United States & Canada: The United States & Canada. 2012. (ENG., Illus.). xx, 230p. 189.00 ***(978-94-007-2155-5(2)***, 9400721552) Springer.

Zivin, Joshua S. Graff & Perloff, Jeffrey M., eds. The Intended & Unintended Effects of U. S. Agricultural & Biotechnology Policies. 2012. (National Bureau of Economic Research Conference Report). (ENG., Illus.). 312p. 99.00 ***(978-0-226-98803-0(1))*** Univ. of Chicago Pr.

2007 Farm Bill Opportunities for Vermont & the Northeast: Hearing Before the Committee on Agriculture, Nutrition, & Forestry, United States Senate, One Hundred Tenth Congress, First Session, March 12, 2007. 2007. (Illus.). iv, 254p. *(978-0-16-078876-5(5)*, 552-070-36005-1) United States Government Printing Office.

AGRICULTURE AND WATER

see Water-Supply, Agricultural

AGRICULTURISTS

see also Agriculture—Vocational Guidance; Farmers; Horticulturists; Women Agriculturists; Women Farmers

Chet. Wolf Prize in Agriculture. 2009. 190.00 *(978-981-283-584-0(9))* World Scientific Publishing Co., Inc.

Clark, Glenn. The Man Who Talks with the Flowers: The Intimate Life Story of Dr. George Washington Carver. 2011. 40p. pap. 6.49 ***(978-1-61720-418-0(8))*** Wilder Pubns., Ltd.

—The Man Who Talks with the Flowers-the Intimate Life Story of Dr George Washington Carver. 2011. 68p. pap. 6.95 ***(978-1-61427-066-9(X))*** Martino Publishing.

Coulter, E. Merton. Daniel Lee, Agriculturist: His Life North & South. 2010. (ENG.). 176p. pap. 22.95 *(978-0-8203-3530-8(4))* Univ. of Georgia Pr.

Escobedo, Héctor J. & Madrigal, Sergio M., eds. Agriculture & Food Science Research Biographical Sketches & Research Summaries. 2012. ***(978-1-62100-934-4(3))*** Nova Science Pubs., Inc.

George Washington Carver National Monument (Mo.) Staff & George Washington Carver Birthplace Association Staff, contrib. by. George Washington Carver: His Life & Legacy. 2010. pap. *(978-1-57864-628-9(6))* Donning Co. Pubs.

Gerasimov, Ilya V. Modernism & Public Reform in Late Imperial Russia: Rural Professionals & Self-Organization, 1905-30. 2009. (ENG., Illus.). 352p. 110.00 *(978-0-230-22947-1(6))* Palgrave Macmillan.

Hesser, Leon. The Man Who Fed the World. 2009. 263p. 24.95 *(978-0-9818486-6-2(4))* 2008. (Illus.). 300p. pap. 15.95 *(978-0-9800067-7-3(5))* Durban House Pr., Inc.

Kremer, Gary R. George Washington Carver: A Biography, 1 vol. 2011. (Greenwood Biographies Ser.). (Illus.). 202p. 35.00 *(978-0-313-34796-2(4)*, GR4796); E-Book *(978-0-313-34797-9(2)*, Greenwood Pr.) Greenwood Publishing Group, Inc.

Lyons, Mark, et al, eds. Espejos y Ventanas/Mirrors & Windows: Historias Orales de Trabajadores Agricolas Mexicanos y Sus Familias/Oral Histories of Mexican Farmworkers & Their Families. 2012. (ENG., Illus.). 318p. per. 15.00 *(978-0-9712996-6-5(8))* New City Community Pr.

Mayberry, B. D., ed. A George Washington Carver Handbook. 2007. 92p. pap. 15.95 *(978-1-60306-016-5(2))* NewSouth, Inc.

Nixon (Ahdanah), Leticia Roa. Blueberry Lady: The Story of Elizabeth Coleman White 1871-1954. 2009. 32p. pap. 12.99 *(978-1-4389-9287-7(4))* AuthorHouse.

Nuthall, Peter L. Farm Business Management: The Human Factor. 2010. (Illus.). 216p. 145.00 *(978-1-84593-598-6(5))* CABI GBR. Dist: Stylus Publishing, LLC.

Rassen, Joshua. From the Shtetl to Americ: Jacob Rassen's Lifetime Journey. 2009. 296p. 31.95 *(978-1-4401-4182-9(7))*; pap. 21.95 *(978-1-4401-4180-5(0))* iUniverse, Inc.

Shilliday, Jim. Canada's Wheat King: The Life & Times of Seager Wheeler. 2007. (Trade Books based in Scholorship(TBS) Ser.). (ENG., Illus.). 177p. pap. 19.95 *(978-0-88977-187-1(1))* Canadian Plains Research Ctr. CAN. Dist: Univ. of Toronto Pr.

Smith, Alvin D. & Edmunds, Henry E. George Washington Carver: Man of God. 2011. 76p. 36.95 ***(978-1-258-06113-5(9))*** Literary Licensing, LLC.

Tirabassi Leonardo. La mia Terra: Intervista storico-politica a Federico Vecchioni. 2011. (ITA., Illus.). 112p. (C). pap. 18.00 ***(978-88-564-0156-1(8))*** Polistampa ITA. Dist: Brown, David Bk. Co., The.

Turnbull, Bill. Confessions of a Bad Beekeeper: What Not to Do When Keeping Bees (with Apologies to My Own) 2011. (ENG., Illus.). 256p. pap. 13.95 *(978-1-61519-032-4(5)*, 1615190325) Experiment LLC, The.

Wade Martins, Susanna. Coke of Norfolk, 1754-1842: A Biography. 2009. (Illus.). 240p. 90.00 *(978-1-84383-426-7(X)*, Boydell Press) Boydell & Brewer, Ltd. GBR. Dist: Boydell & Brewer, Inc.

Zimdahl, Robert L. Agriculture's Ethical Horizon. 2nd ed. 2012. (ENG.). 308p. 53.95 ***(978-0-12-416043-9(3))*** Elsevier Science & Technology Bks.

AGRIPPA I, KING OF JUDEA, 10 B.C.-44 A.D.

see Herod Agrippa I, King of Judea, 10 B.C.-44 A.D.

AGROFORESTRY

Auclair, Daniel & Dupraz, C., eds. Agroforestry for Sustainable Land-Use: Fundamental Research & Modelling with Emphasis on Temperate & Mediterranean Applications. 2010. (Forestry Sciences Ser.). (Illus.). 266p. pap. 189.00 *(978-90-481-5258-2(5)*, 9048152585) Springer.

Ayalew, Yenenesh, et al. Edible Plants: Species diversity & significance to food Security. 2010. 88p. pap. *(978-3-639-24772-5(8))* VDM Verlag Dr. Mueller e.K.

Batish, Daizy Rani, et al, eds. Ecological Basis of Agroforestry. 2007. (ENG., Illus.). 400p. 129.95 *(978-1-4200-4327-3(7)*, CRC Press) Taylor & Francis Group GBR. Dist: Taylor & Francis Group.

Crawford, Martin. Creating a Forest Garden & A Forest Garden Year: Book & DVD Set. 2011. (Illus.). 336p. 64.95 *(978-1-60358-381-7(5))* Green Bks. GBR. Dist: Chelsea Green Publishing.

DeClerck, Fabrice, et al, eds. Ecosystem Services from Agriculture & Agroforestry: Measurement & Payment. 2011. (ENG., Illus.). 448p. 99.95 *(978-1-84971-147-0(X))* Routledge.

Gairola, Yogesh. Winter Annual Flowers under Agroforestry Tree Species. 2010. 64p. pap. *(978-3-8383-4697-7(1))* Lambert Academic Publishing.

Garrett, H. E. "Gene", ed. North American Agroforestry: An Integrated Science & Practice, 2nd Edition. 2nd ed. 2009. lib. bdg. 70.00 *(978-0-89118-163-7(6))* ASA-CSSA-SSSA.

Gholz, H. L., ed. Agroforestry: Realities, Possibilities & Potentials: Realities, Possibilities & Potentials. 2010. 236p. pap. 199.00 *(978-90-481-8306-7(5)*, 9048183065) Springer.

Gitau, Thomas, et al. Integrated Assessment of Health & Sustainability of Agroecosystems. 2008. (Advances in Agroecology Ser.). (ENG., Illus.). 256p. 104.95 *(978-1-4200-7277-8(3)*, CRC Press) Taylor & Francis Group GBR. Dist: Taylor & Francis Group.

John, Jacob. Allelopathic Effect of Trees in the Homesteads of Kerala, Indi. 2010. 76p. pap. *(978-3-8383-8988-2(3))* Lambert Academic Publishing.

Jose, Shibu, ed. Agroforestry for Commodity Production: Ecological & Social Dimensions: Ecological & Social Dimensions. 2009. (ENG.). vi, 250p. 179.00 *(978-90-481-3364-2(5)*, 9048133645) Springer.

—Agroforestry for Ecosystem Services & Environmental Benefits. 2009. (Advances in Agroforestry Ser.). (ENG., Illus.). vi, 266p. 199.00 *(978-90-481-3322-2(X)*, 904813322X) Springer.

Jose, Shibu & Gordon, Andrew M., eds. Toward Agroforestry Design: An Ecological Approach. (Advances in Agroforestry Ser.). 2010. x, 314p. pap. 249.00 *(978-90-481-7671-7(9)*, 9048176719) 2008. (Illus.). 312p. 249.00 *(978-1-4020-6571-2(X))* Springer.

Kellimore, Lawrence R., ed. Handbook on Agroforestry: Management Practices & Environmental Impact. 2010. (Environmental Science, Engineering & Technology Ser.). 195.00 *(978-1-60876-359-7(5))* Nova Science Pubs., Inc.

Khadka, Rigendra. Transition from Slash-and-Burn Farming to Permanent Agroforestry. 2011. 68p. pap. ***(978-3-8443-3073-1(9))*** Lambert Academic Publishing.

Kulshreshtha, Suren N., et al, eds. Agroforestry Development on the Canadian Prairies. 2010. (Agriculture Issues & Policies Ser.). 76p. pap. 43.00 *(978-1-61668-266-8(3))* Nova Science Pubs., Inc.

Kumar, B. M. & Nair, P. K. R. Tropical Homegardens: A Time-Tested Example of Sustainable Agroforestry. 2006. (Advances in Agroforestry Ser.: Vol. 3). (ENG., Illus.). xiii, 377p. 249.00 *(978-1-4020-4947-7(1)*, 1402049471) Springer.

Kumar, B. M. & Nair, P. K. R., eds. Tropical Homegardens: A Time-Tested Example of Sustainable Agroforestry. 2010. (Advances in Agroforestry Ser.). xiii, 377p. pap. 249.00 *(978-90-481-7237-5(3)*, 9048172373) Springer.

Kumar, B. Mohan & Nair, P. K. Ramachandran, eds. Carbon Sequestration Potential of Agroforestry Systems: Opportunities & Challenges. 2011. (Advances in Agroforestry Ser.). (ENG., Illus.). xvii, 530p. 239.00 *(978-94-007-1629-2(X)*, 940071629X) Springer.

Lichtfouse, Eric. Biodiversity, Biofuels, Agroforestry & Conservation Agriculture. Lichtfouse, Eric, ed. 2010. (Sustainable Agriculture Reviews Ser.). (Illus.). x, 390p. 209.00 *(978-90-481-9512-1(8)*, 9048195128) Springer.

Montagnini, Florencia, et al. Agroforestry as a Tool for Landscape Restoration. 2010. (Agriculture Issues & Policies Ser.). 89.00 *(978-1-61728-940-8(X)*, Nova Biomedical Bks.) Nova Science Pubs., Inc.

Munyaradzi, Chitakira. Agroforestry Adoption in African Smallholder Communities: Opportunities, Challenges & Coping Mechanisms. 2011. 88p. pap. ***(978-3-639-32905-6(8))*** VDM Verlag Dr. Mueller e.K.

Nair, P.K. Ramachandran, et al, eds. New Vistas in Agroforestry: A Compendium for 1st World Congress of Agroforestry 2004. 2010. (Advances in Agroforestry Ser.). 488p. pap. 219.00 *(978-90-481-6673-2(X)*, 904816673X) Springer.

Nair, P.K. Ramachandran & Latt, C. R., eds. Directions in Tropical Agroforestry Research. 2010. (Forestry Sciences Ser.). 260p. pap. 219.00 *(978-90-481-5025-0(6)*, 9048150256) Springer.

Namirembe, S. Design of Appropriate Agroforestry Interventions in Uganda: Agroforestry In-Service Training Manual. Agea, J. G., ed. 2007. (Illus.). 140p. pap. *(978-9970-02-677-7(1))* Fountain Pubs. Ltd. UGA. Dist: Michigan State Univ. Pr.

Nuberg, Ian, et al. Agroforestry for Natural Resource Management. 2009. 360p. pap. 79.50 *(978-0-643-09224-2(2))* CSIRO Publishing AUS. Dist: Stylus Publishing, LLC.

Rahman, Syed. Cost Benefit & Livelihood Impacts of Agroforestry in Bangladesh. 2011. 172p. pap. ***(978-3-8433-5484-4(7))*** Lambert Academic Publishing.

Rigueiro Rodríguez, Antonio, et al. Agroforestry in Europe: Current Status & Future Prospects. 2008. (Advances in Agroforestry Ser.). (Illus.). xxii, 450p. 239.00 *(978-1-4020-8271-9(1))* Springer.

Sharma, Ajay. Municipal Effluent Irrigated Agroforestry Plantations. 2010. 292p. pap. *(978-3-639-20600-5(2))* VDM Verlag Dr. Mueller e.K.

Sinclair, Fergus L., ed. Agroforestry: Science, Policy & Practice: Science, Policy & Practice. 2010. (Forestry Sciences Ser.). 296p. pap. 249.00 *(978-90-481-4610-9(0)*, 9048146100) Springer.

Ssekabembe, Charles. The Tenets of Agroforestry. 2011. 528p. pap. ***(978-3-8443-0178-6(X))*** Lambert Academic Publishing.

Trimble, Stanley W. Encyclopedia of Water Science, 2 vols., Set. 2nd rev. ed. 2007. (ENG., Illus.). 1586p. 1100.00 *(978-0-8493-9627-4(1)*, CRC Press) Taylor & Francis Group GBR. Dist: Taylor & Francis Group.

Tschamtke, Teja, et al, eds. Tropical Rainforests & Agroforests under Global Change: Ecological & Socio-economic Valuations. 2010. (Environmental Science & Engineering / Environmental Science Ser.). (ENG., Illus.). xv, 519p. 249.00 *(978-3-642-00492-6(X)*, 364200492X) Springer.

AGRONOMISTS

see Agriculturists

AGRONOMY

see also Crops; Soil Management

Aslam, Muhammad. Chickpea Agronomy. 2011. 276p. pap. ***(978-3-8443-8585-4(1))*** Lambert Academic Publishing.

Fieldsend, Andrew. Evening Primrose. 2011. 108p. pap. ***(978-3-8433-8300-4(6))*** Lambert Academic Publishing.

Gemechu, Dibaba & Aweke, Girma. Application of Spatial ed Model in Agricultural Field Experiment. 2011. 96p. pap. ***(978-3-8443-9315-6(3))*** Lambert Academic Publishing.

Gould, David. Advances in Agronomy, Vol. 95. 2007. (Advances in Agronomy Ser.: 95). (ENG., Illus.). 396p. 182.00 *(978-0-12-374165-3(3)*, Academic Pr.) Elsevier Science & Technology Bks.

Hussain, Nazim. Phosphorous Nutrition in Wheat: A new Approach. 2010. 240p. pap. *(978-3-8383-1554-6(5))* Lambert Academic Publishing.

L. Sparks, Donald, contrib. by. Advances in Agronomy. 2012. (Advances in Agronomy Ser.: 115). (ENG.). 370p. 182.00 ***(978-0-12-394276-0(4)***, Academic Pr.) Elsevier Science & Technology Bks.

Moser, L. E. The American Society of Agronomy: 100 Years of History. 2007. (Illus.). v, 96p. *(978-0-89118-166-8(0))* American Society of Agronomy.

Mutsaers, H. J. W. Peasants, Farmers & Scientists: A Chronicle of Tropical Agricultural Science in the Twentieth Century. 2010. (ENG.). xxviii, 612p. pap. 139.00 *(978-90-481-7555-0(0)*, 9048175550) Springer.

Nair, K. P. Prabhakaran. Agronomy & Economy of Black Pepper & Cardamom: The King & Queen of Spices. 2011. (ENG.). 380p. 140.00 *(978-0-12-391865-9(0))* Elsevier Science & Technology Bks.

—The Agronomy & Economy of Important Tree Crops of the Developing World. 2010. (ENG., Illus.). 368p. 145.00 *(978-0-12-384677-8(3))* Elsevier Science & Technology Bks.

Norman, Ag. Advances in Agronomy. 2011. 450p. pap. 36.75 ***(978-1-175-42287-3(8))*** BiblioBazaar.

Sadras, Victor O. & Calderini, Daniel, eds. Crop Physiology: Applications for Genetic Improvement & Agronomy. 2009. (ENG., Illus.). 1000p. 114.00 *(978-0-12-374431-9(8)*, Academic Pr.) Elsevier Science & Technology Bks.

Sheaffer, Craig C. & Moncada, Kristine M. Introduction to Agronomy: Food, Crops, & Environment. 2nd ed. 2011. (ENG.). 608p. (C). 123.95 *(978-1-111-31233-6(8))* Delmar Cengage Learning.

Sparks, Donald L., contrib. by. Advances in Agronomy. (Advances in Agronomy Ser.: 116). (ENG.). 2012. 284p. 182.00 ***(978-0-12-394277-7(2))*** 2011. 359p. 182.00 ***(978-0-12-386473-4(9))*** 2011. 242p. 182.00 *(978-0-12-385538-1(1))* 2011. 466p. 182.00 *(978-0-12-387689-8(3))* 2011. 380p. 182.00 *(978-0-12-385531-2(4))* 2010. 279p. 182.00 *(978-0-12-385040-9(1))* 2010. 326p. 182.00 *(978-0-12-381031-1(0))* 2010. 232p. 182.00 *(978-0-12-381033-5(7))* 2010. 288p. 182.00 *(978-0-12-381023-6(X))* 2009. 282p. 182.00 *(978-0-12-374820-1(8))* 2009. 234p. 182.00 *(978-0-12-374819-5(4))* 2009. 393p. 182.00 *(978-0-12-374818-8(6))* 2009. 408p. 182.00 *(978-0-12-374817-1(8))* 2008. 272p. 182.00 *(978-0-12-374361-9(3))* 2008. 350p. 182.00 *(978-0-12-374360-2(5))* 2008. 448p. 182.00 *(978-0-12-374355-8(9))* 2007. (Illus.). 442p. 182.00 *(978-0-12-374206-3(4))* 2007. (Illus.). 312p. 182.00 *(978-0-12-374107-3(6))* 2007. (Illus.). 408p. 182.00 *(978-0-12-373987-2(X))* 2007. (Illus.). 264p. 182.00 *(978-0-12-373686-4(2))* Elsevier Science & Technology Bks. (Academic Pr.).

—Advances in Agronomy. 2012. (Advances in Agronomy Ser.: 114). (ENG.). 320p. 182.00 ***(978-0-12-394275-3(6)***, Academic Pr.) Elsevier Science & Technology Bks.

—Advances in Agronomy. 2006. (Advances in Agronomy Ser.: 90). (ENG., Illus.). Vol. 90. 328p. 182.00 *(978-0-12-000808-7(4))* Vol. 91. 504p. 182.00 *(978-0-12-000809-4(2))* Elsevier Science & Technology Bks. (Academic Pr.).

—Advances in Agronomy V106. 2010. (Advances in Agronomy Ser.: 106). (ENG.). 224p. 182.00 *(978-0-12-381035-9(3)*, Academic Pr.) Elsevier Science & Technology Bks.

Ssekabembe, Charles. General Principles of Agronomy. 2011. 372p. pap. ***(978-3-8443-9655-3(1))*** Lambert Academic Publishing.

Sumberg, James & Thompson, John, eds. Contested Agronomy. 2012. (Pathways to Sustainability Ser.). (ENG., Illus.). 232p. (C). pap. 35.95 ***(978-0-415-50714-1(6))*** Routledge.

—Contested Agronomy: Agricultural Research in a Changing World. 2012. (Pathways to Sustainability Ser.). (ENG., Illus.). 232p. (C). 155.00 ***(978-0-415-59806-1(5))*** Routledge.

AGROSTOLOGY

see Grasses

AGUE

see Malaria

AGUIRRE, LOPE DE, D. 1561

Balkan, Evan. The Wrath of God: Lope de Aguirre, Revolutionary of the Americas. 2011. (Illus.). ix, 225p. *(978-0-8263-5045-9(3))* Univ. of New Mexico Pr.

Simón, Pedro. The Expedition of Pedro de Ursua & Lope de Aguirre in Search of el Dorado & Omagua in 1560-1: Translated from Fray Pedro Simon's Sixth Historical Notice of the Conquest of Tierra Firme by William Bollaert. Bollaert, William, tr. 2010. (Cambridge Library Collection- Hakluyt First Ser.). (Illus.). 318p. pap. 28.99 *(978-1-108-01067-2(9))* Cambridge Univ. Pr.

AHMAD, BEY OF TUNIS, 1806-1855

Brown, L. Carl. The Tunisia of Ahmad Bey, 1837-1855. 2008. 436p. pap. 43.00 *(978-1-59740-453-2(5))* ACLS Humanities E-Book.

AHMADIYYA

Ahmad, Ghulam. Our Teaching, Translated from Kashti-Nuh: Hazrat Mirza Ghulam Ahmad, Promised Messiah & Mahdi, Founder of the Ahmadiyya Movement in Islam. 2011. 72p. 36.95 ***(978-1-258-03899-1(4))*** Literary Licensing, LLC.

Allay, Shabir. Decision of the Court: Quadianies Are Not Muslim. 200p. *(978-9960-9036-3-7(X))* Al-Attique Pubs., Inc.

Valentine, Simon Ross. Islam & the Ahmadiyya Jama'at: History, Belief, Practice. 2008. (Columbia/Hurst Ser.). (ENG.). 256p. (gr. 17). 55.00 *(978-0-231-70094-8(6))* Columbia Univ. Pr.

AHMEDABAD

David, Robin. City of Fear. 2008. (ENG.). 264p. (gr. 12-18). 9.00 *(978-0-14-310137-6(4)*, Penguin Global) Penguin Group (USA) Inc.

AID

see United States—Agency for International Development

AID TO DEPENDENT CHILDREN

see Aid to Families with Dependent Children Programs

AID TO DEVELOPING COUNTRIES

see Economic Assistance

AID TO FAMILIES WITH DEPENDENT CHILDREN PROGRAMS

Here are entered works on government programs to provide public assistance to families of welfare recipients that include children. Works on programs to provide financial aid to families with children regardless of eligibility for welfare are entered under Family Allowances.

Chappell, Marisa. The War on Welfare: Family, Poverty, & Politics in Modern America. 2011. (Politics & Culture in Modern America Ser.). (Illus.). 360p. (C). pap. 24.95 *(978-0-8122-2154-1(0))* Univ. of Pennsylvania Pr.

Harris, Deborah. TAFDC Advocacy Guide. 2011. pap. 9.95 ***(978-1-57589-637-3(0))*** Massachusetts Continuing Legal Education, Inc.

Klerman, Jacob Alex & McClure, P. Jane. Sanctions in the CalWORKs Program. 2008. 178p. pap. 31.50 *(978-0-8330-4233-0(5)*, tr-540) RAND Corp., The.

Weiss, Heather & Jacobs, Francine, eds. Evaluating Family Programs: Current Issues in Theory & Policy. 2008. (ENG., Illus.). 588p. pap. 49.95 *(978-0-202-36215-1(9))* Aldine Transaction.

YMCA of the USA Staff. Guidelines for Family Support Practice. 142p. 35.00 *(978-0-7360-1018-4(1)*, YMCA of the U.S.A.) Human Kinetics Pubs.

AID TO UNDERDEVELOPED AREAS
see Technical Assistance

AIDAN, SAINT, D. 651

Troy, Aidan. Out of the Shadow: Responding to Suicide. 2010. (ENG.). 140p. pap. 12.95 *(978-1-84730-175-8(4))* Veritas Pubns. IRL. Dist: Dufour Editions, Inc.

AIDS (DISEASE)
see also AIDS (Disease) in Children; AIDS (Disease) in Infants; AIDS (Disease) in Pregnancy; HIV (Viruses)

Adler, Michael W., et al, eds. ABC of HIV & AIDS. 6th ed. 2012. (ABC Ser.: 40). (ENG.). 144p. pap. 49.95 ***(978-1-4051-5700-1(3))*** Wiley, John & Sons, Inc.

Aggleton, Peter. Education, Vulnerability & HIV/AIDS. 2009. (IOE Inaugural Professional Lectures). (ENG., Illus.). 30p. pap. 9.95 *(978-0-85473-801-4(0))* Institute of Education GBR. Dist: Stylus Publishing, LLC.

Aids Manual. 240p. pap. *(978-0-86840-380-9(6),* UNSW Press) NewSouth Publishing.

Alexander, Ivy L., ed. AIDS Sourcebook: Basic Consumer Health Information about Human Immunodeficiency Virus (HIV) & Acquired Immunodeficiency Syndrome (AIDS), Featuring Updated Statistics & Facts about Risks, Prevention, Screening, Diagnosis, Treatments, Side Effects, & Complications, And. 4th ed. 2007. (Health Reference Ser.). (Illus.). 707p. 87.00 *(978-0-7808-0997-0(1))* Omnigraphics, Inc.

Anderson, Jean R., ed. Guide to the Clinical Care of Women with HIV. 2007. (Illus.). 600p. (C). pap. 75.00 *(978-1-4223-1530-9(4))* DIANE Publishing Co.

Ashton, Paul J. Etched in Hope: A Weekly Journal for Those Living with or Affected by HIV/AIDS. 2007. (Illus.). 112p. per. 9.95 *(978-0-87946-344-1(9))* ACTA Pubns.

Atzberger, Craig. Will Peak Oil Fuel the Aids Epidemic? 2008. 412p. pap. *(978-3-8364-8737-5(3))* VDM Verlag Dr. Mueller e.K.

Baldwin, Peter. Disease & Democracy: The Industrialized World Faces AIDS. 2007. (California/Milbank Books on Health & the Public). 465p. per. 25.95 *(978-0-520-25147-2(4))* Univ. of California Pr.

Bartlett, John G. & Finkbeiner, Ann K. The Guide to Living with HIV Infection: Developed at the Johns Hopkins AIDS Clinic. 6th ed. 2006. (Johns Hopkins Press Health Book Ser.). (ENG.). 408p. 50.00 *(978-0-8018-8485-6(3));* (Illus.). (gr. -1-k). per. 19.95 *(978-0-8018-8486-3(1))* Johns Hopkins Univ. Pr.

Bauer, Henry H. The Origin, Persistence & Failings of HIV/AIDS Theory. 2007. (ENG., Illus.). 296p. per. 35.00 *(978-0-7864-3048-2(6))* McFarland & Co., Inc. Pubs.

Beck, Eduard J., et al. The HIV Pandemic: Local & Global Implications. Beck, Eduard J. et al, eds. 2008. (ENG., Illus.). 840p. pap. 74.95 *(978-0-19-923740-1(9))* Oxford Univ. Pr., Inc.

Bell, Sigall K., ed. AIDS, 1 vol. 2010. (Biographies of Disease Ser.). (Illus.). 151p. 45.00 *(978-0-313-37682-5(4),* GR7682) Greenwood Publishing Group, Inc.

Bell, Sigall K., et al. AIDS. 2011. E-Book ***(978-0-313-37683-2(2),*** Greenwood Pr.) Greenwood Publishing Group, Inc.

Brennan, Mark & Karpiak, Stephen E., eds. Older Adults with HIV: An In-Depth Examination of an Emerging Population. 2010. (HIV/AIDS - Medical, Social & Psychological Aspects Ser.). (Illus.). 141p. 89.00 *(978-1-60876-054-1(5))* Nova Science Pubs., Inc.

Brewer, Vernon & Yeatts, Noel. Children of Hope: Be touched. Be inspired. Be Changed. 2007. per. 14.99 *(978-0-9788041-2-1(0))* World Help Inc.

Cabot, Sandra. Hepatitis & Aids: How to Fight Them Naturally. 2011. (ENG.). 160p. pap. 15.00 ***(978-0-9829336-5-7(7))*** SCB International.

Callahan, Catina. Hiv Risk among Urban, Female Crack Cocaine Users. 2008. 120p. pap. *(978-3-639-06325-7(2))* VDM Verlag Dr. Mueller e.K.

Cameron, Michael. Vicious Circle. 2008. 300p. pap. *(978-3-639-05752-2(X))* VDM Verlag Dr. Mueller e.K.

Chambers, Sylvester, Jr. Has Time Finally Revealed the Whole Truth about Aids? Exposing a Killer. 2008. 75p. pap. 16.95 *(978-1-60474-220-6(8))* PublishAmerica, Inc.

Clark, Rebecca A., et al. A Woman's Guide to Living with HIV Infection: A Comprehensive Guide Emphasizing the Unique Concerns of Women. 2nd ed. 2012. (Johns Hopkins Press Health Book Ser.). (ENG., Illus.). 344p. pap. 18.95 ***(978-1-4214-0549-0(0));*** (gr. 17). 45.00 ***(978-1-4214-0548-3(2))*** Johns Hopkins Univ. Pr.

Conner, Ross F., et al. AIDS: Science & Society. 5th rev. ed. 2007. (Illus.). 249p. per. 84.95 *(978-0-7637-4263-8(5))* Jones & Bartlett Learning, LLC.

Culshaw, Rebecca. Science Sold Out: Does HIV Really Cause AIDS? 2007. (Terra Nova Ser.). (ENG.). 112p. pap. 14.95 *(978-1-55643-642-0(4))* North Atlantic Bks.

Degazon-Johnson, Roli, ed. Gender, HIV/AIDS & the Status of Teachers: Report of the Third Commonwealth Teachers' Research Symposium. 2008. (ENG., Illus.). 76p. pap. 29.95 *(978-0-85092-890-7(7))* Commonwealth Secretariat GBR. Dist: Stylus Publishing, LLC.

Derose, Kathryn Pitkin, et al. The Role of Faith-Based Organizations in HIV Prevention & Care in Central America. 2010. 122p. pap. 24.00 *(978-0-8330-4953-7(4));* 128p. pap. 20.00 *(978-0-8330-4999-5(2))* RAND Corp., The.

Dow, Unity & Essex, Max. Saturday Is for Funerals. 2011. (ENG.). 240p. pap. 14.95 *(978-0-674-06183-5(7))* Harvard Univ. Pr.

Drotman, D. Peter, ed. Hiv/aids: A Reprint from the Journal, Emerging Infectious Diseases. 2006. (Illus.). 99p. (C). pap. 40.00 *(978-1-4223-0686-4(0))* DIANE Publishing Co.

Encyclopaedia Britannica, Inc., compiled by. Choices: Learning about Aids. 2008. 49.95 *(978-1-59339-647-3(3))* Encyclopaedia Britannica, Inc.

—Young People & AIDS. 2008. 49.95 *(978-1-59339-655-8(4))* Encyclopaedia Britannica, Inc.

Eribon, Didier. De la Subversion: Droit, Norme et Politique. 2010. (FRE.). 107p. *(978-2-915842-66-1(3))* Cartouche, Editions.

Esack, Farid. Islam & AIDS: Between Scorn, Pity, & Justice. 2009. (ENG.). 300p. pap. 27.95 *(978-1-85168-633-9(9))* Oneworld Pubns. GBR. Dist: National Bk. Network.

Feldman, Douglas A., ed. AIDS, Culture, & Gay Men. 2010. (ENG., Illus.). 272p. 75.00 *(978-0-8130-3431-7(0))* Univ. Pr. of Florida.

Fogel, Catherine Ingram, et al. Sexually Transmitted Infections, Including HIV: Impact on Women's Reproductive Health. 2006. *(978-0-86525-117-5(7))* March of Dimes Birth Defects Foundation.

Ford, Michael Thomas. Preguntas y Respuestas Sobre el Sida.Tr. of Questions & Answers about AIDS. (SPA.). 9.98 *(978-970-643-300-8(7))* Selector, S.A. de C.V. MEX. Dist: AIMS International Bks., Inc.

Friedman, Lauri S. Aids. 2010. (Writing the Critical Essay: an Opposing Viewpoints Guide Ser.). (Illus.). 128p. 30.85 *(978-0-7377-4802-4(8),* Greenhaven Pr., Inc.) Cengage Gale.

Gaffey, Janice. Witnessing the Pandemic: Irish Print Media & HIV/Aids in Ireland & Sub-Saharan Africa. 2007. (Irish Research Ser.: No. 53). 204p. lib. bdg. 74.95 *(978-1-933146-24-9(9))* Academica Pr., LLC.

Galanda, Claudia D., ed. AIDS-Related Opportunistic Infections. 2008. (Illus.). 207p. 98.00 *(978-1-60692-144-9(4))* Nova Science Pubs., Inc.

Gallant, Joel E. 100 Questions & Answers about HIV & AIDS. 2008. (ENG., Illus.). 209p. per. 22.95 *(978-0-7637-5042-8(5))* Jones & Bartlett Learning, LLC.

Gallant, Joel E. 100 Questions & Answers about HIV & Aids. 2nd ed. 2012. 204p. pap. 22.95 ***(978-1-4496-5517-4(3))*** Jones & Bartlett Learning, LLC.

Gao Yaojie: Physician, Grandmother, & Whistleblower in China's Fight Against HIV/AIDS: Roundtable Before the Congressional-Executive Commission on China, One Hundred Eleventh Congress, First Session, December 3, 2009. 2010. ii, 29p. *(978-0-16-085802-4(X),* 552-070-41019-8) United States Government Printing Office.

Gendelman, Howard E., et al, eds. The Neurology of AIDS, 1 vol. 3rd ed. 2011. (ENG., Illus.). 1160p. 275.00 ***(978-0-19-539934-9(X))*** Oxford Univ. Pr., Inc.

Goettel, Diane, ed. Art & Understanding: 20th Anniversary Anthology. 2012. (ENG.). 250p. pap. 20.00 ***(978-1-936873-12-8(5))*** Black Lawrence Pr.

Gogichadze, G. K. & Gogichadze, T. Karyogamic Theory of Cancer Cell Formation from the View of the XXI Century. 2010. (Cancer Etiology, Diagnosis & Treatments Ser.). 125.00 *(978-1-60876-386-3(2),* Nova Biomedical Bks.) Nova Science Pubs., Inc.

Green, William Iii. Hiv/Aids: African american preachers Respond. 2010. 68p. 24.99 *(978-1-4535-0582-3(2));* pap. 15.99 *(978-1-4535-0581-6(4))* Xlibris Corp.

Guardia, Josefina. Living Hell: The Truth about Aids & Hiv. 2011. 140p. 23.95 *(978-1-4502-8857-6(X));* pap. 13.95 *(978-1-4502-8855-2(3))* iUniverse, Inc.

Guilfoile, Patrick G., et al. Hiv/aids. 2nd rev. ed. 2011. (Deadly Diseases & Epidemics Ser.). (Illus.). 122p. (C). (gr. 9). 34.95 *(978-1-60413-465-0(8),* Chelsea Hse.) Facts On File, Inc.

Habtamu, Mekonnen. Psychosocial Experience of Double Orphaned Children from Hiv/Aids: Children Can Not Live by Bread Alone: Psychosocial Experience of Double Orphans Before & after the Death of Their Parents from Hiv/Aids. 2011. 104p. pap. ***(978-3-639-32793-9(4))*** VDM Verlag Dr. Mueller e.K.

Hall, John C. & Hall, Brian J. Aids in the 21st Century: Treatment, Prevention & Epidemiology. 2011. (Illus.). 700p. ***(978-1-60795-105-6(3))*** PMPH-USA, Ltd.

Hammar, Lawrence James. Sin, Sex & Stigma: Pacific response to HIV & AIDS. 2010. (ENG & ABK., Illus.). 440p. 129.99 *(978-0-9556400-4-9(0))* Kingston, Sean Publishing GBR. Dist: Lightning Source, Inc.

Hardon, Anita & World Health Organization. From Access to Adherence: The Challenges of Antiretroviral Treatment - Studies from Botswana Tanzania & Uganga 2006. 2006. (Nonserial Publication). (ENG., Illus.). 312p. pap. 36.00 *(978-92-4-156328-4(1))* World Health Organization.

Harris, Paul G. & Siplon, Patricia D., eds. The Global Politics of AIDS. 2007. (Illus.). 350p. lib. bdg. 63.00 *(978-1-58826-467-1(X))* Rienner, Lynne Pubs.

Heymann, Jody, et al, eds. Protecting Childhood in the AIDS Pandemic: Finding Solutions that Work, 1 vol. 2012. (ENG., Illus.). 336p. 55.00 ***(978-0-19-976512-6(X))*** Oxford Univ. Pr., Inc.

HIV/AIDS at Work: A Training Program for Federal Workers, Participant's Manual. 51p. pap. 20.00 *(978-0-7881-1587-5(1))* DIANE Publishing Co.

Hot Talk-Starter Videos Series 6: AIDS/Youth Crime/Violence/Occult/Satanism/Teenagers' Views on Parents. pap., tchr. ed. 19.99 incl. VHS *(978-1-55945-487-2(3))* Group Publishing, Inc.

Human Rights Watch (Organization) Staff, contrib. by. An Unbreakable Cycle: Drug Dependency Treatment, Mandatory Confinement, & HIV/AIDS in China's Guangxi Province. 2008. 43p. pap. *(978-1-56432-416-0(8))* Human Rights Watch.

Ingenkamp, Nina. How Hiv/Aids Has Made It - an Analysis of Global Hiv/Aids Agenda-Setting Between 1981 And 2002. 2008. 104p. pap. *(978-3-8364-4481-1(X))* VDM Verlag Dr. Mueller e.K.

JOHNS HOPKINS UNIV. Johns Hopkins Hiv Guide 2010. rev. ed. 2012. 644p. pap. 24.95 *(978-0-7637-8548-2(2))* Jones & Bartlett Learning, LLC.

Johnson, Nancy J. & Vaughan, Jennifer F., eds. AIDS Litigation Digest 1992. 92p. pap. 34.50 *(978-0-9616858-4-3(0))* Strafford Pubns., Inc.

Jones, Molly. AIDS. 2010. (Epidemics & Society Ser.). (ENG.). 80p. (YA). lib. bdg. 30.60 *(978-1-4358-9434-1(0))* Rosen Publishing Group, Inc., The.

Judd, Sandra, ed. AIDS Sourcebook. 5th rev. ed. 2011. (Health Reference Ser.). lib. bdg. 95.00 *(978-0-7808-1147-8(X))* Omnigraphics, Inc.

Kalichman, Seth C. Denying AIDS: Conspiracy Theories, Pseudoscience, & Human Tragedy. 2009. (ENG., Illus.). xxiii, 205p. 25.00 *(978-0-387-79475-4(1))* Springer.

Kamuzora, Faustin. Assessment of Quality of Hiv/Aids Information Systems. 2010. 88p. pap. *(978-3-8383-0198-3(6))* Lambert Academic Publishing.

Kartikeyan, S., et al. HIV & AIDS: Basic Elements & Priorities. 2010. (ENG.). xiv, 418p. pap. 209.00 *(978-90-481-7445-4(7),* 9048174457) Springer.

—HIV & AIDS: Basic Elements & Priorities. 2007. (ENG.). xiv, 418p. 209.00 *(978-1-4020-5788-5(1),* 1402057881) Springer.

Kikyonkyo, Dickson. Role of the Laboratory in Hiv Clinical Care. 2010. 84p. pap. *(978-3-639-25675-8(1))* VDM Verlag Dr. Mueller e.K.

Latin American & Caribbean Campaign on Children & AIDS. 2007. (Illus.). 16p. per. *(978-92-806-4155-4(7))* United Nations Children's Fund, The (UNICEF).

Lee, Sharon Dian, ed. HIV & Aging. 2008. (Illus.). 160p. pap. 99.95 *(978-1-4200-8390-3(2),* Informa Healthcare) Taylor & Francis Group GBR. Dist: Taylor & Francis Group.

Lisk, Franklyn. Global Institutions & the HIV/AIDS Epidemic: Responding to an International Crisis. 2009. (Global Institutions Ser.). (ENG., Illus.). 160p. (C). 28.95 *(978-0-415-44497-2(7));* 118.00 *(978-0-415-44496-5(9))* Routledge.

Lovrien, Everett Winslow. Doctor Guilt? 2010. 500p. 39.95 *(978-1-4502-1684-5(6));* pap. 29.95 *(978-1-4502-1682-1(X))* iUniverse, Inc.

MacFarlane, Katherine, ed. AIDS. 2007. (Perspectives on Diseases & Disorders Ser.). (ENG., Illus.). 144p. (YA). (gr. 10-12). lib. bdg. 37.10 *(978-0-7377-3868-1(5),* LML02109-235105, Greenhaven Pr., Inc.) Cengage Gale.

Maggiore, Christine. What If Everything You Thought You Knew about AIDS Was Wrong? 4th rev. ed. 2006. (ENG., Illus.). 126p. pap. 12.95 *(978-0-9674153-2-1(2))* American Foundation For Aids Alternatives.

Mandell, Gerald L. International Atlas of AIDS. Mildvan, Donna, ed. 4th ed. 2007. (ENG., Illus.). x, 366p. 159.00 *(978-1-57340-274-3(5),* 1573402745) Current Medicine Group LLC.

Mapuranga, Tapiwa Praise. Gender, Hiv & Aids & African Traditional Religion in Zimbabwe. 2011. 164p. pap. ***(978-3-8433-8791-0(5))*** Lambert Academic Publishing.

Masten, James & Schmidtberger, James. Aging with HIV: A Gay Man's Guide, 1 vol. 2011. (ENG., Illus.). 256p. pap. 17.95 *(978-0-19-974058-1(5))* Oxford Univ. Pr., Inc.

Mayes, Stephen & Stein, Lyndall, eds. Positive Lives. (Illus.). 144p. pap. *(978-0-304-33494-0(4),* Burns & Oates) Continuum International Publishing Group, Ltd.

Mazari, Ali A., et al. Data Mining & Modeling of HIV/AIDS Dynamics. 2013. (Nature-Inspired Computing Ser.). (ENG.). 400p. 110.00 *(978-0-470-56708-1(2),* Wiley) Wiley, John & Sons, Inc.

McCree, Donna H., et al, eds. African Americans & HIV/AIDS: Understanding & Addressing the Epidemic. 2010. (ENG., Illus.). xx, 323p. 129.00 *(978-0-387-78320-8(2),* 0387783202) Springer.

Mckenna, Jason. The, Secret of Cancer & Aids: Immunological Tolerance in the Lymph System. 2011. (ENG.). 128p. pap. 14.95 ***(978-1-4327-3977-5(8))*** Outskirts Pr., Inc.

Merino, Noël. AIDS in Developing Countries. 2010. (At Issue Ser.). (Illus.). 128p. pap. 21.85 *(978-0-7377-4672-3(6),* Greenhaven Pr., Inc.) Cengage Gale.

Mildvan, Donna, ed. International Atlas of AIDS. 4th ed. 2009. (ENG.). cd-rom 99.00 *(978-1-57340-322-1(9),* 1573403229) Current Medicine Group LLC.

—International Atlas of AIDS (Consignment) 4th ed. 2009. (ENG.). cd-rom 64.35 *(978-1-57340-348-1(2),* 1573403482) Current Medicine Group LLC.

Mindel, A. Relationship Between HIV & Other Conditions. *(978-0-340-58715-7(6),* Hodder Arnold) Hodder Education.

Moritz, Andreas. Ending the Aids Myth. 2006. pap. 12.95 *(978-0-9767944-9-3(7))* Ener-Chi Wellness Ctr.

Morse, Stephen A., et al. Atlas of Sexually Transmitted Diseases & AIDS. 4th ed. 2010. (ENG., Illus.). 400p. 250.00 *(978-0-7020-4060-3(6),* Saunders) Elsevier - Health Sciences Div.

Munich, Lutz Gürtler, et al, eds. Evolution of Anti-HIV Drug Resistance - Interpretation & Its Therapeutic Progress Vol. 55, No. 2: Special Topic Issue - 'Intervirology 2012. 2012. (ENG., Illus.). 112p. pap. ***(978-3-8055-9902-3(1))*** Karger, S. AG.

Nappe, Rodolfo Oscar. La Enfermedad Que Cur. 2009. 144p. pap. 19.99 *(978-1-4415-4808-5(4))* Xlibris Corp.

Netsanet, Shiferaw, et al. Emotional Distress: Anxiety & Depression among Clients Prior to Hiv-Vct & Pre Initiation of Art in South Ethiopia. 2011. 72p. pap. ***(978-3-639-25622-2(0))*** VDM Verlag Dr. Mueller e.K.

Odek, Antony & James Alan, Oloo. Challenges Facing Home Based Care Programs in Botswan. 2010. 92p. pap. *(978-3-8383-8783-3(X))* Lambert Academic Publishing.

Odets, Walt. In the Shadow of the Epidemic. 314p. pap. *(978-0-304-33544-2(4),* Burns & Oates) Continuum International Publishing Group, Ltd.

Ohioze, Idowu. Access to Essential Medicines for Hiv/Aids Patients. 2010. 108p. pap. *(978-3-8383-7363-8(4))* Lambert Academic Publishing.

O'Leary,, Ann, Ann & Jemmott, Loretta Sweet, eds. Women & AIDS: Coping & Care: Coping & Care. 2010. (Aids Prevention & Mental Health Ser.). 263p. pap. 109.00 *(978-1-4419-3253-2(4),* 1441932534) Springer.

Olsen, Sissel Tove. Turning a Blind Eye to Hiv/Aids? 2011. 328p. pap. ***(978-3-8443-1683-4(3))*** Lambert Academic Publishing.

Onifade, Abdulfatah, et al. Are Herbal Remedies Effective in Hiv Infection? 2011. 200p. pap. ***(978-3-8443-2594-2(8))*** Lambert Academic Publishing.

Orr, Neil M. & Patient, David. Positive Health. 70th ed. 2008. (ENG.). 156p. pap. 6.95 *(978-1-77009-354-6(0))* Jacana Media ZAF. Dist: Independent Pubs. Group.

Parker, Richard G., ed. Culture, Society & Sexuality: A Reader. 2nd ed. 2007. (Sexuality, Culture & Health Ser.). (Illus.). 490p. per. 43.95 *(978-0-415-40456-3(8))* Routledge.

Peck, Nicole & Bock, Jeanne, eds. Stedman's Oncology Words: Includes Hematology, HIV & AIDS. 5th rev. ed. 2006. (Stedman's Word Books). (ENG., Illus.). 769p. per. 43.99 *(978-0-7817-7382-9(2))* Lippincott Williams & Wilkins.

Perez, Venus. I'm Still Here: The History, Testimony, Education, Outcomes, & Strengths of people Living with HIV/AIDS. 2006. (Illus.). 147p. 26.66 *(978-1-4122-0188-9(8))* Trafford Publishing.

Poku, Nana K., et al, eds. AIDS & Governance. 2007. (Global Health Ser.). 286p. 124.95 *(978-0-7546-4579-5(7));* pap. 49.95 *(978-0-7546-4581-8(9))* Ashgate Publishing Co.

Posey, Ronald. How I Became Mr Hiv: The John Henry Turner Story. 2008. 316p. pap. 12.95 *(978-1-4327-2676-8(5))* Outskirts Pr., Inc.

Poz Magazine Staff, photos by. Essays on HIV/AIDS. 2008. (ENG.). 208p. pap. 16.95 *(978-0-9815381-2-9(6))* Hilton Publishing Co.

Pribram, Vivian, ed. Nutrition & HIV. 2010. (ENG., Illus.). 528p. pap. 68.99 *(978-1-4051-8270-6(9),* Wiley-Blackwell) Wiley, John & Sons, Inc.

Pye. Respond to the AIDS Challenge. Date not set. (Illus.). 215p. pap. 40.00 *(978-0-582-06434-8(1))* Addison-Wesley Longman, Ltd. GBR. Dist: Trans-Atlantic Pubns., Inc.

Radlett, Marty & Bennett, Olivia. Triple Jeopardy: Women & AIDS. (Illus.). vii, 104p. pap. 9.95 *(978-1-870670-20-3(5))* Panos Pubns., Ltd. GBR. Dist: Paul & Co. Pubs. Consortium, Inc.

Rasebotsa, Nobantu, et al, eds. Nobody Ever Said AIDS: Poems & Stories from Southern Africa. 2010. (ENG., Illus.). 192p. pap. 22.95 *(978-0-7957-0184-9(5))* NB Pubs. Ltd. ZAF. Dist: International Publishers Marketing.

Ripley, Vaughn. Survivor: One Man's Battle with Hiv, Hemophilia, & Hepatitis C. 2010. 284p. 30.95 *(978-1-4502-6031-2(4));* pap. 20.95 *(978-1-4502-6030-5(6))* iUniverse, Inc.

Rivera, Orlando Mejia. Etica y Sida. (SPA.). 208p. 8.95 *(978-958-607-889-4(2))* Sociedad de San Pablo COL. Dist: St Pauls/Alba Hse. Pubs.

Roberts-Pittman, Bridget. An Analysis of the Social Support Networks of Gay Men Living with Hiv. 2010. 60p. pap. *(978-3-8383-5621-1(7))* Lambert Academic Publishing.

Rubin, Robert H. & Young, Lowell S. Clinical Approach to Infection in the Compromised Host. 5th ed. 2010. 225.00 *(978-0-387-77981-2(7),* 0387779817) Springer.

Sanborn, Jeannie & Harlin, David. AIDS Facts: A Fact-Based Curriculum for Teaching about AIDS. Corriveau, Verna, ed. ring bd. *(978-0-9643269-9-6(X))* AIDS-Free American Foundation.

Sankar, Nathan, et al. Oxford Handbook of Genitourinary Medicine, HIV, & Sexual Health. 2nd ed. 2010. (ENG., Illus.). 648p. 59.95 *(978-0-19-957166-6(X))* Oxford Univ. Pr., Inc.

Sax, Paul E., et al. HIV Essentials 2010. 3rd rev. ed. 2009. 252p. pap. 24.95 *(978-0-7637-7709-8(9))* Jones & Bartlett Learning, LLC.

Schuitemaker, H. & Miedema, Frank, eds. AIDS Pathogenesis. 2010. (Immunology & Medicine Ser.). 294p. pap. 189.00 *(978-90-481-5407-4(3),* 9048154073) Springer.

Sekopane, Momo Andrew. Hiv/Aids Awareness Campaigns. 2008. 84p. pap. *(978-3-8364-9554-7(6))* VDM Verlag Dr. Mueller e.K.

Sharma, Vinod K. Sexually Transmitted Diseases & AIDS. 2nd ed. 2009. (Illus.). 560p. 170.00 *(978-1-84829-019-8(5))* Anshan GBR. Dist: Publishers Storage & Shipping.

Simkhada, Lava. Knowledge & Attitudes of Nepalese Women Towards Hiv/Aids. 2011. 80p. pap. ***(978-3-8443-0717-7(6))*** Lambert Academic Publishing.

Skerritt, Andrew J. Ashamed to Die: Silence, Denial, & the AIDS Epidemic in the South. 2011. (ENG., Illus.). 320p. 24.95 *(978-1-56976-814-3(5),* Hill, Lawrence Bks.) Chicago Review Pr., Inc.

Smallman, Shawn C. The AIDS Pandemic in Latin America. 2007. (ENG., Illus.). 304p. 69.95 *(978-0-8078-3093-2(3));* per. 28.95 *(978-0-8078-5796-0(3))* Univ. of North Carolina Pr.

Sobopha, Siphiwo. I Am the Queen of My Own Body. 2008. 56p. pap. 21.99 *(978-1-4343-5526-3(8))* AuthorHouse.

Stine, Gerald. AIDS Update 2011. 20th ed. 2010. (Textbook Ser.). (ENG., Illus.). 544p. (C). pap. 81.33 *(978-0-07-352763-5(7),* 0073527637, McGraw-Hill/Dushkin) McGraw-Hill Higher Education.

Stine, Gerald. AIDS Update 2012. 21st ed. 2011. (Textbook Ser.). (ENG., Illus.). 560p. (C). pap. 81.33 ***(978-0-07-352765-9(3),*** 0073527653, McGraw-Hill/Dushkin) McGraw-Hill Higher Education.

Taylor, Justine. Sharing the Pain. 2006. 87p. pap. 16.95 *(978-1-4241-4071-8(4))* PublishAmerica, Inc.

The AIDS 2031 Commission. AIDS: Taking a Long-Term View. 2010. (FT Press Science Ser.). (ENG.). 224p. 34.99 *(978-0-13-217259-2(3))* FT Press.

Thomas, Felicity, et al, eds. Mobility Sexuality & Aids. 2012. (ENG., Illus.). 224p. (C). pap. 42.95 ***(978-0-415-53699-8(5))*** Routledge.

Towle, James B. & Towle, Rose-Marie. US National SWAT Sniper Championships: US Shooting Academy, Tulsa, OK June 15-16 2009. 2009. 196p. 24.95 *(978-1-936728-00-8(1))* ATSN (American Trigger Sports Network).

UNAIDS. Global Reach: How Trade Unions are Responding to AIDS: Case Studies of Union Action. 2006. (UNAIDS Publication). (ENG.). 67p. pap. 18.00 *(978-92-9173-519-8(1))* World Health Organization.

—Monitoring the Declaration of Commitmenton HIV/AIDS: Guidelines on Construction of Core Indicators 2008 Reporting. 2007. (Unaids Publication). (ENG.). 139p. pap. 18.00 (978-92-9173-563-1(9)) World Health Organization.

—UNAIDS Outlook Report 2010. 2010. (UNAIDS Publication Ser.). 40p. pap. 15.00 (978-92-9173-839-7(5)) World Health Organization.

—UNAIDS Outlook Report July 2010. 2010. (UNAIDS Publication). 140p. pap. 18.00 (978-92-9173-859-5(X)) World Health Organization.

UNAIDS Inter-agency Task Team on Young People. Preventing HIV/AIDS in young People: A Systematic Review of the Evidence from Developing Countries. Ross, David A. et al, eds. 2006. (Who Technical Report Ser.). (ENG., Illus.). 353p. pap. 24.00 (978-92-4-120938-0(0)) World Health Organization.

United Nations. AIDS At 30: Nations at the Crossroads. 2011. (ENG.). 138p. pap. 30.00 **(978-92-9173-895-3(6))** United Nations Pubns.

Ward, Darrell. A Practical Guide to HIV/AIDS in Africa: The Disease, Its Prevention, & Basic Home Care. 2007. (Illus.). 224p. pap. 20.00 (978-0-8214-1657-0(X)) Ohio Univ. Pr.

Watstein, Sarah Barbara & Stratton, Stephen E. The Encyclopedia of HIV & AIDS. 3rd rev. ed. 2012. (Library of Health & Living Ser.). (C). (gr. 9). 75.00 (978-0-8160-7723-6(1)) Facts On File, Inc.

Weeks, Benjamin S. & Alcamo, I. Edward. AIDS: The Biological Basis. 5th rev. ed. 2009. 360p. pap. 98.95 (978-0-7637-6324-4(1)) Jones & Bartlett Learning, LLC.

Welbourn, Alice, ed. HIV & AIDS. 2008. (Oxfam Working in Gender & Development Ser.). (ENG.). 160p. pap. 29.95 (978-0-85598-603-2(4)) Oxfam Publishing GBR. Dist: Stylus Publishing, LLC.

Whelehan, Patricia. The Anthropology of AIDS: A Global Perspective. 2009. (ENG., Illus.). 320p. pap. 32.00 (978-0-8130-3292-4(X)) Univ. Pr. of Florida.

Whiteside, Alan. HIV/AIDS. 2008. (Very Short Introductions Ser.). (ENG., Illus.). 144p. per. 11.95 (978-0-19-280692-5(0)) Oxford Univ. Pr., Inc.

WHO Regional of Staff. Guidance on Testing & Counselling for HIV in Settings Attended by People Who Inject Drugs: Improving Access to Treatment Care & Prevention. 2010. (WPRO Nonserial Publication Ser.). 87p. pap. 12.00 (978-92-9061-396-5(X)) World Health Organization.

WHO Regional Office for the Western Pacific. HIV/AIDS Care & Treatment for People Who Inject Drugs in Asia & the Pacific. 2009. (WPRO Nonserial Publication Ser.). (ENG.). 64p. pap. 12.00 (978-92-9061-320-6(3)) World Health Organization.

—A Revised Framework to Address TB-HIV Co-infection in the Western Pacific Region. 2009. (WHO Regional Publications Western Pacific Ser.). (ENG.). 85p. pap. 12.00 (978-92-9061-387-9(4)) World Health Organization.

Woldesenbet, Selamawit. Infant Feeding Strategies & Other Determinants. 2011. 128p. pap. **(978-3-8443-0926-3(8))** Lambert Academic Publishing.

World Health Or Staff. 2008 UNAIDS Annual Report. 2010. 68p. pap. 10.00 (978-92-9173-802-1(6)) World Health Organization CHE. Dist: Stylus Publishing, LLC.

World Health Organization. Monitoring Equity in Access to AIDS Treatment Programmes: A Review of Concepts, Models, Methods & Indicators. 2011. 108p. pap. 24.00 (978-92-4-156412-0(1)) World Health Organization.

—2008 UNAIDS Annual Report: Towards Universal Access. 2010. (UNAIDS Publication). 68p. pap. 12.00 (978-92-9173-800-7(X)) World Health Organization.

World Health Organization, Executive Board Staff. Integrating Poverty & Gender into Health Programmes: A Sourcebook for Health Professionals: Module on HIV/AIDS. 2009. (WHO Regional Publications Western Pacific Ser.). (ENG., Illus.). 116p. pap. 12.00 (978-92-9061-388-6(2)) World Health Organization.

Zheng, Tiantian & Wortman, Jack. Hiv/Aids Through an Anthropological Lens. 2nd rev. ed. 2012. (ENG.). 206p. pap. 82.99 **(978-0-7575-9041-2(1))** Kendall Hunt Publishing Co.

2004 HIV Cme. (978-1-56363-494-9(5)) PDR Network, LLC.

AIDS (DISEASE)—BIBLIOGRAPHY

Gross, Melissa. HIV/AIDS in Young Adult Novels: An Annotated Bibliography. 2010. (ENG., Illus.). 246p. (gr. 17). 49.95 (978-0-8108-7443-5(1)) Scarecrow Pr., Inc.

Gross, Melissa, et al. HIV/AIDS in Young Adult Novels: An Annotated Bibliography. 2010. E-Book 49.95 (978-0-8108-7444-2(X)) Scarecrow Pr., Inc.

AIDS (DISEASE)—BIOGRAPHY

see AIDS (Disease)—Patients—Biography

AIDS (DISEASE)—CHEMOTHERAPY

Bodasing, Uvani. Adherence to Heart for Management of Kaposi's Sarcom. 2011. 280p. pap. **(978-3-8433-8727-9(3))** Lambert Academic Publishing.

Gallant, Joel. Antiretroviral Agents in HIV-1 FLASHcard (2011) 2011. 2p. 6.95 **(978-0-9846423-6-6(6))** International Guidelines Ctr., Inc.

Joint United Nations Programme on HIV/AIDS (UNAIDS). 2008 Report on the Global AIDS Epidemic. 2009. (UNAIDS Publication Ser.). (ENG.). 357p. pap. 48.00 (978-92-9173-711-6(9)) World Health Organization.

Skowron, Gail & Ogden, Richard, eds. Reverse Transcriptase Inhibitors in HIV/AIDS Therapy. 2010. (Infectious Disease Ser.). (Illus.). 544p. pap. 159.00 (978-1-61737-695-5(7), 1617376957) Humana Pr.

Ye, Zhi-Wei. Interaction of Hiv Protease Inhibitor with Hepatic Drug Transporters. 2010. 156p. pap. (978-3-8383-5429-3(X)) Lambert Academic Publishing.

AIDS (DISEASE)—COMPLICATIONS

Barbaro, Giuseppe. Cardiovascular Disease in Aids. 2nd ed. 2008. (Illus.). 246p. spiral bd. 199.00 (978-88-470-0760-4(7)) Springer.

Barbaro, Giuseppe, ed. HIV Infection & the Cardiovascular System, Vol. 40. (Advances in Cardiology Ser.: Vol. 40). (Illus.). (978-3-8055-7606-2(4)) Karger, S. AG.

Dittmer, Dirk P. & Krown, Susan E., eds. Molecular Basis for Therapy of AIDS-Defining Cancers. 2010. (ENG., Illus.). ccivi, 200p. 179.00 (978-1-4419-1512-2(5), 1441915125) Springer.

Dittmer, Dirk Peter & Krown, Susan E. Molecular Basis for Therapy of AIDS-Defining Cancers. 2010. (Illus.). xiii, 256p. E-Book **(978-1-4419-1513-9(3))** Springer.

Hendricks, Kristy M., et al. Nutrition Management of HIV & AIDS. 2009. xii, 180p. (978-0-88091-413-0(0)) Academy of Nutrition & Dietetics.

Kohan, Darius, et al. AIDS & the Otolaryngologist. 2nd ed. 2006. (SIPac Ser.). pap. (978-1-56772-101-0(X)) American Academy of Otolaryngology-Head & Neck Surgery Foundation, Inc.

Mersh, T.G.Allen- & Gottesman, Lester, eds. Anorectal Disease in AIDS. (ENG., Illus.). 208p. (978-0-340-54643-7(3), Hodder Arnold) Hodder Education.

Meucci, Olimpia, ed. Chemokine Receptors & Neuroaids: Beyond Co-Receptor Function & Links to Other Neuropathologies. 2010. (ENG., Illus.). xvi, 412p. 209.00 (978-1-4419-0792-9(0), 1441907920) Springer.

Meyers, Craig, ed. AIDS-Associated Viral Oncogenesis. 2010. (Cancer Treatment & Research Ser.). (Illus.). ix, 270p. pap. 159.00 (978-1-4419-4287-6(4), 1441942874) Springer.

Paul, Robert Harris, ed. HIV & the Brain: New Challenges in the Modern Era. 2009. (Current Clinical Neurology Ser.). (Illus.). 360p. 189.00 (978-1-934115-08-4(8)) Humana Pr.

Portegies, Peter & Berger, Joseph R., eds. HIV/AIDS & the Nervous System: Handbook of Clinical Neurology. 2007. (Handbook of Clinical Neurology Ser.: 85). (ENG., Illus.). 384p. pap. 297.00 (978-0-444-52010-4(4)) Elsevier Science & Technology Bks.

Swanepoel, DeWet & Louw, Brenda, eds. HIV/AIDS Related Communication, Hearing & Swallowing Disorders. 2009. (Illus.). 350p. pap. 98.00 (978-1-59756-262-1(9)) Plural Publishing, Inc.

AIDS (DISEASE)—CONGRESSES

Gill, Robin, ed. Reflecting Theologically on AIDS: A Global Challenge. 2007. 208p. per. (978-0-334-04002-6(7)) Hymns Ancient & Modern Ltd.

Primary HIV Infection: Pathology, Diagnosis, Management. 2007. (Illus.). 84p. per. 59.95 (978-1-58890-416-4(4)) Thieme Medical Pubs., Inc.

AIDS (DISEASE)—DIAGNOSIS

ABBE Scientist Research Division Staff. AIDS & HIV in Body Fluids: Index & Medical Analysis of New Clinical & Research Information. 2007. (ENG., Illus.). 160p. ring bd. 69.95 (978-0-7883-4778-8(0)) ABBE Pubs. Assn. of Washington, D.C.

Konyana, Elias G. Making Voluntary Counselling & Testing Worthwhile. 2011. 60p. pap. **(978-3-8443-2295-8(7))** Lambert Academic Publishing.

Levy, Jay A., ed. HIV AIDS: Physician's Reference. 2010. (Infectious Disease Ser.). (ENG.). 1p. cd-rom 99.00 (978-981-4284-02-8(5)) Focus Medica Pte Ltd. SGP. Dist: Independent Pubs. Group.

Murphy, Robert L. Contemporary Diagnosis & Management of HIV/AIDS Infections. 3rd ed. 2009. (Illus.). 268p. pap. 24.99 (978-1-935103-07-3(5), Handbooks in Health Care Co.) Assocs. in Medical Marketing Co., Inc.

Reid, Selbourne. God's Miraculous Healing Power: Divine Healing of Hiv/Aids. 2011. 80p. pap. 9.99 **(978-1-4634-2832-7(4))** AuthorHouse.

AIDS (DISEASE)—DIRECTORIES

Peterson, Marion L. HIV-AIDS Resources the National Directory of Resources on HIV Infection - AIDS. 2nd rev. ed. 650p. pap. 116.00 (978-1-885461-02-5(X)) National Directory CYF.

AIDS (DISEASE)—ECONOMIC ASPECTS

Adato, Michelle & Bassett, Lucy. Social Protection & Cash Transfers to Strengthen Families Affected by HIV & AIDS. 2012. **(978-0-89629-201-7(0))** International Food Policy Research Institute.

Banks, Nancy Turner. AIDS, Opium, Diamonds, & Empire: The Deadly Virus of International Greed. 2010. 484p. pap. 29.95 (978-1-4502-0171-1(7)) iUniverse, Inc.

Chirambo, Kondwani, ed. Examining the Impact of an Epidemic on Ward Councillors. 2008. 124p. pap. (978-1-920118-74-7(8)) IDASA Pubs. ZAF. Dist: Michigan State Univ. Pr.

Condon, Bradly J. Global Lessons from the AIDS Pandemic: Economic, Financial, Legal & Political Implications. 2008. (ENG., Illus.). xxvi, 366p. 159.00 (978-3-540-78391-6(1), 3540783911) Springer.

Condon, Bradly J. & Sinha, Tapen. Global Lessons from the AIDS Pandemic: Economic, Financial, Legal & Political Implications. 2010. (ENG., Illus.). xxvi, 366p. pap. 159.00 (978-3-642-09712-6(X), 364209712X) Springer.

Conroy, Anne C., ed. Poverty, AIDS & Hunger: Breaking the Poverty Trap in Malawi. 2007. (ENG., Illus.). 280p. 95.00 (978-1-4039-9833-0(7)) Palgrave Macmillan.

Coriat, Benjamin. The Political Economy of HIV/AIDS in Developing Countries: TRIPS, Public Health Systems & Free Access. Coriat, Benjamin, ed. 2008. (Illus.). 352p. 150.00 (978-1-84844-077-7(4)) Elgar, Edward Publishing, Inc.

Doss, Cheryl & Conrad, Cecilia, eds. Aids Gender & Economic Development. 2011. (ENG., Illus.). 232p. (C). 125.00 (978-0-415-67327-3(5)); pap. 32.95 (978-0-415-67328-0(3)) Routledge.

Faulk, Saskia & Usunier, Jean-Claude. AIDS & Business. 2009. (Routledge Advances in Management & Business Studies: Vol. 41). (ENG., Illus.). 354p. (C). 166.00 (978-0-415-45463-6(8)) Routledge.

Gillespie, Stuart. AIDS, Poverty, & Hunger: Challenges & Responses. 2006. xii, 376p. (978-0-89629-758-6(6)) International Food Policy Research Institute.

Haacker, Markus & Claeson, Mariam. HIV & AIDS in South Asia: An Economic Development Risk. 2009. (Directions in Development Ser.). (ENG., Illus.). 272p. pap. 30.00 (978-0-8213-7800-7(7), 9780821378007) World Bank Pubns.

Johnston, Deborah. The Sickness of Economics: The Application of Economics to the HIV Pandemic. 2012. (Routledge International Studies in Health Economics Ser.). (ENG.). 224p. (C). 130.00 (978-0-415-68116-2(2)) Routledge.

Kamhanga Beraho, Monica. Living with AIDS in Uganda: Impacts on banana-farming households in two Districts. 2008. (AWLAE Ser.). 372p. pap. 55.00 (978-90-8686-064-7(8)) Wageningen Academic Publishers NLD. Dist: Enfield Publishing & Distribution Co., Inc.

Leoni, Patrick. Economic Challenges in the Fight Against HIV/AIDS. 2010. 208p. 79.00 (978-1-60741-587-9(9)) Nova Science Pubs., Inc.

Lule, Elizabeth & Haacker, Markus. The Fiscal Dimensions of HIV/AIDS in Botswana, South Africa, Swaziland, & Uganda. 2011. (ENG.). 308p. pap. 40.00 **(978-0-8213-8807-5(X)**, 9780821388075); **(978-0-8213-8808-2(8))** World Bank Pubns.

Mugyenyi, Peter. Genocide by Denial: How Profiteering from HIV/AIDS Killed Millions. 2008. (Illus.). xiv, 295p. (978-9970-02-753-8(0)) Fountain Pubs. Ltd. UGA. Dist: Michigan State Univ. Pr.

Organisation for Economic Co-operation and Development Staff. Creditor Reporting System: Aid Activities in Support of Hiv/Aids Control 2003-2006-SystèMe de Notification des Pays CréAnciers: Activités d'Aide Pour la Lutte Contre le Vih/Sida 2003-2006. 2006. 116p. pap. 63.00 (978-92-64-03233-5(5)) Organization for Economic Cooperation & Development.

Pisani, Elizabeth. The Wisdom of Whores: Bureaucrats, Brothels, & the Business of AIDS. 2008. (ENG.). 400p. 25.95 (978-0-393-06662-3(2), 6662) Norton, W. W. & Co., Inc.

Rugalema, Gabriel, et al, eds. AIDS & Rural Livelihoods: Dynamics & Diversity in sub-Saharan Africa. 2010. (ENG., Illus.). 248p. 140.00 (978-1-84971-125-8(9)); pap. 49.95 (978-1-84971-126-5(7)) Routledge.

Sahn, David E., ed. The Socioeconomic Dimensions of HIV/AIDS in Africa. 2010. (United Nations University Ser.). (Illus.). 360p. pap. 29.95 (978-0-8014-7693-8(3)) Cornell Univ. Pr.

Seibold, Mandy. The Economic Impact of Hiv/Aids in Tanzani. 2008. 108p. per. (978-3-8364-6308-9(3)) VDM Verlag Dr. Mueller e.K.

Simbayi, Leickness. The Impact of & Responses to HIV/AIDS in the Private Security & Legal Services Industry in South Africa. 2009. (ENG.). 192p. pap. 19.95 (978-0-7969-2205-2(5)) Human Sciences Research Council ZAF. Dist: Independent Pubs. Group.

Siphambe, Happy, et al. Development Challenges of HIV/AIDS in Small States: Experiences from the Pacific, Southern Africa & the Caribbean. 2011. (ENG., Illus.). 120p. pap. 33.00 **(978-1-84929-058-6(X))** Commonwealth Secretariat GBR. Dist: Stylus Publishing, LLC.

Sonntag, Diana. AIDS & Aid: A Public Good Approach. 2010. (Contributions to Economics Ser.). (ENG.). xii, 200p. 119.00 (978-3-7908-2418-5(6), 3790824186) Physica-Verlag DEU. Dist: Springer.

Uzukwu, Matthew. Factors Influencing the Spread of Hiv/Aids in Nigeri. 2011. 232p. pap. **(978-3-8443-8923-4(7))** Lambert Academic Publishing.

Waring, Marilyn, et al, eds. Who Cares? The Economics of Dignity. 2011. (ENG., Illus.). 200p. pap. 24.95 (978-1-84929-019-7(9)) Commonwealth Secretariat GBR. Dist: Stylus Publishing, LLC.

Welpe, Ingelore & Owino, Philip, eds. The Intersection of Human Capital, Gender & HIV/AIDS in the African Context, Vol. 2. (Illus.). 113p. (C). pap. 26.95 (978-3-631-54068-8(X)) Lang, Peter Publishing, Inc.

World Bank. O Compromisso do Banco Mundial com o VIH/SIDA Em África: O Nosso Plano de Actividades, 2007-2011. 2008. (POR.). 136p. pap. 20.00 (978-0-8213-7466-5(4), 9780821374665) World Bank Pubns.

—Our Commitment French. 2008. (FRE.). 136p. pap. 20.00 (978-0-8213-7464-1(8), 9780821374641) World Bank Pubns.

World Bank Staff. The World Bank's Commitment to HIV/AIDS in Africa: Our Agenda for Action, 2007-2011. 2008. (ENG., Illus.). 144p. pap. 20.00 (978-0-8213-7448-1(6), 9780821374481) World Bank Pubns.

Zheng, Tiantian & Wortman, Jack. Hiv/Aids Through an Anthropological Lens. 2nd rev. ed. 2012. (ENG.). 206p. pap. 82.99 **(978-0-7575-9041-2(1))** Kendall Hunt Publishing Co.

AIDS (DISEASE)—EPIDEMIOLOGY

Bourke, Dale Hanson. Global AIDS Crisis: Tough Questions, Direct Answers. 2007. (Skeptic's Guide Ser.). (ENG., Illus.). 104p. per. 9.99 (978-1-934068-08-3(X)) Authentic Media.

Brier, Jennifer. Infectious Ideas: U. S. Political Responses to the AIDS Crisis. 2009. (ENG., Illus.). 312p. 36.95 (978-0-8078-3314-8(2)) Univ. of North Carolina Pr.

Hunter, Susan. AIDS in America. 2008. (ENG.). 256p. pap. 20.00 (978-1-4039-7650-5(3)) Palgrave Macmillan.

Joint United Nations Programme on HIV/AIDS (UNAIDS). 2006 report on the global AIDS Epidemic: A UNAIDS 10th anniversary special Edition. 10th rev. ed. 2006. (Unaids Publication). (ENG., Illus.). 629p. pap. 40.00 (978-92-9173-479-5(9)) World Health Organization.

—2008 Report on the Global AIDS Epidemic. 2009. (UNAIDS Publication Ser.). (ENG.). 357p. pap. 48.00 (978-92-9173-711-6(9)) World Health Organization.

Joint United Nations Programme on HIV/AIDS (UNAIDS) & World Health Organization. UNAIDS Annual Report 2007: Knowing Your Epidemic. 2009. (UNAIDS Publication Ser.). (ENG., Illus.). 48p. pap. 15.00 (978-92-9173-700-0(3)) World Health Organization.

Messer, Donald E. Names, Not Just Numbers: Facing Global AIDS & World Hunger. 2010. (Speaker's Corner Ser.). (ENG.). 160p. 17.95 (978-1-55591-633-6(3)) Fulcrum Publishing.

Rehle, Thomas, et al. South African National HIV Prevalence, Incidence, Behaviour & Communication Survey 2008: A Turning Tide among Teenagers? 2010. (ENG., Illus.). 120p. pap. 25.95 (978-0-7969-2291-5(8)) Human Sciences Research Council ZAF. Dist: Independent Pubs. Group.

Shakeri, Nezhat. Estimation of Incidence & Survival Function of Doubly Censored Dat. 2009. 132p. pap. (978-3-639-16724-5(4)) VDM Verlag Dr. Mueller e.K.

Tchuenche, Jean Michel & Mukandavire, Zindoga. Advances in Disease Epidemiology. 2009. (Illus.). viii, 299p. 89.00 (978-1-60741-452-0(X), Nova Biomedical Bks.) Nova Science Pubs., Inc.

Thomas, Felicity, et al. Mobility, Sexuality, & AIDS. 2009. (Sexuality, Culture & Health Ser.). (ENG., Illus.). XVI, 224p. 140.00 (978-0-415-47777-2(5)) Routledge.

UNAIDS. AIDS Epidemic Update, December 2007. 2007. (UNAIDS Publication). 50p. pap. 18.00 (978-92-9173-621-8(X)) World Health Organization.

—AIDS Epidemic Update November 2009. 2010. (UNAIDS Publication). (Illus.). 99p. pap. 24.00 (978-92-9173-832-8(8)) World Health Organization.

—AIDS Scorecards: Overview: UNAIDS Report on the Global AIDS Epidemic 2010. 2011. (Illus.). 150p. pap. 12.00 (978-92-9173-878-6(6)) World Health Organization.

—CD-ROM Report on the Global AIDS Epidemic & Document Library: Multilingual English/French/Spanish/Russian. 2009. (UNAIDS Product Ser.). (ENG & FRE.). cd-rom 36.00 (978-92-9173-808-3(5)) World Health Organization.

—Global Report: Unaids Report on the Global Aids Epidemic 2010. 2011. (Illus.). 360p. pap. 24.00 (978-92-9173-871-7(9)) World Health Organization.

—MDG6: Six Things You Need to Know about the AIDS Response Today. 2011. 150p. pap. 12.00 (978-92-9173-887-8(5)) World Health Organization.

—Unaids: The First Ten Years. 2010. (UNAIDS Publication). (ENG.). 286p. pap. 36.00 (978-92-9173-589-1(2)) World Health Organization.

WHO Regional Office for South-East Asia. HIV/AIDS among men who have sex with men & transgender populations in South-East Asia: The current situation & national Responses. 2011. 161p. pap. 36.00 (978-92-9022-381-8(2)) World Health Organization.

Williams, Mary E. AIDS. 2011. (Introducing Issues with Opposing Viewpoints Ser.). 144p. lib. bdg. 35.75 (978-0-7377-5197-0(5), Greenhaven Pr., Inc.) Cengage Gale.

AIDS (DISEASE)—FICTION

Alston, Stephanie R. As I Die Slowly. 2008. 60p. pap. 12.99 (978-1-4389-4072-4(6)) AuthorHouse.

Alvarez, Julia. Saving the World. 2007. (ENG.). 400p. pap. 13.95 (978-1-56512-558-2(4), 1565125584, Shannon Ravenel Bks.) Algonquin Bks. of Chapel Hill.

Anthony, Jeff. Religion Is Fiction. 2007. 352p. per. 26.50 (978-1-4251-1125-0(4)) Trafford Publishing.

Boswell, Robert & Schweidel, David. What Men Call Treasure: The Search for Gold at Victorio Peak. 2008. (ENG., Illus.). 352p. 25.95 (978-1-933693-21-7(5)) Cinco Puntos Pr.

Brown, Carrie. The Rope Walk. Lt. ed. 2007. (Thorndike Reviewers' Choice Ser.). 491p. 29.95 (978-0-7862-9907-2(X)) Thorndike Pr.

Brunt, Carol Rifka. Tell the Wolves I'm Home: A Novel. 2012. (ENG.). 368p. E-Book **(978-0-8129-9292-2(X))**; 25.00 **(978-0-679-64419-4(9))** Random House Publishing Group. (Dial Pr.).

Bundu, Alieu. The Victim. 2011. 68p. pap. 6.99 **(978-1-61667-196-9(3))** Raider Publishing International.

Campos, Marcos Anthony. A Long Wait. 2007. 180p. per. 13.95 (978-0-595-43562-3(9)) iUniverse, Inc.

Canning, Richard, ed. Vital Signs: Essential AIDS Fiction. 2007. (ENG., Illus.). 400p. per. 15.95 (978-0-7867-2009-5(3)) Westview Pr.

Cleage, Pearl. What Looks Like Crazy on an Ordinary Day. 2009. (ENG.). 256p. pap. 13.99 (978-0-06-171038-4(5), William Morrow Paperbacks) HarperCollins Pubs.

Coben, Harlan. Miracle Cure. 2011. (ENG.). 544p. (gr. 12). pap. 9.99 (978-0-451-23491-9(X), Signet) Penguin Group (USA) Inc.

Curtin, Ralph & Curtin, Michael. The Agenda. 2007. 508p. per. 24.95 (978-1-60290-060-8(4)) OakTara Publishing Group LLC.

Danierla, Bcb. Habiba My Habib. 2009. 252p. 25.99 (978-1-4389-5786-9(6)) AuthorHouse.

—Habiba My Habiba. 2009. 252p. pap. 15.99 (978-1-4389-5785-2(8)) AuthorHouse.

Gaitskill, Mary. Veronica. 2006. (Vintage Contemporaries Ser.). (ENG.). 272p. pap. 14.95 (978-0-375-72785-6(X), Vintage) Knopf Doubleday Publishing Group.

Graziano, Michael S. A. The Love Song of Monkey. 2008. (ENG.). 152p. pap. 13.95 (978-0-9815148-0-2(4)) Leapfrog Pr.

Gross, Melissa. HIV/AIDS in Young Adult Novels: An Annotated Bibliography. 2010. (ENG., Illus.). 246p. (gr. 17). 49.95 (978-0-8108-7443-5(1)) Scarecrow Pr., Inc.

Gross, Melissa, et al. HIV/AIDS in Young Adult Novels: An Annotated Bibliography. 2010. E-Book 49.95 (978-0-8108-7444-2(X)) Scarecrow Pr., Inc.

Guzman, R. M. Alzmek: A Fictional Memoir of a Tainted Life. 2008. (ENG.). 335p. pap. 17.95 (978-1-934187-24-1(0)) STARbooks Pr.

Hayward, Glynnis. A Significant Test of Blood. 2007. 275p. pap. 27.95 (978-1-4137-6838-1(5)) PublishAmerica, Inc.

Hemphill, Randolph. Death Angel. 2010. 101p. pap. 16.95 *(978-1-4327-5358-0(4))* Outskirts Pr., Inc.

Julian, Frank S. AIDS: Love's Fight: The Story of Fawn. 2010. pap. 12.95 *(978-0-7414-6266-4(4))* Infinity Publishing.

Kalinoff, Thomas Frederick. Solid Shadows. 2008. 165p. pap. 24.95 *(978-1-60610-753-9(4))* PublishAmerica, Inc.

Kennedy, Thomas. Post mortem - a play in three Acts. 2008. 93p. pap. 14.50 *(978-1-4092-2248-4(9))* Lulu Enterprises Inc.

Kennedy's Brain. 2008. (Vintage Crime/Black Lizard Ser.). (ENG.). 336p. pap. 15.00 *(978-0-307-38591-8(4),* Vintage) Knopf Doubleday Publishing Group.

Kittle, Katrina. Traveling Light. 2008. (P. S. Ser.). (ENG.). 384p. pap. 13.99 *(978-0-06-145137-9(1),* HarperPerennial) HarperCollins Pubs.

Kronlokken, Connie. Pleasure's Only Rule. 2007. 224p. per. 15.95 *(978-0-595-43950-8(0))* iUniverse, Inc.

Lianke, Yan. Dream of Ding Village. Carter, Cindy, tr. from CHI. 2011. (ENG.). 352p. 24.00 *(978-0-8021-1932-2(8),* Grove Pr.) Grove/Atlantic, Inc.

Mathis, Francine C. No one in Particular: A story of hope, Love & HIV... We should all be Concerned. 2007. (Illus.). 176p. per. 13.00 *(978-0-9787159-0-8(X))* Gwada Publishing.

Mckinlay, Marc. Infectious Betrayal. 2007. 316p. per. 18.95 *(978-0-595-45280-4(9))* iUniverse, Inc.

Mur, Nick. Vicarious. 2008. 188p. pap. 12.95 *(978-1-934925-58-4(6),* Eloquent Bks.) AEG Literary Publishing Services, Inc.

Mwangi, Meja. Cross Roads: The Last Plague. 2008. pap. *(978-0-9796476-4-2(9))* HM Bks.

Onyile, Nsedu B. Ten Days with Minor: An Unlikely Story of Love, Sex & the Beauty of Dying. 2011. 176p. pap. 11.70 *(978-1-4567-5986-5(8))* AuthorHouse.

Palmer, Thom. Desire. 2007. 628p. 40.95 *(978-0-595-68211-9(1));* per. 30.95 *(978-0-595-43235-6(2))* iUniverse, Inc.

Peeters, Frederik. Blue Pills: A Positive Love Story. Singh, Anjali, tr. from FRE. 2008. (ENG., Illus.). 192p. 18.95 *(978-0-618-82099-3(X))* Houghton Mifflin Harcourt Publishing Co.

—Píldoras Azules: Blue Pills. 2007. (SPA.). 200p. pap. 25.95 *(978-1-59497-396-3(2))* Public Square Bks.

Pugh, Richard G. Bad Blood Again: First Syphilis, Then AIDS- A Whole New Game. 2009. 276p. pap. 15.49 *(978-1-4389-4039-7(4))* AuthorHouse.

Rasnick, David. Germ of Lies. 2008. 185p. pap. 19.95 *(978-0-615-25128-8(5))* Rasnick, David.

Reinken, Patrick A. Judgment Day. 2011. (ENG.). 384p. pap. 23.99 ***(978-1-4516-7241-1(1))*** Simon & Schuster.

Ryman, Geoff. Was: A Novel. 2012. (ENG.). 384p. pap. 16.00 ***(978-1-931520-73-7(9))*** Small Beer Pr.

Schulman, Sarah. Rat Bohemia. 2008. (ENG.). 240p. pap. 17.95 *(978-1-55152-235-7(7))* Arsenal Pulp Pr. CAN. Dist: Consortium Bk. Sales & Distribution.

Schwartz, Bernard. Unexpected News. 2011. 132p. pap. 24.95 ***(978-1-4560-5688-9(3))*** PublishAmerica, Inc.

Sherman, Charlotte Watson. Touch. 2011. 224p. pap. 14.95 ***(978-1-4502-8204-8(0))*** iUniverse, Inc.

Sirls, Felix. Switch & Sway. 2007. pap. 14.95 *(978-1-932263-35-0(7))* Meyer, Abbott Publishing.

Steel, Danielle. H. R. H. (ENG.). 2008. 336p. pap. 14.00 *(978-0-385-34253-7(5))* 2007. 416p. mass mkt. 7.99 *(978-0-440-24204-8(5))* Random House Publishing Group. (Dell).

Steyn, Johan. Father Michael's Lottery: A Novel of Africa. 2007. (ENG.). 424p. 26.95 *(978-0-9710598-7-0(X))* Schaffner Pr., Inc.

Taylor, Ashlyn Nicole. Sometimes We Fall. 2008. 255p. pap. 27.95 *(978-1-60610-632-7(5))* PublishAmerica, Inc.

Thomas, Teresa. The Beautiful Face of AIDS. 2007. pap. 9.00 *(978-0-8059-8472-9(0))* Dorrance Publishing Co., Inc.

TrinityJas. The Domino Series: Sherry Tate. 2008. 196p. pap. 13.95 *(978-0-7414-4374-8(0))* Infinity Publishing.

Vaughn, Novelist Shamontiel L. Round Trip. 2007. 215p. pap. 14.95 *(978-0-615-15615-6(0))* Vaughn, Shamontiel L.

West, R. Grantham. Ad 2040: Clear & Present Danger. 2011. 352p. 29.99 ***(978-1-4568-7777-4(1));*** pap. 19.99 ***(978-1-4568-7776-7(3))*** Xlibris Corp.

Wolf, Arnold. Chickenhawk. 2008. 390p. pap. 29.95 *(978-1-4241-7491-1(0))* PublishAmerica, Inc.

AIDS (DISEASE)—GOVERNMENT POLICY

Agbodzakey, James. Collaborative Governance & the Implementation of Ryan White Care Act. 2010. 252p. pap. *(978-3-8383-4699-1(8))* Lambert Academic Publishing.

Ayres, Jeffrey McKelvey & Siplon, Patricia D. Divergent Campaigns Towards Global Health Governance: Canadian & U.S. Approaches to the Global HIV/AIDS Pandemic. 2007. 52p. *(978-1-882582-58-7(6))* Canadian-American Ctr.

Brent, Robert J. Setting Priorities for HIV/AIDS Interventions: A Cost-Benefit Approach. 240p. 2011. pap. 20.00 *(978-0-85793-250-1(0))* 2010. (Illus.). 112.00 *(978-1-84720-331-1(0))* Elgar, Edward Publishing, Inc.

Brier, Jennifer. Infectious Ideas: U. S. Political Responses to the AIDS Crisis. (ENG., Illus.). 312p. 2011. pap. 22.95 *(978-0-8078-7211-6(3))* 2009. 36.95 *(978-0-8078-3314-8(2))* Univ. of North Carolina Pr.

Condon, Bradly J. Global Lessons from the AIDS Pandemic: Economic, Financial, Legal & Political Implications. 2008. (ENG., Illus.). xxvi, 366p. 159.00 *(978-3-540-78391-6(1),* 3540783911) Springer.

Condon, Bradly J. & Sinha, Tapen. Global Lessons from the AIDS Pandemic: Economic, Financial, Legal & Political Implications. 2010. (ENG., Illus.). xxvi, 366p. pap. 159.00 *(978-3-642-09712-6(X),* 364209712X) Springer.

Engh, Ida-Eline. Developing Capacity to Realise Socio-Economic Rights: The Example of the Right to Food in the Context of HIV/AIDS in South Africa & Uganda. 2008. 500p. pap. 110.75 *(978-90-5095-766-3(8))* Intersentia Uitgevers N.V. BEL. Dist: International Specialized Bk. Services.

Evans, Ruth & Becker, Saul. Children Caring for Parents with HIV & AIDS: Global Issues & Policy Responses. 2009. (Illus.). 368p. 85.00 *(978-1-84742-022-0(2));* pap. 39.95 *(978-1-84742-021-3(4))* Policy Pr. GBR. Dist: Chicago Distribution Ctr.

Fourie, Pieter. The Political Management of HIV & AIDS in South Africa: One Burden Too Many? 2006. (ENG., Illus.). 264p. 95.00 *(978-0-230-00667-6(1))* Palgrave Macmillan.

Geffen, Nathan. Debunking Delusions: The Inside Story of the Treatment Action Campaign. 2010. (ENG.). 256p. pap. 24.00 *(978-1-77009-781-0(3))* Jacana Media ZAF. Dist: Independent Pubs. Group.

Harman, Sophie. Governance of HIV/AIDS: Making Participation & Accountability Count. Harman, Sophie & Lisk, Franklyn, eds. 2009. (ENG., Illus.). 194p. 140.00 *(978-0-415-48564-7(9))* Routledge.

HIV Prevention: How Effective Is the President's Emergency Plan for AIDS Relief (PEPFAR): Hearing Before the Subcommittee on National Security, Emerging Threats, & International Relations of the Committee on Government Reform, House of Representatives, One Hundred Ninth Congress, Second Session, September 6, 2006. 2007. (Illus.). iii, 157p. *(978-0-16-079038-6(7),* 552-070-36148-1) United States Government Printing Office.

Hyde, Sandra Teresa. Eating Spring Rice: The Cultural Politics of AIDS in Southwest China. 2007. (Illus.). 271p. per. 26.95 *(978-0-520-24715-4(9));* 55.00 *(978-0-520-24714-7(0))* Univ. of California Pr.

Institute of Medicine Staff, creator. PEPFAR Implementation: Progress & Promise. 2007. (ENG., Illus.). 400p. 42.00 *(978-0-309-10982-6(5))* National Academies Pr.

Jensen, Lawrence T. Responding to HIV/AIDS: National Strategies, Plans & Programs. 2011. (Public Health in the 21st Century HIV/AIDS - Medical, Social & Psychological Aspects Ser.). 235p. 185.00 ***(978-1-61324-618-4(8))*** Nova Science Pubs., Inc.

Multi-Drug Resistant Tuberculosis: Assessing the U.S. Response to an Emerging Global Threat: Hearing Before the Subcommittee on Africa & Global Health of the Committee on Foreign Affairs, House of Representatives, One Hundred Tenth Congress, Second Session, February 27, 2008. 2008. iii, 55p. *(978-0-16-082429-6(X),* 552-070-38473-1) United States Government Printing Office.

Myrick, Darrell. The Voting Franchise & Government Spending forHIV/AIDS Policy: HIV/AIDS Policy in South Africa. 2008. 212p. pap. *(978-3-639-08878-6(6))* VDM Verlag Dr. Mueller e.K.

Nattrass, Nicoli. Mortal Combat: AIDS Denialism & the Struggle for Antiretrovirals in South Africa. 2007. (Illus.). 269p. (C). pap. 34.95 *(978-1-86914-132-5(6))* University of Kwazulu-Natal Press ZAF. Dist: International Specialized Bk. Services.

The Next Phase of the Global Fight Against HIV/AIDS: Hearing Before the Committee on Foreign Relations, United States Senate, One Hundred Tenth Congress, First Session, October 24, 2007. 2008. iii, 49p. *(978-0-16-080290-4(3),* 552-070-36985-6) United States Government Printing Office.

Nunn, Amy. The Politics & History of AIDS Treatment in Brazil. 2009. (Illus.). 260p. 79.95 *(978-0-387-09617-9(5))* Springer.

Patterson, Amy S. The Politics of AIDS in Africa. 2006. (Challenge & Change in African Politics Ser.). (Illus.). (C). 200p. lib. bdg. 49.95 *(978-1-58826-452-7(1));* 226p. pap. 22.00 *(978-1-58826-477-0(7))* Rienner, Lynne Pubs.

PEPFAR: An Assessment of Progress & Challenges: Hearing Before the Committee on Foreign Affairs, House of Representatives, One Hundred Tenth Congress, First Session, April 24, 2007. 2007. iii, 46p. *(978-0-16-079052-2(2),* 552-070-36158-8) United States Government Printing Office.

PEPFAR Reauthorization: From Emergency to Sustainability: Hearing Before the Committee on Foreign Affairs, House of Representatives, One Hundred Tenth Congress, First Session, September 25, 2007. 2007. (Illus.). iii, 87p. *(978-0-16-079845-0(0),* 552-070-36739-0) United States Government Printing Office.

Seckinelgin, Hakan. International Politics of Hiv/Aids. 2007. XII, 196p. 37.95 *(978-0-415-41384-8(2))* Routledge.

—International Politics of HIV/AIDS: Global Disease-Local Pain. 2007. 193p. 150.00 *(978-0-415-41383-1(4))* Routledge.

Sonntag, Diana. AIDS & Aid: A Public Good Approach. 2010. (Contributions to Economics Ser.). (ENG.). xii, 200p. 119.00 *(978-3-7908-2418-6(6),* 3790824186) Physica-Verlag DEU. Dist: Springer.

Thom, Hakan & Foller, -Lis, eds. The Politics of AIDS: Globalization, the State & Civil Society. 2008. (ENG., Illus.). 368p. 121.00 *(978-0-230-55402-3(4))* Palgrave Macmillan.

Williams, Mary E. AIDS. 2011. (Introducing Issues with Opposing Viewpoints Ser.). 144p. lib. bdg. 35.75 *(978-0-7377-5197-0(5),* Greenhaven Pr., Inc.) Cengage Gale.

Youde, Jeremy. AIDS South Africa & the Politics of Knowledge. 2007. (Global Health Ser.). 166p. 114.95 *(978-0-7546-7003-2(1))* Ashgate Publishing Co.

AIDS (DISEASE)—HISTORY

Engel, Jonathan. The Epidemic: A Global History of AIDS. 2006. (Illus.). 400p. 28.95 *(978-0-06-114488-2(6))* Smithsonian Institution Pr.

Harden, Victoria A. AIDS At 30: A History. 2012. (Illus.). 340p. 29.95 *(978-1-59797-294-9(0))* Potomac Bks., Inc.

Lawson, Lesley. Side Effects: The Story of AIDS in South Africa. 2008. 352p. pap. 22.95 *(978-1-77013-067-8(5))* Double Storey Bks. ZAF. Dist: International Publishers Marketing.

AIDS (DISEASE)—LAW AND LEGISLATION

Ayalew, Mulugeta. Consensual Sex & Hiv/Aids. 2010. 88p. pap. *(978-3-639-22831-1(6))* VDM Verlag Dr. Mueller e.K.

Chalmers, James. Legal Responses to HIV & AIDS. 2008. 174p. (C). pap. 62.00 *(978-1-84113-726-1(X))* Hart Publishing Ltd. GBR. Dist: International Specialized Bk. Services.

Condon, Bradly J. Global Lessons from the AIDS Pandemic: Economic, Financial, Legal & Political Implications. 2008. (ENG., Illus.). xxvi, 366p. 159.00 *(978-3-540-78391-6(1),* 3540783911) Springer.

Condon, Bradly J. & Sinha, Tapen. Global Lessons from the AIDS Pandemic: Economic, Financial, Legal & Political Implications. 2010. (ENG., Illus.). xxvi, 366p. pap. 159.00 *(978-3-642-09712-6(X),* 364209712X) Springer.

Gable, Lance, et al. Legal Aspects of HIV/AIDS: A Guide for Policy & Law Reform. 2007. (Law, Justice, & Development Ser.). (ENG.). 246p. per. 22.00 *(978-0-8213-7105-3(3),* 9780821371053) World Bank Pubns.

Jasper, Margaret C. AIDS Law. 3rd ed. 2008. (Legal Almanac Ser.). (ENG., Illus.). 208p. 47.00 *(978-0-19-537617-3(X))* Oxford Univ. Pr., Inc.

Weait Matthew. Intimacy & Responsibility: The Criminalisation of HIV Transmission. 2007. 224p. 57.95 *(978-1-904385-70-7(2));* 170.00 *(978-1-904385-71-4(0))* Taylor & Francis Group GBR. (Routledge Cavendish). Dist: Taylor & Francis Group.

Webber, David W. AIDS & the Law. 4th ed. 2007. ring bd. 299.00 *(978-0-7355-6198-4(2),* Aspen Pubs.) Wolters Kluwer Law & Business.

AIDS (DISEASE)—MORAL AND ETHICAL ASPECTS

Alkier, Stefan & Dronsch, Kristina, eds. HIV/Aids - Ethische Perspektiven. 2009. (GER.). XXX, 388p. 81.00 *(978-3-11-020715-6(X))* De Gruyter, Walter Inc.

Haslam, Edward T. Dr. Mary's Monkey: How the Unsolved Murder of a Doctor, a Secret Laboratory in New Orleans & Cancer-Causing Monkey Viruses Are Linked to Lee Harvey Oswald, the JFK Assassination & Emerging Global Epidemics. 2007. (ENG., Illus.). 275p. pap. 19.95 *(978-0-9777953-0-7(6))* Trine Day.

Kopelman, Loretta M. & Van Niekerk, Anton A., eds. Ethics & AIDS in Africa: The Challenge to Our Thinking. 2006. (ENG., Illus.). 240p. pap. 34.95 *(978-1-59874-071-4(7))* Left Coast Pr., Inc.

Loue, Sana & Pike, Earl C., eds. Case Studies in Ethics & HIV Research. 2007. (ENG., Illus.). xii, 344p. 64.95 *(978-0-387-71361-8(1),* 0387713611) Springer.

Van Niekerk, Anton A. Ethics & AIDS in Africa. Kopelman, Loretta M., ed. 2006. (ENG., Illus.). 240p. 94.00 *(978-1-59874-070-7(9))* Left Coast Pr., Inc.

AIDS (DISEASE)—NURSING

Association of Nurses in AIDS Care (ANAC). ANAC's Core Curriculum for HIV / AIDS Nursing. 3rd rev. ed. 2009. 444p. pap. 83.95 *(978-0-7637-5459-4(5))* Jones & Bartlett Learning, LLC.

Association of Nurses in AIDS Care Staff & American Nurses Association Staff, contrib. by. HIV/AIDS Nursing: Scope & Standards of Practice. 2006. pap. *(978-1-55810-236-1(1))* American Nurses Publishing.

Claxton, Rosie & Harrison, Tony, eds. Caring for Children with HIV & AIDS. (Illus.). 224p. pap. *(978-0-340-55256-8(5),* Hodder Arnold) Hodder Education.

Clumeck, N. & Friedland, G. Handbook of Medical Supportive Care of AIDS Patients. Date not set. (Basic & Clinical Oncology Ser.). *(978-0-8247-9299-2(8))* Dekker, Marcel Inc.

Cram101 Textbook Reviews & Cram101 Textbook Reviews. Outlines & Highlights for Anacs Core Curriculum for Hiv / Aids Nursing by Association of Nurses in Aids Care. 2011. 120p. pap. 28.95 ***(978-1-61830-111-6(0))*** Cram101 Inc.

Lashley, Felissa R. & Durham, Jerry D. The Person with HIV/AIDS: Nursing Perspectives. 4th ed. 2009. (Illus.). xvii, 644p. 60.00 *(978-0-8261-2137-0(3))* Springer Publishing Co., Inc.

Minnaar, Ansie & Bodkin, Candice. The Pocket Guide for HIV & AIDS Nursing Care. 2007. (ENG., Illus.). 256p. pap. 31.95 *(978-0-7021-7193-2(X))* Juta Academic ZAF. Dist: Independent Pubs. Group.

Pratt, Robert J. HIV & AIDS: A Strategy for Nursing Care. 4th rev. ed. (ENG., Illus.). 488p. *(978-0-340-59233-5(8),* Hodder Arnold) Hodder Education.

Zelnick, Jennifer R. Who Is Nursing Them? It Is Us: Neoliberalism, HIV/AIDS, & the Occupational Health & Safety of South African Public Sector Nurses. 2011. (ENG., Illus.). 206p. 45.95 *(978-0-89503-327-7(5))* Baywood Publishing Co., Inc.

AIDS (DISEASE)—NUTRITIONAL ASPECTS

Hendricks, Kristy M., et al. Nutrition Management of HIV & AIDS. 2009. xii, 180p. *(978-0-88091-413-0(0))* Academy of Nutrition & Dietetics.

HIV & Nutrition. 2007. pap. *(978-3-8055-8279-7(X))* Karger, S. AG.

Tshuma, Ndumiso. Intergrating Nutrition & Hiv Programmes. 2011. 120p. pap. ***(978-3-8443-9809-0(0))*** Lambert Academic Publishing.

AIDS (DISEASE)—PATIENTS

see also Children of AIDS Patients

Abraham, Dawit & Berhane, Yemane. Assessment of Quality of Vct Services in Addis Ababa, Ethiopi. 2010. 108p. pap. *(978-3-639-23794-8(3))* VDM Verlag Dr. Mueller e.K.

Agbodzakey, James. Collaborative Governance & the Implementation of Ryan White Care Act. 2010. 252p. pap. *(978-3-8383-4699-1(8))* Lambert Academic Publishing.

Alexandrova, Anna, ed. Mobilizing Civil Society's Response to Stigma & Discrimination in Central Asia. 2007. (Sourcebook on Contemporary Controversies Ser.). (ENG., Illus.). 178p. pap. 24.95 *(978-1-932716-34-4(3))* International Debate Education Assn.

Anonymus. Quicksand: HIV/AIDS in Our Lives. 2009. (ENG., Illus.). 112p. (YA). (gr. 5). 16.99 *(978-0-7636-1589-5(7))* Candlewick Pr.

Ashton, Paul J. Etched in Hope: A Weekly Journal for Those Living with or Affected by HIV/AIDS. 2007. (Illus.). 112p. per. 9.95 *(978-0-87946-344-1(9))* ACTA Pubns.

Binaté Fofana, Namizata. Efficacy of micro-financing women's activities in Côte D'Ivoire: Evidence from rural areas & HIV/AIDS-affected Women. 2010. (AWLAE Ser.: 8). 208p. pap. 57.00 *(978-90-8686-125-5(3))* Wageningen Academic Publishers NLD. Dist: Enfield Publishing & Distribution Co., Inc.

Chambré, Susan Maizel. Fighting for Our Lives: New York's AIDS Community & the Politics of Disease. 2006. (Critical Issues in Health & Medicine Ser.). (ENG.). 280p. 68.00 *(978-0-8135-3866-2(1))* Rutgers Univ. Pr.

Chambre, Susan Maizel. Fighting for Our Lives: New York's AIDS Community & the Politics of Disease. annot. ed. 2006. (Critical Issues in Health & Medicine Ser.). (ENG.). 280p. per. 24.95 *(978-0-8135-3867-9(X))* Rutgers Univ. Pr.

Cichocki, Mark. Living with HIV: A Patient's Guide. 2009. (McFarland Health Topics Ser.). (ENG.). 257p. pap. 35.00 *(978-0-7864-3921-8(1))* McFarland & Co., Inc. Pubs.

Clumeck, N. & Friedland, G. Handbook of Medical Supportive Care of AIDS Patients. Date not set. (Basic & Clinical Oncology Ser.). *(978-0-8247-9299-2(8))* Dekker, Marcel Inc.

Cohen, Mary Ann & Gorman, Jack M., eds. Comprehensive Textbook of AIDS Psychiatry. 2007. (ENG., Illus.). 800p. 98.50 *(978-0-19-530435-0(7))* Oxford Univ. Pr., Inc.

Cohen, Mary Ann, et al. Handbook of AIDS Psychiatry. 2010. (ENG., Illus.). 400p. 54.95 *(978-0-19-537257-1(3))* Oxford Univ. Pr., Inc.

Committee on HIV Screening and Access to Care & Institute of Medicine. HIV Screening & Access to Care: Exploring Barriers & Facilitators to Expanded HIV Testing. 2010. (ENG.). 96p. pap. 21.00 *(978-0-309-15661-5(0))* National Academies Pr.

—HIV Screening & Access to Care: Exploring the Impact of Policies on Access to & Provision of HIV Care. 2011. (ENG.). 100p. pap. 30.00 *(978-0-309-16419-1(2))* National Academies Pr.

—HIV Screening & Access to Care: Health Care System Capacity for Increased HIV Testing & Provision of Care. 2011. (ENG.). 114p. pap. 30.00 *(978-0-309-18507-3(6))* National Academies Pr.

Corvinelli, Antonietta. Boredom in Recovery from Substance Use Disorder. 2009. 144p. pap. *(978-3-639-16364-3(8))* VDM Verlag Dr. Mueller e.K.

Diefenbach. Andrea Diefenbach Aids in Odessa. 2008. (ENG., Illus.). 160p. 45.00 *(978-3-7757-2158-5(4))* Hatje Cantz Verlag GmbH & Co KG DEU. Dist: D.A.P./Distributed Art Pubs.

Edkins, Don & Vehkalahti, Iikka. Steps by Steps. 2009. (ENG., Illus.). 240p. pap. 26.00 *(978-1-920196-09-7(9))* Jacana Media ZAF. Dist: Independent Pubs. Group.

Evian, Clive. Primary HIV/AIDS Care: A Practical Guide for Primary Care Personnel in a Clinical & Supportive Setting. 4th ed. 2007. (ENG.). 350p. per. 49.95 *(978-1-77009-198-6(X))* Jacana Media ZAF. Dist: Independent Pubs. Group.

Gable, Lance, et al. Legal Aspects of HIV/AIDS: A Guide for Policy & Law Reform. 2007. (Law, Justice, & Development Ser.). (ENG.). 246p. per. 22.00 *(978-0-8213-7105-3(3),* 9780821371053) World Bank Pubns.

Gobina, Ronald. Lymphomas in Hiv Patients. 2011. 100p. pap. ***(978-3-8443-1411-3(3))*** Lambert Academic Publishing.

HIV: Issues with Mental Health & Illness. 2007. (ENG., Illus.). 180p. 116.00 *(978-0-7890-3409-0(3));* per. 54.50 *(978-0-7890-3410-6(7))* Routledge.

HIV/AIDS Bureau (U.S.) & Health Resources and Services Administration (U.S.), eds. Guide for HIV/AIDS Clinical Care. 2011. (ENG.). 619p. spiral bd. 55.00 ***(978-0-16-087205-1(7),*** Health & Human Services Dept.) United States Government Printing Office.

Kakuru, Doris Muhwezi. The Combat for Gender Equality in Education: Rural Livelihood Pathways in the Context of HIV/AIDS. 2006. (AWLAE Ser.). 224p. pap. 39.00 *(978-90-8686-015-9(X))* Wageningen Academic Publishers NLD. Dist: Enfield Publishing & Distribution Co., Inc.

Karim, Salim Abdool & Karim, Quarraisha Abdool, eds. HIV/AIDS in South Africa. 2nd rev. ed. 2010. (Illus.). 608p. pap. 75.00 *(978-0-521-14793-4(X))* Cambridge Univ. Pr.

Katyal, Veena, et al, eds. Healthcare Management in India: Psycho-Social & Neurological Aspects of HIV/AIDS & Other Physical & Mental Disorders. 2010. 349p. 84.25 *(978-81-7708-244-9(2))* New Century Publications IND. Dist: International Specialized Bk. Services.

Keesee, Marguerite. The Relationship Between Strain, Hiv/Aids Risk- Behavior & Adherence. 2009. 168p. pap. *(978-3-639-12911-3(3))* VDM Verlag Dr. Mueller e.K.

Klaits, Frederick. Death in a Church of Life: Moral Passion During Botswana's Time of AIDS. 2010. (Anthropology of Christianity Ser.). (ENG., Illus.). 368p. pap. 25.95 *(978-0-520-25966-9(1))* Univ. of California Pr.

—Death in a Church of Life: Moral Passion During Botswana's Time of AIDS. 2010. (Anthropology of Christianity Ser.). (ENG., Illus.). 368p. 60.00 (978-0-520-25965-2(3)) Univ. of California Pr.

Lune, Howard. Urban Action Networks: HIV/AIDS & Community Organizing in New York City. 2006. (ENG.). 240p. 92.00 (978-0-7425-4083-5(9)); (Illus.). per. 30.95 (978-0-7425-4084-2(7)) Rowman & Littlefield Publishers, Inc.

Matoane, Matshepo. From Theory to Practice. 2009. 136p. pap. (978-3-639-16661-3(2)) VDM Verlag Dr. Mueller e.K.

McMickle, Marvin Andrew. A Time to Speak: How Black Pastors Can Respond to the HIV/AIDS Pandemic. 2008. 176p. 20.00 (978-0-8298-1803-1(0)) Pilgrim Pr., The/United Church Pr.

Munro, Ian. The Lived Experience of Gay Men Caring for Others with Hiv/Aids. 2008. 324p. pap. (978-3-639-03581-0(X)) VDM Verlag Dr. Mueller e.K.

Musisi, Seggane & Kinyanda, Eugene. Psychiatric Problems of HIV/AIDS & Their Management in Africa. (Illus.). xvii, 369p. (978-9970-02-734-7(4)) Fountain Pubs. Ltd.

O'Neal, Cynthia. Talk Softly: A Memoir. 2010. (ENG.). 240p. 22.00 (978-1-58322-906-4(X)) Seven Stories Pr.

Outreach & Care Approaches to HIV/AIDS along the US-Mexico Border. 2006. (ENG., Illus.). 190p. 116.00 (978-0-7890-3466-3(2)); per. 50.50 (978-0-7890-3467-0(0)) Routledge.

Patton, Lauren L. Clinician's Guide to Treatment of HIV-infected Patients. 2009. 37p. 29.95 (978-1-936176-00-7(9)) American Academy of Oral Medicine.

Payne Foster, Pamela. Is there a Balm in Black America?: Perspectives on HIV/AIDS in the African American Community. 2007. 312p. per. 19.99 (978-1-4303-1670-1(5)) Lulu Enterprises Inc.

PEPFAR: From Emergency to Sustainability & Advances Against HIV/AIDS: Hearing Before the Committee on Foreign Affairs, House of Representatives, One Hundred Eleventh Congress, Second Session, September 29, 2010. 2010. iii, 141p. **(978-0-16-087680-6(X)**, 552-070-42232-3) United States Government Printing Office.

Rohleder, Poul, et al, eds. HIV/AIDS in South Africa 25 Years On: A Psychosocial Perspective. 2009. (ENG., Illus.). xix, 393p. 159.00 (978-1-4419-0305-1(4), 1441903054) Springer.

Simbayi, Leickness. The Impact of & Responses to HIV/AIDS in the Private Security & Legal Services Industry in South Africa. 2009. (ENG.). 192p. pap. 19.95 (978-0-7969-2205-2(5)) Human Sciences Research Council ZAF. Dist: Independent Pubs. Group.

Sonntag, Diana. AIDS & Aid: A Public Good Approach. 2010. (Contributions to Economics Ser.). (ENG.). xii, 209p. 119.00 (978-3-7908-2418-6(6), 3790824186) Physica-Verlag DEU. Dist: Springer.

Stone, Valerie, et al, eds. HIV/AIDS in U. S. Communities of Color. 2009. (ENG., Illus.). x, 310p. 89.95 (978-0-387-98151-2(9), 0387981519) Springer.

Tutu, Desmond, pref. Access to Life. 2009. (ENG., Illus.). 310p. 49.95 (978-1-59711-105-8(8)) Aperture Foundation, Inc.

UNAIDS. CD-ROM Report on the Global AIDS Epidemic & Document Library: Multilingual English/French/Spanish/Russian. 2009. (UNAIDS Product Ser.). (ENG & FRE.). cd-rom 36.00 (978-92-9173-808-3(5)) World Health Organization.

United Nations. Handbook on HIV & Human Rights for National Human Rights Institutions. 2007. (ENG.). 52p. pap. 20.00 (978-92-1-154181-6(6)) United Nations Pubns.

United States, Congress Senate Committee on Homeland Security and Governmental Affairs Subcommittee on Federal Financial Management, Government Information, and International Security Staff, contrib. by. Ensuring Early Diagnosis & Access to Treatment for HIV/AIDS: Can Federal Resources Be More Effectively Targeted?: Hearing Before the Federal Financial Management, Government Information, & International Security Subcommittee of the Committee on Homeland Security & Governmental Affairs, United States Senate, One Hundred Ninth Congress, Second Session, April 26, 2006. 2007. (Illus.). iii, 385p. (978-0-16-078419-4(0), 552-070-35715-7) United States Government Printing Office.

Vass, Jocelyn & Phakathi, Sizwe. Managing HIV in the Workplace: Learning from SMEs. 2007. (Hsrc Research Monograph Ser.). (ENG., Illus.). 104p. pap. 21.95 (978-0-7969-2161-1(X)) Human Sciences Research Council ZAF. Dist: Independent Pubs. Group.

Venus, Perez. I'm Still Here: The History, Testimony, Education, Outcomes, & Strengths of people Living with HIV/AIDS. 2006. (Illus.). 147p. per. 16.50 (978-1-4251-0059-9(7)) Trafford Publishing.

Waring, Marilyn, et al, eds. Who Cares? The Economics of Dignity. 2011. (ENG., Illus.). 200p. pap. 24.95 (978-1-84929-019-7(9)) Commonwealth Secretariat GBR. Dist: Stylus Publishing, LLC.

Wealt Matthew. Intimacy & Responsibility: The Criminalisation of HIV Transmission. 2007. 224p. 57.95 (978-1-904385-70-7(2)); 170.00 (978-1-904385-71-4(0)) Taylor & Francis Group GBR. (Routledge Cavendish). Dist: Taylor & Francis Group.

World Bank Staff. Corporate Responses to HIV/AIDS: Case Studies from India. 2007. (Books Ser.). (ENG., Illus.). 88p. per. 15.00 (978-0-8213-7171-8(1), 9780821371718) World Bank Pubns.

World Health Organization. HIV Stand up for Human Rights. 2011. (Nonserial Publication Ser.). (Illus.). 16p. pap. 6.00 (978-92-4-159991-7(X)) World Health Organization.

Zulu, Princess Kasune. Warrior Princess: Fighting for Life with Courage & Hope. 2009. (ENG.). 272p. 22.00 (978-0-8308-3725-0(6), IVP Bks.) InterVarsity Pr.

AIDS (DISEASE)—PATIENTS—BIOGRAPHY

Beaupre, Norman R. Before All Dignity Is Lost. 2006. pap. 9.95 (978-1-59526-620-0(8)) Aeon Publishing Inc.

Brand, Alan. Positively Alive: Living with HIV & AIDS: A Path to Inner Healing. 2006. (ENG., Illus.). 152p. per. 24.95 (978-1-77009-130-6(0)) Jacana Media ZAF. Dist: Independent Pubs. Group.

Brown, Marvelyn & Martin, Courtney. The Naked Truth: Young, Beautiful, & (HIV) Positive. 2008. 176p. pap. 14.99 (978-0-06-156239-6(4), Harper Paperbacks) HarperCollins Pubs.

Castagnier, Stephanie. Fear to Fire: My Life as an AIDS Orphan. 2007. 124p. per. 13.95 (978-0-595-43304-9(9)) iUniverse, Inc.

Charbonneau, Paul. Why Me? 2010. 132p. pap. 19.99 (978-1-4500-6583-2(X)) Xlibris Corp.

Davis, Scott M. Living Jonathan's Life: A Doctor's Descent into Darkness & Addiction. 2008. (ENG.). 260p. pap. 14.95 (978-0-7573-0649-5(7)) Health Communications, Inc.

Duve, Pascal de. Cargo Vie. (FRE.). 192p. (978-2-7096-1058-2(2)) Lattes, Jean-Claude Editions.

Fisher, TerryAnn & Michaels, Troy. Conversations with My Son: A Diary. 2010. 156p. 23.95 (978-1-4502-3002-5(4)); pap. 13.95 (978-1-4502-2997-5(2)) iUniverse, Inc.

Greene, Melissa Fay. There Is No Me Without You: One Woman's Odyssey to Rescue Africa's Children. 2006. (ENG., Illus.). 480p. 25.95 (978-1-59691-116-1(6)) Bloomsbury Publishing.

—There Is No Me Without You: One Woman's Odyssey to Rescue Her Country's Children. 2007. (ENG., Illus.). 480p. per. 17.00 (978-1-59691-293-9(6)) Bloomsbury Publishing.

Hofmann, Regan. I Have Something to Tell You: A Memoir. 304p. 2011. pap. 15.00 (978-1-4165-9861-9(8)) 2009. (ENG.). 23.00 (978-1-4165-9859-6(6)) Atria Bks. (Beyond Words/Atria Bks.).

Inuwa, Jibrin Idris. My Predicament: A Struggle with HIV. 2011. 274p. pap. 16.95 **(978-1-60976-181-3(2)**, Strategic Bk. Publishing) AEG Literary Publishing Services, Inc.

Jaboro, Majemite. The Ikoyi Prison Narratives: the Spiritualism & Political Philosophy of Fela Kuti. 2009. 199p. pap. 15.50 (978-1-4452-2626-2(X)) Lulu Enterprises Inc.

Jarman, Derek. At Your Own Risk: A Saint's Testament. 2010. (ENG.). 160p. pap. 18.95 (978-0-8166-6592-1(3)) Univ. of Minnesota Pr.

—Smiling in Slow Motion. 2011. (Illus.). 400p. pap. 18.95 (978-0-8166-7453-4(1)) Univ. of Minnesota Pr.

Kearns, Michael. Lasting Connections: Two Plays That Survived the Plague. 2009. 128p. pap. 18.69 (978-0-325-02159-1(7), E02159) Heinemann.

Kudrako, Ron. More Than a Wheelchair, More Than Hiv: Overcoming PML. 2009. 476p. 32.95 (978-1-4490-0330-2(3)); pap. 23.95 (978-1-4490-0331-9(1)) AuthorHouse.

Lambert, Lola. The Brothers Three. 2008. 60p. per. 15.99 (978-1-4363-0182-4(3)) Xlibris Corp.

Margretson, Ngong. Homo Invitus: Memoirs of a Genie. 2011. 58p. pap. 15.99 **(978-1-4628-5754-8(X))** Xlibris Corp.

McColly, Michael. The After-Death Room: Journey into Spiritual Activism. 2006. (ENG.). 384p. per. 15.95 (978-1-932360-92-9(1)) Counterpoint LLC.

McGregor, Liz. Khabzela: The Life & Times of a South African. 2007. (ENG.). 252p. pap. 29.95 (978-1-77009-080-4(0)) Jacana Media ZAF. Dist: Independent Pubs. Group.

Mills, J'Korey. I'm Not Going Mad, I'm Just Coming into Myself, after Living Through Dying Places. 2011. 200p. pap. 16.95 (978-1-4620-0018-0(5)) iUniverse, Inc.

My Story. 2009. 48p. pap. (978-0-217-25999-6(5)) Books LLC.

Nolen, Stephanie. 28: Stories of AIDS in Africa. 2008. (ENG., Illus.). 384p. pap. 15.99 (978-0-8027-1675-0(X)) Walker & Co.

Open Door Clinic, creator. The Legacy Campaign: Personal Accounts of Lives Forever Changed When Diagnosed with HIV/AIDS. 2006. (ENG.). 227p. per. 15.00 (978-0-9789461-0-4(3)) His Rose, Inc.

Pearson, Carol Lynn. Goodbye, I Love You. 2006. 199p. per. 13.99 (978-1-55517-984-7(3)) Cedar Fort, Inc./CFI Distribution.

RODRIGUEZ SORIANO, Maribel. Freddie mercury con la fuerza de un HuracÁn. 2008. 208p. pap. 31.95 (978-1-4092-1180-8(0)) Lulu Enterprises Inc.

Roston, Miles. Taking Away the Distance: A Young Orphan's Journey & the AIDS Epidemic in Africa. 2007. (ENG.). 272p. per. 15.95 (978-0-7867-2082-8(4)) Basic Bks.

Selvage, Ray. Living with the Virus. 2011. pap. 12.99 **(978-1-61777-537-6(1))** Tate Publishing & Enterprises, LLC.

Somuah, Yaa Serwaa. Celebrating God. 2009. 124p. pap. 19.99 (978-1-4415-0346-6(3)) Xlibris Corp.

Stanford, Shane. A Positive Life: Living with HIV as a Pastor, Husband, & Father, 1 vol. 2010. (ENG.). 224p. 19.99 (978-0-310-29292-0(1)) Zondervan.

Sugar, Jennifer & Nelson, Jill C. John Holmes, a Life Measured in Inches. 2008. 584p. pap. 29.95 (978-1-59393-302-9(9)) BearManor Media.

Torgerson, Martha. Mom-He Is Gay & Has Aids: Six Words that Forever Changed my Life. 2011. 80p. pap. 10.95 **(978-1-4327-6640-5(6))** Outskirts Pr., Inc.

Walker, D. Felecia. From Better to Worse: A Memoir of Unconditional Love. 2007. 223p. per. 14.99 (978-1-933725-06-2(0)) Premium Pr. America.

Wilson, Debbie. Brushing Away the Tears. 2009. 200p. pap. 11.95 (978-1-935118-76-3(5)) Bellissima Publishing, LLC.

Wirz, Mario. It's Late, I Can't Breathe: A Nocturnal Narrative. Meyer, Alfred G., ed. 2007. 131p. pap. 12.95 (978-0-9788691-1-3(7)) Meyer, G. Bks.

AIDS (DISEASE)—PATIENTS—FAMILY RELATIONSHIPS

Brookshire, Lajoyce. Faith under Fire: Betrayed by a Thing Called Love. 2009. (ENG.). 272p. pap. 15.00 (978-1-4165-9601-1(1), Gallery Books/Karen Hunter Publishing) Gallery Books/Karen Hunter Publishing.

Dow, Unity & Essex, Max. Saturday Is for Funerals. 2010. 240p. 19.95 (978-0-674-05077-8(0)) Harvard Univ. Pr.

Roth, Marco. The Scientists: A Family Romance, 1 vol. 2012. (ENG.). 208p. 23.00 **(978-0-374-21028-1(4))** Farrar, Straus & Giroux.

United Nations Children's Fund. Caring for Children Affected by HIV & AIDS. 2008. (Insight Innocenti Ser.). (Illus.). 56p. pap. 20.00 (978-88-89129-48-7(4)) United Nations Children's Fund, The (UNICEF).

AIDS (DISEASE)—PERSONAL NARRATIVES

see AIDS (Disease)—Patients—Biography

AIDS (DISEASE)—POETRY

Cowan, Derik. Yearning/the Album of Ecstasy & Agony. 2008. 94p. pap. 10.99 (978-0-557-00239-9(7)) Lulu Enterprises Inc.

Myers, Sonia P. Too Close to Home: AIDS/Violence, 1 vol. 2009. 76p. pap. 16.95 (978-1-60813-791-6(0)) PublishAmerica, Inc.

AIDS (DISEASE)—POLITICAL ASPECTS

Biehl, João. Will to Live: AIDS Therapies & the Politics of Survival. 2007. (In-Formation Ser.). (Illus.). 466p. 32.95 (978-0-691-13008-8(6)) Princeton Univ. Pr.

Brier, Jennifer. Infectious Ideas: U. S. Political Responses to the AIDS Crisis. (ENG., Illus.). 312p. 2011. pap. 22.95 (978-0-8078-7211-6(3)) 2009. 36.95 (978-0-8078-3314-8(2)) Univ. of North Carolina Pr.

Brown, Dan, ed. Is AIDS Genocide? Reflections Associated with Canada's Stephen Lewis Related to the Workings of Capitalist Corporate Globalization. 2006. per. (978-1-897318-11-9(1), Canadian National Newspaper, The) Agora Publishing Consortium.

Chambré, Susan Maizel. Fighting for Our Lives: New York's AIDS Community & the Politics of Disease. 2006. (Critical Issues in Health & Medicine Ser.). (ENG.). 280p. 68.00 (978-0-8135-3866-2(1)) Rutgers Univ. Pr.

Chambre, Susan Maizel. Fighting for Our Lives: New York's AIDS Community & the Politics of Disease. annot. ed. 2006. (Critical Issues in Health & Medicine Ser.). (ENG.). 280p. per. 24.95 (978-0-8135-3867-9(X)) Rutgers Univ. Pr.

Chirambo, Kondwani. The Political Cost of AIDS in Africa: An Overview. 2008. 84p. pap. (978-1-920118-66-2(7)) IDASA Pubs. ZAF. Dist: Michigan State Univ. Pr.

Chirambo, Kondwani, ed. The Political Cost of Aids in Africa Evidence from Six Countries. 2008. 408p. (C). pap. (978-1-920118-65-5(9)) IDASA Pubs. ZAF. Dist: Michigan State Univ. Pr.

Cullinan, Kerry & Thom, Anso, eds. The Virus, Vitamins & Vegetables: The South African HIV/AIDS Mystery. 2010. (ENG.). 211p. pap. 21.00 (978-1-77009-691-2(4)) Jacana Media ZAF. Dist: Independent Pubs. Group.

de Waal, Alex. AIDS & Power: Why There Is No Political Crisis - Yet. 2006. (African Arguments Ser.). (ENG., Illus.). 176p. 75.95 (978-1-84277-706-0(8)); per. 23.95 (978-1-84277-707-7(6)) Zed Bks., Ltd. GBR. Dist: Macmillan.

De Waal, Alexander, et al. HIV/AIDS, Security, & Conflict: New Realities, New Responses: AIDS, Security, & Conflict Initiative. 2010. (978-0-9841257-9-1(5)) Ashgate Publishing, Ltd.

—VIH/SIDA, Seguridad y Conflictos: Nuevas Realidades, Nuevas Respuestas Iniciativa SIDA, Seguridad y Conflictos. 2010. (978-0-9841257-6-0(0)) Ashgate Publishing, Ltd.

Elbe, Stefan. Virus Alert: Security, Governmentality, & the AIDS Pandemic. 2009. (ENG., Illus.). 224p. (gr. 17). 45.00 (978-0-231-14868-9(2)) Columbia Univ. Pr.

Flint, Adrian. HIV/AIDS in Sub-Saharan Africa: Politics, Aid & Globalization. 2011. (ENG., Illus.). 240p. 85.00 (978-0-230-22142-0(4)) Palgrave Macmillan.

Geffen, Nathan. Debunking Delusions: The Inside Story of the Treatment Action Campaign. 2010. (ENG.). 256p. pap. 24.00 (978-1-77009-781-0(3)) Jacana Media ZAF. Dist: Independent Pubs. Group.

Gould, Deborah B. Moving Politics: Emotion & ACT up's Fight against AIDS. 2009. (ENG., Illus.). 536p. 65.00 (978-0-226-30529-5(5)); pap. 23.00 (978-0-226-30530-1(9)) Univ. of Chicago Pr.

Kirp. AIDS in the Industrialized Democracies: Passions, Politics & Policies. 408p. (978-0-7735-0956-6(9)) McGill-Queen's Univ. Pr.

Kontaratos, Nikolas. DISSECTING a DISCOVERY. 2007. (ENG.). 404p. 34.99 (978-1-4257-0628-9(2)); per. 14.00 (978-1-4257-0627-2(4)) Xlibris Corp.

Lieberman, Evan & Lieberman, Evan S. Boundaries of Contagion: How Ethnic Politics Have Shaped Government Responses to AIDS. 2009. (ENG., Illus.). 368p. (C). 70.00 (978-0-691-13286-0(0)) Princeton Univ. Pr.

—Boundaries of Contagion: How Ethnic Politics Have Shaped Government Responses to AIDS. 2009. (ENG., Illus.). 368p. (C). pap. 26.95 (978-0-691-14019-3(7)) Princeton Univ. Pr.

Nattrass, Nicoli. Mortal Combat: AIDS Denialism & the Struggle for Antiretrovirals in South Africa. 2007. (Illus.). 269p. (C). pap. 34.95 (978-1-86914-132-5(6)) University of Kwazulu-Natal Press ZAF. Dist: International Specialized Bk. Services.

Ntarangwi, Mwenda, et al, eds. African Anthropologies: History, Critique & Practice. 2006. (Africa in the New Millennium Ser.). (ENG.). 256p. 123.95 (978-1-84277-762-6(9)); per. 34.95 (978-1-84277-763-3(7)) Zed Bks., Ltd. GBR. Dist: Macmillan.

Seckinelgin, Hakan. International Politics of Hiv/Aids. 2007. XII, 196p. 37.95 (978-0-415-41384-8(2)) Routledge.

Shilts, Randy. And the Band Played On: Politics, People & the AIDS Epidemic. 2nd rev. anniv. ed. 2007. (ENG.). 656p. pap. 18.99 (978-0-312-37463-1(1), St. Martin's Griffin) St. Martin's Pr.

Wambui, Henry Kiragu. The Politics of HIV / AIDS & Implications for Democracy in Kenya. 2006. 256p. (978-0-7734-5649-5(X)) Mellen, Edwin Pr., The.

White, Renee T., et al. HIV/AIDS: Global Frontiers in Prevention/Intervention. (Illus.). 2008. (ENG.). 600p. 155.00 (978-0-415-95382-5(0)) 2007. 624p. 69.95 (978-0-415-95383-2(9)) Routledge.

Youde, Jeremy. AIDS South Africa & the Politics of Knowledge. 2007. (Global Health Ser.). 166p. 114.95 (978-0-7546-7003-2(1)) Ashgate Publishing Co.

Zheng, Tiantian & Wortman, Jack. Hiv/Aids Through an Anthropological Lens. 2nd rev. ed. 2012. (ENG.). 206p. pap. 82.99 **(978-0-7575-9041-2(1))** Kendall Hunt Publishing Co.

AIDS (DISEASE)—PREVENTION

see also Safe Sex in AIDS Prevention

Acharya, Sanghmitra S. Young People & Hiv/Aids- 2011. 104p. pap. **(978-3-8443-9421-4(4))** Lambert Academic Publishing.

Aikman, Sheila, et al, eds. Gender Equality & HIV & AIDS: A Challenge for the Education Sector. 2009. 246p. pap. 29.95 (978-0-85598-579-0(8)) Oxfam Publishing GBR. Dist: Stylus Publishing, LLC.

Alemneh, Aschenaki. Sexual Behaviour & Hiv/Aids: In Community Practicing Widow Inheritance. 2011. 24p. pap. **(978-3-639-18371-9(1))** VDM Verlag Dr. Mueller e.K.

American Association of Colleges for Teacher Education Staff. Humanizing Pedagogy Through HIV & AIDS Prevention: Transforming Teacher Knowledge. 2006. (Series in Critical Narrative). (ENG., Illus.). 404p. per. 60.95 (978-1-59451-260-5(4)) Paradigm Pubs.

Asian Development Bank Staff, et al. Strategic Directions for Human Development in Papua New Guinea. 2007. (Directions in Development Ser.). (ENG., Illus.). 250p. per. 25.00 (978-0-8213-6987-6(3), 9780821369876) World Bank Pubns.

Atlani-Duault, LaëTitia. Humanitarian Aid in Post-Soviet Countries: An Anthropological Perspective. 2008. (Illus.). VIII, 152p. 160.00 (978-0-415-44884-0(0)) Routledge.

Atsepoyi, Prince Gabriel B. The Book of Total Happiness: Total Happiness. 2009. (ENG.). 199p. 19.99 (978-0-9636951-0-9(X)) Blue Sky Pubs., Inc.

Ayim, Ushonye. Hiv/Aids - How Experts Spread the Virus. 2007. 108p. pap. 21.50 (978-1-4116-4446-5(8)) Lulu Enterprises Inc.

Ayres, Jeffrey McKelvey & Siplon, Patricia D. Divergent Campaigns Towards Global Health Governance: Canadian & U.S. Approaches to the Global HIV/AIDS Pandemic. 2007. 52p. (978-1-882582-58-7(6)) Canadian-American Ctr.

Baxen, Jean. Performative Praxis: Teacher Identity & Teaching in the Context of HIV/AIDS. 2010. 338p. pap. (978-3-03911-612-6(6)) Lang, Peter.

Beck, Eduard J., et al, eds. The HIV Pandemic: Local & Global Implications. 2006. (ENG., Illus.). 840p. pap. 139.95 (978-0-19-852843-2(4)) Oxford Univ. Pr., Inc.

Beyrer, Chris, et al. The Global HIV Epidemics among Men who have Sex with Men (MSM) Epidemiology, prevention, access to care, & human Rights. 2011. (Directions in Development Ser.). (ENG., Illus.). 400p. pap. 35.00 (978-0-8213-8726-9(X), 9780821387269) World Bank Pubns.

Bhattarai, Rajan Kumar. Voluntary Hiv Counselling & Testing in Resource Limited Settings. 2010. 80p. pap. (978-3-8383-2488-3(9)) Lambert Academic Publishing.

Boler, Tania, et al. The Politics of Prevention: A Global Crisis in AIDS & Education, 1 vol. 2008. (ENG., Illus.). 176p. 21.00 (978-0-7453-2732-7(X)); lib. bdg. 63.00 (978-0-7453-2733-4(8)) Pluto Pr. GBR. Dist: Macmillan.

Bowser, Benjamin P. & Quimby, Ernest, eds. When Communities Assess their AIDS Epidemics: Results of Rapid Assessment of HIV/AIDS in Eleven U. S. Cities. 2008. (ENG.). 264p. pap. 31.50 (978-0-7391-2949-4(X)) Lexington Bks.

Bowser, Benjamin P., et al. When Communities Assess Their AIDS Epidemics: Results of Rapid Assessment of HIV/AIDS in Eleven U. S. Cities. 2007. (ENG., Illus.). 264p. 68.50 (978-0-7391-0752-2(6)) Lexington Bks.

Building on Success: New Directions in Global Health: Hearing Before the Committee on Foreign Relations, United States Senate, One Hundred Eleventh Congress, Second Session, March 10, 2010. 2010. (Illus.). iii, 44p. (978-0-16-086848-1(3), 552-070-41760-5) United States Government Printing Office.

Bundy, Donald, et al. Accelerating the Education Sector Response to HIV: Five Years of Experience from Sub-Saharan Africa. 2010. (ENG., Illus.). 128p. pap. 15.00 (978-0-8213-7932-5(1), 9780821379325) World Bank Pubns.

Byamugisha, Gideon B. ISG 44: Church Communities Confronting HIV/AIDS. 2010. 128p. pap. **(978-0-281-06239-3(0))** SPCK Publishing.

Card, Josefina J., et al. Tools for Building Culturally Competent HIV Prevention Programs. 2007. 95.00 (978-0-8261-1517-1(9)) Springer Publishing Co., Inc.

Chale, Samwel. Media & Hiv/Aids in Cities-Tanzania Experience. 2011. 64p. pap. **(978-3-8443-0308-7(1))** Lambert Academic Publishing.

CHIBAYA MBUYA PhD, John & Chibaya Mbuya, John. Hiv / Aids Epidemic. 2010. 196p. pap. (978-3-8383-6956-3(4)) Lambert Academic Publishing.

Clossey, Laurene. Hiv/Sti Prevention on the College Campus: Coping with Controversy. 2009. 192p. pap. (978-3-639-13999-0(2)) VDM Verlag Dr. Mueller e.K.

Cohen, Clara, et al. Design Considerations for Evaluating the Impact of PEPFAR: Workshop Summary. 2008. (ENG.). 142p. pap. 36.75 (978-0-309-11672-5(4)) National Academies Pr.

Coleman, Mrs. Octavia, Mhsa & Charity, For the Cause, Inc. The Role of Community Leaders: Finding Solutions to the HIV/AIDS Epidemic. 2010. 140p. pap. 15.00 (978-0-557-24464-5(1)) Lulu Enterprises Inc.

Committee on Planning the Assessment/Evaluation of Programs Implemented Under the U.S. Global Leadership Against HIV/AIDS, Tuberculosis, and Malaria Reauthorization Act of 2008, et al. Strategic Approach to the Evaluation of Programs Implemented under the Tom Lantos & Henry J. Hyde U. S. Global Leadership Against HIV/AIDS, Tuberculosis, & Malaria Reauthorization Act Of 2008. 2010. (ENG.). 216p. pap. 44.25 (978-0-309-15393-5(X)) National Academies Pr.

Committee on the Methodological Challenges in HIV Prevention Trials. Methodological Challenges in Biomedical HIV Prevention Trials. Lagakos, Stephen W. & Gable, Alicia R., eds. 2008. (ENG.). 270p. pap. 56.50 (978-0-309-11430-1(6)) National Academies Pr.

Committee on the Prevention of HIV Infection among Injecting Drug Users in High-Risk Countries. Preventing HIV Infection among Injecting Drug Users in High Risk Countries: An Assessment of the Evidence. 2006. (ENG.). 298p. pap. 61.25 (978-0-309-10280-3(4)) National Academies Pr.

Cortes, Luis. Hay una Respuesta: Cómo Prevenir y Entender el VIH y el SIDA. 2006. (SPA.). 144p. pap. 7.99 (978-0-7432-8995-5(1), Beyond Words/Atria Bks.) Atria Bks.

—There Is an Answer: How to Prevent & Understand HIV/AIDS. 2006. (ENG.). 144p. pap. 10.99 (978-0-7432-8987-0(0), Beyond Words/Atria Bks.) Atria Bks.

D'Adesky, Anne-Christine. Moving Mountains: The Race to Treat Global AIDS. 2006. (ENG.). 496p. per. 23.00 (978-1-84467-543-2(2), 844543) Verso Bks. GBR. Dist: Norton, W. W. & Co., Inc.

De Quina Menezes Cordeiro, Delphine. The Impact of Hiv/Aids Prevention & Promotion Messages. 2011. 92p. pap. (978-3-8443-3061-8(5)) Lambert Academic Publishing.

Dittmann, Dawn. Sports & Hiv/Aids Prevention. 2008. 136p. pap. (978-3-639-00181-5(8)) VDM Verlag Dr. Mueller e.K.

The Domestic Epidemic Is Worse Than We Thought: A Wake-Up Call for HIV Prevention: Hearing Before the Committee on Oversight & Government Reform, House of Representatives, One Hundred Tenth Congress, Second Session, September 16, 2008. 2010. (Illus.). iii, 166p. (978-0-16-086745-3(2), 552-070-41667-6) United States Government Printing Office.

Douste-Blazy, Philippe & Altman, Daniel. Power in Numbers: Unitaid, Innovative Financing, & the Quest for Massive Good. 2010. (ENG., Illus.). 160p. pap. 12.95 (978-1-58648-893-2(7)) PublicAffairs.

Edgar, Timothy, et al. Communication Perspectives on HIV/AIDS for the 21st Century. Edgar, Timothy et al, eds. 2007. (LEA's Communication Ser.). (Illus.). 477p. 110.00 (978-0-8058-5826-6(1)) Erlbaum, Lawrence Assocs., Inc.

Encyclopaedia Britannica, Inc., compiled by. AIDS: Nobody Is Immune. 2008. 49.95 (978-1-59339-656-5(2)) Encyclopaedia Britannica, Inc.

—Y. P. & A. - changing Lifestyles. 2008. 49.95 (978-1-59339-658-9(9)) Encyclopaedia Britannica, Inc.

—Y. P. & A. - the Global Impact. 2008. 49.95 (978-1-59339-657-2(0)) Encyclopaedia Britannica, Inc.

Enhanced Protection for Children Affected by AIDS. 2007. 56p. 15.00 (978-92-806-4152-3(2)) United Nations Children's Fund, The (UNICEF).

Feldman, Douglas A., ed. AIDS, Culture, & Africa. 2008. (ENG., Illus.). 336p. 75.00 (978-0-8130-3253-5(9)) Univ. Pr. of Florida.

Ferreira Do Val, Luciane & Meneghin, Paolo. Aids-Related Factors. 2010. 92p. pap. (978-3-639-26884-3(9)) VDM Verlag Dr. Mueller e.K.

Fiaveh, Daniel Yaw. Male Perspectives on Condom Use. 2011. 164p. pap. (978-3-8443-0941-6(1)) Lambert Academic Publishing.

Freimuth, Vicki S., et al. Communication Perspectives on HIV/AIDS for the 21st Century. Freimuth, Vicki S. et al, eds. 2007. (LEA's Communication Ser.). 477p. per. 45.95 (978-0-8058-5827-3(X)) Erlbaum, Lawrence Assocs., Inc.

Fuller, Linda K. African Women's Unique Vulnerabilities to HIV/AIDS: Communication Perspectives & Promises. 2008. (ENG.). 328p. 105.00 (978-1-4039-8405-0(0)) Palgrave Macmillan.

Gaga, John. The Role of Church Leaders in Hiv & Aids Prevention. 2011. 140p. pap. (978-3-8443-8252-5(6)) Lambert Academic Publishing.

Gardazi, Syed Mudasser Fida. Human Rights Law & Hiv/Aids. 2011. 192p. pap. (978-3-8443-1308-6(7)) Lambert Academic Publishing.

Gebre-Egziabher, Kinfe Abraha. Education & Development: Females' Education & Fertility Reduction. 2010. 132p. pap. (978-3-639-26553-8(X)) VDM Verlag Dr. Mueller e.K.

Genevieve, Keene. Reflexivity with Regards to Sexual Decision Making: A Study of a Group of Adolescents, Living in the Context of an Informal Settlement, in the Eastern Cape of South Africa. 2011. 140p. pap. (978-3-639-32095-4(6)) VDM Verlag Dr. Mueller e.K.

Gill, Peter. Body Count: Fixing the Blame for the Global AIDS Catastrophe. 2006. (ENG.). 208p. per. 14.95 (978-1-56025-943-5(4)) Da Capo Pr., Inc.

Gisselquist, David. Points to Consider: Responses to HIV/AIDS in Africa,Asia, & the Caribbean. 2008. 236p. per. (978-1-905068-45-6(X)) Adonis & Abbey Publishers Ltd.

Githiora, Kuria C. Need for Information on Hiv/Aids among Teenagers in Rural Thik. 2010. 96p. pap. (978-3-639-27558-2(6)) VDM Verlag Dr. Mueller e.K.

Gootnick, David. Global Health: Spending Requirement Presents Challenges for Allocating Prevention Funding under the President's Emergency Plan for AIDS Relief. 2006. (Illus.). 86p. (C). pap. 25.00 (978-1-4223-0702-1(6)) DIANE Publishing Co.

Gorgens-Albino, Marelize, et al. The Africa Multi-Country AIDS Program, 2000-2006: Results of the World Bank's Response to a Development Crisis. 2007. (ENG., Illus.). 188p. per. 15.00 (978-0-8213-7052-0(9), 9780821370520) World Bank Pubns.

—Programme Plurinational de Lutte Contre le Sida en Afrique, 2000-2006: Bilan des Interventions de la Banque Mondiale Face a une Crise de Developpement. 2007. (FRE., Illus.). 208p. per. 15.00 (978-0-8213-7109-1(6), 9780821371091) World Bank Pubns.

Green, Edward C. Broken Promises: How the AIDS Establishment Has Betrayed the Developing World. 2011. (Illus.). 288p. pap. 17.95 (978-1-936227-00-6(2)) Left Coast Pr., Inc.

Green, Edward C. Broken Promises: How the AIDS Establishment has Betrayed the Developing World. 2011. (ENG., Illus.). 288p. (C). pap. 17.95 (978-1-61132-112-8(3)) Left Coast Pr., Inc.

Green, Edward C. & Ruark, Allison Herling. AIDS, Behavior, & Culture: Understanding Evidence-Based Prevention. 2011. (Key Questions in Anthropology Ser.). (ENG., Illus.). 300p. (C). 89.00 (978-1-59874-478-1(X)); pap. 32.95 (978-1-59874-479-8(8)) Left Coast Pr., Inc.

Groeninck, Sandy. Effectiveness of Sport As a Tool for Hiv/Aids Prevention & Awareness. 2010. 216p. pap. (978-3-8383-4643-4(2)) Lambert Academic Publishing.

Guta, Yonas Regassa. Where Is the Change of Behavior? Assessment on Hiv/Aids Education: Where Is the Change of Behavior? Assessment on the Integrated Early School Adolescents' Sexual & Reproductive Health (Hiv/Aids) Education. 2011. 144p. pap. (978-3-639-32052-7(2)) VDM Verlag Dr. Mueller e.K.

Hall, Jyl, et al, eds. A Guide to Acting on AIDS: Understanding the Global AIDS Pandemic & Responding through Faith in Action. 2006. (ENG., Illus.). 90p. per. 9.99 (978-1-932805-80-2(X)) Authentic Media.

Hanley, Matthew & de Irala, Jokin. Affirming Love, Avoiding AIDs: What Africa Can Teach the West. 2009. (ENG.). pap. 17.95 (978-0-935372-56-4(3)) National Catholic Bioethics Ctr., The.

Haricharan, Hanne Jensen. 'to Tell or Not to Tell' 2010. 92p. pap. (978-3-8383-5256-5(4)) Lambert Academic Publishing.

Higgins, Christina & Norton, Bonny, eds. Language & HIV/Aids. 2009. (Critical Language & Literacy Studies). (ENG., Illus.). 280p. 129.95 (978-1-84769-220-7(6)); pap. 44.95 (978-1-84769-219-1(2)) Multilingual Matters GBR. Dist: Univ. of Toronto Pr.

HIV Prevention: How Effective Is the President's Emergency Plan for AIDS Relief (PEPFAR): Hearing Before the Subcommittee on National Security, Emerging Threats, & International Relations of the Committee on Government Reform, House of Representatives, One Hundred Ninth Congress, Second Session, September 6, 2006. 2007. (Illus.). iii, 157p. (978-0-16-079038-6(7), 552-070-36148-1) United States Government Printing Office.

Hubbard, Susan & Suzuki, Tomoko. Building Resilience: Human Security Approaches to AIDS in Africa & Asia. 2008. (ENG.). 120p. pap. 10.00 (978-4-88907-079-8(6)) Japan Ctr. for International Exchange JPN. Dist: Brookings Institution Pr.

Hungwe, Caroline. Hiv/Aids Prevention Television Advertisements in Afric. 2010. 128p. pap. (978-3-8383-4617-5(3)) Lambert Academic Publishing.

Institute of Medicine Staff, creator. PEPFAR Implementation: Progress & Promise. 2007. (ENG., Illus.). 400p. 42.00 (978-0-309-10982-6(5)) National Academies Pr.

International AIDS Vaccine Initiative (IAVI). Imagining A World Without AIDS: A History of the International AIDS Vaccine Initiative. 2007. (978-0-9773126-7-2(4)) International AIDS Vaccine Initiative.

—The Impact of an AIDS Vaccine in Developing Countries: A New Role Model & Preliminary Results. 2006. (978-0-9773126-6-5(6)) International AIDS Vaccine Initiative.

Joint United Nations Programme on HIV/AIDS (UNAIDS). Helping Ourselves: Community Responses to AIDS in Swaziland. 2006. (UNAIDS Publication). (ENG.). 52p. pap. 18.00 (978-92-9173-516-7(7)) World Health Organization.

—2006 report on the global AIDS Epidemic: A UNAIDS 10th anniversary special Edition. 10th rev. ed. 2006. (Unaids Publication). (ENG., Illus.). 629p. pap. 40.00 (978-92-9173-479-5(9)) World Health Organization.

Joint United Nations Programme on HIV/AIDS (UNAIDS) & World Health Organization. UNAIDS Annual Report 2007: Knowing Your Epidemic. 2009. (UNAIDS Publication Ser.). (ENG., Illus.). 48p. pap. 15.00 (978-92-9173-700-0(3)) World Health Organization.

Joint United Nations Programme on HIV/AIDS (UNAIDS) & World Health Organization Staff. UNAIDS Legal & Regulatory Self-Assessment Tool for Male Circumcision in Sub-Saharan Africa. 2010. (UNAIDS Publication). (ENG.). 16p. pap. 12.00 (978-92-9173-734-5(8)) World Health Organization.

Joint United Nations Programme on HIV/AIDS (UNAIDS), et al. Safe, Voluntary, Informed Male Circumcision & Comprehensive HIV Prevention Programming: Guidance for Decision-Makers on Human Rights Ethical & Legal Considerations. 2009. (UNAIDS Publication Ser.). (ENG.). 34p. pap. 18.00 (978-92-9173-680-5(5)) World Health Organization.

Joint United Nations Programme on HIV/AIDS Staff, contrib. by. The Positive Partnerships Program in Thailand: Empowering People Living with HIV. 2007. (UNAIDS Publication). 48p. pap. 18.00 (978-92-9173-593-8(0)) World Health Organization.

Kaguda, Darmarris. Hiv/Aids & the Medi. 2011. 116p. pap. (978-3-8443-9842-7(2)) Lambert Academic Publishing.

Kalichman, Seth C., ed. Positive Prevention: Reducing HIV Transmission among People Living with HIV/AIDS. 2010. (ENG.). xxii, 281p. pap. 79.95 (978-1-4419-3468-0(5), 1441934685) Springer.

Kane, Brigid M. HIV/AIDS Treatment Drugs. Triggle, David J., ed. 2008. (Drugs Ser.). (Illus.). 120p. (C). (gr. 9-12). lib. bdg. 30.00 (978-0-7910-8552-3(X), Chelsea Hse.) Facts On File, Inc.

Karim, Salim Abdool & Karim, Quarraisha Abdool, eds. HIV/AIDS in South Africa. 2nd rev. ed. 2010. (Illus.). 608p. pap. 75.00 (978-0-521-14793-4(X)) Cambridge Univ. Pr.

Kinsman, John. AIDS Policy in Uganda: Evidence, Ideology, & the Making of an African Success Story. 2010. (ENG., Illus.). 258p. 89.00 (978-0-230-10428-0(2)) Palgrave Macmillan.

Kling, Sydney. INSIDE Outside: A Retiree's Peace Corps Journal from South Africa. 2007. 387p. pap. 14.00 (978-0-9794257-1-4(9)) Kling, Sydney.

Kumar, Ashok. Hiv & Aids. 2011. 76p. pap. (978-3-8433-9166-5(1)) Lambert Academic Publishing.

Lemieux, Anthony F. Music Based Hiv Prevention. 2008. 120p. pap. (978-3-639-06367-7(8)) VDM Verlag Dr. Mueller e.K.

Lindner, Mary. Evaluation Study on the Effects of the Child Mind Project. 2010. 298p. pap. 52.00 (978-3-940755-30-8(3)) Budrich-Esser, Barbara DEU. Dist: International Specialized Bk. Services.

Maithya, Harrison. Sexual & Reproductive Issues among the Akamba of Keny. 2009. 236p. pap. (978-3-639-16405-3(9)) VDM Verlag Dr. Mueller e.K.

Makwambeni, Vimbai. A Kap Study to Assess of a Life Skills Program in Zimbabwe. 2011. 80p. pap. (978-3-8383-9588-3(3)) Lambert Academic Publishing.

Mapara, Edwin Mavunika. Aiducation 20-10 Taking Control of Aids. 2010. 290p. pap. 19.99 (978-1-4500-3892-8(1)) Xlibris Corp.

—Aiducation 20-10 Taking Control of Tb: Taking Control of TB. 2010. 298p. pap. 19.99 (978-1-4535-1442-9(2)) Xlibris Corp.

Martin, Noreen. Life after AIDS: Restoring Health Naturally. 2007. 168p. per. 12.95 (978-1-59824-504-2(X)) E-BookTime LLC.

Mayer, Kenneth H. & Pizer, Hank. HIV Prevention: A Comprehensive Approach. Mayer, Kenneth H. & Pizer, H. F., eds. 2008. (ENG., Illus.). 696p. 87.95 (978-0-12-374235-3(8), Academic Pr.) Elsevier Science & Technology Bks.

McCree, Donna H., et al. African Americans & HIV/AIDS: Understanding & Addressing the Epidemic. 2010. (Illus.). xx, 323p. E-Book (978-0-387-78321-5(0)) Springer.

Mehlomakulu, Vuyelwa. Construction of Masculine Sexuality: A Psychological Discourse Analysis. 2010. 84p. pap. (978-3-8383-8252-4(8)) Lambert Academic Publishing.

Messer, Donald E. 52 Ways to Create an AIDS-Free World. 2009. 136p. pap. 9.95 (978-1-935205-04-3(8)) Fresh Air Bks.

Moges, Kassaye Tekola. Immigrants As Risk Group in the Host Country. 2009. 76p. pap. (978-3-639-21318-8(1)) VDM Verlag Dr. Mueller e.K.

Motsi, Petronella Dadirai & MABVURIRA, Vincent. Seeking Balance Between Hiv Prevention Programmes & Tradition. 2011. 56p. pap. (978-3-8443-9071-1(5)) Lambert Academic Publishing.

Mugambi, Hannah Mweru. Nakuru Women's Culture-Dependent Responses to Hiv Prevention. 2009. 196p. pap. (978-3-639-13541-1(5)) VDM Verlag Dr. Mueller e.K.

Multi-Drug Resistant Tuberculosis: Assessing the U.S. Response to an Emerging Global Threat: Hearing Before the Subcommittee on Africa & Global Health of the Committee on Foreign Affairs, House of Representatives, One Hundred Tenth Congress, Second Session, February 27, 2008. 2008. iii, 55p. (978-0-16-082429-6(X), 552-070-38473-1) United States Government Printing Office.

Mwiturubani, Donald Anthony & Gebre, Ayalew. Youth, HIV/AIDS & Social Transformations in Africa. 2009. 142p. pap. (978-2-86978-255-6(1)) Council for the Development of Social Science Research in Africa SEN. Dist: Michigan State Univ. Pr.

Myles, Lessie. African-Americans & Aids: Why are Black People still dying of (AIDS) while other Races are Not? 2009. 156p. 22.99 (978-1-4490-3313-2(X)); pap. 17.99 (978-1-4490-3312-5(1)) AuthorHouse.

Namaste, Viviane. Prevention Possibilities: Bisexual Realities & HIV Educaton in Montreal. 2011. (C). 264p. (978-0-8020-9993-8(9)); pap. (978-0-8020-9717-0(0)) Univ. of Toronto Pr.

The Next Phase of the Global Fight Against HIV/AIDS: Hearing Before the Committee on Foreign Relations, United States Senate, One Hundred Tenth Congress, First Session, October 24, 2007. 2008. iii, 49p. (978-0-16-080290-4(3), 552-070-36985-6) United States Government Printing Office.

Nguyen, Thu Anh, et al. Access to Prevention of Mother-to-Child Transmission Program. 2010. 236p. pap. (978-3-8383-6318-9(3)) Lambert Academic Publishing.

Nigatu, Tilahun. A Test Construction. 2009. 100p. pap. (978-3-639-21489-5(7)) VDM Verlag Dr. Mueller e.K.

Nursien, Ibrahim. Acceptability of Hiv Testing among Tuberculosis Patientsin Addis Abab. 2009. 56p. pap. (978-3-639-19219-3(2)) VDM Verlag Dr. Mueller e.K.

Obisesan, Oladipo. Living Without Aids: Helping families & youth win the fight against AIDS & attaining a new dimension of exceptional Living. 2010. (Illus.). 172p. 25.49 (978-1-4520-0653-6(9)); pap. 13.49 (978-1-4490-8406-6(0)) AuthorHouse.

Opata, Violet Nabwire K. Fighting Hiv/Aids Pandemic Through Education: A Reflection on Hiv/Aids Education Programme in Kenya. 2011. 152p. pap. (978-3-639-32668-0(7)) VDM Verlag Dr. Mueller e.K.

Organisation for Economic Co-operation and Development Staff. Creditor Reporting System: Aid Activities Iin Support of Hiv/Aids Control 2003-2006-SystèMe de Notification des Pays CréAnciers: Activités d'Aide Pour la Lutte Contre le Vih/Sida 2003-2006. 2008. 116p. pap. 63.00 (978-92-64-03283-5(5)) Organization for Economic Cooperation & Development.

Organista, Kurt C., ed. HIV Prevention with Latinos: Theory, Research, & Practice, 1 vol. 2012. (ENG., Illus.). 484p. pap. 59.99 (978-0-19-976430-3(1)) Oxford Univ. Pr., Inc.

Over, A. Mead. Achieving an AIDS Transition: Preventing Infections to Sustain Treatment. 2011. (978-1-933286-62-4(8)) Brookings Institution Pr.

Over, Mead. Achieving an AIDS Transition: Preventing Infections to Sustain Treatment. 2011. (ENG.). 150p. pap. 19.95 (978-1-933286-38-9(5)) Ctr. for Global Development.

PEPFAR: An Assessment of Progress & Challenges: Hearing Before the Committee on Foreign Affairs, House of Representatives, One Hundred Tenth Congress, First Session, April 24, 2007. 2007. iii, 46p. (978-0-16-079052-2(2), 552-070-38158-8) United States Government Printing Office.

PEPFAR: From Emergency to Sustainability & Advances Against HIV/AIDS: Hearing Before the Committee on Foreign Affairs, House of Representatives, One Hundred Eleventh Congress, Second Session, September 29, 2010. 2010. iii, 141p. (978-0-16-087680-6(X), 552-070-42232-3) United States Government Printing Office.

PEPFAR Reauthorization: From Emergency to Sustainability: Hearing Before the Committee on Foreign Affairs, House of Representatives, One Hundred Tenth Congress, First Session, September 25, 2007. 2007. (Illus.). iii, 87p. (978-0-16-079845-0(0), 552-070-36739-0) United States Government Printing Office.

Pequegnat, Willo & Bell, Carl C., eds. Family & HIV/AIDS: Cultural & Contextual Issues in Prevention & Treatment. 2011. (ENG., Illus.). xiv, 364p. 79.95 (978-1-4614-0438-5(X), 146140438X) Springer.

Pisani, Elizabeth. The Wisdom of Whores: Bureaucrats, Brothels, & the Business of AIDS. 2008. (ENG.). 400p. 25.95 (978-0-393-06662-3(2), 6662) Norton, W. W. & Co., Inc.

Pisani, Elizabeth & Pisani. The Wisdom of Whores: Bureaucrats, Brothels & the Business of AIDS. 2009. (ENG., Illus.). 400p. pap. 16.95 (978-0-393-33765-5(0), 33765) Norton, W. W. & Co., Inc.

Revenga, Ana, et al. The Economics of Effective AIDS Treatment: Evaluating Policy Options for Thailand. 2006. (Health, Nutrition, & Population Ser.). (ENG., Illus.). 272p. per. 25.00 (978-0-8213-6755-1(2), 9780821367551) World Bank Pubns.

Roger W. Hoerl And Presha E. Neidermeyer. Use What You Have: Resolving the HIV/AIDS Pandemic. 2009. 186p. 29.99 (978-1-4415-2113-2(5)); pap. 19.99 (978-1-4415-2112-5(7)) Xlibris Corp.

Rowden, Rick. The Deadly Ideas of Neoliberalism: How the IMF Has Undermined Public Health & the Fight Against AIDS. 2009. (ENG.). 288p. 126.95 (978-1-84813-284-9(0)) Zed Bks., Ltd. GBR. Dist: Macmillan.

Samuel Frimpong, Mph. Std/Hiv Prevention Action: Let's Protect Each Other. 2010. 288p. 30.95 (978-0-595-51135-8(X)); pap. 20.95 (978-0-595-52137-1(1)) iUniverse, Inc.

Sharron Kay Jenkins. Aids: Education & Prevention Workbook. 2009. 312p. pap. 60.00 (978-1-4389-9263-1(7)) AuthorHouse.

Sibanda, Laura. Female Students Motivations for Voluntary Counselling & Testing. 2010. 84p. pap. (978-3-8383-6678-4(6)) Lambert Academic Publishing.

Stop AIDS in Prison ACT of 2007, & the Drug Endangered Children ACT of 2007: Hearing Before the Subcommittee on Crime, Terrorism, & Homeland Security of the Committee on the Judiciary, House of Representatives, One Hundred Tenth Congress, First Session, on H.R. 1943 & H.R. 1199, May 22, 2007. 2008. (Illus.). iii, 125p. (978-0-16-081947-6(4), 552-070-38120-1) United States Government Printing Office.

Susser, Ida. AIDS, Sex, & Culture: Global Politics & Survival in Southern Africa. 2009. (ENG., Illus.). 304p. pap. 39.95 (978-1-4051-5587-8(6), Wiley-Blackwell) Wiley, John & Sons, Inc.

Swanepoel, Piet H. & Hoeken, Hans, eds. Adapting Health Communication to Cultural Needs. 2008. (Illus.). 175p. 128.00 (978-90-272-3247-2(4)) Benjamins, John Publishing Co.

Tadele, Gizachew & Gail. Hiv Sero-Prevalence among Premarital Couples in Bahir Dar Town. 2010. 64p. pap. (978-3-639-22025-4(0)) VDM Verlag Dr. Mueller e.K.

Thornton, Robert J. Unimagined Community: Sex, Networks, & AIDS in Uganda & South Africa. 2008. (California Series in Public Anthropology: Vol. 20). (Illus.). 304p. pap. 26.95 (978-0-520-25553-1(4)); 60.00 (978-0-520-25552-4(6)) Univ. of California Pr.

UNAIDS. AIDS Scorecards: Overview: UNAIDS Report on the Global AIDS Epidemic 2010. 2011. (Illus.). 150p. pap. 12.00 (978-92-9173-878-6(6)) World Health Organization.

—CD-ROM Report on the Global AIDS Epidemic & Document Library: Multilingual English/French/Spanish/Russian. 2009. (UNAIDS Product Ser.). (ENG & FRE.). cd-rom 36.00 (978-92-9173-808-3(5)) World Health Organization.

—Collaborating with Traditional Healers for HIV Prevention & Care in Sub-Saharan Africa: Suggestions for Programme Managers & Field Workers. 2006. (UNAIDS Publication). (ENG.). 54p. pap. 18.00 (978-92-9173-342-2(3)) World Health Organization.

—The Far Away from Home Club: HIV Prevention & Policy Implementation Feedback for Migrant & Mobile Populations in the Mekong River Delta, Viet Nam. 2010. (UNAIDS Publication). (ENG.). 27p. pap. 12.00 (978-92-9173-732-1(1)) World Health Organization.

—Getting to Zero: 2011-2015 Strategy Joint United Nations Programme on HIV/AIDS (UNAIDS) 2011. 63p. pap. 12.00 (978-92-9173-883-0(2)) World Health Organization.

—Global Report: Unaids Report on the Global Aids Epidemic 2010. 2011. (Illus.). 360p. pap. 24.00 *(978-92-9173-871-7(9))* World Health Organization.

—High Coverage Sites: HIV Prevention among Injecting Drug Users in Transitional & Developing Countries: Case Studies. 2006. (UNAIDS Publication). (ENG.). 75p. pap. 18.00 *(978-92-9173-531-0(0))* World Health Organization.

—Practical Guidelines for Intensifying HIV Prevention - Towards Universal Access: Five Steps to HIV Prevention Planning & Implementation. 2010. (UNAIDS Publication). (ENG.). 18p. pap. 12.00 *(978-92-9173-751-2(8))* World Health Organization.

UNICEF Staff, et al. Opportunity in Crisis: Preventing HIV from Early Adolescence to Young Adulthood. 2011. (Illus.). 64p. pap. 15.00 ***(978-92-806-4586-6(2))*** United Nations Children's Fund, The (UNICEF).

United Nations. Securing Our Future: Report of the Commission on HIV/AIDS & Governance in Africa. 2008. (ENG.). 250p. pap. 25.00 *(978-92-1-125105-0(2))* United Nations Pubns.

U.S. Investments in HIV/AIDS: Opportunities & Challenges Ahead: Hearing Before the Subcommittee on Africa & Global Health of the Committee on Foreign Affairs, House of Representatives, One Hundred Eleventh Congress, Second Session, March 11, 2010. 2010. iii, 66p. *(978-0-16-086564-0(6)*, 552-070-41562-9) United States Government Printing Office.

Valerio, Alexandria, et al. A Sourcebook of HIV/AIDS Prevention Programs: Education Sector-Wide Approaches. 2nd ed. 2008. (ENG.). 272p. pap. 45.00 *(978-0-8213-7440-5(0)*, 9780821374405) World Bank Pubns.

VIHdeo America (2 DVDs) An Anthology of 10 Years of HIV Spots in the Americas. 2006. (Paho Dvd Ser.). (ENG.). pap. 40.00 *(978-92-75-07396-4(1))* World Health Organization.

Vitellone, Nicole. Object Matters: Condoms, Adolescence & Time. 2008. (ENG.). 160p. 79.00 *(978-0-7190-7568-1(8))* Manchester Univ. Pr. GBR. Dist: Macmillan.

Walden, Vivien Margaret & Yetter, Mary. Humanitarian Programmes & HIV & AIDS: A Practical Approach to Mainstreaming. 2007. (ENG., Illus.). 124p. pap. 25.95 *(978-0-85598-562-2(3))* Oxfam Publishing GBR. Dist: Stylus Publishing, LLC.

Wangulu, Esther, ed. HIV & Culture Confluence: Cross-cultural Experiences on HIV, Gender & Education from the Johannesburg Conference. 2011. 92p. pap. 39.95 *(978-94-6022-141-5(6))* Royal Tropical Institute Pr. (KIT (Koninklijk Instituut voor de Tropen) NLD. Dist: Stylus Publishing, LLC.

WHO Regional Office for South-East Asia. HIV/AIDS among men who have sex with men & transgender populations in South-East Asia: The current situation & national Responses. 2011. 161p. pap. 36.00 *(978-92-9022-381-8(2))* World Health Organization.

WHO Regional Office for the Western Pacific. Harm Reduction - Good Practice in Asia. the Integration of Harm Reduction into Abstinence-Based Therapeutic Communities: A Case Study of We Help Ourselves, Australia. 2006. (Wpro Nonserial Publication). (ENG.). 31p. pap. 12.00 *(978-92-9061-220-9(7))* World Health Organization.

—Priority HIV & Sexual Health Interventions in the Health Sector for Men who have Sex with Men & Transgender People in the Asia-Pacific Region: With CD-ROM. 2010. (WPRO Nonserial Publication Ser.). 125p. pap. 18.00 *(978-92-9061-463-0(3))* World Health Organization.

Williams, Mary E. AIDS. 2011. (Introducing Issues with Opposing Viewpoints Ser.). 144p. lib. bdg. 35.75 *(978-0-7377-5197-0(5)*, Greenhaven Pr., Inc.) Cengage Gale.

Wood, Lesley. Dealing with HIV & AIDS in the Classroom. 2009. (ENG.). 240p. pap. 26.95 *(978-0-7021-7685-2(0))* Juta Academic ZAF. Dist: Independent Pubs. Group.

World Bank Staff. Corporate Responses to HIV/AIDS: Case Studies from India. 2007. (Books Ser.). (ENG., Illus.). 88p. per. 15.00 *(978-0-8213-7171-8(1)*, 9780821371718) World Bank Pubns.

—O Programa Multinacional de Africa Contra a Sida 2000-2006: Resultados Da Resposta Do Banco Mundial a Uma Crise de Desenvolvimento. 2007. (POR., Illus.). 180p. per. 15.00 *(978-0-8213-7229-6(7)*, 9780821372296) World Bank Pubns.

World Health Organization: Regional Office for the Western Pacific. Good Practices in Asia: Effective Paradigm Shifts Towards an Improved National Response to Drugs & HIV/AIDS:; Scale-up of Harm Reduction in Malaysia. 2011. (WPRO Nonserial Publication Ser.). (ENG.). 67p. cd-rom 18.00 ***(978-92-9061-519-4(2))*** WHO Regional Office for the Western Pacific PHL. Dist: World Health Organization.

—Orientation on harm Reduction: One-hour training course; participant Manual. 2007. (WPRO Publication). 49p. pap. 12.00 *(978-92-9061-306-0(8))* World Health Organization.

—Orientation on harm Reduction: Three-hour training course; participant Manual. 2008. (WPRO Publication). 43p. pap. 12.00 *(978-92-9061-308-4(4))* World Health Organization.

AIDS (DISEASE)—PSYCHOLOGICAL ASPECTS

Alexandrova, Anna, ed. Mobilizing Civil Society's Response to Stigma & Discrimination in Central Asia. 2007. (Sourcebook on Contemporary Controversies Ser.). (ENG., Illus.). 178p. pap. 24.95 *(978-1-932716-34-4(3))* International Debate Education Assn.

Asmamaw, Beyene. Hiv/Aids Attitude Scale: Development & Validation. 2011. 80p. pap. ***(978-3-639-33952-9(5))*** VDM Verlag Dr. Mueller e.K.

Berrigan, Daniel. Sorrow Built a Bridge: Friendship & AIDS. 2009. (Daniel Berrigan Reprint Ser.). 248p. (Orig.). pap. 27.00 *(978-1-60608-469-4(0)*, Wipf and Stock) Wipf & Stock Pubs.

Chakrabartty, Arupkumar. Mental Health & Hiv/Aids. 2010. 64p. pap. *(978-3-639-26077-9(5))* VDM Verlag Dr. Mueller e.K.

Cohen, Mary Ann & Gorman, Jack M., eds. Comprehensive Textbook of AIDS Psychiatry. 2007. (ENG., Illus.). 800p. 98.50 *(978-0-19-530435-0(7))* Oxford Univ. Pr., Inc.

Cohen, Mary Ann, et al. Handbook of AIDS Psychiatry. 2010. (ENG., Illus.). 400p. 54.95 *(978-0-19-537257-1(3))* Oxford Univ. Pr., Inc.

Ebersöhn, Liesel, ed. From Microscope to Kaleidoscope: Reconsidering Educational Aspects Related to Children in the HIV & AIDS Pandemic. 2008. 220p. *(978-90-8790-563-7(7))*; pap. *(978-90-8790-562-0(9))* Sense Pubs.

Froman, Paul Kent. After You Say Goodbye: When Someone You Love Dies of AIDS. 2007. 270p. reprint ed. pap. 11.00 *(978-1-4223-6695-0(2))* DIANE Publishing Co.

HIV: Issues with Mental Health & Illness. 2007. (ENG., Illus.). 180p. 116.00 *(978-0-7890-3409-0(3))*; per. 54.50 *(978-0-7890-3410-6(7))* Routledge.

Hong, Yan. Psychological Wellbeing & Hiv Risks of Female Sex Workers in Chin. 2008. 188p. pap. *(978-3-639-10310-6(6))* VDM Verlag Dr. Mueller e.K.

Joint United Nations Programme on HIV/AIDS (UNAIDS) & World Health Organization. Preventing Carer Burnout: Inter-Mission Care & Rehabilitation Society (IMCARES) 2009. (UNAIDS Publication Ser.). (ENG.). 48p. pap. 18.00 *(978-92-9173-638-6(4))* World Health Organization.

Ka'opus, Lana Sue, ed. HIV Treatment Adherence: Challenging for Social Services. 2007. (Illus.). 184p. 175.00 *(978-0-7890-3626-1(6))* Routledge.

Leonard, Erin. Adolescents with HIV: Attachment, Depression, & Medication. 2008. 136p. 89.95 *(978-1-60497-533-8(4))* Cambria Pr.

Lyon, Maureen E., ed. Teenagers, HIV, & AIDS: Insights from Youths Living with the Virus, 1 vol. annot. ed. 2006. (Sex, Love, & Psychology Ser.). (Illus.). 288p. 49.95 *(978-0-275-98892-0(9)*, C8892, Praeger Pubs.) Greenwood Publishing Group, Inc.

Perreault, Yvette. The Presence of Absence: The Effect of HIV Sero-Status on the Bereavement Experiences of Long-Term Survivors of Multiple AIDS-Related Losses. 2008. 228p. pap. *(978-3-8364-8340-7(8))* VDM Verlag Dr. Mueller e.K.

AIDS (DISEASE)—PUBLIC OPINION

Rödlach, Alexander. Witches, Westerners, & HIV: AIDS & Cultures of Blame in Africa. 2006. (Illus.). 258p. (C). 89.00 *(978-1-59874-033-2(4))* Left Coast Pr., Inc.

AIDS (DISEASE)—RELIGIOUS ASPECTS

Archey, Donald. Pastor, How Did You Get AIDS? 2007. 101p. per. 9.99 *(978-1-60247-484-0(2))* Tate Publishing & Enterprises, LLC.

Becker, Felicitas & Geissler, Wessler, eds. Aids & Religious Practice in Africa. 2009. (Studies of Religion in Africa Ser.). (Illus.). vi, 404p. *(978-90-04-16400-0(6))* BRILL.

Bongmba, Elias Kifon. Facing a Pandemic: The African Church & the Crisis of HIV/AIDS. 2007. 350p. per. 39.95 *(978-1-932792-82-9(1))* Baylor Univ. Pr.

Butt, Leslie & Eves, Richard. Making Sense of AIDS: Culture, Sexuality, & Power in Melanesia. 2008. (Illus.). 352p. (C). 60.00 *(978-0-8248-3193-6(4))*; pap. 27.00 *(978-0-8248-3249-0(3))* Univ. of Hawaii Pr.

Byamugisha, Gideon B. ISG 44: Church Communities Confronting HIV/AIDS. 2010. 128p. pap. ***(978-0-281-06239-3(0))*** SPCK Publishing.

Canteon, James. When God Stood Up: A Christian Response to AIDS in Africa. 2007. (ENG.). 256p. per. 24.95 *(978-0-470-83927-0(9)*, Wiley) Wiley, John & Sons, Inc.

Clark, J. Michael. Defying the Darkness: Gay Theology in the Shadows. 2010. 126p. (Orig.). pap. 16.00 *(978-1-60899-204-1(7)*, Resource Pubns.) Wipf & Stock Pubs.

Drayton, Tony Ferdinand. Transformation & the Church: A Push toward Acceptance within the HIV/AIDS Pandemic. 2008. 176p. per. 19.95 *(978-0-9787394-9-2(3))* Protective Hands Communications.

Dube, Musa Wenkosi & Dube Shomanah, Musa W. The HIV & AIDS Bible: Selected Essays. 2008. 175p. pap. 20.00 *(978-1-58966-114-1(1))* Univ. of Scranton Pr.

Gill, Robin, ed. Reflecting Theologically on AIDS: A Global Challenge. 2007. 208p. per. *(978-0-334-04002-6(7))* Hymns Ancient & Modern Ltd.

Haddad, Beverley, ed. Religion & Hiv & Aids: Charting the Terrain. 2011. 448p. pap. 45.00 ***(978-1-86914-207-0(1))*** University of Kwazulu-Natal Press ZAF. Dist: International Specialized Bk. Services.

Harris, Angelique. AIDS, Sexuality, & the Black Church: Making the Wounded Whole. 2010. (Martin Luther King, Jr. Memorial Studies in Religion, Culture, & Social Development Ser.). 198p. (C). 72.95 *(978-1-4331-0943-0(3))* Lang, Peter Publishing, Inc.

Hinga & Hinga, Teresia M. Women, Religion & HIV/AIDS in Africa: Responding to Ethical & Theological Challenges. xviii, 205p. *(978-1-875053-69-8(7))* Cluster Pubns.

Iozzio, Mary Jo, et al. Calling for Justice Throughout the World: Catholic Women Theologians on the HIV/AIDS Pandemic. Roche, Mary M. Doyle, ed. 2009. (ENG.). 288p. 90.00 *(978-0-8264-2863-9(0))*; pap. 34.95 *(978-0-8264-2864-6(9))* Continuum International Publishing Group, Ltd. GBR. Dist: National Bk. Network.

Klaits, Frederick. Death in a Church of Life: Moral Passion During Botswana's Time of AIDS. 2010. (Anthropology of Christianity Ser.). (ENG., Illus.). 368p. pap. 25.95 *(978-0-520-25966-9(1))* Univ. of California Pr.

—Death in a Church of Life: Moral Passion During Botswana's Time of AIDS. 2010. (Anthropology of Christianity Ser.). (ENG., Illus.). 368p. 60.00 *(978-0-520-25965-2(3))* Univ. of California Pr.

Leclercq, Vincent. Blessed are the Vulnerable: Reaching Out to Those with AIDS. 2010. 272p. pap. 29.95 *(978-1-58595-776-7(3))* Twenty-Third Pubns./Bayard.

Masaiti, Bridget Nonde. African Indigenous Churches, Polygamy & Hiv & Aids. 2011. 132p. pap. ***(978-3-8443-9450-4(8))*** Lambert Academic Publishing.

McMickle, Marvin Andrew. A Time to Speak: How Black Pastors Can Respond to the HIV/AIDS Pandemic. 2008. 176p. 20.00 *(978-0-8298-1803-1(0))* Pilgrim Pr., The/United Church Pr.

Mligo, Elia Shabani. Jesus & the Stigmatized: Reading the Gospel of John in a Context of HIV/AIDSÐRelated Stigmatization in Tanzania. 2011. 474p. pap. 52.00 ***(978-1-60899-706-0(5)***, Pickwick Pubns.) Wipf & Stock Pubs.

Moyo, Herbert. Jesus Is Hiv Positive. 2011. 200p. pap. ***(978-3-8443-0326-6(1))*** Lambert Academic Publishing.

Mulligan, Suzanne. Confronting the Challenge: Poverty, Gender, & HIV in South Africa. 2010. 209p. pap. 51.95 *(978-3-03911-938-7(9))* Lang, Peter AG GBR. Dist: Lang, Peter.

Musopole, Augustine. Spirituality, Sexuality & HIV/AIDS in Malawi: Theological Strategies for Behaviour Change. 2007. 64p. pap. *(978-99908-81-02-8(2))* Kachere Series, Bks. on Religion, Theology & Society in Malawi MWI. Dist: Michigan State Univ. Pr.

Palmer, Gerald. The Church Has AIDS: Essays on Sexuality, Sexual Orientation, Taboos, & the Black Church. 2010. 84p. pap. 18.20 *(978-0-557-12464-0(6))* Lulu Enterprises Inc.

Radcliffe, Timothy, et al. Christians & Sexuality in the Time of AIDS. Bowden, John, tr. from FRE. 2008. (ENG.). 152p. 19.95 *(978-0-8264-9911-0(2))* Continuum International Publishing Group, Ltd. GBR. Dist: National Bk. Network.

Sanders, Winnie. My True Revelation Featuring a Possible Cure for Aids. 2010. 62p. pap. 10.49 *(978-1-4490-7272-8(0))* AuthorHouse.

Stanford, Shane. A Positive Life: Living with HIV as a Pastor, Husband, & Father, 1 vol. 2010. (ENG.). 224p. 19.99 *(978-0-310-29292-0(1))* Zondervan.

Trinitapoli, Jenny Ann & Weinreb, Alexander. Religion & AIDS in Africa. 2012. (ENG.). 272p. 29.95 ***(978-0-19-533594-1(5))*** Oxford Univ. Pr., Inc

UNAIDS. A Faith-based Response to HIV in Southern Africa: The Choose to Care Inititative. 2006. (UNAIDS Publication). (ENG.). 75p. pap. 18.00 *(978-92-9173-545-4(9))* World Health Organization.

Williams, D & Dennis, C. An Ecclesiastical Model for Hiv/Aids Ministry. 2010. 100p. pap. 10.49 *(978-1-4520-5708-8(7))* AuthorHouse.

Zigon, Jarrett. HIV Is God's Blessing: Rehabilitating Morality in Neoliberal Russia. 2010. (ENG.). 272p. 60.00 *(978-0-520-26762-6(1))*; pap. 24.95 *(978-0-520-26764-0(8))* Univ. of California Pr.

Zulu, Princess Kasune. Warrior Princess: Fighting for Life with Courage & Hope. 2009. (ENG.). 272p. 22.00 *(978-0-8308-3725-0(6)*, IVP Bks.) InterVarsity Pr.

AIDS (DISEASE)—RESEARCH

ABBE Scientist Research Division Staff. AIDS & HIV in Adolescents: Index & Medical Analysis of New Clinical & Research Information. 2007. (ENG., Illus.). 160p. ring bd. 69.95 *(978-0-7883-5000-9(5))*; ring bd. 69.95 *(978-0-7883-4775-7(6))* ABBE Pubs. Assn. of Washington, D.C.

—AIDS & HIV in Argentina: Index & Medical Analysis of New Clinical & Research Information. 2008. (ENG., Illus.). 160p. ring bd. 69.95 *(978-0-7883-4958-4(9))* ABBE Pubs. Assn. of Washington, D.C.

—AIDS & HIV in Athletes: Index & Medical Analysis of New Clinical & Research Information. 2007. (Illus.). 160p. ring bd. 69.95 *(978-0-7883-4775-4(4))* ABBE Pubs. Assn. of Washington, D.C.

—AIDS & HIV in Australia: Index & Medical Analysis of New Clinical & Research Information. 2008. (ENG., Illus.). 160p. ring bd. 69.95 *(978-0-7883-4959-1(7))* ABBE Pubs. Assn. of Washington, D.C.

—AIDS & HIV in Blood: Index & Medical Analysis of New Clinical & Research Information. 2007. (ENG., Illus.). 160p. ring bd. 69.95 *(978-0-7883-4777-1(2))* ABBE Pubs. Assn. of Washington, D.C.

—AIDS & HIV in Body Fluids: Index & Medical Analysis of New Clinical & Research Information. 2007. (ENG., Illus.). 160p. ring bd. 69.95 *(978-0-7883-4778-8(0))* ABBE Pubs. Assn. of Washington, D.C.

—AIDS & HIV in Brazil: Index & Medical Analysis of New Clinical & Research Information. 2008. (ENG., Illus.). 160p. ring bd. 69.95 *(978-0-7883-4960-7(0))* ABBE Pubs. Assn. of Washington, D.C.

—AIDS & HIV in Canada: Index & Medical Analysis of New Clinical & Research Information. 2008. (ENG., Illus.). 160p. ring bd. 69.95 *(978-0-7883-4951-5(1))* ABBE Pubs. Assn. of Washington, D.C.

—AIDS & HIV in Children: Index & Medical Analysis of New Clinical & Research Information. 2007. (ENG., Illus.). 160p. ring bd. 69.95 *(978-0-7883-4779-5(9))* ABBE Pubs. Assn. of Washington, D.C.

—AIDS & HIV in China: Index & Medical Analysis of New Clinical & Research Information. 2008. (Illus.). 160p. ring bd. 69.95 *(978-0-7883-4961-4(9))* ABBE Pubs. Assn. of Washington, D.C.

—AIDS & HIV in Congo: Index & Medical Analysis of New Clinical Research Information. 2008. (ENG., Illus.). 160p. ring bd. 69.95 *(978-0-7883-4964-5(3))* ABBE Pubs. Assn. of Washington, D.C.

—AIDS & HIV in Employees: Index & Medical Analysis of New Clinical & Research Information. 2007. (ENG., Illus.). 160p. ring bd. 69.95 *(978-0-7883-4780-1(2))* ABBE Pubs. Assn. of Washington, D.C.

—AIDS & HIV in Ethiopia: Index & Medical Analysis of New Clinical & Research Information. 2008. (ENG., Illus.). 160p. ring bd. 69.95 *(978-0-7883-4965-2(1))* ABBE Pubs. Assn. of Washington, D.C.

—AIDS & HIV in France: Index & Medical Analysis of New Clinical & Research Information. 2008. 160p. 69.95 *(978-0-7883-4952-2(X))* ABBE Pubs. Assn. of Washington, D.C.

—AIDS & HIV in Germany: Index & Medical Analysis of New Clinical & Research Information. 2008. (ENG., Illus.). 160p. ring bd. 69.95 *(978-0-7883-4953-9(8))* ABBE Pubs. Assn. of Washington, D.C.

—AIDS & HIV in Human Mouth Infections & Lesions with Index & Medical Analysis of New Clinical Information for All Nations. 2008. (ENG., Illus.). 192p. ring bd. 69.95 *(978-0-7883-4529-6(X))* ABBE Pubs. Assn. of Washington, D.C.

—AIDS & HIV in India: Index & Medical Analysis of New Clinical & Research Information. 2008. 160p. 69.95 *(978-0-7883-4962-1(7))* ABBE Pubs. Assn. of Washington, D.C.

—AIDS & HIV in Indonesia: Index & Medical Analysis of New Clinical & Research Information. 2008. (ENG., Illus.). 160p. ring bd. 69.95 *(978-0-7883-4966-9(X))* ABBE Pubs. Assn. of Washington, D.C.

—AIDS & HIV in Italy: Index & Medical Analysis of New Clinical & Research Information. 2008. (ENG., Illus.). 160p. ring bd. 69.95 *(978-0-7883-4950-8(3))* ABBE Pubs. Assn. of Washington, D.C.

—AIDS & HIV in Japan: Index & Medical Analysis of New Clinical & Research Information. 2008. (ENG., Illus.). 160p. ring bd. 69.95 *(978-0-7883-4963-8(5))* ABBE Pubs. Assn. of Washington, D.C.

—AIDS & HIV in Mexico: Index & Medical Analysis of New Clinical & Research Information. 2008. (ENG., Illus.). 160p. ring bd. 69.95 *(978-0-7883-4954-6(6))* ABBE Pubs. Assn. of Washington, D.C.

—AIDS & HIV in Newborn Babies: Index & Medical Analysis of New Clinical & Research Information. 2007. (Illus.). 160p. ring bd. 69.95 *(978-0-7883-4781-8(0))* ABBE Pubs. Assn. of Washington, D.C.

—AIDS & HIV in Nigeria: Index & Medical Analysis of New Clinical & Research Information. 2008. (ENG., Illus.). 160p. ring bd. 69.95 *(978-0-7883-4957-6(8))* ABBE Pubs. Assn. of Washington, D.C.

—AIDS & HIV in Norway: Index & Medical Analysis of New Clinical & Research Information. 2008. (ENG., Illus.). 160p. ring bd. 69.95 *(978-0-7883-4958-3(6))* ABBE Pubs. Assn. of Washington, D.C.

—AIDS & HIV in Nurses: Index & Medical Analysis of New Clinical & Research Information. 2007. (ENG., Illus.). 160p. ring bd. 69.95 *(978-0-7883-4782-5(9))* ABBE Pubs. Assn. of Washington, D.C.

—AIDS & HIV in Oral Sex with Overview of the Human Race: Index & Medical Analysis of New Clinical Research Information for All Nations. 2008. (ENG., Illus.). 160p. ring bd. 74.50 *(978-0-7883-4566-1(4))* ABBE Pubs. Assn. of Washington, D.C.

—AIDS & HIV in Physicians: Index & Medical Analysis of New Clinical & Research Information. 2007. (Illus.). 160p. ring bd. 69.95 *(978-0-7883-4783-2(7))* ABBE Pubs. Assn. of Washington, D.C.

—AIDS & HIV in Pregnant Women: Index & Medical Analysis of New Clinical & Research Information. 2007. (ENG., Illus.). 160p. 69.95 *(978-0-7883-4784-9(5))* ABBE Pubs. Assn. of Washington, D.C.

—AIDS & HIV in Russia: Index & Medical Analysis of New Clinical & Research Information. 2008. (Illus.). 160p. ring bd. 69.95 *(978-0-7883-4955-3(4))* ABBE Pubs. Assn. of Washington, D.C.

—AIDS & HIV in Saliva: Index & Medical Analysis of New Clinical & Research Information. 2007. (ENG., Illus.). 160p. ring bd. 69.95 *(978-0-7883-4785-6(3))* ABBE Pubs. Assn. of Washington, D.C.

—AIDS & HIV in Spain: Index & Medical Analysis of New Clinical & Research Information. 2008. (ENG., Illus.). 160p. ring bd. 69.95 *(978-0-7883-4969-0(4))* ABBE Pubs. Assn. of Washington, D.C.

—AIDS & HIV in Sports: Index & Medical Analysis of New Clinical & Research Information. 2007. (ENG., Illus.). 160p. ring bd. 69.95 *(978-0-7883-4786-3(1))* ABBE Pubs. Assn. of Washington, D.C.

—AIDS & HIV in SPUTUM: Index & Medical Analysis of New Clinical & Research Information. 2007. (Illus.). 160p. ring bd. 69.95 *(978-0-7883-4787-0(X))* ABBE Pubs. Assn. of Washington, D.C.

—AIDS & HIV in Sweden: Index & Medical Analysis of New Clinical & Research Information. 2008. (ENG., Illus.). 160p. ring bd. 69.95 *(978-0-7883-4970-6(8))* ABBE Pubs. Assn. of Washington, D.C.

—AIDS & HIV in Switzerland: Index & Medical Analysis of New Clinical & Research Information. 2008. (ENG., Illus.). 160p. ring bd. 69.95 *(978-0-7883-4971-3(6))* ABBE Pubs. Assn. of Washington, D.C.

—AIDS & HIV in Teachers: Index & Medical Analysis of New Clinical & Research Information. 2007. (ENG., Illus.). 160p. ring bd. 69.95 *(978-0-7883-4788-7(8))* ABBE Pubs. Assn. of Washington, D.C.

—AIDS & HIV in the United Kingdom: Index & Medical Analysis of New Clinical & Research Information. 2008. (ENG., Illus.). 160p. ring bd. 69.95 *(978-0-7883-4956-0(2))* ABBE Pubs. Assn. of Washington, D.C.

—AIDS & HIV in the United States: Index & Medical Analysis of New Clinical & Research Information. 2008. 160p. 69.95 *(978-0-7883-4957-7(0))* ABBE Pubs. Assn. of Washington, D.C.

—AIDS & HIV in URINE: Index & Medical Analysis of New Clinical & Research Information. 2007. (ENG., Illus.). 160p. ring bd. 69.95 *(978-0-7883-4789-4(6))* ABBE Pubs. Assn. of Washington, D.C.

—HIV as an air-borne Infection: Index, Reference & Medical Analysis of New Reserch Information for All Nations. 2008. (Illus.). 160p. ring bd. 69.95 *(978-0-7883-3876-2(5))* ABBE Pubs. Assn. of Washington, D.C.

Chase, Amanda Jewell. Regulatory Mechanisms Controlling Hiv-1 Induced Immune Activation. 2008. 76p. pap. *(978-3-639-08889-2(1))* VDM Verlag Dr. Mueller e.K.

Einerson, Janet. Sire of Death. 2011. 48p. pap. 39.95 ***(978-1-4634-5006-9(0))*** AuthorHouse.

Esau, Omar. Checkmating Hiv/Aids As a Teacher Researcher. 2011. 264p. pap. (978-3-8443-0702-3(8)) Lambert Academic Publishing.

Githiora, Kuria C. Need for Information on Hiv/Aids among Teenagers in Rural Thik. 2010. 96p. pap. (978-3-639-27558-2(6)) VDM Verlag Dr. Mueller e.K.

Haslam, Edward T. Dr. Mary's Monkey: How the Unsolved Murder of a Doctor, a Secret Laboratory in New Orleans & Cancer-Causing Monkey Viruses Are Linked to Lee Harvey Oswald, the JFK Assassination & Emerging Global Epidemics. 2007. (ENG., Illus.). 275p. pap. 19.95 (978-0-9777953-0-7(6)) Trine Day.

Henderson, Lisa, ed. New Medical Therapies - AIDS HIV. 14p. pap. 14.99 (978-1-930624-10-8(7)) CenterWatch.

Holmberg, Scott D. Scientific Errors & Controversies in the U. S. HIV/AIDS Epidemic: How They Slowed Advances & Were Resolved, 1 vol. 2007. (Illus.). 240p. 49.95 (978-0-313-34717-7(4), C34717, Praeger Pubs.) Greenwood Publishing Group, Inc.

Kendow, Lawrence B. AIDS Vaccines, HIV Receptors, & AIDS Research. 2008. 98.00 (978-1-60692-074-9(X)) Nova Science Pubs., Inc.

Krotz, Larry. Piecing the Puzzle: The Genesis of AIDS Research in Africa. 2012. (ENG., Illus.). 220p. pap. 28.95 (978-0-88755-730-9(0)) Univ. of Manitoba Pr. CAN. Dist: Chicago Distribution Ctr.

Loffredo, John. Cellular Responses to Aids-Virus Infection. 2008. 264p. pap. (978-3-8364-9286-7(5)) VDM Verlag Dr. Mueller e.K.

Schuetz, Volker. Attachment Styles & Hiv-Risk Behavior. 2008. 52p. pap. (978-3-639-06179-6(9)) VDM Verlag Dr. Mueller e.K.

UNAIDS. Good Participatory Practice Guidelines for Biomedical HIV Prevention Trials. 2008. (UNAIDS Publication Ser.). 64p. pap. 18.00 (978-92-9173-634-8(1)) World Health Organization.

AIDS (DISEASE)—SOCIAL ASPECTS

Africa's Orphaned & Vulnerable Generations: Children Affected by AIDS. 2006. (Illus.). 12p. (978-92-806-4034-2(8)) United Nations Children's Fund, The (UNICEF).

Alexandrova, Anna, ed. Mobilizing Civil Society's Response to Stigma & Discrimination in Central Asia. 2007. (Sourcebook on Contemporary Controversies Ser.). (ENG., Illus.). 178p. pap. 24.95 (978-1-932716-34-4(3)) International Debate Education Assn.

Ande, Karen & Richter, Ruthann. Face to Face: Children of the AIDS Crisis in Africa. 2010. 128p. pap. 39.95 (978-1-932717-20-4(X)) Hope Publishing Hse.

Angula, Penehafo. Accessibility of Health Information to Plwh. 2010. 96p. pap. (978-3-8383-7272-3(7)) Lambert Academic Publishing.

Ashburn, Kristen, photos by. I Am Because We Are. 2009. (ENG., Illus.). 180p. 49.95 (978-1-57687-482-0(6)) powerHouse Cultural Entertainment, Inc.

Benz, Sophia. The Killing of the Fittest - a Quantitative Analysis of Hiv/Aids & Conflict. 2008. 144p. pap. (978-3-639-03767-8(7)) VDM Verlag Dr. Mueller e.K.

Berger, Michele Tracy. Workable Sisterhood: The Political Journey of Stigmatized Women with HIV/AIDS. 2006. (ENG., Illus.). 256p. (C). per. 25.95 (978-0-691-12770-5(0)) Princeton Univ. Pr.

Biehl, João. Will to Live: AIDS Therapies & the Politics of Survival. 2009. (In-Formation Ser.). (ENG., Illus.). 480p. (C). pap. 39.95 (978-0-691-14385-9(4)) Princeton Univ. Pr.

Biggs, Nalini Asha. Education & HIV/AIDS. 2012. (ENG., Illus.). 192p. 140.00 (978-1-4411-6895-5(8)); pap. 44.95 (978-1-4411-4778-3(0)) Continuum International Publishing Group, Ltd. GBR. Dist: National Bk. Network.

Boesten, Jelke & Poku, Nana K. Gender & AIDS: Critical Perspectives from the Developing World. 2009. (Global Health Ser.). (Illus.). 216p. 114.95 (978-0-7546-7269-2(7)) Ashgate Publishing Co.

Butt, Leslie & Eves, Richard. Making Sense of AIDS: Culture, Sexuality, & Power in Melanesia. 2008. (Illus.). 352p. (C). 60.00 (978-0-8248-3193-6(4)); pap. 27.00 (978-0-8248-3249-0(3)) Univ. of Hawaii Pr.

Castiglia, Christopher & Reed, Christopher. If Memory Serves: Gay Men, AIDS, & the Promise of the Queer Past. 2011. (ENG., Illus.). 296p. 75.00 (978-0-8166-7610-1(0)); pap. 25.00 (978-0-8166-7611-8(9)) Univ. of Minnesota Pr.

Chambré, Susan Maizel. Fighting for Our Lives: New York's AIDS Community & the Politics of Disease. 2006. (Critical Issues in Health & Medicine Ser.). (ENG.). 280p. 68.00 (978-0-8135-3866-2(1)) Rutgers Univ. Pr.

Chambre, Susan Maizel. Fighting for Our Lives: New York's AIDS Community & the Politics of Disease. annot. ed. 2006. (Critical Issues in Health & Medicine Ser.). (ENG.). 280p. per. 24.95 (978-0-8135-3867-9(X)) Rutgers Univ. Pr.

Chidi Nwachukwu-Udaku, Benedict. SIDA en África: Reflexiones y Propuestas Desde el Pueblo Igbo. 2009. (SPA., Illus.). 374p. (978-84-8468-258-5(7)) Universidad Pontificia Comillas de Madrid.

Conner, Ross F., et al. AIDS: Science & Society. 5th rev. ed. 2007. (Illus.). 249p. per. 84.95 (978-0-7637-4263-8(5)) Jones & Bartlett Learning, LLC.

Conroy, Anne C., ed. Poverty, AIDS & Hunger: Breaking the Poverty Trap in Malawi. 2007. (ENG., Illus.). 280p. 95.00 (978-1-4039-9833-0(7)) Palgrave Macmillan.

Cullinan, Kerry & Thom, Anso, eds. The Virus, Vitamins & Vegetables: The South African HIV/AIDS Mystery. 2010. (ENG.). 211p. pap. 21.00 (978-1-77009-691-2(4)) Jacana Media ZAF. Dist: Independent Pubs. Group.

D'Adesky, Anne-Christine. Moving Mountains: The Race to Treat Global AIDS. 2006. (ENG., Illus.). 496p. per. 23.00 (978-1-84467-543-2(2), 844543) Verso Bks. GBR. Dist: Norton, W. W. & Co., Inc.

Dilger, Hansjörg & Luig, Ute, eds. Morality, Hope & Grief: Anthropologies of AIDS in Africa. 2010. (EH Ser.). (Illus.). 356p. 95.00 (978-1-84545-663-4(7)) Berghahn Bks., Inc.

Doss, Cheryl & Conrad, Cecilia, eds. Aids Gender & Economic Development. 2011. (ENG., Illus.). 232p. (C). 125.00 (978-0-415-67327-3(5)); pap. 32.95 (978-0-415-67328-0(3)) Routledge.

Dow, Unity & Essex, Max. Saturday Is for Funerals. 2010. 240p. 19.95 (978-0-674-05077-8(0)) Harvard Univ. Pr.

Evian, Clive. Primary HIV/AIDS Care: A Practical Guide for Primary Care Personnel in a Clinical & Supportive Setting. 4th ed. 2007. (ENG.). 350p. per. 49.95 (978-1-77009-198-6(X)) Jacana Media ZAF. Dist: Independent Pubs. Group.

Fan, Hung, et al. AIDS: Science & Society. 6th rev. ed. 2010. 240p. pap. 78.95 (978-0-7637-7315-1(8)) Jones & Bartlett Learning, LLC.

Feldman, Douglas A., ed. AIDS, Culture, & Africa. 2011. (ENG., Illus.). 312p. pap. 32.95 (978-0-8130-3721-9(2)) Univ. Pr. of Florida.

Flint, Adrian. HIV/AIDS in Sub-Saharan Africa: Politics, Aid & Globalization. 2011. (ENG., Illus.). 240p. 85.00 (978-0-230-22142-0(4)) Palgrave Macmillan.

Foote, Carrie. HIV/AIDS: A Global Social Problem. 2012. (Framing 21st Century Social Issues Ser.). (ENG.). 64p. pap. 9.95 (978-0-415-50996-1(3)) Routledge.

Francis, Dennis A., ed. Acting on Hiv: Using Drama to Create Possibilities for Change. 2011. 166p. (978-94-6091-593-2(0)); pap. (978-94-6091-592-5(2)) Sense Pubs.

Friedman, Samuel R., et al. Social Networks, Drug Injectors' Lives, & HIV/AIDS. 2010. (Aids Prevention & Mental Health Ser.). 284p. pap. 139.00 (978-1-4419-3313-3(1), 1441933131) Springer.

Gentry, Quinn M. Black Women's Risk for HIV: Rough Living. 2007. (ENG.). 282p. per. 65.95 (978-0-7890-3170-9(1)) Routledge.

Gillespie, Stuart. AIDS, Poverty, & Hunger: Challenges & Responses. 2006. xii, 376p. (978-0-89629-758-6(6)) International Food Policy Research Institute.

Glass, John E. & Stolley, Kathy S. Hiv/aids, 1 vol. 2009. (Health & Medical Issues Today Ser.). (Illus.). 241p. 45.00 (978-0-313-34421-3(3), GR4421) Greenwood Publishing Group, Inc.

Gogwe, Lavender Fadzai. Identity Crisis. 2011. 60p. pap. (978-3-8443-8456-7(1)) Lambert Academic Publishing.

Green, Edward C. & Ruark, Allison Herling. AIDS, Behavior, & Culture: Understanding Evidence-Based Prevention. 2011. (Key Questions in Anthropology Ser.). (ENG., Illus.). 300p. (C). 89.00 (978-1-59874-478-1(X)); pap. 32.95 (978-1-59874-479-8(8)) Left Coast Pr., Inc.

Gumisiriza, Caleb. Towards Hiv/Aids Competent Organisations. 2010. 148p. pap. (978-3-639-22383-5(7)) VDM Verlag Dr. Mueller e.K.

Hammond, Tarana. Media Use, Hiv/Aids Knowledge, & Sexual Beliefs. 2008. 72p. pap. (978-3-639-00175-4(3)) VDM Verlag Dr. Mueller e.K.

Inrig, Stephen J. North Carolina & the Problem of AIDS: Advocacy, Politics, & Race in the South. 2011. (ENG., Illus.). 256p. 45.00 (978-0-8078-3498-5(X)) Univ. of North Carolina Pr.

Iweala, Uzodinma. Our Kind of People: A Continent's Burden, a Country's Hope. 2012. (ENG.). 240p. 24.99 (978-0-06-128490-8(4)) HarperCollins Pubs.

Johansson, Ola. Community Theatre & AIDS. 2011. (Studies in International Performance Ser.). (ENG., Illus.). 248p. 80.00 (978-0-230-20515-4(1)) Palgrave Macmillan.

Josephs, Lauren. Hiv/Aids & Intimate Partner Violence. 2009. 172p. pap. (978-3-639-12289-3(5)) VDM Verlag Dr. Mueller e.K.

Kamhanga Beraho, Monica. Living with AIDS in Uganda: Impacts on banana-farming households in two Districts. 2008. (AWLAE Ser.). 372p. pap. 55.00 (978-90-8686-064-7(8)) Wageningen Academic Publishers NLD. Dist: Enfield Publishing & Distribution Co., Inc.

Katyal, Veena, et al, eds. Healthcare Management in India: Psycho-Social & Neurological Aspects of HIV/AIDS & Other Physical & Mental Disorders. 2010. 349p. 84.25 (978-81-7708-244-9(2)) New Century Publications IND. Dist: International Specialized Bk. Services.

Klot, Jennifer & Nguyen, Vinh-Kim. The Fourth Wave: Violence, Gender, Culture, & HIV in the 21st Century. 2009. (978-0-9841257-1-5(X)) Centre for Research in Ethnic Relations.

Kopp, C. The New Era of AIDS: HIV & Medicine in Times of Transition. 2010. (International Library of Ethics, Law, & the New Medicine Ser.). 212p. pap. 139.00 (978-90-481-6187-4(8), 9048161878) Springer.

Lieberman, Evan & Lieberman, Evan S. Boundaries of Contagion: How Ethnic Politics Have Shaped Government Responses to AIDS. 2009. (ENG., Illus.). 368p. (C). pap. 26.95 (978-0-691-14019-3(7)) Princeton Univ. Pr.

Lloyd, Mary Elizabeth. AIDS Orphans Rising: What You Should Know & What You Can Do to Help Them Succeed. 2008. 120p. per. (978-1-932690-47-7(6)) Loving Healing Pr., Inc.

Lloyd, Sister Mary Elizabeth. Aids Orphans Rising. 2008. 132p. 27.95 (978-1-932690-61-3(1)) Loving Healing Pr., Inc.

Lockhart, Chris. AIDS Is Our Shadow: Sex & Survival among the New Women of Urban Tanzania. 2007. pap. (978-0-89089-376-0(4)) Carolina Academic Pr.

Lune, Howard. Urban Action Networks: HIV/AIDS & Community Organizing in New York City. 2006. (ENG.). 240p. 92.00 (978-0-7425-4083-5(9)); (Illus.). per. 30.95 (978-0-7425-4084-2(7)) Rowman & Littlefield Publishers, Inc.

MacMaster, Samuel A., et al, eds. International Perspectives on Women & HIV. 2009. (ENG.). 214p. 150.00 (978-0-415-99837-6(9)) Routledge.

Maxwell, Janine. It's Not Okay with Me. 2009. 208p. per. 14.99 (978-1-57921-885-0(7)) WinePress Publishing.

McLaughlin, Patrick J. AIDS: A Cause for Concern. (Orig.). pap. (978-0-938279-01-3(7)) Smedley, W.P. Co.

Mligo, Elia Shabani. Jesus & the Stigmatized: Reading the Gospel of John in a Context of HIV/AIDSÐRelated Stigmatization in Tanzania. 2011. 474p. pap. 52.00 (978-1-60899-706-0(5), Pickwick Pubns.) Wipf & Stock Pubs.

Ndinga-Muvumba, Angela & Pharoah, Robyn, eds. HIV/AIDS & Society in South Africa. 2008. 265p. (C). pap. 38.95 (978-1-86914-152-3(0)) University of Kwazulu-Natal Press ZAF. Dist: International Specialized Bk. Services.

Nyirenda, Nkhosikazi-Princess Zindaba. Talakata - the Tears of Afric. 2009. 236p. 30.00 (978-1-934925-51-5(9), Strategic Bk. Publishing) AEG Literary Publishing Services, Inc.

Open Door Clinic, creator. The Legacy Campaign: Personal Accounts of Lives Forever Changed When Diagnosed with HIV/AIDS. 2006. (ENG.). 227p. per. 15.00 (978-0-9789461-0-4(3)) His Rose, Inc.

Patterson, Amy S. The Politics of AIDS in Africa. 2006. (Challenge & Change in African Politics Ser.). (Illus.). (C). 200p. lib. bdg. 49.95 (978-1-58826-452-7(1)); 226p. pap. 22.00 (978-1-58826-477-0(7)) Rienner, Lynne Pubs.

Poindexter, Cynthia Cannon. Handbook of HIV & Social Work: Principles, Practice, & Populations. 2010. (ENG., Illus.). 384p. pap. 52.00 (978-0-470-26093-7(9), Wiley) Wiley, John & Sons, Inc.

Prince, Ruth Jane & Geissler, Paul Wenzel. The Land Is Dying: Contingency, Creativity & Conflict in Western Kenya. 2010. (Epistemologies of Healing Ser.). (Illus.). 444p. 95.00 (978-1-84545-481-4(2)) Berghahn Bks., Inc.

Rehle, Thomas, et al. South African National HIV Prevalence, Incidence, Behaviour & Communication Survey 2008: A Turning Tide among Teenagers? 2010. (ENG., Illus.). 120p. pap. 25.95 (978-0-7969-2291-5(8)) Human Sciences Research Council ZAF. Dist: Independent Pubs. Group.

Rinken, S. The AIDS Crisis & the Modern Self: Biographical Self-Construction in the Awareness of Finitude. 2010. (International Library of Ethics, Law, & the New Medicine Ser.). 260p. pap. 149.00 (978-90-481-5484-5(7), 9048154847) Springer.

Rosengarten, Marsha. HIV Interventions: Biomedicine & the Traffic Between Information & Flesh. 2009. (ENG., Illus.). 148p. pap. 25.00 (978-0-295-98942-6(4)) Univ. of Washington Pr.

—HIV Interventions: Biomedicine & the Traffic between Information & Flesh. 2009. (ENG.). 148p. 60.00 (978-0-925989-59-8(2)); (Illus.). 60.00 (978-0-295-98959-4(9)) Univ. of Washington Pr.

Rugalema, Gabriel, et al, eds. AIDS & Rural Livelihoods: Dynamics & Diversity in sub-Saharan Africa. 2010. (ENG., Illus.). 248p. 140.00 (978-1-84971-125-8(9)); pap. 49.95 (978-1-84971-126-5(7)) Routledge.

Sahn, David E., ed. The Socioeconomic Dimensions of HIV/AIDS in Africa. 2010. (United Nations University Ser.). (Illus.). 360p. pap. 29.95 (978-0-8014-7693-8(3)) Cornell Univ. Pr.

Schulman, Sarah. The Gentrification of the Mind: Witness to a Lost Imagination. 2012. (ENG.). 184p. 27.95 (978-0-520-26477-9(0)) Univ. of California Pr.

Shaba, Lutanga. Secrets of a Woman's Soul. 2006. 115p. pap. (978-1-84401-734-8(6)) Athena Pr.

Shilts, Randy. And the Band Played On: Politics, People & the AIDS Epidemic. 2nd rev. anniv. ed. 2007. (ENG.). 656p. pap. 18.99 (978-0-312-37463-1(1), St. Martin's Griffin) St. Martin's Pr.

Shisana, Olive, et al. South African National HIV Prevalence, HIV Incidence, Behaviour & Communication Survey 2005. 2008. (ENG., Illus.). 156p. pap. 25.95 (978-0-7969-2152-9(0)) Human Sciences Research Council ZAF. Dist: Independent Pubs. Group.

Simbayi, Leickness. The Impact of & Responses to HIV/AIDS in the Private Security & Legal Services Industry in South Africa. 2009. (ENG.). 192p. pap. 19.95 (978-0-7969-2205-2(5)) Human Sciences Research Council ZAF. Dist: Independent Pubs. Group.

Simpson, Anthony. Boys to Men in the Shadow of AIDS: Masculinities & HIV Risk in Zambia. 2009. (ENG.). 252p. 95.00 (978-0-230-61391-1(8)) Palgrave Macmillan.

Stone, Valerie, et al, eds. HIV/AIDS in U. S. Communities of Color. 2009. (ENG., Illus.). x, 310p. 89.95 (978-0-387-98151-2(9), 0387981519) Springer.

Susser, Ida. AIDS, Sex, & Culture: Global Politics & Survival in Southern Africa. 2009. (ENG., Illus.). 304p. 104.95 (978-1-4051-5586-1(8)); pap. 39.95 (978-1-4051-5587-8(6)) Wiley, John & Sons, Inc. (Wiley-Blackwell).

Thorn, Hakan & Foller, -Lis, eds. The Politics of AIDS: Globalization, the State & Civil Society. 2008. (ENG., Illus.). 368p. 121.00 (978-0-230-55402-3(4)) Palgrave Macmillan.

Thornton, Robert J. Unimagined Community: Sex, Networks, & AIDS in Uganda & South Africa. 2008. (California Series in Public Anthropology: Vol. 20). (Illus.). 304p. pap. 26.95 (978-0-520-25553-1(4)); 60.00 (978-0-520-25552-4(6)) Univ. of California Pr.

UNAIDS. CD-ROM Report on the Global AIDS Epidemic & Document Library: Multilingual English/French/Spanish/Russian. 2009. (UNAIDS Product Ser.). (ENG & FRE.). cd-rom 36.00 (978-92-9173-808-3(5)) World Health Organization.

UNICEF Staff. Africa's Orphaned & Vulnerable Generations: Children Affected by AIDS. 2006. (Illus.). 48p. pap. 15.00 (978-92-806-4035-9(6)) United Nations Children's Fund, The (UNICEF).

Varma, Sudhir. Gender, HIV, & Social Work. 2010. (Illus.). 254p. 40.00 (978-81-316-0341-3(5)) Rawat Pubns. IND. Dist: International Specialized Bk. Services.

Wangulu, Esther, ed. HIV & Culture Confluence: Cross-cultural Experiences on HIV, Gender & Education from the Johannesburg Conference. 2011. 92p. pap. 39.95 (978-94-6022-141-5(6)) Royal Tropical Institute Pr. (KIT (Koninklijk Instituut voor de Tropen) NLD. Dist: Stylus Publishing, LLC.

Welpe, Ingelore & Owino, Philip, eds. The Intersection of Human Capital, Gender & HIV/AIDS in the African Context, Vol. 2. (Illus.). 113p. (C). pap. 26.95 (978-3-631-54068-8(X)) Lang, Peter Publishing, Inc.

White, Renee T., et al. HIV/AIDS: Global Frontiers in Prevention/Intervention. (Illus.). 2008. (ENG.). 600p. 155.00 (978-0-415-95382-5(0)) 2007. 624p. 69.95 (978-0-415-95383-2(9)) Routledge.

World Bank Staff. Reducing Vulnerability to HIV/ 2007. (World Bank Working Papers). 352p. pap. 28.00 (978-0-8213-7026-1(X)) World Bank Pubns.

Zheng, Tiantian & Wortman, Jack. Hiv/Aids Through an Anthropological Lens. 2nd rev. ed. 2012. (ENG.). 206p. pap. 82.99 (978-0-7575-9041-2(1)) Kendall Hunt Publishing Co.

AIDS (DISEASE)—STATISTICS

Aids/Hiv. 2010. (Information Plus Reference Ser.). (ENG.). 160p. 58.00 (978-1-4144-4113-9(4)) Cengage Gale.

Alters, Sandra M. Aids/Hiv. 2008. (Information Plus Ser.). (ENG.). 176p. pap. 53.00 (978-1-4144-0742-5(4)) Cengage Gale.

Haacker, Markus & Claeson, Mariam. HIV & AIDS in South Asia: An Economic Development Risk. 2009. (Directions in Development Ser.). (ENG., Illus.). 272p. pap. 30.00 (978-0-8213-7800-7(7), 9780821378007) World Bank Pubns.

Messer, Donald E. Names, Not Just Numbers: Facing Global AIDS & World Hunger. 2010. (Speaker's Corner Ser.). (ENG.). 160p. 17.95 (978-1-55591-633-6(3)) Fulcrum Publishing.

Organisation for Economic Co-operation and Development Staff. Creditor Reporting System: Aid Activities Iin Support of Hiv/Aids Control 2003-2006-SystèMe de Notification des Pays CréAnciers: Activités d'Aide Pour la Lutte Contre le Vih/Sida 2003-2006. 2008. 116p. pap. 63.00 (978-92-64-03283-5(5)) Organization for Economic Cooperation & Development.

Shakeri, Nezhat. Estimation of Incidence & Survival Function of Doubly Censored Dat. 2009. 132p. pap. (978-3-639-16724-5(4)) VDM Verlag Dr. Mueller e.K.

UNAIDS. AIDS Epidemic Update November 2009. 2010. (UNAIDS Publication). (Illus.). 99p. pap. 24.00 (978-92-9173-832-8(8)) World Health Organization.

AIDS (DISEASE)—STUDY AND TEACHING

Aitken, Jayde. Exploring Students' Experiences of an Hiv/Aids Service Learning Module. 2010. 96p. pap. (978-3-8383-5927-4(5)) Lambert Academic Publishing.

Card, Josefina J., et al. The Complete HIV/AIDS Teaching Kit. 2007. (Illus.). 376p. pap. 95.00 incl. cd-rom (978-0-8261-0316-1(2)) Springer Publishing Co., Inc.

—Tools for Building Culturally Competent HIV Prevention Programs. 2007. 95.00 (978-0-8261-1517-1(9)) Springer Publishing Co., Inc.

Higgins, Christina & Norton, Bonny, eds. Language & HIV/Aids. 2009. (Critical Language & Literacy Studies). (ENG., Illus.). 280p. 129.95 (978-1-84769-220-7(6)); pap. 44.95 (978-1-84769-219-1(2)) Multilingual Matters GBR. Dist: Univ. of Toronto Pr.

Kiesbye, Stefan, ed. AIDS. 2008. (Social Issues Firsthand Ser.). (ENG.). 103p. (J). (gr. 4-7). lib. bdg. 31.80 (978-0-7377-4028-8(0), Greenhaven Pr., Inc.) Cengage Gale.

Lindner, Mary. Evaluation Study on the Effects of the Child Mind Project. 2010. 298p. pap. 52.00 (978-3-940755-30-8(3)) Budrich-Esser, Barbara DEU. Dist: International Specialized Bk. Services.

Machawira, Patricia & MacHawira, Patricia. How Is Education Possible in a World with Aids? 2010. 244p. pap. (978-3-8383-5892-5(9)) Lambert Academic Publishing.

Umbrage Editors. Pandemia: Enfrentado el SIDA. 2010. (ENG., Illus.). 45p. 40.00 (978-1-884167-38-6(1)) Umbrage Editions.

Wood, Lesley. Dealing with HIV & AIDS in the Classroom. 2009. (ENG.). 240p. pap. 26.95 (978-0-7021-7685-2(0)) Juta Academic ZAF. Dist: Independent Pubs. Group.

AIDS (DISEASE)—TESTING

Adekeye, Olujide. Psycho-Cultural Variables. 2010. 208p. pap. (978-3-639-27426-4(1)) VDM Verlag Dr. Mueller e.K.

Maru, Melaku. Hiv Testing & Pihct among Tuberculosis Patients in Addis Abab. 2009. 72p. pap. (978-3-639-17420-5(8)) VDM Verlag Dr. Mueller e.K.

Nebiyu, Hiruy & Ahmed, Ali. Hiv Voluntary Testing Uptake Determinants: Factors Affecting Voluntary Testing Uptake among University Students. 2011. 84p. pap. (978-3-639-32248-4(7)) VDM Verlag Dr. Mueller e.K.

AIDS (DISEASE)—TREATMENT

Aginam, O., et al, eds. The Global Governance of HIV/AIDS: Intellectual Property & Access to Essential Medicines. 2012. (Elgar Intellectual Property & Global Development Ser.). (Illus.). 288p. 110.00 (978-1-84980-490-5(7)) Elgar, Edward Publishing, Inc.

Brent, Robert J. Setting Priorities for HIV/AIDS Interventions: A Cost-Benefit Approach. 240p. 2011. pap. 20.00 (978-0-85793-250-1(0)) 2010. (Illus.). 112.00 (978-1-84720-331-1(0)) Elgar, Edward Publishing, Inc.

Browne-Umar, S. D. HIV/AIDS Treatment Strategies. 2010. 178p. pap. (978-1-84748-724-7(6)) Athena Pr.

Castor, Delivette, et al. Hiv-1 Resistance in Supervised Treatment Settings. 2008. 188p. pap. (978-3-639-07491-8(2)) VDM Verlag Dr. Mueller e.K.

Clumeck, N. & Friedland, G. Handbook of Medical Supportive Care of AIDS Patients. Date not set. (Basic & Clinical Oncology Ser.). (978-0-8247-9299-2(8)) Dekker, Marcel Inc.

Committee on Envisioning a Strategy for the Long-Term Burden of HIV/AIDS: African Needs and U.S. Interests & Institute of Medicine. Preparing for the

Future of HIV/AIDS in Africa: A Shared Responsibility. 2011. (ENG.). 228p. pap. 49.50 *(978-0-309-16018-6(9))* National Academies Pr.

Cullinan, Kerry & Thom, Anso, eds. The Virus, Vitamins & Vegetables: The South African HIV/AIDS Mystery. 2010. (ENG.). 211p. pap. 21.00 *(978-1-77009-691-2(4))* Jacana Media ZAF. Dist: Independent Pubs. Group.

D'Adesky, Anne-Christine. Moving Mountains: The Race to Treat Global AIDS. 2006. (ENG.). 496p. per. 23.00 *(978-1-84467-543-2(2)*, 844543) Verso Bks. GBR. Dist: Norton, W. W. & Co., Inc.

Dolin, Raphael, et al. AIDS Therapy. 3rd rev. ed. 2007. (ENG., Illus.). 1204p. 230.00 *(978-0-443-06752-5(X)*, Churchill Livingstone) Elsevier - Health Sciences Div.

Epstein, Helen. The Invisible Cure: Why We Are Losing the Fight Against AIDS in Africa. 2008. (ENG., Illus.). 352p. pap. 17.00 *(978-0-312-42772-6(7))* Picador.

Farber, M. Paul. The Micro Silver Bullet: A Preliminary Scientifically Documented Answer to the Three Largest Epidemics in the World. 5th rev. ed. Date not set. 700p. pap. 29.95 *(978-1-887742-01-6(8))* Professional Physicians Publishing & Health Services, Inc.

Geffen, Nathan. Debunking Delusions: The Inside Story of the Treatment Action Campaign. 2010. (ENG.). 256p. pap. 24.00 *(978-1-77009-781-0(3))* Jacana Media ZAF. Dist: Independent Pubs. Group.

Gilbert, David N., et al, eds. The Sanford Guide to HIV/AIDS Therapy. (Sanford Guide Ser.). (Illus.). 17th ed. 2008. 203p. pap. 39.95 *(978-1-930808-50-8(X))* 18th ed. 2009. 204p. pap. 39.95 *(978-1-930808-58-4(5))* Antimicrobial Therapy, Inc.

Gilbert, David N., et al. The Sanford Guide to Antimicrobial Therapy. 41st ed. 2011. (Sanford Guide to Animicrobial Therapy Ser.). (Illus.). 220p. spiral bd. 34.95 ***(978-1-930808-66-9(6)***, Wiley-Blackwell) Antimicrobial Therapy, Inc.

Hagemeister, Dirk T. The Burden of Care- Health Care Dilemmas in the South African Aids-Pandemic. 2007. 104p. per. *(978-3-8364-3198-9(X))* VDM Verlag Dr. Mueller e.K.

HIV/AIDS Bureau (U.S.) & Health Resources and Services Administration (U.S.), eds. Guide for HIV/AIDS Clinical Care. 2011. (ENG.). 619p. spiral bd. 55.00 ***(978-0-16-087205-1(7)***, Health & Human Services Dept.) United States Government Printing Office.

Joint United Nations Programme on HIV/AIDS Staff, contrib. by. The Positive Partnerships Program in Thailand: Empowering People Living with HIV. 2007. (UNAIDS Publication). 48p. pap. 18.00 *(978-92-9173-593-8(0))* World Health Organization.

Jones, Peris S. & Jones, Peris. AIDS Treatment & Human Rights in Context. 2009. (ENG., Illus.). 224p. 89.00 *(978-0-230-60959-4(7))* Palgrave Macmillan.

Kane, Brigid M. HIV/AIDS Treatment Drugs. 2011. (Understanding Drugs Ser.). (Illus.). 156p. (C). (gr. 9-12). 34.95 *(978-1-60413-541-1(7))* Facts On File, Inc.

Ka'opus, Lana Sue, ed. HIV Treatment Adherence: Challenging for Social Services. 2007. (Illus.). 184p. 175.00 *(978-0-7890-3626-1(6))* Routledge.

Karim, Salim Abdool & Karim, Quarraisha Abdool, eds. HIV/AIDS in South Africa. 2nd rev. ed. 2010. (Illus.). 608p. pap. 75.00 *(978-0-521-14793-4(X))* Cambridge Univ. Pr.

Kopp, C. The New Era of AIDS: HIV & Medicine in Times of Transition. 2010. (International Library of Ethics, Law, & the New Medicine Ser.). 212p. pap. 139.00 *(978-90-481-6187-4(8)*, 9048161878) Springer.

Meucci, Olimpia, ed. Chemokine Receptors & Neuroaids: Beyond Co-Receptor Function & Links to Other Neuropathologies. 2010. (ENG., Illus.). xvi, 412p. 209.00 *(978-1-4419-0792-9(0)*, 1441907920) Springer.

Mills, Robert Parker. Between Rock & a Hard Place: In Defense of Rock Hudson: from the Ashes of Trial to the Light of Truth. 2010. 492p. 33.99 *(978-1-4567-0039-3(1))*; pap. 22.50 *(978-1-4567-0038-6(3))* AuthorHouse.

Nunn, Amy. The Politics & History of AIDS Treatment in Brazil. 2009. (Illus.). 260p. 79.95 *(978-0-387-09617-9(5))* Springer.

Over, Mead. Achieving an AIDS Transition: Preventing Infections to Sustain Treatment. 2011. (ENG.). 150p. pap. 19.95 *(978-1-933286-38-9(5))* Ctr. for Global Development.

PEPFAR: From Emergency to Sustainability & Advances Against HIV/AIDS: Hearing Before the Committee on Foreign Affairs, House of Representatives, One Hundred Eleventh Congress, Second Session, September 29, 2010. 2010. iii, 141p. ***(978-0-16-087680-6(X)***, 552-070-42232-3) United States Government Printing Office.

Petersen, Maya. Application of Causal Inference Methods to Improve Treatment of Hiv Infection. 2008. 124p. pap. *(978-3-639-06629-6(4))* VDM Verlag Dr. Mueller e.K.

Pezi, Sinawe. Township Women's Fears of Hiv Disclosure. 2010. 80p. pap. *(978-3-8383-6616-6(6))* Lambert Academic Publishing.

Quigley, Fran. Walking Together, Walking Far: How a U. S. & African Medical School Partnership Is Winning the Fight Against HIV/AIDS. 2009. (ENG., Illus.). 176p. 50.00 *(978-0-253-35324-5(6)*, 0253353246); pap. 19.95 *(978-0-253-22089-9(0)*, 0253220890) Indiana Univ. Pr.

Revenga, Ana, et al. The Economics of Effective AIDS Treatment: Evaluating Policy Options for Thailand. 2006. (Health, Nutrition, & Population Ser.). (ENG., Illus.). 272p. per. 25.00 *(978-0-8213-6755-1(2)*, 9780821367551) World Bank Pubns.

Rowden, Rick. The Deadly Ideas of Neoliberalism: How the IMF Has Undermined Public Health & the Fight Against AIDS. 2009. (ENG.). 288p. 126.95 *(978-1-84813-284-9(0))* Zed Bks., Ltd. GBR. Dist: Macmillan.

Sande, Pamela. Sanford Guide to HIV/AIDS Therapy 2005 Pocket Edition. 10.50 *(978-1-930808-34-8(8))* Antimicrobial Therapy, Inc.

Sanders, Winnie. My True Revelation Featuring a Possible Cure for Aids. 2010. 62p. pap. 10.49 *(978-1-4490-7272-8(0))* AuthorHouse.

Sanford, Jay P. The Sanford Guide to HIV/AIDS Therapy. Sande, Merle A. et al, eds. 16th ed. 2007. (Illus.). 195p. spiral bd. 29.95 *(978-1-930808-44-7(5))* Antimicrobial Therapy, Inc.

—The Sanford Guide to HIV/AIDS Therapy. Gilbert, David N. et al, eds. 17th ed. 2008. (Sanford Guide Ser.). (Illus.). 204p. pap. 15.25 *(978-1-930808-51-5(8))* Antimicrobial Therapy, Inc.

Sanford, Jay P. & Sande, Merle A. The Sanford Guide to HIV/AIDS Therapy. Gilbert, David N. et al, eds. 18th ed. 2009. (Illus.). 204p. pap. 15.95 *(978-1-930808-57-7(7))* Antimicrobial Therapy, Inc.

Seckinelgin, Hakan. International Politics of Hiv/Aids. 2007. XII, 196p. 37.95 *(978-0-415-41384-8(2))* Routledge.

—International Politics of HIV/AIDS: Global Disease-Local Pain. 2007. 193p. 150.00 *(978-0-415-41383-1(4))* Routledge.

Springs, Daniel Everett. How to Be Healed of Aids & Cancer. 2007. 82p. pap. 10.00 *(978-1-4257-4647-6(0))* Xlibris Corp.

United States, Congress Senate Committee on Homeland Security and Governmental Affairs Subcommittee on Federal Financial Management, Government Information, and International Security Staff, contrib. by. Ensuring Early Diagnosis & Access to Treatment for HIV/AIDS: Can Federal Resources Be More Effectively Targeted?: Hearing Before the Federal Financial Management, Government Information, & International Security Subcommittee of the Committee on Homeland Security & Governmental Affairs, United States Senate, One Hundred Ninth Congress, Second Session, April 26, 2006. 2007. (Illus.). iii, 385p. *(978-0-16-078419-4(0)*, 552-070-357'5-7) United States Government Printing Office.

Volberding, Paul, et al, eds. Sande's HIV/AIDS Medicine: Medical Management of AIDS 2012. 2nd ed. 2012. (ENG., Illus.). 596p. pap. 75.00 ***(978-1-4557-0695-2(7)***, Saunders) Elsevier - Health Sciences Div.

WHO Regional Office for the Western Pacific. Continuum of Care for People Living with HIV/AIDS in Cambodia (the): Linkages & Strengthening in the Public Health System: Case Study. 2006. (Wpro Nonserial Publication). (ENG.). 31p. pap. 12.00 *(978-92-9061-222-3(3))* World Health Organization.

AIDS (DISEASE)—AFRICA

ABBE Scientist Research Division Staff. AIDS & HIV in Congo: Index & Medical Analysis of New Clinical Research Information. 2008. (ENG., Illus.). 160p. ring bd. 69.95 *(978-0-7883-4964-5(3))* ABBE Pubs. Assn. of Washington, D.C.

—AIDS & HIV in Ethiopia: Index & Medical Analysis of New Clinical & Research Information. 2008. (ENG., Illus.). 160p. ring bd. 69.95 *(978-0-7883-4965-2(1))* ABBE Pubs. Assn. of Washington, D.C.

—AIDS & HIV in Nigeria: Index & Medical Analysis of New Clinical & Research Information. 2008. (ENG., Illus.). 160p. ring bd. 69.95 *(978-0-7883-4967-6(8))* ABBE Pubs. Assn. of Washington, D.C.

Abraraw, Chane. Impact of Hiv/Aids on Ethiopian Business: A Managerial Perspective. 2011. 132p. pap. ***(978-3-639-32931-5(7))*** VDM Verlag Dr. Mueller e.K.

Abu-Raddad, Laith, et al. Characterizing the HIV/AIDS Epidemic in the Middle East & North Africa: Time for Strategic Action. 2010. (Orientations in Development Ser.). (ENG., Illus.). 304p. pap. 35.00 *(978-0-8213-8137-3(7)*, 9780821381373) World Bank Pubns.

Adato, Michelle & Bassett, Lucy. Social Protection & Cash Transfers to Strengthen Families Affected by HIV & AIDS. 2012. ***(978-0-89629-201-7(0))*** International Food Policy Research Institute.

Adekeye, Olujide. Psycho-Cultural Variables. 2010. 208p. pap. *(978-3-639-27426-4(1))* VDM Verlag Dr. Mueller e.K.

Africa's Soul Hope: The AIDS Crisis & the Church. 2007. 96p. pap. 8.50 *(978-0-8341-2289-5(8)*, 083-412-2898) Beacon Hill Pr. of Kansas City.

Alemayehu, Bekele. Evaluation of Voluntary Counseling & Testing Service: Counselors' Attitude, Minimum Standard & Client Satisfaction. 2011. 92p. pap. ***(978-3-639-32307-8(6))*** VDM Verlag Dr. Mueller e.K.

Alemneh, Aschenaki. Sexual Behaviour & Hiv/Aids: In Community Practicing Widow Inheritance. 2011. 24p. pap. ***(978-3-639-18371-9(1))*** VDM Verlag Dr. Mueller e.K.

Amde, Woldekidan Kifle. Barriers to Hiv Testing: Investigating Hiv Testing Practices in a Rural District in Ethiopia. 2011. 84p. pap. ***(978-3-639-33707-5(7))*** VDM Verlag Dr. Mueller e.K.

Ande, Karen & Richter, Ruthann. Face to Face: Children of the AIDS Crisis in Africa. 2010. 128p. pap. 39.95 *(978-1-932717-20-4(X))* Hope Publishing Hse.

Ansari, Naseem. Pathology of Hiv/Aids. 2011. 156p. pap. ***(978-3-8443-8091-0(4))*** Lambert Academic Publishing.

Ansumana, Rashid & JAMES SUNDUFU, A. B. U. The Management of Hiv/Aids in Freetown, Sierra Leone. 2010. 76p. pap. *(978-3-8383-8823-6(2))* Lambert Academic Publishing.

Arseneau, Robyn. Factors Shaping Pre-Service Teacher Identities in an Hiv/Aids Context. 2011. 136p. pap. ***(978-3-8433-8381-3(2))*** Lambert Academic Publishing.

Ashburn, Kristen, photos by. I Am Because We Are. 2009. (ENG., Illus.). 180p. 49.95 *(978-1-57687-482-0(6))* powerHouse Cultural Entertainment, Inc.

Ayres, Jeffrey McKelvey & Siplon, Patricia D. Divergent Campaigns Towards Global Health Governance: Canadian & U.S. Approaches to the Global HIV/AIDS Pandemic. 2007. 52p. *(978-1-882582-58-7(6))* Canadian-American Ctr.

Barz, Gregory & Cohen, Judah M., eds. The Culture of AIDS in Africa: Hope & Healing Through Music & the Arts, 1 vol. 2011. (ENG., Illus.). 528p. pap. 49.95 *(978-0-19-974448-0(3))* Oxford Univ. Pr., Inc.

Becker, Felicitas & Geissler, Wessler, eds. Aids & Religious Practice in Africa. 2009. (Studies of Religion in Africa Ser.). (Illus.). vi, 404p. *(978-90-04-16400-0(6))* BRILL.

Bill John, Akutoko. Religious Health Assets, Health Outcomes & Hiv/Aids. 2011. 96p. pap. ***(978-3-8443-1391-8(5))*** Lambert Academic Publishing.

Bongmba, Elias Kifon. Facing a Pandemic: The African Church & the Crisis of HIV/AIDS. 2007. 350p. per. 39.95 *(978-1-932792-82-9(1))* Baylor Univ. Pr.

Cantelon, James. When God Stood Up: A Christian Response to AIDS in Africa. 2007. (ENG.). 256p. per. 24.95 *(978-0-470-83927-0(9)*, Wiley) Wiley, John & Sons, Inc.

Carelse, Roslind. Community Based Hiv & Aids Care. 2009. 88p. pap. *(978-3-639-16379-7(6))* VDM Verlag Dr. Mueller e.K.

Chale, Samwel. Media & Hiv/Aids in Cities-Tanzania Experience. 2011. 64p. pap. ***(978-3-8443-0308-7(1))*** Lambert Academic Publishing.

Chanza, Nelson. Private Sector Response to Hiv/Aids Policy in Zimbabwe. 2011. 88p. pap. ***(978-3-8454-2046-2(4))*** Lambert Academic Publishing.

Chibambo, Lucy Thokozile. Cultural Practices, Hiv & Aids & the Church in Nsanje District - Malawi: Perspectives of the Citizens of Nsanje District in Malawi on Hiv & Aids, Culture & the Church. 2011. 84p. pap. ***(978-3-639-31840-1(4))*** VDM Verlag Dr. Mueller e.K.

Chidi Nwachukwu-Udaku, Benedict. SIDA en África: Reflexiones y Propuestas Desde el Pueblo Igbo. 2009. (SPA., Illus.). 374p. *(978-84-8468-258-5(7))* Universidad Pontificia Comillas de Madrid.

Chimunhu, Jephias. Adolescence Perceptions of the Relevance of Barriers to Vct. 2011. 92p. pap. ***(978-3-8443-1710-7(4))*** Lambert Academic Publishing.

Chirambo, Kondwani. The Political Cost of AIDS in Africa: An Overview. 2008. 84p. pap. *(978-1-920118-66-2(7))* IDASA Pubs. ZAF. Dist: Michigan State Univ. Pr.

Chirambo, Kondwani, ed. Examining the Impact of an Epidemic on Ward Councillors. 2008. 124p. pap. *(978-1-920118-74-7(8))* IDASA Pubs. ZAF. Dist: Michigan State Univ. Pr.

Cohen, Barney & Menken, Jane A., eds. Aging in Sub-Saharan Africa: Recommendations for Furthering Research. 2006. (ENG., Illus.) 368p. pap. 73.25 *(978-0-309-10281-0(2))* National Academies Pr.

Cohen, Judah M. The Culture of AIDS in Africa: Hope & Healing Through Music & the Arts, 1 vol. Barz, Gregory, ed. 2011. (ENG., Illus.). 528p. 150.00 *(978-0-19-974447-3(5))* Oxford Univ. Pr., Inc.

Committee on Envisioning a Strategy for the Long-Term Burden of HIV/AIDS: African Needs and U.S. Interests & Institute of Medicine. Preparing for the Future of HIV/AIDS in Africa: A Shared Responsibility. 2011. (ENG.). 228p. pap. 49.50 *(978-0-309-16018-6(9))* National Academies Pr.

Crush, Jonathan, et al. Linking Migration, Hiv/Aids & Urban Food Security in Southern & Eastern Afric. 2007. (Illus.). 64p. (C). pap. *(978-1-920118-46-4(2))* IDASA Pubs. ZAF. Dist: Michigan State Univ. Pr.

Cullinan, Kerry & Thom, Anso, eds. The Virus, Vitamins & Vegetables: The South African HIV/AIDS Mystery. 2010. (ENG.). 211p. pap. 21.00 *(978-1-77009-691-2(4))* Jacana Media ZAF. Dist: Independent Pubs. Group.

de Waal, Alex. AIDS & Power: Why There Is No Political Crisis - Yet. 2006. (African Arguments Ser.). (ENG., Illus.). 176p. 75.95 *(978-1-84277-706-0(8))*; per. 23.95 *(978-1-84277-707-7(6))* Zed Bks., Ltd. GBR. Dist: Macmillan.

Debra Liebenow Daly. The Kingdom of Roses & Thorns. 2009. 276p. pap. 15.49 *(978-1-4389-5488-2(3))* AuthorHouse.

Dickinson, David. Changing the Course of AIDS: Peer Education in South Africa & Its Lessons for the Global Crisis. 2009. (Culture & Politics of Health Care Work Ser.). (Illus.). 248p. 39.95 *(978-0-8014-4831-7(X)*, ILR Pr.) Cornell Univ. Pr.

Dilger, Hansjörg & Luig, Ute, eds. Morality, Hope & Grief: Anthropologies of AIDS in Africa. 2010. (EH Ser.). (Illus.). 356p. 95.00 *(978-1-84545-663-4(7))* Berghahn Bks., Inc.

Doku, Paul Narh. Hiv/Aids, Orphans & Mental Health: The African Perspective. 2011. 88p. pap. ***(978-3-639-34016-7(7))*** VDM Verlag Dr. Mueller e.K.

Elemo, Ibrahim. Reproductive Health, Hiv/Aids & Gender Perspectives in East Afric. 2009. 168p. pap. *(978-3-639-16758-0(9))* VDM Verlag Dr. Mueller e.K.

Epprecht, Marc. Heterosexual Africa? The History of an Idea from the Age of Exploration to the Age of AIDS. 2008. (New African Histories Ser.). (ENG.). 240p. 39.95 *(978-0-8214-1798-0(3))*; pap. 24.95 *(978-0-8214-1799-7(1))* Ohio Univ. Pr.

—Heterosexual Africa: The History of an Idea from the Age of Exploration to the Age of AIDS. 2008. xiii, 231p. pap. *(978-1-86914-157-8(1))* Univ. of Natal Pr. ZAF. Dist: International Specialized Bk. Services.

Epstein, Helen. The Invisible Cure: Why We Are Losing the Fight Against AIDS in Africa. 2008. (ENG., Illus.). 352p. pap. 17.00 *(978-0-312-42772-6(7))* Picador.

Erin, Hartzell. Living in Africa: The Convergence of Poverty & the Hiv/Aids Epidemic. 2011. 76p. pap. ***(978-3-639-32788-5(8))*** VDM Verlag Dr. Mueller e.K.

Esau, Omar. Checkmating Hiv/Aids As a Teacher Researcher. 2011. 264p. pap. ***(978-3-8443-0702-3(8))*** Lambert Academic Publishing.

Falola, Toyin & Heaton, Matthew M., eds. HIV/AIDS, Illness, & African Well-Being. 2007. (Rochester Studies in African History & the Diaspora Ser.: Volume 27). (Illus.). 428p. 75.00 *(978-1-58046-240-2(5))* Univ. of Rochester Pr.

Feldman, Douglas A., ed. AIDS, Culture, & Africa. (ENG., Illus.). 2011. 312p. pap. 32.95 *(978-0-8130-3721-9(2))* 2008. 336p. 75.00 *(978-0-8130-3253-5(9))* Univ. Pr. of Florida.

Fiaveh, Daniel Yaw. Male Perspectives on Condom Use. 2011. 164p. pap. ***(978-3-8443-0941-6(1))*** Lambert Academic Publishing.

Flint, Adrian. HIV/AIDS in Sub-Saharan Africa: Politics, Aid & Globalization. 2011. (ENG., Illus.). 240p. 85.00 *(978-0-230-22142-0(4))* Palgrave Macmillan.

Fourie, Pieter. The Political Management of HIV & AIDS in South Africa: One Burden Too Many? 2006. (ENG., Illus.). 264p. 95.00 *(978-0-230-00667-6(1))* Palgrave Macmillan.

Gaga, John. The Role of Church Leaders in Hiv & Aids Prevention. 2011. 140p. pap. ***(978-3-8443-8252-5(6))*** Lambert Academic Publishing.

Geffen, Nathan. Debunking Delusions: The Inside Story of the Treatment Action Campaign. 2010. (ENG.). 256p. pap. 24.00 *(978-1-77009-781-0(3))* Jacana Media ZAF. Dist: Independent Pubs. Group.

Gisselquist, David. Points to Consider. 2008. 236p. *(978-1-905068-26-5(3))* Adonis & Abbey Publishers Ltd.

Gobina, Ronald. Lymphomas in Hiv Patients. 2011. 100p. pap. ***(978-3-8443-1411-3(3))*** Lambert Academic Publishing.

Gorgens-Albino, Marelize, et al. The Africa Multi-Country AIDS Program, 2000-2006: Results of the World Bank's Response to a Development Crisis. 2007. (ENG., Illus.). 188p. per. 15.00 *(978-0-8213-7052-0(9)*, 9780821370520) World Bank Pubns.

—Programme Plurinational de Lutte Contre le Sida en Afrique, 2000-2006: Bilan des Interventions de la Banque Mondiale Face a une Crise de Developpement. 2007. (FRE., Illus.). 208p. per. 15.00 *(978-0-8213-7109-1(6)*, 9780821371091) World Bank Pubns.

Grannis, Susanna W. Hope Amidst Despair: HIV/AIDS-Affected Children in Sub-Saharan Africa, 1 vol. 2011. (ENG.). 200p. 25.00 ***(978-0-7453-3153-9(X))***; lib. bdg. 75.00 ***(978-0-7453-3154-6(8))*** Pluto Pr. GBR. Dist: Macmillan.

Green, Edward C. Broken Promises: How the AIDS Establishment Has Betrayed the Developing World. 2011. (Illus.). 288p. pap. 17.95 *(978-1-936227-00-6(2))* Left Coast Pr., Inc.

Green, Edward C. Broken Promises: How the AIDS Establishment has Betrayed the Developing World. 2011. (ENG., Illus.). 288p. (C). pap. 17.95 ***(978-1-61132-112-8(3))*** Left Coast Pr., Inc.

Greene, Melissa Fay. There Is No Me Without You: One Woman's Odyssey to Rescue Africa's Children. 2006. (ENG., Illus.). 480p. 25.95 *(978-1-59691-116-1(6))* Bloomsbury Publishing.

—There Is No Me Without You: One Woman's Odyssey to Rescue Her Country's Children. 2007. (ENG., Illus.). 480p. per. 17.00 *(978-1-59691-293-9(6)*, Bloomsbury Publishing.

Hagemeister, Dirk T. The Burden of Care- Health Care Dilemmas in the South African Aids-Pandemic. 2007. 104p. per. *(978-3-8364-3198-9(X))* VDM Verlag Dr. Mueller e.K.

Halperin, Daniel & Timberg, Craig. Tinderbox: How the West Sparked the AIDS Epidemic & How the World Can Finally Overcome It. 2012. (ENG.). 432p. (gr. 12). 29.95 ***(978-1-59420-327-5(X)***, Penguin Pr. HC, The) Penguin Group (USA) Inc.

Hanley, Matthew & de Irala, Jokin. Affirming Love, Avoiding AIDs: What Africa Can Teach the West. 2009. (ENG.). pap. 17.95 *(978-0-935372-56-4(3))* National Catholic Bioethics Ctr., The.

Haricharan, Hanne Jensen. 'to Tell or Not to Tell' 2010. 92p. pap. *(978-3-8383-5256-5(4))* Lambert Academic Publishing.

Harman, Sophie. The World Bank, Civil Society & HIV/AIDS: Setting a Global Agenda. 2010. (Routledge Advances in International Relations & Global Politics Ser.). (ENG.). 176p. (C). 128.00 *(978-0-415-56290-4(2)*, Routledge) Taylor & Francis Group GBR. Dist: Taylor & Francis Group.

Hattas, Aysha. Religious Leaders,Traditional Healers. 2009. 136p. pap. *(978-3-639-19174-5(9))* VDM Verlag Dr. Mueller e.K.

Henderson, Patricia C. AIDS, Intimacy & Care in Rural KwaZulu-Natal: A Kinship of Bones. 2012. (Care & Welfare Ser.). (ENG.). 256p. pap. ***(978-90-8964-359-9(1))*** Amsterdam Univ. Pr.

Hinga & Hinga, Teresia M. Women, Religion & HIV/AIDS in Africa: Responding to Ethical & Theological Challenges. xviii, 205p. *(978-1-875053-69-8(7))* Cluster Pubns.

Hoad, Neville Wallace. African Intimacies: Race, Homosexuality, & Globalization. 2007. 232p. 60.00 *(978-0-8166-4915-0(4))*; per. 22.50 *(978-0-8166-4916-7(2))* Univ. of Minnesota Pr.

Hubbard, Susan & Suzuki, Tomoko. Building Resilience: Human Security Approaches to AIDS in Africa & Asia. 2008. (ENG.). 120p. pap. 10.00 *(978-4-88907-079-8(6))* Japan Ctr. for International Exchange JPN. Dist: Brookings Institution Pr.

Hunter, Mark. Love in the Time of AIDS: Inequality, Gender, & Rights in South Africa. 2010. (ENG., Illus.). 324p. 70.00 *(978-0-253-35533-1(8)*, 0253355338); pap. 24.95 *(978-0-253-22239-8(7)*, 0253222397) Indiana Univ. Pr.

Ikuteyijo, Lanre. Hiv & Aids in Nigerian Prisons. 2010. 96p. pap. *(978-3-8383-0370-3(9))* Lambert Academic Publishing.

Itano, Nicole. No Place Left to Bury the Dead: Denial, Despair & Hope in the African AIDS Pande. 2010. (ENG.). 352p. pap. 21.99 *(978-1-4516-3454-9(4)*, Beyond Words/Atria Bks.) Atria Bks.

Kaguda, Darmarris. Hiv/Aids & the Medi. 2011. 116p. pap. ***(978-3-8443-9842-7(2))*** Lambert Academic Publishing.

Kaguri, Twesigye Jackson. The Price of Stones: Building a School for My Village. 2010. lib. bdg. *(978-1-60285-836-7(5))* Ctr. Point Large Print.

Kaguri, Twesigye Jackson & Linville, Susan Urbanek. The Price of Stones: Building a School for My Village. 2010. (ENG., Illus.). 288p. (gr. 12). 25.95 *(978-0-670-02184-0(9)*, Viking Adult) Penguin Group (USA) Inc.

A

Kalanzi, Dorothy J. AIDS Crisis Control in Uganda: The Use of HAART. 2011. 166p. *(978-1-60497-787-5(6))* Cambria Pr.

Kalipeni, Ezekiel, et al, eds. Strong Women, Dangerous Times: Gender & HIV/AIDS in Africa. 2009. 79.00 *(978-1-60692-736-6(1))* Nova Science Pubs., Inc.

Kalula, Mpiana. Project of Mpiana Pensioners in South Africa & Hiv/Aids. 2010. 116p. pap. *(978-3-8383-6673-9(5))* Lambert Academic Publishing.

Kanki, Phyllis J. & Marlink, Richard G. A Line Drawn in the Sand: Responses to the AIDS Treatment Crisis in Africa. 2009. (Harvard Series on Population & Development Studies). (Illus.). 300p. pap. 30.00 *(978-0-674-03345-0(0))* Harvard Univ. Pr.

Karim, Salim Abdool & Karim, Quarraisha Abdool, eds. HIV/AIDS in South Africa. 2nd rev. ed. 2010. (Illus.). 608p. pap. 75.00 *(978-0-521-14793-4(X))* Cambridge Univ. Pr.

Kamhanga Beraho, Monica. Living with AIDS in Uganda: Impacts on banana-farming households in two Districts. 2008. (AWLAE Ser.). 372p. pap. 55.00 *(978-90-8686-064-7(8))* Wageningen Academic Publishers NLD. Dist: Enfield Publishing & Distribution Co., Inc.

Katiambo, David. Health Communication. 2011. 308p. pap. ***(978-3-8383-8070-4(3))*** Lambert Academic Publishing.

Kedia, Satish. Annals of Anthropological Practice: Hiv/Aids & Food Insecurity in Sub-Saharan Africa - Challenges & Solutions. 2011. (NAPA Bulletin Ser.). (ENG.). 244p. pap. 25.00 ***(978-1-4443-6155-1(4)***, Wiley-Blackwell) Wiley, John & Sons, Inc.

Kelakazola, Henry Ilunga Kasongo. W H O Recommended Infant Feeding Options. 2011. 108p. pap. ***(978-3-8443-0787-0(7))*** Lambert Academic Publishing.

Kemigisa, Margaret. Social Networks & Health Promotion. 2010. 260p. pap. *(978-3-639-22879-3(0))* VDM Verlag Dr. Mueller e.K.

Keys, Alicia. How Can I Keep from Singing? Transforming the Lives of African Children & Families Affected by AIDS. 2011. (ENG., Illus.). 112p. 25.00 *(978-1-884167-60-7(8))* Umbrage Editions.

Kinsman, John. AIDS Policy in Uganda: Evidence, Ideology, & the Making of an African Success Story. 2010. (ENG., Illus.). 258p. 89.00 *(978-0-230-10428-0(2))* Palgrave Macmillan.

Kling, Sydney. INSIDE Outside: A Retiree's Peace Corps Journal from South Africa. 2007. 387p. pap. 14.00 *(978-0-9794257-1-4(9))* Kling, Sydney.

Konyana, Elias G. Making Voluntary Counselling & Testing Worthwhile. 2011. 60p. pap. ***(978-3-8443-2295-8(7))*** Lambert Academic Publishing.

Krotz, Larry. Piecing the Puzzle: The Genesis of AIDS Research in Africa. 2012. (ENG., Illus.). 220p. pap. 28.95 ***(978-0-88755-730-9(9))*** Univ. of Manitoba Pr. CAN. Dist: Chicago Distribution Ctr.

Langwick, Stacey A. Bodies, Politics, & African Healing: The Matter of Maladies in Tanzania. 2011. (ENG., Illus.). 320p. 70.00 *(978-0-253-35527-0(3)*, 0253355273); pap. 24.95 *(978-0-253-22245-9(1)*, 0253222451) Indiana Univ. Pr.

Lawson, Lesley. Side Effects: The Story of AIDS in South Africa. 2008. 352p. pap. 22.95 *(978-1-77013-067-8(5))* Double Storey Bks. ZAF. Dist: International Publishers Marketing.

Libati, Daniel. Right to Health in Zambi. 2011. 64p. pap. ***(978-3-8443-9606-5(3))*** Lambert Academic Publishing.

Lule, Elizabeth & Haacker, Markus. The Fiscal Dimensions of HIV/AIDS in Botswana, South Africa, Swaziland, & Uganda. 2011. ***(978-0-8213-8808-2(8))*** World Bank Pubns.

Magoro, Mmbangiseni. Hiv, Aids & Arvs. 2011. 116p. pap. ***(978-3-8433-8192-5(5))*** Lambert Academic Publishing.

Maithya, Harrison. Sexual & Reproductive Issues among the Akamba of Keny. 2009. 236p. pap. *(978-3-639-16405-3(9))* VDM Verlag Dr. Mueller e.K.

Makonese, Loveness. Livelihoods & Hiv/Aids. 2009. 104p. pap. *(978-3-639-14296-9(9))* VDM Verlag Dr. Mueller e.K.

Manda, Charles. Who Is My Neighbour? 2011. 128p. pap. ***(978-3-8443-9310-1(2))*** Lambert Academic Publishing.

Mapuranga, Tapiwa Praise. Gender, Hiv & Aids & African Traditional Religion in Zimbabwe. 2011. 164p. pap. ***(978-3-8433-8791-0(5))*** Lambert Academic Publishing.

Maru, Melaku. Hiv Testing & Pihct among Tuberculosis Patients in Addis Abab. 2009. 72p. pap. *(978-3-639-17420-5(8))* VDM Verlag Dr. Mueller e.K.

Masaiti, Bridget Nonde. African Indigenous Churches, Polygamy & Hiv & Aids. 2011. 132p. pap. ***(978-3-8443-9450-4(8))*** Lambert Academic Publishing.

Mashua, Jacinta Sintamei. Institutional Survey of Producers & Analysis of Hiv/Aids Publications. 2010. 72p. pap. *(978-3-8383-6273-1(X))* Lambert Academic Publishing.

Matoane, Matshepo. From Theory to Practice. 2009. 136p. pap. *(978-3-639-16661-3(2))* VDM Verlag Dr. Mueller e.K.

Maxwell, Janine. It's Not Okay with Me. 2009. 208p. per. 14.99 *(978-1-57921-885-0(7))* WinePress Publishing.

Mehlomakulu, Vuyelwa. Construction of Masculine Sexuality: A Psychological Discourse Analysis. 2010. 84p. pap. *(978-3-8383-8252-4(8))* Lambert Academic Publishing.

Minnaar, Ansie & Bodkin, Candice. The Pocket Guide for HIV & AIDS Nursing Care. 2007. (ENG., Illus.). 256p. pap. 31.95 *(978-0-7021-7193-2(X))* Juta Academic ZAF. Dist: Independent Pubs. Group.

Mligo, Elia Shabani. Jesus & the Stigmatized: Reading the Gospel of John in a Context of HIV/AIDSÐRelated Stigmatization in Tanzania. 2011. 474p. pap. 52.00 *(978-1-60899-706-0(5)*, Pickwick Pubns.) Wipf & Stock Pubs.

Mogeni, Emily. Aids in Afric: Aids, Africa's Dilemma! 2011. 216p. 29.99 ***(978-1-4568-9871-7(X))*** Xlibris Corp.

Motsi, Petronella Dadirai & MABVURIRA, Vincent. Seeking Balance Between Hiv Prevention Programmes & Tradition. 2011. 56p. pap. ***(978-3-8443-9071-1(5))*** Lambert Academic Publishing.

Muchiri Murithi, Gideon. Hiv/Aids: Adoption of Urban Agricultural Interventions in Nakuru,Kenya. 2011. 128p. pap. ***(978-3-8454-1126-2(0))*** Lambert Academic Publishing.

Mukudi, Edith & Commins, Stephen K. HIV/AIDS in Africa: Challenges & Impact. 2008. *(978-1-59221-624-6(2))*; pap. *(978-1-59221-625-3(0))* Africa World Pr.

Mulligan, Suzanne. Confronting the Challenge: Poverty, Gender, & HIV in South Africa. 2010. 209p. pap. 51.95 *(978-3-03911-938-7(9))* Lang, Peter AG GBR. Dist: Lang, Peter.

Murfee, Keith R. A Second Chance for Hope: the Story of Nyumbani. 2007. 104p. pap. 19.50 *(978-1-4303-1968-9(2))* Lulu Enterprises Inc.

Muriisa, Roberts. The Aids Pandemic in Ugand. 2009. 344p. pap. *(978-3-639-14634-9(4))* VDM Verlag Dr. Mueller e.K.

Musisi, Seggane & Kinyanda, Eugene. Psychiatric Problems of HIV/AIDS & Their Management in Africa. (Illus.). xvii, 369p. *(978-9970-02-734-7(4))* Fountain Pubs. Ltd.

Musopole, Augustine. Spirituality, Sexuality & HIV/AIDS in Malawi: Theological Strategies for Behaviour Change. 2007. 64p. pap. *(978-99908-81-02-8(2))* Kachere Series, Bks. on Religion, Theology & Society in Malawi MWI. Dist: Michigan State Univ. Pr.

Mwiturubani, Donald Anthony & Gebre, Ayalew. Youth, HIV/AIDS & Social Transformations in Africa. 2009. 142p. pap. *(978-2-86978-255-6(1))* Council for the Development of Social Science Research in Africa SEN. Dist: Michigan State Univ. Pr.

Nakazibwe, Faustine. The Hiv/Aids Orphan Crisis. 2009. 90p. pap. *(978-3-639-18236-1(7))* VDM Verlag Dr. Mueller e.K.

Nattrass, Nicoli. The AIDS Conspiracy: Science Fights Back. 2012. (ENG., Illus.). 240p. (gr. 17). 34.50 ***(978-0-231-14912-9(3))*** Columbia Univ. Pr.

Nattrass, Nicoli. Mortal Combat: AIDS Denialism & the Struggle for Antiretrovirals in South Africa. 2007. (Illus.). 269p. (C). pap. 34.95 *(978-1-86914-132-5(6))* University of Kwazulu-Natal Press ZAF. Dist: International Specialized Bk. Services.

Ndinga-Muvumba, Angela & Pharoah, Robyn, eds. HIV/AIDS & Society in South Africa. 2008. 265p. (C). pap. 38.95 *(978-1-86914-152-3(0))* University of Kwazulu-Natal Press ZAF. Dist: International Specialized Bk. Services.

Nguyen, Vinh-Kim. The Republic of Therapy: Triage & Sovereignty in West Africa's Time of AIDS. 2010. (Body, Commodity, Text Ser.). (ENG.). 256p. pap. 22.95 *(978-0-8223-4874-0(8))*; (Illus.). 79.95 *(978-0-8223-4862-7(4))* Duke Univ. Pr.

Nolen, Stephanie. 28: Stories of AIDS in Africa. (ENG., Illus.). 384p. 2008. pap. 15.99 *(978-0-8027-1675-0(X))* 2007. 25.95 *(978-0-8027-1598-2(2))* Walker & Co.

Ntarangwi, Mwenda, et al, eds. African Anthropologies: History, Critique & Practice. 2006. (Africa in the New Millennium Ser.). (ENG.). 256p. 123.95 *(978-1-84277-762-6(9))*; per. 34.95 *(978-1-84277-763-3(7))* Zed Bks., Ltd. GBR. Dist: Macmillan.

Nwachukwu-Udaku, Benedict Chidi. From What We Should Do to Who We Should Be: Negotiating Theological Reflections & Praxis in the Context of Hiv/Aids among the Igbos of Nigeria. 2011. 432p. pap. 20.50 ***(978-1-4634-1493-1(5))*** AuthorHouse.

Nwanna, Chinwe. Socio-Economic Status & Hiv-Related Discrimination in Lagos, Nigeri. 2011. 308p. pap. ***(978-3-8443-0605-7(6))*** Lambert Academic Publishing.

Nyawasha, Tawanda Sydesky. Citizenship, Social Capital & Hiv/Aids in South Afric. 2011. 316p. pap. ***(978-3-8454-1937-4(7))*** Lambert Academic Publishing.

Nyirenda, Nkhosikazi-Princess Zindaba. Talakata - the Tears of Afric. 2009. 236p. 30.00 *(978-1-934925-51-5(9)*, Strategic Bk. Publishing) AEG Literary Publishing Services, Inc.

Obare, Evans & Evans, Obare. Effects of Hiv/Aids on Sugar Industry in Kenya: A Case Study of Chemelil Sugar Factory, Nyando District. 2011. 68p. pap. ***(978-3-639-32304-7(1))*** VDM Verlag Dr. Mueller e.K.

Okwa, Omolade. Health Status of Women in Tropical Afric. 2011. 156p. pap. ***(978-3-8443-1352-9(4))*** Lambert Academic Publishing.

Opata, Violet Nabwire K. Fighting Hiv/Aids Pandemic Through Education: A Reflection on Hiv/Aids Education Programme in Kenya. 2011. 152p. pap. ***(978-3-639-32668-0(7))*** VDM Verlag Dr. Mueller e.K.

Palitza, Kristin, et al, eds. What Is Left Unsaid: Reporting the South African HIV Epidemic. 2011. (ENG., Illus.). 288p. pap. 31.95 ***(978-1-920196-25-7(0))*** Jacana Media ZAF. Dist: Independent Pubs. Group.

Patterson, Amy S. The Politics of AIDS in Africa. 2006. (Challenge & Change in African Politics Ser.). (Illus.). (C). 200p. lib. bdg. 49.95 *(978-1-58826-452-7(1))*; 226p. pap. 22.00 *(978-1-58826-477-0(7))* Rienner, Lynne Pubs.

Pepin, Jacques. The Origins of AIDS. 2011. (ENG., Illus.). 310p. 85.00 *(978-1-107-00663-8(5))*; pap. 28.99 *(978-0-521-18637-7(4))* Cambridge Univ. Pr.

Pezi, Sinawe. Township Women's Fears of Hiv Disclosure. 2010. 80p. pap. *(978-3-8383-6616-6(6))* Lambert Academic Publishing.

Prince, Bridgette, et al, eds. Skills-building for Gender Mainstreaming in HIV/AIDS: Research & Practice: Seminar Proceedings. 2007. (ENG.). 88p. pap. 11.95 *(978-0-7969-2167-3(9))* Human Sciences Research Council ZAF. Dist: Independent Pubs. Group.

Prince, Ruth Jane & Geissler, Paul Wenzel. The Land Is Dying: Contingency, Creativity & Conflict in Western Kenya. 2010. (Epistemologies of Healing Ser.). (Illus.). 444p. 95.00 *(978-1-84545-481-4(2))* Berghahn Bks., Inc.

Quigley, Fran. Walking Together, Walking Far: How a U. S. & African Medical School Partnership Is Winning the Fight Against HIV/AIDS. 2009. (ENG., Illus.). 176p. 50.00 *(978-0-253-35324-5(6)*, 0253353246); pap. 19.95 *(978-0-253-22089-9(0)*, 0253220890) Indiana Univ. Pr.

Reddy, Vasu, et al, eds. From Social Silence to Social Science: Same-Sex Sexuality, HIV & AIDS & Gender in South Africa. 2010. (ENG., Illus.). 296p. pap. 34.95 *(978-0-7969-2276-2(4))* Human Sciences Research Council ZAF. Dist: Independent Pubs. Group.

Rehle, Thomas, et al. South African National HIV Prevalence, Incidence, Behaviour & Communication Survey 2008: A Turning Tide among Teenagers? 2010. (ENG., Illus.). 120p. pap. 25.95 *(978-0-7969-2291-5(8))* Human Sciences Research Council ZAF. Dist: Independent Pubs. Group.

Rödlach, Alexander. Witches, Westerners, & HIV: AIDS & Cultures of Blame in Africa. 2006. (Illus.). 258p. (C). 89.00 *(978-1-59874-033-2(4))*; (ENG.). pap. 29.95 *(978-1-59874-034-9(2))* Left Coast Pr., Inc.

Roger W. Hoerl And Presha E. Neidermeyer. Use What You Have: Resolving the HIV/AIDS Pandemic. 2009. 186p. 29.99 *(978-1-4415-2113-2(5))*; pap. 19.99 *(978-1-4415-2112-5(7))* Xlibris Corp.

Rohleder, Poul, et al, eds. HIV/AIDs in South Africa 25 Years On: A Psychosocial Perspective. 2009. (ENG., Illus.). xix, 393p. 159.00 *(978-1-4419-0305-1(4)*, 1441903054) Springer.

Rose, Mboya. An Investigation into a Local Church's Response to Hiv in South Africa: Challenges That a Small Local Church Faces When Responding to Hiv in South Africa (1990S-2005) 2011. 84p. pap. ***(978-3-639-33177-6(X))*** VDM Verlag Dr. Mueller e.K.

Ruparanganda, Watch. Genitals Are Assets? 2011. 328p. pap. ***(978-3-8443-3080-9(1))*** Lambert Academic Publishing.

Sahn, David E., ed. The Socioeconomic Dimensions of HIV/AIDS in Africa. 2010. (United Nations University Ser.). (Illus.). 360p. pap. 29.95 *(978-0-8014-7693-8(3))* Cornell Univ. Pr.

Seibold, Mandy. The Economic Impact of Hiv/Aids in Tanzani. 2008. 108p. per. *(978-3-8364-6308-9(3))* VDM Verlag Dr. Mueller e.K.

Sentumbwe, Simon. Correlates of Std & Hiv/Aids Infections among Sex Workers in Ugand. 2010. 68p. pap. *(978-3-639-15387-3(1))* VDM Verlag Dr. Mueller e.K.

Shisana, Olive, et al. South African National HIV Prevalence, HIV Incidence, Behaviour & Communication Survey 2005. 2008. (ENG., Illus.). 156p. pap. 25.95 *(978-0-7969-2152-9(0))* Human Sciences Research Council ZAF. Dist: Independent Pubs. Group.

Simmons, David S. Modernizing Medicine in Zimbabwe: HIV/AIDS & Traditional Healers. 2012. (ENG., Illus.). 248p. 55.00 *(978-0-8265-1807-1(9))* Vanderbilt Univ. Pr.

Simon, Steve. Heroines & Heros: Hope, HIV & Africa, 1 vol. 2006. (ENG., Illus.). 96p. pap. 34.95 *(978-88-8158-610-3(X))* Charta ITA. Dist: D.A.P./Distributed Art Pubs.

Simpson, Anthony. Boys to Men in the Shadow of AIDS: Masculinities & HIV Risk in Zambia. 2009. (ENG.). 252p. 95.00 *(978-0-230-61391-1(8))* Palgrave Macmillan.

Siphambe, Happy, et al. Development Challenges of HIV/AIDS in Small States: Experiences from the Pacific, Southern Africa & the Caribbean. 2011. (ENG., Illus.). 120p. pap. 33.00 ***(978-1-84929-058-6(X))*** Commonwealth Secretariat GBR. Dist: Stylus Publishing, LLC.

Squire, Corinne. HIV in South Africa: Talking about the Big Thing. 2007. 229p. 160.00 *(978-0-415-37209-1(7))*; per. 45.95 *(978-0-415-37210-7(0))* Routledge.

Steinberg, Jonny. Sizwe's Test: A Young Man's Journey Through Africa's AIDS Epidemic. 2010. (ENG., Illus.). 368p. pap. 22.99 *(978-1-4165-5270-3(7))* Simon & Schuster.

Susser, Ida. AIDS, Sex, & Culture: Global Politics & Survival in Southern Africa. 2009. (ENG., Illus.). 304p. 104.95 *(978-1-4051-5586-1(8)*, Wiley-Blackwell) Wiley, John & Sons, Inc.

Tadesse, Derebe. Factors Associated with Late Presentation to Chronic Hiv Care. 2010. 72p. pap. *(978-3-639-22328-6(4))* VDM Verlag Dr. Mueller e.K.

Tesfaye, Anteneh Mekuria. Magnitude & Nature of Hiv/Aids Coverage in the Ethiopian Press. 2009. 104p. pap. *(978-3-639-20697-5(5))* VDM Verlag Dr. Mueller e.K.

Thornton, Robert J. Unimagined Community: Sex, Networks, & AIDS in Uganda & South Africa. 2008. (California Series in Public Anthropology: Vol. 20). (Illus.). 304p. pap. 26.95 *(978-0-520-25553-1(4))*; 60.00 *(978-0-520-25552-4(6))* Univ. of California Pr.

Trinitapoli, Jenny Ann & Weinreb, Alexander. Religion & AIDS in Africa. 2012. (ENG.). 272p. 29.95 ***(978-0-19-533594-1(5))*** Oxford Univ. Pr., Inc.

UNAIDS. Collaborating with Traditional Healers for HIV Prevention & Care in Sub-Saharan Africa: Suggestions for Programme Managers & Field Workers. 2006. (UNAIDS Publication). (ENG.). 54p. pap. 18.00 *(978-92-9173-342-2(3))* World Health Organization.

United Nations. Securing Our Future: Report of the Commission on HIV/AIDS & Governance in Africa. 2008. (ENG.). 250p. pap. 25.00 *(978-92-1-125105-0(2))* United Nations Pubns.

United Nations University Staff. HIV/AIDS in Sub-Saharan Africa: Understanding the Implications of Culture & Context. Baxen, Jean & Breidlid, Anders, eds. 2009. (ENG., Illus.). 160p. pap. 25.00 *(978-92-808-1179-7(7))* United Nations Univ. Pr. JPN. Dist: Brookings Institution Pr.

U.S. Investments in HIV/AIDS: Opportunities & Challenges Ahead: Hearing Before the Subcommittee on Africa & Global Health of the Committee on Foreign Affairs, House of Representatives, One Hundred Eleventh Congress, Second Session, March 11, 2010. 2010. iii, 66p. *(978-0-16-086564-0(6)*, 552-070-41562-9) United States Government Printing Office.

Valerio, Alexandria, et al. A Sourcebook of HIV/AIDS Prevention Programs: Education Sector-Wide Approaches. 2nd ed. 2008. (ENG.). 272p. pap. 45.00 *(978-0-8213-7440-5(0)*, 9780821374405) World Bank Pubns.

Van Niekerk, Anton A. Ethics & AIDS in Africa. Kopelman, Loretta M., ed. 2006. (ENG., Illus.). 240p. 94.00 *(978-1-59874-070-7(9))* Left Coast Pr., Inc.

Vass, Jocelyn & Phakathi, Sizwe. Managing HIV in the Workplace: Learning from SMEs. 2007. (Hsrc Research Monograph Ser.). (ENG., Illus.). 104p. pap. 21.95 *(978-0-7969-2161-1(X))* Human Sciences Research Council ZAF. Dist: Independent Pubs. Group.

Veenstra, Nina. Health Systems in a Context of Hiv/Aids. 2011. 212p. pap. ***(978-3-8443-8245-7(3))*** Lambert Academic Publishing.

Viterbo, Paula & Ngalamulume, Kalala J., eds. Medicine & Health in Africa: Multidisciplinary Perspectives. 2011. (ENG.). 256p. pap. 34.95 *(978-0-87013-991-8(6))* Michigan State Univ. Pr.

Wambui, Henry Kiragu. The Politics of HIV / AIDS & Implications for Democracy in Kenya. 2006. 256p. *(978-0-7734-5649-5(X))* Mellen, Edwin Pr., The.

Watanabe, Seiko. Hiv/Aids in Rural Botswana - Poverty, Gender Inequality, Marginalization, & Stigm. 2008. 100p. pap. *(978-3-639-00077-1(3))* VDM Verlag Dr. Mueller e.K.

Watermeyer, Brian, et al, eds. Disability & Social Change: A South African Agenda. 2007. (ENG., Illus.). 424p. per. 34.95 *(978-0-7969-2137-6(7))* Human Sciences Research Council ZAF. Dist: Independent Pubs. Group.

Welpe, Ingelore & Owino, Philip, eds. The Intersection of Human Capital, Gender & HIV/AIDS in the African Context, Vol. 2. (Illus.). 113p. (C). pap. 26.95 *(978-3-631-54068-8(X))* Lang, Peter Publishing, Inc.

World Bank. O Compromisso do Banco Mundial com o VIH/SIDA Em Africa: O Nosso Plano de Actividades, 2007-2011. 2008. (POR.). 136p. pap. 20.00 *(978-0-8213-7466-5(4)*, 9780821374665) World Bank Pubns.

—Our Commitment French. 2008. (FRE.). 136p. pap. 20.00 *(978-0-8213-7464-1(8)*, 9780821374641) World Bank Pubns.

World Bank Staff. The Changing HIV/AIDS Landscape: Selected Papers for the World Bank's Agenda for Action in Africa, 2007-2011. Lule, Elizabeth L., et al, eds. 2009. (ENG., Illus.). 496p. pap. 40.00 *(978-0-8213-7651-5(9)*, 9780821376515) World Bank Pubns.

—The World Bank's Commitment to HIV/AIDS in Africa: Our Agenda for Action, 2007-2011. 2008. (ENG., Illus.). 144p. pap. 20.00 *(978-0-8213-7448-1(6)*, 9780821374481) World Bank Pubns.

Yonathan, Hailemeskel. Community Participation in Monitoring & Evaluation: Experience, Application & Adoption of Participatory Monitoring & Evaluation. 2011. 76p. pap. ***(978-3-639-32551-5(6))*** VDM Verlag Dr. Mueller e.K.

Youde, Jeremy. AIDS South Africa & the Politics of Knowledge. 2007. (Global Health Ser.). 166p. 114.95 *(978-0-7546-7003-2(1))* Ashgate Publishing Co.

Zelnick, Jennifer R. Who Is Nursing Them? It Is Us: Neoliberalism, HIV/AIDS, & the Occupational Health & Safety of South African Public Sector Nurses. 2011. (ENG., Illus.). 206p. 45.95 *(978-0-89503-327-7(5))* Baywood Publishing Co., Inc.

Zulu, Princess Kasune. Warrior Princess: Fighting for Life with Courage & Hope. 2009. (ENG.). 272p. 22.00 *(978-0-8308-3725-0(6)*, IVP Bks.) InterVarsity Pr.

AIDS (DISEASE)—ASIA

ABBE Scientist Research Division Staff. AIDS & HIV in China: Index & Medical Analysis of New Clinical & Research Information. 2008. (Illus.). 160p. ring bd. 69.95 *(978-0-7883-4961-4(9))* ABBE Pubs. Assn. of Washington, D.C.

—AIDS & HIV in India: Index & Medical Analysis of New Clinical & Research Information. 2008. 160p. 69.95 *(978-0-7883-4962-1(7))* ABBE Pubs. Assn. of Washington, D.C.

—AIDS & HIV in Indonesia: Index & Medical Analysis of New Clinical & Research Information. 2008. (ENG., Illus.). 160p. ring bd. 69.95 *(978-0-7883-4966-9(X))* ABBE Pubs. Assn. of Washington, D.C.

Akhavi, Negar, ed. AIDS Sutra: Untold Stories from India. 2008. (ENG., Illus.). 352p. pap. 13.95 *(978-0-307-45472-0(X)*, Anchor) Knopf Doubleday Publishing Group.

Alexandrova, Anna, ed. Mobilizing Civil Society's Response to Stigma & Discrimination in Central Asia. 2007. (Sourcebook on Contemporary Controversies Ser.). (ENG., Illus.). 178p. pap. 24.95 *(978-1-932716-34-4(3))* International Debate Education Assn.

DuBasky, Valentina, et al, intros. Painting Our Lives: Art by Children Affected by AIDS, Children with AIDS & AIDS Orphans in Cambodia. 2008. (ENG & CAM., Illus.). 116p. pap. 30.00 *(978-0-9801666-0-6(8))* Heron-on-Hudson Pr.

Ebersöhn, Liesel, ed. From Microscope to Kaleidoscope: Reconsidering Educational Aspects Related to Children in the HIV & AIDS Pandemic. 2008. 220p. *(978-90-8790-563-7(7))*; pap. *(978-90-8790-562-0(9))* Sense Pubs.

Fawole, Olufemi & Adegoke, Oluwagbemileke. Hiv/Aids & Sexual Behavior among University Students in Nigeri. 2011. 148p. pap. ***(978-3-8433-8323-3(5))*** Lambert Academic Publishing.

Ghimire, Laxmi. Sexual Health Services. 2011. 288p. pap. ***(978-3-8454-1353-2(0))*** Lambert Academic Publishing.

Glsselquist, David. Points to Consider. 2008. 236p. *(978-1-905068-26-5(3))* Adonis & Abbey Publishers Ltd.

Haacker, Markus & Claeson, Mariam. HIV & AIDS in South Asia: An Economic Development Risk. 2009. (Directions in Development Ser.). (ENG., Illus.).

272p. pap. 30.00 *(978-0-8213-7800-7(7)*, 9780821378007) World Bank Pubns.
Hood, Johanna. HIV/AIDS, Health, & the Media in China: Imagined Immunity Through Racialized Disease. 2011. (Media, Culture & Social Change in Asia Ser.). (ENG., Illus.). 256p. (C). 150.00 *(978-0-415-47198-5(2))* Routledge.
Hubbard, Susan & Suzuki, Tomoko. Building Resilience: Human Security Approaches to AIDS in Africa & Asia. 2008. (ENG.). 120p. pap. 10.00 *(978-4-88907-079-8(6))* Japan Ctr. for International Exchange JPN. Dist: Brookings Institution Pr.
Hyde, Sandra Teresa. Eating Spring Rice: The Cultural Politics of AIDS in Southwest China. 2007. (Illus.). 271p. per. 26.95 *(978-0-520-24715-4(9))*; 55.00 *(978-0-520-24714-7(0))* Univ. of California Pr.
Katyal, Veena, et al, eds. Healthcare Management in India: Psycho-Social & Neurological Aspects of HIV/AIDS & Other Physical & Mental Disorders. 2010. 349p. 84.25 *(978-81-7708-244-9(2))* New Century Publications IND. Dist: International Specialized Bk. Services.
Khanal, Rajesh Prasad. Hiv in South Asi. 2010. 84p. pap. *(978-3-8383-5343-2(9))* Lambert Academic Publishing.
Liu, Shao-hua. Passage to Manhood: Youth Migration, Heroin, & AIDS in Southwest China. 2010. (Studies of the Weatherhead East Asian In Ser.). (ENG., Illus.). 248p. 60.00 *(978-0-8047-7024-8(7))*; pap. 22.95 *(978-0-8047-7025-5(5))* Stanford Univ. Pr.
Lu, Yichen & Essex, Max, eds. AIDS in Asia. 2010. xxvi, 598p. pap. 199.00 *(978-1-4419-3452-9(9)*, 1441934529) Springer.
Moses, Stephen, et al, eds. AIDS in South Asia: Understanding & Responding to a Heterogenous Epidemic. 2006. (Health, Nutrition, & Population Ser.). (ENG., Illus.). 136p. per. 18.00 *(978-0-8213-6757-5(9)*, 9780821367575) World Bank Pubns.
Nepal, Binod. Hiv/Aids in Asi. 2010. 276p. pap. *(978-3-8383-6029-4(X))* Lambert Academic Publishing.
Poston, Dudley L., et al, eds. Gender Policy & HIV in China: Catalyzing Policy Change. 2009. (Springer Series on Demographic Methods & Population Analysis Ser.). (ENG., Illus.). xviii, 226p. 159.00 *(978-1-4020-9899-4(5))* Springer.
Rai, Bishwa. Hiv & Aids-Related Stigma & Discrimination in Nepal. 2010. 64p. pap. *(978-3-8383-6661-6(1))* Lambert Academic Publishing.
Revenga, Ana, et al. The Economics of Effective AIDS Treatment: Evaluating Policy Options for Thailand. 2006. (Health, Nutrition, & Population Ser.). (ENG., Illus.). 272p. per. 25.00 *(978-0-8213-6755-1(2)*, 9780821367551) World Bank Pubns.
Stang, Anne. Tackling HIV-Related Stigma & Discrimination in South Asia. 2010. (Directions in Development Ser.). (ENG., Illus.). 228p. pap. 25.00 *(978-0-8213-8449-7(X)*, 9780821384497) World Bank Pubns.
Sutherland, Dylan. Hiv/Aids in China. 2011. (Routledge Contemporary China Ser.). (ENG., Illus.). 184p. (C). 145.00 *(978-0-415-41875-1(5))* Routledge.
United Nations. HIV & AIDS in Asia & the Pacific: A Review of Progress Towards Universal Access. 2009. (ENG.). 64p. pap. 20.00 *(978-92-1-120573-2(5))* United Nations Pubns.
Varma, Sudhir. Gender, HIV, & Social Work. 2010. (Illus.). 254p. 40.00 *(978-81-316-0341-3(5))* Rawat Pubns. IND. Dist: International Specialized Bk. Services.
WHO Regional Office for South-East Asia. HIV/AIDS among men who have sex with men & transgender populations in South-East Asia: The current situation & national Responses. 2011. 161p. pap. 36.00 *(978-92-9022-381-8(2))* World Health Organization.
WHO Regional Office for the Western Pacific. Continuum of Care for People Living with HIV/AIDS in Cambodia (the): Linkages & Strengthening in the Public Health System: Case Study. 2006. (Wpro Nonserial Publication). (ENG.). 31p. pap. 12.00 *(978-92-9061-222-3(3))* World Health Organization.
World Bank Staff. Corporate Responses to HIV/AIDS: Case Studies from India. 2007. (Books Ser.). (ENG., Illus.). 88p. per. 15.00 *(978-0-8213-7171-8(1)*, 9780821371718) World Bank Pubns.
World Health Organization Staff & United Nations Staff. HIV & Men who Have Sex with Men in Asia & the Pacific. 2006. (Unaids Publication). (ENG.). 68p. pap. 18.00 *(978-92-9173-262-3(1))* World Health Organization.
World Health Organization: Regional Office for the Western Pacific. Good Practices in Asia: Effective Paradigm Shifts Towards an Improved National Response to Drugs & HIV/AIDS:; Scale-up of Harm Reduction in Malaysia. 2011. (WPRO Nonserial Publication Ser.). (ENG.). 67p. cd-rom 18.00 ***(978-92-9061-519-4(2))*** WHO Regional Office for the Western Pacific PHL. Dist: World Health Organization.
Zheng, Tiantian. Ethnographies of Prostitution in Contemporary China: Gender Relations, HIV/AIDS, & Nationalism. (ENG., 256p. 2012. Illus.). pap. 28.00 ***(978-0-230-34099-2(7))*** 2009. 89.00 *(978-0-230-61741-4(7))* Palgrave Macmillan.

AIDS (DISEASE)—AUSTRALIA

ABBE Scientist Research Division Staff. AIDS & HIV in Australia: Index & Medical Analysis of New Clinical & Research Information. 2008. (ENG., Illus.). 160p. ring bd. 69.95 *(978-0-7883-4959-1(7))* ABBE Pubs. Assn. of Washington, D.C.
Munro, Ian. The Lived Experience of Gay Men Caring for Others with Hiv/Aids. 2008. 324p. pap. *(978-3-639-03581-0(X))* VDM Verlag Dr. Mueller e.K.

AIDS (DISEASE)—CANADA

ABBE Scientist Research Division Staff. AIDS & HIV in Canada: Index & Medical Analysis of New Clinical & Research Information. 2008. (ENG., Illus.). 160p. ring bd. 69.95 *(978-0-7883-4951-5(1))* ABBE Pubs. Assn. of Washington, D.C.
Ayres, Jeffrey McKelvey & Sipion, Patricia D. Divergent Campaigns Towards Global Health Governance: Canadian & U.S. Approaches to the Global HIV/AIDS Pandemic. 2007. 52p. *(978-1-882582-59-7(6))* Canadian-American Ctr.
Chongo, Meck. Determinants of Adherence to Highly Active Anti-Retroviral Therapy. 2011. 164p. pap. ***(978-3-8443-3414-2(9))*** Lambert Academic Publishing.
Kirp. AIDS in the Industrialized Democracies: Passions, Politics & Policies. 408p. pap. *(978-0-7735-0957-3(7))* McGill-Queen's Univ. Pr.
Schoueri, Nour. A Hidden Reality. 2008. 220p. per. *(978-3-8364-5692-0(3))* VDM Verlag Dr. Mueller e.K.

AIDS (DISEASE)—CARIBBEAN AREA

Gisselquist, David. Points to Consider: Responses to HIV/AIDS in Africa,Asia, & the Caribbean. 2008. 236p. per. *(978-1-905068-45-6(X))* Adonis & Abbey Publishers Ltd.
Padilla, Mark. Caribbean Pleasure Industry: Tourism, Sexuality, & AIDS in the Dominican Republic. 2007. (Worlds of Desire: the Chicago Series on Sexuality, Gender, & Culture Ser.). (ENG., Illus.). 304p. per. 25.00 *(978-0-226-64436-3(7))* Univ. of Chicago Pr.
Padilla, Mark B. Caribbean Pleasure Industry: Tourism, Sexuality, & AIDS in the Dominican Republic. 2007. (Worlds of Desire: the Chicago Series on Sexuality, Gender, & Culture Ser.). (Illus.). 304p. 60.00 *(978-0-226-64435-6(9))* Univ. of Chicago Pr.
Schuller, Mark. Killing with Kindness: Haiti, International Aid, & NGOs. 2012. 256p. 72.00 ***(978-0-8135-5362-7(8))***; pap. 26.95 ***(978-0-8135-5363-4(6))*** Rutgers Univ. Pr.
Siphambe, Happy, et al. Development Challenges of HIV/AIDS in Small States: Experiences from the Pacific, Southern Africa & the Caribbean. 2011. (ENG., Illus.). 120p. pap. 33.00 ***(978-1-84929-058-6(X))*** Commonwealth Secretariat GBR. Dist: Stylus Publishing, LLC.
World Bank Staff. Strengthening the Education Sector Response to HIV & AIDS in the Caribbean. 2008. (World Bank Working Papers: 137). (ENG.). 44p. pap. 10.00 *(978-0-8213-7476-4(1)*, 9780821374764) World Bank Pubns.

AIDS (DISEASE)—EUROPE

ABBE Scientist Research Division Staff. AIDS & HIV in France: Index & Medical Analysis of New Clinical & Research Information. 2008. 160p. 69.95 *(978-0-7883-4952-2(X))* ABBE Pubs. Assn. of Washington, D.C.
—AIDS & HIV in Italy: Index & Medical Analysis of New Clinical & Research Information. 2008. (ENG., Illus.). 160p. ring bd. 69.95 *(978-0-7883-4950-8(3))* ABBE Pubs. Assn. of Washington, D.C.
—AIDS & HIV in Norway: Index & Medical Analysis of New Clinical & Research Information. 2008. (ENG., Illus.). 160p. ring bd. 69.95 *(978-0-7883-4968-3(6))* ABBE Pubs. Assn. of Washington, D.C.
—AIDS & HIV in Spain: Index & Medical Analysis of New Clinical & Research Information. 2008. (ENG., Illus.). 160p. ring bd. 69.95 *(978-0-7883-4969-0(4))* ABBE Pubs. Assn. of Washington, D.C.
—AIDS & HIV in Sweden: Index & Medical Analysis of New Clinical & Research Information. 2008. (ENG., Illus.). 160p. ring bd. 69.95 *(978-0-7883-4970-6(8))* ABBE Pubs. Assn. of Washington, D.C.
—AIDS & HIV in Switzerland: Index & Medical Analysis of New Clinical & Research Information. 2008. (ENG., Illus.). 160p. ring bd. 69.95 *(978-0-7883-4971-3(6))* ABBE Pubs. Assn. of Washington, D.C.
—AIDS & HIV in the United Kingdom: Index & Medical Analysis of New Clinical & Research Information. 2008. (ENG., Illus.). 160p. ring bd. 69.95 *(978-0-7883-4956-0(2))* ABBE Pubs. Assn. of Washington, D.C.
Kemppainen-Bertram, Katri. Future Strategies for Hiv/Aids Policy. 2008. 96p. per. *(978-3-8364-6702-5(X))* VDM Verlag Dr. Mueller e.K.
Weait Matthew. Intimacy & Responsibility: The Criminalisation of HIV Transmission. 2007. 224p. 57.95 *(978-1-904385-70-7(2))*; 170.00 *(978-1-904385-71-4(0))* Taylor & Francis Group GBR. (Routledge Cavendish). Dist: Taylor & Francis Group.

AIDS (DISEASE)—MEXICO

ABBE Scientist Research Division Staff. AIDS & HIV in Mexico: Index & Medical Analysis of New Clinical & Research Information. 2008. (ENG., Illus.). 160p. ring bd. 69.95 *(978-0-7883-4954-6(6))* ABBE Pubs. Assn. of Washington, D.C.
Hein, Karen, et al. SIDA: Verdades en Lugar.Tr. of AIDS. (SPA.). 17.95 *(978-968-39-0422-5(X))* Editorial Patria Cultural MEX. Dist: AIMS International Bks., Inc.

AIDS (DISEASE)—SOUTH AMERICA

ABBE Scientist Research Division Staff. AIDS & HIV in Argentina: Index & Medical Analysis of New Clinical & Research Information. 2008. (ENG., Illus.). 160p. ring bd. 69.95 *(978-0-7883-4958-4(9))* ABBE Pubs. Assn. of Washington, D.C.
—AIDS & HIV in Brazil: Index & Medical Analysis of New Clinical & Research Information. 2008. (ENG., Illus.). 160p. ring bd. 69.95 *(978-0-7883-4960-7(0))* ABBE Pubs. Assn. of Washington, D.C.
Fassin, Didier. When Bodies Remember: Experiences & Politics of AIDS in South Africa. Jacobs, Amy & Varro, Gabrielle, trs. from FRE. 2007. (California Series in Public Anthropology). 365p. 60.00 *(978-0-520-24467-2(2))*; per. 26.95 *(978-0-520-25027-7(3))* Univ. of California Pr.
Loffler, Anne. Hiv/Aids & the Power of Decision Making - A Gender Study in a Rural Township in South Africa. 2008. 164p. pap. *(978-3-639-00959-0(2))* VDM Verlag Dr. Mueller e.K.

AIDS (DISEASE)—SOVIET UNION

ABBE Scientist Research Division Staff. AIDS & HIV in Russia: Index & Medical Analysis of New Clinical & Research Information. 2008. (Illus.). 160p. ring bd. 69.95 *(978-0-7883-4955-3(4))* ABBE Pubs. Assn. of Washington, D.C.
Atlani-Duault, LaëTitia. Humanitarian Aid in Post-Soviet Countries: An Anthropological Perspective. 2008. (Illus.). VIII, 152p. 160.00 *(978-0-415-44884-0(0))* Routledge.
Twigg, Judyth L. Hiv/Aids in Russia & Eurasia, 2 vols., Vol. 1. 2007. (ENG., Illus.). 240p. 84.00 *(978-1-4039-7057-2(2))* Palgrave Macmillan.
Twigg, Judyth L., ed. HIV/AIDS in Russia & Eurasia, 2 vols., Vol. 2. rev. ed. 2007. (ENG., Illus.). 212p. 84.00 *(978-1-4039-7628-4(7))* Palgrave Macmillan.

AIDS (DISEASE)—UNITED STATES

ABBE Scientist Research Division Staff. AIDS & HIV in the United States: Index & Medical Analysis of New Clinical & Research Information. 2008. 160p. 69.95 *(978-0-7883-4957-7(0))* ABBE Pubs. Assn. of Washington, D.C.
Agbodzakey, James. Collaborative Governance & the Implementation of Ryan White Care Act. 2010. 252p. pap. *(978-3-8383-4699-1(8))* Lambert Academic Publishing.
Anjejo, Dixon. Risk Behaviors of African Born Adolescents in United States of Americ. 2010. 148p. pap. *(978-3-8383-4959-6(8))* Lambert Academic Publishing.
Behrman, Greg. The Invisible People: How the U. S. Has Slept Through the Global AIDS Pan. 2009. (ENG.). 372p. pap. 23.95 *(978-1-4391-5735-0(9)*, Free Pr.) Free Pr.
Bowser, Benjamin P. & Quimby, Ernest, eds. When Communities Assess their AIDS Epidemics: Results of Rapid Assessment of HIV/AIDS in Eleven U. S. Cities. 2008. (ENG.). 264p. pap. 31.50 *(978-0-7391-2949-4(X))* Lexington Bks.
Bowser, Benjamin P., et al. When Communities Assess Their AIDS Epidemics: Results of Rapid Assessment of HIV/AIDS in Eleven U. S. Cities. 2007. (ENG., Illus.). 264p. 68.50 *(978-0-7391-0752-2(6))* Lexington Bks.
Brier, Jennifer. Infectious Ideas: U. S. Political Responses to the AIDS Crisis. (ENG., Illus.). 312p. 2011. pap. 22.95 *(978-0-8078-7211-6(3))* 2009. 36.95 *(978-0-8078-3314-8(2))* Univ. of North Carolina Pr.
Carmody, David R., ed. Global HIV/AIDS Threat & the U. S. Response. 2011. (Public Health in the 21st Century Ser.). 125.00 *(978-1-61324-566-2(8))* Nova Science Pubs., Inc.
Chambré, Susan Maizel. Fighting for Our Lives: New York's AIDS Community & the Politics of Disease. 2006. (Critical Issues in Health & Medicine Ser.). (ENG.). 280p. 68.00 *(978-0-8135-3866-2(1))* Rutgers Univ. Pr.
Chambre, Susan Maizel. Fighting for Our Lives: New York's AIDS Community & the Politics of Disease. annot. ed. 2006. (Critical Issues in Health & Medicine Ser.). (ENG.). 280p. per. 24.95 *(978-0-8135-3867-9(X))* Rutgers Univ. Pr.
Chase, Sabrina. Surviving HIV/AIDS in the Inner City: How Resourceful Latinas Beat the Odds. 2012. (Studies in Medical Anthropology Ser.). (ENG.). 228p. (C). pap. 26.95 ***(978-0-8135-5355-9(5))*** Rutgers Univ. Pr.
Chase, Sabrina Maria. Surviving HIV/AIDS in the Inner City: How Resourceful Latinas Beat the Odds. 2011. (Studies in Medical Anthropology Ser.). (ENG.). 228p. 39.95 *(978-0-8135-4892-0(6))* Rutgers Univ. Pr.
The Domestic Epidemic Is Worse Than We Thought: A Wake-Up Call for HIV Prevention: Hearing Before the Committee on Oversight & Government Reform, House of Representatives, One Hundred Tenth Congress, Second Session, September 16, 2008. 2010. (Illus.). iii, 166p. *(978-0-16-086745-3(2)*, 552-070-41667-6) United States Government Printing Office.
Fisher, TerryAnn & Michaels, Troy. Conversations with My Son: A Diary. 2010. 156p. 23.95 *(978-1-4502-3002-5(4))*; pap. 13.95 *(978-1-4502-2997-5(2))* iUniverse, Inc.
Fleury-Steiner, Benjamin Dov & Crowder, Carla. Dying Inside: The HIV/AIDS Ward at Limestone Prison. 2008. (Law, Meaning, & Violence Ser.). (ENG., Illus.). 248p. 32.95 *(978-0-472-11429-0(8))* Univ. of Michigan Pr.
Gentry & Gentry, Quinn M. Black Women's Risk for HIV: Rough Living. 2008. (ENG.). 282p. (C). 158.00 *(978-0-7890-3169-3(8))* Routledge.
Gentry, Quinn M. Black Women's Risk for HIV: Rough Living. 2007. (ENG.). 282p. per. 65.95 *(978-0-7890-3170-9(1))* Routledge.
Hammond, Tarana. Media Use, Hiv/Aids Knowledge, & Sexual Beliefs. 2008. 72p. pap. *(978-3-639-00175-4(3))* VDM Verlag Dr. Mueller e.K.
Holleran, Andrew. Chronicle of a Plague, Revisited: AIDS & Its Aftermath. 2008. (ENG.). 304p. pap. 16.00 *(978-0-7867-2039-2(5))* Da Capo Pr., Inc.
Holmberg, Scott D. Scientific Errors & Controversies in the U. S. HIV/AIDS Epidemic: How They Slowed Advances & Were Resolved, 1 vol. 2007. (Illus.). 240p. 49.95 *(978-0-313-34717-7(4)*, C34717, Praeger Pubs.) Greenwood Publishing Group, Inc.
Hunter, Susan. AIDS in America. 2008. (ENG.). 256p. pap. 20.00 *(978-1-4039-7650-5(3))* Palgrave Macmillan.
Inrig, Stephen J. North Carolina & the Problem of AIDS: Advocacy, Politics, & Race in the South. 2011. (ENG., Illus.). 256p. 45.00 *(978-0-8078-3498-5(X))* Univ. of North Carolina Pr.
Jensen, Lawrence T. Responding to HIV/AIDS: National Strategies, Plans & Programs. 2011. (Public Health in the 21st Century HIV/AIDS - Medical, Social & Psychological Aspects Ser.). 235p. 185.00 ***(978-1-61324-618-4(8))*** Nova Science Pubs., Inc.
John, Elton. Love Is the Cure: Ending the Global AIDS Epidemic. 2012. (ENG., Illus.). 304p. 27.99 ***(978-0-316-21990-7(8))*** Little Brown & Co.
Lorber, Kim. Transitional Housing & Aids in New York City. 2009. 200p. pap. *(978-3-639-18378-8(9))* VDM Verlag Dr. Mueller e.K.
Loue, Sana. My Nerves Are Bad: Puerto Rican Women Managing Mental Illness & HIV Risk. 2011. (ENG.). 240p. 59.95 *(978-0-8265-1753-1(6))*; pap. 27.95 *(978-0-8265-1754-8(4))* Vanderbilt Univ. Pr.
Lune, Howard. Urban Action Networks: HIV/AIDS & Community Organizing in New York City. 2006. (ENG.). 240p. 92.00 *(978-0-7425-4083-5(9))*; (Illus.). per. 30.95 *(978-0-7425-4084-2(7))* Rowman & Littlefield Publishers, Inc.
McCree, Donna H., et al. African Americans & HIV/AIDS: Understanding & Addressing the Epidemic. 2010. (Illus.). xx, 323p. E-Book ***(978-0-387-78321-5(0))*** Springer.
Mills, Robert Parker. Between Rock & a Hard Place: In Defense of Rock Hudson: from the Ashes of Trial to the Light of Truth. 2010. 492p. 33.99 *(978-1-4567-0039-3(1))*; pap. 22.50 *(978-1-4567-0038-6(3))* AuthorHouse.
Multi-Drug Resistant Tuberculosis: Assessing the U.S. Response to an Emerging Global Threat: Hearing Before the Subcommittee on Africa & Global Health of the Committee on Foreign Affairs, House of Representatives, One Hundred Tenth Congress, Second Session, February 27, 2008. 2008. iii, 55p. *(978-0-16-082429-6(X)*, 552-070-38473-1) United States Government Printing Office.
Myles, Lessie. African-Americans & Aids: Why are Black People still dying of (AIDS) while other Races are Not? 2009. 156p. 22.99 *(978-1-4490-3313-2(X))*; pap. 17.99 *(978-1-4490-3312-5(1))* AuthorHouse.
Nattrass, Nicoli. The AIDS Conspiracy: Science Fights Back. 2012. (ENG., Illus.). 240p. (gr. 17). 34.50 ***(978-0-231-14912-9(3))*** Columbia Univ. Pr.
The Next Phase of the Global Fight Against HIV/AIDS: Hearing Before the Committee on Foreign Relations, United States Senate, One Hundred Tenth Congress, First Session, October 24, 2007. 2008. iii, 49p. *(978-0-16-080290-4(3)*, 552-070-36985-6) United States Government Printing Office.
Organista, Kurt C., ed. HIV Prevention with Latinos: Theory, Research, & Practice, 1 vol. 2012. (ENG., Illus.). 484p. pap. 59.99 ***(978-0-19-976430-3(1))*** Oxford Univ. Pr., Inc.
Outreach & Care Approaches to HIV/AIDS along the US-Mexico Border. 2006. (ENG., Illus.). 190p. 116.00 *(978-0-7890-3466-3(2))*; per. 50.50 *(978-0-7890-3467-0(0))* Routledge.
Payne Foster, Pamela. Is there a Balm in Black America?: Perspectives on HIV/AIDS in the African American Community. 2007. 312p. per. 19.99 *(978-1-4303-1670-1(5))* Lulu Enterprises Inc.
Ramirez-Valles, Jesus. Compañeros: Latino Activists in the Face of AIDS. 2011. (Latinos in Chicago & Midwest Ser.). (ENG., Illus.). 192p. 75.00 ***(978-0-252-03644-6(1))***; 208p. pap. 25.00 ***(978-0-252-07821-7(7))*** Univ. of Illinois Pr.
Robertson, Gil L., IV. Not in My Family: AIDS in the African-American Community. 2006. (ENG.). 300p. per. 16.00 *(978-1-932841-24-4(5))* Agate Publishing, Inc.
Schifter-Sikora, Jacobo. Mongers in Heaven: Sexual Tourism & HIV Risk in Costa Rica & in the United States. 2006. (ENG., Illus.). 212p. per. 37.99 *(978-0-7618-3597-4(0))* Univ. Pr. of America, Inc.
Schulman, Sarah. The Gentrification of the Mind: Witness to a Lost Imagination. 2012. (ENG.). 184p. 27.95 ***(978-0-520-26477-9(0))*** Univ. of California Pr.
Scott, William L. C. & Scott, Donald W. Aids: The Crime Beyond Belief. 2008. 692p. 44.30 *(978-1-4251-4157-8(9))* Trafford Publishing.
Shilts, Randy. And the Band Played On: Politics, People & the AIDS Epidemic. 2nd rev. anniv. ed. 2007. (ENG.). 656p. pap. 18.99 *(978-0-312-37463-1(1)*, St. Martin's Griffin) St. Martin's Pr.
Stop AIDS in Prison ACT of 2007, & the Drug Endangered Children ACT of 2007: Hearing Before the Subcommittee on Crime, Terrorism, & Homeland Security of the Committee on the Judiciary, House of Representatives, One Hundred Tenth Congress, First Session, on H.R. 1943 & H.R. 1199, May 22, 2007. 2008. (Illus.). iii, 125p. *(978-0-16-081947-6(4)*, 552-070-38120-1) United States Government Printing Office.
VIHdeo America (2 DVDs) An Anthology of 10 Years of HIV Spots in the Americas. 2006. (Paho Dvd Ser.). (ENG.). pap. 40.00 *(978-92-75-07396-4(1))* World Health Organization.

AIDS (DISEASE) IN ART

Bordowitz, Gregg. General Idea: Imagevirus. 2010. (One Work Ser.). (ENG., Illus.). 121p. (gr. 17). pap. 16.00 *(978-1-84638-065-5(0))* Afterall Publishing GBR. Dist: MIT Pr.
Ellis, Kelly Norman. The Spaces Between Us: Poetry, Prose & Art on HIV/AIDS. 2010. (ENG.). 203p. pap. 15.95 *(978-0-88378-320-7(7))* Third World Press.
From Media to Metaphor: Art about AIDS. pap. 20.00 *(978-0-916365-34-9(4))* Independent Curators International.
Simon, Steve. Heroines & Heros: Hope, HIV & Africa, 1 vol. 2006. (ENG., Illus.). 96p. pap. 34.95 *(978-88-8158-610-3(X))* Charta ITA. Dist: D.A.P./Distributed Art Pubs.

AIDS (DISEASE) IN CHILDREN

see also AIDS (Disease) in Infants

ABBE Scientist Research Division Staff. AIDS & HIV in Children: Index & Medical Analysis of New Clinical & Research Information. 2007. (ENG., Illus.). 160p. ring bd. 69.95 *(978-0-7883-4779-5(9))* ABBE Pubs. Assn. of Washington, D.C.
American Health Research Institute Staff. HIV in Babies & Children with Index & Medical Analysis of New Research Information for All Nations. 2007. (Illus.). 160p. 69.95 *(978-0-7883-4651-4(2)*, 0-7883-4651-2) ABBE Pubs. Assn. of Washington, D.C.

A

Bethelehem, Newayeselassie, et al. Determination of Cd4+ T-Cells Using Different Systems: Evaluation of Different Systems of Cd4+ T-Cell Percentage Determination by Using Standard Flow Cytometer for Pediatric Hiv Managment. 2011. 72p. pap. ***(978-3-639-32235-4(5))*** VDM Verlag Dr. Mueller e.K.

Bhana, Deevia, et al. Towards Gender Equality: South African Schools during the HIV & AIDS Epidemic. 2009. 223p. pap. 44.00 *(978-1-86914-175-2(X))* Univ. of Natal Pr. ZAF. Dist: International Specialized Bk. Services.

Deacon, Harriet & Stephney, Inez. HIV/AIDS, Stigma & Children: A Literature Review. 2008. (ENG., Illus.). 88p. pap. 16.95 *(978-0-7969-2188-8(1))* Human Sciences Research Council ZAF. Dist: Independent Pubs. Group.

DeSantis, Charles. Smart, Beautiful & Important: Teaching Art to AIDS-affected Orphans in Africa's Largest Slum. 2010. (Illus.). 132p. 42.00 *(978-0-9828061-1-1(6)*, Scarith) New Academia Publishing, LLC.

DuBasky, Valentina, et al, intros. Painting Our Lives: Art by Children Affected by AIDS, Children with AIDS & AIDS Orphans in Cambodia. 2008. (ENG & CAM., Illus.). 116p. pap. 30.00 *(978-0-9801666-0-6(8))* Heron-on-Hudson Pr.

Ebersöhn, Liesel, ed. From Microscope to Kaleidoscope: Reconsidering Educational Aspects Related to Children in the HIV & AIDS Pandemic. 2008. 220p. *(978-90-8790-563-7(7))*; pap. *(978-90-8790-562-0(9))* Sense Pubs.

Matimba, Peter. Analysis of Impact of Hiv on Children's Education in Zambi. 2009. 116p. pap. *(978-3-639-21049-1(2))* VDM Verlag Dr. Mueller e.K.

Moran & Mullick. Systemic Pathology of HIV Infections & AIDS in Children. Date not set. 328p. pap. 62.00 *(978-1-881041-40-5(9))* ARP Pr.

Murfee, Keith R. A Second Chance for Hope: the Story of Nyumbani. 2007. 104p. pap. 19.50 *(978-1-4303-1968-9(2))* Lulu Enterprises Inc.

Thayer, Linda. AIDS & Adolescents. 90p. pap. 2.00 *(978-0-8198-0744-1(3))* Pauline Bks. & Media.

World Health Organization. WHO Recommendations on the Management of Diarrhoea & Pneumonia in HIV Infected Infants & Children: Integrated Management of Childhood Illness (IMCI) 2011. (DOCUMENTS for SALE Ser.). (Illus.). 60p. pap. 36.00 *(978-92-4-154808-3(8))* World Health Organization.

AIDS (DISEASE) IN INFANTS

see also AIDS (Disease) in Children

ABBE Scientist Research Division Staff. AIDS & HIV in Newborn Babies: Index & Medical Analysis of New Clinical & Research Information. 2007. (Illus.). 160p. ring bd. 69.95 *(978-0-7883-4781-8(0))* ABBE Pubs. Assn. of Washington, D.C.

American Health Research Institute Staff. HIV in Babies & Children with Index & Medical Analysis of New Research Information for All Nations. 2007. (Illus.). 160p. 69.95 *(978-0-7883-4651-4(2)*, 0-7883-4651-2) ABBE Pubs. Assn. of Washington, D.C.

Kourtis, Athena P. & Bulterys, Marc. Perinatal HIV/AIDS: Clinics in Perinatology. 2010. (Clinics: Internal Medicine Ser.: 37-4). (ENG., Illus.). xxi, 700p. 105.00 *(978-1-4377-2480-6(9)*, Saunders) Elsevier - Health Sciences Div.

AIDS (DISEASE) IN LITERATURE

Horton, Randall, ed. Fingernails Across the Chalkboard: Poetry & Prose on HIV/AIDS from the Black Diaspora. 2007. (Illus.). 182p. per. 15.95 *(978-0-88378-274-3(X))* Third World Press.

Pearl, Monica B. AIDS Literature & Gay Identity: The Literature of Loss. 2012. (Routledge Studies in Twentieth-Century Literature Ser.). (ENG.). 208p. (C). 125.00 ***(978-0-415-80887-3(1))*** Routledge.

AIDS (DISEASE) IN MASS MEDIA

Edgar, Timothy, et al. Communication Perspectives on HIV/AIDS for the 21st Century. Edgar, Timothy et al, eds. 2007. (LEA's Communication Ser.). (Illus.). 477p. 110.00 *(978-0-8058-5826-6(1))* Erlbaum, Lawrence Assocs., Inc.

Freimuth, Vicki S., et al. Communication Perspectives on HIV/AIDS for the 21st Century. Freimuth, Vicki S. et al, eds. 2007. (LEA's Communication Ser.). 477p. per. 45.95 *(978-0-8058-5827-3(X))* Erlbaum, Lawrence Assocs., Inc.

Gokah, Theophilus K. Contemporary Discourses on IE & C Theory & Practice. 2009. (Illus.). x, 410p. 69.00 *(978-1-60692-360-3(9))* Nova Science Pubs., Inc.

Tesfaye, Anteneh Mekuria. Magnitude & Nature of Hiv/Aids Coverage in the Ethiopian Press. 2009. 104p. pap. *(978-3-639-20697-5(5))* VDM Verlag Dr. Mueller e.K.

AIDS (DISEASE) IN PREGNANCY

see also AIDS (Disease) in Infants

ABBE Scientist Research Division Staff. AIDS & HIV in Pregnant Women: Index & Medical Analysis of New Clinical & Research Information. 2007. (ENG., Illus.). 160p. 69.95 *(978-0-7883-4784-9(5))* ABBE Pubs. Assn. of Washington, D.C.

Farnan, Rose & Enriquez, Maithe. What Nurses Know ... HIV & AIDS. 2012. (What Nurses Know... Ser.). (ENG., Illus.). 208p. pap. 16.95 ***(978-1-936303-19-9(1))*** Demos Medical Publishing, LLC.

Kourtis, Athena P. & Bulterys, Marc. Perinatal HIV/AIDS: Clinics in Perinatology. 2010. (Clinics: Internal Medicine Ser.: 37-4). (ENG., Illus.). xxi, 700p. 105.00 *(978-1-4377-2480-6(9)*, Saunders) Elsevier - Health Sciences Div.

Minnie, Karin (Cs). Best Practice Guidelines - Counselling for Hiv Testing in Pregnancy. 2010. 372p. pap. *(978-3-639-22817-5(0))* VDM Verlag Dr. Mueller e.K.

Quintana-Jefferson, Marlinda. HIV-Infected Pregnant Women: Factors Predictive of Adherence to Antiretroviral Medications. 2008. 84p. pap. *(978-3-639-09197-7(3))* VDM Verlag Dr. Mueller e.K.

AIDS PATIENTS

see AIDS (Disease)—Patients

AIDS PATIENTS' CHILDREN

see Children of AIDS Patients

AIDS TO AIR NAVIGATION

see also Airways; Meteorology in Aeronautics

Casner, Stephen M. Cockpit Automation: For General Aviators & Future Airline Pilots. 2007. (ENG., Illus.). 188p. pap. 29.95 *(978-1-56027-636-4(3))* Aviation Supplies & Academics, Inc.

Clearman, Brian. International Marine AIDS to Navigation. 3rd ed. 2010. (Illus.). 273p. ***(978-0-918941-33-6(4))*** Mount Angel Abbey.

Federal Aviation Administration. Aeronautical Chart Users Guide: National Aeronautical Navigation Services. 9th ed. 2012. (ENG., Illus.). 80p. pap. 12.95 ***(978-1-61608-534-6(7)***, 608534) Skyhorse Publishing Co., Inc.

Federal Aviation Administration. Federal Aviation Regulations: Aeronautical Information Manual 2010. 2009. (ENG., Illus.). 960p. pap. 15.95 *(978-1-60239-728-6(7)*, 239728) Skyhorse Publishing Co., Inc.

Rogers, Robert M. & Rogers, Robert M. Applied Mathematics in Integrated Navigation Systems. 3rd ed. 2007. (AIAA Education Ser.). (Illus.). 408p. 94.95 *(978-1-56347-927-4(3))* American Institute of Aeronautics & Astronautics.

The Science of Flight: A Gateway to New Horizons. 2011. ***(978-1-4496-3065-2(0))*** Jones & Bartlett Publishers.

AIDS TO NAVIGATION

see also Electronics in Navigation; Lighthouses; Nautical Charts; Radar in Navigation; Radio in Navigation

Anon & Anon. Philippine Islands Sailing Directions - Section II - Southwest & South Coasts of Luzon & Adjacent Islands from Manila to San Bernardino Strait. 2011. 70p. pap. 26.45 ***(978-1-4460-6433-7(6))*** Barclay Pr., Inc.

Barbieri, Nicholas. Lenticular Sheet Generated Optical Patterns for Aircraft Navigation. 2009. 116p. pap. *(978-3-639-14232-7(2))* VDM Verlag Dr. Mueller e.K.

Clearman, Brian. Transportation-Markings Database: Marine. 2007. 324p. pap. 31.95 *(978-0-918941-26-8(1))* Mount Angel Abbey.

Coast Guard (U.S.). Light List, 2010, V. 7, Great Lakes, Great Lakes & the St. Lawrence River above the St. Regis River. 2010. (ENG., Illus.). 244p. pap. 37.00 *(978-0-16-084711-0(7)*, Coast Guard) United States Government Printing Office.

Coast Guard (U.S.), compiled by. Light List, 2011, V. 1, Atlantic Coast, St. Croix River, Maine to Shrewsbury River, New Jersey. 2011. (ENG., Illus.). 380p. pap. 53.00 *(978-0-16-087112-2(3)*, Coast Guard) United States Government Printing Office.

Coast Guard (U.S.), ed. Light List, 2010, V. 2, Atlantic Coast, Toms River, New Jersey to Little River, South Carolina. 2010. (ENG., Illus.). 388p. pap. 53.00 *(978-0-16-084706-6(0)*, Coast Guard) United States Government Printing Office.

—Light List, 2010, V. 3, Atlantic & Gulf Coasts, Little River, South Carolina to Econfina River, Florida (Includes Puerto Rico & the U. S. Virgin Islands) 2010. (ENG., Illus.). 520p. pap. 53.00 *(978-0-16-084707-3(9)*, Coast Guard) United States Government Printing Office.

—Light List, 2010, V. 4, Gulf of Mexico, Econfina River, Florida, to the Rio Grande, Texas. 2010. (ENG., Illus.). 370p. pap. 53.00 *(978-0-16-084708-0(7)*, Coast Guard) United States Government Printing Office.

—Light List, 2010, V. 6, Pacific Coast & Outlying Pacific Islands. 2010. (ENG., Illus.). 293p. pap. 43.00 *(978-0-16-084710-3(9)*, Coast Guard) United States Government Printing Office.

—Light List, 2011, V. 2, Atlantic Coast, Toms River, New Jersey to Little River, South Carolina. 2011. (ENG., Illus.). 398p. pap. 53.00 *(978-0-16-087113-9(1)*, Coast Guard) United States Government Printing Office.

—Light List, 2011, V. 3, Atlantic & Gulf Coasts, Little River, South Carolina to Econfina River, Florida (Includes Puerto Rico & the U. S. Virgin Islands) 2011. (ENG., Illus.). 224p. pap. 33.00 ***(978-0-16-087114-6(X)***, Coast Guard) United States Government Printing Office.

—Light List, 2011, V. 4, Gulf of Mexico, Econfina River, Florida, to the Rio Grande, Texas. 2011. (ENG., Illus.). 374p. pap. 53.00 ***(978-0-16-087115-3(8)***, Coast Guard) United States Government Printing Office.

—Light List, 2011, V. 6, Pacific Coast & Outlying Pacific Islands. 2011. (ENG., Illus.). 302p. pap. 44.00 ***(978-0-16-087116-0(6)***, Coast Guard) United States Government Printing Office.

—Light List, 2011, V. 7, Great Lakes & the St. Lawrence River above the St. Regis River. 2011. (ENG., Illus.). 248p. pap. 37.00 ***(978-0-16-087117-7(4)***, Coast Guard) United States Government Printing Office.

Drower, George. Boats, Boffins & Bowlines: The Stories of Sailing Inventors & Innovations. 2011. (ENG., Illus.). 256p. pap. 15.95 *(978-0-7524-6065-9(X))* History Pr. Ltd., The GBR. Dist: Independent Pubs. Group.

List of Lights, Buoys & Fog Signals. 355p. pap. *(978-0-660-15938-6(4))* Canadian Government Publishing.

National Geospatial-Intelligence Agency. NGA List of Lights - Radio Aids & Fog Signals: British Isles, English Channel, & North Sea. 2008. pap. 45.00 *(978-1-57785-718-1(6))* ProStar Pubns., Inc.

—NGA List of Lights - Radio Aids & Fog Signals: Greenland, the East Coasts of North & South America. 2008. pap. 52.00 *(978-1-57785-721-1(6))* ProStar Pubns., Inc.

November 2007 San Francisco Oil Spill: Causes & Response: Field Hearing Before the Subcommittee on Coast Guard & Maritime Transportation of the Committee on Transportation & Infrastructure, House of Representatives, One Hundred Tenth Congress, First Session, November 19, 2007 (San Francisco, CA) 2007. (Illus.). xx, 113p. *(978-0-16-081365-8(4)*, 552-070-37743-3) United States Government Printing Office.

Swanick, Lois. Navigation in Exploration. 2007. 136p. per. *(978-3-8364-2822-4(9))* VDM Verlag Dr. Mueller e.K.

Transport Canada Staff. The Canadian Aids to Navigation System. 2nd ed.Tr. of Le Systeme Canadien d'Aides a la Navigation. (Illus.). 58p. pap. *(978-0-660-16233-1(4))* Canadian Government Publishing.

United Nations: Economic Commission for Europe: Working Party on Inland Water Transport. Signi: Signs & Signals for Inland Waterways. 2011. (ENG., Illus.). 72p. pap. 20.00 ***(978-92-1-117048-1(6))*** United Nations Pubns.

Weintrit, Adam & Neumann, Tomasz, eds. Methods & Algorithms in Navigation. 2011. (ENG.). 218p. pap. 79.95 ***(978-0-415-69114-7(1)***, CRC Press) Taylor & Francis Group GBR. Dist: Taylor & Francis Group.

AIDS VACCINES

Abalaka, Jeremiah O. A. The First Decade of Safe & Effective HIV Vaccines. 2009. pap. 79.00 *(978-1-60741-143-7(1))* Nova Science Pubs., Inc.

Gupta, Indrani, et al. Adoption of Health Technologies in India: Implications for the AIDS Vaccine. 2007. (Studies in Economic & Social Development: No. 68). 236p. (C). pap. 34.00 *(978-0-7619-3590-2(8)*, B35902P) SAGE Pubns., Inc.

International AIDS Vaccine Initiative (IAVI). AIDS Vaccine Blueprint 2006. 2006. *(978-0-9773126-5-8(8))* International AIDS Vaccine Initiative.

—HIV Vaccine Research & Development: Modeling the Path to Speedier Success. 2006. *(978-0-9773126-9-6(0))* International AIDS Vaccine Initiative.

—The Impact of an AIDS Vaccine in Developing Countries: A New Role Model & Preliminary Results. 2006. *(978-0-9773126-6-5(6))* International AIDS Vaccine Initiative.

Kendow, Lawrence B. AIDS Vaccines, HIV Receptors, & AIDS Research. 2008. 98.00 *(978-1-60692-074-9(X))* Nova Science Pubs., Inc.

Koff, Wayne C., et al, eds. AIDS Vaccine Development: Challenges & Opportunities. 2007. (Illus.). 151p. pap. 99.00 *(978-1-904455-11-0(5))* Caister Academic Pr. GBR. Dist: International Specialized Bk. Services.

Loffredo, John. Cellular Responses to Aids-Virus Infection. 2008. 264p. pap. *(978-3-8364-9286-7(5))* VDM Verlag Dr. Mueller e.K.

Pancino, Gianfranco, et al, eds. Models of Protection Against HIV/SIV: Avoiding AIDS in Humans & Monkeys. 2011. (ENG.). 360p. 99.95 ***(978-0-12-387715-4(6)***, Academic Pr.) Elsevier Science & Technology Bks.

AIDS VIRUS

see HIV (Viruses)

AIKEN, CONRAD, 1889-1973

Butscher, Edward. Conrad Aiken: Poet of White Horse Vale. 2010. (ENG.). 544p. pap. 26.95 *(978-0-8203-3620-6(3))* Univ. of Georgia Pr.

Smith, Harry W. Life & Sports at Aiken & Those Who Made It. (Illus.). 237p. reprint ed. lib. bdg. 98.00 *(978-0-7222-0626-3(7))* Library Reprints, Inc.

AIKIDO

Allemann, Bruce. Aikido: The Essential Guide to Mastering the Art. 2006. (ENG., Illus.). 96p. pap. 19.95 *(978-1-58394-164-5(9)*, Blue Snake Bks.) North Atlantic Bks.

Aloia, Michael. How Aikido Can Change the World. 2009. (Illus.). 92p. pap. *(978-0-578-02614-5(7))* March Baby Publishing.

Bearden, Thomas E. Yoseikan Aikido. 2006. per. *(978-0-9725146-9-9(4))* Cheniere Pr.

Crum, Thomas. Magic of Conflict Video Seminar. Warner, Judith, ed. pap. 124.95 incl. audio, VHS *(978-1-877803-07-9(3))* Aiki Works, Inc.

Curtis, Christopher. Ki-Aikido on Maui: A Training Manual. 3rd rev. ed. (Illus.). (Orig.). pap. 25.00 *(978-0-9655021-1-5(2))* MAKS Pubns.

Escobar, Jose Carlos. The Way of Aiki: A Path of Unity, Confluence & Harmony. 2009. 264p. pap. 23.29 *(978-1-4251-7196-4(6))* Trafford Publishing.

Gleason, William. Aikido & Words of Power. 2009. (ENG., Illus.). 1p. pap. *(978-1-59477-245-0(2)*, Destiny Bks.) Inner Traditions International, Ltd.

Greenhalgh, Margaret. Aikido & Spirituality. 2010. 152p. pap. *(978-3-639-22298-2(9))* VDM Verlag Dr. Mueller e.K.

Higashi, Nobuyoshi. Koryu Aikido. Date not set. (Illus.). 152p. pap. 14.95 *(978-0-86568-158-3(9)*, 321) Unique Pubns.

Makiyama, Thomas H. The Power of Aikido. 2011. 190p. 42.95 ***(978-1-258-00827-7(0))*** Literary Licensing, LLC.

—The Techniques of Aikido V1: Fundamentals. 2011. 108p. 39.95 ***(978-1-258-01019-5(4))*** Literary Licensing, LLC.

Nemeroff, David. Enter into Aikido. 2009. pap. 20.99 *(978-1-60799-272-1(8))* Tate Publishing & Enterprises, LLC.

Owen, Peter. Fishing Knots Handbook. 2nd ed. 2006. (Field & Stream Ser.). (ENG., Illus.). 128p. per. 12.95 *(978-1-59228-274-6(1)*, Lyons Pr.) Globe Pequot Pr., The.

Palmer, Wendy. The Intuitive Body: Discovering the Wisdom of Conscious Embodiment & Aikido. 2008. (ENG., Illus.). 224p. pap. 17.95 *(978-1-58394-212-3(2)*, Blue Snake Bks.) North Atlantic Bks.

—The Practice of Freedom: Aikido Principles as a Spiritual Guide. 2010. (ENG.). 256p. pap. 17.95 *(978-1-930485-27-3(1))* Rodmell Pr.

Response Training Programs. Leading Chaos: An Essential Guide to Conflict Management. rev. ed. 2010. (Illus.). 176p. 15.95 *(978-0-615-39507-4(4))* zoomopzoom.

Roedel, Bodo. Aikido: The Basics. 2010. (Illus.). 352p. pap. 19.95 *(978-1-84126-302-1(8))* Meyer & Meyer Sport, Ltd. GBR. Dist: Cardinal Pubs. Group.

Shifflett, C. M. Aikido Exercises for Teaching & Training: Revised Edition. 2nd rev. ed. 2009. (ENG., Illus.). 288p. pap. 19.95 *(978-1-58394-217-8(3)*, Blue Snake Bks.) North Atlantic Bks.

—Ki in Aikido. 2nd ed. 2010. (ENG., Illus.). 256p. pap. 19.95 *(978-0-9778702-1-9(9))* Round Earth Publishing.

Shioda, Gozo & Shioda, Yasuhisa. Aikido: The Complete Basic Techniques, 1 vol. 2006. (ENG., Illus.). 208p. 35.00 *(978-4-7700-3019-1(3))* Kodansha America, Inc.

Stein, Mary. The Gift of Danger: Lessons from Aikido. 2009. (ENG., Illus.). 120p. pap. 14.95 *(978-1-58394-273-4(4)*, Blue Snake Bks.) North Atlantic Bks.

Stevens, John, tr. from JPN. The Secret Teachings of Aikido, 1 vol. 2008. (ENG., Illus.). 152p. 35.00 *(978-4-7700-3030-6(4))* Kodansha America, Inc.

Ueshiba, Kisshomaru, pref. The Spirit of Aikido, 1 vol. 2012. (JPN & ENG.). 176p. 35.00 ***(978-1-56836-409-4(1))*** Kodansha America, Inc.

Ueshiba, Kisshomaru & Ueshiba, Moriteru. A Life in Aikido: The Biography of Founder Morihei Ueshiba, 1 vol. 2008. (ENG., Illus.). 320p. 35.00 *(978-4-7700-2617-0(X))* Kodansha America, Inc.

Ueshiba, Morihei. The Art of Peace. Stevens, John, tr. from JPN. 2010. (ENG., Illus.). 192p. 18.00 *(978-1-59030-892-9(1))* Shambhala Pubns., Inc.

—The Art of Peace. Stevens, John, ed. & tr. by. 2007. (ENG.). 192p. mass mkt. 6.99 *(978-1-59030-448-8(9))* Shambhala Pubns., Inc.

—The Heart of Aikido: The Philosophy of Takemusu Aiki, 1 vol. Takahashi, Hideo, ed. Stevens, John, tr. from JPN. 2010. (ENG., Illus.). 144p. 19.95 *(978-4-7700-3114-3(9))* Kodansha America, Inc.

AIM

see American Indian Movement

AINU

Batchelor, John. The Ainu of Japan: The Religion, Superstitions, & General History of the Hairy Aborigines of Japan. 2010. 342p. pap. 31.75 *(978-1-146-87850-0(8))*; 336p. pap. 31.75 *(978-1-144-55876-3(X))* BiblioBazaar.

Horimoto, Fumiko. From Ainu World to Inner Japan: Changing Notions of Northern Boundaries in Tokugawa Japan. 2008. 240p. pap. *(978-3-639-10360-1(2))* VDM Verlag Dr. Mueller e.K.

Irimoto, Takashi. Ainu No Kumamatsuri. 2010. (JPN., Illus.). ii, 277p. *(978-4-639-02131-5(3))* Yuzankaku Shuppan.

Irish, Ann B. Hokkaido: A History of Ethnic Transition & Development on Japan's Northern Island. 2009. (ENG., Illus.). 378p. pap. 55.00 *(978-0-7864-4449-6(5))* McFarland & Co., Inc. Pubs.

Muñoz González, Yolanda. La Literatura de Resistencia de la Mujeres Ainu. 2008. (Estudios de Asia y África Ser.). (SPA.). 509p. pap. 62.99 *(978-968-12-1279-7(7))* El Colegio de México, A.C., Biblioteca Miguel Cosio Villegas MEX. Dist: Fondo de Cultura Economica USA.

Watson, Mark. Japan's Ainu Minority in Tokyo: Indigeneity & Cultural Politics. 2012. (Japan Anthropology Workshop Ser.). (ENG.). 256p. (C). 145.00 *(978-0-415-68753-9(5))* Routledge.

AINU—FOLKLORE

Chamberlain, Basil Hall. Aino Folk-Tales. 2009. 48p. pap. *(978-0-217-77029-3(0))* Books LLC.

—Aino Folk-Tales. 2009. 52p. pap. *(978-1-4068-8213-1(5))* Echo Library.

—Aino Folk-Tales. 2007. pap. 16.95 *(978-1-4304-5003-0(7))* Kessinger Publishing, LLC.

AIR

see also Aerodynamics; Atmosphere; Bubbles; Ventilation

also headings beginning with the word Atmospheric

Fahy, Frank. Air: The Excellent Canopy. 2009. (ENG., Illus.). 136p. pap. 35.00 *(978-1-904275-42-8(7)*, Horwood Publishing, Ltd.) Woodhead Publishing Ltd. GBR. Dist: Ingram Pub. Services.

Holmes. Gateway Science. 5th ed. tchr. ed., lab manual ed. 10.68 *(978-0-07-029875-0(0))* 5th ed. stu. ed., lab manual ed. 7.47 *(978-0-07-029865-1(3))*Level 5. 4th ed. tchr. ed. 79.77 *(978-0-07-079545-7(2))*Level 5. 5th ed. tchr. ed. 32.91 *(978-0-07-029921-4(8))* Macmillan/McGraw-Hill Schl. Div.

Knechtel, John, ed. Air. 2010. (Alphabet City Ser.). (ENG., Illus.). 272p. (gr. 17). 15.95 *(978-0-262-01466-3(1))* MIT Pr.

Möller, Detlev. Air: Chemistry of the Climate System: Chemistry of the Climate System. 2010. (ENG., Illus.). XVII, 722p. 224.00 *(978-3-11-019791-4(X))* De Gruyter, Walter Inc.

Navarro, Adolfo. El Dominio del Aire. (Ciencia para Todos Ser.). (SPA.). pap. 6.99 *(978-968-16-4373-7(9))* Fondo de Cultura Economica USA.

Sherman, Joe. Gasp! The Swift & Terrible Beauty of Air. 2007. (ENG., Illus.). 416p. per. 16.95 *(978-1-59376-140-0(6))* Counterpoint LLC.

Spellman, Frank R. The Science of Air: Concepts & Applications. 2nd rev. ed. 2008. (ENG., Illus.). 300p. 109.95 *(978-1-4200-7532-8(2)*, CRC Press) Taylor & Francis Group GBR. Dist: Taylor & Francis Group.

Vincent, P., et al. Mastering the Air. Date not set. (Longman Biology Topics Ser.). (Illus.). 32p. pap. 35.67 *(978-0-582-32300-1(2))* Addison-Wesley Longman, Ltd. GBR. Dist: Trans-Atlantic Pubns., Inc.

Walker, Gabrielle. An Ocean of Air: Why the Wind Blows & Other Mysteries of the Atmosphere. (ENG., Illus.). 288p. 2008. pap. 17.95 *(978-0-15-603414-2(X)*, Mariner Bks.) 2007. 25.00 *(978-0-15-101124-7(9))* Houghton Mifflin Harcourt Trade & Reference Pubs.

AIR—ANALYSIS

Heard, Dwayne, ed. Analytical Techniques for Atmospheric Measurement. 2006. (ENG., Illus.). 528p. 240.00 (978-1-4051-2357-0(5), Wiley-Blackwell) Wiley, John & Sons, Inc.

Macdonald, J. D. A Guide to the Microscopical Examination of Drinking Water. 2006. 124p. per. 18.99 (978-1-4255-1430-3(8)) MPublishing.

McCleery, Robert E. Niosh Evaluation of Air Sampling Methodologies for Bacillus Anthracis in a United States Postal Service Processing & Distribution Center, Trenton, New Jersey. 2006. (Illus.). 51p. (C). reprint ed. pap. 20.00 (978-1-4223-0645-1(3)) DIANE Publishing Co.

Ness, Shirley A. Air Monitoring for Toxic Exposures: An Integrated Approach. 2nd ed. 2007. 352p. pap., stu. ed. 20.00 (978-0-471-29222-7(2), Wiley); 640p. 98.95 (978-0-471-29199-2(4)) Wiley, John & Sons, Inc.

AIR—BACTERIOLOGY

see Air—Microbiology

AIR—MICROBIOLOGY

see also Airborne Infection

Flannigan, Brian, et al, eds. Microorganisms in Home & Indoor Work Environments: Diversity, Health Impacts, Investigation & Control. 2nd rev. ed. 2011. (ENG., Illus.). 539p. 149.95 (978-1-4200-9334-6(7), CRC Press) Taylor & Francis Group GBR. Dist: Taylor & Francis Group.

Macdonald, J. D. A Guide to the Microscopical Examination of Drinking Water. 2006. 124p. per. 18.99 (978-1-4255-1430-3(8)) MPublishing.

Mandrioli, Paolo, et al, eds. Cultural Heritage & Aerobiology: Methods & Measurement Techniques for Biodeterioration Monitoring. 2010. 258p. pap. 189.00 (978-90-481-6423-3(0), 9048164230) Springer.

Tyndall, John. Essays on the Floating-Matter of the Air in Relation to Putrefaction & Infection. 2010. 366p. pap. 32.75 (978-1-142-93683-9(X)) BiblioBazaar.

—Essays on the Floating-Matter of the Air in Relation to Putrefaction & Infection. 2009. 202p. pap. 19.99 (978-1-150-66284-3(0)) General Bks. LLC.

AIR—POLLUTION

see also Acid Rain; Air Quality; Automobiles—Motors—Exhaust Gas; Automobiles—Pollution Control Devices; Dust; Indoor Air Pollution; Motor Vehicles—Pollution Control Devices; Radioactive Pollution of the Atmosphere; Smog

ABBE Scientist Research Division Staff. Chemicals in Dust at Home, Office & in Occupations: Index, Reference & Medical Analysis of New Research. 2008. (Illus.). 160p. ring bd. 69.95 (978-0-7883-4679-8(2)) ABBE Pubs. Assn. of Washington, D.C.

Adeeb, Farah. Near-Surface Ozone Concentrations in the City of Auckland, New Zealand. 2010. 316p. pap. (978-3-8383-4608-3(4)) Lambert Academic Publishing.

Air and Waste Management Association (A&WMA) Staff, compiled by. Power Plant Air Pollutant Control Mega Symposium 2006. 2007. 1570p. pap. 281.00 (978-1-60423-719-1(8)) Curran Assocs., Inc.

—Symposium on Air Quality Measurement: Methods & Technology 2006. 2007. 497p. pap. 118.00 (978-1-60423-793-1(7)) Curran Assocs., Inc.

—Symposium on Air Quality Measurement Methods & Technology 2007. 2008. 308p. pap. 115.00 (978-1-60423-900-3(X)) Curran Assocs., Inc.

—99th Annual Conference & Exhibition of the Air & Waste Management Association 2006. 2007. 4513p. pap. 268.00 (978-1-60423-702-3(3)) Curran Assocs., Inc.

Air Pollution: EPA's Progress in Determining the Costs & Benefits of Clean Air Legislation. 39p. pap. 30.00 (978-0-7881-4083-9(3)) DIANE Publishing Co.

Air Pollution & Cancer. 2009. (IARC Scientific Publication No 161 Ser.). (ENG.). pap. 250.00 (978-92-832-2161-6(3)) International Agency for Research on Cancer (IARC) (UN) FRA. Dist: World Health Organization.

Akanni, Cornelius. Transportation & Air Quality Changes in an Urban Environment. 2011. 268p. pap. (978-3-8433-8071-3(6)) Lambert Academic Publishing.

Alexander, Ralph B. Global Warming False Alarm: The Bad Science Behind the United Nations' Assertion that Man-made CO2 Causes Global Warming. 2009. (Illus.). 178p. pap. 18.95 (978-0-9840989-0-3(9)) Canterbury Publishing.

Allin, Craig W., ed. Atmosphere & Air Pollution. 2011. (Encyclopedia of Environmental Issues Ser.). (ENG., Illus.). 151p. pap. 29.95 (978-1-4298-3670-8(9)) Salem Pr., Inc.

Amann, M., et al. Health Risks of Ozone from Long-range Transboundary Air Pollution. 2009. (EURO Nonserial Publication Ser.). (ENG.). 106p. pap. 24.00 (978-92-890-4289-5(3)) World Health Organization.

Ambient Air Pollution. 2007. per. 95.00 (978-0-9792542-0-8(5)) EnviroComp Institute, The.

American Society of Mechanical Engineers Staff, ed. Vehicle & the Environment (Fisita Proceedings), 5 vols. (Illus.). 317p. 116.00 (978-0-85298-833-6(8)) Professional Engineering Publishing GBR. Dist: SAE Intl.

Aviation & the Environment: Emissions [sic]: Hearing Before the Subcommittee on Aviation of the Committee on Transportation & Infrastructure, House of Representatives, One Hundred Tenth Congress, Second Session, May 6, 2008. 2008. (Illus.). xiii, 203p. (978-0-16-083489-9(X), 552-070-39229-1) United States Government Printing Office.

Bajwa, Saima & Ashraf, Wajiha. Sugar Industry in Pakistan & Air Pollution Impacts. 2011. 92p. pap. (978-3-8443-9782-6(5)) Lambert Academic Publishing.

Bakker, Sem H. Ozone Depletion, Chemistry, & Impacts. 2008. 98.00 (978-1-60692-007-7(3)) Nova Science Pubs., Inc.

Baklanov, Alexander, et al, eds. Meteorological & Air Quality Models for Urban Areas. 2009. (ENG., Illus.). xviii, 183p. pap. 109.00 (978-3-642-00297-7(8), 3642002978) Springer.

Balduino, Sergio P. Progress in Air Pollution Research. 2007. 129.00 (978-1-60021-804-0(0)) Nova Science Pubs., Inc.

Baron, Paul A., et al, eds. Aerosol Measurement: Principles, Techniques, & Applications. 3rd ed. 2011. (ENG., Illus.). 904p. 195.00 (978-0-470-38741-2(6), Wiley) Wiley, John & Sons, Inc.

Beniston, Martin & Pielke, Roger, eds. Interactions Between Energy Transformations & Atmospheric Phenomena: A Survey of Recent Research. 2010. 440p. pap. 399.00 (978-90-481-8445-3(2), 9048184452) Springer.

Bloom, Khaled J. Murder of a Landscape: The California Farmer-Smelter War, 1897-1916. 2010. (Western Lands & Waters Ser.). (ENG.). 240p. (C). 34.95 (978-0-87062-396-7(6), Clark, Arthur H. Co., The) Univ. of Oklahoma Pr.

Blumenthal, George T., ed. Aviation & Climate Change. 2010. (Environmental Research Advances Ser.). 115.00 (978-1-60876-757-1(4)) Nova Science Pubs., Inc.

Bodine, Corin G. Air Pollution Research Advances. 2007. 129.00 (978-1-60021-806-4(7)) Nova Science Pubs., Inc.

Borrego, Carlos. Air Pollution Modeling & Its Application XIX. Miranda, Ana Isabel, ed. 2008. (NATO Science for Peace & Security Series C: Environmental Security Ser.). XLIV, 740p. 329.00 (978-1-4020-8451-5(X), 140208451X) Springer.

—Air Pollution Modeling & Its Application XIX. Miranda, Ana Isabel, ed. 2008. (NATO Science for Peace & Security Series C: Environmental Security Ser.). XLIV, 736p. pap. 159.00 (978-1-4020-8452-2(8), 1402084528) Springer.

Borrego, Carlos & Norman, Ann-Lise, eds. Air Pollution Modeling & Its Application XVII. 2006. (Illus.). XX, 746p. 249.00 (978-0-387-28255-8(6), 0387282556) Springer.

Boutin, Jacob, ed. Air Pollution & Ship Emissions. 2010. (Air, Water & Soil Pollution Science & Technology Ser.). 198p. 115.00 (978-1-60876-087-9(1)) Nova Science Pubs., Inc.

Brebbia, C. A. & Longhurst, J. W. S., eds. Air Pollution XVIII. 2010. (WIT Transactions on Ecology & the Environment Ser.: 136). (Illus.). 464p. 352.00 (978-1-84564-450-5(6)) WIT Pr GBR. Dist: WIT Pr.

Brebbia, C. A. & Popov, V., eds. Air Pollution XIX. 2011. (WIT Transactions on Ecology & the Environment Ser.: 147). (Illus.). 496p. lib. bdg. 426.00 (978-1-84564-528-1(6)) WIT Pr GBR. Dist: WIT Pr.

—Air Pollution XVII. 2009. (WIT Transactions on Ecology & the Environment Ser.: 123). (Illus.). 480p. 328.00 (978-1-84564-195-5(7)) WIT Pr GBR. Dist: WIT Pr.

Brebbia, Carlos A. & Borrego, C. A., eds. Air Pollution XV. 2007. (WIT Transactions on Ecology & the Environment Ser.: 101). (Illus.). 624p. 355.00 (978-1-84564-067-5(5)) WIT Pr GBR. Dist: WIT Pr.

Brownell, F. William & Hunton. Clean Air Handbook. 4th ed. 2013. (ENG.). 350p. pap. 115.00 (978-0-86587-022-2(5)) Government Institutes.

Budisulistiorini, Sri Hapsari. Evaluation of Air Quality Management Plans for PM10Control: Jakarta Case Study. 2008. 132p. pap. (978-3-639-09778-8(5)) VDM Verlag Dr. Mueller e.K.

Businger, Steven. Eye to the Sky: Exploring Our Atmosphere. 2006. (C). per., lab manual ed. 42.99 (978-0-9787831-1-2(5)) Novus Publishing, LLC.

Bytnerowicz, Andrzej, et al, eds. Wildland Fires & Air Pollution. 2008. (Developments in Environmental Science Ser.: 8). (ENG., Illus.). 686p. 180.00 (978-0-08-055609-3(4), Elsevier Science) Elsevier Science & Technology Bks.

Calhoun, Yael. The Environment in the News. 2007. (Science News Flash Ser.). (Illus.). 112p. (YA). (gr. 7-12). lib. bdg. 31.95 (978-0-7910-9253-8(4)) Facts On File, Inc.

Carle, David. Introduction to Air in California. 2006. (California Natural History Guides Ser.: Vol. 87). (Illus.). 245p. 45.00 (978-0-520-24531-0(8)); pap. 19.95 (978-0-520-24748-2(5)) Univ. of California Pr.

Carolina Biological Staff, compiled by. Experiencing Air Pollution. 2009. (Inquiries in Science Environmental Ser.). (978-1-4350-0452-8(3)); tchr. ed., spiral bd. (978-1-4350-0451-1(5)) Carolina Biological Supply Co.

Cassee, Flemming R., et al, eds. Cardiovascular Effects of Inhaled Ultrafine & Nano-Sized Particles. 2011. (ENG., Illus.). 585p. 158.00 (978-0-470-43353-9(1), Wiley) Wiley, John & Sons, Inc.

Cheng, Ming & Liu, Wen, eds. Airborne Particulates. 2009. 98.00 (978-1-60692-907-0(0)) Nova Science Pubs., Inc.

Clearing the Smoke: Understanding the Impacts of Black Carbon Pollution: Hearing Before the Select Committee on Energy Independence & Global Warming, House of Representatives, One Hundred Eleventh Congress, Second Session, March 16, 2010. 2010. (Illus.). iii, 116p. (978-0-16-087581-6(1), 552-070-42212-9) United States Government Printing Office.

Colls, Jeremy. Air Pollution. 3rd rev. ed. 2009. (ENG., Illus.). 528p. (C). 165.00 (978-0-415-47933-2(9)); pap. 71.95 (978-0-415-47932-5(0)) Taylor & Francis Group GBR. (CRC Press). Dist: Taylor & Francis Group.

Committee for Review of the DOD's Enhanced Particulate Matter Surveillance Program Report & National Research Council. Review of the Department of Defense Enhanced Particulate Matter Surveillance Program Report. 2010. (ENG.). 106p. pap. 28.75 (978-0-309-15413-0(8)) National Academies Pr.

Committee on Determining a Standard Unit of Measure for Biological Aerosols & National Research Council. A Framework for Assessing the Health Hazard Posed by Bioaerosols. 2008. (ENG.). 100p. pap. 26.00 (978-0-309-11150-8(1)) National Academies Pr.

Committee on Energy Futures and Air Pollution in Urban China and the United States, et al. Energy Futures & Urban Air Pollution: Challenges for China & the United States. 2008. (ENG.). 386p. pap. 76.25 (978-0-309-11140-9(4)) National Academies Pr.

Committee on Estimating Mortality Risk Reduction Benefits from Decreasing Tropospheric Ozone Exposure & National Research Council. Estimating Mortality Risk Reduction & Economic Benefits from Controlling Ozone Air Pollution. 2008. (ENG.). 226p. pap. 49.00 (978-0-309-11994-8(4)) National Academies Pr.

Committee on the Significance of International Transport of Air Pollutants & National Research Council. Global Sources of Local Pollution: An Assessment of Long-Range Transport of Key Air Pollutants to & from the United States. 2010. (ENG.). 248p. pap. 47.00 (978-0-309-14401-8(9)) National Academies Pr.

Connor, Steven. The Matter of Air: Science & Art of the Ethereal. 2010. (Illus.). 374p. 39.00 (978-1-86189-766-4(9)) Reaktion Bks., Ltd. GBR. Dist: Chicago Distribution Ctr.

Cram101 Textbook Reviews. Outlines & Highlights for Fundamentals of Air Pollution by Daniel Vallero, Isbn: 9780123736154 0123736153. 2011. 156p. pap. 29.95 (978-1-61490-203-4(8)) Cram101 Inc.

Cram101 Textbook Reviews Staff. Outlines & Highlights for Earth under Siege: From Air Pollution to Global Change by Turco, Richard P. Turco, Richard P., ISBN. 2009. 240p. pap. 31.95 (978-1-4288-7411-4(9)) Cram101 Inc.

Das, Sandipan Kumar. Pollutant Dispersion Prediction in Airports. 2009. 124p. pap. (978-3-639-12479-8(0)) VDM Verlag Dr. Mueller e.K.

Demidov, Sergey & Bonnet, Jacques. Traffic Related Air Pollution & Internal Combustion Engines. 2009. 129.00 (978-1-60741-145-1(8)) Nova Science Pubs., Inc.

Devinny, Joseph S., et al. Biofiltration for Air Pollution Control. 2nd rev. ed. 2008. (Illus.). 400p. 129.95 (978-0-8493-9776-9(6)) CRC Pr LLC.

Earth Observing System Aura (U.S.), et al, eds. Our Changing Atmosphere: Discoveries from EOS Aura (Booklet) Discoveries from EOS Aura. 2010. (ENG., Illus.). 56p. 10.00 (978-0-16-086587-9(5), U. S. National Aeronautics & Space Administration) United States Government Printing Office.

Ebel, Adolf, et al, eds. Tropospheric Modelling & Emission Estimation: Chemical Transport & Emission Modelling on Regional, Global & Urban Scales Chemistry Chemistry. 2010. (Transport & Chemical Transformation of Pollutants in the Troposphere Ser.). (ENG., Illus.). xxiv, 440p. pap. 239.00 (978-3-642-08319-8(6), 3642083196) Springer.

Epstein, Joshua M & Gupta, Raj. Controlling the Greenhouse Effect: Five Global Regimes Compared. (Brookings Occasional Papers). (Illus.). 40p. pap. 9.95 (978-0-8157-2465-0(9)) Brookings Institution Pr.

Fenger, J., et al, eds. Urban Air Pollution - European Aspects. 2010. (Environmental Pollution Ser.). 492p. pap. 215.00 (978-90-481-5147-9(3), 9048151473) Springer.

Flagan, Richard C., et al. Fundamentals of Air Pollution Engineering. 2012. (Dover Civil & Mechanical Engineering Ser.). (ENG., Illus.). 592p. (C). (gr. 15). pap. 29.95 (978-0-486-48872-1(1)) Dover Pubns., Inc.

Friedrich, Rainer & Reis, Stefan, eds. Emissions of Air Pollutants: Measurements, Calculations & Uncertainties. 2010. (ENG., Illus.). xviii, 335p. pap. 159.00 (978-3-642-05645-1(8), 3642056458) Springer.

From the Wright Brothers to the Right Solutions: Curbing Soaring Aviation Emissions: Hearing Before the Select Committee on Energy Independence & Global Warming, House of Representatives, One Hundred Tenth Congress, Second Session, April 2, 2008. 2010. (Illus.). iii, 128p. (978-0-16-087414-7(9), 552-070-42107-6) United States Government Printing Office.

Gallo, Dean & Mancini, Richard. Environmental & Regional Air Pollution. 2009. (Air, Water & Soil Pollution Science & Technology Ser.). 129.00 (978-1-60692-893-6(7)) Nova Science Pubs., Inc.

Gates, Alexander E., et al. Encyclopedia of Pollution Set: Air, Earth & Water, 2 vols. 2011. (Science Encyclopedia Ser.). (Illus.). 1080p. (C). (gr. 9). 170.00 (978-0-8160-7002-2(4), Facts On File, Inc.

Gehr, Peter, et al, eds. Particle-Lung Interactions, Second Edition. 2nd rev. ed. 2009. (ENG., Illus.). 338p. 300.00 (978-1-4200-7256-3(0), Informa Healthcare) Taylor & Francis Group GBR. Dist: Taylor & Francis Group.

Gelencsér, András. Carbonaceous Aerosol. 2010. (Atmospheric & Oceanographic Sciences Library). ix, 350p. pap. 189.00 (978-90-481-6740-1(X), 904816740X) Springer.

Ghose, Mrinal. Air Quality Impact Assessment. 2011. 208p. pap. (978-3-8433-8780-4(X), Lambert Academic Publishing.

Gonçalves-Ageitos, Maria, et al. Alternatives for a Cleaner Air in Urban Areas: A modelling Study. 2010. 236p. pap. (978-3-639-24766-4(3)) VDM Verlag Dr. Mueller e.K.

Granier, Claire, et al, eds. Emissions of Atmospheric Trace Compounds. 2010. (Advances in Global Change Research Ser.). 560p. pap. 299.00 (978-90-481-6605-3(5), 9048166055) Springer.

Greim, Helmut & Parlar, Harun, eds. Air Monitoring Methods, Vol. 10. 2007. (MAK-Collection for Occupational Health & Safety. Part III: Air Monitoring Methods (DFG) Ser.). (ENG., Illus.). 187p. 185.00 (978-3-527-31601-4(9), Wiley-VCH) Wiley, John & Sons, Inc.

Guideline on Air Quality Models — Applications & FLAG Developments: Applications & FLAG Developments. 2007. cd-rom (978-0-923204-96-9(2)) Air & Waste Management Assn.

Gurjar, Bhola R., et al, eds. Air Pollution: Health & Environmental Impacts. 2010. (ENG., Illus.). 556p. 129.95 (978-1-4398-0962-4(3), CRC Press) Taylor & Francis Group GBR. Dist: Taylor & Francis Group.

Gyr, A. & Rys, Franz-S., eds. Diffusion & Transport of Pollutants in Atmospheric Mesoscale Flow Fields. 2010. (ERCOFTAC Ser.). 232p. pap. 299.00 (978-90-481-4501-0(5), 9048145015) Springer.

Haerens, Margaret. Air Pollution. 2011. (Global Viewpoints Ser.). 224p. pap. 26.50 (978-0-7377-5186-4(X)); lib. bdg. 38.45 (978-0-7377-5185-7(1)) Cengage Gale. (Greenhaven Pr., Inc.).

Hamblyn, Richard. Terra: Tales of the Earth - Four Events That Changed the World. 2010. (ENG., Illus.). 304p. pap. 19.95 (978-0-330-49074-0(5), Picador) Pan Macmillan GBR. Dist: Trans-Atlantic Pubns., Inc.

Harrison, Jill Lindsay. Pesticide Drift & the Pursuit of Environmental Justice. 2011. (Food, Health, & the Environment Ser.). (ENG., Illus.). 296p. (gr. 17). 46.00 (978-0-262-01598-1(6)) MIT Pr.

Harrison, Jill Lindsey. Pesticide Drift & the Pursuit of Environmental Justice. 2011. (Food, Health, & the Environment Ser.). (ENG., Illus.). 296p. (gr. 17). pap. 23.00 (978-0-262-51628-0(4)) MIT Pr.

Harrison, R. M., et al. Air Quality in Urban Environments. Harrison, R. M. & Hester, R. E., eds. 2009. (Issues in Environmental Science & Technology Ser.). (ENG., Illus.). 162p. (C). 96.00 (978-1-84755-907-4(7)) Royal Society of Chemistry, The GBR. Dist: Ingram Pub. Services.

Heumann, William L. Industrial Air Pollution Control Systems. Date not set. (Environmental Science & Pollution Ser.). (978-0-8247-9422-4(2)) Dekker, Marcel Inc.

Ho, Mun S. & Nielsen, Chris P., eds. Clearing the Air: The Health & Economic Damages of Air Pollution in China. 2007. (ENG., Illus.). 405p. (gr. 17). 53.00 (978-0-262-08358-4(2)) MIT Pr.

Hudson, Robert C. Hazardous Materials in the Soil & Atmosphere: Treatment, Removal & Analysis. 2006. (Illus.). 169p. pap. 98.00 (978-1-60021-250-5(6)) Nova Science Pubs., Inc.

The Implications of the Supreme Court's Decision Regarding EPA's Authorities with Respect to Greenhouse Gases under the Clean Air ACT: Hearing Before the Committee on Environment & Public Works, United States Senate, One Hundred Tenth Congress, First Session, April 24, 2007. 2011. iii, 86p. (978-0-16-089899-0(4), 552-070-43745-2) United States Government Printing Office.

International Civil Aviation Organization Staff, contrib. by. Guidance on Aircraft Emissions Charges Related to Local Air Quality. 2007. (978-92-9194-972-4(8)) International Civil Aviation Organization, ICAO.

Jiang, Ningbo. Quality of the Auckland Airshed. 2008. 280p. pap. (978-3-8364-9002-3(1)) VDM Verlag Dr. Mueller e.K.

Juniper, Tony. How Many Lightbulbs Does It Take to Change A Planet? 95 Ways to Save Planet Earth. 2008. (ENG.). 304p. pap. 12.95 (978-1-84724-371-3(1)) Quercus GBR. Dist: Independent Pubs. Group.

Kellie, Shawn. Factors Affecting Mercury Emissions from Coal Fired Combustors. 2008. 132p. pap. (978-3-639-06071-3(7)) VDM Verlag Dr. Mueller e.K.

Kessel, Anthony. Air, the Environment & Public Health. 2010. (ENG., Illus.). 258p. pap. 35.99 (978-0-521-15773-5(0)) Cambridge Univ. Pr.

Khare, Mukesh & Nagendra, S. M. Shiva. Artificial Neural Networks in Vehicular Pollution Modelling. 2010. (Studies in Computational Intelligence Ser.). (Illus.). xvi, 242p. pap. 149.00 (978-3-642-07222-2(4), 3642072224) Springer.

Kim, Young J. & Platt, Ulrich, eds. Advanced Environmental Monitoring. 2010. (ENG., Illus.). xxii, 420p. pap. 239.00 (978-90-481-7615-1(8), 9048176158) Springer.

Knechtel, John, ed. & intro. Fuel. 2008. (Alphabet City Ser.). (ENG., Illus.). 352p. (gr. 17). 15.95 (978-0-262-11325-0(2)) MIT Pr.

Knudsen, Henrik & Rasmussen, Niels. Particulate Matter: Sources, Emission Rates & Health Effects. 2012. (Environmental Science, Engineering & Technology Ser.). 344p. 215.00 (978-1-61470-948-0(3)) Nova Science Pubs., Inc.

Kravets, N. & Parker, J. Linkage of the Third National Health & Nutrition Examination Survey to Air Quality Data. 2008. (DHHS Publication Ser.: Nos. 2009-1349). (978-0-8406-0628-0(1)) National Ctr. for Health Statistics.

Kwiatkowski, Lester. Monitoring & Modelling Emissions of Uk Road Transport. 2011. 88p. pap. (978-3-8443-9895-3(3)) Lambert Academic Publishing.

Larsen, John, et al. Charting the Midwest: An Inventory & Analysis of Greenhouse Gas Emissions in America's Heartland. 2007. (Illus.). xii, 68p. pap. (978-1-56973-664-7(2)) World Resources Institute.

Lave, Lester B. & Seskin, Eugene P. Air Pollution & Human Health. 2011. (RFF Policy & Governance Set Ser.). (ENG.). 368p. 99.95 (978-1-61726-058-2(4), RFF Pr.) Earthscan LLC.

Lazaridis, Mihalis. First Principles of Meteorology & Air Pollution. 2010. (Environmental Pollution Ser.). (Illus.). x, 362p. 179.00 (978-94-007-0161-8(6), 9400701616) Springer.

Lehmann, Christopher. Atmospheric Deposition Monitoring: Assessing Trends for the Continental United States. 2008. 408p. pap. (978-3-639-04614-4(5)) VDM Verlag Dr. Mueller e.K.

Leonard, Barry, ed. Evaluating Ozone Control Programs in the Eastern United States: Focus on the NOx Budget Trading Program 2004. 2006. (Illus.). 51p. (C). reprint ed. pap. 15.00 (978-1-4223-0770-0(0)) DIANE Publishing Co.

Levin, Zev & Cotton, William R. Aerosol Pollution Impact on Precipitation: A Scientific Review. 2008. (Illus.). 486p. 229.00 (978-1-4020-8689-2(X), 140208689X) Springer.

Levin, Zev & Cotton, William R., eds. Aerosol Pollution Impact on Precipitation: A Scientific Review. 2010. (Illus.). xxi, 386p. pap. 229.00 (978-90-481-7953-4(X), 904817953X) Springer.

Lidskog, Rolf & Sundqvist, Goran. Governing the Air: - the Dynamics of Science, Policy, & Citizen Interaction. 2011. (Politics, Science, & the Environment Ser.). (ENG., Illus.). 384p. (gr. 17). pap. 27.00 (978-0-262-51642-6(X)) MIT Pr.

A

—Governing the Air: The Dynamics of Science, Policy, & Citizen Interaction. 2011. (Politics, Science, & the Environment Ser.). (ENG., Illus.). 384p. (gr. 17). 54.00 (978-0-262-01650-6(8)) MIT Pr.

Lieberman, Daniel, et al, eds. Accounting for Climate Change: Uncertainty in Greenhouse Gas Inventories - Verification, Compliance, & Trading. (ENG.). vi, 162p. 2010. pap. 139.00 (978-90-481-7479-9(1), 9048174791) 2007. (Illus.). 139.00 (978-1-4020-5929-2(9), 1402059299) Springer.

Lioy, Paul. Dust: The Inside Story of It's Role in the September 11th Aftermath. 2011. (ENG.). 280p. pap. 18.95 (978-1-4422-0149-1(5)) Rowman & Littlefield Publishers, Inc.

Lioy, Paul J. Dust: The Inside Story of Its Role in the September 11th Aftermath. 2010. (ENG., Illus.). 272p. 37.50 (978-1-4422-0148-4(7)) Rowman & Littlefield Publishers, Inc.

Longhurst, J. W. S. & Brebbia, C. A04, eds. Air Pollution XX. 2012. (Illus.). 500p. lib. bdg. 430.00 (978-1-84564-582-3(0)) WIT Pr GBR. Dist: WIT Pr.

Longhurst, James. Citizen Environmentalists. 2010. (Civil Society: Historical & Contemporary Perspectives Ser.). (ENG., Illus.). 264p. (C). 85.00 (978-1-58465-849-8(5)); pap. 35.00 (978-1-58465-859-7(2)) Univ. Pr. of New England. (Tufts University Press).

Longhurst, James W. S. & Brebbia, C. A. Air Pollution XVI. Brebbia, Carlos A. & Longhurst, James W. S., eds. 2008. (WIT Transactions on Ecology & the Environment Ser.: 116). (Illus.). 672p. 442.00 (978-1-84564-127-6(2)) WIT Pr GBR. Dist: WIT Pr.

Macauslan, Robert. Air Pollution Policy in Singapore, Dalian, & Hong Kong: Contemporary Case Studies Examining the Role of Political Will in Policy Development & Enforcement. 2008. 92p. pap. (978-3-639-10307-6(6)) VDM Verlag Dr. Mueller e.K.

Margui, Eva. Metal Dispersal Around Mining Environments. 2009. 252p. pap. (978-3-639-13617-3(9)) VDM Verlag Dr. Mueller e.K.

Maroni, M., ed. Ventilation & Indoor Air Quality in Hospitals. 2010. (Nato Science Partnership Subseries: 2 (closed) Ser.). 360p. pap. 349.00 (978-90-481-4712-0(3), 9048147123) Springer.

Marsik, Tom & Johnson, Ron. Effect of Outdoor Air Quality on Indoor Air. 2008. 152p. pap. (978-3-8364-8196-0(0)) VDM Verlag Dr. Mueller e.K.

Massachusetts V. U.S. EPA: Implications of the Supreme Court Decision: Hearing Before the Select Committee on Energy Independence & Global Warming, House of Representatives, One Hundred Tenth Congress, First Session, June 8, 2007. 2010. (Illus.). iii, 90p. (978-0-16-086841-2(6), 552-070-41755-9) United States Government Printing Office.

Massachusetts V. U.S. EPA, Part II: Implications of the Supreme Court Decision: Hearing Before the Select Committee on Energy Independence & Global Warming, House of Representatives, One Hundred Tenth Congress, Second Session, March 13, 2008. 2010. (Illus.). iv, 157p. (978-0-16-087422-2(X), 552-070-42115-7) United States Government Printing Office.

McKenna, John D., et al. Fine Particle (2.5 Microns) Emissions: Regulations, Measurement & Control. 2008. (ENG., Illus.). 266p. 94.95 (978-0-471-70963-3(8), Wiley-Interscience) Wiley, John & Sons, Inc.

Miller, Debra A. Pollution. 2007. (Current Controversies Ser.). (ENG.). 219p. (gr. 10-12). 27.50 (978-0-7377-3728-8(X)); (Illus.). (YA). (gr. 9-12). pap. 39.70 (978-0-7377-3727-1(1)) Cengage Gale.

Moreira, Davidson, ed. Air Pollution & Turbulence: Modeling & Applications. 2009. (ENG., Illus.). 354p. 129.95 (978-1-4398-1144-3(X), CRC Press) Taylor & Francis Group GBR. Dist: Taylor & Francis Group.

Moroney, John R. Power Struggle: World Energy in the Twenty-First Century, 1 vol. 2008. (Illus.). 208p. 39.95 (978-0-313-35677-3(7), C35677, Praeger Pubs.) Greenwood Publishing Group, Inc.

Mudakavi, J. R. Principles & Practices of Air Pollution Control & Analysis. 2010. (Illus.). 736p. (C). (978-93-80026-38-1(2)) I.K. International Publishing House Pvt. Ltd.

Mukhopadhyay, Arunangshu, ed. Pulse-Jet Filtration. 2010. (ENG.). pap. 31.95 (978-0-415-59287-1(9), CRC Press) Taylor & Francis Group GBR. Dist: Taylor & Francis Group.

—Pulse-Jet Filtration: an Effective Way to Control Industrial Pollution: Part 1: Theory, Selection & Design of Pulse-Jet Filter. 2010. (Textile Progress Ser.). (ENG.). 128p. pap. 31.95 (978-0-415-58103-5(6), CRC Press) Taylor & Francis Group GBR. Dist: Taylor & Francis Group.

Mukhopadhyay, Kakali. Air Pollution in India & Its Impact on the Health of Different Income Groups. 2008. 79.00 (978-1-60456-935-3(2)) Nova Science Pubs., Inc.

National Research Council (U.S.) Staff, et al, contrib. by. New Source Review for Stationary Sources of Air Pollution. 2006. (ENG., Illus.). 334p. pap. 65.00 (978-0-309-10277-3(4)) National Academies Pr.

Ness, Shirley A. Air Monitoring for Toxic Exposures: An Integrated Approach. 2nd ed. 2007. 352p. pap., stu. ed. 20.00 (978-0-471-29222-7(2), Wiley); 640p. 98.95 (978-0-471-29199-2(4)) Wiley, John & Sons, Inc.

Nicolay, Xavier, ed. Odors in the Food Industry. 2006. (Integrating Safety & Environmental Knowledge into Food Studies towards European Sustainable Development Ser.). (ENG., Illus.). xiv, 162p. 149.00 (978-0-387-33510-0(2), 0387335102) Springer.

Oanh, Nguyen Thi Kim. Integrated Air Quality Mangement. 2012. (ENG., Illus.). 434p. 129.95 (978-1-4398-6225-4(7), CRC Press) Taylor & Francis Group GBR. Dist: Taylor & Francis Group.

O'Dowd, Colin & Wagner, Paul, eds. Nucleation & Atmospheric Aerosols: 17th International Conference, Galway, Ireland 2007. 2007. 1010p. 339.00 (978-1-4020-6474-6(8), 1402064748) Springer.

Onat, Adem. Fugitive Emissions & Seals. 2011. (Environmental Science, Engineering & Technology Ser.). pap. 43.00 (978-1-61122-991-2(X), Nova Novinka) Nova Science Pubs., Inc.

Pantoja Filho, Jorge. Biofiltration for Removal of Air Toxic Compounds - Hydrogen Sulfide. 2010. 80p. pap. (978-3-639-24466-3(4)) VDM Verlag Dr. Mueller e.K.

Parisotto, Emanuele. An Innovative Hvac System Exploiting Vortex Tubes. 2009. 224p. pap. (978-3-639-15046-9(5)) VDM Verlag Dr. Mueller e.K.

Parker, K. J., et al. Linkage of the National Health Interview Survey to Air Quality Data. 2008. (DHHS Publication Ser.: No. 145). (978-0-8406-0619-8(2)) National Ctr. for Health Statistics.

Parlar, Harun, ed. The MAK-Collection for Occupational Health & Safety. 2011. (MAK-Collection for Occupational Health & Safety. Part III: Air Monitoring Methods (DFG) Ser.). (ENG.). 208p. 86.50 (978-3-527-32818-5(1)) Wiley, John & Sons, Inc.

Parlar, Harun & Greim, Helmut, eds. Air Monitoring Methods, Vol. 11, Pt. 3. 2009. (MAK-Collection for Occupational Health & Safety. Part III: Air Monitoring Methods (DFG) Ser.). (ENG.). 196p. 179.00 (978-3-527-31959-6(X), Wiley-VCH) Wiley, John & Sons, Inc.

Pawar, Kishore, et al. Air Pollution Impact on Reproductive Behaviour of Few Tropical Trees. 2011. 68p. pap. (978-3-8433-8835-1(0)) Lambert Academic Publishing.

Peng, Roger D. & Dominici, Francesca. Statistical Methods for Environmental Epidemiology with R: A Case Study in Air Pollution & Health. 2008. (Use R Ser.). (Illus.). 150p. pap. 79.95 (978-0-387-78166-2(8)) Springer.

Peretz, Daniel H., ed. Aerosols: Chemistry, Environmental Impact & Health Effects. 2008. 240p. 89.00 (978-1-60692-925-4(9)) Nova Science Pubs., Inc.

Phalen. Introduction to Air Pollution Science. rev. ed. 2011. (Illus.). 333p. pap. 86.95 (978-0-7637-8044-9(8)) Jones & Bartlett Learning, LLC.

Phalen, Robert F. Inhalation Studies: Foundations & Techniques. 2nd rev. ed. 2008. (ENG., Illus.). 288p. 180.00 (978-0-8493-1400-1(3)) CRC Pr. LLC.

Pulugurtha, Srinivas S. Transportation Planning, Land Use, & Air Quality: Selected Papers of the 2009 Transportation Planning, Land Use, & Air Quality Conference, July 28-29, 2009, Denver, Colorado. 2009. pap. 66.00 (978-0-7844-1059-2(3)) American Society of Civil Engineers.

Pulugurtha, Srinivas S., et al, eds. Transportation Land-Use Planning, & Air Quality Conference 2007: Proceedings of the 2007 Transportation Land-Use Planning, & Air Quality Conference: July 9-11, 2007, Orlando, Florida. 2008. pap. 90.00 (978-0-7844-0960-2(9)) American Society of Civil Engineers.

Ramachandran, Gurumurthy. Assessing Nanoparticle Risks to Human Health. 2011. (Micro & Nano Technologies Ser.). (ENG.). 400p. 175.00 (978-1-4377-7863-2(1)) William Andrew, Inc.

Reis, Stefan. Costs of Air Pollution Control: Analyses of Emission Control Options for Ozone Abatement Strategies. 2010. (ENG., Illus.). xv, 203p. pap. 149.00 (978-3-642-07878-1(8), 3642078788) Springer.

Resosudarmo, Budy P. The Impact of Environmental Policies on a Developing Economy. 2010. 196p. pap. (978-3-639-23523-4(1)) VDM Verlag Dr. Mueller e.K.

Resources for the Future Staff, contrib. by. Measuring the Benefits of Clean Air & Water, 8 vols. 2011. (RFF Environmental & Resource Economics Set Ser.). (ENG.). 159p. 99.95 (978-1-61726-028-5(2), RFF Pr.) Earthscan LLC.

Reuten, Christian. Upslope Flow Systems - Scaling, Structure, & Kinematics in Tank & Atmosphere. 2008. 200p. pap. (978-3-639-00757-2(3)) VDM Verlag Dr. Mueller e.K.

Roberts, Gillian S. Environmental Concerns in Animal Agriculture & Feeding Operations. 2011. (Environmental Science, Engineering & Technology Ser.). 115.00 (978-1-61209-518-9(6)) Nova Science Pubs., Inc.

Romano, Gaia C. & Conti, Alice G. Air Quality in the 21st Century. 2008. 89.00 (978-1-60456-793-9(7)) Nova Science Pubs., Inc.

Romley, John A., et al. The Impact of Air Quality on Hospital Spending. 2010. 76p. pap. 23.00 (978-0-8330-4929-2(1), tr-777) RAND Corp., The.

Saffarian, Saman. A Study of Life Cycle Assessment in Air Pollution Control. 2010. 164p. pap. (978-3-8383-5079-0(0)) Lambert Academic Publishing.

Saponaro, Sabrina, et al, eds. Vapor Emission to Outdoor Air & Enclosed Spaces for Human Health Risk Assessment: Site Characterization, Monitoring & Modeling. 2010. (Chemistry Research & Applications Ser.). 195.00 (978-1-61728-692-6(3), Nova Biomedical Bks.) Nova Science Pubs., Inc.

Schwartz, Joel M. Air Quality in America: A Dose of Reality on Air Pollution Levels, Trends, & Health Risks. 2007. (ENG., Illus.). 275p. per. 20.00 (978-0-8447-7187-8(2), AEI Pr.) American Enterprise Institute for Public Policy Research.

Schwela, Dieter, et al. Urban Air Pollution in Asian Cities: Status, Challenges & Management. 2006. (ENG., Illus.). 296p. 146.00 (978-1-84407-375-7(0)) Routledge.

Sefcik, Lesley T. Biosphere-Atmosphere Interactions: Northern Hardwood Seedling Responses to Anthropogenic Atmospheric Resource Alteration. 2008. 144p. pap. (978-3-8364-8143-4(X)) VDM Verlag Dr. Mueller e.K.

Sharma, Atul Prakash. Air Pollution Management in the Surrounding Areas of Coal-Fired Tpp. 2010. 160p. pap. (978-3-639-25367-2(7)) VDM Verlag Dr. Mueller e.K.

Sheffield, Mark E. Encyclopedia of Air Pollution, 2 vols. 2011. (Series: Air, Water & Soil Pollution Science & Technology Ser.). 395.00 (978-1-61761-833-8(0)) Nova Science Pubs., Inc.

Sheldon, Adam I. & Barnhart, Edward P. Nitrous Oxide Emissions Research Progress. 2009. (Series: Environmental Science, Engineering & Technology Ser.). (Illus.). xii, 280p. 129.00 (978-1-60692-267-5(X)) Nova Science Pubs., Inc.

Simons, Stefaan. Air Pollution. 2009. (ENG., Illus.). 488p. (C). pap. 115.00 (978-1-84755-865-7(8)) Royal Society of Chemistry, The GBR. Dist: Ingram Pub. Services.

Slanina, Sjaak, ed. Biosphere-Atmosphere Exchange of Pollutants & Trace Substances: Experimental & Theoretical Studies of Biogenic Emissions & Pollutant Deposition. 2010. (Transport & Chemical Transformation of Pollutants in the Troposphere Ser.). (Illus.). xxvi, 528p. pap. 289.00 (978-3-642-08273-3(4), 3642082734) Springer.

Soares, A. O., et al, eds. GeoENV I - Geostatistics for Environmental Applications. 2010. (Quantitative Geology & Geostatistics Ser.). 516p. pap. 299.00 (978-90-481-4861-5(8), 9048148618) Springer.

Sokhi, Ranjeet S. World Atlas of Atmospheric Pollution. 2008. (Anthem Atlas & Reference Ser.). (ENG., Illus.). 144p. 250.00 (978-1-84331-289-5(1)) Anthem Pr. GBR. Dist: Books International, Inc.

Sokhi, Ranjeet S., ed. World Atlas of Atmospheric Pollution. 2011. (Anthem Environmental Studies). (ENG., Illus.). 144p. pap. 50.00 (978-1-84331-891-0(1)) Anthem Pr. GBR. Dist: Books International, Inc.

Somerville, Richard. The Forgiving Air: Understanding Environmental Change. 2nd ed. 2008. (Illus.). 224p. pap. 22.00 (978-1-878220-85-1(3)) American Meteorological Society.

Spalding, Frank. Under a Black Cloud: Our Atmosphere under Attack. 2009. (Extreme Environmental Threats Ser.). (ENG., Illus.). 64p. (YA). (gr. 7-12). pap. 12.95 (978-1-4358-5377-5(6)); 64p. (gr. 6-6). 58.50 (978-1-61512-440-4(3)); (YA). (gr. 5-9). lib. bdg. 29.25 (978-1-4358-5021-7(1)) Rosen Publishing Group, Inc., The.

Spitz, N., et al. Prediction of Performance & Pollutant Emission from Pulverized Coal Utility Boilers. 2009. pap. 37.00 (978-1-60741-184-0(9)) Nova Science Pubs., Inc.

Sportisse, Bruno. Fundamentals in Air Pollution: From Processes to Modelling. 2009. (ENG., Illus.). x, 299p. 89.95 (978-90-481-2969-0(9), 9048129699) Springer.

Sportisse, Bruno, ed. Air Pollution Modelling & Simulation. 2010. (ENG., Illus.). xiv, 592p. pap. 259.00 (978-3-642-07637-4(8), 3642076378) Springer.

Steyn, Douw G. & Rao, S. T., eds. Air Pollution Modeling & its Application XX. 2010. (NATO Science for Peace & Security Series C: Environmental Security Ser.). (ENG., Illus.). xlvii, 592p. 319.00 (978-90-481-3810-4(8), 9048138108); pap. 159.00 (978-90-481-3811-1(6), 9048138116) Springer.

Steyn, Douw G. & Trini Castelli, Silvia, eds. Air Pollution Modeling & its Application XXI. 2011. (NATO Science for Peace & Security Series C: Environmental Security Ser.). (ENG., Illus.). lv, 766p. 269.00 (978-94-007-1358-1(4), 9400713584); pap. 129.00 (978-94-007-1361-1(4), 9400713614) Springer.

Stonehouse, B. Arctic Air Pollution. 2009. (Studies in Polar Research Ser.). (ENG.). 348p. pap. 46.00 (978-0-521-09339-2(2)) Cambridge Univ. Pr.

Symposium on Air Quality Measurement Methods & Technology - 2007. 2007. cd-rom (978-0-923204-94-5(6)) Air & Waste Management Assn.

Symposium on Air Quality Measurement Methods & Technology 2006. 2007. cd-rom (978-0-923204-90-7(3)) Air & Waste Management Assn.

Tammemagi, Hans. Air: Our Planet's Ailing Atmosphere. 2009. (ENG., Illus.). 256p. 27.95 (978-0-19-543007-3(7)) Oxford Univ. Pr., Inc.

Technologies for Air Pollution Monitoring, Prevention & Control. 2007. per. 4250.00 (978-1-59623-281-5(1)) BCC Research.

Theodore, Louis. Air Pollution Control Equipment Calculations. 2008. (ENG., Illus.). 574p. 132.00 (978-0-470-20967-7(4), Wiley-Interscience) Wiley, John & Sons, Inc.

Turner, D. Bruce & Schulze, Richard H., eds. A Practical Guide for Atmospheric Dispersion Modeling. 2007. (978-0-923204-92-1(X)) Air & Waste Management Assn.

Uddin, Jaber. Hazardous Air Pollution: Contribution of Transport Sector in Dhaka City. 2011. 120p. pap. (978-3-8433-8765-1(6)) Lambert Academic Publishing.

Uddin, Muhammad Salaha. Urban Planning & Policy Tools Against Climate Change & Air Pollution. 2011. 140p. pap. (978-3-8443-0032-1(5)) Lambert Academic Publishing.

Uekoetter, Frank. The Age of Smoke: Environmental Policy in Germany & the United States, 1880-1970. Dunlap, Thomas, tr. from GER. 2009. (Pittsburgh Hist Urban Environ Ser.). (ENG.). 336p. (C). pap. 26.95 (978-0-8229-6012-6(5)) Univ. of Pittsburgh Pr.

Uekoetter, Frank & Uekötter, Frank. The Age of Smoke: Environmental Policy in Germany & the United States, 1880-1970. Dunlap, Thomas, tr. from GER. 2009. (Pittsburgh Hist Urban Environ Ser.). (ENG., Illus.). 336p. (C). 65.00 (978-0-8229-4364-8(6)) Univ. of Pittsburgh Pr.

United Nations. Hemispheric Transport Air Pollution 2010: Part D - Answers to Policy-Relevant Questions. 2011. (Air Pollution Studies). (ENG.). 56p. pap. 15.00 (978-92-1-117047-4(8)) United Nations Pubns.

—Hemispheric Transport of Air Pollution 2010. 2011. (Air Pollution Studies). (ENG.). 256p. pap. 43.00 (978-92-1-117045-0(1)); 212p. pap. 38.00 (978-92-1-117044-3(3)) United Nations Pubns.

—Hemispheric Transport of Air Pollution 2010: Part A - Tropospheric Ozone & Particulate Matter. 2011. (Air Pollution Studies). (ENG.). 304p. pap. 46.00 (978-92-1-117043-6(5)) United Nations Pubns.

Uzawa, Hirofumi. Economic Theory & Global Warming. 2008. (ENG., Illus.). 292p. pap. 31.99 (978-0-521-06659-4(X)) Cambridge Univ. Pr.

Valério Marques, A. P., ed. Positional Responses in Lichen Transplant Biomonitoring of Trace Element Air Pollution. 2008. 160p. pap. 87.00 (978-1-58603-928-8(8)) IOS Pr., Inc.

Vallero, Daniel A. Fundamentals of Air Pollution. 4th ed. 2007. (ENG., Illus.). 968p. 102.00 (978-0-12-373615-4(3), Academic Pr.) Elsevier Science & Technology Bks.

van Dijk, Harrie F. G., et al, eds. Fate of Pesticides in the Atmosphere - Implications for Environmental Risk Assessment. 2010. 280p. pap. 109.00 (978-90-481-5329-9(8), 9048153298) Springer.

Vasiliev, Daniel G. & Kask, Robert A., eds. Air Pollution Emissions. 2012. (978-1-62100-453-0(8)) Nova Science Pubs., Inc.

Villeneuve, Claude & Richard, Francois. Vivre les Changements Climatiques: Quoi de Neuf? (FRE., Illus.). xxxiii, 382p. (978-2-89544-074-1(3)) Editions MultiMondes.

Wagner, Debi. Over My Head. 2011. 228p. pap. 15.95 (978-1-4269-5465-8(4)) Trafford Publishing.

Wang, Lawrence K., et al, eds. Advanced Air & Noise Pollution Control: Volume 2. 2010. (Handbook of Environmental Engineering Ser.). (Illus.). xviii, 526p. pap. 229.00 (978-1-61737-517-0(9), 1617375179) Humana Pr.

—Air Pollution Control Engineering. 2010. (Handbook of Environmental Engineering Ser.). (Illus.). 528p. pap. 225.00 (978-1-61737-397-8(4), 1617373974) Humana Pr.

Wargo, John. Green Intelligence: Creating Environments That Protect Human Health. 2010. (ENG., Illus.). 400p. pap. 22.00 (978-0-300-16790-0(3)) Yale Univ. Pr.

Wark & Warner & Davis & Cram101 Textbook Reviews Staff. Air Pollution: Its Origin & Control. 2007. 84p. per. 10.95 (978-1-4288-3244-2(0)) Cram101 Inc.

Watt, John, et al, eds. The Effects of Air Pollution on Cultural Heritage. 2009. (ENG., Illus.). xii, 299p. 139.00 (978-0-387-84892-1(4), 0387848924) Springer.

Webb, Sandy, et al. Research Needs Associated with Particulate Emissions at Airports. 2008. (ACRP Report Ser.). (Illus.). 58p. 40.00 (978-0-309-11739-5(9)) Transportation Research Board.

Welfens, Paul J. J., ed. Internationalization of the Economy & Environmental Policy Options. 2010. (Illus.). xiv, 442p. pap. 117.00 (978-3-642-07575-9(4), 3642075754) Springer.

Whitefield, Philip, et al. Summarizing & Interpreting Aircraft Gaseous & Particulate Emissions Data. 2008. (Illus.). 60p. pap. 42.00 (978-0-309-11760-9(7)) Transportation Research Board.

Winslow, Margrethe. Environmental Quality, Economic Growth, & Democracy. 2010. 164p. pap. (978-3-8383-4323-5(9)) Lambert Academic Publishing.

Wood, Ezra, et al. Aircraft & Airport-Related Hazardous Air Pollutants: Research Needs & Analysis. 2008. (ACRP Report Ser.). (Illus.). 56p. pap. 40.00 (978-0-309-11745-6(3)) Transportation Research Board.

World Health Organization Staff, contrib. by. Air Quality Guidelines - Global Update 2005: Particulate Matter, Ozone, Nitrogen Dioxide & Sulfur Dioxide. 2006. (EURO Nonserial Publication). (ENG.). 493p. pap. 120.00 (978-92-890-2192-0(6)) World Health Organization.

Wu, Shiliang. Global Change & Ozone Air Quality. 2008. 116p. pap. (978-3-639-07993-7(0)) VDM Verlag Dr. Mueller e.K.

Yusup, Yusri. Turbulence & Dispersion in the Lowest Atmospheric Layer. 2011. 176p. pap. (978-3-8443-8722-3(6)) Lambert Academic Publishing.

Zaikov, Gennadii Efremovich. Polymer & Biopolymer Analysis & Characterization. 2007. 87p. (C). 89.00 (978-1-60021-609-1(9)) Nova Science Pubs., Inc.

Zannetti, Paolo, ed. Air Quality Modeling: Theories, Methodologies, Computational Techniques, & Available Databases & Software, Vol. III. 2008. pap. (978-0-923204-99-0(7)) Air & Waste Management Assn.

AIR—POLLUTION—GOVERNMENT POLICY

Cohen & Cram101 Textbook Reviews Staff. Washington at Work. 2007. 112p. per. 11.95 (978-1-4288-2560-4(6)) Cram101 Inc.

De Lucia, Caterina. Environmental Policies in the New Europe: A Computable General Equilibrium Model for Transboundary Pollution & Trade. 2010. (Routledge Explorations in Environmental Economics Ser.). (ENG., Illus.). 144p. (C). 120.00 (978-0-415-49814-2(7)) Routledge.

Eisinger, Douglas S. Smog Check: Science, Federalism, & the Politics of Clean Air. 2010. (ENG., Illus.). 252p. 99.95 (978-1-933115-71-9(8)); pap. 34.95 (978-1-933115-72-6(6)) Earthscan LLC. (RFF Pr.).

Gerdes, Louise. Pollution. 2011. (Opposing Viewpoints Ser.). 240p. pap. 26.50 (978-0-7377-5232-8(7)); lib. bdg. 39.70 (978-0-7377-5231-1(9)) Cengage Gale. (Greenhaven Pr., Inc.).

Ho, Mun S. & Nielsen, Chris P., eds. Clearing the Air: The Health & Economic Damages of Air Pollution in China. 2007. (ENG., Illus.). 405p. (gr. 17). 53.00 (978-0-262-08358-4(2)) MIT Pr.

Ternes, Mary Ellen. EPA's Mandatory Greenhouse Gas Reporting Rule. 2010. xvi, 50p. 49.00 (978-1-4224-7592-8(1)) LexisNexis Matthew Bender.

United Nations. Strategies & Policies for Air Pollution Abatement: Review 2006. 2008. (ENG.). 76p. pap. 15.00 (978-92-1-116977-5(1)) United Nations Pubns.

Vasser, Christophe P. & Matsuda, Taisho, eds. Robot Vision: New Research. 2008. 89.00 (978-1-60456-984-1(0)) Nova Science Pubs., Inc.

Whitehead, Mark. State, Science & the Skies: Governmentalities of the British Atmosphere. 2009. (RGS-IBG Book Ser.: 32). (ENG., Illus.). 296p. 94.95 (978-1-4051-9174-6(0)); pap. 39.95 (978-1-4051-9173-9(2)) Wiley, John & Sons, Inc. (Wiley-Blackwell).

AIR—POLLUTION—LAW AND LEGISLATION

Belden, Roy S. The Clean Air ACT. 2nd ed. 2012. (ENG.). 355p. pap. 79.95 (978-1-61438-096-2(1)) American Bar Assn.

Davidson, Jonathan M. & Norbeck, Joseph M. An Interactive History of the Clean Air Act: Scientific & Policy Perspectives. 2011. (ENG.). 162p. 99.95 (978-0-12-416035-4(2)) Elsevier Science & Technology Bks.

Havercroft, Ian, et al, eds. Carbon Capture & Storage: Emerging Legal & Regulatory Issues, 0 vols. 2011. (ENG., Illus.). 390p. 130.00

(978-1-84113-268-6(3)) Hart Publishing Ltd. GBR. Dist: International Specialized Bk. Services.
Jacobson, Mark Z. Air Pollution & Global Warming: History, Science, & Solutions. 2nd ed. 2012. (ENG., Illus.). 406p. (C). pap. 85.00 ***(978-1-107-69115-5(X))*** Cambridge Univ. Pr.
Kaniaru, Donald, ed. The Montreal Protocol: Celebrating 20 Years of Environmental Progress Ozone Layer & Climate Protection. 2007. (Illus.). 355p. pap. 100.00 *(978-1-905017-51-5(0))* Cameron May, Ltd. GBR. Dist: Gaunt, Inc.
Kim, Dong-Young. The Challenges of Consensus Building in a Consolidating Democracy- Diesel Vehicles & Urban Air Pollution in Kore. 2007. 372p. per. *(978-3-8364-2486-8(X))* VDM Verlag Dr. Mueller e.K.
Lincoln-Oswalt, Jessica, ed. Better Air: Benefits & Costs of the Clean Air Act. 2011. (Environmental Science, Engineering & Technology Ser.). 244p. 185.00 ***(978-1-61470-724-0(3))*** Nova Science Pubs., Inc.
Martineau, et al. The Clean Air ACT Handbook. 3rd ed. 2012. (ENG.). 782p. 179.95 ***(978-1-61438-035-1(X))*** American Bar Assn.
Mitschang, Stephan, ed. Gerüche, Feinstaub und Gefahrstoffe in der Bauleitplanung und Bei der Zulassung Von Bauvorhaben. 2011. (Berliner Schriften zur Stadt- und Regionalplanung Ser.). (GER.). 238p. pap. 65.95 ***(978-3-631-62095-3(0))*** Lang, Peter GmbH, Europaischer Verlag der Wissenschaften DEU. Dist: Lang, Peter.
Post, Harry, ed. The Protection of Ambient Air in International & European Law. 2009. 192p. 120.00 *(978-90-77596-63-0(1))* Eleven International Publishing NLD. Dist: International Specialized Bk. Services.
Reitze, Arnold W., Jr. Air Pollution Control & Climate Change Mitigation Law. 2nd ed. 2010. (ENG.). 300p. pap. 109.95 *(978-1-58576-153-1(2))* Environmental Law Institute.
S. 1265: The Diesel Emissions Reduction ACT of 2005: Hearing Before the Subcommittee on Clean Air, Climate Change, & Nuclear Safety of the Committee on Environment & Public Works, United States Senate, One Hundred Ninth Congress, First Session, July 12, 2005. 2007. (Illus.). iii, 108p. *(978-0-16-079812-2(4)*, 552-070-36717-9) United States Government Printing Office.
Sigel, Gabrielle. Emerging Issues in Environmental Law & Climate Change. 2008. pap. *(978-1-4224-2622-7(X))* LexisNexis Matthew Bender.
Strengths & Weaknesses of Regulating Greenhouse Gas Emissions Using Existing Clean Air ACT Authorities: Hearing Before the Subcommittee on Energy & Air Quality of the Committee on Energy & Commerce, House of Representatives, One Hundred Tenth Congress, Second Session, April 10, 2008. 2008. v, 166p. *(978-0-16-084014-2(7)*, 552-070-39686-1) United States Government Printing Office.
United Nations. Montreal Protocol on Substances that Deplete the Ozone Layer: 2006 Assessment Report of the Technology & Economic Assessment Panel. 2007. (ENG.). 162p. pap. 30.00 *(978-92-807-2823-1(7))* United Nations Environment Programme KEN. Dist: National Bk. Network.

AIR—POLLUTION—PHYSIOLOGICAL EFFECT

Balagopalan, Mohan. Air Quality Permitting. Date not set. 55.00 *(978-1-56670-152-5(X))* Lewis Pubs.
Dydek. Health Risks Analysis for Toxic Air Pollutants. Date not set. 69.95 *(978-0-87371-567-6(5)*, L567) Lewis Pubs.
Hoelzemann, Judith. Global Wildland Fires. 2007. 212p. per. *(978-3-8364-1193-6(8))* VDM Verlag Dr. Mueller e.K.
Willis, Alette. Doing Epidemiology As If Space & Place Mattered. 2010. 152p. pap. *(978-3-8383-8353-8(2))* Lambert Academic Publishing.

AIR—POLLUTION—GREAT BRITAIN

Brimblecombe, Peter. The Big Smoke: A History of Air Pollution in London since Medieval Times. 2011. (Routledge Revivals Ser.). (ENG.). 202p. 118.00 *(978-0-415-67183-5(3))* Routledge.
Mosley, Stephen. The Chimney of the World: A History of Smoke Pollution in Victorian & Edwardian Manchester. 2008. (ENG., Illus.). 288p. (C). pap. 43.95 *(978-0-415-47767-3(0))* Routledge.
The Smoke of London: Two Prophecies. Incl. Doom of London. Barr, Robert. Fumifugium or, The Inconvience of the Aer-Smoake of London Dissipated. Evelyn, John. 7.50 o.s.i *(978-0-08-022309-4(5))* Elsevier.
Whitehead, Mark. State, Science & the Skies: Governmentalities of the British Atmosphere. 2009. (RGS-IBG Book Ser.: 32). (ENG., Illus.). 296p. 94.95 *(978-1-4051-9174-6(0))*; pap. 39.95 *(978-1-4051-9173-9(2))* Wiley, John & Sons, Inc. (Wiley-Blackwell).

AIR—PURIFICATION

see also Air Conditioning

Cooper, C. David & Alley, F. C. Air Pollution Control: A Design Approach. 4th ed. 2010. (Illus.). 839p. (C). 104.95 *(978-1-57766-678-3(X))* Waveland Pr., Inc.
Heck, Ronald M., et a. Catalytic Air Pollution Control: Commercial Technology. 3rd ed. 2009. (ENG., Illus.). 544p. 122.00 *(978-0-470-27503-0(0)*, Wiley) Wiley, John & Sons, Inc.
Longhurst, James W. S. & Brebbia, C. A. Air Pollution XVI. Brebbia, Carlos A. & Longhurst, James W. S., eds. 2008. (WIT Transactions on Ecology & the Environment Ser.: 116). (Illus.). 672p. 442.00 *(978-1-84564-127-6(2))* WIT Pr GBR. Dist: WIT Pr.
Ramseur, Jonathan L., et al. Greenhouse Gases: Management, Reduction & Impact. 2008. (Illus.). 77p. pap. 50.00 *(978-1-60456-627-7(2))* Nova Science Pubs., Inc.
Sinha, Rajiv. Green Plants & Pollution. 2010. (Air, Water & Soil Pollution Science & Technology Ser.). 79p. pap. 43.00 *(978-1-61668-147-0(0))* Nova Science Pubs., Inc.
Theodore, Louis. Air Pollution Control Equipment Calculations. 2008. (ENG., Illus.). 574p. 132.00 *(978-0-470-20967-7(4)*, Wiley-Interscience) Wiley, John & Sons, Inc.

AIR—RADIOACTIVE POLLUTION

see Radioactive Pollution of the Atmosphere

AIR, COMPRESSED

see Compressed Air

AIR, IONIZED

see also Ionosphere

Pawar, Subhash. Air ion Variation for Different Atmospheric Conditions. 2011. 224p. pap. ***(978-3-8454-0063-1(3))*** Lambert Academic Publishing.
Periodic Verification of Air Ionizers. (Illus.). 13p. pap. 37.50 *(978-1-878303-90-5(2)*, DSP3.3-1997) EOS/ESD Assn., Inc.

AIR, MOISTURE OF

see Humidity

AIR-AGE EDUCATION

see Aeronautics and Civilization

AIR ATTACHES

see Military Attaches

AIR BASES

see also Intercontinental Ballistic Missile Bases

Amouzegar, Mahyar A., et al. Evaluation of Options for Overseas Combat Support Basin. 2006. (Illus.). 172p. per. 22.50 *(978-0-8330-3874-6(5)*, MG-421) RAND Corp., The.
Aubert, Paul. La Base Aérienne 132, L'adieu. 2010. (FRE., Illus.). 167p. *(978-2-84960-224-9(8))* Bentzinger, Jerome Do., Editeur.
Bauman Taylor, Paula. F. E. Warren Air Force Base. 2012. (Images of America Ser.). (ENG., Illus.). 128p. pap. 21.99 ***(978-0-7385-9225-1(0))*** Arcadia Publishing.
Berryman, David. Action Stations Revisited: The Complete History of Britain's Military Airfields. 2009. (Illus.). 384p. 39.95 *(978-0-85979-121-2(1))* Crecy Publishing GBR. Dist: Partners Pubs. Group, Inc.
Bird, Andrew D. A Separate Little War: The Banff Coastal Command Strike Wing versus the Kriegsmarine & Luftwaffe 1944-1945. 2008. (Illus.). 192p. pap. 24.95 *(978-1-906502-13-3(7))* Grub Street GBR. Dist: Casemate Pubs. & Bk. Distributors, LLC.
Blair, Gordon & Lindsey, Norman. The Boys of Ballykelly. 2010. (Illus.). 301p. 34.95 *(978-1-84624-405-6(6))* Book Guild, Ltd. GBR. Dist: Trans-Atlantic Pubns., Inc.
Bond, Steve & Forder, Richard. Special Ops Liberators: 223 (Bomber Support) Squadron & the Electronic War. 2011. (Illus.). 224p. 39.95 ***(978-1-908117-14-4(1))*** Grub Street GBR. Dist: Casemate Pubs. & Bk. Distributors, LLC.
Bowman, Martin W. Bomber Bases of World War 2 2nd Air Division 8th Air Force USAAF 1942-45: Liberator Squadrons in Norfolk & Suffolk. 2007. (Aviation Heritage Trail Ser.). (Illus.). 196p. per. 19.95 *(978-1-84415-547-7(1))* Pen & Sword Bks. Ltd. GBR. Dist: Casemate Pubs. & Bk. Distributors, LLC.
—Bomber Bases of WW2 3rd Air Division, 8th Air Force USAAF 1942-45: Flying Fortress & Liberator Squadrons in Norfolk & Suffolk. 2009. (Illus.). 192p. pap. 25.99 *(978-1-84415-828-7(4))* Pen & Sword Bks. Ltd. GBR. Dist: Casemate Pubs. & Bk. Distributors, LLC.
—US 8th Army Air Force Fighter Command USAAF, 1943-45: P-38 Lightning, P-47 Thunderbolt & P-51 Mustang Squadrons in East Anglia, Cambridgeshire & Northamptonshire. 2009. (Illus.). 208p. pap. 25.99 *(978-1-84415-905-5(1))* Pen & Sword Bks. Ltd. GBR. Dist: Casemate Pubs. & Bk. Distributors, LLC.
—US 9th Air Force Bases in Essex 1943 - 44. 2010. (Illus.). 208p. pap. 24.95 *(978-1-84884-332-5(1))* Pen & Sword Bks. Ltd. GBR. Dist: Casemate Pubs. & Bk. Distributors, LLC.
—100 Group (Bomber Support) RAF Bomber Command in World War II. 2006. (Aviation Heritage Trail Ser.). (Illus.). 144p. per. 19.95 *(978-1-84415-418-0(1))* Pen & Sword Bks. Ltd. GBR. Dist: Casemate Pubs. & Bk. Distributors, LLC.
Brooks, Robin J. Herefordshire & Worcestershire Airfields in the Second World War. 2006. (British Airfields of World War II Ser.). (Illus.). 252p. per. 29.95 *(978-1-85306-964-0(1))* Countryside Bks. GBR. Dist: Brown, David Bk. Co., The.
Byard, Kyle & Naiman, Tom. McClellan Air Force Base. 2007. (Images of America Ser.). (ENG., Illus.). 128p. per. 19.99 *(978-0-7385-4762-6(X))* Arcadia Publishing.
Chorlton, Martyn. Cumbria Airfields in the Second World War: Including the Isle of Man. 2006. (British Airfields of World War II Ser.). (Illus.). 256p. per. 29.95 *(978-1-85306-983-3(3))* Countryside Bks. GBR. Dist: Brown, David Bk. Co., The.
—Scottish Airfields in the Second World War: Fife & the Central Region. 2009. (British Airfields in the Second World War Ser.). (ENG., Illus.). 180p. (C). pap. 26.95 *(978-1-84674-148-7(3))* Countryside Bks. GBR. Dist: Brown, David Bk. Co., The.
—Scottish Airfields in the Second World War: Vol 3: the Grampians. 2010. (ENG., Illus.). 192p. (C). pap. 29.95 *(978-1-84674-169-2(6))* Countryside Bks. GBR. Dist: Brown, David Bk. Co., The.
—Staffordshire Airfields in the Second World War. 2007. (British Airfields in the Second World War Ser.). (Illus.). 256p. (C). pap. 29.95 *(978-1-84674-056-5(8))* Countryside Bks. GBR. Dist: Brown, David Bk. Co., The.
Dawson, Beverly Roberts. Glenview Naval Air Station. 2007. (Images of America Ser.). (ENG., Illus.). 128p. per. 21.99 *(978-0-7385-4122-8(2))* Arcadia Publishing.
Delve, Ken. Military Airfields of Britain: Scotland & Northern Ireland. 2011. (ENG., Illus.). 272p. 29.95 *(978-1-84797-027-5(3)*, 1847970273) Crowood Pr., Ltd. GBR. Dist: MBI Distribution Services/Quayside Distribution.
—The Military Airfields of Britain - East Midlands: Cambridgeshire, Derbyshire, Leicestershire, Lincolnshire, Nottinghamshire. 2008. (ENG., Illus.). 272p. pap. 29.95 *(978-1-86126-995-9(1)*, 1861269951) Crowood Pr., Ltd. GBR. Dist: MBI Distribution Services/Quayside Distribution.
—The Military Airfields of Britain - Northern England: Co. Durham, Cumbria, Isle of Man, Lancashire, Merseyside, Manchester, Northumberland, Tyne & Wear, Yorkshire. 2006. (Military Airfields of Britain Ser.). (ENG., Illus.). 272p. pap. 29.95 *(978-1-86126-809-9(2)*, 1861268092) Crowood Pr., Ltd. GBR. Dist: MBI Distribution Services/Quayside Distribution.
—The Military Airfields of Britain: Northern Home Counties: Bedfordshire, Berkshire, Buckinghamshire, Essex, Hertfordshire, Middlesex, Oxfordshire. 2007. (Military Airfields of Britain Ser.). (ENG., Illus.). 272p. pap. 29.95 *(978-1-86126-907-2(2)*, 1861269072) Crowood Pr., Ltd. GBR. Dist: MBI Distribution Services/Quayside Distribution.
—Military Airfields of Britain South-Western England: Channel Islands, Cornwall, Devon, Dorset, Gloucestershire, Somerset, Wiltshire. 2006. (Military Airfields of Britain Ser.). (ENG., Illus.). 272p. per. 29.95 *(978-1-86126-810-5(6)*, 1861268106) Crowood Pr., Ltd. GBR. Dist: MBI Distribution Services/Quayside Distribution.
—Wales & West Midlands: Cheshire, Hereford & Worcester, Northamptonshire, Shropshire, Staffordshire, Warwickshire, West Midlands, Wales. 2007. (Military Airfields of Britain Ser.). (ENG., Illus.). 272p. pap. 29.95 *(978-1-86126-917-1(X)*, 186126917X) Crowood Pr., Ltd. GBR. Dist: MBI Distribution Services/Quayside Distribution.
Dolitsky, Alexander. Allies in Wartime: The Alaska-Siberia Airway During World War II. Dolitsky, Alexander, ed. 2007. (Illus.). 160p. 29.95 *(978-0-9653891-6-7(2))* Alaska-Siberia Research Ctr.
Jacobs, Peter. Airfields of the D-Day Invasion Air Force: 2nd Tactical Air Force in South-East England in WWII. 2009. (Illus.). 176p. pap. 25.99 *(978-1-84415-900-0(0))* Pen & Sword Bks. Ltd. GBR. Dist: Casemate Pubs. & Bk. Distributors, LLC.
Jendrysik, Stephen R. Chicopee: 1950ndash;1975. 2012. (Images of America Ser.). (ENG., Illus.). 128p. pap. 21.99 ***(978-0-7385-7661-9(1))*** Arcadia Publishing.
Lambert, John W. The 8th Air Force: A World War II Photo History. 2006. (Illus.). 160p. 39.95 *(978-0-7643-2534-2(5))* Schiffer Publishing, Ltd.
Library, Special Collections of the Sacramento Public. Mather Field. 2012. (Images of America Ser.). (ENG., Illus.). 128p. pap. 21.99 ***(978-0-7385-8877-3(6))*** Arcadia Publishing.
Mailes, Yancy D. Mountain Home Air Force Base. 2007. (Images of America Ser.). (ENG., Illus.). 128p. per. 19.99 *(978-0-7385-4805-0(7))* Arcadia Publishing.
Manrho, John & Pütz, Ron. Bodenplatte: The Luftwaffe's Last Hope. 2010. (Stackpole Military History Ser.). (ENG., Illus.). 576p. pap. 21.95 *(978-0-8117-0686-5(9))* Stackpole Bks.
McGarvey, Ronald G., et al. Global Combat Support Basing: Robust Prepositioning Strategies for Air Force War Reserve Materiel. 2010. 170p. pap. 33.00 *(978-0-8330-4766-3(3)*, mg-902) RAND Corp., The.
O'Neil, Terry. Runways & Racers: Sports Car Races Held on Military Airfields in America, 1952-1954. 2011. (ENG., Illus.). 208p. 69.95 *(978-1-84584-255-0(3)*, 1845842553) Veloce Publishing Ltd. GBR. Dist: MBI Distribution Services/Quayside Distribution.
Phillips, Alan, pseud. Brawdy: Stronghold in the West. 2009. (ENG., Illus.). 128p. pap. 29.95 *(978-0-7524-4923-4(0))* History Pr. Ltd., The GBR. Dist: Independent Pubs. Group.
Simmons, Geoffrey. East Riding Airfields 1915-1920. 2010. (Illus.). 64p. 19.95 *(978-0-9545605-9-1(0))* Flight Recorder Pubns. Ltd. GBR. Dist: Partners Pubs. Group, Inc.
Smith, Blake W. Wings over the Wilderness: They Flew the Trail of '42. 2008. (Illus.). 296p. pap. 39.95 ***(978-0-88839-595-5(7))*** Hancock Hse. Pubs.
Stroud, Jon. Little Book of the RAF. 2011. (Little Book Of Ser.). (ENG., Illus.). 128p. 11.99 *(978-1-907803-11-6(4))* G2 Entertainment Ltd. GBR. Dist: BookMasters Distribution Services (BDS).
Stroup, Robert M. Crossroads of Liberty: A Pictorial Tribute to Lockbourne/Rickenbacker AFB ANGP IAP. 2009. (ENG.). 152p. 32.00 *(978-1-57510-133-0(5)*, Pictorial Histories Publishing Co., Inc.
Thole, Lou. Forgotten Fields of America, Volume IV. 2007. 145p. 21.95 *(978-1-57510-132-3(7)*, Pictorial Histories Publishing Co., Inc.
Tweddle, Paul. Into the Night Sky: RAF Middleton St George: A Bomber Airfield at War. 2007. (ENG., Illus.). 288p. 44.95 *(978-0-7509-4596-7(6))* Sutton Publishing.
U.S.-Japan Relations: Enduring Ties, Recent Developments: Hearing Before the Subcommittee on Asia, the Pacific, & the Global Environment of the Committee on Foreign Affairs, House of Representatives, One Hundred Eleventh Congress, Second Session, March 17, 2010. 2010. iii, 82p. ***(978-0-16-087170-2(0)*** 552-070-42012-6) United States Government Printing Office.
Williams, William A., et al. Preserving Range & Airspace Access for the Air Force Mission: Striving for a Strategic Vantage Point. 2011. (Illus.). 100p. pap. 29.50 *(978-0-8330-5140-0(7))* RAND Corp., The.

AIR-BEARING VEHICLES

see Ground-Effect Machines

AIR-BORNE INFECTION

see Airborne Infection

AIR BRUSH ART

see Airbrush Art

AIR BUILDINGS

see Air-Supported Structures

AIR CARGO

see Aeronautics, Commercial

AIR CARRIERS

see Airlines

AIR-COMPRESSORS

see also Compressed Air

American Society of Mechanical Engineers Staff, ed. Safety Standard for Air Compressor Systems. 36p. 55.00 *(978-0-7918-2352-1(0))* ASME Pr.
British Standards Institute Staff. Compressed-air dryers. Specifications & Testing. 30p. pap. 109.00 *(978-0-580-53867-4(2))* Artech Hse., Inc.
—Filters for compressed air. Test methods. Oil Vapours. 20p. pap. 123.00 *(978-0-580-53131-6(7))* Artech Hse., Inc.

AIR CONDITIONING

see also Dampness in Buildings; Refrigeration and Refrigerating Machinery; Solar Air Conditioning; Ventilation

also specific subjects with or without the subdivision Air Conditioning, e.g. Dwellings—Air Conditioning

Abdullah, Syed Muhammad. Air Conditioning Designing Project. 2011. 152p. pap. ***(978-3-8443-1693-3(0))*** Lambert Academic Publishing.
Ackermann, Marsha. Cool Comfort: America's Romance with Air-Conditioning. 2010. (ENG.). 224p. pap. 29.95 *(978-1-58834-279-9(4))* Smithsonian Institution Pr.
AHRI, Carter, et al. Fundamentals of HVACR. 2nd rev. ed. 2012. (ENG., Illus.). 1536p. (C). 133.33 ***(978-0-13-285961-5(0)***, Prentice Hall) Prentice Hall PTR.
—Lab Manual for Fundamentals of HVACR. 2nd ed. 2012. (ENG.). 362p. (C). pap. 51.80 ***(978-0-13-287974-3(3)***, Prentice Hall) Prentice Hall PTR.
Air Conditioning and Refrigeration Institute Staff, et al. Lab Manual for Fundamentals of HVAC/R. 5th ed. 2009. (ENG.). 416p. (C). pap. 51.80 *(978-0-13-222410-9(C)*, Prentice Hall) Prentice Hall PTR.
Air Conditioning Contractors of America Staff. ACCA Guide to Safety & Loss Control. Date not set. 325p. pap. 100.00 *(978-1-892765-16-1(0))* Air Conditioning Contractors of America.
Althouse, Andrew D., et al. Modern Refrigeration & Air Conditioning. 368p. tchr. ed. 55.00 *(978-1-56637-727-0(7))* Goodheart-Willcox Pub.
—Modern Refrigeration & Air Conditioning. 208p. pap., lab manual ed. 16.00 *(978-1-56637-726-3(9))* Goodheart-Willcox Pub.
—Modern Refrigeration & Air Conditioning: Teacher's Resource Binder. 524p. tchr. ed., ring bd. 138.00 *(978-1-56637-728-7(5))* Goodheart-Willcox Pub.
Alves, Ken. How to Clean Your Old Air Conditioner: So It Runs Like New Again. 2007. 9.95 *(978-0-9794860-7-4(6))* Town & Country Reprographics.
American Contractors Exam Staff. HVAC Code Reference: Based on the International Mechanical Code. 2010. (ENG.). 84p. spiral bd. 19.95 *(978-0-9777183-8-2(7)*, DEWALT) CENGAGE Learning.
American Contractors Exam Staff & Christopherson, Norm. HVAC Technician Certification Exam. 2nd ed. 2008. (ENG.). 272p. pap., instr.'s gde. ed. 39.95 *(978-0-9797403-0-5(4)*, DEWALT) CENGAGE Learning.
American Society of Heating, contrib. by. ASHRAE Pocket Guide for Air-Conditioning, Heating, Ventilation & Refrigeration, 7th Edition: (I-P Edition) 7th ed. 2010. (ENG.). 272p. pap. 45.00 *(978-1-933742-67-0(4))* American Society of Heating, Refrigerating & Air-Conditioning Engineers, Inc.
—ASHRAE Pocket Guide for Air-Conditioning, Heating, Ventilation & Refrigeration, 7th Edition: (SI Edition) 7th ed. 2010. (ENG.). 272p. pap. 45.00 *(978-1-933742-68-7(2))* American Society of Heating, Refrigerating & Air-Conditioning Engineers, Inc.
—2010 ASHRAE Handbook — Refrigeration (I-P) 2010. (ENG.). 758p. 195.00 *(978-1-933742-81-6(X))* American Society of Heating, Refrigerating & Air-Conditioning Engineers, Inc.
Angel, W. Larsen. HVAC Design Sourcebook. 2011. (ENG., Illus.). 400p. 60.00 ***(978-0-07-175303-6(5)***, 0071753036) McGraw-Hill Professional Publishing.
Ashrae. A Practical Guide to Noise & Vibration Control for HVAC Systems, Second Edition (SI Edition) 2nd ed. 2011. pap. 71.00 *(978-1-936504-02-2(2))* American Society of Heating, Refrigerating & Air-Conditioning Engineers, Inc.
Ashrae Press Staff. Air-Conditioning System Design Manual. 2nd ed. 2007. (ENG., Illus.). 416p. 102.00 *(978-1-933742-13-7(5)*, Butterworth-Heinemann) Elsevier Science & Technology Bks.
Bell, Arthur A. & Bell, Arthur A., Jr. HVAC Equations, Data, & Rules of Thumb. 2nd rev. ed. 2007. (ENG., Illus.). 790p. (C). per. 69.95 *(978-0-07-148242-4(3)*, 0071482423) McGraw-Hill Professional Publishing.
Bridgens. Ugly's Hvac References. rev. ed. 2011. spiral bd. 19.95 *(978-0-7637-7783-8(6))* Jones & Bartlett Learning, LLC.
Carpenter, David R. Essentials of HVAC Controls. 2008. 128p. pap. 34.95 *(978-0-7637-5214-9(2))* Jones & Bartlett Learning, LLC.
Coad, William J., et al. Principles of Heating, Ventilating & Air-Conditioning, 6th Edition: Includes RTS Method Load Calculation Spreadsheets CD (I-P) 6th ed. 2010. (ENG.). 576p. 89.00 *(978-1-933742-69-4(0))* American Society of Heating, Refrigerating & Air-Conditioning Engineers, Inc.

Cox, Stan. Losing Our Cool: Uncomfortable Truths about Our Air Conditioned World (And Finding New Ways to Get Through the Summer) 2010. (ENG.). 272p. 24.95 *(978-1-59558-489-2(7))* New Pr., The.

Cox, Stan. Losing Our Cool: Uncomfortable Truths about Our Air-Conditioned World (and Finding New Ways to Get Through the Summer) 2012. (ENG., Illus.). 272p. pap. 17.95 ***(978-1-59558-775-6(6))*** New Pr., The.

Cram101 Textbook Reviews. Outlines & Highlights for Air Conditioning Principles & Systems by Pita, Isbn: 0130928720. 2011. 168p. pap. 29.95 ***(978-1-61812-920-8(1))*** Cram101 Inc.

Cram101 Textbook Reviews & Cram101 Textbook Reviews. Outlines & Highlights for Heating, Cooling, Lighting: Design Methods for Architects by Norbert Lechner. 2011. 350p. pap. 33.95 ***(978-1-61830-975-4(7))*** Cram101 Inc.

DeVore, Russell B. Practical Problems in Mathematics for Heating & Cooling Technicians. (Applied Mathematics Ser.). (ENG.). 320p. 5th ed. 2008. pap. 65.95 *(978-1-4283-2428-2(3))* 6th ed. 2012. (C). pap. 65.95 ***(978-1-111-54135-4(3))*** Delmar Cengage Learning.

Dunlop, Carson. Ashi at Home Training: Air Conditioning & Heating. 245.00 *(978-0-7931-7931-2(9))* Kaplan Publishing.

—Heating & Cooling Systems Testbook. 50.00 *(978-0-7931-8119-3(4))* Kaplan Publishing.

Edwards, Rodger, et al. HVAC & Refrigeration ebook Collection: Heating, Ventilating, Air Conditioning & Refrigeration Ultimate CD. 2008. (ENG.). 1528p. cd-rom 275.00 *(978-1-85617-574-6(X),* Butterworth-Heinemann) Elsevier Science & Technology Bks.

Egg, Jay, et al. Geothermal HVAC. 2010. (ENG., Illus.). 272p. 60.00 *(978-0-07-174610-6(2),* 0071746102) McGraw-Hill Professional Publishing.

Elder, PE, Keith E. Six-Minute Solutions for Mechanical PE Exam HVAC & Refrigeration Problems. 2nd ed. 2008. (ENG.). 66p. pap. 96.00 *(978-1-59126-146-9(5))* Professional Pubns., Inc.

Faber & Kell's Heating & Air-conditioning of Buildings. 10th rev. ed. 2008. (ENG., Illus.). 804p. 134.00 *(978-0-7506-8365-4(1))* Routledge.

Featherstone, Robert & Riojas, Jesse. Guide to the NATE/ICE Certification Exams. 3rd ed. 2008. (ENG.). 408p. (C). pap. 66.80 *(978-0-13-231970-6(5),* Prentice Hall) Prentice Hall PTR.

Graves, Hilary. Cooling Buildings in London: Overcoming the Heat Island. 2010. (ENG., Illus.). 36p. pap. 55.00 *(978-1-86081-526-3(X))* Building Research Establishment GBR. Dist: Taylor & Francis Group.

Gregory, Robert. Texas Air Conditioning & Refrigeration Business & Law Reference Manual. 3rd ed. 2008. (ENG.). 275p. pap. 99.95 *(978-1-4277-8583-1(X))* Kaplan Publishing.

Haines, Roger W. & Myers, Michael. HVAC Systems Design Handbook, Fifth Edition. 5th ed. 2009. (ENG., Illus.). 576p. 115.00 *(978-0-07-162297-4(7),* 0071622977) McGraw-Hill Professional Publishing.

Harriman, Lewis G., 3rd. The ASHRAE Guide for Buildings in Hot & Humid Climates: Section 1, Common Issues. 2008. (ENG.). 123p. pap. 116.00 *(978-1-933742-26-7(7))* American Society of Heating, Refrigerating & Air-Conditioning Engineers, Inc.

Harvey, L. D. Danny, ed. A Handbook on Low-Energy Buildings & District-Energy Systems: Fundamentals, Techniques, & Examples. 2006. (ENG., Illus.). 720p. 290.00 *(978-1-84407-243-9(6))* Routledge.

Hästesko, Tobias & Kiljunen. Air Conditioning Systems: Performance, Environment & Energy Factors. 2009. (Energy Science, Engineering & Technology Ser.). (Illus.). xi, 399p. 129.00 *(978-1-60741-555-8(0))* Nova Science Pubs., Inc.

Hegger, Manfred, et al. Heat. 2012. (Scale Ser.). (ENG., Illus.). 160p. pap. 64.95 *(978-3-0346-0513-7(7))* Birkhauser Verlag AG CHE. Dist: Actar Birkhauser Distribution.

Herman, Stephen L. & Sparkman, Bennie. Electricity & Controls for HVAC-R. 6th ed. 2009. (ENG.). 608p. (C). pap. 186.95 *(978-1-4354-8427-6(4))* Delmar Cengage Learning.

Hohman, John. Hvacr 301. 2010. (ENG.). 384p. (C). pap. 89.95 *(978-1-4180-6666-6(4))* Delmar Cengage Learning.

Howell, Ronald H., et al. Principles of Heating, Ventilating, & Air Conditioning. 6th Edition Solution Manual: A Textbook with Design Data Based on the 2009 ASHRAE Handbook of Fundamentals. 6th ed. 2010. (Illus.). 224p. pap. 89.00 *(978-1-933742-70-0(4))* American Society of Heating, Refrigerating & Air-Conditioning Engineers, Inc.

Hundy, G. F., et al. Refrigeration & Air-Conditioning. 4th ed. 2008. (ENG., Illus.). 392p. 76.95 *(978-0-7506-8519-1(0),* Butterworth-Heinemann) Elsevier Science & Technology Bks.

HVAC Spanish. 2006. 5.00 net. *(978-0-88069-040-9(2))* LAMA Bks.

ICC. 2007 Ohio Mechanical Code. 2007. bds. 84.00 *(978-1-58001-528-8(X))* International Code Council.

ICC/OHIO. 2011 Ohio Mechanical Code. 2011. spiral bd. 86.50 ***(978-1-60983-201-8(9))*** International Code Council.

Joe Gorman. From Contractor to Consumer: The Truth about Heating, Air Conditioning, & Home Comfort Systems. 2009. 72p. pap. 10.95 *(978-1-4401-7817-7(8))* iUniverse, Inc.

Johnson, Bill. BTU Buddy Notebook. 2008. (ENG.). 288p. (C). pap. 52.95 *(978-1-4354-2583-5(9))* Delmar Cengage Learning.

Johnson, Bill, et al. Refrigeration & A/C Technology 6e Lab Manual. 6th ed. 2008. (ENG.). 496p. (C). pap. 64.95 *(978-1-4283-1937-0(9))* Delmar Cengage Learning.

—Refrigeration & Air Conditioning Technology. 6th ed. 2008. (Available Titles CourseMate Ser.). (ENG., Illus.). 1360p. (C). 147.95 *(978-1-4283-1936-3(0))* Delmar Cengage Learning.

Johnson, Jim & prod. Troubleshooting, Servicing & Maintaining Central Air Conditioning Systems. pap., wbk. ed. 99.95 incl. VHS *(978-1-930797-07-9(9))* Appliance Univ.

Kalita, Nitul & Misra, Rahul Dev. Cfd Analysis of Room Air Distribution. 2011. 148p. pap. ***(978-3-8443-8396-6(4))*** Lambert Academic Publishing.

Kissell, Thomas E. Electricity, Electronics, & Control Systems for HVAC. 4th ed. 2007. (ENG., Illus.). 720p. (C). 131.20 *(978-0-13-199568-0(5),* Prentice Hall) Prentice Hall PTR.

Kreider, Jan F., et al. Heating & Cooling of Buildings: Design for Efficiency. 2nd rev. ed. 2009. (Mechanical Engineering Ser.). (ENG., Illus.). 863p. 129.95 *(978-1-4398-1151-1(2),* CRC Press) Taylor & Francis Group GBR. Dist: Taylor & Francis Group.

Kumar, Ritunesh. Stand Alone Liquid Desiccant Air-Conditioning Systems. 2011. 216p. pap. ***(978-3-8443-1174-7(2))*** Lambert Academic Publishing.

Meyer, Leo A. Digital Controls for HVAC Technicians. 2008. pap. 34.00 *(978-0-88069-048-5(8))* LAMA Bks.

Miller, Frank & Moravek, Joseph. Blueprints & Plans for HVAC. 3rd ed. 2008. (ENG.). 320p. (C). pap. 149.95 *(978-1-4283-3520-2(X))* Delmar Cengage Learning.

Miller, Rex. HVAC Troubleshooting Guide. 2009. (ENG., Illus.). 720p. pap. 49.95 *(978-0-07-160499-4(5),* 0071604995) McGraw-Hill Professional Publishing.

Miller, Rex & Miller, Mark. Air Conditioning & Refrigeration 2/E. 2nd ed. 2011. (ENG., Illus.). 624p. pap. 50.00 ***(978-0-07-176139-0(X),*** 007176139X) McGraw-Hill Professional Publishing.

Miller, Rex & Miller, Mark R. Electricity & Electronics for HVAC. 2007. (ENG., Illus.). 380p. (C). pap. 49.95 *(978-0-07-149668-1(8),* 0071496688) McGraw-Hill Professional Publishing.

—HVAC Licensing Study Guide. 2007. (ENG., Illus.). 408p. per. 39.95 *(978-0-07-148640-8(2),* 0071486402) McGraw-Hill Professional Publishing.

Mitchell, John W. & Braun, James E. Heating, Ventilation, & Air Conditioning in Buildings. 2012. (ENG.). 600p. (C). 171.95 ***(978-0-470-62457-9(4),*** Wiley) Wiley, John & Sons, Inc.

Montgomery, Ross & McDowall, Robert. Fundamentals of HVAC Control Systems. 2011. *(978-1-933742-91-5(7)); (978-1-933742-92-2(5))* American Society of Heating, Refrigerating & Air-Conditioning Engineers, Inc.

NCCER. HVAC Level 1. 3rd ed. 2007. (ENG.). 416p. (C). pap. 86.67 *(978-0-13-614416-8(0),* Prentice Hall); 540p. pap. *(978-0-13-614418-2(7))* Prentice Hall PTR.

—HVAC Level 4 Trainee Guide, Perfect Bound. 3rd ed. 2009. (ENG.). 586p. (C). pap. 125.33 *(978-0-13-604494-9(8),* Prentice Hall) Prentice Hall PTR.

—Pro HVAC TG Spiral. 3rd ed. 2008. (C). spiral bd. 120.00 *(978-0-13-607509-7(6),* Prentice Hall) Prentice Hall PTR.

Patterson, John. Build Your Own Air Conditioner or Dehumidifier: Increase the Cooling Effect of your Fan. 2007. 6.99 *(978-0-9794439-0-9(3))* H & S Pantry.

Phcc-Naef Acca Rses Staff & Moravek, Joseph. Hvacr 101. 2008. (ENG.). 352p. (C). pap. 89.95 *(978-1-4180-6663-5(X))* Delmar Cengage Learning.

Phcc-Naef Acca Rses Staff, et al. HVACR 201. 2009. (ENG.). 472p. (C). pap. 89.95 *(978-1-4180-6664-2(8))* Delmar Cengage Learning.

Roman, Luis. Conexiones Electricas Del Aire Acondicionado. 2009. 112p. pap. 17.95 *(978-1-4327-4669-8(3))* Outskirts Pr., Inc.

Rosenberg, Paul & American Contractors Educational Services Staff. HVAC/R Professional Reference. 2006. (DeWalt Ser.). (ENG., Illus.). 768p. per. 24.95 *(978-0-9770003-8-8(9),* DEWALT) CENGAGE Learning.

Rudman, Jack. Air Conditioning & Refrigeration. (Occupational Competency Examination Ser.: Vol. 1). 49.95 *(978-0-8373-5751-5(9),* Passbooks) National Learning Corp.

—Supervising HVAC Plant Operator. (Career Examination Ser.: C-3752). pap. 39.95 *(978-0-8373-3752-4(6))* National Learning Corp.

Rutkowski, Hank. Air Distribution Basics for Residential & Small Commerical Buildings, Manual T. Date not set. (Illus.). 85p. pap. 34.00 *(978-1-892765-06-2(3))* Air Conditioning Contractors of America.

—Commercial Applications, Systems, & Equipment, Manual CS. Date not set. (Illus.). 380p. pap. 68.00 *(978-1-892765-05-5(5))* Air Conditioning Contractors of America.

—Commercial Low Pressure, Low Velocity Duct System Design, Manual Q. Date not set. (Illus.). 316p. pap. 68.00 *(978-1-892765-02-4(0))* Air Conditioning Contractors of America.

—Heat Pump Systems, Principles & Applications, Manual H. 2nd ed. Date not set. (Illus.). 69p. pap. 38.00 *(978-1-892765-07-9(1))* Air Conditioning Contractors of America.

—Residential Equipment Selections, Manual S. 2nd ed. Date not set. (Illus.). 115p. pap. 46.00 *(978-1-892765-03-1(9))* Air Conditioning Contractors of America.

—Residential Load Calculation, Manual J. 7th ed. Date not set. (Illus.). 126p. pap. 45.00 *(978-1-892765-01-7(2))* Air Conditioning Contractors of America.

—Selection of Distribution Systems, Manual G. Date not set. 23p. pap. 23.00 *(978-1-892765-12-3(8))* Air Conditioning Contractors of America.

—What Makes a Good Air Conditioning System?, Manual C. Date not set. (Illus.). 40p. pap. 22.00 *(978-1-892765-13-0(6))* Air Conditioning Contractors of America.

S, Muthuraman. Heating Ventilation Refrigeration & Air Conditioning - Hvacr. 2011. 388p. pap. ***(978-3-8454-1585-7(1))*** Lambert Academic Publishing.

—Hvac & Plumbing. 2011. 96p. pap. ***(978-3-8454-0395-3(0))*** Lambert Academic Publishing.

Santamouris, M. Advances in Passive Cooling. 2007. (BEST (Buildings Energy & Solar Technology) Ser.). (ENG., Illus.). 284p. 152.00 *(978-1-84407-263-7(0))* Routledge.

Skaves, David & Stanfield, Carter. Fundamentals of HVAC/R. 2009. (ENG., Illus.). 1568p. (C). 133.13 *(978-0-13-222367-6(8),* Prentice Hall) Prentice Hall PTR.

Smith, Russell E. Electricity for Refrigeration, Heating & Air Conditioning. 8th ed. 2011. (ENG.). (C). 1408.95 *(978-1-111-03877-9(5))* Delmar Cengage Learning.

—Electricity for Refrigeration, Heating, & Air Conditioning. 8th ed. 2010. (ENG.). 736p. (C). 183.95 *(978-1-111-03874-8(0))* Delmar Cengage Learning.

—Lab Manual for Smith's Electricity for Refrigeration, Heating & Air Conditioning. 8th ed. 2010. (ENG.). 288p. (C). pap. 75.95 *(978-1-111-03875-5(9))* Delmar Cengage Learning.

Song, Qing. Neural Network Control & Optimization. 2009. 146p. pap. *(978-3-639-18179-1(4))* VDM Verlag Dr. Mueller e.K.

Spitler, Jeffrey D. Load Calculation Applications Manual: I-P Edition, RP-1326, with CD. 2009. (ENG.). 342p. 119.00 *(978-1-933742-42-7(9))* American Society of Heating, Refrigerating & Air-Conditioning Engineers, Inc.

—Load Calculation Applications Manual SI Version: With CD. 2010. (ENG.). 347p. 119.00 *(978-1-933742-72-4(0))* American Society of Heating, Refrigerating & Air-Conditioning Engineers, Inc.

Stanford, Herbert W. HVAC Water Chillers & Cooling Towers: Fundamentals, Application, & Operation. 2nd rev. ed. 2011. (Dekker Mechanical Engineering Ser.). (ENG., Illus.). 407p. 149.95 *(978-1-4398-6202-5(8),* CRC Press) Taylor & Francis Group GBR. Dist: Taylor & Francis Group.

Sugarman, Samuel C. HVAC Fundamentals, 2 Edition. 2nd rev. ed. 2007. (ENG.). 300p. 109.95 *(978-1-4200-5245-9(4),* CRC Press) Taylor & Francis Group GBR. Dist: Taylor & Francis Group.

—HVAC Fundamentals. 2nd ed. 2007. *(978-0-88173-559-8(0))* Fairmont Pr., Inc.

Taitano, Mike. Air Conditioning & Refrigeration System Evaluation Guide. 2009. 36p. 19.95 *(978-1-4357-1239-3(0))* Lulu Enterprises Inc.

Thomas, P. C. & Moller, Steven. HVAC System Size - Getting it Right. 2007. (Illus.). 15p. spiral bd. *(978-0-9803503-8-8(7))* Cooperative Research Ctr. for Construction Innovation.

Thomson, James. 2010 National Plumbing & HVAC Estimator. 2010. (Illus.). 464p. pap. 63.25 *(978-1-57218-231-8(8))* Craftsman Bk. Co.

Thomson, James A. National Plumbing & HVAC Estimator. (National Plumbing & HVAC Estimator Ser.). (Illus.). 2008. 459p. pap. 63.25 incl. cd-rom *(978-1-57218-214-1(8))* 16th ed. 2007. 428p. pap. 58.25 incl. cd-rom *(978-1-57218-195-3(8))* Craftsman Bk. Co.

—2007 NATL Plumbing & HVAC Estimator. 2006. 400p. 53.25 *(978-1-57218-180-9(X))* Craftsman Bk. Co.

—2011 National Plumbing & HVAC Estimator. 2010. 464p. pap. 63.25 incl. cd-rom *(978-1-57218-248-6(2))* Craftsman Bk. Co.

Tips for Residental HVAC Installation. 2006. (Indoor Environment Technicians Library). 20.00 *(978-0-88069-039-3(9))* LAMA Bks.

Tomczyk, John, et al. Seguridad y capacitacion universales del R-410A. 2nd ed. 2011. (ESCO Institute's Section 608 Preparatory Manual Ser.).Tr. of Universal R-410A Safety & Training. (SPA., Illus.). 102p. ring bd. 34.95 ***(978-1-930044-30-2(5))*** ESCO PR.

Tomczyk, John A., et al. Tecnologia de Refrigeracion Acondicionado: Un Manual de Referencia en Espanol. 2006. (ENG., Illus.). 448p. (C). per. 87.95 *(978-1-4180-5571-4(9))* Delmar Cengage Learning.

United Nations Environment Programme: Air Conditioning and Heat Pumps Technical Options Committee. Montreal protocol on substances that deplete the ozone Layer: 2006 report of the Refrigeration, Air Conditioning & Heat Pumps Technical Options Committee (RTOC); 2006 Assessment. 2007. (ENG., Illus.). 236p. pap. 50.00 *(978-92-807-2822-4(9))* United Nations Environment Programme KEN. Dist: National Bk. Network.

Whitman, Bill, et al. Refrigeration & Air Conditioning Technology. 6th ed. 2011. (Illus.). 1418p. 158.95 incl. cd-rom *(978-1-111-03372-9(2))* Delmar Cengage Learning.

AIR-CUSHION VEHICLES

see Ground-Effect Machines

AIR DEFENSE ARTILLERY

see Antiaircraft Artillery

AIR DEFENSES

see also Air Raid Shelters; Air Raid Warning Systems; Aircraft Spotting; Antiaircraft Artillery; Radar Defense Networks

Air Sovereignty Alert Operations: Hearing Before the Readiness Subcommittee of the Committee on Armed Services, House of Representatives, One Hundred Eleventh Congress, First Session, Hearing Held April 22, 2009. 2010. (Illus.). iii, 135p. *(978-0-16-085169-8(6),* 552-070-40523-2) United States Government Printing Office.

Diez, Octavio. Specialist Military Aircraft. 2006. (Aircraft Ser.). (ENG., Illus.). 96p. pap. 24.95 *(978-84-934728-1-8(6))* Udyat, S.L. ESP. Dist: Independent Pubs. Group.

Foster, Peter & Mylon, Patrick. Tornado ADV: The Last Cold War Interceptor. 2011. (ENG., Illus.). 120p. pap. 34.95 ***(978-0-7524-5936-3(8))*** History Pr. Ltd.,The GBR. Dist: Independent Pubs. Group.

Green, Tom. Bright Boys: The Making of Information Technology. 2010. (ENG.). 320p. 39.00 *(978-1-56881-476-6(3))* AK Peters, Ltd.

Grube, Michael & Grube, Christel. Ringtreppenturm Rosshafen: Ein Luftschutzturm in Hamburg. 2008. 62p. pap. 18.50 *(978-3-8370-1750-2(8))* Bks. on Demand.

Hamilton, John A. Blazing Skies: Air Defense Artillery on Fort Bliss, Texas, 1940-2009. 2009. (ENG., Illus.). 388p. pap. 74.00 *(978-0-16-082210-0(6),* Dept. of the Army) United States Government Printing Office.

Hearing on National Defense Authorization ACT for Fiscal Year 2009 & Oversight of Previously Authorized Programs Before the Committee on Armed Services, House of Representatives, One Hundred Tenth Congress, Second Session: Strategic Forces Subcommittee Hearings on Budget Request on U.S. Strategic Posture & Budget Request for Strategic Programs, Hearing Held, February 27, 2008. 2008. iii, 98p. *(978-0-16-082581-1(4),* 552-070-38602-5) United States Government Printing Office.

Jackson, Brian A., et al. Evaluating Novel Threats to the Homeland: Unmanned Aerial Vehicles & Cruise Missiles. 2007. 128p. pap. 24.00 *(978-0-8330-4169-2(X),* mg-626) RAND Corp., The.

Jane's Land-Based Air Defence. cd-rom 1150.00 *(978-0-7106-1585-5(X))* Jane's Information Group, Inc.

Jordan, Melissa V. Options for Deploying Missile Defenses in Europe. 2010. (Defense, Security & Strategies Ser.). 184p. 115.00 *(978-1-60741-889-4(4))* Nova Science Pubs., Inc.

Martini, John & Haller, Stephen. The Last Missile Site: An Operational & Physical History of Nike Site SF-88, Fort Barry, California. 2010. (ENG., Illus.). 158p. mass mkt. 19.95 *(978-0-9761494-1-5(9))* Hole in the Head Pr.

Oversight of Missile Defense (Part 3) Questions for the Missile Defense Agency: Hearing Before the Subcommittee on National Security & Foreign Affairs of the Committee on Oversight & Government Reform, House of Representatives, One Hundred Tenth Congress, Second Session, April 30, 2008. 2009. (Illus.). iii, 214p. *(978-0-16-083584-1(4),* 552-070-39302-1) United States Government Printing Office.

Rosenfeld, Susan & Gross, Charles J. Air National Guard at 60: A History: A History. 2007. (ENG., Illus.). 75p. pap. 11.50 *(978-0-16-079501-5(X),* Dept. of the Air Force) United States Government Printing Office.

Samson, Victoria A. American Missile Defense: A Guide to the Issues. 2010. (Contemporary Military, Strategic, & Security Issues Ser.). 242p. instr.'s gde. ed., instr.'s hndbk. ed. 44.95 *(978-0-313-35326-0(3),* C35326, Praeger Pubs.) Greenwood Publishing Group, Inc.

Stocker, Jeremy. The United Kingdom & Nuclear Deterrence. 2007. 240p. 32.50 *(978-0-415-43834-6(9))* Routledge.

Stuart, F. S. Immortal Wings. 2006. 84p. per. *(978-1-4067-2540-7(4),* Hesperides Pr.) Read Bks.

Swicker, Charles C. Theater Ballistic Missile Defense from the Sea: Issues for the Maritime Component Commander. 2006. (Newport Paper Ser.). 103p. per. 10.00 *(978-0-16-076988-7(4),* Defense Dept.) United States Government Printing Office.

U.S. Combat Air Power: Reassessing Plans to Modernize Interdiction Capabilities Could Save Billions. 60p. pap. 30.00 *(978-0-7881-4099-0(X))* DIANE Publishing Co.

Whitcomb, Randall. Cold War Tech War: The Politics of America's Air Defense. 2008. (Apogee Books Space Ser.). (ENG., Illus.). 230p. pap. 29.95 *(978-1-894959-77-3(9))* Collector's Guide Publishing, Inc. CAN. Dist: Independent Pubs. Group.

Wilson, Gordon A. A. NORAD & the Soviet Nuclear Threat: Canada's Secret Electronic Air War. 2012. (ENG., Illus.). 288p. pap. 28.99 ***(978-1-4597-0410-7(X))*** Dundurn CAN. Dist: Ingram Pub. Services.

Wilson, Jim. Launch Pad Uk. 2009. (Illus.). 208p. 39.99 *(978-1-84415-799-0(7))* Pen & Sword Bks. Ltd. GBR. Dist: Casemate Pubs. & Bk. Distributors, LLC.

Withington, Thomas. Wild Weasel Fighter Attack: The Story of the Suppression of Enemy Air Defences. 2008. (Illus.). 256p. 39.95 *(978-1-84415-668-9(0))* Pen & Sword Bks. Ltd. GBR. Dist: Casemate Pubs. & Bk. Distributors, LLC.

AIR DEFENSES, CIVIL

see Air Defenses; Civil Defense

AIR DEFENSES, MILITARY

see Air Defenses

AIR DUCTS

see also Air Conditioning; Ventilation

Felker, Laurence G. & Felker, Travis L. Dampers & Airflow Control. 2010. (ENG.). 306p. pap. 89.00 *(978-1-933742-53-3(4))* American Society of Heating, Refrigerating & Air-Conditioning Engineers, Inc.

Rutkowski, Hank. Commercial Low Pressure, Low Velocity Duct System Design, Manual Q. Date not set. (Illus.). 316p. pap. 68.00 *(978-1-892765-02-4(0))* Air Conditioning Contractors of America.

—Residential Duct Systems, Manual D. 2nd ed. Date not set. (Illus.). 298p. pap. 44.00 *(978-1-892765-00-0(4))* Air Conditioning Contractors of America.

Rutkowski, Hank, ed. Installation Techniques for Perimeter Heating & Cooling, Manual 4. 11th ed. Date not set. (Illus.). 21p. pap. 23.00 *(978-1-892765-09-3(8))* Air Conditioning Contractors of America.

AIR FILTERS

American Society of Heating, contrib. by. Particulate & Gaseous Contamination in Datacom Environments: ASHRAE Datacom Series, Book 8. 2009. (ENG.). 104p. pap. 54.00 *(978-1-933742-60-1(7))* American Society of Heating, Refrigerating & Air-Conditioning Engineers, Inc.

British Standards Institute Staff. Filters for compressed air. Test methods. Oil Vapours. 20p. pap. 123.00 *(978-0-580-53131-6(7))* Artech Hse., Inc.

Choi, Kyung-Ju. Practical Handbook of Air Filtration. 2012. 384p. 125.00 *(978-1-85617-459-6(X),* Elsevier Science) Elsevier Science & Technology Bks.

AIR FLOW

see also Gas Flow; Permeability

Baille, Neil. Modeling Nasal Airflow. 2009. 244p. pap. *(978-3-639-16989-8(1))* VDM Verlag Dr. Mueller e.K.

Barton, Noel G. & Périaux, Jacques. Coupling of Fluids, Structures & Waves in Aeronautics: Proceedings of a French-Australian Workshop in Melbourne, Australia 3-6 December 2001. 2010. (Notes on Numerical Fluid Mechanics & Multidisciplinary Design Ser.). xii, 316p. pap. 289.00 *(978-3-642-07294-9(1),* 3642072941) Springer.

Bettes, Harold. The Engine Airflow HP1537: A Practical Guide to Airflow Theory, Parts Testing, Flow Bench Testing & Analyzing Data to Increase Performance for Any Street or Racing Engine. 2010. (ENG.). 160p. (gr. 12). instr.'s hndbk. ed. 23.95 *(978-1-55788-537-1(0),* HP Trade) Penguin Group (USA) Inc.

Cebeci, Tuncer. An Engineering Approach to the Calculation of Aerodynamic Flows. 2010. (Illus.). xv, 396p. pap. 209.00 *(978-3-642-08543-7(1),* 3642085431) Springer.

Felker, Laurence G. & Felker, Travis L. Dampers & Airflow Control. 2010. (ENG.). 306p. pap. 89.00 *(978-1-933742-53-3(4))* American Society of Heating, Refrigerating & Air-Conditioning Engineers, Inc.

Kirpekar, Sujit. Turbulent Flows in Hard Disk Drives. 2008. 280p. pap. *(978-3-8364-7494-8(8))* VDM Verlag Dr. Mueller e.K.

Roulet, Claude-Alain. Ventilation & Airflow in Buildings: Methods for Diagnosis & Evaluation. 2007. (BEST (Buildings Energy & Solar Technology) Ser.). (ENG., Illus.). 128p. 156.00 *(978-1-84407-451-8(X))* Routledge.

Sturm, Robert. Modeling Deposition & Clearance of Insoluble Particles in Human Lung Airways. 2008. 364p. pap. *(978-3-639-00892-0(8))* VDM Verlag Dr. Mueller e.K.

Sun, Yigang. Volumetric Particle Streak-Tracking Velocimetry & Room Airflow Characterization. 2008. 140p. pap. *(978-3-639-03029-7(X))* VDM Verlag Dr. Mueller e.K.

Swaffield, John A. Transient Airflow in Building Drainage Systems. 2010. (ENG., Illus.). 362p. (C). 130.00 *(978-0-415-49265-2(3))* Routledge.

AIR FORCE SPOUSES

Miller, Laura L., et al. Year of the Air Force Family: 2009 Survey of Active-Duty Spouses, 1 vol. 2011. (Illus.). 100p. (C). pap. 24.00 *(978-0-8330-5096-0(6))* RAND Corp., The.

AIR FORCES

see also subdivision Air Force under names of countries, e.g. United States—Air Force

Air Force, United States & NASA. F-104 Starfighter Pilot's Flight Operating Instructions. 2011. 292p. pap. 28.95 *(978-1-935700-47-0(2))* Periscope Film, LLC.

Breffort, Dominique & Breffort, André. French Aircraft 1939-1942. 2011. (Illus.). 160p. pap. 39.95 *(978-2-35250-197-8(0))* Histoire et Collections FRA. Dist: Casemate Pubs. & Bk. Distributors, LLC.

Cliff, Roger, et al. Shaking the Heavens & Splitting the Earth: Chinese Air Force Employment Concepts in the 21st Century. 2010. 300p. pap. 29.00 *(978-0-8330-4932-2(1),* mg-915) RAND Corp., The.

Edwards, Peter J. The Rise & Fall of the Japanese Imperial Naval Air Service. 2010. (Illus.). 346p. 50.00 *(978-1-84884-307-3(0))* Pen & Sword Bks. Ltd. GBR. Dist: Casemate Pubs. & Bk. Distributors, LLC.

Greenacre, John. Churchill's Spearhead: The Development of Britain's Airborne Forces in World War II. 2010. (Illus.). 256p. 39.95 *(978-1-84884-271-7(6))* Pen & Sword Bks. Ltd. GBR. Dist: Casemate Pubs. & Bk. Distributors, LLC.

Hayward, Greg. D-Day to Ve-Day: With the Second Tactical Air Force 1944-1945. 2009. 60p. pap. 12.99 *(978-1-4389-6760-8(8))* AuthorHouse.

High Stakes Writing. Im- Air Force Jrotc Cult Studies. 2010. pap., instr.'s hndbk. ed., instr.'s planning gde. ed. 999.95 incl. cd-rom *(978-0-7637-8465-2(6))* Jones & Bartlett Learning, LLC.

Jackson, Robert. Baling Out: Amazing Dramas of Military Flying. 2006. (Illus.). 192p. 39.95 *(978-1-84415-347-3(9))* Pen & Sword Bks. Ltd. GBR. Dist: Casemate Pubs. & Bk. Distributors, LLC.

Joseph, Frank. The Axis Air Forces: Flying in Support of the German Luftwaffe, 1 vol. 2011. (Illus.). 312p. 58.00 *(978-0-313-39590-1(X),* A3465C); E-Book *(978-0-313-39591-8(8),* Praeger Pubs.) Greenwood Publishing Group, Inc.

Mann, Robert A. The B-29 Superfortress: A Comprehensive Registry of the Planes & Their Missions. alt. ed. 2009. (ENG.). 288p. pap. 39.95 *(978-0-7864-4458-8(4))* McFarland & Co., Inc. Pubs.

Mason, Tim. The Secret Years. 2010. (Illus.). 320p. *(978-1-902109-14-5(7))* Hikoki Pubns.

McCarthy Jr., Donald J. Those Who Were There: Ninety-Two True Stories of Combat Missions Flown over North Vietnam. 2009. 392p. pap. 35.95 *(978-1-4401-3129-5(5))* iUniverse, Inc.

Olsen, John Andreas, ed. Global Air Power. 2011. 560p. 55.00 *(978-1-59797-555-1(9));* pap. 35.00 *(978-1-59797-680-0(6))* Potomac Bks., Inc.

Resa, Jolinda Bull. Honor Them Always: For the Sacrifice of Their Youth at Bataan. 2011. 60p. pap. 14.95 *(978-1-4327-7555-1(3))* Outskirts Pr., Inc.

Ripley, Tim. Middle East Air Forces in the 21st Century. 2010. (Illus.). 459p. 70.00 *(978-1-84884-099-7(3))* Pen & Sword Bks. Ltd. GBR. Dist: Casemate Pubs. & Bk. Distributors, LLC.

Schnell, James. Meaningful Communication for the Military. 2010. 108p. pap. *(978-3-639-23473-2(1))* VDM Verlag Dr. Mueller e.K.

Stovall, Jr. Wings of Courage. (Illus.). 200p. pap. 12.95 *(978-0-9615206-9-4(8))* MBI Distribution Services/Quayside Distribution.

Stroud, Jon. Little Book of the RAF. 2011. (Little Book Of Ser.). (ENG., Illus.). 128p. 11.99 *(978-1-907803-11-6(4))* G2 Entertainment Ltd. GBR. Dist: BookMasters Distribution Services (BDS).

Tanner, Lean, et al. Brigadier General Lecel Lee: The Toughest Airforce Commander in World War II. 2009. 224p. 25.00 *(978-0-9726133-3-0(1))* Nebo Valley Pr.

Vitarbo, Gregory. Army of the Sky: Russian Military Aviation Before the Great War, 1904-1914. 2012. E-Book *(978-1-4539-0266-0(X));* (C). 80.95 *(978-1-4331-1490-8(9))* Lang, Peter Publishing, Inc.

Wragg, David. Jane's Air Forces of the World: The History & Composition of the World's Air Forces. 2007. 240p. 39.95 *(978-0-06-089070-4(3))* HarperCollins Pubs.

Zidon, Ofer & Aloni, Shlomo. Israeli Air Force Cutting Edge. 2010. 80p. pap. 54.00 *(978-965-7371-03-9(1))* Wizard ISR. Dist: Gefen Bks.

AIR FRAMES

see Airframes

AIR FREIGHT

see Aeronautics, Commercial

AIR GUNS

Atkins, Malcolm. GATS. A Guide to Junior Push in - Pop Out Airguns. 2012. (Illus.). 188p. pap. 25.00 *(978-1-78035-225-1(5),* Fastprint Publishing) Upfront Publishing Ltd. GBR. Dist: Printondemand-worldwide.com.

Barnett, Ian. The Airgun Hunter's Year. 2011. (ENG., Illus.). 224p. 30.00 *(978-1-906122-28-7(8))* Unwin, Merlin Bks. GBR. Dist: SCB Distributors.

Beeman, Robert & Allen, John. Blue Book of Airguns. Fjestad, S. P., ed. 7th ed. 2008. (Illus.). 504p. pap. 29.95 *(978-1-886768-77-2(3))* Blue Bk. Pubns., Inc.

Beeman, Robert & Allen, John B. Blue Book of Airguns. 9th ed. 2011. (Blue Book of Airguns Ser.). (Illus.). 616p. pap. 29.95 *(978-1-936120-13-0(5))* Blue Bk. Pubns., Inc.

Bezzant, John. Advanced Airgun Hunting: A Guide to Equipment, Shooting Techniques & Training. 2012. (ENG., Illus.). 128p. 32.95 *(978-1-84797-294-1(2))* Crowood Pr., Ltd. GBR. Dist: Independent Pubs. Group.

Bezzant, John. Air Rifle Shooting for Pest Control & Rabbiting. 2009. (ENG., Illus.). 192p. 50.00 *(978-1-84797-043-5(5))* Crowood Pr., Ltd. GBR. Dist: Independent Pubs. Group.

Dunathan, A. T. The American B. B. Gun: A Collector's Guide. Date not set. (Illus.). reprint ed. 35.00 *(978-0-9707608-1-4(7))* Rowe Pubns.

Groenewold, John, compiled by. Exploded Airgun Drawings. 2nd ed. 2007. (Illus.). 363p. *(978-0-9674667-2-9(5))* Groenewold, John.

Manning, Mathew. Hunting with Air Rifles: A Complete Guide. 2010. (ENG., Illus.). 192p. 29.95 *(978-0-85716-001-0(X))* Northumbria University Press GBR. Dist: Independent Pubs. Group.

Middleton, Richard. The Practical Guide to Man-Powered Weapons & Ammunition: Experiments with Catapults, Musketballs, Stonebows, Blowpipes, Big Airguns, & Bullet Bows. 2007. (ENG., Illus.). 224p. per. 14.95 *(978-1-60239-147-5(5),* 239147) Skyhorse Publishing Co., Inc.

Smith, W. H. B. Gas, Air, & Spring Guns of the World. 2009. (Classic Gun Bks). (ENG., Illus.). 288p. 34.95 *(978-0-8117-0514-1(5))* Stackpole Bks.

Thrale, Christopher. Webley Air Rifles 1925-2005. 2011. (ENG., Illus.). 272p. 100.00 *(978-0-7090-8910-0(4))* Hale, Robert Ltd. GBR. Dist: Independent Pubs. Group.

Wadeson, Pete. Total Airguns 2nd Edn. 2nd rev. ed. 2012. (Illus.). 304p. 34.95 *(978-1-84689-110-6(8))* Quiller Publishing, Ltd. GBR. Dist: Stackpole Bks.

AIR HOSTESSES

see Flight Attendants

AIR LAW

see Aeronautics—Law and Legislation

AIR LINES

see Airlines

AIR MAIL SERVICE

Hill, Wing Commander. Baghdad Air Mail. 2006. 380p. per. *(978-1-4067-3432-4(2),* Hesperides Pr.) Read Bks.

Rosenberg, Barry & Macaulay, Catherine. Mavericks of the Sky: The First Daring Pilots of the U. S. Air Mail. 2007. (ENG., Illus.). 368p. per. 14.95 *(978-0-06-052950-5(4),* HarperPerennial) HarperCollins Pubs.

AIR NAVIGATION

see Aeronautics; Navigation (Aeronautics)

AIR PILOTS

see also Astronauts; Fighter Pilots; Women in Aeronautics
also subdivision Piloting under special types of aircraft, e.g. Airplanes—Piloting

Abbott, Ace & Morris, Allen Robert. The Rogue Aviator: In the Back Alleys of Aviation. 2011. (ENG., Illus.). 237p. pap. 14.95 *(978-0-578-08508-1(9))* Morris, Allen.

Air Force, United States. U-2 Dragon Lady Pilot's Flight Operating Instructions. 2011. 330p. pap. 29.95 *(978-1-935700-49-4(9))* Periscope Film, LLC.

Aldridge, Edward/Albert, 2nd. Al's Odyssey, from Catonsville MD to Japan: Edward Albert Aldridge II, World War II Letters. 2009. (Illus.). 382p. lib. bdg. *(978-0-9841210-0-7(5))* El's Research Studies.

Alexatos, Michael S. Ramblings from a Cockpit. 2010. 140p. 25.49 *(978-1-4490-5889-0(2));* pap. 13.49 *(978-1-4490-5888-3(4))* AuthorHouse.

Alling, Chuck. A Mighty Fortress: Lead Bomber over Europe. Hildt, Elizabeth Alling, ed. 2006. (Illus.). 186p. per. 19.95 *(978-1-932033-59-5(9))* Casemate Pubs. & Bk. Distributors, LLC.

ASA Test Prep Board Staff, ed. Instrument Rating Test Prep 2011: Study & Prepare for the Instrument Rating, Instrument Flight Instructor (CFII), Instrument Ground Instructor, & Foreign Pilot: Airplane & Helicopter FAA Knowledge Tests. 2010. (Test Prep Ser.). (ENG.). 328p. pap. 21.95 *(978-1-56027-765-1(3))* Aviation Supplies & Academics, Inc.

Aviation Safety: FAA's Role in the Oversight of Commercial Air Carriers: Hearing Before the Subcommittee on Aviation Operations, Safety, & Security of the Committee on Commerce, Science, & Transportation, United States Senate, One Hundred Eleventh Congress, First Session, June 10, 2009. 2010. iii, 81p. *(978-0-16-085627-3(2),* 552-070-40689-0) United States Government Printing Office.

Aviation Safety: One Year after the Crash of Flight 3407: Hearing Before the Subcommittee on Aviation Operations, Safety, & Security of the Committee on Commerce, Science, & Transportation, United States Senate, One Hundred Eleventh Congress, Second Session, February 25, 2010. 2010. (Illus.). iii, 46p. *(978-0-16-086805-4(X),* 552-070-41721-4) United States Government Printing Office.

Aviation Safety: Pilot Fatigue: Hearing Before the Subcommittee on Aviation Operations, Safety, & Security of the Committee on Commerce, Science, & Transportation, United States Senate, One Hundred Eleventh Congress, First Session, December 1, 2009. 2010. (Illus.). iii, 49p. *(978-0-16-086182-6(9),* 552-070-41280-8) United States Government Printing Office.

Bigelow, James H. Balancing Rated Personnel Requirements & Inventories. 2011. 45p. pap. 17.00 *(978-0-8330-5094-6(X),* tr-869) RAND Corp., The.

Blackman, Tony. Vulcan Test Pilot: My experiences in the cockpit of a Cold War Icon. 2009. (Illus.). 224p. pap. 26.95 *(978-1-906502-30-0(7))* Grub Street GBR. Dist: Casemate Pubs. & Bk. Distributors, LLC.

Bowen, Ezra. Knights of the Air. (Illus.). 176p. 24.00 *(978-1-84447-030-3(X))* Time Life Value GBR. Dist: Mercury Bks. Ltd.

Bronnenkant, Lance J. The Imperial German Eagles in World War I, Vol. 2. 2008. (Illus.). 400p. bds. 69.95 *(978-0-7643-2928-9(6))* Schiffer Publishing, Ltd.

—The Imperial German Eagles in World War I: Their Postcards & Pictures, 3 vols. 2011. (Illus.). 464p. 79.99 *(978-0-7643-3764-2(5))* Schiffer Publishing, Ltd.

Brown, Craig. Debrief: A Complete History of U. S. Aerial Engagements - 1981 to the Present. 2007. (Illus.). 224p. pap. 49.95 *(978-0-7643-2785-8(2))* Schiffer Publishing, Ltd.

Brown, Eric. Wings of the Weird & Wonderful. 2010. (Illus.). 208p. *(978-1-902109-16-9(3))* Hikoki Pubns.

Bruder, Gerry. Heroes of the Horizon: Flying Adventures of Alaska's Legendary Bush Pilots. 2007. (ENG., Illus.). 279p. pap. 17.95 *(978-0-88240-363-2(X))* Graphic Arts Ctr. Publishing Co.

Burnett, Claudine. Soaring Skyward: A History of Aviation in & Around Long Beach, California. 2011. 308p. pap. 29.95 *(978-1-4670-3361-9(8))* AuthorHouse.

Byetheway, John. Supersonic Saints. 2007. 192p. 19.95 *(978-1-59038-747-4(3))* Deseret Bk. Co.

Cage, Cheryl A. Reporting Clear? A Pilot's Interview Guide to Background Checks & Presentation of Personal History. 2006. (Professional Aviation Ser.). (ENG.). 94p. per. 19.95 *(978-1-56027-509-1(X))* Aviation Supplies & Academics, Inc.

Civil Aviation Medical Institute Staff. Pilot Medical Handbook: Human Factors for Successful Flying. 2009. (ENG., Illus.). 100p. pap. 16.95 *(978-1-56027-717-0(3))* Aviation Supplies & Academics, Inc.

Collins, Brian J., ed. Behind the Cyberspace Veil: The Hidden Evolution of the Air Force Officer Corps, 1 vol. 2008. (Praeger Security International Ser.). (Illus.). 264p. 54.95 *(978-0-313-34965-2(7),* C34965, Praeger Security International) Greenwood Publishing Group, Inc.

Consumer Dummies Staff, et al. Military Flight Aptitude Tests for Dummies. 2012. (ENG.). 528p. pap. 22.99 *(978-0-470-60032-0(2),* For Dummies) Wiley, John & Sons, Inc.

Cook, Andrew. To Be an Airline Pilot. 2007. (ENG., Illus.). 160p. pap. 22.95 *(978-1-86126-865-5(3),* 1861268653) Crowood Pr., Ltd. GBR. Dist: MBI Distribution Services/Quayside Distribution.

Craft, Stephen G. Embry-Riddle at War: Aviation Training during World War II. 2010. (Florida History & Culture Ser.). (ENG., Illus.). 344p. pap. 24.95 *(978-0-8130-3503-1(1),* Univ. Pr. of Florida.

Dolitsky, Alexander. Allies in Wartime: The Alaska-Siberia Airway During World War II. Dolitsky, Alexander, ed. 2007. (Illus.). 160p. 29.95 *(978-0-9653891-6-7(2),* Alaska-Siberia Research Ctr.

Drew, John G. & Lynch, Kristin F. Options for Meeting the Maintenance Demands of Active Associate Flying Units. 2008. 94p. pap. 24.50 *(978-0-8330-4210-1(6),* mg-611) RAND Corp., The.

Duran, Terry. Barron's Military Flight Aptitude Tests. 2nd rev. ed. 2011. (ENG., Illus.). 552p. pap. 21.99 *(978-0-7641-4573-5(8))* Barron's Educational Series, Inc.

Examining the Federal Aviation Administration's Age 60 Rule: Hearing Before the Subcommittee on Aviation of the Committee on Commerce, Science, & Transportation, United States Senate, One Hundred Ninth Congress, First Session, July 19, 2005. 2011. (Illus.). iii, 61p. *(978-0-16-088032-2(7),* 552-070-42456-0) United States Government Printing Office.

F. Willard Robinson, Lieutenant. Navy Wings of Gold: 3rd Edition. 2010. 356p. pap. 26.66 *(978-1-4269-2449-1(6))* Trafford Publishing.

FAA's Oversight of On-Demand Aircraft Operators: Hearing Before the Subcommittee on Aviation of the Committee on Transportation & Infrastructure, House of Representatives, One Hundred Eleventh Congress, Second Session, March 17, 2010. 2010. (Illus.). xiv, 116p. *(978-0-16-086769-9(X),* 552-070-41690-1) United States Government Printing Office.

Federal Aviation Administration. Aviation Instructor's Handbook: Faa-h-8083-9a. 2009. (FAA Handbooks Ser.). (ENG.). 226p. pap. 19.95 *(978-1-56027-749-1(1),* Aviation Supplies & Academics, Inc.

—Federal Aviation Regulations / Aeronautical Information Manual 2012 (FAR/AIM) 2011. (ENG., Illus.). 960p. pap. 15.95 *(978-1-61608-486-8(3),* 608486) Skyhorse Publishing Co., Inc.

Federal Aviation Administration (FAA). Far/aim 2012: Federal Aviation Regulations/Aeronautical Information Manual. 2011. (FAR/AIM Ser.). (ENG.). 1090p. pap. 16.95 *(978-1-56027-858-0(7))* Aviation Supplies & Academics, Inc.

—Far/amt 2011: Federal Aviation Regulations for Aviation Maintenance Technicians. 2010. (FAR/AIM Ser.). (ENG.). 896p. pap. 24.95 *(978-1-56027-774-3(2),* Aviation Supplies & Academics, Inc.

Federal Aviation Administration Staff. Certified Flight Instructor Test Prep 2010: Study & Prepare for the Ground, Flight & Sport Instructor: Airplane, Helicopter, Glider, Weight-Shift Control, Powered Parachute, Add-on Ratings, Fundamentals of Instructing, & Designated Pilot Examiner FAA Knowledge Exams. ASA Test Prep Board Staff, ed. 2009. (Test Prep Ser.). (ENG.). 464p. pap. 21.95 *(978-1-56027-739-2(4))* Aviation Supplies & Academics, Inc.

The Federal Aviation Administration's Call to Action on Airline Safety & Pilot Training: Hearing Before the Subcommittee on Aviation of the Committee on Transportation & Infrastructure, House of Representatives, One Hundred Eleventh Congress, First Session, September 23, 2009. 2009. xviii, 192p. *(978-0-16-085163-6(7),* 552-070-40517-8) United States Government Printing Office.

Fluet, M. R. Our Brothers in the Skies: The Hidden Truth Revealed. 2009. 312p. pap. 15.49 *(978-1-4389-3663-5(X))* AuthorHouse.

Forney, Joyce Manley, et al, eds. Henry S. Manley (1892-1967) His Life & Writings. 2011. 340p. 33.95 *(978-1-4502-7565-1(6));* pap. 23.95 *(978-1-4502-7548-4(6),* iUniverse, Inc.

Francis, Martin. The Flyer: British Culture & the Royal Air Force, 1939-1945. 2011. (ENG., Illus.). 278p. pap. 45.00 *(978-0-19-960229-2(8))* Oxford Univ. Pr., Inc.

Franks, Norman. British & Commonwealth Aces of World War II: The Pictorial Record. 2006. (Illus.). 240p. 59.95 *(978-0-7643-2525-0(6))* Schiffer Publishing, Ltd.

Fraser, Chelsea. Famous American Flyers. 376p. 2008. 48.95 *(978-1-4367-0308-6(5),* 2007. (ENG.). per. 33.95 *(978-1-4304-9136-1(1))* Kessinger Publishing, LLC.

Gandy, Stewart. Down on the Ground: The Diary of an Enlisted Tuskegee Airman. 2011. 55p. pap. 18.95 *(978-1-4327-7434-9(4))* Outskirts Pr., Inc.

Goss, Chris. Sea Eagles Vol. 2: Luftwaffe Anti-Shipping Units, 1942-45, 2 vols. 2009. (Luftwaffe Colours Ser.). (ENG., Illus.). 96p. pap. 27.95 *(978-1-903223-56-7(3),* Allan, Ian Publishing GBR. Dist: BookMasters Distribution Services (BDS).

Hallock, Austin Bruce. Sky Full of Dreams: The Aviation Exploits, Creations, & Visions of Bruce K. Hallock (Tailless Aircraft Designer, Builder, & Pilot) 2010. (Illus.). 230p. pap. 16.00 *(978-0-9826390-0-9(7))* Elevon Bks.

Hardison, Chaitra M., et al. Incentive Pay for Remotely Piloted Aircraft Career Fields, 1 vol. 2012. (ENG., Illus.). 112p. (C). pap. 25.00 *(978-0-8330-5965-9(3),* RAND Corp., The.

Hart, Peter. Aces Falling: War above the Trenches 1918. (ENG., Illus.). 416p. 2009. pap. 14.95 *(978-0-7538-2407-8(8),* Phoenix) 2007. 34.95 *(978-0-297-84653-6(1),* Weidenfeld & Nicolson) Orion Publishing Group, Ltd. GBR. Dist: Sterling Publishing Co., Inc.

Harvey, Geraint. Management in the Airline Industry. 2008. (Routledge Research in Employment Relations Ser.). (Illus.). 158p. 143.00 *(978-0-415-39078-1(8))* Routledge.

Heide, Rachel Lea. The Politics of British Commonwealth Air Training Plan Base Selection. 2009. 204p. pap. *(978-3-639-14181-8(4))* VDM Verlag Dr. Mueller e.K.

Henard, David Earl. Victory Stolen: The Perspectives of a Helicopter Pilot on the Tet Offensive & Its Aftermath. 2008. 202p. pap. 24.95 *(978-1-60474-929-8(6))* PublishAmerica, Inc.

Jentsch, Florian, et al, eds. Simulation in Aviation Training. 2011. (Critical Essays on Human Factors in Aviation Ser.). (Illus.). 540p. 260.00 *(978-0-7546-2887-3(6),* Ashgate Publishing Co.

Kelly, Shawna. Aviators in Early Hollywood. 2008. (Images of America Ser.). (ENG., Illus.). 128p. pap. 19.99 *(978-0-7385-5902-5(4))* Arcadia Publishing.

Ketley, Barry. Fledgling Eagles: Luftwaffe Training Aircraft 1933. 2010. (ENG., Illus.). 96p. pap. 27.95 *(978-1-905537-05-0(4))* Allan, Ian Publishing GBR. Dist: BookMasters Distribution Services (BDS).

Kudimi, Eric. Essentials of a Successful Flight Instructor Certification Renewal Program: Flight Instructor Refresher Training Course (FIRC) Sharp, Karen, ed. 2008. (Illus.). 339p. ring bd. *(978-1-935657-39-2(9))* M K Conquest International Pr.

Laird, Malcolm & Mackenzie, Steve. The ANZACs. 2011. (Illus.). 72p. pap. 22.00 *(978-0-9864653-0-7(5),* Stratus, Wydawnictwo, Juszczak, Artur POL. Dist: Casemate Pubs. & Bk. Distributors, LLC.

LearningExpress Staff. Military Flight Aptitude Tests. 3rd rev. ed. 2009. (Complete Preparation Guides). (ENG.). 300p. pap. 24.95 *(978-1-57685-688-8(7))* LearningExpress, LLC.

Lovell, Mary S. The Sound of Wings: The Life of Amelia Earhart. 2009. (ENG.). 464p. pap. 17.99 *(978-0-312-58733-8(3),* St. Martin's Griffin) St. Martin's Pr.

Lovell, Mike, ed. & compiled by. Arthur Lovell - Aviation Pioneer & Navigator. 2007. *(978-0-9776414-5-1(7))* LifeReloaded.

Mackersey, Ian. No Empty Chairs: The Young Aviators of the Great War in Their Own Words. 2012. (ENG., Illus.). 304p. 29.95 ***(978-0-297-85994-9(3)***, Weidenfeld & Nicolson) Orion Publishing Group, Ltd. GBR. Dist: Sterling Publishing Co., Inc.

Madden, Ray. Alligators, Freight Trains & near Flying Disasters: How to Fly an Airplane Backwards, & How to Lose over 18 Engines & Live to Retire or Mayday, Ma. 2009. 176p. 22.95 *(978-1-4389-2634-6(0))*; pap. 16.95 *(978-1-4389-2633-9(2))* AuthorHouse.

Mark, Robert P. Professional Pilot's Career Guide. 2nd rev. ed. 2007. (ENG., Illus.). 455p. per. 24.95 *(978-0-07-148553-1(8)*, 0071485538) McGraw-Hill Professional Publishing.

Marrett, George J. Testing Death: Hughes Aircraft Test Pilots & Cold War Weaponry. 2008. (Illus.). 228p. pap. *(978-1-59114-512-7(0))* Naval Institute Pr.

Mason, Mort D. The Alaska Bush Pilot Chronicles: More Adventures & Misadventures from the Big Empty. 2009. (ENG., Illus.). 320p. 25.00 *(978-0-7603-3433-1(1)*, 0760334331, Voyageur Pr) MBI Publishing Co. LLC.

McMahon, Arlynn. Lesson Plans for Train Like You Fly: A Flight Instructor's Reference for Scenario-Based Training. 2011. (Illus.). 182p. pap. 19.95 *(978-1-56027-789-7(0))* Aviation Supplies & Academics, Inc.

Michaelides-Mateou, Sofia & Mateou, Andreas. Flying in the Face of Criminalization: The Safety Implications of Prosecuting Aviation Professionals for Accidents. 2010. (Illus.). 234p. 99.95 *(978-1-4094-0767-6(5))* Ashgate Publishing Co.

Mills, Stephen E. & Phillips, James Wendell. Sourdough Sky: A Pictorial History of Flights & Flyers in the Bush Country. 2011. 178p. 42.95 ***(978-1-258-05235-5(0))*** Literary Licensing, LLC.

Millward, Liz. Women in British Imperial Airspace: 1922-1937. 2007. (ENG., Illus.). 264p. (C). *(978-0-7735-3337-0(0))* McGill-Queen's Univ. Pr.

Mondor, Colleen. The Map of My Dead Pilots: The Dangerous Game of Flying in Alaska. 2011. (ENG.). 256p. 22.95 *(978-0-7627-7361-9(8)*, Lyons Pr.) Globe Pequot Pr., The.

Moye, J. Todd. Freedom Flyers: The Tuskegee Airmen of World War II. 2012. (Oxford Oral History Ser.). (ENG., Illus.). 256p. pap. 17.95 ***(978-0-19-989655-4(0))*** Oxford Univ. Pr., Inc.

Myers, Roger, et al. Fort Wayne Aviation: Baer Field & Beyond. 2012. (Images of Aviation Ser.). (ENG., Illus.). 128p. pap. 21.99 ***(978-0-7385-8860-5(1))*** Arcadia Publishing.

National Research Council (U.S.), Committee on the Effects of Commuting on Pilot Fatigue Staff, et al, contrib. by. Issues in Commuting & Pilot Fatigue: Interim Report. 2011. ix, 29p. ***(978-0-309-18712-1(5))*** National Academies Pr.

Nesbit, Roy C. Missing: Believed Killed: Amelia Earhart, Amy Johnson, Glenn Miller & the Duke of Kent. 2010. (Illus.). 160p. pap. 24.95 *(978-1-84884-319-6(4))* Pen & Sword Bks. Ltd. GBR. Dist: Casemate Pubs. & Bk. Distributors, LLC.

Newman, Rick & Shepperd, Don. Bury Us Upside Down: The Misty Pilots & the Secret Battle for the Ho Chi Minh Trail. 2007. (ENG., Illus.). 512p. pap. 16.95 *(978-0-345-46538-2(5)*, Presidio Pr.) Random House Publishing Group.

Ostrow, Scott A. Master the Military Flight Aptitude Tests: Targeted Test Prep to Jump-Start Your Career. 7th ed. 2009. (ENG.). 384p. (YA). pap. 24.95 *(978-0-7689-2793-1(5)*, Arco) Peterson's.

Page, Charles. Wings of Destiny: Wing Commander Charles Learmonth DFC & Bar, & the Air War in New Guinea. 2008. (Illus.). 416p. pap. 35.00 *(978-1-877058-64-6(5))* Rosenberg Publishing Pty, Ltd. AUS. Dist: International Specialized Bk. Services.

Penberthy, Ian, ed. To Be a Pilot. 6th ed. 2008. (ENG., Illus.). 176p. pap. 22.95 *(978-1-84797-013-8(3)*, 1847970133) Crowood Pr., Ltd. GBR. Dist: MBI Distribution Services/Quayside Distribution.

Piccard, Bertrand, text. A Trace in the Sky. 2010. (ENG., Illus.). 234p. 24.00 *(978-88-544-0471-7(3))* White Star ITA. Dist: Random Hse., Inc.

Pike, Richard. The Lightning Boys. 2011. (Illus.). 224p. 39.95 ***(978-1-908117-15-1(X))*** Grub Street GBR. Dist: Casemate Pubs. & Bk. Distributors, LLC.

A Pilot's Guide to Safety: How to Avoid Moments of Stark Terror. 2006. per. 17.00 net. *(978-0-934754-13-2(6))* Airguide Pubns., Inc.

Pitchfork, Graham. Men Behind the Medals: A New Selection. 2009. (ENG., Illus.). 288p. pap. 32.95 *(978-0-7524-5027-8(1))* History Pr. Ltd.,The GBR. Dist: Independent Pubs. Group.

Pitchfork, Graham, frwd. The Daily Telegraph Airmen's Obituaries: Book Two. 2007. (Daily Telegraph Obituaries Ser.). 416p. 39.95 *(978-1-904943-83-9(7))* Grub Street GBR. Dist: Casemate Pubs. & Bk. Distributors, LLC.

Provensen, Alice & Provensen, Martin. The Glorious Flight: Across the Channel with Louis Bleriot. 2009. (JPN., Illus.). 40p. (J). *(978-4-7764-0353-1(6))* BL Publishing Co., Ltd.

Race, John T. "Jack". I'll Fly Away: A World War II Pilot's Lifetime of Adventures from Biplanes to Jumbo Jets. 2006. (Illus.). 296p. per. 20.00 *(978-1-58966-113-4(3))* Univ. of Scranton Pr.

Randall, Craig & Penn, Rexford. Crew / Cockpit Resource Management, (CRM) A Guide for Professional Pilots. 2010. 73p. pap. 39.90 *(978-0-557-26985-3(7))* Lulu Enterprises Inc.

Reed, Robert. Lost Black Sheep: The Search for WWII Ace Chris Magee. 2006. pap. 17.95 *(978-1-55571-674-5(1))* L & R Publishing.

Reeves, Richard. Daring Young Men: The Heroism & Triumph of the Berlin Airlift-June 1948-May 1949. 2011. (ENG., Illus.). 336p. pap. 16.00 *(978-1-4165-4120-2(9))* Simon & Schuster.

Regional Air Carriers & Pilot Workforce Issues: Hearing Before the Subcommittee on Aviation of the Committee on Transportation & Infrastructure, House of Representatives, One Hundred Eleventh Congress, First Session, June 11, 2009. 2009. (Illus.). xxiii, 219p. *(978-0-16-084406-5(1)*, 552-070-39948-8) United States Government Printing Office.

Rhodes, Suzanne. Angel Flight Mid-Atlantic. 2008. (Images of Aviation Ser.). (ENG., Illus.). 128p. per. 19.99 *(978-0-7385-5296-5(8))* Arcadia Publishing.

Russell, Peter. Flying in Defiance of the Reich: A Lancaster Pilot's Rites of Passage. 2007. (Illus.). 264p. 39.95 *(978-1-84415-576-7(5))* Pen & Sword Bks. Ltd. GBR. Dist: Casemate Pubs. & Bk. Distributors, LLC.

Semple, Clive & Mawby, Alan. Diary of a Night Bomber in World War I. 2008. (ENG., Illus.). 352p. 39.95 *(978-1-86227-452-5(5))* History Pr. Ltd.,The GBR. Dist: Independent Pubs. Group.

Shuff, Derek. Evader: The Epic Story of the First British Airman to Be Rescued by the Comete Escape Line in World War II. 2007. (ENG.). 192p. pap. 27.95 *(978-1-86227-426-0(2))* History Pr. Ltd.,The GBR. Dist: Independent Pubs. Group.

—Evader: The Epic Story of the First British Airman to Be Rescued by the Comète Escape Line in World War II. 2010. (ENG., Illus.). 240p. pap. 16.95 *(978-0-7524-5748-2(9))* History Pr. Ltd.,The GBR. Dist: Independent Pubs. Group.

Spencer, William. Air Force Records: A Guide for Family Historians. 2nd ed. 2008. (Illus.). 160p. pap. 24.95 *(978-1-905615-25-4(6))* National Archives (PRO), The GBR. Dist: International Publishers Marketing.

Stallman, David A. Women in the Wild Blue... Target-Towing WASP at Camp Davis. Stallman, David A. & Hovey, Carol P., eds. 2010. 244p. 24.50 *(978-0-9708239-3-9(2)*, ECHOES Pr.) Stallman, David A.

Stern, Robert. Fire from Sky. 2010. (Illus.). 0400p. 49.95 *(978-1-59114-267-6(9))* Naval Institute Pr.

Stockdale, Jim & Stockdale, Sybil. In Love & War. 2nd rev. ed. (Illus.). 536p. 27.95 *(978-1-55750-784-6(8))* Naval Institute Pr.

Thorburn, Gordon. No Need to Die: American Flyers in RAF Bomber Command. (ENG., Illus.). 2012. 262p. pap. 14.95 ***(978-0-85733-135-9(3)***, 0857331353) 2009. 256p. 34.95 *(978-1-84425-652-5(9)*, 1844256529) Haynes Publishing PLC GBR. Dist: MBI Distribution Services/Quayside Distribution.

Tise, Larry E. Conquering the Sky: The Secret Flights of the Wright Brothers at Kitty Hawk. 2009. (ENG., Illus.). 256p. 25.00 *(978-0-230-61490-1(6))* Palgrave Macmillan.

Townley, Alvin. Fly Navy: Discovering the Extraordinary People & Enduring Spirit of Naval Aviation. 2011. (ENG., Illus.). 352p. 25.99 *(978-0-312-65084-1(1)*, Dunne, Thomas Bks.) St. Martin's Pr.

Van Wormer, Nicholas. The Ultimate Guide to Air Force Basic Training: Tips, Tricks, & Tactics for Surviving Boot Camp. 2010. (Illus.). 192p. pap. 18.95 *(978-1-932714-92-0(8))* Savas Beatie.

Warham, John. The 49ers: The True Story. 2011. (Illus.). 576p. 37.50 *(978-1-84624-587-9(7))* Book Guild, Ltd. GBR. Dist: Trans-Atlantic Pubns., Inc.

Williams, William A., et al. Preserving Range & Airspace Access for the Air Force Mission: Striving for a Strategic Vantage Point. 2011. (Illus.). 100p. pap. 29.50 *(978-0-8330-5140-0(7))* RAND Corp., The.

Wingfield, William. The Aeromedical Certification Examinations Self-Assessment Test. 2008. 293p. pap. 64.94 *(978-0-615-19124-9(X))* ResO Shop, The.

AIR PILOTS—BIOGRAPHY

Abbott, Ace. The Rogue Aviator: In the Back Alleys of Aviation. 2010. 200p. pap. 14.95 *(978-1-4502-5384-0(9))* iUniverse, Inc.

Abney, Arthur E. Wings over Illinois. 2007. (ENG., Illus.). 272p. 50.00 *(978-0-8093-2768-3(6))* Southern Illinois Univ. Pr.

Adlam, Hank. On & off the Flight Deck: Reflections of a Naval Fighter Pilot in World War II: Book 1: the Years 1941-1948. 2008. (Illus.). 237p. *(978-1-84415-629-0(X))* Pen & Sword Bks. Ltd.

Adventures in Aviation: An Autobiography of Capt. Kimball J. Scribner. 24.95 *(978-1-893358-06-5(2)*, 0082) Scribner & Assocs.

Aldrin, Buzz, Jr. & Abraham, Ken. Magnificent Desolation: The Long Journey Home from the Moon. (ENG., Illus.). 2010. 352p. pap. 16.00 *(978-0-307-46346-3(X)*, Three Rivers Pr.) 2009. 336p. 27.00 *(978-0-307-46345-6(1)*, Harmony) Crown Publishing Group.

Ammerman, Gale. An American Glider Pilot's Story. 2008. 272p. 36.95 *(978-1-4357-4953-5(7))*; pap. 19.95 *(978-1-4357-4952-8(9))* Lulu Enterprises Inc.

Anderson, Rocky. Maximum Risk: True Adventures of a Homeland Security Pilot. 2011. 192p. pap. 16.95 *(978-1-4502-8994-8(0))* iUniverse, Inc.

Armstrong, Jim. From POW to Blue Angel: The Story of Commander Dusty Rhodes. 2006. (ENG., Illus.). 317p. 29.95 *(978-0-8061-3764-3(9))* Univ. of Oklahoma Pr.

Armstrong, Rene' Palmer. Wings & a Ring: Letters of War & Love from a WWII Pilot. 2011. pap. 29.99 ***(978-1-61346-310-9(3))*** Tate Publishing & Enterprises, LLC.

Artzer, Eric. Reach for the Sky: How to Get What You Want in Life. 2009. 128p. pap. 14.99 *(978-1-4490-2928-9(0))* AuthorHouse.

Atkins, Edward. Flight Deck. 2006. 28.00 *(978-0-8059-7303-7(6))* Dorrance Publishing Co., Inc.

Atkins, Edward M. Flight Deck: A Pictorial Essay of a Day in the Life of an Airdale with First-Person Comments by Edward Atkins (Part 1) 2006. 34.00 *(978-0-8059-7302-0(8))* Dorrance Publishing Co., Inc.

Ayres, Travis L. The Bomber Boys: Heroes Who Flew the B-17s in World War II. 2009. (ENG., Illus.). 288p. (gr. 12-18). 16.00 *(978-0-451-22871-0(5)*, N A L Trade) Penguin Group (USA) Inc.

Bagley, Mark B. & Stephens, Marianne. The G Stands for Guts: A Glider Pilot Remembers WWII. 2008. pap. 17.95 *(978-1-55571-657-8(1)*, Hellgate Pr.) L & R Publishing.

Bailey, Charles E. If You Fly Don't Crash! 2009. 108p. pap. 15.99 *(978-1-4415-4162-8(4))* Xlibris Corp.

Bak, Richard. The Big Jump: Lindbergh & the Great Atlantic Air Race. 2011. (ENG., Illus.). 336p. 27.95 *(978-0-471-47752-5(4)*, Wiley) Wiley, John & Sons, Inc.

Balzer, Joseph. Flying Drunk: The True Story of a Northwest Airlines Flight, Three Drunk Pilots, & One Man's Fight for Redemption. 2009. 240p. 25.00 *(978-1-932714-71-5(5))* Savas Beatie.

Baranek, Dave "Bio". Topgun Days: Dogfighting, Cheating Death, & Hollywood Glory as One of America's Best Fighter Jocks. 2010. (ENG., Illus.). 320p. 24.95 *(978-1-61608-005-1(1)*, 608005) Skyhorse Publishing Co., Inc.

Bartlett, Les & Jacobs, Peter. Bomb Aimer over Berlin: The Wartime Memoirs of les Bartlett. 2007. (Illus.). 224p. 39.95 *(978-1-84415-596-5(X))* Pen & Sword Bks. Ltd. GBR. Dist: Casemate Pubs. & Bk. Distributors, LLC.

Behrns, William M. The San Joaquin Siren: An American Ace in WWII's CBI. 2011. (Illus.). 252p. pap. 18.95 ***(978-1-935354-61-1(2))*** Amethyst Moon Publishing and Services.

Beldin, Don. Yours for a Meeting in the Air: Sixty Years with God as My Co-Pilot. 2007. (Illus.). 120p. per. 10.99 *(978-1-60247-002-6(2))* Tate Publishing & Enterprises, LLC.

Belisle, Leonard. Back-N-Forth: Recollections of a Crop Duster BACK-N-FORTH. 2008. 176p. pap. 58.50 *(978-0-615-20758-2(8))* Belisle Communications.

Bernheim, Molly. A Sky of My Own. 2011. 252p. 46.95 ***(978-1-258-01352-3(5))*** Literary Licensing, LLC.

Billberg, Rudy. In the Shadow of Eagles: From Barnstormer to Alaska Bush Pilot, a Pilots Story. 2009. (ENG., Illus.). 352p. pap. 16.95 *(978-0-88240-815-6(1)*, Alaska Northwest Bks.) Graphic Arts Ctr. Publishing Co.

Biographiq. Howard Hughes - from Wealth to Madness. 2008. 68p. pap. 9.99 *(978-1-59986-370-2(7)*, Biographiq) Filiquarian Publishing, LLC.

Black, Dale & Gire, Ken. Flight to Heaven: A Plane Crash... A Lone Survivor... A Journey to Heaven — and Back. 2010. (Illus.). 192p. pap. 14.99 *(978-0-7642-0794-5(6))* Bethany Hse. Pubs.

Blackburn, James. Norman: ... A Most Unforgettable Character. 2007. 52p. per. 16.95 *(978-1-4241-7058-6(3))* PublishAmerica, Inc.

Blacker, Stewart & Blacker, Barnaby. The Adventures & Inventions of Stewart Blacker: Soldier, Aviator, Weapons Inventor: An Autobiography of Lieutenant Colonel L.V.S. Blacker. 2006. (Illus.). 206p. 39.95 *(978-1-84415-431-9(9))* Pen & Sword Bks. Ltd. GBR. Dist: Casemate Pubs. & Bk. Distributors, LLC.

Blackman, Tony. Tony Blackman - Test Pilot: My extraordinary life in Flight. 2009. (Illus.). 224p. 39.95 *(978-1-906502-36-2(6))* Grub Street GBR. Dist: Casemate Pubs. & Bk. Distributors, LLC, Littlehampton Bk Services, Ltd.

Bodding, Gerald A. & Cass, William F. Alaska's Father Goose: Captain Gerald A. "Bud" Bodding: A Career in Aviation. 2010. 176p. pap. 19.95 ***(978-0-88839-651-8(1))*** Hancock Hse. Pubs.

Boomhower, Ray E. Fighter Pilot: The World War II Career of Alex Vraciu. 2010. (Illus.). 170p. *(978-0-87195-282-0(3))* Indiana Historical Society.

Bowen, Thomas. Backcountry Pilot: Flying Adventures with Ike Russell. 2010. (Southwest Center Ser.). (ENG., Illus.). 248p. pap. 19.95 *(978-0-8165-2938-4(8))* Univ. of Arizona Pr.

Bowman, Robert Hal. Memoirs of a Pilot. 2011. 184p. 42.95 ***(978-1-258-02963-0(4))*** Literary Licensing, LLC.

Boyd, James R. Follow the Trend: The Story of a Life & Observations from Living It. 2010. 296p. 25.99 *(978-1-4520-8413-8(0))*; pap. 15.49 *(978-1-4520-8412-1(2))* AuthorHouse.

Braatz, Kurt, ed. My Logbook: Reminiscences 1938-2006. aut. ed. 2007. (Illus.). 373p. *(978-3-9807935-8-2(3)*, TwentynineSix, Editions) NeunundzwanzigSechs Verlag.

Bramson, Alan. Pure Luck: The Authorised Biography of Sir Thomas Sopwith. 2007. (Soft Cover Ser.). (ENG.). 288p. pap. *(978-0-85979-106-9(8)*, 0859791068) Crecy Publishing GBR. Dist: MBI Distribution Services/Quayside Distribution.

Bray, Frank. One Lucky Pilot: My Life in Aviation. 2006. *(978-0-9788283-3-2(X))* Acacia Bks.

Briand Jr., Paul L. Daughter of the Sky: The Story of Amelia Earhart. 2011. 258p. 47.95 ***(978-1-258-07648-1(9))*** Literary Licensing, LLC.

Bridgeman, William & Hazard, Jacqueline. The Lonely Sky: The Personal Story of America's Pioneering Experimental Test Pilot. 2009. (ENG.). 308p. 31.95 *(978-1-4401-5871-1(1))* iUniverse, Inc.

—The Lonely Sky: The Personal Story of America's Pioneering Experimental Test Pilot. 2009. (ENG.). 308p. pap. 21.95 *(978-1-4401-5870-4(3))* iUniverse, Inc.

Bright, Darrell. Growing up with Bob. 2009. 292p. 35.95 *(978-1-60594-051-9(8))*; (ENG.). pap. 17.95 *(978-1-60594-050-2(X))* Aeon Publishing Inc. (Llumina Pr.).

Britten, Michael D. Flights of Inspiration. 2009. (Illus.). 256p. pap. 14.49 *(978-1-4389-5223-9(6))* AuthorHouse.

Broadnax, Samuel L. Blue Skies, Black Wings: African American Pioneers of Aviation. 2008. (ENG., Illus.). 208p. pap. 17.95 *(978-0-8032-1774-4(9)*, Bison Bks.) Univ. of Nebraska Pr.

Bronnenkant, Lance J. The Imperial German Eagles in World War I, Vol. 2. 2008. (Illus.). 400p. bds. 69.95 *(978-0-7643-2928-9(6))* Schiffer Publishing, Ltd.

Broughton, Jack. Rupert Red Two: A Fighter Pilot's Life from Thunderbolts to Thunderchiefs. rev. ed. 2008. (ENG., Illus.). 352p. 26.95 *(978-0-7603-3217-7(7)*, 0760332177, Zenith Pr.) MBI Publishing Co. LLC.

Brown, Bill. Fujiyama Honeymoon. 2007. 208p. 32.50 *(978-1-4251-2711-4(8))* Trafford Publishing.

Brown, Eldon. Controlled Crash: An Airline Odyssey, from Eels & Ethics to Blimps & Drunken Bears. 2009. 148p. 24.95 *(978-1-4401-6032-5(5))*; pap. 14.95 *(978-1-4401-6030-1(9))* iUniverse, Inc.

Brown, Lee Frances. Tuskegee Red Tail Fighter Pilot: Calvin J. Spann. 2009. 232p. 28.95 *(978-1-4401-1789-3(6))*; pap. 18.95 *(978-1-4401-1788-6(8))* iUniverse, Inc.

Brown, N. G. Blue Max: Missions & Memories. 2006. (ENG.). 228p. 19.95 *(978-1-59800-666-7(5))*; per. 13.95 *(978-1-59800-498-4(0))* Outskirts Pr., Inc.

Brumbeloe, Renda. Life at 35,000 Feet. 2010. pap. 16.99 *(978-1-61663-848-1(6))* Tate Publishing & Enterprises, LLC.

Buchner, Hermann. Stormbird. 2009. pap. 18.95 *(978-0-85979-140-3(8))* Crecy Publishing GBR. Dist: Partners Pubs. Group, Inc.

Bullen, Annie & Rivas, Brian. John Derry. 2009. (ENG., Illus.). 224p. 39.95 *(978-1-84425-531-3(X)*, 184425531X) Haynes Publishing PLC GBR. Dist: MBI Distribution Services/Quayside Distribution.

Burgess, Colin. Selecting the Mercury Seven: The Search for America's First Astronauts. 2011. (Springer Praxis Books / Space Exploration Ser.). (ENG., Illus.). xxv, 371p. pap. 44.95 *(978-1-4419-8404-3(6)*, 1441984046) Springer.

Butler, Susan. East to the Dawn: The Life of Amelia Earhart. movie tie-in ed. 2009. (ENG.). 520p. pap. 15.95 *(978-0-306-81837-0(X))* Da Capo Pr., Inc.

Butts, Thomas A. Amazing Benefits in Traveling on Someone Else's Dime. 2010. 134p. pap. 45.07 *(978-1-4269-4224-2(9))* Trafford Publishing.

Bytheway, John. Supersonic Saints 2: More Thrilling Stories from LDS Pilots. 2008. 256p. 21.95 *(978-1-59038-911-9(5))* Deseret Bk. Co.

Caidin, Martin. Thunderbolt! 2007. 232p. (ENG.). 29.95 *(978-1-4344-8411-6(4))*; per. 17.95 *(978-1-4344-8410-9(6))* Wildside Pr., LLC.

Campbell, Robert D. REMINISCENCES of a BIRDMAN: The remarkable story of Earle Lewis Ovington, American pioneer aviator & Inventor. Robbins, Beth Ann, ed. 2009. (ENG., Illus.). 432p. 59.99 *(978-0-615-28188-9(5))* Living History Pr., LLC.

Capron, Freddy. Les Carnets du Major Aviateur Firmin Capon. (Belgique en Guerre Ser.: Tome 1). (FRE., Illus.). 80p. pap. 18.95 *(978-90-72547-68-2(3))* De Krijger BEL. Dist: Casemate Pubs. & Bk. Distributors, LLC.

Carswell, Andrew. Over the Wire: A Canadian Pilot's Memoir of War & Survival as a POW. 2011. (ENG., Illus.). 288p. pap. 22.95 *(978-1-118-10969-4(4))*; 27.95 ***(978-1-118-10968-7(6))*** Wiley, John & Sons, Inc. (Wiley).

Casey, Aloysius G. & Casey, Patrick. Velocity: Speed with Direction: The Professional Career of Gen Jerome F. O'Malley. 2007. (Illus.). x, 286p. *(978-1-58566-169-5(4))* Air University Pr.

Celis, Peter. One Who Almost Made It Back: The Remarkable Story of One of World War Two's Unsung Heroes, Sqn Ldr Edward Teddy Blenkinsop, DFC, CdeG (Belge), RCAF. 2008. (Illus.). 224p. 42.95 *(978-1-906502-16-4(1))* Grub Street GBR. Dist: Casemate Pubs. & Bk. Distributors, LLC.

Chapman, Dick. The Story of a Canadian in Aviation: From 1934 To 2009. 2010. 268p. pap. 17.95 *(978-1-4269-2702-7(9))* Trafford Publishing.

Cherry, Dan. My Enemy My Friend. Erickson, Fran, ed. 2009. 80p. 20.00 *(978-0-692-00007-6(0))* Aviation Heritage Park, Inc.

Clouddancer. Clouddancer's Alaskan Chronicles: The Tragedies. 2010. 164p. pap. 15.95 *(978-1-4502-0911-3(4))* iUniverse, Inc.

Coggins, Patrick C. Tuskegee Airman Fighter Pilot: A Story of an Original Tuskegee Pilot Lt. Col. Hiram E. Mann. 2008. 272p. pap. 25.94 *(978-1-4251-4732-7(1))* Trafford Publishing.

Connor, Don W. The Sting of Flight. 2006. (Illus.). 220p. pap. *(978-1-84401-671-6(4))* Athena Pr.

Conrad, Klaus. Canadian Escapades - Kanadische Eskapaden: The true story of the author's 3 escapes from WW2 POW Camps. Franck, Maximilian & Lawton, Scott S., trs. 2009. (ENG & GER., Illus.). 132p. pap. 12.95 *(978-0-9843271-0-2(X))* Germancosm.

Cook, David G. Flying from My Mind. 2007. (Illus.). 256p. 39.95 *(978-1-84415-588-0(9))* Pen & Sword Bks. Ltd. GBR. Dist: Casemate Pubs. & Bk. Distributors, LLC.

Cooper, Ann L. Stars of the Sky, Legends All: Illustrated Histories of Women Aviation Pioneers. 2008. *(978-0-7603-3375-4(0))* MBI Publishing Co. LLC.

Corbin, Jimmy. Last of the Ten Fighter Boys. 2010. (ENG., Illus.). 252p. pap. 18.95 *(978-0-7524-5643-0(1))* History Pr. Ltd.,The GBR. Dist: Independent Pubs. Group.

—Last of the Ten Fighter Boys. 2007. (ENG., Illus.). 256p. 44.95 *(978-0-7509-4805-0(1))* Sutton Publishing.

Covington, William R. War Is Not All Hell: The Story of Comraderie & Friendship Born in Times of War. 2010. 148p. pap. 14.95 *(978-1-4502-3352-1(X))* iUniverse, Inc.

Crean, Thomas. Lieutenant der Reserve Werner Voss & the Pilots of Jasta 10. 2010. 478p. pap. 113.95 *(978-1-4327-4873-9(4))* Outskirts Pr., Inc.

Cross, James U., et al. Around the World with LBJ: My Wild Ride as Air Force One Pilot, White House Aide, & Personal Confidant. 2008. (ENG., Illus.). 218p. 26.95 *(978-0-292-71768-8(7))* Univ. of Texas Pr.

Crummett, Major Richard M. & Crummett, Richard M. Above the Clouds: Memoirs of a B-26 Marauder Pilot. Crummett, Cheryl, ed. 2011. 144p. ***(978-1-77067-291-8(5))***; pap. ***(978-1-77067-292-5(3))*** FriesenPress.

Culver, Kelley. What a Long Strange Trip It's Been. 2006. 352p. pap. 29.95 *(978-1-4241-4151-7(6))* PublishAmerica, Inc.

Daniel, Larry G. They Gave Me Wings. 2009. 292p. 29.99 *(978-1-4415-4300-4(7))*; pap. 19.99 *(978-1-4415-4299-1(X))* Xlibris Corp.

Davies, Richard Bell. Sailor in the Air. 2010. (Illus.). 264p. pap. 19.95 *(978-1-84832-011-6(6))* Pen & Sword Bks. Ltd. GBR. Dist: Casemate Pubs. & Bk. Distributors, LLC.

Davis, Larry. 4th Fighter Group in World War II. 2007. (Illus.). 79p. *(978-0-89747-515-0(1))* Squadron Signal Pubns.

DeBlanc, Jefferson J. The Guadalcanal Air War: Col. Jefferson Deblanc's Story, 1 vol. 2008. (ENG., Illus.). 216p. 24.95 *(978-1-58980-587-3(9))* Pelican Publishing Co., Inc.

Deeter, Robert. Bullseye: Journal of a Black Hawk Pilot. 2009. (ENG.). 192p. 25.99 *(978-1-4490-1463-6(1))*; (ENG.). 192p. pap. 16.99 *(978-1-4490-1462-9(3))*; (Illus.). xii, 176p. *(978-1-4490-1464-3(X))* AuthorHouse.

Denard, James Mitchel. Tally Ho! Friend or Foe: There's Something about a Fighter Pilot. 2011. pap. 19.95 *(978-0-533-16354-0(4))* Vantage Pr., Inc.

Derado, R. Before & Beyond: WW II P-Shooters in North Africa. 2010. (Illus.). 157p. 17.00 *(978-1-4251-1828-0(3))* Trafford Publishing.

Desaulniers, Abel. In Love with Wings: The Story of A Barnstorming Pilot. 2011. 78p. 37.95 ***(978-1-258-08858-3(4))*** Literary Licensing, LLC.

Dick, Ron & Patterson, Dan. 50 Aircraft That Changed the World. 2010. (ENG., Illus.). 208p. pap. 29.95 *(978-1-55407-658-1(7))* Boston Mills Pr. CAN. Dist: Firefly Bks., Ltd.

Donald, Graeme Vivian. Without Fear. 2007. 380p. per. *(978-1-84401-996-0(9))* Athena Pr.

Dorr, Robert F. Mission to Berlin: The American Airmen Who Struck the Heart of Hitler's Reich. 2011. (ENG., Illus.). 336p. 28.00 *(978-0-7603-3898-8(1)*, 0760338981, Zenith Pr.) MBI Publishing Co. LLC.

Doty Jr., Arch. The Diary of a Pilot. 2007. 148p. pap. 13.95 *(978-1-60145-260-3(8))* Booklocker.com, Inc.

Dousset, Ray. Rotor in the Green. 2007. 408p. per. 21.99 *(978-1-60266-316-9(5))* Xulon Pr., Inc.

Doyle, James M. Flying Through Time: A Journey into History in a World War II Biplane. 2008. (ENG.). 282p. pap. 19.00 *(978-1-4223-9553-0(7))* DIANE Publishing Co.

Doylerush, Edward. Rocks in the Clouds: High-Ground Aircraft Crashes of South Wales. 2010. (ENG., Illus.). 112p. pap. 21.95 *(978-1-85780-281-8(0))* Allan, Ian Publishing GBR. Dist: BookMasters Distribution Services (BDS).

Drabier, Jacques & Anomdeplume, J. War Pilot Memoirs: A Mirror On 1939. 2010. 262p. pap. 20.00 *(978-1-881276-13-5(9))* Serey/Jones Pubs.

Driggs, Laurence La Tourette. The High Aces: French, American, British, Italian & Belgian Pilots of the First World War 1914-18. 2010. 280p. *(978-1-84677-956-5(1))*; pap. *(978-1-84677-955-8(3))* Leonaur Ltd.

Drucker, Graham. Wings over the Waves: The Biography & Letters of Lieut. Com. Roy Baker-Falkner DSO DSC RN. 2010. (Illus.). 256p. 50.00 *(978-1-84884-305-9(4))* Pen & Sword Bks. Ltd. GBR. Dist: Casemate Pubs. & Bk. Distributors, LLC.

Duddridge, Lew. The Flying Duddridges of Hanley. 2011. 320p. 29.11 ***(978-1-4269-6654-5(7))***; pap. 19.11 ***(978-1-4269-6653-8(9))*** Trafford Publishing.

Dundas, Hugh. Flying Start. 2011. (Illus.). 224p. pap. 24.95 ***(978-1-84884-442-1(5))*** Pen & Sword Bks. Ltd. GBR. Dist: Casemate Pubs. & Bk. Distributors, LLC.

Durrett, Deanne. Unsung Heroes of World War II: The Story of the Navajo Code Talkers. 2009. (ENG., Illus.). 144p. pap. 14.95 *(978-0-8032-2456-8(7)*, Bison Bks.) Univ. of Nebraska Pr.

Dye, Robert. A Pioneer in Aviation: The Life Story of Brice H. Goldsborough & His Contribution to Aviation Instrumentation. 2011. 240p. 25.95 ***(978-1-4620-2169-7(7))***; pap. 15.95 ***(978-1-4620-2167-3(0))*** iUniverse, Inc.

Eads, Bill. When Flying Was Fun an Autobiographical. 2007. 392p. 29.95 *(978-1-4241-6407-3(9))* PublishAmerica, Inc.

Edgerton, Clyde & Edgerton, Clyde. Solo: My Adventures in the Air. 2006. (ENG., Illus.). 288p. pap. 12.95 *(978-1-56512-546-9(0)*, 1565125460, Shannon Ravenel Bks.) Algonquin Bks. of Chapel Hill.

Edris, Pete & Reid, Raymond. Dying for Another Day. 2010. 104p. pap. 19.95 *(978-1-4520-2300-7(X))* AuthorHouse.

Edwards, Goronwy 'Gron'. Flying to Norway, Grounded in Burma: A Hudson Pilot in World War II. 2009. (Illus.). 208p. 39.99 *(978-1-84415-809-6(8))* Pen & Sword Bks. Ltd. GBR. Dist: Casemate Pubs. & Bk. Distributors, LLC.

Edwards, John Carver. Orville's Aviators: Outstanding Alumni of the Wright Flying School, 1910-1916. 2009. (ENG., Illus.). 195p. pap. 45.00 *(978-0-7864-4227-0(1))* McFarland & Co., Inc. Pubs.

Eeles, Group Tom. A Passion for Flying: 8,000 hours of RAF Flying. 2008. (Illus.). 256p. 39.95 *(978-1-84415-688-7(5))* Pen & Sword Bks. Ltd. GBR. Dist: Casemate Pubs. & Bk. Distributors, LLC.

Eggspuehler, Don. Star Benchwarmers: A Family Memoir. 2011. 336p. pap. 17.99 *(978-1-4520-8310-0(X))* AuthorHouse.

Ehlinger, Dolcie. S. & Ehlinger, Karen G. Letters from my Son: A Texas Boy's Journey to the R. A. F. 2011. (ENG., Illus.). 288p. pap. 22.95 *(978-1-884820-04-5(2))* SAFE GOODS/ATN Publishing.

Elwell, Mary Ellen. With No Extraordinary Power: A Social Worker's Life. 2007. 240p. per. 19.95 net. *(978-0-9742773-5-6(5))* Soleil Pr.

Enrique "Blyhe" Horta. Confessions & Memoirs of an Airline Pilot. 2009. 300p. 25.99 *(978-1-4389-2814-2(9))*; pap. 15.49 *(978-1-4389-2815-9(7))* AuthorHouse.

Erickson, George. Back to the Barrens: On the Wing with Da Vinci & Friends. 2007. (ENG.). 352p. pap. 17.95 *(978-0-88839-642-6(2))* Hancock Hse. Pubs.

Evans, Harvey. From Fox Moths to Jet Rangers: A Bush Pilot's Life. 2009. (ENG., Illus.). 272p. pap. 26.95 *(978-1-55017-463-2(0))* Harbour Publishing Co., Ltd. CAN. Dist: Ingram Pub. Services.

Farmer, Andrew Hollinger. Finding the Way: The Story of a Combat Navigator in World War II. 2nd ed. 2006. (Illus.). viii, 235p. 18.95 *(978-0-9744960-1-6(4))* Farmer, Andrew.

Fisher, Clayton E. Hocked: Tails & Adventures of a TAILHOOK WARRIOR. 2009. (Illus.). 245p. 29.95 *(978-1-4327-3911-9(5))*; pap. 15.95 *(978-1-4327-2279-1(4))* Outskirts Pr., Inc.

Flying Through History. 2010. pap. 14.95 *(978-0-7414-5919-0(1))* Infinity Publishing.

Fogg, Richard & Fogg, Janet. Fogg in the Cockpit: Master Railroad Artist, World War II Fighter Ace. 2011. (Illus.). 256p. 32.95 *(978-1-61200-004-6(5))* Casemate Pubs. & Bk. Distributors, LLC.

Follis, Thomas K. He Wore a Pair of Silver Wings. 2008. 254p. 36.95 *(978-1-4357-5497-3(2))* Lulu Enterprises Inc.

Ford, Dale C. My Two Hot Wars & One Cold War. 2011. pap. 11.99 ***(978-1-61777-153-8(8))*** Tate Publishing & Enterprises, LLC.

Ford, Kenneth W. In Love with Flying. 2007. (Illus.). 240p. 21.95 *(978-0-9794104-0-6(1))*; pap. 14.95 *(978-0-9794104-1-3(X))* H Bar Pr.

Forrester, Larry. Skymen: Heroes of Fifty Years of Flying. 2009. 270p. 42.95 *(978-1-104-84114-0(2))* 2007. (ENG.). 268p. per. 27.95 *(978-0-548-38895-2(4))* Kessinger Publishing, LLC.

Fortuna, David & Burnett, Evelyn. You Betcha, Baby! The Legend of Aviator Vincent "Squeek" Burnett. 2008. (Illus.). ix, 228p. pap. *(978-0-9789337-5-3(3))* Pine Haven Pr., Inc.

Foster, Gary. Phantom in the River: Flight of Linfield Two Zero One. 2010. 175p. pap. 19.95 *(978-1-55571-664-6(4)*, Hellgate Pr.) L & R Publishing.

Foster, R. W. & Franks, Norman. Tally Ho! From the Battle of Britain to the Defence of Darwin. 2008. (Illus.). 224p. 39.95 *(978-1-906502-26-3(9))* Grub Street GBR. Dist: Casemate Pubs. & Bk. Distributors, LLC.

Foutch, Paul. The Show Is on the Podium: The 20th Century Life of Dr. Mark R. Foutch-Eye Doctor, Aviator, Bandleader. 2007. 296p. per. 27.95 *(978-1-4241-6872-9(4))* PublishAmerica, Inc.

Franks, Norman & Saunders, Andy. Mannock: The Life & Death of Major Edward Mannock VC, DSO, MC, RAF. 2008. (Illus.). 192p. 45.00 *(978-1-906502-12-6(9))* Grub Street GBR. Dist: Casemate Pubs. & Bk. Distributors, LLC.

Franzak, Michael. A Nightmare's Prayer: A Marine Harrier Pilot's War in Afghanistan. 2011. (ENG., Illus.). 432p. mass mkt. 7.99 *(978-1-4516-0807-6(1))* Pocket Books.

—A Nightmare's Prayer: A Marine Harrier Pilot's War in Afghanistan. 2010. (ENG., Illus.). 304p. 26.00 *(978-1-4391-9498-0(X)*, Threshold Editions) Threshold Editions.

Frater, Stephen. Hell above Earth: The Incredible True Story of an American WWII Bomber Commander & the Copilot Ordered to Kill Him. 2012. (ENG., Illus.). 320p. 25.99 ***(978-0-312-61792-9(5))*** St. Martin's Pr.

Frilling, Christoph. Elly Beinhorn und Bernd Rosemeyer - Kleiner Grenzverkehr zwischen Resistenz und Kumpanei im Nationalsozialismus: Studien zu Habitus und Sprache prominenter Mitläufer. 2009. (GER.). 478p. pap. 107.95 *(978-3-631-58836-9(4))* Lang, Peter GmbH, Europaischer Verlag der Wissenschaften DEU. Dist: Lang, Peter.

Gagliardi Kindlimann, Oscar Gregorio. Jorge Chávez Dartnell: Centenario de la Hazaña Del Cruce de Los Alpes (1910 - 2010) 2010. (SPA., Illus.). 171p. *(978-9972-210-89-1(8))* Universidad Alas Peruanas.

Gamble, Bruce. Fortress Rabaul: The Battle for the Southwest Pacific, January 1942-April 1943. 2010. (ENG., Illus.). 416p. 28.00 *(978-0-7603-2350-2(X)*, 076032350X, Zenith Pr.) MBI Publishing Co. LLC.

Geere, Stacy T. Lucky Me: The Life & Flights of Veteran Aviator Clay Lacy. 2010. *(978-1-57864-635-7(9))* Donning Co. Pubs.

Giesemann, Suzanne. Living a Dream: A Journey from Aide to the Chairman of the Joint Chiefs of Staff on 9/11 to Full-Time Cruiser. 2008. (Illus.). 300p. pap. 14.95 *(978-0-939837-80-9(3))* Paradise Cay Pubns.

Giffords, Gabrielle & Kelly, Mark. Gabby: A Story of Courage & Hope. 2011. (ENG.). 320p. 26.99 ***(978-1-4516-6106-4(1)***, Scribner) Scribner.

Giffords, Gabrielle & Kelly, Mark E. Gabby: A Story of Courage & Hope. 2012. (ENG., Illus.). 320p. pap. 16.00 ***(978-1-4516-6107-1(X)***, Scribner) Scribner.

Giffords, Gabrielle, et al. Gabby: A Story of Courage & Hope. 2011. ***(978-1-4104-4538-4(0))*** 2012. (ENG.). pap. 16.99 ***(978-1-59413-564-4(9)***, Large Print Pr.) Thorndike Pr.

Gimmi, Russell M. Airman: The Life of Richard F. B. Gimmi. 2009. 398p. 35.95 *(978-1-4401-5313-6(2))*; pap. 25.95 *(978-1-4401-5311-2(6))* iUniverse, Inc.

Girard, Jerry. Checkride: This Pilot's Life. 2011. 496p. 30.79 ***(978-1-4634-2606-4(2))***; pap. 21.00 ***(978-1-4634-2607-1(0))*** AuthorHouse.

Girard, June. Turbulence: Life in the Friendly Skies. 2009. 180p. pap. 14.49 *(978-1-4389-7261-9(X))* AuthorHouse.

Goldstein, Donald M. & Dillon, Katherine V. Amelia: A Life of the Aviation Legend. 2007. (Potomac's Paperback Classics Ser.). (Illus.). 352p. per. 9.95 *(978-1-59797-095-2(6))* Potomac Bks., Inc.

González, Alejandro Roque. Born Motherland or Death. 2012. (ENG.). 300p. pap. 15.99 ***(978-1-4636-5986-8(5))*** CreateSpace.

Gordon Holborn Scott (Usaf, Ret.). My Incredible Journey: A Quest to Conquer the U. S. A. as an 80 Year Old Fighter Pilot. 2011. 256p. 29.99 ***(978-1-4500-8459-8(1))***; pap. 19.99 ***(978-1-4500-8458-1(3))*** Xlibris Corp.

Gordon, Joseph Furbee. Flying Low: And shot down twice during World War II in a spotter Plane. 2006. (Illus.). 224p. pap. 20.00 *(978-0-913337-62-2(5))* Southfarm Pr.

Goyer, Robert, ed. I Learned about Flying from That, Volume 4: First-Hand Accounts of Mishaps to Avoid from Real-Life Pilots. 2007. (I Learned about Flying from That Ser.). (ENG., Illus.). 272p. 18.95 *(978-1-933231-24-2(6))* Filipacchi Publishingsan.

Griffin, John C. Lt. Bill Farrow: Doolittle Raider, 1 vol. 2006. (ENG., Illus.). 272p. 24.95 *(978-1-58980-422-7(8))* Pelican Publishing Co., Inc.

Gross, Malvern. Nine Lives: Adventures of a Lucky Pilot. 2009. (ENG., Illus.). 520p. *(978-0-9760328-4-7(8))* Island In The Sky Publishing Co.

Gross, Malvern J. Nine Lives: Adventures of a Lucky Pilot. 2009. (Illus.). 510p. pap. 19.95 *(978-0-9760328-0-9(5))* Island In The Sky Publishing Co.

Gully, Patti. Sisters of Heaven: China's Barnstorming Aviatrixes: Modernity, Feminism, & Popular Imagination in Asia & the West. 2007. (ENG., Illus.). 448p. per. 24.95 *(978-1-59265-075-0(9))* Long River Pr.

Guth, Gilberta. The Fighter Pilot's Wife: A Military Family's Story. 2006. (Illus.). 376p. per. 19.95 *(978-0-9768678-0-7(X))* Call Sign Pr.

Guy, Sallie. Flying Without Wings: The Story of Carroll Guy - A World War II Bomber Pilot. 2008. 116p. per. 14.95 *(978-1-59858-496-7(0))* Dog Ear Publishing, LLC.

Haakonsen, Ray. An Arrested Heart. 2010. 264p. 29.99 *(978-1-4500-7919-8(9))*; pap. 19.99 *(978-1-4500-7918-1(0))* Xlibris Corp.

Hadley, Peter E. Wings of the Tern: A Flyers Odyssey. 2010. (Illus.). 599p. pap. 22.95 *(978-1-4327-5093-0(3))* Outskirts Pr., Inc.

Halliburton, Richard. The Flying Carpet: Adventures in a Biplane from Timbuktu to Everest & Beyond. 2012. (ENG.). 264p. 17.00 ***(978-1-84885-914-2(7)***, Tauris Parke Paperbacks) I. B. Tauris & Co., Ltd. GBR. Dist: Macmillan.

Hang, Nguyen Minh. Bright Moon. 2006. 239p. pap. 14.95 *(978-0-7414-3597-2(7))* Infinity Publishing.

Harris, Randy. Two Million Five Hundred Thousand Miles Later: To the Moon & Back Five Times. 2007. 52p. per. 16.95 *(978-1-4241-9109-3(2))* PublishAmerica, Inc.

Harwood, Craig S. & Fogel, Gary. Quest for Flight: John J. Montgomery & the Dawn of Aviation in the West. 2012. ***(978-0-8061-4264-7(2))*** Univ. of Oklahoma Pr.

Haun, James Robert, Jr., ed. & prologue by. Spitfire Wingman from Tennessee: My love affair with Flight 2006. Orig. Title: Who Says There Are No Old, Bold, Pilots?! (Illus.). 224p. per. 14.95 *(978-0-9790002-0-1(3))* Stormwatch Pr.

Hawkridge, Audrey and John. To Win or Lose It All. 2008. 224p. pap. 18.95 *(978-1-84799-587-2(X))* Lulu Enterprises Inc.

Haynes, Gerald. My War: With True Rescue Stories. 2007. 80p. per. 16.95 *(978-1-4241-6784-5(1))* PublishAmerica, Inc.

Heartlines Publishing Group. Touch the Sky: ... the story of a Mom, a Wife, an Arishow Pilot & Wingrider. 2010. 19.95 *(978-0-615-38594-5(X))* Heartlines Publishing Group.

Hellman, William. A Pilot's Tale - Flying Helicopters in Vietnam. 2008. 324p. pap. 26.51 *(978-1-4357-1185-3(8))* Lulu Enterprises Inc.

Heimann, Judith M. The Airmen & the Headhunters: A True Story of Lost Soldiers, Heroic Tribesmen & the Unlikeliest Rescue of World War II. 2007. (ENG., Illus.). 304p. 26.00 *(978-0-15-101434-7(5))* Houghton Mifflin Harcourt Trade & Reference Pubs.

Heinrich, Durwood J. Attack Out of the Sun: Lessons from the Red Baron for Our Business & Personal Lives. 2010. 344p. 33.95 *(978-1-4502-5741-1(0))*; pap. 23.95 *(978-1-4502-5740-4(2))* iUniverse, Inc.

Henshaw, Alex. The Flight of the Mew Gull: Record-Breaking Flying in the 1930s. 2008. (ENG., Illus.). 272p. pap. 24.95 *(978-1-84037-021-8(1)*, 1840370211) Crowood Pr., Ltd. GBR. Dist: MBI Distribution Services/Quayside Distribution.

Higgs, Geoffrey. Front-Line & Experimental Flying with the Fleet Air Arm. 2010. (Illus.). 208p. 39.95 *(978-1-84884-262-5(7))* Pen & Sword Bks. Ltd. GBR. Dist: Casemate Pubs. & Bk. Distributors, LLC.

Higston, Michael. Renegade Hero. 2011. (Illus.). 256p. 39.95 ***(978-1-84884-530-5(8))*** Pen & Sword Bks. Ltd. GBR. Dist: Casemate Pubs. & Bk. Distributors, LLC.

Hildebrandt, Erik. Front Row Center 4: Inside the Great American Air Show. 2009. (ENG.). 172p. 39.95 *(978-0-9674040-7-3(X)*, 096740407X) Cleared Hot Media.

Holmes, Bob. The Pilotless Plane, 1 vol. 2009. 76p. pap. 16.95 *(978-1-60836-371-1(6))* PublishAmerica, Inc.

Hooper, Jim. A Hundred Feet over Hell: Flying with the Men of the 220th Recon Airplane Company over I Corps & the DMZ, Vietnam 1968-1969. 2009. (ENG., Illus.). 272p. 25.00 *(978-0-7603-3633-5(4)*, 0760336334, Zenith Pr.) MBI Publishing Co. LLC.

Horrigan, Kenneth V. Coffin Corner: The True Story of Kenneth Horrigan, World War II POW in Stalag 17B. 2010. 152p. 26.50 *(978-1-60911-011-6(0)*, Eloquent Bks.) AEG Literary Publishing Services, Inc.

Hudlow, Rick. Shamrock 22: An Aviator's StoryD. 2011. 428p. 31.99 ***(978-1-4670-2810-3(X))***; pap. 23.95 ***(978-1-4670-2811-0(8))*** AuthorHouse.

Hutchison, Sheryl L. Mentor Inbound: The Authorized Biography of Fred J. Ascani, Major General, USAF Retired. 2009. 280p. pap. 20.95 *(978-1-4389-9974-6(7))* AuthorHouse.

Jackson, Joe. Atlantic Fever: Lindbergh, His Competitors, & the Race to Cross the Atlantic, 1 vol. 2012. (ENG., Illus.). 544p. 30.00 ***(978-0-374-10675-1(4))*** Farrar, Straus & Giroux.

Jackson, Mike & Dixon-Engel, Tara. Naked in Da Nang: A Forward Air Controller in Vietnam. 2010. (ENG., Illus.). 304p. pap. 17.99 *(978-0-7603-3916-9(3)*, 0760339163, Zenith Pr.) MBI Publishing Co. LLC.

Jackson, Robert. Men of Power: The Lives of Rolls-Royce Chief Test Pilots Harvey & Jim Heyworth. 2007. (Illus.). 192p. 39.95 *(978-1-84415-427-2(0))* Pen & Sword Bks. Ltd. GBR. Dist: Casemate Pubs. & Bk. Distributors, LLC.

Jakust, Carl. Doing My Share. 2009. *(978-0-9814539-7-2(X))* Lifetime Chronicle Pr.

Jared, Edmond F. One Hell of a Ride: A Memoir. 2008. 184p. 24.95 *(978-0-9822726-0-2(X))* Interview You, LLC.

Jarrett, Philip. Frank Mcclean: The Godfather of British Naval Aviation. 2011. (Illus.). 192p. 50.00 ***(978-1-84832-109-0(0))*** Pen & Sword Bks. Ltd. GBR. Dist: Casemate Pubs. & Bk. Distributors, LLC.

Jaycox, R. A. A Love Story Good Grief. 2010. 108p. pap. 12.95 *(978-1-4502-4441-1(6))* iUniverse, Inc.

Jefford, Jack. Winging It! Jack Jefford, Pioneer Alaskan Aviator. 2nd ed. 2011. (Caribou Classics Ser.). (ENG., Illus.). 320p. pap. 18.95 *(978-0-88240-816-3(X)*, Alaska Northwest Bks.) Graphic Arts Ctr. Publishing Co.

Jerry Lemieux. One Bird Strike & You're Out! Solutions to Prevent Bird Strikes. 2009. 400p. pap. 19.43 *(978-1-4269-2085-1(7))* Trafford Publishing.

Johnson, Amy. Sky Roads of the World - Amy Johnson's Story about Her Adventurous Flying Career. 2009. 316p. pap. *(978-1-906393-18-2(4))* Trotamundas Pr., Ltd.

Johnson, Eddella. I'm Coming Home. 2010. 188p. pap. 20.00 *(978-1-4251-6856-8(6))* Trafford Publishing.

Johnson, Joe. The Lonely Hours. 2010. 120p. 29.95 *(978-0-557-38699-4(3))* Lulu Enterprises Inc.

Jones, Ira. King of Airfighters. 2008. (Illus.). 256p. 29.95 *(978-1-932033-99-1(8))* Casemate Pubs. & Bk. Distributors, LLC.

Karram, Kerry. Four Degrees Celsius: A Story of Arctic Peril. 2012. (ENG., Illus.). 224p. pap. 22.99 ***(978-1-4597-0051-2(1))*** Natural Heritage/Natural History, Inc. CAN. Dist: Ingram Pub. Services.

Keefe, Howie. Galloping on Wings with the P-51 Mustang Miss America: Diary of an Air Race Pilot. 2007. (ENG., Illus.). 370p. per. 19.95 *(978-1-56027-643-2(6))* Aviation Supplies & Academics, Inc.

Keeffe, James H., III. Two Gold Coins & a Prayer: The Epic Journey of a World War II Bomber Pilot & POW. 2010. (ENG., Illus.). 500p. (gr. 9). pap. 24.95 *(978-0-9843600-0-0(X))* Appell Publishing.

Keller, Keith. Zella's Story. 2010. 304p. *(978-1-926582-52-8(7))*; pap. *(978-1-926582-51-1(9))* Insomniac Pr.

Kelly, Terence. Hurricanes Versus Zeros: Air Battles over Java, Sumatra, & Singapore. 2008. (Illus.). 205p. *(978-1-84415-622-1(2))* Pen & Sword Bks. Ltd.

Kerns, Raymond C. Above the Thunder: Reminiscences of a Field ARtillery Pilot in World War II. 2008. (Illus.). 192p. 24.95 *(978-0-87338-980-8(8))* Kent State Univ. Pr.

Kessner, Thomas. The Flight of the Century: Charles Lindbergh & the Rise of American Aviation. (Pivotal Moments in American History Ser.). (ENG., Illus.). 2012. 336p. pap. 17.95 ***(978-0-19-993117-0(8))*** 2010. 432p. 27.95 *(978-0-19-532019-0(0))* Oxford Univ. Pr., Inc.

Kidston, Martin J. Cromwell Dixon: A Boy & His Plane 1892-1911. 2007. (ENG., Illus.). 168p. per. 14.95 *(978-1-56037-473-2(X))* Farcountry Pr.

King, James Gore. Attending Alaska's Birds: A Wildlife Pilot's Story. 2nd ed. 2010. (Illus.). 474p. pap. 29.95 ***(978-0-88839-656-3(2))*** Hancock Hse. Pubs.

Kittinger, Joe & Ryan, Craig. Come up & Get Me: An Autobiography of Colonel Joe Kittinger. 2011. (ENG., Illus.). 272p. pap. 21.95 *(978-0-8263-4804-3(1))* Univ. of New Mexico Pr.

Kline, Bob. Fasten Your Seatbelt: A Pilot's Memoir. 2008. (Illus.). 368p. pap. 19.95 *(978-0-615-18835-5(4))* Blue Yonder Publishing.

Knight, Bliss. Air Affair. 2008. 392p. pap. 17.99 *(978-1-4389-0270-8(0))* AuthorHouse.

Knight, Max E. Spinning Through Clouds: Tales of an Early Hoosier Aviator. 2007. *(978-0-87195-256-1(4))* Indiana Historical Society.

Knudsen, John James. Off I Went into the Wild Blue Yonder, 1 vol. 2007. (ENG., Illus.). 336p. 24.95 *(978-1-58980-494-4(5))* Pelican Publishing Co., Inc.

Kotler, Alvin E. & Flynn, Jack. We Came to Fight a Warkotler & Flynn. 2009. 148p. 34.95 *(978-0-557-04925-7(3))* Lulu Enterprises Inc.

Ksiazek-Polensky, Henryk. Escape into the Unknown. 2009. 170p. pap. 9.99 *(978-1-935383-52-9(3))* Raider Publishing International.

Kuntz, Jerry. A Pair of Shootists: The Wild West Story of S. F. Cody & Maud Lee. 2010. (ENG.). 224p. (C). 29.95 *(978-0-8061-4149-7(2))* Univ. of Oklahoma Pr.

Kuwahara, Yasuo & Allred, Gordon T. Kamikaze: A Japanese Pilot's Own Spectacular Story of the Famous Suicide Squadrons. 7th ed. 2007. (ENG.). 272p. pap. 16.95 *(978-0-9761547-5-4(7))* American Legacy Media.

Langione, Jon. Bipolar Passages. 2011. 266p. pap. 27.95 ***(978-1-4560-0739-3(4))*** PublishAmerica, Inc.

Launay, Françoise. The Astronomer Jules Janssen: A Globetrotter of Celestial Physics. 2011. (Astrophysics & Space Science Library). (ENG., Illus.). xxix, 220p. 129.00 ***(978-1-4614-0696-9(X)***, 146140696X) Springer.

Layton, Andrew. Wolverines in the Sky. 2007. 172p. per. 13.99 *(978-1-60266-389-3(0))* Xulon Pr., Inc.

Layton, Howard M. Love & Sand. 2008. 24.00 *(978-0-9676008-5-7(5))* Three Spires Publishing.

Leininger, Bruce & Leininger, Andrea. Soul Survivor: The Reincarnation of a World War II Fighter Pilot. 2010. (ENG., Illus.). 272p. pap. 13.99 *(978-0-446-50934-3(5))* Grand Central Publishing.

Lennon, Patrick Anthony. Tony. Metzroth, Almut, ed. 2008. 316p. pap. 17.95 *(978-0-9814956-0-6(5))* Fiction Publishing, Inc.

Lester, Jean, told to. Jorgy: The Life of Native Alaskan Bush Pilot & Airline Captain Holger Jorgy Jorgensen. 2008. (Illus.). 280p. pap. *(978-0-9749221-5-7(3))* Ester Republic Pr.

Levine, Joshua. Fighter Heroes of WWI: The Extraordinary Story of the Pioneering Airmen of the Great War. 2009. (ENG., Illus.). 384p. pap. 15.95 *(978-0-00-727494-9(7))* HarperCollins Pubs. Ltd. GBR. Dist: Independent Pubs. Group.

Levy, Harry. The Dark Side of the Sky. 2007. (Illus.). 220p. per. *(978-1-905006-62-5(4))* London Pr., The.

Lewis Cooper, Ann. Stars of the Sky, Legends All: Illustrated Histories of Women Aviation Pioneers. 2008. (ENG., Illus.). 160p. pap. 24.95 *(978-0-7603-3374-7(2),* 0760333742, Zenith Pr.) MBI Publishing Co. LLC.

Lewis, Julian. Racing Ace: The Fights & Flights of 'Kink' Kinkead DSO, DSC*, DFC* 2011. (Illus.). 288p. 39.95 *(978-1-84884-216-8(3))* Pen & Sword Bks. Ltd. GBR. Dist: Casemate Pubs. & Bk. Distributors, LLC.

Lewis, W. David. Eddie Rickenbacker: An American Hero in the Twentieth Century. 2008. (ENG., Illus.). 720p. pap. 31.00 *(978-0-8018-8972-1(3))* Johns Hopkins Univ. Pr.

Lindbergh, Reeve. Under a Wing. 2009. (ENG., Illus.). 224p. pap. 14.00 *(978-1-4391-4883-9(X))* Simon & Schuster.

Logan, Edward F., Jr. Jump, Damn It, Jump! Memoir of a Downed B-17 Pilot in World War II. 2006. (ENG., Illus.). 244p. per. 29.95 *(978-0-7864-2572-3(5))* McFarland & Co., Inc. Pubs.

Lord, Brigadier Dick. From Tailhooker to Mudmover: An Aviation Career in the Royal Naval Fleet Air Arm, United States Navy, & South African Air Force. 2010. 360p. pap. 29.95 *(978-0-620-30762-8(5))* 30° South Pubs. ZAF. Dist: International Publishers Marketing.

Lovell, Mary S. Straight on till Morning: The Life of Beryl Markham. 2011. (ENG., Illus.). 421p. pap. 15.95 *(978-0-393-33915-4(7),* 33915) Norton, W. W. & Co., Inc.

Lundquist, Wayne. Len, the Pilot. 2011. 524p. 34.99 ***(978-1-4628-5611-4(X))***; pap. 23.99 ***(978-1-4628-5610-7(1))*** Xlibris Corp.

Lussier, Betty. Intrepid Woman: Betty Lussier's Secret War, 1942-1945. 2010. (Illus.). 221p. 34.95 *(978-1-59114-449-6(3))* Naval Institute Pr.

Lynch, Brendan. Yesterday We Were in America: Alcock & Brown - First to Fly the Atlantic Non-Stop. 2009. (ENG., Illus.). 256p. 39.95 *(978-1-84425-681-5(2),* 1844256812) Haynes Publishing PLC GBR. Dist: MBI Distribution Services/Quayside Distribution.

Maccarron, Donal. Letters from an Early Bird: The Life & Letters of Aviation Pioneer Denys Corbett Wilson 1882-1915. 2006. (Illus.). 176p. 39.95 *(978-1-84415-382-4(7))* Pen & Sword Bks. Ltd. GBR. Dist: Casemate Pubs. & Bk. Distributors, LLC.

MacDonell, Donald. From Dogfight to Diplomacy: A Spitfire Pilot's Log 1932-1958. MacDonell, Lois & Mackay, Anne, eds. 2009. (Illus.). 352p. pap. 29.95 *(978-1-84884-198-7(1))* Pen & Sword Bks. Ltd. GBR. Dist: Casemate Pubs. & Bk. Distributors, LLC.

MacKay, Ron. The 31st Fighter Group in World War II. 2007. (Illus.). 80p. pap. *(978-0-89747-514-3(3))* Squadron Signal Pubns.

Mackenzie, S. P. Bader's War: 'Have a Go at Everything' 2008. (ENG., Illus.). 192p. 42.95 *(978-1-86227-467-9(3))* History Pr. Ltd.,The GBR. Dist: Independent Pubs. Group.

Macksey, Kenneth. Kesselring: The Making of the Luftwaffe. 2012. (Illus.). 256p. pap. 24.95 ***(978-1-84832-649-1(1),*** Frontline) Pen & Sword Bks. Ltd. GBR. Dist: Casemate Pubs. & Bk. Distributors, LLC.

Magrady, Charles A. Charlie's Way: Teacher & Pilot - The Rest of the Story. 2008. 158p. pap. 24.95 *(978-1-60703-770-5(X))* PublishAmerica, Inc.

Magruder, Kevin M. Portrait of a Pilot: The Memoirs of Dr. Eugene R. Magruder, Col. , USAF, Ret. 2007. per. *(978-1-59872-972-6(1))* Instant Pub.

Mahurin, Walker Bud. Honest John: The Autobiography of Walker M. Mahurin. 2011. 312p. 50.95 ***(978-1-258-00641-9(3))*** Literary Licensing, LLC.

Manion, Gene. Flying on the Edge. 2011. 384p. 29.99 ***(978-1-4568-4058-7(4))***; pap. 19.99 ***(978-1-4568-4057-0(6))*** Xlibris Corp.

Manthos, Jeff Lee. Steel Beach: My Life as a Naval Aircrewman 1972-1976. 2007. (ENG.). 336p. pap. 17.95 *(978-1-59299-261-4(7))* Inkwater Pr.

Markman, Steven R. Out of the Blue: Curbing Crises, Circumventing the System, & Keeping My Pants on in Russia: Memoirs of a Baffled Bureaucrat. 2007. (ENG.). 284p. pap. 18.95 *(978-1-59663-552-4(5),* Seaboard Pr.) Rock, James A. & Co. Pubs.

Marrett, George J. Howard Hughes: Aviator. (Illus.). 288p. 27.95 *(978-1-59114-510-3(4))* Naval Institute Pr.

—Testing Death: Hughes Aircraft Test Pilots & Cold War Weaponry. 2008. (Illus.). 228p. pap. *(978-1-59114-512-7(0))* Naval Institute Pr.

Martin, Barry S. Forgotten Aviator: The Adventures of Royal Leonard. 2011. 256p. pap. 15.95 ***(978-1-60844-929-3(7))*** Dog Ear Publishing, LLC.

Martin, Edward Trueblood. I Flew Them Home: A Pilot's Story of the Yemenite Airlift. 2011. 64p. 36.95 ***(978-1-258-07649-8(7))*** Literary Licensing, LLC.

Martin, Matt J. & Sasser, Charles W. Predator: The Remote-Control Air War over Iraq & Afghanistan: A Pilot's Story. 2010. (ENG., Illus.). 320p. 28.00 *(978-0-7603-3896-4(5),* 0760338965, Zenith Pr.) MBI Publishing Co. LLC.

Matthews, Hart. Pioneer Aviators of the World: A Biographical Dictionary of the First Pilots of 100 Countries. alt. ed. 2008. (ENG., Illus.). 216p. pap. 39.95 *(978-0-7864-3880-8(0))* McFarland & Co., Inc. Pubs.

Mawer, Allen. Diary of a Spitfire Pilot: Over the English Channel & over Darwin. 2011. (Illus.). 224p. pap. 29.95 *(978-1-921719-18-9(4))* Rosenberg Publishing Pty, Ltd. AUS. Dist: International Specialized Bk. Services.

McCarthy, Bob. Hell at 30,000 Feet: The World War II Experiences of Pittsburgh Lieutenant Fran Goldcamp as a B-24 Bomber Copilot over Europe. 2006. 55p. pap. 16.95 *(978-1-4241-0579-3(X))* PublishAmerica, Inc.

McCarthy Jr., Donald J. Those Who Were There: Ninety-Two True Stories of Combat Missions Flown over North Vietnam. 2009. 392p. pap. 35.95 *(978-1-4401-3129-5(5))* iUniverse, Inc.

McCarville, Mary Michele. American Doctor. 2009. 145p. pap. 23.76 *(978-0-578-00813-4(0))* McCarville, Mary Michele.

McDonough, James L. The Wars of Myron King: A B-17 Pilot Faces WWII & U.S.-Soviet Intrigue. 2009. (ENG.). 32.95 *(978-1-57233-675-9(7))* Univ. of Tennessee Pr.

McGhie, Bruce. Ascent: How One Quadriplegic Fought for a Full Life & Soared. 2007. (ENG., Illus.). 336p. 29.95 *(978-1-932646-28-3(0))* Ruder-Finn Pr.

McKenzie, Dave. The Spirit's Journey. 2011. 424p. 36.95 *(978-1-4502-7220-9(7))*; pap. 26.95 *(978-1-4502-7221-6(5))* iUniverse, Inc.

McMahon, Bryan. Ascend or Die: Richard Crosbie: Pioneer of Balloon Flights. 2012. (ENG., Illus.). 256p. pap. 19.95 ***(978-1-84588-985-2(1))*** History Pr. Ltd.,The GBR. Dist: Independent Pubs. Group.

Meek, Donald J. Seven War Stories. 2011. 120p. pap. 12.95 *(978-1-4269-5457-3(3))* Trafford Publishing.

Meilinger, Phillip S. Hubert R. Harmon: Airman, Officer, Father of the Air Force Academy. 2009. (ENG., Illus.). 374p. 35.00 *(978-1-56373-184-6(3))* Fulcrum Publishing.

Mejía, Libardo Aldana. AK-47: Intriga Internacional. 2006. (SPA., Illus.). 200p. per. 20.00 *(978-1-4251-0423-8(1))* Trafford Publishing.

Melinsky, Hugh. Forming the Pathfinders: The Career of Air Vice-Marshal Sydney Bufton. 2010. (ENG., Illus.). 192p. pap. 24.95 *(978-0-7524-5453-5(6))* History Pr. Ltd.,The GBR. Dist: Independent Pubs. Group.

Merry, Lois K. Women Military Pilots of World War II: A History with Biographies of American, British, Russian & German Aviators. 2010. (ENG., Illus.). 220p. pap. 35.00 *(978-0-7864-4441-0(X))* McFarland & Co., Inc. Pubs.

Miller, Charles Vernon. Smooth Sailing, a Glider Pilot Memoir. 2008. 148p. pap. 12.95 *(978-0-9818683-3-2(9))* Peppertree Pr., The.

Miller, Hank. The Admiral's Son. 2007. 381p. pap. 23.50 *(978-0-615-16505-9(2))* Miller, Hank.

Millman, Nicholas. Ki-44 'Tojo' Aces of World War 2. 2011. (Aircraft of the Aces Ser.). (ENG., Illus.). 96p. pap. 22.95 *(978-1-84908-440-6(8))* Osprey Publishing, Ltd. GBR. Dist: Random Hse., Inc.

Minnesota Marine Air Reserve Staff, contrib. by. Marine Wings: Stories of War & Peace As Written by the Pilots. 2007. (Illus.). 380p. *(978-1-930374-25-6(9))* DeForest Pr.

Modleski, Matthew. The American Dream & What We Must Do to Secure Our Children's Dreams. 2011. 116p. pap. 12.95 ***(978-1-4575-0366-5(2))*** Dog Ear Publishing, LLC.

Morgan, Robert, Usaft & Powers, Ron. The Man Who Flew the Memphis Belle: Memoir of a WWII Bomber Pilot. 2011. (ENG.). 400p. (gr. 12). 15.00 *(978-0-451-23352-3(2),* N A L Trade) Penguin Group (USA) Inc.

Moseley, Willie G. Smoke Jumper, Moon Pilot: The Remarkable Life of Apollo 14 Astronaut Stuart A. Roosa. 2011. ***(978-1-935001-76-8(0))*** Acclaim Pr., Inc.

Moye, J. Todd. Freedom Flyers: The Tuskegee Airmen of World War II, 1 vol. 2010. (Oxford Oral History Ser.). (ENG., Illus.). 256p. 24.95 *(978-0-19-538655-4(8))* Oxford Univ. Pr., Inc.

Mrazek, Robert J. To Kingdom Come: An Epic Saga of Survival in the Air War over Germany. (ENG.). 400p. (gr. 12). 2012. 16.00 ***(978-0-451-23575-6(4),*** N A L Trade) 2011. 25.95 *(978-0-451-23227-4(5),* N A L Hardcover) Penguin Group (USA) Inc.

Murphy, Tom. Reclaiming the Sky: 9/11 & the Untold Story of the Men & Women Who Kept America Flying. 2006. (ENG., Illus.). 224p. 21.95 *(978-0-8144-0909-1(1))* Amacom.

My Navy! 2009. (Illus.). 184p. pap. 12.95 *(978-0-9768545-5-5(4))* Patmos Publishing.

Nelson, Dick. The Contrail Chronicles: An American Family's Journey through War & Peace. 2010. 307p. pap. 23.95 *(978-1-4327-5504-1(8))* Outskirts Pr., Inc.

Newton, James. Armed Action. 2007. (ENG., Illus.). 352p. pap. 12.95 *(978-0-7553-1603-8(7))* Headline Bk. Publishing GBR. Dist: Independent Pubs. Group.

—Armed Action: My War in the Skies with 847 Naval Air Squadron. 2007. (ENG., Illus.). 352p. 35.00 *(978-0-7553-1601-4(0))* Headline Bk. Publishing GBR. Dist: Independent Pubs. Group.

Noecker, Jeff. Callsign: Spectre. 2011. 180p. 26.95 ***(978-1-4620-0483-6(0))***; pap. 16.95 ***(978-1-4620-0482-9(2))*** iUniverse, Inc.

O'Connor, William B. Stealth Fighter: A Year in the Life of an F-117 Pilot. 2012. (ENG., Illus.). 424p. 30.00 ***(978-0-7603-4135-3(4),*** 0760341354, Zenith Pr.) MBI Publishing Co. LLC.

Okerstrom, Dennis R. The Final Mission of Bottoms Up: A World War II Pilot's Story. 2011. (ENG., Illus.). 272p. (gr. 9). 29.95 *(978-0-8262-1948-0(9))* Univ. of Missouri Pr.

Okpe, August. The Last Flight: A Pilot Remembers the Air Force & the Biafran Air Attacks. 2011. 620p. (ENG.). 36.95 *(978-1-4327-6340-4(7))*; pap. 32.95 *(978-1-4327-1102-3(4))* Outskirts Pr., Inc.

Oleson, James A. In Their Own Words - the Final Chapter: True Stories from American Fighter Aces. 2011. 224p. 28.95 *(978-1-4502-9044-9(2))*; pap. 18.95 *(978-1-4502-9045-6(0))* iUniverse, Inc.

Oliver, Ron. Mock Two. 2010. 176p. 24.23 *(978-1-4269-2222-0(1))*; (ENG.). pap. 14.23 *(978-1-4269-2221-3(3))* Trafford Publishing.

Olsen, W. Scott. Hard Air: Adventures from the Edge of Flying. 2008. (ENG., Illus.). 246p. pap. 19.95 *(978-0-8032-1144-5(9),* Bison Bks.) Univ. of Nebraska Pr.

—Never Land: Adventures, Wonder, & One World Record in a Very Small Plane. 2010. (ENG., Illus.). 202p. 24.95 *(978-0-8032-1750-8(1))* Univ. of Nebraska Pr.

O'Mahony, Charles. The Widow Maker. 2010. 81p. pap. 25.95 *(978-1-4327-5455-6(6))* Outskirts Pr., Inc.

Orange, Vincent. Slessor: Bomber Champion - The Life of Marshal of the Royal Air Force Sir John Slessor, GCB, DSO, MC. 2006. (Illus.). 296p. 39.95 *(978-1-904943-57-0(8))* Grub Street GBR. Dist: Casemate Pubs. & Bk. Distributors, LLC.

Ostrye, Norbert. Memoir Pilot Duty Wwii & Beyond. 2006. (Illus.). 213p. 28.00 *(978-1-4122-0208-4(6))* Trafford Publishing.

Otstot, Eric F. Balls O' Fire: The Story of Lt. Kenneth Otstot, a B-242 Pilot with the 5th Bomber 'Barons' Group in the South Pacific During World War II. (Illus.). 157p. pap. 9.95 *(978-0-9718644-0-5(3))* Otstot, Eric F.

Ottaway, Susan. Dambuster: A Life of Guy Gibson, VC, DSO*, DFC. 2007. (Illus.). 196p. per. 24.95 *(978-1-84415-605-4(2))* Pen & Sword Bks. Ltd. GBR. Dist: Casemate Pubs. & Bk. Distributors, LLC.

Palmer, Kel. A Roving Commission. 2011. 556p. 38.95 *(978-1-4502-8084-6(6))*; pap. 28.95 *(978-1-4502-8083-9(8))* iUniverse, Inc.

Parnell, Ben. Air Commandos: The Only Full Account of the Top Secret Special Operations War in Europe During World War II. 2007. 320p. pap. 7.99 *(978-0-7434-9823-4(2))* ibooks, Inc.

Peden, Buck. Baseball, Golf, Wars, Women & Puppies: An Autobiography. 2011. 336p. pap. 28.30 ***(978-1-4567-5844-8(6))*** AuthorHouse.

Pengelly, Colin. Albert Ball VC: The Fighter Pilot Hero of World War I. 2010. (Illus.). 208p. 39.95 *(978-1-84415-904-8(3))* Pen & Sword Bks. Ltd. GBR. Dist: Casemate Pubs. & Bk. Distributors, LLC.

Petter-Bowyer, P. J. H. Winds of Destruction: The Autobiography of a Rhodesian Combat Pilot. 2008. 392p. pap. 35.95 *(978-0-9548490-3-0(5))* 30° South Pubs. ZAF. Dist: International Publishers Marketing.

Pierrot, James R. Beyond Dodge Road: Fighting the Odds & Finding Success. 2011. pap. 12.99 *(978-1-61739-053-1(4))* Tate Publishing & Enterprises, LLC.

Pinson, Lynn R. Butch. Goin' up & Lookin' Down: The Book about Flying, Airplanes, Pilots, Airports, Plane people, & Plane Stuff. 2007. 224p. per. 18.95 *(978-0-595-47685-5(6))* iUniverse, Inc.

Pipes, Robert F. The Playboy Crew 1943-1944 Memoirs of World War II: The Men of B-24 Liberator 41-29399. 2010. 115p. 21.95 *(978-1-4327-5851-6(9))*; (ENG., Illus.). pap. 9.95 *(978-1-4327-5849-3(7))* Outskirts Pr., Inc.

Pisanos, Steve N. The Flying Greek: An Immigrant Fighter Ace's WWII Odyssey with the RAF, USAAF, & French Resistance. 2008. (Illus.). 280p. 34.95 *(978-1-59797-078-5(6))* Potomac Bks., Inc.

Pitt, Steve. Day of the Flying Fox: The True Story of World War II Pilot Charley Fox. 2008. (ENG.). 152p. (YA). (gr. 4). pap. 19.99 *(978-1-55002-808-9(1),* Sandcastle Bks.) Dundurn CAN. Dist: Ingram Pub. Services.

Pogue, William R. But for the Grace of God: An Autobiography of an Aviator & Astronaut. 2011. 338p. pap. 35.00 *(978-0-9814756-6-0(3))* Soar With Eagles.

Pook, Jerry. Flying Freestyle: An RAF Fast Jet Pilot's Story. 2009. (Illus.). 224p. 39.99 *(978-1-84415-824-9(1))* Pen & Sword Bks. Ltd. GBR. Dist: Casemate Pubs. & Bk. Distributors, LLC.

Powell, James Garland. Of Dreams & Coveralls: Daring to Become an Airline Pilot despite the Opposition & Challenges. 2009. 180p. 26.95 *(978-0-595-51715-2(3))*; pap. 16.95 *(978-0-595-52316-0(1))* iUniverse, Inc.

Pumroy, Fredrick L. Born to Live on the Edge. 2006. (Illus.). 105p. pap. 17.99 *(978-1-4120-9055-1(5))* Trafford Publishing.

Queiroz, Manuel. Chasing the Morning Sun. 2011. (Illus.). 160p. 35.00 ***(978-1-908117-09-0(5))*** Grub Street GBR. Dist: Casemate Pubs. & Bk. Distributors, LLC.

Rafford, Paul, Jr. Amelia Earhart's Radio. 2006. (Illus.). 134p. per. 25.00 *(978-1-891030-35-2(3))* Paragon Agency, The.

Rajlich, Jiri. Hurricane Ace Josef Frantisek. 2010. (Illus.). 120p. pap. 24.00 *(978-83-89450-71-5(2))* Stratus, Wydawnictwo, Juszczak, Artur POL. Dist: Casemate Pubs. & Bk. Distributors, LLC.

Ralpapajan. Half a Century in Uniform. 2008. 242p. 46.50 *(978-1-4092-0847-1(8))* Lulu Enterprises Inc.

Reed, Jim. Turning Final, A Life Complete. 2011. 228p. 25.86 *(978-1-4269-6322-3(X))*; pap. 15.86 *(978-1-4269-6319-3(X))* Trafford Publishing.

Reed, Robert T. & Dickinson, Constance C. Lost Black Sheep: The Search for World War II Ace Chris Magee. 2006. 252p. pap. 17.95 *(978-1-55571-647-9(4),* Hellgate Pr.) L & R Publishing.

Rees, Billy. The Sun Does Not Rise in the East. 2008. 264p. 29.95 *(978-1-4251-5109-6(4))* Trafford Publishing.

Reeves, Richard. Daring Young Men: The Heroism & Triumph of the Berlin Airlift, June 1948- May 1949. 2010. (ENG., Illus.). 336p. 28.00 *(978-1-4165-4119-6(5))* Simon & Schuster.

Rehr, Louis S. & Rehr, Carleton R. Marauder: Memoir of a B-26 Pilot in Europe in World War II. alt. l.t. ed. 2009. (ENG.). 353p. pap. 39.95 *(978-0-7864-4367-3(7))* McFarland & Co., Inc. Pubs.

Reitsch, Hanna. The Sky My Kingdom. 2008. 256p. 29.95 *(978-1-932033-97-7(1))* Casemate Pubs. & Bk. Distributors, LLC.

Reshetnikov, Vasily, et al. Bomber Pilot on the Eastern Front: 307 Missions Behind Enemy Lines. 2008. (Illus.). 224p. 39.95 *(978-1-84415-660-3(5))* Pen & Sword Bks. Ltd. GBR. Dist: Casemate Pubs. & Bk. Distributors, LLC.

Revell, Alex. Fighter Aces! the Constable Maxwell Brothers: Fighter Pilots in Two World Wars. 2010. (Illus.). 256p. 39.95 *(978-1-84884-177-2(9))* Pen & Sword Bks. Ltd. GBR. Dist: Casemate Pubs. & Bk. Distributors, LLC.

Reyher, Charles R. Memoirs of a B-29 Pilot. 2008. 228p. pap. 19.95 *(978-1-4357-1508-0(X))*; (Illus.). 34.95 *(978-1-4357-1509-7(8))* Lulu Enterprises Inc.

Reynolds, Steven Craig. Where Do We Get Such Men: The Story of One Such Man. 2009. 252p. 24.99 *(978-1-4389-9299-0(8))* AuthorHouse.

Rich, Doris L. Jackie Cochran: Pilot in the Fastest Lane. 2010. (ENG.). 288p. pap. 24.95 *(978-0-8130-3506-2(6))* Univ. Pr. of Florida.

Rickman, Sarah Byrn. Nancy Batson Crews: Alabama's First Lady of Flight. 2nd ed. 2009. (Alabama Fire Ant Ser.). (ENG., Illus.). 230p. pap. 24.95 *(978-0-8173-5553-1(7))* Univ. of Alabama Pr.

—Nancy Love & the WASP Ferry Pilots of World War II. 2008. (North Texas Military Biography & Memoir Ser.). (ENG., Illus.). 352p. 24.95 *(978-1-57441-241-3(8))* Univ. of North Texas Pr.

Riedel, Jay E. Memories of a Fighter Pilot. 2010. 340p. pap. 24.95 *(978-0-557-38608-6(X))* Lulu Enterprises Inc.

Rines, S. Melvin. Winging Through Wall Street. 2011. 324p. 29.99 ***(978-1-4568-0044-4(2))***; pap. 19.99 ***(978-1-4568-0043-7(4))*** Xlibris Corp.

Rioni, Al. All Time High: A Pilot's Memoirs. 2007. (Illus.). 300p. per. 15.95 *(978-0-9748065-2-5(8))* Rioni, Al.

—Wings & Things: True Flying Stories. 2007. (Illus.). 305p. per. 15.95 *(978-0-9748065-5-6(2))* Rioni, Al.

Rippon, Anton. Gunther Plüschow: Airmen, Escaper & Explorer. 2009. (Illus.). 208p. 39.95 *(978-1-84884-132-1(9))* Pen & Sword Bks. Ltd. GBR. Dist: Casemate Pubs. & Bk. Distributors, LLC.

Roberts, Geo. Impact! 2010. 288p. 26.99 *(978-1-61579-525-3(1))*; pap. 16.99 *(978-1-61579-311-2(9))* Xulon Pr., Inc.

Robertson, Gordon Bennett, Jr. Bringing the Thunder: The Missions of a World War II B-29 Pilot in the Pacific. 2006. (Stackpole Military History Ser.). (ENG., Illus.). 279p. per. 19.95 *(978-0-8117-3333-5(5))* Stackpole Bks.

Robson, Richard. An Airman of the Queen, My Lads. 2010. (Illus.). 256p. pap. *(978-0-7552-1218-7(5))* Authors OnLine, Ltd.

Roesler, Alan Louis. An Arizona Aviator in France: The Life of Ernest A. Love, 147th Aero Squadron, USAS. 2007. 300p. *(978-0-9797919-0-1(1))* Roesler Enterprises Inc.

Rosenberg, Barry & Macaulay, Catherine. Mavericks of the Sky: The First Daring Pilots of the U. S. Air Mail. 2007. (ENG., Illus.). 368p. per. 14.95 *(978-0-06-052950-5(4),* HarperPerennial) HarperCollins Pubs.

Ross, Hamish. Freedom in the Air: A Czech Flyer & His Aircrew Dog. 2007. (Illus.). 227p. 39.95 *(978-1-84415-590-3(0))* Pen & Sword Bks. Ltd. GBR. Dist: Casemate Pubs. & Bk. Distributors, LLC.

Rovetto, Katy. Flying High: Soaring above the Tragedies of Life. 2009. pap. 14.99 *(978-1-60696-307-4(4))* Tate Publishing & Enterprises, LLC.

Rowley, Richard. An Airman's Odyssey: An Air Force Memoir. 2009. 180p. 24.99 *(978-1-4389-5134-8(5))*; pap. 15.99 *(978-1-4389-5133-1(7))* AuthorHouse.

Runways in the Sand: The History of Blythe Army Air Base in World War II. 2008. (Illus.). 128p. 21.95 *(978-0-615-21889-2(X))* Wilson, Art.

Runyon, Damon & Kiernan, Walter. The Life Story of Eddie Rickenbacker. Saxon, Charles D., ed. 2011. 38p. 35.95 ***(978-1-258-01185-7(9))*** Literary Licensing, LLC.

Sage, E. Helene. The Clay Pigeons: A B-17 Pilot's Story of World War II. 2011. (Illus.). 160p. 35.00 ***(978-0-7643-3951-6(6),*** Schiffer Publishing Ltd) Schiffer Publishing, Ltd.

Saint-Exupéry, Antoine de. Flight to Arras. 2007. 260p. per. *(978-1-4067-0579-9(9))* Read Bks.

—Wind, Sand & Stars. Date not set. 250p. 22.95 *(978-0-8488-2596-6(9))* Amereon LTD.

Samuel, Wolfgang W. E. Coming to Colorado: A Young Immigrant's Journey to Become an American Flyer. 2006. (ENG., Illus.). 336p. 30.00 *(978-1-57806-902-6(5))* Univ. Pr. of Mississippi.

—I Always Wanted to Fly: America's Cold War Airmen. 2011. (ENG.). 384p. pap. 25.00 *(978-1-61703-170-0(4))* Univ. Pr. of Mississippi.

Sanner, George Bernard. Your Dreams Can Fly!, 1 vol. 2010. 236p. pap. 24.95 *(978-1-4512-9055-4(1))* PublishAmerica, Inc.

Saunders, Andy. Finding the Few: Some Outstanding Mysteries of the Battle of Britain Investigated & Solved. 2009. (Illus.). 192p. 39.95 *(978-1-906502-55-3(2))* Grub Street GBR. Dist: Casemate Pubs. & Bk. Distributors, LLC.

Schnitzer, George. Panthers over Kore. 2007. 304p. per. 29.95 *(978-1-4241-7942-8(4))* PublishAmerica, Inc.

Sears, David. Such Men as These: The Story of the Navy Pilots Who Flew the Deadly Skies over Korea. 2011. (ENG., Illus.). 432p. pap. 18.00 *(978-0-306-82010-6(2))* Da Capo Pr., Inc.

Sherman, Janann. Walking on Air: The Aerial Adventures of Phoebe Omlie. 2011. (Willie Morris Books in Memoir & Biography Ser.). (ENG., Illus.). 196p. 30.00 *(978-1-61703-124-3(0))* Univ. Pr. of Mississippi.

Shipman, John. One of 'the Few' The Memoirs of Wing Commander Ted 'shippy' Shipman AFC. 2008. (Illus.). 256p. 39.95 *(978-1-84415-687-0(7))* Pen & Sword Bks. Ltd. GBR. Dist: Casemate Pubs. & Bk. Distributors, LLC.

Shouse, Jim. Tale of an Old, Bold Pilot. 2011. 112p. pap. 12.95 *(978-1-4502-8739-5(5))* iUniverse, Inc.

Shrum, Clyde. Five Seconds to Live Two Seconds to Die. 2007. 87p. pap. 16.95 *(978-1-4241-5799-0(4))* PublishAmerica, Inc.

Simon, Anna & Hampton, Ann. Kimberley's Flight. 2012. (Illus.). 304p. 29.95 *(978-1-61200-102-9(5)*, Casemate) Casemate Pubs. & Bk. Distributors, LLC.
Sinko, Benjamin A. Echoes of the Dominator. 2007. 154p. pap. 19.95 *(978-0-615-15898-3(6))* Up North Pr.
Skelton, Dane. Jungle Flight: Spiritual Adventures at the Ends of the Earth. 2009. 104p. pap. 10.99 *(978-1-60791-922-3(2))* Xulon Pr., Inc.
Slaker, Kenneth Hawk. A Military Pilot's Exciting Life & Visit from the Hereafter. 2008. (Illus.). 328p. 39.95 *(978-1-57197-489-1(X)*, Ivy House Publishing Group) Pentland Pr., Inc.
Sloan, Raymond. Ray's Story: An Autobiography. 2006. pap. 15.00 *(978-0-938728-19-1(9))* Collage Bks Inc.
Smith, David S. Lifting the Silence: A World War II RCAF Bomber Pilot Reunites with His Past. 2010. (ENG., Illus.). 248p. pap. 27.99 *(978-1-55488-774-3(7))* Dundurn CAN. Dist: Ingram Pub. Services.
Smith, Graham. Heroes of Bomber Command: Suffolk. 2008. (Heroes of Bomber Command Ser.). (Illus.). 192p. (C). pap. 29.95 *(978-1-84674-103-6(3))* Countryside Bks. GBR. Dist: Brown, David Bk. Co., The.
Smith, Richard K. & Hall, R. Cargill. Five Down, No Glory: Frank G. Tinker, Merenary Ace in the Spanish Civil War. 2011. (Illus.). 385p. 36.95 ***(978-1-61251-054-5(X))*** Naval Institute Pr.
Smith, Robin G. & Clark, James A. A Paid Vacation: Every Pilot's Dream. 2007. 84p. per. 10.00 *(978-1-4257-5356-6(6))* Xlibris Corp.
Smith, Rod. The Spitfire Smiths: A Unique Story of Brothers in Arms. 2008. (Illus.). 224p. 45.00 *(978-1-906502-11-9(0))* Grub Street GBR. Dist: Casemate Pubs. & Bk. Distributors, LLC.
Smoke in the Cockpit: The Flying Adventures of Don Smokey Patry. 2006. (Illus.). 118p. per. *(978-1-897126-07-3(7))* NeWest Pubs., Ltd.
Soucie, David & Cheek, Ozzie. Why Planes Crash: An Accident Investigator Fights for Safe Skies. 2011. (ENG., Illus.). 240p. 24.95 *(978-1-61608-426-4(X)*, 608426) Skyhorse Publishing Co., Inc.
Spector, Iftach. Loud & Clear: The Memoir of an Israeli Fighter Pilot. 2009. (ENG., Illus.). 432p. 30.00 *(978-0-7603-3630-4(X)*, 076033630X, Zenith Pr.) MBI Publishing Co. LLC.
Sprekelmeyer, Linda. These We Honor: The International Aerospace Hall of Fame. 2006. (Illus.). 78p. *(978-1-57864-397-4(X))* Donning Co. Pubs.
Stevens, Steve. Beaufighter over the Balkans: From the Balkan Air Force to the Berlin Airlift. 2007. (Illus.). 204p. 39.95 *(978-1-84415-487-6(4))* Pen & Sword Bks. Ltd. GBR. Dist: Casemate Pubs. & Bk. Distributors, LLC.
Stever, Rex H. How the Lord Smiled on Me During World War II. 2011. (Illus.). 73p. ***(978-0-9658719-3-8(2))*** Stever, Rex H.
Stills, Jim. God Protects the Ignorant... Sometimes: The Memoirs of One Pilot's Journey - Missions in Vietnam, Iran, & on Rescue Missions. 2007. (ENG.). 188p. per. 18.00 *(978-1-933580-33-3(X))* Fifth Estate, Inc.
Strebe, Amy Goodpaster. Flying for Her Country: The American & Soviet Women Military Pilots of World War II. 2009. (Illus.). 146p. pap. 15.95 *(978-1-59797-266-6(5))* Potomac Bks., Inc.
Sullenberger, Chesley B. Highest Duty: My Search for What Really Matters. 2009. (ENG.). 64.99 *(978-1-61587-522-1(0))* Findaway World, LLC.
Sullenberger, Chesley B. & Zaslow, Jeffrey. Highest Duty: My Search for What Really Matters. 2010. (ENG., Illus.). 368p. pap. 15.99 *(978-0-06-192469-9(5)*, William Morrow Paperbacks) 2009. (ENG., Illus.). 352p. 25.99 *(978-0-06-192468-2(7)*, Morrow, William & Co.) 2009. 424p. pap. 25.99 *(978-0-06-192758-4(9)*, HarperLuxe) HarperCollins Pubs.
Sweetman, John. Cavalry of the Clouds: Air War over Europe, 1914-1918. 2010. (ENG.). 224p. 37.95 *(978-0-7524-5503-7(6))* History Pr. Ltd.,The GBR. Dist: Independent Pubs. Group.
Taliaferro, Margaret. A Reckless Grace. 2008. 112p. 24.48 *(978-1-4357-0955-3(1))* Lulu Enterprises Inc.
Tate, Robert. Hans-Joachim Marseille: An Illustrated Tribute to the Luftwaffe's Star of Africa. 2008. (Illus.). 224p. bds. 49.95 *(978-0-7643-2940-1(5))* Schiffer Publishing, Ltd.
Ted Beaudoin. Pilot of Fortune. 2009. 344p. 28.99 *(978-1-4269-2231-2(0))*; pap. 18.99 *(978-1-4269-2230-5(2))* Trafford Publishing.
Terpening, Rex. Bent Props & Blow Pots. unabr. ed. 2006. (ENG., Illus.). 338p. pap. 24.95 *(978-1-55017-381-9(2))* Harbour Publishing Co., Ltd. CAN. Dist: Ingram Pub. Services.
Thomas, Cynda & Thomas, Velvet. Hell of a Ride: A First Person Biography of the 'Gutsy' Test Pilot, Richard G. 'Dick' Thomas, Notorious for His Bold, Daring & Dashing Flight Test Escapades. 2008. 232p. pap. 18.95 *(978-0-595-52878-3(3))* iUniverse, Inc.
Thomas, Harold Eugene. Pilot with a Purpose. 2011. 206p. 29.99 ***(978-1-4535-5402-9(5))***; pap. 19.99 ***(978-1-4535-5401-2(7))*** Xlibris Corp.
Thomas, Nick. RAF Top Gun: The Story of Battle of Britain Ace & World Air Speed Holder Air Cdre E. M. "Teddy" Donaldson CB, CBE, DSO, AFC*, LoM (USA) 2008. (Illus.). 256p. 39.95 *(978-1-84415-685-6(0))* Pen & Sword Bks. Ltd. GBR. Dist: Casemate Pubs. & Bk. Distributors, LLC.
Thompson, Ken. Memoirs of A Wwii Fighter Pilot & Some Modern Political Commentary. 2011. 84p. pap. 8.99 ***(978-1-4269-6775-7(6))*** Trafford Publishing.
Thomsen, Richard. Is God on Our Side? My Side? Your Side? Their Side? 2010. 253p. 29.95 *(978-1-4327-6053-3(X))*; (Illus.). pap. 15.95 *(978-1-4327-6038-0(6))* Outskirts Pr., Inc.
Thorning, Arthur G. The Dambuster Who Cracked the Dam: The story of Melvin 'Dinghy' Young. 2008. (Illus.). 192p. 39.95 *(978-1-84415-667-2(2))* Pen & Sword Bks. Ltd. GBR. Dist: Casemate Pubs. & Bk. Distributors, LLC.
Timofeyeva-Yegorova, Anna. Red Sky, Black Death: A Soviet Woman Pilot's Memoir of the Eastern Front. Ponomaryova, Margarita, tr. 2009. (Illus.). 244p. pap. 29.95 *(978-0-89357-355-3(8))* Slavica Pubs.
Tomaselli, Phil. Tracing Your Air Force Ancestors. 2007. (Illus.). 211p. per. 19.95 *(978-1-84415-573-6(0))* Pen & Sword Bks. Ltd. GBR. Dist: Casemate Pubs. & Bk. Distributors, LLC.
Training the Best: Charles Herbert Flowers, Jr. Tuskegee Airman Flight Instructor. 2009. 120p. (YA). pap. 12.50 *(978-0-9776192-3-8(0))* Robnor Publishing.
Tran, Hoi B. A Vietnamese Fighter Pilot in an American War. 2011. 442p. 34.99 ***(978-1-4568-4724-1(4))***; pap. 23.99 ***(978-1-4568-4723-4(6))*** Xlibris Corp.
Trimble, William F. Hero of the Air: Glenn Curtiss & the Birth of Naval Aviation. 2010. (Illus.). 304p. 37.95 *(978-1-59114-879-1(0))* Naval Institute Pr.
Trubshaw, Brian & Edmondson, Sally. Brian Trubshaw: Test Pilot. 2006. (ENG., Illus.). 224p. per. 16.95 *(978-0-7509-4494-6(3))* Sutton Publishing.
Tucker, Phillip Thomas. Father of the Tuskegee Airmen, John C. Robinson. 2012. (Illus.). 400p. 29.95 *(978-1-59797-487-5(0))* Potomac Bks., Inc.
Utgoff, Vadym V. Pilot Error: A Naval AViator's Career - WWII Black Cats to Korean War PBYs to Annapolis Professor. 2006. (Illus.). 184p. *(978-0-9669904-3-0(9))* NAR Publishing.
Vacher, Polly. Wings Around the World. 2008. (Illus.). 160p. 29.95 *(978-1-904943-99-0(3))* Grub Street GBR. Dist: Casemate Pubs. & Bk. Distributors, LLC.
Van Loan, Dana L. Blue Skies & Tail Winds. 2008. (Illus.). 249p. *(978-0-9717214-1-8(6))* Sunnyside Pr.
Van Pelt, Lori. Amelia Earhart: The Sky's No Limit. 2009. (American Heroes Ser.). (ENG.). 240p. pap. 12.99 *(978-0-7653-2483-2(0)*, Forge Bks.) Doherty, Tom Assocs., LLC.
Venter, Al. Gunship Ace: The Wars of Neall Ellis, Gunship Pilot & Mercenary. 2011. (Illus.). 432p. 32.95 ***(978-1-61200-070-1(3)***, Casemate) Casemate Pubs. & Bk. Distributors, LLC.
Volk, Don W. Tractors, Planes, Golf, & Dames. 2011. 154p. pap. 15.95 *(978-1-58985-192-4(7))* Five Star Pubns., Inc.
von Below, Nicolaus. At Hitler's Side: The Memoirs of Hitler's Luftwaffe Adjutant. 2010. (Illus.). 256p. pap. 24.95 *(978-1-84832-585-2(1)*, Frontline) Pen & Sword Bks. Ltd. GBR. Dist: Casemate Pubs. & Bk. Distributors, LLC.
Walsh, Thomas L. Damnyankee: A WWII Story of Tragedy & Survival off the West of Ireland. 2008. 180p. pap. 17.95 *(978-1-4327-2910-3(1))* Outskirts Pr., Inc.
Warner, Guy. World War One Aircraft Carrier Pioneer: The Story & Diaries of Captain JM Mccleery RNAS/RAF. 2011. (Illus.). 304p. 39.95 *(978-1-84884-255-7(4))* Pen & Sword Bks. Ltd. GBR. Dist: Casemate Pubs. & Bk. Distributors, LLC.
Warsitz, Lutz. The First Jet Pilot: The Story of German Test Pilot Erich Warsitz. 2009. (Illus.). 176p. 39.99 *(978-1-84415-818-8(7))* Pen & Sword Bks. Ltd. GBR. Dist: Casemate Pubs. & Bk. Distributors, LLC.
Weekley, Harold D. & Zazas, James B. The Last of Combat B-17 Drivers. 60th ed. 2006. (Illus.). 334p. 39.95 *(978-0-9785980-1-3(6))* Flying Fortress International.
Wells, Jim. Slow down Daddy. 2009. 142p. 29.99 *(978-1-4415-4646-3(4))*; pap. 19.99 *(978-1-4415-4645-6(6))* Xlibris Corp.
Westfall, Douglas. The Hunt for Amelia Earhart: America's Greatest Search. 2007. (1st Person Account). (Illus.). 270p. per. 35.00 *(978-1-891030-24-6(8)*, Paragon Agency, Pubs., The) Paragon Agency, The.
Westfall, Douglas, ed. The Report of the Earhart Search: By the U. S. Navy & U. S. Coast Guard. 2007. (Illus.). 108p. per. 20.00 *(978-1-891030-66-6(3)*, Paragon Agency, Pubs., The) Paragon Agency, The.
White, Robert M. & Summers, Jack L. Higher & Faster: Memoir of a Pioneering Air Force Test Pilot. 2010. (ENG., Illus.). 295p. pap. 29.95 *(978-0-7864-4989-7(6))* McFarland & Co., Inc. Pubs.
Whiteside, Darren J. Rampant Lion: The Life of Eduard Ritter von Schleich - Germany's 'Black Knight' of WWI. 2007. (Illus.). 389p. 22.50 *(978-0-9791946-0-3(1))* A & S Publishing.
Whitlock, Flint. Turbulence Before Takeoff: The Life & Times of Aviation Pioneer Marlon Dewitt Green. 2009. (Illus.). 420p. 24.95 *(978-1-934980-68-8(8))*; pap. 17.95 *(978-1-934980-67-5(6))* Cable Publishing.
Whitlock, Flint & Barnhart, Terry L. Capt. Jepp & the Little Black Book: How Barnstormer & Aviation Pioneer Elrey B. Jeppeson Made the Skies Safer for Everyone. 2007. (Illus.). 209p. *(978-1-886028-83-8(4))* Savage Pr.
Wilberg, Jim. Rittmeister: A Biography of Manfred von Richthofen. 2007. (YA). per. 29.95 *(978-1-4218-9957-2(4))* 1st World Publishing, Inc.
Wilco, Lt. Roger. To Cratisto. 2008. (ENG., Illus.). 400p. pap. 19.95 *(978-1-934956-04-5(X)*, Red Anvil Pr.) Elderberry Press, Inc.
Wildbergh, Jan Wouter & Forrer, Frits. Suffering with a Smile. 2011. 336p. pap. 19.95 ***(978-0-9822207-3-3(1))*** Holland's Glory.
Williams, Lou. My Fascination with Airplanes: Adventures of a Part Time Aviator, 1 vol. 2010. 56p. pap. 16.95 *(978-1-4489-4174-2(1))* PublishAmerica, Inc.
Williams, Ronald. From Supermarine Seafire XVII to Douglas DC-10. 2012. (Illus.). 256p. 39.95 ***(978-1-84884-647-0(9))*** Pen & Sword Bks. Ltd. GBR. Dist: Casemate Pubs. & Bk. Distributors, LLC.
Willis, Bud. Marble Mountain: A Vietnam Memoir. 2011. 484p. 30.79 *(978-1-4567-4349-9(X))*; pap. 20.23 *(978-1-4567-4348-2(1))* AuthorHouse.
Wingo, Dorcey Alan. The Rise & Fall of Captain Methane: Autobiography of a Maverick. 2010. 371p. 34.95 *(978-1-4327-4518-9(2))*; (ENG., Illus.). pap. 19.95 *(978-1-4327-4828-9(9))* Outskirts Pr., Inc.
Winters, Kathleen C. Amelia Earhart: The Turbulent Life of an American Icon. 2010. (ENG., Illus.). 256p. 25.00 *(978-0-230-61669-1(0))* Palgrave Macmillan.
World War II Fighter-Bomber Pilot, Valiant Multi-Mission Air War, What it Was Like, 3rd Edition. 2007. pap. 24.00 *(978-0-7884-4531-6(6))* Heritage Bks.
Wortz, Eleanor Thompson. Fly Gals of World War II. 2011. 174p. pap. 15.00 ***(978-1-61170-034-3(5))*** Robertson Publishing.
Yellin, Jerry & Grosswald, Sarina J. The Resilient Warrior. 2011. 142p. pap. 14.95 ***(978-1-59095-704-2(0))*** TotalRecall Pubns., Inc.
Zamperini, Louis & Rensin, David. Devil at My Heels: A Heroic Olympian's Astonishing Story of Survival as a Japanese POW in World War II. 2011. (ENG.). 336p. pap. 14.99 ***(978-0-06-211885-1(4)***, William Morrow Paperbacks) HarperCollins Pubs.
ZéPhanie. Diary of A French Girl. 2010. 324p. 28.49 *(978-1-4520-5487-2(8))*; pap. 19.99 *(978-1-4520-5486-5(X))* AuthorHouse.
Zuk, Bill. True-Life Adventures of Canada's Bush Pilots. 2009. (ENG.). 136p. (gr. 6-12). pap. 9.95 *(978-1-55277-409-0(0))* Lorimer, James & Co., Ltd., Pubs. CAN. Dist: Casemate Pubs. & Bk. Distributors, LLC.

AIR PILOTS—CORRESPONDENCE

Franks, Norman & Muggleto. Raw Courage. 2011. (Illus.). 224p. 39.95 ***(978-1-908117-13-7(3))*** Grub Street GBR. Dist: Casemate Pubs. & Bk. Distributors, LLC.
Langenfeld, Robert E. & Langenfeld, Robert. A Young Man's Letters from World War II: "More Than Becoming a Soldier" 2011. (Illus.). 234p. ***(978-0-944318-39-3(8))*** ELT Pr.
Stuart, Gordon Lee & Smalley, Debra Stuart. With This You Have the Works: WWII Airman's Letters. 2007. (ENG., Illus.). 276p. 21.95 *(978-1-4327-0080-5(4))*; per. 13.95 *(978-1-4327-0075-1(8))* Outskirts Pr., Inc.
Sweeney, Emma. As Always, Jack: A World War II Love Story. 2012. (ENG.). 180p. 17.00 ***(978-1-60419-048-9(5))*** Axios Pr.

AIR PILOTS—LICENSES

ASA Test Prep Board Staff. Private Pilot Test Prep 2012: Study & Prepare for the Recreational & Private: Airplane, Helicopter, Gyroplane, Glider, Balloon, Airship, Powered Parachute, & Weight-Shift Control FAA Knowledge Exams. 2011. (Test Prep Ser.). (ENG.). 380p. pap. 16.95 *(978-1-56027-850-4(1))* Aviation Supplies & Academics, Inc.
ASA Test Prep Board Staff, ed. Commercial Pilot Test Prep 2012: Study & Prepare for the Commercial Airplane, Helicopter, Gyroplane, Glider, Balloon, Airship & Military Competency FAA Knowledge Exams. 2011. (Test Prep Ser.). (ENG.). 386p. pap. 19.95 *(978-1-56027-852-8(8))* Aviation Supplies & Academics, Inc.
—Instrument Rating Test Prep 2012: Study & Prepare for the Instrument Rating, Instrument Flight Instructor (CFII), Instrument Ground Instructor, & Foreign Pilot: Airplane & Helicopter FAA Knowledge Exams. 2011. (Test Prep Ser.). (ENG.). 335p. pap. 21.95 *(978-1-56027-851-1(X))* Aviation Supplies & Academics, Inc.
Aviation Theory Centre Ltd. Editorial Team. The Pilot's Manual: Instrument Flying: A Step-by-Step Course Covering All Knowledge Necessary to Pass the FAA Instrument Written & Oral Exams, & the IFR Flight Check. 2010. (Pilot's Manual Ser.). (ENG., Illus.). 696p. 59.95 *(978-1-56027-790-3(4))* Aviation Supplies & Academics, Inc.
Aviation Theory Centre Ltd., Staff, ed. The Pilot's Manual: Ground School: All the Aeronautical Knowledge Required to Pass the FAA Exams & Operate as a Private & Commercial Pilot. 3rd ed. 2007. (Pilot's Manual Ser.). (ENG., Illus.). 686p. 59.95 *(978-1-56027-677-7(0))* Aviation Supplies & Academics, Inc.
Eichenberger, Jerry. Your pilots License 8/e. 8th ed. 2011. (ENG., Illus.). 320p. (C). pap. 25.00 ***(978-0-07-176382-0(1)***, 0071763821) McGraw-Hill Professional Publishing.
Federal Aviation Administration. Private Pilot Test Prep 2009. 2008. 368p. pap. 12.95 *(978-1-60239-325-7(7))* Skyhorse Publishing Co., Inc.
Gardner, Bob. The Complete Advanced Pilot: A Combined Commercial & Instrument Course. 4th ed. 2008. (Complete Pilot Ser.). (ENG., Illus.). 480p. pap. 29.95 *(978-1-56027-718-7(1))* Aviation Supplies & Academics, Inc.
Hamilton, Paul. Sport Pilot Checkride: A Guide to Passing the FAA Practical Flight & Oral Exam. 2008. (Freedom to Fly Ser.). (ENG.). 250p. pap. 24.95 *(978-1-56027-726-2(2))* Aviation Supplies & Academics, Inc.
Hayes, Michael D. Airline Transport Pilot Oral Exam Guide: The Comprehensive Guide to Prepare You for the FAA Checkride. 2nd ed. 2011. (Oral Exam Guide Ser.). (ENG.). 220p. pap. 12.95 *(978-1-56027-863-4(3))* Aviation Supplies & Academics, Inc.
Tiscareño, Froy. Flight Time. 2011. 258p. pap. 27.95 ***(978-1-4560-6911-7(X))*** PublishAmerica, Inc.

AIR PISTOLS

see Air Guns

AIR PLANTS

see Epiphytes

AIR POLLUTION

see Air—Pollution

AIR PORTS

see Airports

AIR POWER

see also Air Forces; Air Warfare

Call, Steve. Selling Air Power: Military Aviation & American Popular Culture after World War II. 2009. (Williams-Ford Texas A&M University Military History Ser.). (ENG.). 240p. pap. 24.95 *(978-1-60344-100-1(X))* Texas A&M Univ. Pr.
Cliff, Roger, et al. Shaking the Heavens & Splitting the Earth: Chinese Air Force Employment Concepts in the 21st Century. 2010. 300p. pap. 29.00 *(978-0-8330-4932-2(1)*, mg-915) RAND Corp., The.
Clodfelter, Mark. Beneficial Bombing: The Progressive Foundations of American Air Power, 1917-1945. 2011. (Studies in War, Society, & the Militar Ser.). (ENG., Illus.). 392p. 40.00 *(978-0-8032-3398-0(1))* Univ. of Nebraska Pr.
Douhet, Giulio. The Command of the Air. Harahan, Joseph P. & Kohn, Richard H., eds. Ferrari, Dino, tr. from ITA. 2nd ed. 2009. (ENG.). 404p. pap. 36.00 *(978-0-8173-5608-8(8))* Univ. of Alabama Pr.
Dyndal, Gjert Lage. Land Based Air Power of Aircraft Carriers? A Case Study of the British Debate about Maritime Air Power in the 1960s. 2012. (Corbett Centre for Maritime Policy Studies). (Illus.). 194p. 114.95 ***(978-1-4094-3335-4(8))*** Ashgate Publishing Co.
Emme, Eugene M., ed. The Impact of Air Power: National Security & World Politics. 2011. 930p. 79.95 ***(978-1-258-07642-9(X))*** Literary Licensing, LLC.
Erickson, Andrew. Chinese Aerospace Power. Goldstein, Lyle, ed. 2011. 512p. 52.96 *(978-1-59114-241-6(5))* Naval Institute Pr.
Fitzpatrick, Jon M. Unmanned Aircraft Systems: U. S. Policy Options & Plans. 2012. (Defense, Security & Strategies Ser.). 182p. 125.00 ***(978-1-61470-972-5(6))*** Nova Science Pubs., Inc.
Government Printing Office Staff. Air & Space Power Journal. per. 32.00 *(978-0-16-010138-0(7))* United States Government Printing Office.
Gray, Colin. Airpower for Strategic Effect. 2012. (Columbia/Hurst Ser.). (ENG.). 288p. (gr. 17). 55.00 ***(978-0-231-70300-0(7))*** Columbia Univ. Pr.
Hall, David Ian. Strategy for Victory: The Development of British Tactical Air Power, 1919-1943, 1 vol. 2007. (Praeger Studies in Diplomacy & Strategic Thought Ser.). (Illus.). 272p. 125.00 *(978-0-275-97767-2(6)*, C7767, Praeger Security International) Greenwood Publishing Group, Inc.
Hinman, Ellwood P., et al. AirLandBattle21: Transformational Concepts for Integrating Twenty-First Century Air & Ground Forces. 2009. (Illus.). 178p. 104.95 *(978-0-7546-7634-8(X))* Ashgate Publishing Co.
Hooton, E. R. War over the Trenches. 2010. (Illus.). 336p. 32.95 *(978-0-7110-3415-0(X))* Midland Publishing Ltd. GBR. Dist: Partners Pubs. Group, Inc.
Jacobs, Jody, et al. Enhancing Fires & Maneuver Capability Through Greater Air-Ground Joint Interdependence. 2009. 124p. pap. 37.00 *(978-0-8330-4605-5(5)*, mg-793) RAND Corp., The.
Johnson, David E. Learning Large Lessons: The Evolving Roles of Ground Power & Air Power in the Post-Cold War Era — Executive Summary. 2006. 100p. pap. 24.00 *(978-0-8330-4029-9(4))* RAND Corp., The.
Locke, Joseph W. Air Superiority at Red Flag: Mass, Technology, & Winning the Next War. 2009. (Illus.). xvii, 210p. *(978-1-58566-201-2(1))* Air University Pr.
Mills, Patrick & Evers, Ken. Supporting Air & Expeditionary Forces: Expanded Operational Architecture for Combat Support Execution Planning & Control. 2006. (Illus.). 107p. pap. 28.00 incl. cd-rom *(978-0-8330-3838-8(9)*, MG-316) RAND Corp., The.
Mitchell, William. Winged Defense: The Development & Possibilities of Modern Air Power — Economic & Military. 2nd ed. 2010. (Alabama Fire Ant Ser.). (ENG., Illus.). 302p. pap. 28.00 *(978-0-8173-5605-7(3))* Univ. of Alabama Pr.
Muscha, William R. Strategic Airpower Elements in Interwar German Air Force Doctrine. 2010. 106p. pap. 15.38 *(978-1-60888-053-9(2))* Nimble Bks. LLC.
Nevin, David. Architects of Air Power. (Illus.). 176p. 24.00 *(978-1-84447-034-1(2))* Time Life Value GBR. Dist: Mercury Bks. Ltd.
O'Connell, John F. The Effectiveness of Airpower in the 20th Century: Part Two (1939-1945) 2007. 352p. per. 23.95 *(978-0-595-45724-3(X))* iUniverse, Inc.
Olsen, John Andreas. John Warden & the Renaissance of American Air Power. 2007. (Illus.). 374p. 32.95 *(978-1-59797-084-6(0))* Potomac Bks., Inc.
Olsen, John Andreas, ed. Global Air Power. 2011. 560p. 55.00 *(978-1-59797-555-1(9))*; pap. 35.00 *(978-1-59797-680-0(6))* Potomac Bks., Inc.
—A History of Air Warfare. 2010. 522p. 55.00 *(978-1-59797-440-0(4))*; (Illus.). pap. 35.00 *(978-1-59797-433-2(1))* Potomac Bks., Inc.
Owen, Robert C. & Mueller, Karl P. Airlift Capabilities for Future U. S. Counterinsurgency Operations. 2007. 88p. pap. 23.00 *(978-0-8330-4038-1(3)*, mg565) RAND Corp., The.
Pelfer, Douglas Carl. Stopping Mass Killings in Africa: Genocide, Airpower, & Intervention. 2008. xiv, 170p. *(978-1-58566-182-4(1))* Air University Pr.
Rice, Rondall R. The Politics of Air Power: From Confrontation to Cooperation in Army Aviation Civil-Military Relations. 2009. (Studies in War, Society, & the Militar Ser.). (ENG.). 308p. pap. 24.95 *(978-0-8032-2496-4(6))* Univ. of Nebraska Pr.
Shaud, John Albert. In Service to the Nation: Air Force Research Institute Strategic Concept for 2018-2023. 2009. (Illus.). vii, 111p. *(978-1-58566-189-3(9))* Air University Pr.
Slessor, John Cotesworth. Air Power & Armies. 2009. (ENG., Illus.). 272p. pap. 28.00 *(978-0-8173-5610-1(X))* Univ. of Alabama Pr.
Terry, Michael Robert, ed. Winged Crusade: The Quest for American Air & Space Power. 2006. per. 24.95 *(978-1-879176-43-0(2))* Imprint Pubns., Inc.
Time-Life Books Staff, contrib. by. New Faces of War Air Strike. (Illus.). 196p. 24.00 *(978-1-84447-224-6(8))* Time Life Value GBR. Dist: Mercury Bks. Ltd.
Van Creveld, Martin. The Age of Airpower. 2011. (ENG., Illus.). 512p. 35.00 *(978-1-58648-981-6(X))* PublicAffairs.
Vick, Alan J., et al. Air Power in the New Counterinsurgency Era: The Strategic Importance of USAF Advisory & Assistance Missions. 2006. (Illus.). 180p. per. 25.00 *(978-0-8330-3963-7(6)*, mg-509) RAND Corp., The.
Westenhoff, Charles M., compiled by. Military Airpower: A Revised Digest of Air Power Opinions & Thoughts. 2007. (Illus.). xii, 261p. *(978-1-58566-163-3(5))* Air University Pr.

Wragg, David. The World Air Power Guide. 2010. (Illus.). 240p. 50.00 *(978-1-84884-282-3(1))* Pen & Sword Bks. Ltd. GBR. Dist: Casemate Pubs. & Bk. Distributors, LLC.

AIR PRESSURE SUPPORT

see Air-Supported Structures

AIR PROPELLERS

see Propellers, Aerial

AIR QUALITY

see also Air—Pollution

Air and Waste Management Association (A&WMA) Staff, compiled by. Indoor Environmental Quality: Problems, Research, & Solutions Conference 2006. 2007. 1082p. pap. 193.00 *(978-1-60423-718-4(X))* Curran Assocs., Inc.

—Symposium on Air Quality Measurement: Methods & Technology 2006. 2007. 497p. pap. 118.00 *(978-1-60423-793-1(7))* Curran Assocs., Inc.

—Symposium on Air Quality Measurement Methods & Technology 2007. 2008. 308p. pap. 115.00 *(978-1-60423-900-3(X))* Curran Assocs., Inc.

American Society for Testing and Materials Staff, contrib. by. ASTM Standards for Indoor Air Quality. 3rd ed. 2007. *(978-0-8031-5524-4(7))* American Society for Testing & Materials.

American Society of Heating, contrib. by. Indoor Air Quality Guide: Best Practices for Design, Construction, & Commissioning. 2010. (ENG.). 176p. pap. 29.00 *(978-1-933742-59-5(3))* American Society of Heating, Refrigerating & Air-Conditioning Engineers, Inc.

American Society of Mechanical Engineers Staff, ed. Vehicle Emissions & Their Impact on European Air Quality. 372p. 84.00 *(978-0-85298-632-5(7))* Professional Engineering Publishing GBR. Dist: SAE Intl.

Baklanov, Alexander, et al, eds. Meteorological & Air Quality Models for Urban Areas. 2009. (ENG., Illus.). xviii, 183p. pap. 109.00 *(978-3-642-00297-7(8),* 3642002978) Springer.

Balagopalan, Mohan. Air Quality Permitting. Date not set. 55.00 *(978-1-56670-152-5(X))* Lewis Pubs.

Balduino, Sergio P. Progress in Air Pollution Research. 2007. 129.00 *(978-1-60021-804-0(0))* Nova Science Pubs., Inc.

Bartacek, Jan, et al, eds. Biotechniques for Air Pollution Control: Proceedings of the 3rd International Congress on Biotechniques for Air Pollution Control. Delft, the Netherlands, September 28-30 2009. 2010. (ENG., Illus.). 350p. 104.95 *(978-0-415-58270-4(9),* CRC Press) Taylor & Francis Group GBR. Dist: Taylor & Francis Group.

Beck, Bill. Air & Waste Management Association: A Centennial History. 2007. *(978-1-57864-435-3(6))* Donning Co. Pubs.

Best, Richard. Emergency & Continuous Exposure Guidance Levels for Selected Submarine Contaminants. 2007. (ENG.). 316p. pap. 64.25 *(978-0-309-09225-8(6))* National Academies Pr.

Boutin, Jacob, ed. Air Pollution & Ship Emissions. 2010. (Air, Water & Soil Pollution Science & Technology Ser.). 198p. 115.00 *(978-1-60876-087-9(1))* Nova Science Pubs., Inc.

Brebbia, C. A. & Longhurst, J. W. S., eds. Air Pollution XVIII. 2010. (WIT Transactions on Ecology & the Environment Ser.: 136). (Illus.). 464p. 352.00 *(978-1-84564-450-5(6))* WIT Pr GBR. Dist: WIT Pr.

Brebbia, C. A. & Popov, V., eds. Air Pollution XIX. 2011. (WIT Transactions on Ecology & the Environment Ser.: 147). (Illus.). 496p. lib. bdg. 426.00 *(978-1-84564-528-1(6))* WIT Pr GBR. Dist: WIT Pr.

—Air Pollution XVII. 2009. (WIT Transactions on Ecology & the Environment Ser.: 123). (Illus.). 480p. 328.00 *(978-1-84564-195-5(7))* WIT Pr GBR. Dist: WIT Pr.

Brebbia, Carlos A. & Borrego, C. A., eds. Air Pollution XV. 2007. (WIT Transactions on Ecology & the Environment Ser.: 101). (Illus.). 624p. 355.00 *(978-1-84564-067-5(5))* WIT Pr GBR. Dist: WIT Pr.

British Standards Institute Staff. Filters for compressed air. Test methods. Oil Vapours. 20p. pap. 123.00 *(978-0-580-53131-6(7))* Artech Hse., Inc.

Budisulistiorini, Sri Hapsari. Evaluation of Air Quality Management Plans for PM10Control: Jakarta Case Study. 2008. 132p. pap. *(978-3-639-09778-8(5))* VDM Verlag Dr. Mueller e.K.

Burney, Nelson E., ed. Carbon Tax & Cap-and-trade Tools: Market-based Approaches for Controlling Greenhouse Gases. 2010. (Climate Change & its Causes, Effects & Prediction Ser.). 69.00 *(978-1-60876-137-1(1))* Nova Science Pubs., Inc.

Burroughs, Barney & Hansen, Shirley J. Managing Indoor Air Quality Fifth Edition. 5th rev. ed. 2011. (ENG.). 350p. 119.95 *(978-1-4398-7014-3(4))* Fairmont Pr., Inc.

Burroughs, H. E. & Hansen, Shirley J. Managing Indoor Air Quality. 4th ed. 2008. (Illus.). xii, 359p. *(978-0-88173-569-7(8))* 5th ed. 2011. *(978-0-88173-662-5(7))* 5th ed. 2011. *(978-0-88173-661-8(9))* Fairmont Pr., Inc.

Cap, Auction, & Trade: Auctions & Revenue Recycling under Carbon Cap & Trade: Hearing Before the Select Committee on Energy Independence & Global Warming, House of Representatives, One Hundred Tenth Congress, Second Session, January 23, 2008. 2010. (Illus.). iii, 217p. *(978-0-16-086997-6(8),* 552-070-41856-3) United States Government Printing Office.

Committee on Emergency and Continuous Exposure Guidance Levels for Selected Submarine Contaminants, et al. Emergency & Continuous Exposure Guidance Levels for Selected Submarine Contaminants. (ENG.). Vol. 2. 2008. 332p. pap. 67.00 *(978-0-309-11273-4(7))* Vol. 3. 2009. 192p. pap. 43.25 *(978-0-309-14379-0(9))* National Academies Pr.

Committee on the Effect of Climate Change on Indoor Air Quality and Public Health & Institute of Medicine. Climate Change, the Indoor Environment, & Health. 2011. (ENG., Illus.). 286p. pap. 49.50 ***(978-0-309-20941-0(2))*** National Academies Pr.

Confronting Freight Challenges in Southern California: Joint Hearing Before the Subcommittee on Highways & Transit & the Subcommittee on Railroads, Pipelines, & Hazardous Materials of the Committee on Transportation & Infrastructure, House of Representatives, One Hundred Eleventh Congress, First Session, February 20, 2009 (Los Angeles, CA) 2009. (Illus.). xxi, 195p. *(978-0-16-084315-0(4),* 552-070-39870-8) United States Government Printing Office.

Connor, Steven. The Matter of Air: Science & Art of the Ethereal. 2010. (Illus.). 374p. 39.00 *(978-1-86189-766-4(9))* Reaktion Bks., Ltd. GBR. Dist: Chicago Distribution Ctr.

Crump, D. A Protocol for the Assessment of Indoor Air Quality. 2010. (ENG., Illus.). 52p. pap. 55.00 *(978-1-86081-590-4(1))* Building Research Establishment GBR. Dist: Taylor & Francis Group.

DePalma, Anthony. City of Dust: Illness, Arrogance, And 9/11. 2010. (FT Press Science Ser.). (ENG.). 352p. 25.99 *(978-0-13-138566-5(6))* FT Press.

DiSano, Joseph. National Air Quality: Status & Trends. 2010. (Air, Water & Soil Pollution Science & Technology Ser.). 115.00 *(978-1-60741-513-8(5))* Nova Science Pubs., Inc.

Drury, Evan K. & Pridgen, Tylor S. Handbook on Environmental Quality. 2009. (Environmental Research Advances Ser.). 195.00 *(978-1-60741-420-9(1))* Nova Science Pubs., Inc.

Earth Observing System Aura (U.S.), et al, eds. Our Changing Atmosphere: Discoveries from EOS Aura (Booklet) Discoveries from EOS Aura. 2010. (ENG., Illus.). 56p. 10.00 *(978-0-16-086587-9(5),* U. S. National Aeronautics & Space Administration) United States Government Printing Office.

Ebel, Adolf. Air, Water & Soil Quality Modelling for Risk & Impact Assessment. 2007. (NATO Science for Peace & Security Series / NATO Science for Peace & Security Series C: Environmental Security Ser.). 380p. 319.00 *(978-1-4020-5875-2(6))* Springer.

EPA's New Ozone Standards: Hearing Before the Committee on Oversight & Government Reform, House of Representatives, One Hundred Tenth Congress, Second Session, May 20, 2008. 2009. (Illus.). iii, 284p. *(978-0-16-082949-9(6),* 552-070-38861-3) United States Government Printing Office.

Ferrey, Steven. Unlocking the Global Warming Toolbox: Key Choices for Carbon Restriction & Sequestration. 2010. (ENG.). 324p. 89.00 *(978-1-59370-213-7(2))* PennWell Corp.

Furumai, Hiroaki, et al. Advanced Monitoring & Numerical Analysis of Coastal Water & Urban Air Environment. 2010. (CSUR-UT Series: Library for Sustainable Urban Regeneration Ser.). (Illus.). 158p. 129.00 *(978-4-431-99719-1(9),* 4431997199) Springer.

Gonçalves-Ageitos, Maria, et al. Alternatives for a Cleaner Air in Urban Areas: A modelling Study. 2010. 236p. pap. *(978-3-639-24766-4(3))* VDM Verlag Dr. Mueller e.K.

Griffin Roger D. Principles of Air Quality Management. 2nd rev. ed. 2006. (ENG., Illus.). 334p. 124.95 *(978-0-8493-7099-1(X),* CRC Press) Taylor & Francis Group GBR. Dist: Taylor & Francis Group.

Grzywacz, Cecily M. Monitoring for Gaseous Pollutants in Museum Environments. 2006. (Scientific Tools for Conservation Ser.). (Illus.). 160p. pap. 65.00 *(978-0-89236-851-8(9))* Oxford Univ. Pr., Inc.

Guideline on Air Quality Models — Applications & FLAG Developments: Applications & FLAG Developments. 2007. cd-rom *(978-0-923204-96-9(2))* Air & Waste Management Assn.

Harrison, R. M., et al. Air Quality in Urban Environments. Harrison, R. M. & Hester, R. E., eds. 2009. (Issues in Environmental Science & Technology Ser.). (ENG., Illus.). 162p. (C). 96.00 ***(978-1-84755-907-4(7))*** Royal Society of Chemistry, The GBR. Dist: Ingram Pub. Services.

Hepher, Michael J., ed. Monitoring & Impact of Air Quality. 2007. (ENG., Illus.). 320p. pap. *(978-1-4051-2530-7(6),* Wiley-Blackwell) Wiley, John & Sons, Ltd.

Hochmair, Katharina. Emissions Trading for Road Transportation. 2008. 116p. pap. *(978-3-639-04136-1(4))* VDM Verlag Dr. Mueller e.K.

Hudson, Robert C. Hazardous Materials in the Soil & Atmosphere: Treatment, Removal & Analysis. 2006. (Illus.). 169p. pap. 98.00 *(978-1-60021-250-5(6))* Nova Science Pubs., Inc.

Jiang, Ningbo. Quality of the Auckland Airshed. 2008. 280p. pap. *(978-3-8364-9002-3(1))* VDM Verlag Dr. Mueller e.K.

Kaniaru, Donald, ed. The Montreal Protocol: Celebrating 20 Years of Environmental Progress Ozone Layer & Climate Protection. 2007. (Illus.). 355p. pap. 100.00 *(978-1-905017-51-5(0))* Cameron May, Ltd. GBR. Dist: Gaunt, Inc.

Kennes, C. & Veiga, M. C., eds. Bioreactors for Waste Gas Treatment. 2010. (Environmental Pollution Ser.). 320p. pap. 179.00 *(978-90-481-5772-3(2),* 9048157722) Springer.

Khodakarami, Jamal. Achieving Thermal Comfort. 2009. 238p. pap. *(978-3-639-18292-7(8))* VDM Verlag Dr. Mueller e.K.

Lazaridis, Mihalis & Colbeck, Ian, eds. Human Exposure to Pollutants via Dermal Absorption & Inhalation. 2010. (Environmental Pollution Ser.). (ENG., Illus.). x, 308p. 199.00 *(978-90-481-8662-4(5),* 9048186625) Springer.

Legge, Allan H., ed. Air Quality & Ecological Impacts: Relating Sources to Effects. 2009. (Developments in Environmental Science Ser.: 9). (ENG., Illus.). 334p. 200.00 *(978-0-08-095201-7(1),* Elsevier Science) Elsevier Science & Technology Bks.

Lidskog, Rolf & Sundqvist, Goran. Governing the Air: - the Dynamics of Science, Policy, & Citizen Interaction. 2011. (Politics, Science, & the Environment Ser.). (ENG., Illus.). 384p. (gr. 17). pap. 27.00 ***(978-0-262-51642-6(X))*** MIT Pr.

—Governing the Air: The Dynamics of Science, Policy, & Citizen Interaction. 2011. (Politics, Science, & the Environment Ser.). (ENG., Illus.). 384p. (gr. 17). 54.00 ***(978-0-262-01650-6(8))*** MIT Pr.

Lincoln-Oswalt, Jessica, ed. Better Air: Benefits & Costs of the Clean Air Act. 2011. (Environmental Science, Engineering & Technology Ser.). 244p. 185.00 ***(978-1-61470-724-0(3))*** Nova Science Pubs., Inc.

Longhurst, J. W. S. & Brebbia, C. A04, eds. Air Pollution XX. 2012. (Illus.). 500p. lib. bdg. 430.00 *(978-1-84564-582-3(0))* WIT Pr GBR. Dist: WIT Pr.

Lynch, Sophie A. & Moore, Leah K. Air Quality: New Research. 2008. (Illus.). xiv, 324p. 129.00 *(978-1-60456-792-2(9))* Nova Science Pubs., Inc.

Markusson, Nils, et al, eds. The Social Dynamics of Carbon Capture & Storage. 2012. (Earthscan Science in Society Ser.). (ENG., Illus.). 352p. 140.00 ***(978-1-84971-314-6(6))***; pap. 49.95 ***(978-1-84971-315-3(4))*** Routledge.

Marsik, Tom & Johnson, Ron. Effect of Outdoor Air Quality on Indoor Air. 2008. 152p. pap. *(978-3-8364-8196-0(0))* VDM Verlag Dr. Mueller e.K.

Martineau, et al. The Clean Air ACT Handbook. 3rd ed. 2012. (ENG.). 782p. 179.95 ***(978-1-61438-035-1(X))*** American Bar Assn.

Meadowcroft, James & Langhelle, Oluf, eds. Caching the Carbon: The Politics & Policy of Carbon Capture & Storage. 2011. 320p. pap. 50.00 *(978-0-85793-387-4(6))* Elgar, Edward Publishing, Inc.

Mihelcic, James R., et al. Field Guide to Environmental Engineering for Development Workers: Water, Sanitation, & Indoor Air. 2009. (Illus.). xiii, 547p. pap. 60.00 *(978-0-7844-0985-5(4))* American Society of Civil Engineers.

Mölders, Nicole. Land-Use & Land-Cover Changes: Impact on Climate & Air Quality. 2011. (Atmospheric & Oceanographic Sciences Library). (ENG., Illus.). ix, 189p. 129.00 *(978-94-007-1526-4(9),* 9400715269) Springer.

Moussiopoulos, Nicolas, ed. Air Quality in Cities. 2010. (ENG., Illus.). x, 298p. pap. 169.00 *(978-3-642-05646-8(6),* 3642056466) Springer.

Oanh, Nguyen Thi Kim. Integrated Air Quality Mangement. 2012. (ENG., Illus.). 434p. 129.95 *(978-1-4398-6225-4(7),* CRC Press) Taylor & Francis Group GBR. Dist: Taylor & Francis Group.

Organisation for Economic Co-operation and Development Staff. Itf Round Tables No. 142: The Cost & Effectiveness of Policies to Reduce Vehicle Emissions. 2009. 184p. pap. 92.00 *(978-92-821-0212-1(2))* Organization for Economic Cooperation & Development.

Oversight of Recent EPA Decisions: Hearing Before the Committee on Environment & Public Works, United States Senate, One Hundred Tenth Congress, First Session, February 6, 2007. 2010. (Illus.). iv, 262p. *(978-0-16-085322-7(2),* 552-070-40652-2) United States Government Printing Office.

Pawar, Subhash. Air Ion Variation for Different Atmospheric Conditions. 2011. 224p. pap. ***(978-3-8454-0063-1(3))*** Lambert Academic Publishing.

Pub, Amer Tech & Gosse, Jonathan F. Indoor Air Quality Solutions for Stationary Engineers. 2009. (Illus.). 390p. *(978-0-8269-0718-9(0))* American Technical Pubs., Inc.

Pulugurtha, Srinivas S., et al, eds. Transportation Land-Use Planning, & Air Quality Conference 2007: Proceedings of the 2007 Transportation Land-Use Planning, & Air Quality Conference: July 9-11, 2007, Orlando, Florida. 2008. pap. 90.00 *(978-0-7844-0960-2(9))* American Society of Civil Engineers.

Radojevic, M. & Harrison, R. M., eds. Atmospheric Acidity: Sources, Consequences & Abatement. 2007. (Illus.). 594p. 339.00 *(978-1-85166-777-2(6))* Springer.

Reis, Stefan. Costs of Air Pollution Control: Analyses of Emission Control Options for Ozone Abatement Strategies. 2010. (ENG., Illus.). xv, 203p. pap. 149.00 ***(978-3-642-07878-1(8),*** 3642078788) Springer.

Romano, Gaia C. & Conti, Alice G. Air Quality in the 21st Century. 2008. 89.00 *(978-1-60456-793-9(7))* Nova Science Pubs., Inc.

S. 1265: The Diesel Emissions Reduction ACT of 2005: Hearing Before the Subcommittee on Clean Air, Climate Change, & Nuclear Safety of the Committee on Environment & Public Works, United States Senate, One Hundred Ninth Congress, First Session, July 12, 2005. 2007. (Illus.). iii, 108p. *(978-0-16-079812-2(4),* 552-070-36717-9) United States Government Printing Office.

Schwela, Dieter, et al. Urban Air Pollution in Asian Cities: Status, Challenges & Management. 2006. (ENG., Illus.). 296p. 146.00 *(978-1-84407-375-7(0))* Routledge.

Symposium on Air Quality Measurement Methods & Technology - 2007. 2007. cd-rom *(978-0-923204-94-5(6))* Air & Waste Management Assn.

Symposium on Air Quality Measurement Methods & Technology 2006. 2007. cd-rom *(978-0-923204-90-7(3))* Air & Waste Management Assn.

Ternes, Mary Ellen. EPA's Mandatory Greenhouse Gas Reporting Rule. 2010. xvi, 50p. 49.00 *(978-1-4224-7592-8(1))* LexisNexis Matthew Bender.

U. S. Indoor Air Quality Market & Trends. 2006. per. 4250.00 *(978-1-59623-227-3(7))* BCC Research.

Uekoetter, Frank. The Age of Smoke: Environmental Policy in Germany & the United States, 1880-1970. Dunlap, Thomas, tr. from GER. 2009. (Pittsburgh Hist Urban Environ Ser.). (ENG.). 336p. (C). pap. 26.95 *(978-0-8229-6012-6(5))* Univ. of Pittsburgh Pr.

Uekoetter, Frank & Uekötter, Frank. The Age of Smoke: Environmental Policy in Germany & the United States, 1880-1970. Dunlap, Thomas, tr. from GER. 2009. (Pittsburgh Hist Urban Environ Ser.). (ENG., Illus.). 336p. (C). 65.00 *(978-0-8229-4364-8(6))* Univ. of Pittsburgh Pr.

Vapor Intrusion — Learning from the Challenges: Learning from the Challenges. 2007. *(978-0-923204-98-3(9))* Air & Waste Management Assn.

Whitefield, Philip, et al. Summarizing & Interpreting Aircraft Gaseous & Particulate Emissions Data. 2008. (Illus.). 60p. pap. 42.00 *(978-0-309-11760-9(7))* Transportation Research Board.

Whitehead, Mark. State, Science & the Skies: Governmentalities of the British Atmosphere. 2009. (RGS-IBG Book Ser.: 32). (ENG., Illus.). 296p. 94.95 *(978-1-4051-9174-6(0))*; pap. 39.95 *(978-1-4051-9173-9(2))* Wiley, John & Sons, Inc. (Wiley-Blackwell).

World Health Organization Staff, contrib. by. Air Quality Guidelines - Global Update 2005: Particulate Matter, Ozone, Nitrogen Dioxide & Sulfur Dioxide. 2006. (EURO Nonserial Publication). (ENG.). 493p. pap. 120.00 *(978-92-890-2192-0(6))* World Health Organization.

World Health Organization: Regional Office for Europe. Who Guidelines for Indoor Air Quality: Selected Pollutants. 2011. 479p. pap. 84.00 *(978-92-890-0213-4(1))* World Health Organization.

Wu, Shiliang. Global Change & Ozone Air Quality. 2008. 116p. pap. *(978-3-639-07993-7(0))* VDM Verlag Dr. Mueller e.K.

AIR RAID DEFENSIVE MEASURES

see Air Defenses

AIR RAID SHELTERS

see also Building, Bombproof; Nuclear Bomb Shelters

Bosma, Koos. Shelter City: Protecting Citizens Against Air Raids. 2012. (Landscape & Heritage Research Ser.). (ENG., Illus.). 308p. pap. *(978-90-8964-211-0(0))* Amsterdam Univ. Pr.

Grube, Michael & Grube, Christel. Ringtreppenturm Rosshafen: Ein Luftschutzturm in Hamburg. 2008. 62p. pap. 18.50 *(978-3-8370-1750-2(8))* Bks. on Demand.

Wade, Stephen. Air Raid Shelters of the Second World War. 2011. (Illus.). 192p. 39.95 ***(978-1-84884-327-1(5))*** Pen & Sword Bks. Ltd. GBR. Dist: Casemate Pubs. & Bk. Distributors, LLC.

AIR RAID WARNING SYSTEMS

see also Radar Defense Networks

Simmen, Robert L. with. Threat Warning for Tactical Aircraft. 2006. (ENG.). 30.99 *(978-1-4257-3672-9(6))*; pap. 20.99 *(978-1-4257-3671-2(8))* Xlibris Corp.

AIR RESCUE SERVICE

see Search and Rescue Operations

AIR RIFLES

see Air Guns

AIR RIGHTS

see Airspace (Law)

AIR-SEA INTERACTION

see Ocean-Atmosphere Interaction

AIR-SEA RESCUE

see Search and Rescue Operations

AIR-SHIPS

see Airships

AIR SPACE (LAW)

see Airspace (Law)

AIR STEWARDESSES

see Flight Attendants

AIR STEWARDS

see Flight Attendants

AIR STRATEGY

see Air Warfare

AIR-SUPPORTED STRUCTURES

American Society of Civil Engineers/Structural Engineering Institute, ed. Tensile Membrane Structures: Asce/sei 55-10. 2010. 54p. pap. 70.00 *(978-0-7844-1097-4(6))* American Society of Civil Engineers.

Drew, Philip. New Tent Architecture. 2008. (ENG., Illus.). 208p. 60.00 *(978-0-500-34243-5(1))* Thames & Hudson.

Krauel, Jacobo. Shaping Space & Form Inflatable Architecture & Design. 2012. (ENG., Illus.). 300p. pap. 39.00 *(978-84-92796-16-8(2))* Links International (Leading International Key Services Barcelona, S.A.) ESP. Dist: National Bk. Network.

Oñate, Eugenio & Kröplin, Bernd, eds. Textile Composites & Inflatable Structures. 2010. (Computational Methods in Applied Sciences Ser.). vii, 322p. pap. 239.00 *(978-90-481-6834-7(1),* 9048168341) Springer.

—Textile Composites & Inflatable Structures II. 2010. (Computational Methods in Applied Sciences Ser.). viii, 272p. pap. 209.00 *(978-90-481-7739-4(1),* 9048177391) Springer.

Seidel, Michael. Tensile Surface Structures: A Practical Guide to Cable & Membrane Construction - Materials, Design, Assembly & Erection. Sturge, David, tr. from GER. 2009. (ENG., Illus.). 240p. 135.00 *(978-3-433-02922-0(9),* Wiley-VCH) Wiley, John & Sons, Inc.

AIR TACTICS

see Air Warfare

AIR TERMINALS

see Airports

AIR TRAFFIC CONTROL

Air Traffic Control Association (ATCA) Staff, compiled by. 51st Air Traffic Control Association Annual Conference & Exposition 2006. 2007. 207p. pap. 75.00 *(978-1-60423-712-2(0))* Curran Assocs., Inc.

—52nd Annual Conference of the Air Traffic Control Association 2007. 2007. 95p. pap. 75.00 *(978-1-60423-950-8(6))* Curran Assocs., Inc.

Air Traffic Control (ATF): Good Progress on Interim Replacement for Outage-Plagued System, but Risks Can Be Further Reduced. 37p. pap. 30.00 *(978-0-7881-4073-0(6))* DIANE Publishing Co.

Air Traffic Control Facility Staffing: Hearing Before the Subcommittee on Aviation of the Committee on Transportation & Infrastructure, House of Representatives, One Hundred Tenth Congress, Second Session, June 11, 2008. 2008. (Illus.). xiv, 186p. *(978-0-16-083487-5(2)*, 552-070-39221-1) United States Government Printing Office.

Airport & Airway Trust Fund: The Future of Aviation Financing: Hearing Before the Committee on Finance, United States Senate, One Hundred Tenth Congress, First Session, July 12, 2007. 2008. (Illus.). iii, 110p. *(978-0-16-080948-4(7)*, 552-070-37478-7) United States Government Printing Office.

Alam, Sameer. Air Traffic Simulation & Modelling. 2009. 288p. pap. *(978-3-639-02255-1(6))* VDM Verlag Dr. Mueller e.K.

ATC Modernization & NextGen Near-Term Achievable Goals: Hearing Before the Subcommittee on Aviation of the Committee on Transportation & Infrastructure, House of Representatives, One Hundred Eleventh Congress, First Session, March 18, 2009. 2009. (Illus.). xx, 313p. *(978-0-16-084362-4(6)*, 552-070-39905-4) United States Government Printing Office.

Berger, Ron. Normal MAYDAY: The Eye in the Sky. 2007. (Illus.). 171p. per. 19.95 *(978-0-9799257-0-2(3))* berger publishing.

Bianco, Lucio, et al, eds. New Concepts & Methods in Air Traffic Management. 2010. (Transportation Analysis Ser.). (ENG., Illus.). x, 224p. pap. 189.00 *(978-3-642-07491-2(X)*, 364207491X) Springer.

Blanchard, Donna M. Next Generation Air Transportation System: The Future of Flight. 2011. (Transportation Infrastructure - Roads, Highways, Bridges, Airports & Mass Transit Ser.). (Illus.). x, 173p. 115.00 *(978-1-61761-936-6(1))* Nova Science Pubs., Inc.

Browning-Freeman. Aviation Foundations I. 2011. (ENG.). 240.00 ***(978-0-7575-9626-1(6))*** Kendall Hunt Publishing Co.

Congestion Management in the New York Airspace: Hearing Before the Subcommittee on Aviation of the Committee on Transportation & Infrastructure, House of Representatives, One Hundred Tenth Congress, Second Session, June 18, 2008. 2008. (Illus.). xii, 127p. *(978-0-16-083868-2(1)*, 552-070-39563-6) United States Government Printing Office.

Coogan, Matthew A. Innovative Approaches to Addressing Aviation Capacity Issues in Coastal Mega-Regions. 2010. (Illus.). 145p. pap. *(978-0-309-11827-9(1))* Transportation Research Board.

Cook, Andrew, ed. European Air Traffic Management: Principles Practice & Research. 2007. (Illus.). 278p. 114.95 *(978-0-7546-7295-1(6))* Ashgate Publishing Co.

Davis, Duane. Controlling Training. 2009. 210p. pap. 19.95 *(978-1-4092-5712-7(6))* Lulu Enterprises Inc.

De Kuyffer, Erik. The Integration of Uavs into Controlled Airspace. 2009. 124p. pap. *(978-3-639-20081-2(0))* VDM Verlag Dr. Mueller e.K.

Deborah A. Boehm-Davis & National Research Council. Assessing the Research & Development Plan for the Next Generation Air Transportation System: Summary of a Workshop. 2008. (ENG.). 38p. pap. 15.00 *(978-0-309-12470-6(0))* National Academies Pr.

Dong, Dujiao, et al. Hang Kong Fa an Li Ping Xi. 2009. (CHI., Illus.). *(978-7-81134-415-8(7))* Univ. of International Business and Economic Pr.

Duke, Graham. Air Traffic Control. 10th rev. ed. 2009. (ENG., Illus.). 111p. pap. 16.95 *(978-1-85780-318-1(3))* Midland Publishing Ltd. GBR. Dist: BookMasters Distribution Services (BDS).

FAA Reauthorization: NextGen & the Benefits of Modernization: Hearing Before the Subcommittee on Aviation Operations, Safety, & Security of the Committee on Commerce, Science, & Transportation, United States Senate, One Hundred Eleventh Congress, First Session, March 25, 2009. 2010. (Illus.). iii, 83p. *(978-0-16-085751-5(1)*, 552-070-40969-6) United States Government Printing Office.

Federal Aviation Administration. Federal Aviation Regulations: Aeronautical Information Manual 2010. 2009. (ENG., Illus.). 960p. pap. 15.95 *(978-1-60239-728-6(7)*, 239728) Skyhorse Publishing Co., Inc.

Federal Aviation Administration Modernization: Hearing Before the Subcommittee on Aviation Operations, Safety, & Security of the Committee on Commerce, Science, & Transportation, United States Senate, One Hundred Tenth Congress, First Session, March 22, 2007. 2010. (Illus.). iii, 61p. *(978-0-16-086661-6(8)*, 552-070-41639-1) United States Government Printing Office.

Flight Safety Foundation Staff, compiled by. 18th Annual European Aviation Safety Seminar (EASS 2006) Safety Means Participating. 2007. 688p. pap. 132.00 *(978-1-60423-384-1(2))* Curran Assocs., Inc.

Gebre-Egiabher, Demoz. Gnss Applications & Methods. Gleason, Scott, ed. 2009. (Illus.). 532p. 149.00 *(978-1-59693-329-3(1))* Artech Hse., Inc.

Gustavsson, Filip N., ed. New Transportation Research Progress. 2008. (C). 185.00 *(978-1-60456-032-9(0))* Nova Science Pubs., Inc.

The Hudson River Airspace & Management of Uncontrolled Airspace Corridors: Hearing Before the Subcommittee on Aviation of the Committee on Transportation & Infrastructure, House of Representatives, One Hundred Eleventh Congress, First Session, September 16, 2009. 2009. (Illus.). xvi, 175p. *(978-0-16-084739-4(7)*, 552-070-40216-1) United States Government Printing Office.

Irwin, Ron. The FAA Will KILL You. 2007. 182p. pap. 14.96 *(978-0-615-14885-4(9))* Irwin, Ronald.

Jamie N. Wright. Air Traffic Safety & Control Issues. 2011. (Series: Transportation Infrastructure - Roads, Highways, Bridges, Airports & Mass Transit Ser.). (Illus.). viii, 213p. 115.00 *(978-1-61761-937-3(X))* Nova Science Pubs., Inc.

Jane's Air Traffic Control: Your Expert Guide to ATC Technology & Market Developments. 470.00 *(978-0-7106-2306-5(2))* Jane's Information Group, Inc.

Jeffrey K. Fozard Cw4 (Ret) Usa. Cleared to Land: Memoirs of an Army Air Traffic Controller Vietnam — Mar 68-Sep 71. 2009. 184p. 24.99 *(978-1-4389-7123-0(0))*; pap. 14.49 *(978-1-4389-7122-3(2))* AuthorHouse.

The Joint Planning & Development Office & the Next Generation Air Transportation System: Status & Issues: Hearing Before the Subcommittee on Space & Aeronautics, Committee on Science & Technology, House of Representatives, One Hundred Tenth Congress, First Session, March 29, 2007. 2007. (Illus.). iv, 78p. *(978-0-16-080101-3(X)*, 552-070-36842-6) United States Government Printing Office.

LearningExpress Editors. Air Traffic Control Test Prep. 2009. (ENG.). 352p. pap. 29.95 *(978-1-57685-665-9(8))* LearningExpress, LLC.

Marlin, Ruth Elizabeth. Advantage of Distributed Capacity in Service Continuity Planning: The Case of Air Traffic Control Facility Consolidation. 2010. 187p. pap. 25.95 *(978-1-4327-3923-2(9))* Outskirts Pr., Inc.

Mattson, Patrick R. Air Traffic Control Career Prep: A Comprehensive Guide to One of the Best-Paying Federal Government Careers, Including Test Preparation for the Initial ATC Exams. 2006. (ENG., Illus.). 240p. pap. 49.95 *(978-1-56027-614-2(2))* Aviation Supplies & Academics, Inc.

McCartin, Joseph A. Collision Course: Ronald Reagan, the Air Traffic Controllers, & the Strike that Changed America, 1 vol. 2011. (ENG., Illus.). 504p. 29.95 *(978-0-19-983678-9(7))* Oxford Univ. Pr., Inc.

Mensen, Heinrich. Moderne Flugsicherung: Organisation, Verfahren, Technik. 3rd ed. 2006. (VDI-Buch Ser.). (Illus.). XXXII, 466p. 69.95 *(978-3-540-20581-4(0)*, 3540205810) Springer.

The Next Generation Air Transportation System: Status & Issues: Hearing Before the Committee on Science & Technology, House of Representatives, One Hundred Tenth Congress, Second Session, September 11, 2008. 2008. (Illus.). iv, 216p. *(978-0-16-082502-6(4)*, 552-070-38540-1) United States Government Printing Office.

NextGen: Area Navigation (RNAV) 2009. (Illus.). xvi, 194p. *(978-0-16-084676-2(5)*, 552-070-40169-5) United States Government Printing Office.

NextGen: Long-Term Planning & Interagency Cooperation: Hearing Before the Subcommittee on Aviation of the Committee on Transportation & Infrastructure, House of Representatives, One Hundred Eleventh Congress, Second Session, April 21, 2010. 2010. (Illus.). xi, 108p. *(978-0-16-086385-1(6)*, 552-070-41464-9) United States Government Printing Office.

Nolan, Michael S. Fundamentals of Air Traffic Control. 5th ed. 2010. (ENG.). 672p. (C). 206.95 *(978-1-4354-8272-2(7))* Delmar Cengage Learning.

Oster, Clinton V. & Strong, John S. Managing the Skies: Public Policy Organization & Financing of Air Traffic Management. 2007. 234p. 99.95 *(978-0-7546-7045-2(7))* Ashgate Publishing Co.

Oversight of the Joint Planning & Development Office: Hearing Before the Subcommittee on Aviation of the Committee on Commerce, Science, & Transportation, United States Senate, One Hundred Ninth Congress, Second Session, July 25, 2006. 2011. (Illus.). iii, 69p. ***(978-0-16-089027-7(6)***, 552-070-43059-8) United States Government Printing Office.

A Review of the Federal Aviation Administration's Research & Development Program: Hearing Before the Subcommittee on Space & Aeronautics, Committee on Science, Space, & Technology, House of Representatives, One Hundred Twelfth Congress, First Session, February 16, 2011. 2011. (Illus.). iii, 67p. ***(978-0-16-088764-2(X)***, 552-070-42904-2) United States Government Printing Office.

Richards, Bob. Secrets from the Tower: An O'Hare Air Traffic Controller's Personal Stories of Life & Aviation. 2007. 376p. per. 25.00 *(978-0-9787113-9-9(4)*, Ithaca Pr.) Authors & Artists Publishers of New York, Inc.

Rider, David. Jane's Air Traffic Control 2005-2006. cd-rom 1150.00 *(978-0-7106-1571-8(X))* Jane's Information Group, Inc.

Rothman, Sidney R., ed. FAA Airspace Redesign & Congestion Management. 2010. 180p. 89.00 *(978-1-60692-710-6(8))* Nova Science Pubs., Inc.

Runway Safety: Hearing Before the Subcommittee on Aviation of the Committee on Transportation & Infrastructure, House of Representatives, One Hundred Tenth Congress, Second Session, February 13, 2008. 2008. (Illus.). vi, 351p. *(978-0-16-082840-9(6)*, 552-070-38820-6) United States Government Printing Office.

Shawcross, Philip. Flightpath Student's Book: Aviation English for Pilots & ATCOs. 2011. (ENG.). 192p. pap., stu. ed. 46.00 incl. DVD, audio compact disk *(978-0-521-17871-6(1))* Cambridge Univ. Pr.

Shawcross, Philip & Day, Jeremy. Flightpath Teacher's Book: Aviation English for Pilots & ATCOs. 2011. (ENG.). 224p. pap., tchr. ed. 50.00 *(978-0-521-17870-9(3))* Cambridge Univ. Pr.

Smith, David J. Air Traffic Control Handbook: The Complete Guide for all Aviation & Air Band Enthusiasts. 9th ed. 2010. (ENG., Illus.). 208p. pap. 29.95 *(978-1-84425-832-1(7)*, 1844258327) Haynes Publishing PLC GBR. Dist: MBI Distribution Services/Quayside Distribution.

Tu, Yufeng. Air Transportation System Performance- Estimation & Comparative Analysis of Departure Delays. 2007. pap. *(978-3-8364-2230-7(1))* VDM Verlag Dr. Mueller e.K.

United States, Congress House Committee on Transportation and Infrastructure Subcommittee on Aviation Staff, contrib. by. Next Generation Air Transportation System Financing Options: Hearing Before the Subcommittee on Aviation of the Committee on Transportation & Infrastructure, House of Representatives, One Hundred Ninth Congress, Second Session, September 27, 2006. 2007. (Illus.). v, 92p. *(978-0-16-078133-9(7)*, 552-070-35533-2) United States Government Printing Office.

VanDrey, Christian. Air Traffic Controller Test Preparation: Development & selected elements, Eurocontrol / FEAST. 2011. 52p. pap. 23.50 ***(978-3-8423-6709-8(0))*** Bks. on Demand.

Weigang, Li & Romani, Italo. Computational Models, Software Engineering, & Advanced Technologies in Air Transportation: Next Generation Applications. Barros, Alexandre de, ed. 2009. (Illus.). 392p. 180.00 *(978-1-60566-800-0(1)*, Engineering Science Reference) IGI Global.

Winston, Clifford & de Rus, Gines, eds. Aviation Infrastructure Performance: A Study in Comparative Political Economy. 2008. (ENG., Illus.). 237p. 59.95 *(978-0-8157-9394-6(4))*; pap. 24.95 *(978-0-8157-9395-3(2))* Brookings Institution Pr.

Wise, J.A., et al, eds. Verification & Validation of Complex Systems: Human Factors Issues - Proceedings of the NATO Advanced Study Institute on Verification & Validation of Complex & Integrated Human-Machine Systems, Held in Vimeiro, Portugal, July 6-17, 1992. 2008. (NATO asi Series / Computer & Systems Sciences Ser.). (Illus.). xiii, 705p. 319.00 *(978-3-540-56574-1(4))* Springer.

Yan, Ruixia. Assessing English Language Proficiency in International Aviation Issues of Reliability, Validity, & Aviation Safety. 2009. 128p. pap. *(978-3-639-10984-9(8))* VDM Verlag Dr. Mueller e.K.

Zhang, Zhaoning, et al. Fei Xing Jian Ge an Quan Ping Gu Yin Lun. 2009. (Illus.). vi, 172p. *(978-7-03-025408-5(2))* Science Pr.

2007 IEEE/AIAA 26th Digital Avionics Systems Conference. 2007. pap. 340.00 *(978-1-4244-1107-8(6)*, 07CH37891) IEEE.

AIR TRANSPORT

see Aeronautics, Commercial

AIR TRANSPORT MANAGEMENT

see Airlines—Management

AIR TRAVEL

see also Airlines

Adey, Peter. Aerial Life: Spaces, Mobilities, Affects. 2010. (RGS-IBG Book Ser.). (ENG., Illus.). 296p. pap. 39.95 *(978-1-4051-8261-4(X))*; 94.95 *(978-1-4051-8262-1(8))* Wiley, John & Sons, Inc. (Wiley-Blackwell).

Altarescu, Joseba & Bai, Taro. Aviation & Passenger Security. 2012. (Transportation Issues, Policies & R & D Ser.). 147p. 95.00 ***(978-1-62100-155-3(5))*** Nova Science Pubs., Inc.

Behrent, Bob. Planes, Pranks & Pepto-Bismol: Tales & Tips from a Seasoned Road Warrior. 2010. 258p. pap. 15.50 *(978-1-60911-383-4(7)*, Eloquent Bks.) AEG Literary Publishing Services, Inc.

Bussa, Michael. NOW BOARDING Confessions of a Stowaway. 2010. 140p. pap. 17.49 *(978-0-557-39049-6(4))* Lulu Enterprises Inc.

Clowers, Anya. Jet with Kids: Taking the Fear Out of Flying... with Your Kids! 2006. 164p. per. 19.95 *(978-0-615-13757-5(1))* Jet Seven, Inc.

Comfort, Ray. 101 Annoying Things about Air Travel. 2007. (Illus.). 135p. per. *(978-0-89221-669-7(7))* New Leaf Pr., Inc.

Cross, James U., et al. Around the World with LBJ: My Wild Ride as Air Force One Pilot, White House Aide, & Personal Confidant. 2008. (ENG., Illus.). 218p. 26.95 *(978-0-292-71768-8(7))* Univ. of Texas Pr.

Cunningham, Agnes. Traveling Graces: A Little Book of Plane Prayers. 2010. *(978-0-7648-1959-9(3))* Liguori Pubns.

Cwerner, Saulo. Aeromobilities. 2010. (Illus.). 260p. pap. 42.95 *(978-0-415-58134-9(6))* Routledge.

Dierikx, Marc & Dierikx, M. L. J. Clipping the Clouds: How Air Travel Changed the World, 1 vol. 2008. (Moving through History: Transportation & Society Ser.). (Illus.). 216p. 49.95 *(978-0-275-98910-1(0)*, C8910, Praeger Pubs.) Greenwood Publishing Group, Inc.

Donohue, George L., et al. Terminal Chaos: Why US Air Travel Is Broken & How to Fix It. 2008. (Library of Flight Ser.). (Illus.). 150p. *(978-1-56347-949-6(4))* American Institute of Aeronautics & Astronautics.

Edwards, Graham & Endres, Gunter. Jane's Airline Recognition Guide. 2006. (Jane's Recognition Guides Ser.). (Illus.). 384p. pap. 24.95 *(978-0-06-113729-7(4)*, HarperPerennial) HarperCollins Pubs.

Erickson, George. Back to the Barrens: On the Wing with Da Vinci & Friends. 2007. (ENG.). 352p. pap. 17.95 *(978-0-88839-642-6(2))* Hancock Hse. Pubs.

Escolme-Schmidt, Libbie. Glamour in the Skies: The Golden Age of the Air Stewardess. 2009. (ENG., Illus.). 224p. 38.95 *(978-0-7524-4904-3(4))* History Pr. Ltd., The GBR. Dist: Independent Pubs. Group.

—Glamour in the Skies: The Golden Age of the Air Stewardess. 2010. (ENG., Illus.). 224p. pap. 23.95 *(978-0-7524-5787-1(X))* History Pr. Ltd., The GBR. Dist: Independent Pubs. Group.

Fellows, Kate L. The Nervous Flyer's Handbook: Your Portable Flight Coach. 2009. 180p. pap. 14.95 *(978-1-60844-299-7(3))* Dog Ear Publishing, LLC.

Foreman & Gerwen. Fly Away Fear: Overcoming Fear Flying. 2008. (Karnac Self Help Ser.). (Illus.). 190p. pap. 26.95 *(978-1-85575-580-2(7))* Karnac Bks. GBR. Dist: Stylus Publishing, LLC.

Green, Larry. One Man's Airline. 2008. 272p. pap. 12.95 *(978-1-4327-0062-1(6))* Outskirts Pr., Inc.

Grounded: How the Air Transportation Crisis Is Hurting Entrepreneurs & the Economy. 2008. v, 70p. *(978-0-16-081793-9(5)*, 552-070-37999-1) United States Government Printing Office.

Havers, Richard & Tiffney, Christopher. In-Flight Confidential. 2009. (Confidential Ser.). (ENG., Illus.). 304p. pap. 10.99 *(978-1-906635-43-5(9)*, 1906635439) G2 Entertainment Ltd. GBR. Dist: MBI Distribution Services/Quayside Distribution.

Hirst, M. The Air Transport System. 2008. 352p. *(978-1-84569-325-1(6))* Woodhead Publishing Ltd.

Hirst, Mike. The Air Transport System. 2008. (Library of Flight). (Illus.). ix, 341p. *(978-1-56347-964-9(8))* American Institute of Aeronautics & Astronautics.

Hunter, Joyce A. Anger in the Air: Combating the Air Rage Phenomenon. 2009. 236p. 124.95 *(978-0-7546-7193-0(3))* Ashgate Publishing Co.

Janic, Milan. The Sustainability of Air Transportation: A Quantitative Analysis & Assessment. 2007. (Illus.). 374p. 124.95 *(978-0-7546-4967-0(9))* Ashgate Publishing Co.

Lavery, Brian. Churchill Goes to War: Winston's Wartime Journeys. 2007. (Illus.). 392p. 34.95 *(978-1-59114-103-7(6))* Naval Institute Pr.

Lonely Planet Staff. Flightless: Incredible Journeys Without Leaving the Ground. 2008. (Travel Literature Ser.). (ENG.). 216p. pap. 14.99 *(978-1-74179-075-7(1))* Lonely Planet Pubns.

Macleay, Victoria. Bon Voyage: Have a Great Adventure. 2008. 48p. 7.95 *(978-0-86435-089-3(5))* Coniston Designs AUS. Dist: Independent Pubs. Group.

Manston, Raf. RAF Manston in Old Photographs. (Illus.). 159p. 13.95 *(978-0-7509-0135-2(7))* Sutton Publishing.

Martinez, Homero E. Dictionary for Air Travel & Tourism Activities: Over 7,100 terms on Airlines, Tourism, Hospitality, Cruises, Car Rentals, GDS, Geography, Climate, E. 2008. 628p. pap. 34.95 *(978-0-595-52709-0(4))* iUniverse, Inc.

Mathews, Daniel & Jackson, James S. America from the Air: A Guide to the Landscape along Your Route. 2007. (ENG., Illus.). 400p. 19.95 *(978-0-618-70603-7(6))* Houghton Mifflin Harcourt Trade & Reference Pubs.

Morris, Doug. From the Flight Deck: Plane Talk & Sky Science. 2007. (ENG., Illus.). 184p. per. 15.95 *(978-1-55022-765-9(3))* ECW Pr. CAN. Dist: Independent Pubs. Group.

Pirie, Gordon. Cultures & Caricatures of British Imperial Flying. 2012. (Studies in Imperialism Ser.). (ENG., Illus.). 256p. 100.00 ***(978-0-7190-8682-3(5))*** Manchester Univ. Pr. GBR. Dist: Macmillan.

Poynter, Dan. Dan Poynter's Air Travel Handbook. 2011. 322p. pap. 14.95 ***(978-1-56860-150-2(6))*** Para Publishing.

Richardson, George. Things that Go Bump in the Flight. 2008. 59p. pap. 30.95 *(978-1-4092-1503-5(2))* Lulu Enterprises Inc.

Rickard, John. Air safety group: a brief History. 2010. 58p. pap. 16.95 *(978-1-4457-6276-0(5))* Lulu Enterprises Inc.

Rust, Daniel L. Flying Across America: The Airline Passenger Experience. 2009. (ENG., Illus.). 272p. 45.00 *(978-0-8061-3870-1(X))* Univ. of Oklahoma Pr.

Seabridge, Allan & Morgan, Shirley. Air Travel & Health: A Systems Perspective. 2010. (Aerospace Ser.). (ENG., Illus.). 248p. 110.00 *(978-0-470-71177-4(9)*, Wiley) Wiley, John & Sons, Inc.

Stambaugh, Hollis, et al. Quarantine Facilities for Arriving Air Travelers: Identification of Planning Needs & Costs. 2008. (ACRP Report Ser.). (Illus.). 34p. 35.00 *(978-0-309-09940-0(4))* Transportation Research Board.

Van Dyke, Donald L. Fortune Favours the Bold. 2009. (Illus.). x, 278p. 161.99 *(978-1-4363-9489-5(5))* Xlibris Corp.

Vink, Peter, ed. Aircraft Interior Comfort & Design. 2011. (ENG., Illus.). 134p. pap. 59.95 *(978-1-4398-6305-3(9)*, CRC Press) Taylor & Francis Group GBR. Dist: Taylor & Francis Group.

Wood, Katie. Fly Europe: The Complete Guide to Budget Airline Destinations. (Illus.). 576p. pap. 19.99 *(978-1-85410-895-1(6))* Aurum Pr., Ltd. GBR. Dist: Trafalgar Square Publishing.

World Health Organization. Tuberculosis & Air Travel: Guidelines for Prevention & Control. 3rd rev. ed. 2008. (Nonserial Publication Ser.). 64p. pap. 12.00 *(978-92-4-154750-5(2))* World Health Organization.

Wysong, James. Flying High with A Frank Steward: More Air Travel Tales from the Flight Crew. 2007. (ENG.). 244p. pap. 14.95 *(978-1-57023-272-5(5))* Impact Pubns.

Youngblood, Dorothy F. The Open Skies. 2008. 160p. 17.99 *(978-0-7858-2442-8(1)*, Chartwell) Book Sales, Inc.

AIR-TURBINES

see Wind Turbines

AIR WARFARE

see also Air Defenses; Air Power; Airplanes, Military; Bombing, Aerial; Chemical Warfare

also subdivision Aerial Operations under names of wars, e.g. World War, 1939-1945—Aerial Operations

Boelcke, Oswald. An Aviator's Field Book. (Great War Ser.: No. 14). (Illus.). 219p. reprint ed. 29.95 *(978-0-89839-163-3(6))* Battery Pr.

Boyne, Walter. How the Helicopter Changed Modern Warfare, 1 vol. 2011. (ENG., Illus.). 384p. 29.95 *(978-1-58980-700-6(6))* Pelican Publishing Co., Inc.

Call, Steve. Selling Air Power: Military Aviation & American Popular Culture after World War II. 2009. (Williams-Ford Texas A&M University Military History Ser.). (ENG.). 240p. pap. 24.95 *(978-1-60344-100-1(X))*; (Illus.). 50.00 *(978-1-60344-091-2(7))* Texas A&M Univ. Pr.

Carlisle, Norman, et al, eds. The Air Forces Reader: Army & Navy Air Forces. 2011. 442p. 56.95 **(978-1-258-08039-6(7))** Literary Licensing, LLC.
Connors, Tracy. Baited Trap: The Ambush of Mission 1890, the Deadliest Helicopter Rescue of the Korean War. 2007. (Illus.). 400p. pap. 19.95 *(978-0-9640138-3-4(5))* BelleAire Pr.
Curley, Robert, ed. War at Sea & in the Air. 2011. (Britannica Guide to War Ser.). (ENG.). 160p. (YA). (gr. 10-12). lib. bdg. 35.25 **(978-1-61530-677-0(3))** Rosen Publishing Group, Inc., The.
Dept. of Defense. Army Aviation Operations. 2009. per. 15.95 *(978-1-60170-035-3(0))* Pentagon Publishing.
—Aviation Brigades. 2009. per. 17.95 *(978-1-60170-036-0(9))* Pentagon Publishing.
Emme, Eugene M., ed. The Impact of Air Power: National Security & World Politics. 2011. 930p. 79.95 **(978-1-258-07642-9(X))** Literary Licensing, LLC.
Feinberg, Amatzia, et al. Supporting Expeditionary Aerospace Forces: Lessons from the Air War over Serbia. 2008. 120p. pap. 15.00 *(978-0-8330-3002-3(7))* RAND Corp., The.
Fisher, David E. A Summer Bright & Terrible: Winston Churchill, Lord Dowding, Radar, & the Impossible Triumph of the Battle of Britain. 2006. (ENG., Illus.). 304p. per. 16.00 *(978-1-59376-116-5(3))* Counterpoint LLC.
Franklin, H. Bruce. War Stars: The Superweapon & the American Imagination. rev. exp. ed. 2008. (Illus.). 280p. pap. 28.95 *(978-1-55849-651-4(3))* Univ. of Massachusetts Pr.
Grosscup, Beau. Strategic Terror: The Politics & Ethics of Aerial Bombardment. 2006. (ENG.). 224p. 94.95 *(978-1-84277-542-4(1))*; per. 31.95 *(978-1-84277-543-1(X))* Zed Bks., Ltd. GBR. Dist: Macmillan.
Hallion, Richard. Strike from the Sky: The History of Battlefield Air Attack, 1910-1945. 2010. *(978-0-8173-8543-9(6))*; 2nd ed. (ENG.). 392p. pap. 35.00 *(978-0-8173-5657-6(6))* Univ. of Alabama Pr.
Hickey, James E. Precision-Guided Munitions & Human Suffering in War. 2012. **(978-1-4094-2952-4(0))**; 200p. **(978-1-4094-2951-7(2))** Ashgate Publishing Co.
Hinman, Ellwood P., et al. AirLandBattle21: Transformational Concepts for Integrating Twenty-First Century Air & Ground Forces. 2009. (Illus.). 178p. 104.95 *(978-0-7546-7634-8(X))* Ashgate Publishing Co.
Jacobs, Jody. Technologies & Tactics for Improved Air-Ground Effectiveness. 2007. 174p. pap. 29.00 *(978-0-8330-4218-7(1))* RAND Corp., The.
Kometer, Michael W. Command in Air War: Centralized Versus Decentralized Control of Combat Airpower. 2007. (Illus.). x, 335p. pap. *(978-1-58566-164-0(3))* Air University Pr.
Lambeth, Benjamin S. Combat Pair: The Evolution of Air Force-Navy Integration in Strike Warfare. 2007. 128p. pap. 22.00 *(978-0-8330-4209-5(2)*, mg655) RAND Corp., The.
Land-Based Air Defence: Evaluate the World's Land-Based Air Defence Systems. 495.00 *(978-0-7106-2320-1(8))* Jane's Information Group, Inc.
Locke, Joseph W. Air Superiority at Red Flag: Mass, Technology, & Winning the Next War. 2009. (Illus.). xvii, 210p. *(978-1-58566-201-2(1))* Air University Pr.
Mars-Proietti, Laura & Grey House Publishing Staff, eds. Air Warfare: An International Encyclopeia 2008, 2 vols. 2nd rev. ed. 2011. 250.00 *(978-1-59237-295-9(3))* Grey Hse. Publishing.
Mills, Patrick & Evers, Ken. Supporting Air & Expeditionary Forces: Expanded Operational Architecture for Combat Support Execution Planning & Control. 2006. (Illus.). 107p. pap. 28.00 incl. cd-rom *(978-0-8330-3838-8(9)*, MG-316) RAND Corp., The.
Murray, Williamson. Strategy for Defeat: The Luftwaffe, 1933-1945. (Illus.). 391p. pap. 12.00 *(978-1-58566-010-0(8))* Air University Pr.
Nordeen, Lon O. Air Warfare in the Missile Age. 2010. (ENG., Illus.). 352p. pap. 24.95 *(978-1-58834-282-9(4))* Smithsonian Institution Pr.
Olsen, John Andreas, ed. A History of Air Warfare. 2010. 522p. 55.00 *(978-1-59797-440-0(4))*; (Illus.). pap. 35.00 *(978-1-59797-433-2(1))* Potomac Bks., Inc.
Price, Alfred. Dogfight: True Stories of Dramatic Air Action. 2010. (ENG.). 360p. pap. 17.95 *(978-0-7524-5470-2(6))* History Pr. Ltd.,The GBR. Dist: Independent Pubs. Group.
Schmitt, Michael N. & Von Heinegg, Wolff Heintschel. The Conduct of Hostilities in International Humanitarian Law: Volume 1. 2012. (Library of Essays in International Humanitarian Law Ser.). 556p. 300.00 **(978-0-7546-2935-1(X))** Ashgate Publishing Co.
Smith, J. Richard, et al. Schlachtflieger: Luftwaffe Ground-Attack Units 1937-1945. 2010. (Luftwaffe Colours Ser.). (ENG., Illus.). 96p. per. 29.95 *(978-1-85780-274-0(8))* Allan, Ian Publishing GBR. Dist: BookMasters Distribution Services (BDS).
Sterrett, James. Soviet Air Force Operational Theory, 1918-45. 2007. (Soviet (Russian) Study of War Ser.). (Illus.). 188p. 170.00 *(978-0-415-77019-4(X))* Routledge.
Stroud, Jon. Little Book of the RAF. 2011. (Little Book Of Ser.). (ENG., Illus.). 128p. 11.99 *(978-1-907803-11-6(4))* G2 Entertainment Ltd. GBR. Dist: BookMasters Distribution Services (BDS).
Thompson, Steve, et al. Air Combat Manoeuvres: The Technique & History of Air Fighting for Flight Simulation. 2008. (ENG., Illus.). 256p. pap. 49.95 **(978-1-903223-94-9(6))** Classic Pubns. GBR. Dist: BookMasters Distribution Services (BDS).
Thompson, Warren & McLaren, David. Mig Alley - Sabres vs. Migs over Korea: Pilot Accounts & the Complete Combat Record of the F-86 Sabre 1950-53. 2010. (Illus.). 288p. 69.95 *(978-1-906033-97-2(8))* Helion & Co., Ltd. GBR. Dist: Casemate Pubs. & Bk. Distributors, LLC.
Time-Life Books Editors. Air Combat. (Illus.). 196p. 24.00 *(978-1-84447-220-8(5))* Time Life Value GBR. Dist: Mercury Bks. Ltd.
Time-Life Books Staff, contrib. by. New Faces of War Air Strike. (Illus.). 196p. 24.00 *(978-1-84447-224-6(8))* Time Life Value GBR. Dist: Mercury Bks. Ltd.
van Schyndel, Heiko. Aviation Code of the Russian Federation. 2010. 192p. 88.00 *(978-90-77596-80-7(1))* Eleven International Publishing NLD. Dist: International Specialized Bk. Services.
Venter, Al. Gunship Ace: The Wars of Neall Ellis, Gunship Pilot & Mercenary. 2011. (Illus.). 432p. 32.95 **(978-1-61200-070-1(3)**, Casemate) Casemate Pubs. & Bk. Distributors, LLC.
Walker, Bryce. Fighting Jets. (Illus.). 176p. 24.00 *(978-1-84447-035-8(0))* Time Life Value GBR. Dist: Mercury Bks. Ltd.
Zinsmeister, Karl. Boots on the Ground: A Month with the 82nd Airborne in the Battle for Iraq. pap. *(978-0-312-32664-7(5)*, St. Martin's Paperbacks) St. Martin's Pr.

AIRBORNE INFECTION

ABBE Scientist Research Division Staff. HIV as an air-borne Infection: Index, Reference & Medical Analysis of New Reserch Information for All Nations. 2008. (Illus.). 160p. ring bd. 69.95 *(978-0-7883-3876-2(5))* ABBE Pubs. Assn. of Washington, D.C.
Kowalski, Wladyslaw J. Hospital Airborne Infection Control. 2011. (ENG., Illus.). 370p. 149.95 *(978-1-4398-2196-1(8)*, CRC Press) Taylor & Francis Group GBR. Dist: Taylor & Francis Group.
National Safety Council (NSC) Staff. Bloodborne & Airborne Pathogens. 2nd ed. 2009. 64p. pap. *(978-0-07-338288-3(4))* McGraw-Hill Cos., The.
Proceedings of the Workshop on Engineering Controls for Preventing Airborne Infections in Workers in Health Care & Related Facilities. 184p. pap. 40.00 *(978-0-7881-3921-5(5))* DIANE Publishing Co.

AIRBORNE TROOPS

see also Parachute Troops

Fauntleroy, Barbara Gavin, et al. The General & His Daughter: The War Time Letters of General James M. Gavin to His Daughter Barbara. Wurst, Gayle, ed. 2nd ed. 2007. (World War II: the Global, Human, & Ethical Dimension Ser.). (ENG., Illus.). 284p. 32.00 *(978-0-8232-2687-0(5))* Fordham Univ. Pr.
Flanagan, Edward M., Jr. 11th Airborne Division. Date not set. (Illus.). 176p. 49.95 *(978-1-56311-111-2(X))* Turner Publishing Co.
Greenwood, John T. & Wright, Robert K. Airborne Forces at War: From Parachute Test Platoon to the 21st Century. 2007. (Illus.). 214p. 39.95 *(978-1-59114-028-3(5))* Naval Institute Pr.
Harclerode, Peter. Wings of War: Airborne Warfare, 1918-1945. 2007. (Cassell Military Paperbacks Ser.). (ENG., Illus.). 656p. pap. 16.95 *(978-0-304-36730-6(3))* Cassell Guides GBR. Dist: Sterling Publishing Co., Inc.
Pushies, Fred. 82nd Airborne Division. 2008. (Military Power Ser.). (ENG., Illus.). 128p. pap. 19.99 *(978-0-7603-3465-2(X)*, 076033465X, Zenith Pr.) MBI Publishing Co. LLC.
Reinhardt, Generalmajor Hellmuth. Airborne Operations in World War II. 2008. 90p. pap. 12.95 *(978-1-4357-5851-3(X))* Lulu Enterprises Inc.
Time-Life Books Staff, contrib. by. Sky Soldiers. (New Face of War Ser.). (Illus.). 196p. 24.00 *(978-1-84447-227-7(2))* Time Life Value GBR. Dist: Mercury Bks. Ltd.
Turner Publishing Company Staff. 82nd Airborne Division: Association History Book. Date not set. (Illus.). 144p. 49.95 *(978-1-56311-272-0(8))* Turner Publishing Co.
War Office Staff. Recognition of Airborne Equipment. 2009. 174p. pap. *(978-1-84734-943-9(9))* Naval & Military Pr., The.
Wright, Stephen L. The Last Drop: Operation Varsity, March 24-25 1945. 2008. (ENG., Illus.). 336p. 29.95 *(978-0-8117-0310-9(X))* Stackpole Bks.
82nd Airborne. 2011. pap. 19.95 *(978-1-59652-773-7(0))* Turner Publishing Co.

AIRBRUSH ART

Here are entered works on spray techniques in art. Technical works on painting using the spray technique are found under Spray painting.

Grosse, Katharina. Eat, Child, Eat! 2011. (ENG & GER., Illus.). 112p. *(978-3-942405-19-5(9))* Die Gestalten Verlag.
Morton, David. The Art of Airbrushing: Techniques & step-by-step projects for the Novice. 2011. (Artists Library). (ENG., Illus.). 64p. pap. 9.95 *(978-1-60058-214-1(1)*, 1600582141) Foster, Walter Publishing, Inc.
Uccellini, Giorgio. The Art of Airbrushing: A Simple Guide to Mastering the Craft. 2011. (ENG., Illus.). 192p. pap. 21.95 *(978-1-86108-830-7(2))* Guild of Master Craftsman Pubns., Ltd. GBR. Dist: Sterling Publishing Co., Inc.

AIRBRUSH ART—TECHNIQUE

Bortles, JoAnn. Airbrush Painting: Advanced Techniques. 2009. (Motorbooks Workshop Ser.). (ENG., Illus.). 176p. pap. 24.99 *(978-0-7603-3503-1(6)*, 0760335036, Motorbooks) MBI Publishing Co. LLC.
—How to Master Airbrush Painting Techniques. rev. ed. 2007. (Motorbooks Workshop Ser.). (ENG., Illus.). 192p. pap. 24.95 *(978-0-7603-2399-1(2)*, 0760323992, Motorbooks) MBI Publishing Co. LLC.
Downie, Robert. How to Use an Airbrush. 2nd ed. 2008. (FineScale Modeler Ser.). (Illus.). 94p. pap. 21.95 *(978-0-89024-706-8(4))* Kalmbach Publishing Co., Bks. Div.
Fraser, Craig. Automotive Cheap Tricks & Special F/X II: Learn How to Paint Cars, Trucks, Motorcycles, Musical Instruments, Surfboards, & R. C. Cars. 2010. (ENG., Illus.). 216p. pap. 34.95 *(978-0-9637336-7-2(2)*, 0963733672) Airbrush Action, Inc.
Hathaway, Norman & Salisbury, Mike. Overspray: Riding High with the Kings of California Airbrush Art, 1 vol. Nadel, Dan, ed. 2008. (ENG., Illus.). 226p. 50.00 *(978-0-9794153-0-2(6))* PictureBox, Inc.
Kuck, Roland. Airbrushing Techniques: Step-by-Step. 2010. (ENG., Illus.). 160p. pap. 29.95 *(978-1-84448-524-6(2))* Search Pr., Ltd. GBR. Dist: Independent Pubs. Group.
Mitchel, Doug. Air Brushing 101. 2008. (Paint Expert Ser.). (ENG., Illus.). 144p. pap. 27.95 *(978-1-929133-67-3(7)*, 1929133677) Wolfgang Pubns., Inc.
Remus, Timothy. Airbrush Bible. 2010. (ENG., Illus.). 176p. pap. 29.95 *(978-1-929133-86-4(3)*, 1929133863) Wolfgang Pubns., Inc.

AIRCRAFT, FIXED WING

see Airplanes

AIRCRAFT, LIGHTER-THAN-AIR

see Airships

AIRCRAFT, NUCLEAR

see Nuclear Aircraft

AIRCRAFT, STEALTH

see Stealth Aircraft

AIRCRAFT ACCIDENTS

see also Korean Air Lines Incident, 1983; Pan Am Flight 103 Bombing Incident, 1988

Ahmed, Rashid. Bird Hazard in Aviation. 2009. 64p. pap. 12.99 *(978-1-4490-3334-7(2))* AuthorHouse.
Argenta, Kregg. The Marshall Miracle: From Aviation Disaster to Gridiron Glory. 2008. 151p. pap. 24.95 *(978-1-60563-521-7(9))* PublishAmerica, Inc.
Arthur, Max. The Busby Babes: Men of Magic. 2008. (ENG., Illus.). 192p. pap. 19.95 *(978-1-84596-341-5(5))* Mainstream Publishing Co., Ltd. GBR. Dist: Independent Pubs. Group.
Aviation Safety: Can NASA Do More to Protect the Public?: Hearings Before the Committee on Science & Technology, House of Representatives, One Hundred Tenth Congress, First Session, October 31, 2007. 2008. (Illus.). v, 404p. *(978-0-16-081270-5(4)*, 552-070-37662-3) United States Government Printing Office.
Aviation Safety: One Year after the Crash of Flight 3407: Hearing Before the Subcommittee on Aviation Operations, Safety, & Security of the Committee on Commerce, Science, & Transportation, United States Senate, One Hundred Eleventh Congress, Second Session, February 25, 2010. 2010. (Illus.). iii, 46p. *(978-0-16-086805-4(X)*, 552-070-41721-4) United States Government Printing Office.
Bibel, George. Beyond the Black Box: The Forensics of Airplane Crashes. 2007. (ENG., Illus.). 408p. 33.00 *(978-0-8018-8631-7(7))* Johns Hopkins Univ. Pr.
Black, Dale & Gire, Ken. Flight to Heaven: A Plane Crash... A Lone Survivor... A Journey to Heaven — and Back. 2010. (Illus.). 192p. pap. 14.99 *(978-0-7642-0794-5(6))* Bethany Hse. Pubs.
Botting, Douglas. Epic of Flight the Giant Airship. 2006. (Illus.). 176p. 24.00 *(978-1-84447-040-2(7))* Time Life Value GBR. Dist: Mercury Bks. Ltd.
Burgess, W. L. The Day I Almost Lost It. 2008. 92p. pap. 16.95 *(978-1-60441-201-7(1))* PublishAmerica, Inc.
Burk, George A. Laugh You Live, Cry You Die... The Sequel to A Bridge Never Crossed — A Survivor's Search for Meaning. A Burn Survivor's Triumph over Tragedy. 2011. (Illus.). pap. 16.95 **(978-1-59630-068-2(X))** Science & Humanities Pr.
Burkill, Peter & Burkill, Maria. Thirty Seconds to Impact. 2010. (Illus.). 340p. pap. 19.99 *(978-1-4490-8858-3(9))* AuthorHouse.
Butts, Thomas A. Amazing Benefits in Traveling on Someone Else's Dime. 2010. 134p. pap. 45.07 *(978-1-4269-4224-2(9))* Trafford Publishing.
Byrne, Gerry. Flight 427: Anatomy of an Air Disaster. 2010. (ENG., Illus.). 312p. pap. 27.50 *(978-1-4419-2923-5(1)*, 1441929231) Springer.
Chorley, W. R. Royal Air Force Bomber Command Losses Vol. 9: Roll of Honour, 1939-1947. 2010. (ENG., Illus.). 494p. pap. 36.95 *(978-1-85780-195-8(4))* Allan, Ian Publishing GBR. Dist: BookMasters Distribution Services (BDS).
Clearwater, John. Broken Arrow #1: The World's First Lost Atomic Bomb. 2008. (Illus.). 160p. pap. 14.95 **(978-0-88839-596-2(5))** Hancock Hse. Pubs.
Cole, Ben. Four down on OLd Peachtree Road. 2006. per. 18.95 *(978-0-9788967-0-6(X))* Crosswind Pubns., Ltd.
Cole, Robert E., ed. The Incident That Could Have Killed Pittsburgh. 2008. (Illus.). 245p. pap. 19.95 *(978-1-55856-495-4(0))* Closson Pr.
Connor, Jeff. Lost Babes: Manchester United & the Forgotten Victims of Munich. 2007. (ENG., Illus.). 320p. pap. 15.95 *(978-0-00-720808-1(1))* HarperCollins Pubs. Ltd. GBR. Dist: Independent Pubs. Group.
Corsetti, Emilio, III. 35 Miles from Shore: The Ditching & Rescue of ALM Flight 980. 2008. (ENG., Illus.). 352p. per. 14.95 *(978-0-9778971-0-0(9))* Odyssey Publishing LLC.
Cramoisi, George. Air Crash Investigations: The Crash of Comair Flight 5191. 2009. 204p. pap. 26.50 *(978-0-557-13648-3(2))* Lulu Enterprises Inc.
—AIR CRASH INVESTIGATIONS: LOST over the ATLANTIC, the Mysterious Disappearance of Air France Flight 447. 2010. 308p. pap. 32.50 *(978-0-557-48194-1(5))* Lulu Enterprises Inc.
—AIR CRASH INVESTIGATIONS: RUNNING OUT of FUEL, How Air Transat 236 Managed to Fly 100 Miles without Fuel & Land Safely. 2010. 196p. pap. 26.50 *(978-0-557-25070-7(6))* Lulu Enterprises Inc.
—The Crash of Comair 5191. 2009. 204p. pap. 26.50 *(978-0-557-11165-7(X))* Lulu Enterprises Inc.
Cross, Wilbur. Disaster at the Pole: The Crash of the Airship Italia-A Harrowing True Tale of Arctic Endurance & Survival. 2010. 348p. pap. 22.95 *(978-1-4401-8674-5(X))* iUniverse, Inc.
Dagtoglou, P. D. & Ehlers, P. Nikolai. Airline Liability: A Seminar on Liability & Claims Handling in the Airline & Aerospace Industries, Munich, 12 May 1997. 109p. *(978-960-232-721-0(9))* Ekdoseis Ant. N. Sakkoyaa.
De Kuyffer, Erik. The Integration of Uavs into Controlled Airspace. 2009. 124p. pap. *(978-3-639-20081-2(0))* VDM Verlag Dr. Mueller e.K.
Dismukes, R. Key. Human Error in Aviation. 2009. (Critical Essays on Human Factors in Aviation Ser.). (Illus.). 604p. 325.00 *(978-0-7546-2831-6(0))* Ashgate Publishing Co.
Dismukes, R. Key, et al. The Limits of Expertise: Rethinking Pilot Error & the Causes of Airline Accidents. 2007. (Ashgate Studies in Human Factors for Flight Operations). (Illus.). 364p. 39.95 *(978-0-7546-4965-6(2))*; 124.95 *(978-0-7546-4964-9(4))* Ashgate Publishing Co.
Doylerush, Edward. Rocks in the Clouds: High-Ground Aircraft Crashes of South Wales. 2010. (ENG., Illus.). 112p. pap. 21.95 *(978-1-85780-281-8(0))* Allan, Ian Publishing GBR. Dist: BookMasters Distribution Services (BDS).
Earhart, Amelia. Last Flight - Amelia Earhart's Flying Adventures. 2009. 260p. pap. *(978-1-906393-14-4(1))* Trotamundas Pr., Ltd.
FAA's Oversight of On-Demand Aircraft Operators: Hearing Before the Subcommittee on Aviation of the Committee on Transportation & Infrastructure, House of Representatives, One Hundred Eleventh Congress, Second Session, March 17, 2010. 2010. (Illus.). xiv, 116p. **(978-0-16-086769-9(X)**, 552-070-41690-1) United States Government Printing Office.
The Federal Aviation Administration's Call to Action on Airline Safety & Pilot Training: Hearing Before the Subcommittee on Aviation of the Committee on Transportation & Infrastructure, House of Representatives, One Hundred Eleventh Congress, First Session, September 23, 2009. 2009. xviii, 192p. *(978-0-16-085163-6(7)*, 552-070-40517-8) United States Government Printing Office.
Firman, Dorothy & Quirk, Kevin. Brace for Impact: Miracle on the Hudson Survivors Share Their Stories of near Death & Hope for New Life. 2010. (ENG.). 288p. pap. 14.95 *(978-0-7573-1357-8(4))* Health Communications, Inc.
Fischer, Harvey L. & Pearce, Jennifer M., eds. Threat of Volcanic Ash to Aviation. 2011. **(978-1-61324-456-2(8))** Nova Science Pubs., Inc.
Fitzgerald, Allistair. Air Crash Investigations: MASS MURDER in the SKY, the Bombing of Air India Flight 182. 2011. 356p. pap. 33.95 **(978-0-557-98184-7(0))** Lulu Enterprises Inc.
—AIR CRASH INVESTIGATIONS: DISASTER in the EVERGLADES the Crash of ValuJet Airlines Flight 592. 2009. 332p. pap. 32.50 *(978-0-557-23626-8(6))* Lulu Enterprises Inc.
—AIR CRASH INVESTIGATIONS: LOCKERBIE, the Bombing of PANAM Flight 103. 2010. 284p. pap. 32.50 *(978-0-557-72932-6(7))* Lulu Enterprises Inc.
—AIR CRASH INVESTIGATIONS: PILOT ERROR KILLS 50 PEOPLE in BUFFALO, the Crash of Colgan Air Flight 3407. 2010. 397p. pap. 35.95 *(978-0-557-39559-0(3))* Lulu Enterprises Inc.
—Air crash investigations: tenerife airport disaster, the world's deadliest plane crash Ever. 2010. 196p. pap. 26.95 *(978-0-557-45179-1(5))* Lulu Enterprises Inc.
—AIR CRASH INVESTIGATIONS: the Crash of Alaska Airlines Flight 261. 2009. 328p. pap. 32.50 *(978-0-557-13911-8(2))* Lulu Enterprises Inc.
Flight Safety Foundation Staff, compiled by. 18th Annual European Aviation Safety Seminar (EASS 2006) Safety Means Participating. 2007. 688p. pap. 132.00 *(978-1-60423-384-1(2))* Curran Assocs., Inc.
—52nd Annual Corporate Aviation Safety Seminar (CASS 2007) The Foundation for Excellence. 2007. 747p. pap. 132.00 *(978-1-60423-385-8(0))* Curran Assocs., Inc.
—59th Annual International Air Safety Seminar & IFA 36th International Conference 2006: Enhancing Safety Worldwide. 2007. 1452p. pap. 125.00 *(978-1-60423-393-3(1))* Curran Assocs., Inc.
Forrester, Peter. Wings over Somerset: Aircraft Crashes since the End of World War II. 2012. (ENG., Illus.). 192p. pap. 24.95 **(978-0-7524-6579-1(1))** History Pr. Ltd.,The GBR. Dist: Independent Pubs. Group.
Forsyth, Robert. Fw 190 Sturmbock vs B-17: Europe 1944-45. 2009. (Duel Ser.). (ENG., Illus.). 80p. pap. 17.95 *(978-1-84603-941-6(X))* Osprey Publishing, Ltd. GBR. Dist: Random Hse., Inc.
Garcia, Michel & Gaynecoetche, Jean-Louis. Aircrash 2000-2009. 2011. (FRE & ENG., Illus.). 48p. pap. 30.00 **(978-2-918590-00-2(2))** Listemann, Philippe FRA. Dist: Casemate Pubs. & Bk. Distributors, LLC.
Gero, David. Aviation Disasters: The World's Major Civil Airliner Crashes Since 1950. 4th ed. 2006. (ENG., Illus.). 368p. 44.95 *(978-0-7509-3146-5(9))* Sutton Publishing.
—Aviation Disasters: The World's Major Civil Airliner Crashes since 1950. 5th ed. 2009. (ENG., Illus.). 368p. pap. 27.95 *(978-0-7524-5039-1(5))* History Pr. Ltd.,The GBR. Dist: Independent Pubs. Group.
—Early Aviation Disasters: The World's Major Airliner Crashes. 2011. (ENG., Illus.). 192p. pap. 22.95 *(978-0-7524-5987-5(2))* History Pr. Ltd.,The GBR. Dist: Independent Pubs. Group.
—Military Aviation Disasters: Significant Losses Since 1908. 2nd ed. 2010. (ENG., Illus.). 192p. 34.95 *(978-1-84425-645-7(6)*, 1844256456) Haynes Publishing PLC GBR. Dist: MBI Distribution Services/Quayside Distribution.
Gill, Robert, et al. Aircraft Accidents: A Practical Guide for Responders. 2007. (ENG., Illus.). 256p. (C). per. 64.95 *(978-1-4018-7910-5(1))* Delmar Cengage Learning.

Gitlin, Martin. The Hudson Plane Landing. 2012. (Essential Events Ser.). 112p. (YA). (gr. 7-12). 34.22 ***(978-1-61783-309-0(6))*** ABDO Publishing Co.
Gowdy, Rex. Crashing Las Vegas: Memoirs of an Aircraft Crash Investigator in the Heyday of Las Vegas. 2007. 76p. per. 16.95 *(978-1-4241-9541-1(1))* PublishAmerica, Inc.
Greenlee, Craig T. November Ever After: A Memoir of Tragedy & Triumph in the Wake of the 1970 Marshall Football Plane Crash. 2011. 168p. pap. 12.95 ***(978-1-4620-0404-1(0))*** iUniverse, Inc.
Griffioen, Hans. AIR CRASH INVESTIGATION: the Crash of Air France Flight 358. 2009. 191p. pap. 25.95 *(978-1-4092-8847-3(1))* Lulu Enterprises Inc.
—Air Crash Investigations: LOST PROPELLER BLADE KILLS 8, the Crash of Atlantic Southeast Airlines Flight 529. 2011. 156p. pap. 25.50 ***(978-1-257-07001-5(0))*** Lulu Enterprises Inc.
—AIR CRASH INVESTIGATIONS: MECHANICAL FAILURE or SUICIDE (1) the Crash of SilkAir Flight 185. 2010. 328p. pap. 32.50 *(978-0-557-67306-3(2))* Lulu Enterprises Inc.
—AIR CRASH INVESTIGATIONS: the Crash of American Airlines Flight 587. 2009. 218p. pap. 27.50 *(978-1-4092-8602-8(9))* Lulu Enterprises Inc.
—AIR CRASH INVESTIGATIONS: the Crash of Helios Airways Flight 522. 2009. 215p. pap. 27.50 *(978-1-4092-8545-8(6))* Lulu Enterprises Inc.
—AIR CRASH INVESTIGATIONS:the Crash of Swissair Flight 111. 2009. (ENG.). 392p. pap. 34.95 *(978-1-4092-8352-2(6))* Lulu Enterprises Inc.
Gunby, David & Temple, Pelham. Royal Air Force Bomber Losses in the Middle East & Mediterranean, 1939-1942, Vol. I. 2007. (ENG.). 224p. pap. 26.95 *(978-1-85780-234-4(9))* Midland Counties Publ.
Henchard Press, creator. The Marshall Story: College Football's Greatest Comeback. 2006. (Illus.). 228p. per. 24.95 *(978-0-9776711-9-9(4))* Henchard Pr., Ltd.
Hood. Dealing with Disaster in Japan. 2011. (Routledge Contemporary Japan Ser.). (ENG., Illus.). 288p. (C). 155.00 *(978-0-415-45662-3(2))* Routledge.
The Hudson River Airspace & Management of Uncontrolled Airspace Corridors: Hearing Before the Subcommittee on Aviation of the Committee on Transportation & Infrastructure, House of Representatives, One Hundred Eleventh Congress, First Session, September 16, 2009. 2009. (Illus.). xvi, 175p. *(978-0-16-084739-4(7)*, 552-070-40216-1) United States Government Printing Office.
Jampoler, Andrew. Adak. 2011. (Illus.). 240p. pap. 17.95 ***(978-1-59114-410-6(8))*** Naval Institute Pr.
Kalafatas, Michael N. Bird Strike: The Crash of the Boston Electra. 2010. (ENG., Illus.). 200p. 24.95 *(978-1-58465-897-9(5)*, Brandeis University Press) Univ. Pr. of New England.
Kelly, Paul W. R. Found in a Foot Locker: The Forgotten Sacrifice of Robert L. Todd. 2009. (Illus.). 220p. pap. 14.49 *(978-1-4389-4253-7(2))* AuthorHouse.
Kenville, Kimberly A. Helping Airport & Air Carrier Employees Cope with Traumatic Events. 2009. (Illus.). 74p. *(978-0-309-11797-5(6))* Transportation Research Board.
Kiefer, Michael. Democrat Down. 2008. 230p. pap. 21.95 *(978-1-4357-4514-8(0))* Lulu Enterprises Inc.
Knott, Richard. Flying Boats of the Empire: The Rise & Fall of the Ships of the Sky. 2011. (ENG., Illus.). 272p. 39.95 ***(978-0-7090-8759-5(4))*** Hale, Robert Ltd. GBR. Dist: Independent Pubs. Group.
Korkuc, Bob. Finding a Fallen Hero: The Death of a Ball Turret Gunner. 2008. (ENG., Illus.). 272p. 24.95 *(978-0-8061-3892-3(0))* Univ. of Oklahoma Pr.
Korovin, Editor Igor & Korovin, Editor. Air Crash Investigations: The WORST SINGLE PLANE CRASH in AMERICAN HISTORY, the Crash of American Airlines Flight 191. 2011. 196p. pap. 26.95 ***(978-1-257-75207-2(3))*** Lulu Enterprises Inc.
Korovin, Igor. Air Crash Investigations: POLISH PRESIDENT DIES in AIR CRASH the Crash of Polish Air Force Flight 101. 2011. 256p. pap. 29.50 ***(978-1-257-02447-6(7))*** Lulu Enterprises Inc.
—Air Crash Investigations: The Crash of Aeroflot Flight 821. 2009. 180p. pap. 25.50 *(978-0-557-13216-4(9))* Lulu Enterprises Inc.
—AIR CRASH INVESTIGATIONS: HARD LANDING KILLS 9, the Crash of Turkish Airlines Flight TK 1951 on Amsterdam Schiphol Airport. 2010. 400p. pap. 36.50 *(978-0-557-52028-2(2))* Lulu Enterprises Inc.
—AIR CRASH INVESTIGATIONS: HORROR in GUAM, the Crash of Korean Air Flight 801. 2010. 324p. pap. 31.95 *(978-0-557-32356-2(8))* Lulu Enterprises Inc.
Langewiesche, William. Fly by Wire. 2010. (ENG., Illus.). 208p. pap. 14.00 *(978-0-312-65538-9(X))* Picador.
—Fly by Wire: The Geese, the Glide, the Miracle on the Hudson. l.t. ed. 2010. (ENG.). 290p. 31.95 *(978-1-4104-2546-1(0))* Thorndike Pr.
Lauing, Daniel A. Manitou, Fountains of the Deep: The Crash of Flight 585, March 3, 1991, Widefield, Colorado. 2012. (ENG.). 320p. 26.50 *(978-0-9641269-0-9(7))* Benchmark Investigative Group, Inc.
Leloudas, George. Risk & Liability in Air Law. 2009. 224p. 612.00 *(978-1-84311-834-3(3))* Informa Professional GBR. Dist: International Specialized Bk. Services.
Logan, Edward F. Jump, Damn It, Jump! Memoir of a Downed B-17 Pilot in World War II. l.t. alt. ed. 2008. (ENG., Illus.). 301p. pap. 35.00 *(978-0-7864-3940-9(8))* McFarland & Co., Inc. Pubs.
Luna, Adrian. Bringing the Inside Out. 2008. 212p. per. *(978-3-8364-3587-1(X))* VDM Verlag Dr. Mueller e.K.
Lupoli, Luis. Organizational Accidents in an Air Force: Brazilian Squadron Commanders' Perceptions. 2008. 168p. pap. *(978-3-8364-8349-0(1))* VDM Verlag Dr. Mueller e.K.
McCauley, Bob. The Still Small Voice. 2011. 340p. pap. 15.95 ***(978-1-60920-022-0(5))*** Ajoyin Publishing, Inc.
McCormick, Barnes Warnock & Papadakis, M. P. Aircraft Accident Reconstruction & Litigation. 4th ed. 2011. *(978-1-933264-76-9(4))* Lawyers & Judges Publishing Co., Inc.
Merlin, Peter & Moore, Tony. X-Plane Crashes: Exploring Experimental, Rocket Plane, & Spycraft Incidents, Accidents & Crash Sites. 2008. (Illus.). 160p. 32.95 *(978-1-58007-121-5(X))* Specialty Pr. Pubs. & Wholesalers, Inc.
Michaelides-Mateou, Sofia & Mateou, Andreas. Flying in the Face of Criminalization: The Safety Implications of Prosecuting Aviation Professionals for Accidents. 2010. (Illus.). 234p. 99.95 *(978-1-4094-0767-6(5))* Ashgate Publishing Co.
Motevalli, Vahid, et al. Evaluation & Mitigation of Aircraft Slide Evacuation Injuries. 2008. (ACRP Report Ser.: Vol. 2). (Illus.). 77p. pap. 47.00 *(978-0-309-09933-2(1))* Transportation Research Board.
The National Transportation Safety Board's Most Wanted Aviation Safety Improvements: Hearing Before the Subcommittee on Aviation of the Committee on Transportation & Infrastructure, House of Representatives, One Hundred Tenth Congress, First Session, June 6, 2007. 2007. xvi, 166p. *(978-0-16-079953-2(8)*, 552-070-36780-2) United States Government Printing Office.
Nesbit, Roy C. Missing: Believed Killed: Amelia Earhart, Amy Johnson, Glenn Miller & the Duke of Kent. 2010. (Illus.). 160p. pap. 24.95 *(978-1-84884-319-6(4))* Pen & Sword Bks. Ltd. GBR. Dist: Casemate Pubs. & Bk. Distributors, LLC.
Nichols, Nikki. Frozen in Time: The Enduring Legacy of the 1961 U. S. Figure Skating Team. 2008. (ENG.). 262p. pap. 15.95 *(978-1-57860-334-3(X))* Clerisy Pr.
Nielson, Stephanie. Heaven Is Here: An Incredible Story of Hope, Triumph, & Everyday Joy. 2012. (ENG.). 277p. 23.99 ***(978-1-4013-4179-4(9))*** Hyperion Pr.
Ollestad, Norman. Crazy for the Storm: A Memoir of Survival. 2009. (Playaway Adult Nonfiction Ser.). 59.99 *(978-1-4332-9097-8(9))* Findaway World, LLC.
—Crazy for the Storm: A Memoir of Survival. 2010. (ENG.). 304p. pap. 14.99 *(978-0-06-176678-7(X)*, Ecco) 2009. (ENG.). 288p. 25.99 *(978-0-06-176672-5(0)*, Ecco) 2009. 360p. pap. 25.99 *(978-0-06-178208-4(4)*, HarperLuxe) HarperCollins Pubs.
Oskins, James C. & Maggelet, Michael H. Broken Arrow - the Declassified History of U. S. Nuclear Weapons Accidents. 2008. 323p. pap. 49.95 *(978-1-4357-0361-2(8))* Lulu Enterprises Inc.
Ottaway, Susan. Fire over Heathrow. 2008. (Illus.). 208p. 45.00 *(978-1-84415-739-6(3))* Pen & Sword Bks. Ltd. GBR. Dist: Casemate Pubs. & Bk. Distributors, LLC.
Parrado, Nando. Miracle in the Andes: 72 Days on the Mountain & My Long Trek Home. 2007. (ENG., Illus.). 291p. 21.60 *(978-0-7569-8847-0(0))* Perfection Learning Corp.
Parrado, Nando & Rause, Vince. Miracle in the Andes. 2011. 14.05 *(978-0-7848-3407-7(5)*, Everbind) Marco Bk. Co.
—Miracle in the Andes: 72 Days on the Mountain & My Long Trek Home. 2007. (ENG., Illus.). 304p. pap. 14.00 *(978-1-4000-9769-2(X)*, Three Rivers Pr.) Crown Publishing Group.
Parry, Simon W. Spitfire Hunters: The Inside Stories Behind the Best of the TV Aircraft Digs. 2010. (ENG., Illus.). 128p. pap. 32.95 *(978-0-9554735-5-5(1))* Red Kite GBR. Dist: BookMasters Distribution Services (BDS).
Penny, Jerry. Down in Charlotte: The Plane, the Train, & the Burning Broom. 2008. (Illus.). 68p. per. 9.95 net. *(978-0-9679041-2-2(9))* Blue Mound Pr.
Prochnau, William, et al. Miracle on the Hudson: The Survivors of Flight 1549 Tell Their Extraordinary Stories of Courage, Faith, & Determination. 2010. (ENG., Illus.). 288p. pap. 15.00 *(978-0-345-52045-6(9)*, Ballantine Bks.) Random House Publishing Group.
Ragan, Bill, MS. Lag: A Look at Circadian Desynchronization. 2007. 126p. pap. 12.95 *(978-1-4357-0221-9(2))* Lulu Enterprises Inc.
Ralph, Barry. The Crash of Little Eva, 1 vol. 2006. (ENG., Illus.). 240p. pap. 19.95 *(978-1-58980-447-0(3))* Pelican Publishing Co., Inc.
Runway Safety: An Update: Hearing Before the Subcommittee on Aviation of the Committee on Transportation & Infrastructure, House of Representatives, One Hundred Tenth Congress, Second Session, September 25, 2008. 2008. (Illus.). xiii, 217p. *(978-0-16-083849-1(5)*, 552-070-39546-6) United States Government Printing Office.
Runway Safety: Hearing Before the Subcommittee on Aviation of the Committee on Transportation & Infrastructure, House of Representatives, One Hundred Tenth Congress, Second Session, February 13, 2008. 2008. (Illus.). vi, 351p. *(978-0-16-082840-9(6)*, 552-070-38820-6) United States Government Printing Office.
Sabbag, Robert. Down Around Midnight: A Memoir of Crash & Survival. 2010. (ENG.). 224p. (gr. 12). 15.00 *(978-0-14-311760-5(2)*, Penguin (Non-Classics)) Penguin Group (USA) Inc.
Saunders, Andy. Finding the Fallen: Outstanding Aircrew Mysteries from the First World War to Desert Storm Investigated & Solved. 2011. (Illus.). 208p. 39.95 ***(978-1-908117-10-6(9))*** Grub Street GBR. Dist: Casemate Pubs. & Bk. Distributors, LLC.
Severn, Theresa. In the Wake of the Storm: Living Beyond the Tragedy of Flight 4184. 2008. (ENG.). 25.00 *(978-0-9796062-0-5(9))* North Cross Pr., Ltd.
Soucie, David & Cheek, Ozzie. Why Planes Crash: An Accident Investigator Fights for Safe Skies. 2011. (ENG., Illus.). 240p. 24.95 *(978-1-61608-426-4(X)*, 608426) Skyhorse Publishing Co., Inc.
Stekel, Peter. Final Flight: The Mystery of a World-War II Plane Crash & the Frozen Airmen in the High Sierra. 2010. (ENG., Illus.). 256p. pap. 15.95 *(978-0-89997-475-0(9))* Wilderness Pr.
Stich, Rodney. Unfriendly Skies. 2007. pap. 25.00 *(978-0-932438-31-7(8))* Silverpeak Enterprises, Inc.
Stone, James E. Plane That Killed Knute Rockne. 2010. 168p. pap. 15.95 *(978-1-935089-13-1(7))* Acacia Publishing, Inc.
Sturkey, Marion F. Mid-Air: Accident Reports & Voice Transcripts from Military & Airline Mid-Air Collisions. Sturkey, Marion F., ed. 2008. (ENG., Illus.). 477p. pap. 19.00 *(978-0-9650814-7-4(8))* Heritage Pr. International.
Sullenberger, Chesley B. Highest Duty: My Search for What Really Matters. 2009. (ENG.). 64.99 *(978-1-61587-522-1(0))* Findaway World, LLC.
Sullenberger, Chesley B. & Zaslow, Jeffrey. Highest Duty: My Search for What Really Matters. 2010. (ENG., Illus.). 368p. pap. 15.99 *(978-0-06-192469-9(5)*, William Morrow Paperbacks) 2009. (ENG., Illus.). 352p. 25.99 *(978-0-06-192468-2(7)*, Morrow, William & Co.) 2009. 424p. pap. 25.99 *(978-0-06-192758-4(9)*, HarperLuxe) HarperCollins Pubs.
Tippets, John M. Hearts of Courage: The Gillam Plane Crash & the Amazing True Story of Survival in the Frozen Wilderness of Alaska. 2008. (Illus.). 144p. pap. 19.95 *(978-1-59433-077-3(8))* Publication Consultants.
U. S. Antional Transportation Safety Board. How & Why Did Flight Five-Fourteen Kill Ninety-two People: An Accident Report. 8.00 *(978-0-405-09161-2(3)*, 19408) Ayer Co. Pubs., Inc.
United States, Congress House Committee on Transportation and Infrastructure Subcommittee on Aviation Staff, contrib. by. Oversight of Federal Aviation Administration Safety Programs: Hearing Before the Subcommittee on Aviation of the Committee on Transportation & Infrastructure, House of Representatives, One Hundred Ninth Congress, Second Session, September 20, 2006. 2007. (Illus.). v, 194p. *(978-0-16-078468-2(9)*, 552-070-35754-8) United States Government Printing Office.
US Airways Flight 1549 Accident: Hearing Before the Subcommittee on Aviation of the Committee on Transportation & Infrastructure, House of Representatives, One Hundred Eleventh Congress, First Session, February 24, 2009. 2009. (Illus.). xvii, 251p. *(978-0-16-084260-3(3)*, 552-070-39830-9) United States Government Printing Office.
Veronico, Nicholas A. Aircraft: A Guide to Finding Aircraft Crash Sites. (Illus.). 76p. pap. 9.95 *(978-0-9636332-0-0(1))* MBI Publishing Co. LLC.
Vierci, Pablo. La sociedad de la Nieve. 2009. (SPA.). 338p. pap. 19.95 *(978-0-307-39281-7(3))* Random House Mondadori ESP. Dist: Random Hse., Inc.
Voogt, Alex De & D'Oliveira, Teresa C. Mechanisms in the Chain of Safety: Research & Operational Experiences in Aviation Psychology. 2012. (Illus.). 150p. 99.95 ***(978-1-4094-1254-0(7))*** Ashgate Publishing Co.
Wagner, Arthur & Braxton, Leon E. Glacier Gooney. 2010. (ENG., Illus.). 160p. pap. 18.00 *(978-0-615-39033-8(1))* Printer's Ink.
Walsh, Thomas L. Damnyankee: A WWII Story of Tragedy & Survival off the West of Ireland. 2008. 180p. pap. 17.95 *(978-1-4327-2910-3(1))* Outskirts Pr., Inc.
Ward, Barbara. Dambuster Raid Crash Sites. 2007. (Illus.). 176p. pap. 24.95 *(978-1-84415-568-2(4))* Pen & Sword Bks. Ltd. GBR. Dist: Casemate Pubs. & Bk. Distributors, LLC.
Waterkeyn, Xavier. Air & Space Disasters of the World. 2009. (ENG.). 320p. 39.95 *(978-1-74110-550-6(1))* New Holland Pubs. Pty, Ltd. AUS. Dist: Tuttle Publishing.
Whetsell, Dewey G. Fire & Ice: Tales from an Alaskan Volunteer Fire Chief. 2nd exp. ed. 2007. (Illus.). 348p. per. 19.95 *(978-0-9789766-8-2(1))* Northbooks.
Whyte, Greg. Fatal Traps for Helicopter Pilots. 2006. (ENG., Illus.). 395p. pap. 39.95 *(978-0-07-148830-3(8)*, 0071488308) McGraw-Hill Professional Publishing.
Widner, Robert. Aircraft Accidents in Florida. 2009. 354p. pap. 32.05 *(978-0-557-03523-6(6))* Lulu Enterprises Inc.
Williams, Charles M. The Crash of TWA Flight 260. 2010. (ENG., Illus.). 264p. pap. 21.95 *(978-0-8263-4807-4(6))* Univ. of New Mexico Pr.
Williamson, Hank, ed. Air Crash Investigations: SUDDENLY FALLING APART the Crash of Lauda Air Flight NG 004. 2011. 128p. pap. 25.95 ***(978-1-257-50540-1(8))*** Lulu Enterprises Inc.
Wotherspoon, C. N., et al. Aircraft Wrecks - A Walker's Guide: Historic Crash Sites on the Moors & Mountains of the British Isles. 2009. (Illus.). 352p. 50.00 *(978-1-84415-910-9(8))* Pen & Sword Bks. Ltd. GBR. Dist: Casemate Pubs. & Bk. Distributors, LLC.
Wotherspoon, Nick. North-West Aircraft Wrecks: New Insights into Dramatic Last Flights. 2007. (Aviation Heritage Trail Ser.). (Illus.). 252p. per. 24.95 *(978-1-84415-478-4(5))* Pen & Sword Bks. Ltd. GBR. Dist: Casemate Pubs. & Bk. Distributors, LLC.
Young, Cindy/ Lou. Out of the Fog: Tragedy on Nantucket. 2008. (Illus.). 162p. per. 14.95 *(978-0-9742815-9-9(X))* Black Lab Publishing LLC.
Zhang, Zhaoning, et al. Fei Xing Jian Ge an Quan Ping Gu Yin Lun. 2009. (Illus.). vi, 172p. *(978-7-03-025408-5(2))* Science Pr.
Zuckoff, Mitchell. Lost in Shangri-La: A True Story of Survival, Adventure, & the Most Incredible Rescue Mission of World War II. (P. S. Ser.). 2012. (ENG.). 448p. pap. 15.99 ***(978-0-06-198835-6(9)***, HarperPerennial) 2011. E-Book 14.99 ***(978-0-06-209166-6(2))*** 2011. (ENG.). 416p. 26.99 *(978-0-06-198834-9(0))* 2011. (ENG.). 400p. pap. ***(978-0-06-209358-5(4))*** HarperCollins Pubs.

AIRCRAFT ACCIDENTS—JUVENILE LITERATURE

Doeden, Matt. The Hindenburg Disaster. 2006. (Graphic Library: Disasters in History Ser.). (ENG., Illus.). 32p. (gr. 3-4). per. 7.95 *(978-0-7368-6876-1(3)*, Graphic Library) Capstone Pr., Inc.

AIRCRAFT CARRIERS

see also names of individual aircraft carriers, e.g. Lexington (Aircraft Carrier: 1943-1991)

Bowman, Martin. Post-War USN Aircraft Carriers. 2010. (Illus.). 256p. pap. *(978-1-84868-494-2(C))* Amberley Publishing.
Buhl, Willard A. Sea-Based Airpower - the Decisive Factor in Expeditionary Operations? 2010. 64p. pap. 16.55 *(978-1-60888-023-2(0))* Nimble Bks. LLC.
Cocker, Maurice. Aircraft-Carrying Ships of the Royal Navy. 2009. (ENG., Illus.). 224p. pap. 36.95 *(978-0-7524-4633-2(9))* History Pr. Ltd., The GBR. Dist: Independent Pubs. Group.
Darling, Kev. US Carrier War. 2011. (Illus.). 312p. 50.00 ***(978-1-84884-185-7(X))*** Pen & Sword Bks. Ltd. GBR. Dist: Casemate Pubs. & Bk. Distributors, LLC.
David, Brown. Carrier Operations in Wwii. 2009. 320p. 72.95 *(978-1-59114-108-2(7))* Naval Institute Pr.
Davies, Richard Bell. Sailor in the Air. 2010. (Illus.). 264p. pap. 19.95 *(978-1-84832-011-6(6))* Pen & Sword Bks. Ltd. GBR. Dist: Casemate Pubs. & Bk. Distributors, LLC.
Dyndal, Gjert Lage. Land Based Air Power of Aircraft Carriers? A Case Study of the British Debate about Maritime Air Power in the 1960s. 2012. (Corbett Centre for Maritime Policy Studies). (Illus.). 194p. 114.95 ***(978-1-4094-3335-4(8))*** Ashgate Publishing Co.
Elward, Brad. Nimitz-Class Aircraft Carriers. 2010. (New Vanguard Ser.). (ENG., Illus.). 48p. pap. 17.95 *(978-1-84603-759-7(X))* Osprey Publishing, Ltd. GBR. Dist: Random Hse., Inc.
Ferrell, Dewitt T. My Heroes. Burns, Megan F., ed. 2011. (Illus.). 432p. 19.95 ***(978-1-935186-19-9(1))*** Waldenhouse Pubs., Inc.
Fontenoy, Paul E. Aircraft Carriers: An Illustrated History of Their Impact. 1 vol. Tucker, Spencer C., ed. 2006. (Weapons & Warfare Ser.). (Illus.). 407p. 85.00 *(978-1-85109-573-5(X)*, AIRCTHC) ABC-CLIO, LLC.
Freeman, Gregory. Troubled Water: Race, Mutiny, & Bravery on the USS Kitty Hawk. (ENG., Illus.). 272p. 2010. pap. 16.00 *(978-0-230-10339-9(1))* 2009. 27.00 *(978-0-230-61361-4(6))* Palgrave Macmillan.
Friedman, Norman. U. S. Aircraft Carriers: An Illustrated Design History. (Illustrated Design Histories Ser.). (Illus.). 428p. 85.00 *(978-0-87021-739-5(9))* Naval Institute Pr.
Goodall, Jim. Nimitz Class Aircraft Carriers. 2009. (Illus.). 80p. pap. ***(978-0-89747-605-8(0))*** Squadron Signal Pubns.
Hearn, Chester G. Carriers in Combat: The Air War at Sea. 2007. (Stackpole Military History Ser.). (ENG., Illus.). 336p. per. 19.95 *(978-0-8117-3398-4(X))* Stackpole Bks.
Hellermann, Rolf. Capacity Options for Revenue Management: Theory & Applications in the Air Cargo Industry. 2006. (Lecture Notes in Economics & Mathematical Systems Ser.). (Illus.). xv, 199p. pap. 139.00 *(978-3-540-34419-3(5)*, 3540344195) Springer.
Holloway, James L. & Holloway, James L., III. Aircraft Carriers at War: A Personal Retrospective of Korea, Vietnam, & the Soviet Confrontation. 2007. (Illus.). 479p. 36.95 *(978-1-59114-391-8(8))* Naval Institute Pr.
Hone, Thomas C., et al. Innovation in Carrier Aviation. Naval War College Press (U.S.), ed. 2011. (Newport Paper Ser.). (ENG., Illus.). 235p. pap. 23.00 ***(978-1-884733-85-7(9)***, Dept. of the Navy) United States Government Printing Office.
Hood, Jean, ed. Carrier: An Anthology of First-Hand Accounts of the War at Sea. 2011. (ENG., Illus.). 456p. 29.95 *(978-1-84486-111-8(2)*, Conway Maritime Pr.) Anova Bks. GBR. Dist: Sterling Publishing Co., Inc.
Ireland, Bernard. Aircraft Carriers of the World: An Illustrated Guide to More Than 140 Ships, with 400 Identification Photographs & Illustrations. from Early Kite Balloon Ships, Zeppelin & Seaplane Carriers to the Many Types of Modern Warships That Carry Variable-Geometry Jets, V/Stol Aircraft & He. 2007. (ENG., Illus.). 160p. pap. 18.99 *(978-1-84476-363-4(3))* Anness Publishing GBR. Dist: National Bk. Network.
Ireland, Bernard & Crosby, Francis. The World Encyclopedia of Aircraft Carriers & Naval Aircraft. 2011. (ENG., Illus.). 512p. 35.00 *(978-0-7548-2327-8(X))* Anness Publishing GBR. Dist: National Bk. Network.
Jones, Barbara/ G. The Role the USS Casablanca (CVE-55) Played in World War II in the Pacific. 2010. (Illus.). vi, 515p. *(978-0-7734-3850-7(5))* Mellen, Edwin Pr., The.
Konstam, Angus. British Aircraft Carriers, 1939-1945. 2010. (New Vanguard Ser.). (ENG., Illus.). 48p. pap. 17.95 *(978-1-84908-079-8(8))* Osprey Publishing, Ltd. GBR. Dist: Random Hse., Inc.
Leahy, J. F. Ask the Chief: Backbone of the Navy. (Illus.). 272p. 29.95 *(978-1-59114-460-1(4)*, Naval Institute Pr.
Marino, Anthony R., ed. Navy Nuclear Aircraft Carrier Homeporting. 2011. ***(978-1-61324-557-6(2))*** Nova Science Pubs., Inc.
Marriott, Leo. Catapult Aircraft: Seaplanes That Flew from Ships Without Flight Decks. 2006. (Illus.). 180p. 39.95 *(978-1-84415-419-7(X))* Pen & Sword Bks. Ltd. GBR. Dist: Casemate Pubs. & Bk. Distributors, LLC.
McGaugh, Scott. USS Midway: America's Shield, 1 vol. 2011. (ENG., Illus.). 192p. pap. 18.95 *(978-1-58980-896-6(7))* Pelican Publishing Co., Inc.
Miller, Richard F. A Carrier at War: On Board the USS Kitty Hawk in the Iraq War. 2007. (Illus.). 272p. per 17.95 *(978-1-59797-047-1(6))* Potomac Bks., Inc.
Morgan, Rick. Tip of the Spear: U. S. Navy Carrier Units & Operations 1974-2000. 2007. (Illus.). 240p. 49.95 *(978-0-7643-2585-4(X))* Schiffer Publishing, Ltd.

Oversight of the Electromagnetic Aircraft Launch System (EMALS) Hearing Before the Seapower & Expeditionary Forces Subcommittee of the Committee on Armed Services, House of Representatives, One Hundred Eleventh Congress, First Session, Hearing Held, July 16, 2009. 2010. (Illus.). iii, 59p. *(978-0-16-086185-7(3)*, 552-070-41283-2) United States Government Printing Office.

Polmar, Norman. Aircraft Carriers Vol. 1: A History of Carrier Aviation & Its Influence on World Events, 1909-1945, 2 vols. 2nd ed. 2006. (Illus.). 576p. 49.95 *(978-1-57488-663-4(0))* Potomac Bks., Inc.

—Aircraft Carriers Vol. 2: A History of Carrier Aviation & Its Influence on World Events, 1946-2006, 2 vols. 2nd ed. 2008. (Illus.). 560p. 49.95 *(978-1-57488-665-8(7))* Potomac Bks., Inc.

Reynolds, Clark G. The Carrier War. (Illus.). 176p. 24.00 *(978-1-84447-036-5(9))* Time Life Value GBR. Dist: Mercury Bks. Ltd.

Schank, John F., et al. Changing Aircraft Carrier Procurement Schedules: Effects That a Five-Year Procurement Cycle Would Have on Cost, Availability, & Shipyard Manpower & Workload, 1 vol. 2011. 100p. (C). pap. 27.00 *(978-0-8330-5145-5(8)*, mg-1073) RAND Corp., The.

Sears, David. Such Men as These: The Story of the Navy Pilots Who Flew the Deadly Skies over Korea. 2011. (ENG., Illus.). 432p. pap. 18.00 *(978-0-306-82010-6(2))* Da Capo Pr., Inc.

Smith, Douglas V. Carrier Battles: Command Decision in Harm's Way. 2006. (Illus.). 346p. 36.95 *(978-1-59114-794-7(8))* Naval Institute Pr.

Southwater & Ireland, Bernard. Aircraft Carriers: An illustrated history of aircraft carriers of the world, from zeppelin & seaplane carriers to vertical/short take-off & landing jet decks & nuclear Carriers. 2010. (ENG., Illus.). 256p. pap. 24.99 *(978-1-84476-938-4(0))* Anness Publishing GBR. Dist: National Bk. Network.

Stern, Robert Cecil. Yorktown-Class Aircraft Carriers. 2007. (Illus.). 51p. pap. *(978-0-89747-543-3(7))* Squadron Signal Pubns.

Stille, Mark. Us Navy Aircraft Carriers, 1942-1945: World War Two Built Ships. 2007. (New Vanguard Ser.: Vol. 130). (ENG., Illus.). 48p. pap. 17.95 *(978-1-84603-037-6(4))* Osprey Publishing, Ltd. GBR. Dist: Random Hse., Inc.

—USN Carriers vs IJN Carriers: The Pacific 1942. 2007. (Duel Ser.). (ENG., Illus.). 80p. pap. 17.95 *(978-1-84603-248-6(2))* Osprey Publishing, Ltd. GBR. Dist: Random Hse., Inc.

Thomason, Tommy H. U. S. Naval Air Superiority: Delevelopment of Shipborne Jet Fighters 1943-1962. 2008. (Illus.). 275p. 46.95 *(978-1-58007-110-9(4))* Specialty Pr. Pubs. & Wholesalers, Inc.

Toosi, Amir. To Downsize or Not Downsize Within Three Airline Carriers. 2009. 116p. pap. *(978-3-639-15675-1(7))* VDM Verlag Dr. Mueller e.K.

Townley, Alvin. Fly Navy: Discovering the Extraordinary People & Enduring Spirit of Naval Aviation. 2011. (ENG., Illus.). 352p. 25.99 *(978-0-312-65084-1(1)*, Dunne, Thomas Bks.) St. Martin's Pr.

Yardley, Roland J. Increasing Aircraft Carrier Forward Presence: Changing the Length of the Maintenance Cycle. 2008. 90p. pap. 23.00 *(978-0-8330-4407-5(9)*, MG-706) RAND Corp., The.

—A Methodology for Estimating the Effect of Aircraft Carrier Operational Cycles on the Maintenance Industrial Base. 2007. 94p. pap. 32.00 *(978-0-8330-4182-1(7)*, TR-480-NAVY) RAND Corp., The.

Zimmerman, W. Frederick. Cvn-68 Nimitz, U S Navy Aircraft Carrier. 2008. 32p. per. 17.36 *(978-1-934840-19-1(X))* Nimble Bks. LLC.

—Cvn-69 Dwight D Eisenhower, U S Navy Aircraft Carrier. 2008. 32p. per. 17.36 *(978-1-934840-20-7(3))* Nimble Bks. LLC.

—Cvn-71 Theodore Roosevelt, U S Navy Aircraft Carrier. 2008. 32p. per. 17.36 *(978-1-934840-22-1(X))* Nimble Bks. LLC.

—Cvn-72 Abraham Lincoln, U S Navy Aircraft Carrier. 2008. 32p. pap. 17.36 *(978-1-934840-23-8(8))* Nimble Bks. LLC.

—Cvn-73 George Washington, U S Navy Aircraft Carrier. 2008. 32p. pap. 17.36 *(978-1-934840-24-5(6))* Nimble Bks. LLC.

—Cvn-74 John C Stennis, U S Navy Aircraft Carrier. 2008. 32p. pap. 17.36 *(978-1-934840-25-2(4))* Nimble Bks. LLC.

—Cvn-75 Harry S Truman, U S Navy Aircraft Carrier. 2008. 40p. pap. 18.36 *(978-1-934840-26-9(2))* Nimble Bks. LLC.

—Cvn-76 Ronald Reagan, U S Navy Aircraft Carrier. 2008. 32p. per. 17.36 *(978-1-934840-08-5(4))* Nimble Bks. LLC.

—Cvn-78 Gerald R Ford, U S Navy Aircraft Carrier. 2007. 32p. per. 17.36 *(978-1-934840-02-3(5))* Nimble Bks. LLC.

—Ddg-81 Winston S Churchill, U S Navy Destroyer. 2008. 32p. pap. 17.36 *(978-1-934840-28-3(9))* Nimble Bks. LLC.

AIRCRAFT ENGINES

see Airplanes—Motors; Airplanes—Turbojet Engines

AIRCRAFT FUELS

see Airplanes—Fuel

AIRCRAFT GAS TURBINES

see also Airplanes—Turbojet Engines

Aircraft Propulsion & Gas Turbine Engines. 2011. (C). 124.95 ***(978-1-4200-0877-7(3)**, CRC Press)* Taylor & Francis Group GBR. Dist: Taylor & Francis Group.

Connors, Jack & Allen, Ned. The Engines of Pratt & Whitney: A Technical History. 2009. 49.95 *(978-1-60086-711-8(1))* American Institute of Aeronautics & Astronautics.

Epstein, A. H. Aircraft & Rocket Turbines - Physics & Design. Vennard, J., ed. 2008. 156p. pap. 74.95 *(978-1-934939-18-5(8))* Wexford College Pr.

Jaw, Link C. & Mattingly, Jack D. Aircraft Engine Controls: Design, System Analysis, & Health Monitoring. 2009. (Illus.). 300p. *(978-1-60086-705-7(7))* American Institute of Aeronautics & Astronautics.

Mattingly, Jack D. Elements of Propulsion: Gas Turbines & Rockets. 2006. (AIAA Education Ser.). (Illus.). 867p. *(978-1-56347-779-9(3))* American Institute of Aeronautics & Astronautics.

Technology Research Editors, ed. Aircraft Gas Turbine Engines: Noise Reduction & Vibration Control, 2007 Ed. 2007. pap. 129.50 *(978-1-60030-142-1(8)*, Search-In-Print) CSA Journal Division.

Vennard, J., pref. Aircraft Gas Turbine Engines - Operation, Components & Systems. 2008. 296p. per. 49.95 *(978-1-934939-13-0(7))* Wexford College Pr.

AIRCRAFT IDENTIFICATION

see Airplanes—Recognition

AIRCRAFT INDUSTRY

see also Airplanes; Used Aircraft

Aircraft Factory 99. pap. 59.95 incl. cd-rom *(978-1-55755-359-1(9))* Abacus.

Alfonso-Gil, Javier, ed. European Aeronautics: The Southwestern Axis. 2010. (ENG., Illus.). x, 277p. pap. 149.00 *(978-3-642-07135-5(X)*, 364207135X) Springer.

Anderson, Michael, Jr. Aviation & Climate Change. 2007. (Routledge Studies in Physical Geography & Environment). (Illus.). 288p. 138.00 *(978-0-415-39705-6(7))* Routledge.

Anderson, Nina E. Flying above the Glass Ceiling: Inspirational Stories of Success from the First Women Pilots to Fly Airline & Corporate Aircraft. Pratt, Bill, ed. 2009. (Illus.). 134p. pap. 14.95 *(978-1-884820-94-6(8))* SAFE GOODS/ATN Publishing.

Anteby, Michel. Moral Gray Zones: Side Productions, Identity, & Regulation in an Aeronautic Plant. 2008. (ENG., Illus.). 248p. (C). 39.95 *(978-0-691-13524-3(X))* Princeton Univ. Pr.

Arnold, Neil. Shadows in the Sky: The Haunted Airways of Britain. 2012. (ENG., Illus.). 192p. pap. 24.95 ***(978-0-7524-6563-0(5))*** History Pr. Ltd., The GBR. Dist: Independent Pubs. Group.

Balasubramaniam, Sangeetha & Huam Hon Tat. Airline Industry. 2011. 156p. pap. ***(978-3-8443-8275-4(5))*** Lambert Academic Publishing.

Bassford, Matt, et al. Sustaining Key Skills in the UK Military Aircraft Industry, 1 vol. 2010. 168p. pap. 27.00 *(978-0-8330-5041-0(9)*, mg-1023) RAND Corp., The.

Bauer, Eugene E. Boeing: The First Century & Beyond. 2nd ed. 2006. (Illus.). 424p. 29.50 *(978-1-879242-09-8(5))* TABA Publishing, Inc.

Birkler, John, et al. Keeping a Competitive U. S. Military Aircraft Industry Aloft: Findings from an Analysis of the Industrial Base. 2012. (ENG.). 142p. pap. 32.50 ***(978-0-8330-5864-5(9))*** RAND Corp., The.

Cadogan, Richard S., ed. U. S. Aerospace Industry: Analysis & Prospects. 2011. (Transportation Infrastructure - Roads, Highways, Bridges, Airports & Mass Transit Business Issues, Competition & Entrepreneurship Ser.). 149p. 95.00 *(978-1-61324-234-6(4))* Nova Science Pubs., Inc.

Coulby, Adam. Fbo Safety & Procedures Guide: A Training & Resource Manual for Line Service Technicians. rev. ed. 2011. (ENG.). 94p. spiral bd. 42.00 *(978-0-7575-8819-8(0))* Kendall Hunt Publishing Co.

Eliasson, Gunnar K. Advanced Public Procurement as Industrial Policy: The Aircraft Industry as a Technical University. 2010. (Economics of Science, Technology & Innovation Ser.). (ENG., Illus.). x, 250p. 159.00 *(978-1-4419-5848-8(7)*, 1441958487) Springer.

Engel, Jeffrey A. Cold War at 30,000 Feet: The Anglo-American Fight for Aviation Supremacy. 2007. (Illus.). 384p. 35.00 *(978-0-674-02461-8(3))* Harvard Univ. Pr.

Eriksson, Sören. Global Shift in the Aircraft Industry: A Study of Airframe Manufacturing with Special Reference to the Asian NIEs. (Illus.). 244p. *(978-91-86472-21-4(6))* Goteborgs Universitet, Kulturgeografiska Institutionen.

Faffelberger, Josef & Josef, Faffelberger. Industry & Competition Analysis of Airbus & Boeing: Measuring the Appropriateness of Time-Series Forecasting for the Aircraft Industry. 2011. 172p. pap. ***(978-3-639-32436-5(6))*** VDM Verlag Dr. Mueller e.K.

Flouris, Triant & Lock, Dennis. Aviation Project Management. 2008. 314p. 99.95 *(978-0-7546-7395-8(2))* Ashgate Publishing Co.

Flouris, Triant G. & Lock, Dennis. Managing Aviation Projects from Concept to Completion. 2009. (Illus.). 528p. 119.95 *(978-0-7546-7615-7(3))* Ashgate Publishing Co.

Fobe. Aviation Products & Insurance in the EU Legal Aspects Ins 2e Rev. 2010. 152.00 *(978-90-411-2803-4(4))* Wolters Kluwer Law & Business.

Freethy, Ron. Memories of the Lancashire Aircraft Industry. 2009. (Memories Ser.). (ENG., Illus.). 176p. (C). pap. 23.95 *(978-1-84674-166-1(1))* Countryside Bks. GBR. Dist: Brown, David Bk. Co., The.

General Electric Aircraft Engines E. H. & S. Reference Manual. Date not set. ring bd. *(978-0-88061-183-1(9))* International Loss Control Institute, Inc.

General Electric Aircraft Engines E. H. & S. Working Copy. Date not set. spiral bd. *(978-0-88061-184-8(7))* International Loss Control Institute, Inc.

General Electric Aircraft Engines Field Verification. Date not set. *(978-0-88061-185-5(5))* International Loss Control Institute, Inc.

Gordon, Yefim & Komissarov, Sergey. German Aircraft in the Soviet Union & Russia. 2010. (ENG., Illus.). 320p. 59.95 *(978-1-85780-292-4(6))* Allan, Ian Publishing GBR. Dist: BookMasters Distribution Services (BDS).

Gunn, Tom. Gunn Sights: Taking Aim on Selling in the High-Stakes Industry of International Aerospace. 2008. (Illus.). 256p. 29.95 *(978-1-59114-346-8(2))* Naval Institute Pr.

Haas, Silke. The European Aviation Industry. 2009. 112p. pap. *(978-3-639-13222-9(X))* VDM Verlag Dr. Mueller e.K.

Henry, Lyell D. Zig-Zag-and-Swirl: Alfred W. Lawson's Quest for Greatness. 2009. (ENG., Illus.). 336p. pap. 27.00 *(978-1-58729-466-2(4))* Univ. of Iowa Pr.

Jackson, Robert. Britain's Greatest Aircraft. 2007. (Illus.). 320p. 50.00 *(978-1-84415-600-9(1))* Pen & Sword Bks. Ltd. GBR. Dist: Casemate Pubs. & Bk. Distributors, LLC.

Jane's Aircraft Upgrades. 14th rev. ed. 2006. (Jane's Aircraft Upgrades Ser.). (Illus.). 826p. *(978-0-7106-2737-7(8))* Jane's Information Group.

Jane's Airports, Equipment & Services: Survey the World's Airport Equipment Suppliers & Manufacturers. 535.00 *(978-0-7106-2305-8(4))* Jane's Information Group, Inc.

Jane's All the World's Aircraft: The Authority on Aircraft under Development or in Production. 560.00 *(978-0-7106-2307-2(0))* Jane's Information Group, Inc.

Jane's Information Group Staff. Trainer Aircraft Markets. (Air-Space Ser.). (Illus.). 151p. 695.00 *(978-0-7106-1835-1(2))* Jane's Information Group, Inc.

Kesseler, Ernst & Guenov, Marin D. Advances in Collaborative Civil Aeronautical Multidisciplinary Design Optimization. 2010. (Illus.). xvii, 436p. 109.95 ***(978-1-60086-725-5(1))*** American Institute of Aeronautics & Astronautics.

Kimura, Seishi. The Challenges of Late Industrialization: The Global Economy & the Japanese Commercial Aircraft Industry. 2007. (ENG., Illus.). 240p. 110.00 *(978-1-4039-9879-8(5))* Palgrave Macmillan.

Leonhardt, Jorg & Vogt, Joachim, eds. Critical Incident Stress Management in Aviation. 2006. (Illus.). 194p. 120.00 *(978-0-7546-4738-6(2))* Ashgate Publishing Co.

Lumpe, Marc-Philippe. Leadership & Organization in the Aviation Industry. 2008. (Illus.). 308p. 124.95 *(978-0-7546-7144-2(5))* Ashgate Publishing Co.

Mortimer, Gavin. Chasing Icarus: The Seventeen Days in 1910 That Forever Changed American Aviation. 2009. (ENG., Illus.). 320p. 26.00 *(978-0-8027-1711-5(X))* Walker & Co.

Nellist, John G. Aircraft Production During World War Ii: Boeing Aircraft of Canada. 2010. 68p. pap. 27.68 *(978-1-4269-3820-7(9))* Trafford Publishing.

Newhouse, John. Boeing versus Airbus: The Inside Story of the Greatest International Competition in Business. 2008. (Vintage Ser.). (ENG.). 272p. pap. 16.00 *(978-1-4000-7872-1(5)*, Vintage) Knopf Doubleday Publishing Group.

Ord-Hume, Arthur. British Private Aircraft: The Re-awakening Years 1946 - 1970. 2012. (Illus.). 600p. 150.00 ***(978-83-61421-46-7(7))*** Stratus, Wydawnictwo, Juszczak, Artur POL. Dist: Casemate Pubs. & Bk. Distributors, LLC.

Parker, Christian. The Care & Maintenance of Heavy Jets. 2008. 205p. pap. 19.95 *(978-0-9815838-0-8(6))* Olympic Dispatch Publishing.

Pauley, Robert F. Michigan Aircraft Manufacturers. 2009. (Images of Aviation Ser.). (ENG., Illus.). 128p. pap. 21.99 *(978-0-7385-5218-7(6))* Arcadia Publishing.

Pescador, Katrina & Aldrich, Mark. Consolidated Aircraft Corporation. 2008. (Images of America Ser.). (ENG., Illus.). 128p. pap. 21.99 *(978-0-7385-5938-4(5))* Arcadia Publishing.

Prather, C. Daniel. General Aviation Marketing & Management: Operating, Marketing, & Managing an FBO. 3rd ed. 2009. (Illus.). 302p. *(978-1-57524-301-6(6))* Krieger Publishing Co.

Rhoades, Dawna L. Evolution of International Aviation: Phoenix Rising. 2nd rev. ed. 2008. (Illus.). 296p. 59.95 *(978-0-7546-7389-7(8))* Ashgate Publishing Co.

Shomo, Linda P. Rosie the Riveter & the Enola Gay: 60 Years after WWII. 2008. 83p. pap. 16.95 *(978-1-60563-506-4(5))* PublishAmerica, Inc.

Skinner, Stephen. British Aircraft Corporation: A History, 1 vol. 2012. (ENG., Illus.). 192p. 39.95 ***(978-1-84797-318-4(3)**,* 1847973183) Crowood Pr., Ltd. GBR. Dist: MBI Distribution Services/Quayside Distribution.

Spong, E. David & Collard, Debbie J. The Making of a World-Class Organization. 2008. (Illus.). 44.00 *(978-0-87389-744-0(7))* ASQ Quality Pr.

Springer, A. M., et al. America by Air. 2007. (ENG., Illus.). 40p. pap. 10.50 *(978-0-16-079431-5(5)*, U. S. National Aeronautics & Space Administration) United States Government Printing Office.

Stoff, Joshua. Long Island Aircraft Manufacturers. 2010. (Images of Aviation Ser.). (ENG., Illus.). 128p. pap. 21.99 *(978-0-7385-7336-6(1))* Arcadia Publishing.

Williams, Paula. Flight Plan to Sales Success: New Media Marketing for the Aviation Industry. 2010. 118p. pap. 17.50 *(978-0-557-56882-6(X))* Lulu Enterprises Inc.

Wilson, Eugene Edward. Slipstream: The Autobiography of an Air Craftsman. 2011. 352p. 51.95 ***(978-1-258-09858-2(X))*** Literary Licensing, LLC.

Yenne, Bill. The American Aircraft Factory in World War II. 2010. (ENG., Illus.). 192p. pap. 24.99 *(978-0-7603-3913-8(9)*, 0760339139, Zenith Pr.) MBI Publishing Co. LLC.

AIRCRAFT INSTRUMENTS

see Aeronautical Instruments

AIRCRAFT INSURANCE

see Aviation Insurance

AIRCRAFT MECHANICS (PERSONS)

see Aviation Mechanics (Persons)

AIRCRAFT NOISE

see Airplanes—Noise

AIRCRAFT PRODUCTION

see Aerospace Industries

AIRCRAFT RECOGNITION

see Airplanes—Recognition

AIRCRAFT SAFETY MEASURES

see Aeronautics—Safety Measures

AIRCRAFT SPOTTING

see also Airplanes—Recognition

Lord, Walter. Lonely Vigil: Coastwatchers of the Solomons. 2006. (Bluejacket Books). (Illus.). 322p. per. 17.95 *(978-1-59114-466-3(3))* Naval Institute Pr.

Lord, Walter, frwd. Coast Watching in World War II: Operations Against the Japanese in the Solomon Islands, 1941-43. 2006. (Stackpole Military History Ser.). (ENG., Illus.). 218p. per. 16.95 *(978-0-8117-3329-8(7))* Stackpole Bks.

AIRCRAFT STRESS ANALYSIS

see Airframes

AIRCRAFT STRUCTURES

see Airframes

AIRDROMES

see Airports

AIREDALE TERRIER

Jarman, Frank. The American Sporting Airedale. 2011. 108p. 29.95 ***(978-1-4634-3169-3(4))***; pap. 19.95 ***(978-1-4634-3170-9(8))*** AuthorHouse.

Linzy, Jan & Pata, Sharae. Airedale Terrier Champions, 2002-2006. 2007. (Illus.). 136p. spiral bd. 46.95 *(978-1-55893-229-6(1))* Camino E.E. & Bk. Co.

Open Court Staff. My Airedale. pap. *(978-0-8126-1007-9(5)*, 61007) Open Court Publishing Co.

AIRFOILS

see also Aerofoils

Agrawal, Anmol. Hingeless Flow Control over an Airfoil. 2011. 84p. pap. ***(978-3-8454-0293-2(8))*** Lambert Academic Publishing.

Akçayöz, Eray. Numerical Investigation of Flow Control over an Airfoil. 2010. 88p. pap. *(978-3-8383-5601-3(2))* Lambert Academic Publishing.

Cebeci, T., et al. Analysis of Low Speed Unsteady Airfoil Flows. 226p. 185.00 *(978-0-9668461-8-8(4))* Horizons Publishing.

Technology Research Editors, ed. Airfoils: Drag, Turbulent Flow, & Vibration Reduction, 2007 Ed. 2007. pap. 128.50 *(978-1-60030-464-4(8)*, Search-In-Print) CSA Journal Division.

Wauquiez, Christian. Shape Optimization of Low Speed Airfoils. 2009. 68p. pap. *(978-3-639-11623-6(2))* VDM Verlag Dr. Mueller e.K.

AIRFRAMES

see also Airplanes—Wings

American Society of Mechanical Engineers, Aerospace Division Staff, contrib. by. Proceedings of the ASME Aerospace Division — 2006: Adaptive Materials & Systems, Aerospace Materials & Structures, General: Presented at 2006 ASME International Mechanical Engineering Congress & Exposition, November 5-10, 2006, Chicago, Illinois, USA. 2007. (Illus.). xix, 664p. *(978-0-7918-4765-7(9))* American Society of Mechanical Engineers, The.

American Society of Mechanical Engineers Staff, ed. Aircraft Structures & Materials. (Illus.). 100p. 72.00 *(978-1-86058-044-4(0))* Professional Engineering Publishing GBR. Dist: SAE Intl.

Backman, B. F. Composite Structures: Safety Management. 2008. (ENG.). 306p. 200.00 *(978-0-08-054809-8(1)*, Elsevier Science) Elsevier Science & Technology Bks.

Bibel, George. Beyond the Black Box: The Forensics of Airplane Crashes. 2007. (ENG., Illus.). 408p. 33.00 *(978-0-8018-8631-7(7))* Johns Hopkins Univ. Pr.

Bos, M. & Bos, M. J., eds. ICAF 2009, Bridging the Gap between Theory & Operational Practice: Proceedings of the 25th Symposium of the International Committee on Aeronautical Fatigue, Rotterdam, the Netherlands, 27-29 May 2009. 2009. (Illus.). xviii, 1370p. 459.00 *(978-90-481-2745-0(9))* Springer.

Cram101 Textbook Reviews & Cram101 Textbook Reviews. Outlines & Highlights for Aircraft Structures for Engineering Students by T H G Megson. 2011. 104p. pap. 28.95 ***(978-1-61830-879-5(3))*** Cram101 Inc.

Crane, Dale. Airframe Test Guide 2012: The Fast-Track to Study for & Pass the FAA Aviation Maintenance Technician (AMT) Airframe Knowledge Exam. Michmerhuizen, Terry, ed. 2011. (Fast Track Ser.). (ENG.). 212p. pap. 14.95 *(978-1-56027-856-6(0))* Aviation Supplies & Academics, Inc.

—Aviation Maintenance Technician - Airframe. 3rd ed. 2008. (Aviation Maintenance Technician Ser.). (ENG.). 540p. 49.95 *(978-1-56027-712-5(2))* Aviation Supplies & Academics, Inc.

—Aviation Maintenance Technician: Airframe: Volume 2: Systems. 3rd ed. 2007. (Aviation Maintenance Technician Ser.). (ENG., Illus.). 492p. pap. 49.95 *(978-1-56027-549-7(9))* Aviation Supplies & Academics, Inc.

Donaldson, Bruce K. Analysis of Aircraft Structures. 2nd rev. ed. 2008. (Cambridge Aerospace Ser.). (ENG., Illus.). 974p. (C). 155.00 *(978-0-521-86583-8(2))* Cambridge Univ. Pr.

Federal Aviation Administration. Aviation Mechanic Practical Test Standards for General, Airframe & Powerplant: FAA-S-8081-26, -27, And -28. 2009. (Practical Test Standards Ser.). (ENG.). 96p. pap. 9.95 *(978-1-56027-751-4(3))* Aviation Supplies & Academics, Inc.

Gebman, Jean R. Opportunities for Systems Engineering to Contribute to Durability & Damage Tolerance of Hybrid Structures for Airframes. 2008. 62p. pap. 20.50 *(978-0-8330-4202-6(5)*, tr489) RAND Corp., The.

Golfman, Yosif, ed. Hybrid Anisotropic Materials for Structural Aviation Parts. 2010. (ENG., Illus.). 339p. 139.95 *(978-1-4398-3680-4(9)*, CRC Press) Taylor & Francis Group GBR. Dist: Taylor & Francis Group.

Kassapoglou, Christos. Design & Analysis of Composite Structures: With Applications to Aerospace Structures. 2010. *(978-1-60086-780-4(4))* American Institute of Aeronautics & Astronautics.

Komorowski, Jerzy, ed. Icaf 2011 Structural Integrity - Influence of Efficiency & Green Imperatives: Proceedings of the 26th Symposium of the International Committee on Aeronautical Fatigue 1-3 June 2011, Montreal, Canada. 2011. (Illus.). xvi, 976p. 399.00 *(978-94-007-1663-6(X)*, 940071663X) Springer.

Lakshmi Narasaiah, G. Aircraft Structures. 2011. (ENG., Illus.). 402p. (C). 129.95 *(978-0-415-66574-2(4)*, CRC Press) Taylor & Francis Group GBR. Dist: Taylor & Francis Group.

Legal Advisory Panel of the Aviation Working Group. Advanced Contract & Opinion Practices under the Cape Town Convention. 2008. (Cape Town Paper Ser.). (ENG.). 66p. pap. 104.00 *(978-1-84113-987-6(4))* Hart Publishing Ltd. GBR. Dist: International Specialized Bk. Services.

Megson, T. H. G. Aircraft Structures for Engineering Students. 5th ed. 2012. (ENG., Illus.). 864p. (C). pap. 120.00 ***(978-0-08-096905-3(4)***, Butterworth-Heinemann) Elsevier Science & Technology Bks.

Megson, T. H. G. Introduction to Aircraft Structural Analysis. 2010. (ENG., Illus.). 648p. (C). pap. 79.95 *(978-1-85617-932-4(X)*, Butterworth-Heinemann) Elsevier Science & Technology Bks.

Megson, T.H.G. Aircraft Structures. 2nd ed. (Illus.). 520p. pap. *(978-0-7131-3681-4(2)*, Hodder Arnold) Hodder Education.

Peery, David J. & Engineering Careers Information Service Staff. Aircraft Structures. 2011. (Dover Books on Aeronautical Engineering Ser.). (ENG.). 576p. pap. 29.95 ***(978-0-486-48580-5(3))*** Dover Pubns., Inc.

AIRGLOW

see also Auroras

Khomich, Vladislav Yu, et al. Airglow As an Indicator of Upper Atmospheric Structure & Dynamics. 2008. (ENG., Illus.). xvi, 740p. 289.00 *(978-3-540-75832-7(1)*, 3540758321) Springer London, Ltd. GBR. Dist: Springer.

Roach, F. The Light of the Night Sky. 2010. 144p. pap. 153.00 *(978-90-481-8339-5(1)*, 9048183391) Springer.

AIRLINE CRASHES

see Aircraft Accidents

AIRLINE HOSTESSES

see Flight Attendants

AIRLINE INDUSTRY

see Airlines

AIRLINE PILOTS

see Air Pilots

AIRLINE RESERVATION SYSTEMS

see Airlines—Reservation Systems

AIRLINE STEWARDESSES

see Flight Attendants

AIRLINE STEWARDS

see Flight Attendants

AIRLINERS

see Transport Planes

AIRLINES

see also Air Pilots; Airways

also names of specific airlines

Airline 500 World Review. *(978-0-944188-18-7(4))* Pyramid Media Group.

Airline Deregulation: Barriers to Entry Continue to Limit Competition in Several Key Domestic Markets. 36p. pap. 30.00 *(978-0-7881-4072-3(8))* DIANE Publishing Co.

Aviation Consumer Issues: Emergency Contingency Planning & Outlook for Summer Travel: Hearing Before the Subcommittee on Aviation of the Committee on Transportation & Infrastructure, House of Representatives, One Hundred Eleventh Congress, First Session, May 20, 2009. 2009. (Illus.). xiii, 139p. *(978-0-16-084374-7(X)*, 552-070-39917-8) United States Government Printing Office.

Aviation Safety: FAA's Role in the Oversight of Commercial Air Carriers: Hearing Before the Subcommittee on Aviation Operations, Safety, & Security of the Committee on Commerce, Science, & Transportation, United States Senate, One Hundred Eleventh Congress, First Session, June 10, 2009. 2010. iii, 81p. *(978-0-16-085627-3(2)*, 552-070-40689-0) United States Government Printing Office.

Balasubramaniam, Sangeetha & Huam Hon Tat. Airline Industry. 2011. 156p. pap. ***(978-3-8443-8275-4(5))*** Lambert Academic Publishing.

Barrett, Sean. Deregulation & the Airline Business in Europe. 2011. (ENG., Illus.). 208p. (C). pap. 44.95 ***(978-0-415-69649-4(6))*** Routledge.

Belobaba, Peter, et al, eds. The Global Airline Industry. 2009. (Aerospace Ser.). (ENG., Illus.). 518p. 120.00 *(978-0-470-74077-4(9)*, Wiley) Wiley, John & Sons, Inc.

Belobaba, Peter, et al. The Global Airline Industry. 2009. 520p. *(978-1-60086-702-6(2))* American Institute of Aeronautics & Astronautics.

Benson, Erik. Aviator of Fortune: Lowell Yerex & the Anglo-American Commercial Rivalry, 1931-1946. 2006. (Louise Lindsey Merrick Natural Environment Ser.: No. 40). (ENG., Illus.). 280p. 45.00 *(978-1-58544-500-4(2))* Texas A&M Univ. Pr.

Branson, Richard. Losing My Virginity: The Autobiography. 2011. (ENG., Illus.). 624p. pap. 17.00 *(978-0-307-72074-0(8)*, Crown Business) Crown Publishing Group.

Bubb, Daniel K. Landing in Las Vegas: Commercial Aviation & the Making of a Tourist City. 2012. (Shepperson Series in Nevada History Ser.). (Illus.). 176p. 34.95 ***(978-0-87417-872-2(X))*** Univ. of Nevada Pr.

Burghouwt, Guillaume. Airline Network Development in Europe & its Implications for Airport Planning. 2007. (Illus.). 300p. 124.95 *(978-0-7546-4506-1(1))* Ashgate Publishing Co.

Cento, Alessandro. The Airline Industry: Challenges in the 21st Century. 2008. (Contributions to Economics Ser.). (ENG., Illus.). xviii, 184p. 129.00 *(978-3-7908-2087-4(3)*, 3790820873) Physica-Verlag DEU. Dist: Springer.

Combating Terrorism: Lessons Learned from London: Hearing Before the Subcommittee on National Security, Emerging Threats, & International Relations of the Committee on Government Reform, House of Representatives, One Hundred Ninth Congress, Second Session, September 19, 2006. 2008. iii, 114p. *(978-0-16-082077-9(4)*, 552-070-38233-0) United States Government Printing Office.

Coscia, Michael. Wings over America: The fact filled guide to the major & regional airlines of the USA. 2009. (Illus.). pap. 24.95 *(978-1-60452-036-1(1))* BluewaterPress, LLC.

Craig, Kodera, et al. From Props to Jets: Commercial Aviation's Transition to the Jet Age 1952-1962. 2010. 160p. 29.95 *(978-1-58007-146-8(5))* Specialty Pr. Pubs. & Wholesalers, Inc.

Cram101 Textbook Reviews & Cram101 Textbook Reviews. Outlines & Highlights for a Europe of the Air: The Airline Industry & European Integration by Martin Staniland. 2011. 520p. pap. 38.95 ***(978-1-61830-836-8(X))*** Cram101 Inc.

Critical Lapses in Federal Aviation Administration Safety Oversight of Airlines: Abuses of Regulatory "Partnership Programs": Hearing Before the Committee on Transportation & Infrastructure, House of Representatives, One Hundred Tenth Congress, Second Session, April 3, 2008. 2008. (Illus.). xxi, 720p. *(978-0-16-083250-5(0)*, 552-070-39078-2) United States Government Printing Office.

Crouch, Gregory. China's Wings: War, Intrigue, Romance, & Adventure in the Middle Kingdom During the Golden Age of Flight. 2012. (ENG., Illus.). 528p. 30.00 ***(978-0-553-80427-0(8))*** Random House Publishing Group.

Cruddas, Colin. 100 Years Advertising in British Aviation. 2008. (ENG., Illus.). 192p. 64.95 *(978-0-7524-4527-4(8))* History Pr. Ltd.,The GBR. Dist: Independent Pubs. Group.

Davies, R. E. G. Airline of the Jet Age: A History. 2011. (ENG., Illus.). 480p. 99.95 *(978-0-9788460-8-4(7))* Smithsonian Institution Scholarly Pr.

Doganis, Rigas. Flying off Course Fourth Edition. 4th ed. 2010. (ENG., Illus.). 352p. 64.95 *(978-0-415-44737-9(2))*; 190.00 *(978-0-415-44736-2(4))* Routledge.

Donohue, George L., et al. Terminal Chaos: Why US Air Travel Is Broken & How to Fix It. 2008. (Library of Flight Ser.). (Illus.). 150p. *(978-1-56347-949-6(4))* American Institute of Aeronautics & Astronautics.

Eller, Richard E. Piedmont Airlines: A Complete History, 1948-1989. (ENG., Illus.). 317p. 2008. 49.95 *(978-0-7864-3147-2(4))* 2012. pap. 25.00 ***(978-0-7864-6914-7(5))*** McFarland & Co., Inc. Pubs.

Essential Air Service & Small Community Air Service Development Programs: Hearing Before the Subcommittee on Aviation of the Committee on Transportation & Infrastructure, House of Representatives, One Hundred Tenth Congress, First Session, April 25, 2007. 2007. (Illus.). xv, 306p. *(978-0-16-079630-2(X)*, 552-070-36587-7) United States Government Printing Office.

Felix J. Mercado. Airline Industry Mergers: Background & Issues. 2011. (Series: Transportation Infrastructure - Roads, Highways, Bridges, Airports & Mass Transit Ser.). (Illus.). ix, 150p. 115.00 *(978-1-61761-993-9(0))* Nova Science Pubs., Inc.

The Financial State of the Airline Industry & the Implications of Consolidation: Hearing Before the Committee on Commerce, Science, & Transportation, United States Senate, One Hundred Eleventh Congress, Second Session, June 17, 2010. 2011. (Illus.). iv, 96p. ***(978-0-16-089628-6(2)***, 552-070-43517-4) United States Government Printing Office.

The Future of TSA's Registered Traveler Program: Hearing Before the Subcommittee on Economic Security, Infrstructure [i.e. Infrastructure] Protection, & Cybersecurity of the Committee on Homeland Security, House of Representatives, One Hundred Ninth Congress, First Session, November 3, 2005. 2007. (Illus.). iv, 84p. *(978-0-16-079483-4(8)*, 552-070-36476-5) United States Government Printing Office.

Glud, Alexander & Wedding, Eivind. Fasten Your Seatbelts. 2011. 140p. pap. ***(978-3-8433-9459-8(8))*** Lambert Academic Publishing.

Gordon, Yefim & Komissarov, Dmitriy. Russian Airliners: Outside Russia. 2008. (Illus.). 160p. per. 32.95 *(978-1-85780-252-8(7))* Midland Publishing Ltd. GBR. Dist: Partners Pubs. Group, Inc.

Green, Larry. One Man's Airline. 2008. 272p. pap. 12.95 *(978-1-4327-0062-1(6))* Outskirts Pr., Inc.

Halford-Macleod, Guy. Britain's Airlines Vol. 3: 1964 to Deregulation. 2010. (ENG., Illus.). 288p. pap. 36.95 *(978-0-7524-5499-3(4))* History Pr. Ltd.,The GBR. Dist: Independent Pubs. Group.

—Britains Airlines, 1951-1964, 2 vols., Vol. 2. 2007. (ENG., Illus.). 264p. pap. 39.95 *(978-0-7524-4276-1(7))* History Pr. Ltd.,The GBR. Dist: Independent Pubs. Group.

Harrison, John. International Aviation & Terrorism: Evolving Threats, Evolving Security. 2009. (Cass Series on Political Violence Ser.). (ENG.). 224p. 140.00 *(978-0-415-48541-8(X))* Routledge.

Havel, Brian F. In Search of Open Skies: Law & Policy for a New Era in International Aviation. 2nd ed. 2009. xxxi, 712p. *(978-90-411-2389-3(X))* Kluwer Law International.

Havers, Richard & Tiffney, Christopher. In-Flight Confidential. 2009. (Confidential Ser.). (ENG., Illus.). 304p. pap. 10.99 *(978-1-906635-43-5(9)*, 1906635439) G2 Entertainment Ltd. GBR. Dist: MBI Distribution Services/Quayside Distribution.

Havers, Richard, et al. Airline Confidential: Lifting the Lid on the Airline Industry. 2007. (ENG., Illus.). 280p. per. 36.95 *(978-0-7509-4380-2(7))* Sutton Publishing.

Hoftbauer, Philip. Market Opportunities for Low-Cost Carriers in Chin. 2010. 108p. pap. *(978-3-639-27857-6(7))* VDM Verlag Dr. Mueller e.K.

Holder, Jean S. Don't Burn Our Bridges: The Case for Owning Airlines. 2010. (Illus.). 296p. pap. *(978-976-640-232-7(9))* Univ. of the West Indies Pr.

Jones, G. & Jones, Geoff. Air France. 2010. (ENG., Illus.). 160p. 36.95 *(978-1-85780-285-6(3))* Allan, Ian Publishing GBR. Dist: BookMasters Distribution Services (BDS).

Kucuk Yilmaz, Ayse. The Best Enterprise Risk Management Practice for Airline & Airport Business. 2008. 228p. per. *(978-3-8364-6789-6(5))* VDM Verlag Dr. Mueller e.K.

Lee, Darin, ed. The Economics of Airline Institutions, Operations & Marketing. 2007. (Advances in Airline Economics Ser.). (Illus.). 413p. 155.95 *(978-0-444-53027-1(4))* Emerald Group Publishing Ltd. GBR. Dist: Turpin Distribution Services Ltd.

Liguori, Michael J. Commercial Airlines: Passenger Fee Issues. 2011. (Illus.). 101p. pap. *(978-1-61761-989-2(2))* Nova Science Pubs., Inc.

Macário, Rosário & Van de Voorde, Eddy, eds. Critical Issues in Air Transport Economics & Business. 2010. (Routledge Studies in the Modern World Economy Ser.). (ENG., Illus.). 432p. (C). 145.00 *(978-0-415-57055-8(7))* Routledge.

Manning, Gerry. Airline Tail Colours. 2012. (ENG., Illus.). 112p. pap. 16.95 *(978-1-85780-350-1(7))* Allan, Ian Publishing GBR. Dist: BookMasters Distribution Services (BDS).

McGee, William J. Attention All Passengers: The Airlines' Dangerous Descent—-And How to Reclaim Our Skies. 2012. (ENG.). 368p. 26.99 ***(978-0-06-208837-6(8))*** HarperCollins Pubs.

Mekawy, Moustafa. Managing Tourist Service Quality in the Airline Industry. 2010. 220p. pap. *(978-3-639-28525-3(5))* VDM Verlag Dr. Mueller e.K.

Milton, Robert A. Straight from the Top: The Truth about Air Canada. annot. ed. 2006. (ENG.). 280p. pap. 18.95 *(978-1-55365-127-7(8)*, Greystone Bks.) D&M Pubs. Inc. CAN. Dist: Perseus-PGW.

Morrell, Peter S. Airline Finance. 3rd rev. ed. 2007. 276p. pap. 59.95 *(978-0-7546-7134-3(8))*; 124.95 *(978-0-7546-7000-1(7))* Ashgate Publishing Co.

Morton, John K. Arrivals & Departures: North American Airlines, 1990-2000. 2010. (ENG., Illus.). 112p. pap. 27.95 *(978-1-85780-200-9(4))* Allan, Ian Publishing GBR. Dist: BookMasters Distribution Services (BDS).

—European Airlines. 2010. (ENG., Illus.). 111p. pap. 27.95 *(978-1-85780-210-8(1))* Allan, Ian Publishing GBR. Dist: BookMasters Distribution Services (BDS).

National Mediation Board Oversight of Elections for Union Representation: Hearing Before the Committee on Transportation & Infrastructure, House of Representatives, One Hundred Tenth Congress, Second Session, September 24, 2008. 2008. ix, 133p. *(978-0-16-083797-5(9)*, 552-070-39499-1) United States Government Printing Office.

Neuscheler, Tillmann. Flughäfen zwischen Regulierung und Wettbewerb: Eine netzökonomische Analyse. 2008. (GER., Illus.). 379p. pap. *(978-3-8329-3737-9(4))* Nomos Verlagsgesellschaft.

O'Connell, John F. & Williams, George, eds. Contemporary Issues in the Air Transport Industry. 2011. (Illus.). 508p. 124.95 *(978-1-4094-0097-4(2))* Ashgate Publishing Co.

Penaloza, Katherine. Great Asian Brands: Singapore Airlines. 2010. 192p. pap. *(978-1-905736-12-6(6))* Marshall Cavendish.

Peoples, James, ed. Pricing Behaviour & Non-Price Characteristics in the Airline Industry. 2012. (Advances in Airline Economics Ser.). (Illus.). 428p. 134.95 ***(978-1-78052-468-9(4))*** Emerald Group Publishing Ltd. GBR. Dist: Turpin Distribution Services Ltd.

Plunkett, Jack W. E-Book Plunkett's Airline, Hotel & Travel Industry Almanac 2008: Airline, Hotel & Travel Industry Market Research, Statistics, Trends & Leading Companies. annuals Plunkett, Jack W., ed. 2007. 497p. E-Book 299.99 incl. cd-rom *(978-1-59392-436-2(4))* Plunkett Research, Ltd.

—Plunkett's Airline, Hotel & Travel Industry Almanac 2007: Airline, Hotel & Travel Industry Market Research, Statistics, Trends & Leading Companies. Plunkett, Jack W., ed. 2006. 460p. pap. 299.99 incl. cd-rom *(978-1-59392-077-7(6))* Plunkett Research, Ltd.

—Plunkett's Airline, Hotel & Travel Industry Almanac 2007 (E-Book) Airline, Hotel & Travel Industry Market Research, Statistics, Trends & Leading Companies. Plunkett, Jack W., ed. 2006. 478p. E-Book 499.99 incl. cd-rom *(978-1-59392-419-5(4))* Plunkett Research, Ltd.

—Plunkett's Airline, Hotel & Travel Industry Almanac 2008: Airline, Hotel & Travel Industry Market Research, Statistics, Trends & Leading Companies. annuals Plunkett, Jack W., ed. 2007. pap. 299.99 incl. cd-rom *(978-1-59392-093-7(8))* Plunkett Research, Ltd.

—Plunkett's Airline, Hotel & Travel Industry Almanac 2010: Airline, Hotel & Travel Industry Market Research, Statistics, Trends & Leading Companies. Plunkett, Jack W., ed. 2009. (Illus.). 498p. pap. 299.99 incl. cd-rom *(978-1-59392-151-4(6))* Plunkett Research, Ltd.

The Proposed Delta/Northwest Merger: The Impact on Workers: Hearing Before the Subcommittee on Health, Employment, Labor & Pensions, Committee on Education & Labor, U.S. House of Representatives, One Hundred Tenth Congress, Second Session, Hearing Held in Washington, DC, July 30, 2008. 2008. iii, 68p. *(978-0-16-082195-0(9)*, 552-070-38329-8) United States Government Printing Office.

Restructuring Canada's Airline Industry. *(978-0-660-61142-6(2))* Canadian Government Publishing.

Reviewing the Department of Transportation's Notice of Proposed Rulemaking That Clarifies the Rules Regarding Foreign Investment in U.S. Air Carriers: Hearing Before the Subcommittee on Aviation of the Committee on Commerce, Science, & Transportation, United States Senate, One Hundred Ninth Congress, Second Session, May 9, 2006. 2011. iii, 73p. ***(978-0-16-088368-2(7)***, 552-070-42641-8) United States Government Printing Office.

Rhoades, Dawna L. Evolution of International Aviation: Phoenix Rising. 2nd rev. ed. 2008. (Illus.). 296p. 59.95 *(978-0-7546-7389-7(8))* Ashgate Publishing Co.

Rickenbacker, Edward V. Rickenbacker. (Airlines History Project Ser.). (Illus.). reprint ed. 57.50 *(978-0-404-19332-4(3))* AMS Pr., Inc.

Rolow, Alicia Lutz. The Plane Truth from an American Airlines Flight Attendant. 2008. 420p. pap. 26.95 *(978-1-4401-0655-2(X))* iUniverse, Inc.

Schank, Joshua. Examining the Cost-Effectiveness of Market-Based Policies. 2010. 176p. pap. *(978-3-639-22684-9(5))* VDM Verlag Dr. Mueller e.K.

Searle, Tex. Golden Years of Flying: As We Remember - Frontier Airlines, 1946-1986. 2008. (ENG.). 300p. pap. 19.95 *(978-1-56027-708-8(4))* Aviation Supplies & Academics, Inc.

Serling, Robert J. The Only Way to Fly: The Story of Western Airlines, America's Senior Air Carrier. (Airlines History Project Ser.). (Illus.). reprint ed. 49.50 *(978-0-404-19334-8(X))* AMS Pr., Inc.

Sheth, Jagdish N., et al. Deregulation & Competition: Lessons from the Airline Industry. 2007. *(978-81-7829-757-6(4))* SAGE Pubns., Inc.

Smith, Barry & Barnhart, Cynthia, eds. Quantitative Problem Solving Methods in the Airline Industry: A Modeling Methodology Handbook. 2011. (International Series in Operations Research & Management Science Ser.). (ENG., Illus.). ix, 458p. 189.00 ***(978-1-4614-1607-4(8)***, 1461416078) Springer.

Snodgrass, Richard. An Uncommon Field: The Flight 93 Temporary Memorial. 2011. (Carnegie Mellon Photography Ser.). (ENG.). 168p. 39.95 ***(978-0-88748-552-7(9))*** Carnegie-Mellon Univ. Pr.

Solomon, Stan. Airlines for the Rest of Us: The Rise & Fall of America's Local Service Airlines. 2008. 168p. pap. 15.95 *(978-0-595-48443-0(3))* iUniverse, Inc.

The Southwest/AirTran Merger & Its Impact on M-7 Businesses, Consumers, & the Local Economy: Hearing Before the Subcommittee on Antitrust, Competition Policy & Consumer Rights of the Committee on the Judiciary, One Hundred Twelfth Congress, First Session, February 25, 2011, Pewaukee, Wisconsin. 2011. ii, 52p. ***(978-0-16-089348-3(8)***, 552-070-43335-0) United States Government Printing Office.

Staniland, Martin. A Europe of the Air? The Airline Industry & European Integration. 2008. (Governance in Europe Ser.). (ENG.). 316p. 80.00 *(978-0-7425-2651-8(8))* Rowman & Littlefield Publishers, Inc.

Starkie, David. Aviation Markets: Studies in Competition & Regulatory Reform. 2008. (Illus.). 246p. pap. 49.95 *(978-0-7546-7388-0(X))* Ashgate Publishing Co.

—Aviation Markets: Studies in Economic Policy. 2008. (Illus.). 246p. 124.95 *(978-0-7546-7360-6(X))* Ashgate Publishing Co.

The State of the Airline Industry: The Potential Impact of Airline Mergers & Industry Consolidation: Hearing Before the Committee on Commerce, Science, & Transportation, United States Senate, One Hundred Tenth Congress, First Session, January 24, 2007. 2010. (Illus.). iv, 113p. ***(978-0-16-086802-3(5)***, 552-070-41718-4) United States Government Printing Office.

Szurovy, Geza & Yenne, Bill. Classic American Airlines. 2007. 360p. pap. 12.99 *(978-0-7603-3206-1(1)*, Zenith Pr.) MBI Publishing Co. LLC.

Taneja, Nawal K. Looking Beyond the Runway: Airlines Innovating with Best Practices While Facing Realities. 2010. (Illus.). 354p. 64.95 *(978-1-4094-0099-8(9))* Ashgate Publishing Co.

Taylor, Michael J. H. The World's Commercial Airlines: An Illustrated History of the Airlines & Their Insignia. 2007. (Illus.). 80p. reprint ed. 25.00 *(978-1-4223-6840-4(8))* DIANE Publishing Co.

Terpstra, Philip. Electric Aircraft Technology. (Illus.). 63p. (Orig.). pap. 12.00 *(978-1-883063-04-7(3))* Spirit Pubns.

Thomas, Andrew R. Aviation Security Management, 3 vols. Thomas, Andrew R., ed. 2008. (Praeger Security International Ser.). (Illus.). 804p. 375.00 *(978-0-313-34652-1(6)*, C34652, Praeger Pubs.) Greenwood Publishing Group, Inc.

Thomas, Andrew R. & Dumont, Gregory M. Soft Landing: Airline Industry Strategy, Service, & Safety. 2011. (ENG.). 220p. pap. 24.99 ***(978-1-4302-3677-1(9))*** Apress L. P.

Truxal, Steven. Competition & Regulation in the Airline Industry: Puppets in Chaos. 2012. (Routledge Research in Competition Law Ser.). (ENG.). 208p. (C). 135.00 *(978-0-415-67196-5(5))* Routledge.

United States, Congress House Committee on Transportation and Infrastructure Subcommittee on Aviation Staff, contrib. by. Commercial Jet Fuel Supply: Impact & Cost on the United States Airline Industry: Hearing Before the Subcommittee on Aviation of the Committee on Transportation & Infrastructure, House of Representatives, One Hundred Ninth Congress, Second Session, February 15, 2006. 2007. (Illus.). v, 124p. *(978-0-16-078047-9(0)*, 552-070-35455-7) United States Government Printing Office.

The United/Continental Airlines Merger: How Will Consumers Fare?: Hearing Before the Subcommittee on Antitrust, Competition Policy, & Consumer Rights of the Committee on the Judiciary, United States Senate, One Hundred Eleventh Congress, Second Session, May 27, 2010. 2010. (Illus.). iii, 121p. *(978-0-16-086983-9(8)*, 552-070-41842-3) United States Government Printing Office.

Van Dyke, Donald L. Fortune Favours the Bold. 2009. (Illus.). x, 278p. 161.99 *(978-1-4363-9489-5(9))* Xlibris Corp.

Vasigh, Bijan, et al. Foundations of Airline Finance: Methodology & Practice. 2010. (Illus.). 444p. 134.95 *(978-0-7546-7769-7(9))*; pap. 49.95 *(978-0-7546-7770-3(2))* Ashgate Publishing Co.

Walsh, Connor R. Airline Industry: Strategies, Operations & Safety. 2011. (Transportation Infrastructure - Roads, Highways, Bridges, Airports & Mass Transit Ser.). (Illus.). x, 242p. 129.00 *(978-1-61122-079-7(3))* Nova Science Pubs., Inc.

Wood, Katie. Fly Europe: The Complete Guide to Budget Airline Destinations. (Illus.). 576p. pap. 19.99 *(978-1-85410-895-1(6))* Aurum Pr., Ltd. GBR. Dist: Trafalgar Square Publishing.

Woodley, Charles. Scotland's Airlines. 2009. (ENG., Illus.). 160p. pap. 32.95 *(978-0-7524-4522-9(7))* History Pr. Ltd.,The GBR. Dist: Independent Pubs. Group.

Wragg, David. The World's Major Airlines. 2nd ed. 2007. (ENG., Illus.). 320p. 44.95 *(978-0-7509-4481-6(1))* Sutton Publishing.

AIRLINES—COLLECTIVE BARGAINING

see Collective Bargaining—Aeronautics

AIRLINES—EMPLOYEES

see also Air Pilots; Collective Bargaining—Aeronautics; Flight Attendants; Flight Crews

Airport Security: The Necessary Improvements to Secure America's Airports: Hearing Before the Subcommittee on Transportation Security & Infrastructure Protection of the Committee on Homeland Security, House of Representatives, One Hundred Tenth Congress, First Session, April 19, 2007. 2009. iii, 47p. *(978-0-16-083536-0(4)*, 552-070-39259-9) United States Government Printing Office.

Bamber, Greg J., et al. Up in the Air: How Airlines Can Improve Performance by Engaging Their Employees. 2009. (Illus.). 224p. 29.95 *(978-0-8014-4747-1(X)*, ILR Pr.) Cornell Univ. Pr.

Beyer, Morten. Flying Higher. 2010. 236p. pap. 18.95 *(978-1-4251-6652-6(0))* Trafford Publishing.

Coulby, Adam. Fbo Safety & Procedures Guide: A Training & Resource Manual for Line Service Technicians. rev. ed. 2011. (ENG.). 94p. spiral bd. 42.00 *(978-0-7575-8819-8(0))* Kendall Hunt Publishing Co.

Eriksen, Carina. Managing Work & Relationships at 35,000 Feet: A Practical Guide for Making Personal Life Fit Aircraft Shift Work, Jetlag, & Absences from Home. 2009. (Karnac Self Help Ser.). (Illus.). 128p. pap. 23.95 *(978-1-85575-578-9(5))* Karnac Bks. GBR. Dist: Stylus Publishing, LLC.

Impact of Consolidation on the Aviation Industry, with a Focus on the Proposed Merger Between Delta Air Lines & Northwest Airlines: Hearing Before the Subcommittee on Aviation of the Committee on Transportation & Infrastructure, House of Representatives, One Hundred Tenth Congress, Second Session, May 14, 2008. 2008. (Illus.). xvi, 307p. *(978-0-16-083853-8(3)*, 552-070-39550-4) United States Government Printing Office.

Kenville, Kimberly A. Helping Airport & Air Carrier Employees Cope with Traumatic Events. 2009. (Illus.). 74p. *(978-0-309-11797-5(6))* Transportation Research Board.

Murphy, Tom. Reclaiming the Sky: 9/11 & the Untold Story of the Men & Women Who Kept America Flying. 2006. (ENG., Illus.). 224p. 21.95 *(978-0-8144-0909-1(1))* Amacom.

Orenic, Liesl Miller. On the Ground: Labor Struggle in the American Airline Industry. 2009. (Working Class in American History Ser.). (ENG., Illus.). 304p. 75.00 *(978-0-252-03433-6(3))*; pap. 26.00 *(978-0-252-07627-5(3))* Univ. of Illinois Pr.

Pascucci, Ron L. The American Airport Screener. 2006. 171p. pap. 19.95 *(978-0-7414-3508-8(X))* Infinity Publishing.

The Proposed United-Continental Merger: Potential Effects for Consumers & Industry: Hearing Before the Subcommittee on Aviation of the Committee on Transportation & Infrastructure, House of Representatives, One Hundred Eleventh Congress, Second Session, June 16, 2010. 2010. (Illus.). xxi, 305p. ***(978-0-16-087093-4(3)***, 552-070-41949-7) United States Government Printing Office.

Protecting Employees in Airline Bankruptcies: Hearing Before the Subcommittee on Commercial & Administrative Law of the Committee on the Judiciary, House of Representatives, One Hundred Eleventh Congress, First Session, December 16, 2009. 2010. iv, 155p. *(978-0-16-085489-7(X)*, 552-070-40740-5) United States Government Printing Office.

Salas, Eduardo, et al, eds. Crew Resource Management: Critical Essays. 2009. (Critical Essays on Human Factors in Aviation Ser.). (Illus.). 448p. 250.00 *(978-0-7546-2829-3(9))* Ashgate Publishing Co.

Seabridge, Allan & Morgan, Shirley. Air Travel & Health: A Systems Perspective. 2010. (Aerospace Ser.). (ENG., Illus.). 248p. 110.00 *(978-0-470-71177-4(9)*, Wiley) Wiley, John & Sons, Inc.

Voogt, Alex De & D'Oliveira, Teresa C. Mechanisms in the Chain of Safety: Research & Operational Experiences in Aviation Psychology. 2012. (Illus.). 150p. 99.95 ***(978-1-4094-1254-0(7))*** Ashgate Publishing Co.

AIRLINES—FLIGHT ATTENDANTS

see Flight Attendants

AIRLINES—HOSTESSES

see Flight Attendants

AIRLINES—LAW AND LEGISLATION

see Aeronautics—Law and Legislation

AIRLINES—MANAGEMENT

Abdelghany, Ahmed F. & Abdelghany, Khaled. Modeling Applications in the Airline Industry. 2010. (Illus.). 290p. 99.95 *(978-0-7546-7874-8(1))* Ashgate Publishing Co.

Abeyratne, Ruwantissa. Airport Business Law. 2009. 284p. 50.00 *(978-1-4490-4768-9(8))*; pap. 50.00 *(978-1-4490-4769-6(6))* AuthorHouse.

Air Traffic Control Facility Staffing: Hearing Before the Subcommittee on Aviation of the Committee on Transportation & Infrastructure, House of Representatives, One Hundred Tenth Congress, Second Session, June 11, 2008. 2008. (Illus.). xiv, 186p. *(978-0-16-083487-5(2)*, 552-070-39221-1) United States Government Printing Office.

Airline Financial Stability: Hearing Before the Subcommittee on Aviation of the Committee on Commerce, Science, & Transportation, United States Senate, One Hundred Ninth Congress, First Session, July 13, 2005. 2010. (Illus.). iii, 53p. ***(978-0-16-087407-9(6)***, 552-070-42100-9) United States Government Printing Office.

Aviation Consumer Issues: Hearing Before the Subcommittee on Aviation of the Committee on Transportation & Infrastructure, House of Representatives, One Hundred Tenth Congress, First Session, April 20, 2007. 2007. (Illus.). xii, 194p. *(978-0-16-079977-8(5)*, 552-070-36802-7) United States Government Printing Office.

Aviation Delays & Consumer Issues: Hearing Before the Subcommittee on Aviation of the Committee on Transportation & Infrastructure, House of Representatives, One Hundred Tenth Congress, Second Session, April 9, 2008. 2008. (Illus.). xii, 194p. *(978-0-16-082967-3(4)*, 552-070-38878-8) United States Government Printing Office.

Barrett, Sean. Deregulation & the Airline Business in Europe. 2009. (Routledge Studies in the European Economy Ser.). (ENG., Illus.). 194p. 140.00 *(978-0-415-44722-5(4))* Routledge.

Bazargan, Massoud. Airline Operations & Scheduling. 2nd rev. ed. 2010. (Illus.). 302p. 89.95 *(978-0-7546-7900-4(4))* Ashgate Publishing Co.

Ben-Yosef, Eldad. The Evolution of the US Airline Industry: Theory, Strategy & Policy. 2010. (Studies in Industrial Organization Ser.). x, 298p. pap. 129.00 *(978-1-4419-3701-8(3)*, 1441937013) Springer.

Beyer, Morten. Flying Higher. 2010. 236p. pap. 18.95 *(978-1-4251-6652-6(0))* Trafford Publishing.

Binder, Philipp. The Iosa Story: Effects of the IATA Operational. 2008. 108p. pap. *(978-3-639-03567-4(4))* VDM Verlag Dr. Mueller e.K.

Cannon, James & Richey, Franklin D. Practical Applications in Business Aviation Management. 2011. (ENG.). (C). (gr. 13-17). 320p. 99.00 ***(978-1-60590-763-5(4))***; 384p. pap. 50.00 ***(978-1-60590-770-3(7))*** Government Institutes.

Cannon, James R. & Richey, Franklin D. Practical Applications in Business Aviation Management. 2011. ***(978-1-60590-764-2(2))*** Government Institutes.

Castro, Raoul. Corporate Aviation Management. 2011. (Illus.). 352p. pap. 25.00 *(978-0-8093-3039-3(3))*; E-Book 25.00 *(978-0-8093-8786-1(7))* Southern Illinois Univ. Pr.

Clark, Paul. Buying the Big Jets: Second edition-fleet planning for Airlines. 2nd rev. ed. 2007. (Illus.). 262p. 144.95 *(978-0-7546-7090-2(2))*; pap. 54.95 *(978-0-7546-7091-9(0))* Ashgate Publishing Co.

Cram101 Textbook Reviews & Cram101 Textbook Reviews. Outlines & Highlights for Air Transportation: A Management Perspective by John Wensveen. 2011. 488p. pap. 37.95 ***(978-1-61830-851-1(3))*** Cram101 Inc.

Cram101 Textbook Reviews Staff. Outlines & Highlights for Do the Right Thing: How Dedicated Employees Create Loyal Customers & Large Profits by Parker, ISBN. 2009. 80p. pap. 10.95 *(978-1-4288-6605-8(1))* Cram101 Inc.

Creaton, Siobhan. Ryanair: How a Small Irish Airline Conquered Europe. (Illus.). 256p. 17.99 *(978-1-85410-992-7(8))* Aurum Pr., Ltd. GBR. Dist: Trafalgar Square Publishing.

—Ryanair: The Full Story of the Controversial Low-Cost Airline. 2007. (ENG.). 272p. pap. 17.95 *(978-1-84513-293-4(9))* Aurum Pr., Ltd. GBR. Dist: Independent Pubs. Group.

Dempsey, Paul Stephen & Gesell, Laurence E. Airline Management: Strategies for te 21st Century, 2nd Ed. 2nd ed. 2006. (ENG.). 1068p. (C). 98.00 *(978-1-890938-09-3(2))* Coast Aire Pubns. & Consulting.

Environmental Management for Airports & Aviation. 2nd ed. (Special Report Ser.). 1040.00 *(978-0-7106-1979-2(0))* Jane's Information Group, Inc.

Gordon, Alastair. Naked Airport: A Cultural History of the World's Most Revolutionary Structure. 2008. (Illus.). 320p. pap. 17.00 *(978-0-226-30456-4(6))* Univ. of Chicago Pr.

Grubesic. The Global Airline Network in the Information Age. 2009. 288p. 150.00 *(978-0-415-77535-9(3))* Routledge.

Harvey, Geraint. Management in the Airline Industry. 2008. (Routledge Research in Employment Relations Ser.). (Illus.). 158p. 143.00 *(978-0-415-39078-1(8))* Routledge.

Heracleous, Loizos, et al. Flying High in a Competitive Industry: Secrets of the World's Leading Airline. 2nd ed. 2008. (ENG., Illus.). 256p. 29.95 *(978-0-07-128196-6(7)*, 0071281967) McGraw-Hill Cos., The.

Hinault-Jambor, Petra. Everything in Orange: Success Story of Easyjet. 2008. 68p. pap. *(978-3-639-03744-9(8))* VDM Verlag Dr. Mueller e.K.

Hirst, M. The Air Transport System. 2008. 352p. *(978-1-84569-325-1(6))* Woodhead Publishing Ltd.

Hirst, Mike. The Air Transport System. 2008. (Library of Flight). (Illus.). ix, 341p. *(978-1-56347-964-9(8))* American Institute of Aeronautics & Astronautics.

Holt, Laurence. Stikky Landings: In One Hour, Learn How to Land a Jet Airplane in an Emergency. 2010. (Stikky Ser.). 256p. pap. 12.00 *(978-1-932974-06-5(7))* Holt, Laurence Bks., Inc.

Hunter, Joyce A. Anger in the Air: Combating the Air Rage Phenomenon. 2009. 236p. 124.95 *(978-0-7546-7193-0(3))* Ashgate Publishing Co.

Iatrou, Kostas & Oretti, Mauro. Airline Choices for the Future: From Alliances to Mergers. 2007. (Illus.). 242p. 114.95 *(978-0-7546-4886-4(9))* Ashgate Publishing Co.

Jaehn, Florian. Robust Flight Gate Assignment. 2008. (Europäische Hochschulschriften. Reihe 5: Volks- und Betriebswirtschaft Ser.). 140p. pap. 39.95 *(978-3-631-57704-2(4))* Lang, Peter GmbH, Europaischer Verlag der Wissenschaften DEU. Dist: Lang, Peter.

Jiang, Ningbo. Quality of the Auckland Airshed. 2008. 280p. pap. *(978-3-8364-9002-3(1))* VDM Verlag Dr. Mueller e.K.

Jones, Lois. EasyJet: The Story of Britain's Biggest Low-Cost Airline. 2nd rev. ed. 2007. (ENG.). 256p. pap. 15.95 *(978-1-84513-247-7(5))* Aurum Pr., Ltd. GBR. Dist: Independent Pubs. Group.

Kaspar, Nina. Low Cost Carriers in Southeast Asi. 2009. 92p. pap. *(978-3-639-08166-4(8))* VDM Verlag Dr. Mueller e.K.

Kuchta, Marek. Viability of the Premium Airline Business Model. 2009. 118p. pap. *(978-3-639-18166-1(2))* VDM Verlag Dr. Mueller e.K.

Kucuk Yilmaz, Ayse. Airport Enterprise Risk Management Model- a Study on Business Management & Airline Management. 2008. (Illus.). 180p. per. *(978-3-8364-2979-5(9))* VDM Verlag Dr. Mueller e.K.

Lauer, Chris. Southwest Airlines, 1 vol. 2010. (Corporations That Changed the World Ser.). 190p. 45.00 *(978-0-313-37863-8(0)*, GR7863) Greenwood Publishing Group, Inc.

Lawton, Thomas C., ed. Strategic Management in Aviation: Critical Essays. 2007. (Illus.). 416p. 225.00 *(978-0-7546-2651-0(2))* Ashgate Publishing Co.

Liu, Pei-Chen Barry. Managing Uncertainty in the Single Airport Ground Holding Problem. 2008. 176p. pap. *(978-3-8364-8445-9(5))* VDM Verlag Dr. Mueller e.K.

Lynes, Jennifer. Motivations for Environmental Commitment in the Airline Industry. 2008. 256p. pap. *(978-3-639-02062-5(6))* VDM Verlag Dr. Mueller e.K.

Masresha, Abebaw Kemaw. Aircraft Scheduling. 2011. 68p. pap. ***(978-3-8443-9571-6(7))*** Lambert Academic Publishing.

Mayo, Anthony, et al. Entrepreneurs, Managers, & Leaders: What the Airline Industry Can Teach Us about Leadership. 2009. (ENG., Illus.). 260p. 58.00 *(978-0-230-61567-0(8))* Palgrave Macmillan.

McGarvey, Ronald G. & Carrillo, Manuel. Analysis of the Air Force Logistics Enterprise: Evaluation of Global Repair Network Options for Supporting the F-16 & KC-135. 2010. 188p. pap. 30.00 *(978-0-8330-4740-3(X)*, mg872) RAND Corp., The.

Oster, Clinton V. & Strong, John S. Managing the Skies: Public Policy Organization & Financing of Air Traffic Management. 2007. 234p. 99.95 *(978-0-7546-7045-2(7))* Ashgate Publishing Co.

Parker, James F. Do the Right Thing: How Dedicated Employees Create Loyal Customers & Large Profits. rev. ed. 2007. (ENG.). 288p. pap. 25.99 ***(978-0-13-276357-8(5))*** Wharton Schl. Publishing.

Rankin, Anna. Quesnel Community Air Shed Improvement Initiatives. 2008. 76p. pap. *(978-3-8364-8583-8(4))* VDM Verlag Dr. Mueller e.K.

Rapajic, Jasenka. Beyond Airline Disruptions. 2009. (Illus.). 184p. 99.95 *(978-0-7546-7440-5(1))* Ashgate Publishing Co.

Rorke, William Buckland. Trek Airways: A South African Adventure. 2007. 200p. per. *(978-1-84401-858-1(X))* Athena Pr.

Shaw, Stepehn. Airline Marketing & Management. 7th rev. ed. 2011. 378p. 144.95 *(978-1-4094-0147-6(2))* Ashgate Publishing Co.

Shaw, Stephen. Airline Marketing & Management. 6th rev. ed. 2007. 336p. pap. 34.95 *(978-0-7546-4820-8(6))* 7th rev. ed. 2011. 378p. pap. 34.95 *(978-1-4094-0149-0(9))* Ashgate Publishing Co.

—Airline Marketing & Management. 6th rev. ed. 2007. 336p. 144.95 *(978-0-7546-4819-2(2))* Ashgate Publishing, Ltd. GBR. Dist: Ashgate Publishing Co.

Taneja, Nawal K. The Passenger Has Gone Digital & Mobile: Accessing & Connecting Through Information & Technology. 2011. (Illus.). 268p. 64.95 ***(978-1-4094-3502-0(4))*** Ashgate Publishing Co.

Taneja, Nawal K. Flying Ahead of the Airplane. 2008. 298p. 69.95 *(978-0-7546-7579-2(3))* Ashgate Publishing Co.

Wensveen, J. G. Wheels Up: Airline Business Plan Development. 2nd ed. 2007. *(978-1-57524-293-4(1))* Krieger Publishing Co.

Wensveen, John G. Air Transportation: A management perpsective:sixth Edition. 6th rev. ed. 2007. (Illus.). 590p. 149.95 *(978-0-7546-7165-7(8))* Ashgate Publishing Co.

—Air Transportation: A Management Perspective. 7th rev. ed. 2011. (Illus.). 604p. 149.95 ***(978-1-4094-3062-9(6))***; pap. 69.95 ***(978-1-4094-3063-6(4))*** Ashgate Publishing Co.

Wensveen, John G. Air Transportation: A management perpsective:sixth Edition. 6th rev. ed. 2007. (Illus.). 590p. pap. 69.95 *(978-0-7546-7171-8(2))* Ashgate Publishing, Ltd. GBR. Dist: Ashgate Publishing Co.

Woodward, Jon M., et al. Aircraft Noise: A Toolkit for Managing Community Expectations. 2009. (Illus.). 151p. pap. ***(978-0-309-11801-9(8))*** Transportation Research Board.

AIRLINES—RATES

Airline Fees: Hearing Before the Subcommittee on Aviation of the Committee on Transportation & Infrastructure, House of Representatives, One Hundred Eleventh Congress, Second Session, July 14, 2010. 2010. (Illus.). xvi, 180p. ***(978-0-16-086995-2(1)***, 552-070-41854-7) United States Government Printing Office.

Boyd, E. Andrew & Boyd, E. A. The Future of Pricing: How Airline Ticket Pricing Has Inspired a Revolution. 2007. (ENG., Illus.). 208p. 59.00 *(978-0-230-60019-5(0))* Palgrave Macmillan.

Calder, Simon. No Frills: The Truth Behind the Low-Cost Revolution in the Skies. 2006. (ENG., Illus.). 352p. pap. *(978-0-7535-1044-5(8))* Macmillan.

Hellermann, Rolf. Capacity Options for Revenue Management: Theory & Applications in the Air Cargo Industry. 2006. (Lecture Notes in Economics & Mathematical Systems Ser.). (Illus.). xv, 199p. pap. 139.00 *(978-3-540-34419-3(5)*, 3540344195) Springer.

Hinault-Jambor, Petra. Everything in Orange: Success Story of Easyjet. 2008. 68p. pap. *(978-3-639-03744-9(8))* VDM Verlag Dr. Mueller e.K.

AIRLINES—RESERVATION SYSTEMS

Bazargan, Massoud. Airline Operations & Scheduling. 2nd rev. ed. 2010. (Illus.). 302p. 89.95 *(978-0-7546-7900-4(4))* Ashgate Publishing Co.

Hanke, Michael. Airline Ecommerce. 2013. (ENG., Illus.). 256p. (C). 166.00 *(978-0-415-77579-3(5))*; pap. 57.00 *(978-0-415-77580-9(9))* Routledge.

Rezamand, Erfan & Sorooshian, Shahryar. E-Ticketing. 2011. 164p. pap. ***(978-3-8454-1058-6(2))*** Lambert Academic Publishing.

AIRLINES—STEWARDESSES

see Flight Attendants

AIRLINES—STEWARDS

see Flight Attendants

AIRPLANE ACCESSORIES

see Airplanes—Equipment and Supplies

AIRPLANE ACCIDENTS

see Aircraft Accidents

AIRPLANE BOMBS

see Bombs

AIRPLANE CARRIERS

see Aircraft Carriers

AIRPLANE COLLISIONS

see Aircraft Accidents

AIRPLANE CRASHES

see Aircraft Accidents

AIRPLANE ENGINES

see Airplanes—Motors

AIRPLANE FUELS

see Airplanes—Fuel

AIRPLANE INDUSTRY

see Aircraft Industry

AIRPLANE MORTGAGES

Nath. Aircraft Repossession Enforcement Practical Aspects Volume Ii. 2010. xxiv, 471p. *(978-90-411-3251-2(1))* Kluwer Law International.

AIRPLANE PHOTOGRAPHY

see Photography of Aircraft

AIRPLANE RACING

Berliner, D. Airplane Racing: A History, 1909-2008. 2010. (ENG., Illus.). 266p. pap. 35.00 *(978-0-7864-4300-0(6))* McFarland & Co., Inc. Pubs.

Bromby, Robin. The Last Great Air Race: London - Christchurch 1953. (Illus.). 47p. pap. 3.95 *(978-0-908616-05-3(8))* Southern Press, Ltd. NZL. Dist: Pacific Island Bks.

Gandt, Robert. Fly Low Fly Fast: Inside the Reno Air Races. 2006. 313p. reprint ed. 27.00 *(978-1-4223-5488-9(1))* DIANE Publishing Co.

Handleman, Philip. Air Racing over Reno: The World's Fastest Motorsport. 2007. (ENG., Illus.). 128p. pap. 24.95 *(978-1-58007-112-3(0))* Specialty Pr. Pubs. & Wholesalers, Inc.

Keefe, Howie. Galloping on Wings with the P-51 Mustang Miss America: Diary of an Air Race Pilot. 2007. (ENG., Illus.). 370p. per. 19.95 *(978-1-56027-643-2(6))* Aviation Supplies & Academics, Inc.

Mayday over the Pacific. 2007. per. *(978-0-9638817-5-5(2))* Roundup Pr.

AIRPLANE RECOGNITION

see Airplanes—Recognition

AIRPLANES

see also Air Mail Service; Aircraft Industry; Amphibian Planes; Autogiros; Bombers; Convertiplanes; Fighter Planes; Flying-Machines; Gliders (Aeronautics); Guided Missiles; Helicopters; Jet Planes; Jet Transports; Rocket Planes; Seaplanes; Short Take-Off and Landing Aircraft; Supersonic Planes; Training Planes; Used Aircraft; Vertically Rising Aircraft

also specific makes of airplanes, e.g. Boeing Bombers; Lockheed Airplanes, and headings beginning with the word Airplane

Abbott, Ace & Morris, Allen Robert. The Rogue Aviator: In the Back Alleys of Aviation. 2011. (ENG., Illus.). 237p. pap. 14.95 ***(978-0-578-08508-1(9))*** Morris, Allen.

Alexander, David E. Why Don't Jumbo Jets Flap Their Wings? Flying Animals, Flying Machines, & How They Are Different. 2009. (ENG., Illus.). 296p. 26.95 (978-0-8135-4479-3(3)) Rutgers Univ. Pr.

Andrup, Norbert. Colorful Aircraft: Unique Paint Schemes on the World's Passenger Airliners. 2010. (Illus.). 144p. 45.00 (978-0-7643-3656-0(8)) Schiffer Publishing, Ltd.

Austin, Reg. Unmanned Aircraft Systems: UAVs Design, Development, & Deployment. 2010. 149.95 (978-1-60086-759-0(6)) Wiley, John & Sons, Inc.

Barber, H. The Aeroplane Speaks. 2008. 228p. 27.99 (978-0-554-95697-8(7)) 2008. 128p. 21.99 (978-0-554-30766-4(9)) 2008. 128p. 24.99 (978-0-554-21463-4(6)) 2008. 228p. pap. 25.75 (978-0-554-95699-2(3)) 2006. (ENG.). 130p. pap. 18.99 (978-1-4264-0069-8(1)) 2006. (ENG.). 124p. pap. 13.99 (978-1-4264-0198-5(1)) BiblioBazaar.

—The Aeroplane Speaks. 2008. 228p. pap. 26.95 (978-1-4370-8477-1(X)) Kessinger Publishing, LLC.

Beaumont, Herve. Garnd Mirage IV: Du Bombardement a la Reconnaissance Strategique. 2007. (Matériels de l'Armée de l'Air 6 Ser.). (Illus.). 66p. pap. 19.95 (978-2-35250-024-7(9)) Histoire et Collections FRA. Dist: Casemate Pubs. & Bk. Distributors, LLC.

Behrent, Bob. Planes, Pranks & Pepto-Bismol: Tales & Tips from a Seasoned Road Warrior. 2010. 258p. pap. 15.50 (978-1-60911-383-4(7), Eloquent Bks.) AEG Literary Publishing Services, Inc.

Benavides, S., ed. Corrosion Control in the Aerospace Industry. 2009. (Illus.). 320p. (978-1-84569-345-9(0)) Woodhead Publishing Ltd.

Blaugher, Michael. Guide to over 900 Aircraft Museums, USA & Canada, 24th Ed. 24th ed. 2007. (ENG., Illus.). 322p. per. 9.00 (978-0-9749772-2-5(5)) Blaugher, Michael A.

Book Sales, Inc. Staff. Illustrated Encyclopedia of the World's Aircraft. 19.98 (978-0-89009-771-7(2)) Book Sales, Inc.

Boone, Aaron. CRJ Aircraft Systems Study Guide. 2007. (ENG.). per. 37.95 (978-0-9790767-2-5(2)) Boone and Rile Co.

Böttger, Tim. Customer Preferences of Very Light Jet Air Taxi Operators. 2009. 94p. pap. 42.00 (978-3-03751-177-0(X)) Dike Verlag AG CHE. Dist: International Specialized Bk. Services.

Bowen, Paul, photos by. Air to Air. 2007. (Illus.). 224p. (978-0-9665095-8-8(7)) North Shore Pr.

Castillo Garcia, Pedro, et al. Modelling & Control of Mini-Flying Machines. 2010. (Advances in Industrial Control Ser.). (Illus.). xvi, 252p. pap. 199.00 (978-1-84996-977-2(9), 1849969779) Springer.

Chen, Tingnan. Fei Ji Fei Xing Xing Neng Pin Zhi Yu Kong Zhi. 2007. (Illus.). xiv, 322p. (978-7-118-04979-4(4)) National Defence Industry Pr.

Clark, Paul. Buying the Big Jets: Second edition-fleet planning for Airlines. 2nd rev. ed. 2007. (Illus.). 262p. 144.95 (978-0-7546-7090-2(2)); pap. 54.95 (978-0-7546-7091-9(0)) Ashgate Publishing Co.

Clarke, R. M. Aircraft: Hawker Typhoon. (Illus.). 70p. pap. 11.95 (978-1-869826-17-8(5)) MBI Publishing Co. LLC.

Claxton, William J. The Mastery of the Air. 2007. 148p. per. (978-1-4065-1385-1(7)) Dodo Pr.

—The Mastery of the Air. 2007. (ENG.). 120p. per. (978-1-4068-4626-3(0)) Echo Library.

Darling, Kev. American X & Y Planes Vol. 2: Experimental Aircraft since 1945, 2 vols. 2010. (ENG., Illus.). 176p. 34.95 (978-1-84797-147-0(4), 1847971474) Crowood Pr., Ltd. GBR. Dist: MBI Distribution Services/Quayside Distribution.

De Florio, Filippo. Airworthiness: An Introduction to Aircraft Certification. 2nd ed. 2010. (ENG., Illus.). 368p. 99.95 (978-0-08-096802-5(3), Butterworth-Heinemann) Elsevier Science & Technology Bks.

Deepwater: Charting a Course for Safer Waters: Joint Hearing Before the Subcommittee on Border, Maritime, & Global Counterterrorism with the Subcommittee on Management, Investigations, & Oversight of the Committee on Homeland Security, House of Representatives, One Hundred Tenth Congress, First Session, May 17, 2007. 2009. (Illus.). iv, 89p. (978-0-16-082706-7(5), 552-070-39413-3) United States Government Printing Office.

Diston, Dominic. Computational Modelling of Aircraft & the Environment. 2009. (Illus.). (978-1-60086-704-0(9)) American Institute of Aeronautics & Astronautics.

Donald, David, ed. The Classic Civil Aircraft Guide: From 1920 to 1964. 2006. (Illus.). 111p. reprint ed. 25.00 (978-1-4223-5513-8(6)) DIANE Publishing Co.

Faffelberger, Josef & Josef, Faffelberger. Industry & Competition Analysis of Airbus & Boeing: Measuring the Appropriateness of Time-Series Forecasting for the Aircraft Industry. 2011. 172p. pap. (978-3-639-32436-5(6)) VDM Verlag Dr. Mueller e.K.

Federal Aviation Administration. Aircraft Weight & Balance Handbook: FAA-H-8083-1A. 2007. (FAA Handbook Ser.). (ENG., Illus.). 92p. per. 9.95 (978-1-56027-676-0(2)) Aviation Supplies & Academics, Inc.

—Aircraft Weight & Balance Handbook: Faa-h-8083-1a. 2011. (ENG., Illus.). 96p. pap. 9.95 (978-1-61608-124-9(4), 608124) Skyhorse Publishing Co., Inc.

Fischer, Harvey L. & Pearce, Jennifer M., eds. Threat of Volcanic Ash to Aviation. 2011. (978-1-61324-456-2(8)) Nova Science Pubs., Inc.

Flintham, Vic. High Stakes: Britain's Air Arms in Action 1945 - 1990. 2009. (Illus.). 432p. 80.00 (978-1-84415-815-7(2)) Pen & Sword Bks. Ltd. GBR. Dist: Casemate Pubs. & Bk. Distributors, LLC.

Fly the Best. pap. 39.95 incl. cd-rom (978-1-55755-377-5(7)) Abacus.

Frawley, Gerard. The International Directory of Civil Aircraft: 2001/2002. 4th rev. ed. 2006. (Illus.). 207p. reprint ed. pap. 22.00 (978-1-4223-5690-6(6)) DIANE Publishing Co.

Gitlin, Martin. The Hudson Plane Landing. 2012. (Essential Events Ser.). 112p. (YA). (gr. 7-12). 34.22 (978-1-61783-309-0(6)) ABDO Publishing Co.

Gordon, Yefim. US Aircraft in the Soviet Union & Russia. 2010. (ENG., Illus.). 335p. 63.95 (978-1-85780-308-2(6)) Allan, Ian Publishing GBR. Dist: BookMasters Distribution Services (BDS).

Gordon, Yefim, et al. Lisunov Li-2: The Soviet DC-3. 2010. (Red Star Ser.). (ENG., Illus.). 127p. pap. 36.95 (978-1-85780-228-3(4)) Allan, Ian Publishing GBR. Dist: BookMasters Distribution Services (BDS).

Hall, Jim, et al. Analysis of Aircraft Overruns & Undershoots for Runway Safety Areas. 2008. (Illus.). 58p. 40.00 (978-0-309-09939-4(0)) Transportation Research Board.

Hayajneh, Luai. The Translation of Allah-Referring Expressions from Arabic to English. 2011. 72p. pap. (978-3-8443-8282-2(8)) Lambert Academic Publishing.

Haynes, Benjamin & Cezzar, Juliette. Paper Pilot: The Paper Airplane Pilot's Manual. 2007. (ENG., Illus.). 144p. pap. 25.00 (978-0-7893-1535-9(1)) Universe Publishing.

Hildebrandt, Erik. Front Row Center 3: Inside the Great American Air Show. 2007. (ENG., Illus.). 160p. 39.95 (978-0-9674040-6-6(1), 0967404061) Cleared Hot Media.

Holmes, Donald B. Wilbur's Story. 2008. 180p. pap. 23.25 (978-1-4092-0100-7(7)) Lulu Enterprises Inc.

Hull, David G. Fundamentals of Airplane Flight Mechanics. 2010. (ENG., Illus.). xiv, 298p. pap. 109.00 (978-3-642-07987-0(3), 3642079873) Springer.

Jane's Aircraft Upgrades. 14th rev. ed. 2006. (Jane's Aircraft Upgrades Ser.). (Illus.). 826p. (978-0-7106-2737-7(8)) Jane's Information Group.

Jane's All the World's Aircraft: The Authority on Aircraft under Development or in Production. 560.00 (978-0-7106-2307-2(0)) Jane's Information Group, Inc.

Jane's All the World's Aircraft 1909. (Illus.). reprint ed. lib. bdg. (978-0-7222-3105-0(9)) Library Reprints, Inc.

Jane's All the World's Aircraft, 1982-1983. 140.00 (978-0-7106-0780-5(6)) Key Bk. Service, Inc.

Lloyd's Aviation Department Staff, compiled by. Aircraft Types & Price Guidelines, 1994-1995. pap. 100.00 (978-1-85044-562-3(1)) LLP, Inc.

Makhlouf, Abdel Salam Hamdy, ed. High Performance Coatings for Automotive & Aerospace Industries. 2010. (Materials Science & Technologies Ser.). (Illus.). vi, 413p. 145.00 (978-1-60876-579-9(2)) Nova Science Pubs., Inc.

Manning, Gerry. Airline Tail Colours. 2012. (ENG., Illus.). 112p. pap. 16.95 (978-1-85780-350-1(7)) Allan, Ian Publishing GBR. Dist: BookMasters Distribution Services (BDS).

—1000 Preserved Aircraft in Colour. 2010. (ENG., Illus.). 160p. pap. 34.95 (978-1-85780-229-0(2)) Allan, Ian Publishing GBR. Dist: BookMasters Distribution Services (BDS).

Mikesh, Robert C. Restoring Museum Aircraft. 2009. (Illus.). 224p. bds. 69.99 (978-0-7643-3234-0(1)) Schiffer Publishing, Ltd.

Milstein, Jeffrey. Aircraft: The Jet As Art. 2007. (ENG., Illus.). 104p. 32.50 (978-0-8109-9285-6(X)) Abrams.

Mueller, Thomas J., et al. Introduction to the Design of Fixed-Wing Micro Air Vehicles: Including Three Case Studies. 2007. (AIAA Education Ser.). (Illus.). 287p. 84.95 (978-1-56347-849-9(8)) American Institute of Aeronautics & Astronautics.

O'Mahony, Charles. The Widow Maker. 2010. 81p. pap. 25.95 (978-1-4327-5455-6(6)) Outskirts Pr., Inc.

O'Rear, James. Aviation Photography: A Pictorial Guide. 2011. 120p. pap. 44.95 (978-1-257-05184-7(9)) Lulu Enterprises Inc.

Paloque, Gerard. Aerobatic Teams. 2011. (Illus.). 128p. pap. 29.95 (978-2-35250-168-8(7)) Histoire et Collections FRA. Dist: Casemate Pubs. & Bk. Distributors, LLC.

Panek, Robert. Henschel Hs 123. 2012. (Illus.). 160p. pap. 38.00 (978-83-61421-48-1(3)) Stratus, Wydawnictwo, Juszczak, Artur POL. Dist: Casemate Pubs. & Bk. Distributors, LLC.

Planes. (Magic Machines Ser.). 5p. bds. (978-1-4054-9205-8(8)) Parragon, Inc.

Pope, Alan. Basic Wing & Airfoil Theory. 2011. 312p. 50.95 (978-1-258-10068-1(1)) Literary Licensing, LLC.

Prather, C. Daniel. General Aviation Marketing & Management: Operating, Marketing, & Managing an FBO. 3rd ed. 2009. (Illus.). 302p. (978-1-57524-301-6(6)) Krieger Publishing Co.

Prochnau, William, et al. Miracle on the Hudson: The Survivors of Flight 1549 Tell Their Extraordinary Stories of Courage, Faith, & Determination. 2010. (ENG., Illus.). 288p. pap. 15.00 (978-0-345-52045-6(9), Ballantine Bks.) Random House Publishing Group.

Queiroz, Manuel. Chasing the Morning Sun. 2011. (Illus.). 160p. 35.00 (978-1-908117-09-0(5)) Grub Street GBR. Dist: Casemate Pubs. & Bk. Distributors, LLC.

Robarge, David. Archangel: CIA's Supersonic A-12 Reconnaissance Aircraft: CIA's Supersonic A-12 Reconnaissance Aircraft. 2008. (ENG., Illus.). 63p. pap. 13.00 (978-1-929667-16-1(7), Central Intelligence Agency) United States Government Printing Office.

Rodden, William P. Theoretical & Computational Aeroelasticity. 2011. (Illus.). xvi, 814p. (978-0-692-01241-3(9)) Bluecliff Publishing.

Rose, Bill. Flying Saucer Technology. 2011. (ENG., Illus.). 160p. 39.95 (978-1-85780-323-5(X), Noodle Bks.) Allan, Ian Publishing GBR. Dist: BookMasters Distribution Services (BDS).

Rose, Bill & Buttler, Tony. Flying Saucer Aircraft. 2007. (ENG., Illus.). 192p. 44.95 (978-1-85780-233-7(0)) Midland Publishing Ltd. GBR. Dist: MBI Distribution Services/Quayside Distribution.

Schafroth, Dario. Aerodynamics, Modeling & Control of an Autonomous Micro Helicopter: Towards the design of a fully autonomous MAV the size & mass of a small bird. 2011. 188p. pap. (978-3-8381-0869-8(8)) Südwestdeutscher Verlag für Hochschulschriften AG & Co. KG.

Segal, Corin. The Scramjet Engine: Processes & Characteristics. 2011. (Cambridge Aerospace Ser.). (ENG., Illus.). 270p. pap. 50.00 (978-1-107-40252-2(2)) Cambridge Univ. Pr.

Sikorsky, Igor I. The Story of the Winged-S: An Autobiography. 2011. 342p. 51.95 (978-1-258-05780-0(8)) Literary Licensing, LLC.

Skulski, Przemyslaw. North American A-36A Apache. 2011. (Illus.). 160p. pap. 27.00 (978-83-61421-45-0(9)) Stratus, Wydawnictwo, Juszczak, Artur POL. Dist: Casemate Pubs. & Bk. Distributors, LLC.

Stekel, Peter. Final Flight: The Mystery of a World-War II Plane Crash & the Frozen Airmen in the High Sierra. 2010. (ENG., Illus.). 256p. pap. 15.95 (978-0-89997-475-0(9)) Wilderness Pr.

United States, Congress House Committee on Transportation and Infrastructure Subcommittee on Aviation Staff, contrib. by. Oversight of Federal Aviation Administration Safety Programs: Hearing Before the Subcommittee on Aviation of the Committee on Transportation & Infrastructure, House of Representatives, One Hundred Ninth Congress, Second Session, September 20, 2006. 2007. (Illus.). v, 194p. (978-0-16-078468-2(9), 552-070-35754-8) United States Government Printing Office.

US Airways Flight 1549 Accident: Hearing Before the Subcommittee on Aviation of the Committee on Transportation & Infrastructure, House of Representatives, One Hundred Eleventh Congress, First Session, February 24, 2009. 2009. (Illus.). xvii, 251p. (978-0-16-084260-3(3), 552-070-39830-9) United States Government Printing Office.

Valavanis, Kimon P., ed. Advances in Unmanned Aerial Vehicles: State of the Art & the Road to Autonomy. 2007. (Intelligent Systems, Control & Automation: Science & Engineering Ser.). xxiv, 543p. 169.00 (978-1-4020-6113-4(7), 1402061137) Springer.

Van Der Linden, Robert F. The Nation's Hangar: Aircraft Treasures of the Smithsonian. 2011. (ENG., Illus.). 256p. pap. 29.95 (978-1-58834-316-1(2)) Smithsonian Institution Pr.

Vink, Peter, ed. Aircraft Interior Comfort & Design. 2011. (ENG., Illus.). 134p. pap. 59.95 (978-1-4398-6305-3(9), CRC Press) Taylor & Francis Group GBR. Dist: Taylor & Francis Group.

Whitefield, Philip, et al. Summarizing & Interpreting Aircraft Gaseous & Particulate Emissions Data. 2008. (Illus.). 60p. pap. 42.00 (978-0-309-11760-9(7)) Transportation Research Board.

Woodroffe, David. Making Paper Airplanes: Make Your Own Aircraft & Watch Them Fly! 2011. (ENG., Illus.). 192p. (J). (gr. 1-3). 14.95 (978-1-61608-147-8(3), 608147) Skyhorse Publishing Co., Inc.

Wright, Allan S. ABC Civil Aircraft Markings 2011. 2011. (ENG., Illus.). 448p. pap. 19.95 (978-1-85780-348-8(5)) Allan, Ian Publishing GBR. Dist: BookMasters Distribution Services (BDS).

Wright, Allan S. & Allan, Ian. Abc Civil Aircraft Markings 2009. 2009. (ENG., Illus.). 432p. pap. 16.95 (978-1-85780-313-6(2)) Midland Publishing Ltd. GBR. Dist: BookMasters Distribution Services (BDS).

Zerbe, James Slough. Aeroplanes. 2008. 168p. 22.99 (978-0-554-35663-1(5)) 2008. 168p. 25.99 (978-0-554-26360-1(2)) 2007. 144p. pap. 18.99 (978-1-4346-0968-7(5)) 2007. (ENG.). 164p. pap. 21.99 (978-1-4346-1067-6(5)) BiblioBazaar.

Zipfel, Peter H. Modeling & Simulation of Aerospace Vehicle Dynamics. 2nd ed. 2007. (AIAA Education Ser.). (Illus.). 567p. (978-1-56347-875-8(7)) American Institute of Aeronautics & Astronautics.

AIRPLANES—ACCIDENTS
see Aircraft Accidents

AIRPLANES—AERODYNAMICS
see Aerodynamics

AIRPLANES—APPARATUS AND SUPPLIES
see Airplanes—Equipment and Supplies

AIRPLANES—CARRIERS
see Aircraft Carriers

AIRPLANES—COLLISIONS WITH BIRDS
see Aircraft Accidents

AIRPLANES—CONTROL SYSTEMS
see also Automatic Pilot (Airplanes)

Bates, Declan & Hagström, Martin, eds. Nonlinear Analysis & Synthesis Techniques for Aircraft Control. 2008. (Lecture Notes in Control & Information Sciences Ser.: Vol. 365). (Illus.). viii, 360p. 179.00 (978-3-540-73718-6(9)) Springer.

Chen, Tingnan. Fei Ji Fei Xing Xing Neng Pin Zhi Yu Kong Zhi. 2007. (Illus.). xiv, 322p. (978-7-118-04979-4(4)) National Defence Industry Pr.

Delves, Peter J. Sense & Avoid in UAS: Research & Applications. Angelov, Plamen, ed. 2nd ed. 2012. (Aerospace Ser.). (ENG.). 384p. 120.00 (978-0-470-97975-4(5), Wiley) Wiley, John & Sons, Inc.

Friedman, Edward J. & Culp, Robert D., eds. Guidance & Control 2009 (Volume 133 in the Advances in the Astronautical Sciences Series) Proceedings, 32nd AAS Rocky Mountain Conference, Breckenridge, CO 2009, 133. 2009. (Advances in the Astronautical Sciences Ser.: 133). (ENG., Illus.). 712p. 190.00 (978-0-87703-553-4(9), American Astronautical Society) Univelt, Inc.

Ginevsky, A. S., et al. Acoustic Control of Turbulent Jets. 2010. (Foundations of Engineering Mechanics Ser.). (ENG., Illus.). xiv, 232p. pap. 169.00 (978-3-642-05764-9(0), 3642057640) Springer.

Guerrero, Josep & Lozano, Rogelio. Flight Formation Control. 2012. (Iste Ser.: 589). (ENG., Illus.). xii, 328p. 145.00 (978-1-84821-323-4(9), Wiley-ISTE) Wiley, John & Sons, Inc.

Langewiesche, William. Fly by Wire. 2010. (ENG., Illus.). 208p. pap. 14.00 (978-0-312-65538-9(X)) Picador.

Langton, Roy. Stability & Control of Aircraft Systems: Introduction to Classical Feedback Control. 2006. (Aerospace Ser.: 10). (ENG., Illus.). 254p. 140.00 (978-0-470-01891-0(7), Wiley) Wiley, John & Sons, Inc.

Lozano, Rogelio. Unmanned Aerial Vehicles Embedded Control. 2010. (Iste Ser.: 407). (ENG., Illus.). 352p. 153.00 (978-1-84821-127-8(9), Wiley-ISTE) Wiley, John & Sons, Inc.

Marschke, Doug, et al. Advanced Control of Aircraft, Spacecraft & Rockets. 2011. (Aerospace Ser.). (ENG., Illus.). 454p. 105.00 (978-0-470-74563-2(0), Wiley) Wiley, John & Sons, Inc.

Mooij, H.A. Criteria for Low-Speed Longitudinal Handling Qualities of Transport Aircraft with Closed-Loop Flight Control Systems. 2010. 170p. pap. 229.00 (978-90-481-8285-5(9), 9048182859) Springer.

Raptis, Ioannis A. & Valavanis, Kimon P. Linear & Nonlinear Control of Small-Scale Unmanned Helicopters. 2010. (Intelligent Systems, Control & Automation: Science & Engineering Ser.). (Illus.). xxv, 206p. 129.00 (978-94-007-0022-2(9), 9400700229) Springer.

Shima, Tal, et al. UAV Cooperative Decision & Control: Challenges & Practical Approaches. 2009. (Advances in Design & Control Ser.). (ENG., Illus.). 198p. 85.00 (978-0-89871-664-1(0)) Society for Industrial and Applied Mathematics.

Siddiqui, Bilal. Reconfigurable Flight Control for Fighter Aircraft Using Mpc. 2010. 216p. pap. (978-3-639-26225-4(5)) VDM Verlag Dr. Mueller e.K.

Valavanis, Kimon, ed. Unmanned Aerial Vehicles. 2011. (Illus.). vi, 586p. 179.00 (978-94-007-1109-9(3), 9400711093) Springer.

Valavanis, Kimon P., ed. Recent Developments in Unmanned Aircraft Systems. 2012. (ENG.). vi, 638p. 229.00 (978-94-007-3032-8(2), 9400730322) Springer.

Verly, Jacques Georges & Guell, Jeff J. Enhanced & Synthetic Vision 2007: 9-10 April 2007, Orlando, Florida, USA. 2007. (Proceedings of SPIE Ser.). (Illus.). 250p. pap. 70.00 (978-0-8194-6681-5(6)) SPIE.

Yanushevsky, Rafael. Guidance of Unmanned Aerial Vehicles. 2011. (ENG., Illus.). 376p. 179.95 (978-1-4398-5095-4(X), CRC Press) Taylor & Francis Group GBR. Dist: Taylor & Francis Group.

Yu, Chao. An Acoustic Intensity-Based Method in Aeroacoustics. 2009. 128p. pap. (978-3-639-16564-7(0)) VDM Verlag Dr. Mueller e.K.

AIRPLANES—CREWS
see Flight Crews

AIRPLANES—DESIGN AND CONSTRUCTION
see also Aeroelasticity; Airframes

Admiralty, War Staff. German Rigid Airships. 2009. 336p. pap. (978-1-84734-997-2(8)) Naval & Military Pr., The.

Air Force, United States. Bell X-1A Rocket Plane Pilot's Flight Operating Instructions. 2007. 48p. pap. 14.95 (978-1-4303-0807-2(9)) Lulu Enterprises Inc.

Al-Malki, Mohammad Fahad. Fault-Tolerant Flight Control: System Design with Application to Bell-205 Helicopter. 2011. 232p. pap. (978-3-639-23928-7(8)) VDM Verlag Dr. Mueller e.K.

Anderson, John. Introduction to Flight. 7th ed. 2011. (ENG., Illus.). 944p. (C). 228.00 (978-0-07-338024-7(5), 0073380245, McGraw-Hill Science, Engineering & Mathematics) McGraw-Hill Higher Education.

Anderson, John D. & Anderson, John D., Jr. Introduction to Flight. 6th ed. 2007. (ENG., Illus.). 912p. (C). 197.50 (978-0-07-352939-4(7), 0073529397, McGraw-Hill Science, Engineering & Mathematics) McGraw-Hill Higher Education.

Austin, Reg. Unmanned Aircraft Systems: UAVS Design, Development & Deployment. 2010. (Aerospace Ser.). (ENG., Illus.). 372p. 125.00 (978-0-470-05819-0(6), Wiley) Wiley, John & Sons, Inc.

Barton, Noel G. & Périaux, Jacques. Coupling of Fluids, Structures & Waves in Aeronautics: Proceedings of a French-Australian Workshop in Melbourne, Australia 3-6 December 2001. 2010. (Notes on Numerical Fluid Mechanics & Multidisciplinary Design Ser.). xii, 316p. pap. 289.00 (978-3-642-07294-9(1), 3642072941) Springer.

Bassford, Matt, et al. Sustaining Key Skills in the UK Military Aircraft Industry. 1 vol. 2010. 168p. pap. 27.00 (978-0-8330-5041-0(9), mg-1023) RAND Corp., The.

Berry, Patrick. Aircraft Conceptual Design Methods. 2010. (Illus.). 88p. pap. (978-3-8433-6485-0(0)) Lambert Academic Publishing.

Boddington, David. Almost Ready to Fly: Radio Control Flying 21st Century Style. 2007. (Illus.). 168p. pap. 42.50 (978-1-85486-242-6(1)) Specialist Interest Model Bks. Ltd. GBR. Dist: Trans-Atlantic Pubns., Inc.

Burke, J. D. Gossamer Condor & Albatross: A Case Study in Aircraft Design. (Illus.). 120p. pap. 23.00 (978-1-56347-305-0(4)) American Institute of Aeronautics & Astronautics.

Caygill, Peter. Javelin from the Cockpit. 2012. (Illus.). 256p. 39.95 (978-1-84884-656-2(8)) Pen & Sword Bks. Ltd. GBR. Dist: Casemate Pubs. & Bk. Distributors, LLC.

Collicott, Steven, et al. Aerodynamics for Engineering Students. 6th ed. 2012. (ENG., Illus.). 740p. pap. 99.95 (978-0-08-096632-8(2), Butterworth-Heinemann) Elsevier Science & Technology Bks.

Committee on Assessment of Aircraft Winglets for Large Aircraft Fuel Efficiency & National Research Council. Assessment of Wingtip Modifications to Increase the Fuel Efficiency of Air Force Aircraft. 2007. (ENG.). 112p. pap. 29.75 (978-0-309-10497-5(1)) National Academies Pr.

Cram101 Textbook Reviews & Cram101 Textbook Reviews. Outlines & Highlights for Introduction to Flight by John D Anderson. 2011. 298p. pap. 32.95 (978-1-61830-956-3(0)) Cram101 Inc.

Crawford, Alex. Hawker Hart Family. 2008. (Illus.). 170p. pap. (978-83-89450-62-3(3)) Stratus, Wydawnictwo, Juszczak, Artur.

Dillmann, Andreas, et al, eds. New Results in Numerical & Experimental Fluid Mechanics VII: Contributions to the 16th STAB/DGLR Symposium Aachen, Germany 2008. 2010. (Notes on Numerical Fluid Mechanics & Multidisciplinary Design Ser.). 610p. 339.00 (978-3-642-14242-0(7), 3642142427) Springer.

Dorstewitz, Andreas. Development & Reporting of Key Performance Indicators (KPI) Applied to a New Development Aircraft Manufacturing Process. 2008. 124p. pap. (978-3-639-03026-6(5)) VDM Verlag Dr. Mueller e.K.

Dyer, Edwin M. Japanese Secret Projects. 2011. (ENG., Illus.). 160p. 39.95 (978-1-85780-317-4(5)) Allan, Ian Publishing GBR. Dist: BookMasters Distribution Services (BDS).

Evenden, Helen. Moving Foward: New Directions in Transport Design. 2007. (ENG., Illus.). 128p. pap. 35.00 (978-1-85177-491-3(2)) V & A Pubns. GBR. Dist: Hachette Bk. Group.

Ferman, M. A. A Wing Design Method for Aerospace Students & Home Builders: Strength, Weight, Flutter, Divergence, Buckling, Deflection, & Twist. 2011. 68p. 55.00 (978-1-4269-7311-6(X)); pap. 45.00 (978-1-4269-7310-9(1)) Trafford Publishing.

Fernande, Jose. Potez 63 Family. 2008. (Illus.). 140p. pap. (978-83-89450-65-4(8)) Stratus, Wydawnictwo, Juszczak, Artur.

Flouris, Triant & Lock, Dennis. Aviation Project Management. 2008. 314p. 99.95 (978-0-7546-7395-8(2)) Ashgate Publishing Co.

Flouris, Triant G. & Lock, Dennis. Managing Aviation Projects from Concept to Completion. 2009. (Illus.). 528p. 119.95 (978-0-7546-7615-7(3)) Ashgate Publishing Co.

Forsyth, Robert & Creek, Eddie J. Heinkel He162 Volksjäger: From Drawing Board to Destruction - The Volksjäger Spatz. 2009. (ENG., Illus.). 208p. 64.95 (978-1-906537-00-5(3)) Allan, Ian Publishing GBR. Dist: BookMasters Distribution Services (BDS).

Fox, Michael C. Knights of the Skies: Armour Protection for British Fighting Aeroplanes. 2006. (ENG., Illus.). 304p. per. (978-1-871187-50-2(8), 1871187508) Air Research Pubns. GBR. Dist: MBI Distribution Services/Quayside Distribution.

Fozard, John W., compiled by. The British Aerospace Harrier Case Study in Aircraft Design. (Illus.). 102p. pap. 23.00 (978-1-56347-306-7(2)) American Institute of Aeronautics & Astronautics.

Fraracci, A., ed. Model-based Failure-modes-and-effects Analysis & its Application to Aircraft Subsystems - Volume 326 Dissertations in Artificial Intelligence. 2010. 218p. pap. 80.00 (978-1-60750-081-0(7)) IOS Pr., Inc.

Freeman, H. R. & Longanecker, G. W. The International Ultraviolet Explorer Case Study in Spacecraft Design. (AIAA Professional Study Ser.). (Illus.). 64p. pap. 23.00 (978-1-56347-314-2(3)) American Institute of Aeronautics & Astronautics.

Garrard, Wilfred. Lockheed C-5 Case Study in Aircraft Design. (Illus.). 28p. pap. 23.00 (978-1-56347-312-8(7)) American Institute of Aeronautics & Astronautics.

Gibbings, David. Fairey Rotodyne. 2009. (ENG., Illus.). 160p. pap. 32.95 (978-0-7524-4916-6(8)) History Pr. Ltd., The GBR. Dist: Independent Pubs. Group.

Gooch, Jan W. & Daher, John K. Electromagnetic Shielding & Corrosion Protection for Aerospace Vehicles. (ENG., Illus.). xii, 130p. 2011. pap. 109.00 (978-1-4419-2358-5(6), 1441923586) 2007. 109.00 (978-0-387-46094-9(2), 0387460942) Springer.

Gordon, Yefim. Lavochkin's Last Jets. Komissarov, Dmitriy, tr. 2010. (Red Star Ser.). (ENG., Illus.). 127p. per. 36.95 (978-1-85780-253-5(5)) Allan, Ian Publishing GBR. Dist: BookMasters Distribution Services (BDS).

Gordon, Yefim & Komissarov, Dmitriy. OKB Sukhoi: A History of the Design Bureau & Its Aircraft. 2010. (ENG., Illus.). 592p. 79.95 (978-1-85780-314-3(0)) Midland Publishing Ltd. GBR. Dist: BookMasters Distribution Services (BDS).

Gordon, Yefim & Komissarov, Sergey. German Aircraft in the Soviet Union & Russia. 2010. (ENG., Illus.). 320p. 59.95 (978-1-85780-292-4(6)) Allan, Ian Publishing GBR. Dist: BookMasters Distribution Services (BDS).

Green, Brett. Aircraft Modelling. 2010. (Modelling Masterclass Ser.). (ENG., Illus.). 192p. 39.95 (978-1-84603-932-4(0)) Osprey Publishing, Ltd. GBR. Dist: Random Hse., Inc.

—Modelling Scale Aircraft. 2008. (Osprey Modelling Ser.). (ENG., Illus.). 80p. pap. 19.95 (978-1-84603-237-0(7)) Osprey Publishing, Ltd. GBR. Dist: Random Hse., Inc.

Gunston, Bill. The Development of Jet & Turbine Aero Engines. 4th ed. 2006. (ENG., Illus.). 272p. per. 22.95 (978-1-85260-618-3(5), 1852606185) Haynes Publishing PLC GBR. Dist: MBI Distribution Services/Quayside Distribution.

—Nimrod: The Centenarian Aircraft. 2010. (ENG.). 192p. pap. 29.95 (978-0-7524-5270-8(3)) History Pr. Ltd., The GBR. Dist: Independent Pubs. Group.

Ha, Kwangtae. A Combined Piezoelectric & Composite Actuator. 2009. 124p. pap. (978-3-639-15523-5(8)) VDM Verlag Dr. Mueller e.K.

Harris, Don. Human Performance on the Flight Deck. 2011. (Illus.). 384p. 144.95 (978-1-4094-2339-3(5)); pap. 69.95 (978-1-4094-2338-6(7)) Ashgate Publishing Co.

Harvey, James. Sharks of the Air: Willi Messerschmitt & How He Built the World's First Operational Jet Fighter. 2010. (Illus.). 352p. 32.95 (978-1-935149-46-0(6)) Casemate Pubs. & Bk. Distributors, LLC.

Havers, Richard. Classic Aircraft: Civilian Aviation from 1906 until the Present Day. 2010. (ENG., Illus.). 128p. 14.95 (978-1-84425-707-2(X), 184425707X) Haynes Publishing PLC GBR. Dist: MBI Distribution Services/Quayside Distribution.

Hawkey, Pat. Building & Detailing Model Aircraft. 2009. (FineScale Modeler Bks.). (Illus.). 95p. pap. 21.95 (978-0-89024-723-5(4)) Kalmbach Publishing Co., Bks. Div.

Heintz, Chris. Flying on Your Own Wings: A Complete Guide to Understanding Light Airplane Design. 2010. (ENG.). 304p. pap. 39.95 (978-1-4251-8828-3(1)) Trafford Publishing.

Hirschel, Ernst H. & Weiland, Claus. Selected Aerothermodynamic Design Problems of Hypersonic Flight Vehicles. 2009. (ENG., Illus.). xvi, 512p. 129.00 (978-3-540-89973-0(1), 3540899731) Springer.

Hoffmann, Jan. Yakovlev Yak-23: The First Yakovlev Jet Fighters. 2008. (Illus.). 128p. pap. (978-83-89450-54-8(2)) Stratus, Wydawnictwo, Juszczak, Artur.

Jackson, Robert. Britain's Greatest Aircraft. 2007. (Illus.). 320p. 50.00 (978-1-84415-600-9(1)) Pen & Sword Bks. Ltd. GBR. Dist: Casemate Pubs. & Bk. Distributors, LLC.

Jaw, Link C. & Mattingly, Jack D. Aircraft Engine Controls: Design, System Analysis, & Health Monitoring. 2009. (Illus.). 300p. (978-1-60086-705-7(7)) American Institute of Aeronautics & Astronautics.

Jones, Barry. British Experimental Turbojet Aircraft. rev. ed. 2007. (Crowood Aviation Ser.). (ENG., Illus.). 208p. pap. 34.95 (978-1-86126-860-0(2), 1861268602) Crowood Pr., Ltd. GBR. Dist: MBI Distribution Services/Quayside Distribution.

Kershaw, Tim. Gloster Gamecock & Grebe. 2010. (Illus.). 160p. pap. 39.00 (978-83-61421-17-7(3)) Stratus, Wydawnictwo, Juszczak, Artur POL. Dist: Casemate Pubs. & Bk. Distributors, LLC.

Kesseler, Ernst & Guenov, Marin D. Advances in Collaborative Civil Aeronautical Multidisciplinary Design Optimization. 2010. (Illus.). xvii, 436p. 109.95 (978-1-60086-725-5(1)) American Institute of Aeronautics & Astronautics.

Kroes, Michael J. & Rardon, James R. Aircraft: Basic Science with Student Study Guide. 7th ed. 2007. (ENG.). (C). pap., pap., pap. 73.00 (978-0-07-723153-8(8), 0077231538) McGraw-Hill Higher Education.

Kroll, Norbert, et al, eds. MEGADESIGN & MegaOpt - German Initiatives for Aerodynamic Simulation & Optimization in Aircraft Design: Results of the closing symposium of the MEGADESIGN & MegaOpt projects, Braunschweig, Germany, May 23 And 24 2007. 2009. (Notes on Numerical Fluid Mechanics & Multidisciplinary Design Ser.). (Illus.). xii, 314p. 289.00 (978-3-642-04092-4(6), 3642040926) Springer.

Kroll, Norbert & Fassbender, Jens K., eds. MEGAFLOW - Numerical Flow Simulation for Aircraft Design: Results of the second phase of the German CFD initiative MEGAFLOW, presented during its closing symposium at DLR, Braunschweig, Germany, December 10 And 11 2002. 2010. (Notes on Numerical Fluid Mechanics & Multidisciplinary Design Ser.). xii, 313p. pap. 289.00 (978-3-642-06365-7(9), 3642063659) Springer.

Kundu, Ajoy. Aircraft Design. 2010. (ENG., Illus.). 648p. (C). 147.00 (978-0-521-88516-4(7)) Cambridge Univ. Pr.

Linehan, Dan. Burt Rutan's Race to Space: The Magician of Mojave & His Flying Innovations. 2011. (Illus.). 160p. 30.00 (978-0-7603-3815-5(9), 0760338159, Zenith Pr.) MBI Publishing Co. LLC.

Lockett, Brian. Flying Aircraft Carriers of the USAF: Mcdonnell XF-85 Goblin. 2009. 52p. pap. 16.95 (978-0-578-03481-2(6)) Lockett, Brian.

—Flying Aircraft Carriers of the USAF: Wing Tip Coupling. 2009. 100p. pap. 21.95 (978-0-578-03186-6(8)) Lockett, Brian.

—Painting Guide for the Boeing Stratofortress Motherships. 2009. 96p. pap. 44.95 (978-0-578-03110-1(8)) Lockett, Brian.

MacLean, Rory. Falling for Icarus: A Journey among the Cretans. 2012. (ENG., Illus.). 352p. pap. 18.00 (978-1-84885-956-2(2), Tauris Parke Paperbacks) I. B. Tauris & Co., Ltd. GBR. Dist: Macmillan.

McLelland, Tim. The Hawker Hunter. 2009. (Illus.). 336p. 49.95 (978-0-85979-123-6(8)) Crecy Publishing GBR. Dist: Partners Pubs. Group, Inc.

Miele, Angelo & Frediani, Aldo, eds. Advanced Design Problems in Aerospace Engineering: Volume 1: Advanced Aerospace Systems. 2010. (Mathematical Concepts & Methods in Science & Engineering Ser.). (Illus.). xii, 188p. pap. 155.00 (978-1-4419-3448-2(0), 1441934480) Springer.

Milstein, Jeffrey. Aircraft: the Jet As Art. 2007. 29.95 (978-88-370-5505-9(6)) Abrams.

Morelli, Eugene A. & Klein, Vladislav. Aircraft System Identification: Theory & Practice. 2006. (AIAA Education Ser.: Vol. 213). (Illus.). 484p. (978-1-56347-832-1(3)) American Institute of Aeronautics & Astronautics.

Motevalli, Vahid, et al. Evaluation & Mitigation of Aircraft Slide Evacuation Injuries. 2008. (ACRP Report Ser.: Vol. 2). (Illus.). 77p. pap. 47.00 (978-0-309-09933-2(1)) Transportation Research Board.

Nadler, Bob. Electric RC Flying for Cheapskates. 2008. (Illus.). 75p. cd-rom 12.00 (978-0-933596-44-3(8)) F/22 Pr.

National Air and Space Museum Staff. In the Cockpit: Inside 50 History-Making Aircraft. 2007. (ENG., Illus.). 144p. 26.99 (978-0-06-114381-6(2), Collins Design) HarperCollins Pubs.

Nicolai, Leland M. & Carichner, Grant. Fundamentals of Aircraft & Airship Design. 2010. (Illus.). xxii, 883p. 119.95 (978-1-60086-751-4(0)) American Institute of Aeronautics & Astronautics.

Nikolaidis, Efstratios, et al, eds. Engineering Design Reliability Applications: For the Aerospace, Automotive & Ship Industries. 2007. (ENG., Illus.). 376p. 145.95 (978-1-4200-5132-2(6), CRC Press) Taylor & Francis Group GBR. Dist: Taylor & Francis Group.

Norvell, Elmer A. Airigami: Realistic Origami Aircraft. 2010. (Dover Origami Papercraft Ser.). (ENG., Illus.). 112p. pap. 14.95 (978-0-486-47502-8(6)) Dover Pubns., Inc.

Obert, E., ed. Aerodynamic Design of Transport Aircraft. 2009. (Illus.). 656p. pap. 109.00 (978-1-58603-970-7(9)) IOS Pr., Inc.

O'Leary, Michael. Building the P-51 Mustang in Original Fa: The Manufacturing Story of North American's Legendary World War II Fighter. 2010. (Illus.). 240p. 39.95 (978-1-58007-152-9(X)) Specialty Pr. Pubs. & Wholesalers, Inc.

Pauley, Robert F. Michigan Aircraft Manufacturers. 2009. (Images of Aviation Ser.). (ENG., Illus.). 128p. pap. 21.99 (978-0-7385-5218-7(6)) Arcadia Publishing.

Pioneer Venus Case Study in Spacecraft Design. 72p. pap. 23.00 (978-1-56347-313-5(5)) American Institute of Aeronautics & Astronautics.

Provensen, Alice & Provensen, Martin. The Glorious Flight: Across the Channel with Louis Bleriot. 2009. (JPN., Illus.). 40p. (J). (978-4-7764-0353-1(6)) BL Publishing Co., Ltd.

Radio Control Airplane Workshop Secrets. 192p. pap. 19.95 (978-0-911295-52-8(6)) Air Age, Inc.

Rallabhandi, Sriram. Sonic Boom Minimization Through Shape Optimization & Acoustic Propagation. 2008. 224p. per. (978-3-8364-6087-3(4)) VDM Verlag Dr. Mueller e.K.

Rambalakos, Andreas. Monte Carlo Simulation Methodology for the Reliability of Aircraft Structures: Reliability of Aircraft Structures Under Damage Tolerance Requirements. 2008. 168p. pap. (978-3-8364-7348-4(8)) VDM Verlag Dr. Mueller e.K.

Rath, Hans Josef, et al, eds. New Results in Numerical & Experimental Fluid Mechanics V: Contributions to the 14th STAB/DGLR Symposium Bremen, Germany 2004. (Notes on Numerical Fluid Mechanics & Multidisciplinary Design Ser.). xiv, 528p. 2010. pap. 409.00 (978-3-642-06995-6(9), 3642069959) 2006. (Illus.). 409.00 (978-3-540-33286-2(3), 3540332863) Springer.

Raymer, Daniel. Living in the Future: The Education & Adventures of an Advanced Aircraft Designer. 2010. 350p. pap. 39.95 (978-0-9722397-2-1(3)) Conceptual Research Corp.

Reyes, Carlos. RCadvisor's Model Airplane Design Made Easy: The Simple Guide to Designing R/C Model Aircraft or Build Your Own Radio Control Flying Model Plane. 2009. (Illus.). 208p. pap. 19.95 (978-0-9822613-2-3(2)) RCadvisor.com.

Rossoni, Philip. Build & Pilot Your Own Walkalong Gliders. 2012. (Build Your Own Ser.). (ENG., Illus.). 224p. pap. 20.00 (978-0-07-179055-0(1), 0071790551, TAB/Electronics) McGraw-Hill Professional Publishing.

Rudman, Jack. Airframe & Powerplant Mechanics. (Occupational Competency Examination Ser.). 49.95 (978-0-8373-5752-2(7), OLE-2, Passbooks) National Learning Corp.

Russo, David. Airplane Rigging. 2007. 208p. per. 29.95 (978-0-9774896-5-7(5)) Aircraft Technical Bk. Co.

Salas, Eduardo & Dietz, Aaron S., eds. Situational Awareness. 2011. (Critical Essays on Human Factors in Aviation Ser.). 544p. 260.00 (978-0-7546-2973-3(2)) Ashgate Publishing Co.

Schiff, Barry. Dream Aircraft: The Most Fascinating Airplanes I've Ever Flown. 2007. (ENG.). 330p. pap. 19.95 (978-1-56027-680-7(0)) Aviation Supplies & Academics, Inc.

Seabridge, Allan & Morgan, Shirley. Air Travel & Health: A Systems Perspective. 2010. (Aerospace Ser.). (ENG., Illus.). 248p. 110.00 (978-0-470-71177-4(9), Wiley) Wiley, John & Sons, Inc.

Shelton, John. Schneider Trophy to Spitfire: The Design Career of R. J. Mitchell. 2009. (ENG., Illus.). 256p. 49.95 (978-1-84425-530-6(1), 1844255301) Haynes Publishing PLC GBR. Dist: MBI Distribution Services/Quayside Distribution.

Skinner, Stephen. British Airliner Prototypes since 1945. 2010. (ENG., Illus.). 224p. 56.95 (978-1-85780-299-3(3)) Allan, Ian Publishing GBR. Dist: BookMasters Distribution Services (BDS).

Slater, Stephen & McKay, Stuart. De Havilland Tiger Moth Manual, 1931-1945: An Insight into Owning, Flying & Maintaining the Legendary British Training Biplane. 2010. (ENG., Illus.). 160p. pap. 32.95 (978-1-84425-586-3(7), 1844255867) Haynes Publishing PLC GBR. Dist: MBI Distribution Services/Quayside Distribution.

Spenser, Jay. The Airplane: How Ideas Gave Us Wings. 2009. (ENG.). 320p. pap. 14.99 (978-0-06-125920-3(9), HarperPerennial) HarperCollins Pubs.

Stoff, Joshua. Long Island Aircraft Manufacturers. 2010. (Images of Aviation Ser.). (ENG., Illus.). 128p. pap. 21.99 (978-0-7385-7336-6(1)) Arcadia Publishing.

Stuart, William. Northrop F-5 Case Study in Aircraft Design. 220p. pap. 23.00 (978-1-56347-309-8(7)) American Institute of Aeronautics & Astronautics.

Technology Research Editors, ed. Corrosion of Aerospace Structures, 2007 Ed. 2007. pap. 118.50 (978-1-60030-145-2(2), Search-In-Print) CSA Journal Division.

—Fatigue of Aircraft & Their Components, 2007 Ed. 2007. pap. 128.50 (978-1-60030-147-6(9), Search-In-Print) CSA Journal Division.

—Metal Matrix Composites for Aerospace Components, 2007 Ed. 2007. pap. 128.50 (978-1-60030-151-3(7), Search-In-Print) CSA Journal Division.

Tropea, Cameron, et al, eds. New Results in Numerical & Experimental Fluid Mechanics VI: Contributions to the 15th STAB/DGLR Symposium Darmstadt, Germany 2006. 2010. (Notes on Numerical Fluid Mechanics & Multidisciplinary Design Ser.). xiv, 472p. pap. 339.00 (978-3-642-09387-6(6), 3642093876) Springer.

Tropea, Carmen, et al, eds. New Results in Numerical & Experimental Fluid Mechanics VI: Contributions to the 15th STAB/DGLR Symposium Darmstadt, Germany 2006. 2007. (Notes on Numerical Fluid Mechanics & Multidisciplinary Design Ser.). 530p. 339.00 (978-3-540-74458-0(4)) Springer.

Valasek, John, ed. Morphing Aerospace Vehicles & Structures. 2nd ed. 2012. (Aerospace Ser.). (ENG., Illus.). 310p. 135.00 (978-0-470-97286-1(6), Wiley) Wiley, John & Sons, Inc.

Wagner, Mark & Norris, Guy. Boeing 787 Dreamliner. 2009. (ENG., Illus.). 160p. 30.00 (978-0-7603-2815-6(3), 0760328153, Zenith Pr.) MBI Publishing Co. LLC.

Wilson, Jeff, compiled by. Classic Combat Aircraft. 2007. (Illus.). 95p. pap. (978-0-89024-696-2(3), Kalmbach Bks.) Kalmbach Publishing Co., Bks. Div.

Windle, Dave & Bowman, Martin. Profiles of Flight: SEPECAT Jaguar: Tactical Support & Maritime Strike Fighter. 2010. (Illus.). 64p. 39.95 (978-1-84884-237-3(6)) Pen & Sword Bks. Ltd. GBR. Dist: Casemate Pubs. & Bk. Distributors, LLC.

Wolf, William. Douglas B-18 Bolo: The Ultimate Look: from Drawing Board to U-Boat Hunter. 2007. (Illus.). 216p. 59.95 (978-0-7643-2581-6(7)) Schiffer Publishing, Ltd.

Younossi, Obaid & Brancato, Kevin. Ending F22A Production: Costs & Industrial Base Implications of Alternative Options 2009. 2011. 116p. pap. 33.00 (978-0-8330-4649-9(7), mg-797) RAND Corp., The.

AIRPLANES—ELECTRIC EQUIPMENT

see also Aeronautical Instruments; Landing Aids (Aeronautics)

British Standards Institute Staff. Aerospace series. Connectors, electrical, rectangular, modular. Operating temperature 175$0DC continuous. Flange mounting receptacle 2 & 4 modules, series 2. Product Standard. 12p. pap. 120.00 (978-0-580-53306-8(9)) Artech Hse., Inc.

—Aerospace series. Connectors, electrical, rectangular, modular. Operating temperature 175$0DC continuous. Plug for 2 & 4 modules, series 2. Product Standard. 12p. pap. 96.00 (978-0-580-53296-2(8)) Artech Hse., Inc.

Eismin, Thomas K. Aircraft: Electricity & Electronics. 5th ed. 2007. (ENG.). (C). pap., pap., pap. 133.33 (978-0-07-723152-1(X), 007723152X) McGraw-Hill Higher Education.

Yan, Dongchao. Fei Ji Gong Dian Xi Tong. 2010. (Illus.). xii, 311p. (978-7-118-06414-8(9)) National Defence Industry Pr.

AIRPLANES—ELECTRONIC EQUIPMENT

see also Landing Aids (Aeronautics)

Eismin, Thomas K. Aircraft: Electricity & Electronics. 5th ed. 2007. (ENG.). (C). pap., pap., pap. 133.33 (978-0-07-723152-1(X), 007723152X) McGraw-Hill Higher Education.

Leech, Christopher. The Pilot's R/T Handbook. 2007. (ENG., Illus.). 96p. per. 24.95 (978-1-86126-853-2(X), 186126853X) Crowood Pr., Ltd. GBR. Dist: MBI Distribution Services/Quayside Distribution.

Moir, Ian & Seabridge, Allan. Aircraft Systems: Mechanical, Electrical & Avionics Subsystems Integration. 3rd ed. 2008. (Aerospace Ser.). (ENG., Illus.). 546p. 130.00 (978-0-470-05996-8(6), Wiley) Wiley, John & Sons, Inc.

Tooley, Mike. Aircraft Digital Electronic & Computer Systems: Principles, Operation & Maintenance. 2007. (ENG., Illus.). 208p. per. 56.95 (978-0-7506-8138-4(1)) Routledge.

AIRPLANES—ENGINES

see Airplanes—Motors

AIRPLANES—EQUIPMENT AND SUPPLIES

Ali, Aidy. Life Extension of Aircraft Components. 2010. 260p. pap. (978-3-639-25831-8(2)) VDM Verlag Dr. Mueller e.K.

British Standards Institute Staff. Aerospace series. Connectors, electrical, rectangular, modular. Operating temperature 175$0DC continuous. Tooling for assembly receptacle coding component. Product Standard. 8p. pap. 197.00 (978-0-580-53299-3(2)) Artech Hse., Inc.

Cram101 Textbook Reviews & Cram101 Textbook Reviews. Outlines & Highlights for Aircraft Systems: Mechanical, Electrical & Avionics Subsystems Integration by Allan Seabridge. 2011. 180p. pap. 29.95 (978-1-61830-877-1(7)) Cram101 Inc.

Griffioen, Hans. AIR CRASH INVESTIGATIONS: the Crash of Helios Airways Flight 522. 2009. 215p. pap. 27.50 (978-1-4092-8545-8(6)) Lulu Enterprises Inc.

—AIR CRASH INVESTIGATIONS:the Crash of Swissair Flight 111. 2009. (ENG.). 392p. pap. 34.95 (978-1-4092-8352-2(6)) Lulu Enterprises Inc.

Peczkowski, Robert. Henschel Hs126. 2008. (Illus.). 128p. pap. (978-83-89450-40-1(2)) Stratus, Wydawnictwo, Juszczak, Artur.

Technology Research Editors, ed. Aircraft Systems: Computer Applications, 2007 Ed. 2007. pap. 128.50 (978-1-60030-143-8(6), Search-In-Print) CSA Journal Division.

AIRPLANES—FLIGHT RECORDERS

see Flight Recorders

AIRPLANES—FLIGHT TESTING

Anton, Phillip S. & Raman, Raj. An Update of the Nation's Long-Term Strategic Needs for NASA's Aeronautics Test Facilities. 2010. 120p. pap. 33.50 (978-0-8330-4493-8(1), db-553) RAND Corp., The.

Aviation, North American, et al. North American X-15 Pilot's Flight Operating Instructions. 2010. 196p. pap. 21.95 (978-1-935327-86-8(0)) Periscope Film, LLC.

Blackman, Tony. Tony Blackman - Test Pilot: My extraordinary life in Flight. 2009. (Illus.). 224p. 39.95 (978-1-906502-36-2(6)) Grub Street GBR. Dist: Casemate Pubs. & Bk. Distributors, LLC, Littlehampton Bk Services, Ltd.

—Vulcan Test Pilot: My experiences in the cockpit of a Cold War Icon. 2009. (Illus.). 224p. pap. 26.95 (978-1-906502-30-0(7)) Grub Street GBR. Dist: Casemate Pubs. & Bk. Distributors, LLC.

Bullen, Annie & Rivas, Brian. John Derry. 2009. (ENG., Illus.). 224p. 39.95 (978-1-84425-531-3(X), 184425531X) Haynes Publishing PLC GBR. Dist: MBI Distribution Services/Quayside Distribution.

Cossement, Mark. Development of a Simulator for the Testing of Avionics Displays. 2009. 128p. pap. (978-3-639-20477-3(8)) VDM Verlag Dr. Mueller e.K.

Hounsfield, Christopher. Trailblazers: Test Pilots in Action: The Most Frightening Moments of the World's Elite. 2008. (Illus.). 208p. 39.95 (978-1-84415-748-8(2)) Pen & Sword Bks. Ltd. GBR. Dist: Casemate Pubs. & Bk. Distributors, LLC.

Marrett, George J. Contrails over the Mojave: The Golden Age of Jet Flight Testing at Edwards Air Force Base. 2008. (Illus.). 230p. 29.95 (978-1-59114-511-0(2)) Naval Institute Pr.

Mason, Tim. The Secret Years. 2010. (Illus.). 320p. (978-1-902109-14-5(7)) Hikoki Pubns.

McCormick, Barnes Warnock & Schetz, Joseph A. Introduction to Flight Testing & Applied Aerodynamics. 2011. (Illus.). ix, 133p. **(978-1-60086-827-6(4))** Virginia Polytechnic Institute & State Univ. Pr.

Meyendorf, Norbert G. H., et al, eds. Nondestructive Materials Characterization: With Applications to Aerospace Materials. 2010. (Springer Series in Materials Science Ser.). (Illus.). xvii, 418p. pap. 219.00 (978-3-642-07350-2(6), 3642073506) Springer.

Ostrow, Scott A. Master the Military Flight Aptitude Tests: Targeted Test Prep to Jump-Start Your Career. 7th ed. 2009. (ENG.). 384p. (YA). pap. 24.95 (978-0-7689-2793-1(5), Arco) Peterson's.

Ward, Donald T., et al. Introduction to Flight Test Engineering, Vol. 2. rev. ed. 2010. (ENG.). 320p. pap. 110.34 (978-0-7575-5151-2(3)) Kendall Hunt Publishing Co.

—Introductions to Flight Test Engineering, Vol. 1. 3rd rev. ed. 2010. (ENG.). 284p. pap. 104.32 (978-0-7575-2934-4(8)) Kendall Hunt Publishing Co.

Warsitz, Lutz. The First Jet Pilot: The Story of German Test Pilot Erich Warsitz. 2009. (Illus.). 176p. 39.99 (978-1-84415-818-8(7)) Pen & Sword Bks. Ltd. GBR. Dist: Casemate Pubs. & Bk. Distributors, LLC.

AIRPLANES—FREIGHT

see Aeronautics, Commercial

AIRPLANES—FUEL

see also Jet Planes—Fuel

Aviation & the Emerging Use of Biofuels: Hearing Before the Subcommittee on Space & Aeronautics, Committee on Science & Technology, House of Representatives, One Hundred Eleventh Congress, First Session, March 26, 2009. 2009. (Illus.). iv, 101p. (978-0-16-084483-6(5), 552-070-40006-1) United States Government Printing Office.

Bowles, Mark D. The Apollo of Aeronautics: NASA's Aircraft Energy Efficiency Program, 1973-1987: NASA's Aircraft Energy Efficiency Program, 1973-1987. National Aeronautics and Space Administration, ed. 2010. (ENG., Illus.). 201p. 24.00 (978-0-16-084295-5(6), U. S. National Aeronautics & Space Administration) United States Government Printing Office.

Committee on Assessment of Aircraft Winglets for Large Aircraft Fuel Efficiency & National Research Council. Assessment of Wingtip Modifications to Increase the Fuel Efficiency of Air Force Aircraft. 2007. (ENG.). 112p. pap. 29.75 (978-0-309-10497-5(1)) National Academies Pr.

Langton, Roy. Aircraft Fuel Systems. 2008. (978-1-56347-963-2(X)) American Institute of Aeronautics & Astronautics.

Langton, Roy, et al. Aircraft Fuel Systems. 2009. (Aerospace Ser.: 13). (ENG.). 366p. 130.00 (978-0-470-05708-7(4), Wiley) Wiley, John & Sons, Inc.

Rehsöft, Markus. Direct Operating Costs of Aircraft Fuel Systems - System Architecture, Analyzing Methods, Contribution of Components. 2008. 96p. pap. (978-3-639-03122-5(9)) VDM Verlag Dr. Mueller e.K.

AIRPLANES—HISTORY

see also Aeronautics—Flights

Angelucci, Enzo & Matricardi, Paolo. Complete Book of World War II Combat Aircraft: With Full-Color Illustrations of Every Fighting Plane from 1933-1945, Including Bombers, Fighters, Assault Aircraft, & Many More. (Illus.). viii, 414p. (978-88-8095-688-4(4)) White Star Publishers, Inc.

Ball, Larry A. The Immortal Twin Beech. 2008. (ENG., Illus.). 240p. 49.99 (978-1-934980-27-9(7)) Cable Publishing.

Berliner, Don. The Paris Air Show. 2006. (Illus.). 68p. reprint ed. pap. 25.00 (978-1-4223-5692-0(2)) DIANE Publishing Co.

Blackman, Tony. Nimrod Rise & Fall. 2012. (Illus.). 224p. 39.95 **(978-1-908117-79-3(6))** Grub Street GBR. Dist: Casemate Pubs. & Bk. Distributors, LLC.

Brown, Eric. Wings of the Weird & Wonderful. 2010. (Illus.). 208p. (978-1-902109-16-9(3)) Hikoki Pubns.

Chant, Christopher. The World's Greatest Aircraft. Taylor, Michael J. H., ed. 2008. (ENG., Illus.). 448p. pap. 12.99 (978-0-7858-2010-9(8), 0785820108) Book Sales, Inc.

Conway, Erik M. Blind Landings: Low-Visibility Operations in American Aviation, 1918-1958. 2006. (ENG., Illus.). 256p. (gr. 17). 48.00 (978-0-8018-8449-8(7)) Johns Hopkins Univ. Pr.

Crawford, Alex. Hawker Hart Family. 2008. (Illus.). 170p. pap. (978-83-89450-62-3(3)) Stratus, Wydawnictwo, Juszczak, Artur.

Dancey, Peter. BOEING Plane-makers of Distinction. 2010. 128p. pap. 30.50 (978-1-4461-5917-0(5)) Lulu Enterprises Inc.

Darling, Kev. American X & Y Planes: Volume 1: Experimental Aircraft To 1945, 1 vol. 2010. (ENG., Illus.). 176p. 34.95 (978-1-84797-141-8(5), 1847971415) Crowood Pr., Ltd. GBR. Dist: MBI Distribution Services/Quayside Distribution.

Dick, Ron & Patterson, Dan. 50 Aircraft That Changed the World. 2010. (ENG., Illus.). 208p. pap. 29.95 (978-1-55407-658-1(7)) Boston Mills Pr. CAN. Dist: Firefly Bks., Ltd.

Endres, Gunter. Airbus A300. 2006. (Illus.). 128p. reprint ed. pap. 25.00 (978-1-4223-5522-0(5)) DIANE Publishing Co.

Film.com, Periscope. P-40 Warhawk Pilot's Flight Operating Manual. 2007. 94p. pap. 19.95 (978-1-4116-9371-5(X)) Lulu Enterprises Inc.

Forczyk, Robert. Fw 200 Condor vs Atlantic Convoy, 1941-1943. 2010. (Duel Ser.). (ENG., Illus.). 80p. pap. 17.95 (978-1-84603-917-1(7)) Osprey Publishing, Ltd. GBR. Dist: Random Hse., Inc.

Foster, David. Tornado: A History. 2008. (ENG.). 120p. pap. 46.95 (978-0-7524-4514-4(6)) History Pr. Ltd.,The GBR. Dist: Independent Pubs. Group.

Gandt, Robert. China Clipper. 2010. (Illus.). 0264p. pap. 18.95 (978-1-59114-303-1(9)) Naval Institute Pr.

Gibbs-Smith, Charles H. Aviation: An Historical Survey from Its Origins to the End of the Second World War. 2nd ed. 2007. (Illus.). 304p. reprint ed. 27.00 (978-1-4223-6825-1(4)) DIANE Publishing Co.

Gordon, Yefim, et al. OKB Tupolev: A History of the Design Bureau & Its Aircraft. 2nd rev. ed. 2010. (ENG., Illus.). 368p. 59.95 (978-1-85780-214-6(4)) Allan, Ian Publishing GBR. Dist: BookMasters Distribution Services (BDS).

Graham, Thomas. Box Top Air Power: The Aviation Art of Model Airplane Boxes. 2008. (Illus.). 192p. pap. 29.99 (978-0-7643-2964-7(2)) Schiffer Publishing, Ltd.

Gunston, Bill. Nimrod: The Centenarian Aircraft. 2010. (ENG.). 192p. pap. 29.95 (978-0-7524-5270-8(3)) History Pr. Ltd.,The GBR. Dist: Independent Pubs. Group.

Harvey, James. Sharks of the Air: Willi Messerschmitt & How He Built the World's First Operational Jet Fighter. 2010. (Illus.). 352p. 32.95 (978-1-935149-46-0(6)) Casemate Pubs. & Bk. Distributors, LLC.

Havers, Richard. Classic Aircraft: Civilian Aviation from 1906 until the Present Day. 2010. (ENG., Illus.). 128p. 14.95 (978-1-84425-707-2(X), 184425707X) Haynes Publishing PLC GBR. Dist: MBI Distribution Services/Quayside Distribution.

Hildebrandt, Erik. Front Row Center 4: Inside the Great American Air Show. 2009. (ENG.). 172p. 39.95 (978-0-9674040-7-3(X), 096740407X) Cleared Hot Media.

Jackson, Robert. Britain's Greatest Aircraft. 2007. (Illus.). 320p. 50.00 (978-1-84415-600-9(1)) Pen & Sword Bks. Ltd. GBR. Dist: Casemate Pubs. & Bk. Distributors, LLC.

Jackson, Robert. Infamous Aircraft. 2012. (Illus.). 176p. pap. 24.95 **(978-1-84884-658-6(4))** Pen & Sword Bks. Ltd. GBR. Dist: Casemate Pubs. & Bk. Distributors, LLC.

Jarrett, Philip. The Color Encyclopedia of Incredible Airplanes. 2012. (ENG.). 360p. 15.95 **(978-0-7566-9575-0(9))** Dorling Kindersley Publishing, Inc.

Jenkins, Dennis R. & Landis, Tony R. Hypersonic: The Story of the North American X-15. rev. ed. 2008. (Illus.). 276p. pap. 28.95 (978-1-58007-131-4(7)) Specialty Pr. Pubs. & Wholesalers, Inc.

Juszczak, Artur. Camouflage & Decals. 2012. (Illus.). 16p. pap. 22.00 **(978-83-61421-54-2(8))** Stratus, Wydawnictwo, Juszczak, Artur POL. Dist: Casemate Pubs. & Bk. Distributors, LLC.

Kinney, Jeremy R. Airplanes: The Life Story of a Technology. 2008. (ENG., Illus.). 184p. (C). (gr. 13-17). pap. 20.95 (978-0-8018-9069-7(1)) Johns Hopkins Univ. Pr.

Lert, Frederic. C160 Transall. 2009. 64p. pap. 22.95 (978-2-35250-092-6(3)) Histoire et Collections FRA. Dist: Casemate Pubs. & Bk. Distributors, LLC.

—F14 Tomcat. 2008. 84p. pap. 19.95 (978-2-35250-073-5(7)) Histoire et Collections FRA. Dist: Casemate Pubs. & Bk. Distributors, LLC.

Lewis, John D. & Cook, LeRoy. Caravan: Cessna's Swiss Army Knife with Wings. 2008. (ENG., Illus.). 235p. pap. 19.95 (978-1-56027-682-1(7)) Aviation Supplies & Academics, Inc.

Lovell, Mike, ed. & compiled by. Arthur Lovell - Aviation Pioneer & Navigator. 2007. (978-0-9776414-5-1(7)) LifeReloaded.

Luisada, Claude G. Queen of the Skies: The Lockheed Constellation. 2010. (Illus.). 608p. 39.95 (978-1-57197-417-4(2), Ivy House Publishing Group) Pentland Pr., Inc.

Marriott, Leo. Jets at Sea: Naval Aviation in Transition 1945 - 55. 2008. (Illus.). 224p. 39.95 (978-1-84415-742-6(3)) Pen & Sword Bks. Ltd. GBR. Dist: Casemate Pubs. & Bk. Distributors, LLC.

Martini, Anthony. Flying Machines over Zion: Aviation Comes to Utah, 1910-1919. 2009. 146p. pap. 11.95 (978-0-557-06798-5(7)) Lulu Enterprises Inc.

Mason, Tim. The Seaplane Years. 2010. (Illus.). 272p. (978-1-902109-13-8(9)) Hikoki Pubns.

—The Secret Years. 2010. (Illus.). 320p. (978-1-902109-14-5(7)) Hikoki Pubns.

Maxwell, David. Airbus A380: Superjumbo on World Tour. rev. ed. 2007. (ENG., Illus.). 160p. 29.95 (978-0-7603-3279-5(7), 0760332797, Zenith Pr.) MBI Publishing Co. LLC.

McKay, Stuart. De Havilland Moths in Detail: Dh60, dh80, dh82, dh83, dh85, dh87, Dh94. 2010. (In Detail Ser.). (ENG., Illus.). 288p. 79.95 (978-1-906133-11-5(5), 1906133115) Herridge & Sons, Ltd. GBR. Dist: MBI Distribution Services/Quayside Distribution.

McLelland, Tim. The Hawker Hunter. 2009. (Illus.). 336p. 49.95 (978-0-85979-123-6(8)) Crecy Publishing GBR. Dist: Partners Pubs. Group, Inc.

Neal, Robert J. A Technical & Operational History of the Liberty Engine: Tanks, Ships & Aircraft 1917-1960. 2008. 616p. 74.95 (978-1-58007-149-9(X)) Specialty Pr. Pubs. & Wholesalers, Inc.

Nijboer, Donald. Cockpit: An Illustrated History of World War II Aircraft Interiors. 2006. (ENG., Illus.). 176p. pap. 24.95 (978-1-55046-488-7(4)) Boston Mills Pr. CAN. Dist: Firefly Bks., Ltd.

Ottaway, Susan. Fire over Heathrow. 2008. (Illus.). 208p. 45.00 (978-1-84415-739-6(3)) Pen & Sword Bks. Ltd. GBR. Dist: Casemate Pubs. & Bk. Distributors, LLC.

Parsons, Dave, et al. Grumman F-14 Tomcat: Bye - Bye Baby...!: Images & Reminiscences from 35 Years of Active Service. 2011. (ENG., Illus.). 200p. pap. 29.99 (978-0-7603-3981-7(3), 0760339813, Zenith Pr.) MBI Publishing Co. LLC.

Pascoe, David. Aircraft. 2006. (Illus.). 240p. reprint ed. pap. 20.00 (978-1-4223-5875-7(5)) DIANE Publishing Co.

Robert E., Bradley. Convair Advanced Designs: Secret Projects from San Diego, 1923-1962. 2010. 176p. 34.95 (978-1-58007-133-8(3)) Specialty Pr. Pubs. & Wholesalers, Inc.

Schiff, Barry. Dream Aircraft: The Most Fascinating Airplanes I've Ever Flown. 2007. (ENG.). 330p. pap. 19.95 (978-1-56027-680-7(0)) Aviation Supplies & Academics, Inc.

Scott, Robert & Heppenheimer, T. A. Flight. 2009. (ENG., Illus.). 256p. pap. 24.95 (978-1-84732-340-8(5)) Carlton Bks., Ltd. GBR. Dist: Sterling Publishing Co., Inc.

Skinner, Stephen. British Airliner Prototypes since 1945. 2010. (ENG., Illus.). 224p. 56.95 (978-1-85780-299-3(3)) Allan, Ian Publishing GBR. Dist: BookMasters Distribution Services (BDS).

Spenser, Jay. The Airplane: How Ideas Gave Us Wings. 2009. (ENG.). 320p. pap. 14.99 (978-0-06-125920-3(9), HarperPerennial) HarperCollins Pubs.

—The Airplane: How Ideas Gave Us Wings. 2008. (ENG., Illus.). 352p. 25.95 (978-0-06-125919-7(5)) Smithsonian Institution Pr.

Sullivan, Mark P. Dependable Engines: The Story of Pratt & Whitney. 2008. (Illus.). ix, 164p. (978-1-56347-957-1(5)); pap. (978-1-56347-958-8(3)) American Institute of Aeronautics & Astronautics.

United States Air Force. B-47 Stratojet Pilot's Flight Operating Instructions. 2008. 103p. pap. 19.96 (978-1-4357-0554-8(8)) Lulu Enterprises Inc.

Weirather, Larry. The China Clipper, Pan American Airways & Popular Culture. 2006. (ENG., Illus.). 351p. per. 35.00 (978-0-7864-2820-5(1)) McFarland & Co., Inc. Pubs.

Wittreich, Paul. Forgotten First Flights. 2009. 360p. 29.99 (978-1-4415-1093-8(1)); pap. 19.99 (978-1-4415-1092-1(3)) Xlibris Corp.

Woodring, Suanne & Woodring, Frank. Fairchild Aircraft. 2007. (Images of Aviation Ser.). (ENG., Illus.). 128p. per. 21.99 (978-0-7385-4439-7(6)) Arcadia Publishing.

Wright, Wilbur, et al. A History of Early Aviation. 2009. 168p. pap. 12.99 (978-1-934941-56-0(5)) Red & Black Pubs.

Yenne, Bill. The Story of the Boeing Company, Updated Edition. rev. ed. 2010. (ENG., Illus.). 288p. 40.00 (978-0-7603-4002-8(1), 0760340021, Zenith Pr.) MBI Publishing Co. LLC.

AIRPLANES—ICE PREVENTION

Aircraft Icing: Hearing Before the Subcommittee on Aviation of the Committee on Transportation & Infrastructure, House of Representatives, One Hundred Eleventh Congress, Second Session, February 24, 2010. 2010. (Illus.). xv, 170p. **(978-0-16-086345-5(7)**, 552-070-41429-1) United States Government Printing Office.

D'Avirro, John & Chaput, Michael D. Optimizing the Use of Aircraft Deicing & Anti-Icing Fluids. 2011. (Illus.). 92p. **(978-0-309-15551-9(7))** Transportation Research Board.

National Research Council (U.S.), Transportation Research Board Staff, et al, contrib. by. Deicing Planning Guidelines & Practices for Stormwater Management Systems. 2009. (Illus.). 40p. (978-0-309-11778-4(X)) Transportation Research Board.

AIRPLANES—INSTRUMENTS

see Aeronautical Instruments

AIRPLANES—JET PROPULSION

see also Airplanes—Turbojet Engines

Anton, Phillip S. & Raman, Raj. An Update of the Nation's Long-Term Strategic Needs for NASA's Aeronautics Test Facilities. 2010. 120p. pap. 33.50 (978-0-8330-4493-8(1), db-553) RAND Corp., The.

Babu, V. Aircraft Propulsion. 2009. (ENG., Illus.). 212p. 139.95 (978-1-4398-1271-6(3), CRC Press) Taylor & Francis Group GBR. Dist: Taylor & Francis Group.

Mattingly, Jack D. Elements of Propulsion: Gas Turbines & Rockets. 2006. (AIAA Education Ser.). (Illus.). 867p. (978-1-56347-779-9(3)) American Institute of Aeronautics & Astronautics.

AIRPLANES—MAINTENANCE AND REPAIR

see also Flight Engineering

Airfield Pavement: Keeping Nation's Runways in Good Condition Could Require Substantially Higher Spending. 30p. pap. 20.00 (978-0-7881-7949-5(7)) DIANE Publishing Co.

Andrews, Brad. How to Land a Top-Paying Aircraft & Avionics Equipment Mechanics & Service Technician Services Job: Your Complete Guide to Opportunities, Resumes & Cover Letters, Interviews, Salaries, Promotions, What to Expect from Recruiters & More! 2010. 151p. pap. (978-1-74244-597-7(7)) Emereo Pty Ltd.

Benavides, S., ed. Corrosion Control in the Aerospace Industry. 2009. 384p. 259.95 (978-1-4200-7965-4(4)) CRC Pr. LLC.

Chenoweth, Mary E., et al. Best Practices in Developing Proactive Supply Strategies for Air Force Low-Demand Service Parts. 2010. (ENG.). 106p. pap. 23.00 (978-0-8330-4878-3(3), mg858) RAND Corp., The.

Cotter, Jarrod & Blackah, Paul. Avro Lancaster Manual: An Insight into Restoring, Servicing & Flying Britain's Legendary World War 2 Bomber. 2008. (ENG., Illus.). 160p. 34.95 (978-1-84425-463-7(1), 1844254631) Haynes Publishing PLC GBR. Dist: MBI Distribution Services/Quayside Distribution.

Crane, Dale. Aviation Maintenance Technician Vol. 2: Systems. 3rd ed. 2008. (Aviation Maintenance Technician Ser.). (ENG.). 492p. 49.95 (978-1-56027-685-2(1)) Aviation Supplies & Academics, Inc.

—Aviation Maintenance Technician - Airframe. 3rd ed. 2008. (Aviation Maintenance Technician Ser.). (ENG.). 540p. 49.95 (978-1-56027-712-5(2)) Aviation Supplies & Academics, Inc.

—Aviation Maintenance Technician: Airframe: Volume 2: Systems. 3rd ed. 2007. (Aviation Maintenance Technician Ser.). (ENG., Illus.). 492p. pap. 49.95 (978-1-56027-549-7(9)) Aviation Supplies & Academics, Inc.

—Aviation Maintenance Technician: General. 3rd ed. 2008. (Aviation Maintenance Technician Ser.). (ENG.). 828p. 59.95 (978-1-56027-711-8(4)) Aviation Supplies & Academics, Inc.

—Aviation Maintenance Technician: Powerplant. 3rd ed. 2011. (Aviation Maintenance Technician Ser.). (ENG., Illus.). 800p. 59.95 **(978-1-56027-862-7(5))** Aviation Supplies & Academics, Inc.

—General Test Guide 2012: The Fast-Track to Study for & Pass the FAA Aviation Maintenance Technician (AMT) General Knowledge Exam. Michmerhuizen, Terry, ed. 2011. (Fast Track Ser.). (ENG.). 180p. pap. 14.95 (978-1-56027-855-9(2)) Aviation Supplies & Academics, Inc.

—Inspection Authorization Test Prep: A Comprehensive Study Tool to Prepare for the FAA Inspection Authorization Knowledge Exam. Michmerhuizen, Terry, ed. 2010. (ENG., Illus.). 735p. pap. 34.95 (978-1-56027-887-0(0)) Aviation Supplies & Academics, Inc.

—Powerplant Test Guide 2012: The Fast-Track to Study for & Pass the FAA Aviation Maintenance Technician (AMT) Powerplant Knowledge Exam. Michmerhuizen, Terry, ed. 2011. (Fast Track Ser.). (ENG.). 212p. pap. 14.95 (978-1-56027-857-3(9)) Aviation Supplies & Academics, Inc.

Crane, Dale, et al. General Test Guide 2009: The Fast-Track to Study for & Pass the FAA Aviation Maintenance Technician General & Designated Mechanic Examiner Knowledge Tests. 2008. (Fast Track Ser.). (ENG., Illus.). 160p. pap. 14.95 (978-1-56027-697-5(5)) Aviation Supplies & Academics, Inc.

Dorworth, Louis C., et al. Essentials of Advanced Composite Fabrication & Repair. 2010. (ENG., Illus.). 325p. 79.95 (978-1-56027-752-1(1)) Aviation Supplies & Academics, Inc.

Drew, John G. & Lynch, Kristin F. Options for Meeting the Maintenance Demands of Active Associate Flying Units. 2008. 94p. pap. 24.50 (978-0-8330-4210-1(6), mg-611) RAND Corp., The.

Duong, Cong N. & Wang, Chun Hui. Composite Repair: Theory & Design. 2007. (ENG., Illus.). 480p. 230.00 (978-0-08-045146-6(2), Elsevier Science) Elsevier Science & Technology Bks.

Federal Aviation Administration. Aviation Mechanic Practical Test Standards for General, Airframe & Powerplant: FAA-S-8081-26, -27, And -28. 2009. (Practical Test Standards Ser.). (ENG.). 96p. pap. 9.95 (978-1-56027-751-4(3)) Aviation Supplies & Academics, Inc.

—Far/amt 2012: Federal Aviation Regulations for Aviation Maintenance Technicians. 2011. (FAR/AIM Ser.). (ENG.). 925p. pap. 24.95 (978-1-56027-860-3(9)) Aviation Supplies & Academics, Inc.

Federal Aviation Administration Staff. Aircraft Inspection & Repair: Acceptable Methods, Techniques, & Practices. 2010. (ENG., Illus.). 768p. pap. 24.95 (978-1-60239-950-1(6), 23995C) Skyhorse Publishing Co., Inc.

—Aircraft Inspection, Repair & Alterations: Acceptable Methods, Techniques, & Practices. 2008. (FAA Handbooks Ser.). (ENG., Illus.). 768p. pap. 24.95 (978-1-56027-728-6(9)) Aviation Supplies & Academics, Inc.

Federal Aviation Administration Staff & Federal Aviation Administration. Aviation Maintenance Technician Handbook-General: Faa-h-8083-30. 2008. (FAA Handbooks Ser.). (ENG.). 660p. pap. 39.95 (978-1-56027-716-3(5)) Aviation Supplies & Academics, Inc.

Flight Safety Foundation Staff, compiled by. 59th Annual International Air Safety Seminar & IFA 36th International Conference 2006: Enhancing Safety Worldwide. 2007. 1452p. pap. 125.00 (978-1-60423-393-3(1)) Curran Assocs., Inc.

Gebman, Jean R. Challenges & Issues with the Further Aging of U. S. Air Force Aircraft: Policy Options for Effective Life-Cycle Management of Resources. 2008. 80p. pap. 41.50 (978-0-8330-4518-8(0), tr560) RAND Corp., The.

Graser, John C., et al. Retaining F-22A Tooling: Options & Costs. 2011. 54p. pap. 15.00 (978-0-8330-5098-4(2), TR-831) RAND Corp., The.

Inspection Authorization Test. 2nd ed. (978-1-56027-367-7(4)) Aviation Supplies & Academics, Inc.

Keeting, Edward G. & Loredo, Elvira N. Valuing Programmed Depot Maintenance Speed: An Analysis of F-15 PDM. 2006. 60p. pap. 20.00 *(978-0-8330-3968-2(7)*, TR-377) RAND Corp., The.

Kochersberger, Kevin. Light Sport Aircraft Inspection Procedures. 2006. per. *(978-1-933189-06-2(1))* Avotek Information Resources.

Kroes, Michael J., et al. Aircraft Maintenance & Repair with Study Guide. 6th ed. 2007. (ENG.). (C). pap., pap., pap. 127.00 *(978-0-07-723154-5(6)*, 0077231546) McGraw-Hill Higher Education.

Loredo, Elvira N., et al. Programmed Depot Maintenance Capacity Assessment Tool: Workloads, Capacity, & Availability. 2007. 118p. pap. 23.00 *(978-0-8330-4015-2(4))* RAND Corp., The.

McGarvey, Ronald G. & Carrillo, Manuel. Analysis of the Air Force Logistics Enterprise: Evaluation of Global Repair Network Options for Supporting the F-16 & KC-135. 2010. 188p. pap. 30.00 *(978-0-8330-4740-3(X)*, mg872) RAND Corp., The.

Nick, Veronico. Amarg: America's Military Aircraft Boneyard - A Photo Scrapbook. 2010. 144p. pap. 24.95 *(978-1-58007-139-0(2))* Specialty Pr. Pubs. & Wholesalers, Inc.

Parker, Christian. The Care & Maintenance of Heavy Jets. 2nd ed. 2009. 204p. pap. 19.95 *(978-0-9815838-3-9(0))* Olympic Dispatch Publishing.

Pyles, Raymond A. & Tripp, Robert S. A Common Operating Picture for Air Force Materiel Sustainment: First Steps. 2008. 140p. pap. 25.00 *(978-0-8330-4128-9(2)*, mg-667) RAND Corp., The.

Rider, David. Aircraft Maintenance & Services. (Transportation Ser.). (Illus.). viii, 189p. 695.00 *(978-0-7106-1600-5(7))* Jane's Information Group, Inc.

Rosello, Anthony D., et al. Assessing the Cost-Effectiveness of Modernizing the KC-10 to Meet Global Air Traffic Management Mandates. 2009. 80p. pap. 23.00 *(978-0-8330-4765-6(5)*, mg-901) RAND Corp., The.

Rudman, Jack. Aircraft Service Worker. (Career Examination Ser.: C-3691). pap. 27.95 *(978-0-8373-3691-6(0))* National Learning Corp.

—Airframe & Powerplant Mechanics. (Occupational Competency Examination Ser.). 49.95 *(978-0-8373-5752-2(7)*, OLE-2, Passbooks) National Learning Corp.

Slater, Stephen & McKay, Stuart. De Havilland Tiger Moth Manual, 1931-1945: An Insight into Owning, Flying & Maintaining the Legendary British Training Biplane. 2010. (ENG., Illus.). 160p. pap. 32.95 *(978-1-84425-586-3(7)*, 1844255867) Haynes Publishing PLC GBR. Dist: MBI Distribution Services/Quayside Distribution.

Technology Research Editors, ed. Maintenance & Repair of Aircraft & their Components, 2007 Ed. 2007. pap. 128.50 *(978-1-60030-150-6(9)*, Search-In-Print) CSA Journal Division.

Tomter Pedersen, Peter. Make it Safe! 2008. 322p. pap. 57.50 *(978-1-84799-454-7(7))* Lulu Enterprises Inc.

Unger, Eric J. An Examination of the Relationship Between Usage & Operating-and-Support Costs of U. S. Air Force Aircraft. 2009. 50p. pap. 22.00 *(978-0-8330-4613-0(6)*, tr594) RAND Corp., The.

Winslade, Richard. The Battle of Britain Memorial Flight. 2010. (ENG., Illus.). 168p. pap. 27.95 *(978-0-7524-5651-5(2))* History Pr. Ltd.,The GBR. Dist: Independent Pubs. Group.

—The Battle of Britain Memorial Flight. 2007. (ENG., Illus.). 160p. 36.95 *(978-0-7509-3151-9(5))* Sutton Publishing.

AIRPLANES—MATERIALS

see also Light Metals

American Society of Mechanical Engineers, Aerospace Division Staff, contrib. by. Proceedings of the ASME Aerospace Division — 2006: Adaptive Materials & Systems, Aerospace Materials & Structures, General: Presented at 2006 ASME International Mechanical Engineering Congress & Exposition, November 5-10, 2006, Chicago, Illinois, USA. 2007. (Illus.). xix, 664p. *(978-0-7918-4765-7(9))* American Society of Mechanical Engineers, The.

American Society of Mechanical Engineers Staff, ed. Flight Vehicle Materials Structures & Dynamics Advanced Metallics Metal Matrix&polymer Matrix Composit, Vol. 2. 472p. 80.00 *(978-0-7918-0660-9(X))* ASME Pr.

Chaturvedi, M. C., ed. Welding & Joining of Aerospace Materials. 2012. (Woodhead Publishing in Materials Ser.). (ENG., Illus.). 448p. 265.00 ***(978-1-84569-532-3(1))*** Woodhead Publishing Ltd. GBR. Dist: Ingram Pub. Services.

Cooper, Jonathan Edward & Wright, Jan Robert. Introduction to Aircraft Aeroelasticity & Loads. 2008. (Aerospace Ser.: 18). (ENG., Illus.). 524p. 155.00 *(978-0-470-85840-0(0)*, Wiley) Wiley, John & Sons, Inc.

Komorowski, Jerzy, ed. Icaf 2011 Structural Integrity - Influence of Efficiency & Green Imperatives: Proceedings of the 26th Symposium of the International Committee on Aeronautical Fatigue 1-3 June 2011, Montreal, Canada. 2011. (Illus.). xvi, 976p. 399.00 *(978-94-007-1663-6(X)*, 940071663X) Springer.

Long, Siyuan. Light Metals, Aerospace Materials & Superconductors, 4 vols. Han, Yafang, ed. 2007. (Progress in Light Metals, Aerospace Materials & Superconductors Ser.: Vols. 546-549). (Illus.). 2420p. *(978-0-87849-432-3(4))* Trans Tech Pubns., Ltd.

Meyendorf, Norbert G. H., et al, eds. Nondestructive Materials Characterization: With Applications to Aerospace Materials. 2010. (Springer Series in Materials Science Ser.). (Illus.). xvii, 418p. pap. 219.00 *(978-3-642-07350-2(6)*, 3642073506) Springer.

Shull, Peter, et al. Nondestructive Characterization for Composite Materials, Aerospace Engineering, Civil Infrastructure, & Homeland Security 2010. 2010. (Proceedings of SPIE Ser.). 492p. pap. 130.00 ***(978-0-8194-8064-4(9))*** SPIE.

Shull, Peter J. Nondestructive Characterization for Composite Materials, Aerospace Engineering, Civil Infrastructure, & Homeland Security 2008: 11-13 March 2008, San Diego, California, USA. 2008. (Proceedings of SPIE Ser.). (Illus.). 380p. pap. 105.00 ***(978-0-8194-7120-8(8))*** SPIE.

Vlot, Ad. Glare: History of the Development of a New Aircraft Material. 2010. (Illus.). 228p. pap. 99.00 *(978-90-481-5870-6(2)*, 9048158702) Springer.

Wright, Jan R. & Cooper, Jonathan E. Introduction to Aircraft Aeroelasticity & Dynamic Loads. 2008. (Aerospace Series (PEP) Ser.). (Illus.). 488p. pap. 85.00 *(978-0-470-85841-7(9))* Wiley, John & Sons, Inc.

Wu, H. Felix. Nondestructive Characterization for Composite Materials, Aerospace Engineering, Civil Infrastructure, & Homeland Security 2009: 9-11 March 2009, San Diego, California, United States. 2009. (Proceedings of SPIE Ser.). (Illus.). 386p. pap. 80.00 *(978-0-8194-7554-1(8))* SPIE.

Wu, H. Felix. Nondestructive Characterization for Composite Materials, Aerospace Engineering, Civil Infrastructure, & Homeland Security 2011. 2011. (Proceedings of SPIE Ser.). 1068p. pap. 190.00 ***(978-0-8194-8545-8(4))*** SPIE.

Wu, H. Felix, et al. Nondestructive Characterization for Composite Materials, Aerospace Engineering, Civil Infrastructure & Homeland Security: 20-22 March 2007, San Diego, California, USA. 2007. (Proceedings of SPIE Ser.). (Illus.). 352p. pap. 90.00 *(978-0-8194-6652-5(2))* SPIE.

AIRPLANES—MODELS

Balsa Gliders Getting Started Teacher's Guide. 2007. spiral bd. 24.95 *(978-1-58651-922-3(0))* Pitsco/Pitsco LEGO Dacta.

Bedson, Colin. Flying Radio-Controlled Model Aircraft. 2007. (ENG., Illus.). 128p. per. 22.95 *(978-1-86126-915-7(3)*, 1861269153) Crowood Pr., Ltd. GBR. Dist: MBI Distribution Services/Quayside Distribution.

Belcarz, Bart?omiej. Camouflage & Decals No. 1: Caudron Cr. 714, MS 406, Hawk H75A. 2010. (Camouflage & Decals Ser.). (Illus.). 16p. pap. 23.00 *(978-83-61421-22-1(X))* Stratus, Wydawnictwo, Juszczak, Artur POL. Dist: Casemate Pubs. & Bk. Distributors, LLC.

Belcarz, Bartomiej. Camouflage & Decals. 2010. (Illus.). 16p. pap. 20.00 *(978-83-61421-31-3(9))* Stratus, Wydawnictwo, Juszczak, Artur POL. Dist: Casemate Pubs. & Bk. Distributors, LLC.

Benjamin, Robert. Hey Mister, Will It Fly? 2010. 200p. pap. 1.00 *(978-0-9841397-7-4(X))* Helm Publishing.

Boddington, David. Almost Ready to Fly: Radio Control Flying 21st Century Style. 2007. (Illus.). 168p. pap. 42.50 *(978-1-85486-242-6(1))* Specialist Interest Model Bks. Ltd. GBR. Dist: Trans-Atlantic Pubns., Inc.

Chambers, Joseph R. Modeling Flight: the Role of Dynamically Scaled Free-Flight Models in Support of NASA's Aerospace Programs: The Role of Dynamically Scaled Free-Flight Models in Support of NASA's Aerospace Programs. National Aeronautics and Space Administration, ed. 2010. (ENG., Illus.). 200p. pap. 35.00 *(978-0-16-084633-5(1)*, U. S. National Aeronautics & Space Administration) United States Government Printing Office.

Dewar, Andrew. Fun & Easy Paper Airplanes. 2008. (ENG., Illus.). 192p. per. 16.95 *(978-0-8048-3888-7(7))* Tuttle Publishing.

Green, Brett. Airbrushing & Finishing Scale Models. 2008. (Modelling Masterclass Ser.). (ENG., Illus.). 192p. 39.95 *(978-1-84603-199-1(0))* Osprey Publishing, Ltd. GBR. Dist: Random Hse., Inc.

—Aircraft Modelling. 2010. (Modelling Masterclass Ser.). (ENG., Illus.). 192p. 39.95 *(978-1-84603-932-4(0))* Osprey Publishing, Ltd. GBR. Dist: Random Hse., Inc.

—The Luftwaffe in the Battle of Britain 1940, Vol. 1. 2010. (ENG., Illus.). 96p. pap. 27.95 *(978-1-906537-11-1(9))* Classic Pubns. GBR. Dist: BookMasters Distribution Services (BDS).

—The Luftwaffe on the Eastern Front, 1943-1945, Vol. 2. 2012. (Classic Modelling Guides). (ENG., Illus.). 96p. pap. 29.95 *(978-1-906537-14-2(3))* Classic Pubns. GBR. Dist: BookMasters Distribution Services (BDS).

—Modelling Scale Aircraft. 2008. (Osprey Modelling Ser.). (ENG., Illus.). 80p. pap. 19.95 *(978-1-84603-237-0(7))* Osprey Publishing, Ltd. GBR. Dist: Random Hse., Inc.

—Modelling the Messerschmitt Bf 109F & Early G Series. 2007. (Osprey Modelling Ser.). (ENG., Illus.). 80p. pap. 19.95 *(978-1-84603-113-7(3))* Osprey Publishing, Ltd. GBR. Dist: Random Hse., Inc.

Hawkey, Pat. Building & Detailing Model Aircraft. 2009. (FineScale Modeler Bks.). (Illus.). 95p. pap. 21.95 *(978-0-89024-723-5(4))* Kalmbach Publishing Co., Bks. Div.

Juszczak, Artur. Camouflage & Decals. 2012. (Illus.). 16p. pap. 22.00 ***(978-83-61421-54-2(8))*** Stratus, Wydawnictwo, Juszczak, Artur POL. Dist: Casemate Pubs. & Bk. Distributors, LLC.

Kamas, Dariusz. Fieseler Fi 156 Storch, 1938-1945. 2012. (Illus.). 148p. pap. 28.00 ***(978-83-61421-47-4(5))*** Stratus, Wydawnictwo, Juszczak, Artur POL. Dist: Casemate Pubs. & Bk. Distributors, LLC.

Kuster, Kevin & Edmundson, Gary. Painting & Finishing Techniques. 2010. (Osprey Modelling Ser.). (ENG., Illus.). 80p. pap. 19.95 *(978-1-84603-263-9(6))* Osprey Publishing, Ltd. GBR. Dist: Random Hse., Inc.

LaFosse, Michael G. & Alexander, Richard L. Planes for Brains: 28 Innovative Origami Airplane Designs. 2011. (ENG., Illus.). 96p. 18.95 *(978-4-8053-1149-3(5))* Tuttle Publishing.

May, James. Toy Stories Airfix. 2010. (ENG., Illus.). 96p. instr.'s hndbk. ed. 14.95 *(978-1-84486-116-3(3)*, Conway Maritime Pr.) Anova Bks. GBR. Dist: Sterling Publishing Co., Inc.

McIlmurray, John. Advanced Aviation Modelling. 2006. (ENG., Illus.). 160p. pap. 29.95 *(978-1-86126-753-5(3)*, 1861267533) Crowood Pr., Ltd. GBR. Dist: MBI Distribution Services/Quayside Distribution.

Model Airplane GS Teacher's Guide. 2006. spiral bd. 24.95 *(978-1-58651-929-2(8))* Pitsco/Pitsco LEGO Dacta.

Morath, Peter. Photo Art for Modellers: Creating Realistic Scenes for Your Aircraft & Train Models. 2008. (Illus.). 96p. pap. 37.50 *(978-1-85486-251-8(0))* Specialist Interest Model Bks. Ltd. GBR. Dist: Trans-Atlantic Pubns., Inc.

—Photo Art for Modellers: Creating Realistic Scenes for Your Aircraft & Train Models. 2008. (ENG., Illus.). 96p. pap. 24.95 *(978-1-877290-73-2(4)*, 1877290734) St. Publishing, Ltd. NZL. Dist: MBI Distribution Services/Quayside Distribution.

Pernes, Emmanuel & Souleys, Olivier. Curtiss P-40: Models & Planes Series. 2008. (Planes & Model Kits Ser.). (Illus.). 84p. pap. 19.95 *(978-2-35250-065-0(6))* Histoire et Collections FRA. Dist: Casemate Pubs. & Bk. Distributors, LLC.

Reyes, Carlos. RCadvisor's Model Airplane Design Made Easy: The Simple Guide to Designing R/C Model Aircraft or Build Your Own Radio Control Flying Model Plane. 2009. (Illus.). 208p. pap. 19.95 *(978-0-9822613-2-3(2))* RCadvisor.com.

—RCadvisor's ModiFly: Design & Build from Scratch Your Own Modern Flying Model Airplane in One Day for Just $5. 2009. (ENG., Illus.). 152p. pap. 19.95 *(978-0-9822613-4-7(9))* RCadvisor.com.

Steiner, Rochelle, text. The New Millennium Paper Airplane Book. 2009. (ENG., Illus.). 104p. pap. 15.95 *(978-0-9608488-5-0(1))* Public Art Fund.

Wang, Patrick. Origami Model Airplanes. 2008. (ENG., Illus.). 160p. 24.95 *(978-4-8053-0999-5(7))* Tuttle Publishing.

Wilson, Jeff, compiled by. Classic Combat Aircraft. 2007. (Illus.). 95p. *(978-0-89024-696-2(3)*, Kalmbach Bks.) Kalmbach Publishing Co., Bks. Div.

AIRPLANES—MOTORS

see also Airplanes—Jet Propulsion; Flight Engineering

Aircraft Propulsion & Gas Turbine Engines. 2011. (C). 124.95 ***(978-1-4200-0877-7(3)***, CRC Press) Taylor & Francis Group GBR. Dist: Taylor & Francis Group.

Bingelis, Tony. Firewall Forward: Airplane Engine Installation Methods. Rivers, David A., ed. (Illus.). 303p. reprint ed. pap. 19.95 *(978-0-940000-93-3(8)*, 21-13950) EAA Aviation Foundation.

Bose, Tarit. Airbreathing Propulsion: An Introduction. 2012. (Springer Aerospace Technology Ser.). (ENG., Illus.). xiv, 206p. 89.95 ***(978-1-4614-3531-0(5)***, 1461435315) Springer.

Connors, Jack & Allen, Ned. The Engines of Pratt & Whitney: A Technical History. 2009. 49.95 *(978-1-60086-711-8(1))* American Institute of Aeronautics & Astronautics.

Crane, Dale. Aviation Maintenance Technician Vol. 2: Systems. 3rd ed. 2008. (Aviation Maintenance Technician Ser.). (ENG.). 492p. 49.95 *(978-1-56027-685-2(1))* Aviation Supplies & Academics, Inc.

—Aviation Maintenance Technician: Powerplant. 3rd ed. 2011. (Aviation Maintenance Technician Ser.). (ENG., Illus.). 800p. 59.95 ***(978-1-56027-862-7(5))*** Aviation Supplies & Academics, Inc.

Crane, Dale. Powerplant Test Guide 2012: The Fast-Track to Study for & Pass the FAA Aviation Maintenance Technician (AMT) Powerplant Knowledge Exam. Michmerhuizen, Terry, ed. 2011. (Fast Track Ser.). (ENG.). 212p. pap. 14.95 *(978-1-56027-857-3(9))* Aviation Supplies & Academics, Inc.

El-Sayed, Ahmed F. Aircraft Propulsion & Gas Turbine Engines. 2008. (ENG., Illus.). 912p. (C). 129.95 *(978-0-8493-9196-5(2)*, CRC Press) Taylor & Francis Group GBR. Dist: Taylor & Francis Group.

Farokhi, Saeed. Aircraft Propulsion. 2008. (ENG., Illus.). 820p. (C). 218.95 *(978-0-470-03906-9(X)*, Wiley) Wiley, John & Sons, Inc.

Greatrix, David R. Powered Flight: The Engineering of Aerospace Propulsion. 2012. (ENG., Illus.). xxii, 519p. 119.00 ***(978-1-4471-2484-9(7)***, 1447124847) Springer.

Gunston, Bill. The Development of Jet & Turbine Aero Engines. 4th ed. 2006. (ENG., Illus.). 272p. per. 22.95 *(978-1-85260-618-3(5)*, 1852606185) Haynes Publishing PLC GBR. Dist: MBI Distribution Services/Quayside Distribution.

—World Encyclopedia of Aero Engines: From the Pioneers to the Present Day. 5th ed. 2006. (ENG., Illus.). 272p. 54.95 *(978-0-7509-4479-3(X))* Sutton Publishing.

International Symposium on Air Breathing Engines, 4th. (Illus.). 444p. 25.00 *(978-1-56347-166-7(3)*, 4-ISABE) American Institute of Aeronautics & Astronautics.

Kroes, Michael J. & Wild, Thomas W. Aircraft: Powerplants. 7th ed. 2007. (ENG.). (C). pap., pap., pap. 124.67 *(978-0-07-723155-2(4)*, 0077231554) McGraw-Hill Higher Education.

Lewis, John D. & Cook, LeRoy. Caravan: Cessna's Swiss Army Knife with Wings. 2008. (ENG., Illus.). 235p. pap. 19.95 *(978-1-56027-682-1(7))* Aviation Supplies & Academics, Inc.

Madden, Ray. Alligators, Freight Trains & near Flying Disasters: How to Fly an Airplane Backwards, & How to Lose over 18 Engines & Live to Retire or Mayday, Ma. 2009. 176p. 22.95 *(978-1-4389-2634-6(0))*; pap. 16.95 *(978-1-4389-2633-9(2))* AuthorHouse.

Michael, Pavelec Sterling. Jet Race & Second World War. 2010. (Illus.). 224p. pap. 19.95 *(978-1-59114-666-7(6))* Naval Institute Pr.

Neal, Robert J. A Technical & Operational History of the Liberty Engine: Tanks, Ships & Aircraft 1917-1960. 2008. 616p. 74.95 *(978-1-58007-149-9(X))* Specialty Pr. Pubs. & Wholesalers, Inc.

Non-fighter Aircraft Staff. Improving the Efficiency of Engines for Large Nonfighter Aircraft. 2007. (ENG., Illus.). 192p. pap. 43.25 *(978-0-309-10399-2(1))* National Academies Pr.

Parker, Christian. The Care & Maintenance of Heavy Jets. 2nd ed. 2009. 204p. pap. 19.95 *(978-0-9815838-3-9(0))* Olympic Dispatch Publishing.

Segal, Corin. The Scramjet Engine: Processes & Characteristics. 2009. (Cambridge Aerospace Ser.). (ENG., Illus.). 270p. 131.00 *(978-0-521-83815-3(0))* Cambridge Univ. Pr.

Seymour, Peter. Wolseley Radial Aero Engines: Lord Nuffield's Venture. 2006. (ENG., Illus.). 192p. pap. 39.95 *(978-0-7524-3915-0(4))* History Pr. Ltd.,The GBR. Dist: Independent Pubs. Group.

Sullivan, Mark P. Dependable Engines: The Story of Pratt & Whitney. 2008. (Illus.). ix, 164p. *(978-1-56347-957-1(5))*; pap. *(978-1-56347-958-8(3))* American Institute of Aeronautics & Astronautics.

Technology Research Editors, ed. Aircraft Engines, 2007 Ed. 2007. pap. 129.50 *(978-1-60030-141-4(X)*, Search-In-Print) CSA Journal Division.

AIRPLANES—NOISE

Attenborough, K., et al. Aircraft Noise Propagation, Exposure & Reduction. 2011. (ENG., Illus.). 432p. (C). 160.00 *(978-0-415-24066-6(2)*, CRC Press) Taylor & Francis Group GBR. Dist: Taylor & Francis Group.

Encyclopaedia Britannica, Inc., compiled by. Aerodynamic Generation of Sound. 2009. 49.00 *(978-1-60835-055-1(X))* Encyclopaedia Britannica, Inc.

Goodman, Jon C., ed. Aviation & the Environment. 2008. (Illus.). x, 515p. 95.00 *(978-1-60692-320-7(X))* Nova Science Pubs., Inc.

Mestre, Vincent. Effects of Aircraft Noise: Research Update on Selected Topics. 2008. (ACRP Synthesis Ser.: Vol. 9). (Illus.). 90p. pap. *(978-0-309-09806-9(8))* Transportation Research Board.

Raman, Ganesh. Jet Aeroacoustics. Raman, Ganesh, ed. 2009. (ENG., Illus.). 570p. pap. 159.95 *(978-0-906522-69-1(2))* Multi Science Publishing Co., Ltd. GBR. Dist: Independent Pubs. Group.

Woodward, Jon M., et al. Aircraft Noise: A Toolkit for Managing Community Expectations. 2009. (Illus.). 151p. pap. ***(978-0-309-11801-9(8))*** Transportation Research Board.

Yu, Chao. An Acoustic Intensity-Based Method in Aeroacoustics. 2009. 128p. pap. *(978-3-639-16564-7(0))* VDM Verlag Dr. Mueller e.K.

AIRPLANES—PERFORMANCE

Diston, Dominic. Computational Modelling of Aircraft & the Environment. 2009. (Illus.). *(978-1-60086-704-0(9))* American Institute of Aeronautics & Astronautics.

Farokhi, Saeed. Aircraft Propulsion. 2008. (ENG., Illus.). 820p. (C). 218.95 *(978-0-470-03906-9(X)*, Wiley) Wiley, John & Sons, Inc.

Gitto, Simone. Measuring the Performance Through Nonparametric Techniques. 2010. 104p. pap. *(978-3-639-24616-2(0))* VDM Verlag Dr. Mueller e.K.

Hitchens, Frank. Range & Endurance: Fuel-Efficient Flying in Light Aircraft. 2007. (ENG., Illus.). 128p. pap. 24.95 *(978-1-86126-920-1(X)*, 186126920X) Crowood Pr., Ltd. GBR. Dist: MBI Distribution Services/Quayside Distribution.

Hurt, H. H. Aerodynamics for Naval Aviators: NAVWEPS 00-8ot-80. 2012. (ENG., Illus.). 432p. pap. 14.95 ***(978-1-61608-439-4(1)***, 608439) Skyhorse Publishing Co., Inc.

McClamroch, N. Harris. Steady Aircraft Flight & Performance. 2011. (ENG., Illus.). 416p. (C). 80.00 *(978-0-691-14719-2(1))* Princeton Univ. Pr.

Saarlas, Maido. Aircraft Performance. 2006. (ENG., Illus.). 296p. 140.00 *(978-0-470-04416-2(0)*, Wiley) Wiley, John & Sons, Inc.

Sadraey, Mohammad. Aircraft Performance. 2009. 476p. pap. *(978-3-639-20013-3(6))* VDM Verlag Dr. Mueller e.K.

Swatton, Peter J. Aircraft Performance: Theory & Practice for Pilots. 2nd ed. 2008. (Aerospace Ser.). (ENG.). 528p. pap. 75.00 *(978-0-470-77313-0(8)*, Wiley-Blackwell) Wiley, John & Sons, Inc.

AIRPLANES—PILOTING

see also Flight Simulators; Flight Training; Instrument Flying; Stunt Flying

Air Force, United States. Convair F-102 Delta Dagger Pilot's Flight Operating Manual. 2007. 450p. pap. 34.95 *(978-1-4303-1046-4(4))* Lulu Enterprises Inc.

—F-111 Aardvark Pilot's Flight Operating Manual. 2007. 298p. pap. 29.95 *(978-1-4303-1212-3(2))* Lulu Enterprises Inc.

—F-86 Sabre Pilot's Flight Operating Manual. 2007. 257p. pap. 24.96 *(978-1-4303-1233-8(5))* Lulu Enterprises Inc.

—Republic F-84 Thunderjet Pilot's Flight Operating Manual. 2007. 427p. pap. 34.94 *(978-1-4303-1044-0(8))* Lulu Enterprises Inc.

ASA Test Prep Board Staff. Private Pilot Test Prep 2012: Study & Prepare for the Recreational & Private: Airplane, Helicopter, Gyroplane, Glider, Balloon, Airship, Powered Parachute, & Weight-Shift Control FAA Knowledge Exams. 2011. (Test Prep Ser.). (ENG.). 380p. pap. 16.95 *(978-1-56027-850-4(1))* Aviation Supplies & Academics, Inc.

ASA Test Prep Board Staff, ed. Certified Flight Instructor Test Prep 2011: Study & Prepare for the Ground, Flight & Sport Instructor: Airplane, Helicopter, Glider, Weight-Shift Control, Powered Parachute, Add-on Ratings, & Fundamentals of Instructing FAA Knowledge Tests. 2010. (Test Prep Ser.). (ENG.). 472p. pap. 21.95 *(978-1-56027-767-5(X))* Aviation Supplies & Academics, Inc.

—Certified Flight Instructor Test Prep 2012: For the Ground, Flight, Military Competency & Sport Instructor: Airplane, Helicopter, Glider, Weight-Shift Control, Powered Parachute, Add-on Ratings, & Fundamentals of Instructing FAA Knowledge Exams. 2011. (Test Prep Ser.). (ENG.). 480p. pap. 21.95 *(978-1-56027-853-5(6))* Aviation Supplies & Academics, Inc.

—Commercial Pilot Test Prep 2012: Study & Prepare for the Commercial Airplane, Helicopter, Gyroplane, Glider, Balloon, Airship & Military Competency FAA Knowledge Exams. 2011. (Test Prep Ser.). (ENG.). 366p. pap. 19.95 *(978-1-56027-852-8(8))* Aviation Supplies & Academics, Inc.

Aviation Supplies & Academics, Inc. Standard Pilot Master Log Book. 2008. (Standard Pilot Logbooks Ser.). (ENG.). 278p. 26.95 *(978-1-56027-727-9(0))* Aviation Supplies & Academics, Inc.

Aviation Supplies and Academics, Inc. Staff. Standard Pilot Log. rev. ed. 2008. (Logbook Ser.). (ENG.). 110p. 12.95 *(978-1-56027-330-1(5)*, ASA-SP-57); 206p. 12.95 *(978-1-56027-329-5(1)*, ASA-SP-40) Aviation Supplies & Academics, Inc.

Aviation Theory Centre, Ltd. The Pilot's Manual: Access to Flight: Integrated Private & Instrument Curriculum. 2009. (Pilot's Manual Ser.). (ENG.). 812p. 74.95 *(978-1-56027-734-7(3))* Aviation Supplies & Academics, Inc.

—The Pilot's Manual: Flight School: How to Fly Your Airplane Through All the FAR/JAR Maneuvers. 2009. (Pilot's Manual Ser.). (ENG.). 670p. 59.95 *(978-1-56027-733-0(5))* Aviation Supplies & Academics, Inc.

Aviation Theory Centre Ltd. Editorial Team. The Pilot's Manual: Instrument Flying: A Step-by-Step Course Covering All Knowledge Necessary to Pass the FAA Instrument Written & Oral Exams, & the IFR Flight Check. 2010. (Pilot's Manual Ser.) (ENG., Illus.). 696p. 59.95 *(978-1-56027-790-3(4))* Aviation Supplies & Academics, Inc.

Aviation Theory Centre Ltd., Staff, ed. The Pilot's Manual: Ground School: All the Aeronautical Knowledge Required to Pass the FAA Exams & Operate as a Private & Commercial Pilot. 3rd ed. 2007. (Pilot's Manual Ser.). (ENG., Illus.). 688p. 59.95 *(978-1-56027-677-7(0))* Aviation Supplies & Academics, Inc.

Ball, James. So, You Want to Be a Pilot, Eh? A Guidebook for Canadian Pilot Training. 2007. *(978-0-9781309-1-6(X))* Writing on Stone Pr., Inc.

Birch, Jane Gardner. They Flew Proud: The Small Town & Airport Training of Cadets & Civilians During World War II. 2007. (Illus.). 190p. 35.00 *(978-1-933858-25-8(7))* Evangel Author Services.

Blackman, Tony. Flight Testing to Win. 2007. 336p. per. *(978-0-9553856-4-3(4))* Blackman Assocs.

Bowen, Thomas. Backcountry Pilot: Flying Adventures with Ike Russell. 2010. (Southwest Center Ser.). (ENG., Illus.). 248p. pap. 19.95 *(978-0-8165-2938-4(8))* Univ. of Arizona Pr.

Bristow, Gary. Ace the Technical Pilot Interview 2/E. 2nd ed. 2012. (ENG., Illus.). 368p. (C). pap. 30.00 ***(978-0-07-179386-5(0)***, 0071793860) McGraw-Hill Professional Publishing.

Burger, Chris. Cockpit Procedures: Effective Routines for Pilots & Virtual Aviators. 2008. (ENG.). 170p. pap. 19.95 *(978-1-56027-721-7(1))* Aviation Supplies & Academics, Inc.

Cook, Andrew. To Be an Airline Pilot. 2007. (ENG., Illus.). 160p. pap. 22.95 *(978-1-86126-865-5(3)*, 1861268653) Crowood Pr., Ltd. GBR. Dist: MBI Distribution Services/Quayside Distribution.

Department Of The Army, Headquarters. Uh-1 Iroquois Pilot's Flight Operating Instructions. 2011. 454p. pap. 39.95 ***(978-1-935700-65-4(0))*** Periscope Film, LLC.

Edwards, Carey. Airmanship. 2008. (ENG., Illus.). 96p. pap. 19.95 *(978-1-86126-980-5(3)*, 1861269803) Crowood Pr., Ltd. GBR. Dist: MBI Distribution Services/Quayside Distribution.

Eichenberger, Jerry. Your pilots License 8/e. 8th ed. 2011. (ENG., Illus.). 320p. (C). pap. 25.00 ***(978-0-07-176382-0(1)***, 0071763821) McGraw-Hill Professional Publishing.

Federal Aviation Administration. Airplane Flying Handbook (FAA-H-8083-3A) 2nd ed. 2011. (ENG., Illus.). 288p. pap. 16.95 *(978-1-61608-338-0(7)*, 608338) Skyhorse Publishing Co., Inc.

—Aviation Instructor's Handbook: Faa-h-8083-9a. 2009. (FAA Handbooks Ser.). (ENG.). 226p. pap. 19.95 *(978-1-56027-749-1(1))* Aviation Supplies & Academics, Inc.

—Federal Aviation Regulations/Aeronautical Information Manual 2009 (FAR/AIM 2009) 2008. (ENG., Illus.). 948p. pap. 12.95 *(978-1-60239-298-4(6)*, 239298) Skyhorse Publishing Co., Inc.

—Flight Instructor Instrument for Airplane & Helicopter Practical Test Standards: Faa-s-8081-9c. 2007. (Practical Test Standards Ser.). (ENG.). 62p. pap. 5.95 *(978-1-56027-675-3(4))* Aviation Supplies & Academics, Inc.

—Pilot's Handbook of Aeronautical Knowledge. 2009. (ENG., Illus.). 368p. pap. 24.95 *(978-1-60239-780-4(5)*, 239780) Skyhorse Publishing Co., Inc.

—Seaplane, Skiplane, & Float/Ski Equipped Helicopter Operations Handbook (FAA-H-8083-23-1) 2011. (ENG., Illus.). 96p. 12.95 *(978-1-61608-202-4(X)*, 608202) Skyhorse Publishing Co., Inc.

—Sport Pilot Practical Test Standards for Airplane, Weight-Shift Control, Powered Parachute, & Flight Instructor: FAA-S-8081-29 And 31. 2008. (Practical Test Standards Ser.). (ENG.). 196p. pap. 9.95 *(978-1-56027-725-5(4))* Aviation Supplies & Academics, Inc.

Federal Aviation Administration (U.S.), compiled by. Airline Transport Pilot & Aircraft Type Rating: Practical Test Standards for Airplane 2008. rev. ed. 2009. (ENG.). 90p. pap. 9.50 *(978-0-16-082215-5(7)*, Federal Aviation Administration) United States Government Printing Office.

Federal Aviation Administration Staff. Federal Aviation Regulations / Aeronautical Information Manual 2011 (FAR/AIM) 2010. (ENG., Illus.). 896p. pap. 15.95 *(978-1-61608-148-5(1)*, 608148) Skyhorse Publishing Co., Inc.

—Flight Instructor for Airplane Multi-Engine Land & Sea: FAA-S-8081-6cm November 2006. 2007. (Practical Test Standards Ser.). (ENG.). 100p. pap. 5.95 *(978-1-56027-673-9(8))* Aviation Supplies & Academics, Inc.

Federal Aviation Administration Staff & Federal Aviation Administration. Airline Transport Pilot & Type Rating Practical Test Standards: For Airplane FAA-S-8081-5F. 2009. (Practical Test Standards Ser.). (ENG.). 95p. pap. 5.95 *(978-1-56027-729-3(7))* Aviation Supplies & Academics, Inc.

The Federal Aviation Administration's Call to Action on Airline Safety & Pilot Training: Hearing Before the Subcommittee on Aviation of the Committee on Transportation & Infrastructure, House of Representatives, One Hundred Eleventh Congress, First Session, September 23, 2009. 2009. xviii, 192p. *(978-0-16-085163-6(7)*, 552-070-40517-8) United States Government Printing Office.

Film.com, Periscope. B-17 Bomber Pilot's Flight Operating Manual. 2007. 175p. pap. 24.95 *(978-1-4116-8725-7(6))* Lulu Enterprises Inc.

—F-4 Phantom Pilot's Flight Operating Manual. 2007. 595p. pap. 44.95 *(978-1-4303-1530-8(X))* Lulu Enterprises Inc.

—P-47 Thunderbolt Pilot's Flight Operating Manual. 2007. 57p. pap. 19.96 *(978-1-4303-1750-0(7))* Lulu Enterprises Inc.

Film.Com, Periscope. Vought f4u-4 Corsair Fighter Pilot's Fli. 2007. 74p. pap. 19.96 *(978-1-4116-8960-2(7))* Lulu Enterprises Inc.

Gardner, Bob. The Complete Advanced Pilot: A Combined Commercial & Instrument Course. 4th ed. 2008. (Complete Pilot Ser.). (ENG., Illus.). 480p. pap. 29.95 *(978-1-56027-718-7(1))* Aviation Supplies & Academics, Inc.

—The Complete Multi-Engine Pilot. 3rd ed. 2009. (Complete Pilot Ser.). (ENG.). 202p. pap. 24.95 *(978-1-56027-732-3(7))* Aviation Supplies & Academics, Inc.

Goyer, Robert, ed. I Learned about Flying from That, Volume 4: First-Hand Accounts of Mishaps to Avoid from Real-Life Pilots. 2007. (I Learned about Flying from That Ser.). (ENG., Illus.). 272p. 18.95 *(978-1-933231-24-2(6))* Filipacchi Publishingsan.

Grim, J. Norman. To Fly the Gentle Giants: The Training of U. S. WW II Glider Pilots. 2009. 340p. 29.95 *(978-1-4389-0484-9(3))*; pap. 19.95 *(978-1-4389-0483-2(5))* AuthorHouse.

Hamilton, Paul. Sport Pilot Checkride: A Guide to Passing the FAA Practical Flight & Oral Exam. 2008. (Freedom to Fly Ser.). (ENG.). 250p. pap. 24.95 *(978-1-56027-726-2(2))* Aviation Supplies & Academics, Inc.

Hayes, Michael D. Airline Transport Pilot Oral Exam Guide: The Comprehensive Guide to Prepare You for the FAA Checkride. 2nd ed. 2011. (Oral Exam Guide Ser.). (ENG.). 220p. pap. 12.95 *(978-1-56027-863-4(3))* Aviation Supplies & Academics, Inc.

Hitchens, Frank. Range & Endurance: Fuel-Efficient Flying in Light Aircraft. 2007. (ENG., Illus.). 128p. pap. 24.95 *(978-1-86126-920-1(X)*, 186126920X) Crowood Pr., Ltd. GBR. Dist: MBI Distribution Services/Quayside Distribution.

Hoy, David. Instrument Flying. 2007. (ENG., Illus.). 256p. pap. 34.95 *(978-1-86126-749-8(5)*, 1861267495) Crowood Pr., Ltd. GBR. Dist: MBI Distribution Services/Quayside Distribution.

The Hudson River Airspace & Management of Uncontrolled Airspace Corridors: Hearing Before the Subcommittee on Aviation of the Committee on Transportation & Infrastructure, House of Representatives, One Hundred Eleventh Congress, First Session, September 16, 2009. 2009. (Illus.). xvi, 175p. *(978-0-16-084739-4(7)*, 552-070-40216-1) United States Government Printing Office.

Hurt, H. H. Aerodynamics for Naval Aviators: NAVWEPS 00-8ot-80. 2012. (ENG., Illus.). 432p. pap. 14.95 ***(978-1-61608-439-4(1)***, 608439) Skyhorse Publishing Co., Inc.

Internet Spyware (I-SPY) Prevention ACT of 2007, & the Securing Aircraft Cockpits Against Lasers ACT of 2007: Hearing Before the Subcommittee on Crime, Terrorism, & Homeland Security of the Committee on the Judiciary, House of Representatives, One Hundred Tenth Congress, First Session, on H.R. 1525 & H.R. 1615, May 1, 2007. 2008. iii, 32p. *(978-0-16-081704-5(8)*, 552-070-37928-2) United States Government Printing Office.

Jordanoff, Assen. Flying & How to Do It! 2011. 112p. 39.95 ***(978-1-258-08266-6(7))*** Literary Licensing, LLC.

Kanki, Barbara G., et al, eds. Crew Resource Management. 2nd ed. 2010. (ENG., Illus.). 528p. pap. 103.00 *(978-0-12-374946-8(8)*, Academic Pr.) Elsevier Science & Technology Bks.

Kearns, Suzanne. E-Learning in Aviation. 2010. (Ashgate Studies in Human Factors for Flight Operations Ser.). (Illus.). 194p. 99.95 *(978-0-7546-7879-3(2))* Ashgate Publishing Co.

Kershner, William K. Student Pilot's Flight Manual: From First Flight to Private Certificate. 10th ed. 2010. (Flight Manuals Ser.). (ENG., Illus.). 450p. pap. 24.95 *(978-1-56027-719-4(X))* Aviation Supplies & Academics, Inc.

Kudimi, Eric. Essentials of a Successful Flight Instructor Certification Renewal Program: Flight Instructor Refresher Training Course (FIRC) Sharp, Karen, ed. 2008. (Illus.). 339p. ring bd. *(978-1-935657-39-2(9))* M K Conquest International Pr.

Lowery, John. Professional Pilot: Proven Tactics & PIC Strategies. 3rd ed. 2008. (ENG.). 350p. pap. 34.95 *(978-1-56027-709-5(2))* Aviation Supplies & Academics, Inc.

Machado, Rod. Rod Machado's Private Pilot Handbook: Learn Everything You Need for Private Pilot Exam & Reviews. Titterington, Diane & Weiss, Brian L., eds. 2nd exp. ed. 2008. (ENG., Illus.). 624p. lib. bdg. 64.95 *(978-0-9631229-9-5(1))* Aviation Speakers Bureau, The.

Mariner, Liz. Cleared for Takeoff: English for Pilots, 2 bks. 2007. (Illus.). Bk. 1. 175p. per., wbk. ed. 48.95 incl. audio compact disk *(978-0-9795068-0-2(8))*Bk. 1 and 2. (ENG., 342p. per. 74.95 incl. audio compact disk *(978-0-9795068-2-6(4))*Bk. 2. (ENG., 167p. per. 48.95 incl. audio compact disk *(978-0-9795068-1-9(6))* A-E-Link Pubns., Ltd.

McMahon, Arlynn. Train Like You Fly: A Flight Instructor's Guide to Scenario-Based Training. 2008. (ENG., Illus.). 235p. pap. 19.95 *(978-1-56027-707-1(6))* Aviation Supplies & Academics, Inc.

Naidoo, Preven. Airline Pilots' Perceptions of Advanced Flight Deck Automation. 2010. 160p. pap. *(978-3-8383-3995-5(9))* Lambert Academic Publishing.

Navy, United States. Douglas SBD Dauntless Dive Bomber Pilot's Flight Manual. 2007. 81p. pap. 19.95 *(978-1-4303-1749-4(3))* Lulu Enterprises Inc.

—PBY Catalina Flying Boat Pilot's Flight Operating Manual. 2007. 114p. pap. 19.95 *(978-1-4303-2160-6(1))* Lulu Enterprises Inc.

—Vought F-8U Crusader Pilot's Flight Operating Manual. 2007. 276p. pap. 29.96 *(978-1-4303-1207-9(6))* Lulu Enterprises Inc.

Olsen, W. Scott. Hard Air: Adventures from the Edge of Flying. 2008. (ENG., Illus.). 246p. pap. 19.95 *(978-0-8032-1144-5(9)*, Bison Bks.) Univ. of Nebraska Pr.

Phillips, Peter & Cole, Robert. The Flying Instructor's Patter Manual: A Word for Word Account of All the Flying Exercises As Spoken in the Air. 2nd ed. 2007. (ENG., Illus.). 304p. per. 34.95 *(978-1-86126-840-2(8)*, 1861268408) Crowood Pr., Ltd. GBR. Dist: MBI Distribution Services/Quayside Distribution.

Regional Air Carriers & Pilot Workforce Issues: Hearing Before the Subcommittee on Aviation of the Committee on Transportation & Infrastructure, House of Representatives, One Hundred Eleventh Congress, First Session, June 11, 2009. 2009. (Illus.). xxiii, 219p. *(978-0-16-084406-5(1)*, 552-070-39948-8) United States Government Printing Office.

Rhodes, Suzanne. Angel Flight Mid-Atlantic. 2008. (Images of Aviation Ser.). (ENG., Illus.). 128p. per. 19.99 *(978-0-7385-5296-5(8))* Arcadia Publishing.

Rossoni, Philip. Build & Pilot Your Own Walkalong Gliders. 2012. (Build Your Own Ser.). (ENG., Illus.). 224p. pap. 20.00 ***(978-0-07-179055-0(1)***, 0071790551, TAB/Electronics) McGraw-Hill Professional Publishing.

Salas, Eduardo, et al, eds. Crew Resource Management: Critical Essays. 2009. (Critical Essays on Human Factors in Aviation Ser.). (Illus.). 448p. 250.00 *(978-0-7546-2829-3(9))* Ashgate Publishing Co.

Shannon, Jack. The 58P. 2008. 91p. pap. 32.50 *(978-0-557-00015-9(7))* Lulu Enterprises Inc.

Shawcross, Philip. Flightpath Student's Book: Aviation English for Pilots & ATCOs. 2011. (ENG.). 192p. pap., stu. ed. 46.00 incl. DVD, audio compact disk *(978-0-521-17871-6(1))* Cambridge Univ. Pr.

Shawcross, Philip & Day, Jeremy. Flightpath Teacher's Book: Aviation English for Pilots & ATCOs. 2011. (ENG.). 224p. pap., tchr. ed. 50.00 *(978-0-521-17870-9(3))* Cambridge Univ. Pr.

Smith, Darren. General Aviation Human Factors. 2010. (Illus.). 125p. spiral bd. 14.95 *(978-0-9823940-9-0(8))* Smith, Darren.

—Visi-Plotter: Simply the Best Flight Planning Plotter Made. 2010. 14.95 *(978-0-9823940-5-2(5))* Smith, Darren.

Smith, John R. Aircraft Performance Explanation for Takeoff from a High Altitude Airport: Takeoff distance, velocity & time are presented as a function of aircraft weight, & provide a practical basis for other reliable information. 2008. 112p. pap. *(978-3-8364-8343-8(2))* VDM Verlag Dr. Mueller e.K.

Spanitz, Jackie. Guide to the Flight Review: Complete Preparation for Issuing or Taking a Flight Review. 2010. (Oral Exam Guide Ser.). (ENG.). 148p. pap. 12.95 *(978-1-56027-778-1(5))* Aviation Supplies & Academics, Inc.

Stewart, Stanley. Flying the Big Jets. 4th ed. 2010. (ENG., Illus.). 292p. pap. 34.95 ***(978-1-84037-422-3(5)***, 1840374225) Crowood/Airlife Publishing Ltd.

Swatton, Peter J. Principles of Flight for Pilots. 2010. (Aerospace Ser.). (ENG., Illus.). 506p. pap. 85.00 *(978-0-470-71073-9(X)*, Wiley) Wiley, John & Sons, Inc.

Terry, Bobby K. Pilots: A Special Breed. 2009. 324p. 29.99 *(978-1-4415-3786-7(4))*; pap. 19.99 *(978-1-4415-3785-0(6))* Xlibris Corp.

Treaty Organization (NATO), North Atlantic. Mikoyan Mig-29 Fulcrum Pilot's Flight Operating Manual (in English) 2007. 496p. pap. 49.95 *(978-1-4303-1349-6(8))* Lulu Enterprises Inc.

Tsourdos, Antonios. Cooperative Path Planning of Unmanned Aerial Vehicles. 2nd ed. 2011. 448p. 120.00 ***(978-1-60086-779-8(0))*** Wiley, John & Sons, Inc.

Vogel, Gib. Flying the Airbus A380. 2009. (ENG., Illus.). 128p. pap. 22.95 *(978-1-84797-124-1(5)*, 1847971245) Crowood Pr., Ltd. GBR. Dist: MBI Distribution Services/Quayside Distribution.

Whitlock, Flint & Barnhart, Terry L. Capt. Jepp & the Little Black Book: How Barnstormer & Aviation Pioneer Elroy B. Jeppeson Made the Skies Safer for Everyone. 2007. (Illus.). 209p. *(978-1-886028-83-8(4))* Savage Pr.

Williams, Bruce P. Scenario-Based Training with X-Plane & Microsoft Flight Simulator: Using PC-Based Flight Simulations Based on FAA & Industry Training Standards. 2012. (ENG.). 624p. pap. 39.99 ***(978-1-118-10502-3(8)***, Wiley) Wiley, John & Sons, Inc.

AIRPLANES—PILOTS

see Air Pilots; Fighter Pilots

AIRPLANES—PROPELLERS

see Propellers, Aerial

AIRPLANES—RACING

see Airplane Racing

AIRPLANES—RADAR EQUIPMENT

Webb, William. My Art Is Where the Ohm Is. 2009. (Illus.). 424p. pap. 97.99 *(978-1-4389-4397-8(0))* AuthorHouse.

AIRPLANES—RECOGNITION

Gething, Michael J. & Endres, Gunter. Jane's Aircraft Recognition Guide. 5th ed. 2007. (Jane's Aircraft Recognition Guide Ser.). (Illus.). 528p. pap. 24.99 *(978-0-06-134619-4(5)*, Harper Paperbacks) HarperCollins Pubs.

Gray, Warren. Mountain Wolf. 2011. 336p. pap. 29.95 ***(978-1-4626-1936-8(3))*** PublishAmerica, Inc.

Mahr, Malcolm D. Murder at the Paradise Sp. 2009. 226p. pap. 14.95 *(978-0-9825086-3-3(8))* Fiction Publishing, Inc.

Newdick, Thomas. Carrier Aircraft: 1917-Present. 2011. (Essential Aircraft Identification Guide Ser.). (Illus.). 192p. 34.95 ***(978-1-907446-97-9(4))*** Amber Bks. GBR. Dist: Casemate Pubs & Bk. Distributors, LLC.

AIRPLANES—SAFETY MEASURES

see Aeronautics—Safety Measures

AIRPLANES—STABILITY

see Stability of Airplanes

AIRPLANES—STRESSES

see Airframes

AIRPLANES—STRUCTURES

see Airframes

AIRPLANES—TURBOJET ENGINES

Air Force, United States & NASA. F-104 Starfighter Pilot's Flight Operating Instructions. 2011. 292p. pap. 28.95 ***(978-1-935700-47-0(2))*** Periscope Film, LLC.

Aircraft Propulsion & Gas Turbine Engines. 2011. (C). 124.95 ***(978-1-4200-0877-7(3)***, CRC Press) Taylor & Francis Group GBR. Dist: Taylor & Francis Group.

Dow, Andrew. Pegasus: The Heart of the Harrier - The History & Development of the World's First Operational Vertical Take-off & Landing Jet Engine. 2009. (Illus.). 528p. 60.00 *(978-1-84884-042-3(X))* Pen & Sword Bks. Ltd. GBR. Dist: Casemate Pubs. & Bk. Distributors, LLC.

El-Sayed, Ahmed F. Aircraft Propulsion & Gas Turbine Engines. 2008. (ENG., Illus.). 912p. (C). 129.95 *(978-0-8493-9196-5(2)*, CRC Press) Taylor & Francis Group GBR. Dist: Taylor & Francis Group.

Ginevsky, A. S., et al. Acoustic Control of Turbulent Jets. 2010. (Foundations of Engineering Mechanics Ser.). (ENG., Illus.). xiv, 232p. pap. 169.00 *(978-3-642-05764-9(0)*, 3642057640) Springer.

Gunston, Bill. The Development of Jet & Turbine Aero Engines. 4th ed. 2006. (ENG., Illus.). 272p. per. 22.95 *(978-1-85260-618-3(5)*, 1852606185) Haynes Publishing PLC GBR. Dist: MBI Distribution Services/Quayside Distribution.

Jaw, Link C. & Mattingly, Jack D. Aircraft Engine Controls: Design, System Analysis, & Health Monitoring. 2009. (Illus.). 300p. *(978-1-60086-705-7(7))* American Institute of Aeronautics & Astronautics.

Kay, Antony L. Turbojet - History & Development, 1930-1960: Great Britain & Germany, 2 vols., Vol. 1. 2007. (ENG., Illus.). 240p. 69.95 *(978-1-86126-912-6(9)*, 1861269129) Crowood Pr., Ltd. GBR. Dist: MBI Distribution Services/Quayside Distribution.

Kulikov, Gennady G. & Thompson, Haydn A., eds. Dynamic Modelling of Gas Turbines: Identification, Simulation, Condition Monitoring & Optimal Control. 2010. (Advances in Industrial Control Ser.). (Illus.). xxvi, 309p. pap. 179.00 *(978-1-84996-914-7(0)*, 1849969140) Springer.

Lacor, Chris & Geurts, Bernard, eds. Les and DNS of Ignition Process & Complex Structure Flames with Local Extinction. 2010. (AIP Conference Proceedings / Mathematical & Statistical Physics Ser.). (Illus.). 158p. pap. 99.00 *(978-0-7354-0726-8(6)*, 0735407266, AIP Pr.) Springer.

Langton, Roy & MacIsaac, Bernie. Gas Turbine Propulsion Systems. 2011. (Aerospace Ser.). (ENG., Illus.). 348p. 125.00 *(978-0-470-06563-1(X)*, Wiley) Wiley, John & Sons, Inc.

Linke-Diesinger, Andreas. Systems of Commercial Turbofan Engines: An Introduction to Systems Functions. 2008. (ENG., Illus.). xvi, 236p. 159.00 *(978-3-540-73618-9(2)*, 3540736182) Springer.

Organ, Allan J., ed. The Air Engine: Stirling Cycle Power for a Sustainable Future. 2007. (Illus.). 276p. 289.95 *(978-1-4200-6672-2(2))* CRC Pr. LLC.

Richter, Hanz. Advanced Control of Turbofan Engines. 2011. (ENG., Illus.). xv, 266p. 139.00 ***(978-1-4614-1170-3(X)***, 146141170X) Springer.

Sullivan, Mark P. Dependable Engines: The Story of Pratt & Whitney. 2008. (Illus.). ix, 164p. *(978-1-56347-957-1(5))*; pap. *(978-1-56347-958-8(3))* American Institute of Aeronautics & Astronautics.

Walpole, Nigel. Best of Breed: The Hawker Hunter FR10. 2006. (Illus.). 215p. 50.00 *(978-1-84415-412-8(2))* Pen & Sword Bks. Ltd. GBR. Dist: Casemate Pubs. & Bk. Distributors, LLC.

AIRPLANES—VIBRATION

see Vibration (Aeronautics)

AIRPLANES—WINGS

Committee on Assessment of Aircraft Winglets for Large Aircraft Fuel Efficiency & National Research Council. Assessment of Wingtip Modifications to Increase the Fuel Efficiency of Air Force Aircraft. 2007. (ENG.). 112p. pap. 29.75 *(978-0-309-10497-5(1))* National Academies Pr.

Lockett, Brian. Flying Aircraft Carriers of the USAF: Wing Tip Coupling. 2009. 100p. pap. 21.95 *(978-0-578-03186-6(8))* Lockett, Brian.

Pope, Alan. Basic Wing & Airfoil Theory. 2009. (Dover Books on Aeronautical Engineering Ser.). (ENG.). 320p. pap. 14.95 *(978-0-486-47188-4(8))* Dover Pubns., Inc.

Valasek, John, ed. Morphing Aerospace Vehicles & Structures. 2nd ed. 2012. (Aerospace Ser.). (ENG., Illus.). 310p. 135.00 ***(978-0-470-97286-1(6)***, Wiley) Wiley, John & Sons, Inc.

Yebi, Adamu & Bazezew (), Alem. Vibration Analysis of Cracked Composite Aircraft Wing Modeled As Shell. 2010. 120p. pap. *(978-3-639-26692-4(7))* VDM Verlag Dr. Mueller e.K.

AIRPLANES, COMPANY

Castro, Raoul. Corporate Aviation Management. 2011. (Illus.). 352p. pap. 25.00 *(978-0-8093-3039-3(3))*; E-Book 25.00 *(978-0-8093-8786-1(7))* Southern Illinois Univ. Pr.

AIRPLANES, JET PROPELLED
see Airplanes—Jet Propulsion; Jet Planes

AIRPLANES, MILITARY
see also Air Warfare; Bombers; Fighter Planes; Hercules (Turboprop Transports); Jet Planes, Military; Stealth Aircraft; Training Planes

Air Force & Army Airlift & Aerial Refueling Fixed-Wing Aircraft Programs: Hearing Before the Air & Land Forces Subcommittee of the Committee on Armed Services, House of Representatives, One Hundred Tenth Congress, First Session, Hearing Held, March 7, 2007. 2008. (Illus.). iv, 165p. *(978-0-16-081373-3(5)*, 552-070-37751-4) United States Government Printing Office.

Air Force, United States. Douglas X-3 Stiletto Pilot's Flight Operating Instructions. 2007. 84p. per. 19.96 *(978-1-4303-0828-7(1))* Lulu Enterprises Inc.

Aloni, Shlomo. Israeli F-15 Eagle Units in Combat. 2006. (Combat Aircraft Ser.: Vol. 67). (ENG., Illus.). 96p. pap. 22.95 *(978-1-84603-047-5(1))* Osprey Publishing, Ltd. GBR. Dist: Random Hse., Inc.

Angelucci, Enzo & Matricardi, Paolo. Complete Book of World War II Combat Aircraft. 2008. (Illus.). 414p. *(978-88-544-0188-4(9))* White Star.

—Complete Book of World War II Combat Aircraft. 2007. (Illus.). 414p. 29.99 *(978-88-540-0829-8(X))* White Star ITA. Dist: Book Sales, Inc.

—Complete Book of World War II Combat Aircraft: With Full-Color Illustrations of Every Fighting Plane from 1933-1945, Including Bombers, Fighters, Assault Aircraft, & Many More. (Illus.). viii, 414p. *(978-88-8095-688-4(4))* White Star Publishers, Inc.

Annett, Roger. Lifeline in Helmland: RAF Front-Line Air Supply in Afghanistan: 1310 Flight in Action. 2010. (Illus.). 288p. 50.00 *(978-1-84884-274-8(0))* Pen & Sword Bks. Ltd. GBR. Dist: Casemate Pubs. & Bk. Distributors, LLC.

Arena, Mark V. & Younossi, Obaid. Why Has the Cost of Fixed-Wing Aircraft Risen? A Macroscopic Examination of the Trends in U. S. Military Aircraft Costs over the Past Several Decades. 2008. (Illus.). 116p. pap. 31.50 *(978-0-8330-4312-2(9)*, mg-696) RAND Corp., The.

Army Air Force, United States. North American B-25 Mitchell Bomber Pilot's Flight Operating Manual. 2007. 183p. pap. 24.96 *(978-1-4303-2198-9(9))* Lulu Enterprises Inc.

Army & Marine Corps Reset Strategies for Ground Equipment & Rotorcraft: Hearing Before the Committee on Armed Services, House of Representatives, One Hundred Ninth Congress, Second Session, Hearing Held, June 27, 2006. 2007. (Illus.). iii, 67p. *(978-0-16-079480-3(3)*, 552-070-36473-1) United States Government Printing Office.

Balzer, Gerald. American Secret Pusher Fighters of World War II: XP-54, XP-55, & XP-56. 2008. (Illus.). 385p. 42.95 *(978-1-58007-125-3(2))* Specialty Pr. Pubs. & Wholesalers, Inc.

Bassford, Matt, et al. Sustaining Key Skills in the UK Military Aircraft Industry, 1 vol. 2010. 168p. pap. 27.00 *(978-0-8330-5041-0(9)*, mg-1023) RAND Corp., The.

Beaumont, Herve. Mirage 2000N. 2011. (Matériel de l'armée de l'air Ser.). (FRE.). 112p. pap. 27.95 ***(978-2-35250-208-1(X))*** Histoire et Collections FRA. Dist: Casemate Pubs. & Bk. Distributors, LLC.

Belcarz, Bart?omiej. Camouflage & Decals No. 1: Caudron Cr. 714, MS 406, Hawk H75A. 2010. (Camouflage & Decals Ser.). (Illus.). 16p. pap. 23.00 *(978-83-61421-22-1(X))* Stratus, Wydawnictwo, Juszczak, Artur POL. Dist: Casemate Pubs. & Bk. Distributors, LLC.

Belcarz, Bartomiej. Camouflage & Decals. 2010. (Illus.). 16p. pap. 20.00 *(978-83-61421-31-3(9))* Stratus, Wydawnictwo, Juszczak, Artur POL. Dist: Casemate Pubs. & Bk. Distributors, LLC.

Birkler, John, et al. Keeping a Competitive U. S. Military Aircraft Industry Aloft: Findings from an Analysis of the Industrial Base. 2012. (ENG.). 142p. pap. 32.50 ***(978-0-8330-5864-5(9))*** RAND Corp., The.

Bowen, Paul, photos by. Air to Air. 2007. (Illus.). 224p. *(978-0-9665095-8-8(7))* North Shore Pr.

Bowers, Peter M. America's Outstanding Aircraft of World War II: Plus Odd Aircraft. 2011. 70p. 36.95 ***(978-1-258-06479-2(0))*** Literary Licensing, LLC.

Bowman, Martin. The Men Who Flew the Mosquito: Compelling Account of the 'Wooden Wonders' Triumphant WW2 Career. 2009. (Illus.). 240p. pap. 25.99 *(978-1-84415-891-1(8))* Pen & Sword Bks. Ltd. GBR. Dist: Casemate Pubs. & Bk. Distributors, LLC.

—Mosquito: Menacing the Reich. 2009. (Illus.). 320p. 50.00 *(978-1-84415-823-2(3))* Pen & Sword Bks. Ltd. GBR. Dist: Casemate Pubs. & Bk. Distributors, LLC.

Bowman, Martin W. Mosquito Mayhem: De Havilland's Wooden Wonder in Action in WWII. 2011. (Illus.). 280p. 50.00 *(978-1-84884-323-3(2))* Pen & Sword Bks. Ltd. GBR. Dist: Casemate Pubs. & Bk. Distributors, LLC.

Bowman, Martin W. The Mosquito Story. 2012. (Story Ser.). (ENG., Illus.). 128p. 14.95 ***(978-0-7524-6192-2(3))*** History Pr. Ltd.,The GBR. Dist: Independent Pubs. Group.

Boyne, Walter. Pushing the Limits. Date not set. 27.50 *(978-0-06-019455-0(3))* HarperCollins Pubs.

Breffort, Dominique. Boeing 707 Kc-135: And Their Derivatives, from Dash 80 to the E-8 J-Stars. 2008. 212p. 49.95 *(978-2-35250-075-9(3))* Histoire et Collections FRA. Dist: Casemate Pubs. & Bk. Distributors, LLC.

Breffort, Dominique & Breffort, André. French Aircraft 1939-1942. 2011. (Illus.). 160p. pap. 39.95 ***(978-2-35250-197-8(0))*** Histoire et Collections FRA. Dist: Casemate Pubs. & Bk. Distributors, LLC.

Brown, Eric. Wings of the Luftwaffe. 2010. (Illus.). 272p. *(978-1-902109-15-2(5))* Hikoki Pubns.

Butler, Phil. War Prizes: The Album. 2010. (ENG., Illus.). 127p. pap. 34.95 *(978-1-85780-244-3(6))* Allan, Ian Publishing GBR. Dist: BookMasters Distribution Services (BDS).

Buttler, Tony. American Secret Projects: Fighters & Interceptors, 1945-1978. 2010. (ENG., Illus.). 240p. 44.95 *(978-1-85780-264-1(0))* Allan, Ian Publishing GBR. Dist: BookMasters Distribution Services (BDS).

Castle, Ian. The Zeppelin Base Raids - Germany 1914. 2011. (Raid Ser.). (ENG., Illus.). 64p. pap. 18.95 *(978-1-84908-243-3(X))* Osprey Publishing, Ltd. GBR. Dist: Random Hse., Inc.

Cea, Eduardo. Aircraft of the Imperial Japanese Army: Land-Based Aviation, 1929-1945 II. (Illus.). 136p. pap. 30.00 *(978-84-96935-24-2(8))* Alcaniz y Fresnos, S.A. ESP. Dist: Casemate Pubs. & Bk. Distributors, LLC.

—Japanese Military Aircraft: Aircraft of the Imperial Japanese Navy. Land-Based Aviation, 1929-1945 (I) Nº4. 2009. (Air Collection Ser.). (Illus.). 104p. pap. 29.00 *(978-84-96935-10-5(8))* Quiron Ediciones ESP. Dist: Casemate Pubs. & Bk. Distributors, LLC.

—Japanese Military Aircraft: Special Attacj Units - Tokubetsu Kogeki Tai. 2011. (Illus.). 195p. pap. 49.00 ***(978-84-96935-37-2(X))*** Quiron Ediciones ESP. Dist: Casemate Pubs. & Bk. Distributors, LLC.

—Japanese Military Aircraft: Special Units of the Imperial Army. 2011. (Illus.). 135p. pap. 42.95 ***(978-84-96935-36-5(1))*** Quiron Ediciones ESP. Dist: Casemate Pubs. & Bk. Distributors, LLC.

Chenoweth, Mary E., et al. Best Practices in Developing Proactive Supply Strategies for Air Force Low-Demand Service Parts. 2010. (ENG.). 106p. pap. 23.00 *(978-0-8330-4878-3(3)*, mg858) RAND Corp., The.

Chorley, W. R. Royal Air Force Bomber Command Losses Vol. 9: Roll of Honour, 1939-1947. 2010. (ENG., Illus.). 494p. pap. 36.95 *(978-1-85780-195-8(4))* Allan, Ian Publishing GBR. Dist: BookMasters Distribution Services (BDS).

Clarke, Bob. Jet Provost: The Little Plane with the Big History. 2009. (Illus.). 208p. 34.95 *(978-1-84868-097-5(X))* Amberley Publishing GBR. Dist: Casemate Pubs. & Bk. Distributors, LLC.

Closing the Gap: Addressing Critical Rotary Wing Shortfalls for U.S. Special Operations Forces in Fiscal Year 2011 & Beyond: Hearing Before the Subcommittee on Terrorism, Unconventional Threats, & Capabilities of the Committee on Armed Services, House of Representatives, One Hundred Eleventh Congress, Second Session, Hearing Held April 27, 2010. 2010. iii, 54p. ***(978-0-16-087385-0(1)***, 552-070-42078-9) United States Government Printing Office.

Cole, Robert E., ed. The Incident That Could Have Killed Pittsburgh. 2008. (Illus.). 245p. pap. 19.95 *(978-1-55856-495-4(0))* Closson Pr.

Committee on Assessment of Aircraft Winglets for Large Aircraft Fuel Efficiency & National Research Council. Assessment of Wingtip Modifications to Increase the Fuel Efficiency of Air Force Aircraft. 2007. (ENG.). 112p. pap. 29.75 *(978-0-309-10497-5(1))* National Academies Pr.

Cotter, Jarrod. The Battle of Britain Memorial Flight: 50 Years of Flying. 2007. (Illus.). 240p. 60.00 *(978-1-84415-566-8(8))* Pen & Sword Bks. Ltd. GBR. Dist: Casemate Pubs. & Bk. Distributors, LLC.

Cram101 Textbook Reviews & Cram101 Textbook Reviews. Outlines & Highlights for Aircraft Systems: Mechanical, Electrical & Avionics Subsystems Integration by Allan Seabridge. 2011. 180p. pap. 29.95 ***(978-1-61830-877-1(7))*** Cram101 Inc.

Crawford, Alex. Hawker Fury (Part 1) 2009. 48p. pap. 21.95 *(978-2-9532544-5-7(5))* Listemann, Philippe FRA. Dist: Casemate Pubs. & Bk. Distributors, LLC.

Crosby, Francis. Fighter Aircraft: Featuring Photographs from the Imperial War Museum. 2011. (ENG., Illus.). 256p. 25.00 *(978-0-7548-0990-6(0))* Anness Publishing GBR. Dist: National Bk. Network.

—The Illustrated Guide to Modern Naval Aircraft: Features a Directory of 55 Aircraft with 330 Identification Photographs. 2012. (ENG., Illus.). 128p. pap. 17.99 *(978-1-84476-991-9(7))* Anness Publishing GBR. Dist: National Bk. Network.

—Naval Aircraft of World Wars I & II: An illustrated history of shipborn fighters & bombers, including the Sopwith Pup, B-25 Mitchell II & many More. 2010. (ENG., Illus.). 128p. pap. 17.99 *(978-1-84476-835-6(X))* Anness Publishing GBR. Dist: National Bk. Network.

—The World Encyclopedia of Naval Aircrafts: An Illustrated History of Shipborne Fighters, Bombers & Helicopters, Including the Sopwith Pup, B-25 Mitchell II, Westland Lynx, Sikorsky Sea King & Many More. 2009. (ENG., Illus.). 256p. (J). 35.00 *(978-0-7548-1670-6(2))* Anness Publishing GBR. Dist: National Bk. Network.

Cruddas, Colin. In Dorset's Skies. 2006. (Images of Aviation Ser.). (ENG., Illus.). 128p. per. 27.50 *(978-0-7524-1734-9(7))* History Pr. Ltd.,The GBR. Dist: Independent Pubs. Group.

Curtis, Des. A Most Secret Squadron: The First Full Story of 618 Squadron & Its Special Detachment Anti-U-Boat Mosquitos. 2009. (Illus.). 308p. 39.95 *(978-1-906502-51-5(X))* Grub Street GBR. Dist: Casemate Pubs. & Bk. Distributors, LLC.

Curtis, Howard J. ABC Military Aircraft Markings 2011. 2011. (ENG., Illus.). 224p. pap. 19.95 *(978-1-85780-347-1(7))* Allan, Ian Publishing GBR. Dist: BookMasters Distribution Services (BDS).

—Military Aircraft Markings 2010. 2010. (ENG., Illus.). 224p. pap. 16.95 *(978-1-85780-327-3(2))* Midland Publishing Ltd. GBR. Dist: BookMasters Distribution Services (BDS).

Curtis, Howard J. & Allan, Ian. Abc Military Aircraft Markings 2009. 2009. (ENG., Illus.). 224p. pap. 16.95 ***(978-1-85780-312-9(4))*** Midland Publishing Ltd. GBR. Dist: BookMasters Distribution Services (BDS).

Department Of The Army, Headquarters. Uh-1 Iroquois Pilot's Flight Operating Instructions. 2011. 454p. pap. 39.95 ***(978-1-935700-65-4(0))*** Periscope Film, LLC.

Department of the Navy & Air Force Combat Aviation Programs: Joint Hearing Before the Air & Land Forces Subcommittee Meeting Jointly with Seapower & Expeditionary Forces Subcommittee of the Committee on Armed Services, House of Representatives, One Hundred Eleventh Congress, Second Session, Hearing Held March 24, 2010. 2010. (Illus.). iv, 228p. ***(978-0-16-086443-8(7)***, 552-070-41502-5) United States Government Printing Office.

Dibbs, John M., photos by. The High Battleground: Air to Air with World War II's Greatest Combat Aircraft. 2006. (Flying Legends Ser.). (ENG., Illus.). 120p. 39.95 *(978-1-55046-492-4(2))* Boston Mills Pr. CAN. Dist: Firefly Bks., Ltd.

Diez, Octavio. Specialist Military Aircraft. 2006. (Aircraft Ser.). (ENG., Illus.). 96p. pap. 24.95 *(978-84-934728-1-8(6))* Udyat, S.L. ESP. Dist: Independent Pubs. Group.

Drendel, Lou. Aviation Art of Lou Drendel. 2008. (Illus.). 64p. pap. ***(978-0-89747-547-1(X))*** Squadron Signal Pubns.

Drew, John G. & Lynch, Kristin F. Options for Meeting the Maintenance Demands of Active Associate Flying Units. 2008. 94p. pap. 24.50 *(978-0-8330-4210-1(6)*, mg-611) RAND Corp., The.

Duffey, Ken. Monino Museum Moscow. 2011. (Illus.). 124p. pap. 37.00 *(978-83-89450-01-2(1))* Stratus, Wydawnictwo, Juszczak, Artur POL. Dist: Casemate Pubs. & Bk. Distributors, LLC.

Duffy, James P. Target: America: Hitler's Plan to Attack the United States. 2011. (ENG., Illus.). 208p. pap. 14.95 *(978-0-7627-7292-6(1)*, Lyons Pr.) Globe Pequot Pr., The.

Dunning, Chris. Courage Alone. 2009. (Illus.). 320p. 56.95 *(978-1-902109-09-1(0))* Hikoki Pubns. GBR. Dist: Partners Pubs. Group, Inc.

—Regia Aeronautica: The Italian Air Force 1923-1945 - an Operational History. 2010. (ENG., Illus.). 224p. 56.95 *(978-1-906537-02-9(X))* Classic Pubns. GBR. Dist: BookMasters Distribution Services (BDS).

Dyer, Edwin M. Japanese Secret Projects. 2011. (ENG., Illus.). 160p. 39.95 *(978-1-85780-317-4(5))* Allan, Ian Publishing GBR. Dist: BookMasters Distribution Services (BDS).

Evans, Tom Parry. Squadron Leader Tommy Broom Dfc** 2012. (Illus.). 192p. pap. 24.95 ***(978-1-84884-582-4(0))*** Pen & Sword Bks. Ltd. GBR. Dist: Casemate Pubs. & Bk. Distributors, LLC.

Fernande, Jose. Potez 63 Family. 2008. (Illus.). 140p. pap. *(978-83-89450-65-4(8))* Stratus, Wydawnictwo, Juszczak, Artur.

Flintham, Vic & Thomas, Andrew. Combat Codes: A full explanation & listing of British, Commonwealth & Allied air force unit codes Since 1938. 2nd ed. 2008. (Illus.). 256p. 60.00 *(978-1-84415-691-7(5))* Pen & Sword Bks. Ltd. GBR. Dist: Casemate Pubs. & Bk. Distributors, LLC.

Forbat, John. Secret World of Vickers Guided Weapons. 2007. (ENG.). 256p. pap. 37.00 *(978-0-7524-3769-9(0))* History Pr. Ltd.,The GBR. Dist: Independent Pubs. Group.

Foster, Peter & Mylon, Patrick. Tornado ADV: The Last Cold War Interceptor. 2011. (ENG., Illus.). 120p. pap. 34.95 ***(978-0-7524-5936-3(8))*** History Pr. Ltd.,The GBR. Dist: Independent Pubs. Group.

Friedman, Norman. Unmanned Combat Air Systems. 2010. (Illus.). 0384p. 52.95 *(978-1-59114-285-0(7))* Naval Institute Pr.

—Unmanned Combat Air Systems: A New Kind of Carrier Aviation. 2010. *(978-1-59114-288-1(1))* Naval Institute Pr.

Gebman, Jean R. Challenges & Issues with the Further Aging of U. S. Air Force Aircraft: Policy Options for Effective Life-Cycle Management of Resources. 2008. 80p. pap. 41.50 *(978-0-8330-4518-8(0)*, tr560) RAND Corp., The.

—Opportunities for Systems Engineering to Contribute to Durability & Damage Tolerance of Hybrid Structures for Airframes. 2008. 62p. pap. 20.50 *(978-0-8330-4202-6(5)*, tr489) RAND Corp., The.

Gero, David. Military Aviation Disasters: Significant Losses Since 1908. 2nd ed. 2010. (ENG., Illus.). 192p. 34.95 *(978-1-84425-645-7(6)*, 1844256456) Haynes Publishing PLC GBR. Dist: MBI Distribution Services/Quayside Distribution.

Gordon, Yefim. Chinese Aircraft: China's Aviation Industry Since 1951. 2008. (Illus.). 264p. 56.95 *(978-1-902109-04-6(X))* Hikoki Pubns. GBR. Dist: Partners Pubs. Group, Inc.

—Famous Russian Aircraft: Ilyushin Il-2. 2010. (ENG., Illus.). 432p. 79.95 *(978-1-85780-322-8(1))* Midland Publishing Ltd. GBR. Dist: BookMasters Distribution Services (BDS).

—Russia's Military Aircraft in the 21st Century. Komissarov, Dmitriy & Komissarov, Sergey, trs. from RUS. 2010. (Red Star Ser.). (ENG., Illus.). 128p. pap. 36.95 *(978-1-85780-224-5(1))* Allan, Ian Publishing GBR. Dist: BookMasters Distribution Services (BDS).

—Soviet Air Power in World War 2. 2010. (ENG., Illus.). 528p. 79.95 *(978-1-85780-304-4(3))* Allan, Ian Publishing GBR. Dist: BookMasters Distribution Services (BDS).

Gordon, Yefim & Davison, Peter. Tupolev Tu-95 Bear, Vol. 43. 2006. (Warbird Tech Ser.: Vol. 43). (ENG., Illus.). 108p. pap. 16.95 *(978-1-58007-102-4(3)*, 1258145) Specialty Pr. Pubs. & Wholesalers, Inc.

Gordon, Yefim & Komissarov, Dmitriy. Ilyushin IL-12 & IL-14: Successors to the Li-2. 2010. (Red Star Ser.). (ENG., Illus.). 127p. pap. 36.95 *(978-1-85780-223-8(3))* Allan, Ian Publishing GBR. Dist: BookMasters Distribution Services (BDS).

—OKB Sukhoi: A History of the Design Bureau & Its Aircraft. 2010. (ENG., Illus.). 592p. 79.95 *(978-1-85780-314-3(0))* Midland Publishing Ltd. GBR. Dist: BookMasters Distribution Services (BDS).

—Russian Air Power: Current Organisation & Aircraft of All Russian Air Forces. 2011. (ENG.). 368p. 79.95 *(978-1-85780-343-3(4))* Allan, Ian Publishing GBR. Dist: BookMasters Distribution Services (BDS).

Gordon, Yefim & Komissarov, Dmitriy. Soviet & Russian Testbed Aircraft. 2011. (Illus.). 416p. ***(978-1-902109-18-3(X))*** Hikoki Pubns.

Gordon, Yefim & Rigmant, Vladimir. Tupolev Tu-104: Aeroflot's First Jet. Komissarov, Dmitriy, tr. from RUS. 2010. (Red Star Ser.). (ENG., Illus.). 127p. pap. 36.95 *(978-1-85780-265-8(9))* Allan, Ian Publishing GBR. Dist: BookMasters Distribution Services (BDS).

Goss, Chris. Sea Eagles Vol. 2: Luftwaffe Anti-Shipping Units, 1942-45, 2 vols. 2009. (Luftwaffe Colours Ser.). (ENG., Illus.). 96p. pap. 27.95 *(978-1-903223-56-7(3))* Allan, Ian Publishing GBR. Dist: BookMasters Distribution Services (BDS).

Graser, John C., et al. Retaining F-22A Tooling: Options & Costs. 2011. 54p. pap. 15.00 *(978-0-8330-5098-4(2)*, TR-831) RAND Corp., The.

Green, Brett. The Luftwaffe in the Battle of Britain 1940, Vol. 1. 2010. (ENG., Illus.). 96p. pap. 27.95 *(978-1-906537-11-1(9))* Classic Pubns. GBR. Dist: BookMasters Distribution Services (BDS).

—The Luftwaffe on the Eastern Front, 1943-1945, Vol. 2. 2012. (Classic Modelling Guides). (ENG., Illus.). 96p. pap. 29.95 *(978-1-906537-14-2(3))* Classic Pubns. GBR. Dist: BookMasters Distribution Services (BDS).

—Modelling the Messerschmitt Bf109B/C/D/E. 2006. (Osprey Modelling Ser.: Vol. 32). (ENG., Illus.). 80p. pap. 19.95 *(978-1-84176-940-0(1))* Osprey Publishing, Ltd. GBR. Dist: Random Hse., Inc.

Greiff, Sophia. Desert Birds. 2nd ed. 2011. (ENG & GER., Illus.). 112p. 45.00 ***(978-3-86828-179-8(7))*** Kehrer Verlag Heidelberg, Klaus Kehrer DEU. Dist: Consortium Bk. Sales & Distribution.

Griehl, Manfred. Last Days of the Luftwaffe: German Luftwaffe Combat Units, 1944-1945. 2009. (Illus.). 320p. 50.00 *(978-1-84832-511-1(8)*, Frontline) Pen & Sword Bks. Ltd. GBR. Dist: Casemate Pubs. & Bk. Distributors, LLC.

Guillemin, Sébastien. Republic p-47 Thunderbolt. 2007. (Illus.). 64p. pap. 22.95 *(978-2-915239-90-4(8))* Histoire et Collections FRA. Dist: Casemate Pubs. & Bk. Distributors, LLC.

Gunby, David & Temple, Pelham. Royal Air Force Bomber Losses in the Middle East & Mediterranean, 1939-1942, Vol. I. 2007. (ENG.). 224p. pap. 26.95 *(978-1-85780-234-4(9))* Midland Counties Publ.

Gurney, Gene. The War in the Air: A Pictorial History of World War II Air Forces in Combat. 2011. 354p. 51.95 ***(978-1-258-10002-5(9))*** Literary Licensing, LLC.

Hagedom, Dan. North American's T-6: A Definitive History of the World's Most Famous Trainer. 2009. 228p. 34.95 *(978-1-58007-124-6(4))* Specialty Pr. Pubs. & Wholesalers, Inc.

Hamady, Theodore. The Nieuport 28: America's First Fighter. 2008. (Illus.). 272p. bds. 59.95 *(978-0-7643-2933-3(2))* Schiffer Publishing, Ltd.

Hancock, Terry. Directory of Britain's Military Aircraft Vol. 1: Fighters, Bombers, Ground Attack, Strike & Over-Land Reconnaissance, 2 vols. 2009. (ENG., Illus.). 288p. 55.00 *(978-0-7524-4525-0(1))* History Pr. Ltd.,The GBR. Dist: Independent Pubs. Group.

Handleman, Philip. Flying Legends of World War II: Archive & Colour Photos of Famous Allied Aircraft. 2011. (Illus.). 112p. pap. 24.95 ***(978-1-84884-308-0(9))*** Pen & Sword Bks. Ltd. GBR. Dist: Casemate Pubs. & Bk. Distributors, LLC.

Harold A. Skaarup. Arizona Warplanes: Updated Edition. 2010. 228p. pap. 25.95 *(978-1-4502-2053-8(3))* iUniverse, Inc.

Haynes, Max. Warbirds. rev. ed. 2006. (Gallery Ser.). (ENG., Illus.). 192p. pap. 17.99 *(978-0-7603-2662-6(2)*, 0760326622, Zenith Pr.) MBI Publishing Co. LLC.

Hearing on National Defense Authorization ACT for Fiscal Year 2011 & Oversight of Previously Authorized Programs Before the Committee on Armed Services, House of Representatives, One Hundred Eleventh Congress, Second Session: Full Committee Hearing on Budget Request from the Department of the Air Force, Hearing Held February 23, 2010. 2010. (Illus.). iii, 88p. ***(978-0-16-087107-8(7)***, 552-070-41963-2) United States Government Printing Office.

Heckman, Charles W. The Phnom Penh Airlift: Confessions of a Pig Pilot in the Early 1970s. alt. ed. 2012. (ENG., Illus.). 240p. pap. 25.00 ***(978-0-7864-6763-1(0))*** McFarland & Co., Inc. Pubs.

Herris, Jack & Pearson, Bob. Aircraft of World War I: 1914-1918. 2010. (Essential Aircraft Identification Guide Ser.). (Illus.). 192p. *(978-1-906626-66-2(9))* Amber Bks.

Hildebrandt, Gregory G. Budget Estimating Relationships for Depot-Level Reparables. 2007. (Illus.). 72p. pap. 23.00 *(978-0-8330-4121-0(5)*, mg355) RAND Corp., The.

Hoeveler, Patrick & Krämer, Adel. Desert Boneyards: Retired Aircraft Storage Facilities n the U. S. 2010. (Illus.). 160p. 45.00 *(978-0-7643-3662-1(2))* Schiffer Publishing, Ltd.

Holmes, Tony. F-14 Tomcat Units of Operation Enduring Freedom. 2008. (Combat Aircraft Ser.). (ENG., Illus.). 96p. pap. 22.95 *(978-1-84603-205-9(9))* Osprey Publishing, Ltd. GBR. Dist: Random Hse., Inc.

—Jane's U. S. Military Aircraft Recognition Guide, The. 2007. (Jane's U. S. Military Aircraft Recognition Guide Ser.). (Illus.). 464p. pap. 24.95 *(978-0-06-113728-0(6)*, HarperPerennial) HarperCollins Pubs.

Holstein, Christina. Fort Vaux. 2012. (Illus.). 320p. pap. 29.95 ***(978-1-84884-660-9(6))*** Pen & Sword Bks. Ltd. GBR. Dist: Casemate Pubs. & Bk. Distributors, LLC.

Huang, Xing Z. & Verhaagen, N. G. Vortex Flow Behavior over Slender Delta Wing Configurations: Experimental Studies, Numerical & Analytical Solutions. 2008. 516p. 289.00 *(978-1-4020-9332-6(2))* Springer.

Hunter, Jamie. Fighting Force: The 90th Anniversary of the Royal Air Force. 2008. (ENG., Illus.). 192p. 39.95 *(978-0-9551020-5-9(7))* Touchstone Bks. Ltd. GBR. Dist: Independent Pubs. Group.

Ireland, Bernard & Crosby, Francis. The World Encyclopedia of Aircraft Carriers & Naval Aircraft. 2011. (ENG., Illus.). 512p. 35.00 *(978-0-7548-2327-8(X))* Anness Publishing GBR. Dist: National Bk. Network.

Jackson, Robert. Encyclopedia of Military Aircraft. (Illus.). 384p. *(978-1-4054-2465-3(6))* Parragon, Inc.

Jakust, Carl. Doing My Share. 2009. *(978-0-9814539-7-2(X))* Lifetime Chronicle Pr.

Jane's Aircraft Upgrades: Your Guide to the World's Aircraft Modernisation Programmes. 495.00 *(978-0-7106-2298-3(8))* Jane's Information Group, Inc.

Johnson, E. R. American Attack Aircraft Since 1926. 2008. (ENG., Illus.). 455p. 95.00 *(978-0-7864-3464-0(3))* McFarland & Co., Inc. Pubs.

—United States Naval Aviation, 1919-1941: Aircraft, Airships & Ships Between the Wars. 2011. (ENG., Illus.). 352p. pap. 45.00 *(978-0-7864-4550-9(5))* McFarland & Co., Inc. Pubs.

Joyce, James. Pucker Factor 10: Memoir of a U. S. Army Helicopter Pilot in Vietnam. alt. l.t. ed. 2009. (ENG., Illus.). 284p. pap. 39.95 *(978-0-7864-4368-0(5))* McFarland & Co., Inc. Pubs.

Juszczak, Artur. Camouflage & Decals. 2012. (Illus.). 16p. pap. 22.00 ***(978-83-61421-54-2(8))*** Stratus, Wydawnictwo, Juszczak, Artur POL. Dist: Casemate Pubs. & Bk. Distributors, LLC.

Karnas, Dariusz. Fieseler Fi 156 Storch, 1938-1945. 2012. (Illus.). 148p. pap. 28.00 ***(978-83-61421-47-4(5))*** Stratus, Wydawnictwo, Juszczak, Artur POL. Dist: Casemate Pubs. & Bk. Distributors, LLC.

Kaufman, Roxanne M. 1912-2012, 100 Years of Marine Corps Aviation: an Illustrated History: 100 Years of Marine Corps Aviation; an Illustrated History. Marine Corps (U.S.), ed. 2011. (ENG., Illus.). 338p. 115.00 ***(978-0-16-089343-8(7)***, Dept. of the Navy) United States Government Printing Office.

Keating, Edward G., et al. Evaluating the Desirability of Navy: F/A-18E/F Service Life Extension Programs. 2011. 60p. pap. 22.00 *(978-0-8330-5104-2(0)*, tr-844) RAND Corp., The.

Ketley, Barry. Austers: A Brief History of the Auster Aircraft in British Military Service. 2006. (ENG., Illus.). 96p. pap. 24.95 *(978-0-9545605-6-0(6))* Flight Recorder Pubns. Ltd. GBR. Dist: MBI Distribution Services/Quayside Distribution.

King, Allan J. Wings on Windermere: The History of the Lake District's Forgotten Flying Boat Factory. 2011. (Illus.). 160p. pap. 59.00 ***(978-83-89450-82-1(8))*** Stratus, Wydawnictwo, Juszczak, Artur POL. Dist: Casemate Pubs. & Bk. Distributors, LLC.

Kirk, Robert F. Warriors at 500 Knots: Intense Stories of Valiant Crews Flying the Legendary F-4 Phantom II in the Vietnam Air War. 2011. 228p. 27.95 ***(978-1-4567-5676-5(1))***; pap. 19.95 ***(978-1-4567-5675-8(3))*** AuthorHouse.

Kloucek, Pavel & Kudlicka, Bohumil. Victory Air Displays: Prague 1946 And '47. 2011. (Illus.). 144p. pap. 25.00 ***(978-83-61421-42-9(4))*** Stratus, Wydawnictwo, Juszczak, Artur POL. Dist: Casemate Pubs. & Bk. Distributors, LLC.

Komissarov, Dmitriy. Tupolev Tu-154: The USSR's Medium-Range Jet Airliner. 2007. (Aerofax Ser.). (ENG., Illus.). 176p. pap. 36.95 *(978-1-85780-241-2(1))* Midland Publishing Ltd. GBR. Dist: MBI Distribution Services/Quayside Distribution.

Krylov, Leonid. Soviet MiG-15 Aces of the Korean War. 2008. (Aircraft of the Aces Ser.). (ENG., Illus.). 96p. pap. 22.95 *(978-1-84603-299-8(7))* Osprey Publishing, Ltd. GBR. Dist: Random Hse., Inc.

Leek, Michael. Military Low-Flying Aircraft. 2011. (Illus.). 272p. 50.00 ***(978-1-84884-223-6(6))*** Pen & Sword Bks. Ltd. GBR. Dist: Casemate Pubs. & Bk. Distributors, LLC.

Lepage, Jean-Denis. Aircraft of the Luftwaffe, 1935-1945: An Illustrated Guide. 2009. (ENG., Illus.). 407p. pap. 65.00 *(978-0-7864-3937-9(8))* McFarland & Co., Inc. Pubs.

Lert, Frederic. C160 Transall. 2009. 64p. pap. 22.95 *(978-2-35250-092-6(3))* Histoire et Collections FRA. Dist: Casemate Pubs. & Bk. Distributors, LLC.

Leversedge, T. F. J. Canadian Combat & Support Aircraft: A Military Compendium. 2007. (Illus.). 348p. 50.00 *(978-1-55125-116-5(7))* Vanwell Publishing, Ltd. CAN. Dist: Casemate Pubs. & Bk. Distributors, LLC.

Listemann, Phil. North AMER B-25 in Australian Service. 2009. 44p. pap. 21.95 *(978-2-9532544-4-0(7))* Listemann, Philippe FRA. Dist: Casemate Pubs. & Bk. Distributors, LLC.

Llewellyn-Jones. British Naval Aviation During the Interwar Era, 1919-1939. 2008. 130.00 *(978-0-415-39182-5(2))* Routledge.

Lovick, Edward. Radar Man: A Personal History of Stealth. 2010. 300p. 31.95 *(978-1-4502-4804-4(7))*; pap. 21.95 *(978-1-4502-4802-0(0))* iUniverse, Inc.

Machat, Mike. World's Fastest Multi-Engine Piston A/C: The Story of Republic's XR-12 Rainbow & the Hughes XF-11. 2011. (Illus.). 144p. 32.95 *(978-1-58007-163-5(5))* Specialty Pr. Pubs. & Wholesalers, Inc.

Mann, Robert A. Aircraft Record Cards of the United States Air Force: How to Read the Codes. 2008. (ENG., Illus.). 288p. pap. 49.95 *(978-0-7864-3782-5(0))* McFarland & Co., Inc. Pubs.

Manning, Gerry. Military Aircraft of the 1970s. 2010. (ENG., Illus.). 144p. pap. 36.95 *(978-1-85780-263-4(2))* Allan, Ian Publishing GBR. Dist: BookMasters Distribution Services (BDS).

March, Peter R., et al. Military Aircraft Markings 2008. 2008. (ENG., Illus.). 224p. pap. 16.95 ***(978-1-85780-290-0(X))*** Midland Publishing Ltd. GBR. Dist: BookMasters Distribution Services (BDS).

Marrett, George J. Contrails over the Mojave: The Golden Age of Jet Flight Testing at Edwards Air Force Base. 2008. (Illus.). 230p. 29.95 *(978-1-59114-511-0(2))* Naval Institute Pr.

—Testing Death: Hughes Aircraft Test Pilots & Cold War Weaponry. 2008. (Illus.). 228p. pap. *(978-1-59114-512-7(0))* Naval Institute Pr.

Marty, Isham & David, McLaren. U. S. Air Force Interceptors: A Military Photo Logbook 1946-1979. 2010. 120p. pap. 24.95 *(978-1-58007-150-5(3))* Specialty Pr. Pubs. & Wholesalers, Inc.

Masser, Barry. The Combat Aircraft Picture Book. 2007. pap. 24.95 net. *(978-1-60402-118-9(7))* Independent Pub.

Matricardi, Paolo. The Great Book of Aircraft. 2007. (Elite Attack Forces Ser.). (Illus.). 431p. 29.99 *(978-88-540-0550-1(9))* White Star ITA. Dist: Book Sales, Inc.

McGarvey, Ronald G. & Carrillo, Manuel. Analysis of the Air Force Logistics Enterprise: Evaluation of Global Repair Network Options for Supporting the F-16 & KC-135. 2010. 188p. pap. 30.00 *(978-0-8330-4740-3(X)*, mg872) RAND Corp., The.

McGarvey, Ronald G. & Masters, James M. Supporting Air & Space Expeditionary Forces: Analysis of CONUS Centralized Intermediate Repair Facilities. 2008. 272p. pap. 34.50 *(978-0-8330-4290-3(4)*, mg-418) RAND Corp., The.

McIlmoyle, Gerald & Bromley, Linda Rios. Remembering the Dragon Lady: Experiences of the Men Who Flew the U-2 Spy Plane. 2011. (Illus.). 400p. 49.95 *(978-1-907677-20-5(8))* Helion & Co., Ltd. GBR. Dist: Casemate Pubs & Bk. Distributors, LLC.

McShea, Robert. Test & Evaluation of Aircraft Avionics & Weapons Systems. 2010. (ENG., Illus.). 700p. 149.00 *(978-1-891121-90-6(1))* SciTech Publishing, Inc.

McShea, Robert E. Test & Evaluation of Aircraft Avionics & Weapon Systems. 2010. 124.95 *(978-1-60086-760-6(X))* SciTech Publishing, Inc.

Mets, David R. Airpower & Technology: Smart & Unmanned Weapons, 1 vol. 2008. (Praeger Security International Ser.). 248p. 49.95 *(978-0-275-99314-6(0)*, C9314, Praeger Security International) Greenwood Publishing Group, Inc.

Mirage III - Tome 1. 2008. 68p. pap. 22.95 *(978-2-35250-090-2(7))* Histoire et Collections FRA. Dist: Casemate Pubs. & Bk. Distributors, LLC.

Mirage III - Tome 2. 2008. 68p. pap. 22.95 *(978-2-35250-091-9(5))* Histoire et Collections FRA. Dist: Casemate Pubs. & Bk. Distributors, LLC.

Mladenov, Alexander. Mil Mi-24 Hind Gunship. 2010. (New Vanguard Ser.). (ENG., Illus.). 48p. pap. 17.95 *(978-1-84603-953-9(3))* Osprey Publishing, Ltd. GBR. Dist: Random Hse., Inc.

Murphy, Justin D., et al. Military Aircraft, 1919-1945: An Illustrated History of Their Impact, 1 vol. Tucker, Spencer C., ed. 2008. (Weapons & Warfare Ser.). (Illus.). 348p. 85.00 *(978-1-85109-498-1(9)*, MLAIR2C) ABC-CLIO, LLC.

Mutza, Wayne. Helicopter Gunships: Deadly Combat Weapon Systems. 2010. (Illus.). 208p. 39.95 *(978-1-58007-154-3(6))* Specialty Pr. Pubs. & Wholesalers, Inc.

—U.S. Army Aviation in Vietnam. 2009. (Illus.). 80p. *(978-0-89747-596-9(8))* Squadron Signal Pubns.

National Air and Space Museum Staff. In the Cockpit II: Inside History-Making Aircraft of World War II. 2010. (Illus.). 144p. 26.99 *(978-0-06-168434-0(1)*, Collins Design) HarperCollins Pubs.

National Research Council (U.S.), Committee on Future Air Force Needs for Survivability Staff, contrib. by. Future Air Force Needs for Survivability. 2006. (ENG., Illus.). 116p. pap. 30.25 *(978-0-309-10219-3(7))* National Academies Pr.

Navy, United States & Aircraft, McDonnell. F-4 Phantom II Pilot's Flight Operating Manual. 2010. 602p. pap. 49.95 *(978-1-935700-41-8(3))* Periscope Film, LLC.

Newdick, Thomas. Aircraft of the Cold War: 1945-1991. 2010. (Essential Aircraft Identification Guide Ser.). (Illus.). 192p. *(978-1-906626-64-8(2))* Amber Bks.

—Modern Military Airpower: 1990-Present. 2010. (Essential Aircraft Identification Guide Ser.). (Illus.). 192p. 34.95 *(978-1-907446-27-6(3))* Amber Bks. GBR. Dist: Casemate Pubs. & Bk. Distributors, LLC.

Nick, Veronico. Amarg: America's Military Aircraft Boneyard - A Photo Scrapbook. 2010. 144p. pap. 24.95 *(978-1-58007-139-0(2))* Specialty Pr. Pubs. & Wholesalers, Inc.

Orlesky, David T., et al. Intratheater Airlift Functional Solution Analysis (FSA), 1 vol. 2011. (ENG.). 214p. pap. 34.00 *(978-0-8330-5085-4(0))* RAND Corp., The.

Orletsky, David T., et al. Intratheater Airlift Functional Area Analysis (FAA) 2009. 65p. pap. 23.00 *(978-0-8330-4417-4(6)*, mg685) RAND Corp., The.

Paloque, Gerard. Mikoyan-Gurevitch MIG 21: Fishbed 1955 - 2010. 2010. (Planes & Pilots 12 Ser.). (Illus.). 96p. pap. 19.95 *(978-2-35250-147-3(4))* Casemate Pubs. & Bk. Distributors, LLC.

—5th Air Force. 2009. pap. 29.95 *(978-2-35250-137-4(7))* Histoire et Collections FRA. Dist: Casemate Pubs. & Bk. Distributors, LLC.

Patterson, Dan. Gil Cohen: Aviation Artist. 2009. (ENG., Illus.). 144p. 49.95 *(978-1-55046-512-9(0))* Boston Mills Pr. CAN. Dist: Firefly Bks., Ltd.

Pautigny, Bruno. Air Warfare 1914-1974: 60 Years of Aerial Warfare. 2010. (Illus.). 164p. 49.95 *(978-2-35250-117-6(2))* Histoire et Collections FRA. Dist: Casemate Pubs. & Bk. Distributors, LLC.

—P-39 Airacobra. 2008. (Illus.). 84p. pap. 19.95 *(978-2-35250-096-4(6))* Histoire et Collections FRA. Dist: Casemate Pubs. & Bk. Distributors, LLC.

Peters, John E., et al. Unmanned Aircraft Systems for Logistics Applications, 1 vol. 2012. (ENG.). 126p. (C). pap. 23.00 *(978-0-8330-5044-1(3)*, mg-978) RAND Corp., The.

Polmar, Norman. The Naval Institute Guide to the Ships & Aircraft of the U. S. Fleet. 18th ed. (Illus.). 672p. 100.00 *(978-1-59114-685-8(2))* Naval Institute Pr.

Pyles, Raymond A. & Tripp, Robert S. A Common Operating Picture for Air Force Materiel Sustainment: First Steps. 2008. 140p. pap. 25.00 *(978-0-8330-4128-9(2)*, mg-667) RAND Corp., The.

Ramey, Timothy L. & Keating, Edward G. United States Air Force Aircraft Fleet Retention Trends: A Historical Analysis. 2009. (Illus.). 48p. pap. 23.00 *(978-0-8330-4794-6(9)*, tr-740) RAND Corp., The.

Ransom, Stephen & Cammann, Hans-Hermann. Me 163 - Rocket Interceptor Vol. 2, Vol. 2. 2008. (Me 163 Ser.). (ENG., Illus.). 224p. 56.95 *(978-1-903223-13-0(X))* Allan, Ian Publishing GBR. Dist: BookMasters Distribution Services (BDS).

The Results of the Investigation by the Department of Defense & the Department of the Air Force into the Release of Proprietary Data in the KC-X Competition: Hearing Before the Committee on Armed Services, United States Senate, One Hundred Twelfth Congress, First Session, January 27, 2011. 2011. iii, 57p. ***(978-0-16-089511-1(1)***, 552-070-43470-4) United States Government Printing Office.

Rininger, Tyson. F-15 Eagle at War. 2009. (At War Ser.). (ENG., Illus.). 160p. pap. 24.99 *(978-0-7603-3350-1(5)*, 0760333505, Zenith Pr.) MBI Publishing Co. LLC.

Ripley, Tim. British Army Aviation in Action. 2012. (Illus.). 224p. 50.00 ***(978-1-84884-670-8(3))*** Pen & Sword Bks. Ltd. GBR. Dist: Casemate Pubs. & Bk. Distributors, LLC.

Roba, Jean-Louis. Foreign Planes in the Service of the Luftwaffe. 2009. (Illus.). 208p. 39.95 *(978-1-84884-081-2(0))* Pen & Sword Bks. Ltd. GBR. Dist: Casemate Pubs. & Bk. Distributors, LLC.

Roberts, Michael L. Aircraft Histories of the Ling-Temco-Vought A-7 Corsair II. 2009. (Illus.). 400p. bds. 69.99 *(978-0-7643-3238-8(4))* Schiffer Publishing, Ltd.

Robinson, Neil. Operation Overlord June - September 1944: Volume I - RAF & Commonwealth Air Forces. 2012. (Camouflage & Markings Ser.). (Illus.). 74p. pap. 30.00 ***(978-0-9569802-0-5(1))*** Airfile Pubns

Robinson, Robert W. Scarface 42: USMC Helicopter support in Close. 2008. (Illus.). 290p. *(978-0-9797704-0-1(8))* Tailwind Pubns., LLC.

Rodrigues, Rick. Aircraft Markings of the Strategic Air Command, 1946-1953. 2006. (ENG., Illus.). 279p. 85.00 *(978-0-7864-2496-2(6))* McFarland & Co., Inc. Pubs.

Rogers, Brian. United States Air Force Unit Designations since 1978. 2010. (ENG., Illus.). 272p. pap. 44.95 *(978-1-85780-197-2(0))* Allan, Ian Publishing GBR. Dist: BookMasters Distribution Services (BDS).

Rosch, Barry. Luftwaffe Support Units & Aircraft: Units, Aircraft, Emblems & Markings, 1933-1945. 2009. (ENG., Illus.). 96p. pap. 27.95 *(978-1-906537-04-3(6))* Allan, Ian Publishing GBR. Dist: BookMasters Distribution Services (BDS).

Ross, Norman. Memoirs of a Tail Gunner II. 2009. 370p. pap. 21.50 *(978-0-557-09629-9(4))* Lulu Enterprises Inc.

Rys, Marek. German Air Projects Volume 4 Bombers, Vol. 4. 2010. (Illus.). 140p. pap. 39.00 *(978-83-89450-31-9(3))* Stratus, Wydawnictwo, Juszczak, Artur POL. Dist: Casemate Pubs. & Bk. Distributors, LLC.

Samuel, Wolfgang W. E. Glory Days: The Untold Story of the Men who Flew the B-66 Destroyer into the Face of Fear. 2008. (Illus.). 464p. bds. 35.00 *(978-0-7643-3086-5(1))* Schiffer Publishing, Ltd.

Shelton, John. Schneider Trophy to Spitfire: The Design Career of R. J. Mitchell. 2009. (ENG., Illus.). 256p. 49.95 *(978-1-84425-530-6(1)*, 1844255301) Haynes Publishing PLC GBR. Dist: MBI Distribution Services/Quayside Distribution.

Shiel, Walt. To Swat A Firefly: How Bureacracy & Politics Wasted Millions in Taxpayer Dollars. 2010. (Illus.). 200p. pap. 14.95 *(978-1-934631-10-2(8))* Slipdown Mountain Pubns. LLC.

Shiel, Walt, et al. T-41 Mescalero: The Military Cessna 172. 2006. (Cessna Warbirds Ser.: 1). (Illus.). 216p. pap. 39.95 *(978-0-9746553-3-8(3))* Slipdown Mountain Pubns. LLC.

Siegel, Barry. Claim of Privilege: A Mysterious Plane Crash, a Landmark Supreme Court Case, & the Rise of State Secrets. 2009. 400p. pap. 15.99 *(978-0-06-077703-6(6)*, HarperPerennial) HarperCollins Pubs.

Simmen, Robert L. with. Threat Warning for Tactical Aircraft. 2006. (ENG.). 30.99 *(978-1-4257-3672-9(6))*; pap. 20.99 *(978-1-4257-3671-2(8))* Xlibris Corp.

Simons, Graham M. Mosquito: The Original Multi-Role Combat Aircraft. 2011. (Illus.). 256p. 50.00 *(978-1-84884-426-1(3))* Pen & Sword Bks. Ltd. GBR. Dist: Casemate Pubs. & Bk. Distributors, LLC.

Skaarup, Harold A. Florida Warplanes. 2010. 420p. pap. 36.95 *(978-1-4502-6444-0(1))* iUniverse, Inc.

Smith, Blake W. Wings over the Wilderness: They Flew the Trail of '42. 2008. (Illus.). 296p. pap. 39.95 ***(978-0-88839-595-5(7))*** Hancock Hse. Pubs.

Smith, Peter. Lockheed Martin Hercules. 2nd ed. 2010. (Illus.). 320p. 49.95 *(978-0-85979-153-3(X))* Crecy Publishing GBR. Dist: Crecy Publishing.

Smith, Peter C. Stuka Volume Two: Luftwaffe Ju 87 Dive-Bomber Units 1942-1945. 2008. (Luftwaffe Colours Ser.). (ENG., Illus.). 96p. pap. 27.95 *(978-1-903223-70-3(9))* Allan, Ian Publishing GBR. Dist: BookMasters Distribution Services (BDS).

Smith, Peter C., et al. Air Combat Manoeuvres: The Technique & History of Air Fighting for Flight Simulation. 2008. (ENG., Illus.). 256p. pap. 24.95 *(978-1-903223-98-7(9))* Allan, Ian Publishing GBR. Dist: BookMasters Distribution Services (BDS).

Solis, William M. & Sullivan, Michael J. Defense Acquisitions: Issues Concerning Airlift & Tanker Programs. 2007. (Illus.). 20p. (C). pap. 15.00 *(978-1-4223-1455-5(3))* DIANE Publishing Co.

Stillion, John, et al. Intratheater Airlift Functional Needs Analysis (FNA) 2009. 100p. pap. 23.00 *(978-0-8330-4755-7(8)*, mg-822) RAND Corp., The.

Stillwell, Paul. Carrier War: Aviation Art of World War II. 2007. (Illus.). 144p. *(978-1-4351-0025-1(5)*, 1081938) Barnes & Noble, Inc.

Stoff, Joshua. Long Island Aircraft Manufacturers. 2010. (Images of Aviation Ser.). (ENG., Illus.). 128p. pap. 21.99 *(978-0-7385-7336-6(1))* Arcadia Publishing.

Thomason, Tommy H. Scooter: The Douglas A-4 Skyhawk Story. 2011. (ENG., Illus.). 272p. pap. ***(978-0-85979-160-1(2))*** Crecy Publishing.

Thompson, Steve, et al. Air Combat Manoeuvres: The Technique & History of Air Fighting for Flight Simulation. 2008. (ENG., Illus.). 256p. pap. 49.95 ***(978-1-903223-94-9(6))*** Classic Pubns. GBR. Dist: BookMasters Distribution Services (BDS).

Timofeeva-Egoro. Over Fields of Fire. 2009. (Illus.). 240p. 49.95 *(978-1-906033-27-9(7))* Helion & Co., Ltd. GBR. Dist: Casemate Pubs. & Bk. Distributors, LLC.

Treadwell, Terry C. British & Allied Aircraft of the First World War. 2011. (Illus.). 256p. pap. 27.95 ***(978-1-4456-0101-4(X))*** Amberley Publishing GBR. Dist: Casemate Pubs. & Bk. Distributors, LLC.

—German & Austrian Aircraft of the First World War. 2011. (Illus.). 256p. pap. 29.95 *(978-1-4456-0102-1(8))* Amberley Publishing GBR. Dist: Casemate Pubs. & Bk. Distributors, LLC.

—Rocket & Jet Aircraft of the Third Reich. 2011. (ENG., Illus.). 192p. 29.95 ***(978-0-7524-6109-0(5))*** History Pr. Ltd.,The GBR. Dist: Independent Pubs. Group.

Treadwell, Terry C. Strike from Beneath the Sea: A History of Aircraft-Carrying Submarines. 2009. (ENG., Illus.). 192p. pap. 29.95 *(978-0-7524-5243-2(6))* History Pr. Ltd.,The GBR. Dist: Independent Pubs. Group.

Tripp, Robert S. & McGarvey, Ronald G. A Repair Network Concept for Air Force Maintenance: Conclusions from Analysis of C-130, F-16 & KC-135 Fleets. 2010. 62p. pap. 22.00 *(978-0-8330-4804-2(X)*, mg919) RAND Corp., The.

Tuttle, Jim. Eject! The Complete History of U. S. Aircraft Escape Systems. 2008. (ENG.). 256p. 30.00 *(978-1-4223-9175-4(2))* DIANE Publishing Co.

Ullmann, Michael. Luftwaffe Colours, 1935-1945. (Illus.). 256p. 60.00 *(978-1-902109-34-3(1))*; 2008. 360p. 56.95 *(978-1-902109-07-7(4))* Hikoki Pubns. GBR. Dist: Howell Pr., Partners Pubs. Group, Inc.

Unger, Eric J. An Examination of the Relationship Between Usage & Operating-and-Support Costs of U. S. Air Force Aircraft. 2009. 50p. pap. 22.00 *(978-0-8330-4613-0(6)*, tr594) RAND Corp., The.

The V-22 Osprey: Costs, Capabilities, & Challenges: Hearing Before the Committee on Oversight & Government Reform, House of Representatives, One Hundred Eleventh Congress, First Session, June 23, 2009. 2009. (Illus.). iii, 98p. *(978-0-16-085203-9(X)*, 552-070-40556-9) United States Government Printing Office.

Van Roo, Ben D., et al. Analysis of the Air Force Logistics Enterprise: Evaluation of Global Repair Network Options for Supporting the C-130, 1 vol. 2011. (ENG.). 92p. pap. 23.00 *(978-0-8330-4957-5(7)*, tr-813) RAND Corp., The.

VanWyngarden, Greg. Pfalz Scout Aces of World War 1. 2006. (Osprey Aircraft of the Aces Ser.: Vol. 71). (ENG., Illus.). 96p. pap. 22.95 *(978-1-84176-998-1(3))* Osprey Publishing, Ltd. GBR. Dist: Random Hse., Inc.

Wadman, David. Aufklarer: Luftwaffe Reconnaissance Aircraft & Units, 1935-1941. 2007. (Luftwaffe Colours Ser.). (ENG., Illus.). 96p. pap. 29.95 *(978-1-903223-74-1(1))* Classic Pubns. GBR. Dist: MBI Distribution Services/Quayside Distribution.

—Aufklarer Vol. 2: Luftwaffe Reconnaissance Aircraft & Units, 1942-1945, 2 vols. 2010. (ENG., Illus.). 96p. pap. 29.95 *(978-1-85780-278-8(0))* Allan, Ian Publishing GBR. Dist: BookMasters Distribution Services (BDS).

Wakefield, Ken. Lightplanes at War. (Illus.). 212p. pap. *(978-0-7524-1727-1(4))* History Pr. Ltd.,The.

Walsh, Thomas L. Damnyankee: A WWII Story of Tragedy & Survival off the West of Ireland. 2008. 180p. pap. 17.95 *(978-1-4327-2910-3(1))* Outskirts Pr., Inc.

Ware, P. World War Two German Trucks. 2009. (Illus.). 240p. 56.95 *(978-0-7110-3249-1(1))* Allan, Ian Publishing GBR. Dist: Casemate Pubs. & Bk. Distributors, LLC.

Warner, Guy. First in the Field. 2011. (Illus.). 304p. 50.00 ***(978-1-84884-263-2(5))*** Pen & Sword Bks. Ltd. GBR. Dist: Casemate Pubs. & Bk. Distributors, LLC.

Warner, Guy. World War One Aircraft Carrier Pioneer: The Story & Diaries of Captain JM Mccleery RNAS/RAF. 2011. (Illus.). 304p. 39.95 *(978-1-84884-255-7(4))* Pen & Sword Bks. Ltd. GBR. Dist: Casemate Pubs. & Bk. Distributors, LLC.

Watkins, Robert A. Battle Colors Insignia & Aircraft Markings of the 8th Air Force in World War II: VIII Fighter Command, Vol. 2. 2006. (Illus.). 144p. 45.00 *(978-0-7643-2535-9(3))* Schiffer Publishing, Ltd.

—Battle Colors Volume 3: Insignia & Tactical Markings of the Ninth Air Force in World War II. 2008. (Illus.). 168p. bds. 45.00 *(978-0-7643-2938-8(3))* Schiffer Publishing, Ltd.

Weal, John. Ju 87 Stukageschwader of the Russian Front. 2008. (Combat Aircraft Ser.). (ENG., Illus.). 96p. pap. 22.95 *(978-1-84603-308-7(X))* Osprey Publishing, Ltd. GBR. Dist: Random Hse., Inc.

—Junkers Ju 88 Kampfgeschwader on the Russian Front. 2010. (Combat Aircraft Ser.). (ENG., Illus.). 96p. pap. 22.95 *(978-1-84603-419-0(1))* Osprey Publishing, Ltd. GBR. Dist: Random Hse., Inc.

Wertheim, Eric. The Naval Institute Guide to Combat Fleets of the World: Their Ships, Aircraft, & Systems. 15th rev. ed. 2007. (Naval Institute Guide to Combat Fleets of the World Ser.). (Illus.). 1058p. 250.00 *(978-1-59114-955-2(X))* Naval Institute Pr.

White, Ian. The History of Air Intercept (AI) Radar & the British Night-Fighter 1935-1959. 2007. (Illus.). 326p. 60.00 *(978-1-84415-532-3(3))* Pen & Sword Bks. Ltd. GBR. Dist: Casemate Pubs. & Bk. Distributors, LLC.

Whittell, Giles. Bridge of Spies: A True Story of the Cold War. 2010. (ENG., Illus.). 304p. 24.99 *(978-0-7679-3107-6(6))* Broadway Bks.

Wilson, Jeff, compiled by. Classic Combat Aircraft. 2007. (Illus.). 95p. *(978-0-89024-696-2(3)*, Kalmbach Bks.) Kalmbach Publishing Co., Bks. Div.

Winchester, Jim. Classic Military Aircraft: The World's Fighting Aircraft, 1914-1945. 2011. (Illus.). 448p. pap. 40.00 *(978-1-907446-39-9(7))* Amber Bks. GBR. Dist: Casemate Pubs. & Bk. Distributors, LLC.

—Jet Fighters Inside Out. 2010. (ENG., Illus.). 320p. 34.95 *(978-1-60710-108-6(4)*, Thunder Bay Pr.) Advantage Pubs. Group.

Winslade, Richard. The Battle of Britain Memorial Flight. 2010. (ENG., Illus.). 168p. pap. 27.95 *(978-0-7524-5651-5(2))* History Pr. Ltd., The GBR. Dist: Independent Pubs. Group.

—The Battle of Britain Memorial Flight. 2007. (ENG., Illus.). 160p. 36.95 *(978-0-7509-3151-9(5))* Sutton Publishing.

Wolf, William. North American B-25 Mitchell: The Ultimate Look: from Drawing Board to Flying Arsenal. 2008. (Illus.). 336p. bds. 69.95 *(978-0-7643-2930-2(8))* Schiffer Publishing, Ltd.

—U. S. Aerial Armament in World War II - the Ultimate Look: Vol. 3: Air Launched Rockets, Mines, Torpedoes, Guided Missiles & Secret Weapons, 3 vols. 2010. (Illus.). 320p. 69.99 *(978-0-7643-3658-4(4))* Schiffer Publishing, Ltd.

—U. S. Aerial Armament in World War II - The Ultimate Look Vol. 2: Bombs, Bombsights, & Bombing, 2 vols. 2010. (Illus.). 320p. 69.99 *(978-0-7643-3524-2(3))* Schiffer Publishing, Ltd.

Woodring, Suanne & Woodring, Frank. Fairchild Aircraft. 2007. (Images of Aviation Ser.). (ENG., Illus.). 128p. per. 21.99 *(978-0-7385-4439-7(6))* Arcadia Publishing.

Woowski, Krzysztof. Bf 109 Late Versions: Camouflage & Markings. 2010. (Illus.). 96p. pap. 37.00 *(978-83-61421-13-9(0))* Stratus, Wydawnictwo, Juszczak, Artur POL. Dist: Casemate Pubs. & Bk. Distributors, LLC.

Yenne, Bill. Birds of Prey: America's Newest Unmanned Aerial Vehicles in Combat. 2010. (Illus.). 160p. pap. 29.95 *(978-1-58007-153-6(8))* Specialty Pr. Pubs. & Wholesalers, Inc.

Zeine, Walter P., ed. Protest & Issues Around the Air Force Refueling Tanker. 2010. (Defense, Security & Strategy Ser.). pap. 43.00 *(978-1-60741-980-8(7))* Nova Science Pubs., Inc.

Zimmerman, W. X-47 Unmanned Combat Air Vehicle. 2007. 36p. per. 17.81 *(978-1-934840-03-0(3))* Nimble Bks. LLC.

AIRPLANES, MILITARY—RECOGNITION
see Airplanes—Recognition

AIRPLANES, PERSONAL
see Airplanes, Private

AIRPLANES, PILOTLESS
see Guided Missiles

AIRPLANES, PRIVATE
see also Beechcraft 17 (Airplanes)

ASTM Committee F37 on Light Sport Staff, contrib. by. ASTM Standards on Light Sport Aircraft. 2nd ed. 2007. *(978-0-8031-4271-8(4))* American Society for Testing & Materials.

Ball, Larry A. Those Incomparable Bonanzas. 2008. (ENG., Illus.). 220p. 49.99 *(978-1-934980-25-5(0))* Cable Publishing.

Benjamin, Robert. Hey Mister, Will It Fly? 2010. 200p. pap. 1.00 *(978-0-9841397-7-4(X))* Helm Publishing.

Campbell, J. R. The Sportplane Resource Guide. 2nd ed. (Illus.). 1100p. pap. 39.95 *(978-1-886743-14-4(2))* Kindred Spirit Pr., Inc.

Federal Aviation Administration. Plane Sense: A Beginner's Guide to Owning & Operating Private Aircraft FAA-H-8083-19A. 2011. (ENG., Illus.). 112p. 12.95 *(978-1-61608-133-1(3)*, 608133) Skyhorse Publishing Co., Inc.

Federal Aviation Administration Aircraft Certification: Alleged Regulatory Lapses in the Certification & Manufacture of the Eclipse EA-500: Hearing Before the Subcommittee on Aviation of the Committee on Transportation & Infrastructure, House of Representatives, One Hundred Tenth Congress, Second Session, September 17, 2008. 2008. (Illus.). xxi, 329p. *(978-0-16-083401-1(5)*, 552-070-39214-9) United States Government Printing Office.

Kuchta, Marek. Viability of the Premium Airline Business Model. 2009. 118p. pap. *(978-3-639-18166-1(2))* VDM Verlag Dr. Mueller e.K.

Ord-Hume, Arthur. British Private Aircraft: The Re-awakening Years 1946 - 1970. 2012. (Illus.). 600p. 150.00 ***(978-83-61421-46-7(7))*** Stratus, Wydawnictwo, Juszczak, Artur POL. Dist: Casemate Pubs. & Bk. Distributors, LLC.

Residential Through-The-Fence Agreements at Public Airports: Action to Date & Challenges Ahead: Hearing Before the Committee on Transportation & Infrastructure, House of Representatives, One Hundred Eleventh Congress, Second Session, September 22, 2010. 2010. (Illus.). xxxi, 112p. ***(978-0-16-088668-3(6)***, 552-070-42834-8) United States Government Printing Office.

AIRPLANES, ROCKET PROPELLED
see Rocket Planes

AIRPLANES, USED
see Used Aircraft

AIRPLANES, VERTICALLY RISING
see Vertically Rising Aircraft

AIRPLANES IN AGRICULTURE
see Aeronautics in Agriculture

AIRPLANES IN ART

Cross, Roy. The Vintage Years of Airfix Box Art. 2009. (ENG., Illus.). 128p. 59.95 *(978-1-84797-076-3(1)*, 1847970761) Crowood Pr., Ltd. GBR. Dist: MBI Distribution Services/Quayside Distribution.

Drendel, Lou. Aviation Art of Lou Drendel. 2008. (Illus.). 64p. pap. ***(978-0-89747-547-1(X))*** Squadron Signal Pubns.

Gordon, Yefim. Tupolev Tu-95/142. 2010. (ENG., Illus.). 416p. 94.95 *(978-1-85780-310-5(8))* Allan, Ian Publishing GBR. Dist: BookMasters Distribution Services (BDS).

Jenkins, Dennis R. & Landis, Tony. USAF Prototype Jet Fighters. 2009. 108p. pap. 22.95 *(978-1-58007-137-6(6))* Specialty Pr. Pubs. & Wholesalers, Inc.

LaFosse, Michael G. & Alexander, Richard L. Planes for Brains: 28 Innovative Origami Airplane Designs. 2011. (ENG., Illus.). 96p. 18.95 *(978-4-8053-1149-3(5))* Tuttle Publishing.

Matowitz, Thomas G. & Matowitz, Thomas G., Jr. Cleveland's Legacy of Flight. 2008. (Images of Aviation Ser.). (ENG., Illus.). 128p. per. 19.99 *(978-0-7385-5177-7(5))* Arcadia Publishing.

Milstein, Jeffrey. Aircraft: the Jet As Art. 2007. 29.95 *(978-88-370-5505-9(6))* Abrams.

Ono, Mari & Ono, Roshin. Fly Origami Fly! 2006. (ENG., Illus.). 128p. pap. 19.95 *(978-1-907030-59-8(X))* CICO Bks. GBR. Dist: Ryland Peters & Small.

Ransom, Stephen & Korrell, Peter. Junkers Ju 287: Germany's Forward Swept Wing Bomber. 2008. (ENG., Illus.). 160p. 49.95 *(978-1-903223-92-5(X))* Allan, Ian Publishing GBR. Dist: BookMasters Distribution Services (BDS).

Whyte, Andrew. How to Draw & Paint Aircraft Like a Pro. 2nd ed. 2008. (Motorbooks Studio Ser.). (ENG., Illus.). 160p. pap. 24.99 *(978-0-7603-3391-4(2)*, 0760333912, Zenith Pr.) MBI Publishing Co. LLC.

AIRPLANES IN FORESTRY
see Aeronautics in Forestry

AIRPORTS
see also Air Bases

Ac-U-Kwik Staff. Acukwik World Edition 2006-2007. 2006. pap. 99.95 *(978-1-59969-048-3(9))* Penton Media, Inc.

Acukwik Staff. Ac-U-Kwik International Airport/Fbo Directory 2007. 2007. pap. *(978-1-59969-069-8(1))* Penton Media, Inc.

—Ac-U-Kwik North American Airport/FBO Directory 2007. 2007. pap. *(978-1-59969-068-1(3))* Penton Media, Inc.

Adamson, Ian J. National Airspace System: Congestion Issues. 2011. (Transportation Infrastructure - Roads, Highways, Bridges, Airports & Mass Transit Ser.). (Illus.). viii, 130p. 89.00 *(978-1-61761-890-1(X))* Nova Science Pubs., Inc.

Aeropuertos y Servicios Auxiliares, creator. Asa: Aeropuertos para la Competitividad y el Desarrollo. 2006. (Coleccion Editorial del Gobierno del Cambio Ser.). (SPA., Illus.). 299p. pap. 24.95 *(978-968-16-8117-3(7))* Fondo de Cultura Economica USA.

Airport Privatization: Issues Related to the Sale or Lease of U.S. Commercial Airports. 55p. pap. 30.00 *(978-0-7881-4062-4(0))* DIANE Publishing Co.

Alley, Bill. Aviation in Southern Oregon. 2011. (Images of Aviation Ser.). (Illus.). 128p. pap. 21.99 *(978-0-7385-8191-0(7))* Arcadia Publishing.

Arrington, Charles W. & Nokes, Garry J. Wings over the Falls: A Century of Aviation in Southern Indiana. 2007. 160p. 24.95 *(978-1-58374-170-2(4))* Chicago Spectrum Pr.

Ashford, Norman J., et al. Airport Engineering: Planning, Design, & Development of 21st Century Airports. 4th ed. 2011. (ENG., Illus.). 768p. 145.00 *(978-0-470-39855-5(8)*, Wiley) Wiley, John & Sons, Inc.

ATC Modernization & NextGen Near-Term Achievable Goals: Hearing Before the Subcommittee on Aviation of the Committee on Transportation & Infrastructure, House of Representatives, One Hundred Eleventh Congress, First Session, March 18, 2009. 2009. (Illus.). xx, 313p. *(978-0-16-084362-4(6)*, 552-070-39905-4) United States Government Printing Office.

Bahrain International Airport: Yearbook 1995-96. (Illus.). 60p. (Orig.). pap. *(978-0-7605-2902-7(7))* Rector Pr., Ltd.

Barger, Jason. Step Back from the Baggage Claim: Change the World, Start at the Airport. 2009. 134p. pap. *(978-0-615-22666-8(3))* One Love Pubs.

Barger, Jason & Barger, Jason V. Step Back from the Baggage Claim: Change the World, Start at the Airport. Idr.'s ed. 2010. 164p. pap. 14.95 *(978-0-615-35738-6(5))* One Love Pubs.

Bergerson, Roger. Winging it at a Country Crossroads: The Ups & Downs of Minnesota's First Real Airport. Date not set. (Illus.). v, 66p. pap. *(978-0-615-22549-4(7))* Bergerson amp; Cunningham.

Bianco, Lucio, et al, eds. New Concepts & Methods in Air Traffic Management. 2010. (Transportation Analysis Ser.). (ENG., Illus.). x, 224p. pap. 189.00 *(978-3-642-07491-2(X)*, 364207491X) Springer.

Bickenbach, Frank, et al. Ausbau der Flughafenstruktur: Konflikte und institutionelle Lösungsansätze. (Kieler Studien - Kiel Studies). (GER.). X, 251p. 119.00 *(978-3-540-29418-4(X)*, 354029418X) Springer.

Birtles, Philip. Battle of Britain Airfields. 2010. (ENG., Illus.). 160p. 32.95 *(978-1-85780-328-0(0))* Midland Publishing Ltd. GBR. Dist: BookMasters Distribution Services (BDS).

Bleakley, Bruce A. Dallas Aviation. 2011. (Images of Aviation Ser.). (Illus.). 128p. pap. 21.99 *(978-0-7385-7988-7(2))* Arcadia Publishing.

Bradley, A. L. W. The Independent Airport Planning Manual. 2010. (Illus.). 162p. 270.00 ***(978-0-85709-035-5(6))*** Woodhead Publishing Ltd. GBR. Dist: Ingram Pub. Services.

Bradley, A. L. W. The Independent Airport Planning Reference Manual. 2010. (ENG., Illus.). 184p. 255.00 *(978-1-84569-713-6(8))* Woodhead Publishing Ltd. GBR. Dist: Ingram Pub. Services.

Branigan, Michael. A History of Chicago's O'Hare Airport. 2011. 160p. pap. 19.99 ***(978-1-60949-434-6(2))*** History Pr., The.

Brebbia, C. A. & Postorino, M. N., eds. Regional Airports. 2009. (WIT Transactions on the Built Environment Ser.). (Illus.). 400p. 264.00 *(978-1-84564-203-7(1))* WIT Pr GBR. Dist: WIT Pr.

Butler, Phil. Liverpool John Lennon Airport. 2008. (ENG.). 160p. pap. 39.95 *(978-0-7524-4511-3(1))* History Pr. Ltd., The GBR. Dist: Independent Pubs. Group.

Calderón, Gabriel V. Airport Improvement Program: Background & Issues. 2011. (Series: Transportation Infrastructure - Roads, Highways, Bridges, Airports & Mass Transit Ser.). (Illus.). viii, 295p. 115.00 *(978-1-61761-894-9(2))* Nova Science Pubs., Inc.

Cassidy, Michael J. & Navarrete, Joseph. Airport Passenger-Related Processing Rates Guidebook. 2009. (Illus.). 116p. pap. *(978-0-309-11805-7(0))* Transportation Research Board.

Caves, Robert E. & Kazda, Antonin. Airport Design & Operation. 2nd ed. 2007. (Illus.). 522p. 151.95 *(978-0-08-045104-6(7))* Emerald Group Publishing Ltd. GBR. Dist: Turpin Distribution Services Ltd.

Ciriani, Tito A., et al, eds. Operations Research in Space & Air. 2010. (Applied Optimization Ser.). 464p. pap. 339.00 *(978-1-4419-5242-4(X)*, 144195242X) Springer.

Clarke, Bob. Archaeology of Airfields. 2007. (ENG., Illus.). 256p. pap. 36.95 *(978-0-7524-4401-7(8))* History Pr. Ltd., The GBR. Dist: Independent Pubs. Group.

Coogan, Matthew A. Planning for Offsite Airport Terminals. 2010. (Illus.). 86p. pap. ***(978-0-309-15488-8(X))*** Transportation Research Board.

Coopman, David T. Quad City International Airport. 2011. (Images of Aviation Ser.). (Illus.). 128p. pap. 21.99 *(978-0-7385-8371-6(5))* Arcadia Publishing.

Crider, Rick. Guidebook for Developing & Leasing Airport Property. 2011. (Illus.). 129p. pap. ***(978-0-309-15556-4(8))*** Transportation Research Board.

Cullen, Laurie. Collaborative Airport Capital Planning Handbook. 2011. (Illus.). ***(978-0-309-21323-3(1))*** Transportation Research Board.

Czerny, Achim & Czerny, Achim I. Airport Slots: International Experiences & Options for Reform. Niemeier, Hans-Martin et al, eds. 2008. 452p. 144.95 *(978-0-7546-7042-1(2))* Ashgate Publishing Co.

de Botton, Alain. A Week at the Airport: A Heathrow Diary. 2010. (Vintage International Original Ser.). (ENG., Illus.). 112p. pap. 15.00 *(978-0-307-73967-4(8)*, Vintage) Knopf Doubleday Publishing Group.

de Harven, Emile. Aerodrame. (FRE.). tchr.'s training gde. ed. 10.95 *(978-0-88436-338-5(4)*, 40812) EMC/Paradigm Publishing.

de Neufville, Richard, et al. Airport Systems: Planning, Design & Management 2/E. 2nd ed. 2012. (ENG., Illus.). 832p. (C). 125.00 ***(978-0-07-177058-3(5)***, 0071770585) McGraw-Hill Professional Publishing.

D'Haenens, Tom. Airport. 2007. 224p. 95.00 *(978-90-209-6811-8(4))* Lannoo N. V., Uitgeverij BEL. Dist: Antique Collectors' Club.

Doherty, Sharon. Heathrow's Terminal 5: History in the Making. 2008. (ENG., Illus.). 372p. 75.00 *(978-0-470-75435-1(4)*, Wiley) Wiley, John & Sons, Inc.

Donohue, George L., et al. Terminal Chaos: Why US Air Travel Is Broken & How to Fix It. 2008. (Library of Flight Ser.). (Illus.). 150p. *(978-1-56347-949-6(4))* American Institute of Aeronautics & Astronautics.

Ebinger, Ginger. The World Connected: DFW International Airport - Taking Flight into the 21st Century. 2007. (ENG., Illus.). 272p. 39.95 *(978-0-9774451-4-1(3))* DSA Publishing & Design, Inc.

Encarnacion, Elizabeth. Airports. 2007. (Qeb Buildings at Work Ser.). (Illus.). 36p. (J). (gr. 4-7). lib. bdg. 19.95 *(978-1-59566-374-0(6))* QEB Publishing Inc.

Flouris, Triant & Lock, Dennis. Aviation Project Management. 2008. 314p. 99.95 *(978-0-7546-7395-8(2))* Ashgate Publishing Co.

Forsyth, Peter, et al. Airport Competition: The European Experience. Müller, Jürgen, ed. 2010. (Illus.). 462p. 134.95 *(978-0-7546-7746-8(X))* Ashgate Publishing Co.

Gallop, Alan. Time Flies: The Heathrow Story. 2012. (ENG., Illus.). 240p. pap. 27.95 ***(978-0-7524-6583-8(X))*** History Pr. Ltd., The GBR. Dist: Independent Pubs. Group.

Galluzzo, John J. & Millville Army Air Field Museum. Millville Army Air Field: America's First Defense Airport. 2011. (Images of Aviation Ser.). (Illus.). 128p. pap. 21.99 *(978-0-7385-7519-3(4))* Arcadia Publishing.

Gesell, Laurence E. & Sobotta, Robin R. The Administration of Public Airports, 5th Ed. 2nd ed. 2007. (ENG.). 1044p. (C). 98.00 *(978-1-890938-10-9(6))* Coast Aire Pubns. & Consulting.

Gonzales, Laurence. One Zero Charlie: Adventures in Grass Roots Aviation. 2007. (ENG.). 272p. pap. 18.95 *(978-1-4165-7641-9(X))* Simon & Schuster.

Gopalakrishnan, Kasthurirangan. Rutting in Flexible Airfield Pavements: Perspectives based on Full-Scale Test Results. 2008. 132p. pap. *(978-3-639-09554-8(5))* VDM Verlag Dr. Mueller e.K.

Gordon, Alastair. Naked Airport: A Cultural History of the World's Most Revolutionary Structure. 2008. (Illus.). 320p. pap. 17.00 *(978-0-226-30456-4(6))* Univ. of Chicago Pr.

Graff, Cory. Boeing Field. 2008. (Images of Aviation Ser.). (ENG., Illus.). 128p. per. 21.99 *(978-0-7385-5615-4(7))* Arcadia Publishing.

Graham, Anne. Managing Airports: An International Perspective. 3rd rev. ed. 2008. (ENG., Illus.). 360p. (C). pap. 55.95 *(978-0-7506-8613-6(8))* Routledge.

Grothaus, James H. Guidebook for Managing Small Airports. 2009. (Illus.). 129p. pap. *(978-0-309-11787-6(9))* Transportation Research Board.

Harding, James R. Wayfinding & Signing Guidelines for Airport Terminals & Landside. 2011. (Illus.). 244p. pap. ***(978-0-309-21346-2(0))*** Transportation Research Board.

Hearing on the Financial Status of the Airport & Airway Trust Fund: Hearing Before the Committee on Ways & Means, U.S. House of Representatives, One Hundred Eleventh Congress, First Session, May 7, 2009. 2009. (Illus.). iii, 60p. *(978-0-16-085690-7(6)*, 552-070-40922-0) United States Government Printing Office.

Hirst, M. The Air Transport System. 2008. 352p. *(978-1-84569-325-1(6))* Woodhead Publishing Ltd.

Hirst, Mike. The Air Transport System. 2008. (Library of Flight). (Illus.). ix, 341p. *(978-1-56347-964-9(8))* American Institute of Aeronautics & Astronautics.

Holden, Henry M. Newark Airport. 2009. (Images of Aviation Ser.). (ENG., Illus.). 128p. pap. 21.99 *(978-0-7385-6522-4(9))* Arcadia Publishing.

Hooks, Mike. Croydon Airport: The Peaceful Years. (ENG., Illus.). 160p. pap. 24.99 *(978-0-7524-2758-4(X))* History Pr. Ltd., The GBR. Dist: Trafalgar Square Publishing.

Horonjeff, Robert M., et al. Planning & Design of Airports, Fifth Edition. 5th rev. ed. 2010. (ENG., Illus.). 688p. (C). 125.00 *(978-0-07-144641-9(9)*, 0071446419) McGraw-Hill Professional Publishing.

Infrastructure Management Group Staff, et al, contrib. by. Developing an Airport Performance-Measurement System. 2010. (Illus.). 144p. pap. ***(978-0-309-15477-2(4))*** Transportation Research Board.

Institution of Civil Engineers Staff, ed. Heathrow Airport Terminal 5: Proceedings of the Institution of Civil Engineers. 2008. (Illus.). 64p. pap. *(978-0-7277-3550-8(0))* Telford, Thomas Ltd.

Jaehn, Florian. Robust Flight Gate Assignment. 2008. (Europäische Hochschulschriften. Reihe 5: Volks- und Betriebswirtschaft Ser.). 140p. pap. 39.95 *(978-3-631-57704-2(4))* Lang, Peter GmbH, Europaischer Verlag der Wissenschaften DEU. Dist: Lang, Peter.

Jahn, Helmut. Suvarnabhumi Airport, Bangkok, Thailand. 2007. (ENG., Illus.). 20.00 *(978-3-89986-088-7(8)*, Avedition Gmbh,Csi) Continental Sales, Inc.

JaniÄ‡, Milan. Greening Airports: Advanced Technology & Operations. 2011. (Green Energy & Technology Ser.). (ENG., Illus.). xiv, 206p. 129.00 *(978-0-85729-657-3(4)*, 0857296574) Springer.

Janic, Milan. Airport Analysis, Planning & Design: Demand, Capacity, & Congestion. 2009. 79.00 *(978-1-60741-308-0(6))* Nova Science Pubs., Inc.

Jones, Will. New Transport Architecture: Travel Hubs in the 21st Century. 2006. (ENG., Illus.). 272p. 50.00 *(978-1-84533-218-1(0)*, Mitchell Beazley) Octopus Publishing Group GBR. Dist: Hachette Bk. Group.

Jovicic, Mile. Two Days till Peace: A Sarajevo Airport Story. 2011. 332p. 28.50 *(978-1-4567-4839-5(4))*; pap. 18.50 *(978-1-4567-4838-8(6))* AuthorHouse.

Kali, Marilyn & Schlapak, Benjamin R. Honolulu International Airport: The First 80 Years. 2007. pap. 35.00 *(978-0-9729540-1-3(5)*, Hot Pixel Pr.) Turner & de Vries, Ltd.

Kasarda, John D. & Lindsay, Greg. Aerotropolis: The Way We'll Live Next. (ENG., Illus.). 480p. 2012. pap. 17.00 ***(978-0-374-53351-9(2))*** 2011. 30.00 *(978-0-374-10019-3(5))* Farrar, Straus & Giroux.

Kenville, Kimberly A. Helping Airport & Air Carrier Employees Cope with Traumatic Events. 2009. (Illus.). 74p. *(978-0-309-11797-5(6))* Transportation Research Board.

Kim, Brian Y. Guidebook on Preparing Airport Greenhouse Gas Emissions Inventories. 2009. (Illus.). 53p. pap. *(978-0-309-11774-6(7))* Transportation Research Board.

Kramer, Lois S. Marketing Guidebook for Small Airports. 2010. (Illus.). 175p. ***(978-0-309-11818-7(2))*** Transportation Research Board.

Kucuk Yilmaz, Ayse. Airport Enterprise Risk Management Model- a Study on Business Management & Airline Management. 2008. (Illus.). 180p. per. *(978-3-8364-2979-5(9))* VDM Verlag Dr. Mueller e.K.

Land, R. A. Americas First Commercial Airfield. 2006. 73p. pap. 10.00 *(978-1-4257-0295-3(3))* Xlibris Corp.

Larauge, Pierre B. & Castille, Martin E. Airports: Performance, Risks, & Problems. 2009. (Illus.). x, 220p. 129.00 *(978-1-60692-393-1(5))* Nova Science Pubs., Inc.

Lawton, Thomas C., ed. Strategic Management in Aviation: Critical Essays. 2007. (Illus.). 416p. 225.00 *(978-0-7546-2651-0(2))* Ashgate Publishing Co.

Liu, Pei-Chen Barry. Managing Uncertainty in the Single Airport Ground Holding Problem. 2008. 176p. pap. *(978-3-8364-8445-9(5))* VDM Verlag Dr. Mueller e.K.

Lobb, Charles. Torrance Airport. 2006. (Images of Aviation Ser.). (ENG., Illus.). 128p. per. 21.99 *(978-0-7385-4662-9(3))* Arcadia Publishing.

Ludwig, Duane A. Safety Management Systems for Airports. 2007. (ACRP Report Ser.: Vol. 1). (Illus.). 30p. 32.00 *(978-0-309-09896-0(3))*; ***(978-0-309-11798-2(4))*** Transportation Research Board.

Lynch, Christopher. When Hollywood Landed at Chicago's Midway Airport: The Photos & Stories of Mike Rotunno. 2012. 160p. pap. 19.99 ***(978-1-60949-592-3(6))*** History Pr., The.

Martins, Edgar. When Light Casts No Shadow. 2010. (ENG., Illus.). 88p. 50.00 ***(978-1-904587-81-1(X))*** Lewis, Dewi Publishing GBR. Dist: Consortium Bk. Sales & Distribution.

Mestre, Vincent. Effects of Aircraft Noise: Research Update on Selected Topics. 2008. (ACRF Synthesis Ser.: Vol. 9). (Illus.). 90p. pap. *(978-0-309-09806-9(8))* Transportation Research Board.

Molar, Barry. Strategies & Financing Opportunities for Airport Environmental Programs. 2011. (Illus.). 218p. pap. ***(978-0-309-14342-4(X))*** Transportation Research Board.

Muia, Maria J. Counting Aircraft Operations at Non-Towered Airports. 2007. (ACRP Synthesis Ser.: Vol. 4). 33p. 34.00 *(978-0-309-09790-1(8))* Transportation Research Board.

National Research Council (U.S.), Transportation Research Board Staff, et al, contrib. by. Guidebook for Planning & Implementing Automated People Mover Systems at Airports. 2010. (Illus.). 218p. pap. ***(978-0-309-15498-7(7))*** Transportation Research Board.

Neuscheler, Tillmann. Flughäfen zwischen Regulierung und Wettbewerb: Eine netzökonomische Analyse. 2008. (GER., Illus.). 379p. pap. *(978-3-8329-3737-9(4))* Nomos Verlagsgesellschaft.

Nichol, Cindy. Innovative Finance & Alternative Sources of Revenue for Airports. 2007. (ACRF Synthesis Ser.: Vol. 1). (Illus.). 43p. 44.00 *(978-0-309-09783-3(5))* Transportation Research Board.

Organisation for Economic Co-operation and Development Staff & Joint Transport Research Centre Staff. Competitive Interaction Between Airports, Airlines & High-Speed Rail. 2009. 208p. pap. 63.00 *(978-92-821-0245-9(9))* Organization for Economic Cooperation & Development.

Osbourne, David L. & Offenhauer, Priscilla. The History of the U. S. Army Battle Command Training Program, 1986-2003. 2007. (ENG., Illus.). 198p. (gr. 9). per. 17.00 *(978-0-16-077797-4(6)*, 552-070-35247-3, Defense Dept.) United States Government Printing Office.

Pedoe, Nadine T. et al. eds. Environmental Management at Airports: Liabilities & Social Responsibilities. (Illus.). 251p. 61.00 *(978-0-7277-2520-2(3))* Telford, Thomas Ltd. GBR. Dist: Routledge, Chapman & Hall, Inc.

Pheng, Low Sui, et al. Just-in-Time Management for Airports. 2010. (Management Science - Theory & Applications Ser.). pap. 43.00 *(978-1-61728-783-1(0)*, Nova Novinka) Nova Science Pubs., Inc.

Postorino, M. N., ed. Regional Airports. 2011. (Illus.). 148p. lib. bdg. 118.00 *(978-1-84564-570-0(7))* WIT Pr GBR. Dist: WIT Pr.

Postorino, Nadia, ed. Development of Regional Airports: Theoretical Analyses & Case Studies. 2010. (Topics in Engineering Ser.: 47). (Illus.). 192p. 146.00 *(978-1-84564-143-6(4))* WIT Pr GBR. Dist: WIT Pr.

Renomination of Charles D. Snelling to Be a Member of the Metropolitan Washington Airports Authority: Hearing Before the Committee on Commerce, Science, & Transportation, United States Senate, One Hundred Tenth Congress, First Session, May 24, 2007. 2007. iii, 11p. *(978-0-16-079289-2(4)*, 552-070-36367-0) United States Government Printing Office.

Residential Through-The-Fence Agreements at Public Airports: Action to Date & Challenges Ahead: Hearing Before the Committee on Transportation & Infrastructure, House of Representatives, One Hundred Eleventh Congress, Second Session, September 22, 2010. 2010. (Illus.). xxxi, 112p. ***(978-0-16-089668-3(6)***, 552-070-42834-8) United States Government Printing Office.

Ricondo & Associates Staff, et al, contrib. by. Handbook to Assess the Impacts of Constrained Parking at Airports. 2010. (Illus.). 101p. pap. ***(978-0-309-15496-3(0))*** Transportation Research Board.

Roche, William K. & Geary, John F. Partnership at Work: The Quest for Radical Organizational Change. 2006. (Routledge Research in Employment Relations Ser.). (ENG., Illus.). 240p. (C). 170.00 *(978-0-415-30434-4(2)*, RU25832) Routledge.

Salk, Ronald D., ed. Airport Transit Guide, 2002: How to Get from the Airport to the City Worldwide. rev. ed. pap. 9.95 *(978-1-890407-05-6(4))* Salk International Travel Premiums, Inc.

Salter, Mark B., ed. Politics at the Airport. 2008. 240p. 60.00 *(978-0-8166-5014-9(4))* Univ. of Minnesota Pr.

Schalk, Susan M. & Schalk, Susan. Planners & Planes: Airports & Land-Use Compatibility. 2011. (Illus.). 125p. pap. 40.00 *(978-1-932364-90-3(0))* American Planning Assn.

Sherwood, Philip. Heathrow: 2,000 Years of History. 2009. (ENG., Illus.). 160p. pap. 27.95 *(978-0-7509-5086-2(2))* History Pr. Ltd, The GBR. Dist: Independent Pubs. Group.

Shrader, Charles R. History of Operations Research in the United States Army, 1942-1962, Vol. 1. 2006. (ENG., Illus.). 221p. per. 28.00 *(978-0-16-072961-4(0)*, 008-029-00433-0 (v. 1), Dept. of the Army) United States Government Printing Office.

Simons, Graham & Bowman, Martin. London's Airports: Useful information on Heathrow, Gatwick, Luton, Stansted & City. 2011. (Illus.). 138p. pap. 29.95 *(978-1-84884-394-3(1))* Pen & Sword Bks. Ltd. GBR. Dist: Casemate Pubs. & Bk. Distributors, LLC.

Smith, Richard C. RAF Duxford: A History in Photographs from 1917 to the Present Day. 2006. (Illus.). 160p. 39.95 *(978-1-904943-59-4(4))* Grub Street GBR. Dist: Casemate Pubs. & Bk. Distributors, LLC.

Spitz, William. Airports & the Newest Generation of General Aviation Aircraft. 2009. (Illus.). *(978-0-309-11795-1(X))* Transportation Research Board.

Spitz, William & Golaszewski, Richard. Airport Aviation Activity Forecasting: A Synthesis of Airport Practice. 2007. (ACRP Synthesis Ser.: Vol. 2). (Illus.). 32p. 44.00 *(978-0-309-09782-6(7))* Transportation Research Board.

Starling, Felipe, et al, eds. Broad Horizons / Larges Horizons: ADPI Architecture & Engineering. 2011. (ENG., Illus.). 176p. 49.95 *(978-1-907317-15-6(5))* Black Dog Publishing Ltd. GBR. Dist: Perseus Distribution.

Stocking, Christine. Integrating Airport Information Systems. 2009. (Illus.). 87p. pap. *(978-0-309-11773-9(9))* Transportation Research Board.

Stoff, Joshua. LaGuardia Airport. 2008. (Images of Aviation Ser.). (ENG., Illus.). 128p. pap. 19.99 *(978-0-7385-5799-1(4))* Arcadia Publishing.

Stroup, Robert M. Crossroads of Liberty: A Pictorial Tribute to Lockbourne/Rickenbacker AFB ANGP IAP. 2009. (ENG.). 152p. 32.00 *(978-1-57510-133-0(5))* Pictorial Histories Publishing Co., Inc.

Taylor, Jennifer. History of Eagle County Airport: How Love of Aviation Formed the Airport - Gypsum, Colorado. 2007. *(978-0-9771135-1-3(2))* Old Gypsum Printer, Inc., The.

'tefánik, Milan. Airport Landside Capacity. 2011. 204p. pap. ***(978-3-8433-3308-9(7))*** Lambert Academic Publishing.

Thomas-Emberson, Steve. Airport Interiors: Design for Business. 2008. (ENG., Illus.). 232p. 85.00 *(978-0-470-03475-0(0)*, Academy Pr.) Wiley, John & Sons, Inc.

Touran, Ali. A Guidebook for Selecting Airport Capital Project Delivery Methods. 2009. (Illus.). 91p. pap. *(978-0-309-11804-0(2))* Transportation Research Board.

Tutumluer, Erol. Bearing Capacity of Roads, Railways & Airfields: Proceedings of the 8th International Conference (BCR2A'09), June 29 - July 2 2009, University of Illinois at Urbana - Champaign, Champaign, Illinois, USA, 2 vols. 2009. (ENG.) 1560p. 440.00 *(978-0-415-87199-0(9)*, CRC Press) Taylor & Francis Group GBR. Dist: Taylor & Francis Group.

Uffelen, Chris van. Airports. 2012. (ENG., Illus.). 272p. 62.50 *(978-3-03768-104-8(7)*, Braun Publish,Csi) Continental Sales, Inc.

Underwood, John. Grand Central Air Terminal. 2006. (Images of America Ser.). (ENG., Illus.). 128p. per. 19.99 *(978-0-7385-4682-7(8))* Arcadia Publishing.

United States & Canada. 150p. 195.00 *(978-0-7876-7326-0(9)*, UXL) Cengage Gale.

United States, Congress House Committee on Transportation and Infrastructure Subcommittee on Aviation Staff, contrib. by. Reforming the Wright Amendment: Hearing Before the Subcommittee on Aviation of the Committee on Transportation & Infrastructure, House of Representatives, One Hundred Ninth Congress, Second Session, July 12, 2006. 2007. vi, 314p. *(978-0-16-078168-1(X)*, 552-070-35566-9) United States Government Printing Office.

Varma, Amily. Aviation, a World of Growth & Change: Proceedings of the 29th International Air Transport Conference, August 19-22, 2007, Irving, Texas. 2007. (Illus.). 253p. pap. 79.00 *(978-0-7844-0938-1(2))* American Society of Civil Engineers.

Visser, H. G & Wijnen, R. A. A. Management of the Environmental Impact at Airport Operations. 2008. pap. 29.00 *(978-1-60456-941-4(7))* Nova Science Pubs., Inc.

Wagner, Olivia. Shopping Paradise Airport. 2008. 168p. pap. *(978-3-639-07589-2(7))* VDM Verlag Dr. Mueller e.K.

Ward, Stephanie A. D. Enhancing Airport Land Use Compatibility, 3 vols. 2010. (Illus.). ***(978-0-309-11823-1(9))***; ***(978-0-309-11824-8(7))*** Transportation Research Board.

Webb, Sandy, et al. Research Needs Associated with Particulate Emissions at Airports. 2008. (ACRP Report Ser.). (Illus.). 58p. 40.00 *(978-0-309-11739-5(9))* Transportation Research Board.

Weigang, Li & Romani, Italo. Computational Models, Software Engineering, & Advanced Technologies in Air Transportation: Next Generation Applications. Barros, Alexandre de, ed. 2009. (Illus.). 392p. 180.00 *(978-1-60566-800-0(1)*, Engineering Science Reference) IGI Global.

Williams, Alan. Developing Strategies for the Modern International Airport: East Asia & Beyond. 2006. 172p. 120.00 *(978-0-7546-4445-3(6))* Ashgate Publishing Co.

Wollersheim, Christoph. On the Provision of Airport Infrastructure in Germany. 2011. 280p. pap. 80.00 *(978-3-8329-6308-8(1))* Nomos Verlagsgesellschaft DEU. Dist: International Specialized Bk. Services.

Wood, Ezra, et al. Aircraft & Airport-Related Hazardous Air Pollutants: Research Needs & Analysis. 2008. (ACRP Report Ser.). (Illus.). 56p. pap. 40.00 *(978-0-309-11745-6(3))* Transportation Research Board.

Woodley, Charles. Heathrow Airport: North Side - The First 25 Years. 2011. (ENG., Illus.). 144p. pap. 24.95 *(978-0-7524-5300-2(9))* History Pr. Ltd., The GBR. Dist: Independent Pubs. Group.

Wragg, David. World's Top 500 Airports. 2010. (ENG., Illus.). 416p. 52.95 *(978-1-84425-632-7(4)*, 1844256324) Haynes Publishing PLC GBR. Dist: MBI Distribution Services/Quayside Distribution.

Yan, Ruixia. Assessing English Language Proficiency in International Aviation Issues of Reliability, Validity, & Aviation Safety. 2009. 128p. pap. *(978-3-639-10984-9(8))* VDM Verlag Dr. Mueller e.K.

Yazici, Riza Onur. Air Passenger Demand Forecasting for Airports. 2011. 152p. pap. ***(978-3-8454-0901-6(0))*** Lambert Academic Publishing.

Young, Seth & Wells, Alexander T. Airport planning & Management 6/e. 6th ed. 2011. (ENG., Illus.). 608p. (C). pap. 70.00 *(978-0-07-175024-0(X)*, 007175024X) McGraw-Hill Professional Publishing.

AIRPORTS—EQUIPMENT AND SUPPLIES

Belliotti, Rick. Common Use Facilities & Equipment at Airports. 2008. (ACRP Synthesis Ser.: Vol. 8). (Illus.). 121p. 52.00 *(978-0-309-09805-2(X))* Transportation Research Board.

Belliotti, Rick. Reference Guide on Understanding Common Use at Airports. 2010. (Illus.). pap. ***(978-0-309-11828-6(X))*** Transportation Research Board.

Butterworth-Hayes, Philip & Birch, Caroline. Airport Equipment Market in China. 62p. 695.00 *(978-0-7106-1221-2(4))* Jane's Information Group, Inc.

The Global Market for Advanced Airport Technologies. 2007. per. 4250.00 *(978-1-59623-286-0(2))* BCC Research.

Jane's Airports, Equipment & Services: Survey the World's Airport Equipment Suppliers & Manufacturers. 535.00 *(978-0-7106-2305-8(4))* Jane's Information Group, Inc.

Rider, David. Jane's Air Traffic Control 2005-2006. cd-rom 1150.00 *(978-0-7106-1571-8(X))* Jane's Information Group, Inc.

Rider, David F. & Bull, Kylie, eds. Jane's Airports, Equipment & Services. 25th rev. ed. 2006. (Jane's Airports, Equipment & Services Ser.). (Illus.). 734p. *(978-0-7106-2744-5(0))* Jane's Information Group, Inc.

Sun Lijun. Dao Lu Yu Ji Chang She Shi Guan Li Xue: Transportation Infrastructure Management System. 2009. (CHI., Illus.). *(978-7-114-07552-0(9))* People's Communications Publishing Hse., The.

United States, Congress House Committee on Transportation and Infrastructure Subcommittee on Aviation Staff, contrib. by. Airline Passenger Baggage Screening: Technology & Airport Deployment Update: Hearing Before the Subcommittee on Aviation of the Committee on Transportation & Infrastructure, House of Representatives, One Hundred Ninth Congress, Second Session, June 29, 2006. 2007. v, 147p. *(978-0-16-078124-7(8)*, 552-070-35525-1) United States Government Printing Office.

AIRPORTS—SECURITY MEASURES

Abeyratne, Ruwantissa. Aviation & the Environment, 1 vol. 2009. 333p. pap. 29.95 *(978-1-60813-707-7(4))* PublishAmerica, Inc.

Ahyudanari, Ervina. Design of Airport Check-in Areas. 2009. 136p. pap. *(978-3-639-12580-1(0))* VDM Verlag Dr. Mueller e.K.

Airport Security: The Necessary Improvements to Secure America's Airports: Hearing Before the Subcommittee on Transportation Security & Infrastructure Protection of the Committee on Homeland Security, House of Representatives, One Hundred Tenth Congress, First Session, April 19, 2007. 2009. iii, 47p. *(978-0-16-083536-0(4)*, 552-070-39259-9) United States Government Printing Office.

Altarescu, Joseba & Bai, Taro. Aviation & Passenger Security. 2012. (Transportation Issues, Policies & R & D Ser.). 147p. 95.00 ***(978-1-62100-155-3(5))*** Nova Science Pubs., Inc.

Aviation Security: An Update: Hearing Before the Subcommittee on Aviation of the Committee on Transportation & Infrastructure, House of Representatives, One Hundred Tenth Congress, Second Session, July 24, 2008. 2008. xv, 193p. *(978-0-16-084017-3(1)*, 552-070-39689-6) United States Government Printing Office.

Aviation Security: Are We Truly Protected?, Part I & a Frontline Perspective on the Need for Enhanced Human Resources & Equipment, Part II: Hearing Before the Subcommittee on Transportation Security & Infrastructure Protection of the Committee on Homeland Security, House of Representatives, One Hundred Tenth Congress, First Session, October 16, 2007 & November 1, 2007. 2009. (Illus.). iv, 117p. *(978-0-16-084141-5(0)*, 552-070-39748-5) United States Government Printing Office.

Brown, David H. Full Body Scam: The Naked View of Current Airport Security. 2011. 260p. pap. 14.95 ***(978-1-4634-2960-7(6))*** AuthorHouse.

Crittenden, Phyllis. Aviation Ground Operation Safety Handbook. 6th ed. 2007. *(978-0-87912-266-9(8))* National Safety Council.

Deb, Sushant. Developing Safety Management Standard for Commercial Airports. 2011. 122p. pap. ***(978-1-84903-097-7(9))*** Schiel & Denver Publishing Ltd.

Elias, Bartholomew. Airport & Aviation Security: U. S. Policy & Strategy in the Age of Global Terrorism. 2009. (ENG., Illus.). 439p. 82.95 *(978-1-4200-7029-3(0))* Auerbach Pubs., Inc.

Flight 253: Learning Lessons from an Averted Tragedy: Hearing Before the Committee on Homeland Security, House of Representatives, One Hundred Eleventh Congress, Second Session, January 27, 2010. 2011. iii, 85p. ***(978-0-16-089494-7(8))*** 552-070-43453-4) United States Government Printing Office.

Flight Safety Foundation Staff, compiled by. 52nd Annual Corporate Aviation Safety Seminar (CASS 2007) The Foundation for Excellence. 2007. 747p. pap. 132.00 *(978-1-60423-385-8(0))* Curran Assocs., Inc.

The Future of the Registered Traveler Program: Hearing Before the Subcommittee on Transportation Security & Infrastructure Protection of the Committee on Homeland Security, House of Representatives, One Hundred Eleventh Congress, First Session, September 30, 2009. 2010. (Illus.). iii, 64p. *(978-0-16-086451-3(8))* 552-070-41508-4) United States Government Printing Office.

General Aviation Security: Assessing Risks & the Road Ahead: Hearing Before the Subcommittee on Transportation Security & Infrastructure Protection of the Committee on Homeland Security, House of Representatives, One Hundred Eleventh Congress, First Session, July 15, 2009. 2009. iv, 81p. *(978-0-16-084857-5(1))* 552-070-40258-6) United States Government Printing Office.

Harrison, John. International Aviation & Terrorism: Evolving Threats, Evolving Security. 2009. (Cass Series on Political Violence Ser.). (ENG.). 224p. 140.00 *(978-0-415-48541-8(X))* Routledge.

Hawley, Kip & Means, Nathan. Permanent Emergency: Inside the TSA & the Fight for the Future of American Security. 2012. (ENG., Illus.). 272p. 27.00 ***(978-0-230-12095-2(4))*** Palgrave Macmillan.

Heitkemper, Lawrence J., et al. Lightning-Warning Systems for Use by Airports. 2008. (Illus.). 71p. *(978-0-309-11752-4(6))* Transportation Research Board.

Hunter, Joyce A. Anger in the Air: Combating the Air Rage Phenomenon. 2009. 236p. 124.95 *(978-0-7546-7193-0(3))* Ashgate Publishing Co.

Ippolito, Natalia. I Might as Well Be Naked! How to Survive Airport Screening with Your Clothes On. 2007. 191p. pap. 15.95 *(978-0-9794484-3-0(3))* Divineisland Bks.

Managing Risk & Increasing Efficiency: An Examination of the Implementation of the Registered Traveler Program: Hearing Before the Subcommittee on Transportation Security & Infrastructure Protection of the Committee on Homeland Security, House of Representatives, One Hundred Tenth Congress, First Session, July 31, 2007. 2009. iii, 44p. *(978-0-16-083977-1(7)*, 552-070-39649-7) United States Government Printing Office.

Markarian, Garik, et al. Aviation Security Engineering: A Holistic Approach. 2011. (Illus.). 280p. 109.00 *(978-1-60807-072-5(7))* Artech Hse., Inc.

Marlin, Ruth Elizabeth. Advantage of Distributed Capacity in Service Continuity Planning: The Case of Air Traffic Control Facility Consolidation. 2010. 187p. pap. 25.95 *(978-1-4327-3923-2(9))* Outskirts Pr., Inc.

Pascucci, Ron L. The American Airport Screener. 2006. 171p. pap. 19.95 *(978-0-7414-3508-8(X))* Infinity Publishing.

Rankin, William. Runway Incursions: The Effectiveness of Airport Driver Training Methods Revealed. 2008. 76p. pap. *(978-3-639-01560-7(6))* VDM Verlag Dr. Mueller e.K.

Salter, Mark B. Politics at the Airport. Salter, Mark B., ed. 2008. 240p. pap. 20.00 *(978-0-8166-5015-6(2))*, Univ. of Minnesota Pr.

Satyamurti, Saty. Simulation of Perimeter Taxiway Operations at Dfw Airport. 2008. 348p. pap. *(978-3-639-09764-1(5))* VDM Verlag Dr. Mueller e.K.

Seidenstat, Paul & Splane, Francis X., eds. Protecting Airline Passengers in the Age of Terrorism, 1 vol. 2009. (Praeger Security International Ser.). (Illus.). 326p. 59.95 *(978-0-313-35453-3(7)*, C35453, Praeger Pubs.) Greenwood Publishing Group, Inc.

Stambaugh, Hollis. An Airport Guide for Regional Emergency Planning for CBRNE Events. 2009. (Illus.). 43p. pap. *(978-0-309-11772-2(0))* Transportation Research Board.

Stambaugh, Hollis, et al. Quarantine Facilities for Arriving Air Travelers: Identification of Planning Needs & Costs. 2008. (ACRP Report Ser.). (Illus.). 34p. 35.00 *(978-0-309-09940-0(4))* Transportation Research Board.

The State of Aviation Security: Is Our Current System Capable of Meeting the Threat?: Hearing Before the Committee on Commerce, Science, & Transportation, United States Senate, One Hundred Eleventh Congress, Second Session, January 20, 2010. 2010. iv, 91p. *(978-0-16-086668-5(5)*, 552-070-41646-3) United States Government Printing Office.

Sweet, Kathleen. Aviation & Airport Security: Terrorism & Safety Concerns, Second Edition. 2nd ed. 2008. (ENG., Illus.). 384p. (C). 83.95 *(978-1-4200-8816-8(5)*, CRC Press) Taylor & Francis Group GBR. Dist: Taylor & Francis Group.

Thomas, Andrew R. Aviation Security Management, 3 vols. Thomas, Andrew R., ed. 2008. (Praeger Security International Ser.). (Illus.). 804p. 375.00 *(978-0-313-34652-1(6)*, C34652, Praeger Pubs.) Greenwood Publishing Group, Inc.

The Transportation Security Administration's Airline Passenger & Baggage Screening: Hearing Before the Committee on Commerce, Science, & Transportation, United States Senate, One Hundred Ninth Congress, Second Session, April 4, 2006. 2011. iii, 73p. ***(978-0-16-087971-5(X)***, 552-070-42422-9) United States Government Printing Office.

United States, Congress House Committee on Homeland Security Subcommittee on Intelligence, Information Sharing, and Terrorism Risk Assessment Staff, contrib. by. Transportation Security Administration's Office of Intelligence: Progress & Challenges. Hearing Before the Subcommittee on Intelligence, Information Sharing, & Terrorism Risk Assessment of the Committee on Homeland Security, U.S. House of Representatives, One Hundred Ninth Congress, Second Session, June 14, 2006. 2007. (Illus.). iii, 64p. *(978-0-16-078439-2(5)*, 552-070-35730-1) United States Government Printing Office.

United States, Congress House Committee on Transportation and Infrastructure Subcommittee on Aviation Staff, contrib. by. Airline Passenger Baggage Screening: Technology & Airport Deployment Update: Hearing Before the Subcommittee on Aviation of the Committee on Transportation & Infrastructure, House of Representatives, One Hundred Ninth Congress, Second Session, June 29, 2006. 2007. v, 147p. *(978-0-16-078124-7(8)*, 552-070-35525-1) United States Government Printing Office.

AIRSHIPS

see also Aeronautics; Balloons

Admiralty, War Staff. German Rigid Airships. 2009. 336p. pap. *(978-1-84734-997-2(8))*, Naval & Military Pr., The.

Althoff, William. Forgotten Weapons. 2009. (Illus.). 432p. 49.95 *(978-1-59114-010-8(2))* Naval Institute Pr.

Aversa, Santiago L. Patrol & ASW Aircraft of the Argentine Navy Vol. I. 2010. 75p. pap. 11.00 *(978-0-557-22402-9(0))* Lulu Enterprises Inc.

Buttlar Brandenfels, Horst Freiherr Treusch von. Zeppelins over England 1914-18. 2011. (Illus.). 152p. 59.95 *(978-1-907677-35-9(6))* Helion & Co., Ltd. GBR. Dist: Casemate Pubs. & Bk. Distributors, LLC.

Castle, Ian. British Airships 1905-30. 2009. (New Vanguard Ser.). (ENG., Illus.). 48p. pap. 17.95 *(978-1-84603-387-2(X))* Osprey Publishing, Ltd. GBR. Dist: Random Hse., Inc.

—London 1914-17: The Zeppelin Menace. 2008. (Campaign Ser.). (ENG., Illus.). 96p. pap. 19.95 *(978-1-84603-245-5(8))* Osprey Publishing, Ltd. GBR. Dist: Random Hse., Inc.

Christopher, John. Transatlantic Airships. 2010. (ENG., Illus.). 192p. 37.95 *(978-1-84797-161-6(X))* Crowood Pr., Ltd. GBR. Dist: Independent Pubs. Group.

—The Zeppelin Story. 2011. (Story Ser.). (ENG., Illus.). 128p. 15.95 *(978-0-7524-5175-6(8))* History Pr. Ltd.,The GBR. Dist: Independent Pubs. Group.

Cross, Wilbur. Disaster at the Pole: The Crash of the Airship Italia-A Harrowing True Tale of Arctic Endurance & Survival. 2010. 348p. pap. 22.95 *(978-1-4401-8674-5(X))* iUniverse, Inc.

Crouch, Tom D. Lighter Than Air: An Illustrated History of Balloons & Airships. 2009. (ENG., Illus.). 192p. 37.00 *(978-0-8018-9127-4(2))* Johns Hopkins Univ. Pr.

Danelek, J. Allan. The Great Airship Of 1897: A Provocative Look at the Most Mysterious Aviation Event in History. 2010. 182p. pap. 16.95 *(978-1-935487-03-6(5))* Adventures Unlimited Pr.

de Syon, Guillaume. Zeppelin! Germany & the Airship, 1900-1939. 2007. (ENG., Illus.). 312p. pap. 25.00 *(978-0-8018-8634-8(1))* Johns Hopkins Univ. Pr.

Faulkner, Neil & Durrani, Nadia. In Search of the Zeppelin War: The Archaeology of the First Blitz. 2008. (ENG., Illus.). 176p. pap. 33.95 *(978-0-7524-4182-5(5))* History Pr. Ltd.,The GBR. Dist: Independent Pubs. Group.

Federal Aviation Administration (U.S.), compiled by. Balloon Flying Handook 2008. 2008. (ENG., Illus.). 237p. pap. 38.00 *(978-0-16-082094-6(4),* Federal Aviation Administration) United States Government Printing Office.

Fioriti, Marco & Chiesa, Sergio. Innovative Solutions for Light, Very Light & Unmanned Aircraft. 2011. 152p. pap. **(978-3-8443-0971-3(3))** Lambert Academic Publishing.

Gardiner, Ian. Flatpack Bombers: The Royal Navy & the Zeppelin Menace. 2009. (Illus.). 176p. 39.99 *(978-1-84884-071-3(3))* Pen & Sword Bks. Ltd. GBR. Dist: Casemate Pubs. & Bk. Distributors, LLC.

George Whale. British Airships: Past, Present & Future. 2006. (ENG.). 128p. pap. 18.99 *(978-1-4264-0074-2(8));* 122p. pap. 13.99 *(978-1-4264-0203-6(1))* BiblioBazaar.

Hylander, Clarence J. Cruisers of the Air: The Story of Lighter Than Air Craft from the Days of Roger Bacon to the Making of the ZRS-4. 2011. 334p. 50.95 **(978-1-258-01611-1(7))** Literary Licensing, LLC.

Jane's All the World's Aircraft: The Authority on Aircraft under Development or in Production. 560.00 *(978-0-7106-2307-2(0))* Jane's Information Group, Inc.

Kochersberger, Kevin. Light Sport Aircraft Inspection Procedures. 2006. per. *(978-1-933189-06-2(1))* Avotek Information Resources.

Le Neve Walmsley, Nick. R101: A Pictorial History. 2nd ed. 2010. (ENG., Illus.). 160p. pap. 29.95 *(978-0-7524-5683-6(0))* History Pr. Ltd.,The GBR. Dist: Independent Pubs. Group.

Mower, Mark. Zeppelin over Suffolk. 2009. pap. 25.99 *(978-1-84415-737-2(7))* Pen & Sword Bks. Ltd. GBR. Dist: Casemate Pubs. & Bk. Distributors, LLC.

Mowthorpe, Ces. Sky Sailors: The Story of the World's Airshipmen. 2011. (ENG.). 192p. pap. 19.95 *(978-0-7524-5879-3(5))* History Pr. Ltd.,The GBR. Dist: Independent Pubs. Group.

Nicolai, Leland M. & Carichner, Grant. Fundamentals of Aircraft & Airship Design. 2010. (Illus.). xxii, 883p. 119.95 *(978-1-60086-751-4(0))* American Institute of Aeronautics & Astronautics.

Powell, John M. Floating to Space: The Airship to Orbit Program. 2008. (Apogee Books Space Ser.). (ENG., Illus.). 204p. pap. 27.95 *(978-1-894959-73-5(6))* Collector's Guide Publishing, Inc. CAN. Dist: Independent Pubs. Group.

Purandare, Ravi. A Buoyancy-Propelled Airship. 2009. 224p. pap. *(978-3-639-13811-5(2))* VDM Verlag Dr. Mueller e.K.

Richards, John. A History of Airships. 2009. (ENG., Illus.). 160p. pap. 32.95 *(978-0-7524-4536-6(7))* History Pr. Ltd.,The GBR. Dist: Independent Pubs. Group.

Ridley-Kitts, Daniel George. The History & Development of the Dirigible Airship in Peace & War. 2012. (ENG., Illus.). 304p. 34.95 **(978-0-7524-6471-8(X))** History Pr. Ltd.,The GBR. Dist: Independent Pubs. Group.

Rosie, George. Flight of the Titan: The Story of the R34. 2010. (ENG., Illus.). 224p. pap. 16.00 *(978-1-84158-863-6(6),* Birlinn) Birlinn, Ltd. GBR. Dist: Interlink Publishing Group, Inc.

Whale, George. British Airships: Past, Present & Future. 2008. 136p. pap. *(978-1-4099-3747-0(X))* Dodo Pr.

AIRSHIPS—JUVENILE LITERATURE

Doeden, Matt. The Hindenburg Disaster. 2006. (Graphic Library: Disasters in History Ser.). (ENG., Illus.). 32p. (gr. 3-4). per. 7.95 *(978-0-7368-6876-1(3),* Graphic Library) Capstone Pr., Inc.

AIRSPACE (LAW)

Banner, Stuart. Who Owns the Sky? The Struggle to Control Airspace from the Wright Brothers On. 2008. (Illus.). 360p. 29.95 *(978-0-674-03082-4(6))* Harvard Univ. Pr.

Beck, Bettina. Die Regelung slots (von Zeitnischen) im Luftverkehrsrecht: Vergabe, Übertragung und Anfechtung in der Schweiz und der EG unter rechtsvergleichender Berücksichtigung US-amerikanischer Normen. 2008. (Studies in Global Economic Law. Studien zum globalen Wirtschaftsrecht. Études en droit économique mondial Ser.). 255p. pap. *(978-3-03911-737-6(8))* Lang, Peter.

Haanappel. Law & Policy of Air, Space & Outer Space, Second Edition Rev. 2nd rev. ed. 2010. 158.00 *(978-90-411-2804-1(2))* Wolters Kluwer Law & Business.

Oduntan, Gbenga. Sovereignty, Jurisdiction, & Exploitation of the Seas, Polar Regions, Airspace & Outer Space: Legal Criteria for Spatial Delimitation. 2011. (Routledge Research in International Law Ser.). (ENG.). 408p. 155.00 *(978-0-415-56212-6(0))* Routledge.

Williams, William A., et al. Preserving Range & Airspace Access for the Air Force Mission: Striving for a Strategic Vantage Point. 2011. (Illus.). 100p. pap. 29.50 *(978-0-8330-5140-0(7))* RAND Corp., The.

AIRWAY (MEDICINE)

American Academy of Orthopaedic Surgeons (AAOS) & Margolis, Gregg. Paramedic: Airway Management. 2011. 332p. pap. 79.95 **(978-1-4496-4259-4(4))** Jones & Bartlett Learning, LLC.

Baur, Dale A. & Rowshan, Henry H. Management of the Airway, an Issue of Atlas of the Oral & Maxillofacial Surgery Clinics. 2010. (Clinics: Dentistry Ser.: 18-1). (ENG., Illus.). viii, 68p. 180.00 *(978-1-4377-1797-6(7),* Saunders) Elsevier - Health Sciences Div.

Benger, Jonathan, et al, eds. Emergency Airway Management. 2008. (ENG., Illus.). 190p. pap. 60.00 *(978-0-521-72729-7(4))* Cambridge Univ. Pr.

Chung, Kian Fan, ed. Airway Smooth Muscle in Asthma & COPD: Biology & Pharmacology. 2008. (ENG., Illus.). 326p. 197.95 *(978-0-470-06066-7(2),* Wiley) Wiley, John & Sons, Inc.

Cram101 Textbook Reviews. Outlines & Highlights for Benumofs Airway Management by Carin Hagberg, Isbn: 9780323022330. 2011. 224p. pap. 30.95 **(978-1-61461-439-5(3))** Cram101 Inc.

Cram101 Textbook Reviews & Cram101 Textbook Reviews. Outlines & Highlights for Core Topics in Airway Management by Adrian Pearce Edited by Ian Calder, Isbn: 9780521869102. 2011. 92p. pap. 27.95 **(978-1-61461-222-3(6))** Cram101 Inc.

Hagberg, Carin A. Benumof's Airway Management. 2nd rev. ed. 2007. (ENG., Illus.). 1344p. 218.00 *(978-0-323-02233-0(2),* Mosby) Elsevier - Health Sciences Div.

Hung, Orlando & Murphy, Michael F. Management of the Difficult & Failed Airway, Second Edition. 2nd ed. 2011. (ENG., Illus.). 608p. 155.00 **(978-0-07-162346-9(9),** 0071623469) McGraw-Hill Professional Publishing.

Kovacs, George & Law, J. Adam. Airway Management in Emergencies. 2nd ed. 2012. (Illus.). 332p. pap. **(978-1-60795-104-9(5))** PMPH-USA. Ltd.

Kovacs, George, et al. Airway Management in Emergencies. 2007. (ENG., Illus.). 312p. pap. 89.00 *(978-0-07-147005-6(0),* 0071470050) McGraw-Hill Professional Publishing.

Murphy, Michael F. Manual of Emergency Airway Management. Murphy, Michael F., ed. 3rd rev. ed. 2008. (ENG., Illus.). 432p. pap. 72.00 *(978-0-7817-8494-8(8))* Lippincott Williams & Wilkins.

Orebaugh, Steven L. & Bigeleisen, Paul E. Atlas of Airway Management: Techniques & Tools. 2nd rev. ed. 2011. (ENG., Illus.). 432p. 124.95 *(978-1-4511-0339-7(5))* Lippincott Williams & Wilkins.

Rich, James Michael. SLAM: Street-Level Airway Management. 2007. (ENG., Illus.). 400p. (C). per. 35.33 *(978-0-13-118320-9(6),* Prentice Hall) Prentice Hall PTR.

Verschakelen, Johny, et al. Computed Tomographic (CT) Imaging for Small Airways Disease: Text & Atlas. 2013. (ENG., Illus.). 160p. pap. 149.95 *(978-0-470-33965-7(9),* Wiley-Blackwell) Wiley, John & Sons, Inc.

Walls, Ron & Murphy, Michael. Manual of Emergency Airway Management. 4th rev. ed. 2012. (ENG., Illus.). 464p. pap. 84.95 **(978-1-4511-4491-8(1))** Lippincott Williams & Wilkins.

Zaccone, Giacomo. Airway Chemoreceptors in the Vertebrates: Structure, Evolution & Function. 2009. (ENG., Illus.). 464p. 139.95 *(978-1-57808-614-6(0))* BIOS Scientific Publishers Ltd. GBR. Dist: Taylor & Francis Group.

AIRWAYS

Here are entered works dealing with air routes along which are maintained aids to air navigation, such as landing fields, beacon lights, etc.

see also Airlines

Bluffield, Robert. Imperial Airways. 2010. (ENG., Illus.). 224p. 56.95 *(978-1-906537-07-4(0))* Allan, Ian Publishing GBR. Dist: BookMasters Distribution Services (BDS).

Markey, Barb & Hunt, Tad. Airways: Rising to the Challenge of Managing COPD. Allen, Susan D. & Holloran, Colleen A., eds. (Illus.). 56p. pap. 3.50 *(978-0-916999-13-1(0))* H E R C, Publishing.

Ottaway, Susan & Ottaway, Ian. Fly with the Stars: British South American Airways: the Rise & Controversial Fall of a Long-Haul Trailblazer. 2007. (ENG., Illus.). 256p. 36.95 *(978-0-7509-4448-9(X))* Sutton Publishing.

Pirie, Gordon. Air Empire: British Imperial Civil Aviation, 1919-39. 2010. (Studies in Imperialism Ser.). (ENG., Illus.). 272p. 89.95 *(978-0-7190-4111-2(2))* Manchester Univ. Pr. GBR. Dist: Macmillan.

Tsourdos, Antonios. Cooperative Path Planning of Unmanned Aerial Vehicles. 2nd ed. 2011. 448p. 120.00 **(978-1-60086-779-8(0))** Wiley, John & Sons, Inc.

AIRY FUNCTIONS

Vallee, Olivier. Airy Functions & Applications to Physics. 2nd ed. 2010. (Illus.). 212p. 70.00 *(978-1-84816-548-9(X))* World Scientific Publishing Co., Inc.

AIX (COMPUTER PROGRAM)

Blanchard, Bruno. Introduction to Workload Partition Management in IBM AIX Version 6.1. 2007. (Illus.). xvi, 276p. *(978-0-7384-8654-3(X))* IBM.

Brandon, Shane. Workload Partition Management in IBM Aix Version 6.1. 2008. (Illus.). xiv, 336p. **(978-0-7384-3207-6(5))** IBM.

Byrd, Janis. Sun Solaris to IBM AIX 5L Migration: A Guide to System Administrators. 2007. (Illus.). xviii, 526p. *(978-0-7384-8973-5(5))* IBM.

Elsetohy, Hassan. NIM from A to Z in AIX 5L. 2007. (Illus.). xvi, 658p. *(978-0-7384-8631-4(0))* IBM.

Franklin, William N., Jr. A Guide to AIX Version 4. Date not set. (Illus.). pap. 44.00 *(978-1-884051-06-7(5))* Metro Information Systems Corp. T/A MIS Pr.

Gilley, Michael, et al. AIX 5L on IBM System I Platform Implementation Guide. 2nd ed. 2007. (Illus.). x, 146p. *(978-0-7384-8614-7(0))* IBM.

Gough, Brad. AIX V6 Advanced Security Features: Introduction & Configuration. 2007. (Illus.). xviii, 394p. *(978-0-7384-8924-7(7))* IBM.

Milberg, Ken. Driving the Power of AIX: Performance Tuning on IBM Power. 2009. (ENG.). 256p. pap. 54.95 *(978-1-58347-098-5(0))* MC Pr., LLC.

AIZOACEAE

Kelaidis, Panayoti. Hardy Ice Plants: A Horticultural Handbook for Hobbyists & Growers. 2009. *(978-1-55566-437-4(7))* Johnson Bks.

AJAX (WEB SITE DEVELOPMENT TECHNOLOGY)

Allen, Richard, et al. Web Development with JavaScript & AJAX Illuminated. 2008. 497p. pap. 83.95 *(978-0-7637-5489-1(7))* Jones & Bartlett Learning, LLC.

Asleson, Ryan & Schutta, Nathaniel T. Pro Ajax & Java Frameworks. 2006. (ENG., Illus.). 336p. per. 49.99 *(978-1-59059-677-7(3))* Apress L. P.

Babin, Lee. Beginning Ajax with PHP. 2006. (Expert's Voice in Open Source Ser.). (ENG., Illus.). 272p. pap. 34.99 *(978-1-59059-667-8(6))* Apress L. P.

Ballard, Phil. Ajax Starter Kit. 2007. (Sams Teach Yourself Ser.). (ENG., Illus.). 224p. pap. 39.99 *(978-0-672-32960-9(3))* Sams.

Bernal, Joey. Web 2.0 & Social Networking for the Enterprise: Guidelines & Examples for Implementation & Management Within Your Organization. 2009. (ENG., Illus.). 312p. pap. 39.99 *(978-0-13-700489-8(3))* Pearson Education.

Brinzarea, Bogdan & Darie, Cristian. AJAX & PHP: Building Modern Web Applications. 2nd ed. 2009. 300p. pap. *(978-1-84719-772-6(8))* Packt Publishing, Ltd.

Calderon, Adam & Rumerman, Joel. Advanced ASP . NET AJAX Server Controls: For . NET 3. 5 Framework 3. 5. 2008. (ENG., Illus.). 648p. pap. 49.99 *(978-0-321-51444-8(0))* Addison Wesley Professional.

Carey, Patrick & Canovatchel, Frank. Instructor Resource CD-ROM for Carey/Canovatchel's New Perspectives on JavaScript & AJAX. 2nd ed. 2009. 175.75 *(978-1-4390-4402-5(3))* Course Technology.

—Review Pack for Carey/Canovatchel's New Perspectives on JavaScript & AJAX. 2nd ed. 2009. (ENG.). 12.95 *(978-1-4390-4401-8(5))* Course Technology.

Chaganti, Prabhakar. Google Web Toolkit GWT Java Ajax Programming: A Practical Guide to Google Web Toolkit for Creating AJAX Applications with Java. 2007. 240p. per. *(978-1-84719-100-7(2))* Packt Publishing, Ltd.

Cram101 Textbook Reviews. Outlines & Highlights for Advanced Ajax: Architecture and Best Practices by Shawn M. Lauriat. 2011. 88p. pap. 27.95 **(978-1-61906-035-7(3))** Cram101 Inc.

Crane, Dave & McCarthy, Phil. Comet & Reverse Ajax: The Next-Generation Ajax 2. 0. 2008. (ENG.). 100p. pap. 19.99 *(978-1-59059-998-3(5))* Apress L. P.

Crane, Dave, et al. Prototype & Scriptaculous in Action. 2007. (ENG., Illus.). 544p. per. 44.99 *(978-1-933988-03-0(7))* Manning Pubns. Co.

Deitel, Paul J. & Deitel, Harvey M. AJAX, Rich Internet Applications, & Web Development for Programmers. 2008. (Deitel Developer Ser.). (ENG., Illus.). 1040p. per. 59.99 *(978-0-13-158738-0(2))* Prentice Hall PTR.

Dewsbury, Ryan. Google Web Toolkit Applications. 2007. (ENG., Illus.). 608p. per. 59.99 *(978-0-321-50196-7(9))* Addison Wesley Professional.

Dwivedi, Himanshu, et al. Hacking Exposed Web 2. 0: Web 2. 0 Security Secrets & Solutions. 2007. (Hacking Exposed Ser.). (ENG., Illus.). 258p. pap. 49.99 *(978-0-07-149461-8(8),* 0071494618) McGraw-Hill Osborne.

Ellis, Matthew. ASP.NET AJAX Programming Tricks. 2007. 388p. pap. 34.99 *(978-0-9703720-0-0(0))* Magma Interactive, LLC.

Esposito, Dino. Microsoft ASP.NET & AJAX: Architecting Web Applications. 2009. (ENG.). 352p. pap. 39.99 *(978-0-7356-2621-8(9))* Microsoft Pr.

Evjen, Bill, et al. ASP.NET 4 in C# & VB. 2010. (ENG., Illus.). 1536p. pap. 59.99 *(978-0-470-50220-4(7),* Wrox) Wiley, John & Sons, Inc.

Ford, Jerry Lee, Jr. Ajax Programming for the Absolute Beginner. 2008. (ENG., Illus.). 320p. pap. 29.99 *(978-1-59863-564-5(6))* Course Technology.

Foster, Robert. ASP.NET 3.5 Ajax. 2008. (Unleashed Ser.). (ENG.). 264p. pap. 39.99 *(978-0-672-32973-9(5))* Sams.

Gallo, Alessandro, et al. ASP. Net Ajax in Action. 2007. (ENG., Illus.). 576p. per. 44.99 *(978-1-933988-14-6(2))* Manning Pubns. Co.

Geary, David. Google Web Toolkit Solutions: More Cool & Useful Stuff. 2007. (ENG., Illus.). 408p. per. 44.99 *(978-0-13-234481-4(5))* Prentice Hall PTR.

Gibbs, Matt & Wahlin, Dan. Professional ASP.NET 2.0 AJAX. 2007. (ENG., Illus.). 336p. per. 39.99 *(978-0-470-10962-5(9),* Wrox) Wiley, John & Sons, Inc.

Gube, Jacob & Cheung, Garrick. Mootools 1 2 Beginners Guide Lite: Getting Started. 2011. 102p. pap. **(978-1-84951-624-2(3))** Packt Publishing, Ltd.

Gumani, Anil. Web Development with TIBCO General Interface: Building AJAX Clients for Enterprise SOA. 2009. (Developer's Library). (ENG., Illus.). 384p. pap. 39.99 *(978-0-321-56329-3(8))* Addison Wesley Professional.

Hadlock, Kris. Ajax for Web Application Developers. 2006. (Developer's Library). (ENG., Illus.). 288p. pap. 44.99 *(978-0-672-32912-8(3))* Sams.

Hanson, Robert & Tacy, Adam. GWT in Action: Easy Ajax with the Google Web Toolkit. 2007. (ENG., Illus.). 600p. per. 49.99 *(978-1-933988-23-8(1))* Manning Pubns. Co.

Harmon, James. Dojo: Using the Dojo JavaScript Library to Build Ajax Applications. 2008. (Developer's Library). (ENG., Illus.). 336p. pap. 44.99 *(978-0-13-235804-0(2))* Addison Wesley Professional.

Harris, Andy. JavaScript & AJAX for Dummies. 2009. (ENG., Illus.). 432p. pap. 29.99 *(978-0-470-41799-7(4),* For Dummies) Wiley, John & Sons, Inc.

Harwani, Bintu. jQuery Recipes: A Problem-Solution Approach. 2010. (ENG.). 456p. pap. 44.99 *(978-1-4302-2709-0(5))* Apress L. P.

Heilmann, Christian. JavaScript with DOM Scripting & Ajax. 2006. (Beginning: from Novice to Professional Ser.). (ENG., Illus.). 512p. per. 39.99 *(978-1-59059-680-7(3))* Apress L. P.

Hoffman, Billy & Sullivan, Bryan. Ajax Security. 2007. (ENG., Illus.). 504p. per. 54.99 *(978-0-321-49193-0(9))* Addison Wesley Professional.

Holzner, Steven. Dojo, Kit. 2008. (Visual QuickStart Guide Ser.). (ENG.). 208p. pap. 24.99 *(978-0-321-60512-2(8))* Peachpit Pr.

Kanjilal, Joydip & Putrevu, Sriram. ASP.NET Ajax. 2008. (Sams Teach Yourself—Hours Ser.). (ENG., Illus.). 432p. pap. 39.99 *(978-0-672-32967-8(0))* Sams.

Katz, Max. Practical RichFaces. 2008. (ENG.). 264p. pap. 39.99 *(978-1-4302-1055-9(9))* Apress L. P.

Katz, Max & Shaikovsky, Ilya. Practical RichFaces. 2nd ed. 2011. (ENG.). 408p. pap. 49.99 *(978-1-4302-3449-4(0))* Apress L. P.

Kaula, Rajeev. Oracle 11g: Developing AJAX Applications with PL/SQL Server Pages. 4th ed. 2008. (ENG.). 528p. (C). pap. 84.33 *(978-0-07-340877-4(8),* 0073408778) McGraw-Hill Cos., The.

Keith, Jeremy. Bulletproof Ajax. 2007. (Voices That Matter Ser.). (ENG., Illus.). 216p. per. 39.99 *(978-0-321-47266-3(7))* New Riders Publishing.

Khosravi, Shahram. ASP.NET AJAX: With ASP. NET 2.0 & ASP.NET 3.5. 2007. (ENG., Illus.). 1522p. per. 59.99 *(978-0-470-10998-4(X),* Wrox) Wiley, John & Sons, Inc.

Lane, Jonathan, et al. Foundation Website Creation with CSS, XHTML, & JavaScript. 2008. (ENG., Illus.). 275p. pap. 34.99 *(978-1-4302-0991-1(7),* Friends of Ed) Apress L. P.

Larson, Daniel. Developing Service-Oriented AJAX Applications on the Microsoft Platform. 2008. (ENG.). 352p. pap. 39.99 *(978-0-7356-2591-4(3))* Microsoft Pr.

Lauriat, Shawn M. Advanced Ajax: Architecture & Best Practices. 2007. (ENG., Illus.). 384p. per. 44.99 *(978-0-13-135064-9(1))* Prentice Hall PTR.

Mahemoff, Michael. Ajax Design Patterns. 2006. (ENG., Illus.). 656p. per. 44.99 *(978-0-596-10180-0(5))* O'Reilly Media, Inc.

Marion, Jim. PeopleSoft PeopleTools Tips & Techniques. 2010. (Oracle Press Ser.). (ENG., Illus.). 640p. pap. 69.99 *(978-0-07-166493-6(9),* 0071664939) McGraw-Hill Osborne.

McClure, Wallace B., et al. Beginning Ajax with ASP. NET. 2006. (ENG., Illus.). 432p. pap. 39.99 *(978-0-471-78544-6(X),* Wrox) Wiley, John & Sons, Inc.

—Beginning ASP.NET 2.0 AJAX. 2007. (ENG., Illus.). 344p. per. 39.99 *(978-0-470-11283-0(2),* Wrox) Wiley, John & Sons, Inc.

Meloni, Julie C., et al. Sams Teach Yourself jQuery in 24 Hours. rev. ed. 2013. (ENG.). 450p. pap. 34.99 **(978-0-672-33556-3(5))** Sams.

Moore, Dana, et al. Professional Rich Internet Applications: AJAX & Beyond. 2007. (ENG., Illus.). 565p. per. 39.99 *(978-0-470-08280-5(1),* Wrox) Wiley, John & Sons, Inc.

Newton, Aaron. MooTools Essentials: The Official MooTools Reference for JavaScript & Ajax Development. 2008. (ENG.). 300p. pap. 19.99 *(978-1-4302-0983-6(6))* Apress L. P.

Olson, Steven Douglas. Ajax on Java. 2007. (ENG., Illus.). 240p. per. 29.99 *(978-0-596-10187-9(2))* O'Reilly Media, Inc.

Powers, David. The Essential Guide to Dreamweaver CS3 with CSS, Ajax, & PHP. 2007. (Friends of ED Adobe Learning Library). (ENG.). 784p. pap. 49.99 *(978-1-59059-859-7(6),* Friends of Ed) Apress L. P.

—The Essential Guide to Dreamweaver CS4 with CSS, Ajax, & PHP. 2008. (ENG.). 1000p. pap. 49.99 *(978-1-4302-1610-0(7),* Friends of Ed) Apress L. P.

Powers, Shelley. Adding Ajax. 2007. (ENG., Illus.). 400p. per. 34.99 *(978-0-596-52936-9(8))* O'Reilly Media, Inc.

Raffer, Georg. Security of Java Based Ajax Frameworks. 2009. 112p. pap. *(978-3-639-14192-4(X))* VDM Verlag Dr. Mueller e.K.

Ramm, Mark, et al. Rapid Web Applications with TurboGears: Using Python to Create Ajax-Powered Sites. 2006. (Prentice Hall Open Source Software Development Ser.). (ENG., Illus.). 504p. per. 54.99 *(978-0-13-243388-4(5))* Prentice Hall PTR.

Raymond, Scott. Ajax on Rails. 2007. (ENG., Illus.). 352p. per. 39.99 *(978-0-596-52744-0(6))* O'Reilly Media, Inc.

Rewis, Greg. Mastering Web Content: Behavior with Ajax, DVD. 2009. (Voices That Matter Ser.). (ENG.). 39.99 *(978-0-321-63691-1(0))* New Riders Publishing.

Riecke, Craig, et al. Mastering Dojo: JavaScript & Ajax Tools for Great Web Experiences. Carter, Jacquelyn, ed. 2008. (Pragmatic Programmers Ser.). (ENG., Illus.). 555p. pap. 38.95 *(978-1-934356-11-1(5),* Pragmatic Bookshelf, The) Pragmatic Programmers, LLC, The.

Riordan, Rebecca M. Head First Ajax. 2008. (Head First Ser.). (ENG., Illus.). 528p. pap. 44.99 *(978-0-596-51578-2(2))* O'Reilly Media, Inc.

Roche, Kyle, et al. Beginning Java Google App Engine. 2009. (ENG.). 264p. pap. 44.99 *(978-1-4302-2553-9(X))* Apress L. P.

Rutter, Jake. Smashing JQuery: Professional Techniques with Ajax & Jquery. 2011. (Smashing Magazine Book Ser.: 7). (ENG.). 336p. pap. 39.99 *(978-0-470-97723-1(X),* Wiley) Wiley, John & Sons, Inc.

Sams Publishing Staff. Sams Teach Yourself JavaScript & Ajax: Video Learning Starter Kit Bundle. 2009. (Sams Teach Yourself Video Learning Ser.). (ENG.). pap. 49.99 *(978-0-672-33090-2(3))* Sams.

Sams Publishing Staff, et al. Sams Teach Yourself JavaScript & Ajax: Video Learning Starter Kit. 2009. (Sams Teach Yourself Ser.). (ENG.). 58p. 39.99 *(978-0-672-33037-7(7))* Sams.

Schalk, Chris & Holzner, Steven. Ajax: A Beginner's Guide. 2008. (Beginner's Guide Ser.). (ENG., Illus.). 475p. pap. 39.99 *(978-0-07-149429-8(4), 0071494294)* McGraw-Hill Osborne.

Smeets, Bram, et al. Beginning Google Web Toolkit. 2008. (Expert's Voice in Web Development Ser.). (ENG., Illus.). 350p. pap. 39.99 *(978-1-4302-1031-3(1))* Apress L. P.

Sonneveld, Jord, et al. Ajax in Practice. 2007. (ENG., Illus.). 456p. per. 44.99 *(978-1-932394-99-3(0))* Manning Pubns. Co.

Spaanjaars, Imar. ASP.NET 4.0: In C# & VB. 2010. (ENG., Illus.). 840p. pap. 44.99 *(978-0-470-50221-1(5)*, Wrox) Wiley, John & Sons, Inc.

Stehling, Brennan & Thomas, Cindi. Embracing JQuery: User Experience Design. 2010. (ENG.). 400p. pap. 39.99 *(978-1-4302-2617-8(X))* Apress L. P.

Tacy, Adam, et al. GWT in Action. 2nd rev. ed. 2012. (ENG.). 500p. pap. 49.99 ***(978-1-935182-84-9(6))*** Manning Pubns. Co.

Teague, Jason Cranford. CSS, DHTML, & Ajax: Visual QuickStart Guide. 4th rev. ed. 2006. (Visual Quickstart Guide Ser.). (ENG., Illus.). 584p. per. 29.99 *(978-0-321-44325-0(X))* Peachpit Pr.

Ullman, Chris & Dykes, Lucinda. Beginning Ajax. 2007. (ENG., Illus.). 498p. per. 39.99 *(978-0-470-10675-4(1)*, Wrox) Wiley, John & Sons, Inc.

Ullman, Larry. Building a Web Site with Ajax. 2007. (Visual QuickProject Guide Ser.). (ENG., Illus.). 176p. pap. 19.99 *(978-0-321-52441-6(1))* Peachpit Pr.

Vohra, Deepak. Ajax in Oracle JDeveloper. 2008. (Illus.). 224p. pap. 69.95 *(978-3-540-77595-9(1), 3540775951)* Springer.

Wells, Christopher. Securing Ajax Applications: Ensuring the Safety of the Dynamic Web. 2007. (ENG., Illus.). 256p. per. 49.99 *(978-0-596-52931-4(7))* O'Reilly Media, Inc.

Wenz, Christian. Programming Atlas. 2006. (ENG., Illus.). 408p. per. 34.99 *(978-0-596-52672-6(5))* O'Reilly Media, Inc.

White, Damien. Hands on ASP. NET AJAX Control Toolkit. 2008. (Wrox Briefs Ser.). 44p. 6.99 *(978-0-470-28664-7(4)*, Wrox) Wiley, John & Sons, Inc.

Woolston, Daniel. Pro Ajax & the . NET 2. 0 Platform. 2006. (Expert's Voice in Web Development Ser.). (ENG., Illus.). 488p. per. 49.99 *(978-1-59059-670-8(6))* Apress L. P.

Woychowsky, Edmond. Ajax: Creating Web Pages with Asynchronous Javascript & Xml. 2006. (Bruce Perens' Open Source Ser.). (ENG.). 408p. pap. 44.99 ***(978-0-13-276422-3(9)***, Prentice Hall) Prentice Hall PTR.

W3Schools. Learn JavaScript & Ajax with W3Schools. 2010. (ENG., Illus.). 264p. pap. 29.99 *(978-0-470-61194-4(4)*, Wiley) Wiley, John & Sons, Inc.

Zakas, Nicholas C., et al. Professional Ajax. 2nd rev. ed. 2007. (ENG., Illus.). 624p. per. 39.99 *(978-0-470-10949-6(1)*, Wrox) Wiley, John & Sons, Inc.

Zammetti, Frank W. Practical Ajax Projects with Java Technology. 2006. (Expert's Voice in Web Development Ser.). (ENG., Illus.). 528p. per. 49.99 *(978-1-59059-695-1(1))* Apress L. P.

AKA LANGUAGE

see Akan Language

AKAN (AFRICAN PEOPLE)

see also Ashanti (African People); Fanti (African People)

Abroquah, Martin. Revelation: The Movement of the Akan People from Kanaan to Ghana. 2010. (Illus.). 532p. pap. 38.49 *(978-1-4490-6251-4(2))* AuthorHouse.

Bahuchet, S., et al, eds. Encyclopédie des Pygmees Aka II. Dictionnaire ethnographique Aka-Francais. Fasc. 9, G-NG-H. 2008. (Societe d'Etudes Linguistiques et Anthropologiques de France Ser.). (AFA & FRE.). 219p. (C). pap. 79.00 *(978-90-429-2099-6(8))* Peeters Pubs. & Booksellers BEL. Dist: Brown, David Bk. Co., The.

Ephirim-Donkor, Anthony. African Religion Defined: A Systematic Study of Ancestor Worship among the Akan. 2010. (Illus.). 160p. pap. 25.50 *(978-0-7618-5328-2(6))* Univ. Pr. of America, Inc.

—African Spirituality: On Becoming Ancestors. 2011. (ENG.). 200p. pap. 29.50 *(978-0-7618-5467-8(3))* Univ. Pr. of America, Inc.

Nkansah-Obrempong, James. Visual Theology. 2010. 296p. pap. *(978-3-639-23087-1(6))* VDM Verlag Dr. Mueller e.K.

Ofosu-Donkoh, Kobina. Human Rights in African Religions & Philosophy. 2010. 204p. pap. *(978-3-8383-4186-6(4))* Lambert Academic Publishing.

Oppong, Christine. Marriage among a Matrilineal Elite: A Family Study of Ghanaian Senior Civil Servants. 2009. (Cambridge Studies in Social & Cultural Anthropology Ser.). (ENG.). 224p. pap. 31.99 *(978-0-521-09318-7(X))* Cambridge Univ. Pr.

AKAN LANGUAGE

Here are entered works dealing collectively with the dialect of the Fanti people and the dialects of the Akuapem, Ashanti, and related peoples who accept the name Twi. Works limited to the dialects of the latter groups are entered under Twi Language.

see also Twi Language

Agyekum, Kofi. Akan Metalanguage & Terminology. 2011. 340p. pap. ***(978-3-8433-7155-1(5))*** Lambert Academic Publishing.

Bahuchet, S., et al, eds. Encyclopedie des Pygmees Aka II. Dictionnaire ethnographique Aka-Francais. Fasc. 9, G-NG-H. 2008. (Societe d'Etudes Linguistiques et Anthropologiques de France Ser.). (AFA & FRE.). 219p. (C). pap. 79.00 *(978-90-429-2099-6(8))* Peeters Pubs. & Booksellers BEL. Dist: Brown, David Bk. Co., The.

Lomotey, Charlotte Fofo. Vowels of Akan. 2010. 232p. pap. *(978-3-639-24947-7(X))* VDM Verlag Dr. Mueller e.K.

Obeng, Samuel Gyasi. Akan Newspaper Reader. 2008. xxv, 148p. *(978-1-931546-52-2(5))* Dunwoody Pr.

Thomas, J. M. C., et al, eds. Encyclopedie des Pygmees AKA II. Dictionnaire Ethnographique AKA-Francais. Fasc. 8, K. 2007. (Société d'Études Linguistiques et Anthropologiques de France Ser.). (ENG.). 385p. (C). pap. 99.00 *(978-90-429-1860-3(8))* Peeters Pubs. & Booksellers BEL. Dist: Brown, David Bk. Co., The.

AKANS (AFRICAN PEOPLE)

see Akan (African People)

AKASHIC RECORDS

Andrews, Synthia & Andrews, Colin. The Complete Idiot's Guide to the Akashic Record. 2010. (Complete Idiot's Guide Ser.). (ENG.). 336p. (gr. 12). 16.95 *(978-1-59257-996-9(5)*, Alpha Bks.) Penguin Group (USA) Inc.

Cori, Patricia. The Cosmos of Soul: A Wake-up Call for Humanity. 2008. (Sirian Revelations Ser.). (ENG., Illus.). 272p. per. 16.95 *(978-1-55643-736-6(6))* North Atlantic Bks.

Dowling, Levi. The Aquarian Gospel of Jesus the Christ. 2007. 268p. 18.95 *(978-1-60206-227-6(7))*; per. 11.45 *(978-1-60206-224-5(2))* Cosimo, Inc.

—The Aquarian Gospel of Jesus the Christ. 2008. 272p. pap. 12.95 *(978-0-486-45776-4(7))* Dover Pubns., Inc.

Dowling, Levi & Dowling, Eva S. The Aquarian Gospel of Jesus the Christ. 2010. 266p. 42.95 *(978-1-161-37075-1(7))* Kessinger Publishing, LLC.

Dowling, Levi H. The Aquarian Gospel of Jesus the Christ. 2009. 560p. 30.99 *(978-0-559-12535-5(6))*; 36.99 *(978-0-559-12524-9(0))*; pap. 42.75 *(978-0-559-12527-0(5))*; pap. 41.75 *(978-0-559-12532-4(1))* BiblioBazaar.

—The Aquarian Gospel of Jesus the Christ. 2006. 264p. per. 19.95 *(978-1-58509-279-6(7))* Book Tree, The.

—The Aquarian Gospel of Jesus the Christ. 2009. pap. 8.95 *(978-1-4209-3382-6(5))* Digireads.com.

—The Aquarian Gospel of Jesus the Christ: The Missing Years. 2010. (Sacred Wisdom Ser.). (ENG.). 192p. 8.95 *(978-1-906787-54-7(9)*, Watkins Publishing) Duncan Baird Pubs. GBR. Dist: Sterling Publishing Co., Inc.

—The Aquarian Gospel of Jesus the Christ: The Philosophic & Practical Basis of the Religion of the Aquarian Age of the World. 2006. 270p. pap. *(978-81-7769-262-4(3))* Pilgrims Publishing.

Dowling, Levi H. & Dowling, Levi. The Aquarian Gospel of Jesus the Christ. 2009. (ENG.). 448p. (gr. 12-18). pap. 10.00 *(978-1-58542-724-6(1)*, Tarcher) Penguin Group (USA) Inc.

Howe, Linda. Healing Through the Akashic Records. 2011. 224p. 21.95 *(978-1-60407-096-5(X))* Sounds True, Inc.

—Healing Through the Akashic Records: Discovering Your Soul's Perfection. 2010. 69.95 *(978-1-59179-913-9(9))* Sounds True, Inc.

—How to Read the Akashic Records: Accessing the Archive of the Soul & Its Journey. unabr. ed. 2010. 224p. pap. 14.95 *(978-1-59179-904-7(X))* Sounds True, Inc.

Laszlo, Ervin. The Akashic Experience: Science & the Cosmic Memory Field. 2009. (ENG.). 1p. pap. 16.95 *(978-1-59477-298-6(3)*, Inner Traditions) Inner Traditions International, Ltd.

—Science & the Akashic Field: An Integral Theory of Everything. 2nd rev. ed. 2007. (ENG., Illus.). 1p. pap. 14.95 *(978-1-59477-181-1(2))* Inner Traditions International, Ltd.

Levi. The Aquarian Gospel of Jesus the Christ. 2010. 264p. pap. 12.95 *(978-1-933993-87-4(1))* Apocryphile Pr.

—The Aquarian Gospel of Jesus the Christ. 2009. 244p. pap. 9.99 *(978-1-60459-879-7(4))* Wilder Pubns., Ltd.

—The Aquarian Gospel of Jesus the Christ: The Philosophic & Practical Basis of the Religion of the Aquarian Age of the World & of the Church Univer. 2010. 266p. pap. 27.75 *(978-1-143-93672-2(8))* BiblioBazaar.

—The Aquarian Gospel of Jesus the Christ: the Philosophic & Practical Basis of the Religion of the Aquarian Age of the World & of the Church. 2010. 274p. pap. 35.26 *(978-1-151-89676-6(4))* General Bks. LLC.

Levi & levi, Dowling S. The Aquarian Gospel of Jesus the Christ. 2011. 266p. pap. 8.95 ***(978-1-61427-041-6(4))*** Martino Publishing.

Levi, Michael I. & Levi. The Aquarian Gospel of Jesus the Christ. 2010. 274p. pap. 35.36 *(978-1-155-05401-8(6))* General Bks. LLC.

AKATHISIA

see Tardive Dyskinesia

AKATZIROI

see Khazars

AKBAR, EMPEROR OF HINDUSTAN, 1542-1605

Blochmann, H., ed. The Ain I Akbari of Abul Fazl 'Allami. 2009. (PER & ENG.). Vol. 1. 710.00 *(978-1-60724-253-6(2))* Vol. 2. 710.00 *(978-1-60724-254-3(0))* Gorgias Pr., LLC.

Blochmann, H., tr. The Ain I Akbari of Abul Fazl 'Allami, Vol. 3. 2009. (PER & ENG.). 710.00 *(978-1-60724-255-0(9))* Gorgias Pr., LLC.

du Jarric, Pierre. Akbar & the Jesuits: An Account of the Jesuit Missions to the Court of Akbar. Payne, C. H., tr. 2007. (Gorgias Historic Travels in the Cradle of Civilization Ser.: 7). 92.00 *(978-1-59333-630-1(6))* Gorgias Pr., LLC.

InterConsult, Lancer. Akbar. 2008. 202p. 18.95 *(978-0-9815378-2-5(0))* Lancer International Inc., The.

Jarrett, H., tr. The Ain I Akbari of Abul Fazl 'Allami. 2009. (PER.). 710.00 *(978-1-60724-256-7(7))*; 710.00 *(978-1-60724-257-4(5))* Gorgias Pr., LLC.

Malleson, George Bruce. Rulers of Indi. 2011. 228p. pap. 28.95 ***(978-1-4460-6911-0(7))*** Research Pr.

Moon, Farzana. Divine Akbar & Holy India. 2011. (ENG.). 264p. pap. 29.95 ***(978-0-7618-5639-9(0))*** Hamilton Bks.

Moura Carvalho, Pedro. Mir'at al-quds(Mirror of Holiness): A Life of Christ for Emperor Akbar: A Commentary on Father Jerome Xavier¿s Text & the Miniatures of Cleveland Museum of Art, Acc. No. 2005. 145. Thackston, Wheeler M., tr. from ARA. 2011. (Muqarnas, Supplements Ser.). (ARA & ENG., Illus.). x, 384p. ***(978-90-04-21149-0(7))*** BRILL.

Steel, Flora Annie. The Adventures of Akbar. 2008. 172p. 22.99 *(978-0-554-33229-1(9))* 2008. 172p. 25.99 *(978-0-554-23926-2(4))* 2007. (ENG.). 154p. pap. 19.99 *(978-1-4264-5161-4(X))* 2007. (ENG.). 170p. pap. 21.99 *(978-1-4264-5462-2(7))* BiblioBazaar.

—The Adventures of Akbar. 2009. (Illus.). 156p. pap. *(978-1-4065-7526-2(7))* Dodo Pr.

—The Adventures of Akbar. 232p. 2008. 41.95 *(978-1-4365-8107-3(9))* 2007. (ENG.). per. 26.95 *(978-0-548-79384-8(0))* Kessinger Publishing, LLC.

Vivekanandan, Jayashree. Indias Strategic Practice. 2011. (War & International Politics in South Asia Ser.). (ENG.). (C). 130.00 *(978-0-415-59812-5(5)*, Routledge India) Taylor & Francis Group GBR. Dist: Taylor & Francis Group.

Wink, Andre. Akbar. 2008. (Makers of the Muslim World Ser.). (ENG., Illus.). 160p. 40.00 *(978-1-85168-605-6(3))* Oneworld Pubns. GBR. Dist: National Bk. Network.

AKELEY, CARL ETHAN, 1864-1926

Kirk, Jay. Kingdom under Glass: A Tale of Obsession, Adventure, & One Man's Quest to Preserve the World's Great Animals. 2010. (ENG., Illus.). 400p. 27.50 *(978-0-8050-9282-0(X))* Holt, Henry & Co.

—Kingdom under Glass: A Tale of Obsession, Adventure, & One Man's Quest to Preserve the World's Great Animals. 2011. (ENG., Illus.). 400p. pap. 18.00 *(978-0-312-61073-9(4))* Picador.

Rodriguez, Louis. From Elephants to Swimming Pools: Carl Akeley, Samuel W. Traylor, & the Development of the Cement Gun. 2006. (Illus.). 160p. per. 15.95 *(978-0-930973-39-1(9)*, Canal History & Technology Pr.) Moore, Hugh Historical Park & Museums, Inc.

AKHENATEN, KING OF EGYPT

Edwards, Margaret Dulles. Child of the Sun a Pharaoh of Egypt. 2007. (ENG.). 126p. 35.95 *(978-0-548-03679-2(9))* Kessinger Publishing, LLC.

Ellis, Ralph. Eden in Egypt: Adam & Eve were Pharaoh Akhenaton & Nefertiti. 2009. 370p. pap. 20.00 *(978-1-931882-95-8(9))* Adventures Unlimited Pr.

Manniche, Lisa. The Akhenaten Colossi of Karnak. 2010. (ENG., Illus.). 208p. 29.95 *(978-977-416-349-4(4))* American Univ. in Cairo Pr. EGY. Dist: Oxford Univ. Pr., Inc.

Silverman, David P., et al. Akhenaten & Tutankhamun: Revolution & Restoration. 2006. (Illus.). 208p. 24.95 *(978-1-931707-90-9(1)*, Univ. of Pennsylvania Museum of Archaeology & Anthropology) Univ. Museum Pubns.

Spieser, C. Offrandes et purification a l'epoque Amarnienne. 2011. (Monographies Reine Elisabeth Ser.). (FRE., Illus.). 213p. (C). pap. 95.00 *(978-2-503-53475-6(9))* Brepols Pubs. BEL. Dist: Brown, David Bk. Co., The.

AKHMATOVA, ANNA ANDREEVNA, 1888-1966

Feinstein, Elaine. Anna of All the Russias: A Life of Anna Akhmatova. 2007. (Vintage Ser.). (ENG., Illus.). 368p. per. 15.95 *(978-1-4000-3378-2(0)*, Vintage) Knopf Doubleday Publishing Group.

Reeder, Roberta. Anna Akhmatova: Poet & Prophet. 2007. (ENG., Illus.). 864p. pap. 30.00 *(978-1-932800-23-4(9))* Figueroa Pr.

AKITA DOG

Killilea, David & Killilea, Jenny. Akita Today. (Illus.). 96p. tchr. ed. 24.95 *(978-1-86054-099-8(6)*, INT033) Ringpress Bks., Ltd. GBR. Dist: TFH Pubns., Inc.

Linzy, Jan. Akita Champions, 2002-2006. 2007. (Illus.). 138p. spiral bd. 46.95 *(978-1-55893-217-3(8))* Camino E.E. & Bk. Co.

Rice D.V.M., Dan. Akitas: Everything about Health, Behavior, Feeding, & Care. 2nd rev. ed. 2007. (Complete Pet Owner's Manual Ser.). (ENG., Illus.). 96p. pap. 8.99 *(978-0-7641-3642-9(9))* Barron's Educational Series, Inc.

Sherrill, Martha. Dog Man: An Uncommon Life on a Faraway Mountain. 2009. (Playaway Adult Nonfiction Ser.). (ENG.). 59.99 *(978-1-61545-734-2(8))* Findaway World, LLC.

—Dog Man: An Uncommon Life on a Faraway Mountain. 2009. (ENG.). 256p. (gr. 12-18). 16.00 *(978-1-59448-390-5(6)*, Riverhead Trade (Paperbacks)) Penguin Group (USA) Inc.

AKKADIAN LANGUAGE

Baker, Heather D. & Jursa, Michael. Le vocabulaire des sentiments dans les textes sumeriens: Recherche sur le lexique sumerien et akkadien. 2006. (Alter Orient und Altes Testament Ser.: Vol. 332). (FRE.). 663p. 152.00 *(978-3-934628-81-6(8))* Ugarit-Verlag DEU. Dist: Eisenbrauns, Inc.

Bezold, Carl. Babylonisch-Assyrisches Glossar. Hanson, K. C., ed. 2008. (Ancient Language Resources Ser.). 362p. pap. 30.00 *(978-1-60608-145-7(4)*, Wipf and Stock) Wipf & Stock Pubs.

Biggs, Robert D., et al, eds. The Assyrian Dictionary of the Oriental Institute of the University of Chicago, Vol. 18, T. 2006. (Assyrian Dictionary of the Oriental Institute of the Univers Ser.). (AKK & ENG.). 510p. (C). 145.00 *(978-1-885923-42-4(2))* Oriental Institute of the Univ. of Chicago, The.

Civil, Miguel. The Lexical Texts in the Schoyen Collection. 2010. (AKK & ENG.). *(978-1-934309-11-7(7)*, CDL Pr.) Univ. Pr. of Maryland.

Dalley, Stephanie. Babylonian Tablets from the First Sealand Dynasty in the Schoyen Collection. 2009. *(978-1-934309-08-7(7)*, CDL Pr.) Univ. Pr. of Maryland.

Deutscher, Guy. Syntactic Change in Akkadian: The Evolution of Sentential Complementation. 2007. (ENG., Illus.). 224p. per. 55.00 *(978-0-19-953222-3(2))* Oxford Univ. Pr., Inc.

Deutscher, Guy & Kowenberg, M. J. C. The Akkadian Language in its Semitic Context: Studies in the Akkadian of the Third & Second Millennium BC Clustered Neighbourhood Settlements of the Central Anatoli, 2006. (Publications de l'Institut historique-archeologique neerlandais de Stamboul Ser.: Vol. 106). (ENG & GER.). 298p. (Orig.). pap. 39.00 *(978-90-6258-317-1(2))* Netherlands Institute for the Near East NLD. Dist: Eisenbrauns, Inc.

Haupt, Paul. The Assyrian E-Vowel. 2009. pap. 72.28 *(978-1-60724-557-5(4))* Gorgias Pr., LLC.

—Open Sesame & Other Studies. 2008. pap. 29.00 *(978-1-60724-048-8(3))* Gorgias Pr., LLC.

Haupt, Paul & Jandora, John. Arabic Tâjir & Assyrian Tamkaru. Rippin, Andrew, ed. 2012. 126.25 *(978-1-60724-045-7(9))* Gorgias Pr., LLC.

Huehnergard, John. The Akkadian of Ugarit. 2011. pap. ***(978-1-57506-940-1(7))*** Eisenbrauns, Inc.

—A Grammar of Akkadian/by John Huehnergard. 2nd ed. 2008. (Harvard Semitic Studies: No. 45). 49.95 *(978-1-57506-922-7(9))* Eisenbrauns, Inc.

Huehnergard, John. A Grammar of Akkadian/By John Huehnergard. 3rd ed. 2011. (ENG & AKK.). ***(978-1-57506-941-8(5))*** Eisenbrauns, Inc.

Johns, C. H. W. Some Secondary Formations among Assyrian Proper Names. 2010. 82.16 *(978-1-61143-531-3(5))* Gorgias Pr., LLC.

Kouwenberg, N. J. C. The Akkadian Verb & Its Semitic Background. 2010. 89.50 *(978-1-57506-193-1(7))* Eisenbrauns, Inc.

Lambert, W. G. Babylonian Oracle Questions. 2007. 49.50 *(978-1-57506-136-8(8))* Eisenbrauns, Inc.

Lenzi, Alan. Akkadian Prayers & Hymns: A Reader. 2011. (AKK & ENG.). ***(978-1-58983-596-2(4))***; ***(978-1-58983-595-5(6))*** Society of Biblical Literature.

Luchsinger, Jurg, et al, eds. Der Lust Hat Am Wort des Herrn!" Festschrift Fur Ernst Jenni Zum 80. Geburtstag. 2007. (Alter Orient und Altes Testament Ser.: 336). 466p. (C). 153.00 *(978-3-934628-87-8(7))* Ugarit-Verlag DEU. Dist: Eisenbrauns, Inc.

Mercer, Samuel A. Assyrian Grammar. (Columbia University, Oriental Studies: No. 29). reprint ed. 27.50 *(978-0-404-50519-6(8))* AMS Pr., Inc.

Muss-Arnolt, William. A Concise Dictionary of the Assyrian Languages, 2 vols., Set. (Ancient Mesopotamian Texts & Studies). (AKK.). reprint ed. 97.50 *(978-0-404-18195-6(3))* AMS Pr., Inc.

—A Concise Dictionary of the Assyrian Languages. 2010. 640p. pap. 45.75 *(978-1-143-83175-1(6))* BiblioBazaar.

Poebel, Arno. Grammatical Texts. 2009. 124p. pap. 20.95 *(978-1-104-17778-2(1))* Kessinger Publishing, LLC.

Poldnikov, D. IU. Languages of the World: The Semitic Languages. 2009. (RUS., Illus.). 840p. 70.00 *(978-5-87444-284-2(7))* Akademija / Academia, Izdatel'stvo RUS. Dist: Eisenbrauns, Inc.

Prince, J. Dyneley. Assyrian Primer: An Inductive Method of Learning the Cuneiform Characters. (Columbia University, Contributions to Oriental History & Philology Ser.: No. 3). reprint ed. 20.00 *(978-0-404-50533-2(3))* AMS Pr., Inc.

Reiner, Erica. A linguistic analysis of Akkadian. (Janua Linguarum. Series Practica Ser.). (ENG.). 155p. 210.00 ***(978-3-11-219503-1(5))***; 135.00 ***(978-3-11-100028-2(1))*** De Gruyter, Mouton DEU. Dist: de Gruyter, Walter GmbH & Co. KG.

Richardson, M. E. J. A Comprehensive Grammar to Hammurabi's Stele. 2006. (Gorgias Handbooks Ser.: 8). 65.00 *(978-1-59333-540-3(7))* Gorgias Pr., LLC.

Richardson, Seth Francis Corning. Texts from the Late Old Babylonian Period. 2010. (Journal of Cuneiform Studies Supplement Ser.). (ENG.). 232p. (C). 75.00 *(978-0-89757-084-8(7))* American Schls. of Oriental Research.

Roth, Martha T., ed. The Assyrian Dictionary of the Oriental Institute of the University of Chicago: Volume 20, U/W. 2010. (Assyrian Dictionary Ser.). (AKK & ENG.). 444p. (C). 150.00 *(978-1-885923-78-3(3))* Oriental Institute of the Univ. of Chicago, The.

Roth, Martha T., et al, eds. Studies Presented to Robert D. Biggs, June 4 2004. 2007. (From the Workshop of the Chicago Assyrian Dictionary Ser.). (ENG., Illus.). 362p. (C). pap. 40.00 *(978-1-885923-44-8(9))* Oriental Institute of the Univ. of Chicago, The.

Roth, Martha T. & McLaman, Linda, eds. The Assyrian Dictionary of the Oriental Institute of the University of Chicago, Vol. 19. 2006. (Assyrian Dictionary of the Oriental Institute of the Univers Ser.). (AKK & ENG.). 170p. (C). 105.00 *(978-1-885923-43-1(0))* Oriental Institute of the Univ. of Chicago, The.

Steinert, Ulrike. Aspekte des Menschseins Im Alten Mesopotamien: Eine Studie Zu Person und Identitat Im 2. und 1. Jt. V. Chr. 2012. ***(978-90-04-22613-5(3))***; E-Book ***(978-90-04-22614-2(1))*** BRILL.

Wasserman, Nathan. Most Probably: Epistemic Modality in Old Babylonian. 2012. (Illus.). xiv, 245p. ***(978-1-57506-198-6(8))*** Eisenbrauns, Inc.

AKKADIAN LANGUAGE—TEXTS

Budge. Annals of the Kings of Assyria. 2012. (ENG.). 256p. pap. 42.95 ***(978-0-415-54089-6(5))*** Routledge.

Esarhaddon & Leichty, Erle. The Royal Inscriptions of Esarhaddon, King of Assyria (680-669 BC) 2011. (AKK & ENG.). *(978-1-57506-209-9(7))* Eisenbrauns, Inc.

Gadotti, Alhena, et al. Cuneiform Texts in the Carl A. Kroch Library, Cornell University. 2010. (978-1-934309-25-4(7), CDL Pr.) Univ. Pr. of Maryland.
Gehlken, Erlend. Weather Omens of Enuma Anu Enlil: Thunderstorms, Wind & Rain (Tablets 44-49) 2012. **(978-90-04-22588-6(9))** BRILL.
George, A. R. Babylonian Literary Texts in the Schoyen Collection. 2009. (978-1-934309-09-4(5), CDL Pr.) Univ. Pr. of Maryland.
—Cuneiform Royal Inscriptions & Related Texts in the Schoyen Collection. 2011. (978-1-934309-33-9(8), CDL Pr.) Univ. Pr. of Maryland.
Grayson, A. Kirk. Assyrian & Babylonian Chronicles. 2008. (Texts from Cuneiform Sources Ser.: Vol. 5). 300p. 79.50 (978-1-57506-049-1(3)) Eisenbrauns, Inc.
Green, Douglas J. I Undertook Great Works: The Ideology of Domestic Achievements in West Semitic Royal Inscriptions. 2010. (Illus.). 368p. pap. 147.50 (978-3-16-150168-5(3)) Mohr Siebeck GmbH & Co. KG DEU. Dist: Coronet Bks.
Hackman, George G. Sumerian & Akkadian Administrative Texts: From Pre-Dynastic Times to the End of the Akkad Dynasty. (Babylonian Inscriptions in the Collection of James B. Nies Ser.: No. 8). reprint ed. 45.00 (978-0-404-60138-6(3)) AMS Pr., Inc.
King, L. Enuma Elish: The Seven Tablets of the History of Creation. 2007. 156p. 19.99 (978-1-59986-701-4(X)) Filiquarian Publishing, LLC.
King, L. W. Enuma Elish: The Seven Tablets of the History of Creation. 2007. pap. 12.99 (978-1-59986-919-3(5)) Filiquarian Publishing, LLC.
Lutz, Henry Frederick. Early Babylonian Letters from Larsa. 2008. 188p. pap. 22.95 (978-1-4368-2725-6(6)) Kessinger Publishing, LLC.
Lutz, Henry Frederick. An Old Babylonian Divination Text. 2011. 16p. pap. 35.95 **(978-1-258-01486-5(6))** Literary Licensing, LLC.
Maidman, M. P. & Guinan, Ann. Nuzi Texts & Their Uses As Historical Evidence. 2010. 296p. (978-90-04-15111-6(7)) BRILL.
Maidman, Maynard P. Nuzi Texts & Their Uses As Historical Evidence. Guinan, Ann K., ed. 2010. (ENG & AKK.). 322p. pap. 34.95 (978-1-58983-213-8(2)) Society of Biblical Literature.
Maiocchi, Massimo. Classical Sargonic Tablets Chiefly from Adab in the Cornell University Collections. 2009. (978-1-934309-12-4(5), CDL Pr.) Univ. Pr. of Maryland.
Maiocchi, Massimo & Visicato, Giuseppe. Classical Sargonic Tablets Chiefly from Adab in the Cornell University Collections. 2012. **(978-1-934309-40-7(0)**, CDL Pr.) Univ. Pr. of Maryland.
Nies, James B. Historical, Religious & Economic Texts & Antiquities. (Babylonian Inscriptions in the Collection of James B. Nies Ser.: No. 2). reprint ed. 37.50 (978-0-404-60132-4(4)) AMS Pr., Inc.
Poebel, Arno. Historical & Grammatical Texts. 2009. 256p. pap. 27.95 (978-1-104-76559-0(4)) Kessinger Publishing, LLC.
Radau, Hugo. Letters to Cassite Kings from the Temple Archives of Nippur. 2009. 356p. pap. 31.95 (978-1-120-31465-9(8)) Kessinger Publishing, LLC.
Rochberg, Francesca. In the Path of the Moon: Babylonian Celestial Divination & Its Legacy. 2010. 445p. (978-90-04-18389-6(2)) BRILL.
Tadmor, Hayim, et al. The Royal Inscriptions of Tiglath-Pileser III (745-727 BC) & Shalmaneser V (726-722 BC), Kings of Assyria. 2011. **(978-1-57506-220-4(8))** Eisenbrauns, Inc.
Ungnad, Arthur. Selected Business Documents of the Neo-Babylonian Period. 2008. 85p. pap. 7.00 (978-1-60608-352-9(X), Wipf and Stock) Wipf & Stock Pubs.
Visicato, Giuseppe & Westenholz, Aage. Early Dynastic & Early Sargonic Tablets from Adab in the Cornell University Collections. 2010. (978-1-934309-10-0(9), CDL Pr.) Univ. Pr. of Maryland.
Westenholz, Joan & Westenholz, Aage. Cuneiform Inscriptions in the Collection of the Bible Lands Museum Jerusalem: The Old Babylonian Inscriptions. 2006. (Illus.). (978-90-04-14710-2(1)) BRILL.

AKKADIANS

De Lafayette, Maximillien. Description & Explanation of Anunnaki, Babylonian, Sumerian, Akkadian, Phoenician Slabs, Inscriptions, Tablets & Symbols. 5th Edition. 2010. 400p. pap. 28.50 (978-0-557-46069-4(7)) Lulu Enterprises Inc.
—Description,Translation,Explanation of Babylonian,Sumerian,Akkadian,Assyrian,Ugaritic,Anunnaki,Phoenician Cylinder Seals,Slabs,Inscriptions,Tablets,Symbols. 2010. 402p. pap. 29.49 (978-0-557-53697-9(9)) Lulu Enterprises Inc.

AKKADIANS (SUMERIANS)

see Sumerians

AKRON (OHIO)

American Map. Atlas Akron Summit Portage Counties OH Atlas. 2008. 80p. 9.95 (978-0-8416-0789-7(3)) American Map Corp.
Gieck, Jack. Early Akron's Industrial Valley: A History of the Cascade Locks. 2007. (Illus.). 84p. per. 11.95 (978-0-87338-928-0(X)) Kent State Univ. Pr.
Hagelberg, Kymberli. Wicked Akron: Tales of Rumrunners, Mobsters, & Other Rubber City Rogues. 2010. (Wicked Ser.). (ENG., Illus.). 128p. pap. 19.99 (978-1-59629-915-3(0)) History Pr., The.
Mavromatis, Kally. Akron Churches: Early Architecture. 2008. (Images of America Ser.). (ENG., Illus.). 128p. pap. 19.99 (978-0-7385-5202-6(X)) Arcadia Publishing.
Miller, Jon, ed. Akron Offering: The Literary Magazine of a Progressive Canal Town (1849-1850), Complete & Annotated. 2011. 384p. pap. 39.95 (978-1-935603-53-5(1)) Univ. of Akron Pr., The.

AKSAKOV, S. T. (SERGEI TIMOFEEVICH), 1791-1851

Aksakov, Sergei. A Russian Schoolboy. Duff, J. D., tr. from RUS. 2009. (ENG.). 200p. pap. 11.95 (978-1-58988-051-1(X)) Dry, Paul Bks., Inc.

AKSUM (ETHIOPIA)

Phillipson, Laurel. Using Stone Tools: The Evidence from Aksum, Ethiopia. 2010. (Bar S Ser.). (ENG., Illus.). 149p. (C). pap. 85.00 (978-1-4073-0408-3(9)) British Archaeological Reports Ltd. GBR. Dist: Brown, David Bk. Co., The.

AKU LANGUAGE

see Yoruba Language

AKUAPEM LANGUAGE

see Twi Language

AKWAPIM LANGUAGE

see Twi Language

AL-ANON

see Al-Anon Family Group Headquarters, Inc.

AL-ANON FAMILY GROUP HEADQUARTERS, INC.

Alcoholics Anonymous. Living with an Alcoholic: With the Help on Al-Anon. 2011. 158p. 41.95 **(978-1-258-02841-1(7))** Literary Licensing, LLC.
Borchert, William G. The Lois Wilson Story: When Love Is Not Enough. (ENG.). 424p. 2010. pap. 15.95 (978-1-59285-980-1(1)) 2008. (Illus.). pap. 15.95 (978-1-59285-598-8(9)) Hazelden Publishing & Educational Services.
Townsend, Kate. The Price of Wisdom. 2009. 244p. pap. (978-1-84748-610-3(X)) Athena Pr.

AL FATAH (ORGANIZATION)

see Fath (Organization)

AL-QAEDA (ORGANIZATION)

see Qaida (Organization)

AL-QAIDA (ORGANIZATION)

see Qaida (Organization)

AL JIB

Blenkinsopp, Joseph. Gibeon & Israel: The Role of Gibeon & the Gibeonites in the Political & Religious History of Early Israel. 2009. (Society for Old Testament Study Monographs). (ENG.). 168p. pap. 28.99 (978-0-521-11541-4(8)) Cambridge Univ. Pr.

ALABADOS

De Aragon, Ray John. The Penitentes of New Mexico: Hermanos de la Luz/ Brothers of the Light. 2006. (ENG & SPA., Illus.). 257p. pap. 24.95 (978-0-86534-504-1(X)) Sunstone Pr.

ALABAMA

Whiting, John Downes. The Trail of Fire: A Story of the Famous Alabama. 2011. 298p. 48.95 **(978-1-258-05691-9(7))** Literary Licensing, LLC.

ALABAMA—ANTIQUITIES

Blitz, John Howard. Moundville. 2nd ed. 2008. (Alabama the Forge of History Ser.). (ENG., Illus.). 128p. pap. 19.95 (978-0-8173-5478-7(6)) Univ. of Alabama Pr.
DeJarnette, David L. Archaeological Salvage in the Walter F. George Basin of the Chattahoochee River. 2nd ed. 2010. (ENG., Illus.). 254p. pap. 32.00 (978-0-8173-5644-6(4)) Univ. of Alabama Pr.
Hornsey, Lara K. The Hunter-Gatherer Use of Caves & Rockshelters in the American Midsouth. 2010. (Bar S Ser.). (Illus.). 101p. (C). pap. 87.50 (978-1-4073-0670-4(7)) British Archaeological Reports Ltd. GBR. Dist: Brown, David Bk. Co., The.
Knight, Vernon J., ed. The Search for Mabila: The Decisive Battle Between Hernando de Soto & Chief Tascalusa. 2nd ed. 2009. (ENG., Illus.). 344p. 57.50 (978-0-8173-1659-4(0)); pap. 37.95 (978-0-8173-5542-5(1)) Univ. of Alabama Pr.
Knight, Vernon James, Jr. & Steponaitis, Vincas P., eds. Archaeology of the Moundville Chiefdom. 2nd rev. ed. 2007. (Illus.). 226p. per. 29.95 (978-0-8173-5421-3(2)) Univ. of Alabama Pr.
Sledge, John S. The Pillared City: Greek Revival Mobile. 2009. (ENG., Illus.). 184p. 42.95 (978-0-8203-3020-4(5)) Univ. of Georgia Pr.
Steponaitis, Vincas P. Ceramics, Chronology, & Community Patterns: An Archaeological Study at Moundville. 2nd ed. 2009. (ENG., Illus.). 400p. pap. 37.50 (978-0-8173-5576-0(6)) Univ. of Alabama Pr.
Wilson, Gregory D. The Archaeology of Everyday Life at Early Moundville. 2nd ed. 2008. (ENG., Illus.). 208p. 55.00 (978-0-8173-1579-5(9)) Univ. of Alabama Pr.
Wimberly, Steve B. Indian Pottery from Clarke County & Mo. 2006. pap. 31.95 (978-1-4286-6318-3(5)) Kessinger Publishing, LLC.

ALABAMA—BIOGRAPHY

Alabama Snow. 2009. (ENG.). 309p. pap. 16.95 (978-0-9767713-1-9(4)) Lighted Tree Pr.
Arrington, Richard. There's Hope for the World: The Memoir of Birmingham, Alabama's First African American Mayor. 2008. (ENG., Illus.). 320p. 29.95 (978-0-8173-1623-5(X)) Univ. of Alabama Pr.
Baldwin, Robert. Life & Death Matters: Seeking the Truth about Capital Punishment. 2008. 24.95 (978-1-58838-234-4(6), NewSouth Bks.) NewSouth, Inc.
Biographiq, Rosa Parks - the Mother of the Modern-Day Civil Rights Movement. 2008. 56p. pap. 9.99 (978-1-59986-101-2(1), Biographiq) Filiquarian Publishing, LLC.
Blackshear, Helen. Mother Was a Rebel: In Praise of Gentle People. 2007. 212p. pap. 19.95 (978-1-60306-037-0(5)) NewSouth, Inc.
Bobo, Thomas. Educator: The Life of Thelma Smiley Morris. 2006. pap. 9.95 (978-0-9785311-2-6(4)) MBF Pr.
Bozeman, Hurdis. Lord, Why Not Me? 2007. per. (978-1-59581-341-1(1), Brentwood Christian Pr.) Brentwood Communications Group.
Bragg, Rick. The Most They Ever Had. 2011. (ENG.). 168p. pap. 14.95 (978-0-8173-5683-5(5)) Univ. of Alabama Pr.
—The Prince of Frogtown. l.t. ed. 2008. (ENG.). 432p. pap. 25.00 (978-0-7393-2796-8(8)) Random Hse. Large Print.
Bright, Darrell. Growing up with Bob. 2009. 292p. 35.95 (978-1-60594-051-9(8)); (ENG.). pap. 17.95 (978-1-60594-050-2(X)) Aeon Publishing Inc. (Llumina Pr.).
Burts, William. How I Got Over. 2006. (ENG.). 48p. per. 16.95 (978-1-4241-5518-7(5)) PublishAmerica, Inc.
Camp, Joseph. An Insight into an Insane Asylum. 2011. (Illus.). x, 120p. (978-0-8173-8533-0(9)); (ENG., 130p. pap. 19.95 (978-0-8173-5651-4(7)) Univ. of Alabama Pr.
Campbell, Benjamin H. A Little Band of Orphans: The Rest of the Story. 2011. 198p. pap. 24.95 **(978-1-4560-4959-1(3))** PublishAmerica, Inc.
Cbaukumunchea "Charley" Babies. To Walk Again after 30 Years: Medical Miracle. 2009. 116p. pap. 15.95 (978-1-4389-8361-5(1)) AuthorHouse.
Chestnut, J. L., Jr. & Cass, Julia. Black in Selma: The Uncommon Life of J. L. Chestnut Jr. Cass, Julia, ed. 2007. (ENG., Illus.). 448p. per. 29.95 (978-0-8173-5461-9(1)) Univ. of Alabama Pr.
Chief: A Biography of Zack Cross. 2009. pap. 19.00 (978-0-615-30320-8(X)) Greater Alabama Council, Boy Scouts of America.
Coggins, Patrick C. Tuskegee Airman Fighter Pilot: A Story of an Original Tuskegee Pilot Lt. Col. Hiram E. Mann. 2008. 272p. 29.82 (978-1-4251-7904-5(5)) Trafford Publishing.
Crawford, Sr Donald. Wheels of Birmingham Civil Rights Movement. 2007. 100p. pap. 18.95 (978-1-60008-025-8(1), Rooftop Publishing) AuthorHouse.
Crosley, Ralph T. My Endearing Love for a Beautiful Maiden, 1 vol. 2009. 80p. pap. 16.95 (978-1-4489-2604-6(1)) PublishAmerica, Inc.
Daniels Jr., Anthony. To Sweeten Alabam: A Story of a Young Man Defying the Odds. 2009. 216p. 25.00 (978-1-4389-4458-6(6)); pap. 17.00 (978-1-4389-4457-9(8)) AuthorHouse.
Delbridge, Melissa J. Family Bible. (Sightline Bks.). (ENG.). 168p. 2010. pap. 17.00 (978-1-58729-874-5(0)) 2008. 23.95 (978-1-58729-651-2(9)) Univ. of Iowa Pr.
Dickson, Foster & Downes. Valerie. I Just Make People Up: Ramblings with Clark Walker. 2008. (978-1-60306-045-5(6), NewSouth Bks.) NewSouth, Inc.
Diouf, Sylviane A. Dreams of Africa in Alabama: The Slave Ship Clotilda & the Story of the Last Africans Brought to America. 2009. (ENG., Illus.). 352p. pap. 19.95 (978-0-19-538293-8(5)) Oxford Univ. Pr., Inc.
Dorsey, Mignette Y. Patrick. Speak Truth to Power: The Story of Charles Patrick, a Civil Rights Pioneer. 2nd ed. 2010. (Alabama Fire Ant Ser.). (ENG., Illus.). 152p. pap. 16.00 (978-0-8173-5556-2(1)) Univ. of Alabama Pr.
Eastland, Lindsey. Let Me Tell You about My Dad & Willard the Squirrel. 2011. 32p. pap. 12.77 **(978-1-4634-2308-7(X))** AuthorHouse.
Eubanks, W. Ralph. The House at the End of the Road: The Story of Three Generations of an Interracial Family in the American South. 2011. (ENG.). 224p. pap. 25.00 **(978-1-61703-081-9(3))** Univ. Pr. of Mississippi.
Feltman, Thomas M. Destination Evil: A Young Man's Journey from Short Creek to the Forgotten War, 1 vol. 2009. 228p. pap. 24.95 (978-1-60703-720-0(3)) PublishAmerica, Inc.
Finch, Jackie Sheckler. It Happened in Alabama. 2011. (It Happened in Ser.). (Illus.). 160p. pap. 14.95 (978-0-7627-6113-5(X)) Globe Pequot Pr., The.
Flynt, Wayne. Keeping the Faith: Ordinary People, Extraordinary Lives. 2011. (Religion & American Culture Ser.). (ENG., Illus.). 416p. 29.95 (978-0-8173-1754-6(6)) Univ. of Alabama Pr.
Gaston, Paul M. Coming of Age in Utopia: The Odyssey of an Idea. 2010. (Illus.). 358p. 27.95 (978-1-58838-225-2(7), NewSouth Bks.) NewSouth, Inc.
Gates, Carolyn Helm. Thursday's Child: A Collection of Short Stories. 2008. 76p. pap. 10.95 (978-0-595-52311-5(0)) iUniverse, Inc.
Gonzales, James Joullian. Gunny: Memoirs of Mobile's South Side Riding Alabama's Tide of White Supremacy. 2007. (Illus.). x, 446p. pap. (978-0-9794714-1-4(9)) Academy Bks.
Hadley, La Verne. Stay in the Race. 2011. 112p. pap. 15.00 (978-1-4567-1302-7(7)) AuthorHouse.
Hall, Wade. Waters of Life from Conecuh Ridge: The Clyde May Story. 2007. 80p. pap. 11.95 (978-1-60306-012-7(X)) NewSouth, Inc.
Harris, Huey. When Everything & More Is Not Enough. 2010. (ENG.). 276p. pap. 18.95 (978-0-944007-19-8(8)) SPI Bks.
Hendon, William. Hendon Brothers in the Civil War: a Divided Family. 2007. (ENG.). 144p. per. 24.95 (978-1-4241-6677-0(2)) PublishAmerica, Inc.
Hendry, Dorothy Diemer & Hendry, Wickliffe B. Looking for Jencey: The Life of Lizzie Elnora Murphy Casebolt. 2007. 488p. (ENG.). 39.95 (978-0-595-67863-1(7)); per. 29.95 (978-0-595-41044-6(8)) iUniverse, Inc.
Heritage of Cullman County, Alabama, Vol. II. 2008. lib. bdg. 60.00 (978-0-9796537-5-9(4)) Heritage Publishing Consultants, Inc.
Hoffman, Roy. Alabama Afternoons: Profiles & Conversations. 2011. (978-0-8173-8560-6(6)); (ENG.). 272p. 29.95 (978-0-8173-1739-3(2)) Univ. of Alabama Pr.
—Back Home: Journeys Through Mobile. 2007. (Illus.). 400p. per. 19.95 (978-0-8173-5431-2(X)) Univ. of Alabama Pr.
Hopkins, Linton C. Biography of Maximilian Bethune Wellborn. 2011. 306p. 48.95 **(978-1-258-06851-6(6))** Literary Licensing, LLC.
Houser, Leon. Only the Strong Shall Survive. 2009. 56p. pap. 10.49 (978-1-4343-7915-3(9)) AuthorHouse.
Howard, Gene. Patterson for Alabama: The Life & Career of John Patterson. 2nd ed. 2008. (ENG., Illus.). 272p. 29.95 (978-0-8173-1605-1(1)) Univ. of Alabama Pr.
Hultquist, Clark & Heatherly, Carey. Montevallo. 2011. (Images of America Ser.). (Illus.). 128p. pap. 21.99 (978-0-7385-8743-1(5)) Arcadia Publishing.
J., M. Living in America as an Undocumented Immigrant: How I Survived the Ordeal. 2010. 100p. pap. 11.95 (978-1-4502-5684-1(8)) iUniverse, Inc.
Jackson, Richie Jean Sherrod. The House by the Side of the Road: The Selma Civil Rights Movement. 2011. (ENG., Illus.). 176p. 24.95 (978-0-8173-1694-5(9)) Univ. of Alabama Pr.
Johnson, William Jerome. The Upstart. 2008. 256p. pap. 21.49 (978-1-4343-8180-4(3)) AuthorHouse.
Jones, Debby Fields. A Rose among the Ashes: Discovering Hope When There Doesn't Seem to Be Any. 2007. (ENG.). 144p. per. 14.99 (978-1-4141-0588-6(6)) Pleasant Word.
Jones, Tommy. Chalkboards & Clipboards: My Thirty-Five Years at the Montgomery Academy. 2011. 136p. 21.95 **(978-1-4620-1347-0(3))**; pap. 11.95 **(978-1-4620-1345-6(7))** iUniverse, Inc.
Kazek, Kelly. Christmas Tales of Alabama. 2011. 128p. pap. 12.99 **(978-1-60949-155-0(6))** History Pr., The.
—Forgotten Tales of Alabama. 2010. 192p. pap. 12.99 (978-1-60949-097-3(5)) History Pr., The.
—A History of Alabama's Deadliest Tornadoes: Disaster in Dixie. 2010. (Disaster Ser.). (ENG., Illus.). 128p. pap. 19.99 (978-1-59629-911-5(8)) History Pr., The.
Lakeman, Sylvia. Jack: "Plane" Life in a Small Town. 2007. (ENG.). 276p. per. 21.99 (978-1-4257-5017-6(6)) Xlibris Corp.
Lawrence, John. Our Proving Ground: Memories of the Good Old Days. 2010. pap. 12.99 (978-1-61566-396-5(7)) Tate Publishing & Enterprises, LLC.
LeBaron, J. Hugh & Coleman, William Goforth. Perry Volunteers in the Mexican War: Perry County, Alabama First Regiment of Alabama Volunteers, 1846-1847 & the Mexican War Diary of Captain William G. Coleman. 2008. (Illus.). 232p. 24.00 (978-0-7884-2267-6(7)) Heritage Bks.
Lopez, Cheyene Montana. Forgotten Storm, 1 vol. 2009. (ENG.). 292p. pap. 27.95 (978-1-61546-255-1(4)) PublishAmerica, Inc.
McClendon, William Augustus. Recollections of War Times: By an Old Veteran While under Stonewall Jackson & Lieutenant General James Longstreet. 2010. (Seeing the Elephant Ser.). (ENG., Illus.). 304p. pap. 22.95 (978-0-8173-5586-9(3)) Univ. of Alabama Pr.
McCormack, John. Field & Pastures New. 2008. 256p. pap. 15.95 (978-1-58818-164-0(2)) Hill Street Pr., LLC.
Mccormack, John. Friend of the Flock. 2008. 256p. pap. 15.95 (978-1-58818-165-7(0)) Hill Street Pr., LLC.
—Hero of the Herd. 2008. 256p. pap. 15.95 (978-1-58818-146-6(4)) Hill Street Pr., LLC.
—Last Cow Doctor. 2008. 256p. pap. 15.95 (978-1-58818-166-4(9)) Hill Street Pr., LLC.
McCrary, Roger. Beam, My Story, A Study Aid. 2006. pap. 9.00 (978-0-8059-7159-0(9)) Dorrance Publishing Co., Inc.
McGinnis, G. Owen. Our Late Great Century, 1900-1999. 2010. 454p. pap. 36.50 (978-0-7884-5168-3(5), Heritage Bks.) Heritage Bks.
McGregor, Bob. Whiskey Bent & Hell Bound: No Holiday for Justice. 2009. 252p. 24.99 (978-1-4490-5144-0(8)); pap. 14.49 (978-1-4490-5143-3(X)) AuthorHouse.
Miliner, Derrick K. From the Projects to the Pulpit: God's Grace Is Sufficient. 2009. 68p. pap. 16.95 (978-1-4389-7711-9(5)) AuthorHouse.
Miller, Hank. The Admiral's Son. 2007. 381p. pap. 23.50 (978-0-615-16505-9(2)) Miller, Hank.
Miller, Panky. Vacation Bible School Dropouts Book ONE. 2008. 116p. pap. 15.50 (978-0-615-16896-8(5)) Miller, Hank.
Mitchell, Tommie Plier. Lovable Courageous Callie. 2011. 164p. 25.01 **(978-1-4520-9763-3(1))**; pap. 13.16 **(978-1-4520-9764-0(X))** AuthorHouse.
Moore, Judge Roy. So Help Me God: The Ten Commandments, Judicial Tyranny, & the Battle for Religious Freedom. 2009. 288p. pap. 16.95 (978-1-935071-22-8(X)) WND Bks, Inc.
Mumpfield, Kimani K. My Soul's Window: An Never Allow Just Anyone Total Access to Who You Are, Is Some Advice I Plan to Keep but If You Want to See One Man's Heart, Mind. 2009. (Illus.). 63p. pap. 17.95 (978-1-4327-3525-8(X)) Outskirts Pr., Inc.
Napier, Christen. Poverty & Prison: Frustrations of My Past. 2010. 220p. pap. 20.00 (978-1-4269-2641-9(3)) Trafford Publishing.
Pate, James P., ed. When This Evil War Is Over: The Correspondence of the Francis Family, 1860-1865. 2006. (ENG., Illus.). 328p. 42.50 (978-0-8173-1517-7(9)) Univ. of Alabama Pr.
Patterson, Horace, Sr. Unbroken & Unbound: A Life Dedicated to God, Justice, & the South. 2007. 208p. pap. 19.95 (978-1-60306-030-1(8)) NewSouth, Inc.
Pettit, Madge. Pioneers & Residents of West Central Alabama Prior to the Civil War. 2008. 354p. (Orig.). pap. 34.00 (978-1-55613-125-7(9)) Heritage Bks.
Phillips, Eddie. The Other Side of Montgomery: Growing up White in the Birthplace of the Civil Rights Movement. 2009. (978-1-60306-055-4(3), NewSouth Bks.) NewSouth, Inc.
Pruitt, Paul M. Taming Alabama: Lawyers & Reformers, 1804-1929. 2010. (ENG., Illus.). 200p. pap. 26.95 (978-0-8173-5601-9(0)); (978-0-8173-8328-2(X)) Univ. of Alabama Pr.
Rankin, John P. Memories of Madison: A Connected Community, 1857-2007. 2007. (Illus.). 143p. pap. 15.95 (978-1-57864-398-1(8)) Donning Co. Pubs.
Reed, Wendy. An Accidental Memoir: How I Killed Someone & Other Stories. 2010. (ENG., Illus.). 208p. pap. 17.95 (978-0-615-27680-9(6)) Jefferson Pr.

Reeves, Jacquelyn Procter. Hidden History of North Alabama. 2010. (Hidden History Ser.). (ENG., Illus.). 128p. pap. 19.99 *(978-1-59629-752-4(2))* History Pr., The.

Richardson, Nell. A Family Home: A History of the President's Mansion at Auburn University. 2009. (ENG., Illus.). 184p. 24.95 *(978-0-8173-1617-4(5))* Univ. of Alabama Pr.

Rickman, Sarah Byrn. Nancy Batson Crews: Alabama's First Lady of Flight. 2nd ed. 2009. (Alabama Fire Ant Ser.). (ENG., Illus.). 230p. pap. 24.95 *(978-0-8173-5553-1(7))* Univ. of Alabama Pr.

Riley, Patsy. Alabama's First Ladies & Their Governors. 2011. (Illus.). 56p. ***(978-1-59421-059-4(4))*** Seacoast Publishing, Inc.

Robertson, Natalie S. The Slave Ship Clotilde & the Making of AfricaTown, USA: Spirit of Our Ancestors, 1 vol. 2008. (Illus.). 272p. 44.95 *(978-0-275-99491-4(0),* C9491, Praeger Pubs.) Greenwood Publishing Group, Inc.

Schake, Lowell M. & Walkinshaw, James R. On the Wings of Cranes: Larry Walkinshaw's Life Story. 2008. 376p. 34.95 *(978-0-595-71999-0(6))*; pap. 24.95 *(978-0-595-48497-3(2))* iUniverse, Inc.

Shaw, John Craig. Life & Times of A Wayward Geologist: A Lifetime of Personal Anecdotes, Adventures, & More... 2011. 224p. 24.59 ***(978-1-4567-6979-6(0))***; pap. 14.03 ***(978-1-4567-6980-2(4))*** AuthorHouse.

Shehane, Susan. Alabama Listening. 2006. per. 15.00 *(978-0-9785401-0-4(7))* Coosa River Bks., L.L.C.

Sikes, Richard. Laughing with the Bear. 2007. 122p. 14.95 *(978-0-9745854-0-6(8))* Old Bay Publishing.

Sikora, Frank. The Judge: The Life & Opinions of Alabamas Frank M. Johnson, JR. 2007. 320p. 29.95 *(978-1-58838-158-3(7),* NewSouth Bks.) NewSouth, Inc.

Smith, Billy D. My Life As I Remember It: Growing up in Alabama. 2009. 260p. 32.00 *(978-1-4490-2399-7(1))*; pap. 23.00 *(978-1-4490-2398-0(3))* AuthorHouse.

Smith, Cpl. (Ret.) Stephen Z. It's More Than Shootouts & Car Chases: Memoirs of a Montgomery Police Officer. 2010. 484p. 30.99 *(978-1-4490-5737-4(3))*; pap. 22.95 *(978-1-4490-5736-7(5))* AuthorHouse.

Smith, Jeffrey K. The Fighting Little Judge: The Life & Times of George C. Wallace. 2009. 236p. pap. 21.50 *(978-1-4490-2318-8(5))*; vi, 226p. *(978-1-4490-2319-5(3))* AuthorHouse.

Smith, Joel P. Candid Comments: Selected Columns from the Eufaula Tribune, 1958-2009. 2011. *(978-1-60306-068-4(5),* NewSouth Bks.) NewSouth, Inc.

Smith, Michael Catfish. Closing the Show: The story of the amazing 1969-70 East Highland High School Indians. 2009. 316p. pap. 20.00 *(978-1-4490-0452-1(0))* AuthorHouse.

Snell, Jacob Randolph & Snell, Marvis Reeder. The Mount Enon Cemetery: A Pioneer Cemetery in Dale County, Alabama First Called Beverett Graveyard. 2009. (Illus.). 217p. 34.89 *(978-0-9707741-1-8(7))* Snell Publishing, Inc.

Speight, Willie. Your Child Support Check Ruined Our Child's Life. 2010. 56p. pap. 10.49 *(978-1-4520-3619-9(5))* AuthorHouse.

Thompson, Elvin. The Blood Running Through My Veins: The Story of the Burns Family from the Slave Plantations of Autauga County Alabama until Today. 2009. 60p. pap. 10.49 *(978-1-4389-9886-2(4))* AuthorHouse.

Thompson, Tammy. A Lively Mind: The Story of Lynn Arthur Smith, A Gifted Teacher. 2007. (Illus.). 170p. pap. 14.95 ***(978-0-9797352-3-3(8))*** Hayes Ferry Pr.

Tim, LaHaye, frwd. Giving an Account: The Life & Ministry of Richard H. Vigneulle. 2009. (Illus.). 334p. 24.95 *(978-1-59421-053-2(5))* Seacoast Publishing, Inc.

Todd, Glenda McWhirter. Heartbreak of a Civil War Widow: Life of Sarah Harper McWhirter, 1825-1883: Including Harper Family Ancestry Traced to Oxfordshire, Noke, England in Early 1500's & Selected Information on the 1st Alabama Cavalry, USV. 2010. (Illus.). xv, 282p. ***(978-0-7884-8484-1(2))***; pap. ***(978-0-7884-5252-9(5))*** Heritage Bks.

Towns, Carl. The Memoirs of Big Head, 1 vol. 2010. 150p. pap. 24.95 *(978-1-4489-4277-0(2))* PublishAmerica, Inc.

Trest, Warren A. Nobody but the People. 2008. 450p. 32.50 *(978-1-58838-221-4(4),* NewSouth Bks.) NewSouth, Inc.

Tucker, Becky. Hang in There¿ Don't Give Up!, 1 vol. 2009. 51p. pap. 16.95 *(978-1-60813-243-0(9))* PublishAmerica, Inc.

Weaver, Lila Quintero. Darkroom: A Memoir in Black & White. 2012. ***(978-0-8173-8619-1(X))***; (ENG.). 264p. pap. 24.95 ***(978-0-8173-5714-6(9))*** Univ. of Alabama Pr.

Whatley, Jim. Auburn, Sweet, Auburn: History, Stories, an Epitaph of Pine Hill Cemetery 1836-2010. 2010. (ENG.). pap. 0.00 *(978-1-4507-3425-7(1))* Independent Pub.

Whelan, Victor. It Gives a Lovely Light a Biography of Chelsea Groves. 2009. 160p. 23.50 *(978-1-60860-968-0(5),* Eloquent Bks.) AEG Literary Publishing Services, Inc.

White, Lois, et al, eds. History of Holly Pond Area, Early Settlers. 2008. lib. bdg. 50.00 *(978-0-9796537-7-3(0))* Heritage Publishing Consultants, Inc.

Williams, Donnie & Greenhaw, Wayne. The Thunder of Angels: The Montgomery Bus Boycott & the People Who Broke the Back of Jim Crow. 2007. (ENG., Illus.). 320p. per. 14.95 *(978-1-55652-676-3(8),* Hill, Lawrence Bks.) Chicago Review Pr., Inc.

Williams, Julie. Wings of Opportunity: The Wright Brothers in Montgomery, Alabama 1910. 2010. (ENG.). 168p. pap. 19.95 *(978-1-58838-168-2(4),* NewSouth Bks.) NewSouth, Inc.

Windham, Kathryn Tucker. Alabama: One Big Front Porch. rev. ed. 2007. (Illus.). 168p. 25.95 *(978-1-58838-219-1(2),* NewSouth Bks.) NewSouth, Inc.

—Twice Blessed. 2007. (Illus.). 156p. per. 20.00 *(978-1-57966-080-2(0))* River City Publishing.

Winston, Donearaum S. Panning for Gold. 2009. 270p. pap. 14.95 *(978-1-4490-0401-9(6))* AuthorHouse.

Woodruff, Chuck. Small Town America. 2008. 78p. pap. 16.95 *(978-1-60610-993-9(6))* PublishAmerica, Inc.

Worthy, Arthur G. The Worthy Way: Memoirs of a Pioneer Black Law Enforcement Officer. 2007. 104p. pap. 15.00 *(978-1-60306-034-9(0))* NewSouth, Inc.

Zellner, Bob & Curry, Constance. The Wrong Side of Murder Creek: A White Southerner in the Freedom Movement. 2008. 350p. 27.95 *(978-1-58838-222-1(2),* NewSouth Bks.) NewSouth, Inc.

ALABAMA—CENSUS

Alabama Census Index, 1880. (Illus.). lib. bdg. *(978-0-89593-164-1(8),* Accelerated Indexing Systems International (AISI)) Genealogical Services.

Alabama State Census Index, 1855. (Illus.). lib. bdg. 90.00 *(978-0-89593-165-8(6),* Accelerated Indexing Systems International (AISI)) Genealogical Services.

Jackson, Ronald V. Alabama Early Census, Vol. 2. (Illus.). lib. bdg. 38.00 *(978-0-89593-718-6(2),* Accelerated Indexing Systems International (AISI)) Genealogical Services.

ALABAMA—DESCRIPTION AND TRAVEL

Adams, Allison Puccetti. Birmingham-Hoover Sketchbook. 2007. (Illus.). 149p. *(978-1-934144-20-6(7))* Indigo.

Alabama Department of Archives and History Staff. The Alabama Guide: Our People, Resources, & Government. Williams, Randall, ed. 2nd ed. 2009. (ENG., Illus.). 600p. 39.95 *(978-0-8173-1656-3(6))* Univ. of Alabama Pr.

—Sweet Home Alabama: Our People, Resources, & Government. Williams, Randall, ed. 2nd ed. 2009. (ENG., Illus.). 600p. pap. 24.95 *(978-0-8173-5537-1(5))* Univ. of Alabama Pr.

Amaki, Amalia K. & Mauter, Katherine R. Tuscaloosa. 2012. (Images of America Ser.). (ENG., Illus.). 128p. pap. 21.99 ***(978-0-7385-8788-2(5))*** Arcadia Publishing.

Aryal, Aimee. Big Al's Journey Through Yellow Hammer State. 2008. 14.95 *(978-1-934787-82-3(5))* Dos Monos Pr.

Bartom, Jessica. Historic Photos of Birmingham in the 50s, 60s, And 70s. 2010. (Historic Photos Ser.). (ENG., Illus.). 206p. 39.95 *(978-1-59652-752-2(8))* Turner Publishing Co.

Bennett, James R. Historic Birmingham & Jefferson County. 2008. (Illus.). 202p. pap. *(978-1-893619-91-3(5))* Historical Publishing Network.

—Historic Birmingham & Jefferson County: An Illustrated History. 2008. (Illus.). 312p. *(978-1-893619-83-8(4))* Historical Publishing Network.

Benton, Jeffrey C., ed. The Very Worst Road: Travellers' Accounts of Crossing Alabama's Old Creek Indian Territory, 1820-1847. 2nd ed. 2009. (Alabama Fire Ant Ser.). (ENG., Illus.). 169p. pap. 17.95 *(978-0-8173-5550-0(2))* Univ. of Alabama Pr.

Bulkeley, Eliphalet Adams, et al. Travel Letters of Eliphalet Adams Bulkeley & Leverett Brainard. 2011. 42p. 35.95 ***(978-1-258-05431-1(0))*** Literary Licensing, LLC.

Burnett, Jason & Bessemer Hall of History Museum. Early Bessemer. 2011. (Images of America Ser.). (Illus.). 128p. pap. 21.99 ***(978-0-7385-8803-2(2))*** Arcadia Publishing.

Carley, Gerald. Sunsets on the Eastern Shore: Evenings on Mobile Bay. 2007. *(978-0-9799992-2-2(7))* Wild Goose Publishing Co.

Chattahoochee Valley Historical Society & Chambers County Museum. Chambers County. 2010. (Images of America Ser.). (Illus.). 128p. pap. 21.99 *(978-0-7385-8640-3(4))* Arcadia Publishing.

Christenberry, William. Kodachromes. 2010. (Illus.). (ENG.). 176p. 65.00 *(978-1-59711-147-8(3))*; ***(978-1-59711-168-3(6))*** Aperture Foundation, Inc.

Clemmons, Vicky, et al. Bibb County. 2008. (Images of America Ser.). (ENG., Illus.). 128p. pap. 21.99 *(978-0-7385-6729-7(9))* Arcadia Publishing.

Collard, Deborah. Haunted Southern Nights, Volume 3, History & Haunting of the Mentone Area. 2009. 168p. pap. 20.00 *(978-0-578-00990-2(0))* Collard, Deborah.

Counts, Patricia Landrum. Landrum Collection of Historical Photographs. Williams, Lisa M., ed. 2010. (Illus.). 200p. 29.99 *(978-0-9792375-4-6(8))* Cypress Creek Publishing.

Daily, Vic. Fall Flight in Alabama: Waterfowling the Tennessee River Valley. 2009. (Illus.). 222p. *(978-0-615-28842-0(1))* Signature Bk. Printing.

Drake, Eleanor C. Perry County. 2010. (Images of America Ser.). (Illus.). 128p. pap. 21.99 *(978-0-7385-8662-5(5))* Arcadia Publishing.

Duncan, Andy. Alabama Curiosities: Quirky Characters, Roadside Oddities & Other Offbeat Stuff. 2nd ed. 2009. (Curiosities Ser.). (ENG., Illus.). 240p. pap. 15.95 *(978-0-7627-4931-7(8))* Globe Pequot Pr., The.

Ellis, Carol & Kirkland, Scotty E. Historic Photos of Mobile. 2008. (Historic Photos Ser.). (ENG., Illus.). 206p. 39.95 *(978-1-59652-434-7(0))* Turner Publishing Co.

—Remembering Mobile. 2010. (Remembering Ser.). (ENG., Illus.). 134p. pap. 16.95 *(978-1-59652-677-8(7))* Turner Publishing Co.

Fleming, David B. & Haynie, Mary Allison. Ensley & Tuxedo Junction. 2011. (Images of America Ser.). (Illus.). 128p. pap. 21.99 *(978-0-7385-8680-9(3))* Arcadia Publishing.

Goodson, Mike. Etowah County. 2009. (Then & Now Ser.). (ENG., Illus.). 96p. pap. 21.99 *(978-0-7385-6720-4(5))* Arcadia Publishing.

Goodson, Mike. Haunted Etowah County, Alabama. 2011. (Illus.). 128p. pap. 19.99 ***(978-1-60949-360-8(5))*** History Pr., The.

Goss, William E. & Pell, Karren. Tallassee. 2008. (Images of America Ser.). (Illus.). 128p. pap. 19.99 *(978-0-7385-5343-6(3))* Arcadia Publishing.

Grimes, Lydia. Brewton & East Brewton. 2011. (Images of America Ser.). (ENG., Illus.). 128p. pap. 21.99 ***(978-0-7385-8751-6(6))*** Arcadia Publishing.

Hanbury-Tenison, Robin. Land of Eagles: Riding through Europe's Forgotten Country. 2009. (ENG., Illus.). 224p. 35.00 *(978-1-84511-855-8(3))* I. B. Tauris & Co., Ltd. GBR. Dist: Macmillan.

Hoffman, Roy. Back Home: Journeys Through Mobile. 2007. (Illus.). 400p. per. 19.95 *(978-0-8173-5431-2(X))* Univ. of Alabama Pr.

Hollis, Tim. Vintage Birmingham Signs. 2008. (Images of America Ser.). (Illus.). 127p. pap. 21.99 *(978-0-7385-5376-4(X))* Arcadia Publishing.

Hultquist, Clark & Heatherly, Carey. Montevallo. 2011. (Images of America Ser.). (Illus.). 128p. pap. 21.99 *(978-0-7385-8743-1(5))* Arcadia Publishing.

Jordan, Mattie May & Jordan, Maya Marcia. Where the Wild Animals is Plentiful: Diary of an Alabama Fur Trader's Daughter, 1912-1914. Baldwin, Elisa Moore, ed. 2nd ed. 2008. (ENG., Illus.). 276p. per. 27.50 *(978-0-8173-5337-7(2))* Univ. of Alabama Pr.

Kazek, Kelly. Athens & Limestone County. 2010. (Images of America Ser.). (Illus.). 128p. pap. 21.99 *(978-0-7385-8614-4(5))* Arcadia Publishing.

Keith, Todd. Birmingham Then & Now. 2009. (Then & Now Thunder Bay Ser.). (ENG.). 144p. 19.95 *(978-1-59223-949-8(8),* Thunder Bay Pr.) Advantage Pubs. Group.

King, Carole A. & Pell, Karren. Montgomery. 2011. (Then & Now Ser.). (Illus.). 96p. pap. 21.99 ***(978-0-7385-8798-1(2))*** Arcadia Publishing.

King, Carole A. & Pell, Karren l. Montgomery's Historic Neighborhoods. 2010. (Images of America Ser.). (ENG., Illus.). 128p. pap. 21.99 *(978-0-7385-8620-5(X))* Arcadia Publishing.

Kirkland, Scotty E., et al. Dothan & Houston County Yesterday, Today & Tomorrow. 2011. (Illus.). 156p. ***(978-0-9796601-3-9(0))*** Beers & Assocs., LLC.

Library History Committee, Gadsden Public Library: 100 Years of Service. 2008. (Images of America Ser.). (ENG., Illus.). 128p. pap. 19.99 *(978-0-7385-5385-6(9))* Arcadia Publishing.

Lyles, John. Phenix City. 2010. (Images of America Ser.). (Illus.). 128p. pap. 21.99 *(978-0-7385-8569-7(6))* Arcadia Publishing.

Maharidge, Dale & Williamson, Michael. And Their Children after Them: The Legacy of Let Us Now Praise Famous Men. 2008. (ENG., Illus.). 264p. pap. 17.95 *(978-1-58322-857-5(5))* Seven Stories Pr.

Marion County Historical Society & Woolbright Carruth, Barbara. Marion County. 2009. (Images of America Ser.). (ENG., Illus.). 128p. pap. 21.99 *(978-0-7385-6849-2(X))* Arcadia Publishing.

McHugh, Eileen, et al. Auburn Correctional Facility. 2010. (Images of America Ser.). (ENG., Illus.). 128p. pap. 21.99 *(978-0-7385-7252-9(7))* Arcadia Publishing.

McMillan, Tom. Escambia County. 2012. (Images of America Ser.). (ENG., Illus.). 128p. pap. 21.99 ***(978-0-7385-9123-0(8))*** Arcadia Publishing.

McWilliams, John L. Tuscumbia. 2012. (Images of America Ser.). (ENG., Illus.). 128p. pap. 21.99 ***(978-0-7385-8820-9(2))*** Arcadia Publishing.

Outlaw, Harriet Brill & Taylor, Penny H. Daphne. 2012. (Images of America Ser.). (ENG., Illus.). 128p. pap. 21.99 ***(978-0-7385-9116-2(5))*** Arcadia Publishing.

Parker, Elizabeth. Haunted Mobile: Apparitions of the Azalea City. 2009. (Haunted America Ser.). 128p. pap. 17.99 *(978-1-59629-713-5(1))* History Pr., The.

Penot, Jessica. Haunted North Alabama. 2010. (Haunted America Ser.). (ENG., Illus.). 128p. pap. 19.99 *(978-1-59629-990-0(8))* History Pr., The.

Philipson, Claire Leila. Alabama. 2010. (ENG., Illus.). 96p. 19.95 *(978-1-55285-908-7(8))* Whitecap Bks., Ltd. CAN. Dist: Midpoint Trade Bks., Inc.

Phillips, Doug. Discovering Alabama Forests. 2006. (Illus.). 120p. 35.00 *(978-0-8173-1525-2(X))* Univ. of Alabama Pr.

Rankin, John P. Memories of Madison: A Connected Community, 1857-2007. 2007. (Illus.). 143p. *(978-1-57864-398-1(8))* Donning Co. Pubs.

Roberts, Mary K. Hueytown. 2010. (Images of America Ser.). (Illus.). 128p. pap. 21.99 *(978-0-7385-8690-8(0))* Arcadia Publishing.

Ruple, Wayne. Cleburne County. 2010. (Images of America Ser.). (Illus.). 128p. pap. 21.99 *(978-0-7385-8645-8(5))* Arcadia Publishing.

Shane Black. The Spirits of Athens: Haunting Tales of an Alabama Town. 2009. 120p. pap. 12.95 *(978-1-4401-7776-7(7))* iUniverse, Inc.

Singleton, Billy J. Mobile Aviation. 2011. (Images of Aviation Ser.). (Illus.). 128p. pap. 21.99 *(978-0-7385-8683-0(8))* Arcadia Publishing.

Spersrud, Jennifer V. Everything You Want to Know about a Gluten-Free Lifestyle in the State of Alabam: Resource Information on Everyday Life for Gluten-Free People. 2009. 196p. pap. 14.49 *(978-1-4389-9585-4(7))* AuthorHouse.

Tapia, Laura Flynn & Lewis, Yoshie. Muscle Shoals. 2007. (Images of America Ser.). (ENG., Illus.). 128p. per. 21.99 *(978-0-7385-5265-1(8))* Arcadia Publishing.

Trammell, Bobbye Baker. Berniston. 2009. (Images of America Ser.). (Illus.). 128p. pap. 21.99 *(978-0-7385-6803-4(1))* Arcadia Publishing.

Trevino, Heather S. & Pastorello, Linda E. Oak Park & the Montgomery Zoo. 2007. (Images of America Ser.). (ENG., Illus.). 128p. per. 19.99 *(978-0-7385-5311-5(5))* Arcadia Publishing.

Utz, Karen R. & Sloss Furnaces Foundation. Sloss Furnaces. 2009. (Images of America Ser.). (ENG., Illus.). 128p. pap. 21.99 *(978-0-7385-6623-8(3))* Arcadia Publishing.

Vogelgesang, Deborah. And the Rivers Rose. 2011. 194p. pap. 18.99 ***(978-1-257-12830-3(2))*** Lulu Enterprises Inc.

Walls, Peggy Jackson & Oliver, Laura Dykes. Alexander City. 2011. (Images of America Ser.). (ENG., Illus.). 128p. pap. 21.99 ***(978-0-7385-8804-9(0))*** Arcadia Publishing.

Watkins, Clarence. Baseball in Birmingham. 2010. (Images of Baseball Ser.). (ENG., Illus.). 128p. pap. 21.99 *(978-0-7385-6686-3(1))* Arcadia Publishing.

What's Cookin' in Alabama! (Orig.). pap. *(978-1-56944-085-8(9))* Terrell Creative.

White, Lois, et al, eds. History of Holly Pond Area, Early Settlers. 2008. lib. bdg. 50.00 *(978-0-9796537-7-3(0))* Heritage Publishing Consultants, Inc.

Wilkerson, Lyn. Slow Travels-Alabama. 2010. 216p. pap. 17.99 *(978-0-557-14055-8(2))* Lulu Enterprises Inc.

Young, Beth Maynor & Hall, John C. Headwaters: A Journey on Alabama Rivers. 2009. (ENG., Illus.). 192p. 39.95 *(978-0-8173-1630-3(2))* Univ. of Alabama Pr.

ALABAMA—DIRECTORIES

Alabama Department of Archives and History Staff. The Alabama Guide: Our People, Resources, & Government. Williams, Randall, ed. 2nd ed. 2009. (ENG., Illus.). 600p. 39.95 *(978-0-8173-1656-3(6))* Univ. of Alabama Pr.

—Sweet Home Alabama: Our People, Resources, & Government. Williams, Randall, ed. 2nd ed. 2009. (ENG., Illus.). 600p. pap. 24.95 *(978-0-8173-5537-1(5))* Univ. of Alabama Pr.

MDR School Directories, 2006-07: Alabama, 51 vols. 29th ed. 2006. 128p. 70.00 *(978-1-57953-485-1(6))* Market Data Retrieval.

ALABAMA—ECONOMIC CONDITIONS

Armes, Ethel. The Story of Coal & Iron in Alabama. 2011. *(978-0-8173-8577-4(0))*; 2nd ed. (ENG., Illus.). 586p. pap. 48.50 *(978-0-8173-5682-8(7))* Univ. of Alabama Pr.

Boyd, Minnie C. Alabama in the Fifties: A Social Study. (Columbia University. Studies in the Social Sciences: No. 353). reprint ed. 32.50 *(978-0-404-51353-5(0))* AMS Pr., Inc.

Bragg, Rick. The Most They Ever Had. 2011. (ENG.). 168p. pap. 14.95 *(978-0-8173-5683-5(5))* Univ. of Alabama Pr.

Hamilton, Deborah, ed. Economic Abstract of Alabama 2000. Date not set. (Printed Ser.: No. 56). (Illus.). 511p. pap. 35.00 *(978-0-943394-14-5(7))* Univ. of Alabama, Ctr. for Business & Economic Research.

ALABAMA—GENEALOGY

Boyd, Gregory A. Family Maps of Butler County, Alabama, Deluxe Edition: With Homesteads, Roads, Waterways, Towns, Cemeteries, Railroads, & More. 2006. (Illus.). 312p. spiral bd. 39.00 *(978-1-4203-0478-7(X))* Arphax Publishing Co.

—Family Maps of Dekalb County, Alabama, Deluxe Edition: With Homesteads, Roads, Waterways, Towns, Cemeteries, Railroads, & More. 2007. (Illus.). 356p. lib. bdg. 54.99 *(978-1-4203-0510-4(7))*; spiral bd. 43.00 *(978-1-4203-0509-8(3))* Arphax Publishing Co.

—Family Maps of Hale County, Alabama, Deluxe Edition: With Homesteads, Roads, Waterways, Towns, Cemeteries, Railroads, & More. 2007. (Illus.). 282p. lib. bdg. 51.99 *(978-1-4203-0655-2(3))*; spiral bd. 38.00 *(978-1-4203-0654-5(5))* Arphax Publishing Co.

—Family Maps of Jefferson County, Alabama, Deluxe Edition: With Homesteads, Roads, Waterways, Towns, Cemeteries, Railroads, & More. 2007. (Illus.). 492p. spiral bd. 46.00 *(978-1-4203-0480-0(1))*; (YA). lib. bdg. 57.99 *(978-1-4203-0481-7(X))* Arphax Publishing Co.

—Family Maps of Limestone County, Alabama, Deluxe Edition: With Homesteads, Roads, Waterways, Towns, Cemeteries, Railroads, & More. 2007. (Illus.). 238p. lib. bdg. 49.99 *(978-1-4203-0645-3(6))*; spiral bd. 36.00 *(978-1-4203-0644-6(8))* Arphax Publishing Co.

—Family Maps of Shelby County, Alabama, Deluxe Edition: With Homesteads, Roads, Waterways, Towns, Cemeteries, Railroads, & More. 2007. (Illus.). 406p. (ENG.). lib. bdg. 57.99 *(978-1-4203-0697-2(9))*; spiral bd. 46.00 *(978-1-4203-0696-5(0))* Arphax Publishing Co.

—Family Maps of Wilcox County, Alabama, Deluxe Edition: With Homesteads, Roads, Waterways, Towns, Cemeteries, Railroads, & More. 2007. (Illus.). 388p. lib. bdg. 54.99 *(978-1-4203-0528-9(X))*; spiral bd. 43.00 *(978-1-4203-0527-2(1))* Arphax Publishing Co.

De Montgomery, B. G. Origin & History of the Montgomerys: Comtes de Montgomery, Ponthieu, Alencon & La Marche; Earls of Arundel, Chichester, Shrewsbury, et al (About Families in Europe) fac. ed. 303p. reprint ed. pap. 47.50 *(978-0-7404-3101-2(3))* Higginson Bk. Co.

Duff, Dorothy Smith. Dekalb County, Alabama, Wills & Estates 1836-1929. 2010. 336p. pap. 29.95 *(978-0-8063-5489-7(5))*; 330p. pap. 30.00 *(978-0-8063-5488-0(7))* Clearfield Co.

Duff, Dorothy Smith, compiled by. DeKalb County, Alabama, Wills & Estates, 1836-1929, 2 vols. 2010. *(978-0-8063-5487-3(9))* Clearfield Co.

Green, Linda L. Alabama 1850 Agricultural & Manufacturing Census, Volume 3 for Autauga, Baldwin, Barbour, Benton, Bibb, Blount, Butler, Chambers, Cherokee, Choctaw, Clarke, Coffee, Conecuh, Coosa, Covington Counties. 2009. 264p. pap. 33.00 *(978-0-7884-4907-9(9))* Heritage Bks.

—Alabama 1860 Agricultural & Manufacturing Census: Volume 4 for Perry, Pickens, Pike, Randolph, Russell, Shelby, St. Clair, Sumter, Tallapoosa, Talladega, Tuscaloosa, Walker, Washington, Wilcox, Winston. 2009. 376p. pap. 41.00 *(978-0-7884-5021-1(2))* Heritage Bks.

Heritage of Cullman County, Alabama, Vol. II. 2008. lib. bdg. 60.00 *(978-0-9796537-5-9(4))* Heritage Publishing Consultants, Inc.

Hill, Henrietta McCormick. The Family Skeleton: A History & Genealogy of the Flewellen, Fontaine, Copeland, Treutlen, Mccormick, Allan & Stuart Families. 2011. 194p. 42.95 ***(978-1-258-09719-6(2))*** Literary Licensing, LLC.

A

Jacobson, Kimberly R. & Greene County Historical Society, The. Greene County & Mesopotamia Cemetery. 2007. (Images of America Ser.). (ENG., Illus.). 128p. per. 19.99 *(978-0-7385-5277-4(1))* Arcadia Publishing.

King, Clinton P. & Barlow, Merlem A. Marriages of Mobile County, Alabama, 1856-1875. 181p. 20.00 *(978-0-943609-02-7(X))* Alabama Ancestors.

Odom, Joyce Smelley. Nichols-Smallwood-Maddox 1638 To 1930: Freeman-Phillips. 2006. (Illus.). 336p. lib. bdg. 60.00 *(978-0-9788481-0-1(1))* Odom, Joyce Smelley.

Russell, Walter A. Descendants of Matthew Russell & Related Families of Jackson County, Alabam: A Collection of Genealogies. 2009. 552p. 38.49 *(978-1-4389-2427-4(5))*; pap. 29.99 *(978-1-4389-2426-7(7))* AuthorHouse.

Sellers, Terry. Iron Butterfly. 2008. (Illus.). 286p. *(978-0-9653313-0-2(X))* Donnell Group, The.

Snell, Jacob Randolph & Snell, Marvis Reeder. The Mount Enon Cemetery: A Pioneer Cemetery in Dale County, Alabama First Called Beverett Graveyard. 2009. (Illus.). 217p. 34.89 *(978-0-9707741-1-8(7))* Snell Publishing, Inc.

Taylor, Frazine K. Researching African American Genealogy in Alabama: A Resource Guide. 2008. *(978-1-60306-044-8(8))*, NewSouth Bks.) NewSouth, Inc.

Thompson, Elvin. The Blood Running Through My Veins: The Story of the Burns Family from the Slave Plantations of Autauga County Alabama until Today. 2009. 60p. pap. 10.49 *(978-1-4389-9886-2(4))* AuthorHouse.

Todd, Glenda McWhirter. Heartbreak of a Civil War Widow: Life of Sarah Harper McWhirter, 1825-1883: Including Harper Family Ancestry Traced to Oxfordshire, Noke, England in Early 1500's & Selected Information on the 1st Alabama Cavalry, USV. 2010. (Illus.). xv, 282p. ***(978-0-7884-8484-1(2))***; pap. *(978-0-7884-5252-9(5))* Heritage Bks.

White, Lois, et al, eds. History of Holly Pond Area, Early Settlers. 2008. lib. bdg. 50.00 *(978-0-9796537-7-3(0))* Heritage Publishing Consultants, Inc.

ALABAMA—GUIDEBOOKS

Chanin, Natalie. Alabama Studio Sewing + Design: A Guide to Hand-Sewing an Alabama Chanin Wardrobe. 2012. (ENG., Illus.). 176p. 35.00 ***(978-1-58479-920-7(X))*** Stewart, Tabori & Chang.

Cuhaj, Joe. Hiking Alabama: A Guide to Alabama's Greatest Hiking Adventures. 3rd ed. 2007. (State Hiking Ser.). (ENG., Illus.). 328p. per. 17.95 *(978-0-7627-4158-8(9)*, Falcon Guides) Globe Pequot Pr., The.

Dabney, Richard. Birmingham's Highland Park. 2006. (Images of America Ser.). (ENG., Illus.). 128p. per. 21.99 *(978-0-7385-4343-7(8))* Arcadia Publishing.

Entertainment Publications, Inc. Staff, compiled by. Birmingham 2009 Entertainment Book. 2008. pap. 25.00 *(978-1-59878-693-4(8))* Entertainment Pubns., Inc.

Haynes, David. Motorcycling Alabama: Fifty Ride Loops Through the Heart of Dixie. 2011. *(978-0-8173-8157-8(0))*; (ENG.). 360p. pap. 29.95 *(978-0-8173-5528-9(6))* Univ. of Alabama Pr.

Helms, Russell. 60 Hikes Within 60 Miles: Birmingham: Including Tuscaloosa, Sipsey Wilderness, Talladega National Forest, & Shelby County. 2nd ed. 2007. (60 Hikes within 60 Miles Ser.). (ENG., Illus.). 266p. pap. 16.95 *(978-0-89732-978-1(3))* Menasha Ridge Pr., Inc.

Kaylor, Mike. The Best of Huntsville, 21st Century. Kaylor, Michael R. & Kaylor, Jennifer W., eds. 3rd ed. 2009. (ENG., Illus.). 124p. mass mkt., act. bk. ed. 15.95 *(978-0-916039-06-6(4))* Kaylor & Kaylor Co.

Keith, Todd. Insiders' Guide to Birmingham. 2011. (Insiders' Guide Ser.). (ENG.). 304p. pap. 18.95 *(978-0-7627-6467-9(8)*, Insiders' Guide) Globe Pequot Pr., The.

Larson, Ron. Mississippi Tenn-Tom River Cruise: Stipaul to Gulf of Mexico. 2008. (Illus.). 197p. 28.00 *(978-0-9640937-3-7(1))*; pap. 19.95 *(978-0-9640937-4-4(X))* Steamboat Pr.

Martin, Gay. Alabama: A Guide to Unique Places. 9th ed. 2009. (Off the Beaten Path Ser.). (ENG., Illus.). 208p. pap. 14.95 *(978-0-7627-5020-7(0))* Globe Pequot Pr., The.

Molloy, Johnny. 50 Hikes in Alabama. 2010. (50 Hikes Ser.). (ENG.). 240p. pap. 18.95 *(978-0-88150-878-9(0)*, 150878) Countryman Pr.

Rand McNally, creator. Rand Mcnally Birmingham Street Guide. 5th ed. 2007. (Rand Mcnally Birmingham Street Guide Ser.). (Illus.). pap. 17.95 *(978-0-528-86793-4(8))* Rand McNally.

Smith, Holly. 101 Things to Do in Alabama: Before You Up & Die. 2009. 5.95 *(978-1-60261-053-8(3))* Sweetwater Pr.

ALABAMA—HISTORY

see also Horseshoe Bend, Battle of, Ala., 1814; Mobile Bay, Battle of, Ala., 1864

Abernethy, Thomas Perkins. The Formative Period in Alabama, 1815-1828. 2010. (ENG.). 192p. pap. 23.75 *(978-1-176-60638-8(7))*; 206p. pap. 24.75 *(978-1-148-01823-2(9))* BiblioBazaar.

—The Formative Period in Alabama, 1815-1828. 2010. 112p. pap. 14.14 *(978-1-152-47286-0(0))* General Bks. LLC.

—The Formative Period in Alabama, 1815-1828. 198p. 2010. pap. 18.36 *(978-1-167-04498-4(3))* 2010. 30.36 ***(978-1-167-08239-9(7))*** 2009. 37.95 *(978-1-120-85415-5(6))* 2009. pap. 22.95 *(978-1-120-75980-1(3))* Kessinger Publishing, LLC.

—The Formative Period in Alabama 1815-1828. 2009. (ENG.). 195p. 30.99 *(978-1-117-25462-3(3))*; (ENG.). 195p. pap. 19.99 *(978-1-117-25464-7(X)*, BiblioLife); 196p. pap. 22.75 *(978-1-117-25463-0(1))* BiblioBazaar.

Alabama. (Proseries Wall Map Ser.). 229.00 *(978-0-528-85855-0(6))* Rand McNally.

Alabama Department of Archives and History Staff. The Alabama Guide: Our People, Resources, & Government. Williams, Randall, ed. 2nd ed. 2009. (ENG., Illus.). 600p. 39.95 *(978-0-8173-1656-3(6))* Univ. of Alabama Pr.

—Sweet Home Alabama: Our People, Resources, & Government. Williams, Randall, ed. 2nd ed. 2009. (ENG., Illus.). 600p. pap. 24.95 *(978-0-8173-5537-1(5))* Univ. of Alabama Pr.

The Alabama Guide, 2011-2014: Our People, Resources, & Government. 2011. ***(978-1-58838-275-7(3))***; pap. ***(978-1-60306-146-9(0))***; pap. ***(978-1-58838-276-4(1))*** NewSouth, Inc. (NewSouth Bks.).

Amaki, Amalia K. & Mauter, Katherine R. Tuscaloosa. 2012. (Images of America Ser.). (ENG., Illus.). 128p. pap. 21.99 ***(978-0-7385-8788-2(5))*** Arcadia Publishing.

Andrews, Christopher. History of the Campaign of Mobile. 2008. (Civil War Ser.). (ENG.). 308p. pap. 19.95 *(978-1-4290-1647-6(7))* Applewood Bks.

Bagget, James & Scouten Bates, Kelsey. Alabama Illustrated Engravings from 19th Century Newspapers. 2009. (ENG.). 98p. 29.95 *(978-1-59652-536-8(3))* Turner Publishing Co.

Bailey, Richard. Neither Carpetbaggers nor Scalawags. 5th ed. 2010. 400p. 29.95 *(978-1-58838-189-7(7))* NewSouth, Inc.

Baldwin, Joseph G. The Flush Times of Alabama & Mississippi. 2009. (Illus.). 244p. pap. *(978-1-4099-7152-8(X))* Dodo Pr.

Bartpm, Jessica. Historic Photos of Birmingham in the 50s, 60s, And 70s. 2010. (Historic Photos Ser.). (ENG., Illus.). 206p. 39.95 *(978-1-59652-752-2(8))* Turner Publishing Co.

Benners, Augustus. Disunion, War, Defeat, & Recovery in Alabama: The Journal of Augustus Benners, 1850-1885. 2007. (Illus.). 357p. 35.00 *(978-0-88146-056-8(7))* Mercer Univ. Pr.

Bennett, James R. Historic Birmingham & Jefferson County. 2008. (Illus.). 202p. pap. *(978-1-893619-91-3(5))* Historical Publishing Network.

—Historic Birmingham & Jefferson County: An Illustrated History. 2008. (Illus.). 312p. *(978-1-893619-83-8(4))* Historical Publishing Network.

Bragg, Rick. The Most They Ever Had. 2009. 250p. *(978-1-59692-361-4(X))* MacAdam/Cage Publishing, Inc.

Burnett, Jason & Bessemer Hall of History Museum. Early Bessemer. 2011. (Images of America Ser.). (Illus.). 128p. pap. 21.99 ***(978-0-7385-8803-2(2))*** Arcadia Publishing.

Burnette, O. Lawrence. Coastal Kingdom: A History of Baldwin County, Alabama. 2006. (ENG.). 436p. per. 29.95 *(978-1-4137-9338-3(X))* PublishAmerica, Inc.

—Historic Baldwin County: A Bicentennial History. 2007. (Illus.). 100p. *(978-1-893619-80-7(X))* Historical Publishing Network.

Carter, Clarence E., ed. The Territory of Alabama, 1817-1819. (Territorial Papers of the United States: Vol. 18). reprint ed. 138.60 *(978-0-404-01468-1(2))* AMS Pr., Inc.

Chattahoochee Valley Historical Society & Chambers County Museum. Chambers County. 2010. (Images of America Ser.). (Illus.). 128p. pap. 21.99 *(978-0-7385-8640-3(4))* Arcadia Publishing.

Clark, E. Culpepper. The Schoolhouse Door: Segregation's Last Stand at the University of Alabama Press. 2007. (Illus.). 352p. 49.95 *(978-0-8173-1570-2(5))* Univ. of Alabama Pr.

Clemmons, Vicky, et al. Bibb County. 2008. (Images of America Ser.). (ENG., Illus.). 128p. pap. 21.99 *(978-0-7385-6729-7(9))* Arcadia Publishing.

Cooper, Nina. Selected Letters of General Woodward Reminiscences: Regarding the Creek, or Musgokee Indians of Alabama & Georgia. 2010. 120p. pap. 14.95 *(978-0-9802175-6-8(3))* Distinction Pr.

Crawford, Sr Donald. Wheels of Birmingham Civil Rights Movement. 2007. 100p. pap. 18.95 *(978-1-60008-025-8(1)*, Rooftop Publishing) AuthorHouse.

Davies, Sharon. Rising Road: A True Tale of Love, Race, & Religion in America, 1 vol. 2011. (ENG., Illus.). 352p. pap. 18.95 *(978-0-19-979445-4(6))* Oxford Univ. Pr., Inc.

Diouf, Sylviane A. Dreams of Africa in Alabama: The Slave Ship Clotilda & the Story of the Last Africans Brought to America. 2009. (ENG., Illus.). 352p. pap. 19.95 *(978-0-19-538293-8(5))* Oxford Univ. Pr., Inc.

Drake, Eleanor C. Perry County. 2010. (Images of America Ser.). (Illus.). 128p. pap. 21.99 *(978-0-7385-8662-5(5))* Arcadia Publishing.

Dykes, Ronald. Building Bridges & Roads in the Korean Conflict: History of Company B, from Scottsboro, Alabama, During the Forgotten War. 2010. 120p. 22.95 *(978-1-4502-2265-5(X))*; pap. 12.95 *(978-1-4502-2264-8(1))* iUniverse, Inc.

East, Don C. A Historical Analysis of the Creek Indian Hillabee Towns: And Personal Reflections on the Landscape & People of Clay County, Alabama. 2008. (Illus.). 280p. 30.95 *(978-1-4401-0163-2(9))*; pap. 20.95 *(978-1-4401-0154-0(X))* iUniverse, Inc.

Ellicott, John Morris. The Life of John Ancrum Winslow, Rear-Admiral of the United States Navy: Who Commanded the U.S. Steamer "Kearsarge" in Her Action with the Confederate Cruiser "Alabama" 281p. reprint ed. 98.00 *(978-0-7222-8216-8(8))* Library Reprints, Inc.

Ellis, Carol & Kirkland, Scotty E. Historic Photos of Mobile. 2008. (Historic Photos Ser.). (ENG., Illus.). 206p. 39.95 *(978-1-59652-434-7(0))* Turner Publishing Co.

—Remembering Mobile. 2010. (Remembering Ser.). (ENG., Illus.). 134p. pap. 16.95 *(978-1-59652-677-8(7))* Turner Publishing Co.

Fallin, Wilson & Fallin, Wilson, Jr. Uplifting the People: Three Centuries of Black Baptists in Alabama. 2007. (Religion & American Culture Ser.). (ENG., Illus.). 352p. 39.95 *(978-0-8173-1569-6(1))* Univ. of Alabama Pr.

Faulkner, Jimmy. Byways of Baldwin: Its People, History, Scenic Attractions & Growth From 1936. 2007. 496p. 35.00 *(978-1-60306-019-6(7))* NewSouth, Inc.

Fleming, Walter Lynwood. The Civil War & Reconstruction in Alabama. 815p. reprint ed. 198.00 *(978-0-7222-8336-3(9))* Library Reprints, Inc.

Flynt, Wayne. Alabama in the Twentieth Century. 2nd ed. 2006. (Modern South Ser.). (Illus.). 642p. per. 36.00 *(978-0-8173-5266-0(X))* Univ. of Alabama Pr.

Gaillard, Frye, et al. In the Path of the Storms: Bayou la Batre, Coden, & the Alabama Coast. 2008. (ENG., Illus.). 140p. pap. 24.95 *(978-0-8173-5504-3(9))* Univ. of Alabama Pr.

Green, Linda L. First, for the Duration: The Story of the Eighth (8th) Alabama Infantry, C. S. A. 2008. pap. 26.00 *(978-0-7884-4553-8(7))* Heritage Bks.

Griffith, Lucille. History of Alabama, 1540-1900: As Recorded in Diaries, Letters, & Papers of the Times. 2011. 468p. 57.95 ***(978-1-258-02918-0(9))*** Literary Licensing, LLC.

Grimes, Lydia. Brewton & East Brewton. 2011. (Images of America Ser.). (ENG., Illus.). 128p. pap. 21.99 ***(978-0-7385-8751-6(6))*** Arcadia Publishing.

Hackney, Sheldon. Populism to Progressivism in Alabama. 2010. (Illus.). 406p. *(978-0-8173-8532-3(0))*; 2nd ed. (ENG., pap. 35.00 *(978-0-8173-5650-7(9))* Univ. of Alabama Pr.

Hague, Parthenia. A Blockaded Family - Life in Southern Al. 2006. 184p. per. *(978-1-4067-9645-2(X)*, Hesperides Pr.) Read Bks.

Heritage of Cullman County, Alabama, Vol. II. 2008. lib. bdg. 60.00 *(978-0-9796537-5-9(4))* Heritage Publishing Consultants, Inc.

Hoffman, Roy. Alabama Afternoons: Profiles & Conversations. 2011. *(978-0-8173-8560-6(6))*; (ENG.). 272p. 29.95 *(978-0-8173-1739-3(2))* Univ. of Alabama Pr.

—Back Home: Journeys Through Mobile. 2007. (Illus.). 400p. per. 19.95 *(978-0-8173-5431-2(X))* Univ. of Alabama Pr.

Hultquist, Clark & Heatherly, Carey. Montevallo. 2011. (Images of America Ser.). (Illus.). 128p. pap. 21.99 *(978-0-7385-8743-1(5))* Arcadia Publishing.

Jackson, Harvey H. The Rise & Decline of the Redneck Riviera: An Insider's History of the Florida-Alabama Coast. 2012. (ENG.). 352p. 28.95 ***(978-0-8203-3400-4(6))*** Univ. of Georgia Pr.

Kadare, Ismail. Albanian Sring. Capouya, Emile, tr. from FRE. 240p. pap. *(978-0-86356-174-0(8))* Saqi Bks.

Kazek, Kelly. Forgotten Tales of Alabama. 2010. 192p. pap. 12.99 *(978-1-60949-097-3(5))* History Pr., The.

—A History of Alabama's Deadliest Tornadoes: Disaster in Dixie. 2010. (Disaster Ser.). (ENG., Illus.). 128p. pap. 19.99 *(978-1-59629-911-5(8))* History Pr., The.

Keenan, Jerry. Wilson's Cavalry Corps: Union Campaigns in the Western Theatre, October 1864 Through Spring 1865. alt. ed. 2006. (ENG., Illus.). 271p. per. 35.00 *(978-0-7864-2732-1(9))* McFarland & Co., Inc. Pubs.

Keith, Todd. Birmingham Then & Now. 2009. (Then & Now Thunder Bay Ser.). (ENG.). 144p. 19.95 *(978-1-59223-949-8(8))*, Thunder Bay Pr.) Advantage Pubs. Group.

King, Carole A. & Pell, Karren. Montgomery. 2011. (Then & Now Ser.). (Illus.). 96p. pap. 21.99 ***(978-0-7385-8798-1(2))*** Arcadia Publishing.

Kinnaman, Stephen Chapin. The Most Perfect Cruiser. 2009. 280p. pap. 14.95 *(978-1-59858-907-8(5))* Dog Ear Publishing, LLC.

LeBaron, J. Hugh & Coleman, William Goforth. Perry Volunteers in the Mexican War: Perry County, Alabama First Regiment of Alabama Volunteers, 1846-1847 & the Mexican War Diary of Captain William G. Coleman. 2008. (Illus.). 232p. 24.00 *(978-0-7884-2267-6(7))* Heritage Bks.

Levine, Mark. F5: Devastation, Survival, & the Most Violent Tornado Outbreak of the Twentieth Century. 2007. (Illus.). 336p. 25.95 *(978-1-4013-5220-2(0))* Miramax Bks.

Lewis, John C. & Brill Outlaw, Harriet. Baldwin County. 2009. (Images of America Ser.). (ENG., Illus.). 128p. pap. 21.99 *(978-0-7385-6834-8(1))* Arcadia Publishing.

Library History Committee. Gadsden Public Library: 100 Years of Service. 2008. (Images of America Ser.). (ENG., Illus.). 128p. pap. 19.99 *(978-0-7385-5385-6(9))* Arcadia Publishing.

Linn, Julius, Jr., et al, eds. Digging Out of the Great Depression: Federal Programs at Work in & Around Birmingham. 2010. (Illus.). 148p. pap. 24.95 *(978-0-943994-35-2(7))* Birmingham Historical Society.

McClellan, William Cowan & Carter, John C. Welcome the Hour of Conflict: William Cowan Mcclellan & the 9th Alabama. 2nd ed. 2007. (ENG., Illus.). 376p. 51.75 *(978-0-8173-1521-4(7))* Univ. of Alabama Pr.

McDonald, William Lindsey. Lore of the River. 3rd exp. ed. 2007. (Illus.). 193p. per. 18.95 *(978-0-9719946-2-1(5))* Bluewater Pubns.

McGinnis, G. Owen. Our Late Great Century, 1900-1999. 2010. 454p. pap. 36.50 *(978-0-7884-5168-3(5)*, Heritage Bks.) Heritage Bks.

McMillan, Tom. Escambia County. 2012. (Images of America Ser.). (ENG., Illus.). 128p. pap. 21.99 ***(978-0-7385-9123-0(8))*** Arcadia Publishing.

McWilliams, John L. Tuscumbia. 2012. (Images of America Ser.). (ENG., Illus.). 128p. pap. 21.99 ***(978-0-7385-8820-9(2))*** Arcadia Publishing.

Meek, A. B. (Alexander Beaufort). Romantic Passages in Southwestern History; Including Orations, Sketches & Essays by a B Meek. 2006. 340p. per. 23.99 *(978-1-4255-3473-8(2))* MPublishing.

Morris, Marilyn K. The Story of the Young Women's Book Club & the Birth of the Scottsboro Public Library. 2009. 56p. pap. 9.95 *(978-1-4401-3142-4(2))* iUniverse, Inc.

Morrison, Pat. Walker County High School Athletics: 1920-2000. 2007. (Images of Sports Ser.). (Illus.). 127p. per. 19.99 *(978-0-7385-4434-2(5))* Arcadia Publishing.

Newton, Wesley Phillips. Montgomery in the Good War: Portrait of a Southern City, 1939-1946. 2010. (ENG., Illus.). 352p. pap. 29.95 *(978-0-8173-5632-3(0))* Univ. of Alabama Pr.

O'Foran, Shelly. Little Zion: A Church Baptized by Fire. 2006. (ENG., Illus.). 288p. 55.95 *(978-0-8078-3048-2(8))*; per. 22.00 *(978-0-8078-5763-2(7))* Univ. of North Carolina Pr.

Olliff, Martin. The Great War in the Heart of Dixie: Alabama During World War I. 2008. (ENG., Illus.). 312p. pap. 29.95 *(978-0-8173-5492-3(1))* Univ. of Alabama Pr.

Outlaw, Harriet Brill & Taylor, Penny H. Daphne. 2012. (Images of America Ser.). (ENG., Illus.). 128p. pap. 21.99 ***(978-0-7385-9116-2(5))*** Arcadia Publishing.

Palmer, Mary S. & Coffman, Elizabeth T. MemoraMOBILEia: Alabama Gulf Coast Potpourri. 195p. pap. 11.95 *(978-0-9639773-0-4(X))* Mobile & Bayside Pr.

Pasquill, Robert G. The Civilian Conservation Corps in Alabama, 1933-1942: A Great & Lasting Good. 2nd ed. 2008. (ENG.). 280p. 29.95 *(978-0-8173-5495-4(6))*; (Illus.). 57.00 *(978-0-8173-1621-1(3))* Univ. of Alabama Pr.

Pate, James P., ed. When This Evil War Is Over: The Correspondence of the Francis Family, 1860-1865. 2006. (ENG., Illus.). 328p. 42.50 *(978-0-8173-1517-7(9))* Univ. of Alabama Pr.

Pepperman, Marcia. Grace Was in Their Steps. 2011. 128p. 29.00 ***(978-1-257-64639-5(7))*** Lulu Enterprises Inc.

Philipson, Claire Leila. Alabama. 2010. (ENG., Illus.). 96p. 19.95 *(978-1-55285-908-7(8))* Whitecap Bks., Ltd. CAN. Dist: Midpoint Trade Bks., Inc.

Pickett, Albert. History of Alabama. 2010. (Historiography Ser.). 411p. pap. 25.95 *(978-1-4290-2304-7(X))* Applewood Bks.

Pickett, Albert James. History of Alabama, & Incidentally of Georgia & Mississippi, from the Earliest Period. 2009. 204p. pap. *(978-1-150-14557-5(9))* Books LLC.

—History of Alabama, & Incidentally of Georgia & Mississippi, from the Earliest Period. 2006. 468p. pap. 29.99 *(978-1-4255-5189-6(0))*; 416p. per. 26.99 *(978-1-4255-4493-5(2))* MPublishing.

Pickett, Albert James & Owen, Thomas McAdory. History of Alabama & Incidentally of Georgia & Mississippi from the Earliest Period; Annals of Alabama 1819-1900. 2007. 772p. per. 52.95 *(978-1-4326-4140-5(9))* Kessinger Publishing, LLC.

Pruitt, Paul M. Taming Alabama: Lawyers & Reformers, 1804-1929. 2010. (ENG., Illus.). 200p. pap. 26.95 *(978-0-8173-5601-9(0))*; *(978-0-8173-8328-2(X))* Univ. of Alabama Pr.

Rankin, John P. Memories of Madison: A Connected Community, 1857-2007. 2007. (Illus.). 143p. *(978-1-57864-398-1(8))* Donning Co. Pubs.

Richardson, Nell. A Family Home: A History of the President's Mansion at Auburn University. 2009. (ENG., Illus.). 184p. 24.95 *(978-0-8173-1617-4(5))* Univ. of Alabama Pr.

Roberts, Mary K. Hueytown. 2010. (Images of America Ser.). (Illus.). 128p. pap. 21.99 *(978-0-7385-8690-8(0))* Arcadia Publishing.

Rogers, William Warren, et al. Alabama: The History of a Deep South State. 2nd ed. 2010. (ENG., Illus.). 790p. 74.50 *(978-0-8173-1699-0(X))*; pap. 39.95 *(978-0-8173-5598-2(7))* Univ. of Alabama Pr.

Ruple, Wayne. Cleburne County. 2010. (Images of America Ser.). (Illus.). 128p. pap. 21.99 *(978-0-7385-8645-8(5))* Arcadia Publishing.

Saugera, Eric. Reborn in America: French Exiles & Refugees in the United States & the Vine & Olive Adventure, 1815-1865. 2011. *(978-0-8173-8511-8(8))* Univ. of Alabama Pr.

—Reborn in America: French Exiles & Refugees in the United States & the Vine & Olive Adventure, 1815-1865. Velguth, Madeleine, tr. 3rd ed. 2011. (Atlantic Crossings Ser.). (ENG., Illus.). 584p. 30.00 *(978-0-8173-1723-2(6))* Univ. of Alabama Pr.

Shane Black. The Spirits of Athens: Haunting Tales of an Alabama Town. 2009. 120p. pap. 12.95 *(978-1-4401-7776-7(7))* iUniverse, Inc.

Singleton, Billy J. Mobile Aviation. 2011. (Images of Aviation Ser.). (Illus.). 128p. pap. 21.99 *(978-0-7385-8683-0(8))* Arcadia Publishing.

Sledge, John S. An Ornament to the City: Old Mobile Ironwork. 2006. (ENG., Illus.). 128p. 36.95 *(978-0-8203-2700-6(X))* Univ. of Georgia Pr.

Smith, Joel P. Candid Comments: Selected Columns from the Eufaula Tribune, 1958-2009. 2011. *(978-1-60306-068-4(5)*, NewSouth Bks.) NewSouth, Inc.

Thompson, Ian. From Green Valley to Hoover Country Club: Fifty Years of Memories. 2010. *(978-1-57864-653-1(7))* Donning Co. Pubs.

Timbes, Mary Lois. The Fair Hope of Heaven: A Hundred Years after Utopia. 2008. 180p. 26.95 *(978-1-4401-0320-9(8))* iUniverse, Inc.

Trammell, Bobbye Baker. Bemiston. 2009. (Images of America Ser.). (Illus.). 128p. pap. 21.99 *(978-0-7385-6803-4(1))* Arcadia Publishing.

Uschan, Michael V. Selma to Montgomery. 2011. (Lucent Library of Black History Ser.). (Illus.). 128p. lib. bdg. 33.45 *(978-1-4205-0571-9(8)*, Lucent Bks.) Cengage Gale.

Utz, Karen R. & Sloss Furnaces Foundation. Sloss Furnaces. 2009. (Images of America Ser.). (ENG., Illus.). 128p. pap. 21.99 *(978-0-7385-6623-8(3))* Arcadia Publishing.

Vogelgesang, Deborah. And the Rivers Rose. 2011. 194p. pap. 18.99 ***(978-1-257-12830-3(2))*** Lulu Enterprises Inc.

Walker, James H. A Cheerful Sadness: The American South During Reconstruction. 2013. 385p. pap. 28.93 *(978-0-9633197-4-6(4))* Indian Heirloom Bks.

Ward, Rufus. The Tombigbee River Steamboats: Rollodores, Dead-Heads, & Side-Wheelers. 2010. (ENG., Illus.). 224p. pap. 22.99 *(978-1-59629-285-7(7))* History Pr., The.

Waselkov, Gregory A. A Conquering Spirit: Fort Mims & the Redstick War Of 1813-1814. 2009. (ENG., Illus.). 424p. pap. 29.95 *(978-0-8173-5573-9(1))* Univ. of Alabama Pr.

Weeks, J. D. Birmingham. 2007. (Then & Now Ser.). (ENG., Illus.). 96p. per. 21.99 *(978-0-7385-4366-6(7))* Arcadia Publishing.

Whatley, Jim. Auburn, Sweet, Auburn: History, Stories, an Epitaph of Pine Hill Lemetery 1836-2010. 2010. (ENG.). pap. 0.00 *(978-1-4507-3425-7(1))* Independent Pub.

White, Lois, et al. eds. History of Holly Pond Area, Early Settlers. 2008. lib. bdg. 50.00 *(978-0-9796537-7-3(0))* Heritage Publishing Consultants, Inc.

Wood, Edward J. A Fierce, Wild Joy: The Civil War Letters of Colonel Edward J. Wood, 48th Indiana Volunteer Infantry Regiment. Towne, Stephen E., ed. 2007. (Voices of the Civil War Ser.). (ENG., Illus.). 320p. 38.00 *(978-1-57233-599-8(8))* Univ. of Tennessee Pr.

Woodard, Aulden & Gunter, V. A. N. Champion Mines: Our fathers¿ Mines. 2011. mass mkt. 24.95 ***(978-1-936533-18-3(9))*** Fifth Estate, Inc.

Wright, Scott. A History of Weiss Lake. 2008. (ENG., Illus.). 128p. pap. 19.99 *(978-1-59629-560-5(0))* History Pr., The.

ALABAMA—HISTORY, LOCAL

Benton, Jeffrey C., ed. The Very Worst Road: Travellers' Accounts of Crossing Alabama's Old Creek Indian Territory, 1820-1847. 2nd ed. 2009. (Alabama Fire Ant Ser.). (ENG., Illus.). 169p. pap. 17.95 *(978-0-8173-5550-0(2))* Univ. of Alabama Pr.

Broyles, Angela. Alabama History in the U. S. Yesterday & Tommorrow. 2007. (Illus.). 257p. per. 39.95 *(978-1-934610-07-7(0))* Bluewater Pubns.

DeJarnette, David L. Archaeological Salvage in the Walter F. George Basin of the Chattahoochee River. 2nd ed. 2010. (ENG., Illus.). 254p. pap. 32.00 *(978-0-8173-5644-6(4))* Univ. of Alabama Pr.

Finch, Jackie Sheckler. It Happened in Alabama. 2011. (It Happened in Ser.). (Illus.). 160p. pap. 14.95 *(978-0-7627-6113-5(X))* Globe Pequot Pr., The.

Goss, William E. & Pell, Karren. Tallassee. 2008. (Images of America Ser.). (Illus.). 128p. pap. 19.99 *(978-0-7385-5343-6(3))* Arcadia Publishing.

Gray, Jacquelyn Procter. Huntsville Sketchbook. 2006. (Illus.). 116p. 39.95 *(978-0-9776711-5-1(1))* Sphinx Publishing.

A History of Baldwin County. Date not set. pap. *(978-0-9660479-0-5(7))* Page & Palette.

Hollis, Tim. Vintage Birmingham Signs. 2008. (Images of America Ser.). (Illus.). 127p. pap. 21.99 *(978-0-7385-5376-4(X))* Arcadia Publishing.

Kaylor, Noel Harold. History of Troy: The University. 2007. 352p. 29.95 *(978-1-890934-05-7(4))* Assn. for Textual Study & Production.

King, Carole A. & Pell, Karren I. Montgomery's Historic Neighborhoods. 2010. (Images of America Ser.). (ENG., Illus.). 128p. pap. 21.99 *(978-0-7385-8620-5(X))* Arcadia Publishing.

Love, Dennis. My City Was Gone: One American Town's Toxic Secret, Its Angry Band of Locals, & a $700 Million Day in Court. 2007. (Illus.). 368p. per. 14.95 *(978-0-06-058551-8(X)*, HarperPerennial) HarperCollins Pubs.

Lyles, John. Phenix City. 2010. (Images of America Ser.). (Illus.). 128p. pap. 21.99 *(978-0-7385-8569-7(6))* Arcadia Publishing.

Marion County Historical Society & Woolbright Carruth, Barbara. Marion County. 2009. (Images of America Ser.). (ENG., Illus.). 128p. pap. 21.99 *(978-0-7385-6849-2(X))* Arcadia Publishing.

McHugh, Eileen, et al. Auburn Correctional Facility. 2010. (Images of America Ser.). (ENG., Illus.). 128p. pap. 21.99 *(978-0-7385-7252-9(7))* Arcadia Publishing.

Oh No! We're Gonna Die Too. 2009. 29.95 net. *(978-1-57833-453-7(5))* Todd Communications.

Reeves, Jacquelyn Procter. Hidden History of North Alabama. 2010. (Hidden History Ser.). (ENG., Illus.). 128p. pap. 19.99 *(978-1-59629-752-4(2))* History Pr., The.

Ryan, Jeanette Dyess. Pig Trails & Open Roads: Stories of Central Baldwin County, Alabama. 2009. 296p. pap. 18.95 *(978-1-4401-1730-5(6))* iUniverse, Inc.

Tapia, Laura Flynn & Lewis, Yoshie. Muscle Shoals. 2007. (Images of America Ser.). (ENG., Illus.). 128p. per. 21.99 *(978-0-7385-5265-1(8))* Arcadia Publishing.

Tuskegee & Its People. 354p. reprint ed. 98.00 *(978-0-7222-9754-4(8))* Library Reprints, Inc.

Walls, Peggy Jackson & Oliver, Laura Dykes. Alexander City. 2011. (Images of America Ser.). (ENG., Illus.). 128p. pap. 21.99 ***(978-0-7385-8804-9(0))*** Arcadia Publishing.

Watkins, Clarence. Baseball in Birmingham. 2010. (Images of Baseball Ser.). (ENG., Illus.). 128p. pap. 21.99 *(978-0-7385-6686-3(1))* Arcadia Publishing.

Young, Beth Maynor & Hall, John C. Headwaters: A Journey on Alabama Rivers. 2009. (ENG., Illus.). 192p. 39.95 *(978-0-8173-1630-3(2))* Univ. of Alabama Pr.

ALABAMA—IMPRINTS

Faulkner, Jimmy. Byways of Baldwin: Its People, History, Scenic Attractions & Growth From 1936. 2007. 496p. 35.00 *(978-1-60306-019-6(7))* NewSouth, Inc.

ALABAMA—JUVENILE LITERATURE

Hoose, Phillip. Claudette Colvin: Twice Toward Justice. 2010. lib. bdg. 20.85 ***(978-0-606-23188-6(9)***, Turtleback) Turtleback Bks.

ALABAMA—MAPS

American Map. Birmingham. 2008. 200p. 17.95 *(978-0-8416-0874-0(1))* American Map Corp.

—Huntsville/Decatur: Alabama. 2008. 192p. 18.95 *(978-0-8416-0878-8(4))* American Map Corp.

—Mobile: Alabama. 2008. 108p. 15.95 *(978-0-8416-0879-5(2))* American Map Corp.

—Montgomery. 2008. 96p. 17.95 *(978-0-8416-0880-1(6))* American Map Corp.

Boyd, Gregory A. Family Maps of Butler County, Alabama, Deluxe Edition: With Homesteads, Roads, Waterways, Towns, Cemeteries, Railroads, & More. 2006. (Illus.). 312p. spiral bd. 39.00 *(978-1-4203-0478-7(X))* Arphax Publishing Co.

—Family Maps of Dekalb County, Alabama, Deluxe Edition: With Homesteads, Roads, Waterways, Towns, Cemeteries, Railroads, & More. 2007. (Illus.). 356p. lib. bdg. 54.99 *(978-1-4203-0510-4(7))*; spiral bd. 43.00 *(978-1-4203-0509-8(3))* Arphax Publishing Co.

—Family Maps of Hale County, Alabama, Deluxe Edition: With Homesteads, Roads, Waterways, Towns, Cemeteries, Railroads, & More. 2007. (Illus.). 282p. lib. bdg. 51.99 *(978-1-4203-0655-2(3))*; spiral bd. 38.00 *(978-1-4203-0654-5(5))* Arphax Publishing Co.

—Family Maps of Jefferson County, Alabama, Deluxe Edition: With Homesteads, Roads, Waterways, Towns, Cemeteries, Railroads, & More. 2007. (Illus.). 492p. spiral bd. 46.00 *(978-1-4203-0480-0(1))*; (YA). lib. bdg. 57.99 *(978-1-4203-0481-7(X))* Arphax Publishing Co.

—Family Maps of Limestone County, Alabama, Deluxe Edition: With Homesteads, Roads, Waterways, Towns, Cemeteries, Railroads, & More. 2007. (Illus.). 238p. lib. bdg. 49.99 *(978-1-4203-0645-3(6))*; spiral bd. 36.00 *(978-1-4203-0644-6(8))* Arphax Publishing Co.

—Family Maps of Shelby County, Alabama, Deluxe Edition: With Homesteads, Roads, Waterways, Towns, Cemeteries, Railroads, & More. 2007. (Illus.). 406p. (ENG.). lib. bdg. 57.99 *(978-1-4203-0697-2(9))*; spiral bd. 46.00 *(978-1-4203-0696-5(0))* Arphax Publishing Co.

—Family Maps of Wilcox County, Alabama, Deluxe Edition: With Homesteads, Roads, Waterways, Towns, Cemeteries, Railroads, & More. 2007. (Illus.). 388p. lib. bdg. 54.99 *(978-1-4203-0528-9(X))*; spiral bd. 43.00 *(978-1-4203-0527-2(1))* Arphax Publishing Co.

Edmondson, Pete, compiled by. Guide to Alabama & Georgia ATV & Dirt Bike Trails. 2nd ed. 2007. (Illus.). 78p. 14.95 *(978-0-9796304-0-8(1))* Atvtrails.org.

Rand McNally, creator. Rand Mcnally Birmingham Street Guide. 5th ed. 2007. (Rand Mcnally Birmingham Street Guide Ser.). (Illus.). pap. 17.95 *(978-0-528-86793-4(8))* Rand McNally.

—Rand Mcnally City Map Book: Southern Alabama Cities. 2010. (Rand Mcnally City Map Bks.). (Illus.). 64p. pap. 7.99 *(978-0-528-88225-8(2))* Rand McNally.

ALABAMA—POLITICS AND GOVERNMENT

Alabama Department of Archives and History Staff. The Alabama Guide: Our People, Resources, & Government. Williams, Randall, ed. 2nd ed. 2009. (ENG., Illus.). 600p. 39.95 *(978-0-8173-1656-3(6))* Univ. of Alabama Pr.

—Sweet Home Alabama: Our People, Resources, & Government. Williams, Randall, ed. 2nd ed. 2009. (ENG., Illus.). 600p. pap. 24.95 *(978-0-8173-5537-1(5))* Univ. of Alabama Pr.

The Alabama Guide, 2011-2014: Our People, Resources, & Government. 2011. ***(978-1-58838-275-7(3))***; pap. ***(978-1-58838-276-4(1))***; pap. ***(978-1-60306-146-9(0))*** NewSouth, Inc. (NewSouth Bks.).

Bailey, Richard. Neither Carpetbaggers nor Scalawags. 5th ed. 2010. 400p. 29.95 *(978-1-58838-189-7(7))* NewSouth, Inc.

Casey, Ron & Thomson, Bailey. For the Love of Alabama: Journalism by Ron Casey & Bailey Thomson. Hodges, Sam, ed. 2nd ed. 2011. (ENG.). 192p. pap. 18.95 *(978-0-8173-5666-8(5))* Univ. of Alabama Pr.

Clark, Cal & Veal, Don-Terry. Public Opinion in Alabama: Looking Beyond the Stereotypes. 2010. *(978-0-7391-4543-2(6))* Lexington Bks.

Clark, Caleb. Public Opinion in Alabama: Looking Beyond the Stereotypes. 2010. (ENG.). 114p. 55.00 *(978-0-7391-4541-8(X))* Lexington Bks.

Formichella, Joe. Murder Creek: The Unfortunate Incident of Annie Jean Barnes. 2008. 286p. 25.95 *(978-1-57966-073-4(8))* River City Publishing.

Frederick, Jeffrey T. Stand up for Alabama: Governor George Wallace. 2nd ed. 2007. (Modern South Ser.). (ENG., Illus.). 504p. 47.50 *(978-0-8173-1574-0(8))* Univ. of Alabama Pr.

Grafton, Carl & Permaloff, Anne. Big Mules & Branchheads: James E. Folsom & Political Power in Alabama. 2008. (ENG.). 336p. pap. 24.95 *(978-0-8203-3188-1(0))* Univ. of Georgia Pr.

Harvey, Gordon E., et al, eds. History & Hope in the Heart of Dixie: Scholarship, Activism, & Wayne Flynt in the Modern South. 2006. (Modern South Ser.). 240p. 50.00 *(978-0-8173-1507-8(1))* Univ. of Alabama Pr.

Jeffries, Hasan. Bloody Lowndes: Civil Rights & Black Power in Alabama's Black Belt. 2009. (ENG., Illus.). 352p. 60.00 *(978-0-8147-4305-8(6))* New York Univ. Pr.

Novkov, Julie Lavonne. Racial Union: Law, Intimacy, & the White State in Alabama, 1865-1954. 2008. (ENG.). 368p. 90.00 *(978-0-472-09885-9(3))* Univ. of Michigan Pr.

—Racial Union: Law, Intimacy, & the White State in Alabama, 1865-1954. 2008. (ENG.). 368p. pap. 29.95 *(978-0-472-06885-2(7))* Univ. of Michigan Pr.

Permaloff, Anne & Grafton, Carl. Political Power in Alabama: The More Things Change ... 2008. (ENG.). 400p. pap. 26.95 *(978-0-8203-3189-8(9))* Univ. of Georgia Pr.

Richardson, Nell. A Family Home: A History of the President's Mansion at Auburn University. 2009. (ENG., Illus.). 184p. 24.95 *(978-0-8173-1617-4(5))* Univ. of Alabama Pr.

Smith, Jeffrey K. The Fighting Little Judge: The Life & Times of George C. Wallace. 2009. vi, 226p. *(978-1-4490-2319-5(3))* AuthorHouse.

Tullos, Allen. Alabama Getaway: The Political Imaginary & the Heart of Dixie. 2011. (Politics & Culture in the Twentieth-Century South Ser.). (ENG.). 380p. 69.95 *(978-0-8203-3048-8(5))*; pap. 24.95 *(978-0-8203-3049-5(3))* Univ. of Georgia Pr.

ALABAMA—SOCIAL CONDITIONS

Boyd, Minnie C. Alabama in the Fifties: A Social Study. (Columbia University, Studies in the Social Sciences: No. 353). reprint ed. 32.50 *(978-0-404-51353-5(0))* AMS Pr., Inc.

Bragg, Rick. The Most They Ever Had. 2011. (ENG.). 168p. pap. 14.95 *(978-0-8173-5683-5(5))* Univ. of Alabama Pr.

CQ Press, ed. Alabama Education in Perspective 2010-2011 Edition, 00 vols. rev. ed. 2010. 24p. pap. 32.00 *(978-1-60871-429-2(2))* CQ Pr.

—Alabama Health Care in Perspective 2010 Edition, 00 vols. rev. ed. 2010. 24p. pap. 32.00 *(978-1-60871-430-8(6))* CQ Pr.

—Alabama in Perspective 2010 Edition, 00 vols. rev. ed. 2010. 24p. pap. 32.00 *(978-1-60871-431-5(4))* CQ Pr.

Flynt, Wayne. Keeping the Faith: Ordinary People, Extraordinary Lives, a Memoir. 2011. (Illus.). x, 400p. ***(978-0-8173-8596-5(7))*** Univ. of Alabama Pr.

Lee, K. G. & Hedgecock, T. S. Flood-Depth Frequency Relations for Rural Streams in Alabama, 2003. 2010. (Illus.). iv, 25p. *(978-1-4113-2844-0(2))* United States Geological Survey.

Love, Dennis. My City Was Gone: One American Town's Toxic Secret, Its Angry Band of Locals, & a $700 Million Day in Court. 2007. (Illus.). 368p. per. 14.95 *(978-0-06-058551-8(X)*, HarperPerennial) HarperCollins Pubs.

Maharidge, Dale & Williamson, Michael. And Their Children after Them: The Legacy of Let Us Now Praise Famous Men. 2008. (ENG., Illus.). 264p. pap. 17.95 *(978-1-58322-857-5(5))* Seven Stories Pr.

Moore, Andrew S. The South's Tolerable Alien: Roman Catholics in Alabama & Georgia, 1945-1970. 2007. 210p. 35.00 *(978-0-8071-3212-8(8))* Louisiana State Univ. Pr.

Morgan, Scott, ed. Alabama in Perspective 2011, 00 vols. rev. ed. 2011. 24p. pap. 32.00 *(978-1-4522-0003-3(3))* CQ Pr.

Novkov, Julie Lavonne. Racial Union: Law, Intimacy, & the White State in Alabama, 1865-1954. 2008. (ENG.). 368p. 90.00 *(978-0-472-09885-9(3))* Univ. of Michigan Pr.

—Racial Union: Law, Intimacy, & the White State in Alabama, 1865-1954. 2008. (ENG.). 368p. pap. 29.95 *(978-0-472-06885-2(7))* Univ. of Michigan Pr.

The One Year Anniversary on [sic] the Tennessee Valley Authority's Kingston Ash Slide: Evaluating Current Cleanup Progress & Assessing Future Environmental Goals: Hearing Before the Subcommittee on Water Resources & Environment of the Committee on Transportation & Infrastructure, House of Representatives, One Hundred Eleventh Congress, First Session, December 9, 2009. 2009. (Illus.). xix, 131p. ***(978-0-16-087077-4(1)***, 552-070-41934-9) United States Government Printing Office.

Pate, James P., ed. When This Evil War is Over: The Correspondence of the Francis Family, 1860-1865. 2006. (ENG., Illus.). 328p. 42.50 *(978-0-8173-1517-7(9))* Univ. of Alabama Pr.

Patterson, Haywood & Conrad, Earl. Scottsboro Boy. 2008. 328p. pap. 32.00 *(978-1-59740-556-0(6))* ACLS Humanities E-Book.

Potts, John A. April 27, 2011 a Generational Storm: The Tornadoes that Hit Alabama. 2011. 108p. pap. 34.29 ***(978-1-4634-4689-5(6))*** AuthorHouse.

Thomas, Richard. Drug Conspiracy: My Persecution by the United States Government: We Only Want the Blacks. 2010. pap. 17.95 *(978-1-60306-064-6(2)*, NewSouth Bks.) NewSouth, Inc.

Todd, Glenda McWhirter. Heartbreak of a Civil War Widow: Life of Sarah Harper McWhirter, 1825-1883: Including Harper Family Ancestry Traced to Oxfordshire, Noke, England in Early 1500's & Selected Information on the 1st Alabama Cavalry, USV. 2010. (Illus.). xv, 282p. ***(978-0-7884-8484-1(2))***; pap. ***(978-0-7884-5252-9(5))*** Heritage Bks.

Weaver, Lila Quintero. Darkroom: A Memoir in Black & White. 2012. ***(978-0-8173-8619-1(X))***; (ENG.). 264p. pap. 24.95 ***(978-0-8173-5714-6(9))*** Univ. of Alabama Pr.

ALABAMA—SOCIAL LIFE AND CUSTOMS

Alabama Department of Archives and History Staff. The Alabama Guide: Our People, Resources, & Government. Williams, Randall, ed. 2nd ed. 2009. (ENG., Illus.). 600p. 39.95 *(978-0-8173-1656-3(6))* Univ. of Alabama Pr.

—Sweet Home Alabama: Our People, Resources, & Government. Williams, Randall, ed. 2nd ed. 2009. (ENG., Illus.). 600p. pap. 24.95 *(978-0-8173-5537-1(5))* Univ. of Alabama Pr.

Allen, Peggy Vonsherie. The Pecan Orchard: Journey of a Sharecropper's Daughter. (ENG., Illus.). 272p. 2011. pap. 18.95 *(978-0-8173-5659-0(2))* 2009. 29.95 *(978-0-8173-1672-3(8))* Univ. of Alabama Pr.

Andrews, Andy. Return to Sawyerton Springs: A Mostly True Tale Filled with Love, Learning, & Laughter. 2009. (ENG.). 160p. 19.99 ***(978-0-9815058-3-1(X))*** Hansen House Publishing, Inc.

—Return to Sawyerton Springs: A Mostly True Tale Filled with Love, Learning, & Laughter. 2009. (ENG.). 160p. 19.99 *(978-0-9819709-1-2(5))* Hay Hse., Inc.

Bagget, James & Scouten Bates, Kelsey. Alabama Illustrated Engravings from 19th Century Newspapers. 2009. (ENG.). 98p. 29.95 *(978-1-59652-536-8(3))* Turner Publishing Co.

Baldwin, Joseph G. (Joseph Glover). The Flush Times of Alabama & Mississippi: A Series of Sketches / by Joseph G. Baldwin. 2006. 368p. per. 26.99 *(978-1-4255-3825-5(8))* MPublishing.

—The Flush Times of Alabama & Mississippi a Series of Sketches. 2006. 372p. per. 26.99 *(978-1-4255-3899-6(1))* MPublishing.

Bartpm, Jessica. Historic Photos of Birmingham in the 50s, 60s, And 70s. 2010. (Historic Photos Ser.). (ENG., Illus.). 206p. 39.95 *(978-1-59652-752-2(8))* Turner Publishing Co.

Brown, Jim, et al. Tributaries Vol. IX: Journal of the Alabama Folklife Association. 2007. (Illus.). 79p. pap. 8.00 *(978-0-9772132-0-7(X))* Alabama Folklife Assn.

Burnett, Jason & Bessemer Hall of History Museum. Early Bessemer. 2011. (Images of America Ser.). (Illus.). 128p. pap. 21.99 ***(978-0-7385-8803-2(2))*** Arcadia Publishing.

Casteel, Dale & Hill, Mary Lou. The Trail That I Traveled. 2010. (Illus.). 208p. ***(978-1-59421-056-3(X))*** Seacoast Publishing, Inc.

Chattahoochee Valley Historical Society & Chambers County Museum. Chambers County. 2010. (Images of America Ser.). (Illus.). 128p. pap. 21.99 *(978-0-7385-8640-3(4))* Arcadia Publishing.

Clemmons, Vicky, et al. Bibb County. 2008. (Images of America Ser.). (ENG., Illus.). 128p. pap. 21.99 *(978-0-7385-6729-7(9))* Arcadia Publishing.

Ellis, Carol & Kirkland, Scotty E. Historic Photos of Mobile. 2008. (Historic Photos Ser.). (ENG., Illus.). 206p. 39.95 *(978-1-59652-434-7(0))* Turner Publishing Co.

—Remembering Mobile. 2010. (Remembering Ser.). (ENG., Illus.). 134p. pap. 16.95 *(978-1-59652-677-8(7))* Turner Publishing Co.

Faulkner, Jimmy. Byways of Baldwin: Its People, History, Scenic Attractions & Growth From 1936. 2007. 496p. 35.00 *(978-1-60306-019-6(7))* NewSouth, Inc.

Feguson, "Riverboat John". The Adventures of Riverboat John: Glimpses of Hunstville in The 1950s. 2009. (American Chronicles Ser.). 128p. pap. 19.99 *(978-1-59629-852-1(9))* History Pr., The.

Fleming, David B. & Haynie, Mary Allison. Ensley & Tuxedo Junction. 2011. (Images of America Ser.). (Illus.). 128p. pap. 21.99 *(978-0-7385-8680-9(3))* Arcadia Publishing.

Grimes, Lydia. Brewton & East Brewton. 2011. (Images of America Ser.). (ENG., Illus.). 128p. pap. 21.99 ***(978-0-7385-8751-6(6))*** Arcadia Publishing.

Hamilton, Virginia Van der Veer. Teddy's Child: Growing up in the Anxious Southern Gentry Between the Great Wars: A Family Memoir. 2009. *(978-1-58838-195-8(1))*; *(978-1-60306-049-3(9))* NewSouth, Inc. (NewSouth Bks.).

Harris, Trudier. Summer Snow: Reflections from a Black Daughter of the South. 2007. (ENG.). 200p. pap. 16.00 *(978-0-8070-7255-4(9))* Beacon Pr.

Hoffman, Roy. Alabama Afternoons: Profiles & Conversations. 2011. *(978-0-8173-8560-6(6))*; (ENG.). 272p. 29.95 *(978-0-8173-1739-3(2))* Univ. of Alabama Pr.

Hunter-Clayton, Victoria Virginia. White & Black under the Old Regime. 195p. reprint ed. 88.00 *(978-0-7222-8233-5(8))* Library Reprints, Inc.

Jackson, Harvey H. The Rise & Decline of the Redneck Riviera: An Insider's History of the Florida-Alabama Coast. 2012. (ENG.). 352p. 28.95 ***(978-0-8203-3400-4(6))*** Univ. of Georgia Pr.

Jordan, Mattie May & Jordan, Maya Marcia. Where the Wild Animals is Plentiful: Diary of an Alabama Fur Trader's Daughter, 1912-1914. Baldwin, Elisa Moore, ed. 2nd ed. 2008. (ENG., Illus.). 276p. per. 27.50 *(978-0-8173-5337-7(2))* Univ. of Alabama Pr.

Kazek, Kelly. Athens & Limestone County. 2010. (Images of America Ser.). (Illus.). 128p. pap. 21.99 *(978-0-7385-8614-4(5))* Arcadia Publishing.

—Christmas Tales of Alabama. 2011. 128p. pap. 12.99 ***(978-1-60949-155-0(6))*** History Pr., The.

Kazek, Kelly. Forgotten Tales of Alabama. 2010. 192p. pap. 12.99 *(978-1-60949-097-3(5))* History Pr., The.

McDonald, William Lindsey. The Old North Field. 2010. (Illus.). 130p. pap. 14.95 *(978-1-934610-05-3(4))* Bluewater Pubns.

McGinnis, G. Owen. Our Late Great Century, 1900-1999. 2010. 454p. pap. 36.50 *(978-0-7884-5168-3(5)*, Heritage Bks.) Heritage Bks.

McWilliams, John L. Tuscumbia. 2012. (Images of America Ser.). (ENG., Illus.). 128p. pap. 21.99 ***(978-0-7385-8820-9(2))*** Arcadia Publishing.

Mills, Michael P. Twice Told Tombigbee Tales. 2007. *(978-1-934193-03-7(9))* Quail Ridge Pr., Inc.

Moates, Marianne. Truman Capote's Southern Years: Stories from a Monroeville Cousin. 2008. (ENG., Illus.). 256p. pap. 19.95 *(978-0-8173-5527-2(8))* Univ. of Alabama Pr.

Phillips, Eddie. The Other Side of Montgomery: Growing up White in the Birthplace of the Civil Rights Movement. 2009. *(978-1-60306-055-4(3)*, NewSouth Bks.) NewSouth, Inc.

Roberts, Mary K. Hueytown. 2010. (Images of America Ser.). (Illus.). 128p. pap. 21.99 *(978-0-7385-8690-8(0))* Arcadia Publishing.

Ruple, Wayne. Cleburne County. 2010. (Images of America Ser.). (Illus.). 128p. pap. 21.99 *(978-0-7385-8645-8(5))* Arcadia Publishing.

Serafin, Faith, et al. Haunted Auburn & Opelika. 2011. (Illus.). 128p. pap. 19.99 ***(978-1-60949-230-4(7))*** History Pr., The.

Smith, Joel P. Candid Comments: Selected Columns from the Eufaula Tribune, 1958-2009. 2011. *(978-1-60306-068-4(5)*, NewSouth Bks.) NewSouth, Inc.

Smith, Robert Leslie. Gone to the Swamp: Raw Materials for the Good Life in the Mobile-Tensaw Delta. 2008. (Alabama Fire Ant Ser.). (ENG., Illus.). 296p. pap. 29.95 *(978-0-8173-5494-7(8))* Univ. of Alabama Pr.

Tuskegee & Its People. 354p. reprint ed. 98.00 *(978-0-7222-9754-4(8))* Library Reprints, Inc.

Wells, Charles Edmon. Ashford: The Depression Years. 2008. (Illus.). 160p. pap. *(978-0-9772337-1-7(5))* Modern Memoirs Publishing.

White, Lois, et al. eds. History of Holly Pond Area, Early Settlers. 2008. lib. bdg. 50.00 *(978-0-9796537-7-3(0))* Heritage Publishing Consultants, Inc.

Windham, Kathryn Tucker. Alabama: One Big Front Porch. rev. ed. 2007. (Illus.). 168p. 25.95 *(978-1-58838-219-1(2)*, NewSouth Bks.) NewSouth, Inc.
—Odd-Egg Editor. 2006. (ENG.). 188p. per. 25.00 *(978-1-934110-01-0(9))* Univ. Pr. of Mississippi.
—She: The Old Woman Who Took over My Life. 2011. (ENG.). 112p. 20.00 ***(978-1-58838-278-8(8)***, NewSouth Bks.) NewSouth, Inc.
Windham, Kathryn Tucker. Twice Blessed. 2007. (Illus.). 156p. per. 20.00 *(978-1-57966-080-2(0))* River City Publishing.

ALABAMA (CONFEDERATE CRUISER)
Semmes, Raphael. The Cruise of the Alabama & the Sumter. 2008. (Civil War Ser.). (ENG.). 332p. pap. 21.95 *(978-1-4290-1611-7(6))* Applewood Bks.
—The Cruise of the Alabama & the Sumter. 2008. 444p. 32.99 *(978-0-554-25127-1(2))* 2008. 444p. 30.99 *(978-0-554-34430-0(0))* 2007. (ENG.). 394p. pap. 25.99 *(978-1-4264-8251-9(5))* BiblioBazaar.
—The Cruise of the Alabama & the Sumter. 2009. 278p. pap. *(978-1-4590-0429-0(9))*; 276p. pap. *(978-1-4590-0425-2(6))*; 184p. pap. *(978-0-217-75356-2(6))* Books LLC.
—The Cruise of the Alabama & the Sumter. 2008. 330p. 45.95 *(978-1-4365-2854-2(2))* 2007. (ENG.). 332p. per. 30.95 *(978-0-548-68989-9(X))* Kessinger Publishing, LLC.
—Cruise of the Alabama & the Sumter. 2006. pap. *(978-1-4068-0452-2(5))* Echo Library.
—The Cruise of the Alabama & the Sumter. l.t. ed. 2007. (ENG.). 442p. pap. 28.99 *(978-1-4264-8288-5(4))* BiblioBazaar.
—Service Afloat. 2009. 574p. pap. *(978-0-217-05168-2(5))* Books LLC.
—Service Afloat. 833p. reprint ed. 198.00 *(978-0-7222-9449-9(2))* Library Reprints, Inc.

ALABAMA CLAIMS
see also Washington, Treaty of, 1871
Beaman, Charles Cotesworth. The National & Private Alabama Claims & Their Final & Amicable Settlement. 2009. (Civil War Ser.). (ENG.). 380p. pap. 23.95 *(978-1-4290-1569-1(1))* Applewood Bks.
—The National & Private Alabama Claims & Their Final & Amicable Settlement / by Charles C Beaman. 2006. 376p. per. 26.99 *(978-1-4255-3928-3(9))* MPublishing.
The Case of the United States. 2006. 208p. per. 20.99 *(978-1-4255-1732-8(3))* MPublishing.
Cushing, Caleb. The Treaty of Washington. 2008. (Civil War Ser.). (ENG.). 284p. pap. 18.95 *(978-1-4290-1564-6(0))* Applewood Bks.
—The Treaty of Washington: Its Negotiation, Execution, & the Discussions Relating Thereto. 2009. 284p. 24.99 *(978-1-103-61375-5(8))*; pap. 18.99 *(978-1-103-61372-4(3))* BiblioBazaar.
—The Treaty of Washington: Its Negotiation, Execution, & the Discussions Relating thereto / by Caleb Cushing. 2006. 284p. per. 23.99 *(978-1-4255-2557-6(1))* MPublishing.
Hill, Frederick Trevor. Decisive Battles of the Law. 2009. 288p. 24.99 *(978-1-103-45849-3(3))*; pap. 18.99 *(978-1-103-45846-2(9))* BiblioBazaar.
—Decisive Battles of the Law. 278p. reprint ed. 98.00 *(978-0-7222-8722-4(4))* Library Reprints, Inc.
State Of Alabama. Statement of the Claim of the State of Alabama Against the United States; with Argument in Support Thereof, & Numerous Precedent from Usage of the G. 2011. 34p. pap. 11.99 ***(978-1-4181-9488-8(3))*** MPublishing.
United States. Dept. of State. Correspondence Concerning Claims Against Great Britain. 2006. 680p. per. 36.99 *(978-1-4255-6814-6(9))* MPublishing.
—Papers Relating to the Treaty of Washington + 2006. 588p. per. 32.99 *(978-1-4255-6374-5(0))*; (ENG.). 676p. per. 36.99 *(978-1-4255-6799-6(1))* MPublishing.

ALABAMA INFANTRY, 15TH REGIMENT, 1861-1865
McClendon, William Augustus. Recollections of War Times. 2010. 252p. pap. 26.75 *(978-1-149-52085-7(X))* BiblioBazaar.
—Recollections of War Times. 2010. 152p. pap. *(978-1-153-12124-8(7))*; 154p. pap. *(978-1-153-12126-2(3))* Books LLC.
—Recollections of War Times: By an Old Veteran While under Stonewall Jackson & Lieutenant General James Longstreet. 2010. (Seeing the Elephant Ser.). (ENG., Illus.). 304p. pap. 22.95 *(978-0-8173-5586-9(3))* Univ. of Alabama Pr.
Oates, William Calvin. The War Between the Union & the Confederacy, & Its Lost Opportunities, with a History of the 15th Alabama Regiment & the Forty-Eight Battles in Which It Was Engaged: The War Between the United States & Spain. 808p. reprint ed. 198.00 *(978-0-7222-7971-7(X))* Library Reprints, Inc.

ALABAMA, UNIVERSITY OF
see University of Alabama

ALACOQUE, MARGUERITE MARIE, SAINT, 1647-1690
Alacoque, Marguerite Marie. The Letters of St Margaret Mary Alacoque. Herbst, Clarence A., tr. 2011. 320p. 50.95 ***(978-1-258-09843-8(1))*** Literary Licensing, LLC.
McKenzie, Janet P. Saint Margaret Mary & the Promises of the Sacred Heart of Jesus Study Guide. 2009. 80p. (J). pap. 7.95 *(978-1-934185-22-3(1))* Biblio Resource Pubns., Inc.
Saint Margaret Mary Alacoque. 2008. 19.95 *(978-1-58002-494-5(7))* Journeys of Faith.

ALALAKH (EXTINCT CITY)
Fink, Amir Sumakai. Late Bronze Age Tell Atchana (Alalakh) 2010. (Bar S Ser.). (ENG., Illus.). 157p. (C). pap. 87.50 *(978-1-4073-0661-2(8))* British Archaeological Reports Ltd. GBR. Dist: Brown, David Bk. Co., The.
Von Dassow, Eva. State & Society in the Late Bronze Age: Alalah under the Mittani Empire. 2008. (C). *(978-1-934309-14-8(1)*, CDL Pr.) Univ. Pr. of Maryland.

ALAMEDA COUNTY (CALIF.)
Christian, Victoria. Alameda County Fair. 2011. (Images of America Ser.). (Illus.). 128p. pap. 21.99 *(978-0-7385-8193-4(3))* Arcadia Publishing.
Friedman, Lawrence M. & Percival, Robert V. The Roots of Justice: Crime & Punishment in Alameda County, California, 1870-1910. 2011. (Studies in Legal History Ser.). (ENG.). 351p. pap. 50.00 ***(978-0-8078-9748-5(5))*** Univ. of North Carolina Pr.

ALAMEIN, BATTLE OF, EGYPT, 1942
see El Alamein, Battle of, Egypt, 1942

ALAMO (SAN ANTONIO, TEX.)
Barr, Amelia E. Remember the Alamo. 2008. 440p. 30.99 *(978-0-559-85986-1(4))* 2008. 440p. pap. 34.75 *(978-0-559-85985-4(6))* 2008. 216p. 27.99 *(978-0-554-21850-2(X))* 2008. 216p. 24.99 *(978-0-554-31153-1(4))* 2006. (ENG.). 222p. pap. 20.99 *(978-1-4264-1078-9(6))* BiblioBazaar.
—Remember the Alamo. 2006. (ENG.). pap. *(978-1-4065-0934-2(5))* Dodo Pr.
—Remember the Alamo. 2010. 222p. 39.95 *(978-1-161-45041-5(6))* Kessinger Publishing, LLC.
—Remember the Alamo. l.t. ed. 2010. (ENG.). 264p. pap. 17.95 *(978-1-61033-393-1(4)*, Texas National Pr.) TGS.
Butterfield, Jack C. Clara Driscoll Rescued: The Alamo. 2011. 20p. pap. 35.95 ***(978-1-258-07653-5(5))*** Literary Licensing, LLC.
Castillo, Mike M. Wrested from This Peaceful Life: Santa Ana at the Alamo. 2008. 79p. pap. 12.96 *(978-1-4357-1891-3(7))* Lulu Enterprises Inc.
Chemerka, William R. C.C. & the Alamo Cats. 2012. ***(978-0-9819904-2-2(8))*** Bright Sky Pr.
Collins, Phil. The Alamo & Beyond: A Collector's Journey. 2012. (ENG.). 416p. 120.00 ***(978-1-933337-50-0(8))*** State Hse. Pr.
Donovan, James. The Blood of Heroes: The 13-Day Struggle for the Alamo — and the Sacrifice That Forged a Nation. 2012. (ENG., Illus.). 512p. 29.99 ***(978-0-316-05374-7(0))*** Little Brown & Co.
Gardner, Raymond. The Cause of Liberty. 2011. 72p. pap. 24.95 ***(978-1-4567-6181-3(1))*** AuthorHouse.
Hatch, Thom. Encyclopedia of the Alamo & the Texas Revolution. alt. ed. 2007. (ENG., Illus.). 237p. per. 49.95 *(978-0-7864-3095-6(8))* McFarland & Co., Inc. Pubs.
Kilgore, Dan & Crisp, James E. How Did Davy Die? & Why Do We Care So Much? enl. ed. 2010. (Elma Dill Russell Spencer Series in the West & Southwest Ser.). (ENG., Illus.). 120p. 18.95 *(978-1-60344-194-0(8))* Texas A&M Univ. Pr.
Travis, Grace W. Lieutenant Colonel William Barret Travis: Commander of the Alamo. 2008. 91p. pap. 16.95 *(978-1-60441-246-8(1))* PublishAmerica, Inc.
Tucker, Phillip. Exodus from the Alamo: The Anatomy of the Last Stand Myth. (Illus.). 2011. 432p. pap. 16.95 ***(978-1-61200-076-3(2)***, Casemate) 2010. 256p. 32.95 *(978-1-932033-93-9(9))* Casemate Pubs. & Bk. Distributors, LLC.
Wallis, Michael. David Crockett: The Lion of the West. (ENG., Illus.). 2012. 400p. pap. 16.95 ***(978-0-393-34227-7(1)***, 34227) 2011. 380p. 27.95 *(978-0-393-06758-3(0)*, 6758) Norton, W. W. & Co., Inc.
Zaboly, Gary S. An Altar for Their Sons: The Alamo & the Texas Revolution in Contemporary Newspaper Accounts. 2011. (ENG., Illus.). 480p. 79.95 ***(978-1-933337-46-3(X))*** State Hse. Pr.

ALAND ISLANDS
Haidari, Benn. Gastronomy from an Ice Cold Paradise: History & Culinary Culture of ÅLand Islands. 2011. (Illus.). 76p. pap. 28.21 ***(978-1-4567-7800-2(5))*** AuthorHouse.

ALARCON, MARTIN DE
Celiz, Francisco. Diary of the Alarcon Expedition into Texas, 1718-1719: Quivira Society Publications, V5. Hoffman, Fritz Leo, tr. 2011. 156p. 41.95 ***(978-1-258-08055-6(9))*** Literary Licensing, LLC.

ALAS, LEOPOLDO, 1852-1901
Alas, Leopoldo. Dona Bert. George, Jr., ed. 2007. (SPA.). 92p. per. 12.95 *(978-1-58977-049-2(8)*, European Masterpieces) LinguaText, Ltd.
Lawless, Geraldine. Modernitys Metonyms: Figuring Time in Nineteenth-Century Spanish Stories. 2011. (ENG.). 338p. 80.00 *(978-1-61148-046-7(9))* Bucknell Univ. Pr.

ALASKA
Baker, Marcus. Extract from Geographic Dictionary of Alaska. (Shorey Historical Ser.). 75p. reprint ed. pap. 10.00 *(978-0-8466-0100-5(1)*, S100) Shorey's Bookstore.
Dall, William H. Alaska & Its Resources. 2007. (ENG.). 668p. 63.95 *(978-0-548-36264-8(5))*; per. 48.95 *(978-0-548-30551-5(X))* Kessinger Publishing, LLC.
Douglass, Don & Hemingway-Douglass, Reanne. Exploring Southeast Alaska: Dixon Entrance to Skagway, 1 vol. 2nd ed. 2007. (ENG.). 544p. pap. *(978-1-932310-24-5(X))* FineEdge.Com LLC.
Hood, D. W., et al, eds. Environmental Studies of Port Valdez. (Occasional Publications: No. 3). 500p. 1.50 *(978-0-914500-01-8(5))* Univ. of Alaska, Institute of Marine Science.
Hood, D. W. & Kelley, E. J., eds. Environmental Studies of Port Valdez, Vol. 1. (Occasional Publications: No. 3a). 800p. 3.00 *(978-0-914500-02-5(3))* Univ. of Alaska, Institute of Marine Science.
Little, Dennise. Untitled Alaskan Anthology. Date not set. mass mkt. *(978-0-312-99083-1(9)*, St. Martin's Paperbacks) St. Martin's Pr.
Orth, Donald J. Dictionary of Alaska Place Names. 210.00 *(978-0-944780-02-2(4))* Glacier Hse. Pubns.
The Ports of Anchorage, Nikisi, Whittier, Seward, Valdez & Ketchkcan,Alalska. per. 10.50 *(978-0-16-001760-5(2))* United States Government Printing Office.
Proposed Fiscal Year 2011 Budgets for Regional Economic Development Commissions, Priorities & Impacts on Regional Economics & Employment: Hearing Before the Subcommittee on Economic Development, Public Buildings, & Emergency Management of the Committee on Transportation & Infrastructure, House of Representatives, One Hundred Eleventh Congress, Second Session, April 29, 2010. 2010. (Illus.). xii, 104p. ***(978-0-16-087946-3(9)***, 552-070-42378-8) United States Government Printing Office.
Ross, Clyde. Valdez Creek Mining District Alaska. 56p. reprint ed. pap. 10.00 *(978-0-8466-0107-4(9)*, S107) Shorey's Bookstore.

ALASKA—ANNEXATION TO THE UNITED STATES
Spicer, George W. The Constitutional Status & Government of Alaska. (Johns Hopkins University. Studies in the Social Sciences, Thirtieth Ser.: 4). reprint ed. 37.50 *(978-0-404-61239-9(3))* AMS Pr., Inc.

ALASKA—ANTIQUITIES
Bielawski, Ellen. In Search of Ancient Alaska: Evidence of Mysteries of the Past. 2006. (ENG., Illus.). 120p. per. 12.95 *(978-0-88240-591-9(8)*, Alaska Northwest Bks.) Graphic Arts Ctr. Publishing Co.
Fienup-Riordan, Ann. Living Tradition of Yupik Mask: Agayuliyararput, Our Way of Making Prayer.Tr. of Our Way of Making Prayer. (Illus.). 320p. pap. 40.00 *(978-0-295-97523-8(7))* Univ. of Washington Pr.
Gronnow, Bjarne, ed. On the Track of the Thule Culture from Bering Strait to East Greenland: Proceedings of the SILA Conference the Thule Culture - New Perspectives in Inuit Prehistory. Papers in honour of Hans Christian Gullov. 2010. (Studies in archaeology & History Ser.). (ENG., Illus.). 263p. (C). 60.00 *(978-87-7602-106-1(8))* Aarhus Universitetsforlag DNK. Dist: ISD.
Knebel, Woody. The Cape Alitak Petroglyphs: From the Old People. 2007. (Illus.). 128p. per. 24.95 *(978-1-57864-212-0(4))* Donning Co. Pubs.
Kramer, Pat. Alaska's Totem Poles, Revised Edition. 3rd ed. 2011. (ENG., Illus.). 104p. pap. 14.95 *(978-0-88240-731-9(7)*, Alaska Northwest Bks.) Graphic Arts Ctr. Publishing Co.
Marsh, Gordon H. Anthropological Papers of the University of Alaska V3, No 1, December 1954. VanStone, James W., ed. 2011. 66p. 36.95 ***(978-1-258-07238-4(6))*** Literary Licensing, LLC.
Mathiassen, Therkel. Archaeological Collections from the Western Eskimos. (Thule Expedition, 5th, 1921-1924 Ser.: Vol. 10, No. 1). reprint ed. 37.50 *(978-0-404-58325-5(3))* AMS Pr., Inc.
—Archaeology of the Central Eskimos, 2 pts. in 1 vol. (Thule Expedition, 5th, 1921-1924 Ser.: No. 4). reprint ed. 137.50 *(978-0-404-58315-6(6))* AMS Pr., Inc.
Oswalt, Wendell H. & Vanstone, James W. The Ethnoarchaeology of Crow Village, Alaska: Bulletin 199. fac. ed. (Smithsonian Institution, Bureau of American Ethnology, Bulletins Ser.). (Illus.). 165p. reprint ed. pap. 18.13 *(978-1-55567-911-8(0))* Coyote Pr.

ALASKA—BIBLIOGRAPHY
Cross Reference Table, Binder 8, Table. *(978-0-327-06381-0(5))* LEXIS Publishing.
Index, Binder 8, Index. *(978-0-327-06382-7(3))* LEXIS Publishing.

ALASKA—BIOGRAPHY
Adams, John Luther. The Place Where You Go to Listen: In Search of an Ecology of Music. 2009. (ENG., Illus.). 180p. pap. 24.95 *(978-0-8195-6903-5(8))* Wesleyan Univ. Pr.
Andrews, Susan B. & Creed, John, eds. Authentic Alaska II: Voices of the Far North. 2008. (Illus.). 416p. pap. 19.95 *(978-0-8032-1564-1(9)*, Bison Bks.) Univ. of Nebraska Pr.
Autobiography: A Brief Glimpse of Life in Alaska 1936-2006. 2007. *(978-0-9778785-2-9(X))* Carson, Michael A.
Benet, Lorenzo. Trailblazer: An Intimate Biography of Sarah Palin. 2010. (ENG., Illus.). 352p. mass mkt. 7.99 *(978-1-4391-8758-6(4))* Pocket Books.
Benson, Kristina. God, Prayer, & Sarah Palin. 2008. 148p. pap. 16.95 *(978-1-60332-062-7(8))* Equity Pr.
Billberg, Rudy. In the Shadow of Eagles: From Barnstormer to Alaska Bush Pilot, a Pilots Story. 2009. (ENG., Illus.). 352p. pap. 16.95 *(978-0-88240-815-6(1)*, Alaska Northwest Bks.) Graphic Arts Ctr. Publishing Co.
Black, Dawn & Petrov, Alexander, eds. Natalia Shelikov: Russian Oligarch of Alaska Commerce. 2010. (University of Alaska Press - Rasmuson Library Historic Translation Ser.). (ENG., Illus.). 250p. pap. 29.95 *(978-1-60223-073-6(0))* Univ. of Alaska Pr.
Bodding, Gerald A. & Cass, William F. Alaska's Father Goose: Captain Gerald A. "Bud" Bodding: A Career in Aviation. 2010. 176p. pap. 19.95 ***(978-0-88839-651-8(1))*** Hancock Hse. Pubs.
Bowers, Don. Fond Memories of Anchorage Pioneers. 29.95 *(978-1-57833-184-0(6))* Todd Communications.
Branson, Jake. More Readings from One Man's Wilderness: The Journals of Richard L. Proenneke, 1974-1980. 2012. (ENG., Illus.). 496p. pap. 18.95 ***(978-1-61608-554-4(1)***, 608554) Skyhorse Publishing Co., Inc.
Brice, Jennifer. Unlearning to Fly. 2010. (ENG.). 224p. pap. 17.95 *(978-0-8032-3428-4(7)*, Bison Bks.) Univ. of Nebraska Pr.
Brokaw, Bill. Hearse to Hoops: Hearsing the Old Alaska Highway & 40 Years of Alaska Men's Basketball. 2006. 176p. per. 14.95 *(978-0-9720604-8-6(0))* Northbooks.
Brower, Charles D., et al. Fifty Years below Zero: A Lifetime of Adventure in the Far North. 352p. 2008. 46.95 *(978-1-4367-0517-2(7))* 2007. (ENG.). per. 31.95 *(978-1-4325-6054-6(9))* Kessinger Publishing, LLC.
Carter, Bill. Red Summer: The Danger & Madness of Commercial Salmon Fishing in Alaska. 2010. (ENG.). 240p. pap. 16.95 *(978-0-9824332-8-7(X))* Schaffner Pr., Inc.
Cheney, Mark. Alask. 2011. 158p. pap. ***(978-1-84549-451-3(2)***, Swirl) arima publishing.
Clouddancer. Clouddancer's Alaskan Chronicles: The Tragedies. 2010. 164p. pap. 15.95 *(978-1-4502-0911-3(4))* iUniverse, Inc.
Coghill, John B. Growing up in Alaska. 2009. pap. 24.95 *(978-0-9823017-1-5(5))* Kayto Communication, Inc.
Cole, Terrence. Fighting for the Forty-Ninth: C. W. Snedden & the Long Struggle for Alaska Statehood. 2010. (ENG., Illus.). 502p. 30.00 *(978-1-883309-06-0(9))* Univ. of Alaska Pr.
Collins, Julie & Collins, Miki. Trapline Twins. 2nd ed. 2010. 212p. pap. 19.95 *(978-1-889963-91-4(7))* Univ. of Alaska Pr.
Conroy, Scott & Walshe, Shushannah. Sarah from Alaska: The Sudden Rise & Brutal Education of a New Conservative Superstar. 2010. (ENG., Illus.). 320p. pap. 15.95 *(978-1-58648-904-5(6))* PublicAffairs.
Dart, Gladys & Wright, Alfred. In Deed, Indeed: Teaching & Learning in a One Room School. 2009. (Illus.). 146p. pap. 32.95 *(978-1-4327-3956-0(5))* Outskirts Pr., Inc.
Dawson, Steven. Delusions of Immortality: Surviving an Unconventional Life. 2007. 372p. per. 16.95 *(978-1-59800-922-4(2))* Outskirts Pr., Inc.
De Vighne, Harry C. Time of My Life. 2006. 244p. per. *(978-1-4067-1587-3(5)*, Hesperides Pr.) Read Bks.
de Yonge, Jack. Boom Town Boy: Coming of Age in Alaska's Lost Frontier. 2010. (ENG., Illus.). 224p. (gr. 9). pap. 14.95 *(978-1-935347-06-4(3))* Epicenter Pr., Inc.
Debogorski, Alex. King of the Road: True Tales from a Legendary Ice Road Trucker. (ENG., Illus.). 2011. 240p. pap. 14.95 ***(978-1-118-14828-0(2))*** 2010. 248p. 24.95 *(978-0-470-64368-6(4))* Wiley, John & Sons, Inc. (Wiley).
Decker, Corky. A Hard Way to Make an Easy Living: From Harpooning for Bluefin Tuna on the East Coast to Fishing the Unpredictable Bering Sea, Relive the Life of one Commercial Fisherman. 2011. 240p. 26.95 *(978-1-4269-5483-2(2))*; pap. 16.95 *(978-1-4269-5482-5(4))* Trafford Publishing.
Dodge, Harry B. Kodiak Tales: Stories of Adventure on Alaska's Emerald Isle. 2010. 168p. 29.99 *(978-1-4490-5600-1(8))*; pap. 19.99 *(978-1-4490-5601-8(6))* AuthorHouse.
Dunn, Charley. Walk with Me Through Alask. 2007. 128p. per. 19.95 *(978-1-4241-9028-7(2))* PublishAmerica, Inc.
Edwards, Carolyn. Answered Prayers in Alask. 2008. 60p. pap. 9.99 *(978-1-60477-981-3(0))* Xulon Pr., Inc.
Eichhorn, J. Martin. Escape from the Cocoon: The true story of how a near-death experience in the wilderness of Alaska propelled the transformation of one man who Despise. 2008. 104p. pap. 12.95 *(978-1-4327-3072-7(X))* Outskirts Pr., Inc.
Elbert, Don. Fascinating Alaska: Inhale the Essence; Intriguing Stories & Facts. (Illus.). 168p. per. 10.00 *(978-1-57833-087-4(4))* Todd Communications.
Fanning, Kay. Kay Fanning's Alaska Story: Memoir of a Pulitzer Prize-Winning Newspaper Publisher on America's Northern Frontier. 2006. (ENG., Illus.). 256p. (gr. 9). per. 17.95 *(978-0-9745014-7-5(6))* Epicenter Pr., Inc.
Fanning, Kay & Field Stephen, Katherine. Kay Fanning's Alaska Story: Memoir of a Pulitzer Prize-Winning Newspaper Publisher on America's Northern Frontier. 2006. (ENG., Illus.). 256p. 24.95 *(978-0-9745014-6-8(8))* Epicenter Pr., Inc.
Fejes, Claire. Cold Starry Night: An Artist's Memoir. 2nd rev. ed. 2007. (ENG., Illus.). 320p. (gr. 9). per. 17.95 *(978-0-9790470-6-0(4))* Epicenter Pr., Inc.
Ferrell, Ed. Biographies of Alaska-Yukon Pioneers, 1850-1950. 2008. 374p. pap. 32.00 *(978-0-7884-0387-3(7)*, F167); Vol. 3. 358p. pap. 31.00 *(978-0-7884-0701-7(5)*, F168) Heritage Bks.
Fields, Leslie Leyland. Surviving the Island of Grace: Life on the Wild Edge of America. 2nd ed. 2008. (ENG., Illus.). 352p. pap. 17.95 *(978-0-9800825-9-3(5))* Epicenter Pr., Inc.
Fienup-Riordan, Ann, ed. Qaluyaarmiuni Nunamtenek Qanemciput / Our Nelson Island Stories: Meanings of Place on the Bering Sea Coast. Rearden, Alice, tr. 2011. (ENG., Illus.). 496p. (C). pap. 50.00 *(978-0-295-99135-1(6))* Univ. of Washington Pr.
Foley, Annette. A Biker's Wife Testimony. 2007. 148p. per. 13.99 *(978-1-60266-874-4(4))* Xulon Pr., Inc.
Gilmore, Robert. Alaska, Where the long trail Led: Chronicles of a Transplanted Okie. 2007. per. 17.95 *(978-1-59433-062-9(X)*, Publishing Consultants) Publication Consultants.
Gilmour, Walter & Hale, Leland E. Butcher, Baker: The Savage Sex Slayer Who Bloodied the Alaskan Landscape: A True Account of a Serial Murderer. 2011. (ENG., Illus.). 348p. pap. 8.99 ***(978-1-57833-544-2(2))*** Todd Communications.
Goulet, Emil Oliver. Rugged Years on the Alaska Frontier. 2011. 328p. 50.95 ***(978-1-258-03772-7(6))*** Literary Licensing, LLC.
Guffey, L. R. Mc Auffe's Arctic. 2009. 176p. pap. 16.25 *(978-1-4269-0341-0(3))* Trafford Publishing.

Guthridge, George. The Kids from Nowhere: The Story Behind the Arctic Educational Miracle. 2006. (ENG., Illus.). 326p. per. 16.95 *(978-0-88240-651-0(5),* Alaska Northwest Bks.) Graphic Arts Ctr. Publishing Co.

Guthrie, Kay. Selling Alaska: The White Collar Adventures of an Advertising Pioneer. 2006. (ENG., Illus.). 160p. (gr. 9). per. 14.95 *(978-0-9745014-8-2(4))* Epicenter Pr., Inc.

Haigh, Jane G. Searching for Fannie Quigley: A Wilderness Life in the Shadow of Mount Mckinley. 2007. (Illus.). 224p. 39.95 *(978-0-8040-1096-2(X));* per. 19.95 *(978-0-8040-1097-9(8))* Swallow Pr.

Haight, Lorrie. Water of Life: Alaska to New Zealand. 2008. (Illus.). 247p. *(978-1-887153-08-9(X))* Floating Pr.

Hand, Carol. Alaska, Oh Alaska: A True to Life Novel of Frontier Alaska. 2011. 156p. pap. 13.49 ***(978-1-4634-2822-8(7))*** AuthorHouse.

Hansen, Sig & Sundeen, Mark. North by Northwestern: A Seafaring Family on Deadly Alaskan Waters. 2010. (ENG., Illus.). 336p. 25.99 *(978-0-312-59114-4(4),* Dunne, Thomas Bks.) St. Martin's Pr.

Harbeson Jr., George. Homesteaders in the Headlights: One family's journey from a Depression-era New Jersey farm to a new life in Wasilla, Alaska. 2010. (Illus.). 312p. pap. 21.50 *(978-0-9789979-8-4(0))* Hardscratch Pr.

Hawley, Charles Caldwell. Wesley Earl Dunkle: Alaska's Flying Miner. 2006. (Illus.). 288p. per. 26.95 *(978-1-889963-93-8(3))* Univ. of Alaska Pr.

Heater, Lucille. Life on the Yentna: Building Rebel's Roost Lodge 1981-1997. 2008. (Illus.). 172p. per. 14.95 *(978-0-9789766-9-9(X))* Northbooks.

Heaton, John. Outlaw Tales of Alaska: True Stories of the Last Frontier's Most Infamous Crooks, Culprits, & Cutthroats. 2010. (Outlaw Tales Ser.). (ENG., Illus.). 208p. pap. 14.95 *(978-0-7627-5326-0(9),* TwoDot) Globe Pequot Pr., The.

Hensley, William L. Iggiagruk. Fifty Miles from Tomorrow: A Memoir of Alaska & the Real People. 2010. (ENG., Illus.). 288p. pap. 15.00 *(978-0-312-42936-2(3))* Picador.

Hillstrand, Johnathan, et al. Time Bandit: Two Brothers, the Bering Sea, & One of the World's Deadliest Jobs. 2009. (ENG., Illus.). 240p. pap. 16.00 *(978-0-345-50412-8(7),* Ballantine Bks.) Random House Publishing Group.

Hitchcock, Mary E. Two Women in the Klondike. 2006. (Illus.). 232p. per. 16.95 *(978-1-889963-96-9(8))* Univ. of Alaska Pr.

—Two Women in the Klondike. 2007. (Illus.). 197p. pap. 24.95 *(978-1-55238-235-6(4))* Univ. of Calgary Pr. CAN. Dist: Michigan State Univ. Pr.

Holleman, Marybeth. The Heart of the Sound: An Alaskan Paradise Found & Nearly Lost. 2011. (ENG., Illus.). 226p. pap. 16.95 *(978-0-8032-3035-4(4),* Bison Bks.) Univ. of Nebraska Pr.

Homer, Jill. Ghost Trails. 2009. 188p. pap. 15.96 *(978-0-557-02407-0(2))* Lulu Enterprises Inc.

Jefford, Jack. Winging It! Jack Jefford, Pioneer Alaskan Aviator. 2nd ed. 2011. (Caribou Classics Ser.). (ENG., Illus.). 320p. pap. 18.95 *(978-0-88240-816-3(X),* Alaska Northwest Bks.) Graphic Arts Ctr. Publishing Co.

Jim, Rearden. Slim Moore: Alaska Master Guide. 2008. 141p. pap. 14.95 *(978-1-57510-139-2(4))* Pictorial Histories Publishing Co., Inc.

John, Sharon. The Road Home. 2007. 52p. per. 9.99 *(978-1-60266-624-5(5))* Xulon Pr., Inc.

Johnson, Kaylene. Sarah: How a Hockey Mom Turned Alaska's Political Establishment Upside Down. 2008. (ENG., Illus.). 164p. (gr. 9). pap. 15.95 *(978-0-9800825-6-2(0));* 3rd ed. 19.95 *(978-0-9790470-8-4(0))* Epicenter Pr., Inc.

—Sarah: How a Hockey Mom Turned Alaska's Political Establishment Upside Down. 2008. (ENG.). 49.99 *(978-1-60640-723-3(6))* Findaway World, LLC.

—A Tender Distance: Raising My Sons in Alaska. 2009. (ENG., Illus.). 208p. pap. 16.95 *(978-0-88240-772-2(4),* Alaska Northwest Bks.) Graphic Arts Ctr. Publishing Co.

Johnston, Levi. Deer in the Headlights: My Life in Sarah Palin's Crosshairs. (ENG., Illus.). 256p. 2012. pap. 15.00 ***(978-1-4516-5166-9(X))*** 2011. 25.00 ***(978-1-4516-5165-2(1))*** Touchstone. (Touchstone).

Kim, Richard & Reed, Betsy, eds. Going Rouge: Sarah Palin: An American Nightmare. 2009. (ENG.). 336p. pap. 15.95 *(978-0-7573-1524-4(0))* Health Communications, Inc.

King, James Gore. Attending Alaska's Birds: A Wildlife Pilot's Story. 2nd ed. 2010. (Illus.). 474p. pap. 29.95 ***(978-0-88839-656-3(2))*** Hancock Hse. Pubs.

King, L. Jo & Janson, Lone. Bird in the Bush. 2008. 236p. pap. 17.50 *(978-1-933973-07-4(2))* KiwE Publishing, Ltd.

Kingrey, Margret. Alaska Stories: A Memoir. 2006. 316p. pap. 17.95 *(978-0-7414-3420-3(2))* Infinity Publishing.

Kinman, Diane, ed. Traveling in Time from the Philippines to Alaska: A Memoir. 2007. per. *(978-0-9763929-1-0(7))* Wimer Publishing Co.

Krakauer, Jon. Into the Wild. movie tie-in ed. 2007. (ENG., Illus.). 224p. pap. 14.95 *(978-0-307-38717-2(5),* Anchor) Knopf Doubleday Publishing Group.

Lambert, Ted. Ted Lambert: The Man Behind the Paintings. 2012. (ENG., Illus.). 176p. pap. 24.95 ***(978-1-60223-165-8(6))*** Univ. of Alaska Pr.

Lende, Heather. Take Good Care of the Garden & the Dogs: A True Story of Bad Breaks & Small Miracles. 2011. (ENG.). 304p. pap. 14.95 *(978-1-61620-051-0(0),* 1616200510) Algonquin Bks. of Chapel Hill.

—Take Good Care of the Garden & the Dogs: Family, Friendships, & Faith in Small-Town Alaska. 2010. (ENG.). 304p. 22.95 *(978-1-56512-568-1(1),* 1565125681) Algonquin Bks. of Chapel Hill.

Lentfer, Hank. Faith of Cranes: Finding Hope & Family in Alaska. 2011. (ENG.). 192p. pap. ***(978-1-59485-639-6(7));*** E-Book ***(978-1-59485-640-2(0))*** Mountaineers Bks., The.

Lester, Jean, told to. Jorgy: The Life of Native Alaskan Bush Pilot & Airline Captain Holger Jorgy Jorgensen. 2008. (Illus.). 280p. pap. *(978-0-9749221-5-7(3))* Ester Republic Pr.

Lindgren, Emory. Adventure in Alaska: I Wouldn't Have Missed It for Anything! 2010. 208p. 27.95 *(978-1-4502-0986-1(6));* (ENG.). pap. 17.95 *(978-1-4502-0984-7(X))* iUniverse, Inc.

Lomen, Carl J. Fifty Years in Alask. 2011. 314p. 50.95 ***(978-1-258-07229-2(7))*** Literary Licensing, LLC.

Mathews, Sandra K. Between Breaths: A Teacher in the Alaskan Bush. 2006. (ENG., Illus.). 250p. pap., tchr. ed. 19.95 *(978-0-8263-3877-8(1))* Univ. of New Mexico Pr.

McGoldrick, John. Alaska Memories: Adventure in the Wilds of Alaska. 2007. 228p. 27.95 *(978-0-595-86111-8(3));* per. 17.95 *(978-0-595-41644-8(6))* iUniverse, Inc.

Mills, Stephen E. & Phillips, James Wendell. Sourdough Sky: A Pictorial History of Flights & Flyers in the Bush Country. 2011. 178p. 42.95 ***(978-1-258-05235-5(0))*** Literary Licensing, LLC.

Moore, Ed. Vagabond Kid: Finds Treasure of God. 2011. 102p. pap. 19.95 ***(978-1-4560-0388-3(7))*** PublishAmerica, Inc.

Morgan, Lael. Art & Eskimo Power: The Life & Times of Alaskan Howard Rock. 2008. (Illus.). 256p. pap. 16.95 *(978-1-60223-021-7(8))* Univ. of Alaska Pr.

—Eskimo Star: From the Tundra to Tinseltown: the Ray Mala Story. 2011. (ENG., Illus.). 144p. (gr. 6). pap. 19.95 *(978-1-935347-12-5(8))* Epicenter Pr., Inc.

Movius, Phyllis Demuth. A Place of Belonging: Five Founding Women of Fairbanks, Alaska. 2009. (ENG., Illus.). 120p. pap. 17.95 *(978-1-60223-064-4(1))* Univ. of Alaska Pr.

Mow, Amy, ed. Snapshots of Seward: A History in Photos. 2010. 102p. pap. 16.95 *(978-0-615-33309-0(5))* Seward Community Library.

Muir, John. Stickeen. 2010. 94p. pap. 18.75 *(978-1-141-08604-7(2))* BiblioBazaar.

Muir, John & Muir, J. Letters from Alaska. Engberg, Robert Martin & Merrell, Bruce, eds. 2009. (ENG., Illus.). 146p. (Orig.). pap. 16.95 *(978-1-60223-055-2(2))* Univ. of Alaska Pr.

Nick, Jans. A Place Beyond: Finding Home in Arctic Alaska. 2nd ed. 2009. (ENG., Illus.). 192p. pap. 16.95 *(978-0-88240-807-1(0),* Alaska Northwest Bks.) Graphic Arts Ctr. Publishing Co.

Noble, Dennis L. & Strobridge, Truman R. Captain Hell Roaring Mike Healy: From American Slave to Arctic Hero. 2009. (New Perspectives on Maritime History & Nautical Archaeology Ser.). (ENG., Illus.). 352p. 34.95 *(978-0-8130-3368-6(3))* Univ. Pr. of Florida.

O'Neill, Patrick H. From Snowshoes to Wingtips: The Life of Patrick O'Neill. 2007. (Illus.). 208p. pap. 19.95 *(978-1-883309-05-3(0))* Univ. of Alaska Pr.

Palin, Bristol & French, Nancy. Not Afraid of Life: My Journey So Far. 2012. (ENG.). 272p. pap. 15.99 ***(978-0-06-208938-0(2),*** William Morrow Paperbacks) HarperCollins Pubs.

Peterson, John. Cottage in the Woods: One Teachers Journey of Discovery from the Alaska Bush to the Oregon Outback. 2007. per. 17.95 *(978-1-59433-059-9(X),* Publishing Consultants) Publication Consultants.

Pioneers of Alaska Men's Igloo 32 and Women's Igloo 14, as told by. In Those Days, Alaska Pioneers of the Lower Kenai Peninsula, Volume II. 2007. (Illus.). 136p. 25.00 *(978-0-9798716-0-3(3))* Erin, Glen Pr.

Rearden, Jim. Sam O. White, Alaskan: Tales of A Legendary Wildlife Agent & Bush Pilot. 2007. pap. 23.95 *(978-1-57510-130-9(0))* Pictorial Histories Publishing Co., Inc.

Renner, Louis. A Kindly Providence: An Alaskan Missionary's Story. 2008. 583p. (J). pap. 16.95 *(978-1-58617-236-7(0))* Ignatius Pr.

Richens, Marvin Gene. Dreams of Reality. 2008. 56p. pap. 15.49 *(978-1-4389-0470-2(3))* AuthorHouse.

Rutzebeck, Hjalmar. My Alaskan Idyll. 2007. (ENG.). 294p. 43.95 *(978-0-548-04728-6(6))* Kessinger Publishing, LLC.

Sanders, Debra. A Matter of Panache: A career in public education. A traumatic brain injury. A memoir of surviving Both. 2008. 344p. pap. 19.95 *(978-1-4327-2816-8(4))* Outskirts Pr., Inc.

Schneider, William. On Time Delivery: The Dog Team Mail Carriers. 2012. (ENG., Illus.). 300p. pap. 24.95 ***(978-1-60223-167-2(2))*** Univ. of Alaska Pr.

Scully, Julia. Outside Passage: A Memoir of an Alaskan Childhood. 2011. 226p. pap. 15.95 *(978-1-60223-129-0(X))* Univ. of Alaska Pr.

Seavey, Mitch. Lead, Follow or Get Out of the Way. 2009. 19.95 net. *(978-1-57833-436-0(5));* pap. 14.95 net. *(978-1-57833-440-7(3))* Todd Communications.

Shumaker, Peggy. Just Breathe Normally. 2009. (American Lives Ser.). (ENG.). 280p. pap. 14.95 *(978-0-8032-2641-8(1),* Bison Bks.) Univ. of Nebraska Pr.

Stout, Jack & Stout, Rita. To Hell with Togetherness: Story of an Alaska Family Living on Remote Homestead West of Anchorage 1957-1962. 2009. pap. 16.95 *(978-0-9815193-4-0(2))* Northbooks.

Strand, Martin R. A Full Life in Sitka Alaska. 2010. 156p. pap. 14.95 *(978-1-4502-5051-1(3))* iUniverse, Inc.

—Transitions from the Sitka, Alaska Wordsmith: Book 3 of the Martin R. Strand, Sr. Trilogy. 2011. 232p. pap. 18.95 *(978-1-4502-8528-5(7))* iUniverse, Inc.

—Voices from the Sitka, Alaska Wordsmith: Book 2 of the Martin R. Strand, Sr. Trilogy. 2010. 260p. pap. 19.95 *(978-1-4502-6918-6(4))* iUniverse, Inc.

Takala, Sherry. My Healing Path. 2007. pap. 12.95 *(978-0-7873-1425-5(0))* Health Research.

Thomas, Tay. My War with Worry. 2011. 154p. pap. 18.00 ***(978-1-61097-036-5(5),*** Resource Pubns.) Wipf & Stock Pubs.

Townsend, Peggy Jean. Alaska Gold Rush Letters & Photographs... (Illus.). 16.95 *(978-0-9657938-4-1(2))* Castle Peak Editions.

Troyer, Will. Bear Wrangler: The Memoirs of an Alaska Pioneer Biologist. (ENG., Illus.). 2010. 256p. pap. 19.95 *(978-1-60223-044-6(7))* 2008. 250p. 26.95 *(978-1-60223-043-9(9))* Univ. of Alaska Pr.

Waldman, Ken. Are You Famous? Touring America with Alaska's Fiddling Poet. 2008. 228p. pap. 15.00 *(978-0-9802081-0-8(6))* Catalyst Bk. Pr.

Waugh, Chris. Misty Memories of Guard Island, Alaska: Ketchikan's Legacy of a Lighthouse Family. 2006. 134p. per. 14.95 *(978-0-9763358-1-8(6))* Alberteen Pr.

Weiss, Miranda. Tide, Feather, Snow: A Life in Alaska. 288p. 2010. (ENG.). pap. 13.99 *(978-0-06-171026-1(1),* HarperPerennial) 2009. 24.99 *(978-0-06-171025-4(3))* HarperCollins Pubs.

Wheeler, Joe L. Togo, the Sled Dog: And Other Great Animal Stories of the North. 2011. pap. 13.99 *(978-0-8163-2431-6(X))* Pacific Pr. Publishing Assn.

Whiting, Fenton B. Grit, grief & Gold. 2008. 176p. pap. 25.00 *(978-0-557-02571-8(0))* Lulu Enterprises Inc.

Wickersham, James & Wickersham, J. Old Yukon: Tales, Trails, & Trials. 2009. (Illus.). 514p. pap. 29.95 *(978-1-60223-051-4(X))* Univ. of Alaska Pr.

Wilder, Edna. The Eskimo Girl & the Englishman. 2008. (ENG., Illus.). 170p. 26.95 *(978-1-60223-016-3(1))* Univ. of Alaska Pr.

—Once upon an Eskimo Time. 2009. (ENG., Illus.). 197p. pap. 17.95 *(978-1-60223-056-9(0))* Univ. of Alaska Pr.

Wilder, Edna & Wilder, E. The Eskimo Girl & the Englishman. 2009. (ENG., Illus.). 166p. pap. 16.95 *(978-1-60223-015-6(3))* Univ. of Alaska Pr.

Wilson, James C. Who Says Life Is Fair? The Story of a Loving Dad. His Life, His Losses, & How He Came Out a Winner. 2010. 352p. 28.49 *(978-1-4490-7640-5(8));* pap. 17.99 *(978-1-4490-7641-2(6))* AuthorHouse.

Windham, Kathryn Tucker. Spit, Scarey Ann, & Sweat Bees: One Thing Leads to Another. 2009. 112p. 20.00 *(978-1-58838-240-5(0),* NewSouth Bks.) NewSouth, Inc.

Winslow, A. D. The Real People: A True Story. 2008. 176p. pap. 13.95 *(978-0-595-51830-2(3))* iUniverse, Inc.

Wood, Deborah. The Legend of River Mahay: Based on a true Alaska adventure story of love, survival & triumph over Adversity. 2007. per. 19.95 *(978-1-59433-057-5(3),* Publishing Consultants) Publication Consultants.

Wood, Ginny & Brewster, Karen. Boots, Bikes, & Bombers: Adventures of Alaska Conservationist Ginny Hill Wood. 2012. (ENG., Illus.). 550p. pap. 29.95 ***(978-1-60223-173-3(7));*** E-Book ***(978-1-60223-174-0(5))*** Univ. of Alaska Pr.

Wyman, Jeffries. Alaska Journal. 2010. (ENG.). 92p. pap. 19.95 *(978-0-9625780-5-2(3))* Protean Publishing Co.

ALASKA—CENSUS

Lindsay, Betty A. & Lindsay, John A. Pribilof Islands, Alaska: Genealogy & Census. 2009. (Illus.). xix, 658p. *(978-1-60319-002-2(3))* United States Government Printing Office.

ALASKA—DESCRIPTION AND TRAVEL

Adams, Dean. Four Thousand Hooks: A True Story of Fishing & Coming of Age on the High Seas of Alaska. 2012. (ENG., Illus.). 280p. 26.95 ***(978-0-295-99197-9(5))*** Univ. of Washington Pr.

Alaska: A Photographic Tour of America's Last Frontier. Date not set. (Illus.). 64p. pap. *(978-1-56944-168-8(5))* Terrell Creative.

Ames, Mary. Surviving Alaska: This Book May Save Your Life. 2008. (ENG., Illus.). 160p. pap. 14.95 *(978-0-9790470-0-8(5))* Epicenter Pr., Inc.

Anderson, Hall. Still Rainin' Still Dreamin' Hall Anderson's Ketchikan. 2010. (ENG., Illus.). 112p. pap. 35.00 *(978-1-889963-90-7(9))* Univ. of Alaska Pr.

Atcheson, Dave. Hidden Alaska: Bristol Bay & Beyond. 2011. (Illus.). 160p. 24.00 *(978-1-4262-0770-9(0),* National Geographic) National Geographic Society.

Barber, Olive. Meet Me in Juneau. 175p. pap. 13.00 *(978-1-57833-024-9(6))* Todd Communications.

Boaz, Robert. Alaskan Quest. 2006. (ENG.). 124p. per. 19.95 *(978-1-4241-4641-3(0))* PublishAmerica, Inc.

Booth, Bonna L. J. Fishing Alaska with Daddy. 2011. 72p. pap. 41.99 ***(978-1-4568-6225-1(1))*** Xlibris Corp.

Branzuela, Lorna J. A Day Without Shadows: Pictures, Poems & True Encounters with Wild Critters of Alaska. 2006. per. 21.95 *(978-0-9777216-0-3(4))* Barnhart Productions.

Breiter, Matthias. Wild Alaska. 2008. (Illus.). 264p. pap. *(978-0-9782432-1-0(8))* BreiterView Publishing

Brownlow, D. B. Pipe Dream: An Alaskan Adventure. 2011. 184p. pap. 16.95 *(978-1-4620-0997-8(2))* iUniverse, Inc.

Burke, Michael D. & Burke, Michael. Same River Twice: A Boatman's Journey Home. 2006. (ENG., Illus.). 224p. pap. 16.95 *(978-0-8165-2531-7(5))* Univ. of Arizona Pr.

Burno, Bucho. Alaska Tide-Findings. 2008. 28p. pap. 24.95 *(978-1-60672-459-0(2))* PublishAmerica, Inc.

Byrd, Dickie. Chandalar 2005. 2008. 193p. pap. 69.50 *(978-1-4357-0723-8(0))* Lulu Enterprises Inc.

Campbell, L. J. Skagway: A Legacy of Gold. Rennick, Penny, ed. (Illus.). 96p. lib. bdg. 24.95 *(978-1-56661-001-8(X),* Alaska Geographic) Graphic Arts Ctr. Publishing Co.

Campbell, Robert. In Darkest Alaska: Travel & Empire along the Inside Passage. 2008. (Nature & Culture in America Ser.). (Illus.). 360p. (C). pap. 24.95 *(978-0-8122-2048-3(X))* Univ. of Pennsylvania Pr.

Campbell, Robert B. In Darkest Alaska: Travel & Empire along the Inside Passage. 2007. (Nature & Culture in America Ser.). (Illus.). 348p. 45.00 *(978-0-8122-4021-4(9))* Univ. of Pennsylvania Pr.

Cole, Dermot. Historic Photos of Alaska. 2008. (Historic Photos Ser.). (ENG., Illus.). 205p. 39.95 *(978-1-59652-424-8(3))* Turner Publishing Co.

Cook, Richard. Cruising in a Big Way. 2009. 102p. pap. 16.95 *(978-0-557-05971-3(2))* Lulu Enterprises Inc.

Deans, Nora L. Wrangell-St. Elias National Park & Preserve. 2007. (Illus.). 14.95 *(978-0-930931-57-5(2))* Alaska Geographic Assn.

Decker, Julie. Expanded View: The New Wing of the Anchorage Museum at Rasmuson Center. 2010. *(978-1-56898-892-4(3))* Princeton Architectural Pr.

Demerjian, Bonnie. Anan, Stream of Living Water. 2007. (ENG., Illus.). 70p. per. 13.95 *(978-0-9776792-1-8(7))* Stikine River Books.

Demerjian, Bonnie. Wrangel. 2011. (Images of America Ser.). (Illus.). 128p. pap. 21.99 ***(978-0-7385-7498-1(8))*** Arcadia Publishing.

Devine, Bob. Lands of the Setting Sun: Discovering Alaska & Western Canada. 2006. (Illus.). 191p. *(978-0-7922-5551-2(8))* National Geographic Society.

Dixon, Jerry. Wild for Alaska: Where Mountains Touch the Sky. 2007. (Illus.). 211p. per. 11.00 *(978-0-9793944-6-1(5))* Entry Way Publishing.

Duncalf, Jean. Born Again Bikers A View from the Pillion. 2011. (Illus.). 120p. pap. 13.32 *(978-1-4567-7193-5(0))* AuthorHouse.

Dunn, Charley. Walk with Me Through Alask. 2007. 128p. per. 19.95 *(978-1-4241-9028-7(2))* PublishAmerica, Inc.

Durr, Bob. The Coldman Cometh: A Family's Adventure in the Alaska Bush. Date not set. pap. *(978-0-312-31180-3(X));* mass mkt. *(978-0-312-98847-0(8))* St. Martin's Pr. (St. Martin's Paperbacks).

Ellis-Knapp, Jody. Ghosts of Alaska. 2009. (Illus.). 160p. pap. 14.99 *(978-0-7643-3303-3(8))* Schiffer Publishing, Ltd.

Ellsworth, Lyman R. Halibut Schooner: An Exciting Account of Present Day Adventure in Alaskan Waters. 2011. 248p. 46.95 ***(978-1-258-07665-8(9))*** Literary Licensing, LLC.

Engelhard, Michael. Cold Flashes: Literary Snapshots of Alaska. 2010. (ENG., Illus.). 210p. pap. 21.95 *(978-1-60223-093-4(5))* Univ. of Alaska Pr.

Fienup-Riordan, Ann, et al. Yupiit Yuraryarait: Yup'ik Ways of Dancing. (ENG., Illus.). 2011. 242p. pap. 35.00 *(978-1-60223-130-6(3))* 2010. 237p. 50.00 *(978-1-60223-082-8(X))* Univ. of Alaska Pr.

Flowers, Pam. Alone Across the Arctic: One Woman's Epic Journey by Dog Team. rev. ed. 2011. (ENG., Illus.). 120p. pap. 12.95 *(978-0-88240-836-1(4),* Alaska Northwest Bks.) Graphic Arts Ctr. Publishing Co.

Foster, Christian. Kongakut River Odyssey 2006. 2008. 248p. pap. 69.95 *(978-1-4327-1154-2(7))* Outskirts Pr., Inc.

Gaede-Penner, Naomi. From Kansas Wheat Fields to Alaska Tundra: A Mennonite Family Finds Home. 2011. pap. 21.99 ***(978-1-61777-202-3(X))*** Tate Publishing & Enterprises, LLC.

Greatland Graphics. Denali Wild: A Nature Portfolio. 2008. (Illus.). 80p. pap. 17.95 *(978-0-9801313-5-2(9))* Greatland Graphics.

Grinev, Andrei Val'terovich. The Tlingit Indians in Russian America, 1741-1867. Bland, Richard L. & Solovjova, Katerina G., trs. from RUS. 2008. (ENG., Illus.). 388p. pap. 24.95 *(978-0-8032-2071-3(5))* Univ. of Nebraska Pr.

Grinnell, George Bird. The Harriman Expedition to Alaska: Encountering the Tlingit & Eskimo in 1899. 2007. (Illus.). 152p. pap. 14.95 *(978-1-889963-98-3(4))* Univ. of Alaska Pr.

Gutkind, Lee. Truckin' with Sam: A Father & Son, the Mick & the Dyl, Rockin' & Rollin', on the Road. 2010. (Excelsior Editions Ser.). (Illus.). 178p. 19.95 *(978-1-4384-3259-5(3),* Suny Pr.) State Univ. of New York Pr.

Hahn, Jennifer. Spirited Waters: Soloing South Through the Inside Passage. 2009. (ENG.). 272p. pap. 16.95 *(978-1-59485-263-3(4))* Mountaineers Bks., The.

Haycox, Stephen & McClanahan, Alexandra J. Alaska Scrapbook: Moments in Alaska History: 1816-1998. 2008. (Illus.). 255p. per. 24.95 *(978-0-938227-08-3(4))* CIRI Foundation, The.

Hirschmann, Fred. Alaska: Portrait of a State. 2006. (Portrait of a Place Ser.). (ENG., Illus.). 112p. 17.95 *(978-1-55868-952-7(4))* Graphic Arts Ctr. Publishing Co.

Hoagland, Edward. Alaskan Travels: Far-Flung Tales of Love & Adventure. 2012. (ENG., Illus.). 208p. 22.95 ***(978-1-61145-503-8(0),*** 611503, Arcade Publishing) Skyhorse Publishing Co., Inc.

Holleman, Marybeth. The Heart of the Sound: An Alaskan Paradise Found & Nearly Lost. 2011. (ENG., Illus.). 226p. pap. 16.95 *(978-0-8032-3035-4(4),* Bison Bks.) Univ. of Nebraska Pr.

Holleman, Marybeth & Coray, Anne. Crosscurrents North: Alaskans on the Environment. Holleman, Marybeth & Coray, Anne, eds. 2008. 320p. pap. 26.95 *(978-1-60223-022-4(6))* Univ. of Alaska Pr.

Hollenbeck, Cliff & Hollenbeck, Nancy. Southeast Aaska. 2010. (Illus.). 112p. *(978-1-57833-480-3(2));* *(978-1-57833-477-3(2))* Todd Communications.

Horacek, Brian P. Where the River Reigns: One Man's Dream for a Log Cabin in the Wild of Alaska. 2008. (Illus.). 171p. pap. 16.99 *(978-0-9802360-3-3(7))* Clear Creek Pubns.

Hoyle, Laurie. Arctic Sanctuary Images of the Arctic National Wildlife Refuge. 2010. (ENG., Illus.). 173p. 35.00 *(978-1-60223-088-0(9))* Univ. of Alaska Pr.

Hrdlicka, Ales. Alaska Diary, 1926-1931. 2011. 432p. 56.95 ***(978-1-258-06753-3(6))*** Literary Licensing, LLC.

Hubbard, Bernard R. Mush, You Malemutes! 2007. (ENG.). 290p. 43.95 *(978-0-548-06423-8(7))* Kessinger Publishing, LLC.

Hudson, Ray. Moments Rightly Placed: An Aleutian Memoir. rev. ed. 2008. (Alaska Book Adventures (Epicenter Press) Ser.). (ENG.). 224p. (gr. 9). pap. 19.95 *(978-0-9790470-7-7(2))* Epicenter Pr., Inc.

Jans, Nick. Alaska. 10th anniv. ed. 2010. (ENG., Illus.). 160p. pap. 29.95 *(978-1-57061-644-0(2))* Sasquatch Bks.

—The Last Light Breaking: Living among Alaska's Inupiat Eskimos. 2007. (ENG., Illus.). 224p. pap. 16.95 *(978-0-88240-458-5(X))* Graphic Arts Ctr. Publishing Co.

Jenkins, Peter. In Alaska. Date not set. *(978-0-312-28581-4(7))* St. Martin's Pr.

Johnson, Madine Maddux. Journey of Enchantment: A Texan's Tall Tale of Alaska. 2011. 66p. 36.95 ***(978-1-258-08502-5(X))*** Literary Licensing, LLC.

Jones, H. Wendy. The Man & the Mountain: Life of Sydney Laurence, Alaskan Painter. 2011. 94p. 38.95 ***(978-1-258-02712-4(7))*** Literary Licensing, LLC.

Jones, Tammy. Alaska Bound: One Man's Dream, One Woman's Nightmare. 2011. (Illus.). 298p. pap. 15.95 *(978-0-615-44237-2(4))* Jones, Tammy.

Kahn, Steve. The Hard Way Home: Alaska Stories of Adventure, Friendship, & the Hunt. 2010. (Outdoor Lives Ser.). (ENG., Illus.). 224p. 22.95 *(978-0-8032-3268-6(3))* Univ. of Nebraska Pr.

Kahn, Steve & Coray, Anne. Lake Clark National Park & Preserve. 2009. pap. 14.95 *(978-0-930931-84-1(X))* Alaska Geographic Assn.

Keenan, Brian. Four Quarters of Light: An Alaskan Journey. 2006. (ENG., Illus.). 384p. pap. 14.00 *(978-0-7679-2325-5(1)*, Broadway) Broadway Bks.

Kelley, Mark. Alaska: A Photographic Excursion. 2007. 34.95 *(978-1-57833-358-5(X))*; pap. 24.95 *(978-1-57833-359-2(8))* Todd Communications.

Kent, Rockwell. Wilderness: A Journal of Quiet Adventure in Alaska. 2010. 236p. pap. 26.75 *(978-1-143-05912-4(3))* 2009. (ENG.). 238p. 32.99 *(978-1-117-03669-4(3))* BiblioBazaar.

King, Robert J. Postcards from Alaska: Souvenir pictures from the Last Frontier, 1890s-1940s. 2007. (Illus.). 176p. pap. 29.95 *(978-0-936425-98-6(9))* Greatland Graphics.

Kirk, Cheryl. Alaska Gold Rush Sudoku. 2006. 108p. per. 9.95 *(978-0-9721764-3-9(8))* ExpandingBooks.com.

Kyi, Tanya Lloyd & Kyi, Tanya Lloyd. Alaska. 2010. (ENG., Illus.). 96p. pap. 12.95 *(978-1-55285-768-7(9))* Whitecap Bks., Ltd. CAN. Dist: Midpoint Trade Bks., Inc.

Lambert, Ted. Ted Lambert: The Man Behind the Paintings. 2012. (ENG., Illus.). 176p. pap. 24.95 ***(978-1-60223-165-8(6))*** Univ. of Alaska Pr.

Lansac, Philippe & London, Jack. Jack London's Grand North. 2007. (ENG., Illus.). 112p. pap. 19.95 *(978-0-7627-4363-6(8))* Globe Pequot Pr., The.

Lindsley, A. L. Sketches of an Excursion to Southern Alaska. fac. ed. (Shorey Historical Ser.). 76p. pap. 10.00 *(978-0-8466-0091-6(9)*, S91) Shorey's Bookstore.

Little, Denise. Untitled Alaskan Anthology. Date not set. *(978-0-312-31702-7(6))* St. Martin's Pr.

Littlepage, Dean. Hiking Alaska: A Guide to Alaska's Greatest Hiking Adventures. 2nd ed. 2006. (Hiking Ser.). (ENG., Illus.). 400p. pap. 19.95 *(978-0-7627-2237-2(1)*, Falcon Guides) Globe Pequot Pr., The.

Lomen, Carl J. Fifty Years in Alask. 2011. 314p. 50.95 ***(978-1-258-07229-2(7))*** Literary Licensing, LLC.

Ludmer, Larry. Cruising Alaska: A Guide to the Ports of Call. 6th ed. 2008. (Illus.). 224p. pap. 14.99 *(978-1-58843-510-1(5))* Hunter Publishing, Inc.

MacHetanz, Sara. Where Else but Alaska? 2011. 224p. 44.95 ***(978-1-258-09681-6(1))*** Literary Licensing, LLC.

MacLeish, Sumner. Seven Words for Wind: Essays & Field Notes from Alaska's Pribilof Islands. 2008. (Illus.). 160p. pap. 14.95 *(978-1-60223-020-0(X))* Univ. of Alaska Pr.

Martin, Anna. Around & about Alask. 2011. 94p. 38.95 ***(978-1-258-06536-2(3))*** Literary Licensing, LLC.

Mason, Mort D. The Alaska Bush Pilot Chronicles: More Adventures & Misadventures from the Big Empty. 2009. (ENG., Illus.). 320p. 25.00 *(978-0-7603-3433-1(1)*, 0760334331, Voyageur Pr) MBI Publishing Co. LLC.

McGinniss, Joe. Going to Extremes. 4th ed. 2010. (ENG.). 306p. (gr. 12). pap. 17.95 *(978-1-935347-03-3(9))* Epicenter Pr., Inc.

McKeown, Martha (Ferguson). Alaska Silver: Another Mont Hawthorne Story. 2011. 286p. 48.95 ***(978-1-258-06585-0(1))*** Literary Licensing, LLC.

McKinley, Jim, et al. Ahtna Travel Narratives: A Demonstration of Shared Geographic Knowledge among Alaska Athabascans. Kari, James, ed. 2011. (ENG., Illus.). 143p. 20.00 *(978-1-55500-105-6(X))* Univ. of Alaska Pr.

Melin, Margaret. Modern Pioneering in Alask. 2011. 98p. 38.95 ***(978-1-258-09282-5(4))*** Literary Licensing, LLC.

Menke, Kathleen M. K. Alaska/Yukon/Arctic Light: Gifts of the Wild. 2007. per. 29.00 *(978-0-9764261-1-0(0))* Crystal Images.

Metz, Dave. Crossing the Gates of Alaska. 2010. (ENG., Illus.). 272p. pap. 15.95 *(978-0-8065-3139-7(8)*, Citadel Pr.) Kensington Publishing Corp.

Miller, Debbie. Midnight Wilderness: Journeys in Alaska's Arctic National Wildlife Refuge. 2011. (ENG., Illus.). 256p. pap. 16.95 *(978-1-59485-633-4(8)*, Braided River) Mountaineers Bks., The.

Misty Fjords National Monument Wilderness. 2007. per. 14.95 *(978-1-57833-368-4(7))* Todd Communications.

Morgan, Chris. Bears of the Last Frontier: The Adventure of a Lifetime among Alaska's Black, Grizzly, & Polar Bears. 2011. (ENG., Illus.). 224p. 35.00 *(978-1-58479-931-3(5))* Stewart, Tabori & Chang.

Muir, John. Travels in Alaska. 2009. (ENG.). 362p. 38.99 *(978-1-117-80872-7(6))* 2009. (ENG.). 362p. pap. 31.75 *(978-1-117-80873-4(4))* 2009. (ENG.). 362p. pap. 25.99 *(978-1-117-80874-1(2)*, BiblioLife) 2009. 366p. 38.99 *(978-1-115-18987-3(5))* 2009. 366p. 33.99 *(978-1-115-18985-9(9))* 2009. 366p. pap. 32.75 *(978-1-115-18984-2(0))* 2009. (ENG.). 364p. pap. 25.99 *(978-1-115-18978-1(6)*, BiblioLife) 2009. (ENG.). 364p. pap. 26.99 *(978-1-115-18980-4(8)*, BiblioLife) 2009. 368p. 26.99 *(978-1-103-94687-7(0))* 2009. 368p. pap. 20.99 *(978-1-103-94678-5(1))* 2008. 248p. 27.99 *(978-0-554-22530-2(1))* 2008. 248p. 24.99 *(978-0-554-31833-2(4))* 2006. 230p. pap. 20.99 *(978-1-4264-2326-0(8))* 2007. (ENG.). 244p. pap. 22.99 *(978-1-4264-2559-2(7))* BiblioBazaar.

—Travels in Alaska. 2009. 194p. pap. *(978-0-217-30194-7(0))*; 196p. pap. *(978-0-217-41089-2(8))*; 190p. pap. *(978-0-217-64775-5(8))* Books LLC.

—Travels in Alaska. 2008. pap. 8.99 *(978-1-4209-3104-4(0))* Digireads.com.

—Travels in Alaska. 2007. (ENG.). 204p. per. *(978-1-4065-8280-2(8))* Dodo Pr.

—Travels in Alaska. 2010. (Illus.). 140p. pap. 22.81 *(978-1-153-74637-3(9))* General Bks. LLC.

—Travels in Alaska. 2010. 172p. pap. *(978-1-4076-4294-9(4))* HardPr.

—Travels in Alaska. 2011. 192p. pap. 25.00 *(978-1-60444-114-7(3))* IndoEuropeanPublishing.com.

—Travels in Alaska. 2008. 430p. 51.95 *(978-0-548-99404-7(8))* 2007. (ENG.). 432p. per. 36.95 *(978-0-548-65282-4(1))* Kessinger Publishing, LLC.

—Travels in Alaska. 2007. (Twelve-Point Ser.). lib. bdg. 25.00 *(978-1-58287-452-4(2))*; lib. bdg. 26.00 *(978-1-58287-937-6(0))* North Bks.

—Travels in Alaska. 176p. 2009. 32.99 *(978-1-59547-562-6(1))* 2007. (ENG.). per. 13.99 *(978-1-59547-865-8(5))* NuVision Pubns., LLC.

Muir, John & Muir, J. Letters from Alaska. Engberg, Robert Martin & Merrell, Bruce, eds. 2009. (ENG., Illus.). 146p. (Orig.). pap. 16.95 *(978-1-60223-055-2(2))* Univ. of Alaska Pr.

Muir, John & Parsons, Marion Randall. Travels in Alaska. 2010. 378p. pap. 33.75 *(978-1-145-10134-0(8))*; 386p. pap. 33.75 *(978-1-142-03747-5(9))* BiblioBazaar.

Oh No! We're Gonna Die Too. 2009. 29.95 net. *(978-1-57833-453-7(5))* Todd Communications.

O'Neill, Dan. A Land Gone Lonesome: An Inland Voyage along the Yukon River. 2007. (ENG., Illus.). 272p. per. 15.95 *(978-1-58243-364-6(X))* Basic Bks.

O'Reilly, Shauna & O'Reilly, Brennan. Alaska Yukon Pacific Exposition. 2009. (Images of America Ser.). (ENG., Illus.). 128p. pap. 21.99 *(978-0-7385-7132-4(6))* Arcadia Publishing.

Peck, Loyd L. The Great Alaskan Quake: First Hand, & Other Cups of Coffee, the True Alaskan Connection. 2011. 76p. pap. 19.95 ***(978-1-4560-6823-3(7))*** PublishAmerica, Inc.

Porter, Chip. Misty Fjords National Monument Wilderness. 2007. 19.95 *(978-1-57833-371-4(7))* Todd Communications.

Powell, Addison M. Trailing & Camping in Alaska. 2006. pap. 36.95 *(978-1-4286-5490-7(9))* Kessinger Publishing, LLC.

Rennicke, Jeff. Alaska: The Last Great American Wilderness. 2010. (ENG., Illus.). 200p. pap. 15.00 *(978-1-4262-0587-3(2)*, National Geographic) National Geographic Society.

Roberts, David. The Mountain of My Fear & Deborah: Two Mountaineering Classics. 2012. (Illus.). (ENG.). 256p. pap. ***(978-1-59485-679-2(6))***; 252p. E-Book ***(978-1-59485-680-8(X))*** Mountaineers Bks., The.

Roland, Cindy. Alaska - Planning Your Own Trip. pap. 10.95 *(978-0-9615245-3-1(7))* Salmonberry Publishing Co.

Roppel, Patricia. Land of Mists: Revillagigedo & Gravina Islands, Misty Fiords National Monument, Alaska. 3rd ed. 60p. pap. 35.00 *(978-1-57833-111-6(0))* Todd Communications.

Rossiter, Harriet. Alaska Calling: A Laugh on Every Page. 2011. 276p. 47.95 ***(978-1-258-06917-9(2))*** Literary Licensing, LLC.

Saulitis, E. V. A. Leaving Resurrection. 2008. 224p. pap. 21.00 *(978-1-59709-091-9(3))* Red Hen Pr.

Schooler, Lynn. Walking Home: A Traveler in the Alaskan Wilderness, a Journey into the Human Heart. (ENG.). 272p. 2011. pap. 16.00 *(978-1-60819-464-3(7))* 2010. 25.00 *(978-1-59691-673-9(7))* Bloomsbury Publishing.

Senkowsky, Sonya & Coyne, Amanda. Alaska Then & Now. 2008. (Then & Now Thunder Bay Ser.). (ENG., Illus.). 144p. 19.95 *(978-1-59223-799-9(1)*, Thunder Bay Pr.) Advantage Pubs. Group.

Sherwonit, Bill. Changing Paths: Travels & Meditations in Alaska's Arctic Wilderness. 2009. (ENG., Illus.). 220p. pap. 21.95 *(978-1-60223-060-6(9))* Univ. of Alaska Pr.

Simpson, Sherry. The Accidental Explorer: Wayfinding in Alaska. 2008. (ENG.). 240p. 23.95 *(978-1-57061-537-5(3))* Sasquatch Bks.

Sipes, Ernest. Into the Savage Land. 2007. (Illus.). 160p. pap. 12.95 *(978-0-88839-562-7(0))* Hancock Hse. Pubs.

Stuck, Hudson. Ascent of Denali. 2007. 136p. per. 12.75 *(978-1-60206-133-0(5))* Cosimo, Inc.

—Ten Thousand Miles with a Dog Sled. 2008. 368p. 29.99 *(978-0-554-39328-5(X))*; 31.99 *(978-0-554-30025-2(7))* BiblioBazaar.

—Ten Thousand Miles with a Dog Sled. 2009. 236p. pap. *(978-1-4588-5775-0(1))* Books LLC.

—Ten Thousand Miles with a Dog Sled. 2008. (Illus.). 332p. pap. *(978-1-4099-2630-6(3))* Dodo Pr.

—Ten Thousand Miles with a Dog Sled. 2010. (Illus.). 196p. pap. 28.01 *(978-1-153-77351-5(1))* General Bks. LLC.

—Ten Thousand Miles with a Dog Sled. 2008. (ENG.). 272p. 97.99 *(978-1-4378-0005-0(X))*; per. 91.99 *(978-1-4378-0032-6(7))* IndyPublish.com.

—Ten Thousand Miles with a Dog Sled: A Narrative of Winter Travel in Interior Alaska. 2007. (ENG.). 364p. pap. 26.99 *(978-1-4346-8981-8(6))*; 324p. pap. 23.99 *(978-1-4346-8980-1(8))* BiblioBazaar.

—Ten Thousand Miles with a Dog Sled: A Narrative of Winter Travel in Interior Alaska. 2007. 504p. per. 24.50 *(978-1-60206-116-3(5))* Cosimo, Inc.

—Ten Thousand Miles with a Dog Sled: A Narrative of Winter Travel in Interior Alaska. 2007. (ENG.). 480p. per. 38.95 *(978-1-4325-7675-2(5))* Kessinger Publishing, LLC.

Sumner, Sandi. Alaska Women's Journey. 2011. (Illus.). 191p. pap. 21.95 *(978-1-58909-903-6(6))* Bookstand Publishing.

U. S. Congress, Senate Committee on Military Affairs. Compilation of Narratives of Explorations in Alaska (1869-1899) Complete with All Folded Maps, Figures & Plates, & indexes to Each Report & a Separate Index of Indian Tribes; with a New Introduction to the AMS Edition by Marvin W. Falk. (Senate Report Ser.: No. 1023). reprint ed. 765.00 *(978-0-404-20323-8(X))* AMS Pr., Inc.

Upton, Joe. Alaska Blues: A Story of Freedom, Risk, & Living Your Dream. 3rd ed. 2008. (ENG., Illus.). 256p. (gr. 9). pap. 14.95 *(978-0-9790470-9-1(9))* Epicenter Pr., Inc.

Ureneck, Lou. Backcast: Fatherhood, Fly-Fishing, & a River Journey Through the Heart of Alaska. 2009. (ENG.). 304p. pap. 13.95 *(978-0-312-38489-0(0)*, St. Martin's Griffin) St. Martin's Pr.

Vanasse, Deb. Picture This, Alaska: Historic Photographs from the Last Frontier. 2009. (ENG., Illus.). 144p. pap. 16.95 *(978-1-57061-584-9(5))* Sasquatch Bks.

Waite, Tom. Wild with Latitude: An Ecologist's Years with Bush Bums, Anarchists, & Other Arctic Wildlife. 2011. 274p. pap. 16.95 ***(978-1-61434-242-7(3))*** Booklocker.com, Inc.

Willems, Sarah Hallock. Psalm of the North: Navigating Life & the Alaska Highway. 2007. (Illus.). 108p. per. 12.00 *(978-0-9777623-2-3(7))* Eveready Letter & Advertising Inc.

Williams, Lorraine, creator. You Know You're in a Small Town When..., Vol. 2. 2007. (Illus.). 84p. pap. 14.95 *(978-0-9797442-0-4(2))* Alaska Independent Pubs.

Wilson, James. Riding the Biscuit Highway. 2008. (Illus.). 212p. pap. *(978-1-84549-306-6(0))* arima publishing.

Witmer, Dennis. Front Street, Kotzebue. 2008. (Illus.). 48p. 50.00 *(978-0-9771028-2-2(3))* Far to The North Pr.

Wohlforth, Charles. Spectacular Alaska. Levy, Dana & O'Connor, Letitia, eds. 2012. (ENG., Illus.). 132p. 29.95 ***(978-0-7893-2429-0(6))*** Universe Publishing.

Wolfe, Art. The Inside Passage to Alaska. 2008. (ENG., Illus.). 160p. 22.95 *(978-1-57061-492-7(X))* Sasquatch Bks.

Wood, Diane F., ed. Alaska Landmark Series, Set. (Orig.). pap. 15.95 *(978-1-886921-05-4(9))* Alaska Pr. Productions.

Wyman, Jeffries. Alaska Journal. 2010. (ENG.). 92p. pap. 19.95 *(978-0-9625780-5-2(3))* Protean Publishing Co.

Young, Anna. The Lost Art of ALASKA FISHING Part One. 2007. 160p. pap. 24.50 *(978-0-615-16852-4(3))* RuggedIsland Publishing.

Young, Samuel Hall. Alaska Days with John Muir by Samuel Hall Young, 1 vol. 2011. 240p. pap. 12.99 *(978-1-4236-0710-6(4))* Gibbs Smith, Publisher.

ALASKA—DIRECTORIES

MDR School Directories, 2006-07: Alaska, 51 vols. 29th ed. 2006. 128p. 52.00 *(978-1-57953-486-8(4))* Market Data Retrieval.

Peterson's Guides Staff. Colleges in the West 2008. Oram, Fern A., ed. 2007. (ENG., Illus.). 288p. pap. 15.00 *(978-0-7689-2420-6(0))* Peterson's.

Wynne, Kate. Guide to Marine Mammals of Alaska. 2008. (Illus.). 75p. (Orig.). pap. 25.00 *(978-1-56612-121-7(3))* Alaska Sea Grant College Program.

ALASKA—ECONOMIC CONDITIONS

Brian, Hosmer. AMER Indians in the Marketplace. 2009. 328p. pap. 19.95 *(978-0-7006-1658-9(6))* Univ. Pr. of Kansas.

Commerce & Economic Development, Binder 1, TITLE 3. *(978-0-327-06371-1(8))* LEXIS Publishing.

Hofmann, Rebecca. The Clash of Economic Decisions in Alask. 2009. 156p. pap. *(978-3-639-13419-3(2))* VDM Verlag Dr. Mueller e.K.

Kimura, Gregory W., ed. Alaska at 50: The Past, Present, & Future of Alaska Statehood. 2009. (ENG., Illus.). 264p. 30.00 *(978-1-60223-061-3(7))* Univ. of Alaska Pr.

—Alaska At 50: The Past, Present, & Future of Alaska Statehood. 2010. (Illus.). 285p. pap. 24.95 *(978-1-60223-081-1(1))* Univ. of Alaska Pr.

McBeath, Jerry, et al. The Political Economy of Oil in Alaska: Multinationals vs. the State. 2008. (Illus.). 240p. 59.95 *(978-1-58826-557-9(9))* Rienner, Lynne Pubs.

McClanahan, Alexandra J. Sakuuktugut. 2006. (Illus.). 200p. pap. 24.95 *(978-0-938227-07-6(6))* CIRI Foundation, The.

Miller, John. The Last Alaskan Barrel: An Arctic Oil Bonanza that Never Was. 2010. (ENG.). 206p. 19.95 *(978-0-9828780-0-2(1))* Caseman Publishing.

Reedy-Maschner, Katherine L. Aleut Identities: Tradition & Modernity in an Indigenous Fishery. 2010. (McGill-Queen's Native & Northern Ser.). (ENG.). 314p. (C). *(978-0-7735-3682-1(5))*; pap. *(978-0-7735-3748-4(1))* McGill-Queen's Univ. Pr.

Revenue, Binder 6, TITLE 15. *(978-0-327-06378-0(5))* LEXIS Publishing.

Rogers, George William. The Future of Alaska: Economic Consequences of Statehood. 2011. (RFF Policy & Governance Set Ser.). (ENG.). 311p. 99.95 *(978-1-61726-068-1(1)*, RFF Pr.) Earthscan LLC.

Shearer, Christine. Kivalina: A Climate Change Story. 2011. (ENG., Illus.). 240p. pap. 16.00 *(978-1-60846-128-8(9))* Haymarket Bks.

ALASKA—GENEALOGY

Ferrell, Ed. Biographies of Alaska-Yukon Pioneers, 1850-1950, Vol. 4. 2008. 354p. pap. 31.00 *(978-0-7884-1500-5(X)*, 1500) Heritage Bks.

Lindsay, Betty A. & Lindsay, John A. Pribilof Islands, Alaska: Genealogy & Census. 2009. (Illus.). xix, 658p. *(978-1-60319-002-2(3))* United States Government Printing Office.

ALASKA—GUIDEBOOKS

Adleman, Jennifer Nicole. Alaska Volcanoes Guidebook for Teachers. 2011. *(978-1-4113-3047-4(1))* United States Geological Survey.

Alaska: Anchorage & South Central. Date not set. pap. *(978-1-56944-151-0(0))* Terrell Creative.

Alaska Princess Cruise Book: Crown Princess. (Orig.). pap. *(978-1-56944-004-9(2))* Terrell Creative.

Alaska Princess Cruise Book: Fair Princess. (Orig.). pap. *(978-1-56944-001-8(8))* Terrell Creative.

Alaska Princess Cruise Book: Regal Princess. (Orig.). pap. *(978-1-56944-003-2(4))* Terrell Creative.

Alaska Princess Cruise Book: Sky Princess. (Orig.). pap. *(978-1-56944-002-5(6))* Terrell Creative.

Alaska Princess Cruise Book: Star Princess. (Orig.). pap. *(978-1-56944-005-6(0))* Terrell Creative.

The Alaska Roadside Angler's Guide. 2007. per. 19.95 *(978-1-57833-376-9(8))* Todd Communications.

Alaska's Inside Passage. pap. *(978-1-56944-074-2(3))* Terrell Creative.

Alaska's Inside Passage. 16.95 *(978-0-942297-14-0(8))* Windham Bay Pr.

Brown, Tricia. The World-Famous Alaska Highway: A Guide to the Alcan & Other Wilderness Roads of the North. 4th ed. 2011. (ENG.). 288p. pap. 22.95 *(978-1-55591-749-4(6))* Fulcrum Publishing.

Cerveny, Lee K. Nature & Tourists in the Last Frontier: Local Encounters with Global Tourism in Coastal Alaska. 2008. (Tourism Dynamics Ser.). *(978-1-882345-53-3(3))* Cognizant Communication Corp.

Chandonnet, Ann. Alaska's Inside Passage. 2nd ed. 2009. (Compass American Guides). (ENG.). 220p. 18.95 *(978-1-4000-0902-2(2)*, Compass America Guides) Fodor's Travel Pubns.

Church, Mike & Church, Terri. Traveler's Guide to Alaskan Camping: Alaska & Yukon Camping with RV or Tent. 5th ed. 2010. (Traveler's Guide Ser.). (ENG., Illus.). 480p. pap. 21.95 *(978-0-9823101-1-3(0))* Rolling Homes Pr.

Crandall, Cass. Bed & Breakfast Alaska Style! 4th ed. (Illus.). 16.95 *(978-0-9626071-5-8(0))* Kachemak Publishing.

Dalby, Ron. Guide to the Alaska Highway. 2nd ed. 2011. (ENG., Illus.). 288p. pap. 19.95 *(978-0-89732-926-2(0))* Menasha Ridge Pr., Inc.

Devaughn, Melissa. Alaska: A Guide to Unique Places. 6th ed. 2008. (Off the Beaten Path Ser.). (ENG., Illus.). 224p. per. 14.95 *(978-0-7627-4534-0(7))* Globe Pequot Pr., The.

DeVaughn, Melissa. Alaska Adventure Guide. 2011. (ENG., Illus.). 448p. pap. 18.95 *(978-0-89732-906-4(6))* Menasha Ridge Pr., Inc.

Devine, Bob & Devine, Robert S. Alaska. 2nd rev. ed. 2009. (ENG., Illus.). 272p. 22.95 *(978-1-4262-0386-2(1)*, National Geographic) National Geographic Society.

DuFresne, Jim. Alaska, 59 vols. 10th rev. ed. 2012. (Regional Guide Ser.). (ENG., Illus.). 448p. pap. 22.99 ***(978-1-74179-696-4(2))*** Lonely Planet Pubns.

Fensterman, Greg. Hiking Alaska's Wrangell-St. Elias National Park & Preserve: From Day Hikes to Backcountry Treks. 2008. (Regional Hiking Ser.). (ENG., Illus.). 272p. pap. 18.95 *(978-0-7627-4319-3(0)*, Falcon Guides) Globe Pequot Pr., The.

Fodor's Travel Publications, Inc. Staff. Fodor's Alaska 2012. 2011. (Full-Color Gold Guides). (ENG., Illus.). 504p. pap. 21.99 *(978-0-679-00955-9(8)*, Fodor's) Fodor's Travel Pubns.

Fowler, Carol. The Alaska Panhandle. 2009. (Great Destinations Ser.). (ENG., Illus.). 336p. pap., instr.'s gde. ed. 19.95 *(978-1-58157-095-3(3)*, 157095) Countryman Pr.

Frazier, Gregory W. Alaska by Motorcycle: How to Motorcycle in Alaska. 2006. 200p. 19.95 *(978-0-935151-48-0(6))* Arrowstar Publishing.

Gates, Nancy, ed. The Alaska Almanac: Facts about Alaska. 33rd rev. ed. 2011. (Alaska Almanac Ser.). (ENG., Illus.). 240p. pap. 14.99 *(978-0-88240-813-2(5)*, Alaska Northwest Bks.) Graphic Arts Ctr. Publishing Co.

Golden, Fran Wenograd & Sloan, Gene. Frommer's Alaska Cruises & Ports of Call. 14th ed. 2012. (Frommer's Color Complete Ser.: 618). (ENG.). 320p. pap. 19.99 ***(978-1-118-04598-5(X)***, Frommers) Wiley, John & Sons, Inc.

Gurney, Michelle & Miller, Mike. Alaska's Southeast: Touring the Inside Passage. 11th ed. 2008. (ENG., Illus.). 304p. pap. 17.95 *(978-0-7627-4535-7(5))* Globe Pequot Pr., The.

Halfpenny, James C. Scats & Tracks of Alaska Including the Yukon & British Columbia: A Field Guide to the Signs of Sixty-Nine Wildlife Species. 2007. (Scats & Tracks Ser.). (ENG., Illus.). 192p. per. 9.95 *(978-0-7627-4230-1(5)*, Falcon Guides) Globe Pequot Pr., The.

Hawk-Bordner, Sharon. Enjoy the Wonders of Alaska. 2010. 288p. pap. 69.99 *(978-1-4520-6130-6(0))* AuthorHouse.

Hicks, Nigel, photos by. DK Eyewitness Travel Guide: Alaska. 2012. (Eyewitness Travel Guide Ser.). (ENG.). 312p. pap. 25.00 *(978-0-7566-8422-8(6))* Dorling Kindersley Publishing, Inc.

Hodges, Montana. Alaska: A Guide to 300 of Alaska's Best Campgrounds. 2009. (State Camping Ser.). (ENG., Illus.). 336p. pap. 19.95 *(978-0-7627-4387-2(5)*, Falcon Guides) Globe Pequot Pr., The.

—Best Easy Day Hikes Fairbanks. 2009. (Best Easy Day Hikes Ser.). (ENG., Illus.). 104p. pap. 9.95 *(978-0-7627-5105-1(3)*, Falcon Guides) Globe Pequot Pr., The.

—Rockhounding Alaska: A Guide to 75 of the State's Best Rockhounding Sites. 2010. (Rockhounding Ser.). (ENG., Illus.). 232p. pap. 16.95 *(978-0-7627-5084-9(7)*, Falcon Guides) Globe Pequot Pr., The.

Insight Guides. Alaska. 8th ed. 2010. (Insight Guides). (ENG., Illus.). 384p. pap. 23.99 *(978-981-282-053-2(1))* APA Publications Services SGP. Dist: Ingram Pub. Services.

Jettmar, Karen. The Alaska River Guide: Canoeing, Kayaking, & Rafting in the Last Frontier. 3rd ed. 2008. (Alaska River Guide: Canoeing, Kayaking, & Rafting in the Last Fronti Ser.). (ENG., Illus.). 328p. pap. 18.95 *(978-0-89732-957-6(0))* Menasha Ridge Pr., Inc.

Joly, Kyle. Outside in the Interior: An Adventure Guide for Central Alaska: More Than 50 Hikes, Bikes, Skis, Strolls & Floats for All Levels of Outdoor Enthusiasts. 2007. (Illus.). 160p. pap. 19.95 *(978-1-889963-99-0(2))* Univ. of Alaska Pr.

Judy Swain Garshelis. The Otter Spotters: A Wildlife Adventure in Alaska. 2009. 192p. 26.95 *(978-1-4401-6128-5(3))*; pap. 16.95 *(978-1-4401-6130-8(5))* iUniverse, Inc.

Kavanagh, James. Alaska Butterflies & Moths: An Introduction to Familiar Species. 2008. (Pocket Naturalist - Waterford Press Ser.). (ENG., Illus.). 1p. 5.95 *(978-1-58355-423-4(8))* Waterford Pr., Inc.

Klancher, Lee & Freeman, Phil. The Adventurous Motorcyclist's Guide to Alaska: Routes, Strategies, Road Food, Dive Bars, off-Beat Destinations, & More. 2012. (Illus.). 192p. pap. 29.95 *(978-0-9829131-2-3(5))* Octane Pr.

Langenscheidt Editorial Staff. Mobil Travel Guide Northwest. 50th anniv. ed. 2008. (Mobil Travel Guide: Northwest & Alaska Ser.). (Illus.). 368p. 18.95 *(978-0-8416-0316-5(2))* Langenscheidt Publishing Group.

Linhart, Elizabeth. Alaska. 9th ed. 2011. (Insight Guides). (Illus.). 384p. pap. 24.99 *(978-1-78005-020-1(8))* APA Publications Services SGP. Dist: Ingram Pub. Services.

Lonely Planet Staff & Bodry, Catherine. Lonely Planet Discover Alaska. 2011. (Full Color Regional Guides). (ENG., Illus.). 350p. pap. 24.99 *(978-1-74220-261-7(6))* Lonely Planet Pubns.

Maclean, Dan. Paddling Alaska: A Guide to the State's Classic Paddling Trips. 2009. (Paddling Ser.). (ENG., Illus.). 160p. pap. 18.95 *(978-0-7627-4229-5(1)*, Falcon Guides) Globe Pequot Pr., The.

Maloney, Lisa. 50 Hikes Around Anchorage. 2010. (50 Hikes Ser.). (ENG., Illus.). 232p. pap. 18.95 *(978-0-88150-905-2(1)*, 150905) Countryman Pr.

Milepost Editors. The Milepost: Legendary Alaska Trip Planner & Alaska Travel Guide to the Highways, Roads, Ferries, Lodgings, Recreation, Sightseeing Attractions & Services along the Alaska Highway to & Within Alaska, Including Alberta, British Columbia, Northwest Territories & the Yukon. 63rd ed. 2011. 784p. pap. 29.95 *(978-1-892154-28-6(5))* Milepost, The.

Mobil Regional Gd. Northwest 2010. 3rd rev. ed. 2009. (Regional Guide Ser.). 336p. pap. 18.99 *(978-0-8416-1423-9(7))* Langenscheidt Publishing Group.

Olthuis, Diane. It Happened in Alaska. 2006. (It Happened in Ser.). (ENG., Illus.). 192p. per. 12.95 *(978-0-7627-3908-0(8)*, TwoDot) Globe Pequot Pr., The.

Paulson, Dennis & Beletsky, Les. Alaska. 2006. (Travelers' Wildlife Guides). (ENG., Illus.). 456p. pap. 27.95 *(978-1-56656-652-0(5))* Interlink Publishing Group, Inc.

Pedersen, Gunnar. Highway Angler V - Fishing Alaska's Road System. 2007. per. 19.95 *(978-1-57833-366-0(0))* Todd Communications.

Pitcher, Don. Anchorage & the Kenai Peninsula. 2009. (Moon Spotlight Ser.). (ENG.). 132p. pap. 8.95 *(978-1-59880-351-8(4))* Avalon Travel Publishing.

—Moon Alaska. 2010. (Moon Handbooks). (ENG., Illus.). 600p. pap. 21.95 *(978-1-59880-350-1(6))* Avalon Travel Publishing.

—Moon Southeast Alaska. 2009. (Moon Spotlight Ser.). (ENG., Illus.). 144p. pap. 9.95 *(978-1-59880-343-3(3))* Avalon Travel Publishing.

Pivar, W. Alaska ASI Guide Set. 33.47 *(978-0-7931-4693-2(3))* Kaplan Publishing.

Readicker-Henderson, Ed & Readicker-Henderson, Lynn. Adventure Guide Alaska Highway. 4th rev. ed. 2006. (Adventure Guide to the Alaska Highway Ser.). (Illus.). 496p. per. 19.99 *(978-1-58843-571-2(7))* Hunter Publishing, Inc.

Tally, Taz. 50 Hikes in Alaska's Kenai Peninsula. 2008. (50 Hikes Ser.). (ENG.). 256p. pap. 16.95 *(978-0-88150-755-3(5)*, 150755) Countryman Pr.

Terpening, T. T. & Terpening, Traveler T. Alaska. 2010. (Bradt Travel Guide Ser.). (ENG., Illus.). 256p. pap. 22.99 *(978-1-84162-298-9(2))* Bradt Travel Guides GBR. Dist: Globe Pequot Pr., The.

Torkildson, Rob. Elbow Room: Wanderings & Musings in the Aleutian Islands. 2008. 120p. 30.99 *(978-1-4257-8929-9(3))*; pap. 20.99 *(978-1-4257-8897-1(1))* Xlibris Corp.

Travel Guide, Forbes. Forbes Travel Guide 2011 Northwest. 2011. (Forbes Travel Guide Regional Guide Ser.). (ENG.). 272p. pap. 18.95 *(978-1-936010-91-2(7))* Five Star Travel Corp., The.

Tyson, John. Best Easy Day Hikes Anchorage. 2009. (Best Easy Day Hikes Ser.). (ENG., Illus.). 96p. pap. 9.95 *(978-0-7627-5102-0(9)*, Falcon Guides) Globe Pequot Pr., The.

—Best Hikes near Anchorage. 2009. (Best Hikes near Ser.). (ENG., Illus.). 176p. pap. 18.95 *(978-0-7627-4356-8(5)*, Falcon Guides) Globe Pequot Pr., The.

Upton, Joe. The Alaska Cruise Handbook: A Mile-by-Mile Guide. 6th rev. ed. 2008. (ENG., Illus.). 288p. (gr. 4). pap. 19.95 *(978-0-9794915-0-4(9))* Coastal Publishing.

Valencia, Kris. The Milepost. 59th ed. 2007. (Milepost Ser.). (Illus.). 800p. per. 27.95 *(978-1-892154-21-7(8))* Morris Communications Co., LLC.

Vanasse, Deb. Anchorage & Southcentral Alaska: Including the Kenai Peninsula, Prince William Sound, & Denali National Park. 2nd ed. 2009. (Insiders' Guide Ser.). (ENG., Illus.). 232p. pap. 18.95 *(978-0-7627-5071-9(5)*, Insiders' Guide) Globe Pequot Pr., The.

West, George C. A Birder's Guide to Alaska. 2nd ed. 2008. (Illus.). x, 662p. pap. *(978-1-878788-48-1(5))* American Birding Assn., Inc.

Whitfield, Paul, et al. Alaska. 3rd ed. 2007. (Rough Guide Travel Guides Ser.). (ENG., Illus.). 608p. pap. 23.99 *(978-1-84353-772-4(9))* Rough Guides, Ltd. GBR. Dist: Dorling Kindersley Publishing, Inc.

Winslow, Kathryn. Alaska Bound. 2011. 320p. 50.95 ***(978-1-258-09824-7(5))*** Literary Licensing, LLC.

Wohlforth, Charles P. Alaska for Dummies. 5th ed. 2011. (Dummies Travel Ser.: 151). (ENG., Illus.). 456p. pap. 21.99 *(978-0-470-88871-1(7)*, For Dummies) Wiley, John & Sons, Inc.

—Frommer's Alaska Day by Day. 2011. (Frommer's Day by Day - Full Size Ser.: 114). (ENG., Illus.). 540p. pap. 27.99 *(978-0-470-56233-8(1)*, Frommers) Wiley, John & Sons, Inc.

Wohlforth, Charles P., et al. Frommer's Alaska. 13th ed. 2012. (Frommer's Color Complete Ser.: 920). (ENG., Illus.). 560p. pap. 21.99 ***(978-1-118-07470-1(X)***, Frommers) Wiley, John & Sons, Inc.

Young, Jan. Alaska by RV. 2009. 152p. pap. 64.95 *(978-0-557-04062-9(0))* Lulu Enterprises Inc.

ALASKA—HISTORY

Allan, June & Charles, Patricia, eds. Spirit! Historic Ketchikan, Alaska. 148p. (Orig.). pap. 12.95 *(978-0-9634438-0-9(1))* Historic Ketchikan, Inc.

Balluta, Andrew. Shtutdaina Daa She Qude: My Forefathers Are Still Walking with Me: Verbal Essays on Qizhjeh & Tsaynen Denaina Traditions. 2008. (Illus.). xii, 147p. pap. *(978-0-9749668-9-2(4))* Dena'inaq' Titaztunt.

Bennett, William P. First Baby in Camp. (Shorey Historical Ser.). 68p. reprint ed. pap. 10.00 *(978-0-8466-0161-6(3)*, S161) Shorey's Bookstore.

Bill, Laurel. Aunt Phil's Trunk, Vol. 2. 2007. pap. *(978-1-57833-343-1(1))* Todd Communications.

—Aunt Phil's Trunk: Volume 3. 2007. per. 19.95 *(978-1-57833-373-8(3))* Todd Communications.

Branson, John & Troll, Tim, eds. Our Story: An Anthology. rev. ed. 2006. Orig. Title: Readings from Southwest Alaska: an Anthology. 222p. pap. 19.95 *(978-0-930931-81-0(5))* Alaska Geographic Assn.

Brinkley Douglas. The Quiet World: Saving Alaska's Wilderness Kingdom, 1879-1960. 2011. (ENG.). 592p. pap. 18.99 ***(978-0-06-200597-7(9)***, HarperPerennial); 29.99 *(978-0-06-200596-0(0))* HarperCollins Pubs.

Brown, Tricia. Silent Storytellers of Totem Bight State Historical Park. 2009. pap. *(978-0-930931-97-1(1))* Alaska Geographic Assn.

Burch, Ernest S., Jr. Social Life in Northwest Alaska: The Structure of Inupiaq Eskimo Nations. 2006. (Illus.). 496p. pap. 29.95 *(978-1-889963-92-1(5))* Univ. of Alaska Pr.

Bushell, Sharon & Jones, Stan. The Spill: Personal Stories from the Exxon Valdez Disaster. 2009. (ENG., Illus.). 289p. pap. 17.95 *(978-0-9800825-8-6(7))* Epicenter Pr., Inc.

Campbell, Robert. In Darkest Alaska: Travel & Empire along the Inside Passage. 2008. (Nature & Culture in America Ser.). (Illus.). 360p. (C). pap. 24.95 *(978-0-8122-2048-3(X))* Univ. of Pennsylvania Pr.

Chandonnet, Fern, ed. Alaska at War, 1941-1945: The Forgotten War Remembered. 2007. (Illus.). 474p. per. 29.95 *(978-1-60223-013-2(7))* Univ. of Alaska Pr.

Chase, Will H., ed. Pioneers of Alask: The Trail Blazers of Bygone Days. 2011. 200p. 44.95 ***(978-1-258-03397-2(6))*** Literary Licensing, LLC.

Coghill, John B. Growing up in Alaska. 2009. pap. 24.95 *(978-0-9823017-1-5(5))* Kayto Communication, Inc.

Cole, Dermot. Fairbanks: A Gold Rush Town That Beat the Odds. 2008. (Illus.). 224p. pap. 14.95 *(978-1-60223-030-9(7))* Univ. of Alaska Pr.

—Historic Photos of Alaska. 2008. (Historic Photos Ser.). (ENG., Illus.). 205p. 39.95 *(978-1-59652-424-8(3))* Turner Publishing Co.

—North to the Future: The Alaska Story, 1959-2009. 2008. (Alaska Book Adventures Ser.). (ENG.). 256p. pap. 14.95 *(978-0-9800825-3-1(6))* Epicenter Pr., Inc.

Dalton, Anthony. Alone Against the Arctic, 1 vol. 2007. (ENG., Illus.). 192p. per. *(978-1-894974-33-2(6))* Heritage Hse.

Dauenhauer, Nora Marks. Anooshi Lingit Aani Ka, Russians in Tlingit America: The Battles of Sitka, 1802 And 1804. Dauenhauer, Richard L. & Black, Lydia T., eds. 2008. (Classics of Tlingit Oral Literature Ser.). (ENG., Illus.). 488p. pap. 35.00 *(978-0-295-98601-2(8))* Univ. of Washington Pr.

David, Cora & Lovick, Olga Charlotte. Teedlay T'iin Naholndak Niign: Stories by the Tetlin People. 2011. (ENG & ATH., Illus.). 160p. pap. 20.00 ***(978-1-55500-114-8(9))*** Alaska Native Language Ctr.

Deans, Nora L. Wrangell-St. Elias National Park & Preserve. 2007. (Illus.). 14.95 *(978-0-930931-57-5(2))* Alaska Geographic Assn.

Demerjian, Bonnie. Anan, Stream of Living Water. 2007. (ENG., Illus.). 70p. per. 13.95 *(978-0-9776792-1-8(7))* Stikine River Books.

Demerjian, Bonnie. Wrangell. 2011. (Images of America Ser.). (Illus.). 128p. pap. 21.99 ***(978-0-7385-7498-1(8))*** Arcadia Publishing.

Denslow, Ray Vaughn. South of the Arctic: A Story of Freemasonry in Alaska. 2011. 26p. 35.95 ***(978-1-258-09644-1(7))*** Literary Licensing, LLC.

Dodge, Harry B. Kodiak Tales: Stories of Adventure on Alaska's Emerald Isle. 2010. 168p. 29.99 *(978-1-4490-5600-1(8))*; pap. 19.99 *(978-1-4490-5601-8(6))* AuthorHouse.

Downing Carlson, Phyllis & Downing Bill, Laurel. Aunt Phil's Trunk, Volume Four. 2009. pap. 19.95 net. *(978-1-57833-435-3(7))* Todd Communications.

Federal Field Commission, compiled by. Where Alaska's Native People Live CD-ROM. 2007. cd-rom 29.95 *(978-1-878051-57-8(1))* Circumpolar Pr.

Fienup-Riordan, Ann. Mission of Change in Southwest Alaska: Conversations with Father René Astruc & Paul Dixon on Their Work with Yup'ik People, 1950-1988. 2012. ***(978-1-60223-162-7(1))*** Univ. of Alaska Pr.

Fienup-Riordan, Ann, ed. Mission of Change in Southwest Alaska: Conversations with Father Rene Astruc & Paul Dixon on Their Work with Yup'ik People. 2012. (ENG., Illus.). 346p. pap. 34.95 ***(978-1-60223-161-0(3))*** Univ. of Alaska Pr.

Fienup-Riordan, Ann, ed. Qaluyaarmiuni Nunamtenek Qanemciput / Our Nelson Island Stories: Meanings of Place on the Bering Sea Coast. Rearden, Alice, tr. 2011. (ENG., Illus.). 496p. (C). pap. 50.00 *(978-0-295-99135-1(6))* Univ. of Washington Pr.

Fletcher, Alder Rye. Maria. 2010. 54p. pap. 10.85 *(978-0-557-47663-3(1))* Lulu Enterprises Inc.

Fradin, Judy & Fradin, Dennis. Earthquakes. 2008. (Witness to Disaster Ser.). (ENG., Illus.). 48p. (J). (gr. 3-6). lib. bdg. 26.90 *(978-1-4263-0212-1(6)*, National Geographic Children's Bks.) National Geographic Society.

Freedman, Lew. Yukon Quest: The Story of the World's Toughest Sled Dog Race. 2010. (ENG.). 224p. (gr. 9). pap. 14.95 *(978-1-935347-05-7(5))* Epicenter Pr., Inc.

Gmelch, Sharon. The Tlingit Encounter with Photography. 2008. (Illus.). 240p. 39.95 *(978-1-934536-10-0(5)*, Univ. of Pennsylvania Museum of Archaeology & Anthropology) Univ. Museum Pubns.

Harbeson Jr., George. Homesteaders in the Headlights: One family's journey from a Depression-era New Jersey farm to a new life in Wasilla, Alaska. 2010. (Illus.). 312p. pap. 21.50 *(978-0-9789979-8-4(0))* Hardscratch Pr.

Haycox, Stephen. Alaska: An American Colony. 2006. (ENG., Illus.). 392p. per. 18.95 *(978-0-295-98629-6(8))* Univ. of Washington Pr.

Haycox, Stephen & McClanahan, Alexandra J. Alaska Scrapbook: Moments in Alaska History: 1816-1998. 2008. (Illus.). 255p. per. 24.95 *(978-0-938227-08-3(4))* CIRI Foundation, The.

Heaton, John. Outlaw Tales of Alaska: True Stories of the Last Frontier's Most Infamous Crooks, Culprits, & Cutthroats. 2010. (Outlaw Tales Ser.). (ENG., Illus.). 208p. pap. 14.95 *(978-0-7627-5326-0(9)*, TwoDot) Globe Pequot Pr., The.

Heroes of Battle Rock. (Shorey Historical Ser.). 24p. reprint ed. pap. 10.00 *(978-0-8466-0067-1(6)*, S67) Shorey's Bookstore.

Hudson, Raymond L. Family after All: Alaska's Jesse Lee Home, Vol. I, Unalaska 1889-1925. 2007. (Illus.). 400p. pap. 33.00 *(978-0-9789979-0-8(5))* Hardscratch Pr.

Hunt, William R. North Of 53: The Wild Days of the Alaska-Yukon Mining Frontier, 1870-1914. 2009. (Illus.). 352p. pap. 23.95 *(978-1-60223-054-5(4))* Univ. of Alaska Pr.

Ingstad, Helge. Nunamiut: Among Alaska's Inland Eskimos. 2006. (ENG., Illus.). 368p. per. 19.95 *(978-0-88150-761-4(X))* Countryman Pr.

Jones, Preston. City for Empire: An Anchorage History, 1914-1941. 2010. (ENG., Illus.). 214p. pap. 26.95 *(978-1-60223-084-2(6))* Univ. of Alaska Pr.

—Empire's Edge: American Society in Nome, Alaska 1898-1934. 2nd ed. 2006. (ENG., Illus.). 176p. pap. 19.95 *(978-1-889963-89-1(5))* Univ. of Alaska Pr.

Kahn, Steve & Coray, Anne. Lake Clark National Park & Preserve. 2009. pap. 14.95 *(978-0-930931-84-1(X))* Alaska Geographic Assn.

Kelly, Sheila. Treadwell Gold: An Alaska Saga of Riches & Ruin. (Illus.). 2011. 288p. pap. 17.95 *(978-1-60223-118-4(4))* 2010. (ENG., 271p. 35.00 *(978-1-60223-075-0(7))* Univ. of Alaska Pr.

Kimura, Gregory W., ed. Alaska at 50: The Past, Present, & Future of Alaska Statehood. 2009. (ENG., Illus.). 264p. 30.00 *(978-1-60223-061-3(7))* Univ. of Alaska Pr.

—Alaska At 50: The Past, Present, & Future of Alaska Statehood. 2010. (Illus.). 285p. pap. 24.95 *(978-1-60223-081-1(1))* Univ. of Alaska Pr.

King, Robert J. Postcards from Alaska: Souvenir pictures from the Last Frontier, 1890s-1940s. 2007. (Illus.). 176p. pap. 29.95 *(978-0-936425-98-6(9))*, Greatland Graphics.

Levi, Steven C. Boom & Bust in the Alaska Goldfields: A Multicultural Adventure, 1 vol. 2007. (Illus.). 268p. 49.95 *(978-0-313-34544-9(9)*, C34544, Praeger Pubs.) Greenwood Publishing Group, Inc.

—The Great Red Scare in World War One Alaska: Elite Panic, Government Hysteria,Supression of Civil Liberties,Unio-Breaking,and Germanophobia, 1915 - 1920. 2010. (Illus.). 264p. pap. *(978-1-933146-96-6(6))* Academica Pr., LLC.

Lifton, Dave. The Sarah Palin Collectors Vault. 2010. 144p. pap. 49.95 *(978-0-7948-3276-6(8),)* Whitman Publishing LLC.

Lively, Brigitte. Matanuska Colony - Sixty Years. pap. 18.95 *(978-1-57833-137-6(4),)* Todd Communications.

Lowenstein, Tom. Ultimate Americans: Point Hope, Alaska, 1826-1909. (ENG., Illus.). 368p. 2010. pap. 36.95 *(978-1-60223-038-5(2))* 2009. 49.95 *(978-1-60223-027-9(7),)* Univ. of Alaska Pr.

Luehrmann, Sonja & Luehrmann, S. Alutiiq Villages under Russian & U. S. Rule. 2009. (Illus.). 224p. pap. 19.95 *(978-1-60223-023-1(4))* Univ. of Alaska Pr.

Mackenzie, Alexander. Mackenzie's Rock. (Shorey Historical Ser.). 39p. reprint ed. pap. 10.00 *(978-0-8466-0048-0(X)*, S48) Shorey's Bookstore.

Mee, Barbara. Senator Ted & Mee. 2010. 208p. pap. 19.95 *(978-1-57833-502-2(7))* Todd Communications.

Miller, Gwenn A. Kodiak Kreol: Communities of Empire in Early Russian America. 2010. (Illus.). 248p. 55.00 *(978-0-8014-4642-9(2))* Cornell Univ. Pr.

Miller, Orlando W. The Frontier in Alaska & the Matanuska Colony. 2009. (Illus.). 341p. pap. 23.95 *(978-1-60223-053-8(6))* Univ. of Alaska Pr.

Mishler, Craig. Black Ducks & Salmon Bellies: An Ethnography of Old Harbor & Ouzinkie, Alaska. 2007. (Illus.). 256p. per. 39.95 *(978-1-57864-218-2(3))* Donning Co. Pubs.

Mondor, Colleen. The Map of My Dead Pilots: The Dangerous Game of Flying in Alaska. 2011. (ENG.). 256p. 22.95 *(978-0-7627-7361-9(8)*, Lyons Pr.) Globe Pequot Pr., The.

Moses, Shirley & Krieg, Holly. Sharing Alaska Native Cultures: Activity... pap. 8.00 *(978-0-931163-12-8(9))*, Univ. of Alaska Museum.

Naske, Claus M. & Slotnick, Herman E. Alaska: A History. 3rd ed. 2011. (ENG., Illus.). 520p. 39.95 *(978-0-8061-4040-7(2))* Univ. of Oklahoma Pr.

Neal, Patricia. Fort Wrangel Alaska: Gateway to the Stikine River: 1834 - 1899. 2007. (Illus.). per. *(978-0-9773871-1-3(9))* Coachlamp Productions.

Noble, Dennis L. & Strobridge, Truman R. Captain Hell Roaring Mike Healy: From American Slave to Arctic Hero. 2009. (New Perspectives on Maritime History & Nautical Archaeology Ser.). (ENG., Illus.). 352p. 34.95 *(978-0-8130-3368-6(3)*, Univ. Pr. of Florida.

Norris, Frank B. & Merrell, Bruce, compiled by. The Alaska 67: A Guide to Alaska's Best History Books. 2006. (Illus.). 95p. per. *(978-0-9678989-9-5(4))* Hardscratch Pr.

O'Hara, Pat. Knik Matanuska Susitna. pap. 28.00 *(978-1-57833-124-6(2))* Todd Communications.

Ott, Riki. Not One Drop & Black Wave (book/dvd Set) 2009. (ENG.). 352p. 39.95 *(978-1-60358-192-9(8))* Chelsea Green Publishing.

Pels, Jacquelin B., ed. & compiled by. Family after All: Alaska's Jesse Lee Home, Vol. II, Seward 1925-1965, 2 vols., Vol. 2. 2008. (Illus.). 800p. pap. 37.00 *(978-0-9789979-1-5(3))* Hardscratch Pr.

Reilly & Vitousek. Alaska Question & Answer Pass Real Estate Exam Set. 32.20 *(978-0-7931-4692-5(5))* Kaplan Publishing.

Remley, David A. Crooked Road: The Story of the Alaska Highway. 2nd ed. 2008. (Illus.). 267p. pap. 21.95 *(978-1-60223-037-8(4))* Univ. of Alaska Pr.

Roppel, Patricia. Land of Mists: Revillagigedo & Gravina Islands, Misty Fiords National Monument, Alaska. 3rd ed. 60p. pap. 35.00 *(978-1-57833-111-6(0))* Todd Communications.

Rossiter, Harriet. Alaska Calling: A Laugh on Every Page. 2011. 276p. 47.95 ***(978-1-258-06917-9(2))*** Literary Licensing, LLC.

Sandler, Martin W. The Impossible Rescue: The True Story of an Amazing Arctic Adventure. 2012. (ENG., Illus.). 176p. (J). (gr. 5-9). 22.99 ***(978-0-7636-5080-3(3))*** Candlewick Pr.

Schneider, William. On Time Delivery: The Dog Team Mail Carriers. 2012. (ENG., Illus.). 300p. pap. 24.95 ***(978-1-60223-167-2(2))*** Univ. of Alaska Pr.

Senkowsky, Sonya & Coyne, Amanda. Alaska Then & Now. 2008. (Then & Now Thunder Bay Ser.). (ENG., Illus.). 144p. 19.95 *(978-1-59223-799-9(1)*, Thunder Bay Pr.) Advantage Pubs. Group.

Sherwood, Morgan. Big Game in Alaska: A History of Wildlife & People. 2008. (Illus.). 224p. pap. 24.95 *(978-1-60223-034-7(X))* Univ. of Alaska Pr.

Smith, Kenneth W. Inupiat Parables. 2009. 132p. pap. 13.95 *(978-1-4401-1310-9(6))* iUniverse, Inc.

Spelaizy, Millie. Mount Marathon: Stories from Alaskas Greatest Foot Race. 2009. (ENG., Illus.). 96p. pap. 14.95 *(978-0-88240-771-5(6)*, Alaska Northwest Bks.) Graphic Arts Ctr. Publishing Co.

Spude, Catherine Holder. Sin & Grace: A Historical Novel of the Skagway, Alaska Sporting Wars. 2007. (Illus.). 220p. pap. 16.95 *(978-0-945284-08-6(X))* Lynn Canal Publishing.

Stephan, Alberta E. The First Athabascans of Alaska: Strawberries. pap. 9.00 *(978-1-57833-150-5(1))* Todd Communications.

Strand, Martin R. Transitions from the Sitka, Alaska Wordsmith: Book 3 of the Martin R. Strand, Sr. Trilogy. 2011. 232p. pap. 18.95 *(978-1-4502-8528-5(7))* iUniverse, Inc.

Taliaferro, John. In a Far Country: The True Story of a Mission, a Marriage, a Murder, & the Remarkable Reindeer Rescue of 1898. 2007. (ENG., Illus.). 424p. per. 15.95 *(978-1-58648-508-5(3))* PublicAffairs.

Thompson, John B. Alaska as It Used to Was. 2006. 199p. per. 13.95 *(978-1-60002-057-5(7)*, 3417) Mountain Valley Publishing, LLC.

Townsend, Peggy Jean. Alaska Gold Rush Letters & Photographs... (Illus.). 34.95 *(978-0-9657938-5-8(0))* Castle Peak Editions.

Turner, Lucien M. An Aleutian Ethnography. Hudson, Raymond L., ed. (Illus.). 2010. (ENG.). 256p. pap. 26.95 *(978-1-60223-039-2(0))* 2008. 175p. 45.00 *(978-1-60223-028-6(5))* Univ. of Alaska Pr.

Underwood, John J. Alaska an Empire in the Making. 2007. (ENG.). 566p. 58.95 *(978-0-548-01931-3(2))* Kessinger Publishing, LLC.

Vanasse, Deb. Picture This, Alaska: Historic Photographs from the Last Frontier. 2009. (ENG., Illus.). 144p. pap. 16.95 *(978-1-57061-584-9(5))* Sasquatch Bks.

Venn, George. Soldier to Advocate: A Soldier's Unpublished Diary, Drawings, Poetry & Letters of Alaska & the Nez Perce Conflict: C. E. S. Wood's 1877 Legacy. 2nd ed. 2006. (Illus.). 98p. pap. 20.00 *(978-1-877655-48-7(1))*, Wordcraft of Oregon, LLC.

Vinkovetsky, Ilya. Russian America: An Overseas Colony of a Continental Empire, 1804-1867, 1 vol. 2011. (ENG., Illus.). 272p. 49.95 *(978-0-19-539128-2(4))* Oxford Univ. Pr., Inc.

Walker, Spike. On the Edge of Survival: A Shipwreck, a Raging Storm, & the Harrowing Alaskan Rescue That Became a Legend. 2011. (ENG., Illus.). 304p. pap. 14.99 *(978-0-312-60459-2(9)*, St. Martin's Griffin) St. Martin's Pr.

Waugh, Chris. Misty Memories of Guard Island, Alaska: Ketchikan's Legacy of a Lighthouse Family. 2006. 134p. per. 14.95 *(978-0-9763358-1-8(6))* Alberteen Pr.

Wickersham, James & Wickersham, J. Old Yukon: Tales, Trails, & Trials. 2009. (Illus.). 514p. pap. 29.95 *(978-1-60223-051-4(X))* Univ. of Alaska Pr.

Williams, Maria Shāa Tlāa, ed. The Alaska Native Reader: History, Culture, Politics. 2009. (World Readers Ser.). (ENG., Illus.). 416p. 94.95 *(978-0-8223-4465-0(3))*; pap. 26.95 *(978-0-8223-4480-3(7))* Duke Univ. Pr.

Wood, Diane F., ed. Alaska Pioneer Series, Set. (Orig.). pap. 15.95 *(978-1-886921-06-1(7))* Alaska Pr. Productions.

Zachry, Joel G. & Zachry, Kathy W. Bears We've Met: Short Stories of Close Encounters. 2010. 178p. 29.99 *(978-1-4520-0821-9(3))*; pap. 21.99 *(978-1-4520-0820-2(5))* AuthorHouse.

The 2006 Prudhoe Bay Shutdown: Will Recent Regulatory Changes & BP Management Reforms Prevent Future Failures?: Hearing Before the Subcommittee on Oversight & Investigations of the Committee on Energy & Commerce, House of Representatives, One Hundred Tenth Congress, First Session, May 16, 2007. 2008. (Illus.). v, 341p. *(978-0-16-081690-1(4), 552-070-37921-5)* United States Government Printing Office.

ALASKA—JUVENILE LITERATURE

Lourie, Peter. Arctic Thaw. 2010. (ENG., Illus.). 48p. pap. 10.95 *(978-1-59078-842-4(7))* Boyds Mills Pr.

ALASKA—MAPS

Alaska Street Master, creator. Fairbanks Road Map. 2008. 4.95 *(978-1-57833-403-2(9))* Todd Communications.

—Matanuska-Susitna Valley Road Map. 2008. 4.95 *(978-1-57833-404-9(7))* Todd Communications.

Great Pacific Map Co. Staff. Recreation Map Southeast Alaska. 2006. 6.95 *(978-0-938011-44-6(8))* Great Pacific Recreation Maps & Guides.

Hodges, Montana. Best Easy Day Hikes Fairbanks. 2009. (Best Easy Day Hikes Ser.). (ENG., Illus.). 104p. pap. 9.95 *(978-0-7627-5105-1(3)*, Falcon Guides) Globe Pequot Pr., The.

Tyson, John. Best Easy Day Hikes Anchorage. 2009. (Best Easy Day Hikes Ser.). (ENG., Illus.). 96p. pap. 9.95 *(978-0-7627-5102-0(9)*, Falcon Guides) Globe Pequot Pr., The.

Waitt, Richard B. & Beget, James E. Volcanic Processes & Geology of Augustine Volcano, Alaska. 2009. (Illus.). vii, 78p. *(978-1-4113-2411-4(0))* United States Geological Survey.

ALASKA—POETRY

Baker, Frank E. Conifered Heights. pap. 10.00 *(978-0-9676964-0-9(2))* Forget-me-not Publishing, Inc.

Conkle, Earl Judson. Alaska Gold. 2011. 86p. 38.95 ***(978-1-258-06820-2(6))*** Literary Licensing, LLC.

Duckworth, Claude H. The Call of Alask. 2011. 90p. 38.95 ***(978-1-258-08541-4(0))*** Literary Licensing, LLC.

Jankowski, Timothy. Misled. 2006. 127p. pap. 19.95 *(978-1-4241-3229-4(0))* PublishAmerica, Inc.

Mullen, Mary. Zephyr. 2011. (ENG.). 68p. pap. 21.95 *(978-1-907056-41-3(6))* Salmon Publishing IRL. Dist: Dufour Editions, Inc.

Sexton, Thomas F. I Think Again of Those Ancient Chinese Poets. 2011. 59p. pap. 14.95 *(978-1-60223-119-1(2))* Univ. of Alaska Pr.

Straley, John. The Rising & the Rain: Collected Poems. 2008. (University of Alaska Press - Alaska Writer Laureate Ser.). 64p. pap. 19.95 *(978-1-60223-033-0(1))* Univ. of Alaska Pr.

ALASKA—POLITICS AND GOVERNMENT

Bailey, Frank, et al. Blind Allegiance to Sarah Palin: A Memoir of Our Tumultuous Years. 2011. (ENG., Illus.). 400p. 26.00 *(978-1-4516-5440-0(5)*, Howard Bks.) Howard Books.

Burch, Ernest S., Jr. Social Life in Northwest Alaska: The Structure of Inupiaq Eskimo Nations. 2006. (Illus.). 496p. pap. 29.95 *(978-1-889963-92-1(5))* Univ. of Alaska Pr.

Cashman, Kay & Nelson, Kristen. Sarah Takes on Big Oil. 2008. 195p. 21.95 *(978-0-9821632-0-7(7))* PNA Publishing.

Coyne, Amanda & Hopfinger, Tony. Crude Awakening: Money, Mavericks, & Mayhem in Alaska. 2011. (ENG.). 304p. (gr. 9). 26.99 *(978-1-56858-447-8(4))* Basic Bks.

Dunn, Geoffrey. The Lies of Sarah Palin: The Untold Story Behind Her Relentless Quest for Power. 2011. (ENG., Illus.). 464p. 26.99 *(978-0-312-60186-7(7))* St. Martin's Pr.

Governor's Office, Binder 3, Title 6. *(978-0-327-06374-2(2))* LEXIS Publishing.

Holen, Davin. Dip Nets, Fish Wheels, & Motor Homes. 2010. 116p. pap. *(978-3-8383-4268-9(2))* Lambert Academic Publishing.

Huhndorf, Shari M. Mapping the Americas: The Transnational Politics of Contemporary Native Culture. 2009. (Illus.). 216p. 39.95 *(978-0-8014-4800-3(X))* Cornell Univ. Pr.

Johnson, Kaylene. Sarah: How a Hockey Mom Turned Alaska's Political Establishment Upside Down. 2008. (ENG., Illus.). 164p. (gr. 9). pap. 15.95 *(978-0-9800825-6-2(0))*; 3rd ed. 19.95 *(978-0-9790470-8-4(0))* Epicenter Pr., Inc.

—Sarah: How a Hockey Mom Turned Alaska's Political Establishment Upside Down. 2008. (ENG.). 49.99 *(978-1-60640-723-3(6))* Findaway World, LLC.

Kennedy, Timothy. Where the Rivers Meet the Sky: A Collaborative Approach to Participatory Development. 2nd ed. 2009. (ENG., Illus.). 210p. pap. 20.00 *(978-983-9054-51-4(1))* Southbound Sdn Bhd Institut Masyarakat MYS. Dist: Chicago Distribution Ctr.

McBeath, Jerry, et al. The Political Economy of Oil in Alaska: Multinationals vs. the State. 2008. (Illus.). 240p. 59.95 *(978-1-58826-557-9(9))* Rienner, Lynne Pubs.

McGinniss, Joe. The Rogue: Searching for the Real Sarah Palin. (ENG.). 336p. 2012. pap. 15.00 ***(978-0-307-71894-5(8))*** 2011. (Illus.). 25.00 *(978-0-307-71892-1(1))* Broadway Bks.

—The Rogue: Searching for the Real Sarah Palin. 2011. (Playaway Adult Nonfiction Ser.). 54.99 ***(978-1-61657-783-4(5))*** Random Hse., Inc.

Mee, Barbara. Senator Ted & Mee. 2010. 208p. pap. 19.95 *(978-1-57833-502-2(7))* Todd Communications.

Miscellaneous Boards & Commissions, Binder 8, TITLE 20. *(978-0-327-06380-3(7))* LEXIS Publishing.

Ott, Riki. Not One Drop & Black Wave (book/dvd Set) 2009. (ENG.). 352p. 39.95 *(978-1-60358-192-9(8))* Chelsea Green Publishing.

Palin, Sarah. Going Rogue: An American Life. 2010. (ENG., Illus.). 432p. pap. 15.99 *(978-0-06-193990-7(0))* Broadside Bks. GBR. Dist: HarperCollins Pubs.

—Going Rogue: An American Life. 2009. (ENG., Illus.). 432p. 28.99 *(978-0-06-193989-1(7))*; 592p. pap. 28.99 *(978-0-06-197955-2(4)*, HarperLuxe) HarperCollins Pubs.

Public Safety, Binder 6, TITLE 13. *(978-0-327-06377-3(7))* LEXIS Publishing.

Spicer, George W. The Constitutional Status & Government of Alaska. (Johns Hopkins University. Studies in the Social Sciences, Thirtieth Ser.: 4). reprint ed. 37.50 *(978-0-404-61239-9(3))* AMS Pr., Inc.

Thomas, Clive S., ed. Alaska Politics & Public Policy: The Dynamics of Beliefs, Institutions, Processes, Personalities, & Power. 2009. (ENG., Illus.). 864p. 40.00 *(978-1-60223-062-0(5))* Univ. of Alaska Pr.

Zellen, Barry Scott. Breaking the Ice: From Land Claims to Tribal Sovereignty in the Arctic. 2008. (ENG.). 450p. 94.50 *(978-0-7391-1941-9(9))*; pap. 47.50 *(978-0-7391-1942-6(7))* Lexington Bks.

—On Thin Ice: The Inuit, the State, & the Challenge of Arctic Sovereignty. 2009. (ENG.). 270p. 73.50 *(978-0-7391-3278-4(4))* Lexington Bks.

ALASKA—SOCIAL CONDITIONS

Andrews, Susan B. & Creed, John, eds. Authentic Alaska II: Voices of the Far North. 2008. (Illus.). 416p. pap. 19.95 *(978-0-8032-1564-1(9)*, Bison Bks.) Univ. of Nebraska Pr.

Balluta, Andrew. Shtutdaina Daa She Qude: My Forefathers Are Still Walking with Me: Verbal Essays on Qizhjeh & Tsaynen Denaina Traditions. 2008. (Illus.). xii, 147p. pap. *(978-0-9749668-9-2(4))* Dena'inaq' Titaztunt.

Barnhardt, Ray, ed. Cross-Cultural Issues in Alaskan Education, Vol. 2, 1982. 206p. 9.95 *(978-1-877962-10-3(4))* Univ. of Alaska Fairbanks, Ctr. for Cross-Cultural Studies (CXCS).

Bates, Clifton & Oleksa, Michael J. Conflicting Landscapes: American Schooling/Alaska Natives. 2008. (Illus.). 264p. pap. 19.95 *(978-1-57833-396-7(2))* Todd Communications.

Collier, Michael. The Melting Edge: Alaska at the Frontier of Climate Change. 2011. *(978-0-9825765-1-9(X))* Alaska Geographic Assn.

CQ Press, ed. Alaska Crime in Perspective 2010 Edition, 00 vols. rev. ed. 2010. 24p. pap. 32.00 *(978-1-60871-432-2(2))* CQ Pr.

—Alaska Education in Perspective 2010-2011 Edition, 00 vols. rev. ed. 2010. 24p. pap. 32.00 *(978-1-60871-433-9(0))* CQ Pr.

—Alaska Health Care in Perspective 2010 Edition, 00 vols. rev. ed. 2010. 24p. pap. 32.00 *(978-1-68071-434-0(1))* CQ Pr.

—Alaska in Perspective 2010 Edition, 00 vols. rev. ed. 2010. 24p. pap. 32.00 *(978-1-60871-435-3(7))* CQ Pr.

Fienup-Riordan, Ann. Mission of Change in Southwest Alaska: Conversations with Father René Astruc & Paul Dixon on Their Work with Yup'ik People, 1950-1988. 2012. ***(978-1-60223-162-7(1))*** Univ. of Alaska Pr.

Fienup-Riordan, Ann, ed. Mission of Change in Southwest Alaska: Conversations with Father Rene Astruc & Paul Dixon on Their Work with Yup'ik People. 2012. (ENG., Illus.). 346p. pap. 34.95 ***(978-1-60223-161-0(3))*** Univ. of Alaska Pr.

Hofmann, Rebecca. The Clash of Economic Decisions in Alask. 2009. 156p. pap. *(978-3-639-13419-3(2))* VDM Verlag Dr. Mueller e.K.

Jones, Preston. City for Empire: An Anchorage History, 1914-1941. 2010. (ENG., Illus.). 214p. pap. 26.95 *(978-1-60223-084-2(6))* Univ. of Alaska Pr.

Kennedy, Timothy. Where the Rivers Meet the Sky: A Collaborative Approach to Participatory Development. 2nd ed. 2009. (ENG., Illus.). 210p. pap. 20.00 *(978-983-9054-51-4(1))* Southbound Sdn Bhd Institut Masyarakat MYS. Dist: Chicago Distribution Ctr.

Kimura, Gregory W., ed. Alaska at 50: The Past, Present, & Future of Alaska Statehood. 2009. (ENG., Illus.). 264p. 30.00 *(978-1-60223-061-3(7))* Univ. of Alaska Pr.

—Alaska At 50: The Past, Present, & Future of Alaska Statehood. 2010. (Illus.). 285p. pap. 24.95 *(978-1-60223-081-1(1))* Univ. of Alaska Pr.

Luehrmann, Sonja & Luehrmann, S. Alutiiq Villages under Russian & U. S. Rule. 2009. (Illus.). 224p. pap. 19.95 *(978-1-60223-023-1(4))* Univ. of Alaska Pr.

McClanahan, Alexandra J. Sakuuktugut. 2006. (Illus.). 200p. pap. 24.95 *(978-0-938227-07-6(6))* CIRI Foundation, The.

Morgan, Scott, ed. Alaska in Perspective 2011, 00 vols. rev. ed. 2011. 24p. pap. 32.00 *(978-1-4522-0007-1(6))* CQ Pr.

National Research Council (U.S.), Transportation Research Board Committee on the Risk of Vessel Accidents and Spills in the Aleutian Islands: A Study to Design a Comprehensive Assessment Staff, contrib. by. Risk of Vessel Accidents & Spills in the Aleutian Islands: Designing a Comprehensive Risk Assessment. 2008. (Illus.). xviii, 225p. *(978-0-309-11332-8(6))* Transportation Research Board.

Oswalt, Wendell H. Bashful No Longer: An Alaskan Eskimo Ethnohistory, 1778-1988. 2011. (Civilization of the American Indian Ser.). (ENG., Illus.). 292p. (C). pap. 19.95 ***(978-0-8061-4250-0(2))*** Univ. of Oklahoma Pr.

Persons, Jean. From Dog Sleds to Float Planes: Alaskan Adventures in Medicine. 2007. (Illus.). 188p. per. 16.95 *(978-0-9789766-2-0(2))* Northbooks.

Power, John A., et al. The 2006 Eruption of Augustine Volcano, Alaska. 2010. ***(978-1-4113-2981-2(3))*** United States Geological Survey.

Salomon, Anne, et al. Imam Cimiucia: Our Changing Sea. 2011. (ENG., Illus.). 105p. 39.95 *(978-1-56612-159-0(0))* Alaska Sea Grant College Program.

Spude, Catherine Holder. Sin & Grace: A Historical Novel of the Skagway, Alaska Sporting Wars. 2007. (Illus.). 220p. pap. 16.95 *(978-0-945284-08-6(X))* Lynn Canal Publishing.

ALASKA—SOCIAL LIFE AND CUSTOMS

Alexander, Evelyn & Weiser, Joshua. Evelyn Alexander: A Life History in Her Own Words. 2007. *(978-1-877962-40-0(6))* Univ. of Alaska Fairbanks, Ctr. for Cross-Cultural Studies (CXCS).

Anderson, Hall. Still Rainin' Still Dreamin' Hall Anderson's Ketchikan. 2010. (ENG., Illus.). 112p. pap. 35.00 *(978-1-889963-90-7(9))* Univ. of Alaska Pr.

Andrew, Frank & Andrew, Frank, Sr. Paitarkiutenka / My Legacy to You. Fienup-Riordan, Ann, ed. Rearden, Alice & Meade, Marie, trs. 2008. (ENG & ESK., Illus.). 360p. pap. *(978-0-295-98780-4(4))* Univ. of Washington Pr.

Andrews, Susan B. & Creed, John, eds. Authentic Alaska II: Voices of the Far North. 2008. (Illus.). 416p. pap. 19.95 *(978-0-8032-1564-1(9)*, Bison Bks.) Univ. of Nebraska Pr.

Autobiography: A Brief Glimpse of Life in Alaska 1936-2006. 2007. *(978-0-9778785-2-9(X))* Carson, Michael A.

Balluta, Andrew. Shtutdaina Daa She Qude: My Forefathers Are Still Walking with Me: Verbal Essays on Qizhjeh & Tsaynen Denaina Traditions. 2008. (Illus.). xii, 147p. pap. *(978-0-9749668-9-2(4))* Dena'inaq' Titaztunt.

Bellinger, Brookelyn. The Frozen Toe Guide to Real Alaskan Livin' Learn How to Survive Moose Attacks, Endless Winters & Life Without Indoor Plumbing. 2007. (ENG., Illus.). 224p. per. 16.95 *(978-1-57061-484-2(9))* Sasquatch Bks.

Branson, John & Troll, Tim, eds. Our Story: An Anthology. rev. ed. 2006. Orig. Title: Readings from Southwest Alaska: an Anthology. 222p. pap. 19.95 *(978-0-930931-81-0(5))* Alaska Geographic Assn.

Brown, Tricia. Children of the Midnight Sun: Young Native Voices of Alaska. 2006. (ENG., Illus.). 47p. (J). (gr. 1-4). pap. 11.95 *(978-0-88240-617-6(5)*, Alaska Northwest Bks.) Graphic Arts Ctr. Publishing Co.

Brown, Tricia & Gates, Nancy. Homesteader Handbook: The Alaska Book of Knowledge. 2012. (ENG., Illus.). 192p. pap. 18.95 *(978-0-88240-811-8(9)*, Alaska Northwest Bks.) Graphic Arts Ctr. Publishing Co.

Burch, Ernest S., Jr. Social Life in Northwest Alaska: The Structure of Inupiaq Eskimo Nations. 2006. (Illus.). 496p. pap. 29.95 *(978-1-889963-92-1(5))* Univ. of Alaska Pr.

Chisham, William E. The Road North: Tales of an Urban Sourdough. 2007. per. 19.95 *(978-0-615-13745-2(8))* Old Red Barn Publishing.

Coghill, John B. Growing up in Alaska. 2009. pap. 24.95 *(978-0-9823017-1-5(5))* Kayto Communication, Inc.

Durr, Bob. The Coldman Cometh: A Family's Adventure in the Alaska Bush. Date not set. pap. *(978-0-312-31180-3(X))*; mass mkt. *(978-0-312-98847-0(8))* St. Martin's Pr. (St. Martin's Paperbacks).

Federal Field Commission, compiled by. Where Alaska's Native People Live CD-ROM. 2007. cd-rom 29.95 *(978-1-878051-57-8(1))* Circumpolar Pr.

Fienup-Riordan, Ann. Mission of Change in Southwest Alaska: Conversations with Father René Astruc & Paul Dixon on Their Work with Yup'ik People, 1950-1988. 2012. ***(978-1-60223-162-7(1))*** Univ. of Alaska Pr.

Fienup-Riordan, Ann, ed. Mission of Change in Southwest Alaska: Conversations with Father Rene Astruc & Paul Dixon on Their Work with Yup'ik People. 2012. (ENG., Illus.). 346p. pap. 34.95 ***(978-1-60223-161-0(3))*** Univ. of Alaska Pr.

Fienup-Riordan, Ann, ed. Qaluyaarmiuni Nunamtenek Qanemciput / Our Nelson Island Stories: Meanings of Place on the Bering Sea Coast. Rearden, Alice, tr. 2011. (ENG., Illus.). 496p. (C). pap. 50.00 *(978-0-295-99135-1(6))* Univ. of Washington Pr.

Fienup-Riordan, Ann, et al. Yupiit Yuraryarait: Yup'ik Ways of Dancing. (ENG., Illus.). 2011. 242p. pap. 35.00 *(978-1-60223-130-6(3))* 2010. 237p. 50.00 *(978-1-60223-082-8(X))* Univ. of Alaska Pr.

Foote, Berit Amestad. Point Hope, Alaska: Life on Frozen Water. 2nd ed. 2009. (ENG., Illus.). 204p. 65.00 *(978-1-60223-065-1(X))* Univ. of Alaska Pr.

Gmelch, Sharon. The Tlingit Encounter with Photography. 2008. (Illus.). 240p. 39.95 *(978-1-934536-10-0(5)*, Univ. of Pennsylvania Museum of Archaeology & Anthropology) Univ. Museum Pubns.

Grinnell, George Bird. The Harriman Expedition to Alaska: Encountering the Tlingit & Eskimo in 1899. 2007. (Illus.). 152p. pap. 14.95 *(978-1-889963-98-3(4))* Univ. of Alaska Pr.

Haakanson, Jr., Sven D., Sven D & Steffian, Amy F., eds. Giinaquq — Like a Face: Suqpiaq Masks of the Kodiak Archipelago. 2009. (Illus.). 200p. pap. 26.95 *(978-1-60223-049-1(8))* Univ. of Alaska Pr.

Harbeson Jr., George. Homesteaders in the Headlights: One family's journey from a Depression-era New Jersey farm to a new life in Wasilla, Alaska. 2010. (Illus.). 312p. pap. 21.50 *(978-0-9789979-8-4(0))* Hardscratch Pr.

Hayes, Ernestine. Blonde Indian: An Alaska Native Memoir. 2006. (Sun Tracks Ser.: Vol. 57). (ENG., Illus.). 200p. 32.95 *(978-0-8165-2538-6(2))*; pap. 16.95 *(978-0-8165-2537-9(4))* Univ. of Arizona Pr.

Hensley, William L. Iggiagruk. Fifty Miles from Tomorrow: A Memoir of Alaska & the Real People. 2010. (ENG., Illus.). 288p. pap. 15.00 *(978-0-312-42936-2(3))* Picador.

Hirschmann, Fred. Alaska: Portrait of a State. 2006. (Portrait of a Place Ser.). (ENG., Illus.). 112p. 17.95 *(978-1-55868-952-7(4))* Graphic Arts Ctr. Publishing Co.

Hudson, Ray. Moments Rightly Placed: An Aleutian Memoir. rev. ed. 2008. (Alaska Book Adventures (Epicenter Press) Ser.). (ENG.). 224p. (gr. 9). pap. 19.95 *(978-0-9790470-7-7(2))* Epicenter Pr., Inc.

Ingstad, Helge. Nunamiut: Among Alaska's Inland Eskimos. 2006. (ENG., Illus.). 368p. per. 19.95 *(978-0-88150-761-4(X))* Countryman Pr.

Johnston, Levi. Deer in the Headlights: My Life in Sarah Palin's Crosshairs. (ENG., Illus.). 256p. 2012. pap. 15.00 ***(978-1-4516-5166-9(X))*** 2011. 25.00 ***(978-1-4516-5165-2(1))*** Touchstone. (Touchstone).

Kelly, Sheila. Treadwell Gold: An Alaska Saga of Riches & Ruin. (Illus.). 2011. 288p. pap. 17.95 *(978-1-60223-118-4(4))* 2010. (ENG., 271p. 35.00 *(978-1-60223-075-0(7))* Univ. of Alaska Pr.

Kremers, Carolyn. Place of the Pretend People: Gifts from a Yup'ik Village. 2011. (ENG., Illus.). 249p. pap. 16.95 *(978-0-88240-855-2(0)*, Alaska Northwest Bks.) Graphic Arts Ctr. Publishing Co.

Martin, Fredericka I. Before the Storm: A Year in the Pribilof Islands, 1941-1942. Hudson, Raymond L., ed. 2010. (ENG., Illus.). 385p. pap. 39.95 *(978-1-60223-076-7(5))* Univ. of Alaska Pr.

Mishler, Craig. Black Ducks & Salmon Bellies: An Ethnography of Old Harbor & Ouzinkie, Alaska. 2007. (Illus.). 256p. per. 39.95 *(978-1-57864-218-2(3))* Donning Co. Pubs.

Moses, Shirley & Krieg, Holly. Sharing Alaska Native Cultures: Activity... pap. 8.00 *(978-0-931163-12-8(9))* Univ. of Alaska Museum.

Movius, Phyllis Demuth. A Place of Belonging: Five Founding Women of Fairbanks, Alaska. 2009. (ENG., Illus.). 120p. pap. 17.95 *(978-1-60223-064-4(1))* Univ. of Alaska Pr.

Mow, Amy, ed. Snapshots of Seward: A History in Photos. 2010. 102p. pap. 16.95 *(978-0-615-33309-0(5))* Seward Community Library.

Olson, R. L. Social Structure & Social Life of the Tlingit in Alaska, Vol. 26. fac. ed. (University of California Publications). 133p. reprint ed. pap. 14.38 *(978-1-55567-937-8(4))* Coyote Pr.

P. E. O. Sisterhood, ed. What! No Igloos? the Diary of a Fairbanks Housewife. 2011. 46p. 35.95 ***(978-1-258-09728-8(1))*** Literary Licensing, LLC.

Pels, Jacquelin B., ed. & compiled by. Family after All: Alaska's Jesse Lee Home, Vol. II, Seward 1925-1965, 2 vols., Vol. 2. 2008. (Illus.). 800p. pap. 37.00 *(978-0-9789979-1-5(3))* Hardscratch Pr.

Pioneers of Alaska Men's Igloo 32 and Women's Igloo 14, as told by. In Those Days, Alaska Pioneers of the Lower Kenai Peninsula, Volume II. 2007. (Illus.). 136p. 25.00 *(978-0-9798716-0-3(3))* Erin, Glen Pr.

Reedy-Maschner, Katherine L. Aleut Identities: Tradition & Modernity in an Indigenous Fishery. 2010. (McGill-Queen's Native & Northern Ser.). (ENG.). 314p. (C). *(978-0-7735-3682-1(5))*; pap. *(978-0-7735-3748-4(1))* McGill-Queen's Univ. Pr.

Salisbury, O. M. The Customs & Legends of the Thlinget Indians of Alask. 2011. 286p. 48.95 ***(978-1-258-04554-8(0))*** Literary Licensing, LLC.

Scully, Julia. Outside Passage: A Memoir of an Alaskan Childhood. 2011. 226p. pap. 15.95 *(978-1-60223-129-0(X))* Univ. of Alaska Pr.

Services for Veterans in Alaska: Field Hearings in Anchorage & Fairbanks: Hearing Before the Committee on Veterans' Affairs, United States Senate, One Hundred Eleventh Congress, Second Session, February 16 & 17, 2010. 2010. iv, 141p. ***(978-0-16-087778-0(4)***, 552-070-42289-7) United States Government Printing Office.

Smith, Kenneth W. Inupiat Parables. 2009. 132p. pap. 13.95 *(978-1-4401-1310-9(6))* iUniverse, Inc.

Stout, Jack & Stout, Rita. To Hell with Togetherness: Story of an Alaska Family Living on Remote Homestead West of Anchorage 1957-1962. 2009. pap. 16.95 *(978-0-9815193-4-0(2))* Northbooks.

Thornton, Thomas F. Being & Place among the Tlingit. 2007. (Culture, Place, & Nature Ser.). (ENG., Illus.). 224p. per. 24.95 *(978-0-295-98749-1(9))* Univ. of Washington Pr.

Turner, Lucien M. An Aleutian Ethnography. Hudson, Raymond L., ed. (Illus.). 2010. (ENG.). 256p. pap. 26.95 *(978-1-60223-039-2(0))* 2008. 175p. 45.00 *(978-1-60223-028-6(5))* Univ. of Alaska Pr.

Vanasse, Deb. Picture This, Alaska: Historic Photographs from the Last Frontier. 2009. (ENG., Illus.). 144p. pap. 16.95 *(978-1-57061-584-9(5))* Sasquatch Bks.

Wilder, Edna. The Eskimo Girl & the Englishman. 2008. (ENG., Illus.). 170p. 26.95 *(978-1-60223-016-3(1))* Univ. of Alaska Pr.

—Once upon an Eskimo Time. 2009. (ENG., Illus.). 197p. pap. 17.95 *(978-1-60223-056-9(0))* Univ. of Alaska Pr.

Wilder, Edna & Wilder, E. The Eskimo Girl & the Englishman. 2009. (ENG., Illus.). 168p. pap. 16.95 *(978-1-60223-015-6(3))* Univ. of Alaska Pr.

Williams, Lorraine, creator. You Know You're in a Small Town When..., Vol. 2. 2007. (Illus.). 84p. pap. 14.95 *(978-0-9797442-0-4(2))* Alaska Independent Pubs.

Windham, Kathryn Tucker. Spit, Scarey Ann, & Sweat Bees: One Thing Leads to Another. 2009. 112p. 20.00 *(978-1-58838-240-5(0)*, NewSouth Bks.) NewSouth, Inc.

Wyman, Jeffries. Alaska Journal. 2010. (ENG.). 92p. pap. 19.95 *(978-0-9625780-5-2(3))* Protean Publishing Co.

ALASKA—UNIVERSITY OF ALASKA (SYSTEM)

see University of Alaska (System)

ALASKA HIGHWAY
Brown, Tricia. The World-Famous Alaska Highway: A Guide to the Alcan & Other Wilderness Roads of the North. 4th ed. 2011. (ENG.). 288p. pap. 22.95 *(978-1-55594-749-4(6))* Fulcrum Publishing.
Dalby, Ron. Guide to the Alaska Highway. 2nd ed. 2011. (ENG., Illus.). 288p. pap. 19.95 *(978-0-89732-926-2(0))* Menasha Ridge Pr., Inc.
Gutkind, Lee. Truckin' with Sam: A Father & Son, the Mick & the Dyl, Rockin' & Rollin', on the Road. 2010. (Excelsior Editions Ser.). (Illus.). 176p. 19.95 *(978-1-4384-3259-5(3),* Suny Pr.) State Univ. of New York Pr.

ALASKA PURCHASE, 1867
see Alaska—Annexation to the United States

ALASKAN MALAMUTE
Kelley, Mary Lu. For the Love of Lilly: Living with Malamutes in Hawaii. 2011. 200p. pap. 14.99 *(978-1-4520-8091-8(7))* AuthorHouse.
Siino, Betsy Sikora. Alaskan Malamutes. 2nd rev. ed. 2007. (Complete Pet Owner's Manual Ser.). (ENG., Illus.). 96p. pap. 8.99 *(978-0-7641-3676-4(3))* Barron's Educational Series, Inc.

ALBANI, ALESSANDRO, CARDINAL, 1692-1779
Vermeule Iii, Cornelius C. The Dal Pozzo-Albani Drawings of Classical Antiquities in the British Museum: Transactions of the American Philosophical Society, V50, Part 5. 2011. 80p. 37.95 ***(978-1-258-10415-3(6))*** Literary Licensing, LLC.

ALBANIA
Icon Group International, Inc. Staff, compiled by. The 2006 Economic & Product Market Databook for Fier, Albania. 2006. 618p. ring bd. 95.00 *(978-0-497-80539-5(1))* Icon Group International, Inc.
van Weenen, John. Task Force Albania. (Illus.). 292p. pap. *(978-0-9517660-7-1(4))* Van Weenen, John GBR. Dist: Vine Hse. Distribution.
Wingfield, William. A Tour in Dalmatia, Albania, & Montenegro with an Historical Sketch of the Republic of Ragusa, from the Earliest Times down to Its Final Fall. 2007. 360p. per. 24.95 *(978-1-60206-288-7(9))* Cosimo, Inc.

ALBANIA—HISTORY
Abbott, Lawrence O. & Abbott, Clinton W. Out of Albania - A True Account of a WWII Underground Rescue Mission. 2010. 296p. (ENG.). 35.00 *(978-0-557-30335-9(4));* pap. 17.95 *(978-0-557-30329-8(X))* Lulu Enterprises Inc.
Alpion, Gëzim I. Encounters with Civilizations: From Alexander the Great to Mother Teresa. 2011. (ENG.). 327p. pap. 34.95 *(978-1-4128-1831-5(1))* Transaction Pubs.
Belegu, Kastriot. Project of Kastriot Mfl & Reduction of Poverty in Rural Albania. 2010. 212p. pap. *(978-3-8383-8690-4(6))* Lambert Academic Publishing.
Bezemer, Dirk J., ed. On Eagle's Wings: The Albanian Economy in Transition. 2008. xiv, 157p. pap. 45.00 *(978-1-60456-546-1(2))* Nova Science Pubs., Inc.
Butterworth, John. God's Secret Listener: The Albanian Army Captain Who Risked Everything. 1 vol. 2011. (Illus.). 224p. pap. 13.99 *(978-1-85424-991-3(6),* Monarch Bks.) Lion Hudson PLC GBR. Dist: Kregel Pubns.
de Loo, Tessa. In Byron's Footsteps. 2011. (Red Bks.). (ENG., Illus.). 220p. 19.95 ***(978-1-906593-77-8(0))*** Haus Publishing GBR. Dist: Consortium Bk. Sales & Distribution.
Destani, Bejtullah & Jasini, Rudina. The Cham Albanians of Greece: A Documentary History. Destani, Bejtullah & Elsie, Robert, eds. 2012. (ENG.). 288p. 90.00 ***(978-1-78076-000-1(0))*** I. B. Tauris & Co., Ltd. GBR. Dist: Macmillan.
Dimo, V., et al. The Complex of Tumuli 9, 10, & 11 in the Necropolis of Apollonia (Albania). 2 vols. 2010. (Bar S Ser.). (ENG., Illus.). 878p. (C). pap. 285.00 *(978-1-4073-0550-9(6))* British Archaeological Reports Ltd. GBR. Dist: Brown, David Bk. Co., The.
d'Istria, Dora & Smith, Morelle. The Land of the Thunderbolt Mountains: The Nineteenth-Century Origins of Albanian National Identity. 2012. (ENG., Illus.). 184p. 47.50 *(978-1-84511-590-6(2))* I. B. Tauris & Co., Ltd. GBR. Dist: Macmillan.
Elsie, Robert. Historical Dictionary of Albania. 2nd ed. 2010. (Historical Dictionaries of Europe Ser.). (ENG., Illus.). 662p. 137.00 *(978-0-8108-6188-6(7))* Scarecrow Pr., Inc.
Esayi Hasan Jalaleants & Bournoutian, George A. A Brief History of the Aghuank Region: Patmutiwn Hamarot Aghuanits Erkri: A History of Karabagh & Ganje from 1702-1723. 2009. (ARM & ENG., Illus.). xi, 124p. *(978-1-56859-171-1(3))* Mazda Pubs., Inc.
Evans, Arthur. Albanian Letters: Nationalism, Independence & the Albanian League. Destani, Bejtullah, ed. 2013. (ENG., Illus.). 224p. 75.00 *(978-1-84511-601-9(1))* I. B. Tauris & Co., Ltd. GBR. Dist: Macmillan.
Gawrych, George W. & Gawrych, George. The Crescent & the Eagle: Ottoman Rule, Islam & the Albanians, 1874-1913. 2006. (Library of Ottoman Studies). (ENG., Illus.). 288p. 94.00 *(978-1-84511-287-5(3))* I. B. Tauris & Co., Ltd. GBR. Dist: Macmillan.
Gloyer, Gillian. Albania. 4th rev. ed. 2012. (Bradt Travel Guide Ser.). (ENG., Illus.). 272p. pap. 25.99 ***(978-1-84162-387-0(3))*** Bradt Travel Guides GBR. Dist: Globe Pequot Pr., The.
Gunning, Jeroen & Kegan Paul, Charles. The Handbook of Albania. 2008. 50.00 *(978-0-7103-1370-6(5))* Kegan Paul International, Ltd. GBR. Dist: Columbia Univ. Pr.
Guy, Nicola. The Birth of Albania: Ethnic Nationalism, the Great Powers of World War I & the Emergence of Albanian Independence. 2012. (ENG.). 288p. 96.00 *(978-1-84885-368-3(8))* I. B. Tauris & Co., Ltd. GBR. Dist: Macmillan.
Hansen, Inge Lyse. Hellenistic & Roman Butrint. 2009. (ENG & ALB., Illus.). 96p. (C). pap. 24.00 *(978-0-9535556-8-0(2))* Butrint Foundation GBR. Dist: Brown, David Bk. Co., The.
Herbert, Aubrey. Albania's Greatest Friend: Aubrey Herbert & the Making of Modern Albania - Diaries & Papers, 1904-1923. Destani, Bejtullah & Tomes, Jason, eds. 2011. (ENG., Illus.). 256p. 55.00 *(978-1-84885-444-4(7))* I. B. Tauris & Co., Ltd. GBR. Dist: Macmillan.
Hodges, Richard. Saranda - Ancient Onchesmos: A Short History & Guide. 2007. (Illus.). 60p. (C). pap. 15.00 *(978-99943-943-6-4(3))* Butrint Foundation GBR. Dist: Brown, David Bk. Co., The.
Jacques, Edwin E. The Albanians: An Ethnic History from Prehistoric Times to the Present. 2 vols. alt. ed. 2009. (ENG.). 748p. pap. 75.00 *(978-0-7864-4238-6(7))* McFarland & Co., Inc. Pubs.
Jost, Hans Peter & Lubonja, Fatos. Albania. 2012. (ENG & ALB., Illus.). 280p. 45.00 ***(978-3-7165-1707-9(0))*** Benteli Verlag CHE. Dist: National Bk. Network.
Kadare. Albanian Spring. 448p. *(978-0-86356-253-2(1))* Saqi Bks.
King, Russell & Vullnetari, Julie. Remittances, Gender & Development: Albania's Society & Economy in Transition. 2011. (Library of Development Studies). (ENG., Illus.). 256p. 92.50 *(978-1-84885-487-1(0),* Tauris Academic Studies) I. B. Tauris & Co., Ltd. GBR. Dist: Macmillan.
Koja, Marjola & Marjola, Koja. Women Entrepreneurship in Albania: A Study of the Motivations & Barriers Behind the Decision to Start & Run a Business. 2011. 80p. pap. ***(978-3-639-32426-6(9))*** VDM Verlag Dr. Mueller e.K.
Konitza, Faik. Albania: The Rock Garden of Southeastern Europe. 2012. (ENG.). 175p. 40.00 *(978-1-84885-562-5(1))* I. B. Tauris & Co., Ltd. GBR. Dist: Macmillan.
Kortsha, Gene X. One Man's Journey to Freedom: Escape from Behind the Iron Curtain. 2010. *(978-1-935356-13-4(5))* Wilderness Adventure Bks.
Lanier, Robert A. The Prisoner of Durazzo: Being a History of Six Months in a Phantom Kingdom & of Armageddon Postponed. 2010. (Illus.). xl, 471p. ***(978-0-615-32523-1(8))*** Zenda Pr.
Leake, William Martin. Researches in Greece & Albania. 2012. (ENG.). 480p. 59.50 *(978-1-84885-128-3(6))* I. B. Tauris & Co., Ltd. GBR. Dist: Macmillan.
Löhr, Hanns Christian. Die Gründung Albaniens: Wilhelm zu Wied und die Balkan-Diplomatie der Großmächte. 1912-1914. 2010. (GER.). 282p. pap. 57.95 *(978-3-631-60117-4(4))* Lang, Peter GmbH, Europaischer Verlag der Wissenschaften DEU. Dist: Lang, Peter.
Lubonja, Fatos. Second Sentence: Inside the Albanian Gulag. Hodgson, John, tr. from ALB. 2009. (ENG.). 224p. 42.00 *(978-1-84511-924-9(X))* I. B. Tauris & Co., Ltd. GBR. Dist: Macmillan.
Lucas, Peter. The OSS in World War II Albania: Covert Operations & Collaboration with Communist Partisans. 2007. (ENG., Illus.). 220p. per. 35.00 *(978-0-7864-2967-7(4))* McFarland & Co., Inc. Pubs.
Organization, World Trade & Bernan Press Staff. Trade Policy Review: Albania 2010. 2010. (ENG.). 161p. pap. 75.00 *(978-1-59888-438-8(7))* Bernan Assocs.
Pano, Nicholas C. Albania. 2009. (Postcommunist States & Nations Ser.). 192p. 130.00 *(978-0-415-27434-0(6))* Routledge.
Pearson, Owen. Albania As Dictatorship & Democracy: From Isolation to the Kosovo War, 1946-98. 2007. (ENG., Illus.). 704p. 89.00 *(978-1-84511-105-2(2))* I. B. Tauris & Co., Ltd. GBR. Dist: Macmillan.
Pettifer, James & Nazarko, Mentor. Strengthening Religious Tolerance for a Secure Civil Society in Albania & the Southern Balkans. 2007. xv, 139p. 150.00 *(978-1-58603-779-6(X))* IOS Pr., Inc.
Pettifer, James & Vickers, Miranda. The Albanian Question: Igniting the Balkans. 2006. (ENG., Illus.). 256p. 58.00 *(978-1-86064-974-5(2))* I. B. Tauris & Co., Ltd. GBR. Dist: Macmillan.
—The Albanian Question: Reshaping the Balkans. 2009. (ENG., Illus.). 288p. pap. 26.95 *(978-1-84885-095-8(6))* I. B. Tauris & Co., Ltd. GBR. Dist: Macmillan.
Pierini, Roberto. Recovering & Improving Elbasan Fortress: An Albanian Citadel from Via Egnatia to No 8 Trans-European Transport Network. 2008. (Illus.). xvii, 241p. *(978-88-8492-587-9(8))* Plus/Pisa University Pr.
Rrumbullaku, Filip. Dekorimet Nga Princ Vidi Deri Sot. 2010. (ALB., Illus.). 296p. *(978-99943-42-80-8(0))* Onufri.
Shetuni, Spiro J. Albanian Traditional Music: An Introduction, with Sheet Music & Lyrics for 48 Songs. 2011. (ALB & ENG., Illus.). 213p. pap. 55.00 *(978-0-7864-6449-4(6))* McFarland & Co., Inc. Pubs.
Tarifa, Fatos, ed. Sociological Analysis: 2007. 2007. per. 50.00 *(978-0-9776662-9-4(8))* Globic Pr.
Winnifrith, T. J. Tribes & Brigands in the Balkans: A History of Northern Albania. 2012. (ENG., Illus.). 200p. 44.95 *(978-1-84511-610-1(0))* I. B. Tauris & Co., Ltd. GBR. Dist: Macmillan.
Woodrum, Robert H. Everybody Was Black down There: Race & Industrial Change in the Alabama Coalfields. 2007. (Politics & Culture in the Twentieth-Century South Ser.). (ENG., Illus.). 328p. 69.95 *(978-0-8203-2735-6(5));* per. 24.95 *(978-0-8203-2879-9(0))* Univ. of Georgia Pr.

ALBANIA—POLITICS AND GOVERNMENT
Behluli, Armend. The Recognition of States: The Case of Kosovo. 2010. 80p. pap. *(978-3-639-23914-0(8))* VDM Verlag Dr. Mueller e.K.
Blockmans, Steven. Tough Love: The European Union's Relations with the Western Balkans. 2007. (ENG.). 400p. 99.00 *(978-90-6704-258-1(7))* T.M.C. Asser Pr. NLD. Dist: Springer.
Blumi, Isa. Rethinking the Late Ottoman Empire. 2010. 105.32 *(978-1-61719-096-4(9))* Gorgias Pr., LLC.
Bogdani, Mirela & Loughlin, John. Albania & the European Union: The Tumultuous Journey Towards Integration & Accession. 2007. (ENG.). 208p. 84.00 *(978-1-84511-308-7(X))* I. B. Tauris & Co., Ltd. GBR. Dist: Macmillan.
Çano, Drini. The Albanian Property Restitution & Compensation Agency. 2009. 60p. pap. *(978-3-639-14265-5(9))* VDM Verlag Dr. Mueller e.K.
Cela, Alba. Orientalism in Service of Contemporary National Identity Building in Albani. 2008. 76p. pap. *(978-3-639-06211-3(6))* VDM Verlag Dr. Mueller e.K.
Cici, Delina. International Organizations & Democracy. 2011. 68p. pap. ***(978-3-8433-9246-4(3))*** Lambert Academic Publishing.
Evans, Arthur. Albanian Letters: Nationalism, Independence & the Albanian League. Destani, Bejtullah, ed. 2013. (ENG., Illus.). 224p. 75.00 *(978-1-84511-601-9(1))* I. B. Tauris & Co., Ltd. GBR. Dist: Macmillan.
Ilirjani, Altin, et al, eds. Albanian Journal of Politics: 2006 2006. 132p. per. 75.00 *(978-0-9776662-6-3(3))* Globic Pr.
—Albanian Journal of Politics: 2007. 2007. per. 75.00 *(978-0-9776662-7-0(1))* Globic Pr.
Irma, Qehajaj. Localizing Democracy in Albania: The Case of Participatory Budgeting. 2011. 72p. pap. ***(978-3-639-32256-9(8))*** VDM Verlag Dr. Mueller e.K.
Kaltsouris, Theodore. The Democratization of Albania: Democracy from Within. 2010. (ENG.). 206p. 89.00 *(978-0-230-10458-7(4))* Palgrave Macmillan.
King & Mai. Out of Albania: From Crisis Migration to Social Inclusion in Italy. 2011. 294p. 34.95 *(978-0-85745-164-4(2))* Berghahn Bks., Inc.
King, Russell & Mai, Nicola. Out of Albania: From Crisis Migration to Social Inclusion in Italy. 2008. (Illus.). 294p. (C). 90.00 *(978-1-84545-544-6(4))* Berghahn Bks., Inc.
Meti, Bledar. Greek Nationalism & the Scope of Its Interrelationship with Albania. 2010. (ALB & ENG., Illus.). 148p. pap. 13.49 *(978-1-4520-0936-0(6))* AuthorHouse.
Pearson, Owen. Albania As Dictatorship & Democracy: From Isolation to the Kosovo War, 1946-98. 2007. (ENG., Illus.). 704p. 89.00 *(978-1-84511-105-2(2))* I. B. Tauris & Co., Ltd. GBR. Dist: Macmillan.
Pettifer, James & Vickers, Miranda. The Albanian Question: Igniting the Balkans. 2006. (ENG., Illus.). 256p. 58.00 *(978-1-86064-974-5(2))* I. B. Tauris & Co., Ltd. GBR. Dist: Macmillan.
—The Albanian Question: Reshaping the Balkans. 2009. (ENG., Illus.). 288p. pap. 26.95 *(978-1-84885-095-8(6))* I. B. Tauris & Co., Ltd. GBR. Dist: Macmillan.
Roselli, Alessandro. Italy & Albania: Financial Relations in the Fascist Period. 2006. (Library of International Relations Ser.). (ENG, SPA & ITA., Illus.). 272p. 100.00 *(978-1-84511-254-7(7))* I. B. Tauris & Co., Ltd. GBR. Dist: Macmillan.
Shaqiri, Albinot. The Economic Well-Being of Albanians: Trust & Social Capital - How do Cultural Values & the Levels of Trust Affect Social Capital & the Robustne. 2008. 92p. pap. *(978-3-639-11536-9(8))* VDM Verlag Dr. Mueller e.K.
Shijaku, Hilda. An Assessment of Monetary Policy in Albania Since 1990. 2010. 388p. pap. *(978-3-8383-5697-6(7))* Lambert Academic Publishing.
van Weenen, John. Task Force Albania. (Illus.). 280p. *(978-0-9517660-8-8(2))* Van Weenen, John GBR. Dist: Vine Hse. Distribution.

ALBANIAN FOLK SONGS
see Folk Songs, Albanien

ALBANIAN LANGUAGE
Bezhani, Laka. Albanian English Dictionary. 2010. 75p. pap. 16.50 *(978-0-557-61580-3(1))* Lulu Enterprises Inc.
Euro Talk. Talk Now! Albanian. 2008. 29.99 *(978-1-84352-346-8(9))* TOPICS Entertainment.
—Vocabulary Builder Albanian. 2008. 24.99 *(978-1-84352-746-6(4))* TOPICS Entertainment.
Icon Group International, Inc. Staff, compiled by. Webster's Albanian - English Thesaurus Dictionary. 2008. 664p. ring bd. 28.95 incl. audio compact disk *(978-0-497-83422-7(7))* Icon Group International, Inc.
Leake, William Martin. Researches in Greece & Albania. 2012. (ENG.). 480p. 59.50 *(978-1-84885-128-3(6))* I. B. Tauris & Co., Ltd. GBR. Dist: Macmillan.
Mayhew, Anila. Beginner's Albanian with 2 Audio Cds. 2012. (ENG & ALB.). 256p. pap. ***(978-0-7818-1280-1(1))*** Hippocrene Bks., Inc.
Mëniku, Linda. Gheg Albanian Reader. 2008. (ALB & ENG., Illus.). l, 196p. *(978-1-931546-47-8(9))* Dunwoody Pr.
Mëniku, Linda & Campos, Héctor. Albanian for Beginners, a Textbook. 2011. (ENG.). 416p. pap. 39.95 *(978-0-299-25084-3(9))* Univ. of Wisconsin Pr.
—Albanian for Beginners Workbook. 2011. (ENG., Illus.). 224p. pap. 19.95 *(978-0-299-25094-2(6))* Univ. of Wisconsin Pr.
—Colloquial Albanian. 2nd rev. ed. 2012. 352p. (ENG & ALB.). 89.95 *(978-0-415-59796-8(X));* (ALB & ENG.). pap. 44.95 *(978-0-415-59795-1(1))* Routledge.
Mëniku, Linda & Campos, Hector. Discovering Albanian I Textbook. 2011. E-Book ***(978-0-299-25083-6(0))*** Univ. of Wisconsin Pr.
Powers, Robert F. English-Albanian Dictionary-Phrasebook for Aid Workers & Military Personnel. Date not set. (ALB & ENG.). pap. 9.95 *(978-1-929482-02-3(7))* Rodnik Publishing Co.
Topalli, Kolec. Sistemi Foljor I Gjuhës Shqipe. 2010. (ALB.). 667p. *(978-99956-57-45-1(7))* Plejad.

ALBANIAN LITERATURE—HISTORY AND CRITICISM
Aliu, Ali. Don Kishoti Shqiptar: Një Histori Ndryshe e Letërsisë Shqipe. 2010. (ALB.). 476p. *(978-99943-1-660-1(5))* Toena.
Cacaj-Shushka, Gjystina. Aspekte Të Veprës Së Atë Anton Harapit. 2010. (ALB.). 124p. *(978-9951-06-320-3(9))* Faik Konica.
Morgan, Peter. Ismail Kadare: The Writer & the Dictatorship 1957-1990. 2010. (Legenda Main Ser.). (ENG., Illus.). 355p. (C). 89.50 *(978-1-906540-51-7(9))* Maney Publishing GBR. Dist: Brown, David Bk. Co., The.
Skendi, Stavro. Albanian & South Slavic Oral Epic Poetry: Memoirs of the American Folklore Society V44. 2011. 228p. 46.95 ***(978-1-258-06372-6(7))*** Literary Licensing, LLC.

ALBANIAN POETRY—HISTORY AND CRITICISM
Llc, Books. Albanian Poets: Aleksander Stavre Drenova, Lasgush Poradeci, Leon Qafzezi, Dritëro Agolli, Muhamet Kyçyku, Masiela Lusha, Andon Zako Çajupi. 2010. 78p. pap. 19.99 *(978-1-155-82721-6(X))* General Bks. LLC.

ALBANIANS
Kapllani, Gazmend. A Short Border Handbook. 2011. (ENG.). 144p. pap. 14.95 *(978-1-84627-150-2(9))* Granta Bks. GBR. Dist: Independent Pubs. Group.
Pekar, Harvey & Roberson, Heather. Macedonia. 2007. (ENG., Illus.). 176p. per. 17.95 *(978-0-345-49899-1(2),* Villard Bks.) Random House Publishing Group.
Troszczynska-Van Genderen, Wanda. Hostages of Tension: Intimidation & Harassment of Ethnic Albanians in Serbia after Kosovo's Declaration of Independence. 2008. 74p. pap. ***(978-1-56432-394-1(3))*** Human Rights Watch.

ALBANIANS—FOREIGN COUNTRIES
Canollari-Baze, Albana. Developing Cultural Identity. 2011. 120p. pap. ***(978-3-8443-2122-7(5))*** Lambert Academic Publishing.
Destani, Bejtullah & Jasini, Rudina. The Cham Albanians of Greece: A Documentary History. Destani, Bejtullah & Elsie, Robert, eds. 2012. (ENG.). 288p. 90.00 ***(978-1-78076-000-1(0))*** I. B. Tauris & Co., Ltd. GBR. Dist: Macmillan.
Judah, Tim. Kosovo: What Everyone Needs to Know. 2008. (What Everyone Needs to Know Ser.). (ENG., Illus.). 192p. pap. 16.95 *(978-0-19-537345-5(6))* Oxford Univ. Pr., Inc.
Kapllani, Gazmend. Shorter Border Handbook. 2009. (ENG., Illus.). 164p. 23.95 *(978-1-84627-149-6(5))* Granta Bks. GBR. Dist: Independent Pubs. Group.
King & Mai. Out of Albania: From Crisis Migration to Social Inclusion in Italy. 2011. 294p. 34.95 *(978-0-85745-164-4(2))* Berghahn Bks., Inc.
King, Russell & Mai, Nicola. Out of Albania: From Crisis Migration to Social Inclusion in Italy. 2008. (Illus.). 294p. (C). 90.00 *(978-1-84545-544-6(4))* Berghahn Bks., Inc.
Pllana-Duli, Abdurrahman. Reentered Banishment. 1 vol. 2009. 169p. pap. 24.95 *(978-1-60749-322-8(5))* PublishAmerica, Inc.

ALBANY (N.Y.)
American Map Staff. Atlas - Albany / Schenectady / Troy NY Atlas. 2009. 112p. pap. 13.99 *(978-0-8416-1689-9(2))* American Map Corp.
Kelly, Arthur C. M. Baptism Records of St. Paul's Lutheran Church, Albany City, Albany Co, NY 1841-1899. 2006. 288p. pap. 56.00 *(978-1-56012-290-6(0))* Kinship.
—Marriage Records of St. Paul's Lutheran Church, Albany City, Albany Co, NY 1841-1899. 2006. 149p. pap. 35.00 *(978-1-56012-291-3(9))* Kinship.
Mayo, A. D. (Amory Dwight). Symbols of the Capital; 2006. 376p. per. 26.99 *(978-1-4255-3904-7(1))* MPublishing.
Michaels, Joanne. The Hudson Valley & Catskill Mountains: Includes Saratoga Springs & Albany. 6th ed. 2007. (Explorer's Guide the Hudson Valley & Catskill Mountains Ser.). (ENG., Illus.). 432p. per. 19.95 *(978-0-88150-772-0(5))* Countryman Pr.
The Port of Albany & Ports on the Hudson River, New York. (Port Ser.: Vol. 6). per. 6.50 *(978-0-16-001740-7(8))* United States Government Printing Office.

ALBANY (N.Y.)—HISTORY
Bailey, Frankie Y. & Green, Alice P. Wicked Albany: Lawlessness & Liquor in the Prohibition ERA. 2009. (Wicked Ser.). (ENG., Illus.). 128p. pap. 19.99 *(978-1-59629-493-6(0))* History Pr., The.
Grant, Anne MacVicar. Memoirs of an American Lady: With Sketches of Manners & Scenes in America, as They Existed Previous to the Revolution. Wilson, James Grant, ed. 2011. (Cambridge Library Collection - Women's Writing Ser.). (ENG., Illus.). 390p. pap. 31.99 ***(978-1-108-03339-8(3))*** Cambridge Univ. Pr.
Grondahl, Paul. Mayor Erastus Corning: Albany Icon, Albany Enigma. 2007. (Illus.). 568p. per. 32.95 *(978-0-7914-7294-1(9))* State Univ. of New York Pr.
Humphreys, Mary G. Catherine Schuyler. (Women of Colonial & Revolutionary Times Ser.). 251p. reprint ed. 98.00 *(978-0-7222-8593-0(0))* Library Reprints, Inc.
Lemak, Jennifer A. Southern Life, Northern City: The History of Albany's Rapp Road Community. 2008. (Illus.). 210p. 25.00 *(978-0-7914-7581-2(6))* State Univ. of New York Pr.
Mercer, Paul, et al. The New York State Capitol & the Great Fire Of 1911. 2011. (Images of America Ser.). (Illus.). 128p. pap. 21.99 *(978-0-7385-7400-4(7))* Arcadia Publishing.
Rittner, Don. Albany Revisited. 2008. (Images of America Ser.). (ENG., Illus.). 128p. pap. 21.99 *(978-0-7385-5652-9(1))* Arcadia Publishing.
—Remembering Albany: Heritage on the Hudson. 2009. (American Chronicles Ser.). 128p. pap. 19.99 *(978-1-59629-770-8(0))* History Pr., The.
Roberts, Warren. A Place in History: Albany in the Age of Revolution, 1775-1825. 2010. (Excelsior Editions Ser.). (ENG., Illus.). 448p. 29.95 *(978-1-4384-3329-5(8))* State Univ. of New York Pr.

A

Salzmann, Kenneth. Albany Scrapbook: A Montage of Life in Albany, New York, Past & Present. 2nd exp. ed. 2006. per. 12.95 *(978-0-9786621-1-0(3))* Gelles-Cole Literary Enterprises.

Sorensen, Karen & Albany Historical Society. Albany. 2007. (Images of America Ser.). (ENG., Illus.). 128p. per. 19.99 *(978-0-7385-4767-1(0))* Arcadia Publishing.

ALBANY AND SUSQUEHANNA RAILROAD

Hicks, Frederick C. High Finance in the Sixties: Chapters from the Early History of the Erie Railway. Hicks, Frederick C., ed. 2011. 432p. 56.95 ***(978-1-258-03085-8(3))*** Literary Licensing, LLC.

ALBAREDA, ANSELM M. (ANSELM MARIA), 1892-1966

Prete, Sesto & Arbesmann, Rudolph. Didascaliae: Studies in Honor of Anselm M. Albareda. Prete, Sesto, ed. 2011. 594p. 64.95 ***(978-1-258-02040-8(8))*** Literary Licensing, LLC.

ALBATROSS D-3 (FIGHTER PLANE)

Guttman, Jon. SE 5a vs Albatros D V: Western Front 1917-18. 2009. (Duel Ser.). (ENG., Illus.). 80p. pap. 17.95 *(978-1-84603-471-8(X))* Osprey Publishing, Ltd. GBR. Dist: Random Hse., Inc.

ALBATROSSES

De Roy, Tui, et al. Albatross: Their World, Their Ways. 2008. (ENG., Illus.). 240p. 49.95 *(978-1-55407-415-0(0))* Firefly Bks., Ltd.

Doughty, Robin W. & Carmichael, Virginia. The Albatross & the Fish: Linked Lives in the Open Seas. 2012. E-Book ***(978-0-292-73763-1(7))*** Univ. of Texas Pr.

Lindsay, Terence. Albatrosses. 2008. (Australian Natural History Ser.). 148p. pap. 35.00 *(978-0-643-09421-5(0))* CSIRO Publishing AUS. Dist: Stylus Publishing, LLC.

Shephard, Hayley. South Solo: Kayaking to Save the Albatross. 2011. (ENG., Illus.). 96p. pap. 19.95 ***(978-1-897411-33-9(2))*** Bayeux Arts, Inc. CAN. Dist: Chicago Distribution Ctr.

ALBEE, EDWARD, 1928-

Albee, Edward. Edward Albee's at Home at the Zoo: Act One - Home Life Act Two - The Zoo Story. 2011. (ENG.). 96p. (gr. 12). 14.00 *(978-1-59020-524-2(3))* Overlook Pr., The.

Cohn. Edward Albee-Aw V77. 2009. pap. 25.00 *(978-0-8166-0527-9(0))* Univ. of Minnesota Pr.

Dircks, Phyllis T. Edward Albee: A Literary Companion. 2010. (McFarland Literary Companions Ser.). (ENG., Illus.). 179p. pap. 39.95 *(978-0-7864-3401-5(5))* McFarland & Co., Inc. Pubs.

Paolucci, Anne. Edward Albee: (the Later Plays) 2010. (ENG.). pap. 20.00 *(978-1-935191-70-4(5))*, Griffon Hse.) ISI Bks.

Solomon, Rakesh H. Albee in Performance. 2010. (ENG., Illus.). 320p. pap. 26.00 *(978-0-253-22205-3(2)*, 0253222052) Indiana Univ. Pr.

Zinman, Toby Silverman & Zinman, Toby. Edward Albee. 2008. (Michigan Modern Dramatists Ser.). (ENG., Illus.). 176p. 64.50 *(978-0-472-09919-1(1))*; pap. 19.95 *(978-0-472-06919-4(5))* Univ. of Michigan Pr.

ALBEMARLE COUNTY (VA.)

Cooper, Jean L. A Guide to Historic Charlottesville & Albemarle County, Virginia. 2007. pap. 19.99 *(978-1-59629-173-7(7))* History Pr., The.

Kern, Susan. The Jeffersons at Shadwell. 2010. (Lamar Series in Western History Ser.). (Illus.). 384p. 30.00 *(978-0-300-15390-3(2))* Yale Univ. Pr.

Woods, Edgar. Albermarle County in Virginia. (Illus.). 412p. reprint ed. lib. bdg. 98.00 *(978-0-7222-0994-3(0))* Library Reprints, Inc.

ALBEMARLE REGION (N.C.)

Johnson, F. Roy. Legends, Myths & Folk Tales of the Roanoke Chowan. 2011. 114p. 39.95 ***(978-1-258-08978-8(5))*** Literary Licensing, LLC.

ALBERS, JOSEF, 1888-1976

Albers, Josef. Josef Albers. 2012. (ENG & ITA., Illus.). 288p. pap. 55.00 ***(978-88-366-2141-5(4))*** Silvana ITA. Dist: D.A.P./Distributed Art Pubs.

Albers, Josef & Judd, Donald. Donald Judd & Josef Albers: Color, Material, Space. 2012. (ENG., Illus.). 128p. 65.00 *(978-3-937572-98-7(8))* Richter Verlag DEU. Dist: D.A.P./Distributed Art Pubs.

—Josef Albers, Donald Judd: Form & Color: January 26-February 24, 2007, PaceWildenstein ... New York. 2007. (Illus.). 83p. *(978-1-930743-69-4(6))* Pace Gallery, The.

Albers, Josef & Weber, Nicholas Fox. Poems & Drawings. 3rd ed. 2006. (GER & ENG., Illus.). 80p. pap. 19.95 *(978-0-300-12033-2(8))* Yale Univ. Pr.

Borchardt-Hume, Achim, ed. Albers & Moholy-Nagy: From the Bauhaus to the New World. 2006. (ENG., Illus.). 192p. 65.00 *(978-0-300-12032-5(X))* Yale Univ. Pr.

Danilowitz, Brenda & Horowitz, Frederick A. Joseph Albers - To Open Eyes: The Bauhaus, Black Mountain College, & Yale. 2006. (ENG., Illus.). 288p. 75.00 *(978-0-7148-4599-9(X))* Phaidon Pr., Inc.

Danilowitz, Brenda & Weber, Nicolas Fox. The Prints of Josef Albers: A Catalogue Raisonné, 1915-1976. 2010. (ENG., Illus.). 240p. 95.00 *(978-1-55595-324-9(7))* Hudson Hills Pr. LLC.

Fox Weber, Nicholas & Danilowitz, Brenda, eds. Josef Albers: Homage to the Square. 2009. (ENG.). 52p. 50.00 *(978-84-92480-38-6(6))* RM Verlag, S.L. ESP. Dist: D.A.P./Distributed Art Pubs.

—The Prints of Anni Albers: Catalogue Raisonne. 2009. (ENG., Illus.). 200p. 70.00 *(978-84-92480-52-4(1))* RM Verlag, S.L. ESP. Dist: D.A.P./Distributed Art Pubs.

Horowitz, Frederick A. & Danilowitz, Brenda. Josef Albers: To Open Eyes. 2009. (ENG., Illus.). 288p. pap. 59.95 *(978-0-7148-4965-2(0))* Phaidon Pr., Inc.

Reinhardt, Ad. Ad Reinhardt: Last Paintings. 2011. (ENG., Illus.). 184p. pap. 60.00 *(978-3-941263-23-9(4))* Richter Verlag DEU. Dist: D.A.P./Distributed Art Pubs.

Semff, Michael & Liesbrock, Heinz, eds. Josef Albers in America: Paintings on Paper. 2011. (ENG., Illus.). 192p. 60.00 *(978-3-7757-2587-3(3))* Hatje Cantz Verlag GmbH & Co KG DEU. Dist: D.A.P./Distributed Art Pubs.

Weber, Nicolas Fox. Josef Albers & Wassily Kandinsky: Friends in Exile - A Decade of Correspondence. 2010. (ENG., Illus.). 160p. pap. 29.95 *(978-1-55595-327-0(1))* Hudson Hills Pr. LLC.

ALBERT, PRINCE CONSORT OF VICTORIA, QUEEN OF GREAT BRITAIN, 1819-1861

Gill, Gillian. We Two: Victoria & Albert: Rulers, Partners, Rivals. 2009. (ENG., Illus.). 480p. pap. 18.00 *(978-0-345-52001-2(7)*, Ballantine Bks.) Random House Publishing Group.

Grey, Charles. The Early Years of His Royal Highness the Prince Consort Comp under the Direction of Her Majesty the Queen, by Lieut.-General the Hon C Grey. 2006. 388p. per. 26.99 *(978-1-4255-4153-8(4))* MPublishing.

Kharibian, Leah. Passionate Patrons: Victoria & Albert & the Arts. 2010. (ENG., Illus.). 192p. pap. 14.95 *(978-1-905686-33-9(1))* Royal Collection Enterprises Ltd. GBR. Dist: Chicago Distribution Ctr.

Marsden, Jonathan, ed. Victoria & Albert: Art & Love. 2010. (Illus.). 480p. 59.95 *(978-1-905686-21-6(8))* Royal Collection Enterprises Ltd. GBR. Dist: Chicago Distribution Ctr.

Martin, Theodore. The Life of His Royal Highness the Prince Consort, by Theodore Martin. 2006. 456p. pap. 29.99 *(978-1-4255-4981-7(0))*; (ENG.). 436p. per. 26.99 *(978-1-4255-4722-6(2))*; (ENG.). 444p. per. 26.99 *(978-1-4255-4897-1(0))*; (ENG.). 448p. per. 26.99 *(978-1-4255-4898-8(9))*; 472p. per. 29.99 *(978-1-4255-5228-2(5))* MPublishing.

Martin, Theodore. The Life of the Prince Consort: Prince Albert & His Times, 5 vols., Vol. 5. 2012. (ENG., Illus.). 2760p. 695.00 ***(978-1-84885-994-4(5))*** I. B. Tauris & Co., Ltd. GBR. Dist: Macmillan.

Rappaport, Helen. A Magnificent Obsession: Victoria, Albert, & the Death That Changed the British Monarchy. 2012. (ENG., Illus.). 352p. 26.99 ***(978-0-312-62105-6(1))*** St. Martin's Pr.

Rimmer, Alfred. The Early Homes of Prince Albert. (ENG.). 392p. 2007. 48.95 *(978-0-548-14191-5(6))* 2006. per. 33.95 *(978-1-4286-5404-4(6))* Kessinger Publishing, LLC.

Stewart, Jules. Albert: A Life. 2011. (ENG., Illus.). 304p. 28.00 ***(978-1-84885-977-7(5))*** I. B. Tauris & Co., Ltd. GBR. Dist: Macmillan.

Weintraub, Stanley. Victorian Yankees at Queen Victoria's Court: American Encounters with Victoria & Albert. 2011. (ENG.). 272p. 70.00 *(978-1-61149-060-2(X))* Univ. of Delaware Pr.

ALBERT, LAKE (CONGO AND UGANDA)

Baker, Samuel W. Albert N'yanzu: Great Basins of the Nile & Explorations of the Nile Sources, 2 vols. reprint ed. 79.00 *(978-0-7812-0732-4(0))* Reprint Services Co.

Baker, Samuel White. In the Heart of Africa. 2008. 260p. 28.99 *(978-0-554-28636-5(X))* 2007. (ENG.). 234p. pap. 20.99 *(978-1-4346-5947-7(X))* 2007. (ENG.). 258p. pap. 23.99 *(978-1-4346-5948-4(8))* BiblioBazaar.

ALBERT NYANZA (CONGO AND UGANDA)

see Albert, Lake (Congo and Uganda)

ALBERTA

Aubrey, Merrily K. Concise/Abridged Place Names of Alberta 2005. 2006. (ENG., Illus.). 398p. pap. 39.95 ***(978-1-55238-210-3(9))*** Univ. of Calgary Pr. CAN. Dist: Chicago Distribution Ctr.

Barrie, Doreen Patricia. The Other Alberta: Decoding a Political Enigma. 2006. (Trade Books based in Scholorship(TBS) Ser.). (ENG., Illus.). 146p. pap. 14.95 *(978-0-88977-192-5(8))* Canadian Plains Research Ctr. CAN. Dist: Univ. of Toronto Pr.

Ford, Catherine. Against the Grain: An Irreverent View of Alberta. 2006. (ENG.). 272p. per. 16.50 *(978-0-7710-4778-7(9)*, McClelland & Stewart) McClelland & Stewart CAN. Dist: Random Hse., Inc.

Jones, Paul. Pembina Country. unabr. ed. (ENG., Illus.). 240p. pap. *(978-0-920576-73-1(7))* Caitlin Pr., Inc.

Paull, Dorothy S. Scarlet Fever: A Story of Early Years in Banff & My Life As a Royal Canadian Mounted Policeman's Wife, 1914-1956. Chvojka, Laural, ed. (Illus.). 122p. 14.95 *(978-0-9697242-0-9(9))* Hancock Hse. Pubs.

Sawchuk, Joe. The Dynamics of Native Politics: The Alberta Metis Experience. 2006. 192p. pap. *(978-1-895830-09-5(5))* Purich Publishing.

Von Heyking, Amy. Creating Citizens: History & Identity in Alberta's Schools, 1905-1980. 2006. (ENG., Illus.). 224p. per. 34.95 *(978-1-55238-144-1(7))* Univ. of Calgary Pr. CAN. Dist: Chicago Distribution Ctr.

ALBERTA—DESCRIPTION AND TRAVEL

Asheton, Pam. Alberta Backcountry Equestrian One-Day Trail Guide, 1 vol. 2007. (ENG., Illus.). 224p. pap. *(978-1-894765-82-4(6))* Rocky Mountain Bks.

Aulenback, Kevin. Identification Guide to the Fossil Plants of the Horseshoe Canyon Formation of Drumheller, Alberta. 2009. (Illus.). 400p. pap. 34.95 *(978-1-55238-247-9(8))* Univ. of Calgary Pr. CAN. Dist: Michigan State Univ. Pr.

Bailey, Mary & Schultz, Judy. The Food Lover's Trail Guide to Alberta, 1 vol. (ENG., Illus.). 256p. pap. *(978-1-894739-02-3(7))* Blue Couch Bks.

Berry, Oliver. Banff, Jasper & Glacier National Parks. 3rd rev. ed. 2012. (National Parks Ser.). (ENG., Illus.). 288p. pap. 19.99 *(978-1-74179-405-2(6))* Lonely Planet Pubns.

Bociurkiw, Marusya. Comfort Food for Breakups: The Memoir of a Hungry Girl. 2007. (ENG., Illus.). 176p. pap. 16.95 *(978-1-55152-219-7(5))* Arsenal Pulp Pr. CAN. Dist: Consortium Bk. Sales & Distribution.

Boissanneault, Dana. The Guests of Itildo Place Bed & Breakfast: A Year's Diary of Our Guests. 2010. 152p. pap. 15.16 *(978-1-4269-2314-2(7))* Trafford Publishing.

Bryan, Liz. Country Roads of Alberta: Exploring the Routes Less Travelled, 1 vol. 2007. (ENG., Illus.). 160p. pap. *(978-1-894974-29-5(8))* Heritage Hse.

Cameron, Ward. Canmore/Kananaskis Recommended. 2007. (Canada Recommended Ser.). (Illus.). 112p. pap. *(978-1-55153-650-7(1))* Altitude Publishing Canada Ltd.

—Hiking in Canmore & Kananaskis Recommended. 2007. (Canada Recommended Ser.). 160p. pap. *(978-1-55153-652-1(8))* Altitude Publishing Canada Ltd.

Copeland, Kathy & Copeland, Craig. Don't Waste Your Time in the Canadian Rockies: The Opinionated Hiking Guide. 6th ed. 2009. (Illus.). 544p. *(978-0-9783427-5-3(5))* hikingcamping.com, Inc.

Corbett, Bill. Day Trips from Calgary. 3rd ed. 2010. (Best of Alberta Ser.). (Illus.). 320p. pap. 24.95 *(978-1-77050-011-2(1))* Whitecap Bks., Ltd. CAN. Dist: Midpoint Trade Bks., Inc.

—Day Trips from Calgary: Best of Alberta. 3rd rev. ed. 2010. (Illus.). 304p. pap. 19.95 *(978-1-55285-766-3(2))* Whitecap Bks., Ltd. CAN. Dist: Midpoint Trade Bks., Inc.

Curran, David. Canoe Trip: North to Athabasca. 2010. pap. 17.95 *(978-1-55571-667-7(9)*, Hellgate Pr.) L & R Publishing.

Daffern, Gillean. Gillean Daffern's Kananaskis Country Trail Guide Vol. 2: West Bragg -The Elbow - The Jumpingpound, 1 vol. 4th ed. 2011. (ENG., Illus.). 280p. pap. *(978-1-897522-77-6(0))* Rocky Mountain Bks.

—Gillean Daffern's Kananaskis Country Trail Guide-4th Edition Vol. 1: Kananaskis Valley — Kananaskis Lakes — Elk Lakes — The Smith-Dorrien, 1 vol. 4th ed. 2010. (ENG., Illus.). 320p. pap. *(978-1-897522-76-9(2))* Rocky Mountain Bks.

—Popular Day Hikes 1: Kananaskis Country, 1 vol. 2007. (ENG., Illus.). 144p. pap. *(978-1-894765-90-9(7))* Rocky Mountain Bks.

Dobson, Thelma Jo. A Ride to Remember: In the Alberta Rockies. 2011. 104p. pap. 11.80 ***(978-1-4269-7075-7(7))*** Trafford Publishing.

Doyle, Pam. Canmore, Kananaskis, & the Canadian Rockies, 1 vol. 2007. (ENG., Illus.). 96p. *(978-1-894765-88-6(5))*; pap. *(978-1-894765-87-9(7))* Rocky Mountain Bks.

Ellis, Bessie Vroom. The Vrooms of the Foothills: When the Work's All Done this Fall. 2011. 132p. pap. 10.50 *(978-1-4269-5626-3(6))* Trafford Publishing.

Ernst, Trent. Northern Alberta: Outdoor Recreation Guide, 1 vol. 2007. (Backroad Mapbooks Ser.). (ENG., Illus.). 36p. spiral bd., spiral bd. *(978-1-897225-12-7(1))* Mussio Ventures, Ltd.

Formac Publishing Company Limited Staff. The Canadian Rockies. Inigo-Jones, Terry, ed. 4th rev. ed. 2010. (Colourguide Travel Ser.). (ENG., Illus.). 208p. pap. 19.95 *(978-0-88780-897-5(2))* Formac Publishing Co., Ltd. CAN. Dist: Casemate Pubs. & Bk. Distributors, LLC.

Gaillard, Frye, et al. Alabama's Civil Rights Trail: An Illustrated Guide to the Cradle of Freedom. 2nd ed. 2010. (Alabama the Forge of History Ser.). (ENG., Illus.). 328p. pap. 24.95 *(978-0-8173-5581-4(2))* Univ. of Alabama Pr.

Galat, Joan Marie. Day Trips from Edmonton. 2010. (Illus.). 192p. pap. 24.95 *(978-1-55285-985-8(1))* Whitecap Bks., Ltd. CAN. Dist: Midpoint Trade Bks., Inc.

Gooch, Jane Lytton. Mount Assiniboine: Images in Art, 1 vol. 2007. (ENG., Illus.). 152p. pap. *(978-1-894765-97-8(4))* Rocky Mountain Bks.

Hempstead, Andrew. Moon Alberta: Including Banff, Jasper & the Canadian Rockies. 2010. (Moon Handbooks). (ENG., Illus.). 544p. pap. 19.95 *(978-1-59880-371-6(9))* Avalon Travel Publishing.

—Moon Canadian Rockies: Including Banff & Jasper National Parks. 2010. (Moon Handbooks). (ENG., Illus.). 352p. pap. 17.95 *(978-1-59880-372-3(7))* Avalon Travel Publishing.

—Moon Spotlight Banff National Park. 2010. (Moon Spotlight Ser.). (ENG.). 80p. pap. 7.95 *(978-1-59880-556-7(8))* Avalon Travel Publishing.

—Moon Spotlight Calgary. 2010. (Moon Spotlight Ser.). (ENG.). 76p. pap. 7.95 *(978-1-59880-554-3(1))* Avalon Travel Publishing.

—Moon Spotlight Edmonton & Northern Alberta. 2010. (Moon Spotlight Ser.). (ENG.). 110p. pap. 8.95 *(978-1-59880-557-4(6))* Avalon Travel Publishing.

Hill, A. S. From Home to Home: Autumn Wanderings in the North-West, 1881-1884, 1 vol. rev. ed. 2009. (ENG., Illus.). 264p. pap. *(978-1-894974-56-1(5))* Heritage Hse.

Holt, Faye Reineberg. Alberta: A History in Photographs, 1 vol. 2009. (History in Photographs Ser.). (ENG., Illus.). 112p. pap. *(978-1-894974-87-5(5))* Heritage Hse.

Isitt, Geraint & Johnson, Graham. Weird Alberta Places. 2006. (ENG., Illus.). 168p. pap. *(978-1-897278-06-2(3))* Blue Bike Bks. CAN. Dist: Lone Pine Publishing.

Jennings, Neil L. In Plain Sight: Exploring the Natural Wonders of Southern Alberta, 1 vol. 2010. (ENG., Illus.). 272p. pap. *(978-1-897522-78-3(9))* Rocky Mountain Bks.

Joubert, Christine. Christine's Found & Shared Country Home Cooking Recipes. 2009. 148p. pap. 41.75 *(978-1-4251-8510-7(X))* Trafford Publishing.

Kershaw, Robert. Exploring the Castle: Discovering the Backbone of the World in Southern Alberta, 1 vol. rev. ed. 2008. (ENG., Illus.). 256p. pap. *(978-1-897522-04-2(5))* Rocky Mountain Bks.

Lakusta, Ernie. Banff & Lake Louise History Explorer. 2007. 160p. pap. *(978-1-55153-643-9(9))* Altitude Publishing Canada Ltd.

Mair, Charles. Through the MacKenzie Basin. 2009. 148p. pap. 24.99 *(978-0-559-05247-7(2))*; 21.99 *(978-0-559-05263-7(4))*; pap. 21.75 *(978-0-559-05253-8(7))*; pap. 20.75 *(978-0-559-05258-3(8))* BiblioBazaar.

—Through the MacKenzie Basin. 2007. (ENG.). 124p. per. *(978-1-4065-8240-6(9))* Dodo Pr.

Marriott, John, photos by. Banff & Lake Louise: Images of Banff National Park. 2007. (Illus.). 80p. *(978-1-894768-01-6(9))* JEM Photography & Consulting.

Massing, Conni L. Roadtripping: On the Move with the Buffalo Gals, 1 vol. 2010. (ENG., Illus.). 264p. pap. *(978-1-897142-47-9(1))* Brindle & Glass Publishing.

McRae, Bill & Olson, Donald. Frommer's British Columbia & the Canadian Rockies. 6th ed. 2010. (Frommer's Complete Guides: 774). (ENG., Illus.). 448p. pap. 20.99 *(978-0-470-59153-6(6)*, Frommers) Wiley, John & Sons, Inc.

Michelin Travel Publications Staff. Alberta & the Rockies. 2009. (Green Guide Ser.). (ENG., Illus.). 288p. pap. 19.95 *(978-1-906261-55-9(5))* Michelin Travel & Lifestyle.

Mobil Regional Gd. Northwest 2010. 3rd rev. ed. 2009. (Regional Guide Ser.). 336p. pap. 18.99 *(978-0-8416-1423-9(7))* Langenscheidt Publishing Group.

Molvar, Erik. Best Easy Day Hikes Glacier & Waterton Lakes National Parks. 2nd ed. 2007. (Best Easy Day Hikes Ser.). (ENG., Illus.). 112p. per. 8.95 *(978-0-7627-3633-1(X)*, Falcon Guides) Globe Pequot Pr., The.

—Hiking Glacier & Waterton Lakes National Parks: A Guide to More Than 60 of the Area's Greatest Hiking Adventures. 3rd ed. 2007. (Regional Hiking Ser.). (ENG., Illus.). 240p. per. 15.95 *(978-0-7627-3632-4(1)*, Falcon Guides) Globe Pequot Pr., The.

Moore, Joyce. A Guide to Alberta Outdoors. 2009. (ENG., Illus.). 96p. 9.95 *(978-1-897411-11-7(1))* Bayeux Arts, Inc. CAN. Dist: Chicago Distribution Ctr.

Murphy, Tim, ed. Journey to the Tar Sands. 2008. (ENG., Illus.). 96p. pap. 19.95 *(978-1-55277-039-9(7))* Lorimer, James & Co., Ltd., Pubs. CAN. Dist: Casemate Pubs. & Bk. Distributors, LLC.

Mussio, Russell & Mussio, Wesley. Southern Alberta. 2008. (Backroad Mapbooks Ser.). (Illus.). 117p. pap. *(978-1-897225-29-5(6))* Mussio Ventures, Ltd.

Nugara, Andrew W. More Scrambles in the Canadian Rockies, 1 vol. 2007. (ENG., Illus.). 264p. pap. *(978-1-894765-86-2(9))* Rocky Mountain Bks.

Oakwell, Mary. Tea Time in Alberta: 54 Great Tea Houses from Grande Prairie to Waterton Lakes. (Illus.). 128p. pap. *(978-1-894739-01-6(9))* Blue Couch Bks.

O'Meara, Dinah. Alberta Book of Musts: The 101 Places Every Albertan MUST See. MacIntyre, John, ed. 2009. (Book of Musts Ser.). (ENG.). 128p. pap. 13.95 *(978-0-9810941-2-0(0))* MacIntyre & Purcell Publishing CAN. Dist: Independent Pubs. Group.

Pashby, Christie. Frommer's Alberta. 2nd ed. 2011. (Frommer's Complete Guides). (ENG., Illus.). 288p. pap. 21.99 *(978-0-470-96422-4(7)*, Frommers) Wiley, John & Sons, Inc.

Rees, Tony. Hope's Last Home: Travels in Milk River Country, 1 vol. (ENG., Illus.). 256p. pap. 14.95 *(978-0-9732481-3-5(0))* Brindle & Glass Publishing CAN. Dist: Literary Pr. Group of Canada.

Sandford, Robert. The Columbia Icefield, 1 vol. 2nd ed. 2009. (SuperGuide Ser.). (ENG., Illus.). 64p. pap. *(978-1-897522-37-0(1))* Rocky Mountain Bks.

Sanford, Emerson & Beck, Janice Sanford. Life of the Trail: Historic Hikes in Eastern Banff National Park, 1 vol. rev. ed. 2008. (Life of the Trail Ser.). (ENG., Illus.). 224p. pap. *(978-1-894765-99-2(0))* Rocky Mountain Bks.

—Life of the Trail 3: The Historic Route from Old Bow Fort to Jasper, 1 vol. 2009. (ENG., Illus.). 224p. pap. *(978-1-897522-41-7(X))* Rocky Mountain Bks.

—Life of the Trail 4: Historic Hikes in Eastern Jasper National Park, 1 vol. 2009. (ENG., Illus.). 216p. pap. *(978-1-897522-42-4(8))* Rocky Mountain Bks.

—Life of the Trail 5: Historic Hikes Around Mount Assiniboine & in Kananaskis Country, 1 vol. 2010. (ENG., Illus.). 224p. pap. *(978-1-897522-80-6(0))* Rocky Mountain Bks.

Schullery, Paul. This High, Wild Country: A Celebration of Waterton-Glacier International Peace Park. 2010. (ENG., Illus.). 142p. pap. 27.95 *(978-0-8263-4602-5(2))* Univ. of New Mexico Pr.

Seton, Ernest Thompson. The Arctic Prairies. 2008. 220p. 27.99 *(978-0-554-23779-4(2))*; 24.99 *(978-0-554-33082-2(2))* BiblioBazaar.

—The Arctic Prairies. 2008. (ENG.). 196p. per. *(978-1-4065-9174-3(2))* Dodo Pr.

—The Arctic Prairies. 2006. pap. *(978-1-84702-461-9(0))* Echo Library.

Steman, Caroline. Southern Alberta for City Folks. 2011. 44p. pap. 21.99 ***(978-1-4568-7472-8(1))*** Xlibris Corp.

Takach, Geo F. Will the Real Alberta Please Stand Up? 2010. (ENG., Illus.). 456p. pap. 34.95 *(978-0-88864-543-2(0))* Univ. of Alberta Pr. CAN. Dist: Michigan State Univ. Pr.

Travel Guide, Forbes. Forbes Travel Guide 2011 Northwest. 2011. (Forbes Travel Guide Regional Guide Ser.). (ENG.). 272p. pap. 18.95 *(978-1-936010-91-2(7))* Five Star Travel Corp., The.

Walls, Martha & Mahaffy, Cheryl. Edmonton Book of Everything: Everything You Wanted to Know about Edmonton & Were Going to Ask Anyway. 2007. (Book of Everything Ser.). (ENG.). 192p. pap. 14.95 *(978-0-9738063-4-2(6))* MacIntyre & Purcell Publishing CAN. Dist: Independent Pubs. Group.

Walls, Martha & McDonald, Roberta. Calgary Book of Everything: Everything You Wanted to Know about Calgary & Were Going to Ask Anyway. 2007. (Book of Everything Ser.). (ENG.). 192p. pap. 14.95 *(978-0-9738063-5-9(4))* MacIntyre & Purcell Publishing CAN. Dist: Independent Pubs. Group.

Webber, George. Last Call, 1 vol. 2010. (ENG., Illus.). 128p. *(978-1-926855-08-0(6))*; *(978-1-926855-02-8(7))* Rocky Mountain Bks.

Williams, Huw, ed. Snowfinder Canada. 2008. (ENG.). 400p. pap. 12.95 *(978-0-9775569-3-9(X))* Wavefinder, Ltd. AUS. Dist: SCB Distributors.

ALBERTA—HISTORY

Alberta, Alberta Community Development Staff & Alberta 2005 Centennial Initiative Staff, contrib. by. Alberta's Centennial. 2006. (ENG., Illus.). 200p. pap. *(978-0-7785-5221-5(7))* Alberta Public Affairs Bureau/Queens Printer CAN. Dist: Lone Pine Publishing.

Armstrong, Christopher, et al. The River Returns: An Environmental History of the Bow. (Illus.). 2011. (ENG.). 506p. pap. *(978-0-7735-3870-2(4))* 2009. 488p. *(978-0-7735-3584-8(5))* McGill-Queen's Univ. Pr.

Bachusky, Johnnie. Ghost Town Stories of the Red Coat Trail: From Renegade to Ruin on the Canadian Prairies, 1 vol. 2010. (Amazing Stories Ser.). (ENG., Illus.). 144p. pap. *(978-1-926613-70-3(8))* Heritage Hse.

Cashman, Tony. When Edmonton Was Young. 2009. (ENG., Illus.). 172p. pap. 19.95 *(978-0-88864-511-1(2))* Univ. of Alberta Pr. CAN. Dist: Michigan State Univ. Pr.

Dobson, Thelma Jo. A Ride to Remember: In the Alberta Rockies. 2011. 104p. pap. 11.80 ***(978-1-4269-7075-7(7))*** Trafford Publishing.

Donovan, Larry & Monto, Tom. Place Names of Alberta. 2007. (ENG.). 240p. pap. *(978-1-896124-11-7(9))* Dragon Hill Publishing CAN. Dist: Lone Pine Publishing.

Dreger, Derek. Clare Drake the Coaches' Coach: Hockey's Quite Revolutionary. 2007. *(978-0-919035-32-4(9))* E.S.P. Marketing & Communications, Ltd. CAN. Dist: Lone Pine Publishing.

Elofson, Warren. Somebody Else's Money: The Walrond Ranch Story, 1883-1907. 2009. (ENG., Illus.). 292p. pap. 34.95 *(978-1-55238-257-8(5))* Univ. of Calgary Pr. CAN. Dist: Chicago Distribution Ctr.

Filax, Gloria. Queer Youth in the Province of the Severely Normal, 1 vol. 2007. (ENG., Illus.). 200p. pap. 29.95 *(978-0-7748-1245-7(X))* UBC Pr. CAN. Dist: Univ. of Washington Pr.

Fromhold, Joachim. Alberta History: Red Deer & Area - 13,000 Years of History Notes. 2010. 457p. pap. 31.99 *(978-0-557-50649-1(2))* Lulu Enterprises Inc.

Holt, Faye Reineberg. Alberta: A History in Photographs, 1 vol. 2009. (History in Photographs Ser.). (ENG., Illus.). 112p. pap. *(978-1-894974-87-5(5))* Heritage Hse.

Kelly, Leroy Victor. The Range Men: Pioneer Ranchers of Alberta, 1 vol. 2010. (ENG., Illus.). 336p. pap. *(978-1-894974-94-3(8))* Heritage Hse.

Langford, Tom. Alberta's Day Care Controversy: From 1908 to 2009 & Beyond. 2011. (ENG.). 330p. pap. 41.95 *(978-1-926836-02-7(2))* UBC Pr. CAN. Dist: Univ. of Washington Pr.

Levesque, Lisa. Investigating Landscape Change & Ecological Restoration. 2008. (Illus.). 136p. pap. *(978-3-639-01372-6(7))* VDM Verlag Dr. Mueller e.K.

Macleod, Roderick. All True Things: A History of the University of Alberta, 1908-2008. 2008. (Centennial Ser.). (ENG., Illus.). 392p. 49.95 *(978-0-88864-444-2(2))* Univ. of Alberta Pr. CAN. Dist: Michigan State Univ. Pr.

Mardon, Ernest G. & Mardon, Austin A. Alberta Election Returns, 1887-1994. 2010. 141p. *(978-1-897472-16-3(1))* Golden Meteorite Pr.

McCormack, Patricia A. Fort Chipewyan & the Shaping of Canadian History, 1788-1920s: We like to be free in this Country. 2011. (ENG., Illus.). 408p. pap. 43.95 *(978-0-7748-1669-4(4))* UBC Pr. CAN. Dist: Univ. of Washington Pr.

McKenzie-Brown, Peter & Rennie, James D. Barbeques, Booms, & Blogs: Fifty Years of Public Relations in Calgary. 2008. (Illus.). 148p. pap. 24.95 *(978-1-55059-363-1(3))* Detselig Enterprises, Ltd. CAN. Dist: Temeron Bks., Inc.

Ore, Florence Bell. The Road Between. 2011. (ENG., Illus.). pap. 12.00 *(978-0-982?377-6-7(9))* Raven Publishing Inc. of Montana.

Orrell, John. Fallen Empires: Lost Theatres of Edmonton 1881-1914. 2nd ed. 2007. (Landmark Editions Ser.). (Illus.). 174p. per. *(978-1-897126-16-5(5))* NeWest Pubs., Ltd.

Outram, James. In the Heart of the Canadian Rockies. 2009. 488p. 53.95 *(978-1-104-21783-9(X))*; pap. 38.95 *(978-1-104-18283-0(1))* Kessinger Publishing, LLC.

—In the Heart of the Canadian Rockies, 1 vol. 2007. (Mountain Classics Collection). (ENG.). 312p. per. *(978-1-894765-96-1(6))* Rocky Mountain Bks.

Portman, Dale. Riding on the Wild Side: Tales of Adventure in the Canadian West, 1 vol. 2009. (Amazing Stories Ser.). (ENG.). 144p. pap. *(978-1-894974-80-6(8))* Heritage Hse.

Scriver, Stephen. Bears on Ice: A History of the University of Alberta Golden Bears. 2007. *(978-0-919035-26-3(4))* E.S.P. Marketing & Communications, Ltd. CAN. Dist: Lone Pine Publishing.

ALBERTA—POLITICS AND GOVERNMENT

Babiuk, Colin. Oil Sands & the Earth: Framing the Environmental Message in the Print News Media. 2008. 52p. pap. *(978-3-639-06241-0(8))* VDM Verlag Dr. Mueller e.K.

Brennan, Brian. The Good Steward: Ernest C. Manning Story, 1 vol. 2009. (ENG., Illus.). 240p. 24.95 *(978-1-897252-16-1(1))* Fitzhenry & Whiteside, Ltd. CAN. Dist: Ingram Pub. Services.

ALBERTA—SOCIAL CONDITIONS

Ellis, Bessie Vroom. The Vrooms of the Foothills: When the Work's All Done this Fall. 2011. 132p. pap. 10.50 *(978-1-4269-5626-3(6))* Trafford Publishing.

Irvine, Kathryn. Substance Misuse among Indigenous Peoples of Canada: The Problem of Inhaling Solvents in the Cree & Blackfoot of Alberta. 2011. 316p. ***(978-0-7734-1595-9(5))*** Mellen, Edwin Pr., The.

Mabindisa, Isaac Kholisile. The Praying Man: Henry Bird Steinhauer, Ojibwe & Methodist Minister. 2011. (ENG.). 420p. (C). pap. 26.95 ***(978-1-926836-06-5(5))*** Athabasca University Pr. CAN. Dist: Univ. of Washington Pr.

MacLeod, Kevin J. Moved by the Tides of Technology. 2010. 144p. pap. *(978-3-8383-5472-9(9))* Lambert Academic Publishing.

Martin, Wayne, et al, eds. Parkinson Disease: A Health Policy Perspective. 2010. (Health Care & Disease Management Ser.: 7). (ENG.). 362p. 169.95 *(978-3-527-32779-9(7))* Wiley-VCH) Wiley, John & Sons, Inc.

Nikiforuk, Andrew. Tar Sands: Dirty Oil & the Future of a Continent. 2nd rev. ed. 2010. (ENG., Illus.). 280p. pap. 17.95 *(978-1-55365-555-8(9))*, Greystone Bks.) D&M Pubs. Inc. CAN. Dist: Perseus-PGW.

ALBERTI, LEON BATTISTA, 1404-1472

Alberti, Leon Battista, et al. Leon Battista Alberti's Delineation of the City of Rome (Descriptio Urbis Romae) 2007. (C). *(978-0-86698-383-9(X))* Arizona State Univ., Arizona Ctr. for Medieval & Renaissance Studies.

Arfanotti, Elisabetta, et al. Corpus epistolare e documentario di Leon Battista Alberti. Benigni, Paola, ed. 2007. (Edizione nazionale opere di leon battista Alberti Ser.) (Illus.). 668p. (C). 99.00 *(978-88-596-0402-0(8))* Edizioni Polistampa ITA. Dist: Brown, David Bk. Co., The.

Cardini, Roberto & Regoliosi, Mariangela. Alberti e la Cultura Del Quattrocento: Atti Del Convegno Internazionale Del Comitato Nazionale VI Centenario Della Nascita Di Leon Battista Alberti, Firenze, 16-17-18 Dicembre 2004, 2 vols. 2007. (Edizione nazionale opere di leon battista Alberti Ser.). (ITA.). 915p. (C). 124.00 *(978-88-596-0352-8(8))* Edizioni Polistampa ITA. Dist: Brown, David Bk. Co., The.

Cardini, Roberto & Regoliosi, Mariangela, eds. Alberti e la Tradizione: Per lo smontaggio dei mosaici Albertiani. 2007. (Edizione nazionale opere di leon battista Alberti Ser.). (ITA., Illus.). 656p. (C). 124.00 *(978-88-596-0380-1(3))* Polistampa ITA. Dist: Brown, David Bk. Co., The.

Kircher, Timothy. Living Well in Renaissance Italy: The Virtues of Humanism & the Irony of Leon Battista Alberti. 2012. ***(978-0-86698-471-3(2))*** Arizona State Univ., Arizona Ctr. for Medieval & Renaissance Studies.

Pearson, Caspar. Humanism & the Urban World: Leon Battista Alberti & the Renaissance City. 2011. (ENG.). 232p. 74.95 *(978-0-271-04855-0(7))* Pennsylvania State Univ. Pr.

Santayana, S. G. Two Renaissance Educators: Alberti & Piccolomini. 2011. 124p. 40.95 ***(978-1-258-06429-7(4))*** Literary Licensing, LLC.

Schöndube, Matthias. Leon Battista Alberti, 'Della tranquillità dell'animo' Eine Interpretation auf dem Hintergrund der antiken Quellen. 2011. (Beiträge zur Altertumskunde Ser.). (GER.). XIII, 171p. 112.00 ***(978-3-11-026062-5(X))*** De Gruyter, Walter Inc.

Williams, Kim, et al. The Mathematical Works of Leon Battista Alberti. 2010. (ENG., Illus.). x, 221p. 109.00 *(978-3-0346-0473-4(4))*, 3034604734) Birkhauser Verlag AG CHE. Dist: Springer.

Wulfram, Hartmut. Literarische Vitruvrezeption in Leon Battista Albertis 'de re Aedificatoria' (Beiträge zur Altertumskunde Ser.). (GER.). 441p. 210.00 ***(978-3-11-184227-1(4))*** De Gruyter, Walter Inc.

ALBERTI, RAFAEL, 1902-1999

Alberti, Rafael, et al. Rafael Alberti: Obras Completas. Marrast, Robert, ed. 2009. (SPA., Illus.). lii, 1273p. pap. *(978-84-322-4057-7(5))* Editorial Seix Barral.

Nahmias, Jean-Fraçois. La Ilusion Catara. 2009. (SPA., Illus.). 320p. *(978-84-322-4051-5(6))* Editorial Seix Barral.

Quirós Fernández, Maria Teresa. Stereophonie der Autobiographie: Autobiographisches Schreiben von Paaren am Beispiel von María Teresa Leon und Rafael Alberti. 2009. (Mimesis Ser.).Tr. of Stereophonic Autobiography. Concept & Model of Autobiographies Written by Couples using the example of María Teresa león & Rafael Alberti. (GER.). VII, 213p. pap. *(978-3-484-55048-3(1))* Verlag Max Niemeyer.

ALBERTUS MAGNUS, SAINT, BISHOP OF RATISBONE, 1193-1280

Cunningham, Stanley B. Reclaiming Moral Agency: The Moral Philosophy of Albert the Great. 2008. 312p. 79.95 *(978-0-8132-1540-2(4))* Catholic Univ. of America Pr.

Hendrix, Scott E. How Albert the Great's Speculum Astronomiae Was Interpreted & Used by Four Centuries of Readers: A Study in Late Medieval Medicine, Astronomy, & Astrology. 2010. iii, 326p. 119.95 *(978-0-7734-3635-0(9))* Mellen, Edwin Pr., The.

Sighart, Joachim. Albert the Great: His Life & Scholastic Labours. Dixon, T. A., tr. from FRE. reprint ed. lib. bdg. 48.00 *(978-0-697-00016-3(8))* Irvington Pubs.

Zambelli, P. The Speculum Astronomiae & its Enigma: Astrology, Theology & Science in Albertus Magnus & his Contemporaries. 2010. (Boston Studies in the Philosophy of Science Ser.). 384p. pap. 254.00 *(978-90-481-4098-5(6)*, 9048140986) Springer.

ALBIGENSES

see also Bogomiles; Waldenses

Bruschi, Caterina. The Wandering Heretics of Languedoc. 2011. (Cambridge Studies in Medieval Life & Thought: Fourth Ser.). (ENG.). 232p. pap. 39.99 *(978-0-521-18227-0(1))* Cambridge Univ. Pr.

Emery, Richard Wilder. Heresy & Inquisition in Narbonne. 2011. 186p. 42.95 ***(978-1-258-02492-5(6))*** Literary Licensing, LLC.

Marvin, Laurence W. The Occitan War: A Military & Political History of the Albigensian Crusade, 1209-1218. (ENG., Illus.). 356p. 2009. pap. 50.00 *(978-0-521-12365-5(8))* 2008. 122.00 *(978-0-521-87240-9(5))* Cambridge Univ. Pr.

Mattingly, Alan. The Cathar Way: A Walker's Guide to the Sentier Cathare, a Trail Linking Cathar Castles in Southern France. 2010. (Illus.). 192p. pap. 19.95 *(978-1-85284-486-8(8))* Cicerone Pr. GBR. Dist: Midpoint Trade Bks., Inc.

O'Shea, Stephen. The Perfect Heresy: The Revolutionary Life & Death of the Medieval Cathars, 1 vol. (ENG., Illus.). 272p. pap. 22.95 *(978-1-55054-873-0(5))* D&M Pubs. Inc. CAN. Dist: Perseus-PGW.

Pegg, Mark Gregory. A Most Holy War: The Albigensian Crusade & the Battle for Christendom. 2009. (Pivotal Moments in World History Ser.). (ENG., Illus.). 288p. pap. 15.95 *(978-0-19-539310-1(4))* Oxford Univ. Pr., Inc.

Rahn, Otto. Crusade Against the Grail: The Struggle Between the Cathars, the Templars, & the Church of Rome. Jones, Christopher, tr. from GER. annot. ed. 2006. (ENG., Illus.). 1p. per. 16.95 *(978-1-59477-135-4(9))* Inner Traditions International, Ltd.

Smith, Damian J. Crusade, Heresy & Inquisition in the Lands of the Crown of Aragon, C. 1167-1276. 2010. (Illus.). 252p. *(978-90-04-18289-9(6))* BRILL.

Wakefield, Walter L. Heresy, Crusade & Inquisition in Southern France, 1100-1250. 2008. 296p. pap. 29.00 *(978-1-59740-490-7(X))* ACLS Humanities E-Book.

Warner, H. J. The Albigensian Heresy. 2007. 96p. per. 12.95 *(978-1-58509-293-2(2))* Book Tree, The.

ALBINOS AND ALBINISM

Baker, Charlotte. Enduring Negativity: Representations of Albinism in the Novels of Didier Destremau, Patrick Grainville & Williams Sassine. 2011. (Illus.). 226p. pap. 55.95 *(978-3-0343-0179-4(0))* Lang, Peter AG GBR. Dist: Lang, Peter.

National Organization for Albinism and Hypopigmentation (U.S.) Staff, contrib. by. Raising a Child with Albinism: A Guide to the Early Years. 2008. (Illus.). 199p. *(978-0-615-20927-2(0))* National Organization for Albinism & Hypopigmentation (NOAH).

ALBION (ILL.)

Flower, Richard. Flower's Letters from Lexington (June 25, 1819) & the Illinois (August 16, 1819) 2007. (Travel in America Ser.). (ENG.). 32p. per. 24.95 *(978-1-4290-0059-8(7))* Applewood Bks.

Sebring, C. & Flower, Richard. Flower's Letters from the Illinois, January 18, 1820 - May 7 1821. 2007. (Travel in America Ser.). (ENG.). 120p. per. 24.95 *(978-1-4290-0077-2(5))* Applewood Bks.

ALBRECHT, ARCHDUKE OF AUSTRIA, GOVERNOR OF THE NETHERLANDS, 1559-1621

Duerloo, Luc. Dynasty & Piety: Archduke Albert (1598-1621) & Habsburg Political Culture in an Age of Religious Wars. 2012. (Illus.). 589p. 144.95 ***(978-0-7546-6904-3(1))*** Ashgate Publishing Co.

ALBRIGHT, MADELEINE KORBEL, 1937-

Albright, Madeleine. Prague Winter: A Personal Story of Remembrance & War, 1937-1948. 2012. (ENG., Illus.). 468p. 29.99 ***(978-0-06-203031-3(0))***; 752p. pap. 29.99 ***(978-0-06-212842-3(6)***, HarperLuxe) HarperCollins Pubs.

Albright, Madeleine. Read My Pins: Stories from a Diplomat's Jewel Box. 2009. (ENG., Illus.). 176p. 40.00 *(978-0-06-089918-9(2))* HarperCollins Pubs.

ALBUMS, POSTAGE-STAMP

see Postage Stamps—Albums

ALBUQUERQUE, ALFONSO DE, 1453-1515

Albuquerque, Afonso de. The Commentaries of the Great Afonso Dalboquerque, Second Viceroy of India, Vol. 2. Birch, Walter de Gray, tr. 2010. (Cambridge Library Collection - Travel & Exploration Ser.). (ENG., Illus.). 400p. pap. 31.99 *(978-1-108-01145-7(4))* Cambridge Univ. Pr.

—The Commentaries of the Great Afonso Dalboquerque, Second Viceroy of India. 2010. 204p. pap. 15.78 *(978-1-154-06622-7(3))* General Bks. LLC.

—The Commentaries of the Great Afonso Dalboquerque, Second Viceroy of India, 1774. Birch, Walter de Gray, tr. 2010. (Cambridge Library Collection - Travel & Exploration Ser.). (ENG., Vol. 1. Illus.). 340p. pap. 28.99 *(978-1-108-01144-0(6))* Vol. 3. 388p. pap. 31.99 *(978-1-108-01154-9(3))* Vol. 4. 376p. pap. 29.99 *(978-1-108-01163-1(2))* Cambridge Univ. Pr.

ALBUQUERQUE (N.M.)

Albuquerque Impressions. 2007. (Impressions (Farcountry Press) Ser.). 80p. pap. 9.95 *(978-1-56037-467-1(5))* Farcountry Pr.

Albuquerque, New Mexico, USA, Resources & Reseach Collections: A guide to selected published materials & archival Resources. 2006. spiral bd. 15.00 *(978-0-9790619-0-5(3))* Legacy Media, Inc.

Atencio, Tomas & Aubele, Jayne, contrib. by. Albuquerque: Portrait of a Western City. 2006. (Illus.). 267p. per. *(978-1-57416-087-1(7))* Clear Light Pubs.

Beman, Joseph E. Water-Level Data for the Albuquerque Basin & Adjacent Areas, Central New Mexico, Period of Record Through September 30, 2008. 2010. (Illus.). iii, 37p. ***(978-1-4113-2923-2(6))*** United States Geological Survey.

Carpio, Myla Vicenti & Hafen, P. Jane. Indigenous Albuquerque. 2011. (Plains Histories Ser.). (ENG., Illus.). 208p. (C). 39.95 *(978-0-89672-678-9(9))* Texas Tech Univ. Pr.

Casselle, Tania. Insiders' Guide to Albuquerque. 2010. (Insiders' Guide Ser.). (ENG.). 256p. pap. 16.95 *(978-0-7627-5341-3(2)*, Insiders' Guide) Globe Pequot Pr., The.

Fodor's Travel Publications, Inc. Staff. Santa Fe, Taos & Albuquerque. 3rd ed. 2011. (Fodor's Gold Guides). (ENG., Illus.). 272p. pap. 17.99 *(978-0-307-48055-2(0)*, Fodor's) Fodor's Travel Pubns.

Garcia, Peter J. Decolonizing Enchantment: Lyricism, Ritual & Echoes of Nuevo Mexicano Popular Music. 2012. (ENG., Illus.). 368p. 50.00 *(978-0-8263-4371-0(6))* Univ. of New Mexico Pr.

Grubbs, Bruce. Best Easy Day Hikes Albuquerque. 2009. (Best Easy Day Hikes Ser.). (ENG., Illus.). 96p. pap. 9.95 *(978-0-7627-5149-5(5)*, Falcon Guides) Globe Pequot Pr., The.

Herron, Gary. Baseball in Albuquerque. 2011. (Images of Baseball Ser.). (Illus.). 128p. pap. 21.99 *(978-0-7385-7964-1(5))* Arcadia Publishing.

King, Lesley S. Frommer's Santa Fe, Taos & Albuquerque. 13th ed. 2010. (Frommer's Complete Guides: 856). (ENG., Illus.). 320p. pap. 17.99 *(978-0-470-64376-1(5)*, Frommers) Wiley, John & Sons, Inc.

Lazell, Carleen & Payne, Melissa. Historic Albuquerque: An Illustrated History. 2007. (Illus.). 112p. *(978-1-893619-75-3(3))* Historical Publishing Network.

Martin, Mary & Wolfgang-Price, Nathaniel. Greetings from Albuquerque. 2007. (Illus.). 128p. pap. 24.95 *(978-0-7643-2383-6(0))* Schiffer Publishing, Ltd.

Morley, Judy Mattivi. Historic Preservation & the Imagined West. 2010. 216p. pap. 19.95 *(978-0-7006-1760-9(4))* Univ. of Kansas Pubns.

O'Neill, Zora. Santa Fe, Taos & Albuquerque. 2nd ed. 2009. (Moon Handbooks). (ENG.). 248p. pap. 17.95 *(978-1-59880-158-3(9))* Avalon Travel Publishing.

Palmer, Mo. Albuquerque Then & Now. 2006. (Then & Now Thunder Bay Ser.). (ENG., Illus.). 144p. 19.95 *(978-1-59223-655-8(3)*, Thunder Bay Pr.) Advantage Pubs. Group.

Randall, Margaret. My Town: A Memoir of Albuquerque, New Mexico in Poems, Prose & Photographs. 2010. *(978-1-60940-004-0(6))*; *(978-1-60940-003-3(8))*; (ENG.). 128p. pap. 16.00 *(978-0-916727-73-4(4))* Wings Pr.

Romero, Arthur & Romero, Cynthia. Albuquerque Trivia. 2007. pap. 14.95 *(978-0-7414-3761-7(9))* Infinity Publishing.

Sánchez, Joseph P. Between Two Rivers: The Atrisco Land Grant in Albuquerque History, 1692-1968. 2008. (ENG., Illus.). 256p. (C). 34.95 *(978-0-8061-3902-9(1))* Univ. of Oklahoma Pr.

Sanchez, Joseph P. & Miller, Larry D. Martineztown, 1823-1950: Hispanics, Italians, Jesuits & Land Investors in New Town Albuquerque. 2008. (Illus.). 228p. 32.95 *(978-1-890689-53-7(X))*; pap. 17.95 *(978-1-890689-44-5(0))* LPD Pr. (Rio Grande Bks.).

Sandweiss, Naomi. Jewish Albuquerque: 1860-1960. 2011. (Images of America Ser.). (Illus.). 128p. pap. 21.99 *(978-0-7385-7977-1(7))* Arcadia Publishing.

Schmader, Matt. Albuquerque's Parks & Open Space. 2011. (Images of America Ser.). (Illus.). 128p. pap. 21.99 ***(978-0-7385-8470-6(3))*** Arcadia Publishing.

Secord, Paul R. Albuquerque Deco & Pueblo. 2012. (Images of America Ser.). (ENG., Illus.). 128p. pap. 21.99 ***(978-0-7385-9526-9(8))*** Arcadia Publishing.

Thornton, Elizabeth, et al. The Best of Everything in Albuquerque. Date not set. (Illus.). 190p. pap. 12.00 *(978-1-878776-01-3(0))* Adobe Publishing Co.

ALCAEUS

Marzullo, Benedetto. Il miraggio di Alceo: Fr. 140 V. 2008. (Beiträge Zur Altertumskunde Ser.). (ITA., Illus.). XXXIX, 173p. 91.00 *(978-3-11-020141-3(0))* De Gruyter, Walter Inc.

ALCALA GALIANO, JUAN VALERA Y, 1824-1905

see Valera, Juan, 1824-1905

ALCALOIDS

see Alkaloids

ALCATRAZ (PENITENTIARY)

see United States Penitentiary, Alcatraz Island, California

ALCATRAZ ISLAND (CALIF.)

see also United States Penitentiary, Alcatraz Island, California

Champion, Jerry Lewis. The Fading Voices of Alcatraz. 2011. 192p. 24.60 *(978-1-4567-1487-1(2))*; pap. 15.00 *(978-1-4567-1488-8(0))* AuthorHouse.

Fortunate Eagle, Adam & Findley, Tim. Heart of the Rock: The Indian Invasion of Alcatraz. 2008. (ENG., Illus.). 232p. pap. 19.95 *(978-0-8061-3989-0(7))* Univ. of Oklahoma Pr.

Johnson, Troy R. The American Indian Occupation of Alcatraz Island: Red Power & Self-Determination. 2008. (ENG., Illus.). 312p. pap. 18.95 *(978-0-8032-1779-9(X))* Univ. of Nebraska Pr.

MacDonald, Donald & Nadel, Ira. Alcatraz: History & Design of a Landmark. 2012. (ENG., Illus.). 144p. 16.95 ***(978-1-4521-0153-8(1))*** Chronicle Bks. LLC.

Van Raaphorst, Donna L. Alcatraz - the History of an Island Prison: From the Development to an American Myth. 2011. (Illus.). 560p. 159.95 ***(978-0-7734-1596-6(3))*** Mellen, Edwin Pr., The.

Vercillo, Kathryn. Ghosts of Alcatraz. 2008. (Illus.). 160p. pap. 14.99 *(978-0-7643-2884-8(0))* Schiffer Publishing, Ltd.

Ward, David. Alcatraz: The Gangster Years. 2010. (ENG., Illus.). 584p. pap. 26.95 *(978-0-520-26596-7(3))* Univ. of California Pr.

Wellman, Gregory L. Alcatraz Island. 2008. (Postcards of America Ser.). (ENG., Illus.). 15p. pap. 7.99 *(978-0-7385-2528-0(6))* Arcadia Publishing.

—A History of Alcatraz Island: 1853-2008. 2008. (Images of America Ser.). (ENG., Illus.). 128p. pap. 21.99 *(978-0-7385-5815-8(X))* Arcadia Publishing.

ALCHEMY

see also Medicine, Magic, Mystic, and Spagiric

Abt, Theodor. Corpus Alchemicum Arabicum Vol. 1B (CALA1 B) Book of the Explanation of the Symbols. 2010. (Corpus Alchemicum Arabicum (CALA) Ser.). 400p. 98.00 *(978-3-9522608-8-3(6))* Daimon Verlag CHE. Dist: AtlasBooks Distribution.

Akins, Steven L. The Lebor Feasa Runda: A Druidic Grammar of Celtic Lore & Magic. 2008. 180p. 26.95 *(978-1-4401-0282-0(1))*; pap. 16.95 *(978-1-4401-0280-6(5))* iUniverse, Inc.

al-Sadiq, Ja'far. Spiritual Gems: The Mystical Qur'an Commentary Ascribed by the Sufis to Imam Ja'far Al-Sadiq (D. 148/765) Mayer, Farhana, tr. 2011. (Fons Vitae Qur'anic Commentary Ser.). (ENG & ARA.). 189p. pap. 24.95 *(978-1-891785-30-6(3))* Fons Vitae of Kentucky, Inc.

Alchemical Society. Journal, Vols. 1-3 In 1. reprint ed. 29.50 *(978-0-404-18445-2(6))* AMS Pr., Inc.

Ashe (Editor), Steven. The Picatrix - the Goal of the Wise. 2007. 435p. 52.50 *(978-1-84753-738-6(3))* Lulu Enterprises Inc.

Bartlett, Robert. Real Alchemy: A Primer of Practical Alchemy. 2006. (Illus.). 220p. pap. 24.95 *(978-0-9788471-0-4(5))* Quinquangle Pr.

Bartlett, Robert Allen. Real Alchemy: A Primer of Practical Alchemy. 3rd ed. 2009. (ENG., Illus.). 1p. pap. 18.95 *(978-0-89254-150-8(4))* Nicolas-Hays, Inc.

—The Way of the Crucible. 2009. Orig. Title: 9780615206820. (ENG.). 1p. pap. 22.95 *(978-0-89254-154-6(7))* Nicolas-Hays, Inc.

Beckley, Tim. Count Saint Germain - The Man Who Lives Forever. 132p. pap. 21.95 *(978-1-892062-20-8(8))* Inner Light - Global Communications.

Benjamine, Elbert & Zain, C. C. Evolution of Life V1, Serial No 125-132. 2011. 270p. 47.95 ***(978-1-258-00634-1(0))*** Literary Licensing, LLC.

—Evolution of Life V2, Serial No 133-140. 2011. 272p. 47.95 ***(978-1-258-00695-2(2))*** Literary Licensing, LLC.

Blackhirst, R. Primordial Alchemy & Modern Religion: Essays on Traditional Cosmology. 2008. pap. *(978-1-59731-083-3(2))* Perennis, Sophia.

Bolton, H. C. Notes on the Early Literature of Chemistry. 2011. 18p. pap. 11.99 ***(978-1-4181-8964-8(2))*** MPublishing.

Bowen-Jones, Ann & Lee, Philippa. Kitchen Alchemy: Transform Yourself Through Food. 2010. (ENG.). 160p. pap. 21.95 *(978-0-9818708-6-1(4))* Spirituality & Health Pub.

Case, Paul Foster. Esoteric Keys of Alchemy. 2008. 156p. *(978-0-9783883-5-5(6))* 2007. pap. *(978-0-9780535-1-2(6))* Ishtar Publishing.

Cavalli, Thom F. Embodying Osiris: The Secrets of Alchemical Transformation. 2010. (ENG., Illus.). 256p. pap. 15.95 *(978-0-8356-0880-0(8)*, Quest Bks.) Theosophical Publishing Hse.

Chia, Mantak. Cosmic Fusion: The Inner Alchemy of the Eight Forces. 2007. (ENG., Illus.). 1p. pap. 18.95 *(978-1-59477-106-4(5)*, Destiny Bks.) Inner Traditions International, Ltd.

Chikashige, Masumi. Alchemy & Other Chemical Achievements of the Ancient Orient. reprint ed. 27.50 *(978-0-404-18456-8(1))* AMS Pr., Inc.

Clucas, Stephen, ed. John Dee: Interdisciplinary Studies in English Renaissance Thought: Interdisciplinary Studies in English Renaissance Thought. 2010. (International Archives of the History of Ideas / archives internationales d'histoire des Idées Ser.). xvii, 366p. pap. 289.00 *(978-90-481-7084-5(2)*, 9048170842) Springer.

Clymer, R. Swinburne. The Science of Spiritual Alchemy. 2011. 240p. 46.95 ***(978-1-258-00949-6(8))*** Literary Licensing, LLC.

Cockren, A. Alchemy Rediscovered & Restored. 2007. (ENG.). 156p. 36.95 *(978-0-548-28056-0(8))* Kessinger Publishing, LLC.

—The Comte de St Germain. 2006. pap. 9.95 *(978-1-4286-7950-4(2))* Kessinger Publishing, LLC.

—Early English Alchemists. 2006. pap. 12.95 *(978-1-4286-7960-3(X))* Kessinger Publishing, LLC.

—Early European Alchemists. 2006. pap. 9.95 *(978-1-4286-7948-1(0))* Kessinger Publishing, LLC.

—Paracelsus a Famous Alchemist. 2006. pap. 9.95 *(978-1-4286-7949-8(9))* Kessinger Publishing, LLC.

Cockren, Archibald. Alchemy Rediscovered & Restored. 2008. 132p. 21.99 *(978-0-554-38910-3(X))* 2008. 132p. 24.99 *(978-0-554-29607-4(1))* 2007. 120p. pap. 18.99 *(978-1-4346-8002-0(9))* 2007. (ENG.). 130p. pap. 19.99 *(978-1-4346-8003-7(7))* BiblioBazaar.

—Alchemy Rediscovered & Restored. 2007. 160p. per. 13.70 *(978-1-60206-104-0(1))* Cosimo, Inc.

Cox, Robert E. The Elixir of Immortality. 2010. (ENG.). 1p. pap. 16.95 *(978-1-59477-303-7(3))* Inner Traditions International, Ltd.

De la Selva, Teresa. De la Alquimia a la Quimica. (Ciencia para Todos Ser.). (SPA.). pap. 6.99 *(978-968-16-3740-8(2))* Fondo de Cultura Economica USA.

DeGivry, Emile Grillot. The Laboratory of the Alchemists & of the Puffers. 2006. pap. 12.95 *(978-1-4286-8451-5(4))* Kessinger Publishing, LLC.

Doreal, M. The Emerald Tablets of Thoth-the-Atlantean. 2006. 204p. 30.00 *(978-1-59858-242-0(9))* Dog Ear Publishing, LLC.

Duffy, Maureen. Alchemy. 2007. (ENG.). 380p. pap. 13.95 *(978-0-00-714966-7(2))* HarperCollins Pubs. Ltd. GBR. Dist: Independent Pubs. Group.

Eamon, William. The Professor of Secrets: Mystery, Medicine, & Alchemy in Renaissance Italy. 2010. (Illus.). 368p. 26.00 *(978-1-4262-0650-4(X)*, National Geographic) National Geographic Society.

Ellwood, Taylor. Inner Alchemy Energy Work & the Magic. 2007. 252p. per. *(978-1-905713-06-6(1))* Megalithica Bks.

Fanning, Philip Ashley. Isaac Newton & the Transmutation of Alchemy: An Alternative View of the Scientific Revolution. 2009. (ENG.). 272p. pap. 18.95 *(978-1-55643-772-4(2))* North Atlantic Bks.

Farrell, Joseph P. The Philosopher's Stone: Alchemy & the Secret Research for Exotic Matter. 2009. (ENG.). 360p. pap. 17.95 *(978-1-932595-40-6(6))* Feral Hse.

Figulus, Benedictus. Certain Verses of an Unknown Writer Concerning the Great Work Of. 2006. pap. 12.95 *(978-1-4286-8687-8(8))* Kessinger Publishing, LLC.

—Concerning the True Medicine of the Most Distinguished Man. 2006. pap. 9.95 *(978-1-4286-8685-4(1))* Kessinger Publishing, LLC.

—A Golden & Blessed Casket of Nature's Marvels. Waite, Arthur Edward, tr. from GER. reprint ed. 42.50 *(978-0-404-18469-8(3))* AMS Pr., Inc.

Goodrick-Clarke, Clare. Alchemical Medicine for the 21st Century. 2010. (ENG.). 1p. pap. 16.95 *(978-1-59477-319-8(X)*, Healing Arts Pr.) Inner Traditions International, Ltd.

Graubard, Mark. Astrology & Alchemy: Two Fossil Sciences. 2011. 394p. 53.95 ***(978-1-258-00162-9(4))*** Literary Licensing, LLC.

Graubard, Mark A. Astrology & Alchemy: Two Fossil Sciences. reprint ed. 40.00 *(978-0-404-18475-9(8))* AMS Pr., Inc.

Gray, Ronald D. Goethe, the Alchemist: A Study of Alchemical Symbolism in Goethe's Literary & Scientific Works. reprint ed. 34.00 *(978-0-404-18476-6(6))* AMS Pr., Inc.

Grund, P. J. Misticall Wordes & Names Infinite. 2011. *(978-0-86698-415-7(1))* ACMRS.

Guiley, Rosemary Ellen. The Encyclopedia of Magic & Alchemy. 2006. (Illus.). 384p. 85.00 *(978-0-8160-6048-1(7))* Facts On File, Inc.

—The Encyclopedia of Magic & Alchemy. 2006. (Illus.). 370p. 37.25 *(978-1-4177-7332-9(4)*, Turtleback) Turtleback Bks.

Hall, Manly P. Orders of the Great Work - Alchemy. (Adepts Ser.). 10.95 *(978-0-89314-534-7(3))* Philosophical Research Society, Inc.

Hamilton-Jones, J. W. Bacstrom's Alchemical Anthology. 2007. (ENG.). 156p. 36.95 *(978-0-548-28057-7(6))* Kessinger Publishing, LLC.

Harding, M. Esther. A Short Review of Dr Jung's Article Redemption Ideas in Alchemy. 2011. 28p. 35.95 ***(978-1-258-00153-7(5))*** Literary Licensing, LLC.

Harkness, Deborah. John Dee's Conversations with Angels: Cabala, Alchemy, & the End of Nature. 2006. (ENG., Illus.). 268p. pap. 53.00 *(978-0-521-02748-9(9))* Cambridge Univ. Pr.

Hartmann, Franz. Paracelsus: Life & Prophecies. 2007. (ENG.). 300p. 43.95 *(978-0-548-28227-4(7))* Kessinger Publishing, LLC.

Hauck, Dennis William. The Complete Idiot's Guide to Alchemy. 2008. (Complete Idiot's Guide Ser.). (ENG., Illus.). 336p. (gr. 12-18). 16.95 *(978-1-59257-735-4(0)*, Alpha Bks.) Penguin Group (USA) Inc.

Hayhurst, Karen J. The Aur: Alchemy of Spirit & Matter. Lessey, Tasha, ed. 2011. 80p. pap. ***(978-1-77067-311-3(3))*** FriesenPress.

Helvetius, John Frederick. The Golden Calf, Which the World Adores, & Desires. 2007. 80p. per. *(978-1-4065-4451-0(5))* Dodo Pr.

—The Golden Calf Which the World Adores & Desires. 2007. 52p. per. *(978-1-4068-1725-6(2))* Echo Library.

Hillman, James. Alchemical Psychology: Uniform Edition, Vol. 5. 2010. (ENG.). 200p. 40.00 *(978-0-88214-583-9(5))* Spring Pubns., Inc.

Ho, Peng Yoke. Explorations in Daoism. 2007. (Needham Research Institute Ser.). (Illus.). XXVIII, 228p. 180.00 *(978-0-415-40460-0(6))* Routledge.

Hogan, Timothy. The Alchemical Keys to Masonic Ritual. 2007. 53p. pap. 14.97 *(978-1-4357-0440-4(1))* Lulu Enterprises Inc.

Hopkins, Arthur John. Alchemy Child of Greek Philosophy. 2007. (ENG.). 292p. 43.95 *(978-0-548-13547-1(9))* 2006. pap. 28.95 *(978-1-4286-4674-2(4))* Kessinger Publishing, LLC.

Hughes, Jonathan. Rise of Alchemy in Fourteenth-Century England: The Plantagenet Kings & the Search for the Philosopher's Stone. 2012. (ENG., Illus.). 296p. pap. 34.95 *(978-1-4411-8183-1(0))* Continuum International Publishing Group, Ltd. GBR. Dist: National Bk. Network.

Ibn Zakariya, Muhammad. Practical Chemistry in the Twelfth Century. Steele, Robert R., ed. Gerard Of Cremona, tr. reprint ed. 37.50 *(978-0-404-18444-5(8))* AMS Pr., Inc.

International Conference on the History of Alchemy and Chymistry & Principe, Lawrence. Chymists & Chymistry: Studies in the History of Alchemy & Early Modern Chemistry. 2007. (Illus.). 287p. 45.00 *(978-0-88135-396-9(5)*, Science History Pubns./USA) Watson Publishing International, LLC.

Jabir, Ibn H. The Works of Geber. reprint ed. 32.50 *(978-0-404-18479-7(0))* AMS Pr., Inc.

Janacek, Bruce. Alchemical Belief: Occultism in the Religious Culture of Early Modern England. 2011. (Magic in History Ser.). (ENG.). 240p. 74.95 ***(978-0-271-05013-3(6))*** Pennsylvania State Univ. Pr.

Junius, Manfred M. Spagyrics: The Alchemical Preparation of Medicinal Essences, Tinctures, & Elixirs. 3rd ed. 2007. (ENG., Illus.). 1p. per. 18.95 *(978-1-59477-179-8(0)*, Healing Arts Pr.) Inner Traditions International, Ltd.

Kahn, Didier. Alchimie et Paracelsisme en France à la Fin de la Renaissance (1567-1625) 2007. (Cahiers d'humanisme et Renaissance Ser.). (FRE.). 808p. (C). pap. 130.00 *(978-2-600-00688-0(5))* Droz, Librairie CHE. Dist: Brown, David Bk. Co., The.

Kohn, Livia & Wang, Robin R., eds. Internal Alchemy: Self, Society, & the Quest for Immortality. 2009. (Illus.). 244p. pap. 29.95 *(978-1-931483-11-7(6))* Three Pines Pr.

Levenda, Peter & Levenda. Stairway to Heaven: Chinese Alchemists, Jewish Kabbalists, & the Art of Spiritual Transformation. 2008. (ENG., Illus.). 272p. pap. 26.95 *(978-0-8264-2850-9(9))* Continuum International Publishing Group, Ltd. GBR. Dist: National Bk. Network.

Linden, Stanton J. Darke Hierogliphicks: Alchemy in English Literature from Chaucer to the Restoration. 2008. (Studies in the English Renaissance Ser.). (ENG., Illus.). 384p. pap. 30.00 *(978-0-8131-9212-3(9))* Univ. Pr. of Kentucky.

Long, Kathleen Perry, ed. Gender & Scientific Discourse in Early Modern Culture. 2010. (Literary & Scientific Cultures of Early Modernity Ser.). (Illus.). 330p. 119.95 *(978-0-7546-6971-5(8))* Ashgate Publishing Co.

MacCoun, Catherine. On Becoming an Alchemist: A Guide for the Modern Magician. 2008. (ENG., Illus.). 272p. pap. 18.95 *(978-1-59030-687-1(2)*, Trumpeter) Shambhala Pubns., Inc.

Marlan, Stanton. The Black Sun: The Alchemy & Art of Darkness. 2008. (Carolyn & Ernest Fay Series in Analytical Psychology Ser.). (ENG.). 288p. pap. 19.95 *(978-1-60344-078-3(X))* Texas A&M Univ. Pr.

Maxwell-Stuart, P. G. Chemical Choir: A History of Alchemy. 2012. (ENG., Illus.). 216p. pap. 27.95 ***(978-1-4411-3297-0(X))*** Continuum International Publishing Group, Ltd. GBR. Dist: National Bk. Network.

Mercer, John E. Alchemy, Its Science & Romance. (Illus.). reprint ed. 27.50 *(978-0-404-18481-0(2))* AMS Pr., Inc.

Moran, Bruce T. Andreas Libavius & the Transformation of Alchemy: Separating Chemical Cultures with Polemical Fire. 2007. (Illus.). 351p. 49.95 *(978-0-88135-395-2(7))* Watson Publishing International, LLC.

—Distilling Knowledge: Alchemy, Chemistry, & the Scientific Revolution. 2006. (New Histories of Science, Technology, & Medicine Ser.). (Illus.). 224p. per. 21.00 *(978-0-674-02249-2(1))* Harvard Univ. Pr.

Morrisson, Mark S. Modern Alchemy: Occultism & the Emergence of Atomic Theory. 2007. (ENG.). 272p. 34.99 *(978-0-19-530696-5(1))* Oxford Univ. Pr., Inc.

Muir, M. M. Pattison. The Alchemical Notion of the Unity & Simplicity of Nature - 2006. pap. 12.95 *(978-1-4304-1437-7(5))* Kessinger Publishing, LLC.

—The Story of Alchemy & the Beginnings of Chemistry. 2008. (Illus.). 172p. 25.99 *(978-0-554-24893-6(X))* 2008. (Illus.). 172p. 22.99 *(978-0-554-34196-5(4))* 2007. 152p. pap. 19.99 *(978-1-4264-7610-5(8))* 2007. (ENG.). 168p. pap. 21.99 *(978-1-4264-7661-7(2))* BiblioBazaar.

—The Story of Alchemy & the Beginnings of Chemistry. 2008. (Illus.). 156p. pap. *(978-1-4099-0388-8(5))* Dodo Pr.

Muir, Matthew M. The Story of Alchemy & the Beginnings of Chemistry. reprint ed. 27.50 *(978-0-404-18482-7(0))* AMS Pr., Inc.

Needham, Tessa. Provocative & Transformative Performance. 2009. 348p. pap. *(978-3-639-14527-4(5))* VDM Verlag Dr. Mueller e.K.

Nummedal, Tara. Alchemy & Authority in the Holy Roman Empire. 2007. (ENG., Illus.). 256p. 40.00 *(978-0-226-60856-3(5))* Univ. of Chicago Pr.

Paracelsus, Philippus Aureolus. The Hermetic & Alchemical Writings of Paracelsus. 2007. 116p. per. 29.99 *(978-1-59547-816-0(7))* NuVision Pubns., LLC.

—Werke, 5 vols., Set. (GER.). reprint ed. 369.60 *(978-3-7965-0471-6(X))* Adler's Foreign Bks., Inc.

Paracelsus, Philippus Aureolus & Waite, Arthur Edward. The Hermetic & Alchemical Writings of Aureolus Philippus Theophrastus Bombast, of Hohenheim, Called Paracelsus the Great, 2 vols. 2008. 800p. 85.00 *(978-1-57898-677-4(X))* Martino Publishing.

Principe, Lawrence M. The Secrets of Alchemy. 2012. (Synthesis Ser.). (Illus.). 288p. 25.00 ***(978-0-226-68295-2(1))*** Univ. of Chicago Pr.

Raleigh, A. S. Woman & SuperWoman. 2006. pap. 20.95 *(978-1-4286-4448-9(2))* Kessinger Publishing, LLC.

Read, John. The Alchemist in Life, Literature, & Art. reprint ed. 37.50 *(978-0-404-18486-5(3))* AMS Pr., Inc.

—Prelude to Chemistry: An Outline of Alchemy, Its Literature & Relationships. (Illus.). reprint ed. 48.00 *(978-0-404-18488-9(X))* AMS Pr., Inc.

Redgrove. Bygone Beliefs, Being a Series of Excursions in the Byways of Thought. 2010. 102p. pap. 20.00 *(978-1-151-94133-6(6))* General Bks. LLC.

Redgrove, H. Stanley. Alchemy: Ancient & Modern. 2009. (Illus.). 154p. pap. *(978-1-4099-8248-7(3))* Dodo Pr.

—Alchemy Ancient & Modern. 2010. 80p. pap. 20.00 *(978-1-153-35159-1(5))* General Bks. LLC.

—Alchemy Ancient & Modern. 2007. (ENG.). 196p. 37.95 *(978-0-548-28054-6(1))* Kessinger Publishing, LLC.

—Alchemy: Ancient & Modern. 2008. 132p. 37.96 *(978-1-4092-3119-6(4))* Lulu Enterprises Inc.

—Bygone Beliefs. 2009. (Illus.). 184p. pap. *(978-1-4099-8249-4(1))* Dodo Pr.

—Bygone Beliefs. 2007. (ENG.). 116p. per. *(978-1-4068-3769-8(5))* Echo Library.

—Bygone Beliefs: Being a series of excursions in the byways of Thought. 180p. 2008. 22.99 *(978-0-554-30739-8(1))* 2006. (ENG.). pap. 19.99 *(978-1-4264-0036-0(5))* BiblioBazaar.

—Bygone Beliefs: Being a Series of Excursions in the Byways of Thought. l.t. ed. 2008. 180p. 25.99 *(978-0-554-21436-8(9))* 2006. (ENG.). 176p. pap. 21.99 *(978-1-4264-0165-7(5))* BiblioBazaar.

—Bygone Beliefs, Being a Series of Excursions in the by Ways of Thought. 2009. 286p. 34.99 *(978-1-116-68072-0(6))*; pap. 28.75 *(978-1-116-68074-4(2))*; pap. 27.75 *(978-1-116-68075-1(0))* BiblioBazaar.

—Bygone Beliefs, Being A Series of Excursions in the by Ways of Thought. 2009. (ENG.). 284p. pap. 21.99 *(978-1-116-68077-5(7)*, BiblioLife) BiblioBazaar.

—Bygone Beliefs; Being a Series of Excursions in the Byways of Thought. 2010. 100p. pap. 20.00 *(978-1-153-59355-7(6))* General Bks. LLC.

Redgrove, H. Stanley. Bygone Beliefs Being a Series of Excursions in the Byways of Thought. 2010. 284p. 35.16 ***(978-1-169-31169-5(5))***; pap. 23.16 ***(978-1-162-57163-8(2))***; 43.95 *(978-1-161-35831-5(5))* Kessinger Publishing, LLC.

Redgrove, H Stanley & Redgrove, H. Stanley. Alchemy Ancient & Modern. 2010. 206p. pap. 24.75 *(978-1-149-26610-6(4))* BiblioBazaar.

Redgrove, H. Stanley 1887-1943. Bygone Beliefs: Being a series of excursions in the byways of Thought. 2010. 296p. pap. 28.75 *(978-1-177-69235-9(X))* BiblioBazaar.

Redgrove, H. Stanley 1887-1943. Bygone Beliefs, Being a Series of Excursions in the Byways of Thought. 2011. 292p. pap. 28.75 ***(978-1-172-85157-7(3))*** BiblioBazaar.

Reeves, William J. Life Alchemy: A Father, A Son & A Transformation. 2009. (Illus.). 138p. pap. 13.95 *(978-1-4327-4097-9(0))* Outskirts Pr., Inc.

Robinet, Isabelle. The World Upside Down: Essays on Taoist Internal Alchemy. 2011. 138p. pap. 15.95 ***(978-0-9843082-6-2(1))*** Golden Elixir Pr.

Roob, Alexander. Alchemie und Mytsik. Sonderausgabe. 25th ed. 2009. (ENG., Illus.). 192p. 7.99 *(978-3-8365-1426-2(5))* TASCHEN DEU. Dist: Ingram Pub. Services.

—Alchemie und Mytsik. Sonderausgabe. 2006. 576p. (FRE.). pap. 12.99 *(978-3-8228-5037-4(3))*; (SPA.). pap. 12.99 *(978-3-8228-5036-7(5))*; (GER.). pap. 12.99 *(978-3-8228-5035-0(7))*; (POR.). pap. 12.99 *(978-3-8228-5216-3(3))*; (DUT.). pap. 12.99 *(978-3-8228-5135-7(3))* Taschen America, LLC.

—Alchemy & Mysticism: The Hermetic Museum. 20th anniv. ed. 2006. (25th Ser.). (ENG., Illus.). 575p. pap. 14.99 *(978-3-8228-5038-1(1))* TASCHEN DEU. Dist: Ingram Pub. Services.

—Alquimia y Mistica. 191p. pap. 13.95 *(978-3-8228-3861-7(6))* TASCHEN DEU. Dist: Libros in Spanish, LLC.

Roos, Anna Maria. The Salt of the Earth: Natural Philosophy, Medicine, & Chymistry in England, 1650-1750. 2007. (History of Science & Medicine Library). 336p. *(978-90-04-16176-4(7))* BRILL.

Ruck, Carl A. P. & Hoffman, Mark Alwin. The Effluents of Deity: Alchemy & Psychoactive Sacraments in Medieval & Renaissance Art. 2012. 372p. 50.00 ***(978-1-61163-041-1(X))*** Carolina Academic Pr.

Russell, Richard. The Alchemical Works of Geber. Date not set. 308p. 24.95 *(978-0-8488-2384-9(2))* Amereon LTD.

Sapere, Aude. Science of Alchymy Spiritual & Materia. 2006. pap. 15.95 *(978-1-4286-6266-7(9))* Kessinger Publishing, LLC.

Schleicher, Peter & Witzigmann, Eckart. The Alchemy of Food: The Secrets of the Great Art of Cooking & the Healing Effects of Fine Cuisine. 2010. (ENG., Illus.). 160p. 12.99 *(978-1-901268-53-9(5)*, 1901268535) Evans Mitchell Bks. GBR. Dist: MBI Distribution Services/Quayside Distribution.

Scruggs. There's a Secret in the Village. 2010. 148p. pap. *(978-3-639-27240-6(4))* VDM Verlag Dr. Mueller e.K.

Shojai, Pedram. Rise & Shine: Awaken Your Energy Body with Taoist Alchemy & Qi Gong. 2011. (ENG., Illus.). 275p. pap. 17.95 ***(978-1-934170-25-0(9))*** Process Packaging.

Silberer, Herbert. Problems of Mysticism & Its Symbolism. 2009. 208p. pap. 20.21 *(978-1-150-47343-2(6))* General Bks. LLC.

—Problems of Mysticism & Its Symbolism. Jelliffe, Smith Ely, tr. 2007. (ENG.). 464p. 52.95 *(978-0-548-11106-2(5))* Kessinger Publishing, LLC.

Smith, Patrick. General Index to the Alchemical Studies Series, Pt. 2, Nos. 14-25. Date not set. (Alchemical Studies Ser.: Vol. 26). pap. 9.95 *(978-1-55818-457-2(0)*, Alchemical Pr.) Holmes Publishing Group, LLC.

Stahl, John Roland, Sr. Hermetic Alchemy & Patterns of Illusion & Change. 2006. pap. 12.00 *(978-0-945303-16-9(5))* Evanescent Pr.

Stavish, Mark. The Path of Alchemy: Energetic Healing & the World of Natural Magic. 2006. (Pathways to Enlightenment Ser.). (ENG., Illus.). 264p. per. 16.95 *(978-0-7387-0903-1(4))* Llewellyn Pubns.

Stein, Walter Johannes. The Death of Merlin: Arthurian Myth & Alchemy, 1 vol. 2008. (ENG.). 240p. pap. *(978-0-86315-641-0(X))* Floris Bks.

Stratford, Jordan. A Dictionary of Western Alchemy. 2011. (ENG., Illus.). 160p. pap. 17.95 *(978-0-8356-0897-8(2)*, Quest Bks.) Theosophical Publishing Hse.

Szulakowska, Urszula. The Sacrificial Body & the Day of Doom: Alchemy & Apocalyptic Discourse in the Protestant Reformation. 2006. (Aries Book Ser.: Vol. 1). (Illus.). 180p. *(978-90-04-15025-6(0))* BRILL.

Taylor, Frank S. A Survey of Greek Alchemy. reprint ed. 31.50 *(978-0-404-18493-3(6))* AMS Pr., Inc.

The Turba Philosophorum. 2007. 76p. per. 9.99 *(978-1-59547-845-0(0))* NuVision Pubns., LLC.

Umail, Muhammad Bin. Corpus Alchemicum Arabicum Vol 1a: Book of the Explantion of the Symbols Kitab Hall Ar-Rumuz — Psychological Commentary by Marie-Louise Von Franz. Abt, Theodor, ed. 2007. (ENG.). 241p. spiral bd. 45.00 *(978-3-9522608-3-8(5))* Daimon Verlag CHE. Dist: AtlasBooks Distribution.

—Three Arabic Treatises on Alchemy. 2006. pap. 26.95 *(978-1-4286-4741-1(4))* Kessinger Publishing, LLC.

Waite, Arthur, tr. The Hermetic Museum, Restored & Enlarged: Most Faithfully Instructing all Disciples of the Sopho-Spagyric Art How that Greatest & Truest Medicine. 2007. 540p. per. 39.99 *(978-1-59547-799-6(3))* NuVision Pubns., LLC.

Waite, Arthur Edward. The Alchemical Writings of Edward Kelly. 2007. (ENG.). 216p. 39.95 *(978-0-548-28060-7(6))* Kessinger Publishing, LLC.

—The Hermetic Museum, Restored & Enlarged: Most Faithfully Instructing all Disciples of the Sopho-Spagyric Art How that Greatest & Truest Medicine. 2009. 538p. 44.99 *(978-1-59547-507-7(9))* NuVision Pubns., LLC.

—The Secret Tradition in Alchemy. 2007. 51.95 *(978-0-548-01063-1(3))* Kessinger Publishing, LLC.

—A Short Tract or Philosophical Summary by Nicholas Flamell - 2006. pap. 9.95 *(978-1-4304-3621-8(2))* Kessinger Publishing, LLC.

Walton, Michael Thomson. Genesis & the Chemical Philosophy: True Christian Science in the Sixteenth & Seventeenth Centuries. 2011. *(978-0-404-62345-6(X))* AMS Pr., Inc.

Watts, Elliott. Alchemy. 2009. 60p. pap. 7.40 *(978-0-557-16888-0(0))* Lulu Enterprises Inc.

Weeks, Andrew, ed. Paracelsus (Theophrastus Bombastus Von Hohenheim, 1493-1541) Essential Theoretical Writings. 2007. (Aries Book Ser.). (GER & ENG.). 975p. *(978-90-04-15756-9(5))* BRILL.

Wilson, William Jerome. The Origin & Development of Greco-Egyptian Alchemy. Rosen, George, ed. 2011. 42p. 35.95 ***(978-1-258-00915-1(3))*** Literary Licensing, LLC.

Woodward, Walter William. Prospero's America: John Winthrop, Jr., Alchemy, & the Creation of New England Culture, 1606-1676. 2010. (Published for the Omohundro Institute of Early American History & Culture, Williamsburg, Virginia Ser.). (ENG., Illus.). 336p. 45.00 *(978-0-8078-3301-8(0))* Univ. of North Carolina Pr.

Zehr, Leslie. The Alchemy of Dance: Sacred Dance as a Path to the Universal Dancer. 2008. 112p. pap. 12.95 *(978-0-595-53052-6(4))* iUniverse, Inc.

ALCHEMY—BIBLIOGRAPHY

Waite, Arthur. Alchemists Through the Ages. 2007. 320p. per. 21.95 *(978-1-60206-315-0(X))* Cosimo, Inc.

Waite, Arthur Edward. Gustenhover, Busardier, an Anonymous Adept, & Albert Belin - 2006. pap. 9.95 *(978-1-4304-3462-7(7))* Kessinger Publishing, LLC.

ALCIATI, ANDREA, 1492-1550

Alciato, Andrea. Held's translation of Alciato's Emblematum Liber (1566) Facsimile Edition Using Glasgow University Library SM 45. Held, Jeremias, ed. 2008. (Imaga Figurata Editions Ser.). (ENG & LAT.). 238p. (C). 109.00 *(978-2-503-52539-6(3))* Brepols Pubs. BEL. Dist: ISD.

Daly, Peter M. Andrea Alciato in England: Aspects of the Reception of Alciato's Emblems in England. 2012. ***(978-0-404-63722-4(1))*** AMS Pr., Inc.

Grimaldi, Alexander. Grimaldis Funeral Oration January 19 155. 2006. pap. 15.95 *(978-1-4286-5836-3(X))* Kessinger Publishing, LLC.

ALCIBIADES

Nepos. Nepos: 3 Lives (Alcibiades, Dion, Atticus) Roebuck, R., ed. 2010. (LAT.). 152p. pap. 17.95 *(978-0-86292-284-9(4))* Bristol Classical Pr. GBR. Dist: International Publishers Marketing.

Plato. Alcibiades I & II. 2009. 126p. 25.99 *(978-1-60512-502-2(4))*; pap. 12.99 *(978-1-60512-524-4(5))* Akasha Publishing, LLC. (Akasha Classics).

Rhodes, P. J. Alcibiades. 2011. (Illus.). 160p. 39.95 ***(978-1-84884-069-0(1))*** Pen & Sword Bks. Ltd. GBR. Dist: Casemate Pubs. & Bk. Distributors, LLC.

Vickers, Michael J. Sophocles & Alcibiades: Athenian Politics in Ancient Greek Literature. 2008. 224p. 47.50 *(978-0-8014-4732-7(1))* Cornell Univ. Pr.

ALCINDOR, LEW, 1947-

see Abdul-Jabbar, Kareem, 1947-

ALCOHOL

see also Alcoholic Beverages; Alcoholism; Distillation; Liquor Industry and Trade; Liquors; Temperance

also names of alcoholic liquors

Afionis, Stavros. Brazil's Ethanol Fuel Program. 2010. 64p. pap. *(978-3-8383-1442-6(5))* Lambert Academic Publishing.

Aldonza, Ken. Bioethanol from Waste Bananas. 2010. 52p. pap. *(978-3-8383-7958-6(6))* Lambert Academic Publishing.

Ali, Hayder Kh. Q. & Al-Azzawi, Zinah. Ethanol Production from Date Syrup. 2010. 88p. pap. *(978-3-8383-6027-0(3))* Lambert Academic Publishing.

Amoabeng, Benedict Kofi. Christianity & Alcohol (Wine) Is It A Sin to Drink Alcohol (Wine) As A Christian? 2010. 28p. pap. 13.99 *(978-1-4490-8621-3(7))* AuthorHouse.

Cardona, C. A., et al. Process Synthesis for Fuel Ethanol Production. 2009. (Biotechnology & Bioprocessing Ser.). (ENG., Illus.). 415p. 129.95 *(978-1-4398-1597-7(6)*, CRC Press) Taylor & Francis Group GBR. Dist: Taylor & Francis Group.

Cho, C. H. & Purohit, Vishnudutt. Alcohol, Tobacco, & Cancer. (Illus.). *(978-3-8055-8107-3(6))* Karger, S. AG.

Curry-Mccoy, Tiana V. & Curry-McCoy, Tiana V. Ethanol Effects on Hepatic Proteolytic Systems. 2010. 140p. pap. *(978-3-8383-5849-9(X))* Lambert Academic Publishing.

Editor. Keep Calm & Drink Up. 2011. (ENG.). 160p. 8.99 *(978-1-4494-0938-8(5))* Andrews McMeel Publishing.

Emerson, Edward Randolph. The History of Alcohol in the Far East - China, Japan, Philippines, Islands of the Pacific. 2011. 46p. pap. 6.95 ***(978-1-4465-3488-5(X))*** Harrison House Pubs.

Faassen, Ernst van & Niemelä, Onni. Biochemistry of Prenatal Alcohol Exposure. 2011. (Series: Pregnancy & Infants: Medical, Psychological & Social Issues Ser.). pap. 43.00 *(978-1-61122-511-2(6))* Nova Science Pubs., Inc.

Feigel, Marcel. Keep Fit with Booze. (Illus.). 64p. pap. 9.95 *(978-1-873658-45-0(7))* Take That Bks. GBR. Dist: Trafalgar Square Publishing.

Friedman, Lauri S. Alcohol. 2010. (Introducing Issues with Opposing Viewpoints Ser.). (Illus.). 144p. (J). 34.70 *(978-0-7377-4730-0(7)*, Greenhaven Pr., Inc.) Cengage Gale.

Galvani, Sarah. Women's Perspectives. 2010. 396p. pap. *(978-3-8383-3959-7(2))* Lambert Academic Publishing.

Gautier, Theophile & Baudelaire, Charles. Hashish, Wine, Opium. Stang, Maurice, tr. from FRE. 2009. (Oneworld Classics Ser.). (ENG.). 200p. pap. 12.95 *(978-1-84749-093-3(X))* Alma Classics GBR. Dist: Independent Pubs. Group.

Gustafsson, Nina-Katri. Bridging the World: Alcohol Policy in Transition & Diverging Alcohol Patterns in Sweden. 2010. (Stockholm Studies in Sociology Ser.). (Illus.). 217p. pap. 62.50 *(978-91-7447-056-7(6))* Stockholms Universitet SWE. Dist: Coronet Bks.

Hames, Gina. Alcohol in World History. 2012. (Themes in World History Ser.). (ENG.). 168p. 29.95 *(978-0-415-31152-6(7))* Routledge.

Khanal, Samir. Anaerobic Biotechnology for Bioenergy Production: Principles & Applications. 2008. (ENG., Illus.). 320p. 237.00 *(978-0-8138-2346-1(3)*, Wiley-Blackwell) Wiley, John & Sons, Inc.

Mannam, Sreedevi & Sekar, Govindasamy. Alcohol Oxidation. 2010. 196p. pap. *(978-3-639-25834-9(7))* VDM Verlag Dr. Mueller e.K.

Miller, Michelle. Polymers in Cementitious Materials. (Illus.). xii, 180p. pap. *(978-1-85957-491-1(2))* iSmithers Rapra Publishing.

Mousdale, David M. Biofuels: Biotechnology, Chemistry, & Sustainable Development. 2008. (ENG., Illus.). 424p. 129.95 *(978-1-4200-5124-7(5)*, CRC Press) Taylor & Francis Group GBR. Dist: Taylor & Francis Group.

Newman, Brett. A Way to Redemption. 2011. 142p. pap. 12.00 ***(978-1-60976-771-6(3)***, Eloquent Bks.) AEG Literary Publishing Services, Inc.

Nimlos, Mark R. & Crowley, Michael F. Computational Modeling in Lignocellulosic Biofuel Production. 2010. (ENG., Illus.). 352p. *(978-0-8412-2571-8(0))* American Chemical Society.

Plant, Martin & Plant, Moira. Binge Britain: Alcohol & the National Response. 2006. (ENG., Illus.). 208p. pap. 50.00 *(978-0-19-929941-6(2))* Oxford Univ. Pr., Inc.

Prasad, Kaushal K, et al. Project of Sonia B Bhardwaj - Effect of Alcohol on Gut. 2010. 152p. pap. *(978-3-8383-5954-0(2))* Lambert Academic Publishing.

Sellers, Robert. An A-Z of Hellraisers: A Comprehensive Compendium of Outrageous Insobriety. 2010. (ENG., Illus.). 432p. 36.95 ***(978-1-84809-244-0(X))*** Random Hse. GBR. Dist: Independent Pubs. Group.

Sher, Leo. Research on the Neurobiology of Alcohol Use Disorders. 2008. (Illus.). xiv, 372p. (C). 79.00 *(978-1-60456-197-5(1)*, Nova Biomedical Bks.) Nova Science Pubs., Inc.

Singer, Manfred V. & Brenner, David. Alcohol & the Gastrointestinal Tract. (Illus.). *(978-3-8055-8114-1(9))* Karger, S. AG.

Strong, R. & Stone, Lauson. Tests of Gasoline & Ethyl Alcohol Combustion in Engines. 2007. 252p. 85.00 *(978-1-4276-1569-5(1))* Wexford College Pr.

Teresi, Louis. Hijacking the Brain: How Drug & Alcohol Addiction Hijacks Our Brains the Science Behind Twelve-Step Recovery. 2011. 308p. 34.95 ***(978-1-4634-4483-9(4))***; pap. 19.95 ***(978-1-4634-4484-6(2))*** AuthorHouse.

Tojo, Gabriel & Fernandez, Marcos I. Oxidation of Alcohols to Aldehydes & Ketones: A Guide to Current Common Practice. 2010. (Basic Reactions in Organic Synthesis Ser.). xx, 375p. pap. 139.00 *(978-1-4419-3642-4(4)*, 1441936424) Springer.

Tojo, Gabriel & Fernández, Marcos I. Oxidation of Primary Alcohols to Carboxylic Acids: A Guide to Current Common Practice. 2006. (Basic Reactions in Organic Synthesis Ser.). (Illus.). xvi, 116p. 99.00 *(978-0-387-35431-6(X)*, 038735431X) Springer.

Welsch, Roger. The Convivial Cup: Conversations about Alcohol. 2011. 190p. pap. 17.95 ***(978-1-257-37484-7(2))*** Lulu Enterprises Inc.

Wilkie, Herman F., et al. Fundamentals of Distillery Practice. 2010. (ENG.). 204p. 65.00 *(978-0-9824055-6-7(1))* White Mule Pr.

Wilson, Hugh T. Drugs, Society, & Behavior 09/10. 24th ed. 2009. (Annual Editions Ser.). (ENG., Illus.). 192p. (C). pap. 40.00 *(978-0-07-812763-2(7)*, 0078127637, McGraw-Hill/Dushkin) McGraw-Hill Higher Education.

World Health Organization. Alcohol & Injuries: Emergency Department Studies in an International Perspective. 2010. (Nonserial Publication Ser.). 296p. pap. 60.00 *(978-92-4-154784-0(7))* World Health Organization.

—Selected 2-Alkoxyethanols. 2011. (Concise International Chemical Assessment Document Ser.) (ENG.). 58p. pap. 36.00 *(978-92-4-153067-5(7))* World Health Organization.

Zacharias, Keith. American Gold Rush in the Twenty-First Century: Corn Ethanol. 2009. 68p. pap. 9.95 *(978-0-595-52781-6(7))* iUniverse, Inc.

ALCOHOL—BIBLIOGRAPHY

International Bibliography of Studies on Alcohol, 3 vols., Set. Incl. Vol. 1. References, 1901-1950. Jordy, Sarah S., compiled by. 1966. 50.00 *(978-0-911290-34-9(6))*; Vol. 2. Indexes, 1901-1950. Jordy, Sarah S. 1968. 50.00 *(978-0-911290-35-6(4))*; Vol. 3. References & Indexes, 1951-1960. Jordy, S. S. & Beck, A. 1981. 100.00 *(978-0-911290-40-0(0))*; 150.00 *(978-0-911290-07-3(9))* Rutgers Ctr. of Alcohol Studies Pubns.

ALCOHOL—LAW AND LEGISLATION

see also Liquor Laws

Alfred W. O'Daire, Jr. Blood Alcohol, Breath Alcohol, Impairment & the Law: A manual for law enforcement, attorneys, & others interested in alcohol issues in law Enforc. 2009. 120p. pap. 22.49 *(978-1-4389-2580-6(8))* AuthorHouse.

Bogart, W. A. Permit but Discourage: Regulating Excessive Consumption, 1 vol. 2010. (ENG.). 366p. 75.00 *(978-0-19-537987-7(X))* Oxford Univ. Pr., Inc.

Comprehensive Alcohol Regulatory Effectiveness (CARE) ACT of 2010: Hearing Before the Committee on the Judiciary, House of Representatives, One Hundred Eleventh Congress, Second Session, on H.R. 5034, September 29, 2010. 2010. iv, 171p. ***(978-0-16-087487-1(4)***, 552-070-42175-1) United States Government Printing Office.

Davis, Marni. Jews & Booze: Becoming American in the Age of Prohibition. 2012. (ENG., Illus.). 272p. 32.00 ***(978-0-8147-2028-8(5))*** 2011. E-Book ***(978-0-8147-8384-9(8))*** 2011. E-Book ***(978-0-8147-4409-3(5))*** New York Univ. Pr.

Garriott, James C. & Aguayo, Erik H. Garriott's Medicolegal Aspects of Alcohol. 5th ed. 2008. 536p. 139.00 *(978-1-933264-58-5(6))* Lawyers & Judges Publishing Co., Inc.

Haney, Johannah. Alcohol. 2012. (J). 32.79 ***(978-0-7614-4966-9(3))*** Marshall Cavendish Corp

Jurkiewicz, Carole L. & Painter, Murphy J. Social & Economic Control of Alcohol: The 21st Amendment in the 21st Century. 2007. (Public Administration & Public Policy Ser.). (ENG., Illus.). 264p. 79.95 *(978-1-4200-5463-7(5)*, CRC Press) Taylor & Francis Group GBR. Dist: Taylor & Francis Group.

Legal Issues Concerning State Alcohol Regulation: Hearing Before the Subcommittee on Courts & Competition Policy of the Committee on the Judiciary, House of Representatives, One Hundred Eleventh Congress, Second Session, March 18, 2010. 2010. (Illus.). iv, 240p. ***(978-0-16-087158-0(1)***, 552-070-42011-1) United States Government Printing Office.

Looseleaf Law Publications, suppl. Alcoholic Beverage Control Law, New York State. 2010. 150p. ring bd. 20.95 *(978-0-930137-62-5(0)*, LLP) Looseleaf Law Pubns., Inc.

Office of the Federal Register (U.S.), compiled by. Code of Federal Regulations, Title 27, Alcohol, Tobacco Products & Firearms, Pt. 1-39, Revised as of April 1, 2011. 2011. (ENG.). 954p. pap. 37.00 ***(978-0-16-088433-7(0)***, Office of the Federal Register) United States Government Printing Office.

—Code of Federal Regulations, Title 27, Alcohol, Tobacco Products & Firearms, Pt. 40-399, Revised as of April 1 2011. rev. ed. 2011. (ENG.). 467p. pap. 67.00 ***(978-0-16-088434-4(9)***, Office of the Federal Register) United States Government Printing Office.

Office of the Federal Register (U.S.), compiled by. Code of Federal Regulations, Title 27, Alcohol, Tobacco Products & Firearms, Pt. 400-End, Revised as of April 1 2010. rev. ed. 2010. (ENG.). 224p. pap. 22.00 *(978-0-16-085418-7(0)*, Office of the Federal Register) United States Government Printing Office.

Robertson, Carol. The Little Red Book of Wine Law: A Case of Legal Issues. 2009. (ENG., Illus.). 200p. pap. 19.95 *(978-1-59031-988-8(5))* American Bar Assn.

ALCOHOL—PHYSIOLOGICAL EFFECT

see also Drinking and Traffic Accidents; Hangover Cures; Wine—Physiological Effect

Alcohol & Other Drugs. pap. *(978-0-86840-038-9(6))* NewSouth Publishing.

Bakewell, Lisa, ed. Alcohol Information for Teens. 2nd rev. ed. 2009. (Teen Health Ser.). 400p. (YA). lib. bdg. 69.00 *(978-0-7808-1043-3(0))* Omnigraphics, Inc.

Bartone, John Charles. Birth Defects Caused by ALCOHOL: Index, Reference & Medical Analysis of New Research Information for All Nations. 2008. (Illus.). 160p. ring bd. 69.95 *(978-0-7883-3830-4(7))* ABBE Pubs. Assn. of Washington, D.C.

Benton, Sarah Allen. Understanding the High-Functioning Alcoholic: Professional Views & Personal Insights. 2010. (ENG.). 224p. pap. 21.95 *(978-1-4422-0390-7(0))* Rowman & Littlefield Publishers, Inc.

Brozner, Elaine Y. New Research on Alcohol Abuse & Alcoholism. 2006. (Illus.). 188p. 129.00 *(978-1-60021-310-6(3))* Nova Science Pubs., Inc.

Dasgupta, Amitava. The Science of Drinking: How Alcohol Affects Your Body & Mind. 2011. (ENG.). 280p. 39.95 *(978-1-4422-0409-6(5))* Rowman & Littlefield Publishers, Inc.

Dasgupta, Amitava & Langman, Loralie J., eds. Pharmacogenomics of Alcohol & Drugs of Abuse. 2012. (ENG., Illus.). 252p. 149.95 *(978-1-4398-5611-6(7)*, CRC Press) Taylor & Francis Group GBR. Dist: Taylor & Francis Group.

Dursun, Ilknur & Jakubowska Dogru, Ewa. Effects of Prenatal Alcohol Exposure in Young Adult Wistar Rats. 2010. 112p. pap. *(978-3-8383-7058-3(9))* Lambert Academic Publishing.

Edwards, Griffith. Alcohol. Date not set. *(978-0-312-28885-3(9))* St. Martin's Pr.

Fox, Anne. 400 Rabbits: The Pleasure & Pain of Drunkenness. MacAvoy, Mike, ed. 2010. (ICAP Series on Alcohol in Society Ser.). (ENG., Illus.). 208p. 63.95 *(978-0-415-99213-8(3))* Routledge.

Graham, Kathryn & Homel, Ross. Raising the Bar: Preventing Aggression in & Around Bars, Pubs & Clubs. 2008. (Crime Science Ser.). (ENG.). 316p. (C). 125.00 *(978-1-84392-318-3(1))* Willan Publishing GBR. Dist: Taylor & Francis Group.

Grant, Bradlee. How to Get a 6-Pack... And Still Drink a 30-Rack Every Weekend: A Drinker's Guide to Getting a Ripped Stomach. 2008. 97p. pap. 16.95 *(978-1-60672-286-2(7))* PublishAmerica, Inc.

Hoffinger, Renee. The Recovery Diet: A Groundbreaking, Scientific Approach to a Healthy Life While Recovering from Alcoholism. 2012. (ENG.). 256p. pap. 14.95 ***(978-1-4405-3026-5(2))*** Adams Media Corp.

Hornsey, Ian S. Alcohol & its Role in the Evolution of Human Society. 2012. (ENG., Illus.). 684p. pap. 48.00 ***(978-1-84973-161-4(6))*** Royal Society of Chemistry, The GBR. Dist: Ingram Pub. Services.

Klopocka, Maria, et al. Information Path Functional & Informational Macrodynamics. 2009. pap. 79.00 *(978-1-60692-139-5(8))* Nova Science Pubs., Inc.

Lolli, Giorgio. Social Drinking: The Effects of Alcohol. 2011. 288p. 48.95 ***(978-1-258-09711-0(7))*** Literary Licensing, LLC.

Mazzei, Adam & D'Arco, Agostina. Alcoholic Beverage Consumption & Health. 2009. (Series: Food & Beverage Consumption & Health Ser.). 106.00 *(978-1-60741-160-4(1))* Nova Science Pubs., Inc.

Myers, Peter & Isralowitz, Richard. Alcohol, 1 vol. 2011. (Health & Medical Issues Today Ser.). (Illus.). 250p. 35.00 *(978-0-313-37247-6(0)*, GR7247) Greenwood Publishing Group, Inc.

Myers, Peter L. & Isralowitz, Richard. Alcohol. 2011. E-Book *(978-0-313-37248-3(9)*, Greenwood Pr.) Greenwood Publishing Group, Inc.

Nagy, Laura E., ed. Alcohol: Methods & Protocols. 2008. (Methods in Molecular Biology Ser.). (Illus.). xx, 420p. pap. 119.00 *(978-1-61737-837-9(2)*, 1617378372) Humana Pr.

—Alcohol: Methods & Protocols. 2008. (Methods in Molecular Biology Ser.). (Illus.). 414p. 119.00 *(978-1-58829-906-2(6)*, 1588299066) Springer.

Preedy, Victor R. Beer in Health & Disease Prevention. Preedy, Victor R., ed. 2008. (ENG., Illus.). 1248p. 200.00 *(978-0-12-373891-2(1)*, Academic Pr.) Elsevier Science & Technology Bks.

Roueche, Berton. Alcohol: Its History, Folklore, Effect on the Human Body. 2011. 156p. 41.95 ***(978-1-258-00968-7(4))*** Literary Licensing, LLC.

Scrivner, Jane. Quick-Fix Hangover Detox: 99 Ways to Feel 100 Times Better. 2010. (ENG.). 112p. pap. 9.99 *(978-1-4022-3807-9(X)*, 1311300) Sourcebooks, Inc.

Singer, Manfred V. & Brenner, David, eds. Alcohol & the Gastrointestinal Tract, Vol. 23. (Illus.). 160p. pap. *(978-3-8055-8030-4(4))* Karger, S. AG.

Siple, Molly. Eating for Recovery: The Essential Nutrition Plan to Reverse the Physical Damage of Alcoholism. 2008. (ENG.). 336p. pap. 17.95 *(978-1-60094-044-6(7)*, Da Capo Lifelong) Da Capo Pr., Inc.

Smart, Lesley, ed. Alcohol & Human Health. 2008. (Introducing Health Science Ser.). (ENG., Illus.). 104p. pap. 55.00 *(978-0-19-923735-7(2))* Oxford Univ. Pr., Inc.

Yoshida, Rin. Trends in Alcohol Abuse & Alcoholism Research. 2006. 300p. 225.00 *(978-1-60021-383-0(9))* Nova Science Pubs., Inc.

ALCOHOL ABUSE

see Alcoholism

ALCOHOL AND YOUTH

see Youth—Alcohol Use

ALCOHOL AS FUEL

Alternative Fuels: Current Status, Proposals for New Standards, & Related Infrastructure Issues: Hearing Before the Subcommittee on Energy & Air Quality of the Committee on Energy & Commerce, House of Representatives, One Hundred Tenth Congress, First Session, May 8, 2007. 2008. (Illus.). v, 190p. *(978-0-16-082626-9(8)*, 552-070-38644-1) United States Government Printing Office.

Alternative Transportation Fuels: An Overview: Hearing Before the Subcommittee on Energy & Air Quality of the Committee on Energy & Commerce, House of Representatives, One Hundred Tenth Congress, First Session April 18, 2007. 2008. (Illus.). v, 119p. *(978-0-16-082387-9(0)*, 552-070-38434-1) United States Government Printing Office.

Bernton, Hal, et al. The Forbidden Fuel: A History of Power Alcohol. 2010. (ENG., Illus.). 328p. pap. 19.95 *(978-0-8032-2808-5(2)*, Bison Bks.) Univ. of Nebraska Pr.

Dewsbury, Suzanne & Dewsbury, Ian M. Ethanol. 2009. (At Issue Ser.). (ENG.). 128p. (J). (gr. 10-12). 22.50 *(978-0-7377-4415-6(4))*; (Illus.). 31.80 *(978-0-7377-4414-9(6))* Cengage Gale. (Greenhaven Pr., Inc.).

Edwards, Mark. Biowar I: Hunger. 2007. 244p. pap. 26.96 *(978-1-4357-0019-2(8))* Lulu Enterprises Inc.

Erbaum, Jason B. Bioethanol: Production, Benefits & Economics. 2009. (Energy Science, Engineering & Technology Ser.). 135.00 *(978-1-60741-697-5(2))* Nova Science Pubs., Inc.

Expanding the Role of Biofuels for America: Field Hearing Before the Committee on Agriculture, Nutrition, & Forestry, United States Senate, One Hundred Eleventh Congress, First Session, September 1, 2009. 2011. (Illus.). iii, 106p. ***(978-0-16-088026-1(2)***, 552-070-42450-4) United States Government Printing Office.

Freudenberger, Richard. Alcohol Fuel: A Guide to Making & Using Ethanol as a Renewable Fuel. 2009. (ENG., Illus.). 288p. pap. 26.95 *(978-0-86571-626-1(9)*, 9780865716261) New Society Pubs., Ltd. CAN. Dist: Consortium Bk. Sales & Distribution.

Fuel from Farms: A Guide to Small-Scale Ethanol Production. 2007. per. 29.95 *(978-1-60322-036-1(4))* Knowledge Pubns. Corp.

Full Committee Hearing on the Impact of Renewable Energy Production in Rural America. 2007. (Illus.). v, 70p. *(978-0-16-080128-0(1)*, 552-070-36867-1) United States Government Printing Office.

Full Committee Hearing on the State of the Renewable Fuels Industry in the Current Economy: Hearing Before the Committee on Small Business, United States House of Representatives, One Hundred Eleventh Congress, First Session, Hearing Held March 4, 2009. 2009. (Illus.). v, 68p. *(978-0-16-083032-7(X)*, 552-070-38927-0) United States Government Printing Office.

Goettemoeller, Jeffrey & Goettemoeller, Adrian. Sustainable Ethanol: Biofuels, Biorefineries, Cellulosic Biomass, Flex-fuel Vehicles, & Sustainable Farming for Energy Independence. 2007. 196p. per. 17.00 *(978-0-9786293-0-4(2))* Prairie Oak Publishing.

Haas, Bratt P., ed. Ethanol Biofuel Production. 2010. (Energy Science, Engineering & Technology Ser.). 115.00 *(978-1-60876-086-2(3))* Nova Science Pubs., Inc.

Hearing to Review Renewable Fuels Standard Implementation & Agriculture Producer Eligibility: Hearing Before the Subcommittee on Conservation, Credit, Energy, & Research of the Committee on Agriculture, House of Representatives, One Hundred Tenth Congress, Second Session, Thursday, July 24, 2008. 2009. (Illus.). iv, 135p. *(978-0-16-083941-2(6)*, 552-070-39630-6) United States Government Printing Office.

Legislative Hearing on Discussion Draft Concerning Alternative Fuels, Infrastructure, & Vehicles: Hearing Before the Subcommittee on Energy & Air Quality of the Committee on Energy & Commerce, House of Representatives, One Hundred Tenth Congress, First Session June 7, 2007. 2008. (Illus.). vi, 255p. *(978-0-16-082363-3(3)*, 552-070-38420-1) United States Government Printing Office.

Marshall, Darlene E., ed. Ethanol Economics & Ethanol's Impact on Food Prices & Greenhouse Gas Emissions. 2010. (Energy Policies, Politics & Prices Ser.). (Illus.). xi, 249p. 130.00 *(978-1-60876-081-7(2))* Nova Science Pubs., Inc.

Mousdale, David M. Biofuels: Biotechnology, Chemistry, & Sustainable Development. 2008. (ENG., Illus.). 424p. 129.95 *(978-1-4200-5124-7(5)*, CRC Press) Taylor & Francis Group GBR. Dist: Taylor & Francis Group.

The Next Generation of Biofuels: Cellulosic Ethanol & the 2007 Farm Bill: Hearing Before the Subcommittee on Energy, Science, & Technology of the Committee on Agriculture, Nutrition, & Forestry, United States Senate, One Hundred Tenth Congress, First Session, April 4, 2007. 2007. (Illus.). iii, 123p. (978-0-16-079621-0(0), 552-070-36578-8) United States Government Printing Office.

Pandey, Ashok. Handbook of Plant-Based Biofuels. 2008. (ENG., Illus.). 312p. 129.95 (978-1-56022-175-3(5), CRC Press) Taylor & Francis Group GBR. Dist: Taylor & Francis Group.

A Path Toward the Broader Use of Biofuels: Enhancing the Federal Commitment to Research & Development to Meet the Growing Need: Hearing Before the Subcommittee on Energy & Environment, Committee on Science & Technology, House of Representatives, One Hundred Tenth Congress, First Session, June 14, 2007. 2008. (Illus.). iv, 88p. (978-0-16-080544-8(9), 552-070-37205-9) United States Government Printing Office.

Patni, Prof. (Ms.) Neha. Biodiesel & Ethanol. 2010. 60p. pap. (978-3-639-25706-9(5)) VDM Verlag Dr. Mueller e.K.

Patzek, Tadeusz W. How Can We Outlive Our Way of Life? 2012. (Synthesis Lectures on Energy & the Environment Ser.). 100p. (C). pap. 35.00 (978-1-59829-848-2(8)) Morgan & Claypool Pubs.

Subcommittee Hearing on Second Generation Biofuels: The New Frontier for Small Businesses. 2008. iii, 61p. (978-0-16-081344-3(1), 552-070-37724-7) United States Government Printing Office.

Transforming Forest Waste to Biofuels & the Renewable Fuels Standard: Field Hearing Before the Committee on Agriculture, Nutrition, & Forestry, United States Senate, One Hundred Tenth Congress, Second Session, August 18, 2008. 2009. iii, 46p. (978-0-16-082724-2(8), 552-070-38734-0) United States Government Printing Office.

Vermerris, Wilfred, ed. Genetic Improvement of Bioenergy Crops. 2010. (ENG., Illus.). xxii, 450p. pap. 169.00 (978-1-4419-2422-3(1), 1441924221) Springer.

Waldron, K., ed. Bioalcohol Production: Biochemical Conversion of Lignocellulosic Biomass. 2010. (Illus.). 496p. (978-1-84569-510-1(0)) Woodhead Publishing Ltd.

Zubrin, Robert. Energy Victory: Winning the War on Terror by Breaking Free of Oil. 2007. (ENG.). 275p. 26.98 (978-1-59102-591-7(5)) Prometheus Bks., Pubs.

Zurbin, Robert. Energy Victory: Winning the War on Terror by Breaking Free of Oil. 2009. (ENG.). 352p. pap. 19.98 (978-1-59102-707-2(1)) Prometheus Bks., Pubs.

ALCOHOL IN THE BODY

Aspatore Books Staff, compiled by. Trends in DUI Discovery: Leading Lawyers on Understanding Scientific Advances, Obtaining & Suppressing Evidence, & Analyzing the Role of Experts (Inside the Minds) 2010. (Illus.). 100p. pap. 95.00 (978-0-314-27119-8(8)) Aspatore Bks.

Aspatore, Inc Staff, contrib. by. Understanding DUI Scientific Evidence: Leading Defense Attorneys on Understanding Chemical & Field Sobriety Testing Procedures, Analyzing the Validity of Results, & Developing Trial Strategies. 2nd ed. 2009. (Illus.). 557p. (978-0-314-90467-6(0)) Aspatore Bks.

Bartell, Donald J. Attacking & Defending Drunk Drinking Tests. 2007. (978-1-58012-116-3(0)) James Publishing, Inc.

Garriott, James C. & Aguayo, Erik H. Garriott's Medicolegal Aspects of Alcohol. 5th ed. 2008. 536p. 139.00 (978-1-933264-58-5(6)) Lawyers & Judges Publishing Co., Inc.

Karch, Steven B., ed. Forensic Issues in Alcohol Testing. 2007. (ENG., Illus.). 154p. 89.95 (978-1-4200-5445-3(7), CRC Press) Taylor & Francis Group GBR. Dist: Taylor & Francis Group.

McCain, Scott. Coded Spectroscopy for Ethanol Detection in Diffuse Medi. 2008. 88p. pap. (978-3-639-05265-7(X)) VDM Verlag Dr. Mueller e.K.

Papafotiou, Katherine. Marijuana, Driving & Impairment Tests. 2009. 140p. pap. (978-3-639-13956-3(9)) VDM Verlag Dr. Mueller e.K.

ALCOHOL INTOXICATION

see Alcohol in the Body; Alcoholism

ALCOHOLIC BEVERAGE CONTROL

see Alcohol—Law and Legislation; Liquor Laws

ALCOHOLIC BEVERAGE INDUSTRY

see Brewing Industry; Distilling Industries; Wine and Wine Making

ALCOHOLIC BEVERAGES

see also Bartending; Beer; Cocktails; Liquors; Temperance; Wine and Wine Making

Allison, Thomas. Moonshine Memories. 2007. 384p. pap. 21.95 (978-1-60306-006-6(5)) NewSouth, Inc.

Atkins, Susy. Make Your Own Drinks: Make Your Own Alcoholic & Non Alcoholic from Fruit Cordials to After-Dinner Liqueurs. 2011. (ENG., Illus.). 160p. 16.99 (978-1-84533-601-1(1), Mitchell Beazley) Octopus Publishing Group GBR. Dist: Hachette Bk. Group.

Black, Rachel. Alcohol in Popular Culture: An Encyclopedia. 2010. (Illus.). xxx, 229p. E-Book (978-0-313-38049-5(X), Greenwood Pr.) Greenwood Publishing Group, Inc.

Black, Rachel, ed. Alcohol in Popular Culture: An Encyclopedia, 1 vol. 2010. (Illus.). 229p. 85.00 (978-0-313-38048-8(1), A2209C) Greenwood Publishing Group, Inc.

Boothby, William T. Cocktail Boothby's American Bartender: The New Anchor Distilling Edition. Burkhart, David, ed. & frwd. by. Maytag, Fritz, frwd. 2009. (Illus.). 152p. pap. 14.95 (978-0-9822473-3-4(8)) Anchor Distilling Co.

Brown, Jared M. & Miller, Anistatia R. The Mixellany Guide to Vermouth & Other Aperitifs. 2011. (Illus.). 240p. pap. (978-1-907434-25-9(9)) Mixellany, Ltd.

Buglass, Alan J., ed. Handbook of Alcoholic Beverages Set: Technical, Analytical & Nutritional Aspects, 2 vols. 2011. (ENG., Illus.). 1204p. 410.00 (978-0-470-51202-9(4), Wiley) Wiley, John & Sons, Inc.

Carriere, Kathryn Marie. Spirits for the Mind & Body: 2101 Cocktail & Alcoholic Beverages. 2009. 548p. pap. 32.22 (978-1-4269-1351-8(6)) Trafford Publishing.

Castella, Krystina & Stone, Terry Lee. Booze Cakes: Confections Spiked with Spirits, Wine, & Beer. 2010. (ENG., Illus.). 144p. pap. 16.95 (978-1-59474-423-5(8)) Quirk Bks.

Charming, Cheryl. Bartender's Book: 750 Recipes for Classic & Mixed Drinks, Trendy Shots, & Non-alcoholic Alternatives. 2nd ed. 2007. (ENG.). 320p. pap. 9.95 (978-1-59869-590-8(8)) Adams Media Corp.

Charming, Cheryl & Resnick, Jane Parker. The Everything Bartender's Book: Your Complete Guide to Cocktails, Martinis, Mixed Drinks, & More! 3rd ed. 2010. (Illus.). xv, 399p. (978-1-4405-0384-9(2)) Adams Media Corp.

Clarke, Ronald J. & Bakker, Jokie. Wine: Flavour Chemistry. 2nd ed. 2011. (ENG., Illus.). 440p. 199.95 (978-1-4443-3042-7(X), Wiley-Blackwell) Wiley, John & Sons, Inc.

Comprehensive Alcohol Regulatory Effectiveness (CARE) ACT of 2010: Hearing Before the Committee on the Judiciary, House of Representatives, One Hundred Eleventh Congress, Second Session, on H.R. 5034, September 29, 2010. 2010. iv, 171p. (978-0-16-087487-1(4), 552-070-42175-1) United States Government Printing Office.

Davis, Marni. Jews & Booze: Becoming American in the Age of Prohibition. 2012. (ENG., Illus.). 272p. 32.00 (978-0-8147-2028-8(5)) 2011. E-Book (978-0-8147-8384-9(8)) 2011. E-Book (978-0-8147-4409-3(5)) New York Univ. Pr.

Fitzgerald, F. Scott. On Booze. 2011. (New Directions Pearls Ser.). (ENG.). 96p. pap. 10.95 (978-0-8112-1926-6(7), 21926) New Directions Publishing Corp.

Foley, Ray. The Ultimate Little Cocktail Book. 2nd ed. 2011. (ENG.). 480p. pap. 11.99 (978-1-4022-5409-3(1)) Sourcebooks, Inc.

—The Ultimate Little Frozen Drinks Book. 2nd ed. 2011. (ENG.). 480p. pap. 11.99 (978-1-4022-5406-2(7)) Sourcebooks, Inc.

—The Ultimate Little Shooter Book. 2nd ed. 2010. (ENG.). 480p. pap. 11.99 (978-1-4022-4265-6(4)) Sourcebooks, Inc.

—The Vodka 1000: The Ultimate Collection of Vodka Cocktails, Recipes, Facts, & Resources. 2007. (Bartender Magazine Ser.). 292p. per. 14.95 (978-1-4022-1056-3(6)) Sourcebooks, Inc.

Fouquet, Louis. Mixellany's Annotated Bariana: A Practical Compendium of All American & British Drinks. Vexenat, Charles, tr. from FRE. & anno. by. annot. ed. 2009. (Illus.). 160p. pap. (978-0-9821074-4-7(7), Mixellany) Mixellany, Ltd.

Gately, Iain. Drink: A Cultural History of Alcohol. 2009. (ENG.). 560p. (gr. 12-18). 22.00 (978-1-59240-464-3(2), Gotham) Penguin Group (USA) Inc.

Glover, Brian & Walton, Stuart. The Illustrated Encyclopedia of Wine, Beer & Spirits: The Definitive Reference Guide to Alchol-Based Drinks & Mixers, & How to Choose, Store & Serve Them. 2006. (ENG., Illus.). 512p. 35.00 (978-0-7548-1649-2(4)) Anness Publishing GBR. Dist: National Bk. Network.

Government Printing Office Staff. Alcohol Health & Research World. pap. 25.00 (978-0-16-010431-2(9)) United States Government Printing Office.

Haney, Johannah. Alcohol. 2012. (J). 32.79 (978-0-7614-4966-9(3)) Marshall Cavendish Corp.

Harvey Collins' Drink Guide. reprint ed. pap. 5.95 (978-0-9657158-0-5(9)) Collins Brothers, Inc.

Hawaii's Best Tropical Food & Drinks. (Illus.). pap. 4.95 (978-0-930492-44-1(7)) Hawaiian Service, Inc.

Jennings, Ryan & Steele, David. Entertaining with Booze: Designer Drinks, Fabulous Food & Inspired Ideas for Your Next Party. 2010. (Illus.). 192p. pap. 29.95 (978-1-55285-930-8(4)) Whitecap Bks., Ltd. CAN. Dist: Midpoint Trade Bks., Inc.

Joseph, Robert. The Complete Encyclopedia of Wine. 2006. (Illus.). 288p. (978-1-84442-108-4(2)) Carlton Bks., Ltd.

Kates, Steven. The Quotable Drunkard: Words of Wit, Wisdom, & Philosophy from the Bottom of the Glass. 2011. (ENG.). 256p. pap. 11.95 (978-1-4405-1264-3(7)) Adams Media Corp.

Knorr, Paul. Big Bad-Ass Book of Cocktails: 1,500 Recipes to Mix It Up! Running Press Staff, ed. 2010. (ENG.). 672p. pap. 14.95 (978-0-7624-3839-6(8), Running Pr.) Running Pr. Bk. Pubs.

Luntz, Perry. Whiskey & Spirits for Dummies. 4th ed. 2007. (ENG., Illus.). 335p. per. 19.99 (978-0-470-11769-9(9), For Dummies) Wiley, John & Sons, Inc.

McGovern, Patrick E. Uncorking the Past: The Quest for Wine, Beer, & Other Alcoholic Beverages. (ENG., Illus.). 348p. 2010. pap. 18.95 (978-0-520-26798-5(2)) 2009. 50.00 (978-0-520-25379-7(5)) Univ. of California Pr.

Nathan-Maister, David. The Absinthe Encyclopedia. 2009. (Illus.). 362p. pap. 162.50 (978-0-9556921-1-6(3)) Oxygenee Ltd. GBR. Dist: Lulu Enterprises Inc.

Nibbe, Dale A. & BarCharts Inc., Staff. Bartender's Guide to Cocktails. 2007. (Quick Study Ser.). (ENG.). 6p. 5.95 (978-1-4232-0323-0(2)) Barcharts, Inc.

Nowosenetz, Tessa. The Construction of Masculinity & Femininity in Alcohol Advertising: A discourse analysis. 2008. 84p. pap. (978-3-639-10706-7(3)) VDM Verlag Dr. Mueller e.K.

Pennock, Pamela E. Advertising Sin & Sickness: The Politics of Alcohol & Tobacco Marketing, 1950-1990. 2007. (Illus.). 290p. 36.00 (978-0-87580-368-5(7)) Northern Illinois Univ. Pr.

Pickford, Louise. Hot Toddies. 2011. (ENG., Illus.). 64p. (978-1-84975-151-3(X)) Ryland Peters & Small.

Piercy, Joseph. Slippery Tipples: A Guide to Weird & Wonderful Spirits & Liqueurs. 2011. (ENG., Illus.). 192p. 17.95 (978-0-7524-5756-7(X)) History Pr. Ltd., The GBR. Dist: Independent Pubs. Group.

Quenet-Chute, Sylvia. At the Cutting Edge: A Lighthearted Anthology on Eating & Drinking. 2010. 168p. 23.50 (978-1-60860-979-6(0), Eloquent Bks.) AEG Literary Publishing Services, Inc.

Scheffel, Sarah & Gaze, Christine. Hot Shots Kit: Flaming Drinks for Daring Drinkers. 2011. (Little Seedling Edition Ser.). (ENG.). 48p. 10.95 (978-1-60433-221-6(2)) Cider Mill Pr. Bk. Pubs., LLC.

Schmidt, William. The Flowing Bowl: When & What to Drink. 2010. 306p. pap. 29.75 (978-1-142-61462-1(X)) BiblioBazaar.

—The Flowing Bowl: When & What to Drink. 2007. 292p. 43.95 (978-0-548-53959-0(6)); (ENG.). per. 28.95 (978-0-548-49192-8(5)) Kessinger Publishing, LLC.

Small, Robert W. Beverage Basics: Understanding & Appreciating Wine, Beer, & Spirits. 2011. (ENG., Illus.). 464p. 65.00 (978-0-470-13883-0(1), Wiley) Wiley, John & Sons, Inc.

Spencer, Edward. The Flowing Bowl - 19th Century Cocktail Bar Recipes. 2007. 260p. 29.95 (978-1-4276-1458-2(X)) Wexford College Pr.

—Flowing Bowl A Treatise on Drinks of Al. 2007. 260p. per. (978-1-4067-8958-4(5), Vintage Cookery Bks.) Read Bks.

Steedman, M. E. Home-Made Summer & Winter Drinks. 2008. 176p. (978-1-4437-3731-9(3), Vintage Cookery Bks.) Read Bks.

Stewart, Scott. Beer: A Quality Perspective. 2008. (Handbook of Alcoholic Beverages Ser.). (ENG., Illus.). 304p. 145.00 (978-0-12-669201-3(7), Academic Pr.) Elsevier Science & Technology Bks.

The International Agency for Research on Cancer. Consumption of Alcoholic Beverages & Ethyl Carbamate. 2011. (IARC Monographs Volume 96 Ser.). (ENG.). 1024p. pap. 66.00 (978-92-832-1296-6(7)) World Health Organization.

Uddin, Jalal. Arrack Drinking. 2011. 56p. pap. (978-3-8433-9291-4(9)) Lambert Academic Publishing.

United Kingdom Bartenders' Guild Staff, creator. The International Guide to Drinks. 2007. (ENG., Illus.). 256p. 19.95 (978-0-09-191202-4(4), Ebury Pr.) Ebury Publishing GBR. Dist: Independent Pubs. Group.

Van Den Bersselaar, Dmitri. The King of Drinks: Schnapps Gin from Modernity to Tradition. 2007. (African Social Studies). (Illus.). 268p. pap. (978-90-04-16091-0(4)) BRILL.

van Outshoorn, Nic. The Hangover Handbook & Boozer's Bible. 2nd ed. (Illus.). 96p. pap. 7.95 (978-1-873668-34-4(1)) Take That Bks. GBR. Dist: Trafalgar Square Publishing.

Vance, Dave A. Martini Madness: 380 recipes to tempt your taste Buds. 2009. 134p. pap. 14.99 (978-0-557-05151-9(7)) Lulu Enterprises Inc.

Walton, Stuart. Vodka Classified: A Vodka Lover's Companion. 2009. (ENG., Illus.). 240p. 24.95 (978-1-86205-803-3(2)) Chrysalis Children's Bks. GBR. Dist: Independent Pubs. Group.

Waters, John K. Bartender's Guide: An A to Z Companion to All Your Favorite Drinks. 2008. (ENG.). 528p. pap. 14.95 (978-1-59869-764-3(1)) Adams Media Corp.

Wolf, David S. & Schuster, Kathryn J. Drug Policies, Addiction & Eradication. 2011. (Substance Abuse Assessment, Interventions & Treatment Ser.). 89.00 (978-1-61209-085-6(0)) Nova Science Pubs., Inc.

Zmirak, John & Matychowiak, Denise. Wine, Whiskey, & Song: A Spirited Look at Catholic Life & Lore from the Apocalypse to Zinfandel. 2007. (Bad Catholic's Guides). (ENG., Illus.). 416p. pap. 14.95 (978-0-8245-2411-1(X), Crossroad) Crossroad Publishing Co., The.

ALCOHOLICS

see also Church Work with Alcoholics; Recovering Alcoholics; Social Work with Alcoholics

ABBE Scientist Research Division Staff. M.M. P. I. Profile of Alcoholics: Index, Reference & Medical Analysis of New Research Information. 2008. (Illus.). 160p. ring bd. 69.95 (978-0-7883-3835-9(8)) ABBE Pubs. Assn. of Washington, D.C.

Anonymous. The Little Red Book. 2010. 90p. pap. 7.49 (978-1-60459-948-0(0)) Wilder Pubns., Ltd.

B., Mel. 101 Meeting Starters: A Guide to Better Twelve Step Discussions. 2007. (ENG.). 224p. pap. 13.95 (978-1-59285-369-4(2)) Hazelden Publishing & Educational Services.

Barry, Nicola. Mother's Ruin. 2008. (ENG.). 304p. pap. 13.95 (978-0-7553-1674-8(6)) Headline Bk. Publishing GBR. Dist: Independent Pubs. Group.

Benton, Sarah Allen. Understanding the High-Functioning Alcoholic: Professional Views & Personal Insights. 2010. (ENG.). 224p. pap. 21.95 (978-1-4422-0390-7(0)) Rowman & Littlefield Publishers, Inc.

Benton, Sarah Allen & Benton, Sarah A. Understanding the High-Functioning Alcoholic: Professional Views & Personal Insights, 1 vol. 2009. (Praeger Series on Contemporary Health & Living Ser.). 224p. 39.95 (978-0-313-35280-5(1), C35280, Praeger Pubs.) Greenwood Publishing Group, Inc.

Bocchieri, Barry. Reflections along the Way: Stories of Recovery & Life from One Who Has Been There. 2007. (978-1-882883-66-0(7)) Idyll Arbor, Inc.

Bollendorf, Robert F., et al. Sober Spring: One Family's Battle with Addiction. 2007. pap. 8.95 (978-1-932514-14-8(7)) College of DuPage Pr.

Butler, Shane. Benign Anarchy: Alcoholics Anonymous in Ireland. 2010. 272p. pap. (978-0-7165-3064-0(3)); (Illus.). 79.95 (978-0-7165-3063-3(5)) Irish Academic Pr. IRL. Dist: International Specialized Bk. Services.

C.A.C., Michael & Shelton, Michael. Gay Men & Substance Abuse: A Basic Guide for Addicts & Those Who Care for Them. 2011. (ENG.). 216p. pap. 14.95 (978-1-59285-889-7(9)) Hazelden Publishing & Educational Services.

Casey, Karen. My Story to Yours: A Guided Memoir for Writing Your Recovery Journey. 2011. E-Book (978-1-61649-163-5(9)); (ENG.). 194p. pap. 14.95 (978-1-61649-094-2(2)) Hazelden Publishing & Educational Services.

Centre de toxicomanie et de santé mentale Staff, contrib. by. Troubles Concomitants et Problèmes Liés à L'usage de Substances et Aux Jeux de Hasard et D'argent en Ontario: Guide Pour les Professionnels Aidants. 2009. (FRE.). (978-0-88868-745-6(1)) Centre for Addiction & Mental Health.

Centre for Addiction and Mental Health Staff, contrib. by. Substance Use, Concurrent Disorders & Gambling Problems in Ontario: A Guide for Helping Professionals. 2008. (978-0-88868-742-5(7)) Centre for Addiction & Mental Health.

Dean, Amy E. Morning Light: A Book of Meditations to Begin Your Day. 2011. (ENG.). 400p. pap. 14.95 (978-1-61649-108-6(6)) Hazelden Publishing & Educational Services.

DiRocco, Stephanie & Derouin, Sandy. A Dangerous Combination: Living with a Bipolar Alcoholic. 2011. pap. 14.99 (978-1-61777-329-7(8)) Tate Publishing & Enterprises, LLC.

Engs, Ruth C., ed. Women: Alcohol & Other Drugs. 2007. (Illus.). 188p. pap. 22.00 (978-1-59752-887-0(0), Resource Pubns.) Wipf & Stock Pubs.

Fairbanks, Robert P. How It Works: Recovering Citizens in Post-Welfare Philadelphia. 2009. (ENG., Illus.). 312p. 70.00 (978-0-226-23408-3(8)); pap. 27.50 (978-0-226-23409-0(6)) Univ. of Chicago Pr.

Fisher, Gary L. & Harrison, Thomas C. Substance Abuse: Information for School Counselors, Social Workers, Therapists & Counselors. 5th rev. ed. 2012. (ENG.). 400p. (C). pap. 109.20 (978-0-13-261324-8(7), Prentice Hall) Prentice Hall PTR.

Flanagan, Leanne Garrett. Swimming in Circles Is Better Than Drowning. 2011. 188p. pap. 15.00 (978-1-4634-0424-6(7)) AuthorHouse.

Foster, John. Quality of Life in Alcohol Dependents: A Longitudinal Study. 2006. 169.00 (978-1-60021-443-1(6)) Nova Science Pubs., Inc.

Fox, Mike & Wilson, Lesley. Counselling Older People with Alcohol Problems. 2011. (ENG., Illus.). 224p. pap. (978-1-84905-117-0(8)) Kingsley, Jessica Ltd.

Gouin, John R. An Unforgettable Salute: Skirmishes, Battlefields, & Making Peace with My Father. 2010. 172p. 25.95 (978-1-4502-3980-6(3)); pap. 15.95 (978-1-4502-3979-0(X)) iUniverse, Inc.

Grant, Judith. Men & Substance Abuse: Narratives of Addiction & Recovery. 2012. 175p. 58.50 (978-1-935049-48-7(8)) FirstForumPress.

Harris, Kitty & Gould, Jodie E. Women & Recovery: Finding Hope. 2012. (ENG.). 256p. pap. 16.95 (978-0-470-94183-6(9), Wiley) Wiley, John & Sons, Inc.

Healing Project Staff. Voices of Alcoholism: The Healing Companion: Stories for Courage, Comfort & Strength. 2008. (Voices Of Ser.). (ENG.). 288p. per. 16.95 (978-1-934184-04-2(7)) Lachance Publishing LLC.

Hoffman, Jeffrey A. Living in Balance: 90 Meditations for Recovery from Addiction. 2011. (ENG.). 128p. pap. 7.95 (978-1-61649-087-4(X)) Hazelden Publishing & Educational Services.

Horner, Craig & Harrold, Edmund. The Diary of Edmund Harrold, Wigmaker of Manchester 1712-15. 2008. (Illus.). 216p. 124.95 (978-0-7546-6172-6(5)) Ashgate Publishing Co.

Humphreys, Keith. Circles of Recovery: Self-Help Organizations for Addictions. 2011. (International Research Monographs in the Addictions Ser.). (ENG., Illus.). 240p. pap. 39.99 (978-0-521-17637-8(9)) Cambridge Univ. Pr.

Iliff, Brenda. A Woman's Guide to Recovery. 2008. (ENG.). 328p. pap. 14.95 (978-1-59285-479-0(6)) Hazelden Publishing & Educational Services.

Irvin, Daniel. The Spirituality of Alcoholics Anonymous: Good or Bad. 2007. 90p. pap. 14.00 (978-0-8059-7582-6(9)) Dorrance Publishing Co., Inc.

Jackson, Arthur M. Raise the Bottom: How to Keep Secret Alcoholics from Damaging Your Business. 2009. 137p. pap. 16.95 (978-0-9820938-2-5(9), Bascom Hill Publishing Group, Ltd.) Hillcrest Publishing Group, Inc.

Jones, Dean C. & Joseph, Michael. Climbing up the Downward Spiral. 2010. 228p. pap. 25.00 (978-1-60899-629-2(8), Resource Pubns.) Wipf & Stock Pubs.

Kosinski, Alan. Successful Sober House: A guide to rescuing alcoholics & drug Addicts. 2010. 244p. (ENG.). 27.95 (978-1-4520-0197-5(9)); pap. 19.95 (978-1-4520-0196-8(0)) AuthorHouse.

Larsen, Earnie. Now That You're Sober: Week-by-Week Guidance from Your Recovery Coach. 2010. (ENG.). 288p. pap. 14.95 (978-1-59285-828-6(7)) Hazelden Publishing & Educational Services.

LeRoux, Pierre & Leroux, Pierre. Immanuel(God with Us)in Recovery. 2011. 216p. 25.99 (978-1-61379-381-7(2)); pap. 15.99 (978-1-61379-380-0(4)) Xulon Pr., Inc.

Linnane, Fergus. Drinking for England: The Great English Drinkers & Their Times. 2008. (ENG., Illus.). 256p. 39.95 (978-1-906217-16-7(5)) Aurum Pr., Ltd. GBR. Dist: Independent Pubs. Group.

Maloney, Ralph. How to Drink Like a Mad Man. 2012. (Dover Humor Ser.). (ENG.). 224p. pap. 9.95 (978-0-486-48352-8(5)) Dover Pubns., Inc.

Miller, David & Miller, Merlene. Staying Clean & Sober: Complementary & Natural Strategies for Healing the Addicted Brain. 2nd rev. ed. 2008. 256p. pap. 16.95 (978-1-58054-124-4(0)) Woodland Publishing, Inc.

Mooney, Geraldine, ed. National Directory of Drug & Alcohol Abuse Treatment Programs. 2008. (ENG.). 665p. (C). pap. 65.00 (978-1-4289-8788-3(6)) DIANE Publishing Co.

Moore, Whitney McKendree. Whit's End: The Biography of a Breakdown. 2011. 120p. 28.95 **(978-1-4497-1645-5(8))**; pap. 11.95 **(978-1-4497-1643-1(1))** Author Solutions, Inc. (WestBow Pr.).
Parr, Martin, ed. Rimaldas Viksraitis: Grimaces of the Weary Village. 2011. (ENG., Illus.). 80p. pap. 49.95 *(978-0-9557394-6-0(2))* White Space Gallery Ltd./The Tarkovsky Foundation GBR. Dist: D.A.P./Distributed Art Pubs.
Partridge, G. E. Studies in the Psychology of Intemperance. 2009. 288p. pap. 27.75 *(978-1-116-21976-0(X))* BiblioBazaar.
Patil, Bajeerao. Insanity - Beyond Understanding. 2010. 364p. pap. 17.50 *(978-1-60976-096-4(0)*, Eloquent Bks.) AEG Literary Publishing Services, Inc.
Paylor, Ian, et al. Social Work & Drug use. 2012. (ENG.). 184p. (C). pap. 47.95 **(978-0-335-23455-4(0)**, 0335234550) McGraw-Hill Education GBR. Dist: McGraw-Hill Cos., The.
Perkinson, Robert R. The Alcoholism & Drug Abuse Client Workbook. 2011. 152p. pap. 26.00 *(978-1-4129-7922-1(6)*, B79221P) SAGE Pubns., Inc.
Purcell, Liz. Seeds of Sobriety: Practical Daily Readings for Alcoholics & Addicts. 2006. (ENG.). 396p. per. 21.95 *(978-1-59800-833-3(1))* Outskirts Pr., Inc.
Rhodes, Richard C. A Counselor Looks at the Big Book: A Clinician's View of the Book Alcoholics Anonymous. 2009. 168p. pap. 19.95 *(978-1-58982-500-0(4)*, Millennial Mind Publishing) American Bk. Publishing Group.
Rini, Patricia Ann. The Power of Choice: The Journey from Addiction - Trial by Fire & Blind Faith. 2008. 300p. pap. 17.99 *(978-1-60477-984-4(5))* Xulon Pr., Inc.
Rogg, Jasmin. To Hell: How to Stay Sober. 2010. pap. 19.95 *(978-0-615-33083-9(5))* Voice of Recovery Pr.
Seed, Gram. One Step Beyond: One Man's Journey from near Death to New Life. 2008. (Illus.). 168p. *(978-1-85345-462-2(1))* Crusade for World Revival.
Sherman, Harold Morrow. Anyone Can Stop Drinking, Even You! 2011. 254p. 47.95 **(978-1-258-06360-3(3))** Literary Licensing, LLC.
Shumway, Sterling T. & Kimball, Thomas G. Six Essentials to Achieve Lasting Recovery. 2012. (ENG.). 200p. pap. 14.95 **(978-1-61649-205-2(8)**, Hazelden) Hazelden Publishing & Educational Services.
Sinister, Bucky. Get Up: A 12-Step Guide to Recovery for Misfits, Freaks, & Weirdos. 2008. (ENG.). 176p. pap. 14.95 *(978-1-57324-366-7(3)*, Conari Pr.) Red Wheel/Weiser.
—Still Standing: Addicts Talk about Living Sober. 2011. (ENG.). 176p. pap. 14.95 *(978-1-57324-476-3(7))* Red Wheel/Weiser.
Slater, Matthew. Carrying the Message. 2011. 108p. 21.23 **(978-1-4634-1862-5(0))**; pap. 10.68 **(978-1-4634-1863-2(9))** AuthorHouse.
Somach, Jeffrey & Busch, Linda. I Cut It Out: An (ex) Drunk's Guide to Sobriety. 2007. 165p. pap. 12.50 *(978-0-9798969-1-0(6))* I Cut It Out, Inc.
Twitchell, Vernon Bronson. Living Without Liquor: How to Help the Problem Drinker. 2011. 86p. 37.95 **(978-1-258-08692-3(1))** Literary Licensing, LLC.
Walle, Alf H. Recovery the Native Way: A Client Reader. 2008. 80p. pap. *(978-1-60752-014-6(1))* Information Age Publishing, Inc.
—Recovery the Native Way: A Therapist's Manual. 2007. pap. *(978-1-59311-833-4(3))* Information Age Publishing, Inc.
Wilhelmson, Brenda. Diary of an Alcoholic Housewife. 2011. 400p. E-Book 11.99 *(978-1-61649-000-3(4))*; (ENG.). pap. 14.95 *(978-1-61649-086-7(1))* Hazelden Publishing & Educational Services.

ALCOHOLICS—BIOGRAPHY

A.A. Grapevine Inc Staff, contrib. by. In Our Own Words: Stories of Young AAs in Recovery: From the Pages of the AA Grapevine. 2007. xi, 164p. pap. *(978-0-933685-64-2(5))* AA Grapevine, Inc.
Aa Services. Alcoholics Anonymous - Big Book Special Edition - Including: New Personal Stories for the Year 2008. 2008. 224p. pap. *(978-956-310-042-6(5))* Editorial Benei Noaj.
AA Services Staff. Alcoholics Anonymous Big Book Special E. 2006. 156p. per. *(978-956-291-357-7(0))* Editorial Benei Noaj.
Alcoholics Anonymous World Services, Inc. Staff. Alcoholics Anonymous Big Book Special E. 2006. 164p. per. *(978-956-291-265-5(5))* Editorial Benei Noaj.
Allen, Steven G. Grace Anonymous. 2010. pap. 9.99 *(978-1-61566-945-5(0))* Tate Publishing & Enterprises, LLC.
Ameisen, Olivier. Heal Thyself: A Doctor at the Peak of His Medical Career, Destroyed by Alcohol — and the Personal Miracle That Brought Him Back. 2009. (ENG., Illus.). 368p. pap. 16.00 *(978-0-374-53220-8(6))* Farrar, Straus & Giroux.
Anderson, Allen. Memoir of an Alcoholic American Spy. 2006. pap. 14.95 *(978-0-9771870-9-6(8))* Arbor Bks.
Anne D. The Best Pharmacist. 2010. 160p. pap. 24.95 *(978-1-4389-5038-9(1))* AuthorHouse.
Anthony, Christopher R. Beat Me Out of Me. 2009. 220p. pap. 19.95 *(978-1-4241-9333-2(8))* PublishAmerica, Inc.
Axe. Bouncing off Guardrails: Somewhere in Life Between Victorious Triumph & Horrific Annihilation. 2010. 224p. pap. 18.95 *(978-1-4502-4236-3(7))* iUniverse, Inc.
Baker, Carolyn. My Issues Touch the Heart of God. 2010. 112p. 21.95 *(978-1-4269-2979-3(X))*; pap. 11.95 *(978-1-4269-2978-6(1))* Trafford Publishing.
Balzer, Joseph. Flying Drunk: The True Story of a Northwest Airlines Flight, Three Drunk Pilots, & One Man's Fight for Redemption. 2009. 240p. 25.00 *(978-1-932714-71-5(5))* Savas Beatie.
Banks, Cynthia. Drunk, for 27 Years: A Story of Victory - Her Choice to Live & Not Die. 2009. 264p. 24.99 *(978-1-4389-9314-0(5))* AuthorHouse.
Barber, Charles Calvin. Life on the Pipe. 2011. 84p. pap. 15.99 **(978-1-4568-6530-6(7))** Xlibris Corp.
Baxter, Meredith. Untied: A Memoir of Family, Fame, & Floundering. (Illus.). 304p. 2012. (ENG.). pap. 15.00 **(978-0-307-71931-7(6)**, Three Rivers Pr.) 2011. 25.00 *(978-0-307-71930-0(8)*, Crown Archetype) Crown Publishing Group.
Bean, Orson. Mail for Mikey. 2008. (ENG.). 128p. 18.95 *(978-1-56980-350-9(1))* Barricade Bks., Inc.
Benson, Luther. Fifteen Years in Hell. rev. ed. 2006. (ENG.). 152p. 26.95 *(978-1-4218-2097-2(8))*; per. 11.95 *(978-1-4218-2197-9(4))* 1st World Publishing, Inc. (1st World Library - Literary Society).
—Fifteen Years in Hell. 2008. 148p. 21.99 *(978-0-554-35442-2(X))*; 24.99 *(978-0-554-26139-3(1))* BiblioBazaar.
—Fifteen Years in Hell. 2007. (ENG.). 120p. per. *(978-1-4065-4836-5(7))* Dodo Pr.
—Fifteen Years in Hell. 2009. (ENG.). 124p. pap. 10.45 *(978-1-4385-2327-9(0)*, Book Jungle) Standard Pubns., Inc.
Bill, Jersey. An Alcoholic's Story. 2010. 48p. pap. 9.98 *(978-1-4269-2967-0(6))* Trafford Publishing.
Braswell, Sterling R. Crazy Town: Money. Marriage. Meth. 2008. (ENG.). 260p. pap. 17.95 *(978-0-9678514-6-4(7))* Kallisti Publishing.
Braxton, Angela. A Woman with an Issue: A Mothers Memior of Addiction & Loss, Redemption & Recovery. 2007. pap. 14.99 *(978-1-59755-097-0(3)*, Advantage Inspirational) Advantage Bks.
Brown, Claude. Manchild in the Promised Land. 2011. (ENG.). 416p. pap. 16.00 *(978-1-4516-3157-9(X)*, Touchstone) Touchstone.
Brown, Nancy. Facing Life. 2008. 183p. per. 24.95 *(978-1-897323-07-6(7))* Penumbra Pr. CAN. Dist: Michigan State Univ. Pr.
Burke, Michael J. Never Enough: One Lawyer's True Story of How He Gambled His Career Away. 2009. (ENG.). 250p. pap. 29.95 *(978-1-59031-991-8(5))* American Bar Assn.
Buttner, George E. An Unsuspecting Trap: One Man's Victory over Alcoholism. 2007. 337p. per. 24.99 *(978-1-60247-258-7(0))* Tate Publishing & Enterprises, LLC.
Byrd, David Lee. Living a Spiritual Life: On the Wings of Eagles. 2006. 91p. pap. 16.95 *(978-1-4241-4302-3(0))* PublishAmerica, Inc.
Campbell, W. Cothran 'Cot'. Memoirs of a Longshot. 2007. 328p. (ENG.). 32.99 *(978-1-4257-4866-9(4))*; (Illus.). per. 22.99 *(978-1-4257-4885-2(6))* Xlibris Corp.
Campion, Christopher John. Escape from Bellevue: A Memoir of Rock 'n' Roll, Recovery, & Redemption. 2009. (ENG.). 384p. (gr. 12-18). 18.00 *(978-1-59240-530-5(4)*, Gotham) Penguin Group (USA) Inc.
Cassidy-Watson, Maxine. Cass: A True Story of Alcoholism & Its Effect on the Alcoholic & the Family. 2008. 48p. pap. 16.95 *(978-1-60563-095-3(0))* PublishAmerica, Inc.
Clima, Terrell. From the Inside Out: True Stories of Changed Lives. 2006. pap. 12.95 *(978-0-9788184-0-1(7))* TLC Nursing, Inc.
Cole, Pastor Carolyn. My Life. 2010. 80p. pap. 14.99 *(978-1-4490-7524-8(X))* AuthorHouse.
Cole, Stuart J. A Message to my Family. 2011. 176p. pap. 14.69 **(978-1-4567-7804-0(8))** AuthorHouse.
Colley, Declan. When Bobby Met Christy: The Story of Bobby Beasley & a Wayward Horse. 2011. (ENG., Illus.). 256p. pap. 26.95 *(978-1-84889-039-8(7))* Collins Pr., The IRL. Dist: Dufour Editions, Inc.
Cooper, Jessica C. Dear Diary, 1 vol. 2010. 200p. pap. 24.95 *(978-1-4512-2444-3(3))* PublishAmerica, Inc.
Cox, Mitch. Fathead Goes to Chico. 2007. 160p. per. 14.95 *(978-0-595-46565-1(X))* iUniverse, Inc.
Critzki, Joe. One Way Trip. 2010. 270p. pap. 19.95 *(978-1-4327-6086-1(6))* Outskirts Pr., Inc.
D, Stan. Stanley Maynard Dooshnik, Jr. with a Name Like That, You'd Drink Too! 2007. (ENG.). 196p. per. 24.95 *(978-1-4241-5128-8(7))* PublishAmerica, Inc.
Davis, Richard Harding. We Can Be Heroes: Get me to the Cooker. 2011. 256p. pap. 27.95 **(978-1-4626-4732-3(4))** PublishAmerica, Inc.
DeClemente, Eileen P. Alive. 2008. 128p. pap. 11.95 *(978-0-7414-4578-0(6))* Infinity Publishing.
Dredla, Larry Michael. Praying for Strength: Memoir of an Ex Suicidal, Alcoholic, Drug Addict. 2011. 124p. pap. 11.68 *(978-1-4567-4749-7(5))* AuthorHouse.
Edick, Mark. Becoming Normal: An Ever-Changing Perspective. 2010. (ENG.). 216p. pap. 14.95 *(978-0-9818482-1-1(4))* Central Recovery Pr.
Ellefson Huray, Melissa. Standing Damaged. 2006. 379p. per. 14.95 *(978-1-59466-097-9(2))* Port Town Publishing.
Ellis, Derrick. From Vodka to Coffee: I Had to Get Sober or Stay Broke. 2010. 132p. pap. 132.00 *(978-1-4520-2383-0(2))* AuthorHouse.
Fante, Dan. Fante: A Family's Legacy of Writing, Drinking & Surviving. 2011. (P. S. Ser.). (ENG.). 288p. pap. 14.99 *(978-0-06-202709-2(3)*, HarperPerennial) HarperCollins Pubs.
Fitzpatrick, Michael & Borchert, William G. 1000 Years of Sobriety: 20 People x 50 Years. 2010. (ENG.). 272p. pap. 14.95 *(978-1-59285-858-3(9))* Hazelden Publishing & Educational Services.
Flanagan, Pam J. You Be the Judge: Evil? Insane? Mildly Masochistic? or, just Plain *itch? 2011. 174p. 29.99 **(978-1-4628-8819-1(4))** Xlibris Corp.
Ford, Felicia. Quiet Desperation, 1 vol. 2009. 203p. pap. 24.95 *(978-1-4489-9848-7(4))* PublishAmerica, Inc.
Francis, Joseph. My Last Drink. 2008. (Cooking in America Ser.). (ENG.). 164p. pap. 12.95 *(978-1-4290-1217-1(X))* Applewood Bks.
Gabriel, Hildy. Where Did the Pain Stop, 1 vol. 2010. 114p. pap. 19.95 *(978-1-4489-6073-6(8))* PublishAmerica, Inc.
Gee, Clare. Hooked: Confessions of a London Call Girl. 2011. (ENG., Illus.). 272p. pap. 13.95 *(978-1-84596-603-4(1))* Mainstream Publishing Co., Ltd. GBR. Dist: Independent Pubs. Group.
Groom, Kelle. I Wore the Ocean in the Shape of a Girl: A Memoir. (ENG.). 2012. 272p. pap. 14.00 *(978-1-4516-1669-9(4))* 2011. 256p. lib. bdg. 23.00 *(978-1-4516-1668-2(6))* Free Pr. (Free Pr.).
Gwilliam, J. Gary. Getting a Winning Verdict in My Personal Life: A Trial Lawyer Finds His Soul. 2007. *(978-1-4243-4283-9(X))* Pavior Publishing.
Hannah, Rufus & Soper, Barry. A Bum Deal: An Unlikely Journey from Hopeless to Humanitarian. 2011. (ENG.). 256p. pap. 15.99 *(978-1-4022-6087-2(3))* Sourcebooks, Inc.
Harm, Dave. Creating Dreams: From the Nightmares of Hell, 1 vol. 2009. 217p. pap. 24.95 *(978-1-60836-802-0(5))* PublishAmerica, Inc.
Hartman. Raising Randy: A Compelling Story of Surviving Child Abuse, Neglect, Alcoholism, & a Dysfunctional Family. 2009. 236p. 28.95 *(978-1-4401-2557-6(8))*; pap. 18.95 *(978-1-4401-2565-2(1))* iUniverse, Inc.
Healy, Thomas. I Have Heard You Calling in the Night. 2007. (ENG.). 224p. per. 13.00 *(978-0-15-603371-8(2)*, Mariner Bks.) Houghton Mifflin Harcourt Trade & Reference Pubs.
Hooten, Claude "Hoot". Drunk & Disorderly, Again: My Name Is Hoot, I'm an Alcoholic. 2009. (ENG.). pap. 17.95 *(978-1-60037-548-4(0))* Morgan James Publishing.
Jack London. John Barleycorn. l.t. ed. 2007. (ENG.). 200p. pap. 21.99 *(978-1-4264-7146-9(7))* BiblioBazaar.
Jensen, George H. Some of the Words are Theirs: A Memoir of an Alcoholic Family. Meyer, Craig A., ed. 2009. 29.95 *(978-0-913785-09-6(1)*, Moon City Pr.) Department of English.
Jericho, Preston. Jaundiced. 2007. (ENG.). 516p. per. 34.95 *(978-1-4241-6237-6(8))* PublishAmerica, Inc.
Karr, Mary. Lit: A Memoir. (P. S. Ser.). 2010. (ENG.). 400p. pap. 14.99 *(978-0-06-059699-6(6)*, HarperPerennial) 2009. 578p. pap. 25.99 *(978-0-06-188547-1(9)*, HarperLuxe) HarperCollins Pubs.
Kathleen, S. Drink Up! How Ten Days Ended a Lifetime of Addiction. 2010. 160p. pap. 14.49 *(978-1-4567-1053-8(2))* AuthorHouse.
Kaufman, Alan. Drunken Angel. 2011. (ENG.). 360p. 25.00 *(978-1-936740-02-4(8)*, Viva Editions) Cleis Pr.
Keck, JR, William C. From Addiction to Miracles. 2007. (Illus.). 292p. per. 18.95 *(978-0-9794424-1-4(9))* Keck, William C.
Kincaid, Robert Luke. Stronger Now: Story of a Recovering Alcoholic & Complete Tetraplegic. 2009. 152p. pap. 14.99 *(978-1-4490-3546-4(9))* AuthorHouse.
Knight, Travis. "Tough Love" - A Life Transforming. 2007. 200p. pap. 7.99 *(978-0-9791604-1-7(3))* Focus On Recovery.
Kucera, Dina. Everything I Never Wanted to Be: A memoir of alcoholism & addiction, faith & family, hope & Humor. 2010. (ENG.). 216p. pap. 14.95 *(978-0-9825794-3-5(6))* Dream of Things.
Lee, Janice. The Sacrifice of Love, 1 vol. 2010. 108p. pap. 19.95 *(978-1-4489-9523-3(X))* PublishAmerica, Inc.
Lee, Jason Kallen. Winter's End. 2007. 100p. per. 11.95 *(978-0-595-47038-9(6))* iUniverse, Inc.
Leitch, Tom. Shamrocks, Trolls, Angels & Drunks. 2011. 344p. pap. 16.95 **(978-1-936400-90-4(1))** Mill City Pr., Inc.
Lewry, David. Angst. 2010. 176p. pap. 21.95 *(978-0-557-34605-9(3))* Lulu Enterprises Inc.
—Head. 2010. 220p. pap. 21.95 *(978-0-557-35867-0(1))* Lulu Enterprises Inc.
London, Jack. John Barleycorn. 2007. (ENG.). 216p. 27.95 *(978-1-4218-3258-6(5))*; per. 12.95 *(978-1-4218-3358-3(1))* 1st World Publishing, Inc. (1st World Library - Literary Society).
—John Barleycorn. 2008. 204p. 25.99 *(978-0-554-24677-2(5))* 2008. 204p. 22.99 *(978-0-554-33980-1(3))* 2007. (ENG.). 182p. pap. 19.99 *(978-1-4264-7070-7(3))* BiblioBazaar.
—John Barleycorn. 2008. (ENG.). 100p. pap. 8.99 *(978-1-4209-3093-1(1))* Digireads.com.
—John Barleycorn. 2007. (ENG.). 176p. per. *(978-1-4065-5221-8(6))* Dodo Pr.
—John Barleycorn. 132p. 2009. pap. *(978-1-4068-7735-9(2))* 2007. (ENG.). per. *(978-1-4068-1491-0(1))* Echo Library.
—John Barleycorn. 2007. (ENG.). 220p. 34.75 *(978-1-934568-09-5(0))* Ellis, Frederick.
—John Barleycorn. 2010. 356p. pap. 22.95 *(978-0-557-50352-0(3))* Lulu Enterprises Inc.
—John Barleycorn. 2008. (Twelve-Point Ser.). lib. bdg. *(978-1-58287-486-9(7))*; lib. bdg. 26.00 *(978-1-58287-969-7(9))* North Bks.
—John Barleycorn. 2008. 184p. pap. 13.99 *(978-1-59547-600-5(8))* NuVision Pubns., LLC.
—John Barleycorn: Alcoholic Memoirs. Sutherland, John, ed. 2009. (Oxford World's Classics Ser.). (ENG.). 288p. pap. 13.95 *(978-0-19-955557-4(5))* Oxford Univ. Pr., Inc.
—John Barleycorn: Alcoholic Memoirs. 2009. 316p. pap. 30.75 **(978-1-113-78205-2(6))** BiblioBazaar.
London, Jack. John Barleycorn: Alcoholic Memoirs. 2009. (ENG.). 313p. pap. 23.99 *(978-1-113-78199-4(8))*; pap. 24.99 *(978-1-113-78201-4(3))* BiblioBazaar. (BiblioLife).
Lorang, Levi. I've Lost My Way. 2010. 328p. pap. 21.98 *(978-0-557-32178-0(6))* Lulu Enterprises Inc.
Lourenço, Antonio Filipe. Adicciones, Paraisos e Infiernos. 2011. (SPA.). 136p. 23.95 **(978-1-4620-3454-3(3))**; pap. 13.95 **(978-1-4620-3455-0(1))** iUniverse, Inc.
Maclean. No, I Tell a Lie, It Was Tuesday. (Illus.). 192p. pap. 22.99 *(978-1-85626-309-2(6))* Cathie, Kyle Ltd. GBR. Dist: Trafalgar Square Publishing.
Madden, Aodhan. Fear & Loathing in Dublin. 2010. (ENG.). 184p. pap. 23.95 *(978-1-905483-82-2(1))* Liberties Pr. IRL. Dist: Dufour Editions, Inc.
McIlwain, Bill. Dancing Naked with the Rolling Stones: A Life in News & a Good-Bye to Booze. 2007. 240p. pap. 18.95 *(978-0-9789736-1-2(5))*; 22.95 *(978-0-9789736-0-5(7))* Winoca Pr.
McMahon, Mike. The Backroads of My Mind: — An Anthology. 2007. 168p. per. 14.95 *(978-1-4251-1155-7(6))* Trafford Publishing.
McPhee, Gregory. Addicted & Convicted. 2011. 152p. pap. 14.95 **(978-1-4620-1853-6(X))** iUniverse, Inc.
Moore, Robert. There's Moore to Life. 2011. 158p. pap. **(978-0-9869152-0-8(3))** Insomniac Pr.
N., Michael & N., Virginia. Hoot 'N Gin. 2008. 312p. 31.95 *(978-0-595-49177-3(4))* iUniverse, Inc.
—Hoot 'N Gin: Write to Recovery. 2008. 312p. pap. 21.95 *(978-0-595-48269-6(4))* iUniverse, Inc.
Nekich, Eric J. Finding 5% of My Life, 1 vol. 2009. 53p. pap. 16.95 *(978-1-4489-2156-0(2))* PublishAmerica, Inc.
O'Brien, Alberta L. Good Morning, Who! 2010. 244p. 29.99 *(978-1-4415-8872-2(8))*; pap. 19.99 *(978-1-4415-8871-5(X))* Xlibris Corp.
Otis, Carre & Schwyzer, Hugo. Beauty, Disrupted: A Memoir. 2011. (ENG.). 256p. 25.99 *(978-0-06-202445-9(0))* HarperCollins Pubs.
Page, Robert. The Presence. 2010. (ENG.). 128p. pap. 19.95 *(978-1-84694-268-6(3))* Hunt, John Publishing Ltd. GBR. Dist: National Bk. Network.
PARKS, RONALD. Only with Vigilance. 2010. 442p. pap. 22.95 *(978-0-557-36008-6(0))* Lulu Enterprises Inc.
Parsons, A. To Hell & Back. 2007. (ENG.). 80p. per. *(978-1-84747-175-8(7))* Chipmunkapublishing.
Poitras, Michele Sandoval. Shattered Pieces, Loving Heart. 2011. 172p. pap. 14.95 *(978-1-4327-6818-8(2))* Outskirts Pr., Inc.
Pruett, Sue. Our Marriage: Surviving Addiction & Thriving in Sobriety. 2010. 256p. 26.99 *(978-1-4520-7589-1(1))*; pap. 16.99 *(978-1-4520-7588-4(3))* AuthorHouse.
Quarteroni, Rosemary. Dead & Moving. 2010. 194p. pap. 14.99 *(978-1-60957-623-3(3))* Xulon Pr., Inc.
REM007. New Beginnings: How God Delivered Me from Alcohol & Drugs! 2011. 100p. pap. 15.00 *(978-1-4269-5298-2(8))* Trafford Publishing.
Rheaume, Jill. Surviving Me: the Personal Journey of a Recovering Alcoholic. 2008. 147p. pap. 14.95 *(978-1-4357-0611-8(0))* Lulu Enterprises Inc.
Rhodes, Richard C. A Counselor Looks at the Big Book: A Clinician's View of the Book Alcoholics Anonymous. 2009. 168p. pap. 19.95 *(978-1-58982-500-0(4)*, Millennial Mind Publishing) American Bk. Publishing Group.
Rich, Marie. Was Lost but Now Found: The Autobiography of Marie Rich. 2011. 208p. pap. 15.04 **(978-1-4269-9428-9(1))** Trafford Publishing.
Ruben, S. From Darkness to Light: A Story of A Soul in Darkness. 2010. 124p. 22.33 *(978-1-4269-4615-8(5))*; pap. 12.33 *(978-1-4269-4539-7(6))* Trafford Publishing.
Rupp, Jeffrey A. Hi, My Name Is Jeff & I'm an Alcoholic¿: The True Life Struggle of a Lonely Alcoholic, 1 vol. 2010. 506p. pap. 34.95 *(978-1-4489-8260-8(X))* PublishAmerica, Inc.
Rusch, Carol Ann. This Lady Here: I'll Drink to That. 2010. 196p. (ENG.). 24.99 *(978-1-4520-2095-2(7))*; pap. 14.49 *(978-1-4520-2094-5(9))* AuthorHouse.
Ruth. Terminal Addiction, 1 vol. 2009. 154p. pap. 24.95 *(978-1-61546-429-6(8))* PublishAmerica, Inc.
Schnerch, Patrick J. & Baldwin, Marc D. The Peaceful Warrior: The Memoirs of a Damaged Mind & Soul. 2006. (ENG.). 212p. per. 17.39 *(978-1-4120-9508-2(5))* Trafford Publishing.
Scoblic, Sacha Z. Unwasted: My Lush Sobriety. 2011. (ENG.). 272p. 14.95 *(978-0-8065-3429-9(X)*, Citadel Pr.) Kensington Publishing Corp.
Serrano, Richard A. My Grandfather's Prison: A Story of Death & Deceit in 1940s Kansas City. 2009. (ENG., Illus.). 168p. (gr. 9). 24.95 *(978-0-8262-1864-3(4))* Univ. of Missouri Pr.
Services, Aa. Alcoholics Anonymous - Big Book - 2007. 192p. *(978-956-291-200-6(0))* Editorial Benei Noaj.
Shelly, Brian. Drunkeneese, 1 vol. 2009. 227p. pap. 24.95 *(978-1-60703-085-0(3))* PublishAmerica, Inc.
Simmons, Parke E. Next to Normal: One Man's Battle with Alcohol & Sexual Addictions. 2010. 552p. 43.50 *(978-1-4269-1237-5(4))*; pap. 33.50 *(978-1-4269-1236-8(5))* Trafford Publishing.
Smith, Nathan. Mom's Idea: A Journey Through Madness. 2010. 108p. 27.50 *(978-1-4269-3745-3(8))*; pap. 17.50 *(978-1-4269-3744-6(X))* Trafford Publishing.
Steinberg, Neil. Drunkard: A Hard-Drinking Life. 2009. (ENG.). 288p. (gr. 12-18). 15.00 *(978-0-452-29543-8(2)*, Plume) Penguin Group (USA) Inc.
Storm, Jennifer. Blackout Girl: Growing up & Drying Out in America. 2008. (ENG.). 280p. pap. 14.95 *(978-1-59285-468-4(0))* Hazelden Publishing & Educational Services.
—Leave the Light On: A Memoir of Recovery & Self-Discovery. 2010. (ENG.). 256p. pap. 14.95 *(978-0-9818482-2-8(2))* Central Recovery Pr.
Toth, John. The Alcoholic Ironman: A Memoir. 2011. pap. 16.99 **(978-1-61346-147-1(X))** Tate Publishing & Enterprises, LLC.
Valle, Stephen J. Della. Rising above the Influence: A True Story about Alcohol, Drugs, & Recovery. 2008. pap. 21.95 *(978-0-9801776-0-2(X))* Oak Ridge Pr.

Velez-Mitchell, Jane. IWant: My Journey from Addition & Overconsumption to a Simpler, Honest Life. 2010. (ENG.). 288p. pap. 14.95 *(978-0-7573-1536-7(4))* Health Communications, Inc.

Wade, Meg Henderson. Confessions of a Southern Baby-Boomer: How I Survived Crack Cocaine Addiction, the Mafia & Other Totally True Tales. 2010. 80p. pap. 10.88 *(978-1-4520-2651-0(3))* AuthorHouse.

Wade, Raleigh. Piney Woods Conman: The Life Story of Raleigh Wade, 1 vol. 2010. 118p. pap. 19.95 *(978-1-4489-4047-9(8))* PublishAmerica, Inc.

Walsh, Laura. Ashamed. 2011. (ENG., Illus.). 240p. pap. 15.95 ***(978-1-84596-763-5(1))*** Mainstream Publishing Co., Ltd. GBR. Dist: Independent Pubs. Group.

Walters, Judy. How it Was & Is for Me. 2011. 116p. 22.95 ***(978-1-4620-5093-2(X))***; pap. 12.95 ***(978-1-4620-5094-9(8))*** iUniverse, Inc.

Ware, Ronald. Seven Thunders Part. 2007. 492p. (ENG.). 35.99 *(978-1-60266-670-2(9))*; per. 23.99 *(978-1-60266-669-6(5))* Xulon Pr., Inc.

Watts, Jack. Hi, My Name Is Jack: One Man's Story of the Tumultuous Road to Sobriety & a Changed Life. 2011. (ENG.). 240p. 22.99 *(978-1-4391-9270-2(7)*, Howard Bks.) Howard Books.

Webster, Michael E. Surviving Life As a Dumbass: It Doesn't Have to be a Life Sentence. 2008. 180p. 26.95 *(978-0-595-71859-7(0))*; pap. 16.95 *(978-0-595-47078-5(5))* iUniverse, Inc.

Wiley, John. Love & Sobriety: Suffering became very difficult, love & sobriety helped me Change. 2007. (Illus.). 160p. per. 15.95 *(978-1-59713-033-2(8))* Goose River Pr.

Williams, Alan. One for the Road! 2010. (Illus.). 228p. pap. *(978-1-84748-733-9(5))* Athena Pr.

Wise, Joe. I Want to Go to Heaven but Not Yet. 2011. 184p. 29.99 ***(978-1-4568-0131-1(7))***; pap. 19.99 ***(978-1-4568-0130-4(9))*** Xlibris Corp.

Zorn, Jack. Never Say Calf Rope: A Grandfather's Legacy. 2009. 244p. 24.99 *(978-1-4490-4663-7(0))*; pap. 15.99 *(978-1-4490-4664-4(9))* AuthorHouse.

ALCOHOLICS—FAMILY RELATIONSHIPS

Al-Anon Family Group Headquarters. Hope for Today. 2007. 379p. 10.00 *(978-0-910034-39-5(7))* Al-Anon Family Group Headquarters, Inc.

Al-Anon Family Group Headquarters, Inc Staff, contrib. by. Discovering Choices: Our Recovery in Relationships. 2008. 336p. *(978-0-9815017-3-4(7))* Al-Anon Family Group Headquarters, Inc.

Alcoholics Anonymous. Living with an Alcoholic: With the Help on Al-Anon. 2011. 158p. 41.95 ***(978-1-258-02841-1(7))*** Literary Licensing, LLC.

Arielle, Lia Marie. Amen: Resurrections of Faith, Hope & Love, 1 vol. 2009. 161p. pap. 24.95 *(978-1-60703-522-0(7))* PublishAmerica, Inc.

Bey, Douglas & Bey, Deborah. Loving an Adult Child of an Alcoholic. 2007. (ENG.). 240p. per. 16.95 *(978-1-59077-117-4(6))* Evans, M. & Co., Inc.

Borchert, William G. The Lois Wilson Story: When Love Is Not Enough. (ENG.). 424p. 2010. pap. 15.95 *(978-1-59285-980-1(1))* 2008. (Illus.). pap. 15.95 *(978-1-59285-598-8(9))* Hazelden Publishing & Educational Services.

Cassidy-Watson, Maxine. Cass: A True Story of Alcoholism & Its Effect on the Alcoholic & the Family. 2008. 48p. pap. 16.95 *(978-1-60563-095-3(0))* PublishAmerica, Inc.

Centre For Addiction And Mental Health. Wishes & Worries: Coping with a Parent Who Drinks Too Much Alcohol. 2011. (Coping Ser.). (ENG., Illus.). 32p. (J). (gr. k-3). 17.95 *(978-1-77049-238-7(0))* Tundra Bks., Inc./Livres Toundra, Inc. CAN. Dist: Random Hse., Inc.

Copeland, Paul. If I Can't Have You. 2009. 98p. pap. 10.67 *(978-0-557-04871-7(0))* Lulu Enterprises Inc.

DeSantis, Richard P. & Manney, Gerald J. Suspended Adolescence: Understanding & Dealing with Teenage Substance Abusers. 2007. (Illus.). 99p. pap. 12.95 *(978-0-9798141-1-2(1))* suspendedadolescence.com.

Encyclopaedia Britannica, Inc., compiled by. When Your Parents Drink. 2008. 49.95 *(978-1-59339-635-0(X))* Encyclopaedia Britannica, Inc.

Ferreira, Melinda. Rays of Grace: A Story of Strength & Spirit. 2010. 148p. pap. 14.99 *(978-0-615-30016-0(2))* Hampton Pr., The.

Fischer, Judith L., et al. Familial Responses to Alcohol Problems. 2007. 163p. per. 49.95 *(978-0-7890-3516-5(2))*; (ENG., Illus.). 182p. 175.00 *(978-0-7890-3515-8(4))* Routledge.

Fitzpatrick, Michael. We Recovered Too: The Family Groups' Beginnings in the Pioneers' Own Words. 2011. (ENG.). 240p. 17.95 ***(978-1-61649-165-9(5))*** Hazelden Publishing & Educational Services.

Forrester, Donald & Harwin, Judith. Parents Who Misuse Drugs & Alcohol: Effective Interventions in Social Work & Child Protection. 2011. (Wiley Child Protection & Policy Ser.). (ENG., Illus.). 262p. pap. 47.95 *(978-0-470-87151-5(2))*; 110.95 *(978-0-470-87150-8(4))* Wiley, John & Sons, Inc. (Wiley).

Graham, K. & Bernards, S. Unhappy Hours: Alcohol & Partner Aggression in the Americas. 2009. (PAHO Scientific Publication No 631 Ser.). 258p. pap. 30.00 *(978-92-75-11631-9(8))* Pan American Health Organization (PAHO).

Harris, Phil. The Concerned Other: New Theory & the Evidence Base for Changing Problematic Drug & Alcohol Users Through Their Family Members. 2011. 136p. pap. 33.95 *(978-1-905541-66-9(X))* Russell Hse. Publishing Ltd. GBR. Dist: International Specialized Bk. Services.

Hartman. Raising Randy: A Compelling Story of Surviving Child Abuse, Neglect, Alcoholism, & a Dysfunctional Family. 2009. 236p. 28.95 *(978-1-4401-2567-6(8))*; pap. 18.95 *(978-1-4401-2565-2(1))* iUniverse, Inc.

Jay, Jeff. Love First: A Family's Guide to Intervention. 2nd rev. ed. 2008. (ENG.). 360p. pap. 15.95 *(978-1-59285-661-9(6))* Hazelden Publishing & Educational Services.

Jensen, George H. Some of the Words are Theirs: A Memoir of an Alcoholic Family. Meyer, Craig A., ed. 2009. 29.95 *(978-0-913785-09-6(1)*, Moon City Pr.) Department of English.

Jones, Kaylie. Lies My Mother Never Told Me: A Memoir. 2010. (ENG.). 400p. pap. 14.99 *(978-0-06-177871-1(0)*, HarperPerennial) HarperCollins Pubs.

Jones, Lou. Happy Days Are Here Again. 2008. 48p. pap. 16.95 *(978-1-60703-163-5(9))* PublishAmerica, Inc.

Karr, Justin. Alcoholism. 2007. (Social Issues Firsthand Ser.). (ENG., Illus.). 142p. (YA). (gr. 8-12). lib. bdg. 31.80 *(978-0-7377-3832-2(4)*, Greenhaven Pr., Inc.) Cengage Gale.

Kraft, William F. When You Love a Functional Alcoholic. 2011. 176p. pap. *(978-0-8091-4679-6(7))* Paulist Pr.

McMahon, John. Bottled Up: How to Survive Living with a Problem Drinker. 2010. (ENG.). 192p. pap. 16.95 *(978-0-7459-5515-5(0))* Lion Hudson PLC GBR. Dist: Independent Pubs. Group.

Middelton-Moz, Jane & Dwinell, Lorie. After the Tears: Helping Adult Children of Alcoholics Heal Their Childhood Trauma. 2nd rev. ed. 2010. (ENG., Illus.). 312p. pap. 14.95 *(978-0-7573-1513-8(5))* Health Communications, Inc.

Morgan, Oliver J. & Litzke, Cheryl H. Family Intervention in Substance Abuse: Current Best Practices. 2008. (Illus.). 247p. (ENG.). 62.95 *(978-0-7890-3758-9(0))*; 125.00 *(978-0-7890-3757-2(2))* Routledge.

O'Connor, Ed. D. I Can Be Me: A Helping Book for Children of Alcoholic Parents. 2009. 184p. pap. 14.95 *(978-1-4259-9899-8(2))* AuthorHouse.

Olsen, Patricia & Levounis, Petros. Sober Siblings: How to Help Your Alcoholic Brother or Sister - And Not Lose Yourself. 2008. (ENG.). 240p. pap. 16.00 *(978-1-60094-055-2(2))* Da Capo Pr., Inc.

Poitras, Michele Sandoval. Shattered Pieces, Loving Heart. 2011. 172p. pap. 14.95 *(978-1-4327-6818-8(2))* Outskirts Pr., Inc.

Pretlow, Louis. Chasing Serenity: Married with Alcohol. 2007. 196p. (ENG.). 16.95 *(978-1-4327-0870-2(8))*; per. 10.95 *(978-1-4327-0823-8(6))* Outskirts Pr., Inc.

Ryan, Gary R. Blessings in Disguise: A Tale of Redemption. 2009. 268p. pap. 20.95 *(978-0-595-53231-5(4))* iUniverse, Inc.

Schaffer, Lesley Ann. Pet People: Surviving the Alcoholic Home. 2006. (ENG.). 23.50 *(978-1-59330-426-3(9))*; pap. 10.95 *(978-1-59330-425-6(0))* Aventine Pr.

Tirbutt, Edmund & Tirbutt, Helen. Beat the Booze: A Comprehensive Guide to Combating Drink Problems in All Walks of Life: Reclaim Your Life. 2008. (ENG.). xi, 289p. per. 19.99 *(978-1-905641-42-0(7))* Harriman Hse. Publishing GBR. Dist: Ingram Pub. Services.

Valle, Stephen J. Della. Rising above the Influence: A True Story about Alcohol, Drugs, & Recovery. 2008. pap. 21.95 *(978-0-9801776-0-2(X))* Oak Ridge Pr.

ALCOHOLICS—PSYCHOLOGY

see Alcoholism—Psychological Aspects

ALCOHOLICS ANONYMOUS

see also Twelve-Step Programs

A.A. Grapevine Inc Staff, contrib. by. In Our Own Words: Stories of Young AAs in Recovery: From the Pages of the AA Grapevine. 2007. xi, 164p. pap. *(978-0-933685-64-2(5))* AA Grapevine, Inc.

AA Services Staff. Alcoholics Anonymous Big Book Special E. 2006. 156p. per. *(978-956-291-357-7(0))* Editorial Benei Noaj.

AA Today. (Illus.). 111p. reprint ed. pap. 5.00 *(978-0-933685-15-4(7))* AA Grapevine, Inc.

Al-Anon Family Group Headquarters. Hope for Today. 2007. 379p. 10.00 *(978-0-910034-39-5(7))* Al-Anon Family Group Headquarters, Inc.

Alcoholics Anonymous First Edition Reprint: By the Anonymous Press. reprint ed. 2009. 416p. 15.00 *(978-1-892959-04-1(6))* 2007. (ENG.). 432p. pap. 4.00 *(978-1-892959-15-7(1))* Anonymous Pr., The.

Alcoholics Anonymous Mini Edition: By the Anonymous Press. 18th ed. 2009. (ENG.). 256p. per. 2.60 *(978-1-892959-01-0(1))* Anonymous Pr., The.

Alcoholics Anonymous Study Edition - Black: By the Anonymous Press. 2nd rev. deluxe ed. 2009. 576p. lthr. 17.00 *(978-1-892959-02-7(X))* Anonymous Pr., The.

Alcoholics Anonymous Study Edition - Black/Gilded: By the Anonymous Press. 2nd rev. deluxe ed. 2007. 576p. lthr. 25.00 *(978-1-892959-11-9(9))* Anonymous Pr., The.

Alcoholics Anonymous Study Edition - Burgundy: By the Anonymous Press. 2nd rev. deluxe ed. 2009. 576p. lthr. 17.00 *(978-1-892959-10-2(0))* Anonymous Pr., The.

Alcoholics Anonymous Study Edition - Burgundy/Gilded: By the Anonymous Press. 2nd rev. deluxe ed. 2007. 576p. lthr. 25.00 *(978-1-892959-12-6(7))* Anonymous Pr., The.

Alcoholics Anonymous Study Edition: By the Anonymous Press. 6th ed. 2007. (ENG.). 576p. pap. 6.25 *(978-1-892959-03-4(8))* Anonymous Pr., The.

Alcoholics Anonymous World Services. A. A. Service Manual Combined with Twelve Concepts for World Service. 2012. (Illus.). 73p. pap. 3.55 *(978-0-916856-14-4(3))* Alcoholics Anonymous World Services, Inc.

Alcoholics Anonymous World Services, Inc. Staff. Alcoholics Anonymous. (ROM.). *(978-0-916856-40-3(2))*; (TAG.). *(978-0-916856-56-4(9))* Alcoholics Anonymous World Services, Inc.

—Alcoholics Anonymous Big Book Special E. 2006. 164p. per. *(978-956-291-265-5(5))* Editorial Benei Noaj.

—E-AA: A reference to Alcoholics Anonymous. 2009. E-Book 20.00 incl. cd-rom *(978-1-892959-08-9(9))* Anonymous Pr., The.

Alcoholics Anonymous World Services, Inc. Staff, contrib. by. Alcohólicos Anónimos: El Relato de Cómo Muchos Miles de Hombres y Mujeres Se Han Recuperado Del Alcoholismo. 3rd ed. 2008. xxxiv, 528p. *(978-1-893007-95-6(2))* Alcoholics Anonymous World Services, Inc.

American Health Research Institute. Alcoholics Anonymous (AA) Activities, Benefits, Therapies for Alcoholism & Values of Self-Help Programs with Index & Medical Analysis of New Research Information for All Nations. 2006. (Illus.). 160p. 69.95 *(978-0-7883-4597-5(4)*, 0-7883-4458-7) ABBE Pubs. Assn. of Washington, D.C.

Anonymous. The Book That Started It All: The Original Working Manuscript of Alcoholics Anonymous. 2010. (ENG.). 248p. 65.00 *(978-1-59285-947-4(X))* Hazelden Publishing & Educational Services.

—The Little Red Book. 2009. 110p. *(978-1-60796-136-9(9))* Editorial Benei Noaj.

—The Little Red Book: An Interpretation of the Twelve Steps of the Alcoholics Anonymous Program. 2010. 160p. pap. 8.50 *(978-1-57898-892-1(6))* Martino Publishing.

B., Mel. 101 Meeting Starters: A Guide to Better Twelve Step Discussions. 2007. (ENG.). 224p. pap. 13.95 *(978-1-59285-369-4(2))* Hazelden Publishing & Educational Services.

Batiuk, Tom. My Name Is Funky... & I'm an Alcoholic: A Story about Alcoholism & Recovery. 1t. ed. 2007. (ENG., Illus.). 152p. pap. 13.95 *(978-1-59285-377-9(3))* Hazelden Publishing & Educational Services.

The Best of the Grapevine, 3 vols. Vol. 1. pap. 7.95 *(978-0-933685-38-3(6))* Vol. 2. pap. 7.95 *(978-0-933685-39-0(4))* Vol. 3. pap. 7.95 *(978-0-933685-40-6(8))* AA Grapevine, Inc.

The Book That Started It All: The Original Working Manuscript of Alcoholics Anonymous. 2010. 125.00 *(978-1-61649-084-3(5))* Hazelden Publishing & Educational Services.

Borchert, William G. The Lois Wilson Story: When Love Is Not Enough. (ENG.). 424p. 2010. pap. 15.95 *(978-1-59285-980-1(1))* 2008. (Illus.). pap. 15.95 *(978-1-59285-598-8(9))* Hazelden Publishing & Educational Services.

Borden, Audrey. The History of Gay People in Alcoholics Anonymous: From the Beginning. 2007. (ENG.). 304p. 125.00 *(978-0-7890-3038-2(1))*; pap. 50.50 *(978-0-7890-3039-9(X))* Routledge.

Broom, Richard. Cocked & Loaded. 2010. (ENG.). 288p. pap. 14.95 *(978-0-7573-1367-7(1))* Health Communications, Inc.

Butler, Shane. Benign Anarchy: Alcoholics Anonymous in Ireland. 2010. 272p. pap. *(978-0-7165-3064-0(3))* Irish Academic Pr. IRL. Dist: International Specialized Bk. Services.

C., Joe. There Is a Solution: A Personal Spiritual Voyage of Recovery from Alcoholism. 2006. pap. 21.99 *(978-1-84728-552-2(X))* Lulu Enterprises Inc.

Fitzpatrick, Michael & Borchert, William G. 1000 Years of Sobriety: 20 People x 50 Years. 2010. (ENG.). 272p. pap. 14.95 *(978-1-59285-858-3(9))* Hazelden Publishing & Educational Services.

Friends of Spirit. Seven Lessons for Living, Learning & Working with Spirit. 2007. 92p. per. 12.95 *(978-0-9796629-0-4(7))* Author One Stop.

Gillespie, James. Finding a Home Group: A Guide to Choosing the Right Twelve Step Meeting for You. 2011. (ENG.). 116p. pap. 9.95 ***(978-1-61649-095-9(0))*** Hazelden Publishing & Educational Services.

Hedblom, Jack H. Last Call: Alcoholism & Recovery. 2007. (ENG., Illus.). 224p. 42.00 *(978-0-8018-8677-5(5))*; per. 18.95 *(978-0-8018-8678-2(3))* Johns Hopkins Univ. Pr.

Hornbacher, Marya. Sane: Mental Illness, Addiction, & the 12 Steps. 2010. (ENG.). 180p. pap. 14.95 *(978-1-59285-824-8(4))* Hazelden Publishing & Educational Services.

Keating, Thomas. Divine Intimacy & Addiction: AA & Centering Prayer. 2009. 128p. 18.00 *(978-1-59056-115-7(5))* Lantern Bks.

Keating, Thomas & S, Tom. Divine Therapy & Addiction: Centering Prayer & the Twelve Steps. 2009. 20.00 *(978-1-59056-144-7(9))* Lantern Bks.

The Little Red Book. 2008. 112p. pap. *(978-956-291-627-1(8))* Editorial Benei Noaj.

Liversage, Jerry J. Responding 12-Step Recovery: Responding to the Truth-Recovery Through Jesus. 2009. 324p. pap. 21.99 *(978-1-60791-915-5(X))* Xulon Pr., Inc.

Manlowe, Jennifer. Loving Life As It Is. 2008. 191p. pap. 21.95 *(978-0-615-16862-3(0))* Life Design Inc,.

Manville, Bill. Cool, Hip, & Sober: 88 Ways to Beat Booze & Drugs. mass mkt. *(978-0-7653-4212-6(X)*, Forge Bks.) Doherty, Tom Assocs., LLC.

O'Halloran, Sean. Talking Oneself Sober: The Discourse of Alcoholics Anonymous. 2008. 109.95 *(978-1-60497-552-9(0))* Cambria Pr.

Rhodes, Richard C. A Counselor Looks at the Big Book: A Clinician's View of the Book Alcoholics Anonymous. 2009. 168p. pap. 19.95 *(978-1-58982-500-0(4)*, Millennial Mind Publishing) American Bk. Publishing Group.

S., Stan. The God Thing in A. A. Sobriety Is Just the Ante. 2010. 156p. pap. 19.95 *(978-1-4490-3937-0(5))* AuthorHouse.

Sanders, Jolene M. Women in Alcoholics Anonymous: Recovery & Empowerment. 2009. 175p. 55.00 *(978-1-935049-08-1(9))* FirstForumPress.

Services, Aa. Alcoholics Anonymous - Big Book - 2007. 192p. *(978-956-291-200-6(0))* Editorial Benei Noaj.

Travis, Trysh. The Language of the Heart: A Cultural History of the Recovery Movement from Alcoholics Anonymous to Oprah Winfrey. 2010. (ENG., Illus.). 376p. 35.00 *(978-0-8078-3319-3(3))* Univ. of North Carolina Pr.

W., Bill. Alcoholics Anonymous: The Original 1939 Edition. 2011. (Dover Empower Your Life Ser.). (ENG.). 432p. pap. 12.95 *(978-0-486-48059-6(3))* Dover Pubns., Inc.

W, Bill. The Little Red Book. 2011. 78p. pap. 7.49 ***(978-1-61720-287-2(8))*** Wilder Pubns., Ltd.

W, Bill, et al. The Little Red Book an Interpretation of the Twelve Steps of the Alcoholics Anonymous Program. 2011. 160p. pap. 6.95 ***(978-1-61427-065-2(1))*** Martino Publishing.

Webster, Edward A. Stools & Bottles: A Study of Character Defects — 31 Daily Meditations. 2010. 160p. pap. 10.00 *(978-1-57898-930-0(2))* Martino Publishing.

Wilson, Larry. The Storytellers. 2009. 188p. 30.52 *(978-0-557-02485-8(4))* Lulu Enterprises Inc.

Ziffer, Ronald. Beyond the Rhetoric: The Truth Will Set You Free. 2008. 128p. pap. 11.99 *(978-1-4389-0323-1(5))* AuthorHouse.

ALCOHOLISM

see also Alcoholics; Children of Alcoholics; Liquor Industry and Trade; Liquor Laws

Aaslid, Flore Singer. Facing the Dragon. 2010. 268p. pap. *(978-3-639-12155-1(4))* VDM Verlag Dr. Mueller e.K.

Adamec, Christine & Gold, Mark S. The Encyclopedia of Alcoholism & Alcohol Abuse. 2010. (Library of Health & Living Ser.). (Illus.). 408p. (C). (gr. 9-18). 75.00 *(978-0-8160-7709-0(6))* Facts On File, Inc.

Adaw. Alcoholism & Drug Abuse Weekly 23 22. 2011. 14.56 *(978-1-118-02085-2(5)*, Wiley) Wiley, John & Sons, Inc.

—Alcoholism & Drug Abuse Weekly 23 23. 2011. 14.56 *(978-1-118-02086-9(3)*, Wiley) Wiley, John & Sons, Inc.

—Alcoholism & Drug Abuse Weekly 23 24. 2011. 14.56 *(978-1-118-02087-6(1)*, Wiley) Wiley, John & Sons, Inc.

—Alcoholism & Drug Abuse Weekly 23 25. 2011. 14.56 *(978-1-118-02088-3(X)*, Wiley) Wiley, John & Sons, Inc.

—Alcoholism & Drug Abuse Weekly 23 26. 2011. 14.56 *(978-1-118-02089-0(8)*, Wiley) Wiley, John & Sons, Inc.

—Alcoholism & Drug Abuse Weekly 23 27. 2011. 14.56 *(978-1-118-02090-6(1)*, Wiley) Wiley, John & Sons, Inc.

—Alcoholism & Drug Abuse Weekly 23 28. 2011. 14.56 *(978-1-118-02091-3(X)*, Wiley) Wiley, John & Sons, Inc.

—Alcoholism & Drug Abuse Weekly 23 29. 2011. 14.56 *(978-1-118-02092-0(8)*, Wiley) Wiley, John & Sons, Inc.

—Alcoholism & Drug Abuse Weekly 23 31. 2011. 14.56 *(978-1-118-02098-2(7)*, Wiley) Wiley, John & Sons, Inc.

—Alcoholism & Drug Abuse Weekly 23 32. 2011. 14.56 *(978-1-118-02093-7(6)*, Wiley) Wiley, John & Sons, Inc.

—Alcoholism & Drug Abuse Weekly 23 33. 2011. 14.56 *(978-1-118-02094-4(4)*, Wiley) Wiley, John & Sons, Inc.

—Alcoholism & Drug Abuse Weekly 23 34. 2011. 14.56 *(978-1-118-02095-1(2)*, Wiley) Wiley, John & Sons, Inc.

—Alcoholism & Drug Abuse Weekly 23 35. 2011. 14.56 *(978-1-118-02096-8(0)*, Wiley) Wiley, John & Sons, Inc.

—Alcoholism & Drug Abuse Weekly 23 36. 2011. 14.56 *(978-1-118-02097-5(9)*, Wiley) Wiley, John & Sons, Inc.

Addenbrooke. Addiction & Recovery. 2011. (ENG., Illus.). 224p. (C). 99.00 *(978-1-58391-724-4(1))* Routledge.

—Survivors of Addiction. 2011. (ENG., Illus.). 224p. (C). pap. 34.95 *(978-1-58391-725-1(X))* Routledge.

Adler, Patricia A., et al, eds. Drugs & the American Dream: An Anthology. 2012. (ENG., Illus.). 456p. pap. 59.95 ***(978-0-470-67027-9(4)***, Wiley-Blackwell) Wiley, John & Sons, Inc.

Alatalo, Päivikki. Markers of Liver Function & Oxidative Stress in Alcohol Consumers with or without Overweight. 2011. (Acta Universitatis Tamperensis Ser.). 104p. pap. 82.50 *(978-951-44-8365-3(0))* Tampere Univ. Pr. FIN. Dist: Coronet Bks.

Alcoholics Anonymous. Living with an Alcoholic: With the Help on Al-Anon. 2011. 158p. 41.95 ***(978-1-258-02841-1(7))*** Literary Licensing, LLC.

ALCOHOLISM & DRUG ABUSE WEEKLY 23 13. 2011. 14.56 *(978-1-118-02076-0(6)*, Wiley) Wiley, John & Sons, Inc.

ALCOHOLISM & DRUG ABUSE WEEKLY 23 14. 2011. 14.56 *(978-1-118-02077-7(4)*, Wiley) Wiley, John & Sons, Inc.

ALCOHOLISM & DRUG ABUSE WEEKLY 23 15. 2011. 14.56 *(978-1-118-02078-4(2)*, Wiley) Wiley, John & Sons, Inc.

ALCOHOLISM & DRUG ABUSE WEEKLY 23 16. 2011. 14.56 *(978-1-118-02079-1(0)*, Wiley) Wiley, John & Sons, Inc.

ALCOHOLISM & DRUG ABUSE WEEKLY 23 17. 2011. 14.56 *(978-1-118-02080-7(4)*, Wiley) Wiley, John & Sons, Inc.

ALCOHOLISM & DRUG ABUSE WEEKLY 23 18. 2011. 14.56 *(978-1-118-02081-4(2)*, Wiley) Wiley, John & Sons, Inc.

ALCOHOLISM & DRUG ABUSE WEEKLY 23 19. 2011. 14.56 *(978-1-118-02082-1(0)*, Wiley) Wiley, John & Sons, Inc.

ALCOHOLISM & DRUG ABUSE WEEKLY 23 20. 2011. 14.56 *(978-1-118-02083-8(9)*, Wiley) Wiley, John & Sons, Inc.

ALCOHOLISM & DRUG ABUSE WEEKLY 23 21. 2011. 14.56 *(978-1-118-02084-5(7)*, Wiley) Wiley, John & Sons, Inc.

Andrew, John Albion. The Errors of Prohibition. 2009. 78p. pap. *(978-0-217-38451-3(X))* Books LLC.

—The Errors of Prohibition. 2009. 110p. pap. 14.14 *(978-1-4589-1736-2(3))* General Bks. LLC.

—The Errors of Prohibition. 2006. 152p. per. 16.99 *(978-1-4255-1125-8(2))* MPublishing.

Anonymous. The Little Red Book: An Interpretation of the Twelve Steps of the Alcoholics Anonymous Program. 2010. 160p. pap. 8.50 *(978-1-57898-892-1(6))* Martino Publishing.

Anonymous. Twenty-Four Hours a Day. 2011. 160p. pap. 7.95 ***(978-1-61427-095-9(3))*** Martino Publishing.

Bancroft, Angus. Drugs, Intoxication & Society. 2009. (ENG.). 224p. 69.95 *(978-0-7456-3533-0(4))*; pap. 26.95 *(978-0-7456-3546-0(6))* Polity Pr. GBR. Dist: Wiley, John & Sons, Inc.

Barrie, Ken. Alcohol: Policy & Practice in Health & Social Care No. 15. 2011. (Illus.). 112p. pap. 29.99 *(978-1-906716-31-8(5))* Dunedin Academic Pr. GBR. Dist: International Specialized Bk. Services.

Bartone, John C., Sr. America & Its No. 1 Social Problem Is Alcoholism with Its Easy Way to Become Sick, Disabled or Diseased — Index of New Research Information for All Nations. 2006. (Illus.). 160p. 75.50 *(978-0-7883-4299-8(1)*, 07883-4299-1) ABBE Pubs. Assn. of Washington, D.C.

Baum, Diane Ganzer. There but for the Grace of God Go I. 2011. 124p. pap. 12.00 ***(978-1-61286-011-4(7))*** Avid Readers Publishing Group.

Behr, Edward. Prohibition: Thirteen Years That Changed America. 2011. (ENG., Illus.). 272p. pap. 14.95 *(978-1-61145-009-5(8)*, 611009, Arcade Publishing) Skyhorse Publishing Co., Inc.

Bell, Kirsten, et al, eds. Alcohol Tobacco & Obesity. 2011. (ENG., Illus.). 248p. (C). 125.00 *(978-0-415-59017-4(5))* Routledge.

Benton, Sarah Allen. Understanding the High-Functioning Alcoholic: Professional Views & Personal Insights. 2010. (ENG.). 224p. pap. 21.95 *(978-1-4422-0390-7(0))* Rowman & Littlefield Publishers, Inc.

Bergmann, Elaine F. Talking to My Mom Is Like Talking to a Brick Wall. 2007. 36p. per. 12.95 *(978-1-4327-0732-3(9))* Outskirts Pr., Inc.

The Best of the Grapevine, 3 vols. Vol. 1. pap. 7.95 *(978-0-933685-38-3(6))* Vol. 2. pap. 7.95 *(978-0-933685-39-0(4))* Vol. 3. pap. 7.95 *(978-0-933685-40-6(8))* AA Grapevine Inc.

Bill, Jersey. An Alcoholic's Story. 2010. 48p. pap. 9.98 *(978-1-4269-2967-0(6))* Trafford Publishing.

Boich, Robert. Excuse Me, Your Life Is Waiting! A Bridge from Addiction to Early Recovery. 2009. 152p. 24.95 *(978-1-4401-2107-4(9))*; pap. 14.95 *(978-1-4401-2105-0(2))* iUniverse, Inc.

The BROWN UNIVERSITY DIGEST of ADDICTION THEORY & APPLICATION, Volume 30, Number 4. 2011. 16.58 *(978-1-118-02002-9(2)*, Wiley) Wiley, John & Sons, Inc.

Brownell, Rachael. Mommy Doesn't Drink Here Anymore: Getting Through the First Year of Sobriety. 2009. (ENG.). 176p. pap. 16.95 *(978-1-57324-409-1(0)*, Conari Pr.) Red Wheel/Weiser.

Browning, Pam. Sobriety, a Love Affair with Life. 2009. 60p. pap. 9.95 *(978-1-60693-951-8(2)*, Eloquent Bks.) AEG Literary Publishing Services, Inc.

Buttner, George E. An Unsuspecting Trap: One Man's Victory over Alcoholism. 2007. 337p. per. 24.99 *(978-1-60247-258-7(0))* Tate Publishing & Enterprises, LLC.

C., Joe. There Is a Solution: A Personal Spiritual Voyage of Recovery from Alcoholism. 2006. pap. 21.99 *(978-1-84728-552-2(X))* Lulu Enterprises Inc.

Caporrimo, Bruno. The Snake in the Glass: The Deceptions of Alcohol Exposed. 2010. 176p. pap. 17.99 *(978-1-4520-2220-8(8))* AuthorHouse.

Carter, John. God, Get Me Out of This One... ! A True Story about Addiction & One Man's Journey Back from Hell. 2009. 292p. pap. 19.95 *(978-0-9814648-1-7(5))* Inkwell Productions, LLC.

Chrzan, Janet. Absolute Anthropology: Alcohol Use in Cultural Context. 2013. (Routledge Series for Creative Teaching & Learning in Cultural Anthropology Ser.). (ENG.). 128p. 110.00 *(978-0-415-89249-0(X))*; pap. 25.95 *(978-0-415-89250-6(3))* Routledge.

Chung, Sulki. The Role of Generational Status in Alcohol Related Disorders. 2010. 176p. pap. *(978-3-8383-4359-4(X))* Lambert Academic Publishing.

COLUCCI. Introduction to Alcohol & Substance Abuse Studies. 2007. (C). pap. 90.67 *(978-0-536-05359-2(8))*; (ENG.). pap., pap. 105.60 *(978-0-536-52933-6(7))* Pearson Learning Solutions.

Cornes, Judy. Alcohol in the Movies, 1898-1962: A Critical History. 2006. (ENG., Illus.). 264p. per. 35.00 *(978-0-7864-2633-1(0))* McFarland & Co., Inc. Pubs.

Cram101 Textbook Reviews & Cram101 Textbook Reviews. Outlines & Highlights for Substance Use & Abuse: Exploring Alcohol & Drug Issues by Sylvia I. Mignon, ISBN. 2011. 176p. pap. 29.95 ***(978-1-4288-5639-4(0))*** Cram101 Inc.

Dade, Penny. Drink Talking: 100 years of alcohol Advertising. 2008. (Popular Culture Ser.). 132p. pap. 23.00 *(978-1-904750-40-6(0))* Libri Publishing Ltd GBR. Dist: Independent Pubs. Group.

Davidson, Todd. The End of Innocence: Looking Back. 2008. 128p. pap. 12.95 *(978-0-615-18466-1(9))* North Harbor Bks.

DeChello, Patrick L., creator. Step Towards Success - Preparation for the Alcohol & Drug Abuse Counselor Written Exam, 2 vols. 2006. 278p. per. 126.00 *(978-1-933661-10-0(0)*, D & S Assocs.

Dewitt, William A. Drinking & What to Do about It. 2011. 192p. 42.95 ***(978-1-258-07543-9(1))*** Literary Licensing, LLC.

Dorchester, Daniel. The Liquor Problem in All Ages. 2009. 538p. pap. *(978-0-217-59697-8(5))* Books LLC.

Dunn, Dan. Nobody Likes a Quitter (and Other Reasons to Avoid Rehab) The Loaded Life of an Outlaw Booze Writer. 2007. (ENG., Illus.). 256p. per. 14.95 *(978-1-56858-366-2(4))* Running Pr. Bk. Pubs.

Encyclopaedia Britannica, Inc., compiled by. Drug Abuse: Sorting It Out. 2008. 49.95 *(978-1-59339-646-5(5))* Encyclopaedia Britannica, Inc.

Everly, Katherine T. & Cosell, Eva M. Social Drinking: Uses, Abuses, & Psychological Factors. 2009. 160.00 *(978-1-60876-219-4(X))* Nova Science Pubs., Inc.

Everly, Katherine T. & Cosell, Eva M., eds. Social Drinking: Uses, Abuses & Psychological Factors. 2009. (Substance Abuse Assessment, Interventions & Treatment Ser.). 129.00 *(978-1-208-76219-8(2)*, Nova Biomedical Bks.) Nova Science Pubs., Inc.

F., Dan. Don't Drink & Go to Meetings: My Journey to Recovery. 2011. 198p. 29.99 ***(978-1-4628-8358-5(3))***; pap. 19.99 ***(978-1-4628-8357-8(5))*** Xlibris Corp.

Feather, Chief Poison. Abused, Addicted, Incarcerated: Canda's Shame. 2011. 452p. pap. 29.95 ***(978-1-4560-7912-3(3))*** PublishAmerica, Inc.

Feeley, J. Patrick. Please Tell Me No. 2009. 264p. 29.99 *(978-1-4415-1273-4(X))*; pap. 19.99 *(978-1-4415-1272-7(1))* Xlibris Corp.

Fleming, John C. Preventing Addiction: What Parents Must Know to Immunize Their Kids Against Drug & Alcohol Addiction. 2007. (ENG., Illus.). 304p. per. 19.95 *(978-0-929292-45-8(6)*, 800-747-0738, CrossHouse Publishing) Hannibal Bks.

Flowers, R. Barri. Drugs, Alcohol & Criminality in American Society. alt. ed. 2008. (ENG., Illus.). 246p. pap. 35.00 *(978-0-7864-3869-3(X))* McFarland & Co., Inc. Pubs.

Flowers, Wax David. Alcoholism/Drug Addiction: A Disease or Not!, What Causes Alcoholism & Drug Addiction: What Causes Alcoholism & Drug Addiction. 2010. 188p. pap. 16.95 *(978-1-4401-8744-5(4))* iUniverse, Inc.

Ford, Gene. The Benefits of Moderate Drinking. 320p. 14.95 *(978-0-932664-60-0(1)*, 6509) Wine Appreciation Guild, Ltd.

Ford, John C. & Ford, John C. Depth Psychology, Morality & Alcoholism. 2011. 90p. 38.95 ***(978-1-258-01449-0(1))*** Literary Licensing, LLC.

Fosdick, Raymond B. & Scott, Albert L. Toward Liquor Control. 2011. (ENG.). reprint ed. pap. 4.99 *(978-0-9823007-0-0(4))* Ctr. for Alcohol Policy.

Foster, John. Quality of Life in Alcohol Dependents: A Longitudinal Study. 2006. 169.00 *(978-1-60021-443-1(6))* Nova Science Pubs., Inc.

Fox, Mike & Wilson, Lesley. Counseling Older People with Alcohol Problems. 2011. (ENG., Illus.). 224p. pap. ***(978-1-84905-117-0(8))*** Kingsley, Jessica Ltd.

Frances, Richard J., et al, eds. Clinical Textbook of Addictive Disorders. 3rd rev. ed. 2011. (ENG.). 684p. pap. 50.00 *(978-1-60918-205-2(7))* Guilford Pubns., Inc.

Galanter, Marc, et al. Research on Alcoholics Anonymous & Spirituality in Addiction: The Twelve-Step Program Model, Spiritually Oriented Recovery, Twelve-Step Membership, Effectiveness & Outcome Research. 2008. (Recent Developments in Alcoholism Ser.). (Illus.). 470p. 329.00 *(978-0-387-77724-5(5))* Springer.

Gamburd, Michele Ruth. Breaking the Ashes: The Culture of Illicit Liquor in Sri Lanka. 2008. (Illus.). 280p. 71.95 *(978-0-8014-4560-3(0))*; pap. 24.95 *(978-0-8014-7432-3(9))* Cornell Univ. Pr.

Garriott, James C. & Aguayo, Erik H. Garriott's Medicolegal Aspects of Alcohol. 5th ed. 2008. 536p. 139.00 *(978-1-933264-58-5(5))* Lawyers & Judges Publishing Co., Inc.

Gifford, Maria L. Alcoholism, 1 vol. 2009. (Biographies of Disease Ser.). (Illus.). 157p. 45.00 *(978-0-313-35908-8(3)*, GR5908) Greenwood Publishing Group, Inc.

Gilpin, Nicholas. Alcohol Abstinence in Vulnerable Subpopulations of Drinkers. 2009. 172p. pap. *(978-3-639-12191-9(0))* VDM Verlag Dr. Mueller e.K.

Groom, Kelle. I Wore the Ocean in the Shape of a Girl: A Memoir. (ENG.). 2012. 272p. pap. 14.00 *(978-1-4516-1669-9(4))* 2011. 256p. lib. bdg. 23.00 *(978-1-4516-1668-2(6))* Free Pr. (Free Pr.).

Haerens, Margaret, ed. Alcohol. 2012. (Global Viewpoints Ser.). (ENG., Illus.). 224p. (gr. 10-12). pap. 39.60 ***(978-0-7377-5643-2(8))***; lib. bdg. 27.30 ***(978-0-7377-5642-5(X))*** Cengage Gale. (Greenhaven Pr., Inc.).

Hames, Peter. Alcohol in World History. 2012. (Themes in World History Ser.). (ENG.). 168p. 115.00 *(978-0-415-31151-9(9))* Routledge.

Hamilton, Marguerite & Carlin, Neal. Reflections for Sufferers of Alcoholism. 2008. pap. 12.95 *(978-1-84730-055-3(3))* Veritas Pubns. IRL. Dist: Dufour Editions, Inc.

Hammond, Adam. Alcohol in the Home: What Should the Church Do? 2010. 124p. pap. 11.95 *(978-1-61507-297-2(7))* Cross Bks. Publishing.

Handmaid. Still Life. 2008. 116p. pap. 19.99 *(978-1-4363-7970-0(9))* Xlibris Corp.

Herrick, Charles & Herrick, Charlotte A. 100 Questions & Answers about Alchoholism. 2007. (Illus.). 290p. per. 22.95 *(978-0-7637-3918-8(9))* Jones & Bartlett Learning, LLC.

Hoffinger, Renee. The Recovery Diet: A Groundbreaking, Scientific Approach to a Healthy Life While Recovering from Alcoholism. 2012. (ENG.). 256p. pap. 14.95 ***(978-1-4405-3026-5(2))*** Adams Media Corp.

Holbrook, Nicholas. 16 Manor Way: The Story of Our Fated Adoptions. 2010. 160p. pap. *(978-1-84991-270-9(X))* Chipmunkapublishing.

Holmes, Ernest. Alcoholism: Its Cause & Cure from the Viewpoint of Science of Mind. 2010. 52p. pap. 6.95 *(978-1-57898-922-5(1))* Martino Publishing.

Hot Talk-Starter Videos Series 5: Alcohol Use/Abuse/Divorce/Gossip/Rumors/Dating Non-Christians. pap., tchr. ed. 19.99 incl. VHS *(978-1-55945-486-5(5))* Group Publishing, Inc.

Hungry Hill: A Memoir. 2007. (Illus.). 284p. 80.00 *(978-1-55849-588-3(6))*; per. 19.95 *(978-1-55849-589-0(4))* Univ. of Massachusetts Pr.

Isaacs, Stephen. To Improve Health & Health Care Vol. 18: The Robert Wood Johnson Foundation Anthology. Colby, David C., ed. 2009. (J-B Public Health/Health Services Text Ser.: 41). (ENG.). 336p. pap. 35.00 *(978-0-470-49663-3(0)*, Jossey-Bass) Wiley, John & Sons, Inc.

J, Adam. Confessions of a Lots-Aholic. 2011. 252p. pap. 16.99 ***(978-0-557-29757-3(5))*** Lulu Enterprises Inc.

J., Jeffrey. Detention: How the Stress of Being A High School Principal Drove Me to Drink. 2011. 168p. 29.99 ***(978-1-4568-9605-8(9))***; pap. 19.99 ***(978-1-4568-9604-1(0))*** Xlibris Corp.

Jamal, M. Mazen, ed. Alcoholic Liver Disease: An Overview. 2009. (Gastroenterology Ser.). (ENG.). 1p. cd-rom 99.00 *(978-981-4206-71-6(7))* Focus Medica Pte Ltd. SGP. Dist: Independent Pubs. Group.

Jellinek, E. M. & Jellinek, E. M. Disease Concept of Alcoholism. 2010. 258p. pap. 13.95 *(978-1-57898-936-2(1))* Martino Publishing.

John, Kevin. Psalms 23 the Key to the Cure of all Addictions. 2011. 84p. 17.99 ***(978-1-61379-547-7(5))*** Xulon Pr., Inc.

Judith Aldridge, Dept Applied So, et al. Illegal Leisure Revisited. 2011. (Adolescence & Society Ser.). (ENG., Illus.). 264p. pap. 42.50 *(978-0-415-49553-0(9))* Routledge.

Jurkiewicz, Carole L. & Painter, Murphy J. Social & Economic Control of Alcohol: The 21st Amendment in the 21st Century. 2007. (Public Administration & Public Policy Ser.). (ENG., Illus.). 264p. 79.95 *(978-1-4200-5463-7(5)*, CRC Press) Taylor & Francis Group GBR. Dist: Taylor & Francis Group.

Karlsson, Kate. My Brother's Shoes: One Families Walk Through Addiction. 2011. 174p. pap. 14.95 ***(978-1-4327-7431-8(X))*** Outskirts Pr., Inc.

Karr, Justin. Alcoholism. 2007. (Social Issues Firsthand Ser.). (ENG., Illus.). 142p. (YA). (gr. 8-12). lib. bdg. 31.80 *(978-0-7377-3832-2(4)*, Greenhaven Pr., Inc.) Cengage Gale.

Karr, Mary. Lit: A Memoir. (P. S. Ser.). 2010. (ENG.). 400p. pap. 14.99 *(978-0-06-059699-6(6)*, HarperPerennial) 2009. 578p. pap. 25.99 *(978-0-06-188547-1(9)*, HarperLuxe) HarperCollins Pubs.

Kiesbye, Stefan. Should the Legal Drinking Age Be Lowered? 2008. (At Issue Ser.). (ENG., 80-128p. Illus.). (YA). (gr. 9-12). pap. 31.80 *(978-0-7377-3934-3(7))*; (gr. 10-12). 22.50 *(978-0-7377-3935-0(5)*, Greenhaven Pr., Inc.) Cengage Gale.

Kiesbye, Stefan, ed. Should the Legal Drinking Age Be Lowered? 2012. (At Issue Ser.). (ENG.). 128p. (gr. 10-12). pap. 23.85 ***(978-0-7377-6204-4(7))***; lib. bdg. 33.70 ***(978-0-7377-6203-7(9))*** Cengage Gale. (Greenhaven Pr., Inc.).

Knight, Adam. Inside the Hurricane: Memories of Alcoholism & Child Abuse. 2010. 260p. pap. 19.95 *(978-1-4502-5613-1(9))* iUniverse, Inc.

Koren, John. Economic Aspects of the Liquor Problem. 2009. 340p. 25.99 *(978-1-103-89223-5(1))*; pap. 19.99 *(978-1-103-89217-4(7))* BiblioBazaar.

—Economic Aspects of the Liquor Problem. 2010. 128p. pap. 15.37 *(978-1-152-64021-4(6))* General Bks. LLC.

Koren, John & Farnham, Henry Walcott. Economic Aspects of the Liquor Problem. 2010. 350p. pap. 32.75 *(978-1-142-87131-4(2))* BiblioBazaar.

Korsmeyer, Pamela & Kranzler, Henry R. Encyclopedia of Drugs, Alcohol & Addictive Behavior, 4 vols. 3rd ed. 2008. (Illus.). *(978-0-02-866067-7(6))*; *(978-0-02-866066-0(8))*; *(978-0-02-866065-3(X))*; *(978-0-02-866068-4(4))*;Set. (C). 711.00 *(978-0-02-866064-6(1))* Cengage Gale. (Macmillan Reference USA).

Kyle, Jeremy. I'M Only Being Honest. 2009. (ENG.). 320p. 27.95 *(978-0-340-98079-8(6)*, Hodder & Stoughton) Hodder General Publishing Div. GBR. Dist: Independent Pubs. Group.

Lankford, Ronald D., ed. Alcohol Abuse. 2007. (At Issue Ser.). (ENG.). 91p. (gr. 8-12). pap. 22.50 *(978-0-7377-3672-4(0)*, Greenhaven Pr., Inc.); (Illus.). 127p. (YA). (gr. 9-12). lib. bdg. 31.80 *(978-0-7377-3671-7(2))* Cengage Gale.

Larsson, Marie. When Women Unite: The Making of the Anti-Liquor Movement in Andhra Pradesh, India. 2006. (Stockholm Studies in Social Anthropology Ser.: Vol. 60). pap. 89.50 *(978-91-7155-249-5(9))* Stockholms Universitet SWE. Dist: Coronet Bks.

Laursen, Gary N. Halfway to Hell & Back: A kick-start for Recovery of Alcohol & Drug Addiction. 2011. 88p. 24.99 ***(978-1-4628-9949-4(8))***; pap. 15.99 ***(978-1-4628-9948-7(X))*** Xlibris Corp.

Lazo, Donald M. Alcoholismo. 144p. 6.95 *(978-958-607-517-6(6))* Sociedad de San Pablo COL. Dist: St Pauls/Alba Hse. Pubs.

Lenters, William R. & Avila, Mariano A. Alcoholismo, Alcohol y Otras Drogas: Una Guia de Estudio y Accion. (SPA.). 115p. pap. 5.95 *(978-1-55883-091-2(X)*, 6765-0220C) Libros Desafio.

Levy, Michael S. Abstinence or Moderation? 2007. (ENG.). 256p. pap. 18.95 *(978-1-59077-099-3(4))* M.Evans & Co.

Lewry, David. Angst. 2010. 176p. pap. 21.95 *(978-0-557-34605-9(3))* Lulu Enterprises Inc.

—Channel of the Broken Gun. 2010. 280p. pap. 21.95 *(978-0-557-32763-8(6))* Lulu Enterprises Inc.

Lowney, Jeremiah. Stoned, Drunk, or Sober? Understanding Alcohol & Drug Use Through Qualitative, Quantitative, & Longitudinal Research. 2008. (Studies in the History of Judaism Ser.). (ENG.). 200p. pap. 36.99 *(978-0-7618-4100-5(8))* Univ. Pr. of America, Inc.

Lund, Bobbi. His Hands, My Heart. 2008. 75p. pap. 16.95 *(978-1-60672-329-6(4))* PublishAmerica, Inc.

Maars, Jeffrey V., ed. Alcohol Dependence & Addiction. 2011. (Series: Substance Abuse Assessment, Interventions & Treatment Ser.). 95.00 *(978-1-61324-719-8(2))* Nova Science Pubs., Inc.

Manzardo, Ann, et al. Alcoholism. 4th ed. 2008. (Facts Ser.). (ENG., Illus.). 200p. pap. 23.95 *(978-0-19-923139-3(7))* Oxford Univ. Pr., Inc.

Marpert, Jo. Don't Park under the Coconut Trees! 2010. 232p. pap. 14.99 *(978-1-60844-589-9(5))* Dog Ear Publishing, LLC.

Martinic, Marjana & Measham, Fiona. Swimming with Crocodiles: The Culture of Extreme Drinking. 2008. (ICAP Series on Alcohol in Society Ser.). (ENG., Illus.). 296p. 73.95 *(978-0-415-95548-5(3))* Routledge.

Mennes, Catherine E. College Drinking. 2008. 220p. pap. *(978-3-639-05790-4(2))* VDM Verlag Dr. Mueller e.K.

Mignon, Sylvia I., et al. Substance Use & Abuse: Exploring Alcohol & Drug Issues. 2009. (Illus.). 350p. (C). *(978-1-58826-620-0(6))*; pap. *(978-1-58826-645-3(1))* Rienner, Lynne Pubs.

Moorman, Dr. Mark Thomas & Moorman, Mark Thomas. Alcohol & Other Drugs. 2010. 104p. pap. *(978-3-8383-9069-5(X))* Lambert Academic Publishing.

Myers, Peter & Isralowitz, Richard. Alcohol, 1 vol. 2011. (Health & Medical Issues Today Ser.). (Illus.). 250p. 35.00 *(978-0-313-37247-6(0)*, GR7247) Greenwood Publishing Group, Inc.

Myers, Peter L. & Isralowitz, Richard. Alcohol. 2011. E-Book *(978-0-313-37248-3(9)*, Greenwood Pr.) Greenwood Publishing Group, Inc.

National Collaborating Centre for Mental Health Staff. Alcohol Use Disorders: The NICE Guideline on the Diagnosis, Assessment & Management of Harmful Drinking & Alcohol Dependence. 2011. (Illus.). 500p. pap. incl. cd-rom *(978-1-904671-26-8(8))* Royal College of Psychiatrists.

Newman, Susan. It Won't Happen to Me. *(978-0-399-51358-9(2))* Penguin Group (USA) Inc.

Oliver, Dan. The Dust of Old Dole Road: From Poverty to Peace. 2011. pap. 21.99 ***(978-1-61777-103-3(1))*** Tate Publishing & Enterprises, LLC.

Olmstead, Mary C., ed. Animal Models of Drug Addiction. 2010. (Neuromethods Ser.). (ENG., Illus.). xii, 484p. 139.00 *(978-1-60761-933-8(4)*, 1607619334) Humana Pr.

Otto, Connie & Bader, Marilyn. Understanding Alcohol, Tobacco & Other Drugs. 16p. stu. ed. 3.45 *(978-0-570-00602-2(3)*, 22-2732); 24p. 4.45 *(978-0-570-00603-9(1)*, 22-2733) Concordia Publishing Hse.

Owen, Olin Marvin. Rum, Rags, & Religion or, in Darkest America & the Way Out. 2007. (ENG.). 128p. 35.95 *(978-0-548-14995-9(X))*; per. 20.95 *(978-1-4304-4321-6(9))* Kessinger Publishing, LLC.

Owens, Lynn. The Burden of Alcohol on the National Health Service. 2010. 328p. pap. *(978-3-8383-6765-1(0))* Lambert Academic Publishing.

Padwa, Howard & Cunningham, Jacob, eds. Addiction: A Reference Encyclopedia, 1 vol. 2010. 398p. 85.00 *(978-1-59884-229-6(3)*, ADDIC) ABC-CLIO, LLC.

Pan American Health Organization. Alcohol, Gender, Culture, & Harms in the Americas: PAHO Multicentric Study Final Report. 2007. (PAHO Occasional Publication Ser.). (ENG.). 68p. pap. 25.00 *(978-92-75-12828-2(6))* World Health Organization.

Parsons, Elaine Frantz. Manhood Lost: Fallen Drunkards & Redeeming Women in the Nineteenth-Century United States. 2009. (New Studies in American Intellectual & Cultural History Ser.). (ENG., Illus.). 256p. (gr. 17). pap. 25.00 *(978-0-8018-9256-1(2))* Johns Hopkins Univ. Pr.

Partridge, G. E. Studies in the Psychology of Intemperance. 2009. 288p. pap. 27.75 *(978-1-116-21976-0(X))* BiblioBazaar.

Pine, Adrienne. Working Hard, Drinking Hard: On Violence & Survival in Honduras. 2008. (Illus.). 272p. 50.00 *(978-0-520-25543-2(7))*; 253p. pap. 24.95 *(978-0-520-25544-9(5))* Univ. of California Pr.

Pivac, Nela, et al. Peripheral Biological Markers in Alcoholism. 2008. (Illus.). viii, 93p. pap. 39.00 *(978-1-60456-617-8(5))*; pap. 39.00 *(978-1-60456-444-0(X)*, Nova Biomedical Bks.) Nova Science Pubs., Inc.

Podolsky, Edward, ed. Management of Addictions. 2011. 430p. 56.95 ***(978-1-258-07131-8(2))*** Literary Licensing, LLC.

Polet, Tom. Finishing Strong! 2009. 122p. pap. 13.16 *(978-0-557-04012-4(4))* Lulu Enterprises Inc.

Renz, Tom. The Tao of Creative Caddying. 2008. 176p. per. 12.99 *(978-1-59858-518-6(5))* Dog Ear Publishing, LLC.

Rogers, Barb. Addiction & Grief: Letting Go of Fear, Anger, & Addiction. 2011. 144p. pap. 14.95 *(978-1-57324-516-6(X)*, Conari Pr.) Red Wheel/Weiser.

Rose, C. Four Years with the Demon Rum. 84p. pap. 5.95 *(978-0-919107-00-7(1))* Acadiensis Pr. CAN. Dist: Goose Lane Editions.

Roth, Marty. Drunk the Night Before: An Anatomy of Intoxication. 2008. 256p. pap. 22.50 *(978-0-8166-4398-1(9))* Univ. of Minnesota Pr.

Royce, James E. & Scratchley, David. Alcoholism & Other Drug Problems. 2007. (ENG., Illus.). 400p. pap. 25.95 *(978-1-4165-6773-8(9)*, Free Pr.) Free Pr.

Rudman, Jack. Drug & Alcohol Abuse. (Dantes Subject Standardized Tests Ser.: Vol. 78). 49.95 *(978-0-8373-6578-7(3)*, Passbooks) National Learning Corp.

Runciman, James. The Ethics of Drink & Other Social Questions. 2008. 284p. 28.99 *(978-0-554-24620-8(1))*; 25.99 *(978-0-554-33923-8(4))* BiblioBazaar.

—The Ethics of Drink & Other Social Questions. 2007. 188p. per. *(978-1-4068-4078-0(5))* Echo Library.

—The Ethics of Drink & Other Social Questions: Joints in Our Social Armour. 2006. (ENG.). 254p. pap. 21.99 *(978-1-4264-6931-2(4))*; 282p. pap. 23.99 *(978-1-4264-7013-4(4))* BiblioBazaar.

Ryan, Gary R. Blessings in Disguise: A Tale of Redemption. 2009. 268p. 30.95 *(978-0-595-63629-7(2))* iUniverse, Inc.

Sage, Sister. Then Came Grace: The Journal Account of How One Family Went from Darkness into Their Destiny. 2011. 148p. 22.23 *(978-1-4520-0680-2(6))*; pap. 11.70 *(978-1-4520-0681-9(4))* AuthorHouse.

Saitz, Richard & Galanter, Marc. Alcohol/Drug Screening & Brief Intervention: Advances in Evidence-Based Practice. 2008. (ENG., Illus.). 100p. pap. 46.00 *(978-0-7890-3749-7(1)*, Informa Healthcare) Taylor & Francis Group.

Schuckit, Marc A. Drug & Alcohol Abuse: A Clinical Guide to Diagnosis & Treatment. 6th ed. 2010. (ENG.). viii, 394p. pap. 89.95 *(978-1-4419-3825-1(7)*, 1441938257) Springer.

Seplesky, Vincent. Wino in a Three Piece Suit. 2010. 92p. 20.00 *(978-1-4134-8064-1(0))* Xlibris Corp.

Sequeira, Alberta H. Please, God, Not Two: This Killer Called Alcoholism. 2010. 343p. pap. 17.95 *(978-0-7414-6029-5(7))* Infinity Publishing.

Setter, Doug. Reduce Your Alcohol Craving. 2010. 124p. pap. 24.00 *(978-0-557-07986-5(1))* Lulu Enterprises Inc.

Shannon, Joyce, ed. Alcoholism Sourcebook. 3rd rev. ed. 2010. (Health Reference Ser.). (Illus.). xx, 633p. lib. bdg. 93.00 (978-0-7808-1141-6(0)) Omnigraphics, Inc.

Sher, Leo, ed. Comorbidity of Depression & Alcohol Use Disorders. 2008. 89.00 (978-1-60692-180-7(0)) Nova Science Pubs., Inc.

Sher, Leo, et al. Alcohol-Related Cognitive Disorders: Research & Clinical Perspectives. 2009. (Illus.). xvi, 378p. 89.00 (978-1-60741-730-9(8), Nova Biomedical Bks.) Nova Science Pubs., Inc.

Shoquist, Cheryl. Drunkenland. 2011. 260p. pap. 19.95 (978-1-61434-270-0(9)) Booklocker.com, Inc.

Shulman, Gerald, et al, eds. ASAM Patient Placement Criteria: Supplement on Pharmacotherapies for Alcohol Use Disorders. 2010. (ENG.). 216p. pap. 59.00 (978-0-7817-9122-9(7)) Lippincott Williams & Wilkins.

Simmons, Richard R. Collateral Damage: The Other Victims. 2009. 308p. pap. 16.95 (978-1-4327-2317-0(0)) Outskirts Pr., Inc.

Smart, Lesley, ed. Alcohol & Human Health. 2008. (Introducing Health Science Ser.). (ENG., Illus.). 104p. pap. 55.00 (978-0-19-923735-7(2)) Oxford Univ. Pr., Inc.

Smith, Barb. Brent's World. 2007. 116p. per. 11.95 (978-1-4327-1629-5(8)) Outskirts Pr., Inc.

Stapleton, Christine. Hoping for a Happy Ending: A journalist's story of depression, bipolar & Alcoholism. 2009. 160p. 22.95 (978-1-4389-9151-1(7)); pap. 14.95 (978-1-4389-9150-4(9)) AuthorHouse.

Stelzle, Charles. Why Prohibition! 2007. (Cooking in America Ser.). (ENG.). 328p. per. 20.95 (978-1-4290-1049-8(5)) Applewood Bks.

—Why Prohibition! 2009. 160p. pap. (978-0-217-41721-1(3)) Books LLC.

—Why Prohibition! 2009. 312p. 45.95 (978-1-104-56777-4(6)); pap. 30.95 (978-1-104-52985-7(8)) Kessinger Publishing, LLC.

Stimson, Gerry V. & Alexander, Barton. Drinking in Context: Patterns, Interventions, & Partnerships. 2006. (ENG., Illus.). 264p. 52.95 (978-0-415-95447-1(9)) Routledge.

Stoneall, Veronica. He Saved My Life: Hope in Recovery. 2011. 120p. pap. 12.00 (978-1-4670-4339-7(7)) AuthorHouse.

Strässle, Thomas & Zumsteg, Simon, eds. Trunkenheit: Kulturen des Rausches. 2008. (GER.). 266p. 78.00 (978-90-420-2323-9(6)) Rodopi.

Substance Abuse and Mental Health Services Administration (U.S.) & Office of Applied Studies (U.S.), compiled by. Treatment Episode Data Set (TEDS) 2006 Highlights: National Admissions to Substastance Abuse Treatment Services: National Admissions to Substastance Abuse Treatment Services. 2008. (ENG.). 38p. pap. 6.00 (978-0-16-080487-8(6), Substance Abuse & Mental Health Services Administration) United States Government Printing Office.

Sugumar, V. Raji & Sathya, G. Social & Clinical Constructs of Alcoholism: A Study. 2011. 100p. pap. (978-3-639-32397-9(1)) VDM Verlag Dr. Mueller e.K.

Sutton, Amy L., ed. Alcoholism Sourcebook. 2nd ed. 2007. (Health Reference Ser.). (Illus.). 653p. 87.00 (978-0-7808-0942-0(4)) Omnigraphics, Inc.

Taub, Shais. God of Our Understanding: Jewish Spirituality & Recovery from Addiction. 2010. 384p. 18.95 (978-1-60280-153-0(3)) Ktav Publishing Hse., Inc.

Thimann, Joseph. The Addictive Drinker: A Manual for the Rehabilitation of Problem Drinkers. 7.95 (978-0-8022-1711-0(7)) Philosophical Library, Inc.

Thompson, Vance. Drink & Be Sober. 2008. 111p. 28.99 (978-0-554-84088-8(X)); 111p. 25.99 (978-0-554-84096-3(0)); 167p. pap. 26.75 (978-0-554-84090-1(1)); 161p. pap. 25.75 (978-0-554-84094-9(4)) BiblioBazaar.

—Drink & Be Sober. 2008. 256p. 42.95 (978-1-4369-4106-8(7)); pap. 27.95 (978-1-4368-2640-2(3)) Kessinger Publishing, LLC.

Tougas, Luke. Meet My Shadow. 2010. 224p. (ENG.). 28.95 (978-1-4502-1280-9(8)); pap. 18.95 (978-1-4502-1278-6(6)) iUniverse, Inc.

Trenk, Marin. Die Milch des Weissen Mannes: Die Indianer Nordamerikas & der Alkohol. (GER.). 232p. (978-3-496-02492-7(5)) Reimer, Dietrich.

Uhl, George R. Addiction Reviews 3. 2011. (Annals of the New York Academy of Sciences Ser.: 72). (ENG., Illus.). 174p. pap. 130.00 (978-1-57331-812-9(4), Wiley-Blackwell) Wiley, John & Sons, Inc.

Vick. Drug & Alcohol in the 21st Century: Theory, Behavior, & Policy. rev. ed. 2010. pap. 68.95 (978-0-7637-7488-2(X)) Jones & Bartlett Learning, LLC.

W, Bill, et al. The Little Red Book an Interpretation of the Twelve Steps of the Alcoholics Anonymous Program. 2011. 160p. pap. 6.95 (978-1-61427-065-2(1)) Martino Publishing.

Wagner, Gerhard. Tears of the Son: An Exposé. 2011. 200p. 26.95 (978-1-4502-9422-5(7)); pap. 16.95 (978-1-4502-9421-8(9)) iUniverse, Inc.

Walcott, Terri A. Drug & Alcohol Abuse Research Focus. 2008. (Illus.). 206p. 129.00 (978-1-60021-808-8(3), Nova Biomedical Bks.) Nova Science Pubs., Inc.

Weaver, Andrew J. & Koenig, Harold G. Pastoral Care of Alcohol Abusers. 2009. (Creative Pastoral Care & Counseling Ser.). 96p. pap. 16.00 (978-0-8006-6261-5(X), Fortress Pr.) Augsburg Fortress, Pubs.

Weber, M. A. Natural Process of Quitting Forever: Explicit Instruction. 2009. 104p. pap. 18.63 (978-1-4343-9776-8(9)) AuthorHouse.

Webster, Edward A. Stools & Bottles: A Study of Character Defects — 31 Daily Meditations. 2010. 160p. pap. 10.00 (978-1-57898-930-0(2)) Martino Publishing.

Welsh, Dianne M., ed. National Epidemiologic Survey on Alcohol & Related Conditions Selected Findings: A Reprint from the Journal, Alcohol Research & Health. 2006. (Illus.). 155p. (C). pap. 35.00 (978-1-4223-0753-3(0)) DIANE Publishing Co.

White, Nancy L. Tiger Pause: Lost in a Jungle called Alcoholism. 2011. 84p. pap. 28.95 (978-1-4634-3550-9(9)) AuthorHouse.

WHO Regional Office for Europe & World Health Organization Staff. European Status Report on Alcohol & Health 2010. 2011. (Illus.). 380p. pap. 60.00 (978-92-890-0206-6(9)) World Health Organization.

WHO Regional Office For the Western Pacific Staff. Addressing the Harmful Use of Alcohol: A Guide to Developing Effective Alcohol Regulation. 2011. (WPRO Nonserial Publication). 118p. pap. 18.00 (978-92-9061-503-3(6)) World Health Organization.

World Health Organization. Global Status Report on Alcohol & Health. 2011. (Illus.). 300p. pap. 72.00 (978-92-4-156415-1(6)) World Health Organization.

Zomar, Jennifer. A Candle for the Children. 2008. 128p. pap. 13.95 (978-0-595-52375-7(7)) iUniverse, Inc.

ALCOHOLISM—BIBLIOGRAPHY

International Bibliography of Studies on Alcohol, 3 vols., Set. Incl. Vol. 1. References, 1901-1950. Jordy, Sarah S., compiled by. 1966. 50.00 (978-0-911290-34-9(6)); Vol. 2. Indexes, 1901-1950. Jordy, Sarah S. 1968. 50.00 (978-0-911290-35-6(4)); Vol. 3. References & Indexes, 1951-1960. Jordy, S. S. & Beck, A. 1981. 100.00 (978-0-911290-40-0(0)); 150.00 (978-0-911290-07-3(9)) Rutgers Ctr. of Alcohol Studies Pubns.

ALCOHOLISM—PREVENTION

An Anonymous Member of A. A. EZ Big Book of Alcoholics Anonymous: A Translation for 21st Century Readers. 2011. 144p. pap. 14.95 (978-1-4502-2795-7(3)) iUniverse, Inc.

Armstrong, Charlotte, ed. Alcohol & Tobacco: An Update: A Reprint from the Journal, Alcohol Research & Health. 2007. (Illus.). 83p. (C). pap. 25.00 (978-1-4223-1480-7(4)) DIANE Publishing Co.

Babor, Thomas F., et al. Alcohol: No Ordinary Commodity: Research & Public Policy. 2nd ed. 2010. (ENG., Illus.). 352p. 59.95 (978-0-19-955114-9(6)) Oxford Univ. Pr., Inc.

Bakewell, Lisa, ed. Alcohol Information for Teens. 2nd rev. ed. 2009. (Teen Health Ser.). 400p. (YA). lib. bdg. 69.00 (978-0-7808-1043-3(0)) Omnigraphics, Inc.

Busch, Linda. I Cut It Out: An (ex) Drunk's Guide to Sobriety. 2007. 164p. pap. 12.00 (978-0-9798969-0-3(8)) I Cut It Out, Inc.

Chaitin, Rebecca D. & Knowlton, Judith M. Detachment & Enabling. 2008. (ENG.). 80p. pap. 9.95 (978-1-59285-746-3(9)) Hazelden Publishing & Educational Services.

Cook, Philip J. Paying the Tab: The Economics of Alcohol Policy. 2007. (ENG., Illus.). 278p. (C). 42.00 (978-0-691-12520-6(1)) Princeton Univ. Pr.

Cram101 Textbook Reviews Staff. Outlines & Highlights for Drugs in Perspective by Richard Fields, Isbn: 9780073380759. 2009. 138p. pap. 28.95 (978-1-4288-7952-2(8)) Cram101 Inc.

Dowdall, George W. College Drinking: Reframing a Social Problem, 1 vol. 2008. 288p. 44.95 (978-0-275-99981-0(5), C9981, Praeger Pubs.) Greenwood Publishing Group, Inc.

Edvin, David & Harald, Samuel. Underage Drinking: Examining & Preventing Youth Use of Alcohol. 2010. (Alcohol & Drug Abuse Ser.). 264p. 79.00 (978-1-60876-141-8(X)) Nova Science Pubs., Inc.

Elise, Christy & Elise, Patricia. The Way up & Out: Recovery from Alcoholism & the Al-Anon Companion Book. 2010. 212p. 24.99 (978-1-4490-3392-7(X)); pap. 15.95 (978-1-4490-3391-0(1)) AuthorHouse.

Engs, Ruth C., ed. Women: Alcohol & Other Drugs. 2007. (Illus.). 188p. pap. 22.00 (978-1-59752-887-0(0), Resource Pubns.) Wipf & Stock Pubs.

Erlandson, Kelly Madigan. Getting Sober: A Practical Guide to Making It Through the First 30 Days. 2007. (ENG.). 208p. per. 15.95 (978-0-07-149377-2(8), 0071493778) McGraw-Hill Cos., The.

Fields, Richard. Drugs in Perspective: Causes, Assessment, Family, Prevention, Intervention, & Treatment. 8th ed. 2012. (ENG., Illus.). 400p. (C). pap. 119.00 (978-0-07-802850-2(7), 0078028507) McGraw-Hill Cos., The.

Fox, Anne. 400 Rabbits: The Pleasure & Pain of Drunkenness. MacAvoy, Mike, ed. 2010. (ICAP Series on Alcohol in Society Ser.). (ENG., Illus.). 208p. 63.95 (978-0-415-99213-8(3)) Routledge.

Giddens, Sandra & Giddens, Owen. Making Smart Choices about Cigarettes, Drugs, & Alcohol. 2008. (Making Smart Choices Ser.). (Illus.). 48p. (YA). (gr. 5-9). lib. bdg. 26.50 (978-1-4042-1388-3(0)) Rosen Publishing Group, Inc., The.

Grant, Marcus & Leverton, Mark, eds. Working Together to Reduce Harmful Drinking: The Producers' Contribution. 2009. (ENG., Illus.). 224p. 73.95 (978-0-415-80087-7(0)) Routledge.

Greenhaven. Teen Drinking & Driving. 2012. (Hot Topics Ser.). (ENG., Illus.). 128p. (gr. 7-10). lib. bdg. 33.45 (978-1-4205-0749-2(4), Lucent Bks.) Cengage Gale.

Hassan, Shereen. Rice Alcohol: A Policy Impact Analysis. 2008. 188p. pap. (978-3-639-04957-2(8)) VDM Verlag Dr. Mueller e.K.

Holder, Harold D. Alcohol & the Community: A Systems Approach to Prevention. 2006. (International Research Monographs in the Addictions Ser.). (ENG.). 200p. pap. 48.00 (978-0-521-03504-0(X)) Cambridge Univ. Pr.

Keune, Kathrin. A Ritual Journey Towards Change. 2010. 108p. pap. (978-3-639-27322-9(2)) VDM Verlag Dr. Mueller e.K.

Klingemann, Harald & Gmel, G., eds. Mapping the Social Consequences of Alcohol Consumption. 2010. 170p. pap. 99.00 (978-90-481-5626-9(2), 9048156262) Springer.

Lawson, Gary & Lawson, Ann W. Alcoholism & Substance Abuse in Diverse Populations. 2nd ed. 2010. 45.00 (978-1-4164-0439-2(2)) PRO-ED, Inc.

Lowe, Ph. D. Nate, et al. Recovery the Road Ahead. 2011. 196p. 27.84 (978-0-557-57107-9(3)) Lulu Enterprises Inc.

Maurice, C. God Is at the Meeting: Spirituality & the Twelve Steps. 2011. 124p. pap. 11.95 (978-1-4497-2623-2(2), WestBow Pr.) Author Solutions, Inc.

McCrady, Barbara S. & Epstein, Elizabeth E. Overcoming Alcohol Problems: A Couples-Focused Program. 2008. (Treatments That Work Ser.). (ENG.). 144p. pap., wbk. ed. 24.95 (978-0-19-532275-0(4)) Oxford Univ. Pr., Inc.

—Overcoming Alcohol Problems: A Couples-Focused Program Therapist Guide. 2008. (Treatments That Work Ser.). (ENG., Illus.). 176p. (C). pap. 35.00 (978-0-19-532287-3(8)) Oxford Univ. Pr., Inc.

Medicine, Beatrice. Drinking & Sobriety among the Lakota Sioux. 2006. (Contemporary Native American Communities Ser.). (ENG., 193p. Illus.). 81.00 (978-0-7591-0570-6(7)); per. 30.95 (978-0-7591-0571-3(5)) AltaMira Pr.

Middelton-Moz, Jane & Dwinell, Lorie. After the Tears: Helping Adult Children of Alcoholics Heal Their Childhood Trauma. 2nd rev. ed. 2010. (ENG., Illus.). 312p. pap. 14.95 (978-0-7573-1513-8(5)) Health Communications, Inc.

Mooney, Geraldine, ed. National Directory of Drug & Alcohol Abuse Treatment Programs. 2008. (ENG.). 665p. (C). pap. 65.00 (978-1-4289-8788-3(6)) DIANE Publishing Co.

Morgan, Thomas R. Journey to Sobriety 34 Years & Counting. 2009. 168p. pap. 12.50 (978-1-59330-601-4(6)) Aventine Pr.

Mountian, Ilana. Drugs, Gender & the Social Imaginary. 2012. (Concepts for Critical Psychology Ser.). (ENG., Illus.). 176p. pap. 39.95 (978-0-415-58386-2(1)); 69.95 (978-0-415-58383-1(7)) Routledge.

Naude, Henri. Escape! from the Clutches of Alcohol. 2008. 320p. 28.50 (978-1-934925-77-5(2), Strategic Bk. Publishing) AEG Literary Publishing Services, Inc.

Noel-Buxton, Martin. Arresting Destruction: Recovery from Alcoholism. 2010. 240p. pap. 25.00 (978-1-4269-3130-7(1)) Trafford Publishing.

Nowinski, Joseph & Doyle, Robert. Almost Alcoholic: Is My (or My Loved One's) Drinking a Problem? 2012. (ENG.). 250p. pap. 14.95 (978-1-61649-159-8(0), Hazelden) Hazelden Publishing & Educational Services.

Nystrom, Richard S., Sr. The Wrath of Grapes! With How to Get off & Stay Off, 1 vol. 2009. 178p. pap. 24.95 (978-1-4489-2665-7(3)) PublishAmerica, Inc.

Press, Central Recovery. My First Year in Recovery: A Journal for the Journey. 2nd rev. ed. 2010. (ENG.). 160p. 19.95 (978-0-9818482-4-2(9)) Central Recovery Pr.

R., John. The 12 Steps Unplugged: A Young Person's Guide to Alcoholics Anonymous. 2011. (ENG.). 136p. pap. 13.95 (978-1-61649-110-9(8)) Hazelden Publishing & Educational Services.

Renebome, Jeffery. How Green Tea Made Me Alcohol Free. 2011. 30p. pap. 16.95 (978-1-4626-2020-3(5)) PublishAmerica, Inc.

Services for the Prevention & Treatment of Dependence on Alcohol & Other Drugs: 14th Report of the WHO Expert Committee on Mental Health. Date not set. (Technical Report Ser.: No. 363). pap. 5.00 (978-92-4-120363-0(3), 1100363) World Health Organization.

Vilalta-Perdomo, Eliseo. What Keeps Us Together & Makes Us Effective? 2010. 244p. pap. (978-3-639-23999-7(7)) VDM Verlag Dr. Mueller e.K.

W., Geno. Sought Through Prayer & Meditation: Wisdom from the Sunday 11th Step Meetings at the Wolfe Street Center in Little Rock. 2008. (ENG.). 216p. pap. 13.95 (978-1-59285-658-9(6)) Hazelden Publishing & Educational Services.

World Health Organization. WHO Expert Committee on Problems Related to Alcohol Consumption: Second Report. 2007. (Technical Report Ser.). (ENG.). 63p. pap. 36.00 (978-92-4-120944-1(5)) World Health Organization.

Youngerman, Barry, et al. Alcohol. 2nd rev. ed. 2010. (Truth about Ser.). (Illus.). 240p. (C). (gr. 9). 35.00 (978-0-8160-7639-0(1)) Facts On File, Inc.

ALCOHOLISM—PSYCHOLOGICAL ASPECTS

ABBE Scientist Research Division Staff. M.M. P. I. Profile of Alcoholics: Index, Reference & Medical Analysis of New Research Information. 2008. (Illus.). 160p. ring bd. 69.95 (978-0-7883-3835-9(8)) ABBE Pubs. Assn. of Washington, D.C.

Adams, A. J. Undrunk: A Skeptic's Guide to AA. 2009. (ENG.). 216p. pap. 14.95 (978-1-59285-720-3(5)) Hazelden Publishing & Educational Services.

Al-Anon Family Group Headquarters. Hope for Today. 2007. 379p. 10.00 (978-0-910034-39-5(7)) Al-Anon Family Group Headquarters, Inc.

Armstrong, Charlotte, ed. Alcohol & Tobacco: An Update: A Reprint from the Journal, Alcohol Research & Health. 2007. (Illus.). 83p. (C). pap. 25.00 (978-1-4223-1480-7(4)) DIANE Publishing Co.

Baudelaire, Charles. On Wine & Hashish. 2010. (On Ser.). (ENG.). 112p. pap. 15.95 (978-1-84391-608-6(8)) Hesperus Pr. GBR. Dist: Independent Pubs. Group.

Benton, Sarah Allen & Benton, Sarah A. Understanding the High-Functioning Alcoholic: Professional Views & Personal Insights, 1 vol. 2009. (Praeger Series on Contemporary Health & Living Ser.). 224p. 39.95 (978-0-313-35280-5(1), C35280, Praeger Pubs.) Greenwood Publishing Group, Inc.

Bergmann, Elaine. Geez! Aren't You Fixed Yet?! 2009. 32p. pap. 11.95 (978-1-4327-1693-6(X)) Outskirts Pr., Inc.

Busch, Linda. I Cut It Out: An (ex) Drunk's Guide to Sobriety. 2007. 164p. pap. 12.00 (978-0-9798969-0-3(8)) I Cut It Out, Inc.

Chaitin, Rebecca D. & Knowlton, Judith M. Detachment & Enabling. 2008. (ENG.). 80p. pap. 9.95 (978-1-59285-746-3(9)) Hazelden Publishing & Educational Services.

Cram101 Textbook Reviews & Cram101 Textbook Reviews. Outlines & Highlights for Alcohol, Other Drugs, & Behavior: Psychological Research Perspectives by John R. Jung, ISBN. 2011. 114p. pap. 28.95 (978-1-61461-031-1(2)) Cram101 Inc.

DeChello, Patrick. The Clinician's Toolbox: Empowering Parents. 2007. per. 34.99 (978-1-933661-11-7(9)) D & S Assocs.

Djos, Matts G. Writing under the Influence: Alcoholism & the Alcoholic Perception from Hemingway to Berryman. 2010. (ENG.). 188p. 79.00 (978-0-230-10260-6(3)) Palgrave Macmillan.

Elster, Jon, et al, eds. Understanding Choice, Explaining Behaviour. 2006. 282p. 59.00 (978-82-7477-237-3(7), Oslo Academic Pr.) Unipub forlag NOR. Dist: International Specialized Bk. Services.

Graves, Clara Jane. Am I a Real Alcoholic?, 1 vol. 2009. 254p. pap. 27.95 (978-1-60813-247-8(1)) PublishAmerica, Inc.

Hedblom, Jack H. Last Call: Alcoholism & Recovery. 2007. (ENG., Illus.). 224p. 42.00 (978-0-8018-8677-5(5)); per. 18.95 (978-0-8018-8678-2(3)) Johns Hopkins Univ. Pr.

Jayne, Mark, et al. (Dis)orderly Geographies: Alcohol Drinking Drunkeness. 2010. (Illus.). 168p. 99.95 (978-0-7546-7160-2(7)) Ashgate Publishing Co.

Jung, John R. Alcohol, Other Drugs, & Behavior: Psychological Research Perspectives. 2nd ed. 2009. (Illus.). 616p. (C). pap. 106.00 (978-1-4129-6764-8(3), B67648P) SAGE Pubns., Inc.

Lesch, Otto-Michael. Alcohol & Nicotine: Medical & Sociological Aspects of Usage, Abuse & Addiction. 2010. (Illus.). 380p. 99.00 (978-3-7091-0145-2(X), 370910145X) Springer.

Maisto, Stephen A., et al. Alcohol Use Disorders. 2007. (Advances in Psychotherapy — Evidence-Based Practice Ser.: Vol. 10). (Illus.). 94p. pap. 29.80 (978-0-88937-317-4(5)) Hogrefe Publishing.

Olsen, Patricia & Levounis, Petros. Sober Siblings: How to Help Your Alcoholic Brother or Sister - And Not Lose Yourself. 2008. (ENG.). 240p. pap. 16.00 (978-1-60094-055-2(2)) Da Capo Pr., Inc.

Ostrowsky, Michael K. Self-Medication & Violent Behavior. 2009. (Criminal Justice). 266p. 70.00 (978-1-59332-299-1(2)) LFB Scholarly Publishing LLC.

Parsons, A. To Hell & Back. 2007. (ENG.). 80p. per. (978-1-84747-175-8(7)) Chipmunkapublishing.

Peavy, Kristie. Centered: How the 12 Steps Brought Me Back from Darkness. 2011. 60p. pap. 12.99 (978-1-4567-5072-5(0)) AuthorHouse.

Rose, Mark Edmund & Cherpitel, Cheryl J. Alcohol: Its History, Pharmacology, & Treatment. 2011. E-Book (978-1-61649-403-2(4)) Hazelden Publishing & Educational Services.

Sandoz, Jeff. Alcoholic Iliad/Recovery Odyssey: Utilizing Myth As Addiction Metaphors in Family Therapy. 2009. 228p. pap. 29.95 (978-1-59942-511-5(4), Brown Walker Pr.) Universal Pubs.

Shelby, Patty. Inside an Anger Management Class. 2006. 136p. per. 9.95 (978-1-60002-257-9(X), 4436) Mountain Valley Publishing, LLC.

Solohub, Roman T. Clear Thinking When Drinking: The Handbook for Responsible Alcohol Consumption. 2006. (Illus.). 160p. per. 15.00 (978-0-9785719-0-0(8)) Empennage Pr.

Volkmann, Chris & Volkmann, Toren. From Binge to Blackout: A Mother & Son Struggle with Teen Drinking. 2006. (ENG.). 432p. (gr. 12-18). 16.00 (978-0-451-21909-1(0), N A L Trade) Penguin Group (USA) Inc.

ALCOHOLISM—RELIGIOUS ASPECTS

Britt, Martin D. Jesus & the Drug: The Bible & Alcohol Drinking. 2007. 80p. pap. (978-0-9719077-3-7(0)) Britt, Martin.

Brotherton, Marcus. Buzz: A Graphic Reality Check for Teens Dealing with Drugs & Alcohol. 2006. (FlipSwitch Ser.). (ENG., Illus.). 64p. pap. 7.00 (978-1-59052-717-7(8), Multnomah) Doubleday Religious Publishing Group, The.

Burrage, Yvonne. Prodigal Wisdom: Lessons Learned from My Son's Addiction. 2011. 152p. pap. 13.95 (978-1-4627-0524-5(3)) Cross Bks. Publishing.

Butler, Joel & Heskett, Randall. Divine Vintage: Following the Wine Trail from Genesis to Modern Times. 2012. (ENG., Illus.). 256p. 25.00 (978-0-230-11243-8(9)) Palgrave Macmillan.

Campbell, Leighton. Why True Biblical Creationists Believe That Jesus Did Not Make Alcohol! 2008. 168p. pap. 13.99 (978-1-60647-206-4(2)) Xulon Pr., Inc.

Collier, Benjamin. Does Optimism Explain How Religiousness Affects Alcohol Use among Students? 2008. 76p. pap. (978-3-639-00880-7(4)) VDM Verlag Dr. Mueller e.K.

Conord, Susan M. Hope for Survivors of Childhood Traum. 2009. 268p. pap. 18.99 (978-1-60791-383-2(6)) Xulon Pr., Inc.

Cook, Christopher C. H. Alcohol, Addiction & Christian Ethics. 2008. (New Studies in Christian Ethics Ser.). (ENG.). 236p. pap. 34.99 (978-0-521-09134-3(9)) Cambridge Univ. Pr.

DeJong, Alexander. Ayuda y Esperanza para el Alcoholico.Tr. of Help & Hope for the Alcoholic. (SPA.). 160p. (978-84-7228-769-3(6), 222200) Clie, Editorial.

DeJong, Alexander & Doot, Martin. Dying for a Drink: A Pastor & a Physician Talk about Alcoholism. pap. 8.00 (978-1-56212-397-0(1), 151120) Faith Alive Christian Resources.

Diel, Sylvanus. From Alcoholism to Moderation. 2007. 52p. per. 9.99 (978-1-60266-946-8(5)) Xulon Pr., Inc.

Dobbs, K. A. There's a Light at the End of the Tunnel: And It's Not a Train! 2009. 132p. pap. 14.99 (978-1-61579-086-9(1)) Xulon Pr., Inc.

Ferriter, Diarmaid. A Nation of Extremes: The Pioneers in Twentieth Century Ireland. 2008. 286p. pap. 32.95 (978-0-7165-2986-6(6)) Irish Academic Pr. IRL. Dist: International Specialized Bk. Services.

Fuller, Robert W. The Baby King Must Die! 2007. 400p. per. 21.99 (978-1-60477-062-9(7)) Xulon Pr., Inc.

Hinson, Harold. Owl Hill. 2009. 152p. 21.49 (978-1-4490-1726-2(6)); pap. 10.99 (978-1-4490-1725-5(8)) AuthorHouse.

Jaeggli, Randy. The Christian & Drinking: A Biblical Perspective on Moderation & Abstinence. 2008. (978-1-59166-919-7(7)) BJU Pr.

John, Kevin. Psalms 23 the Key to the Cure of All Addictions. 2011. 84p. pap. 10.99 **(978-1-61379-546-0(7))** Xulon Pr., Inc.

Kincaid, Robert Luke. Stronger Now: Story of a Recovering Alcoholic & Complete Tetraplegic. 2009. 152p. pap. 14.99 (978-1-4490-3546-4(9)) AuthorHouse.

Kraft, William F. When You Love a Functional Alcoholic. 2011. 176p. pap. (978-0-8091-4679-6(7)) Paulist Pr.

Li, Zhe. We Did Not Drink As Stupidly As Today's Young People. 2011. 188p. pap. **(978-3-8443-1509-7(8))** Lambert Academic Publishing.

Libatique, Kelly. A Toast to the Holy Ghost? a Dispassionate Look at Alcohol & the Bible. 2010. 178p. pap. 12.50 (978-1-60911-347-6(0), Eloquent Bks.) AEG Literary Publishing Services, Inc.

Martin, Bill. Life after the Hangover. 2009. 108p. pap. 11.99 (978-1-60791-832-5(3)) Xulon Pr., Inc.

Murray, Maurice "Mo". Just Snap Your Fingers And... Bingo You're Sober! A "Recovery" Workbook for Alcoholics. 2007. 124p. pap. 10.49 (978-1-4343-2881-6(3)) AuthorHouse.

—Just Snap Your Fingers and... Bingo You're Sober! A "Recovery" Workbook for Alcoholics. 2007. (ENG.). 124p. 21.49 (978-1-4343-5965-0(4)) AuthorHouse.

Nanoff, Patricia D. Rising from the Dead: Stories of Women's Spiritual Journeys to Sobriety. 2007. (ENG.). 136p. 125.00 (978-0-7890-3173-0(6)); per. 50.50 (978-0-7890-3174-7(4)) Routledge.

Oropeza, B. J. Jesus & Paul: Global Perspectives in Honor of James D. G. Dunn for His 70th Birthday. Mohrmann, Douglas C. & Robertson, C. K., eds. 2010. (Library of New Testament Studies, the Ser.). (ENG., Illus.). 272p. 140.00 (978-0-567-62953-1(8), T&T Clark Int'l) Continuum International Publishing Group, Ltd. GBR. Dist: National Bk. Network.

Phillips, Lawrence. Holy Spirit Unveiled: A Revelation in God's Time. 2009. pap. 12.99 (978-1-60799-783-2(5)) Tate Publishing & Enterprises, LLC.

Platt, Nancy Van Dyke & Knudsen, Chilton R. So You Think You Don't Know One? Addiction & Recovery in Clergy & Congregations. 2010. xi, 126p. (978-0-8192-2442-2(1)); E-Book (978-0-8192-2443-9(X)) Church Publishing, Inc. (Morehouse Publishing).

Shuler, Randy. Hand Me a Dr Pepper, Please: A Fresh Look at the Issue of Christians & Social Drinking. 2010. pap. 12.99 (978-1-61566-590-7(0)) Tate Publishing & Enterprises, LLC.

Simply Quit Drinking: An Inspirational Journey from near Death. 2008. 112p. pap. 14.95 (978-0-9816134-0-6(3), Reaching Peak Publishing) Reaching Peak, LLC.

Spirituality & Religiousness & Alcohol/Other Drug Problems: Treatment & Recovery Perspectives. 2006. (ENG., Illus.). 232p. 124.00 (978-0-7890-3299-7(6)) Routledge.

St. Romain, Philip. Freedom from Codependency. 2010. 103p. pap. 12.95 (978-0-557-39592-7(5)) Lulu Enterprises Inc.

Stephens, Charles Paul. Hotels, Motels, Cocktails & Jail-Cells: From Syringe to Salvation in Fort Worth Texas. 2007. 204p. per. 11.95 (978-1-4327-0497-1(4)) Outskirts Pr., Inc.

Sturgis, Colleen. An Act of Grace, 1 vol. 2009. 149p. pap. 24.95 (978-1-60836-692-7(8)) PublishAmerica, Inc.

Turner, Frank. Raised from the Dead: The Personal Testimony of America's First Evangelical Anchorman. 2008. (Illus.). 300p. 24.95 (978-1-934363-27-0(8)) Zoe Life Publishing.

Uddin, Emaj. Cross-Cultural Alcohol & Arrack Drinking. 2011. 148p. pap. **(978-3-8443-0208-0(5))** Lambert Academic Publishing.

Vedella, Joe. That's No Story, That's My Life. 2008. 304p. pap. 18.99 (978-1-60647-492-1(8)) Xulon Pr., Inc.

W., Geno. Sought Through Prayer & Meditation: Wisdom from the Sunday 11th Step Meetings at the Wolfe Street Center in Little Rock. 2008. (ENG.). 216p. pap. 13.95 (978-1-59285-658-9(6)) Hazelden Publishing & Educational Services.

Weber, John Michael. From Junk to Jesus: In the Blink of an Eye. 2007. 76p. per. 16.95 (978-1-4241-8581-8(5)) PublishAmerica, Inc.

Wightman, Julia Bainbrigge. Annals of the Rescued. 2006. 284p. per. 23.99 (978-1-4255-2561-3(X)) MPublishing.

ALCOHOLISM—TREATMENT

see also Twelve-Step Programs

Aa Services. Alcoholics Anonymous - Big Book Special Edition - Including: New Personal Stories for the Year 2008. 2008. 224p. pap. (978-956-310-042-6(5)) Editorial Benei Noaj.

AA Services Staff. Alcoholics Anonymous Big Book Special E. 2006. 156p. per. (978-956-291-357-7(0)) Editorial Benei Noaj.

Adams, A. J. Undrunk: A Skeptic's Guide to AA. 2009. (ENG.). 216p. pap. 14.95 (978-1-59285-720-3(5)) Hazelden Publishing & Educational Services.

Al-Anon Family Group Headquarters. Hope for Today. 2007. 379p. 10.00 (978-0-910034-39-5(7)) Al-Anon Family Group Headquarters, Inc.

Alcoholics Anonymous. 2008. (MLT.). 172p. pap. 7.60 (978-0-916856-20-5(8)) Alcoholics Anonymous World Services, Inc.

Alcoholics Anonymous Study Edition - Black: By the Anonymous Press. 2nd rev. deluxe ed. 2009. 576p. lthr. 17.00 (978-1-892959-02-7(X)) Anonymous Pr., The.

Alcoholics Anonymous Study Edition - Black/Gilded: By the Anonymous Press. 2nd rev. deluxe ed. 2007. 576p. lthr. 25.00 (978-1-892959-11-9(9)) Anonymous Pr., The.

Alcoholics Anonymous Study Edition - Burgundy: By the Anonymous Press. 2nd rev. deluxe ed. 2009. 576p. lthr. 17.00 (978-1-892959-10-2(0)) Anonymous Pr., The.

Alcoholics Anonymous Study Edition - Burgundy/Gilded: By the Anonymous Press. 2nd rev. deluxe ed. 2007. 576p. lthr. 25.00 (978-1-892959-12-6(7)) Anonymous Pr., The.

Alcoholics Anonymous World Services, Inc. Staff. Alcoholics Anonymous Big Book Special E. 2006. 164p. per. (978-956-291-265-5(5)) Editorial Benei Noaj.

Alcoholics Anonymous World Services, Inc. Staff, contrib. by. Alcohólicos Anónimos: El Relato de Cómo Muchos Miles de Hombres y Mujeres Se Han Recuperado Del Alcoholismo. 3rd ed. 2008. xxxiv, 528p. (978-1-893007-95-6(2)) Alcoholics Anonymous World Services, Inc.

Alexander, William. Ordinary Recovery: Mindfulness, Addiction, & the Path of Lifelong Sobriety. 2010. (ENG., Illus.). 160p. pap. 15.95 (978-1-59030-828-8(X)) Shambhala Pubns., Inc.

Allen, David. The Sophisticated Alcoholic. 2011. (ENG.). 221p. pap. 22.95 **(978-1-84694-522-9(4))** Hunt, John Publishing Ltd. GBR. Dist: National Bk. Network.

Ameisen, Olivier. Heal Thyself: A Doctor at the Peak of His Medical Career, Destroyed by Alcohol — and the Personal Miracle That Brought Him Back. 2009. (ENG., Illus.). 368p. pap. 16.00 (978-0-374-53220-8(6)) Farrar, Straus & Giroux.

Anonymous. The Little Red Book. 2009. 110p. (978-1-60796-136-9(9)) Editorial Benei Noaj.

—The Little Red Book. 2010. 90p. pap. 7.49 (978-1-60459-948-0(0)) Wilder Pubns., Ltd.

Babor, Thomas F. & Del Boca, Frances K., eds. Treatment Matching in Alcoholism. 2010. (International Research Monographs in the Addictions Ser.). (ENG., Illus.). 292p. pap. 36.99 (978-0-521-17726-9(X)) Cambridge Univ. Pr.

Babor, Thomas F., et al. Alcohol: No Ordinary Commodity: Research & Public Policy. 2nd ed. 2010. (ENG., Illus.). 352p. 59.95 (978-0-19-955114-9(6)) Oxford Univ. Pr., Inc.

Baye, Douglas R. New Research on Alcoholism. 2006. 89.00 (978-1-60021-245-1(X), Nova Biomedical Bks.) Nova Science Pubs., Inc.

Bill, W. El Lenguaje del Corazon: Los Escritos de Bill W. Para el Grapevine.Tr. of Language of the Heart: Bill W's Grapevine Writings. (SPA.). 435p. pap. 12.00 (978-0-933685-27-7(0)) AA Grapevine, Inc.

Braun-Harvey, Douglas. Sexual Health in Drug & Alcohol Treatment: Group Facilitator's Manual. 2009. 344p. 50.00 (978-0-8261-2015-1(6)) Springer Publishing Co., Inc.

—Sexual Health in Recovery. 2010. 150p. pap. (978-0-8261-2017-5(2)) Springer Publishing Co., Inc.

Brozner, Elaine Y. New Research on Alcohol Abuse & Alcoholism. 2006. (Illus.). 188p. 129.00 (978-1-60021-310-6(3)) Nova Science Pubs., Inc.

C., Joe. There Is a Solution: A Personal Spiritual Voyage of Recovery from Alcoholism. 2006. pap. 21.99 (978-1-84728-552-2(X)) Lulu Enterprises Inc.

Cram101 Textbook Reviews Staff. Outlines & Highlights for Drugs in Perspective by Richard Fields, Isbn: 9780073380759. 2009. 138p. pap. 28.95 (978-1-4288-7952-2(8)) Cram101 Inc.

Cressman, Scott. Drugs: Power over Alcohol & Addiction. 2006. 96p. (YA). pap. 7.99 (978-0-8341-5011-9(5)) Beacon Hill Pr. of Kansas City.

Diel, Sylvanus. From Alcoholism to Moderation. 2007. 52p. per. 9.99 (978-1-60266-946-8(5)) Xulon Pr., Inc.

Edmundson, Eldon, Jr., ed. Implementing Evidence-Based Practices for Treatment of Alcohol & Drug Disorders. 2008. (ENG., Illus.). 115p. per. 19.95 (978-0-7890-3152-5(3)) Routledge.

Ena, compiled by. ENA SBIRT Implementation Toolkit. 2008. cd-rom 0.00 (978-0-9798307-0-9(2)) Emergency Nurses Assn.

Epstein, Elizabeth E. & McCrady, Barbara S. Overcoming Alcohol Abuse Use Problems: A Cognitive-Behavioral Treatment Program Therapist. 2009. (Treatments That Work Ser.). (ENG., Illus.). 272p. (C). pap. 36.50 (978-0-19-532281-1(9)) Oxford Univ. Pr., Inc.

—Overcoming Alcohol Use Problems: A Cognitive-Behavioral Treatment Program Workbook. 2009. (Treatments That Work Ser.). (ENG., Illus.). 208p. pap. 26.00 (978-0-19-532279-8(7)) Oxford Univ. Pr., Inc.

Eskapa, Roy & TaRessa. The Cure for Alcoholism: Drink Your Way Sober Without Willpower, Abstinence or Discomfort. 2008. (ENG., Illus.). 319p. pap. 14.95 (978-1-933771-55-7(0)) BenBella Bks.

Fals-Stewart, William & O'Farrell, Timothy J. Behavioral Couples Therapy for Alcoholism & Drug Abuse. 2006. (ENG., Illus.). 436p. pap. 50.00 (978-1-59385-324-2(6)) Guilford Pubns., Inc.

Fields, Richard. Drugs in Perspective: Causes, Assessment, Family, Prevention, Intervention, & Treatment. 8th ed. 2012. (ENG., Illus.). 400p. (C). pap. 119.00 **(978-0-07-802850-2(7)**, 0078028507) McGraw-Hill Cos., The.

Fischer, Judith L., et al. Familial Responses to Alcohol Problems. 2007. 163p. per. 49.95 (978-0-7890-3516-5(2)); (ENG., Illus.). 182p. 175.00 (978-0-7890-3515-8(4)) Routledge.

Flores, Philip J. Addiction as an Attachment Disorder. 2011. (ENG.). 364p. pap. 38.99 **(978-0-7657-0905-9(8)**, Aronson, Jason) Rowman & Littlefield Publishers, Inc.

Flores, Philip J. Group Psychotherapy with Addicted Populations: An Integration of Twelve-Step & Psychodynamic Theory. 3rd ed. 2007. (ENG.). 796p. 246.95 (978-0-7890-3529-5(4)); 792p. per. 115.00 (978-0-7890-3530-1(8)) Routledge.

Giordano, John J. Proven Holistic Treatment & Addiction. 2006. (Illus.). 186p. per. 12.99 (978-1-59886-375-8(4)) Tate Publishing & Enterprises, LLC.

Government Printing Office Staff. Alcohol Health & Research World. pap. 25.00 (978-0-16-010431-2(9)) United States Government Printing Office.

Grimmett, John O. Barriers Against Recovery. 8p. reprint ed. pap. 1.50 (978-0-89486-009-6(7), 1180B) Hazelden Publishing & Educational Services.

Harris, Phil. The Concerned Other: New Theory & the Evidence Base for Changing Problematic Drug & Alcohol Users Through Their Family Members. 2011. 136p. pap. 33.95 (978-1-905541-66-9(X)) Russell Hse. Publishing Ltd. GBR. Dist: International Specialized Bk. Services.

Healing Project Staff. Voices of Alcoholism: The Healing Companion: Stories for Courage, Comfort & Strength. 2008. (Voices Of Ser.). (ENG.). 288p. per. 16.95 (978-1-934184-04-2(7)) Lachance Publishing LLC.

Hedblom, Jack H. Last Call: Alcoholism & Recovery. 2007. (ENG., Illus.). 224p. 42.00 (978-0-8018-8677-5(5)); per. 18.95 (978-0-8018-8678-2(3)) Johns Hopkins Univ. Pr.

Hepp, Ernst & Hepp, Frances Fulenwider. In Love & War: The Dilemma of an American Girl & a German Diplomat. Christy, Helen & Christy, Gary, eds. 2007. (Illus.). 512p. pap. 16.95 (978-0-938075-96-7(9)); 39.95 (978-0-938075-95-0(0)) Ocean View Bks.

Hill, Robert & Harris, Jennifer, eds. The Principles & Practice of Group Work in Addictions. 2011. (ENG., Illus.). 272p. (C). 99.00 (978-0-415-48684-2(X)); pap. 41.99 (978-0-415-48685-9(8)) Routledge.

Hoffer, Abram & Saul, Andrew W. The Vitamin Cure for Alcoholism: How to Protect Against & Fight Alcoholism Using Nutrition & Vitamin Supplementation, 1 vol. 2009. 144p. pap. (978-1-59120-254-7(X)) Basic Health Pubns., Inc.

Hornbacher, Marya. Sane: Mental Illness, Addiction, & the 12 Steps. 2010. (ENG.). 180p. pap. 14.95 (978-1-59285-824-8(4)) Hazelden Publishing & Educational Services.

Johnson, Bankole. The Rehab Myth: New Medications that Conquer Alcoholism. 2013. (ENG.). 256p. pap. 17.00 (978-0-7382-1426-9(4)) Da Capo Pr., Inc.

Kinney, Jean. Loosening the Grip: A Handbook of Alcohol Information. 9th ed. 2008. (ENG., Illus.). 672p. (C). pap. 108.13 (978-0-07-340465-3(9), 0073404659) McGraw-Hill Cos., The.

—Loosening the Grip: A Handbook of Alcohol Information. 10th ed. 2011. (ENG., Illus.). 688p. (C). pap. 119.00 (978-0-07-340468-4(3), 0073404683) McGraw-Hill Cos., The.

Kleinig, John & Einstein, Stanley, eds. Ethical Challenges for Intervening in Drug Use: Policy, Research & Treatment. 2006. 766p. (978-0-942511-67-3(0)); per. 35.00 (978-0-942511-65-9(4)) Office of International Criminal Justice.

Klopocka, Maria, et al. Information Path Functional & Informational Macrodynamics. 2009. pap. 79.00 (978-1-60692-139-5(8)) Nova Science Pubs., Inc.

Kraft, William F. When You Love a Functional Alcoholic. 2011. 176p. pap. (978-0-8091-4679-6(7)) Paulist Pr.

Kuenzler, Alfred. The Patient's Intimate Partner in Couple Alcohol Treatment - Benefits by Matching Therapy to Partners. 2008. 140p. per. (978-3-8364-5742-2(3)) VDM Verlag Dr. Mueller e.K.

Lawson, Gary & Lawson, Ann W. Alcoholism & Substance Abuse in Diverse Populations. 2nd ed. 2010. 45.00 (978-1-4164-0439-2(2)) PRO-ED, Inc.

Lesch, Otto-Michael. Alcohol & Nicotine: Medical & Sociological Aspects of Usage, Abuse & Addiction. 2010. (Illus.). 380p. 99.00 **(978-3-7091-0145-2(X)**, 370910145X) Springer.

Lessa, Nicholas & Gilbert, Sara. Living with Alcoholism & Drug Addiction. 2009. (Teen's Guides). 168p. (gr. 6-12). pap. 14.95 (978-0-8160-7741-0(X), Checkmark Bks.) Facts On File, Inc.

Levy, Michael S. Take Control of Your Drinking... And You May Not Need to Quit. 2007. (ENG.). 264p. per. 20.95 (978-0-8018-8668-3(6)) Johns Hopkins Univ. Pr.

—Take Control of Your Drinking... & You May Not Need to Quit. 2007. (ENG.). 264p. 42.00 (978-0-8018-8667-6(8)) Johns Hopkins Univ. Pr.

The Little Red Book. 2008. 112p. pap. (978-956-291-627-1(8)) Editorial Benei Noaj.

Mack, Avram H., et al. Clinical Manual for Treatment of Alcoholism & Addictions. 2009. (Illus.). pap. 55.00 (978-1-58562-373-0(3)) American Psychiatric Publishing, Inc.

Maltzman, Irving. Alcoholism: Its Treatments & Mistreatments. 2008. (Illus.). 317p. 146.00 (978-981-277-087-5(9)) World Scientific Publishing Co., Inc.

Marcellino, Dennis. Addiction Free Forever. 2007. 224p. per. 19.95 (978-0-945272-31-1(6)) Lighthouse Publishing.

—Addiction Free Forever Workbook. 2007. 152p. per. 19.95 (978-0-945272-30-4(8)) Lighthouse Publishing.

—How to Naturally & Permanently Cure an Alcohol or Drug Addiction: What to Say "Yes" to That Will Give You the Strength, Peace, & Joy to "Say No to Drugs" 2006. (978-0-945272-28-1(6)) Lighthouse Pubns., Inc.

Marshall, E. Jane, et al. The Treatment of Drinking Problems: A Guide to the Helping Professions. 5th rev. ed. 2010. (ENG., Illus.). 276p. pap. 70.00 (978-0-521-13237-4(1)) Cambridge Univ. Pr.

McIlwain, Bill. Dancing Naked with the Rolling Stones: A Life in News & a Good-Bye to Booze. 2007. 240p. pap. 18.95 (978-0-9789736-1-2(5)); 22.95 (978-0-9789736-0-5(7)) Winoca Pr.

McMahon, John. First Steps out of Problem Drinking. 2010. (First Steps Ser.). (ENG.). 96p. pap. 9.95 (978-0-7459-5397-7(2)) Lion Hudson PLC GBR. Dist: Independent Pubs. Group.

Medicine, Beatrice. Drinking & Sobriety among the Lakota Sioux. 2006. (Contemporary Native American Communities Ser.). (ENG., 193p. Illus.). 81.00 (978-0-7591-0570-6(7)); per. 30.95 (978-0-7591-0571-3(5)) AltaMira Pr.

Morgan, Oliver J. & Litzke, Cheryl H. Family Intervention in Substance Abuse: Current Best Practices. 2008. (Illus.). 247p. (ENG.). 62.95 (978-0-7890-3758-9(0)); 125.00 (978-0-7890-3757-2(2)) Routledge.

Murray, Maurice "Mo". Just Snap Your Fingers And... Bingo You're Sober! A "Recovery" Workbook for Alcoholics. 2007. 124p. pap. 10.49 (978-1-4343-2881-6(3)) AuthorHouse.

—Just Snap Your Fingers and... Bingo You're Sober! A "Recovery" Workbook for Alcoholics. 2007. (ENG.). 124p. 21.49 (978-1-4343-5965-0(4)) AuthorHouse.

Naude, Henri. Escape! from the Clutches of Alcohol. 2008. 320p. 28.50 (978-1-934925-77-5(2), Strategic Bk. Publishing) AEG Literary Publishing Services, Inc.

Nekich, Eric J. Finding 5% of My Life, 1 vol. 2009. 53p. pap. 16.95 (978-1-4489-2156-0(2)) PublishAmerica, Inc.

Nolen-Hoeksema, Susan. Women Conquering Depression: How to Gain Control of Eating, Drinking, & Overthinking & Embrace a Healthier Life. rev. ed. 2010. (ENG.). 272p. pap. 16.00 (978-0-8050-9222-6(6), Holt Paperback) Holt, Henry & Co.

P. H., Cheryl, et al. Alcohol: Its History, Pharmacology, & Treatment. 2011. (ENG.). 260p. pap. 17.95 (978-1-61649-147-5(7)) Hazelden Publishing & Educational Services.

Page, Robert. The Presence. 2010. (ENG.). 128p. pap. 19.95 (978-1-84694-268-6(3)) Hunt, John Publishing Ltd. GBR. Dist: National Bk. Network.

Perkinson, Robert R. The Alcoholism & Drug Abuse Client Workbook. 2011. 152p. pap. 26.00 (978-1-4129-7922-1(6), B79221P) SAGE Pubns., Inc.

Prentiss, Chris. The Alcoholism & Addiction Cure: A Holistic Approach to Total Recovery. 2007. (ENG.). 352p. 24.95 (978-0-943015-54-5(5)) Power Pr.

Raeburn, Susan & Maisel, Eric. Creative Recovery: A Complete Addiction Treatment Program That Uses Your Natural Creativity. 2008. (ENG., Illus.). 312p. pap. 16.95 (978-1-59030-544-7(2), Trumpeter) Shambhala Pubns., Inc.

Railey, Robert R. Half Drunk, Half Sober. 2006. 49p. pap. 16.95 (978-1-4241-1546-4(9)) PublishAmerica, Inc.

Rhodes, Richard C. A Counselor Looks at the Big Book: A Clinician's View of the Book Alcoholics Anonymous. 2009. 168p. pap. 19.95 (978-1-58982-500-0(4), Millennial Mind Publishing) American Bk. Publishing Group.

Rose, Mark Edmund & Cherpitel, Cheryl J. Alcohol: Its History, Pharmacology, & Treatment. 2011. E-Book **(978-1-61649-403-2(4))** Hazelden Publishing & Educational Services.

Sandoz, Jeff. Alcoholic Iliad/Recovery Odyssey: Utilizing Myth As Addiction Metaphors in Family Therapy. 2009. 228p. pap. 29.95 (978-1-59942-511-5(4), Brown Walker Pr.) Universal Pubs.

Scott, Liz. The Sober Kitchen: Recipes & Advice for a Lifetime of Sobriety. 2006. 474p. reprint ed. pap. 20.00 (978-1-4223-5808-5(9)) DIANE Publishing Co.

Services, Aa. Alcoholics Anonymous - Big Book - 2007. 192p. (978-956-291-200-6(0)) Editorial Benei Noaj.

Services for the Prevention & Treatment of Dependence on Alcohol & Other Drugs: 14th Report of the WHO Expert Committee on Mental Health. Date not set. (Technical Report Ser.: No. 363). pap. 5.00 (978-92-4-120363-0(3), 1100363) World Health Organization.

Siple, Molly. Eating for Recovery: The Essential Nutrition Plan to Reverse the Physical Damage of Alcoholism. 2008. (ENG.). 336p. pap. 17.95 (978-1-60094-044-6(7), Da Capo Lifelong) Da Capo Pr., Inc.

Somach, Jeffrey & Busch, Linda. I Cut It Out: An (ex) Drunk's Guide to Sobriety. 2007. 165p. pap. 12.50 (978-0-9798969-1-0(6)) I Cut It Out, Inc.

Substance Abuse and Mental Health Services Administration (U.S.), compiled by. National Survey of Substance Abuse Treatment Services (N-SSATS) 2006: Data on Substance Abuse Treatment Facilities. 2008. (ENG., Illus.). 213p. pap. 31.00 (978-0-16-080714-5(X), 552-070-37307-1); pap. 31.00 (978-0-16-080814-2(6)) United States Government Printing Office. (Substance Abuse & Mental Health Services Administration).

Tatarsky, Andrew. Harm Reduction Psychotherapy: A New Treatment for Drug & Alcohol Problems. 2007. (ENG.). 392p. per. 36.99 (978-0-7657-0373-6(4), Aronson, Jason) Rowman & Littlefield Publishers, Inc.

Teetotaler, Ima. Known Cures for Alcoholism & other Drug Addictions. 2007. per. 5.00 (978-0-9674915-8-5(4)) Day By Day.

Tirbutt, Edmund & Tirbutt, Helen. Beat the Booze: A Comprehensive Guide to Combating Drink Problems in All Walks of Life: Reclaim Your Life. 2008. (ENG.). xi, 289p. per. 19.99 (978-1-905641-42-0(7)) Harriman Hse. Publishing GBR. Dist: Ingram Pub. Services.

Tracy, Sarah W. Alcoholism in America: From Reconstruction to Prohibition. 2007. (ENG.). 384p. (gr. 17). per. 26.00 (978-0-8018-8620-1(1)) Johns Hopkins Univ. Pr.

Urschel, Harold. Healing the Addicted Brain. 2009. (ENG.). 288p. pap. 15.99 (978-1-4022-1844-6(3)) Sourcebooks, Inc.

Vale, Brian & Edwards, Griffith. Physician to the Fleet: The Life & Times of Thomas Trotter, 1760-1832. 2011. (Illus.). 248p. 99.00 (978-1-84383-604-9(1), Boydell Press) Boydell & Brewer, Ltd. GBR. Dist: Boydell & Brewer, Inc.

Velleman, Richard D. B. Counselling for Alcohol Problems. 3rd ed. 2011. (Counselling in Practice Ser.). (Illus.). 208p. (C). 120.00

(978-1-84860-149-9(2), B01492C); pap. 46.00 (978-1-84860-150-5(6), B01492P) SAGE Pubns., Ltd. GBR. Dist: SAGE Pubns., Inc.

W., Bill. Alcoholics Anonymous: The Original 1939 Edition. 2011. (Dover Empower Your Life Ser.). (ENG.). 432p. pap. 12.95 (978-0-486-48059-6(3)) Dover Pubns., Inc.

W, Bill. The Little Red Book. 2011. 78p. pap. 7.49 **(978-1-61720-287-2(8))** Wilder Pubns., Ltd.

Walker, Ida. Alcohol Addiction: Not Worth the Buzz. 2012. **(978-1-4222-2428-1(7))**; pap. **(978-1-4222-2447-2(3))** Mason Crest Pubs.

Walle, Alf H. Recovery the Native Way: A Client Reader. 2008. 80p. pap. (978-1-60752-014-6(1)) Information Age Publishing, Inc.

—Recovery the Native Way: A Therapist's Manual. 2007. pap. (978-1-59311-833-4(3)) Information Age Publishing, Inc.

Washton, Arnold M. & Zweben, Joan E. Treating Alcohol & Drug Problems in Psychotherapy Practice: Doing What Works. 2008. (ENG.). 312p. pap. 30.00 (978-1-59385-980-0(5)) Guilford Pubns., Inc.

Wightman, Julia Bainbrigge. Annals of the Rescued. 2006. 284p. per. 23.99 (978-1-4255-2561-3(X)) MPublishing.

Yoshida, Rin. Trends in Alcohol Abuse & Alcoholism Research. 2006. 300p. 225.00 (978-1-60021-383-0(9)) Nova Science Pubs., Inc.

ALCOHOLISM AND CRIME

see also Drunkenness (Criminal Law)

Graham, K. & Bernards, S. Unhappy Hours: Alcohol & Partner Aggression in the Americas. 2009. (PAHO Scientific Publication No 631 Ser.). 258p. pap. 30.00 (978-92-75-11631-9(8)) Pan American Health Organization (PAHO).

North, Anthony. Descent into Crime: Britian's Century of Lawlessness 1650-1750. (Illus.). 232p. 26.95 (978-1-902809-10-6(6), London Hse.) Allison & Busby, Ltd. GBR. Dist: International Publishers Marketing.

ALCOHOLISM AND EMPLOYMENT

Berger, Lisa. Workplace & Employee Alcohol Problems. 2009. 124p. pap. (978-3-639-13031-7(6)) VDM Verlag Dr. Mueller e.K.

Dasgupta, Amitava. Pre-Employment Drug & Alcohol Testing: A Pocket Guide. 2011. (978-1-59425-110-8(X)) American Assn. for Clinical Chemistry, Inc.

Jackson, Arthur M. Raise the Bottom: How to Keep Secret Alcoholics from Damaging Your Business. 2009. 137p. pap. 16.95 (978-0-9820938-2-5(9), Bascom Hill Publishing Group, Ltd.) Hillcrest Publishing Group, Inc.

National Safety Compliance Services, Inc. Controlled Substance Abuse & Alcohol Misuse Training for Transportation Supervisors. 3rd rev. ed. 2008. (ENG.). 108p. pap. 34.95 (978-0-7872-9528-8(0)) Kendall Hunt Publishing Co.

Tobutt, Clive, ed. Alcohol at Work. 2011. (Illus.). 266p. 124.95 (978-0-566-08694-6(8), Gower Publishing Co., Ltd.) Ashgate Publishing, Ltd. GBR. Dist: Ashgate Publishing Co.

ALCOHOLISM AND MENTAL ILLNESS

see Dual Diagnosis

ALCOHOLISM AND RELIGION

see Alcoholism—Religious Aspects

ALCOHOLISM AND TRAFFIC ACCIDENTS

see Drinking and Traffic Accidents

ALCOHOLS

see also Alcohol; Glycerin

ABBE Scientist Research Division Staff. Analysis of Food Containing ALCOHOL with Index & Medical Analysis of New Clinical & Research Division. 2008. (Illus.). 160p. 69.95 (978-0-7883-4833-4(7)) ABBE Pubs. Assn. of Washington, D.C.

Adam, Waldemar, et al. Oxidation of Organic Compounds by Dioxiranes. 2009. (ENG., Illus.). 670p. pap., Intern't.'s hndbk. ed. 111.00 (978-0-470-45407-7(5), Wiley-Interscience) Wiley, John & Sons, Inc.

Mudge, Stephen M., et al. Fatty Alcohols: Anthropogenic & Natural Occurrence in the Environment. 2008. (ENG., Illus.). 176p. (C). 160.00 **(978-0-85404-152-7(4))** Royal Society of Chemistry, The GBR. Dist: Ingram Pub. Services.

Pandaram, Palanisamy. Synthesis of Polyols from Cardanol. 2011. 64p. pap. **(978-3-8443-0382-7(0))** Lambert Academic Publishing.

Ramasamy, Subramanian. Alcohols Permeability in Nafion Membranes for Direct Alcohol Fuel Cell. 2011. 64p. pap. **(978-3-8433-9050-7(9))** Lambert Academic Publishing.

Tojo, Gabriel & Fernandez, Marcos I. Oxidation of Primary Alcohols to Carboxylic Acids: A Guide to Current Common Practice. 2010. (Basic Reactions in Organic Synthesis Ser.). (Illus.). xvi, 116p. pap. 99.00 (978-1-4419-2254-0(7), 1441922547) Springer.

ALCORAN

see Koran

ALCOTT, AMOS BRONSON, 1799-1888

Alcott, Amos Bronson. Notes of Conversations, 1848-1875: Amos Bronson Alcott. English, Karen, ed. 2007. 288p. (C). 55.00 (978-0-8386-4118-7(0)) Fairleigh Dickinson Univ. Pr.

Cheney, Ednah D. Story of the Alcotts. 2006. pap. 15.95 (978-1-4286-6210-0(3)) Kessinger Publishing, LLC.

Francis, Richard. Fruitlands: The Alcott Family & Their Search for Utopia. (ENG., Illus.). 344p. 2011. pap. 17.00 (978-0-300-17790-9(9)) 2010. 30.00 (978-0-300-14041-5(X)) Yale Univ. Pr.

Hovet, Grace Ann & Hovet Sr., Theodore R. Tableaux Vivants. 2009. 222p. 29.99 (978-1-4415-3453-8(9)); pap. 19.99 (978-1-4415-3452-1(0)) Xlibris Corp.

Peabody, Elizabeth Palmer,. Record of Mr Alcott's School, Exemplifying the Principles & Methods of Moral Culture. 2009. 304p. 24.99 (978-1-103-62316-7(8)); pap. 18.99 (978-1-103-62312-9(5)) BiblioBazaar.

—Record of Mr Alcott's School, Exemplifying the Principles & Methods of Moral Culture. 2006. 300p. per. 23.99 (978-1-4255-2825-6(2)) MPublishing.

Schreiner, Samuel Agnew, Jr., et al. The Concord Quartet: Alcott, Emerson, Hawthorne, Thoreau, & the Friendship That Freed the American Mind. 2006. (ENG., Illus.). 256p. 24.95 (978-0-471-64663-1(6), Wiley) Wiley, John & Sons, Inc.

Sears, Clara Endicott. Bronson Alcott's Fruitlands. 2009. 240p. 23.99 (978-1-103-86894-0(2)); pap. 17.99 (978-1-103-86884-1(5)) BiblioBazaar.

—Bronson Alcott's Fruitlands. 2009. 102p. pap. (978-0-217-45019-5(9)) Books LLC.

Shepard, Odell. Pedlar's Progress: The Life of Bronson Alcott. 580p. 2008. 58.95 (978-1-4366-9584-8(8)) 2007. (ENG.). per. 43.95 (978-1-4325-7028-6(5)) Kessinger Publishing, LLC.

ALCOTT, LOUISA MAY, 1832-1888

Alcott, Louisa May. Hospital Sketches. 2010. 392p. pap. 33.75 (978-1-117-87105-9(3)) 2009. 106p. pap. 19.75 (978-1-116-82701-9(8)) 2009. (ENG.). 105p. pap. 18.99 (978-1-116-82704-0(2), BiblioLife) 2009. (ENG.). 105p. pap. 19.99 (978-1-116-82703-3(4), BiblioLife) 2009. 106p. pap. 19.75 (978-1-116-82702-6(6)) BiblioBazaar.

—Hospital Sketches. 2007. (ENG.). 80p. per. (978-1-4068-4835-9(2)) Echo Library.

—Hospital Sketches. 2010. (Illus.). 52p. pap. 20.00 (978-1-153-62926-3(7)) General Bks. LLC.

—Hospital Sketches. 2010. 68p. pap. 13.56 (978-1-162-66673-0(0)); 25.56 **(978-1-169-21867-3(9))**; 31.95 (978-1-161-43538-2(7)) Kessinger Publishing, LLC.

—Hospital Sketches - an Army Nurses's Tru. 2006. 96p. per. (978-1-4067-9644-5(1), Hesperides Pr.) Read Bks.

—Little Women Abroad: The Alcott Sisters' Letters from Europe, 1870-1871. Shealy, Daniel, ed. 2008. (ENG., Illus.). 376p. 34.95 (978-0-8203-3009-9(4)) Univ. of Georgia Pr.

—Louisa May Alcott: Her Life, Letters, & Journals. 2008. (ENG.). 424p. per. (978-1-4086-7733-9(4)) Read Bks.

Cheever, Susan. American Bloomsbury: Louisa May Alcott, Ralph Waldo Emerson, Margaret Fuller, Nathaniel Hawthorne, & Henry David Thoreau: Their Lives, Their Loves, Their Work. 2007. (ENG., Illus.). 240p. pap. 15.00 (978-0-7432-6462-4(2)) Simon & Schuster.

—Louisa May Alcott. l.t. ed. 2011. 443p. 31.99 (978-1-4104-3552-1(0)) Thorndike Pr.

—Louisa May Alcott: A Personal Biography. 2011. (Playaway Adult Nonfiction Ser.). 79.99 (978-1-61707-009-9(2)) Findaway World, LLC.

—Louisa May Alcott: A Personal Biography. (ENG., Illus.). 320p. 2011. pap. 16.00 (978-1-4165-6992-3(8)) 2010. 26.00 (978-1-4165-6991-6(X)) Simon & Schuster.

Cheney, Ednah, ed. Louisa May Alcott: Her Life, Letters, & Journals. 2010. (ENG., Illus.). 428p. pap. 19.95 (978-1-4290-4460-8(8)) Applewood Bks.

Cheney, Ednah D. Story of the Alcotts. 2006. pap. 15.95 (978-1-4286-6210-0(3)) Kessinger Publishing, LLC.

Clark, Beverly Lyon, ed. Louisa May Alcott: The Contemporary Reviews. 2010. (American Critical Archives Ser.). (ENG.). 419p. pap. 39.99 (978-0-521-15539-7(8)) Cambridge Univ. Pr.

Leopold, Allison. May Alcott: The Real Amy. 2007. (ENG.). 384p. 35.00 (978-0-300-11164-4(9)) Yale Univ. Pr.

Maibor, Carolyn. Labor Pains: Emerson, Hawthorne, & Alcott on Work, Women, & the Development of the Self. 2009. 154p. pap. 39.95 (978-0-415-80350-2(0)) Routledge.

Matteson, John. Eden's Outcasts: The Story of Louisa May Alcott & Her Father. 2008. (ENG., Illus.). 512p. pap. 17.95 (978-0-393-33359-6(0), 33359) 2007. 29.95 (978-0-7930-5964-5(X)) 2007. (ENG., Illus.). 512p. 29.95 (978-0-393-05964-9(2), 5964) Norton, W. W. & Co., Inc.

Reisen, Harriet. Louisa May Alcott: The Woman Behind Little Women. 2009. (ENG.). 384p. 26.00 (978-0-8050-8299-9(9)) Holt, Henry & Co.

—Louisa May Alcott: The Woman Behind Little Women. 2010. (ENG.). 464p. pap. 16.00 (978-0-312-65887-8(7)) Picador.

Stepanski, Lisa M. The Home Schooling of Louisa May Alcott: How Her Father & Her Mother Educated an American Writer. 2011. (Illus.). 180p. 109.95 (978-0-7734-1485-3(1)) Mellen, Edwin Pr., The.

Whitman, Walt. Racial Indigestion: Eating Bodies in the 19th Century. White, William, ed. 2007. (ENG.). 288p. 74.00 **(978-0-8147-7002-3(9))** New York Univ. Pr.

ALCOTT FAMILY

Cheney, Ednah D. Story of the Alcotts. 2006. pap. 15.95 (978-1-4286-6210-0(3)) Kessinger Publishing, LLC.

Gowing, Clara. The Alcotts As I Knew Them. 2007. (ENG.). 160p. 36.95 (978-0-548-43654-7(1)); per. 21.95 (978-0-548-41443-9(2)) Kessinger Publishing, LLC.

Matteson, John. Eden's Outcasts: The Story of Louisa May Alcott & Her Father. 2007. (ENG., Illus.). 512p. 29.95 (978-0-393-05964-9(2), 5964) Norton, W. W. & Co., Inc.

Stepanski, Lisa M. The Home Schooling of Louisa May Alcott: How Her Father & Her Mother Educated an American Writer. 2011. (Illus.). 180p. 109.95 (978-0-7734-1485-3(1)) Mellen, Edwin Pr., The.

ALCUIN, 735-804

Bisogno, Armando. Il Metodo Carolingio: Identità Culturale e Dibattito Teologico Nel Secolo Nono. 2008. (ITA., Illus.). 428p. (978-2-503-52862-5(7)) Brepols Pubs.

Browne, Right Rev G. F. Alcuin of York. 2008. 380p. (978-1-4437-2301-5(0)) 2006. 376p. per. (978-1-4067-1835-5(1)) Read Bks. (Hesperides Pr.).

Scheck, Helene. Reform & Resistance: Formations of Female Subjectivity in Early Medieval Ecclesiastical Culture. (SUNY Series in Medieval Studies). 2009. 224p. pap. 24.95 (978-0-7914-7484-6(4), Suny Pr.) 2008. (Illus.). xii, 238p. (C). 70.00 (978-0-7914-7483-9(6)) State Univ. of New York Pr.

West, Andrew Fleming. Alcuin & the Rise of the Christian Schools. 2009. 218p. 28.99 (978-1-110-40142-0(6)); 28.99 (978-1-110-82407-6(6)); pap. 23.75 (978-1-110-40139-0(6)); pap. 23.75 (978-1-110-82404-5(1)) BiblioBazaar.

—Alcuin & the Rise of the Christian Schools. 2009. 126p. pap. (978-0-217-77096-5(7)); 118p. pap. (978-1-4590-2430-4(3)) Books LLC.

—Alcuin & the Rise of the Christian Schools. 2009. 94p. pap. 19.99 (978-1-151-62259-4(1)) General Bks. LLC.

—Alcuin & the Rise of the Christian Schools. 2007. (ENG.). 214p. 39.95 (978-0-548-15229-4(2)); 216p. per. 24.95 (978-1-4304-4595-1(5)) Kessinger Publishing, LLC.

—Alcuin & the Rise of the Christian Schools. 2008. 212p. pap. (978-1-4097-7664-2(6)) Read Bks.

ALDEHYDES

Mahrwald, Rainer. Aldol Reactions. 2010. (ENG., Illus.). xii, 350p. pap. 239.00 **(978-90-481-7958-9(0)**, 9048179580) Springer.

—Aldol Reactions. Mahrwald, Rainer, ed. 2009. (ENG., Illus.). xii, 350p. 239.00 (978-1-4020-8700-4(4), 1402087004) Springer.

Novartis Foundation Symposium Staff. Acetaldehyde-Related Pathology: Bridging the Trans-Disciplinary Divide. 2007. (Novartis Foundation Symposia Ser.). (ENG., Illus.). 286p. 195.00 (978-0-470-05766-7(1), Wiley) Wiley, John & Sons, Inc.

Shi, Min, et al. The Chemistry of the Morita-Baylis-Hillman Reaction. 2011. (RSC Catalysis Ser.). (ENG., Illus.). 563p. (C). 232.00 (978-1-84973-129-4(2)) Royal Society of Chemistry, The GBR. Dist: Ingram Pub. Services.

Tojo, Gabriel & Fernandez, Marcos I. Oxidation of Alcohols to Aldehydes & Ketones: A Guide to Current Common Practice. 2010. (Basic Reactions in Organic Synthesis Ser.). xx, 375p. pap. 139.00 (978-1-4419-3642-4(4), 1441936424) Springer.

World Health Organization. 2-Butenal. 2009. (Concise International Chemical Assessment Document No 74 Ser.). (ENG.). 59p. pap. 24.00 (978-92-4-153074-3(X)) World Health Organization.

ALDHELM, SAINT, 640?-709

Brooks, Nicholas & Barker, Katherine. Aldhelm & Sherborne: Essays to Celebrate the Founding of the Bishopric. Barker, Katherine, ed. 2010. (ENG., Illus.). 332p. (C). pap. 70.00 (978-1-84217-357-2(X)) Oxbow Bks., Ltd. GBR. Dist: Brown, David Bk. Co., The.

Orchard, Andy. The Poetic Art of Aldhelm. 2006. (Cambridge Studies in Anglo-Saxon England Ser.). (ENG.). 332p. pap. 63.00 (978-0-521-03457-9(4)) Cambridge Univ. Pr.

ALDINGTON, RICHARD, 1892-1962

Aldington, Richard. Life for Life's Sake: A Book of Reminiscences. (Des Imagistes Ser.). 416p. reprint ed. 55.00 (978-0-404-17076-9(5)) AMS Pr., Inc.

Gates, Norman T. Richard Aldington. 2008. pap. 31.95 (978-0-271-02844-6(0)) Pennsylvania State Univ. Pr.

ALDISS, BRIAN WILSON, 1925-

Aldiss, Brian W. An Exile on Planet Earth: Articles & Reflections. 2012. (ENG.). 192p. 35.00 **(978-1-85124-373-0(9))** Bodleian Library GBR. Dist: Chicago Distribution Ctr.

ALDOSTERONE

DeMello, Walmor C. & Frohlich, Edward D., eds. Renin Angiotensin System & Cardiovascular Disease. 2009. (Contemporary Cardiology Ser.). (ENG., Illus.). xii, 248p. 219.00 (978-1-60761-185-1(6), 1607611856) Humana Pr.

Kohn, Taylor. Anp Inhibits the Production of Aldosterone in Rat Adrenal Glands. 2011. 68p. pap. **(978-3-8454-0885-9(5))** Lambert Academic Publishing.

Leung, Po Sing, ed. Frontiers in Research of the Renin-Angiotensin System on Human Disease. 2010. (Proteases in Biology & Disease Ser.). xii, 308p. pap. 199.00 (978-90-481-7617-5(4), 9048176174) Springer.

ALDRICH, THOMAS BAILEY, 1836-1907

Aldrich, Thomas Bailey. Crowding Memories. 2008. 348p. 29.99 (978-0-554-99452-9(6)); 28.99 (978-0-554-99456-7(9)); pap. 31.75 (978-0-554-99455-0(0)); pap. 32.75 (978-0-554-99453-6(4)) BiblioBazaar.

—Crowding Memories. 2007. (ENG.). 352p. 46.95 (978-0-548-08573-8(0)) Kessinger Publishing, LLC.

Duryee, Samuel Sloan. Thomas Bailey Aldrich Inspired Poet of T. 2006. pap. 15.95 (978-1-4286-6073-1(9)) Kessinger Publishing, LLC.

Greenslet, Ferris. The Life of Thomas Bailey Aldrich. 2009. 152p. pap. 19.99 (978-1-150-18657-8(7)) General Bks. LLC.

ALDRIDGE, IRA FREDERICK, D. 1867

Kujawinska Courtney, Krystyna & Lukowska, Maria, eds. Ira Aldridge (1807-1867) The Great Shakespearean Tragedian on the Bicentennial Anniversary of his Birth. 2009. 168p. pap. 50.95 **(978-3-631-57734-9(6))** Lang, Peter GmbH, Europaischer Verlag der Wissenschaften DEU. Dist: Lang, Peter.

Lindfors, Bernth. Ira Aldridge: The Early Years, 1807-1833, 2 vols. 2011. (Rochester Studies in African History & the Diaspora Ser.: Volume 48). (Illus.). 402p. 55.00 (978-1-58046-381-2(9)) Univ. of Rochester Pr.

—Ira Aldridge: The Early Years, 1807-1833 & the Vagabond Years, 1833-1852. 2011. (Rochester Studies in African History & the Diaspora Ser.). 660p. 99.00 (978-1-58046-401-7(7)) Univ. of Rochester Pr.

—Ira Aldridge: The Vagabond Years, 1833-1852, 2 vols. 2011. (Rochester Studies in African History & the Diaspora Ser.: Volume 49). (Illus.). 258p. 55.00 (978-1-58046-394-2(0)) Univ. of Rochester Pr.

Lindfors, Bernth, ed. Ira Aldridge: The African Roscius. 2007. (Rochester Studies in African History & the Diaspora Ser.: Volume 28). (Illus.). 304p. 55.00 (978-1-58046-258-7(8)) Univ. of Rochester Pr.

ALDRIN, BUZZ, 1930-

Aldrin, Buzz, Jr. & Abraham, Ken. Magnificent Desolation: The Long Journey Home from the Moon. (ENG., Illus.). 2010. 352p. pap. 16.00 (978-0-307-46346-3(X), Three Rivers Pr.) 2009. 336p. 27.00 (978-0-307-46345-6(1), Harmony) Crown Publishing Group.

ALDRIN, EDWIN E., 1930-

see Aldrin, Buzz, 1930-

ALDUS PAGEMAKER (COMPUTER PROGRAM)

see Adobe PageMaker (Computer Program)

ALE

see also Beer; Malt

O'Neill, Patrick. Cellermanship. 5th ed. 2011. (ENG., Illus.). 152p. pap. 13.95 (978-1-85249-278-6(3)) Camra Bks. GBR. Dist: Independent Pubs. Group.

Sykes, Walter J. The Principles & Practice of Brewing Beer & Ale. 2008. 532p. pap. 37.95 (978-1-934939-23-9(4)) Wexford College Pr.

Wheeler, Graham. Home Brewing: The Camra Guide. (Illus.). 232p. per. 14.99 (978-1-85249-112-3(4)) Camra Bks. GBR. Dist: All About Beer Magazine.

ALE-HOUSES

see Hotels

ALEKHINE, ALEXANDER, 1892-1946

Bogdanov, Valentin. Play the Alekhine. 2010. (ENG., Illus.). 112p. pap. 19.95 (978-1-906454-15-9(9)) Gambit Pubns., Ltd. GBR. Dist: Perseus Distribution.

ALEMAN, MATEO, 1547-1617

Aleman, Mateo. The Rogue: or The Life of Guzman De Alfarache, 4 vols. Mabbe, James, tr. (Tudor Translations, Second Ser.: No. 2-5). reprint ed. 230.00 (978-0-404-51970-4(9)) AMS Pr., Inc.

Ife, B. W. Reading & Fiction in Golden-Age Spain: A Platonist Critique & Some Picaresque Replies. 2009. (Cambridge Iberian & Latin American Studies). 224p. pap. 33.99 (978-0-521-12120-0(5)) Cambridge Univ. Pr.

ALEMBERT, JEAN LE ROND D', 1717-1783

Bertrand, Joseph. D'Alembert. 2011. 228p. pap. 20.99 **(978-1-4255-7933-3(7))** MPublishing.

ALEPPO (SYRIA)

Boogert, Maurits van den. Aleppo Observed: Ottoman Syria Through the Eyes of Two Scottish Doctors, Alexander & Patrick Russell. 2010. (ENG., Illus.). 160p. 250.00 (978-0-19-958856-5(2)) Oxford Univ. Pr., Inc.

Wilkins, Charles L. Forging Urban Solidarities: Ottoman Aleppo, 1640-1700. 2009. (Illus.). 334p. (978-90-04-16907-4(5)) BRILL.

ALEUTIAN ISLANDS (ALASKA)

Blackford, Mansel G. Pathways to the Present: U. S. Development & Its Consequences in the Pacific. 2007. (Illus.). 267p. 50.00 (978-0-8248-3073-1(3)) Univ. of Hawaii Pr.

Chandonnet, Fern, ed. Alaska at War, 1941-1945: The Forgotten War Remembered. 2007. (Illus.). 474p. per. 29.95 (978-1-60223-013-2(7)) Univ. of Alaska Pr.

ALEUTS

Dumond, Don. The Eskimos & Aleuts. 2011. 184p. 27.00 **(978-1-59740-807-3(7))** ACLS Humanities E-Book.

Fair, Susan W. Alaska Native Art: Tradition, Innovation, Continuity. Blodgett, Jean, ed. 2007. (ENG., Illus.). 312p. pap. 32.95 (978-1-889963-82-2(8)) Univ. of Alaska Pr.

Hudson, Ray. Moments Rightly Placed: An Aleutian Memoir. rev. ed. 2008. (Alaska Book Adventures (Epicenter Press) Ser.). (ENG.). 224p. (gr. 9). pap. 19.95 (978-0-9790470-7-7(2)) Epicenter Pr., Inc.

Lindsay, Betty A. & Lindsay, John A. Pribilof Islands, Alaska: Genealogy & Census. 2009. (Illus.). xix, 658p. (978-1-60319-002-2(3)) United States Government Printing Office.

Martin, Fredericka I. Before the Storm: A Year in the Pribilof Islands, 1941-1942. Hudson, Raymond L., ed. 2010. (ENG., Illus.). 385p. pap. 39.95 (978-1-60223-076-7(5)) Univ. of Alaska Pr.

McClanahan, Alexandra J. & Bissett, Hallie L. Na'eda: Our Friends. Hall, Veldee, ed. 3rd ed. 2008. (Illus.). 128p. pap. 12.95 (978-0-938227-09-0(2)) CIRI Foundation, The.

Oleksa, Michael J., ed. Alaskan Missionary Spirituality. 2nd ed. 2010. (ENG.). 416p. pap. 24.00 (978-0-88141-340-3(2)) St. Vladimir's Seminary Pr.

Reedy-Maschner, Katherine L. Aleut Identities: Tradition & Modernity in an Indigenous Fishery. 2010. (McGill-Queen's Native & Northern Ser.). (ENG.). 314p. (C). (978-0-7735-3682-1(5)); pap. (978-0-7735-3748-4(1)) McGill-Queen's Univ. Pr.

Sutton, Mark Q. Sutton: Introd Native North Americ_4. 4th rev. ed. 2011. (ENG.). 432p. (C). pap. 109.60 *(978-0-205-12156-4(X)*, Prentice Hall) Prentice Hall PTR.

Turner, Lucien M. An Aleutian Ethnography. Hudson, Raymond L., ed. (Illus.). 2010. (ENG.). 256p. pap. 26.95 *(978-1-60223-039-2(0))* 2008. 175p. 45.00 *(978-1-60223-028-6(5))* Univ. of Alaska Pr.

ALEXANDER I, EMPEROR OF RUSSIA, 1777-1825

Paleologue, Maurice. The Enigmatic Czar: The Life of Alexander I of Russia. Muir, Edwin & Muir, Willa, trs. 344p. 2008. 46.95 *(978-1-4366-9793-4(X))* 2007. (ENG.). per. 31.95 *(978-1-4325-7704-9(2))* Kessinger Publishing, LLC.

Vilinbachov, George & Olausson, Magnus, eds. Staging Power: Napoleon, Charles John, Alexander. 2010. 424p. 129.50 *(978-91-7100-824-4(1))* Moderna Museet SWE. Dist: Coronet Bks.

ALEXANDER II, EMPEROR OF RUSSIA, 1818-1881

Beran, Michael Knox. Forge of Empires: Three Revolutionary Statesmen & the World They Made, 1861-1871. 2011. (ENG.). 496p. pap. 28.99 *(978-0-7432-7070-0(3)*, Free Pr.) Free Pr.

Footman, David. Red Prelude: The Life of the Russian Terrorist, Zhelyabov. 284p. 2008. 43.95 *(978-1-4367-0708-4(0))* 2007. (ENG.). per. 28.95 *(978-1-4304-6630-7(8))* Kessinger Publishing, LLC.

Pfeifer Swezey, Marilyn, ed. The Tsar & the President: Alexander II & Abraham Lincoln, Liberator & Emancipator. 2009. (Illus.). 112p. pap. 24.95 *(978-0-9787201-1-7(3))* Univ. of Wisconsin Pr.

Radzinsky, Edvard. Alexander II: The Last Great Tsar. Bouis, Antonina, tr. 2006. (ENG., Illus.). 480p. pap. 17.00 *(978-0-7432-8426-4(7)*, Free Pr.) Free Pr.

Verhoeven, Claudia. The Odd Man Karakozov: Imperial Russia, Modernity, & the Birth of Terrorism. (Illus.). 248p. 2011. pap. 23.95 ***(978-0-8014-7757-7(3))*** 2009. 39.95 *(978-0-8014-4652-8(X))* Cornell Univ. Pr.

ALEXANDER III, EMPEROR OF RUSSIA, 1845-1894

Fiehn, Terry & Corin, Chris. Russia under Tsarism & Communism 1881-1953. 2nd rev. ed. 2011. 402p. pap. 58.50 *(978-1-4441-2423-1(4))* Hodder Education GBR. Dist: Trans-Atlantic Pubns., Inc.

Lowe, Charles. Alexander III of Russia. 2009. 382p. 33.99 *(978-1-110-10367-6(0))*; pap. 32.75 *(978-1-110-10365-2(4))* BiblioBazaar.

—Alexander III of Russia. 2008. 380p. 48.95 *(978-1-4369-8742-4(3))*; pap. 33.95 *(978-1-4367-6359-2(2))* Kessinger Publishing, LLC.

ALEXANDER III, POPE, D. 1181

Clarke, Peter D. & Duggan, Anne J., eds. Pope Alexander III(1159-81) The Art of Survival. 2012. (Church, Faith & Culture in the Medieval West Ser.). (Illus.). 400p. 134.95 ***(978-0-7546-6288-4(8))*** Ashgate Publishing Co.

ALEXANDER VI, POPE, 1431-1503

Anonymous. Pope Alexander VI & His Court: Extracts from the Latin diary of Johannes Burchardus. 2009. 228p. 28.99 *(978-1-116-56221-7(9))*; pap. 25.75 *(978-1-116-56222-4(7))*; pap. 24.75 *(978-1-116-56223-1(5))* BiblioBazaar.

ALEXANDER VII, POPE, 1594-1667

Bargrave, John. Pope Alexander the Seventh & the College of Cardinals. Robertson, James C., ed. (Camden Society, London. Publications, First Ser.: No. 92). reprint ed. 37.50 *(978-0-404-50192-1(3))* AMS Pr., Inc.

—Pope Alexander the Seventh & the College of Cardinals. Robertson, James C., ed. 2007. (ENG.). 172p. 37.95 *(978-0-548-20632-4(5))*; 176p. per. 22.95 *(978-1-4325-2411-1(9))* Kessinger Publishing, LLC.

Caramuel Lobkowitz, Juan & Sabaino, Daniele. Il Tractatus Expendens Propositiones Damnatas Ab Alexandro VII Di Juan Caramuel Lobkowitz: Studio Introduttivo Ed Edizione Critica. 2010. (LAT, ITA & ENG.). 139.95 *(978-0-7734-3608-4(1))* Mellen, Edwin Pr., The.

ALEXANDER, THE GREAT, 356-323 B.C.

Abbott, Jacob. History of Alexander the Great. 2009. 108p. pap. *(978-1-150-66887-6(3))* Books LLC.

Alexander the Great. 2008. 29.90 *(978-1-60591-043-7(0))* Title Player, Inc.

Amitay, Ory. From Alexander to Jesus. 2010. (Hellenistic Culture & Society Ser.). (ENG.). 260p. 49.95 *(978-0-520-26636-0(6))* Univ. of California Pr.

Atkinson, J. E. Curtius Rufus, Histories of Alexander the Great, Book 10. Oxford Staff, ed. Yardley, J. C., tr. from LAT. 2009. (Clarendon Ancient History Ser.). (ENG., Illus.). 320p. 150.00 *(978-0-19-955762-2(4))*; pap. 60.00 *(978-0-19-955763-9(2))* Oxford Univ. Pr., Inc.

Badian, Ernst. Collected Papers on Alexander the Great. 2012. (ENG., Illus.). 560p. (C). 180.00 *(978-0-415-37828-4(1))* Routledge.

Barbour, John, et al. The Buik of the Most Noble & Vailzeand Conqueror Alexander the Great. 2008. 452p. 52.95 *(978-1-4372-7114-0(6))*; 450p. pap. 37.95 *(978-1-4371-4521-2(3))* Kessinger Publishing, LLC.

Birkenholz, A. Thomas. Die Alexander-Geschichte von Charles le Brun: Historische und Stilistische Untersuchungen der Werkentwicklung. (Ars Faciendi Beitrage und Studien zur Kunstgeschichte: Bd. 11). (GER., Illus.). 274p. 47.95 *(978-3-631-37565-5(4))* Lang, Peter Publishing, Inc.

Bonaccorsi, John. Alexander. Miller, Zachary N., ed. 2007. (Ancient Greek Mystery Ser.). (J). pap. 4.95 *(978-1-58659-215-8(7))* Artesian Pr.

Briant, Pierre. Alexander the Great & His Empire. Kuhrt, Amelie, tr. from FRE. 2010. (ENG., Illus.). 216p. (C). 26.95 *(978-0-691-14194-7(0))* Princeton Univ. Pr.

Briant, Pierre. Alexander the Great & His Empire: A Short Introduction. Kuhrt, Amélie, tr. from FRE. 2012. (ENG., Illus.). 216p. (C). pap. 19.95 ***(978-0-691-15445-9(7))*** Princeton Univ. Pr.

Brown, L. R. Heroes. 2008. 260p. pap. 18.50 *(978-1-4357-5918-3(4))* Lulu Enterprises Inc.

Burn, Andrew R. Alexander the Great & the Hellenistic Empire. reprint ed. 33.50 *(978-0-404-20048-0(6))* AMS Pr., Inc.

Cantor, Norman F. Alexander the Great: Journey to the End of the Earth. 2009. 49.99 *(978-1-4332-7691-0(7))* Findaway World, LLC.

—Alexander the Great: Journey to the End of the Earth. 2007. (ENG., Illus.). 192p. pap. 13.95 *(978-0-06-057013-2(X)*, HarperPerennial) HarperCollins Pubs.

Carney, Elizabeth & Ogden, Daniel, eds. Philip II & Alexander the Great: Father & Son, Lives & Afterlives, 1 vol. 2010. (ENG., Illus.). 384p. 85.00 *(978-0-19-973815-1(7))* Oxford Univ. Pr., Inc.

Cheshire, Keyne. Alexander the Great. 2009. (Greece & Rome: Texts & Contexts Ser.). (ENG., Illus.). 198p. pap. 26.00 *(978-0-521-70709-1(9))* Cambridge Univ. Pr.

Chugg, Andrew. Alexander the Great in Afghanistan: A Reconstruction of Cleitarchus. 2011. 212p. pap. ***(978-0-9556790-3-2(6))*** AMC Pubns.

Chugg, Andrew. Alexander the Great in India: A Reconstruction of Cleitarchus. 2009. 200p. pap. 25.50 *(978-0-9556790-1-8(X))* AMC Pubns. GBR. Dist: Lulu Enterprises Inc.

Curtius Rufus, Quintus, Quintus. Q. Curtius Rufus, Historiae Alexandri Magni. Lucarini, Carlo, ed. 2009. (Bibliotheca scriptorum Graecorum et Romanorum Teubneriana (BT) Ser.). (LAT.). LXVI, 383p. 112.00 *(978-3-11-020116-1(X))* De Gruyter, Walter Inc.

Cutrules, Alexander James. Invictus: A History of Alexander the Great. 2011. 348p. 51.95 ***(978-1-258-10131-2(9))*** Literary Licensing, LLC.

Dahmen, Karsten. The Legend of Alexander the Great on Greek & Roman Coins. 2007. (Illus.). 179p. 125.00 *(978-0-415-39451-2(1))*; per. 39.95 *(978-0-415-39452-9(X))* Routledge.

Doufikar-Aerts, Faustina. Alexander Magnus Arabicus: A Survey of the Alexander Tradition through Seven Centuries: from Pseudo-Callisthenes to Suri. 2010. (Mediaevalia Groningana New Ser.). (ENG.). 416p. (C). pap. 95.00 *(978-90-429-2183-2(8))* Peeters Pubs. & Booksellers BEL. Dist: Brown, David Bk. Co., The.

English, Stephen. The Field Campaigns of Alexander the Great. 2011. (Illus.). 192p. 39.95 *(978-1-84884-066-9(7))* Pen & Sword Bks. Ltd. GBR. Dist: Casemate Pubs. & Bk. Distributors, LLC.

English, Stephen. The Sieges of Alexander the Great. 2010. (Illus.). 168p. 39.95 *(978-1-84884-060-7(8))* Pen & Sword Bks. Ltd. GBR. Dist: Casemate Pubs. & Bk. Distributors, LLC.

Freeman, Philip. Alexander the Great. 2011. (ENG., Illus.). 416p. pap. 17.00 *(978-1-4165-9281-5(4))* Simon & Schuster.

Gandeto, J. S. G. The Theft of A King: Who Stole Alexander. 2011. 519p. 31.95 *(978-1-4327-6855-0(5))* Outskirts Pr., Inc.

Grainger, John D. Alexander the Great Failure: The Collapse of the Macedonian Empire. 2009. (ENG., Illus.). 256p. 24.95 *(978-0-8264-4394-6(X))* Continuum International Publishing Group, Ltd. GBR. Dist: National Bk. Network.

Grainger, John D. & Grainger. Alexander the Great Failure: The Collapse of the Macedonian Empire. 2008. (Hambledon Continuum Ser.). (ENG., Illus.). 256p. 80.00 *(978-1-84725-188-6(9))* Continuum International Publishing Group, Ltd. GBR. Dist: National Bk. Network.

Hammond, N. G. L. Sources for Alexander the Great: An Analysis of Plutarch's 'Life' & Arrian's 'Anabasis Alexandrou' 2007. (Cambridge Classical Studies). 361p. pap. 50.00 *(978-0-521-71471-6(0))* Cambridge Univ. Pr.

—Three Historians of Alexander the Great. 2007. (Cambridge Classical Studies). (ENG.). 220p. pap. 46.00 *(978-0-521-03653-5(4))* Cambridge Univ. Pr.

Heckel, Alice. Alexander the Great: A New History. Tritle, Lawrence A. & Heckel, Waldemar, eds. 2009. (ENG., Illus.). 392p. pap. 49.95 *(978-1-4051-3082-0(2)*, Wiley-Blackwell) Wiley, John & Sons, Inc.

—The Conquests of Alexander the Great. 2007. (Key Conflicts of Classical Antiquity Ser.). (ENG., Illus.). 240p. (C). 45.00 *(978-0-521-84247-1(6))* Cambridge Univ. Pr.

Heckel, Alice, et al, eds. Alexander's Empire: Formulation to Decay. 2007. 310p. per. 19.95 *(978-1-930053-45-8(2))* Regina Bks.

Heckel, Waldemar. The Conquests of Alexander the Great. 2010. (Key Conflicts of Classical Antiquity Ser.). 240p. (C). pap. 24.00 *(978-0-521-60323-2(4))* Cambridge Univ. Pr.

Heckel, Waldemar, ed. Who's Who in the Age of Alexander the Great: Prosopography of Alexander's Empire. 2008. (ENG., Illus.). 336p. pap. 49.95 *(978-1-4051-8839-5(1)*, Wiley-Blackwell) Wiley, John & Sons, Inc.

Heckel, Waldemar, et al, eds. Alexander the Great: A New History. 2009. (ENG., Illus.). 392p. 116.95 *(978-1-4051-3081-3(4)*, Wiley-Blackwell) Wiley, John & Sons, Inc.

Hogarth, David G. Philip & Alexander of Macedon: Two Essays in Biography. 2007. (ENG.). 324p. per. 30.95 *(978-1-4304-4268-4(9))* Kessinger Publishing, LLC.

Holt, Frank L. Into the Land of Bones: Alexander the Great in Afghanistan. 2006. (Hellenistic Culture & Society Ser.). (Illus.). 254p. pap. 19.95 *(978-0-520-24993-6(3))* Univ. of California Pr.

Le Rider, Georges. Alexander the Great: Coinage, Finances, & Policy. 2008. *(978-0-87169-261-0(9))* American Philosophical Society.

Lonsdale, David J. Alexander the Great: Lessons in Strategy. 2007. (Strategy & History Ser.). (Illus.). 192p. 150.00 *(978-0-415-35847-7(7))* Routledge.

—Alexander the Great: Lessons in Strategy: Lessons in Strategy. 2009. 198p. pap. 39.95 *(978-0-415-54525-9(0))* Routledge.

Matthews, Rupert. Alexander the Great at the Battle of Granicus: A Campaign in Context. 2008. (Campaign in Context Ser.). (ENG., Illus.). 256p. 42.95 *(978-1-86227-448-8(7))* History Pr. Ltd., The GBR. Dist: Independent Pubs. Group.

Ogden, Daniel. Alexander the Great: Myth, Genesis & Sexuality. 2011. (University of Exeter Press - Exeter Studies in History Ser.). (ENG.). 288p. pap. 37.00 *(978-0-85989-838-6(5))*; (Illus.). 276p. 110.00 *(978-0-85989-837-9(7))* Univ. of Exeter Pr. GBR. Dist: Chicago Distribution Ctr.

Rodgers, Nigel. Alexander the Great - An Illustrated Military History: The Rise of Macedonia, the Battles, Campaigns & Tactics of Alexander, & the Collapse of His Vast Empire after His Early Death, Depicted in More Than 250 Pictures. 2012. (ENG., Illus.). 128p. pap. 17.99 ***(978-1-84476-821-9(X))*** Anness Publishing GBR. Dist: National Bk. Network.

Roisman, Joseph. Alexander's Veterans & the Early Wars of the Successors. 2012. E-Book ***(978-0-292-73597-2(9))***; (ENG., Illus.). 264p. 55.00 ***(978-0-292-73596-5(0))*** Univ. of Texas Pr.

Romm, James. Ghost on the Throne: The Death of Alexander the Great & the War for Crown & Empire. (Vintage Ser.). (ENG., Illus.). 2012. 448p. pap. 17.00 ***(978-0-307-45660-1(9)***, Vintage) 2011. 368p. 28.95 *(978-0-307-27164-8(1)*, Knopf) Knopf Doubleday Publishing Group.

Romm, James, ed. The Landmark Arrian: The Campaigns of Alexander. Mensch, Pamela, tr. from GEC. 2010. (ENG., Illus.). 560p. 40.00 *(978-0-375-42346-8(X)*, Pantheon) Knopf Doubleday Publishing Group.

—The Landmark Arrian: The Campaigns of Alexander. 2012. (ENG., Illus.). 560p. pap. 25.00 *(978-1-4000-7967-4(5)*, Anchor) Knopf Doubleday Publishing Group.

Sheppard, Ruth. Alexander the Great at War: His Army - His Battles - His Enemies. 2011. (General Military Ser.). (ENG., Illus.). 256p. pap. 18.95 *(978-1-84908-480-2(7))*, Osprey Publishing, Ltd. GBR. Dist: Random Hse., Inc.

Skelton, Debra & Dell, Pamela. Empire of Alexander the Great, Revised Edition. 2nd rev. ed. 2009. (Great Empires of the Past Ser.). (Illus.). 152p. (gr. 6-12). 35.00 *(978-1-60413-162-8(4)*, Chelsea Hse.) Facts On File, Inc.

Stark, Freya. Alexander's Path: A Travel Memoir. 2011. 320p. 17.00 *(978-1-59020-523-5(5))* Overlook Pr., The.

Stoneman, Richard. Alexander the Great: A Life in Legend. 2010. (ENG., Illus.). 336p. pap. 23.00 *(978-0-300-16401-5(7))* Yale Univ. Pr.

Stoneman, Richard. Legends of Alexander the Great. 2011. (ENG., Illus.). 192p. pap. 19.95 ***(978-1-84885-785-8(3))*** I. B. Tauris & Co., Ltd. GBR. Dist: Macmillan.

Stoneman, Richard, ed. & tr. from GRE. The Book of Alexander the Great: A Life of the Conqueror. 2012. (ENG., Illus.). 192p. 75.00 ***(978-1-84885-293-8(2))***; pap. 19.95 ***(978-1-84885-294-5(0))*** I. B. Tauris & Co., Ltd. GBR. Dist: Macmillan.

Suhr, Elmer G. Sculptured Portraits of Greek Statesmen with a Special Study of Alexander the Great. Robinson, David M., ed. 2007. (ENG.). 234p. 41.95 *(978-0-548-03676-1(4))* Kessinger Publishing, LLC.

Thomas, Carol G. Alexander the Great in His World. 2006. (Blackwell Ancient Lives Ser.). (ENG., Illus.). 304p. pap. 41.95 *(978-0-631-23246-9(X))*; 116.95 *(978-0-631-23245-2(1))* Wiley, John & Sons, Inc. (Wiley-Blackwell).

Tomo, Grandes de, ed. Los Grandes - Alejandro Magno. 2007. 168p. pap. 5.95 *(978-970-666-543-0(9))* Grupo Editorial Tomo, S.A. de C.V. MEX. Dist: Giron Bks.

Townsend, David. An Epitome of Biblical History: Glosses on Walter of Châtillon's Alexandreis 4.176-274 - Edited from London, British Library, MS. Additional 18217. Townsend, David, tr. 2008. (Toronto Medieval Latin Texts). (LAT & ENG.). 93p. pap. 12.95 *(978-0-88844-480-6(X))* Pontifical Institute of Mediaeval Studies, Dept. of Pubns. CAN. Dist: Univ. of Toronto Pr.

van Donzel, E. J. & Schmidt, A. B. Gog & Magog in Early Syriac & Islamic Sources: Sallam's Quest for Alexander's Wall. 2009. (Brill's Inner Asian Library). (Illus.). 264p. *(978-90-04-17416-0(8))* BRILL.

Worthington, Ian, ed. Alexander the Great. 2nd rev. ed. 2012. (ENG., Illus.). 448p. (C). 140.00 *(978-0-415-66742-5(9))*; pap. 44.95 *(978-0-415-66743-2(7))* Routledge.

Yardley, J. C., tr. Justin Vol. 2: Epitome of the Philippic History of Pompeius Trogus - The Successors to Alexander the Great. 2012. (Clarendon Ancient History Ser.). (ENG., Illus.). 384p. pap. 99.00 ***(978-0-19-927760-5(5))*** Oxford Univ. Pr., Inc.

—Justin Vol. 2,Bk. 13-15: Epitome of the Philippic History of Pompeius Trogus - The Successors to Alexander the Great. 2012. (Clarendon Ancient History Ser.). (Illus.). 300p. 135.00 ***(978-0-19-927759-9(1))*** Oxford Univ. Pr., Inc.

Yenne, Bill. Alexander the Great: Lessons from History's Undefeated General. 2010. (World Generals Ser.). (ENG., Illus.). 224p. 22.00 *(978-0-230-61915-9(0))* Palgrave Macmillan.

ALEXANDER, THE GREAT, 356-323 B.C.—BIBLIOGRAPHY

Cary, George. The Medieval Alexander. Ross, D. J. A., ed. 2009. (ENG., Illus.). 448p. pap. 55.00 *(978-0-521-10877-5(2))* Cambridge Univ. Pr.

ALEXANDER, THE GREAT, 356-323 B.C.—ROMANCES

Ashurst, D. The Ethics of Empire in the Saga of Alexander the Great. 2009. (Studia Islandica Ser.). 324p. (C). pap. 35.00 *(978-9979-54-861-4(4))* Univ. of Iceland Pr. ISL. Dist: Brown, David Bk. Co., The.

Budge. Alexander the Great. 2012. (ENG.). 256p. pap. 42.95 ***(978-0-415-54086-5(0))*** Routledge.

Colin, Gérard. Alexandre le Grand, Héros Chrétien en Éthiopie: Histoire D'Alexandre (Zênâ Eskender) 2007. (ENG & FRE.). *(978-2-87723-966-0(7))* Peeters Pubs. & Booksellers.

—Alexandre le Grand, Héros Chrétien en Éthiopie: Histoire D'Alexandre (Zênâ Eskender) 2007. (ENG & FRE.). 157p. (C). pap. 27.00 *(978-90-429-1890-0(X))* Peeters Pubs. & Booksellers BEL. Dist: Brown, David Bk. Co., The.

Cruse, Mark. Illuminating the Roman d'Alexandre - Oxford, Bodleian Library, MS Bodley 264: The Manuscript as Monument. 2011. (Gallica Ser.: Volume 22). (Illus.). 252p. 99.00 *(978-1-84384-280-4(7)*, D. S. Brewer) Boydell & Brewer, Ltd. GBR. Dist: Boydell & Brewer, Inc.

de Leeuw van Weenen, Andrea. Alexanders Saga: AM 519a 4° in the Arnamagnæan Collection, Copenhagen. 2009. 352p. pap. 138.00 incl. cd-rom *(978-87-635-2604-3(2))* Museum Tusculanum Pr. DNK. Dist: Chicago Distribution Ctr.

De Palerne, Guillaume, et al. The Romance of William of Palerne. 2010. (ENG.). 386p. pap. 33.75 *(978-1-176-95501-1(2))* BiblioBazaar.

Gaullier-Bougassas, Catherine, ed. Les voeux du paon de Jacques de Longuyon: Originalite et Rayonnement. 2011. (Circare Ser.). (FRE.). 352p. (C). pap. 50.00 ***(978-2-252-03775-1(X))*** Klincksieck, Editions FRA. Dist: ISD.

Gautier & Townsend, David. The Alexandreis. 2007. (ENG.). 284p. pap. *(978-1-55111-676-1(6))* Broadview Pr.

ALEXANDER, EDWARD PORTER, 1835-1910

Alexander, E. P. Military Memoirs of a Confederate: A Critical Narrative. 2007. (ENG.). 656p. 63.95 *(978-0-548-09291-0(5))* Kessinger Publishing, LLC.

—Military Memoirs of a Confederate: A Critical Narrative. 634p. reprint ed. lib. bdg. 128.00 *(978-0-7222-4624-5(2))* Library Reprints, Inc.

Alexander, Edward Porter. Military Memoirs of a Confederate: A Critical Narrative. 634p. reprint ed. 128.00 *(978-0-7222-8221-2(4))*; 128.00 *(978-0-7222-8004-1(1))* Library Reprints, Inc.

ALEXANDER, SAMUEL, 1859-1938

Stiernotte, Alfred P. God & Space-Time: Deity in the Philosophy of Samuel Alexander. 2011. 484p. 58.95 ***(978-1-258-06732-8(3))*** Literary Licensing, LLC.

ALEXANDER, WILLIAM, 1726-1783

Duer, William Alexander. The Life of William Alexander. 2009. 172p. pap. *(978-1-150-39094-4(8))* Books LLC.

—The Life of William Alexander: Earl of Stirling. (Illus.). 272p. reprint ed. lib. bdg. 98.00 *(978-0-7222-0242-5(3))* Library Reprints, Inc.

—The Life of William Alexander: Earl of Stirling; Major-General in the Army of the United States, During the Revolution. 2010. 310p. pap. 29.75 *(978-1-142-56386-8(3))* BiblioBazaar.

—The Life of William Alexander, Earl of Stirling. 2008. 300p. 25.99 *(978-0-559-81145-6(4))*; 300p. pap. 28.75 *(978-0-559-81143-2(8))*; 292p. 28.99 *(978-0-554-40930-6(5))*; 292p. 25.99 *(978-0-554-40942-9(9))*; 292p. pap. 27.75 *(978-0-554-40939-9(9))*; 292p. pap. 28.75 *(978-0-554-40935-1(6))* BiblioBazaar.

—The Life of William Alexander, Earl of Stirling: With Selections from His Correspondence. 2007. 296p. 43.95 *(978-0-548-36190-0(8))*; (ENG.). per. 28.95 *(978-0-548-30472-3(6))* Kessinger Publishing, LLC.

—The Life of William Alexander, Earl of Stirling, Major General for the Army of the United States During the Revolution; With. 2009. 156p. pap. 19.99 *(978-1-151-07248-1(6))* General Bks. LLC.

—The Life of William Alexander, Earl of Stirling, Major-General in the Army of the United States Duri. 2009. 296p. 30.99 *(978-1-115-91096-5(5))*; 34.99 *(978-1-115-91095-8(7))*; pap. 27.75 *(978-1-115-91098-9(1))* BiblioBazaar.

—The life of William Alexander, Earl of Stirling, Major-General in the Army of the United States Duri. 2009. 295p. pap. 21.99 *(978-1-115-91100-9(7))*; (ENG.). pap. 23.99 *(978-1-115-91099-6(X))* BiblioBazaar. (BiblioLife).

—The Life of William Alexander, Earl of Stirling, Major-General in the Army of the United States During the Revolution. 2009. 170p. pap. *(978-1-150-16644-0(4))* Books LLC.

—The Life of William Alexander, Earl of Stirling; Major-General in the Army of the United States, During the Revolution: With. 2010. 152p. pap. *(978-1-153-00393-3(7))* Books LLC.

—The Life of William Alexander, Earl of Stirling, Major-General in the Army of the United States During the Revolution: With Selections from His Corres. 2010. 316p. pap. 30.75 *(978-1-146-35866-8(0))*; 304p. pap. 29.75 *(978-1-142-68251-4(X))*; 308p. pap. 29.75 *(978-1-142-05714-5(3))* BiblioBazaar.

—The Life of William Alexander, Earl of Stirling, Major-General in the Army of the United States During the Revolution; with Selections from His. 2010. 148p. pap. *(978-1-153-00391-9(0))* Books LLC.

ALEXANDER, WILLIAM, SIR, 1567 OR 8-1640

see Stirling, William Alexander, Earl of, 1567 or 8-1640

ALEXANDER OF TUNIS, HAROLD RUPERT LEOFRIC GEORGE ALEXANDER, EARL, 1891-1969

Alexander of Tunis, Harold Rupert Leofric George Alexander. The Alexander Memoirs, 1940?1945. 2010. (Illus.). 240p. 39.95 *(978-1-84832-567-8(3)*, Frontline) Pen & Sword Bks. Ltd. GBR. Dist: Casemate Pubs. & Bk. Distributors, LLC.

ALEXANDER TECHNIQUE

Alcantara, Pedro de. Integrated Practice: Coordination, Rhythm & Sound, 1 vol. 2011. (Integrated Musician Ser.). (ENG., Illus.). 336p. pap. 27.95 *(978-0-19-531708-4(4))* Oxford Univ. Pr., Inc.

Balk, Malcolm & Shields, Andrew. Master the Art of Running: Raising Your Performance with the Alexander Technique. 2009. (ENG., Illus.). 160p. pap. 12.95 *(978-1-84340-543-6(1)*, Collins & Brown) Anova Bks. GBR. Dist: Sterling Publishing Co., Inc.

Brennan, Richard. The Alexander Technique Manual: Take Control of Your Posture & Your Life. 2007. (ENG., Illus.). 144p. pap. 17.95

(978-1-85906-163-3(X)) Connections Bk. Publishing, Ltd. GBR. Dist: Red Wheel/Weiser.

—The Alexander Technique Workbook: The Complete Guide to Health, Poise & Fitness. 2011. (ENG., Illus.). 160p. pap. 14.95 *(978-1-84340-594-8(6)*, Collins & Brown) Anova Bks. GBR. Dist: Sterling Publishing Co., Inc.

Craze, Richard. Beat Back Pain with Alexander Technique. 2011. (Teach Yourself Ser.). (ENG., Illus.). 166p. pap. 15.95 *(978-1-4441-0102-7(1)*, Hodder & Stoughton) Hodder General Publishing Div. GBR. Dist: Independent Pubs. Group.

Dimon, Theodore & Dimon, Theodore, Jr. Anatomy of the Moving Body: A Basic Course in Bones, Muscles, & Joints. 2nd rev. ed. 2008. (ENG., Illus.). 280p. pap. 21.95 *(978-1-55643-720-5(X))* North Atlantic Bks.

Harer, John B. & Munden, Sharon. The Alexander Technique Resource Book: A Reference Guide. 2008. (ENG.). 192p. pap. 50.00 *(978-0-8108-5431-4(7))* Scarecrow Pr., Inc.

Miranda, Kathryn, ed. Dare to Be Wrong: The Teaching of Judith Leibowitz. 2007. 32.00 *(978-0-9644352-8-5(4)*, Books that Change) Momum Time Pr.

Netti-Fiol, Rebecca & Vanier, Luc. Dance & the Alexander Technique. 2011. (ENG., Illus.). 216p. 80.00 *(978-0-252-03601-9(8))*; 30.00 *(978-0-252-07793-7(8))* Univ. of Illinois Pr.

Nicholls, Carolyn. Body, Breath & Being: A New Guide to the Alexander Technique. 2008. (ENG., Illus.). 160p. pap. 23.95 *(978-1-904468-42-4(X))* D & B Publishing GBR. Dist: Globe Pequot Pr., The.

Shaw, Steven. Master the Art of Swimming: Raise Your Performance with the Alexander Technique. 2009. (ENG., Illus.). 176p. pap. 12.95 *(978-1-84340-542-9(3)*, Collins & Brown) Anova Bks. GBR. Dist: Sterling Publishing Co., Inc.

Sullivan, Karen. Collins Gem 5-Minute Back Relief: Beat Backache Instantly. 2008. (Collins Gem Ser.). (ENG., Illus.). 192p. pap. 6.95 *(978-0-00-725159-9(9))* HarperCollins Pubs. Ltd. GBR. Dist: Independent Pubs. Group.

Vail, Leland. Secret to Using Your Body. 2010. 124p. pap. 24.95 *(978-0-578-04485-9(4))* Vail, Leland.

Weiss, Maria. The Alexander Technique & the Art of Teaching Voice. 2009. (Illus.). 184p. pap. *(978-3-639-12293-0(3))* VDM Verlag Dr. Mueller e.K.

ALEXANDRA, EMPRESS, CONSORT OF NICHOLAS II, EMPEROR OF RUSSIA, 1872-1918

Brandt, Clydene. Nicholas & Alexandra: Soul Mates: Book II: the Soul Searcher's. 2007. (ENG.). 196p. per. 24.95 *(978-1-4241-2850-1(1))* PublishAmerica, Inc.

Gelardi, Julia. Born to Rule: Five Reigning Consorts, Granddaughters of Queen Victoria. Date not set. mass mkt. *(978-0-312-99516-4(4)*, St. Martin's Paperbacks) St. Martin's Pr.

Massie, Robert K. Nicholas & Alexandra. 2012. (ENG., Illus.). 640p. 24.00 ***(978-0-679-64561-0(6)**,* Modern Library) Random House Publishing Group.

Rounding, Virginia. Alix & Nicky: The Passion of the Last Tsar & Tsarina. 2012. (ENG., Illus.). 400p. 29.99 ***(978-0-312-38100-4(X))*** St. Martin's Pr.

ALEXANDRIA (EGYPT)

Butler, Beverley. Return to Alexandria: An Ethnography of Cultural Heritage, Revivalism, & Museum Memory. 2007. (Publications of the Institute of Archaeology, University Col Ser.). (ENG., Illus.). 299p. per. 34.95 *(978-1-59874-191-9(8))* Left Coast Pr., Inc.

Clarie, Thomas C. Pharos: A Lighthouse for Alexandria. 2009. pap. 29.95 *(978-1-934582-12-1(3))* Back Channel Pr.

Davis, Harold T. Alexandria, the Golden City V1: The City of the Ptolemies. 2011. 256p. 47.95 ***(978-1-258-01542-8(0))*** Literary Licensing, LLC.

—Alexandria, the Golden City V2: Cleopatra's City. 2011. 304p. 48.95 ***(978-1-258-01575-6(7))*** Literary Licensing, LLC.

Ekdahl Ravicz, Marilyn. Alexandri: Cloud-Cuckoo-Town. 2009. 288p. pap. 15.49 *(978-1-4389-7129-2(X))* AuthorHouse.

El-Abbadi, Mostafa & Fathallah, Omnia Mounir, eds. What Happened to the Ancient Library of Alexandria? 2008. (Library of the Written Word Ser.). (FRE & ENG., Illus.). 259p. *(978-90-04-16545-8(2))* BRILL.

Flower, Derek Adie. The Shores of Wisdom. 2009. 204p. pap. *(978-1-84923-499-3(X))* YouWriteOn.

Gambetti, S. The Alexandrian Riots of 38 C. E. & the Persecution of the Jews. A Historical Reconstruction. 2009. (Supplements to the Journal for the Study of Judaism Ser.). 336p. *(978-90-04-13846-9(3))* BRILL.

Haag, Michael. Vintage Alexandria: Photographs of the City, 1860-1960. 2008. (ENG., Illus.). 160p. 39.95 *(978-977-416-192-6(0))* American Univ. in Cairo Pr. EGY. Dist: Oxford Univ. Pr., Inc.

Haas, Christopher. Alexandria in Late Antiquity: Topography & Social Conflict. 2006. (Ancient Society & History Ser.). (ENG., Illus.). 520p. (gr. 17). pap. 37.00 *(978-0-8018-8541-9(8))* Johns Hopkins Univ. Pr.

Harker, Andrew. Loyalty & Dissidence in Roman Egypt: The Case of the Acta Alexandrinorum. 2011. (ENG.). 264p. pap. 35.99 *(978-0-521-18258-4(1))* Cambridge Univ. Pr.

Hinge, George & Krasilnikoff, Jens A., eds. Alexandria: A Cultural & Religious Melting Pot. 2009. (Aarhus Studies in Mediterranean Antiquity). (ENG., Illus.). 176p. (C). 40.00 *(978-87-7934-491-4(7))* Aarhus Universitetsforlag DNK. Dist: ISD.

Kaczvinsky, Donald P. Durrell & the City: Collected Essays on Place. 2011. (ENG.). 232p. 70.00 ***(978-1-61147-453-4(1))*** Lexington Bks.

Khuri-Makdisi, Ilham. The Eastern Mediterranean & the Making of Global Radicalism, 1860-1914. 2010. (California World History Library). (ENG., Illus.). 296p. 50.00 *(978-0-520-26201-0(8))* Univ. of California Pr.

Mojsov, Bojana. Alexandria Lost: From the Advent of Christianity to the Arab Conquest. 2010. (Illus.). 224p. pap. 27.95 *(978-0-7156-3865-1(3))* Duckworth Publishers GBR. Dist: International Publishers Marketing.

Pollard, Justin & Reid, Howard. The Rise & Fall of Alexandria: Birthplace of the Modern World. 2007. (ENG.). 352p. (gr. 12-18). 17.00 *(978-0-14-311251-8(1)*, Penguin (Non-Classics)) Penguin Group (USA) Inc.

Ravicz, Marilyn Ekdahl. Alexandri: Cloud-Cuckoo-Town. 2009. 288p. 25.99 *(978-1-4389-7128-5(1))* AuthorHouse.

Robertson, David. Word & Meaning in Ancient Alexandria: Theories of Language from Philo to Plotinus. 2008. 132p. 99.95 *(978-0-7546-0696-3(1))* Ashgate Publishing Co.

Russell, Norman. Theophilus of Alexandria. 2006. (Early Church Fathers Ser.). 222p. 130.00 *(978-0-415-28914-6(9))*; per. 37.95 *(978-0-415-28915-3(7))* Routledge.

Shehata, Samer S. Shop Floor Culture & Politics in Egypt. (Illus.). 2010. 275p. pap. 24.95 *(978-1-4384-2850-5(2)*, Suny Pr.) 2009. 304p. 80.00 *(978-1-4384-2849-9(9))* State Univ. of New York Pr.

Surovtsov, Vicka Markov. Snow & Sand. 2010. 316p. pap. 22.95 *(978-1-4502-5057-3(2))* iUniverse, Inc.

Tapia, Ricardo Wahby. Memories of Alexandria: From A Void to Nothingness. 2011. (Illus.). 232p. pap. 17.09 ***(978-1-4567-8359-4(9))*** AuthorHouse.

ALEXANDRIA (VA.)

Campbell County Historical & Genealogical Society. Alexandria. 2008. (Images of America Ser.). (ENG., Illus.). 128p. pap. 21.99 *(978-0-7385-5392-4(1))* Arcadia Publishing.

Combs, George K., et al. Alexandria. 2012. (Images of America Ser.). (ENG., Illus.). 128p. pap. 21.99 ***(978-0-7385-9238-1(2))*** Arcadia Publishing.

Lee, Michael Pope. Ghosts of Alexandria. 2010. 112p. pap. 19.99 *(978-1-59629-958-0(4))* History Pr., The.

Mills, Charles A. & Mills, Andrew L. Alexandria: 1861-1865. 2008. (Images of America Ser.). (ENG., Illus.). 128p. pap. 21.99 *(978-0-7385-5344-3(1))* Arcadia Publishing.

Patton, Julie Ballin & Holtz, Rita Williams, texts. Historic Photos of Alexandria. 2008. (Historic Photos Ser.). (ENG., Illus.). 206p. 39.95 *(978-1-59652-413-2(8))* Turner Publishing Co.

Pope, Michael Lee. Hidden History of Alexandria, D.C. 2011. (Illus.). 128p. pap. 19.99 ***(978-1-60949-281-6(1))*** History Pr., The.

The Alexandria Police Association. Alexandria Police Department. 2006. (Images of America Ser.). (ENG., Illus.). 128p. per. 19.99 *(978-0-7385-4340-6(3))* Arcadia Publishing.

Winters, Barb, compiled by. Letters to Virginia: Letters from Three Generations of Virginians from Before, During & after the Civil War. 2010. 24.95 *(978-1-935001-63-8(9))* Acclaim Pr., Inc.

ALEXANDRIAN SCHOOL

see also Neoplatonism

Boughton, Jesse Scott. The Idea of Progress in Philo Judaeus. 2011. 294p. 48.95 ***(978-1-258-05212-6(1))*** Literary Licensing, LLC.

Deakin, Michael A. B. Hypatia of Alexandria: Mathematician & Martyr. 2007. (ENG., Illus.). 1p. 29.98 *(978-1-59102-520-7(6))* Prometheus Bks., Pubs.

Kingsley, Charles. Alexandria & Her Schools. 2007. 92p. per. *(978-1-4065-2853-4(6))* Dodo Pr.

Watt, John & Lossl, Josef. Interpreting the Bible & Aristotle in Late Antiquity: The Alexandrian Commentary Tradition from Rome to Baghdad. 2011. (Illus.). 360p. 134.95 ***(978-1-4094-1007-2(2))*** Ashgate Publishing Co.

ALEXANDRIAN SCHOOL, CHRISTIAN

Here are entered works on the theology of the early Christian church of Alexandria which was sometimes complementary and sometimes opposed to that of Antioch.

see also Antiochian School

Osborn, Eric. Clement of Alexandria. 2008. (ENG.). 344p. (C). pap. 48.00 *(978-0-521-09081-0(4))* Cambridge Univ. Pr.

Sellers, Robert V. Two Ancient Christologies: A Study in the Christological Thought of the Schools of Alexandria & Antioch in the Early History of Christian Doctrine. (Orthodoxies & Heresies in the Early Church Ser.). reprint ed. 39.50 *(978-0-404-62394-4(8))* AMS Pr., Inc.

Watts, Edward Jay. Riot in Alexandria: Tradition & Group Dynamics in Late Antique Pagan & Christian Communities. 2010. (Transformation of the Classical Heritage Ser.). (Illus.). 312p. 55.00 *(978-0-520-26207-2(7))* Univ. of California Pr.

ALEXIN

see Complement (Immunology)

ALEXIS, WILLIBALD

Carpent, Thierry. Willibald Alexis, Intellectuel du Juste milieu: Histoire, Droit et Politique dans l'Allemagne. (Publications Universitaires Europeennes: Vol. 1836). (FRE.). 351p. 51.95 *(978-3-906769-08-0(9))* Lang, Peter CHE. Dist: Lang, Peter Publishing, Inc.

Hobi, Caroline. Willibald Alexis: Rube Ist Die Erste Bürgerpflicht. (GER.). 365p. pap. 75.95 *(978-3-03911-230-2(9))* Lang, Peter Publishing, Inc.

ALEXIUS, SAINT

Chamberas, Peter A., tr. The Life of Saint Alexios the Man of God. 2008. 72p. pap. 7.95 *(978-1-933275-18-5(9)*, Orthodox Research Institute) Cocheco Falls Publishing.

Mancuso, Laurence. Being Good: Responding to Our Faith. 2008. 264p. pap. 17.95 *(978-1-933275-19-2(7)*, Orthodox Research Institute) Cocheco Falls Publishing.

ALEXIUS I COMNENUS, EMPEROR OF THE EAST, 1048-1118

Frankopan, Peter. The First Crusade: The Call from the East. 2012. (ENG., Illus.). 268p. 29.95 ***(978-0-674-05994-8(8)**,* Belknap Pr.) Harvard Univ. Pr.

Komnene, Anna. The Alexiad. Frankopan, Peter, ed. Sewter, E. R. A., tr. from GEC. rev. ed. 2009. (ENG., Illus.). 608p. (gr. 12-18). pap. 18.00 *(978-0-14-045527-4(2)*, Penguin Classics) Penguin Group (USA) Inc.

ALFALFA

Fiala, Jakub & Pospísil, David. Alfalfa & Clovers: Properties, Medicinal Uses & Health Benefits. 2011. (Botanical Research & Practices Ser.). 95.00 ***(978-1-62100-062-4(1))*** Nova Science Pubs., Inc.

Undersander, Dan, et al. Alfalfa Management Guide. 2011. (ENG., Illus.). 63p. 10.00 *(978-0-89118-179-8(2))* ASA-CSSA-SSSA.

ALFA ROMEO AUTOMBILE

Clarke, R. M., compiled by. Alfa Romeo Spider, 1966-1994. 2008. (Ultimate Portfolio Ser.). (ENG., Illus.). 216p. pap. 37.95 *(978-1-85520-755-4(9)*, 1855207559) Brooklands Bks. GBR. Dist: MBI Distribution Services/Quayside Distribution.

Collins, Peter. Alfa Romeo 155/156/147 Competition Touring Cars: The Development & Racing History. 2012. (ENG., Illus.). 224p. 79.95 ***(978-1-84584-342-7(8)**,* 1845843428) Veloce Publishing Ltd. GBR. Dist: MBI Distribution Services/Quayside Distribution.

Sannia, Alessandro. Alfa Romeo, 1 vol. 2010. (ENG & FRE., Illus.). 192p. 12.95 *(978-90-79761-50-0(8))* Tectum B.V.B.A. BEL. Dist: Innovative Logistics.

Stroud, Jon & Groome, Clive. Alfa Romeo. 2011. (Little Book Of Ser.). (ENG., Illus.). 128p. 11.99 *(978-1-907803-23-9(8))* G2 Entertainment Ltd. GBR. Dist: BookMasters Distribution Services (BDS).

Tabucchi, Maurizio & d'Amico, Stefano. Alfa Romeo: Production Cars from 1910. 2008. (ENG., Illus.). 1184p. 300.00 *(978-88-7911-408-0(5)*, 8879114085) Giorgio Nada Editore ITA. Dist: MBI Distribution Services/Quayside Distribution.

Taylor, Bruce. Alfa Romeo Montreal. 2008. (Essential Companion Ser.). (ENG., Illus.). 320p. 130.00 *(978-1-84584-158-4(1)*, 1845841581) Veloce Publishing Ltd. GBR. Dist: MBI Distribution Services/Quayside Distribution.

—Alfa Romeo Montreal: The Dream Car That Came True. 2009. (ENG., Illus.). 208p. 79.95 *(978-1-84584-218-5(9)*, 1845842189) Veloce Publishing Ltd. GBR. Dist: MBI Distribution Services/Quayside Distribution.

Tipler, John. Alfa Romeo Giulia GT & GTA. 3rd rev. enl. ed. 2012. (ENG., Illus.). 224p. 79.95 *(978-1-904788-17-1(3)*, 1904788173) Veloce Publishing Ltd. GBR. Dist: MBI Distribution Services/Quayside Distribution.

ALFARO SIQUEIROS, DAVID, 1896-1974

see Siqueiros, David Alfaro, 1896-1974

ALFIERI, VITTORIO, 1749-1803

Miller, Charles R. D. Alfieri: A Biography. 2011. 272p. 47.95 ***(978-1-258-06596-6(7))*** Literary Licensing, LLC.

Vaughan, Herbert M. The Last Stuart Queen: Louise Countess of Albany, Her Life & Letters. 2006. (ENG.). 408p. per. 34.95 *(978-1-4286-5096-1(2))* Kessinger Publishing, LLC.

ALFONSO V, KING OF ARAGON, 1396-1458

Earenfight, Theresa. The King's Other Body: Maria of Castile & the Crown of Aragon. 2009. (Middle Ages Ser.). (Illus.). 240p. (C). 49.95 *(978-0-8122-4185-3(1))* Univ. of Pennsylvania Pr.

ALFONSO X, KING OF CASTILE AND LEON, 1221-1284

Blum, Andreas. Etymologische Erklärungen in Alfonsinischen Texten. 2007. (Beihefte zur Zeitschrift far romanische Philologie Ser.). (GER.). XIII, 561p. ***(978-3-11-183658-4(4))**;* (Illus.). *(978-3-484-52340-1(9))* Verlag Max Niemeyer.

Niederehe, Hans-Josef. Alfonso X "El Sabio" (Historiografia de la Linguistica Espanola Ser.). (SPA.). 252p. *(978-84-7143-345-9(1))* Sociedad General Espanola de Libreria.

Salvador Martínez, H. Alfonso X, the Learned: A Biography. 2010. *(978-90-04-18147-2(4))* BRILL.

Scarborough, Connie L. A Holy Alliance: Alfonso X's Political Use of Marian Poetry. 2009. (Estudios de Literatura Medieval Ser.: 6). 206p. 22.95 *(978-1-58871-148-9(X)*, Juan de la Cuesta-Hispanic Monographs) LinguaText, Ltd.

Snow, Joseph T. The Poetry of Alfonso X: An Annotated Critical Bibliography (1278-2010) 2012. (Research Bibliographies & Checklists: New Ser.: Volume 10). 466p. pap. 115.00 ***(978-1-85566-239-1(6)**,* Tamesis Bks.) Boydell & Brewer, Ltd. GBR. Dist: Boydell & Brewer, Inc.

ALFORD, HENRY, 1810-1871

Alford, Henry. Life Journals & Letters of Henry Alford, 2 vols., Set. vii, 542p. reprint ed. 69.00 *(978-0-7812-0872-7(6))* Reprint Services Co.

—Life, Journals & Letters of Henry Alford, D D Late Dean of Canterbury, Edited by His Widow. 2006. 560p. per. 32.99 *(978-1-4255-6176-5(4))* MPublishing.

ALFRED, KING OF ENGLAND, 849-899

Besant, Walter. The Story of King Alfred. 2009. 66p. pap. *(978-0-217-37304-3(6))* Books LLC.

—The Story of King Alfred. 2007. (ENG.). 184p. 37.95 *(978-0-548-14908-9(9))*; per. 22.95 *(978-1-4304-4212-7(3))* Kessinger Publishing, LLC.

Bowker, Alfred. Alfred the Great Containing Chapters on. 2006. pap. 28.95 *(978-1-4286-5110-4(1))* Kessinger Publishing, LLC.

Duckett, Eleanor Shipley. Alfred the Great. 2011. 230p. 46.95 ***(978-1-258-01619-7(2))*** Literary Licensing, LLC.

Harrison, Frederic. George Washington & Other American Addresses. 2008. 244p. 25.99 *(978-0-554-68037-8(8))*; 127p. 28.99 *(978-0-554-68025-5(4))*; 401p. pap. 26.75 *(978-0-554-68033-0(5))*; 268p. pap. 27.75 *(978-0-554-68028-6(9))* BiblioBazaar.

—George Washington & Other American Addresses. 2007. 262p. 42.95 *(978-0-548-23827-1(8))*; 264p. per. 27.95 *(978-1-4326-3957-0(9))* Kessinger Publishing, LLC.

—George Washington & Other American Addresses. 252p. reprint ed. 98.00 *(978-0-7222-8932-7(4))*; 98.00 *(978-0-7222-8770-5(4))* Library Reprints, Inc.

Hart, Cyril. Chronicles of the Reign of Alfred the Great: Part I: Introduction & Commentary: the Early Chronicles of England, Volume IV, 2 vols. 2010. (ANG, LAT & ENG., Illus.). 232p. 109.95 *(978-0-7734-3729-6(0))* Mellen, Edwin Pr., The.

—Chronicles of the Reign of Alfred the Great: Part II: the Texts: the Early chronicles of England, Volume IV, 2 vols. 2010. (ENG, ANG & LAT., Illus.). 416p. 129.95 *(978-0-7734-3731-9(2))* Mellen, Edwin Pr., The.

Hill, Paul. The Viking Wars of Alfred the Great. 2009. (ENG.). 208p. 26.00 *(978-1-59416-087-5(2))* Westholme Publishing.

Hinton, David A. The Alfred Jewel: And Other Late Anglo-Saxon Decorated Metalwork. 2008. (ENG., Illus.). 112p. 22.95 *(978-1-85444-229-1(5))* Ashmolean Museum GBR. Dist: Antique Collectors' Club.

Hinton, David A. & Hinton, David Alban. The Alfred Jewel: And Other Late Anglo-Saxon Decorated Metalwork. 2008. (Ashmolean Handbooks). (ENG., Illus.). 112p. pap. 15.95 *(978-1-85444-230-7(9))* Ashmolean Museum GBR. Dist: Antique Collectors' Club.

Horspool, David. King Alfred: Burnt Cakes & Other Legends. 2006. (Profiles in History Ser.). (Illus.). 240p. 19.95 *(978-0-674-02320-8(X))* Harvard Univ. Pr.

Merkle, Benjamin R. White Horse King: The Life of Alfred the Great, 0 vols. 2009. (Illus.). 272p. pap. 14.99 *(978-1-59555-252-5(9))* Nelson, Thomas Inc.

Metcalf, Allan A. Poetic diction in the Old English meters of Boethius. (De Proprietatibus Litterarum. Series Practica Ser.). (ENG.). 168p. 210.00 ***(978-3-11-193042-8(4))**;* 135.00 ***(978-3-11-099164-2(0))*** De Gruyter, Mouton DEU. Dist: de Gruyter, Walter GmbH & Co. KG.

Parker, Joanne. England's Darling: The Victorian Cult of Alfred the Great. 2007. (ENG., Illus.). 256p. 89.00 *(978-0-7190-7356-4(1))* Manchester Univ. Pr. GBR. Dist: Macmillan.

Pauli, Reinhold. The Life of Alfred the Great. Thorpe, B., tr. (Bohn's Antiquarian Library). reprint ed. 46.00 *(978-0-404-50021-4(8))* AMS Pr., Inc.

Pauli, Reinhold & Thorpe, B. The Life of Alfred the Great. 2008. 592p. 59.95 *(978-1-4374-2113-2(X))*; pap. 44.95 *(978-1-4373-3555-2(1))* Kessinger Publishing, LLC.

Plummer, Charles. Life & Times of Alfred the Great. 2006. (ENG.). pap. 26.95 *(978-1-4286-4240-9(4))* Kessinger Publishing, LLC.

—The Life & Times of Alfred the Great. 2007. (ENG.). 248p. 41.95 *(978-0-548-13181-7(3))* Kessinger Publishing, LLC.

Pollard, Justin. Alfred the Great: The Man Who Made England. 2007. (ENG., Illus.). 368p. pap. 17.95 *(978-0-7195-6666-0(5))* Murray, John GBR. Dist: Independent Pubs. Group.

Pratt, David. The Political Thought of King Alfred the Great. (Cambridge Studies in Medieval Life & Thought: Fourth Ser.). (ENG.). 2010. 436p. pap. 42.00 *(978-0-521-12644-1(4))* 2007. 434p. 138.00 *(978-0-521-80350-2(0))* Cambridge Univ. Pr.

ALFRED, KING OF ENGLAND, 849-899—POETRY

Chesterton, G. K. The Ballad of the White Horse. 2010. 162p. pap. 21.75 *(978-1-148-10411-9(9))* 2009. 152p. 22.99 *(978-1-103-97002-5(X))* 2009. 152p. pap. 16.99 *(978-1-103-96997-5(8))* BiblioBazaar.

—The Ballad of the White Horse. reprint ed. lib. bdg. 98.00 *(978-0-7426-3023-9(4))* Classic Bks.

—The Ballad of the White Horse. 2007. (ENG.). 104p. per. 9.50 *(978-1-60206-888-9(7))* Cosimo, Inc.

—The Ballad of the White Horse. 2008. (ENG.). 88p. per. *(978-1-4065-9085-2(1))* Dodo Pr.

—The Ballad of the White Horse. 2010. (ENG.). 144p. pap. 7.95 *(978-0-486-47563-9(8))* Dover Pubns., Inc.

—The Ballad of the White Horse. 2010. 68p. pap. 20.00 *(978-1-153-69386-8(0))* General Bks. LLC.

—The Ballad of the White Horse. 2010. 96p. pap. 15.16 *(978-1-162-68849-7(1))*; 33.95 *(978-1-161-45714-8(3))* Kessinger Publishing, LLC.

—The Ballad of the White Horse. 2007. 84p. per. 11.99 *(978-1-59547-795-8(0))* NuVision Pubns., LLC.

—The Ballad of the White Horse. 2007. 204p. per. *(978-1-4086-3056-3(7))* Read Bks.

—The Ballad of the White Horse. 2007. (ENG.). 116p. pap. 8.45 *(978-1-60424-340-6(6)*, Book Jungle) Standard Pubns., Inc.

—The Ballad of the White Horse. 2009. 92p. pap. 9.99 *(978-1-4344-7934-1(X))* Wildside Pr., LLC.

ALFRED, MOTHER, 1827-1899

Whelan, Ellen. The Sisters' Story Pt. 2: Saint Marys Hospital - Mayo Clinic, 1939 to 1980. 2007. 237p. pap. 19.95 *(978-1-893005-99-0(2))* Mayo Foundation for Medical Education & Research.

ALFRED UNIVERSITY

Davis, Boothe Colwell. Memoirs of Boothe Colwell Davis & of Estelle Hoffman Davis, His Wife. 2011. 344p. 51.95 ***(978-1-258-10350-7(8))*** Literary Licensing, LLC.

Strong, Susan Romney & Strong, Susan Rumsey. Thought Knows No Sex: Women's Rights at Alfred University. 2008. (Illus.). (C). 70.00 *(978-0-7914-7513-3(1))* State Univ. of New York Pr.

Strong, Susan Rumsey. Thought Knows No Sex: Women's Rights at Alfred University. 2008. (Illus.). xii, 217p. (C). pap. 29.95 *(978-0-7914-7514-0(X))* State Univ. of New York Pr.

ALGAE

see also Algology; Chrysophyceae; Diatoms; Marine Algae

also names of families of algae, e.g. Zygnemaceae

Aftab, Javed & Shameel, Mustafa. Phycochemistry & Bioactivity of Some Algae from Miani Hor, Balochistan. 2010. 236p. pap. *(978-3-639-26821-8(0))* VDM Verlag Dr. Mueller e.K.

Alvarez-Murphy, Gerry. Ecological Effects of Removing Ulva Spp from Avon-Heathcote Estuary. 2008. 144p. pap. *(978-3-639-09067-3(5))* VDM Verlag Dr. Mueller e.K.

Amsler, Charles D., ed. Algal Chemical Ecology. (ENG., Illus.). xviii, 313p. 2009. pap. 99.00 *(978-3-540-92998-7(3)*, 3540929983) 2007. 269.00 *(978-3-540-74180-0(1)*, 3540741801) Springer.

Atazadeh, Islam & Sharifi, Mozafar. Algae As Bioindicators. 2010. 116p. pap. *(978-3-8383-7634-9(X))* Lambert Academic Publishing.

Australian Biological Resources Study Staff. Algae of Australia: Introduction. 2007. (Algae of Australia Ser.). (Illus.). 744p. 160.00 *(978-0-643-09377-5(X))* CSIRO Publishing AUS. Dist: Stylus Publishing, LLC.

AWWA Committee, compiled by. Algae: Source to Treatment (M57) 2010. 480p. pap. 250.00 *(978-1-58321-787-0(8))* American Water Works Assn.

Barinova, Sophia. Algal Diversity in the River Ecosystems of the Eastern Mediterranean. 2011. (Environmental Science, Engineering & Technology Ser.). (Illus.). 369p. 95.00 *(978-1-61209-338-3(8))* Nova Science Pubs., Inc.

Barredo, José-Luis, ed. Microbial Carotenoids from Bacteria & Microalgae: Methods & Protocols. 2012. (Methods in Molecular Biology Ser.: 892). (ENG., Illus.). x, 352p. 139.00 ***(978-1-61779-878-8(9)***, 1617798789) Humana Pr.

Bellinger, Edward G. & Sigee, David C. Freshwater Algae: Identification & Use As Bioindicators. 2010. (ENG., Illus.). 284p. 149.95 *(978-0-470-05814-5(5)*, Wiley) Wiley, John & Sons, Inc.

Brodie, Juliet & Lewis, Jane, eds. Unravelling the Algae: The Past, Present, & Future of Algal Systematics. 2007. (Systematics Association Special Volumes Ser.). (ENG., Illus.). 402p. 119.95 *(978-0-8493-7989-5(X)*, CRC Press) Taylor & Francis Group GBR. Dist: Taylor & Francis Group.

Buteyko, Vladimir. Harmful Algal Blooms - Impact & Response. 2010. (Environmental Science, Engineering & Technology Ser.). (Illus.). 259p. 115.00 *(978-1-60741-665-4(4))* Nova Science Pubs., Inc.

Ciugulea, Ionel, et al. A Color Atlas of Photosynthetic Euglenoids. 2010. (ENG.). 204p. 89.95 *(978-0-87013-879-9(0))* Michigan State Univ. Pr.

Cole, Kathleen M. & Sheath, Robert G., eds. Biology of the Red Algae. 2011. (ENG.). 528p. pap. 65.00 *(978-0-521-20246-6(9))* Cambridge Univ. Pr.

Cram101 Textbook Reviews. Outlines & Highlights for Cyanobacterial Harmful Algal Blooms by H Kenneth Hudnell, Isbn: 9780387758640 038775864x. 2011. 76p. pap 27.95 ***(978-1-61490-306-2(9))*** Cram101 Inc.

Cram101 Textbook Reviews & Cram101 Textbook Reviews. Outlines & Highlights for the Chlamydomonas Sourcebook: Cell Motility & Behavior, Vol. 3 by George Witman, ISBN. 2011. 92p. pap. 27.95 ***(978-1-61461-048-9(7))*** Cram101 Inc.

Demirbas, Ayhan & Demirbas, Muhammet Fatih. Algae Energy: Algae as a New Source of Biodiesel. 2010. (Green Energy & Technology Ser.). (ENG., Illus.). xxiv, 280p. 199.00 *(978-1-84996-049-6(6)*, 1849960496) Springer.

Doyle, Alisha M. & Bell, Jayden A., eds. Algal Biofuels: Where We've Been, Where We're Going (with DVD) 2011. (Energy Science, Engineering & Technology Ser.). 207p. 229.00 *(978-1-61209-502-8(X))* Nova Science Pubs., Inc.

Eisler, Ronald. Compendium of Trace Metals & Marine Biota: Volume 1: Plants & Invertebrates, 2 vols. 2009. (ENG.). 638p. 275.00 *(978-0-444-53436-1(9)*, Elsevier Science) Elsevier Science & Technology Bks.

—Compendium of Trace Metals & Marine Biota Vols. 1 & 2: Plants & Invertebrates - Vertebrates, 2 vols. 2009. (ENG.). 1150p. 420.00 *(978-0-444-53439-2(3)*, Elsevier Science) Elsevier Science & Technology Bks.

Entwisle, Timothy J., et al. Algae of Australia: Batrachospermales, Thoreales, Oedogoniales & Zygnemaceae. 2007. (Illus.). 200p. (C). 79.95 *(978-0-643-09431-4(8))* CSIRO Publishing AUS. Dist: Stylus Publishing, LLC.

Ezhilarasi, Anbalagan. Molecular Taxonomic Studies on the Genus Anabaena Bory. 2010. 128p. pap. *(978-3-8383-8818-2(6))* Lambert Academic Publishing.

Feng Chen & Yue Jiang, eds. Algae & their Biotechnological Potential. 2010. 320p. pap. 259.00 *(978-90-481-5886-7(9)*, 9048158869) Springer.

Frey, Jeffrey W. Assessment of Nutrient Enrichment by Use of Algal-, Invertebrate-, & Fish-Community Attributes in Wadeable Streams in Ecoregions Surrounding the Great Lakes. 2011. (Illus.). vii, 49p. ***(978-1-4113-3103-7(6))*** United States Geological Survey.

Fryxell, Greta A., ed. Survival Strategies of the Algae. 2011. (ENG.). 158p. pap. 24.99 *(978-0-521-18008-5(2))* Cambridge Univ. Pr.

Goff, Lynda J., ed. Algal Symbiosis: A Continuum of Interaction Strategies. 2011. (ENG.). 226p. pap. 30.99 *(978-0-521-17742-9(1))* Cambridge Univ. Pr.

Gouveia, Luisa. Microalgae as a Feedstock for Biofuels. 2011. (SpringerBriefs in Microbiology Ser.). (ENG., Illus.). v, 68p. pap. 49.95 *(978-3-642-17996-9(7)*, 3642179967) Springer.

Graham, Linda E., et al. Algae. 2nd ed. 2008. (ENG., Illus.). 720p. (C). 146.53 *(978-0-321-55965-4(7))* Benjamin-Cummings Publishing Co.

Granéli, Edna & Turner Jefferson T. Ecology of Harmful Algae. 2006. (Ecological Studies). (Illus.). xxvi, 413p. 169.00 *(978-3-540-32209-2(4)*, 3540322094) Springer.

Griffiths, Dilwyn J. Microalgal Cell Cycles. 2010. (Cell Biology Research Progress Ser.). (Illus.). viii, 116p. pap. 49.00 *(978-1-60876-787-8(6)*, Nova Novinka) Nova Science Pubs., Inc.

Guha, Shubhra. Microcystis: Killer Algae of Fresh water Habitats. 2011. 220p. pap. ***(978-3-8443-8655-4(6))*** Lambert Academic Publishing.

Gulati, Ramesh D., et al. eds. Biomanipulation - Tool for Water Management. 2011. (Developments in Hydrobiology Ser.). (ENG.). 648p. pap. 629.00 *(978-90-481-4074-9(9)*, 9048140749) Springer.

Hagen, Kristian N., ed. Algae: Nutrition, Pollution Control & Energy Sources. 2008. 89.00 *(978-1-60692-008-4(1))* Nova Science Pubs., Inc.

Harmful Algal Blooms: The Challenges on the Nation's Coastlines: Hearing Before the Subcommittee on Energy & Environment, Committee on Science & Technology, House of Representatives, One Hundred Tenth Congress, Second Session, July 10, 2008. 2008. (Illus.). iv, 124p. *(978-0-16-082634-4(9)*, 552-070-38652-1) United States Government Printing Office.

Harmful Algal Blooms & Hypoxia: Formulating an Action Plan: Hearing Before the Subcommittee on Energy & Environment, Committee on Science & Technology, House of Representatives, One Hundred Eleventh Congress, First Session, September 17, 2009. 2009. (Illus.). iv, 87p. *(978-0-16-084953-4(5)*, 552-070-40343-4) United States Government Printing Office.

Heydt, Matthias. How Do Spores Select Where to Settle? A Holographic Motility Analysis of Ulva Zoospores on Different Surfaces. 2011. (Springer Theses Ser.). (Illus.). xviii, 178p. 129.00 *(978-3-642-17216-8(4)*, 3642172164) Springer.

Huisman, John M. Algae of Australia: Nemaliales. 2006. (Illus.). 164p. 79.95 *(978-0-643-09378-2(8))* CSIRO Publishing AUS. Dist: Stylus Publishing, LLC.

Jitendra, Priya & V.K.Anand, . The Oedogoniales of Jammu , Indi. 2011. 448p. pap. ***(978-3-8383-9763-4(0))*** Lambert Academic Publishing.

Johansen, Melanie N. Microalgae: Biotechnology, Microbiology & Energy. 2011. (Marine Biology Ser.). (Illus.). 489p. 185.00 *(978-1-61324-625-2(0))* Nova Science Pubs., Inc.

Kim, Se-Kwon, ed. Handbook of Marine Macroalgae: Biotechnology & Applied Phycology. 2012. (ENG., Illus.). 592p. 249.95 ***(978-0-470-97918-1(6)***, Wiley) Wiley, John & Sons, Inc.

Kristiansen, Jorgen, ed. Biogeography of Freshwater Algae. 2011. (Developments in Hydrobiology Ser.). 168p. pap. 259.00 *(978-90-481-4756-4(5)*, 9048147565) Springer.

Kromkamp, Jacco C., et al, eds. Functioning of Microphytobenthos in Estuaries. 2007. (Illus.). 400p. pap. 78.00 *(978-90-6984-453-4(2))* Koninklijke Nederlandse Academie van Wetenschappen NLD. Dist: Chicago Distribution Ctr.

Lan, Christopher. Microalgae for Biofuel Production & CO2 Sequestration. Wang, Bei et al, eds. 2010. (Energy Science, Engineering & Technology Ser.). 180p. pap. 69.00 *(978-1-61668-151-7(9))* Nova Science Pubs., Inc.

Lembi, Carole A. & Waaland, J. Robert, eds. Algae & Human Affairs. 2007. (ENG., Illus.). 600p. pap. 111.00 *(978-0-521-04440-0(5))* Cambridge Univ. Pr.

Leon, Rosa, et al, eds. Transgenic Microalgae as Green Cell Factories. 2007. (Advances in Experimental Medicine & Biology Ser.). (ENG., Illus.). 600p. 159.00 *(978-0-387-75531-1(4)*, 0387755314) Springer.

Malcolm Pirnie. Strategies for Controlling & Mitigating Algal Growth Within Water Treatment Plants. 2009. (Illus.). 244p. pap. *(978-1-60573-058-5(0))* Water Research Foundation.

Margulis, Lynn. Handbook of Protoctista. 2nd rev. ed. 2011. 298.95 *(978-0-7637-5710-6(1))* Jones & Bartlett Learning, LLC.

Okaichi, Tomotoshi, ed. Red Tides. 2010. (Ocean Sciences Research Ser.). (ENG.). 432p. pap. 199.00 *(978-90-481-6376-2(5)*, 9048163765) Springer.

Pettersson, Lasse, et al. Monitoring of Harmful Algae Blooms. 2008. (Springer Praxis Books / Marine Science & Coastal Management Ser.). 300p. 189.00 *(978-3-540-22892-9(6)*, 3540228926) Springer.

Reckhow K. Water Quality Indicators: Nutrient Impacts on Chlorophyll or Algae Species Composition:WERF Report: Evaluating Ecosystem Health (02-Eco-1) 2007. (WERF Report 02-ECO-1 Ser.). 84p. (C). pap. *(978-1-84339-747-2(1))* IWA Publishing.

Rogers, Kara. Fungi, Protists, & Algae. 2011. (Biochemistry, Cells, & Life Ser.). (ENG.). 232p. (YA). lib. bdg. 40.00 *(978-1-61530-310-6(3))* Rosen Publishing Group, Inc., The.

Rogers, Kara, ed. Fungi, Algae, & Protists. 2011. (Biochemistry, Cells, & Life Ser.). (Illus.). 232p. (YA). 80.00 *(978-1-61530-464-6(9))* Rosen Publishing Group, Inc., The.

Rowan, K. S. Photosynthetic Pigments of Algae. 2011. (ENG.). 350p. pap. 58.00 ***(978-0-521-10594-1(3))*** Cambridge Univ. Pr.

Sandgren, Craig D., et al, eds. Chrysophyte Algae: Ecology, Phylogeny & Development. 2009. (ENG., Illus.). 416p. pap. 74.00 *(978-0-521-10241-4(3))* Cambridge Univ. Pr.

Seckbach, Joseph, ed. Algae & Cyanobacteria in Extreme Environments. 2007. (Cellular Origin, Life in Extreme Habitats & Astrobiology Ser.). (Illus.). 450p. 399.00 *(978-1-4020-6111-0(0)*, 1402061110) Springer.

Seckbach, Joseph & Chapman, David J., eds. Red Algae in the Genomic Age. 2010. (Cellular Origin, Life in Extreme Habitats & Astrobiology Ser.). (ENG., Illus.). 495p. 239.00 *(978-90-481-3794-7(2)*, 9048137942) Springer.

Solari, Cristian Alejandro. Evolutionary Ecology & the Transition to Multicellularity: Hydrodynamics & the Volvocalean Green Algae as a Model System to Explain the Evolution of Multicellularity & Cellular Differentiation. 2008. pap. *(978-3-8364-9247-8(4))* VDM Verlag Dr. Mueller e.K.

Thierstein, Hans R. & Young, Jeremy R., eds. Coccolithophores: From Molecular Processes to Global Impact. 2010. (ENG., Illus.). xiv, 565p. pap. 269.00 *(978-3-642-06016-8(1)*, 3642060161) Springer.

Valeem, Ehsan Elahi & Shameel, Mustafa. Composition of Fatty Acids in Marine & Freshwater Algae of Sindh. 2010. 240p. pap. *(978-3-639-25103-6(2))* VDM Verlag Dr. Mueller e.K.

West, G. S. Algae: Volume 1, Myxophyceae, Peridinieae, Bacillarieae, Chlorophyceae. 2010. (Cambridge Library Collection - Life Sciences Ser.). (ENG., Illus.). 490p. pap. 35.99 *(978-1-108-01322-2(8))* Cambridge Univ. Pr.

Whitton, B. A., et al, eds. The Freshwater Algal Flora of the British Isles: An Identification Guide to Freshwater & Terrestrial Algae. 2nd rev. ed. 2011. (ENG., Illus.). 896p. 199.00 *(978-0-521-19375-7(3))* Cambridge Univ. Pr.

Wilkinson, A. N., et al. Atlas of Chrysophycean Cysts: Volume II. 2010. (Developments in Hydrobiology Ser.). 180p. pap. 299.00 *(978-90-481-5746-4(3)*, 9048157463) Springer.

Williams, Peter E. Marine & Freshwater Harmful Algal Blooms. 2010. (Environmental Health - Physical, Chemical & Biological Factors Ser.). 145p. 89.00 *(978-1-60741-838-2(X))* Nova Science Pubs., Inc.

Winter, Amos & Siesser, William G., eds. Coccolithophores. 2006. (ENG.). 256p. pap. 56.00 *(978-0-521-03169-1(9))* Cambridge Univ. Pr.

World Catalog of Algae. 88.00 *(978-4-7622-2592-5(4))* Business Ctr. for Academic Societies JPN. Dist: International Specialized Bk. Services.

ALGAE—BIBLIOGRAPHY

Hope, A. B. The Physiology of Giant Algal Cells. 2011. (ENG., Illus.). 226p. pap. 31.99 *(978-0-521-27931-4(3))* Cambridge Univ. Pr.

Whitford, L. A. & Schumacher, George. Manual of Freshwater Algae. 35.00 *(978-0-916822-01-9(X))* Sparks Pr., Inc.

ALGAE, FOSSIL

Mikami, Koji. Porphyra Yezoensis: Frontiers in Physiological & Molecular Biological Research. 2012. (Series: Marine Biology Ser.). 213p. 129.00 *(978-1-61122-304-0(0))* Nova Science Pubs., Inc.

ALGARVE (PORTUGAL)

Anderson, Brian & Anderson, Eileen. Sunflower Guide Landscapes of Algarve: A Countryside Guide. 5th rev. ed. 2007. (Sunflower Guides Algarve Ser.). (Illus.). 136p. pap. 17.99 *(978-1-85691-334-8(1))* Hunter Publishing, Inc.

Branco, Conceicao. Algarve (Illus.). pap. *(978-88-8029-089-6(4))* Casa Editrice Bonechi.

Evans, Brian J. How the Algarve Has Changed: A Reflective Look at This Part of Portugal over the Past Twenty Seven Years. 2011. 144p. pap. 16.52 ***(978-1-4567-8812-4(4))*** AuthorHouse.

Frommer's Staff & Gauldie, Robin. The Algarve with Your Family: The Best of Portugals Southern Coast. 2008. (Frommers with Your Family Ser.: 20). (ENG., Illus.). 256p. pap. 22.99 *(978-0-470-05526-7(X)*, Frommers) Wiley, John & Sons, Inc.

O'Callaghan, Jane. Algarve Travel Pack. 7th ed. 2009. (Globetrotter Travel Packs Ser.). (ENG., Illus.). 128p. 14.95 *(978-1-84773-553-9(3)*, Globetrotter) New Holland Pubs., Ltd. GBR. Dist: Globe Pequot Pr., The.

—The Best of the Algarve. (Illus.). 96p. 8.95 *(978-1-84330-578-1(X))* New Holland Pubs., Ltd. GBR. Dist: Globe Pequot Pr., The.

ALGAZEL

see Ghazali, Al, 1058-1111

ALGEBRA

see also Algorithms; Associative Algebras; Binomial Theorem; Combinations; Combinatorial Analysis; Commutative Algebra; Determinants; Diophantine Analysis; Equations; Forms (Mathematics); Group Theory; Logarithms; Mathematical Analysis; Modules (Algebra); Number Theory; p-Adic Analysis; Partitions (Mathematics); Permutations; Probabilities; Representations of Algebras; Sequences (Mathematics); Series; Spinor Analysis

Abbott, Paul & Neill, Hugh. Understand Algebra. 2011. (Teach Yourself: Reference Ser.). (ENG.). 352p. pap. 15.00 *(978-0-07-175485-9(7)*, 0071754857) McGraw-Hill Cos., The.

Acosta, Gisela & Karwowski, Margie. Activity Workbook with Real-World Applications for College Algebra. rev. ed. 2009. (ENG.). 150p. pap. 31.68 *(978-0-7575-5669-2(8))* Kendall Hunt Publishing Co.

Adams, Barbara. Building a Bridge to Algebra. (C). pap. 35.00 *(978-1-881592-30-3(8))* Hayden-McNeil Publishing, Inc.

Addison-Wesley. MML Student Access Kit for Ad Hoc Valuepacks. 7th ed. (Illus.). xxxii, 1234p. *(978-0-321-26252-3(2))* Addison Wesley.

Addison-Wesley, James S. Elementary Algebra Worksheets for Classroom or Lab Practice. 2008. (ENG.). 344p. (C). pap. 26.67 *(978-0-321-52310-5(5))* Addison Wesley Higher Education.

Addison-Wesley Publishing Staff. Beginning & Intermediate Algebra with Applications & Visualization Worksheets for Classroom or Lab Practice. 2nd ed. 2008. (ENG.). 510p. (C). pap. 31.00 *(978-0-321-53967-0(2))* Addison Wesley.

—Elementary & Intermediate Algebra Worksheets for Classroom or Lab Practice. 2nd ed. 2008. (ENG.). 562p. (C) pap. 31.00 *(978-0-321-52321-1(0))* Addison Wesley.

—Intermediate Algebra with Applications & Visualization Worksheets for Classroom or Lab Practice. 3rd ed. 2008. (ENG.). 490p. (C). pap. 26.67 *(978-0-321-54271-7(1))* Addison Wesley Higher Education.

Adventures in Algebra: Automated Homework Systems for the College Curriculum - Version 2.0. Date not set. (Illus.). 43p. (Orig.). pap. *(978-0-918091-16-1(0))* Hawkes Learning Systems.

Akram, Muhammad & Dar, Karamat. Generalized Fuzzy K-Algebras. 2010. 288p. pap. *(978-3-639-27095-2(9))* VDM Verlag Dr. Mueller e.K.

Akst, Geoffrey, et al, contrib. by. Intermediate Algebra Through Applications. 2008. *(978-0-321-53579-5(0))* Addison-Wesley Longman, Inc.

Akst, Geoffrey & Bragg, Sadie. Intermediate Algebra Through Applications. (MathXL Tutorials on CD Ser.). (ENG., (C). 2nd ed. 2008. Illus.). 984p. pap. 162.00 *(978-0-321-51801-9(2))* 3rd rev. ed. 2012. 488p. pap. 26.67 ***(978-0-321-75975-7(3))*** 3rd rev. ed. 2011. (Illus.). 912p. pap. 162.00 ***(978-0-321-74671-9(6))*** Addison Wesley.

—Intermediate Algebra Through Applications, Books a la Carte Edition plus MyMathLab Student Access Kit. 2012. (ENG.). (C). ring bd. 107.20 ***(978-0-321-72941-5(2))*** Addison Wesley.

—Intermediate Algebra Through Applications plus MyMathLab Student Access Kit. 2012. (ENG.). (C). pap., pap. 172.00 ***(978-0-321-83216-0(7))*** Addison Wesley.

—Introductory Algebra, Books a la Carte Edition plus MyMathLab Student Access Kit. 2012. (ENG.). (C). ring bd. 107.20 ***(978-0-321-72948-4(X))*** Addison Wesley.

—Introductory Algebra Through Applications. (MathXL Tutorials on CD Ser.). (ENG., (C). 2nd ed. 2008. Illus.). 768p. pap. 162.00 *(978-0-321-51802-6(0))* 3rd rev. ed. 2012. 400p. pap. 26.67 ***(978-0-321-75928-3(1))*** 3rd rev. ed. 2011. 744p. pap. 162.00 *(978-0-321-74669-6(4))* Addison Wesley.

—Introductory Algebra Through Applications. 2nd ed. 2008. *(978-0-321-52305-1(9))* Addison-Wesley Longman, Inc.

—Introductory & Intermediate Algebra Through Applications. 2nd ed. 2008. (Akst & Bragg Developmental Mathematics Ser.). (ENG., Illus.). 1104p. (C). pap. 176.00 *(978-0-321-53578-8(2))* Addison Wesley.

—Student Solutions Manual for Introductory & Intermediate Algebra through Applications. 2nd ed. 2008. (ENG.). 432p. (C). pap. 36.67 *(978-0-321-55670-7(4))* Addison Wesley Higher Education.

—Student's Solutions Manual for Intermediate Algebra through Applications. 2nd ed. 2008. (ENG.). 320p. (C). pap. 36.67 *(978-0-321-52819-3(0))* Addison Wesley Higher Education.

Al. Aspects of Infinite Groups (V1) 2008. 104.00 *(978-981-279-340-9(2))* World Scientific Publishing Co., Inc.

Algebra. 9th ed. 2009. (ENG., Illus.). Vol.1. 568p. pap. 35.00 *(978-0-9815320-5-9(5))* Vol.2. 608p. (C). pap. 35.00 *(978-0-9815320-6-6(3))* JRL Enterprises, Inc.

Algebra. Some Current Trends: Proceedings of the 5th National School in Algebra, held in Varna, Bulgaria, Sept. 24 - Oct. 4, 1986. 2008. (Lecture Notes in Mathematics Ser.). pap. 46.00 *(978-3-540-50371-2(4))* Springer.

Algebra Volume 1. 7th rev. ed. 2007. (C). per. 31.95 *(978-0-9789017-7-6(0))* JRL Enterprises, Inc.

Algebra Volume 2. 7th rev. ed. 2007. (C). per. 31.95 *(978-0-9789017-8-3(9))* JRL Enterprises, Inc.

Aluffi, Paolo. Algebra. 2009. (Graduate Studies in Mathematics Ser.). (Illus.). 713p. 89.00 *(978-0-8218-4781-7(3))* American Mathematical Society.

America's Math Teacher. Pre-Algebra Concepts. 2008. (Mastering Essential Math Skills Ser.). (Illus.). 96p. (J). (gr. 6-13). pap. 34.95 *(978-0-9821901-2-8(3))* Math Essentials.

Andersen, Maria H. Intermediate Algebra - Student Workbook. 9th ed. 2011. (ENG.). 492p. (C). pap. 42.95 *(978-1-111-57484-0(7))* Brooks/Cole.

—Prealgebra & Introductory Algebra: An Applied Approach. 2nd ed. 2010. (ENG.). 368p. (C). pap., wbk. ed. 64.95 *(978-0-8400-5351-0(7))* Brooks/Cole.

Andersen, Maria H. & Lockwood, Joanne. Introductory Algebra: An Applied Approach. 8th ed. 2010. (ENG.). 352p. (C). pap., stu. ed., wbk. ed. 42.95 *(978-1-4390-4717-0(0))* Brooks/Cole.

Andersen, Maria H. & Massey, Marilyn. Algebra. 9th ed. 2010. (ENG.). 374p. (C). pap., wbk. ed. 42.95 *(978-1-4390-4745-3(6))* Brooks/Cole.

Anfinson, Cynthia & Clark, Mark. Intermediate Algebra: Concepts Through Applications. 2011. (ENG.). 496p. (C). pap. 44.95 *(978-0-534-49641-8(5))* Brooks/Cole.

—Student Solutions Manual for Algebra: Concepts Through Applications. 2011. (ENG.). 448p. (C). pap. 42.95 *(978-0-534-46533-9(1))* Brooks/Cole.

—Text-Specific Videos-Intermediate Algebra: Concepts through Applications. 2011. (ENG.). (C). 170.95 *(978-0-534-49643-2(1))* Brooks/Cole.

Angel & Angel, Allen R. Elementary & Intermediate Algebra for College Students, A la Carte with MML/MSL Student Access Kit (adhoc for Valuepacks) 4th ed. 2010. (ENG.). (C). ring bd. 116.67 *(978-0-321-70613-3(7))* Addison Wesley.

Angel & Cram101 Textbook Reviews Staff. Elementary Algebra for College Students. 2007. 124p. per. 11.95 *(978-1-4288-3602-0(0))* Cram101 Inc.

—Intermediate Algebra for College Students. 2007. 168p. per. 12.95 *(978-1-4288-3622-8(5))*; 148p. per. 12.95 *(978-1-4288-3522-1(9))* Cram101 Inc.

Angel, Allen R. Algebra for College Students. 3rd ed. 2007. (Angel Developmental Algebra Ser.). (ENG., Illus.). 928p. (C). 168.00 *(978-0-13-612908-0(0)*, Prentice Hall) Prentice Hall PTR.

—Algebra for College Students, Books a la Carte Plus MyMathLab/MyStatLab Student Access Kit. 3rd ed. 2010. (ENG.). (C). ring bd. 110.80 *(978-0-321-74101-1(3))* Addison Wesley.

—Algebra for College Students Value Package (includes MyMathLab/MyStatLab Student Access) 3rd ed. 2010. (ENG.). (C). pap. 178.00 (978-0-321-74724-2(0)) Addison Wesley.

—Elementary Algebra Early Graphing for College Students. 3rd ed. 2007. (Angel Developmental Algebra Ser.). (ENG., Illus.). 704p. (C). 168.00 (978-0-13-613416-9(5), Prentice Hall) Prentice Hall PTR.

—Elementary Algebra for College Students: Early Graphing. 3rd ed. 2008. (ENG.). (C). ring bd. 100.80 (978-0-321-62245-7(6)) Addison Wesley.

—Elementary Algebra for College Students: Early Graphing. 3rd ed. 2007. (978-0-13-613417-6(3)) Pearson Bks.

—Elementary Algebra for College Students, A la Carte with MML/MSL Student Access Kit (adhoc for Valuepacks) 8th ed. 2010. (ENG.). (C). ring bd. 110.00 (978-0-321-70611-9(0)) Addison Wesley.

—Elementary & Intermediate Algebra for College Students. 3rd ed. 2007. 966p. incl. cd-rom (978-0-13-233416-7(X)) Pearson Education Canada.

—Elementary & Intermediate Algebra for College Students, Books a la Carte Edition. 4th ed. 2010. (ENG.). 1088p. (C). ring bd. 104.80 (978-0-321-69251-1(9)) Addison Wesley.

—Intermediate Algebra for College Students. 8th ed. 2010. (ENG.). 576p. (C). pap. 36.67 (978-0-321-65265-2(7), Prentice Hall) Prentice Hall PTR.

—Student's Solutions Manual for Elementary & Intermediate Algebra for College Students. 4th ed. 2010. (ENG.). 624p. (C). pap. 36.67 (978-0-321-65237-9(1), Prentice Hall) Prentice Hall PTR.

Angel, Allen R. & Runde, Dennis. Intermediate Algebra for College Students. 8th ed. 2010. (Angel Developmental Algebra Ser.). (ENG., Illus.). 784p. (C). 168.00 (978-0-321-62091-0(7), Prentice Hall) Prentice Hall PTR.

—Intermediate Algebra for College Students, A la Carte with MML/MSL Student Access Kit (adhoc for Valuepacks) 8th ed. 2010. (ENG.). (C). ring bd. 110.80 (978-0-321-70612-6(9)) Addison Wesley.

—Intermediate Algebra for College Students, Books a la Carte Edition. 8th ed. 2010. (ENG.). 768p. (C). ring bd. 100.80 (978-0-321-69249-8(7)) Addison Wesley.

Angel, Allen R. & Runde, Dennis C. Elementary Algebra for College Students. 8th ed. 2009. tchr. ed. (978-0-321-62877-0(2)) Pearson Education.

—Elementary & Intermediate Algebra for College Students. 4th ed. 2011. tchr. ed. (978-0-321-62875-6(6)) Pearson Education.

—Intermediate Algebra for College Students. 8th ed. 2010. tchr. ed. (978-0-321-62876-3(4)) Pearson Education.

Angel, Allen R. & Ziegler, Michael. Student's Solutions Manual for Elementary Algebra for College Students. 8th ed. 2010. (ENG.). 360p. (C). pap. 36.67 (978-0-321-65313-0(0), Prentice Hall) Prentice Hall PTR.

Angel, Allen R., et al. Elementary Algebra for College Students. 8th ed. 2010. (ENG.). 672p. (C). 168.00 (978-0-321-62093-4(3), Prentice Hall) Prentice Hall PTR.

—Elementary & Intermediate Algebra for College Students. 3rd ed. 2007. (Illus.). (978-0-13-614445-8(4)) Pearson Bks.

—Elementary & Intermediate Algebra for College Students. 4th ed. 2010. (Angel Developmental Algebra Ser.). (ENG., Illus.). 1008p. (C). 176.00 (978-0-321-62092-7(5), Prentice Hall) Prentice Hall PTR.

Arslanov, M. M., et al, eds. Algebra & Analysis: Proceedings of the International Centennial Chebotarev Conference held in Kazan, Russia, June 5-11 1994. (De Gruyter Proceedings in Mathematics Ser.). (ENG.). 163p. 240.00 (978-3-11-177791-7(X)) De Gruyter, Walter Inc.

Arthur, John W. Understanding Geometric Algebra for Electromagnetic Theory. 2011. (IEEE Press Series on Electromagnetic Wave Theory Ser.: 38). (ENG., Illus.). 320p. 125.00 (978-0-470-94163-8(4), Wiley-IEEE Pr.) Wiley, John & Sons, Inc.

Artin & Cram101 Textbook Reviews Staff. Algebr. 2007. 140p. per. 11.95 (978-1-4288-3358-6(7)) Cram101 Inc.

Artin, Emil. Algebra with Galois Theory. 2007. (Courant Lecture Notes Ser.: Vol. 15). (Illus.). 126p. (C). pap. 30.00 (978-0-8218-4129-7(7)) American Mathematical Society.

Artin, Michael. Algebra. 2nd ed. 2010. (ENG., Illus.). 560p. (C). 138.67 (978-0-13-241377-0(9)) Addison Wesley.

Arveson, William. Noncommutative Dynamics & E-Semigroups. 2012. (Springer Monographs in Mathematics Ser.). (ENG.). x, 434p. pap. 149.00 (978-1-4419-1803-1(5), 1441918035) Springer.

Ash, Robert B. Basic Abstract Algebra: For Graduate Students & Advanced Undergraduates. 2006. (Dover Books on Mathematics Ser.). (ENG., Illus.). 432p. per. 24.95 (978-0-486-45356-9(1)) Dover Pubns., Inc.

Atiyah, Steven K. Complete Algebra: Part One. 2010. 596p. pap. 49.95 (978-1-4269-3310-3(X)) Trafford Publishing.

—Complete Algebra: Part Two. 2010. 624p. pap. 49.95 (978-1-4269-3311-0(8)) Trafford Publishing.

—Complete Algebra: Solution Manual. 2010. 408p. pap. 49.95 (978-1-4269-3309-7(6)) Trafford Publishing.

Aufmann, Richard N. College Algebra. 6th ed. 2007. (ENG.). 832p. (C). 200.95 (978-0-618-80371-2(8), 302685) CENGAGE Learning.

Aufmann, Richard N. & Andersen, Maria H. Algebra: Beginning & Intermediate. 2nd ed. 2010. (ENG.). 450p. (C). pap., wbk. ed. 64.95 (978-0-538-73157-7(5)) Brooks/Cole.

Aufmann, Richard N. & Lockwood, Joanne. Algebra: Introductory & Intermediate - An Applied Approach. 5th ed. 2010. (ENG.). 416p. (C). pap. 69.95 (978-0-538-49723-7(8)) Brooks/Cole.

—Intermediate Algebra: An Applied Approach. 8th ed. 2010. (Available Titles CourseMate Ser.). (ENG.). 848p. (C). pap. 195.95 (978-1-4390-4690-6(5)) Brooks/Cole.

—Introductory Algebra. 8th ed. 2010. (ENG.). 304p. (C). pap. 67.95 (978-1-4390-4711-8(1)) Brooks/Cole.

—Mathematics Allied Health Professional. 2012. (ENG.). 608p. (C). pap. 175.95 (978-1-111-98674-2(6)) Brooks/Cole.

—Prealgebra & Introductory Algebra: An Applied Approach. 2nd ed. 2010. (Available 2011 Titles Enhanced Web Assign Ser.). (ENG.). (C). 1008p. pap. 216.95 (978-0-8400-4808-0(4)); 352p. pap. 65.95 (978-0-8400-4930-8(7)) Brooks/Cole.

—Prealgebra, Enhanced Edition (with Enhanced WebAssign 1-Semester Printed Access Card) 5th ed. 2009. (Available 2010 Titles Enhanced Web Assign Ser.). (ENG.). 784p. (C). pap. 193.95 (978-1-4390-4798-9(7)) Brooks/Cole.

Aufmann, Richard N. & Lockwood, Joanne S. Algebra: Beginning & Intermediate. 2nd ed. 2008. (Illus.). xxxii, 834p. (978-0-618-82073-3(6)) Houghton Mifflin Harcourt Publishing Co.

—Algebra for College Students. 2nd ed. 2007. (ENG., Illus.). 1040p. (C). 211.95 (978-0-618-82494-6(4), 301304) Brooks/Cole.

Aufmann, Richard N. & Mosley, Dana. Algebra with Applications. 7th ed. 2007. (ENG.). (C). 63.95 (978-0-618-82071-9(X), 302618) Brooks/Cole.

Aufmann, Richard N., et al. Algebra: Beginning & Intermediate. 2nd ed. 2008. (Available 2010 Titles Enhanced Web Assign Ser.). (ENG.). 984p. (C). 221.95 (978-0-547-19794-4(2)) Brooks/Cole.

—Algebra: Introductory & Intermediate - An Applied Approach. 5th ed. 2010. (Available Titles CourseMate Ser.). (ENG.). 928p. (C). pap. 216.95 (978-1-4390-4695-1(6)) Brooks/Cole.

—Algebra for College Students. 2nd ed. 2008. (Illus.). xxxiv, 888p. (978-0-618-82495-3(2)) Houghton Mifflin Harcourt Publishing Co.

—Beginning Algebra. 2007. 128p. per. 11.95 (978-1-4288-3594-8(6)) Cram101 Inc.

—Beginning Algebra with Applications. 7th ed. 2008. (Available 2010 Titles Enhanced Web Assign Ser.). (ENG.). 792p. (C). 204.95 (978-0-547-19796-8(9)) Brooks/Cole.

—Beginning Algebra with Applications. 7th ed. 2008. (Illus.). xxxii, 664p. (978-0-618-80361-3(0)) Houghton Mifflin Harcourt Publishing Co.

—College Algebra. 7th ed. 2010. (Available 2011 Titles Enhanced Web Assign Ser.). (ENG.). 792p. (C). 200.95 (978-1-4390-4861-0(4)) Brooks/Cole.

—College Algebra & Trigonometry. 6th ed. 2007. (ENG., Illus.). 1152p. (C). 225.95 (978-0-618-82515-8(0), 302451) CENGAGE Learning.

—College Algebra & Trigonometry. 6th ed. 2007. (ENG.). 592p. (C). pap., pupil's gde. ed. 61.95 (978-0-618-82518-9(5), 302453) Brooks/Cole.

—College Algebra & Trigonometry. 7th ed. 2010. (College Algebra & Trigonometry Ser.). (ENG.). 1080p. (C). 225.95 (978-1-4390-4860-3(6)) Brooks/Cole.

—College Algebra: Enhanced Edition. 6th ed. 2009. (ENG.). 864p. (C). 180.95 (978-1-4390-4379-0(5)) Brooks/Cole.

—College Algebra Student Guide & Solutions Manual. 6th ed. 2007. (ENG., Illus.). 432p. (C). per. 65.95 (978-0-618-82498-4(7), 302687) Brooks/Cole.

—Intermediate Algebra. 2007. 156p. per. 12.95 (978-1-4288-3630-3(6)) Cram101 Inc.

—Intermediate Algebra with Applications. 7th ed. 2008. (Illus.). xxxiii, 780p. (978-0-618-80370-5(X)) Houghton Mifflin Harcourt Publishing Co.

—Intermediate Algebra with Applications. 7th ed. 2008. (Available 2010 Titles Enhanced Web Assign Ser.). (ENG.). 936p. (C). 206.95 (978-0-547-19797-5(7)) Brooks/Cole.

—Introductory Algebra: An Applied Approach. 8th ed. 2010. (Available Titles CourseMate Ser.). (ENG.). 680p. (C). pap. 195.95 (978-1-4390-4604-3(2)) Brooks/Cole.

Augustus De Morgan. Trigonometry & Double Algebra - Unabridged. 2007. 188p. 19.95 (978-1-933998-71-8(7), Merchant Bks.) Rough Draft Printing.

Axler, Sheldon. Algebra & Trigonometry. 2011. (ENG., Illus.). 784p. (C). 173.95 (978-0-470-58579-5(X)); pap. 160.95 (978-0-470-47081-7(X)) Wiley, John & Sons, Inc. (Wiley).

—College Algebra. 2010. (ENG.). 528p. (C). pap. 138.95 (978-0-470-47077-0(1)); (Illus.). 160.95 (978-0-470-47076-3(3)) Wiley, John & Sons, Inc. (Wiley).

—College Algebra First Edition Binder Ready Version. 2010. (ENG., Illus.). 528p. (C). pap. 79.95 (978-0-470-47078-7(X), Wiley) Wiley, John & Sons, Inc.

—Precalculus Student Solutions Manual. 2007. pap. 31.95 (978-0-470-14027-7(5)) Wiley, John & Sons, Inc.

Axler, Sheldon Jay. Algebra & Trigonometry First Edition Binder Ready Version. 2011. (Illus.). 784p. (C). ring bd. 96.95 (978-0-470-47082-4(8), Wiley) Wiley, John & Sons, Inc.

Bahturin, Y. Basic Structures of Modern Algebra. 2010. (Mathematics & Its Applications Ser.). 434p. pap. 189.00 (978-90-481-4317-7(9), 9048143179) Springer.

Baldor, Aurelio. Algebra. 2nd ed. 2007. 576p. 39.95 (978-970-817-000-0(3)) Patria.

Baratto, Stefan, et al. Basic Mathematical Skills with Geometry. 7th ed. 2008. (Illus.). xxvi, 866p. 120.00 (978-0-07-325777-8(X)) McGraw-Hill Higher Education.

—Beginning Algebra. 7th rev. ed. 2006. (Streeter Ser.). (Illus.). 988p. per. 134.38 (978-0-07-330960-6(5), 9780073309606, McGraw-Hill Science, Engineering & Mathematics) McGraw-Hill Higher Education.

—Elementary & Intermediate Algebra: A Unified Approach. 3rd ed. 2007. (Streeter Ser.). (Illus.). 1243p. 148.44 (978-0-07-330931-6(1), 9780073309316); per. 148.44 (978-0-07-330961-3(3), 9780073309613) McGraw-Hill Higher Education. (McGraw-Hill Science, Engineering & Mathematics).

—Hutchison's Basic Mathematical Skills with Geometry. 8th ed. 2009. (978-0-07-338417-7(8)) McGraw-Hill Cos., The.

—Hutchison's Beginning Algebra. 8th ed. 2009. (978-0-07-729210-2(3)); (978-0-07-338418-4(6)) McGraw-Hill Cos., The.

—Hutchison's Beginning Algebra. 8th ed. 2009. (ENG.). (C). pap., pap. 165.00 (978-0-07-735475-6(3), 0077354753, McGraw-Hill Science, Engineering & Mathematics) McGraw-Hill Higher Education.

—Hutchison's Elementary & Intermediate Algebra. 4th ed. 2010. (978-0-07-338419-1(4)) McGraw-Hill Cos., The.

—Hutchison's Elementary & Intermediate Algebra. 4th ed. 2010. (ENG.). 1120p. (C). pap. 182.67 (978-0-07-735012-3(X), 007735012X, McGraw-Hill Science, Engineering & Mathematics) McGraw-Hill Higher Education.

—Prealgebra: Media Enhanced. 3rd ed. 2012. (Illus.). xxiv, 866p. (978-0-07-340623-7(6)) McGraw-Hill Cos., The.

Barnett & Ziegler & Byleen & Cram101 Textbook Reviews Staff. College Algebr. 2007. 148p. per. 11.95 (978-1-4288-3376-0(5)) Cram101 Inc.

Barnett, Raymond. Annotated Instructor's Edition College Algebra. 2010. 896p. 110.25 (978-0-07-729713-8(X), WCB/McGraw-Hill) McGraw-Hill Higher Education.

Barnett, Raymond, et al. College Algebra. 9th ed. 2010. (ENG.). 832p. (C). 166.00 (978-0-07-735016-1(2), 0077350162, McGraw-Hill Science, Engineering & Mathematics) McGraw-Hill Higher Education.

—College Algebra with Trigonometry. 9th ed. 2010. (ENG., Illus.). 1088p. (C). 185.67 (978-0-07-735010-9(3), 0077350103, McGraw-Hill Science, Engineering & Mathematics) McGraw-Hill Higher Education.

—Student Solutions Manual College Algebra. 9th ed. 2010. (ENG.). 448p. (C). pap. 67.33 (978-0-07-729718-3(0), 0077297180, McGraw-Hill Science, Engineering & Mathematics) McGraw-Hill Higher Education.

—Student Solutions Manual College Algebra with Trigonometry. 9th ed. 2010. (ENG.). 672p. (C). pap. 73.33 (978-0-07-729725-1(3), 0077297253, McGraw-Hill Science, Engineering & Mathematics) McGraw-Hill Higher Education.

—Student Solutions Manual for use with Precalculus: Graphs & Models. 3rd ed. 2008. (ENG.). 864p. (C). pap. 76.67 (978-0-07-334178-1(9), 0073341789, McGraw-Hill Science, Engineering & Mathematics) McGraw-Hill Higher Education.

Barnett, Raymond A. College Algebra. 9th ed. 2010. (Illus.). 832p. (978-0-07-351949-4(9)) McGraw-Hill Cos., The.

—College Algebra with Trigonometry. 9th ed. 2010. (Illus.). 1088p. (978-0-07-351950-0(2)) McGraw-Hill Cos., The.

—Precalculus with Limits. 2007. 174.06 (978-0-07-336014-0(7)) McGraw-Hill Higher Education.

Barnett, Raymond A., et al. College Algebra. 8th rev. ed. 2007. (Illus.). (C). 920p. 121.25 (978-0-07-286738-1(8), 9780072867381); (ENG., 928p. 146.56 (978-0-07-331262-0(2), 0073312622) McGraw-Hill Higher Education. (McGraw-Hill Science, Engineering & Mathematics).

—College Algebra with Trigonometry. 8th rev. ed. 2007. (Illus.). (C). 1056p. 134.06 (978-0-07-286740-4(X), 9780072867404); (ENG., 1044p. 163.75 (978-0-07-331264-4(9), 0073312649) McGraw-Hill Higher Education. (McGraw-Hill Science, Engineering & Mathematics).

—Precalculus: Functions & Graphs. 6th rev. ed. 2007. 1192p. (C). 134.06 (978-0-07-286739-8(6), 9780072867398, McGraw-Hill Science, Engineering & Mathematics) McGraw-Hill Higher Education.

—Precalculus with Limits. 6th ed. 2007. (ENG.). 1256p. (C). 163.75 (978-0-07-336580-0(7), 0073365807, McGraw-Hill Science, Engineering & Mathematics) McGraw-Hill Higher Education.

Basnet, Dhiren Kumar. Topics in Intuitionistic Fuzzy Algebr. 2011. 80p. pap. (978-3-8443-9147-3(9)) Lambert Academic Publishing.

Bauer, Cameron. Algebra for Athletes, 2nd Edition. 2nd rev. ed. 2008. (Illus.). 39.00 (978-1-60021-925-2(X)) Nova Science Pubs., Inc.

Baur, Ulrike. Control-Oriented Model Reduction for Parabolic System. 2008. 224p. pap. (978-3-639-07417-8(3)) VDM Verlag Dr. Mueller e.K.

Beck, Matthias, et al, eds. Integer Points in Polyhedra: Geometry, Number Theory, Representation Theory, Algebra, Optimization, Statistics. 2008. (Contemporary Mathematics Ser.). (Illus.). 187p. pap. 61.00 (978-0-8218-4173-0(4)) American Mathematical Society.

Beecher & Penna & Bittinger & Cram101 Textbook Reviews Staff. College Algrbr. 2007. 128p. per. 11.95 (978-1-4288-3464-4(8)) Cram101 Inc.

—Precalculus. 2007. 148p. per. 12.95 (978-1-4288-3524-5(5)) Cram101 Inc.

Beecher, Judith, et al. Annotated Instructor's Edition. 3rd rev. ed. 2007. 816p. (978-0-321-28627-7(8)) Pearson Bks.

Beecher, Judith A., et al. Algebra & Trigonometry. 4th rev. ed. 2011. (ENG.). 1120p. (C). 187.33 (978-0-321-69398-3(1)) Addison Wesley.

—Algebra & Trigonometry. 3rd ed. 2007. (Beecher/Penna/Bittinger Ser.). (ENG., Illus.). 1072p. (C). 181.33 (978-0-321-46620-4(9)) Addison-Wesley Longman, Inc.

—Algebra & Trigonometry, Books a la Carte Edition. 4th ed. 2011. (ENG.). 1088p. (C). ring bd. 112.40 (978-0-321-72569-1(7)) Addison Wesley.

—College Algebra. 4th rev. ed. 2011. (ENG.). 800p. (C). 168.67 (978-0-321-69399-0(X)) Addison Wesley.

—College Algebra. 3rd ed. 2007. (Beecher/Penna/Bittinger Ser.). (ENG., (C). Illus.). 800p. 162.67 (978-0-321-46607-5(1));Kit. pap. 172.67 (978-0-321-47926-6(2)) Addison-Wesley Longman, Inc.

—College Algebra, Books a la Carte Edition. 4th ed. 2011. (ENG.). 768p. (C). ring bd. 101.20 (978-0-321-72560-8(3)) Addison Wesley.

—Graphing Calculator Manual for Algebra & Trigonometry & Precalculus. 3rd ed. 2007. (ENG.). 144p. (C). pap. 24.67 (978-0-321-46538-2(5)) Addison Wesley Higher Education.

—Precalculus. 3rd ed. 2007. (Beecher/Penna/Bittinger Ser.). (ENG., Illus.). 1072p. (C). 181.33 (978-0-321-46006-6(5)) Addison-Wesley Longman, Inc.

—Precalculus: A Right Triangle Approach. 4th rev. ed. 2011. (ENG., Illus.). 1120p. (C). 187.33 (978-0-321-69397-6(3)) Addison Wesley.

—Precalculus: A Right Triangle Approach, Books a la Carte Edition. 4th ed. 2011. (ENG.). 1072p. (C). ring bd. 112.40 (978-0-321-72576-9(X)) Addison Wesley.

—Precalculus: A Right Triangle Approach, Books a la Carte Plus MML/MSL Student Access Code Card (for ad hoc Valuepacks) 4th ed. 2011. (ENG.). (C). ring bd. 122.40 (978-0-321-77219-0(9)) Addison Wesley.

—Precalculus: A Right Triangle Approach plus MyMathLab/MyStatLab Student Access Code Card. 4th ed. 2011. (ENG.). (C). pap. 197.33 (978-0-321-75987-0(7)) Addison Wesley.

—Student Solutions Manual for Algebra & Trigonometry: A Right Triangle Approach & Precalculus: A Right Triangle Approach. 4th ed. 2011. (ENG.). 432p. (C). pap. 36.67 (978-0-321-72564-6(6)) Addison Wesley.

—Student Solutions Manual for College Algebra. 4th ed. 2011. 240p. (C). pap. 36.67 (978-0-321-72484-7(4)) Pearson Education.

Beecher, Penna & Bittinger & Cram101 Textbook Reviews Staff. Algebra & Trigonometry. 2007. 168p. per. 12.95 (978-1-4288-3670-9(5)) Cram101 Inc.

Bello, Ignacio. Introductory Algebra. 3rd ed. 2008. (ENG.). 800p. (C). pap. 130.00 (978-0-07-722478-3(7), 0077224787, McGraw-Hill Science, Engineering & Mathematics) McGraw-Hill Higher Education.

—Introductory Algebra: A Real-World Approach. 4th ed. 2011. (ENG., Illus.). 800p. (C). pap. 130.00 (978-0-07-338439-9(9), 0073384399, McGraw-Hill Science, Engineering & Mathematics) McGraw-Hill Higher Education.

—Introductory Algebra w/ Connect Plus Access Card. 4th ed. 2011. (ENG.). (C). pap., pap. 143.33 (978-0-07-752686-3(4), 0077526864, McGraw-Hill Science, Engineering & Mathematics) McGraw-Hill Higher Education.

—Loose Leaf Version for Introductory Algebra. 4th ed. 2011. (ENG.). (C). ring bd. 91.00 (978-0-07-748966-3(7), 0077489667, McGraw-Hill Science, Engineering & Mathematics) McGraw-Hill Higher Education.

—Student Solutions Manual for Introductory Algebra. 4th ed. 2011. (ENG.). 448p. (C). pap. 70.33 (978-0-07-736347-5(7), 0077363477, McGraw-Hill Science, Engineering & Mathematics) McGraw-Hill Higher Education.

Bello, Ignacio & Hopf, Fran. Intermediate Algebra. 3rd ed. 2008. (ENG.). 960p. (C). pap. 130.00 (978-0-07-722480-6(9), 0077224809, McGraw-Hill Science, Engineering & Mathematics) McGraw-Hill Higher Education.

Berg, Claire Vaugelade. Developing Algebraic Thinking in a Community of Inquiry. 2010. 332p. pap. (978-3-639-23142-7(2)) VDM Verlag Dr. Mueller e.K.

Berry, Betsy. Pre-Algebra: NCTM Standards. 2008. (Daily Warm-Ups Ser.). (Illus.). 211p. pap. 24.99 incl. cd-rom (978-0-8251-6460-6(5)) Walch Education.

Berstel, Jean & Reutenauer, Christophe. Noncommutative Rational Series with Applications. 2010. (Encyclopedia of Mathematics & its Applications Ser.). (ENG., Illus.). 262p. 85.00 (978-0-521-19022-0(3)) Cambridge Univ. Pr.

Bhatti, Akhlaq. Chromatic Polynomials & Chromaticity of Graphs & Hypergraphs. 2010. 76p. pap. (978-3-639-25612-3(3)) VDM Verlag Dr. Mueller e.K.

Bhavanari, Satyanarayana. Contributions to near-Ring Theory. 2010. 204p. pap. (978-3-639-22417-7(5)) VDM Verlag Dr. Mueller e.K.

Bialynicki-Birula, A., et al. Algebraic Quotients. Torus Actions & Cohomology. the Adjoint Representation & the Adjoint Action. 2012. (Encyclopaedia of Mathematical Sciences Ser.). (ENG.). v, 242p. pap. 169.00 (978-3-642-07745-6(5), 3642077455) Springer.

Billera, Louis J., et al, eds. New Perspectives in Algebraic Combinatorics. 2011. (Mathematical Sciences Research Institute Publications). (ENG.). 355p. pap. 39.99 (978-0-521-17979-9(3)) Cambridge Univ. Pr.

Bird, J. O. & May, A. J. C. Algebra for Technicians. Date not set. (Longman Technician Ser.). 198p. pap. 181.35 (978-0-582-41258-3(7)) Addison-Wesley Longman, Ltd. GBR. Dist: Trans-Atlantic Pubns., Inc.

Birkhoff, Garrett & Mac Lane, Saunders. A Survey of Modern Algebra. 5th ed. 2008. (ENG., Illus.). 512p. pap. 72.95 (978-1-56881-454-4(2)) AK Peters, Ltd.

Bittinger & Beecher. Developmental Mathematics: College Mathematics & Introductory Algebra. 7th ed. 2006. pap., pap. 156.00 (978-0-321-51072-3(0)) Addison-Wesley Longman, Inc.

Bittinger & Bittinger, Marvin L. Intermediate Algebra, Books a la Carte Edition. 11th ed. 2010. (ENG.). 912p. (C). ring bd. 100.80 (978-0-321-65447-2(1)) Addison Wesley.

Bittinger & Cram101 Textbook Reviews Staff. Introductory Algebr. 2007. 112p. per. 11.95 (978-1-4288-3564-1(4)) Cram101 Inc.

Bittinger & Ellenbogen & Cram101 Textbook Reviews Staff. Elementary Algebr. 2007. 112p. per. 11.95 (978-1-4288-3356-2(0)) Cram101 Inc.

Bittinger, Beecher & Cram101 Textbook Reviews Staff. Introductory & Intermediate Algebr. 2007. 112p. per. 11.95 (978-1-4288-3650-1(0)) Cram101 Inc.

Bittinger, Ellenbogen & Cram101 Textbook Reviews Staff. Elementary Algebr. 2007. 132p. per. 11.95 (978-1-4288-3620-4(9)) Cram101 Inc.

Bittinger, Marvin L. Algebra & Trigonometry: Graphs & Models. 4th ed. 2007. (978-0-321-50150-9(0)) Pearson Bks.

—Intermediate Algebra. 11th ed. 2010. (Bittinger Worktext Ser.). (ENG., Illus.). 912p. (C). pap. 162.00 (978-0-321-61336-3(8)) Addison Wesley.

—Intermediate Algebra. 11th ed. 2010. (ENG.). 448p. (C). pap. 36.67 (978-0-321-61375-2(9)) Addison-Wesley Longman, Inc.

—Intermediate Algebra. 11th ed. 2010. tchr. ed. (978-0-321-61369-1(4)) Pearson Education.

—Intermediate Algerba. 11th ed. 2010. (ENG.). (C). pap., pap. 172.00 (978-0-321-71455-8(5)) Addison Wesley.

—Introductory Algebra. 11th ed. 2010. (ENG.). (C). pap., pap. 172.00 (978-0-321-62440-6(8)); 840p. ring bd. 97.20 (978-0-321-65444-1(7)); 432p. pap. 36.67 (978-0-321-64070-3(5)) Addison Wesley.

—Introductory Algebra, Books a la Carte Plus MathXL 12-month Student Access Kit. 11th ed. 2010. (ENG.). (C). pap., ring bd. 104.67 (978-0-321-73491-4(2)) Addison Wesley.

Bittinger, Marvin L. & Beecher, Judith A. Developmental Mathematics. (Bittinger Developmental Mathematics Ser.). (ENG., Illus.). (C). 7th ed. 2007. 1344p. per. 176.00 (978-0-321-33192-2(3)) 8th rev. ed. 2010. 1280p. pap. 176.00 (978-0-321-73153-1(0)) Addison Wesley.

—Developmental Mathematics. 7th ed. 2007. (Illus.). xxxii, 1234p. (978-0-321-34830-2(3)) Addison-Wesley Longman, Inc.

—Developmental Mathematics: College Mathematics & Introductory Algebra. 7th ed. 2007. (MathXL Tutorials on CD Ser.). (ENG., Illus.). 1344p. (C). per. 176.00 (978-0-321-33191-5(5)) Addison Wesley.

—Developmental Mathematics: College Mathematics & Introductory Algebra. 8th ed. 2011. tchr. ed. **(978-0-321-73082-4(8))** Pearson Education.

—Introductory & Intermediate Algebra. 4th ed. 2010. (Bittinger Worktext Ser.). (ENG.). 1080p. (C). pap. 176.00 (978-0-321-61337-0(6)) Addison Wesley.

—Introductory & Intermediate Algebra. 4th ed. 2010. tchr. ed. (978-0-321-61360-8(0)) Pearson Education.

—Introductory & Intermediate Algebra, A la Carte Edition. 4th ed. 2010. (ENG.). 1080p. (C). ring bd. 105.60 (978-0-321-65428-1(5)) Addison Wesley.

—MyWorkBook for Developmental Mathematics. 8th rev. ed. 2011. (ENG.). 416p. (C). pap. 31.00 (978-0-321-73090-9(9)) Addison Wesley.

—Students Solutions Manual for Introductory & Intermediate Algebra. 4th ed. 2010. (ENG.). 528p. (C). pap. 36.67 (978-0-321-61362-2(7)) Addison-Wesley Longman, Inc.

Bittinger, Marvin L. & Ellenbogen, David. Prealgebra & Introductory Algebra. 3rd ed. 2011. tchr. ed. **(978-0-321-73171-5(9))** Pearson Education.

Bittinger, Marvin L. & Ellenbogen, David J. Elementary Algebra: Concepts & Applications. 8th ed. 2008. (Bittinger Concepts & Applications Ser.). (ENG., Illus.). 688p. (C). 168.00 (978-0-321-55717-9(4)) Addison Wesley.

—Elementary Algebra: Concepts & Applications. 2009. (978-0-321-55945-6(2)) Prentice Hall PTR.

—Elementary Algebra: Concepts & Applications Plus MyMathLab Student Access Kit. 8th ed. 2009. (ENG.). (C). pap. 178.00 (978-0-321-61615-9(4)) Addison Wesley.

—Graphing Calculator Manual for Calculus & Its Applications. 9th ed. 2007. (ENG.). 172p. (C). pap. 24.67 (978-0-321-45582-6(7)) Addison Wesley Higher Education.

—Intermediate Algebra: Concepts & Applications. 8th ed. 2009. (Bittinger Concepts & Applications Ser.). (ENG., Illus.). 840p. (C). 168.00 (978-0-321-55718-6(2)) Addison Wesley.

—Intermediate Algebra: Concepts & Applications. 8th ed. 2009. tchr. ed. (978-0-321-55947-0(9)) Pearson Education.

—Intermediate Algebra: Concepts & Applications, the MyMathLab Edition Package. 8th ed. 2010. (ENG.). (C). pap., spiral bd. 120.00 (978-0-321-64137-3(X)) Addison Wesley.

—Prealgebra & Introductory Algebra. 2nd ed. 2007. (Illus.). xxxi, 1370p. (978-0-321-34826-5(5)) Addison-Wesley Longman, Inc.

—Worksheets for Elementary Algebra: Concepts & Applications. 8th ed. 2009. (ENG.). 320p. (C). pap. 26.67 (978-0-321-59931-5(4)) Addison Wesley.

Bittinger, Marvin L. & Penna, Judith A. Basic College Mathematics: With Early Integers. 2nd ed. 2010. (ENG., Illus.). 672p. (C). ring bd. 97.20 (978-0-321-65441-0(2)) Addison Wesley.

—Basic College Mathematics with Early Integers. 2nd ed. 2010. (Bittinger Worktext Ser.). (ENG.). 816p. (C). pap. 162.00 (978-0-321-61341-7(4)) Addison Wesley

—Basic College Mathematics with Early Integers. 2nd ed. 2010. tchr. ed. (978-0-321-56171-8(6)) Pearson Education.

—Basic College Mathematics with Early Integers, Books a la Carte Plus MyMathLab/MyStatLab Student Access Kit. 2nd ed. 2010. (ENG.). (C). ring bd. 107.20 (978-0-321-75841-5(2)) Addison Wesley.

—Student Solutions Manual for Basic College Mathematics with Early Integers. 2nd ed. 2010. (ENG.). 360p. (C). pap. 36.67 (978-0-321-60544-3(6)) Addison-Wesley Longman, Inc.

Bittinger, Marvin L., et al. Algebra & Trigonometry: Graphs & Models. 4th ed. 2009. (ENG.). 1152p. (C). 187.33 (978-0-321-50112-7(8)) Addison Wesley.

—Algebra & Trigonometry - Precalculus: Graphs & Models. 4th ed. 2008. (ENG.). 432p. (C). pap. 36.67 (978-0-321-53197-1(3)) Addison Wesley.

—Books a la Carte Edition, Intermediate Algebra: Graphs & Models. 4th ed. 2011. (ENG.). (C). ring bd. 100.80 (978-0-321-74604-7(X)) Addison Wesley.

—College Algebra: Graphs & Models with Graphing Calculator Manual Package. 4th ed. 2007. (Bittinger Graphs & Models Ser.). (ENG.). 768p. (C). pap. 168.67 (978-0-321-53192-6(2)) Addison Wesley.

—Elementary & Intermediate Algebra. 3rd ed. 2007. (Illus.). xxx, 976p. (978-0-321-42293-4(7)) Addison-Wesley Longman, Inc.

—Elementary & Intermediate Algebra: Concepts & Applications. 5th ed. 2009. (ENG.). (C). 300p. pap. 36.67 (978-0-321-58623-0(9)); (Illus.). 1120p. 176.00 (978-0-321-55944-9(4)) Addison Wesley.

—Elementary & Intermediate Algebra: Concepts & Applications. 5th ed. 2009. (Illus.). tchr. ed. (978-0-321-56726-0(9)) Pearson Education.

—Elementary & Intermediate Algebra: Concepts & Applications Plus MyMathLab Student Access Kit. 5th ed. 2009. (ENG.). (C). pap. 186.00 (978-0-321-60967-0(0)) Addison Wesley.

—Graphing Calculator Manual for Algebra & Trigonometry: Graphs & Models. 4th ed. 2008. (ENG.). 176p. (C). pap. 24.67 (978-0-321-53198-8(1)) Addison Wesley.

—Graphing Calculator Manual for Elementary & Intermediate Algebra: Graphs & Models. 4th rev. ed. 2011. (ENG.). 144p. (C). pap. 24.67 (978-0-321-73726-7(1)) Pearson Education.

—Graphing Calculator Manual for Intermediate Algebra: Graphs & Models. 4th rev. ed. 2011. (ENG.). 144p. (C). pap. 24.67 (978-0-321-74515-6(9)) Pearson Education.

—Intermediate Algebra: Graphs & Models. 3rd ed. 2007. (978-0-321-42855-4(2)) Addison-Wesley Longman, Inc.

—Intermediate Algebra: Graphs & Models, Books a la Carte Plus MML/MSL Student Access Kit (for ad hoc Valuepacks) 4th ed. 2011. (ENG.). (C). ring bd. 110.80 (978-0-321-77186-5(9)) Addison Wesley.

—Intermediate Algebra: Graphs & Models plus MyMathLab/MyStatLab Student Access Code Card. 4th ed. 2011. (ENG.). (C). pap. 178.00 (978-0-321-76015-9(8)) Addison Wesley.

—MyWorkBook for Prealgebra & Introductory Algebra. 3rd rev. ed. 2011. (ENG.). 300p. (C). pap. 31.00 (978-0-321-73176-0(X)) Addison Wesley.

—Prealgebra. 5th ed. 2007. (978-0-321-33712-2(3)) Addison-Wesley Longman, Inc.

—Prealgebra & Introductory Algebra. 3rd rev. ed. 2011. (ENG., Illus.). 1408p. (C). pap. 176.00 (978-0-321-73163-0(8)) Addison Wesley.

—Prealgebra & Introductory Algebra, Books a la Carte Edition. 3rd ed. 2011. (ENG.). (C). ring bd. 105.60 (978-0-321-73178-4(6)) Addison Wesley.

—Precalculus: Graphs & Models & Graphing Calculator Manual Package. 5th rev. ed. 2012. (ENG.). 1152p. (C). pap. 187.33 **(978-0-321-79566-3(0))** Addison Wesley.

—Precalculus: Graphs & Models, Books a la Carte Edition. 5th ed. 2012. (ENG.). 1152p. (C). ring bd. 112.40 **(978-0-321-82485-1(7))** Addison Wesley.

—Precalculus, Books A la Carte Edition, Algebra & Trigonometry: Graphs & Models. 5th ed. 2012. (ENG.). 1056p. (C). ring bd. 112.40 **(978-0-321-79101-6(0))** Addison Wesley.

—Student Solutions Manual for Prealgebra & Introductory Algebra. 3rd ed. 2011. (ENG.). 648p. (C). pap. 36.67 (978-0-321-73169-2(7)) Pearson Education.

—Student's Solutions Manual for Intermediate Algebra: Graphs & Models. 4th rev. ed. 2011. (ENG.). 624p. (C). pap. 36.67 (978-0-321-72577-6(8)) Pearson Education.

Blair, Jamie, et al. Beginning Algebra. 7th ed. 2008. (Tobey/Slater/Blair Developmental Mathematics Ser.). (ENG.). 736p. (C). pap. 162.00 (978-0-321-57375-9(7), Prentice Hall) Prentice Hall PTR.

—Beginning Algebra. 8th rev. ed. 2011. (ENG.). 720p. (C). pap. 162.00 **(978-0-321-76952-7(X))** Addison Wesley.

—Beginning Algebra, Books a la Carte Edition with MML/MSL Student Access Kit (for ad hoc Valuepacks) 2nd ed. 2011. (ENG.). (C) ring bd. 107.20 **(978-0-321-79037-8(5))** Addison Wesley.

—Beginning & Intermediate Algebra. 3rd ed. 2009. (Tobey/Slater/Blair Developmental Mathematics Ser.). (ENG.). 976p. (C). pap. 176.00 (978-0-321-58796-1(0), Prentice Hall) Prentice Hall PTR.

—Beginning & Intermediate Algebra. 4th rev. ed. 2012. (ENG.). 912p. (C). pap. 178.00 **(978-0-321-78053-9(1))** Addison Wesley.

—Prealgebra. 4th ed. 2008. (978-0-321-57690-3(X)) Pearson Prentice Hall.

—Prealgebra. 4th ed. 2008. (Tobey/Slater/Blair Developmental Mathematics Ser.). (ENG.). 784p. (C) pap. 162.00 (978-0-321-56793-2(5), Prentice Hall) Prentice Hall PTR.

—Student Solutions Manual for Beginning Algebra. 7th ed. 2009. (ENG.). 312p. (C). pap. 36.67 (978-0-321-57376-6(5), Prentice Hall) Prentice Hall PTR.

—Worksheets for Classroom or Lab Practice for Beginning Algebra. 7th ed. 2009. (ENG.). 168p. (C). pap. 26.67 (978-0-321-58950-7(5), Prentice Hall) Prentice Hall PTR.

—Worksheets for Classroom or Lab Practice for Prealgebra. 4th ed. 2009. (ENG.). 144p. (C). pap. 26.67 (978-0-321-58839-5(3), Prentice Hall) Prentice Hall PTR.

Blitzer. Precalculus. 2nd ed. stu. ed. 83.97 (978-0-13-191845-0(1)); 1248p. tchr. ed. 83.97 (978-0-13-101475-6(7)) Prentice Hall (Schl. Div.).

Blitzer & Elitzer, Robert F. Algebra & Trigonometry: An Early Functions Approach Plus MyMathLab/MyStatLab Student Access Code Card. 2nd ed. 2010. (ENG.). (C). pap. 197.33 (978-0-321-74445-6(4)) Addison Wesley.

—College Algebra: An Early Functions Approach Plus MyMathLab/MyStatLab Student Access Code Card. 2nd ed. 2010. (ENG.). (C). pap. 178.67 (978-0-321-74462-3(4)) Addison Wesley.

Blitzer & Cram101 Textbook Reviews Staff. College Algebr. 2007. 180p. per. 12.95 (978-1-4288-3632-7(2)) Cram101 Inc.

—Introductory Algebra for College Students. 2007. 120p. per. 11.95 (978-1-4288-3548-1(2)) Cram101 Inc.

Blitzer, Robert. Precalculus. 4th ed. 2010. (Illus.). xviii, 1087p. (J). (978-0-13-136221-5(6)) Prentice Hall PTR.

Blitzer, Robert F. Algebra & Trigonometry. 4th ed. 2008. (ENG.). 1200p. (C). 187.33 (978-0-321-55985-2(1), Prentice Hall) Prentice Hall PTR.

—Algebra & Trigonometry: An Early Functions Approach. 2nd ed. 2010. (ENG.). (C) ring bd. 112.40 (978-0-321-65644-5(X)) Addison Wesley.

—Algebra & Trigonometry: An Early Functions Approach. 2nd ed. 2009. (ENG.). 1216p. (C). 187.33 (978-0-321-58870-8(3), Prentice Hall) Prentice Hall PTR.

—Algebra & Trigonometry: An Early Functions Approach, Books a la Carte Edition plus MyMathLab (ad hoc for national Valuepacks) 2nd ed. 2011. (ENG.). (C). ring bd 122.40 **(978-0-321-79135-1(5))** Addison Wesley.

—Algebra for College Students. 7th rev. ed. 2012. (ENG.). 1072p. (C). 168.00 (978-0-321-75892-7(7)) Addison Wesley.

—Algebra for College Students. 6th ed. 2008. (Blitzer Developmental Algebra Ser.). (ENG., Illus.). 1056p. (C). 168.67 (978-0-13-601974-9(9), Prentice Hall) Prentice Hall PTR.

—Algebra for College Students, Books a la Carte Edition. 7th ed. 2012. (ENG.). 1056p. (C). ring bd. 100.80 **(978-0-321-76064-7(6))** Addison Wesley.

—Algebra for College Students, Books a la Carte Edition plus MyMathLab Student Access Kit. 2012. (ENG.). (C). ring bd. 110.80 **(978-0-321-83210-8(9))** Addison Wesley.

—Algebra for College Students plus MyMathLab Student Access Kit. 2012. (ENG.). (C). 178.00 **(978-0-321-83771-4(1))** Addison Wesley.

—Algebra for College Students Plus MyMathLab Student Access Kit. 6th ed. 2010. (ENG.). (C). pap. 178.67 (978-0-321-75197-3(3)) Addison Wesley.

—College Algebra. 5th ed. 2008. (ENG.). 848p. (C). 168.67 (978-0-321-55983-8(5), Prentice Hall) Prentice Hall PTR.

—College Algebra: An Early Functions Approach. 2nd ed. 2009. (ENG.). 864p. (C). 168.67 (978-0-321-58797-8(9), Prentice Hall) Prentice Hall PTR.

—College Algebra: International Edition. 4th ed. 2007. 832p. pap. incl. cd-rom (978-0-321-55214-3(8)) 5th ed. 2010. (Illus.). 848p. pap. incl. cd-rom (978-0-321-60940-3(9)) Prentice Hall PTR.

—College Algebra Essentials. 3rd ed. 2008. (ENG.). 640p. (C). 130.67 (978-0-321-57781-8(7), Prentice Hall) Prentice Hall PTR.

—Intermediate Algebra for College Students. 5th ed. 2007. (Blitzer Developmental Algebra Ser.). (ENG., Illus.). 960p. (C). 168.00 (978-0-13-600762-3(7), Prentice Hall) Prentice Hall PTR.

—Intermediate Algebra for College Students. 6th rev. ed. 2011. (ENG.). 976p. (C). 168.00 (978-0-321-75893-4(5)) Addison Wesley.

—Intermediate Algebra for College Students, Books a la Carte Edition. 6th ed. 2012. (ENG.). 992p. (C). ring bd. 100.80 **(978-0-321-76040-1(9))** Addison Wesley.

—Intermediate Algebra for College Students, Books a la Carte Edition plus MyMathLab Student Access Kit. 2012. (ENG.). (C). ring bd. 110.80 **(978-0-321-72928-6(5))** Addison Wesley.

—Intermediate Algebra for College Students, MyMathLab Edition. 5th ed. 2008. (ENG.). 572p. (C). spiral bd. 57.33 (978-0-13-601132-3(2)) Addison Wesley.

—Intermediate Algebra for College Students Plus MyMathLab Student Access Kit. 5th ed. 2010. (ENG.). (C). pap. 178.00 (978-0-321-74706-8(2)) Addison Wesley.

—Introductory Algebra for College Students. 6th rev. ed. 2012. (ENG.). 288p. (C). pap. 26.67 **(978-0-321-76047-0(6))** Addison Wesley.

—Introductory Algebra for College Students. 5th ed. 2007. (Blitzer Developmental Algebra Ser.). (ENG., Illus.). 752p. (C). 168.00 (978-0-13-235679-4(1), Prentice Hall) Prentice Hall PTR.

—Introductory Algebra for College Students. 6th rev. ed. 2011. (ENG.). 768p. (C). 168.00 (978-0-321-75895-8(1)) Addison Wesley.

—Introductory Algebra for College Students, Books a la Carte Edition plus MyMathLab Student Access Kit. 2012. (ENG.). (C). ring bd. 110.80 **(978-0-321-82817-0(8))** Addison Wesley.

—Introductory Algebra for College Students Plus MyMathLab Student Access Kit. 5th ed. 2010. (ENG.). (C). pap. 178.00 (978-0-321-74709-9(7)) Addison Wesley.

—Introductory & Intermediate Algebra for College Students. 3rd ed. 2008. (Blitzer Developmental Algebra Ser.). (ENG., Illus.). 1152p. (C). 176.00 (978-0-13-602895-6(0), Prentice Hall) Prentice Hall PTR.

—Introductory & Intermediate Algebra for College Students. 4th rev. ed. 2012 (ENG.). 1184p. (C). 176.00 (978-0-321-75894-1(3)) Addison Wesley.

—Introductory & Intermediate Algebra for College Students. 4th rev. ed. 2012. (ENG.). 394p. (C). pap. 26.67 **(978-0-321-75607-7(X))** Addison Wesley.

—Introductory & Intermediate Algebra for College Students, Books A la Carte Edition. 4th ed. 2012. (ENG.). 1184p. (C). ring bd. 105.60 **(978-0-321-75608-4(8))** Addison Wesley.

—Introductory & Intermediate Algebra for College Students, Books a la Carte Edition plus MyMathLab Student Access Kit. 2012. (ENG.). (C). ring bd. 116.67 **(978-0-321-72937-8(4))** Addison Wesley.

—Introductory & Intermediate Algebra for College Students plus MyMathLab Student Access Kit. rev. ed. 2012. (ENG.). (C). 186.00 **(978-0-321-72938-5(2))** Addison Wesley.

—Introductory & Intermediate Algebra for College Students Plus MyMathLab Student Access Kit. 3rd ed. 2010. (ENG.). (C). pap. 186.00 (978-0-321-74713-6(5)) Addison Wesley.

—The Learning Guide for Intermediate Algebra for College Students. 6th rev. ed. 2012. (ENG.). 300p. (C). pap. 26.67 **(978-0-321-76042-5(5))** Addison Wesley.

—Precalculus. 4th ed. 2009. (ENG., Illus.). 1232p. (C). 187.33 (978-0-321-55984-5(3), Prentice Hall) Prentice Hall PTR.

—Precalculus Essentials. 3rd ed. 2009. (ENG.). 832p. (C). 148.00 (978-0-321-59403-7(7), Prentice Hall) Prentice Hall PTR.

—Student Solutions Manual for Precalculus. 4th ed. 2009. (ENG.). 984p. (C). pap. 36.67 (978-0-321-57532-6(6), Prentice Hall) Prentice Hall PTR.

—Student's Solutions Manual for Algebra & Trigonometry. 4th ed. 2009. (ENG.). 500p. (C). pap. 36.67 (978-0-321-57544-9(X), Prentice Hall) Prentice Hall PTR.

—Worksheets for Classroom or Lab Practice. 5th ed. 2008. (ENG.). 152p. (C). pap. 26.67 (978-0-13-603164-2(1), Prentice Hall) Prentice Hall PTR.

Bobrow, Jerry. CliffsNotes Algebra I Quick Review. 2nd ed. 2011. (ENG., Illus.). 224p. pap. 9.99 (978-0-470-88028-9(7), Cliff Notes) Wiley, John & Sons, Inc.

Bocher, Maxime. Introduction to Higher Algebra. 321p. reprint ed. lib. bdg. (978-0-7222-3038-1(9)) Library Reprints, Inc.

Bojarski, Bogdan, et al, eds. C*-algebras & Elliptic Theory. 2006. (Trends in Mathematics Ser.). ix, 327p. 139.00 (978-3-7643-7686-4(4), 3764376864) Birkhauser Boston.

Bonfiglioli, Andrea & Fulci, Roberta. Topics in Noncommutative Algebra: The Theorem of Campbell, Baker, Hausdorff & Dynkin. 2011. (Lecture Notes in Mathematics Ser.). (ENG., Illus.). xxii, 539p. pap. 119.00 **(978-3-642-22596-3(9)**, 3642225969) Springer.

Bonnycastle, John. Bonnycastle's Introduction to Algebra; Containing the Indeterminate & Diophantine Analysis, & the Application of Algebra to Geometry Revised, Cor. 2006. 292p. per. 23.99 (978-1-4255-2613-9(6)) MPublishing.

Borkotokey, Surajit. Advanced Topics in Fuzzy Algebr. 2010. 96p. pap. (978-3-639-26400-5(2)) VDM Verlag Dr. Mueller e.K.

Boulabiar, Karim, et al, eds. Positivity. 2007. (Trends in Mathematics Ser.). 279p. 169.00 (978-3-7643-8477-7(8)) Birkhauser Verlag AG CHE. Dist: Springer.

Bowen, K. A. Model Theory for Modal Logic: Kripke Models for Modal Predicate Calculi. 2010. (Synthese Library). 137p. pap. 149.00 (978-90-481-8353-1(7), 9048183537) Springer.

Bowen, Ray M. & Wang, C. -C. Introduction to Vectors & Tensors, 2 vols. in 1. 2nd ed. 2009. (Dover Books on Mathematics Ser.). (ENG.). 560p. pap. 24.95 (978-0-486-46914-0(X)) Dover Pubns., Inc.

Bracken, Laura & Miller, Ed. Elementary Algebra. 2011. (Textbooks Available with Cengage YouBook Ser.). (ENG.). (C). 832p. pap. 90.95 (978-1-111-57409-3(X)); Vol. 2. 160p. pap. 14.95 (978-1-111-98785-5(8)) Brooks/Cole.

—Intermediate Algebra: Class Test Edition. 2011. (Textbooks Available with Cengage YouBook Ser.). (ENG.). 992p. (C). pap. 90.95 (978-1-111-57410-9(3)) Brooks/Cole.

—Intermediate Algebra, Volume 2, Chapters 6-8. 2011. (ENG.). 272p. (C). pap. 14.95 (978-1-111-98787-9(4)) Brooks/Cole.

Bradley, Teresa. Essential Mathematics for Economics & Business, 2 vols. 3rd ed. 2008. (ENG., Illus.). 682p. pap. 74.95 (978-0-470-01856-9(9), Wiley) Wiley, John & Sons, Inc.

Breitenbach, Jerome R. A Mathematics Companion for Science & Engineering Students. 2007. (ENG.). 496p. (C). pap. 34.95 (978-0-19-532775-5(6)) Oxford Univ. Pr., Inc.

Brown & Dolciani & Sorgenfrey & Cole & Cram101 Textbook Reviews Staff. Algebr: Structure & Method Book 1. 2007. 104p. per. 10.95 (978-1-4288-3496-5(6)) Cram101 Inc.

Brown, Susan, et al. Algebra, Volume 1: Chapters 1-6. 2007. (Illus.). 395p. 73.32 (978-0-07-611033-9(8)) McGraw-Hill Cos., The.

—UCSMP Algebra, Volume 2: Chapters 7-13. 2007. (Illus.). 73.32 (978-0-07-615932-1(9)) McGraw-Hill Cos., The.

Brundan, Jonathan & Kleshchëv, A. S. Representations of Shifted Yangians & Finite W-Algebras. 2008. (Memoirs of the American Mathematical Society Ser.). 107p. pap. 65.00 (978-0-8218-4216-4(1)) American Mathematical Society.

Buckley, Michael. Algebra. Saddleback Educational Publishing Staff, ed. 2011. (Mathskills Ser.). (ENG.). 108p. (gr. 6-12). tchr. ed. 39.95 incl. cd-rom **(978-1-61651-505-8(8))** Saddleback Educational Publishing.

—Algebra 2. Saddleback Educational Publishing Staff, ed. 2011. (Mathskills Ser.). (ENG.). 107p. (gr. 6-12). tchr. ed. 39.95 incl. cd-rom **(978-1-61651-507-2(4))** Saddleback Educational Publishing.

—Pre-Algebra. Saddleback Educational Publishing, ed. 2011. (Mathskills Ser.). (ENG.). 109p. (gr. 6-12). tchr. ed. 39.95 incl. cd-rom **(978-1-61651-504-1(X))** Saddleback Educational Publishing.

Bueso, J. L., et al. Algorithmic Methods in Non-Commutative Algebra: Applications to Quantum Groups. 2010. (Mathematical Modelling: Theory & Applications Ser.). 298p. pap. 129.00 (978-90-481-6328-1(5), 9048163285) Springer.

Burger, Christopher James, et al. Pre-Calculus for Dummies. 2008. (ENG., Illus.). 408p. pap. 19.99 (978-0-470-16984-1(2), For Dummies) Wiley, John & Sons, Inc.

Butkovic, Peter. Max-linear Systems: Theory & Algorithms. 2010. (Springer Monographs in Mathematics Ser.). (Illus.). xvii, 275p. 99.00 (978-1-84996-298-8(7), 1849962987) Springer.

Cambridge. New Basic Skills Math Algebra (978-0-8359-4650-6(9)) Cambridge Adult Education.

Cao, Tian Yu. From Current Algebra to Quantum Chromodynamics: A Case for Structural Realism. 2010. (ENG.). 318p. 85.00 (978-0-521-88933-9(2)) Cambridge Univ. Pr.

Carlson, Marilyn P. & Oehrtman, Michael. Precalculus: A Problems Solving Approach. 2nd ed. 2011. (Illus.). 343p. (C). pap. 89.95 **(978-0-9845795-1-8(6))** Rational Reasoning, LLC.

Carson, Tom. Prealgebra, Books a la Carte Edition plus MyMathLab Student Access Kit. 2012. (ENG.). (C). ring bd. 107.20 **(978-0-321-82815-6(1))** Addison Wesley.

—Prealgebra plus MyMathLab Student Access Kit. 2012. (ENG.). (C). pap., pap. 172.00 **(978-0-321-82816-3(X))** Addison Wesley.

Carson, Tom. Worksheets for Classroom or Lab Practice for Prealgebra. 3rd ed. 2008. (ENG.). 288p. (C). pap. 26.67 (978-0-321-53008-0(X)) Addison Wesley Higher Education.

Carson, Tom & Jordan, Bill. Elementary & Intermediate Algebra. 3rd ed. 2010. (ENG., Illus.). 1008p. (C). ring bd. 116.67 (978-0-321-66567-6(8)) Addison Wesley.

—Intermediate Algebra. 3rd ed. 2010. (ENG.). 792p. (C). ring bd. 100.00 *(978-0-321-66551-5(1))* Addison Wesley.

Carson, Tom & Jordan, Bill E. Elementary Algebra. 3rd ed. 2010. (ENG.). (C). 832p. ring bd. 100.80 *(978-0-321-66563-8(5))*; (Illus.). pap. 178.00 *(978-0-321-62438-3(6))* Addison Wesley.

—Elementary & Intermediate Algebra, A la Carte with MML/MSL Student Access Kit (adhoc for Valuepacks) 3rd ed. 2010. (ENG.). (C). ring bd. 126.67 *(978-0-321-70592-1(0))* Addison Wesley.

—Intermediate Algebra. 3rd ed. 2010. (ENG., Illus.). (C). pap. 178.00 *(978-0-321-70897-7(0))* Addison Wesley.

Carson, Tom, et al. Elementary Algebra. 3rd ed. 2010. (Carson Algebra Ser.). (ENG.). 832p. (C). 168.00 *(978-0-321-57729-0(9))* Addison Wesley.

—Elementary & Intermediate Algebra. 3rd ed. 2010. (Carson Algebra Ser.). (ENG., Illus.). 1008p. (C). 176.00 *(978-0-321-62109-2(3))* Addison Wesley.

—Intermediate Algebra. 3rd ed. 2010. (Carson Algebra Ser.). (ENG.). 792p. (C). 168.00 *(978-0-321-60711-9(2))* Addison Wesley.

—Student's Solutions Manual for Elementary & Intermediate Algebra. 3rd ed. 2010. (ENG.). 504p. (C). pap. 36.67 *(978-0-321-62734-6(2))* Addison-Wesley Longman, Inc.

Cattaneo, Alberto S., et al, eds. Higher Structures in Geometry & Physics: In Honor of Murray Gerstenhaber & Jim Stasheff. 2010. (Progress in Mathematics Ser.). (ENG., Illus.). xv, 362p. 124.00 *(978-0-8176-4734-6(1)*, 0817647341) Birkhauser Verlag AG CHE. Dist: Springer.

Cerebellum Academic Team. Light Speed Algebra: The Powers & Functions. 2010. (Light Speed Ser.). cd-rom 14.98 *(978-1-58565-436-9(1))* Cerebellum Corp.

Chadick, Kathleen M., et al. Beginning Algebra. 2nd rev. ed. 2010. (ENG.). 274p. pap. 57.44 *(978-0-7575-2118-8(5)*, 0757521185) Kendall Hunt Publishing Co.

Chapman, Scott T. & Coykendall, Jim. Factorization Problems in Integral Domains & Monoids. 2009. 300p. 139.95 *(978-1-57444-601-2(0)*, DK3855) Taylor & Francis Group.

Cherlin, G. Model Theoretic Algebr. 2008. (Lecture Notes in Mathematics Ser.). 240p. pap. 59.95 *(978-3-540-07696-4(4))* Springer.

Childs, Lindsay. A Concrete Introduction to Higher Algebra. 3rd ed. 2009. (Illus.). xiv, 603p. *(978-0-387-74725-5(7))* Springer.

Childs, Lindsay N. A Concrete Introduction to Higher Algebra. 3rd ed. (Undergraduate Texts in Mathematics Ser.). (Illus.). 2010. (ENG.). xiv, 603p. pap. 69.95 *(978-1-4419-2561-9(9)*, 1441925619) 2008. 570p. 69.95 *(978-0-387-74527-5(0))* Springer.

Chlouveraki, Maria. Blocks & Families for Cyclotomic Hecke Algebras. 2009. (Lecture Notes in Mathematics Ser.). (ENG.). xiii, 166p. pap. 49.95 *(978-3-642-03063-5(7)*, 3642030637) Springer.

Christy, Dennis T., et al. Algebra & Trigonometry for College Students, 2E. 2nd ed. 2008. (ENG.). (C). 117.33 *(978-0-558-05803-6(5))* Pearson Learning Solutions.

Clark, John, et al. Lifting Modules: Supplements & Projectivity in Module Theory. 2006. (Frontiers in Mathematics Ser.). (Illus.). xii, 394p. pap. 69.95 *(978-3-7643-7572-0(8)*, 3764375728) Birkhauser Boston.

Clark, Mark & Anfinson, Cynthia. Beginning Algebra: Concepts Through Applications. 2011. (Textbooks Available with Cengage YouBook Ser.). (ENG.). 944p. (C). 168.95 *(978-0-534-41938-7(0))* Brooks/Cole.

—Cengage Advantage Books: Beginning Algebra: Connecting Concepts through Applications. 2011. (ENG.). 944p. (C). ring bd. 113.95 *(978-1-111-56929-7(0))* Brooks/Cole.

—Cengage Advantage Books: Intermediate Algebra: Connecting Concepts through Applications. 2011. (ENG.). 976p. (C). pap. 113.95 *(978-1-111-56912-9(6))* Brooks/Cole.

—Intermediate Algebra: Connecting Concepts Through Applications. 2011. (Textbooks Available with Cengage YouBook Ser.). (ENG.). (C). 976p. 151.95 *(978-0-534-49636-4(9))*; 414p. pap., wbk. ed. 39.95 *(978-1-111-56889-4(8))* Brooks/Cole.

Clark, Mark, et al. Intermediate Algebra 2010. 2010. (ENG.). 944p. (C). pap. 81.95 *(978-0-538-49872-2(2))* Brooks/Cole.

Close-Punzalan. High School Algebra: A First Course. rev. ed. 2011. (ENG.). 746p. pap. 115.00 ***(978-0-7575-9333-8(X))*** Kendall Hunt Publishing Co.

Coburn. Prealgebra. Date not set. (C). pap. *(978-0-03-032244-0(8))* Dryden Pr.

Coburn, John. Algebra & Trigonometry. 2nd ed. 2009. (ENG.). 1152p. (C). 185.67 *(978-0-07-727651-5(5)*, 0077276515, McGraw-Hill Science, Engineering & Mathematics) McGraw-Hill Higher Education.

—College Algebra. 2nd ed. 2009. (ENG.). 864p. (C). 166.00 *(978-0-07-727649-2(3)*, 0077276493, McGraw-Hill Science, Engineering & Mathematics) McGraw-Hill Higher Education.

—Loose Leaf Version for Algebra & Trigonometry. 2nd ed. 2009. (ENG.). (C). ring bd. 108.13 *(978-0-07-734365-1(4)*, 0077343654, McGraw-Hill Science, Engineering & Mathematics) McGraw-Hill Higher Education.

—Loose Leaf Version for College Algebra. 2nd ed. 2009. (ENG.). (C). ring bd. 116.33 *(978-0-07-736663-6(8)*, 0077366638, McGraw-Hill Science, Engineering & Mathematics) McGraw-Hill Higher Education.

—Loose Leaf Version for College Algebra Essentials. 2nd ed. 2009. (ENG.). (C). ring bd., ring bd. 94.00 *(978-0-07-736656-8(5)*, 0077366565); ring bd. 75.31 *(978-0-07-734366-8(2)*, 0077343662) McGraw-Hill Higher Education. (McGraw-Hill Science, Engineering & Mathematics).

—Student Solutions Manual Algebra & Trigonometry. 2nd ed. 2009. (ENG.). 672p. (C). pap. 55.67 *(978-0-07-723506-2(1)*, 0077235061, McGraw-Hill Science, Engineering & Mathematics) McGraw-Hill Higher Education.

—Student Solutions Manual for College Algebra. 2nd ed. 2009. (ENG.). 480p. (C). pap. 68.33 *(978-0-07-334907-7(0)*, 0073349070, McGraw-Hill Science, Engineering & Mathematics) McGraw-Hill Higher Education.

—Student Solutions Manual t/a College Algebra Essentials. 2nd ed. 2009. (ENG.). 316p. (C). pap. 51.33 *(978-0-07-729197-6(2)*, 0077291972, McGraw-Hill Science, Engineering & Mathematics) McGraw-Hill Higher Education.

Coburn, John & Herdlick, J. D. (John). Package: College Algebra - Graphs & Models with Connect Plus Access Card. 2011. (ENG.). (C). 175.00 *(978-0-07-747570-3(4)*, 0077475704, McGraw-Hill Science, Engineering & Mathematics) McGraw-Hill Higher Education.

Coburn, John W. Algebra & Trigonometry. 2nd ed. 2009. *(978-0-07-351952-4(9))* McGraw-Hill Cos., The.

—College Algebra. 2nd ed. 2009. *(978-0-07-351941-8(3))*; *(978-0-07-334903-9(8))* McGraw-Hill Cos., The.

—College Algebra. 2007. (C). 139.38 *(978-0-07-330542-4(1)*, 9780073305424, McGraw-Hill Science, Engineering & Mathematics) McGraw-Hill Higher Education.

—College Algebra Essentials. 2nd ed. 2010. (Illus.). xxxvii, 555p. *(978-0-07-729201-0(4))* 2009. *(978-0-07-351968-5(5))* McGraw-Hill Cos., The.

—College Algebra Essentials. 2nd ed. 2009. (ENG.). (C). 134.00 *(978-0-07-729790-9(3)*, 0077297903, McGraw-Hill Science, Engineering & Mathematics) McGraw-Hill Higher Education.

Coecke, Bob, ed. New Structures for Physics. 2010. (Lecture Notes in Physics Ser.). (Illus.). xviii, 1000p. pap. 159.00 *(978-3-642-12820-2(3)*, 3642128203) Springer.

Cohen, A. Algorithms in Algebra. 2008. (London Mathematical Society Student Texts: Vol. 30). (Illus.). 250p. (C). pap. 22.95 *(978-0-521-43630-4(3))* Cambridge Univ. Pr.

Cohen, David. College Algebra. 5th ed. 2010. (ENG.). 1p. (C). ring bd. 83.95 *(978-1-111-57889-3(3))* Brooks/Cole.

Cohen, David, et al. Precalculus: A Problems-Oriented Approach. 6th ed. 2009. (Available 2010 Titles Enhanced Web Assign Ser.). (ENG.). 1216p. (C). 208.95 *(978-1-4390-4460-5(0))* Brooks/Cole.

The Concise Handbook of Algebra. 2006. pap. 189.00 *(978-1-4020-0636-4(5)*, 1402006365) Springer.

Connally. College Algebra & Trigonometry. 2014. (ENG.). (C). pap., stu. ed. 32.95 *(978-0-471-70619-9(1)*, Wiley) Wiley, John & Sons, Inc.

Connally & Hughes-Hallett, Deborah. College Algebra. 2nd ed. 2008. (C). pap., stu. ed. 32.95 *(978-0-471-71334-0(1))* Wiley, John & Sons, Inc.

Connally, Eric, et al. Algebra: Form & Function. 2009. (ENG., Illus.). 576p. (C). 159.95 *(978-0-471-70708-0(2)*, Wiley) Wiley, John & Sons, Inc.

Consortium for Foundation Mathematics Staff. Mathematics in Action: Algebraic, Graphical & Trigonometric Problem Solving, Books a la Carte Plus MML/MSL Student Access Kit (for ad hoc Valuepacks) 4th ed. 2010. (ENG.). (C). ring bd. 110.80 *(978-0-321-77183-4(4))* Addison Wesley.

—Mathematics in Action: Algebraic, Graphical, & Trigonometric Problem Solving plus MyMathLab/MyStatLab Student Access Code Card. 4th ed. 2011. (ENG.). (C). pap., pap. 178.00 ***(978-0-321-76005-0(0))*** Addison Wesley.

Consortium for Foundation Mathematics Staff. Worksheets for Classroom or Lab Practice for Mathematics in Action: Algebraic, Graphical, & Trigonometric Problem Solving. 4th rev. ed. 2011. (ENG.). 200p. (C). pap. 26.67 *(978-0-321-73835-6(7))* Pearson Education.

Consortium for Foundation Mathematics Staff, contrib. by. Mathematics in Action. 4th ed. 2010. tchr. ed. *(978-0-321-69290-0(X))* Pearson Education.

—Mathematics in Action: Algebraic, Graphical, & Trigonometric Problem Solving. 4th rev. ed. 2010. (ENG.). 792p. (C). pap. 168.00 *(978-0-321-69861-2(4))* Addison Wesley.

—Mathematics in Action: Algebraic, Graphical, & Trigonometric Problem Solving. 3rd ed. 2007. *(978-0-321-44483-7(3))* Addison-Wesley Longman, Inc.

Consumer Dummies. Algebra II & Geometry Essentials for Dummies Bundle. 2011. (ENG.). pap. 19.98 ***(978-1-118-16144-9(0)***, For Dummies) Wiley, John & Sons, Inc.

Conway, John Horton & Mathematics. Regular Algebra & Finite Machines. 2012. (Dover Books on Mathematics Ser.). (ENG.). 160p. pap. 9.95 ***(978-0-486-48583-6(8))*** Dover Pubns., Inc.

Cook, Jane Warner. Alpha Teach Yourself Algebra I in 24 Hours. 2011. (ENG.). 416p. (gr. 12). 18.95 *(978-1-61564-019-5(3)*, Alpha Bks.) Penguin Group (USA) Inc.

Cooke, Roger. Classical Algebra: Its Nature, Origins, & Uses. 2008. (ENG., Illus.). 224p. per. 68.99 *(978-0-470-25952-8(3)*, Wiley-Interscience) Wiley, John & Sons, Inc.

Corradini, Andrea, et al, eds. Algebra & Coalgebra in Computer Science: 4th International Conference, CALCO 2011, Winchester, UK, August 30 - September 2, 2011, Proceedings. 2011. (Lecture Notes in Computer Science / Theoretical Computer Science & General Issues Ser.). (ENG., Illus.). xi, 420p. pap. 95.00 ***(978-3-642-22943-5(3)***, 3642229433) Springer.

Corso, Alberto, et al, eds. Algebra, Geometry & Their Interactions. 2007. (Contemporary Mathematics Ser.). (Illus.). 270p. (C). pap. 81.00 *(978-0-8218-4094-8(0))* American Mathematical Society.

Cram101 Textbook Reviews. Outlines & Highlights for a Graphical Approach to Algebra & Trigonometry by John Hornsby. 2011. 304p. pap. 32.95 ***(978-1-61905-100-3(1))*** Cram101 Inc.

—Outlines & Highlights for Algebr: Introductory & Intermediate. 2011. 312p. pap. 33.95 ***(978-1-61905-140-9(0))*** Cram101 Inc.

—Outlines & Highlights for Algebra & Number Theory: An Integrated Approach by Martyn Dixon. 2011. 278p. pap. 32.95 ***(978-1-61905-134-8(6))*** Cram101 Inc.

—Outlines & Highlights for Algebra & Trigonometry: Real Mathematics, Real People by Ron Larson. 2011. 302p. pap. 32.95 ***(978-1-61905-149-2(4))*** Cram101 Inc.

—Outlines & Highlights for Algebra & Trigonometry by Cynthia y Young, Isbn: 9780471756835. 2010. 208p. pap. 30.95 *(978-1-61698-046-7(X))* Cram101 Inc.

—Outlines & Highlights for Algebra & Trigonometry by Earl W Swokowski. 2011. 288p. pap. 32.95 ***(978-1-61905-101-0(X))*** Cram101 Inc.

—Outlines & Highlights for Algebra & Trigonometry by James Stewart. 2011. 338p. pap. 33.95 ***(978-1-61905-147-8(8))*** Cram101 Inc.

—Outlines & Highlights for Algebra & Trigonometry by Judith a Beecher. 2011. 356p. pap. 34.95 ***(978-1-61905-160-7(5))*** Cram101 Inc.

—Outlines & Highlights for Algebra & Trigonometry by Ron Larson. 2011. 276p. pap. 32.95 ***(978-1-61905-148-5(6))*** Cram101 Inc.

—Outlines & Highlights for Algebra & Trigonometry by Sheldon Axler. 2011. 196p. pap. 30.95 ***(978-1-61905-122-5(2))*** Cram101 Inc.

—Outlines & Highlights for Algebra by Michael Artin. 2011. 404p. pap. 35.95 ***(978-1-61905-158-4(3))*** Cram101 Inc.

—Outlines & Highlights for Algebra for College Students by Margaret L Lial. 2011. 318p. pap. 33.95 ***(978-1-61905-150-8(8))*** Cram101 Inc.

—Outlines & Highlights for Algebra for College Students by Richard N Aufmann, Isbn: 9780618824946. 2010. 148p. pap. 29.95 *(978-1-61698-047-4(8))* Cram101 Inc.

—Outlines & Highlights for Beginning Algebr: A Text/Workbook by Charles P. Mckeague. 2011. 112p. pap. 28.95 ***(978-1-61905-145-4(1))*** Cram101 Inc.

—Outlines & Highlights for Beginning Algebr: Connecting Concepts Through Applications by Mark Clark. 2011. 188p. pap. 30.95 ***(978-1-61905-113-3(3))*** Cram101 Inc.

—Outlines & Highlights for Beginning Algebr: Non-Media Edition by R. David Gustafson, ISBN. 2010. 106p. pap. 28.95 *(978-1-61698-044-3(3))* Cram101 Inc.

—Outlines & Highlights for Beginning Algebra, 9th Edition by R David Gustafson. 2011. 192p. pap. 30.95 ***(978-1-61905-144-7(3))*** Cram101 Inc.

—Outlines & Highlights for Beginning Algebra by Julie Miller. 2011. 184p. pap. 29.95 ***(978-1-61905-115-7(X))*** Cram101 Inc.

—Outlines & Highlights for Beginning Algebra by Margaret L Lial. 2011. 206p. pap. 30.95 ***(978-1-61905-141-6(9))*** Cram101 Inc.

—Outlines & Highlights for Beginning Algebra by Sherri Messersmith. 2011. 240p. pap. 31.95 ***(978-1-61905-110-2(9))*** Cram101 Inc.

—Outlines & Highlights for Beginning & Intermediate Algebra by Julie Miller. 2011. 274p. pap. 32.95 ***(978-1-61905-146-1(X))*** Cram101 Inc.

—Outlines & Highlights for Beginning & Intermediate Algebra by Margaret L Lial. 2011. 300p. pap. 32.95 ***(978-1-61905-152-2(4))*** Cram101 Inc.

—Outlines & Highlights for Beginning & Intermediate Algebra by Sherri Messersmith. 2011. 296p. pap. 32.95 ***(978-1-61905-116-4(8))*** Cram101 Inc.

—Outlines & Highlights for Classical Algebr: Its Nature, Origins, & Uses by Roger Cooke. 2011. 126p. pap. 28.95 ***(978-1-61905-015-0(3))*** Cram101 Inc.

—Outlines & Highlights for College Algebr: Concepts & Contexts by James Stewart. 2011. 144p. pap. 28.95 ***(978-1-61905-019-8(6))*** Cram101 Inc.

—Outlines & Highlights for College Algebr: Graphing Approach by Ron Larson, ISBN. 2010. 186p. pap. 29.95 *(978-1-61654-622-9(0))* Cram101 Inc.

—Outlines & Highlights for College Algebr: Graphs & Models. 2011. 270p. pap. 32.95 ***(978-1-61905-001-3(3))*** Cram101 Inc.

—Outlines & Highlights for College Algebr: Real Mathematics, Real People by Ron Larson. 2011. 216p. pap. 30.95 ***(978-1-61905-002-0(1))*** Cram101 Inc.

—Outlines & Highlights for College Algebra & Trigonometry: A Unit Circle Approach by Mark Dugopolski. 2011. 314p. pap. 33.95 ***(978-1-61830-999-0(4))*** Cram101 Inc.

—Outlines & Highlights for College Algebra & Trigonometry by J S Ratti. 2011. 322p. pap. 33.95 ***(978-1-61830-930-3(7))*** Cram101 Inc.

—Outlines & Highlights for College Algebra & Trigonometry by Richard N Aufmann. 2011. 286p. pap. 32.95 ***(978-1-61905-017-4(X))*** Cram101 Inc.

—Outlines & Highlights for College Algebra by Dennis G Zill. 2011. 254p. pap. 31.95 ***(978-1-61905-018-1(8))*** Cram101 Inc.

—Outlines & Highlights for College Algebra by Michael Sullivan. 2011. 210p. pap. 30.95 ***(978-1-61905-050-1(1))*** Cram101 Inc.

—Outlines & Highlights for College Algebra by Raymond Barnett. 2011. 230p. pap. 31.95 ***(978-1-61905-033-4(1))*** Cram101 Inc.

—Outlines & Highlights for College Algebra by Raymong a Barnett. 2011. 236p. pap. 31.95 ***(978-1-61905-046-4(3))*** Cram101 Inc.

—Outlines & Highlights for College Algebra by Ron Larson. 2011. 226p. pap. 30.95 ***(978-1-61905-045-7(5))*** Cram101 Inc.

—Outlines & Highlights for College Algebra by Sheldon Axler. 2011. 140p. pap. 28.95 ***(978-1-61905-011-2(0))*** Cram101 Inc.

—Outlines & Highlights for College Algebra by William G Mccallum. 2011. 104p. pap. 28.95 ***(978-1-61905-035-8(8))*** Cram101 Inc.

—Outlines & Highlights for Developmental Mathematics by Marvin L Bittinger. 2011. 318p. pap. 33.95 ***(978-1-61830-157-4(8))*** Cram101 Inc.

—Outlines & Highlights for Elementary Algebra by Charles P Mckeague. 2011. 118p. pap. 28.95 ***(978-1-4672-7239-1(6))***; 114p. pap. 28.95 ***(978-1-61905-034-1(X))*** Cram101 Inc.

—Outlines & Highlights for Elementary Algebra by Jerome E Kaufmann. 2011. 126p. pap. 28.95 ***(978-1-61905-005-1(6))*** Cram101 Inc.

—Outlines & Highlights for Elementary Algebra by Tom Carson. 2011. 166p. pap. 29.95 ***(978-1-61905-020-4(X))*** Cram101 Inc.

—Outlines & Highlights for Elementary Algebra for College Students by Allen R Angel. 2011. 202p. pap. 30.95 ***(978-1-61830-992-1(7))*** Cram101 Inc.

—Outlines & Highlights for Elementary Algebra Person Acad Notebook by Academic Sys Academic Sys. 2011. 238p. pap. 31.95 ***(978-1-61812-164-6(2))*** Cram101 Inc.

—Outlines & Highlights for Elementary & Intermediate Algebr: A Combined Approach by Jerome E. Kaufmann. 2011. 164p. pap. 29.95 ***(978-1-61905-006-8(4))*** Cram101 Inc.

—Outlines & Highlights for Elementary & Intermediate Algebra by Charles P Mckeague. 2011. 140p. pap. 28.95 ***(978-1-61905-008-2(0))*** Cram101 Inc.

—Outlines & Highlights for Elementary & Intermediate Algebra by George Woodbury. 2011. 296p. pap. 32.95 ***(978-1-61830-991-4(9))*** Cram101 Inc.

—Outlines & Highlights for Elementary & Intermediate Algebra by Lehmann. 2011. 236p. pap. 31.95 ***(978-1-61830-965-5(X))*** Cram101 Inc.

—Outlines & Highlights for Elementary & Intermediate Algebra by Mark Dugopolski. 2011. 326p. pap. 33.95 ***(978-1-4672-6691-8(4))*** Cram101 Inc.

—Outlines & Highlights for Elementary & Intermediate Algebra by Tom Carson. 2011. 194p. pap. 30.95 ***(978-1-61905-003-7(X))*** Cram101 Inc.

—Outlines & Highlights for Elementary & Intermediate Algebra for College Students by Allen R Angel. 2011. 330p. pap. 33.95 ***(978-1-61830-931-0(5))*** Cram101 Inc.

—Outlines & Highlights for Essentials of College Algebra by Gary K Rockswold. 2011. 200p. pap. 30.95 ***(978-1-61830-996-9(X))*** Cram101 Inc.

—Outlines & Highlights for Essentials of College Algebra by Margaret L Lial. 2011. 162p. pap. 29.95 ***(978-1-61905-014-3(5))*** Cram101 Inc.

—Outlines & Highlights for Explorations in College Algebra by Linda Almgren Kime. 2011. 162p. pap. 29.95 ***(978-1-61830-932-7(3))*** Cram101 Inc.

—Outlines & Highlights for Film by Phillips. 2011. 352p. pap. 33.95 ***(978-1-61812-914-7(7))*** Cram101 Inc.

—Outlines & Highlights for Intermediate Algebr: Application. . Paperback Student Support Edition by Richard N. Aufmann, ISBN. 2010. 182p. pap. 29.95 *(978-1-61698-059-7(1))* Cram101 Inc.

—Outlines & Highlights for Intermediate Algebr: Concepts & Applications by Bittinger, ISBN. 2010. 126p. pap. 28.95 *(978-1-61698-057-3(5))* Cram101 Inc.

—Outlines & Highlights for Intermediate Algebr: Connecting Concepts through Applications by Mark Clark. 2011. 214p. pap. 30.95 ***(978-1-4672-6594-2(2))*** Cram101 Inc.

—Outlines & Highlights for Intermediate Algebr: Graphs & Models by Marvin L. Bittinger. 2011. 202p. pap. 30.95 ***(978-1-4672-6590-4(X))*** Cram101 Inc.

—Outlines & Highlights for Intermediate Algebr: Hybrid by Jerome E. Kaufmann. 2011. 146p. pap. 29.95 ***(978-1-4672-1982-2(7))*** Cram101 Inc.

—Outlines & Highlights for Intermediate Algebra by Charles P Mckeague. 2011. 162p. pap. 29.95 ***(978-1-4672-6584-3(5))*** Cram101 Inc.

—Outlines & Highlights for Intermediate Algebra by Elayn Martin-Gay. 2011. 258p. pap. 31.95 ***(978-1-4672-6585-0(3))*** Cram101 Inc.

—Outlines & Highlights for Intermediate Algebra by Margaret L Lial. 2011. 260p. pap. 31.95 ***(978-1-4672-6578-2(0))*** Cram101 Inc.

—Outlines & Highlights for Intermediate Algebra by Marvin L Bittinger. 2011. 190p. pap. 30.95 ***(978-1-4672-6593-5(4))*** Cram101 Inc.

—Outlines & Highlights for Intermediate Algebra by Sherri Messersmith. 2011. 278p. pap. 32.95 ***(978-1-4672-6579-9(9))*** Cram101 Inc.

—Outlines & Highlights for Intermediate Algebra by Tom Carson. 2011. 180p. pap. 29.95 ***(978-1-4672-6580-5(2))*** Cram101 Inc.

—Outlines & Highlights for Introductory Algebra by Elayn Martin-Gay. 2011. 176p. pap. 29.95 ***(978-1-4672-6156-2(4))*** Cram101 Inc.

—Outlines & Highlights for Introductory Algebra by Ignacio Bello. 2011. 130p. pap. 28.95 ***(978-1-4672-2467-3(7))*** Cram101 Inc.

—Outlines & Highlights for Introductory Algebra by Marvin L Bittinger. 2011. 150p. pap. 29.95 ***(978-1-4672-6587-4(X))*** Cram101 Inc.

—Outlines & Highlights for Introductory & Intermediate Algebra by Marvin L Bittinger. 2011. 250p. pap. 31.95 ***(978-1-4672-2606-6(8))*** Cram101 Inc.

—Outlines & Highlights for Mathematics in Action: Algebraic, Graphical, & Trigonometric Problem Solving by Consortium for Foundation Mathematics. 2011. 174p. pap. 29.95 ***(978-1-61830-189-5(6))*** Cram101 Inc.

—Outlines & Highlights for Prealgebra & Introductory Algebra by Marvin L Bittinger. 2011. 352p. pap. 33.95 ***(978-1-4672-6577-5(2))*** Cram101 Inc.

—Outlines & Highlights for Prealgebra by Jamie Blair, Isbn: 9780321567932 0321567935. 2011. 198p. pap. 30.95 ***(978-1-4288-5370-6(7))*** Cram101 Inc.

—Outlines & Highlights for Precalculus: Mathematics for Calculus, Enhanced Review Edition by James Stewart. 2010. 416p. pap. 35.95 *(978-1-4288-5074-3(0))* Cram101 Inc.

—Outlines & Highlights for Precalculus, Enhanced Webassign Edition by James Stewart. 2010. 456p. pap. 36.95 *(978-1-4288-5279-2(4))* Cram101 Inc.

—Outlines & Highlights for Tensors: The Mathematics of Relativity Theory & Continuum Mechanics by Anadi Jiban Das. 2011. 192p. pap. 30.95 ***(978-1-61830-121-5(7))*** Cram101 Inc.

Cram101 Textbook Reviews. Outlines & Highlights for Understanding Intermediate Algebr: A Course for College Students by Lewis R. Hirsch, Arthur Goodman, ISBN. 2010. 110p. pap. 28.95 *(978-1-61698-841-8(X))* Cram101 Inc.

Cram101 Textbook Reviews Staff. Outlines & Highlights for Algebr: Beginning & Intermediate, Multimedia Edition by Richard N. Aufmann, Joanne Lockwood, Vernon C. Barker, ISBN. 2009. 122p. pap. 28.95 *(978-1-4288-3730-0(2))* Cram101 Inc.

—Outlines & Highlights for Algebr: Combined Approach by Martin-Gay, K. Elayn, ISBN. 2009. 96p. pap. 27.95 *(978-1-4288-3793-5(0))* Cram101 Inc.

—Outlines & Highlights for Algebr: Introductory & Intermediate by Richard N. Aufmann, ISBN. 2009. 138p. pap. 28.95 *(978-1-4288-2039-5(6))* Cram101 Inc.
—Outlines & Highlights for Algebra & Trigonometry: A Graphing Approach, Enhanced Edition by Larson, ISBN. 2009. 244p. pap. 31.95 *(978-1-4288-2935-0(0))*; 194p. pap. 30.95 *(978-1-4288-8458-8(0))* Cram101 Inc.
—Outlines & Highlights for Algebra & Trigonometry: An Early Functions Approach by Blitzer, ISBN. 2009. 342p. pap. 33.95 *(978-1-4288-2937-4(7))*; 302p. pap. 32.95 *(978-1-4288-8650-6(8))* Cram101 Inc.
—Outlines & Highlights for Algebra & Trigonometry: Graphing Approach by Ron Larson, ISBN. 2009. 160p. pap. 29.95 *(978-1-4288-2077-7(9))* Cram101 Inc.
—Outlines & Highlights for Algebra & Trigonometry by Blitzer, Isbn: 9780321559852. 2009. 238p. pap. 31.95 *(978-1-4288-8461-8(0))* Cram101 Inc.
—Outlines & Highlights for Algebra & Trigonometry by Coburn, Isbn: 9780077276515. 2009. 346p. pap. 33.95 *(978-1-4288-2873-5(7))* Cram101 Inc.
—Outlines & Highlights for Algebra & Trigonometry by Judith a Beecher, Isbn: 9780321466204. 2009. 260p. pap. 31.95 *(978-1-4288-3549-8(0))* Cram101 Inc.
—Outlines & Highlights for Algebra & Trigonometry by Michael Sullivan, Isbn: 9780132329033. 2009. 230p. pap. 31.95 *(978-1-4288-9654-3(6))* Cram101 Inc.
—Outlines & Highlights for Algebra & Trigonometry by Young, Isbn: 9780470222737. 2009. 224p. pap. 30.95 *(978-1-4288-2931-2(8))*; 198p. pap. 30.95 *(978-1-4288-8460-1(2))* Cram101 Inc.
—Outlines & Highlights for Algebra & Trigonometry, Enhanced Edition by Stewart, Redlin, & Watson, Isbn: 9781439047309. 2009. 272p. pap. 32.95 *(978-1-4288-2933-6(4))*; 216p. pap. 30.95 *(978-1-4288-8459-5(9))* Cram101 Inc.
—Outlines & Highlights for Algebra & Trigonometry Enhanced with Graphing Utilities by Michael Sullivan, Isbn: 9780131527393. 2009. 316p. pap. 33.95 *(978-1-4288-3571-9(7))* Cram101 Inc.
—Outlines & Highlights for Algebra & Trigonometry Enhanced with Graphing Utilities by Michael Sullivan, Isbn: 9780136004929. 2009. 336p. pap. 33.95 *(978-1-4288-3577-1(6))* Cram101 Inc.
—Outlines & Highlights for Algebra & Trigonometry with Analytic Geometry by Earl W Swokowski, Jeffery a Cole, Isbn: 9780495108269. 2009. 266p. pap. 31.95 *(978-1-4288-3593-1(8))* Cram101 Inc.
—Outlines & Highlights for Algebra & Trigonometry with Analytic Geometry, Classic Edition by Earl Swokowski, Jeffery a Cole, Isbn: 9780495559719. 2009. 250p. pap. 31.95 *(978-1-4288-2677-9(7))* Cram101 Inc.
—Outlines & Highlights for Algebra & Trigonometry with Modeling & Visualization by Gary K Rockswold, Isbn: 9780321568014. 2009. 234p. pap. 31.95 *(978-1-4288-2681-6(5))*; 230p. pap. 31.95 *(978-1-4288-8727-5(X))* Cram101 Inc.
—Outlines & Highlights for Algebra for College Students by Allen R Angel, Isbn: 9780136129080. 2009. 134p. pap. 28.95 *(978-1-4288-2015-9(9))* Cram101 Inc.
—Outlines & Highlights for Algebra for College Students by Blitzer, Isbn: 9780136019749. 2009. 200p. pap. 30.95 *(978-1-4288-2923-7(7))*; 192p. pap. 30.95 *(978-1-4288-7804-4(1))* Cram101 Inc.
—Outlines & Highlights for Algebra for College Students by Jerome E Kaufmann, Karen L Schwitters, Isbn: 9780495105107. 2009. 156p. pap. 29.95 *(978-1-4288-3735-5(3))*; 96p. pap. 27.95 *(978-1-4288-7664-4(2))* Cram101 Inc.
—Outlines & Highlights for Algebra for College Students by Margaret L Lial, John Hornsby, Terry Mcginnis, Isbn: 9780321442543. 2009. 162p. pap. 29.95 *(978-1-4288-3780-5(9))* Cram101 Inc.
—Outlines & Highlights for Algebra for College Students by Mark Dugopolski, Isbn: 9780077224844. 2009. 158p. pap. 29.95 *(978-1-4288-3736-2(1))* Cram101 Inc.
—Outlines & Highlights for Aufmann Introductory Algebra Paperback Student Support Edition by Richard N Aufmann, Joanne Lockwood, Vernon C Barker, Isb. 2009. 126p. pap. 28.95 *(978-1-4288-3722-5(1))* Cram101 Inc.
—Outlines & Highlights for Basic Mathematical Skills with Geometry by Donald Hutchison, Isbn: 9780073309590. 2009. 128p. pap. 28.95 *(978-1-4288-3896-3(1))* Cram101 Inc.
—Outlines & Highlights for Basic Mathematical Skills with Geometry by Hutchison Isbn. 2007. pap. 9.95 *(978-1-4288-5726-1(5))* Cram101 Inc.
—Outlines & Highlights for Beginning Algebra by Aufmann Isbn: 0618803599. 2008. 60p. per. 9.95 *(978-1-4288-5793-3(1))* Cram101 Inc.
—Outlines & Highlights for Beginning Algebra by Kaufmann & Schwitters, Isbn: 9780495388210. 2009. 68p. pap. 27.95 *(978-1-4288-2941-1(5))*; 64p. pap. 27.95 *(978-1-4288-8456-4(4))* Cram101 Inc.
—Outlines & Highlights for Beginning Algebra by Margaret L Lial, Isbn: 9780321437266. 2009. 114p. pap. 28.95 *(978-1-4288-3744-7(2))* Cram101 Inc.
—Outlines & Highlights for Beginning Algebra by Martin-Gay, Isbn: 9780136007029. 2009. 88p. pap. 27.95 *(978-1-4288-3808-6(2))* Cram101 Inc.
—Outlines & Highlights for Beginning Algebra by Miller, Isbn. 2007. pap. 9.95 *(978-1-4288-5729-2(X))* Cram101 Inc.
—Outlines & Highlights for Beginning Algebra by Stefan Baratto, Isbn: 9780073309606. 2009. 94p. pap. 27.95 *(978-1-4288-2065-4(5))* Cram101 Inc.
—Outlines & Highlights for Beginning Algebra by Tobey, Isbn: 9780321573759. 2009. 92p. pap. 27.95 *(978-1-4288-7605-7(7))* Cram101 Inc.
—Outlines & Highlights for Beginning Algebra with Applications & Visualization by Gary K Rockswold, Terry a Krieger, Isbn: 9780321500045. 2009. 96p. pap. 27.95 *(978-1-4288-3786-7(8))* Cram101 Inc.
—Outlines & Highlights for Beginning & Intermediate Algebr: Building a Foundation by Mckenna, ISBN. 2009. 116p. pap. 28.95 *(978-1-4288-2817-9(6))*; 100p. pap. 27.95 *(978-1-4288-7617-0(0))* Cram101 Inc.
—Outlines & Highlights for Beginning & Intermediate Algebra by Elayn Martin-Gay, Isbn: 9780136007319. 2009. 138p. pap. 28.95 *(978-1-4288-7660-6(X))* Cram101 Inc.
—Outlines & Highlights for Beginning & Intermediate Algebra by John Tobey, Isbn: 9780131492035. 2009. 110p. pap. 28.95 *(978-1-4288-2011-1(6))* Cram101 Inc.
—Outlines & Highlights for Beginning & Intermediate Algebra by Margaret L Lial, John Hornsby, Terry Mcginnis, Isbn: 9780321442338. 2009. 160p. pap. 29.95 *(978-1-4288-3778-2(7))* Cram101 Inc.
—Outlines & Highlights for Beginning & Intermediate Algebra by Miller Isbn. 2007. pap. 9.95 *(978-1-4288-5730-8(3))* Cram101 Inc.
—Outlines & Highlights for Beginning & Intermediate Algebra by R David Gustafson, Peter D Frisk, Isbn: 9780495117933. 2009. 142p. pap. 28.95 *(978-1-4288-3776-8(0))* Cram101 Inc.
—Outlines & Highlights for Beginning & Intermediate Algebra by Tobey & Slater, Isbn: 9780321587961. 2009. 106p. pap. 28.95 *(978-1-4288-2939-8(3))*; 58p. pap. 26.95 *(978-1-4288-8457-1(2))* Cram101 Inc.
—Outlines & Highlights for Beginning & Intermediate Algebra with Applications & Visualization by Gary K Rockswold, Isbn: 9780321500052. 2009. 124p. pap. 28.95 *(978-1-4288-3772-0(8))* Cram101 Inc.
—Outlines & Highlights for College Algebr: An Early Functions Approach by Gail Bcushey, ISBN. 2009. 160p. pap. 29.95 *(978-1-4288-1945-0(2))* Cram101 Inc.
—Outlines & Highlights for College Algebr: An Early Functions Approach by Robert F. Blitzer, ISBN. 2009. 186p. pap. 30.95 *(978-1-4288-2679-3(3))*; 122p. pap. 28.95 *(978-1-4288-8728-2(8))* Cram101 Inc.
—Outlines & Highlights for College Algebr: Building Concepts & Connections by Revathi Narasimhan, ISBN. 2009. 116p. pap. 28.95 *(978-1-4288-2623-6(8))* Cram101 Inc.
—Outlines & Highlights for College Algebr: Concepts & Models by Ron Larson, Robert P. Hostetler, Anne V. Hodgkins, ISBN. 2009. 90p. pap. 27.95 *(978-1-4288-3762-1(0))* Cram101 Inc.
—Outlines & Highlights for College Algebr: Early Functions by Robert F. Blitzer, ISBN. 2009. 176p. pap. 29.95 *(978-1-4288-1961-0(4))* Cram101 Inc.
—Outlines & Highlights for College Algebr: Enhanced Edition by Aufmann, Barker, Nation, ISBN. 2009. 176p. pap. 29.95 *(978-1-4288-2857-5(5))*; 126p. pap. 28.95 *(978-1-4288-8652-0(4))* Cram101 Inc.
—Outlines & Highlights for College Algebra & Calculus: An Applied Approach by Larson, ISBN. 2009. 238p. pap. 31.95 *(978-1-4288-7807-5(6))* Cram101 Inc.
—Outlines & Highlights for College Algebra & Trigonometry: Building Concepts & Connections by Narasimhan, ISBN. 2009. 170p. pap. 29.95 *(978-1-4288-2875-9(3))*; 146p. pap. 29.95 *(978-1-4288-8465-6(3))* Cram101 Inc.
—Outlines & Highlights for College Algebra & Trigonometry by Aufmann, Richard N / Barker, Vernon C / Nation, Richard D , Isbn: 9780618825158. 2009. 256p. pap. 31.95 *(978-1-4288-3539-9(3))* Cram101 Inc.
—Outlines & Highlights for College Algebra & Trigonometry by J S Ratti, Isbn: 9780321296429. 2009. 232p. pap. 31.95 *(978-1-4288-1995-5(9))* Cram101 Inc.
—Outlines & Highlights for College Algebra & Trigonometry by Margaret L Lial, David I Schneider, John Hornsby, Isbn: 9780321497444. 2009. 236p. pap. 31.95 *(978-1-4288-7669-9(3))* Cram101 Inc.
—Outlines & Highlights for College Algebra by Coburn, Isbn: 0072901195. 2007. 92p. per. 10.95 *(978-1-4288-5725-4(7))* Cram101 Inc.
—Outlines & Highlights for College Algebra by Coburn, Isbn: 9780077276492. 2009. 146p. pap. 29.95 *(978-1-4288-2823-0(0))*; 112p. pap. 28.95 *(978-1-4288-7612-5(X))* Cram101 Inc.
—Outlines & Highlights for College Algebra by Coburn, John W , Isbn: 9780073229829. 2009. 152p. pap. 29.95 *(978-1-4288-1965-8(7))* Cram101 Inc.
—Outlines & Highlights for College Algebra by Dugopolski, Mark, Isbn: 9780321356918. 2009. 88p. pap. 27.95 *(978-1-4288-2943-5(1))*; 74p. pap. 27.95 *(978-1-4288-8649-0(4))* Cram101 Inc.
—Outlines & Highlights for College Algebra by Gustafson, Frisk, & Hughes, Isbn: 9780495558880. 2009. 148p. pap. 29.95 *(978-1-4288-2835-3(4))*; 124p. pap. 28.95 *(978-1-4288-7606-4(5))* Cram101 Inc.
—Outlines & Highlights for College Algebra by James Stewart, Lothar Redlin, Saleem Watson, Isbn: 9780495565215. 2009. 148p. pap. 29.95 *(978-1-4288-2737-0(4))*; 114p. pap. 28.95 *(978-1-4288-7916-4(1))* Cram101 Inc.
—Outlines & Highlights for College Algebra by Jerome E Kaufmann, Isbn: 9780495554035. 2009. 102p. pap. 27.95 *(978-1-4288-2713-4(7))*; 82p. pap. 27.95 *(978-1-4288-7921-8(8))* Cram101 Inc.
—Outlines & Highlights for College Algebra by Judith a Beecher, Isbn: 9780321466075. 2009. 112p. pap. 28.95 *(978-1-4288-3755-3(8))* Cram101 Inc.
—Outlines & Highlights for College Algebra by Larson, Ron / Hostetler, Robert P , Isbn: 9780618643103. 2009. 114p. pap. 28.95 *(978-1-4288-3805-5(8))* Cram101 Inc.
—Outlines & Highlights for College Algebra by Margaret L Lial, Isbn: 9780321499134. 2009. 122p. pap. 28.95 *(978-1-4288-2241-2(0))* Cram101 Inc.
—Outlines & Highlights for College Algebra by Michael Sullivan, Isbn: 9780132402866. 2009. 184p. pap. 29.95 *(978-1-4288-3741-6(8))* Cram101 Inc.
—Outlines & Highlights for College Algebra by R David Gustafson, Isbn: 9780495110767. 2009. 124p. pap. 28.95 *(978-1-4288-2303-7(4))*; 132p. pap. 28.95 *(978-1-4288-9908-7(1))* Cram101 Inc.
—Outlines & Highlights for College Algebra by Ratti, Mcwaters, Isbn: 9780321296443. 2009. 136p. pap. 28.95 *(978-1-4288-1963-4(0))* Cram101 Inc.
—Outlines & Highlights for College Algebra by Raymond a Barnett, Isbn: 9780073312620. 2009. 82p. pap. 27.95 *(978-1-4288-1967-2(3))* Cram101 Inc.
—Outlines & Highlights for College Algebra by Robert F Blitzer, Isbn: 9780132191418. 2009. 178p. pap. 29.95 *(978-1-4288-3746-1(9))* Cram101 Inc.
—Outlines & Highlights for College Algebra by Robert F Blitzer, Isbn: 9780321559838. 2009. 146p. pap. 29.95 *(978-1-4288-1991-7(6))* Cram101 Inc.
—Outlines & Highlights for College Algebra by William G Mccallum, Isbn: 9780470226667. 2009. 70p. pap. 27.95 *(978-1-4288-2093-7(0))* Cram101 Inc.
—Outlines & Highlights for College Algebra Enhanced Graphing Utilities by Michael Sullivan, Isbn. 9780136004912. 2009. 150p. pap. 29.95 *(978-1-4288-3773-7(6))* Cram101 Inc.
—Outlines & Highlights for College Algebra Essentials by Coburn & Leaf, Isbn: 9780077366568. 2009. 130p. pap. 28.95 *(978-1-4288-2855-1(9))*; 106p. pap. 28.95 *(978-1-4288-7539-9(9))* Cram101 Inc.
—Outlines & Highlights for College Algebra Essentials by Robert F Blitzer, Isbn: 9780132203135. 2009. 142p. pap. 28.95 *(978-1-4288-2417-1(0))* Cram101 Inc.
—Outlines & Highlights for College Algebra in Context with Applications for the Managerial, Life, & Social Sciences by Harshbarger, Isbn: 97803215706. 2009. 116p. pap. 28.95 *(978-1-4288-2879-7(6))* Cram101 Inc.
—Outlines & Highlights for College Algebra with Applications for Business & Life Sciences by Ron Larson, Anne V Hodgkins, Isbn: 9780547052694. 2009. 144p. pap. 28.95 *(978-1-4288-3753-9(1))* Cram101 Inc.
—Outlines & Highlights for College Algebra with Modeling & Visualization & Access Kit by Gary Rockswold, Isbn: 9780321290076. 2009. 128p. pap. 28.95 *(978-1-4288-2699-1(8))*; 102p. pap. 27.95 *(978-1-4288-7932-4(3))* Cram101 Inc.
—Outlines & Highlights for College Algebra with Modeling & Visualization by Rockswold, Gary K , Isbn: 9780321542304. 2009. 140p. pap. 28.95 *(978-1-4288-1957-3(6))* Cram101 Inc.
—Outlines & Highlights for College Algebra with Trigonometry by Barnett, Raymond / Ziegler, Michael / Byleen, Karl, Isbn: 9780073312644. 2009. 212p. pap. 30.95 *(978-1-4288-2767-7(6))*; 222p. pap. 30.95 *(978-1-4288-9036-7(X))* Cram101 Inc.
—Outlines & Highlights for College Algebra W/Modeling & Visualization by Gary K Rockswold, Isbn: 9780321279088. 2009. 106p. pap. 28.95 *(978-1-4288-3803-1(1))* Cram101 Inc.
—Outlines & Highlights for Developmental Mathematics: Basic Mathematics & Algebra by Lial, Hornsby, Mcginnis, andSalzman, ISBN. 2009. 196p. pap. 30.95 *(978-1-4288-2845-2(1))*; 158p. pap. 29.95 *(978-1-4288-7604-0(9))* Cram101 Inc.
—Outlines & Highlights for Developmental Mathematics by Elayn Martin-Gay, Isbn: 9780132290906. 2009. 156p. pap. 29.95 *(978-1-4288-3869-7(4))* Cram101 Inc.
—Outlines & Highlights for Elementary Algebr: Concepts & Applications by Bittinger, ISBN. 2009. 100p. pap. 27.95 *(978-1-4288-2893-3(1))*; pap. 27.95 *(978-1-4288-7820-4(3))* Cram101 Inc.
—Outlines & Highlights for Elementary Algebra by Bittinger & Ellenbogen, Isbn: 0201719657. 2009. 74p. pap. 27.95 *(978-1-4288-3959-5(3))* Cram101 Inc.
—Outlines & Highlights for Elementary Algebra by George Woodbury, Isbn: 9780321166425. 2009. 102p. pap. 28.95 *(978-1-4288-3769-0(8))* Cram101 Inc.
—Outlines & Highlights for Elementary Algebra by Jerome E Kaufmann, Isbn: 9780495105718. 2009. 60p. pap. 26.95 *(978-1-4288-3167-4(3))* Cram101 Inc.
—Outlines & Highlights for Elementary Algebra by Larson, Hostetler, Isbn: 9780547102276. 2009. 86p. pap. 27.95 *(978-1-4288-2859-9(1))*; 84p. pap. 27.95 *(978-1-4288-7598-2(0))* Cram101 Inc.
—Outlines & Highlights for Elementary Algebra by Mark Dugopolski, Isbn: 9780077224790. 2009. 124p. pap. 28.95 *(978-1-4288-2647-2(5))*; 110p. pap. 28.95 *(978-1-4288-8752-7(0))* Cram101 Inc.
—Outlines & Highlights for Elementary Algebra by Sullivan & Struve, Isbn: 9780321567482. 2009. 120p. pap. 28.95 *(978-1-4288-2847-6(8))*; 118p. pap. 28.95 *(978-1-4288-7600-2(6))* Cram101 Inc.
—Outlines & Highlights for Elementary Algebra by Tom Carson, Bill E Jordan, Ellyn Gillespie, Isbn: 9780321353370. 2009. 120p. pap. 28.95 *(978-1-4288-3721-8(3))* Cram101 Inc.
—Outlines & Highlights for Elementary Algebra Early Graphing for College Students by Allen R Angel, Richard Semmler, Aimee Calhoun, Donna R Petrie, I. 2009. 98p. pap. 27.95 *(978-1-4288-3763-8(9))* Cram101 Inc.
—Outlines & Highlights for Elementary Algebra for College Students by Allen R Angel, Isbn: 9780131994577. 2009. 92p. pap. 27.95 *(978-1-4288-2219-1(4))* Cram101 Inc.
—Outlines & Highlights for Elementary Algebra Student Support System by Ron Larson, Isbn: 9780618753536. 2009. 82p. pap. 27.95 *(978-1-4288-3143-8(6))* Cram101 Inc.
—Outlines & Highlights for Elementary & Intermediate Algebr: Concepts & Applications by Bittinger & Ellenbogen, ISBN. 2009. 164p. pap. 29.95 *(978-1-4288-2895-7(8))*; 148p. pap. 29.95 *(978-1-4288-7819-8(X))* Cram101 Inc.
—Outlines & Highlights for Elementary & Intermediate Algebr: Graphs & Models -with CD by Marvin L. Bittinger, ISBN. 2009. 130p. pap. 28.95 *(978-1-4288-3333-3(1))* Cram101 Inc.
—Outlines & Highlights for Elementary & Intermediate Algebra by Alan S Tussy, Isbn: 9780495389613. 2009. 66p. pap. 27.95 *(978-1-4288-9831-8(X))* Cram101 Inc.
—Outlines & Highlights for Elementary & Intermediate Algebra by Alan S Tussy, R David Gustafson, Isbn: 9780534419325. 2009. 114p. pap. 28.95 *(978-1-4288-3794-2(9))* Cram101 Inc.
—Outlines & Highlights for Elementary & Intermediate Algebra by Bittinger, Marvin / Ellenbogen, David / Johnson, B Bittinger, Marvin / Ellenbogen, D. 2009. 58p. pap. 26.95 *(978-1-4288-9806-6(9))*, Cram101 Inc.
—Outlines & Highlights for Elementary & Intermediate Algebra by Charles P Mckeague, Isbn: 9780495108511. 2009. 88p. pap. 27.95 *(978-1-4288-3781-2(7))* Cram101 Inc.
—Outlines & Highlights for Elementary & Intermediate Algebra by Craine, Timothy / Mcgowan, Jeffrey / Ruben, Thomas, Isbn: 9780618103379. 2009. 84p. pap. 27.95 *(978-1-4288-3337-1(4))* Cram101 Inc.
—Outlines & Highlights for Elementary & Intermediate Algebra by Hutchison, Baratto, & Bergman, Isbn: 0073309613. 2009. 172p. pap. 29.95 *(978-1-4288-3895-6(3))* Cram101 Inc.
—Outlines & Highlights for Elementary & Intermediate Algebra by Michael Sullivan III , Isbn: 9780131915053. 2009. 172p. pap. 29.95 *(978-1-4288-2175-0(9))* Cram101 Inc.
—Outlines & Highlights for Elementary & Intermediate Algebra by Michael Sullivan, Isbn: 9780321593092. 2009. 130p. pap. 28.95 *(978-1-4288-3131-5(2))* Cram101 Inc.
—Outlines & Highlights for Elementary & Intermediate Algebra by Stefan Baratto, Isbn: 9780073309316. 2009. 80p. pap. 27.95 *(978-1-4288-3175-9(4))* Cram101 Inc.
—Outlines & Highlights for Elementary & Intermediate Algebra for College Students by Allen R Angel, Richard Semmler, Aimee Calhoun, Isbn: 9780132337. 2009. 126p. pap. 28.95 *(978-1-4288-3724-9(8))* Cram101 Inc.
—Outlines & Highlights for Elementary Mathematics Modeling-Updated by Mary Ellen Davis, Isbn: 9780136154167. 2009. 64p. pap. 27.95 *(978-1-4288-3033-2(2))* Cram101 Inc.
—Outlines & Highlights for Explorations in College Algebra by Beverly K Michael, Judy Clark, Linda Almgren Kime, Isbn: 9780471916888. 2009. 142p. pap. 28.95 *(978-1-4288-3792-8(2))*; 110p. pap. 28.95 *(978-1-4288-7658-3(8))* Cram101 Inc.
—Outlines & Highlights for Fundamentals of College Algebra by Swokowski, Earl W / Cole, Jeffery a , Isbn: 9780534420864. 2009. 132p. pap. 28.95 *(978-1-4288-3802-4(3))* Cram101 Inc.
—Outlines & Highlights for Integrated Arith & Basic Algebra by Bill E Jordan, William P Palow, Isbn: 9780321442550. 2009. 118p. pap. 28.95 *(978-1-4288-3756-0(6))* Cram101 Inc.
—Outlines & Highlights for Intermediate Agebr: A Graphing Approach by Elayn Martin-Gay, Margaret Greene, ISBN. 2009. 106p. pap. 28.95 *(978-1-4288-3742-3(6))* Cram101 Inc.
—Outlines & Highlights for Intermediate Algebr: An Applied Approach by Aufmann, Richard N. / Barker, Vernon C. / Lockwood, Joanne S. , ISBN. 2009. 148p. pap. 29.95 *(978-1-4288-3791-1(4))* Cram101 Inc.
—Outlines & Highlights for Intermediate Algebr: Concepts & Applications by Marvin L. Bittinger, ISBN. 2009. 108p. pap. 28.95 *(978-1-4288-2573-4(8))*; 106p. pap. 28.95 *(978-1-4288-2355-6(7))*; 106p. pap. 28.95 *(978-1-4288-9106-7(4))*; 128p. pap. 28.95 *(978-1-4288-9801-1(8))* Cram101 Inc.
—Outlines & Highlights for Intermediate Algebr: Graphs & Models by Marvin L. Bittinger, ISBN. 2009. 106p. pap. 28.95 *(978-1-4288-3733-1(7))* Cram101 Inc.
—Outlines & Highlights for Intermediate Algebra by Alan S Tussy, R David Gustafson, Isbn: 9780495389736. 2009. 118p. pap. 28.95 *(978-1-4288-3734-8(5))* Cram101 Inc.
—Outlines & Highlights for Intermediate Algebra by Charles P Mckeague, Isbn: 9780495108405. 2009. 58p. pap. 26.95 *(978-1-4288-9889-9(1))* Cram101 Inc.
—Outlines & Highlights for Intermediate Algebra by Elayn Martin-Gay, Isbn: 9780131868304. 2009. 98p. pap. 27.95 *(978-1-4288-3743-0(4))* Cram101 Inc.
—Outlines & Highlights for Intermediate Algebra by Hutchison et Al , Isbn: 0073406139. 2009. 92p. pap. 27.95 *(978-1-4288-3899-4(6))* Cram101 Inc.
—Outlines & Highlights for Intermediate Algebra by Hutchison, Isbn: 0073406139. 2007. 60p. per. 9.95 *(978-1-4288-5724-7(9))* Cram101 Inc.

—Outlines & Highlights for Intermediate Algebra by Ignacio Bello, Isbn: 9780077224806. 2009. 88p. pap. 27.95 *(978-1-4288-2213-9(5))* Cram101 Inc.

—Outlines & Highlights for Intermediate Algebra by Jerome E Kaufmann, Isbn: 9780495105527. 2009. 88p. pap. 27.95 *(978-1-4288-2205-4(4))* Cram101 Inc.

—Outlines & Highlights for Intermediate Algebra by John Jr Tobey, Jeffrey Slater, Isbn: 9780131490789. 2009. 88p. pap. 27.95 *(978-1-4288-3745-4(0))* Cram101 Inc.

—Outlines & Highlights for Intermediate Algebra by John Tobey, Isbn: 9780131865877. 2009. 72p. pap. 27.95 *(978-1-4288-2693-9(9))*; 74p. pap. 27.95 *(978-1-4288-8712-1(1))* Cram101 Inc.

—Outlines & Highlights for Intermediate Algebra by John Tobey, Isbn: 9780321578297. 2009. 114p. pap. 28.95 *(978-1-4288-2385-3(9))* Cram101 Inc.

—Outlines & Highlights for Intermediate Algebra by Lehmann, Jay, Isbn: 9780131953338. 2009. 114p. pap. 28.95 *(978-1-4288-3720-1(5))* Cram101 Inc.

—Outlines & Highlights for Intermediate Algebra by Margaret L Lial, Isbn: 9780321279200. 2009. 140p. pap. 28.95 *(978-1-4288-3761-4(2))* Cram101 Inc.

—Outlines & Highlights for Intermediate Algebra by Mark Dugopolski, Isbn: 9780077224813. 2009. 182p. pap. 29.95 *(978-1-4288-2153-8(8))* Cram101 Inc.

—Outlines & Highlights for Intermediate Algebra by Martin-Gay, Elayn, Isbn: 9780321572110. 2009. 100p. pap. 27.95 *(978-1-4288-2369-3(7))* Cram101 Inc.

—Outlines & Highlights for Intermediate Algebra by Marvin L Bittinger, Isbn: 9780321319081. 2009. 114p. pap. 28.95 *(978-1-4288-2797-4(8))* Cram101 Inc.

—Outlines & Highlights for Intermediate Algebra by Michael Sullivan, Isbn: 9780321567529. 2009. 118p. pap. 28.95 *(978-1-4288-2579-6(7))*; 114p. pap. 28.95 *(978-1-4288-8874-6(8))* Cram101 Inc.

—Outlines & Highlights for Intermediate Algebra by Miller, Isbn: 0073312681. 2007. 60p. per. 9.95 *(978-1-4288-5728-5(1))* Cram101 Inc.

—Outlines & Highlights for Intermediate Algebra by Nancy Hyde, Isbn: 9780077304256. 2009. 138p. pap. 28.95 *(978-1-4288-2583-3(5))*; 124p. pap. 28.95 *(978-1-4288-8871-5(3))* Cram101 Inc.

—Outlines & Highlights for Intermediate Algebra by Rockswold, Isbn: 9780321500038. 2009. 118p. pap. 28.95 *(978-1-4288-3788-1(4))*; 112p. pap. 28.95 *(978-1-4288-7659-0(6))* Cram101 Inc.

—Outlines & Highlights for Intermediate Algebra by Ron Larson, Isbn: 9780547102177. 2009. 128p. pap. 28.95 *(978-1-4288-2581-9(9))*; 114p. pap. 28.95 *(978-1-4288-8873-9(X))* Cram101 Inc.

—Outlines & Highlights for Intermediate Algebra by Sullivan Isbn: 0131467735. 2008. 60p. per. 9.95 *(978-1-4288-5792-6(3))* Cram101 Inc.

—Outlines & Highlights for Intermediate Algebra by Sullivan, Struve, Isbn: 0131467735. 2009. 164p. pap. 29.95 *(978-1-4288-3887-1(2))* Cram101 Inc.

—Outlines & Highlights for Intermediate Algebra by Tom Carson, Bill E Jordan, Ellyn Gillespie, Isbn: 9780321358356. 2009. 120p. pap. 28.95 *(978-1-4288-3782-9(5))* Cram101 Inc.

—Outlines & Highlights for Intermediate Algebra by Woodbury, Isbn: 9780321166418. 2009. 92p. pap. 27.95 *(978-1-4288-3801-7(5))* Cram101 Inc.

—Outlines & Highlights for Intermediate Algebra by Wright, D Franklin, Isbn: 9780918091789. 2009. 180p. pap. 29.95 *(978-1-4288-2391-4(3))* Cram101 Inc.

—Outlines & Highlights for Intermediate Algebra by Yoshiwara, Katherine / Yoshiwara, Bruce, Isbn: 9780534358259. 2009. 86p. pap. 27.95 *(978-1-4288-3798-0(1))* Cram101 Inc.

—Outlines & Highlights for Intermediate Algebra for College Students by Allen R Angel, Isbn: 9780132383578. 2009. 122p. pap. 28.95 *(978-1-4288-2695-3(5))*; 106p. pap. 28.95 *(978-1-4288-8710-7(5))* Cram101 Inc.

—Outlines & Highlights for Intermediate Algebra for College Students by Robert F Blitzer, Isbn: 9780136007623. 2009. 172p. pap. 29.95 *(978-1-4288-3764-5(7))* Cram101 Inc.

—Outlines & Highlights for Intermediate Algebra Through Applications by Geoffrey Akst, Isbn: 9780321518019. 2009. 84p. pap. 27.95 *(978-1-4288-2533-8(9))*; pap. 27.95 *(978-1-4288-8923-1(X))* Cram101 Inc.

—Outlines & Highlights for Intermediate Algebra with Applications by Richard N Aufmann, Isbn: 9780547197975. 2009. 122p. pap. 28.95 *(978-1-4288-2479-9(0))*; 110p. pap. 28.95 *(978-1-4288-8973-6(6))* Cram101 Inc.

—Outlines & Highlights for Intermediate Algebra with Early Functions & Graphing by Lial, Hornsby, Mcginnis, Isbn: 0321064593. 2009. 118p. pap. 28.95 *(978-1-4288-3954-0(2))* Cram101 Inc.

—Outlines & Highlights for Introductory Algebr: Applied Approach by Aufmann, Richard N. / Barker, Vernon C. / Lockwood, Joanne, ISBN. 2009. 148p. pap. 29.95 *(978-1-4288-3751-5(5))* Cram101 Inc.

—Outlines & Highlights for Introductory Algebra by Elayn Martin-Gay, Isbn: 9780131868434. 2009. 66p. pap. 27.95 *(978-1-4288-3759-1(0))* Cram101 Inc.

—Outlines & Highlights for Introductory Algebra by Ignacio Bello, Isbn: 9780077224783. 2009. 70p. pap. 27.95 *(978-1-4288-3795-9(7))* Cram101 Inc.

—Outlines & Highlights for Introductory Algebra by Julie Miller, Isbn: 9780077366513. 2009. 90p. pap. 27.95 *(978-1-4288-2567-3(3))*; 88p. pap. 27.95 *(978-1-4288-9111-1(0))* Cram101 Inc.

—Outlines & Highlights for Introductory Algebra by Marvin L Bittinger, Isbn: 9780321269478. 2009. 92p. pap. 27.95 *(978-1-4288-3775-1(2))* Cram101 Inc.

—Outlines & Highlights for Introductory Algebra by Miller, Oneill, & Hyde, Isbn: 9780077281120. 2009. 106p. pap. 28.95 *(978-1-4288-2437-9(5))*; 98p. pap. 27.95 *(978-1-4288-9165-4(X))* Cram101 Inc.

—Outlines & Highlights for Introductory Algebra by Tussy, Gustafson, Isbn: 0534436374. 2009. 96p. pap. 27.95 *(978-1-4288-3931-1(3))* Cram101 Inc.

—Outlines & Highlights for Introductory Algebra for College Students by Robert F Blitzer, Isbn: 9780132356794. 2009. 106p. pap. 28.95 *(978-1-4288-2139-2(2))* Cram101 Inc.

—Outlines & Highlights for Introductory Algebra Through Applications by Geoffrey Akst, Sadie Bragg, Isbn: 9780321518026. 2009. 60p. pap. 26.95 *(978-1-4288-3726-3(4))* Cram101 Inc.

—Outlines & Highlights for Introductory & Intermediate Algebra by Lial & Hornsby, Isbn: 9780321575692. 2009. 168p. pap. 29.95 *(978-1-4288-2263-4(1))* Cram101 Inc.

—Outlines & Highlights for Introductory & Intermediate Algebra by Marvin L Bittinger, Judith a Beecher, Isbn: 9780321319098. 2009. 116p. pap. 28.95 *(978-1-4288-3757-7(4))* Cram101 Inc.

—Outlines & Highlights for Introductory & Intermediate Algebra for College Students by Robert F Blitzer, Isbn: 9780136028956. 2009. 184p. pap. 30.95 *(978-1-4288-3783-6(3))* Cram101 Inc.

—Outlines & Highlights for Modeling, Functions, & Graphs: Algebra for College Students by Katherine Yoshiwara, Bruce Yoshiwara, ISBN. 2009. 110p. pap. 28.95 *(978-1-4288-3765-2(5))*; 106p. pap. 28.95 *(978-1-4288-7665-1(0))* Cram101 Inc.

—Outlines & Highlights for Precalculus by J S Ratti, Marcus M Mcwaters, Isbn: 9780321296467. 2009. 304p. pap. 32.95 *(978-1-4288-3657-0(8))* Cram101 Inc.

—Outlines & Highlights for Precalculus by Judith a Beecher, Marvin L Bittinger, Isbn: 9780321460066. 2009. 252p. pap. 31.95 *(978-1-4288-3629-7(2))* Cram101 Inc.

—Outlines & Highlights for Precalculus by Larson, Isbn: 9780618760961. 2009. 196p. pap. 30.95 *(978-1-4288-2101-9(5))* Cram101 Inc.

—Outlines & Highlights for Precalculus by Margaret L Lial, David I Schneider, John Hornsby, Isbn: 9780321528841. 2009. 258p. pap. 31.95 *(978-1-4288-3701-0(9))* Cram101 Inc.

—Outlines & Highlights for Precalculus by Michael Sullivan, Isbn: 9780132256889. 2009. 278p. pap. 32.95 *(978-1-4288-3603-7(9))* Cram101 Inc.

—Outlines & Highlights for Precalculus by Robert F Blitzer, Isbn: 9780321559845. 2009. 58p. pap. 26.95 *(978-1-4288-9913-1(8))* Cram101 Inc.

—Outlines & Highlights for Precalculus, Enhanced Edition by Ron Larson, Isbn: 9781439044575. 2009. 196p. pap. 30.95 *(978-1-4288-2423-2(5))*; 200p. pap. 30.95 *(978-1-4288-9194-4(3))* Cram101 Inc.

—Outlines & Highlights for Precalculus, Enhanced Review Edition by James Stewart, Isbn: 9780495392767. 2009. 254p. pap. 31.95 *(978-1-4288-2509-3(6))*; 252p. pap. 31.95 *(978-1-4288-8953-8(1))* Cram101 Inc.

—Outlines & Highlights for Precalculus Essentials by Robert F Blitzer, Isbn: 9780321594037. 2009. 194p. pap. 30.95 *(978-1-4288-2137-8(6))* Cram101 Inc.

—Outlines & Highlights for Precalculus with Calculus Previews: Expanded Volume by Dennis, G Zill, ISBN. 2009. 148p. pap. 29.95 *(978-1-4288-3675-4(6))* Cram101 Inc.

—Outlines & Highlights for Precalculus with Limits: Enhanced Edition by Ron Larson, ISBN. 2009. 224p. pap. 30.95 *(978-1-4288-2551-2(7))*; 236p. pap. 31.95 *(978-1-4288-8896-8(9))* Cram101 Inc.

Crauder, Bruce, et al. Functions & Change: A Modeling Approach to College Algebra & Trigonometry. 2007. (ENG.). 496p. (C). pap. 60.95 *(978-0-618-85805-7(9)*, 314276) Brooks/Cole.

Crossley, J. N., ed. Algebra & Logic: Papers from the 1974 Summer Research Institute of the Australian Mathematical Society, Monash University, Australia. 2008. (Lecture Notes in Mathematics Ser.). 320p. pap. 59.95 *(978-3-540-07152-5(0))* Springer.

Cuculescu, I. & Oprea, A. G. Noncommutative Probability. 2010. (Mathematics & Its Applications Ser.). 372p. pap. 189.00 *(978-90-481-4470-9(1)*, 9048144701) Springer.

Cummins, Jerry, et al. Algebra: Concepts & Applications. 2007. (ENG., Illus.). 834p. (C). stu. ed. 99.28 *(978-0-07-879912-9(0)*, 0078799120) McGraw-Hill Higher Education.

Damiano, David B. & Little, John B. A Course in Linear Algebra. 2011. (Dover Books on Mathematics Ser.). (ENG.). 464p. pap. 26.95 *(978-0-486-46908-9(5))* Dover Pubns., Inc.

Das, Anadi Jiban. Tensors: The Mathematics of Relativity Theory & Continuum Mechanics. 2010. (ENG., Illus.). xii, 292p. pap. 139.00 *(978-1-4419-2410-0(8)*, 1441924108) Springer.

Davies, Charles. Elementary Algebra: Embracing the First Principles of the Science. by Charles Davies. 2006. 292p. per. 23.99 *(978-1-4255-2694-8(2))* MPublishing.

—Elements of Algebra: On the Basis of M. Bourdon, Embracing Sturm's & Horner's theorems, & Practical Examples. by Charles Davies. 2006. 404p. per. 26.99 *(978-1-4255-4314-3(6))* MPublishing.

—New Elementary Algebra Embracing the First Principles of Science by Charles Davies. 2006. 320p. per. 23.99 *(978-1-4255-3098-3(2))* MPublishing.

Davis, Stephen. Math Games Galore: Algebra & Geometry. 2009. pap. 12.99 *(978-1-59198-982-0(5))* Creative Teaching Pr., Inc.

De Meyer, Frank & Ingraham, Edward. Separable Algebras over Commutative Rings. 2008. (Lecture Notes in Mathematics Ser.). 172p. pap. 39.95 *(978-3-540-05371-2(9)*, 3540053719) Springer.

Demana, Franklin, et al. Precalculus: Graphical, Numerical, Algebraic. 8th ed. 2010. (ENG.). 984p. (C). 187.33 *(978-0-321-65693-3(8))* Addison Wesley.

—Precalculus: Graphical, Numerical, Algebraic, Books a la Carte Edition, Precalculus: Graphical, Numerical, Algebraic. 8th ed. 2010. (ENG.). (C). ring bd. 112.40 *(978-0-321-73208-8(1))* Addison Wesley.

Demana, Franklin D. Precalculus: Graphical, Numerical, Algebraic. 8th ed. 2010. *(978-0-13-136906-1(7))*; *(978-0-13-136907-8(5))* Addison-Wesley Longman, Inc.

—Precalculus: Graphical, Numerical, Algebraic. 7th ed. 2009. (Illus.). xxiv, 1032p. 127.29 *(978-0-13-135962-8(2))*; 127.29 *(978-0-13-245775-0(X))*; 127.29 *(978-0-13-700065-4(0))* Pearson Education.

Demarois, et al. Mathematical Investigations. 2nd rev. ed. 2009. (ENG.). pap. 102.12 *(978-0-7575-5915-0(8))* Kendall Hunt Publishing Co.

Dimitric, R. Slender Modules. 2008. 250p. (C). 64.95 *(978-0-521-66057-0(2))* Cambridge Univ. Pr.

Dixon, Martyn R., et al. Algebra & Number Theory: An Integrated Approach. 2010. (ENG., Illus.). 523p. 139.00 *(978-0-470-49636-7(3)*, Wiley) Wiley, John & Sons, Inc.

Donkin, S. Representations of the Hyperalgebra of a Semisimple Group. 2008. (London Mathematical Society Lecture Note Ser.: No. 219). 250p. (C). 39.95 *(978-0-521-47251-7(2))* Cambridge Univ. Pr.

Downing, Douglas. E-Z Algebra. 5th rev. ed. 2009. (Barron's E-Z Ser.). (ENG., Illus.). 480p. pap. 16.99 *(978-0-7641-4257-4(7))* Barron's Educational Series, Inc.

Drton, Mathias. Lectures on Algebraic Statistics. 2008. (Oberwolfach Seminars Ser.). (Illus.). viii, 171p. pap. 39.95 *(978-3-7643-8904-8(4))* Birkhauser Boston.

Dugopolski & Cram101 Textbook Reviews Staff. Intermediate Algebr. 2007. 156p. per. 12.95 *(978-1-4288-3678-5(0))* Cram101 Inc.

Dugopolski, Mark. Algebra for College Students. 5th ed. 2008. *(978-0-07-353352-0(1))* McGraw-Hill Cos., The.

—Algebra for College Students. (ENG., Illus.). (C). 5th ed. 2008. 880p. 176.67 *(978-0-07-722484-4(1)*, 0077224841) 6th ed. 2011. 992p. 176.67 *(978-0-07-338434-4(8)*, 0073384348) McGraw-Hill Higher Education. (McGraw-Hill Science, Engineering & Mathematics).

—Algebra for College Students w/ Connect Plus Access Card. 6th ed. 2011. (ENG.). (C). 190.00 *(978-0-07-752691-7(0)*, 0077526910, McGraw-Hill Science, Engineering & Mathematics) McGraw-Hill Higher Education.

—College Algebra. 5th ed. 2010. (Dugopolski Precalculus Ser.). (ENG., Illus.). 736p. (C). 168.67 *(978-0-321-64474-9(3))* Addison Wesley.

—College Algebra. 5th ed. 2011. (Illus.). xxiii, 638p. *(978-0-321-64559-3(6))* Addison-Wesley Longman, Inc.

—College Algebra & Trigonometry. 5th ed. 2010. (Dugopolski Precalculus Ser.). (ENG., Illus.). 992p. (C). 187.33 *(978-0-321-64477-0(8))* Addison Wesley.

—College Algebra & Trigonometry. 5th ed. 2010. (Illus.). xxv, 860p. *(978-0-321-64560-9(X))* Addison-Wesley Longman, Inc.

—College Algebra & Trigonometry: A Unit Circle Approach, Books a la Carte Edition. 5th ed. 2010. (ENG.). (C). ring bd. 112.40 *(978-0-321-66534-8(1))* Addison Wesley.

—College Algebra, Books a la Carte Edition. 5th ed. 2010. (ENG.). (C). ring bd. 101.20 *(978-0-321-65542-4(7))* Addison Wesley.

—Elementary Algebra. 6th ed. 2008. *(978-0-07-353350-6(5))* McGraw-Hill Cos., The.

—Elementary Algebra. 6th ed. 2008. (ENG., Illus.). 704p. (C). 177.33 *(978-0-07-722479-0(5)*, 0077224795, McGraw-Hill Science, Engineering & Mathematics) McGraw-Hill Higher Education.

—Elementary & Intermediate Algebra. 3rd ed. 2008. *(978-0-07-353349-0(1))* 4th ed. 2011. *(978-0-07-735329-2(3))* McGraw-Hill Cos., The.

—Elementary & Intermediate Algebra. (ENG., Illus.). (C). 3rd ed. 2008. 1096p. 182.67 *(978-0-07-722482-0(5)*, 0077224825) 4th ed. 2011. 1056p. 182.67 *(978-0-07-338435-1(6)*, 0073384356) McGraw-Hill Higher Education. (McGraw-Hill Science, Engineering & Mathematics).

—Elementary & Intermediate Algebra w/ Connect Plus Access Card. 4th ed. 2011. (ENG.). (C). 196.00 *(978-0-07-752690-0(2)*, 0077526902, McGraw-Hill Science, Engineering & Mathematics) McGraw-Hill Higher Education.

—Intermediate Algebra. 6th ed. 2007. *(978-0-07-353351-3(3))* McGraw-Hill Cos., The.

—Intermediate Algebra. 7th ed. 2011. (ENG., Illus.). 864p. (C). 177.33 *(978-0-07-338457-3(7)*, 0073384577, McGraw-Hill Science, Engineering & Mathematics) McGraw-Hill Higher Education.

—Intermediate Algebra w/ Connect Plus Access Card. 7th ed. 2011. (ENG.). (C). 190.66 *(978-0-07-752688-7(0)*, 0077526880, McGraw-Hill Science, Engineering & Mathematics) McGraw-Hill Higher Education.

—Loose Leaf Version for Algebra for College Students. 6th ed. 2011. (ENG.). (C). ring bd. 123.67 *(978-0-07-743121-9(1)*, 0077431219, McGraw-Hill Science, Engineering & Mathematics) McGraw-Hill Higher Education.

—Loose Leaf Version for Elementary & Intermediate Algebra. 4th ed. 2011. (ENG.). (C). ring bd. 128.00 *(978-0-07-743122-8(7)*, 0077431227, McGraw-Hill Science, Engineering & Mathematics) McGraw-Hill Higher Education.

—Loose leaf version for intermediate Algebra. 7th ed. 2011. (ENG.). (C). ring bd. 124.33 *(978-0-07-747621-2(2)*, 0077476212, McGraw-Hill Science, Engineering & Mathematics) McGraw-Hill Higher Education.

—Precalculus: Functions & Graphs. 3rd ed. 2007. (Dugopolski Precalculus Ser.). (ENG., Illus.). 992p. (C). 187.33 *(978-0-321-50111-0(X))* Addison Wesley.

—Precalculus: Functions & Graphs. 3rd ed. 2007. *(978-0-321-50133-2(0))* Addison-Wesley Longman, Inc.

—Precalculus: Functions & Graphs plus MyMathLab Student Access Kit. 2012. (ENG.). (C). 197.33 ***(978-0-321-83758-5(4))*** Addison Wesley.

—Precalculus: Graphs & Models, Books a la Carte Edition plus MyMathLab Student Access Kit. 2012. (ENG.). (C). ring bd. 122.40 ***(978-0-321-83757-8(6))*** Addison Wesley.

—Student Solution Manual t/a Elementary & Intermediate Algebra. 3rd ed. 2008. (ENG.). 384p. (C). pap. 70.33 *(978-0-07-320599-1(0)*, 0073205990, McGraw-Hill Science, Engineering & Mathematics) McGraw-Hill Higher Education.

—Student's Solutions Manual for College Algebra. 5th ed. 2010. (ENG.). 288p. (C). pap. 36.67 *(978-0-321-65534-9(6))* Addison Wesley.

—Student's Solutions Manual for College Algebra & Trigonometry: A Unit Circle Approach. 5th ed. 2010. (ENG.). 384p. (C). pap. 36.67 *(978-0-321-65578-3(8))* Addison-Wesley Longman, Inc.

—Student's Solutions Manual for use with Elementary Algebra. 6th ed. 2008. (ENG.). 248p. (C). pap. 70.33 *(978-0-07-334075-3(8)*, 0073340758, McGraw-Hill Science, Engineering & Mathematics) McGraw-Hill Higher Education.

—Student's Solutions Manual for use with Intermediate Algebra. 6th ed. 2008. (ENG.). 312p. (C). pap. 70.33 *(978-0-07-320614-1(8)*, 0073206148, McGraw-Hill Science, Engineering & Mathematics) McGraw-Hill Higher Education.

—Student's Solutions Manual for with Algebra for College Students. 5th ed. 2008. (ENG.). 344p. (C). pap. 70.33 *(978-0-07-320623-3(7)*, 0073206237, McGraw-Hill Science, Engineering & Mathematics) McGraw-Hill Higher Education.

Durbin, John R. Modern Algebra: An Introduction. 6th ed. 2008. (ENG., Illus.). 336p. (C). 181.95 *(978-0-470-38443-5(3)*, Wiley) Wiley, John & Sons, Inc.

Dvurecenskij, Anatolij & Pulmannová, Sylvia. New Trends in Quantum Structures. 2010. (Mathematics & Its Applications Ser.). 541p. pap. 219.00 *(978-90-481-5525-5(8)*, 9048155258) Springer.

Dwyer, Diana. College Algebra. 2nd ed. Date not set. (Math). 58.50 net. *(978-0-314-12629-0(5))* Brooks/Cole.

Dzierzon, Christian. Essentially Algebraic Descriptions of Locally Presentable Categories. 2008. 152p. pap. *(978-3-8364-6416-1(0))* VDM Verlag Dr. Mueller e.K.

Ehrig, Hartmut, et al, eds. Mathematical Foundations of Software Development. Proceedings of the International Joint Conference on Theory & Practice of Software Development (TAPSOFT), Berlin, March 25-29, 1985: Volume 1: Colloquium on Trees in Algebra & Programming (CAAP'85) 2007. (Lecture Notes in Computer Science Ser.). 436p. per. 49.95 *(978-3-540-15198-2(2))* Springer.

Elduque, Alberto & Hyo Chyl Myung. Mutations of Alternative Algebras. 2010. (Mathematics & Its Applications Ser.). 244p. pap. 249.00 *(978-90-481-4373-3(X)*, 904814373X) Springer.

Elementary Algebra Student. Date not set. (C). pap. *(978-0-201-35199-6(4))* Addison-Wesley Longman, Inc.

Emekwulu, Paul Chika. Fibonacci Numbers for Research Mathematicians & AI Applications. xiv, 101p. pap. 25.00 *(978-0-9623353-5-8(5))* Novelty Bks.

Encyclopaedia Britannica, Inc. Mathematics in Context: Viva el Algebra 2006 Student Edition (Algebra Rules) 2010. (SPA.). (YA). pap. 9.95 *(978-1-61535-391-0(7))* Encyclopaedia Britannica, Inc.

Encyclopaedia Britannica, Inc., compiled by. Mathematics in Context: Expressions & Formulas. 2008. (gr. 5-8). 8.75 *(978-1-59339-898-9(0))* Encyclopaedia Britannica, Inc.

—Mathematics in Context: Second Chance. 2009. (gr. 5-8). 8.75 *(978-1-59339-981-8(2))* Encyclopaedia Britannica, Inc.

—2010 Mathematics in Context S: Revisiting Number Teacher Guide. 2009. (gr. 8). 36.00 *(978-1-59339-969-6(3))* Encyclopaedia Britannica, Inc.

Esty, Warren W. Precalculus. 4th ed. 2007. (ENG., Illus.). 445p. (C). pap. 113.00 *(978-0-536-08358-6(4))* Pearson Learning Solutions.

Euler, Leonard. Elements of Algebra. Hewlett, John, tr. from FRE. 3rd ed. 2009. (Cambridge Library Collection - Mathematics Ser.). (ENG.). 628p. pap. 43.00 *(978-1-108-00296-7(X))* Cambridge Univ. Pr.

Euler, Leonhard. Elements of Algebra. 2007. 276p. pap. 41.50 *(978-1-899618-79-8(1))* Parkwest Pubns., Inc.

Faciane, Kirby. Statistics for Management. 2007. 217p. pap. 219.95 *(978-0-9788208-8-6(6))* Henry Carey Baird & Co.

Faith, Carl. Lectures on Injective Modules & Quotient Rings. 2007. (Lecture Notes in Mathematics Ser.). 160p. per. 39.95 *(978-3-540-03920-4(1))* Springer.

Fisher, Anna. Pre-Algebra & Word Problem Applications. rev. ed. 2010. (ENG.). 310p. pap. 91.24 *(978-0-7575-4515-3(7))* Kendall Hunt Publishing Co.

Flanders, James, et al. Advanced Algebra: Third Edition Field Trial Version 2006-2007 Chapters 9-10. 2007. pap. *(978-0-936745-32-9(0))* Univ. of Chicago Schl. Mathematics Project.

Fokkink, Wan. Introduction to Process Algebra. 2010. (Texts in Theoretical Computer Science. an EATCS Ser.). (ENG., Illus.). viii, 163p. pap. 89.95 (978-3-642-08584-0(9), 3642085849) Springer.

Fong, Y., et al, eds. First International Tainan-Moscow Algebra Workshop: Proceedings of the International Conference held at National Cheng Kung University Tainan, Taiwan, Republic of China, July 23 - August 22 1994. (De Gruyter Proceedings in Mathematics Ser.). (ENG.). XI, 349p. 266.00 (978-3-11-177122-9(9)) De Gruyter, Walter Inc.

Garling, D. J. H. Clifford Algebras: an Introduction. 2011. (London Mathematical Society Student Texts). (ENG., Illus.). 208p. 99.00 (978-1-107-09638-7(3)); pap. 39.99 (978-1-107-42219-3(1)) Cambridge Univ. Pr.

Gerritzen, Lothar, et al, eds. Algebraic Methods in Cryptography. 2006. (Contemporary Mathematics Ser.). (Illus.). 178p. pap. 61.00 (978-0-8218-4037-5(1)) American Mathematical Society.

Gerver, Robert K. & Sgroi, Richard J. Financial Algebra, Student Edition. 2010. (Applied Mathematics Ser.). (ENG.). 576p. (C). 104.95 (978-0-538-44967-0(5)) Cengage South-Western.

Gilbert, J. & Murray, M. Clifford Algebras & Dirac Operators in Harmonic Analysis. 2008. (Cambridge Studies in Advanced Mathematics Ser.). (ENG.). 344p. pap. 61.00 (978-0-521-07198-7(4)) Cambridge Univ. Pr.

Gille, Philippe, et al. Central Simple Algebras & Galois Cohomology. 2006. (Cambridge Studies in Advanced Mathematics: Vol. 101). (ENG., Illus.). 356p. 97.00 (978-0-521-86103-8(9)) Cambridge Univ. Pr.

Glass, B. R. Algebra I Toolkit: Reproducible Notes for Student Journals. 2011. 102p. pap. 19.95 (978-1-257-04267-8(X)) Lulu Enterprises Inc.

Glencoe McGraw-Hill Staff. Glencoe Precalculus Student Edition. 2010. (ENG.). 1200p. (C). 133.32 (978-0-07-880273-7(3), 0078802733) McGraw-Hill Higher Education.

Glencoe McGraw-Hill Staff, creator. Algebra 1 Skills Practice Workbook. 2007. (ENG., Illus.). 83p. (C). pap. 5.96 (978-0-07-880307-9(1), 0078803071) McGraw-Hill Higher Education.

—Algebra 1 Word Problem Practice Workbook. 2007. (ENG., Illus.). 83p. (C). pap. 5.96 (978-0-07-880308-6(X), 007880308X) McGraw-Hill Higher Education.

—Algebra 2 para California: Libro de Ejercicios para Guia de Estudio E Intervencion. 2007. (ENG., Illus.). 202p. (C). per. 9.32 (978-0-07-879056-0(5), 0078790565) McGraw-Hill Higher Education.

Gobran. Beginning Algebra. Date not set. (Mathematics Ser.). 14.75 net. (978-0-87150-538-5(X), Brooks/Cole) Brooks/Cole.

—Beginning Algebra. (SPA.). pap. (978-968-7270-51-7(9)) CENGAGE Learning.

Goguen, Joseph A. & Malcolm, Grant, eds. Software Engineering with OBJ: Algebraic Specification in Action. 2010. (Advances in Formal Methods Ser.). 440p. pap. 299.00 (978-1-4419-4965-3(8), 1441949658) Springer.

Goldstein, Larry. Algebra & Trigonometry & Their Applications: Instructor's Edition. Date not set. (Illus.). (C). 767p. tchr. ed. (978-1-891304-32-3(1)); 2nd ed. 901p. tchr. ed. (978-1-891304-07-1(0)) Mobius Communications, Ltd.

—Algebra & Trigonometry & Their Applications: Instructor's Solutions Manual. Date not set. 488p. pap., tchr. ed. (978-1-891304-35-4(6)) Mobius Communications, Ltd.

—Algebra & Trigonometry & Their Applications: Student Edition. Date not set. (C). 695p. stu. ed. 44.50 (978-1-891304-31-6(3)); 2nd ed. 835p. stu. ed. 44.50 (978-1-891304-09-5(7)) Mobius Communications, Ltd.

—Algebra & Trigonometry & Their Applications: Student Solutions Manual. Date not set. (Illus.). 249p. (C). pap., stu. ed. 15.00 (978-1-891304-34-7(8)) Mobius Communications, Ltd.

—Algebra & Trigonometry & Their Applications: TIF. Date not set. 321p. (C). pap. (978-1-891304-08-8(9)) Mobius Communications, Ltd.

—Algebra & Trigonometry & Their Applications: Transparency Masters. Date not set. (Illus.). 182p. (C). pap. incl. trans. (978-1-891304-33-0(X)) Mobius Communications, Ltd.

—College Algebra & Its Applications. Date not set. 120p. (C). pap. incl. trans. (978-1-891304-29-3(1)); (Illus.). 276p. (C). pap., tchr. ed. (978-1-891304-27-9(5)); 2nd ed. (Illus.). 661p. tchr. ed. (978-1-891304-20-0(8)) Mobius Communications, Ltd.

—College Algebra & Its Applications: Instructor's Solution Manual. Date not set. (C). 360p. pap., tchr. ed. (978-1-891304-26-2(7)); 2nd ed. 248p. pap., tchr. ed. (978-1-891304-23-1(2)) Mobius Communications, Ltd.

—College Algebra & Its Applications: Student Edition. Date not set. (Illus.). (C). 519p. 44.50 (978-1-891304-25-5(9)); 2nd ed. 682p. stu. ed. 44.50 (978-1-891304-21-7(6)) Mobius Communications, Ltd.

—College Algebra & Its Applications: Student Solutions Manual. Date not set. (C). 204p. pap., stu. ed. 15.00 (978-1-891304-28-6(3)); 2nd ed. 92p. pap., stu. ed. 15.00 (978-1-891304-22-4(4)) Mobius Communications, Ltd.

—College Algebra & Its Applications: Test Item File. Date not set. (C). 246p. pap. (978-1-891304-30-9(5)); 222p. pap. (978-1-891304-24-8(0)) Mobius Communications, Ltd.

—College Algebra for Management, Social, & Biological Sciences. Date not set. (C). 88p. pap., stu. ed. 15.00 (978-1-891304-18-7(6)); (Illus.). 668p. 44.50 (978-1-891304-15-6(1)) Mobius Communications, Ltd.

—College Algebra for Management, Social, & Biological Sciences: Instructor's Edition. Date not set. (Illus.). 708p. (C). pap., tchr. ed. (978-1-891304-17-0(8)) Mobius Communications, Ltd.

—College Algebra for Management, Social, & Biological Sciences: Instructor's Solutions Manual. Date not set. 318p. (C). pap., tchr. ed. (978-1-891304-16-3(X)) Mobius Communications, Ltd.

—College Algebra for Management, Social, & Biological Sciences: Test Item File. Date not set. 271p. (C). pap. (978-1-891304-19-4(4)) Mobius Communications, Ltd.

Goodearl, K. R. New Trends in Noncommutative Algebra. Ara, P. C. et al, eds. 2012. (Contemporary Mathematics Ser.). (Illus.). 297p. pap. 99.00 (978-0-8218-5297-2(3)) American Mathematical Society.

Goodman, Arthur. Understanding Elementary Algebra. 4th ed. Date not set. (C). 62.95 (978-0-534-35327-8(4)) Brooks/Cole.

Gray, Jeremy & Parshall, Karen Hunger. Episodes in the History of Modern Algebra (1800-1950) 2007. (History of Mathematics Ser.). (Illus.). 336p. 71.00 (978-0-8218-4343-7(5)) American Mathematical Society.

Green, Edward L. & Kornbluth, Jerry. A Simple Approach to College Algebra & Trigonometry. 2006. (ENG., Illus.). 200p. (C). pap. 100.95 (978-0-7593-6020-4(0), Cengage Learning) CENGAGE Learning.

Grimaldo, Andreana & Robichaud, Denise. Intro Algebra. rev. ed. 2011. (ENG.). 888p. (C). ring bd. 112.00 (978-0-321-64128-1(0)) Addison Wesley.

—Intro Algebra. 2012. (978-0-321-69036-4(2)); (978-0-321-81610-8(2)) Pearson Education, Ltd.

Gustafson & Frisk & Cram101 Textbook Reviews Staff. College Algebr. 2007. 148p. per. 12.95 (978-1-4288-3598-6(9)) Cram101 Inc.

Gustafson, R. David & Frisk, Peter D. Beginning Algebra. 8th ed. 2008. (Illus.). xxvi, 589p. (978-0-495-31895-8(7)) Brooks/Cole.

—Beginning & Intermediate Algebra: An Integrated Approach. 5th ed. 2008. (Illus.). xxvi, 957p. (978-0-495-31893-4(0)) Brooks/Cole.

—Intetmediate Algebra. 8th ed. 2008. (Illus.). xxviii, 763p. (978-0-495-31896-5(5)) Brooks/Cole.

Gustafson, R. David & Schwitters, Karen L. Beginning Algebra. 2009. (ENG.). 352p. (C). pap. 48.95 (978-0-495-38823-4(8)) Brooks/Cole.

Gustafson, R. David, et al. Beginning Algebra. 9th ed. 2010. (Available 2011 Titles Enhanced Web Assign Ser.). (ENG.). (C). 696p. 206.95 (978-0-495-83141-9(7)); 320p. pap. 75.95 (978-1-4390-4739-2(1)) Brooks/Cole.

—Beginning Algebra. 3rd ed. 2010. (ENG.). 304p. (C). pap. 62.33 (978-0-07-730068-5(8), 0077300688, McGraw-Hill Science, Engineering & Mathematics) McGraw-Hill Higher Education.

—Beginning & Intermediate Algebra: An Integrated Approach. 6th ed. 2010. (Available 2011 Titles Enhanced Web Assign Ser.). (ENG.). (C). 1128p. 221.95 (978-0-495-83143-3(3)); 480p. pap. 72.95 (978-0-538-49533-2(2)) Brooks/Cole.

—College Algebra. 10th ed. 2008. (Available 2010 Titles Enhanced Web Assign Ser.). (ENG.). 816p. (C). 209.95 (978-0-495-55888-0(5)) Brooks/Cole.

—Intermediate Algebra. 9th ed. 2010. (Available 2011 Titles Enhanced Web Assign Ser.). (ENG., Illus.). 912p. (C). 206.95 (978-0-495-83142-6(5)) Brooks/Cole.

Hall, James W. & Mercer, Brian A. Beginning & Intermediate Algebra: The Language & Symbolism of Mathematics. 2nd ed. 2007. (Illus.). xxx, 944p. (978-0-07-293322-2(4)) 3rd ed. 2011. (Illus.). xxxi, 1008p. (978-0-07-729688-9(5)) 3rd ed. 2010. (978-0-07-338424-5(0)) McGraw-Hill Cos., The.

—Beginning & Intermediate Algebra: The Language & Symbolism of Mathematics. 2nd rev. ed. 2007. (Illus.). 944p. 148.44 (978-0-07-322971-3(7), 9780073229713) 3rd ed. 2010. (ENG.). 928p. (C). 182.67 (978-0-07-735004-8(9), 0077350049) McGraw-Hill Higher Education. (McGraw-Hill Science, Engineering & Mathematics).

Hall, Mercer & Cram101 Textbook Reviews Staff. Beginning & Intermediate Algebra the Language & Symbolism of Mathematics. 2007. 152p. per. 12.95 (978-1-4288-3672-3(1)) Cram101 Inc.

Harder, Gunter. Lectures on Algebraic Geometry II: Basic Concepts, Coherent Cohomology, Curves & their Jacobians. 2011. (Aspects of Mathematics Ser.). (ENG.). xiii, 365p. 89.95 (978-3-8348-0432-7(0), 3834804320) Vieweg Verlag, Friedr, & Sohn Verlagsgesellschaft mbH DEU. Dist: Springer.

Hardy, Darel W., et al. Applied Algebra: Codes, Ciphers & Discrete Algorithms, Second Edition. 2nd rev. ed. 2009. (Discrete Mathematics & Its Applications Ser.). (ENG., Illus.). 424p. (C). 107.95 (978-1-4200-7142-9(4), Chapman & Hall/CRC) CRC Pr. LLC.

Harshbarger, Ronald J. & Yocco, Lisa. College Algebra in Context, Books a la Carte Edition plus MyMathLab Student Access Kit. 2012. (ENG.). (C). ring bd. 111.20 (978-0-321-83755-4(X)) Addison Wesley.

—College Algebra in Context plus MyMathLab Student Access Kit. 2012. (ENG.). (C). 178.67 (978-0-321-83756-1(8)) Addison Wesley.

Harshbarger, Ronald J. & Yocco, Lisa S. College Algebra in Context: With Applications for the Managerial, Life, & Social Sciences. 4th rev. ed. 2011. (ENG.). 720p. (C). 168.67 (978-0-321-75626-8(6)) Addison Wesley.

—College Algebra in Context with Applications for the Managerial, Life, & Social Sciences. 3rd ed. 2008. (ENG., Illus.). 768p. (C). 168.67 (978-0-321-57060-4(X)) Addison Wesley.

—College Algebra in Context with Applications for the Managerial, Life, & Social Sciences. 3rd ed. 2008. tchr. ed. (978-0-321-56360-6(3)) Pearson Education.

—College Algebra in Context with Applications for the Managerial, Life, & Social Sciences plus MyMathLab Student Access Kit. 3rd ed. 2009. (ENG.). (C). 178.67 (978-0-321-56972-1(5)) Addison Wesley.

Harshbarger, Ronald J., et al. Additional Skill & Exercise Manual for College Algebra in Context with Applications for the Managerial, Life, & Social Sciences. 3rd ed. 2008. (ENG.). 120p. (C). pap. 36.67 (978-0-321-56970-7(9)) Addison-Wesley Longman, Inc.

—College Algebra in Context with Applications for the Managerial, Life, & Social Sciences. 3rd ed. 2009. (ENG.). (C). pap. 36.67 (978-0-321-56968-4(7)) Addison Wesley.

Harvill, Lawrence. Applied Matrix Algebr. 2011. 568p. 34.99 (978-1-4328-8355-4(9)); pap. 23.99 (978-1-4628-8354-7(0)) Xlibris Corp.

Hass, Lonnie & Taylor, Larry. College Algebra. 6th rev. ed. 2011. (ENG.). 404p. pap. 66.25 (978-0-7575-8977-5(4)) Kendall Hunt Publishing Co.

Hawkes Learning Systems, ed. Introductory & Intermediate Algebra 2nd ed Bundle Hard. 2010. (C). 88.00 net. (978-1-932628-78-4(9)) Hawkes Learning Systems.

—Introductory & Intermediate Algebra 2nd ed Text only Hard. 2010. (C). 70.00 net. (978-1-932628-77-7(0)) Hawkes Learning Systems.

Hazewinkel, M., ed. Handbook of Algebra. (Handbook of Algebra Ser.: 6). (ENG., Illus.). 2009. 592p. 220.00 (978-0-444-53257-2(9)) 2008. 576p. 215.00 (978-0-444-53101-8(7)) Vol. 4. 2006. 542p. 240.00 (978-0-444-52213-9(1)) Elsevier Science & Technology Bks. (North Holland).

Høyrup, Jens. Lengths, Widths, Surfaces: A Portrait of Old Babylonian Algebra & Its Kin. 2010. (Sources & Studies in the History of Mathematics & Physical Sciences Ser.). (Illus.). xiv, 459p. pap. 179.00 (978-1-4419-2945-7(2), 1441929452) Springer.

Heimerl, Joseph M. Basic Arithmetic & Algebra: A Focused Review. 2011. pap. 28.95 (978-0-7414-6012-7(2)) Infinity Publishing.

Hemakul, Wanida & Sy, Polly Wee. Proceedings of the International Conference on Algebra 2010: Advances in Algebraic Structures. 2011. 750p. 220.00 (978-981-4366-30-4(7)) World Scientific Publishing Co., Inc.

Hendricks, Andrea & Chow, Oiyin Pauline. Beginning Algebra. 2012. (ENG., Illus.). 864p. (C). 168.67 (978-0-07-338427-6(5), 0073384275, McGraw-Hill Science, Engineering & Mathematics) McGraw-Hill Higher Education.

—Beginning & Intermediate Algebra. 2012. (ENG., Illus.). 1152p. (C). 173.67 (978-0-07-338453-5(4), 0073384534) McGraw-Hill Cos., The.

—Intermediate Algebra. 2012. (ENG., Illus.). 928p. (C). 168.67 (978-0-07-338426-9(7), 0073384267, McGraw-Hill Science, Engineering & Mathematics) McGraw-Hill Higher Education.

—Student Solutons Manual for Beginning Algebra. 2012. (ENG.). 416p. (C). pap. 56.33 (978-0-07-336666-1(8), 0073366668, McGraw-Hill Science, Engineering & Mathematics) McGraw-Hill Higher Education.

—Student Solutions Manual for Beginning & Intermediate Algebra. 2012. (ENG.). 256p. (C). pap. 42.67 (978-0-07-729709-1(1), 0077297091, McGraw-Hill Science, Engineering & Mathematics) McGraw-Hill Higher Education.

—Student Solutions Manual for Intermediate Algebra. 2012. (ENG.). 416p. (C). pap. 56.33 (978-0-07-336101-7(1), 0073361011, McGraw-Hill Science, Engineering & Mathematics) McGraw-Hill Higher Education.

Herzog, David Alan. Algebra. 2008. (ENG., Illus.). 304p. per. 21.99 (978-0-470-18559-9(7), Visual) Wiley, John & Sons, Inc.

Hilbe, Joseph M. Negative Binomial Regression. 2nd rev. ed. 2011. (ENG., Illus.). 572p. 85.00 (978-0-521-19815-8(1)) Cambridge Univ. Pr.

Holt Rinehart & Winston, creator. Holt Mathematics Algebra Fundamentals. 2008. (Illus.). 293p. pap. 20.00 (978-0-554-02888-0(3)) Holt McDougal.

Holt, Rinehart and Winston Staff. Pre-Algebra Chptr. 8: Resource Book with Answer Key. 4th ed. Date not set. pap. 38.86 (978-0-03-069688-6(7)) Holt McDougal.

Holzapfel. Arithmetic & Geometry Around Hypergeomet. 2007. (Progress in Mathematics Ser.). (Illus.). viii, 437p. 139.00 (978-3-7643-8283-4(X)) Birkhauser Verlag AG CHE. Dist: Springer.

Hornsby & Lial & Rockswold & Cram101 Textbook Reviews Staff. A Graphical Approach to College Algebr. 2007. 160p. per. 12.95 (978-1-4288-3428-6(1)) Cram101 Inc.

Hornsby, E. John, et al. A Graphical Approach to Algebra & Trigonometry. 5th ed. 2010. (978-0-321-65503-5(5)) Addison-Wesley Longman, Inc.

—A Graphical Approach to College Algebra. 5th ed. 2010. (978-0-321-65502-8(8)) Addison-Wesley Longman, Inc.

Hornsby, John, et al. A Graphical Approach to Algebra & Trigonometry, A la Carte with MML/MSL Student Access Kit (adhoc for Valuepacks) 5th ed. 2010. (ENG.). (C). ring bd. 122.40 (978-0-321-69323-5(X)) Addison Wesley.

—Graphical Approach to College Algebra, A, Books a la Carte Edition. 5th ed. 2010. (ENG.). 704p. (C). ring bd. 101.20 (978-0-321-66418-1(3)) Addison Wesley.

Hornsby, John K., et al. A Graphical Approach to College Algebra, A la Carte Plus MyMathLab Student Access Kit. 5th ed. 2010. (ENG.). (C). ring bd. 111.20 (978-0-321-66590-4(2)) Addison Wesley.

Hornsby, John S., et al. A Graphical Approach to Algebra & Trigonometry. 5th ed. 2010. (ENG., 992p. (C). Illus.). ring bd. 112.40 (978-0-321-66419-8(1)); 187.33 (978-0-321-64472-5(7)) Addison Wesley.

—A Graphical Approach to College Algebra. 5th ed. 2010. (Hornsby/Lial/Rockswold Graphical Approach Ser.). (ENG., Illus.). 768p. (C). 168.67 (978-0-321-64476-3(X)) Addison Wesley.

—Student's Solutions Manual for A Graphical Approach to Algebra & Trigonometry. 5th ed. 2010. (ENG.). 600p. (C). pap. 36.67 (978-0-321-66447-1(7)) Addison-Wesley Longman, Inc.

—Student's Solutions Manual for A Graphical Approach to College Algebra. 5th ed. 2010. (ENG.). 432p. (C). pap. 36.67 (978-0-321-66461-7(2)) Addison Wesley.

—Student's Solutions Manual for A Graphical Approach to Precalculus with Limits: A A Unit Circle Approach. 5th ed. 2010. (ENG.). 606p. (C). pap. 36.67 (978-0-321-66488-4(4)) Addison Wesley.

Hosch, William L., ed. The Britannica Guide to Algebra & Trigonometry. 2010. (Math Explained Ser.). (Illus.). 280p. (YA). 90.00 (978-1-61530-222-2(0)) Rosen Publishing Group, Inc., The.

Hostetler, Robert P. & Cram101 Textbook Reviews Staff. College Algebra. 2007. 196p. per. 13.95 (978-1-4288-3554-2(7)) Cram101 Inc.

Hostetler, Robert P. & Falvo, David C. College Algebra. 7th ed. 2007. (Illus.). xvii, 678p. (978-0-618-64311-0(7)) Houghton Mifflin Harcourt Publishing Co.

Hu, Wenchuan. Algebraic Cycles & Lawson Homology. 2008. 120p. pap. (978-3-639-01886-8(9)) VDM Verlag Dr. Mueller e.K.

Hughes-Hallett, Deborah, et al. Algebra: Form & Function. 2008. (ENG., Illus.). 416p. (C). per. 65.95 (978-0-470-22666-7(8), Wiley) Wiley, John & Sons, Inc.

Humphreys, T. P. A Reference Guide to Vector Algebra. 2008. (Illus.). 200p. (C). pap. 50.00 (978-0-87573-095-0(7)) Jain Publishing Company, Inc.

Hutchison, Bergman & Cram101 Textbook Reviews Staff. Beginning Algebr. 2007. 116p. per. 11.95 (978-1-4288-3668-6(3)) Cram101 Inc.

Hutchison, Donald & Baratto, Stefan. Annotated Instructor's Edition Elementary & Intermediate Algebra. 2010. 1120p. pap. 117.50 (978-0-07-729216-4(2), WCB/McGraw-Hill) McGraw-Hill Higher Education.

—Student Solutions Manual Elementary & Intermediate Algebra. 4th ed. 2010. 288p. (C). pap. 55.94 (978-0-07-729218-8(9), 0077292189, WCB/McGraw-Hill) McGraw-Hill Higher Education.

Hutchison, Donald, et al. Basic Math Skills with Geometry. 8th ed. 2009. (ENG.). 192p. (C). pap. 74.67 (978-0-07-729206-5(5), 0077292065, McGraw-Hill Science, Engineering & Mathematics) McGraw-Hill Higher Education.

—Beginning Algebra. 8th ed. 2010. (ENG.). 224p. (C). pap. 74.67 (978-0-07-729213-3(8), 0077292138, McGraw-Hill Science, Engineering & Mathematics) McGraw-Hill Higher Education.

—Intermediate Algebra. 2006. (Streeter Ser.). (ENG.). 1120p. (C). pap., pap. 165.00 (978-0-07-330930-9(3), 0073309303, McGraw-Hill Science, Engineering & Mathematics) McGraw-Hill Higher Education.

—Prealgebra. 3rd ed. 2009. (ENG.). 896p. (C). pap. 165.00 (978-0-07-729962-0(0), 0077299620, McGraw-Hill Science, Engineering & Mathematics) McGraw-Hill Higher Education.

—Student's Solutions Manual Prealgebra. 3rd ed. 2009. (ENG.). 192p. (C). pap. 74.67 (978-0-07-335787-4(1), 0073357871, McGraw-Hill Science, Engineering & Mathematics) McGraw-Hill Higher Education.

Huynh, Dinh V., et al, eds. Algebra & Its Applications. 2006. (Contemporary Mathematics Ser.). (Illus.). 319p. pap. 92.00 (978-0-8218-3842-6(3)) American Mathematical Society.

Hyde, Nancy, et al. Intermediate Algebra. 2nd ed. 2009. (ENG.). 992p. (C). pap., pap. 165.00 (978-0-07-728111-3(X), 007728111X, McGraw-Hill Science, Engineering & Mathematics) McGraw-Hill Higher Education.

—Introductory Algebra. 2nd ed. 2008. (ENG.). 832p. (C). pap., pap. 165.00 (978-0-07-728112-0(8), 0077281128, McGraw-Hill Science, Engineering & Mathematics) McGraw-Hill Higher Education.

Iachello, Francesco. Lie Algebras & Applications. 2006. (Lecture Notes in Physics Ser.: Vol. 708). (Illus.). 196p. 69.95 (978-3-540-36236-4(3), 3540362363) Springer.

Ibrahim Adeku, Musa. A Study of Multiset Algebras. 2011. 144p. pap. (978-3-8443-0901-0(2)) Lambert Academic Publishing.

Introductory Algebra 6th ed Text Only Softcover. 2007. (C). pap. (978-1-932628-32-6(0)) Hawkes Learning Systems.

Introductory Algebra 6th edition Solutions Manual. 2007. (C). pap. (978-1-932628-35-7(5)) Hawkes Learning Systems.

Isaacs, I. Martin. Algebra: A Graduate Course. 2009. (Graduate Studies in Mathematics Ser.). (Illus.). 516p. 79.00 (978-0-8218-4799-2(6)) American Mathematical Society.

Itskov, Mikhail. Tensor Algebra & Tensor Analysis for Engineers: With Applications to Continuum Mechanics. 2nd ed. 2010. (ENG., Illus.). xiii, 247p. pap. 69.95 (978-3-642-10103-8(8), 3642101038) Springer.

Ivanescu, Cristian. Classification of Inductive Limits of Continuous Trace C*-Algebras. 2010. 88p. pap. (978-3-8383-0325-3(3)) Lambert Academic Publishing.

Jacobs, Harold. Elementary Algebra. 2nd ed. Date not set. instr.'s gde. ed. 70.00 incl. cd-rom (978-0-7167-9487-5(X)) Freeman, W. H. & Co.

—Elementary Algebra Computerized Test Bank. 2nd ed. Date not set. 70.00 (978-0-7167-1176-6(1)) Freeman, W. H. & Co.

—Printed Test Bank for Elementary Algebra. 2nd ed. Date not set. pap. 35.00 (978-0-7167-9489-9(6)) Freeman, W. H. & Co.

—Teacher's Guide for Elementary Algebra. 2nd ed. Date not set. 35.00 (978-0-7167-9488-2(8)) Freeman, W. H. & Co.

Jacobs, Harold R. Elementary Algebra. 2nd ed. Date not set. 55.00 (978-0-7167-0952-7(X)) Freeman, W. H. & Co.

Jacobson, Nathan. Basic Algebra I. 2nd ed. 2009. (Dover Books on Mathematics Ser.). (ENG.). 528p. pap. 19.95 (978-0-486-47189-1(6)) Dover Pubns., Inc.

—Basic Algebra II. 2nd ed. 2009. (Dover Books on Mathematics Ser.). (ENG.). 704p. pap. 25.95 (978-0-486-47187-7(X)) Dover Pubns., Inc.

Jamestown. Number Power, Vol. 3. 2nd ed. 224p. (YA). (gr. 7-8). pap. 12.98 (978-0-8092-2388-6(0)) McGraw-Hill/Contemporary.

Jamsen, Jane & Hetler, Gwen. Beginning Algebra: Once & for All. rev. ed. 2008. (ENG.). 498p. pap. 77.67 (978-0-7872-9146-4(3)) Kendall Hunt Publishing Co.

Jandu, Daljit S. NP Completeness for Algebra & Number Theory, Games & Puzzles, Logic & Open Problems. 2010. per. (978-1-933773-07-0(3)) Infinite Bandwidth Publishing.

Jarden, Moshe. Algebraic Patching. 2011. (Springer Monographs in Mathematics Ser.). x, 290p. 99.00 (978-3-642-15127-9(2), 3642151272) Springer.

Jespers, Eric & Okninski, Jan. Noetherian Semigroup Algebras. 2010. (Algebra & Applications Ser.). vii, 366p. pap. 119.00 (978-90-481-7448-5(1), 9048174481) Springer.

John Wesley Young. Lectures on Fundamental Concepts of Algebra & Geometry. 2008. 252p. pap. 13.95 (978-1-60386-117-5(3), Merchant Bks.) Rough Draft Printing.

Johnston & Willis. Intermediate Algebra. 5th ed. Date not set. (Math). tchr. ed. 13.25 net. (978-0-534-14336-7(9)) Brooks/Cole.

Jollenbeck, Michael & Welker, Volkmar. Minimal Resolutions Via Algebraic Discrete Morse Theory. 2009. (Memoirs of the American Mathematical Society Ser.). 74p. pap. 62.00 (978-0-8218-4257-7(9)) American Mathematical Society.

Jones, Andrea D. & Land, Lee C. College Algebra Solutions Guide: Student Edition. rev. ed. 2010. (ENG.). 246p. pap., stu. ed. 39.10 (978-0-7575-7403-0(3)) Kendall Hunt Publishing Co.

Jones, Jane. Learning in Usa Algebra Classes - Instructor Perceptions of Student Learning in Secondary & Postsecondary Algebra Classes. 2008. 152p. pap. (978-3-639-01916-2(4)) VDM Verlag Dr. Mueller e.K.

Jordan, Bill. Integrated Arithmetic & Basic Algebra, Books a la Carte Edition plus MyMathLab Student Access Kit. 2012. (ENG.). (C). ring bd. 107.20 (978-0-321-82813-2(5)) Addison Wesley.

—Integrated Arithmetic & Basic Algebra plus MyMathLab Student Access Kit. 2012. (ENG.). (C). pap., pap. 172.00 (978-0-321-82814-9(3)) Addison Wesley.

Jordan, Bill E. & Palow, William P. Integrated Arithmetic & Basic Algebra. (ENG., Illus.). (C). 4th ed. 2007. 1032p. per. 162.00 (978-0-321-44255-0(5)) 5th rev. ed. 2011. 960p. pap. 162.00 (978-0-321-74738-9(0)) Addison Wesley.

—Integrated Arithmetic & Basic Algebra. 4th ed. 2008. (978-0-321-49173-2(4)) Addison-Wesley Longman, Inc.

Jordan, Palow & Cram101 Textbook Reviews Staff. Integrated Arithmetic & Basic Algebr. 2007. 120p. per. 11.95 (978-1-4288-3642-6(X)) Cram101 Inc.

Joswig, Michael & Takayama, Nobuki, eds. Algebra, Geometry & Software Systems. 2010. (ENG., Illus.). xiii, 331p. pap. 103.00 (978-3-642-05539-3(7), 3642055397) Springer.

Kaise, T. Representations de Weil et GL2 - algebres de dimension GLn: (Vers les corps de classes galoisiens I, II) 2008. (Lecture Notes in Mathematics Ser.). pap. 46.00 (978-3-540-17827-9(9)) Springer.

Kallrath, Josef, ed. Algebraic Modeling Systems: Modeling & Solving Real World Optimization Problems. 2012. (Applied Optimization Ser.). (ENG., Illus.). xxvi, 236p. 139.00 (978-3-642-23591-7(3), 3642235913) Springer.

Kano, Mikio & Akiyama, Jin. Factors & Factorizations of Graphs: Proof Techniques in Factor Theory. 2011. (Lecture Notes in Mathematics Ser.). (Illus.). xii, 353p. pap. 89.95 (978-3-642-21918-4(7), 3642219187) Springer.

Kaput, James J., et al, eds. Algebra in the Early Grades. 2007. (Studies in Mathematical Thinking & Learning). (Illus.). 526p. per. 62.95 (978-0-8058-5473-2(8)) Erlbaum, Lawrence Assocs., Inc.

Kaput, James J., et al. Algebra in the Early Grades. Kaput, James J. et al, eds. 2007. (Studies in Mathematical Thinking & Learning). (ENG., Illus.). 552p. (C). 173.00 (978-0-8058-5472-5(X)) Routledge.

Karwowski, Margie & Acosta, Gisela. Activity Workbook with Real-World Applications for College Algebra. rev. ed. 2010. (ENG.). 150p. pap. 31.68 (978-0-7575-7364-4(9)) Kendall Hunt Publishing Co.

Kaseberg, Alice. Intermediate Algebra. 4th ed. 2007. 696p. (C). 119.95 (978-0-495-10838-2(3)) Brooks/Cole.

—Intermediate Algebra: Everyday Explorations. 4th ed. 2007. (ENG.). 736p. (C). 195.95 (978-0-618-91880-5(9)) CENGAGE Learning.

—Intermediate Algebra: Everyday Explorations. 4th ed. 2008. (Illus.). (978-0-618-92001-3(3)) Houghton Mifflin Harcourt Publishing Co.

—Introductory Algebra. 4th ed. 2007. (C). 119.95 (978-0-495-10841-2(3)); (ENG.). 240p. pap. 59.95 (978-0-618-94699-0(3), 1019862) Brooks/Cole.

—Introductory Algebra: Everyday Explorations. 4th ed. 2008. (Illus.). xxviii, 628p. (978-0-618-92005-1(6)) Houghton Mifflin Harcourt Publishing Co.

—Introductory Algebra 4e. 4th ed. 2007. (ENG.). 656p. (C). 195.95 (978-0-618-91878-2(7)) CENGAGE Learning.

Kaufmann, Jerome E. & Schwitters. Algebra for College Students 1pass. 8th ed. 2007. (Illus.). xvi, 879p. (978-0-495-12757-4(4)) Brooks/Cole.

Kaufmann, Jerome E. & Schwitters, Karen L. Algebra for College Students. 9th ed. 2010. (Available 2011 Titles Enhanced Web Assign Ser.). (ENG.). 832p. (C). 211.95 (978-0-538-73354-0(3)) Brooks/Cole.

—Beginning Algebra. 2008. (Available 2010 Titles Enhanced Web Assign Ser.). (ENG.). 624p. (C). pap. 176.95 (978-0-495-38821-0(1)) Brooks/Cole.

—Cengage Advantage Books: Elementary & Intermediate Algebra: A Combined Approach. 6th ed. 2011. (ENG.). 864p. (C). ring bd. 109.95 (978-1-111-57843-5(5)) Brooks/Cole.

—College Algebra. 7th ed. 2008. (ENG.). (C). 33.95 (978-0-495-55407-3(3)); (Illus.). 752p. 215.95 (978-0-495-55403-5(0)) Brooks/Cole.

—Elementary Algebra. 9th ed. 2010. (Available 2011 Titles Enhanced Web Assign Ser.). (ENG.). 560p. (C). 206.95 (978-1-4390-4917-4(3)) Brooks/Cole.

—Elementary & Intermediate Algebra: A Combined Approach. 6th ed. 2011. (ENG.). 816p. (C). pap. 77.95 (978-1-111-57462-8(6)) Brooks/Cole.

—Intermediate Algebra. (Available 2010 Titles Enhanced Web Assign Ser.). (ENG.). (C). 2009. 832p. pap. 176.95 (978-0-495-38798-5(3)) 9th ed. 2010. 656p. 206.95 (978-1-4390-4900-6(9)) Brooks/Cole.

—Intermediate Algebra: Hybrid. 2011. (Textbooks Available with Cengage YouBook Ser.). (ENG.). 592p. (C). pap. 114.95 (978-0-8400-6591-9(4)) Brooks/Cole.

—Student Solutions Manual for Kaufmann/Schwitters' Algebra for College Students, 9th. 9th ed. 2010. (ENG.). 608p. (C). pap. 66.95 (978-0-538-79876-1(9)) Brooks/Cole.

Kaufmann, Jerome E., et al. Intermediate Algebra. (ENG.). (C). 2010. 472p. pap., stu. ed., wbk. ed. 41.95 (978-0-538-73192-8(3)) 2009. 53.95 (978-0-495-38808-1(4)) Brooks/Cole.

Kaufmann, Jerome E. (Jerome E. Kaufmann) & Schwitters, Karen L. Elementary & Intermediate Algebra: A Combined Approach. 6th ed. 2011. (Textbooks Available with Cengage YouBook Ser.). (ENG.). (C). 864p. 221.95 (978-0-8400-5314-5(2)); 492p. pap., wbk. ed. 64.95 (978-1-111-57461-1(8)) Brooks/Cole.

Keaton, Emily, et al. Algebra for College Students. 2nd ed. 2007. (ENG., Illus.). 416p. (C). per. 65.95 (978-0-618-87424-8(0), 301306) Brooks/Cole.

Kelley, W. Michael. Algebra - The Complete Idiot's Guide. 2nd ed. 2007. (Complete Idiot's Guide Ser.). (ENG., Illus.). 336p. (gr. 12-18). 19.95 (978-1-59257-648-7(6), Alpha Bks.) Penguin Group (USA) Inc.

—The Humongous Book of Basic Math & Pre-Algebra Problems: Translated for People Who Don't Speak Math. 2011. (ENG.). 496p. (gr. 12). 19.95 (978-1-61564-083-6(5), Alpha Bks.) Penguin Group (USA) Inc.

Khatri, Daryao S. & Hughes, Anne. Math Remediation for the College Bound: How Teachers Can Close the Gap, from the Basics Through Algebra. 2011. (ENG.). 272p. 80.00 (978-1-61048-366-7(9)); pap. 39.95 (978-1-61048-367-4(7)) Rowman & Littlefield Education.

Khatri, Daryao S. & Hughes, Anne O. Math Remediation for the College Bound. 2011. (978-1-61048-368-1(5)) Rowman & Littlefield Education.

Kime, Linda Almgren. Explorations in College Algebra. 3rd ed. 2006. pap. 89.00 net. (978-0-470-10156-8(3)) Wiley, John & Sons, Inc.

Kime, Linda Almgren. Explorations in College Algebra 5th Edition with Trig Supplement from Tech Math 4th Edition & WP SA 5. 0 Set. 5th ed. 2011. (C). pap. 167.95 (978-1-118-14211-0(X)) Wiley, John & Sons, Inc.

Kime, Linda Almgren, et al. Explorations in College. 3rd ed. 2006. (Wiley Plus Products Ser.). pap. 131.95 (978-0-470-14599-9(4)) Wiley, John & Sons, Inc.

—Explorations in College Algebra. 4th ed. 2007. (ENG.). 720p. (C). ring bd. 107.95 (978-0-470-27990-8(7)); (Illus.). pap. 178.95 (978-0-471-91688-8(9)) Wiley, John & Sons, Inc. (Wiley).

—Explorations in College Algebra: Printed Test Bank. 4th ed. 2008. 274p. pap. 31.95 (978-0-470-14024-6(0), Wiley) Wiley, John & Sons, Inc.

Kizlik, S. B. & BarCharts Inc., Staff. Algebra. 2006. (Quickstudy: Academic Ser.). (ENG., Illus.). 144p. pap. 6.95 (978-1-4232-0254-7(6)) Barcharts, Inc.

Klein, Félix. Elementary Mathematics from an Advanced Standpoint: Arithmetic, Algebra, Analysis. 2007. (ENG.). 288p. per. 11.95 (978-1-60206-647-2(7)) Cosimo, Inc.

Kleyn, Aleks. Representation Theory. 2011. 96p. pap. (978-3-8443-0072-7(4)) Lambert Academic Publishing.

Klima, Richard E., et al. Applications of Abstract Algebra with Maple & MATLAB. 2nd rev. ed. 2006. (Discrete Mathematics & Its Applications Ser.). (ENG., Illus.). 528p. (C). 107.95 (978-1-58488-610-5(2), Chapman & Hall/CRC) CRC Pr. LLC.

Knapp, Anthony W. Advanced Algebra: Along with a Companion Volume Basic Algebra. 2007. (Cornerstones Ser.). (Illus.). 730p. 79.95 (978-0-8176-4522-9(5), 0817645225) Birkhauser Boston.

—Basic Algebra. 2006. (Cornerstones Ser.). (Illus.). 717p. 79.95 (978-0-8176-3248-9(4), 0817632484) Birkhauser Boston.

—Basic Algebra & Advanced Algebra Set. 2007. (Cornerstones Ser.). (Illus.). XLVI, 1454p. 109.00 (978-0-8176-4533-5(0), 0817645330) Birkhauser Boston.

Kostrikin, A. I. & Shafarevich, I. R., eds. Algebra IV: Infinite Groups. Linear Groups. Wiegold, J., tr. 2010. (Encyclopaedia of Mathematical Sciences Ser.). (Illus.). vii, 203p. pap. 149.00 (978-3-642-08100-2(2), 3642081002) Springer.

—Algebra VI: Combinatorial & Asymptotic Methods of Algebra. Nonassociative Structures. Dimitric, R., tr. 2012. (Encyclopaedia of Mathematical Sciences Ser.). (ENG., Illus.). vii, 287p. pap. 149.00 (978-3-642-08124-8(X), 364208124X) Springer.

Kranjc, Marko & Brinker, Raymond. Intermediate Algebra. 2nd rev. ed. 2009. (ENG.). 302p. pap. 96.91 (978-0-7575-6311-9(2)) Kendall Hunt Publishing Co.

Kurosch, A. G. Curso de Álgebra Superior. (SPA.). 440p. (C). (978-968-18-4938-2(8), Limusa) Noriega Editores.

Kurz, Alexander, et al. Algebra & Coalgebra in Computer Science: Third International Conference, CALCO 2009, Udine, Italy, September 7-10, 2009, Proceedings. 2009. (Lecture Notes in Computer Science / Theoretical Computer Science & General Issues Ser.). xi, 457p. pap. 99.00 (978-3-642-03740-5(2), 3642037402) Springer.

Lang, Serge. Undergraduate Algebra. 3rd ed. 2010. (Undergraduate Texts in Mathematics Ser.). (Illus.). xi, 385p. pap. 74.95 (978-1-4419-1959-5(7), 1441919597) Springer.

Larson, Ron. Algebra & Trigonometry. 8th ed. 2010. (ENG.). 688p. (C). pap. 79.95 (978-1-4390-4851-1(7)) Brooks/Cole.

—Algebra & Trigonometry: Real Mathematics, Real People. 6th ed. 2011. (College Algebra & Trigonometry Ser.). (ENG., Illus.). 1008p. (C). 234.95 (978-1-111-42842-6(5)) Brooks/Cole.

—Algebra & Trigonometry: Real Mathematics, Real People. 6th alt. ed. 2011. (ENG.). 656p. (C). pap. 62.95 (978-1-111-58227-2(0)) Brooks/Cole.

—College Algebra. 8th ed. 2010. (ENG.). (C). 68.95 (978-0-538-73848-4(0)) Brooks/Cole.

—College Algebra: Real Mathematics, Real People. 6th ed. 2011. (Textbooks Available with Cengage YouBook Ser.). (ENG.). 736p. (C). 209.95 (978-1-111-57510-6(X)) Brooks/Cole.

—College Algebra, Alternate. 8th ed. 2011. (ENG.). (C). pap. 204.95 (978-0-495-97065-1(4)) Brooks/Cole.

—College Algebra & Calculus: An Applied Approach. 2nd ed. 2012. (Textbooks Available with Cengage YouBook Ser.). (ENG.). 1200p. (C). pap. 204.95 (978-1-133-10506-0(8)) Brooks/Cole.

Larson, Ron & Hodgkins, Anne V. College Algebra with Applications for Business & Life Sciences. 2nd ed. 2012. (Textbooks Available with Cengage YouBook Ser.). (ENG.). 768p. (C). 200.95 (978-1-133-10849-8(0)) Brooks/Cole.

Larson, Ron & Hodgkins, Anne V. College Algebra with Applications for Business & Life Sciences, Enhanced Edition (with Enhanced WebAssing 1-Semester Printed Access Card) 2009. (Available 2010 Titles Enhanced Web Assign Ser.). (ENG.). 784p. (C). 178.95 (978-1-4390-4788-0(X)) Brooks/Cole.

Larson, Ron & Hostetler, Robert P. Algebra & Trigonometry. 8th ed. 2010. (Available 2011 Titles Enhanced Web Assign Ser.). (ENG.). 1040p. (C). 213.95 (978-1-4390-4847-4(9)) Brooks/Cole.

—College Algebra. 8th ed. 2010. (Available 2011 Titles Enhanced Web Assign Ser.). (ENG.). 800p. (C). 214.95 (978-1-4390-4869-6(X)) Brooks/Cole.

—Elementary Algebra. 5th ed. 2009. (Available 2010 Titles Enhanced Web Assign Ser.). (ENG.). 720p. (C). 206.95 (978-0-547-10227-6(5)) Brooks/Cole.

—Elementary & Intermediate Algebra. 5th ed. 2009. (Available 2010 Titles Enhanced Web Assign Ser.). (ENG., Illus.). 1024p. (C). 221.95 (978-0-547-10216-0(X)) Brooks/Cole.

—Intermediate Algebra. 4th ed. 2008. (Illus.). vi, 47p. (978-0-618-75465-6(2)) Houghton Mifflin Harcourt Publishing Co.

—Intermediate Algebra. 5th ed. 2008. (Available 2010 Titles Enhanced Web Assign Ser.). (ENG.). 880p. (C). 206.95 (978-0-547-10217-7(8)) Brooks/Cole.

—NoteTaking Guide for Larson/Hostetler's Precalculus, 8th. 8th ed. 2010. (ENG.). 192p. (C). pap. 8.95 (978-0-538-73909-2(6)) Brooks/Cole.

—Precalculus. 8th ed. 2010. (Precalculus Ser.). (ENG.). 1040p. (C). 239.95 (978-1-4390-4577-0(1)) Brooks/Cole.

—Precalculus: Building Concepts & Connections. 8th ed. 2010. (ENG.). 672p. (C). pap. 79.95 (978-0-538-73870-5(7)) Brooks/Cole.

—Precalculus with Limits. 2nd ed. 2010. (Available 2011 Titles Enhanced Web Assign Ser.). (ENG.). (C). 1152p. 239.95 (978-1-4390-4909-9(2)); 208p. pap. 8.95 (978-0-538-73864-4(2)) Brooks/Cole.

Larson, Ron & Nolting, Kimberly. Intermediate Algebra. 5th ed. 2010. (Illus.). xxii, 751p. (978-0-547-10220-7(8)) Brooks/Cole.

Larson, Ron & Schwitters, Karen L. Intermediate Algebra. 9th ed. 2010. (ENG.). 480p. (C). pap. 66.95 (978-0-538-79747-4(9)) Brooks/Cole.

Larson, Ron, et al. Algebra & Trigonometry. 2007. 204p. per. 13.95 (978-1-4288-3414-9(1)) Cram101 Inc.

—College Algebra: A Graphing Approach, Enhanced Edition (with Enhanced WebAssign 1-Semester Printed Access Card) 5th ed. 2009. (Available 2010 Titles Enhanced Web Assign Ser.). (ENG.). 896p. (C). 204.95 (978-1-4390-4380-6(9)) Brooks/Cole.

—Intermediate Algebra. 2010. (ENG.). (C). 4th ed. 484p. pap. 67.95 (978-0-538-73402-8(7)) 9th ed. 384p. pap. 74.95 (978-0-538-49546-2(4)) Brooks/Cole.

—Precalculus: A Graphing Approach, Enhanced Edition (with Enhanced WebAssign 1-Semester Printed Access Card) 5th ed. 2009. (Available 2010 Titles Enhanced Web Assign Ser.). (ENG.). 1168p. (C). 204.95 (978-1-4390-4438-4(4)) Brooks/Cole.

—Precalculus: Real Mathematics, Real People. 6th alt. ed. 2011. (Precalculus Ser.). (ENG.). 1008p. (C). 242.95 (978-1-111-42843-3(3)) Brooks/Cole.

—Precalculus Functions & Graphs: A Graphing Approach, Enhanced Edition (with Enhanced WebAssign 1-Semester Printed Access Card) 5th ed. 2009. (Available 2010 Titles Enhanced Web Assign Ser.). (ENG.). 1200p. (C). 204.95 (978-1-4390-4452-0(X)) Brooks/Cole.

LearningExpress Editors. 1001 Algebra Problems. 2011. (ENG.). 256p. pap. 17.95 (978-1-57685-764-9(6)) LearningExpress, LLC.

LearningExpress Staff. Algebra I. 2007. (Express Review Guides). (ENG., Illus.). 304p. per. 12.95 (978-1-57685-594-2(5)) LearningExpress, LLC.

—Algebra II. 2007. (Express Review Guides). (ENG., Illus.). 304p. per. 12.95 (978-1-57685-595-9(3)) LearningExpress, LLC.

—Basic Math & Pre-Algebra. 2007. (Express Review Guides). (ENG., Illus.). 304p. per. 12.95 (978-1-57685-593-5(7)) LearningExpress, LLC.

Lehmann & Lehmann, Jay. Intermediate Algebra: Functions & Authentic Applications, Books a la Carte Edition. 4th ed. 2010. (ENG.). (C). ring bd. 100.80 (978-0-321-69866-7(5)) Addison Wesley.

—Intermediate Algebra: Functions & Authentic Applications, Books a la Carte Plus MyMathLab/MyStatLab Student Access Kit. 4th ed. 2010. (ENG.). (C). ring bd. 110.80 (978-0-321-72207-2(8)) Addison Wesley.

—Intermediate Algebra: Functions & Authentic Applications plus MyMathLab/MyStatLab/MyStatLab Student Code Card. 4th ed. 2010. (ENG.). (C). pap. 178.00 (978-0-321-74447-0(0)) Addison Wesley.

Lehmann, Jay. Elementary Algebra: Graphs & Authentic Applications. 3rd ed. 2007. (ENG., Illus.). 672p. (C). 168.00 (978-0-13-220164-3(X), Prentice Hall) Prentice Hall PTR.

—Elementary & Intermediate Algebra: Functions & Authentic Applications. 2010. (ENG., Illus.). 1040p. (C). 176.00 (978-0-321-62107-8(7), Prentice Hall) Prentice Hall PTR.

—Elementary & Intermediate Algebra: Functions & Authentic Applications, A la Carte with MML/MSL Student Access Kit (adhoc for Valuepacks) 2010. (ENG.). (C). ring bd. 116.67 (978-0-321-69333-4(7)) Addison Wesley.

—Elementary & Intermediate Algebra: Functions & Authentic Applications, Books a la Carte Edition. 2010. (ENG.). 1040p. (C). ring bd. 104.80 (978-0-321-69248-1(9)) Addison Wesley.

—Intermediate Algebra: Functions & Authentic Applications. 4th ed. 2010. (ENG.). 720p. (C). 168.00 (978-0-321-62095-8(X), Prentice Hall) Prentice Hall PTR.

Lemmermeyer, Franz & Lorenz, Falko. Algebra 1: Körper und Galoistheorie. 4th ed. 2007. (Illus.). 390p. per. 39.95 (978-3-8274-1609-4(4)) Springer.

Li. Invariant Algebras & Geometric Reasoning. 2008. (Illus.). (C). 150.00 (978-981-270-808-3(1)) World Scientific Publishing Co., Inc.

Lial, et al. Algebra 2: Digital Video Tutors. 8th ed. 800p. cd-rom 25.97 (978-0-321-28570-6(0)) Prentice Hall PTR.

—Intermediate Algebra. 10th rev. ed. 2007. (ENG., Illus.). (C). 162.67 (978-0-321-55764-3(6)) Pearson Higher Education & Professional Group.

Lial & Hornsby & Cram101 Textbook Reviews Staff. Beginning & Intermediate Algebr. 2007. 140p. per. 11.95 (978-1-4288-3532-0(6)) Cram101 Inc.

Lial & Hornsby & McGinnis & Cram101 Textbook Reviews Staff. Beginning & Intermediate Algebr. 2007. 128p. per. 11.95 (978-1-4288-3538-2(5)) Cram101 Inc.

—Intermediate Algebra with Early Functions & Graphing. 2007. 132p. per. 11.95 (978-1-4288-3420-0(6)) Cram101 Inc.

Lial, Hornsby & Cram101 Textbook Reviews Staff. Beginning Algebr. 2007. 116p. per. 11.95 (978-1-4288-3628-0(4)) Cram101 Inc.

Lial, Hornsby & McGinnis & Cram101 Textbook Reviews Staff. Introductory & Intermediate Algebr. 2007. 124p. per. 11.95 (978-1-4288-3558-0(X)) Cram101 Inc.

Lial, Margaret, et al. College Algebra & Trigonometry, Books a la Carte Edition. 5th ed. 2012. (ENG.). (C). ring bd. 112.40 (978-0-321-79531-1(8)) Addison Wesley.

—College Algebra & Trigonometry, Books a la Carte Edition plus MyMathLab Student Accses Kit. 2012. (ENG.). (C). ring bd. 122.40 (978-0-321-82805-7(4)) Addison Wesley.

—College Algebra & Trigonometry plus MyMathLab Student Access Kit. 2012. (ENG.). (C). 197.33 (978-0-321-82806-4(2)) Addison Wesley.

—College Algebra, Books a la Carte Edition. 11th ed. 2012. (ENG.). 864p. (C). ring bd. 101.20 (978-0-321-79534-2(2)) Addison Wesley.

—College Algebra, Books a la Carte Edition plus MyMathLab Student Access Kit. 2012. (ENG.). (C). ring bd. 111.20 (978-0-321-82811-8(9)) Addison Wesley.

—College Algebra plus MyMathLab Student Access Kit. 2012. (ENG.). (C). 178.67 (978-0-321-82812-5(7)) Addison Wesley.

—Precalculus, Books a la Carte Edition plus MyMathLab Student Access Kit. 2012. (ENG.). (C). ring bd. 122.40 (978-0-321-82807-1(0)) Addison Wesley.

—Precalculus plus MyMathLab Student Access Kit. 2012. (ENG.). (C). 197.33 (978-0-321-82808-8(9)) Addison Wesley.

Lial, Margaret L. Developmental Mathematics: Basic Mathematics & Algebra. 2007. (978-0-321-50664-1(2)) Addison-Wesley Longman, Inc.

—Developmental Mathematics: Basic Mathematics & Algebra. 2nd ed. 2009. tchr. ed. (978-0-321-59965-0(9)) Pearson Education.

—Prealgebra & Introductory Algebra. 3rd ed. 2009. tchr. ed. (978-0-321-59923-0(3)) Pearson Education.

Lial, Margaret L. & Hestwood, Diana L. Prealgebra. 4th ed. 2009. (ENG.). 352p. (C). pap. 36.67 (978-0-321-57478-7(8)) Addison-Wesley Longman, Inc.

—Prealgebra: An Integrated Approach, Books a la Carte Edition. 2010. (ENG.). 768p. (C). ring bd. 97.20 (978-0-321-69404-1(X)) Addison Wesley.

—Prealgebra plus MyMathLab Student Starter Kit. 2007. (ENG.). (C). pap. 172.00 (978-0-321-42963-6(X)) Addison Wesley.

Lial, Margaret L. & Hornsby, E. John. Algebra & Trigonometry for College Readiness. 2010. (978-0-13-136626-8(2)); (978-0-13-136903-0(2)) Addison-Wesley Longman, Inc.

Lial, Margaret L. & Hornsby, John. Intermediate Algebra. 9th ed. 2008. tchr. ed. (978-0-321-57622-4(5)) Pearson Education.

Lial, Margaret L., et al. Algebra, Kit. 6th ed. 2007. (ENG.). (C). pap. 172.67 (978-0-321-50719-8(3)) Pearson Education.

—Algebra for College Students, Books a la Carte Edition. 7th ed. 2011. (ENG.). 985p. (C). ring bd. 100.80 (978-0-321-71555-5(1)) Addison Wesley.

—Beginning Algebra. 11th rev. ed. 2010. (ENG., Illus.). 672p. (C). 168.00 (978-0-321-67348-0(4)) Addison Wesley.

—Beginning Algebra. 10th ed. 2007. (978-0-321-44786-9(7)) Pearson Bks.

—Beginning Algebra. (Lial Developmental Mathematics Ser.). 10th ed. 2007. (ENG., Illus.). 720p. (C). 162.67 (978-0-321-43726-6(8)) 11th ed. 2010. tchr. ed. (978-0-321-67585-9(1)) Pearson Education.

—Beginning Algebra, Books a la Carte Edition. 11th ed. 2010. (ENG.). 672p. (C). ring bd. 100.80 (978-0-321-70253-1(0)) Addison Wesley.

—Beginning & Intermediate Algebra. 5th rev. ed. 2011. (ENG., Illus.). 1008p. (C). 176.00 (978-0-321-71542-5(X)) Addison Wesley.

—Beginning & Intermediate Algebra. 4th ed. 2007. (978-0-321-44105-8(2)) Pearson Bks.

—Beginning & Intermediate Algebra. 5th ed. 2010. tchr. ed. (978-0-321-71569-2(1)) Pearson Education.

—Beginning & Intermediate Algebra, Books a la Carte Edition. 5th ed. 2011. (ENG.). 879p. (C). ring bd. 105.60 (978-0-321-71577-7(2)) Addison Wesley.

—College Algebra. 11th rev. ed. 2012. (ENG., Illus.). 816p. (C). 168.67 (978-0-321-67179-0(1)) Addison Wesley.

—College Algebra & Trigonometry. 5th rev. ed. 2012. (ENG., Illus.). 1200p. (C). 187.33 (978-0-321-67178-3(3)) Addison Wesley.

—College Algebra & Trigonometry: MyMathLab Edition. 3rd ed. 2007. (ENG.). 696p. (C). spiral bd. 62.00 *(978-0-321-51322-9(3))* Pearson Education.
—Developmental Mathematics: Basic Mathematics & Algebra. 2nd ed. 2009. (Lial Paperback Ser.). (ENG.). 1368p. (C). pap. 176.00 *(978-0-321-59920-9(9))* Addison Wesley.
—Developmental Mathematics: Basic Mathematics & Algebra, A la Carte Plus Package. 2nd ed. 2010. (ENG.). (C). ring bd. 115.60 *(978-0-321-59968-1(3))* Addison Wesley.
—Essentials of College Algebra. 2007. (Illus.). *(978-0-321-49985-1(9))* 10th ed. 2010. *(978-0-321-66427-3(2))* Addison-Wesley Longman, Inc.
—Essentials of College Algebra. 10th ed. 2010. (ENG.). (C). pap. 140.67 *(978-0-321-68731-9(0))* Addison Wesley.
—Essentials of College Algebra. 10th ed. 2010. (Lial/Hornsby/Schneider College Algebra Ser.). (ENG.). 720p. (C). 130.67 *(978-0-321-66499-0(X))* Addison Wesley.
—Essentials of College Algebra, A la Carte Plus MyMathLab Student Access Kit. 10th ed. 2010. (ENG.). (C). ring bd. 88.40 *(978-0-321-66597-3(X))* Addison Wesley.
—Essentials of College Algebra, Books a la Carte Edition. 10th ed. 2010. (ENG.). 704p. (C). ring bd. 78.40 *(978-0-321-66422-8(1))* Addison Wesley.
—Intermediate Algebra. (Lial Paperback Ser.). (ENG.). (C). 9th ed. 2008. 904p. pap. 162.00 *(978-0-321-57497-8(4))* 11th rev. ed. 2010. (Illus.). 792p. 168.00 *(978-0-321-71541-8(1))* Addison Wesley.
—Intermediate Algebra. 10th ed. 2007. *(978-0-321-44783-8(2))* Pearson Bks.
—Intermediate Algebra. 11th ed. 2010. tchr. ed. *(978-0-321-71578-4(0))* Pearson Education.
—Intermediate Algebra, Books a la Carte Edition. 11th ed. 2010. (ENG.). 768p. (C). ring bd. 100.80 *(978-0-321-71590-6(X))* Addison Wesley.
—Intermediate Algebra, Books a la Carte Plus MML/MSL Student Access Code Card (for ad hoc Valuepacks) 11th ed. 2010. (ENG.). (C). ring bd. 110.80 *(978-0-321-77201-5(6))* Addison Wesley.
—Intermediate Algebra plus MyMathLab Student Access Kit. 9th ed. 2009. (ENG.). (C). pap., pap. 172.00 *(978-0-321-57632-3(2))* Addison Wesley.
—Introductory Algebra. 9th ed. 2008. (Lial Paperback Ser.). (ENG.). 784p. (C). pap. 162.00 *(978-0-321-55713-1(1))* Addison Wesley.
—Introductory Algebra. 9th ed. 2008. tchr. ed. *(978-0-321-57637-8(3))* Pearson Education.
—Introductory Algebra plus MyMathLab Student Access Kit. 9th ed. 2009. (ENG.). (C). pap., pap. 172.00 *(978-0-321-57646-0(2))* Addison Wesley.
—Introductory & Intermediate Algebra. 4th ed. 2009. (Lial Developmental Mathematics Ser.). (ENG.). (C). 1104p. pap. 176.00 *(978-0-321-57569-2(5))*;Kit. pap., pap. 186.00 *(978-0-321-57615-6(2))* Addison Wesley.
—Introductory & Intermediate Algebra. 4th ed. 2009. (ENG.). 600p. (C). pap., pupil's gde. ed. 36.67 *(978-0-321-57612-5(8))* Addison-Wesley Longman, Inc.
—Introductory & Intermediate Algebra. 4th ed. 2009. tchr. ed. *(978-0-321-57605-7(5))* Pearson Education.
—MyWorkBook for Algebra for College Students. 7th ed. 2011. (ENG.). 96p. (C). pap. 26.67 ***(978-0-321-71552-4(7))*** Pearson Education.
—MyWorkBook for Beginning & Intermediate Algebra. 5th ed. 2011. (ENG.). 744p. (C). pap. 31.00 *(978-0-321-71573-9(X))* Addison Wesley.
—MyWorkBook for Intermediate Algebra. 11th ed. 2011. (ENG.). 600p. (C). pap. 26.67 *(978-0-321-71586-9(1))* Pearson Education.
—Prealgebra & Introductory Algebra. 3rd ed. 2009. (Lial Paperback Ser.). (ENG.). 1344p. (C). pap. 176.00 *(978-0-321-57873-0(2))* Addison Wesley.
—Precalculus. 5th rev. ed. 2012. (ENG.). 1200p. (C). 187.33 ***(978-0-321-78380-6(8))*** Addison Wesley.
—Precalculus: MyMathLab Edition. 3rd ed. 2007. (ENG.). 696p. (C). spiral bd. 65.33 *(978-0-321-51321-2(5))* Addison Wesley.
—Precalculus, Books A la Carte Edition. 5th ed. 2012. (ENG.). 1052p. (C). ring bd. 112.40 ***(978-0-321-79530-4(X))*** Addison Wesley.
—Student Solutions Manual for College Algebra & Trigonometry. 5th rev. ed. 2012. (ENG., Illus.). 672p. (C). pap. 36.67 ***(978-0-321-79136-8(3))*** Addison Wesley.
—Student's Solutions Manual for Algebra for College Students. 7th ed. 2011. (ENG.). 512p. (C). pap. 36.67 *(978-0-321-71549-4(7))* Addison Wesley.
—Student's Solutions Manual for Beginning Algebra. 11th ed. 2011. (ENG.). 408p. (C). pap. 36.67 *(978-0-321-70245-6(X))* Pearson Education.
—Student's Solutions Manual for Beginning & Intermediate Algebra. 5th ed. 2011. (ENG.). 624p. (C). pap. 36.67 *(978-0-321-71565-4(9))* Pearson Education.
—Student's Solutions Manual for Essentials of College Algebra. 10th ed. 2010. (ENG.). 360p. (C). pap. 36.67 *(978-0-321-66421-1(3))* Addison-Wesley Longman, Inc.
—Student's Solutions Manual for Intermediate Algebra. 11th ed. 2011. (ENG.). 480p. (C). pap. 36.67 *(978-0-321-71582-1(9))* Pearson Education.
Lidl, Rudolf & Pilz, Ganter. Applied Abstract Algebra. 2nd ed. 2010. (Undergraduate Texts in Mathematics Ser.). (ENG., Illus.). xvi, 508p. pap. 84.95 *(978-1-4419-3117-7(1),* 1441931171) Springer.
Ljapin, E. S. & Evseev, A. E. The Theory of Partial Algebraic Operations. 2010. (Mathematics & Its Applications Ser.). 248p. pap. 239.00 *(978-90-481-4857-7(7),* 9048148677) Springer.
Long, Lynette. Painless Algebra. 3rd rev. ed. 2011. (Painless Ser.). (ENG.). 304p. pap. 9.99 *(978-0-7641-4715-9(3))* Barron's Educational Series, Inc.
Loomis, Elias. A Treatise on Algebra by Elias Loomis. 2006. 356p. per. 26.99 *(978-1-4255-3819-4(3))*; (ENG.). 388p. per. 26.99 *(978-1-4255-4083-8(X))* MPublishing.
Lorenz, Falko. Algebra: Volume II: Fields with Structure, Algebras & Advanced Topics. Levy, Silvio, tr. from GER. 2007. (Universitext Ser.). (Illus.). 336p. per. 49.95 *(978-0-387-72487-4(7),* 0387724877) Springer.
Luszczek, Piotr. Improving Performance of Sparse Numerical Linear Algebra Computations. 2010. 84p. pap. *(978-3-8383-3469-1(8))* Lambert Academic Publishing.
Maddux, Roger Duncan. Relation Algebras. 2006. (Studies in Logic & the Foundations of Mathematics Ser.: 150). (ENG., Illus.). 758p. 250.00 *(978-0-444-52013-5(9),* Elsevier Science) Elsevier Science & Technology Bks.
Majewicz, Stephen. College Algebra: A Narrative Approach. 2nd ed. 2007. (ENG., Illus.). 489p. (C). per. 99.00 *(978-0-536-44720-3(9))* Pearson Learning Solutions.
—Precalculus: A Narrative Approach. 2007. (ENG., Illus.). 785p. (C). per. 105.00 *(978-0-536-34974-3(6))* Pearson Learning Solutions.
Malliavin, M. Séminaire d'Algèbre Paul Dubreil et Marie-Paul Malliavin: Proceedings Paris 1985 (37ème Année) 2008. (Lecture Notes in Mathematics Ser.). pap. 59.95 *(978-3-540-17185-0(1))* Springer.
—Séminaire d'Algèbre Paul Dubreil et Marie-Paule Malliavin: Proceedings Paris 1982 (35ème Année) 2008. (Lecture Notes in Mathematics Ser.). pap. 46.00 *(978-3-540-12699-7(6))* Springer.
Malliavin, M. P. Séminaire d'Algèbre Paul Dubreil et Marie-Paule Malliavin: Proceedings Paris 1987-1988 (39ème Année) 2008. (Lecture Notes in Mathematics Ser.). pap. 69.95 *(978-3-540-51812-9(6))* Springer.
Malliavin, M. P., ed. Séminaire d'Algèbre Paul Dubreil et Marie-Paule Malliavin: Proceedings. Paris 1981 (34ème Année) 2008. (Lecture Notes in Mathematics Ser.). 488p. pap. 59.00 *(978-3-540-10841-2(6))*; 440p. pap. 59.00 *(978-3-540-09980-2(8))*; 472p. pap. 59.00 *(978-3-540-11496-3(3))* Springer.
Man, Ka Lok, et al. Pafesd: Process Algebras for Electronic System Design. 2010. 132p. pap. *(978-3-8383-6383-7(3))* Lambert Academic Publishing.
Manin, U I., et al. Algebra, Arithmetic, & Geometry: In Honor of Y.I. Manin. 2009. (Illus.). E-Book *(978-0-8176-4745-2(7))* Birkhauser Verlag AG.
Marshall, Jason. The Math Dude's Quick & Dirty Guide to Algebra. 2011. (ENG.). 496p. pap. 19.99 *(978-0-312-56956-3(4),* St. Martin's Griffin) St. Martin's Pr.
Martinez, Jorge, ed. Ordered Algebraic Structures. 2010. (Developments in Mathematics Ser.). 332p. pap. 199.00 *(978-1-4419-5225-7(X),* 144195225X) Springer.
Martin-Gay & Cram101 Textbook Reviews Staff. Beginning Algebr. 2007. 132p. per. 11.95 *(978-1-4288-3600-6(4))* Cram101 Inc.
—Intermediate Algebr. 2007. 144p. per. 11.95 *(978-1-4288-3626-6(8))*; 140p. per. 11.95 *(978-1-4288-3562-7(8))* Cram101 Inc.
Martin-Gay & Martin-Gay, Elayn. Prealgebra & Introductory Algebra, A la Carte with MML/MSL Student Access Kit (adhoc for Valuepacks) 3rd ed. 2010. (ENG.). (C). ring bd. 116.67 *(978-0-321-62379-9(7))* Addison Wesley.
Martin-Gay, Elayn. Algebra: A Combined Approach. 4th ed. 2011. (Martin-Gay Developmental Math Ser.). (ENG.). 1152p. (C). pap. 176.00 *(978-0-321-72639-1(1))* Addison Wesley.
—Algebra: A Combined Approach, Books a la Carte Edition. 4th ed. 2011. (ENG.). (C). ring bd. 105.60 *(978-0-321-74559-0(0))* Addison Wesley.
—Algebra: A Combined Approach, Books a la Carte Plus MML/MSL Student Access Code Card (for ad hoc Valuepacks) 4th ed. 2011. (ENG.). (C). ring bd. 116.67 *(978-0-321-77200-8(8))* Addison Wesley.
—Algebra: A Combined Approach plus MyMathLab/MyStatLab Student Access Code Card. 4th ed. 2011. (ENG.). (C). pap., pap. 136.00 *(978-0-321-76023-4(9))* Addison Wesley.
—Beginning Algebra. 6th rev. ed. 2011. (ENG.). 720p. (C). 168.00 ***(978-0-321-78491-9(X))*** Addison Wesley.
—Beginning Algebra. 5th ed. 2008. (ENG.). 464p. (C). pap., stu. ed. 36.67 *(978-0-13-603108-6(0),* Prentice Hall) Prentice Hall PTR.
—Beginning Algebra, Books a la Carte Edition plus MyMathLab Student Access Kit. 2012. (ENG.). (C). ring bd. 110.80 ***(978-0-321-82803-3(8))*** Addison Wesley.
—Beginning Algebra plus MyMathLab Student Access Kit. 2012. (ENG.). (C). 178.00 ***(978-0-321-72947-7(1))*** Addison Wesley.
—Beginning & Intermediate Algebra. 4th ed. 2008. (Martin-Gay Developmental Algebra Series (hardbacks) Ser.). (ENG., Illus.). 1008p. (C). 176.00 *(978-0-13-600731-9(7),* Prentice Hall) Prentice Hall PTR.
—Beginning & Intermediate Algebra. 5th rev. ed. 2012. (ENG.). 1032p. (C). 176.00 ***(978-0-321-78512-1(6))*** Addison Wesley.
—Beginning & Intermediate Algebra, Books a la Carte Edition. 5th ed. 2012. (ENG.). 1032p. (C). ring bd. 105.60 ***(978-0-321-78586-2(X))*** Addison Wesley.
—Beginning & Intermediate Algebra, Books a la Carte Edition plus MyMathLab Student Access Kit. 2012. (ENG.). (C). ring bd. 116.67 ***(978-0-321-72935-4(8))*** Addison Wesley.
—Beginning & Intermediate Algebra plus MyMathLab Student Access Kit. 2012. (ENG.). (C). 186.00 ***(978-0-321-72936-1(6))*** Addison Wesley.
—Developmental Mathematics. 2nd ed. 2010. (Martin-Gay Paperback Ser.). (ENG., Illus.). 1368p. (C). pap. 176.00 *(978-0-321-65274-4(6),* Prentice Hall) Prentice Hall PTR.
—Intermediate Algebra. 3rd ed. 2006. (Illus.). pap. incl. cd-rom *(978-0-13-175284-9(7))* Pearson Education Canada.
—Intermediate Algebra. 4th ed. 2010. (Martin-Gay Developmental Math Ser.). (ENG.). 912p. (C). pap. 162.00 *(978-0-321-72637-7(5))* Addison Wesley.
—Intermediate Algebra. 5th ed. 2008. (Martin-Gay Developmental Algebra Series (hardbacks) Ser.). (ENG., Illus.). 792p. (C). 168.00 *(978-0-13-600729-6(5),* Prentice Hall) Prentice Hall PTR.
—Intermediate Algebra. 6th rev. ed. 2011. (ENG.). 792p. (C). pap. 168.00 ***(978-0-321-78504-6(5))*** Addison Wesley.
—Intermediate Algebra, Books a la Carte Edition. 4th ed. 2010. (ENG.). 912p. (C). ring bd. 97.20 *(978-0-321-74480-7(2))* Addison Wesley.
—Intermediate Algebra, Books a la Carte Edition plus MyMathLab Student Access Kit. 2012. (ENG.). (C). ring bd. 107.20 ***(978-0-321-72946-0(3))*** Addison Wesley.
—Intermediate Algebra, Books a la Carte Plus MML/MSL Student Access Code Card (for ad hoc Valuepacks) 4th ed. 2010. (ENG.). (C). ring bd. 107.20 *(978-0-321-77198-8(2))* Addison Wesley.
—Intermediate Algebra plus MyMathLab Student Access Kit. 2012. (ENG.). (C). 178.00 ***(978-0-321-72963-7(3))*** Addison Wesley.
—Intermediate Algebra Plus MyMathLab Student Access Kit. 5th ed. 2010. (ENG.). (C). pap. 178.00 *(978-0-321-75190-4(6))* Addison Wesley.
—Introductory Algebra. 4th rev. ed. 2010. (Martin-Gay Developmental Math Ser.). (ENG.). 816p. (C). pap. 162.00 *(978-0-321-72638-4(3))* Addison Wesley.
—Introductory Algebra. 3rd ed. 2006. pap. incl. cd-rom *(978-0-13-239036-1(1))* Pearson Education Canada.
—Prealgebra. 6th ed. 2010. (Martin-Gay Paperback Ser.). (ENG.). 888p. (C). pap. 162.00 *(978-0-321-62886-2(1),* Prentice Hall) Prentice Hall PTR.
—Prealgebra & Introductory Algebra. 3rd ed. 2010. (ENG., Illus.). 1344p. (C). 176.00 *(978-0-321-64947-8(8))* Addison Wesley.
—Prealgebra & Introductory Algebra. 2nd ed. 2007. (Illus.). 1223p. *(978-0-13-600919-1(0))* Pearson Education Canada.
—Prealgebra & Introductory Algebra. 3rd ed. 2010. (Martin-Gay Paperback Ser.). (ENG., Illus.). 1344p. (C). pap. 176.00 *(978-0-321-64490-9(5),* Prentice Hall) Prentice Hall PTR.
—Prealgebra & Introductory Algebra, Books a la Carte Edition. 3rd ed. 2010. (ENG.). 1248p. (C). ring bd. 105.60 *(978-0-321-69253-5(5))* Addison Wesley.
—Prealgebra & Introductory Algebra plus MyMathLab/MyStatLab/MyStatLab Student Access Code Card. 3rd ed. 2010. (ENG.). (C). pap., pap. 186.00 *(978-0-321-74453-1(5))* Addison Wesley.
—Prealgebra, Books a la Carte Plus MathXL 12-month Student Access Kit. 6th ed. 2010. (ENG.). (C). pap., ring bd. 104.67 *(978-0-321-73222-4(7))* Addison Wesley.
—Student Organizer for Beginning Algebra. 2010. 312p. (C). pap. 36.67 *(978-0-321-74631-3(7))* Pearson Education.
—Student Organizer for Beginning & Intermediate Algebra. 2010. (ENG.). 432p. (C). pap. 36.67 *(978-0-321-74628-3(7))* Addison Wesley.
—Student Organizer for Intermediate Algebra. (ENG.). 312p. (C). 2010. pap. 36.67 *(978-0-321-74533-7(3))* 4th rev. ed. 2011. pap. 36.67 *(978-0-321-74479-1(9))* Pearson Education.
—Student Organizer for Prealgebra. 6th ed. 2010. (ENG.). 264p. (C). pap. 36.67 *(978-0-321-63402-3(0),* Prentice Hall) Prentice Hall PTR.
—Student Solutions Manual for Algebra: A Combined Approach. 4th rev. ed. 2011. (ENG.). 784p. (C). pap. 36.67 *(978-0-321-74589-7(2))* Pearson Education.
—Student Solutions Manual for Intermediate Algebra. 4th rev. ed. 2011. (ENG.). 664p. (C). pap. 36.67 *(978-0-321-74546-0(9))* Pearson Education.
—Student Solutions Manual for Introductory Algebra. 4th rev. ed. 2011. (ENG.). 496p. (C). pap. 36.67 ***(978-0-321-74532-3(9))*** Pearson Education.
—Student's Solutions Manual for Prealgebra & Introductory Algebra. 3rd ed. 2010. (ENG.). 396p. (C). pap. 36.67 *(978-0-321-64943-0(5),* Prentice Hall) Prentice Hall PTR.
—Student's Solutions Manual (standalone) for Developmental Mathematics. 2nd ed. 2010. (ENG.). 720p. (C). pap. 36.67 *(978-0-321-65320-8(3),* Prentice Hall) Prentice Hall PTR.
Martin-Gay, Elayn & Greene, Margaret Peg. Intermediate Algebra: A Graphing Approach. 4th ed. 2008. (Martin-Gay Developmental Algebra Series (hardbacks) Ser.). (ENG.). 888p. (C). 168.00 *(978-0-13-600733-3(3),* Prentice Hall) Prentice Hall PTR.
—Intermediate Algebra: A Graphing Approach Plus MyMathLab Student Access Kit. 4th ed. 2010. (ENG.). (C). pap. 178.00 *(978-0-321-75191-1(4))* Addison Wesley.
Martin-Gay, K. Elayn. Algebra: A Combined Approach. 4th ed. 2011. tchr. ed. *(978-0-321-73832-5(2))* Pearson Education.
—Beginning Algebra. 6th ed. 2011. tchr. ed. ***(978-0-321-78528-2(2))*** Pearson Education.
—Beginning Algebra, MyMathLab Edition. 5th ed. 2008. (ENG.). 544p. (C). spiral bd. 57.33 *(978-0-321-56673-7(4))* Addison Wesley.
—Beginning & Intermediate Algebra. 5th ed. 2011. 170.67 ***(978-0-321-78584-8(3))*** Pearson Education.
—Developmental Mathematics. 2nd ed. 2010. tchr. ed. *(978-0-321-65314-7(9))* Pearson Education.
—Intermediate Algebra. 4th ed. 2010. tchr. ed. *(978-0-321-73830-1(6))* 6th ed. 2011. 152.67 ***(978-0-321-78594-7(0))*** Pearson Education.
—Intermediate Algebra. 4th ed. 816p. 70.97 *(978-0-13-191844-3(3))*; tchr. ed. 70.97 *(978-0-13-149894-5(0))* Prentice Hall (Schl. Div.).
—Intermediate Algebra, MyMathLab Edition. 5th ed. 2008. (ENG.). 624p. (C). spiral bd. 57.33 *(978-0-321-56671-3(8))* Addison Wesley.
—Introductory Algebra. 4th ed. 2012. (Illus.). xviii, 730p. ***(978-0-321-73192-0(1))*** Pearson Education.
—Introductory Algebra. 3rd ed. 2006. pap. *(978-0-13-175285-6(5))* Pearson Education Canada.
—Prealgebra & Introductory Algebra. 3rd ed. 2010. tchr. ed. *(978-0-321-64373-5(9))* Pearson Education.
Martin, Hope. Primary Algebra: Student Workbook. 2008. pap. 9.95 *(978-1-59647-273-0(1))* Good Year Bks.
Marx, Andrew. Shortcut Algebra II: A Quick & Easy Way to Increase Your Algebra II Knowledge & Test Scores. 2007. (ENG.). 288p. pap. 12.00 *(978-1-4195-9315-4(3))* Kaplan Publishing.
Mary Everest Boole. Philosophy & Fun of Algebr. 2008. 48p. pap. 7.95 *(978-1-60386-126-7(2),* Merchant Bks.) Rough Draft Printing.
Math 1100 College Algebra Workbook. (C). 2008. pap. *(978-0-9820161-0-7(7))* 2007. per. *(978-0-9774658-6-6(1))* Univ. of North Texas Copy Ctr.
Maxwell, E. A. Advanced Algebra, Part 1. 2009. (ENG.). 324p. pap. 42.00 *(978-0-521-10267-4(7))* Cambridge Univ. Pr.
—Algebraic Structure & Matrices Book 2, 2 vols. 2009. (ENG., Illus.). 336p. pap. 61.00 *(978-0-521-10905-5(1))* Cambridge Univ. Pr.
McCallum, William G., et al. College Algebra. 2010. (ENG.). (C). 158p. pap. 25.00 ***(978-0-470-57088-3(1))***; pap. 63.95 *(978-0-470-57866-7(1))* Wiley, John & Sons, Inc. (Wiley).
McCarthy, Robert. Pathways in Mathematics Beginning Algeb. 2006. pap. 61.70 *(978-1-4303-0116-5(3))* Lulu Enterprises Inc.
McCune, Sandra Luna & Clark, William D. Easy Algebra Step-by-Step. 2011. (Easy Step-By-Step Ser.). (ENG., Illus.). 256p. (C). pap. 14.00 ***(978-0-07-176724-8(X),*** 007176724X) McGraw-Hill Cos., The.
McGraw-Hill Book Company Staff. Precalculus Estudentedition. 2nd ed. 2011. (ENG.). stu. ed. 157.32 incl. cd-rom *(978-0-07-661342-7(9),* 0076613429) McGraw-Hill Higher Education.
McGraw-Hill-Glencoe Staff. Algebra 2 Student Edition CCSS. 2011. (ENG., Illus.). 1152p. (gr. 10-12). 105.28 *(978-0-07-895265-4(4),* 0078952654) McGraw-Hill Higher Education.
—Pre-Algebra 2011. (ENG.). stu. ed. 91.96 incl. cd-rom *(978-0-07-895999-8(3),* 0078959993) McGraw-Hill Higher Education.
—Pre-Algebra Student Edition. 2011. (ENG.). 1112p. 91.96 *(978-0-07-895773-4(7),* 0078957737) McGraw-Hill Higher Education.
McGraw-Hill Staff. Algebra 1, Practice Workbook. 2007. (C). pap. 5.32 *(978-0-07-879047-8(6),* 9780078790478) Glencoe/McGraw-Hill.
—Algebra 1 Practice Workbook. 2007. (ENG., Illus.). 83p. (C). pap. 5.96 *(978-0-07-880306-2(3),* 0078803063) McGraw-Hill Higher Education.
—Algebra 1, Spanish Study Guide & Intervention Workbook. 2007. (ENG.). (C). pap. 9.32 *(978-0-07-879046-1(8),* 0078790468) McGraw-Hill Higher Education.
—Algebra 1, Study Guide & Intervention Workbook. 2007. (ENG.). (C). pap. 9.32 *(978-0-07-880305-5(5),* 0078803055) McGraw-Hill Higher Education.
—Algebra 2: Libro de Ejercicios de Practica. 2007. (ENG., Illus.). 101p. (C). per. 5.96 *(978-0-07-879058-4(1),* 0078790581) McGraw-Hill Higher Education.
—Algebra 2, Practice Workbook. 2007. (ENG.). (C). pap. 5.96 *(978-0-07-879057-7(3),* 0078790573) McGraw-Hill Higher Education.
—Algebra 2 Skills Practice Workbook. 2007. (ENG., Illus.). 101p. (C). pap. 5.96 *(978-0-07-879059-1(X),* 007879059X) McGraw-Hill Higher Education.
—Glencoe Secondary Mathematics to the Common Core State Standards. 2011. (ENG.). 112p. (gr. 8-12). pap. 7.16 ***(978-0-07-661900-9(1),*** 0076619001) McGraw-Hill Higher Education.
—Glencoe Secondary Mathematics to the Common Core State Standards, Algebra 2 Se Supplement. 2011. (ENG.). 80p. (gr. 9-12). pap. 7.16 ***(978-0-07-661902-3(8),*** 0076619028) McGraw-Hill Higher Education.
—Pre-Algebra, Student Edition. (ENG.). (C). 2008. (gr. 7-9). 97.48 *(978-0-07-888515-0(9),* 0078885159) 2007. 93.12 *(978-0-07-873818-0(0),* 0078738180) McGraw-Hill Higher Education.
—Precalculus Study Notebook. 2010. (ENG.). 190p. pap. 14.64 *(978-0-07-893814-6(7),* 0078938147) McGraw-Hill Higher Education.
McGraw-Hill Staff, creator. Algebra 1. 2007. (ENG., Illus.). 773p. (C). stu. ed. 98.32 *(978-0-07-873822-7(9),* 0078738229) McGraw-Hill Higher Education.
—Algebra 1: Libro de Ejercicios de Practica. 2007. (ENG.). 83p. (C). pap. 5.96 *(978-0-07-879048-5(4),* 0078790484) McGraw-Hill Higher Education.
—Algebra 1: Libro de Ejercicios Para Practicar Problemas Planteados en Palabras. 2007. (ENG., Illus.). 83p. (C). pap. 5.96 *(978-0-07-879052-2(2),* 0078790522) McGraw-Hill Higher Education.
—Algebra 2: Interactive Study Notebook with Foldables. 2007. (ENG.). 422p. (C). per. 14.64 *(978-0-07-877352-5(0),* 0078773520) McGraw-Hill Higher Education.
—Algebra 2 Study Guide & Intervention Workbook. 2007. (ENG., Illus.). 202p. (C). per. 9.32 *(978-0-07-879055-3(7),* 0078790557) McGraw-Hill Higher Education.
—Algebra 2 Word Problems Practice. 2007. (ENG.). 101p. (C). per. 5.96 *(978-0-07-879061-4(1),* 0078790611) McGraw-Hill Higher Education.
—California Algebra 1: Skills Practice. 2007. 83p. per. 5.32 *(978-0-07-879049-2(2),* 9780078790492) Glencoe/McGraw-Hill.
—California Algebra 1: Word Problem Practice. 2007. 83p. per. 5.32 *(978-0-07-879051-5(4),* 9780078790515) Glencoe/McGraw-Hill.
—California Algebra 1 Study Guide & Intervention Workbook. 2007. (Illus.). 166p. per. 8.64 *(978-0-07-879045-4(X),* 9780078790454) Glencoe/McGraw-Hill.
Mckeague. Beginning Algebra A Text/Workbook. 9th ed. 2012. (Textbooks Available with Cengage YouBook Ser.). (ENG.). 816p. (C). pap. 189.95 ***(978-1-133-10363-9(4))*** Brooks/Cole.
McKeague & Cram101 Textbook Reviews Staff. Intermediate Algebr. 2007. 140p. per. 11.95 *(978-1-4288-3638-9(1))* Cram101 Inc.
McKeague, Charles P. Algebra with Trigonometry for College Students. 6th rev. ed. 2007. (C). 123.95 *(978-0-534-49583-1(4))* Brooks/Cole.

—Beginning Algebra. 7th ed. 2007. (Illus.). xxiii, 661p. *(978-0-495-17127-0(1))* Brooks/Cole.
—Beginning & Intermediate Algebr. 2007. (Illus.). 7th ed. xxiii, 778p. *(978-0-495-17131-7(X))* 8th rev. ed. (ENG., 736p. (C). 177.95 *(978-0-495-10840-5(5))* Brooks/Cole.
—Elementary Algebra, Non-media Edition. 8th ed. 2007. (ENG.). 592p. (C). 169.95 *(978-0-495-38490-8(9))* Brooks/Cole.
—Elementary & Intermediate Algebra. 4th ed. 2011. (Textbooks Available with Cengage YouBook Ser.). (ENG.). (C). 928p. 221.95 *(978-0-8400-6419-6(5))*; 520p. pap., wbk. ed. 64.95 *(978-1-111-57509-0(6))*; 448p. pap. 69.95 *(978-1-111-57508-3(8))* Brooks/Cole.
—Elementary & Intermediate Algebra: A Combined Course. 3rd ed. 2008. (Illus.). *(978-0-495-39294-1(4))* Brooks/Cole.
—Intermediate Algebra: A Text/Workbook. 9th ed. 2012. (Textbooks Available with Cengage YouBook Ser.). (ENG.). 960p. (C). pap. 189.95 ***(978-1-133-10364-6(2))*** Brooks/Cole.
McKeague, Charles P. Intermediate Algebra Student Solutions Manual. 9th ed. 2011. (ENG.). 400p. (C). pap. 71.95 *(978-1-111-57159-7(7))* Brooks/Cole.
McKeague, Charles P. (Charles P. McKeague). Elementary Algebra. 8th ed. 2008. (Illus.). *(978-0-495-39248-4(0))* 8th rev. ed. 2007. (ENG., Illus.). 560p. (C). 206.95 *(978-0-495-10839-9(1))* 9th ed. 2011. (ENG.). 640p. (C). 206.95 *(978-0-8400-6421-9(7))* 9th ed. 2011. (ENG.). 304p. (C). pap. 68.95 *(978-1-111-57180-1(5))* Brooks/Cole.
McKellar, Danica. Algebra Exposed! 2011. (ENG., Illus.). 432p. (gr. 6-18). 16.00 *(978-0-452-29719-7(2)*, Plume) Penguin Group (USA) Inc.
—Hot X - Algebra Exposed! 2010. (ENG.). 400p. (gr. 6-18). 26.95 *(978-1-59463-070-5(4)*, Hudson Street Pr.) Penguin Group (USA) Inc.
McKenna, Paula & Kirk, Honey. Beginning & Intermediate Algebra. 2009. tchr. ed. *(978-0-321-58831-9(2))* Pearson Education.
—Beginning & Intermediate Algebra: Building a Foundation. 2009. (ENG.). 896p. (C). 176.00 *(978-0-201-78737-5(7))* Addison Wesley.
McWaters, Marcus M. & Ratti, Jogindar. College Algebra. 2007. (Ratti/McWaters Ser.). (ENG., Illus.). 912p. (C). 162.67 *(978-0-321-29644-3(3))* Addison-Wesley Longman, Inc.
McWaters, Marcus S. & Ratti, J. S. College Algebra & Trigonometry. 2nd ed. 2010. (ENG.). 1088p. (C). ring bd. 112.40 *(978-0-321-66570-6(8))* Addison Wesley.
Melnikov, Yuri A. Green's Functions & Infinite Products: Bridging the Divide. 2011. (ENG., Illus.). x, 165p. 59.95 ***(978-0-8176-8279-8(1)***, 0817682791) Birkhauser Verlag AG CHE. Dist: Springer.
Messersmith, Sherri. Beginning Algebra. 2011. (ENG., Illus.). 800p. (C). 168.67 *(978-0-07-340616-9(3)*, 0073406163, McGraw-Hill Science, Engineering & Mathematics) McGraw-Hill Higher Education.
—Beginning & Intermediate Algebra. 2nd ed. 2008. (Illus.). xxiv, 986p. 139.69 *(978-0-07-304775-1(9))* McGraw-Hill Cos., The.
—Beginning & Intermediate Algebra. (ENG.). (C). 2nd ed. 2008. 1152p. 182.67 *(978-0-07-722483-7(3)*, 0077224833) 3rd ed. 2011. (Illus.). 1056p. 182.67 *(978-0-07-338437-5(2)*, 0073384372) McGraw-Hill Higher Education. (McGraw-Hill Science, Engineering & Mathematics).
—Intermediate Algebra. 2011. (ENG., Illus.). 944p. (C). 168.67 *(978-0-07-340617-6(1)*, 0073406171, McGraw-Hill Science, Engineering & Mathematics) McGraw-Hill Higher Education.
—Intermediate Algebra w/ Connect Plus Access Card. 2011. (ENG.). (C). 182.00 *(978-0-07-752687-0(2)*, 0077526872, McGraw-Hill Science, Engineering & Mathematics) McGraw-Hill Higher Education.
—Loose Leaf Beginning Algebra. 2011. (ENG.). (C). ring bd. 118.33 *(978-0-07-743128-0(6)*, 0077431286, McGraw-Hill Science, Engineering & Mathematics) McGraw-Hill Higher Education.
—Loose Leaf Version for Beginning & Intermediate Algebra. 3rd ed. 2011. (ENG.). (C). ring bd. 128.00 *(978-0-07-743131-0(6)*, 0077431316, McGraw-Hill Science, Engineering & Mathematics) McGraw-Hill Higher Education.
—Loose Leaf Version for Intermediate Algebra. 2011. (ENG.). (C). ring bd. 118.33 *(978-0-07-743130-3(8)*, 0077431308, McGraw-Hill Science, Engineering & Mathematics) McGraw-Hill Higher Education.
—Student Solution Manual t/a Beginning & Intermediate Algebra. 2nd ed. 2008. (ENG.). 474p. (C). pap. 70.33 *(978-0-07-322758-0(7)*, 0073227587, McGraw-Hill Science, Engineering & Mathematics) McGraw-Hill Higher Education.
—Student Solutions Manual for Beginning & Intermediate Algebra. 3rd ed. 2011. (ENG.). 512p. (C). pap. 70.33 *(978-0-07-729702-2(4)*, 0077297024, McGraw-Hill Science, Engineering & Mathematics) McGraw-Hill Higher Education.
Michel, Anthony N. & Herget, Charles J. Algebra & Analysis for Engineers & Scientists. 2007. Orig. Title: Mathematical Foundations in Engineering & Science. (Illus.). 484p. per. 54.95 *(978-0-8176-4706-3(6))* Springer.
Millan-Vossler, Silvia. The Lower Algebraic K-Theory of Braid Groups on S2and RP2: Braids. 2008. 76p. pap. *(978-3-639-10919-1(8))* VDM Verlag Dr. Mueller e.K.
Miller, et al. Combo: Intermediate Algebra with MathZone Access Card. 3rd ed. 2011. (ENG.). (C). pap. 185.75 *(978-0-07-798884-5(1)*, 0077988841, McGraw-Hill Science, Engineering & Mathematics) McGraw-Hill Higher Education.
Miller, Bob. Algebra for the Clueless. 2nd rev. ed. 2006. (Bob Miller's Clueless Ser.). (ENG., Illus.). 240p. pap. 16.00 *(978-0-07-147366-8(1)*, 0071473661) McGraw-Hill Cos., The.
Miller, Charles D., et al. Intermediate Algebra. 7th ed. Date not set. (C). pap., stu. ed. 9.00 *(978-0-673-55940-1(8))* Addison-Wesley Educational Pubs., Inc.
Miller, Julie & Hyde, Nancy. Beginning Algebra. 2nd ed. 2006. (Illus.). 745p. 144.38 *(978-0-07-331267-5(3)*, 9780073312675, McGraw-Hill Science, Engineering & Mathematics) McGraw-Hill Higher Education.
Miller, Julie & O'Neill, Molly. Beginning Algebra. 2nd ed. 2007. *(978-0-07-302871-2(1))* 2nd ed. 2007. *(978-0-07-327083-8(0))* 3rd ed. 2010. *(978-0-07-338420-7(8))* McGraw-Hill Cos., The.
—Student Solutions Manual for Intermediate Algebra. 3rd ed. 2010. (ENG.). 448p. (C). pap. 58.67 *(978-0-07-729644-5(3)*, 0077296443, McGraw-Hill Science, Engineering & Mathematics) McGraw-Hill Higher Education.
Miller, Julie, et al. Beginning Algebra. 3rd ed. 2010. (ENG.). 832p. (C). 177.33 *(978-0-07-734993-6(8)*, 0077349938, McGraw-Hill Science, Engineering & Mathematics) McGraw-Hill Higher Education.
—Beginning & Intermediate Algebra. 2nd ed. 2008. (Illus.). (J). *(978-0-07-329793-4(3))* 2nd ed. 2007. (J). *(978-0-07-305281-6(7))* 3rd ed. 2010. (Illus.). *(978-0-07-338421-4(6))* McGraw-Hill Cos., The.
—Beginning & Intermediate Algebra. (Illus.). 2nd ed. 2007. 1044p. 148.44 *(978-0-07-331269-9(X)*, 9780073312699) 3rd ed. 2010. (ENG., (C). 182.67 *(978-0-07-735008-6(1)*, 0077350081) McGraw-Hill Higher Education. (McGraw-Hill Science, Engineering & Mathematics).
—Intermediate Algebra. 2nd ed. 2009. *(978-0-07-730334-1(2))* 2nd ed. 2009. *(978-0-07-335231-2(4))* 2nd ed. 2009. *(978-0-07-730339-6(3))* 2nd ed. 2009. *(978-0-07-340610-7(4))* 2nd ed. 2006. (Illus.). xxvi, 842p. *(978-0-07-302872-9(X))* 3rd ed. 2010. *(978-0-07-338422-1(4))* McGraw-Hill Cos., The.
—Intermediate Algebra. 2nd ed. 2008. (Illus.). 124.00 *(978-0-07-327074-6(1))* McGraw-Hill Higher Education.
—Intermediate Algebra: Media Update. 2nd ed. 2012. (ENG., Illus.). 992p. (C). pap. 165.00 ***(978-0-07-340629-9(5)***, 0073406295, McGraw-Hill Science, Engineering & Mathematics) McGraw-Hill Higher Education.
—Intermediate Algebra (alt ed. Hardcover) 2nd ed. 2009. (ENG.). (C). pap. 177.33 *(978-0-07-730425-6(X)*, 007730425X, McGraw-Hill Science, Engineering & Mathematics) McGraw-Hill Higher Education.
—Intermediate Algebra (Hardcover) 3rd ed. 2010. (ENG.). 976p. (C). 177.33 *(978-0-07-734994-3(6)*, 0077349946, McGraw-Hill Science, Engineering & Mathematics) McGraw-Hill Higher Education.
—Introductory Algebra. 2nd ed. 2009. *(978-0-07-340609-1(0))* 2008. *(978-0-07-730340-2(7))* 2008. *(978-0-07-335701-0(4))* McGraw-Hill Cos., The.
—Introductory Algebra. 2nd ed. 2009. (ENG.). 288p. (C). pap. 50.67 *(978-0-07-335707-2(3)*, 0073357073, McGraw-Hill Science, Engineering & Mathematics) McGraw-Hill Higher Education.
—Introductory Algebra: Media Update. 2nd ed. 2012. (ENG., Illus.). 768p. (C). pap. 165.00 ***(978-0-07-340630-5(9)***, 0073406309, McGraw-Hill Science, Engineering & Mathematics) McGraw-Hill Higher Education.
—Loose Leaf Intermediate Algebra. 3rd ed. 2010. (ENG.). (C). ring bd., ring bd. 124.33 *(978-0-07-740180-1(8)*, 0077401808, McGraw-Hill Science, Engineering & Mathematics) McGraw-Hill Higher Education.
—Loose Leaf Prealgebra. 2010. (ENG.). (C). ring bd., ring bd. 115.67 *(978-0-07-740179-5(4)*, 0077401794, McGraw-Hill Science, Engineering & Mathematics) McGraw-Hill Higher Education.
—Loose Leaf Version Beginning Algebra. 3rd ed. 2010. (C). ring bd. 101.25 *(978-0-07-739965-8(X)*, 007739965X, McGraw-Hill Science, Engineering & Mathematics) McGraw-Hill Higher Education.
—Loose Leaf Version for Intermediate Algebra. 2nd ed. 2009. (ENG.). (C). ring bd., ring bd. 115.66 *(978-0-07-736658-2(1)*, 0077366581, McGraw-Hill Science, Engineering & Mathematics) McGraw-Hill Higher Education.
—Loose Leaf Version for Introductory Algebra. 2nd ed. 2009. (ENG.). (C). ring bd., ring bd. 115.67 *(978-0-07-736651-3(4)*, 0077366514, McGraw-Hill Science, Engineering & Mathematics) McGraw-Hill Higher Education.
—Prealgebra. 2010. (ENG.). (C). pap., pap. 165.00 *(978-0-07-734995-0(4)*, 0077349954, McGraw-Hill Science, Engineering & Mathematics) McGraw-Hill Higher Education.
—Prealgebra & Introductory Algebra. 2012. (ENG., Illus.). 1280p. (C). pap. 176.00 ***(978-0-07-351295-2(8)***, 0073512958, McGraw-Hill Science, Engineering & Mathematics) McGraw-Hill Higher Education.
—Student Solutions Manual for Prealgebra & Introductory Algebra. 2012. (ENG.). 700p. (C). pap. 68.67 ***(978-0-07-758296-8(9)***, 0077582969, McGraw-Hill Science, Engineering & Mathematics) McGraw-Hill Higher Education.
Miller, Julie, et al. Student's Solution Manual Intermediate Algebra. 2nd ed. 2009. (ENG.). 448p. (C). pap. 56.67 *(978-0-07-335237-4(3)*, 0073352373, McGraw-Hill Science, Engineering & Mathematics) McGraw-Hill Higher Education.
Miller, O'Neill & Cram101 Textbook Reviews Staff. Begining Algebr. 2007. 120p. per. 11.95 *(978-1-4288-3682-2(9))* Cram101 Inc.
Mordeson, J. N. & Vinograde, B. Structure of Arbitrary Purely Inseparable Extensions. 2008. (Lecture Notes in Mathematics Ser.). (ENG.). 144p. pap. 26.00 *(978-3-540-05295-1(X)*, 354005295X) Springer.
Mossakowski, Till, et al. Algebra & Coalgebra in Computer Science: Second International Conference, CALCO 2007, Bergen, Norway, August 20-24, 2007, Proceedings. 2007. (Lecture Notes in Computer Science / Theoretical Computer Science & General Issues Ser.). xi, 463p. pap. 109.00 *(978-3-540-73857-2(6))* Springer.
Mueller, Guntram & Brent, Ronald I. Just-in-Time Algebra & Trigonometry for Calculus. 4th ed. 2012. (ENG.). 216p. (C). pap. 26.67 *(978-0-321-67104-2(X))* Addison-Wesley Longman, Inc.
—Just-in-Time Algebra & Trigonometry for Early Transcendentals Calculus. 4th ed. 2012. (ENG.). 216p. (C). pap. 26.67 *(978-0-321-67103-5(1))* Addison-Wesley Longman, Inc.
Mullany, Ruth. The Easiest Book for Understanding Algebra. 2008. (Illus.). 84p. mass mkt. 27.97 incl. cd-rom *(978-0-9710212-3-5(6))* Dynasty Pr.
Munem, Mustafa A. & Yizze, James P. College Algebra. 4th rev. ed. 2007. (ENG.). 550p. pap. 42.00 *(978-0-7575-2125-6(8))* Kendall Hunt Publishing Co.
Napier, John. De Arte Logistica Joannis Naperi Merchistonii, Baronis Libri Qui Supersunt. (Maitland Club, Glasgow Publications: No. 47). reprint ed. 37.50 *(978-0-404-52773-0(6))* AMS Pr., Inc.
Narasimhan. College Algebra & Trigonometry: Building Concepts & Connections. 2009. (Illus.). 600p. *(978-0-618-41290-7(5))* Houghton Mifflin Harcourt Publishing Co.
Narasimhan College Algebra: Functions & Models First Edition Mathspaceweb Booklet for Packages: Functions & Models First Edition Mathspaceweb Booklet for Packages. 2008. (YA). 1.56 *(978-0-547-14059-9(2)*, 1049917) CENGAGE Learning.
Narasimhan, Revathi. College Algebra: Building Concepts & Connections. 2008. (ENG.). 832p. (C). 204.95 *(978-0-618-26035-5(8)*, 309030) CENGAGE Learning.
—College Algebra: Building Concepts & Connections. 2010. (ENG.). 1p. (C). ring bd. 80.95 *(978-1-111-57888-6(5))* Brooks/Cole.
—College Algebra: Building Concepts & Connections. 2009. (Illus.). xxix, 698p. *(978-0-618-26036-2(6))* Houghton Mifflin Harcourt Publishing Co.
—College Algebra & Trigonometry: Building Concepts & Connections. 2008. (Available 2010 Titles Enhanced Web Assign Ser.). (ENG., Illus.). 1128p. (C). 228.95 *(978-0-618-41289-1(1)*, 309050) CENGAGE Learning.
—College Algebra & Trigonometry: Building Concepts & Connections. 2009. (ENG.). 368p. (C). pap., stu. ed. 56.95 *(978-0-618-41291-4(3)*, 309052) Brooks/Cole.
—Precalculus: Building Concepts & Connections. 2008. (Available 2010 Titles Enhanced Web Assign Ser.). (ENG., Illus.). 1112p. (C). 228.95 *(978-0-618-41301-0(4)*, 309060) CENGAGE Learning.
Neher, Erhard, et al, eds. Geometric Representation Theory & Extended Affine Lie Algebras. 2011. (Fields Institute Communications Ser.). (Illus.). 213p. 99.00 ***(978-0-8218-5237-8(X))*** American Mathematical Society.
Newman, M. F. & Richardson, J. S., eds. Topics in Algebra: Proceedings, 18th Summer Research Institute of the Australian Mathematical Society, Australian National University, Canberra, January 9 - February 17, 1978. 2008. (Lecture Notes in Mathematics Ser.). 248p. pap. 59.95 *(978-3-540-09103-5(3))* Springer.
Northcott, D. G. Multilinear Algebra. 2009. (ENG.). 216p. pap. 46.00 *(978-0-521-09060-5(1))* Cambridge Univ. Pr.
O'Daffer, Phares G., et al. Introduccion al Algebra. 2011. (SPA & ENG.). 592p. (C). pap. 106.00 *(978-968-444-292-4(0))* Pearson Education.
Oladunni, Olutayo. Regularized Least Squares Multi-Class Knowledge- Based Kernel MacHines. 2009. 136p. pap. *(978-3-639-14091-0(5))* VDM Verlag Dr. Mueller e.K.
Orlik, Peter & Welker, Volkmar. Algebraic Combinatorics: Lectures at a Summer School in Nordfjordeid, Norway, June 2003. 2007. (Universitext Ser.). (Illus.). 177p. per. 74.95 *(978-3-540-68375-9(5)*, 3540683755) Springer.
Ortner, Jerry. Fundamentals of Math Book 2 Algebra 1: 2nd Edition. 2010. 248p. pap. 16.99 *(978-1-4520-7000-1(8))* AuthorHouse.
Ortner, Jerry. Fundamentals of Math Part 2 Algebra 1. 2nd rev. ed. 2011. 172p. pap. 13.72 ***(978-1-4567-4054-2(7))*** AuthorHouse.
Pacholski, L., et al, eds. Model Theory of Algebra & Arithmetic: Proceedings of the Conference on Applications of Logic to Algebra & Arithmetic held at Karpacz,Poland, September 1-7, 1979. 2008. (Lecture Notes in Mathematics Ser.). 420p. pap. 59.00 *(978-3-540-10269-4(8))* Springer.
Parnell, John E. & Monahan, Christopher D. The Everything Guide to Algebra: A Step-by-Step Guide to the Basics of Algebra - in Plain English! 2011. (ENG.). 304p. pap. 16.95 *(978-1-4405-0458-7(X))* Adams Media Corp.
Passing the Tennessee Gateway in Algebra I. 2007. per. 23.00 *(978-1-59807-127-6(0))* American Bk. Co.
Pearson Education Staff. MyMathWorkbook for Basic Mathematics & Algebra. 2009. (ENG.). 864p. (C). pap. 31.00 *(978-0-321-62849-7(7)*, Prentice Hall) Prentice Hall PTR.
Pearson, John, et al. MyMathWorkbook for Basic Mathematics & Algebra with MyMathLab. 2009. (ENG.). (C). pap. 109.33 *(978-0-321-64453-4(0)*, Prentice Hall) Prentice Hall PTR.
Pearson/Addison Wesley, creator. Prealgebra & Introductory Algebra. 2nd ed. 2007. (Math XL Ser.). cd-rom 26.67 *(978-0-321-44285-7(7))* Addison-Wesley Longman, Inc.
Penna, Judith A. Graphing Calculator Manual for Algebra & Trigonometry: Graphs & Models & Precalculus: Graphs & Models. 5th rev. ed. 2012. (ENG., Illus.). 176p. (C). pap. 24.67 ***(978-0-321-79088-0(X))*** Addison Wesley.
Penna, Judith A., et al. Developmental Mathematics. 7th ed. 2007. (ENG., Illus.). 350p. (C). pap. 36.67 *(978-0-321-34858-6(3))* Addison Wesley.
Perelman, Yakov Isidorovich. Algebra Can Be Fun. Beltyansky, V. G., ed. Yankovsky, George, tr. 2011. (Illus.). 234p. pap. 25.95 ***(978-4-87187-710-7(8))*** Ishi Pr. International.
Petrello, Rena. Elementary Algebra. 9th ed. 2011. (ENG.). (C). 53.95 *(978-0-538-73955-9(X))* Brooks/Cole.
—Intermediate Algebra. 4th ed. 2010. (ENG.). (C). 53.95 *(978-0-538-73400-4(0))* Brooks/Cole.
Pilone, Tracey & Pilone, Dan. Algebra: A Learner's Guide to Algebra I. 2009. (Head First Ser.). (ENG., Illus.). 560p. pap. 29.99 *(978-0-596-51486-0(7))* O'Reilly Media, Inc.
Popescu, Gelu. Operator Theory on Noncommutative Domains. 2010. (Memoirs of the American Mathematical Society Ser.). 124p. pap. 69.00 *(978-0-8218-4710-7(4))* American Mathematical Society.
Popp, H., ed. Classification of Algebraic Varieties & Compact Complex Manifolds. 2008. (Lecture Notes in Mathematics Ser.). 348p. pap. 59.95 *(978-3-540-06951-5(8))* Springer.
Positselski, Leonid. Two Kinds of Derived Categories, Koszul Duality, & Comodule-Contramodule Correspondence. 2011. (Memoirs of the American Mathematical Society Ser.). 133p. pap. 71.00 *(978-0-8218-5296-5(5))* American Mathematical Society.
Prasolov, Victor V. Polynomials. Leites, D., tr. from SLA. 2009. (Algorithms & Computation in Mathematics Ser.). Orig. Title: Mnogochleny. (ENG., Illus.). xiii, 301p. pap. 69.95 *(978-3-642-03979-9(0)*, 3642039790) Springer.
Pre-Algebra. 5th rev. ed. 2007. per. 31.95 *(978-0-9789017-6-9(2))* 7th ed. 2009. (ENG., Illus.). 800p. pap. 35.00 *(978-0-9815320-4-2(7))* JRL Enterprises, Inc.
Prest, Mike. Purity, Spectra & Localisation. 2009. (Encyclopedia of Mathematics & its Applications Ser.). (ENG., Illus.). 798p. (C). 175.00 *(978-0-521-87308-6(8))* Cambridge Univ. Pr.
Previte, Elaine. Essential Algebra: A Workbook Approach. rev. ed. 2008. (ENG.). 306p. spiral bd. 47.89 *(978-0-7575-3704-2(9))* Kendall Hunt Publishing Co.
Prior, Robert. Prealgebra. 2008. (Prior Developmental Mathematics Ser.). (ENG.). 832p. (C). spiral bd. 105.33 *(978-0-321-21378-5(5))* Addison Wesley.
Pycior, Helena M. Symbols, Impossible Numbers, & Geometric Entanglements: British Algebra through the Commentaries on Newton's Universal Arithmetick. 2006. (ENG., Illus.). 344p. pap. 69.00 *(978-0-521-02740-3(3))* Cambridge Univ. Pr.
Qiu. Difference Sets & Their Applications, Vol. 5. 2010. 88.00 *(978-981-4280-76-1(3))* World Scientific Publishing Co., Inc.
Rao, Rama. College Algebra & Trigonometry. 2nd rev. ed. 2007. (ENG.). 94p. pap. 41.75 *(978-0-7575-4449-1(5))* Kendall Hunt Publishing Co.
Rappaport, Josh. Understand Positive & Negative Numbers. 2010. (PreAlgebra Blastoff! Ser.). (Illus.). 128p. pap. 14.95 *(978-0-9659113-6-8(5))* Singing Turtle Pr.
Ratti, et al. Precalculus: A Right Triangle Approach plus MyMathLab/MyStatLab Student Access Code Card. 2nd ed. 2010. (ENG.). (C). pap. 197.33 *(978-0-321-62436-9(X))* Addison Wesley.
Ratti, J. S. & McWaters, Marcus M. College Algebra. 2nd ed. 2010. *(978-0-321-65506-6(0))* Addison-Wesley Longman, Inc.
—College Algebra & Trigonometry. 2nd ed. 2010. *(978-0-321-65507-3(9))* Addison-Wesley Longman, Inc.
—Precalculus: A Right Triangle Approach. 2nd ed. 2010. (Illus.). xxii, 960p. *(978-0-321-65508-0(7))* Addison-Wesley Longman, Inc.
—Precalculus: A Unit Circle Approach. 2009. *(978-0-321-56507-5(X))* Pearson Bks.
Ratti, J. S. & McWaters, Marcus S. College Algebra. 2nd ed. 2010. (ENG.). 832p. (C). 168.67 *(978-0-321-64031-4(4))* Addison Wesley.
—College Algebra, A la Carte + MML. 2009. (ENG.). (C). ring bd. 123.87 *(978-0-321-62843-5(8))* Pearson Education.
—College Algebra & Trigonometry. 2nd ed. 2010. (ENG.). 1088p. (C). 187.33 *(978-0-321-64471-8(9))* Addison Wesley.
—College Algebra, Books a la Carte Edition. 2nd ed. 2010. (ENG.). (C). ring bd. 101.20 *(978-0-321-65569-0(4))* Addison Wesley.
—College Algebra plus MyMathLab Student Access Kit. 2007. (ENG.). (C). pap. 172.67 *(978-0-321-48904-3(7))* Pearson Education.
—Graphing Calculator Manual for College Algebra. 2nd ed. 2010. (ENG.). 72p. (C). pap. 24.67 *(978-0-321-65431-1(5))* Addison-Wesley Longman, Inc.
—Graphing Calculator Manual for College Algebra & Trigonometry/Precalculus: A Right Triangle Approach. 2nd ed. 2010. (ENG.). 90p. (C). pap. 24.67 *(978-0-321-66423-5(X))* Addison Wesley.
—Precalculus: A Right Triangle Approach. 2nd ed. 2010. (ENG., Illus.). 1088p. (C). 187.33 *(978-0-321-64470-1(0))* Addison Wesley.
—Precalculus: A Right Triangle Approach, Books a la Carte Edition. 2nd ed. 2010. (ENG.). (C). ring bd. 112.40 *(978-0-321-65435-9(8))* Addison Wesley.
—Precalculus: A Unit Circle Approach. 2009. (ENG.). 960p. (C). 187.33 *(978-0-321-53709-6(2))* Addison Wesley.
—Precalculus: A Unit Circle Approach, Books a la Carte Edition. 2010. (ENG.). (C). ring bd. 112.40 *(978-0-321-66355-9(1))* Addison Wesley.
—Precalculus: A Unit Circle Approach, Books a la Carte Edition plus MML. 2011. (ENG.). (C). ring bd. 122.40 ***(978-0-321-79062-0(6))*** Addison Wesley.
Ratti, J. S. & McWaters, Marcus S. Student's Solutions Manual for College Algebra. 2nd ed. 2010. (ENG.). 456p. (C). pap. 36.67 *(978-0-321-66471-6(X))* Addison-Wesley Longman, Inc.
Ratti, Jogindar & McWaters, Marcus. College Algebra & Trigonometry/Precalculus: A Right Triangle Approach. 2nd ed. 2010. (ENG.). 360p. (C). pap. 36.67 *(978-0-321-66498-3(1))* Addison Wesley.
—Precalculus: A Right Triangle Approach, A la Carte Plus MyMathLab Student Access Kit. 2nd ed. 2010. (ENG.). (C). ring bd. 122.40 *(978-0-321-66594-2(5))* Addison Wesley.
Ratti, Jogindar & McWaters, Marcus S. College Algebra & Trigonometry, A la Carte Plus MyMathLab Student Access Kit. 2nd ed. 2010. (ENG.). (C). ring bd. 122.40 *(978-0-321-65451-9(X))* Addison Wesley.
Reilly, Norman R. Introduction to Applied Algebraic Systems. 2009. (ENG., Illus.). 464p. (C). 80.00 *(978-0-19-536787-4(1))* Oxford Univ. Pr., Inc.
Reiter, H. L1-Algebras & Segal Algebras. 2008. (Lecture Notes in Mathematics Ser.). 128p. pap. 39.95 *(978-3-540-05651-5(3)*, 3540056513) Springer.

Rhodes, John. Applications of Automata Theory & Algebra: Via the Mathematical Theory of Complexity to Biology, Physics, Psychology, Philosophy, & Games. 2009. (Illus.). 292p. 65.00 *(978-981-283-696-0(9))*; pap. 39.00 *(978-981-283-697-7(7))* World Scientific Publishing Co., Inc.

Rich, Barnett. Schaum's Easy Outline of Elementary Algebra, Second Edition. 2nd ed. 2010. (Schaum's Easy Outlines Ser.). (ENG., Illus.). 144p. (C). pap. 11.00 *(978-0-07-174583-3(1)*, 0071745831) McGraw-Hill Cos., The.

Robbins, Joel. Matrix Algebra. (Illus.). 567p. (C). 44.95 *(978-0-86720-459-9(1))* Jones & Bartlett Learning, LLC.

Robertson. Introductory Algebra. Date not set. pap. 18.95 *(978-0-534-35135-9(2))* Brooks/Cole.

Rock, Nathaniel Max. Standards Driven Math: Combo Book. 2007. 688p. pap. 99.99 *(978-1-59980-033-2(0))* Nathaniel Max Rock.

Rockswold & Cram101 Textbook Reviews Staff. College Algebra with Modeling & Visualization. 2007. 168p. per. 12.95 *(978-1-4288-3606-8(3))* Cram101 Inc.

Rockswold, Gary K. Algebra & Trigonometry with Modeling & Visualization. 4th ed. 2009. (Rockswold Precalculus Ser.). (ENG.). 1176p. (C). 187.33 *(978-0-321-55801-4(X))* Addison Wesley.

—Algebra & Trigonometry with Modeling & Visualization. 4th ed. 2009. *(978-0-321-55509-9(6))* Addison-Wesley Longman, Inc.

—Algebra & Trigonometry with Modeling & Visualization, Books a la Carte Edition. 4th ed. 2010. (ENG.). 1176p. (C). ring bd. 112.40 *(978-0-321-65642-1(3))* Addison Wesley.

—College Algebra with Modeling & Visualization. 4th ed. 2008. (Rockswold Precalculus Ser.). (ENG.). 888p. (C). 168.67 *(978-0-321-54230-4(4))* Addison Wesley.

—College Algebra with Modeling & Visualization. 4th ed. 2009. *(978-0-321-56510-5(X))* Addison-Wesley Longman, Inc.

—Essentials of College Algebra with Modeling & Visualization. 4th ed. 2011. (ENG.). 768p. (C). 130.67 *(978-0-321-71528-9(4))* Addison Wesley.

—Essentials of College Algebra with Modeling & Visualization, Books A la Carte. 4th ed. 2010. (ENG.). 768p. (C). ring bd. 78.40 *(978-0-321-72672-8(3))* Addison Wesley.

—Essentials of College Algebra with Modeling & Visualization, Books a la Carte Plus MML/MSL Student Access Code Card (for ad hoc Valuepacks) 4th ed. 2010. (ENG.). (C). ring bd. 104.67 *(978-0-321-77218-3(0))* Addison Wesley.

—Essentials of College Algebra with Modeling & Visualization plus MyMathLab Student Access Kit. 3rd ed. 2007. (ENG.). (C). pap. 138.00 *(978-0-321-49082-7(7))* Pearson Education.

Rockswold, Gary K. & Krieger, Terry A. Beginning Algebra with Applications & Visualization. (MathXL Tutorials on CD Ser.). (ENG., (C). 2nd ed. 2007. Illus.). 720p. 168.00 *(978-0-321-50004-5(0))* 3rd ed. 2012. 672p. ring bd. 105.60 ***(978-0-321-74803-4(4))*** 3rd rev. ed. 2012. 704p. 168.00 *(978-0-321-77330-2(6))* Addison Wesley.

—Beginning Algebra with Applications & Visualization. 2nd ed. 2008. (Illus.). xxiv, 630p. *(978-0-321-51329-8(0))* Addison-Wesley Longman, Inc.

—Beginning Algebra with Applications & Visualization, Books a la Carte Edition. 2nd ed. 2010. (ENG.). (C). ring bd. 100.80 *(978-0-321-57843-3(0))* Addison Wesley.

—Beginning Algebra with Applications & Visualization, Books a la Carte Edition plus MyMathLab Stude. 2012. (ENG.). (C). ring bd. 115.60 ***(978-0-321-72939-2(0))*** Addison Wesley.

—Beginning Algebra with Applications & Visualization plus MyMathLab Student Access Kit. 2012. (ENG.). (C). pap. 178.00 ***(978-0-321-72940-8(4))*** Addison Wesley.

—Beginning & Intermediate Algebra with Applications & Visualization. (MathXL Tutorials on CD Ser.). (ENG., (C). 2nd ed. 2008. Illus.). 1116p. 176.00 *(978-0-321-50005-2(9))* 3rd rev. ed. 2011. 1072p. 176.00 *(978-0-321-78651-0(7))* Addison Wesley.

—Beginning & Intermediate Algebra with Applications & Visualization. 2nd ed. 2008. *(978-0-321-51331-1(2))* Addison-Wesley Longman, Inc.

—Beginning & Intermediate Algebra with Applications & Visualization, Books a la Carte Edition. 2nd ed. 2010. (ENG.). (C). ring bd. 105.60 *(978-0-321-57799-4(2))* Addison Wesley.

—Beginning & Intermediate Algebra with Applications & Visualization, Books a la Carte Edition plus MyMathLab Student Access Kit. 2012. (ENG.). (C). ring bd. 116.67 ***(978-0-321-72944-6(7))*** Addison Wesley.

—Beginning & Intermediate Algebra with Applications & Visualization plus MyMathLab Student Access Kit. 2012. (ENG.). (C). 186.00 ***(978-0-321-72945-3(5))*** Addison Wesley.

—Intermediate Algebra with Applications & Visualization. (Rockswold Developmental Mathematics Ser.). (ENG., 912p. (C). 3rd ed. 2007. Illus.). 168.00 incl. cd-rom *(978-0-321-50003-8(2))* 4th rev. ed. 2011. 168.00 *(978-0-321-77331-9(4))* Addison Wesley.

—Intermediate Algebra with Applications & Visualization. 3rd ed. 2008. (Illus.). *(978-0-321-51330-4(4))* Addison-Wesley Longman, Inc.

—Intermediate Algebra with Applications & Visualization, Books a la Carte Edition plus MyMathLab Student Access Kit. 2012. (ENG.). (C). ring bd. 110.80 ***(978-0-321-72942-2(0))*** Addison Wesley.

—Intermediate Algebra with Applications & Visualization plus MyMathLab Student Access Kit. 2012. (ENG.). (C). 178.00 ***(978-0-321-72943-9(9))*** Addison Wesley.

—Prealgebra, Books a la Carte Edition plus MyMathLab Student Access Kit. 2012. (ENG.). (C). ring bd. 107.20 ***(978-0-321-72930-9(7))*** Addison Wesley.

—Prealgebra plus MyMathLab Student Access Kit. 2012. (ENG.). (C). pap. 172.00 ***(978-0-321-72931-6(5))*** Addison Wesley.

Roos, J., ed. Algebra, Algebraic Topology & their Interactions: Proceedings of a Conference held in Stockholm, Aug. 3 - 13, 1983, & later developments. 2008. (Lecture Notes in Mathematics Ser.). pap. 59.95 *(978-3-540-16453-1(7))* Springer.

Rosenberg, A. Noncommutative Algebraic Geometry & Representations of Quantized Algebras. 2010. (Mathematics & Its Applications Ser.). 328p. pap. 279.00 *(978-90-481-4577-5(5)*, 9048145775) Springer.

Ross, Debra Anne & Ross, Debra. Algebra. 2nd ed. 2009. (ENG.). 208p. pap. 17.99 *(978-1-59863-980-3(3))* Course Technology.

Rothlauf, Franz. Representations for Genetic & Evolutionary Algorithms. 2nd ed. 2010. (ENG., Illus.). xvi, 325p. pap. 159.00 *(978-3-642-06410-4(8)*, 3642064108) Springer.

Rotman & Cram101 Textbook Reviews Staff. Advanced Modern Algebr. 2007. 196p. per. 13.95 *(978-1-4288-3436-1(2))* Cram101 Inc.

Rotman, Joseph J. Advanced Modern Algebra. 2nd rev. ed. 2010. (Graduate Studies in Mathematics: Vol. 114). (Illus.). 1008p. 99.00 *(978-0-8218-4741-1(4))* American Mathematical Society.

Rusczyk, Richard. Introduction to Algebra. 2007. per. 53.00 *(978-1-934124-01-7(X)*; 2nd ed. 2009. (Illus.). 656p. pap. 53.00 *(978-1-934124-14-7(1))* AoPS Inc.

Rusczyk, Richard & Crawford, Mathew. Intermediate Algebra. 2008. 720p. per. 59.00 *(978-1-934124-04-8(4))* AoPS Inc.

Rusczyk, Richard, et al. Intermediate Algebra Solutions Manual. 2007. per. 12.00 *(978-1-934124-05-5(2))* AoPS Inc.

—Prealgebra. 2011. (Illus.). 608p. pap. 49.00 ***(978-1-934124-21-5(4))*** AoPS Inc.

—Prealgebra Solutions Manual. 2011. (Illus.). 224p. pap. 12.00 ***(978-1-934124-22-2(2))*** AoPS Inc.

Sabadini, Irene & Sommen, F. Hypercomplex Analysis & Applications. 2010. (Trends in Mathematics Ser.). (ENG.). viii, 282p. 124.00 *(978-3-0346-0245-7(6)*, 3034602456) Birkhauser Verlag AG CHE. Dist: Springer.

Safier, Fred. Precalculus. 2nd ed. 2008. (Schaum's Outline Ser.). (ENG.). 426p. (C). pap. 20.00 *(978-0-07-150864-3(3)*, 0071508643) McGraw-Hill Cos., The.

Saracino, D. H. & Weispfenning, V. B., eds. Model Theory & Algebr. 2008. (Lecture Notes in Mathematics Ser.). 480p. pap. 69.95 *(978-3-540-07538-7(0))* Springer.

Saxon, John H., Jr. Homeschool Testing Book Algebra 2. 2nd ed. 2006. (Saxon Algebra Ser.). per. 10.99 *(978-1-60032-014-9(7))* Houghton Mifflin Harcourt Supplemental Pubs.

Scheid, Harald & Schwarz, Wolfgang. Elemente der Arithmetik und Algebra. 5th ed. 2008. (Illus.). 323p. pap. *(978-3-8274-1821-0(6))* Spektrum Akademischer Verlag GmbH.

Schreier, O. & Sperner, E. Introduction to Modern Algebra & Matrix Theory: Second Edition. David, Martin & Hausner, Melvin, trs. from GER. 2011. (Dover Books on Mathematics Ser.). (ENG.). 400p. pap. 24.95 *(978-0-486-48220-0(0))* Dover Pubns., Inc.

Schultz, Et Al. & Cram101 Textbook Reviews Staff. Algebra. 2007. 192p. per. 13.95 *(978-1-4288-3690-7(X))* Cram101 Inc.

Sepanski, Mark R. Algebra. 2010. (Pure & Applied Undergraduate Texts). (Illus.). 255p. 62.00 *(978-0-8218-5294-1(9))* American Mathematical Society.

Sesiano, Jacques. An Introduction to the History of Algebra: Solving Equations from Mesopotamian Times to the Renaissance. 2009. (Mathematical World Ser.). (FRE, MUL & ENG., Illus.). 174p. pap. 35.00 *(978-0-8218-4473-1(3))* American Mathematical Society.

Sharpe. Injective Modules. 2008. (Cambridge Tracts in Mathematics Ser.). (ENG., Illus.). 204p. pap. 48.00 *(978-0-521-09092-6(X))* Cambridge Univ. Pr.

Shaska, Tanush & Elezi, Artur, eds. Albanian Journal of Mathematics: Special Issue on Algebra & Algebraic Geometry. 2007. 350p. lib. bdg. *(978-0-9754541-7-6(X))* AulonaPr.

Shestopaloff, Yuri K. Properties & Interrelationships of Polynomial, Exponential, Logarithmic & Power Functions with Applications to Modeling Natural Phenomena. 2010. (Illus.). 228p. 59.95 *(978-0-9813800-2-5(6))* AKVY Pr. CAN. Dist: Lightning Source, Inc.

Shum. Advances in Algebra & Combinatorics. 2008. 184.00 *(978-981-279-000-2(4))* World Scientific Publishing Co., Inc.

Sinaceur, Hourya. Fields & Models: Based on the French Corps et Mochles. 2006. (Illus.). XXVI, 446p. (C). 99.00 *(978-0-8176-4114-6(9)*, 0817641149) Birkhauser Boston.

Singer, William M. Steenrod Squares in Spectral Sequences. 2006. (Mathematical Surveys & Monographs Ser.). 155p. 57.00 *(978-0-8218-4141-9(6))* American Mathematical Society.

Slater, Jeffrey, et al. Beginning & Intermediate Algebra Plus MyMathLab/MyStatLab Student Access Code Card. 3rd ed. 2010. (ENG.). (C). pap., pap. 186.00 *(978-0-321-74455-5(1))* Addison Wesley.

—Worksheets for Classroom or Lab Practice for Beginning & Intermediate Algebra. 3rd ed. 2009. (ENG.). 188p. (C). pap. 31.00 *(978-0-321-58585-1(2)*, Prentice Hall) Prentice Hall PTR.

Smith. College Algebra. 5th rev. ed. 2010. 149.95 *(978-0-7637-5816-5(7))* Jones & Bartlett Learning, LLC.

Solomon, Ronald. Abstract Algebra. 2009. (Pure & Applied Undergraduate Texts Ser.). (Illus.). 227p. 62.00 *(978-0-8218-4795-4(3))* American Mathematical Society.

Spanish BOP Pre Algebra. 2007. (SPA.). (YA). per. *(978-1-933387-97-0(1))* Knepper Pr. Corp.

Spears, William M. Evolutionary Algorithms: The Role of Mutation & Recombination. 2010. (Natural Computing Ser.). (ENG., Illus.). xiv, 222p. pap. 109.00 *(978-3-642-08624-3(1)*, 3642086241) Springer.

Springer, Tonny A. & Veldkamp, Ferdinand D. Octonions, Jordan Algebras, & Exceptional Groups. 2010. (Springer Monographs in Mathematics Ser.). (ENG., viii, 208p. pap. 129.00 *(978-3-642-08563-5(6)*, 3642085636) Springer.

Squires, John & Wyrick, Karen. Introductory Algebra. 2011. (ENG.). (C). 260p. pap. 26.67 ***(978-0-321-78614-2(9))***; 98.67 ***(978-0-321-67530-9(4))*** Addison Wesley.

—Notebook for Squires / Wyrick Intermediate Algebra. 2012. (ENG.). 312p. (C). pap. 26.67 ***(978-0-321-74602-3(3))*** Addison Wesley.

—Notebook (looseleaf) for Squires / Wyrick Intermediate Algebra. 2012. (ENG.). 200p. (C). pap. 26.67 ***(978-0-321-79500-7(8))*** Addison Wesley.

Statistical Inference, Number Systems, Vol. 11. 144p. 6.95 *(978-0-87891-210-0(X))* Research & Education Assn.

Stedall, Jacqueline. From Cardano's Great Art to Lagrange's Reflections: Filling a Gap in the History of Algebra. 2011. 236p. ***(978-3-03719-092-0(2))*** European Mathematical Society.

Steege, Ray & Bailey, Kerry. Schaum's Outline of Intermediate Algebra, Second Edition. 2nd ed. 2010. (ENG., Illus.). 408p. (C). pap. 18.95 *(978-0-07-162998-0(X)*, 007162998X) McGraw-Hill Cos., The.

Stein, Sherman K. Elementary Algebra: A Guided Inquiry. rev. ed. (Orig.). 21.20 *(978-1-55636-750-2(3))*; tchr. ed. 24.38 *(978-1-55636-751-9(1))*; tchr. ed. 8.22 *(978-1-55636-752-6(X))* Sunburst Communications, Inc.

Steinberg, R. Conjugacy Classes in Algebraic Groups. 2008. (Lecture Notes in Mathematics Ser.). pap. 39.95 *(978-3-540-06657-6(8))*, Springer.

Sterling, Mary Jane. Algebra I, Pack, No.1. 2nd ed. 2010. (ENG.). 360p. pap., wbk. ed. 18.99 *(978-0-470-49596-4(0)*, Cliff Notes) Wiley, John & Sons, Inc.

—Algebra I Essentials for Dummies. 2010. (ENG.). 192p. pap. 9.99 *(978-0-470-61834-9(5)*, For Dummies) Wiley, John & Sons, Inc.

—Algebra I for Dummies. 2nd ed. 2010. (ENG., Illus.). 384p. pap. 19.99 *(978-0-470-55964-2(0)*, For Dummies) Wiley, John & Sons, Inc.

—Algebra II, Pack. 2nd ed. 2010. (ENG.). 264p. pap. 18.99 *(978-0-470-49597-1(9)*, Cliff Notes) Wiley, John & Sons, Inc.

—Algebra II Essentials for Dummies. 2010. (ENG., Illus.). 192p. pap. 9.99 *(978-0-470-61840-0(X)*, For Dummies) Wiley, John & Sons, Inc.

Stewart & Redlin & Watson & Cram101 Textbook Reviews Staff. Algebra & Trigonometry. 2007. 172p. per. 12.95 *(978-1-4288-3502-3(4))* Cram101 Inc.

Stewart, James, et al. Algebra & Trigonometry. (Available 2010 Titles Enhanced Web Assign Ser.). (ENG., (C). 2nd ed. 2009. Illus.). 1120p. 202.95 *(978-1-4390-4730-9(8))* 3rd ed. 2011. 1040p. 227.95 *(978-0-8400-6813-2(1))* Brooks/Cole.

—Algebra & Trigonometry Study Guide. 3rd ed. 2011. (ENG.). 354p. (C). pap. 65.95 *(978-1-111-56810-8(3))* Brooks/Cole.

—College Algebra. 5th ed. 2008. (ENG.). (C). 272p. pap., pupil's gde. ed. 66.95 *(978-0-495-56523-9(7))*; (Illus.). 784p. 219.95 *(978-0-495-56521-5(0))*; 368p. pap. 66.95 *(978-0-495-56524-6(5))* Brooks/Cole.

—College Algebra, Hybrid. 2010. (ENG.). (C). 61.95 *(978-0-538-74031-9(0))*; 480p. pap. 104.95 *(978-0-538-74029-6(9))* Brooks/Cole.

—Note Taking Guide for Precalculus. (ENG.). (C). 5th ed. 2010. 264p. pap. 9.95 *(978-1-4390-4949-5(1))* 6th ed. 2011. 224p. pap. 9.95 *(978-1-111-57259-4(3))* Brooks/Cole.

—Precalculus. 5th ed. 2008. (Available 2010 Titles Enhanced Web Assign Ser.). (ENG.). 1072p. (C). pap. 131.95 *(978-0-495-55750-0(1))* Brooks/Cole.

—Precalculus: Mathematics for Calculus. (ENG.). (C). 5th ed. 2007. 1072p. 231.95 *(978-0-495-39276-7(6))* 5th ed. 2007. (Illus.). 1072p. 219.95 *(978-0-495-39277-4(4))* 6th ed. 2011. 1008p. 221.95 *(978-0-8400-6807-1(7))* Brooks/Cole.

—Student Solutions Manual for Stewart/Redlin/Watson's Algebra & Trigonometry, 3rd. 3rd ed. 2011. (ENG.). 474p. (C). pap. 71.95 *(978-0-8400-6923-8(5))* Brooks/Cole.

Stewart, Redlin & Cram101 Textbook Reviews Staff. College Algebr. 2007. 168p. per. 12.95 *(978-1-4288-3612-9(8))* Cram101 Inc.

Stewart, Scott, et al. College Algebra: Concepts & Contexts. 2010. (Available 2011 Titles Enhanced Web Assign Ser.). (ENG.). 816p. (C). 174.95 *(978-0-495-38789-3(4))* Brooks/Cole.

Stillwell, John. Elements of Algebra: Geometry, Numbers, Equations. 2010. (Undergraduate Texts in Mathematics Ser.). (Illus.). 200p. pap. 69.95 *(978-1-4419-2839-9(1)*, 1441928391) Springer.

Stone, Jacqueline. College Algebra with Applications Resource Manual. 4th rev. ed. 2007. (ENG.). 226p. pap. 18.00 *(978-0-7575-4158-2(5))* Kendall Hunt Publishing Co.

Streeter, Hutchison & Cram101 Textbook Reviews Staff. Prealgebra an Integrated Equations Approach. 2007. 104p. per. 10.95 *(978-1-4288-3676-1(4))* Cram101 Inc.

Subramaniam, Viswanatha. Productivity Redefinition - an Algebraic Model. 2010. 60p. pap. *(978-3-8383-6450-6(3)*, Lambert Academic Publishing.

Sullivan. Precalculus. 7th ed. 1184p. tchr. ed. 83.97 *(978-0-13-143133-1(1))* Prentice Hall (Schl. Div.).

Sullivan & Cram101 Textbook Reviews Staff. Precalculus. 2007. (ENG.). 60p. per. 27.95 *(978-1-4288-3488-0(5))* Cram101 Inc.

Sullivan, Michael. Algebra & Trigonometry, Books a la Carte Plus MML/MSL Student Access Code Card (for ad hoc Valuepacks) 9th ed. 2010. (ENG.). (C). ring bd. 122.40 *(978-0-321-77217-6(2))* Addison Wesley.

—Algebra & Trigonometry. 9th ed. 2011. (ENG.). 1176p. (C). 187.33 *(978-0-321-71656-9(6))* Addison Wesley.

—Algebra & Trigonometry. 8th ed. 2006. (ENG., Illus.). 1176p. (C). 181.33 *(978-0-13-232903-3(4)*, Prentice Hall) Prentice Hall PTR.

—Algebra & Trigonometry, Books a la Carte Edition. 9th ed. 2010. (ENG.). 1176p. (C). ring bd. 112.40 *(978-0-321-71716-0(3))* Addison Wesley.

—Algebra & Trigonometry Enhanced with Graphing Utilities. 5th ed. 2007. (Sullivan Enhanced with Graphing Utilities Ser.). (ENG., Illus.). 1200p. (C). 187.33 *(978-0-13-600492-9(X)*, Prentice Hall) Prentice Hall PTR.

—Algebra & Trigonometry (with MyMathLab Student Access Kit) 8th ed. 2010. (ENG.). (C). pap. 191.33 *(978-0-321-74715-0(1))* Pearson Education.

—College Algebra. 9th rev. ed. 2011. (ENG., Illus.). 840p. (C). 168.67 *(978-0-321-71681-7(7))* Addison Wesley.

—College Algebra. 8th ed. 2007. (ENG., Illus.). 840p. (C). 162.67 *(978-0-13-240286-6(6)*, Prentice Hall) Prentice Hall PTR.

—College Algebra: Concepts Through Functions. (Illus.). 2007. *(978-0-13-243175-0(0))* 2nd ed. 2010. (ENG., 792p. (C). 168.67 *(978-0-321-64107-6(8)*, Prentice Hall) Prentice Hall PTR.

Sullivan, Michael, III. College Algebra: Enhanced with Graphing Utilities. 5th ed. 2007. (Sullivan Enhanced with Graphing Utilities Ser.). (ENG.). 864p. (C). 168.67 *(978-0-13-600491-2(1)*, Prentice Hall) Prentice Hall PTR.

Sullivan, Michael. College Algebra, Books a la Carte Edition. 9th ed. 2011. (ENG.). 848p. (C). ring bd. 101.20 *(978-0-321-71699-6(X))* Addison Wesley.

—Precalculus. 9th rev. ed. 2011. (ENG.). 1152p. (C). 187.33 *(978-0-321-71683-5(3))* Addison Wesley.

—Precalculus. 8th ed. 2007. (ENG.). 1152p. (C). 187.33 *(978-0-13-225688-9(6)*, Prentice Hall) Prentice Hall PTR.

—Precalculus, Books a la Carte Edition. 9th ed. 2011. (ENG.). 1152p. (C). ring bd. 112.40 *(978-0-321-71765-8(1))* Addison Wesley.

—Precalculus Enhanced with Graphing Utilities. 4th ed. 900p. tchr. ed. 83.97 *(978-0-13-149095-6(8))*; stu. ed. 83.97 *(978-0-13-192496-3(6))* Prentice Hall (Schl. Div.).

—Precalculus Value Package (includes MyMathLab/MyStatLab Student Access) 8th ed. 2010. (ENG.). (C). pap. 197.33 *(978-0-321-75185-0(X))* Addison Wesley.

—Standalone for Algebra & Trigonometry. 8th ed. 2009. (ENG.). (C). pap. 36.67 *(978-0-321-62890-9(X)*, Prentice Hall) Prentice Hall PTR.

—Student Solutions Manual for Algebra & Trigonometry. 9th rev. ed. 2011. (ENG.). 960p. (C). pap. 36.67 *(978-0-321-71711-5(2))* Addison Wesley.

—Student Solutions Manual for College Algebra. 9th rev. ed. 2011. (ENG.). 648p. (C). pap. 36.67 *(978-0-321-71687-3(6))* Addison Wesley.

—Student Solutions Manual for College Algebra - Standalone. 8th ed. 2008. (ENG.). 536p. (C). pap. 36.67 *(978-0-321-62105-4(0)*, Prentice Hall) Prentice Hall PTR.

Sullivan, Michael & Struve, Katherine R. Intermediate Algebra. 2nd ed. 2008. (Sullivan/Struve/Mazzarella Algebra Ser.). (ENG.). (C). 888p. 168.00 *(978-0-321-56752-9(8))*; 456p. pap. 26.67 *(978-0-321-59305-4(7))* Prentice Hall PTR. (Prentice Hall).

—Intermediate Algebra Plus MyMathLab/MyStatLab Student Access Code Card. 2nd ed. 2010. (ENG.). (C). pap. 178.00 *(978-0-321-74620-7(1))* Addison Wesley.

—Student Solutions Manual (standalone) for Intermediate Algebra. 2nd ed. 2009. (ENG.). 864p. (C). pap. 36.67 *(978-0-321-58929-3(7)*, Prentice Hall) Prentice Hall PTR.

Sullivan, Michael & Sullivan, Michael, III. Algebra & Trigonometry. 5th ed. 2008. (ENG.). (C). cd-rom 33.33 ***(978-0-13-600539-1(X))*** Addison Wesley.

Sullivan, Michael & Sullivan III, Michael. Trigonometry Enhanced with Graphing Utilities Plus MyMathLab Student Access Kit. 5th ed. 2010. (ENG.). (C). pap. 178.00 *(978-0-321-75196-6(5))* Addison Wesley.

Sullivan, Michael & Sullivan, Michael, III. Precalculus Enhanced with Graphing Utilities. 6th rev. ed. 2012. (ENG., Illus.). 1152p. (C). 187.33 ***(978-0-321-79546-5(6))*** Addison Wesley.

Sullivan, Michael & Sullivan, Michael III. College Algebra: Concepts through Functions, Books a la Carte Edition. 2nd ed. 2010. (ENG.). (C). ring bd. 101.20 *(978-0-321-63670-6(8))* Addison Wesley.

Sullivan, Michael, et al. Elementary Algebra. 2nd ed. 2008. (ENG.). (C). 432p. pap. 26.67 *(978-0-321-59312-2(X))*; (Illus.). 792p. 168.00 *(978-0-321-56748-2(X))* Prentice Hall PTR. (Prentice Hall).

—Elementary & Intermediate Algebra. 2nd ed. 2009. (ENG.). 576p. (C). pap. 31.00 *(978-0-321-59359-7(5)*, Prentice Hall) Prentice Hall PTR.

Sullivan, Michael, III, et al. Elementary & Intermediate Algebra MyMathLab Edition. 2007. (ENG.). 816p. (C). spiral bd. 66.67 *(978-0-13-600868-2(2)*, Prentice Hall) Prentice Hall PTR.

—Intermediate Algebra: Mymathlab Edition. 2007. (Illus.). 559p. spiral bd. 41.33 *(978-0-13-600550-6(0))* Prentice Hall PTR.

Sullivan, Michael, et al. Student Solutions Manual for College Algebra: Concepts through Functions. 2nd ed. 2010. (ENG.). 600p. (C). pap. 36.67 *(978-0-321-63155-8(2)*, Prentice Hall) Prentice Hall PTR.

—Student Solutions Manual (standalone) for Elementary & Intermediate Algebra. 2nd ed. 2009. (ENG.). 1008p. (C). pap. 36.67 *(978-0-321-59351-1(0)*, Prentice Hall) Prentice Hall PTR.

Swarbrick, David. Algebra & its Applications. 2007. ring bd. 30.00 net. *(978-1-892664-07-5(0))* Bell Missions Publishing.

—Fractions, Decimal Numbers, & Percents. 2007. ring bd. 30.00 net. *(978-1-892664-05-1(4))* Bell Missions Publishing.

—Introduction to Algebra. 2007. ring bd. 30.00 net. *(978-1-892664-06-8(2))* Bell Missions Publishing.

—Introduction to Algebra II. 2007. ring bd. 30.00 net. *(978-1-892664-09-9(7))* Bell Missions Publishing.

Swokowski, Cole & Cram101 Textbook Reviews Staff. Algebra & Trigonometry with Analytic Geometry. 2007. 164p. per. 12.95 *(978-1-4288-3658-7(6))* Cram101 Inc.

Swokowski, Earl & Cole, Jeffery A. Algebra & Trigonometry with Analytic Geometry, Classic Edition. 12th ed. 2009. (Available 2010 Titles Enhanced Web Assign Ser.). (ENG.). 912p. (C). 237.95 *(978-0-495-55971-9(7))* Brooks/Cole.

Swokowski, Earl W. & Cole, Jeffery A. Algebra & Trigonometry with Analytic Geometry. (Available Titles CengageNOW Ser.). (ENG., (C). 12th rev. ed. 2007. Illus.). 1024p. 235.95 *(978-0-495-10826-9(X))* 13th ed. 2011. 960p. 235.95 *(978-0-8400-6852-1(2))* Brooks/Cole.

Tabak, John. Algebra. 2nd rev. ed. 2011. (History of Mathematics Ser.). (Illus.). 256p. (C). (gr. 9). 45.00 *(978-0-8160-7944-5(7))* Facts On File, Inc.

Taylor, Harold & Taylor, Loretta. Developing Skills in Algebra 1 Bk. A: Introduction to Algebra, Real Numbers, Solving Linear Equations, 16.50 *(978-0-86651-221-3(7),* DSO1441) Seymour, Dale Pubns.

—Developing Skills in Algebra 1/Applications of Fractions, Ratio & Proportion Bk. C: Graphs of Linear Equations & Inequalities: Linear Systems in Two Variables, 16.50 *(978-0-86651-223-7(3),* DSO1443) Seymour, Dale Pubns.

The Consortium for Foundation Mathematics. Mathematics in Action: Algebraic, Graphical, & Trigonometric Problem Solving. 3rd ed. 2007. (MathXL Tutorials on CD Ser.). (ENG., Illus.). 864p. (C). per. 145.33 *(978-0-321-44780-7(8))* Addison-Wesley Longman, Inc.

Tian, Jianjun Paul. Evolution Algebras & Their Applications. 2007. (Lecture Notes in Mathematics Ser.). (Illus.). 125p. per. 69.95 *(978-3-540-74283-8(2))* Springer.

Timmons, Daniel L., et al. Fundamentals of Algebraic Modeling: An Introduction to Mathematical Modeling with Algebra & Statistics. 5th ed. 2008. (ENG.). 456p. (C). 173.95 *(978-0-495-55509-4(6))* Brooks/Cole.

Tobey, John, Jr., et al. Beginning Algebra. 7th ed. 2008. *(978-0-321-57377-3(3))* Prentice Hall PTR.

—Beginning Algebra: Early Graphing Plus MyMathLab/MyStatLab Student Access Code Card. 2nd ed. 2010. (ENG.). (C). pap., pap. 172.00 *(978-0-321-74461-6(6))* Addison Wesley.

Tobey, John, et al. Beginning & Intermediate Algebra. 3rd ed. 2009. *(978-0-321-58582-0(8))* Prentice Hall PTR.

Tobey, John Jr, et al. Intermediate Algebra. 7th rev. ed. 2012. (ENG.). (C). pap., pap. 172.00 ***(978-0-321-82417-2(2))*** Addison Wesley.

Tobey, John S., Jr. & Slater, Jeffrey L. Worksheets for Classroom or Lab Practice for Intermediate Algebra. 6th ed. 2009. (ENG.). 154p. (C). pap. 26.67 *(978-0-321-59418-1(5),* Prentice Hall) Prentice Hall PTR.

Tobey, John S., et al. Beginning & Intermediate Algebra, Books a la Carte Edition. 4th ed. 2012. (ENG.). 912p. (C). ring bd. 105.60 ***(978-0-321-78062-1(0))*** Addison Wesley.

—Beginning & Intermediate Algebra, Books a la Carte Plus MML/MSL Student Access Code Card (for ad hoc Valuepacks) 4th ed. 2012. (ENG.). (C). ring bd. 115.60 ***(978-0-321-82420-2(2))*** Addison Wesley.

—Beginning & Intermediate Algebra plus MyMathLab/MyStatLab Student Access Code Card. 4th ed. 2012. (ENG.). (C). pap., pap. 186.00 ***(978-0-321-82419-6(9))*** Addison Wesley.

—Intermediate Algebra. 6th ed. 2008. *(978-0-321-57841-9(4))* Prentice Hall PTR.

—Intermediate Algebra. 6th ed. 2008. (Tobey/Slater Developmental Math Ser.). (ENG.). 768p. (C). pap. 162.00 *(978-0-321-57829-7(5),* Prentice Hall) Prentice Hall PTR.

Tobey, John S., Jr., et al. Intermediate Algebra. 7th rev. ed. 2011. (ENG.). 752p. (C). pap. 162.00 ***(978-0-321-76950-3(3))*** Addison Wesley.

Tobey, John S., et al. Intermediate Algebra, Books a la Carte Edition. 7th ed. 2011. (ENG.). 752p. (C). ring bd. 97.20 ***(978-0-321-76972-5(4))*** Addison Wesley.

Tobey, John S., Jr., et al. Student Solutions Manual for Intermediate Algebra. 6th ed. 2009. (ENG.). 336p. (C). pap. 36.67 *(978-0-321-57838-9(4),* Prentice Hall) Prentice Hall PTR.

Todhunter, Isaac. Algebra for Beginners with Numerous Examples. 2010. 336p. pap. 31.45 *(978-1-4455-4914-9(X),* Kent Pr.) Kent Communications, Ltd.

Tom, Mark & Woodbury, George. Instructor's Solutions Manual for Elementary & Intermediate Algebra. 2nd ed. 2009. (Illus.). 1042p. pap. 37.80 *(978-0-321-50673-3(1))* Addison-Wesley Longman, Inc.

Toth, Gabor. Glimpses of Algebra & Geometry. 2nd ed. 2012. (Undergraduate Texts in Mathematics Ser.). (ENG., Illus.). 484p. pap. 79.95 *(978-1-4419-2962-4(2),* 1441929622) Springer.

Trigsted, Kirk. Algebra & Trigonometry. rev. ed. 2011. (ENG.). 1136p. (C). spiral bd. 26.67 *(978-0-321-74421-0(7))* Addison Wesley.

—College Algebra. 2008. (ENG.). (C). 98.67 *(978-0-321-62135-1(2),* Prentice Hall) Prentice Hall PTR.

—Precalculus: A Right Triangle Approach. rev. ed. 2011. (ENG.). (C). 98.67 *(978-0-321-78486-5(3))* Addison Wesley.

Trigsted, Kirk. Precalculus Etext Reference: A Unit Circle Approach. 2012. (ENG.). 932p. (C). spiral bd. 26.67 ***(978-0-321-73683-3(4))*** Addison Wesley.

Trigsted, Kirk, et al. Beginning Algebra: Guided Notebook. rev. ed. 2011. (ENG.). 768p. (C). pap. 26.67 *(978-0-321-73854-7(3))* Addison Wesley.

—Beginning & Intermediate Algebra. rev. ed. 2011. (ENG.). (C). 1580p. 114.67 *(978-0-321-72640-7(5));*Kit. 384p. pap. 31.00 *(978-0-321-73857-8(8))* Addison Wesley.

—Intermediate Algebra. 2010. (ENG.). (C). 350p. spiral bd. 26.67 *(978-0-321-65285-0(1));*Kit. 1400p. stu. ed. 98.67 *(978-0-321-64594-4(4))* Prentice Hall PTR. (Prentice Hall).

Trigsted, Kirk, et al. MyMathLab Beginning & Intermediate Algebra Student Access Kit & eText Reference. 2011. (ENG.). (C). pap., spiral bd. 121.33 ***(978-0-321-78615-9(7))*** Addison Wesley.

Trimble, Cindy & Martin-Gay, Elayn. Introductory Algebra Student Solutions Manual. 3rd ed. 2006. (ENG., Illus.). 496p. (C). per. 36.67 *(978-0-13-227606-1(2))* Pearson Education Canada CAN. Dist: Pearson Education.

Tschinkel, Yuri & Zarhin, Yuri G., eds. Algebra, Arithmetic, & Geometry: Volume I: in Honor of Y. I. Manin. 2009. (Progress in Mathematics Ser.). (Illus.). 600p. 139.00 *(978-0-8176-4744-5(9))* Birkhauser Boston.

—Algebra, Arithmetic, & Geometry: Volume II: in Honor of Y. I. Manin. 2010. (Progress in Mathematics Ser.). (Illus.). 600p. 139.00 *(978-0-8176-4746-9(5))* Birkhauser Verlag AG CHE. Dist: Springer.

Tussy, Alan S., et al. Intermediate Algebra. 4th ed. 2010. (Textbooks Available with Cengage YouBook Ser.). (ENG.). (C). 1024p. pap. 195.95 *(978-1-4390-4436-0(8));* 464p. pap., wbk. ed. 42.95 *(978-0-538-73403-5(5))* Brooks/Cole.

—Introductory Algebra. 4th ed. 2010. (Textbooks Available with Cengage YouBook Ser.). (ENG., Illus.). 864p. (C). pap. 195.95 *(978-1-4390-4787-3(1))* Brooks/Cole.

Tussy, Gustafson & Cram101 Textbook Reviews Staff. Introductory Algebr. 2007. 128p. per. 11.95 *(978-1-4288-3578-8(4))* Cram101 Inc.

Tyne-Franzosa. Algebraic Models in Our World. rev. ed. 2011. (ENG.). 286p. spiral bd. 68.00 ***(978-0-7575-9372-7(0))*** Kendall Hunt Publishing Co.

The University of Chicago School Mathematics Project: Advanced Algebra, 1996. Date not set. stu. ed. 49.97 *(978-0-673-45804-9(0));* tchr. ed. 81.97 *(978-0-673-45807-0(5))* Prentice Hall (Schl. Div.).

Vasantha Kandasamy, W. B. Smarandache Special Definite Algebraic Structures. 2009. pap. 25.00 *(978-1-59973-085-1(5))* Multimedia Larga.

Viete, Francois. The Analytic Art: Nine Studies in Algebra, Geometry & Trigonometry from the Opus Restitutae Mathematicae Analyseos, Seu Algebra Nova. Witmer, T. Richard, tr. from LAT. 2006. (Dover Books on Mathematics Ser.). (ENG., Illus.). 464p. per. 24.95 *(978-0-486-45348-4(0))* Dover Pubns., Inc.

Vince, John A. Geometric Algebra for Computer Graphics. 2010. (Illus.). xvi, 256p. pap. 99.00 *(978-1-84996-697-9(4),* 1849966974) Springer.

Walch Publishing Staff. Academic Support Program for Algebra. 2007. (J). lthr. 395.00 *(978-0-8251-6376-0(5))* Walch Education.

Walker. New Course in Algebra: With Answer. Date not set. pap. 34.65 *(978-0-582-31870-0(X))* Addison-Wesley Longman, Ltd. GBR. Dist: Trans-Atlantic Pubns., Inc.

Wang, Rongdong & Ahangar, Reza. College Algebra Supplement. rev. ed. 2010. (ENG.). 122p. spiral bd. 81.90 *(978-0-7575-7763-5(6))* Kendall Hunt Publishing Co.

Weltman. Beginning Algebra. Date not set. (Math). stu. ed. 21.50 net. *(978-0-534-11779-5(1))* Brooks/Cole.

Wheater, Carolyn. Easy Pre-Calculus Step-by-Step. 2012. (Easy Step-by-Step Ser.). (ENG., Illus.). 336p. (C). pap. 14.00 ***(978-0-07-176767-5(3),*** 0071767673) McGraw-Hill Cos., The.

Wheater, Carolyn. Practice Makes Perfect Algebra. 2010. (ENG., Illus.). 192p. (C). pap. 12.95 *(978-0-07-163819-7(9),* 0071638199) McGraw-Hill Cos., The.

Wheel, Laura. Prealgebra Review Workbook. 2006. (ENG.). 300p. (C). pap. 36.67 *(978-0-321-47332-5(9))* Pearson Education.

Wilson, Delvin, ed. The Verbs of Algebra: Adding Integers: Using the Sea-Level Chart(r) to Manage the Addition of Integers. 2011. 48p. pap. 9.99 ***(978-1-4269-6519-7(2))*** Trafford Publishing.

Wilson, Frank, et al. College Algebra: A Make it Real Approach. 2012. (Textbooks Available with Cengage YouBook Ser.). (ENG.). (C). 155.95 ***(978-0-618-94532-0(6))*** Brooks/Cole.

Witkowski, Joseph & Phillips, Eileen. Applied Algebra & Trigonometry. rev. ed. 2011. (ENG.). 334p. spiral bd. 50.99 *(978-0-7575-8401-5(2))* Kendall Hunt Publishing Co.

Wolter, Kurt. Mathematics Refresher: Easy, Clear, & Right from the Beginning. 2011. 96p. 38.95 ***(978-1-258-07132-5(0))*** Literary Licensing, LLC.

Woodbury, George. Elementary Algebra. 2007. (MathXL Tutorials on CD Ser.). (ENG., Illus.). 688p. (C). 168.00 *(978-0-321-16642-5(6))* Addison Wesley.

—Elementary Algebra. 2008. (Illus.). xix, 610p. *(978-0-321-54204-5(5));* *(978-0-321-46757-7(4))* Addison-Wesley Longman, Inc.

—Elementary Algebra, Books a la Carte Edition. 2010. (ENG.). (C). ring bd. 100.00 *(978-0-321-58820-3(7))* Addison Wesley.

—Elementary & Intermediate Algebra. (MathXL Tutorials on CD Ser.). (ENG., (C). 2nd ed. 2008. Illus.). 1152p. 176.00 *(978-0-321-50006-9(7))* 3rd rev. ed. 2010. 976p. 176.00 *(978-0-321-66548-5(1))* Addison Wesley.

—Elementary & Intermediate Algebra. 2nd ed. 2008. *(978-0-321-50672-6(3))* Addison-Wesley Longman, Inc.

—Elementary & Intermediate Algebra. 3rd ed. 2010. tchr. ed. *(978-0-321-66584-3(8))* Pearson Education.

—Elementary & Intermediate Algebra, Books a la Carte Edition. 3rd ed. 2010. (ENG.). 976p. (C). ring bd. 105.60 *(978-0-321-65330-7(0))* Addison Wesley.

—Elementary & Intermediate Algebra plus MyMathLab Student Access Kit. 2nd ed. 2008. (ENG.). (C). pap. 186.00 *(978-0-321-52318-1(0))* Addison Wesley.

—Guide to Skills & Concepts for Elementary & Intermediate Algebra. 3rd ed. 2011. (ENG.). 670p. (C). pap. 26.67 *(978-0-321-71563-0(2))* Pearson Education.

—Intermediate Algebra. 2008. (MathXL Tutorials on CD Ser.). (ENG.). 976p. (C). 168.00 *(978-0-321-16641-8(8))* Addison Wesley.

—Intermediate Algebra. 2008. *(978-0-321-45955-8(5))* Addison-Wesley Longman, Inc.

—Student Solutions Manual for Elementary & Intermediate Algebra. 3rd rev. ed. 2011. 576p. (C). pap. 36.67 *(978-0-321-71562-3(4))* Pearson Education.

—Student's Solutions Manual for Intermediate Algebra. 2008. (ENG.). 656p. (C). pap. 36.67 *(978-0-321-46756-0(6))* Addison Wesley Higher Education.

Wright, Tony & Cram101 Textbook Reviews Staff. Intermediate Algebr. 2007. 128p. per. 11.95 *(978-1-4288-3588-7(1))* Cram101 Inc.

Wright, Warren S. Student Resource Manual to accompany Algebra & Trigonometry. 3rd ed. 2012. 384p. pap. 60.95 *(978-1-4496-3828-3(7))* Jones & Bartlett Learning, LLC.

—Student Resource Manual to accompany College Algebra. 3rd ed. 2012. 320p. pap. 60.95 *(978-1-4496-3830-6(9))* Jones & Bartlett Learning, LLC.

—Student Resource Manual to accompany Essentials of Precalculus with Calculus Previews. 5th ed. 2011. 264p. pap. 60.95 *(978-1-4496-3826-9(0))* Jones & Bartlett Learning, LLC.

Yisheng, Huang. BCI-Algebra. 2007. (ENG., Illus.). 356p. pap. 103.00 *(978-7-03-015411-6(8),* Elsevier Science) Elsevier Science & Technology Bks.

Yoshiwara, Katherine & Yoshiwara, Bruce. Modeling, Functions, & Graphs. 4th rev. ed. 2006. (ENG., Illus.). 936p. (C). 214.95 *(978-0-495-11306-5(9))* Brooks/Cole.

—Modeling, Functions, & Graphs: Algebra for College Students. 4th ed. (Illus.). 2007. *(978-0-495-19014-1(4))* 2006. (ENG., 936p. (C). 214.95 *(978-0-534-41941-7(0))* Brooks/Cole.

—S. S. M. Modeling Functions & Graphs: Algebra F/Coll Students. 4th ed. 2006. (ENG.). 368p. (C). pap. 75.95 *(978-0-534-41946-2(1))* Brooks/Cole.

Young. College Algebra 2E for Wharton College. 2nd ed. 2011. 896p. (C). pap. 83.95 ***(978-1-118-10333-3(5),*** Wiley) Wiley, John & Sons, Inc.

Young, Cynthia Y. Algebra & Trigonometry. 2007. (ENG., Illus.). 1200p. (C). 199.95 *(978-0-471-75683-5(0),* Wiley) Wiley, John & Sons, Inc.

—Algebra & Trigonometry. 2nd ed. 2008. (ENG.). 98p. (C). pap. 25.95 ***(978-0-470-47913-1(2),*** Wiley) Wiley, John & Sons, Inc.

—Algebra & Trigonometry. 2nd ed. 2009. (ENG.). 936p. (C). pap. 48.95 *(978-0-470-43376-8(0),* Wiley) Wiley, John & Sons, Inc.

—Algebra & Trigonometry. 3rd ed. 2012. (ENG.). (C). pap., stu. ed. 51.95 ***(978-1-118-13758-1(2));*** 1344p. 191.95 ***(978-0-470-64803-2(1))*** Wiley, John & Sons, Inc. (Wiley).

—Algebra & Trigonometry Wileyplus Set. 2007. (Wiley Plus Products Ser.). 132.95 *(978-0-470-13227-2(2))* Wiley, John & Sons, Inc.

—Algebra & Trigonometry with Wiley Plus WebCT Powerpack Set. 2006. (Wiley Plus Products Ser.). 132.95 *(978-0-470-13689-8(8))* Wiley, John & Sons, Inc.

—College Algebra. (Wiley Plus Products Ser.). 2007. pap. 88.95 *(978-0-470-14454-1(8))* 2006. 119.95 *(978-0-470-11918-1(7))* Wiley, John & Sons, Inc.

—College Algebra. 2nd ed. 2008. (ENG., Illus.). 888p. (C). 179.95 *(978-0-470-22272-0(7),* Wiley) Wiley, John & Sons, Inc.

—College Algebra. 2nd ed. 2009. (ENG.). 504p. (C). pap. 61.95 *(978-0-470-41703-4(X),* Wiley) Wiley, John & Sons, Inc.

—College Algebra. 3rd ed. 2012. (ENG.). 976p. (C). 173.95 ***(978-0-470-64801-8(5),*** Wiley) Wiley, John & Sons, Inc.

—College Algebra with Trigonometry & Wiley Plus (2) Set. 2006. (Wiley Plus Products Ser.). 174.95 *(978-0-470-14072-7(0))* Wiley, John & Sons, Inc.

—Intermediate Algebra. 2nd ed. 2009. (ENG.). 960p. (C). 116.95 *(978-0-470-50483-3(8),* Wiley) Wiley, John & Sons, Inc.

—Precalculus Suite Evaluation Package. 2nd ed. 2008. (ENG.). (C). 25.00 *(978-0-470-41504-7(5),* Wiley) Wiley, John & Sons, Inc.

—Precalculus with Limits. 2010. (ENG.). 1249p. (C). ring bd. 113.95 *(978-0-470-57836-0(X),* Wiley) Wiley, John & Sons, Inc.

Young, Cynthia Y., et al. Algebra & Trigonometry. 2nd ed. 2009. (ENG., Illus.). 1344p. (C). 199.95 *(978-0-470-22273-7(5),* Wiley) Wiley, John & Sons, Inc.

—Algebra & Trigonometry Student Solutions Manual. 2007. (ENG., Illus.). 740p. (C). pap., stu. ed. 47.95 *(978-0-471-78846-1(5),* Wiley) Wiley, John & Sons, Inc.

Yuen Fong, et al, eds. Proceedings of the Third International Algebra Conference: June 16-July 1, 2002, Chang Jung Christian University, Tainan, Taiwan. 2010. 280p. pap. 150.00 *(978-90-481-6351-9(X),* 904816351X) Springer.

Zegarelli, Mark T. Basic Math & Pre-Algebra for Dummies. 2007. (ENG., Illus.). 384p. per. 19.99 *(978-0-470-13537-2(9),* For Dummies) Wiley, John & Sons, Inc.

Zill. Algebra & Trigonometry W/ Calc Prev 3E. 3rd rev. ed. 2010. 750p. 167.95 *(978-0-7637-5461-7(7))* Jones & Bartlett Learning, LLC.

Zill, Dennis G. & Dewar, Jacqueline M. College Algebra. 3rd ed. 2010. 544p. 146.95 *(978-1-4496-0602-2(4))* Jones & Bartlett Learning, LLC.

—Essentials of Precalculus with Calculus Previews. 5th ed. 2010. 440p. 146.95 *(978-1-4496-1497-3(3))* Jones & Bartlett Learning, LLC.

ALGEBRA—DATA PROCESSING

Alexander, Michael & Gardner, William. Process Algebra for Parallel & Distributed Processing. Alexander, Michael & Gardner, William, eds. 2008. (Chapman & Hall/CRC Computational Science Ser.). (ENG., Illus.). 440p. 109.95 *(978-1-4200-6486-5(X),* Chapman & Hall/CRC) CRC Pr. LLC.

Algebraic Informatics: Second International Conference, CAI 2007, Thessaloniki, Greece, May 21-25, 2007, Revised Selected & Invited Papers. 2008. (Lecture Notes in Computer Science Ser.). (Illus.). 289p. pap. 79.95 *(978-3-540-75413-8(X))* Springer.

Angel, Allen R. Elementary Algebra Early Graphing for College Students Value Package (includes MyMathLab/MyStatLab Student Access) 3rd ed. 2010. (ENG.). (C). pap. 178.00 *(978-0-321-74719-8(4))* Addison Wesley.

—Elementary Algebra for College Students plus MyMathLab/MyStatLab Student Access Code Card. 8th ed. 2010. (ENG.). (C). pap. 178.00 *(978-0-321-71453-4(9))* Addison Wesley.

Association for Computing Machinery Staff, contrib. by. ISSAC 2008. 2008. (Illus.). x, 338p. pap. ***(978-1-59593-904-3(0))*** Assn. for Computing Machinery.

Autexier, Serge, et al. Intelligent Computer Mathematics: 10th International Conference, AISC 2010, 17th Symposium, Calculemus 2010, & 9th International Conference, MKM 2010, Paris, France, July 5-10, 2010, Proceedings. 2010. (Lecture Notes in Computer Science / Lecture Notes in Artificial Intelligence Ser.). xv, 471p. pap. 99.00 *(978-3-642-14127-0(7),* 3642141277) Springer.

Bayro-Corrochano, Eduardo & Scheuermann, Gerik, eds. Geometric Algebra Computing: In Engineering & Computer Science. 2010. (ENG., Illus.). xvi, 524p. 159.00 *(978-1-84996-107-3(7),* 1849961077) Springer.

Bittinger, et al. Introductory & Intermediate Algebra plus MyMathLab/MyStatLab Student Access Code Card. 4th ed. 2010. (ENG.). (C). pap., pap. 186.00 *(978-0-321-71773-3(2))* Addison Wesley.

Blitzer, Robert F. Algebra & Trigonometry Plus MyMathLab/MyStatLab Student Access Code Card. 4th ed. 2010. (ENG.). (C). pap. 197.33 *(978-0-321-74621-4(X))* Addison Wesley.

—Algebra & Trigonometry, the MyMathLab/MyStatLab Edition, Package. 4th ed. 2010. (ENG.). (C). pap., spiral bd. 125.33 *(978-0-321-74454-8(3))* Addison Wesley.

—College Algebra Essentials Plus MyMathLab/MyStatLab Student Access Code Card. 3rd ed. 2010. (ENG.). (C). pap. 140.67 *(978-0-321-74622-1(8))* Addison Wesley.

—College Algebra Plus MyMathLab Student Access Kit. 5th ed. 2010. (ENG.). (C). pap. 178.67 *(978-0-321-74705-1(4))* Addison Wesley.

—Collge Algebra, the MyMathLab/MyStatLab Edition, Package. 5th ed. 2010. (ENG.). (C). pap., spiral bd. 120.00 *(978-0-321-74460-9(8))* Addison Wesley.

—Precalculus, the MyMathLab/MyStatLab Edition, Package. 4th ed. 2010. (ENG.). (C). pap., spiral bd. 125.33 *(978-0-321-74459-3(4))* Addison Wesley.

Bosma, Wieb & Cannon, John, eds. Discovering Mathematics with Magma: Reducing the Abstract to the Concrete. 2010. (Algorithms & Computation in Mathematics Ser.). (Illus.). xxiv, 374p. pap. 119.00 *(978-3-642-07231-4(3),* 3642072313) Springer.

Bosma, Wieb & van der Poorten, Alf, eds. Computational Algebra & Number Theory. 2010. (Mathematics & Its Applications Ser.). 340p. pap. 279.00 *(978-90-481-4560-7(0),* 9048145600) Springer.

Bozapalidis, Symeon & Rahonis, George. Algebraic Informatics: 3rd International Conference on Algebraic Informatics, CAI 2009, Thessaloniki, Greece, Mai 19-22 2009. 2009. (Lecture Notes in Computer Science / Theoretical Computer Science & General Issues Ser.). (ENG.). x, 361p. pap. 79.95 *(978-3-642-03563-0(9),* 3642035639) Springer.

Bras-Amorós, Maria & Hoholdt, Tom. Applied Algebra, Algebraic Algorithms & Error-Correcting Codes: 18th International Symposium, AAECC-18, Tarragona, Sapin, June 8-12, 2009, Proceedings. 2009. (Lecture Notes in Computer Science / Theoretical Computer Science & General Issues Ser.). xi, 243p. pap. 69.95 *(978-3-642-02180-0(8),* 3642021808) Springer.

Carson, et al. Elementary & Intermediate Algebra plus MyMathLab/MyStatLab Student Access Code Card. 3rd ed. 2010. (ENG.). (C). pap. 186.00 *(978-0-321-62437-6(8))* Addison Wesley.

Cohen, Arjeh M., et al, eds. Some Tapas of Computer Algebra. 2011. (Algorithms & Computation in Mathematics Ser.). (ENG., Illus.). xiv, 352p. pap. 79.95 *(978-3-642-08335-8(8),* 3642083358) Springer.

Dase, Pamela & Dase, Pamela H. TI Graphing Calculator Strategies: Algebra. 2006. (Texas Instruments Graphic Calculator Strategies Ser.). (ENG., Illus.). 238p. (gr. 6-12). pap. 34.99 *(978-1-4258-0024-6(6))* Shell Educational Publishing.

Davenport, James H., et al, eds. Intelligent Computer Mathematics: 18th Symposium, Calculemus 2011, & 10th International Conference, MKM 2011, Bertinoro, Italy, July 18-23, 2011, Proceedings. 2011. (Lecture Notes in Computer Science / Lecture Notes in Artificial Intelligence Ser.). (Illus.). xiv, 312p. pap. 83.00 ***(978-3-642-22672-4(8),*** 3642226728) Springer.

DeWilde, Patrick & Veen, Alle-Jan van der. Time-Varying Systems & Computations. 2010. (ENG.). 474p. pap. 259.00 *(978-1-4419-5045-1(1),* 1441950451) Springer.

Dixon, Lucas, et al. Intelligent Computer Mathematics: 16th Symposium, Calculemus 2009, 8th International Conference, MKM 2009, Grand Bend, Canada, July 6-12, 2009, Proceedings. 2009. (Lecture Notes in Computer Science / Lecture Notes in Artificial Intelligence Ser.). (ENG.). xix, 493p. pap. 109.00 *(978-3-642-02613-3(3),* 3642026133) Springer.

Dugopolski, Mark. College Algebra & Trigonometry: A Unit Circle Approach, A la Carte Plus MyMathLab Student Access Kit. 5th ed. 2010. (ENG.). (C). ring bd. 122.40 *(978-0-321-66404-4(3))* Addison Wesley.

—Graphing Calculator Manual for Precalculus: Functions & Graphs. 3rd ed. 2007. (ENG.). 128p. (C). pap. 24.67 *(978-0-321-53544-3(8))* Addison Wesley Higher Education.

Enns, Richard H. & McGuire, George C. Computer Algebra Recipes: An Advanced Guide to Scientific Modeling. 2007. (ENG., Illus.). x, 374p. 69.95 *(978-0-387-25768-6(3),* 0387257683) Springer.

Futatsugi, Kokichi, et al. Algebra, Meaning, & Computation: Essays dedicated to Joseph A. Goguen on the Occasion of His 65th Birthday. 2006. (Lecture

Notes in Computer Science Ser.: Vol. 4060). (Illus.). XXXVIII, 643p. pap. 129.00 *(978-3-540-35462-8(X)*, 354035462X) Springer.
Ganzha, V. G., et al. Computer Algebra in Scientific Computing: 10th International Workshop, CASC 2007, Bonn, Germany, September 16-20, 2007, Proceedings. 2007. (Lecture Notes in Computer Science / Theoretical Computer Science & General Issues Ser.). xiii, 460p. pap. 89.95 *(978-3-540-75186-1(6))* Springer.
Ganzha, Victor G., et al, eds. Computer Algebra in Scientific Computing: 9th International Workshop, CASC 2006 Chisinau, Moldova, September 11-15, 2006 Proceedings. 2007. (Lecture Notes in Computer Science Ser.). (Illus.). 312p. per. 79.95 *(978-3-540-45182-2(X)*, 354045182X) Springer.
Gerber, Leon. Algebra & Calculus with Excel for Business & Economics. 2007. (C). per. *(978-0-9792926-0-6(3))* Gerber, Leon.
—Precalculus & Calculus with Excel for Science. 2007. (C). per. *(978-0-9792926-2-0(X))* Gerber, Leon.
—Precalculus with Excel. 2007. (C). per. *(978-0-9792926-3-7(8))* Gerber, Leon.
Gerdt, Vladimir P. et al. Computer Algebra in Scientific Computing: 11th International Workshop, CASC 2009, Kobe, Japan, September 13-17, 2009, Proceedings. 2009. (Lecture Notes in Computer Science / Theoretical Computer Science & General Issues Ser.). xi, 393p. pap. 99.00 *(978-3-642-04102-0(7)*, 3642041027) Springer.
Gerdt, Vladimir P. et al, eds. Computer Algebra in Scientific Computing: 12th International Workshop, CASC 2010, Tsakhadzor, Armenia, September 6-12, 2010, Proceedings. 2010. (Lecture Notes in Computer Science / Theoretical Computer Science & General Issues Ser.). xiv, 304p. pap. 83.00 *(978-3-642-15273-3(2)*, 3642152732) Springer.
Gerdt, Vladimir P. et al, eds. Computer Algebra in Scientific Computing: 13th International Workshop, CASC 2011, Kassel, Germany, September 5-9, 2011. Proceedings. 2011. (Lecture Notes in Computer Science / Theoretical Computer Science & General Issues Ser.). (ENG., Illus.). xi, 359p. pap. 83.00 ***(978-3-642-23567-2(0)***, 3642235670) Springer.
Hardy, Yorick. Computer Algebra with SimbolicC++ 2008. pap. 58.00 *(978-981-283-361-7(7))* World Scientific Publishing Co., Inc.
—Computer Algebra with Symbolicc++ 2008. 107.00 *(978-981-283-360-0(9))* World Scientific Publishing Co., Inc.
Horimoto, Katsuhisa, et al, eds. Algebraic & Numeric Biology: 4th International Conference, ANB 2010, Hagenberg, Austria, July 31-August 2, 2010, Revised Selected Papers. 2012. (Lecture Notes in Computer Science / Theoretical Computer Science & General Issues Ser.). (ENG., Illus.). x, 185p. pap. 72.00 ***(978-3-642-28066-5(8)***, 3642280668) Springer.
Hornsby, John, et al. A Graphical Approach to Algebra & Trigonometry plus MyMathLab/MyStatLab Student Access Code Card. 5th ed. 2010. (ENG.). (C). pap. 197.33 *(978-0-321-70896-0(2))* Addison Wesley.
Intelligent Computer Mathematics. 2008. (Lecture Notes in Computer Science / Lecture Notes in Artificial Intelligence Ser.). spiral bd. 109.00 *(978-3-540-85109-7(7))* Springer.
Janßen, Rainer, ed. Trends in Computer Algebra: International Symposium, Bad Neuenahr, May 19-21, 1987. Proceedings. 2007. (Lecture Notes in Computer Science Ser.). 212p. per. 34.95 *(978-3-540-18928-2(9))* Springer.
Kamischke, Eric, et al. Exploring Algebra 1 with Fathom Dynamic Data Software Version 2. 2007. (Illus.). xii, 234p. ***(978-1-55953-801-5(5))*** Key Curriculum Pr.
Kauers, Manuel. Towards Mechanized Mathematical Assistants: 14th Symposium, Calculemus 2007, 6th International Conference, MKM 2007, Hagenberg, Austria, June 27-30, 2007, Proceedings. 2007. (Lecture Notes in Artificial Intelligence Ser.). (Illus.). 406p. pap. 89.95 *(978-3-540-73083-5(4))* Springer.
Kotsireas, Ilias S. & Zima, Eugene V., eds. Computer Algebra: Latest Advances in Symbolic Algorithms - Proceedings of the Waterloo Workshop. 2007. (Illus.). 211p. 82.00 *(978-981-270-200-5(8))* World Scientific Publishing Co., Inc.
Kuich, Werner & Rahonis, George, eds. Algebraic Foundations in Computer Science: Essays Dedicated to Symeon Bozapalidis on the Occasion of His Retirement. 2011. (Lecture Notes in Computer Science / Theoretical Computer Science & General Issues Ser.). (ENG., Illus.). x, 363p. pap. 83.00 ***(978-3-642-24896-2(9)***, 3642248969) Springer.
Kunkel, Paul, et al. Exploring Algebra 2 with the Geometer's Sketchpad. 4th ed. 2007. (Illus.). xvi, 238p. pap. ***(978-1-55953-799-5(X))*** Key Curriculum Pr.
Lehmann, Jay. Elementary Algebra: Graphs & Authentic Applications Value Package (includes MyMathLab/MyStatLab Student Access) 2010. (ENG.). (C). pap. 178.00 *(978-0-321-74721-1(6))* Addison Wesley.
Lu, Hsiao-Feng, ed. Applied Algebra, Algebraic Algorithms & Error-Correcting Codes. 2007. (Lecture Notes in Computer Science Ser.). 368p. pap. 79.95 *(978-3-540-77223-1(5))* Springer.
Machì, Antonio. Algebra for Symbolic Computation: Introduction to Computational Algebra. 2012. (UNITEXT / la Matematica per il 3+2 Ser.). (ENG., Illus.). 190p. pap. 59.95 ***(978-88-470-2396-3(3)***, 8847023963) Springer.
Martin-Gay, Elayn. Beginning Algebra Plus MyMathLab Student Access Kit. 5th ed. 2010. (ENG.). (C). pap. 178.00 *(978-0-321-75186-7(8))* Addison Wesley.
—Beginning & Intermediate Algebra Plus MyMathLab Student Access Kit. 4th ed. 2010. (ENG.). (C). pap. 186.00 *(978-0-321-74706-2(9))* Addison Wesley.
Mulzet, Alfred, text. Using the TI-83 for College Algebra: A Step-by-step Approach. 2006. spiral bd. 30.00 *(978-0-9776973-1-1(2))* Palm Coast Publishing Incorporated
Ng, E. W., ed. Symbolic & Algebraic Computation: Eurosam '79, an International Symposium on Symbolic & Algebraic Manipulation, Marseille, France, June 1979. 2007. (Lecture Notes in Computer Science Ser.). 580p. pap. 49.95 *(978-3-540-09519-4(5)*, 3540095195) Springer.
Nielsen, Mogens, et al. SOFSEM 2009: Theory & Practice of Computer Science: 35th Conference on Current Trends in Theory & Practice of Computer Science, Špindleruv Mlýn, Czech Republic, January 24-30, 2009. Proceedings. 2009. (Lecture Notes in Computer Science / Theoretical Computer Science & General Issues Ser.). (Illus.). xvii, 670p. pap. 119.00 *(978-3-540-95890-1(8))* Springer.
Ratti, Jogindar & McWaters, Marcus S. College Algebra, A la Carte Plus MyMathLab Student Access Kit. 2nd ed. 2010. (ENG.). (C). ring bd. 111.20 *(978-0-321-65450-2(1))* Addison Wesley.
Schmidt, Renate A. Relations & Kleene Algebra in Computer Science: 9th International Conference on Relational Methods in Computer Science & 4th International Workshop on Applications of Kleene Algebra, RelMiCS/AKA 2006, Manchester, UK, August 29 - September 2, 2006, Proceedings. 2006. (Lecture Notes in Computer Science Ser.: Vol. 4136). (Illus.). XI, 433p. pap. 89.95 *(978-3-540-37873-0(1)*, 3540378731) Springer.
Seibt, Peter. Algorithmic Information Theory: Mathematics of Digital Information Processing. 2010. (Signals & Communication Technology Ser.). (Illus.). vi, 444p. pap. 179.00 *(978-3-642-06978-9(9)*, 3642069789) Springer.
Seiler, Werner M. Involution: The Formal Theory of Differential Equations & its Applications in Computer Algebra. 2009. (Algorithms & Computation in Mathematics Ser.). (ENG., Illus.). xxii, 650p. 129.00 *(978-3-642-01286-0(8)*, 3642012868) Springer.
Shingareva, Inna & Lizárraga-Celaya, Carlos. Maple & Mathematica: A Problem Solving Approach for Mathematics. 2007. xiii, 263p. pap. 59.95 *(978-3-211-73264-9(0))* Springer.
Shingareva, Inna K. & Lizárraga-Celaya, Carlos. Maple & Mathematica: A Problem Solving Approach for Mathematics. 2nd ed. 2009. (Illus.). xviii, 483p. 69.95 *(978-3-211-99431-3(9)*, 3211994319) Springer.
Sommer, Gerald, ed. Geometric Computing with Clifford Algebras: Theoretical Foundations & Applications in Computer Vision & Robotics. 2010. (ENG., Illus.). xviii, 551p. pap. 139.00 *(978-3-642-07442-4(1)*, 3642074421) Springer.
Steeb, Willi-Hans & Hardy, Yorick. Quantum Mechanics Using Computer Algebra: Includes Sample Programs in C++, Symbolicc++, Maxima, Maple, & Mathematica (2nd Edition) 2nd ed. 2010. 244p. 62.00 *(978-981-4307-16-1(5))* World Scientific Publishing Co., Inc.
Sullivan, Michael, III. College Algebra Enhanced with Graphing Utilities Plus MyMathLab/MyStatLab Student Access Code Card. 5th ed. 2010. (ENG.). (C). pap. 178.67 *(978-0-321-74464-7(0))* Addison Wesley.
Sullivan, Michael. College Algebra (with MyMathLab & Stickers Package) 8th ed. 2010. (ENG.). (C). pap. 172.67 *(978-0-321-74707-5(0))* Pearson Education.
Sullivan, Michael & SullivanIII, Michael. Algebra & Trigonometry Enhanced with Graphing Utilities Plus MyMathLab Student Access Kit. 5th ed. 2010. (ENG.). (C). pap. 197.33 *(978-0-321-74725-9(9))* Addison Wesley.
Sullivan, Michael, et al. Elementary Algebra Plus MyMathLab/MyStatLab Student Access Code Card. 2nd ed. 2010. (ENG.). (C). pap. 178.00 *(978-0-321-74457-9(8))* Addison Wesley.
—Elementary & Intermediate Algebra plus MyMathLab/MyStatLab/MyStatLab Student Access Code Card. 2nd ed. 2010. (ENG.) (C). pap. 186.00 *(978-0-321-74619-1(8))* Addison Wesley.
Tobey, John S., Jr. & Slater, Jeffrey L. Beginning Algebra Plus MyMathLab/MyStatLab Student Access Code Card. 7th ed. 2010. (ENG.). (C). pap., pap. 172.00 *(978-0-321-74617-7(1))* Addison Wesley.
Vanhulzen, J., ed. Computer Algebra. 2007. (Lecture Notes in Computer Science Ser.). 328p. per. 39.95 *(978-3-540-12868-7(9))* Springer.
Verschelde, J., ed. International Workshop on Symbolic-Numeric Computation (SNC 07) 2007. 203p. pap. 93.00 *(978-1-60423-400-8(8))* Curran Assocs., Inc.
Vorhees, Alice Bedard. Shorter Term Success in Online College Algebr. 2008. 76p. pap. *(978-3-639-05986-1(7))* VDM Verlag Dr. Mueller e.K.
Wester, M. J., et al. Computer Algebra in Education. 2008. (Illus.). 145p. per. 75.00 *(978-0-9754541-9-0(6))* AulonaPr.
Winkler, Franz, ed. Algebraic Informatics: 4th International Conference, CAI 2011, Linz, Austria, June 21-24, 2011, Proceedings. 2011. (Lecture Notes in Computer Science / Theoretical Computer Science & General Issues Ser.). (Illus.). x, 261p. pap. 72.00 ***(978-3-642-21492-9(4)*** 3642214924) Springer.
Wu, Weili & Daescu, Ovidiu, eds. Combinatorial Optimization & Applications: 4th International Conference, COCOA 2010, Kailua-Kona, HI, USA, December 18-20, 2010, Proceedings, Part I. 2010. (Lecture Notes in Computer Science / Theoretical Computer Science & General Issues Ser.). xvi, 424p. pap. 95.00 *(978-3-642-17457-5(4)*, 3642174574) Springer.
Zhang, Fuzhen, ed. The Schur Complement & Its Applications. 2010. (Numerical Methods & Algorithms Ser.). xvi, 296p. pap. 149.00 *(978-1-4419-3712-4(9)*, 1441937129) Springer.

ALGEBRA—EARLY WORKS TO 1800

Al-Khayam, Omar. Essay by the Uniquely Wise 'Abel Fath Omar Bin Al-Khayam on Algebra & Equations: Algebra Wa Al-Muqabala. Khalil, Roshdi, tr. from ARA. 2008. 57p. (Illus.). pap. 34.95 *(978-1-85964-181-1(4))*; (C). 69.95 *(978-1-85964-180-4(6))* Garnet Publishing, Ltd. GBR. Dist: International Specialized Bk. Services.
Cardano, Girolamo. The Rules of Algebra: Ars Magna. Witmer, T. Richard, tr. from LAT 2007. (Dover Books on Mathematics Ser.). (ENG., Illus.). 304p. per. 14.95 *(978-0-486-45873-1(3))* Dover Pubns., Inc.
Hoyrup, Jens. Jacopo da Firenze. Tractatus Algorismi. 2007. (Science Networks. Historical Studies). 500p. 139.00 *(978-3-7643-8390-9(9)*, 3764383909) Birkhauser Verlag AG CHE. Dist: Springer.

ALGEBRA—EXAMINATIONS, QUESTIONS, ETC.

Blitzer. Precalculus: TestGen. 2nd rev. ed. 49.97 *(978-0-13-101925-6(2))* Prentice Hall (Schl. Div.).
Clemens, Meg & Waldner, Bruce C. Algebra 2/Trigonometry Power Pack. 2011. (Regents Power Packs Ser.). (ENG.). pap. 18.99 *(978-0-7641-9732-1(0))* Barron's Educational Series, Inc.
Clemens, Meg, et al. Algebra 2/Trigonometry. 2011. (Barron's Regents Exams & Answers Bks.). (ENG.). 512p. pap. 7.99 *(978-0-7641-4512-4(6))* Barron's Educational Series, Inc.
Day, Erica. Passing the California Algebra 1 End of Course Test. 2007. per. 23.00 *(978-1-59807-141-2(6))* American Bk. Co.
Kohn, Edward & Herzog, David Alan. CliffsNotes Algebra II QuickReview. 2nd ed. 2011. (ENG., Illus.). 288p. pap. 9.99 *(978-0-470-87634-3(4)*, Cliff Notes) Wiley, John & Sons, Inc.
LearningExpress Staff. 501 Algebra Questions. 2nd rev. ed. 2007. (501 Algebra Questions Ser.). (ENG., Illus.). 288p. per. 16.95 *(978-1-57685-552-2(X))* LearningExpress, LLC.
Leff, Lawrence S. Integrated Algebra. 2011. (ENG., Illus.). 496p. pap., pupil's gde. ed. 7.99 *(978-0-7641-3870-6(7))* Barron's Educational Series, Inc.
—Let's Review: Integrated Algebra. 2008. (Let's Review Ser.). (ENG., Illus.). 528p. per. 13.99 *(978-0-7641-3591-0(0))* Barron's Educational Series, Inc.
Lial, Margaret L., et al. Additional Skill & Drill Manual for College Algebra. 10th ed. 2007. (ENG.). 96p. (C). pap. 36.67 *(978-0-321-53048-6(9))* Addison Wesley.
—Additional Skill & Drill Manual for College Algebra & Trigonometry & Precalculus. 4th ed. 2008. (ENG.). 144p. (C). pap. 36.67 *(978-0-321-52929-2(6))* Addison Wesley.
—Additional Skill & Drill Manual for Intermediate Algebra. 10th ed. 2007. (ENG.). 464p. (C). pap. 36.67 *(978-0-321-44637-4(2))* Addison Wesley Higher Education.
—Prealgebra & Introductory Algebra. 3rd ed. 2009. (ENG.). 624p. (C). pap. 36.67 *(978-0-321-59929-2(2))* Addison-Wesley Longman, Inc.
Lipschutz, Seymour. McGraw-Hill's 500 College Linear Algebra Questions to Know by Test Day. 2012. (ENG., Illus.). 192p. pap. 16.00 ***(978-0-07-179799-3(8)***, 0071797998) McGraw-Hill Cos., The.
Low, Yvonne. Kyoodoz Pre-Algebra Multiple Choice Questions. 2010. 200p. (YA). 25.00 *(978-0-9771172-3-9(5))* Kyoodoz.
Manhattan GMAT. Equations, Inequalities, & VIC's, GMAT Preparation Guide, 4th Edition. 4th rev. ed. 2009. (ENG.). 216p. pap. 26.00 *(978-0-9824238-1-3(0))* Manhattan Prep Publishing.
—Word Translations GMAT Preparation Guide, 4th Edition. 4th rev. ed. 2009. (ENG.). 216p. pap. 26.00 *(978-0-9824238-7-5(X))* Manhattan Prep Publishing.
Manhattan GRE. Algebra GRE Strategy Guide, 2nd Edition. 2nd ed. 2011. (ENG.). 144p. pap. 20.00 *(978-1-935707-47-9(7))* Manhattan Prep Publishing.
Marx, Andrew, et al. Shortcut Algebra I: A Quick & Easy Way to Increase Your Algebra I Knowledge & Test Scores. 2007. (ENG., Illus.). 288p. pap. 12.00 *(978-1-4195-5288-5(0))* Kaplan Publishing.
Morrison, Elizabeth & Carleton, Jodie. Florida End-of-Course Assessment - Algebra 1. 2012. (Florida FCAT Test Preparation Ser.). (ENG.). 336p. (J). (gr. 10-12). pap. 15.95 ***(978-0-7386-1022-1(4))*** Research & Education Assn.
Newman, Donald & Boxer, Robert J. College Algebra Exam File. 2nd ed. 2007. (ENG.). 278p. pap. 17.95 *(978-1-4195-1816-4(X))* Kaplan Publishing.
Research and Education Association Staff. CLEP College Algebra. 2012. (CLEP Test Preparation Ser.). (ENG.). 192p. (C). (gr. 13-14). pap. 34.95 ***(978-0-7386-1016-0(X))*** Research & Education Assn.
Rudman, Jack. College Algebra. (College Level Examination Ser.: Vol. 6). 47.95 *(978-0-8373-5356-2(4)*, Passbooks) National Learning Corp.
—College Algebras - Trigonometry. (College Level Examination Ser.: Vol. 7). (C). 47.95 *(978-0-8373-5357-9(2)*, Passbooks) National Learning Corp.
Sullivan. Elementary Algebra: TestGen. 2006. 700p. cd-rom 49.97 *(978-0-13-146819-1(7))* Prentice Hall (Schl. Div.).
Topical Review Book Co. Staff, Illus. Algebra 2/Trigonometry Practice Tests for Regents Examinations. 2010. pap. 2.50 *(978-1-929099-88-7(6))* Topical Review Bk Co., Inc.
—Answer Key for Algebra 2/Trigonometry Practice Tests for Regents Examinations. 2010. 0.25 *(978-1-929099-89-4(4))* Topical Review Bk Co., Inc.
—Single Exams for Algebra 2/Trigonometry Regents Examinations. 2010. 0.30 *(978-1-929099-90-0(8))* Topical Review Bk Co., Inc.
Waldner, Bruce. Let's Review Algebra 2 & Trigonometry. 2009. (Let's Review Ser.). (ENG.). 496p. pap. 13.99 *(978-0-7641-4186-7(4))* Barron's Educational Series, Inc.

ALGEBRA—GRAPHIC METHODS

see also Equations—Numerical Solutions; Geometry, Analytic

Barnett & Ziegler & Byleen & Cram101 Textbook Reviews Staff. Precalculus. 2007. 164p. per. 12.95 *(978-1-4288-3372-2(2))* Cram101 Inc.
Barnett, Raymond A. College Algebra: Graphs & Models. 3rd ed. 2008. (Illus.). *(978-0-07-305195-6(0))* McGraw-Hill Cos., The.
—College Algebra: Graphs & Models. 3rd ed. 2009. (Illus.). 124.50 *(978-0-07-334187-3(8))* McGraw-Hill Higher Education.
—Precalculus. 7th ed. 2010. *(978-0-07-351951-7(0))* McGraw-Hill Cos., The.
Barnett, Raymond A., et al. College Algebra: Graphs & Models. 3rd ed. 2008. (ENG.). 896p. (C). 166.00 *(978-0-07-722128-7(1)*, 0077221281, McGraw-Hill Science, Engineering & Mathematics) McGraw-Hill Higher Education.
—Precalculus. (ENG., (C). 6th ed. 2007. Illus.). 1192p. 163.75 *(978-0-07-331263-7(0)*, 0073312630) 7th ed. 2010. 944p. 185.67 *(978-0-07-734991-2(1)*, 0077349911) McGraw-Hill Higher Education. (McGraw-Hill Science, Engineering & Mathematics).
—Precalculus: Raymond A. Barnett, Michael R. Ziegler, Karl E. Byleen.. 6th ed. 2008. (Illus.). xxiv, 1044p. *(978-0-07-330424-3(7))* McGraw-Hill Cos., The.
—Student's Solutions Manual to Accompany College Algebra: Graphs & Models. 3rd ed. 2008. (ENG., Illus.). 576p. (C). pap. 84.67 *(978-0-07-334185-9(1)*, 0073341851, McGraw-Hill Science, Engineering & Mathematics) McGraw-Hill Higher Education.
Beecher, Judith, et al. Annotated Instructor's Edition. 3rd rev. ed. 2007. 816p. *(978-0-321-28627-7(8))* Pearson Bks.
Beecher, Judith A., et al. College Algebra: Graphing Calculator Manual. 3rd ed. 2007. (ENG., Illus.). 120p. (C). per. 24.67 *(978-0-321-46498-9(2))* Addison-Wesley Longman, Inc.
Bittinger, et al. Elementary & Intermediate Algebra: Graphs & Models, Books a la Carte Plus MML/MSL Student Access Code Card (for ad hoc Valuepacks) 4th ed. 2011. (ENG.). (C). ring bd. 116.67 ***(978-0-321-77187-2(7))*** Addison Wesley.
Bittinger, Marvin L., et al. Algebra & Trigonometry: Graphs & Models. 5th rev. ed. 2012. (ENG., Illus.). 1120p. (C). 187.33 ***(978-0-321-78397-4(2))*** Addison Wesley.
—Algebra & Trigonometry: Graphs & Models & Graphing Calculator Manual Package. (Bittinger Graphs & Models Ser.). (ENG.). (C). 4th ed. 2008. 1052p. pap. 187.33 *(978-0-321-50151-6(9))* 5th rev. ed. 2012. 1152p. pap. 187.33 ***(978-0-321-82422-6(9))*** Addison Wesley.
—Algebra & Trigonometry: Graphs & Models, Books a la Carte plus Graphing Calculator Manual. 5th ed. 2012. (ENG.). (C). pap., ring bd. 112.40 ***(978-0-321-84236-7(7))*** Addison Wesley.
—College Algebra: Graphs & Models. 5th rev. ed. 2011. (ENG.). 800p. (C). 168.67 ***(978-0-321-78395-0(6))*** Addison Wesley.
—College Algebra: Graphs & Models, Books a la Carte plus Graphing Calculator Manual. 5th ed. 2012. (ENG.). (C). pap., ring bd. 101.20 ***(978-0-321-84237-4(5))*** Addison Wesley.
—College Algebra: Graphs & Models with Graphing Calculator Manual Package. 4th ed. 2007. (Bittinger Graphs & Models Ser.). (ENG.). 768p. (C). pap. 168.67 *(978-0-321-53192-6(2))* Addison Wesley.
—Elementary & Intermediate Algebra: Graphs & Models. 4th rev. ed. 2010. (ENG.). 1104p. (C). 176.00 *(978-0-321-72634-6(0))* Addison Wesley.
—Elementary & Intermediate Algebra: Graphs & Models. 4th ed. 2011. tchr. ed. *(978-0-321-72663-6(4))* Pearson Education.
—Elementary & Intermediate Algebra: Graphs & Models plus MyMathLab/MyStatLab Student Access Code Card. 4th ed. 2011. (ENG.). (C). pap. 186.00 *(978-0-321-76021-0(2))* Addison Wesley.
—Intermediate Algebra: Graphs & Models. 4th ed. 2011. (ENG.). 960p. (C). 168.00 *(978-0-321-72555-4(7))* Addison Wesley.
—Intermediate Algebra: Graphs & Models. 4th ed. 2011. tchr. ed. *(978-0-321-72668-1(5))* Pearson Education.
—Precalculus: Graphs & Models. 5th rev. ed. 2012. (ENG.). 1120p. (C). 187.33 ***(978-0-321-78396-7(4))*** Addison Wesley.
—Worksheets for Classroom or Lab Practice for Elementary & Intermediate Algebra: Graphs & Models. 4th ed. 2011. (ENG.). 300p. (C). pap. 31.00 *(978-0-321-72666-7(9))* Addison Wesley.
—Worksheets for Classroom or Lab Practice for Intermediate Algera: Graphs & Models. 4th rev. ed. 2011. (ENG.). 368p. (C). pap. 26.67 *(978-0-321-74607-8(4))* Pearson Education.
Brown, Courtney. Graph Algebra: Mathematical Modeling with a Systems Approach. 2007. (Quantitative Applications in the Social Sciences Ser.: 151). (Illus.). 104p. (C). per. 18.00 *(978-1-4129-4109-9(1)*, B41091P) SAGE Pubns., Inc.
Burgis, Kathy. Investigating College Algebra & Trigonometry with Technology: Trigonometry Chapters 12 And 13. 2008. (ENG.). 90p. (C). pap. 12.95 *(978-0-470-41235-0(6)*, Wiley) Wiley, John & Sons, Inc.
—Investigating College Algebra & Trigonometry with Technology with Trigonometry Chapters 12 & 13 Student CD-ROM & Access Code Card. 2008. (ENG.). 698p. (C). 172.95 *(978-0-470-41332-6(8)*, Wiley) Wiley, John & Sons, Inc.
—Investigating College Algebra with Technology. 2008. (ENG.). 697p. (C). 136.95 *(978-0-470-41249-7(6)*, Wiley) Wiley, John & Sons, Inc.
Burgis, Kathy & Morford, Jeff. Investigating College Algebra & Trigonometry with Technology. 2008. (ENG.). 697p. (C). 178.95 *(978-0-470-41239-8(9)*, Wiley) Wiley, John & Sons, Inc.
—Investigating College Algebra & Trigonometry with Technology, with Student CD-ROM & Access Code Card. 2008. (ENG.). 698p. (C). 178.95 *(978-0-470-41331-9(X)*, Wiley) Wiley, John & Sons, Inc.
—Investigating College Algebra with Technology, Student CD-ROM with Access Code Card. 2008. (ENG.). 697p. (C). 136.95 *(978-0-470-41330-2(1)*, Wiley) Wiley, John & Sons, Inc.
Coburn, John & Herdlick, J. D. (John). Loose Leaf Version for College Algebra: Graphs & Models. 2011. (ENG.). (C). ring bd. 116.33 *(978-0-07-743084-9(0)*, 0077430840, McGraw-Hill Science, Engineering & Mathematics) McGraw-Hill Higher Education.
Coburn, John W. & Herdlick, J. D. (John). Loose Leaf Version for Precalculus: Graphs & Models. 2011. (ENG.). (C). ring bd. 130.00 *(978-0-07-743118-1(9)*, 0077431189, McGraw-Hill Science, Engineering & Mathematics) McGraw-Hill Higher Education.

Coburn, John W. & Herdlick, John D. College Algebra: Graphs & Models. 2011. (ENG., Illus.). 896p. (C). 166.00 *(978-0-07-351954-8(5)*, 0073519545, McGraw-Hill Science, Engineering & Mathematics) McGraw-Hill Higher Education.

Cram101 Textbook Reviews. Outlines & Highlights for Beginning Algebr: Early Graphing by John Tobey. 2011. 134p. pap. 28.95 ***(978-1-61905-117-1(6))*** Cram101 Inc.

—Outlines & Highlights for Elementary & Intermediate Algebr: Graphs & Models by Marvin L. Bittinger. 2011. 246p. pap. 31.95 ***(978-1-61905-007-5(2))*** Cram101 Inc.

Cram101 Textbook Reviews. Outlines & Highlights for Precalculus Functions & Graphs: Graphing Approach by Ron Larson. 2010. 352p. pap. 34.95 *(978-1-4288-5072-9(4))* Cram101 Inc.

Cram101 Textbook Reviews Staff. Outlines & Highlights for College Algebr: Graphs & Models by Bittinger, Marvin L. , ISBN. 2009. 120p. pap. 28.95 *(978-1-4288-3790-4(6))* Cram101 Inc.

—Outlines & Highlights for Experiencing Introductory & Intermediate Algebra Through Functions & Graphs by Thomasson, Joanne / Pesut, Robert, Isbn. 2009. 162p. pap. 29.95 *(978-1-4288-3789-8(2))* Cram101 Inc.

—Outlines & Highlights for Precalculus: A Graphing Approach, Enhanced Edition by Ron Larson, ISBN. 2009. 236p. pap. 31.95 *(978-1-4288-2435-5(9))* Cram101 Inc.

—Outlines & Highlights for Precalculus: Functions & Graphs by Earl Swokowski, ISBN. 2009. 152p. pap. 29.95 *(978-1-4288-2381-5(6))*; 328p. pap. 33.95 *(978-1-4288-9739-7(9))* Cram101 Inc.

—Outlines & Highlights for Precalculus: Graphing Approach by Ron Larson, Bruce H. Edwards, Robert P. Hostetler, ISBN. 2009. 250p. pap. 31.95 *(978-1-4288-3689-1(6))* Cram101 Inc.

Crawford, Jennifer, et al. Beginning Algebra: Early Graphing. 3rd rev. ed. 2012. (ENG.). (C). pap., pap. 172.00 ***(978-0-321-82415-8(6))*** Addison Wesley.

Demarois. Graphing Calculator Manual - Cd. 3rd rev. ed. 2010. (ENG.). 85.00 *(978-0-7575-2919-1(4))* Kendall Hunt Publishing Co.

Dugopolski, Mark. Precalculus: Functions & Graphs. 4th rev. ed. 2011. (ENG.). 960p. (C). 187.33 ***(978-0-321-78943-3(1))*** Addison Wesley.

Dugopolski, Mark. Student's Solutions Manual for Precalculus: Functions & Graphs. 3rd ed. 2007. (ENG.). 360p. (C). pap. 36.67 *(978-0-321-53543-6(X))* Addison Wesley.

Ebersole. Intermediate Algebra: Graphing Approach. 2010. *(978-0-314-20056-3(8))* West Publishing Co., College & Schl. Div.

Hirsh & Goodman. Understanding Intermediate Algebra Using Graphing Tech. 2009. *(978-0-314-20498-1(9))* Aspatore Bks.

Jacobs, Russell F. Algebra II Topics by Design. 2007. (Illus.). *(978-0-918272-38-6(6))* Jacobs Publishing Co.

Larson, Ron. Algebra & Trigonometry: A Graphing Approach. 5th ed. 2007. (ENG.). 656p. (C). pap. 65.95 *(978-0-618-85198-0(4)*, 333393) Brooks/Cole.

—Algebra & Trigonometry: A Graphing Approach, Enhanced Edition (with Enhanced WebAssign 1-Semester Printed Access Card) 5th ed. 2009. (ENG.). 1168p. (C). 204.95 *(978-1-4390-4454-4(6))* Brooks/Cole.

Larson, Ron, et al. Precalculus. 2007. 176p. per. 12.95 *(978-1-4288-3418-7(4))* Cram101 Inc.

Lial, Margaret L., et al. Graphing Calculator Manual for College Algebra. 10th ed. 2008. (ENG.). 120p. (C). pap. 24.67 *(978-0-321-52887-2(5))* Addison Wesley.

—Graphing Calculator Manual for College Algebra & Trigonometry/Precalculus. 4th ed. 2008. (ENG.). 144p. (C). pap. 24.67 *(978-0-321-52925-1(1))* Addison Wesley Higher Education.

Martin-Gay, K. Elayn & Greene, Margaret. Intermediate Algebra: A Graphic Approach. 3rd ed. 2007. pap. *(978-0-13-236447-8(6))* Pearson Education Canada.

Noftsier, Kathleen. Integrated Algebra on the Ti-73. 2011. 308p. pap. 15.33 *(978-1-4269-4329-4(6))* Trafford Publishing.

Penna, Judith A. Graphing Calculator Manual for College Algebra: Graphs & Models. 4th ed. 2008. (ENG.). 144p. (C). pap. 24.67 *(978-0-321-52908-4(1))* Addison Wesley.

Slater, Jeffrey, et al. Beginning Algebra: Early Graphing. 2nd ed. 2009. (ENG.). 288p. (C). pap. 36.67 *(978-0-321-57816-7(3)*, Prentice Hall) Prentice Hall PTR.

Sullivan, Michael & Sullivan, Michael, III. College Algebra Enhanced with Graphing Utilities. 6th rev. ed. 2012. (ENG.). 816p. (C). 168.67 ***(978-0-321-79564-9(4))*** Addison Wesley.

Sullivan, Michael & Sullivan, Michael, III. Algebra & Trigonometry Enhanced with Graphing Utilities. 6th rev. ed. 2011. (ENG.). 1152p. (C). 187.33 ***(978-0-321-78483-4(9))*** Addison Wesley.

Sullivan, Michael & Sullivan, Michael, Iii, III. College Algebra Enhanced with Graphing Utilities. 6th rev. ed. 2012. (ENG.). 550p. (C). pap. 36.67 ***(978-0-321-84506-1(4))*** Addison Wesley.

Sullivan, Michael & Sullivan, Michael Iii. College Algebra Enhanced with Graphing Utilities, Books a la Carte Edition. 6th ed. 2012. (ENG.). 928p. (C). ring bd. 101.20 ***(978-0-321-81647-4(1))*** Addison Wesley.

—College Algebra Enhanced with Graphing Utilities, Books a la Carte Edition plus MyMathLab Student Access Kit. 2012. (ENG.). (C). ring bd. 111.20 ***(978-0-321-83212-2(4))*** Addison Wesley.

—College Algebra Enhanced with Graphing Utilities plus MyMathLab Student Access Kit. 2012. (ENG.). (C). pap. 178.67 ***(978-0-321-83211-5(6))*** Addison Wesley.

—Student Solutions Manual for College Algebra Enhanced with Graphing Utilities. 6th ed. 2012. (ENG.). 536p. (C). pap. 36.67 ***(978-0-321-81655-9(2))*** Addison Wesley.

Swokowski, Earl & Cole, Jeffery. Precalculus: Functions & Graphs. 12th ed. 2011. (Textbooks Available with Cengage YouBook Ser.). (ENG.). 912p. (C). 232.95 *(978-0-8400-6857-6(3))* Brooks/Cole.

—Student's Solutions Manual for Swokowski/Cole's Algebra & Trigonometry with Analytic Geometry, Classic Edition, 12th. 12th ed. 2009. (ENG.). 432p. (C). pap. 74.95 *(978-0-495-56072-2(3))* Brooks/Cole.

Tobey, John, et al. Beginning Algebra: Early Graphing. 2nd ed. 2010. *(978-0-321-57821-1(X))* Prentice Hall PTR.

Tobey, John, Jr., et al. Beginning Algebra: Early Graphing. 3rd rev. ed. 2011. (ENG.). 656p. (C). pap. 162.00 ***(978-0-321-76951-0(1))*** Addison Wesley.

Tobey, John S., Jr., et al. Worksheets for Beginning Algebra: Early Graphing. 2nd ed. 2009. (ENG.). (C). 148p. pap. 26.67 *(978-0-321-57824-2(4))*; 688p. pap. 162.00 *(978-0-321-57796-2(5))* Prentice Hall PTR. (Prentice Hall).

Young, Cynthia Y. Algebra & Trigonometry with Limits: Prepared for Kirkwood Community College. 2007. (Illus.). 1241p. pap. 132.95 *(978-0-470-25844-6(6)*, Wiley) Wiley, John & Sons, Inc.

ALGEBRA—PROBLEMS, EXERCISES, ETC.

Addison-Wesley. Algebra for College Students Worksheets for Classromm or Lab Practice. 6th ed. 2007. (ENG.). 400p. (C). pap. 26.67 *(978-0-321-52326-6(1))* Addison Wesley Higher Education.

—Beginning Algebra Worksheets for Classroom or Lab Practice. 10th ed. 2007. (ENG.). 406p. (C). pap. 26.67 *(978-0-321-49409-2(1))* Addison Wesley Higher Education.

—Intermediate Algebra Worksheets for Classroom or Lab Practice. 10th ed. 2007. (ENG.). 480p. (C). pap. 26.67 *(978-0-321-51686-2(9))* Addison Wesley Higher Education.

—Prealgebra Worksheets for Classroom or Lab Practice. 5th ed. 2007. (ENG.). 352p. (C). pap. 26.67 *(978-0-321-51677-0(X))* Addison Wesley Higher Education.

Addison-Wesley, James S. Intermediate Algebra Worksheets for Classroom or Lab Practice. 2008. (ENG.). 440p. (C). pap. 26.67 *(978-0-321-52315-0(6))* Addison Wesley Higher Education.

Addison-Wesley Publishing Staff. Beginning Algebra with Applications & Visualization Worksheets for Classroom or Lab Practice. 2nd ed. 2008. (ENG.). 344p. (C). pap. 26.67 *(978-0-321-54583-1(4))* Addison Wesley Higher Education.

Addison-Wesley Publishing Staff, et al. Addison-Wesley's Algebra Review. 2nd ed. 6p. 4.97 *(978-0-321-39473-6(9))* Prentice Hall PTR.

Akst, Geoffrey & Bragg, Sadie. Student's Solutions Manual for Intermediate Algebra through Applications. 3rd rev. ed. 2012. (ENG.). 250p. (C). pap. 36.67 ***(978-0-321-75715-9(7))*** Addison Wesley.

—Student's Solutions Manual for Introductory Algebra through Applications. 3rd ed. 2012. (ENG.). 298p. (C). pap. 36.67 ***(978-0-321-75931-3(1))*** Addison Wesley.

Andersen, Maria H. Algebra for College Students. 2nd ed. 2010. (ENG.). 496p. (C). pap., wbk. ed. 42.95 *(978-0-8400-6167-6(6))* Brooks/Cole.

Andersen, Maria H. & Lockwood, Joanne. Algebra: Introductory & Intermediate - An Applied Approach. 5th ed. 2010. (ENG.). 480p. (C). pap., wbk. ed. 64.95 *(978-0-538-49544-8(8))* Brooks/Cole.

—Intermediate Algebra with Applications. 7th ed. 2010. (ENG.). 492p. (C). pap., wbk. ed. 42.95 *(978-0-538-73158-4(3))* Brooks/Cole.

Aufmann, Richard N. & Lockwood, Joanne. Algebra: Introductory & Intermediate - An Applied Approach. 5th ed. 2010. (ENG.). 184p. (C). pap. 40.95 *(978-0-8400-6431-8(4))* Brooks/Cole.

—Beginning Algebra. 2010. (ENG.). 208p. (C). pap. 47.95 *(978-0-8400-5424-1(6))* Brooks/Cole.

—Intermediate Algebra. 2010. (ENG.). 240p. (C). pap. 47.95 *(978-0-8400-5428-9(9))* Brooks/Cole.

—Prealgebra & Introductory Algebra: An Applied Approach. 2nd ed. 2010. (ENG.). 202p. (C). pap. 40.95 *(978-0-8400-6430-1(6))* Brooks/Cole.

Aufmann, Richard N., et al. Beginning Algebra with Applications. 7th ed. 2010. (ENG.). 374p. (C). pap., wbk. ed. 42.95 *(978-0-538-73159-1(1))* Brooks/Cole.

Barnett, Raymond, et al. Student Solutions Manual Precalculus. 7th ed. 2010. (ENG.). 688p. (C). pap. 76.67 *(978-0-07-729754-1(7)*, 0077297547, McGraw-Hill Science, Engineering & Mathematics) McGraw-Hill Higher Education.

Barnett, Raymond A., et al. Student's Solutions Manual to Accompany College Algebra: Graphs & Models. 3rd ed. 2008. (ENG., Illus.). 576p. (C). pap. 84.67 *(978-0-07-334185-9(1)*, 0073341851, McGraw-Hill Science, Engineering & Mathematics) McGraw-Hill Higher Education.

Bittinger, Marvin L. Student's Solutions Manual for Intermediate Algebra: Concepts & Applications. 8th ed. 2009. (ENG.). 300p. (C). pap. 36.67 *(978-0-321-58874-6(6))* Pearson Education.

Bittinger, Marvin L. & Ellenbogen, David J. Student's Solutions Manual for Elementary Algebra: Concepts & Applications. 8th ed. 2009. (ENG.). 288p. (C). pap. 36.67 *(978-0-321-56733-8(1))* Addison Wesley.

Bittinger, Marvin L., et al. College Algebra: Graphs & Models. 4th ed. (ENG., (C). 2009. Illus.). 816p. 168.67 *(978-0-321-52832-2(8))* 2008. pap. 178.67 *(978-0-321-53193-3(0))* Addison Wesley.

—Student's Solutions Manual. 5th rev. ed. 2012. (ENG.). 432p. (C). pap. 36.67 ***(978-0-321-79098-9(7))*** Addison Wesley.

Bittinger, Marvin L., et al. Worksheets for Classroom or Lab Practice for Elementary & Intermediate Algebra: Concepts & Applications. 5th ed. 2009. (ENG.). 504p. (C). pap. 31.00 *(978-0-321-59933-9(0))* Addison Wesley.

Blair, Jamie, et al. Student Solutions Manual for Intermediate Algebra. 7th rev. ed. 2012. (ENG.). 500p. (C). pap. 36.67 ***(978-0-321-75898-9(6))*** Addison Wesley.

—Worksheets with the Math Coach for Beginning Algebra: Early Graphing. 3rd rev. ed. 2012. (ENG.). 314p. (C). pap. 26.67 ***(978-0-321-76989-3(9))*** Addison Wesley.

Blair, Richelle M. Intermediate Algebra. 2006. (Blair Developmental Mathematics Ser.). (ENG., Illus.). 850p. (C). pap. 162.00 *(978-0-201-65887-3(9))* Addison Wesley.

Blitzer, Robert F. Student Solutions Manual for Algebra & Trigonometry: An Early Functions Approach. 2nd ed. 2009. (ENG.). 966p. (C). pap. 36.67 *(978-0-321-58881-4(9)*, Prentice Hall) Prentice Hall PTR.

—Student Solutions Manual for Algebra for College Students. 7th rev. ed. 2012. (ENG.). 888p. (C). pap. 36.67 ***(978-0-321-76060-9(3))*** Addison Wesley.

—Student Solutions Manual for College Algebra. 5th ed. 2009. (ENG.). 616p. (C). pap. 36.67 *(978-0-321-56895-3(8)*, Prentice Hall) Prentice Hall PTR.

—Student Solutions Manual for College Algebra: An Early Functions Approach. 2nd ed. 2009. (ENG.). 632p. (C). pap. 36.67 *(978-0-321-58865-4(7)*, Prentice Hall) Prentice Hall PTR.

—Student Solutions Manual for Intermediate Algebra for College Students. 6th rev. ed. 2012. (ENG.). 500p. (C). pap. 36.67 ***(978-0-321-76033-3(6))*** Addison Wesley.

—Student Solutions Manual for Introductory & Intermediate Algebra for College Students. 4th rev. ed. 2012. (ENG.). 500p. (C). pap. 36.67 ***(978-0-321-76052-4(2))*** Addison Wesley.

—Student Solutions Manual (standalone) 5th ed. 2008. (ENG.). 528p. (C). pap. 36.67 *(978-0-13-603146-8(3)*, Prentice Hall) Prentice Hall PTR.

Blitzer, Robert F. Worksheets for Algebra for College Students. 7th rev. ed. 2012. (ENG.). 328p. (C). pap. 26.67 ***(978-0-321-76061-6(1))*** Addison Wesley.

Carson, Tom, et al. Student Solutions Manual for Intermediate Algebra. 3rd ed. 2010. (ENG.). 408p. (C). pap. 36.67 *(978-0-321-62694-3(X))* Addison-Wesley Longman, Inc.

—Student's Solutions Manual for Elementary Algebra. 3rd ed. 2010. (ENG.). 384p. (C). pap. 36.67 *(978-0-321-62281-5(2))* Addison-Wesley Longman, Inc.

Coburn, John. Algebra & Trigonometry. 2nd ed. 2009. (C). ring bd. 108.13 *(978-0-07-736660-5(3)*, 0077366603, McGraw-Hill Science, Engineering & Mathematics) McGraw-Hill Higher Education.

Coburn, John & Herdlick, J. D. (John). Student Solutions Manual for College Algebra: Graphs & Models. 2011. (ENG.). 496p. (C). pap. 68.33 *(978-0-07-723060-9(4)*, 0077230604, McGraw-Hill Science, Engineering & Mathematics) McGraw-Hill Higher Education.

Cohen, David. Precalculus - Student Soltuions Manual. 7th ed. 2011. (ENG.). 864p. (C). pap. 68.95 *(978-1-111-42824-2(7))* Brooks/Cole.

Connally, Eric, et al. Algebra: Form & Function. 2010. (ENG.). 192p. (C). pap. 39.95 *(978-0-471-71336-4(8)*, Wiley) Wiley, John & Sons, Inc.

Contemporary. Seeking Patterns, Building Rules: Algebraic Thinking. 2011. (ENG.). 176p. (C). (gr. 12-12). pap. 12.00 ***(978-0-07-662088-3(3)***, 0076620883) McGraw-Hill Cos., The.

Cooperstein, Bruce. Advanced Linear Algebra. 2010. (ENG., Illus.). 364p. 83.95 *(978-1-4398-2966-0(7)*, CRC Press) Taylor & Francis Group GBR. Dist: Taylor & Francis Group.

Cram101 Textbook Reviews Staff. Outlines & Highlights for Elementary & Intermediate Algebra by Hutchison Isbn: 0073309613. 2007. 60p. per. 9.95 *(978-1-4288-5727-8(3))* Cram101 Inc.

—Outlines & Highlights for Introduction to Linear Algebra with Applications by James Defranza, Daniel Gagliardi, Isbn: 9780073532356. 2009. 122p. pap. 28.95 *(978-1-4288-3738-6(8))* Cram101 Inc.

Crauder, Bruce, et al. Functions & Change: A Modeling Approach to College Algebra. 4th ed. 2008. (ENG.). 480p. (C). pap. 64.95 *(978-0-547-16567-7(6))* Brooks/Cole.

Dugopolski, Mark. Student's Solutions Manual for Precalculus: Functions & Graphs. 3rd ed. 2007. (ENG.). 360p. (C). pap. 36.67 *(978-0-321-53543-6(X))* Addison Wesley.

Faires, J. Douglas & DeFranza, James. Study Guide with Solutions for Faires/Defranza's Precalculus, 5th. 5th ed. 2010. (ENG.). 416p. (C). pap. 81.95 *(978-1-111-42736-8(4))* Brooks/Cole.

Fischman, Davida, et al. Interactive College Algebra: A Web-Based Course. 2008. (ENG.). (C). 350p. pap., stu. ed. 118.95 *(978-0-470-41351-7(4))*; 349p. pap., stu. ed. 38.95 *(978-0-470-41293-0(3))* Wiley, John & Sons, Inc. (Wiley).

Fotiyeva, Izolda. Algebra Word Problems. 2010. (Complete Idiot's Guide Ser.). (ENG.). 352p. (gr. 12). 18.95 *(978-1-61564-037-9(1)*, Alpha Bks.) Penguin Group (USA) Inc.

Gannon, Terry. Moonshine Beyond the Monster: The Bridge Connecting Algebra, Modular Forms & Physics. 2010. (Cambridge Monographs on Mathematical Physics Ser.). (ENG., Illus.). 492p. pap. 60.00 *(978-0-521-14188-8(5))* Cambridge Univ. Pr.

Gardner, Jane. The Complete Idiot's Guide to Algebra Practice Problems. 2011. (Complete Idiot's Guide Ser.). (ENG.). 320p. (gr. 12). 16.95 *(978-1-61564-091-1(6)*, Alpha Bks.) Penguin Group (USA) Inc.

Gibilisco, Stan. Algebra Know-It-ALL: Beginner to Advanced, & Everything in Between. 2008. (ENG., Illus.). 730p. pap. 29.95 *(978-0-07-154617-1(0)*, 0071546170, TAB/Electronics) McGraw-Hill Professional Publishing.

Goldstein, Larry. Precalculus & Its Applications. Date not set. (Illus.). 234p. (C). pap., stu. ed. 15.00 *(978-1-891304-12-5(7))* Mobius Communications, Ltd.

Gordon, Warren B. Succeeding in Applied Calculus. 2nd ed. 2007. (Illus.). x, 225p. *(978-0-495-22001-5(9))* Brooks/Cole.

Gustafson, R. David, et al. College Algebra. 10th ed. 2009. (ENG.). 384p. (C). pap. 75.95 *(978-0-495-55895-8(8))* Brooks/Cole.

Huettenmueller, Rhonda. Algebra Demystified. 2nd rev. ed. 2010. (Demystified Ser.). (ENG., Illus.). 496p. pap. 20.00 *(978-0-07-174361-7(8)*, 0071743618) McGraw-Hill Professional Publishing.

Hughes-Hallett, Deborah, et al. Algebra: Form & Function. 2009. (ENG., Illus.). 576p. (C). pap. 143.95 *(978-0-470-52143-4(0)*, Wiley) Wiley, John & Sons, Inc.

Kaufmann, Jerome E. & Schwitters, Karen L. Beginning Algebra: Hybrid (with Enhanced Web-Assign with eBook for One Term Math & Science) 2011. (Textbooks Available with Cengage YouBook Ser.). (ENG.). 480p. (C). pap. 114.95 *(978-0-8400-6589-6(2))* Brooks/Cole.

—Elementary Algebra. 8th rev. ed. 2008. (ENG.). 576p. (C). 206.95 *(978-1-4390-4586-2(0))* Brooks/Cole.

—Elementary Algebra Student Solutions Manual. 9th ed. 2010. (ENG.). 608p. (C). pap. 66.95 *(978-0-538-73956-6(8))* Brooks/Cole.

Khatri, Daryao S. & Hughes, Anne. Math Remediation for the College Bound: Homework, Sample Tests, & Answer Keys. 2011. (ENG.). 140p. pap. 24.95 *(978-1-61048-378-0(2))* Rowman & Littlefield Education.

Khatri, Daryao S. & Hughes, Anne O. Math Remediation for the College Bound. 2011. *(978-1-61048-379-7(0))* Rowman & Littlefield Education.

Kime, Linda Almgren, et al. Explorations in College Algebra. (ENG., Illus.). (C). 4th ed. 2007. 720p. pap. 178.95 *(978-0-471-91688-8(9))* 5th ed. 2011. 768p. pap. 170.95 *(978-0-470-46644-5(8))* Wiley, John & Sons, Inc. (Wiley).

Larson, Ron. Precalculus: Real Mathematics, Real People. 6th ed. 2011. (Textbooks Available with Cengage YouBook Ser.). (ENG.). 896p. (C). 234.95 *(978-1-111-42763-4(1))* Brooks/Cole.

Larson, Ron & Hostetler, Robert P. Precalculus: A Concise Course. 2nd ed. 2010. (ENG.). 416p. (C). pap. 68.95 *(978-0-538-73889-7(8))* Brooks/Cole.

—Precalculus with Limits. 2nd ed. 2010. (ENG.). 752p. (C). pap. 79.95 *(978-0-538-73863-7(4))* Brooks/Cole.

Larson, Ron, et al. Precalculus Real Mathematics Real People. 6th ed. 2011. (ENG.). 464p. (C). pap., pupil's gde. ed. 59.95 *(978-1-111-57209-9(7))* Brooks/Cole.

Leff, Lawrence S. Integrated Algebra. 2011. (ENG., Illus.). 496p. pap., pupil's gde. ed. 7.99 *(978-0-7641-3870-6(7))* Barron's Educational Series, Inc.

—Let's Review: Integrated Algebra. 2008. (Let's Review Ser.). (ENG., Illus.). 528p. per. 13.99 *(978-0-7641-3591-0(0))* Barron's Educational Series, Inc.

Lial, Margaret L. & Hestwood, Diana L. Worksheets for Classroom or Lab Practice for Prealgebra. 4th ed. 2008. (ENG.). 416p. (C). pap. 26.67 *(978-0-321-57491-6(5))* Addison-Wesley Longman, Inc.

Lial, Margaret L., et al. Algebra for College Students. 7th ed. 2011. (ENG.). 936p. (C). 168.00 *(978-0-321-71540-1(3))* Addison Wesley.

—Algebra for College Students. 6th ed. 2007. *(978-0-321-44452-3(3))* Addison-Wesley Longman, Inc.

—Algebra for College Students. 7th ed. 2011. tchr. ed. *(978-0-321-71548-7(9))* Pearson Education.

—College Algebra. 10th ed. 2007. (Lial/Hornsby/Schneider College Algebra Ser.). (ENG., Illus.). 864p. (C). 168.67 *(978-0-321-49913-4(1))* Addison Wesley.

—College Algebra. 9th ed. 2007. *(978-0-321-50148-6(9))* Addison-Wesley Longman, Inc.

—College Algebra & Trigonometry. 4th ed. 2008. (Lial/Hornsby/Schneider College Algebra Ser.). (ENG., Illus.). 1264p. (C). 187.33 *(978-0-321-49744-4(9))* Addison Wesley.

—College Algebra & Trigonometry. 4th ed. 2007. *(978-0-321-50149-3(7))* Addison-Wesley Longman, Inc.

—Developmental Mathematics: Basic Mathematics & Algebra. 2nd ed. 2009. (ENG.). 616p. (C). pap. 36.67 *(978-0-321-59970-4(5))* Addison-Wesley Longman, Inc.

—Prealgebra & Introductory Algebra. 3rd ed. 2009. (ENG.). 624p. (C). pap. 36.67 *(978-0-321-59929-2(2))* Addison-Wesley Longman, Inc.

—Student Solutions Manual for College Algebra. 11th rev. ed. 2012. (ENG.). 456p. (C). pap. 36.67 ***(978-0-321-79138-2(X))*** Addison Wesley.

—Student's Solutions Manual for Intermediate Algebra. 9th ed. 2009. (ENG.). 360p. (C). pap. 36.67 *(978-0-321-57629-3(2))* Addison Wesley.

—Student's Solutions Manual for Introductory Algebra. 9th ed. 2009. (ENG.). 432p. (C). pap. 36.67 *(978-0-321-57643-9(8))* Addison-Wesley Longman, Inc.

—Worksheets for Classroom or Lab Practice for Developmental Mathematics: Basic Mathematics & Algebra. 2nd ed. 2009. (ENG.). (C). pap. 31.00 *(978-0-321-59973-5(X))* Addison Wesley.

—Worksheets for Classroom or Lab Practice for Intermediate Algebra. 9th ed. 2009. (ENG.). 512p. (C). pap. 26.67 *(978-0-321-57635-4(7))* Addison-Wesley Longman, Inc.

—Worksheets for Classroom or Lab Practice for Introductory Algebra. 9th ed. 2008. (ENG.). 456p. (C). pap. 26.67 *(978-0-321-57649-1(7))* Addison-Wesley Longman, Inc.

—Worksheets for Classroom or Lab Practice for Introductory & Intermediate Algebra. 4th ed. 2009. (ENG.). 600p. (C). pap. 31.00 *(978-0-321-57618-7(7))* Addison Wesley.

—Worksheets for Classroom or Lab Practice for Prealgebra & Introductory Algebra. 3rd ed. 2009. (ENG.). 762p. (C). pap. 31.00 *(978-0-321-60016-5(9))* Addison Wesley.

Low, Yvonne. Kyoodoz Pre-Algebra Multiple Choice Questions. 2010. 200p. (YA). 25.00 *(978-0-9771172-3-9(5))* Kyoodoz.

Manhattan GRE Word Problems GRE Strategy Guide, 2nd Edition. 2nd ed. 2011. (ENG.). 152p. pap. 20.00 *(978-1-935707-54-7(X))* Manhattan Prep Publishing.

Martin-Gay, Elayn. Beginning Algebra. 5th ed. 2007. (Martin-Gay Developmental Algebra Series (hardbacks) Ser.). (ENG., Illus.). 720p. (C). 168.00 *(978-0-13-600702-9(3)*, Prentice Hall) Prentice Hall PTR.

—Student Solutions Manual for Beginning Algebra. 6th rev. ed. 2012. (ENG.). 480p. (C). pap. 36.67 ***(978-0-321-78523-7(1))*** Addison Wesley.

—Student Solutions Manual for Beginning & Intermediate Algebra. 5th rev. ed. 2012. (ENG.). 768p. (C). pap. 36.67 ***(978-0-321-78574-9(6))*** Addison Wesley.

—Student Solutions Manual for Intermediate Algebra. 6th rev. ed. 2012. (ENG.). 648p. (C). pap. 36.67 ***(978-0-321-78532-9(0))*** Addison Wesley.

Martin-Gay, K. Elayn. Beginning Algebra. 4th ed. 672p. stu. ed. 70.97 *(978-0-13-191842-9(7))*; tchr. ed. 70.97 *(978-0-13-149893-8(2))* Prentice Hall (Schl. Div.).

Mccallum & Hughes-Hallett, Deborah. College Algebra & Trigonometry. 2014. (ENG.). (C). pap. 32.95 *(978-0-471-70618-2(3)*, Wiley) Wiley, John & Sons, Inc.

McGraw-Hill-Glencoe Staff. Algebra 1 Homework Practice Workbook, CCSS. 2nd ed. 2011. (ENG.). 192p. (gr. 8-12). pap. 5.96 *(978-0-07-660291-9(5)*, 0076602915) McGraw-Hill Higher Education.

—Algebra 1, Student Edition CCSS. 2011. (ENG., Illus.). 1056p. (gr. 8-12). 97.96 *(978-0-07-895115-2(1)*, 0078951151) McGraw-Hill Higher Education.

—Algebra 2 eStudentEdition CD. 2011. (ENG.). (gr. 9-12). cd-rom 93.28 *(978-0-07-896049-9(5)*, 0078960495) McGraw-Hill Higher Education.

—Algebra 2 Homework Practice Workbook, CCSS. 2nd ed. 2011. (ENG.). 192p. (gr. 9-12). pap. 5.96 *(978-0-07-660299-5(0)*, 0076602990) McGraw-Hill Higher Education.

—Algebra 2 Spanish Homework Practice Workbook, CCSS. 2nd ed. 2011. (ENG.). 192p. (gr. 9-12). pap. 5.96 *(978-0-07-660300-8(8)*, 0076603008) McGraw-Hill Higher Education.

—Algebra 2 Study Notebook, CCSS. 2nd ed. 2011. (ENG., Illus.). 240p. (gr. 9-12). pap. 14.64 *(978-0-07-660296-4(6)*, 0076602966) McGraw-Hill Higher Education.

McKenna, Paula & Kirk, Helen. Student's Solutions Manual for Beginning & Intermediate Algebra: Building a Foundation. 2009. (ENG.). 570p. (C). pap. 36.67 *(978-0-321-59404-4(5))* Addison Wesley.

—Worksheets for Classroom or Lab Practice for Beginning & Intermediate Algebra: Building a Foundation. 2009. (ENG.). 400p. (C). pap. 31.00 *(978-0-321-59397-9(9))* Addison Wesley.

Medvedovsky, Anna. SparkNotes 101: Algebra. 2006. *(978-1-4114-0334-5(7))* Spark Publishing Group.

Miller, Julie, et al. Loose Leaf Beginning Algebra. 3rd ed. 2010. (ENG.). (C). ring bd., ring bd. 124.33 *(978-0-07-740178-8(6)*, 0077401786, McGraw-Hill Science, Engineering & Mathematics) McGraw-Hill Higher Education.

—Loose Leaf Beginning & Intermediate Algebra. 3rd ed. 2010. (ENG.). (C). ring bd., ring bd. 128.00 *(978-0-07-740181-8(6)*, 0077401816, McGraw-Hill Science, Engineering & Mathematics) McGraw-Hill Higher Education.

Monahan, Christopher. Practice Makes Perfect Algebra II. 2012. (ENG., Illus.). 224p. (J). pap. 14.00 ***(978-0-07-177841-1(1)***, 0071778411) McGraw-Hill Cos., The.

Moyer, Robert & Spiegel, Murray R. College Algebra. 2nd ed. 2010. (Schaum's Easy Outlines Ser.). (ENG., Illus.). 144p. (C). pap. 11.00 *(978-0-07-174584-0(X)*, 007174584X) McGraw-Hill Cos., The.

Narasimhan, Revathi. College Algebra: Enhanced Edition (with Enhanced WebAssign 1-Semester Printed Access Card) 2009. (Available 2010 Titles Enhanced Web Assign Ser.). (ENG.). 864p. (C). 182.95 *(978-0-538-73477-5(9))* Brooks/Cole.

Newman, Donald & Boxer, Robert J. College Algebra Exam File. 2nd ed. 2007. (ENG.). 278p. pap. 17.95 *(978-1-4195-1816-4(X))* Kaplan Publishing.

Olney, Edward. Test Examples in Algebra, Especially Adapted for Use in Connection with Olney's School, or University Algebra by Edward Olney. 2006. 116p. per. 16.99 *(978-1-4255-0742-8(5))* MPublishing.

Ortner, Jerry. Fundamentals of Math Book: Algebra. 2008. 256p. pap. 16.99 *(978-1-4389-2692-6(8))* AuthorHouse.

—Fundamentals of Math Book: Pre-Algebra. 2009. 172p. pap. 13.99 *(978-1-4389-9165-8(7))* AuthorHouse.

Prentice-Hall Staff. Algebra 2. 2nd ed. tchr. ed. 59.47 *(978-0-13-026659-0(0))* Prentice Hall (Schl. Div.).

Qi, Liqun, et al. Semismooth & Smoothing Newton Methods. 2011. (Springer Series in Operations Research & Financial Engineering Ser.). (ENG., Illus.). 238p. 79.95 *(978-0-387-79149-4(3)*, 0387791493) Springer.

Rich, Barnett & Schmidt, Philip. Elementary Algebra. 3rd ed. 2009. (Schaum's Outline Ser.). (ENG., Illus.). 384p. (C). pap. 18.95 *(978-0-07-161163-3(0)*, 0071611630) McGraw-Hill Cos., The.

Rockswold, Gary K. College Algebra with Modeling & Visualization. 4th ed. 2009. (ENG.). 352p. (C). pap. 36.67 *(978-0-321-57702-3(7))* Addison Wesley.

—Student's Solutions Manual for Algebra & Trigonometry/Precalculus with Modeling & Visualization. 4th ed. 2009. (ENG.). 480p. (C). pap. 36.67 *(978-0-321-57709-2(4))* Addison Wesley.

Rockswold, Gary K. & Krieger, Terry A. Student's Solutions Manual for Beginning Algebra with Applications & Visualization. 3rd rev. ed. 2012. (ENG.). 352p. (C). pap. 36.67 ***(978-0-321-74799-0(2))*** Addison Wesley.

—Student's Solutions Manual for Beginning & Intermediate Algebra with Applications & Visualization. 3rd rev. ed. 2012. (ENG.). 534p. (C). pap. 36.67 ***(978-0-321-75655-8(X))*** Addison Wesley.

—Student's Solutions Manual for Intermediate Algebra with Applications & Visualization. 4th rev. ed. 2012. (ENG.). 456p. (C). pap. 36.67 ***(978-0-321-74784-6(4))*** Addison Wesley.

—Worksheets for Beginning Algebra with Applications & Visualization. 3rd rev. ed. 2012. (ENG.). 250p. (C). pap. 26.67 ***(978-0-321-74802-7(6))*** Addison Wesley.

—Worksheets for Beginning & Intermediate Algebra with Applications & Visualization. 3rd rev. ed. 2012. (ENG.). 550p. (C). pap. 31.00 ***(978-0-321-75661-9(4))*** Addison Wesley.

—Worksheets for Intermediate Algebra with Applications & Visualization. 4th rev. ed. 2012. (ENG.). 256p. (C). pap. 26.67 ***(978-0-321-74788-4(7))*** Addison Wesley.

Rusczyk, Richard. Introduction to Algebra Solution Manual. 2007. per. 12.00 *(978-1-934124-02-4(8))* 2nd ed. 2009. (Illus.). 312p. pap. 14.00 *(978-1-934124-15-4(X))* AoPS Inc.

—Precalculus. 2009. 528p. pap. 47.00 *(978-1-934124-16-1(8))* AoPS Inc.

Sato, Naoki & Rusczyk, Richard. Precalculus Solutions Manual. 2009. 272p. pap. 12.00 *(978-1-934124-17-8(6))* AoPS Inc.

Slater, Jeffrey, et al. Worksheets with the Math Coach for Beginning Algebra. 8th rev. ed. 2012. (ENG.). 336p. (C). pap. 26.67 ***(978-0-321-76980-0(5))*** Addison Wesley.

Spiegel, Murray, et al. Schaum's Outline of College Algebra, Third Edition. 3rd ed. 2009. (Schaum's Outline Ser.). (ENG., Illus.). 416p. (C). pap. 20.00 *(978-0-07-163539-4(4)*, 0071635394) McGraw-Hill Cos., The.

Staszkow, Ronald. Math Skills: Arithmetic with Introductory Algebra & Geometry. 7th rev. ed. 2007. (ENG.). 534p. pap. 80.80 *(978-0-7575-4612-9(9))* Kendall Hunt Publishing Co.

Sterling, Mary Jane. Algebra I Workbook for Dummies. 2nd ed. 2011. (ENG., Illus.). 312p. pap. 19.99 *(978-1-118-04922-8(5)*, For Dummies) Wiley, John & Sons, Inc.

—Algebra II Workbook for Dummies. 2007. (ENG., Illus.). 312p. per. 16.99 *(978-0-470-05238-9(4)*, For Dummies) Wiley, John & Sons, Inc.

Strang, Gilbert. Introduction to Linear Algebra 4e. 4th ed. 2009. (ENG., Illus.). 550p. 87.50 *(978-0-9802327-1-4(6))* Wellesley-Cambridge Pr.

Sullivan, Michael. Precalculus, the MyMathLab Edition. 8th ed. 2007. (ENG.). 744p. (C). pap. 65.33 *(978-0-13-612788-8(6)*, Prentice Hall) Prentice Hall PTR.

Sullivan, Michael & Sullivan, Michael, III, III. Student Solutions Manual for Algebra & Trigonometry Enhanced with Graphing Utilities. 6th rev. ed. 2012. (ENG.). 768p. (C). pap. 36.67 ***(978-0-321-78498-8(7))*** Addison Wesley.

Sullivan, Michael & Sullivan, Michael III. Student Solutions Manual for College Algebra Enhanced with Graphing Utilities. 6th ed. 2012. (ENG.). 536p. (C). pap. 36.67 ***(978-0-321-81655-9(2))*** Addison Wesley.

Sullivan, Michael, et al. Elementary & Intermediate Algebra. 2nd ed. 2009. (Sullivan/Struve/Mazzarella Algebra Ser.). (ENG.). 1128p. (C). 176.00 *(978-0-321-59309-2(X)*, Prentice Hall) Prentice Hall PTR.

—Student Solutions Manual, Standalone. 5th ed. 2008. (ENG.). 536p. (C). pap. 36.67 *(978-0-13-600196-6(3)*, Prentice Hall) Prentice Hall PTR.

Swokowski, Earl. Precalculus: Functions & Graphs - Student Solutions Manual. 12th ed. 2011. (ENG.). 448p. (C). pap. 74.95 *(978-1-111-57350-8(6))* Brooks/Cole.

Swokowski, Earl & Cole, Jeffery. Student's Solutions Manual for Swokowski/Cole's Algebra & Trigonometry with Analytic Geometry, Classic Edition, 12th. 12th ed. 2009. (ENG.). 432p. (C). pap. 74.95 *(978-0-495-56072-2(3))* Brooks/Cole.

Swokowski, Earl W. & Cole, Jeffery A. Algebra & Trigonometry with Analytic Geometry. 13th ed. 2011. (ENG.). 464p. (C). pap. 74.95 *(978-1-111-57335-5(2))* Brooks/Cole.

Szecsei, Denise. Homework Helpers: Algebra. 2nd rev. ed. 2011. (Homework Helpers Ser.). (ENG., Illus.). 1p. pap. 14.99 *(978-1-60163-169-5(3))* Career Pr., Inc.

Tobey, John, Jr., et al. Student Solutions Manual for Beginning Algebra. 8th rev. ed. 2012. (ENG.). 312p. (C). pap. 36.67 ***(978-0-321-76973-2(2))*** Addison Wesley.

—Student Solutions Manual for Beginning & Intermediate Algebra. 4th rev. ed. 2012. (ENG.). 500p. (C). pap. 36.67 ***(978-0-321-77343-7(9))*** Addison Wesley.

—Worksheets with the Math Coach for Beginning & Intermediate Algebra. 4th rev. ed. 2012. (ENG.). 400p. (C). pap. 31.00 ***(978-0-321-78055-3(8))*** Addison Wesley.

Tobey, John Jr, et al. Student Solutions Manual for Beginning Algebra: Early Graphing. 3rd rev. ed. 2011. (ENG.). 500p. (C). pap. 36.67 ***(978-0-321-76986-2(4))*** Addison Wesley.

Tobey, John Jr, Jr., et al. Worksheets with the Math Coach for Intermediate Algebra. 7th rev. ed. 2012. (ENG.). 300p. (C). pap. 26.67 ***(978-0-321-75901-6(X))*** Addison Wesley.

Walch Education, creator. Algebra Station Activities for NCTM Standards. 2011. (Illus.). 381p. pap. 39.00 ***(978-0-8251-6223-7(8))*** Walch Education.

Waner, Stefan & Costenoble, Steven. Applied Calculus SSM. 5th ed. 2010. (ENG.). 288p. (C). pap. 52.95 *(978-1-4390-4990-7(4))* Brooks/Cole.

—Finite Math & Applied Calculus. 5th ed. 2010. (ENG.). 588p. (C). pap. 47.95 *(978-0-538-73482-0(5))* Brooks/Cole.

White, Jonathan J., et al. Basic Math & Pre-Algebra, Pack. 2nd ed. 2010. (ENG.). 264p. pap. 18.99 *(978-0-470-53349-9(8)*, Cliff Notes) Wiley, John & Sons, Inc.

Wiley Law Publications Editorial Staff & Zegarelli, Mark. Basic Math & Pre-Algebra for Dummies Education Bundle. 2009. (ENG.). pap. 29.99 *(978-0-470-53700-8(0)*, For Dummies) Wiley, John & Sons, Inc.

Willers, Michael. The Joy of X: How Algebra Shapes Your Daily Life. 2009. (Illus.). 176p. 28.55 *(978-0-550-10523-3(9))* Chambers Harrap Pubs., Ltd. GBR. Dist: Trans-Atlantic Pubns., Inc.

Woodbury, George. Elementary & Intermediate Algebra. 2nd ed. 2008. (ENG.). 720p. (C). pap., stu. ed. 36.67 *(978-0-321-50674-0(X))* Addison Wesley Higher Education.

Yocco, Lisa & Harshbarger, Ronald J. Student's Solutions Manual for College Algebra in Context. 4th rev. ed. 2012. (ENG.). 400p. (C). pap. 36.67 ***(978-0-321-78355-4(7))*** Addison Wesley.

Young, Precalculus Binder Ready Version. 2010. (Illus.). 1175p. (C). ring bd. 125.95 *(978-0-470-55665-8(X)*, Wiley) Wiley, John & Sons, Inc.

Young, Cynthia Y. College Algebra. 3rd ed. 2012. (ENG.). 896p. (C). pap. 44.95 ***(978-1-118-13757-4(4)***, Wiley) Wiley, John & Sons, Inc.

—College Algebra with Wiley Plus WebCT Powerpack Set. 2006. (Wiley Plus Products Ser.). 119.95 *(978-0-470-11547-3(5)*, Wiley) Wiley, John & Sons, Inc.

—Precalculus. 2012. (ENG., Illus.). 1175p. (C). 206.95 *(978-0-471-75684-2(9)*, Wiley) Wiley, John & Sons, Inc.

Zegarelli, Mark. Basic Math & Pre-Algebra for Dummies. 2008. (ENG., Illus.). 312p. pap., wbk. ed. 16.99 *(978-0-470-28817-7(5)*, For Dummies) Wiley, John & Sons, Inc.

Zhang, Fuzhen & Zhang, F. Linear Algebra: Challenging Problems for Students. 2nd ed. 2009. (Johns Hopkins Studies in the Mathematical Sciences Ser.). (ENG., Illus.). 264p. (C). (gr. 13-17). 73.00 *(978-0-8018-9125-0(6))*; pap. 28.00 *(978-0-8018-9126-7(4))* Johns Hopkins Univ. Pr.

ALGEBRA—PROGRAMMED INSTRUCTION

Blitzer, Robert F. MyMathLab Edition. 5th ed. 2008. (ENG.). 560p. (C). spiral bd. 57.33 *(978-0-13-603186-4(2))* Addison Wesley.

Lee, Kuen H. Student's Solution Manual for Elementary Algebra: A Step-by-Step Approach. 3rd exp. ed. Date not set. (Illus.). 524p. pap., stu. ed. 40.25 *(978-0-9618565-5-6(1))* Edmund Publishing Co.

Martin-Gay, K. Elayn. Beginning & Intermediate Algebra, MyMathLab Edition. 4th ed. 2008. (ENG., Illus.). 784p. (C). spiral bd. 65.33 *(978-0-321-56675-1(0))* Addison Wesley.

Miller, Julie & O'Neill, Molly. Student's Solution Manual Beginning & Intermediate Algebra. 3rd ed. 2010. (ENG.). 592p. (C). pap. 62.33 *(978-0-07-729632-2(X)*, 007729632X, McGraw-Hill Science, Engineering & Mathematics) McGraw-Hill Higher Education.

Squires, John & Wyrick, Karen. Introductory Algebra. 2011. (ENG.). 264p. (C). pap. 20.00 ***(978-0-321-74925-0(X))*** Addison Wesley.

Trigsted, Kirk. College Algebra. 2010. (ENG.). 456p. (C). pap. 26.67 *(978-0-321-69352-5(3)*, Prentice Hall) Prentice Hall PTR.

—College Algebra: A Hybrid Approach. 2009. (ENG.). 432p. (C). pap. 26.67 *(978-0-13-174459-1(0)*, Prentice Hall) Prentice Hall PTR.

ALGEBRA—STUDY AND TEACHING

Algebra for Dummies Education Bundle. 2008. pap. 29.99 *(978-0-470-43095-8(8))* Wiley, John & Sons, Inc.

Algebra Readiness Teachers Guide. 2010. spiral bd. 37.27 *(978-1-4488-3812-7(6)*, Rosen Classroom Bks. & Materials) Rosen Publishing Group, Inc., The.

Andersen, Maria H. Algebra. 2010. (ENG.). 356p. (C). pap., stu. ed., wbk. ed. 41.95 *(978-0-538-73193-5(1))* Brooks/Cole.

—Beginning & Intermediate Algebra: An Integrated Approach. 6th ed. 2010. (ENG.). 492p. (C). pap., wbk. ed. 64.95 *(978-0-538-73184-3(2))* Brooks/Cole.

—Elementary Algebra. 5th ed. 2010. (ENG.). 384p. (C). pap., wbk. ed. 42.95 *(978-0-538-49350-4(7))* Brooks/Cole.

—Elementary & Intermediate Algebra. 5th ed. 2010. (ENG.). 496p. (C). pap., wbk. ed. 64.95 *(978-0-538-49358-1(5))* Brooks/Cole.

—Elementary & Intermediate Algebra: A Combined Approach. 5th ed. 2010. (ENG.). 492p. (C). pap., wbk. ed. 64.95 *(978-0-538-49632-2(0))* Brooks/Cole.

—Intermediate Algebra. 5th ed. 2010. (ENG.). 496p. (C). pap., stu. ed., wbk. ed. 42.95 *(978-0-538-49356-7(9))* Brooks/Cole.

—Intermediate Algebra. 8th ed. 2010. (ENG.). 492p. (C). pap., wbk. ed. 42.95 *(978-0-538-49583-7(9))* Brooks/Cole.

—Intermediate Algebra. 9th ed. 2010. (ENG.). 474p. (C). pap., stu. ed., wbk. ed. 42.95 *(978-0-538-73190-4(7))* Brooks/Cole.

—Introductory Algebra. 4th ed. 2010. (ENG.). 384p. (C). pap., wbk. ed. 41.95 *(978-0-538-49545-5(6))* Brooks/Cole.

Andersen, Maria H. & Lockwood, Joanne. Algebra: Introductory & Intermediate - An Applied Approach. 5th ed. 2010. (ENG.). 480p. (C). pap., wbk. ed. 64.95 *(978-0-538-49544-8(8))* Brooks/Cole.

—Intermediate Algebra with Applications. 7th ed. 2010. (ENG.). 492p. (C). pap., wbk. ed. 42.95 *(978-0-538-73158-4(3))* Brooks/Cole.

Andersen, Maria H. & Massey, Marilyn. Intermediate Algebra. 9th ed. 2010. (ENG.). 492p. (C). pap., wbk. ed. 42.95 *(978-0-538-49543-1(X))* Brooks/Cole.

Anderson, Kelly. Algebra Readiness Resource Guide. 2009. pap. 12.95 *(978-1-61584-165-3(2))* Independent Pub.

Andres, Richard J. & Bernstein, Joyce. Preparing for the Regents Examination Integrated Algebra 1. 2006. pap. *(978-1-56765-587-2(4)*, R037W) AMSCO Schl. Pubns., Inc.

Aufmann, Richard N. & Lockwood, Joanne. Intermediate Algebra. 8th ed. 2010. (ENG.). 400p. (C). pap. 67.95 *(978-0-538-49392-5(5))* Brooks/Cole.

Aufmann, Richard N., et al. Beginning Algebra with Applications. 7th ed. 2010. (ENG.). 374p. (C). pap., wbk. ed. 42.95 *(978-0-538-73159-1(1))* Brooks/Cole.

—College Algebra. 7th ed. 2010. (ENG.). 768p. (C). pap., pupil's gde. ed. 65.95 *(978-0-538-75764-5(7))* Brooks/Cole.

—College Algebra & Trigonometry. 7th ed. 2010. (ENG.). 1056p. (C). pap., pupil's gde. ed. 65.95 *(978-0-538-73908-5(8))* Brooks/Cole.

Banu, Flavia, et al. Integrated Algebra. 2008. (ENG., Illus.). 187p. pap., wbk. ed. 9.99 *(978-0-470-16782-3(3)*, Cliff Notes) Wiley, John & Sons, Inc.

Barnett-Clarke, Carne & Ramirez, Alma B. Math Pathways & Pitfalls Fractions & Decimals with Algebra Readiness: Lessons & Teaching Manual Grade 4, Grade 5, & Grade 6. 2009. (ENG.). 368p. (gr. 4-6). pap. 165.00 *(978-0-914409-60-1(3)*, 9780914409601) WestEd.

—Math Pathways & Pitfalls Place Value & Whole Number Operations with Algebra Readiness: Lessons & Teaching Manual Grade 2 & Grade 3. 2009. (ENG.). 352p. (gr. 2-3). pap. 165.00 *(978-0-914409-59-5(X)*, 9780914409595) WestEd.

Bello, Ignacio. Student's Solutions Manual t/a Introductory Algebra. 3rd ed. 2008. (ENG.). 416p. (C). pap. 70.33 *(978-0-07-336095-9(3)*, 0073360953, McGraw-Hill Science, Engineering & Mathematics) McGraw-Hill Higher Education.

Bello, Ignacio & Hopf, Fran. Student's Solutions Manual t/a Intermediate Algebra. 3rd ed. 2008. (ENG.). 504p. (C). pap. 70.33 *(978-0-07-335798-0(7)*, 0073357987, McGraw-Hill Science, Engineering & Mathematics) McGraw-Hill Higher Education.

Bittinger, Marvin L. & Ellenbogen, David J. Worksheets for Classroom or Lab Practice for Intermediate Algebra: Concepts & Applications. 8th ed. 2009. (ENG.). 384p. (C). pap. 26.67 *(978-0-321-59936-0(5))* Addison-Wesley Longman, Inc.

Blahut, Richard E. Algebraic Codes on Lines, Planes, & Curves: An Engineering Approach. 2008. (ENG., Illus.). 576p. 105.00 *(978-0-521-77194-8(3))* Cambridge Univ. Pr.

Blanton, Maria L. Developing Essential Understanding of Algebraic Thinking for Teaching Mathematics in Grades 3-5. 2011. *(978-0-87353-668-4(1))* National Council of Teachers of Mathematics.

Blitzer. Precalculus: Instructor's Solutions Manual. 2nd ed. tchr. ed., per. 18.97 *(978-0-13-101923-2(6))* Prentice Hall (Schl. Div.).

Breeden, Terri & Dillard, Kathryn. The Middle School Mathematician: Challenging Games & Activities That Empower Students to Achieve Success with Rational Numbers, Algebra, & Geometry. 2008. (Illus.). 127p. pap. 21.99 incl. cd-rom *(978-0-86530-505-2(6))* Incentive Pubns., Inc.

Brown, Kyndall. Traditional Versus Reform. 2009. 60p. pap. *(978-3-639-19446-3(2))* VDM Verlag Dr. Mueller e.K.

Brutlag, Dan. Active Algebra: Strategies & Lessons for Successfully Teaching Linear Relationships, Grades 7-10. 2009. 166p. pap. 36.95 *(978-1-935099-05-5(1))* Math Solutions.

Burgis, Kathy & Morford, Jeff. Investigating College Algebra Student Study & Solutions Companion. 2008. (ENG.). 410p. (C). pap. 39.95 *(978-0-470-41250-3(X)*, Wiley) Wiley, John & Sons, Inc.

Cai, Jinfa & Knuth, Eric, eds. Early Algebraization: A Global Dialogue from Multiple Perspectives. 2011. (Advances in Mathematics Education Ser.). (ENG.). xxiii, 623p. 129.00 *(978-3-642-17734-7(4)*, 3642177344) Springer.

Cavanagh, Mary, et al. Algebra Readiness Made Easy: An Essential Part of Every Math Curriculum. 2008. (Best Practices in Action Ser.). (ENG., Illus.). 80p. pap. 18.99 *(978-0-439-83942-6(4)*, Teaching Resources) Scholastic, Inc.

Clark, Mark. Intermediate Algebra: Concepts through Applications, Class Test Volume 1. 2nd ed. 2008. (C). pap. 85.95 *(978-0-495-82842-6(4))* Brooks/Cole.

—Intermediate Algebra: Concepts through Applications, Class Test Volume 2. 2nd ed. 2008. (C). pap. 42.95 *(978-0-495-82843-3(2))* Brooks/Cole.

Close, John & Punzalan, Celestina. Elementary Algebra. rev. ed. 2010. (ENG.). 752p. spiral bd. 83.62 *(978-0-7575-8182-3(X))* Kendall Hunt Publishing Co.

Cobb, Margaret V., et al. Psychology of Algebr. 2011. 494p. 58.95 ***(978-1-258-04619-4(9))*** Literary Licensing, LLC.

Coburn & Coburn, John. Combo: College Algebra with MathZone Access Card. 2nd ed. 2010. (ENG.). (C). pap. 174.42 *(978-0-07-808573-4(X)*, 007808573X, McGraw-Hill Science, Engineering & Mathematics) McGraw-Hill Higher Education.

Collins, Anne & Dacey, Linda Schulman. The Xs & Whys of Algebra: Key Ideas & Common Misconceptions. 2011. pap. ***(978-1-57110-857-9(2))***; E-Book ***(978-1-57110-927-9(7))*** Stenhouse Pubs.

Contemporary. Seeking Patterns, Building Rules: Algebraic Thinking. 2011. (ENG.). 176p. (C). (gr. 12-12). pap. 12.00 ***(978-0-07-662088-3(3)***, 0076620883) McGraw-Hill Cos., The.

Cram101 Textbook Reviews. Outlines & Highlights for Fostering Algebraic Thinking: A Guide for Teachers, Grades 6-10 by Mark Driscoll. 2011. 78p. pap. 27.95 ***(978-1-61812-343-5(2))*** Cram101 Inc.

Cram101 Textbook Reviews. Outlines & Highlights for Holt Pre-Algebra by Jennie M Bennet, Isbn: 9780030934681. 2010. 292p. pap. 32.95 *(978-1-61654-085-2(0))* Cram101 Inc.

Dase, Pamela & Dase, Pamela H. TI Graphing Calculator Strategies: Algebra. 2006. (Texas Instruments Graphic Calculator Strategies Ser.). (ENG., Illus.). 238p. (gr. 6-12). pap. 34.99 *(978-1-4258-0024-6(6))* Shell Educational Publishing.

Dogan-Dunlap, Hamide. Linear Algebra Teaching & Learning: Visualization. 2008. 116p. pap. *(978-3-639-08994-3(4))* VDM Verlag Dr. Mueller e.K.

Dougherty, Barbara, et al. X-Power Interactive. 2007. cd-rom 1000.00 ***(978-1-58351-087-2(7))*** Univ. of Hawaii, Curriculum Research & Development Group.

Encyclopaedia Britannica, Inc., compiled by. Mathematics in Context: Algebra Rules. 2008. (gr. 5-8). 8.75 *(978-1-59339-908-5(1))* Encyclopaedia Britannica, Inc.

—Mathematics in Context: Algebra Rules 2006 Teacher Guide. 2009. (gr. 5-8). 31.75 *(978-1-60835-011-7(8))* Encyclopaedia Britannica, Inc.

—Mathematics in Context: Algebra Tools Teacher Guide. 2009. (gr 5-8). 70.60 *(978-1-59339-916-0(2))* Encyclopaedia Britannica, Inc.

—Mathematics in Context: Algebra Tools Workbook Student Edition. 2009. (gr. 5-8). 9.75 *(978-1-59339-914-6(6))* Encyclopaedia Britannica, Inc.

—Mathematics in Context: Building Formulas 2006 Teacher Guide. 2009. (gr. 5-8). 31.75 *(978-1-60835-006-3(1))* Encyclopaedia Britannica, Inc.

—Mathematics in Context: Comparing Quantities. 2009. (gr. 5-8). 8.75 *(978-1-59339-993-1(6))*; (gr. 6). 8.95 *(978-1-59339-917-7(0))* Encyclopaedia Britannica, Inc.

—Mathematics in Context: Expressions & Formulas 2006 Teacher Guide. 2009. (gr. 5-8). 31.75 *(978-1-60835-001-8(0))* Encyclopaedia Britannica, Inc.

—Mathematics in Context: Graphing Equations. 2009. (gr. 5-8). 8.75 *(978-1-59339-983-2(9))* Encyclopaedia Britannica, Inc.

—Mathematics in Context: Operations. 2008. (gr. 5-8). 8.75 *(978-1-59339-904-7(9))* Encyclopaedia Britannica, Inc.

—Mathematics in Context: Patterns & Figures. 2008. (gr. 5-8). 8.75 *(978-1-59339-911-5(1))* Encyclopaedia Britannica, Inc.

—Mathematics in Context: Patterns & Figures 2006 Teacher Guide. 2009. (gr. 5-8). 31.75 *(978-1-60835-014-8(2))* Encyclopaedia Britannica, Inc.

—Mathematics in Context: Ups & Downs. 2009. (gr. 5-8). 8.75 *(978-1-59339-997-9(9))* Encyclopaedia Britannica, Inc.

—Mathematics in Context: Ups & Downs 2006 Teacher Guide. 2009. (gr. 5-8). 31.75 *(978-1-60835-010-0(X))* Encyclopaedia Britannica, Inc.

—2010 Mathematics in Context: Algebra Rules Student Edition. 2009. (gr. 8). 8.95 *(978-1-59339-957-3(X))* Encyclopaedia Britannica, Inc.

—2010 Mathematics in Context: Algebra Rules Teacher Guide. 2009. (gr. 8). 36.00 *(978-1-59339-972-6(3))* Encyclopaedia Britannica, Inc.

—2010 Mathematics in Context: Building Formulas. 2009. (gr. 7). 8.95 *(978-1-59339-937-5(5))* Encyclopaedia Britannica, Inc.

—2010 Mathematics in Context: Building Formulas Teacher Guide. 2009. (gr. 7). 36.00 *(978-1-59339-946-7(4))* Encyclopaedia Britannica, Inc.

—2010 Mathematics in Context: Comparing Quantities Teacher Guide. 2009. (gr. 6). 36.00 *(978-1-59339-927-6(8))* Encyclopaedia Britannica, Inc.

—2010 Mathematics in Context: Graphing Equations Student Edition. 2009. (gr. 8). 8.95 *(978-1-59339-958-0(8))* Encyclopaedia Britannica, Inc.

—2010 Mathematics in Context: Operations. 2009. (gr. 7). 8.95 *(978-1-59339-940-5(5))* Encyclopaedia Britannica, Inc.

—2010 Mathematics in Context: Operations Teacher Guide. 2009. (gr. 7). 36.00 *(978-1-59339-949-8(9))* Encyclopaedia Britannica, Inc.

—2010 Mathematics in Context: Patterns & Figures Student Edition. 2009. (gr. 8). 8.95 *(978-1-59339-962-7(6))* Encyclopaedia Britannica, Inc.

—2010 Mathematics in Context: Patterns & Figures Teacher Guide. 2009. (gr. 8). 36.00 *(978-1-59339-968-9(5))* Encyclopaedia Britannica, Inc.

—2010 Mathematics in Context: Rates & Ratios. 2009. (gr. 7). 8.95 *(978-1-59339-943-6(X))* Encyclopaedia Britannica, Inc.

—2010 Mathematics in Context: Ups & Downs Student Edition. 2009. (gr. 8). 8.95 *(978-1-59339-956-6(1))* Encyclopaedia Britannica, Inc.

—2010 Mathematics in Context: Ups & Downs Teacher Guide. 2009. (gr. 8). 36.00 *(978-1-59339-971-9(5))* Encyclopaedia Britannica, Inc.

Filloy, Eugenio. Educational Algebra. 2007. (Mathematics Education Library). (Illus.). 312p. (C). 159.00 *(978-0-387-71253-6(4))* Springer.

Filloy, Eugenio, et al. Educational Algebra: A Theoretical & Empirical Approach. 2010. (Mathematics Education Library). (Illus.). xiii, 292p. pap. 159.00 *(978-1-4419-4389-7(7)*, 1441943897) Springer.

Flores, Sergio & Kanim, Stephen E. Student Use of Vectors in Mechanics: Learning Difficulties with Vectors in Introductory Mechanics Courses. 2008. 212p. pap. *(978-3-639-10725-8(X))* VDM Verlag Dr. Mueller e.K.

Fosnot, Catherine Twomey & Jacob, Bill. Young Mathematicians at Work. 2010. (Young Mathematicians at Work Ser.). 224p. pap. 31.25 *(978-0-325-02841-5(9)*, E02841) Heinemann.

Gantert, Ann Xavier. Integrated Algebra 1. 2006. pap. 29.00 net. *(978-1-56765-584-1(X)*, R239P) AMSCO Schl. Pubns., Inc.

—Integrated Algebra 1 Hardbound. 2006. *(978-1-56765-585-8(8)*, R239H) AMSCO Schl. Pubns., Inc.

Gibilisco, Stan. Pre-Calculus Know-It-ALL. 2009. (ENG., Illus.). 608p. pap. 24.95 *(978-0-07-162702-3(2)*, 0071627022, TAB/Electronics) McGraw-Hill Professional Publishing.

Glencoe McGraw-Hill Staff. Algebra 1 eStudentEdition CD. 2011. (ENG.). (gr. 8-12). cd-rom 85.96 *(978-0-07-896029-1(0)*, 0078960290) McGraw-Hill Higher Education.

Gordon-Holliday, Berchie W. California Algebra 1: Concepts, Skills, & Problem Solving. 2008. (Illus.). ***(978-0-07-877853-7(0))*** Glencoe/McGraw-Hill.

Graham, Karen, et al. Focus in High School Mathematics: Reasoning & Sense Making in Algebra. 2010. *(978-0-87353-640-0(1))* National Council of Teachers of Mathematics.

Henry Holt & Company, LLC, creator. Holt California Mathematics, Course 1: Chapter 1 Resource File. 2011. pap. 19.99 ***(978-0-03-094522-9(4))*** Holt, Henry & Co.

High School Success Deluxe. 2009. 49.95 *(978-1-60077-576-5(4))* TOPICS Entertainment.

Holliday, Berchie, et al. Algebra 2. 2006. (ENG., Illus.). 956p. (C). stu. ed. 104.24 *(978-0-07-873830-2(X)*, 007873830X) McGraw-Hill Higher Education.

Holt, Rinehart and Winston Staff. Pre-Algebra: Homework & Practice. 4th ed. Date not set. (SPA.). pap., tchr. ed. 11.00 *(978-0-03-069808-8(1))* Holt McDougal.

—Pre-Algebra: Homework & Practice Workbook. 4th ed. Date not set. (Holt Pre-Algebra Ser.). (SPA.). pap., wbk. ed. 8.40 *(978-0-03-069807-1(3))* Holt McDougal.

Jacobs, Russell F. Algebra II Topics by Design. 2007. (Illus.). *(978-0-918272-38-6(6))* Jacobs Publishing Co.

Kamischke, Eric, et al. Exploring Algebra 1 with Fathom Dynamic Data Software Version 2. 2007. (Illus.). xii, 234p. ***(978-1-55953-801-5(5))*** Key Curriculum Pr.

Katz, Gabriele & Nodelman, Vladimir. The Shape of Algebra: A Visual Exploration of Elementary Algebra & Beyond (with CD-ROM) 2010. 500p. 77.00 *(978-981-4313-59-9(9))* World Scientific Publishing Co., Inc.

Kaufmann, Jerome E. & Schwitters, Karen L. Algebra for College Students. 9th ed. 2010. (ENG.). 492p. (C). pap., stu. ed., wbk. ed. 42.95 *(978-0-538-73186-7(9))* Brooks/Cole.

—Elementary Algebra. 9th ed. 2010. (ENG.). 386p. (C). pap., stu. ed., wbk. ed. 42.95 *(978-0-538-73191-1(5))* Brooks/Cole.

Kunkel, Paul, et al. Exploring Algebra 2 with the Geometer's Sketchpad. 4th ed. 2007. (Illus.). xvi, 238p. pap. ***(978-1-55953-799-5(X))*** Key Curriculum Pr.

Lay, Steven R. & Lay, L. Clark. Prelude to Algebra - Teacher's Edition. 2007. 346p. spiral bd. 80.00 *(978-0-9793087-1-0(2))* Cross Product Pubns.

LearningExpress Editors. Algebra in 15 Minutes a Day. 2009. (Junior Skill Builders in 15 Minutes a Day Ser.). (ENG.). 256p. pap. 12.95 *(978-1-57685-673-4(9))* LearningExpress, LLC.

—Algebra Success in 20 Minutes a Day. 4th rev. ed. 2010. (ENG.). 256p. pap. 18.00 *(978-1-57685-719-9(0))* LearningExpress, LLC.

LearningExpress Staff, creator. Algebra Success in 20 Minutes a Day. 3rd rev. ed. 2007. (Skill Builders in 20 Minutes a Day Ser.). (ENG.). 256p. per. 16.00 *(978-1-57685-607-9(0))* LearningExpress, LLC.

Martin, Hope. Primary Algebra: Teacher Resource. 2008. pap. 9.95 *(978-1-59647-126-9(3))* Good Year Bks.

McDougal Littell, creator. Connecticut Lesson Plans: Math Course 2. 2010. (Illus.). 90p. pap. *(978-0-618-80770-3(5))* Holt McDougal.

McGraw-Hill-Glencoe Staff. Algebra 1 Homework Practice Workbook, CCSS. 2nd ed. 2011. (ENG.). 192p. (gr. 8-12). pap. 5.96 *(978-0-07-660291-9(5)*, 0076602915) McGraw-Hill Higher Education.

—Algebra 1, Student Edition CCSS. 2011. (ENG., Illus.). 1056p. (gr. 8-12). 97.96 *(978-0-07-895115-2(1)*, 0078951151) McGraw-Hill Higher Education.

—Algebra 1 Study Notebook, CCSS. 2nd ed. 2011. (ENG., Illus.). 224p. (gr. 8-12). pap. 14.64 *(978-0-07-660287-2(7)*, 0076602877) McGraw-Hill Higher Education.

—Algebra 2 eStudentEdition CD. 2011. (ENG.). (gr. 9-12). cd-rom 93.28 *(978-0-07-896049-9(5)*, 0078960495) McGraw-Hill Higher Education.

—Algebra 2 Homework Practice Workbook, CCSS. 2nd ed. 2011. (ENG.). 192p. (gr. 9-12). pap. 5.96 *(978-0-07-660299-5(0)*, 0076602990) McGraw-Hill Higher Education.

—Algebra 2 Study Notebook, CCSS. 2nd ed. 2011. (ENG., Illus.). 240p. (gr. 9-12). pap. 14.64 *(978-0-07-660296-4(6)*, 0076602966) McGraw-Hill Higher Education.

McKeague, Charles P. Beginning & Intermediate Algebr. 9th ed. 2011. (Textbooks Available with Cengage YouBook Ser.). (ENG.). 784p. (C). 195.95 *(978-0-8400-6420-2(9))* Brooks/Cole.

McKellar, Danica. Algebra Exposed! 2011. (ENG., Illus.). 432p. (gr. 6-18). 16.00 *(978-0-452-29719-7(2)*, Plume) Penguin Group (USA) Inc.

—Hot X - Algebra Exposed! 2010. (ENG.). 400p. (gr. 6-18). 26.95 *(978-1-59463-070-5(4)*, Hudson Street Pr.) Penguin Group (USA) Inc.

Messersmith, Sherri. Beginning Algebra w/ Connect Plus Access Card. 2011. (ENG.). (C). 182.00 *(978-0-07-752685-6(6)*, 0077526856, McGraw-Hill Science, Engineering & Mathematics) McGraw-Hill Higher Education.

Messersmith, Sherri. Student Solutions Manual for Beginning Algebra. 2011. (ENG.). 384p. (C). pap. 60.67 ***(978-0-07-329716-3(X)***, 007329716X, McGraw-Hill Science, Engineering & Mathematics) McGraw-Hill Higher Education.

Muschla, Judith A., et al. The Algebra Teacher's Guide to Reteaching Essential Concepts & Skills: 150 Mini-Lessons for Correcting Common Mistakes. 2011. (ENG.). 336p. pap. 32.95 ***(978-0-470-87282-6(9)***, Jossey-Bass) Wiley, John & Sons, Inc.

Noftsier, Kathleen. Integrated Algebra on the Ti-73. 2011. 308p. pap. 15.33 *(978-1-4269-4329-4(6))* Trafford Publishing.

Peterson, Matthew. Scope & sequence/ standards Alignment: ST Math Algebra Readiness. 3rd ed. 2008. *(978-1-933787-43-5(0))* MIND Research Institute.

—ST Math Algebra Readiness User Guide. 3rd ed. 2008. spiral bd. incl. cd-rom *(978-1-933787-42-8(2))* MIND Research Institute.

Pezeshki, Hossein. The College Algebra Helper. 2006. 270p. per. 34.95 *(978-0-9786773-2-9(3))* Texas State Technical College Publishing.

Price, Jack. California Algebra Readiness: Concepts, Skills, & Problem Solving. 2007. (Illus.). 557p. lib. bdg. 115.50 *(978-0-07-877737-0(2))* McGraw-Hill Cos., The.

Pylon Education. Pylon Math Grade 6: Pre-Algebra I. 2010. 216p. pap. 24.95 *(978-1-4502-2544-1(6))* iUniverse, Inc.

—Pylon Math Grade 8: Pre-Algebra 2. 2010. 240p. pap. 26.95 *(978-1-4502-3089-6(X))* iUniverse, Inc.

Rouhani, Behnaz. Studentsæ Knowledge of Functions in an Online Mathematics Course. 2008. 112p. pap. *(978-3-639-08576-1(0))* VDM Verlag Dr. Mueller e.K.

Russell, Susan Jo, et al. Connecting Arithmetic to Algebra (Professional Book) Strategies for Building Algebraic Thinking in the Elementary Grades. 2011. 176p. pap. 26.25 ***(978-0-325-04191-9(1)***, E04191) Heinemann.

Schroeder, Michael William. University of Wisconsin - Madison College Algebra Work Text. rev. ed. 2011. (ENG.). 272p. pap. 30.62 *(978-0-7575-8465-7(9))* Kendall Hunt Publishing Co.

SOYGÜ, et al. Misconceptions of Students in Algebra Lessons. 2010. 128p. pap. *(978-3-8383-2180-6(4))* Lambert Academic Publishing.

Spielhagen, Frances R. The Algebra Solution to Mathematics Reform: Completing the Equation. 2011. (ENG., Illus.). 112p. pap. 24.95 *(978-0-8077-5231-9(2))* Teachers College Pr., Teachers College, Columbia Univ.

Stacey, Kaye, et al, eds. The Future of the Teaching & Learning of Algebra: The 12th ICMI Study. 2010. (New ICMI Study Ser.). xiv, 373p. pap. 229.00 *(978-90-481-7787-5(1)*, 9048177871) Springer.

Sterling, Mary Jane. Algebra II for Dummies Education Bundle. 2008. (ENG.). pap. 29.99 *(978-0-470-43098-9(2)*, For Dummies) Wiley, John & Sons, Inc.

Sullivan. Elementary Algebra. 2006. 700p. tchr. ed. 18.97 *(978-0-13-146813-9(8))* Prentice Hall (Schl. Div.).

—Elementary Algebra: Instructor's Resource Manual W/Tests. 2006. 700p. instr.'s lab manual ed. 18.97 *(978-0-13-146814-6(6))* Prentice Hall (Schl. Div.).

—Intermediate Algebra. 2006. 825p. tchr. ed. 18.97 *(978-0-13-146776-7(X))* Prentice Hall (Schl. Div.).

—Intermediate Algebra: Instructor's Resource Manual W/Tests. 2006. 825p. tchr. ed. 18.97 *(978-0-13-146774-3(3))* Prentice Hall (Schl. Div.).

Sullivan, Michael, et al. Student's Solutions Manual (standalone) for Elementary Algebra. 2nd ed. 2009. (ENG.). 624p. (C). pap. 36.67 *(978-0-321-58930-9(0)*, Prentice Hall) Prentice Hall PTR.

Summers, William L. Beginning Algebra: Mastering the Basics. 4th rev. ed. 2010. (ENG.). 424p. ring bd. 44.12 *(978-0-7575-5022-5(3))* Kendall Hunt Publishing Co.

Sutherland, R., et al, eds. Perspectives on School Algebra. 2010. (Mathematics Education Library). 292p. pap. 269.00 *(978-90-481-5522-4(3)*, 9048155223) Springer.

Taylor-Cox, Jennifer. Differentiating in Algebra, PreK-Grade 2: A Content Companion for Ongoing Assessment, Grouping Students, & Targeting Instruction. 2008. 96p. pap. 12.50 *(978-0-325-02184-3(8)*, E02184) Heinemann.

—Differentiating in Geometry, PreK-Grade 2: A Content Companion for Ongoing Assessment, Grouping Students, & Targeting Instruction. 2008. 112p. pap. 12.50 *(978-0-325-02186-7(4)*, E02186) Heinemann.

Teacher Created Materials Staff, ed. Algebra Readiness: Guided Practice Book. 2007. (Active Algebra Ser.). 224p. pap. 9.99 *(978-1-4333-0126-1(1))* Teacher Created Materials, Inc.

Thompson, Frances McBroom. The Algebra Teacher's Activity-a-Day: Over 180 Quick Challenges for Developing Math & Problem-Solving Skills. 2010. (JB-Ed: 5 Minute FUNdamentals Ser.: 16). (ENG., Illus.). 256p. pap., tchr. ed. 19.95 *(978-0-470-50517-5(6)*, Jossey-Bass) Wiley, John & Sons, Inc.

Tintera, Ping-Jung. The Facilitative Role of Graphing Calculators in Learning Col Algebr. 2009. 96p. pap. *(978-3-639-13240-3(8))* VDM Verlag Dr. Mueller e.K.

Tobey, John Jr, et al. Beginning & Intermediate Algebra. 3rd ed. 2009. (ENG.). 386p. (C). pap. 36.67 *(978-0-321-58871-5(1)*, Prentice Hall) Prentice Hall PTR.

Usiskin, Zalman, et al, eds. Future Curricular Trends in School Algebra & Geometry: Proceedings of A Conference (HC) 2010. 346p. 85.99 *(978-1-61735-007-8(9))* Information Age Publishing, Inc.

—Future Curricular Trends in School Algebra & Geometry: Proceedings of A Conference (PB) 2010. 346p. pap. 45.99 *(978-1-61735-006-1(0))* Information Age Publishing, Inc.

Usiskin, Zalman, et al. Future Curricular Trends in School Algebra & Geometry: Proceedings of a Conference. 2010. 334p. *(978-1-60752-473-1(2))*; pap. *(978-1-60752-472-4(4))*; E-Book *(978-1-60752-474-8(0))* Information Age Publishing, Inc.

Walch Education, creator. Algebra Station Activities for NCTM Standards. 2011. (Illus.). 381p. pap. 39.00 ***(978-0-8251-6223-7(8))*** Walch Education.

Wilfrid, Alvin. Relationship Between Teacher Knowledge & Student Performance. 2010. 128p. pap. *(978-3-639-11704-2(2))* VDM Verlag Dr. Mueller e.K.

Williams, Tony G. Reaching Algebra Readiness: Preparing Middle School Students to Succeed in Algebra - the Gateway to Career Success. 2011. 182p. ***(978-94-6091-508-6(6))***; pap. ***(978-94-6091-507-9(8))*** Sense Pubs.

Witzel, Bradley S. & Riccomini, Paul J. Solving Equations: An Algebra Intervention. 2010. (Math Intervention Ser.). (ENG.). 224p. (C). pap. 25.99 *(978-0-205-56740-9(1))* Allyn & Bacon, Inc.

Young, Cynthia Y. College Algebra, Annotated Instructor's Edition. 2nd ed. 2008. (ENG.). 960p. (C). ring bd. 93.95 *(978-0-470-38738-2(6)*, Wiley) Wiley, John & Sons, Inc.

ALGEBRA, ABSTRACT

see also Algebra, Boolean; Algebra, Homological; Algebra, Universal; Algebraic Fields; Finite Fields (Algebra); Group Theory; Jordan Algebras; Lattice Theory; Lie Algebras; Logic, Symbolic and Mathematical; Matrices; Nonassociative Algebras

Abhyankar, S. S. Lectures on Algebra, Volume 1. 2006. (Illus.). 746p. 86.00 *(978-981-256-826-7(3))* World Scientific Publishing Co., Inc.

Abstract Algebra. 2011. (C). 102.95 ***(978-1-4200-9453-4(X)***, CRC Press) Taylor & Francis Group GBR. Dist: Taylor & Francis Group.

Andree, Richard V. Introduction à L'algèbre. Denizot, F., ed. (Mathématiques et Sciences de L'Homme Ser.). (FRE.). XIII, 238p. 135.00 ***(978-3-11-117281-1(3))*** De Gruyter, Mouton DEU. Dist: de Gruyter, Walter GmbH & Co. KG.

Barbey, K. & König, H. Abstract Analytic Function Theory & Hardy Algebras. 2008. (Lecture Notes in Mathematics Ser.). 272p. pap. 46.00 *(978-3-540-08252-1(2))* Springer.

Bergen, Jeffrey. A Concrete Approach to Abstract Algebra: From the Integers to the Insolvability of the Quintic. 2010. (ENG.). 720p. (C). 109.99 *(978-0-12-374941-3(7)*, Academic Pr.) Elsevier Science & Technology Bks.

Cameron, Peter J. Introduction to Algebra. 2nd ed. 2008. (ENG., Illus.). 352p. per. 65.00 *(978-0-19-852793-0(4))* Oxford Univ. Pr., Inc.

Carstensen, Celine, et al. Abstract Algebra. 2011. (De Gruyter Textbook Ser.). (ENG.). XI, 366p. (C). pap. 60.00 ***(978-3-11-025008-4(X))*** De Gruyter, Walter Inc.

Cram101 Textbook Reviews Staff. Outlines & Highlights for a First Course in Abstract Algebra by Rotman, Isbn: 0130115843. 2009. 108p. pap. 28.95 *(978-1-4288-3944-1(5))* Cram101 Inc.

—Outlines & Highlights for Abstract Algebr: An Introduction by Hungerford, ISBN. 2009. 92p. pap. 27.95 *(978-1-4288-2785-1(4))*; 132p. pap. 28.95 *(978-1-4288-7834-1(3))* Cram101 Inc.

—Outlines & Highlights for Abstract Algebra by Beachy, Isbn: 9781577664437. 2009. 188p. pap. 30.95 *(978-1-4288-2049-4(3))* Cram101 Inc.

—Outlines & Highlights for Contemporary Abstract Algebra by Joseph Gallian, Isbn: 9780618514717. 2009. 86p. pap. 27.95 *(978-1-4288-2401-0(4))*; 94p. pap. 27.95 *(978-1-4288-9687-1(2))* Cram101 Inc.

Derbyshire, John. Unknown Quantity: A Real & Imaginary History of Algebra. 2008. (ENG.). 374p. pap. 16.00 *(978-1-4379-5198-1(8))* DIANE Publishing Co.

—Unknown Quantity: A Real & Imaginary History of Algebra. 2007. (ENG., Illus.). 416p. (gr. 12-18). 17.00 *(978-0-452-28853-9(3)*, Plume) Penguin Group (USA) Inc.

Ehrlich, Gertrude & Mathematics Centre Staff. Fundamental Concepts of Abstract Algebra. 2011. (Dover Books on Mathematics Ser.). (ENG.). 352p. pap. 24.95 ***(978-0-486-48589-8(7))*** Dover Pubns., Inc.

Eie, Minking & Chang, Shou-Te. A Course on Abstract Algebra. 2010. (Illus.). 360p. 54.00 *(978-981-4271-88-2(8))* World Scientific Publishing Co., Inc.

Engler, Antonio J. & Prestel, Alexander. Valued Fields. 2010. (Springer Monographs in Mathematics Ser.). x, 208p. pap. 129.00 *(978-3-642-06345-9(4)*, 3642063454) Springer.

Fraleigh & Cram101 Textbook Reviews Staff. A First Course in Abstract Algebr. 2007. 140p. per. 11.95 *(978-1-4288-3392-0(7))* Cram101 Inc.

Gallian & Cram101 Textbook Reviews Staff. Contemporary Abstract Algebr. 2007. 128p. per. 11.95 *(978-1-4288-3404-0(4))* Cram101 Inc.

Gallian, Joseph. Contemporary Abstract Algebra. 7th ed. 2009. (ENG.). 640p. (C). 216.95 *(978-0-547-16509-7(9))* Brooks/Cole.

Garrett, Paul B. Abstract Algebra. 2007. (ENG., Illus.). 472p. (C). 98.95 *(978-1-58488-689-1(7)*, Chapman & Hall/CRC) CRC Pr. LLC.

Ginzburg, D., et al. The Descent Map from Automorphic Representations of Gl(N) to Classical Groups. 2011. (Illus.). 350p. 99.00 *(978-981-4304-98-6(0))* World Scientific Publishing Co., Inc.

Grillet, Pierre Antoine. Abstract Algebra. 2nd ed. (Graduate Texts in Mathematics Ser.). 2010. xii, 676p. pap. 69.95 *(978-1-4419-2450-6(7)*, 1441924507) 2007. (Illus.). 669p. 69.95 *(978-0-387-71567-4(3))* Springer.

Grove, Larry C. Algebra. unabr. ed. 2010. (Dover Books on Mathematics Ser.). (ENG., Illus.). 320p. (C). pap. 19.95 *(978-0-486-43947-1(X))* Dover Pubns., Inc.

Hazra, A. K. Matrix: Algebra, Calculus & Generalized Inverse (Part II) 2007. (ENG.). 508p. per. 145.00 *(978-1-904602-58-3(4))* Cambridge International Science Publishing, Ltd. GBR. Dist: Ingram Pub. Services.

Herstein & Cram101 Textbook Reviews Staff. Abstract Algebr. 2007. 76p. per. 10.95 *(978-1-4288-3388-3(9))* Cram101 Inc.

Kleiner, Israel. History of Abstract Algebra. 2010. (Illus.). 200p. 49.95 *(978-0-387-34050-0(5)*, 0387340505) Springer.

—A History of Abstract Algebra. 2007. (ENG., Illus.). xvi, 168p. pap. 49.95 *(978-0-8176-4684-4(1)*, 0817646841) Birkhauser Boston.

Klima, Richard E., et al. Applications of Abstract Algebra with Maple & Matlab. 2nd ed. 2006. (Discrete Mathematics & Its Applications Ser.). (Illus.). 505p. 102.95 *(978-1-4200-1119-7(7))* Taylor & Francis Group.

Kohlas, Juerg & Pouly, Marc. Generic Inference: A Unifying Theory for Automated Reasoning. 2011. (ENG., Illus.). 484p. 110.00 *(978-0-470-52701-6(3)*, Wiley) Wiley, John & Sons, Inc.

Lidl, Rudolf & Pilz, Ganter. Applied Abstract Algebra. 2nd ed. 2010. (Undergraduate Texts in Mathematics Ser.). (ENG., Illus.). xvi, 508p. pap. 84.95 *(978-1-4419-3117-7(1)*, 1441931171) Springer.

Loomis, Lynn H. Introduction to Abstract Harmonic Analysis. 2011. (Dover Books on Mathematics Ser.). (ENG.). 208p. pap. 19.95 *(978-0-486-48123-4(9))* Dover Pubns., Inc.

Martin, Stuart. Schur Algebras & Representation Theory. 2009. (Cambridge Tracts in Mathematics Ser.). (ENG.). 256p. pap. 51.00 *(978-0-521-10046-5(1))* Cambridge Univ. Pr.

Maxfield, John E. & Maxfield, Margaret W. Abstract Algebra & Solution by Radicals. 2010. (Dover Books on Mathematics Ser.). (ENG.). 224p. pap. 12.95 *(978-0-486-47723-7(1))* Dover Pubns., Inc.

Maxwell, E. A. A Gateway to Abstract Mathematics. 2008. (ENG.). 140p. pap. 31.99 *(978-0-521-09028-5(8))* Cambridge Univ. Pr.

Nicholson, W. Keith. Introduction to Abstract Algebra. 4th ed. 2012. (ENG.). 560p. 135.00 ***(978-1-118-13535-8(0)***, Wiley) Wiley, John & Sons, Inc.

—Introduction to Abstract Algebra. 4th ed. 2012. (ENG.). 160p. pap. 29.95 ***(978-1-118-28815-3(7)***, Wiley) Wiley, John & Sons, Inc.

—Introduction to Abstract Algebra, Set. 4th ed. 2012. (ENG.). 145.00 ***(978-1-118-29603-5(6)***, Wiley) Wiley, John & Sons, Inc.

Paulsen, William. Abstract Algebra: An Interactive Approach. 2009. (Textbooks in Mathematics Ser.). (ENG., Illus.). 560p. (C). 107.95 *(978-1-4200-9452-7(1)*, CRC Press) Taylor & Francis Group GBR. Dist: Taylor & Francis Group.

Petrich, M. Categories of Algebraic Systems. 2008. (Lecture Notes in Mathematics Ser.). 232p. pap. 59.95 *(978-3-540-07998-9(X))* Springer.

Pinter, Charles C. A Book of Abstract Algebra: Second Edition. 2nd ed. 2010. (Dover Books on Mathematics Ser.). (ENG.). 400p. pap. 16.95 *(978-0-486-47417-5(8))* Dover Pubns., Inc.

Reis, Clive. Abstract Algebra: An Introduction to Groups, Rings & Fields. 2011. 520p. 108.00 *(978-981-4335-64-5(9))*; pap. 58.00 *(978-981-4340-28-1(6))* World Scientific Publishing Co., Inc.

Rotman & Cram101 Textbook Reviews Staff. A First Course in Abstract Algebr. 2007. 124p. per. 11.95 *(978-1-4288-3462-0(1))* Cram101 Inc.

Saracino, Dan. Abstract Algebra: A First Course. 2nd ed. 2008. 313p. (C). 57.95 *(978-1-57766-536-6(8))* Waveland Pr., Inc.

Shirshov, A. I. & Bokut, L. A. Selected Works of A. I. Shirshov. Bremner, M. & Kotchetov, M., trs. from RUS. 2009. (Contemporary Mathematicians Ser.). Orig. Title: 19 papers according to the enclosed List. (ENG., Illus.). viii, 242p. 199.00 *(978-3-7643-8857-7(9)*, 3764388579) Birkhauser Boston.

Smith, Jonathan D. H. Introduction to Abstract Algebra. 2008. (Textbooks in Mathematics Ser.). (ENG., Illus.). 344p. (C). 99.95 *(978-1-4200-6371-4(5)*, Chapman & Hall/CRC) CRC Pr. LLC.

ALGEBRA, BOOLEAN

see also Caratheodory Measure; Lattice Theory

Arnold, Bradford Henry & Mathematics Centre Staff. Logic & Boolean Algebra. 2011. (Dover Books on Mathematics Ser.). (ENG.). 160p. pap. 12.95 ***(978-0-486-48385-6(1))*** Dover Pubns., Inc.

Brickenstein, Michael. Boolean Gröbner bases — Theory, Algorithms & Applications. 2010. 160p. pap. *(978-3-8325-2597-2(1))* Logos Verlag Berlin.

Bubeck, U., ed. Model-Based Transformations for Quantified Boolean Formulas. 2010. 226p. pap. 73.00 *(978-1-60750-545-7(2))* IOS Pr., Inc.

Budaghyan, Lilya. The Equivalence of Apn & Ab Functions & Their Generalizations. 2008. 92p. pap. *(978-3-8364-9410-6(8))* VDM Verlag Dr. Mueller e.K.

Caramani, Danièle. Introduction to the Comparative Method with Boolean Algebra. 2008. (Quantitative Applications in the Social Sciences Ser.: 158). (Illus.). 128p. (C). pap. 18.00 *(978-1-4129-0975-4(9)*, B09759P) SAGE Pubns., Inc.

Chakraborty, Sourav. Models of Query Complexity for Boolean Functions. 2010. 132p. pap. *(978-3-8383-9269-1(8))* Lambert Academic Publishing.

Clote, Peter & Kranakis, Evangelos. Boolean Functions & Computation Models. 2010. (Texts in Theoretical Computer Science. an EATCS Ser.). (Illus.). xiv, 601p. pap. 109.00 *(978-3-642-08217-7(3)*, 3642082173) Springer.

Crama, Yves & Hammer, Peter L. Boolean Functions Vol. 1: Theory & Algorithms. 2008. (Encyclopedia of Mathematics & Its Applications Ser.). (Illus.). 700p. 150.00 *(978-0-521-84751-3(6))* Cambridge Univ. Pr.

Crama, Yves & Hammer, Peter L., eds. Boolean Models & Methods in Mathematics, Computer Science, & Engineering. 2010. (Encyclopedia of Mathematics & Its Applications Ser.). (ENG., Illus.). 776p. 175.00 *(978-0-521-84752-0(4))* Cambridge Univ. Pr.

Cusick, Thomas W., et al. Cryptographic Boolean Functions & Applications. 2009. (ENG., Illus.). 248p. 61.95 *(978-0-12-374890-4(9)*, Academic Pr.) Elsevier Science & Technology Bks.

Dalai, Deepak Kumar. On Boolean Functions to Resist Algebraic Attacks. 2010. 152p. pap. *(978-3-639-26685-6(4))* VDM Verlag Dr. Mueller e.K.

Drechsler, Rolf, et al. Test Pattern Generation using Boolean Proof Engines. 2009. (ENG., Illus.). xii, 192p. 139.00 *(978-90-481-2359-9(3)*, 9048123593) Springer.

Ebendt, Rudiger, et al. Advanced BDD Optimization. 2010. (ENG.). x, 222p. pap. 189.00 *(978-1-4419-3796-4(X)*, 144193796X) Springer.

Flament, Claude. L' Analyse Booléenne de Questionnaire. (Méthodes de la Sociologie Ser.). (FRE., Illus.). 299p. 210.00 ***(978-3-11-174667-8(4))*** De Gruyter, Mouton DEU. Dist: de Gruyter, Walter GmbH & Co. KG.

Givant, Steven R. & Halmos, Paul R. Introduction to Boolean Algebras. 2009. (Undergraduate Texts in Mathematics Ser.). (Illus.). xiv, 574p. (ENG.). 59.95 *(978-0-387-40293-2(4))*; 49.95 *(978-0-387-68436-9(0))* Springer.

Goodstein, R. L. Boolean Algebra. 2007. (Dover Books on Mathematics Ser.). (ENG., Illus.). 160p. per. 10.95 *(978-0-486-45894-6(6))* Dover Pubns., Inc.

Jukna, Stasys. Boolean Function Complexity: Advances & Frontiers. 2012. (Algorithms & Combinatorics Ser.). (ENG., Illus.). xv, 617p. 84.95 ***(978-3-642-24507-7(2)***, 3642245072) Springer.

Kleine Buning, Hans. Theory & Applications of Satisfiability Testing - Sat 2008. 2008. (Lecture Notes in Computer Science / Theoretical Computer Science & General Issues Ser.). spiral bd. 79.95 *(978-3-540-79718-0(1)*, 3540797181) Springer.

Kullmann, Oliver. Theory & Applications of Satisfiability Testing - SAT 2009: 12th International Conference, SAT 2009, Swansea, UK, June 30 - July 3, 2009. Proceedings. 2009. (Lecture Notes in Computer Science / Theoretical Computer Science & General Issues Ser.). xii, 540p. pap. 109.00 *(978-3-642-02776-5(8)*, 3642027768) Springer.

Kushilevitz, Eyal & Nisan, Noam. Communication Complexity. 2006. (ENG., Illus.). 208p. pap. 48.00 *(978-0-521-02983-4(X))* Cambridge Univ. Pr.

Loginov, O. A., et al. Boolean Functions in Coding Theory & Cryptography. 2012. (Translations of Mathematical Monographs Ser.). (RUS., Illus.). 334p. 129.00 ***(978-0-8218-4680-3(9))*** American Mathematical Society.

Monk, J. Donald. Cardinal Invariants on Boolean Algebras. 2009. (Modern Birkhäuser Classics Ser.). Orig. Title: 978-3-7643-5402-2 (pm). 308p. pap. 59.95 *(978-3-0346-0333-1(9)*, 3034603339) Birkhauser Verlag AG CHE. Dist: Springer.

The Monodromy Groups of Isolated Singularities of Complete Intersections. 2008. (Lecture Notes in Mathematics Ser.). pap. 39.95 *(978-3-540-18686-1(7))* Springer.

O'Connor, Brian. Satisfiability Checking with Difference Constraints. 2010. 80p. pap. *(978-3-639-14738-4(3))* VDM Verlag Dr. Mueller e.K.

Pinus, A. G. Boolean Constructions in Universal Algebras. 2010. (Mathematics & Its Applications Ser.). (ENG.). 364p. pap. 189.00 *(978-90-481-4239-2(3)*, 9048142393) Springer.

Preneel, Bart & Logachev, Oleg A. Boolean Functions in Cryptology & Information Security. 2008. viii, 355p. 157.00 *(978-1-58603-878-6(8))* IOS Pr., Inc.

Pseudo-Boolean Programming & Applications: Presented at the Colloquium on Mathematics & Cybernetics in the Economy, Berlin, October 1964. 2007. (Lecture Notes in Mathematics Ser.). pap. 26.00 *(978-3-540-03352-3(1))* Springer.

Rudeanu. Axioms for Lattices & Boolean Algebras. 2008. 77.00 *(978-981-283-454-6(0))* World Scientific Publishing Co., Inc.

Sasao, Tsutomu & Butler, Jon T. Progress in Applications of Boolean Functions. 2010. (Synthesis Lectures on Digital Circuits & Systems Ser.). 153p. pap. 40.00 *(978-1-60845-181-4(X))* Morgan & Claypool Pubs.

Sets & Subsets, Boolean Algebra, Boolean Simplification, Vol. 12. 160p. 6.95 *(978-0-87891-211-7(8)*, Research & Education Assn.

Strichman, Ofer & Szeider, Stefan, eds. Theory & Applications of Satisfiability Testing - SAT 2010: 13th International Conference, SAT 2010, Edinburgh, UK, July 11-14, 2010, Proceedings. 2010. (Lecture Notes in Computer Science / Theoretical Computer Science & General Issues Ser.). xiii, 400p. pap. 99.00 *(978-3-642-14185-0(4)*, 3642141854) Springer.

Theory & Applications of Satisfiability Testing - SAT 2007: 10th International Conference, Lisbon, Portugal, May 28-31, 2007 Proceedings. 2007. (Lecture Notes in Computer Science Ser.). (Illus.). 384p. pap. 79.95 *(978-3-540-72787-3(6))* Springer.

Vladimirov, D. A. Boolean Algebras in Analysis. 2010. (Mathematics & Its Applications Ser.). 632p. pap. 359.00 *(978-90-481-5961-1(X)*, 904815961X) Springer.

Vollmer, Heribert. Introduction to Circuit Complexity: A Uniform Approach. 2010. (Texts in Theoretical Computer Science. an EATCS Ser.). (ENG., Illus.). xi, 270p. pap. 119.00 *(978-3-642-08398-3(6)*, 3642083986) Springer.

Whitesitt, J. Eldon. Boolean Algebra & Its Applications. 2010. (Dover Books on Computer Science Ser.). (ENG.). 192p. pap. 10.95 *(978-0-486-47767-1(3))* Dover Pubns., Inc.

ALGEBRA, COMMUTATIVE

see Commutative Algebra

ALGEBRA, DIFFERENCE

see Difference Algebra

ALGEBRA, DIFFERENTIAL

see Differential Algebra

ALGEBRA, HOMOLOGICAL

see also Categories (Mathematics); Functor Theory

Altman, Allen & Kleiman, Steven. Introduction to Grothendieck Duality Theory. 2008. (Lecture Notes in Mathematics Ser.). 188p. pap. 39.95 *(978-3-540-04935-7(5)*, 3540049355) Springer.

Beligiannis, Apostolos & Reiten, Idun. Homological & Homotopical Aspects of Torsion Theories. 2007. (Memoirs of the American Mathematical Society Ser.). 207p. pap. 74.00 *(978-0-8218-3996-6(9))* American Mathematical Society.

Bousfield, A. & Kan, D. Homotopy Limits, Completions & Localizations. 2008. (Lecture Notes in Mathematics Ser.). vp. pap. 46.00 *(978-3-540-06105-2(3))* Springer.

Bridson, Martin R., et al, eds. Geometric & Cohomological Methods in Group Theory. 2009. (London Mathematical Society Lecture Note Ser.). (ENG., Illus.). 330p. pap. 71.00 *(978-0-521-75724-9(X))* Cambridge Univ. Pr.

Brodmann, M. P. & Sharp, R. Y. Local Cohomology: An Algebraic Introduction with Geometric Applications. 2007. (Cambridge Studies in Advanced Mathematics). (ENG., Illus.). 436p. pap. 60.00 *(978-0-521-04758-6(7))* Cambridge Univ. Pr.

Categorical Algebra & its Applications: Proceedings of a Conference, Held in Louvain-la-Neuve, Belgium, July 26 - August 1, 1987. 2008. (Lecture Notes in Mathematics Ser.). pap. 59.95 *(978-3-540-50362-0(5))* Springer.

Corso, Alberto & Polini, Claudia, eds. Commutative Algebra & Its Connections to Geometry. 2011. (Contemporary Mathematics Ser.). (Illus.). 215p. pap. 79.00 ***(978-0-8218-4959-0(X))*** American Mathematical Society.

Gelfand, Sergei I. & Manin, Yuri I. Methods of Homological Algebra. 2nd ed. 2010. (Springer Monographs in Mathematics Ser.). (Illus.). xx, 370p. pap. 119.00 *(978-3-642-07813-2(3)*, 3642078133) Springer.

Geramita, Anthony V., et al. The Hilbert Function of a Level Algebra. 2007. (Memoirs of the American Mathematical Society Ser.: No. 872). (Illus.). 139p. pap. 66.00 *(978-0-8218-3940-9(3))* American Mathematical Society.

Hartshorne, Robin. Local Cohomology. 2007. (Lecture Notes in Mathematics Ser.). 116p. pap. 39.95 *(978-3-540-03912-9(0)*, 3540039120) Springer.

Hodgkin, L. H. & Snaith, V. P. Topics in K-Theory. 2008. (Lecture Notes in Mathematics Ser.). 308p. pap. 59.95 *(978-3-540-07536-3(4))* Springer.

Illusie, L. Complexe Cotangent et Deformations I. 2008. (Lecture Notes in Mathematics Ser.). 368p. per. 46.00 *(978-3-540-05686-7(6))* Springer.

—Complexe Cotangent et Deformations II. 2008. (Lecture Notes in Mathematics Ser.). 320p. per. 46.00 *(978-3-540-05976-9(8))* Springer.

Inassaridze, H. K-theory & Homological Algebra: A Seminar Held at the Razmadze Mathematical Institute in Tbilisi, Georgia, USSR 1987-88. 2008. (Lecture Notes in Mathematics Ser.). (ENG.). v, 313p. pap. 59.95 *(978-3-540-52836-4(9)*, 3540528369) Springer.

Inassaridze, Hvedri. Non-Abelian Homological Algebra & Its Applications. 2010. (Mathematics & Its Applications Ser.). 272p. pap. 279.00 *(978-90-481-4899-8(5)*, 9048148995) Springer.

Iyengar, Srikanth, et al. Twenty-Four Hours of Local Cohomology. 2007. (Graduate Studies in Mathematics Ser.: Vol. 87). (Illus.). 282p. (C). 57.00 *(978-0-8218-4126-6(2))* American Mathematical Society.

Jonsson, Jakob. Simplicial Complexes of Graphs. 2007. (Lecture Notes in Mathematics Ser.). spiral bd. 79.95 *(978-3-540-75858-7(5))* Springer.

Kashiwara, Masaki & Schapira, Pierre. Sheaves on Manifolds: With a Short History les debuts de la theorie des faisceaux by Christian Houzel. 2010. (Grundlehren der mathematischen Wissenschaften Ser.). x, 512p. pap. 139.00 *(978-3-642-08082-1(0)*, 3642080820) Springer.

Khalkhali, Masoud & Yu, Guoliang, eds. Perspectives on Noncommutative Geometry. 2011. (Fields Institute Communications Ser.). (Illus.). 163p. 89.00 ***(978-0-8218-4849-4(6))*** American Mathematical Society.

Kozlov, Dmitry. Combinatorial Algebraic Topology. (Algorithms & Computation in Mathematics Ser.). (Illus.). 389p. 2008. pap. 59.95 *(978-3-540-73051-4(6))* 2007. 109.00 *(978-3-540-71961-8(X))* Springer.

Levy, Lawrence S. & Robson, J. Chris. Hereditary Noetherian Prime Rings & Idealizers. 2011. (Mathematical Surveys & Monographs). (Illus.). 228p. 84.00 *(978-0-8218-5350-4(3))* American Mathematical Society.

Majadas, Javier & Rodicio, Antonio G. Smoothness, Regularity, & Complete Intersection. 2010. (London Mathematical Society Lecture Note Ser.). (ENG.). 140p. pap. 50.00 *(978-0-521-12572-7(3))* Cambridge Univ. Pr.

Northcott, D. G. An Introduction to Homological Algebra. 2009. (ENG.). 300p. pap. 38.99 *(978-0-521-09793-2(2))* Cambridge Univ. Pr.

Olteanu, Anda. Classes of Monomial Ideals. 2010. 124p. pap. *(978-3-8383-5563-4(6))* Lambert Academic Publishing.

Percy, Andrew. Integral Cohomology Algebras. 2010. 152p. pap. *(978-3-8383-5172-8(X))* Lambert Academic Publishing.

Positselski, Leonid. Homological Algebra of Semimodules & Semicontramodules. 2010. (Monografie Matematyczne Ser.). (ENG., Illus.). xxiv, 349p. 109.00 *(978-3-0346-0435-2(1)*, 3034604351) Birkhauser Verlag AG CHE. Dist: Springer.

Quillen, Daniel G. Homotopical Algebr. 2007. (Lecture Notes in Mathematics Ser.). 158p. per. 39.95 *(978-3-540-03914-3(7))* Springer.

Relative Homological Algebra. (De Gruyter Expositions in Mathematics Ser.). 2011. (ENG. Illus.). XII, 96p. 210.00 ***(978-3-11-173442-2(0))*** 2010. (ENG.). 280p. 140.00 *(978-3-11-021522-9(5))* 2nd ed. 2011. (ENG., Illus.). XIII, 359p. 210.00 ***(978-3-11-173685-3(7))*** 2nd ed. 2010. 350p. 140.00 *(978-3-11-021520-5(9))* De Gruyter, Walter Inc.

Rotman, Joseph J. Introduction to Homological Algebra. 2nd ed. 2008. (Universitext Ser.). 650p. (C). pap. 49.95 *(978-0-387-24527-0(8)*, 0387245278) Springer.

Stammbach, Urs. Homology in Group Theory. 2008. (Lecture Notes in Mathematics Ser.). 196p. pap. 39.95 *(978-3-540-06569-2(5)*, 3540065695) Springer.

Strooker, J. R. Introduction to Categories, Homological Algebra & Sheaf Cohomology. 2009. (ENG.). 260p. pap. 36.99 *(978-0-521-09525-9(5))* Cambridge Univ. Pr.

Toën, Bertrand & Vezzosi, Gabriele. Homotopical Algebraic Geometry II: Geometric Stacks & Applications. 2008. (Memoirs of the American Mathematical Society Ser.). 224p. pap. 81.00 *(978-0-8218-4099-3(1))* American Mathematical Society.

Yau, Donald. Lambda-rings. 2010. (Illus.). 204p. 61.00 *(978-981-4299-09-1(X))* World Scientific Publishing Co., Inc.

ALGEBRA, MULTIPLE

see Algebra, Universal

ALGEBRA, UNIVERSAL

see also Algebra, Abstract; Algebras, Linear; Categories (Mathematics); Matrices; Numbers, Complex; Quaternions; Vector Analysis

Behms, Vernon N. An Introduction to the Algebra of Hypernumbers. 2007. 34p. pap. 9.00 *(978-0-8059-7638-0(8))* Dorrance Publishing Co., Inc.

Belohlávek, Radim & Vychodil, Vilem. Fuzzy Equational Logic. 2010. (Studies in Fuzziness & Soft Computing Ser.). (Illus.). xii, 283p. pap. 139.00 *(978-3-642-06575-0(9)*, 3642065759) Springer.

Bergman, Clifford. Universal Algebra. 2011. (Chapman & Hall Pure & Applied Mathematics Ser.). (ENG., Illus.). 320p. 99.95 *(978-1-4398-5129-6(8)*, Chapman & Hall/CRC) CRC Pr. LLC.

Comer, S., ed. Universal Algebra & Lattice Theory: Proceedings of a Conference held at Charleston, July 11-14, 1984. 2008. (Lecture Notes in Mathematics Ser.). pap. 46.00 *(978-3-540-15691-8(7))* Springer.

Denecke, Klaus. Universal Algebra & Coalgebra. 2009. 292p. 69.00 *(978-981-283-745-5(0))* World Scientific Publishing Co., Inc.

Derbyshire, John. Unknown Quantity: A Real & Imaginary History of Algebra. 2008. (ENG.). 374p. pap. 16.00 *(978-1-4379-5198-1(8))* DIANE Publishing Co.

—Unknown Quantity: A Real & Imaginary History of Algebra. 2007. (ENG., Illus.). 416p. (gr. 12-18). 17.00 *(978-0-452-28853-9(3)*, Plume) Penguin Group (USA) Inc.

Doberkat, Ernst-Erich. Coalgebraic Stochastic Logic. 2009. (Monographs in Theoretical Computer Science. an EATCS Ser.). (Illus.). xv, 231p. 129.00 *(978-3-642-02994-3(9)*, 3642029949) Springer.

Erdmann, K. Blocks of Tame Representation Type & Related Algebras. 2008. (Lecture Notes in Mathematics Ser.). pap. 59.95 *(978-3-540-52709-1(5))* Springer.

Freese, R. S. & Garcia, O. C., eds. Universal Algebra & Lattice Theory: Proceedings of the Fourth International Conference Held at Puebla, Mexico, 1982. 2008. (Lecture Notes in Mathematics Ser.). pap. 46.00 *(978-3-540-12329-3(6))* Springer.

Galatos, Nikolaos, et al. Residuated Lattices: An Algebraic Glimpse at Substructural Logics. 2007. (Studies in Logic & the Foundations of Mathematics Ser.: 151). (ENG., Illus.). 532p. 140.00 *(978-0-444-52141-5(0)*, Elsevier Science) Elsevier Science & Technology Bks.

Gottsche, Lothar. Hilbert Schemes of Zero-Dimensional Subschemes of Smooth Varieties. 2008. (Lecture Notes in Mathematics / Mathematisches Institut der Universität und Max-Planck-Institut für Mathematik, Bonn Ser.). 205p. pap. 49.95 *(978-3-540-57814-7(5))* Springer.

Grätzer, George A. Universal Algebra. 2nd ed. 2008. (ENG., Illus.). xx, 588p. pap. 89.95 *(978-0-387-77486-2(6)*, 0387774866) Springer.

Johnstone, P. I., et al. Indexed Categories & Their Applications. 2008. (Lecture Notes in Mathematics Ser.). 272p. pap. 59.95 *(978-3-540-08914-8(4))* Springer.

Jonsson, B. Topics in Universal Algebr. 2008. (Lecture Notes in Mathematics Ser.). 232p. pap. 59.95 *(978-3-540-05722-2(6)*, 3540057226) Springer.

Laumon, Gérard. Cohomology of Drinfeld Modular Varieties: Geometry, Counting of Points & Local Harmonic Analysis, Pt. 1. 2010. (Cambridge Studies in Advanced Mathematics Ser.). 360p. pap. 45.00 *(978-0-521-17274-5(8))* Cambridge Univ. Pr.

Pinus, A. G. Boolean Constructions in Universal Algebras. 2010. (Mathematics & Its Applications Ser.). (ENG.). 364p. pap. 189.00 *(978-90-481-4239-2(3)*, 9048142393) Springer.

Pitkethly, Jane G. & Davey, Brian A. Dualisability: Unary Algebras & Beyond. 2010. (Advances in Mathematics Ser.). (Illus.). xii, 263p. pap. 119.00 *(978-1-4419-3901-2(6)*, 1441939016) Springer.

Rosenberg, Ivo G. & Sabidussi, Gert, eds. Algebras & Orders. 2010. (NATO Science Series C: (closed) Ser.). 576p. pap. 559.00 *(978-90-481-4243-9(1)*, 9048142431) Springer.

Smith, J. D. H. Mal'cev Varieties. 2008. (Lecture Notes in Mathematics Ser.). 176p. pap. 39.95 *(978-3-540-07999-6(8))* Springer.

Whitehead, Alfred North. A Treatise on Universal Algebra: With Applications. 2009. (Cambridge Library Collection - Mathematics Ser.). 620p. pap. 35.99 *(978-1-108-00168-7(8))* Cambridge Univ. Pr.

Xu, Yichao. Theory of Complex Homogeneous Bounded Domains. 2010. (Mathematics & Its Applications Ser.). x, 427p. pap. 119.00 *(978-90-481-6596-4(2)*, 9048165962) Springer.

ALGEBRA OF LOGIC

see Logic, Symbolic and Mathematical

ALGEBRAIC CONFIGURATIONS IN HYPERSPACE

see Hyperspace

ALGEBRAIC CURVES

see Curves, Algebraic

ALGEBRAIC FIELDS

see also Algebraic Number Theory; Differential Algebra; Finite Fields (Algebra); Ideals (Algebra); Number Theory; Quaternions; Rings (Algebra)

Adamson, Iain T. Introduction to Field Theory. 2nd ed. 2007. (Dover Books on Mathematics Ser.). (ENG., Illus.). 192p. per. 11.95 *(978-0-486-46266-0(8))* Dover Pubns., Inc.

Araujo-Gomez, Jesus, et al, eds. Advances in Non-Archimedean Analysis. 2011. (Contemporary Mathematics Ser.). (Illus.). 280p. pap. 99.00 ***(978-0-8218-5291-0(4))*** American Mathematical Society.

Berz, Martin & Shamseddine, Khodr, eds. Advances in P-Adic & Non-Archimedean Analysis. 2010. (Contemporary Mathematics Ser.). (Illus.). 269p. pap. 89.00 *(978-0-8218-4740-4(6))* American Mathematical Society.

Borho, W. & Rentschler, Rudolf. Primideale in Einhüllenden auflösbarer Lie-Algebren: (Beschreibung durch Bahnenräume) 2008. (Lecture Notes in Mathematics Ser.). (GER.). 182p. 29.95 *(978-3-540-06561-6(X))* Springer.

Breuil, Christophe & Paskunas, Vytautas. Towards A Modulo P Langlands Correspondence for Gl$_2$ 2012. (Memoirs of the American Mathematical Society Ser.). 114p. pap. 70.00 ***(978-0-8218-5227-9(2))*** American Mathematical Society.

Buhler, Joe P. & Stevenhagen, P. Algorithmic Number Theory: Lattices, Number Fields, Curves & Cryptography. Buhler, Joe & Stevenhagen, Peter, eds. 2008. (Mathematical Sciences Research Institute Publications). (ENG., Illus.). 662p. 104.00 *(978-0-521-80854-5(5))* Cambridge Univ. Pr.

Bushnell, C. J. & Frohlich, A. Gauss Sums & p-adic Division Algebras. 2008. (Lecture Notes in Mathematics Ser.). pap. 26.00 *(978-3-540-12290-6(7))* Springer.

A

Chambert-Loir, Antoine. A Field Guide to Algebra. 2010. (Undergraduate Texts in Mathematics Ser.). (Illus.). x, 195p. pap. 59.95 (978-1-4419-1947-2(3), 1441919473) Springer.

Childress, Nancy. Algebraic Number Fields & Their Completions. 2012. (Discrete Mathematics & Its Applications Ser.). (ENG., Illus.). 352p. 89.95 **(978-1-4398-5251-4(0)**, Chapman & Hall/CRC) CRC Pr. LLC.

Coates, John, et al, eds. Non-abelian Fundamental Groups & Iwasawa Theory. 2011. (London Mathematical Society Lecture Note Ser.). (ENG., Illus.). 320p. pap. 90.00 **(978-1-107-64885-2(8))** Cambridge Univ. Pr.

Coates, John & Sujatha, R. Cyclotomic Fields & Zeta Values. (Springer Monographs in Mathematics Ser.). x, 116p. 2010. pap. 64.95 (978-3-642-06959-8(2), 3642069592) 2006. (ENG., Illus.). 64.95 (978-3-540-33068-4(2), 3540330682) Springer.

Cohn, P. M. Skew Fields: Theory of General Division Rings. 2008. (Encyclopedia of Mathematics & its Applications Ser.). (ENG.). 520p. pap. 95.00 (978-0-521-06294-7(2)) Cambridge Univ. Pr.

Conner, P. E. Jr. Notes on the Witt Classification of Hermitian Innerproduct Spaces over a Ring of Algebraic Integers. 2012. (ENG.). 158p. pap. 25.00 **(978-0-292-74067-9(0))** Univ. of Texas Pr.

Dixon, G. M. Division Algebras: Octonions Quaternions Complex Numbers & the Algebraic Design of Physics. 2010. (Mathematics & Its Applications Ser.). 248p. pap. 139.00 (978-1-4419-4746-8(9), 1441947469) Springer.

Fried, Michael D. Field Arithmetic. 2008. (Ergebnisse der Mathematik und ihrer Grenzgebiete. 3. Folge / A Series of Modern Surveys in Mathematics Ser.). 219.00 (978-3-540-77269-9(3)) Springer.

Fried, Michael D. & Jarden, Moshe. Field Arithmetic. 3rd ed. 2010. (Ergebnisse der Mathematik und Ihrer Grenzgebiete. 3. Folge a Series of Modern Surveys in Mathematics Ser.). xxiv, 792p. pap. 219.00 (978-3-642-09594-8(1), 3642095941) Springer.

Fuchs, Laszlo. Partially Ordered Algebraic Systems. 2011. (Dover Books on Mathematics Ser.). (ENG.). 240p. pap. 19.95 **(978-0-486-48387-0(8))** Dover Pubns., Inc.

Gerardin, P. Construction de Series Discretes P-Adiques. 2008. (Lecture Notes in Mathematics Ser.). 188p. pap. 26.00 (978-3-540-07172-3(5)) Springer.

Gerritzen, L. & Put, M. van der. Schottky Groups & Mumford Curves. 2008. (Lecture Notes in Mathematics Ser.). 332p. pap. 59.95 (978-3-540-10229-8(9)) Springer.

Greenberg, Ralph. Iwasawa Theory, Projective Modules, & Modular Representations. 2011. (Memoirs of the American Mathematical Society Ser.). 185p. pap. 83.00 (978-0-8218-4931-6(X)) American Mathematical Society.

Hasan, M. Anwar & Helleseth, Tor, eds. Arithmetic of Finite Fields: Third International Workshop, WAIFI 2010, Istanbul, Turkey, June 27-30, 2010, Proceedings. 2010. (Lecture Notes in Computer Science / Theoretical Computer Science & General Issues Ser.). 280p. pap. 72.00 (978-3-642-13796-9(2), 3642137962) Springer.

Haskell, Deirdre, et al, eds. Model Theory, Algebra, & Geometry. 2010. (Mathematical Sciences Research Institute Publications). (ENG., Illus.). 236p. pap. 26.99 (978-0-521-14349-3(7)) Cambridge Univ. Pr.

Hilbert, David. The Theory of Algebraic Number Fields. Adamson, I. T., tr. from GER. 2010. (ENG.). xxxvi, 350p. pap. 119.00 (978-3-642-08306-8(4), 3642083064) Springer.

Hsia, J. S., et al, eds. Proceedings of the Conference on Orders, Group Rings & Related Topics. 2008. (Lecture Notes in Mathematics Ser.). 236p. pap. 46.00 (978-3-540-06518-0(0), 3540065180) Springer.

Hsu, D. F. Cyclic Neofields & Combinatorial Designs. 2008. (Lecture Notes in Mathematics Ser.). 244p. pap. 59.95 (978-3-540-10243-4(4)) Springer.

Ishida, M. The Genus Fields of Algebraic Number Fields. 2008. (Lecture Notes in Mathematics Ser.). 136p. pap. 26.00 (978-3-540-08000-8(7)) Springer.

Kiechle, Hubert, et al, eds. Nearrings & Nearfields: Proceedings of the Conference on Nearrings & Nearfields, Hamburg, Germany July 27 - August 3 2003. 2010. xiv, 319p. pap. 119.00 (978-90-481-6850-7(3), 9048168503) Springer.

Knebusch, Manfred. Specialization of Quadratic & Symmetric Bilinear Forms. Unger, Thomas, tr. from GER. 2010. (Algebra & Applications Ser.). xii, 192p. 109.00 (978-1-84882-241-2(3), 1848822413) Springer.

Koch, Helmut. Galois Theory of P-Extensions. Lemmermeyer, F., tr. from GER. 2010. (Springer Monographs in Mathematics Ser.). (ENG.). xiii, 190p. pap. 139.00 (978-3-642-07817-0(6), 3642078176) Springer.

Lam, T. Y. Serre's Conjecture. 2008. (Lecture Notes in Mathematics Ser.). 244p. pap. 59.95 (978-3-540-08657-4(9)) Springer.

Lectures on Formally Real Fields. 2008. (Lecture Notes in Mathematics Ser.). pap. 39.95 (978-3-540-13885-3(4)) Springer.

Malle, Gunter & Matzat, B. H. Inverse Galois Theory. 2010. (Springer Monographs in Mathematics Ser.). (ENG.). xvi, 436p. pap. 139.00 (978-3-642-08311-2(0), 3642083110) Springer.

Mathiak, K. Valuations of Skew Fields & Projective Hjelmslev Spaces. 2008. (Lecture Notes in Mathematics Ser.). pap. 39.95 (978-3-540-16099-1(X)) Springer.

Mski, S. The Determination of Units in Real Cyclic Sextic Fields. 2008. (Lecture Notes in Mathematics Ser.). 208p. pap. 26.00 (978-3-540-09984-0(0)) Springer.

Neukirch, Jürgen, et al. Cohomology of Number Fields. 2008. (Grundlehren der mathematischen Wissenschaften Ser.). 179.00 (978-3-540-37888-4(X)) Springer.

Oda, Susumu & Yoshida, Ken-ichi. Simple Extensions with the Minimum Degree Relations of Integral Domains. 2007. (Lecture Notes in Pure & Applied Mathematics Ser.: Vol. 253). (ENG., Illus.). 296p. 189.95 (978-1-58488-851-2(2), Chapman & Hall/CRC) CRC Pr. LLC.

Oggier, Frédtrique, et al. Cyclic Division Algebras: A Tool for Space-Time Coding. 2007. 108p. pap. 80.00 (978-1-60198-050-2(7)) Now Pubs.

Prestel, A. Formally p-adic Fields. 2008. (Lecture Notes in Mathematics Ser.). pap. 39.95 (978-3-540-12890-8(5)) Springer.

Reid, Legh Wilber. The Elements of the Theory of Algebraic Numbers. 2007. (ENG.). 476p. per. 37.95 (978-0-548-29131-3(4)) Kessinger Publishing, LLC.

Robert, Alain M. A Course in p-adic Analysis. 2010. (Graduate Texts in Mathematics Ser.). (Illus.). xv, 437p. pap. 84.95 (978-1-4419-3150-4(3), 1441931503) Springer.

Roman, Steven. Field Theory. 2nd ed. 2012. (Graduate Texts in Mathematics Ser.). (ENG., Illus.). xii, 335p. pap. 64.95 (978-1-4419-2095-9(1), 1441920951) Springer.

Room, T. G. & Kirkpatrick, P. B. Miniquaternion Geometry: An Introduction to the Study of Projective Planes. 2008. (Cambridge Tracts in Mathematics Ser.). (ENG., Illus.). 188p. pap. 42.00 (978-0-521-09064-3(4)) Cambridge Univ. Pr.

Rosen, Michael I., ed. Exposition by Emil Artin: A Selection. 2006. (History of Mathematics Ser.). (Illus.). 346p. (C). pap. 61.00 (978-0-8218-4172-3(6)) American Mathematical Society.

Schultz, Claudia. Quantifier Elimination over Real Closed Fields- Mathematical Basis, Solution Techniques, Practical Integrations. 2007. pap. (978-3-8364-1306-0(X)) VDM Verlag Dr. Mueller e.K.

Stichtenoth, Henning. Algebraic Function Fields & Codes. 2nd ed. (Graduate Texts in Mathematics Ser.). (Illus.). xiii, 355p. 2010. (ENG.). pap. 59.95 (978-3-642-09556-6(9), 3642095569) 2008. 59.95 (978-3-540-76877-7(7)) Springer.

Villa Salvador, Gabriel Daniel. Topics in the Theory of Algebraic Function Fields. 2006. (Mathematics: Theory & Applications Ser.). (Illus.). xvi, 652p. (C). 109.00 (978-0-8176-4480-2(6), 0817644806) Birkhauser Boston.

Warshauer, M. L. The Witt Group of Degree k Maps & Asymmetric Inner Product Spaces. 2008. (Lecture Notes in Mathematics Ser.). pap. 46.00 (978-3-540-11201-3(4)) Springer.

Weil, A. Dirichlet Series & Automorphic Forms: Lezioni Fermiane. 2008. (Lecture Notes in Mathematics Ser.). iv, 164p. pap. 39.95 (978-3-540-05382-8(4)) Springer.

Zariski, Oscar. An Introduction to the Theory of Algebraic Surfaces. 2008. (Lecture Notes in Mathematics Ser.). pap. 39.95 (978-3-540-04602-8(X)) Springer.

ALGEBRAIC FUNCTIONS

Cram101 Textbook Reviews. Outlines & Highlights for Essentials of College Algebra by Gary K Rockswold. 2011. 200p. pap. 30.95 **(978-1-61830-996-9(X))** Cram101 Inc.

Cram101 Textbook Reviews Staff. Outlines & Highlights for Experiencing Introductory & Intermediate Algebra Through Functions & Graphs by Thomasson, Joanne / Pesut, Robert, Isbn. 2009. 162p. pap. 29.95 (978-1-4288-3789-8(2)) Cram101 Inc.

Davenport, J. H. On the Integration of Algebraic Functions. 2007. (Lecture Notes in Computer Science Ser.). 197p. pap. 24.95 (978-3-540-10290-8(6), 3540102906) Springer.

Deuring, Max. Lectures on the Theory of Algebraic Functions of One Variable. 2008. (Lecture Notes in Mathematics Ser.). 164p. pap. 39.95 (978-3-540-06152-6(5)) Springer.

Dur, A. Möbius Functions, Incidence Algebras & Power Series Representations. 2008. (Lecture Notes in Mathematics Ser.). pap. 39.95 (978-3-540-16771-6(4)) Springer.

Goldschmidt, David. Algebraic Functions & Projective Curves. 2010. (Graduate Texts in Mathematics Ser.). xvi, 179p. pap. 64.95 (978-1-4419-2995-2(9), 1441929959) Springer.

Knutson, Donald. Algebraic Spaces. 2008. (Lecture Notes in Mathematics Ser.). 272p. pap. 59.95 (978-3-540-05496-2(0), 3540054960) Springer.

Rockswold, Gary K. Essentials of College Algebra with Modeling & Visualization. 4th ed. 2011. (ENG.). 768p. (C). 130.67 (978-0-321-71528-9(4)) Addison Wesley.

—Essentials of College Algebra with Modeling & Visualization, Books A la Carte. 4th ed. 2010. (ENG.). 768p. (C). ring bd. 78.40 (978-0-321-72672-8(3)) Addison Wesley.

—Essentials of College Algebra with Modeling & Visualization, Books a la Carte Plus MML/MSL Student Access Code Card (for ad hoc Valuepacks) 4th ed. 2010. (ENG.). (C). ring bd. 104.67 (978-0-321-77218-3(0)) Addison Wesley.

Sasane, Amol. Algebras of Holomorphic Functions & Control Theory. 2009. (Dover Books on Mathematics Ser.). (ENG.). 160p. pap. 7.95 (978-0-486-47465-6(8)) Dover Pubns., Inc.

Stichtenoth, Henning. Algebraic Function Fields & Codes. 2nd ed. (Graduate Texts in Mathematics Ser.). (Illus.). xiii, 355p. 2010. (ENG.). pap. 59.95 (978-3-642-09556-6(9), 3642095569) 2008. 59.95 (978-3-540-76877-7(7)) Springer.

Sullivan, Michael. College Algebra: Concepts Through Functions. (Illus.). 2007. (978-0-13-243175-0(0)) 2nd ed. 2010. (ENG., 792p. (C). 168.67 (978-0-321-64107-6(8), Prentice Hall) Prentice Hall PTR.

Sullivan, Michael & Sullivan, Michael Iii. College Algebra: Concepts through Functions, Books a la Carte Edition. 2nd ed. 2010. (ENG.). (C). ring bd. 101.20 (978-0-321-63670-6(8)) Addison Wesley.

Villa Salvador, Gabriel Daniel. Topics in the Theory of Algebraic Function Fields. 2006. (Mathematics: Theory & Applications Ser.). (Illus.). xvi, 652p. (C). 109.00 (978-0-8176-4480-2(6), 0817644806) Birkhauser Boston.

ALGEBRAIC GEOMETRY

see Geometry, Algebraic

ALGEBRAIC LOGIC

Aerts, Diederik & Pykacz, Jaroslaw, eds. Quantum Structures & the Nature of Reality: The Indigo Book of 'Einstein Meets Magritte' 2010. (Einstein Meets Magritte: an Interdisciplinary Reflection on Science, Nature, Art, Human Action & Society Ser.). (Illus.). 260p. pap. 199.00 (978-90-481-5243-8(7), 9048152437) Springer.

Andréka, Hajnal, et al. Universal Algebraic Logic: Dedicated to the Unity of Science. 2009. (Studies in Universal Logic Ser.). 260p. pap. 79.95 (978-3-7643-8505-7(7)) Birkhauser Boston.

Barrios, Victor Manuel Garcia. Personalisation Systems. 2008. 216p. pap. (978-3-8364-6623-3(6)) VDM Verlag Dr. Mueller e.K.

Berghammer, Rudolf. Relations & Kleene Algebra in Computer Science. 2008. (Lecture Notes in Computer Science / Theoretical Computer Science & General Issues Ser.). spiral bd. 89.95 (978-3-540-78912-3(X), 354078912X) Springer.

Berghammer, Rudolf, et al. Relations & Kleene Algebra in Computer Science: 11th International Conference on Relational Methods in Computer Science, RelMiCS 2009, & 6th International Conference on Applications of Kleene Algebra, AKA 2009, Doha, Qatar, November 1-5, 2009, Proceedings. 2009. (Lecture Notes in Computer Science / Theoretical Computer Science & General Issues Ser.). viii, 367p. pap. 83.00 (978-3-642-04638-4(X), 364204638X) Springer.

Cohen, A. Algorithms in Algebra. 2008. (London Mathematical Society Student Texts: Vol. 30). (Illus.). 250p. (C). 59.95 (978-0-521-43046-3(1)); pap. 22.95 (978-0-521-43630-4(3)) Cambridge Univ. Pr.

Coherent Systems on Algebraic Curves. 2011. 74.00 (978-981-4304-17-7(4)) World Scientific Publishing Co., Inc.

Craig, William. Semigroups Underlying First-Order Logic. 2006. (Memoirs of the American Mathematical Society Ser.: No. 866). 263p. pap. 85.00 (978-0-8218-4149-5(1)) American Mathematical Society.

Cram101 Textbook Reviews. Outlines & Highlights for Classical Algebr: Its Nature, Origins, & Uses by Roger Cooke. 2011. 126p. pap. 28.95 **(978-1-61905-015-0(3))** Cram101 Inc.

Czelakowski, J. Protoalgebraic Logics. 2010. (Trends in Logic Ser.). 464p. pap. 249.00 (978-90-481-5693-1(9), 9048156939) Springer.

de Swart, Harrie, ed. Relational & Algebraic Methods in Computer Science: 12th International Conference, RAMICS 2011, Rotterdam, the Netherlands, May 30 — June 3, 2011, Proceedings. 2011. (Lecture Notes in Computer Science / Theoretical Computer Science & General Issues Ser.). (Illus.). viii, 363p. pap. 83.00 (978-3-642-21069-3(4), 3642210694) Springer.

Gindikin, Semen G. Algebraic Logic. Silverman, R. H., tr. 2012. (Problem Books in Mathematics Ser.). (ENG.). pap. 119.00 (978-1-4419-3076-7(0), 1441930760) Springer.

Henkin, L., et al. Cylindric Set Algebras. 2008. (Lecture Notes in Mathematics Ser.). 332p. pap. 59.95 (978-3-540-10881-8(5)) Springer.

Loewe, B. Algebra Logic Set Theory. 2007. (GER & ENG., Illus.). viii, 311p. (978-1-904987-28-4(1)) College Pubns.

Loucks, Stuart E. Introductory Physics with Algebra as a Second Language: Mastering Problem-Solving. 2006. (ENG., Illus.). 288p. (C). pap. 44.95 (978-0-471-76250-8(4), Wiley) Wiley, John & Sons, Inc.

Louis Couturat. The Algebra of Logic. Lydia Robinson, tr. 2007. 92p. per. 9.95 (978-1-60386-038-3(X), Merchant Bks.) Rough Draft Printing.

Rédei, Miklós. Quantum Logic in Algebraic Approach. 2010. (Fundamental Theories of Physics Ser.). 260p. pap. 269.00 (978-90-481-4976-6(2), 9048149762) Springer.

Schlaudt, Oliver. Louis Couturat -Traité de Logique Algorithmique. Schlaudt, Oliver & Sakhri, Mohsen, eds. 2010. (Publications des Archives Henri Poincaré Publications of the Henri Poincaré Archives / Science autour de / Around 1900 Ser.). (ENG & FRE., Illus.). viii, 317p. 149.00 (978-3-0346-0410-9(6), 3034604106) Birkhauser Verlag AG CHE. Dist: Springer.

Schliemann, Analucia Dias, et al. Bringing Out the Algebraic Character of Arithmetic: From Children's Ideas to Classroom Practice. 2006. (Studies in Mathematical Thinking & Learning). (Illus.). 144p. 150.00 incl. cd-rom (978-0-8058-4338-5(8)) Erlbaum, Lawrence Assocs., Inc.

—Bringing Out the Algebraic Character of Arithmetic: From Children's Ideas to Classroom Practice. 2006. (Studies in Mathematical Thinking & Learning). (ENG., Illus.). 160p. pap. 27.95 (978-0-8058-5873-0(3)) Routledge.

ALGEBRAIC NUMBER THEORY

see also Algebraic Fields

Ash, Robert B. A Course in Algebraic Number Theory. 2010. (Dover Books on Mathematics Ser.). (ENG.). 128p. pap. 10.95 (978-0-486-47754-1(1)) Dover Pubns., Inc.

Bernstein, L. The Jacobi-Perron Algorithm. 2008. (Lecture Notes in Mathematics Ser.). 164p. pap. 39.95 (978-3-540-05497-9(9), 3540054979) Springer.

Brink, David. Procyclic Galois Extensions of Algebraic Number Fields. 2010. 96p. pap. (978-3-8383-8004-9(5)) Lambert Academic Publishing.

Bugeaud, Yann. Approximation by Algebraic Numbers. 2007. (Cambridge Tracts in Mathematics Ser.). (ENG., Illus.). 292p. pap. 60.00 (978-0-521-04567-4(3)) Cambridge Univ. Pr.

Burns, David, et al, eds. L-Functions & Galois Representations. 2008. (London Mathematical Society Lecture Note Ser.). (ENG., Illus.). 576p. pap. 102.00 (978-0-521-69415-5(9)) Cambridge Univ. Pr.

Bushnell, Colin J. & Henniart, Guy. The Local Langlands Conjecture for GL(2) 2010. (Grundlehren der mathematischen Wissenschaften Ser.). xii, 354p. pap. 125.00 (978-3-642-06853-9(7), 3642068537) Springer.

Cohen, Henri. A Course in Computational Algebraic Number Theory. 2010. (Graduate Texts in Mathematics Ser.). (Illus.). xx, 550p. pap. 89.95 (978-3-642-08142-2(8), 3642081428) Springer.

—Number Theory, Volume 1: Tools & Diophantine Equations, 2 vols. 2007. (Graduate Texts in Mathematics Ser.: Vols. 239-240). (Illus.). 650p. 64.95 (978-0-387-49922-2(9)) Springer.

—Number Theory, Volume 2: Analytic & Modern Tools, 2 vols. 2007. (Graduate Texts in Mathematics Ser.: Vols. 239-240). 596p. 64.95 (978-0-387-49893-5(1)) Springer.

Cram101 Textbook Reviews. Outlines & Highlights for Advanced Algebra by Anthony W Knapp. 2011. 232p. pap. 31.95 **(978-1-61905-106-5(0))** Cram101 Inc.

Diophantine Approximation & Transcendence Theory: Seminar, Bonn (FRG) May - June 1985. 2008. (Lecture Notes in Mathematics Ser.). pap. 59.95 (978-3-540-18597-0(6)) Springer.

Farb, Benson. Problems on Mapping Class Groups & Related Topics. 2006. (Proceedings of Symposia in Pure Mathematics Ser.: Vol. 74). (Illus.). 371p. 92.00 (978-0-8218-3838-9(5)) American Mathematical Society.

Fried, Michael D. Field Arithmetic. 2008. (Ergebnisse der Mathematik und ihrer Grenzgebiete. 3. Folge / A Series of Modern Surveys in Mathematics Ser.). 219.00 (978-3-540-77269-9(3)) Springer.

Fried, Michael D. & Jarden, Moshe. Field Arithmetic. 3rd ed. 2010. (Ergebnisse der Mathematik und Ihrer Grenzgebiete. 3. Folge a Series of Modern Surveys in Mathematics Ser.). xxiv, 792p. pap. 219.00 (978-3-642-09594-8(1), 3642095941) Springer.

Friedlander, Eric M. & Stein, M. R., eds. Algebraic K-Theory. Evanston 1980: Proceedings of the Conference Held at Northwestern University Evanston, March 24-27, 1980. 2008. (Lecture Notes in Mathematics Ser.). 532p. pap. 69.95 (978-3-540-10698-2(7)) Springer.

Godement, Roger & Jacquet, Herve. Zeta Functions of Simple Algebras. 2008. (Lecture Notes in Mathematics Ser.). 204p. pap. 39.95 (978-3-540-05797-0(8), 3540057978) Springer.

Gras, Georges. Class Field Theory: From Theory to Practice. Cohen, H., tr. from FRE. 2010. (Springer Monographs in Mathematics Ser.). xiv, 512p. pap. 129.00 (978-3-642-07908-5(3), 3642079083) Springer.

Hecke, E. T. Lectures on the Theory of Algebraic Numbers. Brauer, G. R. et al, trs. 2010. (Graduate Texts in Mathematics Ser.). 260p. pap. 84.95 (978-1-4419-2814-6(6), 1441928146) Springer.

Ikeda. Multi-Dimensional Langlands Functoriality Principle. 2010. 65.00 (978-981-283-831-5(7)) World Scientific Publishing Co., Inc.

Kiyek, K. & Vicente, J. L. Resolution of Curve & Surface Singularities: In Characteristic Zero. 2010. (Algebra & Applications Ser.). xxii, 484p. pap. 129.00 (978-90-481-6573-5(3), 9048165733) Springer.

Kohno, Toshitake & Morishita, Masanori, eds. Primes & Knots: JAMI Conference, Knots & Primes, March 8-16, 2003, Johns Hopkins University. 2006. (Contemporary Mathematics Ser.). (Illus.). 284p. pap. 81.00 (978-0-8218-3456-5(8)) American Mathematical Society.

Kubert, D. & Lang, S. Modular Units. 2010. (Grundlehren der mathematischen Wissenschaften Ser.). 380p. pap. 145.00 (978-1-4419-2813-9(8), 1441928138) Springer.

Lauter, Kristin E. & Ribet, Kenneth A., eds. Computational Arithmetic Geometry. 2008. (Contemporary Mathematics Ser.). (Illus.). 129p. pap. 50.00 (978-0-8218-4320-8(6)) American Mathematical Society.

Lemmermeyer, Franz. Reciprocity Laws: From Euler to Eisenstein. 2010. (Springer Monographs in Mathematics Ser.). xix, 516p. pap. 135.00 (978-3-642-08628-1(4), 3642086284) Springer.

MacCallum, Malcolm A. H. & Mikhailov, Alexander V., eds. Algebraic Theory of Differential Equations. 2008. (London Mathematical Society Lecture Note Ser.). (ENG., Illus.). 248p. pap. 74.00 (978-0-521-72008-3(7)) Cambridge Univ. Pr.

Marubayashi, H., et al. Non-Commutative Valuation Rings & Semi-Hereditary Orders. 2010. (K-Monographs in Mathematics Ser.). 200p. pap. 189.00 (978-90-481-4853-0(7), 9048148537) Springer.

Mollin, Richard A. Algebraic Number Theory. 2nd rev. ed. 2011. (Discrete Mathematics & Its Applications Ser.). (ENG., Illus.). 442p. 89.95 (978-1-4398-4598-1(0), Chapman & Hall/CRC) CRC Pr. LLC.

Moreno, Carlos Julio. Advanced Analytic Number Theory: L-Functions. 2007. (Mathematical Surveys & Monographs). 291p. pap. 80.00 (978-0-8218-4266-9(8)) American Mathematical Society.

Moroz, B. Analytic Arithmetic in Algebraic Number Fields. 2008. (Lecture Notes in Mathematics Ser.). pap. 39.95 (978-3-540-16784-6(5)) Springer DEU. Dist: Springer.

Murty, M. Ram & Esmonde, Jody (Indigo). Problems in Algebraic Number Theory. 2nd ed. 2010. (Graduate Texts in Mathematics Ser.). xvi, 352p. pap. 74.95 (978-1-4419-1967-0(8), 1441919678) Springer.

Narkiewicz, Wladyslaw. Elementary & Analytic Theory of Algebraic Numbers. 3rd ed. 2010. (Springer Monographs in Mathematics Ser.). (ENG.). xi, 708p. pap. 179.00 (978-3-642-06010-6(2), 3642060102) Springer.

Neukirch, Jargen. Algebraic Number Theory. Schappacher, Norbert, tr. from GER. 2010. (Grundlehren der mathematischen Wissenschaften Ser.). (Illus.). xvii, 571p. pap. 169.00 (978-3-642-08473-7(7), 3642084737) Springer.

Reiner, I. & Roggenkamp, K.W. Integral Representations: Topics in Integral Representation Theory. Integral Representations & Presentations of Finite Groups by Roggenkamp, K. W. 2008. (Lecture Notes in Mathematics Ser.). 284p. pap. 46.00 (978-3-540-09546-0(2)) Springer.

Ribenboim, Paulo. Classical Theory of Algebraic Numbers. 2nd ed. 2010. (Universitext Ser.). (Illus.). xxiv, 681p. pap. 99.00 *(978-1-4419-2870-2(7),* 1441928707) Springer.

Roggenkamp, Klaus W., ed. Integral Representations & Applications: Proceedings of a Conference held at Oberwolfach, Germany, June 22-28, 1980. 2008. (Lecture Notes in Mathematics Ser.). 492p. pap. 59.00 *(978-3-540-10880-1(7))* Springer.

Samuel, Pierre. Algebraic Theory of Numbers: Translated from the French by Allan J. Silberger. Silberger, Allan J., tr. from FRE. 2008. (Dover Books on Mathematics Ser.). (ENG.). 112p. pap. 10.95 *(978-0-486-46666-8(3))* Dover Pubns., Inc.

Schmidt, W.M. Diophantine Approximation. 2008. (Lecture Notes in Mathematics Ser.). xii, 299p. pap. 69.95 *(978-3-540-09762-4(7))* Springer.

Shimura, Goro. Arithmetic of Quadratic Forms. 2010. (Springer Monographs in Mathematics Ser.). (ENG.). xii, 240p. 119.00 *(978-1-4419-1731-7(4),* 1441917314) Springer.

Stein, Michael R., ed. Algebraic K-Theory: Papers presented at the Conference held at Northwestern University, Evanston, January 12-16, 1976. 2008. (Lecture Notes in Mathematics Ser.). 428p. pap. 69.95 *(978-3-540-07996-5(3))* Springer.

Zimmer, H. G. Computational Problems, Methods, & Results in Algebraic Number Theory. 2008. (Lecture Notes in Mathematics Ser.). 112p. pap. 26.00 *(978-3-540-05822-9(2))* Springer.

ALGEBRAIC NUMBERS

see Algebraic Fields

ALGEBRAIC RINGS

see Rings (Algebra)

ALGEBRAIC SPACES

Bergeron, Francois. Algebraic Combinatorics & Coinvariant Spaces. 2009. (ENG.). 230p. 59.00 *(978-1-56881-324-0(4))* AK Peters, Ltd.

Delfs, H. Homology of Locally Semialgebraic Spaces. 2008. (Lecture Notes in Mathematics Ser.). 145p. pap. 26.00 *(978-3-540-54615-3(4))* Springer.

Dubinsky, E. The Structure of Nuclear Frechet Spaces. 2008. (Lecture Notes in Mathematics Ser.). 196p. pap. 26.00 *(978-3-540-09504-0(7))* Springer.

Han, Qing & Hong, Jia-Xing. Isometric Embedding of Riemannian Manifolds in Euclidean Spaces. 2006. (Mathematical Surveys & Monographs Ser.). (Illus.). 260p. 77.00 *(978-0-8218-4071-9(1))* American Mathematical Society.

Hoffman, Kenneth. Analysis in Euclidean Space. 2007. (Dover Books on Mathematics Ser.). (ENG., Illus.). 448p. per. 23.95 *(978-0-486-45804-5(0))* Dover Pubns., Inc.

Johnson, Norman. Combinatorics of Spreads & Parallelisms. 2010. (Pure & Applied Mathematics Ser.). (ENG.). 664p. 199.95 *(978-1-4398-1946-3(7),* CRC Press) Taylor & Francis Group GBR. Dist: Taylor & Francis Group.

Kilford. Computations with Modular Forms. 2008. (Illus.). xii, 224p. 68.00 *(978-1-84816-213-6(8))* Imperial College Pr. GBR. Dist: World Scientific Publishing Co., Inc.

Knutson, Donald. Algebraic Spaces. 2008. (Lecture Notes in Mathematics Ser.). 272p. pap. 59.95 *(978-3-540-05496-2(0),* 3540054960) Springer.

Mathiak, K. Valuations of Skew Fields & Projective Hjelmslev Spaces. 2008. (Lecture Notes in Mathematics Ser.). pap. 39.95 *(978-3-540-16099-1(X))* Springer.

Schwartz, L. Semi-martingales sur des varietes, et martingales conformes sur des varietes analytiques complexes. 2008. (Lecture Notes in Mathematics Ser.). 152p. pap. 26.00 *(978-3-540-09749-5(X))* Springer.

Sigrist, Francois, ed. H - Spaces. 2008. (Lecture Notes in Mathematics Ser.). 172p. pap. 39.95 *(978-3-540-05461-0(8),* 3540054618) Springer.

Stasheff, James. H-Spaces from a Homotopy Point of View. 2008. (Lecture Notes in Mathematics Ser.). 108p. pap. 39.95 *(978-3-540-04940-1(1),* 3540049401) Springer.

Stein, William A. Modular Forms, a Computational Approach. 2007. (Graduate Studies in Mathematics Ser.). (Illus.). 268p. 57.00 *(978-0-8218-3960-7(8))* American Mathematical Society.

Stoyanov, Luchezar N. Scattering Resonances for Several Small Convex Bodies & the Lax-Phillips Conjecture. 2009. (Memoirs of the American Mathematical Society Ser.). 76p. pap. 62.00 *(978-0-8218-4294-2(3))* American Mathematical Society.

Todorcevic, Stevo. Introduction to Ramsey Spaces. 2010. (Annals of Mathematics Studies). (ENG., Illus.). 296p. (C). 89.50 *(978-0-691-14541-9(5));* pap. 45.00 *(978-0-691-14542-6(3))* Princeton Univ. Pr.

Weakly Semialgebraic Spaces. 2008. (Lecture Notes in Mathematics Ser.). pap. 46.00 *(978-3-540-50815-1(5))* Springer.

Wolf, Joseph Albert. Harmonic Analysis on Commutative Spaces. 2007. (Mathematical Surveys & Monographs). 387p. (C). 102.00 *(978-0-8218-4289-8(7))* American Mathematical Society.

ALGEBRAIC SURFACES

see Surfaces, Algebraic

ALGEBRAIC TOPOLOGY

see also Fiber Spaces (Mathematics); Homology Theory; Hopf Algebras; K-Theory; Measure Theory; Sheaves, Theory Of

Adams, J. Frank. The Selected Works of J. Frank Adams, Vol. 2. May, J. Peter & Thomas, Charles B., eds. 2009. (ENG.). 548p. pap. 67.00 *(978-0-521-11068-6(8))* Cambridge Univ. Pr.

—The Selected Works of J. Frank Adams: Volume 1. May, J. Peter & Thomas, Charles B., eds. 2009. (ENG.). 556p. pap. 67.00 *(978-0-521-11067-9(X))* Cambridge Univ. Pr.

Adem, Alejandro, et al. Orbifolds & Stringy Topology. 2007. (Cambridge Tracts in Mathematics Ser.). (ENG., Illus.). 164p. 88.00 *(978-0-521-87004-7(6))* Cambridge Univ. Pr.

Aguade, J. Algebraic Topology: Homotopy & Group Cohomology. 2008. (Lecture Notes in Mathematics Ser.). pap. 59.95 *(978-3-540-55195-9(6))* Springer.

Aguilar, Marcelo, et al. Algebraic Topology from a Homotopical Viewpoint. Sontz, S. B., tr. 2012. (Universitext Ser.). (ENG., Illus.). xxix, 478p. pap. 99.00 *(978-1-4419-3005-7(1),* 1441930051) Springer.

Al. Topology & Physics (V12) 2008. (Nankai Tracts in Mathematics Ser.). 124.00 *(978-981-281-910-9(X))* World Scientific Publishing Co., Inc.

Algebraic Topology & Transformation Groups: Proceedings of a Conference held in Göttingen, FRG, August 23-29, 1987. 2008. (Lecture Notes in Mathematics / Mathematica Gottingensis Ser.). pap. 59.95 *(978-3-540-50528-0(8))* Springer.

Algebraic Topology, Barcelona 1986: Proceedings of a Symposium held in Barcelona, April 2-8, 1986. 2008. (Lecture Notes in Mathematics Ser.). pap. 59.95 *(978-3-540-18729-5(4))* Springer.

Andersen, Jorgen E., et al, eds. Chern-Simons Gauge Theory: 20 Years After. 2011. (Ams/Ip Studies in Advanced Mathematics Ser.). (Illus.). 446p. pap. 130.00 ***(978-0-8218-5353-5(8))*** American Mathematical Society.

Andres, J. & Górniewicz, Lech. Topological Fixed Point Principles for Boundary Value Problems. 2011. (Topological Fixed Point Theory & Its Applications Ser.). (ENG.). 761p. pap. 129.00 *(978-90-481-6318-2(8),* 9048163188) Springer.

Aschbacher, Michael. The Generalized Fitting Subsystem of a Fusion System. 2011. (Memoirs of the American Mathematical Society Ser.). 110p. pap. 70.00 *(978-0-8218-5303-0(1))* American Mathematical Society.

Aschbacher, Michael, et al. Fusion Systems in Algebra & Topology. 2011. (London Mathematical Society Lecture Note Ser.). (ENG., Illus.). 326p. pap. 65.00 ***(978-1-107-60100-0(2))*** Cambridge Univ. Pr.

Ausoni, Christian, et al, eds. Alpine Perspectives on Algebraic Topology. 2009. (Contemporary Mathematics Ser.). 254p. pap. 79.00 *(978-0-8218-4839-5(9))* American Mathematical Society.

Baas, Nils. Algebraic Topology: The Abel Symposium 2007. Baas, Nils et al, eds. 2009. (Abel Symposia Ser.). (ENG., Illus.). xiv, 409p. 139.00 *(978-3-642-01199-3(3),* 3642011993) Springer.

Banagl, Markus & Vogel, Denis, eds. The Mathematics of Knots: Theory & Application. 2010. (Contributions in Mathematical & Computational Sciences Ser.) (Illus.). x, 364p. 149.00 *(978-3-642-15636-6(3),* 3642156363) Springer.

Barmak, Jonathan A. Algebraic Topology of Finite Topological Spaces & Applications. 2011. (Lecture Notes in Mathematics Ser.). (ENG., Illus.). xvii, 170p. pap. 49.95 ***(978-3-642-22002-9(9),*** 3642220029) Springer.

Baues, H. J. Obstruction Theory: On Homotopy Classification of Maps. 2008. (Lecture Notes in Mathematics Ser.). 400p. pap. 59.95 *(978-3-540-08534-8(3))* Springer.

Behrens, Mark & Lawson, Tyler. Topological Automorphic Forms. 2010. (Memoirs of the American Mathematical Society Ser.). (Illus.). 136p. pap. 74.00 *(978-0-8218-4539-4(X))* American Mathematical Society.

Berrick, A. Jon. Braids: Introductory Lectures on Braids, Configurations & Their Applications. 2009. (Illus.). 416p. 111.00 *(978-981-4291-40-8(4))* World Scientific Publishing Co., Inc.

Borisovich, Yu. G., et al. Introduction to Differential & Algebraic Topology. 2010. (Texts in the Mathematical Sciences Ser.). (Illus.). 504p. pap. 109.00 *(978-90-481-4558-4(9),* 9048145589) Springer.

Bott, Raoul & Tu, Loring W. Differential Forms in Algebraic Topology. 2010. (Graduate Texts in Mathematics Ser.). (Illus.). pap. 74.95 *(978-1-4419-2815-3(4),* 1441928154) Springer.

Bott, Raoul, et al. Lectures on Algebraic & Differential Topology, Delivered at the II. ELAM. 2008. (Lecture Notes in Mathematics Ser.). (SPA & ENG.). 174p. 39.95 *(978-3-540-05944-8(X))* Springer.

Bredon, Glen E. Topology & Geometry. 2010. (Graduate Texts in Mathematics Ser.). (ENG., Illus.). xiv, 557p. pap. 79.95 *(978-1-4419-3103-0(1),* 1441931031) Springer.

Brümmer, Guillaume & Gilmour, Christopher, eds. Papers in Honour of Bernhard Banaschewski. 2010. 512p. pap. 189.00 *(978-90-481-5540-8(1),* 9048155401) Springer.

Bruner, Robert & Greenlees, J. P. C. Connective Real K-Theory of Finite Groups. 2010. (Mathematical Surveys & Monographs). (Illus.). 318p. 92.00 *(978-0-8218-5189-0(6))* American Mathematical Society.

Bunke, Ulrich. Index Theory, Eta Forms, & Deligne Cohomology. 2009. (Memoirs of the American Mathematical Society Ser.). 120p. pap. 67.00 *(978-0-8218-4284-3(6))* American Mathematical Society.

Carlsson, G. Algebraic Topology: Proceedings of an International Conference held in Arcata, California, July 27 - August 2, 1986. 2008. (Lecture Notes in Mathematics Ser.). pap. 69.95 *(978-3-540-51118-2(0))* Springer.

Carter, J. Scott. An Excursion in Diagrammatic Algebra: Turning A Sphere from Red to Blue. 2011. 296p. 108.00 ***(978-981-4374-49-1(0))*** World Scientific Publishing Co., Inc.

Carter, J. Scott, et al, eds. Intelligence of Low Dimensional Topology, 2007. (Series on Knots & Everything). (Illus.). 382p. 188.00 *(978-981-270-593-8(7))* World Scientific Publishing Co., Inc.

Cha, Jae Choon. The Structure of the Rational Concordance Group of Knots. 2007. (Memoirs of the American Mathematical Society Ser.). 95p. pap. 62.00 *(978-0-8218-3993-5(4))* American Mathematical Society.

Conner, Pierre E. Lectures on the Action of a Finite Group. 2008. (Lecture Notes in Mathematics Ser.). (ENG.). 132p. pap. 39.95 *(978-3-540-04243-3(1),* 3540042431) Springer.

Craven, David. The Theory of Fusion Systems: An Algebraic Approach. 2011. (Cambridge Studies in Advanced Mathematics Ser.). (ENG., Illus.). 384p. 72.00 *(978-1-107-00596-9(5))* Cambridge Univ. Pr.

Cuntz, Joachim, et al. Topological & Bivariant K-Theory. 2007. (Oberwolfach Seminars Ser.). xi, 262p. pap. 49.95 *(978-3-7643-8398-5(4),* 3764383984) Birkhauser Verlag AG CHE. Dist: Springer.

Dieudonné, Jean. A History of Algebraic & Differential Topology, 1900 - 1960. 2009. (Modern Birkhäuser Classics Ser.). xxiv, 648p. pap. 69.95 *(978-0-8176-4906-7(9))* Birkhauser Verlag AG CHE. Dist: Springer.

Doran, Robert S., et al, eds. Superstrings, Geometry, Topology, & C*-algebras. 2010. (Proceedings of Symposia in Pure Mathematics Ser.). 249p. 63.00 *(978-0-8218-4887-6(9))* American Mathematical Society.

Dupont, J. L. & Madsen, I. H., eds. Algebraic Topology, Aarhus 1978: Proceedings of a Symposium held at Aarhus, Denmark, August 7-12, 1978. 2008. (Lecture Notes in Mathematics Ser.). 708p. pap. 69.95 *(978-3-540-09721-1(X))* Springer.

Elliptic Curves & Modular Forms in Algebraic Topology: Proceedings of a Conference held at the Institute for Advanced Study, Princeton, Sept. 15-17, 1986. 2008. (Lecture Notes in Mathematics Ser.). pap. 59.95 *(978-3-540-19490-3(8))* Springer.

Faddeev, L., ed. Topology: General & Algebraic Topology & Applications. Proceedings of the International Topological Conference held in Leningrad, August 23-27, 1983. 2008. (Lecture Notes in Mathematics Ser.). pap. 46.00 *(978-3-540-13337-7(2))* Springer.

Fuchssteiner, Martin. Transformation Groups And (Co)Homology. 2010. 567p. pap. *(978-3-8325-2524-8(6))* Logos Verlag Berlin.

Geoghegan, Ross. Topological Methods in Group Theory. (Graduate Texts in Mathematics Ser.). (Illus.). 2010. xvi, 473p. pap. 64.95 *(978-1-4419-2564-0(3),* 1441925643) 2008. 476p. 64.95 *(978-0-387-74611-1(0))* Springer.

Giblin, Peter. Graphs, Surfaces & Homology. 3rd ed. 2010. (ENG., Illus.). 272p. (C). 115.00 *(978-0-521-76665-4(6));* pap. 50.00 *(978-0-521-15405-5(7))* Cambridge Univ. Pr.

Gitler, Samuel, et al. Recent Developments in Algebraic Topology: A Conference to Celebrate Sam Gitler's 70th Birthday December 3-6, 2003. 2006. (Contemporary Mathematics Ser.). (Illus.). 191p. pap. 61.00 *(978-0-8218-3676-7(5))* American Mathematical Society.

Goerss, P. G. & Jardine, John F., eds. Algebraic K-Theory & Algebraic Topology. 2010. (NATO Science Series C: (closed) Ser.). 348p. pap. 389.00 *(978-90-481-4302-3(0),* 9048143020) Springer.

Grenander, Ulf. Probabilities on Algebraic Structures. 2008. (Dover Books on Mathematics Ser.). (ENG., Illus.). 224p. per. 12.95 *(978-0-486-46287-5(0))* Dover Pubns., Inc.

Harder, Günter. Lectures on Algebraic Geometry I: Sheaves, Cohomology of Sheaves, & Applications to Riemann Surfaces. 2nd ed. 2011. (Aspects of Mathematics Ser.). (ENG.). xiv, 299p. 79.95 ***(978-3-8348-1844-7(5),*** 3834818445) Vieweg Verlag, Friedr, & Sohn Verlagsgesellschaft mbH DEU. Dist: Springer.

Hilton, P. J., ed. Symposium on Algebraic Topology. 2008. (Lecture Notes in Mathematics Ser.). 124p. pap. 26.00 *(978-3-540-05715-4(3))* Springer.

Hoffman, P., et al, eds. Algebraic Topology. 2008. (Lecture Notes in Mathematics Ser.). 284p. pap. 46.00 *(978-3-540-08930-8(6))* Springer.

Inassaridze, Hvedri, ed. Journal of Homotopy & Related Structures. 2009. 412p. pap. *(978-0-9543006-8-5(8))* College Pubns.

Jackowski, S. Algebraic Topology, Poznan 1989. 2008. (Lecture Notes in Mathematics Ser.). pap. 59.95 *(978-3-540-54098-4(9))* Springer.

Jardine, J. F. Generalized Etale Cohomology Theories. 2010. (Modern Birkhäuser Classics Ser.). x, 317p. pap. 89.95 *(978-3-0348-0065-5(7),* 3034800657) Birkhauser Verlag AG CHE. Dist: Springer.

Kato, Goro. The Heart of Cohomology. 2010. (ENG.). xiii, 195p. pap. 135.00 *(978-90-481-7261-0(6),* 9048172616) Springer.

Kiehl, Reinhardt & Weissauer, Rainer. Weil Conjectures, Perverse Sheaves & l'adic Fourier Transform. 2010. (Ergebnisse der Mathematik und Ihrer Grenzgebiete. 3. Folge a Series of Modern Surveys in Mathematics Ser.). xii, 375p. pap. 209.00 *(978-3-642-07472-1(3),* 3642074723) Springer.

Knauer, Ulrich. Algebraic Graph Theory: Morphisms, Monoids & Matrices. 2011. (De Gruyter Studies in Mathematics Ser.). (ENG., Illus.). XVI, 308p. 168.00 ***(978-3-11-218868-2(3));*** 112.00 ***(978-3-11-025408-2(5))*** De Gruyter, Walter Inc.

Kozlov, Dmitry. Combinatorial Algebraic Topology. (Algorithms & Computation in Mathematics Ser.). (Illus.). 389p. 2008. pap. 59.95 *(978-3-540-73051-4(6))* 2007. 109.00 *(978-3-540-71961-3(X))* Springer.

Kreck, Matthias. Differential Algebraic Topology: From Stratifolds to Exotic Spheres. 2010. (Graduate Studies in Mathematics Ser.). (Illus.). 218p. 55.00 *(978-0-8218-4898-2(4))* American Mathematical Society.

Latiolais, P. Topology & Combinatorial Group Theory: Proceedings of the Fall Foliage Topology Seminars held in New Hampshire 1985-1988. 2008. (Lecture Notes in Mathematics Ser.). pap. 46.00 *(978-3-540-52990-3(X))* Springer.

Laudal, O. A. Formal Moduli of Algebraic Structures. 2008. (Lecture Notes in Mathematics Ser.). 172p. pap. 39.95 *(978-3-540-09702-0(3))* Springer.

Libgober, A. Topology of Algebraic Varieties & Singularities. Cogolludo-Agustin, Jose Ignacio & Hironaka, Eriko, eds. 2011. (Contemporary Mathematics Ser.). (Illus.). 467p. pap. 135.00 *(978-0-8218-4890-6(9))* American Mathematical Society.

Mardesic, S. & Segal, J., eds. Shape Theory & Geometric Topology: Proceedings of a Conference Held at the Inter-University Centre of Postgraduate Studies, Dubrovnik, Yugoslavia, January 19-30, 1981. 2008. (Lecture Notes in Mathematics Ser.). 272p. pap. 59.95 *(978-3-540-10846-7(7))* Springer.

Mathiak, K. Valuations of Skew Fields & Projective Hjelmslev Spaces. 2008. (Lecture Notes in Mathematics Ser.). pap. 39.95 *(978-3-540-16099-1(X))* Springer.

Matousek, J. Using the Borsuk-Ulam Theorem: Lectures on Topological Methods in Combinatorics & Geometry. 2007. (Universitext Ser.). (Illus.). XII, 210p. pap. 69.95 *(978-3-540-00362-5(2),* 3540003622) Springer.

May, J. Peter & Ponto, Kathleen. More Concise Algebraic Topology: Localization, Completion, & Model Categories. 2012. (Chicago Lectures in Mathematics Ser.). (ENG., Illus.). 544p. 65.00 *(978-0-226-51178-8(2))* Univ. of Chicago Pr.

Mcauley, L. F., ed. Algebraic & Geometrical Methods in Topology. 2008. (Lecture Notes in Mathematics Ser.). 300p. pap. 59.95 *(978-3-540-07019-1(2))* Springer.

Miller, H. Algebraic Topology, Seattle 1985: Proceedings of a Workshop held at the University of Washington, Seattle, 1984-85. 2008. (Lecture Notes in Mathematics Ser.). pap. 59.95 *(978-3-540-18481-2(3))* Springer.

Millett, Kenneth C., ed. Algebraic & Geometric Topology: Proceedings of a Symposium held at Santa Barbara in honor of Raymond L. Wilder, July 25 - 29, 1977. 2008. (Lecture Notes in Mathematics Ser.). 256p. pap. 46.00 *(978-3-540-08920-9(9))* Springer.

Mimura, M. Homotopy Theory & Related Topics: Proceedings of the International Conference held at Kinosaki, Japan, August 19-24, 1988. 2008. (Lecture Notes in Mathematics Ser.). v, 241p. pap. 46.00 *(978-3-540-52246-1(8),* 3540522468) Springer.

Neisendorfer, Joseph. Algebraic Methods in Unstable Homotopy Theory. 2010. (New Mathematical Monographs). (ENG., Illus.). 574p. 125.00 *(978-0-521-76037-9(2))* Cambridge Univ. Pr.

Ocampo, Hernan, et al, eds. Geometric & Topological Methods for Quantum Field Theory. 2010. (ENG., Illus.). 434p. 125.00 *(978-0-521-76482-7(3))* Cambridge Univ. Pr.

O'Shea, Donal. The Poincare Conjecture: In Search of the Shape of the Universe. 2007. (ENG., Illus.). 304p. per. 17.00 *(978-0-8027-1654-5(7))* Walker & Co.

—The Poincare Conjecture: In Search of the Shape of the Universe. 2007. (ENG., Illus.). 304p. 26.95 *(978-0-8027-1532-6(X))* Walker & Co.

Outerelo, Enrique & Ruiz, Jesus M. Mapping Degree Theory. 2009. (Graduate Studies in Mathematics Ser.). (Illus.). 244p. 62.00 *(978-0-8218-4915-6(8))* American Mathematical Society.

Paycha, Sylvie & Uribe, B. Geometric & Topological Methods for Quantum Field Theory: Summer School on Geometric & Topological Methods for Quantum Field Theory, July 11-29, 2005, Villa de Leyva, Colombia. 2007. (Contemporary Mathematics Ser.). (Illus.). 255p. pap. 81.00 *(978-0-8218-4062-7(2))* American Mathematical Society.

Pelayo, Alvaro. Symplectic Actions of 2-Tori on 4-Manifolds. 2010. (Memoirs of the American Mathematical Society Ser.). 81p. pap. 64.00 *(978-0-8218-4713-8(9))* American Mathematical Society.

Percy, Andrew. Integral Cohomology Algebras. 2010. 152p. pap. *(978-3-8383-5172-8(X))* Lambert Academic Publishing.

Peterson, F. P., ed. The Steenrod Algebra & Its Applications. 2008. (Lecture Notes in Mathematics Ser.). 332p. pap. 59.95 *(978-3-540-05300-2(X),* 354005300X) Springer.

Poenaru, V. Groupes Discrets. 2008. (Lecture Notes in Mathematics Ser.). 228p. pap. 46.00 *(978-3-540-06967-6(4))* Springer.

Poincaré, Henri. Papers on Topology: Analysis Situs & Its Five Supplements. 2010. (History of Mathematics Ser.). (FRE., Illus.). 228p. pap. 59.00 *(978-0-8218-5234-7(5))* American Mathematical Society.

Ranicki, A., ed. Algebraic & Geometric Topology: Proceedings of a Conference held at Rutgers University, New Brunswick, USA, July 6-13, 1983. 2008. (Lecture Notes in Mathematics Ser.). pap. 59.00 *(978-3-540-15235-4(0))* Springer.

Roos, J., ed. Algebra, Algebraic Topology & their Interactions: Proceedings of a Conference held in Stockholm, Aug. 3 - 13, 1983, & later developments. 2008. (Lecture Notes in Mathematics Ser.). pap. 59.95 *(978-3-540-16453-1(7))* Springer.

Rosenberg, Jonathan. Topology, C*-Algebras, & String Duality. 2009. (CBMS Regional Conference Series in Mathematics Ser.). 110p. pap. 33.00 *(978-0-8218-4922-4(0))* American Mathematical Society.

Sati, Hisham & Schreiber, Urs, eds. Mathematical Foundations of Quantum Field Theory & Perturbative String Theory. 2011. (Proceedings of Symposia in Pure Mathematics Ser.). 354p. 95.00 ***(978-0-8218-5195-1(0))*** American Mathematical Society.

Serre, Jean Pierre. Lectures on N_X(p) 2011. (Chapman & Hall/CRC Research Notes in Mathematics Ser.). (ENG.). 174p. 39.95 ***(978-1-4665-0192-8(8))*** AK Peters, Ltd.

Shick, Paul L. Topology: Point-Set & Geometric. 2007. (Pure & Applied Mathematics: a Wiley Series of Texts, Monographs & Tracts Ser.: 83). (ENG., Illus.). 296p. 128.00 *(978-0-470-09605-5(5),* Wiley-Interscience) Wiley, John & Sons, Inc.

Smith, L., ed. Algebraic Topology, Göttingen 1984: Proceedings of a Conference held in Göttingen, November 9-15, 1984. 2008. (Lecture Notes in Mathematics / Mathematica Gottingensis Ser.). pap. 46.00 *(978-3-540-16061-8(2))* Springer.

Smith, Stephen D. Subgroup Complexes. 2011. (Mathematical Surveys & Monographs Ser.). (ENG., Illus.). 364p. 94.00 (978-0-8218-0501-5(0)) American Mathematical Society.

Strom, Jeffrey. Modern Classical Homotopy Theory. 2011. (Graduate Studies in Mathematics Ser.). (Illus.). 835p. 95.00 (978-0-8218-5286-6(8)) American Mathematical Society.

Usher, Michael, ed. Low-Dimensional & Symplectic Topology. 2011. (Proceedings of Symposia in Pure Mathematics Ser.). 228p. 61.00 (978-0-8218-5235-4(3)) American Mathematical Society.

Verity, Dominic. Complicial Sets Characterising the Simplicial Nerves of Strict [Omega]-Categories. 2008. (Memoirs of the American Mathematical Society Ser.). 184p. pap. 76.00 (978-0-8218-4142-6(4)) American Mathematical Society.

Wallace, Andrew H. Algebraic Topology: Homology & Cohomology. 2007. (Dover Books on Mathematics Ser.). (ENG., Illus.). 288p. per. 15.95 (978-0-486-46239-4(0)) Dover Pubns., Inc.

—An Introduction to Algebraic Topology. 2007. (Dover Books on Mathematics Ser.). (ENG., Illus.). 208p. per. 12.95 (978-0-486-45786-4(9)) Dover Pubns., Inc.

Walsh, Mark P. Metrics of Positive Scalar Curvature & Generalised Morse Functions, Pt. 1. 2011. (Memoirs of the American Mathematical Society Ser.). 80p. pap. 69.00 (978-0-8218-5304-7(X)) American Mathematical Society.

Weissauer, Rainer. Endoscopy for GSp(4) & the Cohomology of Siegel Modular Threefolds. 2009. (Lecture Notes in Mathematics Ser.). (ENG., Illus.). xvii, 368p. pap. 79.95 (978-3-540-89305-9(9)) Springer.

ALGEBRAS, ASSOCIATIVE

see Associative Algebras

ALGEBRAS, BANACH

see Banach Algebras

ALGEBRAS, HILBERT

see Hilbert Algebras

ALGEBRAS, HOPF

see Hopf Algebras

ALGEBRAS, JORDAN

see Jordan Algebras

ALGEBRAS, LIE

see Lie Algebras

ALGEBRAS, LINEAR

see also Complexes; Jordan Algebras; Lie Algebras; Line Geometry; Nonassociative Algebras; Topology; Vector Spaces

Abhyankar, S. S. Lectures on Algebra, Volume 1. 2006. (Illus.). 746p. 86.00 (978-981-256-826-7(3)) World Scientific Publishing Co., Inc.

Adams, Jeffrey, et al, eds. Representation Theory & Mathematical Physics. 2011. (Contemporary Mathematics Ser.). (Illus.). 388p. pap. 125.00 (978-0-8218-5246-0(9)) American Mathematical Society.

Adams, Malcolm & Shifrin, Ted. Linear Algebra: A Geometric Approach. 2nd rev. ed. 2010. (ENG., Illus.). 464p. (C). 153.95 (978-1-4292-1521-3(6)) Freeman, W. H. & Co.

Ahmed, Aden. On Quaternions, Octonions, & the Quantization of Games. 2011. 176p. pap. (978-3-8433-9145-0(9)) Lambert Academic Publishing.

Ahmed, Mohammad Maruf. Generalized Inverse: Properties, representations & Applications. 2011. 80p. pap. (978-3-8433-9348-5(6)) Lambert Academic Publishing.

Aja-Fernández, Santiago, et al, eds. Tensors in Image Processing & Computer Vision. 2009. (Advances in Pattern Recognition Ser.). (Illus.). x, 470p. 149.00 (978-1-84882-298-6(7), 1848822987) Springer.

Aleskerov, Fuad, et al. Linear Algebra for Economists. 2011. (Springer Texts in Business & Economics Ser.). (ENG., Illus.). xii, 279p. 109.00 (978-3-642-20569-9(0), 3642205690) Springer.

Andrilli, Stephen & Hecker, David. Elementary Linear Algebra. 4th ed. 2009. (ENG., Illus.). 768p. (C). 99.95 (978-0-12-374751-8(1), Academic Pr.) Elsevier Science & Technology Bks.

Annin, Scott A. & Goode, Stephen W. Differential Equations & Linear Algebra. 3rd rev. ed. 2007. (ENG., Illus.). 816p. (C). 148.00 (978-0-13-045794-3(9), Prentice Hall) Prentice Hall PTR.

Anthony, Martin & Harvey, Michele. Linear Algebra: Concepts & Methods. 2012. (ENG., Illus.). 536p. (C). pap. 55.00 (978-0-521-27948-2(8)) Cambridge Univ. Pr.

Anton, Howard. Elementary Linear Algebra. 10th ed. 2010. (ENG., (C). Illus.). 592p. 168.95 (978-0-470-45821-1(6)); 592p. ring bd. 106.95 (978-0-470-55991-8(8)); 320p. pap. 38.95 (978-0-470-45823-5(2)) Wiley, John & Sons, Inc. (Wiley).

—Elementary Linear Algebra & Linear Algebra Applications Software Set. 7th ed. 570p. 71.00 net. (978-0-471-00828-6(1), Wiley) Wiley, John & Sons, Inc.

—Elementary Linear Algebra with Applications. 9th rev. ed. 2006. (Wiley Plus Products Ser.). 155.95 (978-0-470-11277-9(8)) Wiley, John & Sons, Inc.

—Elementary Linear Algebra with Applications + Wileyplus/WebCT Access Card. 9th ed. 2006. (Wiley Plus Products Ser.). 125.95 (978-0-470-10480-4(5)) Wiley, John & Sons, Inc.

—Elementary Linear Algebra with Applications with Applications & Wiley Plus Set. 9th rev. ed. 2006. (Wiley Plus Products Ser.). 125.95 (978-0-470-10305-0(1), Sybex) Wiley, John & Sons, Inc.

—Elementary Linear Algebra with Applications with MATLAB Tutorial CD & Wiley Plus Set. 9th rev. ed. 2006. (Wiley Plus Products Ser.). 152.95 (978-0-470-14074-1(7)) Wiley, John & Sons, Inc.

—Elementary Linear Algebra with Applications with Student Access Card for WebCT Set. 9th ed. 2008. (C). 154.95 (978-0-470-39674-2(1)) Wiley, John & Sons, Inc.

—Elementary Linear Algebra with Student Solutions Manual & Wiley Plus Set. 9th ed. 2006. (Wiley Plus Products Ser.). 150.95 (978-0-470-11619-7(6)) Wiley, John & Sons, Inc.

—Elementary Linear Algebra with Wiley Plus Set. 9th ed. 2007. (Wiley Plus Products Ser.). 119.95 (978-0-470-15096-2(3)) Wiley, John & Sons, Inc.

Anton, Howard & Rorres, Chris. Elementary Linear Algebra. 10th ed. 2010. (ENG.). 773p. (C). 173.95 (978-0-470-43205-1(5), Wiley) Wiley, John & Sons, Inc.

—Elementary Linear Algebra with Applications. (Wiley Plus Products Ser.). 9th ed. 2006. pap. 61.95 (978-0-470-07843-3(X)) 9th ed. 2006. pap. 61.95 (978-0-470-07536-4(8)) 10th ed. 2010. (ENG.). 792p. (C). ring bd. 109.95 (978-0-470-55992-5(6), Wiley) Wiley, John & Sons, Inc.

Anton, Howard, et al. Elementary Linear Algebra with Applications. 10th ed. 2010. (ENG.). 288p. (C). pap. 55.95 (978-0-470-45822-8(4), Wiley) Wiley, John & Sons, Inc.

Anwar, Imran, et al. Algebras Associated to Simplicial Complexes. 2010. 72p. pap. (978-3-8383-5895-6(3)) Lambert Academic Publishing.

Bakonyi, Mihaly & Woerdeman, Hugo J. Matrix Completions, Moments, & Sums of Hermitian Squares. 2011. (Princeton Series in Applied Mathematics Ser.). (ENG., Illus.). 536p. (C). 79.50 (978-0-691-12889-4(8)) Princeton Univ. Pr.

Banerjee, Sudipto & Roy, Anindya. Linear Algebra & Matrix Computations for Statistics. 2012. (Chapman & Hall/CRC Texts in Statistical Science Ser.). (ENG., Illus.). 416p. 79.95 (978-1-4200-9538-8(2), Chapman & Hall/CRC) CRC Pr. LLC.

Baranyi, Peter, et al. Tensor Product Model Transformation in Polytopic Model-Based Control. 2012. (Automation & Control Engineering Ser.). (ENG., Illus.). 250p. 129.95 (978-1-4398-1816-9(9), CRC Press) Taylor & Francis Group GBR. Dist: Taylor & Francis Group.

Bartolo, Alfonso Di, et al. Algebraic Groups & Lie Groups with Few Factors. 2008. (Lecture Notes in Mathematics Ser.). XVI, 212p. pap. 69.95 (978-3-540-78583-5(3), 3540785833) Springer.

Bautista, R., et al. Differential Tensor Algebras & their Module Categories. 2009. (London Mathematical Society Lecture Note Ser.). (ENG., Illus.). 462p. pap. 80.00 (978-0-521-75768-3(1)) Cambridge Univ. Pr.

Bayro-Corrochano, Eduardo & Scheuermann, Gerik, eds. Geometric Algebra Computing: In Engineering & Computer Science. 2010. (ENG., Illus.). xvi, 524p. 159.00 (978-1-84996-107-3(7), 1849961077) Springer.

Bock, Dirk de, et al. The Illusion of Linearity: From Analysis to Improvement. 2010. (Mathematics Education Library). (Illus.). xiv, 186p. pap. 129.00 (978-1-4419-4381-1(1), 1441943811) Springer.

Boelkins, Matthew R., et al. Differential Equations with Linear Algebra. 2009. (ENG., Illus.). 576p. 89.95 (978-0-19-538586-1(1)) Oxford Univ. Pr., Inc.

Bogolmony, Marianna. Give Me an Example. 2010. 152p. pap. (978-3-8383-8588-4(8)) Lambert Academic Publishing.

Borovik, Alexander V. & Borovik, Anna. Mirrors & Reflections: The Geometry of Finite Reflection Groups. 2009. (Universitext Ser.). (ENG., Illus.). xii, 172p. pap. 49.95 (978-0-387-79065-7(9), 0387790659) Springer.

Breiar, Matej, et al. Functional Identities. 2007. (Frontiers in Mathematics Ser.). 272p. pap. 59.95 (978-3-7643-7795-3(X)) Birkhauser Verlag AG CHE. Dist: Springer.

Bretscher, Otto. Linear Algebra with Applications. 4th ed. 2008. (ENG.). 504p. (C). 152.00 (978-0-13-600926-9(3), Prentice Hall) Prentice Hall PTR.

—Student Solutions Manual for Linear Algebra with Applications. 4th ed. 2009. (ENG.). 184p. (C). pap. 36.67 (978-0-13-600927-6(1), Prentice Hall) Prentice Hall PTR.

Bronson, Richard & Costa, Gabriel B. Linear Algebra: An Introduction. 2nd rev. ed. 2007. (ENG., Illus.). 520p. (C). per. 76.95 (978-0-12-088784-2(3), Academic Pr.) Elsevier Science & Technology Bks.

—Matrix Methods: Applied Linear Algebra. 3rd ed. 2008. (ENG., Illus.). 432p. (C). 94.95 (978-0-12-374427-2(X), Academic Pr.) Elsevier Science & Technology Bks.

Brualdi, Richard A. The Mutually Beneficial Relationship of Graphs & Matrices. 2011. (CBMS Regional Conference Ser. in Mathematics Ser.). (Illus.). 96p. pap. 34.00 (978-0-8218-5315-3(5)) American Mathematical Society.

Busam, Rolf & Epp, Thomas. Prüfungstrainer Lineare Algebra: 500 Fragen und Antworten für Bachelor und Vordiplom. 2008. (GER., Illus.). 245p. pap. (978-3-8274-1976-7(X)) Spektrum Akademischer Verlag GmbH.

Butt, Rizwan. Applied Linear Algebra & Optimization Using MATLAB. 2011. 800p. 69.95 (978-1-936420-04-9(X)) Mercury Learning & Information.

Buzzi-Ferraris, Guido & Manenti, Flavio. Fundamentals & Linear Algebra for the Chemical Engineer: Solving Numerical Problems. 2010. (ENG., Illus.). 375p. 130.00 (978-3-527-32552-8(2), Wiley-VCH) Wiley, John & Sons, Inc.

Carlen, Eric. Linear Algebra Solution's Manual. 2007. (ENG.). 264p. (C). pap. 51.95 (978-1-4292-0428-6(1)) Freeman, W. H. & Co.

Carlen, Eric, et al. Linear Algebra: From the Beginning. 2006. (ENG.). 504p. (C). pap. 135.95 (978-0-7167-4894-6(0)) Freeman, W. H. & Co.

Chan, Ping-Shun. Invariant Representations of GSp(2) under Tensor Product with a Quadratic Character. 2010. (Memoirs of the American Mathematical Society Ser.). 172p. pap. 77.00 (978-0-8218-4822-7(4)) American Mathematical Society.

Cheney, E. W. & Kincaid, David. Linear Algebra: Theory & Applications. 2nd ed. 2010. 624p. 166.95 (978-1-4496-1352-5(7)) Jones & Bartlett Learning, LLC.

Cheney, Ward & Kincaid, David R. Student Resource Manual to Accompany Linear Algebra: Theory & Application. 2nd ed. 2011. 292p. pap. 50.95 (978-1-4496-3735-4(3)) Jones & Bartlett Learning, LLC.

Colliot-Thélène, Jean-Louis, et al, eds. Quadratic Forms, Linear Algebraic Groups, & Cohomology. 2010. (Developments in Mathematics Ser.). (ENG & FRE., Illus.). x, 348p. 149.00 (978-1-4419-6210-2(7), 1441962107) Springer.

Conner, Pierre E. Seminar on Periodic Maps. 2007. (Lecture Notes in Mathematics Ser.). 124p. per. 26.00 (978-3-540-03917-4(1)) Springer.

Conte, Elio. Advances in Application of Quantum Mechanics in Neuroscience & Psychology: A Clifford Algebraic Approach. 2011. (Physics Research & Technology/Neuroscience Research Progress Ser.). 140.00 (978-1-61470-325-9(6)) Nova Science Pubs., Inc.

Cooperstein, Bruce. Advanced Linear Algebra. 2010. (ENG., Illus.). 364p. 83.95 (978-1-4398-2966-0(7), CRC Press) Taylor & Francis Group GBR. Dist: Taylor & Francis Group.

Cram101 Textbook Reviews. Outlines & Highlights for a Modern Introduction to Linear Algebra by Henry Ricardo. 2011. 320p. pap. 33.95 (978-1-61905-105-8(2)) Cram101 Inc.

—Outlines & Highlights for Advanced Linear Algebra for Engineers by Sohail a Dianat. 2011. 154p. pap. 29.95 (978-1-61905-108-9(7)) Cram101 Inc.

—Outlines & Highlights for Applied Linear Algebra by Peter J Olver, Isbn: 9780131473829. 2010. 644p. pap. 40.95 (978-1-61698-121-1(0)) Cram101 Inc.

—Outlines & Highlights for Elementary Linear Algebra by Howard Anton. 2011. 308p. pap. 32.95 (978-1-61905-012-9(9)) Cram101 Inc.

—Outlines & Highlights for Elementary Linear Algebra by Stephen Andrilli. 2011. 384p. pap. 34.95 (978-1-61905-013-6(7)) Cram101 Inc.

—Outlines & Highlights for Introduction to Linear Algebra by Gilbert Strang. 2011. 196p. pap. 30.95 (978-1-4672-6581-2(0)) Cram101 Inc.

—Outlines & Highlights for Linear Algebr: A Modern Introduction by David Poole. 2011. 274p. pap. 32.95 (978-1-4672-6176-0(9)) Cram101 Inc.

—Outlines & Highlights for Linear Algebr: Theory & Applications by Ward Cheney. 2011. 328p. pap. 33.95 (978-1-4672-3735-2(3)) Cram101 Inc.

—Outlines & Highlights for Principles of Linear Algebra by Kenneth M Shiskowski. 2011. 124p. pap. 28.95 (978-1-4672-3835-9(X)) Cram101 Inc.

Cram101 Textbook Reviews Staff. Outlines & Highlights for Differential Equations & Linear Algebra by C Henry Edwards, Isbn: 9780136054252. 2009. 216p. pap. 30.95 (978-1-4288-2231-3(3)) Cram101 Inc.

—Outlines & Highlights for Differential Equations & Linear Algebra by Stephen W Goode, Isbn: 9780130457943. 2009. 198p. pap. 30.95 (978-1-4288-2057-9(4)) Cram101 Inc.

—Outlines & Highlights for Differential Equations, Dynamical Systems, & an Introduction to Chaos by Morris W Hirsch, Stephen Smale, Robert Devaney. 2009. 98p. pap. 27.95 (978-1-4288-7465-7(8)) Cram101 Inc.

—Outlines & Highlights for Elementary Linear Algebr: A Matrix Approach by Lawrence E. Spence, Stephen H. Friedberg, Arnold J. Insel, ISBN. 2009. 184p. pap. 29.95 (978-1-4288-3731-7(0)) Cram101 Inc.

—Outlines & Highlights for Elementary Linear Algebr: Applications Version by Howard A. Anton, Chris Rorres, ISBN. 2009. 266p. pap. 31.95 (978-1-4288-3718-8(3)) Cram101 Inc.

—Outlines & Highlights for Elementary Linear Algebra by Kolman, Hill, Isbn: 0130457876. 2009. 168p. pap. 29.95 (978-1-4288-3915-1(1)) Cram101 Inc.

—Outlines & Highlights for Elementary Linear Algebra, Enhanced Edition by Ron Larson, Isbn: 9781439044001. 2009. 148p. pap. 29.95 (978-1-4288-2613-7(0)); 114p. pap. 28.95 (978-1-4288-9069-5(6)) Cram101 Inc.

—Outlines & Highlights for Elementary Linear Algebra with Applications by Bernard Kolman, Isbn: 9780132296540. 2009. 124p. pap. 28.95 (978-1-4288-8668-1(0)) Cram101 Inc.

—Outlines & Highlights for Introduction to Linear Algebra with Applications by James Defranza, Daniel Gagliardi, Isbn: 9780073532356. 2009. 122p. pap. 28.95 (978-1-4288-3738-6(8)) Cram101 Inc.

—Outlines & Highlights for Linear Algebr: Modern Introduction by Poole, David, ISBN. 2009. 192p. pap. 30.95 (978-1-4288-3796-6(5)) Cram101 Inc.

—Outlines & Highlights for Linear Algebr: Theory & Applications by Ward Cheney, ISBN. 2009. 176p. pap. 29.95 (978-1-4288-2535-2(5)); 132p. pap. 28.95 (978-1-4288-8921-7(3)) Cram101 Inc.

—Outlines & Highlights for Linear Algebra & Its Application by Strang, Isbn: 9780030105678. 2009. 204p. pap. 30.95 (978-1-4288-2777-6(3)); 152p. pap. 29.95 (978-1-4288-8661-2(3)) Cram101 Inc.

—Outlines & Highlights for Linear Algebra & Its Applications by David C Lay, Isbn: 9780321287137. 2009. 218p. pap. 30.95 (978-1-4288-3760-7(4)) Cram101 Inc.

—Outlines & Highlights for Linear Algebra by Kenneth M Hoffman, Isbn: 9780135367971. 2009. 154p. pap. 29.95 (978-1-4288-3732-4(9)) Cram101 Inc.

—Outlines & Highlights for Linear Algebra with Applications by Gareth Williams, Isbn: 9780763757533. 2009. 156p. pap. 29.95 (978-1-4288-3717-1(5)) Cram101 Inc.

—Outlines & Highlights for Linear Algebra with Applications by Otto Bretscher, Isbn: 9780136009269. 2009. 154p. pap. 29.95 (978-1-4288-3728-7(0)) Cram101 Inc.

—Outlines & Highlights for Linear Algebra with Applications by Steven J Leon, Isbn: 9780131857858. 2009. 132p. pap. 28.95 (978-1-4288-2411-9(1)); 78p. pap. 27.95 (978-1-4288-9650-5(3)) Cram101 Inc.

Crumeyrolle, A. Orthogonal & Symplectic Clifford Algebras: Spinor Structures. 2010. (Mathematics & Its Applications Ser.). 368p. pap. 189.00 (978-90-481-4059-6(5), 9048140595) Springer.

Davis, Ernest. Linear Algebra & Probability for Computer Science Applications. 2012. (ENG.). 431p. 59.95 (978-1-4665-0155-3(3)) AK Peters, Ltd.

De Bock, Dirk, et al. The Illusion of Linearity: From Analysis to Improvement. 2007. (Mathematics Education Library). (Illus.). 200p. 129.00 (978-0-387-71082-2(5)) Springer.

DeWilde, Patrick & Veen, Alle-Jan van der. Time-Varying Systems & Computations. 2010. (ENG.). 474p. pap. 259.00 (978-1-4419-5045-1(1), 1441950451) Springer.

Dianat, Sohail A. Solutions Manual - Advanced Linear Algebra for Engineers with MATLAB. 2009. (978-1-4398-0129-1(0)) CRC Pr. LLC.

Dianat, Sohail A. & Saber, Eli. Advanced Linear Algebra for Engineers with MATLAB. 2009. 99.95 (978-1-4200-9524-1(2)) CRC Pr. LLC.

—Advanced Linear Algebra for Engineers with MATLAB. 2009. (ENG., Illus.). 346p. (C). 107.95 (978-1-4200-9523-4(4), CRC Press) Taylor & Francis Group GBR. Dist: Taylor & Francis Group.

Diestel, Joe, et al. The Metric Theory of Tensor Products: Grothendieck's Résumé Revisited. 2008. (Illus.). 278p. (C). 81.00 (978-0-8218-4440-3(7)) American Mathematical Society.

Dogan-Dunlap, Hamide. Linear Algebra Teaching & Learning: Visualization. 2008. 116p. pap. (978-3-639-08994-3(4)) VDM Verlag Dr. Mueller e.K.

Dolotin, V. & Morozov, A. Introduction to Non-Linear Algebra. 2008. (Illus.). 269p. 69.00 (978-981-270-800-7(6)) World Scientific Publishing Co., Inc.

Dorier, J. -L., ed. On the Teaching of Linear Algebra. 2010. (Mathematics Education Library). 312p. pap. 309.00 (978-90-481-5549-1(5), 9048155495) Springer.

Dorst, Leo & Lasenby, Joan, eds. Guide to Geometric Algebra in Practice. 2011. (ENG., Illus.). xvii, 458p. 129.00 (978-0-85729-810-2(0), 0857298100) Springer.

Dym, Harry. Linear Algebra in Action. 2007. (Graduate Studies in Mathematics: Vol. 78). (Illus.). 545p. (C). 81.00 (978-0-8218-3813-6(X)) American Mathematical Society.

Edwards, C. Henry & Penney, David E. Differential Equations & Linear Algebra. 3rd ed. 2008. (ENG.). 792p. (C). 148.00 (978-0-13-605425-2(0), Prentice Hall) Prentice Hall PTR.

Edwards, Henry. Student's Solutions Manual for Differential Equations & Linear Algebra. 3rd ed. 2008. (ENG.). 340p. (C). pap. 36.67 (978-0-13-605427-6(7), Prentice Hall) Prentice Hall PTR.

Edwards, Henry & Penney, David E. Applications Manual for Differential Equations & Linear Algebra. 3rd ed. 2008. (ENG.). 250p. (C). pap. 36.67 (978-0-321-61525-1(5), Prentice Hall) Prentice Hall PTR.

Faciane, Kirby. Applied Calculus for Finance. 2006. 121p. pap. 299.95 (978-0-9788208-4-8(3)) Henry Carey Baird & Co.

Farlow, Jerry, et al. Differential Equations & Linear Algebra. 2nd rev. ed. 2006. (ENG., Illus.). 800p. (C). 148.00 (978-0-13-186061-2(5), Prentice Hall) Prentice Hall PTR.

—Differential Equations & Linear Algebra, Books a la Carte Edition. 2nd ed. 2010. (ENG.). (C). ring bd. 88.80 (978-0-321-65712-1(8)) Addison Wesley.

Ferris, Michael C., et al. Linear Programming with MATLAB. 2007. (MPS-SIAM Series on Optimization). (ENG.). 280p. (C). pap. 45.00 (978-0-89871-643-6(8)) Society for Industrial and Applied Mathematics.

Finite Dimensional Linear Algebra. 2011. 99.95 (978-1-4398-1564-9(X), CRC Press) Taylor & Francis Group GBR. Dist: Taylor & Francis Group.

Finkbeiner, Daniel T. Introduction to Matrices & Linear Transformations. 2011. (Dover Books on Mathematics Ser.). (ENG.). 480p. pap. 24.95 (978-0-486-48159-3(X)) Dover Pubns., Inc.

Fraleigh & Beauregard & Cram101 Textbook Reviews Staff. Linear Algebr. 2007. 140p. per. 11.95 (978-1-4288-3442-2(7)) Cram101 Inc.

Friedberg & Insel & Spence & Cram101 Textbook Reviews Staff. Linear Algebr. 2007. 100p. per. 10.95 (978-1-4288-3408-8(7)) Cram101 Inc.

Fuhrmann, Paul A. A Polynomial Approach to Linear Algebra. 2nd ed. 2011. (Universitext Ser.). (ENG.). xvi, 411p. pap. 74.95 (978-1-4614-0337-1(5), 1461403375) Springer.

Glazman, I. M. & Ljubic, Ju I. Finite-Dimensional Linear Analysis: A Systematic Presentation in Problem Form. Kuerti, G., ed. Barker, G. P., tr. from RUS. 2006. (Dover Books on Mathematics Ser.). 544p. per. 27.95 (978-0-486-45332-3(4)) Dover Pubns., Inc.

Gockenbach, Mark S. Finite Dimensional Linear Algebra. 2010. (Discrete Mathematics & Its Applications Ser.). (ENG., Illus.). 672p. 99.95 (978-1-4398-1563-2(1), CRC Press) Taylor & Francis Group GBR. Dist: Taylor & Francis Group.

Golan, Jonathan Samuel. Foundations of Linear Algebra. 2010. (Texts in the Mathematical Sciences Ser.). 244p. pap. 130.00 (978-90-481-4592-8(9), 9048145929) Springer.

Gruenberg, K. W. & Weir, A. J. Linear Geometry. 2010. pap. 39.95 (978-1-4419-2806-1(5), 1441928065) Springer.

Halma, Arvid. Interpolation in Conformal Geometric Algebra. 2011. 152p. pap. (978-3-8433-8091-1(0)) Lambert Academic Publishing.

Hart, Roger. The Chinese Roots of Linear Algebra. 2010. (ENG., Illus.). 304p. (gr. 17). 65.00 (978-0-8018-9755-9(6)) Johns Hopkins Univ. Pr.

Harville, D. A. Matrix Algebra from a Statistician's Perspective. 2008. (ENG.). xvi, 636p. pap. 79.95 (978-0-387-78356-7(3), 0387783563) Springer.

Helmstetter, Jacques. Quadratic Mappings & Clifford Algebras. 2008. 400p. 129.00 *(978-3-7643-8605-4(3)*, 3764386053) Birkhauser Verlag AG CHE. Dist: Springer.

Hill & Cram101 Textbook Reviews Staff. Elementary Linear Algebra with Applications. 2007. 76p. per. 10.95 *(978-1-4288-3400-2(1))* Cram101 Inc.

Hirsch, Morris W., et al. Differential Equations, Dynamical Systems, & an Introduction to Chaos. 3rd ed. 2012. (ENG.). 432p. (C). 99.95 ***(978-0-12-382010-5(3)***, Academic Pr.) Elsevier Science & Technology Bks.

Hogben, Leslie, et al, eds. Handbook of Linear Algebra. 2006. (Discrete Mathematics & Its Applications Ser.). (ENG., Illus.). 1400p. 125.95 *(978-1-58488-510-8(6)*, Chapman & Hall/CRC) CRC Pr. LLC.

Hotta, Ryoshi, et al. D-Modules, Perverse Sheaves, & Representation Theory. Takeuchi, Kiyoshi, tr. from JPN. 2007. (Progress in Mathematics Ser.). (Illus.). XII, 412p. (C). 89.95 *(978-0-8176-4363-8(X)*, 081764363X) Springer.

Howland, R. A. Intermediate Dynamics: A Linear Algebraic Approach. 2010. (Mechanical Engineering Ser.). xix, 548p. pap. 104.00 *(978-1-4419-3920-3(2)*, 1441939202) Springer.

Hubbard, John H. & Hubbard, Barbara Burke. Vector Calculus, Linear Algebra, & Differential Forms: A Unified Approach. 4th ed. 2009. *(978-0-9715766-5-0(3))* Matrix Editions.

Hubbard, John Hamal & Hubbard, Barbara Burke. Student Solution Manual 2nd Edition: To accompany 3rd edition of Vector Calculus, Linear Algebra, & Differential Forms: A Unified Approach. 2nd rev. ed. 2007. (Illus.). 268p. (C). per. 33.00 *(978-0-9715766-4-3(5))* Matrix Editions.

—Vector Calculus, Linear Algebra, & Differential Forms: A Unified Approach, 1. 3rd ed. 2007. (Illus.). 802p. (C). 78.00 *(978-0-9715766-3-6(7))* Matrix Editions.

Humphreys, J. E. Arithmetic Groups. 2008. (Lecture Notes in Mathematics Ser.). 168p. pap. 39.95 *(978-3-540-09972-7(7))* Springer.

Iatan, Iuliana. Advanced Lectures on Linear Algebra with Applications. 2011. 356p. pap. ***(978-3-8443-2410-5(0))*** Lambert Academic Publishing.

Insel, Arnold J., et al. Elementary Linear Algebra. 2nd rev. ed. 2007. (ENG., Illus.). 656p. (C). 152.00 *(978-0-13-187141-0(2)*, Prentice Hall) Prentice Hall PTR.

Jantzen, Jens Carsten. Representations of Algebraic Groups. 2nd rev. ed. 2007. (Mathematical Surveys & Monographs). 576p. pap. 104.00 *(978-0-8218-4377-2(X))* American Mathematical Society.

Johnson, Lee, et al. Introduction to Linear Algebra. 6th rev. ed. 2011. (ENG.). 592p. (C). 144.00 *(978-0-321-33445-9(0))* Addison-Wesley Longman, Inc.

Johnson, Lee W., et al. Introduction to Linear Algebra, Books a la Carte Edition. 6th ed. 2011. (C). ring bd. 100.80 *(978-0-321-65672-8(5))* Pearson Education.

—Student's Solutions Manual for Introduction to Linear Algebra. 6th ed. 2011. (ENG.). (C). pap. 36.67 *(978-0-321-38520-8(9))* Addison-Wesley Longman, Inc.

Jsnich, Klaus. Linear Algebr. 2007. 216p. per. 25.00 *(978-3-540-78056-4(4))* Springer.

Jungers, Raphaël. The Joint Spectral Radius: Theory & Applications: Theory & Applications. 2009. (Lecture Notes in Control & Information Sciences Ser.). (ENG., Illus.). xiv, 146p. pap. 139.00 *(978-3-540-95979-3(3))* Springer.

Kambayashi, T., et al. Unipotent Algebraic Groups. 2008. (Lecture Notes in Mathematics Ser.). 176p. pap. 39.95 *(978-3-540-06960-7(7))* Springer.

Kaplan, Wilfred & Lewis, Donald. Calculus & Linear Algebra: Vectors in the Plane & One-Variable Calculus, Vol. 1. 2007. (ENG., Illus.). 712p. (C). per. 24.95 *(978-1-4255-8913-4(8))* MPublishing.

Kapovich, Michael, et al. The Generalized Triangle Inequalities in Symmetric Spaces & Buildings with Applications to Algebra. 2008. (Memoirs of the American Mathematical Society Ser.: No. 896). (Illus.). 83p. pap. 61.00 *(978-0-8218-4054-2(1))* American Mathematical Society.

Katznelson, Yitzhak & Katznelson, Yonatan R. A (Terse) Introduction to Linear Algebra. 2007. (Student Mathematical Library Ser.: Vol. 44). 215p. (C). pap. 36.00 *(978-0-8218-4419-9(9))* American Mathematical Society.

Kepner, Jeremy V. & Gilbert, J. R. Graph Algorithms in the Language of Linear Algebra. 2011. (ENG.). 375p. ***(978-0-89871-990-1(9))*** Society for Industrial and Applied Mathematics.

Kleshchev, Alexander. Linear & Projective Representations of Symmetric Groups. 2009. (Cambridge Tracts in Mathematics Ser.). (ENG.). 292p. pap. 55.00 *(978-0-521-10418-9(1))* Cambridge Univ. Pr.

Knop, Larry E. Linear Algebra: A First Course with Applications. 2008. (Textbooks in Mathematics Ser.). (ENG., Illus.). 752p. (C). 107.95 *(978-1-58488-782-9(6)*, Chapman & Hall/CRC) CRC Pr. LLC.

Kolman, Bernard & Hill, David. Elementary Linear Algebra with Applications. 9th ed. 2007. (ENG.). 720p. (C). 152.00 *(978-0-13-229654-0(3)*, Prentice Hall) Prentice Hall PTR.

Kolman, Bernard & Hill, David R. Elementary Linear Algebra with Applications. 9th ed. 2008. (Illus.). 720p. pap. *(978-0-13-135063-2(3))* Prentice Hall PTR.

Korevaar, Jacob. Mathematical Methods: Linear Algebra, Normed Spaces, Distributions, Integration. 2008. (Dover Books on Mathematics Ser.). (ENG., Illus.). 528p. pap. 24.95 *(978-0-486-46621-7(3))* Dover Pubns., Inc.

Kraus, Johannes & Margenov, Svetozar. Robust Algebraic Multilevel Methods & Algorithms. 2009. (Radon Series on Computational & Applied Mathematics Ser.). (ENG.). X, 246p. 98.00 *(978-3-11-019365-7(5))* De Gruyter, Walter Inc.

Landsberg, J. M. Tensors: Geometry & Applications. 2011. (Graduate Studies in Mathematics Ser.). (Illus.). 439p. 74.00 ***(978-0-8218-6907-9(8))*** American Mathematical Society.

Lang & Lang, Serge. Linear Algebra. 3rd ed. 2010. (Undergraduate Texts in Mathematics Ser.). (Illus.). ix, 296p. pap. 64.95 *(978-1-4419-3081-1(7)*, 1441930817) Springer.

Larson, Ron & Falvo, David C. Elementary Linear Algebra. 6th ed. 2009. (Illus.). *(978-0-547-00481-5(8))* Houghton Mifflin Harcourt Publishing Co.

—Elementary Linear Algebra, Enhanced Edition (with Enhanced WebAssign 1-Semester Printed Access Card) 6th ed. 2009. (Available 2010 Titles Enhanced Web Assign Ser.). (ENG.). 592p. (C). 207.95 *(978-1-4390-4400-1(7))* Brooks/Cole.

Larson, Ron, et al. Elementary Linear Algebra. 2007. 84p. per. 10.95 *(978-1-4288-3426-2(5))* Cram101 Inc.

—Elementary Linear Algebra. 6th ed. 2008. (ENG.). 560p. (C). 233.95 *(978-0-618-78376-2(8))* Brooks/Cole.

Lawther, R. & Testerman, D. M. Centres of Centralizers of Unipotent Elements in Simple Algebraic Groups. 2011. (Memoirs of the American Mathematical Society Ser.). 188p. pap. 83.00 *(978-0-8218-4769-5(4))* American Mathematical Society.

Lax, Peter D. Linear Algebra & Its Applications. 2nd rev. ed. 2007. (Pure & Applied Mathematics: a Wiley Series of Texts, Monographs & Tracts Ser.: 78). (ENG., Illus.). 392p. 94.95 *(978-0-471-75156-4(1)*, Wiley-Interscience) Wiley, John & Sons, Inc.

—Linear Algebra & Its Applications, Second Edition + Functional Analysis Set. 2009. (Pure & Applied Mathematics: a Wiley Series of Texts, Monographs & Tracts Ser.: 97). (ENG.). 1000p. 185.00 *(978-0-470-55554-5(8)*, Wiley) Wiley, John & Sons, Inc.

Lay & Lay, David C. Linear Algebra & Its Applications with Student Study Guide. 4th ed. 2011. (ENG.). (C). pap. 155.33 ***(978-0-321-79154-2(1))*** Addison Wesley.

Lay, David C. Linear Algebra & Its Applications. 4th ed. 2011. (ENG., (C). Illus.). 450p. pap., stu. ed. 36.67 *(978-0-321-38883-4(6))*; 576p. 152.00 *(978-0-321-38517-8(9))* Addison Wesley.

Lay, David C. Linear Algebra & Its Applications, Books a la Carte Edition. 4th ed. 2011. (ENG.). 576p. (C). ring bd. 91.20 ***(978-0-321-78072-0(8))*** Addison Wesley.

Lederer, Eric M. & Lederer, Eric. Linear Algebra Exam File. 2nd ed. 2007. (ENG.). 312p. pap. 17.95 *(978-1-4277-6623-6(1))* Kaplan Publishing.

Leon, Steve. Linear Algebra with Applications. 8th ed. 2009. (ENG., (C). Illus.). 552p. 152.00 *(978-0-13-600929-0(8))*; 415p. pap., stu. ed. 36.67 *(978-0-13-600930-6(1))* Prentice Hall PTR. (Prentice Hall).

Lin, Hsiung. Geometric Linear Algebra. 900p. (C). pap. 125.00 *(978-981-270-775-8(1))* World Scientific Publishing Co., Inc.

Linear Algebra. 2011. (C). 102.95 ***(978-1-58488-783-6(4)***, Chapman & Hall/CRC) CRC Pr. LLC.

Ling, Gerald D., ed. Linear Algebra Research Advances. 2007. 129.00 *(978-1-60021-818-7(0))* Nova Science Pubs., Inc.

Lipschutz, Seymour & Lipson, Marc. Linear Algebra. 4th ed. 2008. (Schaum's Outline Ser.). (ENG., Illus.). 432p. (C). pap. 20.00 *(978-0-07-154352-1(X)*, 007154352X) McGraw-Hill Cos., The.

Lipschutz, Seymour & Lipson, Marc. Schaums Easy Outline of Linear Algebra Revised. 2011. (Schaum's Easy Outlines Ser.). (ENG.). 160p. (C). pap. 11.00 ***(978-0-07-177748-3(2)***, 0071777482) McGraw-Hill Cos., The.

Lipsky, Lester. Queuing Theory: A Linear Algebraic Approach. 2nd ed. 2008. (ENG.). xxii, 554p. 79.95 *(978-0-387-49704-4(8)*, 0387497048) Springer.

Lorenz, Falko. Lineare Algebra II. 3rd ed. 2009. (Illus.). 204p. pap. *(978-3-86025-457-8(X))* Springer Singapore Pte. Ltd.

Maatallah, Prof. Magid. Linear Algebr. 2011. 260p. pap. ***(978-3-8443-0800-6(8))*** Lambert Academic Publishing.

Malle, Gunter & Testerman, Donna. Linear Algebraic Groups & Finite Groups of Lie Type. 2011. (Cambridge Studies in Advanced Mathematics Ser.). (ENG., Illus.). 324p. 75.00 *(978-1-107-00854-0(9))* Cambridge Univ. Pr.

Matousek, Jiri. Thirty-Three Miniatures: Mathematical & Algorithmic Applications of Linear Algebra. 2010. (Student Mathematical Library). (Illus.). 182p. pap. 36.00 *(978-0-8218-4977-4(8))* American Mathematical Society.

Micali, A., et al, eds. Clifford Algebras & their Applications in Mathematical Physics. 2010. (Fundamental Theories of Physics Ser.). 540p. pap. 389.00 *(978-90-481-4130-2(3)*, 9048141303) Springer.

Mitrea, M. Clifford Wavelets, Singular Integrals, & Hardy Spaces. 2008. (Lecture Notes in Mathematics Ser.). 127p. pap. 39.95 *(978-3-540-57884-0(6))* Springer.

Monticelli, Dario Daniele. Maximum Principles & Applications. 2010. 92p. pap. *(978-3-8383-8930-1(1))* Lambert Academic Publishing.

Moonen, M. S., et al, eds. Linear Algebra for Large Scale & Real-Time Applications. 2010. (NATO Science Series E: (closed) Ser.). 456p. pap. 419.00 *(978-90-481-4246-0(6)*, 9048142466) Springer.

Nagle, R., et al. Differential Equations & Linear Algebra. 2007. 704p. (C). 117.33 *(978-0-321-15036-3(8))* Addison-Wesley Longman, Inc.

Niknejad, Amir. Applications of Linear Algebra to Dna Microarrays. 2009. 76p. pap. *(978-3-639-17994-1(3))* VDM Verlag Dr. Mueller e.K.

O'Meara, Kevin, et al. Advanced Topics in Linear Algebra: Weaving Matrix Problems through the Weyr Form, 1 vol. 2011. (ENG., Illus.). 432p. 75.00 *(978-0-19-979373-0(5))* Oxford Univ. Pr., Inc.

O'Sullivan, Peter. The Generalised Jacobson-Morosov Theorem. 2010. (Memoirs of the American Mathematical Society Ser.). 120p. pap. 69.00 *(978-0-8218-4895-1(X))* American Mathematical Society.

Paris, Alessandro De & Vinogradov, Alexandre M. Fat Manifolds & Linear Connections. 2008. 250p. 97.00 *(978-981-281-904-8(5))* World Scientific Publishing Co., Inc.

Parshin, A. N. & Shafarevich, I. R., eds. Algebraic Geometry IV: Linear Algebraic Groups, Invariant Theory. 2010. (Encyclopaedia of Mathematical Sciences Ser.: Tr. of Algebraicheskaia Geometriia IV. (ENG.). vii, 286p. pap. 169.00 *(978-3-642-08115-4(3)*, 3642081193) Springer.

Penney, Richard C. Linear Algebra: Ideas & Applications. 3rd ed. 2008. (ENG., Illus.). 504p. 126.00 *(978-0-470-17884-3(1)*, Wiley-Interscience) Wiley, John & Sons, Inc.

Pinkus, Allan. Totally Positive Matrices. 2009. (Cambridge Tracts in Mathematics Ser.). (ENG.). 194p. 70.00 *(978-0-521-19408-2(3))* Cambridge Univ. Pr.

Piziak, Robert & Odell, P. L. Matrix Theory: From Generalized Inverses to Jordan Form. 2007. (Pure & Applied Mathematics Ser.). (ENG., Illus.). 568p. (C). 104.95 *(978-1-58488-625-9(0)*, Chapman & Hall/CRC) CRC Pr. LLC.

Poole, David. Linear Algebra: A Modern Introduction. 3rd ed. 2010. (Available 2011 Titles Enhanced Web Assign Ser.). (ENG.). 768p. (C). 242.95 *(978-0-538-73545-2(7))* Brooks/Cole.

—Student Solutions Manual with Study Guide for Poole's Linear Algebra: A Modern Introduction, 3rd. 3rd ed. 2011. (ENG.). 592p. (C). pap. 73.95 *(978-0-538-73771-5(9))* Brooks/Cole.

Porteous, Ian R. Clifford Algebras & the Classical Groups. 2009. (Cambridge Studies in Advanced Mathematics Ser.). (ENG.). 308p. pap. 67.00 *(978-0-521-11802-6(6))* Cambridge Univ. Pr.

Prof Khan, M. O. H. D. Z. U. B. A. I. R. Lecturers on linear Algebra. 2008. 256p. pap. 45.00 *(978-1-905740-89-5(1))* Anshan GBR. Dist: Publishers Storage & Shipping.

Ricardo, Henry. A Modern Introduction to Linear Algebra. 2009. (ENG., Illus.). 670p. 104.95 *(978-1-4398-0040-9(5)*, Chapman & Hall/CRC) CRC Pr. LLC.

Riesz, Marcel. Clifford Numbers & Spinors: With Riesz's Private Lectures to E. Folke Bolinder & a Historical Review by Pertti Lounesto. Bolinder, E. F. & Lounesto, P., eds. 2010. (Fundamental Theories of Physics Ser.). (ENG.). 256p. pap. 219.00 *(978-90-481-4279-8(2)*, 9048142792) Springer.

Robbiano, Lorenzo. Linear Algebra for Everyone. 2nd ed. 2010. (UNITEXT / la Matematica per il 3+2 Ser.). xv, 235p. pap. 59.95 *(978-88-470-1838-9(2)*, 8847018382) Springer.

Robinson, Derek J. S. A Course in Linear Algebra with Applications. 2nd ed. 2006. (Illus.). 436p. 121.00 *(978-981-270-023-0(4))*; pap. 60.00 *(978-981-270-024-7(2))* World Scientific Publishing Co., Inc.

Roman, Steven. Advanced Linear Algebra. (Graduate Texts in Mathematics Ser.). 2007. 74.95 *(978-0-387-72828-5(7))* 3rd ed. 2010. (Illus.). xviii, 526p. pap. 74.95 *(978-1-4419-2498-8(1)*, 1441924981) Springer.

Rubio Montaner, Francisco. Àlgebra Lineal Bàsica para Ingenieria Civil. Edicions UPC, ed. 2010. 324p. pap. *(978-84-8301-961-0(2))* UPC, S.L., Edicions.

Ryan, Raymond A. Introduction to Tensor Products of Banach Spaces. 2010. (Springer Monographs in Mathematics Ser.). (Illus.). xiv, 225p. pap. 109.00 *(978-1-84996-872-0(1)*, 1849968721) Springer.

Saavedra Rivano, N. Categories Tannakiennes. 2008. (Lecture Notes in Mathematics Ser.). (FRE.). 424p. per. 59.00 *(978-3-540-05844-1(3))* Springer.

Sabadini, Irene. Hypercomplex Analysis. 2009. (Trends in Mathematics Ser.). (Illus.). vi, 289p. 169.00 *(978-3-7643-9892-7(2))* Birkhauser Boston.

Sadun, Lorenzo. Applied Linear Algebra: The Decoupling Principle. 2nd rev. ed. 2007. (Illus.). 371p. (C). 61.00 *(978-0-8218-4441-0(5))* American Mathematical Society.

Sarma, Bipul. Double Sequence Spaces & the Difference Operator. 2011. 68p. pap. ***(978-3-8433-9191-7(2))*** Lambert Academic Publishing.

Sawyer, W. W. An Engineering Approach to Linear Algebra. 2009. (ENG., Illus.). 316p. pap. 42.00 *(978-0-521-09333-0(3))* Cambridge Univ. Pr.

Schilders, W. H. A, et al. Model Order Reduction: Theory, Research Aspects & Applications. 2008. (Mathematics in Industry / the European Consortium for Mathematics in Industry Ser.). (Illus.). xi, 471p. 159.00 *(978-3-540-78840-9(9)*, 354C788409) Springer.

Schmied, Robert. Lineare Algebra. 2010. (GER.). 135p. pap. *(978-3-8325-2595-8(5))* Logos Verlag Berlin.

Seitz, Gary M. & Liebeck, Martin W. Unipotent & Nilpotent Classes in Simple Algebraic Groups & Lie Algebras. 2012. (Mathematical Surveys & Monographs). 380p. 96.00 ***(978-0-8218-6920-8(5))*** American Mathematical Society.

Shiskowski, Kenneth M. & Frinkle, Karl. Principles of Linear Algebra with Maple. 2010. (Pure & Applied Mathematics: a Wiley Series of Texts, Monographs & Tracts Ser.: 100). (ENG., Illus.). 596p. 116.00 *(978-0-470-63759-3(5)*, Wiley) Wiley, John & Sons, Inc.

—Principles of Linear Algebra with Mathematica. 2011. (Pure & Applied Mathematics: a Wiley Series of Texts, Monographs & Tracts Ser.: 101). (ENG., Illus.). 616p. 115.00 *(978-0-470-63795-1(1)*, Wiley) Wiley, John & Sons, Inc.

Shores, Thomas S. Applied Linear Algebra & Matrix Analysis. (Undergraduate Texts in Mathematics Ser.). (Illus.). 383p. 2007. per. 49.95 *(978-0-387-33195-9(6)*, 0387331956) 3rd ed. 2006. 79.95 *(978-0-387-33194-2(8)*, 0387331948) Springer.

Simon, Leon. Introduction to Multivariable Mathematics. 2008. (Synthesis Lectures on Mathematics & Statistics Ser.). 100p. pap. 40.00 *(978-1-59829-801-7(1))* Morgan & Claypool Pubs.

Singer, Stephanie Frank. Linearity, Symmetry, & Prediction in the Hydrogen Atom. 2010. (Undergraduate Texts in Mathematics Ser.). (Illus.). xiv, 398p. pap. 59.95 *(978-1-4419-2035-5(8)*, 1441920358) Springer.

Slodowy, P. Simple Singularities & Simple Algebraic Groups. 2008. (Lecture Notes in Mathematics Ser.). 192p. pap. 39.95 *(978-3-540-10026-3(1))* Springer.

Smirnov, V. I. Linear Algebra & Group Theory. Silverman, Richard A., tr. from RUS. 2011. (Dover Books on Mathematics Ser.). (ENG.). 480p. pap. 29.95 *(978-0-486-48222-4(7))* Dover Pubns., Inc.

Snygg, John. A New Approach to Differential Geometry using Clifford's Geometric Algebra. 2011. (ENG., Illus.). xvii, 465p. 74.95 ***(978-0-8176-8282-8(1)***, 0817682821) Birkhauser Verlag AG CHE. Dist: Springer.

Spence, Lawrence E., et al. Elementary Linear Algebra: A Matrix Approach, Books a la Carte Edition. 2nd ed. 2010. (ENG.). (C). ring bd. 91.20 *(978-0-321-65600-1(8))* Addison Wesley.

—Elementary Linear Algebra: A Matrix Approach; Instructor's Edition. 2nd ed. 2008. (Illus.). 626p. *(978-0-13-600110-2(6))* Pearson Education Canada.

Springer, T. A. Linear Algebraic Groups. 2nd ed. 2008. (Modern Birkhäuser Classics Ser.). xii, 334p. pap. 49.95 *(978-0-8176-4839-8(9))* Birkhauser Boston.

Sterling, Mary Jane. Linear Algebra for Dummies. 2009. (ENG., Illus.). 384p. pap. 19.99 *(978-0-470-43090-3(7)*, For Dummies) Wiley, John & Sons, Inc.

Sternberg, Shlomo & Mathematics. Curvature in Mathematics & Physics. 2012. (Dover Books on Mathematics Ser.). (ENG.). 416p. pap. 19.95 ***(978-0-486-47855-5(6))*** Dover Pubns., Inc.

Strang & Cram101 Textbook Reviews Staff. Introduction to Linear Algebr. 2007. 124p. per. 11.95 *(978-1-4288-3654-9(3))* Cram101 Inc.

—Linear Algebra & Its Applications. 2007. 132p. per. 11.95 *(978-1-4288-3478-1(8)*, Cram101 Inc.

Strang, Gilbert. Introduction to Linear Algebra 4e. 4th ed. 2009. (ENG., Illus.). 550p. 87.50 *(978-0-9802327-1-4(6))* Wellesley-Cambridge Pr.

Stroud, K. A. & Booth, Dexter. Linear Algebra. 2008. 257p. (C). pap. 39.95 *(978-0-8311-3188-3(8))* Industrial Pr., Inc.

Suprunenko, I. D. The Minimal Polynomials of Unipotent Elements in Irreducible Representations of the Classical Groups in Odd Characteristic. 2009. (Memoirs of the American Mathematical Society Ser.). 154p. pap. 72.00 *(978-0-8218-4369-7(9)*, American Mathematical Society.

Szabo, Fred. Linear Algebra with Mathematica: An Introduction Using Mathematica. 2009. (ENG.). (C). pap. 99.95 *(978-0-12-381401-2(4)*, Academic Pr.) Elsevier Science & Technology Bks.

Tao, Terence. Topics in Random Matrix Theory. 2012. (Graduate Studies in Mathematics Ser.). 64.00 ***(978-0-8218-7430-1(6))*** American Mathematical Society.

Timashev, D. A. Homogeneous Spaces & Equivariant Embeddings. 2011. (Encyclopaedia of Mathematical Sciences Ser.). (Illus.). xxi, 253p. 124.00 *(978-3-642-18398-0(0)*, 3642183980) Springer.

Van Dooren, Paul, et al, eds. Numerical Linear Algebra in Signals, Systems & Control. 2011. (Lecture Notes in Electrical Engineering Ser.). (Illus.). xv, 478p. 179.00 *(978-94-007-0601-9(4)*, 9400706014) Springer.

Varga, Richard S. Gerŝgorin & His Circles. 2010. (Springer Series in Computational Mathematics Ser.). (Illus.). x, 226p. pap. 109.00 *(978-3-642-05928-5(7)*, 3642059287) Springer.

Vasantha Kandasamy, W. B. & Smarandache, Florentin. N-Linear Algebra of Type I & Its Applications. 2008. mass mkt. 20.00 *(978-1-59973-074-5(X))* Multimedia Larga.

—N-Linear Algebra of Type II. 2008. 229p. mass mkt. 35.00 *(978-1-59973-031-8(6))* Multimedia Larga.

—Super Linear Algebra. 2008. pap. 50.00 *(978-1-59973-065-3(0))* Multimedia Larga.

Vasantha Kandasamy, W. B., et al. New Classes of Neutrosophic Linear Algebras. 2010. (Illus.). pap. 39.00 *(978-1-59973-116-2(9))* Multimedia Larga.

—Set Linear Algebra & Set Fuzzy Linear Algebra. 2008. pap. 50.00 *(978-1-59973-029-5(4))* Multimedia Larga.

Vesentini, E., ed. Geometry Seminar 'Luigi Bianchi' Lectures Given at the Scuola Normale Superiore, 1982. 2008. (Lecture Notes in Mathematics Ser.). pap. 26.00 *(978-3-540-12719-2(4))* Springer.

—Geometry Seminar 'Luigi Bianchi' II - 1984: Lectures given at the Scuola Normale Superiore. 2008. (Lecture Notes in Mathematics Ser.). pap. 59.95 *(978-3-540-16048-9(5))* Springer.

Vujicic, Milan. Linear Algebra Thoroughly Explained. Sanderson, Jeffrey, ed. (ENG., Illus.). xii, 288p. 2010. pap. 99.00 *(978-3-642-09410-1(4)*, 3642094104) 2007. 99.00 *(978-3-540-74637-9(4)*, 3540746374) Springer.

Waldspurger, J.-L. L' Endoscopie Tordue n'Est Pas Si Tordue. 2008. (Memoirs of the American Mathematical Society Ser.: No. 908). (FRE.). 261p. pap. 90.00 *(978-0-8218-4469-4(5))* American Mathematical Society.

Weintraub, Steven H. A Guide to Advanced Linear Algebra. 2011. 220p. 49.95 ***(978-0-88385-351-1(5))*** Mathematical Assn. of America.

Wiley & Kring, Ann M. Abnormal Psychology, 2 vols. 11th ed. 2007. (Illus.). xiv, 777p. *(978-0-470-08731-2(5))* Wiley, John & Sons, Inc.

Williams. Ism- Linear Alg W/ Apps 7E Alt Ed Instruct Sol Manual. 7th rev. ed. 2010. pap. 69.95 *(978-0-7637-9617-4(4))* Jones & Bartlett Learning, LLC.

—Ism- Linear Alg W/ Apps 7E Instruc Sol Manual. 7th rev. ed. 2010. pap. 69.95 *(978-0-7637-9616-7(6))* Jones & Bartlett Learning, LLC.

—Linear Algebra with Applications. 7th rev. ed. 2010. pap. 39.95 *(978-0-7637-9089-9(3))*; pap. 39.95 *(978-0-7637-9091-2(5))* Jones & Bartlett Learning, LLC.

Williams, F. L. Tensor Products of Principal Series Representations. 2008. (Lecture Notes in Mathematics Ser.). 144p. pap. 26.00 *(978-3-540-06567-8(9))* Springer.

Williams, Gareth. Linear Algebra with Applications. 6th rev. ed. 2007. 743p. (C). 127.95 *(978-0-7637-4631-5(2))* 7th rev. ed. 2009. 532p. 168.95 *(978-0-7637-8248-1(3))* Jones & Bartlett Learning, LLC.

—Linear Algebra with Applications 6th. 6th rev. ed. 2007. 544p. 200.95 *(978-0-7637-5753-3(5))* Jones & Bartlett Learning, LLC.

—Linear Algebra with Applications, Alternate Edition. 7th rev. ed. 2009. 532p. 168.95 *(978-0-7637-8249-8(1))* Jones & Bartlett Learning, LLC.

Winitzki, Sergei. Linear Algebra via Exterior Products. 2010. 285p. pap. 20.95 *(978-1-4092-9496-2(X))* Lulu Enterprises Inc.

Zhang, Fuzhen, ed. The Schur Complement & Its Applications. 2010. (Numerical Methods & Algorithms Ser.). xvi, 296p. pap. 149.00 *(978-1-4419-3712-4(9), 1441937129)* Springer.

Zhang, Fuzhen & Zhang, F. Linear Algebra: Challenging Problems for Students. 2nd ed. 2009. (Johns Hopkins Studies in the Mathematical Sciences Ser.). (ENG., Illus.). 264p. (C). (gr. 13-17). 73.00 *(978-0-8018-9125-0(6))*; pap. 28.00 *(978-0-8018-9126-7(4))* Johns Hopkins Univ. Pr.

ALGEBRAS, MEASURE
see Measure Algebras

ALGEBRAS, NONASSOCIATIVE
see Nonassociative Algebras

ALGEBRAS, OPERATOR
see Operator Algebras

ALGEBRAS, REPRESENTATIONS OF
see Representations of Algebras

ALGEBRAS, TOPOLOGICAL
see Topological Algebras

ALGEBRAS, VON NEUMANN
see Von Neumann Algebras

ALGEBRAS, W
see C Algebras; Von Neumann Algebras

ALGER, HORATIO, 1834-1899

Alger, Horatio. The Tin Box & What It Contained. 2008. 236p. pap. *(978-1-4099-5798-0(5))* Dodo Pr.

Baxter, Kent. The Modern Age: Turn-of-the-Century American Culture & the Invention of Adolescence. (ENG., Illus.). 200p. 2011. pap. 24.95 ***(978-0-8173-5698-9(3))*** 2008. 39.95 *(978-0-8173-1626-6(4))* Univ. of Alabama Pr.

Seff, Richard. Shine! The Horatio Alger Musical. 2011. 112p. pap. 8.50 *(978-0-573-62928-0(5), 21529)* French, Samuel Inc.

ALGERIA

Harmon, Daniel E. Algeria. Rotberg, Robert I., ed. 2009. (Africa Ser.). (Illus.). 79p. (YA). (gr. 5-18). lib. bdg. 21.95 *(978-1-4222-0081-0(7))* Mason Crest Pubs.

Icon Group International, Inc. Staff, compiled by. The 2006 Economic & Product Market Databook for Constantine, Algeria. 2006. 618p. ring bd. 95.00 *(978-0-497-80405-3(0))* Icon Group International, Inc.

ALGERIA—ANTIQUITIES

Landwehr, Christa, et al. Die Römischen Skulpturen Von Caesarea Mauretaniae: Denkmaler Aus Stein und Bronze, 4 vols. 2008. (Die romischen Skulpturen von Caesarea Mauretaniae Ser.). (GER., Illus.). 165p. (C). 114.00 *(978-3-8053-3940-7(2))* Zabern, Philipp von Verlag, GmbH DEU. Dist: Brown, David Bk. Co., The.

ALGERIA—DESCRIPTION AND TRAVEL

Belloc, Hilaire. Esto Perpetua: Algerian Studies & Impressions. (BCL Ser. I). reprint ed. 39.50 *(978-0-404-00738-6(4))* AMS Pr., Inc.

Betham-Edwards, Matilda. Through Spain to the Sahara. 2010. (Cambridge Library Collection - Women's Writing Ser.). (Illus.). 330p. pap. 28.99 *(978-1-108-02068-8(2))* Cambridge Univ. Pr.

Bourdieu, Pierre. Picturing Algeria. Schultheis, Franz, ed. 2012. (Columbia / SSRC Book Ser.). (ENG., Illus.). 248p. (gr. 17). 27.50 ***(978-0-231-14842-9(9))*** Columbia Univ. Pr.

Bridgman, Frederick Arthur. Winters in Algeria. 2006. 270p. 86.00 *(978-1-59333-599-1(7))* Gorgias Pr., LLC.

de Sosa, Antonio. An Early Modern Dialogue with Islam: Antonio de Sosa's Topography of Algiers (1612) Garces, Maria Antonia, ed. Wilson, Diana de Armas, tr. from SPA. 2011. (History Lang & Cult Spanish Portuguese Ser.). (ENG., Illus.). 432p. pap. 45.00 *(978-0-268-02978-4(4))* Univ. of Notre Dame Pr.

Doucey, Bruno, et al. L'aventurier du Désert: L'itinéraire de Jules Jacques, Entre Désert, Désir et Désertion. 2010. (FRE., Illus.). 167p. *(978-2-35639-051-6(0))* Elytis.

France, Hector. Musk, Hashish, & Blood. 2007. (ENG.). 474p. 52.95 *(978-0-548-24988-8(1))*; 476p. per. 37.95 *(978-1-4326-5244-9(3))* Kessinger Publishing, LLC.

Glass, Jack. How Not to Travel North Africa, Middle East, Israel & Malta & Still Enjoy Yourself. 2010. 384p. pap. *(978-1-84549-431-5(8), Swirl)* arima publishing.

Harrison, Alexander. Challenging de Gaulle: Newly Updated with over 40 Photographs. 2007. per. 29.99 *(978-0-9776155-8-2(8))* Hailer Publishing.

Hilton-Simpson, M. W. Algiers & Beyond. 2010. (Folios Archive Library). (Illus.). 308p. pap. 39.95 *(978-1-85964-229-0(2))* Garnet Publishing, Ltd. GBR. Dist: International Publishers Marketing.

Irwin, Robert. The Summer Of '67. 2012. (ENG., Illus.). 288p. pap. 18.95 ***(978-1-86197-991-9(6))*** Profile Bks. Ltd. GBR. Dist: Consortium Bk. Sales & Distribution.

Locken, E. Travel Journal Algeria. 2010. 192p. pap. 19.99 *(978-0-557-43255-4(3))* Lulu Enterprises Inc.

Maupassant, Guy de. To the Sun. 2009. 37.95 *(978-0-9558525-0-3(1))* Duchy of Lambeth GBR. Dist: Lulu Enterprises Inc.

Oakes, Jonathan. Bradt Travel Guide: Algeria. 2008. (Bradt Travel Guide Ser.). (ENG., Illus.). 352p. pap. 26.99 *(978-1-84162-232-3(X))* Bradt Travel Guides GBR. Dist: Globe Pequot Pr., The.

ALGERIA—FOREIGN RELATIONS

Evans, Martin. Algeria: France's Undeclared War. 2012. (ENG., Illus.). 304p. 35.00 *(978-0-19-280350-4(6))* Oxford Univ. Pr., Inc.

Hannoum, Abdelmajid. Violent Modernity: France in Algeria. 2010. (Harvard Middle Eastern Monographs: 42). (ENG.). 272p. pap. 19.95 *(978-0-674-05328-1(1))* Harvard Univ., Ctr. for Middle Eastern Studies.

Lorcin, Patricia M. E. Algeria & France, 1800-2000: Identity, Memory, Nostalgia. 2006. (Modern Intellectual & Political History of the Middle East Ser.). (Illus.). 335p. 45.00 *(978-0-8156-3074-6(3))* Syracuse Univ. Pr.

Taubert, Fritz. La Guerre D'Algérie et la République Démocratique Allemande: Le Rôle de L'"autre" Allemagne Pendant les "événements", 1954 à 1962. 2010. (FRE.). 301p. *(978-2-915611-69-4(6))* Editions universitaires de Dijon.

ALGERIA—HISTORY

Alleg, Henri. The Question. Calder, John, tr. from FRE. 2006. (ENG.). 1p. pap. 16.95 *(978-0-8032-5960-7(3), Bison Bks.)* Univ. of Nebraska Pr.

Alvermann, Dirk. Algeria, 1 vol. 2012. (ENG., Illus.). 224p. pap. 32.00 ***(978-3-86930-255-3(0))*** Steidl, Gerhard Druckerei und Verlag DEU. Dist: Innovative Logistics.

Amin, Ahmad. Suwar Mushriqah Min Al-Shir Al-Shabi Al-Jazairi: Muhammad Ibn Vaytun, Al-Shaykh Al-Samati, Al-Qadi Abd Allah Ibn Karyu: Dirasat Wa-Namadhij. 2007. (ARA.). 304p. *(978-9961-906-99-6(3))* El Hikma (Souk-Ahras).

Aoudjit, Abdelkader. The Algerian Novel & Colonial Discourse: Witnessing to a Différend. 2010. (Francophone Cultures & Literatures Ser.). 228p. (C). 74.95 *(978-1-4331-1074-0(1))* Lang, Peter Publishing, Inc.

Boudjedra, Rachid. Lettres Algériennes. (FRE.). 205p. *(978-2-246-49091-3(X))* Grasset et Fasquelle.

Bourdieu, Pierre. Picturing Algeria. Schultheis, Franz, ed. 2012. (Columbia / SSRC Book Ser.). (ENG., Illus.). 248p. (gr. 17). 27.50 ***(978-0-231-14842-9(9))*** Columbia Univ. Pr.

Brower, Benjamin C. A Desert Named Peace: The Violence of France's Empire in the Algerian Sahara, 1844-1902. 2009. (History & Society of the Modern Middle East Ser.). (ENG., Illus.). 480p. (gr. 17). 50.00 *(978-0-231-15492-5(5))* Columbia Univ. Pr.

Bruschi, Mark. 13ème RDP: Combats en Algérie de la Kabylie au Constantinois. 2011. (Illus.). 208p. 55.00 *(978-2-84048-293-2(2))* Editions Heimdal FRA. Dist: Casemate Pubs. & Bk. Distributors, LLC.

Christelow, Allan. Algerians without Borders: The Making of a Global Frontier Society. 2012. (ENG., Illus.). 256p. 74.95 *(978-0-8130-3755-4(7))* Univ. Pr. of Florida.

Cixous, Hélène. So Close. 2010. (ENG.). 176p. 59.95 *(978-0-7456-4435-6(X))*; pap. 19.95 *(978-0-7456-4436-3(8))* Polity Pr. GBR. Dist: Wiley, John & Sons, Inc.

[Cler, Jean Joseph Gustave]. Reminiscences of an Officer of Zouaves Tr from the French. 2006. 340p. per. 23.99 *(978-1-4255-3431-8(7))* MPublishing.

Crapanzano, Vincent. The Harkis: The Wound That Never Heals. 2011. (ENG.). 248p. 35.00 *(978-0-226-11876-5(2))* Univ. of Chicago Pr.

Djebar, Assia. Blanc de l Algerie. pap. 16.95 *(978-2-253-15340-5(0))* Librairie Generale Francaise, LGF FRA. Dist: Distribooks, Inc.

—Le Blanc de L'Algérie: Récit. (FRE.). 279p. *(978-2-226-08457-6(6), Branch Line Video)* Albin-Michel, Editions.

Durantin, Jean. Le Commando de Penfentenyo. 2010. (FRE., Illus.). 400p. 85.00 *(978-2-84048-266-6(5))* Editions Heimdal FRA. Dist: Casemate Pubs. & Bk. Distributors, LLC.

Evans, Martin. Algeria: France's Undeclared War. 2012. (ENG., Illus.). 304p. 35.00 *(978-0-19-280350-4(6))* Oxford Univ. Pr., Inc.

Evans, Martin & Phillips, John. Algeria: Anger of the Dispossessed. 2008. (ENG., Illus.). 352p. 35.00 *(978-0-300-10881-1(8))* Yale Univ. Pr.

Fatiah. Algérie: Chronique D'une Femme Dans la Tourmente. (FRE.). 143p. *(978-2-87678-276-1(6))* Editions de l'Aube.

Fughali, Jamal. Sual Al-Kaynunah: Qiraat Fi Jamaliyat Al-Ibda Al-Jazairi Al-Muasar. 2009. (ARA.). 198p. *(978-9961-62-827-0(6))* Entreprise Nationale des Arts Graphiques.

Gallois, William. The Administration of Sickness: Medicine & Ethics in Nineteenth-Century Algeria. 2008. (ENG.). 288p. 89.00 *(978-0-230-50043-3(9))* Palgrave Macmillan.

Galula, David. Pacification in Algeria, 1956-1958. 2006. (Illus.). 324p. per. 28.50 *(978-0-8330-3920-0(2), MG-478)* RAND Corp., The.

Hardman, Ben. Islam & the Métropole: A Case Study of Religion & Rhetoric in Algeria. 2009. (American University Studies VII: Theology & Religion Ser.). (ENG.). 286p. (C). 77.95 *(978-1-4331-0271-4(4))* Lang, Peter Publishing, Inc.

Harrison, Alexander. Challenging de Gaulle: Newly Updated with over 40 Photographs. 2007. per. 29.99 *(978-0-9776155-8-2(8))* Hailer Publishing.

Hesperides. Among the Hill Folk of Algeria. 2007. 304p. per. *(978-1-4067-5164-2(2), Hesperides Pr.)* Read Bks.

Horne, Alistair. A Savage War of Peace: Algeria 1954-1962. 2006. (New York Review Books Classics). (ENG., Illus.). 624p. pap. 19.95 *(978-1-59017-218-6(3), NYRB Classics)* New York Review of Bks., Inc., The.

Jean-Marie, Vivaldi. Collective Ethics & Humanism in Fanon's Wretched of the Earth. 2007. 176p. (C). 63.95 *(978-1-4331-0062-8(2))* Lang, Peter Publishing, Inc.

Jestice, Phyllis & Sherry, Matthew, trs. from FRE. A Life Poured Out: Pierre Claverie of Algeria. 2007. Orig. Title: Pierre claverie: un Algerien par Alliance. (FRE., Illus.). 286p. per. 30.00 *(978-1-57075-706-8(2))* Orbis Bks.

Joffe, George. Algeria: The Failed Revolution. 2009. 192p. 140.00 *(978-0-415-27427-2(3), RoutledgeCurzon)* Taylor & Francis Group.

Khanna, Ranjana. Algeria Cuts: Women & Representation, 1830 to the Present. 2007. (Cultural Memory in the Present Ser.). (ENG., Illus.). 328p. 65.00 *(978-0-8047-5261-9(3))*; per. 24.95 *(978-0-8047-5262-6(1))* Stanford Univ. Pr.

Kiser, John W. Commander of the Faithful: The Life & Times of Emir Abd El-Kader (18081883) 2008. (ENG.). 400p. 28.95 *(978-0-9798828-3-8(4))* Monkfish Bk. Publishing Co.

Laouisset, Djamel Eddine. The Algerian Steel Industry Growth Decade: 1968-1978. 2010. pap. 47.00 *(978-1-61761-190-2(5))* Nova Science Pubs., Inc.

Lazreg, Marnia. Torture & the Twilight of Empire: From Algiers to Baghdad. 2007. (Human Rights & Crimes Against Humanity Ser.). (ENG., Illus.). 354p. (C). 42.00 *(978-0-691-13135-1(X))* Princeton Univ. Pr.

Liverani, Andrea. Civil Society in Algeria: The Political Functions of Associational Life. 2008. (Routledge Studies in Middle Eastern Politics Ser.). (Illus.). XXVIII, 228p. 140.00 *(978-0-415-77583-0(3))* Routledge.

Lorcin, Patricia M. E. Algeria & France, 1800-2000: Identity, Memory, Nostalgia. 2006. (Modern Intellectual & Political History of the Middle East Ser.). (Illus.). 335p. 45.00 *(978-0-8156-3074-6(3))* Syracuse Univ. Pr.

MacMaster, Neil. Burning the Veil: The Algerian War & the 'Emancipation' of Muslim Women, 1954-62. 2010. (ENG., Illus.). 432p. 95.00 *(978-0-7190-7473-8(8))* Manchester Univ. Pr. GBR. Dist: Macmillan.

Malmvig, Helle. State Sovereignty & Intervention: A Discourse Analysis of Interventionary & Non-Interventionary Practices in Kosovo & Algeria. 2011. (ENG., Illus.). 224p. pap. 42.95 ***(978-0-415-66389-2(X))*** Routledge.

Mameri, Khalfa. Les Constitutions Algérienne: Histoire, Textes, Réflexions. 2008. (FRE.). 276p. *(978-9947-834-30-5(1))* Thala.

Maougal, Mohammed & Kassoul, Aïtcha. The Algerian Destiny of Albert Camus: 1940-1962. 2006. 264p. 74.95 *(978-1-930901-58-2(5))* Academica Pr., LLC.

Mathias, Grégor. Galula in Algeria: Counterinsurgency Practice versus Theory, 1 vol. 2011. (Praeger Security International Ser.). (Illus.). 143p. 37.00 *(978-0-313-39575-8(6), A3438C)* Greenwood Publishing Group, Inc.

Mathias, Grégor. Galula in Algeria: Counterinsurgency Practice Versus Theory. 2011. E-Book ***(978-0-313-39576-5(4)***, Praeger Pubs.) Greenwood Publishing Group, Inc.

McCormack, Jo. Collective Memory: France & the Algerian War (1954-1962) 2007. (After the Empire: the Francophone World & Postcolonial France Ser.). (ENG.). 236p. 68.50 *(978-0-7391-0921-2(9))* Lexington Bks.

Mccormack, Jo. Collective Memory: France & the Algerian War, 1954-1962. 2010. (After the Empire: the Francophone World & Postcolonial France Ser.). (ENG.). 236p. pap. 31.50 *(978-0-7391-4562-3(2))* Lexington Bks.

McMaster, Neil. Burning the Veil. 2012. (ENG., Illus.). 432p. pap. 39.95 ***(978-0-7190-8754-7(6))*** Manchester Univ. Pr. GBR. Dist: Macmillan.

Millen, Raymond. Vietnam (1955-63), Algeria (1945-62), & Nicaragua (1967-79) 2008. *(978-1-58487-346-4(9))* Strategic Studies Institute, U.S. Army War College Commandant (AWCC-DSI/Pubns.).

—The Political Context Behind Successful Revolutionary Movements. 2009. 76p. pap. 37.00 *(978-1-60692-809-7(0))* Nova Science Pubs., Inc.

Morgan, Ted. My Battle of Algiers: A Memoir. 2007. (ENG., Illus.). 304p. pap. 14.95 *(978-0-06-120576-7(1), HarperPerennial)* HarperCollins Pubs.

Mukhtar, Hassani. Tarikh Al-Dawlah Al-Ziyaniyah, 3 vols. 2007. (ARA.). *(978-9961-76-758-0(6))* El Hadhara.

—Thawrat Al-Amir Abd Al-Qadir Min Khilal Thalathat Makhtutat. 2007. (ARA.). 230p. *(978-9947-842-01-0(0))* El Hikma (Souk-Ahras).

Musawi, Ahmad. Al-Mawlidiyat Fi Al-Adab Al-Jazairi Al-Qadim: Ahd Tilimsan Al-Zayyaniyah: Dirasah. 2008. (ARA., Illus.). 261p. *(978-9961-62-741-9(5))* Entreprise Nationale des Arts Graphiques.

Naylor, Phillip Chiviges. Historical Dictionary of Algeria. 3rd ed. 2006. (Historical Dictionaries of Africa Ser.: Vol. 102). (ENG., Illus.). 640p. 139.00 *(978-0-8108-5340-9(X))* Scarecrow Pr., Inc.

O'Donnell, James J. Augustine Confessions: Augustine Confessions: Volume 1: Introduction & Text. 2012. (ENG.). 287p. pap. 45.00 ***(978-0-19-966072-8(7))*** Oxford Univ. Pr., Inc.

O'Riley, Michael F. Cinema in an Age of Terror: North Africa, Victimization, & Colonial History. 2010. (France Overseas: Studies in Empire & D Ser.). (ENG.). 208p. 45.00 *(978-0-8032-2809-2(0))* Univ. of Nebraska Pr.

Porter, David, ed. Eyes to the South: French Anarchists & Algeria. 2011. (ENG., Illus.). 550p. pap. 25.00 ***(978-1-84935-076-1(0))*** AK Pr. GBR. Dist: Consortium Bk. Sales & Distribution.

Rachi, Abdelkader. Sous le Soleil: Le Sang... 2011. (FRE.). 312p. pap. 22.29 ***(978-1-4120-9506-8(9))*** Trafford Publishing.

Rahal, Malika. Ali Boumendjel, 1919-1957: Une Affaire Française, une Histoire Algérienne. 2010. (FRE., Illus.). 296p. (C). pap. 41.00 ***(978-2-251-90005-6(5))*** Societe d'edition Les Belles lettres FRA. Dist: ISD.

Rashed, Roshdi, ed. & tr. from ARA. Al-Khwarizmi: The Beginnings of Algebra. 2010. (ENG.). 392p. 100.00 *(978-0-86356-430-7(5))* Saqi Bks. GBR. Dist: Consortium Bk. Sales & Distribution.

Rice, Alison. Polygraphies: Francophone Women Writing Algeria. 2012. (ENG.). 256p. (C). (gr. 13-17). pap. 24.50 ***(978-0-8139-3292-7(0))***; (Illus.). (gr. 17). 55.00 ***(978-0-8139-3291-0(2))*** Univ. Pr. of Virginia.

Scheele, Judith. Smugglers & Saints of the Sahara: Regional Connectivity in the Twentieth Century. 2012. (African Studies: 120). (ENG., Illus.). 120p. 99.00 ***(978-1-107-02212-6(6))*** Cambridge Univ. Pr.

Sessions, Jennifer E. By Sword & Plow: France & the Conquest of Algeria. 2011. (Illus.). 352p. 49.95 ***(978-0-8014-4975-8(8))*** Cornell Univ. Pr.

Shepard, Todd. The Invention of Decolonization: The Algerian War & the Remaking of France. 2008. (Illus.). 288p. per. 23.95 *(978-0-8014-7454-5(X))* Cornell Univ. Pr.

Taubert, Fritz. La Guerre D'Algérie et la République Démocratique Allemande: Le Rôle de L'"autre" Allemagne Pendant les "événements", 1954 à 1962. 2010. (FRE.). 301p. *(978-2-915611-69-4(6))* Editions universitaires de Dijon.

Ulloa, Marie-Pierre. Francis Jeanson: A Dissident Intellectual from the French Resistance to the Algerian War. Todd, Jane, tr. from FRE. 2008. (ENG.). 376p. 60.00 *(978-0-8047-5508-5(6))* Stanford Univ. Pr.

Vétillard, Roger. Sétif, Mai 1945, Massacres en Algérie. 2008. (FRE.). 589p. *(978-2-85162-213-6(7))* Editions de Paris.

Wills, Garry. Augustine's Confessions: The Biography of a Book. 2011. (Lives of Great Religious Bks.). (ENG.). 176p. 19.95 *(978-0-691-14357-6(9))* Princeton Univ. Pr.

Yakubu, Owusu Yaki. Meditations on Frantz Fanon's Wretched of the Earth, Part One: A Study Guide. 2nd ed. 2006. (Illus.). 26p. pap. 5.00 *(978-0-9731432-6-3(6))* Kersplebedeb Publishing CAN. Dist: AK Pr. Distribution.

—Meditations on Frantz Fanon's Wretched of the Earth, Part Two: A Study Guide. 2006. 36p. pap. 5.00 *(978-0-9731432-7-0(4))* Kersplebedeb Publishing CAN. Dist: AK Pr. Distribution.

ALGERIA—POLITICS AND GOVERNMENT

Abi-Mershed, Osama. Apostles of Modernity: Saint-Simonians & the Civilizing Mission in Algeria. 2010. (ENG., Illus.). 344p. 60.00 *(978-0-8047-6909-9(5))* Stanford Univ. Pr.

Cavatorta, Francesco. The International Dimension of the Failed Algerian Transition: Democracy Betrayed? 2009. (Perspectives on Democratic Practice Ser.). (ENG.). 224p. 89.00 *(978-0-7190-7616-9(1))* Manchester Univ. Pr. GBR. Dist: Macmillan.

Christelow, Allan. Algerians without Borders: The Making of a Global Frontier Society. 2012. (ENG., Illus.). 256p. 74.95 *(978-0-8130-3755-4(7))* Univ. Pr. of Florida.

Hannoum, Abdelmajid. Violent Modernity: France in Algeria. 2010. (Harvard Middle Eastern Monographs: 42). (ENG.). 272p. pap. 19.95 *(978-0-674-05328-1(1))* Harvard Univ., Ctr. for Middle Eastern Studies.

Hill, Jonathan N. C. Identity in Algerian Politics: The Legacy of Colonial Rule. 2009. 215p. 55.00 *(978-1-58826-608-8(7))* Rienner, Lynne Pubs.

Ibn Kharf Allah, al-Tahir. Al-Nukhbah Al-Hakimah Fi Al-Jazair (62-89) Bayna Al-Tasawwur Al-Idiyuluji Wa-Al-Mumarisah Al-Siyasiyah, 2 vols. 2007. (ARA.). *(978-9961-65-078-3(6))* Houma.

Joffe, George. Algeria: The Failed Revolution. 2009. 192p. 140.00 *(978-0-415-27427-2(3), RoutledgeCurzon)* Taylor & Francis Group.

Kesseiri, Radia. Algeri: An account of International Politics. 2011. 308p. pap. ***(978-3-8433-8486-5(X))*** Lambert Academic Publishing.

Le Sueur, James D. Algeria since 1989: Between Terror & Democracy. 2010. (Global History of the Present Ser.). (ENG., Illus.). 224p. pap. 29.95 *(978-1-84277-725-1(4))* Zed Bks., Ltd. GBR. Dist: Macmillan.

—Between Terror & Democracy: Algeria since 1989. 2010. (Global History of the Present Ser.). (ENG., Illus.). 224p. 117.95 *(978-1-84277-724-4(6))* Zed Bks., Ltd. GBR. Dist: Macmillan.

Liverani, Andrea. Civil Society in Algeria: The Political Functions of Associational Life. 2008. (Routledge Studies in Middle Eastern Politics Ser.). (Illus.). XXVIII, 228p. 140.00 *(978-0-415-77583-0(3))* Routledge.

Lowi, Miriam R. Oil Wealth & the Poverty of Politics: Algeria Compared. (Cambridge Middle East Studies). (ENG., Illus.). 2011. 252p. pap. 31.99 *(978-1-107-40296-6(4))* 2009. 250p. 93.00 *(978-0-521-11318-2(0))* Cambridge Univ. Pr.

Lunisi, Ibrahim. Al-Sira Al-Siyasi Fi Al-Jazair Khilal Ahd Al-Rais Ahmad Ibn Billah, 1962-1965. 2007. (ARA.). 136p. *(978-9961-65-020-2(4))* Houma.

Maddy-Weitzman, Bruce. The Berber Identity Movement & the Challenge to North African States. 2011. (ENG., Illus.). 304p. 55.00 *(978-0-292-72587-4(6))* Univ. of Texas Pr.

Porter, David, ed. Eyes to the South: French Anarchists & Algeria. 2011. (ENG., Illus.). 550p. pap. 25.00 ***(978-1-84935-076-1(0))*** AK Pr. GBR. Dist: Consortium Bk. Sales & Distribution.

Rachi, Abdelkader. Sous le Soleil: Le Sang... 2011. (FRE.). 312p. pap. 22.29 ***(978-1-4120-9506-8(9))*** Trafford Publishing.

Rahal, Malika. Ali Boumendjel, 1919-1957: Une Affaire Française, une Histoire Algérienne. 2010. (FRE., Illus.). 296p. (C). pap. 41.00 ***(978-2-251-90005-6(5))*** Societe d'edition Les Belles lettres FRA. Dist: ISD.

Scheele, Judith. Village Matters: Knowledge, Politics & Community in Kabylia, Algeria. 2009. (African Anthropology Ser.). (Illus.). 191p. 80.00 *(978-1-84701-205-0(1), Currey, James)* Boydell & Brewer, Ltd. GBR. Dist: Boydell & Brewer, Inc.

Stora, Benjamin. L'Algérie en 1995: La Guerre, L'histoire, la Politique: Essai. (FRE.). 114p. *(978-2-84186-013-5(2))* Michalon, Editions.

Werenfels, Isabelle. Managing Instability in Algeria: Elites & Political Change Since 1995. 2009. 236p. pap. 39.95 *(978-0-415-55886-0(7))* 2007. (ENG., Illus.). 245p. 160.00 *(978-0-415-40344-3(8))* Routledge.

Willis, Michael J. Politics & Power in the Maghreb: Algeria, Tunisia & Morocco from Independence to the Arab Spring. 2012. (Columbia/Hurst Ser.). (ENG.). 320p. (gr. 17). 35.00 ***(978-0-231-70324-6(4))***; ***(978-0-231-80093-8(2))*** Columbia Univ. Pr.

ALGERIA—SOCIAL CONDITIONS

Bourdieu, Pierre. Political Interventions: Social Science & Political Action. Poupeau, Franck & Discepolo, Thierry, eds. Fernbach, David, tr. from FRE. 2008. (ENG.). 400p. 110.00 *(978-1-84467-189-2(5)*, 844189); per. 39.95 *(978-1-84467-190-8(9)*, 844190) Verso Bks. GBR. Dist: Norton, W. W. & Co., Inc.

de Sosa, Antonio. An Early Modern Dialogue with Islam: Antonio de Sosa's Topography of Algiers (1612) Garces, Maria Antonia, ed. Wilson, Diana de Armas, tr. from SPA. 2011. (History Lang & Cult Spanish Portuguese Ser.). (ENG., Illus.). 432p. pap. 45.00 *(978-0-268-02978-4(4))* Univ. of Notre Dame Pr.

Goodman, Jane E. & Silverstein, Paul A., eds. Bourdieu in Algeria: Colonial Politics, Ethnographic Practices, Theoretical Developments. Fogarty, Patricia, tr. 2009. (France Overseas: Studies in Empire & D Ser.). (ENG., Illus.). 290p. pap. 35.00 *(978-0-8032-1362-3(X))* Univ. of Nebraska Pr.

Lowi, Miriam R. Oil Wealth & the Poverty of Politics: Algeria Compared. (Cambridge Middle East Studies). (ENG., Illus.). 2011. 252p. pap. 31.99 *(978-1-107-40296-6(4))* 2009. 250p. 93.00 *(978-0-521-11318-2(0))* Cambridge Univ. Pr.

McDougall, James. History & the Culture of Nationalism in Algeria. 2006. (Cambridge Middle East Studies: Vol. 23). (ENG., Illus.). 284p. 95.00 *(978-0-521-84373-7(1))* Cambridge Univ. Pr.

Mukhtar, Hassani. Tarikh Al-Dawlah Al-Ziyaniyah, 3 vols. 2007. (ARA.). *(978-9961-76-758-0(6))* El Hadhara.

Scheele, Judith. Smugglers & Saints of the Sahara: Regional Connectivity in the Twentieth Century. 2012. (African Studies: 120). (ENG., Illus.). 120p. 99.00 ***(978-1-107-02212-6(6))*** Cambridge Univ. Pr.

Scheele, Judith. Village Matters: Knowledge, Politics & Community in Kabylia, Algeria. 2009. (African Anthropology Ser.). (Illus.). 191p. 80.00 *(978-1-84701-205-0(1)*, Currey, James) Boydell & Brewer, Ltd. GBR. Dist: Boydell & Brewer, Inc.

ALGERIAN WOMEN

see Women—Algeria

ALGOL (COMPUTER PROGRAM LANGUAGE)

Branquart, P., et al. An Optimized Translation Process & Its Application to ALGOL 68. 2007. (Lecture Notes in Computer Science Ser.). (ENG.). 348p. pap. 39.95 *(978-3-540-07545-5(3)*, 3540075453) Springer.

ALGOLOGY

see also Algae

Gantt, Elisabeth, ed. Handbook of Phycological Methods: Developmental & Cytological Methods. 2008. (ENG., Illus.). 440p. pap. 79.00 *(978-0-521-05663-2(2))* Cambridge Univ. Pr.

Hellebust, Johan A. & Craigie, James S., eds. Handbook of Phycological Methods: Physiological & Biological Methods. 2011. (ENG.). 528p. pap. 65.00 *(978-0-521-27942-0(9))* Cambridge Univ. Pr.

Kim, Se-Kwon, ed. Handbook of Marine Macroalgae: Biotechnology & Applied Phycology. 2012. (ENG., Illus.). 592p. 249.95 ***(978-0-470-97918-1(6)***, Wiley) Wiley, John & Sons, Inc.

Lee, Robert. Phycology. 4th rev. ed. 2008. (ENG., Illus.). 560p. (C). pap. 74.00 *(978-0-521-68277-0(0))* Cambridge Univ. Pr.

Littler, Mark M. & Littler, Diane S., eds. Handbook of Phycological Methods: Volume 4: Ecological Field Methods: Macroalgae. 2008. (ENG., Illus.). 632p. pap. 116.00 *(978-0-521-06640-2(9))* Cambridge Univ. Pr.

Stevenson, R. Jan, et al. Advances in Algal Biology: A Commemoration of the Work of Rex Lowe: A Commemoration of the Work of Rex Lowe. 2010. (Developments in Hydrobiology Ser.). viii, 249p. pap. 199.00 *(978-90-481-7194-1(6)*, 9048171946) Springer.

ALGONQUIAN INDIANS

see Indians of North America

ALGONQUIAN LANGUAGES

see also Cheyenne Language; Delaware Language; Massachuset Language; Ojibwa Language; Siksika Language

Bell, Nicole. Just Do It. 2010. 212p. pap. *(978-3-639-14060-6(5))* VDM Verlag Dr. Mueller e.K.

Bross, Kristina & Wyss, Hilary E. Early Native Literacies in New England: A Documentary & Critical Anthology. Bross, Kristina & Wyss, Hilary E., eds. 2008. (Native Americans of the Northeast Ser.). (Illus.). 320p. (ENG.). pap. 29.95 *(978-1-55849-648-4(3))*; lib. bdg. 98.00 *(978-1-55849-647-7(5))* Univ. of Massachusetts Pr.

Frantz, Donald G. Blackfoot Grammar. 2nd ed. 2009. (ENG.). 224p. pap. *(978-1-4426-9987-6(6))* Univ. of Toronto Pr.

Lahontan, Louis Armand de Lom d'Arce. New Voyages to North-America, by the Baron De Lahontan. reprint ed. 250.00 *(978-0-7222-6734-9(7))* Library Reprints, Inc.

Masta, Henry Lorne. Abenaki Indian Legends, Grammar & Place Names. 2008. 116p. pap. *(978-1-897367-18-6(X))* Global Language Press.

Perley, Bernard C. Defying Maliseet Language Death: Emergent Vitalities of Language, Culture, & Identity in Eastern Canada. 2011. (ENG., Illus.). 256p. 60.00 *(978-0-8032-2529-9(6))* Univ. of Nebraska Pr.

ALGONQUIAN LANGUAGES—DICTIONARIES

Francis, David A. & Leavitt, Robert. A Passamaquoddy-Maliseet Dictionary: Peskotomuhkati Wolastoqewi Latuwewakon. 2008. (Illus.). xiii, 1198p. *(978-0-89101-117-0(X))* Univ. of Maine Pr.

Icon Group International, Inc. Staff, compiled by. Webster's Abenaki - English Thesaurus Dictionary. 2008. 60p. ring bd. 28.95 incl. audio compact disk *(978-0-497-83420-3(0))* Icon Group International, Inc.

—Webster's Anishinaabe - English Thesaurus Dictionary. 2008. 38p. ring bd. 28.95 incl. audio compact disk *(978-0-497-83425-8(1))* Icon Group International, Inc.

—Webster's Micmac - English Thesaurus Dictionary. 2008. 249p. ring bd. 28.95 incl. audio compact disk *(978-0-497-83614-6(9))* Icon Group International, Inc.

Maillard, Antoine & Bellenger, Joseph. Grammaire de la Langue Mikmaque. 2007. (MUL.). 104p. per. *(978-1-897367-14-8(7))* Global Language Press.

ALGONQUIAN PROVINCIAL PARK (ONT.)

Runtz, Michael. Algonquin Souvenir. 2007. (ENG., Illus.). 96p. 19.95 *(978-1-55046-494-8(9))* Boston Mills Pr. CAN. Dist: Firefly Bks., Ltd.

—The Explorer's Guide to Algonquin Park. rev. ed. (Illus.). 176p. *(978-1-55046-321-7(7))* Boston Mills Pr.

—The Explorer's Guide to Algonquin Park. rev. ed. 2008. (ENG., Illus.). 224p. pap. 29.95 *(978-1-55046-498-6(1))* Boston Mills Pr. CAN. Dist: Firefly Bks., Ltd.

ALGORITHMIC LANGUAGE

see ALGOL (Computer Program Language)

ALGORITHMS

see also Computer Algorithms; Genetic Algorithms; Machine Theory; Machine Translating; Numerical Analysis; Programming (Mathematics); Programming Languages (Electronic Computers); Recursive Functions; Transformations (Mathematics)

Abdelgawad, Ahmed & Bayoumi, Magdy. Resource-Aware Data Fusion Algorithms for Wireless Sensor Networks. 2012. (Lecture Notes in Electrical Engineering Ser.). (ENG., Illus.). 124p. 129.00 ***(978-1-4614-1349-3(4)***, 1461413494) Springer.

Abera, Fasil. Energy Optimal Control of Interior Permanent Magnet Synchronous Motor. 2010. 96p. pap. *(978-3-639-22799-4(9))* VDM Verlag Dr. Mueller e.K.

Abudalfa, Shadi. Metaheuristic Clustering Algorithm. 2011. 104p. pap. ***(978-3-8443-9574-7(1))*** Lambert Academic Publishing.

Aci, Cigdem. A New Congestion Control Algorithm. 2011. 76p. pap. ***(978-3-8443-9440-5(0))*** Lambert Academic Publishing.

Adjeroh, Donald, et al. The Burrows-Wheeler Transform: Data Compression, Suffix Arrays, & Pattern Matching. 2010. (ENG., Illus.). xii, 352p. pap. 159.00 *(978-1-4419-4628-7(4)*, 1441946284) Springer.

Advances in Computational Algorithms & Data Analysis. 2010. (Lecture Notes in Electrical Engineering Ser.). viii, 588p. pap. 159.00 *(978-90-481-8027-1(9)*, 9048180279) Springer.

Aggarwal, Charu C., ed. Data Streams: Models & Algorithms. 2006. (Advances in Database Systems Ser.). (Illus.). 354p. 149.00 *(978-0-387-28759-1(0)*, 0387287590) Springer.

Aggarwal, Charu C. & Yu, Philip S. Privacy-Preserving Data Mining: Models & Algorithms. Aggarwal, Charu C. & Yu, Philip S., eds. 2008. (Advances in Database Systems Ser.). (Illus.). XXII, 514p. (C). 149.00 *(978-0-387-70991-8(6)*, 0387709916) Springer.

Aha, David W., ed. Lazy Learning. 2010. 432p. pap. 145.00 *(978-90-481-4860-8(X)*, 904814860X) Springer.

Akella, Srinivas. Algorithmic Foundation of Robotics. 2008. (Springer Tracts in Advanced Robotics Ser.). 490p. 219.00 *(978-3-540-68404-6(2))* Springer.

Akella, Srinivas, et al, eds. Algorithmic Foundation of Robotics VII: Selected Contributions of the Seventh International Workshop on the Algorithmic Foundations of Robotics. 2010. (Springer Tracts in Advanced Robotics Ser.). (Illus.). xiv, 526p. pap. 219.00 *(978-3-642-08798-1(1)*, 3642087981) Springer.

Akram, Muhammad & Imran Shafi, Muhammad. Functional Approach Towards Approximation Problems. 2010. 112p. pap. *(978-3-8383-6350-9(7))* Lambert Academic Publishing.

Al-Azemi, Abdullah. Classification Algorithms for Graphs, Digraphs, & Linear Spaces. 2010. 216p. pap. *(978-3-8383-0278-2(8))* Lambert Academic Publishing.

Al Tamim, Asma, et al. Discrete-Time Control Algorithms Design. 2010. 140p. pap. *(978-3-639-27295-6(1))* VDM Verlag Dr. Mueller e.K.

Alexandru, Adajeniuc. Wireless Sensor Networks Simulation. 2010. 80p. pap. *(978-3-8383-8265-4(X))* Lambert Academic Publishing.

Alpert, Charles J., et al, eds. Algorithms for Physical Design Automation. 2008. (ENG., Illus.). 1024p. instr.'s hndbk. ed. 162.95 *(978-0-8493-7242-1(9))* Auerbach Pubs., Inc.

alsadi, jehad & Alsadi, Jehad. New Fault-Tolerant Routing Algorithms for K-Ary N-Cube Networks. 2011. 156p. pap. ***(978-3-8383-5263-3(7))*** Lambert Academic Publishing.

Altman, Russ B. Biocomputing 2008. 2007. 274.00 *(978-981-277-608-2(7))* World Scientific Publishing Co., Inc.

Altman, Russ B., et al, eds. Biocomputing 2009. 2008. 600p. 210.00 *(978-981-283-692-2(6))* World Scientific Publishing Co., Inc.

Alvarez, Carme & Serna, Maria. Experimental & Efficient Algorithms: 5th International Workshop, WEA 2006, Cala Galdana, Menorca, Spain, May 24-27, 2006, Proceedings. 2006. (Lecture Notes in Computer Science Ser.: Vol. 4007). (Illus.). XI, 329p. pap. 79.95 *(978-3-540-34597-8(3)*, 3540345973) Springer.

Antoniou, Andreas & Lu, Wu-Sheng. Practical Optimization: Algorithms & Engineering Applications. 2007. (ENG., Illus.). xx, 676p. 124.00 *(978-0-387-71106-5(6)*, 0387711066) Springer.

Ao, Sio-Iong & Gelman, Len, eds. Advances in Electrical Engineering & Computational Science. 2009. (Lecture Notes in Electrical Engineering Ser.). (ENG., Illus.). xxvi, 726p. 189.00 *(978-90-481-2310-0(0))* Springer.

Ao, Sio-Iong, et al. Advances in Computational Algorithms & Data Analysis. 2008. (Lecture Notes in Electrical Engineering Ser.). (ENG., Illus.). viii, 588p. 159.00 *(978-1-4020-8918-3(X)*, 140208918X) Springer.

Arge, Lars & Freivalds, Rusins. Algorithm Theory — SWAT 2006: 10th Scandinavian Workshop on Algorithm Theory, Riga, Latvia, July 6-8, 2006, Proceedings. 2006. (Lecture Notes in Computer Science Ser.). (Illus.). XII, 436p. pap. 89.95 *(978-3-540-35753-7(X)*, 354035753X) Springer.

Arif, Muhammad & Rahat, Syed. New Algorithms for Multi-Step Ahead Forecasting. 2010. 160p. pap. *(978-3-639-24981-1(X))* VDM Verlag Dr. Mueller e.K.

Arndt, Jörg. Matters Computational: Ideas, Algorithms, Source Code. 2010. (Illus.). xiv, 978p. 199.00 *(978-3-642-14763-0(1)*, 3642147631) Springer.

Ascher, U. M. & Greif, Chen. A First Course in Numerical Methods. 2011. (Illus.). 580p. pap. ***(978-0-89871-997-0(6))*** Society for Industrial and Applied Mathematics.

Astola, Jaakko. Image Processing: Algorithms & Systems VII: 19-20, 22 January 2009, San Jose, California, United States. 2009. (Proceedings of SPIE Ser.). (Illus.). 424p. pap. 105.00 ***(978-0-8194-7495-7(9))*** SPIE.

Astola, Jaakko & Egiazarian, K. Image Processing: Algorithms & Systems VIII: 19-20 January 2010, San Jose, California, United States. 2010. (Proceedings of SPIE Ser.). (Illus.). 310p. pap. 90.00 ***(978-0-8194-7925-9(X))*** SPIE.

Astola, Jaakko & Egiazarian, Karen. Image Processing: Algorithms & Systems IX. 2011. (Proceedings of SPIE Ser.). (Illus.). 414p. pap. 105.00 ***(978-0-8194-8407-9(5))*** SPIE.

Astola, Jaakko, et al. Image Processing: Algorithms & Systems V, 29-30 January 2007, San Jose, California, USA. 2007. (Proceedings of SPIE Ser.). (Illus.). 362p. pap. 90.00 *(978-0-8194-6610-5(7))* SPIE.

—Image Processing: Algorithms & Systems VI: 28-29 January 2008, San Jose, California, USA. 2008. (Proceedings of SPIE Ser.). (Illus.). 504p. pap. 105.00 *(978-0-8194-6984-7(X))* SPIE.

Atallah, Mikhail, et al, eds. Frontiers in Algorithmics & Algorithmic Aspects in Information & Management: Joint International Conference, FEW-AAIM 2011, Jinhua, China, May 28-31, 2011, Proceedings. 2011. (Lecture Notes in Computer Science / Theoretical Computer Science & General Issues Ser.). (Illus.). xiii, 390p. pap. 95.00 *(978-3-642-21203-1(4)*, 3642212034) Springer.

Atallah, Mikhail J. Algorithms & Theory of Computation: Special Topics & Techniques, 2 vols. Blanton, Marina, ed. 2nd ed. 2009. (Chapman & Hall/CRC Applied Algorithms & Data Structures Ser.). (ENG., Illus.). 950p. 124.95 *(978-1-58488-820-8(2)*, Chapman & Hall/CRC) CRC Pr. LLC.

Atti, Venkatraman. Algorithms & Software for Predictive Coding of Speech. 2011. (Synthesis Lectures on Algorithms & Software in Engineering Ser.). 119p. pap. 35.00 *(978-1-60845-387-0(1))* Morgan & Claypool Pubs.

Awal, Tanveer. Resource Partitioning on Planar Graphs. 2010. 64p. pap. *(978-3-639-25083-1(4))* VDM Verlag Dr. Mueller e.K.

Bahi, Jacques M., et al. Parallel Iterative Algorithms: From Sequential to Grid Computing. 2007. (Chapman & Hall/CRC Numerical Analysis & Scientific Computing Ser.). (ENG., Illus.). 240p. 99.95 *(978-1-58488-808-6(3)*, Chapman & Hall/CRC) CRC Pr. LLC.

Baldi, Paolo, ed. Fun with Algorithms: 5th International Conference, FUN 2010, Iscia, Italy, June 2-4, 2010, Proceedings. 2010. (Lecture Notes in Computer Science / Theoretical Computer Science & General Issues Ser.). ix, 382p. pap. 83.00 *(978-3-642-13121-9(2)*, 3642131212) Springer.

Ball, Larry, et al. Hierarchical Innovation Algorithms: A TRIZ Collaboration. Ball, Erika, ed. 2007. (Illus.). 574p. per. 39.95 *(978-1-932657-87-6(8))* Third Millennium Pubns.

Balsamo, Simonetta, et al. Analysis of Queueing Networks with Blocking. 2010. (International Series in Operations Research & Management Science Ser.). 272p. pap. 229.00 *(978-1-4419-5014-7(1)*, 1441950141) Springer.

Bao, Lichun & Garcia-Luna-Aceves, J. J. Neighbor-Aware Control in Ad Hoc Networks. 2010. 144p. pap. *(978-3-8383-4702-8(1))* Lambert Academic Publishing.

Baragona, Roberto, et al. Evolutionary Statistical Procedures. 2011. (Statistics & Computing Ser.). (Illus.). iv, 296p. 79.95 *(978-3-642-16217-6(7)*, 3642162177) Springer.

Basu, Saugata, et al. Algorithms in Real Algebraic Geometry. 2nd ed. 2010. (Algorithms & Computation in Mathematics Ser.). (Illus.). x, 662p. pap. 89.95 *(978-3-642-06964-2(9)*, 3642069649) Springer.

Basu, Tanaya. Coastline Identification & Shift Detection. 2010. 64p. pap. *(978-3-8383-4889-6(3))* Lambert Academic Publishing.

Battaglia, Demian. Survey Propagation Methods. 2010. 156p. pap. *(978-3-8383-5593-1(8))* Lambert Academic Publishing.

Böckenhauer, Hans-Joachim & Bongartz, Dirk. Algorithmic Aspects of Bioinformatics. 2010. (Natural Computing Ser.). (Illus.). x, 396p. pap. 95.00 *(978-3-642-09100-1(8)*, 3642091008) Springer.

Becvar, J., ed. Mathematical Foundations of Computer Science 1975. 2007. (Lecture Notes in Computer Science Ser.). 492p. pap. 27.00 *(978-3-540-07389-5(2)*, 3540073892) Springer.

—Mathematical Foundations of Computer Science 1979. 2007. (Lecture Notes in Computer Science Ser.). 596p. per. 49.95 *(978-3-540-09526-2(8))* Springer.

Bekkerman, Ron, et al, eds. Scaling up Machine Learning: Parallel & Distributed Approaches. 2011. (ENG., Illus.). 496p. 90.00 ***(978-0-521-19224-8(2))*** Cambridge Univ. Pr.

Bernstein, L. The Jacobi-Perron Algorithm. 2008. (Lecture Notes in Mathematics Ser.). 164p. pap. 39.95 *(978-3-540-05497-9(9)*, 3540054979) Springer.

Bhattacharya, Bhargab B., et al, eds. Algorithms, Architectures & Information Systems Security. 2008. (Illus.). 334p. 133.00 *(978-981-283-623-6(3))* World Scientific Publishing Co., Inc.

Bhuyan, Shariful Islam. Combinatorial Generation. 2010. 56p. pap. *(978-3-639-23220-2(8))* VDM Verlag Dr. Mueller e.K.

Biratti, Mauro, et al. Ant Colony Optimization & Swarm Intelligence: 5th International Workshop, ANTS 2006 Brussels, Belgium, September 4-7, 2006 Proceedings. 2006. (Lecture Notes in Computer Science Ser.: Vol. 4150). (Illus.). 526p. pap. 119.00 *(978-3-540-38482-3(0)*, 3540384820) Springer.

Bird, Richard. Pearls of Functional Algorithm Design. 2010. (ENG., Illus.). 290p. 60.00 *(978-0-521-51338-8(3))* Cambridge Univ. Pr.

Blahut, Richard E. Fast Algorithms for Signal Processing. 2010. (ENG., Illus.). 466p. 120.00 *(978-0-521-19049-7(5))* Cambridge Univ. Pr.

Boissonnat, Jean-Daniel, et al. Algorithmic Foundations of Robotics V. 2010. (Springer Tracts in Advanced Robotics Ser.). (ENG., Illus.). xiv, 577p. pap. 199.00 *(978-3-642-07341-0(7)*, 3642073417) Springer.

Bongartz, Dirk & Bockenhauer, Hans-Joachim. Algorithmic Aspects of Bioinformatics. 2007. (Natural Computing Ser.). (Illus.). 396p. 95.00 *(978-3-540-71912-0(1)*, 3540719121) Springer.

Borreggine, Joseph S. The Podiatric Practice Manual: A Guide to Running an Efficient Practice. 2009. *(978-1-57400-129-7(9))* Data Trace Publishing Co.

Boyle, Brandon H. Support Vector Machines: Data Analysis, Machine Learning & Applications. 2011. (Computer Science, Technology & Applications Ser.). (Illus.). 213p. 129.00 *(978-1-61209-342-0(6))* Nova Science Pubs., Inc.

Branco, Antnio, ed. Anaphora: Analysis, Algorithms & Applications: 6th Discourse Anaphora & Anaphor Resolution Colloquium, Daarc 2007, Lagos Portugal, March 29-30, 2007, Selected Papers. 2007. (Lecture Notes in Artificial Intelligence Ser.). (Illus.). 190p. pap. 69.95 *(978-3-540-71411-8(1))* Springer.

Brankovich, L. Proceedings of the International Workshop on Combinatorial Algorithms 2007. 2008. pap. *(978-1-904987-67-3(2))* College Pubns.

Bras-Amorós, Maria & Hoholdt, Tom. Applied Algebra, Algebraic Algorithms & Error-Correcting Codes: 18th International Symposium, AAECC-18, Tarragona, Sapin, June 8-12, 2009, Proceedings. 2009. (Lecture Notes in Computer Science / Theoretical Computer Science & General Issues Ser.). xi, 243p. pap. 69.95 *(978-3-642-02180-0(8)*, 3642021808) Springer.

Brearley, Malcom J. Decision Making in Small Animal Oncology. Argyle, David J. & Turek, Michelle M., eds. 2008. (ENG., Illus.). 392p. pap. 82.99 *(978-0-8138-2275-4(0)*, Wiley-Blackwell) Wiley, John & Sons, Inc.

Bressoud, David & Wagon, Stan. A Course in Computational Number Theory. 2008. (ENG.). 384p. (C). 115.95 *(978-0-470-41215-2(1)*, Wiley) Wiley, John & Sons, Inc.

Britanak, Vladimir, et al. Discrete Cosine & Sine Transforms: General Properties, Fast Algorithms & Integer Approximations. 2nd ed. 2006. (ENG., Illus.). 368p. 205.00 *(978-0-12-373624-6(2)*, Academic Pr.) Elsevier Science & Technology Bks.

Broersma, H. Algorithms & Complexity in Durham 2006. 2006. pap. *(978-1-904987-38-3(9))* College Pubns.

Broersma, H., et al, eds. Algorithms & Complexity: Proceedings of the Third ACID Workshop. 2007. 164p. per. *(978-1-904987-55-0(9))* College Pubns.

BröKer, Reinier. Constructing elliptic curves of prescribed order. 2008. 172p. pap. *(978-3-639-09734-4(3))* VDM Verlag Dr. Mueller e.K.

Broman, Karl W. & Sen, Saunak. A Guide to QTL Mapping with R/qtl. 2009. (Statistics for Biology & Health Ser.). (ENG., Illus.). xii, 400p. 119.00 *(978-0-387-92124-2(9)*, 0387921249) Springer.

Brownlee, Jason. Clever Algorithms: Nature-Inspired Programming Recipes. 2011. 436p. pap. 24.99 ***(978-1-4467-8506-5(8))*** Lulu Enterprises Inc.

Brusco, Michael & Stahl, Stephanie. Branch-and-Bound Applications in Combinatorial Data Analysis. 2010. (Statistics & Computing Ser.). xii, 221p. pap. 109.00 *(978-1-4419-2039-3(0)*, 1441920390) Springer.

Bucher, Philipp, ed. Algorithms in Bioinformatics: 6th International Workshop, WABI 2006, Zurich, Switzerland, September 11-13, 2006, Proceedings. 2007. (Lecture Notes in Computer Science Ser.). (Illus.). 402p. per. 99.00 *(978-3-540-39583-6(0)*, 3540395830) Springer.

Bueso, J. L., et al. Algorithmic Methods in Non-Commutative Algebra: Applications to Quantum Groups. 2010. (Mathematical Modelling: Theory & Applications Ser.). 298p. pap. 129.00 *(978-90-481-6328-1(5)*, 9048163285) Springer.

Buhler, J. P. & Stevenhagen, P., eds. Algorithmic Number Theory: Lattices, Number Fields, Curves & Cryptography. 2011. (Mathematical Sciences Research Institute Publications). (ENG.). 664p. pap. 60.00 *(978-0-521-20833-8(5))* Cambridge Univ. Pr.

Buhler, Joe P. & Stevenhagen, P. Algorithmic Number Theory: Lattices, Number Fields, Curves & Cryptography. Buhler, Joe & Stevenhagen, Peter, eds. 2008. (Mathematical Sciences Research Institute Publications). (ENG., Illus.). 662p. 104.00 *(978-0-521-80854-5(5))* Cambridge Univ. Pr.

Burgin, Mark. Measuring Power of Algorithms, Programs & Automata. 2009. 79.00 *(978-1-60692-381-8(1))* Nova Science Pubs., Inc.

—Super-Recursive Algorithms. 2010. (Monographs in Computer Science Ser.). (Illus.). xiv, 306p. pap. 99.00 *(978-1-4419-3060-6(4)*, 1441930604) Springer.

Byrne, Charles L. Applied Iterative Methods. 2007. (ENG.). 400p. 85.00 *(978-1-56881-342-4(2))* AK Peters, Ltd.

Cai, Jin-Yi, et al. Theory & Applications of Models of Computation: Third International Conference, TAMC 2006, Beijing, China, May 15-20, 2006, Proceedings. 2006. (Lecture Notes in Computer Science Ser.: Vol. 3959). (Illus.). XV, 794p. pap. 139.00 *(978-3-540-34021-8(1)*, 3540340211) Springer.

Calamoneri, Tiziana, et al. Algorithms & Complexity: 6th Italian Conference, CIAC 2006, Rome, Italy, May 29-31, 2006, Proceedings. 2006. (Lecture Notes in

Computer Science Ser.: Vol. 3998). (Illus.). XII, 394p. pap. 89.95 (978-3-540-34375-2(X), 354034375X) Springer.

Caramia, Massimiliano & Dell'Olmo, Paolo. Effective Resource Management in Manufacturing Systems: Optimization Algorithms for Production Planning. 2010. (Springer Series in Advanced Manufacturing Ser.). (Illus.). xxii, 216p. pap. 219.00 (978-1-84996-542-2(0), 1849965420) Springer.

Casanova, Henri, et al. Parallel Algorithms. 2008. (Chapman & Hall/CRC Numerical Analysis & Scientific Computing Ser.). (ENG., Illus.). 360p. (C). 87.95 (978-1-58488-945-8(4), Chapman & Hall/CRC) CRC Pr. LLC.

Chakraborty, Soubhik & Kumar Sourabh, Suman. A Computer Experiment Oriented Approach to Algorithmic Complexity. 2010. 192p. pap. (978-3-8383-7743-8(5)) Lambert Academic Publishing.

Challa, Subhash, et al. Fundamentals of Object Tracking. 2011. (ENG., Illus.). 392p. 90.00 (978-0-521-87628-5(1)) Cambridge Univ. Pr.

Chan, Joseph, et al, eds. London Algorithmics 2008: Theory & Practice. 2009. (Illus.). 214p. pap. (978-1-904987-97-0(4)) College Pubns.

Chen, Bo, ed. Algorithmic Aspects in Information & Management: 6th International Conference, AAIM 2010, Weihai, China, July 19-21, 2010. Proceedings. 2010. (Lecture Notes in Computer Science / Information Systems & Applications, incl. Internet/Web, & HCI Ser.). xi, 336p. pap. 83.00 (978-3-642-14354-0(7), 3642143547) Springer.

Chen, Bo, et al. Combinatorics, Algorithms, Probabilistic & Experimental Methodologies: First International Symposium, ESCAPE 2007 Hangzhou, China, April 7-9, 2007 Revised Selected Papers. 2007. (Lecture Notes in Computer Science Ser.). (Illus.). 530p. pap. 99.00 (978-3-540-74449-8(5)) Springer.

Cheng Siu-Wing Staff. Delaunay Meshing of Surfaces & Volumes Algorithms & Mathemat. 2012. (Chapman & Hall/CRC Computer & Information Science Ser.). (ENG., Illus.). 352p. 89.95 (978-1-58488-730-0(3), Chapman & Hall/CRC) CRC Pr. LLC.

Ching, Wai Ki & Ng, Michael K. Markov Chains: Models, Algorithms & Applications: Models, Algorithms & Applications. 2010. (International Series in Operations Research & Management Science Ser.). (Illus.). xiv, 208p. pap. 144.00 (978-1-4419-3986-9(5), 1441939865) Springer.

Chinneck, John W. Feasibility & Infeasibility in Optimization: Algorithms & Computational Methods. 2007. (International Series in Operations Research & Management Science Ser.). (Illus.). 286p. 129.00 (978-0-387-74931-0(4), 0387749314) Springer.

—Feasibility & Infeasibility in Optimization: Algorithms & Computational Methods. 2010. (International Series in Operations Research & Management Science Ser.). (Illus.). xxii, 274p. pap. 129.00 (978-1-4419-4519-8(9), 1441945199) Springer.

Chiong, Raymond, ed. Nature-Inspired Algorithms for Optimisation. 2009. (Studies in Computational Intelligence Ser.). (ENG., Illus.). xviii, 536p. 269.00 (978-3-642-00266-3(8)) Springer.

—Nature-Inspired Informatics for Intelligent Applications & Knowledge Discovery: Implications in Business, Science, & Engineering. 2009. 500p. 180.00 (978-1-60566-705-8(6)) IGI Global.

Chirikjian, Gregory S., et al, eds. Algorithmic Foundation of Robotics VIII: Selected Contributions of the Eight International Workshop on the Algorithmic Foundations of Robotics. 2010. (Springer Tracts in Advanced Robotics Ser.). (ENG., Illus.). xxvi, 680p. 279.00 (978-3-642-00311-0(7), 3642003117) Springer.

Ciulla, Carlo. Improved Signal & Image Interpolation in Biomedical Applications: The Case of Magnetic Resonance Imaging (MRI) 2009. 640p. 225.00 (978-1-60566-202-2(X)) IGI Global.

Cohen, A. Algorithms in Algebra. 2008. (London Mathematical Society Student Texts: Vol. 30). (Illus.). 250p. (C). 59.95 (978-0-521-43046-3(1)); pap. 22.95 (978-0-521-43630-4(3)) Cambridge Univ. Pr.

Cokuslu, Deniz, et al. Topology Control for Mobile Ad Hoc Networks. 2010. 100p. pap. (978-3-639-25703-8(0)) VDM Verlag Dr. Mueller e.K.

Consoli. Sensorless Control of Ac Motor Drives. 2007. (Synthesis Lectures on Power Electronics Ser.). 40.00 (978-1-59829-278-7(1)) Morgan & Claypool Pubs.

Cormen, Thomas H. & Cormen, T. Introduction to Algorithms. 3rd ed. 2009. (ENG., Illus.). 1312p. pap. 70.00 (978-0-262-53305-8(7)) MIT Pr.

Cormen, Thomas H., et al. Introduction to Algorithms. 3rd ed. 2009. (ENG., Illus.). 1312p. 92.00 (978-0-262-03384-8(4)) MIT Pr.

Crabtree, John. Atomic Reaction Mapping. 2008. 92p. pap. (978-3-639-07358-4(4)) VDM Verlag Dr. Mueller e.K.

Crainic, Teodor Gabriel & Roucairol, Catherine. Parallel Branch & Bound: Algorithms & Libraries. 2010. (ENG.). 300p. 69.95 (978-0-471-74044-5(6), Wiley-Interscience) Wiley, John & Sons, Inc.

Cram101 Textbook Reviews. Outlines & Highlights for Algorithm Design by Jon Kleinberg. 2010. 382p. pap. 34.95 (978-1-4288-5318-8(9)) Cram101 Inc.

Cram101 Textbook Reviews & Cram101 Textbook Reviews. Outlines & Highlights for MacHine Learning: An Algorithmic Perspective by Stephen Marsland, ISBN. 2011. 224p. pap. 30.95 **(978-1-61744-965-9(2))** Cram101 Inc.

Cyganek, Boguslaw & Siebert, J. Paul. An Introduction to 3D Computer Vision Techniques & Algorithms. 2009. (ENG., Illus.). 504p. 140.00 (978-0-470-01704-3(X), Wiley) Wiley, John & Sons, Inc.

Dalkiliç, Gökhan. Statistical Properties of Turkish Words. 2010. 140p. pap. (978-3-8383-5158-2(4)) Lambert Academic Publishing.

Dasgupta, Sanjoy, et al. Algorithms. 2006. (ENG., Illus.). 336p. (C). per. 45.33 (978-0-07-352340-8(2), 0073523402, McGraw-Hill Science, Engineering & Mathematics) McGraw-Hill Higher Education.

Daykin, J., et al, eds. London Algorithmics & Stringology 2006. 2007. (Illus.). vii, 213p. pap. (978-1-904987-41-3(9)) College Pubns.

De Bruyne, Steven. Process, Data & Classifier Models for Accessible Supervised Classification Problem Solving. 2010. (ENG.). 178p. pap. 44.00 (978-90-5487-750-9(2)) VUB Univ. Pr. BEL. Dist: Independent Pubs. Group.

De Koninck, Jean-Marie & Luca, Florian. Analytic Number Theory: Exploring the Anatomy of Integers. 2012. (Graduate Studies in Mathematics Ser.). 420p. 75.00 **(978-0-8218-7577-3(9))** American Mathematical Society.

Deck, Wendall C. Target Tracking with the Zero Instruction Set Computer. 2010. 184p. pap. (978-3-639-22693-5(3)) VDM Verlag Dr. Mueller e.K.

Dehne, Frank, et al, eds. Algorithms & Data Structures: 12th International Symposium, WADS 2011, New York, NY, USA, August 15-17, 2011, Proceedings. 2011. (Lecture Notes in Computer Science / Theoretical Computer Science & General Issues Ser.). (ENG., Illus.). xv, 718p. pap. 131.00 **(978-3-642-22299-3(4)**, 3642222994) Springer.

Delmas, Jean-Francois & Jourdain, Benjamin. Es Aléatoires: Applications Aux Sciences de L'ingénieur et Du Vivant (Mathématiques et Applications) 2006. (Mathématiques et Applications Ser.). (Illus.). XV, 433p. pap. 109.00 (978-3-540-33282-4(0), 3540332820) Springer.

Demetrescu, Camil, et al, eds. The Shortest Path Problem: Ninth DIMACS Implementation Challenge. 2009. (DIMACS: Ser. in Discrete Mathematics & Theoretical Computer Science Ser.). (Illus.). 319p. 104.00 (978-0-8218-4383-3(4)) American Mathematical Society.

Dey, Tamal K. Curve & Surface Reconstruction: Algorithms with Mathematical Analysis. 2006. (Cambridge Monographs on Applied & Computational Mathematics: Vol. 23). (ENG., Illus.). 232p. 83.00 (978-0-521-86370-4(8)) Cambridge Univ. Pr.

Dhake, Pravin. Autonomous Vehicle Test Bed. 2011. 104p. pap. **(978-3-8443-9866-3(X))** Lambert Academic Publishing.

Diaz, Josep & Calamoneri, Tiziana, eds. Algorithms & Complexity: 7th International Conference, CIAC 2010, Rome, Italy, May 26-28, 2010, Proceedings. 2010. (Lecture Notes in Computer Science / Theoretical Computer Science & General Issues Ser.). xi, 384p. pap. 83.00 (978-3-642-13072-4(0), 3642130720) Springer.

Dickenstein, Alicia, et al, eds. Algorithms in Algebraic Geometry. 2010. (IMA Volumes in Mathematics & its Applications Ser.). xii, 164p. pap. 119.00 (978-1-4419-2583-1(X), 144192583X) 2008. (IMA Volumes in Mathematics & its Applications Ser.: Vol. 146). 157p. 119.00 (978-0-387-75154-2(8)) Springer.

Diederich, Joachim, ed. Rule Extraction from Support Vector Machines. 2010. (Studies in Computational Intelligence Ser.). (Illus.). xii, 262p. pap. 179.00 (978-3-642-09463-7(5), 3642094635) Springer.

Dimitrov, Dimitar. Implementation of Signal Processing Algorithms on an Fpo. 2010. 84p. pap. (978-3-639-23035-2(3)) VDM Verlag Dr. Mueller e.K.

Diniz, Paulo S. R. Adaptive Filtering: Algorithms & Practical Implementation. 3rd ed. 2011. (ENG., Illus.). xxiv, 632p. pap. 109.00 (978-1-4419-4062-9(6), 1441940626) Springer.

Diwan, Piyush. Euclidean Distance Transform of 3d Images on L a R P B S Model. 2010. 60p. pap. (978-3-8383-7594-6(7)) Lambert Academic Publishing.

Dogancay, Kutluyil. Partial-Update Adaptive Signal Processing: Design Analysis & Implementation. 2008. (ENG., Illus.). 296p. 135.00 (978-0-12-374196-7(3), Academic Pr.) Elsevier Science & Technology Bks.

Dogancay, Kutluyil & Naylor, Patrick, eds. Adaptive Partial-Update & Sparse System Identification. 2007. 116p. per. 19.00 (978-977-5945-81-5(X)) Hindawi Publishing Corp.

Dorigo, Marco. Ant Colony Optimization & Swarm Intelligence. 2008. (Lecture Notes in Computer Science / Theoretical Computer Science & General Issues Ser.). (Illus.). xv, 416p. 89.95 (978-3-540-87526-0(3)) Springer.

Dorigo, Marco, et al, eds. Swarm Intelligence: 7th International Conference, ANTS 2010, Brussels, Belgium, September 8-10, 2010 Proceedings. 2010. (Lecture Notes in Computer Science / Theoretical Computer Science & General Issues Ser.). xviii, 582p. pap. 119.00 (978-3-642-15460-7(3), 3642154603) Springer.

Drechsler, Rolf. Evolutionary Algorithms for VLSI CAD. 2010. (ENG.). 196p. pap. 209.00 (978-1-4419-5040-6(0), 1441950400) Springer.

Edelsbrunner, Herbert & Harer, John L. Computational Topology: An Introduction. 2009. (Illus.). 241p. 59.00 (978-0-8218-4925-5(5)) American Mathematical Society.

El-Hajj, Wassim. A Distributed Hierarchical Energy-Efficient Scheme. 2010. 212p. pap. (978-3-8383-6388-2(4)) Lambert Academic Publishing.

Elloumi, Mourad & Zomaya, Albert Y. Algorithms in Computational Molecular Biology: Techniques, Approaches & Applications. 2011. (Wiley Series in Bioinformatics Ser.: 16). (ENG., Illus.). 1080p. 158.00 (978-0-470-50519-9(2), Wiley) Wiley, John & Sons, Inc.

Elomaa, Tapio, et al, eds. Algorithms & Applications: Essays Dedicated to Esko Ukkonen on the Occasion of His 60th Birthday. 2010. (Lecture Notes in Computer Science / Theoretical Computer Science & General Issues Ser.). x, 261p. pap. 72.00 (978-3-642-12475-4(5), 3642124755) Springer.

Emanet, Nahit. The Rectilinear Steiner Tree Problem. 2010. 116p. pap. (978-3-8383-4906-0(7)) Lambert Academic Publishing.

Erdmann, Jakob. Dynamischer Lastausgleich für Multi-Domain-Cluster: Prädiktive Algorithmen am Beispiel einer parallelen physikalischen Simulation. 2010. 68p. pap. (978-3-8364-6229-7(X)) VDM Verlag Dr. Mueller e.K.

Erdmann, Michael, et al, eds. Algorithmic Foundations of Robotics VI. 2010. (Springer Tracts in Advanced Robotics Ser.). xiii, 456p. pap. 189.00 (978-3-642-06513-2(9), 3642065139) Springer.

Erlebach, Thomas. Combinatorial & Algorithmic Aspects of Networking: Third Workshop, CAAN 2006, Chester, UK, July 2, 2006: Revised Papers. 2007. (Lecture Notes in Computer Science Ser.: Vol. 4235). (Illus.). VIII, 135p. pap. 69.95 (978-3-540-48822-4(7), 3540488227) Springer.

Erlebach, Thomas, et al, eds. Algorithms for Sensor Systems: 7th International Symposium on Algorithms for Sensor Systems, Wireless Ad Hoc Networks & Autonomous Mobile Entities, ALGOSENSORS 2011, Saarbrücken, Germany, September 8-9, 2011, Revised Selected Papers. 2012. (Lecture Notes in Computer Science / Computer Communication Networks & Telecommunications Ser.). (ENG., Illus.). x, 239p. pap. 72.00 **(978-3-642-28208-9(3)**, 3642282083) Springer.

Ertekin, Seyda. Algorithms for Efficient Learning Systems. 2009. 160p. pap. (978-3-639-21069-9(7)) VDM Verlag Dr. Mueller e.K.

Escalante, René & Raydan, Marcos. Alternating Projection Methods. 2011. (ENG.). 140p. pap. **(978-1-61197-193-4(4))** Society for Industrial and Applied Mathematics.

Even, Shimon. Graph Algorithms. 2nd ed. 2011. (ENG., Illus.). 208p. 90.00 **(978-0-521-51718-8(4))**; pap. 32.99 **(978-0-521-73653-4(6))** Cambridge Univ. Pr.

Faigle, Ulrich, et al. Algorithmic Principles of Mathematical Programming. 2010. (Texts in the Mathematical Sciences Ser.). 352p. pap. 119.00 (978-90-481-6117-1(7), 9048161177) Springer.

Fan, Chun-PO Steve. Analysis of Interval-Censored or Aggregated Point Process Dat. 2010. 112p. pap. (978-3-639-25254-5(3)) VDM Verlag Dr. Mueller e.K.

Fassbender, Heike. Symplectic Methods for the Symplectic Eigen-problem. 2010. (ENG.). 278p. pap. 154.00 (978-1-4419-3346-1(8), 1441933468) Springer.

Feder, Elie. Algorithmic Problems in the Braid Group. 2009. 84p. pap. (978-3-639-13898-6(8)) VDM Verlag Dr. Mueller e.K.

Fernandez-Maloigne, Christine, ed. Advanced Color Image Processing & Analysis. 2012. (ENG., Illus.). x, 489p. 179.00 (978-1-4419-6189-1(5), 1441961895) Springer.

Ferreira, Alfonso & Rolim, José, eds. Parallel Algorithms for Irregular Problems: State of the Art: State of the Art. 2010. (ENG.). 356p. pap. 199.00 (978-1-4419-4747-5(7), 1441947477) Springer.

Flum, J. & Grohe, M. Parameterized Complexity Theory. 2010. (Texts in Theoretical Computer Science. an EATCS Ser.). (Illus.). xiv, 493p. pap. 119.00 (978-3-642-06757-0(3), 3642067573) Springer.

Fomin, Fedor V. & Kratsch, Dieter. Exact Exponential Algorithms. 2010. (Texts in Theoretical Computer Science. an EATCS Ser.). (Illus.). xiv, 204p. 69.95 (978-3-642-16532-0(X), 364216532X) Springer.

Fournel, Thierry & Javidi, Bahram, eds. Information Optics & Photonics: Algorithms, Systems, & Applications. 2010. (ENG., Illus.). xv, 281p. 129.00 (978-1-4419-7379-5(6), 1441973796) Springer.

Frieze, Alan, et al, eds. Algorithms & Models for the Web-Graph: 8th International Workshop, WAW 2011, Atlanta, GA, USA, May 27-29, 2011, Proceedings. 2011. (Lecture Notes in Computer Science / Theoretical Computer Science & General Issues Ser.). (Illus.). ix, 127p. pap. 72.00 (978-3-642-21285-7(9), 3642212859) Springer.

Gabbay, Dov M. & Smets, Philippe, eds. Handbook of Defeasible Reasoning & Uncertainty Management Systems: Volume 5: Algorithms for Uncertainty & Defeasible Reasoning. 2010. (Handbook of Defeasible Reasoning & Uncertainty Management Systems Ser.). 524p. pap. 309.00 (978-90-481-5603-0(3), 9048156033) Springer.

Gama, Joao. On Combining Classification Algorithms. 2009. 200p. pap. (978-3-639-16746-7(5)) VDM Verlag Dr. Mueller e.K.

Gama, Joao & Gaber, Mohamed Medhat, eds. Learning from Data Streams: Processing Techniques in Sensor Networks. (ENG., Illus.). x, 244p. 2010. pap. 109.00 (978-3-642-09285-5(3), 3642092853) 2007. 109.00 (978-3-540-73678-3(6), 3540736786) Springer.

Gammerman, Alex & Shafer, Glenn. Algorithmic Learning in a Random World. 2010. (ENG., Illus.). xvi, 324p. pap. 124.00 (978-1-4419-3471-0(5), 1441934715) Springer.

Gaspers, Serge. Exponential Time Algorithms. 2010. 216p. pap. (978-3-639-21825-1(6)) VDM Verlag Dr. Mueller e.K.

Gebali, Fayez. Algorithms & Parallel Computing. 2011. (Wiley Series on Parallel & Distributed Computing Ser.: 82). (ENG., Illus.). 364p. 105.00 (978-0-470-90210-3(8), Wiley) Wiley, John & Sons, Inc.

Geem, Zong Woo. Recent Advances in Harmony Search Algorithm. 2010. (Studies in Computational Intelligence Ser.). (Illus.). viii, 176p. 159.00 (978-3-642-04316-1(X), 364204316X) Springer.

Geem, Zong Woo, ed. Harmony Search Algorithms for Structural Design: Theory & Applications. 2009. (Studies in Computational Intelligence Ser.). (ENG., Illus.). viii, 228p. 159.00 (978-3-642-03449-7(7), 3642034497) Springer.

Ghosh, Subir Kumar. Visibility Algorithms in the Plane. 2007. (ENG., Illus.). 332p. 122.99 (978-0-521-87574-5(9)) Cambridge Univ. Pr.

Giancarlo, Raffaele & Hannenhalli, Sridhar. Algorithms in Bioinformatics. 2007. (Lecture Notes in Computer Science Ser.). (Illus.). 432p. pap. 89.95 (978-3-540-74125-1(9)) Springer.

Gilbert, J. R. & Karlsson, R., eds. SWAT '90: 2nd Scandinavian Workshop on Algorithm Theory. Bergen, Norway, July 11-14, 1990. Proceedings. 2007. (Lecture Notes in Computer Science Ser.). 432p. per. 79.95 (978-3-540-52846-3(6)) Springer.

Goh, Chi-Keong & Tan, Kay Chen. Evolutionary Multi-objective Optimization in Uncertain Environments: Issues & Algorithms. 2009. (Studies in Computational Intelligence Ser.). (Illus.). xii, 272p. 199.00 (978-3-540-95975-5(0)) Springer.

Goldberg, Andrew & Zhou, Yunhong. Algorithmic Aspects in Information & Management: 5th International Conference, AAIM 2009, San Francisco, CA, USA, June 15-17, 2009, Proceedings. 2009. (Lecture Notes in Computer Science / Information Systems & Applications, incl. Internet/Web, & HCI Ser.). x, 327p. pap. 74.95 (978-3-642-02157-2(3), 3642021573) Springer.

Goldberg, Carolyn & Narayan, Deepak. A New Algorithm for the Management of Dermatofibrosarcoma Protuberans. 2011. 52p. pap. **(978-3-8433-9236-5(6))** Lambert Academic Publishing.

Goldreich, Oded, ed. Property Testing: Current Research & Surveys. 2010. (Lecture Notes in Computer Science / Theoretical Computer Science & General Issues Ser.). xi, 359p. pap. 83.00 (978-3-642-16366-1(1), 3642163661) Springer.

Goodrich & Guibas. Geometric Algorithms. Date not set. (Computer Science Ser.). (C). mass mkt. 49.95 (978-0-534-95069-9(8), Brooks/Cole) Brooks/Cole.

Gopi, E. S. Algorithm Collections for Digital Signal Processing Applications Using Matlab. (ENG.). xv, 190p. 2010. pap. 169.00 (978-90-481-7630-4(1), 9048176301) 2007. 169.00 (978-1-4020-6409-8(8), 1402064098) Springer.

Graph-Theoretic Concepts in Computer Science: 32nd International Workshop, WG 2006, Bergen, Norway, June 22-23, 2006, Revised Papers. 2007. (Lecture Notes in Computer Science Ser.). (Illus.). 358p. pap. 72.00 (978-3-540-48381-6(0)) Springer.

Greene, Daniel H. & Knuth, Donald E. Mathematics for the Analysis of Algorithms. 3rd ed. 2007. (Modern Birkhäuser Classics Ser.). (ENG., Illus.). x, 132p. pap. 44.95 (978-0-8176-4728-5(7), 0817647287) Birkhauser Verlag AG CHE. Dist: Springer.

Gu, Jun, et al. Algorithms for the Satisfiability Problem. 2008. 250p. 44.95 (978-0-521-64041-1(5)) Cambridge Univ. Pr.

Gurvits, Leonid, et al, eds. Randomization, Relaxation, & Complexity in Polynomial Equation Solving. 2011. (Contemporary Mathematics Ser.). (Illus.). 217p. pap. 79.00 **(978-0-8218-5228-6(0))** American Mathematical Society.

Habib, Michel, et al, eds. Probabilistic Methods for Algorithmic Discrete Mathematics. 2010. (Algorithms & Combinatorics Ser.). xvii, 323p. pap. 219.00 (978-3-642-08426-3(5), 3642084265) Springer.

Hanrot, Guillaume, et al. Algorithmic Number Theory: 9th International Symposium, ANTS-IX, Nancy, France, July 19-23, 2010, Proceedings. 2010. (Lecture Notes in Computer Science / Theoretical Computer Science & General Issues Ser.). xi, 397p. pap. 99.00 (978-3-642-14517-9(5), 3642145175) Springer.

Haque, Israat Tanzeena. Randomized Routing Algorithms in Mobile Ad Hoc Networks. 2009. 104p. pap. (978-3-639-14369-0(8)) VDM Verlag Dr. Mueller e.K.

Harel, David & Feldman, Yishai. Algorithmik: Die Kunst des Rechnens. Krieger-Hauwede, M., tr. 2009. 628p. pap. (978-3-642-04338-3(0)) Springer London, Ltd.

Heinze, Glenn. Evolutionary Algorithms Applied to Erds. 2010. 68p. pap. (978-3-8383-7947-0(0)) Lambert Academic Publishing.

Helten, Stephan. Algorithmen zur Berechnung kürzester Wege in Graphen: Optimierungen bei der Implementierung einer Suche für kürzeste Verbindungen zwischen Personen in einem sozialen Internet-Netzwerk. 2010. 120p. pap. (978-3-639-25028-2(1)) VDM Verlag Dr. Mueller e.K.

Hemaspaandra, Lane A. & Torenvliet, Leen. Theory of Semi-Feasible Algorithms. 2010. (Monographs in Theoretical Computer Science. an EATCS Ser.). (Illus.). x, 148p. pap. 99.00 (978-3-642-07581-0(9), 3642075819) Springer.

Hertling, Peter, et al, eds. Reliable Implementation of Real Number Algorithms: Theory & Practice. 2008. (Lecture Notes in Computer Science Ser.). (Illus.). 237p. pap. 69.95 (978-3-540-85520-0(3)) Springer.

Hromkovic, J. Design & Analysis of Randomized Algorithms: Introduction to Design Paradigms. 2010. (Texts in Theoretical Computer Science. an EATCS Ser.). xii, 284p. pap. 74.95 (978-3-642-06300-8(4), 3642063004) Springer.

Hsu, David, et al, eds. Algorithmic Foundations of Robotics IX: Selected Contributions of the Ninth International Workshop on the Algorithmic Foundations of Robotics. 2010. (Springer Tracts in Advanced Robotics Ser.). 392p. 159.00 (978-3-642-17451-3(5), 3642174515) Springer.

Hutter, Marcus. Universal Artificial Intelligence: Sequential Decisions Based on Algorithmic Probability. 2010. (Texts in Theoretical Computer Science. an EATCS Ser.). xx, 280p. pap. 109.00 (978-3-642-06052-6(8), 3642060528) Springer.

Hyer, Tom. Derivatives Algorithms Vol. 1: Bones. 2010. 320p. 58.00 (978-981-4289-80-1(9)) World Scientific Publishing Co., Inc.

Iatan, Iuliana. Statistical Methods for Pattern Recognition. 2010. 176p. pap. (978-3-8383-5147-6(9)) Lambert Academic Publishing.

IEEE Staff. International Conference on Tools with Artificial Intelligence: 19th: 2007: Patras, Greece, 2 vols. 2007. 1118p. pap. 344.00 (978-0-7695-3015-4(X)) IEEE Computer Society Pr.

—2007 Signal Processing Algorithms, Architectures, Arrangements, & Applications. 2007. pap. 180.00 (978-1-4244-1514-4(4)) IEEE.

Iliopoulos, Costas S. & Smyth, William F., eds. Combinatorial Algorithms: 21st International Workshop, IWOCA 2010, London, UK, July 26-28, 2010, Revised Selected Papers. 2011. (Lecture Notes in Computer Science / Theoretical Computer Science & General Issues Ser.). (Illus.). xi, 418p. pap. 95.00 (978-3-642-19221-0(1), 3642192211) Springer.

Iliopoulos, Costas S. & Smyth, William F., eds. Combinatorial Algorithms: 22th International Workshop, IWOCA 2011, Victoria, Canada, July 20-22, 2011, Revised Selected Papers. 2012. (Lecture Notes in Computer Science / Theoretical Computer Science & General Issues Ser.). (ENG., Illus.). xi, 387p. pap. 83.00 **(978-3-642-25010-1(6)**, 3642250106) Springer.

Indoor Localisation: State of the Art & Novel Algorithms. 2010. 152p. pap. *(978-3-8383-4429-4(4))* Lambert Academic Publishing.

Iske, Armin & Levesley, Jeremy. Algorithms for Approximation: Proceedings of the 5th International Conference, Chester, July 2005. 2010. (ENG., Illus.). xiv, 389p. pap. 129.00 *(978-3-642-06994-9(0)*, 3642069940) Springer.

Jachan, Michael. Time-Frequency-Autoregressive-Moving-Average Modeling. 2008. 168p. per. *(978-3-8364-6532-8(9))* VDM Verlag Dr. Mueller e.K.

Jackson, Philip. Selected Works. 2010. (Illus.). 156p. pap. 24.50 *(978-1-4452-7964-0(9))* Lulu Enterprises Inc.

Jaeger, Michael. Self-Managing Publish/Subscribe Systems. 2008. 320p. pap. *(978-3-639-07363-8(0))* VDM Verlag Dr. Mueller e.K.

Janssen, Erwin & van Roermund, Arthur. Look-Ahead Based Sigma-Delta Modulation. 2011. (Analog Circuits & Signal Processing Ser.). (Illus.). xii, 247p. 129.00 *(978-94-007-1386-4(X)*, 940071386X) Springer.

Janssen, Jeannette, ed. Combinatorial & Algorithmic Aspects of Networking: 4th Workshop, CAAN 2007, Halifax, Canada, August 14, 2007, Revised Papers. 2008. (Lecture Notes in Computer Science Ser.). (Illus.). 148p. pap. 59.95 *(978-3-540-77293-4(6))* Springer.

Jouannaud, J., ed. Rewriting Techniques & Applications: Dijon, France, May 20-22, 1985. 2007. (Lecture Notes in Computer Science Ser.). 452p. per. 49.95 *(978-3-540-15976-6(2))* Springer.

Jozefowska, Joanna & Weglarz, Jan, eds. Perspectives in Modern Project Scheduling. 2010. (International Series in Operations Research & Management Science Ser.). (Illus.). xxii, 444p. pap. 149.00 *(978-1-4419-4144-2(4)*, 1441941444) Springer.

Kamvar, S. Numerical Algorithms for Personalized Search in Self-Organizing Information Networks. 2010. (ENG., Illus.). 160p. (C). 45.00 *(978-0-691-14503-7(2))* Princeton Univ. Pr.

Kao, Ming-Yang, ed. Encyclopedia of Algorithms. 2008. (Springer Reference Ser.). (Illus.). 1100p. 399.00 *(978-0-387-30770-1(2)*, 0387307702); 1220p. E-Book 499.00 *(978-0-387-36061-4(1)*, 0387360611) Springer.

Karayiannis, Nicolaos & Venetsanopoulos, Anastasios N. Artificial Neural Networks: Learning Algorithms, Performance Evaluation, & Applications. 2010. (Springer International Series in Engineering & Computer Science Ser.). 460p. pap. 269.00 *(978-1-4419-5132-8(6)*, 1441951326) Springer.

Kartsakli, Elli, et al. Contention-Based Collision-Resolution Medium Access Control Algorithms. 2009. pap. 39.00 *(978-1-60692-580-5(6))* Nova Science Pubs., Inc.

KATOH, Naoki & Kumar, Amit, eds. WALCOM: Algorithms & Computation: 5th International Workshop, WALCOM 2011, New Delhi, India, February 18-20, 2011, Proceedings. 2011. (Lecture Notes in Computer Science / Theoretical Computer Science & General Issues Ser.). (Illus.). xi, 233p. pap. 72.00 *(978-3-642-19093-3(6)*, 3642190936) Springer.

Kemper, Jens. Computation of invariant measures with dimension reduction Methods. 2010. 158p. pap. *(978-3-8325-2452-4(5))* Logos Verlag Berlin.

Khashan, Osama. Implementing Rc5 Encryption Algorithm. 2010. 96p. pap. *(978-3-639-24323-9(4))* VDM Verlag Dr. Mueller e.K.

Kim, Jusub. Volume Rendering: Out-of-Core Algorithms & Parallel Rendering. 2008. (Illus.). 116p. pap. *(978-3-639-09572-2(3))* VDM Verlag Dr. Mueller e.K.

Kimitei, Symon. Algorithms for Toeplitz Matrices with Applications to Image Deblurring. 2011. 84p. pap. ***(978-3-8443-1426-7(1))*** Lambert Academic Publishing.

Kirchner, C., ed. Rewriting Techniques & Applications: 5th International Conference, RTA-93, Montreal, Canada, June 16-18, 1993. Proceedings, 5th. 2007. 512p. per. 69.95 *(978-3-540-56868-1(9))* Springer.

Klazar, Martin, et al. Combinatorics, Graph Theory, Algorithms & Applications: 6th Czech-Slovak International Symposium, Dedicated to Jarik Nešetřil on the Occasion of His 60th Birthday Prague, July 10-15 2006. 2006. (Algorithms & Combinatorics Ser.: Vol. 26). (Illus.). xvi, 627p. 139.00 *(978-3-540-33698-3(2)*, 3540336982) Springer.

Knuth, D.E. Axioms & Hulls. 2007. (Lecture Notes in Computer Science Ser.). 128p. per. 69.95 *(978-3-540-55611-4(7))* Springer.

Kohlas, Juerg & Pouly, Marc. Generic Inference: A Unifying Theory for Automated Reasoning. 2011. (ENG., Illus.). 484p. 110.00 *(978-0-470-52701-6(3)*, Wiley) Wiley, John & Sons, Inc.

Kokkinakis, Kostas & Loizou, Philip. Advances in Modern Blind Signal Separation Algorithms. 2010. (Synthesis Lectures on Algorithms & Software in Engineering Ser.). 100p. pap. 40.00 *(978-1-60845-106-7(2))* Morgan & Claypool Pubs.

Kontogiannis, Spyros, et al, eds. Algorithmic Game Theory: Third International Symposium, SAGT 2010, Athens, Greece, October 18-20, 2010, Proceedings. 2010. (Lecture Notes in Computer Science / Information Systems & Applications, incl. Internet/Web, & HCI Ser.). viii, 359p. pap. 83.00 *(978-3-642-16169-8(3)*, 3642161693) Springer.

Konur, Umut. 3d Mesh Geometry Compression with a Set Partitioning Approach. 2010. 60p. pap. *(978-3-8383-1741-0(6))* Lambert Academic Publishing.

Kosakowski, Adrian. Control System Design for Stirling Engine. 2010. 100p. pap. *(978-3-639-25793-9(6))* VDM Verlag Dr. Mueller e.K.

Kotsireas, Ilias S., et al. D-Optimal Matrices. 2013. (SpringerBriefs in Optimization Ser.). (ENG., Illus.). iv, 104p. pap. 49.95 *(978-1-4419-9343-4(6)*, 1441993436) Springer.

Královic, Rastislav & Niwinski, Damian. Mathematical Foundation of Computer Science 2009: 34th International Symposium, MFCS 2009, Novy Smokovec, High Tatras, Slovakia, August 24-28, 2009, Proceedings. 2009. (Lecture Notes in Computer Science / Theoretical Computer Science & General Issues Ser.). xv, 760p. pap. 139.00 *(978-3-642-03815-0(8)*, 3642038158) Springer.

Kralovic, Richard & Hromkovic, Juraj, eds. Stochastic Algorithms: Foundations & Applications. 2007. (Lecture Notes in Computer Science Ser.). (Illus.). 165p. pap. 69.95 *(978-3-540-74870-0(9))* Springer.

Kroening, Daniel & Strichman, Ofer. Decision Procedures: An Algorithmic Point of View. 2010. (Texts in Theoretical Computer Science. an EATCS Ser.). (Illus.). xvi, 304p. pap. 69.95 *(978-3-642-09344-9(2)*, 3642093442) Springer.

Kulkarni, Sandeep & Schiper, André. Stabilization, Safety, & Security of Distributed Systems: 10th International Symposium, SSS 2008, Detroit, MI, USA, November 21-23, 2008, Proceedings. 2008. (Lecture Notes in Computer Science / Theoretical Computer Science & General Issues Ser.). x, 265p. pap. 69.95 *(978-3-540-89334-9(2))* Springer.

Laurent, Anne & Lesot, Marie-Jeanne, eds. Scalable Fuzzy Algorithms for Data Management & Analysis: Methods & Design. 2009. (Illus.). 380p. 180.00 *(978-1-60566-858-1(3))* IGI Global.

Lavrov, Igor & Maksimova, Larisa. Problems in Set Theory, Mathematical Logic & the Theory of Algorithms. Corsi, Giovanna, ed. Shehtman, Valentin, tr. from RUS. 2007. (University Series in Mathematics). (Illus.). 282p. 229.00 *(978-0-306-47712-6(2)*, 0306477122) Springer.

Lawhead, Pamela & Ferguson, David. Sun Certified Java Programmer Data Structures & Algorithms Lab Manual. 2010. (ENG.). 78p. (C). pap. 60.00 *(978-0-558-75821-9(5))* Pearson Learning Solutions.

Lebedeva, Ekaterina. Hypertree Decompositions for Combinatorial Auctions - Optimal Winner Determination. 2008. 80p. pap. *(978-3-639-02231-5(9))* VDM Verlag Dr. Mueller e.K.

Leiss, Ernst L. A Programmer's Companion to Algorithm Analysis. 2006. (ENG., Illus.). 255p. per. 59.95 *(978-1-58488-673-0(0)*, Chapman & Hall/CRC) CRC Pr. LLC.

Lerner, Jürgen, et al. Algorithmic of Large & Complex Networks. 2009. (Lecture Notes in Computer Science / Theoretical Computer Science & General Issues Ser.). (ENG.). x, 401p. pap. 81.00 *(978-3-642-02093-3(3)*, 3642020933) Springer.

Lescanne, Pierre. Rewriting Techniques & Applications: Bordeaux, France, May 25-27, 1987. Proceedings. 2007. (Lecture Notes in Computer Science Ser.). 296p. per. 39.95 *(978-3-540-17220-8(3))* Springer.

Leshik, Edward & Cralle, Jane. An Introduction to Algorithmic Trading: Basic to Advanced Strategies. 2nd ed. 2011. (Wiley Trading Ser.: 525). (ENG., Illus.). 272p. 80.00 *(978-0-470-68954-7(4)*, Wiley) Wiley, John & Sons, Inc.

Levitin, Anany & Levitin, Maria. Algorithmic Puzzles, 1 vol. 2011. (ENG., Illus.). 280p. pap. 21.95 *(978-0-19-974044-4(5))* Oxford Univ. Pr., Inc.

Li, Xiaoyun. Topology Discovery Using Binary Connectivity Information. 2010. 108p. pap. *(978-3-8383-6934-1(3))* Lambert Academic Publishing.

Li, Zhilin. Algorithmic Foundation of Multi-Scale Spatial Representation. 2006. (ENG., Illus.). 281p. 124.95 *(978-0-8493-9072-2(9)*, CRC Press) Taylor & Francis Group GBR. Dist: Taylor & Francis Group.

Liang, Yizeng & Xu, Qing-Song. Support Vector Machines & Their Application in Chemistry & Biotechnology. 2011. (ENG., Illus.). 211p. 119.95 *(978-1-4398-2127-5(5)*, CRC Press) Taylor & Francis Group GBR. Dist: Taylor & Francis Group.

Lohaka, Hippolyte. Making a Grouped-Data Frequency Table. 2009. 292p. pap. *(978-3-639-16781-8(3))* VDM Verlag Dr. Mueller e.K.

Loizou, Christos & Pattichis, Costas. Despeckle Filtering Algorithms. 2008. (Synthesis Lectures on Algorithms & Software in Engineering Ser.). (Illus.). 100p. pap. 40.00 *(978-1-59829-620-4(5))* Morgan & Claypool Pubs.

Lu, Hsiao-Feng, ed. Applied Algebra, Algebraic Algorithms & Error-Correcting Codes. 2007. (Lecture Notes in Computer Science Ser.). 368p. pap. 79.95 *(978-3-540-77223-1(5))* Springer.

Lu, Linghai. Inverse Modelling & Inverse Simulation for Engineering Applications. 2010. 236p. pap. *(978-3-8383-3733-3(6))* Lambert Academic Publishing.

Luk, Franklin T. Advanced Signal Processing Algorithms, Architectures, & Implementations XVII: 26-27 August 2007, San Diego, California, USA. 2007. (Proceedings of SPIE Ser.). (Illus.). 302p. pap. 80.00 *(978-0-8194-6845-1(2))* SPIE.

Luszczek, Piotr. Improving Performance of Sparse Numerical Linear Algebra Computations. 2010. 84p. pap. *(978-3-8383-3469-1(8))* Lambert Academic Publishing.

Lysaght, Patrick & Rosenstiel, Wolfgang, eds. New Algorithms, Architectures & Applications for Reconfigurable Computing. 2010. (ENG.). xvii, 313p. pap. 179.00 *(978-1-4419-5264-6(0)*, 1441952640) Springer.

Ma, Zhongxia & Klette, Reinhard. Object Segmentation in Depth Maps. 2011. 136p. pap. ***(978-3-8443-2367-2(8))*** Lambert Academic Publishing.

MacHanja, Addmore & B. Bajic, Vladimir. Towards Chereme Based Dynamic Sign Language Gesture Recognition System. 2011. 144p. pap. ***(978-3-8443-1871-5(2))*** Lambert Academic Publishing.

Maheshwari, Uma & Rebello, Santhosh. Fundamental Simulation Methodologies Dwelling in Neural Networks. 2011. 136p. pap. ***(978-3-8443-2579-9(4))*** Lambert Academic Publishing.

Maji, Pallab & Rath, Girija Sankar. Application of Residue Arithmetic. 2011. 92p. pap. ***(978-3-8454-1287-0(9))*** Lambert Academic Publishing.

Malcik, Martin. Fuzzy Approach to Hierarchical Clustering. 2011. 120p. pap. ***(978-3-8433-8864-1(4))*** Lambert Academic Publishing.

Malik, Aamir Saeed, et al. Depth Map & 3D Imaging Applications: Algorithms & Technologies. 2011. (Illus.). xv, 631p. ***(978-1-61350-328-7(8))***; ***(978-1-61350-326-3(1))***; E-Book ***(978-1-61350-327-0(X))*** IGI Global.

Mansoor Umair B. Quasi-Newton Least Mean Fourth Adaptive Algorithm. 2010. 104p. pap. *(978-3-639-26296-4(4))* VDM Verlag Dr. Mueller e.K.

Manyem, Prabhu. Routing Problems in Multicast Networks. 2010. 92p. pap. *(978-3-639-09363-6(1))* VDM Verlag Dr. Mueller e.K.

Markov, A. A. & Nagorny, N. M. The Theory of Algorithms. 2010. (Mathematics & its Applications Ser.). (ENG.). 400p. pap. 189.00 *(978-90-481-8453-8(3)*, 9048184533) Springer.

Mastorakis, Nikos E. Pathway Modeling & Algorithm Research. 2011. (Computer Science, Technology & Applications Ser.). 98.00 *(978-1-61122-757-4(7))* Nova Science Pubs., Inc.

Mathematical Foundations of Computer Science. 2008. (Lecture Notes in Computer Science / Theoretical Computer Science & General Issues Ser.). spiral bd. 109.00 *(978-3-540-85237-7(9))* Springer.

Matthew, Beauregard. Analysis of Elastic Filaments Conveying a Fluid & a Numerical Study: Weakly Nonlinear Analysis of Elastic Filaments Conveying a Fluid & Numerical Approximations to the Static Kirhhoff Equations. 2011. 120p. pap. ***(978-3-639-33621-4(6))*** VDM Verlag Dr. Mueller e.K.

Matti, Mukhlis. Exploring a Bioinformatics Clustering Algorithm - Methodology, Experiments, Analysis. 2008. 172p. pap. *(978-3-639-03335-9(3))* VDM Verlag Dr. Mueller e.K.

Mavronicolas, Marios & Papadoupoulou, Maria. Algorithmic Game Theory: Second International Symposium, SAGT 2009, Paphos, Cyprus, October 18-20, 2009, Proceedings. 2009. (Lecture Notes in Computer Science / Information Systems & Applications, incl. Internet/Web, & HCI Ser.). (Illus.). xi, 359p. pap. 83.00 *(978-3-642-04644-5(4)*, 3642046444) Springer.

McLachlan, Geoffrey J. The Em Algorithm & Extensions, Set. 2nd ed. 2009. (Wiley Series in Probability & Statistics Ser.: 829). (ENG.). 1264p. 355.00 *(978-0-470-55605-4(6)*, Wiley) Wiley, John & Sons, Inc.

McLachlan, Geoffrey J. & Krishnan, Thriyambakam. The EM Algorithm & Extensions. 2nd rev. ed. 2008. (Wiley Series in Probability & Statistics Ser.: 382) (ENG., Illus.). 400p. 137.00 *(978-0-471-20170-0(7)*, Wiley-Interscience) Wiley, John & Sons, Inc.

McMillan, Michael. Data Structures & Algorithms in C# 2007. (ENG., Illus.). 366p. (C). 119.00 *(978-0-521-87691-9(5))* Cambridge Univ. Pr.

—Data Structures & Algorithms Using C# 2007. (ENG., Illus.). 366p. (C). per. 53.99 *(978-0-521-67015-9(2))* Cambridge Univ. Pr.

Mendack, Sascha. Olap Without Cubes - Data Analysis in Non-Cube Systems. 2008. 72p. pap. *(978-3-639-03343-4(4))* VDM Verlag Dr. Mueller e.K.

Mesleh, Abdelwadood. Support Vector MacHine Text Classifier for Arabic Articles. 2010. 132p. pap. *(978-3-639-27141-6(6))* VDM Verlag Dr. Mueller e.K.

Mester, D., et al, eds. Discrete Optimization for TSP-like Genome Mapping Problems. 2010. (Genetics - Research & Issues Ser.). pap. 43.00 *(978-1-61668-170-8(5)*, Nova Biomedical Bks.) Nova Science Pubs., Inc.

Meurant, Gérard A. The Lanczos & Conjugate Gradient Algorithms: From Theory to Finite Precision Computations. 2006. (Software, Environments, Tools Ser.). (ENG., Illus.). 381p. pap. *(978-0-89871-616-0(0))* Society for Industrial and Applied Mathematics.

Michael, T. S. How to Guard an Art Gallery & Other Discrete Mathematical Adventures. 2009 (ENG., Illus.). 272p. (C). (gr. 13-17). 60.00 *(978-0-8018-9298-1(8))*; pap. 25.00 *(978-0-8018-9299-8(6))* Johns Hopkins Univ. Pr.

Michel, Robert. Flexray Applications in Control Loops Focussing on Steer-by-Wire Models. 2008. 108p. pap. *(978-3-639-02985-7(2))* VDM Verlag Dr. Mueller e.K.

Miller, Mirka & Koichi, Wada, eds. Proceedings of the International Workshop on Combinatorial Algorithms 2008. 2010. (Illus.). 280p. pap. *(978-1-904987-74-1(5))* College Pubns.

Mirzal, Andri. Nonnegative Matrix Factorizations for Clustering & Lsi. 2011. 152p. pap. ***(978-3-8443-2489-1(5))*** Lambert Academic Publishing.

Modersitzki, Jan. FAIR: Flexible Algorithms for Image Registration. 2009. (Fundamentals of Algorithms Ser.: 6). (ENG.). 210p. pap. 69.00 *(978-0-89871-690-0(X))* Society for Industrial and Applied Mathematics.

Mohamed, Amr. Utility-Based Resource & Qos Optimization in Packet Networks - Link & Network Level Optimization. 2008. 220p. pap. *(978-3-639-04446-1(0))* VDM Verlag Dr. Mueller e.K.

Mohamed, Yasser Abdelrady I. New Control Algorithms for the Distributed Generation Interface. 2009. 180p. pap. *(978-3-639-19692-4(9))* VDM Verlag Dr. Mueller e.K.

Mohyud-Din, Syed. Variational Iteration Techniques for Boundary Value Problems. 2010. 196p. pap. *(978-3-639-27664-0(7))* VDM Verlag Dr. Mueller e.K.

Molina Lopez, Francisco Javier. Three Clustering Algorithms & Their Application to Microarray Dat. 2010. 96p. pap. *(978-3-8383-4794-3(3))* Lambert Academic Publishing.

Monien, Burkhard. Algorithmic Game Theory: First International Symposium, SAGT 2008, Paderborn, Germany April 30-May 2, 2008. 2008. (Lecture Notes in Computer Science / Information Systems & Applications, incl. Internet/Web, & HCI Ser.). (Illus.). 374p. spiral bd. 79.95 *(978-3-540-79308-3(9)* 3540793089) Springer.

Monmarché, Nicolas, et al. Artificial Ants. 2010. (Iste Ser.: 474). (ENG., Illus.). 576p. 211.00 *(978-1-84821-194-0(5)*, Wiley-ISTE) Wiley, John & Sons, Inc.

Morel, John Henry. Nanogroup Quantum Notebook Series, the Holocomb Theory, Blank Lined. 2009. 160p. pap. 12.99 *(978-1-935436-70-6(8))* Rodaian Pr.

Mozgovoy, Maxim. Algorithms, Languages, Automata, & Compilers: A Practical Approach. 2009. (ENG.). 345p. 139.95 *(978-0-7637-7627-5(0))* Jones & Bartlett Learning, LLC.

Muhammad Asad, Syed. Variable Step-Size Least Mean Fourth Adaptive Algorithm. 2010. 112p. pap. *(978-3-639-24939-2(9))* VDM Verlag Dr. Mueller e.K.

Müller-Hannemann, Matthias & Schirra, Stefan, eds. Algorithm Engineering: Bridging the Gap Between Algorithm Theory & Practice. 2010. (Lecture Notes in Computer Science / Theoretical Computer Science & General Issues Ser.). xvi, 513p. pap. 107.00 *(978-3-642-14865-1(4)*, 3642148654) Springer.

Muruganathan, Siva & Sesay, Abu. Receiver Designs for Ofdm Systems with Space-Frequency Diversity. 2010. 184p. pap. *(978-3-8383-3909-2(6))* Lambert Academic Publishing.

Nagamochi, Hiroshi & Ibaraki, Toshihde. Algorithmic Aspects of Graph Connectivity. 2008. (Encyclopedia of Mathematics & its Applications Ser.). (ENG., Illus.). 392p. 99.00 *(978-0-521-87864-7(0))* Cambridge Univ. Pr.

Nahin, Paul J. Digital Dice: Computational Solutions to Practical Probability Problems. 2008. (ENG., Illus.). 276p. 27.95 *(978-0-691-12698-2(4))* Princeton Univ. Pr.

Naidoo, Richard(Ramu). Algorithms for Hyperbolic Systems & Applications. 2010. 148p. pap. *(978-3-639-27987-0(5))* VDM Verlag Dr. Mueller e.K.

Nakariyakul, Songyot. Feature Selection for Anomaly Detection in Hyperspectral Dat. 2009. 184p. pap. *(978-3-639-16828-0(3))* VDM Verlag Dr. Mueller e.K.

Namboodiri, Vinod. Algorithms. 2009. 128p. pap. *(978-3-639-15702-4(8))* VDM Verlag Dr. Mueller e.K.

Narayanappa, Sada. Geometric Routing. 2009. 132p. pap. *(978-3-639-20218-2(X))* VDM Verlag Dr. Mueller e.K.

Nazareth, John L. Differentiable Optimization & Equation Solving: A Treatise on Algorithmic Science & the Karmarkar Revolution. 2011. (CMS Books in Mathematics Ser.). (ENG., Illus.). xvii, 256p. pap. 99.00 *(978-1-4419-3061-3(2)*, 1441930612) Springer.

Neapolitan, Richard. Foundations of Algorithms using C++ Pseudocode, Third Edition. 3rd ed. 2008. (ENG.). 617p. pap. 116.95 *(978-0-7637-6354-1(3))* Jones & Bartlett Learning, LLC.

Neapolitan, Richard & Naimipour, Kumarss. Foundations of Algorithms. 4th rev. ed. 2009. 627p. 139.95 *(978-0-7637-8250-4(5))* Jones & Bartlett Learning, LLC.

Nguyen, Hung V. Content-Based Mining of Query Replacements. 2008. 76p. pap. *(978-3-639-09121-2(3))* VDM Verlag Dr. Mueller e.K.

Nguyen, Phong Q. & Vallée, Brigitte, eds. The LLL Algorithm: Survey & Applications. 2009. (Information Security & Cryptography Ser.). (ENG., Illus.). xiv, 496p. 159.00 *(978-3-642-02294-4(4)*, 3642022944) Springer.

Nicolae, Cristina. Identification & Resolution of Entity Mentions in Text. 2009. 74p. pap. *(978-3-639-17862-3(9))* VDM Verlag Dr. Mueller e.K.

Nierhaus, Gerhard. Algorithmic Composition. 2008. (ENG., Illus.). x, 287p. 69.95 *(978-3-211-75539-6(X)*, 321175539X) Springer.

Nishizeki, T. & Chiba, N. Planar Graphs: Theory & Algorithms. 2008. (Dover Books on Mathematics Ser.). (ENG.). 240p. pap. 15.95 *(978-0-486-46671-2(X))* Dover Pubns., Inc.

Ogihara, Mitsunori & Tarui, Jun, eds. Theory & Applications of Models of Computation: 8th Annual Conference, TAMC 2011, Tokyo, Japan, May 23-25, 2011, Proceedings. 2011. (Lecture Notes in Computer Science / Theoretical Computer Science & General Issues Ser.). (Illus.). xv, 564p. pap. 107.00 *(978-3-642-20876-8(2)*, 3642208762) Springer.

O'Gorman, Lawrence, et al. Practical Algorithms for Image Analysis with CD-ROM. 2nd ed. 2008. (ENG., Illus.). 360p. 68.00 incl. cd-rom *(978-0-521-88411-2(X))* Cambridge Univ. Pr.

Okun, Oleg. Supervised & Unsupervised Ensemble Methods & Their Applications. 2008. (Studies in Computational Intelligence Ser.). (C). 159.00 *(978-3-540-78980-2(4))* Springer.

Okun, Oleg, ed. Supervised & Unsupervised Ensemble Methods & their Applications. 2010. (Studies in Computational Intelligence Ser.). (Illus.). xiv, 180p. pap. 159.00 *(978-3-642-09776-8(6)*, 3642097766) Springer.

Okun, Oleg, et al, eds. Ensembles in Machine Learning Applications. 2011. (Studies in Computational Intelligence Ser.). (ENG., Illus.). xx, 252p. 129.00 ***(978-3-642-22909-1(3)***, 3642229093) Springer.

Omary, Zanifa. Classifier Workflow. 2010. 148p. pap. *(978-3-8383-4084-5(1))* Lambert Academic Publishing.

Osborne, M. R. Simplicial Algorithms for Minimizing Polyhedral Functions. 2011. (ENG., Illus.). 262p. pap. 50.00 ***(978-1-107-40350-5(2))*** Cambridge Univ. Pr.

Osipenko, George. Dynamical Systems, Graphs, & Algorithms. 2006. (Lecture Notes in Mathematics Ser.). (Illus.). 283p. pap. 69.95 *(978-3-540-35593-9(6)*, 3540355936) Springer.

Osman, Haitham. Evolutionary Algorithms. 2011. 160p. pap. ***(978-3-8443-1854-8(2))*** Lambert Academic Publishing.

Pach, Janos & Sharir, Micha. Combinatorial Geometry & Its Algorithmic Applications: The Alcalá Lectures. 2008. (Mathematical Surveys & Monographs). (Illus.). 235p. 77.00 *(978-0-8218-4691-9(4))* American Mathematical Society.

Palavuzlar, Mehper Cihangir. Random Variate Generation If the Density Is Not Known. 2010. 168p. pap. *(978-3-8383-6208-3(X))* Lambert Academic Publishing.

Pankaj K. Agarwal. Intersection & Decomposition Algorithms for Planar Arrangements. 2010. (ENG.). 293p. pap. 36.99 *(978-0-521-16847-2(3))* Cambridge Univ. Pr.

Paruchuri, Praveen, et al. Keep the Adversary Guessing: Agent Security by Policy Randomization. 2008. 120p. pap. *(978-3-639-01925-4(3))* VDM Verlag Dr. Mueller e.K.

Paulsen, Keith D., et al, eds. Alternative Breast Imaging: Four Model-Based Approaches. 2010. (Springer International Series in Engineering & Computer Science Ser.). (Illus.). xv, 253p. pap. 149.00 *(978-1-4419-3616-5(5)*, 1441936165) Springer.

Pavlu, Viktor. Shape-Based Alias Analysis. 2010. 132p. pap. *(978-3-639-24965-1(8))* VDM Verlag Dr. Mueller e.K.

Penumatcha, Sriram. On the Correlation Clustering Problem. 2010. 64p. pap. *(978-3-8383-1354-2(2))* Lambert Academic Publishing.

Persiano, Giuseppe, ed. Algorithmic Game Theory: 4th International Symposium, SAGT 2011, Amalfi, Italy, October 17-19, 2011. Proceedings. 2011. (Lecture Notes in Computer Science / Information Systems & Applications, incl. Internet/Web, & HCI Ser.). (ENG., Illus.). xi, 327p. pap. 83.00 ***(978-3-642-24828-3(4)**, 3642248284)* Springer.

Pfenning, Frank, ed. Term Rewriting & Applications: 17th International Conference, RTA 2006 Seattle, WA, USA, August 12-14, 2006 Proceedings. 2006. (Lecture Notes in Computer Science Ser.: Vol. 4098). (Illus.). 414p. pap. 99.00 *(978-3-540-36834-2(5)*, 3540368345) Springer.

Phaisangittisagul, Ekachai. Algorithms to Enhance MacHine Olfaction Performance. 2010. 144p. pap. *(978-3-639-27433-2(4))* VDM Verlag Dr. Mueller e.K.

Poorten, Alf J. van der. Algorithmic Number Theory. 2008. (Lecture Notes in Computer Science / Theoretical Computer Science & General Issues Ser.). spiral bd. 99.00 *(978-3-540-79455-4(7))* Springer.

Pralet, Cédric, et al. Sequential Decision-Making Problems: Representation & Solution. 2009. (Iste Ser.: 454). (ENG., Illus.). 384p. 158.00 *(978-1-84821-174-2(0)*, Wiley-ISTE) Wiley, John & Sons, Inc.

Principe, José C. Information Theoretic Learning: Renyi's Entropy & Kernel Perspectives. 2010. (Information Science & Statistics Ser.). (ENG., Illus.). xiv, 448p. 109.00 *(978-1-4419-1569-6(9)*, 1441915699) Springer.

Principe, José C., et al. Kernel Adaptive Filtering: A Comprehensive Introduction. 2010. (Adaptive & Learning Systems for Signal Processing, Communications & Control Ser.: 57). (ENG., Illus.). 209p. 105.00 *(978-0-470-44753-6(2)*, Wiley) Wiley, John & Sons, Inc.

Pytlak, Radosaw. Conjugate Gradient Algorithms in Nonconvex Optimization. 2008. (Nonconvex Optimization & Its Applications Ser.). (Illus.). 500p. 189.00 *(978-3-540-85633-7(1))* Springer.

Rahwan, Talal. Algorithms for Coalition Formation in Multi-Agent Systems. 2009. (Illus.). xiii, 118p. pap. 75.00 *(978-1-906124-14-4(0))* British Computer Society, The GBR. Dist: Turpin Distribution Services Ltd.

Ramachandran, Rohith. Real-Time Signal Processing Algorithms. 2009. 96p. pap. *(978-3-639-14070-5(2))* VDM Verlag Dr. Mueller e.K.

Ranganath, Venkatesh-Prasad. Program Dependences, Slicing, & Verification. 2010. 304p. pap. *(978-3-639-22803-8(0))* VDM Verlag Dr. Mueller e.K.

Rankenburg, Ivan. Application of the Difference Map Algorithm to Protein Structure Prediction. 2008. 204p. per. *(978-3-8364-7106-0(X))* VDM Verlag Dr. Mueller e.K.

Ren, Wei & Beard, Randal. Distributed Consensus in Multi-vehicle Cooperative Control: Theory & Applications. 2010. (Communications & Control Engineering Ser.). (Illus.). xvi, 319p. pap. 159.00 *(978-1-84996-701-3(6)*, 1849967016) Springer.

—Distributed Consensus in Multi-Vehicle Cooperative Control: Theory & Applications. 2007. (Communications & Control Engineering Ser.). (Illus.). 320p. 159.00 *(978-1-84800-014-8(6)*, 1848000146) Springer.

Rish, Irina. Sparse Modeling: Theory, Algorithms, & Applications. 2013. (ENG., Illus.). 250p. 79.95 *(978-1-4398-2869-4(5)*, CRC Press) Taylor & Francis Group GBR. Dist: Taylor & Francis Group.

Rivas-Davalos, Francisco. Evolutionary Algorithms for Power Distribution System Planning. 2010. 168p. pap. *(978-3-8383-7108-5(9))* Lambert Academic Publishing.

Roux, Alet. Options under Transaction Costs. 2008. 156p. pap. *(978-3-8364-9239-3(3))* VDM Verlag Dr. Mueller e.K.

Rößling, Guido. Animal-Farm: An Extensible Framework for Algorithm Visualization. 2008. 224p. pap. *(978-3-639-02776-1(0))* VDM Verlag Dr. Mueller e.K.

Rubtsov, Konstantin & ROMERIO, Giovanni. Hyperoperations for Science & Technology. 2011. 196p. pap. ***(978-3-8443-1516-5(0))*** Lambert Academic Publishing.

Rustin, Randall, ed. Combinatorial Algorithms, Vol. 9. 40.00 Algorithmics, Inc.

Sait, Sadiq M. Parallel Inverse Halftoning Via Look-up Table Partitioning. 2009. 120p. pap. *(978-3-639-05525-2(X))* VDM Verlag Dr. Mueller e.K.

Salman, Mohammad, et al. Adaptive Filters. 2010. 84p. pap. *(978-3-8383-7934-0(9))* Lambert Academic Publishing.

Satya, Ravi Vijaya. Algorithms for Haplotype Inference & Block Partitioning: Perfect Phylogeny Based Approaches for the Haplotype Inference Problem. 2008. 148p. pap. *(978-3-639-11097-5(8))* VDM Verlag Dr. Mueller e.K.

Schapire, Robert E. & Freund, Yoav. Boosting: Foundations & Algorithms. 2012. (Adaptive Computation & Machine Learning Ser.). (ENG., Illus.). 496p. (gr. 17). 50.00 ***(978-0-262-01718-3(0))*** MIT Pr.

Schmalz, Mark S. Mathematics for Signal & Information Processing: 2-5 August 2009, San Diego, California, United States. 2009. (Proceedings of SPIE Ser.). (Illus.). 400p. pap. 80.00 *(978-0-8194-7734-7(6))* SPIE.

Schmidt, E.M. & Skyum, S., eds. Algorithm Theory - SWAT '94: 4th Scandianvian Workshop on Algorithm Theory, Aarhus, Denmark, July 6-8, 1994. Proceedings. 2007. (Lecture Notes in Computer Science Ser.). 408p. per. 59.95 *(978-3-540-58218-2(5))* Springer.

Schweiger, F. The Metrical Theory of Jacobi-Perron Algorithm. 2008. (Lecture Notes in Mathematics Ser.). 124p. pap. 39.95 *(978-3-540-06388-9(9))* Springer.

Sedgewick & Wayne, Kevin. Algorithms. 4th ed. 2011. (ENG., Illus.). 976p. 79.99 *(978-0-321-57351-3(X))* Addison Wesley Professional.

Senawi, Mohd Yusoff. Building Energy Simulation. 2010. 196p. pap. *(978-3-639-27636-7(1))* VDM Verlag Dr. Mueller e.K.

Sepulchre, R., et al. Optimization Algorithms on Matrix Manifolds. 2007. (ENG., Illus.). 240p. (C). 60.00 *(978-0-691-13298-3(4))* Princeton Univ. Pr.

Shackell, John R. Symbolic Asymptotics. 2010. (Algorithms & Computation in Mathematics Ser.). (Illus.). xii, 243p. pap. 129.00 *(978-3-642-05925-4(2)*, 3642059252) Springer.

Shah, Devrarat & Wischik, Damon. Scheduling Algorithms for Switched Networks. 2012. (Synthesis Lectures on Communication Networks Ser.). 100p. pap. 40.00 *(978-1-60845-065-7(1))* Morgan & Claypool Pubs.

Shen, Ruijing, et al. Statistical Performance Analysis & Modeling Techniques for Nanometer VLSI Designs. 2012. (ENG., Illus.). 336p. 129.00 ***(978-1-4614-0787-4(7)**, 1461407877)* Springer.

Shilane, Philip. Shape Distinction for 3D Object Retrieval: Algorithms to Improve Three Dimensional Shape Retrieval by Identifying & Focusing on Distinctive Regions. 2008. 176p. pap. *(978-3-639-09143-4(4))* VDM Verlag Dr. Mueller e.K.

Shpilrain, Vladimir, et al. Group-Based Cryptography. 2008. (Advanced Courses in Mathematics Ser.). 183p. pap. 49.95 *(978-3-7643-8826-3(9))* Birkhauser Boston.

Sobh, Tarek, et al, eds. Novel Algorithms & Techniques in Telecommunications & Networking. 2010. (ENG., Illus.). xv, 517p. 249.00 *(978-90-481-3661-2(X)*, 904813661X) Springer.

Socha, Krzysztof. Ant Colony Optimisation for Continuous & ed-Variable Domains. 2009. 188p. pap. *(978-3-639-16433-6(4))* VDM Verlag Dr. Mueller e.K.

Solnon, Christine. Ant Colony Optimization & Constraint Programming. 2010. (Iste Ser.: 410). (ENG., Illus.). 320p. 142.00 *(978-1-84821-130-8(9)*, Wiley-ISTE) Wiley, John & Sons, Inc.

Soltys, Michael. An Introduction to the Analysis of Algorithms. 2009. 152p. 45.00 *(978-981-4271-40-0(3))* World Scientific Publishing Co., Inc.

Stadel, Joachim. Bounds for Monotone Algorithms. 2010. 96p. pap. *(978-3-639-23993-5(8))* VDM Verlag Dr. Mueller e.K.

Statnikov, Alexander. Gentle Introduction to Support Vector Machines in Biomedicine Vol. 1: Theory & Methods. 2011. 200p. 78.00 *(978-981-4324-38-0(8))* World Scientific Publishing Co., Inc.

Steinberg, Jordan M. Algorithms for the USMLE Step 3. 2015. (First Aid USMLE Ser.). (ENG., Illus.). 352p. pap. 30.00 *(978-0-07-150806-3(6)*, 0071508066) McGraw-Hill Medical Publishing Div.

Steinwart, Ingo & Christmann, Andreas. Support Vector Machines. 2008. (Information Science & Statistics Ser.). (Illus.). 602p. 129.00 *(978-0-387-77241-7(3))* Springer.

Stone, John D. Algorithms for Functional Programming. 2006. (Texts in Computer Science Ser.). 265p. 54.95 *(978-0-387-95570-4(4)*, 0387955704) Springer.

Stützle, Thomas, et al. Engineering Stochastic Local Search Algorithms. Designing, Implementing & Analyzing Effective Heuristics: International Workshop, SLS 2009, Brussels, Belgium, September 3-5, 2009, Proceedings. 2009. (Lecture Notes in Computer Science / Theoretical Computer Science & General Issues Ser.). (Illus.). x, 155p. pap. 69.95 *(978-3-642-03750-4(X)*, 364203750X) Springer.

Sun, Changming. Fast Algorithms for Stereo Matching. 2009. (Illus.). 290p. 54.95 *(978-0-387-95424-0(4)*, 0387954244) Springer.

Sun, Guilin. Development & Evaluation of Novel Fdtd Methods. 2010. 188p. pap. *(978-3-8383-3901-6(0))* Lambert Academic Publishing.

Sundaraj, Kenneth. Real-Time Soft Tissue Simulation. 2009. 152p. pap. *(978-3-639-13432-2(X))* VDM Verlag Dr. Mueller e.K.

Sung, Wing-Kin. Algorithms in Bioinformatics: A Practical Introduction. 2009. (Chapman & Hall/CRC Mathematical & Computational Biology Ser.). (ENG., Illus.). 407p. (C). 87.95 *(978-1-4200-7033-0(9)*, Chapman & Hall/CRC) CRC Pr. LLC.

Takács, Gergely & Roha-Ilkiv, Boris. Model Predictive Vibration Control: Efficient Constrained MPC Vibration Control for Lightly Damped Mechanical Structures. 2012. (ENG., Illus.). xxxvii, 515p. 229.00 ***(978-1-4471-2332-3(8)**, 1447123328)* Springer.

Tan, Liang. Numerical Evaluation of American Options. 2010. 176p. pap. *(978-3-8383-0442-7(X))* Lambert Academic Publishing.

Tapankov, Martin. Managing Dependencies in Knowledge-Based Systems. 2009. 80p. pap. *(978-3-639-18027-5(5))* VDM Verlag Dr. Mueller e.K.

Tapolcai, János. Routing Algorithms in Survivable Telecommunication Networks. 2010. 136p. pap. *(978-3-8383-9297-4(3))* Lambert Academic Publishing.

Tatu, Marta. Discovering Intentions in Text & Semantic Calculus Intention Overview, Classification, Representation, Discovery & Interactions with Other Semant. 2008. 132p. pap. *(978-3-639-07868-8(3))* VDM Verlag Dr. Mueller e.K.

Tempo, Roberto, et al. Randomized Algorithms for Analysis & Control of Uncertain Systems. 2010. (Communications & Control Engineering Ser.). (Illus.). xvii, 344p. pap. 169.00 *(978-1-84996-882-9(9)*, 1849968829) Springer.

Term Rewriting & Applications: 18th International Conference, Rta 2007, Paris, France, June 26-28, 2007, Proceedings. 2007. (Lecture Notes in Computer Science Ser.). (Illus.). 418p. per. 89.95 *(978-3-540-73447-5(3))* Springer.

Theocharidis, Athanasios. Ai Algorithms for a Prototype Game Software in Java 1. 2009. 100p. pap. *(978-3-639-17158-7(6))* VDM Verlag Dr. Mueller e.K.

Tillé, Yves. Sampling Algorithms. 2010. (Springer Series in Statistics Ser.). xi, 216p. pap. 129.00 *(978-1-4419-2155-0(9)*, 1441921559) Springer.

Tomczak, Jakub. Algorithms for Knowledge Extraction Using Relation Identification. 2010. 100p. pap. *(978-3-8383-6347-9(7))* Lambert Academic Publishing.

Tomita, Masaru. Efficient Parsing for Natural Language: A Fast Algorithm for Practical Systems. 2010. (Springer International Series in Engineering & Computer Science Ser.). 225p. pap. 179.00 *(978-1-4419-5198-4(9)*, 1441951989) Springer.

Treinen, Ralf. Rewriting Techniques & Applications: 20th International Conference, RTA 2009 Brasília, Brazil, June 29 - July 1, 2009 Proceedings. 2009. (Lecture Notes in Computer Science / Theoretical Computer Science & General Issues Ser.). xii, 391p. pap. 89.95 *(978-3-642-02347-7(9)*, 3642023479) Springer.

Tsitsiashvili, G. Sh, ed. Efficient Algorithms of Time Series Processing & Their Applications. 2008. 89.00 *(978-1-60692-062-6(6))* Nova Science Pubs., Inc.

Tso-Sutter, Karen H. L. Towards Metadata-Aware Algorithms for Recommender Systems. 2010. (Informationstechnologie Und Ökonomie Ser.). 134p. 43.95 *(978-3-631-59841-2(6))* Lang, Peter GmbH, Europaischer Verlag der Wissenschaften DEU. Dist: Lang, Peter.

Tyugu, E. Algorithms & architectures of artificial Intelligence. 2007. 117.00 *(978-1-58603-770-3(6))* IOS Pr., Inc.

Uspensky, Vladimir & Semenov, A. L. Algorithms: Main Ideas & Applications: Main Ideas & Applications. 2010. (Mathematics & Its Applications Ser.). 288p. pap. 299.00 *(978-90-481-4256-9(3)*, 9048142563) Springer.

Vasilenko, O. N. Number-Theoretic Algorithms in Cryptography. 2006. (Translations of Mathematical Monographs: Vol. 232). (RUS.). 243p. 92.00 *(978-0-8218-4090-0(8))* American Mathematical Society.

Verhaegh, W., et al, eds. Algorithms in Ambient Intelligence. 2010. (Philips Research Book Ser.). 354p. pap. 259.00 *(978-90-481-6490-5(7)*, 9048164907) Springer.

Vladimir, Konoplev & Al, Cheremensky. Aggregative Mechanics: Analysis of Multibody Systems. 2011. 136p. pap. ***(978-3-639-34302-1(6))*** VDM Verlag Dr. Mueller e.K.

Voicu, Mirela Catrinel. Algorithms on Relational Databases. 2010. 188p. pap. *(978-3-8383-9244-8(2))* Lambert Academic Publishing.

Wang, Yue. Vision-Based Lane Detection & Tracking Algorithm. 2009. 140p. pap. *(978-3-639-21391-1(2))* VDM Verlag Dr. Mueller e.K.

Wegener, Ingo. Complexity Theory: Exploring the Limits of Efficient Algorithms. Pruim, R., tr. 2010. (Illus.). xii, 308p. pap. 89.95 *(978-3-642-05914-8(7)*, 3642059147) Springer.

Weiss, Mark A. Data Structures & Algorithm Analysis in Java. 3rd rev. ed. 2011. (ENG.). 640p. (C). 129.00 ***(978-0-13-257627-7(9))*** Addison Wesley.

Welch, Jennifer & Walter, Jennifer. Link Reversal Algorithms. 2011. (Synthesis Lectures on Distributed Computing Theory Ser.). 100p. pap. 40.00 *(978-1-60845-041-1(4))* Morgan & Claypool Pubs.

Whiteson, Shimon. Adaptive Representations for Reinforcement Learning. 2010. (Studies in Computational Intelligence Ser.). (Illus.). 133p. 129.00 *(978-3-642-13931-4(0)*, 3642139310) Springer.

Wilson, Caroline L., ed. Clustering Algorithms & Mathematical Modeling. 2009. (Mathematics Research Developments Ser.). 116.10 *(978-1-61668-681-9(2))* Nova Science Pubs., Inc.

Woltzenlogel Paleo, Bruno. Herbrand Sequent Extraction. 2008. 92p. per. *(978-3-8364-6152-8(8))* VDM Verlag Dr. Mueller e.K.

Wu, Bin. Algorithm Design in Optical Networking. 2009. 240p. pap. *(978-3-639-17889-0(0))* VDM Verlag Dr. Mueller e.K.

Wu, Qiang, et al. Microscope Image Processing. 2008. (ENG., Illus.). 576p. 108.00 *(978-0-12-372578-3(X)*, Academic Pr.) Elsevier Science & Technology Bks.

Wu, Xiaoqing. Conquer Compiler Complexity. 2008. 172p. pap. *(978-3-8364-9856-2(1))* VDM Verlag Dr. Mueller e.K.

Xu, Hua. Data Analysis for Mass Spectrometry-Based Proteomics: Novel Data Analysis Methods & Algorithms forIdentification of Peptides & Proteins by Use ofTandem Mass Spectrometry. 2008. (Illus.). 236p. pap. *(978-3-639-10525-4(7))* VDM Verlag Dr. Mueller e.K.

Yang, Haiqin, et al. Sparse Learning under Regularization Framework. 2011. 152p. pap. ***(978-3-8443-3030-4(5))*** Lambert Academic Publishing.

Yang, Xin-She. Introduction to Computational Mathematics. 2008. (Illus.). 245p. 87.00 *(978-981-281-817-1(0))* World Scientific Publishing Co., Inc.

—Nature-Inspired Metaheuristic Algorithms. 2008. (Illus.). 128p. per. *(978-1-905986-10-1(6))* Luniver Pr.

Yi, Szu-Ting. Robust Semantic Role Labeling. 2010. 168p. pap. *(978-3-639-23903-4(2))* VDM Verlag Dr. Mueller e.K.

Yu, Lean, et al. Bio-Inspired Credit Risk Analysis: Computational Intelligence with Support Vector Machines. 2010. (ENG., Illus.). xvi, 244p. pap. 139.00 *(978-3-642-09655-6(7)*, 3642096557) Springer.

Zazkis, Dov. Considering Symmetries of the Middle Levels Problem. 2009. 108p. pap. *(978-3-639-08684-3(8))* VDM Verlag Dr. Mueller e.K.

Zhang, Jicheng. Bearing Estimation of Seismic Sources from a 3-Axis Seismometer. 2011. 120p. pap. ***(978-3-8443-8001-9(9))*** Lambert Academic Publishing.

Zhang, Yanchun, et al. Web Communities: Analysis & Construction. 2010. (ENG., Illus.). xii, 187p. pap. 109.00 *(978-3-642-06611-5(9)*, 3642066119) Springer.

Zhou, Zhi-Hua. Ensemble Methods for Machine Learning & Pattern Recognition. 2012. (ENG., Illus.). 236p. 79.95 ***(978-1-4398-3003-1(7)**, Chapman & Hall/CRC)* CRC Pr. LLC.

Zhu, Zhigang & Huang, Thomas S., eds. Multimodal Surveillance: Sensors, Algorithms, & Systems. 2007. (Illus.). 428p. 149.00 *(978-1-59693-184-8(1))* Artech Hse., Inc.

Zivkovic, Dejan. Foundations of Algorithm Design & Analysis. 2009. 380p. pap. *(978-3-639-13504-6(0))* VDM Verlag Dr. Mueller e.K.

ALGREN, NELSON, 1909-1981

Shay, Art. Chicago's Nelson Algren. 2007. (ENG., Illus.). 208p. per. 19.95 *(978-1-58322-764-0(4))* Seven Stories Pr.

Ward, Robert. Nelson Algren: A Collection of Critical Essays. 2007. 188p. (C). *(978-0-8386-4108-8(3))* Fairleigh Dickinson Univ. Pr.

ALHAMBRA (GRANADA, SPAIN)

Alkholy, Inas. Alhambra & Gautier. 2010. 212p. pap. *(978-3-639-22854-0(5))* VDM Verlag Dr. Mueller e.K.

Fernandez, Francisco & Jacobs, Michael. Alhambra. 2009. (ENG., Illus.). 192p. pap. 29.95 *(978-0-7112-2518-3(4))* Lincoln, Frances Ltd. GBR. Dist: Perseus-PGW.

Golden Book on Granada/Alhambra. 64p. *(978-88-7009-559-3(2))* Casa Editrice Bonechi.

Irving, Washington. The Alhambr. 2009. 300p. 36.99 *(978-1-59547-522-0(2))* NuVision Pubns., LLC.

—The Alhambra. 2009. (ENG.). 345p. pap. 24.99 *(978-1-110-38270-5(7)*, BiblioLife); (ENG.). 345p. pap. 23.99 *(978-1-110-38268-2(5)*, BiblioLife); 324p. 25.99 *(978-1-103-29219-6(6))*; 324p. pap. 19.99 *(978-1-103-29217-2(X))* BiblioBazaar.

—The Alhambra. 2010. 102p. pap. *(978-1-151-87263-0(6))* 2010. 120p. pap. *(978-1-151-87160-2(5))* 2009. 246p. pap. *(978-1-150-23161-2(0))* Books LLC.

—The Alhambra. 2007. (ENG.). 408p. 22.99 *(978-1-59986-736-6(2))*; per. 14.99 *(978-1-59986-809-7(1))* Filiquarian Publishing, LLC.

—The Alhambra. 2007. (ENG.). 372p. per. 24.45 *(978-1-59462-429-2(1)*, 465, Book Jungle) Standard Pubns., Inc.

—Alhambra. 2008. 228p. 39.95 *(978-1-4369-3002-4(2))*; pap. 24.95 *(978-1-4367-6388-2(6))* Kessinger Publishing, LLC.

—Alhambra. 2007. 304p. per. 29.99 *(978-1-59547-946-4(5))* NuVision Pubns., LLC.

—The Alhambra (New Edition) 2007. 372p. per. 17.45 *(978-1-59462-637-1(5)*, 674, Book Jungle) Standard Pubns., Inc.

Irwin, Robert. The Alhambra. 2011. (Wonders of the World Ser.). (Illus.). 224p. pap. 14.95 *(978-0-674-06033-3(4))* Harvard Univ. Pr.

Jones, Owen. Ornament & Design of the Alhambra. 2008. (ENG., Illus.). 80p. pap. 15.95 *(978-0-486-46524-1(1))* Dover Pubns., Inc.

Serrano Marqués, Mercedes & Piñar Samos, Javier. En Los Confines de un Mismo Mar: Los Palacios de la Alhambra y Topkapi en la Fotografía Del Viaje a Oriente/Ayni Denizin Uçlarinda: Dogu'ya Yolculugun Fotografinda el Hamra Ve Topkapi Saraylari. 2009. (Illus.). 220p. *(978-84-92441-65-5(8))*; *(978-84-96933-33-0(4))* Sociedad Estatal para la Accion Cultural Exterior, S.A.

ALI, MUHAMMAD, 1942-

Abbas, Ali. 2008. (FRE.). 128p. *(978-2-916355-23-8(5))* Editions Intervalles.

Arkush, Michael. The Fight of the Century: Ali vs. Frazier March 8 1971. 2007. (ENG., Illus.). 272p. 25.95 *(978-0-470-05642-4(8)*, Wiley) Wiley, John & Sons, Inc.

Bryar, Thomas A. The Greatest Muhammad Ali Quiz Book: Hundreds of Questions about Muhammad Ali, His Life, His Times & His Opponents. 2011. 224p. pap. 17.09 ***(978-1-4389-7591-7(0))*** AuthorHouse.

Collings, Mark, ed. Muhammad Ali: Through the Eyes of the World. 2007. (Illus.). 481p. per. 19.95 *(978-1-60239-028-7(2))* Skyhorse Publishing Co., Inc.

Cushman, Tom. Muhammad Ali & the Greatest Heavyweight Generation. 2009. 208p. 35.00 *(978-0-9822489-3-5(8))*; pap. 19.00 *(978-0-9822489-2-8(X))* Southeast Missouri State Univ. Pr.

Ezra, Michael. Muhammad Ali: The Making of an Icon. 2009. (Sporting Ser.). (ENG.). 248p. pap. 26.95 *(978-1-59213-662-9(1))*; (Illus.). 71.50 *(978-1-59213-661-2(3))* Temple Univ. Pr.

Haley, Alex & Oates, Joyce Carol. Muhammad Ali: Ringside. 128p. 14.98 *(978-1-56852-717-8(9))* Konecky, William S. Assocs., Inc.

Kidney, Christine. Muhammad Ali: An Illustrated Biography. 2009. (ENG.). 224p. pap. 16.95 *(978-1-56649-997-2(6))* Welcome Rain Pubs.

Kindred, Dave. Sound & Fury: Two Powerful Lives, One Fateful Friendship. 2007. (ENG., Illus.). 384p. pap. 23.99 *(978-0-7432-6212-5(3)*, Free Pr.) Free Pr.

Mee, Bob. Liston & Ali: The Ugly Bear & the Boy Who Would Be King. 2011. (ENG., Illus.). 336p. 24.95 *(978-1-61608-369-4(7)*, 608369) Skyhorse Publishing Co., Inc.

Monaghan, Paddy. Street Fighting Man. 2008. (ENG.). 288p. 34.95 *(978-1-84454-553-7(9))* Blake, John Publishing, Ltd. GBR. Dist: Independent Pubs. Group.

Newsham, Gavin. The Official Treasures of Muhammad Ali. 2010. (ENG., Illus.). 64p. 34.95 *(978-1-84732-671-3(4))* Carlton Bks., Ltd. GBR. Dist: Sterling Publishing Co., Inc.

Rafiq, Fiaz. Muhammad Ali: Conversations. 2011. 352p. 24.95 *(978-0-9562586-4-9(6))* Health 'n' Life Publishing GBR. Dist: Midpoint Trade Bks., Inc.

Satterwhite, Al. Titans: Muhammad Ali & Arnold Schwarzenegger. 2009. (ENG., Illus.). 262p. 89.00 *(978-1-85443-231-5(1)*, 1854432311) Dalton Watson Fine Bks.

Taschen, Benedikt. Greatest of All Time: A Tribute to Muhammad Ali. 2010. (Go Ser.). (ENG., Illus.). 652p. 150.00 *(978-3-8365-2067-6(2))* TASCHEN DEU. Dist: Ingram Pub. Services.

Torres, Jose & Sugar, Bert Randolph. Sting Like a Bee: The Muhammad Ali Story. 2009. (ENG., Illus.). 224p. pap. 17.95 *(978-0-8032-2056-0(1),* Bison Bks.) Univ. of Nebraska Pr.

Winters, Mark. Axis of Greatness: Muhammad Ali, Sugar Ray Leonard & Angelo Dundee. 2008. (ENG., Illus.). 240p. 27.95 *(978-1-906217-60-0(2))* Aurum Pr., Ltd. GBR. Dist: Independent Pubs. Group.

Zirin, Dave. Muhammad Ali Handbook. 2007. (Handbook Ser.). 432p. *(978-1-84072-684-3(9))* M Q Pubns.

—Muhammad Ali Handbook. 2007. (Illus.). 431p. 25.00 *(978-1-84601-155-9(8))* M Q Pubns. GBR. Dist: Ingram Pub. Services.

ALI MUHAMMAD SHIRAZI AL-BAB, 1819-1850

see Bab, Ali Muhammad Shirazi, 1819-1850

ALI PASHA, 1741-1822

Dumas, Alexandre. Ali Pacha. 2008. 88p. pap. *(978-1-4068-7013-8(7))* Echo Library.

ALIBAMU INDIANS

see Indians of North America—East (U.S.)

ALICE, GRAND DUCHESS, CONSORT OF LUDWIG IV, GRAND DUKE OF HESSE-DARMSTADT, 1843-1878

Alice, Grand D. Alice, Grand Duchess of Hess, Princess of Great Britain & Ireland: Biographical Sketch & Letters. 407p. reprint ed. 98.00 *(978-0-7222-1735-1(8))* Library Reprints, Inc.

ALICE (FICTITIOUS CHARACTER: CARROLL)

Batey, Robert H. Under His Hat. 2009. 264p. 27.50 *(978-1-60693-462-3(7),* Strategic Bk. Publishing) AEG Literary Publishing Services, Inc.

Carroll, Lewis, pseud. Alice's Adventures in Wonderland & Through the Looking Glass. 2012. (ENG.). 256p. (gr. 12). 3.95 ***(978-0-451-53200-8(7),*** Signet Classics) Penguin Group (USA) Inc.

Rubin, C M & Rubin, Gabriela. The Real Alice in Wonderland: A Role Model for the Ages. 2010. 144p. 29.95 *(978-1-4490-8131-7(2))* AuthorHouse.

Silberberg, Daniel Doen. Wonderland: The Zen of Alice. 2009. (ENG.). 120p. pap. 12.95 *(978-1-388375-95-4(7))* Parallax Pr.

Smith, Geoffrey. Charles Blackman. 2009. (ENG.). 144p. 34.95 *(978-0-7241-0274-7(4))* National Gallery of Victoria AUS. Dist: National Bk. Network.

Smith, Geoffrey & St John Moore, Felicity. Charles Blackman: Alice in Wonderland. 2007. (ENG., Illus.). 144p. pap. 26.50 *(978-0-7241-0272-3(8))* National Gallery of Victoria AUS. Dist: National Bk. Network.

ALICE SPRINGS (N.T.)

Brooks, David. A Town Like Mparntwe: A Guide to the Dreaming Tracks & Sites of Alice Springs. 2007. (ENG., Illus.). 32p. pap. 11.95 *(978-1-86465-045-7(1))* IAD Pr. AUS. Dist: Independent Pubs. Group.

ALICYCLIC COMPOUNDS

see also Cycloalkenes

Gooden, David. Synthesis & Physical Organic Chemistry of C-Nitroso Compounds. 2009. 168p. pap. *(978-3-639-16056-7(8))* VDM Verlag Dr. Mueller e.K.

Whitmore, Frank C. & Chemistry Associates Staff. Organic Chemistry, Volume One: Part I: Aliphatic Compounds Part II: Alicyclic Compounds. 2011. (Dover Books on Chemistry Ser.). (ENG.). 608p. pap. 24.95 ***(978-0-486-60700-9(3))*** Dover Pubns., Inc.

ALIEN ABDUCTION

Here are entered works on the reported phenomenon of the kidnapping of humans by UFO occupants.

Andrews, Ann. Walking Between Worlds: Belonging to None. 2007. (ENG.). 268p. pap. 19.95 *(978-0-9791750-3-9(8))* Reality Pr.

Brown, Bridget. They Know Us Better Than We Know Ourselves: The History & Politics of Alien Abduction. 2007. (ENG., Illus.). 288p. 75.00 *(978-0-8147-9921-5(3));* per. 24.00 *(978-0-8147-9922-2(1))* New York Univ. Pr.

Clancy, Susan A. Abducted: How People Come to Believe They Were Kidnapped by Aliens. annot. ed. 2007. 192p. per. 19.00 *(978-0-674-02401-4(X))* Harvard Univ. Pr.

De Lafayette, Maximillien. De Lafayette Mega Encyclopedia of Anunnaki, Ulema-Anunnaki, Their Offspring, Their Remnants & Extraterrestrial Civilization on Earth. 2010. 300p. pap. 25.50 *(978-0-557-47930-6(4))* Lulu Enterprises Inc.

—De Lafayette Mega Encyclopedia of Anunnaki, Ulema-Anunnaki, Their Offspring, Their Remnants & Extraterrestrial Civilization on Earth. Vol. 3. 2010. 292p. pap. 24.95 *(978-0-557-48827-8(3))* Lulu Enterprises Inc.

—De Lafayette Mega Encyclopedia of Anunnaki, Ulema-Anunnaki, Their Offspring, Their Remnants & Extraterrestrial Civilization on Earth. Vol. 4. 2010. 316p. pap. 25.98 *(978-0-557-49619-8(5))* Lulu Enterprises Inc.

—De Lafayette Mega Encyclopedia of Anunnaki, Ulema-Anunnaki, Their Offspring, Their Remnants & Extraterrestrial Civilization on Earth. Vol. 5. 2010. 300p. pap. 25.50 *(978-0-557-51041-2(4))* Lulu Enterprises Inc.

—De Lafayette Mega Encyclopedia of Anunnaki, Ulema-Anunnaki, Their Offspring, Their Remnants & Extraterrestrial Civilization on Earth. Vol. 6 (Final Part) 2010. 282p. pap. 24.51 *(978-0-557-51739-8(7))* Lulu Enterprises Inc.

—De Lafayette Mega Encyclopedia of Anunnaki, Ulema-Anunnaki, Their Offspring, Their Remnants & Extraterrestrial Civilization on Earth. Volume 1. Illustrated. 2010. 300p. pap. 25.50 *(978-0-557-48142-2(2))* Lulu Enterprises Inc.

—The Grays, Alien Abductions & Genetic Creation of Humans Hybrids Race. 2010. 322p. pap. 25.97 *(978-0-557-75535-6(2))* Lulu Enterprises Inc.

—INSIDE the EXTRAORDINARY WORLD of the ANUNNAKI & ANUNNAKI-ULEMA: What I saw, what I learned, & what I can teach you. Book 1. 2010. 300p. pap. 25.50 *(978-0-557-47421-9(3))* Lulu Enterprises Inc.

—INSIDE the EXTRAORDINARY WORLD of the ANUNNAKI & ANUNNAKI-ULEMA: What I saw, what I learned, & what I can teach you. Book 2. 2010. 294p. pap. 24.97 *(978-0-557-47472-1(8))* Lulu Enterprises Inc.

Kerner, Nigel. Grey Aliens & the Harvesting of Souls. 2010. (ENG.). 1p. pap. 28.00 *(978-1-59143-103-9(4))* Bear & Co.

Knight-Jadczyk, Laura. High Strangeness: Hyperdimensions & the Process of Alien Abduction. 2nd rev. ed. 2008. (Illus.). 424p. pap. *(978-1-897244-34-0(7))* Red Pill Pr.

Konkolesky, William. Experiencer: Raised in Two Worlds. 2009. 140p. pap. 12.95 *(978-0-557-11580-8(9))* Lulu Enterprises Inc.

LeBeau, Byron. The Curs-Ed Net. 2007. 284p. (ENG.). 25.99 *(978-1-60477-223-4(9));* per. 15.99 *(978-1-60477-149-7(6))* Xulon Pr., Inc.

Mack. Abduction: Human Encounters with Aliens. 2007. (ENG.). 464p. pap. 28.95 *(978-1-4165-7580-1(4),* Scribner) Scribner.

Marden, Kathleen & Friedman, Stanton T. Captured! The Betty & Barney Hill UFO Experience: The True Story of the World's First Documented Alien Abduction. 2007. (ENG., Illus.). 1p. pap. 16.99 *(978-1-56414-971-8(4),* New Page Bks.) Career Pr., Inc.

Morris, Theresa. Alien UFO story by Tj. 2010. 183p. pap. 23.99 *(978-0-557-38566-5(0))* Lulu Enterprises Inc.

Southwell, David. Unsolved Extraterrestrial Mysteries. 2009. (Mysteries & Conspiracies Ser.). (ENG.). 80p. (gr. 10-10). 61.20 *(978-1-61514-746-5(2))* Rosen Publishing Group, Inc., The.

Southwell, David & Twist, Sean. Unsolved Extraterrestrial Mysteries. 2007. (Mysteries & Conspiracies Ser.). (Illus.). 80p. (YA). (gr. 9-12). lib. bdg. 30.50 *(978-1-4042-1080-6(6))* Rosen Publishing Group, Inc., The.

Sparks, Jim. The Keepers: An Alien Message for the Human Race. 2008. 244p. (J). pap. 19.99 *(978-0-926524-68-2(2))* Granite Publishing, LLC.

Streicher, Thomas James. Extra-Planetary Experiences: Alien-Human Contact & the Expansion of Consciousness. 2012. pap. ***(978-1-59143-136-7(0))*** Bear & Co.

Tumminia, Diana G. Alien Worlds: Social & Religious Dimensions of Extraterrestrial Contact. 2007. (Religion & Politics Ser.). (Illus.). 364p. per. 34.95 *(978-0-8156-0858-5(6))* Syracuse Univ. Pr.

whiting, jim. Ufos. 2011. (Extraterrestrial Life Ser.). (Illus.). 80p. (YA). (gr. 7-12). lib. bdg. 27.95 *(978-1-60152-172-9(3))* ReferencePoint Pr., Inc.

ALIEN AND SEDITION LAWS, 1798

see also Kentucky and Virginia Resolutions of 1798

Warfield, Ethelbert Dudley. The Kentucky Resolutions of 1798: An Historical Study. 203p. reprint ed. 98.00 *(978-0-7222-7390-6(8))* Library Reprints, Inc.

ALIEN ANIMALS

see Animal Introduction

ALIEN CRIMINALS

Armed & Dangerous: Confronting the Problem of Border Incursions: Hearing Before the Subcommittee on Investigations of the Committee on Homeland Security, House of Representatives, One Hundred Ninth Congress, Second Session, February 7, 2006. 2007. iii, 61p. *(978-0-16-079515-2(X),* 552-070-36493-5) United States Government Printing Office.

Mars, Gerald, et al, eds. Crime & Immigration. 2nd ed. 2007. (International Library of Criminology, Criminal Justice & Penology Ser.: Vol. 2). (Illus.). 558p. 325.00 *(978-0-7546-2449-3(8))* Ashgate Publishing Co.

Mogire, Edward. Victims as Security Threats: Refugee Impact on Host State Security in Africa. 2011. (Global Security in a Changing World Ser.). (Illus.). 228p. 99.95 *(978-0-7546-7820-5(2))* Ashgate Publishing Co.

William McDonald Staff. Immigration, Crime & Justice. 2009. (Illus.). xxiv, 337p. 144.95 *(978-1-84855-438-2(9))* Emerald Group Publishing Ltd. GBR. Dist: Turpin Distribution Services Ltd.

ALIEN CRIMINALS—UNITED STATES

Comprehensive Immigration Reform: Impact of Immigration on States & Localities: Hearing Before the Subcommittee on Immigration, Citizenship, Refugees, Border Security, & International Law of the Committee on the Judiciary, House of Representatives, One Hundred Tenth Congress, First Session, May 17, 2007. 2007. (Illus.). iv, 151p. *(978-0-16-079276-2(2,* 552-070-36361-1) United States Government Printing Office.

Deportees in Latin America & the Caribbean: Hearing & Briefing Before the Subcommittee on the Western Hemisphere of the Committee on Foreign Affairs, House of Representatives, One Hundred Tenth Congress, First Session, July 24, 2007. 2007. (Illus.). iii, 78p. *(978-0-16-079728-6(4),* 552-070-36654-7) United States Government Printing Office.

Friedman Ramirez, Linda. Cultural Issues in Criminal Defense - 2nd Edition. 2nd ed. 2007. (ENG.). 774p. 150.00 *(978-1-57823-224-6(4))* Juris Publishing, Inc.

Keep Our Communities Safe ACT: Hearing Before the Subcommittee on Immigration Policy & Enforcement of the Committee on the Judiciary, House of Representatives, One Hundred Twelfth Congress, First Session, on H.R. 1932, May 24, 2011. 2011. iii, 194p. ***(978-0-16-089458-9(1),*** 552-070-43422-4) United States Government Printing Office.

Knowles, Wesley B., ed. Organized Crime in the U. s. 2010. (Criminal Justice, Law Enforcement & Corrections Ser.). 117p. 69.00 *(978-1-60741-524-4(0))* Nova Science Pubs., Inc.

No Safe Haven: Accountability for Human Rights Violators in the United States: Hearing Before the Subcommittee on Human Rights & the Law of the Committee on the Judiciary, United States Senate, One Hundred Tenth Congress, First Session, November 14, 2007. 2008. iii, 161p. *(978-0-16-082052-6(9),* 552-070-38211-9) United States Government Printing Office.

United States, Congress House Committee on Homeland Security Subcommittee on Management, Integration, and Oversight Staff, contrib. by. The 287(G) Program: Ensuring the Integrity of America's Border Security System Through Federal-State Partnerships: Hearing Before the Subcommittee on Management, Integration, & Oversight of the Committee on Homeland Security, House of Representatives, One Hundred Ninth Congress, First Session, July 27, 2005. 2007. (Illus.). iii, 69p. *(978-0-16-078411-8(5),* 552-070-35706-9) United States Government Printing Office.

ALIEN ENCOUNTERS WITH HUMANS

see Human-Alien Encounters

ALIEN KIDNAPPING

see Alien Abduction

ALIEN LABOR

see Foreign Workers

ALIEN LABOR CRIMINALS

see Alien Criminals

ALIEN PROPERTY

see also Eminent Domain (International Law); Enemy Property

Bayley, Carl. How to Avoid Tax on Foreign Property. 2008. (Illus.). 308p. per. *(978-1-904608-66-0(3))* Taxcafe UK Ltd.

Kohn, Roger. Adieu, Dordogne. 2008. (ENG.). 137p. pap. *(978-1-85756-608-6(4))* Janus Publishing Co.

O'Mahony, Lorna Fox & Sweeney, James, eds. The law Of 'home' Displacement & Dispossession. 2010. (Law, Property & Society Ser.). (Illus.). 248p. 124.95 *(978-0-7546-7947-9(0))* Ashgate Publishing Co.

Signet, William D. Introduction to the Mexican Real Estate System. 2010. 298p. pap. 35.00 *(978-1-59460-870-4(9))* Carolina Academic Pr.

ALIENATION (LAW)

see Transfer (Law)

ALIENATION (PHILOSOPHY)

Campbell, Sally Howard. Rousseau & the Paradox of Alienation. 2012. (ENG.). 110p. (gr. 17). 50.00 ***(978-0-7391-6632-1(8))*** Lexington Bks.

Dunning, Benjamin H. Aliens & Sojourners: Self as Other in Early Christianity. 2009. (Divinations: Rereading Late Ancient Religion Ser.). 192p. (C). 55.00 *(978-0-8122-4156-3(8))* Univ. of Pennsylvania Pr.

Kubota, Mami. Schiller's Concept of Alienation Revisited. 2008. 116p. pap. *(978-3-639-07243-3(X))* VDM Verlag Dr. Mueller e.K.

Sayers, Sean. Marx & Alienation: Essays on Hegelian Themes. 2011. (ENG.). 208p. 80.00 *(978-0-230-27654-3(7))* Palgrave Macmillan.

Segal, Jerome M. Agency Illusion & Well Being: Essays in Moral Psychology & Philosophical Economics. 2009. (ENG.). 260p. 78.99 *(978-0-7391-2968-5(6))* Lexington Bks.

—Agency Illusion, & Well-Being: Essays in Moral Psychology & Philosophical Economics. 2008. (ENG.). 260p. pap. 31.50 *(978-0-7391-2969-2(4))* Lexington Bks.

Skempton, Simon. Alienation after Derrida. 2011. (ENG.). 246p. pap. 44.95 ***(978-1-4411-0328-4(7))*** Continuum International Publishing Group, Ltd. GBR. Dist: National Bk. Network.

Swamy, Vinay. Interpreting the Republic: Marginalization & Belonging in Contemporary French Novels & Films. 2011. (ENG., Illus.). 208p. 65.00 *(978-0-7391-6536-2(4))* Lexington Bks.

Wendling, Amy. Karl Marx on Technology & Alienation. 2011. (ENG., Illus.). 264p. pap. 32.78 ***(978-0-230-34848-6(3))*** Palgrave Macmillan.

Wendling, Amy & Wendling, Amy E. Karl Marx on Technology & Alienation. 2009. (ENG.). 272p. 89.00 *(978-0-230-22440-7(7))* Palgrave Macmillan.

ALIENATION (SOCIAL PSYCHOLOGY)

see also Social Isolation

Abrams, Robert E. Landscape & Ideology in American Renaissance Literature: Topographies of Skepticism. 2009. (Cambridge Studies in American Literature & Culture Ser.). (ENG., Illus.). 180p. pap. 31.00 *(978-0-521-11988-7(X))* Cambridge Univ. Pr.

Benderson, Bruce. Sex & Isolation: And Other Essays. 2007. (ENG.). 208p. pap. 24.95 *(978-0-299-22314-4(0))* Univ. of Wisconsin Pr.

Borinsky, Alicia. One-Way Tickets: Writers & the Culture of Exile. 2011. (ENG.). 232p. 24.95 *(978-1-59534-070-2(X))* Trinity Univ. Pr.

Braun, Jerome. To Break Our Chains: Social Cohesiveness & Modern Democracy. 2010. (Studies in Critical Social Sciences Ser.). 416p. *(978-90-04-19027-6(9))* BRILL.

Braun, Jerome & Langman, Lauren, eds. Alienation & the Carnivalization of Society. 2011. (Routledge Studies in Social & Political Thought Ser.). (ENG., Illus.). 214p. (C). 125.00 *(978-0-415-88878-3(6))* Routledge.

Brescia, Robert. Disruptive Power in American Discourse: The Trial of the Chicago Seven. 2010. 300p. pap. *(978-3-8383-7590-8(4))* Lambert Academic Publishing.

Casey, Karen. Codependence & the Power of Detachment: How to Set Boundaries & Make Your Life Your Own. 2011. (ENG.). 176p. pap. 15.95 *(978-1-57324-362-9(0),* Conari Pr.) Red Wheel/Weiser.

COLLINGWOOD-WHITTICK, Sheila, ed. The Pain of Unbelonging: Alienation & Identity in Australasian Literature. 2007. (Cross-Cultures Ser.: 91). 256p. 56.70 *(978-90-420-2187-7(X))* Rodopi.

Declark, Robert. Alienation & Marginalisation - a Case Study of the Social Experiences of Men in the Lifehouse Program, Ottawa, Ontario. 2008. 92p. pap. *(978-3-639-05312-8(5))* VDM Verlag Dr. Mueller e.K.

Fidler, Barbara Jo, et al. Children Who Resist Post-Separation Parental Contact: A Differential Approach for Legal & Mental Health Professionals, 1 vol. 2012. (American Psychology-Law Society Ser.). (ENG.). 328p. pap. 75.00 ***(978-0-19-989549-6(X))*** Oxford Univ. Pr., Inc.

Fromm, Erich. On Disobedience: Why Freedom Means Saying No to Power. 2010. (ENG.). 112p. pap. 10.00 *(978-0-06-199045-8(0),* HarperPerennial) HarperCollins Pubs.

Gunton, Colin E. Enlightenment & Alienation: An Essay Towards a Trinitarian Theology. 2006. 174p. pap. 21.00 *(978-1-59752-948-8(6),* Wipf and Stock) Wipf & Stock Pubs.

Houellebecq, Michel. The Art of Struggle. 2012. (ENG., Illus.). 120p. pap. 16.95 ***(978-1-84688-106-0(4))*** Alma Bks. GBR. Dist: Independent Pubs. Group.

Hugs to Heartbreak: A Parent's Journey Through Parental Alienation. 2007. per. 17.95 *(978-0-9796960-0-8(3))* Family's Heartbreak, LLC, A.

Kelly, Philippa & Semler, Liam E. Word & Self Estranged in English Texts, 1550-1660. 2010. (Illus.). 244p. 99.95 *(978-1-4094-0037-0(9))* Ashgate Publishing Co.

Kuntz, Andreas & Pfleiderer, Beatrix. Fremdheit & Migration Band 2: Lebensformen. (GER.). iv, 260p. *(978-3-496-00889-7(X))* Reimer, Dietrich.

Lojeski, Karen Sobel & Reilly, Richard R. Uniting the Virtual Workforce: Transforming Leadership & Innovation in the Globally Integrated Enterprise. 2008. (Microsoft Executive Leadership Ser.: 2). (ENG., Illus.). 204p. 29.95 *(978-0-470-19395-2(6),* Wiley) Wiley, John & Sons, Inc.

MacDonald, Geoff & Jensen-Campbell, Lauri A. Social Pain: Neuropsychological & Health Implications of Loss & Exclusion. 2010. (Illus.). x, 258p. 59.95 *(978-1-4338-0874-6(9))* American Psychological Assn.

Mathur, Saloni, ed. The Migrant's Time: Rethinking Art History & Diaspora. 2011. (Clark Studies in the Visual Arts Ser.). (ENG., Illus.). 272p. pap. 24.95 *(978-0-300-13414-8(2))* Yale Univ. Pr.

Minkova, Radoslava. Zur Problematik des Fremdseins in Thomas Bernhards und Christoph Heins Erzählwerken: Eine Vergleichende Untersuchung. (Europaische Hochschulschriften Ser.). (GER.). 192p. 30.95 *(978-3-631-38544-9(7))* Lang, Peter Publishing, Inc.

Mitra, Ananda. Alien Technology: Coping with Modern Mysteries. 2011. 224p. (C). pap. 30.00 *(978-81-321-0466-7(8),* B04667P) SAGE Pubns., Inc.

Morrison, Brenda. Restoring Safe School Communities: A Whole School Response to Bullying, Violence & Alienation. 2007. (Illus.). 270p. per. *(978-1-86287-477-0(8))* Federation Pr. AUS. Dist: Willan Publishing.

Muratore, Mary Jo. Exiles, Outcasts, Strangers: Icons of Marginalization in Post World War II Narrative. 2011. (ENG.). 208p. 110.00 *(978-1-4411-5611-2(9))* Continuum International Publishing Group, Ltd. GBR. Dist: National Bk. Network.

Noguera, Pedro, et al, eds. Understanding the Disenfranchisement of Latino Men & Boys: Invisible No More. 2011. (ENG., Illus.). 336p. 140.00 *(978-0-415-87778-7(4));* pap. 49.95 *(978-0-415-87779-4(2))* Routledge.

Olson, Kirsten. Wounded by School: Recapturing the Joy in Learning & Standing up to Old School Culture. rev. ed. 2009. (ENG.). 240p. 56.00 *(978-0-8077-4956-2(7));* pap. 21.95 *(978-0-8077-4955-5(9))* Teachers College Pr., Teachers College, Columbia Univ.

Padgett, Barry L. & Padgett. Marx & Alienation in Contemporary Society. 2007. (ENG., Illus.). 176p. 130.00 *(978-0-8264-9029-2(8))* Continuum International Publishing Group, Ltd. GBR. Dist: National Bk. Network.

Porterfield, Jason. How to Beat Social Alienation. 2012. (Beating Bullying Ser.). (ENG., Illus.). 48p. (YA). (gr. 5-8). pap. 11.75 ***(978-1-4488-6821-6(1));*** lib. bdg. 27.95 ***(978-1-4488-6812-4(2))*** Rosen Publishing Group, Inc., The. (Rosen Central).

Reevy, Gretchen & Frydenberg, Erica. Personality, Stress, & Coping: Implications for Education. 2011. ***(978-1-61735-524-0(0));*** pap. ***(978-1-61735-523-3(2));*** E-Book ***(978-1-61735-525-7(9))*** Information Age Publishing, Inc.

Richards, Nancy. Heal & Forgive II: The Journey from Abuse & Estrangement to Reconciliation. 2008. 172p. pap. 16.00 *(978-1-57733-220-6(2))* Blue Dolphin Publishing, Inc.

Robinson, Douglas. Estrangement & the Somatics of Literature: Tolstoy, Shklovsky, Brecht. 2008. (Parallax: Re#45;visions of Culture & Society Ser.). (ENG.). 344p. (gr. 17). 65.00 *(978-0-8018-8796-3(8))* Johns Hopkins Univ. Pr.

Rosa, Hartmut. Alienation & Acceleration: Towards a Critical Theory of Late-Modern Temporality. 2010. (Summertalk Ser.). (ENG.). 111p. (C). pap. 20.00 *(978-87-87564-14-4(9))* Aarhus Universitetsforlag DNK. Dist: ISD.

Samellas, Antigone. Alienation: The Experience of the Eastern Mediterranean, 50-600 A. D. 2010. 556p. pap. *(978-3-03911-789-5(0))* Lang, Peter.

Shenker, Barry. Intentional Communities (Routledge Revivals) Ideology & Alienation in Communal Societies. 2011. (Routledge Revivals Ser.). (ENG.). 296p. 115.00 *(978-0-415-60938-5(0))* Routledge.

Shoham, S.G. Society & the Absurd. 2nd rev. ed. 2006. (ENG., Illus.). 239p. pap. 32.50 *(978-1-84519-067-5(X))* Sussex Academic Pr. GBR. Dist: International Specialized Bk. Services.

Smyth, John. From Silent Witnesses to Active Agents: Student Voice in Re-Engaging with Learning. 2012. (C). pap. 139.95 ***(978-1-4331-1374-1(0));*** pap. 34.95 ***(978-1-4331-1373-4(2),*** Lang, Peter Publishing, Inc.

Wright-Neville, David & Halafoff, Anna, eds. Terrorism & Social Exclusion: Misplaced Risk - Common Security. 2010. (Monash Studies in Global Movements Ser.). 224p. 112.00 *(978-1-84720-816-3(9))* Elgar, Edward Publishing, Inc.

ALIENATION, RESTRAINTS ON

see Restraints on Alienation

ALIENISTS

see Psychiatrists

ALIENS

Here are entered works on persons who are not citizens of the country in which they reside.

see also Alien Property; Citizenship; Corporations, Foreign; Diplomatic Protection; Expatriation; Illegal Aliens; Immigrants; Naturalization; Pilgrims and Pilgrimages; Repatriation; Taxation of Aliens

Allende, Isabel. A House Somewhere: Tales of Life Abroad. George, Don, ed. 2nd rev. ed. 2011. (Travel Literature Ser.). (ENG.). 320p. pap. 14.99 *(978-1-74220-105-4(9))* Lonely Planet Pubns.

Aponte, Wayne/Lionel. The Year of No Money in Tokyo. 2009. 165p. *(978-0-9820550-2-1(1))*; pap. *(978-0-9820550-1-4(3))* Watkins & McKay, LLC.

Asimorov, Victor. A Son of Old Atlantis. 2007. 224p. per. *(978-1-905747-20-7(9))* Experiencers eBooks, Ltd.

Bhabha, Homi K. Our Neighbours, Ourselves: Contemporary Reflections on Survival. 2011. E-Book *(978-3-11-026244-5(4))* De Gruyter, Walter Inc.

Bosniak, Linda. The Citizen & the Alien: Dilemmas of Contemporary Membership. (ENG.). 240p. (C). 2008. pap. 24.95 *(978-0-691-13828-2(1))* 2006. 32.95 *(978-0-691-11622-8(9))* Princeton Univ. Pr.

Brener, Milton E. Walking Through Walls & Other Impossibilities: The Hybrid Agenda. 2011. 306p. 29.99 ***(978-1-4628-8113-0(0))***; pap. 19.99 ***(978-1-4628-8112-3(2))*** Xlibris Corp.

Browne, Kevin. Welfare Benefits Immigration Law 2e. 2007. (Legal Practice Guides Ser.). (Illus.). xxviii, 539p. pap. *(978-1-905391-31-8(5))* College of Law Publishing.

Carlson, Isobel. Ooh la La! 2012. (ENG., Illus.). 96p. 10.95 ***(978-1-84024-665-0(0))*** Summerdale Pubs. GBR. Dist: Independent Pubs. Group.

Cataldo, Chet. Ancient Aliens, the Rapture & the Return of Christ. 2011. 324p. pap. 17.72 ***(978-1-4634-0006-4(3))*** AuthorHouse.

Council of Europe Staff. The position of aliens in relation to the European Convention on Human Rights (2007) 2007. 76p. pap. 20.00 *(978-92-871-6098-0(8))* Council of Europe FRA. Dist: Manhattan Publishing Co.

Dauvergne, Catherine. Making People Illegal: What Globalization Means for Migration & Law. (Law in Context Ser.). (ENG.). 2009. 230p. pap. 32.99 *(978-0-521-71928-5(3))* 2008. 232p. 84.00 *(978-0-521-89508-8(1))* Cambridge Univ. Pr.

De Lafayette, Maximillien. Black Operations, Weapons Systems & Experiments by Extraterrestrials, Grays & Governments. 2010. 320p. pap. 25.94 *(978-0-557-53024-3(5))* Lulu Enterprises Inc.

Ehrman, Mark & Nelson, Cletus. Getting Out: Your Guide to Leaving America. rev. ed. 2012. (Process Self-reliance Ser.). (ENG., Illus.). 460p. pap. 19.95 ***(978-1-934170-29-8(1))*** Process Packaging.

Gruen, Erich S. Rethinking the Other in Antiquity. 2010. (Martin Classical Lectures). (ENG., Illus.). 416p. (C). 39.50 *(978-0-691-14852-6(X))* Princeton Univ. Pr.

Hadnum, Lee. Non-Resident & Offshore Tax Planning: How to Cut Your Tax to Zero. 2010. 244p. pap. *(978-1-907302-21-3(2))* Taxcafe UK Ltd.

Haebich, Anna & Offord, Baden, eds. Landscapes of Exile: Once Perilous, Now Safe. 2008. (Illus.). 283p. pap. 69.95 *(978-3-03911-090-2(X))* Lang, Peter Publishing, Inc.

Harold, Gregory. The Alien Connection. 2009. 176p. pap. 14.95 *(978-1-59858-856-9(7))* Dog Ear Publishing, LLC.

Kopnina, Helen. Migration & Tourism: Formation of New Social Classes. 2007. (Tourism Dynamics Ser.). *(978-1-882345-48-9(7))* Cognizant Communication Corp.

(Kraakar Shem), Chico Penteado. Talking to the Reptilians-A Report from Brazil. 2010. 130p. pap. 14.49 *(978-0-557-57653-1(9))* Lulu Enterprises Inc.

Le Blanc, Guillaume. Dedans, Dehors: La Condition D'étranger. 2010. (FRE.). 217p. *(978-2-02-102884-3(4))* Editions du Seuil.

Leonard, Pauline. Expatriate Identities in Postcolonial Organizations: Working Whiteness. 2010. (Studies in Migration & Diaspora Ser.). 174p. 99.95 *(978-0-7546-7365-1(0))* Ashgate Publishing Co.

Magliveras, Konstantinos D. Migration Law in Greece. 2011. 182p. pap. ***(978-90-411-3441-7(7))*** Kluwer Law International.

Morris-Suzuki, Tessa. Borderline Japan: Foreigners & Frontier Controls in the Postwar Era. 2012. (ENG., Illus.). 286p. pap. 36.99 ***(978-0-521-68310-4(6))*** Cambridge Univ. Pr.

Niessen, J. & Huddleston, T., eds. Legal Frameworks for the Integration of Third-Country Nationals. 2009. (Immigration & Asylum Law & Policy in Europe Ser.). (Illus.). 200p. *(978-90-04-17069-8(3))* BRILL.

Resnik, Judith. Migrations & Mobilities: Citizenship, Borders, & Gender. Benhabib, Seyla, ed. 2009. (ENG., Illus.). 576p. pap. 25.00 *(978-0-8147-7600-1(0))* New York Univ. Pr.

Rough Guides Staff & Bizony, Piers. The Search for Aliens: A Rough Guide to Life on Other Worlds. 2012. (ENG., Illus.). 272p. 18.99 *(978-1-4053-8324-0(0))* Rough Guides, Ltd. GBR. Dist: Dorling Kindersley Publishing, Inc.

Sarat, Austin, et al, eds. Law & the Stranger. 2010. (Amherst Series in Law, Jurisprudence, & Social Thought Ser.). (ENG.). 264p. 65.00 *(978-0-8047-7154-2(5))* Stanford Univ. Pr.

Seklitova, Larisa. Rendezvous with the Invisibles. 2011. 176p. pap. 14.25 ***(978-1-4269-7097-9(8))*** Trafford Publishing.

Spann, Korbinian. Beschreibung und Wahmehmung des Fremden in der rabbinischen Literatur: Eine Interpretation anhand der Traktate Brachot, Schabbat, Jebamot und Sanhedrin. 2010. (Judaica et Christiana Ser.). (GER.). 429p. pap. *(978-3-0343-0484-9(6))* Lang, Peter.

Sterett, Susan, ed. Immigration. 2006. (International Library of Essays in Law & Society). 632p. 350.00 *(978-0-7546-2474-5(9))* Ashgate Publishing Co.

United Nations. The Rights of Non-citizens. 2008. (ARA.). 68p. pap. 10.00 *(978-92-1-654018-0(4))* 2007. (CHI.). 64p. pap. 10.00 *(978-92-1-730101-8(9))* 2007. (RUS.). 92p. pap. 10.00 *(978-92-1-454026-7(8))* United Nations Pubns.

United Nations, Office of the High Commissioner for Human Rights Staff, contrib. by. The Rights of Non-Citizens. 2007. (ENG.). 52p. pap. 10.00 *(978-92-1-154175-5(1))* United Nations Pubns.

U.S. Customs and Border Protection Staff & American Immigration Lawyers Association Staff, contrib. by. CBP Inspector's Field Manual. 2008. (Illus.). 711p. *(978-1-57370-235-5(8))* American Immigration Lawyers Assn.

Weissbrodt, David S. The Human Rights of Non-Citizens. 2008. (ENG.). 300p. 143.00 *(978-0-19-954782-1(3))* Oxford Univ. Pr., Inc.

ALIENS—EMPLOYMENT

see Foreign Workers

ALIENS—AFRICA

Crush, Jonathan, ed. The Perfect Storm: Xenophobia in Contemporary South Africa. 2008. 68p. pap. *(978-1-920118-71-6(3))* IDASA Pubs. ZAF. Dist: Michigan State Univ. Pr.

Khouma, Pap. I Was an Elephant Salesman: Adventures Between Dakar, Paris, & Milan. Pivetta, Oreste, ed. Hopkins, Rebecca, tr. from ITA. 2010. (Global African Voices Ser.). (ENG.). 158p. 55.00 *(978-0-253-35522-5(2),* 0253355222); pap. 18.95 *(978-0-253-22232-9(X),* 025322232X) Indiana Univ. Pr.

Triandafyllidou, Anna & Maroukis, Thanos. Migrant Smuggling: Irregular Migration from Asia & Africa to Europe. 2012. (ENG., Illus.). 256p. 85.00 ***(978-0-230-29637-4(8))*** Palgrave Macmillan.

ALIENS—ASIA

Aponte, Wayne/Lionel. The Year of No Money in Tokyo. 2009. 160p. 19.95 *(978-0-9820550-0-7(5))* Watkins & McKay, LLC.

D'Andrea, Anthony. Global Nomads: Techno & New Age as Transnational Contercultures in Ibiza & Goa. 2007. (International Library of Sociology Ser.). (ENG., Illus.). 264p. (C). 190.00 *(978-0-415-42013-6(X))* Routledge.

—Global Nomads: Techno & New Age as Transnational Countercultures in Ibiza (Spain) & Goa (India) 2009. (Illus.). 256p. 39.95 *(978-0-415-55367-4(9))* Routledge.

Fechter, Anne-Meike. Transnational Lives: Expatriates in Indonesia. 2007. 190p. 114.95 *(978-0-7546-4743-0(9))* Ashgate Publishing Co.

Filc, MD, Dani. Circles of Exclusion: The Politics of Health Care in Israel. 2009. (Culture & Politics of Health Care Work Ser.). 200p. 36.95 *(978-0-8014-4795-2(X))* Cornell Univ. Pr.

Goodman, Roger. Global Japan: The Experience of Japan's New Immigrant & Overseas Communities. 2009. 246p. pap. 39.95 *(978-0-415-54626-3(5))* Routledge.

Hipsher, Scott A. Expatriates in Asia: Breaking Free from the Colonial Paradigm. 2008. (Illus.). 224p. *(978-1-84334-422-3(X),* Chandos Publishing) Woodhead Publishing Ltd.

—Expatriates in Asia: Breaking Free from the Colonial Paradigm. 2008. (Chandos Asian Studies). (ENG., Illus.). 222p. pap. 70.00 *(978-1-84334-421-6(1),* Chandos Publishing) Woodhead Publishing Ltd. GBR. Dist: Ingram Pub. Services.

Triandafyllidou, Anna & Maroukis, Thanos. Migrant Smuggling: Irregular Migration from Asia & Africa to Europe. 2012. (ENG., Illus.). 256p. 85.00 ***(978-0-230-29637-4(8))*** Palgrave Macmillan.

Yi, Sun-Tae. Tamunhwa Sahoe Ui Torae e Ttarun Oegugin Ui Ch'uripkuk MIT Koju e Kwanhan Popche Yon'gu. 2007. (KOR., Illus.). 291p. *(978-89-8323-343-1(5))* Korea Legislation Research Institute.

ALIENS—CHINA

Boyd, Julia. A Dance with the Dragon. 2012. (ENG., Illus.). 288p. 29.00 ***(978-1-78076-052-0(3))*** I. B. Tauris & Co., Ltd. GBR. Dist: Macmillan.

Koo, Vi K. Status of Aliens in China. (Columbia University, Studies in the Social Sciences: No. 126). reprint ed. 35.00 *(978-0-404-51126-5(0))* AMS Pr., Inc.

Sen, Tansen & Mair, Victor H. Traditional China in Asian & World History. 2011. pap. ***(978-0-924304-65-1(0))*** Assn. for Asian Studies, Inc.

Shanghai Daily. Snapshots of New. 2010. 110p. pap. 15.95 *(978-1-60220-400-3(4))* BetterLink Pr., Inc.

Yang, Lu. Living in China. 2008. 344p. pap. 19.95 *(978-7-80228-501-9(1))* New World Pr. CHN. Dist: China Bks. & Periodicals, Inc.

ALIENS—EUROPE

Acosta Arcarazo, Diego. The Long-Term Residence Status As a Subsidiary Form of EU Citizenship: An Analysis of Directive 2003/109. 2011. (Immigration & Asylum Law & Policy in Europe Ser.). (ENG.). XIV, 266p. *(978-90-04-20412-6(1))* BRILL.

Coleman, Nils P. European Readmission Policy: Third Country Interests & Refugee Rights. 2008. (Immigration & Asylum Law & Policy in Europe Ser.). 412p. *(978-90-04-16554-0(1))* BRILL.

D'Andrea, Anthony. Global Nomads: Techno & New Age as Transnational Contercultures in Ibiza & Goa. 2007. (International Library of Sociology Ser.). (ENG., Illus.). 264p. (C). 190.00 *(978-0-415-42013-6(X))* Routledge.

—Global Nomads: Techno & New Age as Transnational Countercultures in Ibiza (Spain) & Goa (India) 2009. (Illus.). 256p. 39.95 *(978-0-415-55367-4(9))* Routledge.

García Vázquez, Sonia & Vázquez, Sonia García. El Estatuto Jurídico-Constitucional Del Extranjero en Espãna. 2007. (SPA.). 445p. *(978-84-8456-894-0(6))* Tirant lo Blanch.

Hurn, Margarete. The Foreigner's Guide to Living in Slovakia. 2007. per. 16.95 net. *(978-0-9790300-3-1(X))* Modra Publishing.

Khouma, Pap. I Was an Elephant Salesman: Adventures Between Dakar, Paris, & Milan. Pivetta, Oreste, ed. Hopkins, Rebecca, tr. from ITA. 2010. (Global African Voices Ser.). (ENG.). 158p. 55.00 *(978-0-253-35522-5(2),* 0253355222); pap. 18.95 *(978-0-253-22232-9(X),* 025322232X) Indiana Univ. Pr.

Kim, Keechang. Aliens in Medieval Law: The Origins of Modern Citizenship. 2011. (Cambridge Studies in English Legal History Ser.). (ENG.). 262p. pap. 50.00 *(978-0-521-17407-7(4))* Cambridge Univ. Pr.

Kirkagac, Nevzat. Verdachtsausweisungen Im Deutschen Rechtsstaat. 2011. (Schriften zum internationalen und zum öffentlichen Recht Ser.). (GER.). 281p. 80.95 ***(978-3-631-62001-4(2))*** Lang, Peter GmbH, Europaischer Verlag der Wissenschaften DEU. Dist: Lang, Peter.

Lautenschläger, Dunja. Der Status ausländischer Personen im deutschen Transplantationssystem. 2008. (Recht & Medizin Ser.). (GRE.). 318p. pap. 74.95 *(978-3-631-58281-7(1))* Lang, Peter GmbH, Europaischer Verlag der Wissenschaften DEU. Dist: Lang, Peter.

Leerkes, Arjen. Illegal Residence & Public Safety in the Netherlands. 2009. (IMISCOE Dissertations Ser.). 256p. pap. *(978-90-8964-049-9(5))* Amsterdam Univ. Pr.

Mathisen, Ralph W. & Shanzer, Danuta R., eds. Romans, Barbarians, & the Transformation of the Roman World: Cultural Interaction & the Creation of Identity in Late Antiquity. 2011. (Illus.). 398p. 99.95 *(978-0-7546-6814-5(2))* Ashgate Publishing Co.

Raphael, Lutz & Uerlings, Herbert, eds. Zwischen Ausschluss und Solidarität: Modi der Inklusion/Exklusion von Fremden und Armen in Europa seit der Spätantike. 2008. (Inklusion/Exklusion. Studien zu Fremdheit und Armut von der Antike bis zur Gegenwart Ser.). (GER., Illus.). 570p. pap. 124.95 *(978-3-631-58204-6(8))* Lang, Peter GmbH, Europaischer Verlag der Wissenschaften DEU. Dist: Lang, Peter.

Selwood, Jacob. Diversity & Difference in Early Modern London. 2010. (Illus.). 226p. 119.95 *(978-0-7546-6375-1(2))* Ashgate Publishing Co.

Stoger, Peter. Eingegrenzt und Ausgegrenzt: Tirol und das Fremde Ein Padagogisch-Historisches Lesebuch zum Thema Fremde, Entfremdung und Fremdbestimmung unter Besonderer Berucksichtigung der Auswanderung nach Lateinamerika und der Geschichte der Judischen Mitburger Mit Einem Vorwort von Bischof Reinhold Stecher 3., Durchgesehene Auflage. (Europaische Hochschulschriften Ser.: Vol. 744). (GER.). 489p. 53.95 *(978-3-631-39554-7(X))* Lang, Peter Publishing, Inc.

Triandafyllidou, Anna & Maroukis, Thanos. Migrant Smuggling: Irregular Migration from Asia & Africa to Europe. 2012. (ENG., Illus.). 256p. 85.00 ***(978-0-230-29637-4(8))*** Palgrave Macmillan.

ALIENS—NORTH AMERICA

Golson, Barry. Gringos in Paradise: An American Couple Builds Their Retirement Dream House in a Seaside Village in Mexico. 2008. (ENG.). 320p. pap. 15.00 *(978-0-7432-7636-8(1),* Scribner) Scribner.

ALIENS—UNITED STATES

Akoh, Harry. How a Country Treats Its Citizens No Longer Exclusive Domestic Concern. 2009. 252p. pap. *(978-3-639-16941-6(7))* VDM Verlag Dr. Mueller e.K.

Assa, Ariel & Hufbauer, Gary Clyde. US Taxation of Foreign Income. 2007. (Illus.). 319p. per. 26.95 *(978-0-88132-405-1(1))* Peterson Institute for International Economics.

Avi-Yonah, Reuven S. & Ring, Diane M. U. S. International Taxation, Cases & Materials, 3d. 3rd rev. ed. 2010. (University Casebook Ser.). 659p. 163.00 *(978-1-59941-376-1(0),* Foundation Pr.) West.

Avi-Yonah, Reuven S., et al. U.S. International Taxation: Cases & Materials. 3rd ed. 2011. (Illus.). xxi, 635p. ***(978-1-59941-651-9(4))*** West.

Bender's Immigration & Nationality Act Service. 2nd rev. ed. ring bd., ring bd. 138.00 *(978-0-8205-2877-9(3))* LexisNexis Matthew Bender.

Bertrand, Lea M., ed. Noncitizen & Illegal Alien Access to Benefits & Assistance. 2010. 137.00 *(978-1-61761-184-1(0))* Nova Science Pubs., Inc.

Borthayre, Blaire. The Tax Preparer's Guide to ITINs: Everything You Need to File an Individual Taxpayer Identification Number. 2008. 96p. 49.95 *(978-0-470-18775-3(1),* Wiley) Wiley, John & Sons, Inc.

Bray, Ilona. Fiance & Marriage Visas: A Couple's Guide to U. S. Immigration. 6th rev. ed. 2010. (ENG.). 512p. pap. 39.99 *(978-1-4133-1254-6(3))* NOLO.

Bray, Ilona & Nicolas Lewis, Loida. How to Get a Green Card. 10th rev. ed. 2012. (ENG.). 352p. pap. 39.99 ***(978-1-4133-1687-2(5))*** NOLO.

Butler, Clark, ed. Guantanamo Bay & the Judicial-Moral Treatment of the Other. 2007. 220p. (C). per. 21.95 *(978-1-55753-427-9(6))* Purdue Univ. Pr.

The Case of Ramos & Compean: The Across-Border Context: Hearing Before the Subcommittee on International Organizations, Human Rights, & Oversight of the Committee on Foreign Affairs, House of Representatives, One Hundred Tenth Congress, First Session, July 31, 2007. 2007. (Illus.). iii, 107p. *(978-0-16-079454-4(4),* 552-070-36457-9) United States Government Printing Office.

Christgau, John. Enemies: World War II Alien Internment. 2009. (ENG., Illus.). 216p. pap. 14.95 *(978-0-8032-2806-1(6),* Bison Bks.) Univ. of Nebraska Pr.

Cram101 Textbook Reviews. Outlines & Highlights for Learning about Immigration Law by Constantinos E Scaros. 2011. 64p. pap. 27.95 ***(978-1-4672-6824-0(0))*** Cram101 Inc.

Davis, Jeffrey. Justice Across Borders: The Struggle for Human Rights in U. S. Courts. 2008. (ENG., Illus.). 318p. 85.00 *(978-0-521-87817-3(9))*; pap. 30.99 *(978-0-521-70240-9(2))* Cambridge Univ. Pr.

Department of Homeland Security (DHS) Staff, compiled by. Yearbook of Immigration Statistics on CD-ROM, 1965 to Present. 2007. cd-rom 627.00 *(978-0-934213-60-8(7))* National Technical Information Service, U.S. Dept. of Commerce.

Doernberg, Donald L. International Taxation in A Nutshell, 9th. 9th rev. ed. 2012. (Nutshell Ser.). 654p. pap. 38.00 ***(978-0-314-27531-8(2),*** West Legalworks) West.

Engle, Eric. The Alien Torts Statute. 2010. 236p. pap. *(978-3-8383-5578-8(4))* Lambert Academic Publishing.

Faro, Michael Mota. Your Complete Guide to Green Card Lottery (Diversity Visa) Easy Do-It-Yourself Immigration books - GreenCard. 2011. (ENG., Illus.). 264p. pap. 23.95 *(978-0-9844543-0-3(6))* Unorth, LLC.

House (U.S.), Office of the Law Revision Counsel Staff, compiled by. United States Code, 2006, V. 4, Title 8, Aliens & Nationality, to Title 10, Armed Forces, Sections 101-1805. 2008. (ENG.). 1440p. 107.00 *(978-0-16-079999-0(6),* Office of the Law Revision Counsel) United States Government Printing Office.

Immigration Statistics Office, ed. 2009 Yearbook of Immigration Statistics. 2010. (ENG.). 109p. pap. 18.00 *(978-0-16-086358-5(9),* Justice Dept.) United States Government Printing Office.

International Organization for Migration Staff, ed. Indigenous Routes: A Framework for Understanding Indigenous Migration. 2008. 84p. pap. 21.00 *(978-92-9068-441-1(0))* International Organization for Migration (IOM) CHE. Dist: Balogh International, Inc.

Isenbergh, Joseph. International Taxation: U. S. Taxation of Foreign Persons & Foreign Income, 4 vols., Vol. 2. 4th rev. ed. 2006. 2400p. 409.00 *(978-0-8080-1618-2(0))* Wolters Kluwer Law & Business.

—International Taxation: U. S. Taxation of Foreign Persons & Foreign Income, 4 vols.; set. 4th rev. ed. 2006. 2400p. 525.00 *(978-0-8080-1616-8(4))*; Vol. 1. 409.00 *(978-0-8080-1617-5(2))*; Vol. 3. 409.00 *(978-0-8080-1619-9(9))*; Vol. 4. 409.00 *(978-0-8080-1620-5(2))* Wolters Kluwer Tax & Accounting. (CCH).

Lathrope, Daniel J. Selected Sections on United States International Taxation, 2009 Ed. 2009th rev. ed. 2009. 593p. pap. 33.00 *(978-1-59941-691-5(3),* Foundation Pr.) West.

—Selected Sections on United States International Taxation 2010. 2010th rev. ed. 2010. 611p. pap. 35.00 *(978-1-59941-836-0(3),* Foundation Pr.) West.

LearningExpress Staff. Lo último en Guías de Obtener Su Tarjeta Verde. 2009. (SPA & ENG.). 256p. pap. 12.95 *(978-1-57685-695-6(X))* LearningExpress, LLC.

—The Ultimate Guide to Getting Your Green Card. 2009. (ENG.). 220p. pap. 14.95 *(978-1-57685-694-9(1))* LearningExpress, LLC.

Lees, Lorraine. Yugoslav-Americans & National Security During World War II. 2007. 288p. 40.00 *(978-0-252-03210-3(1))* Univ. of Illinois Pr.

Lowenstein, Edith. The Alien & the Immigration Law: A Study of 1446 Cases Arising under the Immigration & Naturalization Laws of the United States. 2011. 402p. 54.95 ***(978-1-258-04186-1(3))*** Literary Licensing, LLC.

Marciniak, Katarzyna. Alienhood: Citizenship, Exile, & the Logic of Difference. 2006. (Illus.). 272p. per. 24.50 *(978-0-8166-4577-0(9))* Univ. of Minnesota Pr.

Office of the Federal Register (U.S.), compiled by. Code of Federal Regulations, Title 8, Aliens & Nationality, Revised as of January 1 2011. rev. ed. 2011. (ENG.). 1216p. pap. 69.00 ***(978-0-16-087541-0(2),*** Office of the Federal Register) United States Government Printing Office.

—Code of Federal Regulations, Title 8, Aliens & Nationality, Revised as of January 1 2012. rev. ed. 2012. (ENG.). 1216p. pap. 69.00 ***(978-0-16-090075-4(1),*** Office of the Federal Register) United States Government Printing Office.

Okoro, Ralph. Mistreatment of Aliens in America. 2011. (Illus.). 132p. pap. ***(978-1-908064-06-6(4))*** Grace Publishing Group.

Plascencia, Luis F. B. Disenchanting Citizenship: Mexican Migrants & the Boundaries of Belonging. 2012. (Latinidad: Transnational Cultures in the United States Ser.). (ENG.). 266p. 72.00 ***(978-0-8135-5279-8(6))***; pap. 25.95 ***(978-0-8135-5280-4(X))*** Rutgers Univ. Pr.

Raustiala, Kal. Does the Constitution Follow the Flag? The Evolution of Territoriality in American Law, 1 vol. 2011. (ENG.). 328p. pap. 21.95 ***(978-0-19-985817-0(9))*** Oxford Univ. Pr., Inc.

Renshon, Stanley A. Non-Citizen Voting & American Democracy. 2009. (ENG., Illus.). 148p. 69.00 *(978-0-7425-6265-3(4))* Rowman & Littlefield Publishers, Inc.

Scharf, Irene, et al. The Waivers Book: Advanced Issues in Immigration Law Practice. 2011. (Illus.). xii, 377p. pap. ***(978-1-57370-303-1(6))*** American Immigration Lawyers Assn.

Schotel, Bas. On the Right of Exclusion: Law, Ethics & Immigration Policy. 2011. (ENG.). 232p. 125.00 *(978-0-415-57537-9(0))* Routledge.

Seabrook, William. Americans All. 2006. 288p. per. *(978-1-4067-0029-9(0),* Hesperides Pr.) Read Bks.

Shippen, Katherine Binney. Passage to Americ: The Story of the Great Migrations. 2011. 222p. 44.95 **(978-1-258-09182-8(8))** Literary Licensing, LLC.
Singer, Paula. International Aspects of Individual U. S. Tax Returns. 2008. pap. 250.00 (978-0-9801793-4-7(3)) Windstar Publishing, Inc.
Singer, Paula N. & Dodd-, Linda. International Aspects of Individual U. S. Tax Returns: What You Need to Know about Honorarium Payments & Service Fees. 2010. pap. 100.00 (978-0-9801793-8-5(6)) Windstar Publishing, Inc.
Spiro, Peter J. Beyond Citizenship: American Identity after Globalization. 2008. (ENG.). 208p. 29.95 (978-0-19-515218-0(2)) Oxford Univ. Pr., Inc.
Stephens, Beth. International Human Rights Litigation in U.S. Courts. 2008. xxxiv, 619p. (C). (978-1-57105-353-4(0)) BRILL.
Thangasamy, Andrew. State Policies for Undocumented Immigrants: Policy-Making & Outcomes in the U. S. , 1998-2005. 2010. (New Americans). 262p. 70.00 (978-1-59332-387-5(5)) LFB Scholarly Publishing LLC.
United States, Dept. of State Staff, contrib. by. Admission of Aliens into the United States. 2006. (978-1-57588-910-8(2)) Hein, William S. & Co., Inc.

ALIENS (EXTRATERRESTRIALS)
see Life on Other Planets

ALIENS, ILLEGAL
see Illegal Aliens

ALIENS, TAXATION OF
see Taxation of Aliens

ALIMENTARY CANAL
see also Esophagus; Gastrointestinal System
Consumer Dummies Staff, et al. Anti-Inflammation Diet for Dummies. 2011. (ENG.). 384p. pap. 19.99 (978-1-118-02381-5(1), For Dummies) Wiley, John & Sons, Inc.
Kaestner, Klaus. Development, Differentiation & Disease of the para-Alimentary Tract. 2010. (ENG.). 304p. 161.00 (978-0-12-385233-5(1), Academic Pr.) Elsevier Science & Technology Bks.

ALIMENTARY CANAL—HEMORRHAGE
see Gastrointestinal Hemorrhage

ALIMENTARY CANAL—RADIOGRAPHY
ICRP. Human Alimentary Tract Model for Radiological Protection. 2007. (International Commission on Radiological Protection Ser.). (ENG.). 250p. pap. 355.00 (978-0-08-045063-6(6), Elsevier) Elsevier - Health Sciences Div.

ALIMENTARY CANAL—SURGERY
Yeo, Charles J. Shackelford's Surgery of the Alimentary Tract, 2 vols., Set. 6th rev. ed. 2006. (ENG., Illus.). 2418p. 490.00 (978-1-4160-2357-9(7), Saunders) Elsevier - Health Sciences Div.

ALIMENTARY CANAL—TUMORS
Ploeckinger, U., et al, eds. Consensus Guidelines for the Standard of Care for Patients with Digestive Neuroendocrine Tumors. 2009. (Illus.). 80p. pap. (978-3-8055-9255-0(8)) Karger, S. AG.

ALIMENTATION
see Nutrition

ALIMONY
Dijksterhuis, Bregje. Rechters normeren de Alimentatiehoogte: Een empirisch onderzoek naar rechterlijke samenwerking in de Werkgroep Alimentatienormen (1975-2007) 2008. (LUP Meijersreeks Ser.). (DUT.). 260p. pap. (978-90-8728-045-1(9), Leiden Univ. Pr.) Amsterdam Univ. Pr.
Donovan, Sherri. Hit Him Where It Hurts: The Take-No Prisoners Guide to Divorce — Alimony, Child Support, Custody, & More. 2006. (ENG., Illus.). 304p. per. 16.95 (978-1-59337-739-7(8)) Adams Media Corp.
Florida Bar, Continuing Legal Education Staff, contrib. by. Florida Proceedings after Dissolution of Marriage. (Illus.). 8th ed. 2007. 115.00 (978-0-8205-7322-9(1)) 9th ed. 2009. (978-1-4224-5391-9(X)) 10th ed. 2011. **(978-1-4224-6688-9(4))** Florida Bar Continuing Legal Education Pubns., The.
Garrett, W. Walton. Tennessee Divorce, Alimony, & Child Custody: With Forms, 2 vols. 2nd ed. 2007. (Illus.). (978-0-314-97764-9(3)) West Publishing Co., College & Schl. Div.
Scherpe, Jens, ed. Marital Agreements & Private Autonomy in Comparative Perspective, 0 vols. 2012. (ENG.). 496p. 150.00 (978-1-84946-012-5(4)) Hart Publishing Ltd. GBR. Dist: International Specialized Bk. Services.
Taft, Robert S. & Florescue, Leonard G. Tax Aspects of Divorce & Separation. rev. ed. 700p. (978-1-58852-023-4(4), Law Journal Pr.) Incisive Media.

ALIPHATIC COMPOUNDS
see also Alkanes; Polyamines
Albertsson, A. C., ed. & contrib. by. Degradable Aliphatic Polyesters. 2010. (Advances in Polymer Science Ser.). (Illus.). xi, 179p. pap. 239.00 (978-3-642-07597-1(5), 3642075975) Springer.
Vukovic, Jasna. Hyperbranched Polymers Based on Aliphatic Polyesters: Synthesis & Characterization. 2008. 144p. pap. (978-3-639-06007-2(5)) VDM Verlag Dr. Mueller e.K.
Whitmore, Frank C. & Chemistry Associates Staff. Organic Chemistry, Volume One: Part I: Aliphatic Compounds Part II: Alicyclic Compounds. 2011. (Dover Books on Chemistry Ser.). (ENG.). 608p. pap. 24.95 **(978-0-486-60700-9(3))** Dover Pubns., Inc.

ALIPHATIC-CYCLIC COMPOUNDS
see Alicyclic Compounds

ALKALI LANDS
Öztürk, Munir, et al, eds. Sabkha Ecosystems: Africa & Southern Europe, Vol. III. 2010. (Tasks for Vegetation Science Ser.). (Illus.). xiii, 148p. 189.00 (978-90-481-9672-2(8), 9048196728) Springer.
Barth, H.-J. & Böer, Benno, eds. Sabkha Ecosystems: Volume I: the Arabian Peninsula & Adjacent Countries. 2010. (Tasks for Vegetation Science Ser.). 368p. pap. 235.00 (978-90-481-5972-7(5), 9048159725) Springer.
Khan, M. Ajmal, et al, eds. Sabkha Ecosystems: Volume II: West & Central Asia. 2010. (Tasks for Vegetation Science Ser.). (Illus.). xvi, 263p. pap. 199.00 (978-90-481-7274-0(8), 9048172748) Springer.
—Sabkha Ecosystems Vol. 2: West & Central Asia. 2006. (Tasks for Vegetation Science Ser.: Vol. 42). (ENG., Illus.). xvi, 263p. 199.00 (978-1-4020-5071-9(2), 1402050712) Springer.

ALKALI METALS
Dierolf, Volkmar. Electronic Defect States in Alkali Halides: Effects of Interaction with Molecular Ions. 2010. (Springer Tracts in Modern Physics Ser.). (Illus.). xii, 196p. pap. 239.00 (978-3-642-05594-2(X), 364205594X) Springer.
Lew, Kristi. The Alkali Metals: Lithium, Sodium, Potassium, Rubidium, Cesium, Francium. 2009. (Understanding the Elements of the Periodic Table Ser.). (Illus.). 48p. (YA). (gr. 5-9). 26.50 (978-1-4358-5330-0(X)) Rosen Publishing Group, Inc., The.

ALKALIES
see also Ammonia; Potassium; Sodium
Chapman and Hall Staff. Alkaline Rocks & Carbonatites of the World. (Illus.). 141p. 269.00 (978-0-412-62900-6(3)) Springer London, Ltd. GBR. Dist: Springer.
Fawwaz, Osama. Theoretical Calculation of the Electronic States of the Molecule Narb. 2010. 148p. pap. (978-3-8383-7604-2(8)) Lambert Academic Publishing.

Halka, Monica. Alkali & Alkaline Earth Metals. Nordstrom, Brian, ed. 2010. (Periodic Table of the Elements Ser.). (Illus.). 192p. (C). (gr. 9-18). 40.00 (978-0-8160-7369-6(4)) Facts On File, Inc.
Horikoshi, Koki. Alkaliphiles: Genetic Properties & Applications of Enzymes. 2006. (ENG., Illus.). 270p. 199.00 (978-3-540-33372-2(X), 354033372X) Springer.
López de Recalde, Andrea. Alkali atomic Spectra. 2008. 268p. pap. 29.90 (978-1-4357-1097-9(5)) Lulu Enterprises Inc.
Walker, Denise. Acids & Alkalis. 2006. (Core Chemistry/Evans Brothers Ser.). (Illus.). 48p. (YA). (gr. 5-9). 34.25 (978-1-58340-821-6(5)) Black Rabbit Bks.

ALKALINE EARTH METALS
Cram101 Textbook Reviews & Cram101 Textbook Reviews. Outlines & Highlights for Metal Amide Chemistry by Michael Lappert, Isbn: 9780470721841 0470721847. 2011. 86p. pap. 27.95 **(978-1-61461-998-7(0))** Cram101 Inc.
Halka, Monica. Alkali & Alkaline Earth Metals. Nordstrom, Brian, ed. 2010. (Periodic Table of the Elements Ser.). (Illus.). 192p. (C). (gr. 9-18). 40.00 (978-0-8160-7369-6(4)) Facts On File, Inc.
Heos, Bridget. The Alkaline Earth Metals: Beryllium, Magnesium, Calcium, Strontium, Barium, Radium. 2009. (Understanding the Elements of the Periodic Table Ser.). (ENG., Illus.). 48p. (YA). (gr. 5-9). lib. bdg. 26.50 (978-1-4358-5331-7(8)) Rosen Publishing Group, Inc., The.
Lappert, Michael, et al. Metal Amide Chemistry. 2009. (ENG., Illus.). 370p. 155.00 (978-0-470-72184-1(7), Wiley) Wiley, John & Sons, Inc.

ALKALOIDS
see also names of Alkaloids
Aniszewski, Tadeusz. Alkaloids - Secrets of Life: Aklaloids Chemistry, Biological Significance, Applications & Ecological Role. 2007. (ENG., Illus.). 334p. 320.00 (978-0-444-52736-3(2), Elsevier Science) Elsevier Science & Technology Bks.
Borah, Debajit & Mishra, Vimalendra. Phytochemical Values of Some Traditionally Used Plant Parts in Indi. 2011. 88p. pap. **(978-3-8443-0387-2(1))** Lambert Academic Publishing.
Buckingham, John. Bitter Nemesis: The Intimate History of Strychnine. 2007. (ENG., Illus.). 320p. per. 45.95 (978-1-4200-5315-9(9), CRC Press) Taylor & Francis Group GBR. Dist: Taylor & Francis Group.
Buckingham, John, et al, eds. Dictionary of Alkaloids. 2nd rev. ed. 2010. (ENG., Illus.). 2374p. 795.00 (978-1-4200-7769-8(4), CRC Press) Taylor & Francis Group GBR. Dist: Taylor & Francis Group.
Cassiano, Nicole M., ed. Alkaloids: Properties, Applications & Pharmacological Effects. 2010. (Illus.). 185p. 69.00 **(978-1-61761-130-8(1))** Nova Science Pubs., Inc.
Colquhoun, Ross. The Use of Naltrexone in the Treatment of Opiate Dependency. 2010. 344p. pap. (978-3-8383-3961-0(4)) Lambert Academic Publishing.
Cordell, Geoffrey A., contrib. by. The Alkaloids: Chemistry & Biology. (ENG.). 2010. 622p. 231.00 (978-0-12-381341-1(7)) 2010. 302p. 231.00 (978-0-12-381335-0(2)) 2009. 296p. 231.00 (978-0-12-374785-3(6)) 2008. 276p. 231.00 (978-0-12-374520-0(9)) 2008. 476p. 231.00 (978-0-12-374296-4(X)) 2007. 248p. 231.00 (978-0-12-373911-7(X)) Elsevier Science & Technology Bks. (Academic Pr.).
Cordell, Geoffrey A., ed. Chemistry & Biology. 2006. (Alkaloids Ser.). (ENG., Illus.). 374p. 231.00 (978-0-12-469563-4(9), Academic Pr.) Elsevier Science & Technology Bks.
El-Azab, Adel. Enantiocontrolled Synthesis of Calabar Bean & Aphanophine Alkaloids. 2010. 132p. pap. (978-3-639-24340-6(4)) VDM Verlag Dr. Mueller e.K.
Fattorusso, Ernesto & Taglialatela-Scafati, Orazio, eds. Modern Alkaloids: Structure, Isolation, Synthesis & Biology. 2007. (ENG., Illus.). 689p. 315.00 (978-3-527-31521-5(7), Wiley-VCH) Wiley, John & Sons, Inc.
Knolker, Hans-Joachim. The Alkaloids. 2011. (ENG.). 180p. 231.00 **(978-0-12-391426-2(4)**, Academic Pr.) Elsevier Science & Technology Bks.
Knölker, Hans-Joachim, ed. Alkaloid Synthesis. 2012. (Topics in Current Chemistry Ser.). (ENG., Illus.). xi, 258p. 309.00 **(978-3-642-25528-1(0)**, 3642255280) Springer.
Leeper, Finian J. & Vederas, John C. Biosynthesis: Aromatic Polyketides, Isoprenoids, Alkaloids. 2010. (Topics in Current Chemistry Ser.). (Illus.). x, 247p. pap. 259.00 (978-3-642-08583-3(0), 3642085830) Springer.
Moore, Elaine A. & Wilkinson, Samantha. The Promise of Low Dose Naltrexone Therapy: Potential Benefits in Cancer, Autoimmune, Neurological, & Infectious Disorders. 2008. (McFarland Health Topics Ser.). (ENG., Illus.). 223p. pap. 35.00 (978-0-7864-3715-3(4)) McFarland & Co., Inc. Pubs.
Roberts, Margaret F., ed. Alkaloids: Biochemistry, Ecology,and Medicinal Applications. 2012. (ENG.). 508p. pap. 259.00 (978-1-4419-3263-1(1), 1441932631) Springer.
Shah, U. et al. Total Synthesis of Galbulimima Alkaloids: Himgaline & GB13. 2008. 244p. pap. (978-3-639-00482-3(5)) VDM Verlag Dr. Mueller e.K.
Taraschenko, Olga. 18-Methoxycoronaridine & the Habenulo-Interpeduncular Pathway. 2009. 192p. pap. (978-3-639-13774-3(4)) VDM Verlag Dr. Mueller e.K.

ALKANES
see also Cycloalkanes; Methane
Calvert, Jack G., et al. Mechanisms of Atmospheric Oxidation of the Alkanes. 2008. (Illus.). 1008p. 125.00 (978-0-19-536581-8(X)) Oxford Univ. Pr., Inc.
Derouane, E. G., et al, eds. Catalytic Activation & Functionalisation of Light Alkanes: Advances & Challenges. 2010. (NATO Science Partnership Sub-Series: 3: Ser.). 504p. pap. 419.00 (978-90-481-4999-5(1), 9048149991) Springer.
Pérez, Pedro J. Alkane C-H Activation by Single-Site Metal Catalysis. 2012. (Catalysis by Metal Complexes Ser.: 38). (ENG., Illus.). 210p. 159.00 (978-90-481-3697-1(0), 9048136970) Springer.
Polinek, Jiri. Fermentative Production of Recombinant Haloalkane Dehalogenases. 2010. 76p. pap. (978-3-8383-6539-8(9)) Lambert Academic Publishing.

ALKENES
see also Cumulenes; Ethylene; Unsaturated Fatty Acids
Arjunan, Pal & Friedrich, Christian, eds. Branching in Polyolefins. 2008. (ENG., Illus.). 336p. (C). 150.00 (978-0-8412-3898-5(7)) American Chemical Society.
Boyadjian, Cassia. Oxidative Cracking of N-Hexane. 2011. 144p. pap. **(978-3-8433-8963-1(2))** Lambert Academic Publishing.
CAMPORA, Juan & GIAMBASTIANI, Giuliano, eds. Olefin Upgrading Catalysis by Nitrogen-Based Metal Complexes II: State of the Art & Perspectives, 2 vols. 2011. (Catalysis by Metal Complexes Ser.). (ENG., Illus.). xi, 265p. 129.00 (978-94-007-0695-8(2), 9400706952) Springer.
Chambers, Richard D. Organofluorine Chemistry: Fluorinated Alkenes & Reactive Intermediates. 2010. (Topics in Current Chemistry Ser.). x, 244p. pap. 289.00 (978-3-642-08320-4(X), 364208320X) Springer.
Falqi, Fahad H. Miracle of Petrochemicals: Olefins Industry. 2009. pap. 99.95 (978-1-59942-915-1(2)) Universal Pubs.
Giambastiani, Giuliano & Campora, Juan, eds. Olefin Upgrading Catalysis by Nitrogen-Based Metal Complexes I: State-of-the-Art & Perspectives, 2 vols. 2011. (Catalysis by Metal Complexes Ser.). (ENG., Illus.). xii, 287p. 129.00 (978-90-481-3814-2(0), 9048138140) Springer.
Guan, Zhibin. Metal Catalysts in Olefin Polymerisation. 2009. (Topics in Organometallic Chemistry Ser.). 270p. 309.00 (978-3-540-87750-9(9)) Springer.

Inuki, Shinsuke. Total Synthesis of Bioactive Natural Products by Palladium-Catalyzed Domino Cyclization of Allenes & Related Compounds. 2011. (Springer Theses Ser.). (ENG., Illus.). xvi, 106p. 129.00 **(978-4-431-54042-7(3)**, 4431540423) Springer.
Karger-Kocsis, J., ed. Recent Topics on Polyolefins & Related Blends. (978-965-294-071-1(2)) Freund Publishing Hse., Ltd.
Matsumoto, Gary. Vaccine A: The Covert Government Experiment That's Killing Our Soldiers - And Why GI's Are Only the First Victims. 2010. (ENG.). 384p. (gr. 9). pap. 18.95 (978-0-465-02182-6(4)) Basic Bks.
Mittal, Vikas, ed. Advances in Polyolefin Nanocomposites. 2010. (ENG., Illus.). 414p. 149.95 (978-1-4398-1454-3(6), CRC Press) Taylor & Francis Group GBR. Dist: Taylor & Francis Group.
Nwabunma, Domasius & Kyu, Thein, eds. Polyolefin Blends. 2007. (Wiley Series on Polymer Engineering & Technology Ser.: 1). (ENG., Illus.). 667p. 195.00 (978-0-471-79058-7(3), Wiley-Interscience) Wiley, John & Sons, Inc.
—Polyolefin Blends & Composites, 2 vols., Set. 2008. (ENG.). 1312p. 321.00 (978-0-470-19614-4(9), Wiley-Interscience) Wiley, John & Sons, Inc.
—Polyolefin Composites. 2008. (Wiley Series on Polymer Engineering & Technology Ser.: 2). (ENG., Illus.). 603p. 195.00 (978-0-471-79057-0(5), Wiley-Interscience) Wiley, John & Sons, Inc.
Perera, Rosestela, et al, eds. Main-Chain Modification as a Result of Polyolefin Functionalization by Different Techniques. 2010. (Polymer Science & Technology Ser.). (Illus.). 65p. pap. 49.00 (978-1-61668-781-6(9), Nova Novinka) Nova Science Pubs., Inc.
Severn, John R. & Chadwick, John C., eds. Tailor-Made Polymers: Via Immobilization of Alpha-Olefin Polymerization Catalysts. 2008. (ENG., Illus.). 374p. 235.00 (978-3-527-31782-0(1), Wiley-VCH) Wiley, John & Sons, Inc.
Shiono, Takeshi, et al, eds. Progress in Olefin Polymerization Catalysts & Polyolefin Materials: Proceedings of the First Asian Polyolefin Workshop, Nara, Japan, December 7-9 2005. 2006. (Studies in Surface Science & Catalysis Ser.: 161). (ENG., Illus.). 298p. 240.00 (978-0-444-52751-6(6), Elsevier Science) Elsevier Science & Technology Bks.
Tolinski, Michael. Additives for Polyolefins: Getting the Most Out of Polypropylene, Polyethylene & TPO. 2009. (ENG., Illus.). 304p. 155.00 (978-0-8155-2051-1(4)) William Andrew, Inc.
Wang, Yu-Hsuan. Synthesis of Polycyclic Aromatics with Unusual Architectures. 2009. 250p. pap. (978-3-639-16604-0(3)) VDM Verlag Dr. Mueller e.K.
Zaikov, G. E. & Babkin, V. A. Theoretical Estimation of Acidic Force of Linear Olefins of Cationic Polymerization. 2011. pap. (978-1-61209-578-3(X)) Nova Science Pubs., Inc.

ALKORAN
see Koran

ALKYLATION
Bandini, Marco & Umani-Ronchi, Achille, eds. Catalytic Asymmetric Friedel-Crafts Alkylations. 2009. (ENG., Illus.). 317p. 210.00 (978-3-527-32380-7(5), Wiley-VCH) Wiley, John & Sons, Inc.
Elhag Ahmed, Adil & Adam, Farook. Heterogeneous Catalysts for the Friedel-Crafts Alkylation. 2010. 132p. pap. (978-3-639-24924-8(0)) VDM Verlag Dr. Mueller e.K.
Najera, Carmen & Chinchilla, Rafael A. Transition Metal-Catalyzed Alkynylation Reactions. 2010. (ENG., Illus.). 350p. 159.95 (978-1-4200-7759-9(7)) CRC Pr. LLC.
Neumann, Hans P. Progress in DNA Methylation Research. 2007. (C). 185.00 (978-1-60021-722-7(2)) Nova Science Pubs., Inc.
Plumlee Karl Staff. Solid-Acid Catalyzed Alkylation & Isomerization. 2009. 169.95 (978-1-57444-523-7(5)) CRC Pr. LLC.

ALL-AMERICAN GIRLS PROFESSIONAL BASEBALL LEAGUE
Davis, Pepper Paire. Dirt in the Skirt. 2009. (Illus.). 515p. (978-1-4490-4378-0(X)) AuthorHouse.
Fidler, Merrie A. The Origins & History of the All-American Girls Professional Baseball League. alt. ed. 2010. (ENG., Illus.). 400p. pap. 39.95 (978-0-7864-6089-2(X)) McFarland & Co., Inc. Pubs.
Heaphy, Leslie A. & May, Mel Anthony, eds. Encyclopedia of Women & Baseball. 2006. (Women's Studies). (ENG., Illus.). 448p. 75.00 (978-0-7864-2100-8(2)) McFarland & Co., Inc. Pubs.
Kann, Bob. Joyce Westerman: Baseball Hero. 2012. (Badger Biographies Ser.). (ENG., Illus.). 120p. (J). pap. 12.95 **(978-0-87020-486-9(6))** Wisconsin Historical Society.
Madden, W. C. The All-American Girls Professional Baseball League Record Book: Comprehensive Hitting, Fielding & Pitching Statistics. alt. ed. 2008. (ENG., Illus.). 302p. per. 49.95 (978-0-7864-3747-4(2)) McFarland & Co., Inc. Pubs.
Sargent, Jim & Gorman, Robert M. The South Bend Blue Sox: A History of the All-American Girls Professional Baseball League Team & Its Players 1943-1954. 2011. (ENG.). 302p. pap. 39.95 **(978-0-7864-4647-6(1))** McFarland & Co., Inc. Pubs.

ALL-ENGLAND CHAMPIONSHIPS
see Wimbledon Championships

ALL-ENGLAND LAWN TENNIS CHAMPIONSHIP
see Wimbledon Championships

ALL HALLOWS' EVE
see Halloween

ALL INDIA MUSLIM LEAGUE
Yousaf, Nasim. Hidden Facts Behind British India's Freedom: A Scholarly Look into Allama Mashraqi & Quaid-E-Azam's Political Conflict. 2007. (Illus.). 440p. 39.99 (978-0-9760333-8-7(0)) AMZ Pubns.

ALL TERRAIN BICYLES
see Mountain Bikes

ALL TERRAIN CYCLING
see Mountain Biking

ALL TERRAIN VEHICLES
see also Mountain Bikes
Ahlstrand, Alan. Polaris ATVs Repair Manual, 1998 Thru 2007: 250cc Thru 800cc. 2011. (Owner's Workshop Manual Ser.). (ENG., Illus.). 320p. pap. 36.45 **(978-1-56392-953-3(8)**, 1563929538) Haynes Manuals, Inc.
Chevrefils, Adam. Modeling & Design of an Electric All-Terrain Vehicle. 2010. 108p. pap. (978-3-639-23620-0(3)) VDM Verlag Dr. Mueller e.K.
Clymer Publications Staff. Honda TRX250 Recon & Recon ES, 1997-2007. 2008. pap. 34.95 (978-1-59969-176-3(0)) Clymer Publishing.
—Honda TRX400EX Fourtrax & Sportrax 1999-2007. 2008. pap. 34.95 (978-1-59969-251-7(1)) Clymer Publishing.
—Kawasaki Bayou KLF220 & KLF250 1988-2010. 2011. pap. 34.95 (978-1-59969-376-7(3)) Clymer Publishing.
—Kawasaki KLR650 1987-2007. 2008. pap. 34.95 (978-1-59969-225-8(2)) Clymer Publishing.
—Polaris 400, 450 & 500 Sportsman 1996-2008. 2008. pap. 45.95 (978-1-59969-242-5(2)) Clymer Publishing.
—Polaris Magnum & Big Boss ATVs, 1996-1999. 2008. pap. 34.95 (978-1-59969-224-1(4)) Clymer Publishing.
—Polaris Predator 2003-2007. 2008. pap. 34.95 (978-1-59969-261-6(9)) Clymer Publishing.

—Polaris Sportsman 400, 450 And 500, 1996-2010. 2010. pap. 47.95 *(978-1-59969-336-1(4))* Clymer Publishing.
—Polaris Sportsman 600, 700, & 800 Series 2002-2010. 2010. pap. 47.95 *(978-1-59969-354-5(2))* Clymer Publishing.
—Yamaha YFM80 Moto-4, Badger & Raptor 2001-2008. 2008. pap. 34.95 *(978-1-59969-236-4(8))* Clymer Publishing.
Clymer Publishing, creator. Clymer Powersport Vehicle Blue Book: March 1, 2009-August 31 2009. 2009. (Clymer Powersport Vehicle Blue Book Ser.). 962p. pap. 44.95 *(978-1-59969-267-8(8))* Clymer Publishing.
Corrigan, Brian C. All-Terrain Vehicles. 2010. 130.00 *(978-1-61728-845-6(4))* Nova Science Pubs., Inc.
Haynes Editors & Freund, Ken. Honda Foreman & Rubicon ATVs, 1995 Thru 2007. 2007. (Motorcycle Repair Manual Ser.). (ENG., Illus.). 208p. pap. 36.45 *(978-1-56392-656-3(3)*, 1563926563) Haynes Manuals, Inc.
—Yamaha Kodiak & Grizzlys ATVS: 2-wheel drive & 4-wheel drive 1993 To 2005. 2007. (Owners Workshop Manual Ser.). (ENG., Illus.). 240p. pap. 36.45 *(978-1-56392-567-2(2)*, 1563925672) Haynes Manuals, Inc.
Haynes Manuals Editors. Suzuki, Kawasaki, Artic Cat ATVs 2003 to 2009: LT-Z400, KFX400, DVX400. 2011. (Haynes Repair Manual Ser.). (ENG., Illus.). 208p. 45.45 ***(978-1-56392-910-6(4)***, 1563929104) Haynes Manuals, Inc.
Haynes Manuals Editors, ed. Honda Rancher, Recon & TRX250EX ATV's. 2010. (Owners Workshop Manual Ser.). (ENG., Illus.). 208p. pap. 33.95 *(978-1-56392-778-2(0)*, 1563927780) Haynes Manuals, Inc.
Meyer, Kevin G. A Comprehensive Framework for off-Highway Vehicle Trail Management. Forest Service (U.S.) Staff et al, eds. 2012. (ENG., Illus.). 324p. pap. 53.00 ***(978-0-16-089806-8(4)***, Forest Service) United States Government Printing Office.
Off Road Venture. Michigan off Road Map: Lower Peninsula East. 2007. 1p. *(978-0-9767312-1-4(5))* Off Road Venture.
Ouren, Douglas S. Environmental Effects of off-Highway Vehicles. 2009. 229p. 79.00 *(978-1-60692-936-0(4))* Nova Science Pubs., Inc.
Price Digest Staff. Clymer Powersport Vehicle Blue Book Fall 2006. 2006. pap. 39.95 *(978-1-59969-070-4(5))* Penton Media, Inc.
Price Digests. Clymer Powersport Vehicle Blue Book Spring/Summer 2007. 2007. pap. *(978-1-59969-114-5(0))* Penton Media, Inc.
Trailsource.com, compiled by. Colorado ATV Trails Guidebook: Complete Riding Guide to ATV Trails in Colorado - CO ATV. 2009. pap. 19.99 *(978-0-9767190-4-5(5))* TRAILSOURCE.COM, Inc.
—Florida ATV Trails Guidebook: Complete Riding Guide to ATV in Florida - FL ATV. 2009. pap. 19.99 *(978-0-9767190-8-3(8))* TRAILSOURCE.COM, Inc.
—Georgia ATV Trails Guidebook: Complete Riding Guide to ATV in Georgia - GA ATV. 2009. 19.99 *(978-0-9767190-5-2(3))* TRAILSOURCE.COM, Inc.
—New York ATV Trails Guidebook: Complete Riding Guide to NY ATV - ATV in New York. 2009. pap. 19.99 *(978-0-9767190-1-4(0))* TRAILSOURCE.COM, Inc.
—North Carolina ATV Trails Guidebook: Complete Riding Guide to ATV in NC - NC ATV. 2009. pap. 19.99 *(978-0-9767190-7-6(X))* TRAILSOURCE.COM, Inc.
—Ohio ATV Trails Guidebook: Complete Riding Guide to ATV in Ohio - OH ATV. 2009. pap. 19.99 *(978-0-9767190-2-1(9))* TRAILSOURCE.COM, Inc.
—Pennsylvania ATV Trails Guidebook: Complete Riding Guide to PA ATV - ATV in PA. 2009. pap. 19.99 *(978-0-9767190-3-8(7))* TRAILSOURCE.COM, Inc.
—Texas ATV Trails Guidebook: Complete Riding Guide to ATV Parks & Trails in Texas - TX ATV. 2009. pap. 19.99 *(978-0-9767190-6-9(1))* TRAILSOURCE.COM, Inc.
—Wisconsin ATV Trails Guidebook: Complete Riding Guide to ATV in Wisconsin - WI ATV. 2009. pap. 19.99 *(978-0-9767190-0-7(2))* TRAILSOURCE.COM, Inc.
Wells, Charles. ATV Trails Gde Colorado. 2008. 160p. pap. 19.95 *(978-1-934838-01-3(2))* FunTreks Guidebooks.
Wells, Charles. Norh Colorado Backroads & 4Wd Trails. 2011. pap. 24.95 ***(978-1-934838-05-1(5))*** FunTreks Guidebooks.
Wells, Charles A. & Peterson, Matt. ATV Trails Guide: Colorado: Silverton, Ouray, Lake City, Telluride. 2009. (Illus.). 158p. *(978-1-934838-03-7(9))* FunTreks Guidebooks.

ALL-VOLUNTEER FORCES
see Military Service, Voluntary

ALLAGASH RIVER (ME.)
Gilpatrick, Gil. The Allagash Guide: What You Need to Know to Canoe this Famous Maine Waterway. 2011. (ENG., Illus.). 104p. pap. 11.95 *(978-1-56523-488-8(X))* Fox Chapel Publishing Co., Inc.

ALLAH
see God (Islam)

ALLDEUTSCHER VERBAND
Jackisch, Barry A. The Pan-German League & Radical Nationalist Politics in Interwar Germany 1918-39. 2012. 172p. 104.95 ***(978-1-4094-2761-2(7))*** Ashgate Publishing Co.

ALLEGANY COUNTY (MD.)
Feldstein, Albert L. Allegany County. 2006. (Postcard History Ser.). (ENG., Illus.). 128p. per. 21.99 *(978-0-7385-4381-9(0))* Arcadia Publishing.
Whetzel, Dan. Allegany County. 2011. (Images of America Ser.). (Illus.). 128p. pap. 21.99 *(978-0-7385-8704-2(4))* Arcadia Publishing.
Zumbrun, Francis & Zumbrun, Champ. A History of Green Ridge State Forest. 2010. (ENG., Illus.). 160p. pap. 19.99 *(978-1-59629-902-3(9))* History Pr., The.

ALLEGATIONS AGAINST POLICE
see Police—Complaints Against

ALLEGHENIES
see Allegheny Mountains

ALLEGHENY COUNTY (PA.)
Allegheny City Society, creator. Allegheny City 1840-1907. 2007. (Images of America Ser.). (ENG., Illus.). 128p. per. 21.99 *(978-0-7385-5500-3(2))* Arcadia Publishing.
Archibald, Rae W. & Sleeper, Sally. Government Consolidation & Economic Development in Allegheny County & the City of Pittsburgh. 2008. 62p. pap. 23.00 *(978-0-8330-4463-1(X)*, tr-569) RAND Corp., The.
Brown, Eliza Smith. African American Historic Sites Survey of Allegheny County (Pennsylvania) 2007. (Illus.). 242p. (C). pap. 25.00 *(978-1-4223-1490-6(1))* DIANE Publishing Co.
Grom, Robert M. Braddock, Allegheny County. 2008. (Images of America Ser.). (ENG., Illus.). 128p. pap. 21.99 *(978-0-7385-6302-2(1))* Arcadia Publishing.
Keyser, Donna, et al. Building Bridges: Lessons from a Pittsburgh Partnership to Strengthen Systems of Care for Maternal Depression. 2010. 234p. pap. 45.00 *(978-0-8330-5006-9(0)*, mg-973) RAND Corp., The.
McCullough, Kevin & Meyers, Larry. 2011 Allegheny County Data Book. McCullough, Kevin, ed. 2011. (Illus.). 213p. pap. *(978-1-58036-702-8(X))* Pennsylvania State Data Ctr.

ALLEGHENY MOUNTAINS
Hurst, Dave. Pennsylvania's Allegheny Mountains: The First Frontier. 2009. (Regional Histories Ser.). 128p. pap. 19.99 *(978-1-59629-724-1(7))* History Pr., The.
Jackson, Robert. The Mountain. 2010. (ENG.). 644p. pap. 30.00 *(978-0-271-03643-4(5)*, Metalmark) Pennsylvania State Univ. Pr.
Mellander, Deane. B & O Thunder in the Alleghenies. (Hobby Book Ser.: No. C 97). 84p. 13.95 *(978-0-911868-97-5(8))* Carstens Pubns., Inc.

ALLEGHENY NATIONAL FOREST (PA.)
Mitchell, Jeff. Hiking the Allegheny National Forest: Exploring the Wilderness of Northwestern Pennsylvania. 2007. (ENG., Illus.). 162p. per. 12.95 *(978-0-8117-3372-4(6))* Stackpole Bks.

ALLEGHENY RIVER (PA. AND N.Y.)
Lindell, Piper L., et al. Allegheny River Paddling Guide: From Kinzua Dam to Tionesta. Brant, Tataboline D., ed. 2007. (Illus.). 36p. ring bd. 28.30 *(978-0-9798528-0-0(3))* Lindell, Piper.

ALLEGHENY RIVER VALLEY (PA. AND N.Y.)
Berrizbeitia, Anita, ed. Michael Van Valkenburgh Associates: Reconstructing Urban Landscapes. 2009. (ENG., Illus.). 320p. 65.00 *(978-0-300-13585-5(8))* Yale Univ. Pr.
Williams, Charles E. Along the Allegheny River: The Southern Watershed. 2006. (Postcard History Ser.). (ENG., Illus.). 128p. per. 21.99 *(978-0-7385-3846-4(9))* Arcadia Publishing.

ALLEGIANCE
see also Dual Nationality; Naturalization; Patriotism; Self-Determination, National
Adler, Nanci. Keeping Faith with the Party: Communist Believers Return from the Gulag. 2012. xvi, 237p. ***(978-0-253-00571-7(X))***; (ENG., Illus.). 256p. 70.00 *(978-0-253-35722-9(5)*, 0253357225); (ENG., Illus.). 256p. pap. 25.00 *(978-0-253-22379-1(2)*, 0253223792) Indiana Univ. Pr.
Ellis, Richard J. To the Flag: The Unlikely History of the Pledge of Allegiance. 2007. (Illus.). 297p. per. 15.95 *(978-0-7006-1521-6(0))* Univ. Pr. of Kansas.
Hajnal, Zoltan & Lee, Taeku. Why Americans Don′t Enjoy the Party - Race, Immigration, & the Failure (of Political Parties) to Engage the Electorate. 2011. (ENG., Illus.). 344p. (C). pap. 27.95 *(978-0-691-14879-3(1))* Princeton Univ. Pr.
Hajnal, Zoltan & Lee, Takeu. Why American Don′t Join the Party - Race, Immigration, & the Failure (of Political Parties) to Engage the Electorate. 2011. (ENG., Illus.). 344p. (C). 75.00 *(978-0-691-14878-6(3))* Princeton Univ. Pr.
Hart, Vivien. Distrust & Democracy: Political Distrust in Britain & America. 2010. (ENG.). 272p. pap. 24.99 *(978-0-521-13454-5(4))* Cambridge Univ. Pr.
Jones, Jeffrey & Meyer, Peter. Pledge: A History of the Pledge of Allegiance. 2010. (ENG.). 224p. 23.99 *(978-0-312-35002-4(3)*, Dunne, Thomas Bks.) St. Martin's Pr.
McMichael, Andrew. Atlantic Loyalties: Americans in Spanish West Florida, 1785-1810. 2008. (ENG., Illus.). 240p. 59.95 *(978-0-8203-3004-4(3))*; per. 24.95 *(978-0-8203-3023-5(X))* Univ. of Georgia Pr.
Patterson, Kathy. I Pledge Allegiance to the Flag. 2011. 24p. pap. 14.95 ***(978-1-4567-2816-8(4))*** AuthorHouse.
Sarris, Jonathan Dean. A Separate Civil War: Communities in Conflict in the Mountain South. 2006. (Nation Divided: Studies in the Civil War Era Ser.). (ENG., Illus.). 256p. (gr. 17). 55.00 *(978-0-8139-2549-3(5))* Univ. Pr. of Virginia.

ALLEGORIES
Here are entered collections of allegories. Works on allegory as a literary form are entered under Allegory.
see also Apocalyptic Art; Fables; Parables
Allegorical Narratives, Vol. 28. *(978-0-404-60928-3(7))* AMS Pr., Inc.
Baskins, Cristelle & Rosenthal, Lisa, eds. Allegory in Early Modern Visual Culture: Embodying Meaning. 2007. (Illus.). 316p. 134.95 *(978-0-7546-5760-6(4))* Ashgate Publishing Co.
Bryte, Scott. Tales of the Inner City. 2007. (Illus.). 114p. per. *(978-0-7880-2389-7(6))* CSS Publishing Co.
Clark, Jan. An Invitation to Come. 2008. 292p. pap. 15.99 *(978-1-60647-260-6(7))* Xulon Pr., Inc.
Leach, Amy. Things That Are. 2012. (ENG., Illus.). 192p. 18.00 ***(978-1-57131-334-8(6))*** Milkweed Editions.
Madsen, Deborah L. The Postmodernist Allegories of Thomas Pynchon. (Illus.). 192p. *(978-0-7185-1369-6(X)*, Burns & Oates) Continuum International Publishing Group, Ltd.
McKelvy, Luke. Union. 2007. 116p. (ENG.). 18.99 *(978-1-60266-638-2(5))*; per. 10.99 *(978-1-60266-637-5(7))* Xulon Pr., Inc.
Molotiu, Andrei. Fragonard's Allegories of Love. 2008. (Illus.). 128p. 24.95 *(978-0-89236-897-6(7))* Oxford Univ. Pr., Inc.
Reidemeister, Johann. Superbia und Narziß. 2006. (Ars Nova Ser.). (Illus.). 229p. (C). 145.00 *(978-2-503-52018-6(9))* Brepols Pubs. BEL. Dist: Brown, David Bk. Co., The.
Tapia Y Rivera, Alejandro. Enardo & Rosael: An Allegorical Novella. 2011. 80p. 37.95 ***(978-1-258-07093-9(6))*** Literary Licensing, LLC.
Willwerth, Edwin. The Wind, the Kite, the String. 2007. 284p. (ENG.). 25.99 *(978-1-60266-984-0(8))*; per. 15.99 *(978-1-60266-983-3(X))* Xulon Pr., Inc.

ALLEGORY
Here are entered works on allegory as a literary form. Collections of allegories are entered under Allegories.
see also Personification in Literature; Symbolism in Literature
Borris, Kenneth. Allegory & Epic in English Renaissance Literature: Heroic Form in Sidney, Spenser, & Milton. 2009. (ENG., Illus.). 336p. pap. 46.00 *(978-0-521-10009-0(7))* Cambridge Univ. Pr.
Boughton, Jesse Scott. The Idea of Progress in Philo Judaeus. 2011. 294p. 48.95 ***(978-1-258-05212-6(1))*** Literary Licensing, LLC.
Bregenzer, Don. A Round-Table in Poictesme: A Symposium. 2007. 140p. (ENG.). 24.95 *(978-1-4344-9486-3(1))*; per. 14.95 *(978-1-4344-9485-6(3))* Wildside Pr., LLC.
Brisson, Luc. How Philosophers Saved Myths: Allegorical Interpretation & Classical Mythology. Tihanyi, Catherine, tr. from FRE. 2008. 221p. pap. 19.00 *(978-0-226-07537-2(0))* Univ. of Chicago Pr.
Copeland, Rita & Struck, Peter, eds. The Cambridge Companion to Allegory. 2010. (Cambridge Companions to Literature Ser.). (ENG., Illus.). 324p. (C). 95.00 *(978-0-521-86229-5(9))*; pap. 29.99 *(978-0-521-68082-0(4))* Cambridge Univ. Pr.
D'Angouleme, Marguerite. The Prisons of Marguerite de Navarre. 152p. pap. 22.95 *(978-0-7049-0124-7(2))* Pegasus Pr.
Del Bello, Davide. Forgotten Paths: Etymology & the Allegorical Mindset. 2007. (Illus.). 187p. 64.95 *(978-0-8132-1484-9(X))* Catholic Univ. of America Pr.
Dieke, Ikenna. Allegory & Meaning: Reading African, African American, & Caribbean Literature. 2010. (ENG.). 188p. pap. 28.00 *(978-0-7618-5121-9(6))* Univ. Pr. of America, Inc.
Favoretto, Mara. Alegoria e Ironia Bajo Censura en la Argentina Del Proceso (1976-1983) 2010. (SPA.). 129.95 *(978-0-7734-1292-7(1))* Mellen, Edwin Pr., The.
Fergusson, Francis. Trope & Allegory: Themes Common to Dante & Shakespeare. 2011. (ENG.). 176p. pap. 22.95 ***(978-0-8203-3849-1(4))*** Univ. of Georgia Pr.
Fletcher, Angus. Allegory - the Theory of a Symbolic Mode. 2012. (ENG., Illus.). 496p. (C). pap. 35.00 ***(978-0-691-15180-9(6))*** Princeton Univ. Pr.
Fuller, Alan. The GOSPEL PROPHECY: the Bible as Allegory. 2009. 206p. pap. 18.99 *(978-0-557-06033-7(8))* Lulu Enterprises Inc.
Gibbs Kamath, Stephanie A. Viereck. Authorship & First-Person Allegory in Late Medieval France & England. 2012. (Gallica Ser.: Volume 26). 226p. 90.00 ***(978-1-84384-313-9(7)***, D. S. Brewer) Boydell & Brewer, Ltd. GBR. Dist: Boydell & Brewer, Inc.
González, John Morán. The Outer Edge of the Wave: Negotiating Cultural Identities in Post-Reconstruction America. 2010. cd-rom 14.95 *(978-0-8142-9228-0(3))* Ohio State Univ. Pr.
Greenlaw, Edwin. Studies in Spenser's Historical Allegory. 232p. 2008. 41.95 *(978-1-4366-8845-1(0))* 2007. (ENG.). per. 26.95 *(978-1-4325-4003-8(7))* Kessinger Publishing, LLC.
Guynn, Noah D. & Guynn, Noah. Allegory & Sexual Ethics in the High Middle Ages. annot. ed. 2007. (New Middle Ages Ser.). (ENG.). 232p. 84.00 *(978-1-4039-7147-0(1))* Palgrave Macmillan.
Hauser, Sheri. Dream Dancing with Dad. 2011. (J). spiral bd. 5.95 ***(978-1-60789-261-8(8))*** Glory Bound Bks. Las Vegas.
Holt, Guy. A Bibliography of the Writings of James Branch Cabell. 2007. (ENG.). 76p. per. 17.95 *(978-1-4325-1460-0(1))* Kessinger Publishing, LLC.
Johnson, Gary. The Vitality of Allegory: Figural Narrative in Modern & Contemporary Fiction. 2012. (Theory interpretation Narrativ Ser.). 296p. 49.95 ***(978-0-8142-1182-3(8))***; cd-rom 14.95 ***(978-0-8142-9281-5(X))*** Ohio State Univ. Pr.
KASTEN, Madeleine. In Search of 'Kynde Knowynge'. Piers Plowman & the Origin of Allegory. 2007. (Costerus New Ser.: 168). 260p. per. 70.20 *(978-90-420-2173-0(X))* Rodopi.
Kelley, Theresa M. Reinventing Allegory. 2010. (Cambridge Studies in Romanticism Ser.). (ENG.). 364p. pap. 35.99 *(978-0-521-15777-3(3))* Cambridge Univ. Pr.
Louth, Andrew. Discerning the Mystery: An Essay on the Nature of Theology. 2007. 150p. pap. 25.00 *(978-0-9717483-6-1(5))* Eighth Day Pr.
Machosky, Brenda. Structures of Appearing: Allegory & the Work of Literature. 2012. (ENG.). 256p. 55.00 ***(978-0-8232-4284-9(6))*** Fordham Univ. Pr.
Machosky, Brenda. Thinking Allegory Otherwise. 2009. (ENG., Illus.). 288p. 50.00 *(978-0-8047-6380-6(1))* Stanford Univ. Pr.
Nuttall, A. D. Two Concepts of Allegory: A Study of Shakespeare's the Tempest & the Logic of Allegorical Expression. 2007. (ENG.). 192p. per. 21.00 *(978-0-300-11874-2(0))* Yale Univ. Pr.
Paxson, James J. The Poetics of Personification. 2009. (Literature, Culture, Theory Ser.). (ENG.). 224p. pap. 31.99 *(978-0-521-10631-3(1))* Cambridge Univ. Pr.
Puga, Ana Elena. Memory, Allegory, & Testimony in South American Theater: Upstaging Dictatorship. 2012. (ENG., Illus.). 208p. pap. 39.95 ***(978-0-415-53752-0(5))*** Routledge.
Raskolnikov, Masha. Body Against Soul: Gender & Sowlehele in Middle English Allegory. 2009. (Interventions: New Studies Medieval Cult Ser.). (ENG.). 288p. 61.95 *(978-0-8142-1102-1(X))*; cd-rom 14.95 *(978-0-8142-9200-6(3))* Ohio State Univ. Pr.
, Renford, Renford. The River of Life. 2009. 114p. pap. 17.96 *(978-0-557-08707-5(4))* Lulu Enterprises Inc.
Saintsbury, George. The Flourishing of Romance & the Rise of Allegory. 2009. 364p. 29.99 *(978-0-559-09517-7(1))*; 31.99 *(978-0-559-09503-0(1))*; pap. 20.99 *(978-0-559-09512-2(0))*; pap. 32.75 *(978-0-559-09506-1(6))* BiblioBazaar.
—The Flourishing of Romance & the Rise of Allegory. 2009. 228p. pap. *(978-0-217-29456-0(1))*; pap. *(978-0-217-58642-9(2))* Books LLC.
—The Flourishing of Romance & the Rise of Allegory. 2008. 324p. pap. *(978-1-4099-1921-6(8))* Dodo Pr.
—The Flourishing of Romance & the Rise of Allegory. 2007. (ENG.). 448p. 51.95 *(978-0-548-11589-3(3))* Kessinger Publishing, LLC.
Scrivener, Michael. Seditious Allegories: John Thelwall & Jacobin Writing. 2008. (ENG.). 320p. per. 27.95 *(978-0-271-02847-7(5))* Pennsylvania State Univ. Pr.
Svendsen, Stefan N. Allegory Transformed: The Appropriation of Philonic Hermeneutics in the Letters to the Hebrews. 2009. 273p. pap. 117.50 *(978-3-16-149968-5(9))* Mohr Siebeck GmbH & Co. KG DEU. Dist: Coronet Bks.
TAMBLING. Allegory. 2010. vi, 192p. 95.00 *(978-0-415-34005-2(5))*; pap. 22.95 *(978-0-415-34006-9(3))* Routledge.
Taylor, Jefferey H. Four Levels of Meaning in the York Cycle of Mystery Plays: A Study in Medieval Allegory. 2006. 128p. (C). 89.95 *(978-0-7734-5578-8(7))* Mellen, Edwin Pr., The.
Wheat, Leonard F. Philip Pullman's His Dark Materials: A Multiple Allegory: Attacking Religious Superstition in the Lion, the Witch & the Wardrobe & Paradise Lost. 2007. (ENG.). 376p. per. 21.98 *(978-1-59102-589-4(3))* Prometheus Bks., Pubs.

ALLEGORY (ART)
see Allegories; Symbolism in Art

ALLEGORY IN LITERATURE
Bonhomme, Denise. Allegory in the Esoteric Literature of France. 2010. 118p. pap. 13.95 *(978-1-4327-5059-6(3))* Outskirts Pr., Inc.
Burlinson, Christopher. Allegory, Space & the Material World in the Writings of Edmund Spenser. 2006. (Studies in Renaissance Literature Ser.: Volume 17). (Illus.). 274p. 90.00 *(978-1-84384-078-7(2))* Boydell & Brewer, Inc.
Luebke, Alexandra. The Pilgrim's Progress in American Juvenile Literature 1860-1900. 2007. 84p. per. *(978-3-8364-2300-7(6))* VDM Verlag Dr. Mueller e.K.
McClennen, Joshua. On the Meaning & Function of Allegory in the English Renaissance. 2007. (ENG.). 48p. per. 15.95 *(978-1-4325-5985-4(0))* Kessinger Publishing, LLC.
Sugg, Katherine. Gender & Allegory in Transamerican Fiction & Performance. 2008. (ENG.). 260p. 89.00 *(978-0-230-60476-6(5))* Palgrave Macmillan.

ALLELOPATHY
Avchar, Bapu & Deokule, Subhas. Weed Allelopathy. 2011. 288p. pap. ***(978-3-8433-9385-0(0))*** Lambert Academic Publishing.
Blum, Udo. Plant-Plant Allelopathic Interactions: Phenolic Acids, Cover Crops & Weed Emergence. 2011. (ENG., Illus.). xxix, 200p. 139.00 *(978-94-007-0682-8(0)*, 9400706820) Springer.
Fujii, Yoshiharu & Parvez, M. M. Allelopathy: New Concepts & Methodology. 2007. (ENG., Illus.). 398p. 99.95 *(978-1-57808-446-3(6))* BIOS Scientific Publishers Ltd. GBR. Dist: Taylor & Francis Group.
Reigosa, Manuel J., et al, eds. Allelopathy: A Physiological Process with Ecological Implications. 2010. (ENG.). xiv, 637p. pap. 359.00 *(978-90-481-7095-1(8)*, 9048170958) Springer.
Roshchina, V. V. & Narwal, S. S., eds. Cell Diagnostics: Images, Biophysical & Biochemical Processes in Allelopathy. 2007. (ENG.). 224p. 79.95 *(978-1-57808-510-1(1))* BIOS Scientific Publishers Ltd. GBR. Dist: Taylor & Francis Group.
Sisodia, Swapnal & Siddiqui, M. B. Allelopathic Effects of Croton Bonplandianum Baill. 2011. 220p. pap. ***(978-3-8433-5701-2(3))*** Lambert Academic Publishing.
Uzma, Bashir. Sunflower Allelopathy: Residual Effects on Subsequent Crops. 2011. 216p. pap. ***(978-3-639-33727-3(1))*** VDM Verlag Dr. Mueller e.K.
Willis, R. The History of Allelopathy. 2007. (ENG.). xiv, 316p. 219.00 *(978-1-4020-4092-4(X)*, 140204092X) Springer.
Willis, R. J. The History of Allelopathy. 2010. (ENG.). xiv, 316p. pap. 219.00 *(978-90-481-7039-5(7)*, 9048170397) Springer.

Zeng, Ren Sen, et al, eds. Allelopathy in Sustainable Agriculture & Forestry. 2010. (ENG., Illus.). xiv, 412p. pap. 225.00 *(978-1-4419-2649-4(6)*, 1441926496) Springer.

Zeng, Ren Sen, et al. Allelopathy in Sustainable Agriculture & Forestry. Zeng, Ren Sen et al, eds. 2008. (ENG., Illus.). xiv, 412p. 225.00 *(978-0-387-77336-0(3)*, 0387773363) Springer.

ALLEN, ETHAN, 1738-1789

Allen, Ethan. A Narrative of Colonel Ethan Allen's Captivity. 2009. 62p. pap. *(978-1-151-45129-3(0))* Books LLC.

—A Narrative of Colonel Ethan Allen's Captivity. 2008. 124p. 35.95 *(978-1-4368-9184-4(1))*; pap. 20.95 *(978-1-4367-4141-5(6))* Kessinger Publishing, LLC.

Brown, Charles Walter. Ethan Allen of Green Mountain Fame a Hero of the Revolution. 2009. (ENG.). 296p. 34.99 *(978-1-117-18540-8(0))* BiblioBazaar.

De Puy, Henry W. (Henry Walter). Ethan Allen & the Green-Mountain Heroes of '76 with a Sketch of the Early History of Vermont by Henry W de Puy. 2006. 436p. per. 26.99 *(978-1-4255-4781-3(8))* MPublishing.

Morrissey, Helen. Ethan Allen's Daughter. 236p. 2008. 41.95 *(978-1-4367-0143-3(0))* 2007. per. 26.95 *(978-1-4325-9743-6(4))* Kessinger Publishing, LLC.

Randall, Willard Sterne. Ethan Allen: His Life & Times. 2011. (ENG., Illus.). 617p. 35.00 *(978-0-393-07665-3(2)*, 7665) Norton, W. W. & Co., Inc.

Smith, Richard B. Ethan Allen & the Capture of Fort Ticonderoga: America's First Victory. 2010. (ENG., Illus.). 128p. pap. 19.99 *(978-1-59629-920-7(7))* History Pr., The.

ALLEN, FRANCES MARGARET, 1784-1819

Betz, Eva K. Fanny Allen: Green Mountain Rebel. 2011. 192p. 42.95 ***(978-1-258-07393-0(5))*** Literary Licensing, LLC.

Morrissey, Helen. Ethan Allen's Daughter. 236p. 2008. 41.95 *(978-1-4367-0143-3(0))* 2007. per. 26.95 *(978-1-4325-9743-6(4))* Kessinger Publishing, LLC.

ALLEN, FRED, 1894-1956

Allen, Fred. Much Ado about Me. 402p. reprint ed. lib. bdg. 27.95 *(978-0-88411-291-4(8))* Amereon LTD.

—Much Ado about Me. 2008. 404p. pap. 19.99 *(978-1-4344-7759-0(2))* Wildside Pr., LLC.

—Treadmill to Oblivion. 252p. 2009. 32.95 *(978-1-4344-5413-3(4))* 2009. pap. 19.95 *(978-1-4344-5412-6(6))* 2007. (ENG.). 35.00 *(978-1-4344-0147-2(2))* 2007. per. 19.95 *(978-1-4344-0142-7(1))* Wildside Pr., LLC.

ALLEN, GRACIE, 1906-1964

Burns, George, et al. I Love Her, That's Why! an Autobiography. 2011. 300p. 48.95 ***(978-1-258-01214-4(6))*** Literary Licensing, LLC.

ALLEN, JAMES LANE, 1849-1925

Allen, James L. Mettle of the Pasture. reprint ed. 31.50 *(978-0-404-00328-9(1))* AMS Pr., Inc.

Bancroft, Edith. Jane Allen Junior. 2008. 168p. 22.99 *(978-0-554-31537-9(8))*; 25.99 *(978-0-554-22234-9(5))* BiblioBazaar.

Knight, Grant C. James Lane Allen & the Genteel Tradition. 328p. 2008. 45.95 *(978-1-4366-6322-6(5))* 2007. (ENG.). per. 30.95 *(978-1-4325-9179-3(7))* Kessinger Publishing, LLC.

—James Lane Allen & the Genteel Tradition. 313p. reprint ed. lib. bdg. 98.00 *(978-0-7222-0465-8(5))* Library Reprints, Inc.

Townsend, John Wilson. James Lane Allen A Personal Note. 2006. pap. 21.95 *(978-1-4286-5792-2(4))* Kessinger Publishing, LLC.

ALLEN, RICHARD, 1760-1831

Newman, Richard. Freedom's Prophet: Bishop Richard Allen, the AME Church, & the Black Founding Fathers. 2009. (ENG., Illus.). 368p. pap. 23.00 *(978-0-8147-5857-1(6))* New York Univ. Pr.

ALLEN, WOODY, 1935-

Colombani, Florence. Woody Allen. 2010. (ENG.). 102p. pap. 9.95 *(978-2-86642-566-1(9))* Phaidon Pr., Inc.

Fernengel, Ingmar Angstlich und Gottverlassen: Woody Allen und Ingmar Bergman auf der Suche nach dem Sinn des Lebens. 2010. (GER.). 214p. 57.95 *(978-3-631-60467-0(X))* Lang, Peter GmbH, Europaischer Verlag der Wissenschaften DEU. Dist: Lang, Peter.

Hample, Stuart E. & Allen, Woody. Dread & Superficiality: Woody Allen as Comic Strip. 2009. (ENG., Illus.). 240p. 35.00 *(978-0-8109-5742-8(6))* Abrams.

Harvey, Adam. The Soundtracks of Woody Allen: A Complete Guide to the Songs & Music in Every Film, 1969-2005. 2007. (ENG., Illus.). 228p. per. 49.95 *(978-0-7864-2968-4(2))* McFarland & Co., Inc. Pubs.

Hopp, Glenn. Movie ICONS. Woody Allen. Duncan, Paul, ed. 2009. (Movie Icons Ser.). (ENG., Illus.). 192p. pap. 9.99 *(978-3-8365-0851-3(6))* TASCHEN DEU. Dist: Ingram Pub. Services.

Hosle, Vittorio. Woody Allen: An Essay on the Nature of the Comical. 2007. 88p. per. 18.00 *(978-0-268-03104-6(5))* Univ. of Notre Dame Pr.

Lax, Eric. Conversaciones con Woody Allen/ Conversations With Woody Allen. 2008. (SPA.). 425p. *(978-84-264-1675-9(6))* Editorial Lumen.

—Conversations with Woody Allen: His Films, the Movies, & Moviemaking. 2007. (ENG., Illus.). 416p. 30.00 *(978-0-375-41533-3(5)*, Knopf) Knopf Doubleday Publishing Group.

Silet, Charles L. P. The Films of Woody Allen: Critical Essays. annot. ed. 2006. (ENG.). 358p. 80.00 *(978-0-8108-5736-0(7))* Scarecrow Pr., Inc.

Silet, Charles L. P., ed. The Films of Woody Allen: Critical Essays. annot. ed. 2006. (ENG.). 258p. per. 45.00 *(978-0-8108-5737-7(5))* Scarecrow Pr., Inc.

ALLEN FAMILY

Allen, Peggy Vonsherie. The Pecan Orchard: Journey of a Sharecropper's Daughter. (ENG., Illus.). 272p. 2011. pap. 18.95 *(978-0-8173-5659-0(2))* 2009. 29.95 *(978-0-8173-1672-3(8))* Univ. of Alabama Pr.

Kidder, Frederic. Military Operations in Eastern Maine and. 2006. pap. 31.95 *(978-1-4286-4969-9(7))* Kessinger Publishing, LLC.

Kouris, Diana Allen. Riding the Edge of an ERA: Growing up Cowboy on the Outlaw Trail. 2007. *(978-0-931271-84-7(3))*; pap. *(978-0-931271-85-4(1))* High Plains Pr.

ALLEN RADIATION BELTS

see Van Allen Radiation Belts

ALLENDE, ISABEL, 1942-

Allende, Isabel. Paula: A Memoir. Peden, Margaret Sayers, tr. 2008. (P. S. Ser.). (ENG.). 368p. pap. 14.99 *(978-0-06-156490-1(7)*, HarperPerennial) HarperCollins Pubs.

—Paula: A Memoir. (SPA.). 21.50 *(978-84-01-22514-7(0)*, AS541) Plaza & Janes Editories, S.A. ESP. Dist: Continental Bk. Co., Inc.

—The Sum of Our Days: A Memoir. 2009. (P. S. Ser.).Tr. of Suma de los Dias. 336p. pap. 14.99 *(978-0-06-155184-0(8)*, HarperPerennial) HarperCollins Pubs.

—The Sum of Our Days: A Memoir. Peden, Margaret Sayers, tr. from SPA. 2008.Tr. of Suma de los Dias. (ENG.). 320p. 26.95 *(978-0-06-155183-3(X))*; 528p. pap. 26.95 *(978-0-06-156310-2(2)*, HarperLuxe) HarperCollins Pubs.

—La Suma de los Dias. (SPA & ENG.). 2009. 352p. pap. 14.99 *(978-0-06-155188-8(0))* 2007. 368p. 26.95 *(978-0-06-155187-1(2))* HarperCollins Pubs. (Rayo).

Chandra, Giti. Narrating Violence, Constructing Collective Identities: 'to Witness These Wrongs Unspeakable' 2009. (ENG., Illus.). 216p. 89.00 *(978-0-230-21962-5(4))* Palgrave Macmillan.

Copertari, Gabriela & Martin, Karen Wooley. Isabel Allende's House of the Spirits Trilogy: Narrative Geographies. 2010. (Monografías A Ser.: Volume 285). (Illus.). 286p. 90.00 *(978-1-85566-200-1(0)*, Tamesis Bks.) Boydell & Brewer, Ltd. GBR. Dist: Boydell & Brewer, Inc.

McNeese, Tim. Isabel Allende. 2006. (Great Hispanic Heritage Ser.). (Illus.). 112p. (gr. 6-12). lib. bdg. 35.00 *(978-0-7910-8836-4(7)*, Chelsea Hse.) Facts On File, Inc.

Rodden, John. Isabel Allende. 2010. (Critical Insights Ser.). 366p. 85.00 *(978-1-58765-699-6(X))* Salem Pr., Inc.

ALLENDE, SALVADOR, 1908-1973

see Allende Gossens, Salvador, 1908-1973

ALLENDE GOSSENS, SALVADOR, 1908-1973

Gustafson, Kristian. Hostile Intent: U. S. Covert Operations in Chile, 1964-1974. 2007. (Illus.). 288p. 29.95 *(978-1-59797-097-6(2))* Potomac Bks., Inc.

Muñoz, Heraldo. The Dictator's Shadow: Life under Augusto Pinochet. 2008. (ENG., Illus.). 376p. 27.50 *(978-0-465-00250-4(1))* Perseus Bks. Group.

Qureshi, Lubna Z. Nixon, Kissinger, & Allende: U. S. Involvement in the 1973 Coup in Chile. 2008. (ENG.). 192p. 68.50 *(978-0-7391-2655-4(5))* Lexington Bks.

Qureshi, Lubna Zakia. Nixon, Kissinger, & Allende: U. S. Involvement in the 1973 Coup in Chile. 2009. (ENG.). 192p. pap. 29.50 *(978-0-7391-2656-1(3))* Lexington Bks.

ALLERGENS

Bader, Walter. Toxic Bedrooms: Your Guide to a Safe Night's Sleep. 2007. 156p. per. 12.95 *(978-1-893910-43-0(1))* Freedom Pr., Inc., The.

Boye, Joyce I. & Godefroy, Samuel Benrejeb. Allergen Management in the Food Industry. 2010. (ENG., Illus.). 624p. 158.00 *(978-0-470-22735-0(4)*, Wiley) Wiley, John & Sons, Inc.

Cox, Linda. Allergen Immunotherapy, an Issue of Immunology & Allergy Clinics. 2011. (Clinics: Internal Medicine Ser.: 31-2). (ENG., Illus.). 312p. 110.00 *(978-1-4557-1148-2(9)*, Saunders) Elsevier - Health Sciences Div.

Denburg, Judah A., ed. Allergy & Allergic Diseases: The New Mechanisms & Therapeutics. 2010. (ENG.). 608p. pap. 175.00 *(978-1-61737-026-7(6)*, 1617370266) Humana Pr.

Emerton, Victoria. Food Chain Allergen Management. Emerton, Victoria, ed. 2009. (Special Publication). 300p. 160.00 *(978-1-905224-85-2(0))* Royal Society of Chemistry, The GBR. Dist: Ingram Pub. Services.

Fergus, Cristin L. Mother Necessity Gluten Free/Casein Free Recipes: Your favorite foods allergen Free. 2007. 92p. spiral bd. 19.95 *(978-0-9796579-1-7(1))* Mother Necessity Inc.

Gehr, Peter, et al, eds. Particle-Lung Interactions, Second Edition. 2nd rev. ed. 2009. (ENG., Illus.). 338p. 300.00 *(978-1-4200-7256-3(0)*, Informa Healthcare) Taylor & Francis Group GBR. Dist: Taylor & Francis Group.

Jedrychowski, Lucjan. Chemical & Biological Properties of Food Allergens. 2009. (Chemical & Functional Properties of Food Components Ser.). (ENG., Illus.). 447p. 164.95 *(978-1-4200-5855-0(X)*, CRC Press) Taylor & Francis Group GBR. Dist: Taylor & Francis Group.

Lawley, Richard, et al. Food Safety Hazard Guidebook. 2008. (ENG.). 432p. 224.00 *(978-0-85404-460-3(4))* Royal Society of Chemistry, The GBR. Dist: Ingram Pub. Services.

Lawley, Richard, et al. The Food Safety Hazard Guidebook. 2nd ed. 2012. (ENG., Illus.). 546p. 195.00 ***(978-1-84973-381-6(3))*** Royal Society of Chemistry, The GBR. Dist: Ingram Pub. Services.

Lepoittevin, J. P. & Le Coz, C J. Dictionary of Contact Allergens. 2007. (Illus.). 280p. per. 49.95 *(978-3-540-74164-0(X))* Springer.

Lockey, Richard F. & Ledford, Dennis K., eds. Allergens & Allergen Immunotherapy. 4th rev. ed. 2008. (Clinical Allergy & Immunology Ser.: Vol. 21). (ENG., Illus.). 576p. 250.00 *(978-1-4200-6197-0(6)*, Informa Healthcare) Taylor & Francis Group GBR. Dist: Taylor & Francis Group.

Lutz, Kim. Welcoming Kitchen Allergen-Free Recipes for Snacks & Goodies. 2007. 64p. pap. 12.00 *(978-0-9800728-0-8(8))* Welcoming Kitchen.

Marone, G., ed. Superantigens & Superallergens [Bibliography & Price not Definite.]. 2007. (Chemical Immunology & Allergy Ser.). (Illus.). 242p. *(978-3-8055-8266-7(8))* Karger, S. AG.

Nollet, Leo M. L. & Van Hengel, Arjon, eds. Food Allergens: Analysis Instrumentation & Methods. 2010. (ENG., Illus.). 231p. 149.95 *(978-1-4398-1503-8(8)*, CRC Press) Taylor & Francis Group GBR. Dist: Taylor & Francis Group.

Wiese, Michael. An Characterisation of Jack Jumper Ant Venom - Definition of the Allergic Components & Pharmaceutical Development of Myrmecia Pilosula. 2008. 192p. pap. *(978-3-639-05169-8(6))* VDM Verlag Dr. Mueller e.K.

ALLERGY

see also Allergy in Children; Anaphylaxis; Contact Dermatitis; Food Allergy

Adkinson, N. Franklin, Jr., et al, eds. Middleton's Allergy, 2 vols., Set. 7th ed. 2008. (ENG., Illus.). 1896p. 435.00 *(978-0-323-04884-2(6)*, Mosby) Elsevier - Health Sciences Div.

Adkinson, N. Franklin, et al. Allergy Set: Principles & Practice, 2 vols. Adkinson, N. Franklin et al, eds. 7th ed. 2008. (ENG., Illus.). 1924p. 342.00 *(978-0-323-05659-5(8)*, Mosby) Elsevier - Health Sciences Div.

Agashe, Shripad N. & Caulton, Eric. Pollen & Spores: Applications with Special Emphasis on Aerobiology & Allergy. 2009. (ENG., Illus.). 412p. 119.95 *(978-1-57808-532-3(2))* BIOS Scientific Publishers Ltd. GBR. Dist: Taylor & Francis Group.

Asamoah, Felix. Epidemiology of Allergy Disorders in the Uk from 1985 To 2005. 2010. 96p. pap. *(978-3-639-23995-9(4))* VDM Verlag Dr. Mueller e.K.

Bastone, Antonio, et al, eds. Annual Review of Immunology 2007, Vol. 25. 2007. 880p. 216.00 *(978-0-8243-3025-5(0))* Annual Reviews, Inc.

Bateson-Koch, Carolee. Allergies, Disease in Disguise: How to Heal Your Allergic Condition Permanently & Naturally. (ENG., Illus.). 312p. mass mkt. 15.95 *(978-1-55312-040-7(X))* Books Alive.

Blaser, K., ed. T Cell Regulation in Allergy, Asthma & Atopic Skin Diseases. 2008. (Chemical Immunology & Allergy Ser.). (Illus.). 226p. *(978-3-8055-8628-3(0))* Karger, S. AG.

Breitenbach, Michael, et al, eds. Fungal Allergy & Pathogenicity, Vol. 81. (Chemical Immunology Ser.: Vol. 81). (Illus.). *(978-3-8055-7391-7(X))* Karger, S. AG.

Briner, William & American College of Sports Medicine Staff. Action Plan for Allergies. 2006. (ENG., Illus.). 200p. per. 17.95 *(978-0-7360-6279-4(3))* Human Kinetics Pubs.

Bruce S. Dobozin & Stuart H. Young. Allergies: The Complete Guide to Diagnosis, Treatment, & Daily Management. 2011. 342p. 29.99 ***(978-1-4628-7343-2(X))***; pap. 19.99 ***(978-1-4628-7342-5(1))*** Xlibris Corp.

Burge, H. A. & Solomon, W. Fungi & Allergic Disease: Diagnosis & Treatment. Date not set. (Clinical Allergy & Immunology Ser.). (Illus.). *(978-0-8247-9482-8(6))* Dekker, Marcel Inc.

Capron, Monique & Trottein, François, eds. Parasites & Allergy, Vol. 90. (Chemical Immunology & Allergy Ser.: Vol. 90). (Illus.). *(978-3-8055-7974-2(8))* Karger, S. AG.

Choi, Yongwon. Osteoimmunology: Interactions of the Immune & Skeletal Systems. 2007. (Advances in Experimental Medicine & Biology Ser.). (Illus.). 156p. 189.00 *(978-0-387-72008-1(1))* Springer.

Coding Companion for ENT/Allergy/Pulmonology. 2007. per. 199.95 *(978-1-56337-875-1(2))*, OptumInsight, Inc.

Colectivo de Medicina Natural. La Curacion Natural del Asma y las Alergias.Tr. of Natural Cure for Asthma & Allergies. (SPA., Illus.). 368p. *(978-84-7927-200-5(7))* Robinbk., Ediciones S.L.

Cox, Linda. Allergen Immunotherapy, an Issue of Immunology & Allergy Clinics. 2011. (Clinics: Internal Medicine Ser.: 31-2). (ENG., Illus.). 312p. 110.00 *(978-1-4557-1148-2(9)*, Saunders) Elsevier - Health Sciences Div.

Crameri, Reto, ed. Allergy & Asthma in Modern Society Vol. 91: A Scientific Approach: Dedicated to Kurt Blaser. (Chemical Immunology & Allergy Ser.: Vol. 91). (Illus.). *(978-3-8055-8000-7(2))* Karger, S. AG.

Cram101 Textbook Reviews. Outlines & Highlights for Allergy & Asthm: Practical Diagnosis & Management by Massoud Mahmoudi, ISBN. 2011. 116p. pap. 28.95 ***(978-1-61461-465-1(0))*** Cram101 Inc.

Denburg, Judah A., ed. Allergy & Allergic Diseases: The New Mechanisms & Therapeutics. 2010. (ENG.). 608p. pap. 175.00 *(978-1-61737-026-7(6)*, 1617370266) Humana Pr.

Dochniak, Michael J. & Dunn, Denise H. Allergies & Autism. 2010. (Allergies & Infectious Diseases Ser.). 147p. pap. 43.00 *(978-1-60876-352-8(8))* Nova Science Pubs., Inc.

Doherty, Peter. The Beginner's Guide to Winning the Nobel Prize: Advice for Young Scientists. 2008. (ENG., Illus.). 320p. (gr. 17). pap. 22.95 *(978-0-231-13897-0(0))* Columbia Univ. Pr.

Durham, Stephen R. ABC of Allergies. 2nd rev. ed. 2007. (ABC Ser.). (ENG.). 96p. pap. *(978-1-4051-3958-8(7)*, Wiley-Blackwell) Wiley, John & Sons, Ltd.

Ewan, Pamela. An Atlas of Allergy. 2010. (Encyclopedia of Visual Medicine Ser.). (Illus.). 100p. 120.00 *(978-1-84214-018-5(3)*, Parthenon Publishing) CRC Pr. LLC.

Ferguson, Berrylin J. Ferguson J. Allergies for the Otolaryngologist: Otolaryngologic Clinics of North America. 2011. (Clinics: Surgery Ser.: 44-3). (ENG., Illus.). 344p. 110.00 *(978-1-4557-1051-5(2)*, Saunders) Elsevier - Health Sciences Div.

Fokken, Wystke. Chronic Rhinosinusitis, an Issue of Immunology & Allergy Clinics. 2009. (Clinics: Internal Medicine Ser.: 29-4). (ENG., Illus.). xvi, 622p. 99.00 *(978-1-4377-1230-8(4)*, Saunders) Elsevier - Health Sciences Div.

Fukuda, T., et al, eds. Eosinophils in Allergy & Related Diseases: Workshop, Tokyo, June 2008: Proceedings. 2009. (Illus.). 116p. pap. *(978-3-8055-9186-7(1))* Karger, S. AG.

Fukuda, T., et al, eds. Eosinophils in Allergy & Related Diseases: Workshop, Tokyo, June 2010: Proceedings. Supplement Issue:'International Archives of Allergy & Immunology 2011, Vol. 155, Suppl. 1' 2011. (ENG., Illus.). 152p. pap. ***(978-3-8055-9765-4(7))*** Karger, S. AG.

Furuta, Glen & Atkins, Dan. Eosinophilic Gastrointestinal Diseases, an Issue of Immunology & Allergy Clinics. 2009. (Clinics: Internal Medicine Ser.: 29-1). (ENG., Illus.). 240p. 99.00 *(978-1-4377-0489-1(1)*, Saunders) Elsevier - Health Sciences Div.

Gabler, Maximilian. DNA Replicons: Next-generation Vaccines against Allergy. 2008. 132p. pap. *(978-3-8364-9555-4(4))* VDM Verlag Dr. Mueller e.K.

Georgiev, Vassil St. National Institute of Allergy & Infectious Diseases, NIH. 2008. (Infectious Disease Ser.). (Illus.). 622p. 199.00 *(978-1-60327-296-4(6))* Humana Pr.

Georgiev, Vassil St., ed. National Institute of Allergy & Infectious Diseases, NIH: Volume 1: Frontiers in Research. 2008. (Infectious Disease Ser.). (Illus.). 500p. 259.00 *(978-1-934115-77-0(0))* Humana Pr.

—National Institute of Allergy & Infectious Diseases, NIH: Volume III: Intramural Research. 2010. (Infectious Disease Ser.). (ENG., Illus.). 350p. 229.00 *(978-1-60761-511-8(8)*, 1607615118) Humana Pr.

Greenberger, Paul A. & Patterson, Roy. Patterson's Allergic Diseases. Greenberger, Paul A. & Grammer, Leslie C., eds. 7th rev. ed. 2009. (ENG., Illus.). 736p. 164.99 *(978-0-7817-9425-1(0))* Lippincott Williams & Wilkins.

Hamilos, Daniel L. & Baroody, Faud M., eds. Chronic Rhinosinusitis: Pathogenesis & Medical Management. 2007. (Clinical Allergy & Immunology Ser.: Vol. 20). (ENG., Illus.). 368p. 230.00 *(978-0-8493-4052-9(7))* Taylor & Francis Group.

Hansel, Trevor T. & Barnes, Peter J., eds. New Drugs for Asthma, Allergy & COPD, Vol. 31. (Progress in Respiratory Research Ser.: Vol. 31). (Illus.). *(978-3-8055-6862-3(2))* Karger, S. AG.

Holgate, Stephen T., et al, eds. Cellular & Molecular Targets in Allergy & Clinical Immunology: Proceedings of the 26th Symposium of the Collegium Internationale Allergologicum. 2008. 354p. 88.00 *(978-0-88937-358-7(2))* Hogrefe Publishing.

—Inflammation & Allergy Drug Design. 2011. (ENG., Illus.). 344p. 144.95 *(978-1-4443-3014-4(4)*, Wiley-Blackwell) Wiley, John & Sons, Inc.

Holgate, Stephen T., et al. Allergy. 4th ed. 2011. (ENG., Illus.). 432p. 145.00 *(978-0-7234-3658-4(4)*, Saunders) Elsevier - Health Sciences Div.

Horwitz, Randy & Muller, Daniel. Integrative Rheumatology. 2010. (Weil Integrative Medicine Library). (ENG., Illus.). 350p. 39.95 *(978-0-19-531121-1(3))* Oxford Univ. Pr., Inc.

Iamandescu, I. B., ed. Psychoneuroallergology. 2nd rev. ed. 2007. 398p. pap. *(978-3-8055-8412-8(1))* Karger, S. AG.

Ingenix, creator. Coding Companion for ENT/Allergy/Pulmonology. 2008. (Coding Companion Ser.). (Illus.). 693p. spiral bd. 199.95 *(978-1-60151-171-3(X))* OptumInsight, Inc.

—Coding Companion for ENT/Allergy/Pulmonology: A Comprehensive Illustrated Guide to Coding & Reimbursement. 2007. (Illus.). 587p. spiral bd. 199.95 *(978-1-60151-055-6(1))* OptumInsight, Inc.

Jackson, Mark. Allergy: The History of a Modern Malady. 2007. (ENG., Illus.). 288p. per. 25.00 *(978-1-86189-333-8(7))* Reaktion Bks., Ltd. GBR. Dist: Chicago Distribution Ctr.

Joe, Stephanie. Rhinology & Allergy for the Facial Plastic Surgeon - An Issue of Facial Plastic Surgery Clinics. 2011. (Clinics: Surgery Ser.: 20-1). (ENG., Illus.). 576p. 115.00 ***(978-1-4557-3858-8(1)***, Saunders) Elsevier - Health Sciences Div.

Johansson, S. G. O. & Haahtela, Tari, eds. Prevention of Allergy & Allergic Asthma Vol. 84: World Allergy Organization Project Report & Guidelines. (Chemical Immunology & Allergy Ser.: Vol. 84). (Illus.). 20;212p. *(978-3-8055-7810-3(5))* Karger, S. AG.

Jones, Lon. No More Allergies, Asthma or Sinus Infections: The Revolutionary Approach. 2011. (ENG.). 160p. pap. 15.95 *(978-1-893910-88-1(1))* Freedom Pr., Inc., The.

Jones, Meinir G. & Lympany, Penny, eds. Allergy Methods & Protocols. 2010. (Methods in Molecular Medicine Ser.). (Illus.). xi, 352p. pap. 149.00 *(978-1-61737-243-8(9)*, 1617372439) Humana Pr.

Kaliner, Michael A. Rhinitis, an Issue of Immunology & Allergy Clinics. 2011. (Clinics: Internal Medicine Ser.: 31-3). (ENG., Illus.). 224p. 110.00 *(978-1-4557-1105-5(5)*, Saunders) Elsevier - Health Sciences Div.

Kaplan, Allen & Greaves, Malcolm W., eds. Urticaria & Angioedema, Second Edition. 2nd rev. ed. 2009. (Illus.). 400p. 300.00 *(978-1-4200-7784-1(8)*, Informa Healthcare) Taylor & Francis Group GBR. Dist: Taylor & Francis Group.

Kay, A. Barry, et al, eds. Allergy & Allergic Diseases, 2 vols., Set. 2nd ed. 2008. (ENG., Illus.). 2184p. 469.95 *(978-1-4051-5720-9(8)*, Wiley-Blackwell) Wiley, John & Sons, Inc.

Kiess, W., et al, eds. Atopic Dermatitis in Childhood & Adolescence. 2011. (Pediatric & Adolescent Medicine Ser.). (ENG., Illus.). 162p. ***(978-3-8055-9570-4(0))*** Karger, S. AG.

Krouse, John H., et al. Managing the Allergic Patient. 2007. (ENG., Illus.). 400p. 182.00 *(978-1-4160-3677-7(6)*, Saunders) Elsevier - Health Sciences Div.
Lachapelle, Jean-Marie & Maibach, Howard I. Patch Testing & Prick Testing: A Practical GuideOfficial Publication of the ICDRG. 2nd ed. 2009. (Illus.). xviii, 195p. 59.95 *(978-3-540-92805-8(7))* Springer.
Lewis, Robert E. & Cruse, Julius M. Illustrated Dictionary of Immunology. 3rd rev. ed. 2009. (ENG., Illus.). 816p. 107.95 *(978-0-8493-7987-1(3)*, CRC Press) Taylor & Francis Group GBR. Dist: Taylor & Francis Group.
Lieberman, Phil L. & Anderson, John A. Allergic Diseases: Diagnosis & Treatment. 3rd ed. 2007. (Current Clinical Practice Ser.). (Illus.). 484p. 149.00 *(978-1-58829-603-0(2)*, 1588296032) Humana Pr.
Litt, Jerome Z. Curious Odd Rare & Abnormal Reactions to Medications. 2009. (ENG.). 272p. pap. 15.95 *(978-1-56980-367-7(6))* Barricade Bks., Inc.
Lockey, Richard F. & Ledford, Dennis K., eds. Allergens & Allergen Immunotherapy. 4th rev. ed. 2008. (Clinical Allergy & Immunology Ser.: Vol. 21). (ENG., Illus.). 576p. 250.00 *(978-1-4200-6197-0(6)*, Informa Healthcare) Taylor & Francis Group GBR. Dist: Taylor & Francis Group.
Lympany, Penny & Jones, Meinir G., eds. Allergy Methods & Protocols. 2008. (Methods in Molecular Medicine Ser.). (Illus.). 352p. 149.00 *(978-0-89603-896-7(3)*, 0896038963) Humana Pr.
Mahmoudi, Massoud. Allergy & Asthma: Practical Diagnosis & Management. 2007. (LANGE Clinical Medicine Ser.). (ENG., Illus.). 400p. per. 58.00 *(978-0-07-147173-2(1)*, 0071471731) McGraw-Hill Professional Publishing.
Mahmoudi, Massoud, ed. Challenging Cases in Allergic & Immunologic Diseases of the Skin. 2010. (ENG., Illus.). xiv, 350p. 89.95 *(978-1-60761-295-7(X)*, 160761295X) Springer.
—Challenging Cases in Allergy & Immunology. 2009. (ENG., Illus.). xiv, 334p. 109.00 *(978-1-60327-442-5(1)*, 1603274421) Humana Pr.
Makino, S., et al, eds. Eosinophils in Allergy & Related Diseases: Workshop, Tokyo, June 2003: Proceedings. (Illus.). 4;8p. pap. *(978-3-8055-7768-7(0))* Karger, S. AG.
—Eosinophils in Allergy & Related Diseases: Workshop, Tokyo, June 2006: Proceedings: Supplement Issue: International Archives of Allergy & Immunology 2007, Vol. 143, Suppl. 1. 2007. (Illus.). 114p. pap. *(978-3-8055-8276-6(5))* Karger, S. AG.
—Eosinophils in Allergy & Related Diseases Vol. 146, No. 1: Workshop, Tokyo, June 2007: Proceedings: Supplement Issue: International Archives of Allergy & Immunology 2008. 2008. (Illus.). 92p. pap., suppl. ed. *(978-3-8055-8610-8(8))* Karger, S. AG.
Makino, Sohei, et al, eds. Eosinophils in Allergy & Related Diseases: Proceedings of a Workshop, Tokyo, Japan, June 26, 2004, Vol. 137. (Illus.). *(978-3-8055-7952-0(7))* Karger, S. AG.
—Eosinophils in Allergy & Related Diseases: Proceedings of a Workshop, Tokyo, June 2001. (Allergy & Immunology Ser.: Vol. 128, Suppl. 1). (Illus.). *(978-3-8055-7447-1(9))* Karger, S. AG.
—Eosinophils in Allergy & Related Diseases - Workshop, Tokyo, June 2002: Proceedings, Vol. 131. (Allergy & Immunology Ser.: Vol. 131, Suppl. 1). (Illus.). *(978-3-8055-7593-5(9))* Karger, S. AG.
Male, David, et al. Immunology. 7th ed. 2007. (ENG.). (C). pap. 99.00 *(978-0-323-05448-5(X)*, Mosby) Elsevier - Health Sciences Div.
Markert, Udo R. & Elsner, Peter, eds. Local Immunotherapy in Allergy, Vol. 82. (Chemical Immunology & Allergy Ser.: Vol. 82). (Illus.). *(978-3-8055-7531-7(9))* Karger, S. AG.
Marple, Bradley F. & Mabry, Richard L., eds. Quantitative Skin Testing for Allergy: IDT & MQT. 2006. (ENG., Illus.). 120p. per. 27.99 *(978-1-58890-430-0(X)* Thieme Medical Pubs., Inc.
Miller, Thomas, ed. Allergy: Complete Handbook. 2011. 124p. pap. 14.95 ***(978-1-937354-08-4(3))*** Rapid Publishing LLC.
Nambudripad, Devi S. Eliminate Your Pet's Allergies: Explore NAET. 2006. (Illus.). 244p. per. *(978-0-9759277-7-9(9))* Delta Publishing Co.
—The NAET Guide Book: The Companion to Say Good-Bye to Illness. 2009. (ENG.). 96p. pap. 12.00 *(978-1-934523-09-4(7))* Delta Publishing Co.
—Say Good-Bye to Allergy-Related Autism. 2nd ed. 2007. (Illus.). 286p. per. 18.00 *(978-0-9743915-6-4(5))* Delta Publishing Co.
Nambudripad, Devi S. Say Good-Bye to Allergy-Related Autism NAET. 3rd ed. 2011. (ENG., Illus.). 280p. pap. 18.00 ***(978-1-934523-17-9(8))*** Delta Publishing Co.
Oktenli, Cagatay, ed. Immunology in Clinic Practice. 2010. (Immunology & Immune System Disorders Ser.). 172p. 89.00 *(978-1-60876-644-4(6))* Nova Science Pubs., Inc.
Pawankar, Ruby, et al. Allergy Frontiers:Classification & Pathomechanisms: Classification & Pathomechanisms, 3 vols. 2009. (Allergy Frontiers Ser.). (Illus.). xxii, 606p. 389.00 *(978-4-431-88314-2(2))* Springer.
—Allergy Frontiers:Clinical Manifestations: Clinical Manifestations, 3 vols. 2009. (Allergy Frontiers Ser.). (ENG., Illus.). xxii, 511p. 349.00 *(978-4-431-88316-6(9))* Springer.
—Allergy Frontiers:Future Perspectives: Future Perspectives, 6 vols. 2009. (Allergy Frontiers Ser.). (ENG., Illus.). xx, 324p. 219.00 *(978-4-431-99364-3(9)*, 4431993649) Springer.
—Allergy Frontiers:Therapy & Prevention: Therapy & Prevention, 6 vols. 2009. (Allergy Frontiers Ser.). (Illus.). 800p. 269.00 *(978-4-431-99361-2(4)*, 4431993614) Springer.
—Diagnosis & Health Economics, 6 vols. 2009. (Allergy Frontiers Ser.). (ENG., Illus.). xxii, 554p. 329.00 *(978-4-431-98293-7(0)*, 4431982930) Springer.
Pawankar, Ruby, et al. Allergy Frontiers: Epigenetics to Future Perspectives, 3 vols. 2008. (Allergy Frontiers Ser.). (Illus.). 600p. 249.00 *(978-4-431-72801-6(5))* Springer.
Pichler, Werner. Drug Hypersensitivity, an Issue of Immunology & Allergy Clinics. 2009. (Clinics: Internal Medicine Ser.: 29-3). (ENG., Illus.). xvi, 406p. 99.00 *(978-1-4377-1229-2(0)*, Saunders) Elsevier - Health Sciences Div.
Powell, Jillian. Allergies. 2008. (Feeling Sick? Ser.). (Illus.). 23p. (J). (gr. 2-4). lib. bdg. *(978-1-84234-471-2(4))* Cherrytree Pubns., Inc.
Ravikovich, Felix. L' Asthme et les Allergies: Le Complot du Siecle. Charland, Caroline, tr. from ENG. 2008. (FRE.). 534p. pap. *(978-2-922969-14-6(2))* Editions le mieux-etre CAN. Dist: AtlasBooks Distribution.
Ring, Johannes. Allergy in Practice. 2010. (Illus.). xviii, 276p. pap. 129.00 *(978-3-642-05526-3(5)*, 3642055265) Springer.
Saito, Hirohisa & Okayama, Yoshimichi, eds. Mast Cells in Allergic Diseases, Vol. 87. (Chemical Immunology & Allergy Ser.: Vol. 87). (Illus.). *(978-3-8055-7948-3(9))* Karger, S. AG.
Scott, Michael J. Hypnosis in Skin & Allergic Diseases. 2011. 178p. 42.95 ***(978-1-258-02285-3(0))*** Literary Licensing, LLC.
Scott-Moncrieff, Christina. Overcoming Allergies. 2008. (ENG.). 160p. pap. 20.00 *(978-1-4379-5136-3(8))* DIANE Publishing Co.
Shah, Shilpa. House Dust Mite Allergens: Der p1 & Blo t5 in MATERNAL & CORD-BLOOD. 2011. 160p. pap. ***(978-3-8433-9457-4(1))*** Lambert Academic Publishing.
Sheen, Barbara. Allergies. 2008. (Diseases & Disorders (Lucent Books) Ser.). (ENG., Illus.). 104p. (J). (gr. 4-7). lib. bdg. 33.45 *(978-1-4205-0039-4(2)*, Lucent Bks.) Cengage Gale.
Valenta, Rudolf & Coffman, Robert L., eds. Vaccines against Allergies. 2011. (Current Topics in Microbiology & Immunology Ser.). (ENG., Illus.). xi, 182p. 189.00 *(978-3-642-20053-3(2)*, 3642200532) Springer.
Volcheck, Gerald W. Allergy Diagnosis & Management: A Case-Oriented Approach. Conn, P. Michael, ed. 2008. (Current Clinical Practice Ser.). (Illus.). 300p. 109.00 *(978-1-58829-616-0(4)*, 1588296164) Humana Pr.
Willingham, Theresa. The Florida Allergy Handbook. 2012. (ENG., Illus.). 360p. pap. 24.95 *(978-0-8130-3746-2(8))* Univ. Pr. of Florida.
World Health Organization Staff, et al, contrib. by. Principles & Methods for Assessing Autoimmunity Associated with Exposure to Chemicals. 2006. (Environmental Health Criteria Series,No. 236 Ser.). (ENG., Illus.). 359p. pap. 60.00 *(978-92-4-157236-1(1))* World Health Organization.
Wu, Alan H. B. & Yeo, Kiang-Teck J., eds. Pharmacogenomic Testing in Current Clinical Practice: Implementation in the Clinical Laboratory. 2011. (Molecular & Translational Medicine Ser.). (Illus.). xiv, 272p. 219.00 *(978-1-60761-282-7(8)*, 1607612828) Humana Pr.
Young, Michael C. The Peanut Allergy Answer Book. 2nd rev. ed. 2006. (ENG.). 168p. per. 14.95 *(978-1-59233-233-5(1)*, 1592332331) Quayside.
Zuberbier, Torsten, et al. Urticaria & Angioedema. 2009. (ENG., Illus.). x, 158p. 99.00 *(978-3-540-79047-1(0)*, 3540790470) Springer.

ALLERGY—ALTERNATIVE TREATMENT

Gaffney, Debra. Sensitivities: The Subtle Cause of Suffering, the Hidden Cause of Illness. 2008. (Illus.). 221p. pap. 19.95 *(978-0-9801824-0-8(9))* Smarketing.
Gottlieb, Billy Adam. The Sprouted Peanut Vaccine & Other Stories. 2008. 242p. pap. 16.95 *(978-0-557-01381-4(X))* Lulu Enterprises Inc.
Nambudripad, Devi S. Freedom from Chemical Sensitivities: Explore NAET (Nambudripad's Allergy Elimination Techniques) 2007. (Illus.). 284p. per. 18.00 *(978-0-9759277-8-6(7))* Delta Publishing Co.
—NAETA-2 N: Bowel Disorders. 2007. (Illus.). 80p. *(978-1-934523-04-9(6))* Delta Publishing Co.
—Say Goodbye to Headaches. 2007. (Say Good-Bye To Ser.). (Illus.). 308p. per. *(978-0-9759277-6-2(0))* Delta Publishing Co.
Pescatore, Fred. The Allergy & Asthma Cure: A Complete 8-Step Nutritional Program. 2008. (ENG.). 272p. pap. 15.95 *(978-0-470-27541-2(3)*, Wiley) Wiley, John & Sons, Inc.

ALLERGY—DIET THERAPY

see Food Allergy—Diet Therapy

ALLERGY—POPULAR WORKS

Brown, Sandra, ed. Asthma & Allergy: Handbook for Patient & Family. 2009. 176p. pap. 19.95 *(978-0-9822136-0-5(3))* Rapid Publishing LLC.
Corren, Jonathan. Allergies. rev. ed. 2010. 144p. pap. 22.95 *(978-0-7637-7609-1(2))* Jones & Bartlett Learning, LLC.
Downing, Damien. The Vitamin Cure for Allergies: How to Prevent & Treat Allergies Using Nutrition & Vitamin Supplementation, 1 vol. 2010. (ENG.). 160p. pap. *(978-1-59120-271-4(X))* Basic Health Pubns., Inc.
Mitman, Gregg. Breathing Space: How Allergies Shape Our Lives & Landscapes. 2008. (ENG., Illus.). 336p. pap. 18.00 *(978-0-300-14315-7(X))* Yale Univ. Pr.
Revill, Jo. Allergy Explosion. 2008. (ENG.). 192p. pap. *(978-1-85626-730-4(X))* Cathie, Kyle Ltd. GBR. Dist: Independent Pubs. Group.
Sutton, Amy L. Allergies Sourcebook: Basic Consumer Health Information about the Immune System & Allergic Disorders, Including Rhinitis (Hay Fever), Sinusitis, Conjunctivitis, Asthma, Atopic Dermatitis, & Anaphylaxis, & Allergy Triggers Such As Pollen, Mold, Dust Mites, Animal Dander, Chemicals, Foods & Additives, & Medications: Along with Facts about Allergy Diagnosis & Treatment, Tips on Avoiding Triggers & Preventing. 4th rev. ed. 2011. (Health Reference Ser.). 600p. lib. bdg. 95.00 *(978-0-7808-1144-7(5))* Omnigraphics, Inc.
Sutton, Amy L., ed. Allergies Sourcebook: Basic Consumer Health Information about Allergic Disorders, Such as Anaphylaxis, Hives, Eczema, Rhinitis, Sinusitis, & Conjunctivitis, & Their Triggers, Including Pollen, Mold, Dust Mites, Animal Dander, Insects, Chemicals, Food, Food Additives, & Me. 3rd ed. 2007. (Health Reference Ser.). (Illus.). 616p. 87.00 *(978-0-7808-0950-5(5))* Omnigraphics, Inc.

ALLERGY IN CHILDREN

see also Food Allergy in Children

American Academy of Pediatrics. Your Child's Allergies & Asthma: The American Academy of Pediatrics Guide to Breathing Easy & Bringing up Healthy, Active Children. Welch, Michael J., ed. 2nd ed. 2010. (What Every Parent Needs to Know Ser.). (ENG.). 200p. pap. 14.95 *(978-1-58110-445-5(6))* American Academy of Pediatrics.
Bee, Peta. I Have Asthma. 2010. (Taking Care of Myself Ser.). (ENG.). 32p. (gr. 3-6). lib. bdg. 26.60 *(978-1-4339-3851-1(0)*, Stevens, Gareth Learning Library) Stevens, Gareth Publishing LLLP.
Bever. Allergic Diseases in Children. 2009. 58.00 *(978-981-4273-53-4(8))* World Scientific Publishing Co., Inc.
Cantani, Arnaldo. Pediatric Allergy, Asthma & Immunology. 2008. Orig. Title: Allergologia e immunologia pediatrica - Dall' Infanzia All'Adolescenza. (Illus.). XXXII, 1619p. 809.00 *(978-3-540-20768-9(6)*, 3540207686) Springer.
Ehrlich, Paul & Chiaramonte, Larry. Asthma Allergies Children: A Parent's Guide. 2010. 311p. pap. 18.95 *(978-0-9843832-0-7(4))* Third Avenue Bks.
Gershwin, M. Eric. Taking Charge of Your Child's Allergies: The Informed Parent's Comprehensive Guide. 2010. 256p. pap. 34.95 *(978-1-61737-044-1(4)*, 1617370444) Humana Pr.
Gow, Melanie. Toasters Don't Roast Chickens: The Story of an Ordinary Mum Who Challenged Conventional Medical Thinking & Transformed the Health of Her Chronically-Ill Child. 2008. 224p. 20.00 *(978-1-905862-17-7(2))* How To Books GBR. Dist: Parkwest Pubns., Inc.
Isolauri, Erika & Walker, W. Allan, eds. Allergic Diseases & the Environment Vol. 53: 53rd Nestle Nutrition Workshop, Pediatric Program, Lausanne, April 6-10, 2003. (Nestle Nutrition Workshop Ser.: Vol. 53). (Illus.). *(978-3-8055-7649-9(8))* Karger, S. AG.
Leung, Donald Y. M., et al. Pediatric Allergy: Principles & Practice. 2nd ed. 2010. (ENG., Illus.). 704p. 138.00 *(978-1-4377-0271-2(6)*, Saunders) Elsevier - Health Sciences Div.
Nambudripad, Devi S. Say Good-Bye to Children's Allergies. 2nd ed. 2009. (ENG., Illus.). 348p. pap. 18.00 *(978-1-934523-00-1(3))* Delta Publishing Co.
Nambuusi Bukenya, Betty. Placental Uptake of Environmental Chemicals & Children Allergy. 2010. 84p. pap. *(978-3-8383-5746-1(9))* Lambert Academic Publishing.
Stauth, Cameron & Bock, Kenneth. Healing the New Childhood Epidemics: Autism, ADHD, Asthma, & Allergies: The Groundbreaking Program for the 4-A Disorders. 2008. (ENG., Illus.). 480p. pap. 16.00 *(978-0-345-49451-1(2)*, Ballantine Bks.) Random House Publishing Group.

ALLEYS

see Streets

ALLIANCE, HOLY

see Holy Alliance

ALLIANCE, TRIPLE, 1882

see Triple Alliance, 1882

ALLIANCE FOR PROGRESS

Taffet, Jeffrey. Foreign Aid as Foreign Policy: The Alliance for Progress in Latin America during The 1960s. 2007. (ENG., Illus.). 328p. 135.00 *(978-0-415-97770-8(3))* Routledge.
Taffet, Jeffrey F. Foreign Aid as Foreign Policy: The Alliance for Progress in Latin America. 2007. (ENG., Illus.). 328p. per. 28.95 *(978-0-415-97771-5(1))* Routledge.

ALLIANCES

Cesa, Marco. Allies yet Rivals: International Politics in 18th Century Europe. 2010. (ENG.). 312p. 55.00 *(978-0-8047-6295-3(3))* Stanford Univ. Pr.
Christensen, Thomas J. Worse Than A Monolith - Alliance Politics & Problems of Coercive Diplomacy in Asia. 2011. (Princeton Studies in International History & Politics Ser.). (ENG.). 318p. (C). 70.00 *(978-0-691-14260-9(2))* Princeton Univ. Pr.
—Worse Than A Monolith - Alliance Politics & Problems of Coercive Diplomacy in Asia. 2011. (Princeton Studies in International History & Politics Ser.). (ENG.). 318p. (C). pap. 24.95 *(978-0-691-14261-6(0))* Princeton Univ. Pr.
Ciorciari, John D. The Limits of Alignment: Southeast Asia & the Great Powers since 1975. 2010. (ENG., Illus.). 336p. pap. 32.95 *(978-1-58901-696-5(3))* Georgetown Univ. Pr.
Davidson, Jason W. America's Allies & War: Kosovo, Afghanistan, & Iraq. 2011. (ENG., Illus.). 260p. 85.00 *(978-0-230-61482-6(5))* Palgrave Macmillan.
Dumbrell, John. America's Special Relationships: Allies & Clients. 2009. (Routledge Studies in US Foreign Policy Ser.). (ENG.). 254p. pap. 41.95 *(978-0-415-48375-9(1))* Routledge.
—America's 'Special Relationships' Foreign & Domestic Aspects of the Politics of Alliance. Dumbrell, John & Schäfer, G, eds. 2009. (Routledge Studies in US Foreign Policy Ser.). (ENG.). 254p. 130.00 *(978-0-415-48376-6(X))* Routledge.
Edström, Håkan, et al, eds. NATO: the Power of Partnerships. 2011. (New Security Challenges Ser.). (ENG., Illus.). 240p. 85.00 *(978-0-230-27377-1(7))* Palgrave Macmillan.
Goforth, Sean. Axis of Unity: Venezuela, Iran & the Threat to America. 2011. 234p. 29.95 ***(978-1-61234-015-9(6))*** Potomac Bks., Inc.
Hunt, Peter. War, Peace, & Alliance in Demosthenes' Athens: Debate & the Process of Decision-Making. 2010. (ENG.). 332p. 99.00 *(978-0-521-83551-0(8))* Cambridge Univ. Pr.
Ishibashi, Natsuyo. Alliance Security Dilemmas in the Iraq War: German & Japanese Responses. 2012. (ENG., Illus.). 256p. 85.00 ***(978-0-230-33733-6(3))*** Palgrave Macmillan.
Menon, Rajan. The End of Alliances. 2008. (ENG., Illus.). 280p. pap. 19.95 *(978-0-19-537726-2(5))* Oxford Univ. Pr., Inc.
Miller, Gregory D. The Shadow of the Past. 2012. (Cornell Studies in Security Affairs Ser.). (ENG.). 248p. 45.00 ***(978-0-8014-5031-0(4))*** Cornell Univ. Pr.
Nadkarni, Vidya. Strategic Partnerships in Asia: Balancing Without Alliances. 2010. (ENG., Illus.). 272p. (C). 135.00 *(978-0-415-77774-2(7)*, Routledge) Taylor & Francis Group GBR. Dist: Taylor & Francis Group.
Podany, Amanda H. Brotherhood of Kings: How International Relations Shaped the Ancient Near East, 1 vol. 2012. (ENG., Illus.). 432p. pap. 24.95 ***(978-0-19-985868-2(3))*** Oxford Univ. Pr., Inc.
Pressman, Jeremy. Warring Friends: Alliance Restraint in International Politics. 2008. (Cornell Studies in Security Affairs). 184p. 57.95 *(978-0-8014-4671-9(6))*; pap. 19.95 *(978-0-8014-7443-9(4))* Cornell Univ. Pr.
Reiter, Erich & Gärtner, Heinz, eds. Small States & Alliances. 2010. (ENG., Illus.). v, 194p. pap. 99.00 *(978-3-7908-2492-6(5)*, 3790824925) Physica-Verlag DEU. Dist: Springer.
Sherwood-Randall, Elizabeth. Alliances & American National Security. 2006. (Letort Papers: No. 15). viii, 41p. pap. *(978-1-58487-261-0(6))* Strategic Studies Institute, U.S. Army War College Commandant (AWCC-DSI/Pubns.).
Snyder, Scott. Pursuing a Comprehensive Vision for the U. S. -South Korea Alliance. 2009. pap. 16.95 *(978-0-89206-578-3(8)*, CSIS Pr., The) Ctr. for Strategic & International Studies.
Treaties & Alliances of the World 8th Ed. 8th rev. ed. 2007. 724p. 180.00 *(978-0-9551144-4-1(6))* John Harper Publishing GBR. Dist: Cengage Gale.
Van Gestel, Melissa. Problematic Alliances. 2011. 96p. pap. ***(978-3-8433-9417-8(2))*** Lambert Academic Publishing.
Walldorf, C. William, Jr. Just Politics: Human Rights & the Foreign Policy of Great Powers. 2008. (Cornell Studies in Security Affairs). (Illus.). 248p. 39.95 *(978-0-8014-4633-7(3))* Cornell Univ. Pr.
Yeager, Melissa & Carter, Charles, eds. Pacts & Alliances in History: Diplomatic Strategy & the Politics of Coalitions. 2012. (ENG., Illus.). 320p. 99.00 ***(978-1-84885-773-5(X))*** I. B. Tauris & Co., Ltd. GBR. Dist: Macmillan.

ALLIED AND ASSOCIATED POWERS (1914-1920)

Dawes, Charles Gates. A Journal of the Great War V1. 2008. 502p. 53.95 *(978-1-4366-6745-6(3))*; 504p. pap. 38.95 *(978-0-548-88911-4(2))* Kessinger Publishing, LLC.
Grant, Ulysses S. America's Part in the Supreme War Council During the World War. 2011. 54p. 36.95 ***(978-1-258-01001-0(1))*** Literary Licensing, LLC.
Tunstall, Graydon. Essays on World War I. Pastor, Peter, ed. 2011. (ENG., Illus.). 215p. (gr. 17). 50.00 ***(978-0-88033-686-4(2))*** Eastern European Monographs.

ALLIED HEALTH EDUCATION

see Paramedical Education

ALLIED HEALTH PERSONNEL

see also Emergency Medical Technicians; Medical Assistants; Medical Secretaries; Medical Technologists; Nurses' Aides; Personal Trainers; Physicians' Assistants

Acello, Barbara. Advanced Skills for Health Care Providers. 2nd rev. ed. 2006. (ENG., Illus.). 624p. (C). per. 82.95 *(978-1-4180-0133-9(3))* Delmar Cengage Learning.
Aehlert, Barbara J. Paramedic Practice Today (Revised Reprint) - 2-Volume Text, 2-Volume Workbook (RR), & Virtual Patient Encounters Package: Above & Beyond. 2011. (ENG.). (C). 306.00 *(978-0-323-09739-0(1)*, Mosby/JEMS) Elsevier - Health Sciences Div.
—Paramedic Practice Today (Revised Reprint) - 2-Volume Text & VPE Package: Above & Beyond. 2011. (ENG.). (C). 255.00 *(978-0-323-09740-6(5)*, Mosby/JEMS) Elsevier - Health Sciences Div.
—Virtual Patient Encounters for Paramedic Practice Today - Revised Reprint: Above & Beyond. 2011. (ENG.). 384p. (C). cd-rom 58.95 *(978-0-323-08550-2(4)*, Mosby/JEMS) Elsevier - Health Sciences Div.
American Medical Association Staff, contrib. by. Health Professions Career & Education Directory 2007-2008. 2007. 636p. pap. 70.00 *(978-1-57947-814-8(X))* American Medical Assn.
Anne Nguyen, Lauren Nguyen & Christina Pham. Pharmacy Technician Certified Board Preparation: Comprehensive Review Manual. 2011. 132p. 29.99 ***(978-1-4568-6326-5(6))***; pap. 19.99 ***(978-1-4568-6325-8(8))*** Xlibris Corp.
Armstrong, Pat, et al. Critical to Care: The Invisible Women in Health Services. 2008. (ENG., Illus.). 176p. *(978-0-8020-9333-2(7))*; pap. *(978-0-8020-9608-1(5))* Univ. of Toronto Pr.
Atwal, Anita & Jones, Mandy, eds. Preparing for Professional Practice in Health & Social Care. 2009. (ENG.). 224p. pap. 62.99 *(978-1-4051-7593-7(1)*, Wiley-Blackwell) Wiley, John & Sons, Inc.
Backscheider & Finlay, Linda. Phenomenology for Therapists: Researching the Lived World. 2011. (ENG., Illus.). 312p. 119.95 *(978-0-470-66646-3(3)*, Wiley-Blackwell) Wiley, John & Sons, Inc.
Badasch, Shirley A. & Chesebro, Doreen S. Health Science Fundamentals. 2008. (ENG.). (C). 656p. pap., stu. ed., act. bk ed. 40.60 *(978-0-13-504372-1(7))*; cd-rom 7.80 *(978-0-13-504310-3(7))* Prentice Hall PTR. (Prentice Hall).
—Health Science Fundamentals: Exploring Career Pathways. 2009. (Illus.). xxviii, 931p. *(978-0-13-504306-6(9))* Pearson Bks.
Baffi-Dugan, Carol, ed. Health Professions Admissions Guide: Strategy for Success. (C). 2009. (ENG.). 184p. pap. 44.00 *(978-0-911899-17-7(0))* 7th ed.

2007. 159p. pap. 44.00 (978-0-911899-15-3(4)) National Assn. of Advisors for the Health Professions, Inc.

Barker, Geoff. Health & Social Care Careers. 2010. (In the Workplace Ser.). 48p. lib. bdg. 34.25 (978-1-60753-091-6(0)) Amicus Publishing.

Barker, Geoff P. & Savery, Annabel. Health & Social Care. 2011. (Been There! Ser.). 32p. (J). (gr. 3-6). lib. bdg. 28.50 (978-1-59920-471-0(1)) Black Rabbit Bks.

Beaman, Nina. Pharmacology Clear & Simple: A Drug Classifications & Dosage Calculations Approach. 2007. (Illus.). 464p. pap. 49.95 (978-0-8036-1239-6(7)) Davis, F. A. Co.

Beebe, Richard & Myers. Paramedic Professional, Volume III: EMS Operations. 2011. (Professional Paramedic Ser.). (ENG.). 704p. (C). pap. 69.95 (978-1-4283-2348-3(1)) Delmar Cengage Learning.

Beebe, Richard & Myers, Jeffrey C. Paramedic Professional, Volume II: Medical Emergencies, Maternal Health & Pediatric, 1 vol. 2010. (Professional Paramedic Ser.). (ENG., Illus.). 1024p. (C). pap. 72.95 (978-1-4283-2351-3(1)) Delmar Cengage Learning.

Beebe, Richard W. O. & Myers, Jeffrey W. Paramedic Professional: Foundations of Paramedic Care. 2009. (Professional Paramedic Ser.). (ENG., Illus.). 896p. (C). pap. 77.95 (978-1-4283-2345-2(7)) Delmar Cengage Learning.

Bircher, Wendy D. & Bircher, Wendy. Lukan's Documentation for Physical Therapist Assistants. 3rd rev. ed. 2007. (Illus.). 224p. (C). pap. 38.95 (978-0-8036-1709-4(7)) Davis, F. A. Co.

Blessing, J. Dennis & Forister, J. Glenn. Book Alone: Introduction to Research & Medical Literature for Health Professionals. 3rd ed. 2012. 350p. pap. 62.95 (978-1-4496-0481-3(1)) Jones & Bartlett Learning, LLC.

Booth, Kathryn. Medical Assisting: Administrative & Clinical Procedures. 4th ed. 2010. (ENG., Illus.). lxi, 1458p. (C). 123.67 (978-0-07-739997-9(8), 0077399978) McGraw-Hill Higher Education.

Booth, Kathryn & Whicker, Leesa. Administrative Procedures for Medical Assisting. 4th ed. 2010. 608p. pap. 81.67 (978-0-07-734007-0(8), Career Education) McGraw-Hill Higher Education.

Booth, Kathryn, et al. Medical Assisting: Administrative Procedures with Student CD. 4th ed. 2010. (ENG.). (C). pap. 100.25 incl. cd-rom (978-0-07-739998-6(6), 0077399986) McGraw-Hill Higher Education.

Booth, Kathryn A. Administrative Procedures for Medical Assisting. 3rd ed. 2009. (Illus.). xviii, 469p. (978-0-07-321143-5(5)) McGraw-Hill Cos., The.

—Medical Assisting: Administrative & Clinical Procedures. 2009. (Illus.). xxix, 1162p. (978-0-07-337399-7(0)) McGraw-Hill Cos., The.

Booth, Kathryn A. & Wyman, Terri D. Anatomy, Physiology, & Pathophysiology for Allied Health. 2007. 240p. (C). pap. 52.33 (978-0-07-337393-5(1), 9780073373935, McGraw-Hill Science, Engineering & Mathematics) McGraw-Hill Higher Education.

—Anatomy, Physiology & Pathophysiology for Allied Health. 2nd ed. 2008. (ENG., Illus.). 312p. (C). pap. 64.55 (978-0-07-337395-9(8), 0073373958) McGraw-Hill Higher Education.

Booth, Kathryn A., et al. Medical Assisting: Adminstrative & Clinical Procedures. 2008. (ENG., Illus.). 550p. (C). pap. 70.38 (978-0-07-332410-4(8), 0073324108) McGraw-Hill Higher Education.

—Pocket Guide for Use with Medical Assisting: Administrative & Clinical Procedures with Anatomy & Physiology. 4th ed. 2010. (ENG., Illus.). 322p. (C). spiral bd. 39.14 (978-0-07-734010-0(8), 0077340108) McGraw-Hill Higher Education.

Borcherding, Sherry & Morreale, Marie J. The OTA's Guide to Writing SOAP Notes. 2nd ed. 2006. (ENG.). 240p. (C). per. 46.95 (978-1-55642-779-4(4)) SLACK, Inc.

Breskin, Myrna, et al. Medical Dictionary for Allied Health. 2007. (ENG., Illus.). 656p. (C). pap., pap. 77.94 (978-0-07-334727-1(2), 0073347272) McGraw-Hill Higher Education.

Brooker, Christine. Mosby's Dictionary of Medicine, Nursing, & Health Professions. 2010. (ENG., Illus.). 972p. 41.95 (978-0-7234-3504-4(9), Mosby) Elsevier - Health Sciences Div.

Buchman, Michelle. Clinical Competencies. 2007. (Medical Assisting Made Incredibly Easy Ser.). (ENG., Illus.). 560p. per. 50.99 (978-0-7817-6345-5(2)) Lippincott Williams & Wilkins.

Buff, Sheila. Health Care Providers. 2010. (Career Launcher Ser.). 224p. (C). (gr. 9-18). 34.95 (978-0-8160-7954-4(4), Ferguson Publishing Co.); pap. 14.95 (978-0-8160-7976-6(5), Checkmark Bks.) Facts On File, Inc.

Burzek, Michael C. Blood on My Shirt: Memoirs of a BC Paramedic. 2011. 240p. 26.26 (978-1-4269-5680-5(0)); pap. 16.26 (978-1-4269-5681-2(9)) Trafford Publishing.

Cairns, Carol S. & Pelletier, Sally J. Core Privileges for AHPs: A Practical Approach to Developing & Implementing Criteria-based Privileges. 2008. 319p. pap. 199.00 (978-1-60146-093-6(7)) Opus Communications.

Calderone, Theresa, et al. Handbook of Informatics for Nurses & amp; Healthcare Professionals. 5th rev. ed. 2012. (ENG.). 624p. (C). 62.95 (978-0-13-257495-2(0)) Pearson Education.

Cartwright, Lorin & Pitney, William. Fundamentals of Athletic Training. 3rd ed. 2011. (Illus.). 408p. 71.00 (978-0-7360-8373-7(1)) Human Kinetics Pubs.

Chapleau, Will, et al. The Paramedic with Drug Reference Guide. 2008. (C). 133.67 (978-0-07-320533-5(8), 9780073205335, Career Education) McGraw-Hill Higher Education.

Clynch, Holly M. The Role of the Physical Therapist Assistant: Regulations & Responsibilities. 2011. (Illus.). 320p. pap. 41.95 (978-0-8036-2562-4(6)) Davis, F. A. Co.

Cox, Carol, et al, eds. Advanced Practice in Heathcare. 2011. (ENG., Illus.). 216p. (C). 135.00 (978-0-415-59430-1(8)); pap. 44.95 (978-0-415-59431-8(6)) Routledge.

Cram101 Textbook Reviews. Outlines & Highlights for Administrative Medical Assisting: Foundations & Practices by Christine Malone, Lorraine M. Papazian-Boyce, ISBN. 2011. 304p. pap. 32.95 (978-1-61812-317-6(3)) Cram101 Inc.

—Outlines & Highlights for Advanced Pharmacy Practice for Technicians by Anita a Lambert. 2011. 62p. pap. 27.95 (978-1-61905-991-7(0)) Cram101 Inc.

—Outlines & Highlights for Burtons Microbiology for the Health Sciences by Paul G Engelkirk, Gwendolyn R Burton, Isbn: 9780781771955. 2010. 178p. pap. 29.95 (978-1-61698-637-7(9)) Cram101 Inc.

—Outlines & Highlights for Clinical Medical Assisting: Foundations & Practice by Margaret Frazer, ISBN. 2011. 400p. pap. 35.95 (978-1-61812-309-1(2)) Cram101 Inc.

—Outlines & Highlights for Clinical Medical Assisting, Edition by Judy Kronenberger, Isbn: 9780781797849 0781797845 9781605470696. 2011. 280p. pap. 41.95 (978-1-61490-028-3(0)) Cram101 Inc.

—Outlines & Highlights for Delmars Comprehensive Medical Assisting: Administrative & Clinical Competencies - with CD by Wilburta Q. Lindh, ISBN. 2010. 248p. pap. 31.95 (978-1-61654-731-8(6)) Cram101 Inc.

—Outlines & Highlights for Essentials of Pharmacology for Health Occupations by Ruth Woodrow, Isbn: 9781401889258. 2010. 556p. pap. 38.95 (978-1-61654-184-2(9)) Cram101 Inc.

—Outlines & Highlights for Law, Liability, & Ethics for Medical Office Personnel by Myrtle Flight, Isbn: 9781428359413. 2011. 280p. pap. 32.95 (978-1-61461-467-8(9)) Cram101 Inc.

—Outlines & Highlights for Paramedics by Will Chapleau. 2011. 740p. pap. 43.95 (978-1-61490-798-5(6)) Cram101 Inc.

—Outlines & Highlights for Principles & Techniques of Patient Care by Frank M Pierson. 2011. 92p. pap. 27.95 (978-1-4672-6990-2(5)) Cram101 Inc.

Cram101 Textbook Reviews & Cram101 Textbook Reviews. Outlines & Highlights for Administrative Medical Assisting, 2nd Edition by Laura Southard Durham, Isbn: 9780781797894 0781797896. 2011. 428p. pap. 33.95 (978-1-61490-058-0(2)) Cram101 Inc.

—Outlines & Highlights for Anatomy, Physiology, & Pathophysiology for Allied Health by Kathryn a Booth, Isbn: 9780073373935 0073373931. 2011. 682p. pap. 41.95 (978-1-61490-277-5(1)) Cram101 Inc.

—Outlines & Highlights for Clinical Competencies: Skills from Beginning Through Advanced by Lorraine Fleming-McPhillips, ISBN. 2011. 400p. pap. 35.95 (978-1-61461-358-9(3)) Cram101 Inc.

—Outlines & Highlights for Cognitive Behavioural Interventions in Physiotherapy & Occupational Therapy by Marie Donaghy, Isbn: 9780750688000. 2011. 112p. pap. 28.95 (978-1-4288-6007-0(X)) Cram101 Inc.

—Outlines & Highlights for Introduction to Physical Therapy for Physical Therapist Assistants by Olga Dreeben, Isbn: 0763730459 9780763730451. 2011. 188p. pap. 30.95 (978-1-61461-541-5(1)) Cram101 Inc.

—Outlines & Highlights for Medical Assisting Made Incredibly Easy! Professionalism by Jackie Marshall, Isbn: 9780781772105 0781772109. 2011. 106p. pap. 28.95 (978-1-61490-001-6(9)) Cram101 Inc.

—Outlines & Highlights for Pharmacology: Principles & Applications - Text & Workbook by Eugenia M. Fulcher. 2011. 640p. pap. 40.95 (978-1-61830-775-0(4)) Cram101 Inc.

—Outlines & Highlights for Pharmacology for Pharmacy Technicians by Kathy Moscou. 2011. 546p. pap. 38.95 (978-1-61830-641-8(3)) Cram101 Inc.

—Outlines & Highlights for Pharmacology for Surgical Technologist by Katherine C Snyder. 2011. 234p. pap. 31.95 (978-1-61830-644-9(8)) Cram101 Inc.

—Outlines & Highlights for Sourcebook for Medical Speech Pathology by Lee Ann C Golper, Isbn: 1428340572 9781428340572. 2011. 218p. pap. 30.95 (978-1-61461-634-4(5)) Cram101 Inc.

—Outlines & Highlights for Standards of Practice for the Pharmacy Technician by Mary E Mohr. 2011. 148p. pap. 29.95 (978-1-61830-746-0(0)) Cram101 Inc.

—Outlines & Highlights for Terminology for Allied Health Professionals by Carolee Sormunen, Isbn: 9781428376342 1428376348. 2011. 456p. pap. 36.95 (978-1-61490-588-2(6)) Cram101 Inc.

Cram101 Textbook Reviews Staff. Outlines & Highlights for Understanding Pharmacology for Health Professions by Susan M Turley, Isbn: 9780135145708. 2009. 104p. pap. 28.95 (978-1-4288-6397-0(5)) Cram101 Inc.

Crane, Andrea L. Rx Success National Certification Review Manual for the Pharmacy Technician. 10th ed. 2007. per. 54.95 (978-0-9722464-3-4(7)) Salt & Light Enterprises, LLC.

Cuhulain Kerr & Douglas, Janet. The Safe Approach: Controlling Risk for Workers in the Helping Professions. 2007. (978-1-930461-03-1(8)) Idyll Arbor, Inc.

DeChello, Patrick L., creator. Step Towards Success - Preparation for the Alcohol & Drug Abuse Counselor Written Exam, 2 vols. 2006. 278p. per. 126.00 (978-1-933661-10-0(0)) D & S Assocs.

Delmar Nursing Assisting Student Theater: Interactive Video Program. 2010. (ENG.). (C). 176.95 (978-1-4354-2829-4(3)) Delmar Cengage Learning.

Dimeo, Sandra. A Practical Approach Becoming a Health Care Professional. rev. ed. 2011. (ENG.). 120p. (C). pap. 20.80 (978-0-13-506354-5(X), Prentice Hall) Prentice Hall PTR.

Doolin, Peter J. Lab Competencies. 2007. (Medical Assisting Made Incredibly Easy Ser.). (ENG., Illus.). 295p. per. 50.99 (978-0-7817-6347-9(9)) Lippincott Williams & Wilkins.

Dreeben-Irimia, Olga. Introduction to Physical Therapy for Physical Therapist Assistants. 2nd rev. ed. 2010. 308p. pap. 60.95 (978-0-7637-8130-9(4)) Jones & Bartlett Learning, LLC.

Dreeben-Irimia, Olga. Physical Therapy Clinical Handbook for PTAs. 2nd ed. 2012. 536p. pap. 57.95 (978-1-4496-4758-2(8)) Jones & Bartlett Learning, LLC.

Dreeben, Olga. Physical Therapy Clinical Handbook for PTAs. 2007. (Illus.). 634p. per. 65.95 (978-0-7637-4667-4(3)) Jones & Bartlett Learning, LLC.

Duncan, Danny. Small-Town Fireman. 2007. 61p. pap. 16.95 (978-1-4241-9077-5(0)) PublishAmerica, Inc.

Durham, Laura Southard. Administrative Medical Assisting. 2nd rev. ed. 2008. (ENG., Illus.). 256p. pap., stu. ed. 35.95 (978-0-7817-9791-7(8)) Lippincott Williams & Wilkins.

Durham, Laura Southard & Molle, Elizabeth A. Lippincott Williams & Wilkins' Administrative Medical Assisting. 2nd rev. ed. 2008. (ENG., Illus.). 416p. pap. 79.95 (978-0-7817-9789-4(6)) Lippincott Williams & Wilkins.

Dutton. Orthopaedics for the Physical Therapist Assistant. 2011. 760p. pap. 67.95 (978-0-7637-9755-3(3)) Jones & Bartlett Learning, LLC.

Dutton, Mark. Physical Therapist Assistant Exam Review Guide & JBTest Prep: PTA Exam Review. 2011. 588p. pap. 72.95 (978-1-4496-2850-5(8)) Jones & Bartlett Learning, LLC.

Early, Mary Beth. Physical Dysfunction Practice Skills for the Occupational Therapy Assistant. 3rd ed. 2012. (ENG., Illus.). 752p. (C). 82.95 (978-0-323-05909-1(0), Mosby) Elsevier - Health Sciences Div.

Edmonds, Vesta. Playlady: Tales of a Recreational Therapist. 2011. 267p. pap. 15.95 (978-1-4327-7688-6(6)) Outskirts Pr., Inc.

Electronic Health Records for Hlth Info Techs. 2011. pap. 72.95 (978-0-7637-9536-2(0)) Jones & Bartlett Learning, LLC.

Elling, Bob & Elling, Kirsten M. The Paramedic Exam Review. 2nd rev. ed. 2007. (ENG.). 464p. pap. 52.95 (978-1-4180-3818-2(0)) Delmar Cengage Learning.

Elling, Bob, et al. Paramedic Field Guide. 2007. (ENG., Illus.). 352p. spiral bd. 40.95 (978-0-7637-5122-7(7)) Jones & Bartlett Learning, LLC.

Engelkirk, Paul G. & Duben-Engelkirk, Janet. Microbiology for the Health Sciences. 9th rev. ed. 2010. (ENG.). 560p. pap. 94.99 (978-1-60547-673-5(0)) Lippincott Williams & Wilkins.

Feix, Jeff. Pharmacology Handbook for Surgical Technologists. 2nd ed. 2011. (ENG.). 288p. (C). pap. 71.95 (978-1-111-30665-6(6)) Delmar Cengage Learning.

Finlay, Linda. Phenomenology for Therapists: Researching the Lived World. 2011. (ENG., Illus.). 312p. pap. 49.95 (978-0-470-66645-6(5), Wiley-Blackwell) Wiley, John & Sons, Inc.

Floyd, Patricia A. & Allen, Beverly. Introduction to Careers in Health, Physical Education, & Sport. 2nd rev. ed. 2008. (ENG., Illus.). 208p. (C). per. 48.95 (978-0-495-38839-5(4)) Brooks/Cole.

Foss, Mark A. & Farine, Tony. Science in Nursing & Health Care. 2nd rev. ed. 2007. (ENG., Illus.). 504p. pap. 77.50 (978-0-13-186902-8(7)) Pearson Education, Ltd. GBR. Dist: Trans-Atlantic Pubns., Inc.

Frazier, Margaret Schell & Malone, Christine. Medical Assisting: Foundations & Practices. 2009. (ENG.). 1312p. (C). 107.13 (978-0-13-515058-0(2), Prentice Hall) Prentice Hall PTR.

Frazier, Margaret Schell, et al. Workbook for Medical Assisting: Foundations & Practices. 2009. (ENG.). 1320p. (C). pap. 43.80 (978-0-13-502363-1(7), Prentice Hall) Prentice Hall PTR.

Fulcher, Eugenia M., et al. Pharmacology: Principles & Applications - Text & Workbook Package: A Worktext for Allied Health Professionals. 2nd ed. 2008. (ENG.). (C). 98.91 (978-1-4160-5576-1(2), Saunders) Elsevier - Health Sciences Div.

Fulcher, Eugenia M., et al. Workbook for Pharmacology: Principles & Applications: A Worktext for Allied Health Professionals. 3rd ed. 2011. (ENG., Illus.). 256p. (C). pap. 32.95 (978-1-4557-0640-2(X), Saunders) Elsevier - Health Sciences Div.

Fulcher, Robert M. & Fulcher, Eugenia M. Math Calculations for Pharmacy Technicians: A Worktext. 2nd ed. 2012. (ENG., Illus.). 688p. (C). pap. 64.95 (978-1-4377-2366-3(7), Saunders) Elsevier - Health Sciences Div.

Generali, Joyce A., ed. The Pharmacy Technician's Pocket Drug Reference. 6th ed. 2010. 246p. pap. 23.00 (978-1-58212-157-4(5)) American Pharmacists Assn.

Gerdin, Judith. Health Careers Today. 5th ed. 2011. (ENG., Illus.). 648p. (C). 74.95 (978-0-323-07504-6(5), Mosby) Elsevier - Health Sciences Div.

—Workbook for Health Careers Today. 4th ed. 2007. (ENG., Illus.). 400p. (C). per. 32.95 (978-0-323-04842-2(0), Mosby) Elsevier - Health Sciences Div.

Giordano, Simona. Exercise & Eating Disorders: An Ethical & Legal Analysis. 2010. (Ethics & Sport Ser.). (ENG., Illus.). 240p. (C). 150.00 (978-0-415-47605-8(4)) Routledge.

Govender, Kevin. Paramedic Migration. 2011. 276p. pap. (978-3-8433-9386-7(9)) Lambert Academic Publishing.

Grafft, Joseph A. & Sarff, Ric. EMS for Secure Facilities. 2011. (ENG.). 208p. (C). 22.95 (978-1-4283-1147-3(5)) Delmar Cengage Learning.

Grayson, Steven Kelly. A Paramedic's Story: Life, Death, & Everything in Between. 2010. (ENG.). 336p. pap. 16.00 (978-1-60714-657-5(6)) Kaplan Publishing.

Green, Michelle A. & Bowie, Mary Jo. Essentials of Health Information Management: Principles & Practices. 2nd ed. 2010. (ENG.). (C). 280p. pap., lab manual ed. 60.95 (978-1-4390-6006-3(1)); 392p. E-Book 83.95 (978-1-4390-6018-6(5)) Delmar Cengage Learning.

Gutiérrez-Rodríguez, Encarnación. Migration, Domestic Work & Affect: A Decolonial Approach on Value & the Feminization of Labor. 2010. (Routledge Research in Gender & Society Ser.). (ENG.). 234p. 125.00 (978-0-415-99473-6(X)) Routledge.

Hart. Intro to Human Disease. 5th rev. ed. 2011. 518p. pap. 86.95 (978-0-7637-7766-1(8)) Jones & Bartlett Learning, LLC.

Hebda, Toni Lee, et al. Informatics for Nurses & Health Care Professionals. 4th ed. 2008. (ENG., Illus.). 576p. (C). pap., instr.'s hndbk. ed. 59.95 (978-0-13-504394-3(8), Prentice Hall) Prentice Hall PTR.

Higgins, Chris. Understanding Laboratory Investigations for Nurses & Health Professionals. 2nd rev. ed. 2007. (ENG., Illus.). 368p. per. 53.99 (978-1-4051-3127-8(6), Wiley-Blackwell) Wiley, John & Sons, Inc.

Hirst, Ben A. Paramedic. 2006. 142p. per. 39.95 (978-0-7637-4216-4(3)) Jones & Bartlett Learning, LLC.

HOBET Exam Secrets Test Prep Staff, ed. HOBET Practice Questions: HOBET Practice Tests & Exam Review for the Health Organization Basic Entrance Test. 2011. (C). pap. 34.99 (978-1-61403-559-6(8)) Mometrix Media LLC.

Hopper, Teresa. Mosby's Pharmacy Technician: Principles & Practice. 3rd ed. 2011. (ENG., Illus.). 1136p. (C). pap. 74.95 (978-1-4377-0670-3(3), Saunders) Elsevier - Health Sciences Div.

—Mosby's Pharmacy Technician - Text & Workbook Package: Principles & Practice. 3rd ed. 2011. (ENG.). (C). pap. 107.91 (978-1-4377-0672-7(X), Saunders) Elsevier - Health Sciences Div.

—Workbook & Lab Manual for Mosby's Pharmacy Technician: Principles & Practice. 3rd ed. 2011. (ENG., Illus.). 400p. (C). pap. 44.95 (978-1-4377-0671-0(1), Saunders) Elsevier - Health Sciences Div.

Houser, Helen J. & Wyman, Terri. Administrative Medical Assisting a Workforce Readiness Approach. 2011. (ENG., Illus.). 672p. (C). pap. 93.73 (978-0-07-340215-4(X), 007340215X) McGraw-Hill Higher Education.

Hunt, Sue. Saunders Fundamentals of Medical Assisting - Text (Revised Reprint) & Virtual Medical Office Package. 2006. (C). 92.95 (978-1-4160-4181-8(8), Saunders) Elsevier - Health Sciences Div.

Hunt, Sue A. & Zonderman, Jon H. Fundamentals of Medical Assisting. rev. ed. 2006. (ENG., Illus.). 1120p. (C). reprint ed. 89.95 (978-1-4160-4223-5(7), Saunders) Elsevier - Health Sciences Div.

JIST Publishing Editors. Health-Care CareerVision: View What You'd Do. 2007. (Illus.). 223p. pap. 22.95 (978-1-59357-463-5(0), JIST Works) JIST Publishing.

Kale-Smith, Geri. Administrative Competencies. 2007. (Medical Assisting Made Incredibly Easy Ser.). (ENG., Illus.). 317p. per. 50.99 (978-0-7817-7810-7(7)); 192p. per., pupil's gde. ed. 29.99 (978-0-7817-6401-8(7)) Lippincott Williams & Wilkins.

Kaplan, Norman M. Kaplan's Introduction to Allied Health: Black Module. 2006. (ENG., Illus.). 464p. pap. 38.00 (978-0-7817-7515-1(9)) Lippincott Williams & Wilkins.

Kennamer, Mike. Paramedic Professional - Foundations of Paramedic Care, Vol. 1. 2010. (ENG.). 176p. (C). pap., stu. ed. 35.95 (978-1-4283-2346-9(5)) Delmar Cengage Learning.

Kimball, Cheryl. Start Your Health Care Career. 2007. (ENG., Illus.). 144p. per. 14.95 (978-1-59918-026-7(X), 159918026X) Entrepreneur Pr. dba Entrepreneur Media, Inc.

Klieger, Diane M. Saunders Essentials of Medical Assisting. 2nd ed. 2009. (ENG., Illus.). 1248p. (C). 89.95 (978-1-4160-5674-4(2), Saunders) Elsevier - Health Sciences Div.

—Saunders Essentials of Medical Assisting - Text & Workbook Package, 2 vols. 2nd ed. 2009. (ENG.). (C). 114.21 (978-1-4160-6184-7(3), Saunders) Elsevier - Health Sciences Div.

—Saunders Essentials of Medical Assisting - Text, Workbook, & Virtual Medical Office Package. 2nd ed. 2009. (ENG.). (C). 144.21 (978-1-4377-1558-3(3), Saunders) Elsevier - Health Sciences Div.

—Workbook for Saunders Essentials of Medical Assisting. 2nd ed. 2009. (ENG., Illus.). 1128p. (C). pap. 36.95 (978-1-4160-5675-1(0), Saunders) Elsevier - Health Sciences Div.

Kuntzman, Andrew J. & Tortora, Gerard J. Anatomy & Physiology for the Manual Therapies. 2009. (ENG., Illus.). 848p. (C). 168.95 (978-0-470-04496-4(9), Wiley) Wiley, John & Sons, Inc.

Laruffa, Pascal. Teen-MD. 2011. 374p. 29.99 (978-1-4568-3121-9(6)); pap. 19.99 (978-1-4568-3120-2(8)) Xlibris Corp.

LearningExpress Staff, contrib. by. Becoming a Healthcare Professional. 2010. (ENG.). 256p. pap. 16.95 (978-1-57685-729-8(8)) LearningExpress, LLC.

Leung, Paul, et al, eds. Multicultural Issues in Rehabilitation & Allied Health. 2006. (C). (978-0-9721642-2-1(7)) Aspen Professional Services.

Loke, Jennifer C. F., et al. Critical Discourse Analysis of Interpersonal Online Learning in Health Care Education. 2011. (Series: Education in a Competitive & Globalizing World Ser.). pap. 43.00 (978-1-61122-729-1(1)) Nova Science Pubs., Inc.

Long, Bruce W., et al. Radiography Essentials for Limited Practice. 3rd ed. 2009. (ENG., Illus.). 656p. (C). pap. 75.95 (978-1-4160-5763-5(3), Saunders) Elsevier - Health Sciences Div.

Longe, Jacqueline L. The Gale Encyclopedia of Nursing & Allied Health, 5 vols. 2nd ed. 2006. (Illus.). xxiii, 3093p. (978-1-4144-0379-3(8)); (978-1-4144-0378-6(X)); (978-1-4144-0377-9(1)); (978-1-4144-0375-5(5)); (978-1-4144-0376-2(3)) Cengage Gale.

Malone, Christine. Administrative Medical Assisting: Foundations & Practices. 2009. (ENG.). 528p. (C). pap., wbk. ed. 43.80 (978-0-13-243145-3(9), Prentice Hall) Prentice Hall PTR.

Martin, Colin R. & Preedy, Victor R., eds. Scientific Basis of Healthcare. 2012. (ENG., Illus.). 210p. 69.95 (978-1-57808-731-0(7)) BIOS Scientific Publishers Ltd. GBR. Dist: Taylor & Francis Group.

Matzka, Kathy. The Medical Staff Meeting Companion: Tools & Techniques for Effective Presentations. 2008. (Illus.). ix, 136p. *(978-1-60146-204-6(2))* Opus Communications.

McGee, Paula, ed. Advanced Practice in Nursing & the Allied Health Professions. 3rd ed. 2009. (ENG., Illus.). 280p. pap. 66.99 *(978-1-4051-6239-5(2),* Wiley-Blackwell) Wiley, John & Sons, Inc.

McGuinness, Helen. Anatomy & Physiology: Therapy Basics. 4th rev. ed. 2010. (ENG., Illus.). 352p. pap. 29.95 *(978-1-4441-0923-8(5))* Hodder Arnold Pubs.

—Anatomy & Physiology: Therapy Basics. 3rd ed. 2006. (Illus.). 362p. pap., stu. ed. 44.50 *(978-0-340-90808-2(4),* Hodder Arnold) Hodder Education GBR. Dist: Trans-Atlantic Pubns., Inc.

Miller, Charly D. Paramedic National Standards Self-Test. 5th ed. 2007. (ENG., Illus.). 520p. (C). per. 35.33 *(978-0-13-199987-9(7),* Prentice Hall) Prentice Hall PTR.

Milliken, Mary Elizabeth & Honeycutt, Alyson. Understanding Human Behavior: A Guide for Health Care Providers. 8th ed. 2011. (Communication & Human Behavior for Health Science Ser.). (ENG., Illus.). 480p. (C). pap. 136.95 *(978-1-4354-8660-7(9))* Delmar Cengage Learning.

Moini, Jahangir. Anatomy & Physiology for Health Professionals International Edition. 2011. (Illus.). 424p. pap. 62.95 *(978-1-4496-3229-8(7))* Jones & Bartlett Learning, LLC.

—Anatomy & Physiology for Health Professionals with Companion Web Site. 2011. 424p. pap. 62.95 *(978-1-4496-2214-5(3))* Jones & Bartlett Learning, LLC.

—Focus on Pharmacology. 2nd rev. ed. 2012. (ENG.). 720p. (C). pap. 77.27 ***(978-0-13-249966-8(5),*** Prentice Hall) Prentice Hall PTR.

—Focus on Pharmacology: Essentials for Health Professionals. 2007. (ENG., Illus.). 752p. (C). pap. 83.00 *(978-0-13-171642-1(5),* Prentice Hall) Prentice Hall PTR.

—Medical Assisting Review: Passing the CMA, RMA, & Other Exams. 3rd ed. 2008. (Illus.). 589p. pap. 93.75 incl. cd-rom *(978-0-07-352087-2(X))* McGraw-Hill Cos., The.

—Medical Assisting Review: Passing the CMA, RMA, & CCMA Exams. 4th ed. 2011. (ENG., Illus.). 560p. (C). pap. 96.13 *(978-0-07-337458-1(X),* 007337458X) McGraw-Hill Higher Education.

—The Pharmacy Technician. 2nd ed. 2010. (ENG.). 144p. (C). pap., wbk. ed. 18.95 *(978-1-4354-9940-9(9))* Delmar Cengage Learning.

—Pocket Guide for Pharmacy Technicians. 2007. (ENG., Illus.). 592p. (C). per. 49.95 *(978-1-4180-3221-0(2))* Delmar Cengage Learning.

Moraski. Physics for Allied Health. rev. ed. 2011. (ENG.). 218p. ring bd. 109.99 ***(978-0-7575-8964-5(2))*** Kendall Hunt Publishing Co.

Moss, Bernard. Communication Skills for Health & Social Care. 2007. (Illus.). 224p. (C). 99.95 *(978-1-4129-2284-5(4),* B22844C); per. 47.00 *(978-1-4129-2285-2(2),* B22844P) SAGE Pubns., Ltd. GBR. Dist: SAGE Pubns., Inc.

Moss, Bernard. Communication Skills in Health & Social Care. 2nd ed. 2012. (Illus.). 248p. (C). 99.95 ***(978-1-4462-0818-2(4),*** B08182C); pap. 42.95 ***(978-1-4462-0819-9(2),*** B08182P) SAGE Pubns., Ltd. GBR. Dist: SAGE Pubns., Inc.

Mulholland, Joan & Turnock, Chris. Learning in the Workplace: A Toolkit for Supervisors. 2nd rev. ed. 2012. (ENG., Illus.). 152p. (C). 145.00 ***(978-0-415-53789-6(4));*** pap. 48.95 ***(978-0-415-53790-2(8))*** Routledge.

Muller, Arlene M. How to Survive & Maybe Even Love Health Professions School: Retention & Career Placement Guide. 2011. (Illus.). 320p. pap. 32.95 *(978-0-8036-2365-1(8))* Davis, F. A. Co.

Mundt, Lillian. Perceptions of Scientific Misconduct among Graduate Health Students. 2010. 340p. pap. *(978-3-8383-7939-5(X))* Lambert Academic Publishing.

Nepon, Bruce & Eberly, Barry. Field Training Officer: Tips & Techniques for FTOs, Preceptors, & Mentors. 2007. (ENG., Illus.). 160p. pap. 55.95 *(978-0-7637-4199-0(X))* Jones & Bartlett Learning, LLC.

Neumann, Donald A. & Mansfield, Paul Jackson. Essentials of Kinesiology for the Physical Therapist Assistant. 2008. (ENG., Illus.). 416p. (C). per. 50.95 *(978-0-323-03616-0(3),* Mosby) Elsevier - Health Sciences Div.

Newby, Cynthia. HIPAA for Allied Health Careers. 2008. (ENG., Illus.). 176p. (C). pap. 67.64 *(978-0-07-337412-3(1),* 0073374121) McGraw-Hill Higher Education.

Newmark, Emanuel & O'Hara, Mary A. Ophthalmic Medical Assisting: An Independent Study Course. 5th ed. 2012. ***(978-1-61525-153-7(7))*** American Academy of Ophthalmology.

Nuttall, Dilyse & Rutt-Howard, Jane. The Textbook of Non-Medical Prescribing. 2011. (ENG., Illus.). 368p. pap. 44.99 *(978-1-4051-9935-3(0),* Wiley-Blackwell) Wiley, John & Sons, Inc.

Offredy, Maxine & Vickers, Peter. Developing a Healthcare Research Proposal. 2010. (ENG., Illus.). 296p. pap., stu. ed. 39.99 *(978-1-4051-8337-6(3),* Wiley-Blackwell) Wiley, John & Sons, Inc.

Orum-Alexander, Gail & Mizner, James. Lab Manual to accompany Pharmacy Technician: Practice & Procedures. 2010. 256p. pap. 43.67 *(978-0-07-328111-7(5),* Career Education) McGraw-Hill Higher Education.

—Lab Manual to accompany Pharmacy Technician: Practice & Procedures. 2010. (ENG., Illus.). 224p. (C). pap. 52.53 *(978-0-07-320269-3(X),* 007320269X) McGraw-Hill Higher Education.

Osborne, Carole. Pre- & Perinatal Massage Therapy: A Comprehensive Guide to Prenatal, Labor, & Postpartum Practice. 2nd ed. 2011. (LWW Massage Therapy & Bodywork Educational Ser.). (ENG., Illus.). 214p. pap. 44.95 *(978-1-58255-851-6(5))* Lippincott Williams & Wilkins.

Papazian-Boyce, Lorraine. ICD-10-CM/PCS Coding: A Map for Success. rev. ed. 2012. (MyHealthProfessionsLab Ser.). (ENG.). 576p. (C). pap. 82.60 ***(978-0-13-286036-9(8),*** Prentice Hall) Prentice Hall PTR.

Pettway, Bsn Ms Diane. Paramedic Med-Math Made Easy. 2008. 64p. pap. 8.95 *(978-0-595-50635-4(6))* iUniverse, Inc.

Pfeiffer, Ronald P. & Mangus, Brent C. Concepts of Athletic Training. 2011. (Illus.). xv, 372p. ***(978-1-4496-2875-8(3))*** Jones & Bartlett Publishers.

Pharmacoepidemiology for the Health Care Professional. 2011. pap. 62.95 *(978-0-7637-9362-3(0))* Jones & Bartlett Learning, LLC.

Pierson, Frank M. & Fairchild, Sheryl L. Principles & Techniques of Patient Care. 4th ed. 2007. (Principles & Techniques of Patient Care Ser.). (ENG., Illus.). 400p. (C). spiral bd. 82.95 *(978-1-4160-3119-2(7),* Saunders) Elsevier - Health Sciences Div.

Porterfield, Deborah. Healthcare, Medicine, Science. 2007. (Top Careers in Two Years Ser.). (Illus.). 128p. (C). (gr. 9). 35.00 *(978-0-8160-6901-9(8),* Ferguson Publishing Co.) Facts On File, Inc.

Prendergast, Heather. Front Office Management for the Veterinary Team. 2010. (ENG., Illus.). 488p. (C). pap. 62.95 *(978-1-4377-0446-4(8),* Saunders) Elsevier - Health Sciences Div.

Pryor, John P., et al. Clinician's Guide to Surgical Care. Berman, Abigail Tripp, ed. 2008. (ENG., Illus.). 416p. (C). pap. 62.00 *(978-0-07-147897-7(3),* 0071478973) McGraw-Hill Medical Publishing Div.

Quan, Kathy. The Everything Guide to Careers in Health Care: Find the Job That's Right for You. 2006. (ENG., Illus.). 304p. per. 14.95 *(978-1-59337-725-0(8))* Adams Media Corp.

Rankin, Jane L., et al, eds. Rehabilitation in Cancer Care. 2008. (ENG., Illus.). 360p. pap. 82.99 *(978-1-4051-5997-5(9),* Wiley-Blackwell) Wiley, John & Sons, Inc.

Roland, Lin S. From My Weakness, I Am Strong: One Woman's Relentless Pursuit of Pressing On. 2009. pap. 9.99 *(978-1-60696-625-9(1))* Tate Publishing & Enterprises, LLC.

Ross, Frederic C. Cell Biology & Chemistry for Allied Health Science. 6th rev. ed. 2010. (ENG.). 432p. spiral bd. 79.86 *(978-0-7575-5365-3(6))* Kendall Hunt Publishing Co.

Ross, Susan. Doulas: Why Every Pregnant Woman Deserves One. 2012. (ENG., Illus.). 168p. pap. 22.95 ***(978-1-921295-30-0(9))*** Rockpool Publishing AUS. Dist: Independent Pubs. Group.

Rudman, Jack. Allied Health Professions Admission Test (AHPAT) (Admission Test Ser.: Vol. 99). 49.95 *(978-0-8373-5199-5(5))* National Learning Corp.

—Health Occupations Aptitude Examination (HOAE) (Admission Test Ser.: Vol. 98). 49.95 *(978-0-8373-5198-8(7))* National Learning Corp.

Russo, Ethan B. & Beans, Donald R. The Rhythms of Life. 2009. (Illus.). XIV, 162p. 45.95 *(978-0-7890-3706-0(8));* 150.00 *(978-0-7890-3705-3(X))* Routledge.

Sanders, Mick J. & Theriault, Rob. Mosby's Paramedic Textbook - Revised Reprint & the Canadian Paramedic: an Introduction Package. 2006. (C). 115.00 *(978-0-7796-9930-8(0),* Mosby) Elsevier - Health Sciences Div.

Sanderson, Susan M. Electronic Health Records for Allied Health Careers. 2008. 256p. (C). pap. 42.67 *(978-0-07-340197-3(8),* 978007340197 3) McGraw-Hill Cos., The.

—Electronic Health Records for Allied Health Careers. 2008. (ENG., Illus.). 244p. (C). pap. 75.53 incl. cd-rom *(978-0-07-330978-1(8),* 0073309788) McGraw-Hill Higher Education.

Schreiner, Kathleen. Therapeutic Communications. 2008. (Medical Assisting Made Incredibly Easy Ser.). (ENG., Illus.). 320p. pap. 56.99 *(978-0-7817-7552-6(3))* Lippincott Williams & Wilkins.

Shankman, Gary A. & Manske, Robert C. Fundamental Orthopedic Management for the Physical Therapist Assistant. 3rd ed. 2010. (ENG., Illus.). 536p. (C). pap. 50.95 *(978-0-323-05669-4(5),* Mosby) Elsevier - Health Sciences Div.

Sherman, Carolan & Chmielewski, Mary. Lange Q&A Surgical Technology Examination, Sixth Edition. 6th ed. 2012. (LANGE Q&a Allied Health Ser.). (ENG.). 339p. pap. 59.00 incl. audio compact disk ***(978-0-07-174576-5(9),*** 0071745769) McGraw-Hill Medical Publishing Div.

Simmers, Louise M. Diversified Health Occupations. 7th rev. ed. 2008. (ENG., Illus.). 1104p. (C). 111.95 *(978-1-4180-3021-6(X))* Delmar Cengage Learning.

Simmers, Louise M., et al. Diversified Health Occupations. 7th ed. 2008. (ENG.). 640p. (C). pap., wbk. ed. 46.95 *(978-1-4180-3022-3(8))* Delmar Cengage Learning.

Skinner, Steven B. & McVey, Christina. Clinical Decision Making for the Physical Therapist Assistant. rev. ed. 2010. 192p. pap. 48.95 *(978-0-7637-7125-6(2))* Jones & Bartlett Learning, LLC.

Smith, Linda J. Comprehensive Lactation Consultant Exam Review. 3rd rev. ed. 2010. 310p. pap. 78.95 *(978-0-7637-7616-9(5))* Jones & Bartlett Learning, LLC.

Snyder, Scott R., et al. Critical Care Paramedic Workbook. 2006. (ENG.). 544p. (C). per. 57.33 *(978-0-13-225892-0(7),* Prentice Hall) Prentice Hall PTR.

Sormunen, Carolee. Terminology for Health Professionals, 4 vols. 6th ed. 2009. (ENG., Illus.). 768p. (C). pap. 134.95 *(978-1-4283-7634-2(8))* Delmar Cengage Learning.

Sparks, Lisa & Villagran, Melinda. Patient Provider Interaction. 2010. (ENG.). 196p. 64.95 *(978-0-7456-4536-0(4))* Polity Pr. GBR. Dist: Wiley, John & Sons, Inc.

Springhouse Publishing Company Staff & Gohsman, Robyn. Law & Ethics. 2008. (Medical Assisting Made Incredibly Easy Ser.). (ENG., Illus.). 291p. per. 50.99 *(978-0-7817-7169-6(2))* Lippincott Williams & Wilkins.

Springhouse Publishing Company Staff, et al. Pharmacology. 2008. (Medical Assisting Made Incredibly Easy Ser.). (ENG., Illus.). 176p. pap., pupil's gde. ed. 29.99 *(978-0-7817-7510-6(8))* Lippincott Williams & Wilkins.

Stanfield, Peggy S., et al. Introduction to the Health Professions. 5th rev. ed. 2008. 414p. pap. 110.95 *(978-0-7637-5823-3(X))* 6th ed. 2011. 502p. pap. 93.95 *(978-1-4496-0055-6(7))* Jones & Bartlett Learning, LLC.

Tamparo, Carol D. & Lindh, Wilburta Q. Therapeutic Communications for Health Care. 3rd rev. ed. 2007. (Communication & Human Behavior for Health Science Ser.). (ENG., Illus.). 288p. (C). pap. 108.95 *(978-1-4180-3264-7(6))* Delmar Cengage Learning.

Taylor, Brian. Consultative Selling Skills for Audiologists. 2011. (Core Clinical Concepts in Audiology Ser.). (Illus.). 160p. pap. 55.00 *(978-1-59756-424-3(9))* Plural Publishing, Inc.

Taylor, Renee R. & Taylor, Renèe. The Intentional Relationship: Occupational Therapy & Use of Self. 2008. (Illus.). 480p. pap. 50.95 *(978-0-8036-1365-2(2))* Davis, F. A. Co.

Thaler, Malcolm S. The Only EKG Book You'll Ever Need. 7th rev. ed. 2012. (ENG., Illus.). 352p. pap. 63.95 ***(978-1-4511-1905-3(4))*** Lippincott Williams & Wilkins.

Theis, Jennifer L. Clinical Decision Making: Case Studies for the Occupational Therapy Assistant. 2010. (ENG., Illus.). 272p. (C). pap. 55.95 *(978-1-4354-2576-7(6))* Delmar Cengage Learning.

Thomas-Brogan, Teri. Health Information Technology Basics: A Concise Guide to Principles & Practice. 2008. 180p. pap. 73.95 *(978-0-7637-4687-2(8))* Jones & Bartlett Learning, LLC.

Turner, Marilyn. Introduction to Health Care in a Flash! An Interactive, Flash-Card Approach. 2012. pap. ***(978-0-8036-2586-0(3))*** Davis, F. A. Co.

Van Servellen, Gwen Marram. Communication Skills for the Health Care Professional: Concepts, Practice, & Evidence. 2nd rev. ed. 2008. 485p. pap. 89.95 *(978-0-7637-5557-7(5))* Jones & Bartlett Learning, LLC.

Waddell, Janice, et al. Building Your Health Care Career: A Guide for Students. 2008. (ENG.). 88p. (C). pap. 27.95 *(978-1-897422-17-5(2),* Mosby) Elsevier - Health Sciences Div.

Wetfeet.com, creator. Careers in Health Care. 2006. (Wetfeet Insider Guides). 148p. per. 24.95 *(978-1-58207-533-4(6))* WetFeet, Inc.

Wilbanks, Donnie J. Applied Psychology in Health Care. 2008. (Communication & Human Behavior for Health Science Ser.). (ENG., Illus.). 176p. (C). pap. 60.95 *(978-1-4180-5348-2(1))* Delmar Cengage Learning.

Woodrow, Ruth. Essentials of Pharmacology for Health Occupations. 4th ed. 2007. pap. 16.95 *(978-1-4288-1909-9(2))* Cram101 Inc.

Woodrow, Ruth, et al. Essentials of Pharmacology for Health Occupations. 6th ed. 2010. (New Releases for Health Science Ser.). (ENG., Illus.). 624p. (C). pap. 97.95 *(978-1-4354-8033-9(3))* Delmar Cengage Learning.

—Flashcards for Woodrow/Colbert/Smith's Essentials of Pharmacology for Health Occupations. 6th ed. 2010. (ENG.). 112p. (C). ring bd. 21.95 *(978-1-4354-8038-4(4))* Delmar Cengage Learning.

—Study Guide for Woodrow/Colbert/Smith's Essentials of Pharmacology for Health Occupations. 6th ed. 2010. (ENG.). 176p. (C). pap. 43.95 *(978-1-4354-8037-7(6))* Delmar Cengage Learning.

Workman, M. Linda, et al. Understanding Pharmacology - Text & Study Guide Package: Essentials in Medicine Safety. 2010. (ENG.). (C). 74.61 *(978-1-4377-2604-6(6),* Saunders) Elsevier - Health Sciences Div.

Wozniak, Lisa. Surveillance Stories. 2008. 116p. pap. *(978-3-639-00785-5(9))* VDM Verlag Dr. Mueller e.K.

Zentz, Lorraine. Math for Pharmacy Technicians. 2009. (ENG.). 142p. pap. 52.95 *(978-0-7637-5961-2(9))* Jones & Bartlett Learning, LLC.

ALLIED HEALTH PERSONNEL—EDUCATION

see Paramedical Education

ALLIED MENTAL HEALTH PERSONNEL

Carlstedt, Roland A. Handbook of Integrative Clinical Psychology, Psychiatry, & Behavioral Medicine: Perspectives, Practices, & Research. 2009. (Illus.). 912p. *(978-0-8261-1094-7(0))* Springer.

Monk, Lee-Ann. Attending Madness: At Work in the Australian Colonial Asylum. 2008. 280p. 82.00 *(978-90-420-2419-9(4))* Rodopi.

ALLIED OPERATIONS (MILITARY SCIENCE)

see Combined Operations (Military Science)

ALLIED PSYCHIATRIC PERSONNEL

see Allied Mental Health Personnel

ALLIGATOR PEAR

see Avocado

ALLIGATORS

Here are entered works on the American species of crocodiles. General works are entered under the heading Crocodiles.

Ross, Charles A., ed. Crocodiles & Alligators. (Illus.). 240p. (gr. 9). 35.00 *(978-0-8160-2174-1(0))* Facts On File, Inc.

Sobczak, Charles. Alligators, Sharks & Panthers: Deadly Encounters with Florida's Top Predator — Man. 2006. (Illus.). 323p. per. *(978-0-9676199-0-3(4))* Indigo Pr., LC.

Specner, Donald. A History of the Alligator: Florida's Favorite Reptile. 2008. (Illus.). 144p. pap. 24.99 *(978-0-7643-3083-4(7))* Schiffer Publishing, Ltd.

Thorbjarnarson, John B. & Wang, Xiaoming. The Chinese Alligator: Ecology, Behavior, Conservation, & Culture. 2010. (ENG., Illus.). 288p. (gr. 17). 85.00 *(978-0-8018-9348-3(8))* Johns Hopkins Univ. Pr.

ALLITERATION

Minkova, Donka. Alliteration & Sound Change in Early English. 2006. (Cambridge Studies in Linguistics Ser.). (ENG.). 424p. pap. 83.00 *(978-0-521-03224-7(5))* Cambridge Univ. Pr.

Nagy, Michael S. The Alliterative Tradition in Early Middle English Poetry: Political Complaint & Social Analysis in the Song of the Husbandman & Beyond. 2011. 316p. 129.95 *(978-0-7734-1503-4(3))* Mellen, Edwin Pr., The.

Roper, Jonathan, ed. Alliteration in Culture. 2011. (ENG., Illus.). 256p. 85.00 *(978-0-230-23264-8(7))* Palgrave Macmillan.

Shimomiya, Tadao. Alliteration in the Poetic Edda. 2011. (Studies in Historical Linguistics Ser.). 197p. pap. 55.95 *(978-3-0343-0151-0(0))* Lang, Peter AG GBR. Dist: Lang, Peter.

ALLIUM

Asadujjaman, Mohammad, et al. Phytochemical & Pharmacological Evaluation of Allium Sativum. 2011. 96p. pap. ***(978-3-8443-9795-6(7))*** Lambert Academic Publishing.

Block, Eric. Garlic & Other Alliums: The Lore & the Science. 2010. (ENG., Illus.). 480p. (C). pap. 40.00 ***(978-1-84973-180-5(2))*** Royal Society of Chemistry, The GBR. Dist: Ingram Pub. Services.

TVK, et al. Onions & Other Vegetable Alliums. 2nd ed. 2008. (Crop Production Science in Horticulture Ser.: No. 15). (Illus.). 448p. pap. 70.00 *(978-1-84593-399-9(0))* CABI GBR. Dist: Stylus Publishing, LLC.

ALLOGENIC HOMOGRAFTS

see Homografts

ALLOGRAFTS

see Homografts

ALLORHYTHMIA

see Arrhythmia

ALLOTROPY

Katsnelson, Mikhail I. Graphene: Carbon in Two Dimensions. 2012. (ENG., Illus.). 366p. 80.00 ***(978-0-521-19540-9(3))*** Cambridge Univ. Pr.

ALLOWANCES, FAMILY

see Family Allowances

ALLOYS

see also Brass; Heat Resistant Alloys; Metallic Glasses; Metallurgy; Pewter also aluminum Alloys, Steel Alloys and similar headings

Aaronson, Hubert I., et al. Mechanisms of Diffusional Phase Transformations in Metals & Alloys. 2010. (ENG., Illus.). 685p. (C). 119.95 *(978-1-4200-6299-1(9),* CRC Press) Taylor & Francis Group GBR. Dist: Taylor & Francis Group.

Adachi, Sadao, et al. Properties of Semiconductor Alloys: Group-IV, III-V & II-VI Semiconductors. 2009. (Wiley Series in Materials for Electronic & Optoelectronic Applications Ser.: 29). (ENG., Illus.). 422p. 225.00 *(978-0-470-74369-0(7),* Wiley) Wiley, John & Sons, Inc.

Aizawa, T. Solid-State Synthesis of Magnesium-Based Functional Alloys & Compounds, vols.56. 2009. (Illus.). 100p. pap. *(978-0-87849-478-1(2))* Trans Tech Pubns., Ltd.

Alagan, Viswanathan. Laser Processing on Metals & Metal Alloys. 2010. 88p. pap. *(978-3-639-22838-0(3))* VDM Verlag Dr. Mueller e.K.

Ammar, Hany & Samuel, Fawzy. Casting Imperfections & the Fatigue Life of Al-Si Casting Alloys. 2010. 132p. pap. *(978-3-8383-3429-5(9))* Lambert Academic Publishing.

Annual Book of ASTM Standards 2007: Section 2: Nonferrous Metal Products; v.02.05: Metallic & Inorganic Coatings; Metal Powders & Metal Powder Products. 2007. 963p. pap. 215.00 *(978-0-8031-4306-7(0))* American Society for Testing & Materials.

Belin-Ferre, Esther. Mechanical Properties of Complex Intermetallics. 2010. (Illus.). 450p. 150.00 *(978-981-4322-16-4(4))* World Scientific Publishing Co., Inc.

—Properties & Applications of Complex Intermetallics, Vol. 2. 2009. (Illus.). 460p. 118.00 *(978-981-4261-63-0(7))* World Scientific Publishing Co., Inc.

Belin-ferre, Esther. Surface Properties & Engineering of Complex Intermetallics. 2010. (Illus.). 408p. 118.00 *(978-981-4304-76-4(X))* World Scientific Publishing Co., Inc.

Berdovsky, Yakov N. Intermetallics Research Progress. 2008. (Illus.). (C). 129.00 *(978-1-60021-982-5(9))* Nova Science Pubs., Inc.

Berg, Brian, et al. SMST-2006: Proceedings of the International Conference on Shape Memory & Superelastic Technologies, May 7-11, 2006, Asilomar Conference Center, Pacific Grove, California, USA. 2008. (Illus.). xvii, 864p. *(978-0-87170-862-5(0))* ASM International, Inc.

Borbón, Lauro Oliver Paz. Computational Studies of Transition Metal Nanoalloys. 2011. (Springer Theses Ser.). (ENG., Illus.). xvi, 180p. 129.00 *(978-3-642-18011-8(6),* 3642180116) Springer.

Bozzolo, Guillermo, et al, eds. Applied Computational Materials Modeling: Theory, Simulation & Experiment. 2010. (ENG., Illus.). xvi, 491p. pap. 129.00 *(978-1-4419-3575-5(4),* 1441935754) Springer.

Brandon, D. G., et al, eds. Strength of Metals & Alloys, 2 vols. 1174p. *(978-965-294-054-4(2))* Freund Publishing Hse., Ltd.

Campbell, F. C. Elements of Metallurgy & Engineering Alloys. 2008. (Illus.). xiii, 656p. *(978-0-87170-867-0(1))* ASM International, Inc.

Chang, Y. Austin & Oates, W. Alan. Materials Thermodynamics. 2009. (Wiley Series on Processing of Engineering Materials Ser.: 7). (ENG., Illus.). 293p. 105.00 *(978-0-470-48414-2(4),* Wiley) Wiley, John & Sons, Inc.

Chen, H. R. Shape Memory Alloys: Manufacture, Properties & Applications. 2009. (Materials Science & Technologies Ser.). 145.00 *(978-1-60741-789-7(8))* Nova Science Pubs., Inc.

Chernenko, V. A., ed. Advances in Magnetic Shape Memory Materials (Materials Science Forum) 2011. (Illus.). 234p. pap. ***(978-3-03785-147-0(3))*** Trans Tech Pubns., Ltd.

Chernenko, V. A. & Barandiaran, J. M., eds. Ferromagnetic Shape Memory Alloys II. 2010. (Materials Science Forum Ser.: Vol. 635). (Illus.). 222p. pap. 166.00 *(978-0-87849-295-4(X))* Translatons for Technology.

Chernenko, V.A., ed. Advances in Shape Memory Materials, Vol. 583. 2008. 302p. pap. *(978-0-87849-381-4(6))* Trans Tech Pubns., Ltd.

Chinbat, Batukhan B. & Mori, Sora H., eds. Encyclopedia of Materials Science Research, 2 vols. 2011. (Materials Science & Technologies Ser.). 295.00 *(978-1-61209-954-5(8))* Nova Science Pubs., Inc.

Chmielus, Markus. Composition, Structure & Magneto-Mechanical Properties of ni-Mn-Ga Magnetic Shape-Memory Alloys. 2010. 163p. pap. *(978-3-8325-2531-6(9))* Logos Verlag Berlin.

Ciach, R., ed. Advanced Light Alloys & Composites. 2010. (NATO Science Partnership Sub-Series: 3: Ser.). 532p. pap. 439.00 *(978-90-481-5087-8(6),* 9048150876) Springer.

Contreras Cuevas, Antonio, et al, eds. Structural & Chemical Characterization of Metals, Alloys & Compounds: Volume 1275. 2011. (MRS Proceedings Ser.). (C). 112.00 ***(978-1-60511-252-7(6))*** Cambridge Univ. Pr.

Cottam, Ryan. Superplasticity of Magnesium Alloy Zk60. 2010. 160p. pap. *(978-3-8383-5368-4(X))* Lambert Academic Publishing.

Czerwinski, Frank. Magnesium Injection Molding. (ENG., Illus.). xxii, 586p. 2010. pap. 189.00 *(978-1-4419-4436-8(2),* 1441944362) 2008. 189.00 *(978-0-387-72399-0(4),* 0387723994) Springer.

Dong, H., ed. Surface Engineering of Light Alloys. 2010. (Illus.). 420p. 249.95 *(978-1-4398-2984-4(5),* CRC Press) Taylor & Francis Group GBR. Dist: Taylor & Francis Group.

—Surface Engineering of Light Alloys: Aluminium, Magnesium & Titanium Alloys. 2010. (Illus.). 680p. 270.00 *(978-1-84569-537-8(2))* Woodhead Publishing Ltd. GBR. Dist: Taylor & Francis Group.

Dragnevski, Kalin. Microstructural Evolution of Deeply Undercooled Metallic Melts. 2008. 168p. pap. *(978-3-639-10173-7(1))* VDM Verlag Dr. Mueller e.K.

Dubois, Jean-Marie & Belin-Ferré, Esther, eds. Complex Metallic Alloys: Fundamentals & Applications. 2011. (ENG., Illus.). 434p. 175.00 *(978-3-527-32523-8(9),* Wiley-VCH) Wiley, John & Sons, Inc.

Effenberg, G. & Ilenko, S. Ternary Alloy Systems: Phase Diagrams, Crystallographic & Thermodynamic Data. 2008. (Landolt-Börnstein: Numerical Data & Functional Relationships in Science & Technology Ser.). (Illus.). 8359.00 *(978-3-540-69759-6(4))* Springer.

Effenberg, Ganter, ed. C-Ta-W to Ti-V-W. 2010. (Landolt-Börnstein: Numerical Data & Functional Relationships in Science & Technology Ser.). (Illus.). 660p. 6199.00 *(978-3-642-00770-5(8),* 3642007708) Springer.

—Refractory Metal Systems. 2010. (Landolt-Börnstein: Numerical Data & Functional Relationships in Science & Technology Ser.). (Illus.). 631p. 6069.00 *(978-3-642-02699-7(0),* 3642026990) Springer.

Ehsani, Morteza, et al. New Polymeric Alloys As High Voltage Insulators. 2011. 152p. pap. ***(978-3-8433-9250-1(1))*** Lambert Academic Publishing.

Elliott, Rodney P., ed. Constitution of Binary Alloys: First Supplement. (Illus.). 896p. reprint ed. 135.00 *(978-0-931690-19-8(6))* Genium Publishing Corp.

Elsayed, Fady. Microstructure & Properties of Mg-Sn-Ca Alloys with 3% Al Additions. 2009. 102p. pap. *(978-3-639-18478-5(5))* VDM Verlag Dr. Mueller e.K.

—Thermo-Mechanical Modeling of Az31 Magnesium Alloy During Hot Rolling. 2009. 96p. pap. *(978-3-639-12661-7(0))* VDM Verlag Dr. Mueller e.K.

Franks, Steven M. Rare Earth Minerals: Policies & Issues. 2011. (Series: Earth Sciences in the 21st Century Ser.). 115.00 *(978-1-61122-310-1(5))* Nova Science Pubs., Inc.

Friedrich, Horst E. & Mordike, Barry Leslie, eds. Magnesium Technology: Metallurgy, Design Data, Applications. 2010. (ENG., Illus.). xxii, 677p. pap. 289.00 *(978-3-642-05825-7(6),* 3642058256) Springer.

Galanakis, I. & Dederichs, P. H. Half-Metallic Alloys: Fundamentals & Applications. 2010. (Lecture Notes in Physics Ser.). (Illus.). xi, 313p. pap. 139.00 *(978-3-642-06609-2(7),* 3642066097) Springer.

Green, Kenneth A., et al, eds. Superalloys 2004. (Illus.). 1,012p. 130.00 incl. cd-rom *(978-0-87339-576-2(X),* 04-576X-G) TMS (The Minerals, Metals & Materials Society).

Guettler, AndrT Franccois Victor. A Practical Gudie for the Manufacture of Metallic Alloys; 2006. 308p. per. 23.99 *(978-1-4255-2992-5(5))* MPublishing.

Gungor, Mehmet N., et al, eds. Innovations in Titanium Technology. 2007. (ENG., Illus.). 284p. pap. 108.00 *(978-0-87339-665-3(0),* Wiley) Wiley, John & Sons, Inc.

Hansen, Max & Anderko, Kurt, eds. Constitution of Binary Alloys. 2nd ed. (Illus.). 1305p. reprint ed. pap. 150.00 *(978-0-931690-18-1(8))* Genium Publishing Corp.

Hirt, G., et al, eds. Semi-Solid Processing of Alloys & Composites X, 143 vols. 2008. (Solid State Phenomena Ser.: Vol. 143). (Illus.). 814p. pap. *(978-3-908451-59-4(0))* Trans Tech Pubns., Ltd.

Hunt, Emily M. & Pantoya, Michelle L. Nanostructured Metallic Alloys- Synthesis, Properties & Applications. 2007. 128p. per. *(978-3-8364-3438-6(5))* VDM Verlag Dr. Mueller e.K.

Hussain, Ahmed Khalid. Evaluation of Parameters of Friction Stir Welding for Al 6351 Alloy. 2011. 72p. pap. ***(978-3-8443-9458-0(3))*** Lambert Academic Publishing.

Kasper, E. & Paul, D. J. Silicon Quantum Integrated Circuits: Silicon-Germanium Heterostructure Devices: Basics & Realisations. 2010. (NanoScience & Technology Ser.). (Illus.). xii, 361p. pap. 219.00 *(978-3-642-06038-0(2),* 3642060382) Springer.

Kassner, Michael & Perez-Prado, Maria-Teresa. Fundamentals of Creep in Metals & Alloys. 2nd ed. 2009. (ENG., Illus.). 320p. 240.00 *(978-0-08-047561-5(2),* Elsevier Science) Elsevier Science & Technology Bks.

Kastner, Oliver. Lattice Transformations in Shape Memory Alloys: Molecular Dynamics Simulations. 2012. (Springer Series in Materials Science Ser.: 163). (ENG., Illus.). xv, 169p. 129.00 ***(978-3-642-28618-6(6),*** 3642286186) Springer.

Kaya, Serhat. Advanced Processes for Formability Improvement of Lightweight Sheet. 2010. 156p. pap. *(978-3-639-23249-3(6))* VDM Verlag Dr. Mueller e.K.

Khachatryan, Armen G. Theory of Structural Transformations in Solids. 2008. (Dover Books on Engineering Ser.). (ENG., Illus.). 592p. pap. 34.95 *(978-0-486-46280-6(3))* Dover Pubns., Inc.

Kirkwood, David H., et al. Semi-solid Processing of Alloys. 2009. (Springer Series in Materials Science Ser.). (ENG., Illus.). xii, 172p. 159.00 *(978-3-642-00705-7(8),* 3642007058) Springer.

Kobryn, P. A., et al. Casting Titanium Alloys. 2008. 120p. pap. 49.95 *(978-1-934939-56-7(0))* Wexford College Pr.

Kohl, Manfred. Shape Memory Microactuators. 2010. (Microtechnology & MEMS Ser.). (Illus.). xix, 247p. pap. 219.00 *(978-3-642-05837-0(X),* 364205837X) Springer.

Kowser, Arefin. Superelastic Shape Memory Alloy Cantilever Beam of Variable X-Section. 2010. 128p. pap. *(978-3-8383-8159-6(9))* Lambert Academic Publishing.

Krupp, Ulrich. Fatigue Crack Propagation in Metals & Alloys: Microstructural Aspects & Modelling Concepts. 11th ed. 2007. (ENG., Illus.). 311p. 155.00 *(978-3-527-31537-6(3),* Wiley-VCH) Wiley, John & Sons, Inc.

Lagoudas, Dimitris C., ed. Shape Memory Alloys: Modeling & Engineering Applications. (ENG., Illus.). xx, 436p. 2010. pap. 149.00 *(978-1-4419-4297-5(1),* 1441942971) 2008. 149.00 *(978-0-387-47684-1(9),* 0387476849) Springer.

Landolt, D. & Mischler, S., eds. Tribocorrosion of Passive Metals & Coatings. 2011. (ENG., Illus.). 584p. 280.00 *(978-1-84569-966-6(1))* Woodhead Publishing Ltd. GBR. Dist: Ingram Pub. Services.

Lenggo Ginta, Turnad & Amin, A. K. M. Nurul. Improved MacHinability of Titanium Alloy Ti-6al-4v. 2010. 172p. pap. *(978-3-8383-7307-2(3))* Lambert Academic Publishing.

Linzalone, Joseph. Electrum & the Invention of Coinage. 2011. (Illus.). xv, 231p. ***(978-0-939767-62-5(7))*** McMillan, Dennis Pubns.

Liu, L, ed. Welding & Joining of Magnesium Alloys. 2010. (ENG., Illus.). 422p. 245.00 *(978-1-84569-692-4(1))* Woodhead Publishing Ltd. GBR. Dist: Ingram Pub. Services.

Materials Science and International Team, Msit(R). Selected Systems from C-Cr-Fe to Co-Fe-S. 2008. (Landolt-Börnstein: Numerical Data & Functional Relationships in Science & Technology Ser.). (Illus.). 9029.00 *(978-3-540-74193-0(3))* Springer.

Materials Science International Services Staff, contrib. by. Selected Systems from Co-Fe-Si to Fe-La-Si. 2008. (Landolt-Börnstein: Numerical Data & Functional Relationships in Science & Technology Ser.). (Illus.). 424p. 7279.00 *(978-3-540-74197-8(6))* Springer.

—Selected Systems from Cu-Fe-Si to Fe-N-U. 2008. (Landolt-Börnstein: Numerical Data & Functional Relationships in Science & Technology Ser.). (Illus.). 424p. 6739.00 *(978-3-540-78643-6(0),* 3540786430) Springer.

Mehta, Yashwant & Shefali Trivedi, Smt. Powder Forged Iron-Phosphorous Alloys. 2011. 92p. pap. ***(978-3-8443-0359-9(6))*** Lambert Academic Publishing.

Meza Garcia, Enrique. Extrusion of Magnesium-Zinc Based Alloys. 2011. 172p. pap. ***(978-3-8381-2478-0(2))*** Südwestdeutscher Verlag für Hochschulschriften AG & Co. KG.

Milagres Ferri, Orley. Fatigue Crack Propagation in Ti-6al-4v. 2010. 68p. pap. *(978-3-639-27824-8(0))* VDM Verlag Dr. Mueller e.K.

Minerals, Metals and Materials Society (TMS) Staff. Magnesium Technology 2011. Mathaudhu, Suveen N. et al, eds. 2011. (ENG., Illus.). 668p. 229.00 *(978-1-118-02936-7(4),* Wiley-TMS) Wiley, John & Sons, Inc.

Mishra, Ajay Kumar, ed. Transition Metals: Characteristics, Properties & Uses. 2011. (Chemical Engineering Methods & Technology Ser.). (Illus.). 507p. 215.00 *(978-1-61324-559-0(9))* Nova Science Pubs., Inc.

Miyazaki, Shuichi. SMST-2007: Proceedings of the International Conference on Shape Memory & Superelastic Technologies, December 2-5, 2007, Tsukuba, Japan. 2008. (Illus.). xvi, 707p. *(978-0-87170-722-2(5))* ASM International, Inc.

Miyazaki, Shuichi, et al, eds. Thin Film Shape Memory Alloys: Fundamentals & Device Applications. 2009. (ENG., Illus.). 486p. 145.00 *(978-0-521-88576-8(0))* Cambridge Univ. Pr.

Mizutani, Uichiro. Hume-Rothery Rules for Structurally Complex Alloy Phases. 2010. (ENG., Illus.). 356p. 89.95 *(978-1-4200-9058-1(5),* CRC Press) Taylor & Francis Group GBR. Dist: Taylor & Francis Group.

Mohd Rosli, Zulkifli. Surface Treatment of Titanium Alloy. 2011. 68p. pap. ***(978-3-8443-3252-0(9))*** Lambert Academic Publishing.

MSIT, Materials Science International, Materials Science International. Selected Systems from Al-B-C to B-Hf-W. 2009. (Landolt-Börnstein: Numerical Data & Functional Relationships in Science & Technology Ser.). (Illus.). xvii, 531p. 7819.00 *(978-3-540-88052-3(6))* Springer.

—Selected Systems from Fe-N-V to Fe-Ti-Zr. 2009. (Landolt-Börnstein: Numerical Data & Functional Relationships in Science & Technology Ser.). (Illus.). xix, 531p. 7819.00 *(978-3-540-70885-8(5))* Springer.

Münstermann, Ernst. Ternary Systems. 2009. (Landolt-Börnstein: Numerical Data & Functional Relationships in Science & Technology - New Series / Physical Chemistry Ser.). 300p. 4489.00 *(978-3-540-88153-7(0))* Springer.

Münstermann, Ernst, et al, eds. Binary Systems & Ternary Systems from C-Cr-Fe to Cr-Fe-W Pt. 1: Thermodynamic Properties of Inorganic Materials Compiled by SGTE, Subvolume C - Ternary Steel Systems, Phase Diagrams & Phase Transition Data. 2012. (Landolt-Börnstein: Numerical Data & Functional Relationships in Science & Technology - New Series / Physical Chemistry Ser.: 19C1). (ENG.). xvi, 420p. 6069.00 *(978-3-540-88141-4(7),* 3540881417) Springer.

Murphy, Matthew. The Use of Ion Implantation for Biomedical Applications. 2010. 348p. pap. *(978-3-8383-7895-4(4))* Lambert Academic Publishing.

Ndlovu, Gebhu. Microstructural Study of the Pt-Al-Nb Phase Diagram. 2010. 136p. pap. *(978-3-8383-7371-3(5))* Lambert Academic Publishing.

Ng, Hock Min, et al, eds. GaN & Related Alloys — 2003 Vol. 798: 2003 MRS Fall Meeting Symposium Proceedings. 2009. (Materials Research Society Symposium Proceedings Ser.: 798). (Illus.). 834p. 35.00 *(978-1-55899-736-3(9),* 798-C) Materials Research Society.

Okamoto, H. Desk Handbook: Phase Diagrams for Binary Alloys. 2nd ed. 2010. (Illus.). xliv, 855p. ***(978-1-61503-046-0(8))*** ASM International.

Ovchinnikov, V. V. Mossbauer Analysis of the Atomic & Magnetic Structure of Alloys. 2006. (ENG., Illus.). 260p. 115.00 *(978-1-904602-13-2(4))* Cambridge International Science Publishing, Ltd. GBR. Dist: Ingram Pub. Services.

Palm, M., et al, eds. Advanced Intermetallic-Based Alloys for Extreme Environment & Energy Applications: Volume 1128. 2009. (MRS Proceedings Ser.). (ENG.). 560p. (C). 125.00 *(978-1-60511-100-1(7))* Cambridge Univ. Pr.

Pekguleryuz, Mihriban O., et al, eds. Manesium Technology 2008: Proceedings of a Symposium Sponsored by the Magnesium Committee of the Light Metals Division of the Minerals, Metals & Materials. 2008. (ENG., Illus.). 449p. 314.00 *(978-0-87339-711-7(8),* Wiley) Wiley, John & Sons, Inc.

Pfeiler, Wolfgang, ed. Alloy Physics: A Comprehensive Reference. 2007. (ENG.). 1003p. 485.00 *(978-3-527-31321-1(4),* Wiley-VCH) Wiley, John & Sons, Inc.

Qing-Ping Sun, ed. IUTAM Symposium on Mechanics of Martensitic Phase Transformation in Solids. 2011. (Solid Mechanics & Its Applications Ser.). (ENG.). 276p. pap. 189.00 *(978-90-481-6071-6(5),* 9048160715) Springer.

Rabie, Mohamed. A Kinetic Model for the Oxidation of Silicon Germanium Alloys. 2010. 140p. pap. *(978-3-8383-4857-5(5))* Lambert Academic Publishing.

Rack, H. J., et al, eds. Beta-Titanium Alloys for the 00s. (Illus.). 498p. pap. *(978-0-87339-592-2(1))* TMS (The Minerals, Metals & Materials Society).

Sanchez, Pedro N., ed. Titanium Alloys: Preparation, Properties & Applications. 2010. (Materials Science & Technologies Ser.). 195.00 *(978-1-60876-151-7(7),* Nova Biomedical Bks.) Nova Science Pubs., Inc.

Saravanan, R. & Rani, M. Prema. Metal & Alloy Bonding - an Experimental Analysis: Charge Density in Metals & Alloys. 2011. (ENG., Illus.). xvi, 151p. 129.00 ***(978-1-4471-2203-6(8),*** 1447122038) Springer.

Schutze, M. Protective Systems for High Temperature Applications: From Theory to Industrial Implementation. 2011. (European federation of corrosion Ser.). (ENG., Illus.). 417p. (C). 290.00 *(978-1-906540-35-7(7))* Maney Publishing GBR. Dist: Brown, David Bk. Co., The.

Sha, W. Titanium: Modelling microstructure, properties & Applications. Shaw, I. & Malinov, G., eds. 2009. (Illus.). 500p. 255.95 *(978-1-4398-0148-2(7))* CRC Pr. LLC.

Sha, W. & Malinov, S. Titanium Alloys: Modelling of Microstructure, Properties & Applications. 2009. (Illus.). 560p *(978-1-84569-375-6(2))* Woodhead Publishing Ltd.

Shiraki, Y. & Usami, N., eds. Silicon-Germanium (SiGe) Nanostructures: Production, Properties & Applications in Electronics. 2011. (ENG., Illus.). 664p. 280.00 *(978-1-84569-689-4(1))* Woodhead Publishing Ltd. GBR. Dist: Ingram Pub. Services.

Shunk, Francis A., ed. Constitution of Binary Alloys: Second Supplement. 846p. reprint ed. pap. 135.00 *(978-0-931690-20-4(X))* Genium Publishing Corp.

Spittel, Thilo & Spittel, Marlene. Non-Ferrous Alloys - Heavy Metals: Metal Forming Data. Warlimont, Hans Peter, ed. 2014. (Landolt-Börnstein: Numerical Data & Functional Relationships in Science & Technology - New Series / Physical Chemistry Ser.). (ENG.). 575p. 5659.00 *(978-3-642-14173-7(0),* 3642141730) Springer.

—Part 2: Non-Ferrous Alloys - Light Metals: Subvolume C: Metal Forming Data - Volume 2: Materials - Group Viii: Advanced Materials & Technologies - Landolt-Bã¶Rnstein New Series Warlimont, Hans, ed. 2011. (Landolt-Börnstein: Numerical Data & Functional Relationships in Science & Technology - New Series / Physical Chemistry Ser.). (ENG., Illus.). x, 640p. 4039.00 *(978-3-642-13863-8(2),* 3642138632) Springer.

Srivatsan, T. S. Advances in Understanding the Fatigue Behavior of Materials. 2008. (Key Engineering Materials Ser.: Vol. 378-79). 420p. pap. *(978-0-87849-394-4(8))* Trans Tech Pubns., Ltd.

Strang, Andrew, et al, eds. Microstructural Stability of Creep Resistant Alloys for High Temperature Plant Applications. (Illus.). 492p. *(978-1-86125-045-2(2))* Woodhead Publishing Ltd.

Svetlana, Ebzéeva. Univariant Eutectic Growth: In Ternary Aluminium Alloys. 2011. 184p. pap. ***(978-3-639-32227-9(4))*** VDM Verlag Dr. Mueller e.K.

Takeuchi, Akira, et al. Part 1: Systems from Ag-Al-Ca to Au-Pd-Si: Volume 37: Phase Diagrams & Physical Properties of Nonequilibrium Alloys, Subvolume A: Physical Properties of Ternary Amorphous Alloys. Carow-Watamura, Ursula & Yu, Jing Zhi, eds. 2011. (Landolt-Börnstein: Numerical Data & Functional Relationships in Science & Technology - New Series / Physical Chemistry Ser.). (ENG., Illus.). 409p. 4179.00 *(978-3-642-03480-0(2),* 3642034802) Springer.

—Part 3: Systems from Cr-Fe-P to Si-W-Zr: Volume 37: Phase Diagrams & Physical Properties of Nonequilibrium Alloys, Subvolume C: Physical Properties of Ternary Amorphous Alloys. Carow-Watamura, Ursula & Yu, Jing Zhi, eds. 2011. (Landolt-Börnstein: Numerical Data & Functional Relationships in Science & Technology - New Series / Physical Chemistry Ser.). (ENG., Illus.). 420p. 4179.00 *(978-3-642-14132-4(3),* 3642141323) Springer.

—Systems from B-Be-Fe to Co-W-Zr: Subvolume B: Physical Properties of Ternary Amorphous Alloys - Volume 37: Phase Diagrams & Physical Properties of Nonequilibrium Alloys - Group I: Elementary Particles, Nuclei & Atoms. Carow-Watamura, Ursula & Yu, Jing Zhi, eds. 2011. (Landolt-Börnstein: Numerical Data & Functional Relationships in Science & Technology - New Series / Physical Chemistry Ser.). (Illus.). 450p. 4179.00 *(978-3-642-13849-2(7),* 3642138497) Springer.

Technology Research Editors, ed. Al-Li Alloys, 2007 Ed. 2007. pap. 128.50 *(978-1-60030-161-2(4),* Search-In-Print) CSA Journal Division.

—Electron Beam Welding of Steels & Alloys, 2007 Ed. 2007. pap. 128.50 *(978-1-60030-478-1(8),* Search-In-Print) CSA Journal Division.

—High Performance Alloys Used in Sporting Goods, 2007 Ed. 2007. pap. 128.50 *(978-1-60030-215-2(7),* Search-In-Print) CSA Journal Division.

—Mechanical Properties of Shape Memory Alloys, 2007 Ed. 2007. pap. 128.50 *(978-1-60030-517-7(2),* Search-In-Print) CSA Journal Division.

—Oxidation of Intermetallics, 2007 Ed. 2007. pap. 128.50 *(978-1-60030-189-6(4),* Search-In-Print) CSA Journal Division.

—Polymer Development Through Blending & Alloying, 2007 Ed. 2007. pap. 128.50 *(978-1-60030-227-5(0),* Search-In-Print) CSA Journal Division.

—Shape Memory Alloys, 2007 Ed. 2007. pap. 134.50 *(978-1-60030-555-9(5),* Search-In-Print) CSA Journal Division.

—Ti-6Al-4V & Surgical Implants, 2007 Ed. 2007. pap. 128.50 *(978-1-60030-232-9(7),* Search-In-Print) CSA Journal Division.

Tekkaya, A. Erman & Khalifa, Nooman Ben, eds. Advances on Hot Extrusion & Simulation of Light Alloys. 2010. (Key Engineering Materials: Vol. 424). (Illus.). 294p. pap. 193.00 *(978-0-87849-302-9(6))* Translatons for Technology.

Temel, F. Zeynep. Modeling Chemical Processes in Materials. 2011. 96p. pap. ***(978-3-8443-0681-1(1))*** Lambert Academic Publishing.

Trivedi, Shefali & Mehta, Yashwant. Development of Iron-Phosphorus Alloys Through Hot Powder Forging. 2011. 100p. pap. ***(978-3-8433-9326-3(5))*** Lambert Academic Publishing.

Tuissi, Ausonio, et al, eds. Smst 2008: Proceedings of the International Conference on Shape Memory & Superelastic Technologies. 2009. (ENG.). 500p. 249.00 *(978-1-4419-0845-2(5),* 1441908455) Springer.

Vadiraj, Aravind & Kamaraj, M. ., eds. Surface Modified Biochemical Titanium Alloys. 2010. (Materials Science & Technologies Ser.). 142p. pap. 43.00 *(978-1-60876-581-2(4))* Nova Science Pubs., Inc.

Vairamuthu, Thangaraj & Chitharanjan Hegde, A. Electrodeposition & Characterization of Zn-Fe Group Metal Alloys. 2010. 184p. pap. *(978-3-8383-7710-0(9))* Lambert Academic Publishing.

Vaughan, Martin. Alloy & Phonon Scattering. 2009. 144p. pap. *(978-3-639-13086-7(3))* VDM Verlag Dr. Mueller e.K.

Wang, Yingmin. Bulk Metallic Glass-Forming Alloys. 2010. 188p. pap. *(978-3-639-22463-4(9))* VDM Verlag Dr. Mueller e.K.

Wego, Wang. Eng Alloys Prop & Apps. 2009. 300p. 139.95 *(978-0-8247-2765-9(7))* CRC Pr. LLC.

Wetzel, C., et al, eds. GaN, AlN, InN & Their Alloys: 2004 MRS Fall Meeting Symposium Proceedings, Vol. 831. 2009. (Materials Research Society Symposium Proceedings Ser.: 831). (Illus.). xix, 784p. 35.00 *(978-1-55899-779-0(2))* Materials Research Society.

Whang, S. H., ed. Nanostructured Metals & Alloys: Processing, Microstructure, Mechanical Properties & Applications. 2011. (ENG., Illus.). 800p. 305.00 *(978-1-84569-670-2(0))* Woodhead Publishing Ltd. GBR. Dist: Ingram Pub. Services.

Wiezorek, Jörg. Advanced Intermetallic-Based Alloys: Symposium Held November 27-30, 2006, Boston, Massachusetts, U.S.A. 2007. (Illus.). xv, 588p. *(978-1-55899-937-4(X))* Materials Research Society.

Yamauchi, Kiyoshi, et al, eds. Shape Memory & Superelastic Alloys: Applications & Technologies. 2011. (Woodhead Publishing in Materials Ser.). (ENG., Illus.). 390p. 230.00 *(978-1-84569-707-5(3))* Woodhead Publishing Ltd. GBR. Dist: Ingram Pub. Services.

Yeoh Lee Moi (Nilai University College, Malaysia). Phase Formation & Superconductivity in Copper Oxide Based YBCO & Ru-1212 & Ru-1222 Systems Prepared by Sol-Gel & Coprecipitation Techniques. 2011. (Series: Materials Science & Technologies Ser.). (Illus.). 138p. 69.00 *(978-1-61122-504-4(3))* Nova Science Pubs., Inc.

Zagrebelnyy, Dmytro. MODELING MACROSEGREGATION DURING VAR OF TI-10V-2FE-3AL ALLOY: Macroscopic Approach. 2008. 292p. pap. *(978-3-8364-5948-8(5))* VDM Verlag Dr. Mueller e.K.

Zhanar, Zhumadilova. Development of Damping Multiple Alloyed Steels. 2011. 148p. pap. ***(978-3-8443-3162-2(X))*** Lambert Academic Publishing.

Zlateva, Ganka & Martinova, Zlatanka. Microstructure of Metals & Alloys: An Atlas of Transmission Electron Microscopy Images. 2008. (ENG., Illus.). 192p.

139.95 *(978-1-4200-7556-4(X),* CRC Press) Taylor & Francis Group GBR. Dist: Taylor & Francis Group.

ALLOYS—CORROSION

Beranger, Gerard. Corrosion & Protection of Metals & Alloys. Mazille, Henri, ed. 2010. (ENG.). 640p. 250.00 *(978-1-84821-037-0(X),* Wiley-ISTE) Wiley, John & Sons, Inc.

HDR Engineering. Contribution of Service Line & Plumbing Fixtures to Lead & Copper Rule Compliance Issues. 2008. (Illus.). 112p. pap. *(978-1-60573-031-8(9))* Water Research Foundation.

Hossain, Mohammad. Stress Corrosion Cracking & Hydrogen Embrittlement of Alloy Ep-823. 2010. 200p. pap. *(978-3-8383-6016-4(8))* Lambert Academic Publishing.

Ogundipe, Adebayo. Environmental Release of Tungsten & Other Elements from Tungsten Heavy Alloys. 2008. 216p. pap. *(978-3-8364-8473-2(0))* VDM Verlag Dr. Mueller e.K.

Song, G., ed. Corrosion of Magnesium Alloys. 2011. (Woodhead Publishing in Materials Ser.). (ENG., Illus.). 480p. 255.00 *(978-1-84569-708-2(1))* Woodhead Publishing Ltd. GBR. Dist: Ingram Pub. Services.

Soodi, Mehdi. Surface Recrystallization of Ze41 to Enhance Its Corrosion Behaviour. 2010. 68p. pap. *(978-3-8383-7561-8(0))* Lambert Academic Publishing.

Technology Research Editors, ed. Corrosion Protection of Aluminum & Aluminum Alloys, 2007 Ed. 2007. pap. 118.50 *(978-1-60030-473-6(7),* Search-In-Print) CSA Journal Division.

—Corrosion Resistance of Nickel & Nickel Alloys, 2007 Ed. 2007. pap. 118.50 *(978-1-60030-397-5(8),* Search-In-Print) CSA Journal Division.

ALLPORT, GORDON WILLARD, 1897-1967

Capps, Donald. Striking Out: The Religious Journey of Teenage Boys. 2011. 160p. pap. 18.00 ***(978-1-61097-300-7(3),*** Cascade Bks.) Wipf & Stock Pubs.

Maddi, Salvatore R., et al. Humanism in Personology: Allport, Maslow, & Murray. 2007. (ENG.). 218p. (gr. 11). pap. 24.95 *(978-0-202-36173-4(X))* Aldine Transaction.

ALLSTON, WASHINGTON, 1779-1843

Fuller, Margaret. Art, Literature, & the Drama / by Margaret Fuller Ossoli, Edited by Her Brother, Arthur B Fuller. 2006. 448p. per. 29.99 *(978-1-4255-4993-0(4))* MPublishing.

—Literature & Art by S Margaret Fuller Two Parts in One Volume with an Introduction by Horace Greeley. 2006. 364p. per. 26.99 *(978-1-4255-3774-6(X))* MPublishing.

Lester, Charles Edwards. Artists of America. 2010. (Illus.). 40p. pap. 14.14 *(978-1-154-52401-7(9))* General Bks. LLC.

Ware, William. Lectures on the Works & Genius of Washington Allston by William Ware. 2006. 164p. per. 18.99 *(978-1-4255-1224-8(0))* MPublishing.

ALLUSIONS

see also Terms and Phrases

Brewer, E. Cobham. Character Sketches of Romance, Fiction & the Drama Vol. 1: A Revised American Edition of the Reader's Handbook. 2007. (ENG.). 654p. pap. 32.99 *(978-1-4264-4694-8(2))* 2006. 738p. pap. 35.99 *(978-1-4264-4725-9(6))* BiblioBazaar.

Delahunty, Andrew & Dignen, Sheila. Oxford Dictionary of Reference & Allusion. 3rd ed. 2012. (ENG.). 416p. 18.95 ***(978-0-19-956746-1(8))*** Oxford Univ. Pr., Inc.

Manser, Martin H. The Facts on File Dictionary of Allusions. (Writers Library). 544p. (gr. 6-12). 2009. pap. 18.95 *(978-0-8160-7907-0(2),* Checkmark Bks.) 2008. 75.00 *(978-0-8160-7105-0(5))* Facts On File, Inc.

O'Brien, Kelli S. Use of Scripture in the Markan Passion Narrative. 2010. (Library of New Testament Studies, the Ser.). (ENG.). 352p. 150.00 *(978-0-567-03379-6(1),* T&T Clark Int'l) Continuum International Publishing Group, Ltd. GBR. Dist: National Bk. Network.

Prescott, Deborah Lee. Imagery from Genesis in Holocaust Memoirs: A Critical Study. 2010. (ENG., Illus.). 204p. pap. 45.00 *(978-0-7864-4817-3(2))* McFarland & Co., Inc. Pubs.

Ruffner, Frederick G. & Urdang, Laurence. Allusions - Cultural, Literary, Religious, & Historical: A Thematic Dictionary. 3rd rev. ed. 2009. lib. bdg. 70.00 *(978-0-7808-1122-5(4))* Omnigraphics, Inc.

Ruffner, Frederick G., Jr. & Urdang, Laurence. Ruffner's Allusions: Cultural, Literary, Biblical, & Historical. Gunton, Sharon R. & Harris, Laurie Lanzen, eds. 3rd ed. 2010. (ENG.). 999p. pap. 45.00 *(978-0-7808-1170-6(4))* KWS Pubs.

Thibodeau, Philip. Playing the Farmer: Representations of Rural Life in Vergil's Georgics. 2011. (ENG.). 288p. 60.00 *(978-0-520-26832-6(6))* Univ. of California Pr.

ALMA, BATTLE OF THE, UKRAINE, 1854

Fletcher, Ian & Ishchenko, N. A. Battle of the Alma 1854. 2009. (Illus.). 224p. 39.99 *(978-1-84415-672-6(9))* Pen & Sword Bks. Ltd. GBR. Dist: Casemate Pubs. & Bk. Distributors, LLC.

ALMANACH DE GOTHA

Kennedy, John & James, John E., eds. Almanach de Gotha II Vol. 2: III. Non-Sovereign Princely & Ducal Houses of Europe: The 200 Non-Royal Principle Aristocratic European Families. rev. ed. 2007. (Almanach de Gotha Ser.). 1100p. 105.00 *(978-0-9532142-6-6(5))* Almanach de Gotha, Ltd. GBR. Dist: Boydell & Brewer, Inc.

ALMANACS

see also Calendars; Chronology; Nautical Almanacs; Yearbooks

A & C Black Publishers Ltd Staff, creator. Whitaker's Almanack. 2007. (Whitaker's Almanack Ser.). (Illus.). 1362p. *(978-1-4144-3344-8(1))* A & C Black.

—Whitaker's Almanack. 139th rev. ed. 2006. (Whitaker's Almanack Ser.). (Illus.). 1364p. 135.00 *(978-0-7136-7659-4(0))* A & C Black GBR. Dist: Cengage Gale.

Almanac, Old Farmer's. The Old Farmer's Almanac 2009. 2008. (ENG.). 15.95 *(978-1-57198-461-6(5));* pap. 6.95 *(978-1-57198-453-1(4))* Yankee Publishing, Inc.

—Old Farmer's Almanac Club Store Edition. 2006. 320p. mass mkt. 9.95 *(978-1-57198-397-8(X))* Yankee Publishing, Inc.

Almanac, World. The World Almanac & Book of Facts 2010, 10, Pack, Set. 2009. (World Almanac Ser.). (gr. 6-12). pap. 129.90 *(978-1-60057-129-9(8),* World Almanac Bks.) Facts On File, Inc.

Alvarez, Elizabeth Cruce & Plocheck, Robert, eds. Texas Almanac 2008-2009: The Source for All Things Texan since 1857. 64th ed. 2007. (Texas Almanac Ser.). (ENG., Illus.). 720p. per. 16.95 *(978-0-914511-41-0(6))* Belo, A. H. Corp., The Dallas Morning News.

Alvarez, Elizabeth Cruce & Plocheck, Robert, eds. Texas Almanac 2012-2013. 2011. (Illus.). 736p. pap. 24.95 ***(978-0-87611-248-9(3));*** (ENG., 39.95 *(978-0-87611-247-2(5))* Texas State Historical Assn.

The American Year-Book. reprint ed. 150.00 *(978-0-7222-7268-8(5))* Library Reprints, Inc.

Appleduck, Cosmo. Ignorance Almanac 1997-98: What You Know Ain't So. annuals. 19.95 *(978-0-911505-15-3(6))* Lifecraft.

Barone, Michael & McCutcheon, Chuck. The Almanac of American Politics 2012. 2011. (Almanac of American Politics - Cloth Ser.). (ENG., Illus.). 1856p. 110.00 *(978-0-226-03807-0(6));* pap. 85.00 *(978-0-226-03808-7(4))* Univ. of Chicago Pr.

Bennett, William J. & Cribb, John T. E., Jr. The American Patriot's Almanac: Daily Readings on America. 2010. 592p. 32.99 *(978-1-59555-260-0(X))* Nelson, Thomas Inc.

Bingham, Jane & Whitaker Staff. Whitaker's Almanack Quiz Book. 2nd ed. 2008. (Whitaker's Ser.). (ENG., Illus.). 512p. 19.95 *(978-1-4081-0448-4(2))* A & C Black GBR. Dist: Macmillan.

Booth, Janet. Janet's Plan-its 2007 Celestial Planner: Easy-to-Use Astrology Calendar. 2006. 60p. 12.95 *(978-0-9711903-5-1(6))* Astrology Booth, LLC.

Bruce, Marie. The Witch's Almanac 2009. 2008. (ENG., Illus.). 224p. pap. 19.95 *(978-0-572-03458-0(X))* Foulsham, W. Co., Ltd. GBR. Dist: APG Sales & Distribution Services.

Bunson, Mathew, ed. Our Sunday Visitor's Catholic Almanac. 2007. 640p. per. 6.95 *(978-1-59276-443-3(6))* Our Sunday Visitor, Publishing Div.

Bunson, Matthew E. D. Min. & Bunson, Matthew, DMin. Our Sunday Visitor's 2010 Catholic Almanac. 2009. 640p. pap. 30.95 *(978-1-59276-614-7(5))* Our Sunday Visitor, Publishing Div.

Burke, Edmund. 1758 Annual Register, 2 vols. Langford, Paul, ed. 2009. (Illus.). 185.00 *(978-1-60030-829-1(5))* ProQuest LLC.

Collins Publishers Staff. Where on Earth? (Collins Gem) 2007. 240p. pap. 7.95 *(978-0-06-119764-2(5))* HarperCollins Pubs.

Curth, Louise Hill & Curth, Louise. English Almanacs, Astrology & Popular Medicine, 1550-1700. 2008. (ENG., Illus.). 288p. 89.00 *(978-0-7190-6928-4(9))* Manchester Univ. Pr. GBR. Dist: Macmillan.

Di Vincenzo, Mark. Buy Mustard in May. 2012. (ENG.). 240p. pap. 13.99 ***(978-0-06-211770-0(X),*** William Morrow Paperbacks) HarperCollins Pubs.

Dolan, Allison. Remember That? A Year-by-Year Chronicle of Fun Facts, Headlines, & Your Memories. Family Tree Magazine Staff, ed. 2011. (ENG.). 176p. pap. 16.99 *(978-1-4403-1688-3(0),* Family Tree Bks.) F&W Media, Inc.

Encyclopaedia Britannica, Inc., compiled by. Encyclopaedia Britannica 2009 Deluxe. 2008. DVD 29.95 *(978-1-59339-817-0(4))* Encyclopaedia Britannica, Inc.

—Encyclopaedia Britannica Almanac 2009. 2009. 13.95 *(978-1-59339-839-2(5))* Encyclopaedia Britannica, Inc.

—Time Almanac 2008 Powered by Encyclopaedia Britannica. 2008. 13.95 *(978-1-59339-427-1(6))* Encyclopaedia Britannica, Inc.

Farmers' Almanc 2007. 2007th ed. 2006. pap. 5.99 *(978-1-928720-08-9(0))* Almanac Publishing Co.

Fehlhaber, Jeff, ed. Inventor's Almanac 2007. 2007th ed. 2007. per. 14.95 *(978-0-9791596-0-2(1))* Mindvantage LLC.

Franklin, Benjamin. Poor Richard's Almanack. 2009. 66p. pap. 16.75 *(978-1-110-37009-2(1))* BiblioBazaar.

—Poor Richard's Almanack. 2007. (ENG., Illus.). 96p. 9.95 *(978-1-60239-117-8(3),* 239117) Skyhorse Publishing Co., Inc.

—Poor Richard's Almanack. 2007. (ENG.). 268p. per. 11.95 *(978-1-59462-731-6(2),* Book Jungle) Standard Pubns., Inc.

—Poor Richard's Almanack. 2010. 64p. pap. 17.75 *(978-1-148-49399-2(9))* BiblioBazaar.

—Poor Richard's Almanack. 2010. (Illus.). 32p. pap. 14.14 *(978-1-154-52883-1(9))* General Bks. LLC.

Fredriksen, John C. Civil War Almanac. 2008. (Almanacs of American Wars Ser.). (Illus.). 864p. (C). (gr. 9). pap. 25.95 *(978-0-8160-7554-6(9),* Checkmark Bks.) Facts On File, Inc.

Geiger, Peter & Duncan, Sondra. Farmers' Almanac. 2007. (Farmers' Almanac Ser.). (Illus.). 240p. per. 6.99 *(978-1-928720-09-6(9))* Almanac Publishing Co.

Hammond World Atlas Corporation Staff, ed. World Almanac World Atlas 2010. 2009. 292p. 29.99 *(978-0-8437-1364-0(X))* Hammond World Atlas Corp.

Hill, Laurence, ed. Whitaker's Almanack 2000. (Illus.). 1291p. lthr. 108.00 *(978-0-11-702253-9(5))* Stationery Office, The GBR. Dist: Balogh International, Inc.

Hirsch Almanac Investor Monthly Sub + FREE copy of Stock Trader's Almanac 2011. 2011. (Almanac Investor Ser.). 19.95 *(978-1-118-09457-0(3),* Wiley) Wiley, John & Sons, Inc.

Horrocks, Thomas A. Popular Print & Popular Medicine: Almanacs & Health Advice in Early America. 2008. (Illus.). 224p. (ENG.). pap. 29.95 *(978-1-55849-657-6(2));* lib. bdg. 80.00 *(978-1-55849-656-9(4))* Univ. of Massachusetts Pr.

Huffman, Florence. Clark's Kentucky Almanac & Book of Facts Second Edition. 2006. 29.95 *(978-1-883589-78-3(9))* Clark Publishing, Inc.

Information Publications, creator. Almanac of the 50 States: Basic Data Profiles with Comparative Tables. 2007. (Almanac of the 50 States Ser.). 466p. 118.25 *(978-0-931845-96-3(3));* per. 104.25 *(978-0-931845-95-6(5))* Information Pubns., Inc.

Jackson, Kenneth T. & Kameny, Fred. The Almanac of New York City. Jackson, Kenneth T. & Kameny, Fred, eds. 2008. (ENG., Illus.). 528p. (gr. 17). 45.00 *(978-0-231-14062-1(2))* Columbia Univ. Pr.

Jackson, Kenneth T. & Kameny, Fred, eds. The Almanac of New York City. 2008. (ENG., Illus.). 528p. (gr. 17). pap. 19.95 *(978-0-231-14063-8(0))* Columbia Univ. Pr.

Jolly, Ronald & Bohnak, Karroll. Michigan's Upper Peninsula Almanac. 2009. (ENG.). 600p. pap. 28.95 *(978-0-472-03248-8(8))* Univ. of Michigan Pr.

Judge Roy Bean Almanac. pap. 1.75 *(978-0-910722-06-3(4))* Highland Pr.

Kittredge, George L. The Old Farmer & His Almanack. reprint ed. lib. bdg. 98.00 *(978-0-7222-0652-2(6))* Library Reprints, Inc.

Kluis, Al & Thompson, Katie. The 2012 Al Kluis Farmer's Almanac. 2011. (Illus.). 180p. mass mkt. 15.00 ***(978-0-9830382-0-7(1))*** Kluis Publishing, LLC.

Knauer, Kelly & Time Magazine Editors. Time Almanac 2012. 2011. (ENG., Illus.). 864p. pap. 13.99 *(978-1-60320-901-4(8))* Time Home Entertainment, Inc.

—Time Almanac 2012: Powered by Encyclopedia Britannica. 2011. (ENG., Illus.). 864p. 34.95 *(978-1-60320-206-0(4))* Time Home Entertainment, Inc.

Lang, Robert, ed. Canadian Almanac & Directory. 2011. 350.00 *(978-1-59237-769-5(6))* 2011th rev. ed. 2010. 350.00 *(978-1-59237-589-9(8))* Grey Hse. Publishing.

Lewis, D. S. & Slater, Wendy, eds. The 2009 Annual Register: World Events Key Events Developments form 2008, ., Vol. 250. 2009. (Illus.). 679p. 250.00 *(978-1-60030-828-4(7))* CSA Journal Division.

Lewis, Jonathan A. Almanac357: A Masonic Reader. 1. l.t. ed. 2007. (Illus.). 125p. per. 9.95 *(978-0-9719339-3-4(6))* Paper Tigers Publishing.

Llewellyn. Llewellyn's 2013 Magical Almanac: Practical Magic for Everyday Living. 2012. (Annuals - Magical Almanac Ser.). (ENG.). 360p. pap. 10.99 ***(978-0-7387-1515-5(8))*** Llewellyn Pubns.

—Llewellyn's 2013 Moon Sign Book: Conscious Living by the Cycles of the Moon. 2012. (Annuals - Moon Sign Book Ser.). (ENG.). 312p. pap. 10.99 ***(978-0-7387-1513-1(1))*** Llewellyn Pubns.

—Llewellyn's 2013 Witches' Companion: An Almanac for Contemporary Living. 2012. (Annuals - Witches' Companion Ser.). (ENG.). 288p. pap. 10.99 ***(978-0-7387-1525-4(5))*** Llewellyn Pubns.

Mars-Proietti, Laura, ed. Canadian Almanac & Directory 2009. 2008. 1600p. 325.00 *(978-1-59237-370-3(4))* Grey Hse. Publishing.

—Canadian Almanac & Directory: Repertoire et Almanach Canadien. 161st ed. 2007. (Canadian Almanac & Directory Ser.). (Illus.). 1732p. 315.00 *(978-1-59237-220-1(1))* Grey Hse. Publishing.

—Canadian Almanac & Directory 2010. 2009. 1600p. 325.00 *(978-1-59237-439-7(5))* Grey Hse. Publishing.

McGovern, Bernie, ed. Florida Almanac 2007-2008. 16th ed. 2007. (ENG., Illus.). 592p. per. 17.95 *(978-1-58980-428-9(7))* Pelican Publishing Co., Inc.

—Louisiana Almanac 2008-2009. 18th ed. 2008. (ENG., Illus.). 760p. pap. 16.95 *(978-1-58980-543-9(7))* Pelican Publishing Co., Inc.

McGowen, Charles. Reasoned Elegance: For the Year 1787. 2009. (ENM., Illus.). 176p. pap. 59.95 *(978-0-9772292-1-5(1))* SolREI, Inc.

Nautical Almanac Office (U.S.), compiled by. Astronomical Almanac for the Year 2013 & Its Companion, the Astronomical Almanac Online. 2012. (ENG.). 612p. 40.00 ***(978-0-7077-4128-4(9),*** Dept. of the Navy) United States Government Printing Office.

Nelson, Mike. Colorado Weather Almanac. 2007. (Illus.). 342p. pap. 27.50 *(978-1-55566-401-5(6))* Johnson Bks.

Old Farmer's Almanac Staff. The Old Farmer's Almanac 2011. 2010. (ENG.). 288p. 15.95 *(978-1-57198-517-0(4));* pap. 6.95 *(978-1-57198-516-3(6))* Yankee Publishing, Inc.

—The Old Farmer's Almanac 2012. 2011. (ENG.). 288p. 15.95 *(978-1-57198-545-3(X));* pap. 6.95 *(978-1-57198-544-6(1))* Yankee Publishing, Inc.

Old House Books, creator. Enquire Within upon Everything 1890. 2006. (Illus.). 415p. 28.50 *(978-1-873590-30-0(X))* Old Hse. Bks. GBR. Dist: Parkwest Pubns., Inc.

Olson, Diane. A Nature Lover's Almanac: Kinky Bugs, Stealthy Critters, Prosperous Plants & Celestial Wonders, 1 vol. 2012. (ENG., Illus.). 224p. pap. 12.99 ***(978-1-4236-2224-6(3))*** Gibbs Smith, Publisher.

Renton, N. E. Renton's Dictionary of Stock Exchange: An annotated Guide & Almanac for Share & Property Investors at All Levels. 2009. 300p. pap. 12.00 *(978-81-7806-175-7(9))* Unicorn Bks. Pvt Ltd. IND. Dist: Mahal, Pustak Pubs., Booksellers & Order Suppliers.

Roberts, David L., 1st. The Missouri Almanac: Fact Collection Project. 2006. 320p. pap. 15.00 *(978-0-9705604-1-4(9))* Missouri Valley College.

Rolbein, Seth, ed. The Martha's Vineyard Almanac Second Edition. 2008. 130p. per. 5.50 *(978-0-9773782-4-1(1))* Cape Cod Voice, The.

Sand County Almanac. (Illus.). *(978-0-19-519985-7(5))* Oxford Univ. Pr., Inc.

Shoals, Bethlehem, et al. The Macrophenomenal Pro Basketball Almanac: Styles, Stats, & Stars in Today's Game. 2008. (ENG., Illus.). 224p. 23.00 *(978-1-59691-561-9(7))* Bloomsbury Publishing.

Simon, Mark, ed. The Original Thoroughbred Times Racing Almanac. 2008. (Original Thoroughbred Times Racing Almanac Ser.). (ENG., Illus.). 1006p. pap. 19.95 *(978-1-933958-76-7(6))* BowTie Pr.

Sports Illustrated Editors. Almanac 2009. 2008. (ENG.). 576p. pap. 13.99 *(978-1-60320-792-8(9))* Time Home Entertainment, Inc.

Sports Illustrated Editors, creator. Almanac 2008. 2007. (ENG., Illus.). 816p. pap. 12.99 *(978-1-933821-90-0(6))* Time Home Entertainment, Inc.

Successful Farming Magazine Staff. 2009 Dutch Farmer's Almanac: Charts, historical data, key events, trends, tips & Forecasts. 2008. (Successful Farming Reference Guides). 160p. pap. 15.00 *(978-0-696-24344-8(X))* Meredith Bks.

Theitic. Spring 2011 & Spring 2012. 2010. (Witches' Almanac Ser.: Vol. 30). (ENG.). 152p. pap. 11.95 *(978-0-9824323-0-3(5))* Witches Almanac Ltd., The.

—The Witches' Almanac, Issue 31: Spring 2012-Spring 2013: Radiance of the Sun. 2011. 152p. pap. 11.95 *(978-0-9824323-6-5(4))* Witches Almanac Ltd., The.

Thoroughbred Times Staff. The Original Thoroughbred Times Racing Almanac. 2006. (Original Thoroughbred Times Racing Almanac Ser.). (ENG., Illus.). 158p. per. 19.95 *(978-1-933958-00-2(6))* BowTie Pr.

Time Magazine Editors. Almanac 2008: Powered by Encyclopedia Britannica. rev. ed. 2007. (ENG.). 992p. (YA). (gr. 7-17). pap. 12.99 *(978-1-60320-754-6(6))* Time Home Entertainment, Inc.

—Almanac 2010. 2009. (ENG., Illus.). 864p. 34.95 *(978-1-60320-091-2(6));* pap. 13.99 *(978-1-60320-825-3(9))* Time Home Entertainment, Inc.

Time Magazine Editors, creator. Almanac 2008. 2007. (ENG., Illus.). 992p. (YA). (gr. 10-17). 31.95 *(978-1-933821-21-4(3))* Time Home Entertainment, Inc.

Time Magazine Editors, ed. Almanac 2009. 2008. (ENG.). (YA). 992p. (gr. 10-17). 34.95 *(978-1-60320-042-4(8));* 960p. (gr. 7-17). pap. 13.99 *(978-1-60320-793-5(7))* Time Home Entertainment, Inc.

Time Magazine Staff. Time Almanac 2011. 2010. (ENG., Illus.). 864p. 34.95 *(978-1-60320-164-3(5))* Time Home Entertainment, Inc.

—Time Almanac 2011. 2010. (ENG., Illus.). 864p. pap. 13.99 *(978-1-60320-165-0(3))* Time Home Entertainment, Inc.

Unknown. Whitaker's Almanack Pocket Reference 2012. 2011. (Whitaker's Ser.). (ENG., Illus.). 224p. pap. 12.95 *(978-1-4081-4005-5(5))* A & C Black GBR. Dist: Macmillan.

Wardhaugh, Benjamin. Poor Robin's Prophesies: A curious Almanac, & the everyday mathematics of Georgian England. 2012. (ENG., Illus.). 272p. 34.95 ***(978-0-19-960542-2(4))*** Oxford Univ. Pr., Inc.

Welsh, Douglas F. Doug Welsh's Texas Garden Almanac. (AgriLife Research & Extension Service Ser.). (Illus.). 512p. 2011. pap. 24.95 ***(978-1-60344-478-1(5))*** 2007. per. 24.95 *(978-1-58544-619-3(X))* Texas A&M Univ. Pr.

Whitaker. Concise Almanack 2011. 2010. (ENG., Illus.). 752p. pap. *(978-1-4081-2851-0(9))* A & C Black GBR. Dist: Macmillan.

Whitaker, Joseph. Whitaker's Almanack: Today's World in One Volume. 2008. (Whitaker's Almanack Ser.). (Illus.). 1369p. *(978-1-4144-5572-3(0))* A & C Black.

Whitaker Staff. Whitaker's Almanack Pocket Reference 2011. 2010. (ENG., Illus.). 224p. pap. 9.95 *(978-1-4081-2850-3(0))* A & C Black GBR. Dist: Macmillan.

—Whitaker's Concise Almanack 2010. 2009. (Whitaker's Ser.). (ENG., Illus.). 752p. pap. 34.95 *(978-1-4081-1361-5(9))* A & C Black GBR. Dist: Macmillan.

Whitaker Staff & Russell, Jane. Almanack 2011. 2010. (ENG., Illus.). 1376p. 145.00 *(978-1-4081-2848-0(9))* A & C Black GBR. Dist: Macmillan.

Whitakers. Whitaker's Almanack 2012. 2012. (Whitaker's Ser.). (ENG., Illus.). 1376p. 145.00 ***(978-1-4081-3012-4(2))*** A & C Black GBR. Dist: Macmillan.

World Almanac Editors. The World Almanac & Book of Facts 2010. Janssen, Sarah & Joyce, Alan C., eds. 2009. (World Almanac & Book of Facts Ser.). (ENG., Illus.). 1008p. (gr. 6-12). pap. 12.99 *(978-1-60057-123-7(9),* World Almanac Bks.) Facts On File, Inc.

—The World Almanac & Book of Facts 2011. Janssen, Sarah, ed. 2010. (World Almanac Ser.). (Illus.). 1008p. (gr. 6-12). pap. 12.99 *(978-1-60057-134-3(4),* World Almanac Bks.) Facts On File, Inc.

World Almanac Staff. The World Almanac(r) & Book of Facts 2012. Janssen, Sarah, ed. 2011. (World Almanac Ser.). (Illus.). 1007p. (gr. 6-12). pap. 12.99 *(978-1-60057-148-0(4),* World Almanac Bks.) Facts On File, Inc.

Wright, John. The New York Times Almanac 2011: The Almanac of Record. Wright, John W., ed. rev. ed. 2010. (ENG.). 1024p. (gr. 12). 12.95 *(978-0-14-311894-7(3),* Penguin (Non-Classics)) Penguin Group (USA) Inc.

Yankee Books Staff. The Old Farmer's Almanac Garden, 1992. Date not set. 4.95 *(978-0-89909-234-8(9))* Rodale Pr., Inc.

2009 Saint Paul Almanac. 2008. (Illus.). 368p. per. 11.95 *(978-0-9772651-4-5(5))* Arcata Pr.

ALMOHADES

Al-Sharif, William. The Dearest Quest: A Biography of Ibn Tumart. 2010. 175p. pap. 24.95 *(978-1-4452-7825-4(1))* Lulu Enterprises Inc.

Allen J. Fromherz Staff & Fromherz, Allen J. Almohads: The Rise of an Islamic Empire. 2010. (Library of Middle East History Ser.). (ENG., Illus.). 288p. 92.50 *(978-1-84511-651-4(8))* I. B. Tauris & Co., Ltd. GBR. Dist: Macmillan.

Fierra, Maribel. The Almohad Revolution: Politics & Religion in the Islamic West During the Twelfth-Thirteenth Centuries. 2012. (Variorum Collected Studies). 330p. 154.95 ***(978-1-4094-4053-6(2))*** Ashgate Publishing Co.

ALMOST COMPLEX MANIFOLDS

Duistermaat, J. J. The Heat Kernel Lefschetz Fixed Point Formula for the Spin-c Dirac Operator. 2011. (Modern Birkhäuser Classics Ser.). (ENG.). viii, 247p. pap. 59.95 ***(978-0-8176-8246-0(5)***, 0817682465) Birkhauser Verlag AG CHE. Dist: Springer.

ALMOST PERIODIC FUNCTIONS

Berglund, J. F. & Hofmann, K. H. Compact Semitopological Semigroups & Weakly Almost Periodic Functions. 2007. (Lecture Notes in Mathematics Ser.). (ENG.). 160p. (Orig.). pap. 26.00 *(978-3-540-03913-6(9)*, 3540039139) Springer.

Berglund, J. F., et al. Compact Right Topological Semigroups & Generalizations of Almost Periodicity. 2008. (Lecture Notes in Mathematics Ser.). 256p. pap. 46.00 *(978-3-540-08919-3(5))* Springer.

Corduneanu, Constantin. Almost Periodic Oscillations & Waves. (ENG.). viii, 308p. 2010. pap. 89.95 *(978-1-4419-1890-1(6)*, 1441918906) 2009. 89.95 *(978-0-387-09818-0(6)*, 0387098186) Springer.

Diagana, Toka. Pseudo Almost Periodic Functions in Banach Spaces. 2007. 125.00 *(978-1-60021-637-4(4))* Nova Science Pubs., Inc.

N'Guérékata, Gaston M. Almost Automorphic & Almost Periodic Functions in Abstract Spaces. 2010. 148p. pap. 139.00 *(978-1-4419-3373-7(5)*, 1441933735) Springer.

ALMS AND ALMS-GIVING

see Charities; Charity

ALMSHOUSES

see also Old Age Homes

Cherry, Robert. Moving Working Families Forward: Third Way Policies That Can Work. 2011. (ENG., Illus.). 263p. 39.00 ***(978-0-8147-1718-9(7))*** New York Univ. Pr.

Cherry, Robert D. & Lerman, Robert I. Moving Working Families Forward: Third Way Policies That Can Work. 2011. pap. ***(978-0-8147-9000-7(3))***; (Illus.). 272p. E-Book ***(978-0-8147-7299-7(4))*** New York Univ. Pr.

Crettaz, Eric. Fighting Working Poverty in Postindustrial Economies: Causes, Trade-Offs & Policy Solutions. 2011. (Illus.). 256p. 110.00 ***(978-0-85793-487-1(2))*** Elgar, Edward Publishing, Inc.

Ehrenreich, Barbara. Nickel & Dimed: On (Not) Getting by in America. 2011. (ENG.). 256p. pap. 15.00 *(978-0-312-62668-6(1))* Picador.

Fowler, Simon. Workhouse: People Places Life Behind Door. 2008. (Illus.). 288p. pap. 19.95 *(978-1-905615-28-5(0))* National Archives (PRO), The GBR. Dist: International Publishers Marketing.

—Workhouse: The People, the Places, the Life Behind Doors. 2007. (Illus.). 224p. 34.95 *(978-1-905615-03-2(5))* National Archives (PRO), The GBR. Dist: International Publishers Marketing.

Goose, Nigel & Moden, Leanne. History of Doughty's Hospital, Norwich, 1687-2009. 2010. (ENG., Illus.). 288p. pap. 19.95 *(978-1-905313-93-8(4))* Univ. of Hertfordshire Pr. GBR. Dist: Independent Pubs. Group.

Haines, Richard. Proposals for Building, in Every County, A Working-Alms-House or Hospital. 2007. 48p. per. *(978-1-4065-1563-3(9))* Dodo Pr.

Hallett, Anna. Almshouses. 2008. (Shire Library). (ENG., Illus.). 64p. pap. 12.95 *(978-0-7478-0583-0(0))* Shire Pubns., Ltd. GBR. Dist: Random Hse., Inc.

O'Brien, Erin E. The Politics of Identity: Solidarity Building among America's Working Poor. 2008. (SUNY Series in Public Policy). xiii, 266p. 80.00 *(978-0-7914-7501-0(8))*; pap. 28.95 *(978-0-7914-7502-7(6))* State Univ. of New York Pr.

Poisson, Sara. Silent Voices from the Past: A Chronicle of the Almshouse of Sullivan County. 2010. 116p. pap. 12.95 *(978-1-4502-5907-1(3))* iUniverse, Inc.

Quinby, G. W. (George Washington). The Gallows, the Prison, & the Poor-House. 2006. 332p. per. 23.99 *(978-1-4255-3349-6(3))* MPublishing.

Urbanska, Wanda. Builders of Hope: A Social Entrepreneur's Solution for Rebuilding America. 2011. (Illus.). 224p. pap. 19.95 *(978-0-89587-568-6(3))* Blair, John F. Pub.

Wagner, David. Ordinary People: In & Out of Poverty in the Gilded Age. 264p. 2008. pap. 33.95 *(978-1-59451-461-6(5))* 2007. (Illus.). 125.00 *(978-1-59451-460-9(7))* Paradigm Pubs.

ALOE

see also Aloe Vera

Newton, L. E., et al. Aloes: the Definitive Guide. 2011. (Illus.). 719p. 182.00 *(978-1-84246-439-7(6))* Kew Publishing GBR. Dist: Chicago Distribution Ctr.

Park, Young In & Lee, Seung Ki, eds. New Perspectives on Aloe. 2010. (ENG., Illus.). x, 200p. pap. 159.00 *(978-1-4419-4069-8(3)*, 1441940693) Springer.

Smith, Gideon F. & Van Wyk, Braam. Aloes in Southern Africa. 2011. (Illus.). 136p. pap. 22.00 *(978-1-77007-462-0(7))* Struik Pubs. ZAF. Dist: International Publishers Marketing.

Zago, Romano. Aloe Isn't Medicine, & Yet... It Cures! 2009. 192p. pap. 16.95 *(978-1-4401-2576-8(7))* iUniverse, Inc.

ALOE BARBADENSIS

see Aloe Vera

ALOE VERA

Grace, O. M., et al. The Aloe Names Book. 2012. (Illus.). 232p. 66.00 *(978-1-84246-419-9(1))* Kew Publishing GBR. Dist: Chicago Distribution Ctr.

Terwadkar, Shardul. Aloe Ferox - in View of Ayurveda: A Critical Study of Aloe Ferox in Ayurvedic Perspective. 2011. 152p. pap. 11.76 ***(978-1-4567-8786-8(1))*** AuthorHouse.

ALONZO, ALICIA

Bernier-Grand, Carmen T. & Colón, Raúl. Alicia Alonso: Prima Ballerina Assoluta, 1 vol. 2011. (ENG.). 64p. (J). *(978-0-7614-5562-2(0))* Marshall Cavendish.

ALOPECIA

see Baldness

ALPHA RHYTHM

Fehmi, Les & Robbins, Jim. Dissolving Pain: Simple Brain-Training Exercises for Overcoming Chronic Pain. 2010. (ENG., Illus.). 224p. pap. 17.95 *(978-1-59030-780-9(1)*, Trumpeter) Shambhala Pubns., Inc.

Harris, Jillene. Human Differential Alpha Conditioning: An EEG study. 2008. 248p. pap. *(978-3-639-09783-2(1))* VDM Verlag Dr. Mueller e.K.

ALPHA WAVES

see Alpha Rhythm

ALPHABET

Here are entered general and comparative works dealing with the Semitic alphabet and its ancient and modern derivatives, or with similar series of characters employed to represent the sounds of a language. Works on variations in the style of writing in the past, and especially with ancient and medieval handwriting, are entered under Paleography. Works on written languages as a form of communication or discourse are entered under Written Communication. Works on the process or result of recording language in the form of conventionalized visible marks or graphic signs on a surface are entered under Writing. Works on the writing of a particular language are entered under the name of the language with subdivisions Alphabet and Writing.

see also Alphabets; Cuneiform Writing; Extinct Languages; Initial Teaching Alphabet; Inscriptions, Linear A; Phonetic Alphabet; Runes; Writing

also subdivision Alphabet or Writing under groups of language or under particular languages, e.g. English Language—Alphabet, Chinese Language—Writing

Abulafia, Abraham. Get Ha-Shemot - Divorce of the Names. Din, Talib, ed. Shatil, Sharron, tr. unabr. ed. 2007. (ENG.). 64p. per. *(978-1-897352-03-8(4))* Providence University.

—Ner Elohim - Candle of God. Din, Talib, ed. Shatil, Sharron, tr. unabr. ed. 2007. (ENG.). 180p. per. *(978-1-897352-09-0(3))* Providence University.

Bandt, Cordula. Der Traktat 'Vom Mysterium der Buchstaben' Kritischer Text mit Einleitung, Übersetzung und Anmerkungen. 2007. (Texte und Untersuchungen Zur Geschichte der Altchristlicher Ser.). (GER., Illus.). VIII, 263p. 140.00 *(978-3-11-019606-1(9))* De Gruyter, Walter Inc.

Clodd, Edward. The Story of the Alphabet. 2009. 216p. 23.99 *(978-1-103-01747-8(0))*; pap. 17.99 *(978-1-103-01745-4(4))* BiblioBazaar.

Diringer, David. The Alphabet: A Key to the History of Mankind. 608p. 2008. 59.95 *(978-1-4367-1375-7(7))* 2007. (ENG.). per. 44.95 *(978-1-4325-7602-8(X))* Kessinger Publishing, LLC.

Einhorn, Kama. Teaching with Favorite Alphabet Books: Easy Activities for Using Thematic ABC Books to Teach Alphabet Recognition, Letter Formation, Letter-Sound Correspondence, & More. 2011. (ENG.). 64p. (gr. -1-1). pap. 11.99 *(978-0-545-23695-9(9)*, Teaching Resources) Scholastic, Inc.

Gnanadesikan, Amalia E. The Writing Revolution: Cuneiform to the Internet. 2008. (Language Library). (ENG., Illus.). 328p. pap. 39.95 *(978-1-4051-5407-9(1))*; 104.95 *(978-1-4051-5406-2(3))* Wiley, John & Sons, Inc. (Wiley-Blackwell).

Goodman Games. The Dungeon Alphabet. 2009. 48p. 19.99 *(978-0-9841127-6-0(6))* Goodman Games.

Healey, John & Smith, Rex. A Brief Introduction to the Arabic Alphabet. 2009. (Brief Introduction Ser.). (ENG., Illus.). 116p. pap. 11.95 *(978-0-86356-431-4(3))* Saqi Bks. GBR. Dist: Consortium Bk. Sales & Distribution.

Henry, Lucia Kemp. Now I Know My Alphabet Learning Mats: 50+ Double-Sided Activity Sheets That Help Children Learn the Letters & Sounds of the Alphabet. 2012. (ENG.). 112p. (gr. k-1). pap. 15.99 ***(978-0-545-32061-0(5)***, Teaching Resources) Scholastic, Inc.

Higgins, Godfrey. The Celtic Druids. 2007. 532p. 44.95 *(978-1-60206-671-7(X))*; per. 26.95 *(978-1-60206-670-0(1))* Cosimo, Inc.

Klein, Frederick C. For the Love of the Packers: An A-to-Z Primer for Packers Fans of All Ages. 2010. (For the Love Of... Ser.). (ENG.). 48p. 16.95 *(978-1-60078-530-6(1))* Triumph Bks.

Moseley, Christopher & Campbell, George L. The Routledge Handbook of Scripts & Alphabets. 2nd rev. ed. 2012. (ENG., Illus.). 200p. (C). pap. 45.95 *(978-0-415-56097-9(7))* Routledge.

Pflughaupt, Laurent. Letter by Letter: An Alphabetical Miscellany. Bruhn, Gregory, tr. from FRE. 2008. (ENG., Illus.). 160p. per. 24.95 *(978-1-56898-737-8(4))* Princeton Architectural Pr.

Powell, Barry B. Writing: Theory & History of the Technology of Civilization. (ENG., Illus.). 296p. 2012. pap. 34.95 ***(978-1-118-25532-2(1))*** 2009. 104.95 *(978-1-4051-6256-2(2))* Wiley, John & Sons, Inc. (Wiley-Blackwell).

Roberts, Jane. Guide to Scripts Used in English Writings up to 1500. 2011. (Illus.). 328p. pap. 35.00 *(978-0-7123-0903-5(9))* British Library, The GBR. Dist: Chicago Distribution Ctr.

Taylor, Isaac. Alphabet V1 an Account of the Origin and 2006. pap. 33.95 *(978-1-4286-3678-1(1))* Kessinger Publishing, LLC.

—Alphabet V2 an Account of the Origin and. 2006. pap. 34.95 *(978-1-4286-3679-8(X))* Kessinger Publishing, LLC.

Waddell, Laurence Austine. The Aryan Origin of the Alphabet. 2010. 96p. pap. 10.50 *(978-1-57898-941-6(8))* Martino Publishing.

Zamudio Mesa, Celia María, ed. Las Consecuencias de la Escritura Alfabética en la Teoría Lingüística. 2010. (Estudios Lingüísticos y Literarios Ser.). (SPA.). 263p. pap. 24.99 *(978-607-462-087-0(3))* El Colegio de México, A.C., Biblioteca Miguel Cosio Villegas MEX. Dist: Fondo de Cultura Economica USA.

ALPHABET, INITIAL TEACHING

see Initial Teaching Alphabet

ALPHABET, PHONETIC

see Phonetic Alphabet

ALPHABETING

see Alphabetizing

ALPHABETIZATION

see Alphabetizing

ALPHABETIZING

see also Filing Systems

Caemmerer, Christiane & Jungmayr, Jorg, eds. Flugblätter von der frühen Neuzeit bis zur Gegenwart als kulturhistorische Quellen und bibliothekarische Sondermaterialien. 2010. (GER & ENG., Illus.). 302p. pap. 72.95 *(978-3-631-56122-5(9))* Lang, Peter GmbH, Europäischer Verlag der Wissenschaften DEU. Dist: Lang, Peter.

ALPHABETS

see also Illumination of Books and Manuscripts; Initials; Lettering; Monograms

Cary, Kate. Il Animal Alphabet. 2010. 32p. 12.99 *(978-1-4520-2730-2(7))* AuthorHouse.

Copley, F. O. Set of Alphabets of Various Hands. (Illus.). 40p. 25.00 *(978-0-87556-588-0(3))* Saifer, Albert Pub.

Cote, Julie. I Can See My Abcs. 2011. 56p. pap. 24.99 ***(978-1-4567-2546-4(7))*** AuthorHouse.

D'Aquino, Jason. Circus ABC. 2010. (ENG., Illus.). 60p. 12.95 *(978-1-897476-25-3(6))* Simply Read Bks. CAN. Dist: Perseus-PGW.

Day, Lewis F. Alphabets Old & New. 2010. 286p. 43.95 *(978-1-161-36512-2(5))* Kessinger Publishing, LLC.

Delamotte, F. Examples of Modern Alphabets Plain & Ornamental. 2007. *(978-1-934227-16-9(1))*; pap. *(978-1-934227-17-6(X))* Operina LLC.

Display with Letter, A - Z. 12p. pap. 1.95 *(978-3-8290-6106-3(4))* Konemann.

Douglas, Will. The Bush Alphabet. (Illus.). 32p. *(978-0-86806-406-2(8)*, Hale & Iremonger) GHR Pr., The.

Dover. Dover Digital Design Source #2: Decorative Initials & Alphabets. 2010. (Dover Electronic Clip Art Ser.). (ENG., Illus.). 128p. pap. 19.95 *(978-0-486-99062-0(1))* Dover Pubns., Inc.

HEMINGSON, Vince. Alphabets & Scripts Tattoo Design Directory: The Essential Reference for Body Art. 2010. (ENG., Illus.). 192p. spiral bd. 14.99 *(978-0-7858-2578-4(9)*, 0785825789, Chartwell) Book Sales, Inc.

Hrachowina, Carl & Bry, Johann Theodor de. Model Sheets for Arts & Crafts: Johann Theodor de Bry's Neiw Kunstliches Alphabet, 1595. 2007. (Illus.). *(978-1-934227-07-7(2))*; pap. *(978-1-934227-08-4(0))* Operina LLC.

McCallum, Graham Leslie & McCallum, Graham. 4000 Alphabet & Letter Motifs: A Sourcebook. 2009. (ENG., Illus.). 400p. 17.95 *(978-0-7134-9060-2(8)*, Batsford, B. T. Ltd.) Anova Bks. GBR. Dist: Sterling Publishing Co., Inc.

McCormack, Christine E. & Mason, Jana. Little Books from A to Z. 2008. (ENG., Illus.). 96p. (J). pap. 12.95 *(978-1-59647-261-7(8))* Good Year Bks.

McCorquodale, Duncan, ed. Alphabets: A Miscellany of Letters. 2010. (ENG., Illus.). 240p. 45.00 *(978-1-907317-09-5(0))* Black Dog Publishing Ltd. GBR. Dist: Perseus Distribution.

Noble, Mary & Mehigan, Janet. Calligraphy Alphabets for Beginners: The Easy Way to Learn Lettering & Illumination Techniques. 2008. (ENG., Illus.). 256p. 21.99 *(978-0-7641-6115-5(6))* Barron's Educational Series, Inc.

Rjeily, Rana. Cultural Connectives: Bridging the Latin & Arabic Alphabets. 2011. (ENG., Illus.). 112p. 34.95 *(978-1-935613-13-8(8))* Batty, Mark Pub., LLC.

Taylor, Isaac. The Semitic Alphabets. 2011. 120.00 *(978-1-61143-681-5(3))* Gorgias Pr., LLC.

Teacher Created Resources Staff & Reynolds, Deanna. Alphabet Treasury. 2009. (ENG.). 208p. pap. 19.99 *(978-1-4206-2340-6(0))* Teacher Created Resources, Inc.

Weller, Alan. Photoshop Brushes & Creative Tools: Ornate Letters & Alphabets. 2011. (Electronic Clip Art Photoshop Brushes Ser.). (ENG., Illus.). 48p. pap. 24.95 *(978-0-486-99126-9(1))* Dover Pubns., Inc.

ALPINE ANIMALS

see Mountain Animals

ALPINE FAUNA

see Mountain Animals

ALPINE FLORA

see Mountain Plants

ALPINE GARDENS

Clarke, Graham. Success with Alpine Gardening. 2010. (Success with Gardening Ser.). (ENG., Illus.). 160p. pap. 14.95 *(978-1-86108-639-6(3))* Guild of Master Craftsman Pubns., Ltd. GBR. Dist: Sterling Publishing Co., Inc.

Mitchell, Michael. Alpines: An Essential Guide. 2012. (ENG., Illus.). 144p. 45.00 ***(978-1-84797-295-8(0))*** Crowood Pr., Ltd. GBR. Dist: Independent Pubs. Group.

Scherrer, Pascal. Monitoring Alpine Vegetation Change. 2011. 332p. pap. ***(978-3-8443-9846-5(5))*** Lambert Academic Publishing.

Tatroe, Marcia. Cutting Edge Gardening in the Intermountain West. 2007. (Illus.). 224p. pap. 29.95 *(978-1-55566-387-2(7))* Johnson Bks.

Wilford, Richard. Alpines, from Mountain to Garden. 2010. (Royal Botanic Gardens, Kew-Botanical Magazine Monograph Ser.). (Illus.). 244p. 53.00 *(978-1-84246-172-3(9))* Kew Publishing GBR. Dist: Chicago Distribution Ctr.

ALPS

Henderson, Paul. Cycling in the French Alps. 2nd rev. ed. 2010. (Cycling Guides). (Illus.). 256p. pap. 22.95 *(978-1-85284-551-3(1))* Cicerone Pr. GBR. Dist: Midpoint Trade Bks., Inc.

ALPS—DESCRIPTION AND TRAVEL

All of Nice & Surroundings. 96p. *(978-88-8029-062-9(2))* Casa Editrice Bonechi.

The Alps. 2010. (ENG.). 266p. pap. 27.75 *(978-1-172-43787-0(4))* BiblioBazaar.

Bevin, Darren. Cultural Climbs. 2010. 200p. pap. *(978-3-639-25295-8(0))* VDM Verlag Dr. Mueller e.K.

Clark, Lloyd. Switzerland on All Fours. 2008. 136p. 26.99 *(978-1-4251-8574-9(6))*; 134p. pap. 17.01 *(978-1-4251-7665-9(0))* Trafford Publishing.

Edwards, Amelia B. Untrodden Peaks & Unfrequented Valleys. 2008. (Illus.). 256p. pap. *(978-1-4099-1597-3(2))* Dodo Pr.

Faber. Infinite Ice Traversing the Arctic & the Alps from 1860 to the Present. 2009. (ENG.). 112p. 45.00 *(978-3-7757-2253-7(X))* Hatje Cantz Verlag GmbH & Co KG DEU. Dist: D.A.P./Distributed Art Pubs.

Forbes, James David. Travels through the Alps of Savoy & Other Parts of the Pennine Chain: With Observations on the Phenomena of Glaciers. 2011. (Cambridge Library Collection - Earth Science Ser.). (ENG., Illus.). 468p. pap. 35.99 ***(978-1-108-03766-2(6))*** Cambridge Univ. Pr.

Randall, Will. Another Long Day on the Piste: A Season in the French Alps. 2008. (ENG., Illus.). 288p. pap. 14.95 *(978-0-349-11934-2(1))* Little, Brown Bk. Group Ltd. GBR. Dist: Independent Pubs. Group.

Sondheimer, E., ed. The Alpine Journal, '89. 39.95 *(978-0-09-173770-2(2)*, Arrow Bks., Ltd.) Random Hse. GBR. Dist: Trafalgar Square Publishing.

Tindall, John. The Glaciers of the Alps & Mountaineering in 1861. 2007. 288p. per. *(978-1-4067-8945-4(3)*, Pierides Pr.) Read Bks.

Tyndall, John. The Glaciers of the Alps: Being a Narrative of Excursions & Ascents, an Account of the Origin & Phenomena of Glaciers & an Exposition of the Physical Principles to Which They Are Related. 2011. (Cambridge Library Collection - Earth Science Ser.). (ENG., Illus.). 482p. pap. 35.99 ***(978-1-108-03781-5(X))*** Cambridge Univ. Pr.

Tyndall, John. Hours of Exercise in the Alps. 2009. 502p. pap. 38.75 *(978-1-113-13886-6(6))* BiblioBazaar.

—Hours of Exercise in the Alps. 2009. 268p. pap. *(978-0-217-49106-8(5))* Books LLC.

—Hours of Exercise in the Alps. 2011. (Cambridge Library Collection - Earth Science Ser.). (ENG., Illus.). 508p. pap. 37.99 ***(978-1-108-03782-2(8))*** Cambridge Univ. Pr.

—Hours of Exercise in the Alps. 2008. 536p. 55.95 *(978-1-4370-1153-1(5))*; pap. 40.95 *(978-1-4368-7744-2(X))* Kessinger Publishing, LLC.

—Hours of Exercise in the Alps. 2006. 508p. per. 29.99 *(978-1-4255-5686-0(8))*; per. 29.99 *(978-1-4255-5687-7(6))* MPublishing.

ALPS—GUIDEBOOKS

Bourne, Grant & Korner-Bourne, Sabine. Walking in the Bavarian Alps. 2nd rev. ed. 2010. (Illus.). 320p. per. 22.95 *(978-1-85284-497-4(3))* Cicerone Pr. GBR. Dist: Midpoint Trade Bks., Inc.

Ellis, Colleen. ABCing: Seeing the Alphabet Differently. 2010. (ENG., Illus.). 64p. 24.95 *(978-0-9819600-4-3(9))* Batty, Mark Pub., LLC.

Michelin, creator. French Alps. 3rd rev. ed. 2007. (Michelin Green Guide French Alps Ser.). (Illus.). 660p. 21.95 *(978-2-06-712334-2(3))* Michelin.

Price, Gillian. Across the Eastern Alps E5 - From Lake Constance to Verona. 2010. (Mountain Walking Ser.). (Illus.). 160p. vinyl bd. 19.95 *(978-1-85284-492-9(2))* Cicerone Pr. GBR. Dist: Midpoint Trade Bks., Inc.

—Walks & Treks in the Maritime Alps. 2010. (Illus.). 224p. pap. 24.95 *(978-1-85284-564-3(3))* Cicerone Pr. GBR. Dist: Midpoint Trade Bks., Inc.

Reynolds, Kev. Chamonix to Zermatt: The Walker's Haute Route' 4th rev. ed. 2010. (Mountain Walking Ser.). (Illus.). 240p. pap. 19.95 *(978-1-85284-513-1(9))* Cicerone Pr. GBR. Dist: Midpoint Trade Bks., Inc.

—The Swiss Alps. 2012. (World Mountain Ranges Ser.). (ENG.). 464p. pap. 39.95 ***(978-1-85284-465-3(5))*** Cicerone Pr. GBR. Dist: Midpoint Trade Bks., Inc.

—Trekking in the Alps. 2011. (Illus.). 256p. pap. 29.95 *(978-1-85284-600-8(3))* Cicerone Pr. GBR. Dist: Midpoint Trade Bks., Inc.

—100 Hut Walks in the Alps. 2nd rev. ed. 2010. (Illus.). 256p. pap. 19.95 *(978-1-85284-471-4(X))* Cicerone Pr. GBR. Dist: Midpoint Trade Bks., Inc.

Scola, P. French Alps & Jura. 2008. (Illus.). 192p. pap. 18.99 *(978-1-84306-312-4(3))* Landmark Publishing Ltd. GBR. Dist: Hunter Publishing, Inc.

Sharp, Hilary. Tour of the Matterhorn. 2010. (Illus.). 192p. pap. 19.95 *(978-1-85284-472-1(8))* Cicerone Pr. GBR. Dist: Midpoint Trade Bks., Inc.

Stewart, Alexander. The Walkers' Haute Route: Mont Blanc to the Matterhorn. 2008. (ENG., Illus.). 256p. pap. 22.95 *(978-1-905864-08-9(6))* Trailblazer Pubns. GBR. Dist: Globe Pequot Pr., The.

ALPS—HISTORY

Ørbaek, Jon Børre, et al, eds. Arctic Alpine Ecosystems & People in a Changing Environment. 2010. (ENG., Illus.). xxviii, 434p. pap. 239.00 *(978-3-642-08014-2(6)*, 3642080146) Springer.

Hunt, Patrick. Alpine Archaeology. 2007. per. 37.95 *(978-1-934269-00-8(X))* Univ. Readers.

A

Love, Dane. Jacobite Stories. 2007. (Illus.). 208p. per. 15.00 *(978-1-903238-86-8(2))* Wilson, Neil Publishing, Ltd. GBR. Dist: Interlink Publishing Group, Inc.

MATHIEU, J. O. N. History of the Alps, 1500 - 1900: Environment, development, & Society. 2009. 276p. 95.95 *(978-1-933202-41-9(6))* West Virginia Univ. Pr.

Mathieu, Jon. History of the Alps, 1500-1900: Environment, Development, & Society. 2009. 276p. pap. 37.95 *(978-1-933202-34-1(3))* West Virginia Univ. Pr.

ALPS—SOCIAL CONDITIONS

Coffen, Béatrice & Toffoletti, Waldemar. L'arc Alpin Romanophone: Une Mosaïque D'identités Linguistiques. 2009. (FRE., Illus.). 158p. *(978-2-88474-658-8(7))* Infolio Sarl.

Langer, Josef & Alfirevic, Niksa, eds. Knowledge Region: Alps-Adriatic Challenges: Volume II - Actors & Cases. 2009. 202p. pap. 56.95 *(978-3-631-58557-3(8))* Lang, Peter GmbH, Europaischer Verlag der Wissenschaften DEU. Dist: Lang, Peter.

Langer, Josef & Pavicic, Jurica, eds. Knowledge Region: Alps-Adriatic Challenges: Volume I - General Perspective. 2009. 206p. pap. 56.95 *(978-3-631-58558-0(6))* Lang, Peter GmbH, Europaischer Verlag der Wissenschaften DEU. Dist: Lang, Peter.

Ørbæk, Jon Borre. Arctic Alpine Ecosystems & People in a Changing Environment. 2006. (ENG., Illus.). xxviii, 434p. 239.00 *(978-3-540-48512-4(0)*, 3540485120) Springer.

ALS (DISEASE)

see Amyotrophic Lateral Sclerosis

ALSACE (FRANCE)

Fischer, Christopher J. Alsace to the Alsatians? Visions & Divisions of Alsatian Regionalism, 1870-1939. 2010. (SCEH Ser.). (Illus.). 260p. 90.00 *(978-1-84545-724-2(2))* Berghahn Bks., Inc.

Hummer, Hans J. Politics & Power in Early Medieval Europe: Alsace & the Frankish Realm, 600-1000. 2009. (Cambridge Studies in Medieval Life & Thought: Fourth Ser.). (ENG., Illus.). 320p. pap. 46.00 *(978-0-521-11448-6(9))* Cambridge Univ. Pr.

McGillicuddy, Áine. René Schickele & Alsace: Cultural Identity Between the Borders. 2010. 250p. pap. 67.95 *(978-3-03911-393-4(3))* Lang, Peter Publishing, Inc.

Sütterle, Hans-Peter. Die Salier und das Elsass: Studien zu den Herrschaftsverhältnissen und zu den politischen Kräften in einer Randregion des Reiches (1002-1125) 2009. (Europäische Hochschulschriften. Reihe 3: Geschichte und ihre Hilfswissenschaften Ser.). (GER., Illus.). 328p. pap. 81.95 *(978-3-631-39641-4(4))* Lang, Peter GmbH, Europaischer Verlag der Wissenschaften DEU. Dist: Lang, Peter.

ALSACE (FRANCE)—DESCRIPTION AND TRAVEL

Golden Book on Alsace. 96p. pap. *(978-88-8029-140-4(8))* Casa Editrice Bonechi.

Golden Book on Colmar. 64p. pap. *(978-88-8029-006-3(1))* Casa Editrice Bonechi.

Green, Michelin. Michelin Green Gd Alsace Lorraine Champagne. 5th rev. ed. 2010. (Green Guide Ser.). (ENG., Illus.). 480p. pap. 21.99 *(978-1-906261-72-6(5))* Michelin Travel & Lifestyle.

Ochterbeck, Cynthia Clayton & Watkins, Gaven R., eds. Alsace Lorraine Champagne. 4th rev. ed. 2007. (Michelin Travel Guide Alsace, Lorraine, Champagne Ser.). (Illus.). 480p. 21.95 *(978-1-906261-04-7(0))* Michelin.

ALSATIAN DOG

see German Shepherd Dog

ALSATIAN WOLF DOG

see German Shepherd Dog

ALSATIANS—UNITED STATES

Bardell, Paul H. 300 Years of an Alsatian-American Family: Martin Hauser & Seven Generations of his Descendents. 2011. pap. 29.95 ***(978-0-7414-6540-5(X))*** Infinity Publishing.

ALTAIANS

see Ural-Altaic Peoples

ALTAIC LANGUAGES

see also Korean Language; Manchu Language; Mongolian Languages; Tungus-Manchu Languages; Turkic Languages; Ural-Altaic Languages

Mayrhofer, Manfred. Einiges Zu Den Skythen, Ihrer Sprache, Ihrem Nachleben. 2006. (Sitzungsberichte der Phil. -Hist. Klasse Ser.). (GER.). 48p. (C). pap. 23.00 *(978-3-7001-3731-3(1))* Austrian Academy of Sciences Press AUT. Dist: Brown, David Bk. Co., The.

Miller, Roy Andrew. Languages & History: Japanese,Korean & Altaic. 2006. (ENG., Illus.). 35.00 *(978-974-8299-69-3(4))* Orchid Pr. THA. Dist: National Bk. Network.

Rachewiltz, Rybatzki. Introduction to Altaic Philology: Turkic, Mongolian, Manchu. 2010. (Handbook of Oriental Studies). (Illus.). 500p. *(978-90-04-18528-9(3))* BRILL.

Veit, Veronika, ed. The Role of Women in the Altaic World: Permanent International Altaistic Conference, 44th Meeting, Walberberg, 26-31 August 2001. 2007. (Asiatische Forschungen Ser.). (ENG & GER., Illus.). 335p. (C). 147.00 *(978-3-447-05537-6(5))* Harrassowitz, Otto Verlag DEU. Dist: ISD.

Webb, Edward. Evidences of the Scythian Affinities of the Dravidian Languages. 2010. pap. 19.36 *(978-1-61719-560-0(X))* Gorgias Pr., LLC.

ALTAR BOYS

see Acolytes

ALTAR GILDS

see Altar Guilds

ALTAR GUILDS

Maxwell, Lee A. The Altar Guild Manual: Lutheran Service Book Edition. 2008. (Illus.). 119p. per. 18.99 *(978-0-7586-1376-9(8))* Concordia Publishing Hse.

Storms, Mary Patricia & Turner, Paul. Guide for Ministers of Liturgical Environment. 2009. (Illus.). ix, 97p. pap. *(978-1-56854-747-3(1))* Liturgy Training Pubns.

ALTARPIECES

Assonitis, Alessio & Miller, David A. Bastiano Mainardi: Painter of Alterpieces in Renaissance Tuscany. 2011. (Illus.). 94p. pap. *(978-0-936260-89-1(0))* Indianapolis Museum of Art.

Binski, Paul & Massing, Ann, eds. The Westminster Retable: History, Technique, Conservation. 2010. (Painting & Practice Ser.). (ENG., Illus.). 464p. (C). 196.00 *(978-1-905375-28-8(X))* Miller, Harvey Pubs. GBR. Dist: Brown, David Bk. Co., The.

Fabri, Ria & Hout, Nico van. From Quinten Metsys to Rubens: Masterpieces from the Royal Museum Reunited in the Cathedral, 1 vol. 2010. (ENG., Illus.). 223p. 40.00 *(978-90-8586-537-7(9))* Exhibitions International BEL. Dist: Innovative Logistics.

Fassl, Johanna. Sacred Eloquence: Giambattista Tiepolo & the Rhetoric of the Altarpiece. 2010. (Illus.). 383p. pap. 88.95 *(978-3-0343-0035-3(2))* Lang, Peter Publishing, Inc.

Imhof, Verlag Michael & Sander, Jochen. Kult Bild: Das Altar- und Andachtsbild von Duccio bis Perugino. Begleitbuch zur Ausstellung im Städel in Frankfurt vom 7. Juli bis 22. Oktober 2006. 2007. 312p. 49.95 *(978-3-86568-128-7(X))* Imhof, Michael Verlag GmbH & Co. KG DEU. Dist: Independent Pubs. Group.

Jones, Pamela M. Altarpieces & Their Viewers in the Churches of Rome from Caravaggio to Guido Reni. 2008. (Visual Culture in Early Modernity Ser.). (Illus.). 390p. 134.95 *(978-0-7546-6179-5(2))* Ashgate Publishing Co.

Kahsnitz, Rainer. Carved Splendor: Late Gothic Altarpieces in Southern Germany, Austria, & South Tirol. Stockman, Russell, tr. from GER. 2006. (Illus.). 480p. 150.00 *(978-0-89236-853-2(5))* Oxford Univ. Pr., Inc.

Kroesen, J. E. A. Staging the Liturgy: The Medieval Altarpiece in the Iberian Peninsula. 2009. (Liturgia Condenda Ser.). (ENG.). 607p. (C). pap. 95.00 *(978-90-429-2116-0(1))* Peeters Pubs. & Booksellers BEL. Dist: Brown, David Bk. Co., The.

Mann, Vivian, et al. Uneasy Communion: Jews, Christians, & the Altarpieces of Medieval Spain. 2010. (ENG., Illus.). 176p. 60.00 *(978-1-904832-70-6(9))* Giles, D. Ltd. GBR. Dist: Antique Collectors' Club.

Nethersole, Scott. Devotion by Design: Italian Altarpieces Before 1500. 2011. (ENG., Illus.). 128p. 40.00 *(978-1-85709-525-8(1))* Yale Univ. Pr.

Wolk-Simon, Linda. Raphael at the Metropolitan: The Colonna Altarpiece. 2006. (ENG., Illus.). 76p. per. 19.95 *(978-0-300-11790-5(6))* Yale Univ. Pr.

Woollett, Anne T., et al. Drama & Devotion: Heemskerck¿s Ecce Homo Altarpiece from Warsaw. 2012. (ENG., Illus.). 112p. pap. 25.00 ***(978-1-60606-112-1(7)***, J. Paul Getty Museum) Getty Pubns.

ALTARS

Flores-Peña, Ysamur & Evanchuk, Roberta J. Santería Garments & Altars: Speaking Without a Voice. 2010. (Folk Art & Artists Ser.). (ENG.). 72p. (C). pap. 30.00 *(978-1-61703-067-3(8))* Univ. Pr. of Mississippi.

Hanh, Thich Nhat. Calm, Ease, Smile, Breathe. 2009. (ENG., Illus.). 16p. pap. 18.95 *(978-1-888375-90-9(6))* Parallax Pr.

Kroesen, J. E. A. & Schmidt, Victor M., eds. The Altar & its Environment. 2010. (Studies in the Visual Cultures of the Middle Ages Ser.). (ENG & FRE., Illus.). 314p. (C). pap. 138.00 *(978-2-503-53044-4(3))* Brepols Pubs. BEL. Dist: ISD.

Kynes, Sandra. Your Altar: Creating a Sacred Space for Prayer & Meditation. 2007. (ENG., Illus.). 240p. per. 15.95 *(978-0-7387-1105-8(5))* Llewellyn Pubns.

Milby, Th And Kathleen & Danson, Lex. Native & Garden Plants for the Church Altar. 2009. 124p. pap. 36.99 *(978-1-4389-0798-7(2))* AuthorHouse.

Parris, Pastor Trevor. Rebuilding the Altars in your Life one Prayer at a Time. 2010. 88p. pap. 10.99 *(978-1-60957-606-6(3))* Xulon Pr., Inc.

ALTERATION, CHROMATIC

see Musica Ficta

ALTERED STATES OF CONSCIOUSNESS

see also Trance

Avery, Kenneth S. A Psychology of Early Sufi Sama'. 2011. 256p. pap. 39.95 ***(978-0-415-66507-0(8))*** Routledge.

Coriat, Isador H. Abnormal Psychology. 2009. 446p. 41.99 *(978-1-117-09492-2(8))* BiblioBazaar.

—Abnormal Psychology. 2009. 208p. pap. *(978-0-217-43601-4(3))*; 210p. pap. *(978-1-4588-0129-6(2))* Books LLC.

—Abnormal Psychology. 444p. 2008. 51.95 *(978-1-4366-7254-2(6))* 2007. (ENG.). per. 36.95 *(978-1-4325-7814-5(6))* Kessinger Publishing, LLC.

—Abnormal Psychology. 2008. 444p. pap. *(978-1-4097-7070-1(2))* Read Bks.

Cvetkovic, Dean & Cosic, Irena, eds. States of Consciousness: Experimental Insights into Meditation, Waking, Sleep & Dreams. 2011. (Frontiers Collection). (ENG., Illus.). x, 280p. 79.95 *(978-3-642-18046-0(9)*, 3642180469) Springer.

Franco, Eli, ed. Yogic Perception, Meditation & Altered States of Consciousness. 2009. (Beitrage zur Kultur- und Geistesgeschichte Asiens Ser.). (ENG.). 483p. (C). pap. 63.00 *(978-3-7001-6648-1(6))* Austrian Academy of Sciences Press AUT. Dist: Brown, David Bk. Co., The.

Humm, Alan. Psychology of Prophecy in Early Christianity. 2009. 112.76 *(978-1-60724-618-3(X))* Gorgias Pr., LLC.

Kelly, Edward F. & Locke, Rafael G. Altered States of Consciousness & PSI: An Historical Survey & Research Prospectus. 2010. (Parapsychological Monograph Ser.). 107p. (Orig.). pap. 15.00 *(978-1-931747-31-8(8))* Parapsychology Foundation.

Kessler, Chad. Alterations of Consciousness in the Emergency Department: Emergency Medicine Clinics of North America. 2010. (Clinics: Internal Medicine Ser.: 28-3). (ENG., Illus.). xvi, 440p. 105.00 *(978-1-4377-2444-8(2)*, Saunders) Elsevier - Health Sciences Div.

Patterson, Wm Patrick, et al. The Life & Teachings of Carlos Castaneda. 2008. *(978-1-879514-97-3(4))* Arete Communications.

Powell, Anna. Deleuze, Altered States & Film. 2012. (ENG.). 224p. (gr. 17). pap. 35.00 ***(978-0-7486-4935-8(2))*** Edinburgh Univ. Pr. GBR. Dist: Columbia Univ. Pr.

Saloff, Jamie L. Transformational Healing W/CD: Five Surprisingly Simple Keys Designed to Redirect Your Life Toward Wellness, Purpose, & Prosperity. 2006. (Illus.). 428p. per. 34.95 *(978-0-9740642-1-5(1))* Saloff Enterprises.

Schiff, et al. Disorders of Consciousness. Schiff, Nicholas D., ed. 2009. (Annals of the New York Academy of Sciences Ser.). (ENG., Illus.). 300p. pap. 139.95 *(978-1-57331-743-6(8)*, Wiley-Blackwell) Wiley, John & Sons, Inc.

Schmidt, Bettina & Huskinson, Lucy, eds. Spirit Possession & Trance: New Interdisciplinary Perspectives, Vol. 7. 2010. (Continuum Advances in Religious Studies). (ENG., Illus.). 258p. 120.00 *(978-0-8264-3574-3(2))* Continuum International Publishing Group, Ltd. GBR. Dist: National Bk. Network.

Schmidt, Bettina E. & Huskinson, Lucy, eds. Spirit Possession & Trance: New Interdisciplinary Perspectives. 2012. (ENG., Illus.). 258p. pap. 44.95 ***(978-1-4411-0828-9(9))*** Continuum International Publishing Group, Ltd. GBR. Dist: National Bk. Network.

Taylor, Steve. Waking from Sleep: Why Awakening Experiences Occur & How to Make Them Permanent. 2010. (ENG.). 288p. pap. 14.95 *(978-1-4019-2870-4(6))* Hay Hse., Inc.

Tocquet, Robert. Supercerebro (Super Brain) (SPA.). pap. *(978-84-305-8237-2(1))* Susaeta Ediciones, S.A.

Wier, Dennis. The Way of Trance. 2009. 204p. 24.75 *(978-1-60860-663-4(5)*, Strategic Bk. Publishing) AEG Literary Publishing Services, Inc.

Winkelman, Michael. Shamanism: A Biopsychosocial Paradigm of Consciousness & Healing, 1 vol. 2nd rev. ed. 2010. (Illus.). 309p. 54.95 *(978-0-313-38181-2(X)*, A2593C, Praeger Pubs.) Greenwood Publishing Group, Inc.

ALTERNATE ENERGY SOURCES

see Renewable Energy Sources

ALTERNATING CURRENT MACHINERY

see Electric Machinery—Alternating Current

ALTERNATING CURRENTS

see Electric Currents, Alternating

ALTERNATING GENERATIONS

see Generations, Alternating

ALTERNATIVE AGRICULTURE

see also Permaculture; Sustainable Agriculture

Allen, Will & Wilson, Charles. The Good Food Revolution: Growing Healthy Food, People, & Communities. 2012. (ENG.). 288p. (gr. 12). 26.00 ***(978-1-59240-710-1(2)***, Gotham) Penguin Group (USA) Inc.

Bates, Albert K. The Biochar Solution: Carbon Farming & Climate Change. 2010. (ENG., Illus.). 208p. pap. 17.95 ***(978-0-86571-677-3(3)***, 9780865716773) New Society Pubs., Ltd. CAN. Dist: Consortium Bk. Sales & Distribution.

Bavec Franc & Bavec Martina. Organic Production & Use of Alternative Crops. 2006. (Books in Soils, Plants, & the Environment Ser.: Vol. 115). (ENG., Illus.). 241p. 157.95 *(978-1-57444-617-3(7)*, CRC Press) Taylor & Francis Group GBR. Dist: Taylor & Francis Group.

Chameides, Bill & Willey, Zach, eds. Harnessing Farms & Forests in the Low-Carbon Economy: How to Create, Measure, & Verify Greenhouse Gas Offsets. 2007. (ENG., Illus.). 240p. per. 60.00 *(978-0-8223-4168-0(9))* Duke Univ. Pr.

Despommier, Dickson. The Vertical Farm: Feeding the World in the 21st Century. 2011. (ENG., Illus.). 336p. pap. 16.00 *(978-0-312-61069-2(6))* Picador.

Frey, Darrell. Bioshelter Market Garden: A Permaculture Farm. 2011. (ENG., Illus.). 480p. pap. 34.95 ***(978-0-86571-678-0(1)***, 9780865716780) New Society Pubs., Ltd. CAN. Dist: Consortium Bk. Sales & Distribution.

Friederici, Peter. A New Plateau: Sustaining the Lands & Peoples of Canyon Country. Houk, Rose, ed. 2006. (ENG., Illus.). 159p. 39.95 *(978-0-9713391-5-6(5))* Renewing the Countryside.

—New Plateau: Sustaining the Lands & Peoples of Canyon Country. Friederici, Peter & Houk, Rose, eds. 2006. (ENG., Illus.). 159p. pap. 24.95 *(978-0-9713391-6-3(3))* Renewing the Countryside.

Garcia-Torres, L., et al, eds. Conservation Agriculture: Environment, Farmers Experiences, Innovations, Socio-Economy, Policy. 2010. 516p. pap. 259.00 *(978-90-481-6211-6(4)*, 9048162114) Springer.

Ikerd, John E. Crisis & Opportunity: Sustainability in American Agriculture. 2008. (Our Sustainable Future Ser.). (ENG., Illus.). 342p. pap. 18.95 *(978-0-8032-1142-1(2)*, Bison Bks.) Univ. of Nebraska Pr.

Warner, Keith Douglass. Agroecology in Action: Extending Alternative Agriculture Through Social Networks. 2006. (Food, Health, & the Environment Ser.). (ENG., Illus.). 296p. (gr. 17). 62.00 *(978-0-262-23252-4(9))*; per. 26.00 *(978-0-262-73180-5(0))* MIT Pr.

Wiebe & Wittman. Food Sovereignty in Canada: Creating Just & Sustainable Food Systems. Desmarais, Annette Aurelie & Hannah, A. C., eds. 2012. 232p. pap. 24.95 ***(978-1-55266-443-8(0))*** Fernwood Publishing Co., Ltd. CAN. Dist: Independent Pubs. Group.

ALTERNATIVE DISPUTE RESOLUTION

see Dispute Resolution (Law)

ALTERNATIVE EDUCATION

see Non-Formal Education

ALTERNATIVE ENERGY SOURCES

see Renewable Energy Sources

ALTERNATIVE HOMES

see Ecological Houses

ALTERNATIVE MEDICINE

see also Alternative Veterinary Medicine; Chiropractic; Energy Medicine; Holistic Medicine; Homeopathy; Medicine, Botanic; Medicine, Magic, Mystic, and Spagiric; Medicine, Oriental; Mental Healing; Mesmerism; Naturopathy; Osteopathic Medicine; Radiesthesia; Traditional Medicine

ABBE Research Division Staff. Alternative Medicine in Action & Practice in the 21st Century with Index & Medical Analysis of New Research Information for All Nations. 2007. (Illus.). 160p. *(978-0-7883-4107-6(3)*, 0-7883-4107-3) ABBE Pubs. Assn. of Washington, D.C.

Adam Staff. The Path of the Dreamhealer: The Quantum World of Energy Healing. 2011. (ENG.). 256p. (gr. 12). pap. 15.50 ***(978-0-14-305378-1(7)***, Penguin Global) Penguin Group (USA) Inc.

Adams, Alison. Chronic Fatigue, ME, & Fibromyalgia: The Natural Recovery Plan. 2010. (ENG.). 256p. pap. 19.95 *(978-1-906787-76-9(X)*, Watkins Publishing) Duncan Baird Pubs. GBR. Dist: Sterling Publishing Co., Inc.

Adams, Angela & TOVEY. Complementary & Alter Med Nur Midw. 2007. (Illus.). 192p. 145.00 *(978-0-415-36846-9(4))* Routledge.

Adams, Jon, ed. Researching Complementary & Alternative Medicine. 2006. (Illus.). 153p. 160.00 *(978-0-415-36774-5(3))*; per. 47.95 *(978-0-415-36775-2(1))* Routledge.

Adams, Jon, et al, eds. Traditional, Complementary & Integrative Medicine: An International Reader. 2012. (ENG., Illus.). 296p. (C). pap. 37.00 ***(978-0-230-23265-5(5))*** Palgrave Macmillan.

Adams, Jon & Tovey, Phillip, eds. Complementary & Alter Med Nur Midw. 2007. (ENG., Illus.). 192p. pap. 47.95 *(978-0-415-36847-6(2))* Routledge.

Ahmed, Hanaa, et al. Natural Opportunities & Parkinson's Disease. 2011. 204p. pap. ***(978-3-8443-0388-9(X))*** Lambert Academic Publishing.

Alaoui-Jamali, Moulay. Alternative & Complementary Therapies for Cancer. 2010. (Illus.). xx, 722p. pap., instr.'s gde. ed. 49.95 *(978-1-4419-0019-7(5)*, 1441900195) Springer.

Aldred, Elaine M. A Guide to Starting Your Own Complementary Therapy Practice. 2006. (ENG., Illus.). 304p. pap., instr.'s gde. ed. 55.95 *(978-0-443-10309-4(7)*, Churchill Livingstone) Elsevier - Health Sciences Div.

Allport, Richard. Heal Your Dog the Natural Way. 2010. (Illus.). 208p. pap. 29.95 *(978-1-84468-110-5(6))* Pen & Sword Bks. Ltd. GBR. Dist: Casemate Pubs. & Bk. Distributors, LLC.

American Cancer Society Staff. Complementary & Alternative Cancer Methods: The Essential Guide for You & Your Doctor. 2nd ed. 2009. (American Cancer Society Complete Guide T Ser.). (ENG.). 893p. pap. 24.95 *(978-0-944235-71-3(9)*, 9780944235713) American Cancer Society, Inc.

Anderson, Rich. Cleanse & Purify Thyself: The Definitive Guide to Intestinal Cleansing, Bk. 1. 2007. (Illus.). 199p. pap. 9.95 *(978-0-9664973-3-5(3))* Christobe Publishing.

Angelo, Jack. El Poder de Curar. (SPA., Illus.). 288p. *(978-84-7927-123-7(X))* Robinbk., Ediciones S.L. ESP. Dist: Lectorum Pubns., Inc.

Angwin, Darice A. Feeling Good: An Alternative Approach to Health Care. Date not set. 100p. (Orig.). pap. 9.95 *(978-0-9648088-0-5(3))* Sunset International.

Aranda, Graciela. Escucha los Mensajes de Tu Cuerpo: Una Historia Que te Revelará una Maravillosa Técnica Chamánica de Sanación a Través de los Vórtices. 2007. (SPA.). 192p. per. 12.95 *(978-0-7387-1142-3(X)*, Llewellyn Espanol) Llewellyn Pubns.

Babel, Ken. Mushrooms for Health & Longevity. 2011. (Illus.). 64p. pap. 11.95 *(978-1-55312-047-6(7))* Books Alive.

Badaracco, Claire Hoertz. Prescribing Faith: Medicine, Media, & Religion in American Culture. 2007. (ENG.). 298p. pap. 34.95 *(978-1-932792-89-8(9))* Baylor Univ. Pr.

Badell, Colleen. 6 Myths about Alternative Medicine: Using It Wisely. 2006. (Illus.). 189p. per. 12.95 *(978-0-9761129-1-4(4))* Turning Point Pr.

Badell, Colleen C. A Simple Plan: Alternative Medicine Made Very Easy. 2006. (Illus.). 264p. per. 14.95 *(978-0-9761129-0-7(6))* Turning Point Pr.

Bagetta, Giacinto, et al, eds. Herbal Medicines. 2011. (Clinical Pharmacognosy Ser.). (ENG., Illus.). 519p. 139.95 *(978-1-4398-3768-9(6)*, CRC Press) Taylor & Francis Group GBR. Dist: Taylor & Francis Group.

Bakalova, Elena. Bio-Energy Diagnostics: Methods, procedures, Techniques. 2008. 208p. pap. 17.95 *(978-1-4401-0115-1(9))* iUniverse, Inc.

Barber, Kimberly. The Role of Chronic Illness in Mental Wellbeing. 2010. 120p. pap. *(978-3-8383-0229-4(X))* Lambert Academic Publishing.

Barcan, Ruth. Complementary & Alternative Medicine: Bodies, Therapies, Senses. 2011. (ENG.). 224p. pap. 34.95 (978-1-84520-743-4(2)); (illus.). 99.95 (978-1-84520-742-7(4)) Berg Pubs. GBR. Dist: Macmillan.

BarCharts, Inc. Natural Remedies. 2011. (ENG.). 6p. 5.95 (978-1-4232-1652-0(0)) Barcharts, Inc.

Barron, Jon. Lessons from the Miracle Doctors: A Step-by-Step Guide to Optimum Health & Relief from Catastrophic Illness, 1 vol. 2008. 320p. (978-1-59120-224-0(8)) Basic Health Pubns., Inc.

Bauer, Brent A., et al. Textbook of Complementary & Alternative Medicine. 2nd rev. ed. 2006. (ENG., Illus.). 816p. 420.00 (978-1-84214-297-4(6)) Taylor & Francis Group.

Bausell, R. Barker. Snake Oil Science: The Truth about Complementary & Alternative Medicine. 2009. (ENG., Illus.). 320p. pap. 19.99 (978-0-19-538342-3(7)) Oxford Univ. Pr., Inc.

Beasley, Keith. Reiki - Without Rules. 2007. 231p. pap. 27.50 (978-1-84799-866-8(6)) Lulu Enterprises Inc.

Bellebuono, Holly. The Essential Herbal for Natural Health: How to Transform Easy-to-Find Herbs into Healing Remedies for the Whole Family. 2012. (ENG., Illus.). 304p. pap. 19.95 (978-1-59030-947-6(2), Roost Books) Shambhala Pubns., Inc.

Benjamin, Patricia J. Pearson's Massage Therapy: Blending Art with Science. 2010. (ENG.). 800p. (C). pap. 79.47 (978-0-13-229668-7(3), Prentice Hall) Prentice Hall PTR.

Bertrand, Sharon. Inroads to an Integrative Medicine. 2010. 184p. pap. (978-3-639-24345-1(6)) VDM Verlag Dr. Mueller e.K.

Bivins, Roberta. Alternative Medicine? A History. (ENG., Illus.). 264p. 2010. pap. 22.99 (978-0-19-954376-2(3)) 2008. 37.95 (978-0-19-921887-5(0)) Oxford Univ. Pr., Inc.

Blackburn, Suzanne & Wade, Margaret, eds. Reclaiming Eros: Sacred Whores & Healers. 2008. (Illus.). 248p. pap. 17.95 (978-0-615-16069-6(7)) Suade Publishing.

Bloom, William. The Endorphin Effect: A Breakthrough Strategy for Holistic Health & Spiritual Wellbeing. 2011. (ENG., Illus.). 320p. pap. 15.95 (978-0-7499-4126-0(X)) Piatkus Bks. GBR. Dist: Independent Pubs. Group.

Bodeker, Gerard & Burford, Gemma, eds. Traditional, Complementary & Alternative Medicine: Policy & Public Health Perspectives. 2007. (Illus.). 453p. 146.00 (978-1-86094-616-5(X)) Imperial College Pr. GBR. Dist: World Scientific Publishing Co., Inc.

Boice, Judith. The Green Medicine Chest: Healthy Treasures for the Whole Family. 2011. (ENG., Illus.). 332p. pap. 19.95 (978-1-61448-058-7(3)) Morgan James Publishing.

Bonney, Doland & Couper, Monroe. Nutrition to Live. l.t. ed. (978-0-615-11324-1(9)) Couper Pubs.

Bowden, Jonny. Most Effective Natural Cures on Earth: The Surprising, Unbiased Truth about What Treatments Work & Why. 2008. (ENG., Illus.). 360p. per. 24.99 (978-1-59233-291-5(9), 1592332919) Quayside.

Bowers Jennifer Muir, et al, eds. Integrating Therapeutic & Complementary Nutrition. 2006. (ENG., Illus.). 634p. 102.95 (978-0-8493-1612-8(X), 1612, CRC Press) Taylor & Francis Group GBR. Dist: Taylor & Francis Group.

Brady, David M. Dr. Brady's Health Revolution: Just What You Really Need to Know to Stay Healthy in a Sick World. 2007. (ENG.). 26.95 (978-1-60037-080-9(2)) Morgan James Publishing.

—Dr. Brady's Health Revolution: What You Really Need to Know to Stay Healthy in a Sick World. 2007. (ENG., Illus.). 207p. pap. 16.95 (978-1-60037-081-6(0)) Morgan James Publishing.

Brannon, Linda, et al. Current Perspectives: Readings on Complementary Medicine & Diversity from InfoTrac College Edition for Brannon. 6th ed. 2006. (ENG.). 240p. (C). pap. 64.95 (978-0-495-13020-8(6)) Wadsworth.

Bratman, Steven. Alternative Health Guide. 2007. 672p. pap. 24.95 (978-0-06-113200-1(4)) HarperCollins Pubs.

—Collins Alternative Health Guide. 2007. (ENG.). 672p. pap. 24.95 (978-0-06-112018-3(9)) HarperCollins Pubs.

Brewer, Sarah. Overcoming Arthritis: The Complete Complementary Health Program. 2009. (Natural Health Guru Ser.). (ENG., Illus.). 180p. pap. 14.95 (978-1-84483-728-1(9)) Duncan Baird Pubs. GBR. Dist: Sterling Publishing Co., Inc.

—Overcoming Asthma: The Complete Complementary Health Program. 2009. (Natural Health Guru Ser.). (ENG., Illus.). 180p. pap. 14.95 (978-1-84483-727-4(0)) Duncan Baird Pubs. GBR. Dist: Sterling Publishing Co., Inc.

Brown, Richard, et al. How to Use Herbs, Nutrients & Yoga in Mental Health Care. 2009. (ENG., Illus.). 464p. 34.95 (978-0-393-70525-6(0), 70525) Norton, W. W. & Co., Inc.

Buchman, Dian Dincin. Ancient Healing Secrets: Practical Herbal Remedies from around the World That Work Today. 2006. (Illus.). 173p. reprint ed. 22.00 (978-1-4223-5415-5(6)) DIANE Publishing Co.

Burras, Jon. Return to Nature. 2011. 448p. 34.99 (978-1-4568-5866-7(1)); pap. 23.99 (978-1-4568-5865-0(3)) Xlibris Corp.

Carreno, Rosa. Herbolaria Mexicana. (SPA.). pap. 8.98 (978-970-643-114-1(4), SR10121) Selector, S.A. de C.V. MEX. Dist: AIMS International Bks., Inc.

Cass, Hyla. Supplement Your Prescription: What Your Doctor Doesn't Know about Nutrition. 2008. (ENG.). 192p. pap. 14.95 (978-1-59120-227-1(2)) Basic Health Pubns., Inc.

Cawthorn, Anne & Mackereth, Peter A., eds. Integrative Hypnotherapy: Complementary Approaches in Clinical Care. 2010. (ENG., Illus.). 264p. pap. 49.95 (978-0-7020-3082-6(1), Churchill Livingstone) Elsevier - Health Sciences Div.

Chatwin, et al. Complementary & Alter Med Cancer. 2007. (Illus.). 192p. 150.00 (978-0-415-35993-1(7)) Routledge.

Chemiack, P. & Chemiack, N., eds. Alternative Medicine for the Elderly. 2010. (ENG., Illus.). xviii, 473p. pap. 119.00 (978-3-642-07913-9(X), 364207913X) Springer.

Chikly, Bruno. Silent Waves, Theory & Practice of Lymph Drainage Therapy: With Applications for Lymphedema, Chronic Pain, & Inflammation. (Illus.). 450p. suppl. ed. 65.00 (978-0-9700530-6-0(1)) Upledger Institute, The.

Christensen, David. Journey of the D's. 2010. 248p. pap. 14.98 (978-0-557-23140-9(X)) Lulu Enterprises Inc.

Chu Tow, Mabel S. & Reed, Melissa Ann. Strange Kindness. 2007. (ENG.). 160p. per. 31.50 (978-0-7618-3881-4(3)) Univ. Pr. of America, Inc.

Cimino, Michael. Abimox : Fundamentals of the Eight Therapeutic Modalities:the Ways of Martial Arts Healing. 2007. per. (978-1-932583-40-3(8)) digital@batesjackson llc.

—Abimoxi - the Ways of Martial Arts Healing: Pathology. 2007. per. (978-1-932583-38-0(6)) digital@batesjackson llc.

Cohen, Jay S. Natural Alternatives to Treating Migraines: Using Natural Supplements, Nutrition & Alternative Therapies to Better Manage Migraine Pain. 2011. (ENG.). 196p. pap. 7.95 (978-0-7570-0358-5(3)) Square One Pubs.

Cohen, Michael H. Healing at the Borderland of Medicine & Religion. (Islamic Civilization & Muslim Networks Ser.). 2009. (ENG., Illus.). 248p. pap. 23.00 (978-0-8078-5962-9(1)) 2006. xiii, 229p. pap. (978-0-8078-5760-1(2)) Univ. of North Carolina Pr.

Collective, Sage-Femme. Natural Liberty: Rediscovering Self-Induced Abortion Methods. 2008. (Illus.). x, 454p. (978-0-9645920-0-1(2)) Sage-femme.

Constantine, Storm. Sekhem Hek. 2008. 240p. pap. (978-1-905713-13-4(4)) Megalithica Bks.

Cooper, Edwin L. & Yamaguchi, Nobuo, eds. Complementary & Alternative Approaches to Biomedicine. 2012. (Advances in Experimental Medicine & Biology Ser.). (ENG., Illus.). xxi, 480p. pap. 179.00 (978-1-4419-3441-3(3), 1441934413) Springer.

Coulter, Ian D., et al. Hospital-Based Integrative Medicine: A Case Study of the Barriers & Factors Facilitating the Creation of a Center. 2008. 192p. pap. 31.00 (978-0-8330-4559-1(8), mg-591) RAND Corp., The.

Courteney, Hazel. 500 of the Most Important Health Tips You'll Ever Need. 2011. (Illus.). 432p. pap. 19.95 (978-1-907030-76-5(X)) CICO Bks. GBR. Dist: Ryland Peters & Small.

Cowen, Sandy. Get Well - Even When You've Been Told You Can't: Simple Steps for Finding Perfect Healing Using Methods Outside of Conventional Medicine. 2008. 244p. pap. 16.95 (978-0-9818948-0-5(1)) Booklocker.com, Inc.

Cram101 Textbook Reviews & Cram101 Textbook Reviews. Outlines & Highlights for Clinical Research in Complementary Therapies: Principles, Problems & Solutions by George Thomas Lewith, ISBN. 2011. 290p. pap. 32.95 (978-1-61461-209-4(9)) Cram101 Inc.

—Outlines & Highlights for Complementary & Alternative Therapies for Nursing Practice by Karen Lee Fontaine, Isbn: 9780135102466. 2011. 142p. pap. 28.95 (978-1-61461-695-5(7)) Cram101 Inc.

Crawford, Gregory A. The Medical Library Association Guide to Complementary & Alternative Medicine Information: Authoritative, Patient-Friendly Print & Electronic Resources. 2010. 90.00 (978-1-55570-727-9(0)) Neal-Schuman Pubs., Inc.

Dach, Jeffrey. Biodentical Hormones 101: Bioidentical Hormones, Natural Thyroid, & Natural Medicine. 2011. 592p. 39.95 (978-1-4620-3655-4(4)) iUniverse, Inc.

—Bioidentical Hormones 101. 2011. 592p. pap. 29.95 (978-1-4620-3499-4(3)) iUniverse, Inc.

Dacher, Elliot S. Integral Health: The Path to Human Flourishing. 2006. (Illus.). 184p. per. 17.95 (978-1-59120-190-8(X)) Basic Health Pubns., Inc.

Dahlke, Rudiger. El Mensaje Curativo del Alma. (SPA.). 360p. (978-84-7927-185-5(X)) Robinbk., Ediciones S.L. ESP. Dist: Lectorum Pubns., Inc.

Dalet, Roger. Digitopuntura: Curese Usted Mismo Sus Dolores y Molestias con una Simple Presion de Dedo. 2010. (SPA., Illus.). 160p. pap. (978-5-89315-073-5(2)) Berbera Editores S.A. de C.V.

Danenberg, Jerry. My Heart & I: The True Story of a Personal Resurrection. 2007. (Illus.). 150p. pap. 12.95 (978-1-890109-36-3(3), Xemplar) Crossquarter Publishing Group.

Davis, Carol M. Complementary Therapies in Rehabilitation: Evidence for Efficacy in Therapy, Prevention, & Wellness. 3rd ed. 2008. (ENG., Illus.). 432p. (C). 61.95 (978-1-55642-866-1(9)) SLACK, Inc.

Davis, Ervin. Vaccine Alternatives: How to Prevent & Treat Illness Using Natural Remedies: an Essential Guide for Patients, Parents, Travelers, & Healthcare Workers. 2008. 136p. pap. 14.95 (978-0-615-19347-2(1)) Autumn Hse. Publishing Co.

Davis, W. Marvin. Consumer's Guide to Dietary Supplements & Alternative Medicines. 2006. (ENG., Illus.). 150p. (C). pap. 50.00 (978-0-7890-3041-2(1), Informa Healthcare) Taylor & Francis Group.

—Consumer's Guide to Dietary Supplements & Alternative Medicines: Servings of Hope. 2006. (Illus.). 532p. 50.00 (978-0-7890-3040-5(3), Informa Healthcare) Taylor & Francis Group.

de la Gletais, Caterina. Los Consejos y Remedios de la Abuela. (SPA., Illus.). 200p. (978-84-7927-466-5(2)) Robinbk., Ediciones S.L. ESP. Dist: Lectorum Pubns., Inc.

De Luca, Bernardo N., ed. Mind-Body & Relaxation Research Focus. 2008. 129.00 (978-1-60021-819-4(9), Nova Biomedical Bks.) Nova Science Pubs., Inc.

de Vries, Jan. Jan de Vries: A Life in Healing. 2006. (ENG., Illus.). 356p. 29.95 (978-1-84596-141-2(2)) Mainstream Publishing Co., Ltd. GBR. Dist: Independent Pubs. Group.

de Vries, Jan & De Vries, Jan. Emotional Healing: Complementary Solutions for a Stress-Free Life. 2008. (ENG.). 192p. pap. 14.95 (978-1-84596-271-5(0)) Mainstream Publishing Co., Ltd. GBR. Dist: Independent Pubs. Group.

DeJong, Michael. Clean Cures: The Humble Art of Zen-Curing Yourself. 2009. (ENG., Illus.). 192p. 10.95 (978-1-4027-6697-8(1)) Sterling Publishing Co., Inc.

Deutsch, Judith E. & Anderson, Ellen Zambo. Complementary Therapies for Physical Therapy: A Clinical Decision-Making Approach. 2007. (ENG., Illus.). 352p. 63.95 (978-0-7216-0111-3(1), Saunders) Elsevier - Health Sciences Div.

DeYoung, Eric M. How to Live a Happy, Healthy, Wealthy & Safe Life! The Missing Links in Conventional Medicine. 2011. 116p. 24.95 (978-1-4269-5310-1(0)) Trafford Publishing.

Ditchek, Stuart H., et al. Healthy Child, Whole Child: Integrating the Best of Conventional & Alternative Medicine to Keep Your Kids Healthy. 2009. (ENG.). 352p. pap. 17.99 (978-0-06-168598-9(4), William Morrow Paperbacks) HarperCollins Pubs.

Donahoo, Eddie. Conception of Inquisitive Entities. 2008. 64p. pap. 15.49 (978-1-4389-0702-4(8)) AuthorHouse.

Donofrio, Peter D. Textbook of Peripheral Neuropathy. 2012. 500p. (978-1-936287-10-9(2)) Demos Medical Publishing, LLC.

Doy, Penelope. 183 Remedios Naturales para Aliviar el Dolor (183 Natural Remedies for Healing Pain) (SPA.). 216p. (978-84-305-8839-8(6)) Susaeta Ediciones, S.A.

Dworkin, Ronald W. Artificial Happiness: The Dark Side of the New Happy Class. 2007. (ENG.). 336p. per. 15.95 (978-0-7867-1933-4(8)) Basic Bks.

Dyczek, Henryk. The Development of Alternative Medicine from 1965 To 2000: A keyword & key-concept Approach. 2008. 104p. pap. (978-3-639-04739-4(7)) VDM Verlag Dr. Mueller e.K.

Edelberg, David. The Triple Whammy Cure: The Breakthrough Women's Health Program for Feeling Good Again in 3 Weeks. annot. ed. 2007. (ENG.). 336p. pap. 15.00 (978-0-7432-6908-7(X), Free Pr.) Free Pr.

Ehrler, Doris. Innocence Remembered, a Path to Personal & Global Healing. 2009. 300p. pap. 19.50 (978-0-557-11183-1(8)) Lulu Enterprises Inc.

Elson, Margaret. You'll Never Make Pastry: Your Hands Are Too Hot: To Reiki Master Teacher - And Beyond! 2010. (Illus.). 200p. pap. 14.49 (978-1-4520-1360-2(8)) AuthorHouse.

Elwins, Dennie. How to Treat Yourself with Alternative Medicine & Non-Traditional Healing. 2009. 32p. pap. 16.99 (978-0-557-15416-6(2)) Lulu Enterprises Inc.

Enna, S. J. & Norton, Stata. Herbal Supplements & the Brain: Understanding Their Health Benefits & Hazards. rev. ed. 2012. (FT Press Science Ser.). (ENG.). 272p. 34.99 (978-0-13-282497-2(3)) FT Press.

Erickson, Pamela I. Ethnomedicine. 2007. 124p. (C). pap. 15.50 (978-1-57766-521-2(X)) Waveland Pr., Inc.

Ernst, Edzard, ed. Helaing, Hype or Harm? A Critical Analysis of Complementary or Alternative Medicine. 2008. (Societas Ser.). (ENG.). 178p. pap. 17.90 (978-1-84540-118-4(2)) Imprint Academic GBR. Dist: Ingram Pub. Services.

Ernst, Edzard, et al, eds. The Desktop Guide to Complementary & Alternative Medicine: An Evidence-Based Approach. 2nd rev. ed. 2006. (ENG., Illus.). 576p. pap. 66.95 (978-0-7234-3383-5(6), Mosby) Elsevier - Health Sciences Div.

Ernst, Edzard & Singh, Simon. Trick or Treatment: The Undeniable Facts about Alternative Medicine. 2009. (ENG., Illus.). 352p. pap. 17.95 (978-0-393-33778-5(2), 33778) Norton, W. W. & Co., Inc.

Ernst, Edzard, et al. Oxford Handbook of Complementary Medicine. 2nd ed. 2008. (Oxford Handbooks Ser.). (ENG., Illus.). 512p. 59.95 (978-0-19-920677-3(5)) Oxford Univ. Pr., Inc.

Escobar, Zenaida. Motivando a la Salud: Nutricion y Remedios Caseros. 2010. (SPA.). 84p. pap. 10.49 (978-1-4490-9481-2(3)) AuthorHouse.

Etkin, Nina L. Edible Medicines: An Ethnopharmacology of Food. (ENG., Illus.). 304p. 2008. pap. 24.95 (978-0-8165-2748-9(2)) 2006. 50.00 (978-0-8165-2093-0(3)) Univ. of Arizona Pr.

Ewing, Jim Pathfinder. Healing Plants & Animals from a Distance: Curative Principles & Applications. 2007. (ENG., Illus.). 192p. pap. 16.95 (978-1-84409-111-9(2)) Findhorn Pr. GBR. Dist: Independent Pubs. Group.

Fauchère, Andrée. Nous Sommes- 2007. (FRE., Illus.). 547p. (978-2-8321-0277-0(8)) Slatkine Editions.

Ferguson. Careers in Focus: Complementary & Alternative Health Care, Third Edition. 3rd rev. ed. 2009. (Careers in Focus Ser.). (Illus.). 248p. (gr. 6-12). 32.95 (978-0-8160-7302-3(3), Ferguson Publishing Co.) Facts On File, Inc.

Field, Tiffany. Complementary & Alternative Therapies Research. 2008. (Illus.). 200p. 49.95 (978-1-4338-0401-4(8)) American Psychological Assn.

Fillmore, Charles. Christian Healing. 2010. 172p. (978-1-4455-1549-6(0)); pap. (978-1-4455-1165-8(7)) Read Bks. (Obscure Pr.).

Fontaine, Karen Lee. Complementary & Alternative Therapies for Nursing Practice. 3rd ed. 2010. (ENG., Illus.). 480p. (C). pap. 58.95 (978-0-13-510246-6(4), Prentice Hall) Prentice Hall PTR.

Forclea, Bruce. Unlocking the Healing Code: Discover the 7 Keys to Unlimited Healing Power. 2007. (ENG., Illus.). 216p. per. 14.95 (978-0-7387-1077-8(6)) Llewellyn Pubns.

Forde, Ralph Quinlan. The Book of Tibetan Medicine: How to Use Tibetan Healing for Personal Wellbeing. 2007. (ENG., Illus.). 128p. pap. 19.95 (978-1-85675-276-3(3), Hamlyn) Octopus Publishing Group GBR. Dist: Hachette Bk. Group.

Fornia, Larry & Mary Frances Lyles-Fornia. An Old-New Treatment for Health in the 21st Century, 1 vol. 2009. 90p. pap. 16.95 (978-1-60749-904-6(5)) PublishAmerica, Inc.

Foster, Steven & Johnson, Rebecca. Nature's Medicine. 2008. (ENG., Illus.). 416p. 24.00 (978-1-4262-0293-3(6), National Geographic) National Geographic Society.

Fraser, Peter H. & Massey, Harry. Decoding the Human Body-Field: The New Science of Information as Medicine. 2008. (ENG., Illus.). 1p. pap. 18.95 (978-1-59477-225-2(8), Healing Arts Pr.) Inner Traditions International, Ltd.

Freeman, Lyn W. Mosby's Complementary & Alternative Medicine: A Research-Based Approach. 3rd ed. 2008. (ENG., Illus.). 640p. 78.95 (978-0-323-05346-4(7), Mosby) Elsevier - Health Sciences Div.

Fucci, E. Dr Bach's Flower Essences a Quantum Approach to Prescribing. 2010. 142p. pap. 11.50 (978-1-59330-645-8(8)) Aventine Pr.

Fuentes, Starr. Healing with Energy: The Definitive Guide to Hands-On Techniques from a Master. 2007. (ENG., Illus.). 1p. per. 14.99 (978-1-56414-969-5(2), New Page Bks.) Career Pr., Inc.

Fundukian, Laurie J. The Gale Encyclopedia of Alternative Medicine. 3rd ed. 2008. (978-1-4144-4875-6(9)); (978-1-4144-4874-9(0)); (978-1-4144-4873-2(2)); (978-1-4144-4876-3(7)) Cengage Gale.

Fundukian, Laurie J., ed. Gale Encyclopedia of Alternative Medicine, 4 vols. 3rd rev. ed. 2008. 620.00 (978-1-4144-4872-5(4)) Cengage Gale.

Gaffney, Debra. Keys to a Vibrantyl Healthy, Long Life: Insights & Information on Healing, Health & Well-Being. 2011. 212p. pap. 14.95 (978-0-615-42602-0(6)) Serenity Pass Pr.

Gaia, Bianca & Belair, Gilles. Welcome to the Fifth Dimension: The Quintessence of Being, Ascensions Ultimate Secret. 2010. (ENG., Illus.). 360p. pap. 19.95 (978-1-55643-840-0(0)) North Atlantic Bks.

Gaik, Frances. Qigong As an Alternative & Complimentary Treatment for Depression. 2010. 108p. pap. (978-3-8383-6564-0(X)) Lambert Academic Publishing.

Gangi, Rayna M. Forget the Cures, Find the Cause: Book One. 2006. 140p. pap. 16.95 (978-1-59800-698-8(3)) Outskirts Pr., Inc.

Gearin-Tosh, Michael. Living Proof: A Medical Mutiny. 2007. (ENG.). 336p. pap. 22.95 (978-1-4165-7751-5(3), Scribner) Scribner.

Gerbarg, Patricia L., et al. How to Use Herbs, Nutrients & Yoga in Mental Health. 2012. (ENG.). 464p. pap. 24.95 (978-0-393-70744-1(X), 70744) Norton, W. W. & Co., Inc.

Gerson, Charlotte & Bishop, Beata. Healing the Gerson Way: Defeating Cancer & Other Chronic Diseases (with Blu-Ray) Shwed, Joanne, ed. & des. by. 2011. 488p. pap. 44.95 (978-0-9760186-8-1(3)) Gerson Health Media.

—Healing the Gerson Way (with DVD) Defeating Cancer & Other Chronic Diseases. Shwed, Joanne, ed. Kroschel, Stephen. 2011. 488p. pap. 39.95 (978-0-9760186-9-8(1)) Gerson Health Media.

Glenville, Marilyn. Natural Alternatives for Menopause & Osteoporosis. 192p. 19.95 (978-1-55285-218-7(0), Walrus Bks.) Whitecap Bks., Ltd. CAN. Dist: Graphic Arts Ctr. Publishing Co.

—Natural Alternatives to Dieting: Why Diets Don't Work & What You Can Do That Does. 192p. 19.95 (978-1-55285-219-4(9), Walrus Bks.) Whitecap Bks., Ltd. CAN. Dist: Graphic Arts Ctr. Publishing Co.

Goldberg, Michael E. End of Mood Disorders. 2008. 156p. 29.99 (978-1-4363-2447-2(5)); pap. 19.99 (978-1-4363-2446-5(7)) Xlibris Corp.

Goldberg, N. La Escritura, una Terapia Creativa. (SPA.). 222p. (978-84-95456-41-0(9), 86413) Ediciones Oniro S.A.

Goldstein, Mark A. Your Best Medicine From Conventional & Complementary Medicine — Expert-Endorsed Therapeutic Solutions to Relieve Symptoms & Speed Healing. 2009. pap. 16.95 (978-1-60529-656-2(2)) Rodale Pr., Inc.

Goldstein, Mark A., et al. Your Best Medicine: From Conventional & Complementary Medicine-Expert-Endorsed Therapeutic Solutions to Relieve Symptoms & Speed Healing. 2008. (978-1-59486-826-9(3)) Rodale Pr., Inc.

Goldstein, M.D., Mark A & Goldstein, Myrna Chandler. Healthy Herbs: Fact Versus Fiction, 1 vol. 2012. (Illus.). 305p. 68.00 (978-0-313-39780-6(5), A3595C) Greenwood Publishing Group, Inc.

Goldstein, Myrna Chandler, et al. Your Best Medicine: From Conventional & Complementary Medicine — Expert-Endorsed Therapeutic Solutions to Relieve Symptoms & Speed Healing. 2009. (ENG.). 624p. pap. 23.95 (978-1-59486-849-8(2)) Rodale Pr., Inc.

Gottlieb, Bill. Alternative Cures: More than 1,000 of the Most Effective Natural Home Remedies. 2008. (ENG.). 816p. mass mkt. 7.99 (978-0-345-50539-2(5), Ballantine Bks.) Random House Publishing Group.

Grace, Sandra. Integrative Medicine in Australian Health Care. 2009. 388p. pap. (978-3-639-12959-5(8)) VDM Verlag Dr. Mueller e.K.

Gruver, Kathy. The Alternative Medicine Cabinet. 2010. pap. 11.95 (978-0-7414-5903-9(5)) Infinity Publishing.

Gursche, Siegfried. Fantastic Flax: A Powerful Defense Against Cancer, Heart Disease, & Digestive Disorders. 2007. (ENG., Illus.). 64p. pap. 11.95 (978-1-55312-000-1(0)) Books Alive.

Gursche, Siegfried & Rona, Zolton P. Encyclopedia of Natural Healing. (Illus.). 1488p. 59.95 (978-1-55312-039-1(6)) Books Alive.

Guyol, Gracelyn. Healing Depression & Bipolar Disorder Without Drugs: Inspiring Stories of Restoring Mental Health Through Natural Therapies. 2006. (ENG., Illus.). 192p. per. 14.95 (978-0-8027-1496-1(X)) Walker & Co.

Hadady, D. Ac. Personal Renewal: Your Guide to Vitality, Allure, & a Joyful Life Using Healing Herbs, Diet, Movement, & Visualizations. 2008. 324p. pap. 21.95 *(978-0-595-52230-9(0))* iUniverse, Inc.

Hahnemann, Samuel. Organon of Medicine. 2009. 274p. pap. *(978-0-217-73782-1(X))*; 252p. pap. *(978-0-217-73778-4(1))* Books LLC.

—Organon of Medicine. Dudgeon, R. E., tr. 2007. (ENG.). 334p. 45.95 *(978-0-548-20146-6(3))*; 336p. per. 30.95 *(978-1-4325-1169-2(6))* Kessinger Publishing, LLC.

—Organon of Medicine. 314p. reprint ed. 98.00 *(978-0-7222-9975-3(3))* Library Reprints, Inc.

Haller, John S. Sectarian Reformers in American Medicine, 1800-1910. 2012. ***(978-0-404-64471-0(6))*** AMS Pr., Inc.

Haller, John S. Swedenborg, Mesmer, & the Mind/Body Connection: The Roots of Complementary Medicine. 2010. (Swedenborg Studies). (ENG., Illus.). 344p. 29.95 *(978-0-87785-331-2(2))* Swedenborg Foundation, Inc.

Haller, John S., compiled by. Swedenborg, Mesmer, & the Mind/Body Connection: The Roots of Complementary Medicine. 2010. (Swedenborg Studies). (ENG., Illus.). 344p. pap. 19.95 *(978-0-87785-330-5(4))* Swedenborg Foundation, Inc.

Hardiman, David & Mukharji, Projit Bihari, eds. Medical Power & Subaltern Therapy in South Asia. 2012. (Intersections: Colonial & Postcolonial Histories Ser.). (ENG., Illus.). 224p. (C). 155.00 ***(978-0-415-50241-2(1))*** Routledge.

Harms, Daniel. The Long-Lost Friend: A 19th Century American Grimoire. 2012. (ENG.). 312p. pap. 17.95 ***(978-0-7387-3254-1(0))*** Llewellyn Pubns.

Harold, Steven. Marketing Your Complimentary Ther. 3rd ed. 2008. (Illus.). 207p. 20.00 *(978-1-84528-268-4(X))* How To Books GBR. Dist: Parkwest Pubns., Inc.

Harold, Steven A. Marketing Your Complementary Therapy Practice. 4th rev. ed. 2011. (ENG., Illus.). 204p. pap. 30.00 *(978-1-84528-449-7(6))* How To Books GBR. Dist: Parkwest Pubns., Inc.

Hassan, Intan Idiana, et al. Complementary Alternative Medicines. 2011. 80p. pap. ***(978-3-8443-9971-4(2))*** Lambert Academic Publishing.

Haugen, David M., ed. Alternative Medicine. 2007. (Opposing Viewpoints Ser.). (ENG., Illus.). 222p. (YA). (gr. 10-12). pap. 39.70 *(978-0-7377-3820-9(0), LML02109-234559, Greenhaven Pr., Inc.)* Cengage Gale.

Hawkes, Joyce. Resonance: Nine Practices for Harmonious Health & Vitality. 2012. (ENG., Illus.). 240p. 24.95 ***(978-1-4019-2908-4(7))*** Hay Hse., Inc.

Healing Cancer Peacefully: When the Body's Not a Battlefield, It Can Tell You What It Needs. 2009. (ENG.). 300p. pap. 17.95 *(978-0-9823089-0-5(6))* Round House Pr., The.

Helms, Joseph M. Acupuncture Energetics: A Clinical Approach for Physicians. 2009. (ENG., Illus.). 759p. 175.00 *(978-1-58890-407-2(5))* Thieme Medical Pubs., Inc.

Henningsen, Janet J. How to Achieve Well-Being Using Your Senses. 2008. 164p. pap. 24.95 *(978-1-60610-180-3(3))* PublishAmerica, Inc.

Herriott, Alain. Supercharging Quantum Touch: Advanced Techniques. 2007. (ENG., Illus.). 240p. pap. 19.95 *(978-1-55643-654-3(8))* North Atlantic Bks.

Hill, John W. Natural Treatments for Genital Herpes, Cold Sores & Shingles. 2008. 180p. pap. 16.95 *(978-1-884979-05-7(X))* Clear Springs Pr.

Hill, Rachel Y. Nursing from the Inside-Out: Living & Nursing from the Highest Point of Your Consciousness. rev. ed. 2010. (Illus.). 298p. pap. 56.95 *(978-0-7637-6996-3(7))* Jones & Bartlett Learning, LLC.

Hills, Margaret. Curing Arthritis: More Ways to a Drug-Free Life. 2009. (ENG.). 182p. pap. 29.95 *(978-1-4128-1253-5(4))* Transaction Pubs.

Ho, Bernard & Lee, Aleta. Lord Liu Chun's Secrets of Longevity: 600 Years of Proven Cures. 2010. 188p. (ENG.). 26.95 *(978-1-4502-3534-1(4))*; pap. 16.95 *(978-1-4502-3532-7(8))* iUniverse, Inc.

Hodgson-Ruetz, Deborah. Do All Bugs Need Drugs? Conventional & Herbal Treatments of Common Ailments. 2011. 144p. 24.95 *(978-1-4502-6828-8(5))*; pap. 14.95 *(978-1-4502-6826-4(9))* iUniverse, Inc.

Hoeppner, Pamela. The Breast Stays Put -. 2008. 268p. per. 15.99 *(978-1-60477-103-9(8))* Xulon Pr., Inc.

Hoffman, Ronald L. How to Talk with Your Doctor, 1 vol. 2011. (ENG.). 272p. pap. ***(978-1-59120-289-9(2)***, 1319316) Basic Health Pubns., Inc.

Hoffman, Ronald L. & Fox, Barry. Alternative Cures That Really Work: For the Savvy Health Consumer-A Must-Have Guide to More Than 100 Food Remedies, Herbs, Supplements, & Healing Techniques. 2006. (Illus.). xi, 388p. *(978-1-59486-452-0(7))* Rodale Pr., Inc.

Horden, Peregrine. Hospitals & Healing from Antiquity to the Later Middle Ages. 2008. (Variorum Collected Studies). 352p. 165.00 *(978-0-7546-6181-8(4))* Ashgate Publishing Co.

Horowitz, Leonard G. LOVE the Real Da Vinci CODE. l.t. ed. 2007. (Illus.). 206p. im. lthr. 22.85 *(978-0-923550-66-0(6))* Tetrahedron Publishing LLC.

Hoxsey, Harry. Hoxsey Therapy: When Natural Cures for Cancer Became Illegal; the Authobiography of Harry Hoxsey, ND. 2009. 322p. pap. 19.95 *(978-1-929661-32-9(0))* Transpersonal Publishing.

Huffines, LaUna. Curate Con la Luz. (SPA.). 288p. *(978-84-7927-161-9(2))* Robinbk., Ediciones S.L. ESP. Dist: Lectorum Pubns., Inc.

Human Outcry: Chapbook Collection, 12 vols. Incl. Friends: Two Levels of Consciousness. Mayer, T. Y. pap. 10.00 *(978-1-889008-01-1(X))*; Inside Out Words. Lustig, Laura J. pap. 10.00 *(978-1-889008-07-3(9))*; Love. Smith, Kathleen M. & Mayer, T. Y. pap. 10.00 *(978-1-889008-02-8(8))*; Suddenly Assume. Avery, Pearl. pap. 10.00 *(978-1-889008-08-0(7))*; (Illus.). 20p. 1996. 19.99 *(978-1-889008-06-6(0))* Projects, Inc.

Humar, Yamile. Virtudes Silenciosas de las Plantas. 2008. (SPA., Illus.). 192p. pap. 14.95 *(978-958-709-295-0(3))* Circulo de Lectores S.A. COL. Dist: Random Hse., Inc.

Hungerford, Carole. The Good Body Guide. 2009. (ENG., Illus.). 516p. pap. 17.95 *(978-0-7145-3171-7(5))* Boyars, Marion Pubs., Ltd. GBR. Dist: Consortium Bk. Sales & Distribution.

Iannuzzi-Sucich, Michele & Sanoski, Cynthia A. Herbal Notes: Complementary & Alternative Medicine Pocket Guide. 2011. (Illus.). 288p. spiral bd. 34.95 *(978-0-8036-2049-0(7))* Davis, F. A. Co.

Ingram, Cass. The Respiratory Solution. 2009. (ENG.). 238p. pap. 19.95 *(978-1-931078-32-0(7))* Knowledge Hse. Pubs.

Institute of Medicine. Integrative Medicine & the Health of the Public: A Summary of the February 2009 Summit. 2009. (ENG.). 250p. pap. 52.00 *(978-0-309-13901-4(5))* National Academies Pr.

Inzerillo, John. Passion Beyond Pain. 2008. 232p. 18.95 *(978-0-89334-453-5(2), Humanics Learning)*; pap. 18.95 *(978-0-89334-454-2(0))* Humanics Publishing Group.

Jadresic, Enrique. When Blushing Hurts: Overcoming Abnormal Facial Blushing. 2008. 108p. pap. 12.95 *(978-0-595-52157-9(6))* iUniverse, Inc.

Jeanteur, Philippe. Alternative Splicing & Disease. 2006. (Progress in Molecular & Subcellular Biology Ser.: Vol. 44). (Illus.). xii, 257p. 189.00 *(978-3-540-34448-3(9), 3540344489)* Springer.

Jell, Andreas. Healthy with Tachyon. 144p. 12.95 *(978-0-914955-58-0(6))* Lotus Pr.

Jewell, Penelope. A Master's Path. 508p. 15.50 *(978-0-9664072-3-5(7))* Adirondack Pr.

Judge, William Q. & Crosbie, Robert. The Laws of Healing: Physical & Metaphysical. 2011. 42p. 35.95 ***(978-1-258-00485-9(2))*** Literary Licensing, LLC.

Kailin, David C. Quality in Complementary & Alternative Medicine. 2006. (Illus.). 519p. 74.95 *(978-1-891426-02-5(8))* CMS Pr.

Kamhi, Ellen. Alternative Medicine Magazine's Definitive Guide to Weight Loss: 10 Healthy Ways to Permanently Shed Unwanted Pounds. 2nd rev. ed. 2007. (ENG., Illus.). 328p. pap. 18.95 *(978-1-58761-259-6(3), Celestial Arts)* Ten Speed Pr.

Kayne, Steven B. Complementary & Alternative Medicine, 2nd Edition. 2nd rev. ed. 2008. (Illus.). 448p. pap. 59.99 *(978-0-85369-763-3(9))* Pharmaceutical Pr. GBR. Dist: Smith Fulfillment Services.

—FASTtrack: Complementary & Alternative Medicine. 2008. (Illus.). 160p. pap. 36.99 *(978-0-85369-774-9(4))* Pharmaceutical Pr. GBR. Dist: Smith Fulfillment Services.

Kemper, Kathi J. Mental Health, Naturally: The Family Guide to Holistic Care for a Healthy Mind & Body. 2010. (ENG.). 600p. pap. 19.95 *(978-1-58110-310-6(7))* American Academy of Pediatrics.

Kenton, Leslie. Love Affair. 2011. (ENG., Illus.). 384p. 27.99 *(978-0-312-65908-0(3))* St. Martin's Pr.

Koen, Benjamin, et al, eds. The Oxford Handbook of Medical Ethnomusicology, 1 vol. 2011. (ENG., Illus.). 570p. pap. 45.00 *(978-0-19-975626-1(0))* Oxford Univ. Pr., Inc.

Koen, Benjamin D., et al, eds. The Oxford Handbook of Medical Ethnomusicology, 1 vol. 2008. (ENG., Illus.). 576p. 150.00 *(978-0-19-533707-5(7))* Oxford Univ. Pr., Inc.

Koopsen, Cyndie & Young, Caroline. Integrative Health: A Holistic Approach for Health Professionals. 2008. 359p. pap. 76.95 *(978-0-7637-5761-8(6))* Jones & Bartlett Learning, LLC.

Korn, Leslie E. Treating & Preventing Diabetes, Naturally... 2010. 242p. pap. 24.95 *(978-0-557-06821-0(5))* Lulu Enterprises Inc.

Kortum, John Christopher. The Kortum Technique: How to Access the Human Body's Natural Blueprint for Health & Healing. 2010. 282p. 29.99 *(978-1-4415-9692-5(5))* Xlibris Corp.

Kostovic, Nick. Universe God's Jewel. 2008. 284p. pap. 25.95 *(978-1-4327-1790-2(1))* Outskirts Pr., Inc.

Kratky, Karl W. Complementary Medicine Systems: Comparison & Integration. 2008. (Illus.). xiv, 297p. 98.00 *(978-1-60456-475-4(X))* Nova Science Pubs., Inc.

Kunikiyo, Marvin. Revolutionizing Your Health: Getting Beyond the Programming of Big Medicine. 2010. 219p. pap. 19.95 *(978-1-935586-06-7(8))* Aviva Publishing.

Kurinij, Matthew. 50 Keys to Health. 2008. 300p. pap. 19.95 *(978-1-4357-1849-4(6))* Lulu Enterprises Inc.

Lake, James. Integrative Mental Health Care. 2009. (ENG.). 382p. instr.'s gde. ed., instr.'s hndbk. ed. 34.95 *(978-0-393-70536-2(6), 70536)* Norton, W. W. & Co., Inc.

Larimore, Walt & O'Mathuna, Dónal. Alternative Medicine, 1 vol. rev. exp. ed. 2006. (ENG., Illus.). 512p. (gr. 13). pap. 22.99 *(978-0-310-26999-1(7))* Zondervan.

Larson, Christine A. Alternative Medicine, 1 vol. 2006. (Health & Medical Issues Today Ser.). (Illus.). 240p. 45.00 *(978-0-313-33718-5(7), GR3718, Greenwood Pr.)* Greenwood Publishing Group, Inc.

LaValle, James B. Green Immunity Boosters: Botanicals for Immunity; Beating Colds, Influenza, & Other Germs with Olive Leaf Extract, ARA-Larix, & Andrographis. 2009. 124p. pap. 8.95 *(978-0-7570-0321-9(4))* Square One Pubs.

Lazar, Alan M. & Breecher, Maury M. Beyond the Knife: Alternatives to Surgery. 2011. 136p. 23.95 ***(978-1-4620-1768-3(1))***; pap. 13.95 ***(978-1-4620-1767-6(3))*** iUniverse, Inc.

Lea, Frank. Creative Mindpower Techniques for Healing Yourself & Others: Featuring unique & exclusive bodily healing Methods. 2011. 244p. pap. 16.26 *(978-1-4269-4839-8(5))* Trafford Publishing.

Lee, Ilchi. Healing Chakras: Awaken Your Body's Energy System for Complete Health, Happiness & Peace. 2009. (Illus.). 144p. pap. 21.95 *(978-1-935127-04-8(7))* BEST Life Media.

Leung, Ping-Chung & Fong, Harry, eds. Alternative Treatment for Cancer. 2008. (Annals of Traditional Chinese Medicine Ser.). (Illus.). 363p. 139.00 *(978-981-270-929-5(0))* World Scientific Publishing Co., Inc.

Levinsohn, Sidney H. Witness a Miracle - Your Own: The Fastest Way to Turn Your Life & Health Around!: 12 New Scientific Discoveries That Can Slow down, Stop & Even Reverse Serious Illness-Naturally! 2007. 272p. per. 15.95 *(978-1-932472-63-9(0))* Nodin Pr.

Lewis, Angie. Sugar Overload Syndrome - Healing Mental & Physical Disorders Naturally. 2009. 179p. pap. 17.98 *(978-0-578-01298-8(7))* Heaven Ministries.

Lewith, George Thomas, et al, eds. Clinical Research in Complementary Therapies: Principles, Problems & Solutions. 2nd ed. 2010. (ENG., Illus.). 426p. (C). pap. 79.95 *(978-0-443-06956-7(5), Churchill Livingstone)* Elsevier - Health Sciences Div.

Life Extension Foundation. Disease Prevention & Treatment. Segala, Melanie & Lea, Carolyn, eds. 5th rev. ed. 2008. (ENG.). 1700p. 37.95 *(978-0-9658777-8-7(7), 993-005)* Life Extension.

Lubeck, Walter. Reiki: La Farmacia en Casa. 2010. 176p. pap. *(978-84-7808-743-3(5))* Sirio, Editorial S.A.

Maccaro, Janet. Fabulous at 50: Redefining Midlife - Body, Mind, & Spirit. 2007. (ENG.). 224p. 19.99 *(978-1-59979-167-8(6), Siloam Pr.)* Charisma Media.

MacEoin, Beth. Total Health. xi, 196p. pap. 15.99 *(978-0-340-74582-3(7), Hodder & Stoughton)* Hodder General Publishing Div. GBR. Dist: Trafalgar Square Publishing.

Madan, S. C. Welcome Homeopathy. 2010. 150p. pap. *(978-81-223-1137-2(7))* Mahal, Pustak Pubs., Booksellers & Order Suppliers.

Maizes, Victoria & Low Dog, Tieraona, eds. Integrative Women's Health, 1 vol. 2010. (ENG., Illus.). 576p. 49.95 *(978-0-19-537881-8(4))* Oxford Univ. Pr., Inc.

Mantle, Fiona & Tiran, Denise. A-Z of Complementary & Alternative Medicine: A Guide for Health Professionals. 2009. (ENG., Illus.). 272p. pap. 32.95 *(978-0-443-10329-2(1), Churchill Livingstone)* Elsevier - Health Sciences Div.

Manz, Hedwig. The Art of Cupping. 2008. (ENG., Illus.). 182p. pap. 54.99 *(978-3-13-148601-1(5))* Thieme Medical Pubs., Inc.

May Loo Staff & Loo, May. Integrative Medicine for Children. 2008. (ENG., Illus.). 536p. 75.95 *(978-1-4160-2299-2(6), Saunders)* Elsevier - Health Sciences Div.

Mayo Clinic Staff. Book of Alternative Medicine: Integrating the Best of Natural Therapies with Conventional Medicine. 2nd rev. exp. ed. 2010. (ENG., Illus.). 208p. 25.95 *(978-1-60320-836-9(4))* Time Home Entertainment, Inc.

McBee, Lucia. Mindfulness-Based Elder Care: Communicating & Embodying Mindfulness for Frail Elders & Their Caregivers. 2008. 40.00 *(978-0-8261-1511-9(X))* Springer Publishing Co., Inc.

McClean, Stuart & Green, Michael K. How Do We Create a Philosophical Cosmos for Acting Socially & Being Happy? Marginal Medicine & Mainstream Concerns. 2006. 280p. (C). 109.95 *(978-0-7734-5667-9(8))* Mellen, Edwin Pr., The.

McKay, Noah. Wellness at Warp Speed: Your Health, Your Destiny, Your Choice. 2007. (ENG., Illus.). 128p. 24.95 *(978-1-60109-108-6(7))* Mandala Publishing.

McNeil, James. Medicine Within Our Bodies. 2007. (Illus.). 148p. 17.99 net. *(978-0-9795183-1-7(8))* Little Nine Heaven Production.

Mehl, Lewis E. & Peterson, Gayle H. Mind Body Medicine Vol. 1: The Stages of Healing. (Frontiers of Consciousness Ser.). (Illus.). 250p. *(978-0-8290-2468-5(9))* Irvington Pubs.

Mehl-Madrona, Lewis. Narrative Medicine: The Use of History & Story in the Healing Process. 2007. (ENG.). 1p. per. 20.00 *(978-1-59143-065-0(8))* Bear & Co.

Meidinger, Werner. El Poder Curativo del Limon. (SPA.). 186p. *(978-84-7927-380-4(1))* Robinbk., Ediciones S.L. ESP. Dist: Lectorum Pubns., Inc.

Micozzi, Marc S. Fundamentals of Complementary & Alternative Medicine. 4th ed. 2010. (ENG., Illus.). 624p. 78.95 *(978-1-4377-0577-5(4), Saunders)* Elsevier - Health Sciences Div.

Micozzi, Mark S., ed. Current Review of Complementary Medicine. 2010. 184p. pap. 79.95 *(978-1-57340-997-1(9), 1573409979)* Current Medicine Group LLC.

Milesson, Karen Y. Our Energetic Evolution in Healing: Free Yourself from the Unseen Forces That Can Make You Sick. 2007. 400p. 29.95 *(978-0-9774171-0-0(7))* Energetics Research Publishing.

Milford, Francine. Tuning Forks & Arthritis. 2008. 60p. pap. 12.99 *(978-1-4357-2886-8(6))* Lulu Enterprises Inc.

Milovidov, Grigorii. Energiia Zhizni V Tvoikh Rukakh: Ezotericheskaia Anatomiia I Fiziologiia Cheloveka, Znakomstvo S Ezotericheskoi Astrologiei I Khirologiei Mudry. 2008. (RUS., Illus.). v, 315p. pap. *(978-0-9791791-9-8(X))* Seagul Pr.

Mindell, Earl & Hopkins, Virginia. Prescription Alternatives: Hundreds of Safe, Natural, Prescription-Free Remedies to Restore & Maintain Your Health. 4th ed. 2009. (ENG.). 448p. pap. 21.95 *(978-0-07-160031-6(0), 0071600310)* McGraw-Hill Cos., The.

Mirchandani, Moti. Alternative & Complementary Therapies. 2007. 308p. per. 29.95 *(978-0-9719916-0-6(X))* Traderoute Pubns.

Mischoulon, David & Rosenbaum, Jerrold F., eds. Natural Medications for Psychiatric Disorders: Considering the Alternatives. 2nd rev. ed. 2008. (ENG., Illus.). 336p. pap. 64.99 *(978-0-7817-6762-0(8))* Lippincott Williams & Wilkins.

Monzon, Guadalupe. Asmu, Su Cura Natural.Tr. of Asma Home Cure. (SPA.). 4.98 *(978-968-15-0467-0(4))* Editores Mexicanos Unidos MEX. Dist: Lectorum Pubns., Inc.

Moon, Norman F. Terror in the Medical Office. 29.50 *(978-1-57529-066-9(9))* Kabel Pubs.

Moore, Ronnie & McClean, Stuart, eds. Folk Healing & Health Care Practices in Britain & Ireland: Stethescopes, Wands or Crystals. 2010. (EH Ser.). 288p. 90.00 *(978-1-84545-672-6(6))* Berghahn Bks., Inc.

Morelli, Vincent & Zoorob, Roger. Integrative Medicine in Primary Care Pt. 2: Disease States & Body Systems - An Issue of Primary Care Clinics in Office Practice. 2010. (Clinics: Internal Medicine Ser.: 37-2). (ENG., Illus.). xiv, 214p. 95.00 *(978-1-4377-1866-9(3), Saunders)* Elsevier - Health Sciences Div.

Morrison, Michael E. A Path Less Conventional. 2008. (Illus.). 100p. pap. *(978-1-84748-380-5(1))* Athena Pr.

Moser, Isabelle A. How & When to Be Your Own Doctor. 2009. (ENG.). 252p. pap. 16.95 *(978-1-4385-2689-8(X), Book Jungle)* Standard Pubns., Inc.

Motyka, Elizabeth, et al. The Rapid Recovery: Your Complete Guide to Faster Healing after Surgery. 2006. (ENG., Illus.). 288p. pap., instr.'s hndbk. ed. 15.99 *(978-0-06-074825-8(7), William Morrow Paperbacks)* HarperCollins Pubs.

Mullin, Gerard. Integrative Gastroenterology. 2011. (ENG.). 712p. 49.95 *(978-0-19-537110-9(0))* Oxford Univ. Pr., Inc.

Murray, Michael T. What the Drug Companies Won't Tell You & Your Doctor Doesn't Know: The Alternative Treatments That May Change Your Life — And the Prescriptions That Could Harm You. 2010. (ENG.). 352p. pap. 15.00 *(978-1-4165-4939-0(0), Beyond Words/Atria Bks.)* Atria Bks.

Natural Standard. Natural Standard Herb & Supplement Guide: An Evidence-Based Reference. 2nd ed. 2010. (ENG., Illus.). 896p. 78.95 *(978-0-323-07295-3(X), Mosby)* Elsevier - Health Sciences Div.

Nelson, Bradley B. The Emotion Code. 2007. 408p. pap. 19.95 *(978-0-9795537-0-7(9))* Wellness Unmasked Publishing.

Neustadt, John & Pieczenik, Steve. A Revolution in Health Part: How to Take Charge of Your Health. 2009. 188p. pap. 24.95 *(978-0-595-53216-2(0))* iUniverse, Inc.

New, Old, & Forgotten Remedies: Papers by Many Writers. 386p. reprint ed. 98.00 *(978-0-7222-9986-9(9))* Library Reprints, Inc.

Newman, Robert & Miller, Ruth L. Calm Healing: Methods for a New Era of Medicine. 2006. (ENG.). 400p. pap. 17.95 *(978-1-55643-626-0(2))* North Atlantic Bks.

Ni, Maoshing. Secrets of Self-Healing: Harness Nature's Power to Heal Common Ailments, Boost Vitality, & Achieve Optimum Wellness. 2009. *(978-1-60529-839-9(5))* Rodale Pr., Inc.

Null, Gary. Get Healthy Now! With Gary Null: Prevention, Treatment & Healthy Living. 2nd ed. 2006. (ENG.). 1152p. per. 29.95 *(978-1-58322-753-4(9))* Seven Stories Pr.

O'Donnell, Tony, compiled by. Miracle Red Super Foods that Heal. 2007. 168p. pap. 24.99 *(978-0-9801173-1-8(3))* GW Health.

Oliver, Charles. Complete Manual Therapy: Chiropractic & Physical Therapy in One Approach. 2010. 413p. pap. 79.00 *(978-0-692-00786-0(5))* Integrative Pr. LLC.

Oness, Karen & Culbert, Timothy. Integrative Pediatrics. 2009. (Weil Integrative Medicine Library). (ENG., Illus.). 720p. 49.95 *(978-0-19-538472-7(5))* Oxford Univ. Pr., Inc.

The Optimal Life: Empowering Health, Healing & Longevity. 2008. (Illus.). 255p. per. 24.95 *(978-0-9800116-0-9(4))* Wellness Communications.

Pecurar, Mihail & Krejci, Gavril, eds. Garlic Consumption & Health. 2009. (Food & Beverage Consumption & Health Ser.). 129.00 *(978-1-60741-642-5(5), Nova Biomedical Bks.)* Nova Science Pubs., Inc.

Pagano, John. Healing Psoriasis: The Natural Alternative. 2008. (ENG., Illus.). 352p. pap. 16.95 *(978-0-470-26726-4(7), Wiley)* Wiley, John & Sons, Inc.

Pelletier, Kenneth R. The Best Alternative Medicine. 2007. (ENG.). 448p. pap. 28.95 *(978-1-4165-7521-4(9))* Simon & Schuster.

Perry, Wayne. Sound Medicine: The Complete Guide to Healing with the Human Voice. 2007. (ENG., Illus.). 1p. pap. 21.99 *(978-1-56414-970-1(6), New Page Bks.)* Career Pr., Inc.

Perspectives on Complementary & Alternative Medicines. 2011. 124.00 *(978-1-84816-556-4(0))* World Scientific Publishing Co., Inc.

Phatlane, Stephens. Poverty, Medicine & Disease in South Africa: The Era of High Apartheid, 1948 to 1976. 2008. 292p. pap. *(978-3-639-10582-7(6))* VDM Verlag Dr. Mueller e.K.

Physician's Guide to Alternative Medicine. Vol. IX. 2007. per. *(978-1-933040-77-6(7))* Vol. II. 2009. mass mkt. *(978-1-934863-27-5(0))* AHC Media, LLC.

Pizzorno, Joseph E., Jr. & Murray, Michael T. Textbook of Natural Medicine. 4th ed. 2012. (ENG., Illus.). 2208p. 275.00 ***(978-1-4377-2333-5(0)***, Churchill Livingstone) Elsevier - Health Sciences Div.

Pizzorno, Joseph E., Jr., et al. The Clinician's Handbook of Natural Medicine. 2nd ed. 2007. (ENG., Illus.). 832p. per. 63.95 *(978-0-443-06723-5(6), Churchill Livingstone)* Elsevier - Health Sciences Div.

Polak, Milan & Michaud, Elissa, eds. Los Angeles Healer's Guide: The Best of Holistic Care. 2006. 298p. per. 9.95 *(978-1-4276-0223-7(9))* Aardvark Global Publishing.

Pop, Micheal M. Misunderstanding Addiction: Overcoming Myth, Mysticism, & Misdirection in the Addictions Treatment Industry. 2010. 348p. 33.95 *(978-1-4502-0779-9(0))*; (ENG.). pap. 23.95 *(978-1-4502-0777-5(4))* iUniverse, Inc.

Popovkina, G. S. Znakhari I Znakharstvo U Vostochnykh Slavian Iuga Dalnego Vostoka Rossii. 2008. (RUS., Illus.). 199p. pap. (978-5-8044-0921-1(2)) Dal'nauka, Izdatel'stvo Dalnevostomnogo otdelenija RAN.

Pressman, Alan. Integrative Medicine. Date not set. pap. (978-0-312-27024-7(0), St. Martin's Griffin) St. Martin's Pr.

Radha, Swami Sivananda. The Yoga of Healing. 2006. 117p. pap. 10.95 (978-1-932018-17-2(4)) Timeless Bks.

Reader's Digest Editors. Food Cures: Fight Disease with Your Fork! 2008. (ENG.). 375p. (gr. 12). 17.95 (978-0-7621-0797-1(9)) Reader's Digest Assn., Inc., The.

Reissner, Adam J. Conquering Cancer: Pursuing a Cure via Integral Medicine. 2010. 316p. 32.95 (978-1-4502-2458-1(X)); (ENG.). pap. 22.95 (978-1-4502-2456-7(3)) iUniverse, Inc.

Rindfleisch, J. Adam. Integrative Medicine, Part I: Incorporating Complementary/Alternative Modalities, an Issue of Primary Care Clinics in Office Practice. 2010. (Clinics: Internal Medicine Ser.: 37-1). (ENG., Illus.). 95.00 (978-1-4377-1865-2(5), Saunders) Elsevier - Health Sciences Div.

Rocher, Dominique. Los Remedios Naturales del Dr. Gireaux (Natural Remedies of Doctor Gireaux) (SPA.). 236p. (978-84-8019-262-0(3)) Paidotribo, Editorial S.L.

Rolle, Reno R. 101 Amazing Cures: The Guide for Relieving Ailments & Disease Naturally. 2007. 224p. pap. 14.95 (978-1-57174-508-8(4)) Hampton Roads Publishing Co., Inc.

Rosenbaum, Elana. Being Well (Even When You're Sick) Mindfulness Practices for People with Cancer & Other Serious Illnesses. 2012. (ENG.). 144p. pap. 14.95 **(978-1-61180-000-5(5))** Shambhala Pubns., Inc.

Ross, Anamaria. The Anthropology of Alternative Medicine. 2012. (ENG.). 192p. (C). 99.95 **(978-1-84520-801-1(3))**; pap. 34.95 **(978-1-84520-802-8(1))** Berg Pubs. GBR. Dist: Macmillan.

Roth, Marilyn A. & Kobayashi, Karen M. Complementary & Alternative Medicine among Chinese Canadians. 2010. (Public Health in the 21st Century Ser.). (Illus.). vii, 62p. pap. 43.00 (978-1-61728-014-6(3), Nova Biomedical Bks.) Nova Science Pubs., Inc.

Rothbart, Brian A. & Penzabene, Linda F. Forever Free from Chronic Pain: The Pain Sufferer's Guide to Getting Your Life Back. 2009. 260p. 34.95 (978-1-60005-128-9(6)) Happy About.

Ruggie, Mary, et al. The Practice of Integrative Medicine: A Legal & Operational Guide. annot. ed. 2007. 201p. 55.00 (978-0-8261-0307-9(3)) Springer Publishing Co., Inc.

Sach, Penelope. Natural Children's Health. 2007. (ENG.). 176p. (gr. 12-18). 14.00 (978-0-14-300265-9(1), Penguin Global) Penguin Group (USA) Inc.

Saeger, Jan & Rudolph, Lewis. Building a Healthy Business: For Massage & Alternative Healthcare Practices. 2009. (ENG., Illus.). 272p. (C). pap. 73.67 (978-0-07-340191-1(9), 0073401919) McGraw-Hill Higher Education.

Saloff, Jamie L. Transformational Healing W/CD: Five Surprisingly Simple Keys Designed to Redirect Your Life Toward Wellness, Purpose, & Prosperity. 2006. (Illus.). 428p. per. 34.95 (978-0-9740642-1-5(1)) Saloff Enterprises.

Sanderson, Helen & Lewis, Jaimee. A Practical Guide to Delivering Personalisation: Person-Centred Practice in Health & Social Care. 2012. (ENG., Illus.). 208p. pap. **(978-1-84905-194-1(1))** Kingsley, Jessica Ltd.

Saputo, Len & Belitsos, Byron. A Return to Healing: Radical Health Care Reform & the Future of Medicine. 2009. 267p. 21.95 (978-1-57983-052-6(8)) Origin Pr.

Saxena, Praveen K., ed. Development of Plant-Based Medicines: Conservation, Efficacy & Safety: Conservation, Efficacy & Safety. 2010. 280p. pap. 229.00 (978-90-481-5675-7(0), 9048156750) Springer.

Scheid, Volker & MacPherson, Hugh, eds. Integrating East Asian Medicine into Contemporary Healthcare. 2011. (ENG., Illus.). 256p. pap. 49.95 **(978-0-7020-3021-5(X)**, Churchill Livingstone) Elsevier - Health Sciences Div.

Schenck, David & Churchill, Larry R. Healers: Extraordinary Clinicians at Work, 1 vol. 2011. (ENG., Illus.). 272p. 35.00 (978-0-19-973538-9(7)) Oxford Univ. Pr., Inc.

Shaheen, Dr. Ghazala, et al. Phytotherapy. 2011. 288p. pap. **(978-3-8443-1399-4(0))** Lambert Academic Publishing.

Shahzad, Muhammad. Immunomodulatory Role of Black Seed Oil. 2010. 84p. pap. (978-3-639-21677-6(6)) VDM Verlag Dr. Mueller e.K.

Shapiro, Rose. Suckers: How Alternative Medicine Makes Fools of Us All. 2009. (ENG., Illus.). 304p. pap. 16.95 (978-0-09-952286-7(1)) Random Hse. GBR. Dist: Independent Pubs. Group.

Shea, Michael J. Biocynamic Craniosacral Therapy, 2 vols., Vol. 1. 2007. (ENG., Illus.). 560p. pap. 39.95 (978-1-55643-591-1(6)) North Atlantic Bks.

Sheen, Brian. A Voice of Reason: Alternative Medicine for Healing ADD/ADHD Without Medication - Eleven Case Studies. 2007. per. 29.95 (978-1-928787-20-4(7)) Quan Publishing.

Shibata, Yoshiharu & Wu, Jean. Kampo Treatment for Climacteric Disorders. (Illus.). 274p. (Orig.). (C). 29.95 (978-0-912111-51-3(8)) Paradigm Pubns.

Silva, Gabriel & Sosa Salinas, Ulises. Revolución Terapéutica de las Pirámides. 2009. (SPA.). 328p. pap. 44.15 (978-1-4092-9621-8(0)) Lulu Enterprises Inc.

Silverstein, H. Robert. Maximum Healing: Optimize Your Natural Ability to Heal. 2010. 288p. pap. 16.95 (978-1-55643-922-3(9)) North Atlantic Bks.

Simester, Lisha. The Natural Health Bible: Stay Well, Live Longer. 2007. (Illus.). 288p. pap., pap. 24.95 (978-1-84400-527-7(5)) Quadrille Publishing, Ltd. GBR. Dist: Ingram Pub. Services.

Singh, Simon & Ernst, Edzard. Trick or Treatment: The Undeniable Facts about Alternative Medicine. 2008. (ENG., Illus.). 352p. 25.95 (978-0-393-06661-6(4), 6661) Norton, W. W. & Co., Inc.

Skenderi, Gazmend. Concise Herbal Handbook: A Quick Reference to Constituents, Properties, Uses, Dosages, & Cautions of over 800 Herbs, Spices, Essential Oils, Lipids, Etc. 2nd rev. enl. ed. 2007. Orig. Title: Herbal Vade Mecum. (978-0-9713209-4-9(2)); pap. (978-0-9713209-3-2(4)) Herbacy Pr.

—Handbook of Medicinal Plants & Botanicals: Plants (A to Z by Genera & Species) & Medicinal, Flavoring & Fragrant Botanicals (Constituents, Properties, Uses, Cautions, Etc.) 2009. (978-0-9713209-5-6(0)) Herbacy Pr.

—Self-Help Herbal Healing: A Guide to Common Disorders & Healing Herbs of Choice. 2008. pap. (978-0-9713209-0-1(X)) Herbacy Pr.

Smith, Alan E. Unbreak Your Health: The Complete Guide to Complementary & Alternative Therapies. 2007. (ENG., Illus.). 212p. per. 19.95 (978-1-932690-36-1(0)) Loving Healing Pr., Inc.

Snyder, Lois, ed. Complementary & Alternative Medicine: Ethics, the Patient, & the Physician. 2007. (Biomedical Ethics Reviews Ser.: Vol. 2007). (Illus.). 241p. 119.00 (978-1-58829-584-2(2), 1588295842) Humana Pr.

Snyder, Robert Ed., et al. Complementary & Alternative Therapies in Nursing. 6th ed. 2009. (978-0-8261-2428-9(3)) Springer.

Sointu, Eeva. Theorizing Complementary & Alternative Medicines: Wellbeing, Self, Gender & Class. 2012. (ENG., Illus.). 264p. 85.00 **(978-0-230-30931-9(3))** Palgrave Macmillan.

Spiegel, David & Lake, James, eds. Complementary & Alternative Treatments in Mental Health Care. 2006. (Illus.). 478p. 76.00 (978-1-58562-202-3(8), 62202) American Psychiatric Publishing, Inc.

Sporn, Stephen & Baer, Hans A. Naturopathy Around the World: Variations & Political Dilemmas of an Eclectic Heterdox Medical System. 2008. 79.00 (978-1-60692-590-4(3)) Nova Science Pubs., Inc.

Steiner, Rudolf. The Healing Process: Spirit, Nature, & Our Bodies. Creeger, Catherine E., tr. from GER. 2nd ed. 2010. (Collected Works of Rudolf Steiner: 319). (Illus.). 320p. pap. 25.00 (978-0-88010-641-2(7)) SteinerBooks, Inc.

Stengler, Mark & Balch, James F. Prescription for Natural Cures: A Self-Care Guide for Treating Health Problems with Natural Remedies Including Diet, Nutrition, Supplements, & Other Holistic Methods. 2nd rev. ed. 2011. (ENG., Illus.). 736p. pap. 24.95 (978-0-470-89177-3(7), Wiley) Wiley, John & Sons, Inc.

Stephenson, Clare. The Complementary Therapist's Guide to Conventional Medicine: A Textbook & Study Course. 2011. (ENG., Illus.). 752p. (C). 77.95 (978-0-7020-3428-2(2), Churchill Livingstone) Elsevier - Health Sciences Div.

Stinnett, Gay. A Measure of Joy: Opening to the Energy of Reiki. 2009. (ENG., Illus.). 95p. pap. 30.00 (978-1-934491-13-3(6)) Fresco Fine Art Pubns., LLC.

Stokker, Kathleen. Remedies & Rituals: Folk Medicine in Norway & the New Land. 2007. (Illus.). 260p. 29.95 (978-0-87351-576-4(5)) Minnesota Historical Society Pr.

Stoll, Walt & Diehl, Kathleen M. Beyond Disease Care: When Your TREATMENTS Fail to CURE You... the Truth about How to Prevent & Reverse Today's Most Common Chronic Conditions. 2007. (Illus.). 380p. pap. 19.95 (978-0-9653171-4-6(5)) Sunrise Health Coach Pubns.

Storizer, Anne L., et al. Introduction to Alternative & Complementary Therapies. 2007. 292p. (C). 175.00 (978-0-7890-2205-9(2)) Routledge.

Strand, Ray D. What Your Doctor Doesn't Know about Nutritional Medicine May Be Killing You, 0 vols. 2007. 256p. pap. 14.99 (978-0-7852-8883-1(X)) Nelson, Thomas Inc.

Strand, Ray D., et al. Lo Que su Medico Ignora Acerca de la Medecina Nutricional Puede Estarlo Metando. 2008. (ENG.). 276p. pap. 23.95 (978-2-922969-09-2(6)) Editions le mieux-etre CAN. Dist: AtlasBooks Distribution.

Strozier, Anne L. & Carpenter, Joyce. Introduction to Alternative & Complementary Therapies. Strozier, Anne L., ed. 2007. 297p. per. 58.95 (978-0-7890-2206-6(0)) Routledge.

Sutton, Amy, ed. Complementary & Alternative Medicine Sourcebook. 4th rev. ed. 2010. (Health Reference Ser.). lib. bdg. 93.00 (978-0-7808-1082-2(1)) Omnigraphics, Inc.

Tacey, David. Gods & Diseases. 2012. (ENG.). 256p. 99.00 **(978-0-415-52062-1(2))**; pap. 34.95 **(978-0-415-52063-8(0))** Routledge.

Tan, Joaquin G. Healing Ourselves from Medicine: How Anthroposophy Can Save Your Life. 2011. (ENG., Illus.). 321p. pap. 18.95 **(978-0-9832261-2-3(1))** Goldenstone Pr.

Tenney, MH, Louise. The Immune System. 2nd ed. 2011. (Woodland Health Ser.). 36p. pap. 4.95 **(978-1-58054-164-0(X))** Woodland Publishing, Inc.

Tombak, Mikhail. Cure the Incurable. 2nd ed. 2006. Orig. Title: Uleczyc Nieuleczalne. (POL.). 232p. per. 16.95 (978-0-9727328-3-3(7)) Healthy Life Pr., Inc.

Totilo, Rebecca Park. Healing Oils of Ancient Scripture. 2008. 64p. pap. 14.99 (978-0-9749115-6-4(9)) Rebecca at the Well Foundation.

Tovey, Philip, et al. Traditional, Complementary & Alternative Medicine & Cancer Care: An International Analysis of Grassroots Integration. 2007. (Illus.). 179p. per. 47.95 (978-0-415-35994-8(5)) Routledge.

Tramontana, Joseph. Hypnotically Enhanced Treatment for Addictions: Alcohol Abuse, Drug Abuse, Gambling, Weight Control, & Smoking Cessation. 2009. 160p. pap. (978-0-9823573-6-1(2)) Crown Hse. Publishing.

Trudeau, Kevin. More Natural Cures Revealed: Previously Censored Brand Name Products That Cure Disease. 2008. (ENG.). 368p. per. 7.99 (978-0-9787851-3-0(4)) Westview Pr.

—Natural Cures "They" Don't Want You to Know About. 2006. (ENG.). 592p. per. 7.99 (978-0-9755995-9-4(3)) Westview Pr.

Ulbricht, Catherine. Davis's Pocket Guide to Herbs & Supplements. 2010. (Illus.). 320p. pap. 24.95 (978-0-8036-2303-3(8)) Davis, F. A. Co.

van Wersch, et al. Complementary Medicine & Health Psychology. 2009. (ENG.). 184p. (C). 127.00 (978-0-335-22012-0(6), 0335220126); (Illus.). pap. 47.00 (978-0-335-22011-3(8), 0335220118) McGraw-Hill Education GBR. Dist: McGraw-Hill Cos., The.

Vasey, Christopher. The Healing Power of Fever. 2012. 144p. pap. 12.95 **(978-1-59477-437-9(4))** Inner Traditions International, Ltd.

Vogel, H. C. Nature Doctor: A Manual of Traditional & Complementary Medicine. (GER., Illus.). 704p. reprint ed. 29.98 (978-0-941683-27-2(3)) Instant Improvement, Inc.

Wait, Marianne. Extraordinary Cures: 56 Health Problems Solved! 2007. (Illus.). 192p. (978-0-7621-0788-9(X)) Reader's Digest Assn., Inc., The.

Walter de Gruyter & Co Staff, contrib. by. Pschyrembel Naturheilkunde und alternative Heilverfahren. 4th ed. 2011.Tr. of Pschyrembel Naturopathy. (GER., Illus.). 488p. 49.00 **(978-3-11-025112-8(4))** De Gruyter, Walter Inc.

Watson, Ronald Ross, ed. Complementary & Alternative Therapies & the Aging Population: An Evidence-Based Approach. 2008. (ENG., Illus.). 624p. 82.95 (978-0-12-374228-5(5), Academic Pr.) Elsevier Science & Technology Bks.

Weil, Andrew. Eight Weeks to Optimum Health: A Proven Program for Taking Full Advantage of Your Body's Natural Healing Power. rev. exp. ed. 2006. (ENG.). 320p. 24.95 (978-0-307-26492-3(0), Knopf) Knopf Doubleday Publishing Group.

—Salud Total en 8 Semanas: Un Programa Probado para Aprovechar al Maximo el Poder Curativo Natural de su Cuerpo. 2007. (Vintage Espanol Ser.). (ENG.). 416p. pap. 14.95 (978-0-307-27884-5(0), Vintage) Knopf Doubleday Publishing Group.

—8 Weeks to Optimum Health: A Proven Program for Taking Full Advantage of Your Body's Natural Healing Power. 2007. (ENG.). 320p. pap. 17.00 (978-0-345-49802-1(X), Ballantine Bks.) Random House Publishing Group.

Weintraub, Michael I., et al, eds. Complementary & Integrative Medicine in Pain Management. 2008. (Illus.). 440p. 69.00 (978-0-8261-2874-4(2)) Springer Publishing Co., Inc.

Welch, Claudia. Balance Your Hormones, Balance Your Life: Achieving Optimal Health & Wellness through Ayurveda, Chinese Medicine, & Western Science. 2011. (ENG.). 352p. pap. 18.00 (978-0-7382-1482-5(5)) Da Capo Pr., Inc.

Wells, Marcus. Soul Food for the Soul Sistah: Spiritual Nourishment for All Women of Color. 2010. 217p. pap. 15.99 (978-0-9830239-2-0(1)) tgx, llc.

—Take It off with Thermogenix: The Active Guide for Baby Boomers & Mature Adults. 2010. 270p. pap. 18.00 (978-0-9830239-0-6(5)) tgx, llc.

Whale, Jon. Naked Spirit. 2008. pap. **(978-0-9814851-6-4(2))** Clear Lotus Publishing.

Whittekin, Marie. Natural Alternatives to Nexium, Maalox, Tagament, Prilosec & Other Acid Blockers: What to Use to Relieve Acid Reflux, Heartburn, & Gastric Ailments. 2008. (ENG.). 160p. pap. 7.95 (978-0-7570-0210-6(2)) Square One Pubs.

Wiener, Jack. The Way of the 4th Toe: Into the Feeling Body. 2011. 84p. pap. 14.95 **(978-1-4620-2780-4(6))** iUniverse, Inc.

Wiesenauer, Markus. PhytoPraxis. 2nd ed. 2006. (Illus.). XXIV, 415p. pap. 29.95 (978-3-540-25620-5(2), 3540256202) Springer.

Wilen, Lydia & Wilen, Joan. Healing Remedies: More Than 1,000 Natural Ways to Relieve Common Ailments, from Arthritis & Allergies to Diabetes, Osteoporosis, & Many Others! 2008. (ENG.). 352p. pap. 16.00 (978-0-345-50335-0(X), Ballantine Bks.) Random House Publishing Group.

Wilmovsky, Brian. Dream Health: How to Live a Healthy, Balanced Life in an Unbalanced World. 2006. (ENG., Illus.). 224p. 19.99 (978-1-59979-021-3(1), Siloam Pr.) Charisma Media.

Wilson, Carol A. Healing Power Beyond Medicine. 2011. (ENG.). 363p. pap. 29.95 (978-1-84694-397-3(3)) Hunt, John Publishing Ltd. GBR. Dist: National Bk. Network.

Winston, David & Kuhn, Merrily A. Winston & Kuhn's Herbal Therapy & Supplements: A Scientific & Traditional Approach. 2nd rev. ed. 2007. (ENG., Illus.). 592p. per. 47.99 (978-1-58255-462-4(5)) Lippincott Williams & Wilkins.

Witt, Claudia & Linde, Klaus. Clinical Research: A Practical Training Book. 2012. (ENG.). pap. 84.95 **(978-0-7020-3476-3(2)**, Churchill Livingstone) Elsevier - Health Sciences Div.

Woloshyn, Tom. Beyond the Master Cleanse: The Year-Round Plan for Maximizing the Benefits of the Lemonade Diet. 2009. (ENG.). 160p. pap. 12.95 (978-1-56975-690-4(2)) Ulysses Pr.

—The Complete Master Cleanse: A Step-by-Step Guide to Maximizing the Benefits of the Lemonade Diet. 2007. (ENG., Illus.). 160p. pap. 13.95 (978-1-56975-613-3(9)) Ulysses Pr.

Wong, David Y. & Mitchell, Deborah. Healing What Hurts: Fast Ways to Get Safe Relief from Aches & Pains & Other Everyday Ailments, 1 vol. 2007. (ENG.). 320p. pap. (978-1-59120-192-2(6), 1269231) Basic Health Pubns., Inc.

Wong, William. 10 Natural Treatments You Haven't Heard of until Now: 10 Conditions with Proven Treatment Plans + Four Bonus Treatments. 2nd rev. ed. 2007. (Illus.). 190p. per. 16.95 (978-1-892264-22-0(6)) Timeless Voyager Pr.

Wood, Eve A. 10 Steps to Take Charge of Your Emotional Life: Overcoming Anxiety, Distress, & Depression Through Whole-Person Healing. (ENG.). 256p. 2008. per. 14.95 (978-1-4019-1122-5(6)) 2006. (Illus.). 24.95 (978-1-4019-1121-8(8)) Hay Hse., Inc.

Wright, Lloyd. Hepatitis C Free: Alternative Medicine vs. the Drug Industry: The People Speak. Bryan, Jessica, ed. pap. 15.95 (978-0-9676404-3-3(1)) Wright, Lloyd.

Wu, Chong. Reporting Complementary & Alternative Medicine. 2010. 96p. pap. (978-3-8383-6151-2(2)) Lambert Academic Publishing.

Yea, Steven & Friedman, Scott L. Regulation of the Krüppel-like Factor 6 Tumor Suppressor: Ras Promotes Cancer Cell Growth via Alternative Splicing-Mediated Inactivation of KLF6. 2008. 168p. pap. (978-3-639-10335-9(1)) VDM Verlag Dr. Mueller e.K.

Yeh, Timothy & Yeh, Pearl. The Perfume Medicine & its Perfumery Technology. 2007. per. (978-0-9652967-4-8(1)) Yeh's Ctr. of Natural Medicine, Inc.

Young, Jacqueline. Complementary Medicine for Dummies. 2007. (ENG., Illus.). 448p. pap. 21.99 (978-0-470-02625-0(1), For Dummies) Wiley, John & Sons, Inc.

Zago, Romano. Aloe Isn't Medicine, & Yet... It Cures! 2009. 192p. pap. 16.95 (978-1-4401-2576-8(7)) iUniverse, Inc.

Zhan, Mei. Other-Worldly: Making Chinese Medicine Through Transnational Frames. 2009. (ENG., Illus.). 256p. 84.95 (978-0-8223-4363-9(0)); pap. 23.95 (978-0-8223-4384-4(3)) Duke Univ. Pr.

Zhao, Xiaolan. Inner Beauty: Looking, Feeling & Being Your Best Through Traditional Chinese Healing. (ENG & CHI., Illus.). 320p. 2012. pap. 19.95 **(978-0-307-35881-3(X)**, Vintage Canada) 2011. 27.95 (978-0-307-35880-6(1), Random Hse CAN) Random Hse. of Canada, Ltd. CAN. Dist: Random Hse., Inc.

Zollman, Catherine, et al, eds. ABC of Complementary Medicine. 2nd rev. ed. 2008. (ABC Ser.: 41). (ENG., Illus.). 64p. pap. 47.95 (978-1-4051-3657-0(X)) Wiley, John & Sons, Inc.

Zuluaga, Maria. Headache, Orofacial Pain & Bruxism: Diagnosis & Multidisciplinary Approaches to Management. Selvaratnam, Peter et al, eds. 2009. (ENG., Illus.). 400p. 80.95 (978-0-443-10310-0(0), Churchill Livingstone) Elsevier - Health Sciences Div.

2007 ABC Coding Manual for Integrative Healthcare. annuals 8th ed. 2006. spiral bd. 99.95 net. (978-0-9740863-0-9(4)) ABC Coding Solutions/Alternative Link.

2007 Practitioner's Guide to Billable Interventions Using ABC Codes. annuals 8th ed. 2006. spiral bd. 129.95 net. (978-0-9740863-1-6(2)) ABC Coding Solutions/Alternative Link.

ALTERNATIVE MEDICINE—JUVENILE LITERATURE

Engdahl, Sylvia, ed. Alternative Therapies. 2011. (Current Controversies Ser.). 240p. (YA). (gr. 9-12). 39.70 (978-0-7377-5610-4(1)) Cengage Gale.

ALTERNATIVE MEDICINE—LAW AND LEGISLATION

Jaffe, Richard A. Galileo's Lawyer: Courtroom Battles in Alternative Health, Complementary Medicine & Experimental Treatments. 2008. 289p. pap. 18.00 (978-0-9801183-0-8(1)) Thumbs UP Pr.

Jesson, Lucinda E. & Tovino, Stacey A. Complementary & Alternative Medicine & the Law. 2010. 308p. pap. 40.00 (978-1-59460-767-7(2)) Carolina Academic Pr.

ALTERNATIVE MILITARY SERVICE

see National Service

ALTERNATIVE PUNISHMENTS

see Alternatives to Imprisonment

ALTERNATIVE SCHOOLS

see Free Schools

ALTERNATIVE VETERINARY MEDICINE

see also Holistic Veterinary Medicine

Bromiley, Mary W. Massage Techniques for Horse & Rider, 1 vol. 2010. (ENG., Illus.). 160p. 24.95 (978-1-84797-185-8(0)) Crowood Pr., Ltd. GBR. Dist: Independent Pubs. Group.

Devi, Lila. Flower Essences for Animals: Remedies for Helping the Pets You Love. 2010. (ENG.). 237p. pap. 14.95 (978-1-56589-100-5(7)) Crystal Clarity Pubs.

Homedes, Enric. The Handbook of Bach Flower Remedies for Animals. Kai, Daniel, tr. from SPA. 2011. (ENG., Illus.). 256p. pap. 27.95 (978-1-84819-075-7(1)) Singing Dragon GBR. Dist: Kingsley, Jessica Ltd.

Messonnier, Shawn. Natural Health Bible for Dogs & Cats: Your A-Z Guide to over 200 Conditions, Herbs, Vitamins, & Supplements. 2008. (978-1-60529-947-1(2)) Rodale Pr., Inc.

Preston, Lisa. Natural Healing for Cats, Dogs, Horses, & Other Animals: 150 Alternative Therapies Available to Owners & Caregivers. 2012. (ENG., Illus.). 208p. pap. 14.95 **(978-1-61608-461-5(8)**, 608461) Skyhorse Publishing Co., Inc.

Scanlan, Nancy. Complementary Medicine for Veterinary Technicians & Nurses. 2011. (ENG., Illus.). 380p. pap. 52.99 (978-0-8138-1862-7(1), Wiley-Blackwell) Wiley, John & Sons, Inc.

Xie, Huisheng & Preast, Vanessa. Traditional Chinese Veterinary Medicine - Fundamental Principles. 2007. (Illus.). 639p. 149.00 (978-0-9720045-1-0(3)) Chi Institute of Chinese Medicine.

—Xie's Veterinary Acupuncture. 2007. (ENG., Illus.). 374p. 164.99 (978-0-8138-1247-2(X), Wiley-Blackwell) Wiley, John & Sons, Inc.

Xie, Huisheng & Preast, Vanessa, eds. Xie's Chinese Veterinary Herbology. 2010. (ENG., Illus.). 632p. 143.99 (978-0-8138-0369-2(1), Wiley-Blackwell) Wiley, John & Sons, Inc.

ALTERNATIVES TO IMPRISONMENT

see also Community-Based Corrections; Criminals—Rehabilitation; Fines (Penalties); Parole; Probation

Ben Zvi, Ehud & Levin, Christoph, eds. The Concept of Exile in Ancient Israel & its Historical Contexts. 2011. (Beihefte zur Zeitschrift fur die alttestamentliche Wissenschaft Ser.). (ENG., Illus.). XII, 388p. 210.00 **(978-3-11-173479-8(X))** De Gruyter, Walter Inc.

Berman, Greg, et al, eds. Documenting Results: Research on Problem-Solving Justice. 2007. 398p. per. 13.95 (978-0-9759505-1-7(7), 2,000) Ctr. for Court Innovation.
Blom-Cooper, Louis. The Penalty of Imprisonment: Why 60 per Cent of the Prison Population Should Not Be There. 2008. (ENG.). 128p. 29.95 (978-1-84706-153-9(2)) Continuum International Publishing Group, Ltd. GBR. Dist: National Bk. Network.
Brayford, Jo, et al, eds. What Else Works? Creative Work with Offenders. 2010. (ENG., Illus.). 304p. 89.95 (978-1-84392-767-9(5)); pap. 39.95 (978-1-84392-766-2(7)) Willan Publishing GBR. Dist: Taylor & Francis Group.
Collins, Catherine Fisher. The Imprisonment of African American Women: Causes, Experiences & Effects. 2nd rev. ed. 2010. (ENG., Illus.). 210p. pap. 39.95 (978-0-7864-3384-1(1)) McFarland & Co., Inc. Pubs.
Criminal Justice Reinvestment ACT of 2009, & the Honest Opportunity Probation with Enforcement (HOPE) Initiative ACT of 2009: Hearing Before the Subcommittee on Crime, Terrorism, & Homeland Security of the Committee on the Judiciary, House of Representatives, One Hundred Eleventh Congress, Second Session, on H.R. 4080 & H.R. 4055, May 11, 2010. 2010. (Illus.). iii, 198p. (978-0-16-087155-9(7), 552-070-41998-5) United States Government Printing Office.
Finkel, Stuart. On the Ideological Front: The Russian Intelligentsia & the Making of the Soviet Public Sphere. 2007. (ENG.). 346p. 55.00 (978-0-300-12241-1(1)) Yale Univ. Pr.
Gentes, Andrew A. Exile, Murder & Madness in Siberia, 1823-61. 2010. (ENG.). 304p. 89.00 (978-0-230-27326-9(2)) Palgrave Macmillan.
Green, Ross G. Justice in Aboriginal Communities: Sentencing Alternatives. (Illus.). 192p. pap. (978-1-895830-10-1(9)) Purich Publishing.
Jacobson, Michael. Downsizing Prisons: How to Reduce Crime & End Mass Incarceration. 2006. (ENG., Illus.). 304p. pap. 22.00 (978-0-8147-4291-4(2)) New York Univ. Pr.
Lankford, Ronnie D., ed. Alternatives to Prisons. 2012. (At Issue Ser.). (ENG.). 128p. (gr. 10-12). pap. 33.70 **(978-0-7377-5545-9(8)**, Greenhaven Pr., Inc.); (YA). (gr. 9-12). lib. bdg. 23.85 **(978-0-7377-5544-2(X))** Cengage Gale.
The Local Role of the U.S. Parole Commission: Increasing Public Safety, Reducing Recidivism, & Using Alternatives to Re-Incarceration in the District of Columbia: Hearing Before the Subcommittee on Federal Workforce, Postal Service, & the District of Columbia of the Committee on Oversight & Government Reform, House of Representatives, One Hundred Eleventh Congress, Second Session, February 3, 2010. 2010. iii, 81p. **(978-0-16-086837-5(8)**, 552-070-41751-6) United States Government Printing Office.
Oversight of State-Run Juvenile Correctional Facilities Known As Boot Camps: Hearing Before the Subcommittee on Crime, Terrorism, & Homeland Security of the Committee on the Judiciary, House of Representatives, One Hundred Tenth Congress, First Session, December 13, 2007. 2008. iii, 61p. (978-0-16-082107-3(X), 552-070-38254-2) United States Government Printing Office.
Padfield, Nicola, et al, eds. Release from Prison: European Policy & Practice. 2010. (ENG., Illus.). 480p. 89.95 (978-1-84392-741-9(1)) Willan Publishing GBR. Dist: Taylor & Francis Group.
Pates, Rebecca. The End of Punishment: Philosophical Considerations on an Institution. 132p. pap. 32.95 (978-3-631-56827-9(4)) Lang, Peter GmbH, Europaischer Verlag der Wissenschaften DEU. Dist: Lang, Peter Publishing, Inc.
Saleh-Hanna, Viviane. Colonial Systems of Control: Criminal Justice in Nigeria. 2008. (Alternative Perspectives in Criminology Ser.). (ENG., Illus.). 534p. (978-0-7766-0666-8(2)) Univ. of Ottawa Pr./Presses de l'Universite d'Ottawa.
Sarmento, José Augusto Nogueira. Direitos Humanos e Egressos Do Sistema Penitenciário. 2008. (POR.). 115p. (978-85-7803-002-5(8)) Paka-Tatu, Editora Ltda-Me.
Sevdiren, Öznur. Alternatives to Imprisonment in England & Wales, Germany & Turkey: A Comparative Study. 2011. (ENG., Illus.). xv, 282p. 139.00 (978-3-642-17350-9(0), 3642173500) Springer.
Wimsatt, William Upski & Counterpoint Staff. No More Prisons: Urban Life, Homeschooling, Hip-Hop Leadership, the Cool Rich Kids Movement, a Hitchhiker's Guide to Community Organizing, & Why Philanthropy Is the Greatest Art Form of the 21st Century! rev. ed. 2008. (ENG., Illus.). 192p. pap. 13.95 (978-1-59376-205-6(4), Soft Skull Pr.) Counterpoint LLC.
Youth Prison Reduction Through Opportunities, Mentoring, Intervention, Support, & Education (PROMISE) ACT: Hearing Before the Subcommittee on Crime, Terrorism, & Homeland Security of the Committee on the Judiciary, House of Representatives, One Hundred Eleventh Congress, First Session, on H.R. 1064, July 15, 2009. 2010. (Illus.). iv, 564p. (978-0-16-086175-8(6), 552-070-41275-1) United States Government Printing Office.

ALTGELD, JOHN PETER, 1847-1902

Altgeld, John P. The Mind & Spirit of John Peter Altgeld: Selected Writings & Addresses. Christman, Henry M., ed. (Essay Index Reprint Ser.). 185p. reprint ed. lib. bdg. 17.00 (978-0-8290-0801-2(2)) Irvington Pubs.

ALTITUDE, INFLUENCE OF

see also Anoxemia; Mountain Sickness

Aldashev, Almaz & Naeije, Robert, eds. Problems of High Altitude Medicine & Biology. 2007. (NATO Science for Peace & Security Series / NATO Science for Peace & Security Series A: Chemistry & Biology Ser.). (ENG., Illus.). viii, 306p. per. 99.00 (978-1-4020-6299-5(0), 1402062990); 316p. 219.00 (978-1-4020-6298-8(2)) Springer.
Baker, Paul T., ed. The Biology of High-Altitude Peoples. 2009. (International Biological Programme Synthesis Ser.). (ENG., Illus.). 372p. pap. 51.00 (978-0-521-11195-9(1)) Cambridge Univ. Pr.
Farris, Mike. The Altitude Experience Successful Trekking & Climbing above 8000 Feet: Successful Trekking & Climbing above 8,000 Feet. 2008. (How to Climb Ser.). (ENG., Illus.). 328p. pap. 19.95 (978-0-7627-4358-2(1), Falcon Guides) Globe Pequot Pr., The.
Milledge, James S., et al. High Altitude Medicine & Physiology. 4th ed. 2007. (ENG., Illus.). 480p. 149.50 (978-0-340-91344-4(4)) Hodder Arnold Pubs.
Neme, Gustavo. Cazadores-Recolectores de Altura en los Andes Meridionales. 2007. (SPA., Illus.). 152p. (C). pap. 82.50 (978-1-4073-0007-8(5)) British Archaeological Reports Ltd. GBR. Dist: Brown, David Bk. Co., The.
Roach, Robert C., et al, eds. Hypoxia: From Genes to the Bedside. 2010. (Advances in Experimental Medicine & Biology Ser.). 462p. pap. 179.00 (978-1-4419-3374-4(3), 1441933743) Springer.
Xi, Lei, ed. Intermittent Hypoxia: from Molecular Mechanisms to Clinical Applications. 2009. (Physiology - Laboratory & Clinical Research Ser.). (Illus.). xxxi, 615p. 89.00 (978-1-60876-127-2(4)) Nova Science Pubs., Inc.
Zubieta-Calleja, Gustavo. Human Adaptation to High Altitude & to Sea Level. 2010. 72p. pap. (978-3-639-25276-7(4)) VDM Verlag Dr. Mueller e.K.

ALTITUDES

Fleming, C., et al, eds. Elevation Models for Geoscience. 2010. (Illus.). 160p. (978-1-86239-313-4(3)) Geological Society Publishing Hse.

ALTITUDES—MEASUREMENT

see also Leveling

Kohn, Matthew J., ed. Paleoaltimetry: Geochemical & Thermodynamic Approaches, 66. 2007. (Reviews in Mineralogy & Geochemistry Ser.: 66). (Illus.). 278p. per. 40.00 (978-0-939950-78-2(2)) Mineralogical Society of America.

ALTMAN, ROBERT, 1925-2006

Altman, Robert. Robert Altman's 3 Women. 2011. DVD 39.95 **(978-1-60465-482-0(1))** Criterion Collection.
Armstrong, Rick, ed. Robert Altman: Critical Essays. 2011. (ENG., Illus.). 205p. pap. 40.00 (978-0-7864-4414-4(2)) McFarland & Co., Inc. Pubs.
Zuckoff, Mitchell. Robert Altman: The Oral Biography. 2010. (Illus.). 576p. pap. 18.00 (978-0-307-38791-2(7), Vintage) Knopf Doubleday Publishing Group.

ALTRUISM

see also Charity; Helping Behavior

Allison, Scott T. & Goethals, George R. Heroes: What They Do & Why We Need Them. 2010. (ENG., Illus.). 256p. 27.95 (978-0-19-973974-5(9)) Oxford Univ. Pr., Inc.
Arnold, Eckhart. Explaining Altruism: A Simulation-Based Approach & Its Limits. 2009. (ENG., Illus.). 310p. 134.00 (978-3-86838-007-1(8)) Ontos Verlag DEU. Dist: Transaction Pubs.
Autry, James A. The Spirit of Retirement: Creating a Life of Meaning & Personal Growth. 2008. 193p. pap. 19.99 (978-1-57312-509-3(1)) Smyth & Helwys Publishing, Inc.
Barclay, Pat, ed. Reputation & the Evolution of Generous Behavior. 2010. (Psychology of Emotions, Motivations & Actions Ser.). pap. 43.00 (978-1-61668-153-1(5)) Nova Science Pubs., Inc.
Batson, C. Daniel. Altruism in Humans, 1 vol. 2011. (ENG., Illus.). 336p. 39.95 (978-0-19-534106-5(6)) Oxford Univ. Pr., Inc.
Bienkowski, Andrew & Akers, Mary. One Life to Give: A Path to Finding Yourself by Helping Others. 2010. (ENG., Illus.). 240p. pap. 14.95 (978-1-61519-008-9(2), 1615190082) Experiment LLC, The.
Blum, Laurence A. Friendship, Altruism & Morality. 2009. (Routledge Revivals Ser.). 234p. 110.00 (978-0-415-57090-9(5)) Routledge.
—Friendship Altruism & Morality (Routledge Revivals) 2009. 234p. pap. 39.95 (978-0-415-57292-7(4)) Routledge.
Blum, Lawrence A. Friendship Altruism & Morality (Routledge Revivals) 2009. x, 234p. 105.00 (978-0-203-85730-4(5)) Routledge.
Boehm, Christopher. Moral Origins: The Evolution of Virtue, Altruism, & Shame. 2012. (ENG.). 432p. (gr. 9). 28.99 (978-0-465-02048-5(8)) Basic Bks.
Brown, Gordon & Community Links Staff. Britain's Everyday Heroes. 2007. (ENG., Illus.). 240p. pap. 21.95 (978-1-84596-307-1(5)) Mainstream Publishing Co., Ltd. GBR. Dist: Independent Pubs. Group.
Bruni, Luigino. Reciprocity, Altruism & the Civil Society: In Praise of Heterogeneity. 2008. (Illus.). 176p. 140.00 (978-0-415-42858-3(0)) Routledge.
—Reciprocity Altruism & the Civil Society: In Praise of Heterogeneity. 2009. 160p. pap. 39.95 (978-0-415-56964-4(8)) Routledge.
Burroughs, Jeremiah. Moses' Self-Denial. 2010. 160p. (978-1-60178-094-2(X), Soli Deo Gloria Pubns.) Reformation Heritage Bks.
Charity & Lim, Arthur S. M. Did I Give Back Enough? 2009. 136p. 32.00 (978-981-4289-86-3(8)) World Scientific Publishing Co., Inc.
Climent Durán, Carlos & Durán, Carlos Climent. La Sociedad Esencial: La Democracia Entre el Altruismo y el Autoritarismo. 2007. (SPA.). 278p. (978-84-8456-830-8(X)) Tirant lo Blanch.
De Waal, Frans B. M. Primates & Philosophers: How Morality Evolved. Macedo, Stephen & Ober, Josiah, eds. 2009. (Princeton Science Library). (ENG., Illus.). 232p. pap. 15.95 (978-0-691-14129-9(0)) Princeton Univ. Pr.
—Primates & Philosophers: How Morality Evolved. Macedo, Stephen & Ober, Josiah, eds. 2006. (University Center for Human Values Ser.). (Illus.). 209p. 22.95 (978-0-691-12447-6(7)) Princeton Univ. Pr.
Dixon, Thomas. The Invention of Altruism: Making Moral Meanings in Victorian Britain. 2008. (ENG., Illus.). 280p. 150.00 (978-0-19-726426-3(3)) Oxford Univ. Pr., Inc.
Douglas, Bryan. Doing Good Works! Small Acts That Make a Big Difference. 2009. 131p. pap. 19.95 (978-0-9841890-7-6(6)) Think Big Pr.
Dugatkin, Lee Alan. The Altruism Equation: Seven Scientists Search for the Origins of Goodness. 2006. (ENG., Illus.). 224p. (C). 26.95 (978-0-691-12590-9(2)) Princeton Univ. Pr.
Effler, Erika Summers. Laughing Saints & Righteous Heroes: Emotional Rhythms in Social Movement Groups. 2010. (Morality & Society Ser.). (ENG., Illus.). 256p. 70.00 (978-0-226-18865-2(5)); pap. 23.00 (978-0-226-18866-9(3)) Univ. of Chicago Pr.
Flescher, Andrew Michael & Worthen, Daniel L. The Altruistic Species: Scientific, Philosophical, & Religious Perspectives of Human Benevolence. 2007. (ENG.). 304p. (C). per. 34.95 (978-1-59947-122-8(1)) Templeton Pr.
Goodman, Lenn E. & Goodman, Lenn Evan. Love Thy Neighbor as Thyself. 2008. (ENG.). 256p. 55.00 (978-0-19-532882-0(5)) Oxford Univ. Pr., Inc.
Grant, Colin. Altruism & Christian Ethics. 2009. (New Studies in Christian Ethics Ser.). (ENG.). 288p. pap. 41.00 (978-0-521-09361-3(9)) Cambridge Univ. Pr.
Gunderman, Richard B. We Make a Life by What We Give. (Philanthropic & Nonprofit Studies). (ENG.). 216p. 2009. pap. 16.00 (978-0-253-20029-7(6), 0253200296) 2008. 24.95 (978-0-253-35076-3(X), 025335076X) Indiana Univ. Pr.
Gunderman, Richard B. & Kegley, Jacquelyn Ann K. Josiah Royce in Focus. 2008. (American Philosophy Ser.). (ENG., Illus.). 240p. pap. 19.95 (978-0-253-21959-6(0), 0253219590) Indiana Univ. Pr.
Harman, Oren. The Price of Altruism: George Price & the Search for the Origins of Kindness. 2010. (ENG., Illus.). 464p. 27.95 (978-0-393-06778-1(5), 6778) Norton, W. W. & Co., Inc.
Hirschklau, Larri Deane. Why People Do Good. 2010. 84p. pap. (978-3-639-22859-5(6)) VDM Verlag Dr. Mueller e.K.
Hoch, Wesley A. Dai Uy Hoch: A Legend in Remote Seas - U. S. N. Military Advisor to the Junk Force - The Strangest War Armada in Naval History. 2009. 444p. pap. 22.99 (978-1-61579-394-5(1)) Xulon Pr., Inc.
Jamal, Syed. The Role of Cooperative Behavior in Evolution. 2011. 60p. pap. **(978-3-8433-7540-5(2))** Lambert Academic Publishing.
Keith, Kent M. Do It Anyway: Finding Personal Meaning & Deep Happiness by Living the Paradoxical Commandments. 2008. (ENG.). 208p. pap. 12.95 (978-1-57731-628-2(2)) New World Library.
Keltner, Dacher, et al, eds. The Compassionate Instinct: The Science of Human Goodness. 2010. (ENG., Illus.). 316p. pap. 16.95 (978-0-393-33728-0(6), 33728) Norton, W. W. & Co., Inc.
Keltner, Dacher & Keltner. Born to Be Good: The Science of a Meaningful Life. 2009. (ENG., Illus.). 352p. pap. 16.95 (978-0-393-33713-6(8), 33713) Norton, W. W. & Co., Inc.
Kielburger, Craig & Kielburger, Marc. Me to We: Finding Meaning in a Material World. 2008. (ENG.). 320p. per. 19.99 (978-0-7432-9451-5(3), Touchstone) Touchstone.
Kolm, Serge-Christophe. Reciprocity: An Economics of Social Relations. (Federico Caffè Lectures). (ENG., Illus.). 2009. 404p. pap. 45.00 (978-0-521-12320-4(8)) 2008. 408p. 103.99 (978-0-521-88265-1(6)) Cambridge Univ. Pr.
Kolm, Serge-Christophe & Ythier, Jean Mercier, eds. Handbook of the Economics of Giving, Altruism & Reciprocity Applications, 2 vols., Vol. 2. 2006. (Handbooks in Economics Ser.). (ENG., Illus.). 752p. 150.00 (978-0-444-52145-3(3), North Holland) Elsevier Science & Technology Bks.
Kramer, Bill. Unexpected Grace: Stories of Faith, Science, & Altruism. 2007. (Illus.). 256p. pap. 22.95 (978-1-59947-112-9(4)) Templeton Pr.
Laland, S. G. Historias Entranables de Altruismo y Amor Animal. (SPA.). 214p. 13.40 (978-84-89920-58-3(3), 86510) Ediciones Oniro S.A. ESP. Dist: Lectorum Pubns., Inc.
Lawler, E. J. & Thye, S. R. Altruism & Prosocial Behavior in Groups. 2009. (Illus.). xi, 223p. 124.95 (978-1-84855-572-3(5)) Emerald Group Publishing Ltd. GBR. Dist: Turpin Distribution Services Ltd.
Mikulincer, Mario & Shaver, Phillip R. Prosocial Motives, Emotions, & Behavior: The Better Angels of Our Nature. 2009. (Illus.). 468p. 69.95 (978-1-4338-0546-2(4)) American Psychological Assn.
Miron, Cyril Harry. The Problem of Altruism in the Philosophy of St Thomas: A Study in Social Philosophy. 2011. 142p. 40.95 **(978-1-258-05368-0(3))** Literary Licensing, LLC.
Monroe, Kristen Renwick. The Hand of Compassion: Portraits of Moral Choice During the Holocaust. 2006. (ENG., Illus.). 384p. (C). per. 26.95 (978-0-691-12773-6(5)) Princeton Univ. Pr.
Neimark, Jill & Post, Stephen. Why Good Things Happen to Good People: How to Live a Longer, Healthier, Happier Life by the Simple Act of Giving. 2008. (ENG.). 320p. pap. 15.99 (978-0-7679-2018-6(X)) Broadway Bks.
Oakley, Barbara, et al, eds. Pathological Altruism, 1 vol. 2011. (ENG., Illus.). 496p. 55.00 (978-0-19-973857-1(2)) Oxford Univ. Pr., Inc.
Oliner, Samuel P. Altruism, Intergroup Apology, Forgiveness, & Reconciliation. 2008. (ENG.). 328p. pap. 19.95 (978-1-55778-878-8(2)) Paragon Hse. Pubs.
Oliner, Samuel P. The Nature of Good & Evil: Understanding the Many Acts of Moral & Immoral Behavior. 2011. (ENG.). 392p. pap. 24.95 **(978-1-55778-896-2(0))** Paragon Hse. Pubs.
Oord, Thomas Jay, ed. The Altruism Reader: Selections from Writings on Love, Religion, & Science. 2007. (ENG., Illus.). 320p. (C). per. 39.95 (978-1-59947-127-3(2)) Templeton Pr.
Peter Hochstein. Cigars & Other Passions: The Biography of Edgar M. Cullman. 2010. 404p. 31.96 (978-1-4269-2370-8(8)); pap. 21.96 (978-1-4269-2369-2(4)) Trafford Publishing.
Price, Patrick Hutcheson Jones & Price, Scott Todd. Looking for Goodwill. 2006. (ENG., Illus.). 326p. 30.00 (978-1-57736-374-3(4)) Turner Publishing Co.
Ramia, Nascira. Development of Empathy & Altruism in Latin AmericanStudents: A Case Study Using Service Learning at a Liberal Arts College in Ecuador. 2008. 88p. pap. (978-3-639-09062-8(4)) VDM Verlag Dr. Mueller e.K.
Roseman, Herbert. Altruism, Evolution & Optional Games. 2008. 320p. pap. (978-3-639-06895-5(5)) VDM Verlag Dr. Mueller e.K.
Salvati, Armida. Altruism & Social Capital. 2008. 116p. pap. (978-1-59942-960-1(8)) Universal Pubs.
Schilt, W. Clarence & Schilt, Stephen. A Life to Die For: Discover the Secret of Christ's Transforming Power. 2009. pap. 17.99 (978-0-8163-2308-1(9)) Pacific Pr. Publishing Assn.
Scott, Niall & Seglow, Jonathan. Altruism. 2007. (ENG.). 160p. (C). 162.00 (978-0-335-22250-6(1), 0335222501); pap. 40.00 (978-0-335-22249-0(8), 0335222498) McGraw-Hill Education GBR. Dist: McGraw-Hill Cos., The.
Singer, Peter. Expanding Cirle - Ethics, Evolution & Moral Progress. 2011. (ENG.). 232p. pap. 17.95 (978-0-691-15069-7(9)) Princeton Univ. Pr.
Sinkie, Otto A. The Book of Altruism. 2011. 266p. 47.95 **(978-1-258-04769-6(1))** Literary Licensing, LLC.
Spielberg, Laurel A. & Adams, Lisa V., eds. Africa: A Practical Guide for Global Health Workers. 2011. (Illus.). 304p. pap. 24.95 (978-1-58465-976-1(9), Dartmouth College Press) Univ. Pr. of New England.
Staddon, John. The Malign Hand of the Markets: the Insidious Forces on Wall Street that are Destroying Financial Markets – & What We Can Do about It. 2012. (ENG., Illus.). 304p. 35.00 **(978-0-07-179740-5(8)**, 0071797408) McGraw-Hill Cos., The.
Steinmann, Michael, et al. Altruism Reconsidered: Exploring New Approaches to Property in Human Tissue. 2009. (Medical Law & Ethics Ser.). 324p. 124.95 (978-0-7546-7270-8(0)) Ashgate Publishing Co.
Sussman, Robert W. & Cloninger, C. Robert, eds. Origins of Altruism & Cooperation. 2011. (Developments in Primatology: Progress & Prospects Ser.). (ENG., Illus.). xvi, 428p. 179.00 (978-1-4419-9519-3(6), 1441995196) Springer.
Thibeault, Donald. Grey Area Thinking: The Nexus of Altruism with Beliefs & Science. 2007. 244p. per. 15.95 (978-1-59526-742-9(5), Llumina Pr.) Aeon Publishing Inc.
Tomasello, Michael. Why We Cooperate. 2009. (Boston Review Bks.). (ENG.). 232p. (gr. 17). 14.95 (978-0-262-01359-8(2)) MIT Pr.
van Lodenstein, Jodocus. A Spiritual Appeal to Christ's Bride. Beeke, Joel R., ed. Elshout, Bartel, tr. from DUT. 2010.Tr. of Negen Predikatien over eenige stiffen, welke zeer zelden geleerd en nog minder beoefend Worden. (Illus.). 176p. (978-1-60178-106-2(7)) Reformation Heritage Bks.
Watts, Wayne. The Gift of Giving. 2008. (978-1-59328-181-6(1)) Graham, Billy Evangelistic Assn.
Wispé, Lauren. The Psychology of Sympathy. 2010. (Perspectives in Social Psychology Ser.). 224p. pap. 119.00 (978-1-4419-3218-1(6), 1441932186) Springer.

ALUCONIDAE

see Owls

ALUMINUM

ABBE Scientist Research Division Staff. Aluminum in Health & Disease: Index & Medical Analysis of New Clinical-Research Information for All Nations. 2006. (Illus.). 160p. ring bd. 75.50 (978-0-7883-4533-3(8), 07883-45346) ABBE Pubs. Assn. of Washington, D.C.
Abubakar, Muazu. Effects of Zinc & Magnesium Addition on Aluminium Sacrificial Anode. 2011. 88p. pap. **(978-3-8443-8953-1(9))** Lambert Academic Publishing.
Aldridge, Simon & Downs, Anthony J. The Group 13 Metals Aluminium, Gallium, Indium & Thallium: Chemical Patterns & Peculiarities. 2011. (ENG., Illus.). 726p. 260.00 (978-0-470-68191-6(8), Wiley) Wiley, John & Sons, Inc.
American Welding Society. Welding Aluminum - Questions & Answers (2008) 2008. 2008. (978-0-87171-085-7(4)) American Welding Society.
Berend, Kenrick. Subacute Aluminum Intoxication in Hemodialysis Patients. 2009. 232p. pap. (978-3-639-09308-7(9)) VDM Verlag Dr. Mueller e.K.
Das, Abhishek. Surface Modification of Aluminum by Edm Using Tic/Cu Electrode. 2010. 96p. pap. (978-3-8383-9457-2(7)) Lambert Academic Publishing.
Green, John A. S., ed. Aluminum Recycling & Processing for Energy Conservation & Sustainability. 2007. (Illus.). 267p. 150.00 (978-0-87170-859-5(0)) ASM International.
Guillen, Donna. Oxidation Behavior of Aluminum During Thermal Spray. 2009. 128p. pap. (978-3-639-17475-5(5)) VDM Verlag Dr. Mueller e.K.
Harle, Helen. Create Colorful Aluminum Jewelry: Upcycle cans into vibrant necklaces, rings, earrings, pins, & Bracelets. 2010. (ENG., Illus.). 56p. pap. 14.95 (978-0-87116-404-9(3)) Kalmbach Publishing Co., Bks. Div.
Hasan, Heather. Aluminum. 2006. 52p. pap. 26.50 (978-1-4358-3759-1(2)); (Illus.). 48p. (YA). (gr. 5-9). lib. bdg. 26.50 (978-1-4042-0705-9(8)) Rosen Publishing Group, Inc., The.
Johnson, John A., ed. Light Metals 2010: Proceeding of the Technical Sessions Presented by the TMS Aluminum Committee at the TMS 2010 Annual Meeting & Exhibition. 2010. (ENG.). 1132p. 272.00 (978-0-87339-747-6(9), Wiley) Wiley, John & Sons, Inc.

Katgerman, L. & Scetens, F., eds. New Frontiers in Light Metals: Proceedings of the 11th International Aluminium Conference INALCO 2010. 2010. pap. 131.00 *(978-1-60750-585-3(1))* IOS Pr., Inc.

Lumley, R., ed. Fundamentals of aluminium Metallurgy: Production, processing & Applications. 2010. (ENG., Illus.). 912p. 325.00 *(978-1-84569-654-2(9))* Woodhead Publishing Ltd. GBR. Dist: Ingram Pub. Services.

Minatel, Rogé, et al. Recrystallization Study of Aluminium Sheets. 2010. 80p. pap. *(978-3-639-24789-3(2))* VDM Verlag Dr. Mueller e.K.

Peterson, Warren S. & Miller, Ronald E., eds. Hall-Heroult Centennial: First Century of Aluminum Process Technology, 1886-1986. 2007. (ENG., Illus.). 174p. pap. 71.00 *(978-0-87339-540-3(9)*, 01-5409-E, Wiley) Wiley, John & Sons, Inc.

Qamar, Sayyad Zahid, et al. Modeling & Analysis of Aluminum Extrusion. 2011. 252p. pap. ***(978-3-8443-3158-5(1))*** Lambert Academic Publishing.

Roesky, H. W. & Atwood, David A. Group 13 Chemistry II: Biological Aspects of Aluminum. 2010. (Structure & Bonding Ser.). (Illus.). x, 200p. pap. 239.00 *(978-3-642-07354-5(0)*, 3642078540) Springer.

Schütze, Michael, et al, eds. Corrosion Resistance of Aluminium & Aluminium Alloys. 2010. (Kreysa Continuation Ser.). (ENG., Illus.). 636p. 215.00 *(978-3-527-33001-0(1)*, Wiley-VCH) Wiley, John & Sons, Inc.

Stiles, Clare. Anodized! Brilliant Colors & Bold Designs for Aluminum Jewelry. 2010. (ENG., Illus.). 128p. pap. 19.95 *(978-1-60059-520-2(0))* Lark Bks.

Taylor, John A. & Grandfield, John. Aluminium Cast House Technology XI: Selected, Peer Reviewed Papers from Th International Conference, Organised by the CAST CRC on Behalf of the Aluminium Industry. 2010. (Materials Science Forum Ser.: Vols. 630). (Illus.). xi, 262p. *(978-0-87849-316-6(6))* Trans Tech Pubns., Ltd.

Technology Research Editors, ed. Joining of Steel & Aluminum, 2007 Ed. 2007. pap. 128.50 *(978-1-60030-181-0(9)*, Search-In-Print) CSA Journal Division.

—Welding of Aluminum, 2007 Ed. 2007. pap. 128.50 *(978-1-60030-203-9(3)*, Search-In-Print) CSA Journal Division.

Timmer, Matthias. Ab Initio Theory of Electronic Excitations at Surfaces. 2011. 172p. pap. ***(978-3-8381-2269-4(0))*** Südwestdeutscher Verlag für Hochschulschriften AG & Co. KG.

Wetzel, C., et al, eds. GaN, AlN, InN & Their Alloys: 2004 MRS Fall Meeting Symposium Proceedings, Vol. 831. 2009. (Materials Research Society Symposium Proceedings Ser.: 831). (Illus.). xix, 784p. 35.00 *(978-1-55899-779-0(2))* Materials Research Society.

ALUMINUM, STRUCTURAL

Muller, Ulrich. Introduction to Structural Aluminum Design. 2011. (ENG., Illus.). 192p. pap. 79.95 *(978-1-4398-5468-6(8))* Whittles Publishing GBR. Dist: Taylor & Francis Group.

ALUMINUM ALLOYS

Akinlabi, Esther. Characterisation of Dissimilar Fsw Between Aluminium & Copper. 2011. 320p. pap. ***(978-3-8443-9042-1(1))*** Lambert Academic Publishing.

Aluminum Casting Technology. 2nd ed. 368p. 140.00 *(978-0-87433-157-8(9)*, NF9300) American Foundry Society.

American Welding Society. Welding Aluminum - Questions & Answers (2008) 2008. 2008. *(978-0-87171-085-7(4))* American Welding Society.

Anodizing Aluminum: The Finish of Choice. (Illus.). 60p. (Orig.). pap. *(978-0-7605-1893-9(9))* Rector Pr., Ltd.

Appel, Fritz, et al. Gamma Titanium Aluminide Alloys: Science & Technology. 2011. (ENG., Illus.). 762p. 260.00 ***(978-3-527-31525-3(X)***, Wiley-VCH) Wiley, John & Sons, Inc.

Attallah, Moataz. Friction Stir Welding of Aluminium Alloys. 2011. 324p. pap. ***(978-3-8433-8069-0(4))*** Lambert Academic Publishing.

Banerjee, Arghya N. & Chattopadhyay, Kalyan K. P-Type Transparent Semiconducting Delafossite Cualo2+X Thin Film. 2008. pap. 49.00 *(978-1-60692-032-9(4))* Nova Science Pubs., Inc.

Bauser, M., et al, eds. Extrusion 2nd Edition. 2nd ed. 2006. (ENG., Illus.). 608p. 220.00 *(978-0-87170-837-3(X))* ASM International.

Ber, Leonid B., et al. Heat Treatment of Aluminum Alloys. 2012. (Advances in Metallic Alloys Ser.). (ENG., Illus.). 350p. 179.95 *(978-0-8493-7610-8(6)*, CRC Press) Taylor & Francis Group GBR. Dist: Taylor & Francis Group.

Bloodworth, Thomas. On the Immersed Friction Stir Welding of Aa6061-T6. 2010. 88p. pap. *(978-3-8383-0137-2(4))* Lambert Academic Publishing.

British Standards Institute Staff. Aluminium & aluminium alloys. Requirements for anodised products for use in contact with Foodstuff. 12p. pap. 117.00 *(978-0-580-53127-9(9))* Artech Hse., Inc.

Coucher, Tom. Fundamentals of Quenching Aluminum Alloys. 2009. pap. 40.00 *(978-1-61623-829-2(1))* Independent Pub.

Crepeau, Paul N., et al, eds. Shape Casting: 2nd International Symposium. 2007. (ENG., Illus.). 322p. pap. 75.00 *(978-0-87339-660-8(X)*, Wiley) Wiley, John & Sons, Inc.

Das, Subodh K. & Yin, Weimin. Aluminum Alloys for Transportation, Packaging, Aerospace, & Other Applications. 2007. (ENG., Illus.). 234p. pap. 108.00 *(978-0-87339-662-2(6)*, Wiley) Wiley, John & Sons, Inc.

Driver, J.H. & Dubost, B., eds. Aluminum Alloy ICAAS, Pt. 4. 288p. 90.00 *(978-0-87849-757-7(9))* Trans Tech Pubns., Ltd. CHE. Dist: Enfield Publishing & Distribution Co., Inc.

Erik L. Persson. Aluminum Alloys: Preparation, Properties & Applications. 2011. (Series: Materials Science & Technologies Ser.). (Illus.). 251p. 89.00 *(978-1-61122-311-8(3))* Nova Science Pubs., Inc.

Eskin, Dmitry G. Physical Metallurgy of Direct Chill Casting of Aluminum Alloys. 2008. (Advances in Metallic Alloys Ser.). (ENG., Illus.). 328p. 172.95 *(978-1-4200-6281-6(6)*, CRC Press) Taylor & Francis Group GBR. Dist: Taylor & Francis Group.

Fansler, Charles. Aluminum Nitride Thin Films - Deposition for Fabrication, Characterization & Fabrication of Surface Acoustic Wave Devices. 2008. 124p. pap. *(978-3-8364-6972-2(3))* VDM Verlag Dr. Mueller e.K.

Féron, D. Corrosion behaviour & protection of copper & aluminium alloys in Seawater, EFC 50. (Illus.). 256p. *(978-1-84569-241-4(1))* Woodhead Publishing Ltd.

Féron, D., ed. Corrosion Behaviour & Protection of Copper & Aluminum Alloys in Seawater. 2007. (Illus.). 195p. 219.95 *(978-1-4200-5409-5(0))* CRC Pr. LLC.

Ghali, Edward. Corrosion Resistance of Aluminum & Magnesium Alloys: Understanding, Performance, & Testing. 2010. (Wiley Series in Corrosion Ser.: 7). (ENG., Illus.). 719p. 168.00 *(978-0-471-71576-4(X)*, Wiley) Wiley, John & Sons, Inc.

Hirsch, Jürgen, ed. Virtual Fabrication of Aluminum Products: Microstructural Modeling in Industrial Aluminum Production. 2007. (ENG., Illus.). 405p. 205.00 *(978-3-527-31363-1(X)*, Wiley-VCH) Wiley, John & Sons, Inc.

Hirsch, Jürgen, et al, eds. Aluminium Alloys: Their Physical & Mechanical Properties, 2 vols. 2008. (ENG., Illus.). 2504p. 840.00 *(978-3-527-32367-8(8)*, Wiley-VCH) Wiley, John & Sons, Inc.

Hughes, A. E. & Thompson, G. E. Copper Distributions in Aluminium Alloys. Muster, T. H., ed. 2008. (Illus.). 106p. pap. 39.00 *(978-1-60456-395-5(8))* Nova Science Pubs., Inc.

J, Mcqueen Hugh. Hot Working of Aluminum Alloys: Microstructures, Properties & Processing. 2011. (Manufacturing Engineering & Materials Processing Ser.). (ENG., Illus.). 615p. 199.95 *(978-1-57444-678-4(9)*, CRC Press) Taylor & Francis Group GBR. Dist: Taylor & Francis Group.

Kaufman, J. Gilbert & Kaufman, J. G. Parametric Analyses of High-Temperature Data for Aluminum Alloys. 2008. (Illus.). v, 165p. *(978-0-87170-715-4(2))* ASM International, Inc.

Kaufman JG & Kaufman, J. G. Properties of Aluminum Alloys: Fatigue Data & the Effects of Temperature, Product Form, & Processing. 2008. (Illus.). vii, 559p. *(978-0-87170-839-7(6))* ASM International.

Kim, Young-Won, et al, eds. Structural Aluminides for Elevated Temperatures: Gamma Titanium & Other Metallic Aluminides. 2008. (ENG., Illus.). 430p. pap. 216.00 *(978-0-87339-720-9(7)*, Wiley) Wiley, John & Sons, Inc.

Long, Siyuan. Light Metals, Aerospace Materials & Superconductors, 4 vols. Han, Yafang, ed. 2007. (Progress in Light Metals, Aerospace Materials & Superconductors Ser.: Vols. 546-549). (Illus.). 2420p. *(978-0-87849-432-3(4))* Trans Tech Pubns., Ltd.

Long, Zhengdong. Aluminum Alloys: Fabrication, Characterization & Applications II. Yin, Weimin & Das, Subodh K., eds. 2009. (ENG., Illus.). 228p. pap. 111.00 *(978-0-87339-735-3(5)*, Wiley) Wiley, John & Sons, Inc.

Majumdar, Amitabha. Characteristics of Aa6061-T4 & -T6 Extrusions. 2009. 236p. pap. *(978-3-639-17177-8(2))* VDM Verlag Dr. Mueller e.K.

Onat, Adem. Silicon Carbide Particulate Reinforced Aluminum Alloys Matrix Composites Fabricated by Squeeze Casting Method. 2011. (Materials Science & Technologies Ser.). pap. 43.00 *(978-1-61209-150-1(4))* Nova Science Pubs., Inc.

Peris, Robbie, et al. Effects of Extrusion Process Conditions on Die Pick-up. 2008. 108p. pap. *(978-3-8364-8431-2(5))* VDM Verlag Dr. Mueller e.K.

sarajan, zohair & Sarajan, Zohair. Advancements in Microstructural Modification of Aluminum-Silicon. 2011. 596p. pap. ***(978-3-8443-9225-8(4))*** Lambert Academic Publishing.

Schütze, Michael, et al, eds. Corrosion Resistance of Aluminium & Aluminium Alloys. 2010. (Kreysa Continuation Ser.). (ENG., Illus.). 636p. 215.00 *(978-3-527-33001-0(1)*, Wiley-VCH) Wiley, John & Sons, Inc.

Sheppard, T. Extrusion of Aluminium Alloys. 2010. (ENG., Illus.). 432p. pap. 499.00 *(978-1-4419-4728-4(0)*, 1441947280) Springer.

Technology Research Editors, ed. Cold Rolling of Aluminum Alloys, 2007 Ed. 2007. pap. 128.50 *(978-1-60030-166-7(5)*, Search-In-Print) CSA Journal Division.

—Continuous Casting of Aluminum Alloys, 2007 Ed. 2007. pap. 128.50 *(978-1-60030-168-1(1)*, Search-In-Print) CSA Journal Division.

—Corrosion Protection of Aluminum & Aluminum Alloys, 2007 Ed. 2007. pap. 118.50 *(978-1-60030-473-6(7)*, Search-In-Print) CSA Journal Division.

—Extrusion of Aluminum Alloys, 2007 Ed. 2007. pap. 128.50 *(978-1-60030-174-2(6)*, Search-In-Print) CSA Journal Division.

—Grain Refinement in the Foundry, 2007 Ed. 2007. pap. 128.50 *(978-1-60030-177-3(0)*, Search-In-Print) CSA Journal Division.

—Impact Strength of Aluminum Base Alloys, 2007 Ed. 2007. pap. 128.50 *(978-1-60030-179-7(7)*, Search-In-Print) CSA Journal Division.

—Nondestructive Testing of Aluminum & Its Alloys, 2007 Ed. 2007. pap. 128.50 *(978-1-60030-186-9(6)*, Search-In-Print) CSA Journal Division.

—Powder Technology of Aluminum/Silicon Carbide Composites, 2007 Ed. 2007. pap. 128.50 *(978-1-60030-191-9(6)*, Search-In-Print) CSA Journal Division.

—Solidification Modeling for Aluminum Base Alloys, 2007 Ed. 2007. pap. 128.50 *(978-1-60030-196-4(7)*, Search-In-Print) CSA Journal Division.

Varli, Aziz Egemen. Fatigue Crack Growth Behaviour of Aa6013 Aluminum Alloy. 2009. 104p. pap. *(978-3-639-12976-2(8))* VDM Verlag Dr. Mueller e.K.

Vijayan, Sundaravel. Process Optimization for Friction Stir Welding: On Aa 5083 for Marine Applications. 2011. 144p. pap. ***(978-3-639-34391-5(3))*** VDM Verlag Dr. Mueller e.K.

Wang, Qigui, et al, eds. Simulation of Aluminum Shape Casting Processing: From Alloy Design to Mechanical Properties. 2006. (ENG., Illus.). 398p. pap. 195.00 *(978-0-87339-624-0(3)*, Wiley) Wiley, John & Sons, Inc.

Yin, Weimin & Das, Subodh K., eds. Aluminum Alloys: Fabrication, Characterization & Applications. 2008. (ENG., Illus.). 278p. pap. 158.00 *(978-0-87339-712-4(6)*, Wiley) Wiley, John & Sons, Inc.

Zolotorevsky, Vadim S., et al. Casting Aluminum Alloys. 2007. (ENG., Illus.). 544p. 230.00 *(978-0-08-045370-5(8)*, Elsevier Science) Elsevier Science & Technology Bks.

ALUMINUM COMPANY OF AMERICA

Muller, Charlotte F. Light Metals Monopoly. (Columbia University, Studies in the Social Sciences: No. 519). reprint ed. 22.50 *(978-0-404-51519-5(3))* AMS Pr., Inc.

ALUMINUM CONSTRUCTION

Gizejowski. Progress in Steel, Composite & Aluminium Structures. 2006. (Illus.). xx, 408p. cd-rom *(978-0-415-40123-4(2)*, Taylor & Francis) Taylor & Francis Group GBR. Dist: Taylor & Francis Group.

Muller, Ulrich. Introduction to Structural Aluminum Design. 2011. (ENG., Illus.). 192p. pap. 79.95 *(978-1-4398-5468-6(8))* Whittles Publishing GBR. Dist: Taylor & Francis Group.

Prouvé, Jean. Jean Prouvé: La Maison Tropicale = Jean Prouvé: The Tropical House. 2009. (FRE & ENG., Illus.). 157p. *(978-2-84426-335-3(6))* Centre National d'Art et de Culture Georges Pompidou.

Prouve, Jean. Jean Prouve: the Tropical House. 2011. (ENG., Illus.). 160p. pap. 40.00 *(978-1-935202-49-3(9))* Editions du Centre Pompidou FRA. Dist: D.A.P./Distributed Art Pubs.

ALUMINUM INDUSTRY AND TRADE

Beckum, Janean Mollet-Van & The Washington County Historical Society. Washington County's Aluminum Industry. 2009. 128p. pap. 21.99 *(978-0-7385-6044-1(8))* Arcadia Publishing.

Katgerman, L. Continuous Casting of Aluminum. Date not set. 320p. 90.00 *(978-0-901716-19-4(7))* Institute of Materials GBR. Dist: Ashgate Publishing Co.

Mazumder, B. M. Management of Waste Material Generated by Aluminium Smelter Plants. 2011. (Woodhead Publishing India Ser.). (ENG.). 200p. 135.00 *(978-0-85709-010-2(0))* Woodhead Publishing Ltd. GBR. Dist: Ingram Pub. Services.

ALUMINUM SILICATES

see also Aluminum; Clay

Technology Research Editors, ed. Tribology of Aluminum/Silicon Carbide Particulate Composites, 2007 Ed. 2007. pap. 128.50 *(978-1-60030-200-8(9)*, Search-In-Print) CSA Journal Division.

ALZHEIMER'S DISEASE

Agronin, Marc E. Alzheimer Disease & Other Dementias: A Practical Guide. 2nd rev. ed. 2007. (Practical Guides in Psychiatry Ser.). (ENG., Illus.). 336p. pap. 49.99 *(978-0-7817-6770-5(9))* Lippincott Williams & Wilkins.

Ahmed, Hanaa, et al. Nutraceuticals & Alzheimer's Disease. 2011. 296p. pap. ***(978-3-8443-8113-9(9))*** Lambert Academic Publishing.

Akbar, Celestina. Alzheimer's Disease: A Growing Health Care Issue among the Elderly. 2008. 56p. pap. 15.99 *(978-1-4257-9755-3(5))* Xlibris Corp.

Altman, H. J. & Altman, B. N., eds. Alzheimer's & Parkinson's Diseases: Recent Advances in Research & Clinical Management. (Illus.). 628p. (C). 198.00 *(978-0-306-43482-2(2))* Springer.

Alzheimer's & Parkinson's Diseases. 2007. pap. *(978-3-8055-8282-7(X))* Karger, S. AG.

Alzheimer's Disease: Current & Future Breakthrough Research: Hearing Before the Subcommittee on Retirement & Aging of the Committee on Health, Education, Labor, & Pensions, United States Senate, One Hundred Tenth Congress, First Session on Examining Alzheimer's Disease, Focusing on Current & Future Breakthrough Research, May 15, 2007. 2007. iii, 49p. *(978-0-16-079724-8(1)*, 552-070-36650-4) United States Government Printing Office.

Anbar, Abraham Isaac. Alzheimer's: A Message of Hope. 2006. pap. 18.00 *(978-0-9771870-6-5(3))* Arbor Bks.

Bährer-Kohler, Sabine & Krebs-Roubicek, Eva, eds. Self Management of Chronic Disease: Alzheimer's Disease. 2009. (ENG., Illus.). xiv, 158p. pap. 79.95 *(978-3-642-00325-7(7))* Springer.

Ballenger, Jesse F., et al, eds. Treating Dementia: Do We Have a Pill for It? 2009. (ENG., Illus.). 288p. (gr. 17). 62.00 *(978-0-8018-9365-0(8))* Johns Hopkins Univ. Pr.

Baum Van Ryzin, Christine, et al, eds. Pathways of Hope: Living Well with Cognitive Changes. 2011. (ENG., Illus.). 72p. pap. 18.00 ***(978-0-9761336-3-6(6))*** Univ. of Wisconsin Pr.

Bennett, D. L. Alzheimer's, Depression & Dementi. 2008. 180p. 22.99 *(978-1-60647-744-1(7))*; pap. 14.99 *(978-1-60647-743-4(9))* Xulon Pr., Inc.

Bernhardi, Rommy von. Neurodegenerative Diseases: From Molecular Concepts to Therapeutic Targets. Inestrosa, Nibaldo C., ed. 2008. (C). 129.00 *(978-1-60456-167-8(X))* Nova Science Pubs., Inc.

Bonner, Dede. The 10 Best Questions for Living with Alzheimer's: The Script You Need to Get the Best Care for Your Loved One. 2008. (ENG.). 336p. pap. 20.99 *(978-1-4165-6051-7(3)*, Touchstone) Touchstone.

Bouchillon, Alice L. The Lost Memory: Living with Alzheimer's, 1 vol. 2010. 48p. pap. 16.95 *(978-1-4489-3914-5(3))* PublishAmerica, Inc.

Boyd, Marisa R. Alzheimer's Disease Diagnosis & Treatments. 2011. *(978-1-61122-064-3(5))* Nova Science Pubs., Inc.

Boyer, Kim & Shapiro, Mary. Alzheimer's & Dementia: A Practical & Legal Guide for Nevada Caregivers. 2011. 176p. pap. 21.95 ***(978-0-87417-858-6(4))*** Univ. of Nevada Pr.

Br, Guruprasad & Kumar. C., Sunil. Computational Biology of Alzheimer's Disease. 2010. 128p. pap. *(978-3-639-27177-5(7))* VDM Verlag Dr. Mueller e.K.

Bradbury, Rob & Brodney, Michael A. Alzheimer's Disease. 2010. (Topics in Medicinal Chemistry Ser.). (Illus.). xiv, 179p. pap. 239.00 *(978-3-642-09354-8(X)*, 364209354X) Springer.

Buchman, Sunny & Buchman, Paul. Precious Window of Time: Our Journey with Alzheimer's Disease. 2011. 80p. pap. 9.99 ***(978-1-4670-3771-6(0))*** AuthorHouse.

Bugg, William. Soaring above Adversity. 2006. (ENG.). 128p. per. 19.95 *(978-1-4241-0880-0(2))* PublishAmerica, Inc.

Burns, Jeffrey & Morris, John. Mild Cognitive Impairment & Early Alzheimer's Disease. 2007. (Illus.). 160p. pap. 10.99 *(978-0-470-31937-6(2)*, Wiley) Wiley, John & Sons, Inc.

Burns, Jeffrey M. & Morris, John C. Mild Cognitive Impairment & Early Alzheimer's Disease: Detection & Diagnosis. 2008. (ENG., Illus.). 156p. 82.00 *(978-0-470-31936-9(4)*, Wiley) Wiley, John & Sons, Inc.

California Workgroup on Guidelines for Alzheimer's Disease Management. Alzheimers Disease GUIDELINES Pocketcard: Managing Disease Progression. 2010. 10p. pap. 9.95 *(978-0-9843604-1-3(7))* International Guidelines Ctr., Inc.

Callone, Patricia & Kudlacek, Connie. The Alzheimer's Caregiving Puzzle: Putting Together the Pieces. 2010. (ENG.). 192p. E-Book 16.95 *(978-1-932603-88-0(3))* Demos Medical Publishing, LLC.

Carper, Jean. 100 Simple Things You Can Do to Prevent Alzheimer's. 2010. audio compact disk 29.95 *(978-1-59316-535-2(8))* Listen & Live Audio, Inc.

—100 Simple Things You Can Do to Prevent Alzheimer's & Age-Related Memory Loss. 2010. (ENG.). 336p. 19.99 *(978-0-316-08685-1(1))* Little Brown & Co.

—100 Simple Things You Can Do to Prevent Alzheimer's & Age-Related Memory Loss. Lt. ed. 2011. 384p. 31.99 *(978-1-4104-3420-3(6))* Thorndike Pr.

Carrillo, M. C. & Hampel, H., eds. Alzheimer's Disease - Modernizing Concept, Biological Diagnosis & Therapy. 2012. (Advances in Biological Psychiatry Ser.). (ENG., Illus.). 194p. ***(978-3-8055-9802-6(5))*** Karger, S. AG.

Carter, Michael D. The Development of New Treatments for Alzheimer's Disease. 2008. 232p. pap. *(978-3-639-06649-4(9))* VDM Verlag Dr. Mueller e.K.

Casadesus, G., ed. Handbook of Animal Models in Alzheimer's Disease - Advances in Alzheimer's Disease. 2011. 352p. 218.00 ***(978-1-60750-732-1(3))*** IOS Pr., Inc.

Caselli, Richard J. & Tariot, Pierre N. Alzheimer's Disease & Its Variants: A Diagnostic & Therapeutic Guide, 1 vol. 2010. (Oxford American Neurology Library). (ENG.). 264p. pap. 24.95 *(978-0-19-539338-5(4))* Oxford Univ. Pr., Inc.

Chan, A. P. Alzheimer's Disease Research Trends. 2007. (C). 185.00 *(978-1-60021-712-8(5))* Nova Science Pubs., Inc.

Chiaravalloti, Nancy, ed. Changes in the Brain: Impact on Daily Life. 2010. (ENG.). 200p. 89.95 *(978-0-387-98187-1(X)*, 038798187X) Springer.

Chopra, Kanwaljit. Neurobiology of Depression & Alzheimer's Disease. 2011. 88p. pap. ***(978-3-8443-1518-9(7))*** Lambert Academic Publishing.

Christen, Yves. Diabetes, Insulin & Alzheimer's Disease. 2010. (Research & Perspectives in Alzheimer's Disease Ser.). (Illus.). 250p. 179.00 *(978-3-642-04299-7(6)*, 3642042996) Springer.

Coleman, Loretta. Tips & Suggestions in Caring for Dementia/Alzhemier Loved Ones. 2011. 72p. pap. 10.99 ***(978-1-4670-3703-7(6))*** AuthorHouse.

Corso, Jeremy A. Perspectives on Alzheimer's Disease. 2011. (Neurology - Laboratory & Clinical Research Developments Ser.). (Illus.). 251p. 129.00 *(978-1-61209-449-6(X))* Nova Science Pubs., Inc.

Cram101 Textbook Reviews & Cram101 Textbook Reviews. Outlines & Highlights for Bace: Lead Target for Orchestrated Therapy of Alzheimers Disease by Varghese John, ISBN. 2011. 146p. pap. 29.95 ***(978-1-61461-282-7(X))*** Cram101 Inc.

Cronin-Golomb, Alice & Hof, Patrick R. Vision in Alzheimer's Disease, Vol. 34. (Interdisciplinary Topics in Gerontology Ser.: Vol. 34). (Illus.). *(978-3-8055-7757-1(5))* Karger, S. AG.

Cuello, A. Claudio, ed. Pharmacological Mechanisms in Alzheimer's Therapeutics. (ENG., Illus.). xx, 324p. 2010. pap. 159.00 *(978-1-4419-2446-9(9)*, 1441924469) 2007. 159.00 *(978-0-387-71521-6(5)*, 0387715215) Springer.

Davis, Mary-Ann. Alzheimer's Disease Mortality. 2008. 220p. pap. *(978-3-639-06536-7(0))* VDM Verlag Dr. Mueller e.K.

Dawbarn, David & Allen, Shelley J., eds. Neurobiology of Alzheimer's Disease. 3rd rev. ed. 2007. (Molecular & Cellular Neurobiology Series (BIOS Scientific Publishers) Ser.). (ENG., Illus.). 488p. 135.00 *(978-0-19-856661-8(1))* Oxford Univ. Pr., Inc.

De Klerk-Rubin, Vicki. Validation Techniques for Dementia Care: The Family Guide to Improving Communication. 2007. (Illus.). 132p. per. 18.95 *(978-1-932529-37-1(3))* Health Professions Pr.

De Leon, Mony J., et al, eds. Imaging & the Aging Brain. 2007. (Annals of the New York Academy of Sciences Ser.: Vol. 1095). (ENG., Illus.). 252p. pap. 149.95 *(978-1-57331-659-0(8)*, Wiley-Blackwell) Wiley, John & Sons, Inc.

de Villiers, Gwen. Every Day a New Day. 2011. 96p. pap. 9.95 *(978-0-7963-1018-7(1))* NB Pubs. Ltd. ZAF. Dist: International Publishers Marketing.

Deanna Lueckenotte, Lbsw. Alzheimer's Days Gone By: For Those Caring for Their Loved Ones. 2009. 136p. pap. 12.49 *(978-1-4389-6748-6(9))* AuthorHouse.

A

Deters, Natasha. Tau Pathophysiology in Transgenic Mice. 2009. 148p. pap. (978-3-639-21098-9(0)) VDM Verlag Dr. Mueller e.K.

Dezell, Maureen & Hill, Carrie. The Everything Health Guide to Alzheimer's Disease: A Reassuring, Informative Guide for Families & Caregivers. 2009. (ENG.). 304p. pap. 14.95 (978-1-60550-124-6(7)) Adams Media Corp.

Dierckx, Eva. Early Detection of Alzheimer's Disease: A Neuropsychological Approach. 2008. (ENG.). 145p. pap. 43.00 (978-90-5487-422-5(8)) VUB Univ. Pr. BEL. Dist: Independent Pubs. Group.

Doody, Rachelle, ed. Alzheimer's Dementia. 2007. per. 35.95 (978-0-9769581-2-3(0)) Carma Publishing LLC.

Doody, Rachelle S., ed. Alzheimer's Dementia. 2007. 79.95 (978-0-9769581-8-5(X)) Carma Publishing LLC.

Doraiswamy, P. Murali, et al. The Alzheimer's Action Plan: The Experts' Guide to the Best Diagnosis & Treatment for Memory Problems. 2008. (ENG.). 496p. 26.95 (978-0-312-35539-5(4)) St. Martin's Pr.

Doughty, Olivia. Semantic Memory Impairments in Schizophreni. 2010. 220p. pap. (978-3-8383-7773-5(7)) Lambert Academic Publishing.

Dowler, Brynn C. Endocytosis: Structural Components, Functions & Pathways. 2010. (Cell Biology Research Progress Ser.). (Illus.). 259p. 129.00 (978-1-61668-189-0(6)) Nova Science Pubs., Inc.

Duara Ranjan Staff. Mild Cognitive Impairment Early Diagnosis & Treatment. 2010. (ENG., Illus.). 400p. 169.95 (978-0-8493-3613-3(9), Informa Healthcare) Taylor & Francis Group GBR. Dist: Taylor & Francis Group.

Duchesne, Simon. Computer Aid to Diagnostic in Epilepsy & Alzheimer's Disease. 2010. 244p. pap. (978-3-8383-3250-5(4)) Lambert Academic Publishing.

Ebmeier, K. P., ed. Spect in Dementia, Vol. 22. (Advances in Biological Psychiatry Ser.: Vol. 22). (Illus.). (978-3-8055-7595-9(5)) Karger, S. AG.

Emerich, Dwaine F., et al, eds. Central Nervous System Diseases. 2010. (Contemporary Neuroscience Ser.). 532p. pap. 179.00 (978-1-61737-152-3(1), 1617371521) Humana Pr.

Federal Response to the Alzheimer's Epidemic: Hearing Before the Subcommittee on Retirement & Aging of the Committee on Health, Education, Labor, & Pensions, United States Senate, One Hundred Tenth Congress, First Session on Examining the Federal Response & Advances Being Made Toward Defeating the Epidemic of Alzheimer's Disease, July 17, 2007. 2009. iii, 42p. (978-0-16-082746-4(9), 552-070-38751-0) United States Government Printing Office.

Fehér, Ágnes. Genetic Risk Factors in Alzheimer's Disease. 2011. 60p. pap. (978-3-8433-8868-9(7)) Lambert Academic Publishing.

Feldman, Howard H., ed. Atlas of Alzheimer's Disease. 2007. (Atlas Of... Ser.). (ENG., Illus.). 166p. 200.00 (978-0-415-39045-3(1)) Taylor & Francis Group.

Feria, Marcela I. Alzheimer: Una Experiencia Humana. 2006. (SPA & ENG.). 288p. per. 13.95 (978-968-860-764-0(9)) Editorial Pax MEX. Dist: Independent Pubs. Group.

Fisher, A., et al, eds. Alzheimer's & Parkinson's Diseases: Advances, Concepts & New ChallengesCongress, Prague, March 2009: Abstracts. 2009. cd-rom (978-3-8055-9118-8(7)) Karger, S. AG.

Fisher, Abraham, et al, eds. Advances in Alzheimer's & Parkinson's Disease: Insights, Progress, & Perspectives. (Advances in Behavioral Biology Ser.). (Illus.). 2010. xxx, 450p. pap. 189.00 (978-1-4419-4423-8(0), 1441944230) 2007. 489p. 189.00 (978-0-387-72074-6(X), 038772074X) Springer.

Flanagan, Michael. The Downside of Upright Posture: The Anatomical Causes of Alzheimer's, Parkinson's, & Multiple Sclerosis. 2010. 227p. pap. 24.95 (978-1-935097-69-3(5)) Hillcrest Publishing Group, Inc.

Fleisher, A., ed. Alzheimer's Disease & Mild Cognitive Impairment: New Insights from Imaging - Book Edition of Behavioural Neurology. 2009. 140p. pap. 160.00 (978-1-60750-066-7(3)) IOS Pr., Inc.

Forum on Neuroscience and Nervous System Disorders & Institute of Medicine. Future Opportunities to Leverage the Alzheimer's Disease Neuroimaging Initiative: Workshop Summary. 2011. (ENG.). 40p. pap. 15.00 (978-0-309-16188-6(6)) National Academies Pr.

Forum on Neuroscience and Nervous Systems Disorders & Institute of Medicine. Alzheimer's Diagnostic Guideline Validation: Exploration of Next Steps: Workshop Summary. 2012. (ENG.). 40p. pap. 24.00 (978-0-309-22554-0(X)) National Academies Pr.

Fotenos, Anthony. Structural Neuroimaging Across the Adult Life-Span. 2010. (Illus.). 140p. pap. (978-3-8383-4893-3(1)) Lambert Academic Publishing.

Galimberti, Daniela & Scarpani, Elio. Biomarkers for Early Diagnosis of Alzheimer's Disease. 2008. 98.00 (978-1-60456-991-9(3)) Nova Science Pubs., Inc.

Garzione, Marilynn. Released to the Angels: Discovering the Hidden Gifts of Alzheimer's. 2010. 188p. pap. 13.95 (978-1-936236-20-6(6)) iUniverse, Inc.

Gauthier. Clinical Diagnosis & Management of Alzheimer's Disease. 3rd ed. 2006. (ENG., Illus.). 408p. 209.95 (978-0-415-37299-2(2), Informa Healthcare) Taylor & Francis Group GBR. Dist: Taylor & Francis Group.

Gauthier, Serge & Ballard, Clive. Management of Dementia. 2nd ed. 2009. pap. 200.00 (978-1-84184-672-9(4)); (ENG., Illus.). 176p. pap. 199.95 (978-1-84184-667-5(8)) Taylor & Francis Group. (Informa Healthcare).

Gibbons, Leeza, et al. Take Your Oxygen First: Protecting Your Health & Happiness While Caring for a Loved One with Memory Loss. 2009. (ENG.). 325p. pap. 14.95 (978-1-934184-20-2(9)) Lachance Publishing LLC.

Glegg, Keith C. M. The Brain That Destroys Itself: The Evolutionary Origin of Neurodegenerative Diseases Alzheimer's, Parkinson's & Many Others. 2010. 144p. 24.95 (978-1-4502-6329-0(1)); pap. 14.95 (978-1-4502-6328-3(3)) iUniverse, Inc.

Gracey, Marilyn J. A Story of the OWMC: The Wasted Years. 2008. (978-1-55452-306-1(0)) Essence Publishing.

Grierson, Jane. Knickers in the Fridge. 2008. 196p. pap. 17.95 (978-1-4092-0342-1(5)) Lulu Enterprises Inc.

Grossberg, George T. & Kamat, Sanjeev M. Alzheimer Disease: The Latest Assessment & Treatment Strategies. 2008. (978-1-887537-32-2(5)) Compact Clinicals.

—Alzheimers: The Latest Assessment & Treatment Strategies. rev. ed. 2009. 114p. pap. 39.95 (978-0-7637-6579-8(1)) Jones & Bartlett Learning, LLC.

Growdon, J. H. & Adlkofer, F. X., eds. Diadem: Reports on Early Diagnosis of Alzheimer's Disease & Related Dementias. (Illus.). 92p. (978-3-8055-7853-0(9)) Karger, S. AG.

Haass, C. & Multhaup, G., eds. Cellular Mechanisms of Alzheimer's Disease. (Illus.). 126p. pap. (978-3-8055-8183-7(1)) Karger, S. AG.

Hanin, I., et al, eds. Alzheimer's & Parkinson's Diseases: Progress & New Perspectives: 8th International Conference on AD/PD, Salzburg, March 2007: Proceedings: Special Issue: Neurodegenerative Diseases 2008, Vol. 5, No. 3-4. 2008. (Illus.). 158p. (C). pap. (978-3-8055-8518-7(7)) Karger, S. AG.

Harder. 101 Puzzles, Riddles & Rhymes for Attorneys. 2010. 104p. pap. 10.99 (978-1-61579-839-1(0)) Xulon Pr., Inc.

Harding, Psy D. M. a. Thomas & Harding, Psy. D. You Can Prevent Alzheimer's! 2010. 304p. pap. 17.95 (978-1-59330-686-1(5)) Aventine Pr.

Hartman-Stein, Paula E. & LaRue, Asenath, eds. Enhancing Cognitive Fitness in Adults: A Guide to the Use & Development of Community-Based Programs. 2011. (ENG., Illus.). xxii, 500p. 169.00 (978-1-4419-0635-9(5), 1441906355) Springer.

Henderson, Barbara G. Backyard Musings of an Organic Dabbler: Alzheimer?ÇOs & Organic Gardening: A Journey of Hope & Healing. 2010. 142p. pap. 20.95 (978-1-4327-4317-8(1)) Outskirts Pr., Inc.

Hernandez, Jill. Sunshine & Joy's Big Book of Alzheimer's Activities Volume One. l.t. ed. 2007. (Illus.). 132p. spiral bd. 29.95 (978-0-9793634-0-5(3)) Sunshine & Joy Enterprises.

Hill, Anne P. Unforgettable Journey: Tips to Survive Your Parent's Alzheimer's Disease Second Edition. 2010. 116p. pap. 12.95 (978-1-4502-4176-2(X)) iUniverse, Inc.

Hinson, Harold. Owl Hill. 2009. 152p. 21.49 (978-1-4490-1726-2(6)); pap. 10.99 (978-1-4490-1725-5(8)) AuthorHouse.

Hoblitzelle, Olivia A. The Majesty of Your Loving: A Couple's Journey Through Alzheimer's. 2008. (Illus.). 314p. pap. 16.95 (978-0-9793218-0-1(8)) Green Mountain Bks.

Hoffman, John & Froemke, Susan. The Alzheimer's Project: Momentum in Science. 2010. (ENG., Illus.). 224p. pap. 15.95 (978-1-58648-815-4(5)) PublicAffairs.

Hooper, Nigel M., ed. Alzheimer's Disease: Methods & Protocols. 2010. (Methods in Molecular Medicine Ser.). 424p. pap. 149.00 (978-1-61737-161-5(0), 1617371610) Humana Pr.

Hultsch, David F. & Tuokko, Holly, eds. Mild Cognitive Impairment: International Perspectives. 2006. (Studies on Neuropsychology, Neurology, & Cognition). (ENG., Illus.). 336p. 105.95 (978-1-84169-466-5(5), Psychology Press) Taylor & Francis Group GBR. Dist: Taylor & Francis Group.

Jagust, William & D'Esposito, Mark, eds. Imaging the Aging Brain. 2009. (ENG., Illus.). 384p. 125.00 (978-0-19-532887-5(6)) Oxford Univ. Pr., Inc.

James W. Ramage, M. S. W. A Caregiver's Training Manual for the Elderly: Alzheimer's & other Dementia. 2009. 212p. pap. 19.49 (978-1-4389-2366-6(X)) AuthorHouse.

Jeong, Hyun Sil, ed. Alzheimer's Disease in the Middle-Aged. 2008. (Illus.). xv, 381p. 185.00 (978-1-60456-480-8(6)) Nova Science Pubs., Inc.

John, Varghese. Bace: Lead Target for Orchestrated Therapy of Alzheimer's Disease. 2010. (ENG., Illus.). 266p. 111.00 (978-0-470-29342-3(X), Wiley) Wiley, John & Sons, Inc.

Jones, Michelle Addison. As the Deer Pants for Streams of Water. 2011. 64p. pap. 31.99 (978-1-4568-5195-8(0)) Xlibris Corp.

Jucker, Mathias, et al. Alzheimer: 100 Years & Beyond: 100 Years & Beyond. 2010. (Research & Perspectives in Alzheimer's Disease Ser.). (Illus.). xxxiv, 544p. pap. 269.00 (978-3-642-07232-1(1), 3642072321) Springer.

Kidd, Parris M. Phosphatidylserine (PS) Mental Clarity at Any Age. 2007. (Illus.). 32p. 3.95 (978-0-9788031-1-7(6)) Intramedia Publishing LLC.

Kim, Woojin. Alzheimer's Disease & Abeta Peptide. 2010. 92p. pap. (978-3-639-21515-1(X)) VDM Verlag Dr. Mueller e.K.

Kosik, Kenneth. The Alzheimers Solution. 2010. (ENG.). 224p. pap. (978-1-61614-208-7(1)) Prometheus Bks., Pubs.

Krauthamer, Michael. Walking in Your Shoes: Communicating with Loved Ones Who Have Alzheimer's Disease. 2010. 116p. 23.50 (978-1-4520-5861-0(X)); pap. 17.50 (978-1-4520-5860-3(1)) AuthorHouse.

Kumar, Amrendar & singh, Abhilasha. Alzheimer's Disease. 2011. 128p. pap. (978-3-8443-0266-0(2)) Lambert Academic Publishing.

Lau, Lit-Fui & Brodney, Michael A., eds. Alzheimer's Disease. 2008. (Topics in Medicinal Chemistry Ser.). (Illus.). 179p. 239.00 (978-3-540-74228-9(X)) Springer.

Laws, Annie Kate Gaskins. 66 Ways Caregivers Solve the Alzheimer Puzzle: Solving the Alzheimer Puzzle. 2011. 92p. pap. 10.95 (978-1-4327-7445-5(X)) Outskirts Pr., Inc.

Lillrank, Sonja M. Alzheimer's Disease & Other Dementias. 2007. (Psychological Disorders Ser.). (Illus.). 128p. (YA). (gr. 7-12). lib. bdg. 37.50 (978-0-7910-9005-3(1)) Facts On File, Inc.

Lim, Yun-An. Alzheimer's Disease & Type 2 Diabetes As Conformational Diseases. 2010. 132p. pap. (978-3-639-22397-2(7)) VDM Verlag Dr. Mueller e.K.

Luke, Richard D. The Long Wait: The Caregiver's Guide to Survival. 2011. 96p. pap. 11.95 (978-1-4620-4126-8(4)) iUniverse, Inc.

Maccioni, Ricardo B. & Perry, George. Current Hypotheses & Research Milestones in Alzheimer's Disease. 2009. (Illus.). 240p. 149.00 (978-0-387-87994-9(3)) Springer.

Maccioni, Ricardo B. & Perry, George, eds. Current Hypotheses & Research Milestones in Alzheimer's Disease. 2010. (ENG., Illus.). x, 254p. pap. 149.00 (978-1-4419-4690-4(X), 144194690X) Springer.

Mack D. Jones. Deadly Sleep: Is Your Sleep Killing You? 2009. 92p. pap. 11.95 (978-0-595-52870-7(8)) iUniverse, Inc.

Martin, Gary A. & Sabbagh, Marwan Noel. Palliative Care for Advanced Alzheimer's & Dementia: Guidelines & Standards for Evidence-Based Care. 2010. (Illus.). xviii, 313p. E-Book (978-0-8261-0676-6(5)) Springer Publishing Co., Inc.

Martinez, Ana, ed. Emerging Drugs & Targets for Alzheimer's Disease: Complete Set, 2 vols. 2010. (RSC Drug Discovery Ser.). (ENG., Illus.). 668p. 352.00 (978-1-84973-045-7(8)) Royal Society of Chemistry, The GBR. Dist: Ingram Pub. Services.

—Emerging Drugs & Targets for Alzheimer's Disease: Volume 1: Beta-Amyloid, Tau Protein & Glucose Metabolism, 2 vols. 2010. (RSC Drug Discovery Ser.). (Illus.). 342p. 232.00 (978-1-84973-063-1(6)) Royal Society of Chemistry, The GBR. Dist: Ingram Pub. Services.

—Emerging Drugs & Targets for Alzheimer's Disease: Volume 2: Neuronal Plasticity, Neuronal Protection & Other Miscellaneous Strategies, 2 vols. 2010. (RSC Drug Discovery Ser.). (Illus.). 326p. 232.00 (978-1-84973-064-8(4)) Royal Society of Chemistry, The GBR. Dist: Ingram Pub. Services.

Mast, Benjamin. Whole Person Dementia Assessment. 2011. (Illus.). 232p. pap. 34.95 (978-1-932529-71-5(3)) Health Professions Pr.

Mayo Clinic Staff. Mayo Clinic Guide to Alzheimer's Disease: The Essential Resource for Treatment, Coping & Caregiving. 2006. 352p. pap. 16.95 (978-0-06-084251-2(2)) HarperCollins Pubs.

McCann-Beranger, Judith. A Caregiver's Guide to Alzheimer's & Related Diseases. 2008. (B&B Personal Wellness Ser.). (Illus.). 111p. pap. 10.00 (978-1-933480-20-6(3)) Bunim and Bannigan Ltd.

McCann, Kathleen/Sheller. Dragon Grip: Journey into the grip of the Dragon. 2007. (Illus.). 273p. per. 14.95 (978-0-9800938-0-3(5)) McCann Communications.

McCullough, Judy N. Halfway Home: Living Life with Dad's Alzheimer's. 2011. 198p. 29.99 (978-1-4653-5102-9(7)); pap. 19.99 (978-1-4653-5101-2(9)) Xlibris Corp.

McDonald, Pamela & Dyer, Wayne W. The Perfect Gene Diet: Use Your Body's Own APO E Gene to Treat High Cholesterol, Weight Problems, Heart Disease, Alzheimer's... & More! 2010. (ENG.). 464p. pap. 16.95 (978-1-4019-2848-3(X)) Hay Hse., Inc.

McFadden, Susan H. & McFadden, John T. Aging Together: Dementia, Friendship, & Flourishing Communities. 2011. (ENG.). 256p. (gr. 17). 55.00 (978-0-8018-9986-7(9)) Johns Hopkins Univ. Pr.

McNamara, Patrick, ed. Dementia: History & Incidence, 3 vols. (Brain, Behavior, & Evolution Ser.). (Illus.). 823p. 154.95 (978-0-313-38434-9(7), A2895C, Praeger Pubs.) Greenwood Publishing Group, Inc.

Meyer, Maria M., et al. The Comfort of Home for Alzheimer's Disease: A Guide for Caregivers. 2007. (Comfort of Home Ser.). (ENG., Illus.). 360p. per. 24.95 (978-0-9787903-0-1(8)) CareTrust Pubns., LLC.

Minoshima, Satoshi. Alzheimer's Disease, an Issue of PET Clinics. 2007. (Clinics: Radiology Ser.). 240p. 61.00 (978-1-4160-4357-7(8), Saunders) Elsevier - Health Sciences Div.

Mitchell, Deborah. How to Live Well with Early Alzheimer's: A Complete Program for Enhancing Your Quality of Life. 2010. (Healthy Home Library). (ENG.). 240p. 7.99 (978-0-312-37316-0(3), St. Martin's Paperbacks) St. Martin's Pr.

Mobley, Tracy. Young Hope the Broken Road. 2007. 104p. per. 10.95 (978-1-4327-0595-4(4)) Outskirts Pr., Inc.

Moore, Beverly L. Matters of the Mind... & the Heart. 2008. (ENG.). 200p. per. 14.99 (978-1-59932-063-2(0)) Advantage Media Group.

Moore, Elaine A. & Moore, Lisa. Encyclopedia of Alzheimer's Disease; with Directories of Research, Treatment & Care Facilities, 2d Ed. 2nd rev. ed. 2012. (ENG., Illus.). 456p. pap. 95.00 (978-0-7864-6458-6(5)) McFarland & Co., Inc. Pubs.

Murray, Alison. Imaging in Alzheimer's Disease & Other Dementias: Neuroimaging Clinics of North America. 2012. (Clinics: Radiology Ser.: 22-1). (ENG., Illus.). xiv, 121p. 115.00 (978-1-4557-4207-3(4), Saunders) Elsevier - Health Sciences Div.

Newport, Mary T. Alzheimer's Disease: What If There Was a Cure? 2011. (ENG.). 256p. pap. (978-1-59120-293-6(0)) Basic Health Pubns., Inc.

Olkhov, Victor K. & Rayburn, Sandra N. Leading-Edge Research in Alzheimer's Disease. 2008. 185.00 (978-1-60456-225-5(0)) Nova Science Pubs., Inc.

Otwell, Patricia Anne. Guide to Ministering: To Alzheimer's Patients & Their Families. 2008. (ENG.). 296p. 79.95 (978-0-7890-2902-7(2)); pap. 54.50 (978-0-7890-2903-4(0)) Routledge.

Pfeiffer, Eric. The Art of Caregiving in Alzheimer's Disease. 2011. 136p. pap. 14.95 (978-1-257-76112-8(9)) Lulu Enterprises Inc.

Phillips, Fiona. Before I Forget. 2010. (ENG.). 336p. pap. 23.95 (978-1-84809-267-9(9)); (Illus.). 324p. 34.95 (978-1-84809-266-2(0)) Random Hse. GBR. Dist: Independent Pubs. Group.

Pickton, Pamela. Beautiful Dreamer. 2009. 266p. pap. (978-1-84747-952-5(9)) Chipmunkapublishing.

Pierce, Letting go of the Rice Connie. Letting go of the Rice. 2009. 81p. pap. 9.99 (978-0-557-05760-3(4)) Lulu Enterprises Inc.

Pitzer, Jean. You Too Can Survive: My Journey as an Alzheimer's Caregiver. 2007. 64p. per. 9.95 (978-0-595-41068-2(5)) iUniverse, Inc.

Purtilo, Ruth B. & ten Have, Henk A. M. J., eds. Ethical Foundations of Palliative Care for Alzheimer Disease. 2010. (ENG., Illus.). 396p. (gr. 17). pap. 35.00 (978-0-8018-9839-6(0)) Johns Hopkins Univ. Pr.

Ramphol, Sylvia. Alzheimer's Disease. 2010. 60p. pap. (978-3-639-00113-6(3)) VDM Verlag Dr. Mueller e.K.

Rasgon, Natalie L., ed. Insulin Resistance Syndrome & Neuropsychiatric Disease. 2008. (Medical Psychiatry Ser.: Vol. 38). (ENG., Illus.). 168p. 150.00 (978-0-8493-8208-6(4), Informa Healthcare) Taylor & Francis Group GBR. Dist: Taylor & Francis Group.

Read, Catherine Y., et al, eds. Aging, Biotechnology, & the Future. 2008. (ENG., Illus.). 296p. (gr. 17). 47.00 (978-0-8018-8788-8(7)) Johns Hopkins Univ. Pr.

Reed, Emma. The Other Woman Is AD: A Behavior Log on an Alzheimer's Patient, My Husband. 2011. 100p. pap. 15.49 (978-1-4567-2212-8(3)) AuthorHouse.

Richter, Ralph W. & Zoeller Richter, Brigitte, eds. Alzheimer's Disease. 2nd ed. 2013. (Current Clinical Neurology Ser.). (ENG., Illus.). 600p. 89.95 (978-1-60327-869-0(9), 1603278699) Humana Pr.

Roberson, Erik D. Alzheimer's Disease & Frontotemporal Dementia: Methods & Protocols. 2011. (Illus.). x, 277p. E-Book (978-1-60761-744-0(7)) Humana Pr.

Roberson, Erik D., ed. Alzheimer's Disease & Frontotemporal Dementia. 2010. (Methods in Molecular Biology Ser.). (ENG., Illus.). x, 270p. 119.00 (978-1-60761-743-3(9), 1607617439) Humana Pr.

Ronson, Charles E., ed. Alzheimer's Diagnosis. 2011. (Neuroscience Research Progress Ser.). (Illus.). 276p. 89.00 (978-1-61209-846-3(0)) Nova Science Pubs., Inc.

Rosen, A. & Adamson, M., eds. Handbook of Imaging the Alzheimer Brain. 2011. 824p. 276.00 (978-1-60750-792-5(7)) IOS Pr., Inc.

Rudolph, Alan S. & Wegrzyn, Renee D., eds. Alzheimer's Disease. 2012. (Frontiers in Neuroscience Ser.). (ENG., Illus.). 298p. 149.95 (978-1-4398-2708-6(7), CRC Press) Taylor & Francis Group GBR. Dist: Taylor & Francis Group.

Santulli, Robert. The Alzheimer's Family: Helping Caregivers Cope. 2011. (ENG.). 256p. 29.95 (978-0-393-70577-5(3), 70577) Norton, W. W. & Co., Inc.

Sarah R. Jacobsen. Vascular Dementia: Risk Factors, Diagnosis & Treatment. 2011. (Series: Neuroscience Research Progress Ser.). 129.00 (978-1-61122-313-2(X), Nova Biomedical Bks.) Nova Science Pubs., Inc.

Selkoe, Dennis J., et al, eds. Synaptic Plasticity & the Mechanism of Alzheimer's Disease. 2008. (Research & Perspectives in Alzheimer's Disease Ser.). (Illus.). 182p. 169.00 (978-3-540-76329-1(5)) Springer.

Selkoe, Dennis J. & Triller, Antoine. Synaptic Plasticity & the Mechanism of Alzheimer's Disease. 2010. (Research & Perspectives in Alzheimer's Disease Ser.). (Illus.). xii, 183p. pap. 169.00 (978-3-642-09519-1(4), 3642095194) Springer.

Selkoe, Dennis J., et al. The Biology of Alzheimer Disease. 2011. 135.00 (978-1-936113-44-6(9)) Cold Spring Harbor Laboratory Pr.

Semple, Jane. Alzheimer Disease: A Naturopathic Approach. 2007. (Woodland Health Ser.). 30p. pap. 4.95 (978-1-58054-106-0(2)) Woodland Publishing, Inc.

Shriver, Maria. Alzheimer's in America: The Shriver Report on Women & Alzheimer's. 2011. (ENG., Illus.). 320p. pap. 12.99 (978-1-4516-3987-2(2), Free Pr.) Free Pr.

Silverman, Dan, ed. PET in the Evaluation of Alzheimer's Disease & Related Disorders. 2009. (ENG., Illus.). xiv, 215p. 149.00 (978-0-387-76419-1(4), 0387764194) Springer.

Simard, Joyce. The End-of-Life Namaste Care Program for People with Dementia. 2007. 197p. per. 29.95 (978-1-932529-34-0(9)) Health Professions Pr.

Sisodia, Sangram S. & Tanzi, Rudolph E., eds. Alzheimer's Disease: Advances in Genetics, Molecular & Cellular Biology. (ENG., Illus.). x, 286p. 2010. pap. 149.00 (978-1-4419-4195-4(9), 1441941959) 2007. 149.00 (978-0-387-35134-6(5), 0387351345) Springer.

Sivaraman, D. Neuroprotective Effect of Methanolic Leaf Extract. 2010. 92p. pap. (978-3-8383-7695-0(1)) Lambert Academic Publishing.

Small, David H., ed. Abeta Peptide & Alzheimer's Disease: Celebrating a Century of Research. 2006. (Illus.). 298p. 139.00 (978-1-85233-961-6(6), 1852339616) Springer.

Smith, Diane. Alzheimer's & Diabetes: My Roller Coaster Journey with My Two Best Friends. 2011. (ENG.). 203p. pap. 14.95 (978-1-4327-7720-3(3)) Outskirts Pr., Inc.

Smith, M. A., et al, eds. Signal Transduction in Alzheimer's Disease: Neurosignals, Vol. 11. (Neurosignals Ser.). (Illus.). 68p. (978-3-8055-7533-1(5)) Karger, S. AG.

Sourcebooks. The Alzheimer's Answer Book: Professional Answers to More Than 250 Questions about Alzheimer's & Dementia. 2008. (ENG.). 352p. pap. 14.95 (978-1-4022-1344-1(1)) Sourcebooks, Inc.

Spainhour, Polly L. The Color of Gray: (Living & Dying with Alzheimer's) 2011. 318p. pap. 29.95 (978-1-4560-9134-7(4)) PublishAmerica, Inc.

Stano, Paul J., text. Alzheimer's Survival Guide: 7 Secrets of Estate Planning for People with Memory Loss & Dementia. 2007. 160p. pap. 14.95 (978-0-9795864-0-8(2)) Stano, Paul.

Steinberg. Forgetting the Memories: A Caregiver's Journey Through Alzheimer's Disease. 2010. 120p. 24.49 (978-1-4490-5589-9(3)); pap. 15.95 (978-1-4490-5588-2(5)) AuthorHouse.

Stern, Yaakov. Cognitive Reserve: Theory & Applications. 2006. (Studies on Neuropsychology, Neurology, & Cognition). (ENG., Illus.). 368p. 105.95 (978-1-84169-474-0(6), Psychology Press) Taylor & Francis Group GBR. Dist: Taylor & Francis Group.

Sun, Maio-Kun. Research Progress in Alzheimer's Disease & Dementia, Volume 3. 2007. 185.00 (978-1-60021-960-3(8)) Nova Science Pubs., Inc.

Sun, Miao-Kun. Research Progress in Alzheimer's Disease & Dementia, Vol. 2. 2006. (Illus.). 378p. 89.00 (978-1-60021-271-0(9)) Nova Science Pubs., Inc.

Sun, Miao-Kun, ed. Cognitive Sciences at the Leading Edge. 2008. 82.00 (978-1-60456-051-0(7)) Nova Science Pubs., Inc.

—Research Progress in Alzheimer's Disease & Dementia (vol. 4) 2009. (Research Progress in Alzheimer's Disease & Dementia Ser.). 145.00 (978-1-60876-152-4(5)) Nova Science Pubs., Inc.

Sutton, Amy, ed. Alzheimer Disease Sourcebook. 5th rev. ed. 2011. (Health Reference Ser.). lib. bdg. 95.00 (978-0-7808-1150-8(X)) Omnigraphics, Inc.

Takeda, Masatoshi, et al, eds. Molecular Neurobiology of Alzheimer Disease & Related Disorders. (Illus.). 14;298p. (978-3-8055-7603-1(X)) Karger, S. AG.

Thacker, Herminia. Coping with the Influx of Dementia Patients - the Need to Involve the Communities & Church Groups with Medical & Social. 2007. pap. (978-3-8364-2972-6(1)) VDM Verlag Dr. Mueller e.K.

Townsend, Terry F. Living Alone with Dementia — Alzheimer's. 2008. 106p. pap. 16.95 (978-1-60672-256-5(5)) PublishAmerica, Inc.

Turkington, Carol & Mitchell, Deborah. The A to Z of Alzheimer's Disease. 2010. (Library of Health & Living Ser.). 320p. (C). (gr. 9-18). pap. 19.95 (978-0-8160-8127-1(1), Checkmark Bks.) Facts On File, Inc.

Turkington, Carol, et al. The Encyclopedia of Alzheimer's Disease. 2nd rev. ed. 2010. (Library of Health & Living Ser.). 320p. (C). (gr. 9-18). 75.00 (978-0-8160-7766-3(5)) Facts On File, Inc.

van Dooren, Tom. Biochemical & Immuno-Histochemical Analysis of APP-Processing & Amyloid Pathology in Single & Multiple Transgenic Mice as Models for Alzheimer's Disease. 2006. (Acta Biomedica Lovaniensia Ser.: Vol. 365). (Illus.). pap. 97.50 (978-90-5867-544-6(0)) Leuven Univ. Pr. BEL. Dist: Cornell Univ. Pr.

Verbeek, M. M., et al, eds. Cerebral Amyloid Angiopathy in Alzheimer's Disease & Related Disorders. 2010. 384p. pap. 182.00 (978-90-481-5480-7(4), 9048154804) Springer.

Visser, Anouk M. Alzheimer's Disease: New Research. Visser, Anouk M., ed. 2008. (Illus.). xiv, 266p. (C). 185.00 (978-1-60456-481-5(4)) Nova Science Pubs., Inc.

Wahlund, Lars-Olof, et al. Vascular Cognitive Impairment in Clinical Practice. Wahlund, Lars-Olof et al, eds. 2009. (ENG., Illus.). 254p. 142.00 (978-0-521-87537-0(4)) Cambridge Univ. Pr.

Wang, Xinglong. Mitochondria Abnormalities in Alzheimer's Disease. 2009. 140p. pap. (978-3-639-16974-4(3)) VDM Verlag Dr. Mueller e.K.

The Way Forward: An Update from the Alzheimer's Study Group: Hearing Before the Special Committee on Aging, United States Senate, One Hundred Eleventh Congress, First Session, Washington, DC, March 25, 2009. 2009. (Illus.). iii, 82p. (978-0-16-084115-6(1), 552-070-39722-1) United States Government Printing Office.

Weiner, Myron F. & Lipton, Anne M. The American Psychiatric Publishing Textbook of Alzheimer Disease & Other Dementias. 2009. (Illus.). 560p. 145.00 (978-1-58562-278-8(8)) American Psychiatric Publishing, Inc.

Weiner, Myron F. & Lipton, Anne M. Clinical Manual of Alzheimer Disease & Other Dementias. 2012. pap. **(978-1-58562-422-5(5))** American Psychiatric Publishing, Inc.

Whitehouse, Peter J. The Myth's of Alzheimer's: What You Aren't Being Told about Today's Most Dreaded Diagnosis. lt. ed. 2009. 659p. 31.95 (978-1-4104-1988-0(6)) Thorndike Pr.

Williams, John W. Preventing Alzheimer's Disease & Cognitive Decline. 2010. (Illus.). x, 328p. **(978-1-58763-393-5(0))** Agency for Healthcare Research & Quality.

Windisch, M., et al, eds. Alzheimer's & Parkinson's Diseases: Advances, Concepts & New Challenges - 9th International Conference AD/PD, Prague, March 2009. 2010. (Illus.). 218p. pap. (978-3-8055-9358-8(9)) Karger, S. AG.

Yadav, Arpita & Sonker, Minakshi. Strategies in Design of Alzheimer's Disease Drugs. 2011. 116p. pap. **(978-3-8433-8903-7(9))** Lambert Academic Publishing.

Zhang, Can. Identifying Genes That Encode App Metabolism Modulators. 2010. 156p. pap. (978-3-8383-6089-8(3)) Lambert Academic Publishing.

ALZHEIMER'S DISEASE—PATIENTS

Akbar, Celestina. Alzheimer's Disease: A Growing Health Care Issue among the Elderly. 2011. 58p. 24.99 **(978-1-4568-8338-6(0))** Xlibris Corp.

Alterra, Aaron. The Caregiver: A Life with Alzheimer's. 2008. (Culture & Politics of Health Care Work Ser.). 213p. per. 20.95 (978-0-8014-7434-7(5)) Cornell Univ. Pr.

Artis, Jennifer. A Blessing of Alzheimer's. 2011. 90p. 24.99 **(978-1-4653-4465-6(9))**; pap. 15.99 **(978-1-4653-4464-9(0))** Xlibris Corp.

Asp, Elissa D. & de de Villiers, Jessica. When Language Breaks Down: Analysing Discourse in Clinical Contexts. 2010. (ENG., Illus.). 270p. 110.00 (978-0-521-88978-0(2)) Cambridge Univ. Pr.

Bell, Virginia, et al. The Best Friends Book of Alzheimer's Activities: Volume 2, 2 vols., 2. 2007. (Illus.). 248p. pap. 36.95 (978-1-932529-26-5(8)) Health Professions Pr.

Bertsch, Fred S. "Fritz". Hell & Heaven Revisited. 2010. 240p. pap. 19.95 (978-1-4269-4028-6(9)) Trafford Publishing.

Bielawski, Melvin R. Diagnosis: Alzheimer's - My Travels with Frances. 2010. 116p. pap. 10.99 (978-1-4490-8722-7(1)) AuthorHouse.

Blandford, Anne. My God Is Real. 2007. 150p. pap. 14.95 (978-1-57258-471-6(8), 945-6332) TEACH Services, Inc.

Brackey, Jolene. Creating Moments of Joy: A Journal for Caregivers. 4th ed. 2008. 331p. per. 24.95 (978-1-55753-462-0(4)) Purdue Univ. Pr.

Bradshaw, Diane. I Am Arnold. 2011. 148p. 22.99 **(978-1-4670-2503-4(8))**; pap. 15.99 **(978-1-4670-2504-1(6))** AuthorHouse.

Brewer, Sonja. Surviving Normal. 2009. 332p. pap. 18.95 (978-1-59330-595-6(8)) Aventine Pr.

Bryden, Christine. Who Will I Be When I Die? 2012. (ENG., Illus.). 176p. pap. **(978-1-84905-312-9(X))** Kingsley, Jessica Ltd.

Buckner, Andrew & Stiver, Russell. Into Existence's Immortal Flame: The Autobiographies of Andrew Buckner & Russell Stiver. 2011. 158p. pap. 24.95 **(978-1-4560-2471-0(X))** PublishAmerica, Inc.

Burke, Ruth Marie. Six Pieces of Pie: Dealing with elderly parents as an adult Child. 2009. 144p. pap. 12.99 (978-1-4389-9814-5(7)) AuthorHouse.

Cabin, William. Phantoms of Home Care. 2010. 252p. pap. (978-3-8383-9206-6(X)) Lambert Academic Publishing.

Cabrera, Thomas S. Adults Gone Missing: Alert Systems & Federal Assistance. 2011. pap. **(978-1-62100-085-3(0))** Nova Science Pubs., Inc.

Calo-oy, Starr. Caregiving Tips A-Z: Everything you need to know to care for your loved one at Home! 2007. per. 29.95 (978-0-9753195-2-9(3)) Orchard Pubns.

—Caregiving Tips A-Z Alzheimer's & Other Dementias: Everything you need to know to care for your loved one at Home. 2007. per. 29.95 (978-0-9753195-3-6(1)) Orchard Pubns.

Carey, Louise. The Hedge People: How I Kept My Sanity & Sense of Humor As an Alzheimer's Caregiver. 2009. (ENG.). 128p. pap. 11.99 (978-0-8341-2468-4(8), 9780834124684) Beacon Hill Pr. of Kansas City.

Carter, R. D. My Ladybug's Alzheimer's Journey: She Looked Like My Mother but She Did Not Act Like My Mother. 2011. 204p. pap. 17.95 (978-1-4502-7903-1(1)) iUniverse, Inc.

Cerasoli, Lisa. As Nora Jo Fades Away: Confessions of a Caregiver: A Memoir. 2010. 180p. 15.95 (978-1-58985-190-0(0)) Five Star Pubns., Inc.

Cockey, E. J. Drawn from Memory: A personal story of healing through Art. 2008. 168p. pap. 13.95 (978-1-934925-16-4(0), Strategic Bk. Publishing) AEG Literary Publishing Services, Inc.

Cockey, Elizabeth Jane. Drawn from Memory: A Personal Story of Healing Through Art. 2007. (ENG.). 168p. per. 13.95 (978-0-9790275-1-2(9)) Ovation Bks.

Coste, Joanne Koenig. Learning to Speak Alzheimer's: The New Approach to Living Positively with Alzheimer's Disease. 2007. 244p. reprint ed. pap. 20.00 (978-1-4223-9027-6(6)) DIANE Publishing Co.

Cummings-Lamnek, Earlene. My Parents' Passing: An Inspirational Story for Victims of Alzheimer's & Their Families. 2011. pap. 10.99 (978-1-61739-294-8(4)) Tate Publishing & Enterprises, LLC.

Currie, Diane. Before My Eyes: A Daughter's Personal Journey with her Mother into Alzheimer's Disease. 2010. 88p. pap. 10.95 (978-1-4502-1678-4(1)) iUniverse, Inc.

David, Judith Ames. Set Me Adrift in the Sea of Faith: The Faith Renewing Story of an Alzheimer Patient's Daughter. 2007. 131p. per. 10.99 (978-1-59886-939-2(6)) Tate Publishing & Enterprises, LLC.

Davies, Helen D. & Jensen, Michael P. Alzheimer's Disease: Answers to the Most Asked Questions. 2011. 160p. pap. 19.95 (978-1-886039-99-5(2)) Addicus Bks.

Davis, Boyd H. Alzheimer Talk, Text & Context: Enhancing Communication. 2009. (ENG., Illus.). 276p. pap. 39.00 (978-0-230-20694-6(8)) Palgrave Macmillan.

Debaggio, Thomas. When It Gets Dark: An Enlightened Reflection on Life with Alzheimer's. 2007. (ENG.). 240p. per. 16.95 (978-1-4165-7320-3(8), Free Pr.) Free Pr.

Dowe, Roberta. A Simple Plan. 2008. 176p. pap. (978-1-55452-316-0(8)) Essence Publishing.

Duarte, Cynthia. Yet, I Will Love Thee: The Hard Truth of Alzheimer's Caregiving. 2008. 64p. per. 16.95 (978-1-4241-9904-4(2)) PublishAmerica, Inc.

Dubono, Regine. Mama Bellissima. 2007. 140p. pap. 18.95 (978-1-4303-2407-2(4)) Lulu Enterprises Inc.

—Maman. 2007. 136p. 32.94 (978-1-4303-2980-0(7)) Lulu Enterprises Inc.

Edwards, Caterina. Finding Rosa: A Mother with Alzheimer's, a Daughter in Search of the Past, 1 vol. (ENG.). 2010. 352p. pap. 16.95 (978-1-55365-526-6(5)) 2009. 304p. 24.95 (978-1-55365-389-9(0)) D&M Pubs. Inc. CAN. (Greystone Bks.). Dist: Perseus-PGW.

Farrell, Richard J. Alzheimer's Caregiving: Lessons from a Surviving Spouse. 2011. 92p. pap. 11.95 (978-1-4502-7645-0(8)) iUniverse, Inc.

Fazio, Sam. The Enduring Self in People with Alzheimer's: Getting to the Heart of Individualized Care. 2008. (Illus.). 175p. pap. 26.95 (978-1-932529-38-8(1)) Health Professions Pr.

Fisher, L. S. Alzheimer's Anthology of Unconditional Love. 2007. pap. 10.00 (978-0-7383-8774-1(6)) Booksource, The.

Fox, Judith. I Still Do: Loving & Living with Alzheimer's. 2009. (ENG., Illus.). 144p. 29.95 (978-1-57687-507-0(5), powerHouse Bks.) powerHouse Cultural Entertainment, Inc.

Frank, Rita. Art of the Heart: How to Understand & Help People with Alzheimer's & Related Disorders, Book I. 2008. pap. 11.00 (978-0-8059-8950-2(1)) Dorrance Publishing Co., Inc.

Fuerst, Frank. Alzheimer's Care with Dignity. 2007. 206p. per. 24.95 (978-0-929915-62-3(3)) Headline Bks.

Gentry, G. Douglas. My Parents, Myself Battling Alzheimer's. 2008. 222p. pap. 24.95 (978-1-60672-048-6(1)) PublishAmerica, Inc.

Gillies, Andrea. Keeper: One House, Three Generations, & a Journey into Alzheimer's. 2010. (ENG.). 336p. 25.00 (978-0-307-71911-9(1)) Broadway Bks.

—Keeper: One House, Three Generations, & a Journey into Alzheimer's. 2011. (ENG.). 336p. pap. 15.00 (978-0-307-71912-6(X), Three Rivers Pr.) Crown Publishing Group.

Gogia, Prem P. & Rastogi, Nirek. Clinical Alzheimer Rehabilitation. 2008. (Illus.). 258p. 48.00 (978-0-8261-1707-6(4)) Springer Publishing Co., Inc.

Gray-Davidson, Frena. Alzheimer's 911: Help, Hope, & Healing for the Caregivers. 2009. 192p. pap. 16.95 (978-1-934759-14-1(7)) Reed, Robert D. Pubs.

Green, Mary, et al. The Long Goodbye. 2011. 124p. pap. 10.68 (978-1-4567-4288-1(4)) AuthorHouse.

Greenblat, Cathy. Love, Loss, & Laughter: Seeing Alzheimer's Differently. 2012. (ENG., Illus.). 176p. 24.95 **(978-0-7627-7907-9(1)**, Lyons Pr.) Globe Pequot Pr., The.

Gretchen L. Dausey. Jim's Journey: The Story of a Young Man with Early on-set Alzheimer's. 2010. 96p. pap. 12.95 (978-1-4251-3765-6(2)) Trafford Publishing.

Hayden, Arlene. Angels Watching over Lydia: The Alzheimer's Crunch. 2011. 596p. pap. 26.94 **(978-1-4634-2099-4(4))** AuthorHouse.

Haynal, Carolyn. I Was Once Like You: Before I Got Alzheimer's. 2011. 308p. 24.95 **(978-1-4678-4952-4(9))**; pap. 16.95 **(978-1-4678-4953-1(7))** AuthorHouse.

Hernandez, Jill. Sunshine & Joy's Big Book of Alzheimer's Activities Volume Two. 2007. (Illus.). 125p. spiral bd. 29.95 (978-0-9793634-1-2(1)) Sunshine & Joy Enterprises.

Hill, Jane. Alzheimers & You: A Self Help Guide for Carers & Sufferers. 2010. 80p. pap. 11.49 (978-1-4490-5371-0(8)) AuthorHouse.

Hill, Jean. A New Life in the Country. 2010. (Illus.). 48p. pap. 10.49 (978-1-4520-1751-8(4)) AuthorHouse.

Hoblitzelle, Olivia Ames. Ten Thousand Joys & Ten Thousand Sorrows: A Couple's Journey Through Alzheimer's. 2010. (ENG.). 352p. (gr. 12). 16.95 (978-1-58542-827-4(2), Tarcher) Penguin Group (USA) Inc.

Hoffman, Linda Marie. Why Do You Call Me Mom? The Experience of an Alzheimer's Patient's Caregiver. 2008. 126p. pap. 19.95 (978-1-60672-931-1(4)) PublishAmerica, Inc.

Holland, Gail Bernice. Forget-Me-Not: A Memoir of Anne Bashkiroff's Alzheimer's Crusade. 2006. 193p. per. 19.95 (978-1-55753-425-5(X)) Purdue Univ. Pr.

Hubley, Todd J. The Silent Flute: A Walk in the Footsteps of Alzheimer's Disease. 2009. 116p. 23.95 (978-1-4389-8132-1(5)); pap. 14.95 (978-1-4389-8131-4(7)) AuthorHouse.

Huddleston, Kathryn. There's A Storm Coming: the Journey to Rescue & Save My Father: Helping My Father Achieve His Mental, Physical, & Spiritual Potential During His Alzheimer's Disease. 2010. 372p. 39.95 (978-1-4497-0599-2(5)); pap. 24.95 (978-1-4497-0597-8(9)) Author Solutions, Inc. (WestBow Pr.).

Huebner, Berna G., ed. I Remember Better When I Paint: Art & Alzheimer's: Opening Doors, Making Connections. 2011. (Illus.). 132p. pap. 19.95 net. **(978-0-9761364-4-6(9))** Bethesda Communications Group.

Ican. Ma Is Back! Restoring My Mother's Memory, Memoir of an Alzheimer's Discovery. 2010. (ENG.). 128p. 13.95 (978-0-9830031-0-6(6)) ICAN, Ltd.

James, Oliver. Contented Dementia: 24-Hour Wraparound Care for Lifelong Well-Being. 2010. (ENG.). 304p. pap. 19.95 (978-0-09-190181-3(2)) Ebury Publishing GBR. Dist: Independent Pubs. Group.

Jowell, Kate & Sorour-Morris, Sharon. Something on My Mind: Kate Jowell: A Battle with Alzheimer's. 2011. (Illus.). 272p. pap. 26.00 (978-1-77020-090-6(8)) Random Hse. Struik (Pty.), Ltd. ZAF. Dist: International Publishers Marketing.

Joyce, James J. Walking into Darkness: How to Care for the Alzheimer Patient. 8p. (Orig.). (978-0-9642138-0-7(X)) Joyce Homecare, Inc.

Kehoe, Sandra M. Listen to Me, I Am Still Somebody: Understanding the Alzheimer's Disease Sufferer. 2007. 116p. per. 19.95 (978-1-58112-988-5(2)) Universal Pubs.

Kessler, Lauren. Finding Life in the Land of Alzheimer's: One Daughter's Hopeful Story. 2008. (ENG.). 272p. (gr. 12-18). 14.00 (978-0-14-311368-3(2), Penguin (Non-Classics)) Penguin Group (USA) Inc.

Krautwald, Martina. Methylglyoxal-Lowering Agents As a Treatment for Alzheimer's Disease? 2011. 84p. pap. **(978-3-8443-1618-6(3))** Lambert Academic Publishing.

LeBlanc, Gary Joseph & Leblanc, Gary Joseph. Staying Afloat in a Sea of Forgetfulness: Common Sense Caregiving Expanded Edition. 2011. 332p. 29.99 **(978-1-4628-7706-5(0))**; pap. 19.99 **(978-1-4628-7705-8(2))** Xlibris Corp.

Legal & Financial Issues on Alzheimer's Disease: An Annotated List of Resources. 33p. pap. 20.00 (978-0-7881-3861-4(8)) DIANE Publishing Co.

Leleux, Robert. The Living End: A Memoir of Forgetting & Forgiving. 2012. (ENG.). 160p. 19.99 **(978-0-312-62124-7(8))** St. Martin's Pr.

Lewis, Zoë A. I Hope They Know. the Essential Handbook on Alzheimer's Disease & Care. 2008. (ENG.). 240p. pap. 24.95 (978-1-60264-177-8(3)) Virtualbookworm.com Publishing, Inc.

Lockhart, Sybil. Mother in the Middle: A Biologist's Story of Caring for Parent & Child. 2009. (ENG.). 320p. 25.00 (978-1-4165-4155-4(1), Touchstone) Touchstone.

London, Judith. Connecting the Dots: Breakthroughs in Communication as Alzheimer's Advances. 2009. (ENG.). 232p. pap. 18.95 (978-1-57224-700-0(2)) New Harbinger Pubns.

Lowden, Leigh. With True Affection, Millie B. A Story of Friendship & God's Grace. 2009. pap. 10.99 (978-1-60791-712-0(2)) Xulon Pr., Inc.

Mace, Nancy L. & Rabins, Peter V. The 36-Hour Day: A Family Guide to Caring for People Who Have Alzheimer Disease, Related Dementias, & Memory Loss. 5th ed. 2011. (Johns Hopkins Press Health Book Ser.). (ENG.). 384p. (gr. 17). 45.00 **(978-1-4214-0279-6(3))**; 384p. pap. 16.95 **(978-1-4214-0280-2(7))**; 648p. pap. 21.95 **(978-1-4214-0307-6(2))** Johns Hopkins Univ. Pr.

Mallory, Pat. One of Us Has Alzheimer's!! 2009. 100p. pap. 10.99 (978-1-60791-612-3(6)) Xulon Pr., Inc.

Mcallister, Jane A. Before It's Too Late. 2009. 204p. pap. 14.49 (978-1-4490-2645-5(1)) AuthorHouse.

—Before It's Too Late: Alzheimer's. 2009. 204p. 24.99 (978-1-4490-2646-2(X)) AuthorHouse.

McCann-Beranger, Judith & Alzheimer Society of Prince Edward Island Staff. A Caregiver's Guide for Alzheimer & Related Diseases. 2nd ed. (Illus.). 112p. pap. 16.95 (978-1-894838-11-5(4)) Acorn Pr., The CAN. Dist: Goose Lane Editions.

McLay, Evelyn. Mom's Ok, She Just Forgets: The Alzheimer's Journey from Denial to Acceptance. 2006. (ENG.). 1p. per. 17.98 (978-1-59102-469-9(2)) Prometheus Bks., Pubs.

McLean. The Person in Dementia: Pb. 2007. (Teaching Culture: UTP Ethnographies for the Classroom Ser.). 225p. pap. 29.95 (978-1-55111-606-8(5)) Broadview Pr. CAN. Dist: Univ. of Toronto Pr.

Menzies, Heather. Enter Mourning: A Memoire on Death, Dementia, & Coming Home. 2009. (ENG., Illus.). 240p. pap. 19.95 (978-1-55470-155-1(4)) Key Porter Bks. CAN. Dist: Perseus-PGW.

Moffett, Pat. Ice Cream in the Cupboard: A True Story of Early Onset Alzheimer's. 2007. 232p. 19.95 (978-0-9742278-1-8(1)) Garrison-Savanna Publishing LLC.

—Ice Cream in the Cupboard: A True Story of Early Onset Alzheimer's. 2008. (ENG.). 232p. 23.95 (978-1-60037-416-6(6)) Morgan James Publishing.

Moore, Beverly. Matters of the Mind & the Heart. 2009. 212p. pap. 15.99 (978-1-60860-476-0(4), Strategic Bk. Publishing) AEG Literary Publishing Services, Inc.

National Silver Alert ACT, the Silver Alert Grant Program ACT of 2008, & the Kristen's ACT Reauthorization of 2007: Hearing Before the Subcommittee on Crime, Terrorism, & Homeland Security of the Committee on the Judiciary, House of Representatives, One Hundred Tenth Congress, Second Session, on H.R. 6004, H.R. 5898 & H.R. 423, July 15, 2008. 2008. iii, 47p. (978-0-16-082479-1(6), 552-070-38516-9) United States Government Printing Office.

Òe Rís, Pádraig. Dare to Dream. 2009. (Illus.). 240p. pap. 14.49 (978-1-4490-4624-8(X)) AuthorHouse.

O'Leary, Gwen. When Life Hands You Alzheimer's, Make Aprons! A Daughter's Journal of Her Mother's Last Months. 2011. 176p. pap. 13.50 **(978-1-4567-5040-4(2))** AuthorHouse.

Parsons, Dale. Dementia. 2006. 17.00 (978-0-8059-8813-0(0)) Dorrance Publishing Co., Inc.

Pate, Billie J. Please Take Me Home Before Dark: One Family's Journey with Alzheimer's Disease. 2006. (Illus.). 84p. per. 12.95 (978-1-57736-389-7(2)) Providence Hse Pubs.

Patricia Cox. We Keep Our Potato Chips in the Refrigerator: A Memoir of an Alzheimer's Victim. 2010. 136p. pap. 13.95 (978-1-4502-0256-5(X)) iUniverse, Inc.

Pearce, Nancy. Inside Alzheimer's: How to Hear & Honor Connections with a Person who has Dementia. rev. ed. 2011. (ENG., Illus.). 336p. pap. 19.95 (978-0-9788299-1-9(3)) Forrason Pr.

Petersen, Barry. Jan's Story: Love Lost to the Long Goodbye of Alzheimer's. 2010. (ENG.). 224p. pap. 15.95 (978-1-933016-44-3(2)) Behler Pubns., LLC.

Phillips, Fiona. Before I Forget. 2011. (ENG., Illus.). 328p. pap. 14.95 (978-1-84809-268-6(7)) Random Hse. GBR. Dist: Independent Pubs. Group.

Radell, John. Lucy's Tears: (How Alzheimer's Affected a Life of Faith & Joy) 2007. 112p. per. 19.95 (978-1-4241-7425-6(2)) PublishAmerica, Inc.

Rafool, Gordon J. Communicating for Care: How to Form a Successful Team with the Alzheimer's Patient, Caregiver, & Doctor. 2007. 72p. per. 16.95 (978-1-4241-7718-9(9)) PublishAmerica, Inc.

Rain, Mary Summer. Love Never Sleeps: Living at Home with Alzheimer's. 2007. 371p. reprint ed. pap. 15.00 (978-1-4223-6681-3(2)) DIANE Publishing Co.

Rava, Susan. Swimming Solo: A Daughter's Memoir of Her Parents, His Parents, & Alzheimer's Disease. 2011. (Illus.). 310p. pap. 14.95 (978-0-9814795-0-7(2), Plateau Bks.) Plateau Bks.

Read, Glory. Everything Will Be Alright: An Alzheimer's Memoir. 2007. 112p. 22.95 (978-0-595-68762-6(8)); per. 12.95 (978-0-595-44006-1(1)) iUniverse, Inc.

Reed, Jacci Smith. A Stranger in the House: A Journal of My Life Living the Last Years with My Husband's Alzheimer's. 2011. 112p. 22.06 **(978-1-4269-9475-3(3))**; pap. 12.06 **(978-1-4269-9476-0(1))** Trafford Publishing.

Reiswig, Gary. The Thousand Mile Stare: Living with the Legacy of Alzheimer's. 2010. (ENG.). 240p. 22.00 (978-1-85788-536-1(8)) Ebsco Publishing.

Rodrigues, Tiffany. Sensual Therapy for the Mentally Frail. 2010. 68p. pap (978-3-639-27762-3(7)) VDM Verlag Dr. Mueller e.K.

Ross-Holley, Vera V. Come Back, Julia! A Tale of Love, Loves Lost, Abuse, & the Come Back! 2011. 104p. pap. 11.95 **(978-1-4620-5879-2(5))** iUniverse, Inc.

Rubinstein, Nataly. Alzheimer's Disease & Other Dementias. 2011. 414p. pap. 17.95 (978-1-936198-13-9(4)) Two Harbors Pr., Inc.

Schaber, Patricia. Occupational Therapy Practice Guidelines for Adults with Alzheimer's Disease & Related Disorders. 2010. (Illus.). viii, 198p. pap. (978-1-56900-302-2(5)) American Occupational Therapy Assn., Inc.

Scoggan, Nita. Boost Your Brain. 76p. 2009. 57.95 (978-0-910487-69-6(3)) 2008. pap. 57.95 (978-0-910487-67-2(7)) Royalty Publishing Co.

Seegmiller, Judy. Life with Big Al: Early Alzheimer's; A Caregiver's Diary. 174p. pap. 12.95 (978-1-57636-108-5(X)) SunRise Publishing.

Sell, Colleen. A Cup of Comfort for Families Touched by Alzheimer's: Inspirational Stories of Unconditional Love & Support. 2008. (ENG., Illus.). 336p. pap. 9.95 (978-1-59869-651-6(3)) Adams Media Corp.

Shabahangi, Nader Robert & Szymkiewicz, Bogna. Deeper into the Soul: Beyond Dementia & Alzheimer's: Toward Forgetfulness Care. 2007. (978-0-9758744-8-6(9)) Elders Academy Pr.

Sheehan, James. The Father Who Didn't Know My Name. 2006. pap. 15.95 (978-0-9672801-1-0(7)) Coy Publishing Co.

Shouse, Deborah. Love in the Land of Dementia: Finding Hope in the Caregiver's Journey. 2006. (Illus.). 179p. per. 14.95 (978-0-9777590-4-0(0)) Creativity Connection, The.

Skillin, Joseph. Confessions of a Caregiver: When Alzheimer's Comes to Your Home. 2009. 120p. pap. 10.99 (978-1-60799-503-6(4)) Tate Publishing & Enterprises, LLC.

Skloot, Floyd. A World of Light. 2011. (ENG.). 216p. pap. 16.95 (978-0-8032-3847-3(9), Bison Bks.) Univ. of Nebraska Pr.

Smith M.S., Barbara A., OTR/L. Still Giving Kisses: A Guide to Helping & Enjoying the Alzheimer's Victim You Love. 2008. 136p. pap. 12.50 (978-1-4357-1025-2(8)) Lulu Enterprises Inc.

Snyder, Lisa. Speaking Our Minds: What It's Like to Have Alzheimer's. 2009. 172p. pap. 21.95 (978-1-932529-50-0(0)) Health Professions Pr.

Suchet, John. My Bonnie: How Dementia Stole the Love of My Life. (ENG., Illus.). 288p. 2011. 13.95 (978-0-00-732841-3(9)) 2010. 29.95 (978-0-00-732842-0(7)) HarperCollins Pubs. Ltd. GBR. Dist: Independent Pubs. Group.

Swiston, Nancy. I'm Not in Control: Coping with Alzheimer's Disease. 2007. 72p. per. 9.95 (978-0-595-45013-8(X)) iUniverse, Inc.

Sykes, Lowell Beach. Twenty years with alzheimer's Disease. 2007. 292p. pap. 22.96 (978-1-4357-0382-7(0)) Lulu Enterprises Inc.

Taylor, Richard. Alzheimer's from the Inside Out. 2007. (Illus.). 255p. per. (978-1-932529-23-4(3)) Health Professions Pr.

Terry, Wayne Glenn. Ezekiel's Wheel Vision: The Strengthening of Patients with Dementia. 2011. 342p. pap. 29.95 (978-1-4560-7234-6(X)) PublishAmerica, Inc.

The Healing Project, ed. Voices of Alzheimer's: The Healing Companion: Stories for Courage, Comfort & Strength. 2007. (Voices of Ser.). (ENG., Illus.). 385p. per. 16.95 (978-1-934184-01-1(2)) Lachance Publishing LLC.

Thorndike, John. The Last of His Mind: A Year in the Shadow of Alzheimer's. (ENG., 2011. Illus.). 256p. pap. 14.95 (978-0-8040-1136-5(2)) 2009. 248p. 24.95 (978-0-8040-1122-8(2)) Swallow Pr.

Todd, Linda. Tales from the Third Floor. 2010. 136p. pap. 10.99 (978-1-4520-0343-6(2)) AuthorHouse.

Tornillo, Deborah Ann. 36 Days Apart: A Memoir of a Daughter, her Parents & the Beast Named - Alzheimer's. 2009. 100p. pap. 10.49 (978-1-4389-5233-8(3)) AuthorHouse.

Tucker, Michele L. A Conversation about Alzheimer's. 2008. 84p. pap. 13.95 (978-1-4389-1558-6(6)) AuthorHouse.

Turley, Jack. Alzheimer's: Will I Be Next? I.t. ed. 2009. (ENG.). 402p. pap. 18.99 (978-1-58124-141-9(0), Gentle Heart Bks.) Fiction Works, The.

Until There's a Cure: How to Help Alzheimer's Patients & Families Now: Forum Before the Special Committee on Aging, United States Senate, One Hundred Eleventh Congress, Second Session, Washington, DC, December 8, 2010. 2011. (Illus.). iii, 219p. (978-0-16-088374-3(1), 552-070-42647-7) United States Government Printing Office.

Waldemar, Gunhild & Burns, Alistair, eds. Alzheimer's Disease. 2009. (Oxford Neurology Library). (Illus.). 120p. pap. 24.95 (978-0-19-956985-4(1)) Oxford Univ. Pr., Inc.

Watkins-Leech, Ruth D. You Have to Laugh or Else You'll Cry. 2011. 56p. pap. 10.00 (978-1-60844-951-4(3)) Dog Ear Publishing, LLC.

Wauson, Lois Zook. Looking for a Silver Lining: Staying Positive in an AlzheimerÆs World. 2008. 133p. pap. 24.95 (978-1-60672-105-6(4)) PublishAmerica, Inc.

Wayman, Laura. A Loving Approach to Dementia Care: Making Meaningful Connections with the Person Who Has Alzheimer's Disease or Other Dementia or Memory Loss. 2011. (ENG.). 128p. (gr. 17). 40.00 (978-1-4214-0033-4(2)); pap. 14.95 (978-1-4214-0034-1(0)) Johns Hopkins Univ. Pr.

Weidman, Ruth C. & Becker, John E. Where Did Howdy Go? 2010. 188p. pap. 14.95 (978-1-4490-5878-4(7)) AuthorHouse.

White, Debra. She Touched My Heart. 2007. per. 9.99 (978-1-59886-962-0(0)) Tate Publishing & Enterprises, LLC.

Whouley, Kate. Remembering the Music, Forgetting the Words: Travels with Mom in the Land of Dementia. 2011. (ENG.). 240p. 24.95 (978-0-8070-0319-0(0)) Beacon Pr.

Wilkinson Pergerson, Karen Denise. Paw Paw Can't Remember. 2009. 44p. pap. 20.00 (978-1-4490-3454-2(3)) AuthorHouse.

Wolfelt, Alan D. & Duvall, Kirby J. Healing Your Grieving Heart When Someone You Care about Has Alzheimer's: 100 Practical Ideas for Families, Friends, & Caregivers. 2011. (Healing Your Grieving Heart Ser.). (ENG.). 128p. pap. 11.95 (978-1-61722-148-4(1)) Companion Pr.

Wood, Yvonne. My People: A Memoir of an Attempt to Save a Fading Family Name. 2007. 68p. per. 10.95 (978-1-4327-0811-5(2)) Outskirts Pr., Inc.

Zeisel, John. I'm Still Here: A New Philosophy of Alzheimer's Care. 2009. (ENG.). 272p. (gr. 12-18). 17.00 (978-1-58333-376-1(2), Avery) Penguin Group (USA) Inc.

Ziegler, Rae-Lynn Cebul. Let's Look Together: An Interactive Picture Book for People with Alzheimer's & Other Forms of Memory Loss. 2009. (ENG., Illus.). 58p. pap. 28.95 (978-1-932529-51-7(9)) Health Professions Pr.

Zuniga, Michael A. & Zuniga, Micha'El A. A Special Vow: To Care for & Love Forever. 2009. 72p. pap. 10.99 (978-1-61579-179-8(5)) Xulon Pr., Inc.

ALZHEIMER'S DISEASE—POPULAR WORKS

Activities en Espanol. Activities en Espanol. 2010.Tr. of Acitvities in Spanish. (SPA., Illus.). 107p. 14.95 (978-0-615-37470-3(0)) Fernandez, Alberto.

Adams, Jacqueline. Alzheimer's Disease. 2011. (Diseases & Disorders Ser.). 128p. lib. bdg. 33.45 (978-1-4205-0553-5(X), Lucent Bks.) Cengage Gale.

Bellenir, Karen, ed. Alzheimer Disease Sourcebook. 4th ed. 2008. (Health Reference Ser.). (Illus.). 604p. 87.00 (978-0-7808-1001-3(5)) Omnigraphics, Inc.

Burdick, Lydia. Wishing on a Star: A Read-Aloud Book for Memory-Challenged Adults. 2009. (Two-Lap Bks.: 3). (Illus.). 32p. 19.95 (978-1-932529-43-2(8)) Health Professions Pr.

Carper, Jean. 100 Simple Things You Can Do to Prevent Alzheimer's & Age-Related Memory Loss. 2012. (ENG.). 336p. pap. 13.99 (978-0-316-08684-4(3)) Little Brown & Co.

Davies, Helen D. & Jensen, Michael P. Alzheimer's Disease: Answers to the Most Asked Questions. 2011. 160p. pap. 19.95 (978-1-886039-99-5(2)) Addicus Bks.

Doraiswamy, P. Murali, et al. The Alzheimer's Action Plan: What You Need to Know - And What You Can Do - About Memory Problems, from Prevention to Early Intervention & Care. 2009. (ENG.). 496p. pap. 16.95 (978-0-312-53871-2(5), St. Martin's Griffin) St. Martin's Pr.

Fife, Bruce. Stop Alzheimer's Now: How to Prevent & Reverse Dementia, Parkinson's, ALS, Multiple Sclerosis, & Other Neurodegenerative Disorders. 2011. (Illus.). 352p. pap. 19.95 (978-0-941599-85-6(X)) Piccadilly Bks., Ltd.

Fortanasce, Vincent. The Anti-Alzheimer's Prescription: The Science-Proven Prevention Plan to Start at Any Age. 2009. (ENG.). 352p. (gr. 12-18). 15.00 (978-1-59240-461-2(8), Gotham) Penguin Group (USA) Inc.

Gordeau, Bretten C. & Hillier, Jeffrey G. Alzheimer's Essentials: Practical Skills for Families & Caregivers. 2nd rev. ed. 2007. 144p. per. 13.95 (978-0-9769581-7-8(1), Carma) Carma Publishing LLC.

Halpern, Sue. Can't Remember What I Forgot: Your Memory, Your Mind, Your Future. 2009. (ENG.). 272p. pap. 14.95 (978-0-307-40788-7(8), Three Rivers Pr.) Crown Publishing Group.

Lisa, Snyder. Living Your Best with Early-Stage Alzheimer's: An Essential Guide. 2010. 288p. pap. 19.95 (978-1-934716-03-8(0)) Sunrise River Pr.

Mendelson, Scott D. Beyond Alzheimer's: How to Avoid the Modern Epidemic of Dementia. 2009. (ENG.). 272p. 24.95 (978-1-59077-157-0(5)) Evans, M. & Co., Inc.

Rubinstein, Nataly. Alzheimer's Disease & Other Dementias. 2011. 414p. pap. 17.95 (978-1-936198-13-9(4)) Two Harbors Pr., Inc.

Sabbagh, Marwan. The Alzheimer's Answer: Reduce Your Risk & Keep Your Brain Healthy. 2009. (ENG., Illus.). 320p. pap. 14.95 (978-0-470-52245-5(3), Wiley) Wiley, John & Sons, Inc.

Sabbagh, Marwan Noel & Sabbagh, Marwan. The Alzheimer's Answer: Reduce Your Risk & Keep Your Brain Healthy. 2008. (ENG., Illus.). 320p. 24.95 (978-0-470-04494-0(2), Wiley) Wiley, John & Sons, Inc.

Small, Gary & Vorgan, Gigi. The Alzheimer's Prevention Program: Keep Your Brain Healthy for the Rest of Your Life. 2011. (ENG., Illus.). 288p. 24.95 (978-0-7611-6526-2(6), 0761165266) Workman Publishing Co., Inc.

Smith, Lisa W. Alzheimer's: Where Do We Go from Here? 2007. (ENG.). 119p. per. 13.95 (978-1-60037-010-6(1)) Morgan James Publishing.

Snyder, Lisa. Speaking Our Minds: What It's Like to Have Alzheimer's. 2009. 172p. pap. 21.95 (978-1-932529-50-0(0)) Health Professions Pr.

Voris, Ed, et al. Conversations with Ed: Waiting for Forgetfulness: Why Are We So Afraid of Alzheimer's Disease? 2009. (978-0-9816248-0-8(4)); (978-0-9816248-1-5(2)) Elders Academy Pr.

Whitehouse, Peter J. & George, Daniel. The Myth of Alzheimer's: What You Aren't Being Told about Today's Most Dreaded Diagnosis. 2008. (ENG., Illus.). 336p. pap. 15.95 (978-0-312-36817-3(8), St. Martin's Griffin) St. Martin's Pr.

AMADOR COUNTY (CALIF.)

Baxter, R. Scott & Wooten, Kimberly. Shenandoah Valley & Amador Wine Country. 2008. (Images of America Ser.). (Illus.). 127p. pe. 19.99 (978-0-7385-5603-1(3)) Arcadia Publishing.

Cenotto, Lawrence A. Logan's Alley: Amador County Yesterdays in Picture & Prose, Five. 2006. 39.95 (978-0-938121-16-9(2)) Cenotto Pubns.

Cook, Deborah Coleen. Amador Central Railroad. 2011. (Images of Rail Ser.). (ENG., Illus.). 128p. pap. 21.99 (978-0-7385-7550-6(X)) Arcadia Publishing.

Poultney, John & Amador County Archives. Amador County. 2006. (Images of America Ser.). (ENG., Illus.). 128p. per. 21.99 (978-0-7385-4701-5(8)) Arcadia Publishing.

AMAFINGO (AFRICAN PEOPLE)

see Fingo (African People)

AMALFI (ITALY)

Bonechi, Casa. Italy: Amalfi. 128p. (978-88-7009-758-0(7)) Casa Editrice Bonechi.

Bruno, Nick. The Amalfi Coast & Bay of Naples with Your Family: From Charming Resorts to Roman Ruins. 2009. (Frommers with Your Family Ser.: 1). (ENG., Illus.). 256p. pap. 18.99 (978-0-470-51999-8(1), Frommers) Wiley, John & Sons, Inc.

—Naples & the Amalfi Coast. 2009. (ENG., Illus.). 288p. pap. 21.95 (978-1-906098-60-5(3)) Footprint Handbooks GBR. Dist: Globe Pequot Pr., The.

Fisher, Robert. Close to Paradise: The Gardens of Naples, Capri & the Amalfi Coast. 2011. (ENG., Illus.). 208p. 45.00 (978-0-7112-3038-5(2)) Lincoln, Frances Ltd. GBR. Dist: Perseus-PGW.

Fodor's Travel Publications, Inc. Staff. The Amalfi Coast, Capri & Naples. 6th ed. 2011. (Fodor's Ser.). (ENG., Illus.). 392p. pap. 22.99 (978-0-679-00933-7(7), Fodor's) Fodor's Travel Pubns.

Kennedy, Jeffrey. Top 10 Naples & Amalfi Coast. (Eyewitness top 10 travel Guide Ser.). (ENG.). 144p. 2012. 14.00 (978-0-7566-8536-2(2)) 2010. 14.00 (978-0-7566-6139-7(0)) Dorling Kindersley Publishing, Inc.

Langenscheidt, compiled by. Naples & the Amalfi Coast. 2011. (Step by Step Ser.). (ENG., Illus.). 112p. pap. 16.99 (978-981-282-360-1(3)) APA Publications Services SGP. Dist: Ingram Pub. Services.

Lonely Planet Staff & Bonetto, Cristian. Naples & the Amalfi Coast. 3rd rev. ed. 2010. (Regional Guide Ser.). (ENG., Illus.). 320p. pap. 21.99 (978-1-74104-509-3(6)) Lonely Planet Pubns.

Loye, David. Return to Amalfi. 2007. 229p. pap. 18.95 (978-0-9789827-4-4(6)) Franklin, Benjamin Pr.

Swallow, Nicky. Frommer's the Amalfi Coast with Naples, Capri & Pompeii. 4th ed. 2012. (Frommer's Color Complete Ser.). (ENG., Illus.). 384p. pap. 21.99 (978-1-118-07467-1(X), Frommers) Wiley, John & Sons, Inc.

Swallow, Nicky. Naples & the Amalfi Coast Day by Day. 2010. (Frommer's Day by Day - Pocket Ser.: 117). (ENG., Illus.). 192p. pap. 12.99 (978-0-470-72120-9(0), Frommers) Wiley, John & Sons, Inc.

Thomas Cook Publishing Staff. Naples & the Amalfi Coast. 4th ed. 2010. (Travellers - Thomas Cook Ser.). (ENG., Illus.). 192p. pap. 16.95 (978-1-84848-224-1(8)) Cook, Thomas Publishing GBR. Dist: Globe Pequot Pr., The.

—Neapolitan Riviera. 2nd ed. 2010. (Thomas Cook Pocket Guides). (ENG., Illus.). 128p. pap. 9.95 (978-1-84848-252-4(3)) Cook, Thomas Publishing GBR. Dist: Globe Pequot Pr., The.

Tippett, Julian. Sorrento Amalfi & Capri. 4th rev. ed. (Illus.). 136p. pap. 15.99 (978-1-85691-323-2(6)) Hunter Publishing, Inc.

AMALGAMATED ASSOCIATION OF IRON, STEEL AND TIN WORKERS OF NORTH AMERICA

Robinson, Jesse S. The Amalgamated Association of Iron, Steel & Tin Workers. reprint ed. 49.50 (978-0-404-58510-5(8)) AMS Pr., Inc.

AMALGAMATION

Here are entered works on the separation of precious metals, especially gold, from any accompanying mineral matter by means of mercury. Works on the combination of mercury with other metals, and the resulting amalgams, are entered under the heading Amalgams.

see also Alloys; Mercury

Read, David C. Dinosaurs: An Adventist View. 2009. (Illus.). 684p. 34.95 (978-0-9820305-0-9(9)) Clarion Call Bks.

AMALGAMATION OF CORPORATIONS

see Consolidation and Merger of Corporations

AMALGAMATION OF LAND

see Consolidation of Land Holdings

AMANA SOCIETY

Amana Colonies. (Illus.). 61p. pap. 5.95 (978-1-57216-079-8(9)) Penfield Pr.

Bourret, Joan L., compiled by. Life in Amana 1867-1935: Reporters' Views of the Communal Way. 2011. (ENG., Illus.). 192p. pap. 18.95 (978-1-57216-050-7(0)) Penfield Pr.

Shambaugh, Bertha. Amana the Community of True Inspiration. Schense, Deb, ed. 2010. (ENG., Illus.). 424p. pap. 19.95 (978-1-932043-63-1(2)) Penfield Bks.

AMARIGNA LANGUAGE

see Amharic Language

AMARYLLIS

Babbitt, Natalie. Los Ojos del Amarilis.Tr. of The Eyes of the Amaryllis. (SPA.). (978-84-406-0190-2(5)) Ediciones B ESP. Dist: AIMS International Bks., Inc.

AMATEUR FILMS

Cram101 Textbook Reviews. Outlines & Highlights for Visual Storytelling by Ronald J Osgood. 2011. 122p. pap. 28.95 (978-1-61490-764-0(1)) Cram101 Inc.

Hardy, Paul. Filming on a Microbudget. 2009. (Pocket Essential Ser.). (ENG., Illus.). 288p. pap. 12.95 (978-1-84243-301-0(6)) Pocket Essentials GBR. Dist: Independent Pubs. Group.

Ishizuka, Karen L. & Zimmermann, Patricia Rodden. Mining the Home Movie: Excavations in Histories & Memories. Ishizuka, Karen L. & Zimmermann, Patricia R., eds. 2007. (Illus.). 360p. 60.00 (978-0-520-23087-3(6)); 333p. per. 26.95 (978-0-520-24807-6(4)) Univ. of California Pr.

Osgood, Ronald J. & Hinshaw, M. Joseph. Visual Storytelling: Videography & Post Production in the Digital Age. 2009. (Illus.). xv, 364p. (978-0-534-63793-4(0)) Wadsworth.

Vågnes, Øyvind. The Kennedy Assassination Film in Visual Culture. 2011. (Illus.). 228p. E-Book (978-0-292-73551-4(0)) Univ. of Texas Pr.

Vågnes, Øyvind. Zaprudered: The Kennedy Assassination Film in Visual Culture. 2011. (ENG., Illus.). 228p. 55.00 (978-0-292-72863-9(8)) Univ. of Texas Pr.

Young, Clive & Young. Homemade Hollywood: Fans Behind the Camera. 2008. (ENG., Illus.). 312p. 90.00 (978-0-8264-2922-3(X)) Continuum International Publishing Group, Ltd. GBR. Dist: National Bk. Network.

AMATEUR JOURNALISM

see College and School Journalism; Journalism

AMATEUR MOVING-PICTURES

see Amateur Films

AMATEUR RADIO STATIONS

American Radio Relay League, creator. ARRL's FCC Rules & Regulations for the Amateur Radio Service: Includes the Complete Part 97 Rules from Title 47 of the Code of Federal Regulations: Effective February 23 2007. 2008. (ARRL's FCC Rule Book Ser.). pap. 5.95 (978-0-87259-106-6(9)) American Radio Relay League, Inc.

—FCC Rules & Regulations for the Amateur Radio Service: February 23 2007. 2008. (Illus.). 54p. pap. 5.95 (978-0-87259-123-3(9)) American Radio Relay League, Inc.

Arrl, Inc & Silver, H. Ward. The ARRL Ham Radio License Manual: All You Need to Become an Amateur Radio Operator. 2nd ed. 2010. (Illus.). (978-0-87259-083-0(6)) American Radio Relay League, Inc.

Bartlett, Richard A. The World of Ham Radio, 1901-1950: A Social History. 2007. (ENG., Illus.). 292p. 55.00 (978-0-7864-2966-0(6)) McFarland & Co., Inc. Pubs.

Booth, Nigel, M0cvo. Beyond the Dipole. 2008. 65p. pap. 28.50 (978-1-4092-2459-4(7)) Lulu Enterprises Inc.

—Introducing Short Wave Radio Listening. 2008. 55p. pap. 30.50 (978-1-4092-0997-3(0)) Lulu Enterprises Inc.

Brogdon, Al. Low Profile Amateur Radio: Operating a Ham Station from Almost Anywhere. 2nd ed. 2007. (Illus.). 162p. per. 19.95 (978-0-87259-974-1(4)) American Radio Relay League, Inc.

Fields, Walter. GPS & Amateur Radio. Banzhaf, Walter, ed. 2007. (Illus.). per. 18.95 (978-0-87259-992-5(2)) American Radio Relay League, Inc.

Hallas, Joel R. AARL's Hamspeak: A Dictionary for Radio Amateurs. 2011. (Illus.). 58p. pap. (978-0-87259-842-3(X)) American Radio Relay League, Inc.

Haring, Kristen. Ham Radio's Technical Culture. (Inside Technology Ser.). (ENG., Illus.). 238p. (gr. 17). 2008. per. 17.95 (978-0-262-58276-6(7)) 2006. 29.95 (978-0-262-08355-3(8)) MIT Pr.

Kearman, Jim. The ARRL DXCO Handbook: Worldwide Ham Radio Operating & the ARRL DXCC Award. 2007. (Illus.). per. 19.95 (978-0-87259-988-8(4)) American Radio Relay League, Inc.

Rouse, Peter & Robertson, Bill. Scanners 6. 6th ed. 2009. (Illus.). 245p. pap. 29.50 (978-1-85486-257-0(X)) Specialist Interest Model Bks. Ltd. GBR. Dist: Trans-Atlantic Pubns., Inc.

Silver, Ward, et al. The ARRL's Amateur Extra QandA: Upgrade to an Amateur Extra Class Ham License. 2nd ed. 2008. (Illus.). pap. (978-0-87259-137-0(9)) American Radio Relay League, Inc.

West, Gordon. Technician + General Class books & software Package: 2006-10 Technician + 2007-11 General Class Amateur Radio Elements 2 + 3 FCC License Preparation, 2 bks. 2007. (Illus.). per. 69.95 (978-0-945053-53-8(3), TPG-07) Master Publishing, Inc.

Wolfgang, Larry D. The ARRL's General QandA: Upgrade to a General Class Ham License. 4th ed. 2011. (Illus.). (978-0-87259-808-9(X)) American Radio Relay League, Inc.

AMATEUR THEATER

Here are entered works about, including history and criticism of, productions of plays, skits, recitations, etc. for production by nonprofessionals.

see also Acting; Bible Plays; Charades; Children's Plays; College and School Drama; Improvisation (Acting); Little Theater Movement; Pageants; Tableaux

Backues, Nancy, et al. Drama Ministry: A Guidebook. 2007. (Smyth & Helwys Help! Books). 195p. per. 17.00 (978-1-57312-490-4(7)) Smyth & Helwys Publishing, Inc.

Burton, Sarah. How to Put on a Community Play. 2011. (ENG.). 256p. pap. 28.95 (978-1-906582-15-9(7)) Aurora Metro Pubns. Ltd. GBR. Dist: Consortium Bk. Sales & Distribution.

Cartmell, Van H. The Amateur Theater Handbook. 2009. 222p. 39.95 (978-1-104-83609-2(2)) 2007. (ENG.). 220p. per. 24.95 (978-0-548-38560-9(2)) Kessinger Publishing, LLC.

Collins, Thomas P. Stage-Struck Settlers in the Sun-Kissed Land: The Amateur Theatre in Territorial Prescott, 1868-1903. 2007. 132p. per. 12.95 (978-1-58736-783-0(1)) Wheatmark.

Forsberg, Linnea & Forsberg, Josephine. Improvisation for Speech & Theater. rev. ed. 2010. (ENG.). 212p. pap. 52.00 (978-0-7575-7815-1(2)) Kendall Hunt Publishing Co.

Lev-Aladgem, Shulamith. Theatre in Co-Communities: Articulating Power. Aston, Elaine & Reynolds, Bryan, eds. 2010. (ENG.). 208p. 84.00 (978-0-230-55519-8(5)) Palgrave Macmillan.

Polsky, Milton. Drama Workshop for Seniors: Improv, Games & Scenes. 2011. (Illus.). 110p. pap. 25.00 (978-0-88734-063-5(6)) Players Pr., Inc.

Romero, Edwina Portelle. Footlights in the Foothills: Amateur Theatre of Las Vegas & Fort Union, New Mexico, 1871-1899. 2011. pap. (978-0-86534-826-4(X)) Sunstone Pr.

Ross, Beverly B. & Durgin, Jean P. Junior Broadway: How to Produce Musicals with Children 9 to 13, 2d Ed. 2nd rev. alt. ed. 2011. (ENG., Illus.). 223p. pap. 25.00 **(978-0-7864-6704-4(5))** McFarland & Co., Inc. Pubs.

Spolin, Viola. Theater Games for Rehearsal: A Director's Handbook, Updated Edition. Sills, Carol Bleackley, ed. 2011. (ENG., Illus.). 117p. pap. 21.95 *(978-0-8101-2749-4(0))* Northwestern Univ. Pr.

AMATEUR THEATRICALS

see Amateur Theater

AMATEURISM IN SPORTS

see Professionalism in Sports

AMAUROSIS

see Blindness

AMAZON.COM (FIRM)

Biographiq Business Profile. Amazon. com (Business Profile) 2008. pap. 9.99 *(978-1-59986-259-0(X)*, Biographiq) Filiquarian Publishing, LLC.

Brandt, Richard L. One Click: Jeff Bezos & the Rise of Amazon.Com. 2011. (ENG.). 224p. (gr. 12). 25.95 *(978-1-59184-375-7(8)*, Portfolio (Hardcover)) Penguin Group (USA) Inc.

Cohen, Sharon. Amazon Income: How Anyone of Any Age, Location, And - Or Background Can Build a Highly Profitable Online Business with Amazon. 2009. (ENG.). 336p. pap. 24.95 *(978-1-60138-299-3(5))* Atlantic Publishing Co.

Sampson, Brent. Sell Your Book on Amazon: The Book Marketing COACH Reveals Top-Secret How-to Tips Guaranteed to Increase Sales for Print-on-Demand & Self-Publishing Writers. 2007. (ENG.). 184p. per. 14.95 *(978-1-4327-0196-3(7))* Outskirts Pr., Inc.

Schepp, Brad, et al. Amazon Top Seller Secrets: Insider Tips from Amazon's Most Successful Sellers. 2009. (ENG., Illus.). 320p. pap. 24.95 *(978-0-8144-1034-9(0))* Amacom.

Shanahan, Francis. Amazon. com Mashups. 2007. (ENG., Illus.). 379p. per. 29.99 *(978-0-470-09777-9(9)*, Wrox) Wiley, John & Sons, Inc.

Shepard, Aaron. Aiming at Amazon: The NEW Business of Self Publishing, or How to Publish Your Books with Print on Demand & Online Book Marketing on Amazon. Com. 2007. 208p. pap. 15.00 *(978-0-938497-43-1(X))* Shepard Pubns.

Vliet, Jurg van, et al. Elastic Beanstalk. 2011. (ENG.). 88p. pap. 29.99 **(978-1-4493-0664-9(0))** O'Reilly Media, Inc.

Weber, Steve. Barcode Booty: How I found & sold $2 million of 'junk' on eBay & Amazon, & you can, too, using your Phone. 2011. 156p. pap. 17.95 **(978-1-936560-06-5(2))** Weber Bks.

Weber, Steve. Sell on Amazon: A Guide to Amazon's Marketplace, Seller Central, & Fulfillment by Amazon Programs. 2008. 192p. pap. 18.95 *(978-0-9772406-4-7(9))* Weber Bks.

AMAZON RIVER AND VALLEY

Abell, Sam & Nissen, Torben Ulrik. Amazonia. 2010. (ENG., Illus.). 96p. pap. 30.00 *(978-0-97114-087-6(X))* Univ. of Oregon, Museum of Art.

Acuña, Cristóbal de, et al. Nuevo Descubrimiento Del Gran Rio de Las Amazonas. 2009. (SPA.). 181p. pap. 22.80 *(978-84-8489-445-2(2))* Iberoamericana Vervuert Publishing Corp.

Basto, Fernanda. Brasil. 2007. (Illus.). 119p. *(978-1-877339-91-2(1))* NZVP Bks. & Calendars Ltd.

Bates, Henry. The Naturalist on the River Amazons. 2007. 376p. per. *(978-1-905748-56-3(6))*; 440p. per. *(978-1-905748-57-0(4))* Rediscovery Bks.

—Naturalist on the River Amazons. 2009. (Stanfords Travel Classics Ser.). 424p. pap. 17.95 *(978-1-906780-09-8(9))* Beaufoy, John Publishing GBR. Dist: Midpoint Trade Bks., Inc.

Bates, Henry Walter. The Naturalist on the River Amazon: A Record of Adventures, Habits of Animals, Sketches of Brazilian & Indian Life, & Aspects of Nature under the Equator, during Eleven Years of Travel. 3rd ed. 2009. (Cambridge Library Collection - Life Sciences Ser.). 412p. pap. 31.99 *(978-1-108-00163-2(7))* Cambridge Univ. Pr.

—The Naturalist on the River Amazons. 2010. 446p. pap. 36.75 *(978-1-174-92264-0(8))*; 450p. pap. 36.75 *(978-1-142-55479-8(1))* BiblioBazaar.

—The Naturalist on the River Amazons. 2007. (ENG., Illus.). 300p. *(978-1-4068-2507-7(7))*; per. *(978-1-4068-2502-2(6))* Echo Library.

—The Naturalist on the River Amazons. 2010. (Illus.). 278p. pap. 35.63 *(978-1-153-71468-5(X))* 2009. 208p. pap. 35.63 *(978-1-150-36378-8(9))* General Bks. LLC.

—The Naturalist on the River Amazons. 2010. 370p. 39.16 *(978-1-169-33077-1(0))*; pap. 27.16 *(978-1-162-70318-3(0))*; 48.95 *(978-1-161-47182-3(0))* Kessinger Publishing, LLC.

Beck, Harald. Linking Amazon Forest Dynamics with Mammalian Diversity. 2008. (Illus.). 128p. pap. *(978-3-639-07513-7(7))* VDM Verlag Dr. Mueller e.K.

Bonotto, Daniel Marcos & Silveira, Ene Glória da. The Amazon Rush Gold & Environmental Mercury Contamination. 2009. (Environmental Science, Engineering & Technology Ser.). 69.00 *(978-1-60741-609-8(3))* Nova Science Pubs., Inc.

Da Cunha, Euclides. The Amazon: Land Without History. Sa, Lucia, ed. Sousa, Ronald, tr. from POR. 2006. (Library of Latin America Ser.). (ENG.). 128p. per. 19.95 *(978-0-19-517204-1(3))* Oxford Univ. Pr., Inc.

De Graff, F. W. Up. Head Hunters of the Amazon. 2007. pap. **(978-1-4067-6681-3(X))** Read Bks.

Edwards, William H. A Voyage up the River Amazon: Including a Residence at Pará. 2010. (Cambridge Library Collection - Travel & Exploration Ser.). (ENG.). 224p. pap. 24.00 *(978-1-108-01196-9(9))* Cambridge Univ. Pr.

Elias-Ulloa, Jose. An Acoustic Phonetics of Shipibo-Conibo (Pano) an Endangered Amazonian Language: A New Approach to Documenting Linguistic Data. 2010. (Illus.). ix, 436p. *(978-0-7734-1303-0(0))* Mellen, Edwin Pr., The.

Everett, Daniel L. Don't Sleep, There Are Snakes: Life & Language in the Amazonian Jungle. 2008. (ENG., Illus.). 304p. 26.95 *(978-0-375-42502-8(0)*, Pantheon) Knopf Doubleday Publishing Group.

Fountain, Paul. The River Amazon from Its Sources to the Sea. 321p. reprint ed. 98.00 *(978-0-7222-9552-6(9))* Library Reprints, Inc.

Galeano, Juan Carlos & Uzendoski, Michael. Folktales of the Amazon, 1 vol. 2008. (Illus.). 172p. 40.00 *(978-1-59158-674-6(7)*, LU8674) Libraries Unlimited, Inc.

Gellert, Vance & Bowman, John, photos by. The Ayahuasca Sessions: Conversations with Amazonian Curanderos & Western Shamans. 2010. (Illus.). 280p. mass mkt. *(978-0-9806487-1-3(8))* Icaro Publishing.

Gordon, Nick. Monkeys of the Amazon. 2007. (Wildlife Monographs). (ENG., Illus.). 72p. pap. 16.95 *(978-1-901268-10-2(1)*, 1901268101) Evans Mitchell Bks. GBR. Dist: MBI Distribution Services/Quayside Distribution.

Goulding, M. Man & Fisheries on an Amazon Frontier. 2011. (Developments in Hydrobiology Ser.). 132p. pap. 169.00 *(978-90-481-8520-7(3)*, 9048185203) Springer.

Harrison, John. Up the Creek: An Amazon Adventure. 2012. (ENG., Illus.). 288p. pap. 16.99 **(978-1-84162-384-9(9))** Bradt Travel Guides GBR. Dist: Globe Pequot Pr., The.

Hecht, Susanna & Cockburn, Alexander. The Fate of the Forest: Developers, Destroyers, & Defenders of the Amazon. rev. ed. 2011. (Illus.). 408p. pap. 22.50 *(978-0-226-32272-8(6))* Univ. of Chicago Pr.

Hemming, John. Tree of Rivers: The Story of the Amazon. (ENG., Illus.). 368p. 2009. pap. 24.95 *(978-0-500-28820-7(8)*, 528820) 2008. 39.95 *(978-0-500-51401-6(1))* Thames & Hudson.

Herndon, William Lewis. Exploration of the Valley of the Amazon. 2009. 296p. pap. *(978-1-150-06512-5(5))*; 306p. pap. *(978-1-150-55192-5(5))*; 332p. pap. *(978-0-217-71643-7(1))* Books LLC.

—Exploration of the Valley of the Amazon, Made under Direction of the Navy Department. 2006. 428p. per. 26.99 *(978-1-4255-4704-2(4))*; 424p. per. 26.99 *(978-1-4255-4621-2(8))* MPublishing.

Heyck, Denis. Schools in the Forest: How Grassroots Education Brought Political Empowerment to the Brazilian Amazon. 2010. 196p. 75.00 *(978-1-56549-351-3(6))* Stylus Publishing, LLC.

Jackson, Joe. The Thief at the End of the World: Rubber, Power, & the Seeds of Empire. 2009. (ENG.). 432p. (gr. 12-18). pap. 16.00 *(978-0-14-311461-1(1)*, Penguin (Non-Classics)) Penguin Group (USA) Inc.

Junk, Wolfgang J., et al, eds. Amazonian Floodplain Forests: Ecophysiology, Biodiversity & Sustainable Management. 2010. (Ecological Studies). (Illus.). 500p. 179.00 *(978-90-481-8724-9(9)*, 9048187249) Springer.

Keller, Michael. Amazonia & Global Change. 2009. (Illus.). ix, 565p. *(978-0-87590-476-4(9))* American Geophysical Union.

Kelly, José Antonio. State Healthcare & Yanomami Transformations: A Symmetrical Ethnography. 2011. (First Peoples Ser.). (ENG., Illus.). 280p. 55.00 *(978-0-8165-2920-9(5))* Univ. of Arizona Pr.

Levy, Buddy. River of Darkness: Francisco Orellana's Legendary Voyage of Death & Discovery down the Amazon. 2011. (ENG., Illus.). 352p. 27.00 *(978-0-553-80750-9(1))* Random House Publishing Group.

Manzi, Maya. Peasant Adaptation to Environmental Change. 2008. 180p. pap. *(978-3-639-06692-0(8))* VDM Verlag Dr. Mueller e.K.

Markham, Clements R. Expeditions into the Valley of the Amazons, 1539, 1540 1639. 2010. (Cambridge Library Collection - Travel & Exploration Ser.). (ENG., Illus.). 272p. pap. 23.99 *(978-1-108-00817-4(8))* Cambridge Univ. Pr.

Mohlke, Matthew & Strel, Martin. The Man Who Swam the Amazon: 3,274 Miles on the World's Deadliest River. 2007. (ENG., Illus.). 224p. per. 16.95 *(978-1-59921-358-3(3)*, Lyons Pr.) Globe Pequot Pr., The.

Montgomery, Sy. Journey of the Pink Dolphins: An Amazon Quest. 2009. (ENG., Illus.). 320p. pap. 19.95 *(978-1-60358-060-1(3))* Chelsea Green Publishing.

Negron, Stephen. False Dawn: Recollections of the Amazon. 2006. (Illus.). 88p. lib. bdg. 18.95 *(978-1-59715-015-6(0))* Chapel Hill Pr.

Orton, James. The Andes & the Amazon; or, Across the Continent of South America. 2006. 360p. per. 26.99 *(978-1-4255-3675-6(1))* MPublishing.

Post, Charles J. Across the Andes. 362p. reprint ed. 98.00 *(978-0-7222-9589-2(8))* Library Reprints, Inc.

—Across the Andes. 2008. 388p. pap. *(978-1-4097-7191-3(1))* Read Bks.

—Across the Andres. 362p. reprint ed. 98.00 *(978-0-7222-9561-8(8))* Library Reprints, Inc.

Post, Charles Johnson. Across the Andes A Tale of Wandering Day. 2006. pap. 33.95 *(978-1-4286-5708-3(8))* Kessinger Publishing, LLC.

Rzóska, Julian. On the Nature of Rivers: With Case Stories of Nile, Zaire & Amazon. 2010. 76p. pap. 43.00 *(978-90-481-8517-7(3)*, 9048185173) Springer.

Slater, Candace. The Amazon. 2006. (ENG., Illus.). 320p. 39.95 *(978-0-300-11194-1(0))* Yale Univ. Pr.

Sweeney, Christopher. Riches of the Amazon. 2007. (Timeline Ser.). (Illus.). 48p. pap. 8.99 *(978-1-4190-4398-7(6))* Houghton Mifflin Harcourt Supplemental Pubs.

Tomlinson, H. M. The Sea & the Jungle. 2010. 254p. pap. *(978-1-4099-7378-2(6))* Dodo Pr.

Tomlinson, Henry M. The Sea & the Jungle. 371p. reprint ed. 98.00 *(978-0-7222-9568-7(5))*; 98.00 *(978-0-7222-9601-1(0))* Library Reprints, Inc.

Urrego, Dunia H. Climate Change & History of Western Amazonian Forests. 2009. 152p. pap. *(978-3-639-13505-3(9))* VDM Verlag Dr. Mueller e.K.

Wallace, Alfred Russel. A Narrative of Travels on the Amazon & Rio Negro, with an Account of the Native Tribes, & Observations on the Climate, Geology, & Natural History of the Amazon. 2010. (Cambridge Library Collection - Travel & Exploration Ser.). (ENG., Illus.). 576p. pap. 39.99 *(978-1-108-00729-0(5))* Cambridge Univ. Pr.

Woodroffe, Joseph Froude. The Upper Reaches of the Amazon. 2010. 194p. pap. *(978-1-151-81472-2(5))* Books LLC.

—The Upper Reaches of the Amazon. 304p. reprint ed. 98.00 *(978-0-7222-6485-0(2))*; 98.00 *(978-0-7222-9572-4(3))* Library Reprints, Inc.

AMAZON RIVER AND VALLEY—DESCRIPTION AND TRAVEL

Baron, Walter. Devil Brother. Taubman, H. Howard, ed. 2011. 270p. 47.95 **(978-1-258-01874-0(8))** Literary Licensing, LLC.

Coates, Marcus. Marcus Coates: The Trip. 2011. (ENG., Illus.). 88p. pap. 22.95 **(978-3-86560-985-4(6))** Verlag der Buchhandlung Walther Konig DEU. Dist: D.A.P./Distributed Art Pubs.

De Bruhl, Marshall. The River Sea: The Amazon in History, Myth, & Legend. 2010. (ENG., Illus.). 320p. 26.00 *(978-1-58243-490-2(5)*, Counterpoint) Counterpoint LLC.

De Bruhl, Marshall. River Sea: The Amazon in History, Myth, & Legend. 2011. (ENG.). 256p. pap. 15.95 **(978-1-58243-768-2(8)**, Counterpoint) Counterpoint LLC.

Grann, David. The Lost City of Z: A Tale of Deadly Obsession in the Amazon. (Vintage Departures Ser.). (ENG., Illus.). 2010. 448p. pap. 15.95 *(978-1-4000-7845-5(8)*, Vintage) 2009. 352p. 27.50 *(978-0-385-51353-1(4)*, Doubleday) Knopf Doubleday Publishing Group.

—The Lost City of Z: A Tale of Deadly Obsession in the Amazon. l.t. ed. 2009. (ENG.). 528p. pap. 27.50 *(978-0-7393-2834-7(4))* Random Hse. Large Print.

Robinson, Alex. Brazilian Amazon. 2012. (Footprint Focus Ser.). (ENG., Illus.). 128p. pap. 11.95 **(978-1-908206-65-7(9))** Footprint Handbooks GBR. Dist: Globe Pequot Pr., The.

Smyth, William & Lowe, Frederick. Narrative of a Journey from Lima to para, across the Andes & down the Amazon: Undertaken with a View of Ascertaining the Practicability of a Navigable Communication with the Atlantic, by the Rivers Pachitea, Ucayali, & Amazon. 2011. (Cambridge Library Collection - Travel & Exploration Ser.). (ENG., Illus.). 354p. pap. 29.99 **(978-1-108-03379-4(2))** Cambridge Univ. Pr.

Stafford, Ed. Walking the Amazon: 860 Days. One Step at a Time. 2012. (ENG., Illus.). 320p. (gr. 12). pap. 16.00 **(978-0-452-29826-2(1)**, Plume) Penguin Group (USA) Inc.

Ugarte, Auxiliomar Silva. Sertões de Bárbaros: O Mundo Natural e As Sociedades Indígenas Da Amazônia Na Visão DOS Cronistas Ibéricos (Séculos XVI-XVII) 2009. (POR., Illus.). 601p. *(978-85-7512-266-2(5))* Valer Livraria Editora e Distribuidora Ltda.

Wallace, Scott. The Unconquered: In Search of the Amazon's Last Uncontacted Tribes. (ENG., 512p. 2012. Illus.). pap. 16.00 *(978-0-307-46297-8(8))* 2011. 26.00 *(978-0-307-46296-1(X)*, Crown) Crown Publishing Group.

AMAZON RIVER AND VALLEY—SOCIAL CONDITIONS

Brightman, Marc, et al, eds. Animism in Rainforest & Tundra: Personhood, Animals, Plants & Things in Contemporary Amazonia & Siberia. 2012. (ENG.). 252p. 90.00 **(978-0-85745-468-3(4))** Berghahn Bks., Inc.

Brightman, Marc, et al. Animism in Rainforest & Tundra. Personhood, Animals, Plants & Things in Contemporary Amazonia & Siberia. 2012. E-Book **(978-0-85745-469-0(2))** Berghahn Bks., Inc.

Hawthorne, Walter. From Africa to Brazil: Culture, Identity, & an Atlantic Slave Trade, 1600-1830. 2010. (African Studies). (ENG., Illus.). 280p. 85.00 *(978-0-521-76409-4(2))*; 113p. pap. 25.99 *(978-0-521-15238-9(0))* Cambridge Univ. Pr.

Hutchins, Frank & Wilson, Patrick C., eds. Editing Eden: A Reconsideration of Identity, Politics, & Place in Amazonia. 2010. (ENG., Illus.). 306p. pap. 35.00 *(978-0-8032-1612-9(2))* Univ. of Nebraska Pr.

Junk, Wolfgang J., ed. The Central Amazon Floodplain: Ecology of a Pulsing System. 2010. (Ecological Studies). (Illus.). xxiii, 525p. pap. 319.00 *(978-3-642-08214-6(9)*, 3642082149) Springer.

Marcos. Notes from the Jungle. 2008. 244p. (ENG.). 31.99 *(978-1-4257-5186-9(5))*; per. 21.99 *(978-1-4257-5184-5(9))* Xlibris Corp.

Nugent, Stephen. Scoping the Amazon: Image, Icon & Ethnography. 2007. (ENG., Illus.). 260p. pap. 34.95 *(978-1-59874-177-3(2))* Left Coast Pr., Inc.

—Scoping the Amazon: Image, Icon, & Ethnography. 2007. (ENG., Illus.). 260p. 89.00 *(978-1-59874-176-6(4))* Left Coast Pr., Inc.

Pinedo-Vasquez, Miguel A., et al, eds. The Amazon Várzea: The Decade Past & the Decade Ahead. 2010. (ENG., Illus.). xxxix, 362p. 179.00 *(978-94-007-0145-8(4)*, 9400701454) Springer.

Politis, Gustavo. Nukak: Ethnoarchaeology of an Amazonian People. Alberti, Benjamin, tr. from SPA. 2007. (University College London Institute of Archaeology Publications). (ENG., Illus.). 412p. 94.00 *(978-1-59874-229-9(9))* Left Coast Pr., Inc.

Posey, D. A. Human Impacts on Amazonia: The Role of Traditional Ecological Knowledge in Conservation & Development. Balick, Michael J. & Posey, Darrell A., eds. 2006. (Biology & Resource Management Ser.). (ENG., Illus.). 392p. (gr. 17). 95.00 *(978-0-231-10588-0(6))* Columbia Univ. Pr.

Posey, Darrell A. & Balick, Michael J., eds. Human Impacts on Amazonia: The Role of Traditional Ecological Knowledge in Conservation & Development. 2006. (Biology & Resource Management Ser.). (ENG., Illus.). 392p. (gr. 17). pap. 39.50 *(978-0-231-10589-7(4))* Columbia Univ. Pr.

Santos-Granero, Fernando, ed. The Occult Life of Things: Native Amazonian Theories of Materiality & Personhood. 2009. (ENG., Illus.). 288p. 55.00 *(978-0-8165-2874-5(8))* Univ. of Arizona Pr.

Vadjunec, Jacqueline M. & Schmink, Marianne, eds. Amazonian Geographies: Emerging Identities & Landscapes. 2012. (ENG.). 240p. (C). 125.00 *(978-0-415-60053-8(7))* Routledge.

AMAZONAS (BRAZIL)

Algot Lange. In the Amazon Jungle: Adventures in Remote Parts of the Upper Amazon River Including a Sojourn among Cannibal Indians. 2007. 130p. pap. 18.99 *(978-1-4346-3900-4(2))*; (ENG.). 142p. pap. 19.99 *(978-1-4346-3901-1(0))* BiblioBazaar.

Lange, Algot. Adventures in Remote Parts of the Upper Amazon River, Including a Sojourn among Cannibal Indians. Frederick, D. E. L. L. E. N. B. A. U. G. H., tr. 2007. 112p. per. 12.99 *(978-1-59547-870-2(1))* NuVision Pubns., LLC.

—In the Amazon Jungle Illustrated Edition. 2009. (Illus.). 336p. pap. *(978-1-84830-173-3(1)*, Wildhern Pr.) Echo Library.

AMAZONS

Anderson, Florence M. Religious Cults Associated with the Amazons. reprint ed. 37.50 *(978-0-404-00749-2(X))* AMS Pr., Inc.

Braund, D. Scythians & Amazons. 2009. (Illus.). CCVIIIp. 110.00 *(978-0-415-16306-4(4))* Routledge.

Burton, Richard F. A Mission to Gelele, King of Dahome. 2011. (Cambridge Library Collection - Travel & Exploration Ser.). (ENG.). 424p. pap. 31.99 *(978-1-108-03032-8(7))*; (Illus.). 406p. pap. 31.99 *(978-1-108-03031-1(9))* Cambridge Univ. Pr.

—A Mission to Gelele, King of Dahome. (ENG.). 384p. 2007. 48.95 *(978-0-548-13941-7(5))* 2006. per. 33.95 *(978-1-4286-5121-0(7))* Kessinger Publishing, LLC.

Lange, Algot. In the Amazon Jungle. 2008. 144p. 21.99 *(978-0-554-37045-3(X))*; 24.99 *(978-0-554-27742-4(5))* BiblioBazaar.

—In the Amazon Jungle. 2009. 108p. pap. *(978-0-217-48737-5(8))* Books LLC.

—In the Amazon Jungle. Hauser, J. Odell, ed. 2007. (ENG.). 120p. per. *(978-1-4065-2562-5(6))* Dodo Pr.

—In the Amazon Jungle. 2007. (ENG.). 92p. per. *(978-1-4068-1507-8(1))* Echo Library.

—In the Amazon Jungle. 405p. reprint ed. 98.00 *(978-0-7222-9596-0(0))*; 98.00 *(978-0-7222-6482-9(8))* Library Reprints, Inc.

AMBASSADORS

see also Diplomatic Privileges and Immunities

Albright, Madeleine. Read My Pins: Stories from a Diplomat's Jewel Box. 2009. (ENG., Illus.). 176p. 40.00 *(978-0-06-089918-9(2))* HarperCollins Pubs.

Ambassadors' Memoir: U.S.-Korea Relations Through the Eyes of the Ambassadors. 2009. *(978-0-9747141-5-8(1))* Korea Economic Institute.

Bell, Gary M. A Handlist of British Diplomatic Representatives, 1509-1688. 2011. (Royal Historical Society Guides & Handbooks Ser.). (ENG.). 316p. pap. 60.00 *(978-0-521-28322-9(1))* Cambridge Univ. Pr.

Ben Natan, Asher. The Audacity to Live. Tarmon, Asher, tr. from HEB. 2007. 328p. 29.95 *(978-965-7344-25-2(3))* Mazo Pubs.

Blackwell Herrick, Agnes. Paris Embassy Diary 1921-1922. 2008. (ENG., Illus.). 30p. per. 20.99 *(978-0-7618-3973-8(8))* Hamilton Bks.

Blinken, Vera & Blinken, Donald. Vera & the Ambassador: Escape & Return. 2008. (Illus.). 350p. 24.95 *(978-1-4384-2663-1(1))* State Univ. of New York Pr.

Bolton, John R. & Bolton, John. Surrender Is Not an Option: Defending America at the United Nations. 2008. (ENG., Illus.). 512p. pap. 16.00 *(978-1-4165-5285-7(5)*, Threshold Editions) Threshold Editions.

Boulger, Demetrius Charles. The Life of Sir Halliday Macartney, K. C. M. G. Commander of Li Hung Chang's Trained Force in the Taeping Rebellion, Founder of the First Chinese Arsenals, for Thirty Years Councillor & Secretary to the Chinese Legation in London. 2011. (Cambridge Library Collection - Travel & Exploration Ser.). (Illus.). 571p. pap. 39.99 **(978-1-108-02626-0(5))** Cambridge Univ. Pr.

Brown, Keith L. A Conversation with Ambassador Keith Brown. 2011. 82p. pap. 15.99 **(978-1-4568-5094-4(6))** Xlibris Corp.

Brunner, Annette. Crossing & Living Cultures. 2011. 212p. 24.99 *(978-1-4520-8261-5(8))*; pap. 14.49 *(978-1-4520-8260-8(X))* AuthorHouse.

Carrozza, Anthony R. William D. Pawley: The Extraordinary Life of the Adventurer, Entrepreneur, & Diplomat Who Cofounded the Flying Tigers. 2012. (Illus.). 392p. 34.95 **(978-1-59797-714-2(4))** Potomac Bks., Inc.

Castro, Raul H. & August, Jack L., Jr. Adversity Is My Angel: The Life & Career of Raúl H. Castro. 2009. (ENG., Illus.). 192p. pap. 21.95 *(978-0-87565-378-5(2))* Texas Christian Univ. Pr.

Cellucci, Paul. Unquiet Diplomacy. rev. ed. 2007. (ENG., Illus.). 256p. pap. 16.95 *(978-1-55263-875-0(8)*, Key Porter Bks. CAN. Dist: Perseus-PGW.

Chollet, Derek & Power, Samantha. The Unquiet American: Richard Holbrooke in the World. 2011. (ENG., Illus.). 400p. 29.99 *(978-1-61039-078-1(4))* PublicAffairs.

Congdon, Lee. George Kennan: A Writing Life. Kennan, George, ed. 2008. (ENG.). 225p. (C). 25.00 *(978-1-933859-71-2(7))* ISI Bks.

Cooper, John M. Walter Hines Page: The Southerner As American, 1855-1918. 2011. (ENG.). 504p. pap. 50.00 *(978-0-8078-6522-4(2))* Univ. of North Carolina Pr.

Dale, William N. Living Diplomatically: A Life in the U. S. Foreign Service. 2008. (ENG.). 76p. pap. 24.00 *(978-0-7618-4007-7(9))* Hamilton Bks.

Davidow, Jeffrey. The Bear & the Porcupine: The U.S. & Mexico. 2006. *(978-1-55876-432-3(1))* Weiner, Maureen.
—The Bear & the Porcupine: The US & Mexico. exp. ed. 2006. (Illus.). 320p. per. 24.95 *(978-1-55876-433-0(X))* Wiener, Markus Pubs., Inc.
Davis, Richard Beale. The Abbe Correa in America, 1812-1820: The Contributions of the Diplomat & Natural Philosopher to the Foundations of Our National Life. 2011. 116p. 39.95 ***(978-1-258-04214-1(2))*** Literary Licensing, LLC.
Dean, John Gunther. Danger Zones: A Diplomat's Fight for America's Interests. 2009. 240p. 36.00 *(978-0-9823867-1-2(0))*; pap. 26.00 *(978-0-9823867-0-5(2))* New Academia Publishing, LLC. (Vellum).
Dobbins, James F. After the Taliban: Nation-Building in Afghanistan. 2008. (Illus.). 192p. 24.95 *(978-1-59797-083-9(2))* Potomac Bks., Inc.
Dorsinville, Jean M. Honor Thy Father: An Awakening. 2008. (Illus.). x, 142p. pap. *(978-0-9818765-0-4(1))* Dorsinville, Jean M.
Drown, Merle. In the Arena: Life & Times of William W. Treat. 2009. (Illus.). 384p. 29.95 *(978-0-9801672-3-8(X))* Hobblebush Bks.
Ducci, Lucia. George P. Marsh Correspondence: Images of Italy, 1861-1881. 2011. (ENG.). 242p. (gr. 17). 75.00 ***(978-1-61147-461-9(2))*** Fairleigh Dickinson Univ. Pr.
Emerson, Jason. Giant in the Shadows: The Life of Robert T. Lincoln. 2012. (ENG., Illus.). 640p. 39.95 *(978-0-8093-3055-3(5))* 2011. E-Book 39.95 *(978-0-8093-9071-7(X))* Southern Illinois Univ. Pr.
Eyre, David W. & Cazimero, Momi. Clare: The Honolulu Years. 2007. 256p. 19.95 *(978-1-56647-837-3(5))* Mutual Publishing LLC.
Foo, Yee-Wah. Chiang Kaishek's Last Ambassador to Moscow: The Wartime Diaries of Fu Bingchang. 2011. (ENG., Illus.). 256p. 89.00 *(978-0-230-58477-8(2))* Palgrave Macmillan.
Gaddis, John Lewis. George F. Kennan: An American Life. (ENG., Illus.). 800p. (gr. 12). 2012. pap. 22.00 ***(978-0-14-312215-9(0)***, Penguin (Non-Classics)) 2011. 39.95 *(978-1-59420-312-1(1)*, Penguin Pr. HC, The) Penguin Group (USA) Inc.
Gotlieb, Allan. The Washington Diaries: 1981-1989. 2007. (ENG., Illus.). 656p. pap. 19.95 *(978-0-7710-3563-0(2)*, McClelland & Stewart) McClelland & Stewart CAN. Dist: Random Hse., Inc.
Grady, Henry Francis. The Memoirs of Ambassador Henry F. Grady: From the Great War to the Cold War. McNay, John T., ed. & intro. by. 2009. (ENG.). 232p. (C). 39.95 *(978-0-8262-1832-2(6))* Univ. of Missouri Pr.
Greenwood. Gladwyn Jebb & the Shaping of the Modern World. 2008. 350p. 85.00 *(978-0-85303-776-7(0))*; pap. 35.00 *(978-0-85303-777-4(9))* Vallentine Mitchell Pubs. GBR. Dist: International Specialized Bk. Services.
Greenwood, Sean. Titan at the Foreign Office: Gladwyn Jebb & the Shaping of the Modern World. 2008. (History of International Relations, Diplomacy, & Intelligence Ser.). (Illus.). xxx, 430p. *(978-90-04-16970-8(9))* BRILL.
Grose, Philip G. Looking for Utopia: The Life & Times of John C. West. 2011. 360p. 34.95 *(978-1-57003-978-2(X))* Univ. of South Carolina Pr.
Hopkins, Michael F., et al, eds. The Washington Embassy: British Ambassadors to the United States, 1939-77. 2009. (ENG.). 256p. 89.00 *(978-0-230-52216-9(5))* Palgrave Macmillan.
Hormel, James C. & Martin, Erin. Fit to Serve: Reflections on a Secret Life, Private Struggle, & Public Battle to Become the First Openly Gay U.S. Ambassador. 2011. (ENG., Illus.). 320p. 24.95 *(978-1-61608-398-4(0)*, 608398) Skyhorse Publishing Co., Inc.
Hunt, Swanee. Half-Life of a Zealot. 2006. (ENG., Illus.). 424p. 32.95 *(978-0-8223-3875-8(0))* Duke Univ. Pr.
Katjavivi, Jane. Undisciplined Heart. 322p. pap. *(978-1-920397-04-3(3))* Michigan State Univ. Pr.
Kerrigan, Michael J. Politics with Principle: Ten Characters with Character. 2010. (Illus.). 290p. 46.95 *(978-1-60494-448-8(X))*; pap. 21.95 *(978-1-60494-447-1(1))* Wheatmark.
Knox, Tim. The British Ambassador's Residence in Paris. 2011. (ENG., Illus.). 168p. 65.00 *(978-2-08-020078-5(X))* Flammarion et Cie FRA. Dist: Random Hse., Inc.
Krueger, Robert, et al. From Bloodshed to Hope in Burundi: Our Embassy Years During Genocide. 2007. (Focus on American History Ser.). (ENG., Illus.). 342p. 26.00 *(978-0-292-71486-1(6))* Univ. of Texas Pr.
Levine, Paul A. Raoul Wallenberg in Budapest: Myth, History & Holocaust 1944-1945. 2010. (Illus.). 416p. 74.95 *(978-0-85303-727-9(2))*; pap. 32.95 *(978-0-85303-728-6(0))* Vallentine Mitchell Pubs. GBR. Dist: International Specialized Bk. Services.
Lowe, David Michael. Australian Between Empires: The Life of Percy Spender, 1 vol. 2010. (Empires in Perspective Ser.). (ENG., Illus.). 256p. 99.00 *(978-1-84893-000-1(3))* Pickering & Chatto Pubs., Ltd. GBR. Dist: Ashgate Publishing Co.
Lukacs, John. George Kennan: A Study of Character. 2009. (ENG., Illus.). 224p. pap. 15.00 *(978-0-300-14306-5(0))* Yale Univ. Pr.
MacLaren, Roy. Commissions High: Canada in London, 1870-1971. 2006. (ENG., Illus.). 584p. (C). *(978-0-7735-3036-2(3))* McGill-Queen's Univ. Pr.
Meyer, Christopher. DC Confidential: The Controversial Memoirs of Britain's Ambassador to the U. S. at the Time of 9/11 & the Run-up to the Iraq War. 2006. (ENG., Illus.). 344p. per. 16.95 *(978-0-7538-2091-9(9))* Orion Publishing Group, Ltd. GBR. Dist: Independent Pubs. Group.
Murray, Craig. Dirty Diplomacy: The Rough-and-Tumble Adventures of a Scotch-Drinking, Skirt-Chasing, Dictator-Busting & Thoroughly Unrepentant Ambassador Stuck on the Frontline of the War Against Terror. 2011. (ENG.). 384p. pap. 23.99 *(978-1-4165-4802-7(5)*, Scribner) Scribner.
Neumann, Ronald E. The Other War: Winning & Losing in Afghanistan. 2009. (Illus.). 256p. 27.50 *(978-1-59797-427-1(7))* Potomac Bks., Inc.
Nomination: Hearing Before the Committee on Foreign Relations, United States Senate, One Hundred Eleventh Congress, Second Session, March 16, 2010. 2011. iii, 36p. ***(978-0-16-088532-7(9)***, 552-070-42709-1) United States Government Printing Office.
Nomination: Hearing Before the Committee on Foreign Relations, United States Senate, One Hundred Eleventh Congress, Second Session, September 23, 2010. 2011. iii, 26p. ***(978-0-16-088468-9(3)***, 552-070-42674-4) United States Government Printing Office.
Nomination of Ryan C. Crocker: Hearing Before the Committee on Foreign Relations, United States Senate, One Hundred Twelfth Congress, First Session, June 8, 2011. 2011. iii, 30p. ***(978-0-16-089536-4(7)***, 552-070-43487-9) United States Government Printing Office.
Nominations: Hearing Before the Committee on Foreign Relations, United States Senate, One Hundred Eleventh Congress, First Session, July 7, 2009. 2011. iii, 45p. ***(978-0-16-088553-2(1)***, 552-070-42729-5) United States Government Printing Office.
Nominations of the 110th Congress, Second Session: Hearings Before the Committee on Foreign Relations, United States Senate, One Hundred Tenth Congress, Second Session, January 30 Through September 24, 2008. 2009. v, 754p. *(978-0-16-083589-6(5)*, 552-070-39307-2) United States Government Printing Office.
Packard, George R. Edwin O. Reischauer & the American Discovery of Japan. 2010. (ENG., Illus.). 368p. (gr. 17). 32.50 *(978-0-231-14354-7(0))* Columbia Univ. Pr.
Perkins, Edward J. & Cronley, Connie. Mr. Ambassador: Warrior for Peace. 2009. (ENG.). 576p. pap. 19.95 *(978-0-8061-4094-0(1))* Univ. of Oklahoma Pr.
Phipps, Eric & Johnson, Gaynor. Our Man in Berlin: The Diary of Sir Eric Phipps, 1933-1937. 2008. (ENG., Illus.). 320p. 89.00 *(978-0-230-51787-5(0))* Palgrave Macmillan.
Platt, Nicholas. China Boys: How U. S. Relations with the PRC Began & Grew. A Personal Memoir. 2010. (Illus.). 386p. pap. 28.00 *(978-0-9844062-2-7(0)*, Vellum) New Academia Publishing, LLC.
Podany, Amanda H. Brotherhood of Kings: How International Relations Shaped the Ancient near East, 1 vol. 2012. (ENG., Illus.). 432p. pap. 24.95 ***(978-0-19-985868-2(3))*** Oxford Univ. Pr., Inc.
Price, John. When the White House Calls: From Immigrant Entrepreneur to U. S. Ambassador. 2011. (ENG., Illus.). 712p. (gr. 9). 30.00 *(978-1-60781-143-5(X))* Univ. of Utah Pr.
Qin, Huasun. Chu Shi Lian He Guo: Ambassador's Memoir: Representing China in the UN. 2010. (CHI., Illus.). pap. *(978-7-5011-9136-9(0))* Xinhua Publishing Hse.
Rana, Kishan S. The 21st Century Ambassador: Plenipotentiary to Chief Executive. 2011. (ENG., Illus.). 288p. pap. 27.95 *(978-0-19-806966-9(9))* Oxford Univ. Pr., Inc.
Rohatyn, Felix G. Dealings: A Political & Financial Life. 2010. (ENG., Illus.). 304p. 27.00 *(978-1-4391-8196-6(9))* Simon & Schuster.
Ruud, Charles A. The Constant Diplomat: Robert Ford in Moscow. 2009. (ENG., Illus.). 344p. (C). *(978-0-7735-3585-5(3))* McGill-Queen's Univ. Pr.
Shaw, John. The Ambassador: Inside the Life of a Working Diplomat. 2007. (Capital Currents Ser.). (Illus.). 200p. per. 16.95 *(978-1-933102-42-9(X))* Capital Bks., Inc.
Siv, Sichan. The Golden Bones: An Extraordinary Journey from Hell in Cambodia to a New Life in America. 2009. (ENG.). 352p. pap. 14.99 *(978-0-06-137541-5(1)*, HarperPerennial) HarperCollins Pubs.
Soroka, Marina. Britain Russia & the Road to the First World War: The Fateful Embassy of Count Aleksandr Benckendorff (1903-16) 2011. (Birmingham Studies in First World War History Ser.). (Illus.). 332p. 124.95 *(978-1-4094-2246-4(1))* Ashgate Publishing Co.
Spivakovsky, Erika. Son of the Alhambra: Don Diego Hurtado de Mendoza, 1504-1575. 2011. (ENG., Illus.). 476p. pap. 40.00 ***(978-0-292-74180-5(4))*** Univ. of Texas Pr.
Stapleton, Craig Roberts. Where Liberty Dwells, There Is My Country: The Story of Twentieth-Century American Ambassadors to France. 2010. (ENG.). 220p. pap. 32.00 *(978-0-7618-5143-1(7))* Hamilton Bks.
Stapleton, Craig Roberts & McCready, Louise French. Where Liberty Dwells, There Is My Country: The Story of Twentieth-Century American Ambassadors to France. 2010. 220p. 62.00 *(978-0-7618-5142-4(9))* Hamilton Bks.
Stiller, Jesse. George S. Messersmith: Diplomat of Democracy. 2011. (ENG.). 368p. pap. 50.00 ***(978-0-8078-6620-7(2))*** Univ. of North Carolina Pr.
Stuart, John Leighton & Chen, Lisong. Situ Leideng Ri Ji: Xiang Jian Shi Nan Bie Yi Nan. 2009. (CHI., Illus.). ***(978-7-5461-0241-2(3))*** Huangshan Publishing Hse.
Sutherland, Jeanne. From Moscow to Cuba & Beyond: A Diplomatic Memoir of the Cold War. 2010. (ENG., Illus.). 336p. 55.00 *(978-1-84885-474-1(9)*, Radcliffe Pr., The) I. B. Tauris & Co., Ltd. GBR. Dist: Macmillan.
Sykes, Percy. The Right Honourable Sir Mortimer Durand: a Biography. 2006. (ENG.). 388p. per. 33.95 *(978-1-4286-5524-9(7))* Kessinger Publishing, LLC.
Tarifa, Fatos. To Albania, with Love. 2007. (ENG., Illus.). 288p. per. 45.50 *(978-0-7618-3590-5(3))* Univ. Pr. of America, Inc.
Templeton, Hugh, ed. Mr Ambassador: Memoirs of Sir Carl Berendsen. 2009. (ENG.). 350p. pap. 25.00 *(978-0-86473-584-3(7))* Victoria Univ. Pr. NZL. Dist: Independent Pubs. Group.
Thompson, Nicholas. The Hawk & the Dove: Paul Nitze, George Kennan, & the History of the Cold War. 2010. (ENG., Illus.). 432p. pap. 17.00 *(978-0-312-65886-1(9))* Picador.
Walter, Richard J. Peru & the United States, 1960-1975: How Their Ambassadors Managed Foreign Relations in a Turbulent Era. 2010. (ENG.). 328p. 68.00 *(978-0-271-03631-1(1))* Pennsylvania State Univ. Pr.
Ward, Adolphus William. Sir Henry Wotton: A Biographical Sketch. 2007. (ENG.). 176p. 37.95 *(978-0-548-25011-2(1))*; 180p. per. 22.95 *(978-1-4326-5269-2(9))* Kessinger Publishing, LLC.
Webb, Nigel & Webb, Caroline. The Earl & His Butler in Constantinople: The Secret Diary of an English Servant among the Ottomans. 2008. (ENG., Illus.). 248p. pap. 26.00 *(978-1-84511-782-5(4))* I. B. Tauris & Co., Ltd. GBR. Dist: Macmillan.
Wilkowski, Jean M. Abroad for Her Country: Tales of a Pioneer Woman Ambassador in the U. S. Foreign Service. 2008. (ENG., Illus.). 384p. 30.00 *(978-0-268-04413-8(9))* Univ. of Notre Dame Pr.
Wright, Robert. Our Man in Tehran: The Truth Behind the Secret Mission to Save Six Americans during the Iran Hostage Crisis & the Ambassador Who Worked with the CIA to Bring Them Home. 2011. (ENG., Illus.). 432p. 25.95 *(978-1-59051-413-9(0))* Other Pr., LLC.
Yager, Jane. Ambassador in A Ten-Gallon Hat. 2009. 231p. pap. 12.24 *(978-0-557-02408-7(0))* Lulu Enterprises Inc.
Young, Robert J. American by Degrees: The Extraordinary Lives of French Ambassador Jules Jusserand. 2009. (ENG., Illus.). 368p. (C). *(978-0-7735-3572-5(1))* McGill-Queen's Univ. Pr.

AMBER

Causey, Faya. Amber & the Ancient World. 2012. (ENG., Illus.). 144p. 25.00 ***(978-1-60606-082-7(1)***, J. Paul Getty Museum) Getty Pubns.
Clark, Neil. Amber - Tears of the Gods. 2010. (Illus.). 128p. 45.00 *(978-1-906716-16-5(1))* Dunedin Academic Pr. GBR. Dist: International Specialized Bk. Services.
Hopp, Nancy P. S. Amber: Jewelry, Art, & Science. 2009. (Illus.). 160p. pap. 29.99 *(978-0-7643-3168-8(X))* Schiffer Publishing, Ltd.
Lloyd, Anne. Antiques & Amber. 2011. 118p. 39.95 ***(978-1-258-01463-6(7))*** Literary Licensing, LLC.
Ross, Andrew. Amber: The Natural Time Capsule. 2010. (ENG., Illus.). 112p. 29.95 *(978-1-55407-609-3(9))* Firefly Bks., Ltd.
Stoev, Pavel, ed. Life Caught in a Spider's Web: Papers in Arachnology. 2009. (ZooKeys Ser.). (Illus.). 375p. pap. 187.50 *(978-954-642-502-7(8))* Pensoft Pubs. BGR. Dist: Coronet Bks.

AMBIGUITY

Agirre, Eneko & Edmonds, Philip, eds. Word Sense Disambiguation: Algorithms & Applications. 2006. (Text, Speech, & Language Technology Ser.: Vol. 33). xxii, 364p. 269.00 *(978-1-4020-4808-1(4)*, 1402048084) Springer.
Almela Sanchez, Moises. From Word to Lexical Units: A Corpus-Driven Account of Collocation & Idiomatic Patterning in English & English-Spanish. 2006. (Studien Zur Romanischen Sprachwissenschaft und Interkulturellen Kommunikation Ser.). 421p. pap. *(978-0-8204-8740-3(6))*; pap. *(978-3-631-55759-4(0))* Lang, Peter AG.
Atherton, Catherine. The Stoics on Ambiguity. 2007. (Cambridge Classical Studies). (ENG.). 584p. pap. 79.00 *(978-0-521-04772-2(2))* Cambridge Univ. Pr.
Bauer, Johannes & Harteis, Christian, eds. Human Fallibility: The Ambiguity of Errors for Work & Learning. 2011. (Professional & Practice-based Learning Ser.). (ENG.). 200p. 139.00 *(978-90-481-3940-8(6)*, 9048139406) Springer.
Cohen, Avner. The Worst-Kept Secret: Israel's Bargain with the Bomb. 2012. (ENG.). 416p. (gr. 17). pap. 25.00 ***(978-0-231-13699-0(4))*** Columbia Univ. Pr.
Cutting, Joan, ed. Vague Language Explored. 2007. (ENG.). 272p. 105.00 *(978-1-4039-8817-1(X))* Palgrave Macmillan.
Edmonds, Philip & Agirre, Eneko, eds. Word Sense Disambiguation: Algorithms & Applications. 2007. (Text, Speech & Language Technology Ser.). 392p. per. 49.95 *(978-1-4020-6870-6(0)*, 1402068700) Springer.
Égré, Paul & Klinedinst, Nathan, eds. Vagueness & Language Use. 2011. (ENG., Illus.). 336p. 85.00 *(978-0-230-23861-9(0))* Palgrave Macmillan.
Hogan, Daniel R. $$$ the Entrepreneur's Guide to Start, Grow, & Manage A Profitable Business. 2011. 352p. 33.00 ***(978-1-4567-6524-8(8))*** AuthorHouse.
Kantas, Vasileios. Photo Ambiguity. 2010. 256p. pap. *(978-3-8383-7059-0(7))* Lambert Academic Publishing.
Lu, Ling. Duo Yuan Shi Yu Zhong de Mo Hu Yu Yan Xue: Fuzzy Linguistics: A Multi Disciplinary Perspective. 2010. (Illus.). *(978-7-5097-1305-1(6))* China Social Science Documentation Publishing Hse.
Marchetti, Luca, text. Simplicity: Essential Ambiguities. 2012. (ENG., Illus.). 128p. pap. 40.00 *(978-2-914563-55-0(8))* Dis Voir Editions FRA. Dist: D.A.P./Distributed Art Pubs.
Mathius, Kabagambe. The Gps Ambiguity Problem Resolution & Validation. 2010. 136p. pap. *(978-3-8383-9263-9(9))* Lambert Academic Publishing.
O'Neal, John C. Poetics of Confusion in the French... 2011. *(978-0-87413-064-5(6))* Univ. of Delaware Pr.
—The Progressive Poetics of Confusion in the French Enlightenment. 2011. (ENG.). 240p. 65.00 *(978-1-61149-024-4(3))* Univ. of Delaware Pr.
Pinkal, Manfred. Logic & Lexicon: The Semantics of the Indefinite. Simmons, Geoffrey, tr. from GER. 2010. (Studies in Linguistics & Philosophy Ser.). 404p. pap. 219.00 *(978-90-481-4529-4(5)*, 9048145295) Springer.
Reichenbach, Uwe K.H. Contexts, hierarchies, & Filters: A study of transformational systems as disambiguated Languages. (Linguistische Arbeiten Ser.). (ENG.). 110p. 210.00 ***(978-3-11-210576-4(1))*** De Gruyter, Mouton DEU. Dist: de Gruyter, Walter GmbH & Co. KG.
Roca I Puigvert, Mercè. Reference Dependence in the Face of Ambiguity. 2010. 232p. pap. *(978-3-639-22746-8(8))* VDM Verlag Dr. Mueller e.K.
Scheffler, Israel. Beyond the Letter: A Philosophical Inquiry into Ambiguity, Vagueness & Methaphor in Language. 2010. (Routledge Revivals Ser.). 164p. 95.00 *(978-0-415-58111-0(7)*, Routledge) Taylor & Francis Group GBR. Dist: Taylor & Francis Group.
—Beyond the Letter (Routledge Revivals) 2010. (ENG.). 164p. pap. 39.95 *(978-0-415-58133-2(8))* Routledge.
Search Query Ambiguity. 2010. 180p. pap. *(978-3-8383-0140-2(4))* Lambert Academic Publishing.
Spector, Cecile C. As Far As Words Go: Activities for Understanding Ambiguous Language & Humor, Revised Edition. 2009. 192p. pap. 39.95 *(978-1-59857-056-4(0))* Brookes, Paul H. Publishing Co.
Spector, Cecile Cyrul. Say One Thing, Mean Another. 2007. per. 34.95 *(978-1-58650-811-1(3))* Super Duper Pubns.
Virno, Paolo. Multitude Between Innovation & Negation. Bertoletti, Isabella et al, trs. from ITA. 2008. (Semiotext(e) / Foreign Agents Ser.). (ENG.). 200p. (gr. 17). pap. 14.95 *(978-1-58435-050-7(4))* Semiotexte/Smart Art.
Walton, Douglas. Fallacies Arising from Ambiguity. 2010. (Applied Logic Ser.). 312p. pap. 219.00 *(978-90-481-4717-5(4)*, 9048147174) Springer.

AMBIGUITY IN LITERATURE

Connon, Daisy. Subjects Not-at-home: Emmanuel Carrère, Marie NDiaye, Eugène Savitzkaya.: Forms of the Uncanny in the Contemporary French Novel. 2010. (Illus.). 295p. pap. 83.00 *(978-90-420-3005-3(4))* Rodopi.
McCallam, David. L'art de L'équivoque Chez Laclos. 2008. (BIBLIOTHeQUE des LUMIeRES Ser.). (FRE.). 196p. (C). pap. 123.00 *(978-2-600-01209-6(5))* Droz, Librairie CHE. Dist: Brown, David Bk. Co., The.
Rowe, Joyce A. Equivocal Endings in Classic American Novels: The Scarlet Letter; Adventures of Huckleberry Finn; the Ambassadors; the Great Gatsby. 2008. (ENG.). 172p. pap. 28.00 *(978-0-521-06102-5(4))* Cambridge Univ. Pr.

AMBITION

Beinart, Peter. The Icarus Syndrome: A History of American Hubris. 496p. 2011. (ENG.). pap. 17.99 *(978-0-06-145647-3(0)*, HarperPerennial) 2010. 27.99 *(978-0-06-145646-6(2))* HarperCollins Pubs.
Faulkner, Robert. The Case for Greatness: Honorable Ambition & Its Critics. 2008. (ENG.). 288p. 30.00 *(978-0-300-12393-7(0))* Yale Univ. Pr.
Harvey, Dave. Rescuing Ambition. 2010. 224p. pap. 14.99 *(978-1-4335-1491-3(5))* Crossway.
Harvey, David T. Rescuing Ambition. 2010. *(978-1-4335-1492-0(3))* Crossway.
Hawkins, Mike. Activating Your Ambition: A Guide to Coaching the Best Out of Yourself & Others. 2009. (Illus.). xi, 314p. pap. *(978-1-934812-42-6(0))* Brown Bks. Publishing Group.
Hewitt, Hugh. A Guide to Christian Ambition: Using Career, Politics, & Culture to Influence the World, 0 vols. 2006. 224p. pap. 13.99 *(978-0-7852-8871-8(6))* Nelson, Thomas Inc.
Kete, Kathleen. Making Way for Genius: The Aspiring Self in France from the Old Regime to the New. 2012. (ENG., Illus.). 256p. 38.00 ***(978-0-300-17482-3(9))*** Yale Univ. Pr.
Mahan, Brian J. Forgetting Ourselves on Purpose: Vocation & the Ethics of Ambition. 2010. (ENG.). 240p. pap. 16.95 *(978-0-470-62168-4(0)*, Jossey-Bass) Wiley, John & Sons, Inc.
Marden, Orison Swett. Ambition & Success. 2007. (ENG.). 108p. 33.95 *(978-0-548-11390-5(4))* Kessinger Publishing, LLC.
Margitics, Ferenc & Pauwlik, Zsuzsa, eds. Personal Strivings as a Predictor of Emotional Intelligence. 2010. (Psychology of Emotions, Motivations & Actions Ser.). (Illus.). ix, 79p. pap. 43.00 *(978-1-60876-620-8(9))* Nova Science Pubs., Inc.
Opal, J. M. Beyond the Farm: National Ambitions in Rural New England. (Early American Studies). (Illus.). 280p. (C). 2011. pap. 24.95 *(978-0-8122-2156-5(7))* 2008. 55.00 *(978-0-8122-4062-7(6))* Univ. of Pennsylvania Pr.
Osho, Osho. Fame, Fortune, & Ambition: What Is the Real Meaning of Success? 2010. (Osho Life Essentials Ser.). (ENG.). 224p. pap. 15.99 *(978-0-312-59544-9(1)*, St. Martin's Griffin) St. Martin's Pr.
Persons, Georgia Anne. Beyond the Boundaries: A New Structure of Ambition in African American Politics. Persons, Georgia, ed. 2009. (ENG., Illus.). 284p. pap. 29.95 *(978-1-4128-1048-7(5))* Transaction Pubs.
Ray, James Lee. American Foreign Policy & Political Ambition, 00 vols. rev. ed. 2007. (Illus.). 375p. (C). pap. 88.00 *(978-1-56802-832-3(6))* CQ Pr.
Rubin, Ellie. Ambition: 7 Rules for Getting There. 2008. 236p. pap. *(978-0-9809231-1-7(5))* BPS Bks.
Samuels, David. Ambition, Federalism, & Legislative Politics in Brazil. 2006. (ENG., Illus.). 268p. pap. 53.00 *(978-0-521-03062-5(5))* Cambridge Univ. Pr.
Teodoro, Manuel P. Bureaucratic Ambition: Careers, Motives, & the Innovative Administrator. 2011. (Johns Hopkins Studies in Governance & Public Management Ser.). (ENG., Illus.). 240p. (gr. 17). 45.00 *(978-1-4214-0245-1(9))* Johns Hopkins Univ. Pr.
Zackheim, Victoria. The Face in the Mirror: Writers Reflect on Their Dreams of Youth & the Reality of Age. Zacheim, Victoria, ed. 2009. (ENG., Illus.). 300p. 25.00 *(978-1-59102-752-2(7))* Prometheus Bks., Pubs.

AMBO LANGUAGE (SOUTHWEST AFRICA AND ANGOLA)

see Kuanyama Language

AMBROSE, SAINT, BISHOP OF MILAN, D. 397

Balzaretti, R. The Lands of Saint Ambrose Monks & Society in Carolingian Milan. 2011. (Studies in the Early Middle Ages). (ENG.). 256p. (C). 87.00 *(978-2-503-50977-8(0))* Brepols Pubs. BEL. Dist: Brown, David Bk. Co., The.

Diederich, Mary Doro. Vergil in the Works of St. Ambrose. 2006. pap. 21.95 *(978-1-4286-5885-1(8))* Kessinger Publishing, LLC.

Liebeschuetz, J. H. W. G. Ambrose & John Chrysostom: Clerics between Desert & Empire. 2011. (ENG.). 320p. 110.00 *(978-0-19-959664-5(6))* Oxford Univ. Pr., Inc.

Liebeschuetz, J. H. W. G., ed. Ambrose of Milan: Political Letters & Speeches. Liebeschuetz, Wolfe, tr. from LAT. 2010. (Liverpool University Press - Translated Texts for Historians Ser.). (ENG.). 432p. pap. 39.95 *(978-1-84631-243-4(4))* Liverpool Univ. Pr. GBR. Dist: Chicago Distribution Ctr.

Markschies, Christoph. Origenes und Sein Erbe: Gesammelte Studien. 2007. (Texte und Untersuchungen zur Geschichte der altchristlichen Literatur Ser.). (GER.). X, 283p. 140.00 *(978-3-11-019278-0(0))* De Gruyter, Walter Inc.

Muncey, R. W. The New Testament Text of Saint Ambrose. 2008. (ENG.). 200p. pap. 31.99 *(978-0-521-09149-7(7))* Cambridge Univ. Pr.

Schaff, Philip, ed. Nicene & Post-Nicene Fathers: Second Series, Volume X Ambrose. 2007. 524p. (ENG.). 35.95 *(978-1-60206-526-0(8))*; per. 24.95 *(978-1-60206-525-3(X))* Cosimo, Inc.

Smith, J. Warren. Christian Grace & Pagan Virtue: The Theological Foundation of Ambrose's Ethics. 2010. (Oxford Studies in Historical Theology Ser.). (ENG.). 368p. 74.00 *(978-0-19-536993-9(9))* Oxford Univ. Pr., Inc.

Vumuka-ku-Nange, Cesar. Politische Theologie in Afrika: Das Dogmatisch-Politische Denken des hl Ambrosius von Mailand als Modell fur die Beziehung Zwischen Staat und Kirche im Modernen Afrika. (Europaische Hochschulschriften Ser.: Vol. 744). (GER.). 410p. 53.95 *(978-3-631-39208-9(7))* Lang, Peter Publishing, Inc.

Wills, Garry. Font of Life: Ambrose, Augustine, & the Mystery of Baptism. 2012. (Emblems of Antiquity Ser.). (ENG., Illus.). 208p. 21.95 ***(978-0-19-976851-6(X))*** Oxford Univ. Pr., Inc.

AMBROSIASTER

Di Santo, Emanuele. L'apologetica Dell'Ambrosiaster: Cristiani, Pagani e Giudei Nella Roma Tardoantica. 2008. (ITA.). 607p. *(978-88-7961-121-3(6))* Ist. Patristico Augustinianum.

Lunn-Rockliffe, Sophie. Ambrosiaster's Political Theology. 2007. (Oxford Early Christian Studies). (ENG.). 224p. 99.00 *(978-0-19-923020-4(X))* Oxford Univ. Pr., Inc.

Souter, Alexander. A Study of Ambrosiaster. 2010. 290p. pap. 28.75 *(978-1-177-80240-6(6))* BiblioBazaar.

—A Study of Ambrosiaster. 2010. 176p. pap. 24.05 *(978-1-152-48638-6(1))* General Bks. LLC.

AMBROSIUS, SAINT, BISHOP OF MILAN

see Ambrose, Saint, Bishop of Milan, d. 397

AMBULANCES

Amoako, Gordon. Genetic Algorithm Applied to Ambulance Location. 2011. 100p. pap. ***(978-3-8443-1635-3(3))*** Lambert Academic Publishing.

Bell, Ryan Corbett. The Ambulance: A History. 2008. (ENG., Illus.). 398p. 55.00 *(978-0-7864-3811-2(8))* McFarland & Co., Inc. Pubs.

Culkin, Jennifer. A Final Arc of Sky: A Memoir of Critical Care. (ENG.). 248p. 2010. pap. 16.00 *(978-0-8070-7329-2(6))* 2009. 24.95 *(978-0-8070-7285-1(0))* Beacon Pr.

Enstone, Gordon. Bells, Two Tones & Sirens: 34 Years of Ambulance Stories. 2008. 312p. pap. 15.49 *(978-1-4389-3030-5(5))* AuthorHouse.

Gentner, Stephen H. Ambulance to the Front! My Grandfather in WWI Ambulance Section SSU510. 2011. (ENG., Illus.). 116p. 29.95 ***(978-1-59299-630-8(2))*** Inkwater Pr.

Haller, John S., Jr. Battlefield Medicine: A History of the Military Ambulance from the Napoleonic Wars Through World War I. 2011. (Medical Humanites Ser.). (Illus.). 288p. pap. 18.95 *(978-0-8093-3040-9(7))* Southern Illinois Univ. Pr.

Haller, John S. Battlefield Medicine: A History of the Military Ambulance from the Napoleonic Wars Through World War I. 2011. (Medical Humanites Ser.). (Illus.). 288p. E-Book 18.95 *(978-0-8093-8787-8(5))* Southern Illinois Univ. Pr.

Hurd, William W. & Jernigan, John G., eds. Aeromedical Evacuation: Management of Acute & Stabilized Patient. 2010. (ENG., Illus.). xv, 373p. pap. 159.00 *(978-1-4419-3138-2(4)*, 1441931384) Springer.

Jansen, Ryan E. Air Ambulance: Industry Changes & Safety Concerns. 2011. (Health Care Issues, Costs & Access Ser.). 115.00 *(978-1-61209-124-2(5))* Nova Science Pubs., Inc.

McCall, Walt & McPherson, Tom. Classic American Ambulances & Funeral Vehicles: 1900-1980 Photo Archives. 2007. (Photo Archive Ser.). (ENG., Illus.). 256p. pap. 19.95 *(978-1-58388-206-1(5)*, 1583882065) Iconografix, Inc.

McCall, Walter. Weller Brothers of Memphis. 2010. (American Coachbuilders Ser.). (ENG., Illus.). 128p. pap. 19.95 *(978-1-58388-257-3(X)*, 158388257X) Iconografix, Inc.

Rasmussen, Kelly R. Call 911! True Stories from My Life in Emergency Dispatch. 2012. pap. 16.95 ***(978-1-59079-216-2(5))*** Select Bks.

Reynolds, Tom. Blood, Sweat, & Tea: Real-Life Adventures in an Inner-City Ambulance. 2008. (ENG., Illus.). 288p. pap. 12.99 *(978-0-7407-7119-4(1))* Andrews McMeel Publishing.

Thurnher, Oskar F. A History of Ambulance Service in Santa Clara County. 2008. 84p. per. *(978-0-9801675-0-4(7))* Robertson Publishing.

Walder, Lysa & Hyams. Rapid Response: True Stories of My Life as a Paramedic. 2011. (ENG.). 276p. pap. 12.95 ***(978-1-84358-397-4(6))*** Blake, John Publishing, Ltd. GBR. Dist: Independent Pubs. Group.

Wheatley, Ben. Regionalizing Emergency Care: Workshop Summary. 2010. (ENG.). 166p. pap. 38.75 *(978-0-309-15151-1(1))* National Academies Pr.

Whitcomb, Darrel. Call Sign - Dust off: A History of U. S. Army Aeromedical Evacuation from Conception to Hurricane Katrina: A History of United States Army Aeromedical Evacuation from Conception to Hurricane Katrina. Borden Institute, Walter Reed Army Medical Center, ed. 2011. (ENG., Illus.). 491p. 57.00 ***(978-0-16-087937-1(X)***, Dept. of the Army) United States Government Printing Office.

AMBULATORY CARE

see Ambulatory Medical Care

AMBULATORY MEDICAL CARE

see also Clinics; Hospitals—Outpatient Services

AAACN TNP Standards Task Force. Telehealth Nursing Practice Administration & Practice Standards. 4th ed. 2007. 28p. 34.00 *(978-0-9768125-9-3(2))* Jannetti Pubns., Inc.

Access to U.S. Department of Veterans Affairs Healthcare: How Easy Is It for Veterans: Addressing the Gaps: Hearing Before the Subcommittee on Health of the Committee on Veterans' Affairs, U.S. House of Representatives, One Hundred Tenth Congress, First Session, April 18, 2007. 2008. iv, 77p. *(978-0-16-080845-6(6)*, 552-070-37326-8) United States Government Printing Office.

Beck, G. Ronald, et al, eds. Manual of Outpatient Cardiology. 2011. (ENG., Illus.). xiii, 505p. pap. 49.95 ***(978-0-85729-943-7(3)***, 0857299433) Springer.

Bischel, Margaret. Medical Review Criteria for Managing Care. 2008. (ENG.). 1250p. ring bd. 675.00 *(978-1-893826-89-2(9))* Apollo Managed Care Consultants.

Blair, Melissa, ed. ACCP Ambulatory Care New Practitioner Survival Guide/Resource Manual. 2008. 277p. pap. 35.95 *(978-1-932658-58-3(0))* American College of Clinical Pharmacy.

Chan, Paul. Outpatient & Primary Care Medicine, 2008 Edition. 2008th ed. 2007. pap. *(978-1-934323-06-9(3))* Current Clinical Strategies Publishing.

—Outpatient & Primary Care Medicine CD-ROM, 2008 Edition. 2007. cd-rom *(978-1-934323-07-6(1))* Current Clinical Strategies Publishing.

Characteristics of Office-Based Physicians & Their Practices: United States, 2003-04. 2006. (DHHS Publication Ser.: Nos. 2007-1735). (Illus.). 34p. *(978-0-8406-0611-2(7))* National Ctr. for Health Statistics.

Chaudhuri, Subhasis, et al. Ambulation Analysis in Wearable ECG. 2009. (ENG., Illus.). xi, 153p. 99.00 *(978-1-4419-0723-3(8)*, 1441907238) Springer.

Cox, Carol & Hill, Marie, eds. Professional Issues in Primary Care Nursing. 2010. (ENG., Illus.). 336p. pap. 53.99 *(978-1-4051-8755-8(7)*, Wiley-Blackwell) Wiley, John & Sons, Inc.

Cram101 Textbook Reviews. Outlines & Highlights for Ambulatory Care Procedures for the Nurse Practitioner by Margaret R Colyar, Isbn: 9780803611238 0803611234. 2011. 120p. pap. 28.95 ***(978-1-61812-420-3(X))*** Cram101 Inc.

De Fer, Thomas M., et al, eds. Outpatient Internal Medicine. 2010. (Lippincott Manual Series (Formerly Known As the Spiral Manual Series) Ser.). (ENG., Illus.). 1072p. pap. 47.99 *(978-0-7817-8977-6(X))* Lippincott Williams & Wilkins.

Dutton, Mark. Dutton's Orthopedic Survival Guide: Managing Common Conditions. 2011. (ENG., Illus.). 1056p. pap. 63.00 *(978-0-07-171510-2(X)*, 007171510X) McGraw-Hill Medical Publishing Div.

Egan, Marcia & Kadushin, Goldie. Social Work Practice in Community-Based Health Care. 2007. (Illus.). (ENG.). 272p. per. 49.95 *(978-0-7890-2567-8(1))*; 259p. 175.00 *(978-0-7890-2566-1(3))* Routledge.

Eremia, Sorin, ed. Office-Based Cosmetic Procedures & Techniques. 2010. (ENG., Illus.). 384p. 129.00 *(978-0-521-70652-0(1))* Cambridge Univ. Pr.

Gabbay, John, et al. Organisational Innovation in Health Services: Lessons from the NHS Treatment Centres. 2011. (Illus.). 184p. 80.00 *(978-1-84742-479-2(1))*; pap. 39.95 *(978-1-84742-478-5(3))* Policy Pr. GBR. Dist: Chicago Distribution Ctr.

Garrels, Marti & Oatis, Carol S. Laboratory Testing for Ambulatory Settings: A Guide for Health Care Professionals. 2nd ed. 2010. (ENG., Illus.). 352p. (C). pap. 54.95 *(978-1-4377-1906-2(6)*, Saunders) Elsevier - Health Sciences Div.

—Laboratory Testing for Ambulatory Settings - Text & Workbook Package: A Guide for Health Care Professionals. 2nd ed. 2010. (ENG.). (C). pap. 73.71 *(978-1-4377-1907-9(4)*, Saunders) Elsevier - Health Sciences Div.

—Workbook for Laboratory Testing for Ambulatory Settings: A Guide for Health Care Professionals. 2nd ed. 2010. (ENG., Illus.). 240p. (C). pap. 26.95 *(978-1-4377-1906-6(2)*, Saunders) Elsevier - Health Sciences Div.

Guinane, Carole & Davis, Noreen. Improving Quality in Outpatient Services. 2011. (ENG., Illus.). 300p. 79.95 *(978-1-4398-5060-2(7))* Productivity Pr.

Guinane, Carole & Venturelli, Joseph. 50 Policies & Plans for Outpatient Services. 2011. (ENG., Illus.). 216p. pap. 99.95 *(978-1-4398-6842-3(5))* Productivity Pr.

Hoellein, Andrew R. & Griffith, Charles H. Ambulatory Medicine. 2007. (LANGE First Exposure Ser.). (ENG., Illus.). 384p. (C). pap. 45.00 *(978-0-07-145906-6(6)*, 0071459006) McGraw-Hill Professional Publishing.

Hoskin, Nicholas. Saving Lives, Living the Dream. 2008. 164p. pap. 12.95 *(978-0-615-23858-6(0))* Hoskin, Nicholas.

Howatson-Jones, Lioba & Ellis, Peter, eds. Outpatient, Day Surgery & Ambulatory Care. 2009. (ENG., Illus.). 248p. pap. 66.99 *(978-0-470-51283-8(0)*, Wiley) Wiley, John & Sons, Inc.

Hoy, Kimberly Anderwood, ed. Outpatient Cardiac Rehab: Tools & Best Practices for Reimbursement & Compliance. 2nd ed. 2007. (Illus.). 157p. pap. 149.00 incl. cd-rom *(978-1-57839-960-4(2))* Opus Communications.

Ingenix, creator. Facilities & Ancillary Services. 2007. (Ingenix Learning Ser.). (Illus.). 449p. per. 99.95 *(978-1-60151-076-1(4))* OptumInsight, Inc.

—Facilities & Ancillary Services: Comprehensive Instruction to Effective Facility & Ancillary Coding. 2008. (Coding & Reimbursement Educational Ser.). (Illus.). 475p. pap. 99.95 incl. cd-rom *(978-1-60151-207-9(4))* OptumInsight, Inc.

International Society of Fire Service Instructors. Fire Service Instructor: Principles & Practice. 2008. 296p. pap. 71.95 *(978-0-7637-4910-1(9))* Jones & Bartlett Learning, LLC.

Joint Commission on Accreditation, creator. Comprehensive Accreditation Manual for Ambulatory Care: Effective January 2009. 2008. (Jcr, Comprehensive Accreditation Manual for Ambulatory Care Ser.). 265.00 *(978-1-59940-238-3(6))* Joint Commission Resources.

Kotar, S. L. & Gessler, J. E. The Complete Guide to Ambulatory Cardiac Monitoring & Full Disclosure Telemetry. rev. ed. 2010. 236p. pap. 86.95 *(978-0-7637-8406-5(0))* Jones & Bartlett Learning, LLC.

Leung, Alexander K. C., ed. Common Problems in Ambulatory Pediatrics: Volume 2. 2011. (Pediatrics - Laboratory & Clinical Research Ser.). 391p. 195.00 ***(978-1-62100-356-4(6))*** Nova Science Pubs., Inc.

—Common Problems in Ambulatory Pediatrics: Volume 3. 2012. (Pediatrics - Laboratory & Clinical Research Ser.). 430p. 195.00 ***(978-1-62100-357-1(4))*** Nova Science Pubs., Inc.

—Common Problems in Ambulatory Pediatrics: Volume 4. 2011. (Pediatrics - Laboratory & Clinical Research Ser.). 339p. 195.00 ***(978-1-62100-358-8(2))*** Nova Science Pubs., Inc.

Levans, Lori. APCs for ASCs: Strategies for Success under the New Payment System. 2008. 120p. pap. 149.00 *(978-1-60146-179-7(8))* Opus Communications.

Lewis, Marcia A., et al. Law, Ethics, & Bioethics for the Health Professions. 7th rev. ed. 2012. (Illus.). 256p. pap. 42.95 ***(978-0-8036-2706-2(8))*** Davis, F. A. Co.

Masci, Joseph R. Outpatient Management of HIV Infection, Fourth Edition. 4th ed. 2010. 312p. 200.00 *(978-1-4200-8735-2(5)*, Informa Healthcare) Taylor & Francis Group GBR. Dist: Taylor & Francis Group.

Mastal, Margaret. Ambulatory Care Nursing Administration & Practice Standards. 7th ed. 2007. 34.00 *(978-0-9768125-8-6(4))* Jannetti Pubns., Inc.

McLane, Dawn Q. The AAAHC-Joint Commission-CMS Crosswalk: A Side-by-Side Comparison of Ambulatory Care Requirements. 2007. pap. 149.00 incl. cd-rom *(978-1-60146-015-8(5))* Opus Communications.

Outpatient Waiting Times: Joint Hearing Before the Subcommittee on Health & the Subcommittee on Oversight & Investigations of the Committee on Veterans' Affairs, U.S. House of Representatives, One Hundred Tenth Congress, First Session, December 12, 2007. 2008. (Illus.). iii, 62p. *(978-0-16-081857-8(5)*, 552-070-38032-9) United States Government Printing Office.

Pozgar, George D. Legal & Ethical Issues for Health Care Professionals. 2nd rev. ed. 2009. 426p. pap. 104.95 *(978-0-7637-6473-9(6))* Jones & Bartlett Learning, LLC.

Raofi, Saeid & Schappert, Susan M. Medication Therapy in Ambulatory Medical Care: United States, 2003-04. 2006. (DHHS Publication Ser.: Nos. 2007-1734). (Illus.). 40p. *(978-0-8406-0610-5(9)*, Centers for Disease Control & Prevention) United States Government Printing Office.

Steele, Thomas E. Outpatient Psychiatry: A Beginner's Guide. 2007. (ENG.). 192p. per. 24.95 *(978-0-393-70543-0(9)*, 70543) Norton, W. W. & Co., Inc.

Stephen, W. J. An Analysis of Primary Medical Care: An International Study. 2008. (ENG.). 420p. pap. 53.00 *(978-0-521-10230-8(8))* Cambridge Univ. Pr.

Vance, James E. Patient Safety in the Medical Practice. 2006. 256p. 59.95 *(978-1-57947-674-8(0))* American Medical Assn.

Weinstock, Michael B., et al. The Resident's Guide to Ambulatory Care: Frequently Encountered & Commonly Confused Clinical Conditions. 6th ed. 2009. (Illus.). 502p. pap. 41.00 *(978-1-890018-66-5(X))* Anadem Publishing, Inc.

Williams, Ronald & Kahan, Scott. In A Page Ambulatory Medicine. 2007. (In a Page Ser.). (ENG.). 272p. pap. 41.99 *(978-0-7817-6495-7(5))* Lippincott Williams & Wilkins.

Zieve, Philip D., et al, eds. Principles of Ambulatory Medicine. 7th rev. ed. 2006. (Principles of Ambulatory Medicine (Barker) Ser.). (ENG., Illus.). 1984p. 128.99 *(978-0-7817-6227-4(8))* Lippincott Williams & Wilkins.

AMBULATORY SURGERY

Becker, Scott. Ambulatory Surgery Centers: Legal & Regulatory Issues. 4th ed. 2009. (Illus.). xiv, 279p. *(978-1-4224-6183-9(1))*; pap. *(978-1-4224-6184-6(X))* American Health Lawyers Assn.

Bennett, Gail & Kassai, Marie. Infection Prevention Manual for Ambulatory Surgery Centers. 2011. ring bd. 219.00 ***(978-0-9840795-5-1(6))*** ICP Assocs., Inc.

Competency and Credentialing Institute. Sterilization Competency Assessment Module. 2008. per. 50.00 *(978-0-9717619-8-8(1))* Certification Board Perioperative Nursing.

Glass, Peter S. A. Ambulatory Anesthesia, an Issue of Anesthesiology Clinics. 2010. (Clinics: Surgery Ser.: 28-2). (ENG., Illus.). xviii, 185p. 105.00 *(978-1-4377-1796-9(9)*, Saunders) Elsevier - Health Sciences Div.

Leffell, David J. & Brown, Marc D. Manual of Skin Surgery: A Practical Guide to Dermatologic Procedures. 2nd ed. 2011. (Illus.). 250p. pap. *(978-1-60795-158-2(4))* PMPH-USA, Ltd.

McLane, Dawn Q. The AAAHC-Joint Commission-CMS Crosswalk: A Side-by-Side Comparison of Ambulatory Care Requirements. 2007. pap. 149.00 incl. cd-rom, cd-rom *(978-1-60146-015-8(5))* Opus Communications.

McWhinnie, Douglas, et al, eds. Day Case Surgery. 2012. (ENG., Illus.). 448p. pap. 79.95 ***(978-0-19-958433-8(2))*** Oxford Univ. Pr., Inc.

Raeder, Johan. Clinical Ambulatory Anesthesia. 2010. (ENG., Illus.). 194p. pap. 49.99 *(978-0-521-73781-4(8))* Cambridge Univ. Pr.

Thomas, William E. G. & Senninger, Norbert, eds. Short Stay Surgery. 2012. (Springer Surgery Atlas Ser.). (ENG., Illus.). x, 408p. pap. 319.00 *(978-3-642-07433-2(2)*, 3642074332) Springer.

Timmins, Fiona & McCabe, Catherine. Day Surgery: Contemporary Approaches to Nursing Care. 2009. (Wiley Series in Nursing Ser.). (ENG., Illus.). 190p. pap. 57.99 *(978-0-470-31984-0(4)*, Wiley) Wiley, John & Sons, Inc.

Tuggy, Michael & Garcia, Jorge. Atlas of Essential Procedures. 2010. (ENG., Illus.). 256p. 99.95 *(978-1-4377-1499-9(4)*, Saunders) Elsevier - Health Sciences Div.

Twersky, Rebecca S. & Philip, Beverly K., eds. Handbook of Ambulatory Anesthesia. 2nd rev. ed. 2008. (Illus.). 576p. pap. 89.95 *(978-0-387-73328-9(0))* Springer.

Urman, Richard, et al. Anesthesia Outside of the Operating Room, 1 vol. 2011. (ENG., Illus.). 416p. 110.00 *(978-0-19-539667-6(7))* Oxford Univ. Pr., Inc.

AMC AUTOMOBILES

see American Motors Automobiles

AMEBIASIS

Ashiq, Bilal. Clinical Pharmacology. 2010. 104p. pap. *(978-3-639-25219-4(5))* VDM Verlag Dr. Mueller e.K.

AMENDMENTS, CONSTITUTIONAL

see Constitutional Amendments

AMENHETEP IV, KING OF EGYPT, 1388-1358 B.C.

see Akhenaten, King of Egypt

AMERICA

Here are entered works discussing collectively the lands of the Western Hemisphere.

Fernández-Armesto, Felipe. Amerigo: The Man Who Gave His Name to America. 2008. (ENG., Illus.). 272p. pap. 15.00 *(978-0-8129-7298-6(8))*, Random Hse. Trade Paperbacks) Random House Publishing Group.

Frank Bari With Mark C. Gribben. Under the Williamsburg Bridge: The Story of an American Family. 2009. 116p. 19.95 *(978-1-4269-1816-2(X))* Trafford Publishing.

Hunt, Norman Bancroft. Historical Atlas of Ancient America. 2009. (Illus.). 192p. 25.00 *(978-1-904668-11-4(9))* Mercury Bks. Ltd. GBR. Dist: International Publishers Marketing.

Thorpe, Thomas Bangs. A Voice to America; or, the Model Republic, Its Glory, or Its Fall: With A Review of the Causes of the Decline & Failure of the Republics of South A. 2006. 412p. per. 26.99 *(978-1-4255-4378-5(2))* MPublishing.

AMERICA—ANTIQUITIES

see also Indians—Antiquities; Paleo-Indians

Bandelier, Adolph F. Papers of the Archaeological Institute of America, 6 vols., Set. (American Ser.). reprint ed. 177.00 *(978-0-404-19502-1(4))* AMS Pr., Inc.

Bosqued, Concepcion Glasco & Gomez, Luis Ramos. Poblamiento y Prehistoria de America: Las Culturas Mas Antiguas. (Biblioteca Iberoamericana Ser.). (SPA., Illus.). 128p. 18.95 *(978-84-207-3219-0(2)*, GS029) Grupo Anaya, S.A. ESP. Dist: Continental Bk. Co., Inc.

Bradford, Alexander W. American Antiquities & Researches into the Origin & History of the Red Race. 2008. 438p. 51.95 *(978-0-548-93966-6(7))* 2007. (ENG.). 440p. per. 36.95 *(978-0-548-59053-9(2))* Kessinger Publishing, LLC.

Burger, Richard L. & Rosenswig, Robert M., eds. Early New World Monumentality. 2012. (ENG., Illus.). 416p. 85.00 ***(978-0-8130-3808-7(1))*** Univ. Pr. of Florida.

Campbell, T. N., ed. American Antiquity V28, No 1, July 1962. 2011. 132p. 40.95 ***(978-1-258-06516-4(9))*** Literary Licensing, LLC.

Corona M, Eduardo & Arroyo-Cabrales, Joaquin. Human & Faunal Relationships Reviewed: An Archaeozoological Approach. 2007. (Bar S Ser.). (SPA & ENG., Illus.). 121p. (C). pap. 75.00 *(978-1-4073-0041-2(5))* British Archaeological Reports Ltd. GBR. Dist: Brown, David Bk. Co., The.

Davidson, George. The Tracks & Landfalls of Bering & Chirikof on the Northwest Coast of America. 2009. (ENG.). 50p. pap. 18.99 *(978-1-110-62307-5(0))*; pap. 16.99 *(978-1-110-62306-8(2))* BiblioBazaar. (BiblioLife).

De Nadaillac, Marquis. Prehistoric America. Dall, W. H., ed. D'Anvers, N., tr. 2008. 578p. 58.95 *(978-1-4365-9811-8(7))* 2007. (ENG.). 580p. per. 43.95 *(978-0-548-80549-7(0))* Kessinger Publishing, LLC.

De Roo, Peter. The History of America Before Columbus: According to Documents & Approved Authors. 2 vol., set. reprint ed. 250.00 *(978-0-7222-6416-4(X))* Library Reprints, Inc.

—History of America Before Columbus V1, According to Documents. 2007. (ENG.). 668p. per. 48.95 *(978-1-4304-4387-2(1))* Kessinger Publishing, LLC.

Enock, C. Reginald. The Secret of the Pacific: A Discussion of the Origin of the Early Civilizations of America 1912. 2007. (ENG.). 458p. 52.95 *(978-0-548-05385-0(5))* Kessinger Publishing, LLC.

Fewkes, Jesse W., ed. A Journal of American Ethnology & Archaeology: Hemenway Southwestern Archaeological Expedition, 5 vols., Set. reprint ed. 240.00 *(978-0-404-19528-1(8))* AMS Pr., Inc.

Gemegah, Helga. The First Americans' New World Roots - A Forgotten Question Reconsidered: Critical Review of the Development, Reception & Impact of Origin Concepts. 2009. 212p. 57.95 *(978-3-631-58883-3(6))* Lang, Peter GmbH, Europaischer Verlag der Wissenschaften DEU. Dist: Lang, Peter.

Gordon, B. Le Roy & Gordon, B. L. Chemical Arts & Technologies of Indigenous Americans. 2009. (Bar S Ser.). (Illus.). 167p. (C). bds. 90.00 *(978-1-4073-0390-1(2))* British Archaeological Reports Ltd. GBR. Dist: Brown, David Bk. Co., The.

Hammond, Dorothy. Pictorial Price Guide to American Antiques 2005-2006: And Objects Made for the American Market. rev. ed. 2007. (ENG., Illus.). 288p. pap. *(978-1-85149-485-9(5)*, Antique Collectors Club Dist) Antique Collectors' Club.

Hewett, Edgar L. The Groundwork of American Archaeology. 2007. (ENG.). 8p. per. 15.95 *(978-0-548-68641-6(6))* Kessinger Publishing, LLC.

Jones, E. Alfred. Old Silver of Europe & Americ. 2008. 488p. pap. *(978-1-905217-97-7(8))* Mills, Jeremy Publishing.

Jones, Terry. Polynesians in America: Pre-Columbian Contacts with the New World. 2011. (ENG.). 380p. 85.00 *(978-0-7591-2004-4(8))* AltaMira Pr.

Jones, Terry L. Polynesians in America: Pre-Columbian Contacts with the New World. 2010. *(978-0-7591-2006-8(4))* AltaMira Pr.

Knudson, Kelly J. & Stojanowski, Christopher M., eds. Bioarchaeology & Identity in the Americas. 2010. (Bioarchaeological Interpretations of the Human Past: Local, Regional, & Global Ser.). (ENG., Illus.). 272p. pap. 34.95 *(978-0-8130-3678-6(X))* Univ. Pr. of Florida.

Loker, Aleck. Ancient Explorers of America: From the Ice Age to Columbus. 2009. pap. 16.95 *(978-1-928874-19-5(3))* Solitude Pr.

Mann, Charles C. 1491: New Revelations of the Americas Before Columbus. 2006. (Vintage Ser.). (ENG., Illus.). 576p. pap. 16.95 *(978-1-4000-3205-1(9)*, Vintage) Knopf Doubleday Publishing Group.

Meggers, Betty. Prehistoric America: An Ecological Perspective (Third Expanded Edition) 3rd ed. 2009. (ENG., Illus.). 232p. pap. 29.95 *(978-0-202-36336-3(8))* Aldine Transaction.

Morrow, Juliet E. & Gnecco, Cristobal, eds. Paleoindian Archaeology: A Hemispheric Perspective. (ENG., Illus.). 288p. 2009. pap. 32.95 *(978-0-8130-3389-1(6))* 2007. 65.00 *(978-0-8130-3014-2(5))* Univ. Pr. of Florida.

Ogundiran, Akinwumi & Falola, Toyin, eds. Archaeology of Atlantic Africa & the African Diaspora. 2010. (Blacks in the Diaspora Ser.). (ENG., Illus.). 528p. pap. 29.95 *(978-0-253-22175-9(7)*, 0253221757) Indiana Univ. Pr.

Pillsbury, Joanne. Past Presented: Archaeological Illustration & the Ancient Americas. 2012. (Dumbarton Oaks Pre-Columbian Symposia & Colloquia Ser.). 512p. 65.00 ***(978-0-88402-380-7(X))*** Dumbarton Oaks.

Sabloff, Jeremy A. & Fash, William L., eds. Gordon R. Willey & American Archeology: Contemporary Perspectives. 2007. (ENG., Illus.). 256p. (C). 34.95 *(978-0-8061-3805-3(X))* Univ. of Oklahoma Pr.

Shipp, Barnard. The Indian & Antiquities of America 1897. 2007. (ENG.). 510p. 55.95 *(978-0-548-05582-3(3))* Kessinger Publishing, LLC.

Thompson, Gunnar. Secret Voyages to the New World. 2010. 251p. pap. 21.95 *(978-0-557-23165-2(5))* Lulu Enterprises Inc.

Thompson, Gunnar, creator. Secret Voyages to the New World: Nine True Adventures from the Forbidden Chronicles of American Discovery. 2006. (Illus.). 300p. per. 40.00 *(978-0-9788916-0-2(0)*, SV) New World Discovery Institute.

Trafzer, Clifford E. & Mcmaster, Gerald, eds. Native Universe: Voices of Indian America. 2008. (ENG., Illus.). 320p. 22.00 *(978-1-4262-0335-0(7)*, National Geographic) National Geographic Society.

Wiener, Leo. Africa & the Discovery of America. 2011. (ENG., Illus.). 287p. pap. 15.95 ***(978-1-61759-002-3(9))*** EWorld, Inc.

Wirth, Diane E. Decoding Ancient America: A Guide to the Archaeology of the Book of Mormon. 2007. (Illus.). 119p. per. 12.99 *(978-0-88290-820-5(0))* Cedar Fort, Inc./CFI Distribution.

AMERICA—BIBLIOGRAPHY

Boon, Edward P. Catalogue of Books & Pamphlets Principally Relating to America. 2009. 114p. pap. *(978-0-217-96073-1(1))* Books LLC.

—Catalogue of Books & Pamphlets Principally Relating to America. 2006. 612p. per. 34.99 *(978-1-4255-6552-7(2))* MPublishing.

Brinley, George. Catalogue of the American Library of George Brinley, 5 pts. in 2 vols. Trumbull, J. Hammond, ed. reprint ed. lib. bdg. 125.00 *(978-0-404-01081-2(4))* AMS Pr., Inc.

Field, Thomas. An Indian Bibliography. 2009. (Native American Ser.). (ENG.). 436p. pap. 26.95 *(978-1-4290-2262-0(0))* Applewood Bks.

Griffin, Grace Gardner. Writings on American History, 1909-1911: A Bibliography of Books & Articles on United States & Canadian History. reprint ed. 150.00 *(978-0-7222-7002-8(X))* Library Reprints, Inc.

Larned, J. N. The Literature of American History: A Bibliographical Guide in Which the Scope, Character, & Comparative Worth of Books in Selected Lists Are Set Forth in Brief Notes by Critics of Authority. 588p. reprint ed. 98.00 *(978-0-7222-7008-0(9))* Library Reprints, Inc.

McLaughlin, Andrew Cunningham. Writings on American History: A Bibliography of Books & Articles on United States History Published During the Year 1903. (Carnegie Institution of Washington Ser.). 172p. reprint ed. 88.00 *(978-0-7222-7010-3(0))* Library Reprints, Inc.

Morrell, Thomas H. Catalogue of a Valuable Collection of Books on America. 2006. 180p. per. 18.99 *(978-1-4255-1427-3(8))* MPublishing.

Richardson, Ernest Cushing. Writings on American History, 1902. 294p. reprint ed. 98.00 *(978-0-7222-7015-8(1))* Library Reprints, Inc.

Robert Clarke and Co. Booksellers Staff. Bibliotheca Americana Catalogue of a Valuable Collection of Books & Pamphlets Relating to America. 2006. 188p. per. 18.99 *(978-1-4255-1511-9(8))*; 320p. per. 23.99 *(978-1-4255-3147-8(4))* MPublishing.

Stevens, Henry. Bibliotheca Historica; 2006. 256p. per. 23.99 *(978-1-4255-2200-1(9))* MPublishing.

AMERICA—BIOGRAPHY

Abend, Hallett. The God from the West: A Biography of Frederick Townsend Ward. 2011. 320p. 50.95 ***(978-1-258-09359-4(6))*** Literary Licensing, LLC.

Alvarado, Beth. Anthropologies: A Family Memoir. 2011. (Sightline Bks.). (Illus.). 202p. pap. 19.95 *(978-1-60938-037-5(1))* Univ. of Iowa Pr.

American Crisis Biographies, 20 vol., set. (American Crisis Biographies Ser.). reprint ed. 2500.00 *(978-0-7222-8432-2(2))* Library Reprints, Inc.

Appleton's Cyclopedia of American Biography, 6 vol., set. reprint ed. 750.00 *(978-0-7222-8412-4(8))* Library Reprints, Inc.

Baucom, Eva. Two Worlds, One Heart: Part II. 2010. pap. 15.99 *(978-1-61663-296-0(8))* Tate Publishing & Enterprises, LLC.

Bradley, Michael. The Columbus Conspiracy. 2011. (Illus.). 253p. pap. 14.95 ***(978-1-61759-006-1(1))*** EWorld, Inc.

Burdick, Bruce Stanley. Mathematical Works Printed in the Americas, 1554-1700. 2009. (Johns Hopkins Studies in the History of Mathematics Ser.). (ENG., Illus.). 392p. (gr. 17). 57.00 *(978-0-8018-8823-6(9))* Johns Hopkins Univ. Pr.

Chavez-Silverman, Susana. Killer Cronicas: Bilingual Memories. 2010. (Writing in Latinidad Ser.). (ENG.). 174p. pap. 16.95 *(978-0-299-20224-8(0))* Univ. of Wisconsin Pr.

Clayton, Lawrence A. Bartolomé de las Casas: A Biography. 2012. (ENG., Illus.). 502p. 75.00 ***(978-1-107-00121-3(8))*** Cambridge Univ. Pr.

Ellis, Bill. The Signs Are Good. 2011. 182p. pap. ***(978-1-908147-69-1(5))*** YouWriteOn.

Falkner, Leonard. Painted Lady, Eliza Jumel: Her Life & Times. 2011. 252p. 46.95 ***(978-1-258-09180-4(1))*** Literary Licensing, LLC.

Feiffer, Jules. Backing into Forward: A Memoir. 2012. (ENG.). 456p. pap. 19.00 ***(978-0-226-24035-0(5))*** Univ. of Chicago Pr.

Guerrero, Jose. Bitácora de un Emigrante Gallego. 2011. 428p. 42.95 ***(978-1-61764-932-5(5))***; pap. 27.95 ***(978-1-61764-934-9(1))*** Palibrio.

Guess, Carol. My Father in Water. 2011. 88p. pap. 15.00 ***(978-1-84861-185-6(4))*** Shearsman Bks. GBR. Dist: SPD-Small Pr. Distribution.

Haffner, Gayle. Hands with A Heart: The Personal Biography of Actress Zasu Pitts. 2011. 523p. pap. 28.95 ***(978-1-4327-6209-4(5))*** Outskirts Pr., Inc.

Hale, Mary M. On Uganda's Terms: A Journal by an American Nurse-Midwife Working for Change in Uganda, East Africa During Idi Amin's Regime. 2nd ed. 2009. (Illus.). 140p. pap. *(978-1-926585-13-0(5)*, CCB Publishing) CCB Publishing.

Helps, Arthur. The Life of Columbus. 2007. 144p. per. *(978-1-4065-4450-3(7))* Dodo Pr.

—Life of Columbus. 2006. pap. *(978-1-4068-3570-0(6))* Echo Library.

—Life of Las Casas the Apostle of the Ind. 2006. pap. 30.95 *(978-1-4286-3436-7(3))* Kessinger Publishing, LLC.

Hively, Evelyn Helmick. Darling Ro & the Benet Women. 2011. 160p. 34.95 *(978-1-60635-096-6(X))* Kent State Univ. Pr.

John Russell Frank. On the Road Home: An American Story. 2009. 360p. 33.95 *(978-1-4401-9376-7(2))*; pap. 23.95 *(978-1-4401-9374-3(6))* iUniverse, Inc.

Lee, Joann Faung Jean. Asian Americans in the Twenty-First Century: Oral Histories of First- to Fourth- Generation Americans from China, Japan, India, Korea, the Philippines, Vietnam, & Laos. 2008. (ENG., Illus.). 277p. 24.95 *(978-1-59558-152-5(9))* New Pr., The.

Merrill, Charles J. Colom of Catalonia: Origins of Christopher Columbus Revealed. 2008. (ENG., Illus.). 312p. pap. 16.95 *(978-0-9816002-2-2(0))* Demers Bks. LLC.

Morris, Charles. Heroes of Discovery in America. 344p. reprint ed. 98.00 *(978-0-7222-6422-5(4))* Library Reprints, Inc.

Murray, William H. Memoirs of Governor Murray & True History of Oklahoma V1. 2011. 428p. 56.95 ***(978-1-258-02964-7(2))*** Literary Licensing, LLC.

—Memoirs of Governor Murray & True History of Oklahoma V2. 2011. 604p. 64.95 ***(978-1-258-02987-6(1))*** Literary Licensing, LLC.

Myers, Kathleen Ann. Fernández de Oviedo's Chronicle of America: A New History for a New World. Scott, Nina M., tr. 2010. (ENG., Illus.). 344p. pap. 30.00 *(978-0-292-72612-3(0))* Univ. of Texas Pr.

One Thousand American Men of Mark of Today. 2007. (ENG.). 448p. per. 36.95 *(978-1-4304-9004-3(7))* Kessinger Publishing, LLC.

Ortiz, Joey. Correcting a Wreckless Life. 2011. 250p. pap. 27.95 ***(978-1-4560-4881-5(3))*** PublishAmerica, Inc.

Paffhausen, Jonah & Nieuwsma, Virginia. Reflections on a Spiritual Journey. 2011. ***(978-0-88141-880-4(3))*** St. Vladimir's Seminary Pr.

Paine, Ralph D. Joshua Barney: A Forgotten Hero of Blue Water. 456p. 2008. 52.95 *(978-1-4366-7539-0(1))* 2007. (ENG.). per. 37.95 *(978-1-4325-8671-3(8))* Kessinger Publishing, LLC.

Peake, Sean T. The Travels of David Thompson: The Hudson's Bay Company 1784-1797, the Missouri, Mississippi, & Lake Superior, 1797-1798. 2011. 568p. 42.95 ***(978-1-4620-1779-9(7))***; pap. 32.95 ***(978-1-4620-1777-5(0))*** iUniverse, Inc.

Pilibosian, Helene. My Literary Profile: A Memoir. 2010. (Illus.). 324p. pap. 20.00 *(978-1-929966-08-0(3))* Ohan Pr.

Pritchard, R. E. Captain John Smith & His Brave Adventures. 2008. (ENG., Illus.). 200p. pap. 18.95 *(978-1-905791-25-5(9))* Haus Publishing GBR. Dist: Consortium Bk. Sales & Distribution.

Resa, Jolinda Bull. Honor Them Always: For the Sacrifice of Their Youth at Bataan. 2011. 60p. pap. 14.95 ***(978-1-4327-7555-1(3))*** Outskirts Pr., Inc.

Saunders, Richard. Never Been Rich: The Life & Work of a Southern Ruralist Writer, Harry Harrison Kroll. 2011. (ENG.). 264p. 42.00 ***(978-1-57233-825-8(3))*** Univ. of Tennessee Pr.

Seymour, Charles C. B. Self-Made Men by Chas C B Seymour. 2006. 608p. per. 34.99 *(978-1-4255-6467-4(4))* MPublishing.

Thompson, Don & Thompson, Carol. Seeking the Northwest Passage: The Explorations & Discoveries of Champlain & Hudson. 2008. (Illus.). 88p. (J). pap. 8.50 *(978-1-930098-90-9(1))* Purple Mountain Pr., Ltd.

Tilden Ii, William Tatem. My Story: A Champion's Memoirs. 2011. 338p. 50.95 ***(978-1-258-09166-8(6))*** Literary Licensing, LLC.

Wall, Nancy T. Pulled by the Heart: A Woman's Real-Life Story of Living & Escaping the Middle East. 2009. (Illus.). 196p. pap. 18.95 *(978-1-930374-28-7(3))* DeForest Pr.

Wright, J. Leitch, Jr. William Augustus Bowles: Director General of the Creek Nation. 2010. (ENG.). 226p. pap. 24.95 *(978-0-8203-3558-2(4))* Univ. of Georgia Pr.

AMERICA—CHURCH HISTORY

Garsoïan, Nina G. Studies on the Formation of Christian Armenia. 2010. (Variorum Collected Studies). (FRE & ENG.). 310p. 134.95 ***(978-1-4094-0366-1(1))*** Ashgate Publishing Co.

Krikorian, Haig A. Lives & Times of the Armenian Patriarchs of Jerusalem: Chronological Succession of Tenures. 2009. (Illus.). xiii, 821p. *(978-0-9769107-1-8(3))* Krikorian, Haig A.

MacPherson, D. Neal. Church at a Crossroads: Being the Church after Christendom. 2008. 178p. pap. 20.00 *(978-1-55635-284-3(0))* Wipf & Stock Pubs.

Riffle, Robert M. The Miracle of Independence. 2009. 312p. pap. 18.99 *(978-1-60647-153-1(8))* Xulon Pr., Inc.

Voigt, Lisa. Writing Captivity in the Early Modern Atlantic: Circulations of Knowledge & Authority in the Iberian & English Imperial Worlds. 2009. (Published for the Omohundro Institute of Early American History & Culture, Williamsburg, VA Ser.). (ENG., Illus.). 352p. pap. 26.95 *(978-0-8078-5944-5(3))* Univ. of North Carolina Pr.

AMERICA—CIVILIZATION

Beck, Sanderson. America To 1744: Ethics of Civilization, 11. 2006. 664p. per. 25.00 *(978-0-9762210-7-4(1))* World Peace Communications.

Benessaieh, Afef, ed. Ameriques Transculturelles - Transcultural Americas. 2010. (Cultural Transfers Ser.). (FRE & ENG.). 270p. pap. *(978-2-7603-0721-6(2))* Univ. of Ottawa Pr./Presses de l'Universite d'Ottawa.

Butler, Martin, et al. Ethnicities: Metropolitan Cultures & Ethnic Identities in the Americas. 2011. ***(978-1-931010-81-8(1))***; ***(978-3-86821-310-2(4))*** Bilingual Pr./Editorial Bilingue.

Dei, Hector Daniel. A New World: A Perspective from Ibero America. 2010. pap. *(978-1-56518-263-9(4))* Council for Research in Values & Philosophy.

Engle, Karen. The Elusive Promise of Indigenous Development: Rights, Culture, Strategy. 2010. (ENG.). 424p. 94.95 *(978-0-8223-4750-7(4))*; pap. 26.95 *(978-0-8223-4769-9(5))* Duke Univ. Pr.

Ferrero, Guglielmo. Ancient Rome & Modern America: A Comparative Study. 352p. reprint ed. 98.00 *(978-0-7222-7315-9(0))* Library Reprints, Inc.

Hall, Anthony J. Earth into Property: Colonization, Decolonization, & Capitalism. 2010. (McGill-Queen's Native & Northern Ser.). (Illus.). 934p. *(978-0-7735-3121-5(1))*; (ENG., (C). pap. *(978-0-7735-3122-2(X))* McGill-Queen's Univ. Pr.

Honore, Pierre. In Search of Quetzalcoatl: The Mysterious Heritage of South American Civilization. 2007. (Illus.). 228p. per. 18.95 *(978-1-931882-57-6(6))* Adventures Unlimited Pr.

Jefferson, Thomas. Releasing the Undiscovered Country: Rebirth of Revolution. (American Rebirth Flip Bks.). 110p. 24.95 *(978-1-888407-11-2(5))* Powerhouse Publishing, Inc.

Jones, Charles A. American Civilization. 2007. (ENG.). 104p. per. 20.00 *(978-1-900039-82-6(6))* Institute of Latin American Studies GBR. Dist: Brookings Institution Pr.

Kuiper, Kathleen, ed. Pre-Columbian America: Empires of the New World. 2010. (Britannica Guide to Ancient Civilizations Ser.). (Illus.). 200p. (YA). 80.00 *(978-1-61530-216-1(6))* Rosen Publishing Group, Inc., The.

Kulbacki, Joseph V. America: A Nation That's Lost Its Way. 2010. 308p. pap. 17.95 *(978-1-935018-09-4(4))* International Localization Network.

Levander, Caroline F., ed. Hemispheric American Studies. 2007. (ENG., Illus.). 366p. (C). pap. 27.95 *(978-0-8135-4223-2(5))* Rutgers Univ. Pr.

Levander, Caroline F. & Levine, Robert, eds. Hemispheric American Studies. 2007. (ENG., Illus.). 366p. 70.00 *(978-0-8135-4222-5(7))* Rutgers Univ. Pr.

Lifshey, Adam. Specters of Conquest: Indigenous Absence in Transatlantic Literatures. 2nd ed. 2010. (American Literatures Initiative Ser.). (ENG.). 192p. 60.00 *(978-0-8232-3238-3(7))* Fordham Univ. Pr.

Livergood, Norman D. & Mairesse, Michelle. Realizing a New Culture: Realizing a New America & a New World. 2007. pap. 24.95 *(978-0-9789611-5-2(3))* Dandelion Bks.

Madsen, Deborah L. Visions of America since 1492. (Illus.). xv, 164p. *(978-0-7185-1470-9(X)*, Burns & Oates) Continuum International Publishing Group, Ltd.

Marinho, Marcelo, et al. Américas Imaginadas: Entrelugares Mestiços, Identidades Híbridas. 2007. (POR.). 204p. *(978-85-7598-122-1(6))* Missao Salesiana de Mato Grasso Univ Cat Dom Bosco.

M'Baye, Babacar. The Trickster Comes West: Pan-African Influence in Early Black Diasporan Narratives. (ENG.). 272p. 2011. pap. 30.00 ***(978-1-61703-210-3(7))*** 2009. 50.00 *(978-1-60473-233-7(4))* Univ. Pr. of Mississippi.

Moore, Lois Merriweather, ed. The Dispersion of Africans & African Culture Throughout the World: Essays on the African Diaspora. 2007. 225p. *(978-0-7734-5309-8(1))* Mellen, Edwin Pr., The.

Moses, Bernard. The Spanish Dependencies in South America; An Introduction to the History of Their Civilization, 2 Vols. reprint ed. 250.00 *(978-0-7222-9537-3(5))* Library Reprints, Inc.

Rodríguez, Ana Patricia. Dividing the Isthmus: Central American Transnational Histories, Literatures, & Cultures. 2009. (ENG., Illus.). 308p. 55.00 *(978-0-292-71909-5(4))* Univ. of Texas Pr.

Saldívar, José David. Trans-Americanity: Subaltern Modernities, Global Coloniality, & the Cultures of Greater Mexico. 2011. (New Americanists Ser.). (ENG., Illus.). 304p. 84.95 ***(978-0-8223-5064-4(5))***; pap. 23.95 ***(978-0-8223-5083-5(1))*** Duke Univ. Pr.

Shukla, Sandhya & Tinsman, Heidi, eds. Imagining Our Americas: Toward a Transnational Frame. 2007. (Radical Perspectives Ser.). (ENG., Illus.). 424p. 94.95 *(978-0-8223-3950-2(1))*; per. 25.95 *(978-0-8223-3961-8(7))* Duke Univ. Pr.

Silverman, Helaine & Isbell, William. Handbook of South American Archaeology. 2008. (Illus.). 870p. 206.00 *(978-0-387-74906-8(3))* Springer.

Sorenson, John L. & Johannessen, Carl L. World Trade & Biological Exchanges Before 1492. 2009. 604p. 39.95 *(978-0-595-51392-5(1))*; pap. 29.95 *(978-0-595-52441-9(9))* iUniverse, Inc.

Vaugeois, Denis & Roth, Kathe. America's Gift: What the World Owes to the Americas & Their First Inhabitants. 2nd ed. 2009. (ENG., Illus.). 274p. pap. 22.95 *(978-0-9812405-2-7(6))* Baraka Bks. CAN. Dist: Independent Pubs. Group.

Warner, J. Sterling & Hilliard, Judith. Visions Across the Americas: Short Essays for Composition. 7th ed. 2009. (Available Titles CengageNOW Ser.). (ENG.). 576p. (C). pap. 92.95 *(978-1-4282-6377-2(2))* Wadsworth.

White, Steven F. & Calderon, Esthela. Culture & Customs of Nicaragua, 1 vol. 2008. (Culture & Customs of Latin America & the Caribbean Ser.). (Illus.). 224p. 49.95 *(978-0-313-33994-3(5)*, GR3994, Greenwood Pr.) Greenwood Publishing Group, Inc.

Wiener, Leo. Africa & the Discovery of America. 2011. (ENG., Illus.). 287p. pap. 15.95 ***(978-1-61759-002-3(9))*** EWorld, Inc.

Witkowski, Igor. Axis of the World: The Search for the Oldest American Civilization. 2008. (ENG.). 220p. pap. 18.95 *(978-1-931882-81-1(9))* Adventures Unlimited Pr.

Young, Jason R. Rituals of Resistance: African Atlantic Religion in Kongo & the Lowcountry South in the Era of Slavery. 2007. 258p. *(978-0-8071-3279-1(9))* Louisiana State Univ. Pr.

—Rituals of Resistance (p) African Atlantic Religion in Kongo & the Lowcountry South in the Era of Slavery. 2011. (Illus.). 272p. pap. 21.50 *(978-0-8071-3719-2(7))* Louisiana State Univ. Pr.

AMERICA—COMMERCE

BIA. Essential American Manufacturers: Food, Textile, Clothing, & Chemical Companies. 6th rev. ed. 2006. 400p. (J). pap. 249.00 *(978-1-4187-4235-5(X))* Business Information Agency.

Hanrahan, Charles E., et al. U. S. Agricultural Trade. 2008. pap. 39.00 *(978-1-60456-818-9(6))* Nova Science Pubs., Inc.

Mercer. The Global Manager's Guide to Living & Working Abroad: Eastern Europe & Asia, 1 vol. 2009. 312p. 49.95 *(978-0-313-37590-3(9)*, C37590, Praeger Pubs.) Greenwood Publishing Group, Inc.

Previts, Gary, et al. A Global History of Accounting, Financial Reporting & Public Policy: Americas, 3 vols., Vol. 14. 2011. 205p. ***(978-0-85724-811-4(1))*** Emerald Group Publishing Ltd. GBR. Dist: Ebsco Publishing.

AMERICA—DESCRIPTION AND TRAVEL

Beker, Ana. Ana Beker, Amazona de Las Americas. 2008. 232p. pap. *(978-1-906393-10-6(9))* Trotamundas Pr., Ltd.

Bergreen, Laurence. Columbus: The Four Voyages. 2011. (ENG.). 544p. (gr. 12). 35.00 *(978-0-670-02301-1(9)*, Viking Adult) Penguin Group (USA) Inc.

—Columbus: The Four Voyages. l.t. ed. 2011. 32.99 ***(978-1-4104-4115-7(6))*** Thorndike Pr.

Bushby, Karl. Giant Steps: The Remarkable Story of the Goliath Expedition from Punta Arenas to Russia. 2008. (ENG., Illus.). 432p. pap. 17.95 *(978-0-7515-3695-9(4))* Little, Brown Bk. Group Ltd. GBR. Dist: Independent Pubs. Group.

Crutchfield, James A. Wagons Ho! Glimpses of Vehicular Transportation in Early America. Crutchfield, James A., ed. 2011. (ENG., Illus.). 64p. pap. *(978-0-944275-16-0(8))* Territorial Pr.

Felszer, Henry. Slipping Away. 2009. 248p. pap. 24.95 *(978-1-60749-075-3(7))* PublishAmerica, Inc.

Gill, Dominic. Take a Seat: One Man, One Tandem & Twenty Thousand Miles of Possibilities. 2010. (ENG., Illus.). 288p. pap. 16.95 *(978-0-7627-7069-4(4)*, Falcon Guides) Globe Pequot Pr., The.

Huot, Jadrino. De Terre-Neuve à la Terre de Feu: Les Aventures D'un Globe-Trotter Dans les Trois Amériques. 2010. (FRE., Illus.). 159p. *(978-2-923382-38-8(2)*, Spotlight Poets) Dumont, Bertrand editeur.

Irving, Washington. The Life & Voyages of Christopher Columbus Volume II. l.t. ed. 2007. (ENG.). 582p. pap. 32.99 *(978-1-4264-5282-6(9))* BiblioBazaar.

—The Life & Voyages of Christopher Columbus Volume II: The Life & Voyages of Christopher Columbus Volume II. 2007. (ENG.). 526p. pap. 30.99 *(978-1-4264-4981-9(X))* BiblioBazaar.

Lawrence, Cory. Rebel Blues, 1 vol. 2009. 57p. pap. 12.95 *(978-1-61546-336-7(4))* PublishAmerica, Inc.
Locken, E. Travel Journal America. 2009. 192p. pap. 20.95 *(978-0-557-07959-9(4))* Lulu Enterprises Inc.
McCormick, Herb. One Island, One Ocean: The Epic Environmental Journey Around the Americas. 2011. (ENG.). 240p. 35.00 *(978-1-61628-171-7(5))* Weldon Owen, Inc.
MONACO BOOKS, compiled by. Dream Routes of the Americas, 1 vol. 2010. (ENG., Illus.). 496p. 24.95 *(978-3-89944-667-8(4),* Monaco Bks.) Verlag Wolfgang Kunth GmbH & Co. KG DEU. Dist: Innovative Logistics.
Passman, Roger. Photographs. 2008. 24p. 39.95 *(978-1-4357-5282-5(1))* Lulu Enterprises Inc.
Purdy, Rachael. Homesick. 2009. 60p. pap. 31.50 *(978-1-4092-0611-8(4))* Lulu Enterprises Inc.
Rand McNally Staff, ed. Modern America. 2007. (Debating the Documents Ser.). (gr. 5-12). pap. 161.95 net. *(978-0-528-67657-4(1))* Rand McNally.
Requist, Lois. RVing Solo Across America ... without a cat, dog, man, or Gun. 2010. 225p. pap. 22.76 *(978-0-557-13384-0(X))* Lulu Enterprises Inc.
Slavin, Robert E. Damp Yankees: (Another American Gobsmacked by England) 2011. 68p. pap. 9.95 ***(978-1-4620-4085-8(3))*** iUniverse, Inc.
Solomon, Susan. Armenia: The Essential Guide to Customs & Culture. 2009. (Culture Smart! Ser.). (ENG., Illus.). 168p. pap. 9.95 *(978-1-85733-493-7(0))* Kuperard Pubs. GBR. Dist: Random Hse., Inc.
Stronza, Amanda & Durnam, William H. Ecotourism & Conservation in the Americas. Stronza, A., ed. 2008. (Ecotourism Ser.). (Illus.). 208p. 125.00 *(978-1-84593-400-2(8))* CABI GBR. Dist: Stylus Publishing, LLC.
Stuart-Wortley, Emmeline. Travels in the United States, etc., During 1849 & 1850 by the Lady Emmeline Stuart Wortley. 2006. 484p. per. 29.99 *(978-1-4255-5316-6(8))* MPublishing.
Waterton, Charles. Wanderings in South America, the North-West of the United States, & the Antilles, in the Years 1812, 1816, 1820, And 1824: With Original Instructions for the Perfect Preservation of Birds, etc for Cabinets of Natural History. 2011. (Cambridge Library Collection - Travel & Exploration Ser.). (ENG., Illus.). 354p. pap. 29.99 ***(978-1-108-03415-9(2))*** Cambridge Univ. Pr.
Winterbotham, William. An Historical, Geographical, Commercial & Philosophical View of the American United States. 2009. (Revolutionary War Ser.). (ENG.). 608p. pap. 34.95 *(978-1-4290-1718-3(X));* Vol. 2. 504p. pap. 29.95 *(978-1-4290-1715-2(5))* Applewood Bks.

AMERICA—DISCOVERY AND EXPLORATION

see also United States—Exploring Expeditions

Abbott, John S. C. Ferdinand de Soto: The Discoverer of the Mississippi. (American Pioneers & Patriots Ser.). 351p. reprint ed. 98.00 *(978-0-7222-8372-1(5));* 98.00 *(978-0-7222-8465-0(9))* Library Reprints, Inc.
Adams, Herbert B. & Wood, Henry. Columbus & His Discovery of America. 40p. 2010. pap. 12.76 *(978-1-163-92681-9(7))* 2010. 30.95 *(978-1-161-70123-4(0))* 2007. (ENG.). per. 15.95 *(978-0-548-61478-5(4))* Kessinger Publishing, LLC.
Aguilar Y. Córdoba, Diego De & Aguilar y Córdoba, Diego. El MarañóN: Edición y Estudio de Julián Díez Torres. 2011. (Biblioteca Indiana Ser.). (SPA.). pap. 44.00 ***(978-84-8489-568-8(8))*** Iberoamericana Vervuert Publishing Corp.
Alexander, Philip F., ed. The Discovery of America 1492-1584. 2011. (ENG.). 230p. pap. 22.99 *(978-1-107-60060-7(X))* Cambridge Univ. Pr.
Alexander, Philip Frederick. The Discovery of America, 1492-1584. (Cambridge Travel Bks.). 212p. reprint ed. 98.00 *(978-0-7222-6410-2(0))* Library Reprints, Inc.
Amado, Jorge. A Descoberta Da América Pelos Turcos: Romancinho.Tr. of How the Turks Discovered America. (POR., Illus.). xx, 171p. pap. 18.95 *(978-85-01-04161-6(0))* Distribuidora Record de Servicos de Imprensa SA BRA. Dist: Distribooks, Inc.
Anderson, Charles Loftus Grant. Old Panama & Castilla del Oro: A Narrative History of the Discovery, Conquest, & Settlement by the Spaniards of Panama, Darien, Veragua, Santo Domingo, Santa Marta, Cartegena, Nicaragua, & Peru. 559p. reprint ed. 98.00 *(978-0-7222-9491-8(3))* Library Reprints, Inc.
Arango L, Manuel Antonio. Proceso Histórico-Social en la Literatura de Los Primeros Cronistas de la Conquista de América. 2010. (Currents in Comparative Romance Languages & Literatures Ser.). (SPA.). 213p. 74.95 *(978-1-4331-1079-5(2))* Lang, Peter Publishing, Inc.
Armitage, Merle & Ortega, Peter Ribera. Pagans, Conquistadores, Heroes & Martyrs. 2011. 122p. 40.95 ***(978-1-258-05345-1(4))*** Literary Licensing, LLC.
Asher, George M., ed. Henry hudson the Navigator: The Original Documents in Which His Career Is Recorded. 2007. 534p. reprint ed. pap. 34.95 *(978-1-60105-138-7(7),* 6D7N) Scholar's Bookshelf.
Asher, George Michael, ed. Henry Hudson the Navigator: The Original Documents in which his Career Is Recorded. 2010. (Cambridge Library Collection- Hakluyt First Ser.). (Illus.). 548p. pap. 43.00 *(978-1-108-01048-1(2))* Cambridge Univ. Pr.
Babcock, William H. Early Norse Visits to North America. 2008. 234p. 41.95 *(978-0-548-97838-2(7))* 2007. (ENG.). 236p. per. 26.95 *(978-0-548-66942-6(2))* Kessinger Publishing, LLC.
Babcock, William Henry. Early Norse Visits to North America. 213p. reprint ed. 98.00 *(978-0-7222-6446-1(1))* Library Reprints, Inc.
Bailey, Carolyn Sherwin. Boys & Girls of Discovery Days. 2011. 222p. 44.95 ***(978-1-258-07220-9(3))*** Literary Licensing, LLC.
Baldy, François, ed. Conquerants et Chroniqueurs espagnols en pays Maya (1515-1697) Livre 2: Conquetes. 2011. (roue a Livres Ser.). (FRE., Illus.). 720p. (C). pap. 68.00 ***(978-2-251-33959-7(0))*** Societe d'edition Les Belles lettres FRA. Dist: ISD.
Balkan, Evan. The Wrath of God: Lope de Aguirre, Revolutionary of the Americas. 2011. (Illus.). ix, 225p. *(978-0-8263-5045-9(3))* Univ. of New Mexico Pr.
Balkan, Evan L. The Wrath of God: Lope de Aguirre, Revolutionary of the Americas. 2011. (ENG., Illus.). 236p. (C). 39.95 *(978-0-8263-5043-5(7))* Univ. of New Mexico Pr.
Barnett, James K. Captain Cook in Alaska & the North Pacific. 2008. (Illus.). 304p. pap. *(978-1-57833-408-7(X))* Todd Communications.
Bawlf, Samuel. The Secret Voyage of Sir Francis Drake, 1 vol. (ENG., Illus.). 464p. pap. 24.95 *(978-1-55365-041-6(7))* D&M Pubs. Inc. CAN. Dist: Perseus-PGW.
Baxter, James Phinney. A Memoir of Jacques Cartier, Sieur de Limoilou. 464p. reprint ed. 98.00 *(978-0-7222-6429-4(1))* Library Reprints, Inc.
Beals, Herbert K., et al, eds. Four Travel Journals: The Americas, Antarctica & Africa, 1775-1874. 2008. (Hakluyt Society, Third Series: 18 Ser.). (Illus.). 414p. 99.95 *(978-0-904180-90-9(5))* Hakluyt Society GBR. Dist: Ashgate Publishing Co.
Bergreen, Laurence. Columbus: The Four Voyages. 2011. (ENG.). 544p. (gr. 12). 35.00 *(978-0-670-02301-1(9),* Viking Adult) Penguin Group (USA) Inc.
—Columbus: The Four Voyages. lt. ed. 2011. 32.99 ***(978-1-4104-4115-7(6))*** Thorndike Pr.
—Columbus: The Four Voyages, 1492-1504. 2012. (ENG., Illus.). 448p. (gr. 12). pap. 20.00 ***(978-0-14-312210-4(X),*** Penguin (Non-Classics)) Penguin Group (USA) Inc.
Biographiq. Christopher Columbus - the Man Who Discovered America. 2008. 68p. pap. 9.99 *(978-1-59986-052-7(X),* Biographiq) Filiquarian Publishing, LLC.
Bodega y Cuadra, Juan de la. Voyage to the Northwest Coast of America, 1792: Juan Francisco de la Bodega y Quadra & the Nootka Sound Controversy. Inglis, Robin & Engstrand, Iris H. W., eds. 2012. (Northwest Historical Ser.). (ENG., Illus.). 192p. 34.95 ***(978-0-87062-408-7(3),*** Clark, Arthur H. Co., The) Univ. of Oklahoma Pr.
Bolton, Herbert E. The Spanish Borderlands. 2009. 128p. pap. *(978-1-151-19541-8(3))* Books LLC.
—Spanish Exploration in the Southwest, 1542-1706. 486p. reprint ed. 98.00 *(978-0-7222-9536-6(7))* Library Reprints, Inc.
Bolton, Herbert Eugene. Spanish Exploration in the Southwest, 1542-1706. (Original Narratives of Early American History Ser.). 486p. reprint ed. 98.00 *(978-0-7222-6511-6(5))* Library Reprints, Inc.
Bourne, Edward Gaylord. Spain in America, 1450-1580. 2009. 222p. pap. *(978-1-4588-5273-1(3))* Books LLC.
—Spain in America, 1450-1580. (American Nation Ser.). 350p. reprint ed. 98.00 *(978-0-7222-7176-6(X));* 98.00 *(978-0-7222-6512-3(3))* Library Reprints, Inc.
Bown, Stephen R. 1494: How a Family Feud in Medieval Spain Divided the World in Half. 2012. (ENG., Illus.). 304p. 27.99 ***(978-0-312-61612-0(0),*** Dunne, Thomas Bks.) St. Martin's Pr.
Bradley, Michael. The Columbus Conspiracy. 2011. (Illus.). 253p. pap. 14.95 ***(978-1-61759-006-1(0))*** EWorld, Inc.
—Dawn Voyage: The Black African Discovery of America. 2011. (Illus.). 193p. pap. 14.95 ***(978-1-61759-003-0(7))*** EWorld, Inc.
Bradley, Michael. Swords at Sunset: Last Stand of North America's Grail Knights. 2006. (Illus.). 240p. per. 14.95 *(978-0-9736477-4-7(4),* 400-001) Manor Hse. Publishing, Inc. CAN. Dist: Bookworld Trade, Inc.
Brady, Cyrus Townsend. Colonial Fights & Fighters. 2009. 374p. 29.99 *(978-1-116-99569-5(7));* 31.99 *(978-1-116-99568-8(9));* pap. 32.75 *(978-1-116-99571-8(9));* pap. 33.75 *(978-1-116-99570-1(0))* BiblioBazaar.
—Colonial Fights & Fighters. 341p. reprint ed. 98.00 *(978-0-7222-6873-5(4))* Library Reprints, Inc.
Breazeale, J. W. M. Life as It Is: Or Matters & Things in General. 2009. (ENG.). pap. 29.95 *(978-1-57233-477-9(0))* Univ. of Tennessee Pr.
Brebner, John B. The Explorers of North America, Fourteen Ninety-Two to Eighteen Hundred Six. reprint ed. 67.50 *(978-0-404-20043-5(5))* AMS Pr., Inc.
Brinkbaumer, Klaus, et al. The Voyage of the Vizcaina: The Mystery of Christopher Columbus's Last Ship. Streck, Annette, tr. from GER. 2007. (ENG., Illus.). 336p. pap. 20.95 *(978-0-15-603158-5(2),* Mariner Bks.) Houghton Mifflin Harcourt Trade & Reference Pubs.
Brittain, Alfred. Discovery & Exploration. 2009. (Illus.). 332p. pap. 25.32 *(978-0-217-70933-0(8))* General Bks. LLC.
—Discovery & Exploration. (History of North America Ser.). 511p. reprint ed. 98.00 *(978-0-7222-6412-6(7))* Library Reprints, Inc.
Brooks, Noah. First Across the Continent. 2011. 256p. pap. ***(978-1-84902-295-8(X))*** Benediction Classics.
Brown, I. I. I. Rediscovering Vinland: Evidence of Ancient Viking Presence in America. 2007. 336p. per. 22.95 *(978-0-595-43680-4(3))* iUniverse, Inc.
Brown, Meredith Mason. Frontiersman: Daniel Boone & the Making of America. 2009. (Illus.). 416p. 34.95 *(978-0-8071-3356-9(6))* Louisiana State Univ. Pr.
Brown, Nancy Marie. The Far Traveler: Voyages of a Viking Woman. 2008. (ENG.). 320p. pap. 15.00 *(978-0-15-603397-8(6),* Mariner Bks.) Houghton Mifflin Harcourt Trade & Reference Pubs.
Burgess, Glyn S. & Strijbosch, Clara, eds. The Brendan Legend: Texts & Versions. 2006. (Northern World Ser.: Vol. 24). (Illus.). 400p. *(978-90-04-15247-2(4))* BRILL.
Burrage, Henry Sweetser. Early English & French Voyages, Chiefly from Hakluyt, 1534-1608. (Original Narratives of Early American History Ser.). 451p. reprint ed. 98.00 *(978-0-7222-6413-3(5))* Library Reprints, Inc.
Cabeza de Vaca, Alvar Nunez. Naufragios. 2010. (SPA.). 94p. per. 13.49 *(978-84-96290-86-0(7))* Linkgua Ediciones, S.L. ESP. Dist: AtlasBooks Distribution.
Cabeza De Vaca, Alvar Nunez. The South American Expeditions, 1540-1545. Morrow, Baker H., tr. from SPA. 2011. (ENG., Illus.). 192p. (C). 39.95 ***(978-0-8263-5063-3(1))*** Univ. of New Mexico Pr.
Castanha, Tony. The Myth of Indigenous Caribbean Extinction: Continuity & Reclamation in Borikén (Puerto Rico) 2010. (ENG., Illus.). 200p. 89.00 *(978-0-230-62025-4(6))* Palgrave Macmillan.
Castro, Daniel. Another Face of Empire: Bartolomé de Las Casas, Indigenous Rights, & Ecclesiastical Imperialism. 2007. (Latin America Otherwise Ser.). (ENG.). 248p. 79.95 *(978-0-8223-3930-4(7));* per. 22.95 *(978-0-8223-3939-7(0))* Duke Univ. Pr.
Champlain, Samuel de. The Voyages & Explorations of Samuel de Champlain, 1604-1616. 2009. 252p. 23.99 *(978-1-103-77435-7(2));* pap. 17.99 *(978-1-103-77429-6(8))* BiblioBazaar.
—The Voyages & Explorations of Samuel de Champlain, 1604-1616. 2009. 116p. pap. *(978-1-4590-5514-8(4))* Books LLC.
—The Voyages & Explorations of Samuel de Champlain, 1604-1616: Narrated by Himself, 2 vol., set. (Trail Makers Ser.). reprint ed. 250.00 *(978-0-7222-6430-0(5))* Library Reprints, Inc.
—Voyages of Samuel de Champlain. 2008. 300p. 28.99 *(978-0-554-23731-2(8));* 300p. 25.99 *(978-0-554-33034-1(2));* 212p. 24.99 *(978-0-554-33065-3(7));* 212p. 27.99 *(978-0-554-23782-4(2))* BiblioBazaar.
—Voyages of Samuel de Champlain. 2009. 160p. pap. *(978-0-217-30358-3(7))* Books LLC.
—Voyages of Samuel de Champlain, 1604-1618. 2009. 324p. pap. *(978-0-217-95550-8(9));* 322p. pap. *(978-0-217-95553-9(3));* 276p. pap. *(978-0-217-41644-3(6))* Books LLC.
—Voyages of Samuel de Champlain, 1604-1618. (Original Narratives of Early American History Ser.). 377p. reprint ed. 98.00 *(978-0-7222-6431-7(3))* Library Reprints, Inc.
—Voyages of Samuel de Champlain, Volume 1. 2007. 254p. pap. 21.99 *(978-1-4264-4964-2(X));* (ENG.). 298p. pap. 23.99 *(978-1-4264-5265-9(9))* BiblioBazaar.
—Voyages of Samuel de Champlain, Volume 2. 2006. (ENG.). 238p. pap. 20.99 *(978-1-4264-4989-5(5));* 276p. pap. 23.99 *(978-1-4264-5290-1(X))* BiblioBazaar.
—Voyages of Samuel de Champlain, Volume 3. 2007. (ENG.). 182p. pap. 19.99 *(978-1-4264-5015-0(X));* 208p. pap. 22.99 *(978-1-4264-5316-8(7))* BiblioBazaar.
Champlain, Samuel de & Otis, Charles P. Voyages of Samuel de Champlain. 2008. 280p. 25.99 *(978-0-554-33059-4(8));* 28.99 *(978-0-554-23756-5(3))* BiblioBazaar.
Chang-Rodriguez, Raquel, ed. Beyond Books & Borders: Garcilaso de la Vega & la Florida del Inca. 2006. (Illus.). 197p. 55.00 *(978-0-8387-5651-5(4))* Bucknell Univ. Pr.
Cheyney, Edward Potts. European Background of American History, 1300-1600. (American Nation Ser.). 343p. reprint ed. 98.00 *(978-0-7222-6414-0(3));* 98.00 *(978-0-7222-7179-7(4))* Library Reprints, Inc.
Chipman, Donald E. Álvar Núñez Cabeza de Vaca: The Great Pedestrian of North & South America 2012. (Fred Rider Cotten Popular History Ser.). 120p. pap. 15.95 ***(978-0-87611-251-9(3))*** Texas State Historical Assn.
Clayton, Lawrence A., ed. Bartolomé de Las Casas & the Conquest of the Americas. 2011. (Viewpoints / Puntos de Vista Ser.: 6). (ENG.). 208p. pap. 24.95 *(978-1-4051-9428-0(6));* 90.95 *(978-1-4051-9427-3(8))* Wiley, John & Sons, Inc. (Wiley-Blackwell).
Coleman, E. C. Captain Vancouver: North-West Navigator. 2006. (ENG., Illus.). 160p. pap. 35.00 *(978-0-7524-3892-4(1))* History Pr. Ltd.,The GBR. Dist: Independent Pubs. Group.
Coleman, R. V. The First Frontier: A History of How America Began. 2009. (ENG., Illus.). 458p. 9.99 *(978-0-7858-2081-9(7),* 0785820817, Castle Bks., Inc.) Book Sales, Inc.
Columbus, Christopher. Journal of Christopher Columbus (During His First Voyage, 1492-93) And Documents Relating the Voyages of John Cabot & Gaspar Corte Real. 2010. (Cambridge Library Collection - Travel & Exploration Ser.). (ENG., Illus.). 344p. pap. 31.00 *(978-1-108-01284-3(1))* Cambridge Univ. Pr.
—Select Letters of Christopher Columbus: With Other Original Documents, Relating to His Four Voyages to the New World. 2010. (Cambridge Library Collection - Travel & Exploration Ser.). (ENG.). 346p. pap. 28.99 *(978-1-108-00799-3(6))* Cambridge Univ. Pr.
—Select Letters of Christopher Columbus: With Other Original Documents, Relating to his Four Voyages to the New World. 2010. (Cambridge Library Collection - Hakluyt First Ser.). (Illus.). 424p. pap. 31.99 *(978-1-108-01194-5(2))* Cambridge Univ. Pr.
—Select Letters of Christopher Columbus W. 2006. pap. 26.95 *(978-1-4286-4398-7(2))* Kessinger Publishing, LLC.
Columbus, Christopher & Casas, Bartolomew las. The Log of Christopher Columbus' First Voyage to America in the Year 1492. 2011. 94p. pap. 8.50 ***(978-1-891396-91-5(9))*** Martino Publishing.
Cortés, Hernán. Fifth Letter of Hernan Cortes to the Emperor Charles V: Containing an Account of his Expedition to Honduras. Gayangos, Pascual de, tr. 2010. (Cambridge Library Collection - Hakluyt First Ser.). (ENG.). 180p. pap. 19.99 *(978-1-108-01344-4(9))* Cambridge Univ. Pr.
Cortés, Hugo R., et al. Rebeldes y Aventureros: Del Viejo Al Nuevo Mundo. 2008. (SPA.). 273p. pap. 24.80 *(978-84-8489-390-5(1))* Iberoamericana Vervuert Publishing Corp.
Crespo Cuesta, Eduardo Daniel. Continuidades Medievales en la Conquista de América. 2010. (Illus.). 190p. *(978-84-313-2719-4(7))* Universidad de Navarra, Ediciones, S. A.
Dark, Richard. The Quest of the Indies. 2010. 90p. pap. *(978-1-151-80654-3(4))* Books LLC.
—The Quest of the Indies. 2008. 268p. 42.95 *(978-0-548-98107-8(8))* 2007. (ENG.). 272p. per. 27.95 *(978-0-548-66646-3(6))* Kessinger Publishing, LLC.
—The Quest of the Indies. 241p. reprint ed. 98.00 *(978-0-7222-6415-7(1))* Library Reprints, Inc.
Davidson, George. The Tracks & Landfalls of Bering & Chirikof on the Northwest Coast of America. 2009. (ENG.). 50p. pap. 18.99 *(978-1-110-62307-5(0));* pap. 16.99 *(978-1-110-62306-8(2),* BiblioBazaar. (BiblioLife).
Davis, Graeme. Vikings in America. 2011. (ENG., Illus.). 224p. pap. 23.95 ***(978-1-84158-959-6(4))*** Birlinn, Ltd. GBR. Dist: Independent Pubs. Group.
De Costa, Benjamin Franklin. The Pre-Columbian Discovery of America by the Northmen, Illustrated by Translations from the Icelandic Sagas, Ed with Notes & a General Introductio. 2006. (Illus.). 176p. per. 18.99 *(978-1-4255-1408-2(1))* MPublishing.
De Roo, Peter. The History of America Before Columbus: According to Documents & Approved Authors, 2 vol., set. reprint ed. 250.00 *(978-0-7222-6416-4(X))* Library Reprints, Inc.
—History of America Before Columbus V1, According to Documents. 2007. (ENG.). 668p. per. 48.95 *(978-1-4304-4387-2(1))* Kessinger Publishing, LLC.
Dean, James Seay. Tropics Bound: Elizabeth's Seadogs on the Spanish Main. 2010. (ENG., Illus.). 224p. 34.95 *(978-0-7524-5096-4(4))* History Pr. Ltd.,The GBR. Dist: Independent Pubs. Group.
Delaney, Carol. Columbus & the Quest for Jerusalem. 2011. (ENG.). 336p. 26.00 *(978-1-4391-0232-9(5),* Free Pr.) Free Pr.
Delgado, James P. Across the Top of the World: The Quest for the Northwest Passage. (Illus.). 29.95 *(978-1-55054-734-4(8))* D&M Pubs. Inc. CAN. Dist: Perseus-PGW.
Dellenbaugh, Frederick S. Fremont & 49 the Story of A Remarkable. 2006. pap. 50.95 *(978-1-4286-5184-5(5))* Kessinger Publishing, LLC.
Díaz del Castillo, Bernal. Conquistador! The True Life Adventures of Bernal Diaz & His Part in the Spanish Conquest of the Americas in the Early Sixteenth Century. 2010.Tr. of Historia Verdadera de la Conquista de la Nueva España. Vol. 1. 500p. ***(978-0-85706-292-5(1))*** Vol. 1. 500p. pap. ***(978-0-85706-291-8(3))*** Vol. 2. 492p. ***(978-0-85706-294-9(8))*** Vol. 2. 492p. pap. ***(978-0-85706-293-2(X))*** Leonaur Ltd.
Díaz del Castillo, Bernal. Histoire Véridique de la Conquête de la Nouvelle-Espagne. Jourdanet, Denis, tr. from SPA. 2010.Tr. of Historia Verdadera de la Conquista de la Nueva España. (FRE.). 984p. pap. 64.75 *(978-1-174-28267-6(3))* BiblioBazaar.
Dionne, Hélène, ed. Gold in the Americas. 2008. (ENG., Illus.). 208p. (C). 49.95 *(978-2-89448-552-1(2))* Editions du Septentrion CAN. Dist: McGill-Queen's Univ. Pr.
Dominguez, Luis L. The Conquest of the River Plate. 2009. 330p. 29.99 *(978-1-113-66708-3(7));* pap. 31.75 *(978-1-113-66704-5(4));* pap. 30.75 *(978-1-113-66703-8(6))* BiblioBazaar.
Dominguez, Luis L., ed. Conquest of the River Plate, 1535-1555: Translated for the Hakluyt Society with Notes & an Introduction. 2010. (Cambridge Library Collection - Travel & Exploration Ser.). (ENG., Illus.). 340p. pap. 28.99 *(978-1-108-01350-5(3))* Cambridge Univ. Pr.
Donovan, S. K. Jamaican Rock Stars, 1823-1971: The Geologists Who Explored Jamaica. 2010. 50.00 *(978-0-8137-1205-5(X))* Geological Society of America, Inc.
Durrett, Reuben Thomas. Traditions of the Earliest Visits of Foreigners to North America. 179p. reprint ed. 88.00 *(978-0-7222-6417-1(8))* Library Reprints, Inc.
Dykstra, Rosemary Kerr. The Norwegian Vikings Discover North America. 2007. per. 15.00 *(978-0-9785055-8-5(1),* Dykstra Publishing.
Early Days in America, Vol. 14. Date not set. 32.95 *(978-0-8369-4807-3(6))* Ayer Co. Pubs., Inc.
Edwards, Charles Lester & Vespucci, Amerigo. Amerigo Vespucci. Bridgeman, Keith & Arsham, Tahira, eds. 2009. 164p. pap. 14.30 *(978-1-906421-02-1(1))* Viartis GBR. Dist: Ingram Bk. Co.
Egert, Nina. Tracing Anza's Trail: A Photographer's Journey: Images Accompanying Journal Entries by the First Spaniards to Travel Overland from Arizona to the San Francisco Bay Area. 2008. (SPA & ENG., Illus.). 98p. pap. *(978-1-60725-700-4(9))* Independent Pub.
Emory, W. H. Notes of A Military Reconnoissance from. 2006. pap. 37.95 *(978-1-4286-4754-1(6))* Kessinger Publishing, LLC.
Encyclopaedia Britannica, Inc., compiled by. Learn & Explore Series: Native Peoples of the Americas. 2009. (Learn & Explore Ser.). (Illus.). vi, 122p. (YA). (gr. 9). 29.95 *(978-1-61535-330-9(5))* Encyclopaedia Britannica, Inc.
Fagan, Brian. Fish on Friday: Feasting, Fasting, & the Discovery of the New World. 2010. (ENG.). 338p. pap. 17.00 *(978-1-4379-7316-7(7))* DIANE Publishing Co.
Fagan, Brian M. Fish on Friday: Feasting, Fasting & the Discovery of the New World. 2007. (ENG., Illus.). 368p. per. 16.95 *(978-0-465-02285-4(5))* Basic Bks.
Fay, Samuel Prescott. The Forgotten Explorer: Samuel Prescott Fay's 1914 Expedition to the Northern Rockies, 1 vol. Helm, Charles & Murtha, Mike, eds. (ENG., Illus.). 320p. 2010. pap. *(978-1-897522-55-4(X))* 2009. *(978-1-897522-56-1(8))* Rocky Mountain Bks.

Fernández-Armesto, Felipe. Amerigo: The Man Who Gave His Name to America. 2008. (ENG., Illus.). 272p. pap. 15.00 *(978-0-8129-7296-6(8)*, Random Hse. Trade Paperbacks) Random House Publishing Group.

—Columbus on Himself. 2010. 300p. 44.00 *(978-1-60384-134-4(2))*; pap. 13.95 *(978-1-60384-133-7(4))* Hackett Publishing Co., Inc.

Fernández de Oviedo y Valdés, Gonzalo. Writing from the Edge of the World: The Memoirs of Darien, 1514-1527. 2006. (Illus.). 232p. annot. ed. per. 24.75 *(978-0-8173-5339-1(9))* 2nd annot. ed. 47.00 *(978-0-8173-1518-4(7))* Univ. of Alabama Pr.

Fischer, David Hackett. Champlain's Dream. 2009. (ENG., Illus.). 848p. pap. 18.99 *(978-1-4165-9333-1(0))* Simon & Schuster.

Fiske, John. The Discovery of America. 2009. 576p. 30.99 *(978-1-103-00253-5(8))*; pap. 24.99 *(978-1-103-00249-8(X))* BiblioBazaar.

—The DISCOVERY of AMERICA; with Some Account of Ancient America & the Spanish Conquest, 2 vols. 2007. (Illus.). 102p. reprint ed. pap. 79.95 *(978-1-60105-101-1(8)*, 6D0X) Scholar's Bookshelf.

The Flatey Book & Recently Discovered Vatican Manuscripts Concerning America As Early As the Tenth Century. 2007. (ENG.). 174p. 37.95 *(978-0-548-04657-9(3))* Kessinger Publishing, LLC.

Forbes, Jack D. The American Discovery of Europe. (Illus.). 272p. 2011. pap. 28.00 ***(978-0-252-07836-1(5))*** 2007. 35.95 *(978-0-252-03152-6(0))* Univ. of Illinois Pr.

Fossum, Andrew. The Norse's Discovery of America. reprint ed. 150.00 *(978-0-7222-6447-8(X))* Library Reprints, Inc.

Fowler, Don D. The Glen Canyon Country: A Personal Memoir. 2011. (ENG., Illus.). 448p. (gr. 12). 75.00 *(978-1-60781-127-5(8))* Univ. of Utah Pr.

Fowler, Don D., ed. Cleaving an Unknown World: The Powell Expeditions & the Scientific Exploration of the Colorado Plateau. 2011. (ENG.). 280p. (gr. 9). pap. 24.95 ***(978-1-60781-146-6(4))*** Univ. of Utah Pr.

Fox, Max. American Classic: An Alternate History, Volume 1. 2007. (Illus.). pap. 15.99 *(978-1-932657-96-8(7))* Third Millennium Pubns.

Frémont, John Charles. The Life of Col John Charles Fremont, & His Narrative of Explorations & Adventures, in Kansas, Nebraska, Oregon & California the Memoir by Sam. 2006. 516p. per. 29.99 *(978-1-4255-5723-2(6))* MPublishing.

Fuller, Mary C. Voyages in Print: English Narratives of Travel to America 1576-1624. 2007. (Cambridge Studies in Renaissance Literature & Culture Ser.). (ENG., Illus.). 228p. pap. 46.00 *(978-0-521-03650-4(X))* Cambridge Univ. Pr.

Gamble, Lynn H. Chumash World at European Contact: Power, Trade, & Feasting among Complex Hunter-Gatherers. 2008. (Illus.). 376p. 55.00 *(978-0-520-25441-1(4))* Univ. of California Pr.

Gamboa, Pedro Sarmiento de. History of the Incas. 2007. 212p. per. *(978-1-4065-1748-4(8))* Dodo Pr.

Ganong, William F. Champlain's Island: An Expanded Edition of Ste. Croix (Dochet) Island. exp. ed. (Illus.). 172p. pap. 16.95 *(978-0-919326-57-6(9))* New Brunswick Museum CAN. Dist: Goose Lane Editions.

Gathorne-Hardy, Geoffrey Malcolm. The Norse Discoverer's of America. 304p. reprint ed. 98.00 *(978-0-7222-6448-5(8))* Library Reprints, Inc.

Gaudio, Michael. Engraving the Savage: The New World & Techniques of Civilization. 2008. (Illus.). 240p. 75.00 *(978-0-8166-4846-7(8))*; per. 25.00 *(978-0-8166-4847-4(6))* Univ. of Minnesota Pr.

Gerbi, Antonello. Nature in the New World: From Christopher Columbus to Gonzalo Fernandez de Oviedo. Moyle, Jeremy, tr. from ITA. 2010. (ENG.). 480p. (C). pap. 29.95 *(978-0-8229-6080-5(X))* Univ. of Pittsburgh Pr.

González, Carlos Alberto. New World Literacy: Writing & Culture Across the Atlantic, 1500-1700. 2011. (ENG.). 296p. 75.00 *(978-1-61148-026-9(4))* Bucknell Univ. Pr.

Goodwin, William B. The Truth about Leif Ericsson & the Greenland Voyages. 2007. 448p. per. 36.95 *(978-1-4304-8470-7(5))* Kessinger Publishing, LLC.

Gotay, Michael & Bowman, John S. North American Exploration. 2009. (ENG., Illus.). 528p. 12.99 *(978-0-7858-2258-5(5)*, 0785822585, Castle Bks., Inc.) Book Sales, Inc.

Goudsward, David. Ancient Stone Sites of New England & the Debate over Early European Exploration. 2006. (ENG., Illus.). 248p. per. 35.00 *(978-0-7864-2462-7(1))* McFarland & Co., Inc. Pubs.

—The Westford Knight & Henry Sinclair: Evidence of a 14th Century Scottish Voyage to North America. 2010. (ENG., Illus.). 260p. pap. 35.00 *(978-0-7864-4649-0(8))* McFarland & Co., Inc. Pubs.

Hakluyt, Richard. Divers Voyages Touching the Discovery of America & the Islands Adjacent. 2009. 192p. pap. 19.99 *(978-1-150-21214-7(4))* General Bks. LLC.

—Voyages of the Elizabethan Seamen. 415p. reprint ed. 98.00 *(978-0-7222-6424-9(0))* Library Reprints, Inc.

Hakluyt, Richard, ed. Divers Voyages Touching the Discovery of America & the Islands Adjacent. (Illus.). 171p. reprint ed. lib. bdg. 88.00 *(978-0-7222-0188-6(5))* Library Reprints, Inc.

Hakluyt, Richard & Jones, John Winter, eds. Divers Voyages Touching the Discovery of America & the Islands Adjacent. 2007. (ENG.). 298p. 43.95 *(978-0-548-24297-1(6))*; 300p. per. 28.95 *(978-1-4326-4475-8(0))* Kessinger Publishing, LLC.

Hakluyt, Richard, et al. Divers Voyages Touching the Discovery of America & the Islands Adjacent. 2010. 308p. pap. 29.75 *(978-1-142-62975-5(9))* BiblioBazaar.

Hale, Edward Everett. The Life of Christopher Columbus from His Own Letters & Journals. rev. ed. 2006. 184p. 26.95 *(978-1-4218-2027-9(7))*; per. 11.95 *(978-1-4218-2127-6(3))* 1st World Publishing, Inc. (1st World Library - Literary Society).

Harrisse, Henry. The Discovery of North America: A Critical, Documentary, & Historic Investigation: with an Essay on the Early Cartography of the New World, Including Descriptions of Two Hundred & Fifty Maps or Globes Existing or Lost, Constructed Before the Year 1536: to Which Are Added a Chronology of One Hundred Voyages Westward, Projected, Attempted, or Accomplished Between 1431 & 1504: Biographical Accounts of the Three Hundred Pilots. 2007. (Illus.). 812p. 125.00 *(978-1-57898-596-8(X))* Martino Publishing.

Hawkins, Richard. Observations of Sir Richard Hawkins, Knt in His Voyage into the South Sea in the Year 1593: Reprinted from the Edition Of 1622. Bethune, Charles Ramsay Drinkwater, ed. 2010. (Cambridge Library Collection - Travel & Exploration Ser.). (ENG.). 268p. pap. 23.99 *(978-1-108-00798-6(8))* Cambridge Univ. Pr.

Hayes, Derek. America Discovered: A Historical Atlas of North American Exploration. 2009. (ENG., Illus.). 224p. pap. 35.00 *(978-1-55365-450-6(1))* D&M Pubs. Inc. CAN. Dist: Perseus-PGW.

Haze, Xaviant & Schrag, Paul. The Suppressed History of America. 2011. (ENG., Illus.). 1p. pap. 15.00 *(978-1-59143-122-0(0))* Bear & Co.

Hearne, Samuel. A Journey to the Northern Ocean: The Adventures of Samuel Hearne, 1 vol. 2007. (ENG., Illus.). 320p. per. *(978-1-894898-60-7(5))* TouchWood Editions.

Heidenreich, Conrad. Samuel de Champlain Before 1604: Des Sauvages & other Documents Related to the Period. Ritch, K. Janet, ed. 2010. (FRE & ENG.). 526p. (C). *(978-0-7735-3757-6(0))* McGill-Queen's Univ. Pr.

Helps, Arthur. The Life of Columbus. 2007. 144p. per. *(978-1-4065-4450-3(7))* Dodo Pr.

—Life of Columbus. 2006. pap. *(978-1-4068-3570-0(6))* Echo Library.

Hernández, Mark A. Figural Conquistadors: Rewriting the New World's Discovery & Conquest in Mexican & River Plate Novels of the 1980s & 1990s. 2006. (Bucknell Studies in Latin American Literature & Theory). (Illus.). 194p. 45.00 *(978-0-8387-5645-4(X))* Bucknell Univ. Pr.

Hichborn, Philip. Cruise of the Dashing Wave: Rounding Cape Horn In 1860. Thiesen, William H., ed. 2010. (New Perspectives on Maritime History & Nautical Archaeology Ser.). (ENG., Illus.). 144p. 24.95 *(978-0-8130-3437-9(X))* Univ. Pr. of Florida.

Hine, Robert V. Edward Kern & American Expansion. 2011. 240p. 46.95 ***(978-1-258-07091-5(X))*** Literary Licensing, LLC.

Hoffer, Peter Charles. The Brave New World: A History of Early America. 2nd ed. 2006. (ENG., Illus.). 544p. (C). (gr. 13-17). pap. 26.00 *(978-0-8018-8483-2(7))* Johns Hopkins Univ. Pr.

Holmes, Abiel. American Annals: A Chronological History of America, 2 vol., set. reprint ed. 250.00 *(978-0-7222-7038-7(0))* Library Reprints, Inc.

Horwitz, Tony. A Voyage Long & Strange: On the Trail of Vikings, Conquistadors, Lost Colonists, & Other Adventurers in Early America. 2009. (ENG., Illus.). 464p. pap. 18.00 *(978-0-312-42832-7(4))* Picador.

—A Voyage Long & Strange: Rediscovering the New World. 2008. (ENG., Illus.). 464p. 27.50 *(978-0-8050-7603-5(4))* Holt, Henry & Co.

—A Voyage Long & Strange: Rediscovering the New World. l.t. ed. 2008. 696p. 32.95 *(978-1-4104-0558-6(3))* Thorndike Pr.

Hovgaard, William. Voyages of the Norsemen to America. 304p. reprint ed. 98.00 *(978-0-7222-6449-2(6))* Library Reprints, Inc.

Hume, Stephen. Simon Fraser: In Search of Modern British Columbia. unabr. ed. 2008. (ENG., Illus.). 336p. 36.95 *(978-1-55017-434-2(7))* Harbour Publishing Co., Ltd. CAN. Dist: Ingram Pub. Services.

Hunter, Douglas. Half Moon: Henry Hudson & the Voyage That Redrew the Map of the New World. (ENG., Illus.). 336p. 2010. pap. 18.00 *(978-1-60819-098-0(6))* 2009. 28.00 *(978-1-59691-680-7(X))* Bloomsbury Publishing.

Hunter, Douglas. The Race to the New World: Christopher Columbus, John Cabot, & a Lost History of Discovery. 2012. (ENG.). 288p. pap. 17.00 ***(978-0-230-34165-4(9))*** Palgrave Macmillan.

Irving, Washington. The Life & Voyages of Christopher Columbus. 2008. 584p. 36.99 *(978-0-554-23748-0(2))*; 33.99 *(978-0-554-33051-8(2))* BiblioBazaar.

—The Life & Voyages of Christopher Columbus. 2007. (ENG.). 496p. per. 24.95 *(978-1-60206-378-5(8))*; 520p. per. 24.95 *(978-1-60206-377-8(X))* Cosimo, Inc.

—Voyages & Discoveries of the Companions of Columbus. 2009. 214p. pap. *(978-0-217-41639-9(X))* Books LLC.

—Voyages & Discoveries of the Companions of Columbus. 2007. (ENG.). 416p. per. 24.95 *(978-1-60206-282-5(X))* Cosimo, Inc.

—Voyages & Discoveries of the Companions of Columbus. 2008. 352p. 46.95 *(978-0-548-93298-8(0))* 2007. (ENG.). 356p. per. 31.95 *(978-0-548-56670-1(4))* Kessinger Publishing, LLC.

James's Accounts of S. H. Long's Expedition, 1819-20. 15. 20.00 *(978-0-404-06545-4(7))*16. 20.00 *(978-0-404-06546-1(5))*17. 20.00 *(978-0-404-06547-8(3))*Pts. 1-4. 20.00 *(978-0-404-06544-7(9))* AMS Pr., Inc.

Jane, Cecil, ed. Select Documents illustrating the Four Voyages of Columbus: Including those contained in R. H. Major's Select Letters of Christopher Columbus: the First & Second Voyages. 2010. (Hakluyt Society, Second Ser.). 344p. 69.95 *(978-1-4094-1432-2(9))* Hakluyt Society GBR. Dist: Ashgate Publishing Co.

Jane, Cecil & Taylor, E. G. R., eds. Select Documents illustrating the Four Voyages of Columbus: Including those contained in R. H. Major's Select Letters of Christopher Columbus: the Third & Fourth Voyages. 2010. (Hakluyt Society, Second Ser.). 254p. 69.95 *(978-1-4094-1437-7(X))* Hakluyt Society GBR. Dist: Ashgate Publishing Co.

Jennings, Francis. The Invasion of America: Indians, Colonialism, & the Cant of Conquest. 2010. (Published for the Omohundro Institute of Early American History & Culture, Williamsburg, Virginia Ser.). (ENG., Illus.). 392p. pap. 24.95 *(978-0-8078-7144-7(3))* Univ. of North Carolina Pr.

Jerome. Early Celts in Americ. 2011. 50p. 36.95 ***(978-1-258-01821-4(7))*** Literary Licensing, LLC.

Johnson, Bob & Westin, Janey. The Last Kings of Norse America: Runestone Keys to a Lost Empire. 2012. 29.95 ***(978-1-59298-419-0(3))*** Beaver's Pond Pr., Inc.

Johnson, Christine R. The German Discovery of the World: Renaissance Encounters with the Strange & Marvelous. (Studies in Early Modern German History Ser.). (ENG., 320p. 2009. Illus.). (C). (gr. 13-17). pap. 22.50 *(978-0-8139-2734-3(X))* 2008. (gr. 17). 45.00 *(978-0-8139-2712-1(9))* Univ. Pr. of Virginia.

Johnson, Kirk. Cruisin' the Fossil Freeway. 2007. (ENG., Illus.). 208p. pap. 29.95 *(978-1-55591-451-6(9))* Fulcrum Publishing.

Johnson, William Henry. French Pathfinders in North America. 2008. 196p. 25.99 *(978-0-554-29937-2(2))* 2007. (ENG.). 176p. pap. 19.99 *(978-1-4346-8774-6(0))* 2007. 192p. pap. 21.99 *(978-1-4346-8775-3(9))* BiblioBazaar.

—French Pathfinders in North America. 2008. (Illus.). 188p. pap. *(978-1-4065-9943-5(3))* Dodo Pr.

—French Pathfinders in North America. 2009. 376p. 48.95 *(978-1-120-83119-4(9))*; pap. 33.95 *(978-1-120-62272-3(7))* Kessinger Publishing, LLC.

—French Pathfinders in North America. 347p. reprint ed. 98.00 *(978-0-7222-6418-8(6))* Library Reprints, Inc.

—Pioneer Spaniards in North America. 381p. reprint ed. 98.00 *(978-0-7222-6514-7(X))* Library Reprints, Inc.

Johnston, Harry Hamilton. Pioneers in Tropical America. 320p. reprint ed. 98.00 *(978-0-7222-9533-5(2))*; 98.00 *(978-0-7222-6420-1(8))* Library Reprints, Inc.

—Pioneers in Tropical America. 2006. 340p. per. *(978-1-4067-2269-7(3)*, Hesperides Pr.) Read Bks.

Johnston, Thomas Crawford. Did the Phoenicians Discover America? 2010. 148p. pap. *(978-1-152-23193-1(6))* Books LLC.

—Did the Phoenicians Discover America? 2008. 316p. 45.95 *(978-0-548-95963-3(3))* 2007. (ENG.). 320p. per. 30.95 *(978-0-548-63495-0(5))* Kessinger Publishing, LLC.

—Did the Phoenicians Discover America? 298p. reprint ed. 98.00 *(978-0-7222-6451-5(8))* Library Reprints, Inc.

Jones, Terry. Polynesians in America: Pre-Columbian Contacts with the New World. 2011. (ENG.). 380p. 85.00 *(978-0-7591-2004-4(8))* AltaMira Pr.

Jones, Terry L. Polynesians in America: Pre-Columbian Contacts with the New World. 2010. *(978-0-7591-2006-8(4))* AltaMira Pr.

Kayserling, Meyer. Christopher Columbus & the Participation of the Jews in the Spanish & Portuguese Discoveries. 2009. 128p. pap. *(978-1-150-06215-5(0))* Books LLC.

—Christopher Columbus & the Participation of the Jews in the Spanish & Portuguese Discoveries. Gross, Charles, tr. 2007. (ENG.). 204p. 39.95 *(978-0-548-16606-2(4))*; per. 24.95 *(978-1-4304-6289-7(2))* Kessinger Publishing, LLC.

Kennedy, William. A Short Narrative of the Second Voyage of the Prince Albert , in Search of Sir John Franklin. 2006. (Illus.). 202p. 85.00 *(978-1-57898-587-6(0))* Martino Publishing.

King, Grace. De Soto & His Men in the Land of Florida. 2008. 358p. 46.95 *(978-0-548-98885-5(4))* 2007. (ENG.). 360p. per. 31.95 *(978-0-548-65842-0(0))* Kessinger Publishing, LLC.

—De Soto & His Men in the Land of Florida. (Illus.). 326p. reprint ed. lib. bdg. 98.00 *(978-0-7222-0190-9(7))* Library Reprints, Inc.

Kirke, Henry. The First English Conquest of Canada: With Some Account of the Earlistsettlements in Nova Scotia & Newfoundland. 227p. reprint ed. 98.00 *(978-0-7222-6810-0(6))* Library Reprints, Inc.

Kohut, Karl. Narración y Reflexión: Las Crónicas de Indias y la Teoría Historiográfica. 2007. (Estudios Lingüísticos y Literarios Ser.). (SPA.). 268p. pap. 14.99 *(978-968-12-1295-7(9))* El Colegio de México, A.C., Biblioteca Miguel Cosío Villegas MEX. Dist: Fondo de Cultura Economica USA.

Kruger, F. (Franz). The First Discovery of America, & Its Early Civilization Translated & Enlarged from the German of Dr F Kruger, by W L Wagener, Professor of L. 2006. 140p. per. 16.99 *(978-1-4255-0984-2(3))* MPublishing.

Ladue, Joseph. Klondyke Nuggets. 2007. (ENG.). 82p. per. 16.99 *(978-1-4346-9717-2(7))*; 90p. per. 18.99 *(978-1-4346-9718-9(5))* BiblioBazaar.

—Klondyke Nuggets. 2007. 80p. per. *(978-1-4065-2554-0(5))* Dodo Pr.

—Klondyke Nuggets. 2006. (ENG.). pap. *(978-1-4068-1333-3(8))* Echo Library.

Lamana, Gonzalo. Domination Without Dominance: Inca-Spanish Encounters in Early Colonial Peru. 2008. (Latin America Otherwise Ser.). (ENG.). 304p. pap. 24.95 *(978-0-8223-4311-0(8))*; 89.95 *(978-0-8223-4293-9(6))* Duke Univ. Pr.

Lamb, W. Kaye, ed. The Letters & Journals of Simon Fraser, 1806-1808. 2007. (ENG., Illus.). 328p. pap. 24.99 *(978-1-55002-713-6(1)*, Dundurn Pr.) Dundurn CAN. Dist: Ingram Pub. Services.

Lamprey, L. Days of the Discoverers. 2007. (Illus.). 276p. per. *(978-1-4065-2588-5(X))* Dodo Pr.

—Days of the Discoverers. 2009. 188p. pap. *(978-1-4068-5133-5(7))* Echo Library.

Lane, Kris, ed. Defending the Conquest: Bernardo de Vargas Machuca's Defense & Discourse of the Western Conquests. Johnson, Timothy F., tr. from SPA. 2010. (Latin American Originals Ser.). 160p. pap. 26.95 *(978-0-271-02937-5(4))* Pennsylvania State Univ. Pr.

Laut, Agnes C. Vikings of the Pacific. 2009. 268p. 25.99 *(978-0-559-06389-3(X))*; 28.99 *(978-0-559-06375-6(X))*; pap. 26.75 *(978-0-559-06386-2(5))*; pap. 27.75 *(978-0-559-06379-4(2))* BiblioBazaar.

—Vikings of the Pacific. 2007. (ENG., Illus.). 256p. per. *(978-1-4065-3593-8(1))* Dodo Pr.

Laut, C. Agnes. Vikings of the Pacific. 2007. 208p. (ENG.). 96.99 *(978-1-4280-7647-1(6))*; per. 90.99 *(978-1-4280-7630-3(1))* IndyPublish.com.

Leacock, Stephen. The Dawn of Canadian History: A Chronicle of Aboriginal Canada & the Coming of the White Man. (Chronicles of Canada Ser.). 112p. reprint ed. 88.00 *(978-0-7222-6470-6(4))*; 88.00 *(978-0-7222-6773-8(8))* Library Reprints, Inc.

—The Mariner of St. Malo: Chronicle of the Voyages of Jacques Cartier. (Chronicles of Canada Ser.). 125p. reprint ed. 88.00 *(978-0-7222-6774-5(6))* Library Reprints, Inc.

—The Nonsense Novels & the Dawn of Canadian History. 2008. 192p. 22.99 *(978-0-554-36136-9(1))* 2008. 192p. 25.99 *(978-0-554-26833-0(7))* 2007. (ENG.). 166p. pap. 19.99 *(978-1-4346-1959-4(1))* 2007. (ENG.). 188p. pap. 21.99 *(978-1-4346-1983-9(4))* BiblioBazaar.

Lehmkuhl, Ursula & Rinke, Stefan H. Amerika, Amerikas: Zur Geschichte Eines Namens Von 1507 Bis Zur Gegenwart. 2008. (GER., Illus.). 250p. *(978-3-88099-687-8(3))* Heinz, Hans-Dieter Akademischer Verlag, Verlag.

Leland, Charles. Fusang or, the Discovery of America: By Chinese Buddhist Priests in the Fifth Century. 2007. 236p. per. 20.45 *(978-1-60206-301-3(X))* Cosimo, Inc.

Leland, Charles Godfrey. Fusang: Or, the Discovery of America by Chinese Buddhist Priests in the Fifth Century. 2009. 236p. 23.99 *(978-1-103-80619-5(X))*; pap. 17.99 *(978-1-103-80613-3(0))* BiblioBazaar.

Lescarbot, Marc. History of New France, 3 vol., set. (Publications of the Champlain Society). reprint ed. 375.00 *(978-0-7222-6738-7(X))* Library Reprints, Inc.

Lester, C. Edwards. The Life & Voyages of Americus Vespucius. 2007. (ENG.). 460p. 52.95 *(978-0-548-04572-5(0))* Kessinger Publishing, LLC.

Levy, Buddy. River of Darkness: Francisco Orellana's Legendary Voyage of Death & Discovery down the Amazon. 2011. (ENG., Illus.). 352p. 27.00 *(978-0-553-80750-9(1))* Random House Publishing Group.

Levy, Philip. Fellow Travelers: Indians & Europeans Contesting the Early American Trail. 2007. (ENG.). 216p. 59.95 *(978-0-8130-3058-6(7))* Univ. Pr. of Florida.

Linton, Joan Pong. The Romance of the New World: Gender & the Literary Formations of English Colonialism. 2006. (Cambridge Studies in Renaissance Literature & Culture Ser.). (ENG.). 284p. pap. 60.00 *(978-0-521-59457-8(X))* Cambridge Univ. Pr.

Loker, Aleck. Ancient Explorers of America: From the Ice Age to Columbus. 2009. pap. 16.95 *(978-1-928874-19-5(3))* Solitude Pr.

Lord, Arthur. Plymouth & the Pilgrims. 2009. 188p. 26.99 *(978-1-110-57385-1(5))*; pap. 21.75 *(978-1-110-57384-4(7))*; 22.99 *(978-1-103-40391-2(5))*; pap. 16.99 *(978-1-103-40387-5(7))* BiblioBazaar.

—Plymouth & the Pilgrims. 2007. (ENG.). 186p. 37.95 *(978-0-548-04582-4(8))* Kessinger Publishing, LLC.

—Plymouth & the Pilgrims. 2008. 188p. pap. *(978-1-4097-6662-9(4))* Read Bks.

Lord, Arthur H. Plymouth & the Pilgrims. 177p. reprint ed. 88.00 *(978-0-7222-6683-0(9))* Library Reprints, Inc.

Lowery, Woodbury. The Spanish Settlements Within the Present Limits of the United States. 500p. reprint ed. 98.00 *(978-0-7222-6516-1(6))* Library Reprints, Inc.

—The Spanish Settlements Within the Present Limits of the United States Set, 2 vols. (Illus.). reprint ed. lib. bdg. 250.00 *(978-0-7222-0192-3(3))* Library Reprints, Inc.

—The Spanish Settlements Within the Present Limits of the United States, 1513-1561. 2007. 536p. 57.95 *(978-0-548-56050-1(1))*; (ENG.). per. 42.95 *(978-0-548-50186-3(6))* Kessinger Publishing, LLC.

—The Spanish Settlements Within the Present Limits of the United States, 1513-1561. 515p. reprint ed. 98.00 *(978-0-7222-6515-4(8))* Library Reprints, Inc.

Luca de Tena, Torcuato. America y Sus Enigmas (American & Its Enigmas) (SPA.). 224p. *(978-84-08-00122-5(1))* GeoPlaneta, Editorial, S. A.

Luca, Frederic William. Appendiculae Historicae. 216p. reprint ed. 98.00 *(978-0-7222-6739-4(8))* Library Reprints, Inc.

Lummis, Charles Fletcher. The Spanish Pioneers. 2009. 156p. pap. *(978-1-150-50523-2(0))* Books LLC.

—The Spanish Pioneers. 292p. reprint ed. 98.00 *(978-0-7222-6517-8(4))* Library Reprints, Inc.

Lutz, John S. Myth & Memory: Stories of Indigenous-European Contact. Lutz, John Sutton, ed. 2007. (ENG., Illus.). 248p. *(978-0-7748-1262-7(1))* Univ. of British Columbia Pr.

Magasich-Airola, Jorge & de Beer, Jean-Marc. When Renaissance Europe Thought It Had Conquered Paradise. Sandor, Monica, tr. from FRE. 2nd rev. ed. 2007. (Anthem History Ser.). (ENG., Illus.). 226p. per. 22.95 *(978-1-84331-292-5(1))* Anthem Pr. GBR. Dist: Books International, Inc.

Mancall, Peter & Johnson, Benjamin Heber, eds. Making of the American West: People & Perspectives, 1 vol. 2007. (Perspectives in American Social History Ser.). (Illus.). 372p. 85.00 *(978-1-85109-763-0(5)*, WESTEX1C) ABC-CLIO, LLC.

Mancall, Peter C. Fatal Journey: The Final Expedition of Henry Hudson. 2010. (ENG., Illus.). 320p. (gr. 9). pap. 16.95 *(978-0-465-02031-7(3))* Basic Bks.

Mapp, Paul W. The Elusive West & the Contest for Empire, 1713-1763. 2011. (Published for the Omohundro Institute of Early American History & Culture, Williamsburg, Virginia Ser.). (ENG., Illus.). 472p. 49.95 *(978-0-8078-3395-7(9))* Univ. of North Carolina Pr.

Marchand, Philip. Ghost Empire: How the French Almost Conquered North America, 1 vol. 2007. (Illus.). 480p. 49.95 *(978-0-275-99417-4(1)*, C9417, Praeger Pubs.) Greenwood Publishing Group, Inc.

Marino, Ruggero. Christopher Columbus, the Last Templar. Godwin, Ariel, tr. from ITA. 2007. (ENG., Illus.). 1p. per. 19.95 *(978-1-59477-190-3(1)*, Destiny Bks.) Inner Traditions International, Ltd.

Markham, Clements, ed. Early Spanish Voyages to the Strait of Magellan. 2010. (Hakluyt Society, Second Ser.). 312p. 69.95 *(978-1-4094-1395-0(0))* Hakluyt Society GBR. Dist: Ashgate Publishing Co.

Markham, Clements R. Letters of Amerigo Vespucci & Other Do. 2006. pap. 22.95 *(978-1-4286-4723-7(6))* Kessinger Publishing, LLC.

Martin, Jose Maria Moreno, text. The Malaspina Expedition. 2010. (ENG., Illus.). 160p. 45.00 *(978-84-7506-954-8(1))* Turner, Ediciones S.A. ESP. Dist: D.A.P./Distributed Art Pubs.

Menzies, Gavin. 1421: The Year China Discovered America. 2008. (P. S. Ser.). (Illus.). 672p. pap. 15.99 *(978-0-06-156489-5(3)*, William Morrow Paperbacks) HarperCollins Pubs.

Merrill, Charles J. Colom of Catalonia: Origins of Christopher Columbus Revealed. 2008. (ENG., Illus.). 312p. pap. 16.95 *(978-0-9816002-2-2(0))* Demers Bks. LLC.

Mertz, Henriette. Pale Ink: Two Ancient Records of Chinese Exploration in America. 2008. (ENG.). 158p. pap. 20.75 *(978-1-4375-1907-5(5))*; 174p. pap. 22.75 *(978-1-4375-1908-2(3))* BiblioBazaar.

Miller, David E. Hole in the Rock: An Epic in the Colonization of the Great American West. 2011. 254p. 47.95 ***(978-1-258-08143-0(1))*** Literary Licensing, LLC.

Miller, Robert J. Native America, Discovered & Conquered: Thomas Jefferson, Lewis & Clark, & Manifest Destiny, 1 vol. 2006. (Native America Ser.). 240p. 49.95 *(978-0-275-99011-4(7)*, C9011, Praeger Pubs.) Greenwood Publishing Group, Inc.

Morris, Charles. Heroes of Discovery in America. 344p. reprint ed. 98.00 *(978-0-7222-6422-5(4))* Library Reprints, Inc.

Munduruku, Daniel. Banquete dos Deuses. (POR.). 126p. pap. 19.95 *(978-85-85969-15-8(6))* Angra Ltda, Editora BRA. Dist: Distribooks, Inc.

Murphy, Henry C. The Voyage of Verrazzano. 2008. 160p. 25.99 *(978-0-554-21968-4(9))* 2008. 160p. 22.99 *(978-0-554-31271-2(9))* 2006. (ENG.). 166p. pap. 19.99 *(978-1-4264-1419-0(6))* 2006. (ENG.). 158p. pap. 21.99 *(978-1-4264-1401-5(3))* BiblioBazaar.

Myers, Kathleen Ann. Fernández de Oviedo's Chronicle of America: A New History for a New World. Scott, Nina M., tr. 2010. (ENG., Illus.). 344p. pap. 30.00 *(978-0-292-72612-3(0))* Univ. of Texas Pr.

Nansen, Fridtjof. In Northern Mists: Arctic Exploration in Early Times, 2 vols. Chater, Arthur G., tr. (Illus.). reprint ed. 94.50 *(978-0-404-01955-6(2))* AMS Pr., Inc.

Nash & Cram101 Textbook Reviews Staff. Red, White, & Black: The Peoples of Early North America. 2007. 132p. per. 11.95 *(978-1-4288-2800-1(1))* Cram101 Inc.

Nash, Gary B. Red, White, & Black. 6th ed. 2009. (ENG.). 320p. (C). pap. 78.80 *(978-0-205-69237-8(0)*, Prentice Hall) Prentice Hall PTR.

Nicholls, Steve. Paradise Found: Nature in America at the Time of Discovery. 536p. 2011. (ENG.). pap. 20.00 *(978-0-226-58341-9(4))* 2009. 30.00 *(978-0-226-58340-2(6))* Univ. of Chicago Pr.

Nichols, A. Bryant, Jr. Captain Christopher Newport: Admiral of Virginia. 2007. (Illus.). 210p. per. 18.95 *(978-0-615-14001-8(7))* Sea Venture LLC.

Nichols, Philip. Sir Francis Drake Revived. 2007. (ENG.). 80p. pap. 17.75 *(978-1-4375-0050-9(1))*; 88p. pap. 18.75 *(978-1-4375-0051-6(X))* BiblioBazaar.

—Sir Francis Drake Revived. 2009. 60p. pap. *(978-1-4068-5269-1(4))* Echo Library.

—Sir Francis Drake Revived. 2010. (Illus.). 54p. pap. 20.00 *(978-1-153-73887-3(2))* General Bks. LLC.

—Sir Francis Drake Revived. 2010. 68p. pap. 13.56 *(978-1-162-68402-4(X))*; 25.56 ***(978-1-169-21970-0(5))***; 31.95 *(978-1-161-45267-9(2))* Kessinger Publishing, LLC.

Nichols, Philip, ed. Sir Francis Drake Revived. 2007. (ENG.). 76p. per. *(978-1-4065-4045-1(5))* Dodo Pr.

Nisbet, Jack. Sources of the River: Tracking David Thompson Across Western North America. 2nd ed. 2007. (ENG., Illus.). 288p. per. 16.95 *(978-1-57061-522-1(5))* Sasquatch Bks.

Nordyke, Eleanor C. Pacific Images: Views from Captain Cook's Third Voyage. 2nd rev. ed. 2008. (Illus.). 228p. 75.00 *(978-1-883528-37-9(2))* Ai Pohaku Pr.

The Norse's Discovery of America. (Anglo-Saxon Classics Ser.). 343p. reprint ed. 98.00 *(978-0-7222-6450-8(X))* Library Reprints, Inc.

Nunez Cabeza de Vaca, Alvar. The Journey of Alvar Nunez Cabeza De Vaca & His Companions from Florida to the Pacific, 1528-1536. 231p. reprint ed. 98.00 *(978-0-7222-6442-3(9))* Library Reprints, Inc.

Núñez Cabeza de Vaca, Alvar & Morrow, Baker H. The South American Expeditions, 1540-1545. 2011. ***(978-0-8263-5065-7(8))*** Univ. of New Mexico Pr.

Onderdonk, James Lawrence. Precolumbian Discoveries of America. 2011. 34p. pap. 11.99 ***(978-1-4181-9404-8(2))*** MPublishing.

Original Narratives of Early American History: Reproduced under the Auspices of the American Historical Association, 19 vol., set. reprint ed. 2375.00 *(978-0-7222-7049-3(6))* Library Reprints, Inc.

Page, Thomas, abr. La Plata, the Argentine Confederation, & Paraguay. 2009. (Military History Ser.). (ENG.). 630p. pap. 36.95 *(978-1-4290-2195-1(0))* Applewood Bks.

Parkman, Francis. La Salle & the Discovery of the Great West. 2012. 524p. pap. 40.75 ***(978-1-279-27046-2(2))*** 2011. 308p. pap. 29.75 ***(978-1-178-85206-6(7))*** 2011. 526p. pap. 40.75 ***(978-1-178-85974-4(6))*** 2011. (France & England in North America Ser.: Vol. 3). 552p. pap. 42.75 ***(978-1-178-85493-0(0))*** 2010. (ENG.). 526p. pap. 40.75 *(978-1-171-51081-9(0))* 2010. (ENG.). 564p. pap. 43.75 *(978-1-177-28178-2(3))* 2010. 554p. pap. 42.75 *(978-1-177-52238-0(1))* 2010. 564p. pap. 43.75 *(978-1-177-79285-1(0))* 2010. 568p. pap. 43.75 *(978-1-148-12344-8(X))* 2010. 516p. pap. 39.75 *(978-1-142-10891-5(0))* 2010. (France & England in North America Ser.: Vol. 3). 592p. reprint ed. pap. 44.75 *(978-1-172-31285-6(0))* 2010. 520p. reprint ed. pap. 39.75 *(978-1-147-17858-6(5))* 2009. (France & England in North America Ser.: Pt. 3). 310p. reprint ed. pap. 24.99 *(978-1-116-42346-4(4)*, BiblioLife) 2009. (France & England in North America Ser.: Pt. 3). 310p. reprint ed. pap. 23.99 *(978-1-116-42347-1(2)*, BiblioLife) BiblioBazaar.

—Pioneers of France in the New World. 2010. (France & England in North America Ser.: Pt. 1). 520p. pap. 39.75 *(978-1-146-36349-5(4))* BiblioBazaar.

—Pioneers of France in the New World. 2009. (France & England in North America Ser.: Pt. 1). 460p. reprint ed. pap. 37.95 *(978-1-120-33674-3(0))* Kessinger Publishing, LLC.

—Works, 20 vols. (Illus.). reprint ed. 1395.00 *(978-0-404-04920-1(6))* AMS Pr., Inc.

Payne, Edward John. History of the New World Called America. 2009. 468p. pap. *(978-1-4590-8294-6(X))* Books LLC.

—History of the New World Called America. 2006. pap. 45.95 *(978-1-4286-3812-9(1))*; pap. 45.95 *(978-1-4286-3811-2(3))* Kessinger Publishing, LLC.

Peñaloza Fernanda, et al. Patagonia: Myths & Realities. 2010. 267p. pap. 61.95 *(978-3-03910-917-3(0))* Lang, Peter AG GBR. Dist: Lang, Peter.

Peterson, Barbara Bennett. Peopling of the Americas: Currents, Canoes, & DNA. 2011. (Focus on Civilizations & Cultures Ser.). (Illus.). 319p. 145.00 *(978-1-61122-137-4(4))* Nova Science Pubs., Inc.

Pickett, Margaret F. The European Struggle to Settle North America: Colonizing Attempts by England, France & Spain, 1521-1608. 2011. 38.00 ***(978-0-7864-6221-6(3))*** McFarland Pubs.

Pickett, Margaret F. & Pickett, Dwayne W. The European Struggle to Settle North America: Colonizing Attempts by England, France & Spain, 1521-1608. 2011. (ENG., Illus.). 264p. pap. 38.00 *(978-0-7864-5932-2(8))* McFarland & Co., Inc. Pubs.

Portuondo, Maria M. Secret Science: Spanish Cosmography & the New World. 2009. (Illus.). 360p. 45.00 *(978-0-226-67534-3(3))* Univ. of Chicago Pr.

Priestley, Herbert Ingram, ed. & intro. The Luna Papers, 1559-1561, Vols. 1&2. 2nd ed. 2010. (ENG., Illus.). 738p. pap. 70.00 *(978-0-8173-5606-4(1))* Univ. of Alabama Pr.

Quinn, David Beers, ed. The Roanoke Voyages, 1584-1590: Documents to Illustrate the English Voyages to North America under the Patent granted to Walter Raleigh in 1584. 2010. (Hakluyt Society, Second Ser.). 514p. 69.95 *(978-1-4094-1471-1(X))*; 532p. 69.95 *(978-1-4094-1470-4(1))* Hakluyt Society GBR. Dist: Ashgate Publishing Co.

—The Roanoke Voyages 1584-1590: Documents to Illustrate the English Voyages to North America under the Patent Granted to Walter Realeigh In 1584. 2010. (Hakluyt Society, Second Ser.). 1046p. 120.00 *(978-1-4094-2491-8(X))* Hakluyt Society GBR. Dist: Ashgate Publishing Co.

Ralegh. The Discoverie of the Large, Rich & Bewtiful Empyre of Guiana. (ENG., Illus.). 256p. *(978-0-7190-4899-9(0))* Manchester Univ. Pr.

Raleigh, Walter. The Discoverie of the Large, Rich & Bewtiful Empyre of Guiana. (ENG., Illus.). 256p. pap. *(978-0-7190-5176-0(2))* Manchester Univ. Pr.

—Discovery of the Large, Rich, & Beautiful Empire of Guiana: With a Relation of the Great & Golden City of Manoa... Performed in the Year 1595, by Sir W. Ralegh, Knt. Schomburgk, Robert H., ed. 2010. (Cambridge Library Collection - Travel & Exploration Ser.). (ENG., Illus.). 338p. pap. 28.99 *(978-1-108-00800-6(3))* Cambridge Univ. Pr.

Rand McNally Staff. Rand Mcnally Exploring with Lewis & Clark Big Book: People, Spaces, & Places. 2010. 29.00 *(978-0-528-67765-6(9))* Rand McNally.

Raynal Abbé. A Philosophical & Political History of the Settlements & Trade of the Europeans in the East & West Indies. 2006. 3008p. 1575.00 *(978-0-415-38311-0(0))* Routledge.

Raynolds, W. F. Report on the Exploration of the Yellowstone River. 2006. 180p. per. 18.99 *(978-1-4255-1478-5(2))* MPublishing.

Reel, Monte. The Last of the Tribe: The Epic Quest to Save a Lone Man in the Amazon. 2010. (ENG., Illus.). 288p. 26.00 *(978-1-4165-9474-1(4)*, Scribner) Scribner.

—The Last of the Tribe: The Epic Quest to Save a Lone Man in the Amazon. 2010. *(978-1-4165-9475-8(2)*, Scribner) Simon & Schuster.

Resendez, Andres, et al. A Land So Strange: The Epic Journey of Cabeza de Vaca: The Extraordinary Tale of a Shipwrecked Spaniard Who Walked Across America in the Sixteenth Century. 2009. (ENG., Illus.). 336p. pap. 16.95 *(978-0-465-06841-8(3))* Perseus Bks. Group.

Restall Matthew & Fernandez-Armesto, Felipe. The Conquistadors: A Very Short Introduction, 1 vol. 2012. (Very Short Introductions Ser.). (ENG., Illus.). 128p. pap. 11.95 ***(978-0-19-539229-6(9))*** Oxford Univ. Pr., Inc.

Richman, Irving B. The Spanish Conquerors: A Chronicle of the Dawn of Empire Overseas. (Chronicles of America Ser.). 238p. reprint ed. 98.00 *(978-0-7222-9575-5(8))* Library Reprints, Inc.

Richman, Irving Berdine. The Spanish Conquerors: A Chronicle of the Dawn of Empire Overseas. 2008. 248p. 24.99 *(978-0-559-79495-7(9))*; pap. 25.75 *(978-0-559-79491-9(6))* BiblioBazaar.

—The Spanish Conquerors: A Chronicle of the Dawn of Empire Overseas. (Chronicles of America Ser.). 238p. reprint ed. 98.00 *(978-0-7222-7128-5(X))*; 98.00 *(978-0-7222-6518-5(2))* Library Reprints, Inc.

Rigdon, W. t. Mystic Chain of Discovery. 2011. 476p. 57.95 ***(978-1-258-04982-9(1))*** Literary Licensing, LLC.

Robertson, William. The History of the Discovery & Settlement of America, by William Robertson with an Account of His Life & Writings to Which Are Added Questions F. 2006. 608p. per. 34.99 *(978-1-4255-6500-8(X))* MPublishing.

Rountree, Helen C., et al. John Smith's Chesapeake Voyages, 1607-1609. 2008. (ENG.). 402p. pap. 19.95 *(978-0-8139-2728-2(5))* Univ. Pr. of Virginia.

Ruis. 500 Anos Fregados pero Cristianos.Tr. of 500 Years of Anguish yet Still Christian. (SPA., Illus.). 286p. 12.00 *(978-970-05-0357-8(7))* Grijalbo, Editorial MEX. Dist: Continental Bk. Co., Inc.

Rushforth, Brett & Mapp, Paul. Colonial North America & the Atlantic World: A History in Documents. 2008. (ENG.). 339p. (C). pap. 63.60 *(978-0-13-234237-7(5)*, Prentice Hall) Prentice Hall PTR.

Russell, Steve F. Lewis & Clark Across the Mountains: Mapping the Corps of Discovery Across Idaho. 2007. (Illus.). 120p. spiral bd. 20.00 *(978-0-931406-16-4(1))* Idaho State Historical Society.

Ruymbeke, B. Van, ed. Constructing Early Modern Empires: Proprietary Ventures in the Atlantic World, 1500-1750. 2007. (Atlantic World Ser.). (Illus.). 423p. *(978-90-04-15676-0(3))* BRILL.

Rye, William B., ed. The Discovery & Conquest of Terra Florida, by Don Ferdinando de Soto & Six Hundred Spaniards His Followers: Written by a Gentleman of Elvas, Employed in All the Actions, & Translated out of Portuguese. Hakluyt, Richard, tr. 2010. (Cambridge Library Collection - Travel & Exploration Ser.). (ENG., Illus.). 288p. pap. 23.99 *(978-1-108-00806-8(2))* Cambridge Univ. Pr.

Safier, Neil. Measuring the New World: Enlightenment Science & South America. 2008. (ENG., Illus.). 428p. 45.00 *(978-0-226-73355-5(6))* Univ. of Chicago Pr.

Sánchez Sorondo, Gabriel. Historia Oculta de la Conquista de América. 2009. (SPA., Illus.). 253p. *(978-84-9763-548-6(5))* Nowtilus, S.L., Ediciones.

Sandler Corey. Dreams & Obsession: The Tragic Legacy of the New World's Least Understood Explorer. 2008. (ENG., Illus.). 250p. 14.95 *(978-0-8065-2853-3(2)*, Citadel Pr.) Kensington Publishing Corp.

Santarem, Manuel Francisco de Barros. Researches Respecting Americus Vespucius, & His Voyages by the Viscount Santarem Tr by E V Childe. 2006. 224p. per. 20.99 *(978-1-4255-1889-9(3))* MPublishing.

Sarmiento De Gamboa, Pedro & Sarmiento de Gamboa, Pedro. The History of the Incas. 2007. (Joe R. & Teresa Lozano Long Series in Latin American & Latino Art & Culture). (ENG., Illus.). 284p. pap. 19.95 *(978-0-292-71485-4(8))* Univ. of Texas Pr.

Sauer. The Early Spanish Main. 2008. (ENG., Illus.). 320p. pap. 42.00 *(978-0-521-08848-0(8))* Cambridge Univ. Pr.

Say, Thomas, et al. James's Account. 2007. (Travel in America Ser.). (ENG.). 360p. 49.95 *(978-1-4290-0085-7(6))*; 340p. 49.95 *(978-1-4290-0084-0(8))*; 300p. 49.95 *(978-1-4290-0086-4(4))*; 312p. 49.95 *(978-1-4290-0087-1(2))* Applewood Bks.

—James's Account of S. H. Long's Expedition, Vol. 1. 2007. (Travel in America Ser.). (ENG.). 340p. per. 24.95 *(978-1-4290-0088-8(0))* Applewood Bks.

Schneider, Paul. Brutal Journey: Cabeza de Vaca & the Epic First Crossing of North America. 2007. (ENG., Illus.). 384p. pap. 16.99 *(978-0-8050-8320-0(0)*, Owl Bks.) Holt, Henry & Co.

Schomburgk, Robert H. The Guiana Travels of Robert Schomburgk 1835-1844, 2 vols. Riviere, Peter, ed. 2007. (Hakluyt Society, Third Ser.). (Illus.). 280p. 99.95 *(978-0-904180-88-6(3))* Hakluyt Society GBR. Dist: Ashgate Publishing Co.

Seaver, Kirsten A. The Last Vikings: The Epic Story of the Great Norse Voyagers. 2010. (ENG., Illus.). 288p. 30.00 *(978-1-84511-869-3(3))* I. B. Tauris & Co., Ltd. GBR. Dist: Macmillan.

Shipp, Barnard. The History of Hernando de Soto & Florida. (Illus.). reprint ed. lib. bdg. 125.00 *(978-0-7222-0186-2(9))* Library Reprints, Inc.

Simpson, Thomas. Narrative of the Discoveries on the North Coast of America, Effected by the Officers of the Hudson's Bay Company During the Years 1836-39. reprint ed. 52.50 *(978-0-404-11685-9(X))* AMS Pr., Inc.

Slafter, Edmund F., ed. Sir William Alexander & American Colonization: Including Three Royal Charters. 2007. (ENG.). 290p. 43.95 *(978-0-548-21515-9(4))*; 292p. per. 28.95 *(978-1-4325-3488-2(2))* Kessinger Publishing, LLC.

Slafter, Edmund Farwell. Sir William Alexander & American Colonization. 2009. 300p. 24.99 *(978-1-103-52040-4(7))*; pap. 18.99 *(978-1-103-52036-7(9))* BiblioBazaar.

—Sir William Alexander & American Colonization. 2009. 182p. pap. 19.99 *(978-0-217-79134-2(4))* General Bks. LLC.

Slafter, Edmund Farwell, et al. Sir William Alexander & American Colonization: Including Three Royal Charters; a Tract on Colonization; a Patent of the County of Canada & of Lo. 2010. 314p. pap. 29.75 *(978-1-146-57595-6(3))* BiblioBazaar.

Sloan, Kim. A New World: England's First View of America. 2007. (ENG., Illus.). 256p. 69.95 *(978-0-8078-3125-0(5))*; pap. 34.95 *(978-0-8078-5825-7(0))* Univ. of North Carolina Pr.

Smith, John E. & Horn, James. Captain John Smith Writings: With Selected Narratives of the Exploration & Settlement of Virginia. Horn, James, ed. 2007. (ENG., Illus.). 1200p. (gr. 12). 45.00 *(978-1-59853-001-8(1))* Library of America, The.

Spanish Explorers in the Southern United States, 1528-1543. (Original Narratives of Early American History Ser.). 411p. reprint ed. 98.00 *(978-0-7222-6519-2(0))* Library Reprints, Inc.

Stanley, Richard T. A Humorous Account of America's Past: 986 To 1898. 2009. (Illus.). 612p. pap. 34.95 *(978-1-4401-3041-0(8))* iUniverse, Inc.

Stansbury, Howard. An Expedition to the Valley of the Great Salt Lake of Utah: Including a Description of its Geography, Natural History & Minerals, & an Analysis of its Waters, with an Authentic Account of the Mormon Settlement. 2011. (Cambridge Library Collection - Travel & Exploration Ser.). (ENG., Illus.). 610p. pap. 43.00 ***(978-1-108-03336-7(9))*** Cambridge Univ. Pr.

Stewart, Chris. Seven Miracles That Saved America. 2010. 43.99 *(978-1-60641-867-3(X))* 2009. 356p. 27.95 *(978-1-60641-144-5(6))* Deseret Bk. Co. (Shadow Mountain).

Stock, Eugene. Metlakahtla & the North Pacific Mission of the Church Missionary Society. 2008. 168p. 25.99 *(978-0-554-25563-7(4))* 2008. 168p. 22.99 *(978-0-554-34866-7(7))* 2007. (ENG.). 152p. pap. 19.99 *(978-1-4264-9458-1(0))* 2007. (ENG.). 166p. pap. 21.99 *(978-1-4264-9551-9(X))* BiblioBazaar.

Strachey, William. Historie of Travaile into Virginia Britannia: Expressing the Cosmographie & Comodities of the Country, Together with the Manners & Customes of the People. 2010. (Cambridge Library Collection - Travel & Exploration Ser.). (ENG., Illus.). 274p. pap. 23.99 *(978-1-108-00803-7(8))* Cambridge Univ. Pr.

Taylor, E. G. R. Select Documents Illustrating the Four Voyages of Columbus: Including Those Contained in R. H. Major's Select Letters of Christopher Columbus. Jane, Cecil, ed. 2010. (Hakluyt Society, Second Ser.). 598p. 120.00 *(978-1-4094-2484-0(7))* Hakluyt Society GBR. Dist: Ashgate Publishing Co.

Thomas, Hugh. The Golden Empire: Spain, Charles V, & the Creation of America. 2011. (ENG., Illus.). 672p. 35.00 *(978-1-4000-6125-9(3))* Random Hse., Inc.

Thompson, Gunnar. Secret Voyages to the New World. 2010. 251p. pap. 21.95 *(978-0-557-23165-2(5))* Lulu Enterprises Inc.

Thompson, Gunnar, creator. Secret Voyages to the New World: Nine True Adventures from the Forbidden Chronicles of American Discovery. 2006. (Illus.). 300p. per. 40.00 *(978-0-9788916-0-2(0)*, SV) New World Discovery Institute.

Thwaites, Reuben Gold. Early Western Travels, 1748-1846: Part I of James' Account of S. H. Long's Expedition, 1819-1820, Vol. XIV. 2007. cd-rom 15.95 *(978-0-7884-4416-6(6))* Heritage Bks.

—Early Western Travels, 1748-1846 Part II of James' Account of S. H. Long's Expedition, 1819-1820, Vol. XV. 2007. cd-rom 15.95 *(978-0-7884-4414-2(X))* Heritage Bks.

—Early Western Travels, 1748-1846 Part III of James's Account of S. H. Long's Expedition, 1819-1820, Vol. XVI. 2007. cd-rom 15.95 *(978-0-7884-4426-5(3))* Heritage Bks.

—Early Western Travels, 1748-1846 Part IV of James' Account of S. H. Long's Expedition, 1819-1820, Vol. XVII. 2007. cd-rom 15.95 *(978-0-7884-4424-1(7))* Heritage Bks.

Ulloa, Antonio de. A Voyage to South America: Describing at Large the Spanish Cities, Towns, Provinces, etc. on that Extensive Continent. 2011. (Cambridge Library Collection - Travel & Exploration Ser.). (ENG., Illus.). 536p. pap. 39.99 *(978-1-108-03168-4(4))* Cambridge Univ. Pr.

United States. Army. Corps Of Engineers. Report of a Reconnaissance of the Black Hills of Dakota, Made in the Summer of 1874 by William Ludlow, Captain of Engineers, Bvt Lieut Colonel, U S. 2011. 128p. pap. 16.99 ***(978-1-4255-0886-9(3))*** MPublishing.

United States. War Dept. Exploration of the Red River of Louisiana, in the Year 1852. 2006. 436p. per. 26.99 *(978-1-4255-4765-3(6))* MPublishing.

—Exploration of the Red River of Louisiana in the Year 1852, by Randolph B Marcy; Assisted by George B Mcclellan with Reports on the Natural History. 2006. 392p. per. 26.99 *(978-1-4255-4155-2(0))* MPublishing.

—Report of an Expedition up the Yellowstone River Made in 1875, by James W Forsyth & F D Grant, under the Orders of Lieutenantgeneral P H Sheridan. 2011. 28p. pap. 11.99 ***(978-1-4181-9258-7(9))*** MPublishing.

—Reports of Explorations & Surveys, to Ascertain the Most Practicable & Economical Route for a Railroad from the Mississippi River to the Pacific O. 2011. 22p. pap. 11.99 ***(978-1-4181-9109-2(4))*** MPublishing.

Valdés, Gonzalo Fernández de Oviedo y. Misfortunes & Shipwrecks in the Seas of the Indies, Islands, & Mainland of the Ocean Sea (1513-1548) Book Fifty of theGeneral & Natural History of the Indies. 2011. (ENG., Illus.). 240p. 69.95 *(978-0-8130-3540-6(6))* Univ. Pr. of Florida.

Vespucci, Amerigo. The First Four Voyages of Amerigo Vespucci. Kearney, Michael, tr. 2007. (ENG.). 84p. per. 17.95 *(978-0-548-61840-0(2))* Kessinger Publishing, LLC.

—The First Four Voyages of Amerigo Vespucci. 2007. 45p. pap. 24.95 *(978-1-60105-139-4(5)*, 6D7P) Scholar's Bookshelf.

—Letters of Amerigo Vespucci, & Other Documents Illustrative of his Career. Markham, Clements R., tr. 2010. (Cambridge Library Collection - Travel & Exploration Ser.). (ENG.). 180p. pap. 19.99 *(978-1-108-01286-7(8))* Cambridge Univ. Pr.

Vignaud, Henry. The Columbian Tradition on the Discovery of America & of the Part Played Therin by the Astronomer Toscanelli: A Memoir Addressed to the Professor's Hermann Wagner of the University of Gottingen & Carlo Errara. 62p. reprint ed. 88.00 (978-0-7222-6439-3(9)) Library Reprints, Inc.

—Toscanelli & Columbus. 2009. 314p. pap. 20.12 (978-0-217-76811-5(3)) General Bks. LLC.

Viles, Donald M. Hidden Heritage of New Spain. 2006. (Illus.). 220p. per. 15.95 (978-1-892076-25-0(X)) Dancing Moon Pr.

Wagner, Henry Raup. Spanish Voyages to the Northwest Coast of America in the Sixteenth Century. 2009. 110.00 (978-1-57898-714-6(8)) Martino Publishing.

Wallace, David Rains. The Monkey's Bridge: Mysteries of Evolution in Central America. 2007. (ENG., Illus.). 280p. per. 18.95 (978-1-59534-040-5(8)) Trinity Univ. Pr.

Weber, David J. Barbaros: Spaniards & Their Savages in the Age of Enlightenment. 2006. (Lamar Series in Western History). (ENG., Illus.). 480p. per. 23.00 (978-0-300-11991-6(7)) Yale Univ. Pr.

Weekes, Don & Banks, Kerry. Hockey's Top 100: The Game's Greatest Records, 1 vol. 2008. (ENG., Illus.). 168p. pap. 15.95 (978-1-55365-274-8(6), Greystone Bks.) D&M Pubs. Inc. CAN. Dist: Perseus-PGW.

Weston Woods Staff, creator. Where Do You Think You're Going Chris. Columbus? 2011. 18.95 (978-0-439-72910-9(6)); 38.75 (978-0-439-72911-6(4)) Weston Woods Studios, Inc.

—Where Do You Think You're Going, Chris. Columbus? 2011. 29.95 (978-0-439-73527-8(0)) Weston Woods Studios, Inc.

Westward Expansion. tchr. ed. 149.00 incl. cd-rom (978-0-382-44442-5(6)) Cobblestone Publishing Co.

Wey-Gómez, Nicolás & Gomez, N. W. The Tropics of Empire: Why Columbus Sailed South to the Indies. 2008. (Transformations: Studies in the History of Science & Technology Ser.). (ENG., Illus.). 616p. (gr. 17). 42.95 (978-0-262-23264-7(2)) MIT Pr.

Whitehead, Neil L. Of Cannibals & Kings: Primal Anthropology in the Americas. 2010. (Latin American Originals Ser.). (Illus.). 136p. pap. 25.95 (978-0-271-03799-8(7)) Pennsylvania State Univ. Pr.

Wiener, Leo. Africa & the Discovery of America. 2009. 176p. pap. (978-1-151-73256-9(7)); 176p. pap. (978-1-151-73252-1(4)); 194p. pap. (978-1-151-73254-5(0)) Books LLC.

—Africa & the Discovery of America. 2011. (ENG., Illus.). 287p. pap. 15.95 (978-1-61759-002-3(9)) EWorld, Inc.

—Africa & the Discovery of America, 3 vol., set. reprint ed. 375.00 (978-0-7222-6426-3(7)) Library Reprints, Inc.

Williams, William Carlos. In the American Grain. 2nd ed. 2009. (ENG.). 272p. pap. 13.95 (978-0-8112-1849-8(X), 21849) New Directions Publishing Corp.

Williamson, James A. & Skelton, R. A., eds. The Cabot Voyages & Bristol Discovery under Henry VII. 2010. (Hakluyt Society, Second Ser.). 348p. 69.95 (978-1-4094-1486-5(8)) Hakluyt Society GBR. Dist: Ashgate Publishing Co.

Willingham, Elizabeth Moore. The Mythical Indies & Columbus's Apocalyptic Letter: Imagining the Americas in the Late Middle Ages. 2012. (ENG., Illus.). 256p. 82.50 (978-1-84519-497-0(7)); pap. 39.95 (978-1-84519-498-7(5)) Sussex Academic Pr. GBR. Dist: International Specialized Bk. Services.

Winsor, Justin. Narrative & Critical History of America. 2010. 588p. pap. (978-1-152-85148-1(9)) 2010. 710p. pap. (978-1-151-75086-0(7)) 2009. 626p. pap. (978-1-151-75084-6(0)) Books LLC.

—Narrative & Critical History of America, 8 vol., set. reprint ed. 1000.00 (978-0-7222-6428-7(3)) Library Reprints, Inc.

Winsor, Justin, ed. Narrative & Critical History of America, 8 vols. reprint ed. 700.00 (978-0-404-07010-6(8)) AMS Pr., Inc.

Wolter, Scott. The Hooked X: Key to the Secret History of North America. 2009. pap. 18.95 (978-0-87839-312-1(9)) North Star Pr. of St. Cloud.

Wright, Irene A. Futher English Voyages to Spanish Americ. 2006. 428p. per. (978-1-4067-1780-8(0), Hesperides Pr.) Read Bks.

Wright, Irene A., ed. Documents concerning English Voyages to the Spanish Main, 1569-1580: I . Spanish Documents selected from the Archives of the Indies at Seville; II. English Accounts, Sir Francis Drake revived, & Others Reprinted. 2010. (Hakluyt Society, Second Ser.). 412p. 69.95 (978-1-4094-1438-4(8)) Hakluyt Society GBR. Dist: Ashgate Publishing Co.

—Further English Voyages to Spanish America, 1583-1594: Documents from the Archives of the Indies at Seville illustrating English Voyages to the Caribbean, the Spanish Main, Florida, & Virginia. 2010. (Hakluyt Society, Second Ser.). 408p. 69.95 (978-1-4094-1465-0(5)) Hakluyt Society GBR. Dist: Ashgate Publishing Co.

—Global & Regional Problems: Towards an Interdisciplinary Study. 2010. (Hakluyt Society, Second Ser.). 224p. 69.95 (978-1-4094-1429-2(9)) Hakluyt Society GBR. Dist: Ashgate Publishing Co.

Zahm, John A. The Quest of el Dorado: The Most Romantic Episode in the History of South American Conquest. 2007. 280p. 42.95 (978-0-548-53829-6(8)); (ENG.). per. 27.95 (978-0-548-49472-1(X)) Kessinger Publishing, LLC.

—The Quest of el Dorado: The Most Romantic Episode in the History of South American Conquest. 260p. reprint ed. 98.00 (978-0-7222-9574-8(X)) Library Reprints, Inc.

AMERICA—DISCOVERY AND EXPLORATION—BIBLIOGRAPHY

Church, Elihu Dwight. A Catalogue of Books Relating to the Discovery & Early History of North & South America Forming a Part of the Library of E.D. Church, 5 vol., set. reprint ed. 625.00 (978-0-7222-6409-6(7)) Library Reprints, Inc.

Fumagalli, Giuseppe & Amat di S Filippo, Pietro. Bibliografia degli scritti italiani o stampati in Italia sopra Cristoforo Colombo, la scoperta del Nuovo Mondo, e i viaggi degli Italiani in America. 2007. (ITA.). 218p. 110.00 (978-1-57898-620-0(6)) Martino Publishing.

AMERICA—DISCOVERY AND EXPLORATION—JUVENILE LITERATURE

Christopher Columbus. pap. 6.95 (978-0-516-24781-6(6), Children's Pr.) Scholastic Library Publishing.

Drake, Samuel Adams. The Making of the Great West: 1512-1883. 2010. 360p. pap. 32.75 (978-1-177-89123-3(9)) BiblioBazaar.

—The Making of the Great West, 1512-1883. 2011. 370p. pap. 32.75 (978-1-175-57716-0(2)) 2010. 364p. pap. 32.75 (978-1-142-80311-7(2)) BiblioBazaar.

Drake, Samuel Adams. The Making of the Great West; 1512-1883. 2010. 364p. pap. 32.75 (978-1-178-06296-0(1)) 2010. 360p. pap. 32.75 (978-1-177-78991-2(4)) 2009. 356p. 33.99 (978-1-110-96051-4(4)) 2009. 356p. pap. 31.75 (978-1-110-96049-1(2)) 2009. (ENG.). 354p. pap. 26.99 (978-1-110-96046-0(8), BiblioLife) 2009. (ENG.). 354p. pap. 25.99 (978-1-110-96045-3(X), BiblioLife) BiblioBazaar.

Garces, Fernando & Julve, Oscar. Cristobal Colon. 2010. (Me Llamo... Ser.). (SPA., Illus.). 63p. (J). pap. (978-84-342-3462-8(9)) Parramon Ediciones S.A.

Ollhoff, Jim. Building a New World. 2011. (Hispanic American History Ser.). (Illus.). 32p. (YA). (gr. 5-9). 27.07 (978-1-61783-053-2(4)) ABDO Publishing Co.

AMERICA—ECONOMIC CONDITIONS

Berkshire Encyclopedia of Sustainability Vol. 8: The Americas & Oceania: Assessing Sustainability. 2009. 512p. lib. bdg. 150.00 (978-1-933782-18-8(8)) Berkshire Publishing Group.

Bernecker, Walther L. & Tobler, Hans W., eds. Development & Underdevelopment in America: Contrasts of Economic Growth in North & Latin America in Historical Perspective. (De Gruyter Studies on North America Ser.). (ENG.). VI, 336p. 225.00 (978-3-11-180653-2(7)) De Gruyter, Walter Inc.

Burch, Henry Reed. American Economic Life in Its Civil And Social Aspects. 533p. reprint ed. 98.00 (978-0-7222-7458-3(0)) Library Reprints, Inc.

Cavataio, Rita Bangert & White, Mark. The Trophy Generation: What Every American Can Do about the Education Crisis. 2011. pap. 15.99 (978-1-61346-276-8(X)) Tate Publishing & Enterprises, LLC.

Eltis, David, et al, eds. Slavery in the Development of the Americas. 2010. (ENG.). 384p. pap. 36.99 (978-0-521-17267-7(5)) Cambridge Univ. Pr.

Engerman, Stanley L. & Sokoloff, Kenneth L. Economic Development in the Americas Since 1500: Endowments & Institutions. 2011. (Illus.). 420p. (C). 99.00 (978-1-107-00955-4(3)); pap. 34.99 (978-0-521-25137-2(0)) Cambridge Univ. Pr.

F, Hall. The Importance of the British Plantations in America to This Kingdom: With the State of Their Trade, & Methods for Improving It; As Also A Descrip. 2010. 128p. pap. 20.75 (978-1-171-91400-6(8)) BiblioBazaar.

McKee, Chris, ed. International Country Risk Guide Annual - 2006 Vol. 1: The Americas. 2006. (C). per. (978-1-933539-20-1(8)) PRS Group Inc., The.

Mckinney, Joseph A. & Gardner, H. Stephen, eds. Economic Integration in the Americas. 2009. 254p. pap. 39.95 (978-0-415-78002-5(0)) Routledge.

O'Keefe, Thomas Andrew. Latin American & Caribbean Trade Agreements: Keys to a Prosperous Community of the Americas. 2009. 511p. pap. (978-90-04-16488-8(X)) BRILL.

Peña Young, Sabrina. Dream the Dreams of God: 99 Ways You Can End Poverty. 2010. 35p. pap. 14.99 (978-0-557-36222-6(9)) Lulu Enterprises Inc.

Perez-Caldentey, Esteban, ed. Ideas, Policies & Economic Development in the Americas. 2007. (Routledge Studies in Development Economics Ser.). (Illus.). 242p. 160.00 (978-0-415-77055-2(6)) Routledge.

Royo, Sebastián. Varieties of Capitalism in Spain: Remaking the Spanish Economy for the New Century. 2008. (ENG., Illus.). 268p. 105.00 (978-1-4039-6412-0(2)) Palgrave Macmillan.

Sánchez-Ancochea, Diego & Shadlen, Kenneth C., eds. The Political Economy of Hemispheric Integration: Responding to Globalization in the Americas. 2008. (Studies of the Americas Ser.). (ENG., Illus.). 304p. 100.00 (978-0-230-60657-9(1)) Palgrave Macmillan.

Slate, Chuck. The Demise of Americ: (As We KNEW It) 2008. 484p. 36.95 (978-1-4251-7034-9(X)) Trafford Publishing.

Westfried, Alex Huxley. The Splendor, Wonder, Vision & Courage of America: A Promising Future. 2011. 136p. pap. 11.95 (978-1-4620-1731-7(2)) iUniverse, Inc.

AMERICA—FOREIGN RELATIONS

Here are entered works on relations, concerted or otherwise, between the Americas and single countries, or groups of countries, outside the western hemisphere.

Gleeson, David T., ed. The Irish in the Atlantic World. 2010. (Carolina Lowcountry & the Atlantic World Ser.). (Illus.). 344p. 69.95 (978-1-57003-908-9(9)) Univ. of South Carolina Pr.

Hilaire, Max. The United States & International Law. rev. ed. 2009. (ENG.). 494p. pap. 99.94 (978-0-7575-6069-9(5)) Kendall Hunt Publishing Co.

Howsam, Leslie & Raven, James, eds. Books between Europe & the Americas: Connections & Communities, 1620-1860. 2011. (ENG., Illus.). 352p. 85.00 (978-0-230-28567-5(8)) Palgrave Macmillan.

Juang, Richard M. & Morrissette, Noelle, eds. Africa & the Americas: Culture, Politics, & History, 3 vols. 2008. (Transatlantic Relations Ser.). (Illus.). 1215p. 270.00 (978-1-85109-441-7(5), AFATRLC) ABC-CLIO, LLC.

Murdoch, Alexander. Scotland & America, C. 1600-C. 1800. 2010. (ENG.). 224p. pap. 34.95 (978-0-230-51649-6(1)) Palgrave Macmillan.

Pritchard, James. In Search of Empire: The French in the Americas, 1670-1730. 2007. (ENG., Illus.). 512p. pap. 30.99 (978-0-521-71111-1(8)) Cambridge Univ. Pr.

Sánchez-Ancochea, Diego & Shadlen, Kenneth C., eds. The Political Economy of Hemispheric Integration: Responding to Globalization in the Americas. 2008. (Studies of the Americas Ser.). (ENG., Illus.). 304p. 100.00 (978-0-230-60657-9(1)) Palgrave Macmillan.

Spitta, Silvia. Misplaced Objects: Migrating Collections & Recollections in Europe & the Americas. 2009. (ENG., Illus.). 294p. 50.00 (978-0-292-71897-5(7)) Univ. of Texas Pr.

Worger, William, et al. Africa & the West: A Documentary History: Volume 2: from Colonialism to Independence, 1875 to the Present, 1 vol. 2nd ed. 2010. (ENG., Illus.). 328p. (C). pap. 24.95 (978-0-19-537313-4(8)) Oxford Univ. Pr., Inc.

Worger, William H., et al. Africa & the West: A Documentary History: Volume 1: from the Slave Trade to Conquest, 1441-1905, 1 vol. 2nd ed. 2010. (ENG., Illus.). 312p. (C). pap. 24.95 (978-0-19-537348-6(0)) Oxford Univ. Pr., Inc.

AMERICA—HISTORY

Andrews, Kenneth R., ed. English Privateering Voyages to the West Indies, 1588-1595: Documents relating to English voyages to the West Indies, from the defeat of the Armada to the last voyage of Sir Francis Drake, including Spanish documents contributed by Irene A. Wright. 2010. (Hakluyt Society, Second Ser.). 448p. 69.95 (978-1-4094-1477-3(9)) Hakluyt Society GBR. Dist: Ashgate Publishing Co.

Armitage, David. The British Atlantic World, 1500-1800. Braddick, Michael J., ed. 2nd rev. ed. 2009. (ENG., Illus.). 384p. pap. 32.00 (978-0-230-20235-1(7)) Palgrave Macmillan.

Armitage, David & Braddick, Michael J., eds. The British Atlantic World, 1500-1800. 2nd rev. ed. 2009. (ENG., Illus.). 384p. 100.00 (978-0-230-20234-4(9)) Palgrave Macmillan.

Beck, Sanderson. America To 1744: Ethics of Civilization, 11. 2006. 664p. per. 25.00 (978-0-9762210-7-4(1)) World Peace Communications.

Briggs, Ronald. Tropes of Enlightenment in the Age of Bolivar: Simon Rodriguez & the American Essay at Revolution. 2010. (ENG., Illus.). 256p. 55.00 (978-0-8265-1693-0(9)) Vanderbilt Univ. Pr.

Burke, Edmund. An Account of the European Settlements in America, 6 pts. in 2 vols., Set. reprint ed. 30.00 (978-0-404-01237-3(X)) AMS Pr., Inc.

—An Account of the European Settlements in America. 2007. (ENG.). 508p. per. 38.95 (978-0-548-59152-9(0)) Kessinger Publishing, LLC.

Clausen, Helene Balslev, et al, eds. Projections of Power in the Americas. 2012. (ENG.). 260p. (C). 125.00 (978-0-415-51747-8(8)) Routledge.

Coll, Kathleen M. Remaking Citizenship: Latina Immigrants & New American Politics. 2010. (ENG.). 248p. 65.00 (978-0-8047-5821-5(2)); pap. 22.95 (978-0-8047-5822-2(0)) Stanford Univ. Pr.

Crespo Cuesta, Eduardo Daniel. Continuidades Medievales en la Conquista de América. 2010. (Illus.). 190p. (978-84-313-2719-4(7)) Universidad de Navarra, Ediciones, S. A.

De León, Pedro De Cieza. Travels of Pedro de Cieza de Leòn, A. D. 1532-50: Contained in the First Part of His Chronicle of Peru. Markham, Clements R., tr. 2010. (Cambridge Library Collection - Travel & Exploration Ser.). (ENG., Illus.). 524p. pap. 39.99 (978-1-108-01334-5(1)) Cambridge Univ. Pr.

Downey, Tika. Michigan: The Great Lakes State. 2010. (Our Amazing States Ser.). (ENG.). 24p. (J). pap. 8.25 (978-1-4358-9802-8(8)); lib. bdg. 21.25 (978-1-4358-9353-5(0)) Rosen Publishing Group, Inc., The. (PowerKids Pr.).

—Minnesota: Land of 10,000 Lakes. 2010. (Our Amazing States Ser.). (ENG.). 24p. (J). pap. 8.25 (978-1-4358-9804-2(4)); lib. bdg. 21.25 (978-1-4358-9354-2(9)) Rosen Publishing Group, Inc., The. (PowerKids Pr.).

Early Days in America, Vol. 14. Date not set. 32.95 (978-0-8369-4807-3(6)) Ayer Co. Pubs., Inc.

Elliott, FBA, John H. Empires of the Atlantic World: Britain & Spain in America 1492-1830. 2007. (ENG., Illus.). 608p. pap. 29.00 (978-0-300-12399-9(X)) Yale Univ. Pr.

Ericson, Carolyn & Ingmire, Frances, eds. Early Doctors of Nacogdoches County, Texas, Vol. II. 2012. (ENG., Illus.). 92p. pap. 25.00 (978-0-911317-11-4(2)) Ericson Bks.

Galeano, Eduardo. Century of the Wind Vol. 3. 2010. (ENG.). 336p. (gr. 9). pap. 15.95 (978-1-56858-446-1(6)) Basic Bks.

—Faces & Masks Vol. 2, Vol. 2. 2010. (ENG.). 312p. (gr. 9). pap. 15.95 (978-1-56858-445-4(8)) Basic Bks.

Gardner, Mark L. To Hell on a Fast Horse: Billy the Kid, Pat Garrett, & the Epic Chase to Justice in the Old West. 2010. 336p. 26.99 (978-0-06-136827-1(X), Morrow, William & Co.) HarperCollins Pubs.

Garretson-Persans, Christine. The Smalbanac: An Opinionated Guide to New York's Capital District. 2010. (Excelsior Editions Ser.). (Illus.). 144p. pap. 9.25 (978-1-4384-3150-5(3), Suny Pr.) State Univ. of New York Pr.

Gerbi, Antonello. The Dispute of the New World: The History of a Polemic, 1750-1900. Moyle, Jeremy, tr. from ITA. 2010. (ENG.). 720p. (C). pap. 29.95 (978-0-8229-6081-2(8)) Univ. of Pittsburgh Pr.

Gillotte, Helen P. & Gregory, Jan. Readings Across American Cultures. 2nd rev. ed. 2007. (ENG.). 400p. per. 80.29 (978-0-7872-9458-8(6)) Kendall Hunt Publishing Co.

Glaser, Jason. North Carolina: The Tar Heel State. 2010. (Our Amazing States Ser.). (ENG.). 24p. (J). pap. 8.25 (978-1-4358-9780-9(3)); lib. bdg. 21.25 (978-1-4358-9394-8(8)) Rosen Publishing Group, Inc., The. (PowerKids Pr.).

—South Carolina: The Palmetto State. 2010. (Our Amazing States Ser.). (ENG.). 24p. (J). 21.25 (978-1-4358-9345-0(X)); pap. 8.25 (978-1-4358-9778-6(1)) Rosen Publishing Group, Inc., The. (PowerKids Pr.).

Great Britain Sovereigns Staff. British Royal Proclamations Relating to America, 1603-1783. (Transactions & Collections of the American Antiquarian Society Ser.: 12). 268p. reprint ed. 98.00 (978-0-7222-6524-6(7)) Library Reprints, Inc.

Harkins, John E. Memphis Chronicles: Bits of History from the Best Times. 2009. (American Chronicles Ser.). 128p. pap. 19.99 (978-1-59629-714-2(X)) History Pr., The.

Hawkins, Martha. Finding Martha's Place: My Journey Through Sin, Salvation, & Lots of Soul Food. 2010. (ENG., Illus.). 256p. 21.99 (978-1-4391-3781-9(1), Touchstone) Touchstone.

High, Steven & High, Steven C. Base Colonies in the Western Hemisphere, 1940-1967. 2008. (Studies of the Americas Ser.). (ENG., Illus.). 320p. 105.00 (978-0-230-60943-3(0)) Palgrave Macmillan.

Humphrey, Thomas J. & Smolenski, John, eds. New World Orders: Violence, Sanction, & Authority in the Colonial Americas. 2007. (Early American Studies). (Illus.). 376p. (C). pap. 26.50 (978-0-8122-1922-7(8)) Univ. of Pennsylvania Pr.

Kahn, Ava Fran, et al. Jews of the Pacific Coast: Reinventing Community on America's Edge. 2010. (Samuel & Althea Stroum Book Ser.). (Illus.). 336p. 50.00 (978-0-295-98965-5(3)) Univ. of Washington Pr.

Kier, David B. Pathways of Learning: Essays in American & European History. 2011. 312p. pap. 20.00 (978-1-4269-5590-7(1)) Trafford Publishing.

Kleinberg, Eliot. Wicked Palm Beach: Lifestyles of the Rich & Heinous. 2009. (Wicked Ser.). (ENG., Illus.). 128p. pap. 19.99 (978-1-59629-794-4(8)) History Pr., The.

Korieh, Chima J. Olaudah Equiano & the Igbo World. 2008. 296p. (978-1-59221-664-2(1)); pap. (978-1-59221-665-9(X)) Africa World Pr.

Lehmkuhl, Ursula & Rinke, Stefan H. Amerika, Amerikas: Zur Geschichte Eines Namens Von 1507 Bis Zur Gegenwart. 2008. (GER., Illus.). 250p. (978-3-88099-687-8(3)) Heinz, Hans-Dieter Akademischer Verlag, Verlag.

Lien, Hans Olav. The Discovery of America - the Deception of the Millennium. 2008. 562p. pap. 39.96 (978-1-4092-1056-6(1)) Lulu Enterprises Inc.

Little, John. Loyalties in Conflict: A Canadian Borderland in War & Rebellion, 1812-1840. 2008. (ENG., Illus.). 192p. pap. (978-0-8020-9525-1(9)) Univ. of Toronto Pr.

Lüsted, Marcia Amidon. Arizona: The Grand Canyon State. 2010. (Our Amazing States Ser.). (ENG.). 24p. (J). pap. 8.25 (978-1-4358-9788-5(9)); lib. bdg. 21.25 (978-1-4358-9347-4(6)) Rosen Publishing Group, Inc., The. (PowerKids Pr.).

Mallon, Florencia E. Decolonizing Native Histories: Collaboration, Knowledge, & Language in the Americas. McCormick, Gladys Irene, tr. 2011. (Narrating Native Histories Ser.). (ENG., Illus.). 272p. 89.95 (978-0-8223-5137-5(4)); pap. 24.95 (978-0-8223-5152-8(8)) Duke Univ. Pr.

Mancall, Peter C., ed. The Atlantic World & Virginia, 1550-1624. 2007. (ENG., Illus.). 608p. per. 31.95 (978-0-8078-5848-6(X)) Univ. of North Carolina Pr.

Marley, David F. Wars of the Americas Set: A Chronology of Armed Conflict in the Western Hemisphere, 2 vols. 2nd rev. ed. 2008. (Illus.). 1112p. 195.00 (978-1-59884-100-8(9), WARAME2C) ABC-CLIO, LLC.

Mattern, Joanne. New Jersey: Past & Present. 2010. (United States: Past & Present Ser.). (ENG., Illus.). 48p. (J). pap. 11.75 (978-1-4358-8500-4(7)); lib. bdg. 26.50 (978-1-4358-3525-2(5)) Rosen Publishing Group, Inc., The. (Rosen Central).

Merediz, Eyda M. Approaches to Teaching the Writings of Bartolomé de Las Casas. Arias, Santa, ed. 2008. (SPA & ENG.). 37.50 (978-0-87352-944-0(8)); pap. 19.75 (978-0-87352-945-7(6)) Modern Language Assn. of America.

Morritt, Robert. Ancient Migrations to the Americas. 2011. 136p. pap. (978-3-8443-9972-1(0)) Lambert Academic Publishing.

The Norse's Discovery of America. (Anglo-Saxon Classics Ser.). 343p. reprint ed. 98.00 (978-0-7222-6450-8(X)) Library Reprints, Inc.

El Pensamiento en America. No. 3. pap. 1.00 (978-0-8270-5895-8(0))No. 4. pap. 1.00 (978-0-8270-5890-3(X)) Organization of American States.

Richter, Daniel K. Before the Revolution: America's Ancient Pasts. 2011. (Illus.). 560p. 35.00 (978-0-674-05580-3(2), Belknap Pr.) Harvard Univ. Pr.

Robertson, William. The History of the Discovery & Settlement of America, by William Robertson with an Account of His Life & Writings to Which Are Added Questions F. 2006. 608p. per. 34.99 (978-1-4255-6500-8(X)) MPublishing.

Seaver, Kirsten A. The Last Vikings: The Epic Story of the Great Norse Voyagers. 2010. (ENG., Illus.). 288p. 30.00 (978-1-84511-869-3(3)) I. B. Tauris & Co., Ltd. GBR. Dist: Macmillan.

Seeman, Erik R. Death in the New World: Cross-Cultural Encounters, 1492-1800. (Early American Studies). (Illus.). 384p. (C). 2011. pap. 24.95 (978-0-8122-2194-7(X)) 2010. 45.00 (978-0-8122-4229-4(7)) Univ. of Pennsylvania Pr.

Sheridan, Thomas E. Arizona: A History. rev. ed. 2012. (Southwest Center Ser.). (ENG., Illus.). 488p. 50.00 (978-0-8165-0687-3(6)) Univ. of Arizona Pr.

Stade, Hans. Captivity of Hans Stade of Hesse in A. D. 1547-1555, among the Wild Tribes of Eastern Brazil. Burton, Richard F., ed. Tootal, Albert, tr. 2010. (Cambridge Library Collection - Travel & Exploration Ser.). (ENG.). 280p. pap. 23.99 (978-1-108-01237-9(X)) Cambridge Univ. Pr.

Stanley, Richard T. A Humorous Account of America's Past: 986 To 1898. 2009. (Illus.). 612p. pap. 34.95 (978-1-4401-3041-0(8)) iUniverse, Inc.

Trinkle, Dennis A. & Merriman, Scott A. The American History Highway: A Guide to Internet Resources on U.S., Canadian, & Latin American History. Trinkle, Dennis A. & Merriman, Scott A., eds. 2007. (History Highway Ser.). (ENG.). 440p. pap. 39.95 (978-0-7656-1629-6(7)) Sharpe, M.E. Inc.

Weber, David J. Barbaros: Spaniards & Their Savages in the Age of Enlightenment. 2006. (Lamar Series in Western History). (ENG., Illus.). 480p. per. 23.00 (978-0-300-11991-6(7)) Yale Univ. Pr.

Weidensaul, Scott. The First Frontier: The Forgotten History of Struggle, Savagery, & Endurance in Early America. 2012. (ENG., Illus.). 496p. 30.00 (978-0-15-101515-3(5)) Houghton Mifflin Harcourt Trade & Reference Pubs.

Wilkinson, Charles. The Fourth West. 2010. (ENG.). 20p. pap. 4.95 (978-1-60781-025-4(5)) Univ. of Utah Pr.

Winsor, Justin. Narrative & Critical History of America. 2010. 588p. pap. (978-1-152-85148-1(9)) 2010. 710p. pap. (978-1-151-75086-0(7)) 2009. 626p. pap. (978-1-151-75084-6(0)) Books LLC.

—Narrative & Critical History of America, 8 vol., set. reprint ed. 1000.00 (978-0-7222-6428-7(3)) Library Reprints, Inc.

Winsor, Justin, ed. Narrative & Critical History of America, 8 vols. reprint ed. 700.00 (978-0-404-07010-6(8)) AMS Pr., Inc.

York, Robert & York, Gigi. Slings & Slingstones: The Forgotten Weapons of Oceania & the Americas. 2011. 224p. 55.00 (978-1-60635-107-9(9)) Kent State Univ. Pr.

AMERICA—HISTORY—BIBLIOGRAPHY

Church, Elihu Dwight. A Catalogue of Books Relating to the Discovery & Early History of North & South America Forming a Part of the Library of E.D. Church, 5 vol., set. reprint ed. 625.00 (978-0-7222-6409-6(7)) Library Reprints, Inc.

Richardson, Ernest Cushing. Writings on American History, 1902. 294p. reprint ed. 98.00 (978-0-7222-7015-8(1)) Library Reprints, Inc.

AMERICA—IN LITERATURE

Buccini, Stefania. The Americas in Italian Literature & Culture, 1700-1825. 2008. (ENG.). 244p. per. 26.95 (978-0-271-02778-4(9)) Pennsylvania State Univ. Pr.

Cote, Jean-Francois, ed. The Function of Contemporary Travel Narratives in the French, Anglo, & Latin Americas: Mixing & Expanding Cultural Identity. 2011. 184p. 109.95 (978-0-7734-1545-4(9)) Mellen, Edwin Pr., The.

Diggins, John P. Eugene O'Neill's America: Desire under Democracy. 2007. 288p. 29.00 (978-0-226-14880-9(7)) Univ. of Chicago Pr.

Gerbi, Antonello. The Dispute of the New World: The History of a Polemic, 1750-1900. Moyle, Jeremy, tr. from ITA. 2010. (ENG.). 720p. (C). pap. 29.95 (978-0-8229-6081-2(8)) Univ. of Pittsburgh Pr.

Guiddal, Jesper. Anti-Americanism in European Literature. 2011. (Studies in European Culture & History Ser.). (ENG., Illus.). 252p. 85.00 (978-0-230-12082-2(2)) Palgrave Macmillan.

Holmes, Oliver Wendell. The Autocrat of the Breakfast Table. 2009. 336p. 25.99 (978-1-103-76553-9(1)); pap. 19.99 (978-1-103-76548-5(5)) BiblioBazaar.

—The Autocrat of the Breakfast Table. 2010. 90p. pap. (978-1-151-90714-1(6)) 2010. 96p. pap. (978-1-151-90717-2(0)) 2009. 156p. pap. (978-0-217-88605-5(1)) Books LLC.

—The Autocrat of the Breakfast Table. 2008. 232p. pap. (978-1-4065-6122-7(3)) Dodo Pr.

—The Autocrat of the Breakfast Table. 2008. 308p. pap. (978-1-4097-6304-8(8)) Read Bks.

—The Autocrat of the Breakfast Table. 2008. 396p. 29.95 (978-1-4344-6901-4(8)); pap. 14.95 (978-1-4344-6900-7(X)) Wildside Pr., LLC.

—The Autocrat of the Breakfast-Table. 2009. 340p. 25.99 (978-1-103-03878-7(8)) 2009. 340p. pap. 19.99 (978-1-103-03875-6(3)) 2008. (ENG.). 344p. 32.99 (978-1-4264-7894-9(1)) 2008. (ENG.). 344p. 36.99 (978-1-4264-7878-9(X)) 2008. (ENG.). 344p. pap. 32.75 (978-1-4264-7883-3(6)) 2008. (ENG.). 344p. pap. 31.75 (978-1-4264-7889-5(5)) BiblioBazaar.

—The Autocrat of the Breakfast-Table. 2009. 228p. pap. (978-1-4588-5984-6(3)); 216p. pap. (978-0-217-62124-3(4)) Books LLC.

—The Autocrat of the Breakfast-Table. 2009. 214p. pap. (978-1-4446-6193-4(0), Pomona Pr.) Read Bks.

Kiening, Christian. Das Wilde Subjekt: Kleine Poetik der Neuen Welt. 2006. (Historische Semantik Ser.). (GER., Illus.). 311p. (C). 48.00 (978-3-525-36709-4(0)) Vandenhoeck & Ruprecht GmbH & Co. KG DEU. Dist: ISD.

Lifshey, Adam. Specters of Conquest: Indigenous Absence in Transatlantic Literatures. 2nd ed. 2010. (American Literatures Initiative Ser.). (ENG.). 192p. 60.00 (978-0-8232-3238-3(7)) Fordham Univ. Pr.

Miller, Brook. America & the British Imaginary in Turn-of-the-Twentieth-Century Literature. 2010. (ENG., Illus.). 256p. 84.00 (978-0-230-10376-4(6)) Palgrave Macmillan.

Perrone, Charles A. Brazil, Lyric, & the Americas. 2010. (ENG., Illus.). 240p. 69.95 (978-0-8130-3421-3(3)) Univ. Pr. of Florida.

Phelan, James. Experiencing Fiction: Judgments, Progressions, & the Rhetorical Theory of Narrative. 2007. (Theory & Interpretation of Narrative Ser.). 249p. (978-0-8142-1065-9(1)); 249p. per. (978-0-8142-5162-1(5)); cd-rom 9.95 (978-0-8142-9145-0(7)) Ohio State Univ. Pr.

Shosun, Nagahara. Lament in the Night. 2012. (ENG., Illus.). 150p. pap. 16.95 (978-1-885030-48-1(7)) Muae Publishing, Inc.

Todd, Dennis. Defoe's America. 2010. (ENG.). 240p. 95.00 (978-0-521-19581-2(0)) Cambridge Univ. Pr.

AMERICA—INTELLECTUAL LIFE

Bauer, Ralph. The Cultural Geography of Colonial American Literatures: Empire, Travel, Modernity. 2009. (Cambridge Studies in American Literature & Culture Ser.). (ENG., Illus.). 316p. pap. 44.00 (978-0-521-10032-8(1)) Cambridge Univ. Pr.

Bringhurst, Robert. The Tree of Meaning: Language, Mind & Ecology. 2007. (ENG., Illus.). 336p. 28.00 (978-1-59376-179-0(1)) Counterpoint LLC.

Ewalt, Margaret R. Peripheral Wonders: Nature, Knowledge, & Enlightenment in the Eighteenth-Century Orinoco. 2008. (Illus.). 264p. 55.00 (978-0-8387-5689-3(1)) Bucknell Univ. Pr.

Iannini, Christopher. Fatal Revolutions: Natural History, West Indian Slavery, & the Routes of American Literature. 2012. (Published for the Omohundro Institute of Early American History & Culture, Williamsburg, Virginia Ser.). (ENG., Illus.). 376p. 45.00 (978-0-8078-3556-2(0)) Univ. of North Carolina Pr.

Sinclair, Mary B. Mining the Sounds of Silence: Therapy in American Life. 2011. 62p. pap. 19.95 (978-1-4626-3360-9(9)) PublishAmerica, Inc.

Zabel, Darcy. Arabs in the Americas: Interdisciplinary Essays on the Arab Diaspora. 2006. 248p. (C). pap. 31.95 (978-0-8204-8111-1(4)) Lang, Peter Publishing, Inc.

AMERICA—MAPS

Lester, Toby. The Fourth Part of the World: An Astonishing Epic of Global Discovery, Imperial Ambition, & the Birth of America. 2010. (ENG., Illus.). 496p. pap. 16.99 (978-1-4165-3534-8(9), Free Pr.) Free Pr.

Thompson, Gunnar. Secret Voyages to the New World. 2010. 251p. pap. 21.95 (978-0-557-23165-2(5)) Lulu Enterprises Inc.

AMERICA—MAPS—EARLY WORKS TO 1800

De Blanca, Blanca & Ocaña, Diego de. Viaje Por el Nuevo Mundo: de Guadalupe a Potosí, 1599-1605. 2010. (Biblioteca Indiana Ser.). (SPA., Illus.). 504p. pap. 44.00 (978-84-8489-505-3(X)) Iberoamericana Vervuert Publishing Corp.

Diego & Madroñal Durán, Abraham. Viaje Por el Nuevo Mundo: De Guadalupe a Potosí, 1599-1605. López de Mariscal, Blanca, ed. & tr. by. 2010. (SPA., Illus.). 504p. (978-3-86527-551-6(6)); (978-607-7588-21-4(0)) Universidad de Navarra, Ediciones, S. A.

AMERICA—POLITICS AND GOVERNMENT

Here are entered comprehensive works on politics and government in the western hemisphere or in three or more countries of the two Americas.

see also Pan-Americanism

Beck, Jeffrey. America's New Strategy in Afghanistan. 2010. 172p. pap. (978-3-639-23500-5(2)) VDM Verlag Dr. Mueller e.K.

Brewer, Mark D. & Stonecash, Jeffrey M. Dynamics of American Political Parties. 2009. (ENG., Illus.). 256p. (C). pap. 25.99 (978-0-521-70887-6(7)); 75.00 (978-0-521-88230-9(3)) Cambridge Univ. Pr.

Chomsky, Noam. New World of Indigenous Resistance. Meyer, Lois & Maldonado, Benjamin, eds. 2010. (City Lights Open Media Ser.). (ENG.). 300p. pap. 18.95 (978-0-87286-533-4(9)) City Lights Bks.

Gaede, Bill. America Has Lost Its Way... Again! 2008. 96p. pap. 9.99 (978-1-60462-898-2(7)) Tate Publishing & Enterprises, LLC.

Gale. CourseReader 0-60: American Government Printed Access Card. 2010. (ENG.). (C). 80.95 (978-1-111-68056-5(6)) Wadsworth.

Guo, Rongxing. The Land & Maritime Boundary Disputes of the Americas. 2009. (American Politica, Economic, & Security Issues Ser.). pap. 89.00 (978-1-60741-636-4(0)) Nova Science Pubs., Inc.

Kelter, Bill. Veeps: Profiles in Insignificance. 2008. (Illus.). 180p. 19.95 (978-1-60309-003-2(7)) Top Shelf Productions.

Koff, Harlan, ed. Social Cohesion in Europe & the Americas: Power, Time & Space. 2009. (Regional Integration & Social Cohesion Ser.). (ENG & SPA., Illus.). 370p. pap. 68.95 (978-90-5201-568-2(6)) PIE - Peter Lang BEL. Dist: Lang, Peter.

Lierse, Hanna. The Evolution of the European Economic Governance System: Monetary & Business Tax Cooperation from A Discursive Institutionalist Perspective. 2011. 306p. pap. 71.00 (978-3-8329-6663-8(3)) Nomos Verlagsgesellschaft DEU. Dist: International Specialized Bk. Services.

Niebler, Dieter. Bamboozle: America at war in the name of God, Country, & the need to buy a flat screen TV. 2011. 354p. pap. 29.95 (978-1-4626-4659-3(X)) PublishAmerica, Inc.

Pavlopoulos, Theodore. A Matter of Life & Death: The American Bureaucracy. 2008. (ENG.). 260p. 29.95 (978-0-595-69357-3(1)); per. 19.95 (978-0-595-45279-8(5)) iUniverse, Inc.

Powell, Kevin. Someday We'll All Be Free. 2006. (ENG.). 160p. per. 13.95 (978-1-933368-57-3(8)) Counterpoint LLC.

Royo, Sebastián. Varieties of Capitalism in Spain: Remaking the Spanish Economy for the New Century. 2008. (ENG., Illus.). 268p. 105.00 (978-1-4039-6412-0(2)) Palgrave Macmillan.

Schorr, Daniel. Come to Think of It: Commentaries from National Public Radio's Senior News Analyst. 2008. (ENG.). 416p. (gr. 12-18). 16.00 (978-0-14-311447-5(6), Penguin (Non-Classics)) Penguin Group (USA) Inc.

Slate, Chuck. The Demise of Americ: (As We KNEW It) 2008. 484p. 36.95 (978-1-4251-7034-9(X)) Trafford Publishing.

Taft, Jessica. Rebel Girls: Youth Activism & Social Change Across the Americas. 2011. (ENG.). 256p. 70.00 (978-0-8147-8324-5(4)); pap. 22.00 (978-0-8147-8325-2(2)) New York Univ. Pr.

Thompson, Heather. Speaking Out: Activism & Protest in the 1960's And 1970's. 2009. (ENG.). 288p. (C). pap. 49.80 (978-0-13-194214-1(X), Prentice Hall) Prentice Hall PTR.

Zhang, Charles. Redrawing World Map: Exploration of Unification Between Countries. 2010. (Illus.). 224p. (978-1-4512-9489-7(1)); pap. (978-1-4489-5805-4(9)) PublishAmerica, Inc.

AMERICA—RACE RELATIONS

Braziel, Jan Evans & Joseph, Young, eds. Erasing Public Memory: Race, Aesthetics, & Cultural Amnesia in the Americas. 2007. 350p. pap. 30.00 (978-0-88146-056-2(3)) Mercer Univ. Pr.

Braziel, Jan Evans & Young, Joseph, eds. Erasing Public Memory: Race, Aesthetics, & Cultural Amnesia in the Americas. 2007. 350p. 60.00 (978-0-88146-076-6(1)) Mercer Univ. Pr.

Casaús Arzú, Marta Elena. Guatemala: Linaje y Racismo. 2007. 339p. pap. (978-99922-61-53-8(6)) F & G Editores.

King, Stewart R. Encyclopedia of Free Blacks & People of Color in the Americas, 2 vols., Set. 2012. 1034p. (C). (gr. 9-18). 185.00 (978-0-8160-7212-5(4)) Facts On File, Inc.

Levander, Caroline F., ed. Hemispheric American Studies. 2007. (ENG., Illus.). 366p. (C). pap. 27.95 (978-0-8135-4223-2(5)) Rutgers Univ. Pr.

Levander, Caroline F. & Levine, Robert, eds. Hemispheric American Studies. 2007. (ENG., Illus.). 366p. 70.00 (978-0-8135-4222-5(7)) Rutgers Univ. Pr.

Nash & Cram101 Textbook Reviews Staff. Red, White, & Black: The Peoples of Early North America. 2007. 132p. per. 11.95 (978-1-4288-2800-1(1)) Cram101 Inc.

Nash, Gary B. Red, White, & Black. 6th ed. 2009. (ENG.). 320p. (C). pap. 78.80 (978-0-205-69237-8(0), Prentice Hall) Prentice Hall PTR.

Oboe, Annalisa & Scacchi, Anna, eds. Recharting the Black Atlantic: Modern Cultures, Local Communities, Global Connections. 2008. (ENG., Illus.). 438p. 125.00 (978-0-415-96111-0(4)) Routledge.

AMERICA—STATISTICS

Mitchell, B. R. & Mitchell, Brian R. Americas, 1750-2005, 3 vols. 6th rev. ed. 2007. (ENG., Illus.). 1120p. 400.00 (978-0-230-00513-6(6)) Palgrave Macmillan.

AMERICA IN LITERATURE

see America—In Literature

AMERICA ONLINE (ONLINE SERVICE)

Bild Staff AOL ganz Einfach. (Computer Bild Ser.). (GER.). 112p. pap. (978-3-548-41149-1(5)) Ullstein-Taschenbuch-Verlag DEU. Dist: International Bk. Import Service, Inc.

AMERICAN ABORIGINES

see Indians; Indians of North America; Indians of South America

AMERICAN ACADEMY IN ROME

Talbott, Mona & Misenti, Mirella. Biscotti: Recipes from the Kitchen of the American Academy in Rome, the Rome Sustainable Food Project. 2010. (Rome Sustainable Food Project Ser.). (ENG., Illus.). 128p. 18.95 (978-1-892145-89-5(8)) Little Bookroom.

AMERICAN ALLIANCE FOR LABOR AND DEMOCRACY

Dennis, Michael. The Memorial Day Massacre: Chicago, Labor, & the Movement for Industrial Democracy. 2010. (ENG.). 288p. 89.00 (978-0-230-61821-3(9)) Palgrave Macmillan.

Okimoto, Daniel I. & Oksenberg, Michel, eds. America's Alliances with Japan & Korea in a Changing Northeast Asia. (978-0-8047-3759-3(2)) Stanford Univ. Pr.

AMERICAN ANTI-SLAVERY SOCIETY

Muelder, Owen W. Theodore Dwight Weld & the American Anti-Slavery Society. 2011. (ENG.). 236p. pap. 45.00 (978-0-7864-6396-1(1)) McFarland & Co., Inc. Pubs.

AMERICAN ART

see Art, American

AMERICAN ART POTTERY

see Art Pottery, American

AMERICAN ASSOCIATION OF GROUP WORKERS

Greengard, Samuel. Finding the Work You Love: The Essential Guide to Reinventing Your Life. 2008. (AARP Ser.). (ENG.). 352p. pap. 14.95 (978-1-4027-5240-7(7)) Sterling Publishing Co., Inc.

AMERICAN ASSOCIATION OF JUNIOR COLLEGES

Nelson, Cary. No University Is an Island: Saving Academic Freedom. 2010. (ENG.). 288p. 65.00 (978-0-8147-5859-5(2)) New York Univ. Pr.

AMERICAN AUTHORS

see Authors, American

AMERICAN BALLADS AND SONGS

see Ballads, American; Folk Songs, American; Songs, American

AMERICAN BAR ASSOCIATION

Beck, Bill. The Young Lawyers of the American Bar Association: Celebrating 75 Years of Excellence. 2010. (978-1-57864-624-1(3)) Donning Co. Pubs.

Fox, Lawrence J., et al. A Century of Legal Ethics: Trial Lawyers & the ABA Canons of Professional Ethics. 2009. xxxv, 413p. (978-1-60442-494-2(X)) American Bar Assn.

Olson, Kurt & Velvel, Lawrence R. The Gathering Peasants Revolt. 2008. 112p. pap. 12.95 (978-0-9778089-3-9(5)) Doukathsan Pr.

Price, John R. Conflicts, Confidentiality, & Other Ethical Considerations in Estate Planning, 801-2nd. 2nd ed. 2007. (Tax Management Portfolios Ser.: 801-2nd). spiral bd. 400.00 (978-1-55871-574-5(6)) Tax Management, Inc.

Tamanaha, Brian Z. Failing Law Schools. 2012. (Chicago Series in Law & Society Ser.). (Illus.). 216p. 25.00 (978-0-226-92361-1(4)) Univ. of Chicago Pr.

Warren, Charles. A History of the American Bar. 2009. 600p. 37.99 (978-1-115-56560-8(5)); pap. 43.75 (978-1-115-56562-2(1)) BiblioBazaar.

—A History of the American Bar. 2009. 370p. pap. (978-0-217-42608-4(5)) Books LLC.

—A History of the American Bar. 2006. (ENG.). pap. 29.95 (978-1-59605-990-0(7), Cosimo Classics) Cosimo, Inc.

AMERICAN BISON

Here are entered works on the American buffalo. Works on buffaloes of the eastern hemisphere are entered under Buffaloes.

Cook, John R. The Border & the Buffalo: An Untold Story of the Southwest Plains. 2009. (ENG., Illus.). 384p. pap. 23.95 (978-1-933337-28-9(1)) State Hse. Pr.

Hornaday, William Temple. The Extermination of the American Bison. 2009. 308p. 28.99 (978-0-559-06468-5(3)); 29.99 (978-0-559-06460-9(8)); pap. 23.75 (978-0-559-06465-4(9)); pap. 29.75 (978-0-559-06462-3(4)) BiblioBazaar.

—The Extermination of the American Bison. 2008. (Illus.). 276p. per. (978-1-4065-6853-0(8)) Dodo Pr.

Punke, Michael. Last Stand: George Bird Grinnell, the Battle to Save the Buffalo, & the Birth of the New West. 2008. 304p. pap. 14.95 (978-0-06-089791-8(0)) HarperCollins Pubs.

—Last Stand: George Bird Grinnell, the Battle to Save the Buffalo, & the Birth of the New West. 2009. (ENG.). 304p. pap. 18.95 (978-0-8032-2680-7(2), Bison Bks.) Univ. of Nebraska Pr.

Rinella, Steven. American Buffalo: In Search of a Lost Icon. 2009. (ENG., Illus.). 304p. pap. 15.00 (978-0-385-52169-7(3)) Spiegel & Grau.

Rosen, R. D. A Buffalo in the House: The Extraordinary Story of Charlie & His Family. 2008. (ENG., Illus.). 272p. pap. 14.00 (978-0-8129-7888-9(9), Random Hse. Trade Paperbacks) Random House Publishing Group.

—A Buffalo in the House: The True Story about a Man, an Animal, & the American West. 2007. (ENG., Illus.). 242p. 24.95 (978-1-59558-165-5(0)) New Pr., The.

Sandoz, Mari. The Buffalo Hunters: The Story of the Hide Men. 2nd ed. 2008. (ENG., Illus.). 384p. pap. 16.95 (978-0-8032-1880-2(X), Bison Bks.) Univ. of Nebraska Pr.

Whitney, Caspar. Musk Ox, Bison, Sheep & Goat. 2007. (ENG.). 280p. 42.95 (978-0-548-03987-8(9)) Kessinger Publishing, LLC.

Yellowstone National Park Bison: Oversight Hearing Before the Subcommittee on National Parks, Forests, & Public Lands of the Committee on Natural Resources, U.S. House of Representatives, One Hundred Tenth Congress, First Session, March 20, 2007. 2007. iii, 75p. (978-0-16-078965-6(6), 552-070-36083-2) United States Government Printing Office.

Zontek, Ken. Buffalo Nation: American Indian Efforts to Restore the Bison. 2007. (Bison Original Ser.). (ENG., Illus.). 256p. pap. 19.95 (978-0-8032-9922-1(2), Bison Bks.) Univ. of Nebraska Pr.

AMERICAN BLACK DIALECT

see Black English

AMERICAN BOARD OF COMMISSIONERS FOR FOREIGN MISSIONS

Anderson, Rufus. History of the Missions of the American Board of Commissioners for Foreign Missions, in India by Rufus Anderson. 2006. 476p. per. 29.99 (978-1-4255-5267-1(6)) MPublishing.

—Memorial Volume of the Firsty Fifty Years of the American Board of Commissioners for Foreign Missions. 2006. 468p. per. 29.99 (978-1-4255-5192-6(0)) MPublishing.

Breath, Sarah Ann. A Journey from Boston to Urmia: The Journal of Sarah Ann Breath. 2008. (978-1-59333-783-4(3)) Gorgias Pr., LLC.

Leimdorfer, Karen. Cultural Imperialism or Cultural Encounters. 2008. 212p. pap. (978-3-8364-3667-0(1)) VDM Verlag Dr. Mueller e.K.

Makdisi, Ussama. Artillery of Heaven: American Missionaries & the Failed Conversion of the Middle East. (United States in the World Ser.). (Illus.). 2009. 280p. pap. 19.95 (978-0-8014-7575-7(9)) 2007. 262p. 60.95 (978-0-8014-4621-4(X)) Cornell Univ. Pr.

Peabody, Andrew. [Christian Pamphlets. 2006. 624p. per. 34.99 (978-1-4255-6665-4(0)) MPublishing.

Whipple, Charles King. Relation of the American Board of Commissioners for Foreign Missions to Slavery by Charles K Whipple. 2006. 252p. per. 20.99 (978-1-4255-2123-3(1)) MPublishing.

Wilder, Royal Gould. Mission Schools in India of the American Board of Commissioners for Foreign Missions, with Sketches of the Missions among the North American Indians. 2006. 448p. per. 29.99 (978-1-4255-5032-5(0)) MPublishing.

AMERICAN BROADCASTING COMPANY

Cozma, Codrina. The Power of the Spoken Word - Literature in the American Broadcasting & Film Industry of The 1990s. 2008. 140p. pap. (978-3-639-01256-9(9)) VDM Verlag Dr. Mueller e.K.

AMERICAN BULL TERRIER

see American Pit Bull Terrier; American Staffordshire Terrier

AMERICAN CHEMICAL SOCIETY

Inman, Henry J. & Inman, Henry. Rubber Mirror: Reflections of the Rubber Division's First 100 Years. 2009. (ENG.). 344p. 29.95 (978-1-931968-60-7(8)) Univ. of Akron Pr., The.

AMERICAN CIVIL LIBERTIES UNION

Askin, Frank. Defending Rights: A Life in Law & Politics. 224p. 56.98 (978-1-57392-622-5(1)); (ENG.). 1p. pap. 26.98 (978-1-57392-300-2(1)) Prometheus Bks., Pubs. (Humanity Bks.).

Bangarth, Stephanie. Voices Raised in Protest: Defending Citizens of Japanese Ancestry, 1942-49. 2009. (Illus.). 280p. pap. 32.95 (978-0-295-98828-3(2)) Univ. of Washington Pr.

Kaminer, Wendy. Worst Instincts: Cowardice, Conformity, & the ACLU, 1 vol. 2010. (ENG.). 160p. pap. 16.00 (978-0-8070-4436-0(9)) Beacon Pr.

Kastensmidt, Sam. Indefensible: 10 Ways the ACLU Is Destroying America. 2006. pap. 13.00 *(978-1-929626-28-1(2))* Coral Ridge Ministries Media, Inc.
Kutulas, Judy. The American Civil Liberties Union: And the Making of Modern Liberalism, 1930-1960. 2006. (ENG.). 320p. 38.95 *(978-0-8078-3036-9(4))* Univ. of North Carolina Pr.

AMERICAN CIVIL WAR, 1861-1865
see United States—History—Civil War, 1861-1865

AMERICAN COCKER SPANIEL
see Cocker Spaniels

AMERICAN COLLEGE OF SURGEONS
American College of Surgeons Staff. A List of Fellows, 1913. ix, 187p. reprint ed. 39.00 *(978-0-932051-29-5(4))* Reprint Services Co.

AMERICAN COLLEGE TESTING ASSESSMENT
see ACT Assessment

AMERICAN COLONIZATION SOCIETY
Brown, Isaac Van Arsdale. Biography of Robert Finley, of Basking Ridge, New Jersey: With an Account of His Agency As the Author of the American Colonization Society (1857) 2009. 340p. 46.95 *(978-1-4374-8642-1(8))*; pap. 31.95 *(978-1-4374-8166-2(3))* Kessinger Publishing, LLC.
Burin, Eric. Slavery & the Peculiar Solution: A History of the American Colonization Society. 2008. (Southern Dissent Ser.). (ENG., Illus.). 240p. pap. 24.95 *(978-0-8130-3273-3(3))* Univ. Pr. of Florida.
The Sixteenth Annual Report of the American Society for Colonizing the Free People of Colour from the United States. 2010. pap. 18.88 *(978-1-61143-183-4(2))* Gorgias Pr., LLC.
Thomas, Perry. From Slave to Governor: The Unlikely Life of Lott Cary. 2010. (ENG.). 228p. (YA). pap. 12.50 *(978-0-9786567-9-9(2))* Parson Place Pr., LLC.
Tyler-McGraw, Marie. An African Republic: Black & White Virginians in the Making of Liberia. 2007. (ENG., Illus.). 264p. 39.95 *(978-0-8078-3167-0(0))* Univ. of North Carolina Pr.

AMERICAN DENTAL ASSOCIATION
Beck, Bill. 150 Years of the American Dental Association: A Pictorial History. 2009. *(978-1-57864-592-3(1))* Donning Co. Pubs.

AMERICAN DIARIES
Fea, John. Way of Improvement Leads Home: Philip Vickers Fithian & the Rural Enlightenment in Early America. 2008. (Early American Studies). (Illus.). 280p. (C). 39.95 *(978-0-8122-4109-9(6))* Univ. of Pennsylvania Pr.
Hafen, Leroy R., ed. Overland Routes to the Gold Fields 1859: From Contemporary Diaries. 2011. 324p. 50.95 ***(978-1-258-08707-4(3))*** Literary Licensing, LLC.
Lyman, Leo, ed. Candid Insights of a Mormon Apostle: The Diaries of Abraham H. Cannon, 1889-1895. 2010. 800p. 125.00 *(978-1-56085-210-0(0))* Signature Bks., LLC.
Matthews, William. American Diaries: An Annotated Bibliography of American Diaries Written Prior To 1861. Matthews, William et al, eds. 2011. 396p. 54.95 ***(978-1-258-06477-8(4))*** Literary Licensing, LLC.

AMERICAN DRAMA
see also One-Act Plays
American Theatre Magazine Staff, ed. The American Theatre Reader: 25 Years from American Theatre. 2009. (ENG.). 600p. pap. 24.95 *(978-1-55936-346-4(0))* Theatre Communications Group, Inc.
Attweiler, Robert, et al. Plays & Playwrights 2008. Denton, Martin, ed. 2008. pap. 18.00 *(978-0-9794852-1-3(5))* New York Theatre Experience, Inc., The.
Baker, George P. Modern American Plays. 2008. 556p. 57.95 *(978-0-548-94400-4(8))* 2007. (ENG.). 560p. per. 42.95 *(978-0-548-59393-6(0))* Kessinger Publishing, LLC.
Brougham, John. Love & Murder: A farce, in one act. by John Brougham. to which are added, a description of the costumecast of the characters ... & the whole of Th. 2011. 22p. pap. 11.99 ***(978-1-4181-9167-2(1))*** MPublishing.
Bryer, Jackson R. & Hartig, Mary C. The Facts on File Companion to American Drama. 2nd rev. ed. 2010. (Companion to Literature Ser.). 656p. (C). (gr. 9-18). 85.00 *(978-0-8160-7748-9(7))* Facts On File, Inc.
Clark, Connie. 12 Fun & Easy Plays for Middle Schoolers. 2010. 176p. pap. 19.95 *(978-1-58595-764-4(X))* Twenty-Third Pubns./Bayard.
Cleaver, Heather. A Children's Play of the Stations of the Cross: An Adaptation from the Holy Bible. 2011. 112p. pap. 14.99 *(978-1-4567-3051-2(7))* AuthorHouse.
Knowles, Richard & Mojica, Monique. Staging Coyote's Dream, Volume 2: An Anthology of First Nations Drama in English, Volume 2. 2009. (ENG.). 380p. pap. 29.95 *(978-0-88754-735-5(4))* Playwrights Canada Pr. CAN. Dist: Consortium Bk. Sales & Distribution.
Lane, Eric & Shengold, Nina, eds. Shorter, Faster, Funnier: Comic Plays & Monologues. 2011. (Vintage Original Ser.). 544p. pap. 16.95 *(978-0-307-47664-7(2)*, Vintage) Knopf Doubleday Publishing Group.
Moeller, Terence James, et al. Dramas of Kalalau. 2007. 192p. pap. 13.95 *(978-1-56647-827-4(8))* Mutual Publishing LLC.
Moses, Montrose J. Representative Plays by American Dramatists. 2009. 688p. 32.99 *(978-1-103-72317-1(0))*; pap. 26.99 *(978-1-103-72313-3(8))* BiblioBazaar.
One Time Blind. Think Again! Modern Scripts for Worship. 2008. (ENG.). 38p. pap. 19.99 *(978-0-8341-7658-4(0)*, 9780834176584) Lillenas Publishing Co.
Palmer, R. Barton & Bray, William Robert. Hollywood's Tennessee: The Williams Films & Postwar America. 2009. (ENG., Illus.). 344p. pap. 30.00 *(978-0-292-72304-7(0))* Univ. of Texas Pr.
Pereira, Paulo A., et al. Two Portuguese-American Plays: Amarelo & Through a Portagee Gate. Thomas, Patricia A., ed. 2007. (Portuguese in the Americas Ser.). 170p. pap. 17.95 *(978-1-933227-21-4(4))* Tagus Pr.
Stowe, Brook. New York Theater Review 2009. 2009. 352p. pap. 19.95 *(978-0-578-02284-0(2))* Black Wave Pr.
Whittell, Crispin. Darwin in Malibu. 2007. 52p. pap. 7.50 *(978-0-8222-2196-8(9))* Dramatists Play Service, Inc.

AMERICAN DRAMA—19TH CENTURY
Fisher, James & Londre, Felicia Hardison. The A to Z of American Theater: Modernism. 97th ed. 2009. (A to Z Guide Ser.: No. 97). (ENG.). 616p. pap. 34.45 *(978-0-8108-6884-7(9))* Scarecrow Pr., Inc.
Fisher, James L. & Londre, Felicia Hardison. Historical Dictionary of American Theater: Modernism. 2007. (Historical Dictionaries of Literature & the Arts Ser.). (ENG.). 616p. 139.00 *(978-0-8108-5533-5(X))* Scarecrow Pr., Inc.
Matlaw, Myron. Nineteenth Century American Plays: Seven Plays Including the Black Crook. Date not set. 272p. 22.95 *(978-0-8488-2367-2(2))* Amereon LTD.
Mitchell, Koritha. Living with Lynching: Afrincan American Lynching Plays, Performance, & Citizenship, 1890-1930. 2011. (New Black Studies Ser.). (ENG., Illus.). 272p. 40.00 ***(978-0-252-03649-1(2))*** Univ. of Illinois Pr.

AMERICAN DRAMA—20TH CENTURY
Alexander, Doris. Eugene O'Neill's Creative Struggle: The Decisive Decade, 1924 - 1933. 2008. 352p. per. 26.95 *(978-0-271-02796-8(7))* Pennsylvania State Univ. Pr.
Ballet. Playwrights for Tomorrow V 2. 2009. pap. 50.00 *(978-0-8166-0383-1(9))* Univ. of Minnesota Pr.
—Playwrights for Tomorrow V 3. 2009. (ENG.). 352p. pap. 60.00 *(978-0-8166-0431-9(2))* Univ. of Minnesota Pr.
—Playwrights for Tomorrow V 4. 2009. pap. 60.00 *(978-0-8166-0433-3(9))* Univ. of Minnesota Pr.
—Playwrights for Tomorrow V 5. 2009. pap. 40.00 *(978-0-8166-0535-4(1))* Univ. of Minnesota Pr.
—Playwrights for Tomorrow V 6. 2009. pap. 40.00 *(978-0-8166-0538-5(6))* Univ. of Minnesota Pr.
—Playwrights for Tomorrow V 8. 2009. pap. 50.00 *(978-0-8166-0652-8(8))* Univ. of Minnesota Pr.
—Playwrights for Tomorrow V 9. 2009. pap. 50.00 *(978-0-8166-0654-2(4))* Univ. of Minnesota Pr.
—Playwrights for Tomorrow V1. 2009. pap. 50.00 *(978-0-8166-0381-7(2))* Univ. of Minnesota Pr.
—Playwrights for Tomorrow V11. 2009. pap. 50.00 *(978-0-8166-0697-9(8))* Univ. of Minnesota Pr.
—Playwrights for Tomorrow V12. 2009. pap. 50.00 *(978-0-8166-0749-5(4))* Univ. of Minnesota Pr.
—Playwrights for Tomorrow V13. 2009. pap. 60.00 *(978-0-8166-0751-8(6))* Univ. of Minnesota Pr.
Barlow, Judith E. Women Writers of the Provincetown Players. 2009. (Excelsior Editions Ser.). 320p. pap. 29.95 *(978-1-4384-2790-4(5)*, Suny Pr.) State Univ. of New York Pr.
—Women Writers of the Provincetown Players: A Collection of Short Works. 2009. (Excelsior Editions Ser.). 320p. 75.00 *(978-1-4384-2789-8(1)*, Suny Pr.) State Univ. of New York Pr.
Birimisa, George. Return to the Caffe Cino. 2006. (Illus.). 500p. 44.95 *(978-0-9774214-1-1(4))* Moving Finger Pr.
Bottoms, Stephen J. Playing Underground: A Critical History of the 1960s off-off-Broadway Movement. 2006. (Theater: Theory/Text/Performance Ser.). (ENG., Illus.). 448p. pap. 22.95 *(978-0-472-03194-8(5))* Univ. of Michigan Pr.
Cohen, Sarah Blacher & Koch, Joanne, intros. Shared Stages: Ten American Dramas of Blacks & Jews. 2007. (SUNY Series in Modern Jewish Literature & Culture). (Illus.). 556p. pap. 29.95 *(978-0-7914-7282-8(5))*; 74.50 *(978-0-7914-7281-1(7))* State Univ. of New York Pr.
Cole, Norma & Elliott, Naneki. Just Desserts. Date not set. 40p. pap. 4.25 *(978-1-58342-018-8(5)*, J37) Dramatic Publishing Co.
Detrick, Erin, ed. Monologues for Men. 2008. (Actor's Choice Ser.). (ENG.). 152p. per. 14.95 *(978-0-9709046-5-2(7))* Playscripts, Inc.
—Monologues for Teens. 2008. (Actor's Choice Ser.). (ENG.). 136p. (gr. 7-18). per. 14.95 *(978-0-9709046-6-9(5))* Playscripts, Inc.
—Monologues for Women. 2008. (Actor's Choice Ser.). (ENG.). 152p. per. 14.95 *(978-0-9709046-4-5(9))* Playscripts, Inc.
Dixon, Michael Bigelow & Engelman, Liz. Ten-Minute Plays, Vol. 4. 266p. pap. *(978-0-573-63367-6(3))* French, Samuel Inc.
Drama for Students, No. 28. 2011. 124.00 *(978-0-7876-8124-1(5))* Cengage Gale.
Fisher, James & Londre, Felicia Hardison. The A to Z of American Theater: Modernism. 97th ed. 2009. (A to Z Guide Ser.: No. 97). (ENG.). 616p. pap. 34.45 *(978-0-8108-6884-7(9))* Scarecrow Pr., Inc.
Fisher, James L. & Londre, Felicia Hardison. Historical Dictionary of American Theater: Modernism. 2007. (Historical Dictionaries of Literature & the Arts Ser.). (ENG.). 616p. 139.00 *(978-0-8108-5533-5(X))* Scarecrow Pr., Inc.
Friesen, Lauren, ed. Best Student One Acts, Vol. 5. Date not set. 263p. pap. 16.95 *(978-1-58342-000-3(2)*, B89) Dramatic Publishing Co.
Gassner, John & Barnes, Clive, eds. Best American Plays. (Sixth Ser. 1963-1967). 34.95 *(978-0-88411-639-4(5))* Amereon LTD.
Gutierrez, Sandra M., et al, eds. Teatro Chicana: A Collective Memoir & Selected Plays. 2008. (Chicana Matters Ser.). (ENG., Illus.). 328p. pap. 27.95 *(978-0-292-71744-2(X))* Univ. of Texas Pr.
Hansel, Adrien-Alice & Dubiner, Julie Felise, eds. Humana Festival 2006: The Complete Plays. 30th anniv. ed. 2009. (ENG.). 400p. pap. 19.95 *(978-0-9709046-1-4(4))* Playscripts, Inc.
Huston-Findley, Shirley Annette & Howard, Rebecca, eds. Footpaths & Bridges: Voices from the Native American Women Playwrights Archive. 2008. (CRE & ENG.). 304p. 90.00 *(978-0-472-11613-3(4))* Univ. of Michigan Pr.
Jones, Bret. Masculinity in Pulitzer Prize-Winning Plays 1982-2002. 2008. 336p. pap. *(978-3-639-08409-2(8))* VDM Verlag Dr. Mueller e.K.
Lane, Stewart F. In the Wings: The New Romantic Comedy about Show Business. 2008. (ENG.). 96p. pap. 10.95 *(978-1-55783-738-7(4)*, 1557837384, Applause Theatre & Cinema) Leonard, Hal Corp.
Lee, Josephine, et al, eds. Asian American Plays for a New Generation. 2011. (ENG., Illus.). 360p. 84.50 *(978-1-4399-0515-9(0))* Temple Univ. Pr.
Papa, Lee. Staged Action: Six Plays from the American Workers' Theatre. 2009. 288p. 71.95 *(978-0-8014-4688-7(0))*; pap. 22.95 *(978-0-8014-7523-8(6))* Cornell Univ. Pr. (ILR Pr.).
Ratliff, Gerald Lee, ed. Young Women's Monologues from Contemporary Plays #2: Professional Auditions for Aspiring Actresses, 1 vol., 2. 2008. (ENG.). 248p. pap. 15.95 *(978-1-56608-153-5(X))* Meriwether Publishing, Ltd.
Saddik, Annette J. & Saddik, Annette. Contemporary American Drama. 2007. (Edinburgh Critical Guides to Literature Ser.). (ENG., Illus.). 224p. (gr. 17). pap. 30.00 *(978-0-7486-2494-2(5))* Edinburgh Univ. Pr. GBR. Dist: Columbia Univ. Pr.
—Contemporary American Drama. Halliwell, Martin & Mousley, Andy, eds. 2007. (Edinburgh Critical Guides to Literature Ser.). (ENG., Illus.). 224p. (gr. 17). 120.00 *(978-0-7486-2493-5(7))* Edinburgh Univ. Pr. GBR. Dist: Columbia Univ. Pr.
Sanchez, Sonia. I'm Black When I'm Singing, I'm Blue When I Ain't & Other Plays. Wood, Jacqueline, ed. 2010. (ENG.). 196p. 69.95 *(978-0-8223-4757-6(1))*; pap. 19.95 *(978-0-8223-4778-1(4))* Duke Univ. Pr.
Saroyan, William. The Time of Your Life. 2008. (Modern Plays Ser.). (ENG.). 112p. pap. 14.95 *(978-1-4081-1394-3(5)*, Methuen Drama) A & C Black GBR. Dist: Macmillan.
Susoyev, Steve & Birimisa, George. Return to the Caffe Cino. 2006. (Illus.). 500p. per. 24.95 *(978-0-9774214-0-4(6))* Moving Finger Pr.
Trevens, Francine L., et al. Short Plays to Long Remember. Trevens, Francine L., ed. 2010. (Illus.). 436p. pap. 16.95 *(978-1-886586-14-7(4)*, T 'n' T Bks.) T 'n' T Classic Bks.

AMERICAN DRAMA—21ST CENTURY
August, Ian, et al. Off-Off Broadway Festival Plays: 31st Series. 2007. (Illus.). 104p. per. 8.95 *(978-0-573-64242-5(7))* French, Samuel Inc.
Brunstetter, Bekah, et al. Off-off broadway festival Plays: 33rd Series. 2009. 100p. mass mkt. 9.00 *(978-0-573-67036-7(6))* French, Samuel Inc.
Cohen, Sarah Blacher & Koch, Joanne, intros. Shared Stages: Ten American Dramas of Blacks & Jews. 2007. (SUNY Series in Modern Jewish Literature & Culture). (Illus.). 556p. pap. 29.95 *(978-0-7914-7282-8(5))*; 74.50 *(978-0-7914-7281-1(7))* State Univ. of New York Pr.
Drama for Students, No. 28. 2011. 124.00 *(978-0-7876-8124-1(5))* Cengage Gale.
Fisher, Van Dirk, compiled by. The Best Plays from the Strawberry One-Act Festival: Volume Five. 2008. 144p. pap. 11.95 *(978-0-595-51323-9(9))* iUniverse, Inc.
Hal Leonard Corporation Staff. The Best American Short Plays 2007-2008. Parisi, Barbara, ed. 2009. (ENG.). 384p. pap. 18.99 *(978-1-55783-749-3(X)*, 155783749X); 34.99 *(978-1-55783-750-9(3)*, 1557837503) Leonard, Hal Corp. (Applause Theatre & Cinema).
Hansel, Adrien-Alice. Humana Festival 2010: the Complete Plays. Hansel, Adrien-Alice, ed. 2011. (ENG.). 400p. pap. 19.95 ***(978-0-9819099-6-7(5))*** Playscripts, Inc.
Kelty, Matthew, et al. Off-off Broadway Festival Plays: Thirty-Second Series. 2008. 82p. mass mkt. 9.95 *(978-0-573-66023-8(9))* French, Samuel Inc.
Lee, Josephine, et al, eds. Asian American Plays for a New Generation. 2011. (ENG., Illus.). 360p. 84.50 *(978-1-4399-0515-9(0))* Temple Univ. Pr.
Parisi, Barbara. The Best American Short Plays 2004-2005. 2008. (ENG.). 336p. 32.95 *(978-1-55783-711-0(2)*, 1557837112); 332p. pap. 16.95 *(978-1-55783-712-7(0)*, 1557837120) Leonard, Hal Corp. (Applause Theatre & Cinema).
Parisi, Barbara, ed. The Best American Short Plays 2005-2006. 2008. (ENG.). 384p. 32.95 *(978-1-55783-713-4(9)*, 1557837139); pap. 18.95 *(978-1-55783-714-1(7)*, 1557837147) Leonard, Hal Corp. (Applause Theatre & Cinema).
—The Best American Short Plays 2006-2007, 1 vol. 2010. (ENG.). 382p. 34.99 *(978-1-55783-747-9(3)*, 1557837473); 380p. pap. 18.99 *(978-1-55783-748-6(1)*, 1557837481) Leonard, Hal Corp. (Applause Theatre & Cinema).
—Best American Short Plays 2008-2009. 2010. (ENG.). 358p. 32.99 *(978-1-55783-761-5(9)*, 1557837619, Applause Theatre & Cinema) Leonard, Hal Corp.
Ribalow, M. Z. Plays from New River 1. 2011. (New River Play Ser.). (ENG.). 198p. pap. 35.00 *(978-0-7864-6502-6(6))* McFarland & Co., Inc. Pubs.
Trevens, Francine L., et al. Short Plays to Long Remember. Trevens, Francine L., ed. 2010. (Illus.). 436p. pap. 16.95 *(978-1-886586-14-7(4)*, T 'n' T Bks.) T 'n' T Classic Bks.
Young, Glenn. The Best American Short Plays. 2007. (Best American Short Plays Ser.). (ENG.). 218p. 32.95 *(978-1-55783-704-2(X)*, 155783704X, Applause Theatre & Cinema) Leonard, Hal Corp.
—The Best American Short Plays 2003-2004. 2006. (ENG.). 268p. 32.95 *(978-1-55783-695-3(7)*, 1557836957); 312p. per. 16.95 *(978-1-55783-696-0(5)*, 1557836965) Leonard, Hal Corp. (Applause Theatre & Cinema).
Young, Glenn, ed. The Best American Short Plays. 2007. (Best American Short Plays Ser.). (ENG.). 216p. per. 16.95 *(978-1-55783-705-9(8)*, 1557837058, Applause Theatre & Cinema) Leonard, Hal Corp.
—The Best American Short Plays 2002-2003. 2010. (ENG.). 352p. 32.99 *(978-1-55783-719-6(8)*, 1557837198); pap. 18.99 *(978-1-55783-720-2(1)*, 1557837201) Leonard, Hal Corp. (Applause Theatre & Cinema).

AMERICAN DRAMA—AFRICAN AMERICAN AUTHORS
Amkpa. Theatre & Postcolonial Desires. 2007. 224p. 36.00 *(978-0-415-43544-4(7))* Routledge.
Asong, Linus. Stranger in his Homeland. 2010. 366p. pap. *(978-9956-616-46-6(X))* Langaa Research & Publishing Common Initiative Group CMR. Dist: Michigan State Univ. Pr.
Bada, Valérie. Mnemopoetics: Memory & Slavery in African American Drama. 2008. (Dramaturgies. Textes, Cultures et Représentations. Texts, Cultures & Performances Ser.). 226p. pap. 53.95 *(978-90-5201-276-6(8))* PIE - Peter Lang BEL. Dist: Lang, Peter.
Banks, Daniel. Say Word! Voices from Hip Hop Theater. 2011. (Critical Performances Ser.). (ENG., Illus.). 400p. (C). 95.00 *(978-0-472-07132-6(7))*; pap. 40.00 *(978-0-472-05132-8(6))* Univ. of Michigan Pr.
bilgin tekin, inci & Bilgin Tekin, Inci. Ntozake Shange's Choreo-Poetry: Celebration of an Authentic Form. 2011. 84p. pap. ***(978-3-8443-1257-7(9))*** Lambert Academic Publishing.
Brown, William Wells. The Escape; or, a Leap for Freedom. 2007. 108p. per. 12.45 *(978-1-60206-645-8(0))* Cosimo, Inc.
Cohen, Sarah Blacher & Koch, Joanne, intros. Shared Stages: Ten American Dramas of Blacks & Jews. 2007. (SUNY Series in Modern Jewish Literature & Culture). (Illus.). 556p. pap. 29.95 *(978-0-7914-7282-8(5))*; 74.50 *(978-0-7914-7281-1(7))* State Univ. of New York Pr.
Hall, Katori. Katori Hall Plays One: Hoodoo Love - Hurt Village - The Mountaintop - Saturday Night - Sunday Morning. 2011. (Modern Plays Ser.). (ENG.). 352p. pap. 23.95 ***(978-1-4081-4702-3(5)***, Methuen Drama) A & C Black GBR. Dist: Macmillan.
Hardie, Mg. It Ain't Just the Size. 2010. 282p. pap. 16.50 *(978-1-59330-647-2(4))* Aventine Pr.
Jiang, Tsui-fen. The American Dream in African American, Asian American, & Hispanic American Drama: August Wilson, Frank Chin, & Luis Valdez. 2009. 180p. 99.95 *(978-0-7734-4656-4(7))* Mellen, Edwin Pr., The.
Lihamba, Amandina, frwd. African Women Playwrights. 2008. (ENG., Illus.). 384p. pap. 26.00 *(978-0-252-07573-5(0))* Univ. of Illinois Pr.
Perkins, Kathy A., intro. African Women Playwrights. 2008. (Illus.). 280p. 65.00 *(978-0-252-03387-2(6))* Univ. of Illinois Pr.
Richardson, Willis. Plays & Pageants from the Life of the Negro. 384p. 2008. 48.95 *(978-1-4366-8518-4(4))* 2007. (ENG.). per. 33.95 *(978-1-4325-6765-1(9))* Kessinger Publishing, LLC.
Richardson, Willis, ed. Plays & Pageants from the Life of the Negro. 2007. (ENG.). 420p. per. 25.00 *(978-1-934110-55-3(8))* Univ. Pr. of Mississippi.
Sanchez, Sonia. I'm Black When I'm Singing, I'm Blue When I Ain't & Other Plays. Wood, Jacqueline, ed. 2010. (ENG.). 196p. 69.95 *(978-0-8223-4757-6(1))*; pap. 19.95 *(978-0-8223-4778-1(4))* Duke Univ. Pr.
Wolfe, George C. The Colored Museum. pap. 7.50 *(978-0-8222-2434-1(8))* Dramatists Play Service, Inc.

AMERICAN DRAMA—AFRICAN AMERICAN AUTHORS—HISTORY AND CRITICISM
Anadolu-Okur, Nilgun. Contemporary African American Theater: Afrocentricity in the Works of Larry Neal, Amiri Baraka, & Charles Fuller. 2010. (ENG.). 236p. pap. 39.95 *(978-0-415-88324-5(5))* Routledge.
Anderson, Lisa M. Black Feminism in Contemporary Drama. 2008. (Illus.). 152p. 37.00 *(978-0-252-03228-8(4))* Univ. of Illinois Pr.
Hagood, Taylor. Secrecy, Magic, & the One-Act Plays of Harlem Renaissance Women Writers. 2010. (Black Performance & Cultural Criticism Ser.). (ENG.). 232p. 44.95 *(978-0-8142-1121-2(6))*; cd-rom 14.95 *(978-0-8142-9219-8(4))* Ohio State Univ. Pr.
Harris-Lopez, Trudier. Reading Contemporary African American Drama: Fragments of History, Fragments of Self. 2007. (African-American Literature & Culture Ser.: Vol. 15). (C). 29.95 *(978-0-8204-8887-5(9))*; xvii, 223p. pap. 29.95 *(978-0-8204-8886-8(0))* Lang, Peter Publishing, Inc.
Kolin, Philip C., ed. Contemporary African American Women Playwrights: A Casebook. (Casebooks on Modern Dramatists Ser.). 2012. (ENG.). 224p. (C). pap. 42.95 ***(978-0-415-54112-1(3))*** 2007. X, 214p. 120.00 *(978-0-415-97826-2(2))* Routledge.
Kolin, Philip C., ed. Suzan-Lori Parks: Essays on the Plays & Other Works. 2010. (ENG., Illus.). 219p. pap. 39.95 *(978-0-7864-4167-9(4))* McFarland & Co., Inc. Pubs.
Miller, Henry D. Theorizing Black Theatre: Art Versus Protest in Critical Writings, 1898-1965. 2010. (ENG., Illus.). 284p. pap. 65.00 *(978-0-7864-5937-7(9))* McFarland & Co., Inc. Pubs.
Mitchell, Koritha. Living with Lynching: Afrincan American Lynching Plays, Performance, & Citizenship, 1890-1930. 2011. (New Black Studies Ser.). (ENG., Illus.). 272p. 40.00 ***(978-0-252-03649-1(2))*** Univ. of Illinois Pr.

Williams-Witherspoon, Kimmika. The Secret Messages in African American Theater: Hidden Meanings Embedded in Public Discourse. 2006. 336p. (978-0-7734-5642-5(2)) Mellen, Edwin Pr., The.

Wilson, James F. Bulldaggers, Pansies, & Chocolate Babies: Performance, Race, & Sexuality in the Harlem Renaissance. (Triangulations: Lesbian/Gay/Queer Theater/Drama/Performance Ser.). (Illus.). 2011. (ENG.). 262p. pap. 27.95 (978-0-472-03489-5(8)) 2010. ix, 260p. E-Book 29.95 (978-0-472-02696-8(8)) Univ. of Michigan Pr.

AMERICAN DRAMA—AFRO-AMERICAN AUTHORS

see American Drama—African American Authors

AMERICAN DRAMA—ASIAN AMERICAN AUTHORS

Bose, Neilesh, ed. Beyond Bollywood & Broadway: Plays from the South Asian Diaspora. 2009. (ENG.). 520p. 75.00 (978-0-253-35300-9(9), 0253353009); pap. 29.95 (978-0-253-22068-4(8), 0253220688) Indiana Univ. Pr.

Jiang, Tsui-fen. The American Dream in African American, Asian American, & Hispanic American Drama: August Wilson, Frank Chin, & Luis Valdez. 2009. 180p. 99.95 (978-0-7734-4656-4(7)) Mellen, Edwin Pr., The.

AMERICAN DRAMA—BIBLIOGRAPHY

Hesperides. American Plays Printed 1714-1830 - a Bibliographical Record. 2007. 168p. per. (978-1-4067-5127-7(8), Hesperides Pr.) Read Bks.

Lerzundi, Patricio, ed. El Gobernador Prudent the Prudent Governor by Gaspar de Avila. 2009. (SPA.). 156p. 99.95 (978-0-7734-4813-1(6)) Mellen, Edwin Pr., The.

Roden, Robert F. Later American Plays, 1831-1900. 2009. 146p. 35.95 (978-1-120-35014-5(X)); pap. 20.95 (978-1-120-31120-7(9)) Kessinger Publishing, LLC.

Wegelin, Oscar. Early American Plays, 1714-1830. 2009. 66p. pap. 12.16 (978-1-151-56141-1(X)) General Bks. LLC.

AMERICAN DRAMA—HISPANIC AMERICAN AUTHORS

Bixler, Jacqueline & Seda, Laurietz, eds. Trans/Acting: Latin American & Latino Performing Arts. 2009. 58.50 (978-0-8387-5726-0(X)) Bucknell Univ. Pr.

Flores, Yolanda. The Drama of Gender: Feminist Theater by Women of the Americas. March, Kathleen N., ed. (Worlds of Change Ser.: Vol. 38). viii, 132p. pap. 32.95 (978-0-8204-6243-1(8)) Lang, Peter Publishing, Inc.

Jiang, Tsui-fen. The American Dream in African American, Asian American, & Hispanic American Drama: August Wilson, Frank Chin, & Luis Valdez. 2009. 180p. 99.95 (978-0-7734-4656-4(7)) Mellen, Edwin Pr., The.

Ramirez, Elizabeth C. & Casiano, Catherine, eds. La Voz Latina: Contemporary Plays & Performance Pieces by Latinas. 2011. (ENG., Illus.). 368p. 60.00 (978-0-252-03622-4(0)) Univ. of Illinois Pr.

Rossini, Jon D. Contemporary Latina/o Theater: Wrighting Ethnicity. 2008. (Theater in the Americas Ser.). (ENG.). 272p. pap. 37.50 (978-0-8093-2830-7(5)) Southern Illinois Univ. Pr.

AMERICAN DRAMA—HISTORY AND CRITICISM

Anthony, M. Susan. Gothic Plays & American Society, 1794-1830. 2008. (ENG., Illus.). 203p. pap. 39.95 (978-0-7864-3337-7(X)) McFarland & Co., Inc. Pubs.

Balakian, Jan. Reading the Plays of Wendy Wasserstein, 1 vol. 2010. (ENG., Illus.). 244p. pap. 19.99 (978-1-55783-725-7(2), 1557837252, Applause Theatre & Cinema) Leonard, Hal Corp.

Bloom, Harold, ed. August Wilson. 2009. (Bloom's Modern Critical Views Ser.). 200p. (C). (gr. 9-18). 45.00 (978-1-60413-393-6(7), Chelsea Hse.) Facts On File, Inc.

Bond, Frederick W. The Negro & the Drama: The Direct & Indirect Contribution Which the American Negro Has Made to Drama & the Legitimate Stage. 28.95 (978-0-405-18492-5(1)) Ayer Co. Pubs., Inc.

Burton, Richard. New American Drama. 2006. pap. 28.95 (978-1-4286-3766-5(4)) Kessinger Publishing, LLC.

Cardullo, Robert. The Death of Salesmen. 2010. 188p. pap. (978-3-8383-2177-6(4)) Lambert Academic Publishing.

Coscio, Elizabeth. The Dramatic Political Allegories of the Spanish Exile Félix Mexía Published in Philadelphia, Pennsylvania in 1826: Refugees from the Inquisition. 2006. 256p. (978-0-7734-5582-5(5)) Mellen, Edwin Pr., The.

Dickinson, Thomas H. Playwrights of the New American Theater. 2007. (ENG.). 338p. 46.95 (978-0-548-03313-5(7)) Kessinger Publishing, LLC.

Eastman, Fred. Christ in the Drama: A Study of the Influence of Christ on the Drama of England & America. 2007. (ENG.). 196p. per. 22.95 (978-1-4304-5921-7(2)) Kessinger Publishing, LLC.

Engle, Sherry D. & Engle, Sherry. New Women Dramatists in America, 1890-1920. 2007. (ENG., Illus.). 288p. 95.00 (978-1-4039-7320-7(2)) Palgrave Macmillan.

Favorini, Attilio. Memory in Play: From Aeschylus to Sam Shepard. 2008. (Palgrave Studies in Theatre & Performance History Ser.). (ENG.). 336p. 89.00 (978-0-230-60464-3(1)) Palgrave Macmillan.

Fisher, Judith L. & Watt, Stephen, eds. When They Weren't Doing Shakespeare: Essays on Nineteenth-Century British & American Theatre. 2011. (ENG.). 372p. pap. 24.95 (978-0-8203-3692-3(0)) Univ. of Georgia Pr.

Fletcher, Anne. Rediscovering Mordecai Gorelik: Scene Design & the American Theatre. 2009. (Theater in the Americas Ser.). (Illus.). 304p. pap. 37.50 (978-0-8093-2880-2(1)) Southern Illinois Univ. Pr.

Frick, John W. Theatre, Culture & Temperance Reform in Nineteenth-Century America. 2008. (Cambridge Studies in American Theatre & Drama Ser.). (ENG., Illus.). 272p. pap. 37.99 (978-0-521-07220-5(4)) Cambridge Univ. Pr.

Friedman, Jonathan C., ed. Performing Difference: Representations of the Other in Film & Theatre. 2008. (ENG.). 310p. pap. 47.50 (978-0-7618-4154-8(7)) Univ. Pr. of America, Inc.

Friedman, Sharon, ed. Feminist Theatrical Revisions of Classic Works: Critical Essays. 2008. (ENG., Illus.). 300p. pap. 45.00 (978-0-7864-3425-1(2)) McFarland & Co., Inc. Pubs.

Gallagher, Kathleen. The Theatre of Urban: Youth & Schooling in Dangerous Times. 2007. (ENG., Illus.). 192p. (978-0-8020-9291-5(8)) Univ. of Toronto Pr.

Grondin, Michael & James, Scarlett. Burlesque: The True Art of Seduction. 2011. 335p. pap. 34.95 (978-1-926893-41-9(7)) Cogito Media Grp. CAN. Dist: Midpoint Trade Bks., Inc.

Hall, Roger A. Performing the American Frontier, 1870-1906. 2006. (Cambridge Studies in American Theatre & Drama Ser.). (ENG., Illus.). 296p. pap. 60.00 (978-0-521-03517-0(1)) Cambridge Univ. Pr.

Harris, Geraldine. Beyond Representation: Television drama & the politics & aesthetics of identity. 2011. (ENG.). 214p. pap. 25.95 (978-0-7190-7459-2(2)) Manchester Univ. Pr. GBR. Dist: Macmillan.

Henry, Barbara J. Rewriting Russia: Jacob Gordin's Yiddish Drama. 2011. (ENG., Illus.). 276p. (C). pap. 35.00 (978-0-295-99133-7(X)) Univ. of Washington Pr.

Herrmann, Eileen J. & Dowling, Robert M., eds. Eugene O'Neill & His Early Contemporaries: Bohemians, Radicals, Progressives & the Avant Garde. 2011. (ENG., Illus.). 324p. pap. 45.00 (978-0-7864-4557-8(2)) McFarland & Co., Inc. Pubs.

Hopkins, Lisa. The Lady's Trial. 2011. (Revels Plays Ser.). (ENG., Illus.). 240p. 80.00 (978-0-7190-7895-8(4)) Manchester Univ. Pr. GBR. Dist: Macmillan.

Jestrovic, Silvija. Performance, Exile And 'America' Meerzon, Yana, ed. 2009. (Studies in International Performance Ser.). (ENG., Illus.). 240p. 89.00 (978-0-230-57456-4(4)) Palgrave Macmillan.

Jiang, Tsui-fen. The American Dream in African American, Asian American, & Hispanic American Drama: August Wilson, Frank Chin, & Luis Valdez. 2009. 180p. 99.95 (978-0-7734-4656-4(7)) Mellen, Edwin Pr., The.

Kerr, Gordon. Everyman & Mankind. Rasmussen, Eric & Bruster, Douglas, eds. 2009. (Arden Early Modern Drama Ser.). (ENG.). 256p. pap. 18.00 (978-1-904271-62-8(6), Arden Shakespeare) A & C Black GBR. Dist: Macmillan.

Kraszewski, Jon. The New Entrepreneurs: An Institutional History of Television Anthology Writers. 2010. (Wesleyan Film Ser.). (Illus.). (ENG.). 236p. 40.00 (978-0-8195-6946-2(1)); xi, 213p. pap. (978-0-8195-6947-9(X)) Wesleyan Univ Pr.

Lazer, Hank. Lyric & Spirit: Selected Essays, 1996-2008. 2008. (ENG., Illus.). 352p. per. 19.95 (978-1-890650-32-2(3)) Omnidawn Publishing.

Mancini, Candice. Freedom of Thought in Jerome Lawrence & Robert Edwin Lee's Inherit the Wind. 2010. (Social Issues in Literature Ser.). (ENG.). 144-224p. 38.45 (978-0-7377-5014-0(6)); pap. 26.50 (978-0-7377-5015-7(4)) Cengage Gale. (Greenhaven Pr., Inc.).

Miller, Tice L. Entertaining the Nation: American Drama in the Eighteenth & Nineteenth Centuries. 2007. (Theater in the Americas Ser.). (ENG.). 238p. per. 37.50 (978-0-8093-2778-2(3)) Southern Illinois Univ. Pr.

Murphy, Brenda, ed. Death of a Salesman, by Arthur Miller. 2009. (Critical Insights Ser.). 352p. lib. bdg. 85.00 (978-1-58765-610-1(8)) Salem Pr., Inc.

—A Streetcar Named Desire, by Tennessee Williams. 2009. (Critical Insights Ser.). 336p. lib. bdg. 85.00 (978-1-58765-628-6(0)) Salem Pr., Inc.

Paolucci, Anne. Edward Albee: (the Later Plays) 2010. (ENG.). pap. 20.00 (978-1-935191-70-4(5), Griffon Hse.) ISI Bks.

Rebhorn Matthew. Pioneer Performances: Staging the Frontier, 1 vol. 2012. (ENG., Illus.). 288p. 65.00 (978-0-19-975130-3(7)) Oxford Univ. Pr., Inc.

Richardson, Dorothy B. Moving Diorama in Play: William Dunlap's Comedy A Trip to Niagara (1828) 2010. 472p. 29.99 (978-1-934844-15-1(2)); pap. 49.99 (978-1-934844-16-8(0)) Teneo Pr.

Richardson, Dorothy B. & Dunlop, William. Moving Diorama in Play: William Dunlap's Comedy, a Trip to Niagara (1828) 2010. (978-1-60497-656-4(X)) Cambria Pr.

Robinson, Marc. The American Play: 1787-2000. 2010. (Illus.). 416p. (C). pap. 28.00 (978-0-300-17004-7(1)) Yale Univ. Pr.

Sami, Gholamreza. Ragged Individualism: America in the Political Drama of The 1930s. 2011. 272p. pap. 15.19 (978-1-4490-8983-2(6)) AuthorHouse.

Senelick, Lawrence, ed. The American Stage: Writing on Theater from Washington Irving to Tony Kushner. movie tie-in ed. 2010. (ENG., Illus.). 850p. (gr. 12-18). 40.00 (978-1-59853-069-8(0)) Library of America, The.

Shapiro, Norman R. Labiche & Co: Fourteen One-Acts by a French Comic Master. 2009. (ENG.). 498p. pap. 26.99 (978-1-55783-757-8(0), 1557837570, Applause Theatre & Cinema) Leonard, Hal Corp.

Shea, Laura. A Moon for the Misbegotten on the American Stage: A History of the Major Productions. 2008. (ENG., Illus.). 190p. per. 45.00 (978-0-7864-3563-0(1)) McFarland & Co., Inc. Pubs.

Smith, Susan Harris. American Drama: The Bastard Art. 2006. (Cambridge Studies in American Theatre & Drama Ser.). (ENG., Illus.). 260p. pap. 53.00 (978-0-521-03242-1(3)) Cambridge Univ. Pr.

—Plays in American Periodicals, 1890-1918. 2007. (Palgrave Studies in Theatre & Performance History Ser.). (ENG., Illus.). 244p. 89.00 (978-1-4039-7765-6(8)) Palgrave Macmillan.

Stanlake, Christy. Native American Drama: A Critical Perspective. 2009. (ENG., Illus.). 254p. 102.00 (978-0-521-51980-9(2)) Cambridge Univ. Pr.

Viagas Robert, ed. The Alchemy of Theatre - the Divine Science: Essays on Theatre & the Art of Collaboration. 2006. (ENG., Illus.). 296p. 29.95 (978-1-55783-698-4(1), 1557836981, Applause Theatre & Cinema) Leonard, Hal Corp.

Watson, Charles S. The History of Southern Drama. 2009. (ENG.). 304p. pap. 30.00 (978-0-8131-9307-6(9)) Univ. Pr. of Kentucky.

Wetmore Jr, Kevin J. & Smith-Howard, Alycia, eds. Suzan-Lori Parks: A Casebook. 2012. (Casebooks on Modern Dramatists Ser.). (ENG.). 176p. pap. 42.95 (978-0-415-54226-5(X)) Routledge.

Widener, Charlene. The Changing Face of American Theatre. 2008. 208p. pap. (978-3-8364-3767-7(8)) VDM Verlag Dr. Mueller e.K.

Zarhy-Levo, Yael. The Making of Theatrical Reputations: Studies from the Modern London Theatre. 2008. (Studies Theatre Hist & Culture Ser.). (ENG., Illus.). 304p. 42.50 (978-1-58729-626-0(8)) Univ. of Iowa Pr.

AMERICAN DRAMA—HISTORY AND CRITICISM—BIBLIOGRAPHY

Murphy, Brenda. American Realism & American Drama, 1880-1940. 2008. (Cambridge Studies in American Literature & Culture Ser.). (ENG., Illus.). 248p. pap. 34.99 (978-0-521-06766-9(9)) Cambridge Univ. Pr.

AMERICAN DRAMA—HISTORY AND CRITICISM—20TH CENTURY

Al-Khalili Raja. The Dialectic of Theatrical Space & Domestic Space. 2008. 264p. pap. (978-3-639-09222-6(8)) VDM Verlag Dr. Mueller e.K.

Altschuler, Bruce E. Acting Presidents: 100 Years of Plays about the Presidency. 2010. (Evolving American Presidency Ser.). (ENG., Illus.). 208p. 89.00 (978-0-230-11017-5(7)) Palgrave Macmillan.

Altwein, Sabine. The Quest for American Manhood - Issues of Race & Gender in David Rabe's Vietnam Trilogy. 2008. 116p. per. (978-3-8364-6903-6(0)) VDM Verlag Dr. Mueller e.K.

Anadolu-Okur, Nilgun. Contemporary African American Theater: Afrocentricity in the Works of Larry Neal, Amiri Baraka, & Charles Fuller. 2010. (ENG.). 236p. pap. 39.95 (978-0-415-88324-5(5)) Routledge.

Anderson, Donald R. Shadowed Cocktails: The Plays of Philip Barry from Paris Bound to the Philadelphia Story. 2010. 238p. pap. 45.00 (978-0-8093-2991-5(3)) Southern Illinois Univ. Pr.

Bechtel, Roger. Past Performance: American Theatre & the Historical Imagination. 2007. 288p. (C). 56.50 (978-0-8387-5649-2(2)) Bucknell Univ. Pr.

Bennett, Michael & Carson, Benjamin D., eds. Eugene O'Neill's One-Act Plays: New Critical Perspectives. 2012. (ENG., Illus.). 240p. 85.00 (978-0-230-33981-1(6)) Palgrave Macmillan.

Bigsby, Christopher. The Cambridge Companion to August Wilson. 2007. (Cambridge Companions to Literature Ser.). (ENG.). 290p. per. 30.99 (978-0-521-68506-1(0)); 240p. (C). 95.00 (978-0-521-86606-4(5)) Cambridge Univ. Pr.

Bixler, Jacqueline & Seda, Laurietz, eds. Trans/Acting: Latin American & Latino Performing Arts. 2009. 58.50 (978-0-8387-5726-0(X)) Bucknell Univ. Pr.

Bloom, Harold. The Crucible. 2nd rev. ed. 2010. (Bloom's Guides). 110p. (C). (gr. 9-18). 30.00 (978-1-60413-815-3(7), Chelsea Hse.) Facts On File, Inc.

—The Crucible - Arthur Miller. 2nd rev. ed. 2008. (Modern Critical Interpretations Ser.). 240p. (C). (gr. 9). 45.00 (978-0-7910-9828-8(1), Chelsea Hse.) Facts On File, Inc.

Bóta, Judit. Tennessee Williams' Maggie, the Cat. 2009. 64p. pap. (978-3-639-12513-9(4)) VDM Verlag Dr. Mueller e.K.

Brietzke, Zander. American Drama in the Age of Film. 2007. (ENG.). 296p. 39.95 (978-0-8173-1571-9(3)) Univ. of Alabama Pr.

Ceballos Muñoz, Alfonso, et al, eds. Violence in American Drama: Essays on Its Staging, Meanings & Effects. 2011. (ENG.). 296p. pap. 55.00 (978-0-7864-6393-0(7)) McFarland & Co., Inc. Pubs.

Cohn, Ruby. Anglo-American Interplay in Recent Drama. 2006. (ENG.). 204p. pap. 50.00 (978-0-521-03528-6(7)) Cambridge Univ. Pr.

DiGaetani, John Louis. Stages of Struggle: Modern Playwrights & Their Psychological Inspirations. 2008. (ENG., Illus.). 206p. per. 35.00 (978-0-7864-3157-1(1)) McFarland & Co., Inc. Pubs.

Dircks, Phyllis T. Edward Albee: A Literary Companion. 2010. (McFarland Literary Companions Ser.). (ENG., Illus.). 179p. pap. 39.95 (978-0-7864-3401-5(5)) McFarland & Co., Inc. Pubs.

Fahy, Thomas. Staging Modern American Life: Popular Culture in the Experimental Theater of Millay, Cummings, & Dos Passos. 2011. (What Is Theatre? Ser.). (ENG., Illus.). 224p. 80.00 (978-0-230-11595-8(0)) Palgrave Macmillan.

Fearnow, Mark. The American Stage & the Great Depression: A Cultural History of the Grotesque. 2007. (Cambridge Studies in American Theatre & Drama Ser.). (ENG., Illus.). 228p. pap. 48.00 (978-0-521-03362-6(4)) Cambridge Univ. Pr.

Fischer, Heinz Dietrich & Fischer, Erika J. Chronicle of the Pulitzer Prizes for Drama: Discussions, Decisions & Documents. 2008. (ENG.). XV, 432p. (978-3-598-30192-6(8)) Saur, K. G. Verlag GmbH & Co.

Fischer, Iris Smith. Interrogating America through Theatre & Performance. Demastes, William W., ed. 2009. (Palgrave Studies in Theatre & Performance History Ser.). (ENG., Illus.). 320p pap. 30.00 (978-0-230-61901-2(0)) Palgrave Macmillan.

Fischer, Iris Smith & Demastes, William. Interrogating America Through Theatre & Performance. Demastes, William W., ed. 2006. (Palgrave Studies in Theatre & Performance History). (ENG.). 312p. 89.00 (978-1-4039-7474-7(8)) Palgrave Macmillan.

Fisher, James, ed. "We Will Be Citizens" New Essays on Gay & Lesbian Theatre. 2008. (ENG.). 232p. pap. 39.95 (978-0-7864-3418-3(X)) McFarland & Co., Inc. Pubs.

Gannon, Paul W. Monarch Notes on O'Neill's Desire under the Elms. Date not set. (Illus.). pap. 3.25 (978-0-671-00750-8(5), Arco) Peterson's.

Gassner. Eugene Oneill, Vol. 45. 2009. pap. 25.00 (978-0-8166-0349-7(9)) Univ. of Minnesota Pr.

Hagood, Taylor. Secrecy, Magic, & the One-Act Plays of Harlem Renaissance Women Writers. 2010. (Black Performance & Cultural Criticism Ser.). (ENG.). 232p. 44.95 (978-0-8142-1121-2(6)); cd-rom 14.95 (978-0-8142-9219-8(4)) Ohio State Univ. Pr.

Hall, Roger A. Performing the American Frontier, 1870-1906. 2006. (Cambridge Studies in American Theatre & Drama Ser.). (ENG., Illus.). 296p. pap. 60.00 (978-0-521-03517-0(1)) Cambridge Univ. Pr.

Harding, James & Rosenthal, Cindy, eds. The Rise of Performance Studies: Rethinking Richard Schechner's Broad Spectrum. 2011. (Studies in International Performance Ser.). (ENG., Illus.). 272p. 90.00 (978-0-230-24291-3(X)) Palgrave Macmillan.

Haynes, Robert W. The Major Plays of Horton Foote: The Trip to Bountiful, the Young Man from Atlanta, & the Orphans' Home Cycle. 2010. vii, 197p. 109.95 (978-0-7734-3594-0(8)) Mellen, Edwin Pr., The.

Johnson, Katie N. Sisters in Sin: Brothel Drama in America, 1900-1920. 2009. (Cambridge Studies in American Theatre & Drama Ser.). (ENG., Illus.). 280p. pap. 33.00 (978-0-521-10513-2(7)) Cambridge Univ. Pr.

Kolin, Philip C., ed. Contemporary African American Women Playwrights: A Casebook. (Casebooks on Modern Dramatists Ser.). 2012. (ENG.). 224p. (C). pap. 42.95 (978-0-415-54112-1(3)) 2007. X, 214p. 120.00 (978-0-415-97826-2(2)) Routledge.

Kolin, Philip C., ed. The Influence of Tennessee Williams: Essays on Fifteen American Playwrights. 2008. (ENG.). 239p. pap. 39.95 (978-0-7864-3475-6(9)) McFarland & Co., Inc. Pubs.

Kornstein, Daniel J. Unlikely Muse: Legal Thinking & Artistic Imagination. 2010. 304p. 25.99 (978-1-4490-3297-5(4)); pap. 15.49 (978-1-4490-3298-2(2)) AuthorHouse.

Kovalcik, Timothy M. The Great Passion Play. 2008. (Images of America Ser.). (ENG., Illus.). 128p. pap. 19.99 (978-0-7385-5324-5(7)) Arcadia Publishing.

Krasner, David. American Drama, 1945-2000: An Introduction. 2006. (Blackwell Introductions to Literature Ser.: 23). (ENG., Illus.). 224p. per. 38.95 (978-1-4051-2087-6(8)); 110.95 (978-1-4051-2086-9(X)) Wiley, John & Sons, Inc. (Wiley-Blackwell).

Krasner, David, ed. A Companion to Twentieth-Century American Drama. 2007. (Blackwell Companions to Literature & Culture Ser.: 57). (ENG., Illus.). 600p. per. 55.95 (978-1-4051-6368-2(2), Wiley-Blackwell) Wiley, John & Sons, Inc.

Mason, Jeffrey D. Stone Tower: The Political Theater of Arthur Miller. 2008. (ENG., Illus.). 328p. 59.50 (978-0-472-11650-8(9)) Univ. of Michigan Pr.

Maufort, Marc. Labyrinth of Hybridities: Avatars of O'Neillian Realism in Multi-ethnic American Drama (1972-2003) 2010. (Dramaturgies. Textes, Cultures et Représentations. Texts, Cultures & Performances Ser.). 241p. pap. 43.95 (978-90-5201-033-5(1)) PIE - Peter Lang BEL. Dist: Lang, Peter.

Maufort, Marc & De Wagter, Caroline eds. Signatures of the Past: Cultural Memory in Contemporary Anglophone North American Drama. 2008. (Illus.). 312p. pap. 54.95 (978-90-5201-454-8(X)) PIE - Peter Lang BEL. Dist: Lang, Peter.

Miller, Henry D. Theorizing Black Theatre: Art Versus Protest in Critical Writings, 1898-1965. 2010. (ENG., Illus.). 284p. pap. 65.00 (978-0-7864-5937-7(9)) McFarland & Co., Inc. Pubs.

Mitchell, Koritha. Living with Lynching: Afrincan American Lynching Plays, Performance, & Citizenship, 1890-1930. 2011. (New Black Studies Ser.). (ENG., Illus.). 272p. 40.00 (978-0-252-03649-1(2)) Univ. of Illinois Pr.

Murphy, Brenda. American Realism & American Drama, 1880-1940. 2008. (Cambridge Studies in American Literature & Culture Ser.). (ENG., Illus.). 248p. pap. 34.99 (978-0-521-06766-9(9)) Cambridge Univ. Pr.

Murphy, Brenda, ed. Twentieth-Century American Drama, 4 vols. rev. ed. 2006. (Critical Concepts in Literary & Cultural Studies). (ENG.). 1728p. 1450.00 (978-0-415-34270-4(8)) Routledge.

Murphy, Daniel. Twentieth Century American Drama: Crit Concepts in LitCult Vol1, 4 vols. 2006. 448p. 220.00 (978-0-415-34271-1(6)) Routledge.

—Twentieth Century American Drama: Crit Concepts Lit & Cult Vol3, 4 vols. 2006. 416p. 220.00 (978-0-415-34273-5(2)) Routledge.

—Twentieth Century American Drama: Crit Concepts Lit & Cult Vol4, 4 vols. 2006. 448p. 220.00 (978-0-415-34274-2(0)) Routledge.

—Twentieth Century American Drama: Crit Concepts Lit Cult Vol2, 4 vols. 2006. 416p. 220.00 (978-0-415-34272-8(4)) Routledge.

Nielsen, Kenneth F. & Nielsen. Tony Kushner's Angels in America. 2008. (Modern Theatre Guides). (ENG.). 148p. 90.00 (978-0-8264-9503-7(6)) Continuum International Publishing Group, Ltd. GBR. Dist: National Bk. Network.

Nielsen, Kent & Nielsen. Tony Kushner's Angels in America. 2008. (Modern Theatre Guides). (ENG.). 148p. 17.95 (978-0-8264-9504-4(4)) Continuum International Publishing Group, Ltd. GBR. Dist: National Bk. Network.

Nourse, Joan T. Monarch Notes on Miller's Crucible & View from the Bridge. (C). 3.95 (978-0-671-00687-7(8), Arco) Peterson's.

Novick, Julius. Beyond the Golden Door: Jewish American Drama & Jewish American Experience. (Palgrave Studies in Theatre & Performance History Ser.). (ENG.). 200p. 2009. pap. 29.00 (978-0-230-61966-1(5)) 2008. 84.00 (978-1-4039-7009-1(2)) Palgrave Macmillan.

Ozieblo, Barbara & Dickey, Jerry. Susan Glaspell & Sophie Treadwell. 2008. (Routledge Modern & Contemporary Dramatists Ser.). (Illus.). XII, 228p. 29.95 (978-0-415-40484-6(3)) Routledge.

—Susan Glaspell & Sophie Treadwell: American Modernist Women Dramatists. 2008. (Routledge Modern & Contemporary Dramatists Ser.). (Illus.). XII, 228p. 110.00 (978-0-415-40485-3(1)) Routledge.

Ozieblo, Barbara & Hernando-Real, Noelia, eds. Performing Gender Violence: Plays by Contemporary American Women Dramatists. 2011. (ENG., Illus.). 204p. 80.00 **(978-0-230-33995-8(6))** Palgrave Macmillan.

Ozieblo Rajkowska, Bárbara & Narbona-Carrión, María Dolores. Codifying the National Self: Spectators, Actors, & the American Dramatic Text. 2006. (Dramaturgies Ser.: No. 17). 299p. pap. 57.95 *(978-90-5201-028-1(5))* Lang, Peter Publishing, Inc.

Prosser, William & Sherin, Edwin. The Late Plays of Tennessee Williams. 2008. (ENG.). 306p. pap. 60.00 *(978-0-8108-6361-3(8))* Scarecrow Pr., Inc.

Quick & VALK. Wooster Group Book. 2007. (ENG., Illus.). 288p. 120.00 *(978-0-415-35333-5(5))*; 46.95 *(978-0-415-35334-2(3))* Routledge.

Rollyson, Carl E. Lillian Hellman. 2011. **(978-1-58765-829-7(1))** Salem Pr., Inc.

Rossini, Jon D. Contemporary Latina/o Theater: Wrighting Ethnicity. 2008. (Theater in the Americas Ser.). (ENG.). 272p. pap. 37.50 *(978-0-8093-2830-7(5))* Southern Illinois Univ. Pr.

Sauer, David K. American Drama & the Postmodern. 2011. *(978-1-60497-757-8(4))* Cambria Pr.

Schwartz, Michael. Broadway & Corporate Capitalism: The Rise of the Professional-Managerial Class, 1900-1920. 2009. (Palgrave Studies in Theatre & Performance History Ser.). (ENG.). 228p. 95.00 *(978-0-230-61657-8(7))* Palgrave Macmillan.

Tichler, Rosemarie & Kaplan, Barry Jay. The Playwright at Work: Conversations. 2012. (ENG.). 352p. pap. 24.95 **(978-0-8101-2762-3(8))** Northwestern Univ. Pr.

Von Szeliski, John. Tragedy & Fear: Why Modern Tragic Drama Fails. 2011. (ENG.). 240p. pap. 40.00 **(978-0-8078-9803-1(1))** Univ. of North Carolina Pr.

Walker, Julia A. Expressionism & Modernism in the American Theatre: Bodies, Voices, Words. 2009. (Cambridge Studies in American Theatre & Drama Ser.). (ENG., Illus.). 316p. pap. 42.00 *(978-0-521-10891-1(8))* Cambridge Univ. Pr.

Wattenberg, Richard. Early Twentieth-Century Frontier Dramas on Broadway: Situating the Western Experience in Performing Arts. 2011. (Palgrave Studies in Theatre & Performance History Ser.). (ENG., Illus.). 280p. 85.00 *(978-0-230-11144-8(0))* Palgrave Macmillan.

Weiss, Kathryn. The Kent State Memorial to the Slain Vietnam War Protestors: Interpreting the Site & Visitor's Responses. 2007. (SPA & ENG.). 184p. 99.95 *(978-0-7734-5203-9(6))* Mellen, Edwin Pr., The.

Westgate, J. Chris. Urban Drama: The Metropolis in Contemporary North American Plays. 2011. (ENG.). 252p. 85.00 *(978-0-230-11453-1(9))* Palgrave Macmillan.

Wilmer, S. E. Native American Performance & Representation. 2011. (ENG.). 296p. pap. 29.95 *(978-0-8165-0240-0(4))* Univ. of Arizona Pr.

Wilmer, S. E., ed. Native American Performance & Representation. 2009. (ENG., Illus.). 296p. (C). 49.95 *(978-0-8165-2646-8(X))* Univ. of Arizona Pr.

Wilson, James F. Bulldaggers, Pansies, & Chocolate Babies: Performance, Race, & Sexuality in the Harlem Renaissance. (Triangulations: Lesbian/Gay/Queer Theater/Drama/Performance Ser.). (Illus.). 2011. (ENG.). 262p. pap. 27.95 **(978-0-472-03489-5(8))** 2010. ix, 260p. E-Book 29.95 *(978-0-472-02696-8(8))* Univ. of Michigan Pr.

Wolff, Tamsen. Mendel's Theatre: Heredity, Eugenics, & Early Twentieth-Century American Drama. 2009. (Palgrave Studies in Theatre & Performance History Ser.). (ENG., Illus.). 288p. 100.00 *(978-0-230-61585-4(6))* Palgrave Macmillan.

AMERICAN DRAMA—HISTORY AND CRITICISM—21ST CENTURY

Hansel, Adrien-Alice & Dubiner, Julie Felise, eds. Humana Festival 2007: The Complete Plays. 2008. (Humana Festival Ser.). (ENG., Illus.). 400p. per. 19.95 *(978-0-9709046-3-8(0))* Playscripts, Inc.

Harding, James & Rosenthal, Cindy, eds. The Rise of Performance Studies: Rethinking Richard Schechner's Broad Spectrum. 2011. (Studies in International Performance Ser.). (ENG., Illus.). 272p. 90.00 *(978-0-230-24291-3(X))* Palgrave Macmillan.

Nadel, Alan, ed. August Wilson: Completing the Twentieth-Century Cycle. 2010. (ENG.). 248p. pap. 29.95 *(978-1-58729-875-2(9))* Univ. of Iowa Pr.

Nielsen, Kenneth F. & Nielsen. Tony Kushner's Angels in America. 2008. (Modern Theatre Guides). (ENG.). 148p. 90.00 *(978-0-8264-9503-7(6))* Continuum International Publishing Group, Ltd. GBR. Dist: National Bk. Network.

Nielsen, Kent & Nielsen. Tony Kushner's Angels in America. 2008. (Modern Theatre Guides). (ENG.). 148p. 17.95 *(978-0-8264-9504-4(4))* Continuum International Publishing Group, Ltd. GBR. Dist: National Bk. Network.

Ozieblo Rajkowska, Bárbara & Narbona-Carrión, María Dolores. Codifying the National Self: Spectators, Actors, & the American Dramatic Text. 2006. (Dramaturgies Ser.: No. 17). 299p. pap. 57.95 *(978-90-5201-028-1(5))* Lang, Peter Publishing, Inc.

Singh, Shweta. A Thematic Study of the Plays of Arthur Miller. 2011. 160p. pap. 23.50 **(978-1-4520-6286-0(2))** AuthorHouse.

Stowe, Brook. New York Theater Review 2008. 2008. 336p. pap. 19.95 *(978-0-615-20056-9(7))* Black Wave Pr.

AMERICAN DRAMA—INDIAN AUTHORS

Wilmer, S. E. Native American Performance & Representation. 2011. (ENG.). 296p. pap. 29.95 *(978-0-8165-0240-0(4))* Univ. of Arizona Pr.

AMERICAN DRAMA—JEWISH AUTHORS

As-Sawi, Wael. The Politics of Subversion. 2010. 176p. pap. *(978-3-639-26108-0(9))* VDM Verlag Dr. Mueller e.K.

Cohen, Sarah Blacher & Koch, Joanne, intros. Shared Stages: Ten American Dramas of Blacks & Jews. 2007. (SUNY Series in Modern Jewish Literature & Culture). (Illus.). 556p. pap. 29.95 *(978-0-7914-7282-8(5))*; 74.50 *(978-0-7914-7281-1(7))* State Univ. of New York Pr.

Novick, Julius. Beyond the Golden Door: Jewish American Drama & Jewish American Experience. (Palgrave Studies in Theatre & Performance History Ser.). (ENG.). 200p. 2009. pap. 29.00 *(978-0-230-61966-1(5))* 2008. 84.00 *(978-1-4039-7009-1(2))* Palgrave Macmillan.

AMERICAN DRAMA—MEXICAN AMERICAN AUTHORS

Gutierrez, Sandra M., et al, eds. Teatro Chicana: A Collective Memoir & Selected Plays. 2008. (Chicana Matters Ser.). (ENG., Illus.). 328p. pap. 27.95 *(978-0-292-71744-2(X))* Univ. of Texas Pr.

AMERICAN DRAMA—WOMEN AUTHORS

Anderson, Lisa M. Black Feminism in Contemporary Drama. 2008. (Illus.). 152p. 37.00 *(978-0-252-03228-8(4))* Univ. of Illinois Pr.

Armstrong, Ann Elizabeth, et al. Performing Words into Being: Native American Women's Theater. 2009. 193p. pap. 29.99 *(978-1-4243-3112-3(9))* Miami Univ. Pr.

Barlow, Judith E. Women Writers of the Provincetown Players. 2009. (Excelsior Editions Ser.). 320p. pap. 29.95 *(978-1-4384-2790-4(5)*, Suny Pr.) State Univ. of New York Pr.

—Women Writers of the Provincetown Players: A Collection of Short Works. 2009. (Excelsior Editions Ser.). 320p. 75.00 *(978-1-4384-2789-8(1)*, Suny Pr.) State Univ. of New York Pr.

Engle, Sherry D. & Engle, Sherry. New Women Dramatists in America, 1890-1920. 2007. (ENG., Illus.). 288p. 95.00 *(978-1-4039-7320-7(2))* Palgrave Macmillan.

Flores, Yolanda. The Drama of Gender: Feminist Theater by Women of the Americas. March, Kathleen N., ed. (Worlds of Change Ser.: Vol. 38). viii, 132p. pap. 32.95 *(978-0-8204-6243-1(8))* Lang, Peter Publishing, Inc.

Greene, Alexis & Lauro, Shirley. Front Lines: Political Plays by American Women. Greene, Alexis & Lauro, Shirley, eds. 2009. (ENG., Illus.). 288p. pap. 20.95 *(978-1-59558-424-3(2)*, 955424) New Pr., The.

Gutierrez, Sandra M., et al, eds. Teatro Chicana: A Collective Memoir & Selected Plays. 2008. (Chicana Matters Ser.). (ENG., Illus.). 328p. pap. 27.95 *(978-0-292-71744-2(X))* Univ. of Texas Pr.

Hagood, Taylor. Secrecy, Magic, & the One-Act Plays of Harlem Renaissance Women Writers. 2010. (Black Performance & Cultural Criticism Ser.). (ENG.). 232p. 44.95 *(978-0-8142-1121-2(6))*; cd-rom 14.95 *(978-0-8142-9219-8(4))* Ohio State Univ. Pr.

Huston-Findley, Shirley Annette & Howard, Rebecca, eds. Footpaths & Bridges: Voices from the Native American Women Playwrights Archive. 2008. (CRE & ENG.). 304p. 90.00 *(978-0-472-11613-3(4))* Univ. of Michigan Pr.

Kolin, Philip C., ed. Contemporary African American Women Playwrights: A Casebook. (Casebooks on Modern Dramatists Ser.). 2012. (ENG.). 224p. (C). pap. 42.95 **(978-0-415-54112-1(3))** 2007. X, 214p. 120.00 *(978-0-415-97826-2(2))* Routledge.

Lihamba, Amandina, frwd. African Women Playwrights. 2008. (ENG., Illus.). 384p. pap. 26.00 *(978-0-252-07573-5(0))* Univ. of Illinois Pr.

Ozieblo, Barbara & Hernando-Real, Noelia, eds. Performing Gender Violence: Plays by Contemporary American Women Dramatists. 2011. (ENG., Illus.). 204p. 80.00 **(978-0-230-33995-8(6))** Palgrave Macmillan.

Perkins, Kathy A., intro. African Women Playwrights. 2008. (Illus.). 280p. 65.00 *(978-0-252-03387-2(6))* Univ. of Illinois Pr.

Sanchez, Sonia. I'm Black When I'm Singing, I'm Blue When I Ain't & Other Plays. Wood, Jacqueline, ed. 2010. (ENG.). 196p. 69.95 *(978-0-8223-4757-6(1))*; pap. 19.95 *(978-0-8223-4778-1(4))* Duke Univ. Pr.

AMERICAN DRAWING

see Drawing, American

AMERICAN EAGLE

see Bald Eagle

AMERICAN EDUCATION FELLOWSHIP

Garcia, Charles P. Leadership Lessons of the White House Fellows: Learn How to Inspire Others, Achieve Greatness & Find Success in Any Organization. 2009. (ENG.). 304p. 24.95 *(978-0-07-159848-4(0)*, 0071598480) McGraw-Hill Cos., The.

AMERICAN ENGLISH

see English Language—United States

AMERICAN ESCADRILLE

see France—Armee—Escadrille Lafayette

AMERICAN ESSAYS

Agee, Jonis. Riding Shotgun: Women Write about Their Mothers. 2008. (ENG., Illus.). 248p. 24.95 *(978-0-87351-614-3(1)*, Borealis Bk.) Minnesota Historical Society Pr.

Albert, Elisa. Freud's Blind Spot: 23 Original Essays on Cherished, Estranged, Lost, Hurtful, Hopeful, Complicated Siblings. 2010. (ENG.). 288p. pap. 15.00 *(978-1-4391-5472-4(4)*, Free Pr.) Free Pr.

Berry, Wendell. Imagination in Place. 2011. (ENG.). 208p. pap. 14.95 *(978-1-58243-706-4(8)*, Counterpoint) Counterpoint LLC.

Castle, Terry. The Professor: A Sentimental Education. 2011. (ENG.). 352p. pap. 14.99 *(978-0-06-167092-3(8)*, HarperPerennial) HarperCollins Pubs.

Cohen & Cohen, Samuel. 50 Essays: A Portable Anthology. 3rd ed. 2010. (ENG.). 560p. (C). pap. 30.95 *(978-0-312-60965-8(5))* Bedford/Saint Martin's.

Cohen, Samuel S. 50 Essays: A Portable Anthology. 3rd ed. 2011. xxx, 473p. *(978-0-312-67543-1(7))* Bedford/Saint Martin's.

Eggers, Dave, ed. The Best American Nonrequired Reading 2009. 2009. (Best American Ser.). (ENG.). 432p. pap. 14.95 *(978-0-547-24160-9(7)*, Mariner Bks.) Houghton Mifflin Harcourt Trade & Reference Pubs.

Emerson, Ralph Waldo. The Laws of Nature: Excerpts from the Writings of Ralph Waldo Emerson. McLaughlin, Walt, ed. 2010. (ENG., Illus.). 96p. pap. 16.95 *(978-1-55643-931-5(8))* North Atlantic Bks.

—Nature. 2009. 48p. pap. *(978-1-4099-6835-1(9))* Dodo Pr.

—Nature. 2007. (ENG.). 96p. pap. 5.00 *(978-0-9796283-0-6(X))* Ledgend Corp., The.

—Nature. 2009. (Penguin Great Ideas Ser.). (ENG.). 128p. (gr. 12-18). 10.00 *(978-0-14-104248-0(6)*, Penguin (Non-Classics)) Penguin Group (USA) Inc.

—Nature. 2008. 96p. pap. *(978-1-4086-8902-8(2))* Read Bks.

Fleming, David. Other Words: A Writer's Reader. rev. ed. 2011. (ENG.). 342p. pap. 40.00 *(978-0-7575-6555-7(7))* Kendall Hunt Publishing Co.

Guitkind, Lee. Hurricanes & Carnivals: Essays by Chicanos, Pochos, Pachucos, Mexicanos, & Expatriates. 2007. (ENG.). 216p. pap. 17.95 *(978-0-8165-2625-3(7))* Univ. of Arizona Pr.

Haydn, Hiram Collins & Saunders, Betsy. The American Scholar Reader. 2012. (ENG.). 543p. pap. 39.95 **(978-1-4128-4295-2(6))** Transaction Pubs.

Higginson, Thomas Wentworth. Atlantic Essays. 2009. 350p. 32.99 *(978-1-110-17813-1(1))*; pap. 31.75 *(978-1-110-17809-4(3))* BiblioBazaar.

—Atlantic Essays. 2009. 66p. pap. *(978-0-217-17807-5(3))* Books LLC.

Jepson, Rw. New & Old Essays. 2006. 240p. per. *(978-1-4067-3444-7(6)*, Hesperides Pr.) Read Bks.

Jones, Jacqueline. The Best American History Essays 2007. 2007. (ENG.). 304p. 100.00 *(978-1-4039-7659-8(7))*; (Illus.). pap. 27.00 *(978-1-4039-7660-4(0))* Palgrave Macmillan.

Matthews, Brander. The Oxford Book of American Essays. 2009. 324p. pap. 23.93 *(978-1-4589-9845-3(2))* General Bks. LLC.

—The Oxford Book of American Essays. 2008. 524p. 39.95 *(978-1-4344-6569-6(1))*; pap. 24.95 *(978-1-4344-6568-9(3))* Wildside Pr., LLC.

Matthews, Brander, ed. The Oxford Book of American Essays. 2007. (ENG.). 524p. 55.95 *(978-0-548-42812-2(3))*; per. 40.95 *(978-0-548-40513-0(1))* Kessinger Publishing, LLC.

McPhee, John & Rigolot, Carol. Princeton Reader: Contemporary Essays by Writers & Journalists at Princeton University. 2010. (ENG., Illus.). 408p. (C). pap. 35.00 *(978-0-691-14308-8(0))* Princeton Univ. Pr.

—Princeton Reader: Contemporary Essays by Writers & Journalists at Princeton University. 2010. (ENG., Illus.). 408p. (C). 90.00 *(978-0-691-14307-1(2))* Princeton Univ. Pr.

Mute, creator. Mute Magazine - 2008. 104p. pap. *(978-1-906496-31-9(5))* Nute Publishing, Ltd.

Parnwell, E. C. Victorian Essays. 2006. 196p. per. *(978-1-4067-3318-1(0)*, Hesperides Pr.) Read Bks.

The Patriotic Thinker. 2010. 120p. 13.95 *(978-1-60747-755-6(6))* Phoenix Bks., Inc.

Pickering, Sam. Dreamtime: A Happy Book. 2011. 168p. pap. 24.95 **(978-1-61117-038-2(9))** Univ. of South Carolina Pr.

Rice, Allen Thorndike, ed. Essays from the North American Review. 2008. 496p. 53.95 *(978-1-4370-0822-7(4))*; pap. 38.95 *(978-1-4368-3787-3(1))* Kessinger Publishing, LLC.

Thoreau, Henry David. Civil Disobedience & Other Essays. 2009. 140p. pap. *(978-1-60796-103-1(2))* Editorial Benei Noaj.

Tilton, Warren. Trifleton Papers by Trifle & the Editor [Pseuds of Warren Tilton & Wm a Crafts]. 2006. 320p. per. 23.99 *(978-1-4255-3092-1(3))* MPublishing.

Twain, Mark, pseud. A Tramp Abroad. 2010. 330p. 36.99 *(978-1-140-18371-6(0))* 2010. 330p. pap. 31.75 *(978-1-140-18372-3(9))* 2010. 648p. pap. 46.75 *(978-1-144-00448-2(9))* 2010. 344p. pap. 31.75 *(978-1-142-15526-1(9))* 2010. 586p. pap. 44.75 *(978-1-142-50454-0(9))* 2009. 332p. 25.99 *(978-1-103-76213-2(3))* 2009. 332p. pap. 19.99 *(978-1-103-76208-8(7))* 2009. 336p. 25.99 *(978-1-103-56685-3(7))* 2009. 336p. pap. 19.99 *(978-1-103-56684-6(9))* 2008. 656p. 35.99 *(978-0-554-36127-7(2))* 2008. 656p. 39.99 *(978-0-554-26824-8(8))* 2007. (ENG.). 588p. per. 30.99 *(978-1-4346-3849-6(9))* 2007. (ENG.). 654p. per. 34.99 *(978-1-4346-1951-8(6))* BiblioBazaar.

—A Tramp Abroad. 2010. 140p. pap. *(978-1-151-90352-5(3))* 2009. 338p. pap. *(978-0-217-31277-6(2))* 2009. 178p. pap. *(978-1-4432-9981-7(2))* Books LLC.

—A Tramp Abroad. 2007. (ENG.). 248p. per. 11.99 *(978-1-4209-3018-4(4))* Digireads.com.

—A Tramp Abroad. 2008. (ENG., Illus.). 676p. per. *(978-1-4065-7144-8(X))* Dodo Pr.

—A Tramp Abroad. 2010. 28p. pap. 14.14 *(978-1-153-58911-6(7))*; 34p. pap. 14.14 *(978-1-153-58912-3(5))*; 42p. pap. 14.14 *(978-1-153-58913-0(3))*; 46p. pap. 14.14 *(978-1-153-58915-4(X))*; 48p. pap. 14.14 *(978-1-153-58916-1(8))*; (Illus.). 284p. pap. 26.30 *(978-1-4432-0055-4(7))*; 126p. pap. 26.30 *(978-1-152-07627-3(2))* General Bks. LLC.

—A Tramp Abroad. 2010. 372p. 39.16 *(978-1-169-33088-7(6))*; pap. 27.16 *(978-1-162-65063-0(X))*; 48.95 *(978-1-161-41928-3(4))* Kessinger Publishing, LLC.

—A Tramp Abroad. 2008. 324p. pap. *(978-1-4437-0416-8(4)*, Pomona Pr.) Read Bks.

Twain, Mark, pseud, et al. A Tramp Abroad. 2010. (ENG.). 656p. pap. 46.75 *(978-1-171-51659-0(2))* BiblioBazaar.

Weinberger, Eliot. Oranges & Peanuts for Sale. 2009. (ENG.). 272p. pap. 16.95 *(978-0-8112-1834-4(1)*, 21834) New Directions Publishing Corp.

AMERICAN ESSAYS—HISTORY AND CRITICISM

Avent, John M., ed. The Book of Modern Essays. 2007. (ENG.). 256p. 42.95 *(978-0-548-05864-0(4))* Kessinger Publishing, LLC.

Gutkind, Lee. The Best Creative Nonfiction, Vol. 1. Gutkind, Lee, ed. 2007. (ENG., Illus.). 352p. per. 15.95 *(978-0-393-33003-8(6)*, 33003) Norton, W. W. & Co., Inc.

Kaufman, Alan, ed. The Outlaw Bible of American Essays. 2006. (ENG., Illus.). 384p. pap. 16.95 *(978-1-56025-935-0(3))* Basic Bks.

Leer, David Van & Van Leer, David. Emerson's Epistemology: The Argument of the Essays. 2009. (ENG.). 304p. pap. 42.00 *(978-0-521-11431-8(4))* Cambridge Univ. Pr.

AMERICAN ESSAYS—20TH CENTURY

Anaya, Rudolfo A. The Essays. 2009. (Chicana & Chicano Visions of the Americas Ser.). (ENG.). 320p. (C). 24.95 *(978-0-8061-4023-0(2))* Univ. of Oklahoma Pr.

Atkins, G. Douglas. E. B. White: The Essayist as First-Class Writer. 2012. (ENG., Illus.). 192p. 80.00 **(978-0-230-34066-4(0))** Palgrave Macmillan.

Atwan, Robert. The Best American Essays. 6th ed. 2010. (ENG.). 464p. (C). pap. 78.95 *(978-1-4390-8387-1(8))* Wadsworth.

Atwan, Robert & Brooks, David, eds. The Best American Essays 2012. 2012. (Best American Series (R) Ser.). (ENG.). 304p. pap. 14.95 **(978-0-547-84009-3(8)**, Mariner Bks.) Houghton Mifflin Harcourt Trade & Reference Pubs.

Baldwin, James. The Cross of Redemption: Uncollected Writings. Kenan, Randall, ed. 2011. (Vintage International Original Ser.). (ENG.). 400p. pap. 16.00 *(978-0-307-27596-7(5)*, Vintage) Knopf Doubleday Publishing Group.

Barthelme, Donald. Not-Knowing: The Essays & Interviews. Herzinger, Kim, ed. & pref. by. 2008. (ENG.). 352p. per. 15.95 *(978-1-59376-173-8(2))* Basic Bks.

Brandi, John. Reflections in the Lizard's Eye: Notes from the High Desert. (ENG & SPA., Illus.). 208p. pap. 14.95 *(978-1-889921-08-2(4)*, 1079) Western Edge Pr.

Cole, Norma. To Be at Music: Essays & Talks. 2010. (ENG., Illus.). 200p. pap. 16.95 *(978-1-890650-44-5(7))* Omnidawn Publishing.

Cooper, Dennis. Smothered in Hugs: Essays, Interviews, Feedback, & Obituaries. 2010. (ENG.). 400p. pap. 14.99 *(978-0-06-171561-7(1)*, HarperPerennial) HarperCollins Pubs.

Dodds, Jack. Dodds Ready Reference Handbook Fourth Edition Plus Atwan Best Americanessays Fifth Edition. 4th ed. 2007. pap. 89.56 *(978-0-547-09054-2(4)*, 1044096) CENGAGE Learning.

Hitchens, Christopher. The Best American Essays 2010. Atwan, Robert, ed. 2010. (Best American Ser.). (ENG.). 304p. pap. 14.95 *(978-0-547-39451-0(9)*, Mariner Bks.) Houghton Mifflin Harcourt Trade & Reference Pubs.

Hoffer, Eric. In Our Time. 2008. (ENG.). 96p. pap. 13.95 *(978-1-933435-28-2(3))* Hopewell Pubns., LLC.

Mencken, H. L. Prejudices: A Selection. 2006. (ENG.). 288p. pap. 27.00 *(978-0-8018-8535-8(3))* Johns Hopkins Univ. Pr.

Root, Robert L., Jr., ed. & intro. Landscapes with Figures: The Nonfiction of Place. 2007. (ENG.). 294p. pap. 21.95 *(978-0-8032-5983-6(2)*, Bison Bks.) Univ. of Nebraska Pr.

Thompson, et al. Sticks & Stones & Other Student Essays. 7th ed. 2010. (ENG.). 240p. (C). pap. 16.95 *(978-0-312-59622-4(7))* Bedford/Saint Martin's.

Wesley, John Milton. Salvos. 2011. (J). 29.95 *(978-1-885942-85-2(0)*, 650) Cune Pr., LLC.

AMERICAN ESSAYS—21ST CENTURY

Alphin, Rex. The Nature of Things: Stories from the Land. 2010. (Illus.). xiv, 173p. *(978-1-883911-89-8(3))* Brandylane Pubs., Inc.

Atwan, Robert, et al, eds. The Best American Essays 2007. 2007. (Best American Ser.). (ENG.). 336p. pap. 18.95 *(978-0-618-70927-4(4))* Houghton Mifflin Harcourt Trade & Reference Pubs.

Atwan, Robert & Gopnik, Adam, eds. The Best American Essays 2008. 2008. (Best American Ser.). (ENG.). 320p. pap. 14.00 *(978-0-618-98322-3(8))* Houghton Mifflin Harcourt Trade & Reference Pubs.

Atwan, Robert & Slater, Lauren, eds. The Best American Essays 2006. 2006. (Best American Ser.). (ENG.). 304p. 28.00 *(978-0-618-70531-3(7))*; pap. 26.95 *(978-0-618-70529-0(5))* Houghton Mifflin Harcourt Trade & Reference Pubs.

Cadle, Lanette & Feyh, Lori. Composing Ourselves: Writing from the Composition Program at Missouri State University. 2007. (C). pap. *(978-0-913785-08-9(3)*, Moon City Pr.) Department of English.

Caswell, Kurt, et al, eds. To Everything on Earth: New Writing on Fate, Community, & Nature. 2010. 160p. pap. 21.95 *(978-0-89672-655-0(X))* Texas Tech Univ. Pr.

Chinn, Sarah & Oza, Rupaul, eds. Ruin: Volume 39, Numbers 3&4 Fall/Winter 2011. 2011. (Women's Studies Quarterly Ser.). (ENG.). 320p. pap. 25.00 **(978-1-55861-750-6(7))** Feminist Pr. at The City Univ. of New York.

Cole, Norma. To Be at Music: Essays & Talks. 2010. (ENG., Illus.). 200p. pap. 16.95 *(978-1-890650-44-5(7))* Omnidawn Publishing.

Danticat, Edwidge & Atwan, Robert, eds. The Best American Essays 2011. 2011. (Best American Ser.). (ENG.). 272p. pap. 14.95 *(978-0-547-47977-4(8)*, Mariner Bks.) Houghton Mifflin Harcourt Trade & Reference Pubs.

Early, Gerald. Best African American Essays 2010. 2009. (ENG.). 400p. pap. 16.00 *(978-0-553-38537-3(2)*, One World/Ballantine) Random House Publishing Group.

Eggers, Dave, ed. The Best American Nonrequired Reading 2011. 2011. (Best American R Ser.). (ENG.). 528p. pap. 14.95 *(978-0-547-57743-2(5),* Mariner Bks.) Houghton Mifflin Harcourt Trade & Reference Pubs.

Goldwasser, Amy. Red: The Next Generation of American Writers — Teenage Girls — On What Fires up Their Lives Today. 2007. (ENG.). 288p. (gr. 12-18). 21.95 *(978-1-59463-040-8(2),* Hudson Street Pr.) Penguin Group (USA) Inc.

Goldwasser, Amy, ed. Red: Teenage Girls in America Write on What Fires up Their Lives Today. 2008. (ENG.). 288p. (gr. 12-18). 14.00 *(978-0-452-28983-3(1),* Plume) Penguin Group (USA) Inc.

Gutkind, Lee. Our Roots Are Deep with Passion: Creative Nonfiction Collects New Essays by Italian-American Writers. Herman, Joanna Clapps, ed. 2006. (ENG.). 312p. pap. 15.95 *(978-1-59051-242-5(1))* Other Pr., LLC.

Kellogg, Matt & Quint, Jillian, eds. Twenty Something Essays by Twenty Something Writers. 2006. (ENG., Illus.). 304p. pap. 14.95 *(978-0-8129-7566-6(9),* Random Hse. Trade Paperbacks) Random House Publishing Group.

Lethem, Jonathan. The Ecstasy of Influence: Nonfictions, Etc. 2012. (Vintage Contemporaries Ser.). (ENG.). 464p. pap. 16.95 ***(978-0-307-74450-0(7),*** Vintage) Knopf Doubleday Publishing Group.

Morford, Mark. Daring Spectacle: Adventures in Deviant Journalism. 2010. 346p. pap. 20.00 *(978-0-9842997-0-6(X))* Rapture Machine.

Organization of American Historians, et al. The Best American History Essays 2008. 2008. (ENG., Illus.). 288p. 95.00 *(978-0-230-60590-9(7));* pap. 30.00 *(978-0-230-60591-6(5))* Palgrave Macmillan.

Perry, Jennifer. Dog Coffee. 2008. 108p. pap. 10.95 *(978-1-59858-836-1(2))* Dog Ear Publishing, LLC.

Redwine, James M. Gavel Gamut Greetings from Jpeg Ranch. 2009. 344p. pap. 23.50 *(978-1-4490-1626-5(X))* AuthorHouse.

Root, Robert L., Jr., ed. & intro. Landscapes with Figures: The Nonfiction of Place. 2007. (ENG.). 294p. pap. 21.95 *(978-0-8032-5983-6(2),* Bison Bks.) Univ. of Nebraska Pr.

St. Germain, Sheryl & Whitford, Margaret, eds. Between Song & Story: Essays for the Twenty-first Century. 2011. 410p. pap. 34.95 *(978-1-932870-50-3(4))* Autumn Hse. Pr.

Wolwode, Larry. Words Made Fresh: Essays on Literature & Culture. 2011. 192p. 24.99 *(978-1-4335-2740-1(5))* Crossway.

AMERICAN FEDERATION OF LABOR AND CONGRESS OF INDUSTRIAL ORGANIZATIONS

Fletcher, Bill, Jr. & Gapasin, Fernando. Solidarity Divided: The Crisis in Organized Labor & a New Path Toward Social Justice. 2009. 324p. pap. 19.95 *(978-0-520-26156-3(9))* Univ. of California Pr.

Gapasin, Fernando & Fletcher, Bill, Jr. Solidarity Divided: The Crisis in Organized Labor & a New Path Toward Social Justice. 2008. 292p. 40.00 *(978-0-520-25525-8(9))* Univ. of California Pr.

Greene, Julie. Pure & Simple Politics: The American Federation of Labor & Political Activism, 1881-1917. 2006. 312p. (C). pap. 61.00 *(978-0-521-02880-6(9))* Cambridge Univ. Pr.

Hughes, Quenby Olmsted. In the Interest of Democracy: The Rise & Fall of the Early Cold War Alliance Between the American Federation of Labor & the Central Intelligence Agency. 2011. (Trade Unions Past, Present & Future Ser.). 204p. pap. 55.95 *(978-3-0343-0212-8(6))* Lang, Peter AG GBR. Dist: Lang, Peter.

Kersten, Andrew. Labor's Home Front: The American Federation of Labor During World War II. 2009. (ENG.). 288p. pap. 23.00 *(978-0-8147-4824-4(4))* New York Univ. Pr.

Murray, Philip. Only One War: There Is Only One War That I Am Interested in at the Present Moment, & That Is the War to Defeat Hitler & His Axis Partners. 2011. 20p. pap. 35.95 ***(978-1-258-03451-1(4))*** Literary Licensing, LLC.

Palladino, Grace. Skilled Hands, Strong Spirits: A Century of Building Trades History. 2007. (Illus.). 274p. per. 21.00 *(978-0-8014-7414-9(0),* ILR Pr.) Cornell Univ. Pr.

Scipes, Kim. AFL-CIO's Secret War against Developing Country Workers: Solidarity or Sabotage? 2011. (ENG.). 274p. pap. 34.95 ***(978-0-7391-3502-0(3))*** Lexington Bks.

Scipes, Kim. AFL-CIO's Secret War against Developing Country Workers:Solidarity or Sabotage? 2010. (ENG.). 278p. 65.00 *(978-0-7391-3501-3(5))* Lexington Bks.

Van Tine, Warren R. In the Workers' Interest: A History of the Ohio AFL-CIO, 1958-1998. 206p. pap. 16.95 *(978-0-9666284-1-8(1))* Ohio State Univ., Ctr. for Labor Research.

AMERICAN FEDERATION OF TEACHERS

Kahlenberg, Richard D. Tough Liberal: Albert Shanker & the Battles over Schools, Unions, Race, & Democracy. 2009. (Columbia Studies in Contemporary American History Ser.). (ENG.). 552p. (gr. 17). pap. 22.50 *(978-0-231-13497-2(5))* Columbia Univ. Pr.

Kahlenberg, Richard D. & Keene, Richard D. Tough Liberal: Albert Shanker & the Battles over Schools, Unions, Race, & Democracy. 2007. (Columbia Studies in Contemporary American History Ser.). (ENG., Illus.). 552p. (gr. 17). 29.95 *(978-0-231-13496-5(7))* Columbia Univ. Pr.

AMERICAN FICTION (COLLECTIONS)

see also Dime Novels; Science Fiction, American; Short Stories, American; Western Stories

Allen-Agostini, Lisa & Mason, Jeanne. Trinidad Noir. Allen-Agostini, Lisa & Mason, Jeanne, eds. 2008. (Akashic Noir Ser.). (ENG., Illus.). 300p. pap. 15.95 *(978-1-933354-55-2(0))* Akashic Bks.

Arment, Chad. Shadows from a Veiled Creation: Classic Tales of Supernatural Fiction in the Christian Tradition. 2006. *(978-1-930585-26-3(8))* Coachwhip Pubns.

Ashley, Mike, ed. The Dreaming Sex: Tales of Scientific Wonder & Dread. 2011. (ENG.). 256p. pap. 15.95 *(978-0-7206-1354-4(X))* Owen, Peter Ltd. GBR. Dist: Independent Pubs. Group.

Burnett, Frances Hodgson. The One I Knew Best of All - a Memory of the Mind of a Child. 2010. 338p. pap. 31.45 *(978-1-4446-9485-7(5))* Audubon Pr. & Christian Bk. Service.

Clements, S. A., ed. Torqued Tales. 2007. 332p. pap. 15.95 *(978-1-60370-035-1(8))* Torquere Pr.

Corey, Stephen, et al, eds. Stories Wanting Only to Be Heard: Selected Fiction from Six Decades of the Georgia Review. 2012. (ENG.). 384p. pap. 24.95 ***(978-0-8203-4254-2(8))*** Univ. of Georgia Pr.

Cortez, Sarah & Martinez, Liz, eds. Indian Country Noir. 2010. (Akashic Noir Ser.). (ENG.). 300p. pap. 15.95 *(978-1-936070-05-3(7))* Akashic Bks.

Douglass, Frederick, et al. Three Great African-American Novels: The Heroic Slave, Clotel & Our Nig. 2008. (ENG.). 304p. pap. 10.95 *(978-0-486-46851-8(8))* Dover Pubns., Inc.

Eggleston, George Cary. Southern Soldier Stories. 2009. 288p. 28.99 *(978-1-117-27374-7(1));* (ENG.). 272p. 34.99 *(978-1-117-04398-2(3));* 288p. pap. 27.75 *(978-1-117-27375-4(X));* 276p. 24.99 *(978-1-103-62637-3(X));* 276p. pap. 18.99 *(978-1-103-62632-8(9))* BiblioBazaar.

—Southern Soldier Stories. 2009. 132p. pap. *(978-0-217-05435-5(8))* Books LLC.

—Southern Soldier Stories. 2008. 272p. 42.95 *(978-0-548-98137-5(X))* 2007. (ENG.). 276p. per. 27.95 *(978-0-548-66606-7(7))* Kessinger Publishing, LLC.

—Southern Soldier Stories. 251p. reprint ed. 98.00 *(978-0-7222-8251-9(6))* Library Reprints, Inc.

Elrod, P. N., ed. Strange Brew. 2009. (ENG.). 384p. pap. 14.99 *(978-0-312-38336-7(3),* St. Martin's Griffin) St. Martin's Pr.

Frye, Steven, ed. The Tales of Edgar Allan Poe. 2009. (Critical Insights Ser.). 304p. lib. bdg. 85.00 *(978-1-58765-616-3(7))* Salem Pr., Inc.

Gale, Kate. Los Angeles Review, Vol. 7. 2010. (ENG.). 296p. pap. 20.00 *(978-1-59709-474-0(9))* Red Hen Pr.

Gordon, Lindsay, ed. Sex & Shopping: The Sexiest Wicked Words Stories Ever! 2006. (Wicked Words Ser.). (ENG.). 272p. mass mkt. 14.95 *(978-0-352-34076-4(2),* Black Lace) Virgin Bks. Ltd. GBR. Dist: Independent Pubs. Group.

Hamilton, Denise, ed. Los Angeles Noir 2: The Classics. 2010. (Akashic Noir Ser.). (ENG.). 300p. pap. 15.95 *(978-1-936070-02-2(2))* Akashic Bks.

Hawthorne, Nathaniel, et al. Four Classic American Novels: The Scarlet Letter - The Adventures of Huckleberry Finn - The Red Badge of Courage - Billy Budd, Sailor. 2007. (ENG.). 752p. (gr. 12-18). 7.95 *(978-0-451-53055-4(1),* Signet Classics) Penguin Group (USA) Inc.

Hines, Jim C. The Mermaid's Madness, 2 vols. 2009. (Princess Novels Ser.). (ENG.). 352p. (gr. 12-18). pap. 7.99 *(978-0-7564-0583-0(1),* D A W Bks., Inc.) Penguin Group (USA) Inc.

Johnson, Ginger. Tales of Masks & Mayhem - Volume III. 2006. 391p. per. *(978-1-59824-395-4(3))* E-BookTime LLC.

Keene, Jarret & Pierce, Todd James, eds. Las Vegas Noir. 2008. (Akashic Noir Ser.). (ENG., Illus.). 300p. pap. 15.95 *(978-1-933354-49-1(6))* Akashic Bks.

Lima, Lazaro & Picano, Felice, eds. Ambientes: New Queer Latino Writing. 2011. (ENG.). 220p. pap. 22.95 *(978-0-299-28224-0(4))* Univ. of Wisconsin Pr.

Meriwether, Sean & Wharton, Greg, eds. Men of Mystery: Homoerotic Tales of Intrigue & Suspense. 2007. 281p. per. *(978-1-56023-663-4(9),* Southern Tier Editions) Haworth Pr., Inc., The.

Montenoso, Augusto, et al. Los Centroamericanos. (SPA.). 376p. pap. 19.95 *(978-99922-788-0-2(3),* Alfaguara) Santillana USA Publishing Co., Inc.

Phillips, Gary, ed. Orange County Noir. 2010. (Akashic Noir Ser.). (ENG.). 300p. pap. 15.95 *(978-1-936070-03-9(0))* Akashic Bks.

Recyled Teenagers Write Again. Rednecks & Roses II. 2006. (ENG.). 172p. per. 12.95 *(978-0-7414-3248-3(X))* Infinity Publishing.

Vassilakos, Jill H. & Vassilakos-Long, Paul. Strange Cases: A Selective Guide to Speculative Mystery Fiction, 1 vol. 2009. 676p. 60.00 *(978-1-59158-421-6(3),* LU3421) Libraries Unlimited, Inc.

AMERICAN FICTION (COLLECTIONS)—20TH CENTURY

Ashley, Mike, ed. & intro. Unforgettable Ghost Stories by Women Writers. 2008. (ENG.). 320p. pap. 10.95 *(978-0-486-46797-9(X))* Dover Pubns., Inc.

Bausch, Richard. Best New American Voices 2008: Fresh Fiction from Top Writing Programs. Kulka, John & Danford, Natalie, eds. 2007. (Best New American Voices Ser.). (ENG.). 432p. pap. 24.95 *(978-0-15-603149-3(3),* Mariner Bks.) Houghton Mifflin Harcourt Trade & Reference Pubs.

Beagle, Peter S., ed. The Secret History of Fantasy. 2010. (ENG.). 432p. pap. 15.95 *(978-1-892391-99-5(6))* Tachyon Pubns.

Betancourt, John Gregory. The Ultimate Collection of 20th-Century Adventure Tales, Volume One. 2007. (Illus.). 320p. pap. 13.95 *(978-0-8095-7213-7(3))* Diamond Bk. Distributors.

Bonner, Thomas, et al. Silver Threads: 25 Years of Fiction from Xavier Review. 2009. 214p. pap. ***(978-1-883275-20-4(2))*** Xavier Review Pr.

Bosman, Ellen, et al. Gay, Lesbian, Bisexual, & Transgendered Literature: A Genre Guide, 1 vol. 2008. (Genreflecting Advisory Ser.). 440p. 60.00 *(978-1-59158-194-9(X),* LU194X) Libraries Unlimited, Inc.

Canning, Richard, ed. Between Men 2: Original Fiction by Today's Best Gay Writers. 2009. (ENG.). 288p. pap. 15.95 *(978-1-59350-114-3(5))* Alyson Pubns.

Cox, J. Randolph, intro. & notes. Dashing Diamond Dick & Other Classic Dime Novels. 2007. (ENG., Illus.). 384p. (gr. 12-18). 15.00 *(978-0-14-310497-1(7),* Penguin Classics) Penguin Group (USA) Inc.

Ellroy, James & Penzler, Otto, eds. The Best American Noir of the Century. (ENG.). 752p. 2011. pap. 16.95 *(978-0-547-57744-9(3),* Mariner Bks.) 2010. (Illus.). 30.00 *(978-0-547-33077-8(4))* Houghton Mifflin Harcourt Trade & Reference Pubs.

Farah, Nuruddin. Crossbones: A Novel. 2012. (ENG.). 400p. (gr. 12). pap. 16.00 ***(978-0-14-312253-1(3),*** Penguin (Non-Classics)) Penguin Group (USA) Inc.

Hamilton, Geoff & Jones, Brian. Encyclopedia of American Popular Fiction. 2009. (Literary Movements Ser.). 416p. (C). (gr. 9-18). 75.00 *(978-0-8160-7157-9(8))* Facts On File, Inc.

Harvey, Samuel R., et al. The Wonders of Would Be Writers. Kasper, John D. & Ebnet, Rosemary, eds. Date not set. 105p. (Orig.). pap., spiral bd. 10.00 *(978-0-9633798-1-8(X))* Harvey Publishing.

Hemmingson, Michael. Gordon Lish & His Influence on Twentieth-Century American Liter. 2009. (Studies in Major Literary Authors Ser.). (ENG.). 256p. (C). 125.00 *(978-0-415-99177-3(3))* Routledge.

Joshi, S. T., contrib. by. American Supernatural Tales. 2007. (Penguin Classics Ser.). (ENG.). 432p. (gr. 12-18). 16.00 *(978-0-14-310504-6(3),* Penguin Classics) Penguin Group (USA) Inc.

Kaldas, Pauline & Mattawa, Khaled, eds. Dinarzad's Children: An Anthology of Contemporary Arab American Fiction. 2009. (ENG.). 380p. pap. 24.95 *(978-1-55728-912-4(3))* Univ. of Arkansas Pr.

Penzler, Otto, ed. & frwd. The Black Lizard Big Book of Black Mask Stories. 2010. (Vintage Crime/Black Lizard Original Ser.). (ENG., Illus.). 1136p. pap. 25.00 *(978-0-307-45543-7(2),* Vintage) Knopf Doubleday Publishing Group.

Schmidt, Gary & Felch, Susan, eds. The Emmaus Readers: More Listening for God in Contemporary Fiction. 2009. (ENG.). 214p. (gr. 13). pap. 17.99 *(978-1-55725-544-0(X))* Paraclete Pr., Inc.

Schmidt, Gary & Felch, Susan M., eds. The Emmaus Readers: Listening for God in Contemporary Fiction. 2008. (ENG.). 208p. (gr. 13). pap. 17.95 *(978-1-55725-543-3(1))* Paraclete Pr., Inc.

Seed, David. Cinematic Fictions: The Impact of the Cinema on the American Novel up to World War II. 2011. (ENG.). 288p. 95.00 *(978-1-84631-212-0(4))* Liverpool Univ. Pr. GBR. Dist: Chicago Distribution Ctr.

Smith, Zak. Pictures Showing What Happens on Each Page of Thomas Pynchon's Novel Gravity's Rainbow. 2006. (ENG., Illus.). 784p. pap. 39.95 *(978-0-9773127-9-5(8))* Tin Hse. Bks., LLC.

Tóibín, Colm & Callil, Carmen. A Brief Guide to the Modern Library. 2011. (ENG.). 320p. pap. 13.95 *(978-0-7624-4276-8(X))* Running Pr. Bk. Pubs.

Vizenor, Gerald, ed. & intro. Native Stories: Five Selections. 2009. (Native Storiers: a Series of American Narratives Ser.). (ENG.). 206p. pap. 25.00 *(978-0-8032-1717-1(X))* Univ. of Nebraska Pr.

Weis, Margaret & Greenberg, Martin, eds. Treasury of Fantasy. Date not set. mass mkt. *(978-0-06-105240-8(X))* HarperCollins Pubs.

Wolfe, Thomas. The Magical Campus: University of North Carolina Writings, 1917-1920. Bruccoli, Matthew J. & Magi, Aldo P., eds. 2008. (Illus.). 134p. 22.50 *(978-1-57003-734-4(5))* Univ. of South Carolina Pr.

AMERICAN FICTION (COLLECTIONS)—21ST CENTURY

Adams, Erica, intro. The Mutation of Fortune. 2011. 127p. pap. 20.00 ***(978-1-4507-4209-2(2))*** Green Lantern Pr.

Aylett, Steve, et al. The Bizarro Starter Kit. 2007. 244p. per. 10.00 *(978-1-933929-62-0(6))* Eraserhead Pr.

Beagle, Peter S., ed. The Secret History of Fantasy. 2010. (ENG.). 432p. pap. 15.95 *(978-1-892391-99-5(6))* Tachyon Pubns.

Bonner, Thomas, et al. Silver Threads: 25 Years of Fiction from Xavier Review. 2009. 214p. pap. ***(978-1-883275-20-4(2))*** Xavier Review Pr.

Brooks, Geraldine & Pitlor, Heidi, eds. The Best American Short Stories 2011. 2011. (Best American R Ser.). (ENG.). 384p. 28.00 *(978-0-547-24208-8(5));* pap. 14.95 *(978-0-547-24216-3(6),* Mariner Bks.) Houghton Mifflin Harcourt Trade & Reference Pubs.

Butler, Blake & Hoang, Lily K. 30 under 30: An Anthology of Innovative Fiction by Younger Writers. 2011. (ENG.). 210p. pap. 20.00 ***(978-0-9842133-3-7(3))*** Starcherone Bks.

Carroll, Jonathan & Hand, Elizabeth. Conjunctions: 54, Shadow Selves. Morrow, Bradford, ed. 2010. (ENG., Illus.). 364p. pap. 15.00 *(978-0-941964-70-8(1))* Bard College Pubns. Office.

Early, Gerald. Best African American Fiction 2010. 2009. (ENG.). 336p. pap. 16.00 *(978-0-553-38535-9(6),* One World/Ballantine) Random House Publishing Group.

Emerald Envisage: A Collection of Short Stories by EXtasy's Finest Authors. 2009. *(978-1-55487-147-6(6))* eXtasy Bks.

Fisher/Woronoff, ed. Historical Dictionary of Contemporary American Theater, 1930-2010, 2 vols. 2011. (Historical Dictionaries of Literature & the Arts Ser.: 2 Volumes). (ENG.). 1002p. 175.00 *(978-0-8108-5532-8(1))* Scarecrow Pr., Inc.

Galef, David & Weinhouse, Beth, eds. 20 Over 40. 2006. (ENG.). 382p. per. 25.00 *(978-1-57806-903-3(3))* Univ. Pr. of Mississippi.

Gottlieb, Daphne, ed. Fucking Daphne: Mostly True Stories & Fictions. 2008. (ENG.). 256p. pap. 15.95 *(978-1-58005-235-1(5))* Westview Pr.

Gurganus, Allan, ed. New Stories from the South: The Year's Best 2006. 2006. (ENG., Illus.). 336p. (Orig.). pap. 14.95 *(978-1-56512-531-5(2),* 1565125312) Algonquin Bks. of Chapel Hill.

Hart, Arianna, et al. Bad Girls Have More Fun. 2008. (Ellora's Cave Ser.). (ENG.). 304p. pap. 19.99 *(978-1-4165-7769-0(6))* Pocket Books.

Hicks, Robert, et al, eds. A Guitar & a Pen: Stories by Country Music's Greatest Songwriters. 2008. (ENG.). 272p. 28.99 *(978-1-59995-064-8(2))* Center St.

Horton, Rich. Fantasy 2008. 2008. 368p. pap. 13.95 *(978-0-8095-7251-9(6))* Prime.

—Science Fiction: the Best of the Year, 2008 Edition: The Best of the Year, 2008 Edition. 2009. 368p. pap. 13.95 *(978-0-8095-7250-2(8))* Prime.

Jack, Ian, ed. Best of Young American Novelists 2. 2007. (Granta: the Magazine of New Writing Ser.). (ENG., Illus.). 320p. per. 14.95 *(978-1-929001-27-9(4))* Grove/Atlantic, Inc.

Jones, Edward P. New Stories from the South 2007: The Year's Best. 2007. (ENG.). 384p. pap. 14.95 *(978-1-56512-556-8(8),* 1565125568) Algonquin Bks. of Chapel Hill.

Joshi, S. T., contrib. by. American Supernatural Tales. 2007. (Penguin Classics Ser.). (ENG.). 432p. (gr. 12-18). 16.00 *(978-0-14-310504-6(3),* Penguin Classics) Penguin Group (USA) Inc.

Kaldas, Pauline & Mattawa, Khaled, eds. Dinarzad's Children: An Anthology of Contemporary Arab American Fiction. 2009. (ENG.). 380p. pap. 24.95 *(978-1-55728-912-4(3))* Univ. of Arkansas Pr.

King, Stephen & Pitlor, Heidi, eds. The Best American Short Stories 2007. 2007. (Best American Ser.). (ENG.). 448p. pap. 24.95 *(978-0-618-71348-6(4),* Mariner Bks.) Houghton Mifflin Harcourt Trade & Reference Pubs.

Kolosov, Jacqueline & Lunstrum, Kirsten Sundberg, eds. The Sincerest Form of Flattery: Contemporary Writers on Forerunners in Fiction. 2008. 388p. per. 20.00 *(978-0-911015-66-9(3))* Sandhills Pr., Inc.

Pitlor, Heidi & Perrotta, Tom, eds. The Best American Short Stories 2012. 2012. (Best American R Ser.). (ENG.). 320p. pap. 14.95 *(978-0-547-24210-1(7))* Houghton Mifflin Harcourt Trade & Reference Pubs.

Pitlor, Heidi & Rushdie, Salman, eds. The Best American Short Stories 2008. 2008. (Best American Ser.). (ENG.). 384p. pap. 14.00 *(978-0-618-78877-4(8))* Houghton Mifflin Harcourt Trade & Reference Pubs.

Pitlor, Heidi & Sebold, Alice. The Best American Short Stories 2009. Sebold, Alice, ed. 2009. (Best American Ser.). (ENG.). 368p. pap. 14.00 *(978-0-618-79225-2(2),* Mariner Bks.) Houghton Mifflin Harcourt Trade & Reference Pubs.

Russo, Richard. The Best American Short Stories 2010. Pitlor, Heidi, ed. 2010. (Best American Ser.). (ENG.). 443p. 28.00 *(978-0-547-05528-2(5));* pap. 14.95 *(978-0-547-05532-9(3),* Mariner Bks.) Houghton Mifflin Harcourt Trade & Reference Pubs.

Sebold, Alice. The Best American Short Stories 2009. Pitlor, Heidi, ed. & contrib. by. Sebold, Alice, ed. 2009. (Best American Ser.). (ENG.). 368p. 28.00 *(978-0-618-79224-5(4))* Houghton Mifflin Harcourt Trade & Reference Pubs.

Sussman, Ellen, ed. Bad Girls: 26 Writers Misbehave. 2008. (ENG.). 320p. pap. 14.95 *(978-0-393-33195-0(4),* 33195) Norton, W. W. & Co., Inc.

Taylor, Joe, ed. Tartts Four: Incisive Fiction from Emerging Writers. 2008. 286p. 26.00 *(978-1-60489-017-4(7))* Livingston Pr.

Wallace, Sean & Mamatas, Nick. Realms: The First Year of Clarkesworld Magazine. 2008. 248p. 29.95 *(978-0-8095-7258-8(3));* pap. 13.95 *(978-0-8095-7248-9(6))* Wyrm Publishing.

AMERICAN FICTION—AFRICAN AMERICAN AUTHORS

Brown, William Wells. The Works of William Wells Brown: Using His Strong, Manly Voice. Robbins, Hollis & Garrett, Paula, eds. annot. ed. 2006. (ENG., Illus.). 519p. 115.00 *(978-0-19-530963-3(4))* Oxford Univ. Pr., Inc.

Byerman, Keith E. Fingering the Jagged Grain: Tradition & Form in Recent Black Fiction. 2010. (ENG.). 322p. pap. 24.95 *(978-0-8203-3776-0(5))* Univ. of Georgia Pr.

Diggs, Anita D. Denzel's Lips. 2010. (ENG.). 304p. 6.99 *(978-0-7582-2610-5(1),* Dafina) Kensington Publishing Corp.

Early, Gerald & Harris, E. Lynn, eds. Best African American Fiction. 2009. (ENG.). 336p. pap. 16.00 *(978-0-553-38534-2(8))* Random House Publishing Group.

Hill, Donna. How to Write African American Ficiton: Avoiding the Stereotype. Date not set. pap. *(978-0-312-31754-6(9),* St. Martin's Paperbacks) St. Martin's Pr.

Jackson, Sandra & Moody Freeman, Julie, eds. The Black Imagination, Science Fiction & the Speculative. 2010. (ENG.). 176p. (C). 125.00 *(978-0-415-61482-5(1),* Routledge.

Jenkins-Bridgers, Josephine. Little Mirror. 2011. 48p. pap. 9.95 ***(978-1-936513-07-9(2))*** PearlStone Publishing, Inc.

AMERICAN FICTION—AFRICAN AMERICAN AUTHORS—HISTORY AND CRITICISM

Akolæma, Chiji. Folklore in New World Black Fiction: Writing & the Oral Traditional Aesthetics. 2007. x, 162p. cd-rom 9.95 *(978-0-8142-9148-1(1))* Ohio State Univ. Pr.

Akoma, Chiji. Folklore in New World Black Fiction: Writing & the Oral Traditional Aesthetics. 2007. (ENG.). 162p. 36.95 *(978-0-8142-1071-0(6))* Ohio State Univ. Pr.

Bailey, Frankie Y. African American Mystery Writers: A Historical & Thematic Study. 2008. (ENG.). 277p. pap. 35.00 *(978-0-7864-3339-1(6))* McFarland & Co., Inc. Pubs.

Barr, Marlene S., ed. Afro-Future Females: Black Writers Chart Science Fiction's Newest New-Wave Trajectory. 2008. (ENG.). 304p. 64.95 *(978-0-8142-1078-9(3));* cd-rom 14.95 *(978-0-8142-9156-6(2))* Ohio State Univ. Pr.

Brown, Stephanie. The Postwar African American Novel: Protest & Discontent, 1945-1950. 2011. (Margaret Walker Alexander Series in African American Studies). (ENG.). 176p. 55.00 *(978-1-60473-973-2(8))* Univ. Pr. of Mississippi.

Cataliotti, Robert H. The Songs Became the Stories: The Music in African American Fiction, 1970-2005. (African American Literature & Culture: Expanding & Exploding the Boundaries Ser.). 280p. (C). pap. 32.95 (978-0-8204-8850-9(X)) Lang, Peter Publishing, Inc.

Demirturk, Emine/Lale. How Black Writers Deal with Whiteness: Characterization Through Deconstructing Color. 2008. 242p. 109.95 (978-0-7734-5073-8(4)) Mellen, Edwin Pr., The.

Drake, Kimberly S. Subjectivity in the American Protest Novel. 2011. (ENG.). 264p. 85.00 (978-0-230-10716-8(8)) Palgrave Macmillan.

Eaton, Kalenda C. Womanism, Literature, & the Transformation of the Black Community, 1965-1980. 2007. (Studies in African American History & Culture Ser.). (ENG.). 122p. 125.00 (978-0-415-96129-5(7), 0415961297) Routledge.

Eaton, Kalenda C. Womanism, Literature, & the Transformation of the Black Community, 1965ndash;1980. 2012. (Studies in African American History & Culture Ser.). (ENG.). 122p. pap. 42.95 (978-0-415-54080-3(1)) Routledge.

Fisch, Audrey A., ed. The Cambridge Companion to the African American Slave Narrative. 2007. (Cambridge Companions to Literature Ser.). (ENG.). 290p. per. 28.99 (978-0-521-61526-6(7)); 91.00 (978-0-521-85019-3(3)) Cambridge Univ. Pr.

Greene, J. Lee. The Diasporan Self: Unbreaking the Circle in Western Black Novels. 2008. (ENG.). 264p. (C). (gr. 13-17). pap. 19.50 (978-0-8139-2740-4(4)); (gr. 17). 55.00 (978-0-8139-2739-8(0)) Univ. Pr. of Virginia.

Hebbar, Reshmi J. Modeling Minority Women. 2010. 288p. pap. 39.95 (978-0-415-88243-9(5)) Routledge.

Ikard, David. Breaking the Silence: Toward a Black Male Feminist Criticism. 2007. 191p. 35.00 (978-0-8071-3213-5(6)) Louisiana State Univ. Pr.

Jackson, Sandra & Moody-Freeman, Julie E. The Black Imagination, Science Fiction, Futurism & the Speculative. 2011. (Black Studies & Critical Thinking Ser.). (C). 129.95 (978-1-4331-1242-3(6)); pap. 32.95 (978-1-4331-1241-6(8)) Lang, Peter Publishing, Inc.

Jeon, Joseph Jonghyun. Racial Things, Racial Forms: Objecthood in Avant-Garde Asian American Poetry. 2012. (Contemporary North American Poetry Ser.). (ENG., Illus.). 240p. pap. 39.95 (978-1-60938-086-1(X)) Univ. of Iowa Pr.

King, Lovalerie. The Cambridge Introduction to Zora Neale Hurston. 2008. (Cambridge Introductions to Literature Ser.). (ENG.). 160p. (C). 63.00 (978-0-521-85457-3(1)); pap. 20.99 (978-0-521-67095-1(0)) Cambridge Univ. Pr.

Knight, Alisha R. Pauline Hopkins & the American Dream: An African American Writer's (Re)Visionary Gospel of Success. 2012. (ENG., Illus.). 152p. 45.00 (978-1-57233-852-4(0)) Univ. of Tennessee Pr.

Leiter, Andrew B. In the Shadow of the Black Beast: African American Masculinity in the Harlem & Southern Renaissances. 2010. (Southern Literary Studies). 296p. 39.95 (978-0-8071-3587-7(9)) Louisiana State Univ. Pr.

Luczak, Ewa / Barbara. How Their Living Outside America Affected Five African American Authors: Toward a Theory of Expatriate Literature. 2010. ix, 250p. (978-0-7734-3748-7(7)) Mellen, Edwin Pr., The.

Nunes, Ana. African American Women Writers' Historical Fiction. 2011. (ENG.). 258p. 85.00 (978-0-230-11253-7(6)) Palgrave Macmillan.

Pillow, Gloria Thomas. Motherlove in Shades of Black: The Maternal Psyche in the Novels of African American Women. 2010. (ENG., Illus.). 199p. pap. 38.00 (978-0-7864-3533-3(X)) McFarland & Co., Inc. Pubs.

Ramsey, Priscilla. Postmodernism, Culture & Class in John Edgar Wideman's Selected Fiction. 2009. 288p. pap. 20.95 (978-1-4327-1856-5(8)) Outskirts Pr., Inc.

Raphael-Hernandez, Heike. The Utopian Aesthetics of Three African American Women (Toni Morrison, Gloria Naylor, Julie Dash) The Principle of Hope. 2008. 188p. 99.95 (978-0-7734-4936-7(1)) Mellen, Edwin Pr., The.

Scott, Darieck. Extravagant Abjection: Blackness, Power, & Sexuality in the African American Literary Imagination. 2010. (ENG.). 320p. pap. 22.00 (978-0-8147-4095-8(2)) New York Univ. Pr.

Stockton, Kathryn Bond. Beautiful Bottom, Beautiful Shame: Where Black Meets Queer. 2006. (Series Q). (ENG., Illus.). 288p. (C). 84.95 (978-0-8223-3783-6(5)); per. 23.95 (978-0-8223-3796-6(7)) Duke Univ. Pr.

Thaler, Ingrid. Black Atlantic Speculative Fictions: Octavia E. Butler, Jewelle Gomez, & Nalo Hopkinson. 2010. (ENG.). 204p. (C). 125.00 (978-0-415-80441-7(8)) Routledge.

Vertb, -Gnes. African American Cultural Clash on the Basis of Alex Haley's Roots. 2008. 64p. pap. (978-3-639-01627-7(0)) VDM Verlag Dr. Mueller e.K.

Wardi, Anissa J. Water & African American Memory: An Ecocritical Perspective. 2011. (ENG., Illus.). 160p. 74.95 (978-0-8130-3745-5(X)) Univ. Pr. of Florida.

West, Elizabeth J. African Spirituality in Black Women's Fiction: Threaded Visions of Memory, Community, Nature, & Being. 2012. E-Book (978-0-7391-6886-8(X)) Lexington Bks.

—African Spirituality in Black Women's Fiction: Threaded Visions of Memory, Community, Nature & Being. 2011. (ENG.). 192p. (gr. 17). 60.00 (978-0-7391-6885-1(1)) Lexington Bks.

WILLIAMS, Dana A., ed. Contemporary African American Fiction: New Critical Essays. 2009. (ENG.). 208p. cd-rom 14.95 (978-0-8142-9183-2(X)) Ohio State Univ. Pr.

AMERICAN FICTION—AFRO-AMERICAN AUTHORS

see American Fiction—African American Authors

AMERICAN FICTION—BIBLIOGRAPHY

Bienvenue, Paul R. The Book Collector's Guide to L. Frank Baum & Oz. 2009. (Illus.). 408p. 75.00 (978-0-615-24725-0(3)) March Hare Bks.

Bosman, Ellen, et al. Gay, Lesbian, Bisexual, & Transgendered Literature: A Genre Guide, 1 vol. 2008. (Genreflecting Advisory Ser.). 440p. 60.00 (978-1-59158-194-9(X), LU194X) Libraries Unlimited, Inc.

Brewer, Frances Joan, et al. James Branch Cabell: A Bibliography of His Writings, Biography & Criticism. 2011. 208p. 44.95 (978-1-258-09030-2(9)) Literary Licensing, LLC.

Bridges, Karl. 100 Great American Novels You've (Probably) Never Read, 1 vol. 2007. 264p. 52.00 (978-1-59158-165-9(6), LU1656) Libraries Unlimited, Inc.

Brooks, Justin. Stephen King: A Primary Bibliography of the World's Most Popular Author. (Illus.). 553p. 2008. 40.00 (978-1-58767-190-6(5)) 2006. pap. 25.00 (978-1-58767-153-1(0)) Cemetery Dance Pubns.

Giles, Wanda H. & Giles, James Richard. Dlb 350 21St Cen Am Nvlsts. 2009. (Dictionary of Literary Biography Ser.). (ENG., Illus.). 512p. 315.00 (978-0-7876-8168-5(7)) Cengage Gale.

Hamilton, Geoff & Jones, Brian. Encyclopedia of Contemporary Writers & Their Work. 2010. (Literary Movements Ser.). 432p. (C). (gr. 9-18). 75.00 (978-0-8160-7578-2(6)) Facts On File, Inc.

Herald, Diana Tixier. Teen Genreflecting: A Guide to Reading Interests, 1 vol. 3rd rev. ed. 2010. (Genreflecting Advisory Ser.). 377p. 48.00 (978-1-59158-729-3(8), LU8729) Libraries Unlimited, Inc.

Hill, Nanci. Reading Women: A Book Club Guide for Women's Fiction, 1 vol. 2012. 221p. pap. 35.00 (978-1-59158-802-3(2), LU8802) Libraries Unlimited, Inc.

Hill, Nanci Milone. Reading Women: A Book Club Guide for Women's Fiction. 2012. E-Book (978-1-59158-806-1(5)) ABC-CLIO, LLC.

Honig, Megan. Urban Grit: A Guide to Street Lit, 1 vol. 2010. (Genreflecting Advisory Ser.). 251p. 55.00 (978-1-59158-857-3(X), LU8857) Libraries Unlimited, Inc.

Johnson, Kevin. The Dark Page II: Books That Inspired American Film Noir, (1950-1965) 2009. (Illus.). 272p. 95.00 (978-1-58456-259-7(5)) Oak Knoll Pr.

—The Dark Page II: Books That Inspired American Film Noir, 1950-1965. deluxe ed. 2009. (Illus.). 272p. 375.00 (978-1-58456-260-3(9)) Oak Knoll Pr.

Johnson, Sarah L., ed. Historical Fiction II: A Guide to the Genre, 1 vol. 2nd rev. ed. 2009. (Genreflecting Advisory Ser.). 738p. 65.00 (978-1-59158-624-1(0), LU8624) Libraries Unlimited, Inc.

Knight, Rachelle Rogers. Read, Remember, Recommend. 2010. (ENG.). 320p. pap. 15.99 (978-1-4022-3718-8(9)) Sourcebooks, Inc.

Lindsay, Elizabeth Blakesley. Great Women Mystery Writers, 1 vol. 2nd rev. ed. 2006. 352p. 65.00 (978-0-313-33428-3(5), GR3428, Greenwood Pr.) Greenwood Publishing Group, Inc.

Meloni, Christine. Teen Chick Lit: A Guide to Reading Interests, 1 vol. (Genreflecting Advisory Ser.). 211p. 45.00 (978-1-59158-756-9(5), LU8756) Libraries Unlimited, Inc.

Mengel, Brad & Mengel, Bradley. Serial Vigilantes of Paperback Fiction: An Encyclopedia from Able Team to Z-Comm. 2009. (ENG., Illus.). 233p. pap. 45.00 (978-0-7864-4165-5(8)) McFarland & Co., Inc. Pubs.

Patricia, O'Brien Mathews. Fang-tastic Fiction: Twenty-First-Century Paranormal Reads. 2010. 160p. pap. (978-0-8389-1073-3(4)) American Library Assn.

Powell, William S., ed. North Carolina Fiction, 1734-1957: An Annotated Bibliography. 2011. 206p. 44.95 (978-1-258-07893-5(7)) Literary Licensing, LLC.

Schraufnagel, Noel. The Baseball Novel: A History & Annotated Bibliography of Adult Fiction. 2008. (ENG.). 254p. pap. 39.95 (978-0-7864-3557-9(7)) McFarland & Co., Inc. Pubs.

Slocum, Robert B. New York State in Fiction (1751-1999) & New York City in Fiction (1751-1930) An Annotated Bibliography. 2008. (978-1-59531-019-4(3)) North Country Bks., Inc.

—Pennsylvania, New Jersey, Delaware & Maryland in Fiction, 1792-2000: An Annotated Bibliography. 2009. (ENG.). 732p. pap. 53.95 (978-1-4401-9337-8(1)) iUniverse, Inc.

Smith, Geoffrey D. American Fiction, 1901-1925 2 Part Set: A Bibliography, 2 vols. 2011. (ENG.). 1056p. pap. 80.00 (978-0-521-16614-0(4)) Cambridge Univ. Pr.

Varner, Paul. Historical Dictionary of Westerns in Literature. 2010. (Historical Dictionaries of Literature & the Arts Ser.). (ENG.). 408p. 95.00 (978-0-8108-6092-6(9)); E-Book (978-0-8108-7486-2(5)) Scarecrow Pr., Inc.

Vnuk, Rebecca. Read on... Women's Fiction: Reading Lists for Every Taste, 1 vol. 2009. (Read on Ser.). (Illus.). 126p. pap. 30.00 (978-1-59158-634-0(8), LU8634) Libraries Unlimited, Inc.

—Women's Fiction Authors: A Research Guide, 1 vol. 2009. (Author Research Ser.). 163p. pap. 40.00 (978-1-59158-642-5(9), LU8642) Libraries Unlimited, Inc.

Webber, Carlisle K. Gay, Lesbian, Bisexual, Transgender & Questioning Teen Literature: A Guide to Reading Interests, 1 vol. 2010. (Genreflecting Advisory Ser.). 131p. 45.00 (978-1-59158-506-0(6), LU5066) Libraries Unlimited, Inc.

White, Barbara A. American Women's Fiction, 1790-1870: A Reference Guide, Volume 15. 2012. (RLE: Women, Feminism & Literature Ser.). (ENG.). 320p. (C). 130.00 (978-0-415-53310-2(4)) Routledge.

AMERICAN FICTION—HISTORY AND CRITICISM

Aldama, Frederick Luis. A User's Guide to Postcolonial & Latino Borderland Fiction. 2010. (ENG.). 208p. pap. 19.95 (978-0-292-72577-5(9)) Univ. of Texas Pr.

Ascari, Maurizio. A Counter-History of Crime Fiction: Supernatural, Gothic, Sensational. 2009. (Crime Files Ser.). (ENG.). 224p. pap. 37.00 (978-0-230-59462-3(X)) Palgrave Macmillan.

Baiada, Christa. Living Death. 2007. 200p. per. (978-3-8364-2709-8(5)) VDM Verlag Dr. Mueller e.K.

Baker, Dorothy Z. America's Gothic Fiction: The Legacy of Magnalia Christi Americana. 2007. (ENG.). 161p. 37.95 (978-0-8142-1060-4(0)) Ohio State Univ. Pr.

Baker, Dorothy Zayatz. America's Gothic Fiction: The Legacy of Magnalia Christi Americana. 2007. (978-0-8142-9144-3(9)) Ohio State Univ. Pr.

Balaev, Michelle. The Nature of Trauma in American Novels. 2012. (ENG.). 152p. 79.95 (978-0-8101-2819-4(5)); pap. 29.95 (978-0-8101-2820-0(9)) Northwestern Univ. Pr.

Barca, Dane. The Human Is Flesh. 2008. 300p. pap. (978-3-639-04490-4(8)) VDM Verlag Dr. Mueller e.K.

BarCharts, Inc. Quicklit:the Catcher in the Rye. 2011. (ENG.). 6p. 5.95 (978-1-4232-1663-6(6)) Barcharts, Inc.

Barkley, Christine. Stephen R. Donaldson & the Epic Vision: A Critical Study of the Chronicles of Thomas Covenant Novels. Palumbo, Donald E. & Sullivan, C. W., III, eds. 2009. (Critical Explorations in Science Fiction & Fantasy Ser.). (ENG.). 223p. pap. 35.00 (978-0-7864-4288-1(3)) McFarland & Co., Inc. Pubs.

Beidler, Peter G. A Reader's Companion to J. D. Salinger's the Catcher in the Rye. 2nd rev. ed. 2011. 290p. 25.95 (978-1-60381-037-1(4), Coffeetown Pr.) Coffeetown Enterprises, Inc.

—A Reader's Companion to J. D. Salinger's the Catcher in the Rye: Second Edition. 2nd rev. ed. 2011. 292p. pap. 17.95 (978-1-60381-013-5(7), Coffeetown Pr.) Coffeetown Enterprises, Inc.

Belletto, Steven. No Accident, Comrade: Chance & Design in Cold War American Narratives, 1 vol. 2011. (ENG., Illus.). 224p. 65.00 (978-0-19-982688-9(9)) Oxford Univ. Pr., Inc.

Bendixen, Alfred, ed. A Companion to the American Novel. 2012. (Blackwell Companions to Literature & Culture Ser.). (ENG.). 704p. 199.95 (978-1-4051-0119-6(9), Wiley-Blackwell) Wiley, John & Sons, Inc.

Bentley, Nancy. The Ethnography of Manners: Hawthorne, James & Wharton. 2007. (Cambridge Studies in American Literature & Culture Ser.). (ENG.). 260p. pap. 56.00 (978-0-521-03966-6(5)) Cambridge Univ. Pr.

Betz, Phyllis M. The Lesbian Fantastic: A Critical Study of Science Fiction, Fantasy, Paranormal & Gothic Writings. 2011. (ENG.). 211p. pap. 40.00 (978-0-7864-5885-1(2)) McFarland & Co., Inc. Pubs.

—Lesbian Romance Novels: A History & Critical Analysis. 2009. (ENG.). 227p. pap. 35.00 (978-0-7864-3836-5(3)) McFarland & Co., Inc. Pubs.

Beverly, William. On the Lam: Narratives of Flight in J. Edgar Hoover's America. 2008. (ENG.). 236p. pap. 25.00 (978-1-60473-183-5(4)) Univ. Pr. of Mississippi.

Bewernick, Hanne. The Storyteller's Memory Palace: A Method of Interpretation Based on the Function of Memory Systems in Literature. 2010. (Europäische Hochschulschriften. Reihe 14: Angelsächsische Sprache und Literatur Ser.). 254p. pap. 64.95 (978-3-631-60470-0(X)) Lang, Peter GmbH, Europaischer Verlag der Wissenschaften DEU. Dist: Lang, Peter.

Bloom, Harold. The Sound & the Fury - William Faulkner. 2nd rev. ed. 2008. (Modern Critical Interpretations Ser.). 240p. (C). (gr. 9). 45.00 (978-0-7910-9627-7(0), Chelsea Hse.) Facts On File, Inc.

Bloom, Harold, ed. Catch-22. 2009. (Bloom's Guides). 152p. (C). (gr. 9-18). 30.00 (978-1-60413-201-4(9), Chelsea Hse.) Facts On File, Inc.

—Toni Morrison's Beloved. 2nd rev. ed. 2009. (Bloom's Modern Critical Interpretations Ser.). 232p. (C). (gr. 9-18). 45.00 (978-1-60413-184-0(5), Chelsea Hse.) Facts On File, Inc.

Bloom, Harold, ed. & intro. Slaughterhouse-Five. 2nd rev. ed. 2009. (Bloom's Modern Critical Interpretations Ser.). 192p. (C). (gr. 9-18). 45.00 (978-1-60413-585-5(9), Chelsea Hse.) Facts On File, Inc.

Bodart, Joni Richards. They Suck, They Bite, They Eat, They Kill: The Meaning of Supernatural Monsters in Young Adult Fiction. 2012. xxxi, 268p. E-Book (978-0-8108-8228-7(0)) Scarecrow Pr., Inc.

Booker, M. Keith & Thomas, Anne-Marie. The Science Fiction Handbook. 2009. (Blackwell Guides to Literature Ser.). (ENG., Illus.). 360p. instr.'s hndbk. ed. 116.95 (978-1-4051-6205-0(8)); 356p. pap. 34.95 (978-1-4051-6206-7(6)) Wiley, John & Sons, Inc. (Wiley-Blackwell).

Bostrom, Melissa. Sex, Race, & Family in Contemporary American Short Stories. 2007. (American Literature Readings in the Twenty-First Century Ser.). (ENG.). 232p. 84.00 (978-1-4039-7990-2(1)) Palgrave Macmillan.

Braziel, Jana Evans. Caribbean Genesis: Jamaica Kincaid & the Writing of New Worlds. 2009. 256p. 75.00 (978-0-7914-7653-6(7)) State Univ. of New York Pr.

Brown, Julia Prewitt. The Bourgeois Interior. 2008. (ENG., Illus.). 208p. (gr. 17). 30.00 (978-0-8139-2710-7(2)) Univ. Pr. of Virginia.

Bulson, Eric. Novels, Maps, Modernity: The Spatial Imagination, 1850-2000. 2009. (ENG., Illus.). 192p. pap. 40.00 (978-0-415-80053-2(6)) Routledge.

Burling, William J., et al, eds. Kim Stanley Robinson Maps the Unimaginable: Critical Essays. 2009. (Critical Explorations in Science Fiction & Fantasy Ser.). (ENG.). 312p. pap. 45.00 (978-0-7864-3369-8(8)) McFarland & Co., Inc. Pubs.

Burn, Stephen J. David Foster Wallace's Infinite Jest: A Reader's Guide. 2nd ed. 2012. (ENG.). 144p. pap. 19.95 (978-1-4411-5707-2(7)) Continuum International Publishing Group, Ltd. GBR. Dist: National Bk. Network.

Campbell, Lori M. Portals of Power: Magical Agency & Transformation in Literary Fantasy. Palumbo, Donald E. & Sullivan, C. W., III, eds. 2010. (Critical Explorations in Science Fiction & Fantasy Ser.). (ENG.). 226p. pap. 35.00 (978-0-7864-4645-2(5)) McFarland & Co., Inc. Pubs.

Capitani, Diane N. Truthful Pictures: Slavery Ordained by God in the Domestic, Sentimental Novel of the Nineteenth Century South. 2009. (ENG., Illus.). 156p. 57.99 (978-0-7391-1232-8(5)) Lexington Bks.

Carpan, Carolyn. Sisters, Schoolgirls, & Sleuths: Girls' Series Books in America. 2008. (Scarecrow Studies in Young Adult Literature Ser.). (ENG.). 184p. 45.00 (978-0-8108-5756-8(1)) Scarecrow Pr., Inc.

Carstens, R. W. Falling into Grace: The Fiction of Andrew Greeley. 2008. 316p. 32.95 (978-0-595-49239-8(8)); pap. 22.95 (978-0-595-49421-7(8)) iUniverse, Inc.

Cart, Michael. Young Adult Literature: From Romance to Realism. 2010. 288p. 60.00 (978-0-8389-1045-0(9)) American Library Assn.

Cassuto, Leonard. Hard-Boiled Sentimentality: The Secret History of American Crime Stories. 2008. (ENG., Illus.). 344p. (gr. 17). 79.50 (978-0-231-12690-8(5)); pap. 27.50 (978-0-231-12691-5(3)) Columbia Univ. Pr.

Cassuto, Leonard, ed. The Cambridge History of the American Novel. 2011. (Illus.). 1272p. 185.00 (978-0-521-89907-9(9)) Cambridge Univ. Pr.

Caton, Lou Freitas. Reading American Novels & Multicultural Aesthetics: Romancing the Postmodern Novel. 2007. (ENG.). 284p. 100.00 (978-1-4039-8486-9(7)) Palgrave Macmillan.

Cella, Matthew J. C. Bad Land Pastoralism in Great Plains Fiction. 2010. (American Land & Life Ser.). 254p. pap. 34.95 (978-1-58729-907-0(0)) Univ. of Iowa Pr.

Center for Learning Staff. The Adventures of Huckleberry Finn: Curriculum Unit. 2007. (Novel Ser.). 82p. (YA). spiral bd. 19.95 (978-1-56077-878-3(4)) Center for Learning, The.

Christensen, Jorgen, ed. Marvellous Fantasy. 2009. (Illus.). 296p. pap. 54.95 (978-87-7307-962-1(6)) Aalborg Universitetsforlag DNK. Dist: International Specialized Bk. Services.

Ciccoricco, David. Reading Network Fiction. 2007. (ENG., Illus.). 256p. 39.95 (978-0-8173-1589-4(6)) Univ. of Alabama Pr.

Clark, David Lee. Brockden Brown & the Rights of Women. 2009. 52p. pap. 17.75 (978-1-113-63433-7(2)); pap. 16.75 (978-1-113-63432-0(4)) BiblioBazaar.

—Brockden Brown & the Rights of Women. 2007. (ENG.). 52p. per. 16.95 (978-0-548-57416-4(2)) Kessinger Publishing, LLC.

Clarke, Amy M. Ursula K. le Guin's Journey to Post-Feminism. Sullivan, C. W., III & Palumbo, Donald E., eds. 2010. (Critical Explorations in Science Fiction & Fantasy Ser.). (ENG., Illus.). 219p. pap. 35.00 (978-0-7864-4277-5(8)) McFarland & Co., Inc. Pubs.

Click, Melissa A. Bitten by Twilight: Youth Culture, Media, & the Vampire Franchise. 2010. (Mediated Youth Ser.). (Illus.). 312p. (C). 32.95 (978-1-4331-0893-8(3)); pap. 129.95 (978-1-4331-0894-5(1)) Lang, Peter Publishing, Inc.

Colavito, Jason, ed. A Hideous Bit of Morbidity: An Anthology of Horror Criticism from the Enlightenment to World War I. alt. ed. 2012. (ENG., Illus.). 384p. pap. 25.00 (978-0-7864-6909-3(9)) McFarland & Co., Inc. Pubs.

Connor, Ralph. The Sky Pilot. 2009. 90p. pap. (978-1-151-37965-8(4)) Books LLC.

—The Sky Pilot. 2007. (ENG.). 100p. per. (978-1-4068-4803-8(4)) Echo Library.

—The Sky Pilot. 2008. (ENG.). 296p. 32.95 (978-1-4344-6057-8(6)); per. 19.95 (978-1-4344-6056-1(8)) Wildside Pr., LLC.

Cook, Barbara J., ed. Women Writing Nature: A Feminist View. 2007. (After the Empire: the Francophone World & Postcolonial France Ser.). (ENG.). 152p. 62.99 (978-0-7391-1912-9(5)); per. 26.50 (978-0-7391-1913-6(3)) Lexington Bks.

Cook, Linda Byrd. Dancing in the Flames: Spiritual Journey in the Novels of Lee Smith. 2009. (ENG.). 248p. pap. 39.95 (978-0-7864-4110-5(0)) McFarland & Co., Inc. Pubs.

Cooper, L. Andrew. Gothic Realities: The Impact of Horror Fiction on Modern Culture. 2010. (ENG., Illus.). 248p. pap. 35.00 (978-0-7864-4835-7(0)) McFarland & Co., Inc. Pubs.

Cornelius, Michael G. & Gregg, Melanie E., eds. Nancy Drew & Her Sister Sleuths: Essays on the Fiction of Girl Detectives. 2008. (ENG.). 216p. pap. 35.00 (978-0-7864-3995-9(5)) McFarland & Co., Inc. Pubs.

Curtis, Claire. Postapocalyptic Fiction & the Social Contract: We'll Not Go Home Again. 2010. (ENG.). 210p. 65.00 (978-0-7391-4203-5(8)) Lexington Bks.

Dahl, Roald. Fantastic Mr. Fox. 2007. (ENG., Illus.). 96p. (J). (gr. 2-18). 6.99 (978-0-14-241034-9(9), Puffin) Penguin Group (USA) Inc.

Daniels, Patsy J. Understanding American Fiction As Postcolonial Literature: Literature in the Historical Development of a Fluctuating Cultural Identity. 2010. 180p. 99.95 (978-0-7734-1435-8(5)) Mellen, Edwin Pr., The.

Davis, Richard S. The Best of Davis: Selections from the Writings of Richard S. Davis. 2011. 130p. 40.95 (978-1-258-04453-4(6)) Literary Licensing, LLC.

de la Durantaye, Leland. Style Is Matter: The Moral Art of Vladimir Nabokov. 2007. (Illus.). 296p. 43.95 (978-0-8014-4563-7(9)) Cornell Univ. Pr.

Deardorff, Donald Lee, II. Hero & Anti-hero in the American Football Novel: Changing Conceptions of Masculinity from the 19th Century to the 21st Century. 2006. 152p. 99.95 (978-0-7734-5554-2(X)) Mellen, Edwin Pr., The.

Di Leo, Jeffrey R., ed. Federman's Fictions: Innovation, Theory, & the Holocaust. 2011. (ENG.). 336p. 80.00 (978-1-4384-3381-3(6)) State Univ. of New York Pr.

Dong, Lan, ed. Transnationalism & the Asian American Heroine: Essays on Literature, Film, Myth & Media. 2010. (ENG., Illus.). 239p. pap. 55.00 (978-0-7864-4632-2(3)) McFarland & Co., Inc. Pubs.

Doyle, Laura. Freedom's Empire: Race & the Rise of the Novel in Atlantic Modernity, 1640-1940. 2008. (ENG.). 592p. 109.95 (978-0-8223-4135-2(2)); per. 29.95 (978-0-8223-4159-8(X)) Duke Univ. Pr.

Dupre, Joan. Fighting Fathers/Saving Sons. 2009. 144p. pap. *(978-3-639-13459-9(1))* VDM Verlag Dr. Mueller e.K.

Elliott, Jane. Popular Feminist Fiction As American Allegory: Representing National Time. 2008. (ENG.). 240p. 89.00 *(978-0-230-60542-8(7))* Palgrave Macmillan.

Fishkin, Benjamin Hart. The Undependable Bonds of Blood. 2011. 140p. pap. ***(978-3-8443-2290-3(6))*** Lambert Academic Publishing.

Fiske, Horace Spencer. Provincial Types in American Fiction. 2008. 288p. 25.99 *(978-0-559-53395-2(0))*; pap. 27.75 *(978-0-559-53391-4(8))* BiblioBazaar.

—Provincial Types in American Fiction. 2009. 144p. pap. *(978-0-217-74622-9(5))* Books LLC.

—Provincial Types in American Fiction. 2009. 144p. pap. 19.99 *(978-1-4588-4508-5(7))* General Bks. LLC.

—Provincial Types in American Fiction. 2007. (ENG.). 282p. 43.95 *(978-0-548-03063-9(4))* Kessinger Publishing, LLC.

Fitzpatrick, Kathleen. The Anxiety of Obsolescence: The American Novel in the Age of Television. 2006. (ENG., Illus.). 288p. (C). per. 34.95 *(978-0-8265-1520-9(7))* Vanderbilt Univ. Pr.

Frantz, Sarah. Women Constructing Men: Female Novelists & Their Male Characters, 1750D2000. 2011. (ENG.). 280p. pap. 32.95 *(978-0-7391-3366-8(7))* Lexington Bks.

Frantz, Sarah & Rennhak, Katharina. Women Constructing Men: Female Novelists & Their Male Characters, 1750-2000. 2009. (ENG.). 280p. 73.50 *(978-0-7391-3365-1(9))* Lexington Bks.

Gandolfo, Anita. Faith & Fiction: Christian Literature in America Today, 1 vol. 2007. 208p. 44.95 *(978-0-275-99196-8(2)*, C9196, Praeger Pubs.) Greenwood Publishing Group, Inc.

Gauthier, Marni. Amnesia & Redress in Contemporary American Fiction: Counterhistory. 2011. (American Literature Readings in the Twenty-First Century Ser.). (ENG., Illus.). 266p. 85.00 *(978-0-230-11577-4(2))* Palgrave Macmillan.

Geherin, David. Scene of the Crime: The Importance of Place in Crime & Mystery Fiction. 2008. (ENG.). 223p. per. 35.00 *(978-0-7864-3298-1(5))* McFarland & Co., Inc. Pubs.

Giannone, Richard. Flannery O'Connor, Hermit Novelist: With a New Preface by the Author. 2010. 312p. pap. 29.95 *(978-1-57003-910-2(0))* Univ. of South Carolina Pr.

Gibbs, Alan. Henry Roth's Semi-Autobiographical Tetralogy Mercy of a Rude Stream (1994-1998) The Second Career of an American Novelist. 2008. 276p. 109.95 *(978-0-7734-5101-8(3))* Mellen, Edwin Pr., The.

Gillis, Stacy. Crime Fiction. 2009. (ENG.). 224p. (gr. 17). 90.00 *(978-0-7486-2320-4(5))*; pap. 29.50 *(978-0-7486-2319-8(1))* Edinburgh Univ. Pr. GBR. Dist: Columbia Univ. Pr.

Gleason, Paul William. Understanding T.C. Boyle. 2009. (Understanding Contemporary American Literature Ser.). 200p. *(978-1-57003-780-1(9))* Univ. of South Carolina Pr.

Golden, Catherine J. Images of the Woman Reader in Victorian British & American Fiction. 2009. (ENG., Illus.). 304p. (C). pap. 29.50 *(978-1-61610-119-0(9))* Orange Grove Bks.

Goodman. Policing Narratives & the State of Terror. 2010. 219p. pap. 23.95 *(978-1-4384-2904-5(5)*, Suny Pr.) State Univ. of New York Pr.

Goodman, Robin Truth. Policing Narratives & the State of Terror. 2009. 208p. 70.00 *(978-1-4384-2903-8(7))* State Univ. of New York Pr.

Grausam, Daniel. On Endings: American Postmodern Fiction & the Cold War. 2011. viii, 196p. E-Book *(978-0-8139-3166-1(5))*; (ENG.). 208p. (C). (gr. 13-17). pap. 22.50 *(978-0-8139-3162-3(2))*; (ENG.). 208p. (gr. 17). 49.50 *(978-0-8139-3161-6(4))* Univ. Pr. of Virginia.

Green, Mary. Diamela Eltit: Reading the Mother. 2007. (Monografías A Ser.: Volume 249). 180p. 90.00 *(978-1-85566-155-4(1)*, Tamesis Bks.) Boydell & Brewer, Ltd. GBR. Dist: Boydell & Brewer, Inc.

Gregoriou, Christiana. Deviance in Contemporary Crime Fiction. 2007. (Crime Files Ser.). (ENG.). 200p. 84.00 *(978-0-230-00339-2(7))* Palgrave Macmillan.

Grice, Helena. Asian American Fiction, History & Life Writing: International Encounters. 2009. (Routledge Transnational Perspectives on American Literature Ser.). (ENG.). 186p. (C). 125.00 *(978-0-415-38475-9(3))* Routledge.

Hamilton, Patrick L. Of Space & Mind: Cognitive Mappings of Contemporary Chicano - A Fiction. 2011. (ENG.). 234p. 55.00 *(978-0-292-72363-4(6))* Univ. of Texas Pr.

Harrington, Ellen Burton. Scribbling Women & the Short Story Form: Approaches by American & British Women Writers. 2008. 216p. (C). pap. 33.95 *(978-1-4331-0077-2(0))* Lang, Peter Publishing, Inc.

Harzewski, Stephanie. Chick Lit & Postfeminism. 2011. (Cultural Frames, Framing Culture Ser.). (ENG., Illus.). 264p. (C). (gr. 13-17). pap. 19.50 *(978-0-8139-3072-5(3))* Univ. Pr. of Virginia.

Hearne, Betsy & Trites, Roberta Seelinger, eds. A Narrative Compass: Stories That Guide Women's Lives. 2009. (ENG., Illus.). 269p. 67.00 *(978-0-252-03407-7(4))*; 264p. pap. 26.00 *(978-0-252-07611-4(7))* Univ. of Illinois Pr.

Herbert, Marilyn. Bookclub-in-a-Box Discusses Abraham Verghese's Novel, Cutting for Stone: The Complete Package for Readers & Leaders. 2011. 74p. pap. 19.95 *(978-1-897082-65-2(7))* Bookclub-in-a-Box CAN. Dist: AtlasBooks Distribution.

—Bookclub-in-a-Box Presents: Water for Elephants by Sara Gruen. 2008. 84p. pap. 19.95 *(978-1-897082-49-2(5))* Bookclub-in-a-Box CAN. Dist: AtlasBooks Distribution.

Hilfer, Anthony Channell. The Ethics of Intensity in American Fiction. 2011. (ENG.). 224p. pap. 25.00 ***(978-0-292-74113-3(8))*** Univ. of Texas Pr.

Hill, Donna. How to Write African American Ficiton: Avoiding the Stereotype. Date not set. pap. *(978-0-312-31754-6(9)*, St. Martin's Paperbacks) St. Martin's Pr.

Hogan, Walter. Animals in Young Adult Fiction. 2009. (Scarecrow Studies in Young Adult Literature Ser.). (ENG.). 268p. 50.00 *(978-0-8108-5994-4(7))* Scarecrow Pr., Inc.

Holman, C. Hugh. The Immoderate Past: The Southern Writer & History. 2008. (ENG.). 128p. pap. 22.95 *(978-0-8203-3357-1(3))* Univ. of Georgia Pr.

Hopkins, Ellen & Wilson, Leah. A New Dawn: Your Favorite Authors on Stephenie Meyer's Twilight Series. 2008. x, 174p. *(978-0-9792331-5-9(1))* BenBella Bks.

Houston, Lynn Marie & Warren, Jennifer. Reading Barbara Kingsolver, 1 vol. 2009. (Pop Lit Book Club Ser.). 149p. 39.95 *(978-0-313-36291-0(2)*, GR6291, Greenwood Pr.) Greenwood Publishing Group, Inc.

Howard, June. Form & History in American Literary Naturalism. 2011. (ENG.). 224p. pap. 40.00 *(978-0-8078-6547-7(8))* Univ. of North Carolina Pr.

Howe, Alexander N. & Jackson, Christine A., eds. Marcia Muller & the Female Private Eye: Essays on the Novels That Defined a Subgenre. 2008. (ENG.). 203p. pap. 35.00 *(978-0-7864-3825-9(8))* McFarland & Co., Inc. Pubs.

Howells, William Dean. Criticism & Fiction. 2007. (ENG.). 76p. per. *(978-1-4065-2279-2(1))* Dodo Pr.

—Criticism & Fiction. 2008. 196p. pap. *(978-1-4086-8003-2(3))*; pap. *(978-1-4086-8004-9(1))* Read Bks.

Hume, Kathryn. Aggressive Fictions: Reading the Contemporary American Novel. 2011. 224p. 45.00 ***(978-0-8014-5001-3(2))*** Cornell Univ. Pr.

Hunt, Alex. The Geographical Imagination of Annie Proulx: Rethinking Regionalism. (ENG.). 2010. 228p. pap. 29.95 *(978-0-7391-2395-9(5))* 2008. 229p. 62.99 *(978-0-7391-2394-2(7))* Lexington Bks.

Isaac, Megan Lynn. Suzanne Fisher Staples: The Setting Is the Story. 2009. (Scarecrow Studies in Young Adult Literature Ser.). (ENG., Illus.). 192p. 50.00 *(978-0-8108-5757-5(X))* Scarecrow Pr., Inc.

Johnson, Kevin. The Dark Page: Books That Inspired American Film Noir, 1940-1949. 2007. (Illus.). 384p. 95.00 *(978-1-58456-217-7(X))*; 450.00 *(978-1-58456-218-4(8))* Oak Knoll Pr.

Jorif, Rolando Leodore. How Slave Narratives Influenced American Literature: A Source for Herman Melville's Billy Budd. 2009. (ENG.). 128p. 89.95 *(978-0-7734-4826-1(8))* Mellen, Edwin Pr., The.

Keener, Joseph B. Shakespeare & Masculinity in Southern Fiction: Faulkner, Simms, Page, & Dixon. 2008. (ENG.). 224p. 84.00 *(978-0-230-60320-2(3))* Palgrave Macmillan.

Kelly, Alison. Understanding Lorrie Moore. 2009. *(978-1-57003-823-5(6))* Univ. of South Carolina Pr.

Kelton, Kevin. Priestly Problems. 2008. 356p. pap. *(978-3-639-01381-8(6))* VDM Verlag Dr. Mueller e.K.

Khair, Tabish. The Gothic, Postcolonialism & Otherness: Ghosts from Elsewhere. 2009. (ENG.). 208p. 84.00 *(978-0-230-23406-2(2))* Palgrave Macmillan.

King, Stephen. He Is Legend: An Anthology Celebrating Richard Matheson. Conlon, Christopher, ed. 2009. 364p. 60.00 *(978-1-887368-10-0(8))* Gauntlet, Inc.

Koloski, Bernard, ed. Awakenings: The Story of the Kate Chopin Revival. (Southern Literary Studies). 2012. 240p. pap. 18.95 ***(978-0-8071-4366-7(9))*** 2009. 232p. 35.00 *(978-0-8071-3495-5(3))* Louisiana State Univ. Pr.

Kuhn, Cynthia & Rubin, Lance, eds. Reading Chuck Palahniuk: American Monsters & Literary Mayhem. (ENG.). (C). 2012. 232p. pap. 39.95 ***(978-0-415-63424-3(5))*** 2009. 246p. 125.00 *(978-0-415-99810-9(7))* Routledge.

Kurnick, David. Empty Houses - Theatrical Failure & the Novel. 2011. (ENG., Illus.). 280p. (C). pap. 32.50 ***(978-0-691-15316-2(7))*** Princeton Univ. Pr.

—Empty Houses - Theatrical Failure & the Novel of Interiority. 2011. (ENG., Illus.). 280p. (C). 75.00 ***(978-0-691-15151-9(2))*** Princeton Univ. Pr.

Lambert, Joshua N. American Jewish Fiction: A JPS Guide. 2009. (JPS Guides). (ENG., Illus.). 250p. pap. 18.00 *(978-0-8276-0883-2(7))* Jewish Pubn. Society.

Landon, Brooks. Understanding Thomas Berger. 2009. (Understanding Contemporary American Literature Ser.). 280p. 39.95 *(978-1-57003-828-0(7))* Univ. of South Carolina Pr.

Lavender, Isiah, III. Race in American Science Fiction. 2011. (ENG., Illus.). 286p. pap. 24.95 *(978-0-253-22259-6(1)*, 0253222591) Indiana Univ. Pr.

Leavis, Q. D. Collected Essays, 3 vols., Vol. 3. Singh, G., ed. 2009. (ENG.). 356p. pap. 48.00 *(978-0-521-31826-6(2))* Cambridge Univ. Pr.

Lee, Hermione. Philip Roth (Routledge Revivals) 2009. (ENG.). 96p. 100.00 *(978-0-415-56241-6(4))* Routledge.

Lemke, Sieglinde. The Vernacular Matters of American Literature. 2009. (ENG.). 208p. 89.00 *(978-0-230-62093-3(0))* Palgrave Macmillan.

Lever, Charles James. Arthur O'Leary: His Wanderings & Ponderings in Many Lands. 2010. 528p. pap. 40.75 *(978-1-143-02675-1(6))* 2009. 520p. 36.99 *(978-1-115-80495-0(2))* 2009. 520p. pap. 38.75 *(978-1-115-80497-4(9))* 2009. 428p. pap. 35.75 *(978-1-115-80490-5(1))* 2009. 520p. pap. 39.75 *(978-1-115-80496-7(0))* 2009. 520p. 44.99 ***(978-1-115-80494-3(4))*** 2009. 308p. 25.99 *(978-1-103-45478-5(1))* 2009. 308p. pap. 19.99 *(978-1-103-45477-8(3))* 2008. 508p. 32.99 *(978-0-559-80946-0(8))* 2008. 508p. pap. 38.75 *(978-0-559-80944-6(1))* BiblioBazaar.

—Arthur O'Leary: His Wanderings & Ponderings in Many Lands. 2009. 368p. pap. *(978-0-217-72493-7(0))* Books LLC.

—Arthur O'Leary: His wanderings & ponderings in many Lands. 2011. 306p. pap. 29.75 ***(978-1-174-56965-4(4))*** 2010. 546p. pap. 41.75 *(978-1-178-37470-4(X))* BiblioBazaar.

—Arthur O'Leary: His Wanderings & Ponderings in Many Lands. 2009. (ENG.). 428p. pap. 26.99 *(978-1-115-80493-6(6)*, BiblioLife) BiblioBazaar.

—Arthur O'Leary: His Wanderings & Ponderings in Many Lands. 2010. 112p. pap. 19.99 *(978-1-154-07611-0(3))*; (Illus.). 98p. pap. 20.00 *(978-1-155-00566-9(X))*; (Illus.). 98p. pap. 19.99 *(978-1-154-33587-3(9))*; (Illus.). 110p. pap. 20.12 *(978-1-155-05111-6(4))* General Bks. LLC.

—Arthur O'Leary: His Wanderings & Ponderings in Many Lands. 2009. (ENG.). 518p. pap. 31.99 *(978-1-115-80498-1(7))*; pap. 30.99 *(978-1-115-80499-8(5))* BiblioBazaar. (BiblioLife).

—Arthur O'Leary His Wanderings & Ponderings in Many Lands. 2010. 304p. pap. 12.17 *(978-1-153-65075-5(4))* General Bks. LLC.

Lever, Charles James & Cruikshank, George. Arthur O'Leary: His wanderings & ponderings in many Lands. 2010. 398p. pap. 33.75 *(978-1-177-92850-2(7))* BiblioBazaar.

Leypoldt, Günter. Cultural Authority in the Age of Whitman: A Transnational Perspectives. Manning, Susan & Taylor, Andrew, eds. 2009. (Edinburgh Critical Studies in Transatlantic Literature Ser.). (ENG.). 312p. (gr. 17). 95.00 *(978-0-7486-3574-0(2))* Edinburgh Univ. Pr. GBR. Dist: Columbia Univ. Pr.

Limon, John. The Place of Fiction in the Time of Science: A Disciplinary History of American Writing. 2009. (Cambridge Studies in American Literature & Culture Ser.). (ENG.). 236p. pap. 34.99 *(978-0-521-10763-1(6))* Cambridge Univ. Pr.

Ling, Jinqi. Across Meridians: History & Figuration in Karen Tei Yamashita's Transnational Novels. 2012. (Asian America Ser.). (ENG.). 248p. 50.00 ***(978-0-8047-7801-5(9))*** Stanford Univ. Pr.

Locke, Richard. Critical Children: The Use of Childhood in Ten Great Novels. 2011. (Illus.). (ENG.). 232p. (gr. 17). 29.50 *(978-0-231-15782-7(7))*; 218p. E-Book *(978-0-231-52799-6(3))* Columbia Univ. Pr.

Luce, Dianne C. Reading the World: Cormac McCarthy's Tennessee Period. 2009. 336p. 49.95 *(978-1-57003-824-2(4))* Univ. of South Carolina Pr.

Lugar, Austin & Huang, Jim, eds. Organizing Crime: The Mystery Company's Guide to Series. 2009. 170p. spiral bd. 15.00 *(978-1-932325-09-6(3)*, Mystery Co., The) Crum Creek Pr.

Manjikian, Mary. Apocalypse & Post-Politics: The Romance of the End. 2012. (ENG.). 344p. (gr. 17). 75.00 ***(978-0-7391-6622-2(0))*** Lexington Bks.

March-Russell, Paul. The Short Story: An Introduction. 2009. (ENG., Illus.). 256p. (gr. 17). 85.00 *(978-0-7486-2773-8(1))*; pap. 28.50 *(978-0-7486-2774-5(X))* Edinburgh Univ. Pr. GBR. Dist: Columbia Univ. Pr.

Margolies, Edward. New York & the Literary Imagination: The City in Twentieth Century Fiction & Drama. 2007. (ENG.). 206p. per. 35.00 *(978-0-7864-3071-0(0))* McFarland & Co., Inc. Pubs.

Martin, Harold C., ed. Style in Prose Fiction. reprint ed. AMS Pr., Inc.

Martin, Robert K. & Savoy, Eric, eds. American Gothic: New Interventions in a National Narrative. 2009. (ENG., Illus.). 278p. pap. 19.95 *(978-1-58729-349-8(8))* Univ. of Iowa Pr.

McAleer, Patrick. Inside the Dark Tower Series: Art, Evil, & Intertextuality in the Stephen King Novels. 2009. (ENG.). 200p. pap. 35.00 *(978-0-7864-3977-5(7))* McFarland & Co., Inc. Pubs.

McDonald, Craig, ed. Rogue Males: Conversations & Confrontations about the Writing Life. 2009. 320p. pap. 14.95 *(978-1-932557-45-9(8))* Bleak Hse. Bks., Inc.

Morace, Robert A. John Cheever. 2011. ***(978-1-58765-827-3(5))*** Salem Pr., Inc.

Morey, Anne. Genre, Reception, & Adaptation in the Twilight Series. 2012. (Ashgate Studies in Childhood, 1700 to the Present Ser.). 245p. 99.95 ***(978-1-4094-3682-1(4))*** Ashgate Publishing Co.

Morris, Nicola. The Golem in Jewish American Literature: Risks & Responsibilities in the Fiction of Thane Rosenbaum, Nomi Eve & Steve Stern. 2007. (Twentieth-Century American Jewish Writers Ser.). 158p. (C). 60.95 *(978-0-8204-6384-1(1))* Lang, Peter Publishing, Inc.

Morris, Vanessa Irvin. The Readers' Advisory Guide to Street Literature. 2011. (Illus.). 144p. ***(978-0-8389-1110-5(2))*** American Library Assn.

Mullan, John. How Novels Work. 368p. 2008. (ENG.). pap. 15.95 *(978-0-19-928178-7(5))* 2006. 35.00 *(978-0-19-928177-0(7))* Oxford Univ. Pr., Inc.

Naparsteck, Martin. Richard Yates up Close: The Writer & His Works. 2011. (ENG., Illus.). 203p. pap. 45.00 *(978-0-7864-6059-5(8))* McFarland & Co., Inc. Pubs.

Newman, Judie. Fictions of America: Narratives of Global Empire. 2007. (ENG.). 208p. 34.95 *(978-0-415-33384-6(9))*; 120.00 *(978-0-415-33383-2(0))* Routledge.

Nickerson, Catherine Ross, ed. The Cambridge Companion to American Crime Fiction. 2010. (Cambridge Companions to Literature Ser.). (ENG.). 208p. (C). 75.00 *(978-0-521-19937-7(0))* Cambridge Univ. Pr.

Nisly, Lamar. Wingless Chickens, Bayou Catholics, & Pilgrim Wayfarers: Constructions of Audience & Tone in O'Connor, Percy, & Gautreaux. 2011. (Flannery O'Connor Ser.). (Illus.). 256p. 35.00 *(978-0-88146-214-2(4))* Mercer Univ. Pr.

Nolan, Michelle. Ball Tales: A Study of Baseball, Basketball & Football Fiction of the 1930s Through 1960s. 2010. (ENG., Illus.). 287p. pap. 35.00 *(978-0-7864-3985-0(8))* McFarland & Co., Inc. Pubs.

Oakley, Helen. From Revolution to Migration: A Study of Contemporary Cuban & Cuban American Crime Fiction. 2011. (Hispanic Studies: Culture & Ideas Ser.). (ENG.). 186p. pap. 53.95 ***(978-3-03911-021-6(7))*** Lang, Peter AG GBR. Dist: Lang, Peter.

O'Brien, Daniel. Hannibal Files: The Unauthorised Guide to the Hannibal Lecter Trilogy. 2009. (ENG., Illus.). 202p. pap. 23.95 *(978-1-905287-70-3(4))* Reynolds & Hearn GBR. Dist: Independent Pubs. Group.

O'Connell, Jennifer, et al. Everything I Needed to Know about Being a Girl I Learned from Judy Blume. 2009. (ENG.). 288p. pap. 14.00 *(978-1-4391-0265-7(1))* Gallery Pr., The IRL. Dist: Simon & Schuster, Inc.

Oh, Seung Ah. Recontextualizing Asian American Domesticity: From Madame Butterfly to My American Wife. 2008. (ENG.). 208p. 68.50 *(978-0-7391-2278-5(9))* Lexington Bks.

Okker, Patricia. Transnationalism & American Serial Fiction. 2011. (Routledge Transnational Perspectives on American Literature Ser.). (ENG., Illus.). 266p. (C). 125.00 *(978-0-415-88886-8(7))* Routledge.

Owen, James A. & Wilson, Leah. Secrets of the Dragon Riders: Your Favorite Authors on Christopher Paolini's Inheritance Cycle. 2008. *(978-0-9792331-6-6(X))* BenBella Bks.

Padilla, Yajaira M. Changing Women, Changing Nation: Female Agency, Nationhood, & Identity in Trans-Salvadoran Narratives. 2012. (SUNY series in Latin American & Iberian Thought & Culture Ser.). (ENG.). 192p. 70.00 ***(978-1-4384-4277-8(7))*** State Univ. of New York Pr.

Paloge, Helen. The Silent Echo: The Middle-Aged Female Body in Contemporary Women's Fiction. 2007. (ENG.). 200p. 73.50 *(978-0-7391-2172-6(3))* Lexington Bks.

Paulauskienė, Aušra. Lost & Found: The Discovery of Lithuania in American Fiction. 2007. (Illus.). 184p. per. 50.00 *(978-90-420-2266-9(3))* Rodopi.

Peacock, James. Jonathan Lethem. 2012. (Contemporary American & Canadian Novelists Ser.). (ENG.). 208p. 95.00 ***(978-0-7190-8267-2(6))*** Manchester Univ. Pr. GBR. Dist: Macmillan.

Powers, Kimberly. Escaping the Vampire: Desperate for the Immortal Hero, 1 vol. 2009. (ENG.). 192p. (YA). pap. 12.99 *(978-1-4347-0061-2(5))* Cook, David C.

Pulitano, Elvira, ed. Transatlantic Voices: Interpretations of Native North American Literatures. 2007. (ENG.). 336p. pap. 26.95 *(978-0-8032-6034-4(2))* Univ. of Nebraska Pr.

Punday, Daniel. Five Strands of Fictionality: The Institutional Construction of Contemporary American Fiction. 2010. (ENG.). 288p. 44.95 *(978-0-8142-1114-4(3))*; cd-rom 14.95 *(978-0-8142-9212-9(7))* Ohio State Univ. Pr.

Purdy, John Lloyd. Writing Indian, Native Conversations. 2009. (ENG.). 302p. 45.00 *(978-0-8032-2287-8(4))* Univ. of Nebraska Pr.

Quirk, Tom. Mark Twain & Human Nature. 2011. (MARK TWAIN & HIS CIRCLE Ser.). (ENG.). 312p. (C). (gr. 13). pap. 30.00 *(978-0-8262-1966-4(7))* Univ. of Missouri Pr.

A Reader's Guide to Blood Meridian. 111th annot. ed. 2006. (C). per. 29.99 *(978-0-9788349-0-6(9))* Bon Mot Publishing.

Reagin, Nancy. Twilight & History. 2010. (Wiley Pop Culture & History Ser.). (ENG.). 288p. pap. 17.95 *(978-0-470-58178-0(6)*, Wiley) Wiley, John & Sons, Inc.

Rehak, Melanie. Girl Sleuth: Nancy Drew & the Women Who Created Her. 2006. (ENG., Illus.). 384p. (gr. 9). pap. 14.00 *(978-0-15-603056-4(X)*, Mariner Bks.) Houghton Mifflin Harcourt Trade & Reference Pubs.

Rennison, Nick & Wood, Ed. 100 Must-Read American Novels: Discover Your Next Great Read... 2010. (ENG.). 224p. pap. 9.99 *(978-1-4081-2912-8(4))* A & C Black GBR. Dist: Macmillan.

Riordan, Rick & Wilson, Leah. Demigods & Monsters: Your Favorite Authors on Rick Riordan's Percy Jackson & the Olympians Series. 2008. *(978-0-9792331-4-2(3))* BenBella Bks.

Riordan, Rick & Wilson, Leah, eds. Demigods & Monsters: Your Favorite Authors on Rick Riordan's Percy Jackson & the Olympians Series. 2009. (ENG.). 196p. (J). (gr. 6-11). pap. 14.95 *(978-1-933771-83-0(6))* BenBella Bks.

Roden, Frederick S., et al, eds. Catholic Figures, Queer Narratives. 2007. (ENG., Illus.). 240p. 100.00 *(978-0-230-00831-1(3))* Palgrave Macmillan.

Rody, Caroline. The Interethnic Imagination: Roots & Passages in Contemporary Asian American Fiction. 2009. (Imagining the Americas Ser.). (ENG.). 216p. 65.00 *(978-0-19-537736-1(2))* Oxford Univ. Pr., Inc.

Rollyson, Carl E. Notable American Novelists. 2007. (Magill's Choice Ser.). 73.00 *(978-1-58765-396-4(6))*; 73.00 *(978-1-58765-395-7(8))*; 73.00 *(978-1-58765-394-0(X))* Salem Pr., Inc.

Romero Garcia, Luz V. Claudia. 119p. 9.95 *(978-1-56758-017-4(3))* Editorial Cultural, Inc.

Rowe, Joyce A. Equivocal Endings in Classic American Novels: The Scarlet Letter; Adventures of Huckleberry Finn; the Ambassadors; the Great Gatsby. 2008. (ENG.). 172p. pap. 28.00 *(978-0-521-06102-5(4))* Cambridge Univ. Pr.

Rubel, Nora L. Doubting the Devout: The Ultra-Orthodox in the Jewish American Imagination. 2009. (Religion & American Culture Ser.). (ENG.). 224p. (gr. 17). pap. 24.50 *(978-0-231-14187-1(4))*; (Illus.). 79.50 *(978-0-231-14186-4(6))* Columbia Univ. Pr.

Rubin Jr., Louis D. Two Ladies of the South: The Sewanee Review, October 1955. 2011. 16p. pap. 35.95 ***(978-1-258-04738-2(1))*** Literary Licensing, LLC.

Rushing, S. Kittrell. Memory & Myth: The Civil War in Fact & Fiction from Uncle Tom's Cabin to Cold Mountain. Sachsman, David & Morris, Roy, Jr., eds. 2007. 307p. (C). spiral bd. 62.95 *(978-1-55753-439-2(X))* Purdue Univ. Pr.

—Memory & Myth: The Civil War in Fiction & Film from Uncle Tom's Cabin to Cold Mountain. Sachsman, David B. & Morris, Roy, Jr., eds. 2007. 307p. (C). per. 29.95 *(978-1-55753-440-8(3))* Purdue Univ. Pr.

Sachs, Viola. The Myth of America: Essays in the Structures of Literary Imagination. (ENG.). 162p. 210.00 ***(978-3-11-175409-3(X))*** De Gruyter, Mouton DEU. Dist: de Gruyter, Walter GmbH & Co. KG.

Samuels, Shirley, ed. A Companion to American Fiction, 1780-1865. 2006. (Blackwell Companions to Literature & Culture Ser.: 59). (ENG., Illus.). 488p. per. 51.95 (978-1-4051-5891-6(3), Wiley-Blackwell) Wiley, John & Sons, Inc.

Sawhney, Brajesh, ed. Studies in the Literary Achievement of Louise Erdrich, Native American Writer: Fifteen Critical Essays. 2009. 312p. 119.95 (978-0-7734-4911-4(6)) Mellen, Edwin Pr., The.

Schmidt, Peter. Sitting in Darkness: New South Fiction, Education, & the Rise of Jim Crow Colonialism, 1865-1920. (ENG.). 2011. pap. 30.00 (978-1-61703-207-3(7)) 2008. (Illus.). 259p. 50.00 (978-1-934110-39-3(6)) Univ. Pr. of Mississippi.

Schuchardt, Read Mercer, ed. You Do Not Talk about Fight Club: I Am Jack's Completely Unauthorized Essay Collection. 2008. (Smart Pop Ser.). (ENG.). 216p. pap. 14.95 (978-1-933771-52-6(6)) BenBella Bks.

Schweighauser, Philipp & Schneck, Peter, eds. Terrorism, Media, & the Ethics of Fiction: Transatlantic Perspectives on Don Delillo. 2010. (ENG., Illus.). 264p. 110.00 (978-1-4411-3993-1(1)) Continuum International Publishing Group, Ltd. GBR. Dist: National Bk. Network.

Schweitzer, Darrell. The Robert E. Howard Reader. Schweitzer, Darrell, ed. 2008. (Illus.). 248p. pap. 14.95 (978-0-8095-7167-3(6)) Wildside Pr., LLC.

—The Robert E. Howard Reader. 2007. 248p. 35.00 (978-0-8095-7166-6(8)) Wildside Pr., LLC.

Shapiro, Stephen. The Culture & Commerce of the Early American Novel: Reading the Atlantic World-System. (ENG.). 368p. 2009. pap. 27.50 (978-0-271-03291-7(X)) 2008. (Illus.). 55.00 (978-0-271-03290-0(1)) Pennsylvania State Univ. Pr.

Short, Mick & Leech, Geoffrey. Style in Fiction: A Linguistic Introduction to English Fictional Prose. 2nd rev. ed. 2007. (English Language Ser.). (ENG., Illus.). 424p. (C). pap. 45.65 (978-0-582-78409-3(3)) Prentice Hall, ESL Dept.

Showalter, Elaine. Faculty Towers: The Academic Novel & Its Discontents. 2009. (Personal Takes Ser.). 152p. (C). pap. 19.95 (978-0-8122-2085-8(4)) Univ. of Pennsylvania Pr.

Sing down the Moon. pap., stu. ed. (978-0-13-017559-5(5)) Prentice Hall (Schl. Div.).

Sky, Melissa. Twilight Tales. 2010. 440p. pap. (978-3-639-22636-2(4)) VDM Verlag Dr. Mueller e.K.

Smith, Caroline J. Cosmopolitan Culture & Consumerism in Chick Lit. 2007. (Literary Criticism & Cultural Theory Ser.). (ENG.). 192p. 125.00 (978-0-415-95662-8(5)) Routledge.

Smith, Caroline J. & Smith, Caroline. Cosmopolitan Culture & Consumerism in Chick Lit. 2009. 188p. 39.95 (978-0-415-80626-8(7)) Routledge.

Smith, Shawn. Pynchon & History: Metahistorical Rhetoric & Postmodern Narrative Form in the Novels of Thomas Pynchon. 2009. 256p. pap. 39.95 (978-0-415-80337-3(3)) Routledge.

Smyczynska, Katarzyna. The World According to Bridget Jones: Discourses of Identity in Chicklit Fictions. 2007. (Literary & Cultural Theory Ser.: Vol. 27). 195p. (C). pap. 46.95 (978-0-8204-8703-8(1)) Lang, Peter Publishing, Inc.

Snodgrass, Mary Ellen. Jamaica Kincaid: A Literary Companion. 2008. (McFarland Literary Companion Ser.: 6). (ENG., Illus.). 304p. pap. 39.95 (978-0-7864-3580-7(1)) McFarland & Co., Inc. Pubs.

—Kaye Gibbons: A Literary Companion. 2007. (McFarland Literary Companions Ser.: Vol. 5). (ENG., Illus.). 379p. per. 39.95 (978-0-7864-2943-1(7)) McFarland & Co., Inc. Pubs.

Snyder, Mary H. Analyzing Literature-to-Film Adaptations: A Novelist's Exploration & Guide. 2011. (ENG., Illus.). 320p. 100.00 (978-1-4411-4998-5(8)); pap. 32.95 (978-1-4411-6818-4(4)) Continuum International Publishing Group, Ltd. GBR. Dist: National Bk. Network.

Spatz, Jonas. Hollywood in Fiction: Some versions of the American Myth. (Studies in American Literature Ser.). (ENG.). 148p. 210.00 (978-3-11-192533-2(1)); 135.00 (978-3-11-101371-8(5)) De Gruyter, Mouton DEU. Dist: de Gruyter, Walter GmbH & Co. KG.

Speiser, Margit. Ennobling the Trivial. 2008. 112p. pap. (978-3-639-02494-4(X)) VDM Verlag Dr. Mueller e.K.

Spooner, Catherine & McEvoy, Emma, eds. The Routledge Companion to Gothic. 2007. (Routledge Companions Ser.). 290p. per. 30.95 (978-0-415-39843-5(6)) Routledge.

Stafford, William T. Books Speaking to Books: A Contextual Approach to American Fiction. 2011. (ENG.). 176p. pap. 30.00 (978-0-8078-9785-0(X)) Univ. of North Carolina Pr.

Statlander, Jane. Philip Roth's Postmodern American Romance: Critical Essays on Selected Works. 2010. (Twentieth-Century American Jewish Writers Ser.). 118p. (C). 62.95 (978-1-4331-0598-2(5)) Lang, Peter Publishing, Inc.

Stein, William Bysshe. Hawthorne's Faust: A Study of the Devil Archetype. 2011. 182p. 42.95 (978-1-258-02412-3(8)) Literary Licensing, LLC.

Stouffer, Tere & CliffsNotes Staff. CliffsNotes on Sparks' A Walk to Remember. 2009. (ENG.). 72p. pap. 5.99 (978-0-470-46022-1(9), Cliff Notes) Wiley, John & Sons, Inc.

Stouffer, Tere & Wasowski, Richard P. On Nicholas Sparks the Notebook. 2009. (ENG.). 72p. pap. 5.99 (978-0-470-46009-2(1), Cliff Notes) Wiley, John & Sons, Inc.

Strehle, Susan. Transnational Women's Fiction: Unsettling Home & Homeland. 2008. (ENG.). 256p. 89.00 (978-0-230-53687-6(5)) Palgrave Macmillan.

Teuton, Sean Kicummah. Red Land, Red Power: Grounding Knowledge in the American Indian Novel. 2008. (New Americanists Ser.). (ENG.). 312p. (C). pap. 24.95 (978-0-8223-4241-0(3)) Duke Univ. Pr.

—Red Land, Red Power: Grounding Knowledge in the American Indian Novel. 2008. (New Americanists Ser.). (ENG.). 312p. (C). 89.95 (978-0-8223-4223-6(5)) Duke Univ. Pr.

Thrailkill, Jane F. Affecting Fictions: Mind, Body, & Emotion in American Literary Realism. annot. ed. 2007. 320p. 51.50 (978-0-674-02512-7(1)) Harvard Univ. Pr.

Tichelaar, Tyler R. The Gothic Wanderer: From Transgression to Redemption: Gothic Literature from 1794 - Present. 2012. (978-1-61599-139-6(5)); pap. (978-1-61599-138-9(7)) Loving Healing Pr., Inc. (Modern History Pr.).

Todorut, Luminita. The Steinbeck Hero: Forces of Good & Evil that Shape his Character. 2008. 60p. pap. (978-3-639-09573-9(1)) VDM Verlag Dr. Mueller e.K.

Trefzer, Annette. Disturbing Indians: The Archaeology of Southern Fiction. 2nd ed. 2006. 240p. 38.50 (978-0-8173-1542-9(X)) Univ. of Alabama Pr.

Treuer, David. Native American Fiction: A User's Manual. 2006. (ENG.). 224p. pap. 15.00 (978-1-55597-452-7(X)) Graywolf Pr.

Tricomi, Albert H. Missionary Positions: Evangelicalism & Empire in American Fiction. 2011. (ENG., Illus.). 240p. 74.95 (978-0-8130-3545-1(7)) Univ. Pr. of Florida.

Underwood, Doug. Journalism & the Novel: Truth & Fiction, 1700-2000. 2010. (ENG.). 278p. pap. 36.99 (978-0-521-18754-1(0)) Cambridge Univ. Pr.

Underwood, Douglas. Journalism & the Novel: Truth & Fiction, 1700-2000. 2008. (ENG.). 280p. 95.00 (978-0-521-89952-9(4)) Cambridge Univ. Pr.

Urbanski, Heather. Plagues, Apocalypses & Bug-Eyed Monsters: How Speculative Fiction Shows Us Our Nightmares. 2007. (ENG., Illus.). 264p. per. 35.00 (978-0-7864-2916-5(X)) McFarland & Co., Inc. Pubs.

Van Doren, Carl. American Novel. 2006. 416p. per. (978-1-4067-3359-4(8), Hesperides Pr.) Read Bks.

Vilas, Martin Samuel. Charles Brockden Brown: A Study of Early American Fiction. 2009. 70p. pap. 16.75 (978-1-110-07576-8(6)) BiblioBazaar.

Walhead, Celia M. A.S. Byatt: Essays on the Short Fiction. 2007. 234p. 75.95 (978-3-03911-158-9(2)); pap. 75.95 (978-0-8204-8385-6(0)) Lang, Peter Publishing, Inc.

Walrath, Douglas Alan. Displacing the Divine: The Minister in the Mirror of American Fiction. 2010. (Religion & American Culture Ser.). (ENG., Illus.). 400p. (gr. 17). 55.00 (978-0-231-15106-1(3)) Columbia Univ. Pr.

Walter, James Frank. Reading Marriage in the American Romance: Remembering Love as Destiny. 2007. (ENG.). 298p. 80.00 (978-0-7391-2178-8(2)) Lexington Bks.

Warner, Matthew. Horror Isn't a 4-Letter Word: Essays on Writing & Appreciating the Genre. 2008. 172p. 29.95 (978-1-933293-68-4(3), Guide Dog Bks.) Raw Dog Screaming Pr.

Warren, Craig A. Scars to Prove It: The Civil War Soldier & American Fiction. 2009. x, 223p. pap. (978-1-60635-015-7(3)) Kent State Univ. Pr.

Watson, Jay. Reading for the Body: The Recalcitrant Materiality of Southern Fiction, 1893-1985. 2012. (New Southern Studies). (ENG., Illus.). 472p. 69.95 (978-0-8203-4336-5(6)); pap. 26.95 (978-0-8203-4338-9(2)) Univ. of Georgia Pr.

Werlock, Abby H. P. The American Short Story, 2 vols., Set. 2nd rev. ed. 2009. (Companion to Literature Ser.). 864p. (C). (gr. 9-18). 150.00 (978-0-8160-6895-1(X)) Facts On File, Inc.

Wight, Ernest. The Long Way Home. 92p. mass mkt. (978-0-9724528-2-3(6)) Mothwing.com.

Williams, John. Back to the Badlands: Crime Writing in the USA. 2007. (ENG.). 273p. per. 14.95 (978-1-85242-921-8(6)) Serpent's Tail Ltd. GBR. Dist: Consortium Bk. Sales & Distribution.

Wilson, Natalie. Seduced by Twilight: The Allure & Contradictory Messages of the Popular Saga. 2011. (ENG., Illus.). 242p. pap. 35.00 (978-0-7864-6042-7(3)) McFarland & Co., Inc. Pubs.

Woodman, Thomas & Knight, Mark, eds. Biblical Religion & the Novel 1700-2000. 2006. 170p. 110.00 (978-0-7546-5117-8(7)) Ashgate Publishing Co.

Wyatt, David. Secret Histories: Reading Twentieth-Century American Literature. 2010. (ENG., Illus.). 424p. (C). (gr. 13-17). 70.00 (978-0-8018-9711-5(4)); pap. 35.00 (978-0-8018-9712-2(2)) Johns Hopkins Univ. Pr.

Yang, Ginger. Women's Freedom of Choice in Marge Piercy's Three Women. 2008. 96p. pap. (978-3-8364-8539-5(7)) VDM Verlag Dr. Mueller e.K.

Youngquist, Paul. Cyberfiction: After the Future. 2010. (ENG., Illus.). 272p. 84.00 (978-0-230-62151-0(1)) Palgrave Macmillan.

AMERICAN FICTION—HISTORY AND CRITICISM—19TH CENTURY

Abate, Michelle Ann. Tomboys: A Literary & Cultural History. 2008. (ENG., Illus.). 328p. 69.00 (978-1-59213-722-0(9)) Temple Univ. Pr.

Alemán, Jesse, ed. Empire & the Literature of Sensation: An Anthology of Nineteenth-Century Popular Fiction. 2007. (Multi-Ethnic Literatures of the Americas Ser.). (ENG.). 336p. per. 28.95 (978-0-8135-4076-4(3)) Rutgers Univ. Pr.

Alvis, John. Nathaniel Hawthorne as Political Philosopher: Revolutionary Principles Domesticated & Personalied. 2011. (ENG.). 291p. 49.95 (978-1-4128-4247-1(6)) Transaction Pubs.

Anderson Cordell, Sigrid. Fictions of Dissent: Reclaiming Authority in Transatlantic Women's Writing of the Late Nineteenth Century, 1 vol. 2010. (Gender & Genre Ser.). (ENG.). 160p. 99.00 (978-1-84893-023-0(2)) Pickering & Chatto Pubs., Ltd. GBR. Dist: Ashgate Publishing Co.

Anesko, Michael & Brookes, N. Christine. The French Face of Nathaniel Hawthorne: Monsieur de L'Aubepine & His Second Empire Critics. 2011. 352p. 52.95 (978-0-8142-1143-4(7)); cd-rom 14.95 (978-0-8142-9246-4(1)) Ohio State Univ. Pr.

Avril, Chloe. The Feminist Utopian Novels of Charlotte Perkins Gilman: Themes of Sexuality, Marriage, & Motherhood. 2008. 220p. 109.95 (978-0-7734-4969-5(8)) Mellen, Edwin Pr., The.

Banyai, Melinda. Experiencing Awakening with Kate Chopin: A Personal Reading of Kate Chopin's The Awakening. 2008. 64p. pap. (978-3-639-09761-0(0)) VDM Verlag Dr. Mueller e.K.

Barnes, Elizabeth. Love's Whipping Boy: Violence & Sentimentality in the American Imagination. 2011. (ENG., Illus.). 224p. 49.95 (978-0-8078-3456-5(4)) Univ. of North Carolina Pr.

Barrish, Phillip. American Literary Realism, Critical Theory, & Intellectual Prestige, 1880-1995. 2008. (Cambridge Studies in American Literature & Culture Ser.). (ENG.). 224p. pap. 34.00 (978-0-521-10380-0(0)) Cambridge Univ. Pr.

Barrish, Phillip J. The Cambridge Introduction to American Literary Realism. 2011. (Cambridge Introductions to Literature Ser.). (ENG., Illus.). 240p. (C). 85.00 (978-0-521-89769-3(6)); pap. 24.99 (978-0-521-05010-4(3)) Cambridge Univ. Pr.

Beam, Dorri. Style, Gender, & Fantasy in Nineteenth-Century American Women's Writing. 2010. (Cambridge Studies in American Literature & Culture Ser.). (ENG.). 268p. 89.00 (978-0-521-76968-6(X)) Cambridge Univ. Pr.

Behling, Laura L. Gross Anatomies: Fictions of the Physical in American Literature. 2008. (ENG., Illus.). 244p. 53.50 (978-1-57591-119-9(1)) Susquehanna Univ. Pr.

Boswell, Parley Ann. Edith Wharton on Film. 3rd ed. 2007. (ENG., Illus.). 248p. 45.00 (978-0-8093-2757-7(0)) Southern Illinois Univ. Pr.

Brennan, Matthew C. The Poet's Holy Craft: William Gilmore Simms & Romantic Verse Traditions. 2010. 168p. 49.95 (978-1-57003-888-4(0)) Univ. of South Carolina Pr.

Buchenau, Barbara. Der Fruhe Amerikanische Historische Roman im Transatlantischen Vergleich, Vol. 2. (GER.). 488p. 68.95 (978-3-631-38938-6(8)) Lang, Peter Publishing, Inc.

Burbick, Joan. Healing the Republic: The Language of Health & the Culture of Nationalism in Nineteenth-Century America. 2009. (Cambridge Studies in American Literature & Culture Ser.). (ENG.). 368p. pap. 48.00 (978-0-521-10673-3(7)) Cambridge Univ. Pr.

Burrows, Stuart. A Familiar Strangeness: American Fiction & the Language of Photography, 1839-1945. (ENG.). 304p. 2010. pap. 24.95 (978-0-8203-3521-6(5)) 2008. lib. bdg. 34.95 (978-0-8203-3174-4(0)) Univ. of Georgia Pr.

Camden, Jennifer B. Secondary Heroines in Nineteenth-Century British & American Novels. 2010. 190p. 99.95 (978-0-7546-6679-0(4)) Ashgate Publishing Co.

Canada, Mark. Literature & Journalism in Antebellum America: Thoreau, Stowe, & Their Contemporaries Respond to the Rise of the Commercial Press. 2011. (ENG., Illus.). 214p. 80.00 (978-0-230-11094-6(0)) Palgrave Macmillan.

Case, Alison & Shaw, Harry E. Austen to Eliot. 2008. (Reading the Novel Ser.). (ENG.). 232p. 104.95 (978-0-631-23149-3(8), Wiley-Blackwell) Wiley, John & Sons, Inc.

Claybaugh, Amanda. The Novel of Purpose: Literature & Social Reform in the Anglo-American World. 2006. 246p. 49.95 (978-0-8014-4480-7(2), ILR Pr.) Cornell Univ. Pr.

Comes, Judy. Madness & the Loss of Identity in Nineteenth Century Fiction. 2007. (ENG.). 224p. per. 39.95 (978-0-7864-3224-0(1)) McFarland & Co., Inc. Pubs.

Crane, Gregg D. The Cambridge Introduction to the Nineteenth-Century American Novel. 2007. (Cambridge Introductions to Literature Ser.). (ENG.). 248p. 87.99 (978-0-521-84325-6(1)); per. 27.99 (978-0-521-60399-7(4)) Cambridge Univ. Pr.

Dinius, Marcy J. The Camera & the Press: American Visual & Print Culture in the Age of the Daguerreotype. 2012. (Material Texts). (Illus.). 320p. (C). 49.95 (978-0-8122-4404-5(4)) Univ. of Pennsylvania Pr.

Dow, William. Narrating Class in American Fiction. 2008. (American Literature Readings in the Twenty-First Century Ser.). (ENG.). 288p. 105.00 (978-0-230-60982-2(1)) Palgrave Macmillan.

Dowling, Robert & Dowling, Robert M. Slumming in New York: From the Waterfront to Mythic Harlem. 2008. (ENG., Illus.). 232p. pap. 21.00 (978-0-252-07632-9(X)) Univ. of Illinois Pr.

Dowling, Robert M. Slumming in New York: From the Waterfront to Mythic Harlem. 2007. (Illus.). 232p. 37.00 (978-0-252-03194-6(0)) Univ. of Illinois Pr.

Elahi, Babak. The Fabric of American Literary Realism: Readymade Clothing, Social Mobility, & Assimilation. 2009. (ENG.). 228p. pap. 39.95 (978-0-7864-4119-8(4)) McFarland & Co., Inc. Pubs.

Fagg, John. On the Cusp: Stephen Crane, George Bellows, & Modernism. 2nd ed. 2009. (Amer Lit Realism & Naturalism Ser.). (ENG., Illus.). 280p. 49.95 (978-0-8173-1651-8(5)) Univ. of Alabama Pr.

Fernie, Deanna. Hawthorne Sculpture & the Question of American Art. 2011. (Illus.). 294p. 99.95 (978-0-7546-5479-7(6)) Ashgate Publishing Co.

Flint, Russ & Irving, Washington. The Legend of Sleepy Hollow. 2008. (ENG., Illus.). 32p. (J). (gr. k-3). 9.99 (978-0-8249-5603-5(6), Ideals Children's Bks.) Ideals Pubns.

Germana, Michael. Standards of Value: Money, Race, & Literature in America. 2009. (ENG., Illus.). 202p. 39.95 (978-1-58729-818-9(X)) Univ. of Iowa Pr.

González, John Morán. The Outer Edge of the Wave: Negotiating Cultural Identities in Post-Reconstruction America. 2010. 44.95 (978-0-8142-1129-8(1)); cd-rom 14.95 (978-0-8142-9228-0(3)) Ohio State Univ. Pr.

Hayes, Kevin J., ed. Henry James: The Contemporary Reviews. 2010. (American Critical Archives Ser.). (ENG.). 503p. pap. 40.00 (978-0-521-15540-3(1)) Cambridge Univ. Pr.

Heaberlin, Dick. Fountain Wells. 2008. 184p. pap. 19.95 (978-0-9794964-4-8(6)) Orange Hse. Bks.

Heneghan, Bridget T. Whitewashing America: Material Culture & Race in the Antebellum Imagination. 2007. (ENG., Illus.). 204p. per. 25.00 (978-1-934110-99-7(X)) Univ. Pr. of Mississippi.

Hoeller, Hildegard. From Gift to Commodity: Capitalism & Sacrifice in Nineteenth-Century American Fiction. 2012. (Becoming Modern: New Nineteenth-Century Studies). (ENG.). 296p. (C). 85.00 (978-1-61168-307-3(6)); pap. 40.00 (978-1-61168-310-3(6)) Univ. Pr. of New England.

Hubbard, Shelagh. Pride & Prejudice, Pack. 2010. (Illus.). 200p. spiral bd. 210.00 (978-1-4441-1037-1(3)) Hodder Education GBR. Dist: Trans-Atlantic Pubns., Inc.

Hughes, R. Ethics, Aesthetics, & the Beyond of Language. 2010. (SUNY series, Insinuations: Philosophy, Psychoanalysis, Literature Ser.). (ENG., Illus.). 240p. 75.00 (978-1-4384-3193-2(7)) State Univ. of New York Pr.

Hughes, Robert. Ethics, Aesthetics, & the Beyond of Language. 2011. (Illus.). 243p. pap. 24.95 (978-1-4384-3194-9(5), Suny Pr.) State Univ. of New York Pr.

Hutchison, Anthony. Writing the Republic: Liberalism & Morality in American Political Fiction. 2007. (ENG., Illus.). 256p. (gr. 17). 55.00 (978-0-231-14138-3(6)) Columbia Univ. Pr.

Ilyts, Csaba. Hemingway's Critical Heritage Then & Now. 2008. 56p. pap. (978-3-8364-9631-5(3)) VDM Verlag Dr. Mueller e.K.

Johnson, Joel A. Beyond Practical Virtue: A Defense of Liberal Democracy Through Literature. 2007. (ENG.). 208p. (C). 39.95 (978-0-8262-1711-0(7)) Univ. of Missouri Pr.

Jones, Anna Maria. Problem Novels: Victorian Fiction Theorizes the Sensational Self. 2007. (Victorian critical Interventio Ser.). viii, 163p. cd-rom 14.95 (978-0-8142-9133-7(3)); 200p. 51.95 (978-0-8142-1053-6(8)) Ohio State Univ. Pr.

Kaplan, Harold. Henry Adams & the American Naturalist Tradition. 2010. (ENG.). 197p. pap. 24.95 (978-1-4128-1423-2(5)) Transaction Pubs.

Kearns, Katherine. Nineteenth-Century Literary Realism: Through the Looking Glass. 2010. 322p. pap. 32.99 (978-0-521-15272-3(0)) Cambridge Univ. Pr.

Krauthammer, Anna. The Representation of the Savage in James Fenimore Cooper & Herman Melville. 2008. 130p. (C). 67.95 (978-0-8204-6810-5(X)) Lang, Peter Publishing, Inc.

Kuhlmann, Susan. Knave, Fool, & Genius: The Confidence Man as He Appears in Nineteenth-Century American Fiction. 2011. (ENG.). 150p. pap. 30.00 (978-0-8078-9703-4(5)) Univ. of North Carolina Pr.

Lamb, Robert Paul & Thompson, G. R., eds. A Companion to American Fiction, 1865-1914. 2009. (Blackwell Companions to Literature & Culture Ser.: 122). (ENG., Illus.). 640p. pap. 52.95 (978-1-4051-9553-9(3), Wiley-Blackwell) Wiley, John & Sons, Inc.

Lang, Amy Schrager. The Syntax of Class: Writing Inequality in Nineteenth-Century America. 2006. (Class: Culture Ser.). (ENG.). 168p. per. 23.95 (978-0-472-03181-8(3)) Univ. of Michigan Pr.

Lawson, Andrew. Downwardly Mobile: The Changing Fortunes of American Realism, 1 vol. 2012. (ENG., Illus.). 224p. 65.00 (978-0-19-982805-0(9)) Oxford Univ. Pr., Inc.

LeMenager, Stephanie. Manifest & Other Destinies: Territorial Fictions of the Nineteenth-Century United States. 2008. (Postwestern Horizons Ser.). (ENG.). 286p. pap. 24.95 (978-0-8032-1845-1(1)) Univ. of Nebraska Pr.

Leroux, Jean-Francois. Dlb 349 Se Asian Wrtrs. 2009. (Dictionary of Literary Biography Ser.). (ENG.). 503p. 315.00 (978-0-7876-8167-8(9)) Cengage Gale.

Levander, Caroline Field. Voices of the Nation: Women & Public Speech in Nineteenth-Century American Literature & Culture. 2009. (Cambridge Studies in American Literature & Culture Ser.). (ENG.). 204p. pap. 31.99 (978-0-521-10252-0(9)) Cambridge Univ. Pr.

Lewes, Darby. Auto-Poetica: Representations of the Creative Process in Nineteenth-Century British & American Fiction. Lewes, Darby, ed. 2006. (ENG.). 264p. 71.50 (978-0-7391-1651-7(7)) AltaMira Pr.

Machor, James L. Reading Fiction in Antebellum America: Informed Response & Reception Histories, 1820-1865. 2011. (ENG.). 424p. (gr. 17). 75.00 (978-0-8018-9874-7(9)) Johns Hopkins Univ. Pr.

Macneil. Novel Judgments. 2011. (ENG.). 256p. 125.00 (978-0-415-45914-3(1)); pap. 41.95 (978-0-415-45915-0(X)) Taylor & Francis Group GBR. (Routledge Cavendish). Dist: Taylor & Francis Group.

McWhirter, David. Desire & Love in Henry James: A Study of the Late Novels. 2009. (ENG.). 236p. pap. 27.99 (978-0-521-12717-2(3)) Cambridge Univ. Pr.

Mitchell, Douglas L. A Disturbing & Alien Memory: Southern Novelists Writing History. 2009. (978-0-8071-3373-6(6)) Louisiana State Univ. Pr.

Murphy, Gretchen. Shadowing the White Man's Burden: U.S. Imperialism & the Problem of the Color Line. 2010. (ENG., Illus.). 288p. 75.00 (978-0-8147-9598-9(6)); pap. 25.00 (978-0-8147-9599-6(4)) New York Univ. Pr.

Murphy, Jillmarie. Monstrous Kinships: Realism & Attachment Theory in the Nineteenth & Early Twentieth Century Novel. 2011. (ENG.). 208p. 60.00 (978-1-61149-050-3(2)) Univ. of Delaware Pr.

Newitz, Annalee. Pretend We're Dead: Capitalist Monsters in American Pop Culture. 2006. (ENG., Illus.). 232p. 79.95 (978-0-8223-3733-1(9)); per. 22.95 (978-0-8223-3745-4(2)) Duke Univ. Pr.

Nissen, Axel. Manly Love: Romantic Friendship in American Fiction, 1850-1900. 2009. (ENG.). 240p. 45.00 (978-0-226-58666-3(9)) Univ. of Chicago Pr.

Noel, Mary. Villains Galore: The Heyday of the Popular Story Weekly. 2011. 340p. 51.95 (978-1-258-05768-8(9)) Literary Licensing, LLC.

O'Brien, John & Searls, Damion, eds. The Review of Contemporary Fiction - Special Fiction Issue, Herman Melville: Summer 2009. 2009. (Review of Contemporary Fiction Ser.). (ENG.). 384p. pap. 8.00 (978-1-56478-590-9(4), 478590) Dalkey Archive Pr.

Olwell, Victoria. The Genius of Democracy: Fictions of Gender & Citizenship in the United States, 1860-1945. 2011. 304p. (C). 59.95 (978-0-8122-4324-6(2)) Univ. of Pennsylvania Pr.

Orr, Stanley. Darkly Perfect World: Colonial Adventure, Postmodernism, & American Noir. 2010. (ENG.). 296p. 49.95 (978-0-8142-1125-0(9)); cd-rom 14.95 (978-0-8142-9223-5(2)) Ohio State Univ. Pr.

Palleau-Papin, Françoise, et al. Willa Cather Vol. 8: A Writer's Worlds. Murphy, John J. & Thacker, Robert, eds. 2010. (Cather Studies). (ENG., Illus.). 492p. pap. 40.00 (978-0-8032-3025-5(7)) Univ. of Nebraska Pr.

Palmer, R. Barton, ed. Nineteenth-Century American Fiction on Screen. 2007. (ENG., Illus.). 276p. 90.99 (978-0-521-84221-1(2)); per. 35.99 (978-0-521-60316-4(1)) Cambridge Univ. Pr.

Panek, Leroy Lad. Before Sherlock Holmes: How Magazines & Newspapers Invented the Detective Story. 2011. (ENG.). 227p. pap. 40.00 (978-0-7864-6787-7(8)) McFarland & Co., Inc. Pubs.

Panek, Leroy Lad. The Origins of the American Detective Story. 2006. (ENG., Illus.). 235p. per. 35.00 (978-0-7864-2776-5(0)) McFarland & Co., Inc. Pubs.

Pardes, Ilana. Melville's Bibles. 2008. (Illus.). 202p. 65.00 (978-0-520-25454-1(6)); 192p. per. 26.95 (978-0-520-25455-8(4)) Univ. of California Pr.

Parille, Ken. Boys at Home: Discipline, Masculinity, & the Boy-Problem in Nineteenth-Century American Literature. 2011. (ENG.). 184p. pap. 21.00 (978-1-57233-787-9(7)) Univ. of Tennessee Pr.

Patterson, Martha H. Beyond the Gibson Girl: Reimagining the American New Woman, 1895-1915. 2008. (ENG., Illus.). 248p. pap. 26.00 (978-0-252-07563-6(3)) Univ. of Illinois Pr.

Petty, Leslie. Romancing the Vote: Feminist Activism in American Fiction, 1870-1920. 2006. (ENG.). 240p. 44.95 (978-0-8203-2858-4(8)) Univ. of Georgia Pr.

Phegley, Jennifer, et al. Transatlantic Sensations. 2012. (Ashgate Ser. in Nineteenth-Century Transatlantic Studies). (Illus.). 266p. 104.95 (978-1-4094-2715-5(3)) Ashgate Publishing Co.

Poe, Edgar Allan & Connelly, Michael. In the Shadow of the Master. 2009. (ENG., Illus.). 416p. 25.99 (978-0-06-169039-6(2), Morrow, William & Co.) HarperCollins Pubs.

Puckett, Kent. Bad Form: Social Mistakes & the Nineteenth-Century Novel. 2008. (ENG., Illus.). 192p. 45.00 (978-0-19-533275-9(X)) Oxford Univ. Pr., Inc.

Puskar, Jason Robert. Accident Society: Fiction, Collectivity, & the Production of Chance. 2012. (ENG.). 280p. 60.00 (978-0-8047-7535-9(4)) Stanford Univ. Pr.

Red Badge of Courage, Grades 6-12. pap., tchr. ed. 4.95 (978-0-8359-0464-3(4)) Globe Fearon Educational Publishing.

Rieder, John. Colonialism & the Emergence of Science Fiction. 2008. (Early Classics of Science Fiction Ser.). (ENG., Illus.). 200p. lib. bdg. 70.00 (978-0-8195-6873-1(2)) Wesleyan Univ. Pr.

Robertson, Ben P. Inchbald, Hawthorne & the Romantic Moral Romance: Little Histories & Neutral Territories, 1 vol. 2009. (ENG., Illus.). 288p. 99.00 (978-1-85196-627-1(7)) Pickering & Chatto Pubs., Ltd. GBR. Dist: Ashgate Publishing Co.

Salazar, James. Bodies of Reform: The Rhetoric of Character in Gilded Age America. 2010. (ENG., Illus.). 304p. 75.00 (978-0-8147-4130-6(4)); pap. 25.00 (978-0-8147-4131-3(2)) New York Univ. Pr.

Samuels, Shirley. Reading the American Novel, 1780-1865. 2012. (Reading the Novel Ser.: 8). (ENG.). 208p. 99.95 (978-0-631-23287-2(7), Wiley-Blackwell) Wiley, John & Sons, Inc.

Sanchez, Maria Carla. Reforming the World: Social Activism & the Problem of Fiction in Nineteenth-Century America. 2009. (ENG.). 256p. 39.95 (978-1-58729-694-9(2)) Univ. of Iowa Pr.

Sanders, Joe Sutliff. Disciplining Girls: Understanding the Origins of the Classic Orphan Girl Story. 2011. (ENG.). 240p. (gr. 17). 60.00 (978-1-4214-0318-2(8)) Johns Hopkins Univ. Pr.

Sasa, Ghada. The Femme Fatale in American Naturalism. 2008. 99.95 (978-1-60497-535-2(0)) Cambria Pr.

Satterwhite, Emily. Dear Appalachia: Readers, Identity, & Popular Fiction Since 1878. 2011. (ENG., Illus.). 396p. 40.00 (978-0-8131-3010-1(7)) Univ. Pr. of Kentucky.

Sebag-Montefiore, Mary. Women Writers of Children's Classics. 2007. (Writers & Their Work Ser.). (ENG.). 154p. (C). pap. 26.00 (978-0-7463-1157-8(5)) Northcote Hse. Publishers, Ltd. GBR. Dist: Brown, David Bk. Co., The.

Serrano, Gabriela. The Feminine Ancestral Footsteps. 2009. 148p. pap. (978-3-639-18385-6(1)) VDM Verlag Dr. Mueller e.K.

Shelley, Lorna. Female Journalists of the Fin de Siècle. 2010. (978-4-86166-130-3(7)) Routledge.

—Shelley: Female Journalists of the Fin de SièCle Vol. I. 2010. (978-0-415-55950-8(2)) Routledge.

—Shelley: Female Journalists of the Fin de SièCle Vol. Ii. 2010. (978-0-415-55951-5(0)) Routledge.

—Shelley: Female Journalists of the Fin de SièCle Vol. Iii. 2010. (978-0-415-55952-2(9)) Routledge.

—Shelley: Female Journalists of the Fin de SièCle Vol. Iv. 2010. (978-0-415-55953-9(7)) Routledge.

Shelley, Lorna, ed. Shelley: Female Journalists of the Fin de SièCle 4-Vol. Set, 4 vols. 2010. (History of Feminism Ser.). (ENG.). 1712p. (C). 1025.00 (978-0-415-55949-2(9)) Routledge.

Simms, William Gilmore. Confession. 2011. 398p. pap. 29.95 (978-1-61117-026-9(5)) Univ. of South Carolina Pr.

Snyder, Katherine V. Bachelors, Manhood, & the Novel, 1850-1925. 2009. (ENG.). 296p. pap. 41.00 (978-0-521-10096-0(8)) Cambridge Univ. Pr.

Spanos, William V. The Exceptionalist State & the State of Exception: Herman Melville's Billy Budd, Sailor. 2010. (Rethinking Theory Ser.). (ENG.). 232p. (gr. 17). 65.00 (978-0-8018-9849-5(8)) Johns Hopkins Univ. Pr.

Spotts, Carle Brocks. Development of Fiction on the Missouri Frontier, 1830-1860. (Illus.). 70p. reprint ed. lib. bdg. 88.00 (978-0-7222-0628-7(3)) Library Reprints, Inc.

Stoneley, Peter. Consumerism & American Girls' Literature, 1860-1940. 2007. (Cambridge Studies in American Literature & Culture Ser.). (ENG., Illus.). 180p. pap. 44.00 (978-0-521-03575-0(9)) Cambridge Univ. Pr.

Streeby, Shelley, ed. Empire & the Literature of Sensation: An Anthology of Nineteenth-Century Popular Fiction. 2007. (Multi-Ethnic Literatures of the Americas Ser.). (ENG.). 336p. 70.00 (978-0-8135-4075-7(5)) Rutgers Univ. Pr.

Sussex, Lucy. Women Writers & Detectives in Nineteenth-Century Crime Fiction: The Mothers of the Mystery Genre. 2010. (Crime Files Ser.). (ENG., Illus.). 224p. 84.00 (978-0-230-27229-3(0)) Palgrave Macmillan.

Swann, Charles. Nathaniel Hawthorne: Tradition & Revolution. 2009. (Cambridge Studies in American Literature & Culture Ser.). (ENG.). 296p. pap. 38.99 (978-0-521-10993-2(0)) Cambridge Univ. Pr.

Szumskyj, Benjamin, ed. The Man Who Collected Psychos: Critical Essays on Robert Bloch. 2009. (ENG., Illus.). 262p. pap. 35.00 (978-0-7864-4208-9(5)) McFarland & Co., Inc. Pubs.

Tawil, Ezra. The Making of Racial Sentiment: Slavery & the Birth of the Frontier Romance. (Cambridge Studies in American Literature & Culture Ser.). (ENG.). 256p. 2008. pap. 37.99 (978-0-521-07304-2(9)) 2006. 106.00 (978-0-521-86539-5(5)) Cambridge Univ. Pr.

Thomas, Brook. Civic Myths: A Law-and-Literature Approach to Citizenship. 2007. (ENG., Illus.). 320p. per. 23.95 (978-0-8078-5846-2(3)) Univ. of North Carolina Pr.

Thompson, G. R. eading the American Novel, 1865-1914. 2012. (Reading the Novel Ser.: 4). (ENG.). 462p. 144.95 (978-0-631-23406-7(3), Wiley-Blackwell) Wiley, John & Sons, Inc.

van Leeuwen, Evert Jan. Alchemical Construction of Genders in Anglo-American Fiction, 1799-1852: Visions of Utopia as Androgynous. 2011. 339p. 129.95 (978-0-7734-1532-4(7)) Mellen, Edwin Pr., The.

Vickery, Sukey. Emily Hamilton & Other Writings. Slawinski, Scott, ed. 2009. (Legacies of Nineteenth-Century American Women Writers Ser.). (ENG.). 278p. pap. 30.00 (978-0-8032-1785-0(4)) Univ. of Nebraska Pr.

Wakana, Maya Higashi. Performing the Everday in Henry James's Late Novels. 2009. 204p. 99.95 (978-0-7546-6744-5(8)) Ashgate Publishing Co.

Walker, Jeffrey. Leather-Stocking Redux, or, Old Tales, New Essays. 2008. (978-0-404-64473-4(2)); pap. (978-0-404-62643-3(2)) AMS Pr., Inc.

Weinstein, Cindy. The Literature of Labor & the Labors of Literature: Allegory in Nineteenth-Century American Fiction. 2008. (Cambridge Studies in American Literature & Culture Ser.). (ENG.). 284p. pap. 36.00 (978-0-521-05458-4(3)) Cambridge Univ. Pr.

Wells, Jeremy. Romances of the White Man's Burden: Race, Empire, & the Plantation in American Literature, 1880-1936. 2011. (ENG., Illus.). 264p. 55.00 (978-0-8265-1756-2(0)) Vanderbilt Univ. Pr.

Willey, Nicole L. Creating a New Ideal of Masculinity for American Men: The Achievement of Sentimental Women Writers in the Mid-Nineteenth Century. 2007. 316p. 119.95 (978-0-7734-5204-6(4)) Mellen, Edwin Pr., The.

Yarington, Earl Frank, II. The Portrayal of Woman's Sentimental Power in American Domestic Fiction: The Novels of Mary Jane Holmes, 1825-1907. 2006. 224p. 109.95 (978-0-7734-5438-5(1)) Mellen, Edwin Pr., The.

AMERICAN FICTION—HISTORY AND CRITICISM—20TH CENTURY

Abate, Michelle Ann. Tomboys: A Literary & Cultural History. 2008. (ENG., Illus.). 338p. pap. 29.95 (978-1-59213-723-7(7)); 328p. 69.00 (978-1-59213-722-0(9)) Temple Univ. Pr.

Abel, Marco. Violent Affect: Literature, Cinema, & Critique after Representation. 2009. (ENG.). 312p. pap. 24.95 (978-0-8032-2481-0(8)) Univ. of Nebraska Pr.

Aboul-Ela, Hosam M. Other South: Faulkner, Coloniality, & the Mariátegui Tradition. 2007. (Pitt Illuminations Ser.). (ENG.). 224p. (C). per. 24.95 (978-0-8229-5976-2(3)) Univ. of Pittsburgh Pr.

Abraham, Julie. Are Girls Necessary? Lesbian Writing & Modern Histories. 2008. 240p. pap. 22.50 (978-0-8166-5676-9(2)) Univ. of Minnesota Pr.

Adair, Gilbert & Tabbi, Joseph. The American Epic Novel in the Late Twentieth Century: The Super Genre of the Imperial State. 2008. 304p. (C). 119.95 (978-0-7734-5213-8(3)) Mellen, Edwin Pr., The.

Adams, Don. Alternative Paradigms of Literary Realism. 2009. (ENG.). 212p. 89.00 (978-0-230-62186-2(4)) Palgrave Macmillan.

Adelman, Gary. Sorrow's Rigging: The Novels of Cormac Mccarthy, Don Delillo, & Robert Stone. 2012. (ENG.). 200p. (C). (978-0-7735-3978-5(6)) McGill-Queen's Univ. Pr.

Alber, Jan. Narrating the Prison: Role & Representation in Charles Dickens's Novels, Twentieth-Century Fiction, & Film. 2007. 316p. (C). 109.95 (978-1-934043-60-8(5)) Cambria Pr.

Alexander, Charlotte A. Monarch Notes Grapes of Wrath. (C). 3.95 (978-0-671-00692-1(4), Arco) Peterson's.

Ames, Christopher. The Life of the Party: Festive Vision in Modern Fiction. 2010. (ENG.). 358p. pap. 24.95 (978-0-8203-3690-9(4)) Univ. of Georgia Pr.

Annesley, James. Fictions of Globalization: Consumption, the Market & the Contemporary American Novel. 2009. (Continuum Literary Studies). (ENG.). 208p. 39.95 (978-0-8264-3316-9(2)) Continuum International Publishing Group, Ltd. GBR. Dist: National Bk. Network.

Armengol, Josep M. Richard Ford & the Fiction of Masculinities. 2010. (Modern American Literature: New Approaches Ser.). 154p. (C). pap. 69.95 (978-1-4331-1086-3(5)) Lang, Peter Publishing, Inc.

Avril, Chloe. The Feminist Utopian Novels of Charlotte Perkins Gilman: Themes of Sexuality, Marriage, & Motherhood. 2008. 220p. 109.95 (978-0-7734-4969-5(8)) Mellen, Edwin Pr., The.

Bachner, Sally. The Prestige of Violence: American Fiction, 1962-2007. 2011. (ENG.). 184p. 59.95 (978-0-8203-3889-7(3)); pap. 24.95 (978-0-8203-3910-8(5)) Univ. of Georgia Pr.

Baker, Brian. Masculinity in Fiction & Film: Representing Men in Popular Genres, 1945-2000. 2008. (Continuum Literary Studies). (ENG.). 186p. pap. 49.95 (978-1-84706-262-8(8)) Continuum International Publishing Group, Ltd. GBR. Dist: National Bk. Network.

Baker, Charles. William Faulkner's Postcolonial South. Hakutani, Yoshinobu, ed. 2nd ed. (Modern American Literature Ser.). 163p. pap. 31.95 (978-0-8204-5825-0(2)) Lang, Peter Publishing, Inc.

Baker, Charley, et al. Madness in Post-1945 British & American Fiction. 2010. (ENG., Illus.). 240p. 84.00 (978-0-230-21975-5(6)) Palgrave Macmillan.

Bakker, J. Fiction As Survival Strategy: A Comparative Study of the Major Works of Ernest Hemingway & Saul Bellow. 2009. 220p. pap. 39.00 (978-90-6203-924-1(3)) Rodopi.

Bakos, Judit. Painting & Writing. 2009. (Illus.). 144p. pap. (978-3-639-13500-8(8)) VDM Verlag Dr. Mueller e.K.

Barrish, Phillip. American Literary Realism, Critical Theory, & Intellectual Prestige, 1880-1995. 2008. (Cambridge Studies in American Literature & Culture Ser.). (ENG.). 224p. pap. 34.00 (978-0-521-10380-0(0)) Cambridge Univ. Pr.

Barrish, Phillip J. The Cambridge Introduction to American Literary Realism. 2011. (Cambridge Introductions to Literature Ser.). (ENG., Illus.). 240p. (C). 85.00 (978-0-521-89769-3(6)); pap. 24.99 (978-0-521-05010-4(3)) Cambridge Univ. Pr.

Baumann, Ursula. Sklavenhalter wider Willen und ein Krieg zwischen Cause und Chaos: Amerikanische Bürgerkriegsromane am Ende des 20. Jahrhunderts. 2009. (Regensburger Arbeiten zur Anglistik und Amerikanistik Ser.). (GER.). 262p. 72.95 (978-3-631-58928-1(X)) Lang, Peter GmbH, Europaischer Verlag der Wissenschaften DEU. Dist: Lang, Peter.

Baxter, Charles. Burning down the House. 2nd ed. 2008. (ENG.). 288p. pap. 15.00 (978-1-55597-508-1(9)) Graywolf Pr.

Becker, Audrey, et al, eds. Welsh Mythology & Folklore in Popular Culture: Essays on Adaptations in Literature, Film, Television & Digital Media. 2011. (Critical Explorations in Science Fiction & Fantasy Ser.). (ENG., Illus.). 234p. pap. 35.00 (978-0-7864-6170-7(5)) McFarland & Co., Inc. Pubs.

Behling, Laura L. Gross Anatomies: Fictions of the Physical in American Literature. 2008. (ENG., Illus.). 244p. 53.50 (978-1-57591-119-9(1)) Susquehanna Univ. Pr.

Bell, Kevin. Ashes Taken for Fire: Aesthetic Modernism & the Critique of Identity. 2007. 240p. 67.50 (978-0-8166-4900-6(6)); per. 24.50 (978-0-8166-4901-3(4)) Univ. of Minnesota Pr.

Berman, Jessica. Modernist Fiction, Cosmopolitanism & the Politics of Community. 2007. (ENG.). 256p. pap. 58.00 (978-0-521-03299-5(7)) Cambridge Univ. Pr.

Berman, Ronald. Translating Modernism: Fitzgerald & Hemingway. 2010. (ENG.). 202p. pap. 19.95 (978-0-8173-5655-1(7)) Univ. of Alabama Pr.

Beuka, Robert. American Icon: Fitzgerald's the Great Gatsby in Critical & Cultural Context. 2011. (Literary Criticism in Perspective Ser.). 172p. 75.00 (978-1-57113-371-7(2)) Camden Hse.

Beyer, Jr., Thomas R., Thomas R. 33 Keys to Unlocking the Lost Symbol: A Reader's Companion to the Dan Brown Novel. 2009. (ENG., Illus.). 176p. pap. 14.95 (978-1-55704-919-3(X), William Morrow Paperbacks) HarperCollins Pubs.

Bibler, Michael P. Cotton's Queer Relations: Same-Sex Intimacy & the Literature of the Southern Plantation, 1936-1968. 2009. (ENG.). 312p. (C). (gr. 13-17). pap. 22.50 (978-0-8139-2792-3(7)); (gr. 17). 55.00 (978-0-8139-2791-6(9)) Univ. Pr. of Virginia.

Billboc, Zs=Fia. Caddy Compson: An Absent Presence. 2008. 88p. pap. (978-3-639-10245-1(2)) VDM Verlag Dr. Mueller e.K.

Black, Shameem. Fiction Across Borders: Imagining the Lives of Others in Late-Twentieth-Century Novels. 2010. (ENG., Illus.). 332p. (gr. 17). 84.50 (978-0-231-14978-5(6)); pap. 26.50 (978-0-231-14979-2(4)) Columbia Univ. Pr.

Bloom, Harold. The Great Gatsby - F. Scott Fitzgerald. 2nd rev. ed. 2010. (Bloom's Modern Critical Interpretations Ser.). 190p. (C). (gr. 9-18). 45.00 (978-1-60413-820-7(3), Chelsea Hse.) Facts On File, Inc.

—Jack London. 2011. (Bloom's Modern Critical Views Ser.). 166p. (C). 45.00 (978-1-60413-366-0(X), Bloom's Literary Criticism) Facts On File, Inc.

Bloom, Harold, ed. Ernest Hemingway's the Sun Also Rises. annot. ed. 2007. (Bloom's Guides). 112p. (YA). (gr. 9-12). lib. bdg. 30.00 (978-0-7910-9359-7(X)) Facts On File, Inc.

Bonadonna, Reed. Served This Soldiering Through. 2010. 224p. pap. (978-3-639-21312-6(2)) VDM Verlag Dr. Mueller e.K.

Bosco, Mark & Connor, Kimberly Rae, eds. Academic Novels as Satire: Critical Studies of an Emerging Genre. 2007. 164p. 99.95 (978-0-7734-5418-7(7)) Mellen, Edwin Pr., The.

Boswell, Parley Ann. Edith Wharton on Film. 3rd ed. 2007. (ENG., Illus.). 248p. 45.00 (978-0-8093-2757-7(0)) Southern Illinois Univ. Pr.

Brady, Owen E. & Maus, Derek C., eds. Finding a Way Home: A Critical Assessment of Walter Mosley's Fiction. 2011. (ENG.). 224p. pap. 30.00 (978-1-61703-065-9(1)) Univ. Pr. of Mississippi.

Brauner, David. Contemporary American Fiction. 2010. (Edinburgh Critical Guides to Literature Ser.). (ENG.). 224p. (gr. 17). 90.00 (978-0-7486-2267-2(5)); pap. 30.00 (978-0-7486-2268-9(3)) Edinburgh Univ. Pr. GBR. Dist: Columbia Univ. Pr.

—Philip Roth. 2007. (Contemporary American & Canadian Novelists Ser.). (ENG.). 256p. 79.00 (978-0-7190-7424-0(X)); pap. 26.00 (978-0-7190-7425-7(8)) Manchester Univ. Pr. GBR. Dist: Macmillan.

Braziel, Jana Evans. Caribbean Genesis: Jamaica Kincaid & the Writing of New Worlds. 2010. 245p. pap. 24.95 (978-0-7914-7654-3(5), Suny Pr.) State Univ. of New York Pr.

Bridges, Karl. 100 Great American Novels You've (Probably) Never Read, 1 vol. 2007. 264p. 52.00 (978-1-59158-165-9(6), LU1656) Libraries Unlimited, Inc.

Brier, Evan. A Novel Marketplace: Mass Culture, the Book Trade, & Postwar American Fiction. 2009. (Illus.). 224p. (C). 49.95 (978-0-8122-4207-2(6)) Univ. of Pennsylvania Pr.

Brivic, Sheldon. Tears of Rage: The Racial Interface of Modern American Fiction: Faulkner, Wright, Pynchon, Morrison. 2009. xiii, 252p. (978-0-8071-3354-5(X)) Louisiana State Univ. Pr.

Broer, Lawrence R. Vonnegut & Hemingway: Writers at War. 2011. (ENG.). 240p. 39.95 (978-1-61117-035-1(4)) Univ. of South Carolina Pr.

Brookes, Les. Gay Male Fiction since Stonewall. 2010. 230p. 39.95 (978-0-415-88073-2(4)) Routledge.

Brown, Stephanie. The Postwar African American Novel: Protest & Discontent, 1945-1950. 2011. (Margaret Walker Alexander Series in African American Studies). (ENG.). 176p. 55.00 (978-1-60473-973-2(8)) Univ. Pr. of Mississippi.

Burn, Stephen J. Jonathan Franzen at the End of Postmodernism. (ENG.). 176p. 2011. pap. 44.95 (978-1-4411-9130-7(3)) 2009. 120.00 (978-1-84706-248-2(2)) Continuum International Publishing Group, Ltd. GBR. Dist: National Bk. Network.

Burn, Stephen J. & Dempsey, Peter, eds. Intersections: Essays on Richard Powers. 2008. (Dalkey Archive Scholarly Ser.). 380p. pap. 29.95 (978-1-56478-508-4(4)) Dalkey Archive Pr.

Burrows, Stuart. A Familiar Strangeness: American Fiction & the Language of Photography, 1839-1945. (ENG.). 304p. 2010. pap. 24.95 (978-0-8203-3521-6(5)) 2008. lib. bdg. 34.95 (978-0-8203-3174-4(0)) Univ. of Georgia Pr.

Burstein, Daniel & De Keijzer, Arne. Secrets of the Lost Symbol: The Unauthorized Guide to the Mysteries Behind the Da Vinci Code Sequel. 2010. 432p. 25.99 (978-0-06-196495-4(6), Morrow, William & Co.) HarperCollins Pubs.

Byerman, Keith E. Fingering the Jagged Grain: Tradition & Form in Recent Black Fiction. 2010. (ENG.). 322p. pap. 24.95 (978-0-8203-3776-0(5)) Univ. of Georgia Pr.

Cabell, James Branch. The Jewel Merchants. 2010. 48p. pap. (978-1-4076-5477-5(2)) HardPr.

Capo, Beth Widmaier. Textual Contraception: Birth Control & Modern American Fiction. 2007. (ENG.). 220p. 42.95 (978-0-8142-1059-8(7)); cd-rom 9.95 (978-0-8142-9139-9(2)) Ohio State Univ. Pr.

Cappell, Ezra. American Talmud: The Cultural Work of Jewish American Fiction. 2008. (Suny Series, Modern Jewish Literature & Culture Ser.). 233p. per. 29.95 (978-0-7914-7124-1(1)) State Univ. of New York Pr.

Carl Van Doren. Contemporary American Novelists. 2007. 124p. pap. 18.99 (978-1-4346-0017-2(3)); (ENG.). 138p. pap. 19.99 (978-1-4346-0020-2(3)) BiblioBazaar.

Carr, Nick. America's Secret Service Ace: The Operator 5 Story. 2007. (ENG.). 64p. per. 14.95 (978-1-4344-9043-3(3), Borgo Pr.) Wildside Pr., LLC.

Carroll, Pamela Sissi. Sharon Creech. 1 vol. 2007. (Teen Reads: Student Companions to Young Adult Literature Ser.). 216p. 45.00 (978-0-313-33598-3(2), GR3598 Greenwood Pr.) Greenwood Publishing Group, Inc.

Casey, Janet Gallingani. A New Heartland: Women, Modernity, & the Agrarian Ideal in America. 2009. (ENG., Illus.). 264p. 65.00 (978-0-19-533895-9(2)) Oxford Univ. Pr., Inc.

Caso, Nicole. Practicing Memory in Central American Literature. 2010. (ENG.). 300p. 84.00 (978-0-230-62036-0(1)) Palgrave Macmillan.

Cather Studies. Willa Cather & Modern Cultures. Reynolds, Guy J. & Homestead, Melissa J., eds. 2011. (Cather Studies). (ENG., Illus.). 328p. pap. 40.00 (978-0-8032-3772-8(3)) Univ. of Nebraska Pr.

Cerasulo, Tom. Authors Out Here: Fitzgerald, West, Parker, & Schulberg in Hollywood. rev. ed. 2010. (Illus.). 216p. 29.95 (978-1-57003-903-4(8)) Univ. of South Carolina Pr.

Cheng, John. Astounding Wonder: Imagining Science & Science Fiction in Interwar America. 2012. (Illus.). 384p. (C). 45.00 (978-0-8122-4383-3(8)) Univ. of Pennsylvania Pr.

Cheng, William Joaquin. La Reevaluacion de la Figura de Simón Bolívar en las Postrimerias del Siglo XX: Las Novelas Sobre el Libertador. 2007. (SPA.). 200p. *(978-0-7734-5377-7(6))* Mellen, Edwin Pr., The.

Chinery, Mary C. Carnival in the Novels of Willa Cather: When the World Becomes Grotesque. 2011. 165p. 109.95 *(978-0-7734-1550-8(5))* Mellen, Edwin Pr., The.

Chu, Seo-Young. Do Metaphors Dream of Literal Sleep? A Science-Fictional Theory of Representation. 2011. (ENG.). 316p. 39.95 *(978-0-674-05517-9(9))* Harvard Univ. Pr.

Clarke, Amy M., et al, eds. The Twilight Mystique: Critical Essays on the Novels & Films. 2010. (Critical Explorations in Science Fiction & Fantasy Ser.). (ENG., Illus.). 247p. pap. 29.95 *(978-0-7864-4998-9(5))* McFarland & Co., Inc. Pubs.

Clontz, Ted. Wilderness City: The Post-War American Urban Novel from Nelson Algren to John Edger Wideman. 2009. 170p. 39.95 *(978-0-415-80307-6(1))* Routledge.

Codde, Philippe. The Jewish American Novel. 2007. (Comparative Cultural Studies). 279p. per. 34.95 *(978-1-55753-437-8(3))* Purdue Univ. Pr.

Cohen, Samuel S. After the End of History: American Fiction in the 1990s. 2009. (ENG.). 250p. 39.95 *(978-1-58729-815-8(5))* Univ. of Iowa Pr.

Cohen, Samuel S. & Konstantinou, Lee. The Legacy of David Foster Wallace. 2012. (New American Canon Ser.). (ENG.). 244p. pap. 19.95 ***(978-1-60938-082-3(7))*** Univ. of Iowa Pr.

Colby, Georgina. Bret Easton Ellis: Underwriting the Contemporary. 2011. (American Literature Readings in the Twenty-First Century Ser.). (ENG., Illus.). 240p. 85.00 *(978-0-230-11698-6(1))* Palgrave Macmillan.

Conner, Marc C. & Nash, William R., eds. Charles Johnson: The Novelist as Philosopher. 2010. (ENG.). 240p. pap. 25.00 *(978-1-60473-506-2(6))* Univ. Pr. of Mississippi.

Cornelius, Michael G., ed. The Boy Detectives: Essays on the Hardy Boys & Others. 2010. (ENG., Illus.). 220p. pap. 35.00 *(978-0-7864-6033-5(4))* McFarland & Co., Inc. Pubs.

Costello, Brannon. Plantation Airs: Racial Paternalism & the Transformations of Class in Southern Fiction, 1945-1971. 2007. (Southern Literary Studies). 203p. 35.00 *(978-0-8071-3270-8(5))* Louisiana State Univ. Pr.

Cotter, Robert Michael Bobb. A History of the Doc Savage Adventures in Pulps, Paperbacks, Comics, Fanzines, Radio & Film. 2009. (ENG., Illus.). 239p. 55.00 *(978-0-7864-4135-8(6))* McFarland & Co., Inc. Pubs.

Cox, James H. Muting White Noise: Native American & European American Novel Traditions. (ENG.). 352p. (C). 2009. (American Indian Literature & Critical Studies). pap. 24.95 *(978-0-8061-4021-6(6))* 2006. (American Indian Literature & Critical Studies: Vol. 51). 29.95 *(978-0-8061-3679-0(0))* Univ. of Oklahoma Pr.

Crisler, Jesse S., et al. John Steinbeck: The Contemporary Reviews. McElrath, Jr, Joseph R., Joseph R & Crisler, Jesse S., eds. Shillinglaw, Susan, ed. 2009. (American Critical Archives Ser.). (ENG.). 592p. pap. 58.00 *(978-0-521-11409-7(8))* Cambridge Univ. Pr.

Crosthwaite, Paul. Trauma, Postmodernism & the Aftermath of World War II. 2009. (ENG.). 240p. 95.00 *(978-0-230-20295-5(0))* Palgrave Macmillan.

Cservtk, Zita. Jack London's Naturalism. 2008. 84p. pap. *(978-3-639-01944-5(X))* VDM Verlag Dr. Mueller e.K.

Dacey-Groth, Camilla E. Representations of American Slavery in Post-Civil Rights Fiction & Film: How Literature Shapes Politics. 2009. 184p. 99.95 *(978-0-7734-4739-4(3))* Mellen, Edwin Pr., The.

Davis, Graeme. The Lost Symbol — Found: Unauthorized Analysis of Dan Brown's Novel. 2009. 144p. pap. 15.93 *(978-1-60888-011-9(7))* Nimble Bks. LLC.

de Angulo, Jaime. The Lariat: And Other Writings. Miller, David, ed. 2010. (ENG.). 208p. pap. 14.95 *(978-1-58243-596-1(0)*, Counterpoint Pr.) Basic Bks. GBR. Dist: Perseus-PGW.

Delfino, Andrew Steven. Becoming the New Man in Post-Postmodernist Fiction - Portrayals of Masculinities in David Foster Wallace's Infinite Jest and. 2008. 100p. per. *(978-3-8364-3735-6(X))* VDM Verlag Dr. Mueller e.K.

Demiturk, Emine/Lale. How Black Writers Deal with Whiteness: Characterization Through Deconstructing Color. 2008. 242p. 109.95 *(978-0-7734-5073-8(4))* Mellen, Edwin Pr., The.

Dennis, Jeffery P. We Boys Together: Teenagers in Love Before Girl-Craziness, 1 vol. 2007. (ENG., Illus.). 256p. lib. bdg. 59.95 *(978-0-8265-1556-8(8))*; per. 24.95 *(978-0-8265-1557-5(6))* Vanderbilt Univ. Pr.

doCarmo, Stephen N. History & Refusal: Consumer Culture & Postmodern Theory in the Contemporary American Novel. 2009. 232p. 53.00 *(978-0-9801496-1-6(4))* Lehigh Univ. Pr.

Domínguez, Frank & Greenia, George D. Castilian Writers, 1200-1400. 2007. (Dictionary of Literary Biography Ser.: Vol. 337). (ENG.). 528p. 315.00 *(978-0-7876-8155-5(5))* Cengage Gale.

Donovan, Christopher. Postmodern Counternarratives: Irony & Audience in the Novels of Paul Auster, Don Delillo, Charles Johnson, & Tim O'Brien. 2009. 10p. 39.95 *(978-0-415-80344-1(6))* Routledge.

Dow, William. Narrating Class in American Fiction. 2008. (American Literature Readings in the Twenty-First Century Ser.). (ENG.). 288p. 105.00 *(978-0-230-60982-2(1))* Palgrave Macmillan.

Dowling, Robert & Dowling, Robert M. Slumming in New York: From the Waterfront to Mythic Harlem. 2008. (ENG., Illus.). 232p. pap. 21.00 *(978-0-252-07632-9(X))* Univ. of Illinois Pr.

Dowling, Robert M. Slumming in New York: From the Waterfront to Mythic Harlem. 2007. (Illus.). 232p. 37.00 *(978-0-252-03194-6(6))* Univ. of Illinois Pr.

Drake, Kimberly S. Subjectivity in the American Protest Novel. 2011. (ENG.). 264p. 85.00 *(978-0-230-10716-8(8))* Palgrave Macmillan.

Durand, Kevin K. J. & Leigh, Mary K., eds. The Universe of Oz: Essays on Baum's Series & Its Progeny. 2010. (ENG., Illus.). 258p. pap. 35.00 *(978-0-7864-4628-5(5))* McFarland & Co., Inc. Pubs.

Duvall, John N. Race & White Identity in Southern Fiction: From Faulkner to Morrison. (ENG., Illus.). 224p. 2012. pap. 28.00 ***(978-0-230-34044-2(X))*** 2008. 89.00 *(978-1-4039-8387-9(9))* Palgrave Macmillan.

Duvall, John N., ed. The Cambridge Companion to American Fiction After 1945. 2011. (Cambridge Companions to Literature Ser.). (ENG., Illus.). 292p. (C). 90.00 ***(978-0-521-19631-4(0))***; pap. 24.99 ***(978-0-521-12347-1(X))*** Cambridge Univ. Pr.

Duvall, John N., ed. Faulkner & His Critics. 2010. (Modern Fiction Studies Book Ser.). (ENG., Illus.). 408p. (C). (gr. 13-17). pap. 30.00 *(978-0-8018-9699-6(1))*; 65.00 *(978-0-8018-9698-9(3))* Johns Hopkins Univ. Pr.

Eaton, Kalenda C. Womanism, Literature, & the Transformation of the Black Community, 1965-1980. 2007. (Studies in African American History & Culture Ser.). (ENG.). 122p. 125.00 *(978-0-415-96129-5(7)*, 0415961297) Routledge.

Eaton, Kalenda C. Womanism, Literature, & the Transformation of the Black Community, 1965ndash;1980. 2012. (Studies in African American History & Culture Ser.). (ENG.). 122p. pap. 42.95 ***(978-0-415-54080-3(1))*** Routledge.

Edmunds, Susan. Grotesque Relations: Modernist Domestic Fiction & the U. S. Welfare State. 2008. (ENG.). 272p. 55.00 *(978-0-19-533853-9(7))* Oxford Univ. Pr., Inc.

Edwards, Justin D. Understanding Jamaica Kincaid. 2007. (Understanding Contemporary American Literature Ser.). 159p. 39.95 *(978-1-57003-688-0(8))* Univ. of South Carolina Pr.

Effron, Malcah, ed. The Millennial Detective: Essays on Trends in Crime Fiction, Film & Television, 1990-2010. 2011. (ENG.). 200p. pap. 40.00 ***(978-0-7864-5851-6(8))*** McFarland & Co., Inc. Pubs.

Elahi, Babak. The Fabric of American Literary Realism: Readymade Clothing, Social Mobility, & Assimilation. 2009. (ENG.). 228p. pap. 39.95 *(978-0-7864-4119-8(4))* McFarland & Co., Inc. Pubs.

Ellis, Sherry, ed. Illuminating Fiction. 2009. (ENG.). 224p. pap. 19.95 *(978-1-59709-068-1(9))* Red Hen Pr.

Engel, Leonard, ed. A Divided Conscience: Essays on the Fiction of James Lee Burke. 2010. (ENG., Illus.). 224p. pap. 38.00 *(978-0-7864-4723-7(0))* McFarland & Co., Inc. Pubs.

Entin, Joseph B. Sensational Modernism: Experimental Fiction & Photography in Thirties America. 2007. (ENG., Illus.). 320p. per. 24.95 *(978-0-8078-5834-9(X))* Univ. of North Carolina Pr.

Erik, Mears. To Generate the Free Brain: Pantheism & Altered Being in Kenneth Patchen's the Journal of Albion Moonlight. 2011. 56p. pap. ***(978-3-639-30069-7(6))*** VDM Verlag Dr. Mueller e.K.

Erisman, Fred. Boys' Books, Boys' Dreams, & the Mystique of Flight. 2006. (ENG., Illus.). 300p. 29.95 *(978-0-87565-330-3(8))* Texas Christian Univ. Pr.

—From Birdwomen to Skygirls: American Girls' Aviation Stories. 2009. (ENG., Illus.). 192p. 29.95 *(978-0-87565-397-6(9))* Texas Christian Univ. Pr.

Fahy, Thomas. Freak Shows & the Modern American Imagination: Constructing the Damaged Body from Willa Cather to Truman Capote. (American Literature Readings in the Twenty-First Century Ser.). (ENG., Illus.). 2011. 288p. pap. 28.00 *(978-0-230-12098-3(9))* 2006. 204p. 84.00 *(978-1-4039-7403-7(9))* Palgrave Macmillan.

Female Force: Anne Rice: Anne Rice. 2010. (Illus.). 40p. pap. 3.99 *(978-1-61623-946-6(8))* Bluewater Productions, Inc.

Ferretter, Luke. Sylvia Plath's Fiction: A Critical Study. 2012. (ENG.). 256p. (gr. 17). pap. 30.00 ***(978-0-7486-2510-9(0))*** Edinburgh Univ. Pr. GBR. Dist: Columbia Univ. Pr.

Ferretter, Luke. Sylvia Plath's Fiction: A Critical Study. 2010. (ENG.). 256p. (gr. 17). 105.00 *(978-0-7486-2509-3(7))* Edinburgh Univ. Pr. GBR. Dist: Columbia Univ. Pr.

Fischer, Heinz D. & Fischer, Erika J., eds. Chronicle of the Pulitzer Prizes for Fiction: Discussions, Decisions & Documents. 2007. (ENG.). XVI, 460p. ***(978-3-11-183333-0(X))*** Saur, K. G. Verlag GmbH & Co.

Fischer, Heinz Dietrich & Fischer, Erika J. Chronicle of the Pulitzer Prizes for Fiction: Discussions, Decisions, & Documents. 2007. (ENG., Illus.). XVI, 460p. *(978-3-598-30191-9(X))* Saur, K. G. Verlag GmbH & Co.

Fitzgerald, F. Scott. The Great Gatsby. Crow, Anne, ed. 2010. (Illus.). 96p. pap. 24.95 *(978-1-4441-1621-2(5))* Hodder Education GBR. Dist: Trans-Atlantic Pubns., Inc.

Fitzgerald, F. Scott. This Side of Paradise. West, III, James L. W., James LW, ed. 2012. (Cambridge Edition of the Works of F. Scott Fitzgerald Ser.). (ENG., Illus.). 560p. pap. 29.99 ***(978-0-521-17047-5(8))*** Cambridge Univ. Pr.

Flis, Leonora. Factual Fictions: Narrative Truth & the Contemporary American Documentary Novel. 2010. (Illus.). 250p. *(978-1-4438-2413-2(5))* Cambridge Scholors Pub.

Flora, Joseph M. Reading Hemingway's Men Without Women: Glossary & Commentary. 2008. (Reading Hemingway Ser.). (Illus.). 224p. pap. 24.95 *(978-0-87338-943-3(3))* Kent State Univ. Pr.

Foley, Barbara. Wrestling with the Left: The Making of Ralph Ellison's Invisible Man. 2010. (ENG.). 464p. 99.95 *(978-0-8223-4817-7(9))*; pap. 29.95 *(978-0-8223-4829-0(2))* Duke Univ. Pr.

Forter, Greg. Gender, Race, & Mourning in American Modernism. 2011. (ENG.). 226p. 90.00 *(978-1-107-00472-6(1))* Cambridge Univ. Pr.

Fortin, David Terrance. Architecture & Science-Fiction Film: Philip K. Dick & the Spectacle of Home. 2011. (Ashgate Studies in Architecture Ser.). (Illus.). 250p. 89.95 *(978-1-4094-0748-5(9))* Ashgate Publishing Co.

Frye, Steven. Understanding Cormac Mccarthy. 2011. 240p. pap. 21.95 *(978-1-61117-018-4(4))* Univ. of South Carolina Pr.

Galloway, Stan. The Teenage Tarzan: A Literary Analysis of Edgar Rice Burroughs' Jungle Tales of Tarzan. 2010. (ENG., Illus.). 275p. pap. 35.00 *(978-0-7864-3853-2(3))* McFarland & Co., Inc. Pubs.

Gandal, Keith. The Gun & the Pen: Hemingway, Fitzgerald, Faulkner, & the Fiction of Mobilization, 1 vol. 2010. (ENG., Illus.). 288p. pap. 24.95 *(978-0-19-974457-2(2))* Oxford Univ. Pr., Inc.

Ganser, Alexandra. Roads of Her Own: Gendered Space & Mobility in American Women's Road Narratives, 1970-2000. 2009. (Illus.). 339p. 95.00 *(978-90-420-2552-3(2))* Rodopi.

Germana, Michael. Standards of Value: Money, Race, & Literature in America. 2009. (ENG., Illus.). 202p. 39.95 *(978-1-58729-818-9(X))* Univ. of Iowa Pr.

Gillard, Shan. The Bronze Bow Novel Guide. 2006. spiral bd. 15.95 *(978-1-933579-34-4(X))* Novel Insights.

Girgus, Sam B. The New Covenant: Jewish Writers & the American Idea. 2011. (ENG.). 233p. pap. 40.00 ***(978-0-8078-9670-9(5))*** Univ. of North Carolina Pr.

Godden, Richard. Fictions of Capital: The American Novel from James to Mailer. 2008. (Cambridge Studies in American Literature & Culture Ser.). (ENG.). 304p. pap. 34.99 *(978-0-521-06403-3(1))* Cambridge Univ. Pr.

Gómez-Galisteo, M. Carmen. The Wind Is Never Gone: Sequels, Parodies & Rewritings of Gone with the Wind. 2011. (ENG., Illus.). 216p. pap. 35.00 *(978-0-7864-5927-8(1))* McFarland & Co., Inc. Pubs.

Goulart, Ron. Cheap Thrills: The Amazing! Thrilling! Astonishing! History. 2007. (Illus.). 208p. (YA). 49.99 *(978-1-932563-75-7(X))* Hermes Pr.

Graham-Bertolini, Alison. Vigilante Women in Contemporary American Fiction. 2011. (American Literature Readings in the Twenty-First Century Ser.). (ENG., Illus.). 208p. 80.00 *(978-0-230-11090-8(8))* Palgrave Macmillan.

Grams, Martin. The Twilight Zone: Unlocking the Door to a Television Classic. 2008. 816p. pap. 44.95 *(978-0-9703310-9-0(6))* O T R Publishing.

Grant, J. Kerry. A Companion to the Crying of Lot 49. 2nd ed. 2008. (ENG.). 208p. 54.95 *(978-0-8203-3207-9(0))*; pap. 22.95 *(978-0-8203-3208-6(9))* Univ. of Georgia Pr.

Gray, Richard J. A Web of Words: The Great Dialogue of Southern Literature. 2007. (Mercer University Lamar Memorial Lectures). (ENG.). 296p. 44.95 *(978-0-8203-3005-1(1))* Univ. of Georgia Pr.

Greenwood, Willard P. Reading Cormac McCarthy, 1 vol. 2009. (Pop Lit Book Club Ser.). 141p. 39.95 *(978-0-313-35664-3(5)*, GR5664, Greenwood Pr.) Greenwood Publishing Group, Inc.

Gregson, Ian. Character & Satire in Post War Fiction. 2008. (Continuum Literary Studies). (ENG.). 192p. 39.95 *(978-1-84706-265-9(2))* Continuum International Publishing Group, Ltd. GBR. Dist: National Bk. Network.

Gretlund, Jan No & Westarp, Karl-He, eds. Flannery O'Connors Radical Reality. 2007. 216p. pap. 21.95 *(978-1-57003-717-7(5))* Univ. of South Carolina Pr.

Haesendonck, Kristian van. Encanto o Espanto? Identidad y Nación en la Novela Puertorriqueña Actual. 2008. 256p. pap. 36.00 *(978-84-8489-330-1(8))* Iberoamericana Vervuert Publishing Corp.

Hall, Alice. Disability & Modern Fiction: Faulkner, Morrison, Coetzee & the Nobel Prize for Literature. 2011. (ENG., Illus.). 232p. 85.00 ***(978-0-230-29209-3(7))*** Palgrave Macmillan.

Hall, Glinda / F. The Creators of Women's Popular Romance Fiction: The Authors Who Gave to Women a Genre of Their Own. 2009. vi, 228p. *(978-0-7734-3841-5(6))* Mellen, Edwin Pr., The.

Halldorson, Stephanie S. & Halldorson, Stephanie. The Hero in Contemporary American Fiction: The Works of Saul Bellow & Don Delillo. 2007. (American Literature Readings in the Twenty-First Century Ser.). (ENG.). 240p. 95.00 *(978-1-4039-8388-6(7))* Palgrave Macmillan.

Hamilton, Patrick L. Of Space & Mind: Cognitive Mappings of Contemporary Chicano/a Fiction. 2012. (ENG.). 224p. pap. 25.00 ***(978-0-292-74397-7(1))*** Univ. of Texas Pr.

Hardy, Donald E. The Body in Flannery O'Connor's Fiction: Computational Technique & Linguistic Voice. 2008. (Illus.). 187p. 39.95 *(978-1-57003-698-9(5))* Univ. of South Carolina Pr.

Harker, Jaime. America the Middlebrow: Women's Novels, Progressivism, & Middlebrow Authorship between the Wars. 2007. (Studies in Print Culture & the History of the Book). (Illus.). 208p. lib. bdg. 80.00 *(978-1-55849-596-8(7))* Univ. of Massachusetts Pr.

—America the Middlebrow: Women's Novels, Progressivism, & Middlebrow Authorship Between the Wars. 2007. (Studies in Print Culture & the History of the Book). (Illus.). 182p. per. 24.95 *(978-1-55849-597-5(5))* Univ. of Massachusetts Pr.

Hauschildt, Patricia M. & Monseau, Virginia R. Teaching the Selected Works of Chris Crutcher. 2008. (Young Adult Literature Ser.). (Illus.). 104p. pap. 21.25 *(978-0-325-01032-8(3)*, E01032) Heinemann.

Heffernan, Teres & Duffin, Jacalyn. History of Medicine: A Scandalously Short Introduction. 2nd ed. 2008. (ENG., Illus.). 480p. *(978-0-8020-9825-2(8))* Univ. of Toronto Pr.

Heffernan, Teresa. Post-Apocalyptic Culture: Modernism, Postmodernism, & the Twentieth-Century Novel. 2008. (ENG.). 224p. *(978-0-8020-9815-3(0))* Univ. of Toronto Pr.

Heilmann, Ann & Llewellyn, Mark. Metafiction & Metahistory in Contemporary Women's Writing. Heilmann, Ann, ed. 2007. (ENG., Illus.). 256p. 84.00 *(978-0-230-00504-4(7))* Palgrave Macmillan.

Heinert, Jennifer. Narrative Conventions & Race in the Novels of Toni Morrison. 2008. (Studies in Major Literary Authors Ser.). (ENG.). 128p. 125.00 *(978-0-415-96148-6(3))* Routledge.

Hepburn, Allan. Enchanted Objects: Visual Art in Contemporary Fiction. 2010. (Illus.). 288p. *(978-1-4426-4100-6(2))* Univ. of Toronto Pr.

Hicks, Heather J. The Culture of Soft Work: Labor, Gender, & Race in Postmodern American Narrative. 2008. (American Literature Readings in the Twenty-First Century Ser.). (ENG., Illus.). 288p. 100.00 *(978-0-230-60823-8(X))* Palgrave Macmillan.

Hinnov, Emily M. Encountering Choran Community: Literary Modernism, Visual Culture, & Political Aesthetics in the Interwar Years. 2009. (ENG., Illus.). 246p. 54.00 *(978-1-57591-130-4(2))* Susquehanna Univ. Pr.

Hnske, Annike B. The Cultural Ecology of the Postmodern American Novel. 2008. 128p. pap. *(978-3-639-01090-9(6))* VDM Verlag Dr. Mueller e.K.

Hollo, Attila. Citylization - the American Idol - City Life As a Symbol of the Modern World in 20th Century American Fiction. 2008. 52p. pap. *(978-3-639-01093-0(0))* VDM Verlag Dr. Mueller e.K.

Hollowell, John. Fact & Fiction: The New Journalism & the Nonfiction Novel. 2011. (ENG.). 204p. pap. 40.00 ***(978-0-8078-9688-4(8))*** Univ. of North Carolina Pr.

Holman, C. Hugh. Three Modes of Modern Southern Fiction: Ellen Glasgow, William Faulkner, Thomas Wolfe. 2008. (Mercer University Lamar Memorial Lectures). (ENG.). 112p. pap. 22.95 *(978-0-8203-3358-8(1))* Univ. of Georgia Pr.

Horsley, Lee. The Noir Thriller. 2nd ed. 2009. (Crime Files Ser.). (ENG., Illus.). 328p. pap. 35.00 *(978-0-230-21886-4(5))* Palgrave Macmillan.

Hovis, George. Vale of Humility: Plain Folk in Contemporary North Carolina Fiction. 2007. 325p. *(978-1-57003-696-5(9))* Univ. of South Carolina Pr.

Howe, Alexander N. It Didn't Mean Anything: A Psychoanalytic Reading of American Detective Fiction. 2008. (ENG.). 296p. per. 39.95 *(978-0-7864-3454-1(6))* McFarland & Co., Inc. Pubs.

Hurst, Mary Jane. Language, Gender, & Community in Late Twentieth-Century Fiction: American Voices & American Identities. 2011. (American Literature Readings in the Twenty-First Century Ser.). (ENG.). 250p. 85.00 *(978-0-230-11045-8(2))* Palgrave Macmillan.

Hutchinson, Colin. Reaganism, Thatcherism & the Social Novel. 2008. (ENG.). 224p. 100.00 *(978-0-230-21045-5(7))* Palgrave Macmillan.

Hutchison, Anthony. Writing the Republic: Liberalism & Morality in American Political Fiction. 2007. (ENG., Illus.). 256p. (gr. 17). 55.00 *(978-0-231-14138-3(6))* Columbia Univ. Pr.

Hutchison, Don. The Great Pulp Heroes. 2007. (ENG., Illus.). 288p. pap. 12.95 *(978-1-58042-184-3(9)*, Book Republic Pr.) Cardoza Publishing.

Hutner, Gordon. What America Read: Taste, Class, & the Novel, 1920-1960. (ENG.). 2011. 464p. pap. 26.95 *(978-0-8078-7212-3(1))* 2009. (Illus.). 432p. 41.95 *(978-0-8078-3227-1(8))* Univ. of North Carolina Pr.

Inge, M. Thomas, ed. William Faulkner: The Contemporary Reviews. 2008. (American Critical Archives Ser.). (ENG.). 604p. pap. 79.00 *(978-0-521-06003-5(6))* Cambridge Univ. Pr.

Irr, Caren. Pink Pirates: Contemporary American Women Writers & Copyright. 2010. 348p. pap. 34.95 *(978-1-58729-912-4(7))* Univ. of Iowa Pr.

Jackson, Anna. Diary Poetics: Form & Style in Writers' Diaries, 1915-1962. 2010. (Routledge Studies in Twentieth-Century Literature Ser.). (ENG.). 198p. (C). 125.00 *(978-0-415-99831-4(X))* Routledge.

Jacobson, Kristin J. Neodomestic American Fiction. 2010. 49.95 *(978-0-8142-1132-8(1))*; cd-rom 14.95 *(978-0-8142-9231-0(3))* Ohio State Univ. Pr.

Jsntti, Saara. Possible Subversions. 2008. 108p. pap. *(978-3-639-04710-3(9))* VDM Verlag Dr. Mueller e.K.

Kadavakollu, Tejaswani. Worlds Attainable. 2011. 236p. pap. ***(978-3-8383-2902-4(3))*** Lambert Academic Publishing.

Kandiyoti, Dalia. Migrant Sites: America, Place, & Diaspora Literatures. 2009. (Reencounters with Colonialism: New Perspectives on the Americas Ser.). (ENG.). 256p. pap. 39.95 *(978-1-58465-846-7(0)*, Dartmouth College Press) Univ. Pr. of New England.

Karl, Alissa G. Modernism & the Marketplace: Literary Culture & Consumer Capitalism in Rhys, Woolf, Stein, & Nella Larsen. 2012. (Literary Criticism & Cultural Theory Ser.). (ENG.). 198p. pap. 42.95 ***(978-0-415-54290-6(1))*** Routledge.

Kennedy, J. Gerald, ed. Modern American Short Story Sequences: Composite Fictions & Fictive Communities. 2011. (ENG.). 240p. pap. 31.99 *(978-0-521-17262-2(4))* Cambridge Univ. Pr.

Kensington Ladies' Erotica Society Staff. Ladies' Own Erotica: Tales, Recipes, & Other Mischiefs by Older Women. 2006. (Illus.). 229p. reprint ed. pap. 20.00 *(978-1-4223-5674-6(4))* DIANE Publishing Co.

Kerouac, Jack. Jack Kerouac - Road Novels 1957 to 1960: On the Road, the Dharma Bums, the Subterraneans, Tristessa, Lonesome Traveler, from the Journals, 1949-1954. 2007. (ENG.). 900p. (gr. 12). 35.00 *(978-1-59853-012-4(7))* Library of America, The.

Kevane, Bridget. Profane & Sacred: Latino/a American Writers Reveal the Interplay of the Secular & the Religious. 2007. (Celebrating Faith Ser.). (ENG.). 160p. 59.00 *(978-0-7425-4314-0(5))*; per. 23.95 *(978-0-7425-4315-7(3))* Rowman & Littlefield Publishers, Inc.

Kimmage, Michael. In History's Grip: Philip Roth's Newark Trilogy. 2012. (Stanford Studies in Jewish History & C Ser.). (ENG.). 224p. 50.00 ***(978-0-8047-8182-4(6))*** Stanford Univ. Pr.

Klinkowitz, Jerome. Kurt Vonnegut's America. 2009. 160p. 34.95 *(978-1-57003-826-6(0))* Univ. of South Carolina Pr.

Klonsky, E. David & Black, Alexis, eds. The Psychology of Twilight. 2011. (ENG., Illus.). 272p. pap. 14.95 *(978-1-936661-12-1(8))* BenBella Bks.

Kostihova, Marcela. How to Analyze the Works of Stephenie Meyer. 2011. (Essential Critiques Set 2 Ser.). (Illus.). 112p. (YA). (gr. 7-12). 34.22 *(978-1-61783-094-5(1))* ABDO Publishing Co.

Kreyling, Michael. Understanding Euroda Welty. 2011. 272p. pap. 21.95 *(978-1-61117-019-1(2))* Univ. of South Carolina Pr.

Kronenberg, Michael & Spurlock, J. David. Spies, Vixens, & Masters of Kung Fu: The Art of Paul Gulacy, 1 vol. 2007. (ENG., Illus.). 128p. 34.95 *(978-1-887591-75-1(3))* Vanguard Productions.

Kronenberg, Michael & Spurlock, J. David, eds. Spies, Vixens, & Masters of Kung Fu: The Art of Paul Gulacy, 1 vol. 2007. (ENG., Illus.). 128p. 49.95 ***(978-1-887591-76-8(1))*** Vanguard Productions.

Ladd, Barbara. Resisting History: Gender, Modernity, & Authorship in William Faulkner, Zora Neale Hurston, & Eudora Welty. (Southern Literary Studies). 2012. 184p. pap. 18.95 ***(978-0-8071-4369-8(3))*** 2007. 175p. 40.00 *(978-0-8071-3223-4(3))* Louisiana State Univ. Pr.

Lamb, Robert Paul & Thompson, G. R., eds. A Companion to American Fiction, 1865-1914. 2009. (Blackwell Companions to Literature & Culture Ser.: 122). (ENG., Illus.). 640p. pap. 52.95 *(978-1-4051-9553-9(3)*, Wiley-Blackwell) Wiley, John & Sons, Inc.

Lawson, Andrew. Downwardly Mobile: The Changing Fortunes of American Realism, 1 vol. 2012. (ENG., Illus.). 224p. 65.00 ***(978-0-19-982805-0(9))*** Oxford Univ. Pr., Inc.

Leder, Priscilla Gay, ed. Seeds of Change: Critical Essays on Barbara Kingsolver. 2010. (ENG.). 320p. 46.00 *(978-1-57233-719-0(2))* Univ. of Tennessee Pr.

Lee, Hermione. Philip Roth (Routledge Revivals) 2011. (ENG.). 96p. pap. 39.95 *(978-0-415-56799-2(8))* Routledge.

Lee, Sue-Im. A Body of Individuals: The Paradox of Community in Contemporary Fiction. 2009. (ENG.). 49.95 *(978-0-8142-0407-8(4))*; cd-rom 14.95 *(978-0-8142-9181-8(3))* Ohio State Univ. Pr.

Leigh, S.J., David J. Apocalyptic Patterns in Twentieth-Century Fiction. 2008. (ENG.). 288p. pap. 28.00 *(978-0-268-03380-4(3))* Univ. of Notre Dame Pr.

Leiter, Andrew B. In the Shadow of the Black Beast: African American Masculinity in the Harlem & Southern Renaissances. 2010. (Southern Literary Studies). 296p. 39.95 *(978-0-8071-3587-7(9))* Louisiana State Univ. Pr.

Lennard, John. Of Sex & Faerie: Furthet Essays on Genre Fiction. 2010. (Illus.). 396p. *(978-1-84760-173-5(1))* Troubadour Publishing Ltd.

Levin, Stephen M. The Contemporary Anglophone Travel Novel: The Aesthetics of Self-Fashioning in the Era of Globalization. 2012. (Literary Criticism & Cultural Theory Ser.). (ENG.). 200p. (C). pap. 42.95 ***(978-0-415-54233-3(2))*** Routledge.

Leving, Yuri. Keys to the Gift: A Guide to Vladimir Nabokov's Novel. 2011. (Studies in Russian & Slavic Literatures, Cultures, & History Ser.). (ENG.). 350p. 75.00 *(978-1-934843-11-6(3))* Academic Studies Pr.

L'Heureux, John & Karagueuzian, Dikran. Conversations with John L'Heureux. 2010. (ENG., Illus.). 200p. 27.00 *(978-1-57586-601-7(3))* CSLI Pubns.

Lincoln, Kenneth. Cormac McCarthy: American Canticles. 2009. (American Literature Readings in the Twenty-First Century Ser.). (ENG.). 192p. pap. 30.00 *(978-0-230-61967-8(3))* Palgrave Macmillan.

Link, Eric C. Understanding Philip K. Dick. 2010. (Understanding Contemporary American Literature Ser.). 224p. 39.95 *(978-1-57003-855-6(4))* Univ. of South Carolina Pr.

Loichot, Valérie. Orphan Narratives: The Postplantation Literature of Faulkner, Glissant, Morrison, & Saint-John Perse. 2007. (New World Studies). (ENG., Illus.). 256p. (gr. 17). 45.00 *(978-0-8139-2640-7(8))* Univ. Pr. of Virginia.

Lombardi, William & Houston, Lynn Marie. Reading Joan Didion, 1 vol. 2009. (Pop Lit Book Club Ser.). 159p. 35.00 *(978-0-313-36403-7(6)*, GR6403) Greenwood Publishing Group, Inc.

Loudermilk, Kim A. Fictional Feminism: How American Bestsellers Affect the Movement for Women's Equality. 2009. 232p. 39.95 *(978-0-415-80345-8(4))* Routledge.

Lozano, Miguel Lopez. Utopian Dreams, Apocalyptic Nightmares: Globilization in Recent Mexican & Chicano Narrative. 2007. (Purdue Studies in Romance Literatures Ser.). 294p. per. 43.95 *(978-1-55753-484-2(5))* Purdue Univ. Pr.

Lubin, Alex, ed. Revising the Blueprint: Ann Petry & the Literary Left. 2011. (ENG.). pap. 30.00 *(978-1-61703-039-0(2))* Univ. Pr. of Mississippi.

Luce, Dianne C. Reading the World: Cormac Mccarthy's Tennessee Period. 2011. 328p. pap. 24.95 *(978-1-57003-988-1(7))* Univ. of South Carolina Pr.

Ludwig. Recent American Novelists. 2009. pap. 25.00 *(978-0-8166-0279-7(4))* Univ. of Minnesota Pr.

Lukin, Josh, ed. Invisible Suburbs: Recovering Protest Fiction in the 1950s United States. 2008. (ENG.). 240p. 50.00 *(978-1-934110-87-4(6))* Univ. Pr. of Mississippi.

MacFarlane, Scott. The Hippie Narrative: A Literary Perspective on the Counterculture. 2007. (ENG., Illus.). 263p. per. 35.00 *(978-0-7864-2915-8(1))* McFarland & Co., Inc. Pubs.

MacGowan, Christopher. The Twentieth-Century American Fiction. 2011. (ENG.). 408p. 94.95 *(978-1-4051-6023-0(3)*, Wiley-Blackwell) Wiley, John & Sons, Inc.

—The Twentieth-Century American Fiction Handbook. 2011. (ENG.). 408p. pap. 31.95 *(978-1-4051-6024-7(1)*, Wiley-Blackwell) Wiley, John & Sons, Inc.

Madsen, Deborah L. The Postmodernist Allegories of Thomas Pynchon. (Illus.). 192p. *(978-0-7185-1369-6(X)*, Burns & Oates) Continuum International Publishing Group, Ltd.

Magistrale, Tony. Stephen King: America's Storyteller, 1 vol. 2009. 181p. 44.95 *(978-0-313-35228-7(3)*, C35228, Praeger Pubs.) Greenwood Publishing Group, Inc.

Mandel, Naomi. Against the Unspeakable: Complicity, the Holocaust, & Slavery in America. 2007. (Cultural Frames, Framing Culture Ser.). (ENG., Illus.). 304p. (gr. 17). 59.50 *(978-0-8139-2580-6(0))* Univ. Pr. of Virginia.

—Bret Easton Ellis: American Psycho, Glamorama, Lunar Park. 2011. (Continuum Studies in Contemporary North American Fiction Ser.). (ENG.). 192p. 29.95 *(978-0-8264-3562-0(9))* Continuum International Publishing Group, Ltd. GBR. Dist: National Bk. Network.

Mantooth, Wes. You Factory Folks Who Sing This Song Will Surely Understand. 2006. (Literary Criticism & Cultural Theory Ser.). (ENG.). 240p. 125.00 *(978-0-415-97758-6(4))* Routledge.

Masuga, Katy. The Secret Violence of Henry Miller. 2011. (Studies in American Literature & Culture Ser.). 240p. 70.00 *(978-1-57113-484-4(0))* Camden Hse.

Matthews, John T. & Matthews. A Companion to the Modern American Novel, 1900-1950. Matthews, John T., ed. 2009. (Blackwell Companions to Literature & Culture Ser.: 151). (ENG., Illus.). 616p. 219.95 *(978-0-631-20687-3(6)*, Wiley-Blackwell) Wiley, John & Sons, Inc.

Maus, Derek C. Unvarnishing Reality: Subversive Russian & American Cold War Satire. 2011. 264p. 49.95 *(978-1-57003-985-0(2))* Univ. of South Carolina Pr.

McAleer, Patrick. The Writing Family of Stephen King: A Critical Study of the Fiction of Tabitha King, Joe Hill & Owen King. 2011. (ENG., Illus.). 207p. pap. 35.00 *(978-0-7864-4850-0(4))* McFarland & Co., Inc. Pubs.

McCann, Paul. Race, Music, & National Identity: Images of Jazz in American Fiction, 1920-1960. 2008. 192p. 42.00 *(978-0-8386-4140-8(7))* Fairleigh Dickinson Univ. Pr.

McClure, John A. Partial Faiths: Postsecular Fiction in the Age of Pynchon & Morrison. 2007. (ENG.). 224p. per. 24.95 *(978-0-8203-3033-4(7))* Univ. of Georgia Pr.

McGurl, Mark. The Program Era: Postwar Fiction & the Rise of Creative Writing. (Illus.). 480p. 2011. (ENG.). pap. 19.95 *(978-0-674-06209-2(4))* 2009. 37.00 *(978-0-674-03319-1(1))* Harvard Univ. Pr.

McHugh, Susan. Animal Stories: Narrating Across Species Lines. 2011. (Posthumanities Ser.). (Illus.). 336p. 75.00 *(978-0-8166-7032-1(3))*; pap. 25.00 *(978-0-8166-7033-8(1))* Univ. of Minnesota Pr.

McLennan, Rachael & Mclennan, Rachael. Adolescence, America & Postwar Fiction: Developing Figures. 2008. (ENG.). 232p. 89.00 *(978-0-230-20551-2(8))* Palgrave Macmillan.

Mercer, Erin. Repression & Realism in Post-War American Literature. 2011. (American Literature Readings in the Twenty-First Century Ser.). (ENG.). 253p. 85.00 *(978-0-230-11166-0(1))* Palgrave Macmillan.

Meyer, Michael J. Harper Lee's To Kill a Mockingbird: New Essays. 2010. (Illus.). xxiii, 265p. E-Book 49.95 *(978-0-8108-7723-8(6))* Scarecrow Pr., Inc.

Michael, Magali Cornier. New Visions of Community in Contemporary American Fiction: Tan, Kingsolver, Castillo, Morrison. 2006. 256p. (C). per. 21.00 *(978-1-58729-511-9(3))* Univ. of Iowa Pr.

Millard, Kenneth. Coming of Age in Contemporary American Fiction. 2007. (ENG.). 200p. (gr. 17). 144.00 *(978-0-7486-2173-6(3))*; pap. 34.00 *(978-0-7486-2174-3(1))* Edinburgh Univ. Pr. GBR. Dist: Columbia Univ. Pr.

Miller, D. Quentin. A Criminal Power: James Baldwin & the Law. 2012. 224p. 45.95 ***(978-0-8142-1175-5(5))***; (ENG.). cd-rom 14.95 ***(978-0-8142-9276-1(3))*** Ohio State Univ. Pr.

Mitchell, Douglas L. A Disturbing & Alien Memory: Southern Novelists Writing History. 2009. *(978-0-8071-3373-6(6))* Louisiana State Univ. Pr.

Monk, Nicholas, ed. Interdisciplinary & Intertextual Approaches to Cormac Mccarthy. 2011. (Routledge Studies in Contemporary Literature Ser.). (ENG., Illus.). 208p. (C). 125.00 *(978-0-415-89549-1(9))* Routledge.

Montgomery, Maxine Lavon. The Fiction of Gloria Naylor: Houses & Spaces of Resistance. 2010. (ENG.). 144p. 35.00 *(978-1-57233-722-0(2))* Univ. of Tennessee Pr.

Morrison, Jago & Watkins, Susan, eds. Scandalous Fictions: The Twentieth-Century Novel in the Public Sphere. 2007. (ENG., Illus.). 224p. 84.00 *(978-1-4039-9584-1(2))* Palgrave Macmillan.

Murphy, Gretchen. Shadowing the White Man's Burden: U.S. Imperialism & the Problem of the Color Line. 2010. (ENG., Illus.). 288p. 75.00 *(978-0-8147-9598-9(6))*; pap. 25.00 *(978-0-8147-9599-6(4))* New York Univ. Pr.

Murphy, Jillmarie. Monstrous Kinships: Realism & Attachment Theory in the Nineteenth & Early Twentieth Century Novel. 2011. (ENG.). 208p. 60.00 *(978-1-61149-050-3(2))* Univ. of Delaware Pr.

Murphy, Mary McDonagh. Scout, Atticus, & Boo: A Celebration of Fifty Years of to Kill a Mockingbird. 2010. (ENG.). 160p. 24.99 *(978-0-06-192407-1(5))*; 300p. pap. 24.99 *(978-0-06-197958-3(9)*, HarperLuxe) HarperCollins Pubs.

—Scout, Atticus & Boo: A Celebration of to Kill a Mockingbird. 2011. (P. S. Ser.). (ENG.). 160p. pap. 14.99 *(978-0-06-192412-5(1)*, HarperPerennial) HarperCollins Pubs.

Nesson, Liam. Jack London & the American Literary Naturalist Movement. 2008. 64p. pap. *(978-3-639-06412-4(7))* VDM Verlag Dr. Mueller e.K.

Newitz, Annalee. Pretend We're Dead: Capitalist Monsters in American Pop Culture. 2006. (ENG., Illus.). 232p. 79.95 *(978-0-8223-3733-1(9))*; per. 22.95 *(978-0-8223-3745-4(2))* Duke Univ. Pr.

Nicol, Bran, et al, eds. Crime Cultures: Figuring Criminality in Fiction & Film. 2011. (Continuum Literary Studies). (ENG., Illus.). 256p. 120.00 *(978-0-8264-3235-3(2))* Continuum International Publishing Group, Ltd. GBR. Dist: National Bk. Network.

Noble, Don, ed. F. Scott Fitzgerald. 2010. (Critical Insights Ser.). 350p. 85.00 *(978-1-58765-693-4(0))* Salem Pr., Inc.

Nunes, Ana. African American Women Writers' Historical Fiction. 2011. (ENG.). 258p. 85.00 *(978-0-230-11253-7(6))* Palgrave Macmillan.

O'Connor, William Van, ed. Seven Modern American Novelists: An Introduction. 2009. (ENG.). 312p. pap. 60.00 *(978-0-8166-5840-4(4))* Univ. of Minnesota Pr.

O'Donnell, Patrick. The American Novel Now: Reading Contemporary American Fiction since 1980. 2010. (ENG.). 248p. pap. 39.95 *(978-1-4051-6755-0(6)*, Wiley-Blackwell) Wiley, John & Sons, Inc.

—American Novel Now: Reading Contemporary American Fiction since 1980. 2010. (ENG.). 248p. 94.95 *(978-1-4051-6757-4(2)*, Wiley-Blackwell) Wiley, John & Sons, Inc.

Olster, Stacey. Reminiscence & Re-creation in Contemporary American Fiction. 2009. (ENG.). 232p. pap. 34.99 *(978-0-521-10980-2(9))* Cambridge Univ. Pr.

Olwell, Victoria. The Genius of Democracy: Fictions of Gender & Citizenship in the United States, 1860-1945. 2011. 304p. (C). 59.95 *(978-0-8122-4324-6(2))* Univ. of Pennsylvania Pr.

Orr, Stanley. Darkly Perfect World: Colonial Adventure, Postmodernism, & American Noir. 2010. (ENG.). 296p. 49.95 *(978-0-8142-1125-0(9))*; cd-rom 14.95 *(978-0-8142-9223-5(2))* Ohio State Univ. Pr.

Osório, Salomé. Reading Roth Reading Roth. 2010. 104p. pap. *(978-3-639-24535-6(0))* VDM Verlag Dr. Mueller e.K.

Page, Max. The City's End: Two Centuries of Fantasies, Fears & Premonitions of New York's Destruction. 2010. (ENG., Illus.). 280p. pap. 25.00 *(978-0-300-16446-6(7))* Yale Univ. Pr.

Palleau-Papin, Françoise, et al. Willa Cather Vol. 8: A Writer's Worlds. Murphy, John J. & Thacker, Robert, eds. 2010. (Cather Studies). (ENG., Illus.). 492p. pap. 40.00 *(978-0-8032-3025-5(7))* Univ. of Nebraska Pr.

Palmer, R. Barton, ed. Twentieth-Century American Fiction on Screen. 2007. (ENG., Illus.). 270p. 101.00 *(978-0-521-83444-5(9))*; pap. 35.99 *(978-0-521-54230-2(8))* Cambridge Univ. Pr.

Panek, Leroy Lad. The Origins of the American Detective Story. 2006. (ENG., Illus.). 235p. per. 35.00 *(978-0-7864-2776-5(0))* McFarland & Co., Inc. Pubs.

Park, Jinim. Narratives of the Vietnam War by Korean & American Writers. 2006. (Illus.). (C). 62.95 *(978-0-8204-8615-4(9))* Lang, Peter Publishing, Inc.

Patterson, Laura Sloan. Stirring the Pot: The Kitchen & Domesticity in the Fiction of Southern Women. 2008. (ENG.). 240p. pap. 39.95 *(978-0-7864-3523-4(2))* McFarland & Co., Inc. Pubs.

Patterson, Martha H. Beyond the Gibson Girl: Reimagining the American New Woman, 1895-1915. 2008. (ENG., Illus.). 248p. pap. 26.00 *(978-0-252-07563-6(3))* Univ. of Illinois Pr.

Peat, Alexandra. Travel & Modernist Literature: Sacred & Ethical Journeys. 2010. (Routledge Studies in Twentieth-Century Literature Ser.). (ENG.). 210p. (C). 125.00 *(978-0-415-87233-1(2))* Routledge.

Perrakis, Phyllis Sternberg. Adventures of the Spirit: The Older Woman in the Works of Doris Lessing, Margaret Atwood, & Other Contemporary Women Writers. 2007. (ENG.). 321p. 49.95 *(978-0-8142-1064-2(3))* 2006. cd-rom 9.95 *(978-0-8142-9142-9(2))* Ohio State Univ. Pr.

Perriman, Wendy K. Willa Cather & the Dance: A Most Satisfying Elegance. 2009. 75.00 *(978-0-8386-4203-0(9))* Fairleigh Dickinson Univ. Pr.

Persaud, Christopher H. K. The Da Vinci Code Revisited: A conclusive refutation of the sinister, widespread Lie. 2010. 346p. 29.99 *(978-1-4500-3488-3(8))*; pap. 19.99 *(978-1-4500-3487-6(X))* Xlibris Corp.

Petty, Leslie. Romancing the Vote: Feminist Activism in American Fiction, 1870-1920. 2006. (ENG.). 240p. 44.95 *(978-0-8203-2858-4(8))* Univ. of Georgia Pr.

Phelan, James. Experiencing Fiction: Judgments, Progressions, & the Rhetorical Theory of Narrative. 2007. (Theory & Interpretation of Narrative Ser.). 249p. *(978-0-8142-1065-9(1))*; 249p. per. *(978-0-8142-5162-1(5))*; cd-rom 9.95 *(978-0-8142-9145-0(7))* Ohio State Univ. Pr.

Philips, Deborah & Philips. Women's Fiction 1945-2005: Writing Romance. 2008. (Continuum Literary Studies). (ENG.). 170p. 27.95 *(978-0-8264-9996-7(1))* Continuum International Publishing Group, Ltd. GBR. Dist: National Bk. Network.

Piatti-Farnell, Lorna. Food & Culture in Contemporary American Fiction. 2011. (Routledge Studies in Contemporary Literature Ser.). (ENG.). 202p. (C). 125.00 *(978-0-415-88422-8(5))* Routledge.

Prescott, Orville. In My Opinion: An Inquiry into the Contemporary Novel. 2011. 258p. 47.95 ***(978-1-258-08153-9(9))*** Literary Licensing, LLC.

Prosser, Jay. American Fiction of the 1990s: Reflections of History & Culture. 2008. 249p. 39.95 *(978-0-415-43567-3(6))* Routledge.

—American Fiction of the 1990s: Reflections of History & Culture. Prosser, Jay, ed. 2008. 249p. 120.00 *(978-0-415-43566-6(8))* Routledge.

Puckett, Kent. Bad Form: Social Mistakes & the Nineteenth-Century Novel. 2008. (ENG., Illus.). 192p. 45.00 *(978-0-19-533275-9(X))* Oxford Univ. Pr., Inc.

Puskar, Jason Robert. Accident Society: Fiction, Collectivity, & the Production of Chance. 2012. (ENG.). 280p. 60.00 ***(978-0-8047-7535-9(4))*** Stanford Univ. Pr.

Ramsey, G. Lee, Jr. Preachers & Misfits, Prophets & Thieves: The Minister in Southern Fiction. 2008. (ENG.). 208p. pap. 20.00 *(978-0-664-23224-5(8))* Westminster John Knox Pr.

Randall, Bryony. Modernism, Daily Time & Everyday Life. 2011. (ENG.). 232p. pap. 39.99 *(978-0-521-17441-1(4))* Cambridge Univ. Pr.

A Reader's Guide to Blood Meridian. 2nd ed. 2008. (Illus.). 361p. per. 36.95 *(978-0-9788349-1-3(7))* Bon Mot Publishing.

Rebein, Robert. Hicks, Tribes, & Dirty Realists: American Fiction after Postmodernism. 2009. (ENG., Illus.). 216p. pap. 30.00 *(978-0-8131-9234-5(X))* Univ. Pr. of Kentucky.

Rhodes, Chip. Politics, Desire, & the Hollywood Novel. 2008. (ENG.). 198p. 34.95 *(978-1-58729-629-1(2))* Univ. of Iowa Pr.

Rhodes, Ron. Unlocking the Mysteries of The Lost Symbol. 2009. pap. *(978-0-7369-1886-2(8))* Harvest Hse. Pubs.

Rich, Charlotte J. Transcending the New Woman: Multiethnic Narratives in the Progressive ERA. 2009. (ENG.). 240p. (C). 39.95 *(978-0-8262-1826-1(1))* Univ. of Missouri Pr.

Rich, Mark. C. M. Kornbluth: The Life & Works of a Science Fiction Visionary. 2009. (ENG., Illus.). 451p. pap. 39.95 *(978-0-7864-4393-2(6))* McFarland & Co., Inc. Pubs.

Rieder, John. Colonialism & the Emergence of Science Fiction. 2008. (Early Classics of Science Fiction Ser.). (ENG., Illus.). 200p. lib. bdg. 70.00 *(978-0-8195-6873-1(2))*; pap. 24.95 *(978-0-8195-6874-8(0))* Wesleyan Univ. Pr.

Rieger, Christopher. Clear-Cutting Eden: Ecology & the Pastoral in Southern Literature. 2009. (ENG.). 264p. 39.75 *(978-0-8173-1641-9(8))* Univ. of Alabama Pr.

Robertson, Sarah. The Secret Country: Decoding Jayne Anne Phillips' Cryptic Fiction. 2007. (Costerus New Ser.: 165). 300p. pap. 78.00 *(978-90-420-2140-2(3))* Rodopi.

Robinson, Frank M. & Davidson, Lawrence. Pulp Culture: The Art of Fiction Magazines. 2007. (Illus.). 206p. pap. *(978-1-933112-30-5(1))* Collectors Pr., Inc.

Rollyson, Carl. Uses of the Past in the Novels of William Faulkner. 2007. (ENG.). 300p. per. 20.95 *(978-0-595-45474-7(7)*, Backinprint.com) iUniverse, Inc.

Rosen, Elizabeth K. Apocalyptic Transformation: Apocalypse & the Postmodern Imagination. 2008. (ENG.). 240p. 83.99 *(978-0-7391-1790-3(4))*; per. 36.99 *(978-0-7391-1791-0(2))* Lexington Bks.

Rowe, John Carlos. Afterlives of Modernism: Liberalism, Transnationalism, & Political Critique. 2011. (Re-Mapping the Transnational: a Dartmouth Series in American Studies). 224p. (C). 85.00 *(978-1-58465-995-2(5))*; pap. 35.00 *(978-1-58465-996-9(3))* Univ. Pr. of New England. (Dartmouth College Press).

Rundle, Christopher. Publishing Translations in Fascist Italy. 2009. 268p. 58.95 *(978-3-03911-831-1(5))* Lang, Peter Publishing, Inc.

Russell, Danielle. Between the Angle & the Curve: Mapping Gender, Race, Space, & Identity in Willa Cather & Toni Morrison. 2009. 230p. 39.95 *(978-0-415-80296-3(2))* Routledge.

Russell, Emily. Reading Embodied Citizenship: Disability, Narrative, & the Body Politic. 2011. (Mellon-ALI Ser.). (ENG.). 264p. (C). 44.95 *(978-0-8135-4939-2(6))* Rutgers Univ. Pr.

Ryan, Tim A. Calls & Responses: The American Novel of Slavery since Gone with the Wind. 2008. (Southern Literary Studies). 260p. 37.50 *(978-0-8071-3322-4(1))* Louisiana State Univ. Pr.

Saguaro, Shelley. Garden Plots: The Politics & Poetics of Gardens. 2006. (Illus.). 264p. 120.00 *(978-0-7546-3753-0(0))* Ashgate Publishing Co.

Salaita, Steven. Modern Arab American Fiction: A Reader's Guide. 2011. 176p. *(978-0-8156-3277-1(0))*; pap. *(978-0-8156-3253-5(3))* Syracuse Univ. Pr.

Salter, James & Phelps, Robert. Memorable Days: The Selected Letters of James Salter & Robert Phelps. McIntyre, John, ed. 2011. (ENG.). 240p. pap. 15.95 *(978-1-58243-726-2(2)*, Counterpoint) Counterpoint LLC.

Sanders, Joe Sutliff. Disciplining Girls: Understanding the Origins of the Classic Orphan Girl Story. 2011. (ENG.). 240p. (gr. 17). 60.00 *(978-1-4214-0318-2(8))* Johns Hopkins Univ. Pr.

Savu, Laura E. Postmortem Postmodernists: The Afterlife of the Author in Recent Narrative. 2009. 63.00 *(978-0-8386-4181-1(4))* Fairleigh Dickinson Univ. Pr.

Savvas, Theophilus. American Postmodernist Fiction & the Past. 2011. (ENG., Illus.). 224p. 85.00 *(978-0-230-29834-7(6))* Palgrave Macmillan.

Saxena, Vandana. The Subversive Harry Potter: Adolescent Rebellion & Containment in the J. K. Rowling Novels. 2012. (ENG.). pap. 40.00 ***(978-0-7864-6674-0(X))*** McFarland & Co., Inc. Pubs.

Schryer, Stephen. Fantasies of the New Class: Ideologies of Professionalism in Post-World War II American Fiction. 2011. (ENG.). 288p. (gr. 17). 79.50 *(978-0-231-15756-8(8))*; pap. 26.50 *(978-0-231-15757-5(6))* Columbia Univ. Pr.

Scott, William. Troublemakers: Power, Representation, & the Fiction of the Mass Worker. 2011. (Mellon-ALI Ser.). (ENG., Illus.). 296p. (C). pap. 24.95 *(978-0-8135-5190-6(0))*; 72.00 *(978-0-8135-5189-0(7))* Rutgers Univ. Pr.

Seed, David, ed. A Companion to Twentieth-Century United States Fiction. 2009. (Blackwell Companions to Literature & Culture Ser.: 105). (ENG.). 608p. 219.95 *(978-1-4051-4691-3(5)*, Wiley-Blackwell) Wiley, John & Sons, Inc.

A Separate Peace Guide. 16.47 *(978-0-13-050207-0(3))* Prentice Hall PTR.

Sepich, John. Notes on Blood Meridian. 2nd rev. exp. ed. 2008. (Southwestern Writers Collection). (ENG., Illus.). 240p. (Orig.). 45.00 *(978-0-292-71820-3(9))*; pap. 22.95 *(978-0-292-71821-0(7))* Univ. of Texas Pr.

Shaffer, Brian W. The Encyclopedia of Twentieth-Century Fiction, 3 vols. 2011. (Wiley-Blackwell Encyclopedia of Literature Ser.: 1). (ENG.). 1584p. 595.00 *(978-1-4051-9244-6(5)*, Wiley-Blackwell) Wiley, John & Sons, Inc.

Shaw, Denise R. The Rape Narrative in the American South: A Psychoanalytical Examination of Sexual Violence & the Melancholic Internalization of Loss in the Modern Southern Novel. 2007. 158p. 99.95 *(978-0-7734-5301-2(6))* Mellen, Edwin Pr., The.

Sheehan, Bill. At the Foot of the Story Tree: An Inquiry into the Fiction of Peter Straub. 350p. 40.00 *(978-1-892284-77-8(4))* Subterranean Pr.

Shiach, Morag, ed. The Cambridge Companion to the Modernist Novel. 2007. (Cambridge Companions to Literature Ser.). (ENG.). 272p. 99.99

(978-0-521-85444-3(X)); 249p. per. 35.99 *(978-0-521-67074-6(8))* Cambridge Univ. Pr.

Shostak, Debra. Philip Roth: American Pastoral, the Human Stain, the Plot Against America. Shostak, Debra, ed. 2011. (Continuum Studies Contem N American Fiction Ser.). (ENG.). 208p. 100.00 *(978-0-8264-2631-4(X))*; pap. 29.95 *(978-0-8264-2227-9(6))* Continuum International Publishing Group, Ltd. GBR. Dist: National Bk. Network.

Shugarts, David A. Secrets of the Widow's Son: The Real History Behind the Lost Symbol. Burstein, Dan, ed. 2009. (ENG.). 224p. pap. 12.95 *(978-1-4027-7729-5(9))* Sterling Publishing Co., Inc.

Simmons, David. The Anti-Hero in the American Novel: From Joseph Heller to Kurt Vonnegut. 2008. (American Literature Readings in the Twenty-First Century Ser.). (ENG.). 216p. 84.00 *(978-0-230-60323-3(8))* Palgrave Macmillan.

Simon, Reeva Spector. Spies & Holy Wars: The Middle East in 20th-Century Crime Fiction. (ENG., Illus.). 224p. 2011. pap. 25.00 ***(978-0-292-73757-0(2))*** 2010. 55.00 *(978-0-292-72300-9(8))* Univ. of Texas Pr.

Sivan, Miriam. Belonging Too Well: Portraits of Identity in Cynthia Ozick's Fiction. 2010. (SUNY series in Modern Jewish Literature & Culture Ser.). 246p. pap. 24.95 *(978-1-4384-2506-1(6)*, Suny Pr.) State Univ. of New York Pr.

Smith, Cynthia. Walter Miller's Canticle for Leibowitz: A Study of Apocalyptic Cycles. 2009. 100p. pap. *(978-3-639-13282-3(3))* VDM Verlag Dr. Mueller e.K.

Smith, Zak. Pictures Showing What Happens on Each Page of Thomas Pynchon's Novel Gravity's Rainbow. 2006. (ENG., Illus.). 784p. 69.95 *(978-0-9773127-8-8(X))* Tin Hse. Bks., LLC.

Solomon, William. Literature, Amusement, & Technology in the Great Depression. 2009. (Cambridge Studies in American Literature & Culture Ser.). (ENG., Illus.). 284p. pap. 42.00 *(978-0-521-12091-3(8))* Cambridge Univ. Pr.

Spencer, Nicholas. After Utopia: The Rise of Critical Space in Twentieth-Century American Fiction. (ENG.). 276p. 2008. pap. 24.95 *(978-0-8032-2076-8(6))* 2006. 24.95 *(978-0-8032-4301-9(4))* Univ. of Nebraska Pr.

Stallings, LaMonda H. & Thomas, Greg, eds. Word Hustle: Critical Essays & Reflections on the Works of Donald Goines. 2011. (ENG.). 250p. pap. 24.95 *(978-1-58073-046-4(9))* Black Classic Pr.

Steinbeck, John. Monarch Notes on Steinbeck's Major Novels. (C). 4.50 *(978-0-671-00647-1(9)*, Arco) Peterson's.

Stockton, Kathryn Bond. Beautiful Bottom, Beautiful Shame: Where Black Meets Queer. 2006. (Series Q). (ENG., Illus.). 288p. (C). 84.95 *(978-0-8223-3783-6(5))*; per. 23.95 *(978-0-8223-3796-6(7))* Duke Univ. Pr.

Stoneley, Peter. Consumerism & American Girls' Literature, 1860-1940. 2007. (Cambridge Studies in American Literature & Culture Ser.). (ENG., Illus.). 180p. pap. 44.00 *(978-0-521-03575-0(9))* Cambridge Univ. Pr.

Stringer, Dorothy. Not Even Past: Race, Historical Trauma, & Subjectivity in Faulkner, Larsen, & Van Vechten. 2009. (American Literatures Initiative Ser.). (ENG.). 272p. 48.00 *(978-0-8232-3147-8(X))* Fordham Univ. Pr.

Sutherland, John. Bestsellers: A Very Short Introduction. 2007. (Very Short Introductions Ser.). (ENG., Illus.). 144p. per. 11.95 *(978-0-19-921489-1(1))* Oxford Univ. Pr., Inc.

Swirski, Peter. American Utopia & Social Engineering in Literature, Social Thought, & Political History. 2011. (Routledge Transnational Perspectives on American Literature Ser.). (ENG., Illus.). 270p. (C). 125.00 *(978-0-415-89192-9(2))* Routledge.

—I Sing the Body Politic: History as Prophecy in Contemporary American Literature. 2009. (ENG.). 216p. (C). *(978-0-7735-3603-6(5))*; pap. *(978-0-7735-3633-3(7))* McGill-Queen's Univ. Pr.

Szumskyj, Benjamin. American Exorcist: Critical Essays on William Peter Blatty. Szumskyj, Benjamin, ed. 2008. (ENG.). 204p. pap. 35.00 *(978-0-7864-3597-5(6))* McFarland & Co., Inc. Pubs.

Szumskyj, Benjamin, ed. Dissecting Hannibal Lecter: Essays on the Novels of Thomas Harris. 2008. (ENG.). 239p. per. 35.00 *(978-0-7864-3275-2(6))* McFarland & Co., Inc. Pubs.

Tate, Andrew. Contemporary Fiction & Christianity. 2010. (Continuum Literary Studies). (ENG.). 168p. 44.95 *(978-1-4411-6175-8(9))* Continuum International Publishing Group, Ltd. GBR. Dist: National Bk. Network.

Tate, Andrew & Tate. Contemporary Fiction & Christianity. 2008. (Continuum Literary Studies). (ENG.). 168p. 120.00 *(978-0-8264-8907-4(9))* Continuum International Publishing Group, Ltd. GBR. Dist: National Bk. Network.

Teslenko, Tatiana. Feminist Utopian Novels of The 1970s: Joanna Russ & Dorothy Bryant. 2009. 202p. 39.95 *(978-0-415-80351-9(9))* Routledge.

Thaler, Ingrid. Black Atlantic Speculative Fictions: Octavia E. Butler, Jewelle Gomez, & Nalo Hopkinson. 2010. (ENG.). 204p. (C). 125.00 *(978-0-415-80441-7(8))* Routledge.

Theobald, Tom. Existentialism & Baseball. 2010. 288p. pap. *(978-3-8383-4896-4(6))* Lambert Academic Publishing.

Thomas, Bronwen. Fictional Dialogue: Speech & Conversation in the Modern & Postmodern Novel. 2012. (Frontiers of Narrative Ser.). (ENG., Illus.). 232p. 50.00 ***(978-0-8032-4451-1(7))*** Univ. of Nebraska Pr.

Thomas, Samuel. Pynchon & the Political. 2007. (Studies in Major Literary Authors Ser.). (ENG.). 214p. 125.00 *(978-0-415-95646-8(3))* Routledge.

Thompson, G. R. eading the American Novel, 1865-1914. 2012. (Reading the Novel Ser.: 4). (ENG.). 462p. 144.95 *(978-0-631-23406-7(3)*, Wiley-Blackwell) Wiley, John & Sons, Inc.

Timmer, Nicoline. Do You Feel It Too? The Post-Postmodern Syndrome in American Fiction at the Turn of the Millennium. 2010. (Illus.). 388p. pap. 115.00 *(978-90-420-2930-9(7))* Rodopi.

Tolchin, Karen. Part Blood, Part Ketchup: Coming of Age in American Literature & Film. annot. ed. 2006. (ENG.). 142p. 68.50 *(978-0-7391-1436-0(0))* Lexington Bks.

Tolchin, Karen R. Part Blood, Part Ketchup: Coming of Age in American Literature & Film. 2006. (ENG.). 142p. per. 26.50 *(978-0-7391-1437-7(9))* Lexington Bks.

Van Dover, J. K. Making the Detective Story American: Biggers, Van Dine & Hammett & the Turning Point of the Genre, 1925-1930. 2010. (ENG., Illus.). 231p. pap. 35.00 *(978-0-7864-4895-1(4))* McFarland & Co., Inc. Pubs.

Venegas, Jose Luis. Decolonizing Modernism: James Joyce & the Development of Spanish American Fiction. 2010. (Legenda Main Ser.). (ENG.). 160p. (C). 89.50 *(978-1-906540-46-3(2))* Maney Publishing GBR. Dist: Brown, David Bk. Co., The.

Viala, Fabienne. Marguerite Yourcenar, Alejo Carpentier: Ecritures de L'histoire. 2008. (Yourcenar Ser.). (FRE & SPA.). 185p. pap. 54.95 *(978-90-5201-400-5(0))* PIE - Peter Lang BEL. Dist: Lang, Peter.

Vickery, John B. The Prose Elegy: An Exploration of Modern American & British Fiction. 2009. 200p. 32.00 *(978-0-8071-3392-7(2))* Louisiana State Univ. Pr.

Vint, Sherryl. Bodies of Tomorrow: Technology, Subjectivity, Science Fiction. 2007. (ENG.). 304p. *(978-0-8020-9052-2(4))* Univ. of Toronto Pr.

Wakana, Maya Higashi. Performing the Everday in Henry James's Late Novels. 2009. 204p. 99.95 *(978-0-7546-6744-5(8))* Ashgate Publishing Co.

Walsch, Frances M. Intelligence in Contemporary Media. 2011. (Intelligence & Counterintelligence Studies). pap. 43.00 *(978-1-61122-651-5(1))* Nova Science Pubs., Inc.

Walsh, Richard. Novel Arguments: Reading Innovative American Fiction. 2009. (Cambridge Studies in American Literature & Culture Ser.). (ENG.). 200p. pap. 33.00 *(978-0-521-10703-7(2))* Cambridge Univ. Pr.

Ward, Joseph Anthony & James, Henry. The Imagination of Disaster: Evil in the Fiction of Henry James. 2011. 198p. 42.95 ***(978-1-258-08770-8(7))*** Literary Licensing, LLC.

Weinstein, Cindy & Stoneley, Peter, eds. A Concise Companion to American Fiction, 1900-1950. 2008. (Concise Companions to Literature & Culture Ser.). (ENG.). 328p. 116.95 *(978-1-4051-3367-8(8)*, Wiley-Blackwell) Wiley, John & Sons, Inc.

Westling, Louise H. Sacred Groves & Ravaged Gardens: The Fiction of Eudora Welty, Carson Mccullers, & Flannery O'Connor. 2008. (ENG.). 232p. pap. 22.95 *(978-0-8203-3202-4(X))* Univ. of Georgia Pr.

Whaley, Annemarie Koning. The Trouble with Dreiser: Harper & the Editing of Jennie Gerhardt. 2009. 248p. 104.99 *(978-1-60497-643-4(8))* Cambria Pr.

Whitebrook, Maureen. Identity, Narrative & Politics. 256p. *(978-1-85728-776-9(2))* Taylor & Francis Group.

Wilson, Christopher P. The Labor of Words: Literary Professionalism in the Progressive Era. 2010. (ENG.). 268p. pap. 24.95 *(978-0-8203-3698-5(X))* Univ. of Georgia Pr.

Wirth-Nesher, Hana. City Codes: Reading the Modern Urban Novel. 2008. (ENG., Illus.). 260p. pap. 53.00 *(978-0-521-06004-2(4))* Cambridge Univ. Pr.

Wright, Charlotte M. Plain & Ugly Janes: The Rise of the Ugly Woman in Contemporary American Fiction. 2006. 152p. (C). pap. 19.95 *(978-0-87745-994-1(0))* Univ. of Iowa Pr.

Wright, Terry R. The Genesis of Fiction: The Modern Novel As Biblical Exegesis. 2007. 200p. 99.95 *(978-0-7546-1668-9(1))* Ashgate Publishing Co.

Ya-hui, Irenna Chang & Chang, Ya-Hui Irenna. How What You Eat Defines Who You Are: The Food Theme in Four American Women Writers. 2009. v, 192p. *(978-0-7734-4906-0(X))* Mellen, Edwin Pr., The.

Yaszek, Lisa. Galactic Suburbia: Recovering Women's Science Fiction. 2008. (ENG.). 256p. 71.95 *(978-0-8142-1075-8(9))*; 256p. pap. 22.95 *(978-0-8142-5164-5(1))*; cd-rom 9.95 *(978-0-8142-9153-5(8))* Ohio State Univ. Pr.

Zamora, Lois Parkinson. The Usable Past: The Imagination of History in Recent Fiction of the Americas. 2008. (ENG.). 276p. pap. 53.00 *(978-0-521-05809-4(0))* Cambridge Univ. Pr.

AMERICAN FICTION—HISTORY AND CRITICISM—21ST CENTURY

Bauer, Margaret Donovan. Understanding Tim Gautreaux. 2010. (Understanding Contemporary American Literature Ser.). 272p. 39.95 *(978-1-57003-859-4(7))* Univ. of South Carolina Pr.

Beahm, George. Discovering the Golden Compass: A Guide to Philip Pullman's Dark Materials. 2007. (ENG., Illus.). 248p. (YA). (gr. 7-12). per. 16.95 *(978-1-57174-506-4(8))* Hampton Roads Publishing Co., Inc.

Berry, R. M. Forms at War: FC2, 1999-2009. Berry, Ralph M., ed. 2009. (ENG., Illus.). 432p. pap. 25.95 *(978-1-57366-806-4(0))* Fiction Collective Two, Inc.

Brauner, David. Contemporary American Fiction. 2010. (Edinburgh Critical Guides to Literature Ser.). (ENG.). 224p. (gr. 17). 90.00 *(978-0-7486-2267-2(5))*; pap. 30.00 *(978-0-7486-2268-9(3))* Edinburgh Univ. Pr. GBR. Dist: Columbia Univ. Pr.

Carroll, Rachel. Rereading Heterosexuality: Feminism, Queer Theory & Contemporary Fiction. 2012. (ENG.). 240p. (gr. 17). 95.00 ***(978-0-7486-3955-7(1))*** Edinburgh Univ. Pr. GBR. Dist: Columbia Univ. Pr.

Çirakli, Mustafa Zeki. Narrative Strategies & Meaning. 2010. 188p. pap. *(978-3-639-19520-0(5))* VDM Verlag Dr. Mueller e.K.

Collins, Tim. Behind the Lost Symbol. 2010. (ENG., Illus.). 224p. (gr. 12). 15.00 *(978-0-425-23721-2(4)*, Berkley Trade) Penguin Group (USA) Inc.

Davis, Graeme. The Lost Symbol — Found: Unauthorized Analysis of Dan Brown's Novel. 2009. 144p. pap. 15.93 *(978-1-60888-011-9(7))* Nimble Bks. LLC.

Delfino, Andrew Steven. Becoming the New Man in Post-Postmodernist Fiction - Portrayals of Masculinities in David Foster Wallace's Infinite Jest and. 2008. 100p. per. *(978-3-8364-3735-6(X))* VDM Verlag Dr. Mueller e.K.

Dell, Kerstin. The Family Novel in North America from Post-War to Post-Millennium - a Study in Genre. 2007. 248p. per. *(978-3-8364-4773-7(8))* VDM Verlag Dr. Mueller e.K.

Dix, Andrew, et al. The Contemporary American Novel in Context. 2011. (Texts & Contexts Ser.). (ENG.). 192p. 80.00 *(978-0-8264-1969-9(0))*; pap. 24.95 *(978-0-8264-3696-2(X))* Continuum International Publishing Group, Ltd. GBR. Dist: National Bk. Network.

Duvall, John N., ed. The Cambridge Companion to American Fiction After 1945. 2011. (Cambridge Companions to Literature Ser.). (ENG., Illus.). 292p. (C). 90.00 ***(978-0-521-19631-4(0))***; pap. 24.99 ***(978-0-521-12347-1(X))*** Cambridge Univ. Pr.

Effron, Malcah, ed. The Millennial Detective: Essays on Trends in Crime Fiction, Film & Television, 1990-2010. 2011. (ENG.). 200p. pap. 40.00 ***(978-0-7864-5851-6(8))*** McFarland & Co., Inc. Pubs.

Ellis, Sherry, ed. Illuminating Fiction. 2009. (ENG.). 224p. pap. 19.95 *(978-1-59709-068-1(9))* Red Hen Pr.

Farrell, Susan Elizabeth. Critical Companion to Tim O'Brien. 2011. (Critical Companion to Ser.). 488p. (C). (gr. 9). 75.00 *(978-0-8160-7870-7(X))* Facts On File, Inc.

Flanagan, Mary & Booth, Austin, eds. Re - Skin. 2009. (ENG., Illus.). 376p. (gr. 17). pap. 21.00 *(978-0-262-51249-7(1))* MIT Pr.

Greenwood, Willard P. Reading Cormac McCarthy, 1 vol. 2009. (Pop Lit Book Club Ser.). 141p. 39.95 *(978-0-313-35664-3(5)*, GR5664, Greenwood Pr.) Greenwood Publishing Group, Inc.

Gretlund, Jan Nordby, ed. Still in Print: The Southern Novel Today. 2010. 59.95 *(978-1-57003-943-0(7))*; pap. 29.95 *(978-1-57003-944-7(5))* Univ. of South Carolina Pr.

Hampton, Gregory. Changing Bodies in the Fiction of Octavia Butler: Slaves, Aliens, & Vampires. 2010. (ENG.). 200p. 60.00 *(978-0-7391-3787-1(5))* Lexington Bks.

Hepburn, Allan. Enchanted Objects: Visual Art in Contemporary Fiction. 2010. (Illus.). 288p. *(978-1-4426-4100-6(2))* Univ. of Toronto Pr.

Jacobson, Kristin J. Neodomestic American Fiction. 2010. 49.95 *(978-0-8142-1132-8(1))*; cd-rom 14.95 *(978-0-8142-9231-0(3))* Ohio State Univ. Pr.

Kessel, Tyler H. Reading Landscape in American Literature: The Outside in the Fiction of Don Delillo. 2011. *(978-1-60497-755-4(8))* Cambria Pr.

Kevane, Bridget. Profane & Sacred: Latino/a American Writers Reveal the Interplay of the Secular & the Religious. 2007. (Celebrating Faith Ser.). (ENG.). 160p. 59.00 *(978-0-7425-4314-0(5))*; per. 23.95 *(978-0-7425-4315-7(3))* Rowman & Littlefield Publishers, Inc.

Klinkowitz, Jerome. Kurt Vonnegut's America. 2009. 160p. 34.95 *(978-1-57003-826-6(0))* Univ. of South Carolina Pr.

Kronenberg, Michael & Spurlock, J. David. Spies, Vixens, & Masters of Kung Fu: The Art of Paul Gulacy, 1 vol. 2007. (ENG., Illus.). 128p. 34.95 *(978-1-887591-75-1(3))* Vanguard Productions.

Kronenberg, Michael & Spurlock, J. David, eds. Spies, Vixens, & Masters of Kung Fu: The Art of Paul Gulacy, 1 vol. 2007. (ENG., Illus.). 128p. 49.95 ***(978-1-887591-76-8(1))*** Vanguard Productions.

Lincoln, Kenneth. Cormac McCarthy: American Canticles. 2009. (American Literature Readings in the Twenty-First Century Ser.). (ENG.). 192p. pap. 30.00 *(978-0-230-61967-8(3))* Palgrave Macmillan.

Lombardi, William & Houston, Lynn Marie. Reading Joan Didion, 1 vol. 2009. (Pop Lit Book Club Ser.). 159p. 35.00 *(978-0-313-36403-7(6)*, GR6403) Greenwood Publishing Group, Inc.

McClure, John A. Partial Faiths: Postsecular Fiction in the Age of Pynchon & Morrison. 2007. (ENG.). 224p. per. 24.95 *(978-0-8203-3033-4(7))* Univ. of Georgia Pr.

Meyers, Helene. Reading Michael Chabon, 1 vol. 2010. (Pop Lit Book Club Ser.). 130p. 35.00 *(978-0-313-35550-9(9)*, GR5550) Greenwood Publishing Group, Inc.

Moynihan, Sinéad. Passing into the Present: Contemporary American Fiction of Racial & Gender Passing. 2011. (Contemporary American & Canadian Novelists Ser.). (ENG.). 256p. 85.00 *(978-0-7190-8229-0(3))* Manchester Univ. Pr. GBR. Dist: Macmillan.

Munro, Martin, ed. Edwidge Danticat: A Reader's Guide. 2010. (ENG.). 232p. (gr. 17). 55.00 *(978-0-8139-3021-3(9))*; (Illus.). (C). (gr. 13-17). pap. 22.50 *(978-0-8139-3022-0(7))* Univ. Pr. of Virginia.

Perrakis, Phyllis Sternberg. Adventures of the Spirit: The Older Woman in the Works of Doris Lessing, Margaret Atwood, & Other Contemporary Women Writers. 2007. (ENG.). 321p. 49.95 *(978-0-8142-1064-2(3))* 2006. cd-rom 9.95 *(978-0-8142-9142-9(2))* Ohio State Univ. Pr.

Philips, Deborah & Philips. Women's Fiction 1945-2005: Writing Romance. 2008. (Continuum Literary Studies). (ENG.). 170p. 27.95 *(978-0-8264-9996-7(1))* Continuum International Publishing Group, Ltd. GBR. Dist: National Bk. Network.

Piatti-Farnell, Lorna. Food & Culture in Contemporary American Fiction. 2011. (Routledge Studies in Contemporary Literature Ser.). (ENG.). 202p. (C). 125.00 *(978-0-415-88422-8(5))* Routledge.

Pokras, Barbara & Yariv, Fran Pokras. Feeding Mrs. Moskowitz & The Caregiver: Two Stories. 2010. *(978-0-8156-0978-0(7))* Syracuse Univ. Pr.

Punday, Daniel. Writing at the Limit: The Novel in the New Media Ecology. 2012. (Frontiers of Narrative Ser.). (ENG., Illus.). 280p. 60.00 ***(978-0-8032-3646-2(8))*** Univ. of Nebraska Pr.

Ramsey, G. Lee, Jr. Preachers & Misfits, Prophets & Thieves: The Minister in Southern Fiction. 2008. (ENG.). 208p. pap. 20.00 *(978-0-664-23224-5(8))* Westminster John Knox Pr.

Rosenthal, Caroline. New York & Toronto Novels after Postmodernism: Explorations of the Urban Symbolic Urban Spaces. 2011. (European Studies in North American Literature & Culture Ser.). 322p. 80.00 *(978-1-57113-489-9(1))* Camden Hse.

Savu, Laura E. Postmortem Postmodernists: The Afterlife of the Author in Recent Narrative. 2009. 63.00 *(978-0-8386-4181-1(4))* Fairleigh Dickinson Univ. Pr.

Shivani, Anis. Against the Workshop: Provocations, Polemics, Controversies. 2011. 272p. pap. 24.95 ***(978-1-933896-72-4(8))*** Texas Review Pr.

Siegel, Ben. Playful & Serious: Philip Roth as a Comic Writer. 2009. (ENG.). 56.00 *(978-1-61149-147-0(9))* Univ. of Delaware Pr.

Siegel, Ben & Halio, Jay L. Playful & Serious: Philip Roth As a Comic Writer. 2010. 56.00 *(978-0-87413-094-2(8))* Univ. of Delaware Pr.

Simpson, Philip L. Making Murder: The Fiction of Thomas Harris, 1 vol. 2010. 358p. 54.95 *(978-0-313-35624-7(6)*, C35624) Greenwood Publishing Group, Inc.

Snodgrass, Mary Ellen. Reading Nora Roberts, 1 vol. 2009. (Pop Lit Book Club Ser.). 155p. 35.00 *(978-0-313-36293-4(9)*, GR6293) Greenwood Publishing Group, Inc.

Strong, Amy L. Race & Identity in Hemingway's Fiction. 2008. (American Literature Readings in the Twenty-First Century Ser.). (ENG.). 192p. 89.00 *(978-1-4039-7205-7(2))* Palgrave Macmillan.

Sun-Kleinberger, Nathan. The Children of Holden. 2009. 68p. pap. *(978-3-639-16371-1(0))* VDM Verlag Dr. Mueller e.K.

Timmer, Nicoline. Do You Feel It Too? The Post-Postmodern Syndrome in American Fiction at the Turn of the Millennium. 2010. (Illus.). 388p. pap. 115.00 *(978-90-420-2930-9(7))* Rodopi.

Van Herk, Aritha. Carol Shields: Evocation & Echo. Steenman-Marcusse, Conny, ed. 2009. (Canada Cahiers Ser.). (ENG.). 146p. (C). pap. 28.00 ***(978-90-77922-51-4(2))*** Barkhuis Publishing NLD. Dist: Brown, David Bk. Co., The.

Varvogli, Aliki. Travel & Dislocation in Contemporary American Fiction. 2011. (Routledge Transnational Perspectives on American Literature Ser.). (ENG.). 180p. (C). 125.00 *(978-0-415-99582-5(5))* Routledge.

Watkiss, Joanne. Gothic Contemporaries: The Haunted Text. 2012. (University of Wales Press - Gothic Literary Studies). (ENG.). 176p. pap. 25.00 ***(978-0-7083-2456-1(8))*** Univ. of Wales Pr. GBR. Dist: Chicago Distribution Ctr.

Whalen-Bridge, John. Later Fictions: Ancient Evenings Through Castle in the Forest. 2010. (American Literature Readings in the Twenty-First Century Ser.). (ENG.). 224p. 79.00 *(978-0-230-10024-4(4))* Palgrave Macmillan.

Wood, Tat. About Time, 1985-1989: The Unauthorized Guide to Doctor Who. 2007. (About Time Ser.). 416p. per. 24.95 *(978-0-9759446-5-3(7))* Mad Norwegian Pr.

AMERICAN FICTION—JEWISH AUTHORS

Beagle, Peter S., et al. People of the Book: A Decade of Jewish Science Fiction & Fantasy. 2010. 352p. pap. 14.95 *(978-1-60701-238-2(3))* Prime.

Cappell, Ezra. American Talmud: The Cultural Work of Jewish American Fiction. 2008. (Suny Series, Modern Jewish Literature & Culture Ser.). 233p. per. 29.95 *(978-0-7914-7124-1(1))* State Univ. of New York Pr.

Codde, Philippe. The Jewish American Novel. 2007. (Comparative Cultural Studies). 279p. per. 34.95 *(978-1-55753-437-8(3))* Purdue Univ. Pr.

Girgus, Sam B. The New Covenant: Jewish Writers & the American Idea. 2011. (ENG.). 233p. pap. 40.00 ***(978-0-8078-9670-9(5))*** Univ. of North Carolina Pr.

Lambert, Joshua N. American Jewish Fiction: A JPS Guide. 2009. (JPS Guides). (ENG., Illus.). 250p. pap. 18.00 *(978-0-8276-0883-2(7))* Jewish Pubn. Society.

Pokras, Barbara & Yariv, Fran Pokras. Feeding Mrs. Moskowitz & The Caregiver: Two Stories. 2010. *(978-0-8156-0978-0(7))* Syracuse Univ. Pr.

Rubel, Nora L. Doubting the Devout: The Ultra-Orthodox in the Jewish American Imagination. 2009. (Religion & American Culture Ser.). (ENG.). 224p. (gr. 17). pap. 24.50 *(978-0-231-14187-1(4))*; (Illus.). 79.50 *(978-0-231-14186-4(6))* Columbia Univ. Pr.

Rubinstein, Rachel. Members of the Tribe: Native America in the Jewish Imagination. 2010. 268p. pap. 27.95 *(978-0-8143-3434-8(2))* Wayne State Univ. Pr.

Statlander, Jane. Philip Roth's Postmodern American Romance: Critical Essays on Selected Works. 2010. (Twentieth-Century American Jewish Writers Ser.). 118p. (C). 62.95 *(978-1-4331-0598-2(5))* Lang, Peter Publishing, Inc.

AMERICAN FICTION—WOMEN AUTHORS

Abraham, Julie. Are Girls Necessary? Lesbian Writing & Modern Histories. 2008. 240p. pap. 22.50 *(978-0-8166-5676-9(2))* Univ. of Minnesota Pr.

Anderson Cordell, Sigrid. Fictions of Dissent: Reclaiming Authority in Transatlantic Women's Writing of the Late Nineteenth Century, 1 vol. 2010. (Gender & Genre Ser.). (ENG.). 160p. 99.00 *(978-1-84893-023-0(2))* Pickering & Chatto Pubs., Ltd. GBR. Dist: Ashgate Publishing Co.

Ashley, Mike, ed. & intro. Unforgettable Ghost Stories by Women Writers. 2008. (ENG.). 320p. pap. 10.95 *(978-0-486-46797-9(X))* Dover Pubns., Inc.

Barr, Marlene S., ed. Afro-Future Females: Black Writers Chart Science Fiction's Newest New-Wave Trajectory. 2008. (ENG.). 304p. 64.95

(978-0-8142-1078-9(3)); cd-rom 14.95 (978-0-8142-9156-6(2)) Ohio State Univ. Pr.

Beam, Dorri. Style, Gender, & Fantasy in Nineteenth-Century American Women's Writing. 2010. (Cambridge Studies in American Literature & Culture Ser.). (ENG.). 268p. 89.00 (978-0-521-76968-6(X)) Cambridge Univ. Pr.

Betz, Phyllis M. Lesbian Detective Fiction: Woman as Author, Subject & Reader. 2006. (ENG., Illus.). 207p. per. 35.00 (978-0-7864-2548-8(2)) McFarland & Co., Inc. Pubs.

—The Lesbian Fantastic: A Critical Study of Science Fiction, Fantasy, Paranormal & Gothic Writings. 2011. (ENG.). 211p. pap. 40.00 (978-0-7864-5885-1(2)) McFarland & Co., Inc. Pubs.

Black Lace Publishing Staff, creator. Black Lace Quickies 1. 2007. (ENG.). 128p. mass mkt. 4.99 (978-0-352-34126-6(2), Black Lace) Virgin Bks. Ltd. GBR. Dist: Independent Pubs. Group.

—Black Lace Quickies 2. 2007. (ENG.). 128p. mass mkt. 4.99 (978-0-352-34127-3(0), Black Lace) Virgin Bks. Ltd. GBR. Dist: Independent Pubs. Group.

Blue, Violet, ed. Best Women's Erotica 2011. 2010. (ENG.). 256p. pap. 15.95 (978-1-57344-423-1(5)) Cleis Pr.

Bona, Mary Jo & BONA, Mary Jo, eds. The Voices We Carry: Recent Italian American Women's Fiction. 2nd ed. 2006. (Picas Ser.: 32). (ENG.). 346p. 18.00 (978-1-55071-099-1(0)) Guernica Editions, Inc. CAN. Dist: Univ. of Toronto Pr.

Capitani, Diane N. Truthful Pictures: Slavery Ordained by God in the Domestic, Sentimental Novel of the Nineteenth Century South. 2009. (ENG., Illus.). 156p. 57.99 (978-0-7391-1232-8(5)) Lexington Bks.

Chen, Li'ang. Hybridizing Identity: Louise Erdrich as Mixed-blood. 2010. 136p. pap. (978-3-8383-5713-3(2)) Lambert Academic Publishing.

Clark, Amy L., et al. A Peculiar Feeling of Restlessness: Four Chapbooks of Short Short Fiction by Four Women. 2008. 224p. pap. 16.00 (978-0-9789848-3-0(8)) Rose Metal Pr., Inc.

Cook, Barbara J., ed. Women Writing Nature: A Feminist View. 2007. (After the Empire: the Francophone World & Postcolonial France Ser.). (ENG.). 152p. 62.99 (978-0-7391-1912-9(5)); per. 26.50 (978-0-7391-1913-6(3)) Lexington Bks.

Dong, Lan, ed. Transnationalism & the Asian American Heroine: Essays on Literature, Film, Myth & Media. 2010. (ENG., Illus.). 239p. pap. 55.00 (978-0-7864-4632-2(3)) McFarland & Co., Inc. Pubs.

Dresner, Lisa M. The Female Investigator in Literature, Film, & Popular Culture. 2006. (ENG.). 240p. per. 35.00 (978-0-7864-2654-6(3)) McFarland & Co., Inc. Pubs.

Eaton, Kalenda C. Womanism, Literature, & the Transformation of the Black Community, 1965ndash;1980. 2012. (Studies in African American History & Culture Ser.). (ENG.). 122p. pap. 42.95 (978-0-415-54080-3(1)) Routledge.

Ferretter, Luke. Sylvia Plath's Fiction: A Critical Study. 2012. (ENG.). 256p. (gr. 17). pap. 30.00 (978-0-7486-2510-9(0)) Edinburgh Univ. Pr. GBR. Dist: Columbia Univ. Pr.

Ferretter, Luke. Sylvia Plath's Fiction: A Critical Study. 2010. (ENG.). 256p. (gr. 17). 105.00 (978-0-7486-2509-3(7)) Edinburgh Univ. Pr. GBR. Dist: Columbia Univ. Pr.

Frantz, Sarah. Women Constructing Men: Female Novelists & Their Male Characters, 1750D2000. 2011. (ENG.). 280p. pap. 32.95 (978-0-7391-3366-8(7)) Lexington Bks.

Frantz, Sarah & Rennhak, Katharina. Women Constructing Men: Female Novelists & Their Male Characters, 1750-2000. 2009. (ENG.). 280p. 73.50 (978-0-7391-3365-1(9)) Lexington Bks.

Ganser, Alexandra. Roads of Her Own: Gendered Space & Mobility in American Women's Road Narratives, 1970-2000. 2009. (Illus.). 339p. 95.00 (978-90-420-2552-3(2)) Rodopi.

Gordon, Lindsay, ed. Love on the Dark Side: A Collection of Paranormal Erotica from Black Lace. 2007. (ENG., Illus.). 288p. mass mkt. (978-0-352-34132-7(7), Black Lace) Virgin Bks. Ltd. GBR. Dist: Independent Pubs. Group.

Hall, Glinda / F. The Creators of Women's Popular Romance Fiction: The Authors Who Gave to Women a Genre of Their Own. 2009. vi, 228p. (978-0-7734-3841-5(6)) Mellen, Edwin Pr., The.

Harker, Jaime. America the Middlebrow: Women's Novels, Progressivism, & Middlebrow Authorship between the Wars. 2007. (Studies in Print Culture & the History of the Book). (Illus.). 208p. lib. bdg. 80.00 (978-1-55849-596-8(7)) Univ. of Massachusetts Pr.

—America the Middlebrow: Women's Novels, Progressivism, & Middlebrow Authorship Between the Wars. 2007. (Studies in Print Culture & the History of the Book). (Illus.). 182p. per. 24.95 (978-1-55849-597-5(5)) Univ. of Massachusetts Pr.

Harrington, Ellen Burton. Scribbling Women & the Short Story Form: Approaches by American & British Women Writers. 2008. 216p. (C). pap. 33.95 (978-1-4331-0077-2(0)) Lang, Peter Publishing, Inc.

Harzewski, Stephanie. Chick Lit & Postfeminism. 2011. (Cultural Frames, Framing Culture Ser.). (ENG., Illus.). 264p. (C). (gr. 13-17). pap. 19.50 (978-0-8139-3072-5(3)) Univ. Pr. of Virginia.

Hearne, Betsy & Trites, Roberta Seelinger, eds. A Narrative Compass: Stories That Guide Women's Lives. 2009. (ENG., Illus.). 269p. 67.00 (978-0-252-03407-7(4)); 264p. pap. 26.00 (978-0-252-07611-4(7)) Univ. of Illinois Pr.

Heilmann, Ann & Llewellyn, Mark. Metafiction & Metahistory in Contemporary Women's Writing. Heilmann, Ann, ed. 2007. (ENG., Illus.). 256p. 84.00 (978-0-230-00504-4(7)) Palgrave Macmillan.

Hill, Nanci. Reading Women: A Book Club Guide for Women's Fiction, 1 vol. 2012. 221p. pap. 35.00 (978-1-59158-802-3(2), LU8802) Libraries Unlimited, Inc.

Hill, Nanci Milone. Reading Women: A Book Club Guide for Women's Fiction. 2012. E-Book (978-1-59158-806-1(5)) ABC-CLIO, LLC.

Hunt, Alex. The Geographical Imagination of Annie Proulx: Rethinking Regionalism. (ENG.). 2010. 228p. pap. 29.95 (978-0-7391-2395-9(5)) 2008. 229p. 62.99 (978-0-7391-2394-2(7)) Lexington Bks.

Irr, Caren. Pink Pirates: Contemporary American Women Writers & Copyright. 2010. 348p. pap. 34.95 (978-1-58729-912-4(7)) Univ. of Iowa Pr.

Kensington Ladies' Erotica Society Staff. Ladies' Own Erotica: Tales, Recipes, & Other Mischiefs by Older Women. 2006. (Illus.). 229p. reprint ed. pap. 20.00 (978-1-4223-5674-6(4)) DIANE Publishing Co.

Knight, Alisha R. Pauline Hopkins & the American Dream: An African American Writer's (Re)Visionary Gospel of Success. 2012. (ENG., Illus.). 152p. 45.00 (978-1-57233-852-4(0)) Univ. of Tennessee Pr.

Michael, Magali Cornier. New Visions of Community in Contemporary American Fiction: Tan, Kingsolver, Castillo, Morrison. 2006. 256p. (C). pap. 21.00 (978-1-58729-511-9(3)) Univ. of Iowa Pr.

Nunes, Ana. African American Women Writers' Historical Fiction. 2011. (ENG.). 258p. 85.00 (978-0-230-11253-7(6)) Palgrave Macmillan.

Oh, Seung Ah. Recontextualizing Asian American Domesticity: From Madame Butterfly to My American Wife. 2008. (ENG.). 208p. 68.50 (978-0-7391-2278-5(9)) Lexington Bks.

Olwell, Victoria. The Genius of Democracy: Fictions of Gender & Citizenship in the United States, 1860-1945. 2011. 304p. (C). 59.95 (978-0-8122-4324-6(2)) Univ. of Pennsylvania Pr.

Paloge, Helen. The Silent Echo: The Middle-Aged Female Body in Contemporary Women's Fiction. 2007. (ENG.). 200p. 73.50 (978-0-7391-2172-6(3)) Lexington Bks.

Patterson, Laura Sloan. Stirring the Pot: The Kitchen & Domesticity in the Fiction of Southern Women. 2008. (ENG.). 240p. pap. 39.95 (978-0-7864-3523-4(2)) McFarland & Co., Inc. Pubs.

Patterson, Martha H. Beyond the Gibson Girl: Reimagining the American New Woman, 1895-1915. 2008. (ENG., Illus.). 248p. pap. 26.00 (978-0-252-07563-6(3)) Univ. of Illinois Pr.

Perrakis, Phyllis Sternberg. Adventures of the Spirit: The Older Woman in the Works of Doris Lessing, Margaret Atwood, & Other Contemporary Women Writers. 2007. (ENG.). 321p. 49.95 (978-0-8142-1064-2(3)) 2006. cd-rom 9.95 (978-0-8142-9142-9(2)) Ohio State Univ. Pr.

Pillow, Gloria Thomas. Motherlove in Shades of Black: The Maternal Psyche in the Novels of African American Women. 2010. (ENG., Illus.). 199p. pap. 38.00 (978-0-7864-3533-3(X)) McFarland & Co., Inc. Pubs.

Raphael-Hernandez, Heike. The Utopian Aesthetics of Three African American Women (Toni Morrison, Gloria Naylor, Julie Dash) The Principle of Hope. 2008. 188p. 99.95 (978-0-7734-4936-7(1)) Mellen, Edwin Pr., The.

Rehak, Melanie. Girl Sleuth: Nancy Drew & the Women Who Created Her. 2008. (ENG.). 364p. 25.00 (978-1-4223-9543-1(X)) DIANE Publishing Co.

—Girl Sleuth: Nancy Drew & the Women Who Created Her. 2006. (ENG., Illus.). 384p. (gr. 9). pap. 14.00 (978-0-15-603056-4(X), Mariner Bks.) Houghton Mifflin Harcourt Trade & Reference Pubs.

Rich, Charlotte J. Transcending the New Woman: Multiethnic Narratives in the Progressive ERA. 2009. (ENG.). 240p. (C). 39.95 (978-0-8262-1826-1(1)) Univ. of Missouri Pr.

Rubin Jr., Louis D. Two Ladies of the South: The Sewanee Review, October 1955. 2011. 16p. pap. 35.95 (978-1-258-04738-2(1)) Literary Licensing, LLC.

Sebag-Montefiore, Mary. Women Writers of Children's Classics. 2007. (Writers & Their Work Ser.). (ENG.). 154p. (C). pap. 26.00 (978-0-7463-1157-8(5)) Northcote Hse. Publishers, Ltd. GBR. Dist: Brown, David Bk. Co., The.

Smith, Caroline J. Cosmopolitan Culture & Consumerism in Chick Lit. 2007. (Literary Criticism & Cultural Theory Ser.). (ENG.). 192p. 125.00 (978-0-415-95662-8(5)) Routledge.

Smith, Caroline J. & Smith, Caroline. Cosmopolitan Culture & Consumerism in Chick Lit. 2009. 188p. 39.95 (978-0-415-80626-8(7)) Routledge.

Smith, Deborah, et al. More Sweet Tea. l.t. ed. 2008. 314p. (YA). 29.95 (978-1-4104-0815-0(9)) Thorndike Pr.

Spillman, Rob, ed. Fantastic Women: 18 Tales of the Surreal & the Sublime from Tin House. 2011. (ENG.). 270p. pap. 18.95 (978-1-935639-10-7(2)) Tin Hse. Bks., LLC.

Stoneley, Peter. Consumerism & American Girls' Literature, 1860-1940. 2007. (Cambridge Studies in American Literature & Culture Ser.). (ENG., Illus.). 180p. pap. 44.00 (978-0-521-03575-0(9)) Cambridge Univ. Pr.

Strehle, Susan. Transnational Women's Fiction: Unsettling Home & Homeland. 2008. (ENG.). 256p. 89.00 (978-0-230-53687-6(5)) Palgrave Macmillan.

Sussex, Lucy. Women Writers & Detectives in Nineteenth-Century Crime Fiction: The Mothers of the Mystery Genre. 2010. (Crime Files Ser.). (ENG., Illus.). 224p. 84.00 (978-0-230-27229-3(0)) Palgrave Macmillan.

Sussman, Ellen, ed. Bad Girls: 26 Writers Misbehave. 2008. (ENG.). 320p. pap. 14.95 (978-0-393-33195-0(4), 33195) Norton, W. W. & Co., Inc.

Svrljuga, Zeljka. Hysteria & Melancholy as Literary Style in the Works of Charlotte Perkins Gilman, Kate Chopin, Zelda Fitzgerald, & Djuna Barnes. 2011. (Illus.). 280p. 129.95 (978-0-7734-1517-1(3)) Mellen, Edwin Pr., The.

Teslenko, Tatiana. Feminist Utopian Novels of The 1970s: Joanna Russ & Dorothy Bryant. 2009. 202p. 39.95 (978-0-415-80351-9(9)) Routledge.

Thaler, Ingrid. Black Atlantic Speculative Fictions: Octavia E. Butler, Jewelle Gomez, & Nalo Hopkinson. 2010. (ENG.). 204p. (C). 125.00 (978-0-415-80441-7(8)) Routledge.

Vickery, Sukey. Emily Hamilton & Other Writings. Slawinski, Scott, ed. 2009. (Legacies of Nineteenth-Century American Women Writers Ser.). (ENG.). 278p. pap. 30.00 (978-0-8032-1785-0(4)) Univ. of Nebraska Pr.

Vnuk, Rebecca. Read on... Women's Fiction: Reading Lists for Every Taste, 1 vol. 2009. (Read on Ser.). (Illus.). 126p. pap. 30.00 (978-1-59158-634-0(8), LU8634) Libraries Unlimited, Inc.

—Women's Fiction Authors: A Research Guide, 1 vol. 2009. (Author Research Ser.). 163p. pap. 40.00 (978-1-59158-642-5(9), LU8642) Libraries Unlimited, Inc.

Weinstock, Jeffrey Andrew. Scare Tactics: Supernatural Fiction by American Women. 2nd ed. 2008. (ENG.). 200p. 55.00 (978-0-8232-2985-7(8)) Fordham Univ. Pr.

West, Elizabeth J. African Spirituality in Black Women's Fiction: Threaded Visions of Memory, Community, Nature & Being. 2011. (ENG.). 192p. (gr. 17). 60.00 (978-0-7391-6885-1(1)) Lexington Bks.

Westling, Louise H. Sacred Groves & Ravaged Gardens: The Fiction of Eudora Welty, Carson Mccullers, & Flannery O'Connor. 2008. (ENG.). 232p. pap. 22.95 (978-0-8203-3202-4(X)) Univ. of Georgia Pr.

White, Barbara A. American Women's Fiction, 1790-1870: A Reference Guide, Volume 15. 2012. (RLE: Women, Feminism & Literature Ser.). (ENG.). 320p. (C). 130.00 (978-0-415-53310-2(4)) Routledge.

Willey, Nicole L. Creating a New Ideal of Masculinity for American Men: The Achievement of Sentimental Women Writers in the Mid-Nineteenth Century. 2007. 316p. 119.95 (978-0-7734-5204-6(4)) Mellen, Edwin Pr., The.

Wright, Kristina, ed. Fairy Tale Lust: Erotic Fantasies for Women. 2010. (ENG.). 256p. pap. 14.95 (978-1-57344-397-5(2)) Cleis Pr.

Ya-hui, Irenna Chang & Chang, Ya-Hui Irenna. How What You Eat Defines Who You Are: The Food Theme in Four American Women Writers. 2009. v, 192p. (978-0-7734-4906-0(X)) Mellen, Edwin Pr., The.

Yaszek, Lisa. Galactic Suburbia: Recovering Women's Science Fiction. 2008. (ENG.). 256p. 71.95 (978-0-8142-1075-8(9)); 256p. pap. 22.95 (978-0-8142-5164-5(1)); cd-rom 9.95 (978-0-8142-9153-5(8)) Ohio State Univ. Pr.

AMERICAN FIELD SERVICE

Bryan, Julien H. Ambulance 464 Encore des Blessés: The Experiences of an American Volunteer with the French Army During the First World War. 2010. 144p. (978-0-85706-180-5(1)); pap. (978-0-85706-179-9(8)) Leonaur Ltd.

Buswell, Leslie. Ambulance Number 10 Personal Letters from the Front. 2007. (ENG.). 214p. 39.95 (978-0-548-03104-9(5)) Kessinger Publishing, LLC.

AMERICAN FLYING SQUADRON

see France—Armee—Escadrille Lafayette

AMERICAN FOLK SONGS

see Folk Songs, American

AMERICAN FOOTBALL LEAGUE

National Football League, creator. NFL Record & Fact Book 2007. rev. ed. 2007. (ENG., Illus.). 784p. (YA). (gr. 2-8). pap. 17.95 (978-1-933821-85-6(X)) Hachette Bk. Group.

Page, Joseph S. Pro Football Championships Before the Super Bowl: A Year-by-Year History, 1926-1965. 2010. (ENG., Illus.). 232p. pap. 35.00 (978-0-7864-4809-8(1)) McFarland & Co., Inc. Pubs.

Rappoport, Ken. The Little League That Could: A History of the American Football League. 2010. (ENG.). 232p. 22.95 (978-1-58979-462-7(1)) Taylor Trade Publishing.

Richey, Tom. Lamar Hunt & the Founding of the American Football League. 2009. (Illus.). 210p. 24.95 (978-0-9817405-3-9(7)) Richey Resources Pubns.

Ryczek, William J. Crash of the Titans: The Early Years of the New York Jets & the AFL. rev. ed. 2009. (ENG., Illus.). 330p. pap. 29.95 (978-0-7864-4126-6(7)) McFarland & Co., Inc. Pubs.

Sharkey, Frederick. Ladies' Football Guide. 2011. 46p. pap. 25.00 (978-1-60746-681-9(3)) FastPrncl, Inc.

Smith, Scott B. The Orange Bowl: A Photographic Journey & Architectural Survey. 2009. 132p. pap. 49.50 (978-1-4389-9611-0(X)) AuthorHouse.

Sporting News Staff. 2007 Pro Football Guide: The Ultimate Football Almanac. 2007. (ENG.). 456p. pap. 18.95 (978-0-89204-874-8(3)) Sporting News Publishing Co.

Super Bowl New Orlean Saints. 2010. pap. 19.95 (978-0-615-35072-1(0)) Sport-Publishing llc.

AMERICAN FOXHOUNDS

see Foxhounds

AMERICAN FRIENDS SERVICE COMMITTEE

Wahrhaftig, Paul. Rev. James D. Mcmanus - the Civil Rights Years: The Movement in Microcosm. 2007. (Illus.). 192p. per. 19.95 net. (978-0-9792463-0-2(X)) Fickle Pr

Yount, David. How the Quakers Invented America. 2007. (ENG.). 192p. 21.95 (978-0-7425-5833-5(9)) Rowman & Littlefield Publishers, Inc.

AMERICAN FUR COMPANY

Larsen, Lawrence H. & Cottrell, Barbara J. Steamboats West: The 1859 American Fur Company Missouri River Expedition. 2010. (Western Lands & Water Ser.). (ENG.). 256p. (C). 34.95 (978-0-87062-385-1(0), Clark, Arthur H. Co., The) Univ. of Oklahoma Pr.

AMERICAN HISTORY

see United States—History

AMERICAN INDIAN MOVEMENT

Brave Bird, Mary. Ohitika Woman. 2009. (ENG.). 304p. pap. 14.00 (978-0-8021-4339-6(3), Grove Pr) Grove/Atlantic, Inc.

Hendricks, Steve. The Unquiet Grave The FBI & the Struggle for the Soul of Indian Country. 2007. (ENG., Illus.). 512p. per. 18.95 (978-1-56858-364-8(8)) Da Capo Pr., Inc.

Johnson, Troy R. Red Power: The Native American Civil Rights Movement. 2007. (Landmark Events in Native American History Ser.). (Illus.). 112p. (YA). (gr. 9-12). lib. bdg. 35.00 (978-0-7910-9341-2(7)) Facts On File, Inc.

Loyer, Marcella. Credo for the American Indian Movement International: Chapters & Divisions on a Worldwide Level. 2009. 328p. pap. 19.99 (978-1-4490-0034-9(7)) AuthorHouse.

Trimbach, Joseph H. & Trimbach, John M. American Indian Mafia: An FBI Agent's True Story about Wounded Knee, Leonard Peltier, & the American Indian Movement (AIM) 2008. (Illus.). ix, 631p. pap. 35.95 (978-1-4327-0778-1(7)) 2007. 652p. per. 28.95 (978-0-9795855-0-0(3)) Outskirts Pr., Inc.

Wilkins, David E., ed. The Hank Adams Reader: An Exemplary Native Activist & the Unleashing of Indigenous Sovereignty. 2011. (ENG.). 280p. pap. 19.95 (978-1-55591-447-9(0)) Fulcrum Publishing.

AMERICAN INDIANS

see Indians; Indians of North America; Indians of South America

AMERICAN INSTITUTE OF CERTIFIED PUBLIC ACCOUNTANTS

Weiss, Judith. GAAP Guide Levels B, C, & D (2009) 2008. 1200p. pap. 185.00 (978-0-8080-9221-6(9)) Toolkit Media Group.

AMERICAN INVASION OF PANAMA, 1989

see Panama—History—American Invasion, 1989

AMERICAN JEWISH JOINT DISTRIBUTION COMMITTEE

Epstein (Epi), Seymour. From Couscous to Kasha: Reporting from the Field of Jewish Community Work. 2009. (Illus.). 171p. 22.95 (978-965-524-017-7(7)) Urim Pubns. ISR. Dist: Lambda Pubs., Inc.

Mark I. Rosen. Mission, Meaning, & Money. 2010. 204p. 27.95 (978-1-4401-6743-0(5)) iUniverse, Inc.

AMERICAN LEAGUE OF PROFESSIONAL BASEBALL CLUBS

Armour, Mark L. Joe Cronin: A Life in Baseball. 2010. (ENG., Illus.). 432p. 31.95 (978-0-8032-2530-5(X)) Univ. of Nebraska Pr.

Gorman, Robert. In Your Face - In Your Heart: The Story of Joe Cronin. 2007. pap. 14.95 (978-0-9792287-0-4(0)) Baldwin Bks.

Jones, David, ed. Deadball Stars of the American League: The Society for American Baseball Research. 2007. (Illus.). 416p. per. 24.95 (978-1-57488-982-6(6)) Potomac Bks., Inc.

Lieb, Frederick G. The Detroit Tigers. 2008. (Writing Sports Ser.). (Illus.). 312p. pap. 18.00 (978-0-87338-958-7(1)) Kent State Univ. Pr.

Lynch, Michael T., Jr. Harry Frazee, Ban Johnson & the Feud That Nearly Destroyed the American League. 2008. (ENG., Illus.). 282p. pap. 29.95 (978-0-7864-3330-8(2)) McFarland & Co., Inc. Pubs.

Porterfield, Jason. Baseball in the American League Central Division. 2009. (Inside Major League Baseball Ser.). (Illus.). 48p. (gr. 5-8). (ENG.). (YA). pap. 11.75 (978-1-4358-5416-1(0)); (J). lib. bdg. 26.50 (978-1-4358-5042-2(4)) Rosen Publishing Group, Inc., The.

AMERICAN LEGION

Bimber, Bruce A., et al. Collective Action in Organizations: Interaction & Engagement in an ERA of Technological Change. 2012. (Communication, Society & Politics Ser.). (ENG., Illus.). 240p. 99.00 (978-0-521-19172-2(6)); pap. 29.99 (978-0-521-13963-2(5)) Cambridge Univ. Pr.

George Seay Wheat. The Story of the American Legion. l.t. ed. 2007. 240p. pap. 23.99 (978-1-4264-8078-2(4)) BiblioBazaar.

United States, Congress Senate Committee on Veterans' Affairs Staff, contrib. by. The Legislative Presentation of the American Legion: Hearing Before the Committee on Veterans' Affairs, United States Senate, One Hundred Ninth Congress, Second Session, September 20, 2006. 2007. iii, 54p. (978-0-16-078130-8(2), 552-070-35530-8) United States Government Printing Office.

AMERICAN LETTERS

Adler, Stephen J. & Grunwald, Lisa, eds. Women's Letters: America from the Revolutionary War to the Present. 2008. (ENG.). 832p. pap. 18.00 (978-0-385-33556-0(3)) Random House Publishing Group.

Bacon, Margaret Hope & Lapsansky-Werner, Emma, eds. Back to Africa: Benjamin Coates & the Colonization Movement in America, 1848-1880. 2007. (ENG.). 368p. pap. 27.00 (978-0-271-02763-0(0)) Pennsylvania State Univ. Pr.

Baker, Richard. Letters from Across the Big Divide: The Ghost Writings of Charles M. Russell. 2008. 240p. pap. 15.95 (978-0-595-50111-3(7)) iUniverse, Inc.

Baldwin, Barbara. Dear Soldier, 0 vols. 2009. 12.99 (978-1-59955-213-6(8)) Nelson, Thomas Inc.

Beach, Sylvia. The Letters of Sylvia Beach. Walsh, Keri, ed. 2010. (ENG., Illus.). 376p. (gr. 17). 29.95 (978-0-231-14536-7(5)) Columbia Univ. Pr.

Beers, Henry A. Initial Studies in American Letters. 2009. 284p. 34.99 (978-1-116-31253-9(0)) 2009. 284p. pap. 28.75 (978-1-116-31255-3(7)) 2009. 284p. pap. 27.75 (978-1-116-31256-0(5)) 2008. 284p. 25.99 (978-0-554-34752-3(0)) 2008. 284p. 28.99 (978-0-554-25449-4(2)) 2007. (ENG.). 250p. pap. 20.99 (978-1-4264-9084-2(4)) 2007. 282p. pap. 23.99 (978-1-4264-9138-2(7)) BiblioBazaar.

—Initial Studies in American Letters. 2007. (ENG.). 244p. per. *(978-1-4065-3734-5(9))* Dodo Pr.

—Initial Studies in American Letters. 2007. (ENG.). 280p. 42.95 *(978-0-548-02366-2(2))* Kessinger Publishing, LLC.

Carroll, Andrew. Behind the Lines: Powerful & Revealing American & Foreign War Letters — and One Man's Search to Find Them. 2006. (ENG., Illus.). 512p. pap. 29.99 *(978-0-7432-5617-9(4)*, Scribner) Scribner.

—Grace under Fire: Letters of Faith in Times of War. 2007. (ENG., Illus.). 160p. 16.95 *(978-1-4000-7337-5(5)*, WaterBrook Pr.) Doubleday Religious Publishing Group, The.

Christie, Thomas, et al. Brother of Mine: The Civil War Letters of Thomas & William Christie. 2010. E-Book *(978-0-87351-810-9(1))* Minnesota Historical Society Pr.

Dehmer, Everett. My Letters to the Editor, 1977-1986. *(978-0-9619584-1-1(3))* Caril Co.

Dickinson, John. Letters from a Farmer in Pennsylvania to the Inhabitants of the British Colonies. 2008. 214p. 39.95 *(978-0-548-97689-0(9))* 2007. (ENG.). 216p. per. 24.95 *(978-0-548-67091-0(9))* Kessinger Publishing, LLC.

Dierks, Konstantin. In My Power: Letter Writing & Communications in Early America. (Early American Studies). (Illus.). 376p. (C). 2011. pap. 24.95 ***(978-0-8122-2181-7(8))*** 2009. 55.00 *(978-0-8122-4153-2(3))* Univ. of Pennsylvania Pr.

Eberwein, Jane Donahue & MacKenzie, Cindy, eds. Reading Emily Dickinson's Letters: Critical Essays. (Illus.). 2011. 293p. pap. 26.95 *(978-1-55849-901-0(6))* 2009. 304p. 39.95 net. *(978-1-55849-741-2(2))* Univ. of Massachusetts Pr.

Farkas, Art. Letters to Ebay: Hilarious Auctions, Crazy Emails, & Bongos for Grandma. 2007. (Illus.). 234p. per. 13.99 *(978-0-446-69958-7(6))* Grand Central Publishing.

Fitzgerald, Edward. Letters of Edward FitzGerald to Fanny Kemble: 1871-1883. 2007. (ENG.). 268p. pap. 21.99 *(978-1-4346-8458-5(X))*; 284p. pap. 23.99 *(978-1-4346-8459-2(8))* BiblioBazaar.

Gaul, Theresa Strouth & Harris, Sharon M. Letters & Cultural Transformations in the U. S., 1760-1860. 2009. (Illus.). 290p. 114.95 *(978-0-7546-6622-6(0))* Ashgate Publishing Co.

Green, Elna C., ed. Looking for the New Deal: Florida Women's Letters During the Great Depression. 2007. (Women's Diaries & Letters of the South Ser.). (Illus.). 243p. 39.95 *(978-1-57003-658-3(6))* Univ. of South Carolina Pr.

Grunwald, Lisa & Adler, Stephen J., eds. Letters of the Century: America 1900-1999. 2008. (ENG., Illus.). 752p. pap. 18.00 *(978-0-385-31593-7(7))* Random House Publishing Group.

Hooper, Jackie. The Things You Would Have Said: The Chance to Say What You Always Wanted Them to Know. 2012. (ENG.). 208p. (gr. 12). 21.95 ***(978-1-59463-086-6(0)***, Hudson Street Pr.) Penguin Group (USA) Inc.

Johnson, Margaret, et al. Dear First Lady: Letters to the White House - From the Collections of the Library of Congress & National Archives. Johnson, Margaret & Young, Dwight, eds. 2009. (ENG., Illus.). 208p. 14.95 *(978-1-4262-0410-4(8)*, National Geographic) National Geographic Society.

Lawson, Dorie McCullough. Posterity: Letters of Great Americans to Their Children. 2008. (ENG.). 336p. pap. 14.95 *(978-0-7679-0904-4(6))* Broadway Bks.

Lincoln, Abraham. The Wit & Wisdom of Abraham Lincoln: As Reflected in His Briefer Letters & Speeches. Lang, H. Jack, ed. 2011. 286p. 48.95 ***(978-1-258-05501-1(5))*** Literary Licensing, LLC.

McElvaine, Robert S., ed. Down & Out in the Great Depression: Letters from the Forgotten Man. 25th ed. 2008. (ENG., Illus.). 280p. per. 20.95 *(978-0-8078-5891-2(9))* Univ. of North Carolina Pr.

Meredith, Suzanne. With a True God Bless: Civil War Letters. 2008. (Illus.). vi, 124p. pap. *(978-0-7884-4471-5(9))* Heritage Bks.

Murray, James. Letters of James Murray, Loyalist. 324p. reprint ed. 98.00 *(978-0-7222-6537-6(9))* Library Reprints, Inc.

Nesbitt, Henrietta. White House Diary. 320p. 2008. 45.95 *(978-1-4367-1531-7(8))* 2007. (ENG.). per. 30.95 *(978-1-4325-6237-3(1))* Kessinger Publishing, LLC.

Opdycke, John B., ed. The Literature of Letters: Famous Literary Letters As Related to Life, to the History of Literature & to the Art of Composition. 2011. 510p. 60.95 ***(978-1-258-05025-2(0))*** Literary Licensing, LLC.

Robbins, Carole Banks, ed. A Railroad Family in the Early 1920s. 2007. pap. *(978-0-615-17228-6(8))* Robbins, Carole Banks.

Serra, Ilaria. The Imagined Immigrant: The Imago of Italian Emigration to the United States Between 1890 And 1924. 2009. 313p. 65.00 *(978-0-8386-4198-9(9))* Fairleigh Dickinson Univ. Pr.

Smith, Hampton, ed. Brother of Mine: The Civil War Letters of Thomas & William Christie. 2010. (ENG.). 336p. pap. 19.95 *(978-0-87351-781-2(4))* Minnesota Historical Society Pr.

Taintor, Sarah Augusta. The Book of Modern Letters. Taintor, Sarah Augusta & Monro, Kate M., eds. 2011. 366p. 53.95 ***(978-1-258-04490-9(0))*** Literary Licensing, LLC.

Young, Dwight, ed. Dear Mr. President: Letters to the Oval Office from the Files of the National Archives. 2007. (ENG., Illus.). 192p. per. 11.95 *(978-1-4262-0020-5(X)*, National Geographic) National Geographic Society.

Young, Dwight & Johnson, Margaret, eds. Dear First Lady: Letters to the White House. 2008. (ENG., Illus.). 208p. 25.00 *(978-1-4262-0087-8(0))* National Geographic Society.

AMERICAN LIBRARY ASSOCIATION

Bluh, Pamela. Commemorating the Past, Celebrating the Present, Creating the Future: Papers in Observance of the 50th Anniversary of the Association for Library Collections & Technical Services. 2007. 38.50 *(978-0-8389-8431-4(2))* American Library Assn.

Koch, Theodore Wesley. War Libraries & Allied Studies. 2009. 158p. pap. 19.99 *(978-1-151-30124-6(8))* General Bks. LLC.

AMERICAN LITERATURE

Adler, Bill. Letters from Camp. 2011. 122p. 39.95 ***(978-1-258-08688-6(3))*** Literary Licensing, LLC.

Alexander, Will. Compression & Purity. 2011. (City Lights Spotlight Ser.). (ENG.). 100p. pap. 13.95 *(978-0-87286-541-9(X))* City Lights Bks.

American Literature Quick Reference Guide. 2007. *(978-1-934529-06-5(0))* Innovative Academic Solutions.

American Literature Workbook. 2007. *(978-1-934529-05-8(2))* Innovative Academic Solutions.

Appleman, Philip. Perfidious Proverbs & Other Poems: A Satirical Look at the Bible. 2011. (Gateway Bookshelf Ser.). (ENG.). 100p. pap. 14.00 *(978-1-61614-385-5(1))* Prometheus Bks., Pubs.

Arthur, Sarah. At the Still Point: A Literary Guide to Prayer in Ordinary Time. 2011. (ENG.). 200p. (gr. 13). pap. 16.99 *(978-1-55725-785-7(X))* Paraclete Pr., Inc.

Austenfeld, Thomas, ed. Barbara Kingsolver. 2009. (Critical Insights Ser.). 336p. lib. bdg. 85.00 *(978-1-58765-642-2(6))* Salem Pr., Inc.

Barone, Dennis. America / Trattabili. 2011. 212p. pap. 18.00 ***(978-1-59954-018-4(5))*** Bordighera Incorporated.

Baym, N. Norton Anthology American Literature 7e Course Guide. 2008. pap. *(978-0-393-92992-8(2))* Norton, W. W. & Co., Inc.

Beers, Terry. Califlora: A Literary Field Guide. 2012. pap. ***(978-1-59714-161-1(5))*** Santa Clara Univ., de Saisset Museum.

Begout, Bruce. Common Place: the American Motel. 2010. 137p. pap. 12.95 *(978-0-9796177-8-2(2))* Seismicity Editions.

Belasco, Susan & Johnson, Linck. The Bedford Anthology of American Literature 1865 Vol. 1: Beginnings to the Civil War. 2007. (ENG., Illus.). 1376p. (C). per. 64.95 *(978-0-312-48299-2(X))* Bedford/Saint Martin's.

Bello, A. Kyce. The Return of the River: Writers, Scholars, & Citizens Speak on Behalf of the Santa Fe River. 2011. pap. *(978-0-86534-781-6(6))* Sunstone Pr.

Bender, Karen E. Choice: True Stories of Birth, Contraception, Infertility, Adoption, Single Parenthood, & Abortion. de Gramont, Nina, ed. 2007. (ENG.). 350p. *(978-1-59692-063-7(7))* MacAdam/Cage Publishing, Inc.

Bercovitch, Sacvan. The Puritan Origins of the American Self: With a New Perface. 2011. (ENG.). 304p. pap. 22.00 *(978-0-300-17241-6(9))* Yale Univ. Pr.

Blackstone, Charles & Talbot, Jill, eds. The Art of Friction: Where (Non) Fictions Come Together. 2008. (ENG.). 242p. 60.00 *(978-0-292-71879-1(9))* Univ. of Texas Pr.

—The Art of Friction: Where (Non)Fictions Come Together. 2008. (ENG.). 242p. pap. 24.95 *(978-0-292-71891-3(8))* Univ. of Texas Pr.

Bowers, John. Love in Tennessee. 2009. (ENG.). 208p. pap. 18.95 *(978-1-59709-456-6(0))* Red Hen Pr.

Brown, Caroline. The Black Female Body in American Literature & Art. 2011. (Routledge Interdisciplinary Perspectives on Literature Ser.). (ENG., Illus.). 308p. (C). 125.00 *(978-0-415-89550-7(2))* Routledge.

Browne, Iain, photos by. Domo in the World. 2011. (ENG., Illus.). 32p. bds. 12.95 *(978-0-8109-9815-5(7)*, Abrams Image) Abrams.

Burgess, Gelett. Le Petit Journal des Refusées. 2009. *(978-0-89263-012-7(4))*; *(978-0-89263-013-4(2))*; *(978-0-89263-014-1(0))* Rice Univ. Pr.

Burritt, Elihu. Thoughts & Notes at Home & Abroad. 2011. (Cambridge Library Collection - Literary Studies). (ENG.). 326p. pap. 24.99 ***(978-1-108-03265-0(6))*** Cambridge Univ. Pr.

Camboni, Marina & Carosso, Andrea, eds. Translating America: The Circulation of Narratives, Commodities, & Ideas Between Italy, Europe, & the United States. 2011. (Transatlantic Aesthetics & Culture Ser.). 377p. pap. ***(978-3-0343-0395-8(5))*** Lang, Peter.

Carr. Riverine: An Anthology of Hudson Valley Writers. Carr, Laurence, ed. 2010. (Codhill Press Ser.). 314p. pap. 20.00 *(978-1-930337-32-9(9)*, Suny Pr.) State Univ. of New York Pr.

Carruth, William H. Kansas in Literature, 2 vols., Set. reprint ed. lib. bdg. 250.00 *(978-0-7222-4891-1(1))* Library Reprints, Inc.

Chevigny, Bell Gale. Doing Time: 25 Years of Prison Writing. 2011. (ENG.). 384p. pap. 17.95 *(978-1-61145-144-3(2)*, 611144, Arcade Publishing) Skyhorse Publishing Co., Inc.

Clark, John Lee, ed. Deaf American Poetry: An Anthology. 2009. (ENG.). 280p. pap. 35.00 *(978-1-56368-413-5(6))* Gallaudet Univ. Pr.

Clark, Lewis Gaylord. Knick-Knacks from an Editor's Table by L Gaylord Clark. 2006. 352p. per. 23.99 *(978-1-4255-3556-8(9))* MPublishing.

Coles, Nicholas & Zandy, Janet, eds. American Working-Class Literature: An Anthology. 2006. (ENG., Illus.). 960p. (C). per. 64.95 *(978-0-19-514456-7(2))* Oxford Univ. Pr., Inc.

Colley, Robert, et al, eds. Stone Canoe, Number 4: A Journal of Arts & Ideas from Upstate New York. 2010. (Stone Canoe Ser.). (Illus.). 327p. pap. *(978-0-9791944-3-6(1))* Syracuse Univ. Pr.

Cronin, Gloria L., et al. Encyclopedia of American Ethnic Literature, 5-Volume Set. 2009. (Encyclopedia of American Ethnic Literature Ser.). 2200p. (C). (gr. 9). 375.00 *(978-0-8160-6083-2(5))* Facts On File, Inc.

Currie, Goldie, ed. Noises from Typewriter Keys: A Literary Collection. 2011. (Offbeat Ser.). (ENG.). 84p. pap. 8.50 *(978-0-87013-988-8(6))* Michigan State Univ. Pr.

Dahlberg, Edward. Alms for Oblivion. 2009. 180p. pap. 40.00 *(978-0-8166-5738-4(6))* Univ. of Minnesota Pr.

Davenport, William H., et al. Dominant Types in British & American Literature V1: Poetry & Drama. 2011. 668p. 68.95 ***(978-1-258-07541-5(5))*** Literary Licensing, LLC.

—Dominant Types in British & American Literature V2: Essay, Biography, Fiction. 2011. 620p. 65.95 ***(978-1-258-07605-4(5))*** Literary Licensing, LLC.

Dessart, Jamie & Gambill, James Bradley, eds. The Word in the English Classroom: Best Practices of Faith Integration. 2009. pap. 24.99 *(978-0-89112-536-5(1)*, ACU Pr.) Abilene Christian Univ. Pr.

Dickstein, Morris, ed. The Great Gatsby, by F. Scott Fitzgerald. 2009. (Critical Insights Ser.). 304p. lib. bdg. 85.00 *(978-1-58765-608-8(6))* Salem Pr., Inc.

—Robert Frost. 2009. (Critical Insights Ser.). 440p. lib. bdg. 85.00 *(978-1-58765-636-1(1))* Salem Pr., Inc.

Diedrich, Maria I. Cornelia James Cannon & the Future American Race. 2011. (Illus.). 288p. pap. 28.95 *(978-1-55849-841-9(9))* Univ. of Massachusetts Pr.

—Cornelia James Cannon & the Future of the American Race. 2011. (Illus.). 288p. lib. bdg. 80.00 *(978-1-55849-840-2(0))* Univ. of Massachusetts Pr.

Drumm, Sally, ed. Milspeak: Warriors, Veterans, Family, & Friends Writing the Military Experience. 2009. 474p. pap. 25.00 *(978-0-9824416-2-6(2))* Press 53, LLC.

Eggers, Dave, ed. The Best American Nonrequired Reading 2009. 2009. (Best American Ser.). (ENG.). 432p. pap. 14.95 *(978-0-547-24160-9(7)*, Mariner Bks.) Houghton Mifflin Harcourt Trade & Reference Pubs.

Emerson, Ralph Waldo. Emerson: The Basic Writings of America's Sage. Lindeman, Eduard C., ed. 2011. 194p. 42.95 ***(978-1-258-02248-8(6))*** Literary Licensing, LLC.

Evans, Chris. Ashes of a Black Frost. 2012. (ENG.). 480p. 9.99 ***(978-1-4391-8067-9(9))*** Pocket Books.

Ewell, Alice Maude. Alice Maude Ewell's Manuscripts & Miscellaneous Writings: Facsimile Reproductions. 2008. *(978-0-8201-1559-7(2))* Scholars' Facsimiles & Reprints.

Fish, Peter, ed. California's Best: Two Centuries of Great Writing from the Golden State. 2009. 360p. pap. 18.95 *(978-1-56037-494-7(2))* Farcountry Pr.

Forgotten Bread: First-Generation Armenian American Writers. 2007. (Illus.). 481p. *(978-1-59714-069-0(4))* Heyday.

Fortier, Alcee. Louisiana Studies. 2010. 314p. pap. 30.95 *(978-1-4455-7763-0(1)*, Kent Pr.) Kent Communications, Ltd.

Fox, Paula. News from the World: Stories & Essays. 2012. (ENG.). 224p. pap. 14.95 ***(978-0-393-34234-5(4)***, 34234) Norton, W. W. & Co., Inc.

Franklin, Benjamin. Poor Richard's Almanack & Other Writings. 2012. (ENG.). 256p. pap. 9.95 ***(978-0-486-48449-5(1))*** Dover Pubns., Inc.

French, Allen. Old Concord. 2009. 200p. 22.99 *(978-1-103-00163-7(9))*; pap. 16.99 *(978-1-103-00161-3(2))* BiblioBazaar.

Fuller, Randall. Emerson's Ghosts: Literature, Politics, & the Making of Americanists. 2011. (ENG.). 240p. pap. 24.95 *(978-0-19-975201-0(X))* Oxford Univ. Pr., Inc.

Fusselman, Amy. 8: All True - Unbelievable. 2007. (ENG.). 144p. 17.00 *(978-1-58243-368-4(2)*, Counterpoint Pr.) Basic Bks. GBR. Dist: Perseus-PGW.

Gale, Kate. Los Angeles Review, Vol. 7. 2010. (ENG.). 296p. pap. 20.00 *(978-1-59709-474-0(9))* Red Hen Pr.

Gwynn, R. S. Literature: A Pocket Anthology. 3rd rev. ed. 2006. (Penguin Academics Ser.). 1376p. per. 50.20 *(978-0-321-36629-0(8))* Longman Publishing.

—Literature: A Pocket Anthology. 5th ed. 2011. (ENG.). 1376p. (C). pap. 50.00 *(978-0-205-03219-8(2)*, Prentice Hall) Prentice Hall PTR.

The Hapless Orphan: Innocent Victim of Revenge, 2 vols. reprint ed. 75.00 *(978-0-404-17260-2(1))* AMS Pr., Inc.

Harner, James L. Literary Research Guide: An Annotated Listing of Reference Sources in English Literary Studies. 5th annot. ed. 2008. (ENG.). 838p. pap. 37.50 *(978-0-87352-808-5(5))* Modern Language Assn. of America.

Harper's New Monthly Magazine December 1881 to February 1882. 2007. (ENG.). 490p. 53.95 *(978-0-548-06162-6(9))* Kessinger Publishing, LLC.

Hesperides. Heart Throbs - in Prose & Verse. 2007. 448p. per. *(978-1-4067-6686-8(0)*, Hesperides Pr.) Read Bks.

Honig, Donald. Blue & Gray: An Anthology of Great Writings on the Civil War. Honig, Donald, ed. 2011. 178p. 42.95 ***(978-1-258-00159-9(4))*** Literary Licensing, LLC.

Hopkins, David & Martindale, Charles, eds. The Oxford History of Classical Reception in English Literature: Volume 3 (1660-1790) 2012. (Oxford History of Classical Reception in English Literature Ser.). (ENG.). 776p. 185.00 ***(978-0-19-921981-0(8))*** Oxford Univ. Pr., Inc.

Jack, Zachary Michael, ed. Iowa, the Definitive Collection: Classic & contemporary readings by Iowans, for Iowans. 2009. 532p. pap. 26.95 *(978-1-888160-38-3(1)*, Tall Corn Bks.) Ice Cube Pr.

Jesse, Richard H. Missouri Literature. 2009. 260p. pap. *(978-0-217-23678-2(2))* Books LLC.

—Missouri Literature. Allen, E. A., ed. 382p. reprint ed. lib. bdg. 98.00 *(978-0-7222-0720-8(4))* Library Reprints, Inc.

—Missouri Literature. 2007. (ENG.). 396p. per. *(978-1-4067-3790-5(9))* Read Bks.

Jesse, Richard H. & Allen, Edward A., eds. Missouri Literature. 2008. 392p. 48.95 *(978-1-4365-6631-5(2))* 2007. (ENG.). 396p. per. 33.95 *(978-0-548-76153-3(1))* Kessinger Publishing, LLC.

Jones, H. Wendy. The Man & the Mountain: Life of Sydney Laurence, Alaskan Painter. 2011. 94p. 38.95 ***(978-1-258-02712-4(7))*** Literary Licensing, LLC.

Kalfopoulou, Adrianne. Passion Maps. 2009. (ENG.). 104p. pap. 17.95 *(978-1-59709-158-9(8))* Red Hen Pr.

Kay, Judith & Gelshenen, Rosemary. Adventures in Composition: Improving Writing Skills Through Literature. 2007. (ENG., Illus.). 232p. per. 24.95 *(978-0-472-03204-4(6))* Univ. of Michigan Pr.

Laine, Christine & Lacombe, Michael A., eds. On Being a Doctor 3. 2007. 366p. *(978-1-930513-88-4(7))* American College of Physicians.

Lee, Joe. Dante for Beginners. 2011. (For Beginners Ser.). (ENG., Illus.). 192p. pap. 16.99 *(978-1-934389-67-6(6)*, For Beginners) Steerforth Pr.

Link, Samuel A. Pioneers of Southern Literature Set, 2 vols. (Illus.). reprint ed. lib. bdg. 250.00 *(978-0-7222-4850-8(4))* Library Reprints, Inc.

Link, Samuel Albert. Pioneers of Southern Literature. 2008. 324p. 28.99 *(978-0-559-24550-3(5))*; pap. 29.75 *(978-0-559-24548-0(3))* BiblioBazaar.

—Pioneers of Southern Literature. 2009. 82p. pap. *(978-1-151-58772-5(9))* Books LLC.

—Pioneers of Southern Literature. 2009. 82p. pap. 14.14 *(978-1-151-71667-5(7))*; pap. 14.14 *(978-1-151-67077-9(4))* General Bks. LLC.

Lynch, Jack, ed. Benjamin Franklin. 2009. (Critical Insights Ser.). 328p. lib. bdg. 85.00 *(978-1-58765-640-8(X))* Salem Pr., Inc.

Manning, Corinne. Apartment D: Five Years of Writers in Residence. 2011. *(978-1-891885-85-3(5))* Hub City Writers Project.

Marrin, Richard B. The Retaking of America. 2008. 273p. *(978-0-7884-7251-0(8)*, Fireside Fiction); pap. 25.00 *(978-0-7884-3378-8(4))* Heritage Bks.

Marshall, J. W. Meaning a Cloud. 2008. (Field Poetry Ser.: 21). 79p. per. 15.95 *(978-0-932440-32-7(0))* Oberlin College Pr.

Martiat, François-Xavier, et al. Le Bouquin Martiat Durnez, Architectes + Frédéric Saenen, écrivain: The Book Martiat Durnez Architects + Frédéric Saenen Writer, 1 vol. 2011. (ENG & FRE., Illus.). 158p. pap. 20.00 *(978-2-9600475-8-5(3))* Centre International Pour La Ville, L'Architecture Et Le Paysage BEL. Dist: Innovative Logistics.

Martin, Benjamin Nicholas. Choice Specimens of American Literature, & Literary Reader, Being Selections from the Chief American Writers by Benj N Martin. 2006. 540p. per. 29.99 *(978-1-4255-5994-6(8))* MPublishing.

McClintock, Russell. Lincoln & the Decision for War: The Northern Response to Secession. 2008. (ENG.). 400p. 39.95 *(978-0-8078-3188-5(3))* Univ. of North Carolina Pr.

McGarrah, James, et al, eds. Southern Indiana Review. Vol. 8, No. 1. (Illus.). 146p. pap. 10.00 *(978-1-930508-00-2(X))* Vol. 8, No. 2. 121p. pap. 10.00 *(978-1-930508-01-9(8))* Univ. of Southern Indiana.

McGlothin, Victor. The Secrets of Newberry. 2010. (ENG.). 384p. pap. 13.99 *(978-0-446-17813-6(6))* Grand Central Publishing.

Meadow Brook Writing Project. In the Company of Writers 2007. 2009. 156p. pap. 14.95 *(978-1-4401-5916-9(5))* iUniverse, Inc.

Mencken, H. L. Prejudices: First Series. 2007. 252p. 29.95 *(978-1-4344-9598-3(1))*; per. 19.95 *(978-1-4344-9597-6(3))* Wildside Pr., LLC.

—Prejudices: Second Series. 2007. (ENG.). 252p. 41.95 *(978-0-548-09157-9(9))* Kessinger Publishing, LLC.

Meyer, Paul Georg: English & American Studies in German. Jahrgang 2009: [Print + Online]. 2010. (GER.). *(978-3-484-43123-2(7))* Verlag Max Niemeyer.

Mickle, Mildred R., ed. I Know Why the Caged Bird Sings, by Maya Angelou. 2009. (Critical Insights Ser.). 296p. lib. bdg. 85.00 *(978-1-58765-624-8(8))* Salem Pr., Inc.

Moser, Robert Henry & Tosta, Antonio Luciano de Andrade, eds. Luso-American Literature: Writings by Portuguese-Speaking Authors in North America. 2011. (Multi-Ethnic Literatures of the Americas (MELA) Ser.). (ENG.). 416p. (C). pap. 34.95 *(978-0-8135-5058-9(0))*; (Illus.). 79.00 *(978-0-8135-5057-2(2))* Rutgers Univ. Pr.

Nicholson, Meredith. The Hoosiers. 2009. 144p. pap. 19.99 *(978-0-217-59192-8(2))* General Bks. LLC.

—The Hoosiers. (Illus.). 296p. reprint ed. lib. bdg. 98.00 *(978-0-7222-0831-1(6))* Library Reprints, Inc.

Noy, Gary & Heide, Rick. The Illuminated Landscape: A Sierra Nevada Anthology. 2010. 352p. pap. 19.95 *(978-1-59714-128-4(3))* Heyday.

Olson, Ted, ed. CrossRoads: A Southern Culture Annual 2009. 2009. (Illus.). 300p. pap. 30.00 *(978-0-88146-095-7(8))* Mercer Univ. Pr.

Osteen, Joel. Your Best Life Begins Each Morning: Devotions to Start Every Day of the Year. 2008. (ENG.). 384p. 13.99 *(978-0-446-54509-9(0))* FaithWords.

Pizer, Donald. American Naturalism & the Jews: Garland, Norris, Dreiser, Wharton, & Cather. 2008. (ENG.). 112p. 31.00 *(978-0-252-03343-8(4))* Univ. of Illinois Pr.

Potamkin, Harry Alan. The Guardian, V1 No 1, November 1924: A Monthly Journal of Life, Art & Letters. Potamkin, Harry Alan et al, eds. 2011. 38p. 35.95 ***(978-1-258-04849-5(3))*** Literary Licensing, LLC.

Preston, Carrie J. Modernism's Mythic Pose: Gender, Genre, Solo Performance, 1 vol. 2011. (Modernist Literature & Culture Ser.). (Illus.). 384p. 49.95 *(978-0-19-976626-0(6))* Oxford Univ. Pr., Inc.

Reynier, Christine, ed. Cross-Cultural Encounters Between the Mediterranean & the English-Speaking Worlds. 2011. (Transatlantic Aesthetics & Culture Ser.). 216p. pap. *(978-3-0343-0604-1(0))* Lang, Peter.

Riley, James Whitcomb. Old-Fashioned Roses, by James Whitcomb Riley. 2006. 160p. per. 18.99 *(978-1-4255-1190-6(2))* MPublishing.

Rosenberger, Francis C. Virginia Reader: A Treasury of Writings. lib. bdg. 33.95 *(978-0-8488-2108-1(4))* Amereon LTD.

San Francisco W, Conference. More Bridges. 2006. 208p. per. 14.95 *(978-0-595-42829-8(0))* iUniverse, Inc.

Saunders, Richard. Never Been Rich: The Life & Work of a Southern Ruralist Writer, Harry Harrison Kroll. 2011. (ENG.). 264p. 42.00 ***(978-1-57233-825-8(3))*** Univ. of Tennessee Pr.
Schakel, Peter & Ridl, Jack. Approaching Literature with 2009 MLA Update: Writing, Reading, & Thinking. 2nd ed. 2010. (ENG.). 1696p. (C). pap. 57.95 *(978-0-312-54397-6(2))* Bedford/Saint Martin's.
Schakel, Peter J. & Ridl, Jack. Approaching Literature: Reading + Thinking + Writing. 3rd ed. 2012. (Illus.). xxxix, 1508p. ***(978-0-312-60698-5(2))*** Bedford/Saint Martin's.
Schilb, John & Clifford, John. Making Literature Matter: An Anthology for Readers & Writers. 5th ed. 2011. (ENG.). 1712p. (C). pap. 82.95 *(978-0-312-65354-5(9))* Bedford/Saint Martin's.
Schmuhl, Robert. In So Many More Words: Arguments & Adventures. 2nd ed. 2010. (ENG.). 288p. pap. 22.00 *(978-0-268-04134-2(2))* Univ. of Notre Dame Pr.
Scieszka, Jon. Guys Write for Guys Read: Boys' Favorite Authors Write about Being Boys. 2008. (J). (gr. 6). 16.99 *(978-0-670-01143-8(6))*; (ENG., Illus.). 272p. 11.99 *(978-0-670-01144-5(4))* Penguin Group (USA) Inc. (Viking Juvenile).
Segreti, Greg & Gilliland, Carol. Introductory American Studies Reader. rev. ed. 2011. (ENG.). 250p. pap. 59.95 *(978-0-7575-8200-4(1))* Kendall Hunt Publishing Co.
Simic, Charles. Master of Disguises. 2010. (ENG.). 96p. 22.00 *(978-0-547-39709-2(7))* Houghton Mifflin Harcourt Trade & Reference Pubs.
Smit, Teresa, et al, eds. Lit Kids: Mama Bird & the Electric Rabbit. 2007. 244p. pap. 12.95 *(978-1-934248-34-8(7))* Mill City Pr., Inc.
Spainhour, Polly L. The Color of Gray: (Living & Dying with Alzheimer's) 2011. 318p. pap. 29.95 ***(978-1-4560-9134-7(4))*** PublishAmerica, Inc.
Stewart, Carla. Chasing Lilacs. 2010. (ENG.). 304p. pap. 13.99 *(978-0-446-55655-2(6))* FaithWords.
Story, William Wetmore. Graffiti D'Italia, by W W Story. 2006. 424p. per. 26.99 *(978-1-4255-4596-3(3))* MPublishing.
Stoyanov, Metodi. Mid-Nineteenth Century British & American Nature Art. 2011. 144p. pap. ***(978-3-8454-1068-5(X))*** Lambert Academic Publishing.
Tagirova-Daley, Tetiana A. Claude McKay's Liberating Narrative: Russian & Anglophone Caribbean Literary Connection. 2012. 156p. (C). 70.95 ***(978-1-4331-1820-3(3))*** Lang, Peter Publishing, Inc.
Teegarden, George M. When I Am Dead: The Writings of George M. Teegarden. Luczak, Raymond, ed. 2007. (Gallaudet Classics Deaf Studie Ser.). (ENG.). 160p. per. 29.95 *(978-1-56368-348-0(2))* Gallaudet Univ. Pr.
Townsend, J. W. Kentucky in American Letters Set, 2 vols. reprint ed. lib. bdg. 250.00 *(978-0-7222-4941-3(1))* Library Reprints, Inc.
Unger, David. Ni Chicha, Ni Limonada. Ortiz, Hector et al, trs. from ENG. 2009. (SPA.). 212p. pap. *(978-99939-84-02-3(7))* F & G Editores.
Vail, Henry H. A History of the Mcguffey Readers. 2007. 56p. per. *(978-1-4068-3812-1(8))* Echo Library.
Victor, Metta Victoria (Fuller). Miss Slimmens' Window: And Other Papers / by Mrs. Mark Peabody [Pseud.]. 2006. 316p. per. 23.99 *(978-1-4255-3034-1(6))* MPublishing.
Wallhead, Celia M., ed. Writers of the Spanish Civil War: The Testimony of Their Auto/Biographies. 2011. (Spanish Perspectives on English & American Literature, Communication & Culture Ser.). 331p. pap. ***(978-3-0343-0696-6(2))*** Lang, Peter.
Wauchope, George Armstrong. The Writers of South Carolina. 420p. reprint ed. lib. bdg. 98.00 *(978-0-7222-4579-8(3))* Library Reprints, Inc.
Whicher, George, ed. Poetry of the New England Renaissance, 1790-1890. 2011. 504p. 58.95 ***(978-1-258-04247-9(9))*** Literary Licensing, LLC.
Wolf, Emma & Cantalupo, Barbara. Emma Wolf's Short Stories in The Smart Set. 2009. *(978-0-404-61597-0(X))* AMS Pr., Inc.

AMERICAN LITERATURE (COLLECTIONS)

Here are entered only collections from several authors. For collections of a particular period, see appropriate subdivision below, e.g. American Literature (Collections)—20th Century.

see also College Readers; German American Literature; Latin American Literature

Allen, Janet, et al. McDougal Littell Literature: Pennsylvania. 2008. (Illus.). 1303p. 78.48 *(978-0-618-94443-9(5))* Holt McDougal.
American Authors, . Gifts of Genius. 2007. 176p. pap. 19.99 *(978-1-4346-1314-1(3))* BiblioBazaar.
—Gifts of Genius. Lt. ed. 2007. (ENG.). 198p. pap. 21.99 *(978-1-4346-1366-0(6))* BiblioBazaar.
Arnold, Oren, ed. Roundup of Western Literature: An Anthology for Young Readers. 2007. (ENG.). 334p. 45.95 *(978-0-548-06627-0(2))* Kessinger Publishing, LLC.
Authors Without Borders. Loose Ends. 2010. pap. 11.95 *(978-0-7414-6071-4(8))* Infinity Publishing.
Barnes, Djuna, et al. Unmuzzled Ox Anthology, No. 15. Andre, Michael, ed. (Illus.). pap. 19.95 *(978-0-934450-08-9(0))* Unmuzzled Ox Pr.
Baughman, Rhonda K. Fusion Open Mind Open Heart Open Book. 2006. pap. 20.99 *(978-1-4257-4722-0(1))* Xlibris Corp.
Baym. Norton Anth of American Literature, Vol. A. 8th ed. 2011. (ENG.). 992p. (C). pap. 34.00 net. ***(978-0-393-93476-2(4)***, 93476) Norton, W. W. & Co., Inc.
Baym, N. Norton Anthology of American Literature 7e V A. 7th ed. 2007. (ENG.). 976p. (C). pap. 34.00 net. *(978-0-393-92739-9(3)*, 92739) Norton, W. W. & Co., Inc.
Baym, Nina. Norton Anthology of AMER Literature, Seventh Edition. 2007. pap. 29.00 *(978-0-7939-2739-5(0))*; pap. 29.00 *(978-0-7939-2740-1(4))*; pap. 29.00 *(978-0-7939-2741-8(2))*; pap. 39.00 *(978-0-7939-2743-2(9))*; pap. 29.00 *(978-0-7939-2742-5(0))* Norton, W. W. & Co., Inc.
—Norton Anthology of AMER Literature, Seventh Edition, Package 1. 2007. pap. 48.00 *(978-0-7939-2993-1(8))* Norton, W. W. & Co., Inc.
—Norton Anthology of AMER Literature, Seventh Edition, Package 2. 2007. pap. 48.00 *(978-0-7939-2994-8(6))* Norton, W. W. & Co., Inc.
Baym, Nina, ed. Norton Anthology of American Literature, 1914-1945. 7th ed. 2007. (ENG., Illus.). 960p. (C). per. 34.00 net. *(978-0-393-92742-9(3)*, 92742) Norton, W. W. & Co., Inc.
Baym, Nina, et al. Norton Anthology of American Literature, Vol. C. Gura, Philip F. et al, eds. 8th ed. 2011. (ENG.). 1232p. (C). pap. 34.00 net. ***(978-0-393-93478-6(0)***, 93478) Norton, W. W. & Co., Inc.
Belasco, Susan & Johnson, Linck. The Bedford Anthology of American Literature, Vol. 2. 2008. (ENG., Illus.). 1632p. (C). pap. 64.95 *(978-0-312-41208-1(8))* Bedford/Saint Martin's.
Bergquist, Kathie. Windy City Queer: LGBTQ Dispatches from the Third Coast. 2011. (ENG.) 168p. pap. 24.95 ***(978-0-299-28404-6(2))*** Univ. of Wisconsin Pr.
Botta, Anne C. Lynch (Anne Charlotte Lyn. The Rhode-Island Book: Selections in Prose & Verse, from the Writings of Rhode-Island Citizens. by Anne C. Lynch. 2006. 364p. per. 26.99 *(978-1-4255-3733-3(2))* MPublishing.
Callaghan, Morley. The New Yorker Stories. 2008. (Exile Classics Ser.). (ENG.). 158p. pap. 19.95 *(978-1-55096-110-2(1))* Exile Editions, Ltd. CAN. Dist: Independent Pubs. Group.
Campbell, Kathy, ed. Musings of Clay City, U. S. A. Book II. 2007. 164p. pap. 15.00 *(978-0-9777688-5-1(6))* TICO Publishing.
Catfish Stew: The Anthology of the South Carolina Writers Workshop. 2006. per. 12.00 *(978-0-9714618-3-3(X))* South Carolina Writers Workshop.
Chock, Eric & Lum, Darrell, eds. Bamboo Ridge Journal #94. 2009. 285p. pap. 18.00 *(978-0-910043-80-9(9))* Bamboo Ridge Pr.
Covert, Diane, ed. The American Standard: A Collection of Classic American Literature. 2007. 672p. pap. 38.00 net. *(978-0-9800878-0-2(5))* Bond Street Publishing, LLC.
Cuba, Nan & Robinson, Riley. Art at Our Doorstep: San Antonio Writers & Artists. 2008. (ENG., Illus.). 224p. pap. 29.95 *(978-1-59534-049-8(1))* Trinity Univ. Pr.
Cumming, Jr. Joseph B. & Cumming, Jr. Bylines: Writings from the American South, 1963-1997. 2009. 264p. pap. 24.99 *(978-1-4490-2310-2(X))*; pap. 14.99 *(978-1-4490-2309-6(6))* AuthorHouse.
Daudistel, Marcia Hatfield, ed. Literary el Paso. 2009. (SPA & ENG., Illus.). 442p. 29.50 *(978-0-87565-387-7(1))* Texas Christian Univ. Pr.
Daws, Gavan & Hymer, Bennett, eds. Honolulu Stories: Voices of the Town Through the Years: Two Centuries of Writing. 2008. 1185p. pap. 35.00 *(978-1-56647-843-4(X))*; 45.00 *(978-1-56647-851-9(0))* Mutual Publishing LLC.
Demey, Kristen B., ed. Tell Me Everything: A Literary Collection. 2007. (Offbeat Ser.). (ENG., Illus.). 148p. per. 6.50 *(978-0-87013-826-3(X))* Michigan State Univ. Pr.
Deseret Book Company Staff, contrib. by. Sharing Christmas: Stories for the Season. 2008. (Illus.). 112p. 21.95 *(978-1-59038-969-0(7))* Deseret Bk. Co.
Engelhard, Michael. Cold Flashes: Literary Snapshots of Alaska. 2010. (ENG., Illus.). 210p. pap. 21.95 *(978-1-60223-093-4(5))* Univ. of Alaska Pr.
English & American Studies in German, Jahrgang 2008. 2009. *(978-3-484-43116-8(0))* Verlag Max Niemeyer.
Finch, Robert, ed. A Place Apart: A Cape Cod Reader. 2009. (ENG.). 464p. pap. 21.95 *(978-0-88150-859-8(4)*, 150859) Countryman Pr.
Firestone Hahn, Susan. TriQuarterly 135. 2009. 256p. pap. 11.95 *(978-0-8101-5934-1(1))* Northwestern Univ. Pr.
Franklin, et al. The Norton Anthology of American Literature, Vol. 2. Krupat, Arnold et al, eds. 7th ed. 2007. (ENG.). 1808p. (C). pap. 47.00 net. *(978-0-393-93055-9(6)*, 93055) Norton, W. W. & Co., Inc.
Franklin, Wayne, et al, eds. Northon Anthology of American Literature, Vol. E. 8th ed. 2011. (ENG.). 1328p. (C). pap. 42.00 net. ***(978-0-393-93480-9(2)***, 93480) Norton, W. W. & Co., Inc.
—The Norton Anthology American Literature: Beginnings to 1865. 7th ed. 2007. (ENG.). 1312p. (C). pap. 47.00 net. *(978-0-393-93056-6(4)*, 93056) Norton, W. W. & Co., Inc.
—The Norton Anthology of American Literature. 7th ed. 2007. (ENG., Illus.). 3008p. (C). pap. 67.50 *(978-0-393-93057-3(2)*, 93057) Norton, W. W. & Co., Inc.
—The Norton Anthology of American Literature, 2 vols., Set. 7th ed. 2007. (ENG.). 1746p. (C). pap. 65.00 *(978-0-393-93058-0(0)*, 93058) Norton, W. W. & Co., Inc.
—The Norton Anthology of American Literature, 2 vols., Vol. 1, Pks. A & B. 8th ed. 2011. (ENG.). 1p. (C). pap. 54.00 net. ***(978-0-393-91309-5(0)***, 91309) Norton, W. W. & Co., Inc.
—Norton Anthology of American Literature, 3 vols. 8th ed. 2011. (ENG.). (C). Vol. C, D. E. pap. 54.00 net. ***(978-0-393-91310-1(4)***, 91310) Vol. B. 1808p. pap. 34.00 net. ***(978-0-393-93477-9(2)***, 93477) Norton, W. W. & Co., Inc.
Franklin, Wayne, et al, eds. The Norton Anthology of American Literature, Vols. A & B. 7th ed. 2007 (ENG.). 2600p. (C). pap. 54.00 net. *(978-0-393-92993-5(0)*, 92993) Norton, W. W. & Co., Inc.
Fred Weissman. The Curmudgeon Speaks. 2010. 176p. pap. 19.95 *(978-1-4269-2045-5(8))* Trafford Publishing.
GALE, Kate, ed. The Los Angeles Review No. 5. 5th ed. 2008. 192p. pap. 20.00 *(978-1-59709-148-0(0))* Red Hen Pr.
Glotfelty, Cheryll, ed. Literary Nevada: Writings from the Silver State. 2008. (Western Literature Ser.). (ENG., Illus.). 896p. 60.00 *(978-0-87417-755-8(3))*; pap. 29.95 *(978-0-87417-759-6(6))* Univ. of Nevada Pr.
Gulf Coast Writers G Staff. As It Is Written. 2006. pap. 14.95 *(978-1-934246-17-7(4))* Peppertree Pr., The.
Gura, Philip F. Norton Anthology of American Literature, Vol. D. Franklin, Wayne et al, eds. 8th ed. 2011. (ENG.). 976p. (C). pap. 34.00 net. ***(978-0-393-93479-3(9)***, 93479) Norton, W. W. & Co., Inc.
Guyol, Deborah. Elderberry Wine Vintage 2010: Writings from the Clark College Mature Learning Program. 2011. 456p. 33.58 *(978-1-4269-5276-0(7))*; pap. 23.58 *(978-1-4269-5274-6(0))* Trafford Publishing.
Henderson Writers' Group & Henderson Writers' Group, compiled by. Writer's Bloc: A Las Vegas Valley Authors' Showcase. 2006. pap. 17.97 *(978-0-9727840-6-1(3))* Mystic Pubs.
Herren, Greg & Willis, Paul, eds. Love, Bourbon Street: Reflections of New Orleans. 2006. (ENG.). 320p. 24.95 *(978-1-55583-981-9(9))* Alyson Pubns.
Hix, H. L. Lines of Inquiry. 2011. (ENG.). 141p. pap. 17.00 ***(978-0-9832944-0-5(2))*** Etruscan Pr.
Hornung, Alfred. Lexikon Amerikanische Literatur. (GER.). 366p. *(978-3-411-07701-4(8))* Bibliographisches Institut & F. A. Brockhaus AG DEU. Dist: i. b. d., Ltd.
Iowa Authors and Artists Staff. Prairie Gold. reprint ed. lib. bdg. 98.00 *(978-0-7222-4811-9(3))* Library Reprints, Inc.
Justice, William E., ed. He Flies Through the Air with the Greatest of Ease: A William Saroyan Reader. 2008. 700p. pap. 24.95 *(978-1-59714-090-4(2))* Heyday.
Kahler, Ericka, ed. Stories & Poems? We're All Forum: The Best of the Northwest Ohio Writers' Forum. 2006. v, 188p. kivar 19.95 *(978-0-9788701-0-2(7))* Northwest Ohio Writers Forum.
Klinkowitz, Jerome, et al, eds. The Norton Anthology American Literature. 7th ed. 2007. (ENG.). 2870p. (C). pap. 75.08 *(978-0-393-92994-2(9)*, 92994) Norton, W. W. & Co., Inc.
—Norton Anthology of American Literature 7e V E. 7th ed. 2007. (ENG.). 1264p. (C). pap. 42.00 net. *(978-0-393-92743-6(1)*, 92743) Norton, W. W. & Co., Inc.
Krupat, Arnold & Levine, Robert S., eds. The Norton Anthology of American Literature, Vol. B. 7th ed. 2007. (ENG.). 1760p. (C). pap. 34.00 net. *(978-0-393-92740-5(7)*, 92740) Norton, W. W. & Co., Inc.
Krupat, Arnold & Reesman, Jeanne Campbell, eds. Norton Anthology of American Literature, 1865-1914. 7th ed. 2007. (ENG., Illus.). 1248p. (C). per. 34.00 net. *(978-0-393-92741-2(5)*, 92741) Norton, W. W. & Co., Inc.
Lamb, Wally & I'll Fly Away Contributors. I'll Fly Away: Further Testimonies from the Women of York Prison. 2008. (P. S. Ser.). (ENG.). 288p. pap. 14.99 *(978-0-06-162639-5(2)*, HarperPerennial) HarperCollins Pubs.
Lauter, Paul, et al. American Literature Vol. E: Contemporary Period. 6th ed. 2009. (Heath Anthologies Ser.). (ENG.). 1424p. (C). pap. 74.95 *(978-0-547-20180-1(X))* Cengage Heinle.
Matthias, John & O'Rourke, William, eds. Notre Dame Review: The First Ten Years. 2009. (ENG.). 576p. pap. 30.00 *(978-0-268-03512-9(1))* Univ. of Notre Dame Pr.
McCord, Charline R. & Tucker, Judy H., eds. Christmas Memories from Mississippi. 2010. (ENG.). 192p. 28.00 *(978-1-60473-755-4(7))* Univ. Pr. of Mississippi.
McMichael, George & Leonard, James S. Concise Anthology of American Literature. 6th ed. 2006. pap. *(978-0-13-239490-1(1))* Pearson Education Canada.
McMichael, George, et al. Anthology of American Literature, Volume I. 10th ed. 2010. (ENG.). 2256p. (C). pap. 103.00 *(978-0-205-77939-0(5))* Longman Publishing Group.
Meyer, Paul Georg. English & American Studies in German. Jahrgang 2006: [Print + Online]. 2009. *(978-3-484-43120-1(2))* Verlag Max Niemeyer.
Morton, Lisa. A Hallowe'en Anthology: Literary & Historical Writings over the Centuries. 2008. (ENG., Illus.). 244p. per. 25.00 *(978-0-7864-3684-2(0))* McFarland & Co., Inc. Pubs.
Native American Literature Guide: Special Anthologies. 16.47 *(978-0-13-437212-9(3))* Prentice Hall PTR.
Perkins, George & Perkins, Barbara. The American Tradition in Literature. 12th ed. 2008. (ENG., (C). Illus.). 2352p. pap. 118.67 *(978-0-07-338489-4(5)*, 0073384895); Vol. 1. 2040p. pap. 115.67 *(978-0-07-723904-6(0)*, 0077239040); Vol. 2. 2160p. pap. 115.67 *(978-0-07-723905-3(9)*, 0077239059) McGraw-Hill Cos., The.
Ponikvar, John. Reading the Scarlet Letter. 2009. 72p. pap. 15.95 *(978-1-4327-2420-7(7))* Outskirts Pr., Inc.
Prentice-Hall Staff. The American Express, Grade 11. 3rd ed. tchr. ed. 431.47 *(978-0-13-722604-7(7))* Prentice Hall (Schl. Div.).
Rattray, Laura, ed. The Unpublished Writing of Edith Wharton, 2 vols. 2009. (Pickering Masters Ser.). (ENG.). 512p. 350.00 *(978-1-85196-897-8(0))* Pickering & Chatto Pubs., Ltd. GBR. Dist: Ashgate Publishing Co.
Robinson, Riley & Cuba, Nan, eds. Art at Our Doorstep: San Antonio Writers & Artists. 2008. (ENG., Illus.). 224p. 50.00 *(978-1-59534-039-9(4))* Trinity Univ. Pr.
Rogers, Mary. Dancing Naked: Memorable Encounters with Unforgettable Texans. 2008. (ENG., Illus.). 280p. 27.50 *(978-0-87565-383-9(9))* Texas Christian Univ. Pr.
Rowland, Russell. West of 98: Living & Writing the New American West. 2011. 380p. E-Book ***(978-0-292-73585-9(5))*** Univ. of Texas Pr.
Schlueter, Paul. Names & American Literature. (International Library of Names). 250p. 29.95 *(978-0-8290-1284-2(2))* Irvington Pubs.
Scott, Whitney S. Fearsome Fascinations. 2009. 170p. pap. 18.95 *(978-0-9712903-6-5(9))* Outrider Pr.
Scudder, Horace E., ed. Masterpieces of American Literature. (Granger Index Reprint Ser.). 504p. reprint ed. lib. bdg. 28.50 *(978-0-8290-0519-6(6))* Irvington Pubs.
Sedgwick, Eve Kosofsky. The Weather in Proust. Goldberg, Jonathan, ed. 2011. (Series Q Ser.). (ENG., Illus.). 240p. 84.95 ***(978-0-8223-5144-3(7))***; pap. 23.95 ***(978-0-8223-5158-0(7))*** Duke Univ. Pr.
Shigekuni, Julie, ed. Blue Mesa Review, No. 19. 2007. (ENG.). 255p. pap. 12.00 *(978-1-885290-19-9(5))* Univ. of New Mexico English Dept.
Southern Review, Set. reprint ed. lib. bdg. 1912.50 *(978-0-404-19558-8(X))* AMS Pr., Inc.
Southern Review. 2009. 472p. pap. *(978-0-217-87315-4(4))*; 470p. pap. *(978-0-217-05422-5(6))*; 530p. pap. *(978-0-217-99804-8(6))*; 488p. pap. *(978-0-217-99810-9(0))*; 410p. pap. *(978-0-217-99807-9(0))* Books LLC.
Stegner, Lynn & Rowland, Russell, eds. West Of 98: Living & Writing the New American West. 2011. (ENG., Illus.). 380p. 45.00 *(978-0-292-72343-6(1))*; pap. 21.95 *(978-0-292-72686-4(4))* Univ. of Texas Pr.
Steinberg, Nicole, ed. Forgotten Borough: Writers Come to Terms with Queens. 2011. (Excelsior Editions Ser.). (ENG.). 256p. 21.95 *(978-1-4384-3583-1(5))* State Univ. of New York Pr.
Tales & Sketches for the Fireside, by the Best American Authors Selected from Putnam's Magazine. 2006. 676p. per. 36.99 *(978-1-4255-6802-3(5))* MPublishing.
Theis, David, ed. Literary Houston. 2011. (ENG., Illus.). 544p. pap. 24.95 *(978-0-87565-440-9(1))* Texas Christian Univ. Pr.
Travalini, Billie & Brown, Fleda, eds. On the Mason-Dixon Line: An Anthology of Contemporary Delaware Writers. 2008. 280p. 37.50 *(978-0-87413-030-0(1))* Univ. of Delaware Pr.
Vallese, Joe, ed. What's Your Exit? A Literary Detour Through New Jersey. 2010. (ENG.). pap. 25.00 *(978-0-9779343-5-5(7))* Word Riot Pr.
Virginia Writers Club, Charlottesville Chapter, compiled by. The Blue Ridge Anthology: Poetry & Prose by Central Virginia Writers. 2007. per. 16.95 *(978-0-9790205-4-4(9))*, Cedar Creek Publishing.
Wattawa, Gayle, ed. Inlandia: A Literary Journey Through California's Inland Empire. 2006. (California Legacy Ser.). 433p. per. 18.95 *(978-1-59714-037-9(6))*, Heyday.
Weisberg, Jacob. The Best American Magazine Writing 2008. American Society of Magazine Editors & The American Society of Magazine Editors, eds. 2008. (ENG., Illus.). 568p. (gr. 17). pap. 16.95 *(978-0-231-14714-9(7))* Columbia Univ. Pr.
Wolff, Rebecca, ed. A Best of Fence: The First Nine Years, Volume 2, Fiction & Nonfiction, 2 vols. 2009. (ENG.). 480p. pap. 29.95 *(978-1-934200-04-9(2)*, Fence Bks.) Fence Magazine, Inc.
—A Best of Fence: The First Nine Years, Volumes 1 And 2, 2 vols. 2009. (ENG.). 960p. pap. 45.00 *(978-1-934200-30-8(1)*, Fence Bks.) Fence Magazine, Inc.
Works: A Quarterly of Writing, Vol. 1-4, No. 3. reprint ed. rng bd. 87.00 *(978-0-404-19564-9(4))* AMS Pr., Inc.
Writers of Madison County. Writers of Madison County (Montana), 2007 Anthology. 2007. (Illus.). 102p. spiral bd. 10.00 *(978-0-9797490-0-1(X))* Original Works Publishing.
Writers of Modern America, Vol. 18. Date not set. 32.95 *(978-0-8369-4809-7(2))* Ayer Co. Pubs., Inc.
Writers of the American Midwest: Anthology. 8.97 *(978-0-13-050125-7(5))* Prentice Hall PTR.
Writers of the American Midwest Guide: Special Anthologies. 16.47 *(978-0-13-050126-4(3))* Prentice Hall PTR.
Young, Liz, ed. Offbeat / 2: Only to Reappear. 2009. (ENG.). 130p. pap. 8.50 *(978-0-87013-871-3(5))* Michigan State Univ. Pr.
Young Voices of Loudon County: The Stories They Tell... the Lessons We Learn. 2006. (Young Voices of America Ser.: 1). 255p. (J). per. 12.95 *(978-0-9776613-0-5(X)*, YVLC1) Community Voice Media, LLC.

AMERICAN LITERATURE (COLLECTIONS)—COLONIAL PERIOD, CA. 1600-1775

Bauer, Ralph & Parini, Jay. Contested Nations in the Early Americas. 2008. (ENG.). 80p. (C). pap. 12.95 *(978-1-4282-6255-3(5))* Cengage Heinle.
—Empire, Science, & Economy in the Americas, Vol. 1. 2008. (ENG., Illus.). 96p. (C). pap. 12.95 *(978-1-4282-6240-9(7))* Cengage Heinle.
Drexler, Michael J. & White, Ed. Beyond Douglass: New Perspectives on Early African-American Literature. 2008. 192p. (C). pap. 25.00 *(978-0-8387-5711-6(1))*, Bucknell Univ. Pr.
Lauter, Paul, et al. Heath Anthology of American Literature, Beginnings to 1800 Vol. A. 6th ed. 2008. (Heath Anthologies Ser.). (ENG.). 1488p. (C). pap. 68.95 *(978-0-618-89799-5(2))* Wadsworth.
Merediz, Eyda M. Approaches to Teaching the Writings of Bartolomé de Las Casas. Arias, Santa, ed. 2008. (SPA & ENG.). 37.50 *(978-0-87352-944-0(8))*; pap. 19.75 *(978-0-87352-945-7(5))* Modern Language Assn. of America.
Parini, Jay & Bauer, Ralph. Between Cultures: Native American Traditions & the European Medium. 2008. (ENG., Illus.). 112p. (C). pap. 12.95 *(978-1-4282-6238-6(5))* Cengage Heinle.
—Spirituality, Church, & State in the Colonial Americas. 2008. (ENG., Illus.). 96p. (C). pap. 12.95 *(978-1-4282-6239-3(3))* Cengage Heinle.
Scanlan, Thomas J. Colonial Writing & the New World, 1583-1671: Allegories of Desire. 2006. (ENG., Illus.). 264p. pap. 53.00 *(978-0-521-03519-4(8))* Cambridge Univ. Pr.

AMERICAN LITERATURE (COLLECTIONS)—19TH CENTURY

Armstrong, Julie Buckner, ed. The Civil Rights Reader: American Literature from Jim Crow to Reconciliation. 2009. (ENG.). 392p. pap. 24.95 (978-0-8203-3225-3(9)); lib. bdg. 69.95 (978-0-8203-3181-2(3)) Univ. of Georgia Pr.

Boyd, Anne E., ed. Wielding the Pen: Writings on Authorship by American Women of the Nineteenth Century. 2009. (ENG.). 488p. (C). (gr. 13-17). 77.00 (978-0-8018-9274-5(0)); pap. 36.00 (978-0-8018-9275-2(9)) Johns Hopkins Univ. Pr.

Haile, C. M. C. M. Haile's Pardon Jones Letters: Old Southwest Humor from Antebellum Louisiana. Piacentino, Edward, ed. 2009. (Southern Literary Studies). 264p. 37.50 (978-0-8071-3437-5(6)) Louisiana State Univ. Pr.

Hansen, Ellen, ed. The New England Transcendentalists: Life of the Mind & of the Spirit. 2nd ed. 2006. (Perspectives on History Ser.). (ENG.). 44p. (YA). pap. 7.95 (978-1-932663-17-4(7)) History Compass, LLC.

Howells, William Dean. Collected Works. reprint ed. lib. bdg. 75.00 (978-0-7812-3226-5(0)) Reprint Services Co.

Ingersoll, Robert. Some Mistakes of Moses. 2007. (ENG.). 136p. per. 19.99 (978-1-59547-932-7(5)) NuVision Pubns., LLC.

Lauter, Paul, et al. The Heath Anthology of American Literature Vol. C: Late Nineteenth Century, 1865-1910. Cheung, King-Kok & Curnutt, Kirk, eds. 6th ed. 2009. (Heath Anthologies Ser.). (ENG., Illus.). 1136p. (C). pap. 74.95 (978-0-547-20166-5(4)) Wadsworth.

—Heath Anthology of American Literature Vol. B: Early Nineteenth Century, 1800-1865. 6th ed. 2008. (Heath Anthologies Ser.). (ENG.). 1792p. (C). pap. 68.95 (978-0-547-20419-2(1)) Wadsworth.

Maffly-Kipp, Laurie F. & Lofton, Kathryn. Women's Work: An Anthology of African-American Women's Historical Writings from the Era of Slavery to the Harlem Renaissance. 2010. (ENG.). 256p. pap. 19.95 (978-0-19-533199-8(0)) Oxford Univ. Pr., Inc.

McCulloch, Jeanne, et al, eds. The World Within: Writers Talk Ambition, Angst, Aesthetics, Bones, Books, Beautiful Bodies, Censorship, Cheats, Comics, Darkness, Democracy, Death, Exile, Failure, Guns, Misery, Muses, Movies, Old Boys' Network, Oprah, Outcasts, Sex, Suicide, Smoking, Strippers, Torture, Vi. 2007. (ENG., Illus.). 350p. per. 16.95 (978-0-9776989-6-7(3)) Tin Hse. Bks., LLC.

McMichael, George L., et al. Anthology of American Literature, Vol. II. 10th ed. 2010. (ENG., Illus.). 2368p. (C). pap. 102.00 (978-0-205-77936-9(0)) Longman Publishing Group.

Parini, Jay & Bendixen, Alfred. Crime, Mystery, & Detection. 2008. (ENG.). 96p. (C). pap. 12.95 (978-1-4282-6247-8(4)) Cengage Heinle.

—Imagining Gender. 2008. (ENG.). 80p. (C). pap. 12.95 (978-1-4282-6244-7(X)) Cengage Heinle.

—The Wadsworth Themes American Literature Series, 1865-1915: Immigration, Ethnicity, & Race. 2008. (ENG.). 96p. (C). pap. 12.95 (978-1-4282-6246-1(6)) Cengage Heinle.

Parini, Jay & Samuels, Shirley. Confronting Race, 1800-1865, Vol. 2. 2008. (ENG.). 80p. (C). pap. 12.95 (978-1-4282-6241-6(5)) Cengage Heinle.

Peyer, Bernd C. The Thinking Indian: Native American Writers, 1850S-1920S. 2007. 384p. pap. 65.95 (978-0-8204-8766-3(X)) Lang, Peter Publishing, Inc.

Ramsey, Jarold & Burlingame, Lori, eds. In Beauty I Walk: The Literary Roots of Modern Native American Writing. 2008. (ENG.). 395p. (C). pap. 29.95 (978-0-8263-4369-7(4)) Univ. of New Mexico Pr.

Repplier, Agnes. American Austen: The Forgotten Writing of Agnes Repplier. Lukacs, John, ed. 2009. (ENG.). 450p. 25.00 (978-1-933859-86-6(5)) ISI Bks.

Smith, Thomas Ruys, ed. Blacklegs, Card Sharps, & Confidence Men: Nineteenth-Century Mississippi River Gambling Stories. 2010. (Southern Literary Studies). 304p. 39.95 (978-0-8071-3636-2(0)) Louisiana State Univ. Pr.

Stedman, Edmund Clarence. American Anthology, 1787-1900. reprint ed. 75.00 (978-0-7812-0791-1(6)) Reprint Services Co.

Stein, Linda, et al. Literary Research & the American Realism & Naturalism Period: Strategies & Sources. 2008. (Literary Research: Strategies & Sources Ser.: 4). (ENG., Illus.). 332p. pap. 50.00 (978-0-8108-6141-1(0)) Scarecrow Pr., Inc.

Thompson, Ralph. American Literary Annuals & Gift Book 1825-1865. 2007. 192p. per. (978-1-4067-5110-9(3)) Read Bks.

Wineapple, Brenda, ed. 19th Century American Writers on Writing. 2010. (Writer's World Ser.). (ENG.). 320p. pap. 18.95 (978-1-59534-069-6(6)); lib. bdg. 60.00 (978-1-59534-068-9(8)) Trinity Univ. Pr.

AMERICAN LITERATURE (COLLECTIONS)—20TH CENTURY

Albert, Susan Wittig, et al, eds. What Wildness Is This: Women Write about the Southwest. 2007. (Southwestern Writers Collection). (ENG.). 336p. pap. 19.95 (978-0-292-71630-8(3)) Univ. of Texas Pr.

Armstrong, Julie Buckner, ed. The Civil Rights Reader: American Literature from Jim Crow to Reconciliation. 2009. (ENG.). 392p. pap. 24.95 (978-0-8203-3225-3(9)); lib. bdg. 69.95 (978-0-8203-3181-2(3)) Univ. of Georgia Pr.

Bamboo Ridge Quarterly. No. 52. pap. 4.00 (978-0-681-27911-7(7))No. 57. pap. 5.00 (978-0-681-27912-4(5)) Booklines Hawaii, Ltd.

Bartholomy, David K., ed. Open 24 Hours 2008. 2008. pap. 10.00 (978-0-9777052-2-1(6)) Brescia Writers Group.

Bartholomy, David Keith, ed. Open 24 Hours 2007. 2007. per. 10.00 (978-0-9777052-1-4(8)) Brescia Writers Group.

Bishop, John Peale & Wilson Jr., Edmund. The Undertaker's Garland. 2007. 192p. 37.95 (978-0-548-52709-2(1)); (ENG.). per. 22.95 (978-0-548-50020-0(7)) Kessinger Publishing, LLC.

Carducci, Joe. Life Against Dementia: Essays, Reviews, Interviews 1975-2011. 2012. (Illus.). per. 22.95 (978-0-9627612-2-5(2)) Redoubt Pr.

A Christmas Treasury, Volume 2: Another collection of joyful holiday Readings. 2007. pap. 5.95 (978-0-9779681-1-4(1)) Mann Media, Inc.

Cintron, Esperanza, ed. Seeds: The Literary Journals of the Sisters of Color. unabr. ed. Date not set. Vol. V. pap. (978-1-892730-00-8(6)) Vol. VIII. pap. (978-1-892730-03-9(0)) Vol. IX. pap. (978-1-892730-04-6(9)) Vol. X. pap. (978-1-892730-05-3(7)) Vol. XI. pap. (978-1-892730-06-0(5)) Vol. XII. pap. (978-1-892730-07-7(3)) Vol. XIII. pap. (978-1-892730-08-4(1)) Vol. XIV. pap. (978-1-892730-09-1(X)) Sisters of Color, The.

Cintron, Esperanza, et al, eds. Seeds: The Literary Journals of the Sisters of Color, Vol. VII. unabr. ed. Date not set. pap. 10.00 (978-1-892730-02-2(2)) Sisters of Color, The.

Csernai, Rita. Reporting Techniques in the Great Gatsby & Citizen Kane. 2008. 88p. pap. (978-3-639-00601-8(1)) VDM Verlag Dr. Mueller e.K.

DANBURY, I. I. I. Dan River Anthology 2007. 2006. 192p. per. 16.98 (978-0-89754-223-4(1)) Dan River Pr.

Danbury, I. I. I., compiled by. Dan River Anthology 2007. 2006. 192p. 39.95 (978-0-89754-224-1(X)) Dan River Pr.

Danbury, Iii, compiled by. Dan River Anthology 08. 2007. 172p. 39.95 (978-0-89754-232-6(0)) Dan River Pr.

—Dan River Anthology 2008. 2007. 172p. per. 16.95 (978-0-89754-231-9(2)) Dan River Pr.

Donnelly, Joe & Ochoa, Laurie, eds. Slake: The Los Angeles Quarterly. 2010. (ENG.). 232p. pap. 18.00 (978-0-9845635-0-0(4)) Slake Media Publishing.

Edinburgh University Press. A Historical Companion to Postcolonial Thought in English. Poddar, Prem & Johnson, David, eds. 2007. (ENG., Illus.). 544p. (gr. 17). pap. 32.50 (978-0-231-13507-8(6)) Columbia Univ. Pr.

Fisher/Woronoff, ed. Historical Dictionary of Contemporary American Theater, 1930-2010, 2 vols. 2011. (Historical Dictionaries of Literature & the Arts Ser.: 2 Volumes). (ENG.). 1002p. 175.00 (978-0-8108-5532-8(1)) Scarecrow Pr., Inc.

Grapes, Jack, ed. Onthebus Issue No. 15/16: A Literary Anthology Double. pap. 15.00 (978-0-941017-11-4(7)) Bombshelter Pr.

Hahn, Susan, ed. TriQuarterly 132. 2008. 256p. pap. 11.95 (978-0-8101-5931-0(7), TriQuarterly Bks.) Northwestern Univ. Pr.

—TriQuarterly 137. 2010. 250p. pap. 11.95 (978-0-8101-2707-4(5), TriQuarterly Bks.) Northwestern Univ. Pr.

Harmon, Kristen & Nelson, Jennifer. Deaf American Prose 1980-2010. 2012. E-Book (978-1-56368-524-8(8)) Gallaudet Univ. Pr.

Harmon, Kristen & Nelson, Jennifer, eds. Deaf American Prose: 1980-2010. 2012. (Gallaudet Deaf Literature Ser.). (ENG.). 336p. pap. 60.00 (978-1-56368-523-1(X)) Gallaudet Univ. Pr.

Harter, Christopher. An Author Index to Little Magazines of the Mimeograph Revolution, 1958-1980. 2008. (ENG.). 752p. 150.00 (978-0-8108-6113-8(5)) Scarecrow Pr., Inc.

Janette, Michele. My Viet: Vietnamese American Literature in English, 1962-Present. 2011. xxvii, 250p. 55.00 (978-0-8248-3446-3(1)); pap. 25.00 (978-0-8248-3550-7(6)) Univ. of Hawai'i Pr.

Jarrett, Vicky, ed. A Christmas Treasury: A Collection of Joyful Holiday Readings. 2006. 96p. mass mkt. 5.95 (978-0-9779681-0-7(3), Our State Magazine) Mann Media, Inc.

Kaluta, Michael Wm. The Art of Michael Wm. Kaluta. 2008. 256p. 49.99 (978-0-9801479-7-1(2)); 79.99 (978-0-9801479-8-8(0)) Desperado Publishing.

Kazmierczak, Elka, ed. & des. Art of Survival: Women, Healing, & the Arts. 1600th ed. 2006. (Illus.). 32p. 12.95 (978-0-9778478-0-8(2)) Elka Bks.

Kemal, Salim & Gaskell, Ivan, eds. Performance & Authenticity in the Arts. 2010. (Cambridge Studies in Philosophy & the Arts Ser.). (ENG.). 286p. pap. 29.99 (978-0-521-14743-9(3)) Cambridge Univ. Pr.

Kline, Lisa Williams. Only Connect: The Charlotte Writers' Club Anthology. 2007. xv, 264p. pap. (978-1-59948-087-9(5)) Main Street Rag Publishing Co.

Kuhne, Dave, et al, eds. Fifty Years of Descant: The Literary Journal of Texas Christian University. 2008. (ENG., Illus.). 256p. 26.50 (978-0-87565-348-8(0)) Texas Christian Univ. Pr.

Lauter, Paul, et al. American Literature Vol. D: Modern Period (1910-1945) 6th ed. 2009. (Heath Anthologies Ser.). (ENG.). 1184p. (C). pap. 74.95 (978-0-547-20194-8(X)) Cengage Heinle.

Maffly-Kipp, Laurie F. & Lofton, Kathryn. Women's Work: An Anthology of African-American Women's Historical Writings from the Era of Slavery to the Harlem Renaissance. 2010. (ENG.). 256p. pap. 19.95 (978-0-19-533199-8(0)) Oxford Univ. Pr., Inc.

Martz, Sandra. I Shall Wear Purple. 2nd l.t. rev. ed. 2010. (Illus.). 217p. per. 19.95 (978-1-57601-079-2(1), Papier-Mache Pr.) Moyer Bell.

Martz, Sandra, ed. I Shall Wear Purple. 4th ed. 2007. (Illus.). 204p. pap. 14.95 (978-1-57601-078-5(3), Papier-Mache Pr.) Moyer Bell.

Matuozzi, Robert & Lindsay, B. Literary Research & the American Modernist Era: Strategies & Sources. 2008. (Literary Research: Strategies & Sources Ser.). (ENG.). 186p. pap. 45.00 (978-0-8108-6116-9(X)) Scarecrow Pr., Inc.

McMichael, George L., et al. Anthology of American Literature, Vol. II. 10th ed. 2010. (ENG., Illus.). 2368p. (C). pap. 102.00 (978-0-205-77936-9(0)) Longman Publishing Group.

Musawa, narrated by. In the Spirit of We'Moon: Celebrating 30 Years. 2011. (ENG., Illus.). 255p. pap. 25.95 (978-1-890931-75-9(6)) Mother Tongue Ink.

Nel, Philip & Zipes, Jack. Tales for Little Rebels: A Collection of Radical Children's Literature. Mickenberg, Julia, ed. 2010. (ENG., Illus.). 313p. pap. 26.00 (978-0-8147-5721-5(9)) New York Univ. Pr.

New York Magazine Staff. New York Stories: Landmark Writing from Four Decades of New York Magazine. 2008. (ENG.). 624p. pap. 17.00 (978-0-8129-7992-3(3), Random Hse. Trade Paperbacks) Random House Publishing Group.

Notre Dame Review: Long Stories/Lean Poems, 1. 2007. 320p. per. 8.00 (978-1-892492-22-7(9)) Notre Dame Review.

Olivas, Daniel A., ed. Latinos in Lotusland: An Anthology of Contemporary Southern California Literature. 2008. 310p. 30.00 (978-1-931010-46-7(3)); pap. 20.00 (978-1-931010-47-4(1)) Bilingual Pr./Editorial Bilingue.

Olmsted, Robert, compiled by. 4th Annual Northwoods Anthology. 2007. 132p. 39.95 (978-0-89002-388-4(3)) Northwoods Pr.

—4th Anual Norhwoods Anthology. 2007. 136p. per. 16.95 (978-0-89002-387-7(5)) Northwoods Pr.

Olson, Charles. The Principle of Measure in Composition by Field: Projective Verse Ii. 2010. 56p. pap. 15.00 (978-0-925904-95-9(3)) Chax Pr.

Parini, Jay & Bendixen, Alfred. Crime, Mystery, & Detection. 2008. (ENG.). 96p. (C). pap. 12.95 (978-1-4282-6247-8(4)) Cengage Heinle.

—Imagining Gender. 2008. (ENG.). 80p. (C). pap. 12.95 (978-1-4282-6244-7(X)) Cengage Heinle.

—The Wadsworth Themes American Literature Series, 1865-1915: Immigration, Ethnicity, & Race. 2008. (ENG.). 96p. (C). pap. 12.95 (978-1-4282-6246-1(6)) Cengage Heinle.

Parini, Jay & Cutter, Martha. The Wadsworth Themes American Literature Series, 1910-1945. 2008. (ENG.). 112p. (C). pap. 12.95 (978-1-4282-6258-4(X)) Cengage Heinle.

Parini, Jay & Cutter, Martha J. The Making of the New Woman & the New Man. 2008. (ENG.). 96p. (C). pap. 12.95 (978-1-4282-6257-7(1)) Cengage Heinle.

—Modernism & the Literary Left Vol. IV: Class, Money & Power. 2008. (ENG.). 96p. (C). pap. 12.95 (978-1-4282-6256-0(3)) Cengage Heinle.

—Poetry & Fiction of War & Social Conflict. 2008. (ENG.). 96p. (C). pap. 12.95 (978-1-4282-6260-7(1)) Cengage Heinle.

Parini, Jay & Hart, Henry. Class Conflicts & the American Dream, Vol. V. 2008. (ENG.). 80p. (C). pap. 12.95 (978-1-4282-6250-8(4)) Cengage Heinle.

—Exploring Gender & Sexual Norms. 2008. (ENG.). 96p. (C). pap. 12.95 (978-1-4282-6252-2(0)) Cengage Heinle.

—Race & Ethnicity in the Melting Pot. 2008. (ENG.). 112p. (C). pap. 12.95 (978-1-4282-6249-2(0)) Cengage Heinle.

—Religion & Spirituality. 2008. (ENG.). 80p. (C). pap. 12.95 (978-1-4282-6254-6(7)) Cengage Heinle.

—Witnessing War. 2008. (ENG.). 96p. (C). pap. 12.95 (978-1-4282-6253-9(9)) Cengage Heinle.

Peddie, Ian. The Hunted Revolutionaries. 2009. 188p. pap. (978-3-639-13055-3(3)) VDM Verlag Dr. Mueller e.K.

Peyer, Bernd C. The Thinking Indian: Native American Writers, 1850S-1920S. 2007. 384p. pap. 65.95 (978-0-8204-8766-3(X)) Lang, Peter Publishing, Inc.

Ramsey, Jarold & Burlingame, Lori, eds. In Beauty I Walk: The Literary Roots of Modern Native American Writing. 2008. (ENG.). 395p. (C). pap. 29.95 (978-0-8263-4369-7(4)) Univ. of New Mexico Pr.

Repplier, Agnes. American Austen: The Forgotten Writing of Agnes Repplier. Lukacs, John, ed. 2009. (ENG.). 450p. 25.00 (978-1-933859-86-6(5)) ISI Bks.

Rivera, Louis Reyes & George, Bruce, eds. The Bandana Republic: A Literary Anthology by Gang Members & Their Affiliates. 2008. (ENG.). 288p. pap. 16.95 (978-1-59376-194-3(5), Soft Skull Pr.) Counterpoint LLC.

Shigekuni, Julie, ed. Blue Mesa Review, No. 18. 2006. (ENG.). 256p. per. 10.00 (978-1-885290-18-2(7)) Univ. of New Mexico Creative Writing Ctr.

Shirinian, Lorne. The Blue Heron Press Anthology: New Voices from Kingston. (978-0-920266-20-5(7)) Blue Heron Pr.

Stine, Peter, ed. The Best of Witness, 1987-2004. 2008. (ENG.). 367p. pap. 24.95 (978-0-87013-829-4(4)) Michigan State Univ. Pr.

Sweeney, Chad, ed. Days I Moved Through Ordinary Sounds: The Extraordinary Work of WritersCorps Teachers. 2009. (ENG., Illus.). 200p. pap. 17.95 (978-1-931404-10-5(0)) City Lights Foundation.

Varner, Paul. Historical Dictionary of the Beat Movement. 2012. (Historical Dictionaries of Literature & the Arts Ser.). (ENG.). 400p. 95.00 (978-0-8108-7189-2(0)) Scarecrow Pr., Inc.

Weiland, Vicki, ed. Building Bridges from Writers to Readers: The 2009 San Francisco Writers Conference Anthology. 2009. 148p. pap. 12.95 (978-1-4401-3813-3(3)) iUniverse, Inc.

Wolff, Rebecca, ed. A Best of Fence: The First Nine Years, 2 vols. 2009. (ENG.). 480p. pap. 29.95 (978-1-934200-06-3(9), Fence Bks.) Fence Magazine, Inc.

Writers, Redwood. Vintage Voices. 2008. 144p. pap. 11.95 (978-0-595-52778-6(7)) iUniverse, Inc.

AMERICAN LITERATURE (COLLECTIONS)—21ST CENTURY

Adler, Frances Payne, et al, eds. Fire & Ink: An Anthology of Social Action Writing. 2009. (ENG.). 448p. pap. 32.95 (978-0-8165-2793-9(8)) Univ. of Arizona Pr.

Albert, Susan Wittig, et al, eds. What Wildness Is This: Women Write about the Southwest. 2007. (Southwestern Writers Collection). (ENG.). 336p. pap. 19.95 (978-0-292-71630-8(3)) Univ. of Texas Pr.

Anderson, Erik. The Poetics of Trespass. 2010. 104p. pap. 12.95 (978-0-9796177-7-5(4)) Seismicity Editions.

Ang, Arlene, et al, eds. The Red Room: Writings from Press 1. 2010. 160p. pap. 16.00 (978-0-9773786-6-1(7)) Straw Gate Pr.

Bender, Karen. Choice: True Stories of Birth, Contraception, Infertility, Adoption, Single Parenthood, & Abortion. de Gramont, Nina, ed. 2007. (ENG.). 350p. per. (978-1-59692-062-0(9)) MacAdam/Cage Publishing, Inc.

Brown, Rebecca & Knecht, Mary Jane, eds. Looking Together: Writers on Art. 2009. (ENG., Illus.). 104p. pap. (978-0-295-98882-5(7)) Univ. of Washington Pr.

Burns, Michael, ed. Moon City Review, 8. 2007. pap. 5.00 (978-0-913785-07-2(5), Moon City Pr.) Department of English.

Cadle, Lanette & Cafagna, Marcus, eds. Moon City Review 2010: An Annual of Poetry, Story, Art, & Criticism. annuals 2010. (ENG., Illus.). 200p. pap. 15.95 (978-0-913785-30-0(X)) Department of English.

Calica, Lovella. Warrior Writers: Re-Making Sense: A Collection of Artwork. 2008. (Illus.). 208p. pap. (978-0-9801665-0-7(0)) Iraq Veterans Against the War.

Carducci, Joe. Life Against Dementia: Essays, Reviews, Interviews 1975-2011. 2012. (Illus.). per. 22.95 (978-0-9627612-2-5(2)) Redoubt Pr.

Caswell, David. Indiana Authors 2007 Inspiration from the Heartland. 2007. (Illus.). 220p. per. (978-0-9768052-3-6(5)) New Century Publishing, LLC.

Clarke, Jaime & Cotton, Mary, eds. No near Exit: Writers Select Their Favorite Work from Post Road Magazine. 2011. (ENG.). 332p. pap. 18.00 (978-0-9826318-4-3(7)) Dzanc Bks.

Cowser, Robert, ed. Why We're Here. 2010. xii, 219p. pap. 19.95 (978-0-912568-22-5(4)) Colgate Univ. Pr.

de Caro, Frank, ed. Folklore Muse: Poetry, Fiction, & Other Reflections by Folklorists. 2008. (ENG.). 296p. (gr. 13). 29.95 (978-0-87421-726-1(1), Utah State Univ. Pr.) Univ. Pr. of Colorado.

Eggers, Dave. The Best American Nonrequired Reading 2010. 2010. (Best American Ser.). (ENG.). 512p. pap. 14.95 (978-0-547-24163-0(1), Mariner Bks.) Houghton Mifflin Harcourt Trade & Reference Pubs.

Eggers, Dave, ed. The Best American Nonrequired Reading 2006. 2006. (Best American Ser.). (ENG., Illus.). 400p. pap. 21.95 (978-0-618-57051-5(9)) Houghton Mifflin Harcourt Trade & Reference Pubs.

—The Best American Nonrequired Reading 2007. 2007. (Best American Ser.). (ENG., Illus.). 384p. pap. 30.95 (978-0-618-90281-1(3)) Houghton Mifflin Harcourt Publishing Co.

Forrest, Emma. Damage Control: Women on the Therapists, Beauticians, & Trainers Who Navigate Their Bodies. 2007. (ENG.). 288p. per. 13.95 (978-0-06-117535-0(8), William Morrow Paperbacks) HarperCollins Pubs.

Gerard, Philip & Gerard, Jill, eds. Chautauqua: Nature & the Natural World. 2011. 264p. pap. 14.95 (978-0-9845922-4-1(5)) Publishing Laboratory at UNC Wilmington, The.

Gessner, David. Ecotone: Reimagining Place. 2007. (ENG.). 216p. per. 9.00 (978-0-9791403-5-8(8)) 2007. (ENG.). 196p. per. 9.00 (978-0-9791403-1-0(5)) 2006. 180p. per. 9.00 (978-0-9791403-0-3(7)) Publishing Laboratory at UNC Wilmington, The.

—Ecotone: Reimagining Place Vol. 3 No. 2. 2008. 224p. per. 9.00 (978-0-9791403-8-9(2)) Publishing Laboratory at UNC Wilmington, The.

Gilb, Dagoberto. Hecho en Tejas: An Anthology of Texas Mexican Literature. 2008. (Southwestern Writers Collection). (ENG., Illus.). 544p. pap. 29.95 (978-0-8263-4126-6(8)) Univ. of New Mexico Pr.

Gutkind, Lee, ed. The Best Creative Nonfiction, Vol. 3. 2009. (ENG.). 272p. pap. 16.95 (978-0-393-33025-0(7), 33025) Norton, W. W. & Co., Inc.

Henderson, Bill. Best of the Small Presses. The Pushcart Prize Editors, ed. 2010. (Pushcart Prize Ser.). (ENG.). 580p. 35.00 (978-1-888889-59-8(4), 888959); pap. 18.95 (978-1-888889-60-4(8), 888960) Pushcart Pr., The.

—Pushcart Prize XXXII: Best of the Small Presses. 2007. (Pushcart Prize: Best of the Small Presses Ser.). (ENG.). 550p. per. 16.95 (978-1-888889-46-8(2)) Pushcart Pr., The.

—The Pushcart Prize Xxxiii: Best of the Small Presses. The Pushcart Prize Editors, ed. 2008. (Pushcart Prize Ser.). (ENG.). 595p. pap. 16.95 (978-1-888889-51-2(9), 888951) Pushcart Pr., The.

—The Pushcart Prize XXXVI: Best of the Small Presses. The Pushcart Prize Editors, ed. 2011. (Pushcart Prize Ser.). (ENG.). 600p. pap. 18.95 (978-1-888889-63-5(2), 888963) Pushcart Pr., The.

Henderson, Bill & The Pushcart Prize Editors, eds. The Pushcart Prize XXXVI: Best of the Small Presses. 2011. (Pushcart Prize Ser.). (ENG.). 600p. 35.00 (978-1-888889-64-2(0), 888964) Pushcart Pr., The.

Hill, Joanna. Kaleidoscope: Lenses on Reality. Lawson, Carol S. & Lawson, Robert F., eds. 2009. (Chrysalis Readers Ser.). (ENG., Illus.). 232p. pap. 15.95 (978-0-87785-240-7(5)) Swedenborg Foundation, Inc.

Hoogestraat, Jane & Cadle, Lanette, eds. Moon City Review 2009: An Annual of Poetry, Story, Art, & Criticism. 2009. (Illus.). 150p. pap. 15.95 (978-0-913785-20-1(2), Moon City Pr.) Department of English.

Janette, Michele. My Viet: Vietnamese American Literature in English, 1962-Present. 2011. xxvii, 250p. 55.00 (978-0-8248-3446-3(1)); pap. 25.00 (978-0-8248-3550-7(6)) Univ. of Hawai'i Pr.

Jasper, Sam & Folse, Mark, eds. A Howling in the Wires: An Anthology of Writings from Postdiluvian New Orleans. 2010. 160p. 15.00 (978-0-615-38879-3(5)) Gallatin and Toulouse Pr.

Kallet, Marilyn & Byer, Kathryn Stripling. The Movable Nest: A Mother/Daughter Companion. 2007. pap. (978-1-884235-39-9(5)) Helicon 9 Editions.

Kuhne, Dave, et al, eds. Fifty Years of Descant: The Literary Journal of Texas Christian University. 2008. (ENG., Illus.). 256p. 26.50 (978-0-87565-348-8(0)) Texas Christian Univ. Pr.

Lakebay Writers. A Collection of Writing: Discovering Inspiration. 2008. (ENG.). 176p. pap. 12.95 (978-0-9822112-2-9(8)) Lakebay Writers.

Lawson, Carol. Imagine That! Breaking Through to Other Worlds. Lawson, Robert F., ed. 2007. (Chrysalis Readers Ser.). (ENG., Illus.). 192p. pap. 15.95 (978-0-87785-238-4(3)) Swedenborg Foundation, Inc.

—Passages: Timeless Voyages of Spirit. Lawson, Robert F., ed. 2006. (Chrysalis Reader Ser.: 13). (ENG., Illus.). 176p. per. 15.95 (978-0-87785-237-7(5), 325-158) Swedenborg Foundation, Inc.

Lawson, Robert F. & Lawson, Carol S., eds. It's a Deal! Dynamic Transactions. 2011. (Chrysalis Readers Ser.). (ENG., Illus.). 224p. pap. 15.95 (978-0-87785-243-8(X)) Swedenborg Foundation, Inc.

McMichael, George L., et al. Anthology of American Literature, Vol. II. 10th ed. 2010. (ENG., Illus.). 2368p. (C). pap. 102.00 (978-0-205-77936-9(0)) Longman Publishing Group.

Melissa Quintero Perez & Alexandro Medrano. My Family, My Story. 2009. 84p. pap. 10.49 (978-1-4389-5564-3(2)) AuthorHouse.

Messerli, Douglas. My Year 2003: Voice without a Voice. 2012. (ENG.). 300p. (gr. 4). pap. 15.95 (978-1-55713-418-9(9)) Green Integer.

Miller, Sean & Verma, Shveta, eds. Riffing on Strings: Creative Writing Inspired by String Theory. 2008. (Illus.). 312p. pap. 20.00 (978-0-9802114-0-5(9), Scriblerus Pr.) Banyan Institute.

Musawa, narrated by. In the Spirit of We'Moon: Celebrating 30 Years. 2011. (ENG., Illus.). 255p. pap. 25.95 (978-1-890931-75-9(6)) Mother Tongue Ink.

Nagelsen, Susan, ed. Exiled Voice, Portals of Discovery. 2008. (Illus.). 272p. 35.00 (978-0-9790130-1-0(1)) New England College Pr.

Narrative Magazine Fall 2007. 2007. 198p. pap. 14.95 (978-0-9798727-0-9(7)) Narrative Magazine.

Narrative Magazine Spring Issue 2008. 2008. 200p. pap. (978-0-9798727-3-0(1)) Narrative Magazine.

Narrative Magazine January 2008 Issue. 2008. 200p. (J). pap. (978-0-9798727-2-3(3)) Narrative Magazine.

New Century Publishing. Indiana Authors 2007 Stories from the Heartland for Children. 2007. (Illus.). 190p. per. 24.95 (978-0-9768052-5-0(1)) New Century Publishing, LLC.

New York Magazine Staff. New York Stories: Landmark Writing from Four Decades of New York Magazine. 2008. (ENG.). 624p. pap. 17.00 (978-0-8129-7992-3(3), Random Hse. Trade Paperbacks) Random House Publishing Group.

Nnoromele, Salome & Day-Lindsay, Lisa. Journeys Home: An Anthology of Contemporary African Diasporic Experience (Poems & Personal Narratives) 2009. (978-1-59221-712-0(5)); 182p. pap. (978-1-59221-713-7(3)) Africa World Pr.

O'Connell, Shaun. Boston: Voices & Visions. 2010. 384p. pap. 29.95 (978-1-55849-820-4(6)); lib. bdg. 80.00 (978-1-55849-819-8(2)) Univ. of Massachusetts Pr.

Palate, Harpur, et al. Harpur Palate. 2009. pap. 10.00 (978-1-61584-374-9(4)) Independent Pub.

Pushcart Prize Editors. Pushcart Prize XXXII: Best of the Small Presses. 2007. (Pushcart Prize: Best of the Small Presses Ser.). (ENG.). 550p. 35.00 (978-1-888889-48-2(9)) Pushcart Pr., The.

Pushcart Prize Editors, told to. Pushcart Prize XXXI: Best of the Small Presses. 2006. (Pushcart Prize: Best of the Small Presses Ser.). (ENG.). 550p. 35.00 (978-1-888889-43-7(8)); per. 16.95 (978-1-888889-44-4(6)) Pushcart Pr., The.

Rivera, Louis Reyes & George, Bruce, eds. The Bandana Republic: A Literary Anthology by Gang Members & Their Affiliates. 2008. (ENG.). 288p. pap. 16.95 (978-1-59376-194-3(5), Soft Skull Pr.) Counterpoint LLC.

Saturday Writers. Culvre River Anthology, 3 vols., Vol. III. Turner, Louella et al, eds. 2007. 171p. pap. 13.95 (978-0-937660-39-3(6)) AWOC.COM.

Sine Cera: 95 Pennies & a Nickel, Seven. 2006. 7.50 (978-0-9789581-6-9(0)) SLCC Community Writing Ctr.

Sine Cera: So They Said. 2007. per. 7.50 (978-0-9789581-7-6(9)) SLCC Community Writing Ctr.

Stewart, Christine. Freshly Squeezed: A Write Here, Write Now Anthology. 2008. 256p. (978-1-934074-32-9(2)) Apprentice Hse.

Stine, Peter, ed. The Best of Witness, 1987-2004. 2008. (ENG.). 367p. pap. 24.95 (978-0-87013-829-4(4)) Michigan State Univ. Pr.

Sweeney, Chad, ed. Days I Moved Through Ordinary Sounds: The Extraordinary Work of WritersCorps Teachers. 2009. (ENG., Illus.). 200p. pap. 17.95 (978-1-931404-10-5(0)) City Lights Foundation.

UNC Wilmington Department of Creative Writing, ed. Show & Tell: Writers on Writing, Revisited & Expanded. 6th rev. ed. 2009. 432p. pap. 19.95 (978-0-9823382-0-9(1)) Publishing Laboratory at UNC Wilmington, The.

Zaleski, Philip, ed. The Best American Spiritual Writing 2007. 2007. (Best American Ser.). (ENG.). 336p. 28.00 (978-0-618-83333-7(1)); pap. 14.00 (978-0-618-83346-7(3)) Houghton Mifflin Harcourt Trade & Reference Pubs.

—The Best Spiritual Writing 2012. 2011. (ENG.). 304p. (gr. 12). 17.00 (978-0-14-311990-5(7), Penguin (Non-Classics)) Penguin Group (USA) Inc.

18 Lies & 3 Truths. 2007. 219p. pap. 14.95 (978-0-9798727-1-6(5)) Narrative Magazine.

AMERICAN LITERATURE (SELECTIONS: EXTRACTS, ETC.)

Lowell, James Russell. Complete Writings, 16 vols., Set. Norton, Charles E., ed. reprint ed. (978-0-404-04070-3(5)) AMS Pr., Inc.

Trent, William P. Colonial Prose & Poetry. 2009. 352p. 25.99 (978-1-103-53234-6(0)); pap. 19.99 (978-1-103-53228-5(6)) BiblioBazaar.

AMERICAN LITERATURE—AFRICAN AMERICAN AUTHORS

see also Harlem Renaissance

Al-Atawneh, Adel. Who Shall Command the Skylark Not to Sing? The Poetics of Love, Hate, & Hope in the East & West. 2010. pap. 16.99 (978-1-61566-101-5(8)) Tate Publishing & Enterprises, LLC.

Archer, William. Through Afro-America. 295p. reprint ed. 98.00 (978-0-7222-9703-2(3)) Library Reprints, Inc.

—Through Afro-America. (Works of William Archer). xvi, 295p. reprint ed. 49.00 (978-0-932051-75-2(8)) Reprint Services Co.

Armstrong, Julie Buckner, ed. The Civil Rights Reader: American Literature from Jim Crow to Reconciliation. 2009. (ENG.). 392p. pap. 24.95 (978-0-8203-3225-3(9)); lib. bdg. 69.95 (978-0-8203-3181-2(3)) Univ. of Georgia Pr.

Beam, Joseph, ed. In the Life: A Black Gay Anthology. 2nd ed. 2007. (Illus.). 585p. per. 17.00 (978-0-9786251-2-2(9)) RedBone Pr.

Black, Kimberly. What Books by African American Women Were Acquired by American Academic Libraries? A Study of Institutional Legitimation, Exclusion, & Implicit Censorship. 2010. iii, 211p. (978-0-7734-3792-0(4)) Mellen, Edwin Pr., The.

Brown, Cheryl M. L. Black American Literature. 2010. 196p. pap. (978-3-639-23232-5(1)) VDM Verlag Dr. Mueller e.K.

Browne, Juanita. African American Literature. 30.00 (978-0-9638296-3-4(7)) Imani Kuumba College & Graduate Schl.

Callahan, Monique-Adelle. Between the Lines: Literary Transnationalism & African American Poetics, 1 vol. 2011. (Imagining the Americas Ser.). 208p. 74.00 (978-0-19-974306-3(1)) Oxford Univ. Pr., Inc.

Carpio, Glenda R. Laughing Fit to Kill: Black Humor in the Fictions of Slavery. 2008. (ENG., Illus.). 304p. 74.00 (978-0-19-530470-1(5)); pap. 19.95 (978-0-19-530469-5(1)) Oxford Univ. Pr., Inc.

Davidson, Adenike Marie. The Black Nation Novel: Imagining Homeplaces in Early African American Literature. 2008. (ENG.). 192p. pap. 16.95 (978-0-88378-281-1(2)) Third World Press.

Davis, Thadious. Southscapes: Geographies of Race, Region, & Literature. 2011. (New Directions in Southern Studies). (ENG., Illus.). 416p. 39.95 (978-0-8078-3521-0(8)) Univ. of North Carolina Pr.

Ferguson, SallyAnn H. Nineteenth-Century Black Women's Literary Emergence: Evolutionary Spirituality, Sexuality, & Identity: An Anthology. 2008. (African American Literature & Culture: Expanding & Exploding the Boundaries Ser.: Vol. 17). 352p. (C). 119.95 (978-1-4331-0158-8(0)); pap. 34.95 (978-1-4331-0157-1(2)) Lang, Peter Publishing, Inc.

Foster, Frances Smith. Love & Marriage in Early African America. Foster, Frances Smith, ed. 2007. (Northeastern Library of Black Literature Ser.). (ENG., Illus.). 360p. pap. 27.95 (978-1-55553-677-0(8)); lib. bdg. 65.00 (978-1-55553-676-3(X)) Univ. Pr. of New England. (Northeastern University Pr.).

Golden, Marita. It's All Love: Black Writers on Soul Mates, Family & Friends. 2009. (ENG.). 432p. pap. 16.95 (978-0-7679-1686-8(7)) Broadway Bks.

—The Word: Black Writers Talk about the Transformative Power of Reading & Writing. 2011. 224p. pap. 14.99 (978-0-7679-2991-2(8)) Broadway Bks.

Green, Malik. The Black-Print: Black America's Blueprint for Achieving Wealth, Prosperity & Respect. 2009. 188p. pap. 19.95 (978-1-4327-4386-4(4)) Outskirts Pr., Inc.

Guthrie, Dorothy Littlejohn. Integrating African American Literature in the Library & Classroom. 2011. E-Book (978-1-59884-752-9(X)) Libraries Unlimited, Inc.

Hemphill, Essex, ed. Brother to Brother: New Writings by Black Gay Men. 2nd ed. 2007. 389p. per. 17.00 (978-0-9786251-1-5(0)) RedBone Pr.

Holt Rinehart & Winston, creator. Holt African American Literature. 2009. (ENG., Illus.). 416p. (gr. 6-6). pap. 27.85 (978-0-554-00030-5(X)) Houghton Mifflin Harcourt Publishing Co.

Hughes, Langston, et al. African-American Classics: Stories & Poems from America's Earliest Black Writers, Vol. 22. 2012. 144p. (YA). pap. 17.95 (978-0-9825630-4-5(3)) Eureka Productions.

Jarrett, Gene Andrew, ed. A Companion to African American Literature. 2010. (Blackwell Companions to Literature & Culture Ser.: 121). (ENG., Illus.). 488p. 159.95 (978-1-4051-8862-3(6), Wiley-Blackwell) Wiley, John & Sons, Inc.

King, Lovalerie & Scott, Lynn Orilla, eds. James Baldwin & Toni Morrison: Comparative Critical & Theoretical Essays. 2006. (ENG.). 312p. 89.00 (978-1-4039-7073-2(4)) Palgrave Macmillan.

Knoerrich Isabel & Hammad, Lamia Khalil. U.S. Women of Color Theorize Subversion Through Cross-Genre Writing: Contemporary Perspectives on Race, Gender, Culture. 2009. 196p. pap. (978-3-639-03797-5(9)) VDM Verlag Dr. Mueller e.K.

Lamothe, Daphne. Inventing the New Negro: Narrative, Culture, & Ethnography. 2008. 240p. (C). 59.95 (978-0-8122-4093-1(6)) Univ. of Pennsylvania Pr.

Lee, A. Robert, ed. African American Writing, 5 vols. 2012. (ENG.). 1736p. (C). 1425.00 (978-0-415-68048-6(4)) Routledge.

Liggins-Hill, Patricia. Anthology African-American Literature, Vol. 2. Date not set. (C). pap. 32.76 (978-0-395-80964-8(9)) CENGAGE Learning.

—Anthology of African-American Literature, Vol. 2. Date not set. (C). 34.76 (978-0-395-80963-1(0)) CENGAGE Learning.

Maffly-Kipp, Laurie F. & Lofton, Kathryn. Women's Work: An Anthology of African-American Women's Historical Writings from the Era of Slavery to the Harlem Renaissance. 2010. (ENG.). 256p. pap. 19.95 (978-0-19-533199-8(0)) Oxford Univ. Pr., Inc.

Mars-Proietti, Laura & Hatcher, Sherry L., eds. Encyclopedia of African American Writing. 2nd rev. ed. 2009. 856p. (gr. 4-6). 135.00 (978-1-59237-291-1(0)) Grey Hse. Publishing.

Miller, R. Baxter. A Literary Criticism of Five Generations of African American Writing: The Artistry of Memory. 2008. 328p. 119.95 (978-0-7734-4966-4(3)) Mellen, Edwin Pr., The.

Mitchell, Angelyn & Taylor, Danille K., eds. The Cambridge Companion to African American Women's Literature. 2009. (Cambridge Companions to Literature Ser.). (ENG.). 336p. (C). 98.00 (978-0-521-85888-5(7)); pap. 29.99 (978-0-521-67582-6(0)) Cambridge Univ. Pr.

Mohammed, Ovey N. Trials, Tribulations, & Celebrations: Past, Present, Future. Secundy, Marion Gray, ed. 2008. 150p. pap. 19.00 (978-1-59244-917-0(4), Wipf and Stock) Wipf & Stock Pubs.

Murphy, Barbara Thrash & Murphy, Deborah. Black Authors & Illustrators of Books for Children & Young Adults: A Biographical Dictionary. Murphy, Barbara T. & Murphy, Deborah L., eds. 4th rev. ed. 2006. (Illus.). 568p. 110.00 (978-0-415-97219-2(1)) Routledge.

Murray, Rolland. Our Living Manhood: Literature, Black Power, & Masculine Ideology. 2006. 160p. (C). 49.95 (978-0-8122-3972-0(5)) Univ. of Pennsylvania Pr.

Nanda, Aparajita. Black California: A Literary Anthology. 2011. pap. (978-1-59714-146-8(1)) Santa Clara Univ., de Saisset Museum.

Nnoromele, Salome & Day-Lindsay, Lisa. Journeys Home: An Anthology of Contemporary African Diasporic Experience (Poems & Personal Narratives) 2009. (978-1-59221-712-0(5)); 182p. pap. (978-1-59221-713-7(3)) Africa World Pr.

Odhiambo, George. Faces of Christianity. 2011. 152p. pap. (978-3-8443-1652-0(3)) Lambert Academic Publishing.

Okonkwo, Christopher N. A Spirit of Dialogue: Incarnations of Ogbanje, the Born-to-Die, in African American Literature. 2008. (ENG.). 266p. 48.00 (978-1-57233-615-5(3)) Univ. of Tennessee Pr.

Parham, Marisa. Haunting & Displacement in African American Literature & Culture. 2008. (Literary Criticism & Cultural Theory Ser.). (ENG., Illus.). 162p. (C). 125.00 (978-0-415-99094-3(7)) Routledge.

Pomplun, Tom, ed. Graphic Classics Robert Louis Stevenson: Graphic Classics(r) Volume 9. 2012. (ENG., Illus.). 144p. (YA). pap. 12.95 (978-0-9825630-3-8(5), Graphic Classics) Eureka Productions.

Smith, Katharine Capshaw. Children's Literature of the Harlem Renaissance. 2006. (Blacks in the Diaspora Ser.). (ENG., Illus.). 368p. pap. 21.95 (978-0-253-21888-9(8), 0253218888) Indiana Univ. Pr.

Soto, Michael. Teaching the Harlem Renaissance: Course Design & Classroom Strategies. (African American Literature & Culture: Expanding & Exploding the Boundaries Ser.). 2008. 268p. (C). 99.95 (978-1-4331-0391-9(5)) 2007. pap. 34.95 (978-0-8204-9724-2(X)) Lang, Peter Publishing, Inc.

Stanley, Tarshia L., ed. Encyclopedia of Hip Hop Literature, 1 vol. 2008. 312p. 69.95 (978-0-313-34389-6(6), GR4389, Greenwood Pr.) Greenwood Publishing Group Inc.

Stepto, Robert B. A Home Elsewhere: Reading African-American Classics in the Age of Obama. 2010. (W. E. B. du Bois Lectures). (Illus.). 192p. 22.95 (978-0-674-05096-9(7)) Harvard Univ. Pr.

Walters, Tracey L. African American Literature & the Classicist Tradition: Black Women Writers from Wheatley to Morrison. 2007. (ENG.). 224p. 89.00 (978-0-230-60022-5(0)) Palgrave Macmillan.

Warhol, Andy. Andy Warhol: Ladies & Gentlemen. 2010. (ENG., Illus.). 80p. 30.00 (978-1-61623-717-2(1)) Skarstedt Fine Art.

Williams, Tyrone. African American Literature, 4 vols. 2008. (Masterplots Ser.). 1800p. lib. bdg. 404.00 (978-1-58765-438-1(5)) Salem Pr., Inc.

—Masterplots II. 2008. 101.00 (978-1-58765-442-8(3)); 101.00 (978-1-58765-441-1(5)); 101.00 (978-1-58765-439-8(3)); 101.00 (978-1-58765-440-4(7)) Salem Pr., Inc.

Wisker, Gina. Teaching African American Women's Writing. Knights, C. B. & Wisker, Gina, eds. 2010. (Teaching the New English Ser.). (ENG.). 224p. 95.00 (978-0-230-00346-0(X)); pap. 30.00 (978-0-230-00348-4(6)) Palgrave Macmillan.

Yenika-Agbaw, Vivian. African & African-American Children's & Adolescent Literature in the Classroom: A Critical Guide. 2011. (Black Studies & Critical Thinking Ser.). 318p. (C). 129.95 (978-1-4331-1196-9(9)) Lang, Peter Publishing, Inc.

—African & African American Children's & Adolescent Literature in the Classroom: A Critical Guide. 2011. (Black Studies & Critical Thinking Ser.). 320p. (C). pap. 32.95 (978-1-4331-1195-2(0)) Lang, Peter Publishing, Inc.

AMERICAN LITERATURE—AFRICAN AMERICAN AUTHORS—BIBLIOGRAPHY

Bader, Philip. African-American Writers. 2nd rev. ed. 2010. (A to Z of African Americans Ser.). (Illus.). 352p. (C). (gr. 9-18). 49.50 (978-0-8160-8141-7(7)) Facts On File, Inc.

Drew, Bernard A. 100 Most Popular African American Authors: Biographical Sketches & Bibliographies, 1 vol. 2006. (Popular Authors Ser.). (Illus.). 372p. 55.00 (978-1-59158-322-6(5), LU3225) Libraries Unlimited, Inc.

Guthrie, Dorothy Littlejohn. Integrating African American Literature in the Library & Classroom, 1 vol. 2011. 294p. pap. 40.00 (978-1-59884-751-2(1), A3360P) Pearson Education GBR. Dist: ABC-CLIO, LLC.

Harris-Lopez, Trudier. The Scary Mason-Dixon Line: African American Writers & the South. 2009. (Southern Literary Studies). 256p. 37.50 (978-0-8071-3395-8(7)) Louisiana State Univ. Pr.

Scally, Mary Anthony. Negro Catholic Writers 1900 - 1943: A Bio-Bibliography. 2006. pap. 21.95 (978-1-4286-5451-8(8)) Kessinger Publishing, LLC.

Smith, Henrietta M. The Coretta Scott King Awards, 1970-2009. 4th ed. 2009. (Illus.). xiii, 131p. (978-0-8389-3534-2(2)) American Library Assn.

AMERICAN LITERATURE—AFRICAN AMERICAN AUTHORS—HISTORY AND CRITICISM

Ahad, Badia Sahar. Freud Upside Down: African American Literature & Psychoanalytic Culture. 2010. (New Black Studies Ser.). (ENG., Illus.). 216p. 40.00 (978-0-252-03566-1(6)) Univ. of Illinois Pr.

Ahlin, Lena. "New Negro" in the Old World: Culture & Performance in James Weldon Johnson, Jessie Fauset, & Nella Larsen. 2006. (Lund Studies in English: Vol. 111). 111p. (C). pap. 79.50 (978-91-975158-0-1(9)) Lund Univ. Pr., Sweden SWE. Dist: Coronet Bks.

Archer, Jermaine O. Antebellum Slave Narratives: Cultural & Political Expressions of Africa. 2008. (Studies in American Popular History & Culture Ser.). (ENG.). 142p. 125.00 (978-0-415-99027-1(0)) Routledge.

Aymer, Margaret & Aymer. First Pure, Then Peaceable: Frederick Douglass Reads James. 2008. (Library of New Testament Studies, the Ser.). (ENG.). 164p. 130.00 (978-0-567-03307-9(4), T&T Clark Int'l) Continuum International Publishing Group, Ltd. GBR. Dist: National Bk. Network.

Bailey, Julius. Race Patriotism: Protest & Print Culture in the A.M.E. Church. 2012. (ENG., Illus.). 192p. 47.00 (978-1-57233-845-6(8)) Univ. of Tennessee Pr.

Baker, Houston A. I Don't Hate the South: Reflections on Faulkner, Family, & the South. 2007. (ENG.). 224p. 125.00 (978-0-19-508429-0(2)) Oxford Univ. Pr., Inc.

Basu, Biman. The Commerce of Peoples: Sadomasochism & African American Literature. 2012. (ENG.). 206p. (gr. 17). 60.00 (978-0-7391-6743-4(X)) Lexington Bks.

Bell, Bernard W. Bearing Witness to African American Literature: Validating & Valorizing Its Authority, Authenticity, & Agency. 2012. pap. 29.95 (978-0-8143-3714-1(7)); E-Book (978-0-8143-3715-8(5)) Wayne State Univ. Pr.

Black Literature Criticism: Classic & Emerging Authors since 1950, 3 vols., Set. 2nd rev. ed. 2008. (ENG.). 544p. 552.00 (978-1-4144-3170-3(8)) Cengage Gale.

Blair, Sara. Harlem Crossroads: Black Writers & the Photograph in the Twentieth Century. 2007. (ENG., Illus.). 376p. (C). 42.00 (978-0-691-13087-3(6)) Princeton Univ. Pr.

Bloom, Harold, ed. Invisible Man - Ralph Ellison, New Edition. 2nd rev. ed. 2009. (Bloom's Modern Critical Interpretations Ser.). 216p. (C). (gr. 9-18). 45.00 (978-1-60413-584-8(0), Chelsea Hse.) Facts On File, Inc.

Brooks, Wanda M. Embracing, Evaluating, & Examining African American Children's & Young Adult Literature. McNair, Jonda C., ed. 2007. (ENG., Illus.). 262p. per. 55.00 (978-0-8108-6027-8(9)) Scarecrow Pr., Inc.

Brown, Kimberly Nichele. Writing the Black Revolutionary Diva: Women's Subjectivity & the Decolonizing Text. 2010. (Blacks in the Diaspora Ser.). (ENG.). 294p. 70.00 (978-0-253-35525-6(7), 0253355257); pap. 24.95 (978-0-253-22246-6(X), 025322246X) Indiana Univ. Pr.

Brown, Lois. Encyclopedia of the Harlem Literary Renaissance: The Essential Guide to the Lives & Works of the Harlem Renaissance Writers. 2006. (Literary Movements Ser.). (Illus.). 624p. per. 21.95 (978-0-8160-6925-5(5), Checkmark Bks.) Facts On File, Inc.

Campbell, James. Syncopations: Beats, New Yorkers, & Writers in the Dark. 2008. 251p. pap. 24.95 (978-0-520-25237-0(3)) Univ. of California Pr.

Cancel, Robert & Woodhull, Winifred. African Diasporas: Ancestors, Migrations & Borders. 2008. (978-1-59221-648-2(X)); pap. (978-1-59221-649-9(8)) Africa World Pr.

Carter, Tomeiko Ashford. Powers Divine: Spiritual Autobiography & Black Women's Writing. 2008. (ENG.). 194p. pap. 36.99 (978-0-7618-4184-5(9)) Univ. Pr. of America, Inc.

Chaney, Michael A. Fugitive Vision: Slave Image & Black Identity in Antebellum Narrative. 2009. (Blacks in the Diaspora Ser.). (ENG., Illus.). 272p. pap. 19.95 (978-0-253-22108-7(0), 0253221080) Indiana Univ. Pr.

Chang, Yoonmee. Writing the Ghetto: Class, Authorship, & the Asian American Ethnic Enclave. 2011. (Mellon-ALI Ser.). (ENG., Illus.). 252p. pap. 24.95 (978-0-8135-5175-3(7)) Rutgers Univ. Pr.

Christian, Barbara. New Black Feminist Criticism, 1985-2000. Bowles, Gloria et al, eds. 2007. 272p. 35.00 (978-0-252-03180-9(6)) Univ. of Illinois Pr.

Clabough, Casey. Gayl Jones: The Language of Voice & Freedom in Her Writings. 2008. (ENG.). 216p. pap. 35.00 (978-0-7864-3379-7(5)) McFarland & Co., Inc. Pubs.

Cohen, Lara Langer & Stein, Jordan Alexander, eds. Early African American Print Culture. 2012. (Material Texts). (Illus.). 432p. (C). 55.00 (978-0-8122-4425-0(7)) Univ. of Pennsylvania Pr.

Colbert, Soyica Diggs. The African American Theatrical Body: Reception, Performance, & the Stage. 2011. (ENG., Illus.). 344p. 99.00 (978-1-107-01438-1(7)) Cambridge Univ. Pr.

Cook, William W. & Tatum, James. African American Writers & Classical Tradition. (ENG.). 464p. 2012. pap. 25.00 (978-0-226-78997-2(7)) 2010. 45.00 (978-0-226-78996-5(9)) Univ. of Chicago Pr.

Davis, Frank Marshall. Writings of Frank Marshall Davis: A Voice of the Black Press. Tidwell, John Edgar, ed. 2006. (ENG., Illus.). 221p. 45.00 (978-1-57806-921-7(1)) Univ. Pr. of Mississippi.

Dawahare, Anthony. Nationalism, Marxism, & African American Literature Between the Wars: A New Pandora's Box. 2007. (ENG.). 172p. per. 25.00 (978-1-934110-51-5(5)) Univ. Pr. of Mississippi.

Dieke, Ikenna. Allegory & Meaning: Reading African, African American, & Caribbean Literature. 2010. (ENG.). 188p. pap. 28.00 (978-0-7618-5121-9(6)) Univ. Pr. of America, Inc.

Dixon, Melvin. A Melvin Dixon Critical Reader. Joyce, Justin A. & McBride, Dwight A., eds. 2006. (ENG.). 159p. 45.00 *(978-1-57806-866-1(5))* Univ. Pr. of Mississippi.

Dodson, Howard & Palmer, Colin, eds. Cultural Life. 2007. (Schomburg Studies on the Black Experience). (ENG., Illus.). 395p. per. 19.95 *(978-0-87013-808-9(1))* Michigan State Univ. Pr.

Dolinar, Brian. The Black Cultural Front: Black Writers & Artists of the Depression Generation. 2012. (Margaret Walker Alexander Series in African American Studies). (ENG.). 288p. 60.00 ***(978-1-61703-269-1(7))*** Univ. Pr. of Mississippi.

Douglas, Robert L. Resistance, Insurgence, & Identity: The Art of Mari Evans, Nelson Stevens, & the Black Arts Movement. 2008. *(978-1-59221-564-5(5))*; 376p. pap. *(978-1-59221-565-2(3))* Africa World Pr.

Drexler, Michael J. & White, Ed. Beyond Douglass: New Perspectives on Early African-American Literature. 2008. 192p. (C). pap. 25.00 *(978-0-8387-5711-6(1))* Bucknell Univ. Pr.

Edwards, Erica R. Black Charisma: Fictions of Political Leadership. 2012. (Difference Incorporated Ser.). (Illus.). 288p. 75.00 ***(978-0-8166-7545-6(7))*** Univ. of Minnesota Pr.

—Charisma & the Fictions of Black Leadership. 2012. (Difference Incorporated Ser.). (Illus.). 288p. pap. 25.00 ***(978-0-8166-7546-3(5))*** Univ. of Minnesota Pr.

Elizabeth & Young, Elizabeth. Black Frankenstein: The Making of an American Metaphor. 2008. (ENG.). 336p. (C). pap. 24.00 *(978-0-8147-9716-7(4))* New York Univ. Pr.

Ernest, John. Chaotic Justice: Rethinking African American Literary History. 2009. (ENG.). 336p. 62.95 *(978-0-8078-3337-7(1))*; pap. 23.95 *(978-0-8078-5983-4(4))* Univ. of North Carolina Pr.

Fisher, Maisha. Black Literate Lives: Historical & Contemporary Perspectives. 2008. (Critical Social Thought Ser.). (Illus.). XXII, 178p. 135.00 *(978-0-415-95864-6(4))* Routledge.

Foreman, P. Gabrielle. Activist Sentiments: Reading Black Women in the Nineteenth Century. 2009. (New Black Studies Ser.). (ENG., Illus.). 280p. 75.00 *(978-0-252-03474-9(0))*; pap. 25.00 *(978-0-252-07664-0(8))* Univ. of Illinois Pr.

Franco, Dean J. Ethnic American Literature: Comparing Chicano, Jewish, & African American Writing. 2006. (ENG.). 224p. (gr. 17). lib. bdg. 49.50 *(978-0-8139-2559-2(2))*; per. 19.50 *(978-0-8139-2560-8(6))* Univ. Pr. of Virginia.

Friedel, Tania. Racial Discourse & Cosmopolitanism in Twentieth-Century African American Writing. (Studies in African American History & Culture Ser.). (ENG.). 214p. 2012. pap. 42.95 ***(978-0-415-54308-8(8))*** 2007. 133.00 *(978-0-415-96355-8(9)*, 0415963559) Routledge.

Garcia, Jay. Psychology Comes to Harlem: Rethinking the Race Question in Twentieth-Century America. 2012. (New Studies in American Intellectual & Cultural History Ser.). (ENG.). 232p. (gr. 17). 50.00 ***(978-1-4214-0519-3(9))*** Johns Hopkins Univ. Pr.

Gardner, Eric. Unexpected Places: Relocating Nineteenth-Century African American Literature. (Margaret Walker Alexander Series in African American Studies). (ENG.). 272p. 2011. pap. 30.00 ***(978-1-61703-211-0(5))*** 2009. 50.00 *(978-1-60473-283-2(0))* Univ. Pr. of Mississippi.

Gates, Henry Louis, Jr. The Henry Louis Gates, Jr. Reader. Wolf, Abby De, ed. 2012. (ENG.). 656p. (gr. 9). 29.99 ***(978-0-465-02831-3(4))*** Basic Bks.

Gates, Henry Louis, Jr. Signifying Monkey: A Theory of African American Literary Criticism. 2010. (ENG., Illus.). 336p. pap. 19.95 *(978-0-19-513647-0(0))* Oxford Univ. Pr., Inc.

Gates, Henry Louis, Jr. & Jarrett, Gene Andrew. The New Negro: Readings on Race, Representation, & African American Culture, 1892-1938. Gates, Henry Louis, Jr. & Jarrett, Gene Andrew, eds. 2007. (Illus.). 591p. 75.00 *(978-0-691-12651-7(8))*; (ENG.). 608p. (C). pap. 35.00 *(978-0-691-12652-4(6))* Princeton Univ. Pr.

Gayle, Addison, Jr. The Addison Gayle Jr. Reader. Norment, Nathaniel, Jr., ed. 2009. (ENG., Illus.). 504p. pap. 37.00 *(978-0-252-07610-7(9))* Univ. of Illinois Pr.

Gayle, Addison, Jr. & Gayle, Addison. The Addison Gayle Jr. Reader. Norment, Nathaniel, Jr. & Norment, Nathaniel, eds. 2009. (ENG., Illus.). 504p. 78.00 *(978-0-252-03408-4(2))* Univ. of Illinois Pr.

Gerstner, David A. Queer Pollen: White Seduction, Black Male Homosexuality, & the Cinematic. 2011. (New Black Studies Ser.). (ENG., Illus.). 216p. 80.00 *(978-0-252-03590-6(9))*; pap. 25.00 *(978-0-252-07787-6(3))* Univ. of Illinois Pr.

Goyal, Yogita. Romance, Diaspora, & Black Atlantic Literature. 2010. (Cambridge Studies in American Literature & Culture Ser.). (ENG.). 288p. 89.00 *(978-0-521-76359-2(2))* Cambridge Univ. Pr.

Grassian, Daniel. Writing the Future of Black America: Literature of the Hip-Hop Generation. 2009. 208p. *(978-1-57003-781-8(7))* Univ. of South Carolina Pr.

Green, Tara T., ed. From the Plantation to the Prison: African American Confinement Literature. 2008. (Voices of the African Diaspora Ser.). 176p. 35.00 *(978-0-88146-090-2(7))* Mercer Univ. Pr.

Greene, Brenda M. The African Presence & Influence on the Cultures of the Americas. 2010. 195p. *(978-1-4438-2216-9(7))* Cambridge Scholors Pub.

Greene, Brenda M. & Beauford, Fred, eds. Meditations & Ascensions: Black Writers on Writing. 2008. 204p. pap. 18.95 *(978-0-88378-296-5(0))* Third World Press.

Greenidge-Copprue, Delano. At the Crossroads. 2008. 52p. pap. *(978-3-639-08104-6(8))* VDM Verlag Dr. Mueller e.K.

Griffiths, Jennifer L. Traumatic Possessions: The Body & Memory in African American Women's Writing & Performance. 2010. (ENG.). 144p. (C). (gr. 13-17). pap. 19.50 *(978-0-8139-2884-5(2))*; (gr. 17). 39.50 *(978-0-8139-2883-8(4))* Univ. Pr. of Virginia.

Gruesser, Wallinger. Loopholes & Retreats: African American Writers & the Nineteenth Century. Gruesser, John & Wallinger, Hanna, eds. 2009. (ENG.). 208p. pap. 44.95 *(978-3-8258-1892-0(6))* Lit Verlag DEU. Dist: Transaction Pubs.

Hakutani, Yoshinobu. Cross-Cultural Visions in African American Literature: West Meets East. Hakutani, Yoshinobu, ed. 2011. (ENG.). 242p. 85.00 *(978-0-230-11341-1(9))* Palgrave Macmillan.

—Cross-Cultural Visions in African American Modernism: From Spatial Narrative to Jazz Haiku. 2006. 251p. 69.95 *(978-0-8142-1030-7(9))*; ix, 251p. cd-rom 9.95 *(978-0-8142-9107-8(4))* Ohio State Univ. Pr.

Hall, Stephen G. A Faithful Account of the Race: African American Historical Writing in Nineteenth-Century America. 2009. (John Hope Franklin Series in African American History & Culture Ser.). (ENG.). 352p. 69.95 *(978-0-8078-3305-6(3))*; pap. 23.95 *(978-0-8078-5967-4(2))* Univ. of North Carolina Pr.

Harris-Lopez, Trudier. The Scary Mason-Dixon Line: African American Writers & the South. 2009. *(978-0-8018-3395-3(7))* Louisiana State Univ. Pr.

Harris, Norman. Connecting Times: The Sixties in Afro-American Fiction. 2007. (ENG.). 197p. pap. 25.00 *(978-1-934110-59-1(0))* Univ. Pr. of Mississippi.

Hawkins, Alfonso. Jazz Trope: A Theory of African American Literary & Vernacular Culture. 2008. (African American Cultural Theory Ser.). (ENG.). 270p. pap. 55.00 *(978-0-8108-6126-8(7))* Scarecrow Pr., Inc.

Hendrick, Veronica C. Servants, Slaves, & Savages: Reflections of Law in American Literature. 2012. pap. ***(978-1-59460-442-3(8))*** Carolina Academic Pr.

Holloway, Karla F. C. Bookmarks: Reading in Black & White. 2008. (ENG.). 240p. pap. 19.95 *(978-0-8135-4351-2(7))* Rutgers Univ. Pr.

—BookMarks: Reading in Black & White. 2006. (ENG., Illus.). 240p. 24.95 *(978-0-8135-3907-2(2))* Rutgers Univ. Pr.

Holmes, David G. Revisiting Racialized Voice: African American Ethos in Language & Literature. 2007. (ENG.). 144p. per. 30.00 *(978-0-8093-2767-6(8))* Southern Illinois Univ. Pr.

Holmes, Linda Janet & Wall, Cheryl A., eds. Savoring the Salt: The Legacy of Toni Cade Bambara. 2007. (ENG., Illus.). 320p. 81.50 *(978-1-59213-624-7(9))*; per. 26.95 *(978-1-59213-625-4(7))* Temple Univ. Pr.

Horton-Stallings, LaMonda. Mutha Is Half a Word: Intersections of Folklore, Vernacular, Myth, & Queerness in Black Female Literature. 2007. (Black Performance & Cultural Criticism Ser.). cd-rom 9.95 *(978-0-8142-9135-1(X))* Ohio State Univ. Pr.

Hutchinson, George, ed. The Cambridge Companion to the Harlem Renaissance. 2007. (Cambridge Companions to Literature Ser.). (ENG.). 296p. per. 34.00 *(978-0-521-67368-6(2))* Cambridge Univ. Pr.

Jackson, Lawrence Patrick. The Indignant Generation: A Narrative History of African American Writers & Critics, 1934-1960. 2010. (ENG., Illus.). 608p. (C). 35.00 *(978-0-691-14135-0(5))* Princeton Univ. Pr.

James, Jennifer C. A Freedom Bought with Blood: African American War Literature from the Civil War to World War II. 2007. (ENG., Illus.). 384p. 73.95 *(978-0-8078-3116-8(6))*; per. 27.95 *(978-0-8078-5807-3(2))* Univ. of North Carolina Pr.

Japtok, Martin. Authentic Blackness/ Real Blackness: Essays on the Meaning of Blackness in Culture & Literature (CB) 2011. (C). 129.95 *(978-1-4331-1509-7(3))* Lang, Peter Publishing, Inc.

—Authentic Blackness/ Real Blackness: Essays on the Meaning of Blackness in Literature & Culture. 2011. (C). pap. 34.95 *(978-1-4331-1508-0(5))* Lang, Peter Publishing, Inc.

Jarrett, Gene. Representing the Race: A New Political History of African American Literature. 2011. (ENG.). 280p. 70.00 *(978-0-8147-4338-6(2))*; pap. 22.00 *(978-0-8147-4339-3(0))* New York Univ. Pr.

Jarrett, Gene Andrew. Deans & Truants: Race & Realism in African American Literature. 2006. (Illus.). 232p. (C). 55.00 *(978-0-8122-3973-7(3))* Univ. of Pennsylvania Pr.

—Representing the Race: A New Political History of African American Literature. 2011. 256p. E-Book *(978-0-8147-4340-9(4))* New York Univ. Pr.

Johnson, Sherita & Johnson, Sherita L. Black Women in New South Literature & Culture. 2009. (Studies in American Popular History & Culture Ser.). (ENG., Illus.). 172p. 125.00 *(978-0-415-99220-6(6))* Routledge.

Joyce, Justin A. & McBride, Dwight A., eds. A Melvin Dixon Critical Reader. 2010. (ENG.). 190p. pap. 25.00 *(978-1-60473-863-6(4))* Univ. Pr. of Mississippi.

Kent, Alicia A. & Kent, Alicia. African, Native, & Jewish American Literature & the Reshaping of Modernism. 2007. (ENG., Illus.). 240p. 84.00 *(978-1-4039-7797-7(6))* Palgrave Macmillan.

King, Lovalerie. Race, Theft, & Ethics: Property Matters in African American Literature. 2007. (Southern Literary Studies). (Illus.). 187p. 35.00 *(978-0-8071-3257-9(8))* Louisiana State Univ. Pr.

King, Lovalerie & Moody-Turner, Shirley, eds. Contemporary African American Literature: The Living Canon. 2012. (Blacks in the Diaspora Ser.). (ENG.). 336p. pap. 30.00 ***(978-0-253-00626-4(0)***, 0253006260); (Illus.). 85.00 ***(978-0-253-00625-7(2)***, 0253006252) Indiana Univ. Pr.

King, Lovalerie & Selzer, Linda F., eds. New Essays on the African American Novel: From Hurston & Ellison to Morrison & Whitehead. 2008. (ENG.). 292p. 95.00 *(978-0-230-60327-1(0))* Palgrave Macmillan.

Knadler, Stephen & Knadler, Stephen P. Remapping Citizenship & the Nation in African-American Literature. 2009. (Routledge Transnational Perspectives on American Literature Ser.). (ENG.). 248p. (C). 125.00 *(978-0-415-99631-0(7))* Routledge.

Kramer, Victor A., ed. Georgia State Literary Studies, 12 vols. *(978-0-404-63200-7(9))* AMS Pr., Inc.

Krstovic, Jelena O. Black Literature Criticism: Classic & Emerging Authors since 1950, 3 vols. 2008. (Illus.). *(978-1-4144-3173-4(2))*; *(978-1-4144-3172-7(4))*; *(978-1-4144-3171-0(6))* Cengage Gale.

Lackey, Michael. African American Atheists & Political Liberation: A Study of the Sociocultural Dynamics of Faith. 2007. (History of African-American Religions Ser.). (ENG., Illus.). 192p. 59.95 *(978-0-8130-3035-7(8))* Univ. Pr. of Florida.

—African American Atheists & Political Liberation: A Study of the Sociocultural Dynamics of Faith. 2008. (History of African-American Religions Ser.). (ENG., Illus.). 192p. pap. 29.95 *(978-0-8130-3318-1(7))* Univ. Pr. of Florida.

Langley, April C. E. The Black Aesthetic Unbound: Theorizing the Dilemma of Eighteenth-Century African American Literature. 2008. (ENG.). 63.95 *(978-0-8142-1077-2(5))*; cd-rom 14.95 *(978-0-8142-9157-3(0))* Ohio State Univ. Pr.

Lee, Julia. Interracial Encounters: Reciprocal Representations in African & Asian American Literatures, 1896-1937. 2011. (ENG.). 228p. 75.00 ***(978-0-8147-5255-5(1))***; pap. 23.00 ***(978-0-8147-5256-2(X))*** New York Univ. Pr.

Lee, Julia H. Interracial Encounters: Reciprocal Representations in African American & Asian American Literatures, 1896-1937. 2011. E-Book ***(978-0-8147-5328-6(0))***; E-Book ***(978-0-8147-5257-9(8))*** New York Univ. Pr.

A Legacy of African American Literature: 2006. 2006. per. 9.95 *(978-0-9786253-0-6(7))* Writer's Block Publishing Co., The.

Lester, Neal A. Once upon a Time in a Different World: Issues & Ideas in African American Children's Literature. 2007. (Children's Literature & Culture Ser.). 304p. 131.00 *(978-0-415-98019-7(4))* Routledge.

Levecq, Christine. Slavery & Sentiment: The Politics of Feeling in Black Atlantic Antislavery Writing, 1770-1850. 2008. (Becoming Modern: New Nineteenth-Century Studies). (ENG.). 324p. lib. bdg. 35.00 *(978-1-58465-734-7(0)*, University of New Hampshire Press) Univ. Pr. of New England.

Lewis, Leslie W. Telling Narratives: Secrets in African American Literature. 2007. (Illus.). 232p. 42.00 *(978-0-252-03211-0(X))* Univ. of Illinois Pr.

Li, Stephanie. Something Akin to Freedom: The Choice of Bondage in Narratives by African American Women. 2011. 172p. pap. 23.95 *(978-1-4384-2970-0(3)*, Suny Pr.) 2010. 160p. 60.00 *(978-1-4384-2971-7(1))* State Univ. of New York Pr.

Lock, Graham & Murray, David, eds. Thriving on a Riff: Jazz & Blues Influences in African American Literature & Film. 2009. (ENG., Illus.). 288p. 99.00 *(978-0-19-533702-0(6))*; pap. 24.95 *(978-0-19-533709-9(3))* Oxford Univ. Pr., Inc.

Locke, Alain LeRoy. The Works of Alain Locke, 1 vol. Molesworth, Charles, ed. 2012. (Collected Black Writings). 624p. 45.00 ***(978-0-19-979504-8(5))*** Oxford Univ. Pr., Inc.

Lockridge, Aisha Damali. Tipping on a Tight Rope: Divas in African American Literature. 2012. (C). pap. 89.95 ***(978-1-4331-0575-3(6))*** Lang, Peter Publishing, Inc.

Major, Clarence. The Dark & the Feeling. 12.95 *(978-0-89388-119-1(8))* Okpaku Communications Corp.

May, Cedrick. Evangelism & Resistance in the Black Atlantic, 1760-1835. 2008. (ENG.). 168p. 39.95 *(978-0-8203-2798-3(0))* Univ. of Georgia Pr.

Mays, Benjamin E. The Negro's God. 2010. 282p. pap. 31.00 *(978-1-60899-777-0(4)*, Wipf and Stock) Wipf & Stock Pubs.

M'Baye, Babacar. The Trickster Comes West: Pan-African Influence in Early Black Diasporan Narratives. (ENG.). 272p. 2011. pap. 30.00 ***(978-1-61703-210-3(7))*** 2009. 50.00 *(978-1-60473-233-7(4))* Univ. Pr. of Mississippi.

Miller, R. Baxter. A Literary Criticism of Five Generations of African American Writing: The Artistry of Memory. 2008. 328p. 119.95 *(978-0-7734-4966-4(3))* Mellen, Edwin Pr., The.

Miller, R. Baxter. On the Ruins of Modernity: New Chicago Renaissance from Wright to Kent. 2011. pap. ***(978-1-86335-969-6(9))*** Common Ground Publishing Pty, Ltd.

Mitchell, Verner D. & Davis, Cynthia. Literary Sisters: Dorothy West & Her Circle, a Biography of the Harlem Renaissance. 2011. (ENG.). 216p. (C). pap. 24.95 *(978-0-8135-5146-3(3))*; (Illus.). 208p. 72.00 *(978-0-8135-5145-6(5))* Rutgers Univ. Pr.

Moses, Sibyl E. African American Women Writers in New Jersey, 1836-2000: A Biographical Dictionary & Bibliographic Guide. 2006. (ENG., Illus.). 256p. per. 29.95 *(978-0-8135-4019-1(4))* Rutgers Univ. Pr.

Muyumba, Walton M. The Shadow & the Act: Black Intellectual Practice, Jazz Improvisation, & Philosophical Pragmatism. 2009. (ENG.). 232p. 48.00 *(978-0-226-55423-5(6))*; pap. 18.00 *(978-0-226-55424-2(4))* Univ. of Chicago Pr.

Norman, Brian. Neo-Segregation Narratives: Jim Crow in Post-Civil Rights American Literature. 2010. (ENG., Illus.). 212p. 59.95 *(978-0-8203-3596-4(7))*; pap. 24.95 *(978-0-8203-3597-1(5))* Univ. of Georgia Pr.

—Representing Segregation: Toward an Aesthetics of Living Jim Crow, & Other Forms of Racial Division. Williams, Piper Kendrix, ed. 2010. (Illus.). 320p. 80.00 *(978-1-4384-3033-1(7))*; pap. 29.95 *(978-1-4384-3032-4(9))* State Univ. of New York Pr.

Omry, Keren. Cross-Rhythms: Jazz Aesthetics in African-American Literature. 2011. (ENG.). 196p. pap. 44.95 ***(978-1-4411-0295-9(7))*** Continuum International Publishing Group, Ltd. GBR. Dist: National Bk. Network.

Omry, Keren & Omry. Cross-Rhythms: Jazz Aesthetics in African-American Literature. 2009. (Continuum Literary Studies). (ENG.). 196p. 130.00 *(978-0-8264-9743-7(8))* Continuum International Publishing Group, Ltd. GBR. Dist: National Bk. Network.

Opoku-Agyemang, Naana Jane, et al. Africa & Trans-Atlantic Memories: Literary & Aesthetic Manifestations of Diaspora & History. 2008. 496p. *(978-1-59221-633-8(1))*; pap. *(978-1-59221-632-1(3))* Africa World Pr.

Page, Yolanda Williams. Icons of African American Literature: The Black Literary World. 2011. E-Book ***(978-0-313-35204-1(6)***, Greenwood Pr.) Greenwood Publishing Group, Inc.

Page, Yolanda Williams, ed. Icons of African American Literature: The Black Literary World, 1 vol. 2011. (Greenwood Icons Ser.). (Illus.). 519p. 100.00 *(978-0-313-35203-4(8)*, GR5203) Greenwood Publishing Group, Inc.

Pinckney, Darryl. Sold & Gone: African American Literature & U. S. Society. 2007. 320p. 26.00 *(978-0-374-28188-5(2))* Farrar, Straus & Giroux.

Polyßk, Mariann. Isolation. 2008. 56p. pap. *(978-3-639-02089-2(8))* VDM Verlag Dr. Mueller e.K.

Porter, Eric. The Problem of the Future World: W. E. B. du Bois & the Race Concept at Midcentury. 2010. (ENG.). 256p. 84.95 *(978-0-8223-4812-2(8))*; pap. 23.95 *(978-0-8223-4808-5(X))* Duke Univ. Pr.

Quashie, Kevin Everod. The Sovereignty of Quiet: Beyond Resistance in Black Culture. 2012. (ENG.). 200p. (C). pap. 24.95 ***(978-0-8135-5310-8(5))***; E-Book ***(978-0-8135-5311-5(3))***; (ENG.). 200p. (C). 72.00 ***(978-0-8135-5309-2(1))*** Rutgers Univ. Pr.

Rankine, Patrice D. Ulysses in Black: Ralph Ellison, Classicism, & African American Literature. 2008. (Wisconsin Studies in Classics Ser.). (ENG.). 272p. pap. 24.95 *(978-0-299-22004-4(4))* Univ. of Wisconsin Pr.

Redding, Jay S. To Make a Poet Black. 8.00 *(978-0-405-18495-6(6))* Ayer Co. Pubs., Inc.

Reddy, Chandan. Freedom with Violence: Race, Sexuality, & the US State. 2011. (Perverse Modernities Ser.). (ENG.). 320p. 84.95 *(978-0-8223-5091-0(2))*; pap. 23.95 *(978-0-8223-5105-4(6))* Duke Univ. Pr.

Retman, Sonnet H. Real Folks: Race & Genre in the Great Depression. 2011. (ENG., Illus.). 336p. 89.95 *(978-0-8223-4925-9(6))*; pap. 24.95 *(978-0-8223-4944-0(2))* Duke Univ. Pr.

Rountree, Wendy. The Boys Club: Male Protagonists in Contemporary African American Young Adult Literature. 2011. 134p. (C). 67.95 *(978-1-4331-0574-6(8))* Lang, Peter Publishing, Inc.

Ruffin, Kimberly N. Black on Earth: African American Ecoliterary Traditions. 2010. (ENG., Illus.). 192p. 59.95 *(978-0-8203-2856-0(1))*; pap. 22.95 *(978-0-8203-3720-3(X))* Univ. of Georgia Pr.

Russell, Heather. Legba's Crossing: Narratology in the African Atlantic. (ENG.). 216p. 2011. pap. 24.95 *(978-0-8203-3879-8(6))* 2009. 44.95 *(978-0-8203-2867-6(7))* Univ. of Georgia Pr.

Russell, Heather & Bassard, Katherine Clay. Transforming Scriptures: African American Women Writers & the Bible. 2010. (ENG.). 180p. 44.95 *(978-0-8203-3090-7(6))* Univ. of Georgia Pr.

Sachs, Wulf. Black Hamlet. 2008. 280p. *(978-1-4437-2469-2(6))* 2006. (ENG.). 276p. per. *(978-1-4067-3058-6(0))* Read Bks. (Hesperides Pr.).

Scruggs, Charles & Holcomb, Gary Edward. Hemingway & the Black Renaissance. 2012. (ENG.). ***(978-0-8142-1177-9(1))***; 296p. cd-rom 14.95 ***(978-0-8142-9278-5(X))*** Ohio State Univ. Pr.

Shields, John C. Phillis Wheatley & the Romantics. 2010. (ENG.). 34.95 *(978-1-57233-705-3(2))* Univ. of Tennessee Pr.

—Phillis Wheatley's Poetics of Liberation: Backgrounds & Contexts. 2008. (ENG.). 37.95 *(978-1-57233-499-1(1))* Univ. of Tennessee Pr.

Shields, John C. & Lamore, Eric D., eds. New Essays on Phillis Wheatley. 2011. (ENG.). 60.00 *(978-1-57233-726-8(5))* Univ. of Tennessee Pr.

Sidbury, James. Becoming African in America: Race & Nation in the Early Black Atlantic. (ENG., Illus.). 2009. 304p. pap. 19.95 *(978-0-19-538294-5(3))* 2007. 320p. 99.00 *(978-0-19-532010-7(7))* Oxford Univ. Pr., Inc.

Smethurst, James. The African American Roots of Modernism: From Reconstruction to the Harlem Renaissance. 2011. (John Hope Franklin Series in African American History & Culture Ser.). (ENG.). 272p. 65.00 *(978-0-8078-3463-3(7))*; pap. 26.95 *(978-0-8078-7185-0(0))* Univ. of North Carolina Pr.

Sollors, Werner. Ethnic Modernism. 2008. 336p. pap. 21.00 *(978-0-674-03091-6(5))* Harvard Univ. Pr.

Spencer Maor, Faye. Lifting Word by Word. 2008. 84p. pap. *(978-3-639-06233-5(7))* VDM Verlag Dr. Mueller e.K.

Stallings, L H. Mutha Is Half a Word: Intersections of Folklore, Vernacular, Myth, & Queerness in Black Female Culture. 2007. (Black Performance & Cultural Criticism Ser.). (ENG.). 334p. 49.95 *(978-0-8142-1056-7(2))* Ohio State Univ. Pr.

Szmanko, Klara. Invisiblity in African American & Asian American Literature: A Comparative Study. 2008. (ENG.). 220p. pap. 45.00 *(978-0-7864-3952-2(1))* McFarland & Co., Inc. Pubs.

Thaggert, Miriam. Images of Black Modernism: Verbal & Visual Strategies of the Harlem Renaissance. 2010. (Illus.). 256p. (ENG.). pap. 28.95 *(978-1-55849-831-0(1))*; lib. bdg. 80.00 *(978-1-55849-830-3(3))* Univ. of Massachusetts Pr.

Thompson, Carlyle Van. Eating the Black Body: Miscegenation As Sexual Consumption in African American Literature & Culture. 2006. (African-American Literature & Culture Ser.: Vol. 10). (C). pap. 29.95 *(978-0-8204-7931-6(4))* Lang, Peter Publishing, Inc.

Thompson, Mark Christian. Black Fascisms: African American Literature & Culture Between the Wars. 2007. (ENG.). 240p. (gr. 17). 57.50 *(978-0-8139-2670-4(X))*; per. 19.50 *(978-0-8139-2671-1(8))* Univ. Pr. of Virginia.

Tolson, Nancy. Black Children's Literature Got de Blues: The Creativity of Black Writers & Illustrators. 2008. (Illus.). xi, 116p. pap. 24.95 *(978-0-8204-6332-2(9))* Lang, Peter Publishing, Inc.

Turpin, Cherie Ann. How Three Black Women Writers Combined Spiritual & Sensual Love: Rhetorically Transcending the Boundaries of Language (Audre Lorde, Toni Morrison, & Dionne Brand) 2010. 120p. 89.95 *(978-0-7734-3839-2(4))* Mellen, Edwin Pr., The.

Ward, Jerry W. & Butler, Robert J., eds. The Richard Wright Encyclopedia, 1 vol. 2008. 472p. 125.00 *(978-0-313-31239-7(7)*, GR1239, Greenwood Pr.) Greenwood Publishing Group, Inc.

Ward, Jerry Washington. The Cambridge History of African American Literature. Graham, Maryemma, ed. 2011. 860p. 165.00 *(978-0-521-87217-1(0))* Cambridge Univ. Pr.

Warren, Kenneth W. What Was African American Literature? 2011. (W. E. B. du Bois Lectures). (ENG.). 192p. 22.95 *(978-0-674-04922-2(5))* Harvard Univ. Pr.

Watkins, Rychetta. Black Power, Yellow Power, & the Making of Revolutionary Identities. 2012. (ENG.). 176p. 55.00 ***(978-1-61703-161-8(5))*** Univ. Pr. of Mississippi.

Watts, Eric King. Hearing the Hurt: Rhetoric, Aesthetics, & Politics of the New Negro Movement. 2012. (Albma Rhetoric Cult & Soc Crit Ser.). (ENG.). 253p. (C). 39.95 ***(978-0-8173-1766-9(X))*** Univ. of Alabama Pr.

Whalan, Mark. The Great War & the Culture of the New Negro. 2008. (ENG., Illus.). 336p. 65.00 *(978-0-8130-3206-1(7))* Univ. Pr. of Florida.

Whitted, Qiana J. A God of Justice? The Problem of Evil in Twentieth-Century Black Literature. 2009. (ENG.). 240p. (C). (gr. 13-17). pap. 21.50 *(978-0-8139-2797-8(8))*; (gr. 17). 55.00 *(978-0-8139-2796-1(X))* Univ. Pr. of Virginia.

Williams, Daniel. Transatlantic Exchange: African Americans & the Welsh, 1845-1945. 2012. (University of Wales Press - Writing Wales in English Ser.). (ENG.). 432p. pap. 40.00 ***(978-0-7083-1987-1(4))*** Univ. of Wales Pr. GBR. Dist: Chicago Distribution Ctr.

Wilson, Ivy G. Specters of Democracy: Blackness & the Aesthetics of Politics in the Antebellum U. S., 1 vol. 2011. (ENG., Illus.). 256p. pap. 29.95 *(978-0-19-534035-3(3))* Oxford Univ. Pr., Inc.

Wong, Edlie L. Neither Fugitive nor Free: Atlantic Slavery, Freedom Suits, & the Legal Culture of Travel. 2009. (ENG., Illus.). 368p. 75.00 *(978-0-8147-9455-5(6))* New York Univ. Pr.

Xu, Dejin. Race & Form: Towards a Contextualized Narratology of African American Autobiography. 226p. pap. 47.95 *(978-3-03911-003-2(9))* Lang, Peter Publishing, Inc.

Young, John K. Black Writers, White Publishers: Marketplace Politics in Twentieth-Century African American Literature. 2010. (ENG., Illus.). 242p. pap. 25.00 *(978-1-60473-548-2(1))* Univ. Pr. of Mississippi.

Young, Kevin. The Grey Album: On the Blackness of Blackness, 1 vol. 2012. (ENG.). 476p. pap. 25.00 ***(978-1-55597-607-1(7))*** Graywolf Pr.

Zamir, Shamoon, ed. The Cambridge Companion to W. E. B. du Bois. 2008. (Cambridge Companions to American Studies). (ENG.). 192p. (C). 81.00 *(978-0-521-87151-8(4))* Cambridge Univ. Pr.

—The Cambridge Companion to W.E.B. Du Bois. 2008. (Cambridge Companions to American Studies). (ENG.). 192p. (C). pap. 25.99 *(978-0-521-69205-2(9))* Cambridge Univ. Pr. GBR. Dist: Cambridge Univ. Pr.

Zamora, Maria C. Nation, Race & History in Asian American Literature: Re-Membering the Body. 2008. (Modern American Literature: New Approaches Ser.). 140p. (C). 35.95 *(978-1-4331-0268-4(4))* Lang, Peter Publishing, Inc.

Zauchner, Sabine, et al. African Diasporas: Afro-German Literature in the Context of the African American Experience. 2007. (ENG.). 144p. (gr. 11). pap. 39.95 *(978-3-8258-9612-6(9))* Lit Verlag DEU. Dist: Transaction Pubs.

AMERICAN LITERATURE—AFRO-AMERICAN AUTHORS

see American Literature—African American Authors

AMERICAN LITERATURE—ASIAN AMERICAN AUTHORS

Banerjee, Neelanjana, et al, eds. Indivisible: An Anthology of Contemporary South Asian American Poetry. 2010. (ENG.). 220p. 65.00 *(978-1-55728-932-2(8))*; pap. 24.95 *(978-1-55728-931-5(X))* Univ. of Arkansas Pr.

Chen, Thomas C., ed. Asian American Studies Now: A Critical Reader. 2010. (ENG.). 672p. (C). pap. 37.50 *(978-0-8135-4575-2(7))* Rutgers Univ. Pr.

Grice, Helena. As an American Fiction, History & Life Writing: International Encounters. 2009. (Routledge Transnational Perspectives on American Literature Ser.). (ENG.). 166p. (C). 125.00 *(978-0-415-38475-9(3))* Routledge.

Huang, Guiyou, ed. The Greenwood Encyclopedia of Asian American Literature, 3 vols. 2008. 1256p. 299.95 *(978-0-313-34157-1(5)*, GR4157, Greenwood Pr.) Greenwood Publishing Group, Inc.

Kherdian, David, ed. Forgotten Bread: First-Generation Armenian American Writers. 2008. (Illus.). 481p. pap. 21.95 *(978-1-59714-068-3(6))* Heyday.

Ninh, Erin. Ingratitude: The Debt-Bound Daughter in Asian American Literature. 2011. (ENG.). 224p. 70.00 *(978-0-8147-5844-1(4))*; pap. 23.00 *(978-0-8147-5845-8(2))* New York Univ. Pr.

Oh, Seiwoong. Encyclopedia of Asian American Literature. 2007. (Encyclopedia of American Ethnic Literature Ser.). 400p. (C). (gr. 9). 75.00 *(978-0-8160-6086-3(X))* Facts On File, Inc.

Saed, Zohra & Muradi, Sahar, eds. One Story, Thirty Stories: An Anthology of Contemporary Afghan American Literature. 2010. (ENG.). 290p. 65.00 *(978-1-55728-946-9(8))*; pap. 24.95 *(978-1-55728-945-2(X))* Univ. of Arkansas Pr.

Shaughnessy, Brenda. Human Dark with Sugar. 2008. (ENG.). 96p. pap. 15.00 *(978-1-55659-276-8(0))* Copper Canyon Pr.

Wu, Jean Yu-wen Shen & Chen, Thomas C., eds. Asian American Studies Now: A Critical Reader. 2010. (ENG.). 672p. (C). 80.00 *(978-0-8135-4574-5(9))* Rutgers Univ. Pr.

Xu, Wenying. Historical Dictionary of Asian American Literature & Theater. 2012. (Historical Dictionaries of Literature & the Arts Ser.). (ENG.). 410p. 99.00 ***(978-0-8108-5577-9(1))*** Scarecrow Pr., Inc.

AMERICAN LITERATURE—ASIAN AMERICAN AUTHORS—HISTORY AND CRITICISM

Adams, Bella. Asian American Literature. Halliwell, Martin & Mousley, Andy, eds. 2008. (Edinburgh Critical Guides to Literature Ser.). (ENG.). 224p. (gr. 17). 70.00 *(978-0-7486-2271-9(3))*; pap. 22.00 *(978-0-7486-2272-6(1))* Edinburgh Univ. Pr. GBR. Dist: Columbia Univ. Pr.

Chae, Youngsuk. Politicizing Asian American Literature: Towards a Critical Multiculturalism. 2007. (Studies in Asian Americans Ser.). (ENG.). 182p. 125.00 *(978-0-415-96099-1(1))* Routledge.

Chang, Yoonmee. Writing the Ghetto: Class, Authorship, & the Asian American Ethnic Enclave. 2010. (American Literatures Initiative Ser.). (ENG., Illus.). 252p. 45.00 *(978-0-8135-4801-2(2))* Rutgers Univ. Pr.

East-West Montage: Reflections on Asian Bodies in Diaspora. 2007. (Illus.). 302p. per. 29.00 *(978-0-8248-3181-3(0))* Univ. of Hawaii Pr.

Hock, Andrew. Asian Gothic: Essays on Literature, Film & Anime. 2008. (ENG.). 252p. per. 35.00 *(978-0-7864-3335-3(3))* McFarland & Co., Inc. Pubs.

Huang, Betsy. Contesting Genres in Contemporary Asian American Fiction. 2010. (ENG.). 192p. 79.00 *(978-0-230-10831-8(8))* Palgrave Macmillan.

Huang, Yunte. Transpacific Imaginations: History, Literature, Counterpoetics. 2008. (Illus.). 202p. 40.50 *(978-0-674-02637-7(3))* Harvard Univ. Pr.

Jenkins, Candice M. Private Lives, Proper Relations: Regulating Black Intimacy. 2007. 240p. 67.50 *(978-0-8166-4787-3(9))*; per. 23.50 *(978-0-8166-4788-0(7))* Univ. of Minnesota Pr.

Kardux, Johanna C. & Einsiedel, Doris. Moving Migration: Narrative Transformations in Asian American Literature. 2011. (ENG.). 280p. pap. 41.95 *(978-3-643-10573-8(8))* Lit Verlag DEU. Dist: Transaction Pubs.

Lee, Christopher. The Semblance of Identity: Aesthetic Mediation in Asian American Literature. 2012. (Asian America Ser.). (ENG.). 208p. 50.00 ***(978-0-8047-7870-1(1))*** Stanford Univ. Pr.

Lee, Julia. Interracial Encounters: Reciprocal Representations in African & Asian American Literatures, 1896-1937. 2011. (ENG.). 228p. 75.00 ***(978-0-8147-5255-5(1))***; pap. 23.00 ***(978-0-8147-5256-2(X))*** New York Univ. Pr.

Lee, Julia H. Interracial Encounters: Reciprocal Representations in African American & Asian American Literatures, 1896-1937. 2011. E-Book ***(978-0-8147-5328-6(0))***; E-Book ***(978-0-8147-5257-9(8))*** New York Univ. Pr.

Leiwei Li, David, ed. Leiwei Li Set: Asian American Literature, 4 vols. 2012. (ENG.). 2240p. (C). 975.00 ***(978-0-415-49887-6(2))*** Routledge.

Ma, Sheng-mei. Asian Diaspora Literature & Visual Culture. 2010. (Routledge Contemporary Asia Ser.). (ENG.). 192p. (C). 125.00 *(978-0-415-59426-4(X))* Routledge.

—Diaspora Literature & Visual Culture: Asia in Flight. 2011. 183p. (C). 125.00 *(978-0-203-84077-1(1))* Routledge.

Mani, Bakirathi. Aspiring to Home: South Asians in America. 2012. (Asian America Ser.). (ENG.). 328p. 85.00 ***(978-0-8047-7799-5(3))***; pap. 27.95 ***(978-0-8047-7800-8(0))*** Stanford Univ. Pr.

Maxey, Ruth. South Asian Atlantic Literature, 1970-2010. 2012. (Edinburgh Critical Studies in Transatlantic Literature Ser.). (ENG.). 272p. (gr. 17). 105.00 ***(978-0-7486-4186-8(2))*** Edinburgh Univ. Pr. GBR. Dist: Columbia Univ. Pr.

Ng, Andrew Hock-Soon. Interrogating Interstices: Gothic Aesthetics in Postcolonial Asian & Asian American Literature. 289p. pap. 63.95 *(978-3-03911-006-3(3))* Lang, Peter Publishing, Inc.

Park, Josephine. Apparitions of Asia: Modernist Form & Asian American Poetics. 2008. (ENG.). 224p. 55.00 *(978-0-19-533273-5(3))* Oxford Univ. Pr., Inc.

Partridge, Jeffrey F. L. Beyond Literary Chinatown. 2007. (American Ethnic & Cultural Studies). (ENG.). 272p. per. 27.95 *(978-0-295-98706-4(5))* Univ. of Washington Pr.

Schlund-Vials, Cathy. Modeling Citizenship: Jewish & Asian American Writing. 2011. (ENG.). 248p. 68.50 *(978-1-4399-0317-9(4))*; pap. 24.95 *(978-1-4399-0318-6(2))* Temple Univ. Pr.

Schueller, Malini Johar. Locating Race: Global Sites of Post-Colonial Citizenship. 2009. (SUNY Series, Explorations in Postcolonial Studies). 240p. 74.50 *(978-0-7914-7681-9(2))*; pap. 29.95 *(978-0-7914-7682-6(0))* State Univ. of New York Pr.

Schultermandl, Silvia. Transnational Matrilineage: Mother-Daughter Conflicts in Asian American Literature. 2011. 240p. pap. 41.95 *(978-3-8258-1262-1(6))* Lit Verlag DEU. Dist: Transaction Pubs.

Szmanko, Klara. Invisibility in African American & Asian American Literature: A Comparative Study. 2008. (ENG.). 220p. pap. 45.00 *(978-0-7864-3952-2(1))* McFarland & Co., Inc. Pubs.

Ty, Eleanor Rose. Unfastened: Globality & Asian North American Narratives. 2010. (Illus.). 216p. 67.50 *(978-0-8166-6507-5(9))*; (ENG., pap. 22.50 *(978-0-8166-6508-2(7))* Univ. of Minnesota Pr.

Watkins, Rychetta. Black Power, Yellow Power, & the Making of Revolutionary Identities. 2012. (ENG.). 176p. 55.00 ***(978-1-61703-161-8(5))*** Univ. Pr. of Mississippi.

Xu, Wenying. Eating Identities: Reading Food in Asian American Literature. 2008. 259p. per. 31.00 *(978-0-8248-3195-0(0))* Univ. of Hawaii Pr.

AMERICAN LITERATURE—BIBLIOGRAPHY

Association for Library Service to Children Staff. The Newbery & Caldecott Awards: A Guide to the Medal Honor Books. 2009. 168p. pap. 25.00 *(978-0-8389-3585-9(0))* American Library Assn.

Bonner, John W., Jr. Bibliography of Georgia Authors, 1949-1965. 2010. (ENG.). 278p. pap. 24.95 *(978-0-8203-3526-1(6))* Univ. of Georgia Pr.

Brinley, George. Catalogue of the American Library of George Brinley, 5 pts. in 2 vols. Trumbull, J. Hammond, ed. reprint ed. lib. bdg. 125.00 *(978-0-404-01081-2(4))* AMS Pr., Inc.

Brooks, Justin. Stephen King: A Primary Bibliography of the World's Most Popular Author. (Illus.). 553p. 2008. 40.00 *(978-1-58767-190-6(5))* 2006. pap. 25.00 *(978-1-58767-153-1(0))* Cemetery Dance Pubns.

Bruccoli, Matthew J. & Baughman, Judith. F. Scott Fitzgerald in the Marketplace: The Auction & Dealer Catalogues, 1935-2006. 2009. (Illus.). 320p. *(978-1-57003-799-3(X))* Univ. of South Carolina Pr.

Ferguson, John D. American Literature in Spain. reprint ed. 37.50 *(978-0-404-02377-5(0))* AMS Pr., Inc.

Foster, Thomas C. Twenty-Five Books That Shaped America. 2011. (ENG.). 352p. pap. 14.99 *(978-0-06-183440-0(8)*, Harper Paperbacks) HarperCollins Pubs.

Hanna, A. J. A Bibliography of the Writings of Irving Bacheller. 2007. (ENG.). 48p. per. 15.95 *(978-1-4325-9992-8(5))* Kessinger Publishing, LLC.

Hare, John. A Prospering Society: Wiltshire on the Later Society. 2011. (Studies in Regional & Local History Ser.). (ENG., Illus.). 288p. 79.95 ***(978-1-902806-84-6(0))*** Univ. of Hertfordshire Pr. GBR. Dist: Independent Pubs. Group.

Hassell, Susan Whitcomb. A Hundred & Sixty Books by Washington Authors. 2009. 44p. pap. 15.95 *(978-1-120-11998-8(7))* Kessinger Publishing, LLC.

—A Hundred & Sixty Books by Washington Authors. 40p. reprint ed. lib. bdg. 88.00 *(978-0-7222-4721-1(4))* Library Reprints, Inc.

Hazeltine, Mary E. One Hundred Years of Wisconsin Authorship, 1836-1937: A Contribution to a Bibliography of Books by Wisconsin Authors. reprint ed. lib. bdg. 125.00 *(978-0-7222-0323-1(3))* Library Reprints, Inc.

Hemmingson, Michael. William T. Vollmann: An Annotated Bibliography. 2011. (ENG.). 114p. (gr. 17). 50.00 ***(978-0-8108-8224-9(8))*** Scarecrow Pr., Inc.

Herman, Paul. The Neverending Hunt: A Bibliography of Robert E. Howard: A Bibliography of Robert E. Howard. 2011. (Illus.). 400p. pap. 19.95 *(978-0-8095-6256-5(1))* Wildside Pr., LLC.

Herman, Paul & Lord, Glenn. The Neverending Hunt: A Bibliography of Robert E. Howard: A Bibliography of Robert E. Howard. 2011. (Illus.). 400p. 35.00 *(978-0-8095-6262-6(6))* Wildside Pr., LLC.

Matuozzi, Robert & Lindsay, B. Literary Research & the American Modernist Era: Strategies & Sources. 2008. (Literary Research: Strategies & Sources Ser.). (ENG.). 186p. pap. 45.00 *(978-0-8108-6116-9(X))* Scarecrow Pr., Inc.

McWhirter, Cameron, compiled by. Omar Shakespear Pound: A Bibliography. 2008. (Illus.). 36p. 5.00 *(978-0-9796448-2-5(8))* Couper Pr., Richard W.

Morgan, Phyllis S. N. Scott Momaday: Remembering Ancestors, Earth, & Traditions - An Annotated Bio-Bibliography. annot. ed. 2010. (American Indian Literature & Critical Studies Ser.). (ENG.). 400p. (C). 60.00 *(978-0-8061-4054-4(2))* Univ. of Oklahoma Pr.

Schon, Isabel. Recommended Books in Spanish for Children & Young Adults, 2004-2008. 2008. (ENG.). 424p. 65.00 *(978-0-8108-6386-6(3))* Scarecrow Pr., Inc.

Wakeman, Stephen & Wakeman, Alice L. James. The Stephen H Wakeman Collection of Books of Nineteenth Century American Writers. 2011. 260p. 47.95 ***(978-1-258-04996-6(1))*** Literary Licensing, LLC.

Weiner, Robert G. Marvel Graphic Novels & Related Publications: An Annotated Guide to Comics, Prose Novels, Children's Books, Articles, Criticism & Reference Works, 1965-2005. 2008. (ENG.). 399p. 49.95 *(978-0-7864-2500-6(8))* McFarland & Co., Inc. Pubs.

York, Sherry. Booktalking Authentic Multicultural Literature: Fiction & History for Young Readers, 1 vol. 2009. 160p. pap. 39.95 *(978-1-58683-300-8(6)*, A2458P) Linworth Publishing, Inc.

AMERICAN LITERATURE—BIBLIOGRAPHY—CATALOGS

Bryer, Jackson R. & Kopley, Richard, eds. Resources for American Literary Study, Vol. 32. 2009. 372p. 187.50 *(978-0-404-64632-5(8))* AMS Pr., Inc.

State Historical Society of Wisconsin. ... Catalogue of the Library of the State Historical Society of Wisconsin Prepared by Daniel S Durrie, Librarian, & Isabel Durrie, Assistant. 2006. 644p. per. 34.99 *(978-1-4255-6656-2(1))* MPublishing.

AMERICAN LITERATURE—BIO-BIBLIOGRAPHY

Adams, Oscar Fay. A Brief Handbook of American Authors. 2009. 222p. 28.99 *(978-1-110-41659-2(8))* 2009. 222p. pap. 23.75 *(978-1-110-41655-4(5))* 2008. 204p. 24.99 *(978-0-559-26988-2(9))* 2008. 204p. pap. 23.75 *(978-0-559-26987-5(0))* BiblioBazaar.

—A Dictionary of American Authors. 2007. (ENG.). 598p. 59.95 *(978-0-548-26352-5(3))*; 600p. per. 44.95 *(978-1-4326-6764-1(5))* Kessinger Publishing, LLC.

Allibone, S. Austin. A Critical Dictionary of English Literature & British & American Authors Living & Deceased Vol. 1: From the Earliest Accounts to the Latter Half of the Nineteenth Century Abb to Duf Part Two. 2006. pap. 42.95 *(978-1-4286-4586-8(1))* Kessinger Publishing, LLC.

—A Critical Dictionary of English Literature & British & American Authors Living & Deceased Vol. 2: From the Earliest Accounts to the Latter Half of the Nineteenth Century Mab to Rad. 2006. pap. 43.95 *(978-1-4286-4582-0(9))* Kessinger Publishing, LLC.

—A Critical Dictionary of English Literature & British & American Authors Living & Deceased Vol. 2: From the Earliest Accounts to the Latter Half of the Nineteenth Century Rad to Szy Part Two. 2006. pap. 44.95 *(978-1-4286-4583-7(7))* Kessinger Publishing, LLC.

—A Critical Dictionary of English Literature & British & American Authors Living & Deceased Vol. 3: From the Earliest Accounts to the Latter Half of the Nineteenth Century Taa to Wil Part One. 2006. pap. 36.95 *(978-1-4286-4588-2(8))* Kessinger Publishing, LLC.

—A Critical Dictionary of English Literature & British & American Authors Living & Deceased Vol. 3: From the Earliest Accounts to the Latter Half of the Nineteenth Century Wil to Zwe Part Two. 2006. pap. 33.95 *(978-1-4286-4589-9(6))* Kessinger Publishing, LLC.

Augustyn, Adam, ed. American Literature from 1600 Through the 1850s. 2010. (Britannica Guide to World Literature Ser.). (ENG.). 240p. (YA). lib. bdg. 45.00 *(978-1-61530-124-9(0))* Rosen Publishing Group, Inc., The.

—American Literature from 1600 Through The 1850S. 2010. (Britannica Guide to World Literature Ser.). (Illus.). 240p. (YA). 90.00 *(978-1-61530-236-9(0))* Rosen Publishing Group, Inc., The.

—American Literature from 1945 Through Today. 2010. (Britannica Guide to World Literature Ser.). 240p. (YA). (ENG.). lib. bdg. 45.00 *(978-1-61530-133-1(X))*; (Illus.). 90.00 *(978-1-61530-237-6(9))* Rosen Publishing Group, Inc., The.

—American Literature from the 1850s to 1945. 2010. (Illus.). 248p. (YA). lib. bdg. 45.00 *(978-1-61530-132-4(1))* Rosen Publishing Group, Inc., The.

—American Literature from the 1850S To 1945. 2010. (Britannica Guide to World Literature Ser.). (Illus.). 248p. (YA). 90.00 *(978-1-61530-238-3(7))* Rosen Publishing Group, Inc., The.

Baym, Nina. Women Writers of the American West, 1833-1927. 2011. (ENG.). 384p. 40.00 *(978-0-252-03597-5(6))* Univ. of Illinois Pr.

Bryson, J. Scott & Thompson, Roger. American Nature Poets. 2008. (Dictionary of Literary Biography Ser.). (ENG., Illus.). 496p. 315.00 *(978-0-7876-8160-9(1))* Cengage Gale.

Drew, Bernard A. 100 Most Popular Thriller & Suspense Authors: Biographical Sketches & Bibliographies, 1 vol. 2009. (Popular Authors Ser.). 468p. 65.00 *(978-1-59158-699-9(2)*, LU8699, Libraries Unlimited, Inc.

Eisler, Garrett. 20th Century American Dramatists. 2008. (Dictionary of Literary Biography Ser.: Vol. 341). (ENG.). 464p. 315.00 *(978-0-7876-8159-3(8))* Cengage Gale.

Fitzgerald, Carol & Fitzgerald, Jean. Series Americana: Post Depression-Era Regional Literature, 1938-1980, 2 vols. 2009. (Illus.). xxxvi, 978p. 125.00 *(978-1-58456-252-8(8))* Oak Knoll Pr.

Furey, Hester Lee. American Radical & Reform Writers. 2008. (Dictionary of Literary Biography Ser.: Vol. 345). (ENG.). 426p. 315.00 *(978-0-7876-8163-0(6))* Cengage Gale.

Gale Editor, ed. American Writers: Supplement XXII. 22nd ed. 2011. lib. bcg. 218.00 *(978-1-4144-8024-4(5)*, Charles Scribner's Sons) Cengage Gale.

Hacht, Anne Marie & Hayes, Dwayne D. Gale Contextual Encyclopedia of American Literature. 2009. *(978-1-4144-3133-8(3))*; *(978-1-4144-3132-1(5))*; *(978-1-4144-3134-5(1))*; (Illus.). 1819p. 495.00 *(978-1-4144-3131-4(7))* Cengage Gale.

Haralson, Eric, ed. Encyclopedia of American Poetry: The Nineteenth Century. 2011. 549p. pap. 59.95 *(978-0-415-89076-2(4))* Routledge.

—Encyclopedia of American Poetry: The Twentieth Century. 2013. (ENG.). 866p. pap. 59.95 *(978-0-415-89077-9(2))* Routledge.

Kaser, James. The Chicago of Fiction: A Resource Guide. 2011. (ENG.). 672p. 100.00 *(978-0-8108-7724-5(4))* Scarecrow Pr., Inc.

Kellman, Steven G., ed. Magill's Survey of American Literature, 6 vols., Set. rev. ed. 2006. (Illus.). 2866p. (YA). (gr. 9-18). lib. bdg. 499.00 *(978-1-58765-285-1(4))* Salem Pr., Inc.

—Magill's Survey of American Literature Vol. 2: Sandra Cisneros — John Guare, 6 vols. rev. ed. 2006. (Illus.). 2600p. lib. bdg. 83.00 *(978-1-58765-287-5(0))* Salem Pr., Inc.

—Magill's Survey of American Literature Vol. 3: H. D. — Nella Larsen, 6 vols. rev. ed. 2006. (Illus.). 2600p. lib. bdg. 83.00 *(978-1-58765-288-2(9))* Salem Pr., Inc.

—Magill's Survey of American Literature Vol. 4: Stephen Leacock — Flannery O'Connor, 6 vols. rev. ed. 2006. (Illus.). 2600p. lib. bdg. 83.00 *(978-1-58765-289-9(7))* Salem Pr., Inc.

—Magill's Survey of American Literature Vol. 5: Clifford Odets — Gertrude Stein, 6 vols. rev. ed. 2006. (Illus.). 2600p. lib. bdg. 83.00 *(978-1-58765-290-5(0))* Salem Pr., Inc.

—Magill's Survey of American Literature, Revised Edition, Volume 1 Vol. 1: Edward Abbey — Kate Chopin, 6 vols. rev. ed. 2006. (Illus.). 2600p. lib. bdg. 83.00 *(978-1-58765-286-8(2))* Salem Pr., Inc.

—Magill's Survey of American Literature, Volume 6: Steinbeck-Zindel, 6 vols. rev. ed. 2006. (Magill's Survey of American Literature Ser.). (Illus.). 500p. 83.00 *(978-1-58765-291-2(9))* Salem Pr., Inc.

Moses, Sibyl E. African American Women Writers in New Jersey, 1836-2000: A Biographical Dictionary & Bibliographic Guide. 2006. (ENG., Illus.). 256p. per. 29.95 *(978-0-8135-4019-1(4))* Rutgers Univ. Pr.

A

Nelson, Emmanuel S., ed. Encyclopedia of Contemporary LGBTQ Literature of the United States, 2 vols. 2009. 762p. 195.00 *(978-0-313-34859-4(6),* GR4859) Greenwood Publishing Group, Inc.

Parini, Jay. American Writers Supplement. 18th rev. ed. 2008. (American Writers Ser.). (ENG.). 592p. 218.00 *(978-0-684-31552-2(1),* Charles Scribner's Sons) Cengage Gale.

Parini, Jay, ed. American Writers: A Collection of Literary Biographies. 16th ed. 2006. (American Writers: Supplement Ser.). (ENG.). 624p. 218.00 *(978-0-684-31510-2(6),* Charles Scribner's Sons) Cengage Gale.

Patterson, Daniel. Early American Nature Writers: A Biographical Encyclopedia, 1 vol. Thompson, Roger & Bryson, Scott, eds. 2007. 448p. 125.00 *(978-0-313-34680-4(1),* GR4680, Greenwood Pr.) Greenwood Publishing Group, Inc.

Rollyson, Carl, ed. Notable American Novelists, 3 vols., Set. 2007. (Magill's Choice Ser.). (Illus.). 1536p. lib. bdg. 217.00 *(978-1-58765-393-3(1),* Magill's Choice) Salem Pr., Inc.

Rollyson, Carl E. Notable American Novelists. 2007. (Magill's Choice Ser.). 73.00 *(978-1-58765-395-7(8));* 73.00 *(978-1-58765-394-0(X));* 73.00 *(978-1-58765-396-4(6))* Salem Pr., Inc.

Salem Press Staff, ed. American Ethnic Writers, 3 vols. 2008. (Magill's Choice Ser.). (Illus.). 1000p. 217.00 *(978-1-58765-462-6(8))* Salem Pr., Inc.

Toruño-Haensly, Rhina. Crossing Cultures: Hispanic Authors & the Challenges They Overcame in the United States = Cruzando Culturas: Autores Hispanos y Sus Desafíos Superados en Los Estados Unidos. 2011. (Currents in Comparative Romance Languages & Literatures Ser.). (SPA & ENG., Illus.). 214p. (C). 76.95 *(978-1-4331-1253-9(1))* Lang, Peter Publishing, Inc.

Varner, Paul. Historical Dictionary of the Beat Movement. 2012. (Historical Dictionaries of Literature & the Arts Ser.). (ENG.). 400p. 95.00 ***(978-0-8108-7189-2(0))*** Scarecrow Pr., Inc.

Xu, Wenying. Historical Dictionary of Asian American Literature & Theater. 2012. (Historical Dictionaries of Literature & the Arts Ser.). (ENG.). 410p. 99.00 ***(978-0-8108-5577-9(1))*** Scarecrow Pr., Inc.

AMERICAN LITERATURE—CATHOLIC AUTHORS

DelRosso, Jeana, et al, eds. The Catholic Church & Unruly Women Writers: Critical Essays. 2007. (ENG.). 272p. 100.00 *(978-0-230-60025-6(5))* Palgrave Macmillan.

Finotti, Joseph Maria. Bibliographia Catholica Americana: A List of Works Written by Catholic Authors, 2006. 324p. per. 23.99 *(978-1-4255-3207-9(1))* MPublishing.

Giles, Paul. American Catholic Arts & Fictions: Culture, Ideology, Aesthetics. 2008. (Cambridge Studies in American Literature & Culture Ser.). (ENG.). 564p. pap. 74.00 *(978-0-521-05773-8(6))* Cambridge Univ. Pr.

O'Gorman, Farrell. Peculiar Crossroads: Flannery O'Connor, Walker Percy, & Catholic Vision in Postwar Southern Fiction. 2007. (Southern Literary Studies). 272p. pap. 22.95 *(978-0-8071-3335-4(3))* Louisiana State Univ. Pr.

Reichardt, Mary R., ed. Between Human & Divine: The Catholic Vision in Contemporary Literature. 2010. (ENG.). 304p. 69.95 *(978-0-8132-1739-0(3))* Catholic Univ. of America Pr.

Scally, Mary Anthony. Negro Catholic Writers 1900 - 1943: A Bio-Bibliography. 2006. pap. 21.95 *(978-1-4286-5451-8(8))* Kessinger Publishing, LLC.

Waldmeir, John C. Cathedrals of Bone: The Role of the Body in Contemporary Catholic Literature. 3rd ed. 2009. (ENG.). 224p. 55.00 *(978-0-8232-3060-0(0))* Fordham Univ. Pr.

AMERICAN LITERATURE—CUBAN AMERICAN AUTHORS

Borland, Isabel Alvarez. Cuban-American Literature & Art: Negotiating Identities. Bosch, Lynette M. F., ed. 2010. (SUNY series in Latin American & Iberian Thought & Culture Ser.). 234p. pap. 25.95 *(978-0-7914-9374-8(1),* Suny Pr.) State Univ. of New York Pr.

Borland, Isabel Alvarez & Bosch, Lynette M. F., eds. Cuban-American Literature & Art: Negotiating Identities. 2009. (SUNY series in Latin American & Iberian Thought & Culture Ser.). 240p. 70.00 *(978-0-7914-9373-1(3))* State Univ. of New York Pr.

Bosch, Lynette M. F. & Borland, Isabel Alvarez, eds. Identity, Memory, & Diaspora: Voices of Cuban-American Artists, Writers, & Philosophers. 2008. (SUNY Series in Latin American & Iberian Thought & Culture). (Illus.). 284p. 70.00 *(978-0-7914-7317-7(1))* State Univ. of New York Pr.

del Rio, Eduardo R. One Island, Many Voices: Conversations with Cuban-American Writers. 2008. (ENG.). 176p. pap. 22.95 *(978-0-8165-2806-6(3));* (Illus.). 216p. (C). 40.00 *(978-0-8165-2714-4(8))* Univ. of Arizona Pr.

Gracia, Jorge J. E. Identity, Memory, & Diaspora: Voices of Cuban-American Artists, Writers, & Philosophers. Bosch, Lynette M. F. & Borland, Isabel Alvarez, eds. 2009. 296p. pap. 29.95 *(978-0-7914-7318-4(X))* State Univ. of New York Pr.

Ortiz, Ricardo L. Cultural Erotics in Cuban America. 2007. 328p. 72.00 *(978-0-8166-4795-8(X));* per. 25.50 *(978-0-8166-4796-5(8))* Univ. of Minnesota Pr.

AMERICAN LITERATURE—DICTIONARIES

Allibone, S. Austin. A Critical Dictionary of English Literature & British & American Authors Living & Deceased Vol. 1: From the Earliest Accounts to the Latter Half of the Nineteenth Century Abb to Duf Part Two. 2006. pap. 42.95 *(978-1-4286-4586-8(1))* Kessinger Publishing, LLC.

—A Critical Dictionary of English Literature & British & American Authors Living & Deceased Vol. 2: From the Earliest Accounts to the Latter Half of the Nineteenth Century Mab to Rad. 2006. pap. 43.95 *(978-1-4286-4582-0(9))* Kessinger Publishing, LLC.

—A Critical Dictionary of English Literature & British & American Authors Living & Deceased Vol. 2: From the Earliest Accounts to the Latter Half of the Nineteenth Century Rad to Szy Part Two. 2006. pap. 44.95 *(978-1-4286-4583-7(7))* Kessinger Publishing, LLC.

—A Critical Dictionary of English Literature & British & American Authors Living & Deceased Vol. 3: From the Earliest Accounts to the Latter Half of the Nineteenth Century Taa to Wil Part One. 2006. pap. 36.95 *(978-1-4286-4588-2(8))* Kessinger Publishing, LLC.

—A Critical Dictionary of English Literature & British & American Authors Living & Deceased Vol. 3: From the Earliest Accounts to the Latter Half of the Nineteenth Century Wil to Zwe Part Two. 2006. pap. 33.95 *(978-1-4286-4589-9(6))* Kessinger Publishing, LLC.

Barnett, Colleen. Mystery Women: an Encyclopedia of Leading Women Characters in Mystery Fiction: Volume Three (1990-1999) (Revised) Volume Three (1990-1999) (Revised) 2010. 700p. pap. 39.95 *(978-1-59058-422-4(8))* Poisoned Pen Pr.

Conyers, James L., et al, eds. The Frederick Douglass Encyclopedia, 1 vol. 2009. (Illus.). 246p. 85.00 *(978-0-313-31988-4(X),* GR1988) Greenwood Publishing Group, Inc.

Drabble, Margaret, et al, eds. The Concise Oxford Companion to English Literature. 3rd ed. 2007. (Oxford Paperback Reference Ser.). (ENG.). 816p. pap. 15.95 *(978-0-19-921492-1(1))* Oxford Univ. Pr., Inc.

Drew, Bernard A. 100 Most Popular Thriller & Suspense Authors: Biographical Sketches & Bibliographies, 1 vol. 2009. (Popular Authors Ser.). 468p. 65.00 *(978-1-59158-699-9(2),* LU8699) Libraries Unlimited, Inc.

Fisher/Woronoff, ed. Historical Dictionary of Contemporary American Theater, 1930-2010, 2 vols. 2011. (Historical Dictionaries of Literature & the Arts Ser.: 2 Volumes). (ENG.). 1002p. 175.00 *(978-0-8108-5532-8(1))* Scarecrow Pr., Inc.

Furey, Hester Lee. American Radical & Reform Writers. 2008. (Dictionary of Literary Biography Ser.: Vol. 345). (ENG.). 426p. 315.00 *(978-0-7876-8163-0(6))* Cengage Gale.

Gale, Robert L. Truman Capote Encyclopedia. 2010. (ENG., Illus.). 187p. 75.00 *(978-0-7864-4296-6(4))* McFarland & Co., Inc. Pubs.

Hacht, Anne Marie & Hayes, Dwayne D. Gale Contextual Encyclopedia of American Literature. 2009. *(978-1-4144-3134-5(1)); (978-1-4144-3133-8(3)); (978-1-4144-3132-1(5));* (Illus.). 1819p. 495.00 *(978-1-4144-3131-4(7))* Cengage Gale.

Inge, M. Thomas & Wilson, Charles Reagan, eds. The New Encyclopedia of Southern Culture: Literature. 2008. (ENG., Illus.). 536p. 49.95 *(978-0-8078-3190-8(5));* pap. 27.95 *(978-0-8078-5875-2(7))* Univ. of North Carolina Pr.

Kellman, Steven G., ed. Magill's Survey of American Literature, 6 vols., Set. rev. ed. 2006. (Illus.). 2866p. (YA). (gr. 9-18). lib. bdg. 499.00 *(978-1-58765-285-1(4))* Salem Pr., Inc.

—Magill's Survey of American Literature Vol. 2: Sandra Cisneros — John Guare, 6 vols. rev. ed. 2006. (Illus.). 2600p. lib. bdg. 83.00 *(978-1-58765-287-5(0))* Salem Pr., Inc.

—Magill's Survey of American Literature Vol. 3: H. D. — Nella Larsen, 6 vols. rev. ed. 2006. (Illus.). 2600p. lib. bdg. 83.00 *(978-1-58765-288-2(9))* Salem Pr., Inc.

—Magill's Survey of American Literature Vol. 4: Stephen Leacock — Flannery O'Connor, 6 vols. rev. ed. 2006. (Illus.). 2600p. lib. bdg. 83.00 *(978-1-58765-289-9(7))* Salem Pr., Inc.

—Magill's Survey of American Literature Vol. 5: Clifford Odets — Gertrude Stein, 6 vols. rev. ed. 2006. (Illus.). 2600p. lib. bdg. 83.00 *(978-1-58765-290-5(0))* Salem Pr., Inc.

—Magill's Survey of American Literature, Revised Edition, Volume 1 Vol. 1: Edward Abbey — Kate Chopin, 6 vols. rev. ed. 2006. (Illus.). 2600p. lib. bdg. 83.00 *(978-1-58765-286-8(2))* Salem Pr., Inc.

—Magill's Survey of American Literature, Volume 6: Steinbeck-Zindel, 6 vols. rev. ed. 2006. (Magill's Survey of American Literature Ser.). (Illus.). 500p. 83.00 *(978-1-58765-291-2(9))* Salem Pr., Inc.

Kort, Carol. A to Z of American Women Writers. 2nd rev. ed. 2007. (A to Z of Women Ser.). (Illus.). 416p. (C). (gr. 9). 60.00 *(978-0-8160-6693-3(0))* Facts On File, Inc.

McClinton-Temple, Jennifer. Encyclopedia of Themes in Literature, 3 vols., Set. 2010. 1264p. (C). (gr. 9-18). 195.00 *(978-0-8160-7161-6(6))* Facts On File, Inc.

Nelson, Emmanuel S., ed. Encyclopedia of Contemporary LGBTQ Literature of the United States, 2 vols. 2009. 762p. 195.00 *(978-0-313-34859-4(6),* GR4859) Greenwood Publishing Group, Inc.

Page, Yolanda Williams, ed. Encyclopedia of African American Women Writers, 2 vols., Set. 2007. (Illus.). 728p. 175.00 *(978-0-313-33429-0(3),* GR3429, Greenwood Pr.) Greenwood Publishing Group, Inc.

Room, Adrian. Literally Entitled: A Dictionary of the Origins of the Titles of More Than 1300 Major Literary Works of the Nineteenth & Twentieth Centuries. alt. ed. 2008. (ENG.). 255p. pap. 35.00 *(978-0-7864-4093-1(7))* McFarland & Co., Inc. Pubs.

Stanley, Tarshia L., ed. Encyclopedia of Hip Hop Literature, 1 vol. 2008. 312p. 69.95 *(978-0-313-34389-6(6),* GR4389, Greenwood Pr.) Greenwood Publishing Group, Inc.

Varner, Paul. Historical Dictionary of the Beat Movement. 2012. (Historical Dictionaries of Literature & the Arts Ser.). (ENG.). 400p. 95.00 ***(978-0-8108-7189-2(0))*** Scarecrow Pr., Inc.

Werlock, Abby H. P. The American Short Story, 2 vols., Set. 2nd rev. ed. 2009. (Companion to Literature Ser.). 864p. (C). (gr. 9-18). 150.00 *(978-0-8160-6895-1(X))* Facts On File, Inc.

Xu, Wenying. Historical Dictionary of Asian American Literature & Theater. 2012. (Historical Dictionaries of Literature & the Arts Ser.). (ENG.). 410p. 99.00 ***(978-0-8108-5577-9(1))*** Scarecrow Pr., Inc.

AMERICAN LITERATURE—EXAMINATIONS, QUESTIONS, ETC.

Brinkmeyer, Robert H., Jr., ed. Three Catholic Writers of the Modern South. 2008. (ENG.). 190p. pap. 25.00 *(978-1-60473-168-2(0))* Univ. Pr. of Mississippi.

Kramer, Mary Eleanor. One Thousand Literary Questions & Answers. 2009. 296p. 30.99 *(978-1-113-21087-6(7));* pap. 27.75 *(978-1-113-21085-2(0))* BiblioBazaar.

—One Thousand Literary Questions & Answers. 2009. 322p. pap. 19.99 *(978-1-4588-3702-8(5))* General Bks. LLC.

—One Thousand Literary Questions & Answers. 308p. 2008. 43.95 *(978-1-4365-8541-5(4))* 2007. (ENG.). per. 28.95 *(978-0-548-78772-4(7))* Kessinger Publishing, LLC.

—One Thousand Literary Questions & Answers. 2007. (ENG.). 300p. per. *(978-1-4067-4205-3(8))* Read Bks.

Princeton Review Staff. Cracking the SAT Literature Subject Test, 2011-2012 Edition. 2011. (College Test Preparation Ser.). 256p. pap. 19.99 *(978-0-375-42811-1(9),* Princeton Review) Random Hse. Information Group.

Rudman, Jack. American Literature. (College Level Examination Ser.: Vol. 3). 49.95 *(978-0-8373-5353-1(X));* (Regents College Proficiency Examination Ser.: Vol. 4). (C). 49.95 *(978-0-8373-5454-5(4))* National Learning Corp. (Passbooks).

—American Literature: Civil War to the Present. (Regents College Proficiency Examination Ser.: Vol. 27). (C). 49.95 *(978-0-8373-5477-4(3),* Passbooks) National Learning Corp.

—American Literature: The Beginnings to the Civil War. (C). (ACT Proficiency Examination Program Ser.: Vol. 2). 49.95 *(978-0-8373-5552-8(4));* (Regents College Proficiency Examination Ser.: Vol. 26). 49.95 *(978-0-8373-5476-7(5))* National Learning Corp. (Passbooks).

—American Literature: The Civil War to the Present. (ACT Proficiency Examination Program Ser.: Vol. 3). (C). 49.95 *(978-0-8373-5553-5(2),* Passbooks) National Learning Corp.

Stratman, Jacob. CLEP American Literature w/CD-ROM (REA) - The Best Test Prep for the CLEP American Literature. 2010. pap. 34.95 *(978-0-7386-0559-3(X))* Research & Education Assn.

AMERICAN LITERATURE—FOREIGN INFLUENCES

Brickhouse, Anna. Transamerican Literary Relations & the Nineteenth-Century Public Sphere. 2009. (Cambridge Studies in American Literature & Culture Ser.). (ENG.). 344p. pap. 46.00 *(978-0-521-10101-1(8))* Cambridge Univ. Pr.

Buell, Lawrence, ed. Shades of the Planet: American Literature as World Literature. 2007. (ENG., Illus.). 312p. (C). per. 29.95 *(978-0-691-12852-8(9))* Princeton Univ. Pr.

Buell, Lawrence & Dimock, Wai-Chee, eds. Shades of the Planet: American Literature as World Literature. 2007. (Illus.). 304p. 75.00 *(978-0-691-12851-1(0))* Princeton Univ. Pr.

Cook, William W. & Tatum, James. African American Writers & Classical Tradition. (ENG.). 464p. 2012. pap. 25.00 ***(978-0-226-78997-2(7))*** 2010. 45.00 *(978-0-226-78996-5(9))* Univ. of Chicago Pr.

Dimock, Wai C. Through Other Continents: American Literature Across Deep Time. 2008. (ENG., Illus.). 264p. (C). pap. 26.95 *(978-0-691-11450-7(1))* Princeton Univ. Pr.

Dimock, Wai-Chee. Through Other Continents: American Literature Across Deep Time. 2006. (Illus.). 243p. 35.00 *(978-0-691-11449-1(8))* Princeton Univ. Pr.

Dong, Lan. Mulan's Legend & Legacy in China & the United States. 2010. (ENG., Illus.). 280p. 70.50 *(978-1-59213-970-5(1));* pap. 27.95 *(978-1-59213-971-2(X))* Temple Univ. Pr.

Egan, Michael. Henrik Ibsen. 2009. 524p. pap. 45.00 *(978-0-415-56902-6(8))* Routledge.

Ellis, Steve. Dante & English Poetry: Shelley to T. S. Eliot. 2010. (ENG.). 300p. pap. 30.99 *(978-0-521-12866-7(8))* Cambridge Univ. Pr.

González Moreno, Beatriz & Rigal Aragón, Margarita. A Descent into Edgar Allan Poe & His Works: The Bicentennial. 2010. (Illus.). 170p. pap. *(978-3-0343-0089-6(1))* Lang, Peter.

Gray, Richard & Zacharasiewicz, Waldemar, eds. Transatlantic Exchanges: The American South in Europe, Europe in the American South. 2007. (Sitzungsberichte der Phil. -Hist. Klasse Ser.). 600p. (C). pap. 98.00 *(978-3-7001-3954-6(3))* Austrian Academy of Sciences Press AUT. Dist: Brown, David Bk. Co., The.

Hakutani, Yoshinobu. Cross-Cultural Visions in African American Modernism: From Spatial Narrative to Jazz Haiku. 2006. 251p. 69.95 *(978-0-8142-1030-7(9));* ix, 251p. cd-rom 9.95 *(978-0-8142-9107-8(4))* Ohio State Univ. Pr.

Horton, Merrill. Hunting the Sun: Faulkner's Borrowings from Balzac's the Human Comedy & Droll Stories. 2010. (Modern American Literature: New Approaches Ser.). 290p. (C). 80.95 *(978-1-4331-1003-0(2))* Lang, Peter Publishing, Inc.

Huang, Yunte. Transpacific Imaginations: History, Literature, Counterpoetics. 2008. (Illus.). 202p. 40.50 *(978-0-674-02637-7(3))* Harvard Univ. Pr.

Jaksic, Iván. The Hispanic World & American Intellectual Life, 1820-1880. 2012. (Studies of the Americas Ser.). (ENG., Illus.). 266p. pap. 36.00 ***(978-0-230-33749-7(X))*** Palgrave Macmillan.

Lease, Benjamin. Anglo-American Encounters: England & the Rise of American Literature. 2009. (ENG.). 316p. pap. 42.00 *(978-0-521-10852-2(7))* Cambridge Univ. Pr.

Mathieu, Bertrand. Orpheus in Brooklyn. 2006. pap. 18.95 *(978-1-933993-16-4(2))* Apocryphile Pr.

Rankine, Patrice D. Ulysses in Black: Ralph Ellison, Classicism, & African American Literature. 2008. (Wisconsin Studies in Classics Ser.). (ENG.). 272p. pap. 24.95 *(978-0-299-22004-4(4))* Univ. of Wisconsin Pr.

Reynolds, Guy J. Apostles of Modernity: American Writers in the Age of Development. 2008. (ENG., Illus.). 278p. (C). 50.00 *(978-0-8032-1377-7(8))* Univ. of Nebraska Pr.

Richards, Page. Distancing English: A Chapter in the History of the Inexpressible. 2009. (ENG.). 208p. 52.95 *(978-0-8142-0741-3(3));* cd-rom 14.95 *(978-0-8142-9187-0(2))* Ohio State Univ. Pr.

Rood, T. The Sea! the Sea! 2006. 272p. 12.99 *(978-0-7156-3571-1(9))* Duckworth Publishers GBR. Dist: International Publishers Marketing.

Shields, John C. Phillis Wheatley's Poetics of Liberation: Backgrounds & Contexts. 2008. (ENG.). 37.95 *(978-1-57233-499-1(1))* Univ. of Tennessee Pr.

Staley, Gregory A., ed. American Women & Classical Myths. 2008. (ENG., Illus.). 300p. (C). pap. 34.95 *(978-1-932792-85-0(6))* Baylor Univ. Pr.

Stalling, Jonathan. Poetics of Emptiness: Transformations of Asian Thought in American Poetry. 2010. (American Literatures Initiative Ser.). (ENG., Illus.). 288p. 45.00 *(978-0-8232-3144-7(5))* Fordham Univ. Pr.

Stoltzfus, Ben. Hemingway & French Writers. 2009. 42.00 *(978-1-60635-039-3(0))* Kent State Univ. Pr.

Stowe, Harriet Beecher & Pearce, Joseph. Uncle Tom's Cabin. 2009. 525p. (J). pap. 11.95 *(978-1-58617-334-0(0))* Ignatius Pr.

Theobald, Tom. Existentialism & Baseball. 2010. 288p. pap. *(978-3-8383-4896-4(6))* Lambert Academic Publishing.

Trubek, Anne. A Skeptic's Guide to Writers' Houses. 2010. (Illus.). 176p. 24.95 *(978-0-8122-4292-8(0))* Univ. of Pennsylvania Pr.

Virtanen, Beth L. Finnish-North American Literature in English: A Concise Anthology. 2009. viii, 578p. *(978-0-7734-3818-7(1))* Mellen, Edwin Pr., The.

Whalen-Bridge, John & Storhoff, Gary, eds. The Emergence of Buddhist American Literature. 2009. (SUNY series in Buddhism & American Culture Ser.). 272p. 80.00 *(978-1-4384-2653-2(4))* State Univ. of New York Pr.

AMERICAN LITERATURE—HISPANIC AMERICAN AUTHORS

Benítez Rojo, Antonio. El Mar de las Lentejas. (SPA.). 312p. 23.95 *(978-84-923649-5-4(5),* PEA11749) Casiopea ESP. Dist: Lectorum Pubns., Inc.

Chacón, Eusebio, et al. The Writings of Eusebio Chacón. 2012. (SPA.). ***(978-0-8263-5102-9(6))*** Univ. of New Mexico Pr.

Fetta, Stefanie, ed. The Chicano/Latino Literary Prize: An Anthology of Prize-Winning Fiction, Poetry & Drama. 2008. 320p. pap. 21.95 *(978-1-55885-511-3(4))* Arte Publico Pr.

González, Rigoberto, ed. Camino del Sol: Fifteen Years on Latina & Latino Writing. 2010. (Camino del Sol Ser.). (ENG., Illus.). 368p. pap. 24.95 *(978-0-8165-2813-4(6))* Univ. of Arizona Pr.

Kanellos, Nicolás. The Greenwood Encyclopedia of Latino Literature, 3 vols., Set. Kanellos, Nicolás, ed. 2008. (Illus.). 1456p. 299.95 *(978-0-313-33970-7(8),* GR3970, Greenwood Pr.) Greenwood Publishing Group, Inc.

Kanellos, Nicolás, ed. Short Fiction by Hispanic Writers of the United States. 228p. pap. 15.95 *(978-1-55885-044-6(9))* Arte Publico Pr.

Martínez, Sara. Latino Literature: A Guide to Reading Interests, 1 vol. 2009. (Genreflecting Advisory Ser.). 364p. 60.00 *(978-1-59158-292-2(X),* LU292X) Libraries Unlimited, Inc.

Meléndez, A. Gabriel & Lomelí, Francisco A., eds. The Writings of Eusebio Chacón. 2012. (Pasó por Aquí Series on the Nuevomexicano Literary Heritage Ser.). (SPA & ENG., Illus.). 288p. (C). 45.00 ***(978-0-8263-5100-5(X))*** Univ. of New Mexico Pr.

Mendoza, Louis G. & Toni, Nelson Herrera, eds. Telling Tongues: A Latin@ Anthology on Language Experience. 2007. (ENG & SPA.). 224p. per. 15.00 *(978-0-9717035-8-2(2))* Calaca Pr.

Olivares, Julian, ed. Cuentos hispanos de los Estados Unidos. 2nd ed. (SPA.). 240p. pap. 16.95 *(978-1-55885-260-0(3))* Arte Publico Pr.

Olivas, Daniel A., ed. Latinos in Lotusland: An Anthology of Contemporary Southern California Literature. 2008. 310p. 30.00 *(978-1-931010-46-7(3));* pap. 20.00 *(978-1-931010-47-4(1))* Bilingual Pr./Editorial Bilingue.

Pedraza Jiménez, Felipe B. & Rodriguez Caceres, Milagros. Manual de Literatura Hispanoamericana, 4 vols. Cenlit Ediciones Staff, ed. (SPA.). 1250p. 268.00 *(978-84-85511-26-6(3))* Cénlit Ediciones ESP. Dist: LEA Bk. Distributors (Libros Espana y America).

Rosario, Vanessa Y. Pérez, ed. Hispanic Caribbean Literature of Migration: Narratives of Displacement. 2010. (New Concepts in Latino American Cultures Ser.). (ENG., Illus.). 256p. 89.00 *(978-0-230-62065-0(5))* Palgrave Macmillan.

Shapard, Robert. Sudden Fiction Latino: Short-Short Stories from the United States & Latin America. Gonzales, Ray et al, eds. 2010. (ENG.). 336p. pap. 15.95 *(978-0-393-33645-0(X),* 33645) Norton, W. W. & Co., Inc.

Stavans, Ilan. The Norton Anthology of Latino Literature. Acosta-Belén, Edna et al, eds. 2010. (ENG.). 2489p. 59.95 *(978-0-393-08007-0(2),* 8007) Norton, W. W. & Co., Inc.

Stavans, Ilan & Augenbraum, Harold, eds. Lengua Fresca: Latinos Writing on the Edge. 2006. (ENG., Illus.). 256p. pap. 13.00 *(978-0-618-65670-7(7))* Houghton Mifflin Harcourt Publishing Co.

Toruño-Haensly, Rhina. Crossing Cultures: Hispanic Authors & the Challenges They Overcame in the United States = Cruzando Culturas: Autores Hispanos y Sus Desafíos Superados en Los Estados Unidos. 2011. (Currents in Comparative Romance Languages & Literatures Ser.). (SPA & ENG., Illus.). 214p. (C). 76.95 *(978-1-4331-1253-9(1))* Lang, Peter Publishing, Inc.

AMERICAN LITERATURE—HISPANIC AMERICAN AUTHORS—HISTORY AND CRITICISM

Bloom, Harold, ed. & intro. Hispanic - American Writers: Bloom's Modern Critical Views. 2006. 230p. reprint ed. pap. 27.00 *(978-1-4223-5542-8(X))* DIANE Publishing Co.

Brignoni, Evangelina. Authors in a Latino Family: Communication, Transformation, & the Exception to the Rule. 2008. 156p. pap. *(978-3-639-01255-2(0))* VDM Verlag Dr. Mueller e.K.

Caminero-Santangelo, Marta. On Latinidad: U. S. Latino Literature & the Construction of Ethnicity. 2009. (ENG., Illus.). 336p. pap. 29.95 *(978-0-8130-3448-5(5))* Univ. Pr. of Florida.

—On Latinidad: U.S. Latino Literature & the Construction of Ethnicity. 2007. (ENG.). 336p. 59.95 *(978-0-8130-3083-8(8))* Univ. Pr. of Florida.

Castaneda, Antonia & Melendez, A. Gabriel, eds. Recovering the U. S. Hispanic Literary Heritage: Volume VI, Vol. 6. annot. ed. 2006. (Recovering the U. S. Hispanic Literary Heritage Ser.). 217p. 39.95 *(978-1-55885-478-9(9))* Arte Publico Pr.

Dalleo, Raphael & Machado Sáez, Elena. The Latino - A Canon & the Emergence of Post-Sixties Literature. annot. ed. 2007. (ENG.). 216p. 84.00 *(978-1-4039-7796-0(8))* Palgrave Macmillan.

Danielson, Marivel. Homecoming Queers: Desire & Difference in Chicana Latina Cultural Production. 2009. (Latinidad Ser.). (ENG.). 242p. 72.00 *(978-0-8135-4571-4(4))* Rutgers Univ. Pr.

—Homecoming Queers: Desire & Difference in Chicana Latina Cultural Production. 2009. (Latinidad Ser.). (ENG.). 224p. pap. 23.95 *(978-0-8135-4572-1(2))* Rutgers Univ. Pr.

DeGuzmán, María. Buenas Noches, American Culture: Latina/o Aesthetics of Night. 2012. (ENG., Illus.). 310p. 80.00 ***(978-0-253-00179-5(X)***, 025300179X); pap. 28.00 ***(978-0-253-00189-4(7)***, 0253001897) Indiana Univ. Pr.

Diedwardo, Maryann Pasda. The Fourth R: A Book to Promote the Journey through Hispanic American Literary History to Develop Language Skills. 2008. 60p. pap. 10.49 *(978-1-4343-9847-5(1))* AuthorHouse.

Heredia, Juanita. Transnational Latina Narratives in the Twenty-First Century: The Politics of Gender, Race, & Migrations. 2009. (ENG.). 192p. 84.00 *(978-0-230-61737-7(9))* Palgrave Macmillan.

Kanellos, Nicolás. Hispanic Immigrant Literature: El Sueño del Retorno. (ENG., Illus.). 211p. 2012. pap. 25.00 ***(978-0-292-74394-6(7))*** 2011. 55.00 *(978-0-292-72640-6(6))* Univ. of Texas Pr.

Kevane, Bridget. Profane & Sacred: Latino/a American Writers Reveal the Interplay of the Secular & the Religious. 2007. (Celebrating Faith Ser.). (ENG.). 160p. 59.00 *(978-0-7425-4314-0(5))*; per. 23.95 *(978-0-7425-4315-7(3))* Rowman & Littlefield Publishers, Inc.

Lomas, Clara. Recovering the U. S. Hispanic Literary Heritage. Ventura, Gabriela Baeza, ed. 2011. (Recovering the U. S. Hispanic Literary Heritage Ser.: Vol. 8). 27.95 *(978-1-55885-604-2(8))* Arte Publico Pr.

Mirabal, Nancy Raquel & Lao-Montes, Agustin, eds. Technofuturos: Critical Interventions in Latina/O Studies. 2007. (ENG., Illus.). 430p. 157.50 *(978-0-7391-0895-6(6))* Lexington Bks.

—Technofuturos: Critical Interventions in Latina/o Studies. 2007. (ENG., Illus.). 430p. per. 41.99 *(978-0-7391-2578-6(8))* Lexington Bks.

Perez, Richard & Sandin, Lyn Di Iorio, eds. Contemporary U. S. Latino/A Literary Criticism. 2007. (American Literature Readings in the Twenty-First Century Ser.). (ENG.). 304p. 100.00 *(978-1-4039-7999-5(5))* Palgrave Macmillan.

Poyo, Gerald E. & Ybarra-Frausto, Tomás, eds. Recovering U. S. Hispanic Literary Heritage, Vol. 7. 2009. (ENG.). 160p. 27.95 *(978-1-55885-526-7(2)*, Piñata Books) Arte Publico Pr.

Sandin, Lyn Di Iorio. Killing Spanish: Literary Essays on Ambivalent U. S. Latino - A Identity. 2009. (ENG.). 208p. pap. 32.00 *(978-0-230-61751-3(4))* Palgrave Macmillan.

Scott, Renee & Chiclana y Gonzalez, Arleen, eds. Unveiling the Body in Hispanic Women's Literature: From Nineteenth-Century Spain to Twenty-First-Century United States. 2006. 240p. (C). 109.95 *(978-0-7734-5673-0(2))* Mellen, Edwin Pr., The.

Stavans, Ilan. A Critic's Journey. 2009. (Writers on Writing Ser.). (ENG.). 208p. 65.00 *(978-0-472-11706-2(8))*; pap. 25.95 *(978-0-472-03382-9(4))* Univ. of Michigan Pr.

Suzanne, Bost & Frances, Aparicio, eds. Companion to Latino Literature. 2012. (Routledge Companions Ser.). (ENG.). 544p. 200.00 *(978-0-415-66606-0(6))* Routledge.

AMERICAN LITERATURE—HISTORY AND CRITICISM

Aaron, Daniel. The Americanist. 2007. (ENG.). 208p. 29.95 *(978-0-472-11577-8(4))* Univ. of Michigan Pr.

Abate, Michelle Ann. Raising Your Kids Right: Children's Literature & American Political Conservatism. 2010. (Rutgers Series in Childhood Studies). (ENG., Illus.). 260p. 42.95 *(978-0-8135-4798-5(9))* Rutgers Univ. Pr.

Abdelrazek, Amal Talaat. Contemporary Arab American Women Writers: Hyphenated Identities & Border Crossings. 2007. (C). 104.95 *(978-1-934043-71-4(0))* Cambria Pr.

Abraham, Julie. Metropolitan Lovers: The Homosexuality of Cities. 2009. (Illus.). 344p. 29.95 *(978-0-8166-3818-5(7))* 2008. pap. *(978-0-8166-3819-2(5))* Univ. of Minnesota Pr.

Accilien, Cécile, et al, eds. Just below South: Intercultural Performance in the Caribbean & the U. S. South. 2007. (New World Studies). (ENG.). 288p. (gr. 17). 59.50 *(978-0-8139-2599-8(1))* Univ. Pr. of Virginia.

Ahmad, Dohra. Landscapes of Hope: Anti-Colonial Utopianism in America. 2009. (ENG.). 272p. 65.00 *(978-0-19-533276-6(8))* Oxford Univ. Pr., Inc.

Aiken, Charles S. William Faulkner & the Southern Landscape. 2009. (Center Books on the American South Ser.). (ENG., Illus.). 304p. 34.95 *(978-0-8203-3219-2(4))* Univ. of Georgia Pr.

Al-Shamma, James. Sarah Ruhl: A Critical Study of the Plays. 2011. (ENG., Illus.). 228p. pap. 45.00 *(978-0-7864-5887-5(9))* McFarland & Co., Inc. Pubs.

Alarcón, Norma, et al. El Mundo Zurdo: Selected Works from the Meetings of the Society for the Study of Gloria Anzaldúa, 2007 & 2009. 2010. *(978-1-879960-83-1(4))* Aunt Lute Bks.

Aldridge, Robert C. Telling it Like it Is, Whether You Like it or Not. 2011. 244p. pap. 15.99 ***(978-1-61215-461-9(1))*** Xulon Pr., Inc.

Allen, Patrick, ed. Literary Nashville. 2011. (Literary Cities Ser.). (ENG.). 296p. pap. 16.95 *(978-1-59534-077-1(7))* Trinity Univ. Pr.

—Literary Savannah. 2011. (Literary Cities Ser.). (ENG.). 296p. pap. 16.95 *(978-1-59534-076-4(9))* Trinity Univ. Pr.

Alonzo, Juan José. Badmen, Bandits, & Folk Heroes: The Ambivalence of Mexican American Identity in Literature & Film. 2009. (ENG., Illus.). 208p. 49.95 *(978-0-8165-2868-4(3))*; pap. *(978-0-8165-2812-7(8))* Univ. of Arizona Pr.

Alter, Robert. Pen of Iron: American Prose & the King James Bible. 2010. (ENG.). 208p. 19.95 *(978-0-691-12881-8(2))* Princeton Univ. Pr.

Alvarez, Alma Rosa. Liberation Theology in Chicana/O Literature: Manifestations of Feminist & Gay Identities. 2007. (Latino Communities: Emerging Voices - Political, Social, Cultural & Legal Issues Ser.). (ENG.). 176p. 138.00 *(978-0-415-95557-7(2))* Routledge.

Alvarez, Alma Rosa. Liberation Theology in Chicana/o Literature: Manifestations of Feminist & Gay Identities. 2012. (Latino Communities: Emerging Voices - Political, Social, Cultural & Legal Issues Ser.). (ENG.). 176p. pap. 42.95 ***(978-0-415-54163-3(8))*** Routledge.

The American Tradition in Letters, Vol. 17. Date not set. 32.95 *(978-0-8369-4808-0(4))* Ayer Co. Pubs., Inc.

Ammons, Elizabeth. Brave New Words: How Literature Will Save the Planet. 2010. (ENG.). 168p. pap. 20.00 *(978-1-58729-861-5(9))* Univ. of Iowa Pr.

Ancevski, Zoran. Za Tradicijata: Vrz Tvoreckiot Opit Na T. S. Eliot I Blaze Koneski. 2007. (MAC., Illus.). 315p. *(978-9989-183-21-8(X))* Magor, Bob.

Anderson, Douglas. A House Undivided: Domesticity & Community in American Literature. 2009. (Cambridge Studies in American Literature & Culture Ser.). (ENG.). 252p. pap. 36.00 *(978-0-521-10730-3(X))* Cambridge Univ. Pr.

Andreach, Robert. Len Jenkin's Theatre: Wonder & Heart. 2010. (ENG.). 150p. pap. 25.00 *(978-0-7618-5323-7(5))* Univ. Pr. of America, Inc.

Arango L. Manuel Antonio. Proceso Histórico-Social en la Literatura de Los Primeros Cronistas de la Conquista de América. 2010. (Currents in Comparative Romance Languages & Literatures Ser.). (SPA.). 213p. 74.95 *(978-1-4331-1079-5(2))* Lang, Peter Publishing, Inc.

Arbery, Glenn C. The Southern Critics: An Anthology. 2010. (ENG.). pap. 22.00 *(978-1-935191-80-3(2))* ISI Bks.

Arsic, Branka. Passive Constitutions or 7 1/2 Times Bartleby. 2007. (ENG., Illus.). 224p. 60.00 *(978-0-8047-5393-7(8))* Stanford Univ. Pr.

Atkinson, Jay. Paradise Road: Jack Kerouac's Lost Highway & My Search for America. 2010. (ENG.). 272p. 25.95 *(978-0-470-23769-4(4)*, Wiley) Wiley, John & Sons, Inc.

Augustyn, Adam, ed. American Literature from 1600 Through the 1850s. 2010. (Britannica Guide to World Literature Ser.). (ENG.). 240p. (YA). lib. bdg. 45.00 *(978-1-61530-124-9(0))* Rosen Publishing Group, Inc., The.

—American Literature from 1600 Through The 1850S. 2010. (Britannica Guide to World Literature Ser.). (Illus.). 240p. (YA). 90.00 *(978-1-61530-236-9(0))* Rosen Publishing Group, Inc., The.

Ayers, David. Literary Theory: A Reintroduction. 2008. (ENG.). 256p. 99.95 *(978-1-4051-3602-0(2))*; pap. 32.95 *(978-1-4051-3601-3(4))* Wiley, John & Sons, Inc. (Wiley-Blackwell).

Azzarello, Robert. Queer Environmentality: Ecology, Evolution, & Sexuality in American Literature. 2012. 160p. 89.95 ***(978-1-4094-2665-3(3))*** Ashgate Publishing Co.

Baelo-Allue, Sonia. Bret Easton Ellis's Controversial Fiction: Writing Between High & Low Culture. 2011. (Continuum Literary Studies). (ENG.). 240p. 110.00 *(978-1-4411-0791-6(6))* Continuum International Publishing Group, Ltd. GBR. Dist: National Bk. Network.

Bailey De Luise, Rachel. A Confluence of Literary Devices in Early American Literature. 2011. 72p. pap. ***(978-3-8443-1699-5(X))*** Lambert Academic Publishing.

Baker, Anne. Heartless Immensity: Literature, Culture, & Geography in Antebellum America. 2006. (ENG., Illus.). 184p. 75.00 *(978-0-472-11570-9(7))* Univ. of Michigan Pr.

Balaam, Peter. Misery's Mathematics: Mourning, Compensation & Reality in Antebellum American Literature. 2009. (Literary Criticism & Cultural Theory Ser.). (ENG., Illus.). 200p. 125.00 *(978-0-415-96807-2(0)*, RT8070) Routledge.

Banach, Jennifer. Bloom's How to Write about Arthur Miller. 2012. (Bloom's How to Write about Literature Ser.). 250p. (C). 45.00 *(978-1-60413-747-7(9)*, Chelsea Hse.) Facts On File, Inc.

—Blooms How to Write about Tennessee Williams. 2009. (Bloom's How to Write about Literature Ser.). 248p. (C). (gr. 9-18). 45.00 *(978-1-60413-346-2(5)*, Chelsea Hse.) Facts On File, Inc.

Banco, Lindsey & Banco, Lindsey Michael. Travel & Drugs in Twentieth-Century Literature. 2009. (Routledge Studies in Twentieth-Century Literature Ser.). (ENG.). 198p. (C). 125.00 *(978-0-415-99861-1(1))* Routledge.

Bannet, Eve Tavor & Manning, Susan, eds. Transatlantic Literary Studies, 1660-1830. 2011. (ENG.). 296p. 90.00 ***(978-1-107-00157-2(9))*** Cambridge Univ. Pr.

Barge, Laura Inez Deavenport. Exploring Worldviews in Literature: From William Wordsworth to Edward Albee. 2009. pap. 19.95 *(978-0-89112-538-9(8)*, ACU Pr.) Abilene Christian Univ. Pr.

Baron, Robert C. & Junkin, Elizabeth Darby. Of Discovery & Destiny: An Anthology of American Writers & the American Land. 2006. (Illus.). 414p. reprint ed. 20.00 *(978-1-4223-5802-3(X))* DIANE Publishing Co.

Barzilai, Lyn Graham. George Oppen: A Critical Study. 2006. (ENG., Illus.). 231p. per. 45.00 *(978-0-7864-2549-5(0))* McFarland & Co., Inc. Pubs.

Baskervill, William Malone. Southern Writers: Biographical & Critical Studies. 2009. (ENG.). 415p. 41.99 *(978-1-117-13656-1(6))* 2009. (ENG.). 415p. pap. 33.75 *(978-1-117-13657-8(4))* 2008. 416p. 30.99 *(978-0-559-32703-2(X))* 2008. 416p. pap. 33.75 *(978-0-559-32702-5(1))* BiblioBazaar.

—Southern Writers: Biographical & Critical Studies. 2009. 98p. pap. *(978-0-217-55675-0(2))* Books LLC.

—Southern Writers Set, 2 vols. reprint ed. lib. bdg. 250.00 *(978-0-7222-4845-4(8))* Library Reprints, Inc.

Bassard, Katherine Clay. Transforming Scriptures: African American Women Writers & the Bible. 2011. (ENG., Illus.). 180p. pap. 22.95 *(978-0-8203-3880-4(X))* Univ. of Georgia Pr.

Bauer, Dale. Sex Expression & American Women Writers, 1860-1940. 2009. (ENG., Illus.). 256p. 57.95 *(978-0-8078-3230-1(8))* Univ. of North Carolina Pr.

Bauer, Dale, ed. The Cambridge History of American Women's Literature. 2012. (ENG., Illus.). 728p. 180.00 ***(978-1-107-00137-4(4))*** Cambridge Univ. Pr.

Bauer, Dale & Bauer, Dale M. Sex Expression & American Women Writers, 1860-1940. 2009. (ENG., Illus.). 256p. pap. 23.00 *(978-0-8078-5906-3(0))* Univ. of North Carolina Pr.

Baym, Nina. Women Writers of the American West, 1833-1927. 2011. (ENG.). 364p. 40.00 *(978-0-252-03597-5(6))* Univ. of Illinois Pr.

Beaver, Lauren. The Offbeat-Words upon the Way: A Literary Collection. 2011. (ENG.). 117p. pap. 8.50 ***(978-1-61186-059-7(8))*** Michigan State Univ. Pr.

Beck, Charlotte H. Robert Penn Warren - Critic. 2006. 224p. 38.00 *(978-1-57233-474-8(6))* Univ. of Tennessee Pr.

Beebee, Thomas O. Millennial Literatures of the Americas, 1492-2002. 2008. (Imagining the Americas Ser.). (Illus.). 264p. 65.00 *(978-0-19-533938-3(X))* Oxford Univ. Pr., Inc.

Beem, Edgar Allen. Backyard Maine: Local Essays. 2010. 209p. pap. 15.00 *(978-0-88448-317-5(7))* Tilbury Hse. Pubs.

Beers, Henry A. Brief History of English & American Literature. 2008. 436p. 30.99 *(978-0-554-38610-2(0))* 2008. 436p. 32.99 *(978-0-554-29307-3(2))* 2007. (ENG.). 388p. per. 25.99 *(978-1-4346-7350-3(2))* 2007. (ENG.). 432p. per. 28.99 *(978-1-4346-7351-0(0))* BiblioBazaar.

Beers, Henry A. & Hurst, John Fletcher. Brief History of English & American Literature. 2007. 356p. per. *(978-1-4065-3730-7(6))* Dodo Pr.

Bellin, Joshua David. Medicine Bundle: Indian Sacred Performance & American Literature, 1824-1932. 2007. 272p. (C). 59.95 *(978-0-8122-4034-4(0))* Univ. of Pennsylvania Pr.

Benedict, Ruth. An Anthropologist at Work. 2011. (ENG., Illus.). 605p. pap. 39.95 *(978-1-4128-1850-6(8))* Transaction Pubs.

Benfey, Christopher. American Audacity: Literary Essays North & South. 2009. (Writers on Writing Ser.). (ENG.). 256p. pap. 23.95 *(978-0-472-03399-7(9))* Univ. of Michigan Pr.

Benito, Jesus, et al. Uncertain Mirrors: Magical Realism in US Ethnic Literatures. 2009. (Illus.). 276p. pap. 74.00 *(978-90-420-2600-1(6))* Rodopi.

Berkove, Lawrence I. Jack London. 2011. ***(978-1-58765-830-3(5))*** Salem Pr., Inc.

Berman, Ronald. Fitzgerald's Mentors: Edmund Wilson, H. L. Mencken, & Gerald Murphy. 2012. (ENG.). 128p. (C). 29.95 ***(978-0-8173-1761-4(9))*** Univ. of Alabama Pr.

—Fitzgerald's Mentors: Edmund Wilson, H.L. Mencken, & Gerald Murphy. 2012. ***(978-0-8173-5693-4(2))***; 119p. ***(978-0-8173-8638-2(6))*** Univ. of Alabama Pr.

Bernath, Michael T. Confederate Minds: The Struggle for Intellectual Independence in the Civil War South. 2010. (Civil War America Ser.). (ENG., Illus.). 464p. 39.95 *(978-0-8078-3391-9(6))* Univ. of North Carolina Pr.

Bernheimer, Kate, ed. Brothers & Beasts: An Anthology of Men on Fairy Tales. 2007. (Series in Fairy-Tale Studies). 208p. pap. 15.95 *(978-0-8143-3267-2(6))* Wayne State Univ. Pr.

Bierfelt, Kristin. The North Shore Literary Trail: From Bradstreet's Andover to Hawthorne's Salem. 2008. 19.99 *(978-1-59629-520-9(1))* History Pr., The.

Bierowski, Thomas R. Kerouac in Ecstasy: Shamanic Expression in the Writings. 2011. (ENG., Illus.). 211p. pap. 45.00 *(978-0-7864-5967-4(0))* McFarland & Co., Inc. Pubs.

Birnbaum, Michele. Race, Work, & Desire in American Literature, 1860-1930. 2009. (Cambridge Studies in American Literature & Culture Ser.). (ENG.). 208p. pap. 32.99 *(978-0-521-12019-7(5))* Cambridge Univ. Pr.

Birns, Nicholas. Willa Cather. 2011. ***(978-1-58765-826-6(7))*** Salem Pr., Inc.

Blackburn, Brandon. Natural History As Dissent. 2010. 68p. pap. *(978-3-8383-4049-4(3))* Lambert Academic Publishing.

Blasing, Mutlu Konuk. The Art of Life: Studies in American Autobiographical Literature. 2011. (ENG.). 222p. pap. 25.00 *(978-0-292-72932-2(4))* Univ. of Texas Pr.

Bliss, Perry. The American Spirit in Literature: Chronicles of America series; V. 34. 2009. 172p. pap. 25.50 *(978-1-60444-038-6(4))* IndoEuropeanPublishing.com.

Bloom, Harold. The House on Mango Street. 2nd rev. ed. 2010. (Bloom's Guides). 122p. (C). (gr. 9-18). 30.00 *(978-1-60413-812-2(2)*, Chelsea Hse.) Facts On File, Inc.

—Richard Wright's Native Son. annot. ed. 2007. (Bloom's Guides). 136p. (YA). (gr. 9-12). lib. bdg. 30.00 *(978-0-7910-9368-9(9))* Facts On File, Inc.

Bloom, Harold, ed. The Adventures of Tom Sawyer. 2011. (Bloom's Guides). 124p. (C). (gr. 9). 30.00 *(978-1-61753-000-5(X)*, Chelsea Hse.) Facts On File, Inc.

—A Farewell to Arms. 2009. (Bloom's Guides). 136p. (C). (gr. 9-18). 30.00 *(978-1-60413-572-5(7)*, Chelsea Hse.) Facts On File, Inc.

—J. D. Salinger's Short Stories. 2011. (Bloom's Modern Critical Interpretations Ser.). 150p. (C). (gr. 9). 45.00 *(978-1-60413-272-4(8)*, Chelsea Hse.) Facts On File, Inc.

—John Steinbeck's Short Stories. 2011. (Bloom's Modern Critical Interpretations Ser.). 146p. (C). (gr. 9). 45.00 *(978-1-60413-271-7(X)*, Chelsea Hse.) Facts On File, Inc.

—Ralph Ellison. 2nd rev. ed. 2009. (Bloom's Modern Critical Views Ser.). 246p. (C). (gr. 9-18). 45.00 *(978-1-60413-578-7(6)*, Bloom's Literary Criticism) Facts On File, Inc.

—The Tell-Tale Heart & Other Stories - Edgar Allan Poe, New Edition. 2nd rev. ed. 2009. (Bloom's Modern Critical Interpretations Ser.). 220p. (C). (gr. 9-18). 45.00 *(978-1-60413-388-2(0)*, Chelsea Hse.) Facts On File, Inc.

Bloom, Harold, ed. & intro. Joy Luck Club. 2009. (Bloom's Guides). 146p. (C). (gr. 9-18). 30.00 *(978-1-60413-574-9(3)*, Chelsea Hse.) Facts On File, Inc.

Bock, Jannika. Concorde in Massachusetts, Discord in the World: The Writings of Henry Thoreau & John Cage. 2008. (American Culture Ser.). (Illus.). 286p. pap. 74.95 *(978-3-631-58413-2(X))* Lang, Peter GmbH, Europaischer Verlag der Wissenschaften DEU. Dist: Lang, Peter.

Bogumil, Mary L. Understanding August Wilson. rev. ed. 2011. (ENG.). 184p. pap. 24.95 *(978-1-57003-979-9(8))* Univ. of South Carolina Pr.

Bollobás, Enikő. They Aren't, until I Call Them: Performing the Subject in American Literature. 2010. 236p. pap. 66.95 *(978-3-631-58982-3(4))* Lang, Peter GmbH, Europaischer Verlag der Wissenschaften DEU. Dist: Lang, Peter.

Boone, Joseph A. & Cadden, Michael, eds. Engendering Men Rle, Volume 3. 2012. (RLE: Women, Feminism & Literature Ser.). (ENG.). 344p. (C). 130.00 ***(978-0-415-52329-5(X))*** Routledge.

Borbála, Bökös. The World is an Illusion: Four Essays on Paul Auster. 2008. 80p. pap. *(978-3-639-09512-8(X))* VDM Verlag Dr. Mueller e.K.

Borland, Isabel Alvarez. Cuban-American Literature & Art: Negotiating Identities. Bosch, Lynette M. F., ed. 2010. (SUNY series in Latin American & Iberian Thought & Culture Ser.). 234p. pap. 25.95 *(978-0-7914-9374-8(1)*, Suny Pr.) State Univ. of New York Pr.

Borland, Isabel Alvarez & Bosch, Lynette M. F., eds. Cuban-American Literature & Art: Negotiating Identities. 2009. (SUNY series in Latin American & Iberian Thought & Culture Ser.). 240p. 70.00 *(978-0-7914-9373-1(3))* State Univ. of New York Pr.

Boston Miscellany of Literature & Fashion, 3 vols. reprint ed. lib. bdg. 180.00 *(978-0-404-19505-2(9))* AMS Pr., Inc.

Boulukos, George. The Grateful Slave: The Emergence of Race in Eighteenth-Century British & American Culture. 2011. (ENG., Illus.). 288p. pap. 36.99 *(978-0-521-18866-1(0))* Cambridge Univ. Pr.

Bouson, J. Brooks. Embodied Shame: Uncovering Female Shame in Contemporary Women's Writings. 2010. 236p. pap. 24.95 *(978-1-4384-2728-7(X)*, Suny Pr.) 2009. 256p. 70.00 *(978-1-4384-2727-0(1))* State Univ. of New York Pr.

Boyden, Michael. Predicting the Past: The Paradoxes of American Literary History. 2009. 214p. 55.00 *(978-90-5867-731-0(1))* Leuven Univ. Pr. BEL. Dist: Cornell Univ. Pr.

Boynton, Percy H. A History of American Literature. 524p. 2008. 55.95 *(978-0-548-96784-3(9))* 2007. (ENG.). per. 40.95 *(978-0-548-64345-7(8))* Kessinger Publishing, LLC.

Bradbury, John M. Renaissance in the South: A Critical History of the Literature, 1920-1960. 2011. (ENG.). 222p. pap. 40.00 ***(978-0-8078-9628-0(4))*** Univ. of North Carolina Pr.

Braziel, Jana Evans. Duvalier's Ghosts: Race, Diaspora, & U. S. Imperialism in Haitian Literatures. 2010. (ENG., Illus.). 320p. 69.95 *(978-0-8130-3457-7(4))* Univ. Pr. of Florida.

Bredahl, A. Carl, Jr., ACarl. New Ground: Western American Narrative & the Literary Canon. 2011. (ENG.). 208p. pap. 40.00 ***(978-0-8078-5641-3(X))*** Univ. of North Carolina Pr.

Breen, Margaret Sönser. Narratives of Queer Desire: Deserts of the Heart. 2009. (ENG., Illus.). 216p. 84.00 *(978-0-230-22388-2(5))* Palgrave Macmillan.

Breitwieser, Mitchell. National Melancholy: Mourning & Opportunity in Classic American Literature. 2007. (ENG.). 336p. 60.00 *(978-0-8047-5581-8(7))* Stanford Univ. Pr.

Brezina, Corona. Johnny Tremain & the American Revolution. 2009. (Looking at Literature Through Primary Sources Ser.). 64p. (gr. 5-8). 58.50 *(978-1-61514-304-7(1))* Rosen Publishing Group, Inc., The.

Brinkmeyer, Robert H. The Fourth Ghost: White Southern Writers & European Fascism, 1930-1950. 2009. *(978-0-8071-3383-5(3))* Louisiana State Univ. Pr.

Brinkmeyer, Robert H., Jr. Remapping Southern Literature: Contemporary Southern Writers & the West. 2007. (Mercer University Lamar Memorial Lecture Ser.). (ENG.). 152p. per. 22.95 *(978-0-8203-2997-0(5))* Univ. of Georgia Pr.

Brittin, Norman A. Emerson & the Metaphysical Poets. 2011. 24p. 35.95 ***(978-1-258-01025-6(9))*** Literary Licensing, LLC.

Bronson, Walter C. A Short History of American Literature. 2009. 388p. 26.99 *(978-1-103-92885-9(6))*; pap. 20.99 *(978-1-103-92877-4(5))* BiblioBazaar.

Brooks, Cleanth. The Language of the American South. 2007. (Mercer University Lamar Memorial Lectures). (ENG.). 72p. per. 18.95 *(978-0-8203-3123-2(6))* Univ. of Georgia Pr.

Brown, Doug. An Interpretation of the Social Theories & Novels of Daniel Quinn: How Can We Create a Sustainable Society? 2009. (Illus.). 172p. 99.95 *(978-0-7734-4652-6(4))* Mellen, Edwin Pr., The.

Brown, Laura. Homeless Dogs & Melancholy Apes: Humans & Other Animals in the Modern Literary Imagination. 2010. (Illus.). 176p. 35.00 *(978-0-8014-4828-7(X))* Cornell Univ. Pr.

Brownell, William C. Standards. 2010. 158p. pap. 17.56 *(978-1-163-76404-6(3))* 2007. 156p. 36.95 *(978-0-548-52317-9(7))* 2007. (ENG.). 156p. per. 21.95 *(978-0-548-50771-1(6))* Kessinger Publishing, LLC.

Brückner, Martin & Hsu, Hsuan L. American Literary Geographies: Spatial Practice & Cultural Production, 1500-1900. Bruckner, Martin, ed. 2007. (Illus.). 367p. *(978-0-87413-980-8(5))* Univ. of Delaware Pr.

Bryant, John L. Melville Unfolding: Sexuality, Politics, & the Versions of Typee. 2008. (ENG., Illus.). 480p. 90.00 *(978-0-472-11592-1(8))* Univ. of Michigan Pr.

Buell, Lawrence, ed. Shades of the Planet: American Literature as World Literature. 2007. (ENG., Illus.). 312p. (C). per. 29.95 *(978-0-691-12852-8(9))* Princeton Univ. Pr.

Buell, Lawrence & Dimock, Wai-Chee, eds. Shades of the Planet: American Literature as World Literature. 2007. (Illus.). 304p. 75.00 *(978-0-691-12851-1(0))* Princeton Univ. Pr.

Burlinson, Christopher. Allegory, Space & the Material World in the Writings of Edmund Spenser. 2006. (Studies in Renaissance Literature Ser.: Volume 17). (Illus.). 274p. 90.00 *(978-1-84384-078-7(2))* Boydell & Brewer, Inc.

Bush, Clive. Holding the Line: Selected Essays in American Literature & Culture. 2009. 376p. 68.95 *(978-3-03911-571-6(5))* Lang, Peter AG GBR. Dist: Lang, Peter.

Caleshu, Anthony. Reconfiguring the Modern American Lyric: The Poetry of James Tate. 2011. 220p. pap. *(978-3-0343-0174-9(X))* Lang, Peter Publishing, Inc.

Callahan, Monique-Adelle. Between the Lines: Literary Transnationalism & African American Poetics, 1 vol. 2011. (Imagining the Americas Ser.). 208p. 74.00 *(978-0-19-974306-3(1))* Oxford Univ. Pr., Inc.

Calvo-Pascual, Mónica. Chaos & Madness: The Politics of Fiction in Stephen Marlowe¿s Historical Narratives. 2011. (ENG., Illus.). 218p. pap. 62.00 *(978-90-420-3301-6(0))* Rodopi.

Cameron, Sharon. Impersonality: Seven Essays. 2007. (ENG., Illus.). 272p. 70.00 *(978-0-226-09131-0(7))* Univ. of Chicago Pr.

Canby, Henry Seidel. Definitions. 2007. (ENG.). 140p. per. *(978-1-4068-4191-6(9))* Echo Library.

—Definitions Essays in Contemporary Criti. 2007. pap. *(978-1-4065-1255-7(9))* Dodo Pr.

Carden, Mary Paniccia. Sons & Daughters of Self-Made Men: Improvising Gender, Place, Nation in American Literature. 2010. 56.50 *(978-0-8387-5754-3(5))* Bucknell Univ. Pr.

—Sons & Daughters of Self-Made Men: Improvising Gender, Place, Nation in American Literature. 2009. (ENG.). 255p. 65.00 *(978-1-61148-344-4(1))* Bucknell Univ. Pr.

Carruthers, Jo & Tate, Andrew, eds. Spiritual Identities: Literature & Post-Secular Imagination. 2009. 236p. pap. 58.95 *(978-3-03911-925-7(7))* Lang, Peter AG GBR. Dist: Lang, Peter.

Carter, Everett. The American Idea: The Literary Response to American Optimism. 2011. (ENG.). 285p. pap. 40.00 ***(978-0-8078-9634-1(9))*** Univ. of North Carolina Pr.

Casale, Frank D. Bloom's How to Write about Walt Whitman. 2009. (Bloom's How to Write about Literature Ser.). 272p. (C). (gr. 9-18). 45.00 *(978-1-60413-310-3(4)*, Chelsea Hse.) Facts On File, Inc.

Castillo, Susan. American Literature in Context to 1865. 2010. (ENG., Illus.). 204p. 94.95 *(978-1-4051-8864-7(2))*; pap. 24.95 *(978-1-4051-8863-0(4))* Wiley, John & Sons, Inc. (Wiley-Blackwell).

Caverlee, William. Amid the Swirling Ghosts & Other Essays. 2009. 214p. pap. 20.00 *(978-1-887366-92-2(X))* Univ. of Louisiana at Lafayette Pr.

Cecere, Gregory. Nobles & Savages. 2009. 96p. pap. *(978-3-639-18196-8(4))* VDM Verlag Dr. Mueller e.K.

Chambers, Douglas B., ed. The Past Is Not Dead: Essays from the Southern Quarterly. 2012. (ENG.). 352p. 65.00 ***(978-1-61703-303-2(0))***; pap. 30.00 ***(978-1-61703-304-9(9))*** Univ. Pr. of Mississippi.

—Personal Souths: Interviews from the Southern Quarterly. 2012. (ENG.). 352p. 65.00 ***(978-1-61703-290-5(5))***; 312p. pap. 30.00 ***(978-1-61703-291-2(3))*** Univ. Pr. of Mississippi.

Chasles, Philar Fte. Anglo-American Literature & Manners: From the French of Philar +te Chasles. 2006. 328p. per. 23.99 *(978-1-4255-3197-3(0))* MPublishing.

Chavkin, Allan Richard. Saul Bellow. 2011. ***(978-1-58765-824-2(0))*** Salem Pr., Inc.

Childs, Peter. Ian Mcewen's Enduring Love. 2007. (Routledge Guides to Literature Ser.). (ENG.). 160p. per. 28.95 *(978-0-415-34559-0(6))* Routledge.

—Rout Guid End Love Cont & Crit. 2007. (Routledge Guides to Literature Ser.). (ENG.). 160p. 95.00 *(978-0-415-34558-3(8))* Routledge.

Ching, Barbara & Wagner-Lawlor, Jennifer A., eds. The Scandal of Susan Sontag. 2009. (Gender & Culture Ser.). (ENG., Illus.). 280p. (gr. 17). 79.50 *(978-0-231-14916-7(6))*; pap. 24.50 *(978-0-231-14917-4(4))* Columbia Univ. Pr.

Chock, Eric & Lum, Darrell H. Y., eds. Bamboo Ridge No. 98. 2011. 256p. pap. 18.00 ***(978-0-910043-84-7(1))*** Bamboo Ridge Pr.

Chu, Patricia E. Race, Nationalism & the State in British & American Modernism. (ENG.). 2009. 212p. pap. 32.99 *(978-0-521-12381-5(X))* 2007. 208p. 107.99 *(978-0-521-86966-9(8))* Cambridge Univ. Pr.

Clabough, Casey. The Art of the Magic Striptease: The Literary Layers of George Garrett. 2009. (ENG., Illus.). 224p. pap. 29.95 *(978-0-8130-3453-9(1))* Univ. Pr. of Florida.

Cohen, Daniel A. Pillars of Salt, Monuments of Grace: New England Crime Literature & the Origins of American Popular Culture, 1674-1860. 2006. (Commonwealth Center Studies in American Culture Ser.). (Illus.). 350p. per. 19.95 *(978-1-55849-529-6(0))* Univ. of Massachusetts Pr.

Cohen, Lara Langer. The Fabrication of American Literature: Fraudulence & Antebellum Print Culture. 2011. (Material Texts). (Illus.). 256p. (C). 59.95 ***(978-0-8122-4369-7(2))*** Univ. of Pennsylvania Pr.

Coles, Robert. Handing One Another Along: Literature & Social Reflection. Hall, Trevor & Kennedy, Vicki, eds. 2010. (ENG., Illus.). 304p. 27.00 *(978-1-4000-6203-4(9))* Random Hse., Inc.

Collins, W. Lucas. Lucian. 2009. 188p. 26.99 *(978-1-110-87032-5(9))*; pap. 21.75 *(978-1-110-87029-5(9))* BiblioBazaar.

Connery, Thomas B. Journalism & Realism: Rendering American Life. 2011. (ENG.). 306p. pap. 24.95 *(978-0-8101-2733-3(4))* Northwestern Univ. Pr.

Contreras, Sheila Marie. Blood Lines: Myth, Indigenism, & Chicana - O Literature. 2008. (Chicana Matters Ser.). (ENG.). 232p. (C). pap. 22.95 *(978-0-292-71797-8(0))* Univ. of Texas Pr.

—Blood Lines: Myth, Indigenism, & Chicana/O Literature. 2008. (Chicana Matters Ser.). (ENG.). 232p. (C). 55.00 *(978-0-292-71796-1(2))* Univ. of Texas Pr.

Cook, Paul. American Literature from the Colonies to the Civil War. rev. ed. 2008. (ENG.). 448p. pap. 77.96 *(978-0-7575-5848-1(8))* Kendall Hunt Publishing Co.

Cook, Richard M. Alfred Kazin: A Biography. 2008. (ENG., Illus.). 464p. 35.00 *(978-0-300-11505-5(9))* Yale Univ. Pr.

Cooper, James Fenimore. Knights of the Brush: The Hudson River School & the Moral Landscape. 2008. (ENG., Illus.). 112p. 35.00 *(978-0-9818663-0-7(1))* Newington Cropsey Cultural Studies Ctr.

Cooper, William Emons. James Fenimore Cooper: Social Historian of the Landed Gentry in New York State in His Littlepage Novels. 2010. 54p. pap. 14.95 *(978-1-4327-6142-4(0))* Outskirts Pr., Inc.

Copeland, Rita & Struck, Peter, eds. The Cambridge Companion to Allegory. 2010. (Cambridge Companions to Literature Ser.). (ENG., Illus.). 324p. (C). pap. 29.99 *(978-0-521-68082-0(4))* Cambridge Univ. Pr.

Copertari, Gabriela & Martin, Karen Wooley. Isabel Allende's House of the Spirits Trilogy: Narrative Geographies. 2010. (Monografías A Ser.: Volume 285). (Illus.). 206p. 90.00 *(978-1-85566-200-1(0)*, Tamesis Bks.) Boydell & Brewer, Ltd. GBR. Dist: Boydell & Brewer, Inc.

Cox, Simon. Decoding the Lost Symbol: The Unauthorized Expert Guide to the Facts Behind the Fiction. 2009. (ENG., Illus.). 256p. pap. 14.99 *(978-0-7432-8727-2(4)*, Touchstone) Touchstone.

Crable, Bryan. Ralph Ellison & Kenneth Burke: At the Roots of the Racial Divide. 2011. (ENG., Illus.). 264p. (C). (gr. 13-17). pap. 22.50 ***(978-0-8139-3216-3(5))*** Univ. Pr. of Virginia.

—Ralph Ellison & Kenneth Burke at the Roots of the Racial Divide. 2012. E-Book ***(978-0-8139-3217-0(3))*** 2011. (ENG.). 264p. (gr. 17). 49.50 ***(978-0-8139-3215-6(7))*** Univ. Pr. of Virginia.

Crane, Stephen. The Blue Hotel. 2008. 48p. pap. *(978-1-4099-0277-5(3))* Dodo Pr.

—The Blue Hotel. 2007. (Tale Blazers: American Literature Ser.). (ENG.). 70p. pap. 3.30 *(978-0-89598-688-7(4))* Perfection Learning Corp.

Crazzolara, Monica. Borders in Chicana Literature: Gloria Anzaldúa & Sandra Cisneros. 2008. 104p. pap. *(978-3-8364-9418-2(3))* VDM Verlag Dr. Mueller e.K.

Creed, John & Andrews, Susan. Purely Alaska: Authentic Voices of the Far North. 2010. (ENG.). 304p. (gr. 7). pap. 17.95 *(978-1-935347-10-1(1))* Epicenter Pr., Inc.

Crowell, Ellen & Hogg, James. The Dandy in Irish & American Southern Fiction: Aristocratic Drag. Manning, Susan et al, eds. 2008. (Edinburgh Critical Studies in Transatlantic Literature Ser.). (ENG., Illus.). 240p. (gr. 17). 90.00 *(978-0-7486-2548-2(8))* Edinburgh Univ. Pr. GBR. Dist: Columbia Univ. Pr.

Daiya, Kavita. Violent Belongings: Partition, Gender, & National Culture in Postcolonial India. (ENG., Illus.). 274p. 2011. pap. 27.95 *(978-1-59213-744-2(X))* 2008. (C). 58.50 *(978-1-59213-743-5(1))* Temple Univ. Pr.

Dallmann, Antje & Isensee, Reinhard, eds. Envisioning American Utopias: Fictions of Science & Politics in Literature & Visual Culture. 2011. 240p. pap. 57.95 *(978-3-631-57513-0(0))* Lang, Peter GmbH, Europaischer Verlag der Wissenschaften DEU. Dist: Lang, Peter.

Dalsgaard, Inger H., et al, eds. The Cambridge Companion to Thomas Pynchon. 2011. (Cambridge Companions to Literature Ser.). (ENG.). 212p. (C). 90.00 ***(978-0-521-76974-7(4))***; pap. 27.99 ***(978-0-521-17304-9(3))*** Cambridge Univ. Pr.

Daniel, Lucy. Gertrude Stein. 2009. (Reaktion Books - Critical Lives Ser.). (ENG., Illus.). 192p. pap. 16.95 *(978-1-86189-516-5(X))* Reaktion Bks., Ltd. GBR. Dist: Chicago Distribution Ctr.

Davidson, Donald. Southern Writers in the Modern World: Eugenia Dorothy Blount Lamar Memorial Lectures 1957. 2011. 88p. 38.95 ***(978-1-258-08535-3(6))*** Literary Licensing, LLC.

Dawn M., Skorczewski. Anne Sexton's Secrets: Inside the Therapy of Anne Sexton. 2012. (ENG.). 268p. (C). 90.00 *(978-0-415-88746-5(1))*; pap. 35.95 *(978-0-415-88747-2(X))* Routledge.

De Saavedra, Miguel Cervantes. Varias Obras inéditas de Cervantes: Sacadas de Códices de la Biblioteca Colombina, con Nuevas Ilustraciones Sobre la Vida Del Autor Y el Quijote. 2010. 524p. pap. 40.75 *(978-1-149-01468-4(7))* BiblioBazaar.

Dean, John Emory. Travel Narratives from New Mexico: Reconstructing Identity & Truth. 2009. 104.99 *(978-1-60497-631-1(4))* Cambria Pr.

Delgadillo, Theresa. Spiritual Mestizaje: Religion, Gender, Race, & Nation in Contemporary Chicana Narrative. 2011. (Latin America Otherwise Ser.). (ENG., Illus.). 296p. pap. 23.95 *(978-0-8223-5046-0(7))*; 84.95 *(978-0-8223-5029-3(7))* Duke Univ. Pr.

Deme, Mariam Konate. Heroism & the Supernatural in the African Epic. 2010. (African Studies). (ENG.). 148p. 125.00 *(978-0-415-87492-2(0))* Routledge.

Deming, Richard. Listening on All Sides: Toward an Emersonian Ethics of Reading. 2008. (ENG.). 192p. 50.00 *(978-0-8047-5738-6(0))* Stanford Univ. Pr.

Denny, Margaret & Gilman, William H., eds. The American Writer & the European Tradition. 2009. (ENG.). 208p. pap. 50.00 *(978-0-8166-5741-4(6))* Univ. of Minnesota Pr.

Derleth, August. Wisconsin Writers & Writing. pap. 16.00 *(978-1-896648-98-9(3))* Battered Silicon Dispatch Box, The.

Dewan, Pauline. The Art of Place in Literature for Children & Young Adults: How Locale Shapes a Story. 2010. 412p. 129.95 *(978-0-7734-3762-3(2))* Mellen, Edwin Pr., The.

Dickens, Charles. A Child's Dream of a Star. 2009. (ENG.). 50p. pap. 16.75 *(978-1-116-99742-2(8))*; pap. 15.75 *(978-1-116-99743-9(6))* BiblioBazaar.

Dickstein, Morris. James Baldwin. 2010. (Critical Insights Ser.). 455p. (C). 85.00 *(978-1-58765-701-6(5))* Salem Pr., Inc.

Dierks, Konstantin. In My Power: Letter Writing & Communications in Early America. (Early American Studies). (Illus.). 376p. (C). 2011. pap. 24.95 ***(978-0-8122-2181-7(8))*** 2009. 55.00 *(978-0-8122-4153-2(3))* Univ. of Pennsylvania Pr.

Dimock, W. C. Through Other Continents: American Literature Across Deep Time. 2008. (ENG., Illus.). 264p. (C). pap. 26.95 *(978-0-691-11450-7(1))* Princeton Univ. Pr.

Dimock, Wai-Chee. Through Other Continents: American Literature Across Deep Time. 2006. (Illus.). 243p. 35.00 *(978-0-691-11449-1(8))* Princeton Univ. Pr.

Dines, Martin. Gay Suburban Narratives in American & British Culture: Homecoming Queens. 2009. (ENG., Illus.). 232p. 95.00 *(978-0-230-23324-9(4))* Palgrave Macmillan.

Dobson, Austin. At Prior Park & Other Papers. 2010. 116p. pap. *(978-1-151-90349-5(3))* Books LLC.

—At Prior Park & Other Papers. 2007. (ENG.). 328p. 45.95 *(978-0-548-04228-1(4))* Kessinger Publishing, LLC.

Dolan, Neal. Emerson's Liberalism. 2009. (Studies in American Thought & Culture). pap. *(978-0-299-22800-2(2))* Univ. of Wisconsin Pr.

Dong, Lan. Reading Amy Tan, 1 vol. 2009. (Pop Lit Book Club Ser.). 138p. 40.00 *(978-0-313-35546-2(0*, GR5546) Greenwood Publishing Group, Inc.

Dowd, Chris. The Construction of Irish Identity in American Literature. 2010. (Routledge Transnational Perspectives on American Literature Ser.). (ENG., Illus.). 234p. (C). 133.00 *(978-0-415-88043-5(2))* Routledge.

Drake, Kimberly S. Subjectivity in the American Protest Novel. 2011. (ENG.). 264p. 85.00 *(978-0-230-10716-8(8))* Palgrave Macmillan.

Dreisinger, Baz. Near Black: White-To-Black Passing in American Culture. 2008. 224p. pap. 24.95 net. *(978-1-55849-675-0(0))*; pap. 24.95 *(978-1-55849-674-3(2))* Univ. of Massachusetts Pr.

Duke, David C. Writers & Miners: Activism & Imagery in America. 2009. (ENG.). 288p. pap. 30.00 *(978-0-8131-9347-2(8))* Univ. Pr. of Kentucky.

Dunne, Eamonn. J. Hillis Miller & the Possibilities of Reading: Literature after Deconstruction. (ENG.). 176p. 2012. pap. 29.95 ***(978-1-4411-3639-8(8))*** 2010. 100.00 *(978-1-4411-9405-3(3))* Continuum International Publishing Group, Ltd. GBR. Dist: National Bk. Network.

Duvall, John N. & Abadie, Ann J., eds. Faulkner & Postmodernism. 2009. (Faulkner & Yoknapatawpha Ser.). (ENG.). 232p. pap. 25.00 *(978-1-60473-253-5(9))* Univ. Pr. of Mississippi.

Dworkin, Ira, ed. Alif 31: The Other Americas. 2011. pap. 24.95 *(978-977-416-451-4(2))* Oxford Univ. Pr., Inc.

Earhart, Amy & Jewell, Andrew. The American Literature Scholar in the Digital Age. 2010. (Editorial Theory & Literary Criticism Ser.). (ENG., Illus.). 302p. pap. 37.50 *(978-0-472-05119-9(9))*; (C). 90.00 *(978-0-472-07119-7(X))* Univ. of Michigan Pr.

Eddy, Steve, ed. Of Mice & Men. 2010. (Philip Allan Literature Guide Ser.). (Illus.). 88p. pap. 19.50 *(978-1-4441-0872-9(7))*;Pack. 200p. 210.00 *(978-1-4441-0873-6(5))* Hodder Education GBR. Dist: Trans-Atlantic Pubns., Inc.

Eisenhauer, Robert. Aftermyths: Hysteria, Colloquialism, & Caricature in the Age of Doubt. 2006. (Studies on Themes & Motifs in Literature: Vol. 87). (Illus.). 270p. (C). 71.95 *(978-0-8204-8697-0(3))* Lang, Peter Publishing, Inc.

Eliot, Marc. Song of Brooklyn: An Oral History of America's Favorite Borough. 2010. 269p. 27.00 *(978-1-4379-7455-3(4))* DIANE Publishing Co.

Ellis, Jay. No Place for Home: Spatial Constraint & Character Flight in the Novels of Cormac Mccarthy. 2009. 362p. 39.95 *(978-0-415-80293-2(8))* 2006. 356p. 131.00 *(978-0-415-97734-0(7))* Routledge.

Elmer, Jonathan. On Lingering & Being Last: Race & Sovereignty in the New World. 2nd ed. 2008. (ENG.). 256p. pap. 28.00 *(978-0-8232-2941-3(6))*; (Illus.). 80.00 *(978-0-8232-2940-6(8))* Fordham Univ. Pr.

Emerson, Ralph Waldo. The Collected Works of Ralph Waldo Emerson Vol. 7: Society & Solitude, Volume VII. Wilson, Douglas Emory, ed. 2008. (Collected Works of Ralph Waldo Emerson Ser.). (Illus.). 542p. 97.50 *(978-0-674-02627-8(6)*, Belknap Pr.) Harvard Univ. Pr.

—Complete Works. 2009. 142p. pap. *(978-1-4588-2208-6(7))*; 264p. pap. *(978-0-217-91593-9(0))*; 112p. pap. *(978-1-4590-6378-5(3))*; 108p. pap. *(978-1-4590-6348-8(1))*; 134p. pap. *(978-1-4590-6346-4(5))* Books LLC.

—The Complete Works of Ralph Waldo Emerson. 2008. 556p. 33.99 *(978-0-559-88048-3(0))*; pap. 41.75 *(978-0-559-88046-9(4))* BiblioBazaar.

—The Complete Works of Ralph Waldo Emerson. 2009. 154p. pap. *(978-0-217-57811-0(X))*; 250p. pap. *(978-0-217-31993-5(9))*; 196p. pap. *(978-0-217-32000-9(7))*; 150p. pap. *(978-0-217-31996-6(3))*; 194p. pap. *(978-0-217-31987-4(4))*; 194p. pap. *(978-1-4589-7857-8(5))*; 148p. pap. *(978-1-4589-7856-1(7))*; 322p. pap. *(978-0-217-07341-7(7))*; 162p. pap. *(978-0-217-07339-4(5))*; 192p. pap. *(978-0-217-31990-4(4))*; 232p. pap. *(978-0-217-34551-4(4))*; 62p. pap. *(978-0-217-34552-1(2))*; 222p. pap. *(978-0-217-57813-4(6))*; 154p. pap. *(978-0-217-62461-9(8))* Books LLC.

—The Complete Works of Ralph Waldo Emerson. 2009. 184p. pap. 19.99 *(978-1-4590-0164-0(8))*; 232p. pap. 22.81 *(978-1-4589-7859-2(1))*; 200p. pap. 19.99 *(978-1-4589-7854-7(0))*; 224p. pap. 19.99 *(978-0-217-62466-4(9))* General Bks. LLC.

—Letters & Social Aims. 2009. 322p. 32.99 *(978-1-116-30228-8(4))* 2009. 322p. pap. 30.75 *(978-1-116-30229-5(2))* 2009. 270p. 30.99 *(978-1-110-54397-7(2))* 2009. 270p. pap. 26.75 *(978-1-110-54395-3(6))* 2009. 292p. 24.99 *(978-1-103-82713-8(8))* 2009. 292p. pap. 18.99 *(978-1-103-82706-0(5))* 2008. 288p. 25.99 *(978-0-559-58804-4(6))* 2008. 288p. pap. 27.75 *(978-0-559-58801-3(1))* BiblioBazaar.

—Letters & Social Aims. 2009. 196p. pap. *(978-0-217-00935-5(2))* Books LLC.

—Letters & Social Aims, Volume VIII. Johnson, Glen M. & Myerson, Joel, eds. 2010. (Collected Works of Ralph Waldo Emerson Ser.). (Illus.). 670p. 100.00 *(978-0-674-03560-7(7)*, Belknap Pr.) Harvard Univ. Pr.

—Letters & Social Aims. 2007. (ENG.). 516p. 55.95 *(978-0-548-17455-5(5))*; per. 40.95 *(978-1-4304-7346-6(0))* Kessinger Publishing, LLC.

Espejo, Ramon, et al, eds. Critical Essays on Chicano Studies. 2007. 268p. pap. 58.95 *(978-3-03911-281-4(3))* Lang, Peter Publishing, Inc.

Esposito, Mario. Studies in Hiberno-Latin Literature. Gorman, Michael M., ed. 2006. (Variorum Collected Studies Ser.). (ENG & FRE., Illus.). 320p. 154.95 *(978-0-86078-966-6(7))* Ashgate Publishing Co.

Fagin, N. Bryllion. The Phenomenon of Sherwood Anderson: A Study in American Life & Letters. 2011. 170p. 41.95 ***(978-1-258-05346-8(2))*** Literary Licensing, LLC.

Fender, Stephen. Nature Class & New Deal Literature. 2011. (Routledge Transnational Perspectives on American Literature Ser.). (ENG., Illus.). 244p. (C). 125.00 *(978-0-415-89678-8(9))* Routledge.

Feng, Pin-Chia. Diasporic Representations: Reading Chinese American Women's Fiction. 2011. 200p. pap. 49.95 ***(978-3-643-10831-9(1))*** Lit Verlag DEU. Dist: Transaction Pubs.

Ferguson, Frank & MacMaster, Richard, eds. Ulster-Scots & America: Diaspora Literature, History & Migration, 1750-2000. 2012. 288p. 65.00 *(978-1-84682-242-1(4))* Four Courts Pr. IRL. Dist: International Specialized Bk. Services.

Fernández, Bélen. The Imperial Messenger: Thomas Friedman at Work. 2011. (Counterblasts Ser.). (ENG.). 240p. pap. 16.95 *(978-1-84467-749-8(4)*, 844749) Verso Bks. GBR. Dist: Norton, W. W. & Co., Inc.

Fessenden, Tracy. Culture & Redemption: Religion, the Secular, & American Literature. 2006. (ENG., Illus.). 352p. (C). 42.00 *(978-0-691-04963-2(7))* Princeton Univ. Pr.

Fiedler, Leslie. The Devil Gets His Due: The Uncollected Essays of Leslie Fiedler. Pardini, Samuele F. S., ed. 2009. (ENG.). 352p. pap. 16.95 *(978-1-59376-266-7(6)*, Soft Skull Pr.) Counterpoint LLC.

Field, Douglas. James Baldwin. 2012. (Writers & Their Work Ser.). (ENG.). 128p. (C). 80.00 *(978-0-7463-1202-5(4))*; pap. 26.00 *(978-0-7463-1207-0(5))* Northcote Hse. Publishers, Ltd. GBR. Dist: Brown, David Bk. Co., The.

Field, Jonathan Beecher. Errands into the Metropolis: New England Dissidents in Revolutionary London. 2009. (Reencounters with Colonialism: New Perspectives on the Americas Ser.). (ENG., Illus.). 176p. lib. bdg. 85.00 *(978-1-58465-774-3(X)*, Dartmouth College Press) Univ. Pr. of New England.

Fields, Annie. Under the Olive. 2010. 336p. pap. 31.75 *(978-1-175-83827-8(6))* 2009. (ENG.). 323p. 29.99 *(978-1-117-55492-1(9)*, BiblioLife) 2009. (ENG.). 323p. pap. 23.99 *(978-1-117-55494-5(5)*, BiblioLife) 2009. (ENG.). 323p. pap. 29.75 *(978-1-117-55493-8(7)*, BiblioLife) BiblioBazaar.

—Under the Olive. 2009. 120p. pap. 21.05 *(978-1-150-32180-1(6))* General Bks. LLC.

—Under the Olive. 2007. 324p. 45.95 *(978-0-548-54502-7(2))*; (ENG.). per. 30.95 *(978-0-548-46335-2(2))* Kessinger Publishing, LLC.

Finseth, Ian Frederick. Shades of Green: Visions of Nature in the Literature of American Slavery, 1770-1860. 2011. (ENG., Illus.). 360p. pap. 24.95 *(978-0-8203-3780-7(3))* Univ. of Georgia Pr.

Fishkin, Shelley Fisher. Feminist Engagements: Forays into American Literature & Culture. 2009. (ENG.). 288p. pap. 30.00 *(978-0-230-61594-6(5))* Palgrave Macmillan.

Flota, Brian. A Survey of Multicultural San Francisco Bay Literature, 1955-1979: Ishnael Reed, Maxine Hong Kingston, Frank Chin & the Beat Generation. 2009. v, 326p. *(978-0-7734-3828-6(9))* Mellen, Edwin Pr., The.

Fluck, Winfried, et al, eds. Re-Framing the Transnational Turn in American Studies. 2011. (Re-Mapping the Transnational: a Dartmouth Series in American Studies). (Illus.). 472p. (C). 85.00 *(978-1-61168-189-5(8))*; pap. 35.00 *(978-1-61168-190-1(1))* Univ. Pr. of New England. (Dartmouth College Press).

Focus on the Fabulous: Colorado Glbt Voices. 2007. (Illus.). 167p. per. 17.00 *(978-1-55566-398-8(2))* Johnson Bks.

Fogle, Sarah D. Martha Grimes Walks into a Pub: Essays on the Ensuing Fiction. Fogle, Sarah D., ed. 2010. (ENG., Illus.). 206p. pap. 40.00 *(978-0-7864-4286-7(7))* McFarland & Co., Inc. Pubs.

Folks, Jeffrey J. Heartland of the Imagination: Conservative Values in American Literature from Poe to O'Connor to Haruf. 2011. (ENG.). 212p. pap. 40.00 ***(978-0-7864-5976-6(X))*** McFarland & Co., Inc. Pubs.

Fort, Charles. The Fortean Collection: The Five Surviving Books of Charles Fort. 2011. 882p. pap. 29.99 ***(978-1-61203-057-9(2))*** Bottom of the Hill Publishing.

Foster, Dennis A. Sublime Enjoyment: On the Perverse Motive in American Literature. 2009. (Cambridge Studies in American Literature & Culture Ser.). (ENG.). 196p. pap. 31.99 *(978-0-521-10818-8(7))* Cambridge Univ. Pr.

Foster, Thomas C. Twenty-Five Books That Shaped America. 2011. (ENG.). 352p. pap. 14.99 *(978-0-06-183440-0(8),* Harper Paperbacks) HarperCollins Pubs.

Francavilla, Joseph. Harlan Ellison. 2011. ***(978-1-58765-828-0(3))*** Salem Pr., Inc.

Francescato, Simone. Collecting & Appreciating: Henry James & the Transformation of Aesthetics in the Age of Consumption. 2010. 217p. pap. 51.95 *(978-3-0343-0163-3(4))* Lang, Peter AG GBR. Dist: Lang, Peter.

Franco, Dean J. Race, Rights, & Recognition: Jewish American Literature Since 1969. 2012. (ENG.). 248p. 49.95 ***(978-0-8014-5087-7(X))*** Cornell Univ. Pr.

Frank, Albert J. von. The Sacred Game: Provincialism & Frontier Consciousness in American Literature, 1630-1860. 2008. (Cambridge Studies in American Literature & Culture Ser.). (ENG.). 200p. pap. 31.99 *(978-0-521-09000-1(8))* Cambridge Univ. Pr.

Fuller, Margaret. Art, Literature, & the Drama / by Margaret Fuller Ossoli, Edited by Her Brother, Arthur B Fuller. 2006. 448p. per. 29.99 *(978-1-4255-4993-0(4))* MPublishing.

—Literature & Art by S Margaret Fuller Two Parts in One Volume with an Introduction by Horace Greeley. 2006. 364p. per. 26.99 *(978-1-4255-3774-6(X))* MPublishing.

Fuller, Randall. Emerson's Ghosts: Literature, Politics, & the Making of Americanists. 2011. (ENG.). 240p. pap. 24.95 *(978-0-19-975201-0(X))* Oxford Univ. Pr., Inc.

G?s y Prietas: Celebrating 20 Years of Borderlands/la Frontera. 2009. (Illus.). 10.00 *(978-0-9786820-0-2(9))* Adelante Project.

Gale Editor, ed. American Writers: Supplement XXII. 22nd ed. 2011. lib. bdg. 218.00 *(978-1-4144-8024-4(5),* Charles Scribner's Sons) Cengage Gale.

GALE, Kate & Davio, Kelly, eds. Los Angeles Review No. 9. 2011. 296p. pap. 20.00 *(978-1-59709-112-1(X))* Red Hen Pr.

Gallo, Donald. Richard Peck: The Past Is Paramount. 2008. (Scarecrow Studies in Young Adult Literature Ser.). (ENG.). 220p. 45.00 *(978-0-8108-5848-0(7))* Scarecrow Pr., Inc.

Garcia-Corales, Guillermo. El Debate Cultural y la Literatura Chilena Actual: Un Dialogo con Cinco Generaciones de Escritores. 2007. (SPA.). 276p. *(978-0-7734-5431-5(4))* Mellen, Edwin Pr., The.

Gardaphe, Fred. The Art of Reading Italian American. 2011. 212p. pap. 15.00 ***(978-1-59954-019-1(3))*** Bordighera Incorporated.

Gardner, Sarah E. Blood & Irony: Southern White Women's Narratives of the Civil War, 1861-1937. 2006. (ENG., Illus.). 325p. per. 23.95 *(978-0-8078-5767-0(X))* Univ. of North Carolina Pr.

Garner, Stanton. The Two Intertwined Narratives in Herman Melville's Billy Budd: A Study of an Author's Literary Methods. 2010. xi, 195p. *(978-0-7734-3707-4(X))* Mellen, Edwin Pr., The.

Garrigue, Marianne Moore-Aw V50. 2009. pap. 25.00 *(978-0-8166-0365-7(0))* Univ. of Minnesota Pr.

Gascoigne, George & Cunliffe, John William. Complete Works. 2010. (ENG.). 518p. pap. 39.75 *(978-1-176-55852-6(8))* BiblioBazaar.

Gastil, Raymond D. & Singer, Barnett. The Pacific Northwest: Growth of a Regional Identity. 2010. (ENG., Illus.). 227p. pap. 38.00 *(978-0-7864-4540-0(8))* McFarland & Co., Inc. Pubs.

Gidley, Mick, ed. Writing with Light: Words & Photographs in American Texts. 2009. (Illus.). 287p. pap. 63.95 *(978-3-03911-572-3(3))* Lang, Peter AG GBR. Dist: Lang, Peter.

Gilbar, Steven. Not Forgotten: American Writers Remember the Lives of Literary Mentors, Friends, & Rivals. 2006. (ENG.). 227p. pap. 17.95 *(978-1-56792-294-3(5))* Godine, David R. Pub.

Gilbert, Sandra M. Rereading Women: Thirty Years of Exploring Our Literary Traditions. 2011. (ENG.). 380p. 29.95 *(978-0-393-06764-4(5),* 6764) Norton, W. W. & Co., Inc.

Giles, Paul. The Global Remapping of American Literature. 2011. (ENG., Illus.). 340p. (C). 39.50 *(978-0-691-13613-4(0))* Princeton Univ. Pr.

Gillam, Ken & Lor, Feyn, eds. Composing Ourselves: Writing from the Composition Program at Missouri State University Second Edition. 2nd ed. 2009. pap. *(978-0-913785-16-4(4),* Moon City Pr.) Department of English.

Giordano, Paolo A. & Tamburri, Anthony Julian, eds. Italian Americans in the Third Millennium. 2009. 232p. pap. 16.00 *(978-0-934675-58-1(9))* Bordighera Incorporated.

Glenday, Michael K., ed. F. Scott Fitzgerald. 2012. (ENG.). 208p. 75.00 *(978-0-333-65899-3(5))*; pap. 24.95 *(978-0-333-66900-6(2))* Palgrave Macmillan.

Goldsby, Jacqueline. A Spectacular Secret: Lynching in American Life & Literature. 2006. (Illus.). 384p. 72.50 *(978-0-226-30137-2(0))*; per. 30.00 *(978-0-226-30138-9(9))* Univ. of Chicago Pr.

Goldstein, Ann. Voices of Italian America: A History of Early Italian American Literature with a Critical Anthology. Marazzi, Martino, ed. 2011. (ENG.). 348p. pap. 25.00 ***(978-0-8232-3973-3(X))*** Fordham Univ. Pr.

Goldstein, Philip & Goldstein, Philip. Modern American Reading Practices: Between Aesthetics & History. 2008. (ENG.). 192p. 89.00 *(978-0-230-61225-9(3))* Palgrave Macmillan.

Goldstein, Philip & Machor, James L. New Directions in American Reception Study. 2008. (ENG., Illus.). 544p. per. 45.00 *(978-0-19-532088-6(3))* Oxford Univ. Pr., Inc.

Gonzalez, Marcial. Chicano Novels & the Politics of Form: Race, Class, & Reification. 2008. (Class: Culture Ser.). (ENG.). 280p. 80.00 *(978-0-472-07045-9(2))*; pap. 32.50 *(978-0-472-05045-1(1))* Univ. of Michigan Pr.

González Moreno, Beatriz & Rigal Aragón, Margarita. A Descent into Edgar Allan Poe & His Works: The Bicentennial. 2010. (Illus.). 170p. pap. *(978-3-0343-0089-6(1))* Lang, Peter.

Gooblar, David. The Major Phases of Philip Roth. 2011. (ENG.). 208p. 100.00 *(978-1-4411-7540-3(7))*; pap. 29.95 *(978-1-4411-6970-9(9))* Continuum International Publishing Group, Ltd. GBR. Dist: National Bk. Network.

Goodheart, Eugene, ed. Ernest Hemingway. 2009. (Critical Insights Ser.). 384p. lib. bdg. 85.00 *(978-1-58765-630-9(2))* Salem Pr., Inc.

Goodspeed-Chadwick, Julie. Modernist Women Writers & War: Trauma & the Female Body in Djuna Barnes, H.D., & Gertrude Stein. 2011. 184p. 35.00 *(978-0-8071-3681-2(6))* Louisiana State Univ. Pr.

Gornick, Vivian. The Men in My Life. 2008. (Boston Review Bks.). (ENG.). 216p. (gr. 1?). 14.95 *(978-0-262-07303-5(X))* MIT Pr.

Grace, Sherrill. Strange Comfort: Essays on the Work of Malcolm Lowry. 2009. (ENG.). 224p. pap. 19.95 *(978-0-88922-618-0(0))* Talonbooks, Ltd. CAN. Dist: Consortium Bk. Sales & Distribution.

Graham, Don. State of Minds: Texas Culture & Its Discontents. 2011. (ENG.). 196p. 29.95 *(978-0-292-72361-0(X))* Univ. of Texas Pr.

Gray, Carol & Gray, Richard. A History of American Literature. 2nd ed. 2011. (ENG.). 928p. 124.95 ***(978-1-4051-9229-3(1),*** Wiley-Blackwell) Wiley, John & Sons, Inc.

Gray, Richard. A Brief History of American Literature. 2011. (ENG., Illus.). 424p. 104.95 *(978-1-4051-9231-6(3))*; pap. 35.95 *(978-1-4051-9230-9(5))* Wiley, John & Sons, Inc. (Wiley-Blackwell).

Gray, Richard. A History of American Literature. 2nd ed. 2012. (ENG.). 952p. pap. 49.95 ***(978-1-4051-9228-6(3),*** Wiley-Blackwell) Wiley, John & Sons, Inc.

Gray, Richard & Robinson, Owen. A Companion to the Literature & Culture of the American South. 2007. (Blackwell Companions to Literature & Culture Ser.: 58) (ENG., Illus.). 672p. per. 55.95 *(978-1-4051-6369-9(0),* Wiley-Blackwell) Wiley, John & Sons, Inc.

Greeson, Jennifer Rae. Our South: Geographic Fantasy & the Rise of National Literature. 2010. (ENG., Illus.). 368p. 39.95 *(978-0-674-02428-1(1))* Harvard Univ. Pr.

Grenby, Matthew. Children's Literature. 2008. (Edinburgh Critical Guides to Literature Ser.). (ENG., Illus.). 224p. (gr. 17). 90.00 *(978-0-7486-2273-3(X))*; pap. 29.50 *(978-0-7486-2274-0(8))* Edinburgh Univ. Pr. GBR. Dist: Columbia Univ. Pr.

Griffin, Joseph. America's Social Classes in the Writings of Edith Wharton: An Analysis of Her Short Stories. 2009. 464p. *(978-0-7734-4682-3(6))* Mellen, Edwin Pr., The.

Guilbert, Pascale, ed. Reflective Landscapes of the Anglophone Countries. 2011. (Illus.). 310p. pap. 90.00 *(978-90-420-3261-3(8))* Rodopi.

Guzzio, Tracie Church. All Stories Are True: History, Myth, & Trauma in the Work of John Edgar Wideman. 2011. (Margaret Walker Alexander Series in African American Studies). (ENG.). 352p. 60.00 *(978-1-61703-004-8(X))* Univ. Pr. of Mississippi.

Hacht, Anne Marie. Literary Themes for Students: The American Dream: Examining Diverse Literature to Understand & Compare Universal Themes. 2007. *(978-1-4144-0285-7(6))*; *(978-1-4144-0286-4(4))* Cengage Gale.

Hacht, Anne Marie & Hayes, Dwayne D. Gale Contextual Encyclopedia of American Literature. 2009. *(978-1-4144-3134-5(1))*; *(978-1-4144-3132-1(5))*; *(978-1-4144-3133-8(3))*; (Illus.). 1819p. 495.00 *(978-1-4144-3131-4(7))* Cengage Gale.

Hajjar, Nijmeh. The Politics & Poetics of Ameen Rihani: The Humanist Ideology of an Arab-American Intellectual & Activist. 2010. (ENG.). 336p. 98.50 *(978-1-84885-266-2(5),* Tauris Academic Studies) I. B. Tauris & Co., Ltd. GBR. Dist: Macmillan.

Hall, H. Lark. V. L. Parrington: Through the Avenue of Art. 2011. (ENG., Illus.). 377p. pap. 39.95 *(978-1-4128-4218-1(2))* Transaction Pubs.

Halleck, Reuben P. History of American Literature. 2006. (ENG.). pap. *(978-1-4068-1092-9(4))* Echo Library.

Halliday, Iain. Huck Finn in Italian, Pinocchio in English: Theory & Praxis of Literary Translation. 2009. 187p. 47.50 *(978-0-8386-4193-4(8))* Fairleigh Dickinson Univ Pr.

Hara, Mavis. An Offering of Rice. 2007. 169p. per. 15.00 *(978-0-910043-76-2(0))* Bamboo Ridge Pr.

Harriet Beecher Stowe. Uncle Tom's Cabin. lt. ed. 2007. 162p. pap. 32.99 *(978-1-4264-6630-4(7))* BiblioBazaar.

Harrison, Brady, ed. All Our Stories Are Here: Critical Perspectives on Montana Literature. 2009. (ENG.). 296p. 50.00 *(978-0-8032-1390-6(5))* Univ. of Nebraska Pr.

Hartley, Maxine A. Guide to the Works of Isaac Bashevis Singer. 2009. (ENG.). 183p. pap. 15.00 *(978-0-533-16031-0(6))* Vantage Pr., Inc.

Harvey, Bob. Moby Dick. Laurel Associates Inc Staff, ed. 2008. (Graphic Novels Ser.). (ENG., Illus.). 16p. (YA). (gr. 9-12). tchr. ed., pupil's gde. ed. 7.95 incl. cd-rom *(978-1-59905-305-9(5))* Saddleback Educational Publishing.

Harvey, Bob & Melville, Herman. Moby Dick. 2007. (punta del Iceberg Ser.). (ENG., Illus.). 192p. (J). (gr. 4-7). 9.95 *(978-84-9786-280-6(5))* Edimat Libros, S. A. ESP. Dist: Independent Pubs. Group.

Hassan, Wail S. Immigrant Narratives: Orientalism & Cultural Translation in Arab-American & Arab-British Literature, 1 vol. 2011. (ENG.). 288p. 65.00 *(978-0-19-979206-1(2))* Oxford Univ. Pr., Inc.

Hawthorne, Nathaniel. Grandfather's Chair. 2008. 208p. 24.99 *(978-0-554-38216-6(4))*; 27.99 *(978-0-554-28913-7(X))* BiblioBazaar.

—Grandfather's Chair. 2007. (ENG.). 172p. per. *(978-1-4065-4380-3(2))* Dodo Pr.

—Grandfather's Chair. 2009. 132p. pap. *(978-1-4068-9277-2(7))* Echo Library.

Hayes, Kevin J. A Journey Through American Literature, 1 vol. 2012. (ENG., Illus.). 240p. pap. 17.95 ***(978-0-19-986206-1(0))*** Oxford Univ. Pr., Inc.

Hayne, Paul H. Legends & Lyrics. 2009. 186p. 26.99 *(978-1-110-86564-2(3))*; pap. 21.75 *(978-1-110-86563-5(5))* BiblioBazaar.

—Legends & Lyrics. 2007. (ENG.). 184p. 37.95 *(978-0-548-41864-2(0))*; per. 22.95 *(978-0-548-39529-5(2))* Kessinger Publishing, LLC.

—Legends & Lyrics. 2008. 184p. pap. *(978-1-4437-1499-0(2))* Read Bks.

Hebel, Udo J., ed. Transnational American Memories. 2009. (Media & Cultural Memory / Medien und kulturelle Erinnerung Ser.). (ENG., VII, 460p. Illus.). 140.00 *(978-3-11-022420-7(8))*; 210.00 ***(978-3-11-174217-5(2))*** De Gruyter, Walter Inc.

Hebert-Leiter, Maria. Becoming Cajun, Becoming American: The Acadian in American Literature from Longfellow to James Lee Burke. 2009. (Southern Literary Studies). 216p. 32.50 *(978-0-8071-3435-1(X))* Louisiana State Univ. Pr.

Hedley, Jane. I Made You to Find Me: The Coming of Age of the Woman Poet & the Politics of Poetic Address. 2009. (ENG.). 199p. 44.95 *(978-0-8142-1101-4(1))* Ohio State Univ. Pr.

Heit, Jamey. Vader, Voldemort & Other Villains: Essays on Evil in Popular Media. Heit, Jamey, ed. 2011. (ENG., Illus.). 233p. pap. 35.00 *(978-0-7864-5845-5(3))* McFarland & Co., Inc. Pubs.

Held, Jacob M. Dr. Seuss & Philosophy: Oh, the Thinks You Can Think! 2011. (ENG.). 288p. pap. 18.95 *(978-1-4422-0311-2(0))* Rowman & Littlefield Publishers, Inc.

Hellman, Caroline. Domesticity & Design in American Womens Lives & Literature. 2011. (Routledge Studies in Nineteenth Century Literature Ser.). (ENG., Illus.). 146p. (C). 125.00 *(978-0-415-88272-9(9))* Routledge.

Henry, O. Waifs & Strays & Series Index - the Complete Works of O Henry - 2008. 72p. pap. 26.45 *(978-1-4437-8186-2(X))* Barclay Pr., Inc.

Herd, David. Enthusiast! Essays on Modern American Literature. 2008. (ENG.). 224p. 79.00 *(978-0-7190-7428-8(2))* Manchester Univ. Pr. GBR. Dist: Macmillan.

Hermansson, Casie E. Bluebeard: A Reader's Guide to the English Tradition. 2009. (ENG., Illus.). 304p. 60.00 *(978-1-60473-230-6(X))*; pap. 30.00 *(978-1-60473-231-3(8))* Univ. Pr. of Mississippi.

Hernández, Ellie D. Postnationalism in Chicana - O Literature & Culture. 2010. (ENG.). 255p. pap. 25.00 *(978-0-292-72346-7(6))* Univ. of Texas Pr.

Hernandez, Guillermo. Chicano Satire: A Study in Literary Culture. 2012. (ENG.). 166p. pap. 19.95 ***(978-0-292-74112-6(X))*** Univ. of Texas Pr.

Hesperides. The Development of American Literary Criticism. 2007. 276p. per. *(978-1-4067-6256-3(3),* Hesperides Pr.) Read Bks.

Hewitt, Elizabeth. Correspondence & American Literature, 1770-1865. 2009. (Cambridge Studies in American Literature & Culture Ser.). (ENG.). 244p. pap. 36.99 *(978-0-521-12373-0(9))* Cambridge Univ. Pr.

Higginson, Thomas Wentworth. A Reader's History of American Literature. 2009. 174p. pap. *(978-1-4432-9369-3(5))* Books LLC.

Hinojosa, Rolando. A Voice of My Own: Essays & Stories. 2011. pap. 19.95 *(978-1-55885-712-4(5))* Arte Publico Pr.

Hoeveler, Diane Long & Schuster, Donna Decker, eds. Women's Literary Creativity & the Female Body. 2007. (ENG.). 228p. 89.00 *(978-1-4039-8383-1(6))* Palgrave Macmillan.

Hoffman, Warren. The Passing Game: Queering Jewish American Culture. 2009. (Judaic Traditions in Literature, Music, & Art Ser.). (Illus.). 216p. 24.95 *(978-0-8156-3202-3(9))* Syracuse Univ. Pr.

Holman, C. Hugh. The Roots of Southern Writing: Essays on the Literature of the American South. 2008. (ENG.). 252p. pap. 24.95 *(978-0-8203-3359-5(X))* Univ. of Georgia Pr.

Hope-Hawkins, Anthony. A Change of Air. 2009. 166p. pap. *(978-1-4432-5975-0(6))* Books LLC.

—A Change of Air. 2008. 262p. 42.95 *(978-1-4365-1915-1(2))* 2007. (ENG.). 264p. per. 27.95 *(978-0-548-72485-9(7))* Kessinger Publishing, LLC.

—A Change of Air. 2008. 264p. pap. *(978-1-4097-9254-3(4))* Read Bks.

—A Change of Air. 2008. 252p. 32.95 *(978-1-4344-7360-8(0))*; pap. 19.95 *(978-1-4344-7359-2(7))* Wildside Pr., LLC.

Hopley, Claire. Literary Tea Times. 2009. (Illus.). 224p. pap. 29.99 *(978-1-84468-030-6(4))* Pen & Sword Bks. Ltd. GBR. Dist: Casemate Pubs. & Bk. Distributors, LLC.

Hoppenstand, Gary. Stephen King. 2010. (Critical Insights Ser.). 344p. (C). 85.00 *(978-1-58765-685-9(X))* Salem Pr., Inc.

Horne, Jackie C. & Sanders, Joe Sutliff. Frances Hodgson Burnett's The Secret Garden: A Children's Classic at 100. 2011. (Children's Literature Association Centennial Studies). (ENG.). 312p. 65.00 *(978-0-8108-8187-7(X))* Scarecrow Pr., Inc.

Hovet, Grace Ann & Hovet Sr., Theodore R. Tableaux Vivants. 2009. 222p. 29.99 *(978-1-4415-3453-8(9))*; pap. 19.99 *(978-1-4415-3452-1(0))* Xlibris Corp.

Howard, Hugh. Writers of the American South: Their Literary Landscapes. 2011. (ENG.). 9.98 *(978-0-7893-2414-6(8),* Rizzoli Universe Promotional Bks.) Rizzoli International Pubns., Inc.

Howe, Julia Ward. At Sunset. 2009. 138p. 22.99 *(978-1-103-85372-4(4))*; pap. 16.99 *(978-1-103-85371-7(6))* BiblioBazaar.

—At Sunset. 2008. 160p. 36.95 *(978-1-4366-2651-4(X))*; pap. 21.95 *(978-0-548-90174-8(0))* Kessinger Publishing, LLC.

Hoyt, Joseph Gibson. Miscellaneous Writings; Addresses, Lectures, & Reviews by Joseph G Hoyt, LI D. 2006. 316p. per. 23.99 *(978-1-4255-3041-9(9))* MPublishing.

Hubbell, Jay B. The South in American Literature, 1607-1900. 2011. 1006p. 81.95 ***(978-1-258-08559-9(3))*** Literary Licensing, LLC.

Hubbell, Jay B., ed. American Literature, V8, No 1, March 1936: A Journal of Literary History, Criticism, & Bibliography. 2011. 126p. 40.95 ***(978-1-258-01043-0(7))*** Literary Licensing, LLC.

Hughes, Evan. Literary Brooklyn: The Writers of Brooklyn & the Story of American City Life. 2011. (ENG., Illus.). 352p. pap. 17.00 *(978-0-8050-8986-8(1),* Holt Paperback) Holt, Henry & Co.

Hunter, Jeffrey W. Contemporary Literary Criticism: Excerpts from Criticism of the Works of Today's Novelists, Poets, Playwrights, Short Story Writers, Scriptwriters, & Other Creative Writers. 2011. 462p. 328.00 *(978-1-4144-5854-0(1),* Cengage Gale.

Huntington, Thomas. A Miscellany Containing Some Essays on Literature with Some of the Arts & Sciences. 2007. 130p. 35.95 *(978-0-548-04457-5(0))* Kessinger Publishing, LLC.

Husband, Julie. Antislavery Discourse & Nineteenth-Century American Literature: Incendiary Pictures. 2010. (ENG., Illus.). 192p. 84.00 *(978-0-230-62148-0(1))* Palgrave Macmillan.

Hutchison, Coleman. Apples & Ashes: Literature, Nationalism, & the Confederate States of America. 2012. (New Southern Studies). (ENG.). 288p. 59.95 ***(978-0-8203-3731-9(5))***; (Illus.). pap. 24.95 ***(978-0-8203-4244-3(0))*** Univ. of Georgia Pr.

Hutchison, Hazel. Seeing & Believing: Henry James & the Spiritual World. 2006. (ENG., Illus.). 224p. 84.00 *(978-1-4039-6926-2(4))* Palgrave Macmillan.

Hutton, Laurence. Other Times & Other Seasons. 2008. 196p. 22.99 *(978-0-559-53510-9(4))*; pap. 22.75 *(978-0-559-53508-6(2))* BiblioBazaar.

—Other Times & Other Seasons. 2009. 80p. pap. *(978-0-217-02672-7(9))* Books LLC.

—Other Times & Other Seasons. 2007. (ENG.). 192p. 37.95 *(978-0-548-42818-4(2))*; per. 22.95 *(978-0-548-40520-8(4))* Kessinger Publishing, LLC.

—Other Times & Other Seasons. 2009. 192p. pap. 27.95 *(978-1-4446-0849-6(5))* Palmer Pr., The.

Ikegami, Hiroko & Rauschenberg, Robert. The Great Migrator: Robert Rauschenberg & the Global Rise of American Art. 2010. (ENG., Illus.). 296p. (gr. 17). 29.95 *(978-0-262-01425-0(4))* MIT Pr.

Inscoe, John C. & Ruppersburg, Hugh, eds. The New Georgia Encyclopedia Companion to Georgia Literature. 2007. (ENG.). 472p. per. 24.95 *(978-0-8203-2876-8(6))* Univ. of Georgia Pr.

Insdorf, Annette. Philip Kaufman. 2012. E-Book ***(978-0-252-09397-5(6))***; (ENG., Illus.). 176p. pap. 22.00 ***(978-0-252-07846-0(2))***; (ENG., Illus.). 176p. 70.00 ***(978-0-252-03685-9(9))*** Univ. of Illinois Pr.

Jackson, Gregory S. The Word & Its Witness: The Spiritualization of American Realism. 2009. (Illus.). 424p. 80.00 *(978-0-226-39003-1(9))*; 336p. pap. 29.00 *(978-0-226-39004-8(7))* Univ. of Chicago Pr.

Jackson, Helen Hunt. A Separate Star: Selected Writings of Helen Hunt Jackson. 2008. (California Legacy Ser.). 299p. per. *(978-1-59714-074-4(0))* Santa Clara Univ., de Saisset Museum.

Jahner, Elaine A. Spaces of the Mind: Narrative & Community in the American West. 2008. (Frontiers of Narrative Ser.). (ENG.). 212p. pap. 19.95 *(978-0-8032-1833-8(8))* Univ. of Nebraska Pr.

Jameson, W. C., ed. Notes from Texas: On Writing in the Lone Star State. 2008. (ENG., Illus.). 250p. 27.95 *(978-0-87565-358-7(8))* Texas Christian Univ. Pr.

Jamie, Colwell. Katherine Anne Porter's Adaptation of Joycean Paralysis: An Analysis of Connections. 2011. 76p. pap. ***(978-3-639-32080-0(8))*** VDM Verlag Dr. Mueller e.K.

Johannessen, Lene M. Horizons of Enchantment: Essays in the American Imaginary. 2011. (Re-Mapping the Transnational: a Dartmouth Series in American Studies). 168p. pap. 35.00 *(978-1-61168-000-3(X),* Dartmouth College Press) Univ. Pr. of New England.

Johnson, Claudia D. Racism in Maya Angelou's I Know Why the Caged Bird Sings. 2007. (Social Issues in Literature Ser.). (ENG., Illus.). 150p. (YA). (gr.

10-12). 26.50 (978-0-7377-3905-3(3), LML02109-238410); pap. 38.45 (978-0-7377-3901-5(0), LML02109-238371) Cengage Gale. (Greenhaven Pr., Inc.).

Johnson, Curt. Jalud. 2007. 216p. pap. 15.00 (978-1-889460-16-1(8)) Cross+Roads Pr.

Johnson, David T. Richard Linklater. 2012. E-Book **(978-0-252-09404-0(2))**; (ENG., Illus.). 200p. 70.00 **(978-0-252-03692-7(1))**; (ENG., Illus.). 200p. pap. 22.00 **(978-0-252-07850-7(0))** Univ. of Illinois Pr.

Jones, William Alfred. Characters & Criticisms by W Alfred Jones. 2006. 304p. per. 23.99 (978-1-4255-2900-0(3)); 280p. per. 23.99 (978-1-4255-2535-4(0)) MPublishing.

Joseph, Philip. American Literary Regionalism in a Global Age. 2006. (Illus.). 232p. 45.00 (978-0-8071-3188-6(1)) Louisiana State Univ. Pr.

Josipovici, Gabriel. What Ever Happened to Modernism? (ENG., Illus.). 224p. 2011. pap. 18.00 (978-0-300-17800-5(X)) 2010. 28.00 (978-0-300-16577-7(3)) Yale Univ. Pr.

Joslin, Katherine. Edith Wharton & the Making of Fashion. 2009. (Becoming Modern: New Nineteenth-Century Studies). (ENG., Illus.). 248p. lib. bdg. 75.00 (978-1-58465-779-8(0), University of New Hampshire Press) Univ. Pr. of New England.

Joyce, Elisabeth W. The Small Space of a Pause: Susan Howe's Poetry & the Space Between. 2010. (ENG.). 297p. 65.00 (978-1-61148-349-9(2)) Bucknell Univ. Pr.

Karell, Linda. Writing Together - Writing Apart: Collaboration in Western American Literature. 2008. (ENG.). 219p. pap. 19.95 (978-0-8032-1834-5(6)) Univ. of Nebraska Pr.

Kates, Ronald E. & Tormey, Warren, eds. Baseball/Literature/Culture: Essays, 2006-2007. 2008. (Baseball in Literature & American Culture Conference Ser.). (ENG., Illus.). 210p. per. 45.00 (978-0-7864-3680-4(8)) McFarland & Co., Inc. Pubs.

—Baseball/Literature/Culture: Essays, 2008-2009. 2010. (Baseball in Literature & American Culture Conference Ser.). (ENG., Illus.). 243p. pap. 39.95 (978-0-7864-3681-1(6)) McFarland & Co., Inc. Pubs.

Kennedy, Mark. Life Stories. 2008. 292p. pap. 21.95 (978-0-9816172-3-7(9)) Westview Publishing Co., Inc.

Kennedy, Thomas E. & Cummins, Walter, eds. Writers on the Job: Tales of the Non-Writing Life. 2008. 244p. pap. 15.95 (978-1-933435-21-3(6)) Hopewell Pubns., LLC.

Kilmer, Joyce. Literature in the Making, by Some of Its Makers. 2009. 98p. pap. (978-1-151-32016-2(1)) Books LLC.

—Literature in the Making, by Some of Its Makers. 336p. 2008. 45.95 (978-0-548-93168-4(2)) 2007. per. 30.95 (978-0-548-59569-5(0)) Kessinger Publishing, LLC.

Kinser, Brent E. & Tarr, Rodger L., eds. Marjorie Kinnan Rawlings's Cross Creek Sampler: A Book of Quotations. 2011. (ENG., Illus.). 224p. 22.50 (978-0-8130-3724-0(7)) Univ. Pr. of Florida.

Kleppien, Axel-Bjö. Der Krieg in der amerikanischen Literatur: Untersuchung des Wandels von Beschreibung, Bewertung und Leserlenkung in der nordamerikanischen War Prose und War Poetry während des Zeltraums vom Unabhängigkeitskrieg bis zum Irakkrieg. 2010. (GER.). 636p. 146.95 (978-3-631-61040-4(8)) Lang, Peter GmbH, Europaischer Verlag der Wissenschaften DEU. Dist: Lang, Peter.

Knadler, Stephen P. The Fugitive Race: Minority Writers Resisting Whiteness. 2007. (ENG.). 280p. per. 25.00 (978-1-934110-34-8(5)) Univ. Pr. of Mississippi.

Knights, Pamela. The Cambridge Introduction to Edith Wharton. 2009. (Cambridge Introductions to Literature Ser.). (ENG., Illus.). 170p. (C). 65.99 (978-0-521-86765-8(7)); pap. 20.99 (978-0-521-68719-5(5)) Cambridge Univ. Pr.

Kochhar-Lindgren, Kanta, et al, eds. The Exquisite Corpse: Chance & Collaboration in Surrealism's Parlor Game. 2009. (Texts & Contexts Ser.). (ENG., Illus.). 368p. 55.00 (978-0-8032-2781-1(7)) Univ. of Nebraska Pr.

Koeninger, Anthony. A Democracy of Ghosts. rev. ed. 2007. (ENG.). 318p. pap. 72.78 (978-0-7575-4143-8(7)) Kendall Hunt Publishing Co.

Kohlert, Frederik Byrn. The Chicago Literary Experience: Writing the City, 1893-1953. 2011. (Illus.). 190p. pap. 25.00 (978-87-635-0776-9(5)) Museum Tusculanum Pr. DNK. Dist: Chicago Distribution Ctr.

Kolin, Philip C., ed. Shakespeare & Southern Writers: A Study in Influence. 2011. (ENG.). 177p. pap. 30.00 **(978-1-61703-206-6(9))** Univ. Pr. of Mississippi.

Kollin, Susan, ed. Postwestern Cultures: Literature, Theory, Space. 2007. (Postwestern Horizons Ser.). (ENG., Illus.). 288p. pap. 19.95 (978-0-8032-6044-3(X)) Univ. of Nebraska Pr.

Kramer, Michael P. & Goodman, Nan. The Turn Around Religion in America: Literature Culture & the Work of Sacvan Bercovitch. 2011. (Illus.). 488p. 124.95 **(978-1-4094-3018-6(9))** Ashgate Publishing Co.

Kreyling, Michael. The South That Wasn't There: Postsouthern Memory & History. 2010. (Southern Literary Studies). 256p. 48.00 (978-0-8071-3648-5(4)) Louisiana State Univ. Pr.

Krick-Aigner, Kirsten. Unredeemed Past: Themes of War & Womanhood in the Works of Post-World War II Austrian Women Writers. 2011. 276p. pap. **(978-1-57241-179-1(1))** Ariadne Pr.

Kuhn, Cynthia G. & Carlson, Cindy L. Styling Texts: Dress & Fashion in Literature. 2007. (Illus.). xvi, 429p. 124.95 (978-1-934043-83-7(4)) Cambria Pr.

Kumamoto, Sadahiro & Ito, Hiroyuki. Stylistic Studies of Literature: In Honour of Professor Hiroyuki Ito. Hori, Masahiro & Tabata, Tomoji, eds. 2009. 257p. pap. (978-3-03911-816-8(1)) Lang, Peter.

Kurucz, Anikó. Mother-Daughter Relationship & Cultural Inheritance. 2008. 52p. pap. (978-3-639-00347-5(0)) VDM Verlag Dr. Mueller e.K.

Kyne, Peter. The Three Godfathers. 2007. 96p. per. 14.50 (978-1-60206-755-4(4)) Cosimo, Inc.

Ladyga, Zuzanna. Rethinking Postmodern Subjectivity: Emmanuel Levinas & the Ethics of Referentiality in the Work of Donald Barthelme. 2009. (Anglo-amerikanische Studien - Anglo-American Studies). 192p. pap. 56.95 (978-3-631-59109-3(8)) Lang, Peter GmbH, Europaischer Verlag der Wissenschaften DEU. Dist: Lang, Peter.

Lambright, Anne. Creating the Hybrid Intellectual: Subject, Space, & the Feminine in the Narrative of Jose Maria Arguedas. 2007. (Bucknell Studies in Latin American Literature & Theory). (ENG.). 308p. 62.50 (978-0-8387-5683-6(2)) Bucknell Univ. Pr.

Lambrou, Marina. Contemporary Stylistics. Stockwell, Peter, ed. 2008. (Contemporary Studies in Linguistics Ser.). (ENG., Illus.). 302p. 170.00 (978-0-8264-9385-9(8)) Continuum International Publishing Group, Ltd. GBR. Dist: National Bk. Network.

Lambrou, Marina & Stockwell, Peter, eds. Contemporary Stylistics. 2010. (Contemporary Studies in Linguistics Ser.). (ENG.). 304p. 44.95 (978-1-4411-8384-2(1)) Continuum International Publishing Group, Ltd. GBR. Dist: National Bk. Network.

Lancaster, Ashley Craig. The Angelic Mother & the Predatory Seductress: Poor White Women in Southern Literature of the Great Depression. 2012. (Southern Literary Studies). 240p. 39.95 **(978-0-8071-4445-9(2))** Louisiana State Univ. Pr.

Lane, Mark R. Sandspurs: Notes from a Coastal Columnist. 2008. (Florida History & Culture Ser.). (ENG., Illus.). 160p. 24.95 (978-0-8130-3234-4(2)) Univ. Pr. of Florida.

Lang, John, ed. Appalachia & Beyond: Conversations with Writers from the Mountain South. 2006. (Illus.). 352p. per. 24.95 (978-1-57233-535-6(1)) Univ. of Tennessee Pr.

Lauter, Paul. Companion to American Literature & Culture. 2010. (Blackwell Companions to Literature & Culture Ser.: 111). (ENG., Illus.). 712p. 209.95 (978-0-631-20892-1(5), Wiley-Blackwell) Wiley, John & Sons, Inc.

Lauter, Paul, ed. Lauter American Literature IV & Moby Dick, 3 vols. 3rd ed. Date not set. (American Heritage Library). (C). 60.76 (978-0-395-90168-7(5)) CENGAGE Learning.

Lawrence, D. H. Studies in Classic American Literature. 2011. 196p. pap. **(978-1-84861-158-0(7))** Shearsman Bks.

Layman, Bruccoli-Clark & Anderson, George Parker. American Modernism, 1914-1945, 7 vols. 2010. (Research Guide to American Literature Ser.). 328p. (C). (gr. 9-18). 50.00 (978-0-8160-7865-3(3)) Facts On File, Inc.

Layman, Bruccoli-Clark & Cusatis, John. Post-War Literature, 1945-1970, 7 vols. 2010. (Research Guide to American Literature Ser.). 272p. (C). (gr. 9-18). 50.00 (978-0-8160-7866-0(1)) Facts On File, Inc.

Layman, Bruccoli-Clark & Franklin, Benjamin. Colonial Literature, 1607-1776, 7 vols. 2010. (Research Guide to American Literature Ser.). 264p. (C). (gr. 9-18). 50.00 (978-0-8160-7861-5(0)) Facts On File, Inc.

Layman, Bruccoli-Clark & Vietto, Angela. Early American Literature, 1776-1820, 7 vols. 2010. (Research Guide to American Literature Ser.). 224p. (C). (gr. 9-18). 50.00 (978-0-8160-7862-2(9)) Facts On File, Inc.

Layman, Bruccoli-Clark, et al. Contemporary Literature, 1970-Present, 7 vols. 2010. (Research Guide to American Literature Ser.). 432p. (C). (gr. 9-18). 50.00 (978-0-8160-7867-7(X)) Facts On File, Inc.

—Realism & Regionalism, 1865-1914, 7 vols. 2010. (Research Guide to American Literature Ser.). 248p. (C). (gr. 9-18). 50.00 (978-0-8160-7864-6(5)) Facts On File, Inc.

—Romanticism & Transcendentalism, 1820-1865, 7 vols. 2010. (Research Guide to American Literature Ser.). 248p. (C). (gr. 9-18). 50.00 (978-0-8160-7863-9(7)) Facts On File, Inc.

Levander, Caroline F. & Levine, Robert S., eds. A Companion to American Literary Studies. 2011. (Blackwell Companions to Literature & Culture Ser.: 136). (ENG.). 592p. 199.95 **(978-1-4051-9881-3(8)**, Wiley-Blackwell) Wiley, John & Sons, Inc.

Lever, Charles James. Barrington. 2009. 230p. pap. (978-0-217-18009-2(4)) Books LLC.

—The Fortunes of Glencore. 2009. 516p. pap. (978-0-217-62576-0(2)) Books LLC.

—Maurice Tiernay: The soldier of Fortune. 2010. (ENG.). 564p. pap. 43.75 (978-1-172-33966-2(X)); (ENG.). 514p. pap. 39.75 (978-1-172-34042-2(0)); 574p. pap. 43.75 (978-1-171-84952-0(4)) BiblioBazaar.

Lever, Charles James. Maurice Tiernay Soldier of Fortune. 2010. 396p. pap. **(978-1-4068-5728-3(9))** Echo Library.

—Maurice Tiernay Soldier of Fortune. 2010. 342p. pap. 13.33 (978-1-153-65077-9(0)) General Bks. LLC.

Levins, Lynn Gartrell. Faulkner's Heroic Design: The Yoknapatawpha Novels. 2008. (ENG.). 216p. pap. 24.95 (978-0-8203-3362-5(X)) Univ. of Georgia Pr.

Lewis, Grover. Splendor in the Short Grass: The Grover Lewis Reader. Reid, Jan & Stratton, W. K., eds. 2009. (ENG.). 291p. pap. 25.00 (978-0-292-72230-9(3)) Univ. of Texas Pr.

Lewis, Leon. Sherman Alexie. 2011. **(978-1-58765-823-5(2))**; **(978-1-58765-822-8(4))** Salem Pr., Inc.

Lewis, Nathaniel. Unsettling the Literary West: Authenticity & Authorship. 2008. (Postwestern Horizons Ser.). (ENG.). 297p. pap. 24.95 (978-0-8032-1846-8(X)) Univ. of Nebraska Pr.

Lewis, Nghana tamu. Entitled to the Pedestal: Place, Race, & Progress in White Southern Women's Writing,1920-1945. 2007. 224p. 37.95 (978-1-58729-529-4(6)) Univ. of Iowa Pr.

Li, Stephanie. Something Akin to Freedom: The Choice of Bondage in Narratives by African American Women. 2011. 172p. pap. 23.95 (978-1-4384-2970-0(3), Suny Pr.) State Univ. of New York Pr.

Limpßr, Ildik=. The American Dream - Reconsidered New World Motifs in Shakespeare's the Tempest & Their Transformations in American Literature. 2008. 172p. pap. (978-3-639-11396-9(9)) VDM Verlag Dr. Mueller e.K.

Listé-Noya, Jose. American Secrets: The Politics & Poetics of Secrecy in the Literature & Culture of the United States. 2011. (ENG.). 274p. 70.00 **(978-1-61147-006-2(4))** Fairleigh Dickinson Univ. Pr.

Locklear, Erica Abrams. Negotiating a Perilous Empowerment: Appalachian Women's Literacies. 2011. (Race, Ethnicity & Gender in Appalachia Ser.). (ENG., Illus.). 272p. 49.95 (978-0-8214-1965-6(X)) Ohio Univ. Pr.

Long, William J. Outlines of English & American Literature. 2009. 600p. 33.99 (978-0-559-09246-6(6)); 36.99 (978-0-559-09233-6(4)); pap. 43.75 (978-0-559-09243-5(1)); pap. 31.99 (978-0-559-09237-4(7)) BiblioBazaar.

López-Calvo, Ignacio. Latino Los Angeles in Film & Fiction: The Cultural Production of Social Anxiety. 2011. (ENG., Illus.). 264p. 50.00 (978-0-8165-2926-1(4)) Univ. of Arizona Pr.

Lopez, Marissa. Chicano Nations: The Hemispheric Origins of Mexican American Literature. 2011. (ENG., Illus.). 269p. 75.00 **(978-0-8147-5261-6(6))**; pap. 24.00 **(978-0-8147-5262-3(4))** New York Univ. Pr.

López, Marissa K. Chicano Nations: The Hemispheric Origins of Mexican American Literature. 2011. (Illus.). x, 258p. E-Book **(978-0-8147-5263-0(2))**; E-Book **(978-0-8147-5329-3(9))** New York Univ. Pr.

López-Peláez Casellas, Milagros. What about the Girls? Estrategias Narrativas de Resistencia en la Primera Literatura Chicana. 2011. (Hispanic Studies: Culture & Ideas Ser.). (SPA & ENG.). 253p. pap. 58.95 **(978-3-0343-0264-7(9))** Lang, Peter AG GBR. Dist: Lang, Peter.

Lopez, Sam. Post-Revolutionary Chicana Literature: Memoir, Folklore, & Fiction of the Border, 1900-1950. 2006. (Latino Communities: Emerging Voices — Political, Social, Cultural & Legal Issues Ser.). (Illus.). 140p. 138.00 (978-0-415-95553-9(X)) Routledge.

Lowe, John. Louisiana Culture from the Colonial ERA to Katrina. 2009. ix, 327p. (978-0-8071-3337-8(X)) Louisiana State Univ. Pr.

Luebke, Alexandra. The Pilgrim's Progress in American Juvenile Literature 1860-1900. 2007. 84p. per. (978-3-8364-2300-7(6)) VDM Verlag Dr. Mueller e.K.

Lundin, Roger. From Nature to Experience: The American Search for Cultural Authority. Lundin, Roger, ed. 2007. (American Intellectual Culture Ser.). (ENG.). 278p. pap. 30.95 (978-0-7425-4840-4(6)) Rowman & Littlefield Publishers, Inc.

Lundin, Roger, ed. Invisible Conversations: Religion in the Literature of America. 2009. (ENG.). 205p. 39.95 (978-1-60258-147-0(9)) Baylor Univ. Pr.

Lynch, Tom. Xerophilia: Ecocritical Explorations in Southwestern Literature. 2008. (Illus.). 282p. 35.00 (978-0-89672-638-3(X)) Texas Tech Univ. Pr.

Mabie, Hamilton Wright. American Ideals, Character & Life. 2009. 344p. 25.99 (978-1-103-79530-7(9)); 25.99 (978-1-103-83881-3(4)); pap. 19.99 (978-1-103-83875-2(X)); pap. 19.99 (978-1-103-79517-8(1)) BiblioBazaar.

—American Ideals, Character & Life. 2009. 152p. pap. (978-0-217-68267-1(7)) Books LLC.

—American Ideals, Character & Life. 2007. (ENG.). 352p. 46.95 (978-0-548-38168-7(2)); per. 31.95 (978-0-548-32517-9(0)) Kessinger Publishing, LLC.

—American Ideals, Character & Life. 341p. reprint ed. 98.00 (978-0-7222-7320-3(7)) Library Reprints, Inc.

Mac Arthur, Pamela Carol. John O'Hara: The Wastrel from Pottsville. 2009. 304p. 61.95 (978-3-03910-515-1(9)) Lang, Peter AG GBR. Dist: Lang, Peter.

MacNeil, Denise Mary. The Emergence of the American Frontier Hero 1682-1826: Gender, Action, & Emotion. 2009. (American Literature Readings in the Twenty-First Century Ser.). (ENG.). 240p. 89.00 (978-0-230-62150-3(3)) Palgrave Macmillan.

Macy, John. The Spirit of American Literature. 2007. (ENG.). 356p. 46.95 (978-0-548-01386-1(1)) Kessinger Publishing, LLC.

Macy, John Albert. The Spirit of American Literature. 2009. 360p. 26.99 (978-1-103-78056-3(5)); pap. 20.99 (978-1-103-78050-1(6)) BiblioBazaar.

Madsen, Deborah L. Louise Erdrich: Tracks, the Last Report on the Miracles at Little No Horse, the Plague of Doves. 2011. (Continuum Studies Contem N American Fiction Ser.). (ENG.). 208p. 100.00 (978-1-4411-1045-9(3)) Continuum International Publishing Group, Ltd. GBR. Dist: National Bk. Network.

Madsen, Deborah L., ed. Louise Erdrich: Tracks, the Last Report on the Miracles at Little No Horse, the Plague of Doves. 2011. (Continuum Studies Contem N American Fiction Ser.). (ENG.). 208p. pap. 29.95 (978-1-4411-0097-9(0)) Continuum International Publishing Group, Ltd. GBR. Dist: National Bk. Network.

Maffly-Kipp, Laurie F. American Scriptures: An Anthology of Sacred Writings. 2010. (ENG.). 432p. (gr. 12). 16.00 (978-0-14-310619-7(8), Penguin Classics) Penguin Group (USA) Inc.

Magistrale, Tony. Approaches to Teaching Poe's Prose & Poetry. Weinstock, Jeffrey Andrew, ed. 2008. (ENG.). xix, 241p. pap. 19.75 (978-1-60329-012-8(5)) Modern Language Assn. of America.

Manzanas, Ana Mª, ed. Border Transits: Literature & Culture across the Line. 2007. (Illus.). 312p. per. 88.00 (978-90-420-2249-2(3)) Rodopi.

Marcus, Greil. A New Literary History of America. Sollors, Werner, ed. 2009. (Harvard University Press Reference Library). (Illus.). 1128p. 49.95 (978-0-674-03594-2(1), Belknap Pr.) Harvard Univ. Pr.

Marcus, Greil & Sollors, Werner, eds. A New Literary History of America. 2012. (Harvard University Press Reference Library). (ENG., Illus.). 1128p. pap. 24.95 **(978-0-674-06410-2(0)**, Belknap Pr.) Harvard Univ. Pr.

Marius, Richard. Reading Faulkner: Introductions to the First Thirteen Novels. Anderson, Nancy Grisham, ed. 2007. (ENG., Illus.). 224p. per. 19.95 (978-1-57233-603-2(X)) Univ. of Tennessee Pr.

Marshall, Bridget M. The Transatlantic Gothic Novel & the Law, 1790-1860. 2010. 214p. 99.95 (978-0-7546-6995-1(5)) Ashgate Publishing Co.

Martin, Gretchen. The Frontier Roots of American Realism: Southwest Humor & the Loophole of Literary Propriety. 2007. (Studies on Themes & Motifs in Literature: Vol. 89). 148p. (C). 58.95 (978-0-8204-8811-0(9)) Lang, Peter Publishing, Inc.

Martin, Holly E. Writing Between Cultures: A Study of Hybrid Narratives in Ethnic Literature of the United States. 2011. (ENG.). 216p. pap. 40.00 **(978-0-7864-6660-3(X))** McFarland & Co., Inc. Pubs.

Martucci, Elise. The Environmental Unconscious in the Fiction of Don Delillo. 2009. 196p. 39.95 (978-0-415-80304-5(7)) Routledge.

Mathes, Virgil. Pistols at High Noon. 2008. 208p. per. (978-3-8364-6325-6(3)) VDM Verlag Dr. Mueller e.K.

Matthews, Brander. Americanisms & Briticisms. 2009. 76p. pap. 14.14 (978-1-151-65065-8(X)) General Bks. LLC.

—An Introduction to the Study of American Literature. 2008. 227p. 28.99 (978-0-554-73250-3(5)); 184p. 25.99 (978-0-554-73262-6(9)); 227p. pap. 26.75 (978-0-554-73254-1(8)); 184p. pap. 25.75 (978-0-554-73260-2(2)) BiblioBazaar.

—An Introduction to the Study of American Literature. 2009. 174p. pap. (978-0-217-77534-2(9)) Books LLC.

—An Introduction to the Study of American Literature. 2007. (ENG.). 256p. 42.95 (978-0-548-02046-3(9)) Kessinger Publishing, LLC.

—Recreations of an Anthologist. 2009. 236p. 23.99 (978-1-103-59732-1(9)); pap. 17.99 (978-1-103-59728-4(0)) BiblioBazaar.

—Recreations of an Anthologist. 2008. 234p. 41.95 (978-0-548-92095-4(8)) 2007. 236p. per. 26.95 (978-0-548-59680-7(8)) Kessinger Publishing, LLC.

—Recreations of an Anthologist. 2008. 236p. pap. (978-1-4097-8779-2(6)) Read Bks.

Maxwell, William & Carduff, Christopher. William Maxwell. Carduff, Christopher, ed. 2008. (ENG.). 920p. (gr. 12). 35.00 (978-1-59853-016-2(X)) Library of America, The.

May, Charles E. Flannery O'Connor. 2011. **(978-1-58765-831-0(3))** Salem Pr., Inc.

McClennen, Sophia A. Ariel Dorfman: An Aesthetics of Hope. 2010. (ENG., Illus.). 408p. 94.95 (978-0-8223-4586-2(2)); pap. 26.95 (978-0-8223-4604-3(4)) Duke Univ. Pr.

McDonald, Kathlene. Feminism, the Left, & Postwar Literary Culture. 2012. (ENG.). 160p. 55.00 **(978-1-61703-301-8(4))** Univ. Pr. of Mississippi.

McIntyre, D. L. Poets, Prophets, Healers - an integrated approach to Literature. 2007. 113p. pap. 14.95 (978-0-615-16213-3(4)) Words & Music.

McKusick, James. Green Writing: Romanticism & Ecology. 2nd ed. 2010. (ENG.). 284p. pap. 28.00 (978-0-230-10561-4(0)) Palgrave Macmillan.

McLoughlin, Kate, ed. The Cambridge Companion to War Writing. 2009. (Cambridge Companions to Literature Ser.). (ENG.). 290p. (C). 88.00 (978-0-521-89568-2(5)); pap. 29.99 (978-0-521-72004-5(4)) Cambridge Univ. Pr.

McMichael, George L., et al. Concise Anthology of American Literature. 7th ed. 2010. (ENG.). 2368p. (C). pap. 103.00 (978-0-205-76310-8(3), Prentice Hall) Prentice Hall PTR.

McMillin, T. S. The Meaning of Rivers: Flow & Reflection in American Literature. 2011. (American Land & Life Ser.). 240p. pap. 34.95 (978-1-58729-977-3(1)) Univ. of Iowa Pr.

McNamara, Kevin R., ed. The Cambridge Companion to the Literature of Los Angeles. 2010. (Cambridge Companions to Literature Ser.). (ENG.). 248p. (C). 85.00 (978-0-521-51470-5(3)); pap. 24.99 (978-0-521-73554-4(8)) Cambridge Univ. Pr.

Melville, Herman. Moby Dick. 2007. (Twelve-Point Ser.). lib. bdg. 30.00 (978-1-58287-443-2(3)) North Bks.

Mencken, H. A Book of Prefaces. 2006. pap. 13.95 (978-1-55742-985-8(5)) Wildside Pr., LLC.

Mencken, H. L. A Book of Prefaces. 2011. 294p. pap. 28.75 **(978-1-178-92827-3(6))** 2010. (ENG.). 296p. pap. 28.75 (978-1-171-73272-3(4)) 2010. 298p. pap. 28.75 (978-1-177-52556-5(9)) 2010. (ENG.). 292p. pap. 28.75 (978-1-177-39574-8(6)) 2010. 294p. pap. 28.75 (978-1-177-79805-1(0)) 2010. (ENG.). 294p. pap. 28.75 (978-1-176-35076-2(5)) 2010. 294p. pap. 28.75 (978-1-144-29795-2(8)) 2009. 286p. 30.99 (978-1-110-02808-5(3)) 2009. 286p. pap. 27.75 (978-1-110-02806-1(7)) 2009. (ENG.). 284p. pap. 23.99 (978-1-110-02804-7(0), BiblioLife) 2009. (ENG.). 284p. pap. 21.99 (978-1-110-02803-0(2), BiblioLife) 2008. 176p. 25.99 (978-0-554-25054-0(3)) 2008. 176p. 22.99 (978-0-554-34357-0(6)) 2007. (ENG.). 152p. pap. 19.99 (978-1-4264-9660-8(5)) BiblioBazaar.

—A Book of Prefaces. 2009. 108p. pap. (978-1-4589-9478-3(3)) Books LLC.

—A Book of Prefaces. 2010. 56p. pap. 20.00 (978-1-77045-956-4(1)) General Bks. LLC.

—A Book of Prefaces. 290p. 2011. 43.95 **(978-1-169-87921-8(7))** 2010. 35.16 (978-1-163-20782-6(9)) 2010. pap. 23.16 (978-1-162-77309-4(X)) Kessinger Publishing, LLC.

Mentak, Said. A (Mis)reading of Kurt Vonnegut. 2010. (Focus on Civilizations & Cultures Ser.). 225p. 175.00 *(978-1-61668-595-9(6))* Nova Science Pubs., Inc.

Mermann-Jozwiak, Elisabeth & Sullivan, Nancy. Conversations with Mexican American Writers: Languages & Literatures in the Borderlands. 2009. (ENG.). 192p. 50.00 *(978-1-60473-214-6(8))*; pap. 22.00 *(978-1-60473-215-3(6))* Univ. Pr. of Mississippi.

Meyers, Jeffrey. Ernest Hemingway. 2009. 610p. pap. 45.00 *(978-0-415-56892-0(7))* Routledge.

Mickenberg, Julia L. & Vallone, Lynne, eds. The Oxford Handbook of Children's Literature, 1 vol. 2011. (Oxford Handbooks Ser.). (ENG., Illus.). 608p. 150.00 *(978-0-19-537978-5(0))* Oxford Univ. Pr., Inc.

Miller, Charles E. Bibliography on Early Modernism in American Literature. 2008. 172p. pap. 13.95 *(978-1-4401-0597-5(9))* iUniverse, Inc.

Miller, Eugene G. Essays on German, American & English Literature. 2007. (ENG.). 102p. per. 25.50 *(978-0-7618-3219-5(X))* Univ. Pr. of America, Inc.

Millgate, Michael. Faulkner's Place. 2009. (ENG.). 168p. pap. 22.95 *(978-0-8203-3371-7(9))* Univ. of Georgia Pr.

Moning, Karen Marie. Zauber der Begierde. (GER.). pap. *(978-3-548-24890-5(X))* Ullstein-Taschenbuch-Verlag DEU. Dist: International Bk. Import Service, Inc.

Monteiro, George. Stephen Crane: The Contemporary Reviews. 2009. (American Critical Archives Ser.). (ENG.). 304p. 135.00 *(978-0-521-38265-6(3))* Cambridge Univ. Pr.

Moore, L. B. & Moore, Bryan L. Ecology & Literature: Ecocentric Personification from Antiquity to the Twenty-First Century. 2008. (ENG.). 260p. 89.00 *(978-0-230-60569-2(5))* Palgrave Macmillan.

More, Paul E. Selected Shelburne Essays. reprint ed. 39.00 *(978-0-403-07240-8(9))* Somerset Pubs., Inc.

Morey, Ann-Janine. Religion & Sexuality in American Literature. 2008. (Cambridge Studies in American Literature & Culture Ser.). (ENG.). 292p. pap. 38.99 *(978-0-521-10376-3(2))* Cambridge Univ. Pr.

Morgan, John Matthew & Morgan, Jack. New World Irish: Notes on One Hundred Years of Lives & Letters in American Culture. 2011. (New Directions in Irish & Irish American Literature Ser.). (ENG., Illus.). 256p. 85.00 *(978-0-230-11696-2(5))* Palgrave Macmillan.

Morley, Christopher. The Powder of Sympathy. 2008. (ENG.). 320p. 32.95 *(978-1-4344-9692-2(1))*; per. 19.95 *(978-1-4344-9891-5(3))* Wildside Pr., LLC.

Morris, Christopher D. The Figure of the Road: Deconstructive Studies in Humanities Disciplines. 2006. 288p. (C). 74.95 *(978-0-8204-8857-8(7))* Lang, Peter Publishing, Inc.

Morton, Clay. The Oral Character of Southern Literature: Explaining the Distinctiveness of Regional Texts. 2008. 330p. 119.95 *(978-0-7734-4944-2(2))* Mellen, Edwin Pr., The.

Morton, Timothy. Ecology Without Nature: Rethinking Environmental Aesthetics. 2009. 264p. pap. 24.50 *(978-0-674-03485-3(6))* 2007. 262p. 54.50 *(978-0-674-02434-2(6))* Harvard Univ. Pr.

Mosser, Jason. The Participatory Journalism of Michael Herr, Norman Mailer, Hunter S. Thompson, & Joan Didion: Creating New Reporting Styles. 2012. (ENG.). 268p. 139.95 ***(978-0-7734-2599-6(3))*** Mellen, Edwin Pr., The.

Mossinger, Ingrid & Ette, Wolfram, eds. Bob Dylan 5 Songs: Vorträge zur Ausstellung Bob Dylan. The Drawn Blank Series. in den Kunstsammlungen Chemnitz. 2009. (ENG., Illus.). 288p. 55.00 *(978-3-86678-245-7(4))* Kerber Verlag DEU. Dist: D.A.P./Distributed Art Pubs.

Moulton, C. W. Library of Literary Criticism of English & American Authors. 45.00 *(978-0-8446-7155-0(X))*; Vol. 2. 45.00 *(978-0-8446-7156-7(8))*; Vol. 3. 45.00 *(978-0-8446-7157-4(6))*; Vol. 4. 45.00 *(978-0-8446-7158-1(4))*; Vol. 5. 45.00 *(978-0-8446-7159-8(2))*; Vol. 6. 45.00 *(978-0-8446-7160-4(6))*; Vol. 7. 45.00 *(978-0-8446-7161-1(4))*; Vol. 8. 45.00 *(978-0-8446-7162-8(2))* Smith, Peter Pub., Inc.

Murphy, Brenda. Understanding David Mamet. 2011. (Understanding Contemporary American Literature Ser.). (ENG.). 160p. 39.95 *(978-1-61117-002-3(8))* Univ. of South Carolina Pr.

Murphy, Michael. Proust & America. 2008. (ENG., Illus.). 380p. 65.00 *(978-1-84631-114-7(4))* Liverpool Univ. Pr. GBR. Dist: Chicago Distribution Ctr.

Murphy, Patrick. Ecocritical Explorations in Literary & Cultural Studies: Fences, Boundaries, & Fields. 2010. (ENG.). 230p. pap. 29.95 *(978-0-7391-3174-9(5))* Lexington Bks.

Murphy, Patrick D. Ecocritical Explorations in Literary & Cultural Studies: Fences, Boundaries, & Fields. 2009. (ENG.). 230p. 62.99 *(978-0-7391-3173-2(7))* Lexington Bks.

Murray, Stuart. Representing Autism: Culture, Narrative, Fascination. 2008. (Liverpool University Press - Representations: Health, Disability, Culture & So Ser.). (ENG., Illus.). 288p. 80.00 *(978-1-84631-091-1(1))*; pap. 35.00 *(978-1-84631-092-8(X))* Liverpool Univ. Pr. GBR. Dist: Chicago Distribution Ctr.

Nahson, Claudia J. The Snowy Day & the Art of Ezra Jack Keats. 2011. (ENG., Illus.). 104p. 27.50 *(978-0-300-17022-1(X))* Yale Univ. Pr.

Nel, Philip. Crockett Johnson & Ruth Krauss: How an Unlikely Couple Found Love, Dodged the FBI, & Transformed Children's Literature. 2012. (Children's Literature Association Ser.). (ENG., Illus.). 368p. 70.00 ***(978-1-61703-624-8(2))***; pap. 40.00 ***(978-1-61703-636-1(6))*** Univ. Pr. of Mississippi.

Neudecker, Claudia. Implanting Foreignness: The Literacy Construction of Korean/American Realities. 226p. pap. 47.95 *(978-3-631-54859-2(1))* Lang, Peter Publishing, Inc.

Neville, Susan & Neville, Susan S. Sailing the Inland Sea: On Writing, Literature, & Land. 2007. (ENG.). 240p. 50.00 *(978-0-253-34867-8(6)*, 0253348676); pap. 19.95 *(978-0-253-21902-2(7)*, 0253219027) Indiana Univ. Pr. (Quarry Bks.).

Newlin, Keith, ed. The Oxford Handbook of American Literary Naturalism, 1 vol. 2011. (Oxford Handbooks Ser.). (ENG., Illus.). 536p. 150.00 *(978-0-19-536893-2(2))* Oxford Univ. Pr., Inc.

Nichol, John. American Literature: An Historical Sketch, 1620-1880. 2010. 492p. pap. 38.75 *(978-1-146-61596-9(5))* BiblioBazaar.

Nieland, Justus. David Lynch. 2012. E-Book ***(978-0-252-09405-7(0))***; (ENG., Illus.). 216p. 70.00 ***(978-0-252-03693-4(X))***; (ENG., Illus.). 216p. pap. 22.00 ***(978-0-252-07851-4(9))*** Univ. of Illinois Pr.

Nixon, Rob. Slow Violence & the Environmentalism of the Poor. 2011. (ENG., Illus.). 370p. 45.00 *(978-0-674-04930-7(6))* Harvard Univ. Pr.

Noble, Donald R. John Steinbeck. 2011. (Critical Insights Ser.). 414p. 85.00 *(978-1-58765-703-0(1))* Salem Pr., Inc.

Nolan, Michelle. Love on the Racks: A History of American Romance Comics. 2008. (ENG., Illus.). 246p. 49.95 *(978-0-7864-3519-7(4))* McFarland & Co., Inc. Pubs.

Norton, Donna E. Multicultural Children's Literature: Through the Eyes of Many Children. 4th rev. ed. 2012. (ENG.). 360p. (C). pap. 53.80 ***(978-0-13-263576-4(0))*** Allyn & Bacon, Inc.

—Multicultural Children's Literature: Through the Eyes of Many Children. 3rd ed. 2008. (ENG., Illus.). 368p. (C). pap. 53.80 *(978-0-13-514528-9(7)*, Prentice Hall) Prentice Hall PTR.

Novak, Barbara. Voyages of the Self: Pairs, Parallels & Patterns in American Art & Literature. 2009. (ENG., Illus.). 232p. pap. 24.95 *(978-0-19-538791-9(0))* Oxford Univ. Pr., Inc.

O'Brien, Michael. Placing the South. 2011. (ENG.). pap. 30.00 ***(978-1-61703-202-8(6))*** Univ. Pr. of Mississippi.

Oehlschlaeger, Fritz. The Achievement of Wendell Berry: The Hard History of Love. 2011. (Culture of the Land Ser.). (ENG.). 336p. 40.00 *(978-0-8131-3007-1(7))* Univ. Pr. of Kentucky.

Ohi, Kevin. Henry James & the Queerness of Style. 2011. 248p. pap. 25.00 *(978-0-8166-6511-2(7))* Univ. of Minnesota Pr.

Ohler, Paul J. Edith Wharton's Evolutionary Conception. 2010. 212p. pap. 39.95 *(978-0-415-88006-0(8))* Routledge.

O'Neill, Edward Hayes. A History of American Biography, 1800-1935. 2011. 440p. 56.95 ***(978-1-258-06237-8(2))*** Literary Licensing, LLC.

Oriard, Michael. Sporting with the Gods: The Rhetoric of Play & Game in American Literature. 2008. (Cambridge Studies in American Literature & Culture Ser.). (ENG.). 600p. pap. 74.00 *(978-0-521-10156-1(5))* Cambridge Univ. Pr.

Ortiz, Ricardo L. Cultural Erotics in Cuban America. 2007. 328p. 72.00 *(978-0-8166-4795-8(X))* Univ. of Minnesota Pr.

Paliwoda, Daniel. Melville & the Theme of Boredom. 2009. (ENG., Illus.). 247p. pap. 45.00 *(978-0-7864-4154-9(2))* McFarland & Co., Inc. Pubs.

Pancoast, Henry S. An Introduction to American Literature. 2008. 434p. 51.95 *(978-0-548-99435-1(8))* 2007. (ENG.). 436p. per. 36.95 *(978-0-548-65257-2(0))* Kessinger Publishing, LLC.

Parikh, Crystal. An Ethics of Betrayal: The Politics of Otherness in Emergent U. S. Literatures & Culture. 4th ed. 2009. (American Literatures Initiative Ser.). (ENG.). 256p. 70.00 *(978-0-8232-3042-6(2))*; pap. 26.00 *(978-0-8232-3043-3(0))* Fordham Univ. Pr.

Parini, Jay. Promised Land: Thirteen Books That Changed America. 2010. (ENG & ABK., Illus.). 400p. pap. 16.95 *(978-0-307-38618-2(X)*, Anchor) Knopf Doubleday Publishing Group.

Parini, Jay, ed. American Writers: A Collection of Literary Biographies. 16th ed. 2006. (American Writers: Supplement Ser.). (ENG.). 624p. 218.00 *(978-0-684-31510-2(6)*, Charles Scribner's Sons) Cengage Gale.

Parker, David B. Alias Bill Arp: Charles Henry Smith & the South's Goodly Heritage. 2009. 220p. pap. 24.95 *(978-0-8203-3450-9(2))* Univ. of Georgia Pr.

Parrington, Vernon Louis. Liberalism, Puritanism & the Colonial Mind: Main Currents in American Thought. 2011. (ENG.). 452p. pap. 39.95 *(978-1-4128-1868-1(0))* Transaction Pubs.

Parry, Albert. Garrets & Pretenders: Bohemian Life in America from Poe to Kerouac. 2012. (New York City Ser.). (ENG.). 480p. pap. 16.95 ***(978-0-486-48605-5(2))*** Dover Pubns., Inc.

Patell, Cyrus R. K. & Waterman, Bryan, eds. The Cambridge Companion to the Literature of New York. 2010. (Cambridge Companions to Literature Ser.). (ENG., Illus.). 282p. (C). 78.00 *(978-0-521-51471-2(1))*; pap. 24.99 *(978-0-521-73555-1(6))* Cambridge Univ. Pr.

Pattee, Amy. Reading the Adolescent Romance: Sweet Valley High & the Popular Young Adult Romance Novel. 2010. (Children's Literature & Culture Ser.). (ENG.). 202p. (C). 125.00 *(978-0-415-87594-3(3))* Routledge.

Patterson, Anita. Race, American Literature & Transnational Modernisms. 2008. (Cambridge Studies in American Literature & Culture Ser.). (ENG.). 248p. 84.00 *(978-0-521-88405-1(5))* Cambridge Univ. Pr.

Paulson, Ronald. Sin & Evil: Moral Values in Literature. 2007. (ENG., Illus.). 432p. (C). 45.00 *(978-0-300-12014-1(1))* Yale Univ. Pr.

Pazicky, Diana Loercher. Cultural Orphans in America. 2008. (ENG.). 232p. pap. 25.00 *(978-1-60473-192-7(3))* Univ. Pr. of Mississippi.

Pearce, Roy Harvey. Hawthorne & the Sense of the Past: Or the Immortality of Major Molineux. 2011. 26p. 35.95 ***(978-1-258-02226-6(5))*** Literary Licensing, LLC.

Pelaud, Isabelle Thuy. This Is All I Choose to Tell: History & Hybridity in Vietnamese American Literature. 2010. (Asian American History & Cultu Ser.) (ENG., Illus.). 216p. 61.50 *(978-1-4399-0216-5(X))*; pap. 22.95 *(978-1-4399-0217-2(8))* Temple Univ. Pr.

Perez, Vincent & Pérez, Vincent. Remembering the Hacienda: History & Memory in the Mexican American Southwest. 2006. (Rio Grande/Rio Bravo Ser.: 11). (ENG., Illus.). 264p. 49.95 *(978-1-58544-511-0(8))*; per. 24.95 *(978-1-58544-546-2(0))* Texas A&M Univ. Pr.

Perkins, James A., ed. David Madden: A Writer for All Genres. 2006. (Illus.). 178p. 34.95 *(978-1-57233-460-1(6))* Univ. of Tennessee Pr.

Perry, Bliss. The American Spirit in Literature. 2009. (ENG.). 288p. 34.99 *(978-1-117-26133-1(6))*; 290p. pap. 27.75 *(978-1-117-26134-8(4))*; 336p. 36.99 *(978-1-115-42280-2(4))*; 336p. 32.99 *(978-1-115-42278-9(2))*; 336p. pap. 31.75 *(978-1-115-42276-5(6))*; 336p. pap. 30.75 *(978-1-115-42274-1(X))* BiblioBazaar.

—The American Spirit in Literature. 2009. 158p. pap. *(978-1-4588-6089-7(2))* Books LLC.

—The American Spirit in Literature. (Chronicles of America Ser.). 281p. reprint ed. 98.00 *(978-0-7222-7127-8(1))* Library Reprints, Inc.

—The American Spirit in Literature: A Chronicle of Great Interpreters. 2010. 288p. pap. 28.75 *(978-1-146-92767-3(3))* 2010. 288p. pap. 28.75 *(978-1-145-83748-5(4))* 2010. 348p. pap. 32.75 *(978-1-142-98397-0(8))* 2008. 316p. 28.99 *(978-0-559-75183-7(4))* 2008. 316p. pap. 28.75 *(978-0-559-75181-3(8))* BiblioBazaar.

—The American Spirit in Literature: A Chronicle of Great Interpreters. 2008. 136p. pap. *(978-1-4099-4150-7(7))* Dodo Pr.

—The American Spirit in Literature: A chronicle of great interpreters. 2010. (ENG.). 304p. pap. 29.75 *(978-1-176-46862-7(6))* BiblioBazaar.

Perry, Bliss. The American Spirit in Literature: A Chronicle of Great Interpreters... 2012. 310p. pap. 29.75 ***(978-1-276-84524-3(3))*** BiblioBazaar.

Pescollderungg, Irene. The Concept of the Self in E E Cummings. 2008. 128p. pap. *(978-3-639-05580-1(2))* VDM Verlag Dr. Mueller e.K.

Pinsky, Robert & Pinsky, R. Thousands of Broadways: Dreams & Nightmares of the American Small Town. 2009. (Campbell Lectures). (Illus.). 106p. 16.00 *(978-0-226-66944-1(0))* Univ. of Chicago Pr.

Pitt, Kristin E. Body, Nation, & Narrative in the Americas. 2010. (ENG.). 220p. 84.00 *(978-0-230-10713-7(3))* Palgrave Macmillan.

Pizer, Donald. The Novels of Theodore Dreiser: A Critical Study. 2009. (ENG.). 400p. pap. 60.00 *(978-0-8166-5851-0(X))* Univ. of Minnesota Pr.

Poe, Edgar Allan. Fall of the House of Usher & Other Tales. 2009. (ENG.). 245p. pap. 24.95 *(978-1-4128-1257-3(7))* Transaction Pubs.

Polk, Noel. Faulkner & Welty & the Southern Literary Tradition. 2008. (ENG.). 240p. 50.00 *(978-1-934110-84-3(1))* Univ. Pr. of Mississippi.

Poll, Ryan. Main Street & Empire: The Fictional Small Town in the Age of Globalization. 2012. E-Book ***(978-0-8135-5294-1(X))***; 238p. 72.00 ***(978-0-8135-5289-7(3))***; (ENG.). 238p. (C). pap. 24.95 ***(978-0-8135-5290-3(7))*** Rutgers Univ. Pr.

Pollard, Percival. Their Day in Court. 2010. 492p. pap. 38.75 *(978-1-177-25043-6(8))*; 490p. pap. 38.75 *(978-1-147-20160-4(9))*; 500p. pap. 38.75 *(978-1-142-17022-6(5))* BiblioBazaar.

—Their Day in Court. 2009. 270p. pap. 19.94 *(978-1-151-25356-9(1))* General Bks. LLC.

Pontuale, Francesco. In Their Own Terms: American Literary Historiography in the United States & Italy. 2008. (Studies on Themes & Motifs in Literature Ser.: Vol. 95). 246p. (C). 70.95 *(978-1-4331-0188-5(2))* Lang, Peter Publishing, Inc.

Potter, Lois & Calhoun, Joshua. Images of Robin Hood: Medieval to Modern. 2008. (Illus.). 288p. (C). 75.00 *(978-0-87413-003-4(4))* Univ. of Delaware Pr.

Pound, Ezra. The Analyst, No. Mayo, Robert, ed. 2011. 16p. pap. 35.95 ***(978-1-258-04945-4(7))*** Literary Licensing, LLC.

Pound, Ezra & Glenn, E. M. The Analyst, No. Mayo, Robert, ed. 2011. 26p. 35.95 ***(978-1-258-04946-1(5))*** Literary Licensing, LLC.

Pound, Ezra, et al. The Analyst, No 1-8. 2011. 116p. 39.95 ***(978-1-258-10261-6(7))*** Literary Licensing, LLC.

Pozorski, Aimee. Roth & Trauma: The Problem of History in the Later Works (1995-2010) 2011. (ENG.). 192p. 100.00 *(978-1-4411-8511-2(9))* Continuum International Publishing Group, Ltd. GBR. Dist: National Bk. Network.

Rader, Pamela/J. Multi-Ethnicity as a Resource for the Literary Imagination: The Creative Achievements of Women Artists, Poets, & Novelists. 2009. 156p. *(978-0-7734-3893-4(9))* Mellen, Edwin Pr., The.

Rainey, Lawrence. American Literature & Culture: 1914 to the Present. rev. ed. 2007. 250p. (ENG.). 59.95 *(978-0-7456-2765-6(X))*; pap. *(978-0-7456-2766-3(8))* Polity Pr. GBR. Dist: Wiley, John & Sons, Inc.

Rapp, Claudia. Mapping Contemporary Literature from Hawai'I. 2008. 240p. pap. *(978-3-639-05197-1(1))* VDM Verlag Dr. Mueller e.K.

Rathmell, George. Realms of Gold: The Colorful Writers of San Francisco 1850-1950. 2008. 223p. pap. 17.95 *(978-0-7414-4537-7(9))* Infinity Publishing.

Rausch, Andrew J. The Wit & Wisdom of Stephen King. Rausch, Andrew J., ed. 2011. 146p. pap. 14.95 ***(978-1-59393-648-8(6))*** BearManor Media.

Raw, Laurence, et al, eds. The Theme of Cultural Adaptation in American History, Literature, & Film: Cases When the Discourse Changed. 2009. (Illus.). vi, 553p. *(978-0-7734-3876-7(9))* Mellen, Edwin Pr., The.

Rawlings, Peter. American Theorists of the Novel: Henry James, Lionel Trilling, Wayne C. Booth. 2006. (Routledge Critical Thinkers Ser.). 171p. 95.00 *(978-0-415-28544-5(5))*; (Illus.). per. 23.95 *(978-0-415-28545-2(3))* Routledge.

Raymond, Ida. Southland Writers Biographical & Critical Sketches of the Living Female Writers of the South with Extracts from Their Writings by Ida Raymond Vo. 2006. (ENG.). 524p. per. 29.99 *(978-1-4255-5804-8(6))*; 464p. per. 29.99 *(978-1-4255-5136-0(X))* MPublishing.

Redding, Arthur F. Haints: American Ghosts, Millennial Passions, & Contemporary Gothic Fictions. 2011. *(978-0-8173-8572-9(X))*; (ENG.). 168p. (C). 27.50 *(978-0-8173-1746-1(5))* Univ. of Alabama Pr.

Reesman, Jeanne Campbell, ed. Speaking the Other Self: American Women Writers. 2011. (ENG.). 352p. pap. 24.95 ***(978-0-8203-3798-2(6))*** Univ. of Georgia Pr.

Reichardt, Mary R., ed. Between Human & Divine: The Catholic Vision in Contemporary Literature. 2010. (ENG.). 304p. 69.95 *(978-0-8132-1739-0(3))* Catholic Univ. of America Pr.

Reichert Powell, Douglas. Critical Regionalism: Connecting Politics & Culture in the American Landscape. 2007. (ENG., Illus.). 280p. 69.95 *(978-0-8078-3091-8(7))*; per. 27.95 *(978-0-8078-5794-6(7))* Univ. of North Carolina Pr.

Renker, Elizabeth. The Origins of American Literature Studies: An Institutional History. (Cambridge Studies in American Literature & Culture Ser.). (ENG.). 232p. 2010. pap. 34.99 *(978-0-521-14199-4(0))* 2007. 98.00 *(978-0-521-88345-0(8))* Cambridge Univ. Pr.

Research Guide to American Literature, 7 vols., Set. 2010. (Research Guide to American Literature Ser). (C). (gr. 9). 350.00 *(978-0-8160-8307-7(X))*, Facts On File, Inc.

Richardson, Charles F. A Primer of American Literature. 120p. 2008. 34.95 *(978-0-548-94651-0(5))* 2007. (ENG.). per. 19.95 *(978-0-548-62124-0(1))* Kessinger Publishing, LLC.

Richardson, Mark. Zen & Now: On the Trail of Robert Pirsig & the Art of Motorcycle Maintenance. 2009. (Vintage Departures Ser.). (ENG., Illus.). 288p. pap. 15.00 *(978-0-307-39069-1(1)*, Vintage) Knopf Doubleday Publishing Group.

Rickels, Laurence A. I Think I Am: Philip K. Dick. 2010. 432p. 75.00 *(978-0-8166-6665-2(2))*; pap. 25.00 *(978-0-8166-6666-9(0))* Univ. of Minnesota Pr.

RIDLEY. 'Relations Stop Nowhere'. The Common Literary Foundations of German & American Literature 1830-1917. 2007. (IFAVL Ser.: 109). 320p. per. 86.00 *(978-90-420-2183-9(7))* Rodopi.

Rivera, Milagros. The Use of Ghosts in Beloved & Beyond the Limbo Silence. 2010. 76p. pap. *(978-3-8383-6248-9(9))* Lambert Academic Publishing.

Rivers, William & Dennis, Everette. Other Voices: The New Journalism in America. 2010. (ENG.). 236p. pap. 29.95 *(978-1-4128-1455-3(3))* Transaction Pubs.

Robertson, Ben P., ed. Themes of Conflict in the Nineteenth- & Twentieth-Century Literature of the American South: The Proceedings of the 2004 Conflict in Southern Writing Conference. 2007. 420p. 128.95 *(978-0-7734-5375-3(X))* Mellen, Edwin Pr., The.

Robinson, Jeffrey C. The Walk: Notes on a Romantic Image. 2nd ed. 2006. (Dalkey Archive Scholarly Ser.). (Illus.). 144p. reprint ed. per. 19.95 *(978-1-56478-459-9(2))* Dalkey Archive Pr.

Robisch, S. K. Wolves & the Wolf Myth in American Literature. 2009. (ENG.). 512p. pap. 29.95 *(978-0-87417-773-2(1))*; 49.95 *(978-0-87417-772-5(3))* Univ. of Nevada Pr.

Rodden, John. Isabel Allende. 2010. (Critical Insights Ser.). 366p. 85.00 *(978-1-58765-699-6(X))* Salem Pr., Inc.

Rodden, John, ed. The Worlds of Irving Howe: The Critical Legacy. 2007. (ENG., Illus.). 390p. pap. 54.95 *(978-1-59451-025-0(3))* Paradigm Pubs.

Rodden, John, ed. & intro. Irving Howe & the Critics: Celebrations & Attacks. 2008. (ENG.). 237p. pap. 24.95 *(978-0-8032-1836-9(2))* Univ. of Nebraska Pr.

Rodgers, Johannah. The Social Construction of Authorship. 2009. 164p. pap. *(978-3-639-13997-6(6))* VDM Verlag Dr. Mueller e.K.

Rohy. Anachronism & Its Others: Sexuality, Race, Temporality. 2010. 194p. pap. 23.95 *(978-1-4384-2864-2(2)*, Suny Pr.) State Univ. of New York Pr.

Rohy, Valerie. Anachronism & Its Others: Sexuality, Race, Temporality. 2009. 224p. 70.00 *(978-1-4384-2865-9(0))* State Univ. of New York Pr.

Ronda, Bruce A. Reading the Old Man: John Brown in American Culture. 2008. (ENG., Illus.). 218p. 39.95 *(978-1-57233-620-9(X))* Univ. of Tennessee Pr.

Rosenthal, Sarah, ed. A Community Writing Itself: Conversations with Vanguard Writers of the Bay Area. 2010. (Dalkey Archive Scholarly Ser.). (ENG.). 420p. pap. 29.95 *(978-1-56478-584-8(X)*, 478584) Dalkey Archive Pr.

Rosenwald, Lawrence. Multilingual America: Language & the Making of American Literature. 2008. (Cambridge Studies in American Literature & Culture Ser.). (ENG.). 216p. 91.00 *(978-0-521-89686-3(X))*; pap. 34.00 *(978-0-521-72161-5(X))* Cambridge Univ. Pr.

Rounds, Charles R. Wisconsin Authors & Their Works. 400p. reprint ed. lib. bdg. 98.00 *(978-0-7222-0324-8(1))* Library Reprints, Inc.

Rourke, Constance. American Humor: A Study of the National Character. 2008. 260p. pap. 25.00 *(978-1-59740-585-0(X))* ACLS Humanities E-Book.

Roza, Mathilde Helene. Following Strangers: The Life & Literary Works of Robert M. Coates. 2011. 344p. 49.95 *(978-1-57003-981-2(X))* Univ. of South Carolina Pr.

Rubin, Joan Shelley. Songs of Ourselves: The Uses of Poetry in America. 2010. (Illus.). 488p. pap. 20.00 *(978-0-674-03512-6(7)*, Belknap Pr.) Harvard Univ. Pr.

Rubin, Louis Decimus Jr., et al. Southern Literary Study: Problems & Possibilities. 2011. (ENG.). 248p. pap. 40.00 ***(978-0-8078-9767-6(1))*** Univ. of North Carolina Pr.

Rusak, Justyna. Poe & Psychoanalysis. 2011. 116p. pap. ***(978-3-639-32383-2(1))*** VDM Verlag Dr. Mueller e.K.

A

Saber, Yomna Mohamed. Brave to Be Involved: Shifting Positions in the Poetry of Gwendolyn Brooks. 2010. 211p. pap. 57.95 *(978-3-0343-0504-4(4))* Lang, Peter Publishing, Inc.

Sabry, Somaya Sami. Arab-American Women's Writing & Performance: Orientalism, Race & the Idea of the Arabian Nights. 2011. (International Library of Cultural Studies). (ENG., Illus.). 224p. 88.00 *(978-1-84885-568-7(0),* Tauris Academic Studies) I. B. Tauris & Co., Ltd. GBR. Dist: Macmillan.

Saloman, Randi. Virginia Woolf's Essayism. 2012. (ENG.). 224p. (gr. 17). 105.00 ***(978-0-7486-4648-7(5))*** Edinburgh Univ. Pr. GBR. Dist: Columbia Univ. Pr.

Salomon, Roger B. Desperate Storytelling: Post-Romantic Elaborations of the Mock-Heroic Mode. 2008. (ENG.). 312p. pap. 24.95 *(978-0-8203-3262-8(3))* Univ. of Georgia Pr.

Sanborn, Franklin Benjamin. Recollections of Seventy Years. 2009. 124p. pap. *(978-1-151-27703-9(7))* Books LLC.

—Recollections of Seventy Years. 2009. 246p. pap. 19.99 *(978-0-217-98129-3(1))* General Bks. LLC.

—Recollections of Seventy Years, 2 vol., set. reprint ed. 250.00 *(978-0-7222-9004-0(7))* Library Reprints, Inc.

Sanborn, Geoffrey & Otter, Sam. Melville & Aesthetics. 2011. (ENG., Illus.). 272p. 85.00 *(978-0-230-11379-4(6))* Palgrave Macmillan.

Sanchez-Blake, Elvira & Lirot, Julie, eds. El Universo Literario de Laura Restrepo. 2007. 383p. per. 24.99 *(978-958-704-573-4(4))* Alfaguara, Ediciones, S.A.-Grupo Santillana ESP. Dist: Santillana USA Publishing Co., Inc.

Sandoval, Anna Marie. Toward a Latina Feminism of the Americas: Repression & Resistance in Chicana & Mexicana Literature. Castañeda, Antonia & González, Deena J., eds. 2009. (ENG.). 144p. pap. 19.95 *(978-0-292-72166-1(8))* Univ. of Texas Pr.

Schaberg, Christopher. The Textual Life of Airports: Reading the Culture of Flight. 2011. (ENG., Illus.). 192p. (gr. 17). 100.00 ***(978-1-4411-7521-2(0))*** Continuum International Publishing Group, Ltd. GBR. Dist: National Bk. Network.

Schafer, Edith Nalle. Literary Circles of Washington. 2008. (ENG., Illus.). 79p. pap. 12.95 *(978-1-55709-081-2(5))* Applewood Bks.

Schiesari, Juliana. Polymorphous Domesticities: Pets, Bodies, & Desire in Four Modern Writers. 2012. (FlashPoints Ser.). (ENG.). 152p. pap. 39.95 ***(978-0-520-27084-8(3))*** Univ. of California Pr.

Schirmer, Walter Franz. Geschichte der Englischen und Amerikanischen Literatur: Von den Anfängen bis zur Gegenwart. Esch, Arno, ed. 5th ed. (GER.). XVI, 838p. 478.00 ***(978-3-11-217653-5(7))*** De Gruyter, Mouton DEU. Dist: de Gruyter, Walter GmbH & Co. KG.

Schlueter, Nathan & Mitchell, Mark T., eds. Humane Vision of Wendell Berry. 2011. (ENG.). 336p. 29.95 *(978-1-61017-001-7(6))* ISI Bks.

Schlund-Vials, Cathy. Modeling Citizenship: Jewish & Asian American Writing. 2011. (ENG.). 248p. 68.50 *(978-1-4399-0317-9(4))*; pap. 24.95 *(978-1-4399-0318-6(2))* Temple Univ. Pr.

Schneck, Peter. Rhetoric & Evidence: Legal Conflict & Literary Representation in U. S. American Culture. 2011. (Law & Literature Ser.). (ENG., Illus.). VII, 291p. 210.00 ***(978-3-11-219029-6(7))***; 140.00 ***(978-3-11-025376-4(3))*** De Gruyter, Walter Inc.

Schocket, Eric. Vanishing Moments: Class & American Literature. 2006. (Class: Culture Ser.). (ENG., Illus.). 320p. 90.00 *(978-0-472-11569-3(3))*; per. 37.50 *(978-0-472-03187-0(2))* Univ. of Michigan Pr.

Scholnick, Robert, ed. American Literature & Science. 2010. (ENG.). 296p. pap. 30.00 *(978-0-8131-9341-0(9))* Univ. Pr. of Kentucky.

Schreiber, Evelyn Jaffe. Race, Trauma, & Home in the Novels of Toni Morrison. 2010. (Southern Literary Studies). 256p. 42.50 *(978-0-8071-3649-2(2))* Louisiana State Univ. Pr.

Schweitzer, Ivy. Perfecting Friendship: Politics & Affiliation in Early American Literature. 2006. (ENG., Illus.). 288p. 55.95 *(978-0-8078-3069-7(0))*; per. 22.00 *(978-0-8078-5778-6(5))* Univ. of North Carolina Pr.

Scialabba, George. The Modern Predicament. 2011. 149p. pap. 14.00 ***(978-0-9831975-6-0(3))*** Pressed Wafer Pr.

Scudder, Horace E. Men & Letters: Essays in Characterization & Criticism. 2007. 248p. 41.95 *(978-0-548-11625-8(3))* Kessinger Publishing, LLC.

Sears, Lorenzo. American Literature in the Colonial & National Periods. 2010. (ENG.). 502p. pap. 39.75 *(978-1-176-18146-5(7))* 2010. 490p. pap. 38.75 *(978-1-147-89927-6(4))* 2010. 502p. pap. 38.75 *(978-1-144-94088-9(5))* 2010. 504p. pap. 38.75 *(978-1-145-76425-5(8))* 2009. 496p. pap. 37.75 *(978-1-116-43115-5(7))* 2009. 496p. pap. 38.75 *(978-1-116-43114-8(9))* BiblioBazaar.

—American Literature in the Colonial & National Periods. 2009. 276p. pap. 22.54 *(978-1-150-33300-2(6))* General Bks. LLC.

—American Literature in the Colonial & National Periods. 2010. 494p. pap. 31.16 *(978-1-163-91927-9(6))* 2008. 492p. 53.95 *(978-0-548-94227-7(7))* 2007. (ENG.). 496p. per. 38.95 *(978-0-548-58284-8(X))* Kessinger Publishing, LLC.

Selzer, Linda Furgerson. Charles Johnson in Context. 2009. (Illus.). 320p. 80.00 net. *(978-1-55849-698-9(X))*; (ENG., pap. 29.95 net. *(978-1-55849-723-8(4))* Univ. of Massachusetts Pr.

Sesnic, Jelena. From Shadow to Presence: Representations of Ethnicity in Contemporary American Literature. 2007. 288p. per. 80.00 *(978-90-420-2217-1(5))* Rodopi.

Shaw, Thomas B. (Thomas Budd). A Complete Manual of English Literature / by Thomas B Shaw; Edited with Notes & Illustrations, by William Smith; with a Sketch of American Litera. 2006. 544p. per. 29.99 *(978-1-4255-6005-8(9))* MPublishing.

—Outlines of English Literature, by Thomas B Shaw with a Sketch of American Literature by Henry T Tuckerman. 2006. 484p. per. 29.99 *(978-1-4255-5362-3(1))* MPublishing.

Shemak, April. Asylum Speakers: Caribbean Refugees & Testimonial Discourse. 2nd ed. 2010. (American Literatures Initiative Ser.). (ENG., Illus.). 320p. 48.00 *(978-0-8232-3355-7(3))* Fordham Univ. Pr.

Sherman, Stuart P. Americans. 2010. 352p. pap. 25.56 *(978-1-163-94870-5(5))* 2008. 350p. 46.95 *(978-0-548-96177-3(8))* 2007. (ENG.). 352p. per. 31.95 *(978-0-548-63719-7(9))* Kessinger Publishing, LLC.

Showalter, Elaine. A Jury of Her Peers: Celebrating American Women Writers from Anne Bradstreet to Annie Proulx. 2010. (Vintage Ser.). (ENG.). 608p. pap. 16.95 *(978-1-4000-3442-0(6),* Vintage) Knopf Doubleday Publishing Group.

Shrubsall, Dennis. The Writings of W. H. Hudson, the First Literary Environmentalist, 1841-1922: A Critical Survey. 2007. 372p. 119.95 *(978-0-7734-5312-8(1))* Mellen, Edwin Pr., The.

Shuffelton, Frank, ed. The Cambridge Companion to Thomas Jefferson. 2009. (Cambridge Companions to American Studies). (ENG.). 228p. (C). pap. 23.99 *(978-0-521-68697-6(0))* Cambridge Univ. Pr.

Sienkiewicz, Henryk. Life & Death & Other Legends & Stories. Curtin, Jeremiah, tr. 2011. 34p. pap. 7.95 ***(978-1-60664-587-1(0))*** Rodgers, Alan Bks.

Simms, William Gilmore. Views & Reviews, First & Second Series in 1 Volume. 2011. (ENG.). 422p. pap. 29.95 ***(978-1-61117-056-6(7))*** Univ. of South Carolina Pr.

Simms, William Gilmore. Views & Reviews in American Literature, History & Fiction. 2009. 248p. 23.99 *(978-1-103-60648-1(4))*; pap. 17.99 *(978-1-103-60644-3(1))* BiblioBazaar.

Simpson, Lewis P. Imagining Our Time: Recollections & Reflections on American Writing. 2007. (Southern Literary Studies). 265p. 45.00 *(978-0-8071-3202-9(0))* Louisiana State Univ. Pr.

Singley, Carol J. Adopting America: Childhood, Kinship, & National Identity in Literature. 2011. (ENG.). 304p. 65.00 *(978-0-19-977939-0(2))* Oxford Univ. Pr., Inc.

Sivils, Matthew Wynn & Walker, Jeffrey, eds. Literature in the Early American Republic: Annual Studies on Cooper & His Contemporaries. 2009. 308p. 125.00 *(978-0-404-63911-2(9))* AMS Pr., Inc.

Skaggs, Carmen Trammell. Overtones of Opera in American Literature from Whitman to Wharton. 2010. 176p. 29.95 *(978-0-8071-3491-7(0))* Louisiana State Univ. Pr.

Skaggs, Merrill Maguire. Axes: Willa Cather & William Faulkner. 2009. (ENG., Illus.). 224p. pap. 24.95 *(978-0-8032-2801-6(5))* Univ. of Nebraska Pr.

Slovic, Scott. Going Away to Think: Engagement, Retreat, & Ecocritical Responsibility. 2008. (ENG.). 264p. pap. 24.95 *(978-0-87417-756-5(1))* Univ. of Nevada Pr.

Smith, Caleb. The Prison & the American Imagination. 2011. (Yale Studies in English Ser.). (ENG., Illus.). 272p. pap. 25.00 *(978-0-300-17149-5(8))* Yale Univ. Pr.

Smith, Lindsey Claire. Indians, Environment, & Identity on the Borders of American Literature: From Faulkner & Morrison to Walker & Silko. 2008. (American Literature Readings in the 21st Century Ser.). (ENG.). 208p. 84.00 *(978-0-230-60541-1(9))* Palgrave Macmillan.

Smith, Stan, ed. Globalisation & Its Discontents: Writing the Global Culture. 2006. (Essays & Studies: Volume 59). 224p. 50.00 *(978-1-84384-075-6(8))* Boydell & Brewer, Inc.

Snodgrass, Mary Ellen. Leslie Marmon Silko: A Literary Companion. 2011. (McFarland Literary Companions Ser.). (ENG., Illus.). 411p. pap. 39.95 *(978-0-7864-4853-1(9))* McFarland & Co., Inc. Pubs.

Solotaroff, Ted. The Literary Community: Selected Essays 1967-2007. 2008. 310p. pap. 18.95 *(978-1-931357-59-3(5))* Sheep Meadow Pr., The.

SöZalan, ÖZden. The American Nightmare: Don Delillo's Falling Man & Cormac Mccarthy's the Road. 2011. 132p. pap. 13.32 ***(978-1-4567-9814-7(6))*** AuthorHouse.

Spanos, William V. American Exceptionalism in the Age of Globalization: The Spector of Vietnam. 2008. 321p. per. 31.95 *(978-0-7914-7290-3(6))*; 89.50 *(978-0-7914-7289-7(2))* State Univ. of New York Pr.

Srikanth, Rajini. Constructing the Enemy: Empathy/Antipathy in U. S. Literature & Law. 2011. (ENG.). 220p. 87.50 *(978-1-4399-0323-0(9))*; pap. 28.95 *(978-1-4399-0324-7(7))* Temple Univ. Pr.

Srikanth, Rajini. Constructing the Enemy: Empathy/Antipathy in U.S. Literature & Law. 2011. E-Book ***(978-1-4399-0325-4(5))*** Temple Univ. Pr.

Staub, Susan C., ed. The Literary Mother: Essays on Representations of Maternity & Child Care. 2007. (ENG.). 273p. per. 39.95 *(978-0-7864-3046-8(X))* McFarland & Co., Inc. Pubs.

Stephens, Lori Ann. The Literary Grotesque & Motherhood - Mothers & Daughters in Southern Literature. 2008. 124p. pap. *(978-3-639-05284-8(6))* VDM Verlag Dr. Mueller e.K.

Stephenson, Neal. Some Remarks. 2012. (ENG.). 288p. 25.99 ***(978-0-06-202443-5(4),*** Morrow, William & Co.) HarperCollins Pubs.

Stern, Frederick C. F. O. Matthiessen: Christian Socialist as Critic. 2011. (ENG.). 304p. pap. 40.00 ***(978-0-8078-9787-4(6))*** Univ. of North Carolina Pr.

Sternlicht, Sanford. Masterpieces of Jewish American Literature, 1 vol. 2007. (Greenwood Introduces Literary Masterpieces Ser.). 152p. 49.95 *(978-0-313-33857-1(4),* GR3857, Greenwood Pr.) Greenwood Publishing Group, Inc.

Stewart, Michelle Pagni & Atkinson, Yvonne, eds. Ethnic Literary Traditions in American Children's Literature. 2009. (ENG.). 268p. 89.00 *(978-0-230-61875-6(8))* Palgrave Macmillan.

Stokes, Claudia. Writers in Retrospect: The Rise of American Literary History, 1875-1910. 2006. (ENG., Illus.). 256p. per. 22.00 *(978-0-8078-5720-5(3))* Univ. of North Carolina Pr.

Stoneback, H. R. & Florczyk, Steven, eds. Elizabeth Madox Roberts: Essays of Reassessment & Reclamation. 2008. 348p. pap. 20.00 *(978-1-893239-77-7(2))* Wind Pubns.

Sugg, Katherine. Gender & Allegory in Transamerican Fiction & Performance. 2008. (ENG.). 260p. 89.00 *(978-0-230-60476-6(5))* Palgrave Macmillan.

Sumner, Gregory D. Unstuck in Time: A Journey Through Kurt Vonnegut's Life & Novels. 2011. (ENG., Illus.). 368p. 24.95 *(978-1-60980-349-0(3))* Seven Stories Pr.

Sykes, John D. Flannery O'Connor, Walker Percy, & the Aesthetic of Revelation. 2007. (ENG.). 208p. (C). 39.95 *(978-0-8262-1757-8(5))* Univ. of Missouri Pr.

Tafoya, Eddie. The Legacy of the Wisecrack: Stand-up Comedy as the Great American Literary Form. 2009. 240p. pap. 25.95 *(978-1-59942-495-8(9),* Brown Walker Pr.) Universal Pubs.

Tally, Robert T., Jr. & Tally, Robert T. Melville, Mapping & Globalization: Literary Cartography in the American Baroque Writer. 2009. (Continuum Literary Studies). (ENG.). 192p. 120.00 *(978-0-8264-7151-2(X))* Continuum International Publishing Group, Ltd. GBR. Dist: National Bk. Network.

Tanfer, Tunc. Feminism's Unfinished Legacy: Critiques of Gender & Racial Inequality in Contemporary American Women's Literature. 2011. 208p. pap. ***(978-3-639-33607-8(0))*** VDM Verlag Dr. Mueller e.K.

Tatum, Charles M. Chicano & Chicana Literature: Otra Voz del Pueblo. 2006. (Mexican American Experience Ser.). (ENG., Illus.). 232p. pap. 17.95 *(978-0-8165-2427-3(0))* Univ. of Arizona Pr.

Taylor, Andrew. Thinking America: New England Intellectuals & the Varieties of American Identity. 2010. (ENG.). 244p. 55.00 *(978-1-58465-862-7(2),* University of New Hampshire Press) Univ. Pr. of New England.

Taylor, Bayard. Critical Essays & Literary Notes. 2009. 396p. 26.99 *(978-1-103-12790-0(X))*; pap. 20.99 *(978-1-103-12786-3(1))* BiblioBazaar.

—Critical Essays & Literary Notes. 2009. 182p. pap. *(978-0-217-19609-3(8))*; 154p. pap. *(978-0-217-69743-9(7))* Books LLC.

—The Story of Kennett. 2010. (ENG.). 534p. pap. 40.75 *(978-1-171-72990-7(1))* 2010. (ENG.). 438p. pap. 35.75 *(978-1-177-38952-5(5))* 2010. 442p. pap. 35.75 *(978-1-177-86730-6(3))* 2010. 440p. pap. 35.75 *(978-1-146-42927-6(4))* 2010. 444p. pap. 35.75 *(978-1-144-39153-7(9))* 2008. 428p. 30.99 *(978-0-559-43708-3(0))* 2008. 428p. pap. 34.75 *(978-0-559-43706-9(4))* 2008. 400p. 29.99 *(978-0-554-32176-9(9))* 2008. 400p. 31.99 *(978-0-554-22873-0(4))* BiblioBazaar.

—The Story of Kennett. 2010. 230p. pap. 31.26 *(978-1-153-72197-4(X))* 2009. 256p. pap. 31.26 *(978-1-150-17554-1(0))* General Bks. LLC.

—The Story of Kennett. 2010. 320p. pap. *(978-1-4076-4998-6(1))* HardPr.

—The Story of Kennett. 2010. 346p. 37.56 *(978-1-169-32567-8(X))*; pap. 25.56 *(978-1-162-70937-6(5))*; 46.95 *(978-1-161-47801-3(9))* Kessinger Publishing, LLC.

Taylor, Walter Fuller. A History of American Letters. 2011. 476p. 57.95 ***(978-1-258-00865-9(3))*** Literary Licensing, LLC.

—The Story of American Letters. 2011. 512p. 60.95 ***(978-1-258-05826-5(X))*** Literary Licensing, LLC.

Tennenhouse, Leonard. The Importance of Feeling English: American Literature & the British Diaspora, 1750-1850. 2007. (ENG.). 170p. (C). 42.00 *(978-0-691-09681-0(3))* Princeton Univ. Pr.

Texas Advisory Board Staff & Gilb, Dagberto. Texas Literature: A Case Study. 2009. (ENG.). 224p. (C). pap. 14.95 *(978-0-312-57604-2(8))* Bedford/Saint Martin's.

Tharaud, Barry. Emerson for the Twenty-First Century: Global Perspectives on an American Icon. 2010. (ENG.). 610p. 110.00 *(978-1-61149-145-6(2))* Univ. of Delaware Pr.

Thompson, Jon. After Paradise - Essays on the Fate of American Writing. 2009. 136p. pap. *(978-1-84861-041-5(6))* Shearsman Bks.

Thorp, Willard. Lost Tradition of American Letters. 2006. pap. 15.95 *(978-1-4286-5791-5(6))* Kessinger Publishing, LLC.

Tietchen, Todd F. The Cubalogues. 2010. (ENG., Illus.). 192p. 29.95 *(978-0-8130-3520-8(1))* Univ. Pr. of Florida.

Tillet, Rebecca. Contemporary Native American Literature. 2008. (BAAS Paperbacks Ser.). (ENG.). 184p. (gr. 17). pap. 34.00 *(978-0-7486-2149-1(0))* Edinburgh Univ. Pr. GBR. Dist: Columbia Univ. Pr.

Tolentino, Cynthia H. & Ferguson, Roderick A. America's Experts: Race & the Fictions of Sociology. 2009. (ENG.). 200p. 67.50 *(978-0-8166-5110-8(8))*; pap. 22.50 *(978-0-8166-5111-5(6))* Univ. of Minnesota Pr.

Torres, Hector A. Conversations with Contemporary Chicana & Chicano Writers. 2007. (ENG.). 367p. pap. 29.95 *(978-0-8263-4088-7(1))* Univ. of New Mexico Pr.

Torres-Padilla, José L. & Rivera, Carmen Haydee, eds. Writing off the Hyphen: New Perspectives on the Literature of the Puerto Rican Diaspora. 2008. (American Ethnic & Cultural Studies). (ENG.). 368p. (C). 65.00 *(978-0-295-98813-9(4))* Univ. of Washington Pr.

—Writing off the Hyphen: New Perspectives on the Literature of the Puerto Rican Diaspora. 2008. (American Ethnic & Cultural Studies). (ENG.). 368p. pap. 30.00 *(978-0-295-98824-5(X))* Univ. of Washington Pr.

Toulmin, Harry Aubrey. Social Historians. 2009. 72p. pap. 14.14 *(978-0-217-55333-9(8))* General Bks. LLC.

Traber, Daniel S. & Traber, Daniel. Whiteness, Otherness, & the Individualism Paradox from Huck to Punk. annot. ed. 2007. (ENG.). 216p. 84.00 *(978-1-4039-7614-7(7))* Palgrave Macmillan.

Trachtenberg, Alan. Lincoln's Smile: And Other Enigmas. 2009. 378p. 30.00 *(978-1-4379-6842-2(2))* DIANE Publishing Co.

—Lincoln's Smile: And Other Enigmas. 2008. (ENG., Illus.). 400p. pap. 30.00 *(978-0-8090-6573-8(8),* Hill & Wang) Farrar, Straus & Giroux.

Trilling, Lionel. The Moral Obligation to Be Intelligent: Selected Essays. Wieseltier, Leon, ed. 2009. (ENG.). 592p. pap. 19.95 *(978-0-8101-2488-2(2))* Northwestern Univ. Pr.

Trodd, Zoe, ed. American Protest Literature. 2008. (John Harvard Library). (Illus.). 576p. pap. 25.50 *(978-0-674-02763-3(9),* Belknap Pr.) Harvard Univ. Pr.

Twain, Mark, pseud. Fenimore Cooper's Literary Offences & Is Shakespeare Dead? 2011. 80p. ***(978-1-84902-308-5(5))*** Benediction Classics.

—The Wit & Wisdom of Mark Twain. Blaisdell, Bob, ed. 2012. (ENG.). 256p. pap. 9.95 ***(978-0-486-48923-0(X))*** Dover Pubns., Inc.

Twelbeck, Kirsten. No Korean Is Whole - Wherever He or She May Be: Erfindungen von Korean America seit 1965. (Europaische Hochschulschriften Ser.: Vol. 393). (GER., Illus.). 310p. 39.95 *(978-3-631-38122-9(0))* Lang, Peter Publishing, Inc.

Unrue, Darlene Harbour. Truth & Vision in Katherine Anne Porter's Fiction. 2008. (ENG.). 288p. pap. 24.95 *(978-0-8203-3354-0(9))* Univ. of Georgia Pr.

Van Anglen, K. P. The New England Milton: Literary Reception & Cultural Authority in the Early Republic. 2008. (ENG.). 276p. per. 27.95 *(978-0-271-02827-9(0))* Pennsylvania State Univ. Pr.

Vázquez, David J. Triangulations: Narrative Strategies for Navigating Latino Identity. 2011. (Critical American Studies). (ENG.). 248p. 75.00 *(978-0-8166-7326-1(8))*; pap. 25.00 *(978-0-8166-7327-8(6))* Univ. of Minnesota Pr.

Velasquez, Antonio. Las Novelas de Claribel Alegria: Historia, Sociedad, y Re-Vision de la Estetica Literaria Centroamericana. Varona-Lacey, Gladys M., ed. (Latin America Ser.: Vol. 4). (FRE.). 207p. 54.95 *(978-0-8204-5843-4(0))* Lang, Peter Publishing, Inc.

Venable, W. H. CD: Beginnings of Literary Culture in the Ohio Valley, Historical & Biographical Sketches. 2007. cd-rom 19.95 *(978-0-7884-2658-2(3))* Heritage Bks.

Veres, Bernadett. The Fall of the American Dream: In Theodore Dreiser's Sister Carrie & An American Tragedy. 2008. 68p. pap. *(978-3-639-09551-7(0))* VDM Verlag Dr. Mueller e.K.

Vetter, Lara Elizabeth. Approaches to Teaching H. D.'s Poetry & Prose. Debo, Annette, ed. 2011. (ENG.). 208p. 37.50 ***(978-1-60329-102-6(4))*** Modern Language Assn. of America.

Vick, Frances Brannen, ed. Literary Dallas. 2008. (ENG.). 384p. 29.50 *(978-0-87565-382-2(0))* Texas Christian Univ. Pr.

Vidal, César. Camino del Sur. 2007. (SPA., Illus.). 304p. incl. audio compact disk *(978-84-270-3316-0(8))* Ediciones Martínez Roca.

Visser, Irene & Wilcox, Helen. Transforming Holiness: Representations of Holiness in English & American Literary Texts. Visser, I. & Wilcox, H, eds. 2006. (Groningen Studies in Cultural Change: Vol. 20). (ENG., Illus.). 217p. (C). 66.00 *(978-90-429-1755-2(5))* Peeters Pubs. & Booksellers BEL. Dist: Brown, David Bk. Co., The.

Waage, Frederick O. Raintree County, the Foremost American Environmental Novel: Uncovering the Deep Message of an Undervalued Text. 2011. 300p. 119.95 *(978-0-7734-1516-4(5))* Mellen, Edwin Pr., The.

Wallace, H. B. (Horace Binney). Literary Criticisms & Other Papers by the Late Horace Binney Wallace. 2006. 468p. per. 29.99 *(978-1-4255-5186-5(6))* MPublishing.

Walsh, William J. Speak So I Shall Know Thee: Interviews with Southern Writers. alt. ed. 2012. (ENG.). 328p. pap. 25.00 ***(978-0-7864-6749-5(5))*** McFarland & Co., Inc. Pubs.

Walters, Tracey L. African American Literature & the Classicist Tradition: Black Women Writers from Wheatley to Morrison. 2007. (ENG.). 224p. 89.00 *(978-0-230-60022-5(0))* Palgrave Macmillan.

Warner, Charles Dudley. As We Go. 2008. (ENG.). 84p. per. *(978-1-4065-7633-7(6))* Dodo Pr.

—As We Go. 2007. (ENG.). 200p. 39.95 *(978-0-548-01857-6(X))* Kessinger Publishing, LLC.

—As We Go. 2009. 200p. pap. 27.95 *(978-1-4446-2136-5(X))* Palmer Pr., The.

—Fashions in Literature: And Other Literary & Social Essays & Addresses. 2007. 348p. 46.95 *(978-0-548-37369-9(8))*; per. 31.95 *(978-0-548-31688-7(0))* Kessinger Publishing, LLC.

Wasowski, Richard P. Cliffsnotes on Nicholas Sparks & Micah Sparts' Three Weeks with My Brother. 2011. (ENG., Illus.). 72p. pap. 5.99 *(978-0-470-94573-5(7),* Cliff Notes) Wiley, John & Sons, Inc.

—CliffsNotes on Nicholas Sparks' the Last Song. 2011. (ENG., Illus.). 96p. pap. 5.99 *(978-0-470-94574-2(5),* Cliff Notes) Wiley, John & Sons, Inc.

—The Last Song. 2010. (ENG.). 96p. pap., tchr. ed. 19.99 *(978-0-470-94576-6(1),* Cliff Notes) Wiley, John & Sons, Inc.

Watson, Jay, ed. Conversations with Larry Brown. 2007. (ENG.). 202p. 50.00 *(978-1-57806-949-1(1))*; (Illus.). per. 22.00 *(978-1-57806-950-7(5))* Univ. Pr. of Mississippi.

Watson, Ritchie Devon, Jr. Normans & Saxons: Southern Race Mythology & the Intellectual History of the American Civil War. 2008. (Southern Literary Studies). 286p. 40.00 *(978-0-8071-3312-5(4))* Louisiana State Univ. Pr.

Weaver, Wesley J. Personajes en Busca de una Realidad: Aproximaciones a la Literatura de Jorge Márquez. 2010. (SPA.). 214p. *(978-84-7798-285-2(6))* Diputacion Provincial de Sevilla. Servicio de Publicaciones.

Wedin, Carolyn. Bloom's How to Write about Maya Angelou. 2011. (Bloom's How to Write about Literature Ser.). 228p. (C). (gr. 9). 45.00 (978-1-60413-891-7(2), Chelsea Hse.) Facts On File, Inc.

Weese, Katherine J. Feminist Narrative & the Supernatural: The Function of Fantastic Devices in Seven Recent Novels. Palumbo, Donald E. & Sullivan, C. W., III, eds. 2008. (Critical Explorations in Science Fiction & Fantasy Ser.). (ENG.). 234p. pap. 35.00 (978-0-7864-3615-6(8)) McFarland & Co., Inc. Pubs.

Weingrad, Michael. American Hebrew Literature: Writing Jewish National Identity in the United States. 2010. 280p. 34.95 (978-0-8156-3251-1(7)) Syracuse Univ. Pr.

Weinstein, Cindy & Looby, Christopher. American Literature's Aesthetic Dimensions. 2012. 432p. **(978-0-231-52077-5(8))** Columbia Univ. Pr.

Weinstein, Cindy & Looby, Christopher, eds. American Literature's Aesthetic Dimensions. 2012. (ENG., Illus.). 440p. (gr. 17). 104.50 **(978-0-231-15616-5(2))**; pap. 34.50 **(978-0-231-15617-2(0))** Columbia Univ. Pr.

Weinstock, Jeffrey Andrew & Magistrale, Tony. Approaches to Teaching Poe's Prose & Poetry. 2008. (ENG.). xix, 241p. 37.50 (978-1-60329-011-1(7)) Modern Language Assn. of America.

Weir, David. American Orient: Imagining the East from the Colonial Era through the Twentieth Century. 2011. 304p. (ENG.). pap. 26.95 (978-1-55849-879-2(6)); lib. bdg. 80.00 (978-1-55849-878-5(8)) Univ. of Massachusetts Pr.

—Decadent Culture in the United States: Art & Literature Against the American Grain, 1890-1926. 2007. (SUNY Series, Studies in the Long Nineteenth Century). (Illus.). 233p. 75.00 (978-0-7914-7277-4(9)) State Univ. of New York Pr.

—Decadent Culture in the United States: Art & Literature against the American Grain, 1890-1926. 2009. (SUNY Series, Studies in the Long Nineteenth Century). 256p. pap. 29.95 (978-0-7914-7278-1(7)) State Univ. of New York Pr.

Wells, Jeremy. Romances of the White Man's Burden: Race, Empire, & the Plantation in American Literature, 1880-1936. 2011. (ENG., Illus.). 264p. 55.00 (978-0-8265-1756-2(0)) Vanderbilt Univ. Pr.

Wendell, Barrett. A Literary History of America. 2006. (ENG.). 576p. per. 32.99 (978-1-4181-8904-4(9)) MPublishing.

Wendell, Barrett & Greenough, Chester Noyes. A History of Literature in America. 2008. 462p. 52.95 (978-0-548-94089-1(4)) 2007. (ENG.). 464p. per. 37.95 (978-0-548-57741-7(2)) Kessinger Publishing, LLC.

West, James L. W., III. Making the Archives Talk: New & Selected Essays in Bibliography, Editing, & Book History. 2011. (Penn State Studies in the History of the Book Ser.). 208p. 54.95 **(978-0-271-05067-6(5))** Pennsylvania State Univ. Pr.

Whalen-Bridge, John & Storhoff, Gary. Writing as Enlightenment: Buddhist American Literature into the Twenty-First Century. 2011. (SUNY series in Buddhism & American Culture Ser.). (ENG.). 224p. 75.00 (978-1-4384-3919-8(9)) State Univ. of New York Pr.

Whalen-Bridge, John & Storhoff, Gary, eds. Writing as Enlightenment: Buddhist American Literature into the Twenty-First Century. 2011. (SUNY series in Buddhism & American Culture Ser.). (ENG.). 224p. pap. 29.95 (978-1-4384-3920-4(2)) State Univ. of New York Pr.

Wharton, Edith. The Age of Innocence. 2007. (ENG.). 388p. per. 15.95 (978-1-4218-9637-3(0), 1st World Library - Literary Society) 1st World Publishing, Inc.

—The Age of Innocence. 2009. 234p. pap. (978-0-217-57005-3(4)); 240p. pap. (978-1-4588-5669-2(0)) Books LLC.

—The Age of Innocence. 2008. (Signet Classics Ser.). 316p. 15.95 (978-1-4178-2395-6(X), Turtleback) Turtleback Bks.

Whipple, Edwin Percy. Essays & Reviews by Edwin P Whipple. 2006. 412p. per. 26.99 (978-1-4255-4425-6(8)); (ENG.). 432p. per. 26.99 (978-1-4255-4724-0(9)) MPublishing.

Whitcomb, Selden L. Chronological Outlines of American Literature. 2010. 296p. 35.16 (978-1-163-36947-0(0)) 2010. 296p. pap. 23.16 (978-1-162-78575-2(6)) 2007. (ENG.). 294p. 43.95 (978-0-548-05933-3(0)) Kessinger Publishing, LLC.

Whitla, William. The English Handbook: A Guide to Literary Studies. 2009. (ENG., Illus.). 360p. 99.95 (978-1-4051-8376-5(4)); pap., instr.'s hndbk. ed. 32.95 (978-1-4051-8375-8(6)) Wiley, John & Sons, Inc. (Wiley-Blackwell).

Whitlock, Reta Ugena. This Corner of Canaan: Curriculum Studies of Place & the Reconstruction of the South. 2007. 190p. (C). pap. 29.95 (978-0-8204-8651-2(5)) Lang, Peter Publishing, Inc.

Whittier, John Greenleaf. Whittier on Writers & Writing: The Uncollected Critical Writings of John Greenleaf Whittier. Cady, Edwin Harrison & Clark, Harry Hayden, eds. 2011. 226p. 46.95 **(978-1-258-06202-6(X))** Literary Licensing, LLC.

Wilks, Jennifer M., et al. Race, Gender, & Comparative Black Modernism: Suzanne Lacascade, Marita Bonner, Suzanne Césaire, Dorothy West. 2009. (Illus.). x, 259p. (978-0-8071-3364-4(7)) Louisiana State Univ. Pr.

Williams, Stanley T. American Literature. 2006. (ENG.). 164p. per. (978-1-4067-3183-5(8), Hesperides Pr.) Read Bks.

Williamson, Eric. Say It Hot: Essays on American Writers Living, Dying, & Dead. 2011. (Illus.). 224p. pap. 24.95 (978-1-933896-38-0(8)) Texas Review Pr.

Willis, Lloyd. Environmental Evasion: The Literary, Critical, & Cultural Politics of Nature's Nation. 2011. 275p. 75.00 (978-1-4384-3281-6(X)) State Univ. of New York Pr.

Winter, Molly Crumpton. American Narratives: Multiethnic Writing in the Age of Realism. 2007. 204p. 36.50 (978-0-8071-3225-8(X)) Louisiana State Univ. Pr.

Wirth-Nesher, Hana. Call It English: The Languages of Jewish American Literature. 2008. (ENG., Illus.). 240p. (C). pap. 24.95 (978-0-691-13844-2(3)) Princeton Univ. Pr.

Witschi, Nicolas S., ed. A Companion to the Literature & Culture of the American West. 2011. (Blackwell Companions to Literature & Culture Ser.: 129). (ENG., Illus.). 576p. 199.95 (978-1-4051-8733-6(6), Wiley-Blackwell) Wiley, John & Sons, Inc.

Wolfe, Cary. The Limits of American Literary Ideology in Pound & Emerson. 2009. (Cambridge Studies in American Literature & Culture Ser.). (ENG.). 308p. (C). pap. 42.00 (978-0-521-10732-7(6)) Cambridge Univ. Pr.

Womack, Kenneth, ed. Books & Beyond: The Greenwood Encyclopedia of New American Reading. 4 vols. 2008. 1352p. 399.95 (978-0-313-33738-3(1), GR3738) Greenwood Publishing Group, Inc.

Worthington, Curtis, ed. Literary Charleston & the Lowcountry. 2nd ed. 2012. (Literary Cities Ser.). (ENG.). 352p. pap. 16.95 (978-1-59534-079-5(3)) Trinity Univ. Pr.

Wright, Nicky. The Classic Era of American Comics. 2009. (ENG., Illus.). 230p. 17.99 (978-1-85375-336-7(X), 185375336X) Prion GBR. Dist: Book Sales, Inc.

Wright, T. G. Literary Culture in Early New England, 1620-1730. (Illus.). reprint ed. lib. bdg. 98.00 (978-0-7222-0665-2(8)) Library Reprints, Inc.

Yang, Xiao-Ming. Hundred Flowers Blossoming: A Collection of Literary Essays. 2009. (ENG.). 142p. pap. 26.50 (978-0-7618-4776-2(6)) Univ. Pr. of America, Inc.

—Hundred Flowers Blossoming: A Collection of Literary Essays Written by Chinese Scholars. 2009. (ENG.). 142p. 50.50 (978-0-7618-4775-5(8)) Univ. Pr. of America, Inc.

Yardley, Jonathan. Second Reading. 2011. (ENG.). 256p. (gr. 12). 16.00 (978-1-60945-008-3(6)) Europa Editions, Inc.

Young, Philip. American Fiction, American Myth: Essays by Philip Young. Morell, David & Spanier, Sandra, eds. 2008. (ENG.). 320p. per. 23.95 (978-0-271-02777-7(0)) Pennsylvania State Univ. Pr.

Zabel, Darcy. Arabs in the Americas: Interdisciplinary Essays on the Arab Diaspora. 2006. 248p. (C). pap. 31.95 (978-0-8204-8111-1(4)) Lang, Peter Publishing, Inc.

Zheng, Jianqing, ed. The Other World of Richard Wright: Perspectives on His Haiku. 2011. (Margaret Walker Alexander Series in African American Studies). (ENG.). 176p. 55.00 (978-1-61703-022-2(8)) Univ. Pr. of Mississippi.

Zygadlo, Grazyna. Culture Matters: Chicanas' Identity in Contemporary USA. 2006. 166p. pap. (978-0-8204-9883-6(1)); pap. (978-3-631-55096-0(0)) Lang, Peter AG.

AMERICAN LITERATURE—HISTORY AND CRITICISM—BIBLIOGRAPHY

Bryer, Jackson R. & Kopley, Richard, eds. Resources for American Literary Study, Vol. 32. 2009. 372p. 187.50 (978-0-404-64632-5(8)) AMS Pr., Inc.

Hubbell, Jay B. American Literature, V10, No 2, May 1938: A Journal of Literary History, Criticism, & Bibliography. Hubbell, Jay B. et al, eds. 2011. 160p. 41.95 **(978-1-258-03674-4(6))** Literary Licensing, LLC.

Oreggioni, Alberto F. Nuevo Diccionario de Literatura Uruguaya, 2001, 2 vols. (SPA., Illus.). (978-9974-1-0217-0(0)) Bow Historical Bks.

AMERICAN LITERATURE—HISTORY AND CRITICISM—COLONIAL PERIOD, CA. 1600-1775

Baker, Jennifer J. Securing the Commonwealth: Debt, Speculation, & Writing in the Making of Early America. 2007. (ENG., Illus.). 232p. (gr. 17). pap. 25.00 (978-0-8018-8969-1(3)) Johns Hopkins Univ. Pr.

Bauer, Ralph. The Cultural Geography of Colonial American Literatures: Empire, Travel, Modernity. 2009. (Cambridge Studies in American Literature & Culture Ser.) (ENG., Illus.). 316p. pap. 44.00 (978-0-521-10032-8(1)) Cambridge Univ. Pr.

Burnham, Michelle. Folded Selves: Colonial New England Writing in the World System. 2007. (Reencounters with Colonialism: New Perspectives on the Americas Ser.). (Illus.). 232p. per. 30.00 (978-1-58465-618-0(2)) Univ. Pr. of New England.

Carruth, Mary C., ed. & contrib. by. Feminist Interventions in Early American Studies. 2006. (Illus.). 352p. 65.00 (978-0-8173-1523-8(3)) Univ. of Alabama Pr.

Egan, Jim. Oriental Shadows: The Presence of the East in Early American Literature. 2011. (Transoceanic Ser.). 192p. 44.95 **(978-0-8142-1161-8(5))**; cd-rom 14.95 **(978-0-8142-9262-4(3))** Ohio State Univ. Pr.

Ferguson, Robert A. Reading the Early Republic. 2006. 370p. per. 25.00 (978-0-674-02236-2(X)) Harvard Univ. Pr.

Hayes, Kevin J., ed. The Oxford Handbook of Early American Literature. 2008. (Oxford Handbooks Ser.). (ENG.). 640p. 150.00 (978-0-19-518727-4(X)) Oxford Univ. Pr., Inc.

Jackson, M. Katherine. Outlines of the Literary History of Colonial Pennsylvania. reprint ed. 35.00 (978-0-404-03542-6(6)) AMS Pr., Inc.

Langley, April C. E. The Black Aesthetic Unbound: Theorizing the Dilemma of Eighteenth-Century African American Literature. 2008. (ENG.). 63.95 (978-0-8142-1077-2(5)); cd-rom 14.95 (978-0-8142-9157-3(0)) Ohio State Univ. Pr.

Lopenzina, Drew. Red Ink. 2012. (Native Traces Ser.). (ENG., Illus.). 432p. 95.00 (978-1-4384-3979-2(2)) State Univ. of New York Pr.

Marlowe, Christopher. The Complete Works of Christopher Marlowe, Vol . I: All Ovids Elegies, Lucans First Booke, Dido Queene of Carthage, Hero & Leander. 2010. 280p. pap. 48.50 (978-1-4092-1152-5(5)) Lulu Enterprises Inc.

Meyers, Karen. Colonialism & the Revolutionary Period, Beginnings - 1800. 2nd rev. ed. 2010. (Backgrounds to American Literature Ser.). (Illus.). 128p. (gr. 6-12). 40.00 (978-1-60413-485-8(2), Chelsea Hse.) Facts On File, Inc.

Parrington, Vernon L. Colonial Mind. 442p. 28.95 (978-0-8488-2572-0(1)) Amereon LTD.

Tenney, Tabitha G. Female Quixotism: Exhibited in the Romantic Opinions & Extravagant Adventures of Dorcasina Sheldon, 2 vols. in 1. reprint ed. 37.50 (978-0-404-17397-5(7)) AMS Pr., Inc.

Waller, George M., ed. Puritanism in Early Americ: Problems in American Civilization. 2011. 126p. 40.95 **(978-1-258-03579-2(0))** Literary Licensing, LLC.

AMERICAN LITERATURE—HISTORY AND CRITICISM—REVOLUTIONARY PERIOD, 1775-1783

Bauer, Ralph & Parini, Jay. Contested Nations in the Early Americas. 2008. (ENG.). 80p. (C). pap. 12.95 (978-1-4282-6255-3(5)) Cengage Heinle.

—Empire, Science, & Economy in the Americas, Vol. 1. 2008. (ENG., Illus.). 96p. (C). pap. 12.95 (978-1-4282-6240-9(7)) Cengage Heinle.

Drexler, Michael J. & White, Ed. Beyond Douglass: New Perspectives on Early African-American Literature. 2008. 192p. (C). pap. 25.00 (978-0-8387-5711-6(1)) Bucknell Univ. Pr.

Gardner, Jared. The Rise & Fall of Early American Magazine Culture. 2012. (History of Communication Ser.). (ENG., Illus.). 224p. 50.00 **(978-0-252-03670-5(0))** Univ. of Illinois Pr.

Hayes, Kevin J., ed. The Oxford Handbook of Early American Literature. 2008. (Oxford Handbooks Ser.). (ENG.). 640p. 150.00 (978-0-19-518727-4(X)) Oxford Univ. Pr., Inc.

Langley, April C. E. The Black Aesthetic Unbound: Theorizing the Dilemma of Eighteenth-Century African American Literature. 2008. (ENG.). 63.95 (978-0-8142-1077-2(5)); cd-rom 14.95 (978-0-8142-9157-3(0)) Ohio State Univ. Pr.

Lawson-Peebles, Robert. Landscape & Written Expression in Revolutionary America: The World Turned Upside Down. 2008. (Cambridge Studies in American Literature & Culture Ser.). (ENG.). 400p. pap. 53.00 (978-0-521-07080-5(5)) Cambridge Univ. Pr.

McWilliams, Jr, John P., John P. The American Epic: Transforming a Genre, 1770-1860. 2009. (Cambridge Studies in American Literature & Culture Ser.). (ENG.). 296p. pap. 41.00 (978-0-521-10702-0(4)) Cambridge Univ. Pr.

Meyers, Karen. Colonialism & the Revolutionary Period, Beginnings - 1800. 2nd rev. ed. 2010. (Backgrounds to American Literature Ser.). (Illus.). 128p. (gr. 6-12). 40.00 (978-1-60413-485-8(2), Chelsea Hse.) Facts On File, Inc.

Parini, Jay & Bauer, Ralph. Between Cultures: Native American Traditions & the European Medium. 2008. (ENG., Illus.). 112p. (C). pap. 12.95 (978-1-4282-6238-6(5)) Cengage Heinle.

—Spirituality, Church, & State in the Colonial Americas. 2008. (ENG., Illus.). 96p. (C). pap. 12.95 (978-1-4282-6239-3(3)) Cengage Heinle.

Pollard, Finn. The Literary Quest for an American National Character. 2010. 272p. pap. 39.95 (978-0-415-88402-0(0)) Routledge.

Shields, David S. & Meléndez, Mariselle. Liberty! Egalité! Independencia! Print Culture, Enlightenment, & Revolution in the Americas, 1776-1838: Papers from a Conference at the American Antiquarian Society in June 2006 [and] the James Russell Wiggins Lecture, "We Declare You Independent Whether You Wish It or Not": The Print Culture of Early Filibusterism. 2007. 25.00 (978-1-929545-46-9(0)) American Antiquarian Society.

Tenney, Tabitha G. Female Quixotism: Exhibited in the Romantic Opinions & Extravagant Adventures of Dorcasina Sheldon, 2 vols. in 1. reprint ed. 37.50 (978-0-404-17397-5(7)) AMS Pr., Inc.

Trent, William P. Colonial Prose & Poetry. 2009. 352p. 25.99 (978-1-103-53234-6(0)); pap. 19.99 (978-1-103-53228-5(6)) BiblioBazaar.

Tyler, Moses Coit. The Literary History of the American Revolution, 1763-1783. 2009. 560p. 37.99 (978-1-116-48143-3(X)); 560p. pap. 41.75 (978-1-116-48145-7(6)); 560p. 44.99 (978-1-116-48142-6(1)); 560p. pap. 42.75 (978-1-116-48144-0(8)); 556p. 30.99 (978-0-559-91254-2(4)); 556p. pap. 24.99 (978-0-559-91251-1(X)) BiblioBazaar.

—The Literary History of the American Revolution, 1763-1783. 2009. 348p. pap. (978-1-151-11976-6(8)); 346p. pap. (978-1-150-51713-6(1)) Books LLC.

—The Literary History of the American Revolution, 1763-1783, 2 vol., set. reprint ed. 250.00 (978-0-7222-7601-3(X)) Library Reprints, Inc.

—Literary History of the American Revolution, 1763-1783. by Moses Coit Tyler. 2006. xix, 527p. pap. 32.99 (978-1-4255-7372-0(X)) MPublishing.

AMERICAN LITERATURE—HISTORY AND CRITICISM—1783-1850

Boggs, Colleen G. Transnationalism & American Literature: Literary Translation, 1773-1892. 2009. (Routledge Transnational Perspectives on American Literature Ser.). (ENG., Illus.). 224p. (C). pap. 35.95 (978-0-415-99989-2(8)) Routledge.

Cairns, William B. British Criticisms of American Writings, 1815-1833: A Contribution to the Study of Anglo-American Literary Relationships. 2007. 324p. 45.95 (978-0-548-54479-2(4)); (ENG.). per. 30.95 (978-0-548-48296-4(9)) Kessinger Publishing, LLC.

Carruth, Mary C., ed. Feminist Interventions in Early American Studies. 2006. (Illus.). 352p. pap. 36.50 (978-0-8173-5342-1(9)) Univ. of Alabama Pr.

Carruth, Mary C., ed. & contrib. by. Feminist Interventions in Early American Studies. 2006. (Illus.). 352p. 65.00 (978-0-8173-1523-8(3)) Univ. of Alabama Pr.

Cheng, Eileen Ka-May. The Plain & Noble Garb of Truth: Nationalism & Impartiality in American Historical Writing, 1784-1860. (ENG.). 376p. 2011. pap. 24.95 (978-0-8203-3877-4(X)) 2008. 44.95 (978-0-8203-3073-0(6)) Univ. of Georgia Pr.

Courtney, Angela. Literary Research & the Era of American Nationalism & Romanticism: Strategy & Sources. 2007. (Literary Research Ser.). (ENG., Illus.). 264p. per. 55.00 (978-0-8108-6035-3(X)) Scarecrow Pr., Inc.

Glenney Boggs, Coleen & Boggs, Coleen Glenney. Transnationalism & American Literature: Literary Translation 1773-1892. annot. ed. 2007. (Routledge Transnational Perspectives on American Literature Ser.). (ENG., Illus.). 212p. (C). 135.00 (978-0-415-77068-2(3)) Routledge.

Howard, Leon. The Connecticut Wits. reprint ed. 40.00 (978-0-404-20125-8(3)) AMS Pr., Inc.

Ickringill, Steve. The Early Republic: The Making of a Nation, the Making of a Culture. 305p. 54.75 (978-90-6256-710-2(X)); pap. 27.75 (978-90-6256-709-6(6)) VU Univ. Pr. NLD. Dist: Paul & Co. Pubs. Consortium, Inc.

Kohut, Karl. Narración y Reflexión: Las Crónicas de Indias y la Teoría Historiográfica. 2007. (Estudios Lingüísticos y Literarios Ser.). (SPA.). 268p. pap. 14.99 (978-968-12-1295-7(9)) El Colegio de México, A.C., Biblioteca Miguel Cosío Villegas MEX. Dist: Fondo de Cultura Economica USA.

Langley, April C. E. The Black Aesthetic Unbound: Theorizing the Dilemma of Eighteenth-Century African American Literature. 2008. (ENG.). 63.95 (978-0-8142-1077-2(5)); cd-rom 14.95 (978-0-8142-9157-3(0)) Ohio State Univ. Pr.

McWilliams, John. New England's Crises & Cultural Memory: Literature, Politics, History, Religion, 1620-1860. 2009. (Cambridge Studies in American Literature & Culture Ser.). (ENG.). 380p. pap. 51.00 (978-0-521-10129-5(8)) Cambridge Univ. Pr.

McWilliams, Jr, John P., John P. The American Epic: Transforming a Genre, 1770-1860. 2009. (Cambridge Studies in American Literature & Culture Ser.). (ENG.). 296p. pap. 41.00 (978-0-521-10702-0(4)) Cambridge Univ. Pr.

Parini, Jay & Bauer, Ralph. Between Cultures: Native American Traditions & the European Medium. 2008. (ENG., Illus.). 112p. (C). pap. 12.95 (978-1-4282-6238-6(5)) Cengage Heinle.

Pollard, Finn. The Literary Quest for an American National Character. 2010. 272p. pap. 39.95 (978-0-415-88402-0(0)) Routledge.

Rodríguez, Jaime Javier. The Literatures of the U. S.- Mexican War: Narrative, Time, & Identity. 2010. (ENG., Illus.). 320p. 65.00 (978-0-292-72245-3(1)) Univ. of Texas Pr.

—The Literatures of the U. S. -Mexican War: Narrative, Time, & Identity. 2011. (ENG., Illus.). 320p. pap. 30.00 (978-0-292-72893-6(X)) Univ. of Texas Pr.

Shields, David S. & Meléndez, Mariselle. Liberty! Egalité! Independencia! Print Culture, Enlightenment, & Revolution in the Americas, 1776-1838: Papers from a Conference at the American Antiquarian Society in June 2006 [and] the James Russell Wiggins Lecture, "We Declare You Independent Whether You Wish It or Not": The Print Culture of Early Filibusterism. 2007. 25.00 (978-1-929545-46-9(0)) American Antiquarian Society.

Smith, Thomas Ruys. River of Dreams: Imagining the Mississippi Before Mark Twain. 2007. (Southern Literary Studies). (Illus.). 232p. 38.00 (978-0-8071-3233-3(0)) Louisiana State Univ. Pr.

Tenney, Tabitha G. Female Quixotism: Exhibited in the Romantic Opinions & Extravagant Adventures of Dorcasina Sheldon, 2 vols. in 1. reprint ed. 37.50 (978-0-404-17397-5(7)) AMS Pr. Inc.

Waterman, Bryan. Republic of Intellect: The Friendly Club of New York City & the Making of American Literature. 2007. (New Studies in American Intellectual & Cultural History Ser.). (ENG., Illus.). 344p. (gr. 17). 57.00 (978-0-8018-8566-2(3)) Johns Hopkins Univ. Pr.

Watkin, Amy. Bloom's How to Write about Harper Lee. 2011. (Bloom's How to Write about Literature Ser.). 118p. (C). (gr. 9). 45.00 (978-1-60413-746-0(0), Chelsea Hse.) Facts On File, Inc.

AMERICAN LITERATURE—HISTORY AND CRITICISM—19TH CENTURY

Abrams, Robert E. Landscape & Ideology in American Renaissance Literature: Topographies of Skepticism. 2009. (Cambridge Studies in American Literature & Culture Ser.). (ENG., Illus.). 180p. pap. 31.00 (978-0-521-11988-7(X)) Cambridge Univ. Pr.

Allen, Francis H. Thoreau's Editors: History & Reminiscence. 2011. 28p. 35.95 **(978-1-258-00761-4(4))** Literary Licensing, LLC.

Allen, Thomas M. A Republic in Time: Temporality & Social Imagination in Nineteenth-Century America. 2008. (ENG., Illus.). 292p. per. 24.95 (978-0-8078-5865-3(X)) Univ. of North Carolina Pr.

Alves, Jaime. Fictions of Female Education in the Nineteenth Century. 2009. (Studies in American Popular History & Culture Ser.). (ENG., Illus.). 204p. 125.00 (978-0-415-99676-1(7)) Routledge.

Andriotis, Katerina. Walt Whitman & Odysseus Elytis: Beyond Being & Time. 2010. pap. 12.99 (978-1-61566-070-4(4)) Tate Publishing & Enterprises, LLC.

Anolik, Ruth Bienstock, ed. Horrifying Sex: Essays on Sexual Difference in Gothic Literature. 2007. (ENG.). 276p. per. 39.95 (978-0-7864-3014-7(1)) McFarland & Co., Inc. Pubs.

Anthony, David. Paper Money Men: Commerce, Manhood, & the Sensational Public Sphere in Antebellum America. 2009. (ENG.). 288p. 53.95 (978-0-8142-1110-6(0)); cd-rom 14.95 (978-0-8142-9207-5(0)) Ohio State Univ. Pr.

Arsic, Branka. On Leaving: A Reading in Emerson. 2010. 404p. 49.95 (978-0-674-05073-0(8)) Harvard Univ. Pr.

Augustyn, Adam, ed. American Literature from the 1850s to 1945. 2010. (Illus.). 248p. (YA). lib. bdg. 45.00 (978-1-61530-132-4(1)) Rosen Publishing Group, Inc., The.

—American Literature from the 1850S To 1945. 2010. (Britannica Guide to World Literature Ser.). (Illus.). 248p. (YA). 90.00 (978-1-61530-238-3(7)) Rosen Publishing Group, Inc., The.

Bayley, Sally. Home on the Horizon: America's Search for Place, from Emily Dickinson to Bob Dylan. 2010. (Illus.). 256p. (978-1-906165-15-4(7)) Lang, Peter Publishing, Inc.

Beach, Joseph Warren. The Method of Henry James. 2007. 292p. 43.95 (978-0-548-53962-0(6)); (ENG.). per. 28.95 (978-0-548-50003-3(7)) Kessinger Publishing, LLC.

Bellis, Peter J. Writing Revolution: Aesthetics & Politics in Hawthorne, Whitman, & Thoreau. 2010. (ENG.). 232p. pap. 24.95 (978-0-8203-3461-5(8)) Univ. of Georgia Pr.

Bennett, Bridget. Transatlantic Spiritualism & Nineteenth-Century American Literature. 2007. (ENG.). 260p. 89.00 (978-1-4039-7800-4(X)) Palgrave Macmillan.

Bentley, Nancy. Frantic Panoramas: American Literature & Mass Culture, 1870-1920. 2009. 376p. (C). 59.95 (978-0-8122-4174-7(6)) Univ. of Pennsylvania Pr.

Berman, Jacob Rama. American Arabesque: Arabs, Islam, & the 19th-Century Imaginary. 2012. E-Book (978-0-8147-8951-3(X)); E-Book (978-0-8147-2321-0(7)) New York Univ. Pr.

Betjemann, Peter. Talking Shop: The Language of Craft in an Age of Consumption. 2011. (Illus.). ix, 267p. E-Book (978-0-8139-3169-2(X)); (ENG.). 280p. (gr. 17). 35.00 (978-0-8139-3121-0(5)) Univ. Pr. of Virginia.

Bierce, Ambrose. Essential Bierce: A Selection of the Writings of Ambrose Bierce. 2007. (California Legacy Ser.). 168p. per. (978-1-59714-054-6(6)) Santa Clara Univ., de Saisset Museum.

Bloom, Harold, ed. Stephen Crane. 2009. (Bloom's Classic Critical Views Ser.). 220p. (C). (gr. 9-18). 45.00 (978-1-60413-432-2(1), Chelsea Hse.) Facts On File, Inc.

Bloom, Harold & Ironside, Fabian, eds. Mark Twain. 2008. (Bloom's Classic Critical Views Ser.). 472p. (YA). (gr. 9-12). 45.00 (978-1-60413-134-5(9)) Facts On File, Inc.

Bloom, Harold & Prono, Luca, eds. Henry David Thoreau. 2008. (Bloom's Classic Critical Views Ser.). 208p. (YA). (gr. 9-12). 45.00 (978-1-60413-141-3(1)) Facts On File, Inc.

Blum, Hester. The View from the Masthead: Maritime Imagination & Antebellum American Sea Narratives. 2008. (ENG., Illus.). 288p. per. 24.95 (978-0-8078-5855-4(2)) Univ. of North Carolina Pr.

Boggs, Colleen G. Transnationalism & American Literature: Literary Translation, 1773-1892. 2009. (Routledge Transnational Perspectives on American Literature Ser.). (ENG., Illus.). 224p. (C). pap. 35.95 (978-0-415-99989-2(8)) Routledge.

Borgstrom, Michael. Minority Reports: Identity & Social Knowledge in Nineteenth-Century American Literature. 2010. (Future of Minority Studies). (ENG.). 200p. 84.00 (978-0-230-62263-0(1)) Palgrave Macmillan.

Boyd, Anne E. Writing for Immortality: Women & the Emergence of High Literary Culture in America. 2009. (ENG., Illus.). 326p. (gr. 17). pap. 30.00 (978-0-8018-9401-5(8)) Johns Hopkins Univ. Pr.

Brand, Dana. The Spectator & the City in Nineteenth Century American Literature. 2010. 254p. (C). pap. 36.99 (978-0-521-15274-7(7)) Cambridge Univ. Pr.

Brickhouse, Anna. Transamerican Literary Relations & the Nineteenth-Century Public Sphere. 2009. (Cambridge Studies in American Literature & Culture Ser.). (ENG.). 344p. pap. 46.00 (978-0-521-10101-1(8)) Cambridge Univ. Pr.

Brooks, Van Wyck. The Flowering of New England, 1815-1865. reprint ed. 45.00 (978-0-404-18007-2(8)) AMS Pr., Inc.

—The Flowering of New England, 1815-1865. 27.95 (978-0-8488-0251-6(9)) Amereon LTD.

—The Flowering of New England, 1815-1865. (Illus.). 468p. reprint ed. lib. bdg. 98.00 (978-0-7222-0379-8(9)) Library Reprints, Inc.

—New England Indian Summer, 1865-1915. Date not set. 575p. 33.95 (978-0-8488-2219-4(6)) Amereon LTD.

—The Times of Melville & Whitman. 2007. (ENG.). 494p. 53.95 (978-0-548-07180-9(2)) Kessinger Publishing, LLC.

Burnham, Walter Dean. Voting in American Elections: The Shaping of the American Political Universe Since 1788. Ferguson, Thomas & Ferleger, Louis, eds. 2009. 464p. pap. (978-1-933146-69-0(9)) Academica Pr., LLC.

Cabanas, Miguel A. The Cultural Other in Nineteenth-Century Travel Narratives: How the United States & Latin America Described Each Other. 2008. (Illus.). 324p. (978-0-7734-5240-4(0)) Mellen, Edwin Pr., The.

Cameron, Kenneth Walter. The Emerson Society Quarterly, 1955-1963: A Journal of the American Renaissance, Miscellaneous Selected. Cameron, Kenneth Walter, ed. 2011. 500p. 58.95 (978-1-258-06987-2(3)) Literary Licensing, LLC.

Cameron, Kenneth Walter, ed. The Emerson Society Quarterly: No. 1, Quarter 4 1955. 2011. 20p. pap. 35.95 (978-1-258-07011-3(1)) Literary Licensing, LLC.

—The Emerson Society Quarterly: No. 13, Quarter 4 1958. 2011. 52p. 36.95 (978-1-258-07013-7(8)) Literary Licensing, LLC.

—The Emerson Society Quarterly: No. 14, Quarter 1 1959. 2011. 100p. 39.95 (978-1-258-07014-4(6)) Literary Licensing, LLC.

—The Emerson Society Quarterly: No. 19, Quarter 2 1960. 2011. 52p. 36.95 (978-1-258-07015-1(4)) Literary Licensing, LLC.

—The Emerson Society Quarterly: No. 22, Part 2, Quarter 1 1961. 2011. 46p. 35.95 (978-1-258-07016-8(2)) Literary Licensing, LLC.

—The Emerson Society Quarterly: No. 28, Part 3 1962. 2011. 32p. 35.95 (978-1-258-07017-5(0)) Literary Licensing, LLC.

—The Emerson Society Quarterly: No. 31, Quarter 2 1963. 2011. 82p. 37.95 (978-1-258-07018-2(9)) Literary Licensing, LLC.

—The Emerson Society Quarterly: No. 32, Quarter 3, Part 3 1963. 2011. 82p. 37.95 (978-1-258-07019-9(7)) Literary Licensing, LLC.

—The Emerson Society Quarterly: No. 6, Quarter 1 1957. 2011. 50p. 35.95 (978-1-258-07012-0(X)) Literary Licensing, LLC.

Cappello, Mary. Awkward: A Detour. 2007. (ENG.). 224p. per. 16.95 (978-1-934137-01-7(4)) Bellevue Literary Pr.

Carosso, Andrea, ed. Urban Cultures of/in the United States: Comparative Perspectives. 2010. 183p. pap. (978-3-0343-0082-7(4)) Lang, Peter.

Carroll, Lorrayne A. Rhetorical Drag: Gender Impersonation, Captivity, & the Writing of History. 2006. (Illus.). 251p. 24.95 (978-0-87338-882-5(8)) Kent State Univ. Pr.

Castiglia, Christopher. Interior States: Institutional Consciousness & the Inner Life of Democracy in the Antebellum United States. 2008. (New Americanists Ser.). (ENG.). 400p. (C). pap. 26.95 (978-0-8223-4267-0(7)); (Illus.). 94.95 (978-0-8223-4244-1(8)) Duke Univ. Pr.

Castronovo, Russ. The Oxford Handbook of Nineteenth-Century American Literature, 1 vol. 2012. (Oxford Handbooks Ser.). (ENG., Illus.). 496p. 150.00 (978-0-19-973043-8(1)) Oxford Univ. Pr., Inc.

Chaney, Michael A. Fugitive Vision: Slave Image & Black Identity in Antebellum Narrative. 2009. (Blacks in the Diaspora Ser.). (ENG., Illus.). 272p. pap. 19.95 (978-0-253-22108-7(0), 0253221080) Indiana Univ. Pr.

Cheng, Eileen Ka-May. The Plain & Noble Garb of Truth: Nationalism & Impartiality in American Historical Writing, 1784-1860. (ENG.). 376p. 2011. pap. 24.95 (978-0-8203-3877-4(X)) 2008. 44.95 (978-0-8203-3073-0(6)) Univ. of Georgia Pr.

Christianson, Frank & Hogg, James. Philanthropy in British & American Fiction: Dickens, Hawthorne, Eliot & Howells. Garside, Peter, ed. 2008. (Edinburgh Critical Studies in Transatlantic Literature Ser.). (ENG.). 256p. (gr. 17). 90.00 (978-0-7486-2508-6(9)) Edinburgh Univ. Pr. GBR. Dist: Columbia Univ. Pr.

Clark, Beverly Lyon, ed. Louisa May Alcott: The Contemporary Reviews. 2010. (American Critical Archives Ser.). (ENG.). 419p. pap. 39.99 (978-0-521-15539-7(8)) Cambridge Univ. Pr.

Cook, Jennifer C. Machine & Metaphor: The Ethics of Language in American Realism. 2006. (Literary Criticism & Cultural Theory Ser.). (ENG.). 128p. 125.00 (978-0-415-97835-4(1)) Routledge.

Cook, Sylvia Jenkins. Working Women, Literary Ladies: The Industrial Revolution & Female Aspiration. 2008. (ENG.). 336p. 99.00 (978-0-19-532780-9(2)); pap. 24.95 (978-0-19-532781-6(0)) Oxford Univ. Pr., Inc.

Corporaal, Marguérite & van Leeuwen, Evert Jan, eds. The Literary Utopias of Cultural Communities, 1790-1910. 2010. (Illus.). 285p. 81.00 (978-90-420-2999-6(4)) Rodopi.

Corrigan, John Michael. American Metempsychosis: Emerson, Whitman, & the New Poetry. 2012. (ENG.). 272p. 55.00 (978-0-8232-4234-4(X)) Fordham Univ. Pr.

Courtney, Angela. Literary Research & the Era of American Nationalism & Romanticism: Strategy & Sources. 2007. (Literary Research Ser.). (ENG., Illus.). 264p. per. 55.00 (978-0-8108-6035-3(X)) Scarecrow Pr., Inc.

Crumbley, Paul. Winds of Will: Emily Dickinson & the Sovereignty of Democratic Thought. 2nd ed. 2010. (ENG., Illus.). 296p. 53.00 (978-0-8173-1703-4(1)) Univ. of Alabama Pr.

Darwin, Charles. American Arabesque: Arabs & Islam in the Nineteenth Century Imaginary. 2012. (ENG.). 288p. 65.00 (978-0-8147-8950-6(1)) New York Univ. Pr.

Davis, Theo. Formalism, Experience & the Making of American Literature in the Nineteenth Century. 2007. (Cambridge Studies in American Literature & Culture Ser.). (ENG.). 210p. 91.00 (978-0-521-87296-6(0)) Cambridge Univ. Pr.

—Formalism, Experience, & the Making of American Literature in the Nineteenth Century. 2010. (Cambridge Studies in American Literature & Culture Ser.). (ENG.). 212p. pap. 29.00 (978-0-521-14200-7(8)) Cambridge Univ. Pr.

del Pilar Blanco, Maria. Ghost-Watching American Modernity: Haunting, Landscape, & the Hemispheric Imagination. 2012. (ENG.). 256p. 45.00 (978-0-8232-4214-6(5)) Fordham Univ. Pr.

Domville, Eric W., ed. Editing British & American Literature, 1880-1920: Papers Given at the Tenth Annual Conference on Editorial Problems, University of Toronto, November, 1974. (Conference on Editorial Problems Ser.: No. 10). reprint ed. 42.50 (978-0-404-63660-9(8)) AMS Pr., Inc.

Dooley, Patrick K. A Community of Inquiry: Conversations Between Classical American Philosophy & American Literature. 2008. 255p. pap. 45.00 (978-0-87338-915-0(8)) Kent State Univ. Pr.

Dowling, David. The Business of Literary Circles in Nineteenth-Century America. 2011. (Nineteenth-Century Major Lives & Letters Ser.). (ENG.). 304p. 89.00 (978-0-230-11046-5(0)) Palgrave Macmillan.

—Capital Letters: Authorship in the Antebellum Literary Market. 2009. (ENG., Illus.). 226p. 39.95 (978-1-58729-784-7(1)) Univ. of Iowa Pr.

Dowling, David. Literary Partnerships & the Marketplace: Writers & Mentors in Nineteenth-Century America. 2012. 248p. 39.95 (978-0-8071-3847-2(9)) Louisiana State Univ. Pr.

Drexler, Michael J. & White, Ed. Beyond Douglass: New Perspectives on Early African-American Literature. 2008. 192p. (C). pap. 25.00 (978-0-8387-5711-6(1)) Bucknell Univ. Pr.

Duquette, Elizabeth. Loyal Subjects: Bonds of Nation, Race, & Allegiance in Nineteenth-Century America. 2010. (American Literatures Initiative Ser.). (ENG., Illus.). 288p. 72.00 (978-0-8135-4780-0(6)); pap. 24.95 (978-0-8135-4781-7(4)) Rutgers Univ. Pr.

Elbert, Monika & Drews, Marie, eds. Culinary Aesthetics & Practices in Nineteenth-Century American Literature. 2009. (Nineteenth-Century Major Lives & Letters Ser.). (ENG., Illus.). 276p. 84.00 (978-0-230-61628-8(3)) Palgrave Macmillan.

Elbert, Monika M., ed. Enterprising Youth: Social Values & Acculturation in Nineteenth-Century American Children's Literature. 2009. 286p. pap. 39.95 (978-0-415-87667-4(2)) Routledge.

Emerson, Ralph Waldo, et al. The Annotated Emerson. 2012. (ENG., Illus.). 576p. 35.00 (978-0-674-04923-9(3), Belknap Pr.) Harvard Univ. Pr.

Evans, Robert C., ed. The Joy Luck Club, by Amy Tan. 2009. (Critical Insights Ser.). 336p. lib. bdg. 85.00 (978-1-58765-626-2(4)) Salem Pr., Inc.

Faflik, David. Boarding Out: Inhabiting the American Urban Literary Imagination, 1840-1860. 2012. (ENG., Illus.). 368p. pap. 29.95 (978-0-8101-2838-5(1)) Northwestern Univ. Pr.

Farkas, Julia. The Artist & the Scientist in Hawthorne's Short Stories. 2008. 100p. pap. (978-3-639-00314-7(4)) VDM Verlag Dr. Mueller e.K.

Fender, Stephen. Plotting the Golden West: American Literature & the Rhetoric of the California Trail. 2010. (ENG., Illus.). 256p. pap. 27.99 (978-0-521-13571-9(0)) Cambridge Univ. Pr.

Fenton, Elizabeth. Religious Liberties: Anti-Catholicism & Liberal Democracy in Nineteenth-Century U. S. Literature & Culture, 1 vol. 2011. (Imagining the Americas Ser.). 192p. 65.00 (978-0-19-538409-3(1)) Oxford Univ. Pr., Inc.

Ferguson, John D. American Literature in Spain. reprint ed. 37.50 (978-0-404-02377-5(0)) AMS Pr., Inc.

Feusahrens, Eilen. Exercising Influence, Hoping for Change. 2008. 72p. pap. (978-3-639-01466-2(9)) VDM Verlag Dr. Mueller e.K.

Flatley, Jonathan. Affective Mapping: Melancholia & the Politics of Modernism. 2008. 272p. 49.00 (978-0-674-03078-7(8)) Harvard Univ. Pr.

François, Anne-Lise. Open Secrets: The Literature of Uncounted Experience. 2007. (Meridian: Crossing Aesthetics Ser.). (ENG.). 328p. 65.00 (978-0-8047-5253-4(2)) Stanford Univ. Pr.

Francois, Anne-Lise. Open Secrets: The Literature of Uncounted Experience. 2007. (Meridian: Crossing Aesthetics Ser.). (ENG.). 328p. per. 24.95 (978-0-8047-5289-3(3)) Stanford Univ. Pr.

Frank, Lucy, ed. Representations of Death in Nineteenth-Century US Writing & Culture. 2007. (Warwick Studies in the Humanities Ser.). (Illus.). 246p. 99.95 (978-0-7546-5528-2(8)) Ashgate Publishing Co.

Fraser, John. America & the Patterns of Chivalry. 2009. (ENG.). 312p. pap. 42.00 (978-0-521-11009-9(2)) Cambridge Univ. Pr.

Freeman, James A. Clarence Hawkes: America's Blind Naturalist & the World He Lived In. 2009. pap. (978-1-935052-21-0(7)) White River Pr.

Fulford, Tim & Hutchings, Kevin, eds. Native Americans & Anglo-American Culture, 1750-1850: The Indian Atlantic. 2009. (ENG., Illus.). 276p. 99.00 (978-0-521-88848-6(4)) Cambridge Univ. Pr.

Fuller, Randall. Emerson's Ghosts: Literature, Politics, & the Making of Americanists, 1 vol. 2007. (ENG.). 240p. 55.00 (978-0-19-531392-5(5)) Oxford Univ. Pr., Inc.

—From Battlefields Rising: How the Civil War Transformed American Literature. 2011. (ENG., Illus.). 288p. 29.95 (978-0-19-534230-7(5)) Oxford Univ. Pr., Inc.

Galvan, Jill Nicole. The Sympathetic Medium: Feminine Channeling, the Occult, & Communication Technologies, 1859-1919. 2010. (Illus.). 224p. 45.00 (978-0-8014-4801-0(8)) Cornell Univ. Pr.

Gardner, Eric. Unexpected Places: Relocating Nineteenth-Century African American Literature. (Margaret Walker Alexander Series in African American Studies). (ENG.). 272p. 2011. pap. 30.00 (978-1-61703-211-0(5)) 2009. 50.00 (978-1-60473-283-2(0)) Univ. Pr. of Mississippi.

Garland, Hamlin. Hamlin Garland, Prairie Radical: Writings from The 1890s. Pizer, Donald, ed. 2010. (ENG., Illus.). 192p. 45.00 (978-0-252-03509-8(7)) Univ. of Illinois Pr.

Gersdorf, Catrin. The Poetics & Politics of the Desert: Landscape & the Construction of America. 2009. (Illus.). 360p. 104.00 (978-90-420-2496-0(8)) Rodopi.

Gifford, James J. Glances Backward: An Anthology of American Homosexual Writing, 1830-1920. 2007. (ENG., Illus.). 388p. pap. (978-1-55111-728-7(2)) Broadview Pr.

Gilmore, Paul. Aesthetic Materialism: Electricity & American Romanticism. 2008. (ENG.). 256p. 60.00 (978-0-8047-6123-9(X)) Stanford Univ. Pr.

Gleason, William. Sites Unseen: Architecture, Race, & American Literature. 2011. (ENG., Illus.). 288p. 65.00 (978-0-8147-3246-5(1)); pap. 22.00 (978-0-8147-3247-2(X)) New York Univ. Pr.

Gleason, William A. Sites Unseen: Architecture, Race, & American Literature. 2011. (Illus.). 288p. E-Book (978-0-8147-3248-9(8)) New York Univ. Pr.

Glenney Boggs, Coleen & Boggs, Colleen Glenney. Transnationalism & American Literature: Literary Translation 1773-1892. annot. ed. 2007. (Routledge Transnational Perspectives on American Literature Ser.). (ENG., Illus.). 212p. (C). 135.00 (978-0-415-77068-2(8)) Routledge.

Goldstein, David S. & Thacker, Audrey B., eds. Complicating Constructions: Race, Ethnicity, & Hybridity in American Texts. 2007. (American Ethnic & Cultural Studies). (ENG.). 352p. 50.00 (978-0-295-98681-4(6)) Univ. of Washington Pr.

González, John Morán. The Outer Edge of the Wave: Negotiating Cultural Identities in Post-Reconstruction America. 2010. 44.95 (978-0-8142-1129-8(1)); cd-rom 14.95 (978-0-8142-9228-0(3)) Ohio State Univ. Pr.

Grant, David. Political Anti-Slavery Discourse & American Literature of the 1850s. 2012. (ENG.). 236p. (gr. 17). 70.00 (978-1-61149-383-2(8)) Univ. of Delaware Pr.

Gray, George Arthur. Leatherstocking. 2011. 336p. 50.95 (978-1-258-09225-2(5)) Literary Licensing, LLC.

Greiman, Jennifer. Democracy's Spectacle: Sovereignty & Public Life in Antebellum American Writing. 2nd ed. 2010. (American Literatures Initiative Ser.). (ENG.). 256p. pap. 26.00 (978-0-8232-3100-3(3)); 48.00 (978-0-8232-3099-0(6)) Fordham Univ. Pr.

Gruesser, Wallinger. Loopholes & Retreats: African American Writers & the Nineteenth Century. Gruesser, John & Wallinger, Hanna, eds. 2009. (ENG.). 208p. pap. 44.95 (978-3-8258-1892-0(6)) Lit Verlag DEU. Dist: Transaction Pubs.

Gustafson, Thomas. Representative Words: Politics, Literature, & the American Language, 1776-1865. 2008. (Cambridge Studies in American Literature & Culture Ser.). (ENG.). 488p. pap. 61.00 (978-0-521-06564-1(X)) Cambridge Univ. Pr.

Gyopár, László. Thoreau's Ideas for Modern Times: An Analysis of Walden & 'Civil Disobedience' 2008. 80p. pap. (978-3-639-10508-7(7)) VDM Verlag Dr. Mueller e.K.

Halliburton, David. The Color of the Sky: A Study of Stephen Crane. 2008. (Cambridge Studies in American Literature & Culture Ser.). (ENG.). 360p. pap. 53.00 (978-0-521-06565-8(8)) Cambridge Univ. Pr.

Haralson, Eric. Henry James & Queer Modernity. 2007. (Cambridge Studies in American Literature & Culture Ser.). (ENG.). 280p. pap. 62.00 (978-0-521-03621-4(6)) Cambridge Univ. Pr.

Harrison, Les. The Temple & the Forum: American Museum & Cultural Authority in Hawthorne, Melville, Stowe, & Whitman. 2007. (Illus.). 296p. 42.50 (978-0-8173-1563-4(2)) Univ. of Alabama Pr.

Hawkins, Alfonso. Jazz Trope: A Theory of African American Literary & Vernacular Culture. 2008. (African American Cultural Theory Ser.). (ENG.). 270p. pap. 55.00 (978-0-8108-6126-8(7)) Scarecrow Pr., Inc.

Hayes, Kevin J. Poe & the Printed Word. 2009. (Cambridge Studies in American Literature & Culture Ser.). (ENG.). 168p. pap. 31.99 (978-0-521-10962-8(0)) Cambridge Univ. Pr.

Hellwig, Harold H. Mark Twain's Travel Literature: The Odyssey of a Mind. 2008. (ENG., Illus.). 227p. pap. 35.00 (978-0-7864-3651-4(4)) McFarland & Co., Inc. Pubs.

Henderson. America & the Black Body. 2009. 69.50 (978-0-8386-4132-3(6)) Fairleigh Dickinson Univ. Pr.

Henderson, Desirée. Grief & Genre in American Literature 1790-1870. 2011. (Illus.). 200p. 99.95 (978-1-4094-2086-6(8)) Ashgate Publishing Co.

Henry, Katherine. Liberalism & the Culture of Security: The Nineteenth-Century Rhetoric of Reform. 2011. (ENG.). 232p. 36.50 (978-0-8173-1722-5(8)); (978-0-8173-8510-1(X)) Univ. of Alabama Pr.

Herrmann, Steven B. Walt Whitman: Shamanism, Spiritual Democracy, & the World Soul. 2010. 326p. 28.95 (978-1-60911-699-6(2), Eloquent Bks.) AEG Literary Publishing Services, Inc.

Hetherington, Hugh W. Melville's Reviewers: British & American, 1846-1891. 2011. 320p. 50.95 (978-1-258-07834-8(1)) Literary Licensing, LLC.

Hochman, Barbara. Uncle Tom's Cabin & the Reading Revolution: Race, Literacy, Childhood & Fiction, 1851¿1911. 2011. (Illus.). 352p. (ENG.). pap. 28.95 (978-1-55849-894-5(X)); lib. bdg. 80.00 (978-1-55849-893-8(1)) Univ. of Massachusetts Pr.

Hoeltje, Hubert H. Inward Sky: The Mind & Heart of Nathaniel Hawthorne. 2011. 616p. 64.95 (978-1-258-02728-5(3)) Literary Licensing, LLC.

Homestead, Melissa J. American Women Authors & Literary Property, 1822-1869. 2010. (ENG.). 286p. pap. 38.00 (978-0-521-15475-8(8)) Cambridge Univ. Pr.

Howells, William Dean. Literary Friends & Acquaintances: A Personal Retrospect of American Authorship. 2008. 448p. 30.99 (978-0-559-26972-1(2)) 2008. 448p. pap. 35.75 (978-0-559-26970-7(6)) 2008. 288p. 28.99 (978-0-554-21958-5(1)) 2008. 288p. 25.99 (978-0-554-31261-3(1)) 2007. (ENG.). 298p. pap. 21.99 (978-1-4264-1355-1(6)) 2006. 296p. pap. 23.99 (978-1-4264-1366-7(1)) BiblioBazaar.

—Literary Friends & Acquaintances: A Personal Retrospect of American Authorship. 2006. (ENG.). pap. (978-1-4068-1444-6(X)) Echo Library.

—Literary Friends & Acquaintances: A Personal Retrospect of American Authorship. 2007. (ENG.). 296p. 43.95 (978-0-548-18629-9(4)); 300p. per. 28.95 (978-1-4304-8960-3(X)) Kessinger Publishing, LLC.

Hsu, Hsuan L. Geography & the Production of Space in Nineteenth-Century American Literature. 2010. (Cambridge Studies in American Literature & Culture Ser.). (ENG., Illus.). 270p. 89.00 (978-0-521-19706-9(6)) Cambridge Univ. Pr.

Huang, Yunte. Transpacific Imaginations: History, Literature, Counterpoetics. 2008. (Illus.). 202p. 40.50 (978-0-674-02637-7(3)) Harvard Univ. Pr.

Hughes, Rowland, ed. 19th Century American Literature. 2011. (York Notes Companions Ser.). 365p. pap. 33.95 (978-1-4082-6663-2(6)) Longman Publishing Group.

Hunter, Jerry. Sons of Arthur, Children of Lincoln: Welsh Writing from the American Civil War. 2007. 498p. 85.00 (978-0-7083-2020-4(1)); per. 35.00

(978-0-7083-2019-8(8)) Univ. of Wales Pr. GBR. Dist: Chicago Distribution Ctr.

Hutchings, Kevin & Wright, Julia M. Transatlantic Literary Exchanges 1790-1870: Gender Race & Nation. 2011. (Ashgate Ser. in Nineteenth-Century Transatlantic Studies). 226p. 99.95 **(978-1-4094-0953-3(8))** Ashgate Publishing Co.

Idol, Jr, John L., John L & Jones, Buford, eds. Nathaniel Hawthorne: The Contemporary Reviews. 2008. (American Critical Archives Ser.). (ENG.). 564p. pap. 69.00 (978-0-521-06938-0(6)) Cambridge Univ. Pr.

Iyasere, Solomon Ogbede & Iyasere, Marla W., eds. Toni Morrison. 2009. (Critical Insights Ser.). 352p. lib. bdg. 85.00 (978-1-58765-622-4(1)) Salem Pr., Inc.

Jackson, Leon. The Business of Letters: Authorial Economies in Antebellum America. 2007. (ENG.). 344p. 35.00 (978-0-8047-5705-8(4)) Stanford Univ. Pr.

Jaksic, Iván. The Hispanic World & American Intellectual Life, 1820-1880. (Studies of the Americas Ser.). (ENG., 2012. Illus.). 266p. pap. 36.00 **(978-0-230-33749-7(X))** 2007. 272p. 95.00 (978-1-4039-8079-3(9)) Palgrave Macmillan.

Johns, J. Adam. The Assault on Progress: Technology & Time in American Literature. 2008. (ENG.). 280p. 45.00 (978-0-8173-1625-9(6)) Univ. of Alabama Pr.

Jones, Gavin. American Hungers: The Problem of Poverty in U. S. Literature, 1840-1945. (20/21 Ser.). (ENG., Illus.). 248p. (C). 2009. pap. 25.95 (978-0-691-14331-6(5)) 2007. 52.50 (978-0-691-12753-8(0)) Princeton Univ. Pr.

Kaiser, Birgit Mara. Figures of Simplicity: Sensation & Thinking in Kleist & Melville. 2011. (SUNY series, Intersections: Philosophy & Critical Theory Ser.). 192p. 75.00 (978-1-4384-3229-8(1)) State Univ. of New York Pr.

Katz, Daniel. American Modernism's Expatriate Scene: The Labour of Translation. 2007. (Edinburgh Critical Studies in Transatlantic Literature Ser.). (ENG.). 208p. (gr. 17). 90.00 (978-0-7486-2526-0(7)) Edinburgh Univ. Pr. GBR. Dist: Columbia Univ. Pr.

Kearns, Michael S. Writing for the Street, Writing in the Garret: Melville, Dickinson, & Private Publication. 2010. 45.95 (978-0-8142-1140-3(2)); cd-rom 14.95 (978-0-8142-9239-6(9)) Ohio State Univ. Pr.

Kete, Mary Louise. Sentimental Collaborations: Mourning & Middle Class Identity in Nineteenth-Century America. 2007. (Illus.). 280p. pap. 24.00 (978-1-4223-6527-1(8)) DIANE Publishing Co.

King, Joseph L. Doctor George William Bagby. reprint ed. 20.00 (978-0-404-03693-5(7)) AMS Pr., Inc.

Kopley, Richard. Edgar Allan Poe & the Dupin Mysteries. 2008. (ENG.). 272p. 85.00 (978-0-230-60470-4(6)) Palgrave Macmillan.

Kovács, Ágnes Zsófia. The Function of the Imagination in the Writings of Henry James: The Production of a Civilized Experience. 2006. iv, 261p. (C). 119.95 (978-0-7734-5787-4(9)) Mellen, Edwin Pr., The.

Krentz, Christopher. Writing Deafness: The Hearing Line in Nineteenth-Century American Literature. 2007. (ENG., Illus.). 280p. 69.95 (978-0-8078-3118-2(2)); per. 22.00 (978-0-8078-5810-3(2)) Univ. of North Carolina Pr.

Ladd, Andrew & Meyers, Karen. Romanticism & Transcendentalism, 1800-1860. 2nd rev. ed. 2010. (Backgrounds to American Literature Ser.). (Illus.). 128p. (gr. 6-12). 40.00 (978-1-60413-486-5(0), Chelsea Hse.) Facts On File, Inc.

Laffrado, Laura. Uncommon Women: Gender & Representation in Nineteenth-Century U. S. Women's Writing. 2009. (ENG.). 216p. 47.95 (978-0-8142-0618-8(2)); 214p. cd-rom 14.95 (978-0-8142-9186-3(4)) Ohio State Univ. Pr.

Larson, Kerry. Imagining Equality in Nineteenth-Century American Literature. 2008. (Cambridge Studies in American Literature & Culture Ser.). (ENG.). 220p. 90.00 (978-0-521-89803-4(X)) Cambridge Univ. Pr.

Lathbury, Roger & Meyers, Karen. Realism & Regionalism, 1860-1910. 2nd rev. ed. 2010. (Backgrounds to American Literature Ser.). (Illus.). 128p. (gr. 6-12). 40.00 (978-1-60413-487-2(9), Chelsea Hse.) Facts On File, Inc.

Lease, Benjamin. Anglo-American Encounters: England & the Rise of American Literature. 2009. (ENG.). 316p. pap. 42.00 (978-0-521-10852-2(7)) Cambridge Univ. Pr.

Lee, Harper. To Kill a Mockingbird. Noble, Donald R., ed. 2009. (Critical Insights Ser.). 344p. lib. bdg. 85.00 (978-1-58765-618-7(3)) Salem Pr., Inc.

Lee, Maurice S. Slavery, Philosophy, & American Literature, 1830-1860. 2010. (Cambridge Studies in American Literature & Culture Ser.). 234p. pap. 34.99 (978-0-521-15268-6(2)) Cambridge Univ. Pr.

—Uncertain Chances: Science, Skepticism, & Belief in Nineteenth-Century American Literature, 1 vol. 2011. (ENG.). 256p. 65.00 (978-0-19-979757-8(9)) Oxford Univ. Pr., Inc.

Legler, Henry Eduard. Walt Whitman, Yesterday & Today. 2007. (ENG.). 108p. 31.95 (978-0-548-42369-1(5)); 72p. per. 16.95 (978-0-548-40049-4(0)) Kessinger Publishing, LLC.

Lemire, Elise. Miscegenation: Making Race in America. 2009. (Illus.). 216p. (C). pap. 24.95 (978-0-8122-2064-3(1)) Univ. of Pennsylvania Pr.

Levecq, Christine. Slavery & Sentiment: The Politics of Feeling in Black Atlantic Antislavery Writing, 1770-1850. 2008. (Becoming Modern: New Nineteenth-Century Studies). (ENG.). 324p. lib. bdg. 35.00 (978-1-58465-734-7(0), University of New Hampshire Press) Univ. Pr. of New England.

Levin, Joanna. Bohemia in America, 1858-1920. 2009. (ENG., Illus.). 480p. 65.00 (978-0-8047-6083-6(7)) Stanford Univ. Pr.

Levine, Robert S. Dislocating Race & Nation: Episodes in Nineteenth-Century American Literary Nationalism. 2008. (ENG., Illus.). 336p. 66.50 (978-0-8078-3226-4(X)); pap. 23.95 (978-0-8078-5903-2(6)) Univ. of North Carolina Pr.

Lewes, Darby. Double Vision: Literary Palimpsests of the Eighteenth & Nineteenth Centuries. 2008. (ENG., Illus.). 296p. 78.99 (978-0-7391-2569-4(9)) Lexington Bks.

Lothstein, Arthur S. & Brodrick, Michael, eds. New Morning: Emerson in the Twenty-First Century. 2008. (Illus.). xv, 218p. 74.50 (978-0-7914-7527-0(1)); pap. 29.95 (978-0-7914-7528-7(X)) State Univ. of New York Pr.

Lounsbery, Anne. Thin Culture, High Art: Gogol, Hawthorne, & Authorship in Nineteenth-Century Russia & America. 2007. (Harvard Studies in Comparative Literature Ser.: 51). 312p. pap. 27.50 (978-0-674-02382-6(X)); (Illus.). 45.00 (978-0-674-02381-9(1)) Harvard Univ. Pr.

Lovett, Robert Morss. Edith Wharton. 2007. (ENG.). 96p. per. 18.95 (978-1-4325-5397-5(6)) Kessinger Publishing, LLC.

Loving, Jerome. Emerson, Whitman, & the American Muse. 2011. (ENG.). 232p. pap. 40.00 (978-0-8078-9714-0(0)) Univ. of North Carolina Pr.

Lowell, James Russell. A Fable for Critics. 2008. 104p. pap. 18.75 (978-0-559-16877-2(2)) BiblioBazaar.

Luciano, Dana. Arranging Grief: Sacred Time & the Body in Nineteenth-Century America. 2007. (ENG.). 368p. (C). 75.00 (978-0-8147-5222-7(5)); per. 25.00 (978-0-8147-5223-4(3)) New York Univ. Pr.

Lundin, Roger, ed. There Before Us: Religion, Literature, & Culture from Emerson to Wendell Berry. 2006. 250p. per. 18.00 (978-0-8028-2963-4(5)) Eerdmans, William B. Publishing Co.

Lynch, Jack, ed. Nathaniel Hawthorne. 2009. (Critical Insights Ser.). 344p. lib. bdg. 85.00 (978-1-58765-604-0(3)) Salem Pr., Inc.

Maibor, Carolyn. Labor Pains: Emerson, Hawthorne, & Alcott on Work, Women, & the Development of the Self. 2009. 154p. pap. 39.95 (978-0-415-80350-2(0)) Routledge.

Manning, Susan. The Puritan-Provincial Vision: Scottish & American Literature in the Nineteenth Century. 2009. (Cambridge Studies in American Literature & Culture Ser.). (ENG.). 256p. pap. 36.99 (978-0-521-10701-3(6)) Cambridge Univ. Pr.

Mark, Cirino & Mark, Ott, eds. Ernest Hemingway & Geography. 2011. 208p. 45.00 (978-1-60635-042-3(0)) Kent State Univ. Pr.

Mark, Noonan. Reading Century ILLUS Mo. 2011. (Illus.). 256p. 65.00 (978-1-60635-063-8(3)) Kent State Univ. Pr.

Matthews, Brander. Americanisms & Briticisms, with Other Essays on Other Isms. 2009. 200p. 26.99 (978-1-116-77646-1(4)); 30.99 (978-1-116-77645-4(6)); pap. 23.75 (978-1-116-77648-5(0)); pap. 24.75 (978-1-116-77647-8(2)) BiblioBazaar.

Matthiessen, Francis Otto. American Renaissance Art & Expression. 2006. pap. 50.95 (978-1-4286-3790-0(7)) Kessinger Publishing, LLC.

Mayer, Sylvia. Beyond Uncle Tom's Cabin: Essays on the Writing of Harriet Beecher Stowe. 2011. (ENG.). 254p. 80.00 (978-1-61147-004-8(8)) Fairleigh Dickinson Univ. Pr.

McBride, Christopher. The Colonizer Abroad: Island Representations in American Prose from Herman Melville to Jack London. 2009. 170p. 39.95 (978-0-415-80343-4(8)) Routledge.

McGill, Meredith L. American Literature & the Culture of Reprinting, 1834-1853. 2007. (Material Texts). (Illus.). 376p. (C). pap. 24.95 (978-0-8122-1995-1(3)) Univ. of Pennsylvania Pr.

McParland, Robert. Charles Dickens's American Audience. 2011. (ENG.). 260p. pap. 34.99 **(978-0-7391-1858-0(7))** Lexington Bks.

Mielke, Laura L. Moving Encounters: Sympathy & the Indian Question in Antebellum Literature. 2008. (Native Americans of the Northeast Ser.). 3328p. lib. bdg. 80.00 net. (978-1-55849-630-9(0)); (Illus.). 255p. pap. 26.95 (978-1-55849-631-6(9)) Univ. of Massachusetts Pr.

Miller, David. Dark Eden: The Swamp in Nineteenth-Century American Culture. 2010. (Cambridge Studies in American Literature & Culture Ser.). (ENG.). 350p. (C). pap. 36.00 (978-0-521-14746-0(8)) Cambridge Univ. Pr.

Miller, Jon. Sketches at Home & Abroad: A Critical Edition of Selections from the Writings of Nathaniel Parker Willis. 2010. (ENG.). 190p. pap. 15.95 (978-1-931968-75-1(6)) Univ. of Akron Pr., The.

Miller, Matthew. Collage of Myself: Walt Whitman & the Making of Leaves of Grass. 2010. (ENG., Illus.). 320p. 40.00 (978-0-8032-2534-3(2)) Univ. of Nebraska Pr.

Mitchell, Een, ed. Ruben Trejo: Beyond Boundaries, Aztlan y mas Alla. 2010. (Jacob Lawrence Series on American Artists Ser.). (ENG., Illus.). 160p. pap. 35.00 (978-0-295-99004-0(X)) Univ. of Washington Pr.

Mizruchi, Susan L. The Rise of Multicultural America: Economy & Print Culture, 1865-1915. 2009. (ENG., Illus.). 352p. 69.95 (978-0-8078-3250-9(2)); pap. 26.95 (978-0-8078-5912-4(5)) Univ. of North Carolina Pr.

Murison, Justine. The Politics of Anxiety in Nineteenth-Century American Literature. 2011. (Cambridge Studies in American Literature & Culture Ser.). (ENG.). 228p. 90.00 (978-1-107-00791-8(7)) Cambridge Univ. Pr.

Murray, Aife. Maid as Muse: How Servants Changed Emily Dickinson's Life & Language. 2010. (Revisiting New England Ser.). (ENG., Illus.). 324p. 35.00 (978-1-58465-674-6(3), University of New Hampshire Press) Univ. Pr. of New England.

Myerson, Joel, ed. Emerson & Thoreau: The Contemporary Reviews. 2009. (American Critical Archives Ser.). (ENG.). 484p. pap. 51.00 (978-0-521-11410-3(1)) Cambridge Univ. Pr.

Myerson, Joel, et al, eds. The Oxford Handbook of Transcendentalism. 2010. (Oxford Handbook Ser.). (ENG., Illus.). 864p. 150.00 (978-0-19-533103-5(6)) Oxford Univ. Pr., Inc.

Nonomura. Books for Children & Youth in Nineteenth-Century America Series. 2008. 3300p. 1195.00 (978-4-86166-044-3(0)) Synapse, Edition JPN. Dist: Taylor & Francis Group.

Norman, Brian. The American Protest Essay & National Belonging: Addressing Division. 2007. (Illus.). 222p. per. 29.95 (978-0-7914-7236-1(1)); 74.50 (978-0-7914-7235-4(3)) State Univ. of New York Pr.

Noyes, Carleton Eldredge. An Approach to Walt Whitman. 2009. 248p. 28.99 (978-1-110-23078-5(8)); pap. 25.75 (978-1-110-23073-0(7)) BiblioBazaar.

Otter, Samuel. Philadelphia Stories: America's Literature of Race & Freedom, 1 vol. 2010. (Illus.). 408p. 35.00 (978-0-19-539592-1(1)) Oxford Univ. Pr., Inc.

Otter, Samuel & Levine, Robert S., eds. Frederick Douglass & Herman Melville: Essays in Relation. 2008. (ENG., Illus.). 488p. per. 27.95 (978-0-8078-5872-1(2)) Univ. of North Carolina Pr.

Packer, Barbara L. The Transcendentalists. 2007. (ENG.). 320p. 69.95 (978-0-8203-2957-4(6)); per. 24.95 (978-0-8203-2958-1(4)) Univ. of Georgia Pr.

Palmer, Stephanie C. Together by Accident: American Local Color Literature & the Middle Class. 2008. (ENG.). 234p. 68.50 (978-0-7391-2494-9(3)) Lexington Bks.

Parini, Jay & Bendixen, Alfred. Questions of Social & Economic Justice. 2008. (ENG.). 96p. (C). pap. 12.95 (978-1-4282-6245-4(8)) Cengage Heinle.

Parini, Jay & Samuels, Shirley. Manifest Destiny & the Quest for the West, 1800-1865, Vol. 2. 2008. (ENG.). 96p. (C). pap. 12.95 (978-1-4282-6242-3(3)) Cengage Heinle.

—Views on War, Vol. 2. 2008. (ENG.). 80p. (C). pap. 12.95 (978-1-4282-6243-0(1)) Cengage Heinle.

—The Woman Question & the Bachelor's Reveries, Vol. 2. 2008. (ENG.). 80p. (C). pap. 12.95 (978-1-4282-6259-1(8)) Cengage Heinle.

Parks, Edd Winfield. Edgar Allan Poe As Literary Critic. 2010. (Mercer University Lamar Memorial Lectures). (ENG.). 128p. pap. 22.95 (978-0-8203-3485-1(5)) Univ. of Georgia Pr.

Parrington, Vernon Louis. The Romantic Revolution in America, 1800-1860 Vol. 2: Main Currents in American Thought. 2012. (ENG.). 540p. pap. 44.95 (978-1-4128-4599-1(8)) Transaction Pubs.

Paryz, Marek. The Postcolonial & Imperial Experience in American Transcendentalism. 2012. (ENG., Illus.). 250p. 85.00 **(978-0-230-33874-6(7))** Palgrave Macmillan.

Paulin, Diana Rebekkah. Imperfect Unions: Staging Miscegenation in U. S. Drama & Fiction. 2012. (Illus.). 336p. 75.00 **(978-0-8166-7098-7(6))**; pap. 25.00 **(978-0-8166-7095-4(4))** Univ. of Minnesota Pr.

Pavese, Cesare. American Literature: Essays & Opinions. Fussell, Edwin, tr. from ITA. & intro. by. 2010. (ENG.). 244p. pap. 29.95 (978-1-4128-1073-9(6)) Transaction Pubs.

Perry, Dennis R. Adapting Poe: Re-Imaginings in Popular Culture. Perry, Dennis R. & Sederholm, Carl H., eds. 2012. (ENG., Illus.). 304p. 90.00 **(978-0-230-12086-0(5))** Palgrave Macmillan.

Pfitzer, Gregory M. Popular History & the Literary Marketplace, 1840-1920. 2008. (Studies in Print Culture & the History of the Book). (Illus.). 464p. lib. bdg. 98.00 net. (978-1-55849-624-8(6)); 469p. per. 29.95 net. (978-1-55849-625-5(4)) Univ. of Massachusetts Pr.

Poe, Edgar Allan. Edgar Allan Poe: Collected Stories & a Selection of his Best Loved Poems. 2009. (ENG.). 460p. (gr. 12-18). pap. 14.95 (978-1-59853-056-8(9)) Library of America, The.

Poe, Harry Lee. Evermore: Edgar Allan Poe & the Mystery of the Universe. 2012. (ENG.). 175p. 24.95 **(978-1-60258-322-1(6))** Baylor Univ. Pr.

Porte, Joel. In Respect to Egotism: Studies in American Romantic Writing. 2009. (Cambridge Studies in American Literature & Culture Ser.). (ENG.). 336p. (C). pap. 38.00 (978-0-521-11000-6(9)) Cambridge Univ. Pr.

Powell, Thomas. The Living Authors of America. 2008. 370p. 48.95 (978-0-548-93480-7(0)) 2007. (ENG.). 372p. per. 33.95 (978-0-548-57155-2(4)) Kessinger Publishing, LLC.

Pratt, Lloyd. Archives of American Time: Literature & Modernity in the Nineteenth Century. 2009. (Illus.). 248p. (C). 55.00 (978-0-8122-4208-9(4)) Univ. of Pennsylvania Pr.

Putzi, Jennifer. Identifying Marks: Race, Gender, & the Marked Body in Nineteenth-Century America. (ENG.). 208p. 2012. pap. 24.95 **(978-0-8203-4344-0(7))** 2006. (Illus.). 44.95 (978-0-8203-2812-6(X)) Univ. of Georgia Pr.

A

Railton, Ben. Contesting the Past, Reconstructing the Nation: American Literature & Culture in the Gilded Age, 1876-1893. 2008. (Amer Lit Realism & Naturalism Ser.). (ENG.). 336p. 45.00 (978-0-8173-1580-1(2)) Univ. of Alabama Pr.

Rein, David M. Edgar Allan Poe: The Inner Pattern. 2011. 142p. 40.95 **(978-1-258-07448-7(6))** Literary Licensing, LLC.

Reyes, Raquel A. G. Love, Passion & Patriotism: Sexuality & the Philippine Propaganda Movement, 1882-1892. 2008. (ENG.). 336p. pap. (978-0-295-98805-4(3)) Univ. of Washington Pr.

Reynolds, David S. Beneath the American Renaissance: The Subversive Imagination in the Age of Emerson & Melville, 1 vol. 2011. (ENG., Illus.). 656p. pap. 24.95 (978-0-19-978284-0(9)) Oxford Univ. Pr., Inc.

Rifkin, Mark. Manifesting America: The Imperial Construction of U. S. National Space. 2009. (ENG.). 288p. 65.00 (978-0-19-538717-9(1)) Oxford Univ. Pr., Inc.

Riquelme, John Paul, ed. T. S. Eliot. 2009. (Critical Insights Ser.). 360p. lib. bdg. 85.00 (978-1-58765-606-4(X)) Salem Pr., Inc.

Riss, Arthur. Race, Slavery, & Liberalism in Nineteenth-Century American Literature. (Cambridge Studies in American Literature & Culture Ser.). (ENG.). 2009. 248p. pap. 38.00 (978-0-521-12020-3(9)) 2006. 246p. 102.00 (978-0-521-85674-4(4)) Cambridge Univ. Pr.

Roberson, Susan. Antebellum American Women Writers & the Road. 2010. (Routledge Studies in Nineteenth Century Literature Ser.). (ENG., Illus.). 200p. (C). 125.00 (978-0-415-88354-2(7)) Routledge.

Robinson, Douglas. Estrangement & the Somatics of Literature: Tolstoy, Shklovsky, Brecht. 2008. (Parallax: Re#45;visions of Culture & Society Ser.). (ENG.). 344p. (gr. 17). 65.00 (978-0-8018-8796-3(8)) Johns Hopkins Univ. Pr.

Rodriguez-Arenas, Flor Maria. Periodicos literarios y generos narrativos Menores: Fabula, anecdota y carta ficticia Colombia (1792- 1850) 2007. (SPA.). 268p. per. 27.00 (978-1-934768-05-1(7)) Stockcero, Inc.

Schoenbach, Lisi. Pragmatic Modernism, 1 vol. 2011. (Modernist Literature & Culture Ser.). (ENG.). 224p. 45.00 (978-0-19-538984-5(0)) Oxford Univ. Pr., Inc.

Seery, John E., ed. A Political Companion to Walt Whitman. 2010. (Political Companions to Great American Authors Ser.). (ENG., Illus.). 368p. 40.00 (978-0-8131-2654-8(1)) Univ. Pr. of Kentucky.

Seitler, Dana. Atavistic Tendencies: The Culture of Science in American Modernity. 2008. (Illus.). 320p. pap. 22.50 (978-0-8166-5124-5(8)) Univ. of Minnesota Pr.

Seitler, Dana & Seitler. Atavistic Tendencies: The Culture of Science in American Modernity. 2008. (Illus.). 320p. 67.50 (978-0-8166-5123-8(X)) Univ. of Minnesota Pr.

Shaheen, Aaron. Androgynous Democracy: Modern American Literature & the Dual-Sexed Body Politic. 2010. (ENG.). 45.95 (978-1-57233-686-5(2)) Univ. of Tennessee Pr.

Silva, Reinaldo Francisco. Portuguese American Literature. 2010. 116p. pap. (978-1-84760-108-7(1)) Troubadour Publishing Ltd.

—Representations of the Portuguese in American Literature. 2008. (Portuguese in the Americas Ser.). 228p. pap. 19.95 (978-1-933227-18-4(4)) Tagus Pr.

Silverman, Gillian. Bodies & Books: Reading & the Fantasy of Communion in Nineteenth-Century America. 2012. (Illus.). 256p. (C). 55.00 **(978-0-8122-4415-1(X))** Univ. of Pennsylvania Pr.

Simpson, Erik. Literary Minstrelsy, 1770-1830: Minstrels & Improvisers in British, Irish, & American Literature. 2008. (Palgrave Studies in the Enlightenment, Romanticism & the Cultures of Print Ser.). (ENG.). 256p. 89.00 (978-0-230-20051-7(6)) Palgrave Macmillan.

—Mercenaries in British & American Literature, 1790-1830: Writing, Fighting, & Marrying for Money. 2010. (Edinburgh Critical Studies in Transatlantic Literature Ser.). (ENG.). 240p. (gr. 17). 90.00 (978-0-7486-3644-0(7)) Edinburgh Univ. Pr. GBR. Dist: Columbia Univ. Pr.

Sloan, De Villo. The Crimsoned Hills of Onondaga: Romantic Antiquarians & the Euro-American Invention of Native American Prehistory. 2008. 264p. (C). 104.95 (978-1-60497-503-1(2)) Cambria Pr.

Smith, Joyce Caldwell. Bloom's How to Write about Stephen Crane. 2nd rev. ed. 2011. (Bloom's How to Write about Literature Ser.). (C). (gr. 9). 45.00 (978-1-60413-751-4(7), Chelsea Hse.) Facts On File, Inc.

Smith, Judy. Yellowbird. 2007. 192p. per. 16.00 (978-0-911015-59-1(0)) Sandhills Pr., Inc.

Smith, Thomas Ruys. River of Dreams: Imagining the Mississippi Before Mark Twain. 2007. (Southern Literary Studies). (Illus.). 232p. 38.00 (978-0-8071-3233-3(0)) Louisiana State Univ. Pr.

Stoneham, Michae. John Brown & the Era of Literary Confrontation. 2009. (Studies in American Popular History & Culture Ser.). (ENG.). 240p. 125.00 (978-0-415-99682-2(1)) Routledge.

Strand, Amy Dunham. Language, Gender, & Citizenship in American Literature, 1789-1919. 2008. (Studies in American Popular History & Culture Ser.). (ENG.). 274p. 125.00 (978-0-415-99193-3(5)) Routledge.

Strand, Amy Dunham. Language, Gender, & Citizenship in American Literature, 1789ndash;1919. 2012. (Studies in American Popular History & Culture Ser.). (ENG.). 274p. pap. 42.95 **(978-0-415-54161-9(1))** Routledge.

Tally, Robert T., Jr. Melville, Mapping & Globalization: Literary Cartography in the American Baroque Writer. 2011. (ENG.). 186p. pap. 44.95 **(978-1-4411-6321-9(2))** Continuum International Publishing Group, Ltd. GBR. Dist: National Bk. Network.

Taylor, Andrew. Thinking America: New England Intellectuals & the Varieties of American Identity. 2011. (Becoming Modern: New Nineteenth-Century Studies). 244p. pap. 29.95 (978-1-58465-863-4(0)) Univ. Pr. of New England.

Thomson, Shawn. The Fortress of American Solitude: Robinson Crusoe & Antebellum Culture. 2009. 54.50 (978-0-8386-4217-7(9)); (ENG.). 234p. 54.50 (978-1-61147-421-3(3)) Fairleigh Dickinson Univ. Pr.

Tinnemeyer, Andrea. Identity Politics of the Captivity Narrative After 1848. 2008. (ENG.). 160p. pap. 19.95 (978-0-8032-2067-6(7)) Univ. of Nebraska Pr.

Tomc, Sandra. Industry & the Creative Mind: The Eccentric Writer in American Literature & Entertainment, 1790-1860. 2012. (ENG.). 328p. (C). 80.00 **(978-0-472-11836-6(6))** Univ. of Michigan Pr.

Tuttleton, James W., et al, eds. Edith Wharton: The Contemporary Reviews. 2010. (American Critical Archives Ser.). (ENG.). 588p. (C). pap. 57.00 (978-0-521-12678-6(9)) Cambridge Univ. Pr.

Voelz, Johannes. Transcendental Resistance: The New Americanists & Emerson's Challenge. 2010. (Re-Mapping the Transnational: a Dartmouth Series in American Studies). 336p. (C). 85.00 (978-1-58465-936-5(X)); pap. 39.95 (978-1-58465-937-2(8)) Univ. Pr. of New England. (Dartmouth College Press).

Wachtell, Cynthia. War No More: The Antiwar Impulse in American Literature, 1861-1914. 2012. 248p. pap. 18.95 **(978-0-8071-4564-7(5))** 2010. 240p. 35.00 (978-0-8071-3562-4(3)) Louisiana State Univ. Pr.

Wadsworth, Sarah. In the Company of Books: Literature & Its Classes in Nineteenth-Century America. 2006. (Studies in Print Culture & the History of the Book). (Illus.). 278p. 80.00 (978-1-55849-540-1(1)); per. 24.95 (978-1-55849-541-8(X)) Univ. of Massachusetts Pr.

Wardrop, Daneen. Emily Dickinson & the Labor of Clothing. 2009. (Becoming Modern: New Nineteenth-Century Studies). (ENG., Illus.). 268p. lib. bdg. 35.00 (978-1-58465-780-4(4), University of New Hampshire Press) Univ. Pr. of New England.

Wearn, Mary McCartin. Negotiating Motherhood in Nineteenth-Century American Literature. (Studies in American Popular History & Culture Ser.). (ENG.). 2012. 178p. pap. 42.95 (978-0-415-54180-0(8)) 2007. 218p. 125.00 (978-0-415-98104-0(2)) Routledge.

Weber, Brenda R. Women & Literary Celebrity in the Nineteenth Century: The Transatlantic Production of Fame & Gender. 2012. (Ashgate Ser. in Nineteenth-Century Transatlantic Studies). (Illus.). 220p. 99.95 (978-1-4094-0074-5(3)); 99.95 (978-1-4094-0073-8(5)) Ashgate Publishing Co.

Weinstein, Cindy. Family, Kinship, & Sympathy in Nineteenth-Century American Literature. 2006. (Cambridge Studies in American Literature & Culture Ser.). (ENG.). 256p. pap. 38.99 (978-0-521-03126-4(5)) Cambridge Univ. Pr.

Wesling, Meg. Empire's Proxy: American Literature & U. S. Imperialism in the Philippines. 2011. (ENG., Illus.). 248p. 65.00 (978-0-8147-9476-0(9)); pap. 21.00 (978-0-8147-9477-7(7)) New York Univ. Pr.

Wesling, Meg. Empire's Proxy: American Literature & U.S. Imperialism in the Philippines. 2011. (Illus.). xii, 235p. E-Book (978-0-8147-9478-4(5)) New York Univ. Pr.

Whitt, Jan. Settling the Borderline: Other Voices in Literary Journalism. 2008. (ENG.). 164p. pap. 35.99 (978-0-7618-4093-0(1)) Univ. Pr. of America, Inc.

Whittier, John Greenleaf. Criticism, Part 4, from Volume Vii, the Works of Whittier: The Conflict with Slavery, Politics, & Reform, the Inner Life & Criticism. 2010. 48p. pap. (978-1-4076-5365-5(2)) HardPr.

Wiener, Gary. The Environment in Henry David Thoreau's Walden. 2010. (Social Issues in Literature Ser.). 224p. pap. 25.70 (978-0-7377-4655-6(6)); (Illus.). 37.30 (978-0-7377-4654-9(8)) Cengage Gale. (Greenhaven Pr., Inc.).

Williams, Daniel. Transatlantic Exchange: African Americans & the Welsh, 1845-1945. 2012. (University of Wales Press - Writing Wales in English Ser.). (ENG.). 432p. pap. 40.00 (978-0-7083-1987-1(4)) Univ. of Wales Pr. GBR. Dist: Chicago Distribution Ctr.

Wilson, Christopher P. White Collar Fictions: Class & Social Representation in American Literature, 1885-1925. 2010. (ENG.). 340p. pap. 24.95 (978-0-8203-3697-8(1)) Univ. of Georgia Pr.

Wilson, Eric G. The Spiritual History of Ice: Romanticism, Science, & the Imagination. 2009. (ENG.). 288p. pap. 30.00 (978-0-230-61971-5(1)) Palgrave Macmillan.

Wong, Edlie L. Neither Fugitive nor Free: Atlantic Slavery, Freedom Suits, & the Legal Culture of Travel. 2009. (ENG., Illus.). 368p. 75.00 (978-0-8147-9455-5(6)) New York Univ. Pr.

Yablon, Nick. Untimely Ruins: An Archaeology of American Urban Modernity, 1819-1919. 2010. (ENG., Illus.). 400p. pap. 25.00 (978-0-226-94664-1(9)) Univ. of Chicago Pr.

Yannella, Philip R. American Literature in Context From, 1865-1929. 2010. (ENG.). 168p. 94.95 (978-1-4051-6781-9(5)); pap. 24.95 (978-1-4051-6780-2(7)) Wiley, John & Sons, Inc. (Wiley-Blackwell).

Yothers, Brian. Melville's Mirrors: Literary Criticism & America's Most Elusive Author. 2011. (Literary Criticism in Perspective Ser.). 222p. 75.00 (978-1-57113-509-4(X)) Camden Hse.

Zieger, Susan. Inventing the Addict: Drugs, Race, & Sexuality in Nineteenth-Century British & American Literature. 2008. 360p. lib. bdg. 98.00 net. (978-1-55849-679-8(3)) Univ. of Massachusetts Pr.

Zieger, Susan & Zieger, Susan Marjorie. Inventing the Addict: Drugs, Race, & Sexuality in Nineteenth-Century British & American Literature. 2008. (ENG.). 360p. pap. 34.95 (978-1-55849-680-4(7)) Univ. of Massachusetts Pr.

AMERICAN LITERATURE—HISTORY AND CRITICISM—20TH CENTURY

Ahlin, Lena. "New Negro" in the Old World: Culture & Performance in James Weldon Johnson, Jessie Fauset, & Nella Larsen. 2006. (Lund Studies in English: Vol. 111). 111p. (C). pap. 79.50 (978-91-975158-0-1(9)) Lund Univ. Pr., Sweden SWE. Dist: Coronet Bks.

Alberts, Crystal, et al, eds. William Gaddis, the Last of Something: Critical Essays. 2009. (ENG., Illus.). 216p. pap. 45.00 (978-0-7864-4309-3(X)) McFarland & Co., Inc. Pubs.

Allen, William Rodney. Understanding Kurt Vonnegut. 2009. (Understanding Contemporary American Literature Ser.). 208p. pap. 21.95 (978-1-57003-886-0(4)) Univ. of South Carolina Pr.

Allred, Jeff. American Modernism & Depression Documentary. 2009. (ENG., Illus.). 288p. 65.00 (978-0-19-533568-2(6)) Oxford Univ. Pr., Inc.

Amir, Ayala. The Visual Poetics of Raymond Carver. 2010. (ENG., Illus.). 230p. 65.00 (978-0-7391-3921-9(5)) Lexington Bks.

Andersson, Daniel. Nothing That Is: The Structure of Consciousness in the Poetry of Wallace Stevens. 2006. 241p. pap. (978-91-554-6457-8(2)) Uppsala Universitet/Acta Universitatis Uppsaliensis.

Anolik, Ruth Bienstock, ed. Horrifying Sex: Essays on Sexual Difference in Gothic Literature. 2007. (ENG.). 276p. per. 39.95 (978-0-7864-3014-7(1)) McFarland & Co., Inc. Pubs.

Ariki, Kyoko. John Steinbeck's Global Dimensions. Pugh, Scott, ed. 2007. (ENG.). 228p. per. 45.00 (978-0-8108-6012-4(0)) Scarecrow Pr., Inc.

Armada, Pawel & Gornisiewicz, Arkadiusz, eds. Modernity & What Has Been Lost. 2011. (ENG.). 256p. pap. 27.00 (978-1-58731-511-4(4)) St. Augustine's Pr., Inc.

Armengol, Josep M. Richard Ford & the Fiction of Masculinities. 2010. (Modern American Literature: New Approaches Ser.). 154p. (C). 35.95 (978-1-4331-1051-1(2)) Lang, Peter Publishing, Inc.

Arsanjani, Mahnoush H. & Cogan, Jacob Katz, eds. Looking to the Future: Essays on International Law in Honor of W. Michael Reisman. 2010. 1153p. (978-90-04-17361-3(7)) BRILL.

Atkins, G. Douglas. E. B. White: The Essayist as First-Class Writer. 2012. (ENG., Illus.). 192p. 80.00 (978-0-230-34066-4(0)) Palgrave Macmillan.

Augustyn, Adam, ed. American Literature from 1945 Through Today. 2010. (Britannica Guide to World Literature Ser.). 240p. (YA). (ENG.). lib. bdg. 45.00 (978-1-61530-133-1(X)); (Illus.). 90.00 (978-1-61530-237-6(9)) Rosen Publishing Group, Inc., The.

—American Literature from the 1850s to 1945. 2010. (Illus.). 248p. (YA). lib. bdg. 45.00 (978-1-61530-132-4(1)) Rosen Publishing Group, Inc., The.

—American Literature from the 1850S To 1945. 2010. (Britannica Guide to World Literature Ser.). (Illus.). 248p. (YA). 90.00 (978-1-61530-238-3(7)) Rosen Publishing Group, Inc., The.

Avery, Evelyn, ed. Modern Jewish Women Writers in America. 2007. (ENG.). 288p. 110.00 (978-1-4039-7799-1(2)); pap. 32.00 (978-1-4039-7804-2(2)) Palgrave Macmillan.

Backgrounds to American Literature, 5 vols., Set. 2010. (Backgrounds to American Literature Ser.). (gr. 6-12). 200.00 (978-1-60413-962-4(5)) Facts On File, Inc.

Banach, Jennifer. Bloom's How to Write about Kurt Vonnegut. 2012. (Bloom's How to Write about Literature Ser.). 250p. (C). (gr. 9). 45.00 (978-1-60413-856-6(4), Chelsea Hse.) Facts On File, Inc.

Banco, Lindsey Michael. Travel & Drugs in Twentieth-Century Literature. 2012. (ENG.). 188p. (C). pap. 39.95 (978-0-415-63423-6(7)) Routledge.

Banerjee, A. Humanistic Interpretations of Modern British & American Writers: Essays in Literary Criticism. 2006. 332p. (C). 119.95 (978-0-7734-5732-4(1)) Mellen, Edwin Pr., The.

Barnard, Rita. The Great Depression & the Culture of Abundance: Kenneth Fearing, Nathanael West, & Mass Culture in The 1930s. 2009. (Cambridge Studies in American Literature & Culture Ser.). (ENG., Illus.). 284p. pap. 38.99 (978-0-521-10222-3(7)) Cambridge Univ. Pr.

Bassett, John Earl. William Faulkner: An Annotated Bibliography of Criticism since 1988. 2009. (ENG.). 602p. 115.00 (978-0-8108-6741-3(9)) Scarecrow Pr., Inc.

Baumli, Diana. Truman Capote, The Fascination of Gothic: Gothic Characters & Motifs Inspired by Reality. 2008. 68p. pap. (978-3-639-07024-8(0)) VDM Verlag Dr. Mueller e.K.

Bayley, Sally. Home on the Horizon: America's Search for Place, from Emily Dickinson to Bob Dylan. 2010. (Illus.). 256p. (978-1-906165-15-4(7)) Lang, Peter Publishing, Inc.

Beck, John. Dirty Wars: Landscape, Power, & Waste in Western American Literature. 2009. (Postwestern Horizons Ser.). (ENG.). 378p. 55.00 (978-0-8032-2631-9(4)) Univ. of Nebraska Pr.

Becnel, Kim. The Rise of Corporate Publishing & Its Effects on Authorship in Early Twentieth-Century America. 2007. (Literary Criticism & Cultural Theory Ser.). 149p. 131.00 (978-0-415-95555-3(6)) Routledge.

Beidler, Philip D. American Literature & the Experience of Vietnam. 2007. (ENG.). 240p. per. 24.95 (978-0-8203-3024-2(8)) Univ. of Georgia Pr.

Bentley, Nancy. Frantic Panoramas: American Literature & Mass Culture, 1870-1920. 2009. 376p. (C). 59.95 (978-0-8122-4174-7(6)) Univ. of Pennsylvania Pr.

Berberich, Christine, et al, eds. Land & Identity: Theory, Memory, & Practice. 2012. (Illus.). 318p. pap. 86.00 (978-90-420-3460-0(2)) Rodopi.

Berger, Alan, ed. Saul Kripke. 2011. (ENG.). 382p. pap. 36.99 (978-0-521-67498-0(0)) Cambridge Univ. Pr.

Berglund, Jeff & Roush, Jan, eds. Sherman Alexie: A Collection of Critical Essays. 2010. (ENG., Illus.). 344p. (gr. 13). pap. 24.95 (978-1-60781-008-7(5)) Univ. of Utah Pr.

Betjemann, Peter. Talking Shop: The Language of Craft in an Age of Consumption. 2011. (Illus.). ix, 267p. E-Book (978-0-8139-3169-2(X)); (ENG., 280p. (gr. 17). 35.00 (978-0-8139-3121-0(5)) Univ. Pr. of Virginia.

Bierce, Ambrose. Essential Bierce: A Selection of the Writings of Ambrose Bierce. 2007. (California Legacy Ser.). 168p. per. (978-1-59714-054-6(6)) Santa Clara Univ., de Saisset Museum.

Bigsby, Christopher, ed. The Cambridge Companion to Arthur Miller. 2nd rev. ed. 2010. (Cambridge Companions to Literature Ser.). (Illus.). 326p. (C). (ENG.). 85.00 (978-0-521-76874-0(8)); pap. 29.99 (978-0-521-74538-3(1)) Cambridge Univ. Pr.

Blades, Andrew, ed. 20th Century American Literature. 2011. (York Notes Companions Ser.). 311p. pap. 33.95 (978-1-4082-6664-9(4)) Longman Publishing Group.

Blair, Amy. Reading Up: Middle-Class Readers & the Culture of Success in the Early Twentieth-Century United States. 2011. (ENG.). 256p. 76.50 (978-1-4399-0667-5(X)); pap. 28.95 (978-1-4399-0668-2(8)) Temple Univ. Pr.

Blauman, Wendy S. Explaining the Bilingual & Bicultural Poetry & Narratives of Julia Alvarez: A Case Study in the Expansion of the English Language. 2011. (ENG.). 252p. 119.95 (978-0-7734-2552-1(7)) Mellen, Edwin Pr., The.

Bloom, Harold. The Awakening - Kate Chopin. 2011. (Bloom's Modern Critical Interpretations Ser.). 194p. (C). (gr. 9). 45.00 (978-1-60413-363-9(5), Chelsea Hse.) Facts On File, Inc.

—Ernest Hemingway. 2nd ed. 2011. (Bloom's Modern Critical Views Ser.). 214p. (C). (gr. 9). 45.00 (978-1-60413-364-6(3), Bloom's Literary Criticism) Facts On File, Inc.

—Night - Elie Wiesel. 2nd rev. ed. 2010. (Bloom's Modern Critical Interpretations Ser.). 206p. (C). (gr. 9). 45.00 (978-1-60413-867-2(X), Chelsea Hse.) Facts On File, Inc.

Bloom, Harold, ed. Black Boy. 2009. (Bloom's Guides). 130p. (C). (gr. 9-18). 30.00 (978-1-60413-575-6(1), Chelsea Hse.) Facts On File, Inc.

—Carson Mccullers, New Edition. 2nd rev. ed. 2009. (Bloom's Modern Critical Views Ser.). 200p. (C). (gr. 9-18). 45.00 (978-1-60413-394-3(5), Chelsea Hse.) Facts On File, Inc.

—Cormac Mccarthy, New Edition. 2nd rev. ed. 2009. (Bloom's Modern Critical Views Ser.). 224p. (C). (gr. 9-18). 45.00 (978-1-60413-395-0(3), Chelsea Hse.) Facts On File, Inc.

—James Baldwin. 2nd rev. ed. 2007. (Modern Critical Views Ser.). 240p. (C). (gr. 9-12). 45.00 (978-0-7910-9365-8(4), Chelsea Hse.) Facts On File, Inc.

—A Separate Peace - John Knowles, New Edition. 2nd rev. ed. 2009. (Bloom's Modern Critical Interpretations Ser.). 132p. (C). (gr. 9-18). 45.00 (978-1-60413-185-7(3), Chelsea Hse.) Facts On File, Inc.

—A Streetcar Named Desire - Tennessee Williams, New Edition. 2nd rev. ed. 2009. (Bloom's Modern Critical Interpretations Ser.). 188p. (C). (gr. 9-18). 45.00 (978-1-60413-389-9(9), Chelsea Hse.) Facts On File, Inc.

Bloom, Harold, ed. & intro. Flannery O'Connor. 2nd rev. ed. 2009. (Bloom's Modern Critical Views Ser.). 194p. (C). (gr. 9-18). 45.00 (978-1-60413-589-3(1), Chelsea Hse.) Facts On File, Inc.

Bone, Robert & Courage, Richard A. The Muse in Bronzeville: African American Creative Expression in Chicago, 1932-1950. 2011. (ENG., Illus.). 336p. (C). 75.00 (978-0-8135-5043-5(2)); pap. 29.95 (978-0-8135-5044-2(0)) Rutgers Univ. Pr.

Books, D. W. J., et al. American Modernism, 1910-1945. 2nd rev. ed. 2010. (Backgrounds to American Literature Ser.). (Illus.). 128p. (gr. 6-12). 40.00 (978-1-60413-488-9(7), Chelsea Hse.) Facts On File, Inc.

Bouchard, Donald F. Hemingway: So Far from Simple. 2010. (ENG.). 190p. pap. 19.00 (978-1-59102-756-0(X)) Prometheus Bks., Pubs.

Bowden, Charles. The Charles Bowden Reader. Almeranti, Erin & Miles, Mary Martha, eds. 2010. (ENG., Illus.). 286p. 40.00 (978-0-292-72322-1(9)); 311p. pap. 24.95 (978-0-292-72198-2(6)) Univ. of Texas Pr.

Boyle, Brenda M. Masculinity in Vietnam War Narratives: A Critical Study of Fiction, Films & Nonfiction Writings. 2009. (ENG.). 211p. pap. 45.00 (978-0-7864-4538-7(6)) McFarland & Co., Inc. Pubs.

Bradley, Adam. Ralph Ellison in Progress: From Invisible Man to Three Days Before the Shooting ... 2010. (ENG., Illus.). 256p. 27.50 (978-0-300-14713-1(9)) Yale Univ. Pr.

Bram, Christopher. Eminent Outlaws: The Gay Writers Who Changed America. 2012. (ENG., Illus.). 384p. 27.99 (978-0-446-56313-0(7), Twelve) Grand Central Publishing.

Bray, Joe & Gibbons, Alison, eds. Mark Z. Danielewski. 2011. (Contemporary American & Canadian Novelists Ser.). (ENG., Illus.). 208p. 80.00 (978-0-7190-8262-7(5)) Manchester Univ. Pr. GBR. Dist: Macmillan.

Brevda, William. Signs of the Signs: The Literary Lights of Incandescence & Neon. 2011. (ENG., Illus.). 405p. 85.00 (978-1-61148-042-9(6)) Bucknell Univ. Pr.

Brewton, Butler E. Richard Wright's Women: The Thematic Treatment of women in UNCLE TOM'S CHILDREN, BLACK BOY & NATIVE SON. 2010. (Illus.). 164p. lib. bdg. (978-1-933146-93-5(1)) Academica Pr., LLC.

Brooks, Van Wyck. New England Indian Summer, 1865-1915. Date not set. 575p. 33.95 (978-0-8488-2219-4(6)) Amereon LTD.

Brown, Cheryl M. L. Black American Literature. 2010. 196p. pap. (978-3-639-23232-5(1)) VDM Verlag Dr. Mueller e.K.

Brown, Joanne. Immigration Narratives in Young Adult Literature: Crossing Borders. 2011. x, 164p. E-Book (978-0-8108-7767-2(8)) 2010. (ENG.). 174p. 40.00 (978-0-8108-6056-8(2)) Scarecrow Pr., Inc.

Brown, Judith. Glamour in Six Dimensions: Modernism & the Radiance of Form. 2009. (Illus.). 224p. 39.95 (978-0-8014-4779-2(8)) Cornell Univ. Pr.

Brown, Mark. Paul Auster. 2008. (Contemporary American & Canadian Novelists Ser.). (ENG.). 224p. pap. 26.00 (978-0-7190-7397-7(9)) Manchester Univ. Pr. GBR. Dist: Macmillan.

Brown, Peter & Irwin, Michael, eds. Literature & Place, 1800-2000. 2nd rev. ed. 2008. 235p. pap. 76.95 (978-1-03-911570-5(5)) Lang, Peter AG GBR. Dist: Lang, Peter.

Bruccoli, Matthew J. On Books & Writers: Selected Essays. Unrue, John C., ed. 2010. 320p. 39.95 (978-1-57003-902-7(X)) Univ. of South Carolina Pr.

Bruszt, Katalin. The American Dream in John Steinbeck's of Mice & Men. 2008. 64p. pap. (978-3-639-02373-2(0)) VDM Verlag Dr. Mueller e.K.

Bryer, Jackson R. & Kopley, Richard, eds. Resources for American Literary Study, Vol. 31. 2007. 416p. 187.50 (978-0-404-64631-8(X)) AMS Pr., Inc.

Bryfonski, Dedria. Mental Illness in Ken Kesey's One Flew over the Cuckoo's Nest. 2010. (Social Issues in Literature Ser.). (ENG., Illus.). 224p. 38.45 (978-0-7377-5018-8(9)); 218p. pap. 26.50 (978-0-7377-5019-5(7)) Cengage Gale. (Greenhaven Pr., Inc.).

Budd, Louis. Mark Twain: The Contemporary Reviews. 2011. (American Critical Archives Ser.). (ENG.). 670p. pap. 60.00 (978-0-521-15380-5(8)) Cambridge Univ. Pr.

Bush, Clive. The Century's Midnight: Dissenting European & American Writers of the Second World War. 2009. (Illus.). 608p. (978-1-906165-25-3(4)) Lang, Peter AG.

Cant, John. Cormac McCarthy & the Myth of American Exceptionalism. 2009. 368p. pap. 39.95 (978-0-415-87567-7(6)) 2007. (ENG.). 380p. 125.00 (978-0-415-98142-2(5)) Routledge.

Carosso, Andrea, ed. Urban Cultures of/in the United States: Comparative Perspectives. 2010. 183p. pap. (978-3-0343-0082-7(4)) Lang, Peter.

Caster, Peter. Prisons, Race, & Masculinity in Twentieth-Century U. S. Literature & Film. 2008. (Black Performance & Cultural Criticism Ser.). (ENG.). 296p. 69.95 (978-0-8142-1073-4(2)); cd-rom 14.95 (978-0-8142-9150-4(3)) Ohio State Univ. Pr.

Cheever, Abigail. Real Phonies: Cultures of Authenticity in Post-World War II America. 2010. (ENG., Illus.). 256p. pap. 24.95 (978-0-8203-3429-5(4)); lib. bdg. 59.95 (978-0-8203-3283-3(6)) Univ. of Georgia Pr.

Chirila, Alexander. Manifest Individuation. 2011. 244p. pap. (978-3-8433-9138-2(6)) Lambert Academic Publishing.

Chodat, Robert. Worldly Acts & Sentient Things: The Persistence of Agency from Stein to Delillo. 2008. 254p. 41.95 (978-0-8014-4678-8(3)) Cornell Univ. Pr.

Chomsky, Noam. New World of Indigenous Resistance. Meyer, Lois & Maldonado, Benjamín, eds. 2010. (City Lights Open Media Ser.). (ENG.). 300p. pap. 18.95 (978-0-87286-533-4(9)) City Lights Bks.

Christian, Barbara. New Black Feminist Criticism, 1985-2000. Bowles, Gloria et al, eds. 2007. 272p. 35.00 (978-0-252-03180-9(6)) Univ. of Illinois Pr.

Christodoulides, Nephie J. & Mackay, Polina, eds. The Cambridge Companion to H. D. 2011. (Cambridge Companions to Literature Ser.). (ENG.). 208p. 85.00 (978-0-521-76908-2(6)); pap. 29.99 (978-0-521-18755-8(9)) Cambridge Univ. Pr.

Cianci, Giovanni & Harding, Jason, eds. T. S. Eliot & the Concept of Tradition. 2009. (ENG., Illus.). 248p. pap. 36.99 (978-0-521-12143-9(4)) Cambridge Univ. Pr.

—T.S. Eliot & the Concept of Tradition. 2007. (ENG., Illus.). 246p. 121.00 (978-0-521-88002-2(5)) Cambridge Univ. Pr.

Cianci, Giovanni, et al. Transits: The Nomadic Geographies of Anglo-American Modernism. 2010. (Illus.). xvii, 316p. 68.95 (978-3-03911-949-3(4)) Lang, Peter Publishing, Inc.

Cirino, Mark. Ernest Hemingway: Thought in Action. 2012. E-Book (978-0-299-28653-8(3)); (ENG.). 176p. pap. 26.95 (978-0-299-28654-5(1)) Univ. of Wisconsin Pr.

Ciuba, Gary M. Desire, Violence & Divinity in Modern Southern Fiction: Katherine Anne Porter, Flannery O'Connor, Cormac Mccarthy, Walker Percy. 2007. 287p. 47.50 (978-0-8071-3175-6(X)) Louisiana State Univ. Pr.

—Desire, Violence, & Divinity (p) Katherine Anne Porter, Flannery O'Connor, Cormac Mccarthy, Walker Percy. 2011. (Southern Literary Studies). 304p. pap. 19.95 (978-0-8071-3863-2(0)) Louisiana State Univ. Pr.

Clabough, Casey. The Art of the Magic Striptease: The Literary Layers of George Garrett. 2008. (ENG.). 224p. 39.95 (978-0-8130-3176-7(1)) Univ. Pr. of Florida.

Claridge: Ernest Hemingway Vol. I. 2011. (978-0-415-49121-1(5)) Routledge.

Claridge: Ernest Hemingway Vol. Ii. 2011. (978-0-415-49122-8(3)) Routledge.

Claridge: Ernest Hemingway Vol. Iii. 2011. (978-0-415-49123-5(1)) Routledge.

Claridge: Ernest Hemingway Vol. Iv. 2011. (978-0-415-49124-2(X)) Routledge.

Claridge, Henry, ed. Ernest Hemingway, 4 vols., Set. 2011. (Critical Assessments of Major Writers Ser.). (ENG.). 1368p. (C). 1295.00 (978-0-415-49120-4(7)) Routledge.

Cleghorn, Angus J., et al, eds. Elizabeth Bishop in the Twenty-First Century. 2012. (ENG., Illus.). 320p. (C). (gr. 13-17). pap. 35.00 (978-0-8139-3274-3(2)); (gr. 17). 70.00 (978-0-8139-3261-3(0)) Univ. Pr. of Virginia.

Cleghorn, Angus J., et al. Elizabeth Bishop in the Twenty-First Century. 2012. E-Book (978-0-8139-3296-5(3)) Univ. Pr. of Virginia.

Clune, Michael. American Literature & the Free Market, 1945-2000. 2009. (Cambridge Studies in American Literature & Culture Ser.). (ENG.). 220p. 89.00 (978-0-521-51399-9(5)) Cambridge Univ. Pr.

Coblentz, Stanton Arthur. The Literary Revolution. (BCL Ser.: No. I). reprint ed. 20.00 (978-0-404-01579-4(4)) AMS Pr., Inc.

Coffman, Christine. Insane Passions: Lesbianism & Psychosis in Literature & Film. 2006. (ENG.). 308p. lib. bdg. 49.95 (978-0-8195-6819-9(8)) Wesleyan Univ. Pr.

Conn, Peter. The American 1930s: A Literary History. 2009. (ENG., Illus.). 280p. 83.00 (978-0-521-51640-2(4)) Cambridge Univ. Pr.

Conn, Peter & Conn, Peter J. The American 1930s: A Literary History. 2009. (ENG., Illus.). 280p. pap. 30.00 (978-0-521-73431-8(2)) Cambridge Univ. Pr.

Cook, Jennifer C. Machine & Metaphor: The Ethics of Language in American Realism. 2006. (Literary Criticism & Cultural Theory Ser.). (ENG.). 128p. 125.00 (978-0-415-97835-4(1)) Routledge.

Cook, Sylvia Jenkins. Working Women, Literary Ladies: The Industrial Revolution & Female Aspiration. 2008. (ENG.). 336p. 99.00 (978-0-19-532780-9(2)); pap. 24.95 (978-0-19-532781-6(0)) Oxford Univ. Pr., Inc.

Cooper, Brendan. Dark Airs: John Berryman & the Spiritual Politics of Cold War American Poetry. 2009. (Modern Poetry Ser.). 262p. 66.95 (978-3-03911-861-8(7)) Lang, Peter AG GBR. Dist: Lang, Peter.

Cooper, John Xiros. Modernism & the Culture of Market Society. 2009. (ENG.). 300p. pap. 44.00 (978-0-521-12011-1(X)) Cambridge Univ. Pr.

Cortez, Jenny. Female Freedom Fighters. 2009. 52p. pap. (978-3-639-15760-4(5)) VDM Verlag Dr. Mueller e.K.

Crawford, Margo Natalie. Dilution Anxiety & the Black Phallus. 2008. (ENG.). 224p. 64.95 (978-0-8142-1091-8(0)); 224p. pap. 29.95

(978-0-8142-5168-3(4)); cd-rom 14.95 (978-0-8142-9171-9(6)) Ohio State Univ. Pr.

Crowley, Kim. Bloom's How to Write about Sylvia Plath. 2012. (Bloom's How to Write about Literature Ser.). 250p. (C). (gr. 9). 45.00 (978-1-60413-767-5(3), Chelsea Hse.) Facts On File, Inc.

Cuadra, Pablo Antonio, et al. Seven Trees Against the Dying Light: A Bilingual Edition. 2007. (AGM Collection). (SPA & ENG.). (978-0-8101-2473-8(4)) Northwestern Univ. Pr.

Culleton, Claire A. & Leick, Karen, eds. Modernism on File: Writers, Artists, & the FBI, 1920-1950. 2008. (ENG.). 280p. 89.00 (978-0-230-60135-2(9)) Palgrave Macmillan.

Cumberland, Debra L., ed. Willa Cather's the Song of the Lark. 2010. (Illus.). 306p. pap. 84.00 (978-90-420-3203-3(0)) Rodopi.

Dalessio, William R. Are We What We Eat? Food & Identity in Late Twentieth-Century American Ethnic Literature. 2012. **(978-1-60497-801-8(5))** Cambria Pr.

Dalleo, Raphael & Machado Sáez, Elena. The Latino - A Canon & the Emergence of Post-Sixties Literature. annot. ed. 2007. (ENG.). 216p. 84.00 (978-1-4039-7796-0(8)) Palgrave Macmillan.

Davidson, Guy. Queer Commodities: Contemporary US Fiction, Consumer Capitalism, & Gay & Lesbian Subcultures. 2012. (American Literature Readings in the Twenty-First Century Ser.). (ENG., Illus.). 208p. 85.00 **(978-0-230-34049-7(0))** Palgrave Macmillan.

Davidson, Marianne, et al. Critical Perspectives on Bell Hooks. 2009. (Critical Social Thought Ser.). (ENG.). 242p. pap. 41.95 (978-0-415-98981-7(7)) Routledge.

Davis, James C. Commerce in Color: Race, Consumer Culture, & American Literature, 1893-1933. 2007. (Class: Culture Ser.). (ENG., Illus.). 312p. 75.00 (978-0-472-09987-0(6)); per. 27.95 (978-0-472-06987-3(X)) Univ. of Michigan Pr.

Davis, Todd F. & Womack, Kenneth. Postmodern Humanism in Contemporary Literature & Culture: Reconciling the Void. 2006. (ENG.). 224p. 84.00 (978-1-4039-4681-2(7)) Palgrave Macmillan.

Davison, Neil. Jewishness & Masculinity from the Modern to the Postmodern. 2010. (Routledge Studies in Twentieth-Century Literature Ser.). (ENG.). 274p. (C). 125.00 (978-0-415-87586-8(2)) Routledge.

De Bourcier, Simon. Pynchon & Relativity: Narrative Time in Thomas Pynchon's Later Novels. 2012. (Continuum Literary Studies). (ENG.). 240p. 110.00 **(978-1-4411-3009-9(8))** Continuum International Publishing Group, Ltd. GBR. Dist: National Bk. Network.

Debo, Annette. The American H. D. 2012. (ENG., Illus.). 246p. pap. 39.95 **(978-1-60938-083-0(5))** Univ. of Iowa Pr.

del Pilar Blanco, Maria. Ghost-Watching American Modernity: Haunting, Landscape, & the Hemispheric Imagination. 2012. (ENG.). 256p. 45.00 **(978-0-8232-4214-6(5))** Fordham Univ. Pr.

Dennis, Helen May. Native American Literature. 2009. 236p. pap. 34.00 (978-0-415-54416-0(5)) Routledge.

—Native American Literature: Towards a Spatialized Reading. annot. ed. 2006. (Routledge Transnational Perspectives on American Literature Ser.). (ENG.). 256p. (C). 161.00 (978-0-415-39702-5(2)) Routledge.

Despotopoulou, Anna & Reed, Kimberly C., eds. Henry James & the Supernatural. 2011. (ENG.). 212p. 85.00 (978-0-230-11526-2(8)) Palgrave Macmillan.

DeTora, Lisa M., ed. Heroes of Film, Comics & American Culture: Essays on Real & Fictional Defenders of Home. 2009. (ENG., Illus.). 347p. pap. 39.95 (978-0-7864-3827-3(4)) McFarland & Co., Inc. Pubs.

Diamond, Suzanne. Compelling Confessions: The Politics of Personal Disclosure. 2010. 230p. (ENG.). 65.00 (978-1-61147-042-0(0)); (978-0-8386-4265-8(9)) Fairleigh Dickinson Univ. Pr.

Dickel, Simon. Black/Gay: The Harlem Renaissance, the Protest Era, & the Constructions of Black Gay Identity in the 1980s & 90s. 2012. (ENG.). 308p. pap. 34.95 (978-1-61186-009-2(1)) Michigan State Univ. Pr.

Dittman, Michael J. Masterpieces of Beat Literature, 1 vol. 2006. (Greenwood Introduces Literary Masterpieces Ser.). 136p. 49.95 (978-0-313-33283-8(5), GR3283, Greenwood Pr.) Greenwood Publishing Group, Inc.

Djos, Matts G. Writing under the Influence: Alcoholism & the Alcoholic Perception from Hemingway to Berryman. 2010. (ENG.). 188p. 79.00 (978-0-230-10260-6(3)) Palgrave Macmillan.

Dolinar, Brian. The Black Cultural Front: Black Writers & Artists of the Depression Generation. 2012. (Margaret Walker Alexander Series in African American Studies). (ENG.). 288p. 60.00 **(978-1-61703-269-1(7))** Univ. Pr. of Mississippi.

Domville, Eric W., ed. Editing British & American Literature, 1880-1920: Papers Given at the Tenth Annual Conference on Editorial Problems, University of Toronto, November, 1974. (Conference on Editorial Problems Ser.: No. 10). reprint ed. 42.50 (978-0-404-63660-9(8)) AMS Pr., Inc.

Donaldson, Scott. Fitzgerald & Hemingway: Works & Days. 2011. (ENG., Illus.). 520p. (gr. 17). pap. 22.50 (978-0-231-14817-7(8)) Columbia Univ. Pr.

Dooley, Patrick K. A Community of Inquiry: Conversations Between Classical American Philosophy & American Literature. 2008. 255p. pap. 45.00 (978-0-87338-915-0(8)) Kent State Univ. Pr.

Douglas, Christopher. A Genealogy of Literary Multiculturalism. 2011. 384p. pap. 24.95 (978-0-8014-7711-9(5)) Cornell Univ. Pr.

Dow, William & Craven, Alice, eds. Richard Wright: New Readings in the 21st Century. 2011. (Signs of Race Ser.). (ENG., Illus.). 304p. 85.00 (978-0-230-11281-0(1)) Palgrave Macmillan.

Dreiser, Theodore. Political Writings. Davies, Jude, ed. 2011. (ENG., Illus.). 352p. 50.00 (978-0-252-03585-2(2)) Univ. of Illinois Pr.

Duck, Leigh Anne. The Nation's Region: Southern Modernism, Segregation, & U. S. Nationalism. 2006. (New Southern Studies). (ENG.). 352p. 44.95 (978-0-8203-2810-2(3)) Univ. of Georgia Pr.

Duffey, Bernard I. The Chicago Renaissance in American Letters: A Critical History. 2011. 294p. 48.95 **(978-1-258-04728-3(4))** Literary Licensing, LLC.

Duong, Lan P. Treacherous Subjects: Gender, Culture, & Trans-Vietnamese Feminism. 2012. (Asian American History & Cultu Ser.). (ENG., Illus.). 264p. 78.50 **(978-1-4399-0177-9(5))**; pap. 26.95 **(978-1-4399-0178-6(3))** Temple Univ. Pr.

Duteil, H. J. The Great American Parade. 2007. (ENG.). 626p. 60.95 (978-0-548-06922-6(0)) Kessinger Publishing, LLC.

Duvall, John N. The Cambridge Companion to Don Delillo. 2008. (Cambridge Companions to Literature Ser.). (ENG.). (C). 218p. 84.99 (978-0-521-87065-8(8)); 224p. pap. 25.99 (978-0-521-69089-8(7)) Cambridge Univ. Pr.

Dyck, Reginald, et al. Crisscrossing Borders in Literature of the American West. 2009. (ENG.). 256p. 95.00 (978-0-230-61343-0(8)) Palgrave Macmillan.

Ebest, Sally Barr & McInerney, Kathleen, eds. Too Smart to Be Sentimental: Contemporary Irish American Women Writers. 2008. (ENG.). 288p. per. 29.00 (978-0-268-02773-5(0)) Univ. of Notre Dame Pr.

Elkholy, Sharin N., ed. The Philosophy of the Beats. 2012. (Philosophy of Popular Culture Ser.). (ENG.). 300p. 40.00 **(978-0-8131-3580-9(X))** Univ. Pr. of Kentucky.

English, Parker. What We Say, Who We Are: Leopold Senghor, Zora Neale Hurston, & the Philosophy of Language. 2009. (ENG.). 134p. 57.99 (978-0-7391-2651-6(2)) Lexington Bks.

Enright, Kelly. The Maximum of Wilderness: The Jungle in the American Imagination. 2012. (Illus.). x, 187p. E-Book **(978-0-8139-3243-9(2))**; (ENG.), 200p. 29.95 **(978-0-8139-3228-6(9))** Univ. Pr. of Virginia.

Entzminger, Betina. Contemporary Reconfigurations of American Literary Classics: The Origin & Evolution of American Stories. 2012. (Routledge Studies in Twentieth-Century Literature Ser.). (ENG.). 228p. (C). 125.00 **(978-0-415-53964-7(1))** Routledge.

Evans, David H. William Faulkner, William James, & the American Pragmatic Tradition. 2008. (Southern Literary Studies). 289p. 40.00 (978-0-8071-3315-6(9)) Louisiana State Univ. Pr.

F Schneider, Thomas, ed. Huns vs. Corned Beef: Representations of the Other in American & German Literature & Film on World War I. 2007. (Schriften des Erich Maria Remarque-Archivs Ser.). (GER., Illus.). 224p. (C). 63.00 (978-3-89971-385-5(0)) Vandenhoeck & Ruprecht GmbH & Co. KG DEU. Dist: ISD.

Farrell, Kirby. Berserk Style in American Culture. 2011. (ENG., Illus.). 262p. 85.00 (978-0-230-11663-4(9)) Palgrave Macmillan.

Fensch, Thomas. Essential Elements of Steinbeck. 2009. 140p. 22.95 (978-1-4401-4793-7(0)); pap. 12.95 (978-1-4401-4705-0(1)) iUniverse, Inc.

Ferrall, Charles. Modernist Writing & Reactionary Politics. 2009. (ENG.). 212p. pap. 33.99 (978-0-521-12082-1(9)) Cambridge Univ. Pr.

Feusahrens, Ellen. Exercising Influence, Hoping for Change. 2008. 72p. pap. (978-3-639-01466-2(9)) VDM Verlag Dr. Mueller e.K.

Fiedler, Leslie A. Devil Gets His Due. Pardini, Samuele, ed. 2007. 336p. pap. (978-1-933368-86-7(8)) Counterpoint LLC.

—The Devil Gets His Due: The Uncollected Essays of Leslie Fiedler. Pardini, Samuele F. S., ed. 2008. (ENG.). 336p. 26.00 (978-1-59376-188-2(0)) Counterpoint LLC.

Field, Douglas. A Historical Guide to James Baldwin. 2009. (History Gds American Ser.). (ENG., Illus.). 304p. pap. 27.95 (978-0-19-536654-9(9)) Oxford Univ. Pr., Inc.

Figueroa, José Luis, ed. El Monstruo. 2008.Tr. of Monster. (SPA.). pap. 13.00 (978-0-9755453-3-1(7)) E2.

Fiore, Kyle. Santa Fe & Taos: The Writer's ERA, 1916-1941. 2008. 264p. per. 28.95 (978-0-86534-650-5(X)) Sunstone Pr.

Fisher, James L. Understanding Tony Kushner. 2008. (Understanding Contemporary American Literature Ser.). 208p. 39.95 (978-1-57003-749-8(3)) Univ. of South Carolina Pr.

Flannery, Kathryn Thoms. Feminist Literacies, 1968-75. 2010. (ENG., Illus.). 280p. pap. 25.00 (978-0-252-07728-9(8)) Univ. of Illinois Pr.

Flatley, Jonathan. Affective Mapping: Melancholia & the Politics of Modernism. 2008. 272p. 49.00 (978-0-674-03078-7(8)) Harvard Univ. Pr.

Foertsch, Jacqueline. Bracing Accounts: The Literature & Culture of Polio in Postwar America. 2008. (Illus.). 223p. 50.00 (978-0-8386-4173-6(3)) Fairleigh Dickinson Univ. Pr.

Fowler, Doreen & Abadie, Ann J., eds. Faulkner & the Southern Renaissance. 2008. (ENG.). 284p. pap. 25.00 (978-1-60473-201-6(6)) Univ. Pr. of Mississippi.

Fowler, Karen Joy & Notkin, Debbie, eds. 80! Memories & Reflections on Ursula K. le Guin. 2010. (Illus.). 239p. pap. 19.00 (978-1-933500-43-0(3)) Aqueduct Pr.

Fraser, John. America & the Patterns of Chivalry. 2009. (ENG.). 312p. pap. 42.00 (978-0-521-11009-9(2)) Cambridge Univ. Pr.

Friedel, Tania. Racial Discourse & Cosmopolitanism in Twentieth-Century African American Writing. (Studies in African American History & Culture Ser.). (ENG.). 214p. 2012. pap. 42.95 **(978-0-415-54308-8(8))** 2007. 133.00 (978-0-415-96355-8(9), 0415963559) Routledge.

Fruscione, Joseph. Faulkner & Hemingway: Biography of a Literary Rivalry. 2012. 304p. 49.95 **(978-0-8142-1174-8(7))**; cd-rom 14.95 **(978-0-8142-9275-4(5))** Ohio State Univ. Pr.

Frye, Steven. Understanding Cormac McCarthy. 2009. (Understanding Contemporary American Literature Ser.). 240p. 39.95 (978-1-57003-839-6(2)) Univ. of South Carolina Pr.

Fuchs, Regula. Remembering Viet Nam: Gustav Hasford, Ron Kovic, Tim O'Brien & the Fabrication of American Cultural Memory. 2010. 66.95 (978-3-0343-0565-3(9)) Lang, Peter Publishing, Inc.

Fulton, Lorie Watkins. William Faulkner, Gavin Stevens, & the Cavalier Tradition. 2011. 120p. **(978-1-4331-1155-6(1))** Lang, Peter Publishing, Inc.

Gale. Contemporary Literary Criticism: Excerpts from Criticism of the Works of Today's Novelists, Poets, Playwrights, Short Story Writers, Scriptwriters, & Other Creative Writers. 2012. (Contemporary Literary Criticism Ser.). (ENG.). 592p. lib. bdg. 326.00 **(978-1-4144-7089-4(4))**; lib. bdg. 328.00 **(978-1-4144-7090-0(8))** Cengage Gale.

Galow, Timothy W. Writing Celebrity: Stein, Fitzgerald, & the Modern(ist) Art of Self-Fashioning. 2011. (American Literature Readings in the Twenty-First Century Ser.). (ENG.). 252p. 85.00 (978-0-230-11271-1(4)) Palgrave Macmillan.

Ganz, Shoshannah, et al, eds. The Ivory Thought: Essays on Al Purdy. 2008. (Reappraisals: Canadian Writers Ser.). (ENG., Illus.). 282p. pap. (978-0-7766-0665-1(4)) Univ. of Ottawa Pr./Presses de l'Universite d'Ottawa.

García, Cristina. Bordering Fires: The Vintage Book of Contemporary Mexican & Chicano/a Literature. 2006. (Vintage Original Ser.). 304p. pap. 13.95 (978-1-4000-7716-2(4), Vintage) Knopf Doubleday Publishing Group.

Garey, Anita Ilta & Hansen, Karen V., eds. At the Heart of Work & Family: Engaging the Ideas of Arlie Hochschild. 2011. (Families in Focus Ser.). (ENG.). 304p. (C). 75.00 (978-0-8135-4955-2(8)); pap. 27.95 (978-0-8135-4956-9(6)) Rutgers Univ. Pr.

Gelfant, Blanche H. Cross-Cultural Reckonings: A Triptych of Russian, American & Canadian Texts. 2009. (Cambridge Studies in American Literature & Culture Ser.). (ENG.). 208p. pap. 31.99 (978-0-521-10675-7(3)) Cambridge Univ. Pr.

Genz, Stephanie & Brabon, Benjamin A., eds. Postfeminist Gothic: Critical Interventions in Contemporary Culture. 2007. (ENG.). 256p. 84.00 (978-0-230-00542-6(X)) Palgrave Macmillan.

Gersdorf, Catrin. The Poetics & Politics of the Desert: Landscape & the Construction of America. 2009. (Illus.). 360p. 104.00 (978-90-420-2496-0(8)) Rodopi.

Gertz, Stephen J. Dope Menace: The Sensational World of Drug Paperbacks, 1900-1975. 2008. (ENG., Illus.). 250p. pap. 24.95 (978-1-932595-34-5(1)) Feral Hse.

Gifford, James J. Glances Backward: An Anthology of American Homosexual Writing, 1830-1920. 2007. (ENG., Illus.). 388p. pap. (978-1-55111-728-7(2)) Broadview Pr.

Giles, Paul. Transnationalism in Practice: Essays on American Studies, Literature & Religion. 2011. (Edinburgh Critical Studies in Transatlantic Literature Ser.). (ENG., Illus.). 336p. (gr. 17). 120.00 (978-0-7486-4049-2(5)) Edinburgh Univ. Pr. GBR. Dist: Columbia Univ. Pr.

Gill, Jo, ed. Modern Confessional Writing. 2009. 208p. pap. 34.00 (978-0-415-54414-6(9)) Routledge.

Gilman, Owen W., Jr. Vietnam & the Southern Imagination. 2008. (ENG.). 204p. pap. 25.00 (978-1-60473-169-9(9)) Univ. Pr. of Mississippi.

Ginn, Sherry. Power & Control in the Television Worlds of Joss Whedon. 2012. (ENG.). 198p. pap. 35.00 **(978-0-7864-5858-5(5))** McFarland & Co., Inc. Pubs.

Girgus, Sam B. The Law of the Heart: Individualism & the Modern Self in American Literature. 2011. (ENG.). 192p. pap. 19.95 **(978-0-292-73969-7(9))** Univ. of Texas Pr.

Gleason, William. Sites Unseen: Architecture, Race, & American Literature. 2011. (ENG., Illus.). 288p. 65.00 (978-0-8147-3246-5(1)); pap. 22.00 (978-0-8147-3247-2(X)) New York Univ. Pr.

Gleason, William A. Sites Unseen: Architecture, Race, & American Literature. 2011. (Illus.). 288p. E-Book **(978-0-8147-3248-9(8))** New York Univ. Pr.

Goble, Mark. Beautiful Circuits: Modernism & the Mediated Life. 2010. (ENG., Illus.). 392p. (gr. 17). 40.00 (978-0-231-14670-8(1)) Columbia Univ. Pr.

Goldman, Jonathan. Modernism Is the Literature of Celebrity. (ENG., Illus.). 2012. 216p. pap. 25.00 **(978-0-292-74404-2(8))** 2011. 220p. 55.00 (978-0-292-72339-9(3)) Univ. of Texas Pr.

Goldstein, David S. & Thacker, Audrey B., eds. Complicating Constructions: Race, Ethnicity, & Hybridity in American Texts. 2007. (American Ethnic & Cultural Studies). (ENG.). 352p. 50.00 (978-0-295-98681-4(6)) Univ. of Washington Pr.

Goody, Alex. Modernist Articulations: A Cultural Study of Djuna Barnes, Mina Loy & Gertrude Stein. 2007. (ENG., Illus.). 256p. 84.00 (978-0-230-50049-5(8)) Palgrave Macmillan.

—Technology, Literature & Culture. 2011. (PTLC - Polity Themes in 20th & 21st Century Literature Ser.: 3). (ENG.). 200p. 69.95 (978-0-7456-3953-6(4)); pap. 24.95 (978-0-7456-3954-3(2)) Polity Pr. GBR. Dist: Wiley, John & Sons, Inc.

Gosmann, Uta. Poetic Memory: Sylvia Plath, Susan Howe, Ellen Hinsey, Louise Glück. 2011. (ENG.). 256p. 80.00 (978-1-61147-036-9(6)) Fairleigh Dickinson Univ. Pr.

Gottfried, Paul E. Leo Strauss & the Conservative Movement in America. 2011. (ENG.). 200p. pap. **(978-1-107-67571-1(5))**; 192p. 90.00 **(978-1-107-01724-5(6))** Cambridge Univ. Pr.

Goulimari, Pelagia & Pelagia. Toni Morrison. 2011. (Routledge Guides to Literature Ser.). (ENG.). 288p. (C). pap. 26.95 (978-0-415-42074-7(1)) Routledge.

Gourevitch, Philip. The Paris Review Interviews. 2007. (Illus.). 528p. pap. (978-1-84195-925-2(1)) Canongate Bks.

Gourevitch, Philip, ed. The Paris Review Interviews. 2007. Vol. 2. (Illus.). 448p. (978-1-84767-033-5(4)) Vol. 181. 184p. pap. (978-1-84767-077-9(6)) Canongate Bks.

Grace, Nancy M. & Skerl, Jennie, eds. The Transnational Beat Generation. 2012. (ENG., Illus.). 294p. 95.00 **(978-0-230-10840-0(7))**; pap. 27.00 **(978-0-230-10841-7(5))** Palgrave Macmillan.

Greenhaven. Women's Issues in Zora Neale Hurston's Their Eyes Were Watching God. 2012. (Social Issues in Literature Ser.). (ENG., Illus.). 224p. (gr. 10-12). pap. 39.60 **(978-0-7377-5822-1(8)**, Greenhaven Pr., Inc.); (YA). (gr. 9-12). lib. bdg. 27.30 **(978-0-7377-5821-4(X))** Cengage Gale.

Gretlund, Jan Nordby, ed. The Southern State of Mind. 2010. 256p. pap. 24.95 (978-1-57003-899-0(6)) Univ. of South Carolina Pr.

Griffin, Alice. Understanding Tennessee Williams. 2011. 288p. pap. 21.95 (978-1-61117-006-1(0)) Univ. of South Carolina Pr.

Griffith, Jean Carol. The Color of Democracy in Women's Regional Writing. 2009. (American Literary Realism & Naturalism Ser.). (ENG., Illus.). 280p. 49.50 (978-0-8173-1661-7(2)) Univ. of Alabama Pr.

Gruber, Eva, ed. Thomas King: Works & Impact. 2012. (European Studies in North American Literature & Culture Ser.). (Illus.). 364p. 90.00 **(978-1-57113-435-6(2))** Camden Hse.

Haines, Colin. "Frightened by a Word" Shirley Jackson & Lesbian Gothic. 2007. (Acta Universitatis Upsaliensis Ser.: Vol. 133). 234p. pap. (978-91-554-6844-6(6)) Uppsala Universitet/Acta Universitatis Upsaliensis.

Halas, Elzbieta. Towards the World Culture Society: Florian Znaniecki's Culturalism. 2010. (Studies in Sociology: Symbols, Theory & Society Ser.). 260p. 60.95 (978-3-631-59946-4(3)) Lang, Peter GmbH, Europaischer Verlag der Wissenschaften DEU. Dist: Lang, Peter.

Harkins, Gillian. Everybody's Family Romance: Reading Incest in Neoliberal America. 2009. (ENG., Illus.). 336p. 75.00 (978-0-8166-5347-8(X)); pap. 25.00 (978-0-8166-5348-5(8)) Univ. of Minnesota Pr.

Harris, Melanie L. Gifts of Virtue, Alice Walker, & Womanist Ethics. 2010. (Black Religion/Womanist Thought/Social Justice Ser.). (ENG.). 190p. 84.00 (978-0-230-61511-3(2)) Palgrave Macmillan.

Harrison-Kahan, Lori. The White Negress: Literature, Minstrelsy, & the Black-Jewish Imaginary. 2011. (American Literatures Initiative Ser.). (ENG., Illus.). 240p. 65.00 (978-0-8135-4782-4(2)); pap. 24.95 (978-0-8135-4783-1(0)) Rutgers Univ. Pr.

Hasan, Rabiul. Rediscovering Hemingway in Bangladesh & India, 1971-2006. 2010. (ENG.). 136p. pap. 24.50 (978-0-7618-5154-7(2)) Univ. Pr. of America, Inc.

Hatfield, Charles. Hand of Fire: The Comics Art of Jack Kirby. 2011. (Great Comics Artists Ser.). (ENG., Illus.). 304p. 65.00 **(978-1-61703-177-9(1))**; pap. 25.00 **(978-1-61703-178-6(X))** Univ. Pr. of Mississippi.

Hawkins, Alfonso. Jazz Trope: A Theory of African American Literary & Vernacular Culture. 2008. (African American Cultural Theory Ser.). (ENG.). 270p. pap. 55.00 (978-0-8108-6126-8(7)) Scarecrow Pr., Inc.

Hawkins, Ty. Reading Vietnam amid the War on Terror. 2012. (American Literature Readings in the Twenty-First Century Ser.). (ENG., Illus.). 224p. 85.00 **(978-0-230-34002-2(4))** Palgrave Macmillan.

Hays, Peter L. The Critical Reception of Hemingway's the Sun Also Rises. 2011. (Literary Criticism in Perspective Ser.). 358p. 75.00 (978-1-57113-366-3(6)) Camden Hse.

Heavilin, Barbara A. & George, Stephen K. A John Steinbeck Reader: Essays in Honor of Stephen K. George. 2009. (ENG.). 204p. pap. 45.00 (978-0-8108-6699-7(4)) Scarecrow Pr., Inc.

Heise, Thomas. Urban Underworlds: A Geography of Twentieth-Century American Literature & Culture. 2010. (American Literatures Initiative Ser.). (ENG., Illus.). 308p. 72.00 (978-0-8135-4784-8(9)); pap. 24.95 (978-0-8135-4785-5(7)) Rutgers Univ. Pr.

Hemminghaus, Edgar H. Mark Twain in Germany: Columbia University Germanic Studies V9. Fife, Robert Herndon, ed. 2011. 180p. 42.95 **(978-1-258-03278-4(3))** Literary Licensing, LLC.

Henderson. America & the Black Body. 2009. 69.50 (978-0-8386-4132-3(6)) Fairleigh Dickinson Univ. Pr.

Henderson, Bill. The Pushcart Prize Xxxiv 2010: Best of the Small Presses. Henderson, Bill, ed. 2009. (ENG.). 600p. pap. 18.95 (978-1-888889-54-3(3), 888954) Pushcart Pr., The.

—The Pushcart Prize XXXIV 2010: Best of the Small Presses. Henderson, Bill, ed. 2009. (ENG.). 600p. 35.00 (978-1-888889-55-0(1), 888955) Pushcart Pr., The.

Hernando-Real, Noelia. Self & Space in the Theater of Susan Glaspell. 2011. (ENG.). 214p. pap. 55.00 **(978-0-7864-6394-7(5))** McFarland & Co., Inc. Pubs.

Herring, Scott. Queering the Underworld: Slumming, Literature, & the Undoing of Lesbian & Gay History. 2007. (Illus.). 272p. 67.50 (978-0-226-32790-7(6)); per. 30.00 (978-0-226-32791-4(4)) Univ. of Chicago Pr.

Hewitt, Avis. Flannery O'Connor in the Age of Terrorism: Essays on Violence & Grace. Donahoo, Robert, ed. 2011. 392p. pap. 26.95 **(978-1-57233-879-1(2))** Univ. of Tennessee Pr.

Hogue, W. Lawrence. Postmodern American Literature & Its Other. 2008. (ENG.). 232p. 47.00 (978-0-252-03383-4(3)) Univ. of Illinois Pr.

Holman. Thomas Wolfe, Vol. 6. 2009. pap. 25.00 *(978-0-8166-0208-7(5))* Univ. of Minnesota Pr.

Hooper, Michael S. D. Sexual Politics in the Work of Tennessee Williams: Desire over Protest. 2012. (ENG., Illus.). 260p. 99.00 ***(978-1-107-01536-4(7))*** Cambridge Univ. Pr.

Horton, Merrill. Hunting the Sun: Faulkner's Borrowings from Balzac's the Human Comedy & Droll Stories. 2010. (Modern American Literature: New Approaches Ser.). 290p. (C). 80.95 *(978-1-4331-1003-0(2))* Lang, Peter Publishing, Inc.

Houen, Alex. Powers of Possibility: Experimental American Writing since The 1960s. 2012. 304p. 99.00 ***(978-0-19-960929-1(2))*** Oxford Univ. Pr., Inc.

Hricko, Mary. The Genesis of the Chicago Renaissance: Theodore Dreiser, Langston Hughes, Richard Wright, & James T. Farrell. (Literary Criticism & Cultural Theory Ser.). (ENG.). 250p. 2012. pap. 42.95 ***(978-0-415-54236-4(7))*** 2008. 125.00 *(978-0-415-95792-2(3))* Routledge.

Huang, Yunte. Transpacific Imaginations: History, Literature, Counterpoetics. 2008. (Illus.). 202p. 40.50 *(978-0-674-02637-7(3))* Harvard Univ. Pr.

Huehls, Mitchum. Qualified Hope: A Postmodern Politics of Time. 2009. *(978-0-8142-0617-1(4))*; (ENG.). cd-rom 14.95 *(978-0-8142-9184-9(8))* Ohio State Univ. Pr.

Hungerford, Amy. Postmodern: American Literature & Religion since 1960. 2010. (20/21 Ser.). (ENG.). 224p. (C). 65.00 *(978-0-691-13508-3(8))*; pap. 27.95 *(978-0-691-14575-4(X))* Princeton Univ. Pr.

Hunter, Jeffrey W. Contemporary Literary Criticism: Excerpts from Criticism of the Works of Today's Novelists, Poets, Playwrights, Short Story Writers, Scriptwriters, & Other Creative Writers. 2011. (ENG.). 475p. 328.00 *(978-1-4144-4928-9(3))*; 481p. 328.00 *(978-1-4144-4927-2(5))* Cengage Gale.

Hutchinson, George, ed. The Cambridge Companion to the Harlem Renaissance. 2007. (Cambridge Companions to Literature Ser.). (ENG.). 296p. per. 34.00 *(978-0-521-67368-6(2))* Cambridge Univ. Pr.

Izzo, David Garrett. The Influence of Mysticism on 20th Century British & American Literature. 2009. (ENG.). 191p. pap. 39.95 *(978-0-7864-4106-8(2))* McFarland & Co., Inc. Pubs.

Jacobs, Elizabeth. Mexican American Literature. 2009. 180p. pap. 34.00 *(978-0-415-54406-1(8))* Routledge.

Jeffery, Ben. Anti-Matter: Michel Houellebecq & Depressive Realism. 2011. (ENG.). 105p. pap. 14.95 ***(978-1-84694-922-7(X))*** O Bks., John Hunt.

Jennings, La Vinia Delois. Toni Morrison & the Idea of Africa. 2010. (ENG.). 258p. pap. 35.99 *(978-0-521-17339-1(6))* Cambridge Univ. Pr.

Johns, J. Adam. The Assault on Progress: Technology & Time in American Literature. 2008. (ENG.). 280p. 45.00 *(978-0-8173-1625-9(6))* Univ. of Alabama Pr.

Johnson, Kendall. Henry James & the Visual. 2011. (ENG., Illus.). 264p. pap. 50.00 *(978-0-521-28339-7(6))* Cambridge Univ. Pr.

Jolas, Eugene. Eugene Jolas: Critical Writings, 1924-1951. Kiefer, Klaus H. & Rumold, Rainer, eds. 2009. (Avant-Garde & Modernism Collection). (ENG.). 624p. pap. 32.95 *(978-0-8101-2581-0(1))* Northwestern Univ. Pr.

Jones, Darryl, et al, eds. It Came from The 1950s! Popular Culture, Popular Anxieties. 2011. (ENG., Illus.). 284p. 85.00 *(978-0-230-27221-7(5))* Palgrave Macmillan.

Jones, Gavin. American Hungers: The Problem of Poverty in U. S. Literature, 1840-1945. (20/21 Ser.). (ENG., Illus.). 248p. (C). 2009. pap. 25.95 *(978-0-691-14331-6(5))* 2007. 52.50 *(978-0-691-12753-8(0))* Princeton Univ. Pr.

Jones, Norman W. Gay & Lesbian Historical Fiction: Sexual Mystery & Post-Secular Narrative. annot. ed. 2007. (ENG.). 232p. 84.00 *(978-1-4039-7655-0(4))* Palgrave Macmillan.

Jongh, James de. Vicious Modernism: Black Harlem & the Literary Imagination. 2009. (ENG., Illus.). 292p. (C). pap. 42.00 *(978-0-521-12330-3(5))* Cambridge Univ. Pr.

Joslin, Katherine. Edith Wharton & the Making of Fashion. 2011. (Becoming Modern: New Nineteenth-Century Studies). (Illus.). 248p. pap. 40.00 *(978-1-61168-218-2(5)*, University of New Hampshire Press) Univ. Pr. of New England.

Josyph, Peter. Adventures in Reading Cormac McCarthy. 2010. (ENG.). 256p. (gr. 17). pap. 35.00 *(978-0-8108-7707-8(4))* Scarecrow Pr., Inc.

Joyce, William & O'Joyce, Guillermo. Miller, Bukowski & Their Enemies: Essays on Contemporary Culture. 2nd ed. 2011. 160p. pap. 15.00 *(978-1-905177-27-1(5))* Pinter & Martin Ltd. GBR. Dist: National Bk. Network.

Junker, Carsten. Frames of Friction: Black Genealogies, White Hegemony, & the Essay as Critical Intervention. 2010. 294p. pap. 49.00 *(978-3-593-39099-4(X))* Campus Verlag GmbH DEU. Dist: Chicago Distribution Ctr.

Jurecic, Ann. Illness as Narrative. 2012. (Pitt Comp Literacy Culture Ser.). (ENG.). 224p. pap. 24.95 ***(978-0-8229-6190-1(3))*** Univ. of Pittsburgh Pr.

Kaplan, Cora & Schwarz, Bill. James Baldwin: America & Beyond. 2011. (Illus.). 288p. E-Book ***(978-0-472-02761-3(1))*** Univ. of Michigan Pr.

Karem, Jeff. The Purloined Island: Caribbean-U. S. Crosscurrents in Literature & Culture, 1880-1959. 2011. (New World Studies). (ENG., Illus.). 320p. (gr. 17). 69.50 *(978-0-8139-3086-2(3))* Univ. Pr. of Virginia.

—The Purloined Islands: Caribbean-U. S, Crosscurrents in Literature & Culture, 1880-1959. 2011. (New World Studies). (ENG., Illus.). 320p. (C). (gr. 13-17). pap. 35.00 *(978-0-8139-3087-9(1))* Univ. Pr. of Virginia.

Katz, Daniel. American Modernism's Expatriate Scene: The Labour of Translation. 2007. (Edinburgh Critical Studies in Transatlantic Literature Ser.). (ENG.). 208p. (gr. 17). 90.00 *(978-0-7486-2526-0(7))* Edinburgh Univ. Pr. GBR. Dist: Columbia Univ. Pr.

Kennedy, Tanya Ann. "Keeping up Her Geography" Women's Writing & Geocultural Space in Twentieth-Century U.S. Literature & Culture. annot. ed. 2006. (Literary Criticism & Cultural Theory Ser.). (ENG.). 160p. 156.00 *(978-0-415-97949-8(8))* Routledge.

Kent, Alicia A. & Kent, Alicia. African, Native, & Jewish American Literature & the Reshaping of Modernism. 2007. (ENG., Illus.). 240p. 84.00 *(978-1-4039-7797-7(6))* Palgrave Macmillan.

Kercher, Stephen E. Revel with a Cause: Liberal Satire in Postwar America. 2006. (Illus.). 572p. 35.00 *(978-0-226-43164-2(9))* Univ. of Chicago Pr.

Keresztesi, Rita. Strangers at Home: American Ethnic Modernism Between the World Wars. 2009. (ENG., Illus.). 248p. pap. 24.95 *(978-0-8032-2792-7(2))* Univ. of Nebraska Pr.

Keyser, Catherine. Playing Smart: New York Women Writers & Modern Magazine Culture. (Mellon-ALI Ser.). (ENG., 242p. 2011. Illus.). pap. 23.95 ***(978-0-8135-5178-4(1))*** 2010. 39.95 *(978-0-8135-4786-2(5))* Rutgers Univ. Pr.

Kime Scott Staff. Gender & Modernism V1, 4 vols. 2008. (Illus.). XXVI, 366p. *(978-0-415-38093-5(6))* Routledge.

—Gender & Modernism V2, 4 vols. 2008. (Illus.). VIII, 384p. *(978-0-415-38094-2(4))* Routledge.

Klinkowitz, Jerome. The Vonnegut Effect. 2011. 232p. pap. 21.95 *(978-1-61117-007-8(9))* Univ. of South Carolina Pr.

Knoerrich Isabel & Hammad, Lamia Khalil. U.S. Women of Color Theorize Subversion Through Cross-Genre Writing: Contemporary Perspectives on Race, Gender, Culture. 2009. 196p. pap. 78.00 *(978-3-639-03797-5(9))* VDM Verlag Dr. Mueller e.K.

Kocela, Christopher. Fetishism & Its Discontents in Post-1960 American Fiction. 2010. (American Literature Readings in the Twenty-First Century Ser.). (ENG.). 288p. 84.00 *(978-0-230-10290-3(5))* Palgrave Macmillan.

Koritz, Amy. Culture Makers: Urban Performance & Literature in the 1920s. 2nd ed. 2008. (ENG., Illus.). 216p. 42.00 *(978-0-252-03384-1(1))* Univ. of Illinois Pr.

Kramer, Victor A., ed. Georgia State Literary Studies, 12 vols. *(978-0-404-63200-7(9))* AMS Pr., Inc.

Kundu, Gautam. Fitzgerald & the Influence of Film: The Language of Cinema in the Novels. 2007. (ENG.). 203p. per. 35.00 *(978-0-7864-3134-2(2))* McFarland & Co., Inc. Pubs.

Landles, Iain. The Case for Cummings. 2008. 360p. pap. *(978-3-639-09250-9(3))* VDM Verlag Dr. Mueller e.K.

Last Name Staff. Gender & Modernism V3, 4 vols. 2008. (Illus.). VIII, 384p. *(978-0-415-38095-9(2))* Routledge.

Lathbury, Roger & Meyers, Karen. Realism & Regionalism, 1860-1910. 2nd rev. ed. 2010. (Backgrounds to American Literature Ser.). (Illus.). 128p. (gr. 6-12). 40.00 *(978-1-60413-487-2(9)*, Chelsea Hse.) Facts On File, Inc.

Lee, A. Robert. Modern American Counter Writing. 2011. (ENG.). 296p. pap. 39.95 ***(978-0-415-89650-4(9))*** Routledge.

Lee, A. Robert. Modern American Counter Writing: Beats, Outriders, Ethnics. 2010. (Literary Criticism & Cultural Theory Ser.). (ENG.). 308p. (C). 125.00 *(978-0-415-99811-6(5))* Routledge.

Lee, Christopher. The Semblance of Identity: Aesthetic Mediation in Asian American Literature. 2012. (Asian America Ser.). (ENG.). 208p. 50.00 ***(978-0-3047-7870-1(1))*** Stanford Univ. Pr.

Leitch, Vincent B. American Literary Criticism since The 1930s. 2nd ed. 2009. (ENG.). 420p. 35.95 *(978-0-415-77818-3(2))*; 135.00 *(978-0-415-77817-6(4))* Routledge.

Lennon, Brian. In Babel's Shadow: Multilingual Literatures, Monolingual States. 2010. 256p. 75.00 *(978-0-8166-6501-3(X))*; pap. 25.00 *(978-0-8166-6502-0(8))* Univ. of Minnesota Pr.

Levin, Joanna. Bohemia in America, 1858-1920. 2009. (ENG., Illus.). 480p. 65.00 *(978-0-8047-6083-6(7))* Stanford Univ. Pr.

Light, James F. Nathanael West: An Interpretive Study. 2011. 236p. 46.95 ***(978-1-258-03220-3(1))*** Literary Licensing, LLC.

Limón, José Eduardo. Américo Paredes: Culture & Critique. 2012. (ENG.). 246p. 55.00 ***(978-0-292-73877-5(3))*** Univ. of Texas Pr.

Lincoln, Kenneth. Cormac McCarthy: American Canticles. 2008. (American Literature Readings in the Twenty-First Century Ser.). (ENG.). 208p. 95.00 *(978-0-230-61226-6(1))* Palgrave Macmillan.

Lindsey, Ben B. The Beast. 2010. 360p. pap. 32.75 *(978-1-143-46265-8(3))* BiblioBazaar.

Lindsey, Ben B. & O'Higgins, Harvey J. The Beast. 2010. 356p. 37.56 ***(978-1-163-65536-8(8))***; pap. 25.56 ***(978-1-163-62275-9(3))*** Kessinger Publishing, LLC.

Lindsey, Ben Barr. The Beast. 2009. 158p. pap. *(978-1-150-71437-5(9))* Books LLC.

Lindsey, Benjain B. & O'Higgins, Harvey J. The Beast. 2009. (Timberline Ser.). (ENG., Illus.). 354p. pap. 21.95 *(978-0-87081-953-7(4))* Univ. Pr. of Colorado.

Lindsey, Benjamin Barr & O'Higgins, Harvey Jerrold. The Beast. 2010. 364p. pap. 32.75 *(978-1-177-77353-9(8))* BiblioBazaar.

Lock, Graham & Murray, David, eds. Thriving on a Riff: Jazz & Blues Influences in African American Literature & Film. 2009. (ENG., Illus.). 288p. 99.00 *(978-0-19-533702-0(6))*; pap. 24.95 *(978-0-19-533709-9(3))* Oxford Univ. Pr., Inc.

Lofaro, Michael, ed. Agee at 100: Centennial Essays on the Works of James Agee. 2012. (ENG., Illus.). 304p. 49.00 ***(978-1-57233-853-1(9))*** Univ. of Tennessee Pr.

Lough, James & Herron, Patricia, eds. Spheres of Awareness: A Wilberian Integral Approach to Literature, Philosophy, Psychology, & Art. 2009. (ENG.). 208p. pap. 33.99 *(978-0-7618-4804-2(5))* Univ. Pr. of America, Inc.

Lovering, Joseph P. The Well-Made Historical Novels of American Regionlist Charles A. Brady, 1912-1995: Defender of the Moral Fabric of Local Cultures. 2006. (Illus.). 196p. 99.95 *(978-0-7734-5778-2(X))* Mellen, Edwin Pr., The.

Lovett, Robert Morss. Edith Wharton. 2007. (ENG.). 96p. per. 18.95 *(978-1-4325-5397-5(6))* Kessinger Publishing, LLC.

Luccock, Halford E. The Questing Spirit: Religion in the Literature of Our Time. 2007. (ENG.). 716p. 65.95 *(978-0-548-07091-8(1))* Kessinger Publishing, LLC.

Luccock, Halford E. & Brentano, Frances, eds. The Questing Spirit: Religion in the Literature of Our Time. 2007. (ENG.). 716p. per. 50.95 *(978-1-4325-8390-3(5))* Kessinger Publishing, LLC.

Lundin, Roger, ed. There Before Us: Religion, Literature, & Culture from Emerson to Wendell Berry. 2006. 250p. per. 18.00 *(978-0-8028-2963-4(5))* Eerdmans, William B. Publishing Co.

Luszczynska, Ana M. The Ethics of Community: Nancy, Derrida, Morrison, & Menendez. 2011. (ENG.). 192p. (gr. 17). 100.00 ***(978-1-4411-2885-0(9))*** Continuum International Publishing Group, Ltd. GBR. Dist: National Bk. Network.

Lynch, Tom & Maher, Susan N., eds. Artifacts & Illuminations: Critical Essays on Loren Eiseley. 2012. (ENG.). 384p. pap. 40.00 ***(978-0-8032-3403-1(1))*** Univ. of Nebraska Pr.

MacKay, James, ed. The Salt Companion to Diane Glancy. 2010. (ENG., Illus.). 220p. pap. *(978-1-84471-428-5(4))* Salt Publishing.

Mackey, Nathaniel. Discrepant Engagement: Dissonance, Cross-Culturality & Experimental Writing. 2009. (Cambridge Studies in American Literature & Culture Ser.). (ENG.). 328p. pap. 42.00 *(978-0-521-10999-4(X))* Cambridge Univ. Pr.

Macpherson, Heidi Slettedahl. Courting Failure: Women & the Law in Twentieth-Century Literature. 2007. (Series on Law, Politics, & Society). 292p. 52.95 *(978-1-931968-47-8(0))*; pap. 24.95 *(978-1-931968-48-5(9))* Univ. of Akron Pr., The.

MacPherson, Heidi Slettedahl. Transatlantic Women's Literature. 2009. (Edinburgh Critical Studies in Transatlantic Literature Ser.). (ENG.). 192p. (gr. 17). 85.00 *(978-0-7486-2445-4(7))* Edinburgh Univ. Pr. GBR. Dist: Columbia Univ. Pr.

Madden, Ed. Tiresian Poetics: Modernism, Sexuality, Voice, 1888-2001. 2008. 408p. (C). 80.00 *(978-0-8386-3937-5(2))* Fairleigh Dickinson Univ. Pr.

Madsen, Deborah. Understanding Gerald Vizenor. 2009. (Understanding Contemporary American Literature Ser.). 216p. 39.95 *(978-1-57003-856-3(2))* Univ. of South Carolina Pr.

Madsen, Deborah & Lee, A. Robert. Gerald Vizenor: Texts & Contexts. 2011. (ENG., Illus.). 448p. (C). 39.95 *(978-0-8263-4915-6(3))* Univ. of New Mexico Pr.

Magome, Kyoko. The Influence of Music on American Literature since 1890: A History of Aesthetic Counterpoint. 296p. 109.95 *(978-0-7734-5135-3(8))* Mellen, Edwin Pr., The.

Mahan, Henry. The Works of Henry Mahan. 2008. 484p. 37.36 *(978-1-4357-0619-4(6))*; (ENG.). 628p. 43.50 *(978-1-4357-0621-7(8))*; (ENG.). 616p. 42.64 *(978-1-4357-0623-1(4))* Lulu Enterprises Inc.

Mandel, Miriam B., ed. Hemingway & Africa. 2011. (Studies in American Literature & Culture Ser.). (Illus.). 426p. 80.00 *(978-1-57113-483-7(2))* Camden Hse.

Manzanas, Ana M. & Benito Sanchez, Jesús. Cities, Borders & Spaces in Intercultural American Literature & Film. 2011. (Routledge Transnational Perspectives on American Literature Ser.). (ENG.). 176p. (C). 125.00 *(978-0-415-88721-2(6))* Routledge.

Marcus, Morton. Striking Through the Masks: A Literary Memoir. 2008. (Illus.). 590p. pap. 18.95 *(978-0-932319-09-8(2))* Capitola Bk. Co.

Margolies, Edward. New York & the Literary Imagination: The City in Twentieth Century Fiction & Drama. 2007. (ENG.). 206p. per. 35.00 *(978-0-7864-3071-0(0))* McFarland & Co., Inc. Pubs.

Mark, Cirino & Mark, Ott, eds. Ernest Hemingway & Geography. 2011. 208p. 45.00 *(978-1-60635-042-3(0))* Kent State Univ. Pr.

Mark, Noonan. Reading Century ILLUS Mo. 2011. (Illus.). 256p. 65.00 *(978-1-60635-063-8(3))* Kent State Univ. Pr.

Mason, Yvonne. Reading, Learning, Teaching Clyde Edgerton. 2008. (Confronting the Text, Confronting the World Ser.). 176p. (C). 32.95 *(978-0-8204-8143-2(2))* Lang, Peter Publishing, Inc.

Matthews, Brander. Bookshelf of Brander Matthews. reprint ed. 31.50 *(978-0-404-04268-4(6))* AMS Pr., Inc.

Matthews, John T. William Faulkner: Seeing Through the South. 2012. (Blackwell Introductions to Literature Ser.: 44). (ENG., Illus.). 320p. pap. 29.95 ***(978-0-470-67240-2(4)***, Wiley-Blackwell) Wiley, John & Sons, Inc.

Matthews, Steven. Modernism. Matthews, Steven, ed. 2008. (ENG., Illus.). 336p. 100.00 *(978-1-4039-9829-3(9))* Palgrave Macmillan.

—Modernism: A Sourcebook. Matthews, Steven, ed. 2008. (ENG., Illus.). 336p. pap. 31.00 *(978-1-4039-9830-9(2))* Palgrave Macmillan.

McBride, Christopher. The Colonizer Abroad: Island Representations in American Prose from Herman Melville to Jack London. 2009. 170p. 39.95 *(978-0-415-80343-4(8))* Routledge.

McCann, Sean. A Pinnacle of Feeling: American Literature & Presidential Government. 2008. (20/21 Ser.). (ENG.). 248p. (C). 39.95 *(978-0-691-13695-0(5))* Princeton Univ. Pr.

McDonald, Gail. American Literature & Culture, 1900-1960. 2006. (Blackwell Introductions to Literature Ser.: 22). (ENG., Illus.). 264p. pap. 41.95 *(978-1-4051-0127-1(X))*; 110.95 *(978-1-4051-0126-4(1))* Wiley, John & Sons, Inc. (Wiley-Blackwell).

McEneaney, Kevin T. Russell Banks: In Search of Freedom, 1 vol. 2010. 221p. 44.95 *(978-0-313-38165-2(8)*, A2591C, Praeger Pubs.) Greenwood Publishing Group, Inc.

McHaney, Thomas L., ed. Faulkner Studies in Japan. 2008. (ENG.). 232p. pap. 24.95 *(978-0-8203-3363-2(8))* Univ. of Georgia Pr.

McMahon, Gary. Kurt Vonnegut & the Centrifugal Force of Fate. 2009. (ENG., Illus.). 259p. pap. 39.95 *(978-0-7864-3993-5(9))* McFarland & Co., Inc. Pubs.

Mencken, H. L. Mencken: Prejudices. Rodgers, Marion, ed. 2010. (ENG.). (gr. 12). 624p. 35.00 *(978-1-59853-074-2(7))*; 656p. 35.00 *(978-1-59853-075-9(5))* Library of America, The.

Mendlesohn, Farah, ed. On Joanna Russ. 2009. (ENG.). 304p. (C). lib. bdg. 85.00 *(978-0-8195-6901-1(1))*; pap. 29.95 *(978-0-8195-6902-8(X))* Wesleyan Univ. Pr.

Meyers, Karen & Rangno, Erik V. R. Contemporary American Literature, 1945 - Present. 2nd rev. ed. 2010. (Backgrounds to American Literature Ser.). (Illus.). 128p. (gr. 6-12). 40.00 *(978-1-60413-489-6(5)*, Chelsea Hse.) Facts On File, Inc.

Michaels, Walter Benn. The Shape of the Signifier: 1967 to the End of History. 2006. (ENG., Illus.). 232p. (C). per. 21.95 *(978-0-691-12618-0(6))* Princeton Univ. Pr.

Mickle, Mildred R., ed. Gwendolyn Brooks. 2009. (Critical Insights Ser.). 416p. lib. bdg. 85.00 *(978-1-58765-632-3(9))* Salem Pr., Inc.

Miller, J.Hillis. The Medium Is the Maker: Browning, Freud, Derrida, & the New Telepathic Ecotechnologies. 2009. (ENG., Illus.). 93p. pap. 27.50 *(978-1-84519-319-5(9))* Sussex Academic Pr. GBR. Dist: International Specialized Bk. Services.

Miller, Joshua L. Accented America: The Cultural Politics of Multilingual Modernism, 1 vol. 2011. (Modernist Literature & Culture Ser.). (ENG., Illus.). 432p. pap. 24.95 *(978-0-19-533700-6(X))* Oxford Univ. Pr., Inc.

Miller, Karl. Tretower to Clyro: Essays. 2011. (ENG., Illus.). 272p. 29.95 ***(978-0-85738-580-2(1))*** Quercus GBR. Dist: Independent Pubs. Group.

Millichap, Joseph R. A Backward Glance: The Southern Renascence, the Autobiographical Epic, & the Classical Legacy. 2009. (ENG.). 256p. 39.95 *(978-1-57233-659-9(5))* Univ. of Tennessee Pr.

Minnick, Lisa Cohen. Dialect & Dichotomy: Literary Representations of African American Speech. 2nd ed. 2007. 216p. pap. 22.50 *(978-0-8173-5423-7(9))* Univ. of Alabama Pr.

Mitchell, Jonathan. Revisions of the American Adam: Innocence, Identity & Masculinity in Twentieth Century America. 2012. (Continuum Literary Studies). (ENG., Illus.). 172p. 110.00 *(978-1-4411-8707-9(3))* Continuum International Publishing Group, Ltd. GBR. Dist: National Bk. Network.

Moffett, Joe. Understanding Charles Wright. 2008. 176p. 34.95 *(978-1-57003-778-8(7))* Univ. of South Carolina Pr.

Moglen, Seth. Mourning Modernity: Literary Modernism & the Injuries of American Capitalism. 2007. (ENG.). 344p. 65.00 *(978-0-8047-5418-7(7))*; per. 24.95 *(978-0-8047-5419-4(5))* Stanford Univ. Pr.

Monteiro, George. Essays on Portuguese-American Culture. 2008. *(978-1-933227-25-2(7))* Univ. of Massachusetts Dartmouth.

Montgomery, Marion. With Walker Percy at the Tupperware Party: In Company with Flannery O'Connor, T. S. Eliot, & Others. 2009. (ENG.). 420p. 45.00 *(978-1-58731-928-0(4))* St. Augustine's Pr., Inc.

Moraru, Christian. Cosmodernism: American Narrative, Late Globalization, & the New Cultural Imaginary. 2010. (ENG.). 440p. (C). 90.00 *(978-0-472-07129-6(7))*; pap. 37.50 *(978-0-472-05129-8(6))* Univ. of Michigan Pr.

Morgan, Bill. The Typewriter Is Holy: The Complete, Uncensored History of the Beat Generation. 2011. (ENG., Illus.). 352p. pap. 15.95 *(978-1-58243-738-5(6)*, Counterpoint) Counterpoint LLC.

Morgan, Bill & Morgan, William. The Typewriter Is Holy: The Complete, Uncensored History of the Beat Generation. 2010. (ENG., Illus.). 320p. 28.00 *(978-1-4165-9242-6(3)*, Free Pr.) Free Pr.

Morley, Catherine. Modern American Lierature. 2012. (Edinburgh Critical Guides to Literature Ser.). (ENG.). 304p. (gr. 17). 105.00 ***(978-0-7486-2506-2(2))*** Edinburgh Univ. Pr. GBR. Dist: Columbia Univ. Pr.

—Modern American Literature. 2012. (Edinburgh Critical Guides to Literature Ser.). (ENG.). 304p. (gr. 17). pap. 27.50 ***(978-0-7486-2507-9(0))*** Edinburgh Univ. Pr. GBR. Dist: Columbia Univ. Pr.

Morley, Catherine W. The Quest for Epic in Contemporary American Fiction. 2008. (Routledge Transnational Perspectives on American Literature Ser.). (ENG.). 226p. 125.00 *(978-0-415-96113-4(0))* Routledge.

Mortenson, Erik Ronald. Capturing the Beat Moment: Cultural Politics & the Poetics of Presence. 2010. E-Book *(978-0-8093-8613-0(5))*; (Illus.). 240p. pap. 35.00 *(978-0-8093-3013-3(X))* Southern Illinois Univ. Pr.

Murphy, Bernice. The Suburban Gothic in American Popular Culture, 1948-2008. 2009. (ENG.). 256p. 95.00 *(978-0-230-21810-9(5))* Palgrave Macmillan.

Murphy, Brenda, ed. Tennessee Williams. 2010. (Critical Insights Ser.). 350p. 85.00 *(978-1-58765-687-3(6))* Salem Pr., Inc.

Nadel, Alan & Griffin, Susan M., eds. The Men Who Knew Too Much: Henry James & Alfred Hitchcock, 1 vol. 2012. (ENG., Illus.). 272p. pap. 27.95 ***(978-0-19-976443-3(3))*** Oxford Univ. Pr., Inc.

Nadel, Ira B., ed. Ezra Pound in Context. 2010. (Literature in Context Ser.). (ENG.). 530p. 110.00 *(978-0-521-51507-8(6))* Cambridge Univ. Pr.

Nakadate, Neil. Understanding Jane Smiley: Revised Edition. 2nd rev. ed. 2009. (Understanding Contemporary American Literature Ser.). 296p. pap. 24.95 (978-1-57003-858-7(9)) Univ. of South Carolina Pr.

Nel, Philip. The Avant-Garde & American Postmodernity: Small Incisive Shocks. 2009. (ENG.). 265p. pap. 25.00 (978-1-60473-252-8(0)) Univ. Pr. of Mississippi.

Nel, Philip & Zipes, Jack. Tales for Little Rebels: A Collection of Radical Children's Literature. Mickenberg, Julia L., ed. 2008. (ENG., Illus.). 313p. 65.00 (978-0-8147-5720-8(0)) New York Univ. Pr.

Newen, Albert & Riel, Raphael van. Identity, Language, & Mind: Introduction to the Philosophy of John Perry. 2012. (Center for the Study of Language & Information - Lecture Notes Ser.). 174p. 45.00 (978-1-57586-643-7(9)); pap. 25.00 (978-1-57586-642-0(0)) CSLI Pubns.

Ngugi wa Thiong'o. Decolonizing the Mind: The Politics of Language in African Literature. 2009. (Studies in African Literature Ser.). 128p. pap. 24.95 (978-0-85255-501-9(6), Currey, James) Boydell & Brewer, Ltd. GBR. Dist: Boydell & Brewer, Inc.

Norman, Brian. The American Protest Essay & National Belonging: Addressing Division. 2007. (Illus.). 222p. per. 29.95 (978-0-7914-7236-1(1)); 74.50 (978-0-7914-7235-4(3)) State Univ. of New York Pr.

—Neo-Segregation Narratives: Jim Crow in Post-Civil Rights American Literature. 2010. (ENG., Illus.). 212p. 59.95 (978-0-8203-3596-4(7)); pap. 24.95 (978-0-8203-3597-1(5)) Univ. of Georgia Pr.

—Representing Segregation: Toward an Aesthetics of Living Jim Crow, & Other Forms of Racial Division. Williams, Piper Kendrix, ed. 2010. (Illus.). 320p. 80.00 (978-1-4384-3033-1(7)); pap. 29.95 (978-1-4384-3032-4(9)) State Univ. of New York Pr.

Obourn, Megan. Reconstituting Americans: Liberal Multiculturalism & Identity Difference in Post-1960s Literature. 2011. (ENG.). 240p. 85.00 (978-0-230-11247-6(1)) Palgrave Macmillan.

O'Connor, Flannery & Gordon, Sarah. Flannery O'Connor: In Celebration of Genius. 2010. (ENG.). pap. 21.95 (978-1-57003-934-8(8)) Univ. of South Carolina Pr.

O'Connor, William Van. The Tangled Fire of William Faulkner. 2009. 204p. pap. 50.00 (978-0-8166-5997-5(4)) Univ. of Minnesota Pr.

Oglesby, Catherine. Corra Harris & the Divided Mind of the New South. 2008. (ENG., Illus.). 272p. 59.95 (978-0-8130-3247-4(4)) Univ. Pr. of Florida.

Oliva, Juan Ignacio. The Painful Chrysalis: Essays on Contemporary Cultural & Literary Identity. 2011. (Spanish Perspectives on English & American Literature, Communication & Culture Ser.). (ENG.). 276p. pap. (978-3-0343-0666-9(0)) Lang, Peter.

Olson, Ted & Olson, Kathy H., eds. James Still: Critical Essays on the Dean of Appalachian Literature. 2007. (Contributions to Southern Appalachian Studies: 17). (ENG., Illus.). 260p. pap. 39.95 (978-0-7864-3076-5(1)) McFarland & Co., Inc. Pubs.

Omry, Keren. Cross-Rhythms: Jazz Aesthetics in African-American Literature. 2011. (ENG.). 196p. pap. 44.95 (978-1-4411-0295-9(7)) Continuum International Publishing Group, Ltd. GBR. Dist: National Bk. Network.

Omry, Keren & Omry. Cross-Rhythms: Jazz Aesthetics in African-American Literature. 2009. (Continuum Literary Studies). (ENG.). 196p. 130.00 (978-0-8264-9743-7(8)) Continuum International Publishing Group, Ltd. GBR. Dist: National Bk. Network.

O'Neill, Eugene. An Wilderness & Days Without End. 2008. 276p. (978-1-4437-2564-4(1)) 2006. 272p. per. (978-1-4067-3620-5(1)) Read Bks. (Hesperides Pr.).

O'Rourke, William. Confessions of a Guilty Freelancer. 2012. (Break Away Bks.). (ENG.). 368p. pap. 29.00 (978-0-253-00181-8(1), 0253001811) Indiana Univ. Pr.

Orr, Gregg & Torrey, Beef. Jim Harrison: A Comprehensive Bibliography, 1964-2008. 2009. (ENG., Illus.). 376p. 65.00 (978-0-8032-1614-3(9)) Univ. of Nebraska Pr.

Orr, Lisa. Transforming American Realism: Working-Class Women Writers of the Twentieth Century. 2006. (ENG.). 148p. per. 30.50 (978-0-7618-3611-7(X)) Univ. Pr. of America, Inc.

Ott, Mark P. A Sea of Change: Ernest Hemingway & the Gulf Stream: A Contextual Biography. 2008. (Illus.). 151p. 29.00 (978-0-87338-923-5(9)) Kent State Univ. Pr.

Overton, Grant. Cargoes for Crusoes. 2007. (ENG.). 430p. 51.95 (978-0-548-01849-1(9)) Kessinger Publishing, LLC.

Pabisch, Peter & Greisenegger, Wolfgang, eds. Von Eierschwammerlhöhen zur D. H. Lawrence Ranch: Österreichisches Literaturgeschehen in den Rockys? 2010. (Jahrbuch für Internationale Germanistik. Reihe A: Kongressberichte Ser.). (GER.). 264p. pap. (978-3-0343-0334-7(3)) Lang, Peter.

Palmer, Stephanie C. Together by Accident: American Local Color Literature & the Middle Class. 2008. (ENG.). 234p. 68.50 (978-0-7391-2494-9(3)) Lexington Bks.

Parini, Jay & Bendixen, Alfred. Questions of Social & Economic Justice. 2008. (ENG.). 96p. (C). pap. 12.95 (978-1-4282-6245-4(8)) Cengage Heinle.

Parrish, Timothy. From the Civil War to the Apocalypse: Postmodern History & American Fiction. 2007. 320p. lib. bdg. 80.00 net. (978-1-55849-626-2(2)); 308p. per. 28.95 net. (978-1-55849-627-9(0)) Univ. of Massachusetts Pr.

Parrish, Timothy. Ralph Ellison & the Genius of America. 2011. (ENG.). 280p. pap. 26.95 (978-1-55849-922-5(9)); lib. bdg. 80.00 (978-1-55849-921-8(0)) Univ. of Massachusetts Pr.

Paulin, Diana Rebekkah. Imperfect Unions: Staging Miscegenation in U. S. Drama & Fiction. 2012. (Illus.). 336p. 75.00 (978-0-8166-7098-7(6)); pap. 25.00 (978-0-8166-7099-4(4)) Univ. of Minnesota Pr.

Pavese, Cesare. American Literature: Essays & Opinions. Fussell, Edwin, tr. from ITA. & intro. by. 2010. (ENG.). 244p. pap. 29.95 (978-1-4128-1073-9(6)) Transaction Pubs.

Peacock, James. Understanding Paul Auster. (Understanding Contemporary American Literature Ser.). 264p. 2011. (ENG.). pap. 21.95 (978-1-61117-052-8(4)) 2010. 39.95 (978-1-57003-864-8(3)) Univ. of South Carolina Pr.

Pearson, Neil. Obelisk: A History of Jack Kahane & the Obelisk Press. 2008. (ENG., Illus.). 528p. 39.00 (978-1-84631-101-7(2)) Liverpool Univ. Pr. GBR. Dist: Chicago Distribution Ctr.

Peeler, David P. Hope among Us Yet: Social Criticism & Social Solace in Depression America. 2008. (ENG.). 360p. per. 26.95 (978-0-8203-3140-9(6)) Univ. of Georgia Pr.

Penner, James. Pinks, Pansies, & Punks: The Rhetoric of Masculinity in American Literary Culture. 2010. (ENG., Illus.). 318p. pap. 24.95 (978-0-253-22251-0(6), 0253222516) Indiana Univ. Pr.

Perdigao, Lisa K. & Pizzato, Mark. Death in Twentieth-Century American Texts & Performances: Corpses Ghosts & the Reanimated Dead. 2010. 228p. 99.95 (978-0-7546-6907-4(6)) Ashgate Publishing Co.

Perez, George. Art of George Perez. 2012. (Illus.). 256p. (YA). 49.99 (978-1-60010-859-4(8)) Idea & Design Works, LLC.

—Art of George Perez S&N Limited Edition. 2012. (Illus.). 256p. (YA). 79.99 (978-1-60010-860-0(1)) Idea & Design Works, LLC.

Perez, Richard & Sandin, Lyn Di Iorio, eds. Contemporary U. S. Latino/A Literary Criticism. 2007. (American Literature Readings in the Twenty-First Century Ser.). (ENG.). 304p. 100.00 (978-1-4039-7999-5(5)) Palgrave Macmillan.

Petry, Alice Hall, ed. On Harper Lee: Essays & Reflections. 2008. (ENG.). 224p. pap. 21.95 (978-1-57233-642-1(0)) Univ. of Tennessee Pr.

Pfitzer, Gregory M. Popular History & the Literary Marketplace, 1840-1920. 2008. (Studies in Print Culture & the History of the Book). (Illus.). 464p. lib. bdg. 98.00 net. (978-1-55849-624-8(6)); 469p. per. 29.95 net. (978-1-55849-625-5(4)) Univ. of Massachusetts Pr.

Phillips, Kathy J. Manipulating Masculinity: War & Gender in Modern British & American Literature. 2010. (ENG.). 240p. pap. 29.00 (978-0-230-62303-3(4)) Palgrave Macmillan.

Piette, Adam. The Edinburgh Companion to Twentieth-Century British & American War Literature. 2013. (ENG., Illus.). 600p. (gr. 17). 240.00 (978-0-7486-3874-1(1)) Edinburgh Univ. Pr. GBR. Dist: Columbia Univ. Pr.

Plant, Rebecca Jo. Mom: The Transformation of Motherhood in Modern America. (ENG.). 264p. 2012. pap. 17.50 (978-0-226-67022-5(8)) 2010. 37.50 (978-0-226-67020-1(1)) Univ. of Chicago Pr.

Pollack, Harriet & Metress, Christopher, eds. Emmett till in Literary Memory & Imagination. 2008. (Southern Literary Studies). 262p. per. 22.50 (978-0-8071-3281-4(0)) Louisiana State Univ. Pr.

Polley, Jason S. Jane Smiley, Jonathan Franzen, Don Delillo: Narratives of Everyday Justice. 2011. (Modern American Literature: New Approaches Ser.). 272p. (C). 81.95 (978-1-4331-1294-2(9)) Lang, Peter Publishing, Inc.

—Jane Smiley, Jonathan Franzen, Don DeLillo: Narratives of Everyday Justice. 2012. viii, 263p. E-Book (978-1-4539-0191-5(4)) Lang, Peter Publishing, Inc.

Poteet, William Mark. Gay Men in Modern Southern Literature: Ritual, Initiation, & the Construction of Masculinity. 2006. 240p. (C). pap. 31.95 (978-0-8204-8691-8(4)) Lang, Peter Publishing, Inc.

Powell, Tara. The Intellectual in Twentieth-Century Southern Literature. 2012. (Southern Literary Studies). 288p. 42.50 (978-0-8071-3898-4(3)) Louisiana State Univ. Pr.

Pozada-Burga, Mario A. Politica y Literatura en la Obra de Antenor Orrego. 2009. (SPA.). 150p. 99.95 (978-0-7734-4651-9(6)) Mellen, Edwin Pr., The.

Price, Steven. The Plays, Screenplays & Films of David Mamet. Tredell, Nicolas, ed. 2008. (Readers' Guides to Essential Criticism Ser.). (ENG.). 192p. (C). pap. 25.00 (978-0-230-55535-8(7)) Palgrave Macmillan.

Quirk, Thomas. Bergson & American Culture: The Worlds of Willa Cather & Wallace Stevens. 2011. (ENG.). 318p. pap. 40.00 (978-0-8078-9756-0(6)) Univ. of North Carolina Pr.

Rabaka, Reiland. Forms of Fanonism: Frantz Fanon's Critical Theory & the Dialectics of Decolonization. 2011. (ENG.). 420p. pap. 39.95 (978-0-7391-4034-5(5)) Lexington Bks.

Radford, Andrew. Romantic Presences in the Twentieth-Century. Sandy, Mark, ed. 2012. (Nineteenth Century Ser.). 215p. E-Book 99.95 (978-0-7546-6992-0(0)) Ashgate Publishing Co.

Rae, Patricia. Modernism & Mourning. 2006. (Illus.). 312p. 62.50 (978-0-8387-5617-1(4)) Bucknell Univ. Pr.

Rampton, David. William Faulkner: A Literary Life. 2008. (Literary Lives Ser.). (ENG.). 248p. 84.00 (978-1-4039-4680-5(9)) Palgrave Macmillan.

Rand, Ayn. Notes on the History of American Free Enterprise. 2011. 12p. pap. 35.95 (978-1-258-00839-0(4)) Literary Licensing, LLC.

Rattray, Laura, ed. Edith Wharton's the Custom of the Country: A Reassessment, 1 vol. 2010. (Gender & Genre Ser.). (ENG., Illus.). 208p. 99.00 (978-1-85196-224-2(7)) Pickering & Chatto Pubs., Ltd. GBR. Dist: Ashgate Publishing Co.

Redding, Arthur. Turncoats, Traitors, & Fellow Travelers: Culture & Politics of the Early Cold War. 2008. (ENG.). 224p. 50.00 (978-1-60473-005-0(6)) Univ. Pr. of Mississippi.

Regier, Willis Goth. Book of the Sphinx. 2007. (Texts & Contexts Ser.). (ENG., Illus.). 301p. per. 19.95 (978-0-8032-1597-9(5), Bison Bks.) Univ. of Nebraska Pr.

Retman, Sonnet H. Real Folks: Race & Genre in the Great Depression. 2011. (ENG., Illus.). 336p. 89.95 (978-0-8223-4925-9(6)); pap. 24.95 (978-0-8223-4944-0(2)) Duke Univ. Pr.

Reynolds, Guy J. Apostles of Modernity: American Writers in the Age of Development. 2008. (ENG., Illus.). 278p. (C). 50.00 (978-0-8032-1377-7(8)) Univ. of Nebraska Pr.

Ringnalda, Donald. Fighting & Writing the Vietnam War. 2008. (ENG.). 260p. pap. 25.00 (978-1-60473-182-8(6)) Univ. Pr. of Mississippi.

Roberts, Nicholas. Poetry & Loss: The Work of Eugenio Montejo. 2009. (Monografías A Ser.: Volume 280). (Illus.). 244p. 90.00 (978-1-85566-193-6(4), Tamesis Bks.) Boydell & Brewer, Ltd. GBR. Dist: Boydell & Brewer, Inc.

Röckl, Barbara. Through A Glass Darkly: The Mirror Metaphor in Texts by Richard Wright, James Baldwin, & Ralph Ellison. 2009. (Europäische Hochschulschriften. Reihe 14: Angelsächsische Sprache und Literatur Ser.). 290p. pap. 72.95 (978-3-631-59214-4(0)) Lang, Peter GmbH, Europaischer Verlag der Wissenschaften DEU. Dist: Lang, Peter.

Romine, Scott. The Real South: Southern Narrative in the Age of Cultural Reproduction. 2008. (Southern Literary Studies). 284p. 42.50 (978-0-8071-3329-3(9)) Louisiana State Univ. Pr.

Rosen, Alan. Sounds of Defiance: The Holocaust, Multilingualism, & the Problem of English. 2008. (ENG.). 250p. pap. 24.95 (978-0-8032-2068-3(5)) Univ. of Nebraska Pr.

Rosenfeld, Alvin H., ed. The Writer Uprooted: Contemporary Jewish Exile Literature. 2008. (Jewish Literature & Culture Ser.). (ENG.). 272p. 50.00 (978-0-253-35144-9(8), 0253351448); pap. 19.95 (978-0-253-21981-7(7), 0253219817) Indiana Univ. Pr.

Rosenquist, Rod. Modernism, the Market & the Institution of the New. 2009. (ENG.). 220p. 98.00 (978-0-521-51619-8(6)) Cambridge Univ. Pr.

Ross, Patricia. The Spell Cast by Remains: The Myth of Wilderness in Modern American Literature. 2009. 182p. 39.95 (978-0-415-80290-1(3)) Routledge.

Rottenberg, Catherine. Performing Americanness: Race, Class, & Gender in Modern African-American & Jewish-American Literature. 2008. (ENG., Illus.). 192p. 50.00 (978-1-58465-682-1(4)) Univ. Pr. of New England.

Rowe, John Carlos & Haralson, Eric, eds. A Historical Guide to Henry James, 1 vol. 2012. (Historical Guides to American Authors Ser.). (ENG., Illus.). 240p. 99.00 (978-0-19-512135-3(X)); pap. 27.95 (978-0-19-512134-6(1)) Oxford Univ. Pr., Inc.

Russ, Elizabeth Christine. The Plantation in the Postslavery Imagination. 2009. (Imagining the Americas Ser.). (ENG.). 224p. 65.00 (978-0-19-537715-6(X)) Oxford Univ. Pr., Inc.

Ryan, Maureen. The Other Side of Grief: The Home Front & the Aftermath in American Narratives of the Vietnam War. 2008. 368p. (ENG.). pap. 34.95 (978-1-55849-686-6(6)); lib. bdg. 98.00 net. (978-1-55849-685-9(8)) Univ. of Massachusetts Pr.

Ryden, Kent C. Sum of the Parts: The Mathematics & Politics of Region, Place, & Writing. 2011. (American Land & Life Ser.). (ENG., Illus.). 176p. pap. 25.00 (978-1-58729-987-2(9)) Univ. of Iowa Pr.

Saito, Naoko & Standish, Paul, eds. Stanley Cavell & the Education of Grownups. 2012. (American Philosophy Ser.). (ENG.). 288p. 80.00 (978-0-8232-3473-8(8)); pap. 28.00 (978-0-8232-3474-5(6)) Fordham Univ. Pr.

Samuels, Peggy. Deep Skin: Elizabeth Bishop & Visual Art. 2010. (Illus.). 256p. 39.95 (978-0-8014-4826-3(3)) Cornell Univ. Pr.

Samowski, Joe/E. The Literary Achievement of the American Poet Robert Penn Warren: His Life-Long Struggles with Morality, Myth, & Modernity. 2009. iv, 251p. (978-0-7734-3897-2(1)) Mellen, Edwin Pr., The.

Savelson, Kim. Where the World Is Not: Cultural Authority & Democratic Desire in Modern American Literature. 2009. (ENG.). 248p. cd-rom 14.95 (978-0-8142-9189-4(9)) Ohio State Univ. Pr.

Scambray, Kenneth. Queen Calafia's Paradise: California & the Italian American Novel. 2007. 211p. 46.50 (978-0-8386-4117-0(2)) Fairleigh Dickinson Univ. Pr.

Schelling, Felix E. Appraisements & Asperities. 2009. (ENG.). 199p. 30.99 (978-1-117-16539-4(6)); pap. 23.75 (978-1-117-16540-0(X)); pap. 19.99 (978-1-117-16541-7(8), BiblioLife) BiblioBazaar.

Schoenbach, Lisi. Pragmatic Modernism, 1 vol. 2011. (Modernist Literature & Culture Ser.). (ENG.). 224p. 45.00 (978-0-19-538984-5(0)) Oxford Univ. Pr., Inc.

Schreier, Benjamin. The Power of Negative Thinking: Cynicism & the History of Modern American Literature. 2009. (ENG., Illus.). 256p. (gr. 17). 39.50 (978-0-8139-2812-8(5)) Univ. Pr. of Virginia.

Schubert, William Henry. Love, Justice & Education: John Dewey & the Utopians. 2009. (978-1-60752-239-3(X)); pap. (978-1-60752-238-6(1)) Information Age Publishing, Inc.

Schuster, Marc. Practical Ambivalence: Don DeLillo, Jean Baudrillard, & the Consumer Conundrum. 2008. 232p. (C). 99.95 (978-1-60497-504-8(0)) Cambria Pr.

Schwarz, Bill & Kaplan, Cora. James Baldwin: America & Beyond. 2011. (ENG., Illus.). 268p. (C). 80.00 (978-0-472-07152-4(1)); pap. 29.95 (978-0-472-05152-6(0)) Univ. of Michigan Pr.

Scott, Bonnie Kime, ed. Gender & Modernism, 4 vols. 2008. (Critical Concepts in Literary & Cultural Studies). (Illus.). L, 1494p. 1445.00 (978-0-415-38092-8(8)) Routledge.

—Gender in Modernism: New Geographies, Complex Intersections. 2007. (Illus.). 896p. 100.00 (978-0-252-03171-7(7)) Univ. of Illinois Pr.

Seitler, Dana. Atavistic Tendencies: The Culture of Science in American Modernity. 2008. (Illus.). 320p. pap. 22.50 (978-0-8166-5124-5(8)) Univ. of Minnesota Pr.

Seitler, Dana & Seitler. Atavistic Tendencies: The Culture of Science in American Modernity. 2008. (Illus.). 320p. 67.50 (978-0-8166-5123-8(X)) Univ. of Minnesota Pr.

Selzer, Jack & Wess, Robert. Kenneth Burke & His Circles. 2008. (978-1-60235-067-0(1)); 272p. pap. (978-1-60235-066-3(3)) Parlor Pr.

Shaheen, Aaron. Androgynous Democracy: Modern American Literature & the Dual-Sexed Body Politic. 2010. (ENG.). 45.95 (978-1-57233-686-5(2)) Univ. of Tennessee Pr.

Sherman, Stuart. The Main Stream. 2007. (ENG.). 252p. 41.95 (978-0-548-01057-0(9)) Kessinger Publishing, LLC.

Shynnagh, Frank. Song Broken, Song: The Work of Frederic Will. 2008. 248p. 109.95 (978-0-7734-5154-4(4)) Mellen, Edwin Pr., The.

Siklósi, Zsuzsanna. Endurance: The Development of the Individual Through Hardships in The Grapes of Wrath & the Old Man & The Sea. 2008. 68p. pap. (978-3-639-04809-4(1)) VDM Verlag Dr. Mueller e.K.

Silva, Reinaldo Francisco. Portuguese American Literature. 2010. 116p. pap. (978-1-84760-108-7(1)) Troubadour Publishing Ltd.

—Representations of the Portuguese in American Literature. 2008. (Portuguese in the Americas Ser.). 228p. pap. 19.95 (978-1-933227-18-4(4)) Tagus Pr.

Siraganian, Lisa. Modernism's Other Work: The Art Object's Political Life, 1 vol. 2012. (ENG., Illus.). 304p. 65.00 (978-0-19-979655-7(6)) Oxford Univ. Pr., Inc.

Smith, Jeff. The Presidents We Imagine: Two Centuries of White House Fictions on the Page, on the Stage, Onscreen, & Online. 2009. (Studies in American Thought & Culture). (978-0-299-23180-4(1)); (ENG., Illus.). 406p. pap. 26.95 (978-0-299-23184-2(4)) Univ. of Wisconsin Pr.

Smith, Richard G. & Smith, Valerie. Toni Morrison: Writing the Moral Imagination. 2012. (Blackwell Introductions to Literature Ser.). (ENG.). 208p. 74.95 (978-1-4051-6033-9(0), Wiley-Blackwell) Wiley, John & Sons, Inc.

Smith, William Jay. My Friend Tom: The Poet-Playwright Tennessee Williams. 2012. (ENG.). 192p. 28.00 (978-1-61703-175-5(5)) Univ. Pr. of Mississippi.

Sollors, Werner. Ethnic Modernism. 2008. 336p. pap. 21.00 (978-0-674-03091-6(5)) Harvard Univ. Pr.

Spurgeon, Sara. Cormac McCarthy: All the Pretty Horses, No Country for Old Men, the Road. Spurgeon, Sara, ed. 2011. (Continuum Studies in Contemporary North American Fiction Ser.). (ENG.). 226p. 100.00 (978-0-8264-3221-6(2)); pap. 29.95 (978-0-8264-3820-1(2)) Continuum International Publishing Group, Ltd. GBR. Dist: National Bk. Network.

Staub, Michael E. Voices of Persuasion. 2009. (Cambridge Studies in American Literature & Culture Ser.). (ENG.) 192p. pap. 31.00 (978-0-521-11194-2(3)) Cambridge Univ. Pr.

Stecopoulos, Harilaos. Reconstructing the World: Southern Fictions & U. S. Imperialisms, 1898-1976. 2008. (Illus.). 248p. pap. 23.95 (978-0-8014-7502-3(3)) Cornell Univ. Pr.

Stecopoulos, Harilaos & Stecopoulos, Harry. Reconstructing the World: Southern Fictions & U.S. Imperialisms, 1893-1976. 2008. (Illus.). 248p. 76.95 (978-0-8014-4685-6(6)) Cornell Univ. Pr.

Steiner, Dorothea & Danner, Sabine, eds. Exploring Spaces: Practices & Perspectives. 2011. (ENG., Illus.) 296p. pap. 34.95 (978-3-643-50094-6(7)) Lit Verlag DEU. Dist: Transaction Pubs.

Stephenson, Gregory. The Daybreak Boys: Essays on the Literature of the Beat Generation. 2009. (ENG.). 232p. pap. 25.00 (978-0-8093-2949-6(2)) Southern Illinois Univ. Pr.

Stirrup, David. Louise Erdrich. 2011. (Contemporary American & Canadian Novelists Ser.). (ENG.). 224p. 90.00 (978-0-7190-7426-4(6)) Manchester Univ. Pr. GBR. Dist: Macmillan.

Stoltzfus, Ben. Hemingway & French Writers. 2009. 42.00 (978-1-60635-039-3(0)) Kent State Univ. Pr.

Stone-Richards, Michael. Logics of Separation: Exile & Transcendence in Aesthetic Modernity. 2011. (American Studies: Culture, Society & the Arts Ser.). 430p. pap. 77.95 (978-3-03911-008-7(X)) Lang, Peter AG GBR. Dist: Lang, Peter.

Storhoff, Gary & Whalen-Bridge, John, eds. Emergence of Buddhist American Literature. 2010. (SUNY series in Buddhism & American Culture Ser.). 272p. pap. 24.95 (978-1-4384-2654-9(2), Suny Pr.) State Univ. of New York Pr.

Sturgis, Amy H. & Oberhelman, David D., eds. The Intersection of Fantasy & Native America: From H. P. Lovecraft to Leslie Marmon Silko: Edited by Amy H. Sturgis & David D. Oberhelman. 2009. 185p. 23.00 (978-1-887726-12-2(8)) Mythopoeic Pr., The.

Sultan, Stanley. Interpreting Modernis: Writers: Macro History, Personal History, & Manuscript History. 356p. (C). 119.95 (978-0-7734-5108-7(0)) Mellen, Edwin Pr., The.

Surette, Leon. The Modern Dilemma: Wallace Stevens, T. S. Eliot, & Humanism. 2008. (ENG.). 430p. (C). (978-0-7735-3363-9(X)) McGill-Queen's Univ. Pr.

Swiggart, Peter & Faulkner, William. The Art of Faulkner's Novels. 2011. 240p. 46.95 (978-1-258-08539-1(9)) Literary Licensing, LLC.

Swirski, Peter. All Roads Lead to the American City. 2007. (ENG., Illus.). 162p. (gr. 17). 50.00 (978-962-209-862-6(2)) Hong Kong Univ. Pr. HKG. Dist: Columbia Univ. Pr.

—All Roads Lead to the American City. 2007. (ENG., Illus.). 162p. (gr. 17). per. 24.95 (978-962-209-863-3(0)) Hong Kong Univ. Pr. HKG. Dist: Columbia Univ. Pr.

—Ars Americana, Ars Politica: Partisan Expression in Contemporary American Literature & Culture. 2010. (ENG.). 221p. (C). (978-0-7735-3765-1(1)); pap. (978-0-7735-3766-8(X)) McGill-Queen's Univ. Pr.

Taylor, Melanie Benson. Disturbing Calculations: The Economics of Identity in Postcolonial Southern Literature, 1912-2002. 2008. (New Southern Studies Ser.). (ENG.). 280p. pap. 24.95 *(978-0-8203-3112-6(0))*; lib. bdg. 59.95 *(978-0-8203-2972-7(X))* Univ. of Georgia Pr.

Thesing, William B. Reading, Learning, Teaching James Dickey. 2008. (Confronting the Text, Confronting the World Ser.). 176p. (C). 32.95 *(978-0-8204-8177-7(7))* Lang, Peter Publishing, Inc.

Thesing, William B. & Wrede, Theda. The Way We Read James Dickey: Critical Approaches for the Twenty-First Century. 2009. (Illus.). 264p. *(978-1-57003-803-7(1))* Univ. of South Carolina Pr.

Tobias, Linda. Hemingway's Code Hero & the Postmodern Everyman in Fight Club: The Drama of Identity in Hemingway's World & in David Fincher's Fight Club. 2008. 64p. pap. *(978-3-639-10063-1(8))* VDM Verlag Dr. Mueller e.K.

Tokarczyk, Michelle, ed. Critical Approaches to American Working-Class Literature: Critiquing Class. 2011. (Routledge Studies in Twentieth-Century Literature Ser.). (ENG., Illus.). 266p. (C). 125.00 *(978-0-415-88546-1(9))* Routledge.

Tokarczyk, Michelle M. Class Definitions: On the Lives & Writings of Maxine Hong Kingston, Sandra Cisneros, & Dorothy Allison. 2008. (ENG.). 257p. 57.50 *(978-1-57591-121-2(3))* Susquehanna Univ. Pr.

Trefzer, Annette & Abadie, Ann J., eds. Faulkner & Formalism: Returns of the Text. 2012. (Faulkner & Yoknapatawpha Ser.). (ENG.). 240p. 60.00 ***(978-1-61703-256-1(5))*** Univ. Pr. of Mississippi.

Trefzer, Annette & Abadie, Ann J., eds. Faulkner's Sexualities. 2010. (Faulkner & Yoknapatawpha Ser.). (ENG., Illus.). 224p. 65.00 *(978-1-60473-560-4(0))* Univ. Pr. of Mississippi.

Trout, Steven. Memorial Fictions: Willa Cather & the First World War. 2008. (ENG.). 225p. pap. 19.95 *(978-0-8032-1837-6(0))* Univ. of Nebraska Pr.

Tully, David. Terry Southern & the American Grotesque. 2010. (ENG., Illus.). 232p. pap. 35.00 *(978-0-7864-4450-2(9))* McFarland & Co., Inc. Pubs.

Tuttle, Jennifer S. Charlotte Perkins Gilman: New Texts, New Contexts. Kessler, Carol Farley, ed. 2011. cd-rom 14.95 *(978-0-8142-9243-3(7))* Ohio State Univ. Pr.

Tuttle, Jennifer S. & Kessler, Carol Farley, intros. Charlotte Perkins Gilman: New Texts, New Contexts. 2011. 288p. 44.95 *(978-0-8142-1144-1(5))* Ohio State Univ. Pr.

Tuttleton, James W., et al, eds. Edith Wharton: The Contemporary Reviews. 2010. (American Critical Archives Ser.). (ENG.). 588p. (C). pap. 57.00 *(978-0-521-12678-6(9))* Cambridge Univ. Pr.

Urquijo-Ruiz, Rita E. Wild Tongues: Transnational Mexican Popular Culture. 2012. (ENG., Illus.). 236p. 55.00 ***(978-0-292-72384-9(9))*** Univ. of Texas Pr.

Usandizaga, Aranzazu & Monnickendam, Andrew, eds. Back to Peace: Reconciliation & Retribution in the Postwar Period. 2007. 320p. per. 35.00 *(978-0-268-04452-7(X))* Univ. of Notre Dame Pr.

Vannatta, Seth, ed. Chuck Klosterman & Philosophy. 2012. (Popular Culture & Philosophy Ser.). (ENG.). 288p. pap. 19.95 ***(978-0-8126-9762-9(6))*** Open Court Publishing Co.

Vest, Jason & Vest, Jason P. The Postmodern Humanism of Philip K. Dick. 2009. (ENG.). 248p. pap. 60.00 *(978-0-8108-6212-8(3))* Scarecrow Pr., Inc.

Vetter, Lara. Modernist Writings & Religio-Scientific Discourse: H. D., Loy, & Toomer. 2010. (Modern & Contemporary Poetry & Poetics Ser.). (ENG., Illus.). 236p. 84.00 *(978-0-230-62122-0(8))* Palgrave Macmillan.

Vials, Chris. Realism for the Masses: Aesthetics, Popular Front Pluralism, & U. S. Culture, 1935-1947. 2009. (ENG.). 288p. 50.00 *(978-1-60473-123-1(0))* Univ. Pr. of Mississippi.

Vinciguerra, Thomas & Gibbs, Wolcott. Backward Ran Sentences: The Best of Wolcott Gibbs from the New Yorker. 2011. (ENG.). 688p. pap. 22.00 *(978-1-60819-550-3(3))* Bloomsbury Publishing.

Wachtell, Cynthia. War No More: The Antiwar Impulse in American Literature, 1861-1914. 2012. 248p. pap. 18.95 ***(978-0-8071-4564-7(5))*** 2010. 240p. 35.00 *(978-0-8071-3562-4(3))* Louisiana State Univ. Pr.

Wald, Alan M. Trinity of Passion: The Literary Left & the Antifascist Crusade. 2007. (ENG., Illus.). 344p. 38.95 *(978-0-8078-3075-8(5))* Univ. of North Carolina Pr.

Waldmeir, John C. Cathedrals of Bone: The Role of the Body in Contemporary Catholic Literature. 3rd ed. 2009. (ENG.). 224p. 55.00 *(978-0-8232-3060-0(0))* Fordham Univ. Pr.

Wallace-Sanders, Kimberly Gisele. Mammy: A Century of Race, Gender, & Southern Memory. 2009. (ENG., Illus.). 224p. (C). pap. 26.95 *(978-0-472-03401-7(4))* Univ. of Michigan Pr.

Wallhead, Celia M., ed. Writers of the Spanish Civil War: The Testimony of Their Auto/Biographies. 2011. (Spanish Perspectives on English & American Literature, Communication & Culture Ser.). 331p. pap. ***(978-3-0343-0696-6(2))*** Lang, Peter.

Walonen, Michael K. Writing Tangier in the Postcolonial Transition: Space & Power in Expatriate & North African Literature. 2011. (Illus.). 176p. 99.95 ***(978-1-4094-3381-1(1))*** Ashgate Publishing Co.

Walter, Roland. Narrative Identities: (Inter) Cultural In-Betweenness in the Americas. 395p. pap. 55.95 *(978-3-906770-79-6(6))* Lang, Peter CHE. Dist: Lang, Peter Publishing, Inc.

Ward, Robert. Understanding James Leo Herlihy. 2012. (Understanding Contemporary American Literature Ser.). (ENG.). 128p. 39.95 ***(978-1-61117-074-0(5))*** Univ. of South Carolina Pr.

Webster, Patrick. Love & Death in Kubrick: A Critical Study of the Films from Lolita through Eyes Wide Shut. 2010. (ENG., Illus.). 334p. pap. 45.00 *(978-0-7864-5916-2(6))* McFarland & Co., Inc. Pubs.

Wells, Jeremy. Romances of the White Man's Burden: Race, Empire, & the Plantation in American Literature, 1880-1936. 2011. (ENG., Illus.). 264p. 55.00 *(978-0-8265-1756-2(0))* Vanderbilt Univ. Pr.

Wernblad, Annette. The Passion of Martin Scorsese: A Critical Study of the Films. 2010. (ENG., Illus.). 267p. pap. 45.00 *(978-0-7864-4946-0(2))* McFarland & Co., Inc. Pubs.

Whalen-Bridge, John & Storhoff, Gary, eds. The Emergence of Buddhist American Literature. 2009. (SUNY series in Buddhism & American Culture Ser.). 272p. 80.00 *(978-1-4384-2653-2(4))* State Univ. of New York Pr.

Whalen, Tom. The Birth of Death & Other Comedies: The Novels of Russell H. Greenan. 2011. (Scholarly Ser.). (ENG.). 200p. pap. 23.95 *(978-1-56478-640-1(4)*, 478640) Dalkey Archive Pr.

Whedonistas: A Celebration of the Worlds of Joss Whedon by the Women Who Love Them. 2011. pap. 14.95 *(978-1-935234-10-4(2))* Mad Norwegian Pr.

Whitt, Jan. Settling the Borderline: Other Voices in Literary Journalism. 2008. (ENG.). 164p. pap. 35.99 *(978-0-7618-4093-0(1))* Univ. Pr. of America, Inc.

Whitted, Qiana J. A God of Justice? The Problem of Evil in Twentieth-Century Black Literature. 2009. (ENG.). 240p. (C). (gr. 13-17). pap. 21.50 *(978-0-8139-2797-8(8))*; (gr. 17). 55.00 *(978-0-8139-2796-1(X))* Univ. Pr. of Virginia.

Widiss, Benjamin Leigh. Obscure Invitations: The Persistence of the Author in Twentieth-Century American Literature. 2011. (ENG.). 224p. 65.00 *(978-0-8047-7322-5(X))*; pap. 21.95 *(978-0-8047-7323-2(8))* Stanford Univ. Pr.

Wiest, Andrew & Doidge, Michael, eds. Triumph Revisited: Historians Battle for the Vietnam War. 2010. (ENG.). 256p. 125.00 *(978-0-415-80020-4(X))*; pap. 36.95 *(978-0-415-80021-1(8))* Routledge.

Williams, Tennessee. The Glass Menagerie. Bloom, Harold, ed. 2007. (Bloom's Guides). 120p. (YA). (gr. 9-12). lib. bdg. 30.00 *(978-0-7910-9297-2(6))* Facts On File, Inc.

Wilson, Andrew. Norman Mailer: An American Aesthetic. 2008. 272p. pap. 66.95 *(978-3-03911-406-1(9))* Lang, Peter AG GBR. Dist: Lang, Peter.

Wilson, Christopher P. White Collar Fictions: Class & Social Representation in American Literature, 1885-1925. 2010. (ENG.). 340p. pap. 24.95 *(978-0-8203-3697-8(1))* Univ. of Georgia Pr.

Wilson, Edmund. Edmund Wilson - Literary Essays & Reviews of the 1920s & 30s: The Shores of Light/Axel's Castle/Uncollected Reviews. Dabney, Lewis M., ed. 2007. (ENG.). 1025p. (gr. 12). 40.00 *(978-1-59853-013-1(5))* Library of America, The.

Wilson, Edmund & Wilson, Edmund. Edmund Wilson: Literary Essays & Reviews of the 1930s & 1940s. Dabney, Lewis M., ed. 2007. (ENG.). 1000p. (gr. 12). 40.00 *(978-1-59853-014-8(3))* Library of America, The.

Wilson, Sarah. Melting-Pot Modernism. 2010. (Illus.). 264p. 45.00 *(978-0-8014-4816-4(6))* Cornell Univ. Pr.

Winspur, Steven. La Poésie du Lieu: Segalen, Thoreau, Guillevic, Ponge. 2006. (Chiasma Ser.: 20). (FRE.). 179p. pap. 47.00 *(978-90-420-2103-7(9))* Rodopi.

Wolf, Felix. The Art of Navigation: Travels with Carlos Castaneda & Beyond. 2010. (ENG.). 324p. pap. 20.00 *(978-0-9822900-1-9(2))* Millichap Bks., LLC.

Wolitz, Seth L., ed. The Hidden Isaac Bashevis Singer. 2011. (ENG., Illus.). 280p. pap. 25.00 *(978-0-292-72868-4(9))* Univ. of Texas Pr.

Worthington, Leslie Harper. Cormac McCarthy & the Ghost of Huck Finn. 2012. (ENG.). 223p. pap. 40.00 ***(978-0-7864-6641-2(3))*** McFarland & Co., Inc. Pubs.

Wright, Susan Prothro & Glass, Ernestine Pickens, eds. Passing in the Works of Charles W. Chesnutt. 2010. (Margaret Walker Alexander Series in African American Studies). (ENG.). 160p. 50.00 *(978-1-60473-416-4(7))* Univ. Pr. of Mississippi.

Yannella, Philip R. American Literature in Context after 1929. 2010. (ENG.). 168p. 94.95 *(978-1-4051-8599-8(6))*; pap. 24.95 *(978-1-4051-8600-1(3))* Wiley, John & Sons, Inc. (Wiley-Blackwell).

—American Literature in Context From, 1865-1929. 2010. (ENG.). 168p. 94.95 *(978-1-4051-6781-9(5))*; pap. 24.95 *(978-1-4051-6780-2(7))* Wiley, John & Sons, Inc. (Wiley-Blackwell).

Yavarian, Reza. De-Mythologising Popular American Myths: Critical Reading of David Mamet's Plays. 2010. 228p. pap. 14.49 *(978-1-4490-3616-4(3))* AuthorHouse.

Zamir, Shamoon, ed. The Cambridge Companion to W. E. B. du Bois. 2008. (Cambridge Companions to American Studies). (ENG.). 192p. (C). 81.00 *(978-0-521-87151-8(4))* Cambridge Univ. Pr.

—The Cambridge Companion to W.E.B. Du Bois. 2008. (Cambridge Companions to American Studies). (ENG.). 192p. (C). pap. 25.99 *(978-0-521-69205-2(9))* Cambridge Univ. Pr. GBR. Dist: Cambridge Univ. Pr.

Zhanial, Susanne. Monsters on the Margin - the Abject in Literature. 2009. 188p. pap. *(978-3-639-14798-8(7))* VDM Verlag Dr. Mueller e.K.

Zwagerman, Sean. Wits End: Women's Humor as Rhetorical & Performative Strategy. 2010. (Pitt Comp Literacy Culture Ser.). (ENG.). 264p. pap. 24.95 *(978-0-8229-6074-4(5))* Univ. of Pittsburgh Pr.

AMERICAN LITERATURE—HISTORY AND CRITICISM—21ST CENTURY

Allen, William Rodney. Understanding Kurt Vonnegut. 2009. (Understanding Contemporary American Literature Ser.). 208p. pap. 21.95 *(978-1-57003-886-0(4))* Univ. of South Carolina Pr.

Augustyn, Adam, ed. American Literature from 1945 Through Today. 2010. (Britannica Guide to World Literature Ser.). 240p. (YA). (ENG.). lib. bdg. 45.00 *(978-1-61530-133-1(X))*; (Illus.). 90.00 *(978-1-61530-237-6(9))* Rosen Publishing Group, Inc., The.

Beers, Terry & Elrod, Emily. Califauna: A Literary Field Guide. 2007. (California Legacy Ser.). (Illus.). 293p. per. *(978-1-59714-049-2(X))* Santa Clara Univ., de Saisset Museum.

Blackstone, Charles & Talbot, Jill, eds. The Art of Friction: Where (Non) Fictions Come Together. 2008. (ENG.). 242p. 60.00 *(978-0-292-71879-1(9))* Univ. of Texas Pr.

—The Art of Friction: Where (Non)Fictions Come Together. 2008. (ENG.). 242p. pap. 24.95 *(978-0-292-71891-3(8))* Univ. of Texas Pr.

Bradbury, Malcolm. Saul Bellow (Routledge Revivals) 2010. (ENG.). 110p. pap. 39.95 *(978-0-415-56802-9(1))* Routledge.

Bryfonski, Dedria. Mental Illness in Ken Kesey's One Flew over the Cuckoo's Nest. 2010. (Social Issues in Literature Ser.). (ENG., Illus.). 224p. 38.45 *(978-0-7377-5018-8(9))*; 218p. pap. 26.50 *(978-0-7377-5019-5(7))* Cengage Gale. (Greenhaven Pr., Inc.).

Callahan, Cynthia. Kin of Another Kind: Transracial Adoption in American Literature. 2010. (ENG.). 200p. 70.00 *(978-0-472-11758-1(0))* Univ. of Michigan Pr.

Cant, John. Cormac McCarthy & the Myth of American Exceptionalism. 2009. 368p. pap. 39.95 *(978-0-415-87567-7(6))* Routledge.

Cash, Jean W. & Perry, Keith, eds. Larry Brown & the Blue-Collar South. 2008. (ENG.). 240p. 50.00 *(978-1-934110-75-1(2))* Univ. Pr. of Mississippi.

Coleman, James W. Writing Blackness: John Edgar Wideman's Art & Experimentation. 2010. 216p. 37.50 *(978-0-8071-3644-7(1))* Louisiana State Univ. Pr.

Dalleo, Raphael & Machado Sáez, Elena. The Latino - A Canon & the Emergence of Post-Sixties Literature. annot. ed. 2007. (ENG.). 216p. 84.00 *(978-1-4039-7796-0(8))* Palgrave Macmillan.

Dana, Robert. Paris on the Flats: Versions of a Literary Life. 2010. *(978-1-59732-072-6(2))*; pap. *(978-1-59732-073-3(0))* Univ. of Tampa Pr.

Davidson, Guy. Queer Commodities: Contemporary US Fiction, Consumer Capitalism, & Gay & Lesbian Subcultures. 2012. (American Literature Readings in the Twenty-First Century Ser.). (ENG., Illus.). 208p. 85.00 ***(978-0-230-34049-7(0))*** Palgrave Macmillan.

Davidson, Marianne, et al. Critical Perspectives on Bell Hooks. 2009. (Critical Social Thought Ser.). (ENG.). 242p. pap. 41.95 *(978-0-415-98981-7(7))* Routledge.

Duong, Lan P. Treacherous Subjects: Gender, Culture, & Trans-Vietnamese Feminism. 2012. (Asian American History & Cultu Ser.). (ENG., Illus.). 264p. 78.50 ***(978-1-4399-0177-9(5))***; pap. 26.95 ***(978-1-4399-0178-6(3))*** Temple Univ. Pr.

Eagleton, Terry. Reason, Faith, & Revolution: Reflections on the God Debate. 2010. (Terry Lectures Ser.). (ENG.). 200p. pap. 16.00 *(978-0-300-16453-4(X))* Yale Univ. Pr.

Edwards, Jason. Eve Kosofsky Sedgwick. 2008. XVI, 184p. 22.95 *(978-0-415-35845-3(0))*; 95.00 *(978-0-415-35844-6(2))* Routledge.

Elam, Michele. The Souls of Mixed Folk: Race, Politics, & Aesthetics in the New Millennium. 2011. (ENG., Illus.). 308p. 75.00 *(978-0-8047-5629-7(5))*; pap. 24.95 *(978-0-8047-5630-3(9))* Stanford Univ. Pr.

Fawcett, Brian & Persky, Stan. Robin Blaser. 2010. (ENG., Illus.). 128p. pap. 16.00 *(978-1-55420-052-8(0))* New Star Bks., Ltd. CAN. Dist: SPD-Small Pr. Distribution.

Gale. Contemporary Literary Criticism: Excerpts from Criticism of the Works of Today's Novelists, Poets, Playwrights, Short Story Writers, Scriptwriters, & Other Creative Writers. 2012. (Contemporary Literary Criticism Ser.). (ENG.). 592p. lib. bdg. 328.00 ***(978-1-4144-7089-4(4))***; lib. bdg. 328.00 ***(978-1-4144-7090-0(8))*** Cengage Gale.

Gannon, Thomas C. Skylark Meets Meadowlark: Reimagining the Bird in British Romantic & Contemporary Native American Literature. 2009. (ENG.). 436p. 50.00 *(978-0-8032-2057-7(X))* Univ. of Nebraska Pr.

Geis, Deborah R. Suzan-Lori Parks. 2008. (Michigan Modern Dramatists Ser.). (ENG., Illus.). 184p. (C). pap. 19.95 *(978-0-472-06946-0(2))*; 59.50 *(978-0-472-09946-7(9))* Univ. of Michigan Pr.

Gilb, Dagoberto. Hecho en Tejas: An Anthology of Texas-Mexican Literature. 2006. (Southwestern Writers Collection). (ENG & SPA., Illus.). 544p. 39.95 *(978-0-8263-4125-9(X))* Univ. of New Mexico Pr.

Giles, Paul. Transnationalism in Practice: Essays on American Studies, Literature & Religion. 2011. (Edinburgh Critical Studies in Transatlantic Literature Ser.). (ENG., Illus.). 336p. (gr. 17). 120.00 *(978-0-7486-4049-2(5))* Edinburgh Univ. Pr. GBR. Dist: Columbia Univ. Pr.

Graham, Don, ed. Literary Austin. 2007. (ENG.). 448p. 29.50 *(978-0-87565-342-6(1))* Texas Christian Univ. Pr.

Hamilton, Caroline. One Man Zeitgeist: Dave Eggers, Publishing & Publicity. 2010. (ENG.). 144p. 110.00 *(978-1-4411-6696-8(3))* Continuum International Publishing Group, Ltd. GBR. Dist: National Bk. Network.

Hamilton, Caroline D. One Man Zeitgeist: Dave Eggers, Publishing & Publicity. 2012. (ENG.). 144p. pap. 34.95 ***(978-1-4411-1737-3(7))*** Continuum International Publishing Group, Ltd. GBR. Dist: National Bk. Network.

Hampton, Gregory Jerome. Changing Bodies in the Fiction of Octavia Butler: Slaves, Aliens, & Vampires. 2010. xxvii, 157p. E-Book *(978-0-7391-3789-5(1))* Lexington Bks.

Hawkins, Ty. Reading Vietnam amid the War on Terror. 2012. (American Literature Readings in the Twenty-First Century Ser.). (ENG., Illus.). 224p. 85.00 ***(978-0-230-34002-2(4))*** Palgrave Macmillan.

Heredia, Juanita. Transnational Latina Narratives in the Twenty-First Century: The Politics of Gender, Race, & Migrations. 2009. (ENG.). 192p. 84.00 *(978-0-230-61737-7(9))* Palgrave Macmillan.

Huehls, Mitchum. Qualified Hope: A Postmodern Politics of Time. 2009. *(978-0-8142-0617-1(4))*; (ENG.). cd-rom 14.95 *(978-0-8142-9184-9(8))* Ohio State Univ. Pr.

Iskandar, Adel & Rustom, Hakem, eds. Edward Said: A Legacy of Emancipation & Representation. 2010. (ENG.). 568p. 65.00 *(978-0-520-24546-4(6))*; pap. 29.95 *(978-0-520-25890-7(8))* Univ. of California Pr.

Julavits, Heidi, et al, eds. Read Hard: Five Years of Great Writing from the Believer. 2009. (ENG., Illus.). 336p. pap. 18.00 *(978-1-934781-39-5(8))* McSweeney's Publishing.

Keniston, Ann & Quinn, Jeanne Follansbee, eds. Literature After 9/11. 2010. (Illus.). 314p. pap. 39.95 *(978-0-415-88398-6(9))* Routledge.

Kilicci, Esra. J D Salinger's Characters As Existential Heroes. 2010. 116p. pap. *(978-3-639-26830-0(X))* VDM Verlag Dr. Mueller e.K.

Kocela, Christopher. Fetishism & Its Discontents in Post-1960 American Fiction. 2010. (American Literature Readings in the Twenty-First Century Ser.). (ENG.). 288p. 84.00 *(978-0-230-10290-3(5))* Palgrave Macmillan.

Laszlo, Ervin. Thomas Berry, Dreamer of the Earth. 2011. (ENG.). 1p. pap. 14.95 *(978-1-59477-395-2(5))* Inner Traditions International, Ltd.

Li, Stephanie. Signifying Without Specifying: Racial Discourse in the Age of Obama. 2011. (ENG.). 208p. 72.00 *(978-0-8135-5143-2(9))*; (Illus.). 218p. (C). pap. 24.95 *(978-0-8135-5144-9(7))* Rutgers Univ. Pr.

Lough, James & Herron, Patricia, eds. Spheres of Awareness: A Wilberian Integral Approach to Literature, Philosophy, Psychology, & Art. 2009. (ENG.). 208p. pap. 33.99 *(978-0-7618-4804-2(5))* Univ. Pr. of America, Inc.

Madsen, Deborah. Understanding Gerald Vizenor. 2009. (Understanding Contemporary American Literature Ser.). 216p. 39.95 *(978-1-57003-856-3(2))* Univ. of South Carolina Pr.

Manzanas, Ana M. & Benito Sanchez, Jesús. Cities, Borders & Spaces in Intercultural American Literature & Film. 2011. (Routledge Transnational Perspectives on American Literature Ser.). (ENG.). 176p. (C). 125.00 *(978-0-415-88721-2(6))* Routledge.

McCarthy, Shaun & Weatherall, Jeanette. The Crucible. 2011. (Philip Allan Literature Guide for A-Level Ser.). 92p. (gr. 10-12). 19.95 ***(978-1-4441-2142-1(1))*** Trans-Atlantic Pubns., Inc.

McHaney, Pearl Amelia, ed. Eudora Welty: The Contemporary Reviews. 2010. (American Critical Archives Ser.). (ENG., Illus.). 422p. pap. 42.00 *(978-0-521-15377-5(8))* Cambridge Univ. Pr.

Michaels, Walter Benn. The Shape of the Signifier: 1967 to the End of History. 2006. (ENG., Illus.). 232p. (C). per. 21.95 *(978-0-691-12618-0(6))* Princeton Univ. Pr.

Morgan, Michael. George Gerbner: A Critical Introduction to Media & Communication Theory. (Illus.). viii, 176p. 2012. E-Book ***(978-1-4539-0189-2(2))*** 2011. (C). pap. 129.95 ***(978-1-4331-1701-5(0))*** 2011. (C). pap. 34.95 ***(978-1-4331-0987-4(5))*** Lang, Peter Publishing, Inc.

Murphy, Brenda, ed. Arthur Miller. 2010. (Critical Insights Ser.). 350p. 85.00 *(978-1-58765-697-2(3))* Salem Pr., Inc.

Oboum, Megan. Reconstituting Americans: Liberal Multiculturalism & Identity Difference in Post-1960s Literature. 2011. (ENG.). 224p. 85.00 *(978-0-230-11247-6(1))* Palgrave Macmillan.

Pollack, Harriet & Metress, Christopher, eds. Emmett till in Literary Memory & Imagination. 2008. (Southern Literary Studies). 262p. per. 22.50 *(978-0-8071-3281-4(0))* Louisiana State Univ. Pr.

Polley, Jason S. Jane Smiley, Jonathan Franzen, Don Delillo: Narratives of Everyday Justice. 2011. (Modern American Literature: New Approaches Ser.). 272p. (C). 81.95 ***(978-1-4331-1294-2(9))*** Lang, Peter Publishing, Inc.

—Jane Smiley, Jonathan Franzen, Don DeLillo: Narratives of Everyday Justice. 2012. viii, 263p. E-Book ***(978-1-4539-0191-5(4))*** Lang, Peter Publishing, Inc.

Randall, Martin. 9/11 & the Literature of Terror. 2011. (ENG.). 224p. (gr. 17). 100.00 *(978-0-7486-3852-9(0))* Edinburgh Univ. Pr. GBR. Dist: Columbia Univ. Pr.

Rottenberg, Catherine. Performing Americanness: Race, Class, & Gender in Modern African-American & Jewish-American Literature. 2008. (ENG., Illus.). 192p. 50.00 *(978-1-58465-682-1(4))* Univ. Pr. of New England.

Salaita, Steven. Arab American Literary Fictions, Cultures, & Politics. 2006. (ENG.). 208p. 84.00 *(978-1-4039-7620-8(1))* Palgrave Macmillan.

Silverberg, Robert. Musings & Meditations: Essays & Thoughts. 2010. (ENG.). 416p. pap. 18.95 *(978-1-933065-20-5(6))* Nonstop Pr.

Spaeth, George L. Family Voices. 2011. 588p. 34.99 ***(978-1-4535-4539-3(5))***; pap. 23.99 ***(978-1-4535-4538-6(7))*** Xlibris Corp.

Theroux, Alexander. The Strange Case of Edward Gorey. 2011. (ENG., Illus.). 168p. 19.99 *(978-1-60699-384-2(4)*, 699384) Fantagraphics Bks.

Thompson, Jeff. House of Dan Curtis: The Television Mysteries of the Dark Shadows Auteur. 2010. 204p. 35.00 *(978-1-935271-60-4(1))* Published by Westview, Inc.

Trupe, Alice. Reading Julia Alvarez, 1 vol. 2011. (Pop Lit Book Club Ser.). 181p. 35.00 *(978-0-313-38395-3(2)*, A2880C); E-Book *(978-0-313-38396-0(0))* Libraries Unlimited, Inc.

Walker Bergström, Catharine. Intuition of an Infinite Obligation: Narrative Ethics & Postmodern Gnostics in the Fiction of E. L. Doctorow. 2010. (Anglo-amerikanische Studien - Anglo-American Studies). 190p. 61.95 *(978-3-631-58749-2(X))* Lang, Peter GmbH, Europaischer Verlag der Wissenschaften DEU. Dist: Lang, Peter.

Walsh, J. Christopher. In the Wake of the Sun: Navigating the Southern Works of Cormac Mccarthy. 2010. (ENG.). pap. 22.95 *(978-0-9797292-7-0(0))* Univ. of Tennessee, Libraries of Newfound Pr.

AMERICAN LITERATURE—INDIAN AUTHORS

Bellin, Joshua David & Mielke, Laura L., eds. Native Acts: Indian Performance, 1603-1832. 2012. (ENG.). 344p. pap. 35.00 *(978-0-8032-2632-6(2))* Univ. of Nebraska Pr.

Brehm, Victoria, ed. Star Songs & Water Spirits: A Great Lakes Native Reader. 2010. (ENG., Illus.). 425p. pap. 27.95 *(978-0-9843340-0-1(9))* Lady Slipper Pr.

Driskill, Qwo-Li, et al, eds. Sovereign Erotics: A Collection of Two-Spirit Literature. 2011. (First Peoples: New Directions in Indigenous Studies). (ENG.). 248p. pap. 26.95 *(978-0-8165-0242-4(0))* Univ. of Arizona Pr.

Gansworth, Eric. Sovereign Bones: New Native American Writing. 2007. (New Native American Writing Ser.). (ENG.). 352p. per. 17.95 *(978-1-56858-357-0(5)*, Nation Bks.) Basic Bks.

Hobson, Geary, et al, eds. The People Who Stayed: Southeastern Indian Writing after Removal. 2010. (ENG.). 404p. (C). pap. 24.95 *(978-0-8061-4136-7(0))* Univ. of Oklahoma Pr.

Howe, Craig Phillip, et al. He Sapa Woihanble: Black Hills Dream. 2011.Tr. of Black Hills Dream. (DAK., Illus.). pap. 20.00 ***(978-0-9721886-9-2(X))*** Living Justice Pr.

Martinez, David. Dakota Philosopher: Charles Eastman & American Indian Thought. 2009. (ENG., Illus.). 224p. pap. 19.95 *(978-0-87351-629-7(X))* Minnesota Historical Society Pr.

Mathews, John Joseph. Twenty Thousand Mornings: An Autobiography. Kalter, Susan, ed. 2012. (American Indian Literature & Critical Studies Ser.). (ENG., Illus.). 352p. 29.95 ***(978-0-8061-4253-1(7))*** Univ. of Oklahoma Pr.

McLaughlin, Timothy P., ed. Walking on Earth & Touching the Sky: Poetry & Prose by Lakota Youth at Red Cloud Indian School. 2012. (ENG., Illus.). 80p. (J). (gr. 3-9). 19.95 ***(978-1-4197-0179-5(7)***, Abrams Bks. for Young Readers) Abrams.

Miller, Susan A. & Riding In, James. Native Historians Write Back: Decolonizing American Indian History. 2011. 384p. 65.00 ***(978-0-89672-732-8(7))***; pap. 45.00 ***(978-0-89672-699-4(1))*** Texas Tech Univ. Pr.

Native American Rights Fund, Native American Rights Fund. Visions for the Future: Volume 1: A Celebration of Young Native American Artists. Native American Rights Fund (Narf), ed. 2007. (ENG., Illus.). 96p. pap. 16.95 *(978-1-55591-655-8(4))* Fulcrum Publishing.

Peyer, Bernd C. The Thinking Indian: Native American Writers, 1850S-1920S. 2007. 384p. pap. 65.95 *(978-0-8204-8766-3(X))* Lang, Peter Publishing, Inc.

Ramsey, Jarold & Burlingame, Lori, eds. In Beauty I Walk: The Literary Roots of Modern Native American Writing. 2008. (ENG.). 395p. (C). pap. 29.95 *(978-0-8263-4369-7(4))* Univ. of New Mexico Pr.

Tigerman, Kathleen, ed. Wisconsin Indian Literature: Anthology of Native Voices. 2006. (Illus.). 426p. per. 26.95 *(978-0-299-22064-8(8))* Univ. of Wisconsin Pr.

Tillet, Rebecca. Contemporary Native American Literature. 2008. (BAAS Paperbacks Ser.). (ENG.). 184p. (gr. 17). pap. 34.00 *(978-0-7486-2149-1(0))* Edinburgh Univ. Pr. GBR. Dist: Columbia Univ. Pr.

Treuer, Anton & Eagle, Melvin. Oshkaabewis Native Journal. 2011. 170p. pap. 14.95 ***(978-1-257-02280-9(6))*** Lulu Enterprises Inc.

Treuer, Anton & Gibbs, Anne. Oshkaabewis Native Journal. 2011. 186p. pap. 14.95 ***(978-1-257-10875-6(1))*** Lulu Enterprises Inc.

Treuer, Anton & Mosay, Archie. Oshkaabewis Native Journal. 2011. 136p. pap. 14.95 ***(978-1-257-02254-0(7))*** Lulu Enterprises Inc.

Treuer, Anton & Stillday, Thomas. Oshkaabewis Native Journal. 2011. 196p. pap. 14.95 ***(978-1-4583-6299-5(X))*** Lulu Enterprises Inc.

Treuer, Anton, et al. Oshkaabewis Native Journal. 2011. 210p. pap. 14.95 ***(978-1-257-02261-8(X))***; 154p. pap. 14.95 ***(978-1-257-02200-7(8))***; 148p. pap. 14.95 ***(978-1-257-01072-1(7))***; 108p. pap. 14.95 ***(978-1-257-01015-8(8))***; 176p. pap. 14.95 ***(978-1-257-02266-3(0))***; 202p. pap. 14.95 ***(978-1-257-01026-4(3))*** Lulu Enterprises Inc.

Zenko, Darren. Native Ghost Stories. rev. ed. 2006. (ENG., Illus.). 216p. pap. *(978-1-894877-76-3(4))* Ghost Hse. Bks CAN. Dist: Lone Pine Publishing.

AMERICAN LITERATURE—INDIAN AUTHORS—HISTORY AND CRITICISM

Acoose, Janice, et al, contrib. by. Reasoning Together: The Native Critics Collective. 2008. (ENG.). 448p. (C). per. 24.95 *(978-0-8061-3887-9(4))* Univ. of Oklahoma Pr.

Bartelt, Guillermo. N. Scott Momaday's Native American Ideology in House Made of Dawn (1968) Stylolinguistic Analyses of Defamiliarization in Contemporary American Indian Literature. 2010. 140p. 99.95 *(978-0-7734-1419-8(3))* Mellen, Edwin Pr., The.

Benson Taylor, Melanie. Reconstructing the Native South: American Indian Literature & the Lost Cause. 2012. (New Southern Studies). (ENG.). 248p. 59.95 ***(978-0-8203-3884-2(2))***; pap. 24.95 ***(978-0-8203-4066-1(9))*** Univ. of Georgia Pr.

Bloom, Harold. Native American Writers. 2nd rev. ed. 2010. (Bloom's Modern Critical Views Ser.). 292p. (C). (gr. 9-18). 45.00 *(978-1-60413-591-6(3)*, Chelsea Hse.) Facts On File, Inc.

Bringhurst, Robert. The Tree of Meaning: Language, Mind & Ecology. 2007. (ENG., Illus.). 336p. 28.00 *(978-1-59376-179-0(1))* Counterpoint LLC.

Carpenter, Cari M. Seeing Red: Anger, Sentimentality, & American Indians. 2008. (ENG., Illus.). 208p. 49.95 *(978-0-8142-1079-6(1))*; xiv, 177p. cd-rom 14.95 *(978-0-8142-9158-0(9))* Ohio State Univ. Pr.

Christie, Stuart. Plural Sovereignties & Contemporary Indigenous Literature. 2009. (ENG., Illus.). 296p. 100.00 *(978-0-230-61342-3(X))* Palgrave Macmillan.

Coulombe, Joseph L. An Introduction to Native American Literature. 2011. (ENG.). 200p. 120.00 *(978-0-415-57942-1(2))*; pap. 29.95 *(978-0-415-57943-8(0))* Routledge.

Dennis, Helen May. Native American Literature. 2009. 236p. pap. 34.00 *(978-0-415-54416-0(5))* Routledge.

—Native American Literature: Towards a Spatialized Reading. annot. ed. 2006. (Routledge Transnational Perspectives on American Literature Ser.). (ENG.). 256p. (C). 161.00 *(978-0-415-39702-5(2))* Routledge.

Donohue, Betty Booth. Bradford's Indian Book: Being the True Roote & Rise of American Letters as Revealed by the Native Text Embedded in of Plimoth Plantation. 2011. (ENG., Illus.). 176p. 69.95 *(978-0-8130-3737-0(9))* Univ. Pr. of Florida.

Flint, Kate & Flint, K. The Transatlantic Indian, 1776-1930. 2008. (ENG., Illus.). 394p. (C). 45.00 *(978-0-691-13120-7(1))* Princeton Univ. Pr.

Fulford, Tim & Hutchings, Kevin, eds. Native Americans & Anglo-American Culture, 1750-1850: The Indian Atlantic. 2009. (ENG., Illus.). 276p. 99.00 *(978-0-521-88848-6(4))* Cambridge Univ. Pr.

Gannon, Thomas C. Skylark Meets Meadowlark: Reimagining the Bird in British Romantic & Contemporary Native American Literature. 2009. (ENG.). 436p. 50.00 *(978-0-8032-2057-7(X))* Univ. of Nebraska Pr.

Henry, Gordon, et al. Stories Through Theories/Theories Through Stories: North American Indian Writing, Storytelling, & Critique. 2009. (American Indian Studies). (ENG.). 327p. pap. 34.95 *(978-0-87013-841-6(3))* Michigan State Univ. Pr.

Herman, Matthew D. Politics & Aesthetics in Contemporary Native American Literature: Across Every Border. 2009. (Indigenous Peoples & Politics Ser.). (ENG.). 154p. 125.00 *(978-0-415-80474-5(4))* Routledge.

Katanski, Amelia V. Learning to Write Indian: The Boarding-School Experience & American Indian Literature. 2007. (ENG., Illus.). 283p. (C). per. 19.95 *(978-0-8061-3852-7(1))* Univ. of Oklahoma Pr.

Kelsey, Penelope Myrte. Tribal Theory in Native American Literature: Dakota & Haudenosaunee Writing & Indigenous Worldviews. 2010. (ENG., Illus.). 192p. pap. 24.95 *(978-0-8032-3273-0(X))* Univ. of Nebraska Pr.

Kent, Alica A. & Kent, Alicia. African, Native, & Jewish American Literature & the Reshaping of Modernism. 2007. (ENG., Illus.). 240p. 84.00 *(978-1-4039-7797-7(6))* Palgrave Macmillan.

Krupat, Arnold. All That Remains: Varieties of Indigenous Expression. 2009. (ENG.). 248p. pap. 25.00 *(978-0-8032-1890-1(7))* Univ. of Nebraska Pr.

Lee, A. Robert, ed. Native American Writing, 4 vols., Set. 2011. (ENG.). 1736p. (C). 1295.00 *(978-0-415-58895-9(2))* Routledge.

Lincoln, Kenneth. Speak Like Singing: Classics of Native American Literature. (ENG.). 383p. (C). 2009. pap. 24.95 *(978-0-8263-4170-9(5))* 2007. 39.95 *(978-0-8263-4169-3(1))* Univ. of New Mexico Pr.

Lopenzina, Drew. Red Ink. 2012. (Native Traces Ser.). (ENG., Illus.). 432p. 95.00 *(978-1-4384-3979-2(2))* State Univ. of New York Pr.

Madsen, Deborah L. Native Authenticity: Transnational Perspectives on Native American Literary Studies. 2010. 192p. 65.00 *(978-1-4384-3167-3(8))*; pap. 24.95 *(978-1-4384-3168-0(6))* State Univ. of New York Pr.

Rader, Dean. Engaged Resistance: American Indian Art, Literature, & Film from Alcatraz to the NMAI. 2011. (ENG., Illus.). 304p. 60.00 *(978-0-292-72399-3(7))*; pap. 29.95 *(978-0-292-72696-3(1))* Univ. of Texas Pr.

Rifkin, Mark. Erotics of Sovereignty: Queer Native Writing in the Era of Self-Determination. 2012. 328p. 75.00 ***(978-0-8166-7782-5(4))***; pap. 25.00 ***(978-0-8166-7783-2(2))*** Univ. of Minnesota Pr.

Rifkin, Mark. When Did Indians Become Straight? Kinship, the History of Sexuality, & Native Sovereignty, 1 vol. 2011. (ENG.). 416p. pap. 35.00 *(978-0-19-975546-2(9))* Oxford Univ. Pr., Inc.

Sadowski-Smith, Claudia. Border Fictions: Globalization, Empire, & Writing at the Boundaries of the United States. 2008. (New World Studies). (ENG.). 208p. (C). (gr. 13-17). per. 22.50 *(978-0-8139-2678-0(5))* Univ. Pr. of Virginia.

Schoolcraft, Jane Johnston. The Sound the Stars Make Rushing Through the Sky: The Writings of Jane Johnston Schoolcraft. Parker, Robert Dale, ed. 2007. (Illus.). 288p. (C). 34.95 *(978-0-8122-3981-2(4))* Univ. of Pennsylvania Pr.

Schweninger, Lee. Listening to the Land: Native American Literary Responses to the Landscape. 2008. (ENG.). 256p. pap. 24.95 *(978-0-8203-3059-4(0))*; lib. bdg. 59.95 *(978-0-8203-3058-7(2))* Univ. of Georgia Pr.

Shumaker, Conrad. Southwestern American Indian Literature — In the Classroom & Beyond. 2007. (American Indian Studies). 128p. (C). pap. 24.95 *(978-0-8204-6344-5(2))* Lang, Peter Publishing, Inc.

Sturgis, Amy H. & Oberhelman, David D., eds. The Intersection of Fantasy & Native America: From H. P. Lovecraft to Leslie Marmon Silko: Edited by Amy H. Sturgis & David D. Oberhelman. 2009. 185p. 23.00 *(978-1-887726-12-2(8))* Mythopoeic Pr., The.

Teuton, Christopher B. Deep Waters: The Textual Continuum in American Indian Literature. 2010. (ENG.). 272p. 40.00 *(978-0-8032-2849-8(X))* Univ. of Nebraska Pr.

Vizenor, Gerald, ed. Survivance: Narratives of Native Presence. 2008. (ENG.). 396p. pap. 29.95 *(978-0-8032-1083-7(3))* Univ. of Nebraska Pr.

Weaver, Jace, et al. American Indian Literary Nationalism. annot. ed. 2006. (ENG.). 296p. pap. 27.95 *(978-0-8263-4073-3(3))* Univ. of New Mexico Pr.

West, Rinda. Out of the Shadow: Ecopsychology, Story, & Encounters with the Land. 2007. (Under the Sign of Nature Ser.). (ENG.). 304p. (gr. 17). 65.00 *(978-0-8139-2655-1(6))*; pap. 24.50 *(978-0-8139-2656-8(4))* Univ. Pr. of Virginia.

Wilson, Michael D. Writing Home: Indigenous Narratives of Resistance. 2008. (American Indian Studies). (ENG.). 188p. pap. 24.95 *(978-0-87013-818-8(9))* Michigan State Univ. Pr.

Womack, Craig S. Art as Performance, Story as Criticism: Reflections on Native Literary Aesthetics. 2009. (ENG.). 376p. (C). 39.95 *(978-0-8061-4064-3(X))*; pap. 24.95 *(978-0-8061-4065-0(8))* Univ. of Oklahoma Pr.

AMERICAN LITERATURE—ITALIAN AMERICAN AUTHORS

Bona, Mary Jo. By the Breath of Their Mouths: Narratives of Resistance in Italian America. 2010. (SUNY series in Italian/American Culture Ser.). 305p. 75.00 *(978-1-4384-2995-3(9))* State Univ. of New York Pr.

Bona, Mary Jo, ed. By the Breath of Their Mouths: Narratives of Resistance in Italian America. 2010. (SUNY series in Italian/American Culture Ser.). 305p. pap. 24.95 *(978-1-4384-2996-0(7))* State Univ. of New York Pr.

Fazio, Venera & De Santis, Delia. Sweet Lemons 2: International Writings with a Sicilian Accent. 2010. pap. *(978-1-881901-76-1(9))* LEGAS.

Giordano, Paolo A. & Tamburri, Anthony Julian, eds. Italian Americans in the Third Millennium. 2009. 232p. pap. 16.00 *(978-0-934675-58-1(9))* Bordighera Incorporated.

McCormick, Kathleen. Teaching Italian American Literature, Film, & Popular Culture. Giunta, Edvige, ed. 2010. (ENG.). 40.00 *(978-1-60329-066-1(4))*; pap. 25.00 *(978-1-60329-067-8(2))* Modern Language Assn. of America.

Scambray, Kenneth. Queen Calafia's Paradise: California & the Italian American Novel. 2007. 211p. 46.50 *(978-0-8386-4117-0(2))* Fairleigh Dickinson Univ. Pr.

AMERICAN LITERATURE—JEWISH AUTHORS

see also American Drama—Jewish Authors; American Fiction—Jewish Authors; American Poetry—Jewish Authors

Avery, Evelyn, ed. Modern Jewish Women Writers in America. 2007. (ENG.). 288p. 110.00 *(978-1-4039-7799-1(2))*; pap. 32.00 *(978-1-4039-7804-2(2))* Palgrave Macmillan.

Bilik, Dorothy. Immigrant-Survivors: Post-Holocaust Consciousness in Recent Jewish American Fiction. 10.95 *(978-0-931848-87-2(3))* Dryad Pr.

Cronin, Gloria L. & Berger, Alan. Jewish-American Literature. 2009. (Encyclopedia of American Ethnic Literature Ser.). 416p. (C). (gr. 9-18). 75.00 *(978-0-8160-6085-6(1))* Facts On File, Inc.

Franco, Dean J. Ethnic American Literature: Comparing Chicano, Jewish, & African American Writing. 2006. (ENG.). 224p. (gr. 17). lib. bdg. 49.50 *(978-0-8139-2559-2(2))*; per. 19.50 *(978-0-8139-2560-8(6))* Univ. Pr. of Virginia.

Franco, Dean J. Race, Rights, & Recognition: Jewish American Literature Since 1969. 2012. (ENG.). 248p. 49.95 ***(978-0-8014-5087-7(X))*** Cornell Univ. Pr.

Hoffman, Warren. The Passing Game: Queering Jewish American Culture. 2009. (Judaic Traditions in Literature, Music, & Art Ser.). (Illus.). 216p. 24.95 *(978-0-8156-3202-3(9))* Syracuse Univ. Pr.

Kent, Alica A. & Kent, Alicia. African, Native, & Jewish American Literature & the Reshaping of Modernism. 2007. (ENG., Illus.). 240p. 84.00 *(978-1-4039-7797-7(6))* Palgrave Macmillan.

Kessner, Carole & Shapiro, Ann, eds. Studies in American Jewish Literature in Honor of Sarah Blacher Cohen. 2010. (Studies in American Jewish Literature 29 (2010) Ser.). 249p. pap. 35.00 *(978-1-55753-589-4(2))* Purdue Univ. Pr.

Levinson, Julian. Exiles on Main Street: Jewish American Writers & American Literary Culture. 2008. (Jewish Literature & Culture Ser.). (ENG., Illus.). 256p. 24.95 *(978-0-253-35081-7(6)*, 0253350816) Indiana Univ. Pr.

Meyers, Helene. Identity Papers: Contemporary Narratives of American Jewishness. 2011. 200p. 70.00 *(978-1-4384-3923-5(7))* State Univ. of New York Pr.

Polyak, Alina. Tradition & Modernity in Contemporary Jewish American Literature. 2010. 124p. pap. *(978-3-639-26265-0(4))* VDM Verlag Dr. Mueller e.K.

Rosenfeld, Alvin H., ed. The Writer Uprooted: Contemporary Jewish Exile Literature. 2008. (Jewish Literature & Culture Ser.). (ENG.). 272p. 50.00 *(978-0-253-35144-9(8)*, 0253351448); pap. 19.95 *(978-0-253-21981-7(7)*, 0253219817) Indiana Univ. Pr.

Royal, Derek Parker, ed. Unfinalized Moments: Essays in the Development of Contemporary Jewish American Narrative. 2011. (Shofar Supplements in Jewish Studies). 267p. pap. 45.00 *(978-1-55753-584-9(1))* Purdue Univ. Pr.

Schlund-Vials, Cathy. Modeling Citizenship: Jewish & Asian American Writing. 2011. (ENG.). 248p. 68.50 *(978-1-4399-0317-9(4))*; pap. 24.95 *(978-1-4399-0318-6(2))* Temple Univ. Pr.

Stahler, Axel. Anglophone Jewish Literatures. 2007. (Routledge Studies in Twentieth-Century Literature Ser.). (ENG.). 304p. 160.00 *(978-0-415-41464-7(4))* Routledge.

Sternlicht, Sanford. Masterpieces of Jewish American Literature, 1 vol. 2007. (Greenwood Introduces Literary Masterpieces Ser.). 152p. 49.95 *(978-0-313-33857-1(4)*, GR3857, Greenwood Pr.) Greenwood Publishing Group, Inc.

Wald, Alan M. Trinity of Passion: The Literary Left & the Antifascist Crusade. 2007. (ENG., Illus.). 344p. 38.95 *(978-0-8078-3075-8(5))* Univ. of North Carolina Pr.

Wertheim, Sally H. & Bennett, Alan, eds. Remembering: Cleveland's Jewish Voices. 2011. (Voices of Diversity Ser.). 352p. pap. 24.00 *(978-1-60635-074-4(9))* Kent State Univ. Pr.

Wirth-Nesher, Hana. Call It English: The Languages of Jewish American Literature. 2008. (ENG., Illus.). 240p. (C). pap. 24.95 *(978-0-691-13844-2(3))* Princeton Univ. Pr.

AMERICAN LITERATURE—LATIN AMERICAN AUTHORS

see American Literature—Hispanic American Authors

AMERICAN LITERATURE—MEXICAN AMERICAN AUTHORS

Alvarez, Alma Rosa. Liberation Theology in Chicana/O Literature: Manifestations of Feminist & Gay Identities. 2007. (Latino Communities: Emerging Voices - Political, Social, Cultural & Legal Issues Ser.). (ENG.). 176p. 138.00 *(978-0-415-95557-7(2))* Routledge.

Alvarez, Alma Rosa. Liberation Theology in Chicana/o Literature: Manifestations of Feminist & Gay Identities. 2012. (Latino Communities: Emerging Voices - Political, Social, Cultural & Legal Issues Ser.). (ENG.). 176p. pap. 42.95 ***(978-0-415-54163-3(8))*** Routledge.

Contreras, Sheila Marie. Blood Lines: Myth, Indigenism, & Chicana - O Literature. 2008. (Chicana Matters Ser.). (ENG.). 232p. (C). pap. 22.95 *(978-0-292-71797-8(0))* Univ. of Texas Pr.

—Blood Lines: Myth, Indigenism, & Chicana/O Literature. 2008. (Chicana Matters Ser.). (ENG.). 232p. (C). 55.00 *(978-0-292-71796-1(2))* Univ. of Texas Pr.

Crazzolara, Monica. Borders in Chicana Literature: Gloria Anzaldúa & Sandra Cisneros. 2008. 104p. pap. *(978-3-8364-9418-2(3))* VDM Verlag Dr. Mueller e.K.

Dean, Jenny. Latina Filmmakers & Writers: The Notion of Chicanisma Through Films & Novellas. 2007. 248p. per. 26.95 *(978-0-9796457-1-6(9))* Floricanto Pr.

Delgadillo, Theresa. Spiritual Mestizaje: Religion, Gender, Race, & Nation in Contemporary Chicana Narrative. 2011. (Latin America Otherwise Ser.). (ENG., Illus.). 296p. pap. 23.95 *(978-0-8223-5046-0(7))*; 84.95 *(978-0-8223-5029-3(7))* Duke Univ. Pr.

Espejo, Ramon, et al, eds. Critical Essays on Chicano Studies. 2007. 268p. pap. 58.95 *(978-3-03911-281-4(3))* Lang, Peter Publishing, Inc.

Fetta, Stefanie, ed. The Chicano/Latino Literary Prize: An Anthology of Prize-Winning Fiction, Poetry & Drama. 2008. 320p. pap. 21.95 *(978-1-55885-511-3(4))* Arte Publico Pr.

Franco, Dean J. Ethnic American Literature: Comparing Chicano, Jewish, & African American Writing. 2006. (ENG.). 224p. (gr. 17). lib. bdg. 49.50 *(978-0-8139-2559-2(2))*; per. 19.50 *(978-0-8139-2560-8(6))* Univ. Pr. of Virginia.

G?s y Prietas: Celebrating 20 Years of Borderlands/la Frontera. 2009. (Illus.). 10.00 *(978-0-9786820-0-2(9))* Adelante Project.

García, Cristina. Bordering Fires: The Vintage Book of Contemporary Mexican & Chicano/a Literature. 2006. (Vintage Original Ser.). 304p. pap. 13.95 *(978-1-4000-7718-2(4)*, Vintage) Knopf Doubleday Publishing Group.

Gilb, Dagoberto. Hecho en Tejas: An Anthology of Texas-Mexican Literature. 2006. (Southwestern Writers Collection). (ENG & SPA., Illus.). 544p. 39.95 *(978-0-8263-4125-9(X))* Univ. of New Mexico Pr.

—Hecho en Tejas: An Anthology of Texas Mexican Literature. 2008. (Southwestern Writers Collection). (ENG., Illus.). 544p. pap. 29.95 *(978-0-8263-4126-6(8))* Univ. of New Mexico Pr.

González, John Morán. Border Renaissance: The Texas Centennial & the Emergence of Mexican American Literature. 2010. (ENG., Illus.). 275p. pap. 25.00 *(978-0-292-72579-9(5))* Univ. of Texas Pr.

Heredia, Juanita. Transnational Latina Narratives in the Twenty-First Century: The Politics of Gender, Race, & Migrations. 2009. (ENG.). 192p. 84.00 *(978-0-230-61737-7(9))* Palgrave Macmillan.

Hernández, Ellie D. Postnationalism in Chicana - O Literature & Culture. 2010. (ENG.). 255p. pap. 25.00 *(978-0-292-72346-7(6))* Univ. of Texas Pr.

Hernandez, Guillermo. Chicano Satire: A Study in Literary Culture. 2012. (ENG.). 166p. pap. 19.95 ***(978-0-292-74112-6(X))*** Univ. of Texas Pr.

Jacobs, Elizabeth. Mexican American Literature. 2009. 180p. pap. 34.00 *(978-0-415-54406-1(8))* Routledge.

López-Calvo, Ignacio. Latino Los Angeles in Film & Fiction: The Cultural Production of Social Anxiety. 2011. (ENG., Illus.). 264p. 50.00 *(978-0-8165-2926-1(4))* Univ. of Arizona Pr.

Lopez, Marissa. Chicano Nations: The Hemispheric Origins of Mexican American Literature. 2011. (ENG., Illus.). 269p. 75.00 ***(978-0-8147-5261-6(6))***; pap. 24.00 ***(978-0-8147-5262-3(4))*** New York Univ. Pr.

López, Marissa K. Chicano Nations: The Hemispheric Origins of Mexican American Literature. 2011. (Illus.). x, 258p. E-Book ***(978-0-8147-5263-0(2))***; E-Book ***(978-0-8147-5329-3(9))*** New York Univ. Pr.

Lopez, Sam. Post-Revolutionary Chicana Literature: Memoir, Folklore, & Fiction of the Border, 1900-1950. 2006. (Latino Communities: Emerging Voices — Political, Social, Cultural & Legal Issues Ser.). (Illus.). 140p. 138.00 *(978-0-415-95553-9(X))* Routledge.

Lozano, Miguel Lopez. Utopian Dreams, Apocalyptic Nightmares: Globilization in Recent Mexican & Chicano Narrative. 2007. (Purdue Studies in Romance Literatures Ser.). 294p. per. 43.95 *(978-1-55753-484-2(5))* Purdue Univ. Pr.

Mermann-Jozwiak, Elisabeth & Sullivan, Nancy. Conversations with Mexican American Writers: Languages & Literatures in the Borderlands. 2009. (ENG.). 192p. 50.00 *(978-1-60473-214-6(8))*; pap. 22.00 *(978-1-60473-215-3(6))* Univ. Pr. of Mississippi.

Moraga, Cherríe L. A Xicana Codex of Changing Consciousness: Writings, 2000-2010. 2011. (ENG., Illus.). 280p. pap. 22.95 *(978-0-8223-4977-8(9))* Duke Univ. Pr.

—A Xicana Codex of Changing Consciousness: Writings, 2000-2010. 2011. (ENG., Illus.). 280p. 79.95 *(978-0-8223-4962-4(0))* Duke Univ. Pr.

Perez, Vincent & Pérez, Vincent. Remembering the Hacienda: History & Memory in the Mexican American Southwest. 2006. (Rio Grande/Río Bravo Ser.: 11). (ENG., Illus.). 264p. 49.95 *(978-1-58544-511-0(8))*; per. 24.95 *(978-1-58544-546-2(0))* Texas A&M Univ. Pr.

Sadowski-Smith, Claudia. Border Fictions: Globalization, Empire, & Writing at the Boundaries of the United States. 2008. (New World Studies). (ENG.). 208p. (C). (gr. 13-17). per. 22.50 *(978-0-8139-2678-0(5))* Univ. Pr. of Virginia.

Sandoval, Anna Marie. Toward a Latina Feminism of the Americas: Repression & Resistance in Chicana & Mexicana Literature. Castañeda, Antonia & González, Deena J., eds. 2009. (ENG.). 144p. pap. 19.95 *(978-0-292-72166-1(8))* Univ. of Texas Pr.

Solorzano, Rosalia & Hernandez, Francisca James. Chicana Studies Vol. 1: An Introduction. rev. ed. 2010. (ENG.). 458p. pap. 92.10 *(978-0-7575-7825-0(X))* Kendall Hunt Publishing Co.

Tatum, Charles M. Chicano & Chicana Literature: Otra Voz del Pueblo. 2006. (Mexican American Experience Ser.). (ENG., Illus.). 232p. pap. 17.95 *(978-0-8165-2427-3(0))* Univ. of Arizona Pr.

Torres, Hector A. Conversations with Contemporary Chicana & Chicano Writers. 2007. (ENG.). 367p. pap. 29.95 *(978-0-8263-4088-7(1))* Univ. of New Mexico Pr.

Trinity University Press Staff. Mexican Writers on Writing. Peden, Margaret Sayers, ed. 2007. (Writer's World Ser.). (ENG.). 320p. lib. bdg. 60.00 *(978-1-59534-028-3(9))*; per. 24.95 *(978-1-59534-034-4(3))* Trinity Univ. Pr.

Zygadlo, Grazyna. Culture Matters: Chicanas' Identity in Contemporary USA. 2006. 166p. pap. *(978-0-8204-9883-6(1))*; pap. *(978-3-631-55096-0(0))* Lang, Peter AG.

AMERICAN LITERATURE—MINORITY AUTHORS

see also American Literature—African American Authors; American Literature—Indian Authors

Benito, Jesus, et al. Uncertain Mirrors: Magical Realism in US Ethnic Literatures. 2009. (Illus.). 276p. pap. 74.00 *(978-90-420-2600-1(6))* Rodopi.

Bogomolny, Abby, ed. New to North America: Writing by U. S. Immigrants, Their Children & Grandchildren, Second Edition. 2nd ed. 2007. (ENG.). 358p. 29.95 *(978-0-9650665-6-3(8))* Burning Bush Pubns.

Dalessio, William R. Are We What We Eat? Food & Identity in Late Twentieth-Century American Ethnic Literature. 2012. ***(978-1-60497-801-8(5))*** Cambria Pr.

Douglas, Christopher. A Genealogy of Literary Multiculturalism. 2011. 384p. pap. 24.95 *(978-0-8014-7711-9(5))* Cornell Univ. Pr.

Douglas, Christopher & Douglas, C. A Genealogy of Literary Multiculturalism. 2009. (Illus.). 360p. 59.95 *(978-0-8014-4769-3(0))* Cornell Univ. Pr.

Fishkin, Shelley Fisher. Feminist Engagements: Forays into American Literature & Culture. 2009. (ENG.). 288p. pap. 30.00 *(978-0-230-61594-6(5))* Palgrave Macmillan.

Franco, Dean J. Ethnic American Literature: Comparing Chicano, Jewish, & African American Writing. 2006. (ENG.). 224p. (gr. 17). lib. bdg. 49.50 *(978-0-8139-2559-2(2))*; per. 19.50 *(978-0-8139-2560-8(6))* Univ. Pr. of Virginia.

Frosch, Mary, ed. Coming of Age in the 21st Century: Growing up in America Today. 2008. (ENG.). 319p. pap. 17.95 *(978-1-59558-055-9(7))* New Pr., The.

Gilton, Donna L. Multicultural & Ethnic Children's Literature in the United States. 2007. (ENG.). 244p. per. 55.00 *(978-0-8108-5672-1(7))* Scarecrow Pr., Inc.

Hinton, KaaVonia & Dickinson, Gail K. Integrating Multicultural Literature in Libraries & Classrooms in Secondary Schools, 1 vol. 2007. 112p. per. 24.95 *(978-1-58683-218-6(2)*, A2475P) Linworth Publishing, Inc.

Keresztesi, Rita. Strangers at Home: American Ethnic Modernism Between the World Wars. 2009. (ENG., Illus.). 248p. pap. 24.95 *(978-0-8032-2792-7(2))* Univ. of Nebraska Pr.

Knadler, Stephen P. The Fugitive Race: Minority Writers Resisting Whiteness. 2007. (ENG.). 280p. per. 25.00 *(978-1-934110-34-8(5))* Univ. Pr. of Mississippi.

Lee, A. Robert. Multicultural American Literature: Comparative Black, Native, Latino/a, & Asian American Fictions. 2008. (ENG.). 307p. pap. 25.00 *(978-1-57806-645-2(X))* Univ. Pr. of Mississippi.

Manzanas, Ana M. & Benito Sanchez, Jesús. Cities, Borders & Spaces in Intercultural American Literature & Film. 2011. (Routledge Transnational Perspectives on American Literature Ser.). (ENG.). 176p. (C). 125.00 *(978-0-415-88721-2(6))* Routledge.

Manzanas, Ana Mª, ed. Border Transits: Literature & Culture across the Line. 2007. (Illus.). 312p. per. 88.00 *(978-90-420-2249-2(3))* Rodopi.

Martin, Holly E. Writing Between Cultures: A Study of Hybrid Narratives in Ethnic Literature of the United States. 2011. (ENG.). 216p. pap. 40.00 ***(978-0-7864-6660-3(X))*** McFarland & Co., Inc. Pubs.

McDonald, Kathlene. Feminism, the Left, & Postwar Literary Culture. 2012. (ENG.). 160p. 55.00 ***(978-1-61703-301-8(4))*** Univ. Pr. of Mississippi.

Michael, Magali Cornier. New Visions of Community in Contemporary American Fiction: Tan, Kingsolver, Castillo, Morrison. 2006. 256p. (C). per. 21.00 *(978-1-58729-511-9(3))* Univ. of Iowa Pr.

Moraru, Christian. Cosmodernism: American Narrative, Late Globalization, & the New Cultural Imaginary. 2010. (ENG.). 440p. (C). 90.00 *(978-0-472-07129-6(7))*; pap. 37.50 *(978-0-472-05129-8(6))* Univ. of Michigan Pr.

Norton, Donna E. Multicultural Children's Literature: Through the Eyes of Many Children. 4th rev. ed. 2012. (ENG.). 360p. (C). pap. 53.80 ***(978-0-13-268576-4(0))*** Allyn & Bacon, Inc.

—Multicultural Children's Literature: Through the Eyes of Many Children. 3rd ed. 2008. (ENG., Illus.). 368p. (C). pap. 53.80 *(978-0-13-514528-9(7)*, Prentice Hall) Prentice Hall PTR.

Obourn, Megan. Reconstituting Americans: Liberal Multiculturalism & Identity Difference in Post-1960s Literature. 2011. (ENG.). 240p. 85.00 *(978-0-230-11247-6(1))* Palgrave Macmillan.

Prchal, Tim, ed. Visions & Divisions: American Immigration Literature, 1870-1930. 2008. (Multi-Ethnic Literatures of the Americas (Mela) Ser.). (ENG.). 408p. per. 26.95 *(978-0-8135-4234-8(0))* Rutgers Univ. Pr.

Prchal, Tim, intro. Visions & Divisions: American Immigration Literature, 1870-1930. 2008. (Multi-Ethnic Literatures of the Americas (MELA) Ser.). (ENG.). 408p. pap. 70.00 *(978-0-8135-4233-1(2))* Rutgers Univ. Pr.

Rader, Pamela/J. Multi-Ethnicity as a Resource for the Literary Imagination: The Creative Achievements of Women Artists, Poets, & Novelists. 2009. 156p. *(978-0-7734-3893-4(9))* Mellen, Edwin Pr., The.

Rottenberg, Catherine. Performing Americanness: Race, Class, & Gender in Modern African-American & Jewish-American Literature. 2008. (ENG., Illus.). 192p. 50.00 *(978-1-58465-682-1(4))* Univ. Pr. of New England.

Salem Press Staff, contrib. by. American Ethnic Writers, 3 vols. 2008. (Magill's Choice Ser.). (Illus.). xxxvi, 1295p. 73.00 *(978-1-58765-465-7(2))*; 73.00 *(978-1-58765-464-0(4))*; 73.00 *(978-1-58765-463-3(6))* Salem Pr., Inc.

Salem Press Staff, ed. American Ethnic Writers, 3 vols. 2008. (Magill's Choice Ser.). (Illus.). 1000p. 217.00 *(978-1-58765-462-6(8))* Salem Pr., Inc.

Smolen, Lynn Atkinson & Oswald, Ruth A. Multicultural Literature & Response: Affirming Diverse Voices. 2010. E-Book *(978-1-59884-475-7(X))* Libraries Unlimited, Inc.

Smolen, Lynn Atkinson & Oswald, Ruth A., eds. Multicultural Literature & Response: Affirming Diverse Voices, 1 vol. (Illus.). 453p. pap. 45.00 *(978-1-59884-474-0(1)*, A2943P) Libraries Unlimited, Inc.

Sollors, Werner. Ethnic Modernism. 2008. 336p. pap. 21.00 *(978-0-674-03091-6(5))* Harvard Univ. Pr.

Tolentino, Cynthia H. & Ferguson, Roderick A. America's Experts: Race & the Fictions of Sociology. 2009. (ENG.). 200p. 67.50 *(978-0-8166-5110-8(8))*; pap. 22.50 *(978-0-8166-5111-5(6))* Univ. of Minnesota Pr.

Walter, Roland. Narrative Identities: (Inter) Cultural In-Betweenness in the Americas. 395p. pap. 55.95 *(978-3-906770-79-6(6))* Lang, Peter CHE. Dist: Lang, Peter Publishing, Inc.

Winter, Molly Crumpton. American Narratives: Multiethnic Writing in the Age of Realism. 2007. 204p. 36.50 *(978-0-8071-3225-8(X))* Louisiana State Univ. Pr.

York, Sherry. Booktalking Authentic Multicultural Literature: Fiction & History for Young Readers, 1 vol. 2009. 160p. pap. 39.95 *(978-1-58683-300-8(6)*, A2458P) Linworth Publishing, Inc.

—Booktalking Authentic Multicultural Literature: Fiction, History, & Memoirs for Teens, 1 vol. 2008. 160p. pap. 39.95 *(978-1-58683-299-5(9)*, A2446P) Linworth Publishing, Inc.

AMERICAN LITERATURE—ORIENTAL AUTHORS

see American Literature—Asian American Authors

AMERICAN LITERATURE—OUTLINES, SYLLABI, ETC.

BarCharts, Inc. Quicklit:the Great Gatsby. 2011. (ENG.). 6p. 5.95 *(978-1-4232-1664-3(4))* Barcharts, Inc.

—Quicklit:to Kill A Mockingbird. 2011. (ENG.). 6p. 5.95 *(978-1-4232-1665-0(2))* Barcharts, Inc.

Cram101 Textbook Reviews. Outlines & Highlights for American Passages, Compact Edition by Edward L Ayers. 2010. 582p. pap. 39.95 *(978-1-4288-5320-1(0))* Cram101 Inc.

Kopley, Richard & Cantalupo, Barbara. Prospects for the Study of American Literature (II) 2009. *(978-0-404-61598-7(8))* AMS Pr., Inc.

AMERICAN LITERATURE—STUDY AND TEACHING

Allen, Janet et al. McDougal Littell Literature: Pennsylvania. 2008. (Illus.). 1303p. 78.48 *(978-0-618-94443-9(5))* Holt McDougal.

Appleman, Deborah. Critical Encounters in High School English: Teaching Literary Theory to Adolescents. 2nd ed. 2009. (ENG.). 256p. pap. 24.95 *(978-0-8077-4892-3(7))* Teachers College Pr., Teachers College, Columbia Univ.

Bellas, Gale Joyce. A Dialogic Approach to Reading & Teaching Ethnic American Texts. 2006. 156p. 99.95 *(978-0-7734-5728-7(3))* Mellen, Edwin Pr., The.

Bruce, Heather E., et al. Sherman Alexie in the Classroom: This Is Not a Silent Movie. Our Voices Will Save Our Lives. 2008. pap. *(978-0-8141-4457-2(8))* National Council of Teachers of English.

Center for Learning Staff. The Member of the Wedding/A Christmas Memory: Curriculum Unit. 2007. (Novel Ser.). 65p. (YA). spiral bd. 19.95 *(978-1-56077-850-9(4))* Center for Learning, The.

—The Scarlet Letter: Curriculum Unit. 2006. (Novel Ser.). 78p. (YA). spiral bd. 19.95 *(978-1-56077-749-6(4))* Center for Learning, The.

—Their Eyes Were Watching God: Curriculum Unit. 2007. (Novel Ser.). 59p. (YA). spiral bd. 19.95 *(978-1-56077-879-0(2))* Center for Learning, The.

Dahl, Roald. Fantastic Mr. Fox. 2007. (ENG., Illus.). 96p. (J). (gr. 2-18). 6.99 *(978-0-14-241034-9(9)*, Puffin) Penguin Group (USA) Inc.

Drexler, Michael J. & White, Ed. Beyond Douglass: New Perspectives on Early African-American Literature. 2008. 192p. (C). pap. 25.00 *(978-0-8387-5711-6(1))* Bucknell Univ. Pr.

Earhart, Amy & Jewell, Andrew. The American Literature Scholar in the Digital Age. 2010. (Editorial Theory & Literary Criticism Ser.). (ENG., Illus.). 302p. pap. 37.50 *(978-0-472-05119-9(9))*; (C). 90.00 *(978-0-472-07119-7(X))* Univ. of Michigan Pr.

Evans, Robert C. The American Novel, 2 vols., Set. 2011. (Understanding Literature through Close Reading Ser.). 1024p. (C). (gr. 9). 150.00 *(978-0-8160-7675-8(8))* Facts On File, Inc.

Gibbons, Louel C. To Kill a Mockingbird in the Classroom. 2009. pap. *(978-0-8141-2551-9(4))* National Council of Teachers of English.

Gilmore, Barry & Kaplan, Alexander. Tim O'Brien in the Classroom: This too Is true: Stories can save Us. 2007. (NCTE High School Literature Ser.). pap. *(978-0-8141-5466-3(2))* National Council of Teachers of English.

Gregory, Marshall. Shaped by Stories: The Ethical Power of Narratives. 2009. (ENG.) 208p. pap. 25.00 *(978-0-268-02974-6(1))* Univ. of Notre Dame Pr.

Hauschildt, Patricia M. & Monseau, Virginia R. Teaching the Selected Works of Chris Crutcher. 2008. (Young Adult Literature Ser.). (Illus.). 104p. pap. 21.25 *(978-0-325-01032-8(3)*, E01032) Heinemann.

Hays, Peter L., ed. Teaching Hemingway's *the Sun Also Rises. 2008. (Teaching Hemingway Ser.). (Illus.). 403p. 39.95 (978-0-87338-954-9(9))* Kent State Univ. Pr.

Kopley, Richard & Cantalupo, Barbara. Prospects for the Study of American Literature (II) 2009. *(978-0-404-61598-7(8))* AMS Pr., Inc.

Linkon, Sherry Lee. Literary Learning: Teaching the English Major. 2011. (Scholarship of Teaching & Learning Ser.). (ENG.). 182p. 70.00 *(978-0-253-35699-4(7)*, 0253356997); pap. 24.95 *(978-0-253-22356-2(3)*, 0253223563) Indiana Univ. Pr.

Long, Mark C. & Waage, Frederick O. Teaching North American Environmental Literature. Christensen, Laird, ed. 2008. (ENG.). 40.00 *(978-0-87352-809-2(3))*; pap. 22.00 *(978-0-87352-810-8(7))* Modern Language Assn. of America.

Magistrale, Tony. Approaches to Teaching Poe's Prose & Poetry. Weinstock, Jeffrey Andrew, ed. 2008. (ENG.). xix, 241p. pap. 19.75 *(978-1-60329-012-8(5))* Modern Language Assn. of America.

Mason, Yvonne. Reading, Learning, Teaching Clyde Edgerton. 2008. (Confronting the Text, Confronting the World Ser.). 176p. (C). 32.95 *(978-0-8204-8143-2(2))* Lang, Peter Publishing, Inc.

McCormick, Kathleen. Teaching Italian American Literature, Film, & Popular Culture. Giunta, Edvige, ed. 2010. (ENG.). 40.00 *(978-1-60329-066-1(4))*; pap. 25.00 *(978-1-60329-067-8(2))* Modern Language Assn. of America.

Merediz, Eyda M. Approaches to Teaching the Writings of Bartolomé de Las Casas. Arias, Santa, ed. 2008. (SPA & ENG.). 37.50 *(978-0-87352-944-0(8))*; pap. 19.75 *(978-0-87352-945-7(6))* Modern Language Assn. of America.

Milner, Joseph O. & Pope, Carol A. Engaging American Novels: Lessons from the Classroom. 2011. pap. *(978-0-8141-1358-5(3))* National Council of Teachers of English.

Novel Units, Inc. Staff, creator. A Tree Grows in Brooklyn Student Packet. 2007. (YA). stu. ed. 12.99 *(978-1-58130-953-9(8))* Novel Units, Inc.

—A Tree Grows in Brooklyn Teacher Guide. 2007. (YA). 11.99 *(978-1-58130-952-2(X))* Novel Units, Inc.

The Pearl. 8.97 *(978-0-673-58331-4(7))* Addison-Wesley Longman, Inc.

Pearson, creator. Prentice Hall Literature Reader's Notebook, Grade Six. 2010. (Illus.). 443p. pap. 17.50 *(978-0-13-366673-1(5)*, Scott Foresman) Addison Wesley Schl.

Polette, Nancy J. Mysteries in the Classroom, 1 vol. 2009. 215p. pap. 40.00 *(978-1-59158-931-0(2)*, A2609P) Libraries Unlimited, Inc.

Princeton Review Staff. Cracking the SAT Literature Subject Test, 2011-2012 Edition. 2011. (College Test Preparation Ser.). 256p. pap. 19.99 *(978-0-375-42811-1(9)*, Princeton Review) Random Hse. Information Group.

Raymond, Richard C. Teaching American Literature at an East European University: Explicating the Rhetoric of Liberty. 2006. (Illus.). 216p. (C). 109.95 *(978-0-7734-5641-9(4))* Mellen, Edwin Pr., The.

Renker, Elizabeth. The Origins of American Literature Studies: An Institutional History. (Cambridge Studies in American Literature & Culture Ser.). (ENG.). 232p. 2010. pap. 34.99 *(978-0-521-14199-4(0))* 2007. 98.00 *(978-0-521-88345-0(8))* Cambridge Univ. Pr.

Samet, Elizabeth D. Soldier's Heart: Reading Literature Through Peace & War at West Point. 2008. (ENG.). 288p. pap. 16.00 *(978-0-312-42782-5(4))* Picador.

Shumaker, Conrad. Southwestern American Indian Literature — In the Classroom & Beyond. 2007. (American Indian Studies). 128p. (C). pap. 24.95 *(978-0-8204-6344-5(2))* Lang, Peter Publishing, Inc.

Sing down the Moon. pap., stu. ed. *(978-0-13-017559-5(5))* Prentice Hall (Schl. Div.).

Smolen, Lynn Atkinson & Oswald, Ruth A. Multicultural Literature & Response: Affirming Diverse Voices. 2010. E-Book *(978-1-59884-475-7(X))* Libraries Unlimited, Inc.

Smolen, Lynn Atkinson & Oswald, Ruth A., eds. Multicultural Literature & Response: Affirming Diverse Voices, 1 vol. (Illus.). 453p. pap. 45.00 *(978-1-59884-474-0(1)*, A2943P) Libraries Unlimited, Inc.

Soto, Michael. Teaching the Harlem Renaissance: Course Design & Classroom Strategies. (African American Literature & Culture: Expanding & Exploding the Boundaries Ser.). 2008. 268p. (C). 99.95 *(978-1-4331-0391-9(5))* 2007. pap. 34.95 *(978-0-8204-9724-2(X))* Lang, Peter Publishing, Inc.

Tyler, Lisa, ed. Teaching Hemingway's *A Farewell to Arms. 2008. (Teaching Hemingway Ser.). 257p. per. 36.00 (978-0-87338-917-4(4))* Kent State Univ. Pr.

Weinstock, Jeffrey Andrew & Magistrale, Tony. Approaches to Teaching Poe's Prose & Poetry. 2008. (ENG.). xix, 241p. 37.50 *(978-1-60329-011-1(7))* Modern Language Assn. of America.

Wilhelm, Jeffrey D., et al. Glencoe Literature: American Literature. 2008. (Glencoe Literature Ser.). (Illus.). 1365p. (J). 144.50 *(978-0-07-877980-0(4))* McGraw-Hill Cos., The.

Wisker, Gina. Teaching African American Women's Writing. Knights, C. B. & Wisker, Gina, eds. 2010. (Teaching the New English Ser.). (ENG.). 224p. 95.00 *(978-0-230-00346-0(X))*; pap. 30.00 *(978-0-230-00348-4(6))* Palgrave Macmillan.

Yenika-Agbaw, Vivian. African & African-American Children's & Adolescent Literature in the Classroom: A Critical Guide. 2011. (Black Studies & Critical Thinking Ser.). 318p. (C). 129.95 ***(978-1-4331-1196-9(9))*** Lang, Peter Publishing, Inc.

—African & African American Children's & Adolescent Literature in the Classroom: A Critical Guide. 2011. (Black Studies & Critical Thinking Ser.). 320p. (C). pap. 32.95 ***(978-1-4331-1195-2(0))*** Lang, Peter Publishing, Inc.

AMERICAN LITERATURE—TRANSLATIONS INTO GERMAN

Boecker, Eberhard. William Faulkner's later novels in German: A study in the theory & practice of Translation. (Linguistische Arbeiten Ser.). (ENG.). X, 236p. 210.00 ***(978-3-11-205609-7(4))*** De Gruyter, Mouton DEU. Dist: de Gruyter, Walter GmbH & Co. KG.

Hemminghaus, Edgar H. Mark Twain in Germany: Columbia University Germanic Studies V9. Fife, Robert Herndon, ed. 2011. 180p. 42.95 ***(978-1-258-03278-4(3))*** Literary Licensing, LLC.

AMERICAN LITERATURE—WOMEN AUTHORS

Abdelrazek, Amal Talaat. Contemporary Arab American Women Writers: Hyphenated Identities & Border Crossings. 2007. (C). 104.95 *(978-1-934043-71-4(0))* Cambria Pr.

Abramowitz, Janvier, et al. Magic in Black & White. 2009. pap. *(978-1-934333-14-3(X))* Eagle Bk. Bindery.

Acampora, Christa Davis & Cotten, Angela L. Cultural Sites of Critical Insight: Philosophy, Aesthetics, & African American & Native American Women's Writings. Acampora, Christa Davis & Cotten, Angela L., eds. 2007. 216p. per. 29.95 *(978-0-7914-6980-4(8))* State Univ. of New York Pr.

Albert, Susan Wittig, et al, eds. What Wildness Is This: Women Write about the Southwest. 2007. (Southwestern Writers Collection). (ENG.). 336p. pap. 19.95 *(978-0-292-71630-8(3))* Univ. of Texas Pr.

Avery, Evelyn, ed. Modern Jewish Women Writers in America. 2007. (ENG.). 288p. 110.00 *(978-1-4039-7799-1(2))*; pap. 32.00 *(978-1-4039-7804-2(2))* Palgrave Macmillan.

Bassard, Katherine Clay. Transforming Scriptures: African American Women Writers & the Bible. 2011. (ENG., Illus.). 180p. pap. 22.95 *(978-0-8203-3880-4(X))* Univ. of Georgia Pr.

Bauer, Dale. Sex Expression & American Women Writers, 1860-1940. 2009. (ENG., Illus.). 256p. 57.95 *(978-0-8078-3230-1(8))* Univ. of North Carolina Pr.

Bauer, Dale, ed. The Cambridge History of American Women's Literature. 2012. (ENG., Illus.). 728p. 180.00 ***(978-1-107-00137-4(4))*** Cambridge Univ. Pr.

Bauer, Dale & Bauer, Dale M. Sex Expression & American Women Writers, 1860-1940. 2009. (ENG., Illus.). 256p. pap. 23.00 *(978-0-8078-5906-3(0))* Univ. of North Carolina Pr.

Bender, Karen. Choice: True Stories of Birth, Contraception, Infertility, Adoption, Single Parenthood, & Abortion. de Gramont, Nina, ed. 2007. (ENG.). 350p. per. *(978-1-59692-062-0(9))* MacAdam/Cage Publishing, Inc.

Bender, Karen E. Choice: True Stories of Birth, Contraception, Infertility, Adoption, Single Parenthood, & Abortion. de Gramont, Nina, ed. 2007. (ENG.). 350p. *(978-1-59692-063-7(7))* MacAdam/Cage Publishing, Inc.

Bloom, Harold, ed. Carson Mccullers, New Edition. 2nd rev. ed. 2009. (Bloom's Modern Critical Views Ser.). 200p. (C). (gr. 9-18). 45.00 *(978-1-60413-394-3(5)*, Chelsea Hse.) Facts On File, Inc.

Bouson, J. Brooks. Embodied Shame: Uncovering Female Shame in Contemporary Women's Writings. 2010. 236p. pap. 24.95 *(978-1-4384-2728-7(X)*, Suny Pr.) 2009. 256p. 70.00 *(978-1-4384-2727-0(1))* State Univ. of New York Pr.

Boyd, Anne E. Writing for Immortality: Women & the Emergence of High Literary Culture in America. 2009. (ENG., Illus.). 326p. (gr. 17). pap. 30.00 *(978-0-8018-9401-5(8))* Johns Hopkins Univ. Pr.

Boyd, Anne E., ed. Wielding the Pen: Writings on Authorship by American Women of the Nineteenth Century. 2009. (ENG.). 488p. (C). (gr. 13-17). 77.00 *(978-0-8018-9274-5(0))*; pap. 36.00 *(978-0-8018-9275-2(9))* Johns Hopkins Univ. Pr.

Brooks, Joanna, et al, eds. Transatlantic Feminisms in the Age of Revolutions, 1 vol. 2012. (ENG., Illus.). 432p. 99.00 *(978-0-19-974348-3(7))*; 360p. pap. 34.95 *(978-0-19-974349-0(5))* Oxford Univ. Pr., Inc.

Carpenter, Cari M. Seeing Red: Anger, Sentimentality, & American Indians. 2008. (ENG., Illus.). 208p. 49.95 *(978-0-8142-1079-6(1))*; xiv, 177p. cd-rom 14.95 *(978-0-8142-9158-0(9))* Ohio State Univ. Pr.

Carruth, Mary C., ed. Feminist Interventions in Early American Studies. 2006. (Illus.). 352p. pap. 36.50 *(978-0-8173-5342-1(9))* Univ. of Alabama Pr.

Carruth, Mary C., ed. & contrib. by. Feminist Interventions in Early American Studies. 2006. (Illus.). 352p. 65.00 *(978-0-8173-1523-8(3))* Univ. of Alabama Pr.

Carter, Tomeiko Ashford. Powers Divine: Spiritual Autobiography & Black Women's Writing. 2008. (ENG.). 194p. pap. 36.99 *(978-0-7618-4184-5(9))* Univ. Pr. of America, Inc.

Chandra, Giti. Narrating Violence, Constructing Collective Identities: 'to Witness These Wrongs Unspeakable' 2009. (ENG., Illus.). 216p. 89.00 *(978-0-230-21962-5(4))* Palgrave Macmillan.

Cook, Sylvia Jenkins. Working Women, Literary Ladies: The Industrial Revolution & Female Aspiration. 2008. (ENG.). 336p. 99.00 *(978-0-19-532780-9(2))*; pap. 24.95 *(978-0-19-532781-6(0))* Oxford Univ. Pr., Inc.

Corbett, Katie. Through This Reporter's Eyes: A collection of Articles by Katie Corbett. 2006. per. 10.00 *(978-0-9788447-7-6(7))* Printmedia Bks.

Cotera, María Eugenia. Native Speakers: Ella Deloria, Zora Neale Hurston, Jovita Gonzalez, & the Poetics of Culture. 2010. (ENG., Illus.). 300p. pap. 25.00 *(978-0-292-72161-6(7))* Univ. of Texas Pr.

Crazzolara, Monica. Borders in Chicana Literature: Gloria Anzaldúa & Sandra Cisneros. 2008. 104p. pap. (978-3-8364-9418-2(3)) VDM Verlag Dr. Mueller e.K.

Danielson, Marivel. Homecoming Queers: Desire & Difference in Chicana Latina Cultural Production. 2009. (Latinidad Ser.). (ENG.). 242p. 72.00 (978-0-8135-4571-4(4)) Rutgers Univ. Pr.

—Homecoming Queers: Desire & Difference in Chicana Latina Cultural Production. 2009. (Latinidad Ser.). (ENG.). 224p. pap. 23.95 (978-0-8135-4572-1(2)) Rutgers Univ. Pr.

Dean, Jenny. Latina Filmmakers & Writers: The Notion of Chicanisma Through Films & Novellas. 2007. 248p. per. 26.95 (978-0-9796457-1-6(9)) Floricanto Pr.

Eaton, Kalenda C. Womanism, Literature, & the Transformation of the Black Community, 1965-1980. 2007. (Studies in African American History & Culture Ser.). (ENG.). 122p. 125.00 (978-0-415-96129-5(7), 0415961297) Routledge.

Ebest, Sally Barr & McInerney, Kathleen, eds. Too Smart to Be Sentimental: Contemporary Irish American Women Writers. 2008. (ENG.). 288p. per. 29.00 (978-0-268-02773-5(0)) Univ. of Notre Dame Pr.

Elbert, Monika M., et al, eds. Reinventing the Peabody Sisters. annot. ed. 2006. 294p. (C). 39.95 (978-1-58729-504-1(0)) Univ. of Iowa Pr.

Engberg, null & Engberg, Kathrynn Se. The Right to Write: The Literary Politics of Anne Bradstreet & Phillis Wheatley. 2009. (ENG.). 110p. pap. 22.50 (978-0-7618-4609-3(3)) Univ. Pr. of America, Inc.

Feng, Pin-Chia. Diasporic Representations: Reading Chinese American Women's Fiction. 2011. 200p. pap. 49.95 **(978-3-643-10831-9(1))** Lit Verlag DEU. Dist: Transaction Pubs.

Ferguson, SallyAnn H. Nineteenth-Century Black Women's Literary Emergence: Evolutionary Spirituality, Sexuality, & Identity: An Anthology. 2008. (African American Literature & Culture: Expanding & Exploding the Boundaries Ser.: Vol. 17). 352p. (C). 119.95 (978-1-4331-0158-8(0)); pap. 34.95 (978-1-4331-0157-1(2)) Lang, Peter Publishing, Inc.

Fishkin, Shelley Fisher. Feminist Engagements: Forays into American Literature & Culture. 2009. (ENG.). 288p. pap. 30.00 (978-0-230-61594-6(5)) Palgrave Macmillan.

Flannery, Kathryn Thoms. Feminist Literacies, 1968-75. 2010. (ENG., Illus.). 280p. pap. 25.00 (978-0-252-07728-9(6)) Univ. of Illinois Pr.

Foreman, P. Gabrielle. Activist Sentiments: Reading Black Women in the Nineteenth Century. 2009. (New Black Studies Ser.). (ENG., Illus.). 280p. 75.00 (978-0-252-03474-9(0)); pap. 25.00 (978-0-252-07664-0(8)) Univ. of Illinois Pr.

Forrest, Emma. Damage Control: Women on the Therapists, Beauticians, & Trainers Who Navigate Their Bodies. 2007. (ENG.). 288p. per. 13.95 (978-0-06-117535-0(8), William Morrow Paperbacks) HarperCollins Pubs.

Freeman, Julia. Women of the South Distinguished in Literature. 2008. (Civil War Ser.). (ENG.). 536p. pap. 32.95 (978-1-4290-1572-1(1)) Applewood Bks.

G?ts y Prietas: Celebrating 20 Years of Borderlands/la Frontera. 2009. (Illus.). 10.00 (978-0-9786520-0-2(9)) Adelante Project.

Geis, Deborah R. Suzan-Lori Parks. 2008. (Michigan Modern Dramatists Ser.). (ENG., Illus.). 184p. (C). pap. 19.95 (978-0-472-06946-0(2)); 59.50 (978-0-472-09946-7(9)) Univ. of Michigan Pr.

Gilbert, Sandra M. Rereading Women: Thirty Years of Exploring Our Literary Traditions. 2011. (ENG.). 380p. 29.95 (978-0-393-06764-4(5), 6764) Norton, W. W. & Co., Inc.

Gilbert, Sandra M. & Gubar, Susan. The Norton Anthology of Literature by Women: The Traditions in English, 2 vols. 3rd ed. 2007. (ENG., Illus.). (C). 1504p. pap. 47.00 net. (978-0-393-93013-9(0), 93013); 1616p. pap. 47.00 net. (978-0-393-93014-6(9), 93014) Norton, W. W. & Co., Inc.

Gilbert, Sandra M. & Gubar, Susan, eds. The Norton Anthology of Literature by Women: The Traditions in English, 2 vols. 3rd ed. 2007. (ENG., Illus.). 2452p. (C). pap. 63.00 net. (978-0-393-93015-3(7), 93015) Norton, W. W. & Co., Inc.

Goodspeed-Chadwick, Julie. Modernist Women Writers & War: Trauma & the Female Body in Djuna Barnes, H.D., & Gertrude Stein. 2011. 184p. 35.00 (978-0-8071-3681-2(6)) Louisiana State Univ. Pr.

Griffith, Jean Carol. The Color of Democracy in Women's Regional Writing. 2009. (American Literary Realism & Naturalism Ser.). (ENG., Illus.). 280p. 49.50 (978-0-8173-1661-7(2)) Univ. of Alabama Pr.

Griffiths, Jennifer L. Traumatic Possessions: The Body & Memory in African American Women's Writing & Performance. 2010. (ENG.). 144p. (C). (gr. 13-17). pap. 19.50 (978-0-8139-2884-5(2)); (gr. 17). 39.50 (978-0-8139-2883-8(4)) Univ. Pr. of Virginia.

Hammill, Faye. Women, Celebrity, & Literary Culture between the Wars. 2010. (ENG.). 271p. pap. 25.00 (978-0-292-72606-2(6)) Univ. of Texas Pr.

Hart, Sue, intro. Montana Women Writers: A Geography of the Heart. 2006. 395p. (978-1-56037-405-3(5)) Farcountry Pr.

—Montana Women Writers: A Geography of the Heart. 2006. 395p. per. (978-1-56037-379-7(2)) Farcountry Pr.

Hedley, Jane. I Made You to Find Me: The Coming of Age of the Woman Poet & the Politics of Poetic Address. 2009. (ENG.). 199p. 44.95 (978-0-8142-1101-4(1)) Ohio State Univ. Pr.

Hellman, Caroline. Domesticity & Design in American Womens Lives & Literature. 2011. (Routledge Studies in Nineteenth Century Literature Ser.). (ENG., Illus.). 146p. (C). 125.00 (978-0-415-88272-9(9)) Routledge.

Heredia, Juanita. Transnational Latina Narratives in the Twenty-First Century: The Politics of Gender, Race, & Migrations. 2009. (ENG.). 192p. 84.00 (978-0-230-61737-7(9)) Palgrave Macmillan.

Hoeveler, Diane Long & Schuster, Donna Decker, eds. Women's Literary Creativity & the Female Body. 2007. (ENG.). 228p. 89.00 (978-1-4039-8383-1(6)) Palgrave Macmillan.

Hogeland, Lisa Maria, et al, eds. The Aunt Lute Anthology of U. S. Women Writers, Volume Two: The 20th Century. 2007. (ENG.). 1416p. pap. 45.00 (978-1-879960-77-C(X)) Aunt Lute Bks.

Homestead, Melissa J. American Women Authors & Literary Property, 1822-1869. 2010. (ENG.). 288p. pap. 38.00 (978-0-521-15475-8(8)) Cambridge Univ. Pr.

Horton-Stallings, LaMonda. Mutha Is Half a Word: Intersections of Folklore, Vernacular, Myth, & Queerness in Black Female Literature. 2007. (Black Performance & Cultural Criticism Ser.). cd-rom 9.95 (978-0-8142-9135-1(X)) Ohio State Univ. Pr.

Kallet, Marilyn & Byer, Kathryn Stripling. The Movable Nest: A Mother/Daughter Companion. 2007. pap. (978-1-884235-39-9(5)) Helicon 9 Editions.

Kazmierczak, Elka, ed. & des. Art of Survival: Women, Healing, & the Arts. 1600th ed. 2006. (Illus.). 32p. 12.95 (978-0-9778478-0-8(2)) Elka Bks.

Kennedy, Mark. Life Stories. 2008. 292p. pap. 21.95 (978-0-9816172-3-7(9)) Westview Publishing Co., Inc.

Keyser, Catherine. Playing Smart: New York Women Writers & Modern Magazine Culture. (Mellon-ALI Ser.). (ENG., 242p. 2011. Illus.). pap. 23.95 **(978-0-8135-5178-4(1))** 2010. 39.95 (978-0-8135-4786-2(5)) Rutgers Univ. Pr.

Kinser, Brent E. & Tarr, Rodger L., eds. Marjorie Kinnan Rawlings's Cross Creek Sampler: A Book of Quotations. 2011. (ENG., Illus.). 224p. 22.50 (978-0-8130-3724-0(7)) Univ. Pr. of Florida.

Knight, Charles. Mind Amongst the Spindles. 2010. 244p. pap. 16.95 (978-1-4290-4131-7(5)) Applewood Bks.

Knoerrich Isabel & Hammad, Lamia Khalil. U.S. Women of Color Theorize Subversion Through Cross-Genre Writing: Contemporary Perspectives on Race, Gender, Culture. 2009. 196p. pap. (978-3-639-03797-5(9)) VDM Verlag Dr. Mueller e.K.

Kort, Carol. A to Z of American Women Writers. 2nd rev. ed. 2007. (A to Z of Women Ser.). (Illus.). 416p. (C). (gr. 9). 60.00 (978-0-8160-6693-3(0)) Facts On File, Inc.

Krick-Aigner, Kirsten. Unredeemed Past: Themes of War & Womanhood in the Works of Post-World War II Austrian Women Writers. 2011. 276p. pap. **(978-1-57241-179-1(1))** Ariadne Pr.

Kurucz, Anikó. Mother-Daughter Relationship & Cultural Inheritance. 2008. 52p. pap. (978-3-639-00347-5(0)) VDM Verlag Dr. Mueller e.K.

Labatt, Laura M., et al, eds. Risk, Courage, & Women: Contemporary Voices in Prose & Poetry. 2007. (ENG.). 384p. pap. 19.95 (978-1-57441-234-5(5)) Univ. of North Texas Pr.

LaGreca, Nancy. Rewriting Womanhood: Feminism, Subjectivity, & the Angel of the House in the Latin American Novel, 1887-1903. 2009. (Penn State Romance Studies). (ENG.). 200p. 65.00 (978-0-271-03438-6(6)); pap. 35.00 (978-0-271-03439-3(4)) Pennsylvania State Univ. Pr.

Lawrence, Deborah. Writing the Trail: Five Women's Frontier Narratives. 2006. (Illus.). 158p. 29.95 (978-1-58729-509-6(1)) Univ. of Iowa Pr.

Lewis, Nghana tamu. Entitled to the Pedestal: Place, Race, & Progress in White Southern Women's Writing,1920-1945. 2007. 224p. 37.95 (978-1-58729-529-4(6)) Univ. of Iowa Pr.

Li, Stephanie. Something Akin to Freedom: The Choice of Bondage in Narratives by African American Women. 2011. 172p. pap. 23.95 (978-1-4384-2970-0(3), Suny Pr.) 2010. 160p. 60.00 (978-1-4384-2971-7(1)) State Univ. of New York Pr.

Lopez, Sam. Post-Revolutionary Chicana Literature: Memoir, Folklore, & Fiction of the Border, 1900-1950. 2006. (Latino Communities: Emerging Voices — Political, Social, Cultural & Legal Issues Ser.). (Illus.). 140p. 138.00 (978-0-415-95553-9(X)) Routledge.

MacPherson, Heidi Slettedahl. Transatlantic Women's Literature. 2009. (Edinburgh Critical Studies in Transatlantic Literature Ser.). (ENG.). 192p. (gr. 17). 85.00 (978-0-7486-2445-4(7)) Edinburgh Univ. Pr. GBR. Dist: Columbia Univ. Pr.

Maffly-Kipp, Laurie F. & Lofton, Kathryn. Women's Work: An Anthology of African-American Women's Historical Writings from the Era of Slavery to the Harlem Renaissance. 2010. (ENG.). 256p. pap. 19.95 (978-0-19-533199-8(0)) Oxford Univ. Pr., Inc.

Marsh, Nicky. Democracy in Contemporary U. S. Women's Poetry. 2007. (American Literature Readings in the Twenty-First Century Ser.). (ENG.). 228p. 89.00 (978-0-230-60026-3(3)) Palgrave Macmillan.

Mastrangelo, Lisa. Writing a Progressive Past: Women Teaching & Writing in the Progressive ERA. 2012. pap. **(978-1-60235-258-2(5))** Parlor Pr.

McDonald, Kathlene. Feminism, the Left, & Postwar Literary Culture. 2012. (ENG.). 160p. 55.00 **(978-1-61703-301-8(4))** Univ. Pr. of Mississippi.

Mitchell, Angelyn & Taylor, Danille K., eds. The Cambridge Companion to African American Women's Literature. 2009. (Cambridge Companions to Literature Ser.). (ENG.). 336p. (C). 98.00 (978-0-521-85888-5(7)); pap. 29.99 (978-0-521-67582-6(0)) Cambridge Univ. Pr.

Mitchell, Verner D. & Davis, Cynthia. Literary Sisters: Dorothy West & Her Circle, a Biography of the Harlem Renaissance. 2011. (ENG.). 216p. (C). pap. 24.95 (978-0-8135-5146-3(3)); (Illus.). 208p. 72.00 (978-0-8135-5145-6(5)) Rutgers Univ. Pr.

Musawa, narrated by. In the Spirit of We'Moon: Celebrating 30 Years. 2011. (ENG., Illus.). 255p. pap. 25.95 **(978-1-890931-75-9(6))** Mother Tongue Ink.

Nieves-Colón, Myrna E. Breaking Ground: Anthology of Puerto Rican Women Writers in New York, 1980-2010 = Antología de Escritoras Puertorriqueñas en Nueva York, 1980-2010. 2011. (SPA & ENG.). pap. **(978-1-934370-16-2(9))** Editorial Campana.

Orr, Lisa. Transforming American Realism: Working-Class Women Writers of the Twentieth Century. 2006. (ENG.). 148p. per. 30.50 (978-0-7618-3611-7(X)) Univ. Pr. of America, Inc.

Rader, Pamela/J. Multi-Ethnicity as a Resource for the Literary Imagination: The Creative Achievements of Women Artists, Poets, & Novelists. 2009. 156p. (978-0-7734-3893-4(9)) Mellen, Edwin Pr., The.

Raymond, Ida. Southland Writers Biographical & Critical Sketches of the Living Female Writers of the South with Extracts from Their Writings by Ida Raymond Vo. 2006. 464p. per. 29.99 (978-1-4255-5136-0(X)); (ENG.). 524p. per. 29.99 (978-1-4255-5804-8(6)) MPublishing.

Reesman, Jeanne Campbell, ed. Speaking the Other Self: American Women Writers. 2011. (ENG.). 352p. pap. 24.95 **(978-0-8203-3798-2(6))** Univ. of Georgia Pr.

Russell, Heather & Bassard, Katherine Clay. Transforming Scriptures: African American Women Writers & the Bible. 2010. (ENG.). 180p. 44.95 (978-0-8203-3090-7(6)) Univ. of Georgia Pr.

Sabry, Somaya Sami. Arab-American Women's Writing & Performance: Orientalism, Race & the Idea of the Arabian Nights. 2011. (International Library of Cultural Studies). (ENG., Illus.). 224p. 88.00 (978-1-84885-568-7(0), Tauris Academic Studies) I. B. Tauris & Co., Ltd. GBR. Dist: Macmillan.

Sandoval, Anna Marie. Toward a Latina Feminism of the Americas: Repression & Resistance in Chicana & Mexicana Literature. Castañeda, Antonia & González, Deena J., eds. 2009. (ENG.). 144p. pap. 19.95 (978-0-292-72166-1(8)) Univ. of Texas Pr.

Scott, Renee & Chiclana y Gonzalez, Arleen, eds. Unveiling the Body in Hispanic Women's Literature: From Nineteenth-Century Spain to Twenty-First-Century United States. 2006. 240p. (C). 109.95 (978-0-7734-5673-0(2)) Mellen, Edwin Pr., The.

Showalter, Elaine. A Jury of Her Peers: Celebrating American Women Writers from Anne Bradstreet to Annie Proulx. 2010. (Vintage Ser.). (ENG.). 608p. pap. 16.95 (978-1-4000-3442-0(6), Vintage) Knopf Doubleday Publishing Group.

—The Vintage Book of American Women Writers. 2011. (Vintage Ser.). 848p. pap. 18.95 (978-1-4000-3445-1(0), Vintage) Knopf Doubleday Publishing Group.

Spencer Maor, Faye. Lifting Word by Word. 2008. 84p. pap. (978-3-639-06233-5(7)) VDM Verlag Dr. Mueller e.K.

Staley, Gregory A., ed. American Women & Classical Myths. 2008. (ENG., Illus.). 300p. (C). pap. 34.95 (978-1-932792-85-0(6)) Baylor Univ. Pr.

Stallings, L. H. Mutha Is Half a Word: Intersections of Folklore, Vernacular, Myth, & Queerness in Black Female Culture. 2007. (Black Performance & Cultural Criticism Ser.). (ENG.). 334p. 49.95 (978-0-8142-1056-7(2)) Ohio State Univ. Pr.

Sugano, Miyoko. Ho'okupu: An Offering of Literature. 2009. pap. 12.95 (978-1-56647-902-8(9)) Mutual Publishing LLC.

Tenney, Tabitha G. Female Quixotism: Exhibited in the Romantic Opinions & Extravagant Adventures of Dorcasina Sheldon, 2 vols. in 1. reprint ed. 37.50 (978-0-404-17397-5(7)) AMS Pr., Inc.

Turpin, Cherie Ann. How Three Black Women Writers Combined Spiritual & Sensual Love: Rhetorically Transcending the Boundaries of Language (Audre Lorde, Toni Morrison, & Dionne Brand) 2010. 120p. 89.95 (978-0-7734-3839-2(4)) Mellen, Edwin Pr., The.

Vetter, Lara. Modernist Writings & Religio-Scientific Discourse: H. D., Loy, & Toomer. 2010. (Modern & Contemporary Poetry & Poetics Ser.). (ENG., Illus.) 236p. 84.00 (978-0-230-62122-0(8)) Palgrave Macmillan.

Waldron, Karen A., et al, eds. Risk, Courage, & Women: Contemporary Voices in Prose & Poetry. 2007. (ENG.). 384p. 34.95 (978-1-57441-233-8(7)) Univ. of North Texas Pr.

Walters, Tracey L. African American Literature & the Classicist Tradition: Black Women Writers from Wheatley to Morrison. 2007. (ENG.). 224p. 89.00 (978-0-230-60022-5(0)) Palgrave Macmillan.

Weber, Brenda R. Women & Literary Celebrity in the Nineteenth Century: The Transatlantic Production of Fame & Gender. 2012. (Ashgate Ser. in Nineteenth-Century Transatlantic Studies). (Illus.). 220p. 99.95 **(978-1-4094-0074-5(3))**; 99.95 **(978-1-4094-0073-8(5))** Ashgate Publishing Co.

Weese, Katherine J. Feminist Narrative & the Supernatural: The Function of Fantastic Devices in Seven Recent Novels. Palumbo, Donald E. & Sullivan, C. W., III, eds. 2008. (Critical Explorations in Science Fiction & Fantasy Ser.). (ENG.). 234p. pap. 35.00 (978-0-7864-3615-6(8)) McFarland & Co., Inc. Pubs.

Wilks, Jennifer M., et al. Race, Gender, & Comparative Black Modernism: Suzanne Lacascade, Marita Bonner, Suzanne Césaire, Dorothy West. 2009. (Illus.). x, 259p. (978-0-8071-3364-4(7)) Louisiana State Univ. Pr.

Winter, Kari J. Subjects of Slavery, Agents of Change: Women & Power in Gothic Novels & Slave Narratives, 1790-1865. 2010. (ENG.). 186p. pap. 22.95 (978-0-8203-3699-2(8)) Univ. of Georgia Pr.

Zygadlo, Grazyna. Culture Matters: Chicanas' Identity in Contemporary USA. 2006. 166p. pap. (978-3-631-55096-0(0)) Lang, Peter AG.

AMERICAN LOYALISTS

Here are entered works on Americans whose allegiance remained with Great Britain during the Revolution. Works on American Loyalists who emigrated to Canada before 1789 are entered under United Empire Loyalists.

see also United Empire Loyalists

Allen, Thomas B. Tories: Fighting for the King in America's First Civil War. (ENG.). 2011. 496p. pap. 16.99 (978-0-06-124181-9(4), Harper Paperbacks) 2010. 480p. 26.99 (978-0-06-124180-2(6)) HarperCollins Pubs.

Calhoon, Robert M., et al. Tory Insurgents: The Loyalist Perception & Other Essays, Revised & Expanded Edition. 2nd rev. ed. 2010. (ENG.). 416p. 29.95 (978-1-57003-920-1(8)); pap. 59.95 (978-1-57003-890-7(2)) Univ. of South Carolina Pr.

Chopra, Ruma. Unnatural Rebellion: Loyalists in New York City During the Revolution. 2011. (Jeffersonian America Ser.). (ENG.). 320p. (gr. 17). 35.00 (978-0-8139-3109-8(6)) Univ. Pr. of Virginia.

Clift, G. Glenn. Loyalists in the American Revolution. cd-rom 19.99 (978-0-8063-9711-5(X)) Genealogical Publishing Co., Inc.

Cooke, Jacob E. Tench Coxe & the Early Republic. 2011. (Published for the Omohundro Institute of Early American History & Culture, Williamsburg Virginia Ser.). (ENG.). 587p. pap. 50.00 (978-0-8078-9639-6(X)) Univ. of North Carolina Pr.

Cruikshank, Ernest, et al. Butler's Rangers: Three Accounts of the American War of Independence. 2011. 168p. **(978-0-85706-711-1(7))**; pap. **(978-0-85706-712-8(5))** Leonaur Ltd.

Curwen, Samuel. Journal & Letters of the Late Samuel Curwen Judge of Admiralty, Etc. 2009. (Revolutionary War Ser.). (ENG.). 592p. pap. 34.95 (978-1-4290-1729-9(5)) Applewood Bks.

De Lancey's Brigade, Oliver. Orderly Book of the Three Battalions of Loyalists Commanded by Brigadier General Oliver De Lancey 1776-1778. 147p. reprint ed. 88.00 (978-0-7222-7667-7(7)) Library Reprints, Inc.

Dornfest, Walter T. Military Loyalists of the American Revolution: Officers & Regiments, 1775-1783. 2010. (ENG., Illus.). 524p. pap. 125.00 (978-0-7864-4815-9(6)) McFarland & Co., Inc. Pubs.

Eddis, William. Letters from America. 2009. (Revolutionary War Ser.). (ENG.). 472p. pap. 28.95 (978-1-4290-1608-7(6)) Applewood Bks.

Elson, Bryan. Nelson's Yankee Captain: The Life of Boston Loyalist Sir Benjamin Hallowell. 2008. (ENG., Illus.). 416p. 29.95 (978-0-88780-751-0(8)) Formac Publishing Co., Ltd. CAN. Dist: Casemate Pubs. & Bk. Distributors, LLC.

Ferguson, Henry. Essays in American History. 2009. 88p. pap. (978-0-217-47227-2(3)) Books LLC.

—Essays in American History. 2009. 214p. 39.95 (978-1-104-80057-4(8)); pap. 24.95 (978-1-104-74405-2(8)) Kessinger Publishing, LLC.

Fingerhut, Eugene R., et al, eds. The Other Loyalists: Ordinary People, Royalism, & the Revolution in the Middle Colonies, 1763-1787. 2010. (Illus.). 220p. pap. 23.95 (978-1-4384-2590-0(2), Suny Pr.) State Univ. of New York Pr.

Flick, Alexander Clarence. Loyalism in New York During the American Revolution. 2010. 138p. pap. (978-1-151-54448-3(5)) Books LLC.

—Loyalism in New York During the American Revolution. 2008. 280p. 42.95 (978-0-548-95725-7(8)) 2007. (ENG.). 284p. per. 27.95 (978-0-548-63246-8(4)) Kessinger Publishing, LLC.

—Loyalism in New York During the American Revolution. 284p. reprint ed. 98.00 (978-0-7222-7675-4(3)) Library Reprints, Inc.

Fox, Ebenezer, et al. Three Views of Independence: Firsthand Accounts of the Revolutionary War from an American Patriot, an American Tory, & a French Volunteer. 2011. 270p. pap. (978-1-61001-014-6(0)) Red & Black Pubs.

Galloway, Joseph. The Claim of the American Loyalists Reviewed & Maintained upon Incontrovertible Principles of Law & Justice. 2009. 62p. pap. 14.14 (978-1-151-46432-3(5)) General Bks. LLC.

Gould, Dudley C. Benedict Arnold. 2006. (Illus.). 72p. pap. 9.95 (978-0-913337-61-5(7)) Southfarm Pr.

Harrell, Isaac S. Loyalism in Virginia: Chapters in the Economic History of the Revolution. reprint ed. 32.50 (978-0-404-03135-0(8)) AMS Pr., Inc.

Harrell, Isaac Samuel. Loyalism in Virginia: Chapters in the Economic History of the Revolution. 2011. 212p. 44.95 **(978-1-258-10374-3(5))** Literary Licensing, LLC.

Ingersoll, Jared. Papers. reprint ed. 150.00 (978-0-7222-6533-8(6)) Library Reprints, Inc.

Jasanoff, Maya. Liberty's Exiles: American Loyalists in the Revolutionary World. 2011. (ENG., Illus.). 480p. 30.00 (978-1-4000-4168-8(6), Knopf) Knopf Doubleday Publishing Group.

Jodoin, Mark. Shadow Soldiers of the American Revolution: Loyalist Tales from New York to Canada. 2009. (Regional Histories Ser.). 160p. pap. 21.99 (978-1-59629-726-5(3)) History Pr., The.

Johnson, Uzal, et al. Captured at Kings Mountain: The Journal of Uzal Johnson, a Loyalist Surgeon. Weir, Robert M. ed. 2011. (ENG., Illus.). 248p. 39.95 (978-1-57003-961-4(5)) Univ. of South Carolina Pr.

Jones, Thomas. History of New York During the Revolutionary War. 2009. 354p. pap. (978-0-217-00127-4(0)); 348p. pap. (978-0-217-84110-8(4)); 482p. pap. (978-0-217-84106-1(6)) Books LLC.

—History of New York During the Revolutionary War, 2 vol., set. reprint ed. 250.00 (978-0-7222-7683-9(4)) Library Reprints, Inc.

Lovelace, Daniel D. Tory Spy: A New York Frontier Family's War Against the American Revolution. 2009. pap. 31.00 (978-0-7884-5025-9(5)) Heritage Bks.

Lovelace, Daniel Dudley. Tory Spy: A New York Frontier Family's War Against the American Revolution. 2009. (Illus.). xvi, 334p. (978-0-7884-8293-9(9)) Heritage Bks.

McNealy, Terry A. The Doan Gang: The Remarkable History of America's Most Notorious Loyalist Outlaws. 2012. (ENG., Illus.). 400p. 29.95 (978-1-59416-062-2(7)) Westholme Publishing.

Murray, James. Letters of James Murray, Loyalist. 324p. reprint ed. 98.00 *(978-0-7222-6537-6(9))* Library Reprints, Inc.

Palmer, Dave Richard. George Washington & Benedict Arnold: A Tale of Two Patriots. 2010. (ENG.). 424p. pap. 18.95 *(978-1-59698-640-4(9))* Regnery Publishing, Inc., An Eagle Publishing Co.

Piecuch, Jim. Three Peoples, One King: Loyalists, Indians, & Slaves in the Revolutionary South, 1775-1782. 2008. (Illus.). 456p. 39.95 *(978-1-57003-737-5(X))* Univ. of South Carolina Pr.

Pond, Edgar Le Roy. The Tories of Chippeny Hill, Connecticut: A Brief Account of the Loyalists of Bristol, Plymouth & Harwinton, Who Founded St. Matthew's Church in East Plymouth in 1791. 92p. reprint ed. 88.00 *(978-0-7222-7676-1(1))* Library Reprints, Inc.

Raymond, William Odber. Winslow Papers, A.D. 1776-1826. 732p. reprint ed. 148.00 *(978-0-7222-6750-9(9))* Library Reprints, Inc.

Sabine, Lorenzo. The American Loyalists: Biographical Sketches of Adherents to the British Crown in the War of the Revolution, Alphabetically Arranged, with a Preliminary Historical Essay. 733p. reprint ed. 148.00 *(978-0-7222-7677-8(X))* Library Reprints, Inc.

—Biographical Sketches of Loyalists of Th. 2006. (ENG.). pap. 45.95 *(978-1-4286-4102-0(5))*; pap. 44.95 *(978-1-4286-4088-7(6))* Kessinger Publishing, LLC.

—Biographical Sketches of Loyalists of the American Revolution. 2009. (Revolutionary War Ser.). (ENG.). Vol. 2. 624p. pap. 35.95 *(978-1-4290-1697-1(3))* Vol. 3. 608p. pap. 34.95 *(978-1-4290-1953-8(0))* Applewood Bks.

—Biographical Sketches of Loyalists of the American Revolution. 2009. 428p. pap. *(978-1-151-73776-2(3))*; 350p. pap. *(978-1-151-73775-5(5))*; 380p. pap. *(978-0-217-44652-5(3))*; 130p. pap. *(978-0-217-44654-9(X))*; 356p. pap. *(978-1-4590-5078-5(9))* Books LLC.

Sabine, Lorenzo. Biographical Sketches of Loyalists of the American Revolution In. 2011. 606p. pap. 52.50 ***(978-0-8063-0863-0(X))***; 626p. pap. 52.50 ***(978-0-8063-0862-3(1))*** Clearfield Co.

Siebert, Wilbur H. Loyalists in East Florida, 1774-1785: The Most Important Documents Pertaining Thereto..., 2 vols., 1. (American Revolutionary Ser.). (Illus.). 734p. reprint ed. lib. bdg. 63.00 *(978-0-8290-1684-0(8))* Irvington Pubs.

Siebert, Wilbur Henry. The Loyalists of Pennsylvania. 117p. reprint ed. 88.00 *(978-0-7222-7678-5(8))* Library Reprints, Inc.

Sparks, Jared. The Life & Treason of Benedict Arnold. 2009. 360p. 26.99 *(978-1-103-41390-4(2))* 2009. 360p. pap. 20.99 *(978-1-103-41387-4(2))* 2008. 361p. 29.99 *(978-0-559-02552-5(1))* 2008. 361p. 31.99 *(978-0-559-02537-2(8))* 2008. 361p. pap. 31.75 *(978-0-559-02546-4(7))* 2008. 361p. pap. 32.75 *(978-0-559-02539-6(4))* BiblioBazaar.

—The Life & Treason of Benedict Arnold. 2008. 348p. 46.95 *(978-1-4374-0565-1(7))*; pap. 31.95 *(978-1-4373-1834-0(7))* Kessinger Publishing, LLC.

—The Life & Treason of Benedict Arnold. 335p. reprint ed. 98.00 *(978-0-7222-8554-1(X))*; 98.00 *(978-0-7222-9269-3(4))* Library Reprints, Inc.

Stark, James Henry. The Loyalists of Massachusetts & the Other Side of the American Revolution. 2009. 546p. pap. *(978-1-150-31446-9(X))* Books LLC.

—The Loyalists of Massachusetts & the Other Side of the American Revolution. 509p. reprint ed. 98.00 *(978-0-7222-7679-2(6))* Library Reprints, Inc.

Thompson, Kent. The Man Who Said No: Reading Jacob Bailey, Loyalist. 2008. (ENG.). 288p. pap. *(978-1-55447-055-6(2))* Gaspereau Pr.

Tiedemann, Joseph S. The Other Loyalists: Ordinary People, Royalism, & the Revolution in the Middle Colonies, 1763-1787. Fingerhut, Eugene R. & Venables, Robert W., eds. 2009. (Illus.). 224p. 70.00 *(978-1-4384-2589-4(9))* State Univ. of New York Pr.

Van Tyne, Claude Halstead. The Loyalists in the American Revolution. 2008. 370p. 48.95 *(978-0-548-96292-3(8))* 2007. (ENG.). 372p. per. 33.95 *(978-0-548-63835-4(7))* Kessinger Publishing, LLC.

—The Loyalists in the American Revolution. 360p. reprint ed. 98.00 *(978-0-7222-7680-8(X))* Library Reprints, Inc.

Wallace, William Stewart. The United Empire Loyalists: A Chronicle of the Great Migration. (Chronicles of Canada Ser.). 148p. reprint ed. 88.00 *(978-0-7222-6784-4(3))* Library Reprints, Inc.

Yoshpe, Harry B. Disposition of Loyalist Estates in the Southern District of the State of New York. (Columbia University, Studies in the Social Sciences: No. 458). reprint ed. 21.50 *(978-0-404-51458-7(8))* AMS Pr., Inc.

AMERICAN LUTHERAN CHURCH (1961-1987)

see also Evangelical Lutheran Church In America

Preus, David W. Pastor & President: Reflections of a Lutheran Churchman. 2012. (ENG., Illus.). 192p. pap. 18.00 ***(978-1-932688-64-1(1),*** Lutheran Univ. Pr.) Kirk Hse. Pubs.

AMERICAN MEDICAL ASSOCIATION

Ameringer, Carl F. The Health Care Revolution: From Medical Monopoly to Market Competition. 2008. (California/Milbank Books on Health & the Public: Vol. 19). (Illus.). 253p. 60.00 *(978-0-520-25480-0(5))* Univ. of California Pr.

Cooper, Melvin. Social Construction of Ama Code of Ethics. 2009. 318p. pap. *(978-3-639-17715-2(0))* VDM Verlag Dr. Mueller e.K.

AMERICAN MERCURY

Fitzgerald, F. Scott. Absolution: American Mercury V2, No. 6, June 1924. Mencken, H. I. & Nathan, George Jean, eds. 2011. 12p. pap. 35.95 ***(978-1-258-01704-0(0))*** Literary Licensing, LLC.

Singleton, Marvin Kenneth. H L Mencken & the American Mercury Adventure. 2011. 282p. 48.95 ***(978-1-258-02571-7(X))*** Literary Licensing, LLC.

Spivak, Lawrence E. & Angoff, Charles, eds. The American Mercury Reader. 27.95 *(978-0-8488-0119-9(9))* Amereon LTD.

—The American Mercury Reader. 2010. 384p. 39.16 *(978-1-163-37747-5(3))* 2010. 384p. pap. 27.16 *(978-1-162-77681-1(1))* 2007. (ENG.). 382p. 48.95 *(978-0-548-06777-2(5))* Kessinger Publishing, LLC.

AMERICAN-MEXICAN BORDER REGION

see Mexican-American Border Region

AMERICAN MISSIONARY ASSOCIATION

Anderson, Toni P. Tell Them We Are Singing for Jesus: The Original Fisk Jubilee Singers & Christian Reconstruction, 1871- 2009. (Illus.). 352p. 45.00 *(978-0-88146-112-1(1))* Mercer Univ. Pr.

Richardson, Joe Martin. Christian Reconstruction: The American Missionary Association & Southern Blacks, 1861-1890. 2009. (ENG., Illus.). 374p. pap. 37.50 *(978-0-8173-5538-8(3))* Univ. of Alabama Pr.

Richardson, Joe Martin & Jones, Maxine Deloris. Education for Liberation: The American Missionary Association & African Americans, 1890 to the Civil Rights Movement. 2009. (ENG., Illus.). 328p. 49.50 *(978-0-8173-1657-0(4))* Univ. of Alabama Pr.

AMERICAN MOTORS AUTOMOBILES

see also Jeep Automobile

Cranswick, Marc. The Cars of American Motors: An Illustrated History. 2011. (ENG., Illus.). 364p. pap. 38.00 *(978-0-7864-4672-8(2))* McFarland & Co., Inc. Pubs.

Foster, Patrick R. Hudson Automobiles. 2010. (Illustrated History Ser.). (ENG., Illus.). 128p. pap. 34.95 *(978-1-58388-266-5(9),* 1583882669) Iconografix, Inc.

Holmstrom, Darwin & Newhardt, David. Gto: Pontiac's Great One. 2009. (ENG., Illus.). 336p. 50.00 *(978-0-7603-3515-4(X),* 076033515X, Motorbooks) MBI Publishing Co. LLC.

Swygert, Frank, compiled by. The Red, White & Blue Book: An American Motors Numbers Guide, 1955-1988. 2007. (Illus.). 70p. spiral bd. 14.95 *(978-0-9821372-0-8(6))* FARNA Systems Publishing.

AMERICAN MUSEUM OF NATURAL HISTORY

Freed, Stanley A. Anthropology Unmasked: Museums, Science, & Politics in New York City. 2011. *(978-1-933197-84-5(6))*; 80.00 *(978-1-933197-83-8(8))* Orange Frazer Pr.

Glass, Aaron. Objects of Exchange: Social & Material Transformation on the Late Nineteenth-Century Northwest Coast. Glass, Aaron, ed. 2011. (Illus.). 256p. pap. *(978-0-9824680-0-5(8))* Bard Graduate Ctr., Exhibitions Dept.

Kirk, Jay. Kingdom under Glass: A Tale of Obsession, Adventure, & One Man's Quest to Preserve the World's Great Animals. 2011. (ENG., Illus.). 400p. pap. 18.00 *(978-0-312-61073-9(4))* Picador.

Williamson, Laila & Young, Serinity, eds. Body & Spirit: Tibetan Medical Paintings. 2009. (ENG., Illus.). 264p. pap. 45.00 *(978-0-295-98869-6(X))* Univ. of Washington Pr.

AMERICAN MUSIC

see Music, American

AMERICAN NATIONAL CHARACTERISTICS

see National Characteristics, American

AMERICAN NATIONAL RED CROSS

Barton, William E. Life of Clara Barton, 2 vols. reprint ed. 78.50 *(978-0-404-00730-0(9))* AMS Pr., Inc.

Bosley, Paul S., ed. Mass Care in Disasters - FEMA, the Red Cross & Volunteers. 2008. 69.00 *(978-1-60692-725-0(6))* Nova Science Pubs., Inc.

Federal Emergency Management Agency's Response to the 2008 Hurricane Season & the National Housing Strategy: Hearing Before the Subcommittee on Economic Development, Public Buildings, & Emergency Management of the Committee on Transportation & Infrastructure, House of Representatives, One Hundred Tenth Congress, Second Session, September 23, 2008. 2008. (Illus.). x, 167p. *(978-0-16-083237-6(3),* 552-070-39065-1) United States Government Printing Office.

Madison, James H. Slinging Doughnuts for the Boys: An American Woman in World War II. (Illus.). 2008. (ENG.). 320p. pap. 20.95 *(978-0-253-22107-0(2),* 0253221072) 2007. 300p. 24.95 *(978-0-253-35047-3(6))* Indiana Univ. Pr.

Marko, Eva. Clara Barton. 2006. (ENG.). 240p. (C). pap. 13.95 *(978-1-4240-0532-1(9))* Cengage Heinle.

United States, Congress House Committee on Foreign Affairs Staff, contrib. by. The American Red Cross Governance Reform: Hearing Before the Committee on Foreign Affairs, House of Representatives, One Hundred Tenth Congress, First Session, March 14, 2007. 2007. (Illus.). iii, 51p. *(978-0-16-078673-0(8),* 552-070-35904-4) United States Government Printing Office.

Warneka, Timothy. Healing Katrina: Volunteering in Post-Hurricane Mississippi. 2007. 124p. (ENG.). per. 19.95 *(978-0-9768627-3-4(5))*; (Illus.). per. 29.95 net. *(978-0-9768627-7-2(8))* Asogomi Publishing International.

Weber, Astrid. Ist die Rotkreuzschwester Arbeitnehmerin ihrer Schwesternschaft? Zugleich eine Untersuchung der Arbeitnehmereigenschaft mithilfe der AGB-Kontrolle. 2009. (Schriften zum Deutschen und Europäischen Arbeits- und Sozialrecht Ser.). (GER.). 326p. 86.95 *(978-3-631-58610-5(8))* Lang, Peter GmbH, Europaischer Verlag der Wissenschaften DEU. Dist: Lang, Peter.

AMERICAN NEWSPAPER PUBLISHERS ASSOCIATION

Emery, Edwin, ed. History of the American Newspaper Publishers Association. 2009. (ENG.). 271p. pap. 50.00 *(978-0-8166-5979-1(6))* Univ. of Minnesota Pr.

AMERICAN NEWSPAPERS

see also German American Newspapers

also names of specific American newspapers

Almiron, Nuria. Journalism in Crisis: Corporate Media & Financialization. 2010. xii, 199p. *(978-1-57273-981-9(9))*; *(978-1-57273-980-2(0))* Hampton Pr., Inc.

Barfuss, Natalie. An Integrated Marketing Communication Case Study of a Small Daily Newspaper. 2008. 268p. pap. *(978-3-8364-7970-7(2))* VDM Verlag Dr. Mueller e.K.

Barnes, Robert W. Missing Relatives & Lost Friends. 2008. pap. 26.50 *(978-0-8063-5368-5(6))* Clearfield Co.

Baumgartner, Apollinaris W. Catholic Journalism. (BCL Ser. I). reprint ed. 21.50 *(978-0-404-00693-8(0))* AMS Pr., Inc.

Beauchamp, William. Early Marriages from Newspapers Published in Central New York. by William M. Beauchamp, Selected & Arranged by Grace Beauchamp Lodder of the Syracuse Public Library with an Appendix: Manlius, New York Obituaries & Marriages in the early 1800s, Supplied by H. C. Durston, Village Historian, Manlius, New York. 2007. pap. 15.00 *(978-1-58549-832-1(7))* Heritage Bks.

Becker, Ulrich. Esperanto in the New York Times. 2010. 286p. pap. 23.95 *(978-1-59569-169-9(3))* Mondial.

Belding, Russell. Hidden History of Barre, Vermont. 2011. 128p. pap. 19.99 *(978-1-60949-092-8(4))* History Pr., The.

Bennett, Gordon, ed. Newspaper Obituaries 1991 & part Of 1990,, 19 bks., Bk,8. 3rd ed. 2009. (Illus.). 312p. pap. 56.00 net. *(978-1-931167-49-9(4))* Cherokee County Genealogical Society.

—Newspaper Obituaries 1992, Cherokee County, Texas, 19 Bks., Bk. 9. 2nd ed. 2009. (Illus.). 194p. pap. 16.00 net. *(978-1-931167-51-2(6))* Cherokee County Genealogical Society.

Blair, Jayne L. Viva Las Vegas: Newspaper Columns. 2009. 52p. pap. 15.99 *(978-1-4415-9240-8(7))* Xlibris Corp.

Bowman, John D. Guide to Selections from the Montgomery County Sentinel, Jan. 1 1909 - Dec. 27 1912. 2011. 270p. pap. 26.50 ***(978-0-7884-5241-3(X))*** Heritage Bks.

—Guide to Selections from the Montgomery County Sentinel, Maryland, January 1, 1897 - December 31 1901. 2007. pap. 29.00 *(978-0-7884-4393-0(3))* Heritage Bks.

—Guide to Selections from the Montgomery County Sentinel, Maryland, January 1, 1905 - December 31 1908. 2009. 258p. pap. 26.00 *(978-0-7884-5011-2(5))* Heritage Bks.

—Guide to Selections from the Montgomery County Sentinel, Maryland, January 1, 1905-December 31, 1908. 2009. 174p. *(978-0-7884-8205-2(X))* Heritage Bks.

Bowman, John D. Guide to Selections from the Montgomery County Sentinel, Maryland, January 1, 1909-December 27, 1912. 2010. 184p. ***(978-0-7884-8481-0(8))*** Heritage Bks.

Boyle, Joseph Lee. Drinks Hard, & Swears Much: White Maryland Runaways, 1770-1774. 2010. 378p. pap. 35.00 ***(978-0-8063-5503-0(4))*** Clearfield Co.

Boyle, Joseph Lee. "He Loves a Good Deal of Rum — " Military Desertions During the American Revolution, 1775-1783, 2 vols. 2009. *(978-0-8063-5403-3(8))*; *(978-0-8063-5404-0(6))* Clearfield Co.

Boyle, Joseph Lee, compiled by. When Drunk Is Very Bold: White Maryland Runaways, 1763-1769. 2011. 394p. pap. 35.00 ***(978-0-8063-5545-0(X))*** Clearfield Co.

Bracken, Donagh. The Words of War: The Civil War Battle Reportage of the New York Times & the Charleston Mercury... & What Historians Say Really Happened. 2007. (Illus.). 326p. 24.95 *(978-1-933909-32-5(3))* History Publishing Co., LLC.

Caplan, Colin M. Westville: Tales from a Connecticut Hamlet. 2009. (American Chronicles Ser.). (ENG., Illus.). 128p. pap. 19.99 *(978-1-59629-538-4(4))* History Pr., The.

Carbonell, John. The Early Printings of Abraham Lincoln's Gettysburg Address & What They Reveal about His Spoken Words. 2008. 19.95 *(978-1-58456-256-6(0))* Oak Knoll Pr.

Chambers, Lenoir & Shank, Joseph E. Salt Water & Printer's Ink: Norfolk & Its Newspapers, 1865-1965. 2011. (ENG.). 432p. pap. 50.00 ***(978-0-8078-7830-9(8))*** Univ. of North Carolina Pr.

Chapman, Marcia, compiled by. Columbia County, Arkansas Obituary Index, 1948-2004. 2008. 50.00 *(978-0-9816451-1-7(9))* Arkansas Genealogical Society, Inc.

Chernomas, Robert & Hudson, Ian. The Gatekeeper: 60 Years of Economics According to the New York Times, 1 vol. 2011. 256p. 105.00 *(978-1-59451-682-5(0))* Paradigm Pubs.

Cook, Elizabeth Christine. Literary Influences in Colonial Newspapers, 1704-1750. 296p. 2009. 24.99 *(978-1-103-21494-5(2))* 2009. pap. 18.99 *(978-1-103-21491-4(8))* 2008. 25.99 *(978-0-559-46066-1(X))* 2008. pap. 27.75 *(978-0-559-46062-3(7))* BiblioBazaar.

—Literary Influences in Colonial Newspapers, 1704-1750. 2009. 150p. pap. 19.99 *(978-1-150-00313-4(8))*; 152p. pap. 19.99 *(978-1-150-15069-2(6))* General Bks. LLC.

—Literary Influences in Colonial Newspapers, 1704-1750. 2008. 290p. 43.95 *(978-1-4372-3318-6(X))*; pap. 28.95 *(978-1-4371-0486-8(X))* Kessinger Publishing, LLC.

CQ Press, ed. Media Contact Directory 2010, 00 vols. rev. ed. 2010. 1344p. pap. 499.00 *(978-0-87289-656-7(0))* CQ Pr.

Dixon, Joan M. National Intelligencer Newspaper Abstracts 1851. 2008. pap. 47.00 *(978-0-7884-4569-9(3))* Heritage Bks.

—National Intelligencer Newspaper Abstracts 1852. 2008. pap. 47.00 *(978-0-7884-4570-5(7))* Heritage Bks.

Dumas, Karen. In Other Words: A Collection of Thoughts & Columns. 2009. 128p. pap. 15.95 *(978-1-4327-1130-6(X))* Outskirts Pr., Inc.

Duncan, Patricia B. Genealogical Abstracts from The Democratic Mirror & The Mirror, Loudoun County, Virginia, 4 vols. 2008. *(978-0-7884-7659-4(9))*; *(978-0-7884-7660-0(2))*; *(978-0-7884-7661-7(0))*; *(978-0-7884-7658-7(0))* Heritage Bks.

Farrell, Mike. Newspapers: A Complete Guide to the Industry. 2010. (Media Industries Ser.). 240p. (C). pap. 32.95 *(978-0-8204-8153-1(X))* Lang, Peter Publishing, Inc.

—Newspapers: A Complete Guide to the Industry (HB) 2010. (Media Industries Ser.). 240p. (C). 119.95 *(978-0-8204-9509-5(3))* Lang, Peter Publishing, Inc.

Gale Directory of Publications & Broadcast Media. 147th ed. 2011. 1297.00 *(978-1-4144-4715-5(9))* Cengage Gale.

Greenman, Robert & Greenman, Carol. More Words That Make a Difference. 2007. *(978-1-929154-28-9(3))* Levenger Pr.

Hays, Robert G. Editorializing the Indian Problem: The New York Times on Native Americans, 1860-1900. 2007. (ENG.). 392p. per. 22.95 *(978-0-8093-2762-1(7))* Southern Illinois Univ. Pr.

Heyd, Uriel. Reading Newspapers: Press & Public in Eighteenth-century Britain & America. 2012. (ENG., Illus.). 320p. pap. ***(978-0-7294-1042-7(0))*** Voltaire Foundation.

Hinshaw, Gregory P. Hinshaw's Historical Index of Winchester, Indiana, Newspapers, 1857-1984. 2009. 458p. pap. 37.00 *(978-0-7884-5013-6(1))* Heritage Bks.

—Hinshaw's Historical Index of Winchester, Indiana Newspapers, 1857-1984. 2009. ix, 448p. *(978-0-7884-8211-3(4))* Heritage Bks.

An Historical Digest of the Provincial Press. 63p. reprint ed. 88.00 *(978-0-7222-7058-5(5))* Library Reprints, Inc.

Kansas State Historical Society Staff. History of Kansas Newspapers. (Illus.). 320p. reprint ed. lib. bdg. 98.00 *(978-0-7222-4913-0(6))* Library Reprints, Inc.

Latimer, James C., ed. Virginia Newspaper Directory & Market Information. 60p. reprint ed. lib. bdg. 88.00 *(978-0-7222-0608-9(9))* Library Reprints, Inc.

Lucier, Armand Francis. Newspaper Datelines of the American Revolution, Vol. 2. 2008. (Illus.). pap. 32.00 *(978-0-7884-1940-9(4))* Heritage Bks.

Madigan, Charles M. 30: The Collapse of the Great American Newspaper. 2007. (ENG.). 256p. 26.00 *(978-1-56663-742-8(2))* Dee, Ivan R. Pub.

Marrin, Richard B. Abstracts from the Clarksville Standard (Formerly the Northern Standard) Texas: Volume 7: August 6, 1859 - May 25 1861. 2010. pap. 24.50 *(978-0-7884-5178-2(2))* Heritage Bks.

—Abstracts from the New London Gazette Covering Southeastern Connecticut. 2007. ***(978-0-7884-7598-6(3))***; ***(978-0-7884-8397-4(8))***; pap. ***(978-0-7884-5017-4(4))***; pap. ***(978-0-7884-4784-6(0))*** Heritage Bks.

Marrin, Richard B. Abstracts from the New London Gazette Covering Southeastern Connecticut, 1763-1769. 2007. iv, 330p. pap. *(978-0-7884-4171-4(X))* Heritage Bks.

Marrin, Richard B. & Sheppard, Lorna Geer. Abstracts from the Northern Standard & the Red River District [Texas]: August 26, 1848-December 20 1851. 2007. pap. 35.00 *(978-0-7884-4454-8(9))* Heritage Bks.

Marth, Marty, ed. Marth's Florida Guide - 2007. 17th ed. 2007. 248p. spiral bd. *(978-1-885034-21-2(0))* Suwannee River Pr.

Martin, David G., ed. "Tossed Around" the World War II Writings of PFC. George Foster Dennis. 2007. (Illus.). 185p. pap. 20.00 *(978-0-944413-71-5(4))* Longstreet Hse.

New York Times Guides Staff & Barron, James. The New York Times' Book of New York: 549 Stories of the People, the Events & the Life of the City - Past & Present. Barron, James, ed. 2009. (ENG., Illus.). 463p. 27.95 *(978-1-57912-801-2(7),* 1579128017) Black Dog & Leventhal Pubs., Inc.

O'Shea, James. The Deal from Hell: How Moguls & Wall Street Plundered Great American Newspapers. 2011. *(978-1-58648-865-9(1))*; (ENG., Illus.). 416p. 28.99 *(978-1-58648-791-1(4))* PublicAffairs.

Park, Robert Ezra. The Immigrant Press & Its Control. 2009. 296p. pap. *(978-1-150-72232-5(0))* Books LLC.

Poss, Faye Stone. Early Jefferson County, Georgia Newspaper Abstracts, 1799-1811. 2011. xii, 353p. ***(978-0-9716808-8-3(4))*** Poss, Faye S.

—Jackson County, Georgia Newspaper Clippings, Jackson Herald, February 1881 to December 1882. 2007. (Illus.). xii, 418p. 35.00 *(978-0-9716808-5-2(X))* Poss, Faye S.

—The Southern Watchman Athens, Georgia: Civil War Home Front Coverage, 1861-1865. 2008. (Illus.). xiv, 586p. 42.00 *(978-0-9716808-6-9(8))* Poss, Faye S.

ProQuest Editorial Staff, ed. Bowker News Media Directory, 3 vols.; set. 58th ed. 2007. 635.00 *(978-1-60030-109-4(6))* CSA Journal Division.

ProQuest LLC Staff, ed. News Media Directory 2009, 3 vols.; Set. 2008. 668.00 *(978-1-60030-120-9(7))* ProQuest LLC.

—News Media Directory 2009: Magazine & Newsletter Directory, Vol. 2. 2008. 385.00 *(978-1-60030-118-6(5))* ProQuest LLC.

—News Media Directory 2009: Newspaper Directory, Vol. 1. 2008. 385.00 *(978-1-60030-117-9(7))* ProQuest LLC.

Rademacher, Tom. Splitting Wood. 2010. pap. 14.99 *(978-0-9843392-0-4(5))* Lake Michigan Bks.

Ruppert, Gary B. The German Correspondent, Baltimore, Maryland: Translation & Transcription of Marriages, Deaths & Selected Articles of Genealogical Interest, 2 vols. 2008. pap. *(978-0-7884-4603-0(7))*; pap. *(978-0-7884-4602-3(9))* Heritage Bks.

Sarasohn, David. Failing Grade: Oregon's Higher Education System Goes Begging. 2010. (ENG.). 203p. pap. 12.95 *(978-0-9825691-7-7(3))* Tin Hse. Bks., LLC.

Schmitt, Jo Ann. Fighting Editors: The Story of Editors Who Faced Six-Shooters with Pens & Won. 2011. 244p. 46.95 ***(978-1-258-02398-0(9))*** Literary Licensing, LLC.

Schwab, Carolyn. Newspaper Extracts from "The Hoosier State" Newspapers: Newport, Vermillion County, Indiana, January 1, 1890 - December 30, 1891. 2008. pap. 38.50 *(978-0-7884-4673-3(8))* Heritage Bks.

—Newspaper Extracts from "The Hoosier State" Newspapers: Newport, Vermillion County, Indiana, January 4, 1888 - December 25, 1889. 2008. pap. 31.00 *(978-0-7884-4674-0(6))* Heritage Bks.

Sheppard, Joseph E. Waters. The True Republican, or, American Whig: "The Truth Our Guide — The Public Good Our End," 1809 CE, Wilmington, North Carolina, USA: Newspaper Transcription with Historical & Genealogical Notes. 2008. 85p. *(978-0-7884-7690-7(4))* Heritage Bks.

Sonoma County Genealogical Society. Index to Vital Data in Local Newspapers of Sonoma County, California, Volume V: 1891-1899. 2007. pap. 50.00 *(978-0-7884-4287-2(2))* Heritage Bks.

—Index to Vital Data in Local Newspapers of Sonoma County, California, Volume VI: 1900-1903. 2007. pap. 49.50 *(978-0-7884-4358-9(5))* Heritage Bks.

—Index to Vital Data in Local Newspapers of Sonoma County, California, Volume VII: 1904-1906. 2008. pap. 46.50 *(978-0-7884-4512-5(X))* Heritage Bks.

—Index to Vital Data in Local Newspapers of Sonoma County, California, Volume VIII: 1907-1909. 2009. pap. 49.50 *(978-0-7884-4940-6(0))* Heritage Bks.

Tidyman, John H. Gimme Rewrite, Sweetheart ... Tales from the Last Glory Days of Cleveland Newspapers, Told by the Men & Women Who Reported the News. 2009. 256p. 24.95 *(978-1-59851-016-4(9))* Gray and Company, Publishers.

Varouhakis, Miron. U S Newspaper Coverage of Arab Americans Pre- & Post-9/11. 2010. 128p. pap. *(978-3-8383-6340-0(3))* Lambert Academic Publishing.

Weeks, Lyman H. & Bacon, Edwin M., eds. Historical Digest of the Provincial Press: Massachusetts Ser. 1689-1707. reprint ed. 39.50 *(978-0-404-06888-2(X))* AMS Pr., Inc.

Williams, Michael. 44th: The Commemorative Edition. 2008. pap. 69.95 *(978-0-615-26585-8(5))* Author Collective.

Winters-Ibrahim, Rachelle. Newspaper Excerpts from the Maysville Eagle, Mason County, Kentucky, 1827-1847. 2007. 124p. pap. *(978-0-7884-3648-2(1))* Heritage Bks.

Woodward, Julian L. Foreign News in American Morning Newspapers. (Columbia University, Studies in the Social Sciences: No. 332). reprint ed. 21.50 *(978-0-404-51332-0(8))* AMS Pr., Inc.

Wright, F. Edward. Abstracts of South Central Pennsylvania Newspapers: 1785-1790. 2007. 177p. per. 18.00 *(978-1-888265-93-4(0))* Heritage Bks.

—Newspaper Abstracts of Cecil & Harford Counties, Maryland: 1822-1830. 2008. 81p. per. 11.00 *(978-1-58549-075-2(X))* Heritage Bks.

Wright, Steven L. Kentucky Soldiers & Their Regiments in the Civil War: Abstracted from the Pages of Contemporary Kentucky Newspapers, 5 vols. 2009. (Illus.). ***(978-0-9819741-2-5(0))***; ***(978-0-9819741-3-2(9))***; ***(978-0-9819741-4-9(7))***; ***(978-0-9819741-1-8(2))*** Miller, Lois N. Genealogical Pubns.

Wright, Steven L., compiled by. Kentucky Soldiers & Their Regiments in the Civil War: Abstracted from the Pages of Contemporary Newspapers, Volume I 1861, 5 vols., Vol. 1. 2009. (Illus.). 25.00 *(978-0-9819741-0-1(4))* Steve's Bks.

Yakubek, Dorothy & McCarty, DeWayne C. Columbiana Ledger, Volume #1: Newspaper Abstracts from the Village of Columbiana, Ohio: Covering the Years 7/18/1862-12/26/1930. 2009. 790p. pap. ***(978-1-55856-507-4(8))*** Closson Pr.

AMERICAN NEWSPAPERS—BIBLIOGRAPHY

Gregory, Winifred. Union List of Newspapers. 791p. reprint ed. lib. bdg. 148.00 *(978-0-7222-0330-9(6))* Library Reprints, Inc.

Howell (George P.) and company, New York. Centennial Newspaper Exhibition, 1876 a Complete List of American Newspapers a Statement of the Industries, Characteristics, Population & Location. 2006. 308p. per. 23.99 *(978-1-4255-2888-1(0))* MPublishing.

Michigan. Board of state building commis. Proceedings at the Laying of the Corner Stone of the New Capitol of Michigan, on the 2d Day of October, 1873, at the City of Lansing. 2006. 140p. per. 16.99 *(978-1-4255-0985-9(1))* MPublishing.

Sgambettera, Mark, et al. Newspaper Titles of the Bronx. 2nd ed. 2007. 32p. *(978-0-941980-55-5(3))* Bronx County Historical Society, The.

AMERICAN NEWSPAPERS—HISTORY

Ali, Ghayda/Abbas. How Arabic Journalists Translate English-Language Newspaper Headlines: Case Studies in Cross-Cultural Understanding. 2009. (ARA & ENG., Illus.). x, 347p. *(978-0-7734-3838-5(6))* Mellen, Edwin Pr., The.

Black, Susan Easton, ed. The St. Louis Luminary. 2010. (ENG., Illus.). 192p. 21.95 *(978-0-8425-2752-1(4))*, Brigham Young Univ. Studies) Brigham Young Univ.

Brisbane, Arthur. Editorials from the Hearst Newspapers. 2009. 230p. pap. *(978-0-217-20541-2(0))* Books LLC.

—Editorials from the Hearst Newspapers. 2008. 416p. pap. *(978-1-4097-0201-6(4))* Read Bks.

Buckingham, Joseph T. (Joseph Tinker). Specimens of Newspaper Literature: With Personal Memoirs, Anecdotes, & Reminiscences / by Joseph T. Buckingham. Vol. 1. 2006. 368p. per. 26.99 *(978-1-4255-3906-1(8))* MPublishing.

—Specimens of Newspaper Literature: With Personal Memoirs, Anecdotes, & Reminiscences / by Joseph T. Buckingham. Vol. 2. 2006. 368p. per. 26.99 *(978-1-4255-3878-1(9))* MPublishing.

Burns, Eric. Infamous Scribblers: The Founding Fathers & the Rowdy Beginnings of American Journalism. 2007. 467p. 27.00 *(978-1-4223-6706-3(1))* DIANE Publishing Co.

—Infamous Scribblers: The Founding Fathers & the Rowdy Beginnings of American Journalism. 2007. (ENG., Illus.). 480p. per. 15.95 *(978-1-58648-428-6(1))* PublicAffairs.

Canada, Mark. Literature & Journalism in Antebellum America: Thoreau, Stowe, & Their Contemporaries Respond to the Rise of the Commercial Press. 2011. (ENG., Illus.). 214p. 80.00 *(978-0-230-11094-6(0))* Palgrave Macmillan.

Cloud, Barbara. The Coming of the Frontier Press: How the West Was Really Won. 2008. (Medill Visions of the American Press Ser.). (ENG.). 296p. pap. 24.95 *(978-0-8101-2508-7(0))* Northwestern Univ. Pr.

Collins, Paul. The Murder of the Century: The Gilded Age Crime That Scandalized a City & Sparked the Tabloid Wars. (Illus.). 336p. 2012. (ENG.). pap. 16.00 ***(978-0-307-59221-7(9))*** 2011. 26.00 *(978-0-307-59220-0(0)*, Crown) Crown Publishing Group.

Coopersmith, Andrew S. Fighting Words: An Illustrated History of Newspaper Accounts of the Civil War. 2006. (ENG., Illus.). 325p. per. 24.95 *(978-1-59558-141-9(3))* New Pr., The.

Cram101 Textbook Reviews. Outlines & Highlights for the Press & America by Emery & Emery & Roberts, Isbn: 0205295576. 2011. 544p. pap. 38.95 ***(978-1-61812-778-5(0))*** Cram101 Inc.

Dicken-Garcia, Hazel & Dell'Orto, Giovanna. Hated Ideas & the American Civil War Press. 2007. (Illus.). 350p. 79.95 *(978-0-922993-89-5(0))*; per. 39.95 *(978-0-922993-88-8(2))* Marquette Bks., LLC.

Ellison, Sarah. War at the Wall Street Journal: Inside the Struggle to Control an American Business Empire. 2010. (ENG., Illus.). 304p. 27.00 *(978-0-547-15243-1(4))* Houghton Mifflin Harcourt Trade & Reference Pubs.

Ford, Edwin H. & Emery, Edwin, eds. Highlights in the History of the American Press: A Book of Readings. 2009. (ENG.). 414p. pap. 60.00 *(978-0-8166-5769-8(6))* Univ. of Minnesota Pr.

Harp, Dustin. Desperately Seeking Women Readers: U. S. Newspapers & the Construction of a Female Readership. 2007. (ENG.). 136p. 57.99 *(978-0-7391-1490-2(5))* Lexington Bks.

—Desperately Seeking Women Readers: U. S. Newspapers & the Construction of a Female Readership. Harp, Dustin, ed. 2007. (ENG.). 136p. pap. 26.50 *(978-0-7391-1491-9(3))* Lexington Bks.

Herber, Lori. Iraq War Through the Lens of Nationality. 2009. 60p. pap. *(978-3-639-16218-9(8))* VDM Verlag Dr. Mueller e.K.

Louis, Errol, et al, eds. Deadline Artists: America's Greatest Newspaper Columns. 2011. (ENG.). 432p. (gr. 12). 29.95 *(978-1-59020-429-0(8))* Overlook Pr., The.

Lovoll, Odd S. Norwegian Newspapers in America: Connecting Norway & the New Land. 2010. (ENG., Illus.). 400p. pap. 24.95 *(978-0-87351-772-0(5))* Minnesota Historical Society Pr.

McChesney, Robert W. & Nichols, John. The Death & Life of American Journalism: The Media Revolution That Will Begin the World Again. 2010. (ENG., Illus.). 352p. (gr. 9). 26.95 *(978-1-56858-605-2(1))* Basic Bks.

Mencken, H. L. Newspaper Days: Mencken's Autobiography: 1899-1906, Volume 2. 2006. (ENG.). 336p. pap. 27.00 *(978-0-8018-8534-1(5))* Johns Hopkins Univ. Pr.

Morton, Paula E. Tabloid Valley: Supermarket News & American Culture. 2009. (ENG., Illus.). 224p. 24.95 *(978-0-8130-3364-8(0))* Univ. Pr. of Florida.

Nord, David Paul. Communities of Journalism: A History of American Newspapers & Their Readers. 2006. (History of Communication Ser.). 312p. per. 22.00 *(978-0-252-07404-2(1))* Univ. of Illinois Pr.

Payne, George Henry. History of Journalism in the United States. 2009. 318p. pap. *(978-1-150-22193-4(3))* Books LLC.

—History of Journalism in the United States. 2009. 476p. 52.95 *(978-1-104-82583-6(X))*; pap. 37.95 *(978-1-104-76660-3(4))* Kessinger Publishing, LLC.

Pinnick, Timothy N. Finding & Using African American Newspapers. 2008. (ENG., Illus.). 73p. per. 12.00 *(978-0-944619-85-8(1)*, AD2186SB); 74p. 25.00 *(978-0-944619-89-6(4)*, AD2186HB) Gregath Publishing Co.

Ratner, Lorman, et al. Paradoxes of Prosperity: Wealth Seeking in Pre-Civil War America. 2009. (ENG.). 168p. 40.00 *(978-0-252-03453-4(8))* Univ. of Illinois Pr.

Risley, Ford. Abolition & the Press: The Moral Struggle Against Slavery. 2008. (Medill Visions of the American Press Ser.). (ENG.). 248p. pap. 24.95 *(978-0-8101-2507-0(2))* Northwestern Univ. Pr.

Sachsman, David. Words at War: The Civil War & American Journalism. Rushing, S. Kittrell & Morris, Roy, Jr., eds. 2008. 412p. pap. 29.95 *(978-1-55753-494-1(2))* Purdue Univ. Pr.

Sachsman, David B., et al. Words at War: The Civil War & American Journalism. 2008. (Illus.). 412p. 64.95 *(978-1-55753-490-3(X))* Purdue Univ. Pr.

Smith, Lisa. The First Great Awakening in Colonial American Newspapers: A Shifting Story. 2012. (ENG.). 194p. (gr. 17). 60.00 ***(978-0-7391-7274-2(3))*** Lexington Bks.

Welky, David. Everything Was Better in America: Print Culture in the Great Depression. 2008. (History of Communication Ser.). (ENG., Illus.). 280p. 67.00 *(978-0-252-03299-8(3))*; pap. 26.00 *(978-0-252-07504-9(8))* Univ. of Illinois Pr.

Whyte, Kenneth. The Uncrowned King: The Sensational Rise of William Randolph Hearst. 2009. (ENG.). 512p. pap. 17.95 *(978-1-58243-554-1(5)*, Counterpoint Pr.) Basic Bks. GBR. Dist: Perseus-PGW.

AMERICAN ORATIONS

see Speeches, Addresses, etc., American

AMERICAN PAINTING

see Painting, American

AMERICAN PARTY

Brownlow, William Gannaway. Americanism Contrasted with Foreignism, Romanism, & Bogus Democracy, in the Light of Reason, History, & Scripture; in Which Certain Demagogues In. 2006. 224p. per. 20.99 *(978-1-4255-1843-1(5))* MPublishing.

Morse, Samuel Finley Breese. Imminent Dangers to the Free Institutions of the United States Through Foreign Immigration, & the Present State of the Naturalization Laws. 2011. 34p. 35.95 ***(978-1-258-08152-2(0))*** Literary Licensing, LLC.

Whitney, Thomas Richard. A Defence of the American Policy, As Opposed to the Encroachments of Foreign Influence, & Especially to the Interference of the Papacy in the Polti. 2006. 376p. per. 26.99 *(978-1-4255-3910-8(6))* MPublishing.

AMERICAN PERIODICALS

see also Latin American Periodicals

also names of specific American periodicals

Adams, Peter H. The Musical Courier, 1880-1940, 2 vols. 2009. (Native American Resources Ser.). (ENG.). 1632p. (gr. 17). 237.00 *(978-0-8108-6658-4(7))* Scarecrow Pr., Inc.

Anderson, James D. & Català, Rafael. Index of American Periodical Verse 2004. 2006. (Index of American Periodical Verse Ser.). (ENG.). 744p. 150.00 *(978-0-8108-5860-2(6))* Scarecrow Pr., Inc.

Balint, Benjamin. Running Commentary: The Contentious Magazine That Transformed the Jewish Left into the Neoconservative Right. 2010. (ENG., Illus.). 304p. 26.95 *(978-1-58648-749-2(3))* PublicAffairs.

Baumgartner, Apollinaris W. Catholic Journalism. (BCL Ser. I). reprint ed. 21.50 *(978-0-404-00693-8(0))* AMS Pr., Inc.

Catala, Rafael & Anderson, James D. Index of American Periodical Verse 2005. 2007. (Index of American Periodical Verse Ser.). (ENG.). 744p. 150.00 *(978-0-8108-6009-4(0))* Scarecrow Pr., Inc.

Chambers, Douglas B., ed. The Past Is Not Dead: Essays from the Southern Quarterly. 2012. (ENG.). 352p. 65.00 ***(978-1-61703-303-2(0))***; pap. 30.00 ***(978-1-61703-304-9(9))*** Univ. Pr. of Mississippi.

Clear, Richard E. Old Magazine Advertisements, 1890-1950. 2006. (ENG., Illus.). 320p. per. 24.95 *(978-1-57432-521-8(3)*, 1574325213) Collector Bks.

Cohen, Patricia Cline et al. The Flash Press: Sporting Male Weeklies in 1840s New York. 2008. (Historical Studies of Urban America Ser.). (ENG., Illus.). 288p. 50.00 *(978-0-226-11233-6(0))* Univ. of Chicago Pr.

Cometbus, Aaron. Add Toner: A Cometbus Collection. 2011. (ENG., Illus.). 368p. pap. 12.00 *(978-0-86719-753-2(6))* Last Gasp of San Francisco.

Conway, Moncure Daniel, ed. Dial: A Monthly Magazine for Literature, Philosophy & Religion, Vol. 1, Nos. 1-12. reprint ed. lib. bdg. 76.50 *(978-0-404-19515-1(6))* AMS Pr., Inc.

Flanders, Bertram Holland. Early Georgia Magazines: Literary Periodicals To 1865. 2010. (ENG.). 304p. pap. 24.95 *(978-0-8203-3536-0(3))* Univ. of Georgia Pr.

Gale Directory of Publications & Broadcast Media. 147th ed. 2011. 1297.00 *(978-1-4144-4715-5(9))* Cengage Gale.

Gardner, Jared. The Rise & Fall of Early American Magazine Culture. 2012. (History of Communication Ser.). (ENG., Illus.). 224p. 50.00 ***(978-0-252-03670-5(0))*** Univ. of Illinois Pr.

Gilfoyle, Timothy J., et al. The Flash Press: Sporting Male Weeklies in 1840s New York. 2008. (Historical Studies of Urban America Ser.). (ENG., Illus.). 288p. pap. 20.00 *(978-0-226-11234-3(9))* Univ. of Chicago Pr.

Harter, Christopher. An Author Index to Little Magazines of the Mimeograph Revolution, 1958-1980. 2008. (ENG.). 752p. 150.00 *(978-0-8108-6113-8(5))* Scarecrow Pr., Inc.

Holland, F. G., ed. Scribner's Monthly Illustrated Magazine November 1878 to January 1879. 2007. (ENG., Illus.). 472p. 52.95 *(978-0-548-06650-8(7))* Kessinger Publishing, LLC.

Johnson, Sammye & Prijatel, Patricia. The Magazine from Cover to Cover. 2nd rev. ed. 2006. (ENG., Illus.). 416p. (C). per. 64.95 *(978-0-19-530417-5(9))* 3rd ed. 2012. ***(978-0-19-982984-2(5))*** Oxford Univ. Pr., Inc.

Jones, Robert Kenneth. The Shudder Pulps: A History of the Weird Menace Magazines of The 1930s. 2007. 256p. (ENG.). 29.95 *(978-1-4344-8625-7(7))*; per. 17.95 *(978-1-4344-8624-0(9))* Wildside Pr., LLC.

Kansas State Historical Society Staff. History of Kansas Newspapers. (Illus.). 320p. reprint ed. lib. bdg. 98.00 *(978-0-7222-4913-0(6))* Library Reprints, Inc.

Keyser, Catherine. Playing Smart: New York Women Writers & Modern Magazine Culture. (Mellon-ALI Ser.). (ENG., 242p. 2011. Illus.). pap. 23.95 ***(978-0-8135-5178-4(1))*** 2010. 39.95 *(978-0-8135-4786-2(5))* Rutgers Univ. Pr.

Life Magazine Editors. LIFE 75 Years: The Very Best of LIFE. 2011. (ENG., Illus.). 224p. 36.95 *(978-1-60320-212-1(9))* Time Home Entertainment, Inc.

Lippincott's Magazine of Popular Literature & Science. 2008. 268p. 28.99 *(978-0-554-24517-1(5))* 2008. 268p. 25.99 *(978-0-554-34233-7(2))* 2008. 260p. 25.99 *(978-0-554-33872-9(6))* 2008. 264p. 25.99 *(978-0-554-34399-0(1))* 2008. 272p. 25.99 *(978-0-554-34128-6(X))* 2008. 268p. 28.99 *(978-0-554-24822-6(0))* 2008. 264p. 25.99 *(978-0-554-34237-5(5))* 2008. 248p. 24.99 *(978-0-554-34235-1(9))* 2008. 260p. 28.99 *(978-0-554-24569-0(8))* 2008. 260p. 28.99 *(978-0-554-25131-8(0))* 2008. 256p. 28.99 *(978-0-554-24790-8(9))* 2008. 268p. 28.99 *(978-0-554-24930-8(8))* 2008. 248p. 27.99 *(978-0-554-24932-2(4))* 2008. 264p. 28.99 *(978-0-554-24934-6(0))* 2008. 252p. 27.99 *(978-0-554-24848-6(4))* 2008. 244p. 24.99 *(978-0-554-33852-1(1))* 2008. 244p. 27.99 *(978-0-554-24549-2(3))* 2008. 256p. 28.99 *(978-0-554-25093-9(4))* 2008. 264p. 28.99 *(978-0-554-25096-0(9))* 2008. 272p. 28.99 *(978-0-554-24825-7(5))* 2008. 260p. 28.99 *(978-0-554-24452-5(7))* 2008. 268p. 25.99 *(978-0-554-34125-5(5))* 2008. 260p. 25.99 *(978-0-554-34434-8(3))* 2008. 268p. 25.99 *(978-0-554-33820-0(3))* 2008. 252p. 24.99 *(978-0-554-34151-4(4))* 2008. 260p. 25.99 *(978-0-554-33755-5(X))* 2008. 256p. 25.99 *(978-0-554-34093-7(3))* 2008. 256p. 25.99 *(978-0-554-34396-9(7))* 2007. 252p. pap. 23.99 *(978-1-4264-8218-2(3))* 2007. 262p. pap. 23.99 *(978-1-4264-7759-1(7))* 2007. (ENG.). 228p. pap. 22.99 *(978-1-4264-8145-8(2))* 2007. (ENG.). 264p. pap. 23.99 *(978-1-4264-7755-3(4))* 2007. (ENG.). 234p. pap. 22.99 *(978-1-4264-7701-0(5))* BiblioBazaar.

Lippincott's Magazine of Popular Literature & Science. 2008. (Illus.). 256p. pap. *(978-1-4099-0302-4(8))* Dodo Pr.

Mark, Noonan. Reading Century ILLUS Mo. 2011. (Illus.). 256p. 65.00 *(978-1-60635-063-8(3))* Kent State Univ. Pr.

Noel, Mary. Villains Galore: The Heyday of the Popular Story Weekly. 2011. 340p. 51.95 ***(978-1-258-05768-8(9))*** Literary Licensing, LLC.

Panek, Leroy Lad. Before Sherlock Holmes: How Magazines & Newspapers Invented the Detective Story. 2011. (ENG.). 227p. pap. 40.00 ***(978-0-7864-6787-7(8))*** McFarland & Co., Inc. Pubs.

Ratner, Lorman, et al. Paradoxes of Prosperity: Wealth Seeking in Pre-Civil War America. 2009. (ENG.). 168p. 40.00 *(978-0-252-03453-4(8))* Univ. of Illinois Pr.

Richardson, Peter. A Bomb in Every Issue: How the Short, Unruly Life of Ramparts Magazine Changed America. 2009. (ENG., Illus.). 272p. 25.95 *(978-1-59558-439-7(0))* New Pr., The.

Smith, Susan Harris. Plays in American Periodicals, 1890-1918. 2007. (Palgrave Studies in Theatre & Performance History Ser.). (ENG., Illus.). 244p. 89.00 *(978-1-4039-7765-6(8))* Palgrave Macmillan.

Sumner, David E. The Magazine Century: American Magazines Since 1900. 2010. (Mediating American History Ser.). (Illus.). 256p. (C). pap. 34.95 *(978-1-4331-0493-0(8))* Lang, Peter Publishing, Inc.

—The Magazine Century: American Magazines since 1900 HB. 2010. (Mediating American History Ser.). (Illus.). 250p. (C). 119.95 *(978-1-4331-0494-7(6))* Lang, Peter Publishing, Inc.

Thayer, John Adams. Astir: A Publisher's Life Story. 2007. (ENG.). 316p. 45.95 *(978-0-548-04796-5(0))* Kessinger Publishing, LLC.

Thompson, Eleanor Wolf. Education for Ladies 1830-1860 - Ideas on Education in Magazines for Women. 2007. 168p. per. *(978-1-4067-6479-6(5))* Read Bks.

Weber, Ronald. News of Paris: American Journalists in the City of Light Between the Wars. 2007. (ENG., Illus.). 352p. per. 16.95 *(978-1-56663-732-9(5))* Dee, Ivan R. Pub.

Witte, Randy. The History of Western Horseman: 75 Years of the World's Leading Horse Magazine. 2011. (ENG.). 160p. 29.95 *(978-0-7627-7753-2(2))* Western Horseman.

AMERICAN PERIODICALS—BIBLIOGRAPHY

Council of Literary Magazines and Presses, ed. CLMP Literary Press & Magazine Directory 2009/2010. 2009. (ENG.). 440p. pap. 23.95 *(978-1-59709-152-7(9))* Red Hen Pr.

Nevins, Jess. Pulp Magazine Holdings Directory: Library Collections in North America & Europe. 2007. (ENG., Illus.). 241p. per. 49.95 *(978-0-7864-3068-0(0))* McFarland & Co., Inc. Pubs.

AMERICAN PERIODICALS—DIRECTORIES

Brewer, Robert Lee. 2010 Poet's Market. 22nd ed. 2009. (ENG.). 576p. pap. 29.99 *(978-1-58297-582-5(5)*, Writer's Digest Bks.) F&W Media, Inc.

CSA Journal Staff. Bowker's News Media Directory 2007, 3 vols.; set. 57th ed. 2006. pap. 600.00 *(978-1-60030-101-8(0))* CSA Journal Division.

—Bowker's News Media Directory 2007: Magazine & Newsletter, 3 vols., Vol. 2. 57th ed. 2006. pap. 345.00 *(978-1-60030-099-8(5))* CSA Journal Division.

ProQuest Editorial Staff, ed. Bowker News Media Directory, 3 vols.; set. 58th ed. 2007. 635.00 *(978-1-60030-109-4(6))* CSA Journal Division.

ProQuest LLC Staff, ed. News Media Directory 2009, 3 vols.; Set. 2008. 668.00 *(978-1-60030-120-9(7))* ProQuest LLC.

—News Media Directory 2009: Magazine & Newsletter Directory, Vol. 2. 2008. 385.00 *(978-1-60030-118-6(5))* ProQuest LLC.

—News Media Directory 2009: Newspaper Directory, Vol. 1. 2008. 385.00 *(978-1-60030-117-9(7))* ProQuest LLC.

AMERICAN PHILOSOPHERS

see Philosophers—United States

AMERICAN PHILOSOPHICAL SOCIETY

American Philosophical Society. Proceedings of the American Philosophical Society, V100, No 6, December 17 1956. American Philosophical Society, ed. 2011. 98p. 38.95 ***(978-1-258-06515-7(0))*** Literary Licensing, LLC.

—Proceedings of the American Philosophical Society, V102, No 1, February 17 1958. 2011. 108p. 39.95 ***(978-1-258-10063-6(0))*** Literary Licensing, LLC.

Chinard, Gilbert. Random Notes on Two Bagatelles: Proceedings of the American Philosophical Society, V103, No. 6, December 15 1959. 2011. 38p. 35.95 ***(978-1-258-09510-9(6))*** Literary Licensing, LLC.

Robbins, William J., ed. Proceedings of the American Philosophical Society, V103, No 6, December 15 1959. 2011. 104p. 39.95 ***(978-1-258-09556-7(4))*** Literary Licensing, LLC.

AMERICAN PHILOSOPHY

see Philosophy, American

AMERICAN PIT BULL TERRIER

see also American Staffordshire Terrier; Staffordshire Bull Terrier

Dog Fancy Magazine, compiled by. American Pit Bull Terrier. 2010. (Smart Owner's Guide Ser.). (ENG.). 176p. (gr. 6). 17.95 *(978-1-59378-759-2(6))* Kennel Club Bks.

Dog Fancy Staff, compiled by. American Pit Bull Terrier. 2010. (Smart Owner's Guide Ser.). (ENG.). 176p. (gr. 6). pap. 15.95 *(978-1-59378-745-5(6))* Kennel Club Bks.

Ewing, Susan M. American Pit Bull Terrier. 2012. ***(978-0-7938-3724-3(3))*** TFH Pubns., Inc.

Frey, James. American Pitbull, 1 vol. 2008. (ENG., Illus.). 248p. per. 25.00 *(978-3-86521-094-4(5))* Steidl, Gerhard Druckerei und Verlag DEU. Dist: Innovative Logistics.

Shojai, Amy. American Pit Bull Terrier, 1 vol. 2010. (DogLife Ser.). (ENG., Illus.). 224p. 19.95 *(978-0-7938-3600-0(X))* TFH Pubns., Inc.

Stahlkuppe, Joe. American Pit Bull Terriers/American Staffordshire Terriers. 3rd rev. ed. 2010. (Complete Pet Owner's Manuals Ser.). (ENG., Illus.). 96p. pap. 8.99 *(978-0-7641-4322-9(0))* Barron's Educational Series, Inc.

Waldorf Gewirtz, Elaine. American Pit Bull Terriers. 2006. (Animal Planet Pet Care Library). (Illus.). 111p. 11.95 *(978-0-7938-3758-8(8))* TFH Pubns., Inc.

AMERICAN POETRY (COLLECTIONS)

see also College Verse; Latin American Poetry

A Blue Moutain Arts Collection. The Love Between a Mother & Daughter Is Forever. 2010. (ENG.). 96p. pap. 13.95 *(978-1-59842-529-1(3))* Blue Mountain Arts Inc.

Anagnopoulos, Kostas. Moving Blanket. 2010. 80p. pap. 15.00 *(978-1-933254-69-2(6))* Ugly Duckling Presse.

Bleakney, Elaine & Kelly, Elaine K., eds. Poem in Your Pocket: 200 Poems to Read & Carry. 2009. (ENG.). 224p. 14.95 *(978-0-8109-0636-5(8)*, Abrams Image) Abrams.

Boynton, Percy H. American Poetry. 736p. 2008. 66.95 *(978-1-4365-5132-8(3))* 2007. (ENG.). per. 51.95 *(978-0-548-68751-2(X))* Kessinger Publishing, LLC.

Bromige, David, et al. Petaluma Poetry Walk 10-Year Anthology: 1996 To 2005. Digiorno, Geri & Vartnaw, Bill, eds. 2007. 134p. pap. 20.00 *(978-0-931552-15-1(X))* Taurean Horn Pr.

Bromwich, David, ed. American Sonnets: An Anthology. 2007. (ENG.). 224p. (gr. 12). 20.00 *(978-1-59853-015-5(1))* Library of America, The.

Buckley, Christopher & Young, Gary, eds. Bear Flag Republic: Prose Poems & Poetics from California. 2008. (Illus.). 421p. pap. 24.95 *(978-0-9655239-4-3(2))* Greenhouse Review Pr.

Burt, Mary E. Poems Every Child Should Know A Selectio. 2006. pap. 33.95 *(978-1-4286-3727-6(3))* Kessinger Publishing, LLC.

Burt, Stephen. Something Understood: Essays & Poetry for Helen Vendler. Halpern, Nick, ed. 2009. (ENG.). 352p. pap. 22.50 *(978-0-8139-2785-5(4))*; (gr. 17). 59.50 *(978-0-8139-2784-8(6))* Univ. Pr. of Virginia.

Chase, Mary M., ed. & illus. Oklahoma Centennial Heritage Collection. 2007. 106p. per. 22.95 *(978-1-930293-57-1(7))* PoetWorks Pr.

Clerisy Press, creator. Haiku on 42nd Street: A Celebration of Urban Poetry & Art. 2008. (ENG., Illus.). 26p. pap. 9.95 *(978-1-57860-315-2(3))* Clerisy Pr.

Coblentz, A. Stanton, ed. The Music Makers: An Anthology of Recent American Poetry. 2007. (ENG.). 310p. 45.95 *(978-0-548-07043-7(1))* Kessinger Publishing, LLC.

Cody, Sherwin, ed. A Selection from the Great English Poets. (Granger Index Reprint Ser.). 576p. reprint ed. lib. bdg. 20.50 *(978-0-8290-0516-5(1))* Irvington Pubs.

Coe, Marian. Between Us: Women Sharing Moments from Lives. 2007. (Illus.). 112p. 14.95 *(978-1-932158-31-1(6))* Ingalls Publishing Group, Inc.

Collins, Billy, ed. Bright Wings: An Illustrated Anthology of Poems about Birds. 2009. (ENG., Illus.). 288p. (gr. 17). 22.95 *(978-0-231-15084-2(9))* Columbia Univ. Pr.

Combs, J. H., ed. All That's Kentucky. 285p. reprint ed. lib. bdg. 98.00 *(978-0-7222-4943-7(8))* Library Reprints, Inc.

Creative Communication, ed. Celebrating What Is Important to Me - East 4-6 Spring 2006. 2006. (J). 21.95 *(978-1-60050-017-6(X))* Creative Communication.

—Celebrating What Is Important to Me - East 7-12 Spring 2006. 2006. (YA). 21.95 *(978-1-60050-022-0(6))* Creative Communication.

—Celebrating What Is Important to Me - Great Lakes 7-12 Spring 2006. 2006. (YA). 21.95 *(978-1-60050-023-7(4))* Creative Communication.

—Celebrating What Is Important to Me - South 4-6 Spring 2006. 2006. (J). 21.95 *(978-1-60050-018-3(8))* Creative Communication.

Czury, Craig. American Know How. 2008. (Illus.). 64p. per. 10.00 *(978-0-9725942-7-1(2))* Paper Kite Pr.

Eastman, Max. Enjoyment of Poetry. 2010. 276p. pap. 27.75 *(978-1-143-09953-3(2))* 2010. 274p. pap. 27.75 *(978-1-141-83372-6(7))* 2009. 246p. 28.99 *(978-1-113-99666-4(8))* 2009. 246p. pap. 25.75 *(978-1-113-99662-6(5))* 2009. 240p. 23.99 *(978-1-103-83093-0(7))* 2009. 240p. pap. 17.99 *(978-1-103-83087-9(2))* 2008. 272p. 25.99 *(978-0-559-63565-6(6))* 2008. 272p. pap. 26.75 *(978-0-559-63562-5(1))* BiblioBazaar.

—Enjoyment of Poetry. 2009. 130p. pap. *(978-1-4588-2702-9(X))*; pap. *(978-0-217-71794-6(2))* Books LLC.

—Enjoyment of Poetry. 2008. 272p. 42.95 *(978-1-4369-4774-9(X))*; pap. 27.95 *(978-1-4368-3650-0(6))* Kessinger Publishing, LLC.

Farr, Maureen E. Eggemoggin Reach Review, Volume II: An Anthology of Prose & Poetry by Members of the Deer Isle Writer's Groups. 2007. 176p. pap. 17.95 *(978-0-9755586-1-4(7))* Eggemoggin Reach Review.

Forward! Best young Poets University of Wisconsin-Madison 2007. 2007. *(978-1-893311-91-6(0))* Univ. of Wisconsin-Madison, General Library System.

Gale, Kate. Los Angeles Review, Vol. 7. 2010. (ENG.). 296p. pap. 20.00 *(978-1-59709-474-0(9))* Red Hen Pr.

Gardner, Stephen & Wright, William, eds. The Southern Poetry Anthology Vol. 1: South Carolina. 2007. (ENG.). 300p. pap. 24.95 *(978-1-933896-06-9(X))* Texas Review Pr.

—The Southern Poetry Anthology, Volume II: Mississippi. 2010. 200p. pap. 26.95 *(978-1-933896-24-3(8))* Texas Review Pr.

Garin, Marita, ed. Southern Appalachian Poetry: An Anthology of Works by 37 Poets. 2008. (Contributions to Southern Appalachian Studies). (ENG., Illus.). 275p. pap. 39.95 *(978-0-7864-3429-9(5))* McFarland & Co., Inc. Pubs.

Gelineau, Christine & Bedell, Jack, eds. French Connections: A Gathering of Franco-American Poets. 2007. per. 24.95 *(978-0-945083-01-6(7))* Louisiana Literature Pr.

Gems of Poetry. 2006. 264p. per. 23.99 *(978-1-4255-2338-1(2))* MPublishing.

Green, Timothy, ed. Embracing Candace: Anthology One. 2007. 240p. pap. 17.77 *(978-0-9766787-9-3(9))* Candalyse Publishing.

Hammond, Raymond. The New York Quarterly, Number 59. 2007. (ENG.). 132p. reprint ed. per. 12.00 *(978-1-934423-59-2(9))* New York Quarterly Foundation, Inc., The.

—The New York Quarterly, Number 61. 2007. (ENG.). 176p. reprint ed. per. 12.00 *(978-1-934423-61-5(0))* New York Quarterly Foundation, Inc., The.

—The New York Quarterly, Number 62. 2007. (ENG.). 180p. reprint ed. per. 12.00 *(978-1-934423-62-2(9))* New York Quarterly Foundation, Inc., The.

Harrison, Henry. An Anthology of 48 Living Writers: Indiana Poets. 160p. reprint ed. lib. bdg. 88.00 *(978-0-7222-0587-7(2))* Library Reprints, Inc.

Hedin, Robert, ed. Where One Voice Ends Another Begins: 150 Years of Minnesota Poetry. 2007. 304p. 28.95 *(978-0-87351-584-9(6))* Minnesota Historical Society Pr.

Hemenway, Abby Maria. Poets & Poetry of Vermont. 2009. 330p. pap. *(978-0-217-84666-0(1))*; 364p. pap. *(978-1-4588-9395-6(2))* Books LLC.

—Poets & Poetry of Vermont. 2009. 414p. pap. 20.12 *(978-1-4588-9397-0(9))* General Bks. LLC.

—Poets & Poetry of Vermont. 2008. 412p. 49.95 *(978-0-548-96468-2(8))* 2007. (ENG.). 416p. per. 34.95 *(978-0-548-64016-6(5))* Kessinger Publishing, LLC.

—Poets & Poetry of Vermont. 2006. 524p. per. 29.99 *(978-1-4255-5796-6(1))* MPublishing.

Hudgens, Ruth & Smith, Michael, eds. Yes Poetry. 2007. pap. *(978-0-9794736-0-9(8))* Fast Bks.

Hutton, Laurence. Occasional Addresses. 2009. 100p. pap. *(978-0-217-52155-0(X))* Books LLC.

—Occasional Addresses. 2008. 152p. pap. *(978-1-4097-0688-5(5))* Read Bks.

Katsimpalis, Tom. Improv: An Anthology of Colorado Poets. 2007. 115p. per. 12.00 *(978-0-9776017-5-2(7))* Green Fuse Poetic Arts Assn.

Katz, Daniel R., ed. Why Freedom Matters. 2006. 413p. reprint ed. 25.00 *(978-1-4223-5577-0(2))* DIANE Publishing Co.

Katz, Joy & Prufer, Kevin, eds. Dark Horses: Poets on Overlooked Poems. 2006. (Illus.). 232p. per. 20.95 *(978-0-252-07287-1(1))* Univ. of Illinois Pr.

, kcmetroverse, kcmetroverse. Kansas City Metropolitan Verse Volume 4 - 2010. 2010. 97p. pap. 10.00 *(978-0-557-37285-0(2))* Lulu Enterprises Inc.

Keillor, Garrison. Good Poems, American Places. 2011. (ENG.). 512p. (gr. 12). 28.95 *(978-0-670-02254-0(3)*, Viking Adult) Penguin Group (USA) Inc.

Kennedy, X. J. & Gioia, Dana. An Introduction to Poetry. 13th ed. 2009. (ENG.). 720p. (C). pap. 88.20 *(978-0-205-68612-4(5))* Longman Publishing Group.

Knowles, Frederic Lawrence. The Golden Treasury of American Songs & Lyrics. 2009. 332p. 25.99 *(978-0-559-96205-9(3))* 2009. 332p. pap. 19.99 *(978-0-559-96203-5(7))* 2008. 316p. 29.99 *(978-0-554-25825-6(0))* 2008. 316p. 23.99 *(978-0-554-35128-5(5))* 2007. (ENG.). 280p. pap. 21.99 *(978-1-4264-9558-8(7))* 2007. (ENG.). 312p. pap. 24.99 *(978-1-4264-9939-5(6))* BiblioBazaar.

—The Golden Treasury of American Songs & Lyrics. 2009. 202p. pap. *(978-0-217-58564-4(7))* Books LLC.

—Poems of American Patriotism, 1776-1898. 2008. 460p. 31.99 *(978-0-559-83307-6(5))*; pap. 35.75 *(978-0-559-83303-8(2))* BiblioBazaar.

—Poems of American Patriotism, 1776-1898. 421p. reprint ed. 98.00 *(978-0-7222-6406-5(2))* Library Reprints, Inc.

Knowles, Frederic Lawrence, ed. The Golden Treasury of American Songs & Lyrics. 2008. 340p. 46.95 *(978-1-4374-0445-6(6))*; pap. 31.95 *(978-1-4373-1709-1(X))* Kessinger Publishing, LLC.

Kronenberger, Louis. An Anthology of Light Verse. 2007. (ENG.). 324p. per. *(978-1-4067-5213-7(4))* Read Bks.

Learned, Walter. A Treasury of Favorite Poems. 2009. 304p. pap. *(978-1-151-11146-3(5))* Books LLC.

Lehman, David. The Best American Erotic Poems: From 1800 to the Present. Lehman, David, ed. 2008. (ENG.). 336p. pap. 16.00 *(978-1-4165-3746-5(5)*, Scribner) Scribner.

Life, Liberty, & the Lord: Poetic Parables. 2008. pap. *(978-0-9819254-0-0(5))* Marion (ME) Enterprises LLC.

Lomax, John A., ed. Songs of the Cattle Trail & Cow Camp. 2009. 140p. pap. *(978-1-4099-6280-9(6))* Dodo Pr.

Long, Augustus White. American Poems 1776-1900: with Notes & Biographies. 2007. pap. 33.95 *(978-1-4304-7056-4(9))* Kessinger Publishing, LLC.

Matthews, Brander. Poems of American Patriotism. 2008. 304p. 25.99 *(978-0-559-71291-3(X))* 2008. 304p. pap. 28.75 *(978-0-559-71287-6(1))* 2008. 304p. 25.99 *(978-0-559-58997-3(2))* 2008. 304p. pap. 28.75 *(978-0-559-58994-2(8))* 2008. 312p. 28.99 *(978-0-559-35894-4(6))* 2008. 312p. pap. 28.75 *(978-0-559-35893-7(8))* 2008. 236p. 27.99 *(978-0-554-23684-1(2))* 2008. 236p. 24.99 *(978-0-554-32987-1(5))* 2007. (ENG.). 208p. pap. 20.99 *(978-1-4264-4916-1(X))* 2007. (ENG.). 232p. pap. 22.99 *(978-1-4264-5217-8(9))* BiblioBazaar.

—Poems of American Patriotism. 2009. 166p. pap. *(978-0-217-03158-5(7))* Books LLC.

—Poems of American Patriotism. 2009. (ENG.). 190p. pap. 13.95 *(978-1-4385-2607-2(5)*, Book Jungle) Standard Pubns., Inc.

McClatchy, J. D., ed. & intro. The Four Seasons: Poems. 2008. (Everyman's Library Pocket Poets). (ENG.). 256p. 13.50 *(978-0-307-26834-1(9)*, Everyman's Library) Knopf Doubleday Publishing Group.

McDonald. Favourite Poems. (Illus.). 256p. 24.95 *(978-1-85479-201-3(6))* O'Mara, Michael Bks., Ltd. GBR. Dist: Trans-Atlantic Pubns., Inc.

—Favourite Poems. pap. 15.95 *(978-1-85479-287-7(3))* Trafalgar Square Publishing.

McDonnell, Kilian. Wrestling with God. 2011. 80p. pap. 10.95 ***(978-0-9740992-8-6(7))*** St. John's Univ. Pr.

Menes, Orlando Ricardo. The Open Light: Poets from Notre Dame, 1991-2008. 2011. (ENG.). 304p. pap. 30.00 *(978-0-268-03521-1(0))* Univ. of Notre Dame Pr.

Meyer, Michael. Poetry: An Introduction. 6th ed. 2009. (ENG.). 848p. (C). pap. 66.95 *(978-0-312-53919-1(3))* Bedford/Saint Martin's.

Moore, Frank. Songs & Ballads of the Southern People, 1861-1865. 324p. reprint ed. 98.00 *(978-0-7222-8311-0(3))* Library Reprints, Inc.

Moore, Frank, ed. Songs & Ballads of the Southern People, 1861-1865. 2007. 328p. 45.95 *(978-0-548-11046-1(8))* Kessinger Publishing, LLC.

Moran, Francisco, ed. Island of My Hunger: Cuban Poetry Today. 2007. (ENG.). 225p. per. 16.95 *(978-0-87286-459-7(6))* City Lights Bks.

Morris, Joseph & Adams, St Clair. It Can Be Done. 2008. 328p. 28.99 *(978-0-554-32719-8(8))*; 29.99 *(978-0-554-23416-8(5))* BiblioBazaar.

National Library of Poetry Staff. A Passage in Time. Date not set. 326p. 69.95 *(978-1-57553-042-0(2))* Watermark Pr.

Neale, Walter. Masterpieces of the Southern Poets. 2009. 280p. 24.99 *(978-1-103-00506-2(5))*; pap. 18.99 *(978-1-103-00504-8(9))* BiblioBazaar.

—Masterpieces of the Southern Poets. 2009. 152p. pap. 14.14 *(978-1-151-09026-3(3))* General Bks. LLC.

Packard, William. The New York Quarterly, Number 58. 2007. (ENG.). 132p. reprint ed. per. 12.00 *(978-1-934423-58-5(0))* New York Quarterly Foundation, Inc., The.

Pagels, Douglas, ed. Estos Son los Dones Que Quisíera Darte: Un Libro Que Es Fuente de Dicha y Aliento.Tr. of These Are the Gifts I'd Like to Give to You. (SPA., Illus.). 64p. pap. 10.95 *(978-0-88396-647-1(6)*, B6476, Blue Mountain Pr.) Blue Mountain Arts Inc.

Painter, Franklin V. N. Poets of the South. 2007. (ENG.). 170p. pap. 19.99 *(978-1-4264-8892-4(0))* BiblioBazaar.

Palgrave, Francis Turner. The Golden Treasury of the Best Songs & Lyrical Poems in the English Language. 2008. 460p. 31.99 *(978-0-554-31806-6(7))* 2008. 460p. 33.99 *(978-0-554-22503-6(4))* 2007. 382p. pap. 25.99 *(978-1-4264-9626-4(5))* 2007. (ENG.). 456p. pap. 30.99 *(978-1-4264-2506-6(6))* BiblioBazaar.

—The Golden Treasury of the Best Songs & Lyrical Poems in the English Language. 2009. 358p. pap. *(978-1-150-60672-4(X))* Books LLC.

Parker, Benjamin S. Poets & Poetry of Indiana. Heiney, Enos B., ed. (Illus.). 464p. reprint ed. lib. bdg. 98.00 *(978-0-7222-0809-0(X))* Library Reprints, Inc.

Peattie, Elia W. Poems You Ought to Know. 2008. 244p. 24.99 *(978-0-559-64978-3(9))*; pap. 25.75 *(978-0-559-64973-8(8))* BiblioBazaar.

—Poems You Ought to Know. 240p. 2008. 41.95 *(978-1-4365-8152-3(4))* 2007. (ENG.). per. 26.95 *(978-0-548-79386-2(7))* Kessinger Publishing, LLC.

Peterson, Devon, ed. The FM. Literary Anthology: Celebrating 10 years of Literary Harassment. 2008. (Illus.). 185p. per. 15.00 *(978-0-9789597-2-2(8))* Poetic Matrix Pr.

Pockell, Leslie M. 100 Essential American Poems. 2010. (ENG.). 304p. pap. 14.99 *(978-0-312-62397-5(6)*, St. Martin's Griffin) St. Martin's Pr.

Poetry for the People, compiled by. And after the Tanks Came. 2007. *(978-0-9747131-7-5(1))* Poetry for the People Pr.

Poetry of the Fields: Passages from the Poets Descriptive of Pastoral Scenes, etc. , Etc... . 2006. 132p. per. 16.99 *(978-1-4255-0921-7(5))* MPublishing.

The Poets & Poetry of Cecil County, Maryland. 2007. (ENG.). 328p. pap. 23.99 *(978-1-4264-6042-5(2))*; 384p. pap. 26.99 *(978-1-4264-6113-2(5))* BiblioBazaar.

Repplier, Agnes. A Book of Famous Verse. 2009. 256p. 24.99 *(978-1-103-69784-7(6))*; 24.99 *(978-1-103-60630-6(1))*; pap. 18.99 *(978-1-103-60629-0(8))*; pap. 18.99 *(978-1-103-69780-9(3))*; 24.99 *(978-1-103-35338-5(1))*; pap. 18.99 *(978-1-103-35336-1(5))*; 24.99 *(978-1-103-06825-8(3))*; pap. 18.99 *(978-1-103-06823-4(7))* BiblioBazaar.

—A Book of Famous Verse. 2009. 238p. pap. *(978-0-217-42356-4(6))* Books LLC.

Repplier, Agnes, ed. A Book of Famous Verse. 2007. (ENG.). 252p. 41.95 *(978-0-548-27755-3(9))*; 256p. per. 26.95 *(978-1-4326-8269-9(5))* Kessinger Publishing, LLC.

Rickert, Edith. American Lyrics. 2009. 262p. pap. *(978-1-150-53959-6(3))* Books LLC.

Rickert, Edith & Paton, Jessie. American Lyrics. 2010. 594p. pap. 44.75 *(978-1-147-02265-0(8))* BiblioBazaar.

—American Lyrics. 2010. 588p. pap. 35.16 *(978-1-163-92158-6(0))* 2008. 586p. 58.95 *(978-0-548-94452-3(0))* 2007. (ENG.). 588p. per. 43.95 *(978-0-548-59507-7(0))* Kessinger Publishing, LLC.

Robarchek, Doug. The Best of the World's Worst Poetry: 20 Very Odd Years of OutFrontery. 2008. 120p. pap. 14.00 *(978-1-59948-127-2(8))* Main Street Rag Publishing Co.

Russo, Carl, ed. Silkworm 2007: The Annual Review of the Florence Poets Society. 2007. 120p. per. 15.00 *(978-0-9800095-0-7(2))* Florence Poets Society Pr.

Sargent, Winthrop. The Loyalist Poetry of the Revolution. 2010. 88p. pap. *(978-1-153-02155-5(2))* Books LLC.

Schakel, Peter & Ridl, Jack. 250 Poems: A Portable Anthology. 2nd ed. 2008. (ENG.). 448p. (C). pap. 30.95 *(978-0-312-46616-9(1))* Bedford/Saint Martin's.

Schwenker, Gretchen L. & Kessler, Mathew J., intros. Hidden Graces: Poems for Crisis, Struggle, & Renewal. 2010. x, 130p. *(978-0-7648-1965-0(8))* Liguori Pubns.

Scollard, Clinton. Ballads of American Bravery. 2010. (ENG.). 246p. pap. 26.75 *(978-1-176-21156-8(0))*; 244p. pap. 26.75 *(978-1-147-68372-1(7))*; 246p. pap. 26.75 *(978-1-145-53383-7(3))* BiblioBazaar.

—Ballads of American Bravery. 2009. 242p. pap. *(978-0-217-17912-6(6))* Books LLC.

Scollard, Clinton, ed. Ballads of American Bravery. 2010. 244p. pap. 21.56 *(978-1-163-94146-1(8))* 2008. 242p. 41.95 *(978-0-548-95459-1(3))* 2007. 244p. per. 26.95 *(978-0-548-62968-0(4))* Kessinger Publishing, LLC.

Shields, David. American Poetry: The Seventeenth & Eighteenth Centuries. Sheilds, David, ed. 2007. (ENG.). 900p. (gr. 12). 40.00 *(978-1-931082-90-7(1))* Library of America, The.

Simms, William & Gilmore, William. War Poetry of the South. 2008. (Civil War Ser.). (ENG.). 500p. pap. 29.95 *(978-1-4290-1667-4(1))* Applewood Bks.

Smith, Henry F., Jr. & Smith, Henry F., photos by. Pennsylvania Seasons: Commonwealth Images & Poetry. 2008. (Illus.). 140p. pap. 35.00 *(978-1-58966-168-4(0))* Univ. of Scranton Pr.

Snoddy, James S. A Little Book of Missouri Verse. 200p. reprint ed. lib. bdg. 98.00 *(978-0-7222-0712-3(3))* Library Reprints, Inc.

Southern Minnesota Poets. WordWalk 2009: The Mankato Sidewalk Poetry Project. 2009. pap. *(978-1-61623-375-4(3))* Independent Pub.

Stalling, Jonathan. Poetics of Emptiness: Transformations of Asion Thought in American Poetry. 2011. (ENG., Illus.). 288p. pap. 18.00 ***(978-0-8232-3145-4(3))*** Fordham Univ. Pr.

Timin, Carole, ed. Penumbra 2007. 2007. 76p. pap. 12.95 *(978-0-9672585-5-3(3))* CyPress Pubns.

Tobin, Daniel, ed. The Book of Irish American Poetry: From the Eighteenth Century to the Present. 2007. 760p. 65.00 *(978-0-268-04230-1(6))* Univ. of Notre Dame Pr.

Twyman, Sheila Mullen, ed. City Lights: An Anthology of Poetry & Art. 2009. (Illus.). 96p. pap. 15.00 *(978-0-9840679-1-6(4))* Beachcomber Pr.

Untermeyer, Louis. Modern American Poetry: An Introduction. 192p. 2009. 22.99 *(978-1-103-30220-8(5))* 2009. pap. 16.99 *(978-1-103-30216-1(7))* 2008. 22.99 *(978-0-559-66164-8(9))* 2008. pap. 22.75 *(978-0-559-66161-7(4))* BiblioBazaar.

Vendler, Helen. Poems, Poets, Poetry: An Introduction & Anthology. 3rd ed. 2009. (ENG.). 752p. (C). pap. 66.95 *(978-0-312-46319-9(7))* Bedford/Saint Martin's.

Verses from the Harvard Advocate. 2006. 264p. per. 23.99 *(978-1-4255-2476-0(1))* MPublishing.

Wagner Buyer, Laurie & Jameson, W. C., eds. Open Range: Poetry of the Reimagined West. 2007. 117p. pap. 13.95 *(978-0-9789456-6-4(2)*, Ghost Road Pr.) Ghost Road Publishing Group, Inc.

Webb, Jack, ed. The Best of Border Voices: Poet Laureates, Pulitzer Prize Winners & the Wisdom of Kids. 2007. (Illus.). 328p. 24.95 *(978-1-933769-24-0(6))* Level 4 Press, Inc.

Whittier, John Greenleaf. Songs of Three Centuries. 2009. 384p. 33.99 *(978-1-116-50921-2(0))*; 38.99 *(978-1-116-50920-5(2))*; pap. 32.75 *(978-1-116-50923-6(7))* BiblioBazaar.

Whittier, John Greenleaf, ed. Songs of Three Centuries. 2008. 382p. 48.95 *(978-1-4372-6035-9(7))*; pap. 33.95 *(978-1-4371-3345-5(2))* Kessinger Publishing, LLC.

Wilkinson, Marguerite. Golden Songs of the Golden State. 2009. 180p. 30.99 *(978-1-116-94476-1(6))*; (ENG.). 178p. 26.99 *(978-1-116-94477-8(4))*; (ENG.). 178p. pap. 22.75 *(978-1-116-94478-5(2))*; (ENG.). 178p. pap. 21.75 *(978-1-116-94479-2(0))* BiblioBazaar.

Wilkinson, Marguerite, ed. Golden Songs of the Golden State. 2007. (ENG.). 176p. 37.95 (978-0-548-42885-6(9)); per. 22.95 (978-0-548-40589-5(1)) Kessinger Publishing, LLC.

Wilson, Ian Randall, ed. 88: A Journal of Contemporary American Poetry - Issue 6. 2006. 140p. per. 13.95 (978-0-9772298-6-4(6)) Hollyridge Pr.

Wiman, Christian & Share, Don, eds. The Open Door: One Hundred Poems, One Hundred Years of Poetry Magazine. 2012. 224p. 20.00 (978-0-226-75070-5(1)) Univ. of Chicago Pr.

Wright, William. The Southern Poetry Anthology: Contemporary Appalachia, Vol. 3. Graves, Jesse & Ruffin, Paul, eds. 2011. 320p. pap. 26.95 (978-1-933896-64-9(7)) Texas Review Pr.

AMERICAN POETRY (COLLECTIONS)—19TH CENTURY

Kane, Paul. Poetry of the American Renaissance: A Diverse Anthology from the Romantic Period. Kane, Paul, ed. 2012. (ENG.). 383p. pap. 19.95 (978-0-8076-1619-2(2), 761619) Braziller, George Inc.

Moore, Frank. Personal & Political Ballads, Arranged & Ed by Frank Moore. 2006. 384p. per. 26.99 (978-1-4255-4029-6(5)) MPublishing.

Parisi, Joseph. 100 Essential Modern Poems by Women. 2008. (ENG.). 304p. 24.95 (978-1-56663-741-1(4)) Dee, Ivan R. Pub.

Parks, Edd W., ed. Southern Poets. 419p. reprint ed. lib. bdg. 98.00 (978-0-7222-0490-0(6)) Library Reprints, Inc.

Ricks, Christopher, ed. The New Oxford Book of Victorian Verse. 2008. (ENG.). 688p. pap. 25.95 (978-0-19-955631-1(8)) Oxford Univ. Pr., Inc.

Simms, William Gilmore. War Poetry of the South Edited by William Gilmore Simms. 2006. 496p. per. 29.99 (978-1-4255-5557-3(8)) MPublishing.

Untermeyer, Louis. Modern American Poetry. 2009. 174p. pap. (978-0-217-02422-8(X)); 348p. pap. (978-0-217-23721-5(5)); 354p. pap. (978-0-217-96521-7(0)) Books LLC.

Whicher, George, ed. Poetry of the New England Renaissance, 1790-1890. 2011. 504p. 58.95 (978-1-258-04247-9(9)) Literary Licensing, LLC.

Whitfield, James Monroe. The Works of James M. Whitfield: America & Other Writings by a Nineteenth-Century African American Poet. Levine, Robert S. & Wilson, Ivy G., eds. 2011. (ENG.). 256p. 65.00 (978-0-8078-3445-9(9)); pap. 26.95 (978-0-8078-7178-2(8)) Univ. of North Carolina Pr.

AMERICAN POETRY (COLLECTIONS)—20TH CENTURY

American Writers in a New Millennium: The Voice of American Poets & Short Story Writers. Date not set. pap. 24.95 (978-1-885519-68-9(0)) DDDD Pubns.

Anderson, Maggie. The Next of Us Is about to Be Born. 2009. 216p. pap. (978-1-60635-021-8(8)) Kent State Univ. Pr.

Axelrod, Steven Gould, et al, eds. The New Anthology of American Poetry: Vol. III: Postmodernisms 1950-Present. 2012. (ENG.). 592p. pap. 35.95 (978-0-8135-5156-2(0)) Rutgers Univ. Pr.

Baer, William, ed. Rhyming Poems: A Contemporary Antrology. 2007. 173p. pap. 15.00 (978-0-930982-64-5(9)) Univ. of Evansville Pr.

Banerjee, Neelanjana, et al, eds. Indivisible: An Anthology of Contemporary South Asian American Poetry. 2010. (ENG.). 220p. 65.00 (978-1-55728-932-2(8)); pap. 24.95 (978-1-55728-931-5(X)) Univ. of Arkansas Pr.

Beckman, Joshua & Zapruder, Matthew, eds. State of the Union: 50 Political Poems. 2008. 112p. 14.00 (978-1-933517-34-6(4)) Wave Bks.

—State of the Union: Fifty Political Poems. 2008. (ENG.). 144p. pap. 14.00 (978-1-933517-33-9(6)) Wave Bks.

Blais, Marie-Claire. Deaf to the City. 2007. (Exile Classics Ser.). (ENG.). 200p. pap. 17.95 (978-1-55096-013-6(X)) Exile Editions, Ltd. CAN. Dist: Independent Pubs. Group.

Blaisdell, Bob, ed. Imagist Poetry: An Anthology. 2011. (Dover Thrift Editions Ser.). (ENG.). 176p. (gr. 9). pap. 3.50 (978-0-486-40875-0(2)) Dover Pubns., Inc.

Blue Mountain Arts(r) Collection Staff. Take Each Day One Step at a Time. 2007. (ENG.). 56p. 5.95 (978-1-59842-201-6(4), Blue Mountain Pr.) Blue Mountain Arts Inc.

Bourgeois, Louise & Indiana, Gary. To Whom It May Concern. 2011. (ENG., Illus.). 76p. 75.00 (978-1-900828-36-9(7)) Violette Editions GBR. Dist: D.A.P./Distributed Art Pubs.

Brady, Philip. By Heart: Reflections of a Rust Belt Bard. 2008. (ENG.). 180p. 29.95 (978-1-57233-632-2(3)) Univ. of Tennessee Pr.

Braithwaite, William S. Anthology of Magazine Verse & Year Book of American Poetry, 6 Vols. 140.95 (978-0-8369-9358-5(6), 19729) Ayer Co. Pubs., Inc.

Brown, Kurt & Schechter, Harold, eds. Killer Verse: Poems of Murder & Mayhem. 2011. (ENG.). 256p. 13.50 (978-0-307-70093-3(3), Everyman's Library) Knopf Doubleday Publishing Group.

The Cancer Poetry Project: Poems by Cancer Patients & Those Who Love Them. 2007. 248p. per. 18.95 (978-0-9789946-8-6(X)) Tasora Bks.

Chronicle of the Pulitzer Prizes for Poetry: Discussions, Decisions & Documents. 2009. (ENG.) XV, 484p. (978-3-11-023007-9(0)) Saur, K. G. Verlag GmbH & Co.

Davis, Todd & Murphy, Erin, eds. Making Poems: Forty Poems with Commentary by the Poets. 2010. (Excelsior Editions Ser.). 144p. (ENG.). 60.00 (978-1-4384-3175-8(9)); pap. 23.95 (978-1-4384-3176-5(7)) State Univ. of New York Pr.

Dungey, Melba, ed. WVPS, 1995 Contest Winners: West. 88p. (978-0-9643688-1-9(2)) West Virginia Poetry Society.

Fishman, Charles Adés, ed. Blood to Remember: American Poets on the Holocaust. 2nd ed. 2007. 642p. 42.50 (978-1-56809-112-9(5)); pap. 27.95 (978-1-56809-113-6(3)) Time Being Bks. (Time Being Pr.).

Freeman, Barbara Claire, et al. An Instance: Three Chapbooks. 2010. 80p. pap. 15.00 (978-0-9679854-8-0(X)) Instance Pr.

Frost, Robert. The Prophets Really Prophecy As Mystics: The Commentators Merely by Statistics. 2011. 12p. pap. 35.95 (978-1-258-05371-0(3)) Literary Licensing, LLC.

Furr, Derek. Recorded Poetry & Poetic Reception from Edna Millay to the Circle of Robert Lowell. 2010. (ENG., Illus.). 206p. 79.00 (978-0-230-10377-1(4)) Palgrave Macmillan.

Gordon, Marilyn, ed. The Northeast Bronx Poets & Writers Forum Anthology, Vol. 1. 48p. (C). 4.50 (978-0-9609542-1-6(X)) Gordon, Marilyn Pub.

Grubbs, Morris A. & Vance, Jane Gentry. What Comes down to Us: 25 Contemporary Kentucky Poets. Worley, Jeff, ed. 2009. (ENG., Illus.). 288p. 29.95 (978-0-8131-2557-2(X)) Univ. Pr. of Kentucky.

Harter, Christopher. An Author Index to Little Magazines of the Mimeograph Revolution, 1958-1980. 2008. (ENG.). 752p. 150.00 (978-0-8108-6113-8(5)) Scarecrow Pr., Inc.

Harvey, Samuel R., et al. The Wonders of Would Be Writers. Kasper, John D. & Ebnet, Rosemary, eds. Date not set. 105p. (Orig.). pap., spiral bd. 10.00 (978-0-9633798-1-8(X)) Harvey Publishing.

Hicks, Patrick, et al. A Harvest of Words: Contemporary South Dakota Poetry. Hicks, Patrick, ed. 2010. (ENG.). 270p. pap. 20.00 (978-0-931170-03-4(6)) Ctr. for Western Studies.

Hollander, John & Weber, Joanna, eds. Words for Images: A Gallery of Poems. 2006. (ENG., Illus.). 103p. 35.00 (978-0-89467-096-1(4)) Yale Univ. Art Gallery.

Honey, Maureen, ed. Shadowed Dreams: Women's Poetry of the Harlem Renaissance. 2nd ed. 2006. (Multi-Ethnic Literatures of the Americas Ser.). (ENG., Illus.). 374p. per. 24.95 (978-0-8135-3886-0(6)) Rutgers Univ. Pr.

Inspirations. 2007. (Engagement Ser.). 13.99 (978-1-59868-163-5(X), 0700609) Avalanche Publishing, Inc.

Larsen, Wally. Selected Utah Poets of the Year: 1965-1982, 1984-1987, 1989-1992, 1994-1997. 2007. (978-0-8425-2674-6(9)) Brigham Young Univ.

Maio, Samuel, ed. Dramatic Monologues: A Contemporary Anthology. 2008. 301p. 25.00 (978-0-930982-67-6(3)) Univ. of Evansville Pr.

McIver, Don & Renz, Mikaela. A Bigger Boat: The Unlikely Success of the Albuquerque Poetry Slam Scene. McAllister, Susan et al, eds. 2008. (Mary Burritt Christiansen Poetry Ser.). (ENG., Illus.). 248p. pap. 19.95 (978-0-8263-4483-0(6)) Univ. of New Mexico Pr.

Merwin, W. S. Lament for the Makers: A Memorial Anthology. 2010. (ENG., Illus.). 96p. pap. 14.95 (978-1-58243-732-3(7), Counterpoint Pr.) Basic Bks. GBR. Dist: Perseus-PGW.

Olmsted, Robert W., compiled by. 5th Annual Northwoods Anthology. 2008. 164p. 39.95 (978-0-89002-392-1(1)); pap. 16.95 (978-0-89002-391-4(3)) Northwoods Pr.

Parks, Edd W., ed. Southern Poets. 419p. reprint ed. lib. bdg. 98.00 (978-0-7222-0490-0(6)) Library Reprints, Inc.

Reflections on a Gift of Watermelon Pickle & Other Modern Verse: Anthology. 8.97 (978-0-673-29423-4(4)) Addison-Wesley Longman, Inc.

Ricks, Christopher, ed. Joining Music with Reason: 34 Poets, British & American Oxford, 2004-2009. 2011. (ENG.). 440p. pap. 23.95 (978-1-904130-40-6(2)) Waywiser Pr., The GBR. Dist: Dufour Editions, Inc.

Schmidt, Elizabeth Hun. The Poets Laureate Anthology. 2010. (ENG., Illus.). 762p. 39.95 (978-0-393-06181-9(7), 6181) Norton, W. W. & Co., Inc.

Smith, James. Don't Leave Hungry: 50 Years of Southern Poetry Review. 2009. 380p. 54.95 (978-1-55728-892-9(5)); pap. 24.95 (978-1-55728-893-6(3)) Univ. of Arkansas Pr.

Sonnenberg, Kerri & Kim, Dennis, eds. Columbia Poetry Review, Vol. 13. Date not set. pap. 6.00 (978-0-932026-54-5(0)) Columbia College Chicago.

Suddeth, Ruth E., ed. An Atlanta Argosy. 175p. reprint ed. lib. bdg. 88.00 (978-0-7222-0630-0(5)) Library Reprints, Inc.

Sweeney, Chad, ed. Days I Moved Through Ordinary Sounds: The Extraordinary Work of WritersCorps Teachers. 2009. (ENG., Illus.). 200p. pap. 17.95 (978-1-931404-10-5(0)) City Lights Foundation.

Twichell, Chase. An Ausable Reader: A Decade of Poetry Against the Current, 1999-2008. 2008. (978-1-931337-45-8(4)) Ausable Pr.

Untermeyer, Louis. Modern American Poetry. 2009. 174p. pap. (978-0-217-02422-8(X)); 354p. pap. (978-0-217-96521-7(0)); 348p. pap. (978-0-217-23721-5(5)) Books LLC.

Waldman, Anne, ed. The Beat Book: Writings from the Beat Generation. 2nd rev. ed. 2007. (ENG.). 400p. pap. 16.95 (978-1-59030-455-6(1)) Shambhala Pubns., Inc.

AMERICAN POETRY (COLLECTIONS)—21ST CENTURY

Addonizio, Kim, ed. Best New Poets 2009: 50 Poems from Emerging Writers. 2009. (Best New Poets Ser.). (ENG.). 144p. pap. 11.95 (978-0-9766296-4-1(X)) Univ. Pr. of Virginia.

Allegrezza, William & Bianchi, Raymond, eds. The City Visible: Chicago Poetry for the New Century. 2007. 256p. per. 22.95 (978-0-9786440-1-7(8)) Cracked Slab Bks.

ALOP, compiled by. Excellence: 2006 Poetry Collection. 2006. (YA). per. 60.95 (978-0-9773662-1-7(9)) America Library of Poetry.

Anderson, Erik. The Poetics of Trespass. 2010. 104p. pap. 12.95 (978-0-9796177-7-5(4)) Seismicity Editions.

Anderson, James & Catal, Rafael, eds. Index of American Periodical Verse 2006. 2008. (Index of American Periodical Verse Ser.). (ENG.). 760p. 150.00 (978-0-8108-6176-3(3)) Scarecrow Pr., Inc.

Anderson, Maggie. The Next of Us Is about to Be Born. 2009. 216p. pap. (978-1-60635-021-8(8)) Kent State Univ. Pr.

Anthology of Poetry by Young Americans. 2006. 176p. 12.95 (978-1-883931-59-9(2)); pap. 6.95 (978-1-883931-60-5(6)) Anthology of Poetry, Inc.

Anthology of Poetry by Young Americans: 2008 Edition. 2008. 176p. 13.95 (978-1-883931-70-4(3)); pap. 7.95 (978-1-883931-71-1(1)) Anthology of Poetry, Inc.

Astley, Neil, ed. Bloodaxe Poetry Introductions 3. 2008. (ENG., Illus.). 96p. pap. 22.95 (978-1-85224-767-6(3)) Bloodaxe Bks. GBR. Dist: Dufour Editions, Inc.

Axelrod, Steven Gould, et al, eds. The New Anthology of American Poetry: Vol. III: Postmodernisms 1950-Present. 2012. (ENG.). 592p. pap. 35.95 (978-0-8135-5156-2(0)) Rutgers Univ. Pr.

Baer, William, ed. Rhyming Poems: A Contemporary Antrology. 2007. 173p. pap. 15.00 (978-0-930982-64-5(9)) Univ. of Evansville Pr.

Baker, David. Talk Poetry: Poems & Interviews with Nine American Poets. 2012. (ENG., Illus.). 172p. pap. 19.95 (978-1-55728-981-0(6)) Univ. of Arkansas Pr.

Banerjee, Neelanjana, et al, eds. Indivisible: An Anthology of Contemporary South Asian American Poetry. 2010. (ENG.). 220p. 65.00 (978-1-55728-932-2(8)); pap. 24.95 (978-1-55728-931-5(X)) Univ. of Arkansas Pr.

Beckman, Joshua & Zapruder, Matthew, eds. State of the Union: 50 Political Poems. 2008. 112p. 14.00 (978-1-933517-34-6(4)) Wave Bks.

—State of the Union: Fifty Political Poems. 2008. (ENG.). 144p. pap. 14.00 (978-1-933517-33-9(6)) Wave Bks.

Belli, Angela & Coulehan, Jack, eds. Primary Care: More Poems by Physicians. 2006. 152p. per. 19.95 (978-1-58729-503-4(2)) Univ. of Iowa Pr.

Blue Mountain Arts(r) Collection Staff. Take Each Day One Step at a Time. 2007. (ENG.). 56p. 5.95 (978-1-59842-201-6(4), Blue Mountain Pr.) Blue Mountain Arts Inc.

Bobo, Emily, et al. New Poets-Short Books, Vol. 3. Bell, Marvin, ed. 2011. (ENG.). 76p. pap. 16.95 (978-0-9800289-2-8(2)) Lost Horse Pr.

Boller, Diane & Selby, Don. Poetry Daily Essentials 2007. 2007. 244p. per. 14.95 (978-1-4022-0927-7(4)) Sourcebooks, Inc.

Bonta, Dave, et al. The Book of Ystwyth: Six Poets on the Art of Clive Hicks-Jenkins. Wakelin, Peter, ed. 2011. (Illus.). 96p. pap. 15.95 (978-0-932112-89-7(7)) Carolina Wren Pr.

Bourgeois, Louise & Indiana, Gary. To Whom It May Concern. 2011. (ENG., Illus.). 76p. 75.00 (978-1-900828-36-9(7)) Violette Editions GBR. Dist: D.A.P./Distributed Art Pubs.

Cantwell, Kevin, ed. Writing on Napkins at the Sunshine Club: An Anthology of Poets Writing in Macon. 2011. 256p. pap. 27.00 (978-0-88146-251-7(9)) Mercer Univ. Pr.

Carr, Gladys Justin, et al. Edge by Edge. 2007. 80p. per. 14.00 (978-0-9766405-2-3(X)) Toadlily Pr.

Carroll, Jonathan & Hand, Elizabeth. Conjunctions: 54, Shadow Selves. Morrow, Bradford, ed. 2010. (ENG., Illus.). 364p. pap. 15.00 (978-0-941964-70-8(1)) Bard College Pubns. Office.

Charara, Hayan, ed. Inclined to Speak: An Anthology of Contemporary Arab American Poetry. 2008. 333p. 65.00 (978-1-55728-866-0(6)); (ENG.). 328p. pap. 24.95 (978-1-55728-867-7(4)) Univ. of Arkansas Pr.

Clark, Stephanie Brown, et al, eds. Body Language: Poems of the Medical Training Experience. 2006. (BOA Anthology Ser.: No. 2). (ENG., Illus.). 159p. per. 21.95 (978-1-929918-86-7(0)) BOA Editions, Ltd.

Colley, Robert, et al, eds. Stone Canoe, Number 4: A Journal of Arts & Ideas from Upstate New York. 2010. (Stone Canoe Ser.). (Illus.). 327p. pap. (978-0-9791944-3-6(1)) Syracuse Univ. Pr.

Collins, Billy. The Best American Poetry 2006. Lehman, David, ed. 2006. (ENG.). 224p. 30.00 (978-0-7432-2967-8(3)); pap. 16.00 (978-0-7432-5759-6(6)) Scribner. (Scribner).

Davis, Brad, ed. Sunken Garden Poetry: 1992-2011. 2012. (ENG., Illus.). 280p. 24.95 (978-0-8195-7290-5(X)); pap. 16.95 (978-0-8195-7291-2(8)) Wesleyan Univ. Pr.

Davis, Todd & Murphy, Erin, eds. Making Poems: Forty Poems with Commentary by the Poets. 2010. (Excelsior Editions Ser.). 144p. (ENG.). 60.00 (978-1-4384-3175-8(9)); pap. 23.95 (978-1-4384-3176-5(7)) State Univ. of New York Pr.

Dawes, Kwame Senu Neville. Home Is Where: An Anthology of African American Poetry from the Carolinas. 2011. pap. (978-1-891885-80-8(4)) Hub City Writers Project.

A Field of Verse: New Jersey Poetry Society, Inc. Anthology 2007. 2007. 71p. pap. 11.95 (978-0-9767942-2-6(5)) New Jersey Poetry Society, Inc.

Gerstler, Amy & Lehman, David, eds. The Best American Poetry 2010: Series Editor David Lehman. 2010. (ENG.). 256p. 35.00 (978-1-4391-8147-8(0)); pap. 16.00 (978-1-4391-8145-4(4)) Scribner. (Scribner).

Glaz, Sarah & Growney, JoAnne Simpson. Strange Attractors: Poems of Love & Mathematics. 2008. (ENG.). 250p. 39.00 (978-1-56881-341-7(4)) AK Peters, Ltd.

Hamby, Barbara & Kirby, David, eds. Seriously Funny: Poems about Love, Death, Religion, Art, Politics, Sex, & Everything Else. 2010. (ENG.). 440p. 69.95 (978-0-8203-3087-7(6)); pap. 24.95 (978-0-8203-3569-8(X)) Univ. of Georgia Pr.

Hicks, Patrick, et al. A Harvest of Words: Contemporary South Dakota Poetry. Hicks, Patrick, ed. 2010. (ENG.). 270p. pap. 20.00 (978-0-931170-03-4(6)) Ctr. for Western Studies.

Honold, Kevin. Men As Trees Walking. 2010. (Osu journal award Poetry Ser.). cd-rom 14.95 (978-0-8142-9242-6(9)) Ohio State Univ. Pr.

—Men as Trees Walking. 2010. (Osu journal award Poetry Ser.). pap. 13.95 (978-0-8142-5176-8(5)) Ohio State Univ. Pr.

Howell, Christopher. Dreamless & Possible: Poems New & Selected. 2010. 224p. pap. 24.95 (978-0-295-99012-5(0)) Univ. of Washington Pr.

Junge, Mary. The Quiet Eye: Thirteen Ways of Looking at Nature. 2009. (978-0-9787973-4-8(5)) Laurel Poetry Collective.

Kolin, Philip C. & Swartwout, Susan, eds. Hurricane Blues: Poems about Katrina & Rita. 2006. 184p. pap. 17.00 (978-0-9760413-5-1(9)) Southeast Missouri State Univ. Pr.

Krcmarik, Tim & Krcmarik, Tim. Lost Horse Press Vol. II. Bell, Marvin, ed. 2011. (ENG.). 88p. pap. 16.95 (978-0-9800289-0-4(6)) Lost Horse Pr.

Kwasny, Melissa & Smoker, M. L., eds. I Go to the Ruined Place Vol. 1: Contemporary Poems in Support of Global Human Rights. 2009. (ENG.). 152p. pap. 18.00 (978-0-9800289-7-3(3)) Lost Horse Pr.

Lehman, David. The Best American Poetry 2008. Wright, Charles & Lehman, David, eds. 2008. (ENG.). 224p. pap. 16.00 (978-0-7432-9975-6(2), Scribner) Scribner.

Lehman, David & McHugh, Heather, eds. The Best American Poetry 2007. 2007. (ENG.). 192p. 30.00 (978-0-7432-9972-5(8), Scribner) Scribner.

Lehman, David & Young, Kevin, eds. The Best American Poetry 2011. 2011. (ENG.). 240p. pap. 16.00 (978-1-4391-8149-2(7)); lib. bdg. 35.00 (978-1-4391-8150-8(0)) Scribner. (Scribner).

Livingood, Jeb & Pankey, Eric, eds. Best New Poets 2006: 50 Poems from Emerging Writers. 2006. (Best New Poets Ser.). (ENG.). 144p. pap. 11.95 (978-0-9766296-1-0(5)) Samovar Pr.

Lloyd, David, ed. Other Land: Contemporary Poems on Wales & Welsh-American Experience. 2008. (ENG.). 140p. pap. 15.95 (978-1-905762-22-4(4)) Parthian Bks. GBR. Dist: Independent Pubs. Group.

Maio, Samuel, ed. Dramatic Monologues: A Contemporary Anthology. 2008. 301p. 25.00 (978-0-930982-67-6(3)) Univ. of Evansville Pr.

McIver, Don & Renz, Mikaela. A Bigger Boat: The Unlikely Success of the Albuquerque Poetry Slam Scene. McAllister, Susan et al, eds. 2008. (Mary Burritt Christiansen Poetry Ser.). (ENG., Illus.). 248p. pap. 19.95 (978-0-8263-4483-0(6)) Univ. of New Mexico Pr.

Melhhem. Art Politics Politics Art. 2010. 80p. pap. 9.95 (978-0-8156-0976-6(0)) Syracuse Univ. Pr.

Mengert, Christina & Wilkinson, Joshua Marie, eds. 12 X 12: Conversations in 21st-Century Poetry & Poetics. 2009. (ENG.). 284p. pap. 29.95 (978-1-58729-791-5(4)) Univ. of Iowa Pr.

Minar, Scott, ed. The Working Poet: Seventy Five Writing Exercises & a Poetry Anthology. 2009. 400p. (C). pap. 29.95 (978-1-932870-32-9(6)) Autumn Hse. Pr.

Minnick, Norman, ed. Between Water & Song: New Poets for the Twenty-First Century. 2010. (ENG.). 260p. pap. 17.00 (978-1-935210-07-8(6)) White Pine Pr.

Neubauer, Alexander. Poetry in Person: Twenty-five Years of Conversation with America's Poets. 2011. (ENG., Illus.). 368p. pap. 18.00 (978-0-375-71175-6(9), Knopf) Knopf Doubleday Publishing Group.

Neubauer, Alexander, ed. Poetry in Person: Twenty-Five Years of Conversations with America's Poets. 2010. (ENG., Illus.). 368p. 27.95 (978-0-307-26967-6(1), Knopf) Knopf Doubleday Publishing Group.

Northern Printmakers Alliance & Lake Superior Writers. Trail Guide to the Northland Experience in Prints & Poetry. 2008. (Illus.). 103p. pap. 19.95 (978-0-9819294-0-8(0)) Calyx Pr.

Phillipson, Larry. Paths & Poetry. 2008. (Illus.). 150p. per. (978-0-9748680-9-7(4)) Heins Pubns.

Rankine, Claudia & Sewell, Lisa, eds. Eleven More American Women Poets in the 21st Century: Poetics Across North America. 2nd ed. 2012. (American Poets in the 21st Century Ser.). (ENG.) 464p. (C). 80.00 (978-0-8195-7234-9(9)); pap. 24.95 (978-0-8195-7235-6(7)) Wesleyan Univ. Pr.

Shaughnessy, Brenda. Human Dark with Sugar. 2008. (ENG.). 96p. pap. 15.00 (978-1-55659-276-8(0)) Copper Canyon Pr.

Smith, James. Don't Leave Hungry: 50 Years of Southern Poetry Review. 2009. 380p. 54.95 (978-1-55728-892-9(5)); pap. 24.95 (978-1-55728-893-6(3)) Univ. of Arkansas Pr.

Strand, Mark, ed. Best New Poets 2008: 50 Poems from Emerging Writers. 2008. (Best New Poets Ser.). (ENG.). 144p. pap. 11.95 (978-0-9766296-3-4(1)) Univ. Pr. of Virginia.

Sweeney, Chad, ed. Days I Moved Through Ordinary Sounds: The Extraordinary Work of WritersCorps Teachers. 2009. (ENG., Illus.). 200p. pap. 17.95 (978-1-931404-10-5(0)) City Lights Foundation.

Swensen, Cole & St. John, David. American Hybrid: A Norton Anthology of New Poetry. St. John, David, ed. 2009. (ENG., Illus.). 560p. pap. 25.95 (978-0-393-33375-6(2), 33375) Norton, W. W. & Co., Inc.

Taylor, Richard Allen, ed. Kakalak 2007: Anthology of Carolina Poets. 2007. 138p. per. 12.00 (978-1-59948-078-7(6)) Main Street Rag Publishing Co.

Tehani Sarreal, Jennifer. Sarreal Visions: Reflections & Journeys. 2010. 110p. pap. 24.95 (978-1-60844-435-9(X)) Dog Ear Publishing, LLC.

Twichell, Chase. An Ausable Reader: A Decade of Poetry Against the Current, 1999-2008. 2008. (978-1-931337-45-8(4)) Ausable Pr.

Unrein, Sonya, ed. Open Windows 2006. 2006. pap. 15.95 (978-0-9789456-2-6(X), Ghost Road Pr.) Ghost Road Publishing Group, Inc.

Wagoner, David & Lehman, David, eds. The Best American Poetry 2009. 2009. (ENG.). 240p. pap. 16.00 (978-0-7432-9977-0(9), Scribner) Scribner.

—The Best American Poetry 2009: Series Editor David Lehman. 2009. (ENG.). 240p. 35.00 (978-0-7432-9976-3(0), Scribner) Scribner.

Walker, Frank X., ed. America, What's My Name? The Other Poets Unfurl the Flag. 2007. 126p. per. 16.95 (978-1-893239-63-0(2)) Wind Pubns.

A

Walker, Sue Brannan & Chambers, J. William, eds. Whatever Remembers Us: An Anthology of Alabama Poetry. 2007. 320p. 30.00 *(978-0-942544-62-6(5))*; pap. 24.00 *(978-0-942544-60-2(9))* Negative Capability Pr.

Wasylyshyn, Karol M. Standing on Marbles: Three Leader Types in Verse & Imagery. 2011. (ENG., Illus.). 120p. pap. 26.99 *(978-0-9824683-4-0(2))* TrueNorth Pr.

Watson, Randall, ed. The Weight of Addition, an anthology of Texas Poetry. 2007. 288p. per. 19.95 *(978-0-9729432-3-9(4))* Mutabilis Pr.

Webb, Kenneth. Essences. 2007. 19.00 *(978-0-8059-8876-5(9))* Dorrance Publishing Co., Inc.

Williams-Evans, Shiphrah, et al. Struggles. 2010. (Illus.). 50p. lib. bdg. *(978-0-9800956-0-9(3))* Williams College Pr.

Wright, Charles & Lehman, David, eds. The Best American Poetry 2008. 2008. (ENG.). 224p. 35.00 *(978-0-7432-9974-9(4)*, Scribner) Scribner.

Write Group (Massachusetts) Staff, contrib. by. Moments Falling Open: The Write Group Anthology. 2007. (ENG.). 108p. per. 14.95 *(978-0-9749291-4-9(X)*, Pear Tree Publishing) Obert, Christopher Publishing.

Xavier, Emanuel. Me No Habla with Acento: Contemporary Latino/A Poetry. 2010. pap. *(978-1-60864-039-3(6))* Rebel Satori Pr.

Yezzi, David, ed. The Swallow Anthology of New American Poets. 2009. (ENG.). 360p. 49.95 *(978-0-8040-1120-4(6))*; pap. 19.95 *(978-0-8040-1121-1(4))* Swallow Pr.

Zucker, Rachel & Greenberg, Arielle, eds. Starting Today: 100 Poems for Obama's First 100 Days. 2010. (ENG.). 210p. pap. 20.00 *(978-1-58729-871-4(6))* Univ. of Iowa Pr.

AMERICAN POETRY—AFRICAN AMERICAN AUTHORS

African American Poetry Interest Level 6-12: Teachers Manual. (Illus.). pap., tchr. ed. 8.50 *(978-0-8359-0534-3(9))* Globe Fearon Educational Publishing.

Dawes, Kwame Senu Neville. Home Is Where: An Anthology of African American Poetry from the Carolinas. 2011. pap. ***(978-1-891885-80-8(4))*** Hub City Writers Project.

Dungy, Camille T., ed. Black Nature: Four Centuries of African American Nature Poetry. 2009. (ENG.). 432p. pap. 24.95 *(978-0-8203-3431-8(6))*; lib. bdg. 69.95 *(978-0-8203-3277-2(1))* Univ. of Georgia Pr.

Finney, Nikky, ed. The Ringing Ear: Black Poets Lean South. 2007. (ENG.). 432p. 69.95 *(978-0-8203-2925-3(8))*; per. 22.95 *(978-0-8203-2926-0(6))* Univ. of Georgia Pr.

Honey, Maureen, ed. Shadowed Dreams: Women's Poetry of the Harlem Renaissance. 2nd ed. 2006. (Multi-Ethnic Literatures of the Americas Ser.). (ENG., Illus.). 374p. per. 24.95 *(978-0-8135-3886-0(6))* Rutgers Univ. Pr.

Jenkins-Bridgers, Josephine. Little Mirror. 2011. 48p. pap. 9.95 ***(978-1-936513-07-9(2))*** PearlStone Publishing, Inc.

Jennings, Regina. Malcolm X & the Poetics of Haki Madhubuti. 2006. (ENG.). 296p. per. 45.00 *(978-0-7864-2619-5(5))* McFarland & Co., Inc. Pubs.

Johnson, James Weldon. The Book of American Negro Poetry. 2007. 194p. pap. 19.99 *(978-1-4264-5755-5(3))*; (ENG.). 218p. pap. 22.99 *(978-1-4264-5815-6(0))* BiblioBazaar.

Miller, E. Ethelbert. The 5th Inning. 2012. (Busboys & Poets Ser.). (ENG., Illus.). 176p. pap. 15.95 ***(978-1-60486-521-9(0))*** PM Pr.

Patterson, Anita. Race, American Literature & Transnational Modernisms. 2011. (Cambridge Studies in American Literature & Culture Ser.). (ENG.). 248p. pap. 48.00 *(978-0-521-34956-7(7))* Cambridge Univ. Pr.

Rowell, Charles Henry, ed. Angles of Ascent: A Norton Anthology of Contemporary African American Poetry. 2013. (ENG.). 608p. pap. 24.95 *(978-0-393-33940-6(8)*, 33940) Norton, W. W. & Co., Inc.

Shakesword, Festus. Lyric Poems from Around the World: Epic Thinks Beyond Feelings. 2011. 700p. 34.99 ***(978-1-4568-9526-6(5))***; pap. 23.99 ***(978-1-4568-9525-9(7))*** Xlibris Corp.

Talley, Thomas W. Negro Folk Rhymes Wise & Otherwise Wit. 2006. pap. 31.95 *(978-1-4286-3579-1(3))* Kessinger Publishing, LLC.

Whitfield, James Monroe. The Works of James M. Whitfield: America & Other Writings by a Nineteenth-Century African American Poet. Levine, Robert S. & Wilson, Ivy G., eds. 2011. (ENG.). 256p. 65.00 *(978-0-8078-3445-9(9))*; pap. 26.95 *(978-0-8078-7178-2(8))* Univ. of North Carolina Pr.

AMERICAN POETRY—AFRICAN AMERICAN AUTHORS—HISTORY AND CRITICISM

Bloom, Harold. African-American Poets, 2 vols., Vol. 2. 2nd rev. ed. 2010. (Bloom's Modern Critical Views Ser.). 202p. (C). (gr. 9-18). 45.00 *(978-1-60413-810-8(6)*, Chelsea Hse.) Facts On File, Inc.

Bloom, Harold, ed. African-American Poets: Volume 1, New Edition, 2 vols. 2nd rev. ed. 2009. (Bloom's Modern Critical Views Ser.). 272p. (C). (gr. 9-18). 45.00 *(978-1-60413-400-1(3)*, Chelsea Hse.) Facts On File, Inc.

Hoffman, Tyler. American Poetry in Performance: From Walt Whitman to Hip Hop. 2011. (ENG.). 282p. (C). 45.00 *(978-0-472-11781-9(5))* Univ. of Michigan Pr.

Jacques, Geoffrey. A Change in the Weather: Modernist Imagination, African American Imaginary. 2009. 240p. (ENG.). pap. 28.95 *(978-1-55849-688-0(2))*; lib. bdg. 80.00 net. *(978-1-55849-687-3(4))* Univ. of Massachusetts Pr.

Jones, Meta DuEwa. The Muse Is Music: Jazz Poetry from the Harlem Renaissance to Spoken Word. 2011. (New Black Studies Ser.). (ENG., Illus.). 304p. 55.00 *(978-0-252-03621-7(2))* Univ. of Illinois Pr.

Kitta, Gergely. Gwendolyn Brooks's Poetry. 2008. 64p. pap. *(978-3-639-00599-8(6))* VDM Verlag Dr. Mueller e.K.

Mance, Ajuan Maria. Inventing Black Women: African American Women Poets & Self-Representation, 1877-2000. 2008. (ENG.). 216p. pap. 24.95 *(978-1-57233-651-3(X))* 2007. 248p. 36.00 *(978-1-57233-492-2(4))* Univ. of Tennessee Pr.

Marcoux, Jean-Philippe. Jazz Griots: Music as History in the 1960s African American Poem. 2012. (ENG.). 240p. (gr. 17). 65.00 ***(978-0-7391-6673-4(5))*** Lexington Bks.

Pereira, Malin, ed. Into a Light Both Brilliant & Unseen: Conversations with Contemporary Black Poets. 2010. (ENG.). 260p. 59.95 *(978-0-8203-3107-2(4))*; pap. 19.95 *(978-0-8203-3713-5(7))* Univ. of Georgia Pr.

Phillips, Rowan Ricardo. When Blackness Rhymes with Blackness. 2010. (Dalkey Archive Scholarly Ser.). (ENG.). 160p. pap. 25.95 *(978-1-56478-583-1(1)*, 478583) Dalkey Archive Pr.

Rambsy, Howard. The Black Arts Enterprise & the Production of African American Poetry. 2011. (ENG., Illus.). 198p. 60.00 *(978-0-472-11733-8(5))* Univ. of Michigan Pr.

Ramey, Lauri. Slave Songs & the Birth of African American Poetry. (ENG.). 216p. 2010. pap. 28.00 *(978-0-230-10034-3(1))* 2008. 84.00 *(978-1-4039-7569-0(8))* Palgrave Macmillan.

Ramey, Lauri, ed. The Heritage Series of Black Poetry, 1962-1975: A Research Compendium. 2008. (Illus.). 388p. 124.95 *(978-0-7546-5782-8(5))* Ashgate Publishing Co.

Ryan, Jennifer D. Post-Jazz Poetics: A Social History. 2010. (ENG., Illus.). 240p. 84.00 *(978-0-230-62315-6(8))* Palgrave Macmillan.

Schultz, Kathy Lou. The Afro-Modernist Epic & Literary History: Tolson, Hughes, Baraka. 2013. (Modern & Contemporary Poetry & Poetics Ser.). (ENG., Illus.). 256p. 80.00 ***(978-0-230-33873-9(9))*** Palgrave Macmillan.

Shockley, Evie. Renegade Poetics: Black Aesthetics & Formal Innovation in African American Poetry. 2011. (Contemporary North American Poetry Ser.). (ENG.). 264p. pap. 39.95 ***(978-1-60938-058-8(4))*** Univ. of Iowa Pr.

Woodson, Jon. Anthems, Sonnets, & Chants: Recovering the African American Poetry of the 1930s. 2011. 312p. 55.95 *(978-0-8142-1146-5(1))*; cd-rom 14.95 *(978-0-8142-9245-7(3))* Ohio State Univ. Pr.

AMERICAN POETRY—AFRO-AMERICAN AUTHORS

see American Poetry—African American Authors

AMERICAN POETRY—BIBLIOGRAPHY

Cooke, George Willis. A Bibliography of James Russell Lowell. 2009. 180p. pap. *(978-0-217-65968-0(3))* Books LLC.

Davis, Gwenn. Poetry by Women to 1900. *(978-0-7201-2016-5(0)*, Burns & Oates) Continuum International Publishing Group, Ltd.

Johnson, Merle, ed. You Know These Lines: A Bibliography of the Most Quoted Verses in American Poetry. 2011. 216p. 44.95 ***(978-1-258-06131-9(7))*** Literary Licensing, LLC.

Wandrei, Donald. A Concordance to the Poetry of Donald Wandrei. 2008. 464p. 50.00 *(978-0-9814888-2-0(X))* Hippocampus Pr.

Whitesell, David R. A Bibliographical Description of Books & Pamphlets of American Verse Printed from 1610 Through 1820. 2012. (ENG.). 720p. ***(978-0-271-05221-2(X))*** Pennsylvania State Univ. Pr.

AMERICAN POETRY—CATHOLIC AUTHORS

see American Literature—Catholic Authors

AMERICAN POETRY—DICTIONARIES, INDEXES, ETC.

Haralson, Eric, ed. Encyclopedia of American Poetry: The Nineteenth Century. 2011. 549p. pap. 59.95 *(978-0-415-89076-2(4))* Routledge.

—Encyclopedia of American Poetry: The Twentieth Century. 2013. (ENG.). 866p. pap. 59.95 *(978-0-415-89077-9(2))* Routledge.

AMERICAN POETRY—HISTORY AND CRITICISM

Andrews, Jennifer. In the Belly of a Laughing God. 2010. *(978-0-8020-3567-7(1))* Univ. of Toronto Pr.

Aptowicz, Cristin O'Keefe. Words in Your Face: A Guided Tour Through Twenty Years of the New York City Poetry Slam. 2007. (ENG., Illus.). 288p. per. 17.95 *(978-1-933368-82-5(9))* Counterpoint LLC.

Arsic, Branka & Wolfe, Cary, eds. The Other Emerson. 2010. (ENG.). 360p. 82.50 *(978-0-8166-6747-5(0))*; pap. 27.50 *(978-0-8166-6748-2(9))* Univ. of Minnesota Pr.

Atkins, Elizabeth. The Poet's Poet: Essays on the Character & Mission of the Poet As Interpreted in English Verse of the Last One Hundred & Fifty Years. 2010. 390p. pap. 33.75 *(978-1-143-91019-7(2))* BiblioBazaar.

—The Poet's Poet: Essays on the Character & Mission of the Poet As Interpreted in English Verse of the Last One Hundred & Fifty Years. 2010. 186p. 30.36 *(978-1-169-72805-9(7))*; pap. 18.36 *(978-1-162-70500-2(0))*; 37.95 *(978-1-161-47364-3(5))* Kessinger Publishing, LLC.

—The Poet's Poet; Essays on the Character & Mission of the Poet As Interpreted in English Verse of the Last One Hundred & Fifty Years. 2010. 392p. pap. 33.75 *(978-1-178-34992-4(6))*; (ENG.). 388p. pap. 33.75 *(978-1-178-04543-7(9))*; (ENG.). 388p. pap. 33.75 *(978-1-177-35190-4(0))* BiblioBazaar.

—The Poet's Poet; Essays on the Character & Mission of the Poet As Interpreted in English Verse of the Last One Hundred & Fifty Years. 2010. (Illus.). 180p. pap. 26.62 *(978-1-153-71709-0(3))* General Bks. LLC.

Bazin, Victoria. Marianne Moore & the Cultures of Modernity. 2010. (Illus.). 228p. 99.95 *(978-0-7546-6232-7(2))* Ashgate Publishing Co.

Bergé, Carol, intro. Light Years: An Anthology on Sociocultural Happenings (Multimedia in the East Village, 1960-1966) 2010. (ENG., Illus.). 632p. pap. 40.00 *(978-1-933132-46-4(9))* Spuyten Duyvil.

Berry, Wendell. The Poetry of William Carlos Williams of Rutherford. 2011. (ENG.). 176p. 24.00 *(978-1-58243-714-9(9)*, Counterpoint) Counterpoint LLC.

Billitteri, Carla. Language & the Renewal of Society in Walt Whitman, Laura (Riding) Jackson, & Charles Olson: The American Cratylus. 2009. (Modern & Contemporary Poetry & Poetics Ser.). (ENG., Illus.). 240p. 89.00 *(978-0-230-60836-8(1))* Palgrave Macmillan.

Blake, David Haven & Robertson, Michael, eds. Walt Whitman, Where the Future Becomes Present. 2008. (Iowa Whitman Ser.). (ENG., Illus.). 200p. 39.95 *(978-1-58729-638-3(1))* Univ. of Iowa Pr.

Boschman, Robert. In the Way of Nature: Ecology & Westward Expansion in the Poetry of Anne Bradstreet, Elizabeth Bishop & Amy Clampitt. 2009. (ENG.). 236p. pap. 39.95 *(978-0-7864-3356-8(6))* McFarland & Co., Inc. Pubs.

Braham, Jeanne. The Light Within the Light: Portraits of Donald Hall, Richard Wilbur, Maxine Kumin, & Stanley Kunitz. 2007. (ENG., Illus.). 90p. 24.95 *(978-1-56792-316-2(X))* Godine, David R. Pub.

Bruns, Gerald L. What Are Poets For? An Anthropology of Contemporary Poetry & Poetics. 2012. (Contemp North American Poetry Ser.). (ENG., Illus.). 260p. pap. 39.95 ***(978-1-60938-080-9(0))*** Univ. of Iowa Pr.

Caplan, David. Poetic Form: An Introduction. 2006. (Pearson English Value Textbook Ser.). (ENG., Illus.). 250p. (C). per. 30.20 *(978-0-321-19820-4(4))* Longman Publishing Group.

Caselli, Daniela & La Penna, Daniela. Twentieth-Century Poetic Translation: Literary Cultures in Italian & English. La Penna, Daniela, ed. 2008. (ENG.). 236p. 120.00 *(978-1-84706-003-7(X))* Continuum International Publishing Group, Ltd. GBR. Dist: National Bk. Network.

Cavitch, Max. American Elegy: The Poetry of Mourning from the Puritans to Whitman. 2007. (Illus.). 336p. 67.50 *(978-0-8166-4892-4(1))*; per. 24.00 *(978-0-8166-4893-1(X))* Univ. of Minnesota Pr.

Christensen, Lena. Editing Emily Dickinson: The Production of an Author. 2012. (Studies in Major Literary Authors Ser.). (ENG.). 200p. pap. 42.95 ***(978-0-415-54122-0(0))*** Routledge.

Christensen, Paul. Strangers in Paradise: A Memoir of Provence. 2007. (ENG., Illus.). 224p. per. 17.95 *(978-0-916727-28-4(9))* Wings Pr.

Dace, Letitia. Langston Hughes: The Contemporary Reviews. Dace, Letitia & Dace, Tish, eds. 2009. (American Critical Archives Ser.). (ENG.). 788p. pap. 74.00 *(978-0-521-11430-1(6))* Cambridge Univ. Pr.

Duncan, Joseph E. The Revival of Metaphysical Poetry: The History of Style, 1800 to the Present. 2009. (ENG.). 238p. pap. 50.00 *(978-0-8166-6033-9(6))* Univ. of Minnesota Pr.

Dungy, Camille T., ed. Black Nature: Four Centuries of African American Nature Poetry. 2009. (ENG.). 432p. pap. 24.95 *(978-0-8203-3431-8(6))*; lib. bdg. 69.95 *(978-0-8203-3277-2(1))* Univ. of Georgia Pr.

Eagleton, Terry. How to Read a Poem. 2006. (ENG.). 192p. per. 24.95 *(978-1-4051-5141-2(2))*; (Illus.). 89.95 *(978-1-4051-5140-5(4))* Wiley, John & Sons, Inc. (Wiley-Blackwell).

Felstiner, John. Can Poetry Save the Earth? A Field Guide to Nature Poems. 2010. (ENG., Illus.). 440p. pap. 20.00 *(978-0-300-16813-6(6))* Yale Univ. Pr.

Felstiner, John & Felstiner, J. Can Poetry Save the Earth? A Field Guide to Nature Poems. 2009. (ENG., Illus.). 440p. 35.00 *(978-0-300-13750-7(8))* Yale Univ. Pr.

Finch, Annie Ridley Crane. A Poet's Ear: A Handbook of Meter & Form. 2011. (ENG.). 496p. (C). 85.00 *(978-0-472-07066-4(5))*; pap. 35.00 *(978-0-472-05066-6(4))* Univ. of Michigan Pr.

Finnerty, Paraic. Emily Dickinson's Shakespeare. 2008. (ENG.). 280p. pap. 28.95 *(978-1-55849-670-5(X))* Univ. of Massachusetts Pr.

Foley, Jack. Visions & Affiliations: A California Literary Time Line Part Two. 2011. 716p. pap. 50.00 ***(978-1-61364-068-5(4))*** Pantograph Pr.

FOX, ALAN. Rattle Conversations. 2008. 286p. pap. 19.95 *(978-1-59709-095-7(6))* Red Hen Pr.

Fredman, Stephen. The Grounding of American Poetry: Charles Olson & the Emersonian Tradition. 2009. (Cambridge Studies in American Literature & Culture Ser.). (ENG.). 188p. pap. 28.00 *(978-0-521-10674-0(5))* Cambridge Univ. Pr.

Freitag, Kornelia & Vester, Katharina, eds. Another Language: Poetic Experiments in Britain & North America. 2009. (ENG., Illus.). 304p. pap. 44.95 *(978-3-8258-1210-2(3))* Lit Verlag DEU. Dist: Transaction Pubs.

Frye, Steven. The Poetry of Edgar Allan Poe. 2010. *(978-1-58765-705-4(8))* Salem Pr., Inc.

Gardner, Thomas. John in the Company of Poets: The Gospel in Literary Imagination. 2011. (Studies in Christianity & Literature Ser.). (ENG.). 236p. 69.95 *(978-1-60258-315-3(3))* Baylor Univ. Pr.

Gillan, Maria Mazziotti. Maria Mazziotti Gillan: Essays on Her Works. Dougherty, Sean Thomas & DOUGHTERY, Seam Thomas, eds. 2006. (Writers Ser.). (ENG.). 200p. 15.00 *(978-1-55071-250-6(0))* Guernica Editions, Inc. CAN. Dist: Univ. of Toronto Pr.

Gross, Irena Grudzinska. Czeslaw Milosz & Joseph Brodsky: Fellowship of Poets. 2009. (ENG.). 384p. 40.00 *(978-0-300-14937-1(9))* Yale Univ. Pr.

Gubar, Susan. Poetry after Auschwitz: Remembering What One Never Knew. 2006. (Jewish Literature & Culture Ser.). (ENG., Illus.). 340p. pap. 24.95 *(978-0-253-21887-2(X)*, 025321887X) Indiana Univ. Pr.

Harshav, Benjamin. American Yiddish Poetry: A Bilingual Anthology. 2007. (ENG.). 840p. pap. 35.00 *(978-0-8047-5170-4(6))* Stanford Univ. Pr.

Hill, Geoffrey. Clavics. 2011. (ENG., Illus.). 48p. 29.95 *(978-1-907587-11-5(X))* Enitharmon Pr. GBR. Dist: Dufour Editions, Inc.

—Collected Critical Writings. Haynes, Kenneth, ed. 2009. (ENG.). 832p. pap. 34.95 *(978-0-19-923448-6(5))* Oxford Univ. Pr., Inc.

Hoffman, Tyler. American Poetry in Performance: From Walt Whitman to Hip Hop. 2011. (ENG.). 282p. (C). 45.00 *(978-0-472-11781-9(5))* Univ. of Michigan Pr.

Holander, Stefan. Wallace Stevens & the Realities of Poetic Language. 2008. (Studies in Major Literary Authors Ser.). (ENG.). 248p. (C). 125.00 *(978-0-415-95596-6(3))* Routledge.

Huff, Adrianne. The Flow of Absence. 2008. 116p. pap. *(978-3-639-04842-1(3))* VDM Verlag Dr. Mueller e.K.

Jakel, Olaf. Sokratisches Textgespräch: Ein Modell zur Schülerorientierten Gedichtinterpretation im Englischunterricht mit Fortgeschrittenen. (Fremdsprachendidaktik Inhalts und Lernerorientiert Ser.). (GER., Illus.). 144p. 26.95 *(978-3-631-37736-9(3))* Lang, Peter Publishing, Inc.

Jenkins, Matthew G. Poetic Obligation: Ethics in Experimental American Poetry After 1945. 2008. (ENG., Illus.). 282p. 42.50 *(978-1-58729-635-2(7))* Univ. of Iowa Pr.

Jennings, Regina. Malcolm X & the Poetics of Haki Madhubuti. 2006. (ENG.). 296p. per. 45.00 *(978-0-7864-2619-5(5))* McFarland & Co., Inc. Pubs.

Jeon, Joseph Jonghyun. Racial Things, Racial Forms: Objecthood in Avant-Garde Asian American Poetry. 2012. (Contemporary North American Poetry Ser.). (ENG., Illus.). 240p. pap. 39.95 ***(978-1-60938-086-1(X))*** Univ. of Iowa Pr.

Joron, Andrew. The Cry at Zero: Selected Prose. 2007. (ENG.). 120p. per. 14.95 *(978-1-933996-02-8(1))* Counterpath Pr.

Kane, Daniel. We Saw the Light: Conversations Between the New American Cinema & Poetry. 2009. (Contemporary North American Poetry Ser.). (ENG., Illus.). 252p. 39.95 *(978-1-58729-788-5(4))* Univ. of Iowa Pr.

Keller, Jim. Writing Plural Worlds in Contemporary U. S. Poetry: Innovative Identities. 2009. (ENG.). 240p. 84.00 *(978-0-230-61220-4(2))* Palgrave Macmillan.

Kerekes, Borbála. A Purgatory of Freedom: Allen Ginsberg's Fight for Spiritual Liberation in Howl. 2008. 72p. pap. *(978-3-639-10987-0(2))* VDM Verlag Dr. Mueller e.K.

Kimmelman, Burt, et al. The Facts on File Companion to American Poetry, 2 vols., Set. 2007. (Companion to Literature Ser.). 1200p. (C). (gr. 9). 150.00 *(978-0-8160-6950-7(6))* Facts On File, Inc.

Klock, Geoff & Klock. Imaginary Biographies: Misreading the Lives of the Poets. 2007. (Continuum Literary Studies). (ENG.). 288p. 130.00 *(978-0-8264-2802-8(9))* Continuum International Publishing Group, Ltd. GBR. Dist: National Bk. Network.

Kreymborg, Alfred. Our Singing Strength: An Outline of American Poetry (1620-1930) (Des Imagistes). reprint ed. 45.00 *(978-0-404-17123-0(0))* AMS Pr., Inc.

Larson, Kerry, ed. The Cambridge Companion to Nineteenth-Century American Poetry. 2011. (Cambridge Companions to Literature Ser.). (ENG.). 310p. 95.00 ***(978-0-521-76369-1(X))*** Cambridge Univ. Pr.

Leitch Rowlinson, Dorothy. Along the Way. 2009. 100p. pap. 28.99 *(978-1-4389-4962-8(6))* AuthorHouse.

Lerner, Laurence. Reading Women's Poetry. 2009. (ENG.). 194p. 69.95 *(978-1-84519-337-9(7))*; pap. 34.95 *(978-1-84519-334-8(2))* Sussex Academic Pr. GBR. Dist: International Specialized Bk. Services.

Lewis, Ethan. The Importance of Reading Unknown Poets in Relation to Those Who Are Known: The Achievement of the Poets of Sangamon, Illinois. 2007. 280p. 109.95 *(978-0-7734-5777-5(1))* Mellen, Edwin Pr., The.

Litz, Frances A. Father Tabb: A Study of His Life & Works with Uncollected & Unpublished Poems. 2007. (ENG.). 312p. 45.95 *(978-0-548-03775-1(2))* Kessinger Publishing, LLC.

Logan, William A. The Undiscovered Country: Poetry in the Age of Tin. 2008. (ENG.). 400p. (gr. 17). pap. 26.00 *(978-0-231-13639-6(0))* Columbia Univ. Pr.

Lowell, Amy. Tendencies in Modern American Poetry. 2010. 376p. pap. 32.75 *(978-1-117-88153-9(9))* 2010. 390p. pap. 33.75 *(978-1-142-77009-9(5))* 2009. 378p. 33.99 *(978-1-113-47581-7(1))* 2009. 378p. pap. 32.75 *(978-1-113-47579-4(X))* BiblioBazaar.

—Tendencies in Modern American Poetry. 2009. 178p. pap. *(978-0-217-56648-3(0))* Books LLC.

—Tendencies in Modern American Poetry. 2008. 382p. 48.95 *(978-1-4365-9072-3(8))* 2007. (ENG.). 384p. per. 33.95 *(978-0-548-80651-7(9))* Kessinger Publishing, LLC.

Maecka, Katarzyna. Death in the Works of Galway Kinnell. 2008. 104.95 *(978-1-60497-572-7(5))* Cambria Pr.

Mahanta, Tora. T E Hulme. 2010. 188p. pap. *(978-3-639-27337-3(0))* VDM Verlag Dr. Mueller e.K.

Mamunes, George. So Has a Daisy Vanished: Emily Dickinson & Tuberculosis. 2007. (ENG.). 211p. per. 39.95 *(978-0-7864-3227-1(6))* McFarland & Co., Inc. Pubs.

Matthias, John. Who Was Cousin Alice? & Other Questions. 2011. 370p. pap. ***(978-1-84861-168-9(4))*** Shearsman Bks.

Maynard, James. (Re:)Working the Ground: Essays on the Late Writings of Robert Duncan. Maynard, James, ed. 2011. (Modern & Contemporary Poetry & Poetics Ser.). (ENG.). 264p. 85.00 *(978-0-230-10810-3(5))* Palgrave Macmillan.

Melville, Herman. John Marr & Other Sailors with Some Sea-Pieces. Robillard, Douglas, ed. 2006. (Illus.). 235p. 34.95 *(978-0-87338-877-1(1))* Kent State Univ. Pr.

Michelucci, Stefania. The Poetry of Thom Gunn: A Critical Study. Franks, Jill, tr. from ITA. 2008. (ENG., Illus.). 222p. pap. 39.95 *(978-0-7864-3687-3(5))* McFarland & Co., Inc. Pubs.

Mikkelsen, Ann Marie. Pastoral, Pragmatism, & Twentieth-Century American Poetry. 2011. (Modern & Contemporary Poetry & Poetics Ser.). (ENG.). 254p. 89.00 *(978-0-230-10583-6(1))* Palgrave Macmillan.

Miles, Josephine. Renaissance, Eighteenth Century & Modern Language in English Poetry: A Tabular View. 2011. 78p. 37.95 (978-1-258-04033-8(6)) Literary Licensing, LLC.
Montgomery, William. The Poetry of Susan Howe: History, Theology, Authority. 2010. (Modern & Contemporary Poetry & Poetics Ser.). (ENG., Illus.). 246p. 84.00 (978-0-230-62197-8(X)) Palgrave Macmillan.
Moody, A. David. Tracing T. S. Eliot's Spirit: Essays on his Poetry & Thought. 2008. (ENG.). 220p. pap. 31.00 (978-0-521-06096-7(6)) Cambridge Univ. Pr.
Mookerjee, Robin. Identity & Society in American Poetry: The Romantic Tradition. 2008. 304p. (C). 109.95 (978-1-60497-508-6(3)) Cambria Pr.
New, Elisa. The Regenerate Lyric: Theology & Innovation in American Poetry. 2009. (Cambridge Studies in American Literature & Culture Ser.). (ENG.). 292p. (C). pap. 38.99 (978-0-521-10731-0(8)) Cambridge Univ. Pr.
Nicholls, Peter. Postwar American Poetry. rev. ed. 2007. 250p. (978-0-7456-2626-0(2)); pap. (978-0-7456-2627-7(0)) Polity Pr. GBR. Dist: Wiley, John & Sons, Inc.
Nyberg, Lennart. Bodies of Poems: Graphic Poetics in a Historical Perspective. 2008. (Illus.). 187p. pap. 66.95 (978-3-03911-343-9(7)) Lang, Peter AG GBR. Dist: Lang, Peter.
Painter, F. V. N. Poets of Virginia. (Illus.). 336p. reprint ed. lib. bdg. 98.00 (978-0-7222-4617-7(X)) Library Reprints, Inc.
Pastore, Stephen R. New Theories of Contemporary Poetry. 2007. 75.00 (978-0-9798547-2-9(5)) Harvard Pr.
Patke, Rajeev S. The Long Poems of Wallace Stevens: An Interpretative Study. 2009. (ENG.) 280p. pap. 42.00 (978-0-521-11513-1(2)) Cambridge Univ. Pr.
Patterson, Samuel White. The Spirit of the American Revolution As Revealed in the Poetry of the Period: A Study of American Patriotic Verse from 1760 to 1783. 235p. reprint ed. 98.00 (978-0-7222-7734-8(2)) Library Reprints, Inc.
Poetry Criticism. 2011. (Poetry Criticism Ser.). 245.00 (978-1-4144-7124-2(6)); (ENG.). 245.00 (978-1-4144-7128-0(9)); (ENG.). 245.00 (978-1-4144-7129-7(7)); (ENG.). 245.00 (978-1-4144-7127-3(0)); (ENG.). 245.00 (978-1-4144-7126-6(2)); (ENG.). 245.00 (978-1-4144-7125-9(4)) Cengage Gale.
Rascouailles, Myriam. Learned Chaucer. 2009. 76p. pap. (978-3-639-16214-1(5)) VDM Verlag Dr. Mueller e.K.
Raymond, Claire. The Posthumous Voice in Women's Writing Form Mary Shelly to Sylvia Plath. 2006. 270p. 120.00 (978-0-7546-5535-0(0)) Ashgate Publishing Co.
Read, Justin. Modern Poetics & Hemispheric American Cultural Studies. 2009. (Studies of the Americas Ser.). (ENG., Illus.). 272p. 100.00 (978-0-230-61596-0(1)) Palgrave Macmillan.
Rowe, Karen E. Saint & Singer: Edward Taylor's Typology & the Poetics of Meditation. 2009. (Cambridge Studies in American Literature & Culture Ser.). (ENG.). 360p. (C). pap. 50.00 (978-0-521-10819-5(5)) Cambridge Univ. Pr.
Savitt, Todd L. Race & Medicine in Nineteenth- & Early-Twentieth-Century America. 2006. (Illus.). 453p. 49.00 (978-0-87338-878-8(X)) Kent State Univ. Pr.
Sedarat, Roger. New England Landscape History in American Poetry: A Lacanian View. 2011. (978-1-60497-742-4(6)) Cambria Pr.
Serio, John N., ed. The Cambridge Companion to Wallace Stevens. 2007. (Cambridge Companions to Literature Ser.). (ENG.). (C). 240p. 85.00 (978-0-521-84956-2(X)); 244p. per. 32.99 (978-0-521-61482-5(1)) Cambridge Univ. Pr.
Shaver, Molly. Poetic Speech in Carl Sandburg's Rootabaga Stories Bridging the Divide Between Oral Discourse & Poetic Language. 2008. 68p. pap. (978-3-639-08928-8(6)) VDM Verlag Dr. Mueller e.K.
Sielke, Sabine & Kloeckner, Christian, eds. Orient & Orientalisms in US-American Poetry & Poetics. 2009. (Transcription. Cultures Concepts Controversies. Kulturen Konzepte Kontroversen Ser.). (Illus.). 360p. pap. 72.95 (978-3-631-57608-3(0)) Lang, Peter GmbH, Europaischer Verlag der Wissenschaften DEU. Dist: Lang, Peter.
Slavitt, David R. Re Verse: Essays on Poetry & Poets. 2009. (ENG.). 224p. pap. 15.95 (978-0-8101-2647-3(8)) Northwestern Univ. Pr.
Snediker, Michael D. Queer Optimism: Lyric Personhood & Other Felicitous Persuasions. 2008. 288p. 75.00 (978-0-8166-4999-0(5)); pap. 25.00 (978-0-8166-5000-2(4)) Univ. of Minnesota Pr.
Spiegelman, Willard. Imaginative Transcripts: Selected Literary Essays. 2008. (ENG.). 336p. 45.00 (978-0-19-536813-0(4)) Oxford Univ. Pr., Inc.
Stedman, Edmund Clarence. Poets of America. 13.00 (978-0-403-00058-6(0)) Scholarly Pr., Inc.
Suttie, Paul. Self-Interpretation in the Faerie Queene. 2006. (Studies in Renaissance Literature Ser.: Volume 18). 240p. 90.00 (978-1-84384-087-9(1)) Boydell & Brewer, Inc.
Tobin, Daniel. Awake in America: On Irish American Poetry. 2011. (ENG.). 424p. pap. 38.00 (978-0-268-04237-0(3)) Univ. of Notre Dame Pr.
Vendler, Helen. Invisible Listeners: Lyric Intimacy in Herbert, Whitman, & Ashbery. 2007. (ENG.). 112p. per. 15.95 (978-0-691-13474-1(X)) Princeton Univ. Pr.
Vendler, Helen & Dickinson, Emily. Dickinson: Selected Poems & Commentaries. 2010. 560p. 35.00 (978-0-674-04867-6(9), Belknap Pr.) Harvard Univ. Pr.
Vincent, John Emil, ed. After Spicer: Critical Essays. 2011. (ENG.). 240p. (C). 80.00 (978-0-8195-6941-7(0)); pap. 24.95 (978-0-8195-6942-4(9)) Wesleyan Univ. Pr.
Vitzthum, Richard C. Land & Sea: The Lyric Poetry of Philip Freneau. 2009. (ENG.). 208p. pap. 50.00 (978-0-8166-5884-8(6)) Univ. of Minnesota Pr.
Von Der Heydt, James E. At the Brink of Infinity: Poetic Humility in Boundless American Space. 2008. (ENG.). 262p. 42.50 (978-1-58729-628-4(4)) Univ. of Iowa Pr.
Wainwright, Jeffrey. Poetry: The Basics. 2nd rev. ed. 2011. (Basics Ser.). (ENG., Illus.). 288p. 90.00 (978-0-415-56615-5(0)); pap. 19.95 (978-0-415-56616-2(9)) Routledge.
Weiner, J. J. At the Barriers. Weiner, Joshua, ed. 2009. (ENG.). 344p. 70.00 (978-0-226-89043-2(0)) Univ. of Chicago Pr.
Weiner, Joshua, ed. At the Barriers: On the Poetry of Thom Gunn. 2009. 344p. pap. 25.00 (978-0-226-89044-9(9)) Univ. of Chicago Pr.
Williams, Miller. Making a Poem: Some Thoughts about Poetry & the People Who Write It. 2006. 127p. per. 18.95 (978-0-8071-3132-9(6)) Louisiana State Univ. Pr.
Young, Stephen. Between the Lines: A History of Poetry in Letters, Part II: 1962-2002. 2006. (ENG., Illus.). 480p. 35.00 (978-1-56663-656-8(6)) Dee, Ivan R. Pub.
Yu, Timothy. Race & the Avant-Garde: Experimental & Asian American Poetry since 1965. 2009. (Asian America Ser.). (ENG.). 208p. 25.00 (978-0-8047-5997-7(9)) Stanford Univ. Pr.
Zhang, Benzi. Asian Diaspora Poetry in North America. 2007. (Literary Criticism & Cultural Theory Ser.). (ENG.). 194p. 125.00 (978-0-415-95717-5(6)) Routledge.
Zwinger, Lynda Marie. Approaches to Teaching Faulkner's As I Lay Dying. O'Donnell, Patrick, ed. 2011. (ENG.). vi, 218p. pap. 19.75 (978-1-60329-085-2(0)); 37.50 (978-1-60329-084-5(2)) Modern Language Assn. of America.

AMERICAN POETRY—HISTORY AND CRITICISM—COLONIAL PERIOD, CA. 1600-1775

Hammond, Jeffrey A. The American Puritan Elegy: A Literary & Cultural Study. 2006. (Cambridge Studies in American Literature & Culture Ser.). (ENG.). 284p. pap. 53.00 (978-0-521-10381-7(9)) Cambridge Univ. Pr.
Otis, William Bradley. American Verse, 1625-1807: A History. 2010. 322p. pap. 30.75 (978-1-146-85526-6(5)) BiblioBazaar.
—American Verse, 1625-1807: A History (1909) 2008. 320p. 45.95 (978-1-4369-6543-9(8)); pap. 30.95 (978-1-4367-6620-3(6)) Kessinger Publishing, LLC.
—American Verse, 1625-1807; a History. 2009. (Illus.). 136p. pap. 19.99 (978-1-150-76766-1(9)) General Bks. LLC.
Padilla, Genaro. The Daring Flight of My Pen: Cultural Politics & Gaspar Perez de Villagra's Historia de la Nueva Mexico 1610. 2011. (Paso Por Aqui Ser. in the Nuevomexicano Literary Heritage Ser.). (ENG., Illus.). 167p. (C). 29.95 (978-0-8263-4970-5(6)) Univ. of New Mexico Pr.

AMERICAN POETRY—HISTORY AND CRITICISM—19TH CENTURY

Attila, Nagy Gtza. 'This is my letter to the World' Mis-interpreting Emily Dickinson. 2006. 68p. pap. (978-3-639-09605-7(3)) VDM Verlag Dr. Mueller e.K.
Benton, Joel. Emerson As a Poet. 2009. 70p. pap. (978-1-4588-2567-4(1)) Books LLC.
—Emerson As a Poet. 2008. 134p. 35.95 (978-0-548-94754-8(6)) 2007. 136p. per. 20.95 (978-0-548-62231-5(0)) Kessinger Publishing, LLC.
Bloom, Harold. Robert Frost. 2nd rev. ed. 2011. (Bloom's Modern Critical Views Ser.). 196p. (C). (gr. 9). 45.00 (978-1-60413-872-6(6), Chelsea Hse.) Facts On File, Inc.
Bouson, J. Brooks, ed. Emily Dickinson. 2010. (Critical Insights Ser.). 350p. 85.00 (978-1-58765-695-8(7)) Salem Pr., Inc.
Brennan, Matthew C. The Poet's Holy Craft: William Gilmore Simms & Romantic Verse Traditions. 2010. 168p. 49.95 (978-1-57003-888-4(0)) Univ. of South Carolina Pr.
Chase, Lewis Nathaniel. Poe & His Poetry. 2008. 132p. 35.95 (978-1-4366-2320-9(0)); pap. 20.95 (978-0-548-86648-1(1)) Kessinger Publishing, LLC.
Ford, Mark. Mr & Mrs Stevens & Other Essays. 2011. (Illus.). 259p. 86.95 (978-3-0343-0247-0(9)) Lang, Peter AG GBR. Dist: Lang, Peter.
Fruit, John Phelps. The Mind & Art of Poe's Poetry. 2008. 150p. 36.95 (978-1-4365-0506-2(2)) 2007. (ENG.). 152p. per. 21.95 (978-0-548-68680-5(7)) Kessinger Publishing, LLC.
Frusciame, Denise Marie. The Poet Figure in the Poetry of Wallace Stevens: Disentangling the Multiplicity of Selves. 2008. 292p. 109.95 (978-0-7734-4992-3(2)) Mellen, Edwin Pr., The.
Grant, Michael. T. S. Eliot Volume 2. 2009. 424p. pap. 45.00 (978-0-415-56897-5(8)) Routledge.
—T. S. Eliot Volume I. 2009. 408p. pap. 45.00 (978-0-415-56896-8(X)) Routledge.
Gray, Timothy. Urban Pastoral: Natural Currents in the New York School. 2010. (Contemporary North American Poetry Ser.). (Illus.). 302p. pap. 34.95 (978-1-58729-909-4(7)) Univ. of Iowa Pr.
Handley, George B. New World Poetics: Nature & the Adamic Imagination of Whitman, Neruda, & Walcott. (ENG.). 456p. 2010. pap. 26.95 (978-0-8203-3520-9(7)) 2007. 39.95 (978-0-8203-2864-5(2)) Univ. of Georgia Pr.
Hart, Josephine. Catching Life by the Throat: How to Read Poetry & Why. 2008. (ENG., Illus.). 256p. 26.95 (978-0-393-06607-4(X), 6607) Norton, W. W. & Co., Inc.
Hass, Robert. Song of Myself: And Other Poems by Walt Whitman. 2010. (ENG.). 320p. 23.00 (978-1-58243-571-8(5), Counterpoint Pr.) Basic Bks. GBR. Dist: Perseus-PGW.
Henderson Murphy, Peggy. Isolated but Not Oblivious. 2010. 64p. pap. (978-3-639-23230-1(5)) VDM Verlag Dr. Mueller e.K.
Heuston, Sean. Modern Poetry & Ethnography: Yeats, Frost, Warren, Heaney, & the Poet as Anthropologist. 2011. (ENG., Illus.). 240p. 85.00 (978-0-230-11167-7(X)) Palgrave Macmillan.
Holmes, John & Springbord, Robert. Darwin's Bards: British & American Poetry in the Age of Evolution. 2009. (ENG.). 352p. (gr. 17). 95.00 (978-0-7486-3940-3(3)) Edinburgh Univ. Pr. GBR. Dist: Columbia Univ. Pr.
Joel, Benton. Emerson As a Poet. 2009. 138p. 24.99 (978-1-110-32058-5(2)); pap. 19.75 (978-1-110-32052-3(3)) BiblioBazaar.
Kern, Robert. Orientalism, Modernism, & the American Poem. 2009. (Cambridge Studies in American Literature & Culture Ser.). (ENG.). 336p. pap. 46.00 (978-0-521-10555-2(2)) Cambridge Univ. Pr.
Kreymborg, Alfred. Our Singing Strength: An Outline of American Poetry (1620-1930) (Des Imagistes). reprint ed. 45.00 (978-0-404-17123-0(0)) AMS Pr., Inc.
Ladin, Joy. Soldering the Abyss. 2010. 196p. pap. (978-3-639-15896-0(2)) VDM Verlag Dr. Mueller e.K.
Laing, Jeanie M. Notes on Superstition & Folk Lore. 2008. 116p. 21.99 (978-0-559-43436-5(7)); pap. 19.75 (978-0-559-43435-8(9)) BiblioBazaar.
—Notes on Superstition & Folk Lore. 2008. 112p. 34.95 (978-1-4371-7462-5(0)); pap. 19.95 (978-1-4370-4270-2(8)) Kessinger Publishing, LLC.
Larson, Kerry, ed. The Cambridge Companion to Nineteenth-Century American Poetry. 2011. (Cambridge Companions to Literature Ser.). (ENG.). 310p. pap. 27.99 (978-0-521-14580-0(5)) Cambridge Univ. Pr.
Leighton, Angela. On Form: Poetry, Aestheticism, & the Legacy of a Word. 2007. (ENG.). 304p. 75.00 (978-0-19-929060-4(1)) Oxford Univ. Pr., Inc.
LeMaster, J. R. & Jahan, Sabahat. Walt Whitman & the Persian Poets: A Study in Literature & Religion. 2009. 98.00 (978-1-58814-062-3(8)) Ibex Pubs., Inc.
MacKenzie, Cindy, ed. Wider Than the Sky: Essays & Meditations on the Healing Power of Emily Dickinson. 2007. (Literature & Medicine Ser.). (Illus.). 150p. per. 18.00 (978-0-87338-919-8(0)) Kent State Univ. Pr.
Magda, Paizs. Whitman & Ginsberg: American Bards: The Romantic Ancestor & the Postmodern Follower. 2008. 64p. pap. (978-3-639-09508-1(1)) VDM Verlag Dr. Mueller e.K.
Marshall, Alan. American Experimental Poetry & Democratic Thought. 2009. (ENG.). 320p. 95.00 (978-0-19-956192-6(3)) Oxford Univ. Pr., Inc.
McCue, Frances. The Car That Brought You Here Still Runs: Revisiting the Northwest Towns of Richard Hugo. 2010. (Samuel & Althea Stroum Book Ser.). (ENG., Illus.). 260p. 27.95 (978-0-295-98964-8(5)) Univ. of Washington Pr.
McGill, Meredith L., ed. The Traffic in Poems: Nineteenth-Century Poetry & Transatlantic Exchange. 2008. (ENG., Illus.). 276p. per. 24.95 (978-0-8135-4230-0(8)) Rutgers Univ. Pr.
McSweeney, Kerry. What's the Import? Nineteenth-Century Literary Works & Contemporary Critical Practice. 2007. (ENG.). 192p. (C). (978-0-7735-3202-1(1)) McGill-Queen's Univ. Pr.
Miller, Cristanne. Reading in Time: Emily Dickinson in the Nineteenth Century. 2012. pap. (978-1-55849-951-5(2)); lib. bdg. (978-1-55849-950-8(4)) Univ. of Massachusetts Pr.
Mitchell, Domhnall. International Reception of Emily Dickinson. Stuart, Maria, ed. 2009. (Continuum Reception Studies). (ENG.). 334p. 150.00 (978-0-8264-9715-4(2)) Continuum International Publishing Group, Ltd. GBR. Dist: National Bk. Network.
Mitchell, Domhnall & Stuart, Maria, eds. The International Reception of Emily Dickinson. 2011. (ENG.). 334p. pap. 49.95 (978-1-4411-2202-5(8)) Continuum International Publishing Group, Ltd. GBR. Dist: National Bk. Network.
Otis, William Bradley. American Verse, 1625-1807: A History. 2010. 322p. pap. 30.75 (978-1-146-85526-6(5)) BiblioBazaar.
—American Verse, 1625-1807: A History (1909) 2008. 320p. 45.95 (978-1-4369-6543-9(8)); pap. 30.95 (978-1-4367-6620-3(6)) Kessinger Publishing, LLC.
—American Verse, 1625-1807; a History. 2009. (Illus.). 136p. pap. 19.99 (978-1-150-76766-1(9)) General Bks. LLC.
Painter, Franklin V. N. Poets of the South. 2007. (ENG.). 170p. pap. 19.99 (978-1-4264-8892-4(0)) BiblioBazaar.
Peel, Robin. Emily Dickinson & the Hill of Science. 2010. (ENG.). 92.50 (978-1-61147-425-1(6)); 92.50 (978-0-8386-4221-4(7)) Fairleigh Dickinson Univ. Pr.
Poe, Edgar Allan, et al. Critical Theory: The Major Documents. Levine, Stuart & Levine, Susan F., eds. 2008. (ENG.). 248p. 52.00 (978-0-252-03123-6(7)) Univ. of Illinois Pr.
Richards, Eliza. Gender & the Poetics of Reception in Poe's Circle. 2010. (Cambridge Studies in American Literature & Culture Ser.). (ENG.). 256p. pap. 36.00 (978-0-521-17439-8(2)) Cambridge Univ. Pr.
Rogal, Samuel J. Congregational Hymns from the Poetry of John Greenleaf Whittier: A Comparative Study of the Sources & Final Works, with a Bibliographic Catalog of the Hymns. 2009. (ENG., Illus.). 174p. pap. 45.00 (978-0-7864-4478-6(9)) McFarland & Co., Inc. Pubs.
Rothenberg, Jerome. Poetics & Polemics, 1980-2005. Clay, Steven, ed. 2008. (Modern & Contemporary Poetics Ser.). (ENG., Illus.). 360p. 62.50 (978-0-8173-1627-3(2)); pap. 29.95 (978-0-8173-5507-4(3)) Univ. of Alabama Pr.
Specimens of the American Poets. 2009. 172p. pap. 19.99 (978-0-217-55829-7(1)) General Bks. LLC.
Spengemann, William C. Three American Poets: Walt Whitman, Emily Dickinson, & Herman Melville. 2010. (ENG.). 232p. pap. 28.00 (978-0-268-04132-8(6)) Univ. of Notre Dame Pr.
Strong, Augustus Hopkins. American Poets & Their Theology. 2009. 404p. pap. (978-1-4588-0574-4(3)) Books LLC.
—American Poets & Their Theology. 2007. (ENG.). 510p. 55.95 (978-0-548-15302-4(7)); 512p. per. 40.95 (978-1-4304-4682-8(X)) Kessinger Publishing, LLC.
—American Poets & Their Theology. 2008. 508p. pap. (978-1-4097-7912-4(2)); pap. (978-1-4097-7911-7(4)) Read Bks.
Tharaud, Barry. Emerson for the Twenty-First Century. 2010. (Illus.). 624p. 110.00 (978-0-87413-091-1(3)) Univ. of Delaware Pr.
Walpert, Bryan. Resistance to Science in Contemporary American Poetry. 2011. (Routledge Interdisciplinary Perspectives on Literature Ser.). (ENG.). 232p. (C). 125.00 (978-0-415-89334-3(8)) Routledge.
White, Fred D. Approaching Emily Dickinson: Critical Currents & Crosscurrents Since 1960. 2008. (Literary Criticism in Perspective Ser.). 239p. 75.00 (978-1-57113-316-8(X)) Camden Hse.
Whittier, John Greenleaf. Reform & Politics, Part 2, from Volume Vii, the Works of Whittier: The Conflict with Slavery, Politics, & Reform, the Inner Life & Criticism. 2010. 48p. pap. (978-1-4076-5363-1(6)) HardPr.
Wolosky, Shira. Poetry & Public Discourse in Nineteenth-Century America. 2010. (Nineteenth-Century Major Lives & Letters Ser.). (ENG.). 266p. 84.00 (978-0-230-10431-0(2)) Palgrave Macmillan.

AMERICAN POETRY—HISTORY AND CRITICISM—20TH CENTURY

Ali, Kazim & Hoppenthaler, John. Jean Valentine: This-World Company. 2012. (Under Discussion Ser.). (ENG.). 252p. 80.00 (978-0-472-07183-8(1)); pap. 29.95 (978-0-472-05183-0(0)) Univ. of Michigan Pr.
Altieri, Charles. The Art of Twentieth-Century American Poetry: Modernism & After. rev. ed. 2009. (Blackwell Introductions to Literature Ser.: 1). (ENG., Illus.). 264p. per. 46.95 (978-1-4051-2107-1(6), Wiley-Blackwell) Wiley, John & Sons, Inc.
—Painterly Abstraction in Modernist American Poetry: The Contemporaneity of Modernism. 2009. (Cambridge Studies in American Literature & Culture Ser.). (ENG.). 540p. (C). pap. 57.00 (978-0-521-10729-7(6)) Cambridge Univ. Pr.
Antin, David. Radical Coherency: Selected Essays on Art & Literature 1966 to 2005. 2011. (ENG.). 384p. 75.00 (978-0-226-02096-9(7)); pap. 25.00 (978-0-226-02097-6(5)) Univ. of Chicago Pr.
Archambeau, Robert. Laureates & Heretics: Six Careers in American Poetry. 2010. (ENG.). 264p. pap. 35.00 (978-0-268-02036-1(1)) Univ. of Notre Dame Pr.
Ashton, Jennifer. From Modernism to Postmodernism: American Poetry & Theory in the Twentieth Century. 2008. (Cambridge Studies in American Literature & Culture Ser.). (ENG.). 212p. pap. 32.99 (978-0-521-10155-4(7)) Cambridge Univ. Pr.
Auden, W. H. The Complete Works of W. H Auden,1956-1962, Vol. 4. 2010. (Complete Works of W. H. Auden Ser.). (ENG., Illus.). 1056p. (C). 65.00 (978-0-691-14755-0(8)) Princeton Univ. Pr.
Babcock, Matthew J. Private Fire: Robert Francis's Ecopoetry & Prose. 2011. (ENG.). 65.00 (978-1-61149-022-0(7)) Univ. of Delaware Pr.
Babcock, Matthew James. Private Fire: Robert Francis's Ecopoetry & Prose. 2010. (978-0-87413-501-5(X)) Univ. of Delaware Pr.
Baer, William. Fourteen on Form: Conversations with Poets. 2009. (ENG.). 265p. pap. 25.00 (978-1-60473-256-6(3)) Univ. Pr. of Mississippi.
Baladouni, Vahé & Gery, John. Hmayeak Shems: A Poet of Pure Spirit. 2010. (ENG., Illus.). 134p. pap. 24.50 (978-0-7618-5054-0(6)) Univ. Pr. of America, Inc.
Bauer, Grace & Kane, Julie, eds. Umpteen Ways of Looking at a Possum: Critical & Creative Responses to Everette Maddox. 2006. per. 25.95 (978-1-883275-16-7(4)) Xavier Review Pr.
Beach, Joseph Warren. Obsessive Images: Symbolism in Poetry of the 1930s & 1940s. O'Connor, William Van, ed. 2009. (ENG.). 416p. pap. 60.00 (978-0-8166-5705-6(X)) Univ. of Minnesota Pr.
Bernstein, Charles. American Poetry After 1975. 2009. (ENG.). 225p. pap. 14.00 (978-0-8223-6719-2(X)) Duke Univ. Pr.
Berry, Susan. Simon J. Ortiz: A Poetic Legacy of Indigenous Continuance. Lucero, Evelina Zuni, ed. 2009. (ENG., Illus.). 440p. (C). pap. 29.95 (978-0-8263-3988-1(3)) Univ. of New Mexico Pr.
Bertholf, Robert J. & Gelpi, Albert, eds. Robert Duncan & Denise Levertov: The Poetry of Politics, the Politics of Poetry. 2006. (ENG., Illus.). 232p. per. 21.95 (978-0-8047-5131-5(5)) Stanford Univ. Pr.
Bettridge, Joel & Selinger, Eric Murphy. Ronald Johnson: Life & Works. 2008. 656p. 49.95 (978-0-943373-76-8(X)); pap. 34.95 (978-0-943373-75-1(1)) National Poetry Foundation.
Biddinger, Mary, ed. Monkey & the Wrench: Essays into Contemporary Poetics. 2011. 176p. pap. 14.95 (978-1-931968-91-1(8)) Univ. of Akron Pr., The.
Blasing, Mutlu Konuk. Politics & Form in Postmodern Poetry: O'Hara, Bishop, Ashbery, & Merrill. 2009. (Cambridge Studies in American Literature & Culture Ser.). (ENG.). 236p. pap. 36.00 (978-0-521-10613-9(3)) Cambridge Univ. Pr.
Blazer, Alex E. I Am Otherwise: The Romance Between Poetry & Theory after the Death of the Subject. 2007. (Dalkey Archive Scholarly Ser.). (ENG.). 246p. per. 34.95 (978-1-56478-458-2(4)) Dalkey Archive Pr.
Blistein, Burton. The Design of 'The Waste Land' 2008. (Illus.). xii, 405p. (978-0-7618-4217-0(9)) Univ. Pr. of America, Inc.

Bloom, Harold. American Modernist Poets. 2011. (Bloom's Modern Critical Views Ser.). 274p. (C). (gr. 9). 45.00 (978-1-60413-275-5(2), Bloom's Literary Criticism) Facts On File, Inc.

Bloom, Harold, ed. American Women Poets. 2011. (Bloom's Modern Critical Views Ser.). 254p. (C). (gr. 9). 45.00 (978-1-60413-991-4(9), Chelsea Hse.) Facts On File, Inc.

Brito, Manuel. Market Fructification of Innovative American Poetry in the Late 20th Century. 2010. 182p. pap. 50.95 (978-3-0343-0444-3(7)) Lang, Peter Publishing, Inc.

Bullough, Geoffrey. Trend of Modern Poetry. 2006. 292p. per. (978-1-4067-3624-3(4), Hesperides Pr.) Read Bks.

Burt, Stephen. The Forms of Youth: Twentieth-Century Poetry & Adolescence. 2007. (ENG.). 280p. (gr. 17). 40.00 (978-0-231-14142-0(4)) Columbia Univ. Pr.

Cambon. Recent American Poetry, Vol. 16. 2009. pap. 25.00 (978-0-8166-0268-1(9)) Univ. of Minnesota Pr.

Campbell, James. Syncopations: Beats, New Yorkers, & Writers in the Dark. 2008. 251p. pap. 24.95 (978-0-520-25237-0(3)) Univ. of California Pr.

Case, Kristen. American Pragmatism & Poetic Practice: Crosscurrents from Ralph Waldo Emerson to Susan Howe. 2011. (Mind & American Literature Ser.). (Illus.). 178p. 75.00 (978-1-57113-485-1(9)) Camden Hse.

Chasar, Mike. Everyday Reading: Poetry & Popular Culture in Modern America. 2012. (ENG., Illus.). 320p. (gr. 17). 84.50 (978-0-231-15864-0(5)); pap. 27.50 (978-0-231-15865-7(3)) Columbia Univ. Pr.

Chiasson, Dan. One Kind of Everything: Poem & Person in Contemporary America. 208p. 2011. pap. 20.00 (978-0-226-10383-9(8)) 2007. 27.50 (978-0-226-10381-5(1)) Univ. of Chicago Pr.

Churchill, Suzanne W. The Little Magazine Others & the Renovation of American Poetry. 2006. (Illus.). 304p. 130.00 (978-0-7546-5332-5(3)) Ashgate Publishing Co.

Cohen, Milton A. Beleaguered Poets & Leftist Critics: Stevens, Cummings, Frost, & Williams in the 1930s. 2011. (ENG.). 280p. 32.50 (978-0-8173-1713-3(9)) 2010. (978-0-8173-8445-6(6)) Univ. of Alabama Pr.

Collins, Michael. Understanding Etheridge Knight. 2012. (Understanding Contemporary American Literature Ser.). 168p. 39.95 (978-1-61117-066-5(4)) Univ. of South Carolina Pr.

Contemporary American Poets. pap. (978-0-86663-701-5(X)); lib. bdg. (978-0-86663-700-8(1)) Ide Hse., Inc.

Cooper, Philip. The Autobiographical Myth of Robert Lowell. 2011. (ENG.). 208p. pap. 40.00 (978-0-8078-9640-2(3)) Univ. of North Carolina Pr.

Copestake, Ian D. The Ethics of William Carlos Williams's Poetry. 2010. (Studies in American Literature & Culture Ser.). (Illus.). 180p. 75.00 (978-1-57113-481-3(6)) Camden Hse.

Corn, Alfred. Atlas: Selected Essays, 1989-2007. 2008. (Poets on Poetry Ser.). (ENG.). 192p. 70.00 (978-0-472-07050-3(9)); pap. 23.95 (978-0-472-05050-5(8)) Univ. of Michigan Pr.

Costello, Bonnie. Planets on Tables: Poetry, Still Life, & the Turning World. 2008. (Illus.). 205p. 32.95 (978-0-8014-4613-9(9)) Cornell Univ. Pr.

Creeley, Robert. Robert Creeley: Selected Poems, 1945-2005. Friedlander, Benjamin, ed. 2007. 338p. 60.00 (978-0-520-25195-3(4)) Univ. of California Pr.

—Selected Poems, 1945-2005. Friedlander, Benjamin, ed. 2008. (Illus.). 338p. per. 26.95 (978-0-520-25196-0(2)) Univ. of California Pr.

Csaszar, Renata. Fusion of Zen & Cubism in E. E. Cummings's Poetry. 2008. 60p. pap. (978-3-639-02289-6(0)) VDM Verlag Dr. Mueller e.K.

Cucinella, Catherine. Poetics of the Body: Edna St. Vincent Millay, Elizabeth Bishop, Marilyn Chin, & Marilyn Hacker. 2010. (ENG.). 190p. 79.00 (978-0-230-62088-9(4)) Palgrave Macmillan.

Damon, Maria. Postliterary America: From Bagel Shop Jazz to Micropoetries. 2011. (Contemporary North American Poetry Ser.). (ENG., Illus.). 280p. pap. 39.95 (978-1-58729-957-5(7)) Univ. of Iowa Pr.

Davidson, Ian. Ideas of Space in Contemporary Poetry. 2007. (ENG., Illus.). 224p. 84.00 (978-1-4039-9771-5(3)) Palgrave Macmillan.

Davies, Damian Walford & Turley, Richard Marggraf, eds. The Monstrous Debt: Modalities of Romantic Influence in Twentieth-Century Literature. 2006. (Illus.). 247p. 45.95 (978-0-8143-3058-6(4)) Wayne State Univ. Pr.

Davis, Alex & Jenkins, Lee M., eds. Locations of Literary Modernism: Region & Nation in British & American Modernist Poetry. 2011. (ENG.). 308p. (C). pap. 39.99 (978-0-521-18739-8(7)) Cambridge Univ. Pr.

Davis, Garrick, ed. Praising It New: The Best of the New Criticism. 2008. (ENG.). 288p. 36.95 (978-0-8040-1108-2(7)) Swallow Pr.

Del Vizo, Hortensia Ruiz & Sanchez-Boudy, Jose. El Orbe Negro en la Poesía: Cuba, Hispanoamérica y Estados Unidos. 2007. (Coleccion Polymita Ser.). 129p. pap. 16.00 (978-1-59388-106-1(1)) Ediciones Universal.

Denham, Robert D. The Early Poetry of Charles Wright: A Companion, 1960-1990. 2009. (ENG.). 199p. pap. 39.95 (978-0-7864-4198-3(4)) McFarland & Co., Inc. Pubs.

Denham, Robert D., ed. Charles Wright: A Companion to the Late Poetry, 1988-2007. 2007. (ENG.). 260p. per. 39.95 (978-0-7864-3242-4(X)) McFarland & Co., Inc. Pubs.

Deshmane, Chetan. Wallace Stevens: A Lacanian Reading. 2012. (ENG.). 248p. pap. 55.00 (978-0-7864-6457-9(7)) McFarland & Co., Inc. Pubs.

Dewey, Anne Day. Beyond Maximus: The Construction of Public Voice in Black Mountain Poetry. 2007. (ENG.). 304p. 60.00 (978-0-8047-5647-1(3)) Stanford Univ. Pr.

Doerr, Joe Francis, ed. The Salt Companion to John Matthias. 2011. (ENG.). 256p. pap. (978-1-84471-897-9(2)) Salt Publishing.

Dowdy, Michael. American Political Poetry in the 21st Century. 2007. (American Literature Readings in the Twenty-First Century Ser.). (ENG.). 248p. 84.00 (978-1-4039-7644-4(9)) Palgrave Macmillan.

Duplessis, Rachel Blau. Blue Studios: Poetry & Its Cultural Work. 2006. (Modern & Contemporary Poetics Ser.). (Illus.). 312p. 68.75 (978-0-8173-1508-5(X)) Univ. of Alabama Pr.

DuPlessis, Rachel Blau. Purple Passages: Pound, Eliot, Zukofsky, Olson, Creeley, & the Ends of Patriarchal Poetry. 2012. (Contemporary North American Poetry Ser.). (ENG.). 256p. pap. 39.95 (978-1-60938-084-7(3)) Univ. of Iowa Pr.

Ellis, Steve. Dante & English Poetry: Shelley to T. S. Eliot. 2010. (ENG.). 300p. pap. 30.99 (978-0-521-12866-7(8)) Cambridge Univ. Pr.

Erkkila, Betsy. Ezra Pound: The Contemporary Reviews. 2011. (American Critical Archives Ser.). (ENG.). 480p. 120.00 (978-0-521-40139-5(9)) Cambridge Univ. Pr.

Farahbakhsh, Alireza & Heidary Moghaddam, Zeinab. Dominant Themes in Ezra Pound's 1930s & 1940s Cantos. 2010. 276p. pap. (978-3-8383-4745-5(5)) Lambert Academic Publishing.

Filreis, Alan. Counter-Revolution of the Word: The Conservative Attack on Modern Poetry, 1945-1960. 2008. (ENG., Illus.). 448p. 44.00 (978-0-8078-3162-5(X)) Univ. of North Carolina Pr.

Fink, Thomas & Lease, Joseph. "Burning Interiors" David Shapiro's Poetry & Poetics. 2007. (C). (978-0-8386-4155-2(5)) Fairleigh Dickinson Univ. Pr.

Finkelstein, Norman. On Mount Vision: Forms of the Sacred in Contemporary American Poetry. 2010. (Contemporary North American Poetry Ser.). (ENG.). 294p. 39.95 (978-1-58729-857-8(0)) Univ. of Iowa Pr.

Ford, Karen Jackson. Gender & the Poetics of Excess: Moments of Brocade. 2009. (ENG.). 272p. pap. 25.00 (978-1-60473-255-9(5)) Univ. Pr. of Mississippi.

Ford, Mark. Mr & Mrs Stevens & Other Essays. 2011. (Illus.). 259p. 86.95 (978-3-0343-0247-0(9)) Lang, Peter AG GBR. Dist: Lang, Peter.

Fredman, Stephen. Contextual Practice: Assemblage & the Erotic in Postwar Poetry & Art. 2010. (ENG., Illus.). 240p. 55.00 (978-0-8047-6358-5(5)) Stanford Univ. Pr.

Frost, Elisabeth A. & Hogue, Cynthia, eds. Innovative Women Poets: An Anthology of Contemporary Poetry & Interviews. 2007. (Illus.). 422p. (C). per. 29.95 (978-1-58729-507-2(5)) Univ. of Iowa Pr.

Géfin, Laszlo K. Ideogram: History of a Poetic Method. 2012. (ENG.). 182p. pap. 19.95 (978-0-292-74097-6(2)) Univ. of Texas Pr.

Gelpi, Albert & Bertholf, Robert J., eds. Robert Duncan & Denise Levertov: The Poetry of Politics, the Politics of Poetry. 2006. (ENG., Illus.). 232p. 60.00 (978-0-8047-5130-8(7)) Stanford Univ. Pr.

Gery, John & Pratt, William. Ezra Pound, Ends & Beginnings: Essays & Poems from the Ezra Pound International Conference Venice, 2007. 2011. xiii, 234p. (978-0-404-65530-3(0)) AMS Pr., Inc.

Goldfarb, Lisa & Eeckhout, Bart, eds. Wallace Stevens, New York, & Modernism. 2012. (Routledge Studies in Twentieth-Century Literature Ser.). (ENG., Illus.). 194p. (C). 125.00 (978-0-415-89910-9(9)) Routledge.

Golston, Michael. Rhythm & Race in Modernist Poetry & Science. 2007. (ENG., Illus.). 296p. (gr. 17). 55.00 (978-0-231-14276-2(5)) Columbia Univ. Pr.

Grant, Michael. T. S. Eliot Volume 2. 2009. 424p. pap. 45.00 (978-0-415-56897-5(8)) Routledge.

—T. S. Eliot Volume I. 2009. 408p. pap. 45.00 (978-0-415-56896-8(X)) Routledge.

Hair, Ross. Ronald Johnson's Modernist Collage Poetry. 2010. (Modern & Contemporary Poetry & Poetics Ser.). (ENG., Illus.). 270p. 84.00 (978-0-230-10869-1(5)) Palgrave Macmillan.

Hargrove, Nancy Duvall. T. S. Eliot's Parisian Year. 2010. (ENG., Illus.). 336p. pap. 29.95 (978-0-8130-3553-6(8)) Univ. Pr. of Florida.

Harmon, William. Time in Ezra Pound's Work. 2011. (ENG.). 178p. pap. 30.00 (978-0-8078-9678-5(0)) Univ. of North Carolina Pr.

Harrell, Willie J., Jr. We Wear the Mask: Paul Laurence Dunbar & the Politics of Representative Reality. 2011. (Illus.). 256p. 45.00 (978-1-60635-046-1(3)) Kent State Univ. Pr.

Harrison, S. J. Living Classics: Greece & Rome in Contemporary Poetry in English. 2009. (Classical Presences Ser.). (ENG.). 360p. 125.00 (978-0-19-923373-1(X)) Oxford Univ. Pr., Inc.

Hart, Josephine. Catching Life by the Throat: How to Read Poetry & Why. 2008. (ENG., Illus.). 256p. 26.95 (978-0-393-06607-4(X), 6607) Norton, W. W. & Co., Inc.

Hart, Matthew. Nations of Nothing but Poetry: Modernism, Transnationalism, & Synthetic Vernacular Writing. 2010. (Modernist Literature & Culture Ser.). (ENG.). 288p. 55.00 (978-0-19-539033-9(4)) Oxford Univ. Pr., Inc.

Hedley, Jane. I Made You to Find Me: The Coming of Age of the Woman Poet & the Politics of Poetic Address. 2009. (ENG.). 199p. 44.95 (978-0-8142-1101-4(1)); cd-rom 14.95 (978-0-8142-9199-3(6)) Ohio State Univ. Pr.

Hedley, Jane, et al. In the Frame: Women's Ekphrastic Poetry from Marianne Moore to Susan Wheeler. 2009. 60.00 (978-0-87413-046-1(8)) Univ. of Delaware Pr.

Heller, Michael. Speaking the Estranged: Essays on the Work of George Oppen. 2008. (ENG.). 152p. pap. (978-1-84471-440-7(3)) Salt Publishing.

Henneberg, Sylvia. The Creative Crone: Aging & the Poetry of May Sarton & Adrienne Rich. 2010. (ENG.). 220p. (C). 44.95 (978-0-8262-1861-2(X)) Univ. of Missouri Pr.

Herd, David. John Ashbery & American Poetry. 2009. (ENG.). 245p. pap. 26.00 (978-0-7190-8059-3(2)) Manchester Univ. Pr. GBR. Dist: Macmillan.

—John Ashbery & American Poetry: Fit to Cope with Our Occasions. (Illus.). 208p. (978-0-7190-5597-3(0)) Manchester Univ. Pr.

Hicok, Bethany. Degrees of Freedom: American Women Poets & the Women's College, 1905-1955. 2008. (Illus.). 224p. (C). 51.50 (978-0-8387-5693-5(X)) Bucknell Univ. Pr.

Hill, Norma Ferguson. Dr. Martin Luther King Jr.'s Chronicle & Creative Poems. 2007. pap. 9.00 (978-0-8059-8624-2(3)) Dorrance Publishing Co., Inc.

Holander, Stefan. Wallace Stevens & the Realities of Poetic Language. 2009. 234p. 39.95 (978-0-415-87665-0(6)) Routledge.

Holden, Jonathan. The Fate of American Poetry. 2008. (ENG.). 160p. pap. 22.95 (978-0-8203-3311-3(5)) Univ. of Georgia Pr.

Holmes, John & Springbord, Robert. Darwin's Bards: British & American Poetry in the Age of Evolution. 2009. (ENG.). 352p. (gr. 17). 95.00 (978-0-7486-3940-3(3)) Edinburgh Univ. Pr. GBR. Dist: Columbia Univ. Pr.

Howarth, Peter. The Cambridge Introduction to Modernist Poetry. 2011. (Cambridge Introductions to Literature Ser.). (ENG., Illus.). (C). 276p. 95.00 (978-0-521-76447-6(5)); 280p. pap. 27.99 (978-0-521-14785-9(9)) Cambridge Univ. Pr.

Humphrey, Walter Beach. Walter Beach Humphrey's "Hovey Murals" at Dartmouth College: A Cultural History. Kennedy, Brian P., ed. 2011. (Illus.). 164p. pap. 39.95 (978-1-61168-029-4(8)) Hood Museum of Art & Univ. Pr. of New England.

Huntsperger, David W. Procedural Form in Postmodern American Poetry: Berrigan, Antin, Silliman, & Hejinian. 2010. (Modern & Contemporary Poetry & Poetics Ser.). (ENG.). 206p. 79.00 (978-0-230-62202-9(X)) Palgrave Macmillan.

Jacques, Geoffrey. A Change in the Weather: Modernist Imagination, African American Imaginary. 2009. 240p. (ENG.). pap. 28.95 (978-1-55849-688-0(2)); lib. bdg. 80.00 net. (978-1-55849-687-3(4)) Univ. of Massachusetts Pr.

Jaeger, Peter. Theorists of Postmodernist Poetry. 2007. (Routledge Critical Thinkers Ser.). 22.95 (978-0-415-33380-1(6)); 95.00 (978-0-415-33379-5(2)) Routledge.

Jennison, Ruth. The Zukofsky Era: Modernity, Margins, & the Avant-Garde. 2012. (Hopkins Studies in Modernism Ser.). (ENG., Illus.). 248p. (gr. 17). 60.00 (978-1-4214-0529-2(6)) Johns Hopkins Univ. Pr.

Johnson, Jeannine. Why Write Poetry? Modern Poets Defending Their Art. 2007. (Illus.). 320p. 59.50 (978-0-8386-4105-7(9)) Fairleigh Dickinson Univ. Pr.

Jones, Meta DuEwa. The Muse Is Music: Jazz Poetry from the Harlem Renaissance to Spoken Word. 2011. (New Black Studies Ser.). (ENG., Illus.). 304p. 55.00 (978-0-252-03621-7(2)) Univ. of Illinois Pr.

Joyce, Elisabeth W. The Small Space of a Pause: Susan Howe's Poetry & the Spaces Between. 2010. 65.00 (978-0-8387-5762-8(6)) Bucknell Univ. Pr.

Kane, Daniel. We Saw the Light: Conversations Between the New American Cinema & Poetry. 2009. (Contemporary North American Poetry Ser.). (ENG., Illus.). 252p. 39.95 (978-1-58729-788-5(4)) Univ. of Iowa Pr.

Kane, Daniel, ed. Don't Ever Get Famous: Essays on New York Writing after the New York School. annot. ed. 2006. (Dalkey Archive Scholarly Ser.). (ENG.). 376p. per. 34.95 (978-1-56478-460-5(6), 478460) Dalkey Archive Pr.

Keller, Lynn. Re-making it New: Contemporary American Poetry & the Modernist Tradition. 2009. (Cambridge Studies in American Literature & Culture Ser.). (ENG.). 312p. pap. 42.00 (978-0-521-10677-1(X)) Cambridge Univ. Pr.

Kendall, Tim. The Art of Robert Frost. 2012. (ENG.). 408p. 35.00 (978-0-300-11813-1(9)) Yale Univ. Pr.

Kern, Robert. Orientalism, Modernism, & the American Poem. 2009. (Cambridge Studies in American Literature & Culture Ser.). (ENG.). 336p. pap. 46.00 (978-0-521-10555-2(2)) Cambridge Univ. Pr.

Keyes, Claire. Aesthetics of Power: The Poetry of Adrienne Rich. 2008. (ENG.). 232p. pap. 24.95 (978-0-8203-3351-9(4)) Univ. of Georgia Pr.

Kim, Dal-Yong. Mystical Themes & Occult Symbolism in Modern Poetry: Wordsworth, Whitman, Hopkins, Yeats, Pound, Eliot, & Plath. 2010. xv, 261p. (978-0-7734-3780-7(0)) Mellen, Edwin Pr., The.

Kornstein, Daniel J. Unlikely Muse: Legal Thinking & Artistic Imagination. 2010. 304p. 25.99 (978-1-4490-3297-5(4)); pap. 15.49 (978-1-4490-3296-2(2)) AuthorHouse.

Kreymborg, Alfred. Our Singing Strength: An Outline of American Poetry (1620-1930) (Des Imagistes). reprint ed. 45.00 (978-0-404-17123-0(0)) AMS Pr., Inc.

Kuzma, Greg, ed. A Book of Rereadings. 2006. 493p. pap. 10.00 (978-0-9788482-0-0(9)) Best Cellar Pr., The.

Lavoie, Steve & Nolan, Pat, eds. Life of Crime: Documents in the Guerrilla War Against Language Poetry. 2010. 144p. pap. 19.95 (978-0-918395-26-9(7)) Poltroon Pr.

Leighton, Angela. On Form: Poetry, Aestheticism, & the Legacy of a Word. 2007. (ENG.). 304p. 75.00 (978-0-19-929060-4(1)) Oxford Univ. Pr., Inc.

Lewis, Ethan. Modernist Image: Rhythmic & Perceptual Resonance in the Works of Ezra Pound & T. S. Eliot. 252p. 109.95 (978-0-7734-5758-4(5)) Mellen, Edwin Pr., The.

Logan, William. Our Savage Art: Poetry & the Civil Tongue. 2012. (ENG.). 368p. (gr. 17). pap. 24.00 (978-0-231-14733-0(3)) Columbia Univ. Pr.

Logan, William A. Our Savage Art: Poetry & the Civil Tongue. 2009. (ENG., Illus.). 368p. (gr. 17). 29.50 (978-0-231-14732-3(5)) Columbia Univ. Pr.

Loizeaux, Elizabeth Bergmann. Twentieth-Century Poetry & the Visual Arts. (ENG., Illus.). 274p. 2011. pap. 35.99 (978-0-521-18020-7(1)) 2008. 93.00 (978-0-521-88795-3(X)) Cambridge Univ. Pr.

Lowney, John. History, Memory, & the Literary Left: Modern American Poetry, 1935-1968. 2006. (Contemporary North American Poetry Ser.). 287p. 39.95 (978-1-58729-508-9(3)) Univ. of Iowa Pr.

Ma, Ming-Qian. Poetry as Re-Reading: American Avant-Garde Poetry & the Poetics of Counter-Method. 2008. (Avant-Garde & Modernism Studies). (ENG.). 320p. (C). 69.95 (978-0-8101-2483-7(1)); pap. 32.95 (978-0-8101-2485-1(8)) Northwestern Univ. Pr.

MacArthur, Marit J. The American Landscape in the Poetry of Frost, Bishop, & Ashbery: The House Abandoned. 2008. (American Literature Readings in the Twenty-First Century Ser.). (ENG.). 272p. 89.00 (978-0-230-60322-6(X)) Palgrave Macmillan.

Magda, Paizs. Whitman & Ginsberg: American Bards: The Romantic Ancestor & the Postmodern Follower. 2008. 64p. pap. (978-3-639-09508-1(1)) VDM Verlag Dr. Mueller e.K.

Malone, Ted. Ted Malone's Scrapbook: Favorite Selections from Between the Bookends. 2007. (ENG.). 384p. 48.95 (978-0-548-06765-9(1)) Kessinger Publishing, LLC.

Marcinkiewicz, Pawel. The Rhetoric of the City: Robinson Jeffers & A. R. Ammons. 2009. (Literary & Cultural Theory Ser.). 208p. 61.95 (978-3-631-59755-2(X)) Lang, Peter GmbH, Europaischer Verlag der Wissenschaften DEU. Dist: Lang, Peter.

Marsh, Alec. Money & Modernity: Pound, Williams, & the Spirit of Jefferson. 2011. (ENG.). 312p. pap. 27.50 (978-0-8173-5695-8(9)) Univ. of Alabama Pr.

Marsh, John. Hog Butchers, Beggars, & Busboys: Poverty, Labor, & the Making of Modern American Poetry. 2011. (Class: Culture Ser.). (ENG.). 280p. 80.00 (978-0-472-07157-9(2)); pap. 35.00 (978-0-472-05157-1(1)) Univ. of Michigan Pr.

Marsh, Nicky. Democracy in Contemporary U. S. Women's Poetry. 2007. (American Literature Readings in the Twenty-First Century Ser.). (ENG.). 228p. 89.00 (978-0-230-60026-3(3)) Palgrave Macmillan.

Marshall, Alan. American Experimental Poetry & Democratic Thought. 2009. (ENG.). 320p. 95.00 (978-0-19-956192-6(3)) Oxford Univ. Pr., Inc.

Mason, David. Two Minds of a Western Poet. 2011. (Poets on Poetry Ser.). (ENG.). 178p. 70.00 (978-0-472-07142-5(4)); pap. 27.95 (978-0-472-05142-7(3)) Univ. of Michigan Pr.

Mayhew, Jonathan & Mayhew, J. Apocryphal Lorca: Translation, Parody, Kitsch. 2009. (ENG.). 240p. 45.00 (978-0-226-51203-7(7)) Univ. of Chicago Pr.

McCabe, Susan. Cinematic Modernism: Modernist Poetry & Film. 2009. (ENG., Illus.). 296p. pap. 42.00 (978-0-521-11483-7(7)) Cambridge Univ. Pr.

McFee, Michael. The Napkin Manuscripts: Selected Essays & an Interview. 2006. 200p. 29.95 (978-1-57233-540-0(8)) Univ. of Tennessee Pr.

McGann, Jerome J. The Point Is to Change It: Poetry & Criticism in the Continuing Present. 2nd ed. 2007. (Modern & Contemporary Poetics Ser.). 288p. (ENG.). 60.00 (978-0-8173-1551-1(9)); per. 32.95 (978-0-8173-5408-4(5)) Univ. of Alabama Pr.

McGill, Arthur C. The Celebration of the Flesh: Poetry in Christian Life. 2008. 190p. pap. 22.00 (978-1-60608-298-0(1), Wipf and Stock) Wipf & Stock Pubs.

Metres, Philip. Behind the Lines: War Resistance Poetry on the American Home Front Since 1941. 2007. (Contemporary North American Poetry Ser.). (Illus.). 298p. 39.95 (978-0-87745-998-9(3)) Univ. of Iowa Pr.

Miller, Stephen Paul & Morris, Daniel, eds. Radical Poetics & Secular Jewish Culture. 2nd ed. 2009. (Modern & Contemporary Poetics Ser.). (ENG., Illus.). 552p. 67.50 (978-0-8173-1675-4(2)); pap. 39.95 (978-0-8173-5563-0(4)) Univ. of Alabama Pr.

Moffett, Joe. A Bakhtinian Reading of Three Postmodern Long Poems. 2008. 56p. pap. (978-3-639-02764-8(7)) VDM Verlag Dr. Mueller e.K.

Mohr, Bill. Hold-Outs: The Los Angeles Poetry Renaissance, 1948-1992. 2011. (Contemporary North American Poetry Ser.). (ENG.). 296p. pap. 39.95 (978-1-60938-073-1(8)) Univ. of Iowa Pr.

Monroe, Harriet. Poetry, a Magazine of Verse, V43, No 4, January 1934. Monroe, Harriet, ed. 2011. 70p. 36.95 (978-1-258-07668-9(3)) Literary Licensing, LLC.

Montgomery, Will & Hampson, Robert, eds. Frank O'Hara Now: New Essays on the New York Poet. 2010. (ENG., Illus.). 255p. pap. 29.95 (978-1-84631-233-5(7)) Liverpool Univ. Pr. GBR. Dist: Chicago Distribution Ctr.

Morgan, Bill & Peters, Nancy J., eds. Howl on Trial: The Battle for Free Expression. 2006. (ENG., Illus.). 224p. per. 14.95 (978-0-87286-479-5(0)) City Lights Bks.

Morris, Adalaide. How to Live/What to Do: H. D.'s Cultural Poetics. 2006. (ENG., Illus.). 280p. pap. 26.00 (978-0-252-07591-9(9)) Univ. of Illinois Pr.

Morris, Daniel. The Poetry of Louise Gluck: A Thematic Introduction. 2006. (ENG., Illus.). 288p. (C). 44.95 (978-0-8262-1693-9(5)) Univ. of Missouri Pr.

Mossin, Andrew. Male Subjectivity & Poetic Form in New American Poetry. 2010. (Modern & Contemporary Poetry & Poetics Ser.). (ENG., Illus.). 246p. 84.00 (978-0-230-61732-2(8)) Palgrave Macmillan.

Msalmi, Manel. The Pastoral in Robert Frost's Poetry. 2010. 136p. pap. (978-3-8383-6262-5(4)) Lambert Academic Publishing.

Nealon, Christopher S. The Matter of Capital: Poetry & Crisis in the American Century. 2011. 172p. E-Book 35.00 (978-0-674-06116-3(0)); (ENG.). 202p. 35.00 (978-0-674-05872-9(0)) Harvard Univ. Pr.

Nelson, Cary, ed. The Oxford Handbook of Modern & Contemporary American Poetry, 1 vol. 2012. (Oxford Handbooks Ser.). (ENG., Illus.). 744p. 150.00 (978-0-19-539877-9(7)) Oxford Univ. Pr., Inc.

Newcomb, John Timberman. How Did Poetry Survive? The Making of Modern American Verse. 2012. E-Book **(978-0-252-09390-6(9))**; (ENG., Illus.). 352p. 75.00 **(978-0-252-03679-8(4))** Univ. of Illinois Pr.
Nicholls, Peter. George Oppen & the Fate of Modernism. 2007. (ENG., Illus.). 240p. 110.00 *(978-0-19-921826-4(9))* Oxford Univ. Pr., Inc.
Nichols, Miriam. Radical Affections: Essays on the Poetics of Outside. 2010. *(978-0-8173-8441-8(3))* 2nd ed. 2011. (ENG., Illus.). 368p. 55.00 *(978-0-8173-1711-9(2))* 2nd ed. 2011. (ENG., Illus.). 368p. pap. 34.95 *(978-0-8173-5621-7(5))* Univ. of Alabama Pr.
Nickels, Joel. Poetry of the Possible: Spontaneity, Modernism, & the Multitude. 2012. 296p. 75.00 **(978-0-8166-7608-8(9))**; pap. 25.00 **(978-0-8166-7609-5(7))** Univ. of Minnesota Pr.
O'Brien, Timothy. Names, Proverbs, Riddles, & Material Text in Robert Frost. 2010. (ENG., Illus.). 220p. 84.00 *(978-0-230-10265-1(4))* Palgrave Macmillan.
O'Neill, Michael. The All-Sustaining Air: Romantic Legacies & Renewals in British, American, & Irish Poetry Since 1900. (ENG.). 224p. 2012. pap. 45.00 **(978-0-19-965305-8(4))** 2007. 110.00 *(978-0-19-929928-7(5))* Oxford Univ. Pr., Inc.
Oostdijk, Diederik. Among the Nightmare Fighters: American Poets of World War II. 2011. 304p. 49.95 *(978-1-57003-995-9(X))* Univ. of South Carolina Pr.
Oppen, George & Cope, Stephen. Selected Prose, Daybooks, & Papers. Cope, Stephen, ed. 2007. (Illus.). 276p. per. 25.95 *(978-0-520-25232-5(2))*; 55.00 *(978-0-520-23579-3(7))* Univ. of California Pr.
Park, Josephine. Apparitions of Asia: Modernist Form & Asian American Poetics. 2008. (ENG.). 224p. 55.00 *(978-0-19-533273-5(3))* Oxford Univ. Pr., Inc.
Parry, Amie Elizabeth. Interventions into Modernist Cultures: Poetry from Beyond the Empty Screen. 2007. (Perverse Modernities Ser.). (ENG., Illus.). 200p. 79.95 *(978-0-8223-3803-1(3))* Duke Univ. Pr.
Patea, Viorica & Derrick, Paul Scott, eds. Modernism Revisited: Transgressing Boundaries & Strategies of Renewal in American Poetry. 2007. (ENG., Illus.). 252p. 70.00 *(978-90-420-2263-8(9))* Rodopi.
Patterson, Anita. Race, American Literature & Transnational Modernisms. 2011. (Cambridge Studies in American Literature & Culture Ser.). (ENG.). 248p. pap. 48.00 *(978-0-521-34956-7(7))* Cambridge Univ. Pr.
Petrosky, Anthony R. Contemporary American Poetry. Date not set. pap. *(978-0-312-03086-5(X))* St. Martin's Pr.
Phelps, William Lyon. The Advance of English Poetry in the Twentieth Century. 2006. 268p. pap. 21.99 *(978-1-4264-2670-4(4))* BiblioBazaar.
Phillips, Siobhan. The Poetics of the Everyday: Creative Repetition in Modern American Verse. 2010. 304p. E-Book *(978-0-231-52029-4(8))* 2009. (ENG., Illus.). 336p. (gr. 17). 45.00 *(978-0-231-14930-3(1))* Columbia Univ. Pr.
Preston, Carrie J. Modernism's Mythic Pose: Gender, Genre, Solo Performance, 1 vol. 2011. (Modernist Literature & Culture Ser.). (Illus.). 384p. 49.95 *(978-0-19-976626-0(6))* Oxford Univ. Pr., Inc.
Primeau, Ronald. Beyond Spoon River: The Legacy of Edgar Lee Masters. 2011. (ENG.). 232p. pap. 25.00 *(978-0-292-72925-4(1))* Univ. of Texas Pr.
Pryor, Sean. W. B. Yeats Ezra Pound & the Poetry of Paradise. 2011. 240p. 99.95 *(978-1-4094-0660-0(1))* Ashgate Publishing Co.
Quartermain, Peter. Disjunctive Poetics: From Gertrude Stein & Louis Zukofsky to Susan Howe. 2009. (Cambridge Studies in American Literature & Culture Ser.). (ENG.). 256p. pap. 36.99 **(978-0-521-10130-1(1))** Cambridge Univ. Pr.
Raiziss, Sona. The Metaphysical Passion: Seven Modern American Poets & the Seventeenth Century Tradition. 2011. 344p. 51.95 **(978-1-258-04958-4(9))** Literary Licensing, LLC.
Ramey, Lauri, ed. The Heritage Series of Black Poetry, 1962-1975: A Research Compendium. 2008. (Illus.). 388p. 124.95 *(978-0-7546-5782-8(5))* Ashgate Publishing Co.
Reddy, Srikanth. Changing Subjects: Digressions in Modern American Poetry, 1 vol. 2012. (ENG.). 208p. 35.00 **(978-0-19-979102-6(3))** Oxford Univ. Pr., Inc.
Ricks, Christopher. True Friendship: Geoffrey Hill, Anthony Hecht, & Robert Lowell under the Sign of Eliot & Pound. 2011. (Anthony Hecht Lectures in the Humanities Ser.). (ENG.). 272p. pap. 18.00 *(978-0-300-17146-4(3))* Yale Univ. Pr.
Ricks, Christopher B. True Friendship: Geoffrey Hill, Anthony Hecht, & Robert Lowell under the Sign of Eliot & Pound. 2010. (Anthony Hecht Lectures in the Humanities Ser.). 272p. 28.00 *(978-0-300-13429-2(0))* Yale Univ. Pr.
Rosenbaum, Susan B. Professing Sincerity: Modern Lyric Poetry, Commercial Culture, & the Crisis in Reading. 2007. (ENG.). 320p. (gr. 17). 39.50 *(978-0-8139-2610-0(6))* Univ. Pr. of Virginia.
Rothenberg, Jerome. Poetics & Polemics, 1980-2005. Clay, Steven, ed. 2008. (Modern & Contemporary Poetics Ser.). (ENG., Illus.). 360p. 62.50 *(978-0-8173-1627-3(2))*; pap. 29.95 *(978-0-8173-5507-4(3))* Univ. of Alabama Pr.
Sadoff, Ira. History Matters: Contemporary Poetry on the Margins of American Culture. 2009. (ENG., Illus.). 228p. 39.95 *(978-1-58729-797-7(3))* Univ. of Iowa Pr.
Sastri, Reena. James Merrill. 2007. (Studies in Major Literary Authors Ser.). 327p. 131.00 *(978-0-415-95592-8(0))* Routledge.
Schmidt, Michael, ed. The Great Modern Poets. 2009. (ENG., Illus.). 208p. 12.99 *(978-1-905204-32-8(9))*, 1905204329) Quercus GBR. Dist: Book Sales, Inc.
Schultz, Kathy Lou. The Afro-Modernist Epic & Literary History: Tolson, Hughes, Baraka. 2013. (Modern & Contemporary Poetry & Poetics Ser.). (ENG., Illus.). 256p. 80.00 **(978-0-230-33873-9(9))** Palgrave Macmillan.
Sereg, Viktória. Jim Morrison - the Poet & the Singer. 2008. 72p. pap. *(978-3-8364-9850-0(2))* VDM Verlag Dr. Mueller e.K.
Shoemaker, Steve, ed. & contrib. by. Thinking Poetics: Essays on George Oppen. 2009. (Modern & Contemporary Poetics Ser.). (ENG., Illus.). 320p. 54.50 *(978-0-8173-1662-4(0))*; pap. 34.95 *(978-0-8173-5546-3(4))* Univ. of Alabama Pr.
Sigg, Eric. The American T. S. Eliot: A Study of the Early Writings. 2009. (Cambridge Studies in American Literature & Culture Ser.). (ENG.). 280p. pap. 41.00 *(978-0-521-11003-7(3))* Cambridge Univ. Pr.
Silverberg, Mark. The New York School Poets & the Neo-Avant-Garde: Between Radical Art & Radical Chic. 2010. (Illus.). 296p. 104.95 *(978-0-7546-6298-3(5))* Ashgate Publishing Co.
Sister Barbara Sudol Csfn. Mystical Elements in the Poetry of T S Eliot. 2008. 192p. pap. *(978-3-639-07725-4(3))* VDM Verlag Dr. Mueller e.K.
Smith, Dale. Poets Beyond the Barricade: Rhetoric, Citizenship, & Dissent After 1960. 2012. (Albma Rhetoric Cult & Soc Crit Ser.). (ENG., Illus.). 200p. 28.95 **(978-0-8173-1749-2(X))** Univ. of Alabama Pr.
—Poets Beyond the Barricade: Rhetoric, Citizenship, & Dissent after 1960. 2012. **(978-0-8173-8592-7(4))** Univ. of Alabama Pr.
Smith, Dave. Hunting Men: Reflections on a Life in American Poetry. 2006. 299p. per. 25.00 *(978-0-8071-3182-4(2))* Louisiana State Univ. Pr.
Somers-Willett, Susan B. A. The Cultural Politics of Slam Poetry: Race, Identity, & the Performance of Popular Verse in America. 2009. (ENG., Illus.). 208p. 70.00 *(978-0-472-07059-6(2))*; pap. 23.95 *(978-0-472-05059-8(1))* Univ. of Michigan Pr.
Stambuk, Andrew. The Man Who Is & Is Not There: The Poetry & Prose of Robert Francis. 2011. 184p. lib. bdg. 80.00 *(978-1-55849-897-6(4))* Univ. of Massachusetts Pr.
—The Man Who Is & Is Not There: The Poetry & Prose of Robert Francis. 2011. 184p. pap. 24.95 *(978-1-55849-898-3(2))* Univ. of Massachusetts Pr.
Stein, Gertrude. Stanzas in Meditation: And Other Poems, 1929-1933. Hollister, Susannah & Setina, Emily, eds. 2012. (ENG., Illus.). 400p. pap. 22.00 *(978-0-300-15309-5(0))* Yale Univ. Pr.
Stein, Kevin. Poetry's Afterlife: Verse in the Digital Age. 2010. (Digitalculturebooks Ser.). (ENG.). 276p. (C). pap. 26.95 *(978-0-472-05099-4(0))* Univ. of Michigan Pr.
Stidger, William Le Roy. Giant Hours with Poet Preachers. 2008. 92p. pap. *(978-1-4099-3732-6(1))* Dodo Pr.
Swanberg, Ingrid & Smith, Larry, eds. D. A. levy & the mimeograph Revolution. 2007. (ENG., Illus.). 264p. (C). pap. 25.00 *(978-1-933964-07-2(3))* Bottom Dog Pr.
Swigg, Richard. Quick, Said the Bird: Williams, Eliot, Moore, & the Spoken Word. 2012. (ENG.). 224p. pap. 39.95 **(978-1-60938-079-3(7))** Univ. of Iowa Pr.
Szefel, Lisa. The Gospel of Beauty in the Progressive Era: Reforming American Verse & Values. 2011. (Palgrave Studies in Cultural & Intellectual History Ser.). (ENG., Illus.). 296p. 85.00 *(978-0-230-11284-1(6))* Palgrave Macmillan.
Thomas, Joseph T. Poetry's Playground: The Culture of Contemporary American Children's Poetry. 2007. (Landscapes of Childhood Ser.). (Illus.). 180p. per. 24.95 *(978-0-8143-3296-2(X))* Wayne State Univ. Pr.
Thurston, Michael. The Underworld in Twentieth-Century Poetry: From Pound & Eliot to Heaney & Walcott. 2009. (ENG.). 228p. 89.00 *(978-0-230-62046-9(9))* Palgrave Macmillan.
Untermeyer, Louis. The New Era in American Poetry. 2009. 226p. pap. 19.99 *(978-1-150-51890-4(1))* General Bks. LLC.
Vaughan, David K. Words to Measure a War: Nine American Poets of World War II. 2009. (ENG.). 204p. pap. 35.00 *(978-0-7864-4306-2(5))* McFarland & Co., Inc. Pubs.
Vendler, Helen. Last Looks, Last Books: Stevens, Plath, Lowell, Bishop, Merrill. 2010. (A. W. Mellon Lectures in the Fine Arts Ser.). (ENG.). 176p. 19.95 *(978-0-691-14534-1(2))* Princeton Univ. Pr.
Viala, Fabienne. Marguerite Yourcenar, Alejo Carpentier: Ecritures de L'histoire. 2008. (Yourcenar Ser.). (FRE & SPA.). 185p. pap. 54.95 *(978-90-5201-400-5(0))* PIE - Peter Lang BEL. Dist: Lang, Peter.
Von Damlem, Nina. The Man Who Heard the Song of Truth - Love As E E Cummings' Concept of Reality. 2007. 132p. per. *(978-3-8364-5015-7(1))* VDM Verlag Dr. Mueller e.K.
Wacior, Slawomir. Explaining Imagism: The Imagist Movement in Poetry & Art. 2007. 316p. *(978-0-7734-5427-9(6))* Mellen, Edwin Pr., The.
Wagner-Martin, Linda, ed. Hemingway: Eight Decades of Criticism. 2008. (ENG.). 531p. pap. 34.95 *(978-0-87013-839-3(1))* Michigan State Univ. Pr.
Wald, Alan M. The Revolutionary Imagination: The Poetry & Politics of John Wheelwright & Sherry Mangan. 2011. (ENG.). 312p. pap. 40.00 *(978-0-8078-6632-0(6))* Univ. of North Carolina Pr.
Walsh, William, ed. David Bottoms: Critical Essays & Interviews. 2010. (ENG., Illus.). 286p. pap. 35.00 *(978-0-7864-4729-9(X))* McFarland & Co., Inc. Pubs.
Wandrei, Donald. A Concordance to the Poetry of Donald Wandrei. 2008. 464p. 50.00 *(978-0-9814888-2-0(X))* Hippocampus Pr.
Wasley, A. The Age of Auden - Postwar Poetry & the American Scene. 2010. (ENG.). 280p. (C). 35.00 *(978-0-691-13679-0(3))* Princeton Univ. Pr.
Weinfield, Henry. The Music of Thought in the Poetry of George Oppen & William Bronk. 2009. (ENG.). 252p. 37.50 *(978-1-58729-781-6(7))* Univ. of Iowa Pr.
Whitworth, Michael H. Reading Modernist Poetry. 2010. (Blackwell Reading Poetry Ser.: 3). (ENG.). 256p. 110.95 *(978-1-4051-6731-4(9)*, Wiley-Blackwell) Wiley, John & Sons, Inc.
Wienen, Mark W. van. Partisans & Poets: The Political Work of American Poetry in the Great War. 2009. (Cambridge Studies in American Literature & Culture Ser.). (ENG., Illus.). 332p. pap. 36.99 *(978-0-521-11006-8(8))* Cambridge Univ. Pr.
Williams, Louise Blakeney. Modernism & the Ideology of History: Literature, Politics, & the Past. 2009. (ENG.). 276p. pap. 38.99 *(978-0-521-12093-7(4))* Cambridge Univ. Pr.
Wójcik-Leese, Elzbieta. Cognitive Poetic Readings in Elizabeth Bishop: Portrait of a Mind Thinking. 2010. (Applications of Cognitive Linguistics [ACL] Ser.). (ENG.). VIII, 317p. 140.00 *(978-3-11-018610-9(1))* De Gruyter, Mouton DEU. Dist: de Gruyter, Walter GmbH & Co. KG.
Wrighton, John. Ethics & Politics in Modern American Poetry. 2009. (Literary Criticism & Cultural Theory Ser.). (ENG., Illus.). 236p. (C). 133.00 *(978-0-415-80122-5(2))* Routledge.
Yao, Steven G. Foreign Accents: Chinese American Verse from Exclusion to Postethnicity, 1 vol. 2010. (Global Asias Ser.). (ENG., Illus.). 352p. 65.00 *(978-0-19-973033-9(4))* Oxford Univ. Pr., Inc.
Zaller, Robert. Robinson Jeffers & the American Sublime. 2012. (ENG.). 424p. 65.00 **(978-0-8047-7563-2(X))** Stanford Univ. Pr.

AMERICAN POETRY—HISTORY AND CRITICISM—21ST CENTURY

Bernstein, Charles. American Poetry After 1975. 2009. (ENG.). 225p. pap. 14.00 *(978-0-8223-6719-2(X))* Duke Univ. Pr.
Biddinger, Mary, ed. Monkey & the Wrench: Essays into Contemporary Poetics. 2011. 176p. pap. 14.95 *(978-1-931968-91-1(8))* Univ. of Akron Pr., The.
Carlson, Burton L. Begging Is Just the Beginning. 2010. 80p. pap. 10.49 *(978-1-4490-4864-8(1))* AuthorHouse.
Corn, Alfred. Atlas: Selected Essays, 1989-2007. 2008. (Poets on Poetry Ser.). (ENG.). 192p. 70.00 *(978-0-472-07050-3(9))*; pap. 23.95 *(978-0-472-05050-5(8))* Univ. of Michigan Pr.
Damon, Maria. Postliterary America: From Bagel Shop Jazz to Micropoetries. 2011. (Contemporary North American Poetry Ser.). (ENG., Illus.). 280p. pap. 39.95 *(978-1-58729-957-5(7))* Univ. of Iowa Pr.
Davidson, Ian. Ideas of Space in Contemporary Poetry. 2007. (ENG., Illus.). 224p. 84.00 *(978-1-4039-9771-5(3))* Palgrave Macmillan.
Dowdy, Michael. American Political Poetry in the 21st Century. 2007. (American Literature Readings in the Twenty-First Century Ser.). (ENG.). 248p. 84.00 *(978-1-4039-7644-4(9))* Palgrave Macmillan.
Finkelstein, Norman. On Mount Vision: Forms of the Sacred in Contemporary American Poetry. 2010. (Contemporary North American Poetry Ser.). (ENG.). 294p. 39.95 *(978-1-58729-857-8(0))* Univ. of Iowa Pr.
Finney, Nikky, ed. The Ringing Ear: Black Poets Lean South. 2007. (ENG.). 432p. 69.95 *(978-0-8203-2925-3(8))*; per. 22.95 *(978-0-8203-2926-0(6))* Univ. of Georgia Pr.
Fredman, Stephen & McCaffery, Steve, eds. Form, Power, & Person in Robert Creeley's Life & Work. 2010. (Contemporary North American Poetry Ser.). (ENG.). 272p. 39.95 *(978-1-58729-859-2(7))* Univ. of Iowa Pr.
Gens, Jacqueline, Editor, Jacqueline. Tygerburning Inaugural Issue. 2010. 198p. pap. 15.00 *(978-1-934851-20-3(5))* Marick Pr.
Harp, Jerry. For Us, What Music? The Life & Poetry of Donald Justice. 2010. 198p. pap. 32.95 *(978-1-58729-911-7(9))* Univ. of Iowa Pr.
Keller, Lynn. Thinking Poetry: Readings in Contemporary Women's Exploratory Poetics. 2009. (ENG., Illus.). 274p. 34.95 *(978-1-58729-867-7(8))* Univ. of Iowa Pr.
Kurteous Kitsch. The Yin Yang of Yo Yos. 2010. 52p. pap. 8.95 *(978-1-4502-0386-9(8))* iUniverse, Inc.
Miller, Stephen Paul & Morris, Daniel, eds. Radical Poetics & Secular Jewish Culture. 2nd ed. 2009. (Modern & Contemporary Poetics Ser.). (ENG., Illus.). 552p. 67.50 *(978-0-8173-1675-4(2))*; pap. 39.95 *(978-0-8173-5563-0(4))* Univ. of Alabama Pr.
Nealon, Christopher S. The Matter of Capital: Poetry & Crisis in the American Century. 2011. 172p. E-Book 35.00 **(978-0-674-06116-3(0))**; (ENG.). 202p. 35.00 *(978-0-674-05872-9(0))* Harvard Univ. Pr.
Nichols, Miriam. Radical Affections: Essays on the Poetics of Outside. 2010. *(978-0-8173-8441-8(3))* 2nd ed. 2011. (ENG., Illus.). 368p. 55.00 *(978-0-8173-1711-9(2))* 2nd ed. 2011. (ENG., Illus.). 368p. pap. 34.95 *(978-0-8173-5621-7(5))* Univ. of Alabama Pr.
O'Neill, Michael. The All-Sustaining Air: Romantic Legacies & Renewals in British, American, & Irish Poetry Since 1900. 2012. (ENG.). 224p. pap. 45.00 **(978-0-19-965305-8(4))** Oxford Univ. Pr., Inc.
Rodriguez y Gibson, Eliza, ed. Stunned into Being: Essays on the Poetry of Loma Dee Cervantes. 2012. (ENG.). 244p. pap. 17.95 **(978-0-916727-88-6(2))** Wings Pr.
Sadoff, Ira. History Matters: Contemporary Poetry on the Margins of American Culture. 2009. (ENG., Illus.). 228p. 39.95 *(978-1-58729-797-7(3))* Univ. of Iowa Pr.
Smith, Dale. Poets Beyond the Barricade: Rhetoric, Citizenship, & Dissent After 1960. 2012. (Albma Rhetoric Cult & Soc Crit Ser.). (ENG., Illus.). 200p. 28.95 **(978-0-8173-1749-2(X))** Univ. of Alabama Pr.
—Poets Beyond the Barricade: Rhetoric, Citizenship, & Dissent after 1960. 2012. **(978-0-8173-8592-7(4))** Univ. of Alabama Pr.
Stein, Kevin. Poetry's Afterlife: Verse in the Digital Age. 2010. (Digitalculturebooks Ser.). (ENG.). 276p. (C). pap. 26.95 *(978-0-472-05099-4(0))* Univ. of Michigan Pr.
Thomas, Joseph T. Poetry's Playground: The Culture of Contemporary American Children's Poetry. 2007. (Landscapes of Childhood Ser.). (Illus.). 180p. per. 24.95 *(978-0-8143-3296-2(X))* Wayne State Univ. Pr.
Wilner, Eleanor. Tourist in Hell. 2010. (Phoenix Poets Ser.). 120p. pap. 18.00 *(978-0-226-90032-2(0))* Univ. of Chicago Pr.

AMERICAN POETRY—INDIAN AUTHORS

Hedge Coke, Allison Adelle. Sing: Poetry from the Indigenous Americas. 2011. (Sun Tracks Ser.). (ENG.). 352p. pap. 29.95 *(978-0-8165-2891-2(8))* Univ. of Arizona Pr.
Plenty, Trevino L. Brings, et al. Shedding Skins: Four Sioux Poets. Louis, Adrian C., ed. 2008. (American Indian Studies). (ENG., Illus.). 124p. per. 15.95 *(978-0-87013-823-2(5))* Michigan State Univ. Pr.

AMERICAN POETRY—JEWISH AUTHORS

Gubar, Susan. Poetry after Auschwitz: Remembering What One Never Knew. 2006. (Jewish Literature & Culture Ser.). (ENG., Illus.). 340p. pap. 24.95 *(978-0-253-21887-2(X)*, 025321887X) Indiana Univ. Pr.
Harshav, Benjamin. Sing, Stranger: A Century of American Yiddish Poetry - A Historical Anthology. 2006. (ENG., Illus.). 760p. 80.00 *(978-0-8047-5183-4(8))* Stanford Univ. Pr.
Miller, Stephen Paul & Morris, Daniel, eds. Radical Poetics & Secular Jewish Culture. 2nd ed. 2009. (Modern & Contemporary Poetics Ser.). (ENG., Illus.). 552p. 67.50 *(978-0-8173-1675-4(2))*; pap. 39.95 *(978-0-8173-5563-0(4))* Univ. of Alabama Pr.

AMERICAN POETRY—WOMEN AUTHORS

Astley, Neil, ed. Bloodaxe Poetry Introductions 3. 2008. (ENG., Illus.). 96p. pap. 22.95 *(978-1-85224-767-6(3))* Bloodaxe Bks. GBR. Dist: Dufour Editions, Inc.
Bloom, Harold, ed. American Women Poets. 2011. (Bloom's Modern Critical Views Ser.). 254p. (C). (gr. 9). 45.00 *(978-1-60413-991-4(9)*, Chelsea Hse.) Facts On File, Inc.
Boschman, Robert. In the Way of Nature: Ecology & Westward Expansion in the Poetry of Anne Bradstreet, Elizabeth Bishop & Amy Clampitt. 2009. (ENG.). 236p. pap. 39.95 *(978-0-7864-3356-8(6))* McFarland & Co., Inc. Pubs.
Cucinella, Catherine. Poetics of the Body: Edna St. Vincent Millay, Elizabeth Bishop, Marilyn Chin, & Marilyn Hacker. 2010. (ENG.). 190p. 79.00 *(978-0-230-62088-9(4))* Palgrave Macmillan.
Davis, Gwenn. Poetry by Women to 1900. *(978-0-7201-2016-5(0)*, Burns & Oates) Continuum International Publishing Group, Ltd.
Duplessis, Rachel Blau. Blue Studios: Poetry & Its Cultural Work. 2006. (Modern & Contemporary Poetics Ser.). (Illus.). 312p. 68.75 *(978-0-8173-1508-5(X))* Univ. of Alabama Pr.
DuPlessis, Rachel Blau. Blue Studios: Poetry & Its Cultural Work. 2006. (Modern & Contemporary Poetics Ser.). (Illus.). 312p. per. 37.95 *(978-0-8173-5321-6(6))* Univ. of Alabama Pr.
Field, Thalia. Bird Lovers, Backyard. 2010. (ENG., Illus.). 144p. pap. 16.95 *(978-0-8112-1840-5(6)*, 21840) New Directions Publishing Corp.
Ford, Karen Jackson. Gender & the Poetics of Excess: Moments of Brocade. 2009. (ENG.). 272p. pap. 25.00 *(978-1-60473-255-9(5))* Univ. Pr. of Mississippi.
Frost, Elisabeth A. & Hogue, Cynthia, eds. Innovative Women Poets: An Anthology of Contemporary Poetry & Interviews. 2007. (Illus.). 422p. (C). per. 29.95 *(978-1-58729-507-2(5))* Univ. of Iowa Pr.
Hedley, Jane. I Made You to Find Me: The Coming of Age of the Woman Poet & the Politics of Poetic Address. 2009. (ENG.). 199p. 44.95 *(978-0-8142-1101-4(1))*; cd-rom 14.95 *(978-0-8142-9199-3(6))* Ohio State Univ. Pr.
Hedley, Jane, et al. In the Frame: Women's Ekphrastic Poetry from Marianne Moore to Susan Wheeler. 2009. 60.00 *(978-0-87413-046-1(8))* Univ. of Delaware Pr.
Henneberg, Sylvia. The Creative Crone: Aging & the Poetry of May Sarton & Adrienne Rich. 2010. (ENG.). 220p. (C). 44.95 *(978-0-8262-1861-2(X))* Univ. of Missouri Pr.
Hicok, Bethany. Degrees of Freedom: American Women Poets & the Women's College, 1905-1955. 2008. (Illus.). 224p. (C). 51.50 *(978-0-8387-5693-5(X))* Bucknell Univ. Pr.
Honey, Maureen, ed. Shadowed Dreams: Women's Poetry of the Harlem Renaissance. 2nd ed. 2006. (Multi-Ethnic Literatures of the Americas Ser.). (ENG., Illus.). 374p. per. 24.95 *(978-0-8135-3886-0(6))* Rutgers Univ. Pr.
Keller, Lynn. Thinking Poetry: Readings in Contemporary Women's Exploratory Poetics. 2009. (ENG., Illus.). 274p. 34.95 *(978-1-58729-867-7(8))* Univ. of Iowa Pr.
Kinnahan, Linda A. Poetics of the Feminine: Authority & Literary Tradition in William Carlos Williams, Mina Loy, Denise Levertov, & Kathleen Fraser. 2008. (Cambridge Studies in American Literature & Culture Ser.). (ENG.). 304p. pap. 42.00 *(978-0-521-10157-8(3))* Cambridge Univ. Pr.
Lerner, Laurence. Reading Women's Poetry. 2009. (ENG.). 194p. 69.95 *(978-1-84519-337-9(7))*; pap. 34.95 *(978-1-84519-334-8(2))* Sussex Academic Pr. GBR. Dist: International Specialized Bk. Services.
Machado, Trena, ed. What I Want from You: Voices of East Bay Lesbian Poets. 2006. (ENG.). 145p. pap. 14.00 *(978-0-9729185-5-8(8))* Raw Art Pr.
Mamunes, George. So Has a Daisy Vanished: Emily Dickinson & Tuberculosis. 2007. (ENG.). 211p. per. 39.95 *(978-0-7864-3227-1(6))* McFarland & Co., Inc. Pubs.
Mance, Ajuan Maria. Inventing Black Women: African American Women Poets & Self-Representation, 1877-2000. 2008. (ENG.). 216p. pap. 24.95 *(978-1-57233-651-3(X))* Univ. of Tennessee Pr.
Miller, Brett Candlish. Flawed Light: American Women Poets & Alcohol. 2009. (ENG.). 168p. 40.00 *(978-0-252-03461-9(9))* Univ. of Illinois Pr.
Parisi, Joseph. 100 Essential Modern Poems by Women. 2008. (ENG.). 304p. 24.95 *(978-1-56663-741-1(4))* Dee, Ivan R. Pub.

Peel, Robin. Emily Dickinson & the Hill of Science. 2010. (ENG.). 92.50 *(978-1-61147-425-1(6))*; 92.50 *(978-0-8386-4221-4(7))* Fairleigh Dickinson Univ. Pr.

Rankine, Claudia & Sewell, Lisa, eds. Eleven More American Women Poets in the 21st Century: Poetics Across North America. 2nd ed. 2012. (American Poets in the 21st Century Ser.). (ENG.). 464p. (C). 80.00 ***(978-0-8195-7234-9(9))***; pap. 24.95 ***(978-0-8195-7235-6(7))*** Wesleyan Univ. Pr.

Raymond, Claire. The Posthumous Voice in Women's Writing Form Mary Shelly to Sylvia Plath. 2006. 270p. 120.00 *(978-0-7546-5535-0(0))* Ashgate Publishing Co.

Richards, Eliza. Gender & the Poetics of Reception in Poe's Circle. 2010. (Cambridge Studies in American Literature & Culture Ser.). (ENG.). 256p. pap. 36.00 *(978-0-521-17439-8(2))* Cambridge Univ. Pr.

Ryan, Jennifer D. Post-Jazz Poetics: A Social History. 2010. (ENG., Illus.). 240p. 84.00 *(978-0-230-62315-6(8))* Palgrave Macmillan.

Schulman, Grace. First Loves & Other Adventures. 2010. (Poets on Poetry Ser.). (ENG.). 168p. 70.00 *(978-0-472-07087-9(8))*; pap. 23.95 *(978-0-472-05087-1(7))* Univ. of Michigan Pr.

Shaughnessy, Brenda. Human Dark with Sugar. 2008. (ENG.). 96p. pap. 15.00 *(978-1-55659-276-8(0))* Copper Canyon Pr.

Write Group (Massachusetts) Staff, contrib. by. Moments Falling Open: The Write Group Anthology. 2007. (ENG.). 108p. per. 14.95 *(978-0-9749291-4-9(X)*, Pear Tree Publishing) Obert, Christopher Publishing.

Zawinski, Andrena, ed. Turning a Train of Thought Upside Down: An Anthology of Women's Poetry. 2012. (ENG.). 112p. pap. 18.00 ***(978-0-9768676-2-3(1))*** Scarlet Tanager Bks.

AMERICAN PORTRAITS

see Portraits

AMERICAN POTTERY

see Pottery, American

AMERICAN PROPAGANDA

see Propaganda, American

AMERICAN PROSE LITERATURE

see also American Essays; American Fiction (Collections); College Prose; Short Stories, American

American Society of Magazine Editors, ed. The Best American Magazine Writing 2007. 2007. (ENG.). 520p. (gr. 17). pap. 16.95 *(978-0-231-14391-2(5))* Columbia Univ. Pr.

—The Best American Magazine Writing 2009. 2009. (ENG., Illus.). 472p. (gr. 17). pap. 16.95 *(978-0-231-14796-5(1))* Columbia Univ. Pr.

—The Best American Magazine Writing 2010. 2010. (ENG., Illus.). 520p. (gr. 17). pap. 16.95 *(978-0-231-15753-7(3))* Columbia Univ. Pr.

Association of Alternative Newsweeklies Staff. Best AltWeekly Writing 2009 And 2010. 2011. 450p. pap. 19.95 *(978-0-8101-2737-1(7))* Northwestern Univ. Pr.

Beals, R. a. Readings in Description & Narration. Beals, R. a. et al, eds. 2011. 394p. 53.95 ***(978-1-258-03696-6(7))*** Literary Licensing, LLC.

Best AltWeekly Writing & Design 2006. 2006th ed. 2007. pap. *(978-0-9770471-1-6(3))* Assn. of Alternative Newsweeklies.

Caswell, Kurt, et al, eds. To Everything on Earth: New Writing on Fate, Community, & Nature. 2010. 160p. pap. 21.95 *(978-0-89672-655-0(X))* Texas Tech Univ. Pr.

Chase, Mary Ellen & Plaine, Frances K. Del. The Art of Narration. 2007. (ENG.). 508p. 55.95 *(978-0-548-06782-6(1))* Kessinger Publishing, LLC.

Eggers, Dave, ed. The Best American Nonrequired Reading 2006. 2006. (Best American Ser.). (ENG., Illus.). 400p. pap. 21.95 *(978-0-618-57051-5(9))* Houghton Mifflin Harcourt Trade & Reference Pubs.

—The Best American Nonrequired Reading 2009. 2009. (Best American Ser.). (ENG.). 432p. pap. 14.95 *(978-0-547-24160-9(7)*, Mariner Bks.) Houghton Mifflin Harcourt Trade & Reference Pubs.

—The Best American Nonrequired Reading 2011. 2011. (Best American R Ser.). (ENG.). 528p. pap. 14.95 *(978-0-547-57743-2(5)*, Mariner Bks.) Houghton Mifflin Harcourt Trade & Reference Pubs.

Farr, Maureen E. Eggemoggin Reach Review, Volume II: An Anthology of Prose & Poetry by Members of the Deer Isle Writer's Groups. 2007. 176p. pap. 17.95 *(978-0-9755586-1-4(7))* Eggemoggin Reach Review.

Foerster, Norman. The Chief American Prose Writers. 2009. 426p. pap. *(978-0-217-75159-9(8))* Books LLC.

Frymer, Benjamin. Censored 2011. Project Censored Staff et al, eds. 2010. (ENG.). 480p. pap. 19.95 ***(978-1-58322-920-0(5))*** Seven Stories Pr.

Gladwell, Malcolm. Malcolm Gladwell. 2011. (ENG., Illus.). 768p. 80.00 *(978-0-316-12309-9(9))* Little Brown & Co.

Gutkind, Lee. The Best Creative Nonfiction, Vol. 2. 2008. (ENG.). 368p. pap. 15.95 *(978-0-393-33024-3(9)*, 33024) Norton, W. W. & Co., Inc.

Gutkind, Lee, ed. The Best Creative Nonfiction, Vol. 3. 2009. (ENG.). 272p. pap. 16.95 *(978-0-393-33025-0(7)*, 33025) Norton, W. W. & Co., Inc.

Holt, Sid. The Best American Magazine Writing 2011. American Society of Magazine Editors, ed. 2011. (ENG.). 600p. (gr. 17). pap. 16.95 ***(978-0-231-15940-1(4))*** Columbia Univ. Pr.

Katz, Daniel R., ed. Why Freedom Matters. 2006. 413p. reprint ed. 25.00 *(978-1-4223-5577-0(2))* DIANE Publishing Co.

Keeble, Richard & Wheeler, Sharon. The Literary Journalists. 2007. (Illus.). 176p. pap. 36.95 *(978-0-415-41724-2(4))* Routledge.

Kuldell, Heather & Whiten, Jon, eds. Best of AltWeekly Writing & Design 2007. 2007. 304p. pap. 20.00 *(978-0-9770471-2-3(1))* Assn. of Alternative Newsweeklies.

Martínez, David, ed. & contrib. by. The American Indian Intellectual Tradition: An Anthology of Writings from 1772 To 1972. 2011. 424p. 79.95 *(978-0-8014-4928-4(6))* Cornell Univ. Pr.

—The American Indian Intellectual Tradition: An Anthology of Writings from 1772 to 1972. 2011. 424p. pap. 29.95 *(978-0-8014-7654-9(2))* Cornell Univ. Pr.

McNair, Wesley. A Place Called Maine: 24 Authors on the Maine Experience. 2008. (ENG.). 320p. 25.00 *(978-0-89272-760-5(8))* Down East Bks.

Melhhem. Art Politics Politics Art. 2010. 80p. pap. 9.95 *(978-0-8156-0976-6(0))* Syracuse Univ. Pr.

Peyer, Bernd C., ed. American Indian Nonfiction: An Anthology of Writings, 1760s-1930s. 2007. (ENG.). 448p. (C). per. 26.95 *(978-0-8061-3798-8(3))* Univ. of Oklahoma Pr.

Phelps, William Lyon. Selected Readings from Much Loved Books. 2007. (ENG.). 382p. 48.95 *(978-0-548-06658-4(2))* Kessinger Publishing, LLC.

Phillips, Peter. Censored 2008: The Top 25 Censored Stories Of 2006-07. 2007. (Illus.). 432p. 40.00 *(978-1-58322-773-2(3))* Seven Stories Pr.

Rees, Byron Johnson. Modern American Prose Selections. 2009. 196p. pap. 16.99 *(978-1-103-74662-0(6))* 2008. 176p. 25.99 *(978-0-554-27509-3(0))* 2008. 176p. 22.99 *(978-0-554-36812-2(9))* 2007. (ENG.). 156p. pap. 19.99 *(978-1-4346-3372-9(1))* 2007. 172p. pap. 21.99 *(978-1-4346-3373-6(X))* BiblioBazaar.

—Modern American Prose Selections. 2009. 114p. pap. *(978-0-217-02424-2(6))* Books LLC.

Rees, Byron Johnson, ed. Modern American Prose Selections. 2009. 196p. pap. 22.99 *(978-1-103-74668-2(5))* BiblioBazaar.

—Modern American Prose Selections. 2008. 194p. 37.95 *(978-0-548-95120-0(9))* 2007. (ENG.). 196p. per. 22.95 *(978-0-548-62615-3(4))* Kessinger Publishing, LLC.

Rees, Johnson Byron, ed. Modern American Prose Selections. 2007. 144p. 95.99 *(978-1-4280-7602-0(6))*; per. 88.99 *(978-1-4280-7595-5(X))* IndyPublish.com.

Roth, Andrew & Phillips, Peter, eds. Censored 2008: The Top 25 Censored Stories of 2007-07. 2007. (Censored Ser.). (ENG., Illus.). 400p. per. 18.95 *(978-1-58322-772-5(5))* Seven Stories Pr.

Samuels, David. Only Love Can Break Your Heart. 2009. (ENG.). 400p. pap. 16.95 *(978-1-58243-503-9(0)*, Counterpoint Pr.) Basic Bks. GBR. Dist: Perseus-PGW.

Scudder, Horace E. American Prose. 2010. 436p. 41.99 *(978-1-140-17178-2(X))*; pap. 35.75 *(978-1-140-17179-9(8))* BiblioBazaar.

Starkey, David, ed. Living Blue in the Red States. 2007. (ENG.). 356p. pap. 19.95 *(978-0-8032-6008-5(3)*, Bison Bks.) Univ. of Nebraska Pr.

Swan, Alison, ed. Fresh Water: Women Writing on the Great Lakes. 2006. (ENG.). 256p. per. 26.95 *(978-0-87013-789-1(1))* Michigan State Univ. Pr.

The American Society of Magazine Editors, ed. The Best American Magazine Writing 2006. 2006. (Columbia Contemporary American Religion Ser.). (ENG.). 464p. (gr. 17). pap. 18.95 *(978-0-231-13993-9(4))* Columbia Univ. Pr.

Tushinski, Jim & Van Buskirk, Jim. Identity Envy: Wanting to Be Who We're Not: Creative Nonfiction by Queer Writers. 2006. (ENG.). 282p. 125.00 *(978-1-56023-586-6(1))*; pap. 49.95 *(978-1-56023-587-3(X))* Routledge.

Watt, Homer A. & Cargill, Oscar. Biography & Exposition: College Reader. 2011. 498p. 58.95 ***(978-1-258-06609-3(2))*** Literary Licensing, LLC.

AMERICAN PROSE LITERATURE—BIBLIOGRAPHY

Drew, Bernard A. 100 Most Popular Nonfiction Authors: Biographical Sketches & Bibliographies, 1 vol. 2007. (Popular Authors Ser.). (Illus.). 452p. 65.00 *(978-1-59158-487-2(6)*, LU4876) Libraries Unlimited, Inc.

AMERICAN PROSE LITERATURE—HISTORY AND CRITICISM

Adams, Timothy Dow. Telling Lies in Modern American Autobiography. 2011. (ENG.). 224p. pap. 40.00 *(978-0-8078-5995-7(8))* Univ. of North Carolina Pr.

Bendixen, Alfred & Hamera, Judith. The Cambridge Companion to American Travel Writing. Bendixen, Alfred & Hamera, Judith, eds. 2009. (Cambridge Companions to Literature Ser.). (ENG.). 314p. (C). 81.00 *(978-0-521-86109-0(8))* Cambridge Univ. Pr.

Bendixen, Alfred & Hamera, Judith, eds. The Cambridge Companion to American Travel Writing. 2009. (Cambridge Companions to Literature Ser.). (ENG.). 314p. (C). pap. 29.99 *(978-0-521-67831-5(5))* Cambridge Univ. Pr.

Burbick, Joan. Healing the Republic: The Language of Health & the Culture of Nationalism in Nineteenth-Century America. 2009. (Cambridge Studies in American Literature & Culture Ser.). (ENG.). 368p. pap. 48.00 *(978-0-521-10673-3(7))* Cambridge Univ. Pr.

D'Amore, Jonathan. American Authorship & Autobiographical Narrative: Mailer, Wideman, Eggers. 2012. (American Literature Readings in the Twenty-First Century Ser.). (ENG., Illus.). 224p. 80.00 ***(978-0-230-39067-6(6))*** Palgrave Macmillan.

Dobree, Bonamy. Modern Prose Style. 2007. (ENG.). 264p. per. *(978-1-4067-3836-0(0))* Read Bks.

Fichtelberg, Joseph. Risk Culture: Performance & Danger in Early America. 2010. (ENG., Illus.). 264p. (C). 75.00 *(978-0-472-07094-7(0))*; pap. 29.95 *(978-0-472-05094-9(X))* Univ. of Michigan Pr.

Finnegan, Jordana. Narrating the American West: New Forms of Historical Memory. 2008. 224p. 99.95 *(978-1-60497-519-2(9))* Cambria Pr.

Fis, Leonora. Factual Fictions: Narrative Truth & the Contemporary American Documentary Novel. 2010. (Illus.). 250p. *(978-1-4438-2413-2(5))* Cambridge Scholars Pub.

Frus, Phyllis. The Politics & Poetics of Journalistic Narrative. 2009. (ENG.). 320p. pap. 42.00 *(978-0-521-10274-2(X))* Cambridge Univ. Pr.

Grassian, Daniel. Writing the Future of Black America: Literature of the Hip-Hop Generation. 2009. 208p. *(978-1-57003-781-8(7))* Univ. of South Carolina Pr.

Gutkind, Lee. The Best Creative Nonfiction, Vol. 1. Gutkind, Lee, ed. 2007. (ENG., Illus.). 352p. per. 15.95 *(978-0-393-33003-8(6)*, 33003) Norton, W. W. & Co., Inc.

Habich, Robert D. Building Their Own Waldos: Emerson's First Biographers & the Politics of Life-Writing in the Gilded Age. 2011. (ENG.). 248p. pap. 29.95 *(978-1-58729-962-9(3))* Univ. of Iowa Pr.

Hall, Calvin L. & Hall, Clavin L. African American Journalists: Autobiography as Memoir & Manifesto. 2009. (ENG.). 146p. pap. 40.00 *(978-0-8108-6930-1(6))* Scarecrow Pr., Inc., The.

Harrell, Willie J. Origins of the African American Jeremiad: The Rhetorical Strategies of Social Protest & Activism, 1760-1861. 2011. (ENG.). 239p. pap. 55.00 ***(978-0-7864-6689-4(8))*** McFarland & Co., Inc. Pubs.

Hollowell, John. Fact & Fiction: The New Journalism & the Nonfiction Novel. 2011. (ENG.). 204p. pap. 40.00 ***(978-0-8078-9688-4(8))*** Univ. of North Carolina Pr.

Humphries, David. Different Dispatches. 2009. 260p. pap. *(978-3-639-18050-3(X))* VDM Verlag Dr. Mueller e.K.

Kibbey, Ann. The Interpretation of Material Shapes in Puritanism: A Study of Rhetoric, Prejudice, & Violence. 2009. (Cambridge Studies in American Literature & Culture Ser.). (ENG.). 216p. pap. 31.99 *(978-0-521-10788-4(1))* Cambridge Univ. Pr.

Kleppien, Axel-Bjö. Der Krieg in der amerikanischen Literatur: Untersuchung des Wandels von Beschreibung, Bewertung und Leserlenkung in der nordamerikanischen War Prose und War Poetry während des Zeitraums vom Unabhängigkeitskrieg bis zum Irakkrieg. 2010. (GER.). 636p. 146.95 *(978-3-631-61040-4(8))* Lang, Peter GmbH, Europaischer Verlag der Wissenschaften DEU. Dist: Lang, Peter.

Lauters, Amy Mattson, ed. The Rediscovered Writings of Rose Wilder Lane: Literary Journalist. 2007. (ENG.). 176p. (C). 29.95 *(978-0-8262-1721-9(4))* Univ. of Missouri Pr.

Lopate, Phillip, ed. Writing New York: A Literary Anthology. 10th ed. 2008. (ENG.). 1050p. (gr. 12). pap. 24.95 *(978-1-59853-021-6(6))* Library of America, The.

Marcus, James & Columbia Journalism Review Editors, eds. Second Read: Writers Look Back at Classic Works of Reportage. 2011. (Columbia Journalism Review Ser.). (ENG., Illus.). 208p. (gr. 17). pap. 24.50 ***(978-0-231-15931-9(5))*** Columbia Univ. Pr.

Marcus, James & Columbia Journalism Review Staff, eds. Second Read: Writers Look Back at Classic Works of Reportage. 2011. (Columbia Journalism Review Ser.). (ENG., Illus.). 208p. (gr. 17). 74.50 ***(978-0-231-15930-2(7))*** Columbia Univ. Pr.

Meehan, Sean Ross. Mediating American Autobiography: Photography in Emerson, Thoreau, Douglass, & Whitman. 2008. (ENG., Illus.). 264p. (C). 39.95 *(978-0-8262-1792-9(3))* Univ. of Missouri Pr.

Mosser, Jason. The Paticipatory Journalism of Michael Herr, Norman Mailer, Hunter S. Thompson, & Joan Didion: Creating New Reporting Styles. 2012. (ENG.). 268p. 139.95 ***(978-0-7734-2599-6(3))*** Mellen, Edwin Pr., The.

Mulvey, Christopher. Anglo-American Landscapes: A Study of Nineteenth-Century Anglo-American Travel Literature. 2009. (ENG.). 312p. pap. 46.00 *(978-0-521-11580-3(9))* Cambridge Univ. Pr.

—Transatlantic Manners: Social Patterns in Nineteenth-Century Anglo-American Travel Literature. 2008. (ENG., Illus.). 256p. pap. 37.99 *(978-0-521-05561-1(X))* Cambridge Univ. Pr.

Oliver, Egbert S., ed. Readings for Ideas & Form. 2007. (ENG.). 544p. 57.95 *(978-0-548-06584-6(5))* Kessinger Publishing, LLC.

Prenshaw, Peggy Whitman. Composing Selves: Southern Women & Autobiography. 2011. (Southern Literary Studies). 368p. 45.00 *(978-0-8071-3791-8(X))* Louisiana State Univ. Pr.

Price, John. Not Just Any Land: A Personal & Literary Journey into the American Grasslands. 2007. (ENG.). 240p. pap. 14.95 *(978-0-8032-6026-9(1)*, Bison Bks.) Univ. of Nebraska Pr.

Roberson, Susan. Antebellum American Women Writers & the Road. 2010. (Routledge Studies in Nineteenth Century Literature Ser.). (ENG., Illus.). 200p. (C). 125.00 *(978-0-415-88354-2(7))* Routledge.

Rusk, Lauren. The Life Writing of Otherness: Woolf, Baldwin, Kingston, & Winterson. 2009. 204p. 39.95 *(978-0-415-80353-3(5))* Routledge.

Shamir, Milette. Inexpressible Privacy: The Interior Life of Antebellum American Literature. 2008. (Illus.). 296p. (C). pap. 22.50 *(978-0-8122-2023-0(4))* Univ. of Pennsylvania Pr.

Shapiro, Stephanie. Reinventing the Feature Story Mythic Cyc. 2006. 128p. per. 16.95 *(978-1-934074-06-0(3))* Apprentice Hse.

Sims, Norman, ed. Literary Journalism in the Twentieth Century. 2008. (Medill Visions of the American Press Ser.). (ENG., Illus.). 296p. pap. 24.95 *(978-0-8101-2519-3(6))* Northwestern Univ. Pr.

Spongberg, Mary, et al. Companion to Women's Historical Writing. 2009. (ENG.). 736p. pap. 33.00 *(978-0-230-23999-9(4))* Palgrave Macmillan.

Steadman, Jennifer Bernhardt. Traveling Economies: American Women's Travel Writing. 2007. (ENG.). cd-rom 9.95 *(978-0-8142-9143-6(0))*; (Illus.). 208p. 37.95 *(978-0-8142-1066-6(X))* Ohio State Univ. Pr.

Straight, Nathan. Autobiography, Ecology, & the Well-Placed Self: The Growth of Natural Biography in Contemporary American Life Writing. 2011. 157p. (C). 70.95 ***(978-1-4331-1225-6(6))*** Lang, Peter Publishing, Inc.

Stuckey-French, Ned. The American Essay in the American Century. 2011. (ENG., Illus.). 272p. (C). (gr. 13). 60.00 *(978-0-8262-1925-1(X))* Univ. of Missouri Pr.

Suzuki, Noriko. The Re-Invention of the American West: Women's Periodicals & Gendered Geography in the Late Nineteenth-Century United States. 2009. (Illus.). 304p. 109.95 *(978-0-7734-4847-6(0))* Mellen, Edwin Pr., The.

Walker, Madeline Ruth. The Trouble with Sauling Around: Conversion in Ethnic American Autobiography, 1965-2002. 2011. (ENG.). 240p. pap. 35.00 ***(978-1-60938-063-2(0))*** Univ. of Iowa Pr.

Wilson, Christopher P. The Labor of Words: Literary Professionalism in the Progressive Era. 2010. (ENG.). 268p. pap. 24.95 *(978-0-8203-3698-5(X))* Univ. of Georgia Pr.

Xu, Dejin. Race & Form: Towards a Contextualized Narratology of African American Autobiography. 226p. pap. 47.95 *(978-3-03911-003-2(9))* Lang, Peter Publishing, Inc.

Yothers, Brian. The Romance of the Holy Land in American Travel Writing, 1790-1876. 2007. 156p. 99.95 *(978-0-7546-5492-6(3))* Ashgate Publishing Co.

Zdovc, Sonja Merljak. Literary Journalism in the United States of America & Slovenia. 2008. (ENG.). 168p. pap. 32.99 *(978-0-7618-4156-2(3))* Univ. Pr. of America, Inc.

AMERICAN PROSE LITERATURE—WOMEN AUTHORS

Adams, Katherine. Owning Up: Privacy, Property, & Belonging in U. S. Women's Life Writing, 1840-1890. 2009. (ENG., Illus.). 304p. 65.00 *(978-0-19-533680-1(1))* Oxford Univ. Pr., Inc.

Davis, Gwenn & Joyce, Beverly A., eds. Personal Writings by Women 1990. (Illus.). 314p. *(978-0-7201-1885-8(9)*, Burns & Oates) Continuum International Publishing Group, Ltd.

DelRosso, Jeana, et al, eds. The Catholic Church & Unruly Women Writers: Critical Essays. 2007. (ENG.). 272p. 100.00 *(978-0-230-60025-6(5))* Palgrave Macmillan.

Hart, John S. (John Seely). The Female Prose Writers of America: With Portraits, Biographical Notices, & Specimens of their Writings. 2006. 552p. per. 32.99 *(978-1-4255-6099-7(7))* MPublishing.

Kack-Brice, Valerie, ed. For She Is the Tree of Life: Grandmothers through the Eyes of Women Writers. 2006. (Illus.). 197p. reprint ed. 22.00 *(978-1-4223-5815-3(1))* DIANE Publishing Co.

Prenshaw, Peggy Whitman. Composing Selves: Southern Women & Autobiography. 2011. (Southern Literary Studies). 368p. 45.00 *(978-0-8071-3791-8(X))* Louisiana State Univ. Pr.

Renek, Nava. Wreckage of Reason: An Anthology of Contemporary Xxperimental Prose by Women Writers. 2008. 324p. pap. 20.00 *(978-1-933132-63-1(9))* Spuyten Duyvil.

Roberson, Susan. Antebellum American Women Writers & the Road. 2010. (Routledge Studies in Nineteenth Century Literature Ser.). (ENG., Illus.). 200p. (C). 125.00 *(978-0-415-88354-2(7))* Routledge.

Steadman, Jennifer Bernhardt. Traveling Economies: American Women's Travel Writing. 2007. (ENG.). cd-rom 9.95 *(978-0-8142-9143-6(0))*; (Illus.). 208p. 37.95 *(978-0-8142-1066-6(X))* Ohio State Univ. Pr.

Suzuki, Noriko. The Re-Invention of the American West: Women's Periodicals & Gendered Geography in the Late Nineteenth-Century United States. 2009. (Illus.). 304p. 109.95 *(978-0-7734-4847-6(0))* Mellen, Edwin Pr., The.

AMERICAN PROTECTIVE LEAGUE

Hough, Emerson. The Web. 2010. 514p. pap. 39.75 *(978-1-142-08987-0(8))* 2009. (ENG.). 516p. 43.99 *(978-1-117-58215-3(9))* 2009. (ENG.). 516p. pap. 30.99 *(978-1-117-58217-7(5)*, BiblioLife) 2009. (ENG.). 516p. pap. 38.75 *(978-1-117-58216-0(7))* BiblioBazaar.

—The Web. 2009. 330p. pap. *(978-1-150-50751-9(9))* Books LLC.

—The Web. 2009. 362p. pap. 38.00 *(978-1-150-98413-6(9))* General Bks. LLC.

—The Web. 2008. 510p. 55.95 *(978-0-548-94288-6(9))* 2007. (ENG.). 512p. per. 40.95 *(978-0-548-58912-0(7))* Kessinger Publishing, LLC.

AMERICAN REPUBLICS

see America; America—Foreign Relations; America—Politics and Government; Pan-Americanism

AMERICAN REVOLUTION

see United States—History—Revolution, 1775-1783

AMERICAN REVOLUTION BICENTENNIAL, 1776-1976

Elkins Med, Keith A. Mr. E. 2003: Manifest Lessons from Ohio's Bicentennial Celebration. 2011. 368p. 34.95 ***(978-1-4620-4893-9(5))***; pap. 24.95 ***(978-1-4620-4891-5(9))*** iUniverse, Inc.

Gray, Timothy & Powell, Scott. Adventures in Exodus Study Set: Called to Freedom. 2007. ring bd. 22.95 *(978-1-934217-09-2(3))* Ascension Pr.

Taylor, Bayard. Story of Kennett. 2006. pap. *(978-1-4068-0756-1(7))* Echo Library.

—The Story of Kennett by Bayard Taylor. 2006. 432p. per. 26.99 *(978-1-4255-4651-9(X))* MPublishing.

AMERICAN SAMOA

see Samoan Islands

AMERICAN SATIRE

see Satire, American

AMERICAN SCHOOL OF CLASSICAL STUDIES AT ATHENS

Vogeikoff-Brogan, Natalia. Triumph over Time 1947: The American School of Classical Studies at Athens in Post-War Greece. 2007. (ENG., Illus.). 24p. pap. 15.00 *(978-0-87661-964-3(2))* American Schl. of Classical Studies at Athens.

AMERICAN SCULPTURE

see Sculpture—United States

AMERICAN SIGN LANGUAGE

Alcorn, Bob J. & Kanda, Jan. One, Two, Buckle Your Shoe: Numbering Systems in American Sign Language. 39.95 *(978-0-9640367-4-1(6))* H&H Publishing Co.

Armstrong, David F., et al, eds. The Study of Signed Languages: Essays in Honor of William C. Stokoe. 2011. 264p. pap. 72.95 *(978-1-56368-510-1(8))* Gallaudet Univ. Pr.

Arnold, Robert. American Sign Language Writing: Learning how to write in ASL. 2010.Tr. of American Sign Language. 184p. 35.00 *(978-0-615-38774-1(8))* si5s.

Bernstein Fant, Barbara & Fant, Lou. The American Sign Language Phrase: Features More Than 500 Video Demonstrations of ASL Phrases. 2011. (ENG., Illus.). 400p. pap. 25.00 *(978-0-07-175932-8(8)*, 0071759328) McGraw-Hill Cos., The.

Bernstein Fant, Barbara, et al. The American Sign Language Phrase Book. 3rd ed. 2008. (ENG., Illus.). 416p. pap. 18.95 *(978-0-07-149713-8(7)*, 0071497137) McGraw-Hill Cos., The.

Bingham, Sara. The Baby Signing Book: Includes 350 ASL Signs for Babies & Toddlers. 2007. (ENG., Illus.). 256p. pap. 22.95 *(978-0-7788-0163-4(2))* Rose, Robert Inc. CAN. Dist: Firefly Bks., Ltd.

Boles, David W. & Sweenie, Janna M. Picture Yourself Learning American Sign Language. 2008. (ENG., Illus.). 208p. pap. 34.99 *(978-1-59863-516-4(6))* Course Technology.

Briant, Monta Z. Baby Sign Language Basics: Early Communication for Hearing Babies & Toddlers. rev. exp. ed. 2009. (ENG.). 496p. 19.95 *(978-1-4019-2159-0(0))* Hay Hse., Inc.

Byrom, Franklin. Basic Asl Dictionary. 2008. 172p. 29.99 *(978-1-4363-4794-5(7))*; pap. 19.99 *(978-1-4363-4793-8(9))* Xlibris Corp.

Cadjan, Nancy. Baby Signing 1 2 3: The Easy-to-Use Illustrated Guide for Every Stage & Every Age. 2007. (ENG., Illus.). 288p. pap. 16.99 *(978-1-4022-0978-9(9))* Sourcebooks, Inc.

—More Please! 2008. (ENG., Illus.). 28p. (J). (gr. -1-k). bds. 6.99 *(978-1-4022-1165-2(1)*, Sourcebooks Jabberwocky) Sourcebooks, Inc.

Cerney, Janet. Deaf Education in America: Voices of Children from Inclusion Settings. 2007. (ENG., Illus.). 224p. 49.95 *(978-1-56368-362-6(8))* Gallaudet Univ. Pr.

Chafin, Suzie. American Sign Language: A Step-by-Step Guide to Signing. 2009. (Knack: Make It Easy Ser.). (ENG., Illus.). 256p. pap. 19.95 *(978-1-59921-514-3(4)*, Knack) Globe Pequot Pr., The.

Coleman, Janet/Renee & Wolf, Elizabeth/England. Advanced Sign Language Vocabulary — Raising Exectations: A Resource Text for Educators, Interpreters, Parents, & Sign Language Instructors. 2nd ed. 2009. 208p. spiral bd. 39.95 *(978-0-398-07901-7(3))* Thomas, Charles C. Pub., Ltd.

Costello, Elaine. American Sign Language Dictionary. 3rd l.t. ed. 2008. (ENG., Illus.). 624p. pap. 21.99 *(978-0-375-72277-6(7)*, Random House Reference) Random Hse. Information Group.

—Random House Webster's American Sign Language Dictionary. unabr. l.t. ed. 2008. (ENG., Illus.). 1232p. 55.00 *(978-0-375-42616-2(7)*, Random House Reference) Random Hse. Information Group.

—Random House Webster's Pocket American Sign Language Dictionary. 2nd l.t. ed. 2008. (ENG., Illus.). 432p. pap. 7.95 *(978-0-375-72278-3(5)*, Random House Reference) Random Hse. Information Group.

—Religious Signing: A Comprehensive Guide for All Faiths. 2009. (ENG.). 352p. pap. 22.00 *(978-0-553-38619-6(0))* Random House Publishing Group.

Costello, Elaine & Living Language Staff. Getting Started in Signing: A Complete Visual Course in American Sign Language. unabr. l.t. ed. 2007. (Sign Language Ser.). (ENG., Illus.). 208p. 29.95 *(978-1-4000-2354-7(8)*, Living Language) Random Hse. Information Group.

Duke, Irene. The Everything Sign Language Book: American Sign Language Made Easy. 2nd ed. 2009. (ENG.). 304p. pap. 15.95 *(978-1-59869-883-1(4))* Adams Media Corp.

—Learn Sign Language in a Hurry: Grasp the Basics of American Sign Language Quickly & Easily. 2009. (ENG.). 192p. pap. 8.95 *(978-1-59869-868-8(0))* Adams Media Corp.

Fant, Lou, et al. Perfect Phrases in American Sign Language for Beginners. 2009. (Perfect Phrases Ser.). (ENG., Illus.). 176p. pap. 13.00 *(978-0-07-159877-4(4)*, 0071598774) McGraw-Hill Cos., The.

Fant, Louie J., Jr. Ameslan - An Introduction to American Sign Language. 11.95 *(978-0-917002-37-3(7))* Joyce Media, Inc.

Flodin, Mickey. Signing Everyday Phrases. 2007. (ENG., Illus.). 288p. (gr. 12-18). 14.95 *(978-0-399-53309-9(5)*, Perigee Trade) Penguin Group (USA) Inc.

Flora, Sherrill B. Sing, Sign, & Learn! 2010. (ENG.). 64p. pap. 11.99 *(978-1-60268-080-7(9)*, Key Education Publishing Company, LLC) Carson-Dellosa Publishing, LLC.

Forestal, Lawrence. Attitudes of American Deaf Leaders Toward Sign Language Interpreters. 2009. 136p. pap. *(978-3-639-17181-5(0))* VDM Verlag Dr. Mueller e.K.

Hatherleigh Press Staff. Why Save Africa? Voices from Around the World. Eding, June, ed. 2011. (Little Book. Big Idea Ser.). (ENG.). 176p. pap. 12.00 *(978-1-57826-308-0(5))* Hatherleigh Co., Ltd., The.

Hoza, Jack. It's Not What You Sign, It's How You Sign It: Politeness in American Sign Language. 2007. (ENG., Illus.). 248p. (C). 49.95 *(978-1-56368-352-7(0))* Gallaudet Univ. Pr.

Humphrey, Janice H. Decisions? Decisions! A Practical Guide for Sign Language Professionals. 267p. 49.95 *(978-0-9640367-8-9(9)*, T-3) H&H Publishing Co.

Humphrey, Janice H. & Alcorn, Bob J. So You Want to Be an Interpreter? An Introduction to Sign Language Interpreting. Date not set. 2nd ed. 423p. reprint ed. pap. 49.95 *(978-0-9640367-3-4(8))* 3rd ed. 416p. 49.95 *(978-0-9640367-7-2(0))* H&H Publishing Co.

Kelly, Arlene B. How Deaf Women Construct Teaching, Language. 2009. 280p. pap. *(978-3-639-15590-7(4))* VDM Verlag Dr. Mueller e.K.

Lindgren, Kristin A., et al, eds. Signs & Voices: Deaf Culture, Identity, Language, & Arts. 2008. (ENG., Illus.). 244p. 80.00 *(978-1-56368-363-3(6))* Gallaudet Univ. Pr.

Livingston, Sue. Working Text: Teaching Deaf & Second-Language Students to Be Better Writers. 2010. (ENG., Illus.). 224p. 45.00 *(978-1-56368-466-1(7))* Gallaudet Univ. Pr.

MacDougall, Cinne. Number Signs for Everyone: Numbering in American Sign Language. 2008. (Illus.). xii, 95p. *(978-1-58121-057-6(4))* DawnSignPress.

Maher, Jane. Seeing Language in Sign: The Work of William C. Stokoe. 2010. (ENG.). 216p. (C). pap. 34.50 *(978-1-56368-470-8(5))* Gallaudet Univ. Pr.

McCaskill, Carolyn. The Hidden Treasure of Black ASL: Its History & Structure. 2011. E-Book *(978-1-56368-490-6(X))* Gallaudet Univ. Pr.

McCaskill, Carolyn, et al. The Hidden Treasure of Black ASL: Its History & Structure. 2011. (ENG., Illus.). 240p. (C). 75.00 *(978-1-56368-489-0(6))* Gallaudet Univ. Pr.

Metzger, Melanie. Sign Language Interpreting: Deconstructing the Myth of Neutrality. 2011. 216p. pap. 75.00 *(978-1-56368-344-2(X))* Gallaudet Univ. Pr.

Mulrooney, Kristin. American Sign Language Demystified with DVD. 2009. (Demystified Ser.). (Illus.). 304p. pap. 24.95 incl. DVD *(978-0-07-160137-5(6)*, 0071601376) McGraw-Hill Cos., The.

Mulrooney, Kristin J. Extraordinary from the Ordinary: Personal Experience Narratives in American Sign Language. 2009. (Gallaudet Sociolinguistics Ser.). (ENG., Illus.). 200p. 85.00 *(978-1-56368-416-6(0))* Gallaudet Univ. Pr.

Murray, Carol Garboden. Simple Signing with Young Children: A Guide for Infant, Toddler, & Preschool Teachers. 2007. (Early Childhood Education Ser.). (ENG., Illus.). 272p. per. 24.95 *(978-0-87659-033-1(4))* Gryphon Hse., Inc.

NICKENS, Carol. The History of American Sign Language. 2008. 179p. pap. 15.00 *(978-1-4357-4077-8(7))* Lulu Enterprises Inc.

Nicodemus, Brenda. Prosodic Markers & Utterance Boundaries in American Sign Language Interpretation. 2009. (Gallaudet Studies in Interpret Ser.). (ENG.). 112p. 65.00 *(978-1-56368-412-8(8))* Gallaudet Univ. Pr.

Padden, Carol A. & Humphries, Tom L. Inside Deaf Culture. 2006. (Illus.). 224p. per. 20.50 *(978-0-674-02252-2(1))* Harvard Univ. Pr.

Patrie, et al. ASL Skills Development. 2007. (Effective Interpreting Ser.). (Illus.). xiii, 142p. pap. *(978-1-58121-108-5(2))* DAWN SIGN PRESS.

Penilla, Adan R., II. Signing for Dummies. 2nd ed. 2012. (ENG.). 384p. pap. 22.99 *(978-1-118-11758-3(1)*, For Dummies) Wiley, John & Sons, Inc.

Poor, Geoffrey. 1,000 Words to Sign. 2010. (ENG.). 256p. pap. 24.95 *(978-1-60710-193-2(9)*, Thunder Bay Pr.) Advantage Pubs. Group.

Poor, Geoffrey S. Barron's 500 Flash Cards of American Sign Language. 2009. (ENG.). 500p. 24.99 *(978-0-7641-6222-0(5))* Barron's Educational Series, Inc.

Registry Of Interpreters For The Deaf. Asl to English Interpretation: Say It Like They Mean It. 2007. 132p. (C). spiral bd. 39.95 *(978-0-916883-38-6(8))* Kendall Hunt Publishing Co.

Scheetz, Nanci A. Building ASL Interpreting & Translation Skills: Narratives for Practice. 2008. (ENG., Illus.). 360p. (C). spiral bd. 77.40 *(978-0-205-47025-9(4))* Allyn & Bacon, Inc.

Sebrey, Leann. The Parents' Guide to Baby Signs: Early Communication with Your Infant. 2009. (ENG., Illus.). 128p. (gr. k — 1). pap. 19.95 *(978-1-56368-398-5(9))* Gallaudet Univ. Pr.

Segal, Justin. The American Sign Language Puzzle Book, Vol. 2. 2006. (ENG., Illus.). 160p. per. 12.95 *(978-0-07-147595-2(8)*, 0071475958) McGraw-Hill Cos., The.

Smith, Adonia K. & Jacobowitz, E. Lynn. Have You Ever Seen...? An American Sign Language Handshape. 2006. (Illus.). 77p. 85.00 incl. DVD *(978-0-9764640-0-6(4))* E. Lynn Jacobowitz/Adonia K. Smith.

Snoddon, Kristin. American Sign Language & Early Literacy: A Model Parent-Child Program. 2012. (ENG., Illus.). 144p. 55.00 *(978-1-56368-527-9(2))* Gallaudet Univ. Pr.

Stewart Ed.D., David A., et al. E-Z American Sign Language. 3rd ed. 2011. (Barron's E-Z Ser.). (ENG., Illus.). 504p. pap. 16.99 *(978-0-7641-4458-5(8))* Barron's Educational Series, Inc.

Swabey, Laurie & Malcolm, Karen, eds. In Our Hands: Educating Healthcare Interpreters. 2012. (Interpreter Education Ser.). (ENG., Illus.). 272p. (C). 70.00 *(978-1-56368-521-7(3))* Gallaudet Univ. Pr.

Tabak, John. Significant Gestures: A History of American Sign Language, 1 vol. 2006. (Illus.). 240p. 44.95 *(978-0-275-98974-3(7)*, C8974, Praeger Pubs.) Greenwood Publishing Group, Inc.

Taub, Sarah F. Language from the Body: Iconicity & Metaphor in American Sign Language. 2010. (ENG.). 274p. pap. 17.99 *(978-0-521-15860-2(5))* Cambridge Univ. Pr.

Taylor-Dieva, Kimberly. Once upon a Sign: Using American Sign Language to Engage, Entertain, & Teach All Children, 1 vol. 2011. (Illus.). 270p. pap. 38.00 *(978-1-59884-476-4(8)*, A2946P) Libraries Unlimited, Inc.

Tennant, Richard A. & Brown, Marianne Gluszak. The American Sign Language Handshape Dictionary. 2nd ed. 2010. (ENG., Illus.). 456p. 49.95 *(978-1-56368-444-9(6))* Gallaudet Univ. Pr.

Tucker, Bethanie. Reading by Age 5. 2007. per. 22.00 *(978-1-929229-79-6(8))*; per. 39.00 incl. DVD *(978-1-929229-80-2(1))* aha! Process, Inc.

Valli, Clayton. Linguistics of American Sign Language: An Introduction. 5th ed. 2011. E-Book *(978-1-56368-508-8(6))* Gallaudet Univ. Pr.

Valli, Clayton, et al. Linguistics of American Sign Language: An Introduction. 5th ed. 2011. (ENG.). 584p. (C). 80.00 *(978-1-56368-507-1(8))* Gallaudet Univ. Pr.

Wyant, Brad. Rhyming Signing: Proper Handshapes with Precise Movements for American Sign Language. 2010. (ENG., Illus.). 248p. pap. 24.95 *(978-0-9817210-0-2(1))* BW Images, Inc.

AMERICAN SONGS

see Songs, American

AMERICAN-SPANISH WAR, 1898

see Spanish-American War, 1898

AMERICAN SPEECHES

see Speeches, Addresses, etc., American

AMERICAN STAFFORDSHIRE TERRIER

see also American Pit Bull Terrier; Staffordshire Bull Terrier

Linzy, Jan. American Staffordshire Terrier Champions, 2002-2006. 2007. (Illus.). 129p. spiral bd. 46.95 *(978-1-55893-218-0(6))* Camino E.E. & Bk. Co.

Stahlkuppe, Joe. American Pit Bull Terriers/American Staffordshire Terriers. 3rd rev. ed. 2010. (Complete Pet Owner's Manuals Ser.). (ENG., Illus.). 96p. pap. 8.99 *(978-0-7641-4322-9(0))* Barron's Educational Series, Inc.

AMERICAN STANDARD TOOL COMPANY

Nutter, Waldo E. Manhattan Firearms, 1 vol. 2008. (Stackpole Classic Gun Book Ser.). (ENG., Illus.). 256p. 29.95 *(978-0-8117-0469-4(6))* Stackpole Bks.

AMERICAN STATESMEN

see Statesmen—United States

AMERICAN STOCK EXCHANGE

The American Stock Exchange: Constitution & Rules as of 3/31/2000. 1160p. pap. 39.50 *(978-0-8080-0506-3(5))* Toolkit Media Group.

The American Stock Exchange: Directors March 2000. pap. 30.00 *(978-0-8080-0513-1(8))* Toolkit Media Group.

Bruchey, Stuart. The Modernization of the American Stock Exchange 1971-1989 (Routledge Revivals) 2011. (Routledge Revivals Ser.). (ENG.). 228p. 120.00 *(978-0-415-50625-0(5))* Routledge.

AMERICAN STUDENTS

Frank, Romano. Storm over Morocco. Strozier, M. Stefan & Torke, Kyle, eds. 2010. 362p. 20.00 *(978-1-935444-61-9(1))* World Audience Pubs.

Pomfret, John. Chinese Lessons: Five Classmates & the Story of the New China. 2007. (ENG., Illus.). 336p. pap. 16.99 *(978-0-8050-8664-5(1)*, Holt Paperback) Holt, Henry & Co.

Spencer, Sarah E. & Tuma, Kathy. The Guide to Successful Short-Term Programs Abroad. 2nd ed. 2007. *(978-0-912207-91-9(4))* NAFSA: Assn. of International Educators.

Wadsworth. American History Resource Center with InfoTrac 2-Semester Printed Access Card. 2nd ed. 2010. (ENG.). (C). 20.95 *(978-1-111-66806-8(X))* Wadsworth.

AMERICAN STUDENTS—FOREIGN COUNTRIES

Anguio, Sarah. Trading Cultures, Transforming Lives: Positive Change During Study Abroad. 2008. 140p. pap. *(978-3-639-10120-1(0))* VDM Verlag Dr. Mueller e.K.

Ary, Brian Scott. Study Abroad Unauthorized. 2007. 192p. per. 24.95 *(978-1-4241-8909-0(8))* PublishAmerica, Inc.

Frost, Maya. The New Global Student: Skip the SAT, Save Thousands on Tuition, & Get a Truly International Education. 2009. (ENG.). 336p. pap. 14.95 *(978-0-307-45062-3(7)*, Three Rivers Pr.) Crown Publishing Group.

Open Doors: Report on International Educational Exchange. 96 p. *(978-0-87206-276-4(7))* Bow Historical Bks.

Romano, Frank. Storm over Morocco. Strozier, M. Stefan & Torke, Kyle, eds. 2009. 356p. pap. 15.99 *(978-1-935444-25-1(5))* World Audience Pubs.

—Storm over Morocco. Strozier, M., ed. 2007. 276p. per. 17.99 *(978-1-934209-43-1(0))* World Audience Pubs.

AMERICAN STUDIES

see United States—Study and Teaching

AMERICAN TELEPHONE AND TELEGRAPH COMPANY

Prescott, George B. Bell's Electric Speaking Telephone: Its Invention, Construction, Application, Modification & History. 2007. (ENG.). 544p. 57.95 *(978-0-548-20809-0(3))*; 548p. per. 42.95 *(978-1-4325-2643-6(X))* Kessinger Publishing, LLC.

AMERICAN THOROUGHBRED HORSE

see Thoroughbred Horse

AMERICAN TOBACCO COMPANY

Cox, Reavis. Competition in the American Tobacco Industry, 1911-1932. (Columbia University, Studies in the Social Sciences: No. 381). reprint ed. 84.50 *(978-0-404-51381-8(6))* AMS Pr., Inc.

AMERICAN UNIVERSITY (WASHINGTON, D.C.)

Hosking, Ian & Schubach, Alanna. American University 2012: Off the Record. 2011. 188p. pap. 16.95 *(978-1-4274-0329-2(5))* College Prowler, Inc.

AMERICAN UNIVERSITY OF BEIRUT

Anderson, Betty S. The American University of Beirut: Arab Nationalism & Liberal Education. 2011. (Illus.). xii, 254p. E-Book *(978-0-292-73498-2(0))* Univ. of Texas Pr.

Vandemark, Brian. American Sheikhs: Two Families, Four Generations, & the Story of America's Influence in the Middle East. 2012. (ENG., Illus.). 250p. 25.00 *(978-1-61614-476-0(9))* Prometheus Bks., Pubs.

AMERICAN WAR-SONGS

see War-Songs, American

AMERICAN WIT AND HUMOR

Here are entered collections from several authors and individual authors who have not written in other literary forms.

see also African American Wit and Humor

Ambrose Bierce. The Collected Works of Ambrose Bierce. l.t. ed. 2007. (ENG.). 216p. pap. 22.99 *(978-1-4264-8760-6(6))* BiblioBazaar.

Amsterdam, Morey. Keep Laughing. 2011. 144p. 40.95 *(978-1-258-08596-4(8))* Literary Licensing, LLC.

Andersen, Kurt, et al. Spy: The Funny Years. 2006. (Illus.). 304p. 39.95 *(978-1-4013-5239-4(1))* Miramax Bks.

Apatow, Judd, ed. I Found This Funny: My Favorite Pieces of Humor & Some That May Not Be Funny at All. 2011. (ENG.). 480p. pap. 16.00 *(978-1-936365-24-1(3))* McSweeney's Publishing.

Armentrout, Donald Lee. Chuckles: Mild to Severe. 2011. 84p. pap. 10.95 *(978-1-4620-1782-9(7))* iUniverse, Inc.

Arquette, Cliff. Charley Weaver's Letters from Mamm. 2011. 64p. 36.95 *(978-1-258-07004-5(9))* Literary Licensing, LLC.

Aswell, James R. Native American Humor. 2007. (ENG.). 412p. 49.95 *(978-0-548-06445-0(8))* Kessinger Publishing, LLC.

Baedeker, Robert, et al. Weddings of the Times: A Parody. 2009. (ENG., Illus.). 128p. pap. 15.99 *(978-0-312-38091-5(7)*, St. Martin's Griffin) St. Martin's Pr.

Barbour Publishing Staff. The Big Book of Church Jokes. 2009. (ENG.). 368p. pap. 9.99 *(978-1-60260-386-8(3)*, Barbour Bks.) Barbour Publishing, Inc.

Bathroom Readers' Institute. Uncle John's 24-Karat Gold Bathroom Reader. 2011. (ENG.). 540p. pap. 18.95 *(978-1-60710-320-2(6)*, Portable Pr.) Advantage Pubs. Group.

—Uncle John's Bathroom Reader History's Lists. 2010. (ENG.). 522p. pap. 18.95 *(978-1-60710-180-2(7)*, Portable Pr.) Advantage Pubs. Group.

—Uncle John's Bathroom Reader Vroom! 2011. (ENG.). 544p. pap. 18.95 *(978-1-60710-184-0(X)*, Portable Pr.) Advantage Pubs. Group.

—Uncle John's Briefs: Quick Hits of Fascinating Facts & Amazing Trivia. 2010. (ENG.). 288p. pap. 9.95 *(978-1-60710-178-9(5)*, Portable Pr.) Advantage Pubs. Group.

—Uncle John's Heavy Duty Bathroom Reader. 2010. (ENG.). 540p. pap. 18.95 *(978-1-60710-183-3(1)*, Portable Pr.) Advantage Pubs. Group.

Bathroom Reader's Institute. Uncle John's Slightly Irregular Bathroom Reader: The Minature Edition. 2011. (ENG.). 192p. 5.95 *(978-0-7624-4079-5(1))* Running Pr. Bk. Pubs.

Bathroom Readers' Institute. Uncle John's True Crime: A Classic Collection of Crooks, Cops, & Capers. 2011. (ENG.). 224p. pap. 9.95 *(978-1-60710-318-9(4)*, Portable Pr.) Advantage Pubs. Group.

Bathroom Readers' Institute Staff. Triumphant. 20th rev. anniv. ed. 2007. (ENG., Illus.). 600p. per. 18.95 *(978-1-59223-093-8(8)*, Portable Pr.) Advantage Pubs. Group.

—Uncle John's 4-Ply Bathroom Reader. 2010. (ENG.). 896p. 17.99 *(978-0-312-66841-9(4)*, St. Martin's Griffin) St. Martin's Pr.

—Uncle John's Bathroom Reader for Girls Only: Mystery, History, Gossip, & Secrets. 2011. (ENG., Illus.). 288p. (gr. 4-8). pap. 12.95 *(978-1-60710-179-6(3)*, Portable Pr.) Advantage Pubs. Group.

—Uncle John's Bathroom Reader the World's Gone Crazy. 2010. (ENG.). 432p. pap. 18.95 *(978-1-60710-101-7(7)*, Portable Pr.) Advantage Pubs. Group.

—Uncle John's Certified Organic Bathroom Reader. 2009. (ENG.). 288p. pap. 12.95 *(978-1-59223-981-8(1)*, Portable Pr.) Advantage Pubs. Group.

Bathroom Readers' Institute Staff & BTMS-Portable Press Staff. Uncle John's Endlessly Engrossing Bathroom Reader. 2009. (ENG.). 540p. pap. 18.95 *(978-1-60710-036-2(3)*, Portable Pr.) Advantage Pubs. Group.

Bauer, Wright & Hobart, George V. Cinders: The Diary of A Drummer. 2007. (ENG.). 134p. 35.95 *(978-0-548-03812-3(0))* Kessinger Publishing, LLC.

Bayan, Rick. The Cynic's Dictionary. 1990p. 7.99 *(978-0-7858-1713-0(1))* Book Sales, Inc.

Believer Editors. You're a Horrible Person, but I Like You: The Believer Book of Advice. 2010. (Vintage Original Ser.). (ENG.). 224p. pap. 13.95 *(978-0-307-47523-7(9)*, Vintage) Knopf Doubleday Publishing Group.

Benchley, Nat & Fitzpatrick, Kevin C., eds. The Lost Algonquin Round Table: Humor, Fiction, Journalism, Criticism & Poetry from America's Most Famous Literary Circle. 2009. 300p. 28.95 *(978-1-4401-5152-1(0))*; pap. 18.95 *(978-1-4401-5151-4(2))* iUniverse, Inc.

Bierce, Ambrose. Ambrose Bierce: the Devil's Dictionary, Tales, & Memoirs: The Devil's Dictionary, Tales, & Memoirs. Joshi, S. T., ed. 2011. (ENG.). 864p. (gr. 12). 35.00 *(978-1-59853-102-2(6))* Library of America, The.

—The Collected Works of Ambrose Bierce. 2008. 428p. 30.99 *(978-0-559-77293-1(9))* 2008. 376p. 29.99 *(978-0-559-75986-4(X))* 2008. 376p. pap. 32.75 *(978-0-559-75984-0(3))* 2008. 428p. pap. 34.75 *(978-0-559-77289-4(0))* 2008. 380p. 29.99 *(978-0-559-52629-9(6))* 2008. 380p. pap. 32.75 *(978-0-559-52625-1(3))* 2008. 220p. 27.99 *(978-0-554-25350-3(X))* 2008. 224p. 27.99 *(978-0-554-24683-3(X))* 2008. 244p. 27.99 *(978-0-554-24608-6(2))* 2008. 220p. 24.99 *(978-0-554-34653-3(2))* 2008. 224p. 24.99 *(978-0-554-33986-3(2))* 2008. 244p. 24.99 *(978-0-554-33911-5(0))* 1. 2006. (ENG.). 220p. pap. 22.99 *(978-1-4264-7152-0(1))* BiblioBazaar.

—The Collected Works of Ambrose Bierce. 2008. Vol. 1. 188p. pap. (978-1-4065-9586-4(1)) Vol. 2. 232p. pap. (978-1-4065-9587-1(X)) Vol. 8. 204p. pap. (978-1-4065-9588-8(8)) Dodo Pr.

—The Collected Works of Ambrose Bierce, Volume 1. 2006. (ENG.). 196p. pap. 19.99 (978-1-4264-7076-9(2)) BiblioBazaar.

—The Collected Works of Ambrose Bierce Volume 8. rev. ed. 2007. (ENG.). 194p. pap. 19.99 (978-1-4264-8705-7(3)) BiblioBazaar.

—The Collected Works of Ambrose Bierce, Volume II: In the Midst of Life: Tales of Soldiers & Civili. 2006. (ENG.). 220p. pap. 20.99 (978-1-4264-6920-6(9)) BiblioBazaar.

—The Devil's Dictionary. 2006. (ENG.). 228p. per. 14.95 (978-1-59818-992-6(1)); 26.95 (978-1-59818-655-0(8)) Aegypan.

—The Devil's Dictionary. 2008. 272p. 28.99 (978-0-554-26089-1(1)) 2008. 272p. 25.99 (978-0-554-35392-0(X)) 2007. (ENG.). 236p. pap. 20.99 (978-1-4346-0369-2(5)) BiblioBazaar.

—The Devil's Dictionary. 2007. (ENG.). 172p. per. 6.99 (978-1-4209-3004-7(4)) Digireads.com.

—The Devil's Dictionary. 2007. 228p. (978-1-4068-2275-5(2)); (ENG.). 416p. (978-1-84702-791-7(1)) Echo Library.

—The Devil's Dictionary. 2007. (ENG.). 284p. 19.99 (978-1-59986-687-1(0)) Filiquarian Publishing, LLC.

—The Devil's Dictionary. 2009. 204p. 32.99 (978-1-59547-538-1(9)) NuVision Pubns., LLC.

—The Devil's Dictionary. 2007. (ENG.). 292p. per. 20.45 (978-1-60424-036-8(9), Book Jungle) Standard Pubns., Inc.

—Devils Dictionary. 2007. 204p. per. 16.99 (978-1-59547-940-2(6)) NuVision Pubns., LLC.

—The Devil's Dictionary. 2010. (ENG.). 388p. pap. 33.75 (978-1-171-82557-9(9)) BiblioBazaar.

—The Devil's Dictionary. 2011. (ENG.). 352p. pap. 12.95 (978-0-486-48224-8(3)) Dover Pubns., Inc.

—The Devil's Dictionary. 2010. (Illus.). 148p. pap. 23.65 (978-1-153-69994-5(X)) General Bks. LLC.

—The Devil's Dictionary. 2010. 226p. 31.96 (978-1-169-29435-6(9)); pap. 19.96 (978-1-162-69261-6(8)); 39.95 (978-1-161-46126-8(4)) Kessinger Publishing, LLC.

—The Devil's Dictionary. 2010. 122p. pap. 7.95 (978-1-57898-983-6(3)) Martino Publishing.

—The Devil's Dictionary. 2010. (ENG.). 227p. pap. 6.95 (978-1-61600-203-9(4)) Mizzou Media - Univ. BookStores.

—Devil's Dictionary. 2010. 378p. 39.16 **(978-1-169-33121-1(1))**; pap. 27.16 **(978-1-162-58440-9(8))**; 48.95 (978-1-161-36791-1(8)) Kessinger Publishing, LLC.

—The Devil's Dictionary. 376p. reprint ed. lib. bdg. 23.95 (978-0-89190-186-0(8)) Amereon LTD.

—The Devil's Dictionary. l.t. ed. 2007. (ENG.). 270p. pap. 23.99 (978-1-4346-0442-2(X)) BiblioBazaar.

—The Devil's Dictionary [Facsimile Edition]. 2008. 376p. pap. 14.95 (978-1-4344-7372-1(4)) Wildside Pr., LLC.

—The Devil's Dictionary [Facsimile Edition]. 2008. 376p. 29.95 (978-1-4344-7371-4(6)) Wildside Pr., LLC.

—The Devil's Dictionary of Ambrose Bierce - Complete & Unabridged - Special Edition. Ford, James H., ed. 2010. (ENG.). 232p. pap. 14.95 (978-1-934255-29-2(7)) El Paso Norte Pr.

Borowitz, Andy, ed. The 50 Funniest American Writers. 2011. (ENG.). 504p. (gr. 12). 27.95 (978-1-59853-107-7(7)) Library of America, The.

Boylan, Gerry. Gerry Tales: How I Lived Happily Ever after, Despite Stabbing Myself in the Back, Scalding My Cojones, & Really Pissing off My Wife During Childbirth. 2010. pap. 16.95 (978-0-9843879-3-9(5), GWB Bks.) Midpoint Trade Bks., Inc.

Butler, Ellis Parker. The Adventures of a Suburbanite. 2007. (ENG.). 264p. 42.95 (978-0-548-43502-1(2)); per. 27.95 (978-0-548-41281-7(2)) Kessinger Publishing, LLC.

BYU Students. The Book of Y: Let There Be Laughter. 2008. (Illus.). pap. 14.99 (978-0-8425-2704-0(4), Brigham Young Univ. Pr.) Brigham Young Univ.

Carolla, Adam. In Fifty Years We'll All Be Chicks: ... & Other Complaints from an Angry Middle-Aged White Guy. 2011. (ENG.). 272p. pap. 15.00 (978-0-307-71738-2(0), Three Rivers Pr.) Crown Publishing Group.

Chelsea's Family, Friends Staff. Lies That Chelsea Handler Told Me. 2011. (Borderline Amazing/A Chelsea Handler Book Ser.). (ENG., Illus.). 304p. 24.99 (978-0-446-58471-5(1)) Grand Central Publishing.

Cho, Margaret. I Have Chosen to Stay & Fight. 2008. (ENG.). 262p. pap. 14.00 (978-1-4379-5223-0(2)) DIANE Publishing Co.

Cliff Road Books Staff, contrib. by. Squeaky Clean Jokes. 2007. 544p. (978-1-60261-276-5(1)) Cliff Road Bks.

Cobb, Irvan S. A Plea for Old Cap Collier. 2010. 70p. pap. 17.75 (978-1-141-25558-0(8)) BiblioBazaar.

Cobb, Irvin S. The Abandoned Farmers. 2007. (ENG.). 246p. 41.95 (978-0-548-04180-2(6)) Kessinger Publishing, LLC.

—Irvin Cobb at His Best. 2007. (ENG.). 338p. 46.95 (978-0-548-01520-9(1)) Kessinger Publishing, LLC.

—A Plea for Old Cap Collier. 2007. 48p. per. (978-1-4065-1398-1(9)) Dodo Pr.

—A Plea for Old Cap Collier. 2010. 76p. pap. 17.75 (978-1-140-44813-6(7)) BiblioBazaar.

—A Plea for Old Cap Collier. 2010. 22p. pap. 12.76 (978-1-162-64971-9(2)); 24.76 **(978-1-169-15753-8(X))**; 30.95 (978-1-161-41836-1(9)) Kessinger Publishing, LLC.

Cobb, Irvin S. (Irvin Shrewsbury), creator. A Plea for Old Cap Collier. 2011. 70p. pap. 17.75 **(978-1-246-16843-3(X))** BiblioBazaar.

Cobb, Irvin S. 1876-1944. A Plea for Old Cap Collier. 2010. (ENG.). 70p. pap. 17.75 (978-1-171-78843-0(6)) BiblioBazaar.

Cobb, Irvin Shrewsbury. A Plea for Old Cap Collier. 2011. 72p. pap. 17.75 **(978-1-246-47068-0(3))** 2010. 70p. pap. 17.75 (978-1-147-35755-4(2)) BiblioBazaar.

Colbert, Stephen. I Am America (and So Can You!) 2009. (ENG.). 240p. pap. 15.99 (978-0-446-58218-6(2)) Grand Central Publishing.

Colbert, Stephen, et al. I Am America (and So Can You!) Dahm, Richard, ed. rev. ed. 2007. (ENG., Illus.). 240p. 26.99 (978-0-446-58050-2(3)) Grand Central Publishing.

Communication Architects, ed. & compiled by. Rejoice! Clean Humor: It's good medicine & GREAT Exercise! 2007. (Illus.). 170p. per. 12.95 (978-0-935597-06-6(9)) Communication Architects.

Cosby, Bill. I Didn't Ask to Be Born: But I'm Glad Is Was. 2011. (ENG., Illus.). 208p. 21.99 (978-0-89296-920-3(2)) Center St.

—I Didn't Ask to Be Born (But I'm Glad I Was) l.t. ed. 2011. (ENG., Illus.). 272p. 23.99 (978-1-4555-0735-1(0)) Center St.

Crockett, Davy. Davy Crockett: American Comic Legend. Dorson, Richard, ed. 2011. 200p. 44.95 **(978-1-258-01652-4(4))** Literary Licensing, LLC.

Department of the Army Headquarter Staff. U.S. Army Zombie Combat Skills. 2009. (ENG., Illus.). 256p. pap. 14.95 (978-1-59921-909-7(3), Lyons Pr.) Globe Pequot Pr., The.

Dickson, Paul. The Official Rules: More than 4000 Principles, Laws, Axioms & Observations for Survival in the Balance of the 21st Century. 2012. (Dover Humor Ser.). 384p. 24.95 (978-0-486-48210-1(3)) Dover Pubns., Inc.

Dogwood Press. Shocco Tales: (Shavin's under a Southern Shade Tree. 2008. (ENG., Illus.). 176p. 22.95 (978-0-9721611-4-5(7)) Dogwood Pr., LLC.

Duck. Bad Boys Jokes. (Illus.). 128p. pap. 7.95 (978-1-85479-285-3(7)) O'Mara, Michael Bks., Ltd. GBR. Dist: Trans-Atlantic Pubns., Inc.

Edmund, Peggy & Harold W. Williams. Toaster's Handbook: Jokes, Stories, & Quotations. 2007. (ENG.). 510p. pap. 30.99 (978-1-4264-6064-7(3)); 588p. pap. 32.99 (978-1-4264-6135-4(6)) BiblioBazaar.

Ephron, Nora. I Remember Nothing: And Other Reflections. (Vintage Ser.). (ENG.). 160p. 2011. pap. 14.00 (978-0-307-74280-3(6), Vintage) 2010. 22.95 (978-0-307-59560-7(9), Knopf) Knopf Doubleday Publishing Group.

—I Remember Nothing: And Other Reflections. l.t. ed. 2010. (ENG.). 160p. pap. 23.00 (978-0-7393-7804-5(X)) Random Hse. Large Print.

Fallon, Jimmy & Late Night with David Letterman Writers Staff. Thank You Notes. 2011. (ENG., Illus.). 176p. pap., pap. 12.99 (978-0-89296-741-4(2)) Grand Central Publishing.

Fenner, Phyllis R., ed. Fun, Fun, Fun: Stories of Fantasy & Farce, Mischief & Mirth, Whimsy & Nonsense. 2011. 280p. 47.95 **(978-1-258-06544-7(4))** Literary Licensing, LLC.

Fey, Tina. Bossypants. (ENG., Illus.). 2012. 304p. pap. 15.99 (978-0-316-05687-8(1), Back Bay Bks.) 2011. 288p. 26.99 (978-0-316-05686-1(3)) 2011. 352p. 28.99 (978-0-316-17789-4(X)) Little Brown & Co.

Fey, Tina & The Author. Bossypants. 2011. 44.99 (978-1-60941-720-8(8), Sound Library) AudioGO.

Ford, Ed, et al. Cream of the Crop. 2011. 280p. 47.95 **(978-1-258-07558-3(X))** Literary Licensing, LLC.

Foxx, Daniel. I Only Laugh When It Hurts: A Collection of Hard & Hilarious Lessons, 1 vol. 2009. (ENG.). 208p. pap. 12.95 (978-1-58980-635-1(2)) Pelican Publishing Co., Inc.

Frazier, Ian. Humor Me: An Anthology of Funny Contemporary Writing - Plus Some Great Old Stuff Too. 2011. (ENG., Illus.). 336p. pap. 14.99 (978-0-06-172895-2(0), Ecco) HarperCollins Pubs.

Friars Club Staff. The Friars Club Encyclopedia of Jokes: Over 2,000 One-Liners, Straight Lines, Stories, Gags, Roasts, Ribs, & Put-Downs. rev. ed. 2009. (ENG.). 512p. pap. 14.95 (978-1-57912-804-3(1), 1579128041) Black Dog & Leventhal Pubs., Inc.

Geist, William. Way off the Road: Discovering the Peculiar Charms of Small Town America. l.t. ed. 2007. (Laugh Lines Ser.). (Illus.). 343p. 29.95 (978-0-7862-9643-9(7)) Thorndike Pr.

Geist, William & Geist, Bill. Way off the Road: Discovering the Peculiar Charms of Small-Town America. 2008. (ENG., Illus.). 256p. pap. 13.95 (978-0-7679-2273-9(5)) Broadway Bks.

Gethard, Chris. A Bad Idea I'm about to Do: True Tales of Seriously Poor Judgment & Stunningly Awkward Adventure. 2012. (ENG.). 264p. pap. 16.00 (978-0-306-82030-4(7)) Da Capo Pr., Inc.

Gibbs Smith Publisher Staff. Little Western Humor Books, No. 24. 166.80 (978-0-87905-678-0(9)) Gibbs Smith, Publisher.

Gillespie, Dan. Bob & Ray & Tom. 2008. 68p. pap. 8.95 (978-1-59393-009-7(7)) BearManor Media.

Gottfried, Gilbert. Rubber Balls & Liquor. 2011. (ENG., Illus.). 288p. 24.99 (978-0-312-66811-2(2)) St. Martin's Pr.

Gray, Spalding. Sex & Death to the Age 14. 2008. (ENG.). 48p. pap. 8.50 (978-0-8222-1558-3-570-1(5)) Dramatic Publishing Co.

Green, Joey, ed. Lunacy: The Best of the Cornell Lunatic. 2008. (ENG., Illus.). 224p. per. 14.95 (978-0-9772590-3-8(X)) Lunatic Pr.

Gross, Milton. Nize Baby. (Classics of Modern American Humor Ser.). reprint ed. 28.00 (978-0-404-19932-6(1)) AMS Pr., Inc.

Halpern, Justin. Sh*t My Dad Says. 2010. (ENG.). 176p. 15.99 (978-0-06-199270-4(4)) HarperCollins Pubs.

Handler, Chelsea. Chelsea Chelsea Bang Bang. (ENG.). 256p. 2011. pap. 15.99 (978-0-446-55243-1(7)) 2010. (Illus.). 25.99 (978-0-446-55244-8(5)) Grand Central Publishing.

—Lies That Chelsea Handler Told Me. 2011. 39.99 (978-1-61113-660-9(1), Sound Library) AudioGO.

Handler, Chelsea, intro. Lies That Chelsea Handler Told Me. 2012. (Chelsea Handler Book/Borderline Amazing Publishing Ser.). (ENG.). 304p. pap. 14.99 **(978-0-446-58470-8(3))** Grand Central Publishing.

Heimberg, Justin & Gomberg, David. Over 300 Diabolically Deranged Dilemmas to Ponder. 2008. (Would You Rather... ? Ser.). (ENG., Illus.). 184p. per. 9.95 (978-0-9788178-3-1(4)) Seven Footer Pr.

—Would You Rather... ?'s Read It & Wipe: Condensed Comedy for the Can. 2009. (Would You Rather... ? Ser.). (ENG.). 240p. pap. 12.95 (978-1-934734-10-0(1)) Seven Footer Pr.

Hightower, Jim. Swim Against the Current: Even a Dead Fish Can Go with the Flow. 2008. (ENG., Illus.). 224p. 25.95 (978-0-470-12151-1(3), Wiley) Wiley, John & Sons, Inc.

Hillbilly Laugh. 2.95 (978-0-936672-42-7(0)) Aerial Photography Services, Inc.

Hodgman, John. The Areas of My Expertise. 2006. (ENG., Illus.). 256p. (gr. 12-18). 14.00 (978-1-59448-222-9(5), Riverhead Trade (Paperbacks)) Penguin Group (USA) Inc.

Hollingsworth, Mary, ed. And God Said... Let There Be Laughter! Humorous & Inspiring Stories, Quotes & Quips. 2008. (ENG.). 256p. per. 14.99 (978-0-8249-4736-1(3), GuidepostsBooks) Ideals Pubns.

House, Boyce. Texas: Proud & Loud. 2007. (ENG.). 110p. 34.95 (978-0-548-06770-3(8)) Kessinger Publishing, LLC.

Howard Books Staff. Humor for a Boomer's Heart: Stories, Quips, & Quotes to Lift the Heart. 2008. (ENG., Illus.). 224p. pap. 15.99 (978-1-4165-7908-3(7), Howard Bks.) Howard Books.

Inge, M. Thomas & Piacentino, Edward, eds. Southern Frontier Humor: An Anthology. 2010. (ENG.). 360p. (C). pap. 26.95 (978-0-8262-1886-5(5)) Univ. of Missouri Pr.

Ingraham, Laura. Of Thee I Zing: America's Cultural Decline from Muffin Tops to Body Shots. (ENG., Illus.). 320p. 2012. pap. 16.00 **(978-1-4516-4205-6(9))** 2011. 25.00 (978-1-4516-4204-9(0)) Threshold Editions. (Threshold Editions).

Irwin L. Gordon. Who Was Who 5000 B. C. to Date: Biographical Dictionary of the Famous & Those Who Wanted to Be. 2006. (ENG.). 92p. pap. 16.99 (978-1-4264-0057-5(8)); 1p. pap. 12.99 (978-1-4264-0186-2(8)) BiblioBazaar.

Jillette, Penn. Every Day Is an Atheist Holiday. 2012. (ENG.). 272p. (gr. 12). 25.95 **(978-0-399-16156-8(2)**, Blue Rider Pr.) Penguin Group (USA) Inc.

Jillette, Penn. God, No! Signs You May Already Be an Atheist & Other Magical Tales. (ENG.). 256p. 2012. pap. 15.00 **(978-1-4516-1037-6(8))** 2011. 24.99 (978-1-4516-1036-9(X)) Simon & Schuster.

Johnson, Barbara. Humor Me, 0 vols. 2009. 96p. pap. 8.99 (978-0-7852-9738-3(3)) Nelson, Thomas Inc.

Keasler, John. Dear George: Presenting Himself, Expert on Everything & Advice Columnist Extraordinary. 2011. 128p. 40.95 **(978-1-258-00151-3(9))** Literary Licensing, LLC.

King, Alexander. May This House Be Safe from Tigers. Date not set. lib. bdg. 22.95 (978-0-8488-2151-7(3)) Amereon LTD.

Kohen, Yael. We Killed: The Rise of Women in American Comedy, 1 vol. 2012. (ENG., Illus.). 352p. 27.00 **(978-0-374-28723-8(6))** Farrar, Straus & Giroux.

Kostick, Anne, et al. 3650 Jokes, Puns, & Riddles. 2nd ed. 2009. (ENG.). 544p. 14.95 (978-1-57912-843-2(2), 1579128432) Black Dog & Leventhal Pubs., Inc.

Lander, Christian. Stuff White People Like: A Definitive Guide to the Unique Taste of Millions. 2008. (ENG., Illus.). 224p. pap. 15.00 (978-0-8129-7991-6(5), Random Hse. Trade Paperbacks) Random House Publishing Group.

Landon, Melville D. Wise, Witty, Eloquent Kings of the Platform & Pulpit. 2007. (ENG.). 568p. 58.95 (978-0-548-17179-0(3)); 572p. per. 43.95 (978-1-4304-6992-6(7)) Kessinger Publishing, LLC.

Lawson, Jenny. Let's Pretend This Never Happened: (A Mostly True Memoir) 2012. (ENG., Illus.). 336p. (gr. 12). 25.95 **(978-0-399-15901-5(0)**, Putnam Adult) Penguin Group (USA) Inc.

Leary, Denis. Why We Suck: A Feel Good Guide to Staying Fat, Loud, Lazy & Stupid. 2009. (ENG.). 256p. (gr. 12-18). pap. 16.00 (978-0-452-29564-3(5), Plume) Penguin Group (USA) Inc.

Liebers, Arthur & Hoss, Norman, eds. Laughs for Teens. 2011. 130p. 40.95 **(978-1-258-08797-5(9))** Literary Licensing, LLC.

Lionel. Everyone's Crazy Except You & Me... And I'm Not So Sure about You - America's Favorite Contrarian Cuts Loose. 2008. 272p. 22.95 (978-1-4013-0366-2(8)) Hyperion Pr.

Magliozzi, Tom. Ask Click & Clack: Answers from Car Talk. 2008. (ENG.). 208p. pap. 16.95 (978-0-8118-6477-0(4)) Chronicle Bks. LLC.

Mahony, Patrick. Barbed Wit & Malicious Humor. 2011. 190p. 42.95 **(978-1-258-06925-4(3))** Literary Licensing, LLC.

Marshall Pinckney Wilder. The Wit & Humor of America. l.t. ed. 2007. Vol. 1. (ENG.). 246p. pap. 22.99 (978-1-4264-9697-4(4)) Vol. 2. 186p. pap. 21.99 (978-1-4264-9698-1(2)) Vol. 3. (ENG.). 190p. pap. 21.99 (978-1-4264-9805-3(5)) Vol. 4. 216p. pap. 22.99 (978-1-4264-9823-7(3)) Vol. 5. (ENG.). 208p. pap. 22.99 (978-1-4264-6952-7(7)) Vol. 6. 232p. pap. 22.99 (978-1-4264-4345-9(5)) BiblioBazaar.

—The Wit & Humor of America Volume I. 2007. 220p. pap. 20.99 (978-1-4264-9316-4(9)) BiblioBazaar.

—The Wit & Humor of America Volume II. 2007. 170p. pap. 19.99 (978-1-4264-9317-1(7)) BiblioBazaar.

—The Wit & Humor of America Volume III. 2007. 172p. pap. 19.99 (978-1-4264-9424-6(6)) BiblioBazaar.

—The Wit & Humor of America Volume IV. 2007. (ENG.). 190p. pap. 19.99 (978-1-4264-9442-0(4)) BiblioBazaar.

—The Wit & Humor of America Volume V. 2007. 190p. pap. 19.99 (978-1-4264-9649-3(4)) BiblioBazaar.

—The Wit & Humor of America Volume VI. 2007. 212p. pap. 20.99 (978-1-4264-9650-9(8)) BiblioBazaar.

Martin, Demetri. This Is a Book. (ENG.). 288p. 2012. pap. 14.99 **(978-0-446-53969-2(4))** 2011. (Illus.). 24.99 (978-0-446-53970-8(8)) Grand Central Publishing.

Mason, Edward T. Humorous Masterpieces from American Literature. 2008. 184p. 25.99 (978-0-554-28528-3(2)) 2008. 184p. 22.99 (978-0-554-37831-2(0)) 2007. (ENG.). 168p. pap. 19.99 (978-1-4346-5641-4(1)) 2007. (ENG.). 182p. pap. 21.99 (978-1-4346-5642-1(X)) BiblioBazaar.

Masson, Thomas L. Our American Humorists. 2008. 470p. 52.95 (978-0-548-96663-1(X)) 2007. (ENG.). 472p. per. 37.95 (978-0-548-64216-0(8)) Kessinger Publishing, LLC.

McCormick, Elsie. The Unexpurgated Diary of a Shanghai Baby. 2007. 114p. pap. 27.50 (978-988-99874-8-0(1)) China Economic Review Publishing HKG. Dist: Trans-Atlantic Pubns., Inc.

McGuire, Margaret, compiled by. The Quotable Douchebag: A Treasury of Spectacularly Stupid Remarks. 2009. (ENG., Illus.). 144p. pap. 12.95 (978-1-59474-425-9(4)) Quirk Bks.

McInnes, Gavin. How to Piss in Public: From Teenage Rebellion to the Hangover of Adulthood. 2012. (ENG.). 288p. 24.00 **(978-1-4516-1417-6(9)**, Scribner) Scribner.

Meyerowitz, Rick. Drunk Stoned Brilliant Dead: The Writers & Artists Who Made the National Lampoon Insanely Great. 2010. (ENG., Illus.). 320p. 40.00 (978-0-8109-8848-4(8)) Abrams.

Mills, Robert L. The Laugh Makers. 2009. 368p. pap. 24.95 (978-1-59393-323-4(1)) BearManor Media.

Monsen, Avery, et al. K Is for Knifeball: An Alphabet of Terrible Advice. 2012. (ENG.). 80p. 9.95 **(978-1-4521-0331-0(3))** Chronicle Bks. LLC.

Montana, Gladiola. Never Ask a Man the Size of His Spread: A Cowgirl's Guide to Life, 1 vol. 2009. (ENG.). 144p. pap. 7.99 (978-1-4236-0705-2(8)) Gibbs Smith, Publisher.

Nadelberg, David. Mortified: Love Is a Battlefield. 2008. (ENG.). 304p. pap. 14.95 (978-1-4169-5479-8(1)) Gallery Pr., The IRL. Dist: Simon & Schuster, Inc.

Nancy, Ted L. All New Letters from a Nut: Includes Lunatic Email Exchanges. 2010. (ENG.). 256p. 19.00 (978-0-307-71628-6(7)) Broadway Bks.

—Hello Junk Mail! 2008. (ENG.). 226p. (978-0-9800592-1-2(6)) National Lampoon.

Nester, Daniel. How to Be Inappropriate. 2009. (ENG.). 272p. pap. 14.95 (978-1-59376-253-7(4), Soft Skull Pr.) Counterpoint LLC.

Nix, Elizabeth. Everything You Thought You 'd Know by Now. mass mkt. (978-0-312-98724-4(2), St. Martin's Paperbacks) St. Martin's Pr.

—Everything You Thought You'd Know by Now. Date not set. pap. (978-0-312-30941-1(4), St. Martin's Griffin) St. Martin's Pr.

Noland, C. F. M. Cavorting on the Devil's Fork: The Pete Whetstone Letters of C. F. M. Noland. Williams, Leonard, ed. 2006. (Illus.). 281p. per. 22.50 (978-1-55728-834-9(8)) Univ. of Arkansas Pr.

Notaro, Laurie. It Looked Different on the Model: Epic Tales of Impending Shame & Infamy. 2011. 240p. pap. 15.00 (978-0-345-51099-0(2), Villard Bks.) Random House Publishing Group.

Nye, Bill. Bill Nye's Red Book. 2009. 166p. pap. 19.99 (978-1-150-33670-6(6)) General Bks. LLC.

—Bill Nye's Red Book. 2007. (ENG.). 390p. 48.95 (978-0-548-02232-0(1)) Kessinger Publishing, LLC.

O'Mara, Lesley. Which Way to the Vomitorium? Date not set. pap. (978-0-312-28067-3(X), St. Martin's Griffin) St. Martin's Pr.

Onion Staff & Williams, Brian. Our Front Pages: 21 Years of Greatness, Virtue, & Moral Rectitude from America's Finest News Source. 2009. (ENG., Illus.). 304p. 28.00 (978-1-4391-5692-6(1), Scribner) Scribner.

Parker, Dorothy. The Best of Dorothy Parker. 26.95 (978-0-8488-0117-5(2)) Amereon LTD.

—Dorothy Parker's Favorites. 18.95 (978-0-8488-0095-6(8)) Amereon LTD.

Perelman, Sidney J. Favorites of S. J. Perelman. 24.95 (978-0-8488-1123-5(2)) Amereon LTD.

Pollack, Merrill. How to Cope With. 2011. 144p. 40.95 **(978-1-258-08148-5(2))** Literary Licensing, LLC.

Poundstone, Paula. There's Nothing in This Book That I Meant to Say. 2007. (ENG.). 288p. per. 15.00 (978-0-307-38228-3(1), Three Rivers Pr.) Crown Publishing Group.

Price, Steven D. 1001 Funniest Things Ever Said. 2010. (1001 Ser.). (ENG.). 352p. pap. 9.95 (978-1-59921-195-4(5), Lyons Pr.) Globe Pequot Pr., The.

—1001 Funniest Things Ever Said. Price, Steven D., ed. 2006. (1001 Ser.). (ENG., Illus.). 352p. 14.95 (978-1-59228-443-6(4), Lyons Pr.) Globe Pequot Pr., The.

Reader's Digest Association Staff, contrib. by. Laughter, the Best Medicine. 2006. (Illus.). 366p. (978-0-7621-0545-8(3)) Reader's Digest Assn., Inc., The.

Reader's Digest Editors & Jackson, Gram. Laughter Really Is the Best Medicine: America's Funniest Jokes, Stories, & Cartoons. 2011. (ENG.). 216p. (gr. 12). 9.95 (978-1-60652-204-2(3)) Reader's Digest Assn., Inc., The.

Reagan, Ronald. The Notes: Ronald Reagan's Private Collection of Stories & Wisdom. (ENG.). 256p. 2012. pap. 16.99 (978-0-06-206514-8(9), HarperPerennial) 2011. 25.99 (978-0-06-206513-1(0)) 2011. pap. 25.99 (978-0-06-206655-8(2), HarperLuxe) HarperCollins Pubs.

Reese, Taylor. Humor & a Little Bit More. 2009. pap. 12.95 (978-1-59712-320-4(X)) Catawba Publishing Co.

Rich, Simon. Free-Range Chickens. 2009. (ENG.). 144p. pap. 13.00 (978-0-8129-7711-0(4), Random Hse. Trade Paperbacks) Random House Publishing Group.

Richards, J. C. & Undead, Zee. 501 Things to Do with a Zombie. 2010. (ENG., Illus.). 256p. pap. 9.95 (978-1-4405-0564-5(0)) Adams Media Corp.

Robertson, Carleton J. Robby's Revelry. Vernon, Sidney, ed. (Illus.). (Orig.). pap. 7.00 (978-0-943150-12-3(4)) Rovern Pr.

Rogers, Will. The Illiterate Digest. 2010. 354p. 37.56 (978-1-169-77218-2(8)); pap. 25.56 (978-1-162-59156-8(0)); 46.95 (978-1-161-37486-5(8)) Kessinger Publishing, LLC.

Rogers, Will. Twelve Radio Talks. 2011. 48p. 35.95 (978-1-258-01153-6(0)) Literary Licensing, LLC.

Rooney, Andrew. Andy Rooney. rev. l.t. ed. 2010. 514p. 31.95 (978-1-4104-2284-2(4)) Thorndike Pr.

Rooney, Andy. Andy Rooney: 60 Years of Wisdom & Wit. 2010. (ENG., Illus.). 320p. pap. 15.95 (978-1-58648-903-8(8)) PublicAffairs.

Rothbart, Davy. My Heart Is an Idiot: Essays, 1 vol. 2012. (ENG.). 304p. 26.00 (978-0-374-28084-0(3)) Farrar, Straus & Giroux.

Schwarz, William. Confessions of a Crabgrass Cowboy: From Lincoln Logs to Lava Lamps. 2007. 252p. per. 19.95 (978-0-595-45169-2(1)) iUniverse, Inc.

Seinfeld, Jerry & Seinfeld, Jerry. Seinlanguage. 2008. (ENG., Illus.). 192p. pap. 15.00 (978-0-553-38573-1(9), Bantam) Random House Publishing Group.

Shaberman, Ben A. The Vegan Monologues: The Collected Essays of Ben A. Shaberman. 2009. (978-1-934074-36-7(5)) Apprentice Hse.

Shillaber, Benjamin Penhallow. Partingtonian Patchwork Blifkins the Martyr: The Domestic Trials of A Model Husband. the Modern Syntax. 2006. 380p. per. 26.99 (978-1-4255-3995-5(5)) MPublishing.

Showalter, Michael. Mr. Funny Pants. 2011. (ENG., Illus.). 288p. 24.99 (978-0-446-54210-4(5)) Grand Central Publishing.

—Mr. Funny Pants: A Memoir of False Starts. 2012. (ENG.). 288p. pap. 14.99 (978-0-446-54211-1(3)) Grand Central Publishing.

Simard, Wendy, et al. F U Haiku: Pissed-Off Poetry for Every Occasion. Munier, Paula, ed. 2010. (ENG.). 224p. pap. 9.95 (978-1-4405-0181-4(5)) Adams Media Corp.

Steiner, Paul. How to Be Offensive to Practically Everybody. 2011. 64p. 36.95 (978-1-258-07952-9(6)) Literary Licensing, LLC.

Sulkin, Alec, et al. Robots Feel Nothing When They Hold Hands. 2012. (ENG., Illus.). 192p. pap. 14.95 (978-0-8118-7883-8(X)) Chronicle Bks. LLC.

Thurber, James. Fables for Our Time & Famous Poems. 18.95 (978-0-8488-1206-5(9)) Amereon LTD.

—My World & Welcome to It. reprint ed. lib. bdg. 20.95 (978-0-89190-269-0(4), Rivercity Pr.) Amereon LTD.

Twain, Mark, pseud. Animals. Fishkin, Shelley Fisher, ed. 2009. (Jumping Frogs: Undiscovered, Rediscovered, & Celebrated Writings of Mark Twain Ser.). (Illus.). 340p. 50.00 (978-0-520-24855-7(4)) Univ. of California Pr.

—Mark Twain's Book of Animals. Fishkin, Shelley Fisher, ed. 2011. (Jumping Frogs: Undiscovered, Rediscovered, & Celebrated Writings of Mark Twain Ser.). (ENG., Illus.). 344p. pap. 21.95 (978-0-520-27152-4(1)) Univ. of California Pr.

—Wit & Wisdom. Date not set. 286p. 23.95 (978-0-8488-2499-0(7)) Amereon LTD.

Uptight Seattleite Staff. A Sensitive Liberal's Guide to Life: How to Banter with Your Barista, Hug Mindfully, & Relate to Friends Who Choose Kids over Dogs. 2010. (ENG.). 224p. (gr. 12-18). 15.00 (978-1-59240-529-9(0), Gotham) Penguin Group (USA) Inc.

Welch, Robert & Editor Of American Opinion. Bullets & Confetti: From the Pages of American Opinion. 2011. 160p. 41.95 (978-1-258-02335-5(0)) Literary Licensing, LLC.

Wilson, Fred G. Say What? Colloquialisms. 2008. 100p. pap. 11.95 (978-1-4327-2792-5(3)) Outskirts Pr., Inc.

Wilson, Gahan & Bierce, Ambrose. The Devil's Dictionary & Other Works. (Classics Illustrated Ser.). (Illus.). 52p. pap. 4.95 (978-1-57209-018-7(9)) Classics International Entertainment, Inc.

Yankee Dictionary. 2.95 (978-0-936672-29-8(3)) Aerial Photography Services, Inc.

Zevin, Dan. Dan Gets a Minivan: Life at the Intersection of Dude & Dad. 2012. (ENG.). 240p. 24.00 (978-1-4516-0646-1(X), Scribner) Scribner.

AMERICAN WIT AND HUMOR—ANIMALS

Becker, Suzy. All I Need to Know I Learned from My Cat: (And Then Some) 2nd collector's ed. 2007. (ENG., Illus.). 144p. pap. 8.95 (978-0-7611-4766-4(7), 0761147667) Workman Publishing Co., Inc.

Bender, Texas Bix. Laughing Stock: A Cow's Guide to Life, 1 vol. 2009. (ENG.). 128p. pap. 7.99 (978-1-4236-0704-5(X)) Gibbs Smith, Publisher.

Burka, Joan. Caribou Crossing. pap. 8.95 (978-1-882185-49-8(8)) Cornerstone Publishing, Inc.

Huneck, Stephen. My Dog's Brain. 2009. (ENG., Illus.). 104p. 14.95 (978-0-8109-8287-1(0), Abrams Image) Abrams.

Valci, Grazia. How to Obey Your Cat: The Ultimate Handbook for the Slavish Cat Owner. (Illus.). 120p. pap. (978-88-7301-469-0(0)) Gremese Editore.

AMERICAN WIT AND HUMOR—ARTS AND LETTERS

Benson, Ophelia & Stangroom, Jeremy. The Dictionary of Fashionable Nonsense: A Guide for Edgy People. 2006. (ENG.). 128p. 9.95 (978-0-285-63714-6(2)) Souvenir Pr. Ltd. GBR. Dist: Independent Pubs. Group.

Walston, John. The Buzzword Dictionary: 1,000 Phrases Translated from Pompous to English. 2006. (How America Speaks Ser.). (ENG., Illus.). 230p. per. 12.95 (978-1-933338-07-1(5), Marion Street Pr.) Acorn Guild Pr., LLC.

Wurdz, Gideon. The Foolish Dictionary. 2008. 136p. 21.99 (978-0-554-37404-8(8)) 2008. 136p. 24.99 (978-0-554-28101-8(5)) 2007. (ENG.). 116p. pap. 18.99 (978-1-4346-4693-4(9)) 2007. (ENG.). 134p. pap. 19.99 (978-1-4346-4694-1(7)) BiblioBazaar.

—The Foolish Dictionary. 2008. (ENG.). 116p. per. (978-1-4065-9414-0(8)) Dodo Pr.

AMERICAN WIT AND HUMOR—ARTS AND SCIENCE

Beckford, William. Biographical Memoirs of Extraordinary Painters. 2010. (ENG.). 164p. pap. 21.75 (978-1-177-39415-4(4)); 168p. pap. 21.75 (978-1-170-58117-9(X), Gale ECCO, Print Editions); 172p. pap. 21.75 (978-1-146-60744-5(X)); 168p. pap. 21.75 (978-1-141-86118-7(6)); 166p. pap. 21.75 (978-1-141-70761-4(6)) BiblioBazaar.

—Biographical Memoirs of Extraordinary Painters. 2009. 48p. pap. 14.14 (978-1-151-31203-7(7)) General Bks. LLC.

—Biographical Memoirs of Extraordinary Painters. 2007. (ENG.). 152p. 36.95 (978-0-548-16351-1(0)); 156p. per. 21.95 (978-1-4304-5970-5(0)) Kessinger Publishing, LLC.

AMERICAN WIT AND HUMOR—BUSINESS, PROFESSIONS, ETC.

Dilks, Kenneth R. If the Job Were Easy, I Wouldn't Need You. pap. 10.95 (978-1-882185-30-6(7)) Cornerstone Publishing, Inc.

Lang, Adele. Bosstrology. mass mkt. (978-0-312-98743-5(9), St. Martin's Paperbacks) St. Martin's Pr.

Mankoff, Robert, ed. The New Yorker Book of Business Cartoons. 2010. (New Yorker Ser.: 8). (ENG., Illus.). 128p. pap. 12.00 (978-1-57660-042-9(4), Bloomberg Pr.) Wiley, John & Sons, Inc.

Peter, Laurence J. & Hull, Raymond. The Peter Principle. Date not set. lib. bdg. 19.95 (978-0-8488-2156-2(4)) Amereon LTD.

—The Peter Principle: Why Things Always Go Wrong. 2009. (ENG.). 192p. 19.99 (978-0-06-169906-1(3), Collins) HarperCollins Pubs.

AMERICAN WIT AND HUMOR—CHURCH AND CLERGY

Colaianni, James F. Pulpit Humor. 320p. (Orig.). pap. 14.95 (978-0-941685-05-4(5)) Voicings Pubns.

AMERICAN WIT AND HUMOR—EDUCATION

Wilder, Robert. Tales from the Teachers' Lounge: What I Learned in School the Second Time Around-One Man's Irreverent Look at Being a Teacher Today. 2008. (ENG.). 320p. pap. 14.00 (978-0-385-33928-5(3), Delta) Random House Publishing Group.

AMERICAN WIT AND HUMOR—HISTORY AND CRITICISM

Baumgartner, Jody C. Laughing Matters: Humor & American Politics in the Media Age. 2007. (Illus.). 362p. 143.00 (978-0-415-95747-2(8)) Routledge.

Baumgartner, Jody C. & Morris, Jonathan S. Laughing Matters: Humor & American Politics in the Media Age. 2007. (ENG.). 392p. per. 41.95 (978-0-415-95748-9(6)) Routledge.

Carter, Steven. Little House of Oxymorons: With Commentaries. 2010. (ENG.). 92p. pap. 19.99 (978-0-7618-5103-5(8)) Hamilton Bks.

Clemens, Will M. Famous Funny Fellows. 2008. 216p. pap. 27.95 (978-1-4437-7725-4(0), Kent Pr.) Kent Communications, Ltd.

Crandall, Arthur George. New England Joke Lore: The Tonic of Yankee Humor. 2009. 304p. 25.99 (978-1-103-76996-4(0)); pap. 19.99 (978-1-103-76989-6(8)) BiblioBazaar.

Dundes, Alan. The Kushmaker & Other Essays on Folk Speech & Folk Humor. Alan Dundes. Mieder, Wolfgang, ed. 2008. (Supplement Series of Proverbium). (Illus.). 206p. per. 10.00 (978-0-9770731-9-1(X)) Proverbium.

Frank, Russell. Newslore: Contemporary Folklore on the Internet. 2011. (ENG., Illus.). 224p. 55.00 (978-1-60473-928-2(2)) Univ. Pr. of Mississippi.

Franklyn, Blair. Towards a Theory of Postmodern Humour. 2008. 116p. pap. (978-3-639-03793-7(6)) VDM Verlag Dr. Mueller e.K.

Haile, C. M. C. M. Haile's Pardon Jones Letters: Old Southwest Humor from Antebellum Louisiana. Piacentino, Edward, ed. 2009. (Southern Literary Studies). 264p. 37.50 (978-0-8071-3437-5(6)) Louisiana State Univ. Pr.

Harriman, Margaret Case. The Vicious Circle: The Story of the Algonquin Round Table. 2011. 320p. 50.95 (978-1-258-10551-8(9)) Literary Licensing, LLC.

Haweis, H. R. American Humorists. 2007. (ENG.). 194p. 37.95 (978-0-548-04402-5(3)) Kessinger Publishing, LLC.

Hollis, Tim. Ain't That a Knee-Slapper: Rural Comedy in the Twentieth Century. 2008. (ENG., Illus.). 256p. 50.00 (978-1-934110-72-0(8)); pap. 25.00 (978-1-934110-73-7(6)) Univ. Pr. of Mississippi.

Karp, Josh. A Futile & Stupid Gesture: How Doug Kenney & National Lampoon Changed Comedy Forever. (ENG., Illus.). 416p. 2008. pap. 16.95 (978-1-55652-762-3(4)) 2006. 24.95 (978-1-55652-602-2(4)) Chicago Review Pr., Inc.

Kessel, Martina & Merziger, Patrick, eds. The Politics of Humour. 2012. (German & European Studies). (ENG., Illus.). 232p. (978-1-4426-4292-8(0)) Univ. of Toronto Pr.

Lee, Judith Yaross. Garrison Keillor: A Voice of America. 2006. (ENG., Illus.). 230p. pap. 25.00 (978-0-87805-473-2(1)) Univ. Pr. of Mississippi.

Lewis, Paul. Cracking Up: American Humor in a Time of Conflict. 2006. (Illus.). 224p. 25.00 (978-0-226-47699-5(5)) Univ. of Chicago Pr.

Marciniak, Vwadek P. Politics, Humor & the Counterculture: Laughter in the Age of Decay. 2008. 164p. (C). 61.95 (978-1-4331-0359-9(1)) Lang, Peter Publishing, Inc.

Martin, Gretchen. The Frontier Roots of American Realism: Southwest Humor & the Loophole of Literary Propriety. 2007. (Studies on Themes & Motifs in Literature: Vol. 89). 148p. (C). 58.95 (978-0-8204-8811-0(9)) Lang, Peter Publishing, Inc.

Morris, Linda A. Gender Play in Mark Twain: Cross-Dressing & Transgression. (MARK TWAIN & HIS CIRCLE Ser.). (ENG., Illus.). 200p. (C). 2011. (gr. 13). pap. 25.00 (978-0-8262-1963-3(2)) 2007. 34.95 (978-0-8262-1759-2(1)) Univ. of Missouri Pr.

Nickels, Cameron C. Civil War Humor. 2010. (ENG., Illus.). 160p. 28.00 (978-1-60473-747-9(6)) Univ. Pr. of Mississippi.

Pascal, John R. Artemus Ward. 2009. 72p. pap. (978-3-639-13329-5(3)) VDM Verlag Dr. Mueller e.K.

Rourke, Constance. American Humor: A Study of the National Character. 2008. 260p. pap. 25.00 (978-1-59740-585-0(X)) ACLS Humanities E-Book.

Thorp. American Humorists, Vol. 42. 2009. pap. 25.00 (978-0-8166-0334-3(0)) Univ. of Minnesota Pr.

Zwagerman, Sean. Wits End: Women's Humor as Rhetorical & Performative Strategy. 2010. (Pitt Comp Literacy Culture Ser.). (ENG.). 264p. pap. 24.95 (978-0-8229-6074-4(5)) Univ. of Pittsburgh Pr.

AMERICAN WIT AND HUMOR—LAW

Galanter, Marc. Lowering the Bar: Lawyer Jokes & Legal Culture. 2006. (Illus.). 448p. per. 26.95 (978-0-299-21354-1(4)) Univ. of Wisconsin Pr.

AMERICAN WIT AND HUMOR—MARRIAGE AND FAMILY LIFE

Cosby, Bill. Fatherhood. 2008. (ENG.). 178p. pap. 13.00 (978-1-4379-5093-9(0)) DIANE Publishing Co.

Downs, Tim. The Laylo Papers: The Complete Guide to Relationships. Date not set. (Illus.). 136p. (Orig.). pap. 8.99 (978-0-9623125-0-2(9)) Downs, Tim.

Hamilton, Cathy. Dadisms: What He Says & What He Really Means. 2008. (ENG.). 104p. pap. 5.99 (978-0-7407-7232-0(5)) Andrews McMeel Publishing.

—Momisms: What She Says & What She Really Means. 2008. (ENG.). 120p. pap. 5.99 (978-0-7407-7239-9(2)) Andrews McMeel Publishing.

Marquis, Don. Hermione & Her Little Group of Serious Thinkers. 2009. 200p. 26.99 (978-1-115-57510-2(4)) 2009. 200p. pap. 23.75 (978-1-115-57512-6(0)) 2009. 200p. pap. 24.75 (978-1-115-57511-9(2)) 2008. 208p. 24.99 (978-0-554-30991-0(2)) 2008. 208p. 27.99 (978-0-554-21688-1(4)) BiblioBazaar.

—Hermione & Her Little Group of Serious Thinkers. 2009. 164p. pap. (978-1-4099-3025-9(4)) Dodo Pr.

—Hermione & Her Little Group of Serious Thinkers. 2009. 98p. pap. 20.00 (978-0-217-40991-9(1)) General Bks. LLC.

—Hermione & Her Little Group of Serious Thinkers. 2007. (ENG.). 200p. per. (978-1-4086-2231-5(9)) Read Bks.

—Hermione & Her Little Group of Serious Thinkers. 2009. 184p. pap. 13.45 (978-1-4385-1617-2(7), Book Jungle) Standard Pubns., Inc.

O'Donnell, Sharon. House of Testosterone: One Mom's Survival in a Household of Males. 2007. (ENG.). 224p. 19.95 (978-0-9778086-0-1(2)) Jefferson Pr.

Peel, Kathy. The Stomach Virus & Other Forms of Family Bonding, 0 vols. 2008. 240p. pap. 14.99 (978-0-7852-9685-0(9)) Nelson, Thomas Inc.

Reed, Steve, illus. You Won't Get Fooled Again: More Than 101 Brilliant Ways to Bust Any Bald-Faced Liar (Even If the Liar Is Lying Beside You!) 2006. 124p. per. 10.95 (978-0-9739277-0-2(4)) FingerTip Press CAN. Dist: Independent Pubs. Group.

Smith, Margaret. What Was I Thinking? How Being a Stand up Did Nothing to Prepare Me to Become a Single Mother. 2008. (ENG.). 191p. pap. 16.95 (978-0-8245-2285-8(0)) Crossroad Publishing Co., The.

Wyse, Lois & Rae, Sheilah. Funny, You Don't Look Like a Grandmother. 2009. 80p. mass mkt. 9.95 (978-0-573-69684-8(5)) French, Samuel Inc.

AMERICAN WIT AND HUMOR—POLITICS, GOVERNMENT, ARMED SERVICES

Brummett, Curt. My Dog's a Democrat. (Illus.). 96p. reprint ed. pap. 6.95 (978-1-879894-01-3(7)) Saratoga Publishing Group, Inc.

Feiffer. Political Cartoon Collection, Vol. 1. Date not set. pap. (978-0-7653-0439-1(2), Forge Bks.) Doherty, Tom Assocs., LLC.

Fish, creator. Go Fish. 2011. (ENG., Illus.). 224p. pap. 18.95 (978-1-61775-014-4(X)) Akashic Bks.

Luckovich, Mike. Four More Wars! 2006. (ENG., Illus.). 248p. per. 16.95 (978-1-55022-737-6(8)) ECW Pr. CAN. Dist: Independent Pubs. Group.

Stewart, Jon, et al. America: A Citizen's Guide to Democracy Inaction. 2006. (ENG., Illus.). 240p. pap., tchr. ed. 15.99 (978-0-446-69186-4(0)) Grand Central Publishing.

Threshold Editions. Sh*t My Vice President Says: With Bonus Material from the Obama White House, Democratic Congress, & Other Special Friends! 2010. (ENG.). 128p. pap. 10.00 (978-1-4516-2763-3(7), Threshold Editions) Threshold Editions.

AMERICAN WIT AND HUMOR—SCIENCE

Harris, Sidney. There Goes the Neighborhood: Cartoons on the Environment. 2008. (ENG.). 152p. pap. 22.95 (978-0-8203-3243-7(7)) Univ. of Georgia Pr.

Sperling, Norman, ed. This Book Warps Space & Time: Selections from the Journal of Irreproducible Results. 2008. (ENG.). 288p. pap. 12.99 (978-0-7407-7713-4(0)) Andrews McMeel Publishing.

AMERICAN WIT AND HUMOR—SOCIAL LIFE AND CUSTOMS

Andrews, Jaime & Doherty, Jessica. Things You Can Do While You're Naked. 2006. (ENG., Illus.). 112p. per. 12.95 (978-1-59580-016-9(6)) Santa Monica Pr.

Benchley, Robert. Benchley Roundup. 25.95 (978-0-8488-0915-7(7)) Amereon LTD.

Bender, Texas Bix. Hats & the Cowboys Who Wear Them. 96p. (Illus.). 69.50 (978-1-58685-225-2(6)); 2009. (ENG.). pap. 7.99 (978-1-4236-0702-1(3)) Gibbs Smith, Publisher.

Chupack, Cindy. The Between Boyfriends Book: A Collection of Cautiously Hopeful Essays. mass mkt. (978-0-312-98692-6(0), St. Martin's Paperbacks) St. Martin's Pr.

Cobb, Irvin S. The Escape of Mr Trimm: His Plight & Other Plights. 2007. (ENG.). 284p. 43.95 (978-0-548-25494-3(X)); per. 28.95 (978-1-4326-5830-4(1)) Kessinger Publishing, LLC.

—The Escape of Mr Trimm: His Plight & Other Plights. 2010. 284p. pap. 23.16 (978-1-163-27467-5(4)); 35.16 (978-1-163-55601-6(7)) Kessinger Publishing, LLC.

—Local Color. 2008. 458p. 52.95 (978-0-548-94071-6(1)) 2007. (ENG.). 460p. per. 37.95 (978-0-548-57000-5(0)) Kessinger Publishing, LLC.

—Local Color. 2008. 456p. pap. (978-1-4086-8477-1(2)) Read Bks.

—One Third Off. 2007. (ENG.). 148p. 35.95 (978-0-548-41961-8(2)); per. 20.95 (978-0-548-39632-2(9)) Kessinger Publishing, LLC.

—Sundry Accounts. 2009. 284p. pap. (978-1-4099-5676-1(8)) Dodo Pr.

—Sundry Accounts. 2007. (ENG.). 436p. 51.95 (978-0-548-41894-9(2)); per. 36.95 (978-0-548-39559-2(4)) Kessinger Publishing, LLC.

Cobb, Irvin S. 1876-1944. The Escape of Mr Trimm; His Plight & Other Plights. 2010. (ENG.). 292p. pap. 28.75 (978-1-176-59662-7(4)) BiblioBazaar.

Cobb, Irvin Shrewsbury. The Escape of Mr Trimm: His Plight & Other Plights. 2010. 292p. pap. 28.75 (978-1-145-78672-1(3)) 2008. 288p. 25.99 (978-0-559-70200-6(0)) 2008. 288p. pap. 27.75 (978-0-559-70198-6(5)) BiblioBazaar.

DeGeneres, Ellen. My Point... & I Do Have One. 2007. (ENG., Illus.). 224p. pap. 14.00 (978-0-553-38422-2(8), Bantam) Random House Publishing Group.

Florentine, Jim. Chicks: A Man's Guide to Gettin' Some. 118p. pap. 7.95 (978-0-9645555-0-1(6)) Florentine Publishing.

Foxworthy, Jeff. Jeff Foxworthy's Complete Redneck Dictionary: All the Words You Thought You Knew the Meaning Of. 2008. (Illus.). 384p. 20.00 (978-0-345-50702-0(9), Villard Bks.) Random House Publishing Group.

—Jeff Foxworthy's Redneck Dictionary: Words You Thought You Knew the Meaning Of. 2006. (ENG., Illus.). 160p. mass mkt. 6.99 (978-0-345-49327-9(3), Fawcett) Random House Publishing Group.

—Jeff Foxworthy's Redneck Dictionary II: More Words You Thought You Knew the Meaning Of. 2007. (ENG., Illus.). 160p. mass mkt. 6.99 (978-0-345-49424-5(5), Ballantine Bks.) Random House Publishing Group.

—Jeff Foxworthy's Redneck Dictionary III: Learning to Talk More Gooder Fastly. 2008. (ENG.). 160p. mass mkt. 6.99 (978-0-345-49849-6(6), Ballantine Bks.) Random House Publishing Group.

Friedman, Francine Pappadis. MatchDotBomb: A Midlife Journey through Internet Dating. 2007. (ENG.). 184p. per. 15.95 (978-1-58736-699-4(1)) Wheatmark.

Harmon, Rick, ed. Never Turn Your Back on Kudzu & Other Southern Wisdom. 244p. (Orig.). pap. 9.95 (978-1-882616-02-2(2)) Advertiser Co.

Lafargue, Paul. The Right to Be Lazy. 2009. 72p. pap. (978-1-4589-9802-6(9)) Books LLC.

Marquis, Don. Hermione & Her Little Group of Serious Thinkers. 2009. 200p. 26.99 (978-1-115-57510-2(4)) 2009. 200p. pap. 24.75 (978-1-115-57511-9(2)) 2009. 200p. pap. 23.75 (978-1-115-57512-6(0)) 2008. 208p. 24.99 (978-0-554-30991-0(2)) 2008. 208p. 27.99 (978-0-554-21688-1(4)) BiblioBazaar.

—Hermione & Her Little Group of Serious Thinkers. 2009. 164p. pap. (978-1-4099-3025-9(4)) Dodo Pr.

—Hermione & Her Little Group of Serious Thinkers. 2009. 98p. pap. 20.00 (978-0-217-40991-9(1)) General Bks. LLC.

—Hermione & Her Little Group of Serious Thinkers. 2007. (ENG.). 200p. per. (978-1-4086-2231-5(9)) Read Bks.

—Hermione & Her Little Group of Serious Thinkers. 2009. 184p. pap. 13.45 (978-1-4385-1617-2(7), Book Jungle) Standard Pubns., Inc.

Miller, Will. Why We Watch: Killing the Gilligan Within. 2008. pap. (978-1-935052-01-2(2)) White River Pr.

Newell, Peter. The Hole Book. 2008. (ENG.). 56p. per. 16.95 (978-0-548-81197-9(0)) Kessinger Publishing, LLC.

Price, Patrick. Drama Queen: The Gay Man's Guide to an Uncomplicated Life. Date not set. (978-0-312-27723-9(7)) St. Martin's Pr.

Rakoff, David. Don't Get Too Comfortable: The Indignities of Coach Class, the Torments of Low Thread Count, the Never-Ending Quest for Artisanal Olive Oil, & Other First World Problems. 2006. (ENG.). 240p. pap. 14.00 (978-0-7679-1603-5(4), Broadway) Broadway Bks.

Riley, Marjorie. The Wife of Riley, Vol. I. Riley, Wyman, ed. 2nd ed. (Illus.). 173p. reprint ed. 16.95 (978-0-9623624-0-8(9)) Levee Hse. Bks.

Samuels, Kim. He's Just NOT: Dating Deal Breakers. 2007. (ENG.). 108p. per. 11.95 (978-1-58736-735-9(1)) Wheatmark.

Schroeder, Don. Air Raid Nights & Radio Days. 2009. 264p. 14.99 (978-1-60696-034-9(2)) Tate Publishing & Enterprises, LLC.

Schultz, Connie. Life Happens: And Other Unavoidable Truths. 2007. (ENG.). 320p. per. 13.95 (978-0-8129-7568-0(5), Random Hse. Trade Paperbacks) Random House Publishing Group.

Skinner, Cornelia Otis. Excuse It Please. 21.95 *(978-0-8488-0702-3(2))* Amereon LTD.
Stern, Howard. Miss America. 2010. (ENG.). 496p. pap. 16.99 *(978-0-06-188555-6(X))* HarperCollins Pubs.
White, Bailey. Mama Makes up Her Mind: And Other Dangers of Southern Living. 2009. (ENG.). 240p. pap. 14.99 *(978-0-306-81802-8(7))* Da Capo Pr., Inc.
Wood, Clark. Wood Chips. Crookham, Arthur L., ed. 2009. 110p. 34.95 *(978-1-104-85126-2(1))* 2007. (ENG.). 108p. per. 19.95 *(978-0-548-44055-1(7))* Kessinger Publishing, LLC.
Zola, Meguido. Noodle, Nitwit, Numskull. 2007. (Illus.). 29p. (J). reprint ed. 13.00 *(978-1-4223-9086-3(1))* DIANE Publishing Co.

AMERICAN WIT AND HUMOR—SPORTS AND GAMES

Migaly, Peter. The Best Cartoons for Health & Fitness. Date not set. 100p. (Orig.). pap. 4.65 *(978-0-9647363-3-7(0))* Migaly, Peter.
Wilson, Scott & Hanks, E. Wayne. The Next Level First at Firewheel Edition: A message of hope for hard Times. 2009. (Bubba Ser.). 224p. (Orig.). 24.95 *(978-1-888237-07-8(4))* Baxter Pr.
Wilson, Scott & Hennessy, Shawn. The Next Level Real Life Edition: A message of hope for hard Times. 2009. (Bubba Ser.). 224p. (Orig.). pap. 24.95 *(978-1-888237-08-5(2))* Baxter Pr.
Wilson, Scott & Springle, Patrick. The Next Level Generic Edition: A message of hope for hard Times. 2009. (Bubba Ser.). 224p. (Orig.). pap. 24.95 *(978-1-888237-06-1(6))* Baxter Pr.

AMERICAN WIT AND HUMOR—TRAVEL

Cobb, Irvin S. Europe Revised. 2008. 276p. 25.99 *(978-0-554-38294-4(6))* 2008. 276p. 28.99 *(978-0-554-28991-5(1))* 2007. 242p. pap. 20.99 *(978-1-4346-6696-3(4))* 2007. (ENG.). 272p. pap. 23.99 *(978-1-4346-6697-0(2))* BiblioBazaar.
—Europe Revised. 2007. (ENG.). 232p. per. *(978-1-4065-1395-0(4))* Dodo Pr.
—Europe Revised. 2007. (ENG.). 176p. per. *(978-1-4068-4644-7(9))* Echo Library.
—Roughing It De Luxe. 2007. (ENG., Illus.). 96p. per. *(978-1-4065-1399-8(7))* Dodo Pr.
Trovato, Ben. Ben Trovato's Art of Survival. 2008. (ENG., Illus.). 200p. pap. 23.00 *(978-1-77009-161-0(0))* Jacana Media ZAF. Dist: Independent Pubs. Group.

AMERICAN WIT AND HUMOR, PICTORIAL

see also Comic Books, Strips, etc.

Adler, Bill & Reisner, Bob. Western on Wry. 2011. 64p. 36.95 ***(978-1-258-08847-7(9))*** Literary Licensing, LLC.
Barry, Lynda. Everything, Vol. 1. 2011. (ENG., Illus.). 176p. 24.95 *(978-1-77046-052-2(7))* Drawn & Quarterly Pubns. CAN. Dist: Macmillan.
—Picture This: The Near-Sighted Monkey Book. 2010. (ENG., Illus.). 96p. 29.95 *(978-1-897299-64-7(8))* Drawn & Quarterly Pubns. CAN. Dist: Macmillan.
Benson, John. The Sincerest Form of Parody: The Best 1950s Mad Inspired Satirical Comics. 2012. (ENG., Illus.). 208p. pap. 24.99 *(978-1-60699-511-2(1),* 699511) Fantagraphics Bks.
Brainard, Joe. The Nancy Book. 2008. (ENG., Illus.). 144p. 39.50 *(978-0-9799562-0-1(X))* Siglio Pr.
Brooks, Charles, ed. Best Editorial Cartoons of the Year: 2009 Edition, 1 vol. 2009th ed. 2008. (Best Editorial Cartoons Ser.). (ENG., Illus.). 208p. pap. 14.95 *(978-1-58980-665-8(4))* Pelican Publishing Co., Inc.
—Best Editorial Cartoons of the Year 2010. 2009. (Best Editorial Cartoons of the Year Ser.). (ENG., Illus.). 208p. pap. 14.95 *(978-1-58980-753-2(7))* Pelican Publishing Co., Inc.
Brunetti, Ivan, ed. An Anthology of Graphic Fiction, Cartoons, & True Stories. 2006. (ENG., Illus.). 400p. 28.00 *(978-0-300-11170-5(3))* Yale Univ. Pr.
—An Anthology of Graphic Fiction, Cartoons & True Stories, Vol. 2. 2008. (ENG., Illus.). 400p. 28.00 *(978-0-300-12671-6(9))* Yale Univ. Pr.
Burciaga, José Antonia. Last Supper of Chicano Heroes: Selected Works of Jose Antonio Burciaga. Gladstein, Mimi R. & Chacon, Daniel, eds. 2008. (Camino del Sol Ser.). (ENG., Illus.). 256p. pap. 16.95 *(978-0-8165-2662-8(1))* Univ. of Arizona Pr.
Burciaga, Jose Antonio. Last Supper of Chicano Heroes: Selected Works of Jose Antonio Burciaga. Gladstein, Mimi R. & Chacon, Daniel, eds. 2008. (Camino del Sol Ser.). (ENG., Illus.). 256p. 35.00 *(978-0-8165-2661-1(3))* Univ. of Arizona Pr.
Cagle, Daryl & Fairrington, Brian. The Best Political Cartoons of the Year 2009. annuals 2008. (ENG., Illus.). 288p. pap. 16.99 *(978-0-7897-3815-8(5))* Que.
—The Best Political Cartoons of the Year 2010. 2009. (ENG.). 240p. pap. 12.99 *(978-0-7897-4241-4(1))* Que.
—The Big Book of Campaign 2008 Cartoons. 2008. (ENG., Illus.). 256p. pap. 16.99 *(978-0-7897-3809-7(0))* Que.
Carlson, George. Perfect Nonsense: The Chaotic Comics & Goofy Games of George Carlson. Marschall, Rick & Yezbick, Daniel, eds. 2012. (ENG., Illus.). 224p. 39.99 ***(978-1-60699-508-2(1),*** 699508) Fantagraphics Bks.
Chast, Roz. Theories of Everything: Selected, Collected, & Health-Inspected Cartoons, 1978-2006. 2008. (ENG., Illus.). 400p. pap. 30.00 *(978-1-59691-540-4(4))* Bloomsbury Publishing.
—Theories of Everything: Selected, Collected, Health-Inspected, Copyright-Protected Cartoons, 1978-2006. 2006. (ENG., Illus.). 400p. 45.00 *(978-1-58234-423-2(X))* Bloomsbury Publishing.
Davis, Jim. Garfield Brings Home the Bacon: His 53rd Book. 2012. (ENG., Illus.). 96p. pap. 14.00 ***(978-0-345-52586-4(8),*** Ballantine Bks.) Random House Publishing Group.
—Garfield Left Speechless. 2012. (ENG., Illus.). 128p. pap. 14.00 ***(978-0-345-53058-5(6),*** Ballantine Bks.) Random House Publishing Group.
Dewey, Donald. The Art of Ill Will: The Story of American Political Cartoons. 2008. (ENG., Illus.). 264p. pap. 26.00 *(978-0-8147-2015-8(3))* New York Univ. Pr.
Diffee, Matthew. The Best of the Rejection Collection: 293 Cartoons That Were Too Dumb, Too Dark, or Too Naughty for the New Yorker. 2011. (ENG., Illus.). 320p. pap. 13.95 ***(978-0-7611-6578-1(9),*** 0761165789) Workman Publishing Co., Inc.
Diffee, Matthew, ed. The Rejection Collection: Cartoons You Never Saw, & Never Will See, in the New Yorker. 2006. (ENG., Illus.). 272p. 22.95 *(978-1-4169-3339-7(5))* Gallery Pr., The IRL. Dist: Simon & Schuster, Inc.
—The Rejection Collection Vol. 2: The Cream of the Crap. 2007. (ENG., Illus.). 304p. 22.95 *(978-1-4169-3401-1(4))* Gallery Pr., The IRL. Dist: Simon & Schuster, Inc.
Feiffer. Political Cartoon Collection, Vol. 1. Date not set. pap. *(978-0-7653-0439-1(2),* Forge Bks.) Doherty, Tom Assocs., LLC.
Feiffer, Jules. Explainers: The Complete Village Voice Strips, 1956-66. 2008. (ENG., Illus.). 528p. 35.00 *(978-1-56097-835-0(X),* 56835) Fantagraphics Bks.
Fischer, Ed. Over-The-Hill & Lovin' It. 2008. *(978-0-88166-536-9(3))* Meadowbrook Pr.
Fish, creator. Go Fish. 2011. (ENG., Illus.). 224p. pap. 18.95 ***(978-1-61775-014-4(X))*** Akashic Bks.
Goldberg, David, illus. & intro. Superbad: The Drawings 4 Copy Pre-Pack. movie tie-in ed. 2008. 96p. 60.00 *(978-1-55704-823-3(1))* Newmarket Pr.
Gorey, Edward & Gorey, Edward. Amphigorey Again. (ENG., Illus.). 260p. 2007. pap. 22.00 *(978-0-15-603021-2(7),* Mariner Bks.) 2006. 35.00 *(978-0-15-101107-0(9))* Houghton Mifflin Harcourt Trade & Reference Pubs.
—The Utter Zoo: An Alphabet. 2010. (Illus.). 56p. 14.95 *(978-0-7649-5508-2(X))* Pomegranate Communications, Inc.
Gottschalk, Peter & Greenberg, Gabriel. Islamophobia: Making Muslims the Enemy. 2007. (ENG., Illus.). 192p. 24.95 *(978-0-7425-5286-9(1))* Rowman & Littlefield Publishers, Inc.
Greene, Ward, ed. Laugh Parade: A Collection of the Funniest Cartoons of the Day. 2011. 130p. 40.95 ***(978-1-258-10369-9(9))*** Literary Licensing, LLC.
Griffith, Bill. Connect the Polka Dots. 2006. (Illus.). 160p. pap. 18.95 *(978-1-56097-777-3(9))* Fantagraphics Bks.
Groening, Matt. Chief Wiggum's Book of Crime & Punishment: The Simpsons Library of Wisdom. 2010. (ENG.). 96p. 9.99 *(978-0-06-178743-0(4),* Collins Design) HarperCollins Pubs.
Jaffee, Al. Tall Tales. 2008. (ENG., Illus.). 128p. 16.95 *(978-0-8109-7272-8(7))* Abrams.
Jamie, Smith. It's Gonna Be A Long Winter... 2008. (Illus.). 128p. pap. *(978-0-9749221-1-9(0))* Ester Republic Pr.
—Nuggets: A big ol' pile of cartoons from Alaska. 2008. (Illus.). 128p. pap. 9.95 *(978-0-9749221-2-6(9))* Ester Republic Pr.
Ketcham, Hank. Complete Dennis the Menace 1959-1960, Vol. 5. 2009. (Dennis the Menace Ser.). (ENG.). 672p. 24.99 *(978-1-56097-966-1(6),* 56966) Fantagraphics Bks.
Kirkman, Rick & Scott, Jerry. Cut! 2011. (ENG.). 128p. pap. 14.99 *(978-1-4494-0182-5(1))* Andrews McMeel Publishing.
Koffman, Deb. Soul Support Book (Ppck 8) pap. 79.60 *(978-1-58017-898-3(7),* 67898, Storey Kids) Storey Publishing, LLC.
Kraus, Jerelle. All the Art That's Fit to Print: Inside the New York Times Op-Ed Page. 2008. (ENG., Illus.). 280p. (gr. 17). 49.95 *(978-0-231-13824-6(5))* Columbia Univ. Pr.
Kurtzman, Harvey & Roth, Arnold. Humbug, 2 vols. 2009. (ENG., Illus.). 476p. 60.00 *(978-1-56097-933-3(X),* 56933) Fantagraphics Bks.
Kurtzman, Harvey, et al. Humbug. aut. ltd. ed. 2009. (ENG., Illus.). 476p. 100.00 *(978-1-60699-179-4(5),* 699179) Fantagraphics Bks.
Lewin, J. G. & Huff, P. J. Lines of Contention: Political Cartoons of the Civil War. 2007. (ENG., Illus.). 224p. per. 19.95 *(978-0-06-113788-4(X),* HarperPerennial) HarperCollins Pubs.
Luckovich, Mike. Four More Wars! 2006. (ENG., Illus.). 248p. per. 16.95 *(978-1-55022-737-6(8))* ECW Pr. CAN. Dist: Independent Pubs. Group.
Mankoff, Robert, ed. The New Yorker Book of Business Cartoons. 2010. (New Yorker Ser.: 8). (ENG., Illus.). 128p. pap. 12.00 *(978-1-57660-042-9(4),* Bloomberg Pr.) Wiley, John & Sons, Inc.
Mankoff, Robert & Gopnik, Adam, eds. The Complete Cartoons of the New Yorker. rev. ed. 2006. (ENG., Illus.). 672p. 35.00 *(978-1-57912-620-9(0),* 1579126200) Black Dog & Leventhal Pubs., Inc.
Mauldin, Bill. Up Front. (Illus.). 240p. 21.95 *(978-0-89190-896-8(X))* Amereon LTD.
—Willie & Joe: Back Home. 25.95 *(978-0-89190-856-2(0))* Amereon LTD.
McCay, Winsor. Early Works. 2007. (Winsor Mccay: Early Works). 200p. Vol. 9. (Illus.). pap. 19.95 *(978-1-933160-07-8(1))* Vol. 10. pap. 19.95 *(978-1-933160-08-5(X))* Devil's Due Digital, Inc. - A Checker Digital Co.
Meyerowitz, Rick. Drunk Stoned Brilliant Dead: The Writers & Artists Who Made the National Lampoon Insanely Great. 2010. (ENG., Illus.). 320p. 40.00 *(978-0-8109-8848-4(8))* Abrams.
Miller, Mark Crispin. Misunderestimated & Overunderappreciated: The George W. Bush Administration As Seen Through the Eyes of the Tribune's Syndicated Editorial Cartoonists. 2007. (Illus.). 328p. *(978-1-4351-0017-6(4))* Metro Bks.
Mokris, Drew & Boyd, Justin. A Dose of Awkward: Left-Handed Toons (by Right-Handed People) 2009. (ENG.). 192p. pap. 9.99 *(978-1-60061-303-6(9),* HOW Bks.) F&W Media, Inc.
Monsen, Avery, et al. All My Friends Are Dead. 2010. (ENG., Illus.). 96p. 9.95 *(978-0-8118-7455-7(9))* Chronicle Bks. LLC.
Mouly, Françoise. Blown Covers: New Yorker Covers You Were Never Meant to See. 2012. (ENG., Illus.). 128p. 24.95 ***(978-1-4197-0209-9(2))*** Abrams.
Nahson, Claudia J., ed. The Art of William Steig. 2007. (ENG., Illus.). 208p. 40.00 *(978-0-300-12478-1(3))* Yale Univ. Pr.
Niemann, Christoph. Abstract City. 2012. (ENG., Illus.). 256p. 24.95 ***(978-1-4197-0207-5(6))*** Abrams.
Opper, Frederick Burr. Happy Hooligan. 2008. (Forever Nuts Ser.). (ENG., Illus.). 110p. 24.95 *(978-1-56163-542-9(1))* NBM Publishing Co.
Palmer, Donald. Looking at Philosophy: The Unbearable Heaviness of Philosophy Made Lighter. 5th ed. 2009. (ENG., Illus.). 464p. (C). pap. 56.67 *(978-0-07-340748-7(8),* 0073407488) McGraw-Hill Cos., The.
Pettibon, Raymond. Raymond Pettibon. Rugoff, Ralph, ed. 2012. (ENG., Illus.). 384p. 135.00 *(978-0-8478-3500-3(6))* Rizzoli International Pubns., Inc.
Phi Delta Kappa International. Head of the Class: The Collected Kappan Cartoons for Educators. 2009. 176p. pap. 16.95 *(978-1-935249-36-8(3))* Solution Tree.
Price, George. Good Humor Man: A Happy Array of Cartoons, Sketches & A Gay Diary. McCallister, Richard, ed. 2011. 126p. 40.95 ***(978-1-258-10445-0(8))*** Literary Licensing, LLC.
Rezwin, Max. Please Don't Eat the Crab Grass. 2011. 64p. 36.95 ***(978-1-258-08826-2(6))*** Literary Licensing, LLC.
Sachs, Harley L. Irma Quarterdeck Reports. 2nd ed. 2007. per. 21.95 *(978-0-9789350-6-1(3))* Nautical Publishing Co.
Schulz, Charles M. Schulz's Youth. 2007. (Illus.). 296p. *(978-0-9790750-1-8(7))* About Comics.
Scott, Jerry & Kirkman, Rick. Ambushed! in the Family Room: Scrapbook #26. 2010. (ENG.). 128p. pap. 12.99 *(978-0-7407-9740-8(9))* Andrews McMeel Publishing.
Sherman, Hal. The Little Friar. 2011. 130p. 40.95 ***(978-1-258-09697-7(8))*** Literary Licensing, LLC.
Sorensen, Jen. Slowpoke: One Nation, Oh My God! 2008. (ENG., Illus.). 150p. pap. 13.95 *(978-0-9788431-6-8(9))* Ig Publishing, Inc.
Swinnerton, James Guilford. James Swinnerton's Canyon Country Kiddies. 2011. 80p. pap. 24.95 ***(978-1-61646-070-9(9))*** Coachwhip Pubns.
Tananbaum, Duane, ed. & intro. Drawn to Service: Political Cartoons from the Papers of Herbert H. Lehman. 2008. 1.00 *(978-0-9789037-2-5(2))* Columbia Univ. Libraries.
Thomas, Cory. Watch Your Head. 2008. (ENG., Illus.). 128p. pap. 12.99 *(978-0-7407-7103-3(5))* Andrews McMeel Publishing.
Topps Company Staff. Wacky Packages. 2008. (ENG., Illus.). 240p. 19.95 *(978-0-8109-9531-4(X))* Abrams.
Wheeler, Shannon. Screw Heaven, When I Die I'm Going to Mars. 2007. (Illus.). 144p. pap. 12.95 *(978-1-59307-820-1(X))* Dark Horse Comics.
Williams, Lorraine, creator. You Know You're in a Small Town When..., Vol. 2. 2007. (Illus.). 84p. pap. 14.95 *(978-0-9797442-0-4(2))* Alaska Independent Pubs.
Wilson, Tom. Zig-Zagging: Loving Madly, Losing Badly - How Ziggy Saved My Life. 2009. (ENG., Illus.). 212p. 17.95 *(978-0-7573-0793-5(0))* Health Communications, Inc.
—Ziggy. 2011. (ENG., Illus.). 304p. 24.99 *(978-1-4494-0108-5(2))* Andrews McMeel Publishing.
Wolfe, Maynard Frank. Rube Goldberg: Inventions! 2011. (ENG.). 192p. pap. 20.95 *(978-1-4516-4663-4(1))* Simon & Schuster.

AMERICAN WOODCOCK

see Woodcock

AMERICAN WORKERS IN FOREIGN COUNTRIES

see Americans—Employment—Foreign Countries

AMERICANA

see also African Americans—Collectibles; United States—History—Civil War, 1861-1865—Collectibles; West (U.S.)—Collectibles

Americana Bounty. 2006. 44p. 10.95 *(978-1-60140-101-4(9))* Leisure Arts, Inc.
Americana Library, 6 bks. & 6 cass., Set. 39.95 *(978-0-86545-165-0(6))* Spizzirri Pr., Inc.
Arkins, Diane C. & Arkins, Diane. The Glorious Fourth of July: Old-Fashioned Treats & Treasures from America's Patriotic Past, 1 vol. 2009. (ENG., Illus.). 128p. 19.95 *(978-1-58980-611-5(5))* Pelican Publishing Co., Inc.
Barson, Michael. True West: An Illustrated Guide to the Heyday of the Western. 2008. (Illus.). 175p. pap. 29.95 *(978-0-87565-379-2(0))* Texas Christian Univ. Pr.
Del Bianco, Fred John, Jr. Late Boomer: The Things I Grew up With. 2009. 176p. pap. 12.95 *(978-1-4343-8214-6(1))* AuthorHouse.
Field, Thomas W. Catalogue of the Library Belonging to Mr. Thomas W. Field. 2007. 385p. 65.00 *(978-1-57898-493-0(9))* Martino Publishing.
Hilfiger, Tommy & Keeps, David A. All American: A Style Book. 2006. (Illus.). 198p. reprint ed. 35.00 *(978-1-4223-5193-2(9))* DIANE Publishing Co.
Hoskinson, Rob. Bridges in Time: Keepsakes Celebrating the Covered Bridges of Madison County. Johnston, Becky W., ed. (Illus.). 64p. 10.95 *(978-0-9646870-0-4(3))* Landauer Publishing, LLC.
Katcher, Jane, et al. Expressions of Innocence & Eloquence: Selections from the Jane Katcher Collection of Americana, Volume II. 2011. (ENG., Illus.). 452p. 95.00 *(978-0-300-17580-6(9))* Yale Univ. Pr.
Larrabee, Linda. Good Morning It's. 2009. 116p. 27.49 *(978-1-4389-8082-9(5))*; pap. 16.49 *(978-1-4389-8083-6(3))* AuthorHouse.
Marchman, Judy. Kentucky Derby Glasses Price Guide. 4th ed. 2008. (ENG., Illus.). 104p. pap. 16.95 *(978-1-58150-183-4(8),* Eclipse Pr.) Blood-Horse, Inc., The.
Mauzy, Barbara. African-Americana. 2008. (Illus.). 192p. 39.99 *(978-0-7643-3144-2(2))* Schiffer Publishing, Ltd.
Minick, Polly. The Americana Collection: Hooked Rugs. 2007. (That Patchwork Place Ser.). (ENG., Illus.). 80p. per. 24.95 *(978-1-56477-752-2(9),* That Patchwork Place) Martingale & Co.
Pina, Leslie. Fostoria American Line 2056. 3rd rev. ed. 2006. (Schiffer Book for Collectors Ser.). (Illus.). 160p. 29.95 *(978-0-7643-2469-7(1))* Schiffer Publishing, Ltd.
Reighley, Kurt B. United States of Americana: Backyard Chickens, Burlesque Beauties, & Handmade Bitters - A Field Guide to the New American Roots Movement. 2010. (ENG., Illus.). 256p. pap. 14.99 *(978-0-06-194649-3(4),* HarperPerennial) HarperCollins Pubs.
Seeley, Mary Evans. Season's Greetings from the White House: The Collection of Presidential Christmas Cards, Messages & Gifts. 6th ed. 2007. 272p. 40.00 *(978-0-9657684-7-4(3))* Presidential Christmas, A.
Sundman, David. 100 Greatest Stamps. 2007. 144p. pap. 29.95 *(978-0-7948-2248-4(7))* Whitman Publishing LLC.

AMERICANISM (CATHOLIC CONTROVERSY)

see also Modernism (Christian Theology)—Catholic Church

Slawson, Douglas J. Ambition & Arrogance: Cardinal William O'Connell of Boston & the American Catholic Church. 2007. (ENG.). 248p. per. *(978-0-9787855-0-5(9))* Cobalt Productions.

AMERICANISMS

Adelson-Goldstein, Jayme. Oxford Picture Dictionary, Pack. Oxford University Press Staff, ed. 2nd ed. 2008. (Oxford Picture Dictionary 2E Ser.). (ENG.). 123.75 *(978-0-19-430196-1(6))* Oxford Univ. Pr., Inc.
Adelson-Goldstein, Jayme, frwd. Oxford Basic American Dictionary for Learners of English. 2011. (ENG.). pap. 31.25 *(978-0-19-439969-2(9))* Oxford Univ. Pr., Inc.
American Heritage Dictionaries Editors, ed. The American Heritage Abbreviations Dictionary: A Compilation of Today's Acronyms & Abbreviations Including Cyberspeak. 3rd ed. 2007. (American Heritage Bks.). (ENG.). 304p. 6.95 *(978-0-618-85747-0(8))* Houghton Mifflin Harcourt Trade & Reference Pubs.
Atwood, E. Bagby. The Regional Vocabulary of Texas. 2011. 286p. 48.95 ***(978-1-258-08647-3(6))*** Literary Licensing, LLC.
Bailey, Richard W. Speaking American: A History of English in the United States, 1 vol. 2012. (ENG., Illus.). 320p. 27.95 *(978-0-19-517934-7(X))* Oxford Univ. Pr., Inc.
Baranowski, Maciej. Phonological Variation & Change in the Dialect of Charleston, South Carolina. 2007. (Publication of the American Dialect Society). (ENG., Illus.). 268p. 20.00 *(978-0-8223-6692-8(4))* Duke Univ. Pr.
Blevins, Winfred. Dictionary of the American West: Over 5,000 Terms & Expressions from Aarigaa! to Zopilote. 2nd ed. 2008. (ENG., Illus.). 429p. pap. 19.95 *(978-0-87565-373-0(1))* Texas Christian Univ. Pr.
Boyd Zimmerman, Cheryl, frwd. Oxford Advanced American Dictionary for Learners of English. 2011. (ENG.). 1736p. 49.38 *(978-0-19-439966-1(4))* Oxford Univ. Pr., Inc.
Brophy, Patrick. Border Speech: Words & Phrases of the Western Border in the Light of Its History. 2007. 101p. pap. 30.00 *(978-1-893046-17-7(6))* Vernon County Historical Society.
Cassidy, Daniel. How the Irish Invented Slang: The Secret Language of the Crossroads. 2007. (Counterpunch Ser.). (ENG., Illus.). 224p. per. 18.95 *(978-1-904859-60-4(7))* AK Pr. GBR. Dist: Consortium Bk. Sales & Distribution.
Chapman, Robert L. & Kipfer, Barbara Ann. Dictionary of American Slang. 4th ed. 2008. 640p. pap. 16.00 *(978-0-06-117663-0(X))* HarperCollins Pubs.
Chapman, Robert L., et al. Dictionary of American Slang. 4th ed. 2007. 608p. 45.00 *(978-0-06-117646-3(X))* HarperCollins Pubs.
COLLIS. 101 American Idioms 2/e. 2nd rev. ed. 2007. (Illus.). vi, 104p. pap. *(978-0-07-148773-3(5))* McGraw-Hill Cos., The.
Collis, Harry. Get with It: 101-Plus Pop Culture Idioms & Expressions. 2008. (ENG., Illus.). 130p. pap. *(978-1-932383-15-7(8))* Alta Bk. Ctr. Pubs.
Dalzell & Victor. New Partridge Dict Sex Slang. 2007. 17.95 *(978-0-415-34673-3(8))* Routledge.
Dalzell, Tom, ed. The Routledge Dictionary of Modern American Slang & Unconventional English. 2008. 1124p. 52.95 *(978-0-415-37182-7(1))* Routledge.
DeCapua, Andrea. Grammar for Teachers: A Guide to American English for Native & Non-Native Speakers. 2010. (ENG.). xviii, 444p. pap. 69.95 *(978-1-4419-4549-5(0),* 1441945490) Springer.
Dickson, Paul. Slang: The Topical Dictionary of Americanisms. 2006. (ENG., Illus.). 464p. 24.95 *(978-0-8027-1531-9(1))* Walker & Co.
Dillard, Joey L., ed. Perspectives on American English. (Contributions to the Sociology of Language [CSL] Ser.). (ENG.). VIII, 467p. 210.00 ***(978-3-11-174822-1(7))*** De Gruyter, Mouton DEU. Dist: de Gruyter, Walter GmbH & Co. KG.
Ehrat, David N. Dialect Emergence in Waumandee English. 2008. (New German-American Studies / Neue Deutsch-Amerikanische Studien Ser.). 214p. pap. 66.95 *(978-3-03910-911-1(1))* Lang, Peter AG GBR. Dist: Lang, Peter.
Foster, Herbert L. The First Yiddish & Jive Dictionary: A Lexicon of the Yiddish & Jive Words in Common Usage. Date not set. (Orig.). pap. *(978-0-9624847-1-1(7))* Foster, Herbert L. Assocs., Inc.
Frandsen, Wendy Jean. Speaking Southern, Writing English: Essential Grammar Skills. 2009. 120p. pap. 22.00 *(978-1-59460-553-6(X))* Carolina Academic Pr.

Fridlund, Anneli. Svensk-Amerikanska Falska Vänner - A Swedish-American False Friends Dictionary. 2007.Tr. of Swedish-American False Friends Dictionary. (SWE.). 224p. pap. 11.00 net. *(978-0-9797941-0-0(2))* Rem Tene Pubns., Inc.

Garner, Bryan. Garner's Modern American Usage. 3rd ed. 2009. (ENG., Illus.). 960p. 45.00 *(978-0-19-538275-4(7))* Oxford Univ. Pr., Inc.

Garrison, Webb, Sr. & Garrison, Cheryl. Civil War Dictionary: An Illustrated Guide to the Everyday Language of Soldiers & Civilians. 2008. (ENG., Illus.). 350p. pap. 16.95 *(978-1-58182-675-3(3))* Turner Publishing Co.

Garrison, Webb & Garrison, Cheryl. Encyclopedia of Civil War Usage. 2009. (ENG.). 274p. 9.99 *(978-0-7858-2346-9(8)*, 0785823468, Castle Bks., Inc.) Book Sales, Inc.

Hall, Joan Houston. Dictionary of American Regional English, Volume V: Sl-Z, 5 vols., Volume V. 2012. (ENG., Illus.). 1296p. 85.00 ***(978-0-674-04735-8(4)***, Belknap Pr.) Harvard Univ. Pr.

Hall, Joseph S. Smoky Mountain Folks & Their Lore. 2011. 74p. 36.95 ***(978-1-258-04010-9(7))*** Literary Licensing, LLC.

Hall, Joseph Sargent. Phonetics of Great Smoky Mountain Speech. 2006. pap. 20.95 *(978-1-4286-6111-0(5))* Kessinger Publishing, LLC.

Harrison, Mim. Wicked Good Words: From Johnnycakes to Jug Handles, a Roundup of America's Regionalisms. 2011. (ENG.). 208p. (gr. 12). 12.95 *(978-0-399-53676-2(0)*, Perigee Trade) Penguin Group (USA) Inc.

Helterbran, Valeri R. Exploring Idioms: A Critical-Thinking Resource for Grades 4-8. 2008. 133p. per. 19.95 *(978-1-934338-14-8(1))* Maupin Hse. Publishing.

Hendrickson, Robert. Yankee Talk: A Dictionary of New England Expressions. 255p. 8.99 *(978-0-7858-1555-6(4))* Book Sales, Inc.

Hobbs, James B., compiled by. Homophones & Homographs: An American Dictionary. 4th rev. ed. 2006. (ENG., Illus.). 376p. 55.00 *(978-0-7864-2488-7(5))* McFarland & Co., Inc. Pubs.

Holm, Thomas Campanius, compiled by. A Vocabulary of Susquehannock. 2nd rev. exp. ed. 2006. (American Language Reprints Ser.: No. 2). 50p. pap. 17.95 *(978-1-889758-85-5(X)*, Evolution Publishing & Manufacturing) Arx Publishing.

Howard, Thomas W., ed. The Dixie Dictionary: Your Complete Guide to the Southern Language. 2006. (ENG.). 144p. per. *(978-1-57587-283-4(8))* Crane Hill Pubs.

Iorio, Mary G. & Beyer, Charles E. ABC Pronunciary: American English Pronunciation Dictionary. (Illus.). 113p. 29.95 incl. audio, VHS Vocalis, Ltd.

Jewell, Elizabeth. The Oxford Desk Dictionary & Thesaurus. 2nd ed. 2007. *(978-1-4114-0508-0(0))* Oxford Univ. Pr., Inc.

Kautzsch, Alexander. The Historical Evolution of Earlier African American English: An Empirical Comparison of Early Sources. (Topics in English Linguistics [TiEL] Ser.). (ENG.). XV, 335p. 180.00 ***(978-3-11-179679-6(5))*** De Gruyter, Mouton DEU. Dist: de Gruyter, Walter GmbH & Co. KG.

Kearse, Randy. Street Talk: Da Official Guide to Hip-Hop & Urban Slanguage. 2006. 686p. per. 19.95 *(978-1-56980-320-2(X))* Barricade Bks., Inc.

Kipfer, Barbara Ann & Chapman, Robert L. American Slang. 4th ed. 2008. 576p. pap. 19.99 *(978-0-06-117947-1(7))* HarperCollins Pubs.

Little, Elizabeth. Trip of the Tongue: Cross-Country Travels in Search of America's Languages. 2012. (ENG.). 288p. 25.00 *(978-1-59691-656-2(7))* Bloomsbury Publishing.

Liu, Dilin. Idioms: Description, Comprehension, Acquisition, & Pedagogy. 2007. (ESL & Applied Linguistics Professional Ser.). (ENG., Illus.). 224p. 45.95 *(978-0-8058-6346-3(X))*; 140.00 *(978-0-8058-6345-1(1))* Routledge.

Lopez, Barry. Home Ground: Language for an American Landscape. Gwartney, Debra, ed. 2010. (ENG.). 480p. pap. 19.95 *(978-1-59534-057-3(2))* Trinity Univ. Pr.

Lujan, Beverly A. The American Accent Guide: A Comprehensive Course on the Sound System of American English/book & MP3 audio (nearly 8 Hours) Wallia, C J S, ed. 2nd ed. 2008. (Illus.). 237p. pap. 59.00 incl. audio compact disk *(978-0-9634139-0-1(2))* Lingual Arts.

Matthews, Brander. Americanisms & Briticisms, with Other Essays on Other Isms. 2009. 200p. 26.99 *(978-1-116-77646-1(4))*; 30.99 *(978-1-116-77645-4(6))*; pap. 24.75 *(978-1-116-77647-8(2))*; pap. 23.75 *(978-1-116-77648-5(0))* BiblioBazaar.

Metcalf, Allan. Ok: The Improbable Story of America's Greatest Word. 2012. (ENG.). 240p. pap. 13.95 ***(978-0-19-989253-2(9))*** Oxford Univ. Pr., Inc.

Metcalf, Allan. OK: The Improbable Story of America's Greatest Word. 2010. (ENG., Illus.). 240p. 18.95 *(978-0-19-537793-4(1))* Oxford Univ. Pr., Inc.

mountainscape Press. American-English Function Words: A Fresh View of American-English Syntax. 2010. (Illus.). 294p. pap. 24.95 net. *(978-0-9799813-0-2(1))* Mountainscape Pr.

Mountainscape Press. American English Phrasal Verbs: Plus Enhanced Diagraming Methods. 2010. 424p. pap. 34.95 net. *(978-0-9799813-1-9(X))* Mountainscape Pr.

Murtha, Sheila MacKechnie & O'Connor, Jane Airey. English the American Way: A Fun ESL Guide to Language & Culture in the U. S. 2011. (English As a Second Language Ser.). (ENG.). 288p. pap. 17.95 *(978-0-7386-0676-7(6))* Research & Education Assn.

Newman, Edwin. Strictly Speaking: Will America Be the Death of English? 2010. (ENG.). 240p. pap. 29.95 *(978-1-4128-1327-3(1))* Transaction Pubs.

Ostler, Rosemarie. Let's Talk Turkey: The Stories Behind America's Favorite Expressions. 2008. (ENG., Illus.). 240p. pap. 18.98 *(978-1-59102-625-9(3))* Prometheus Bks., Pubs.

Oxford, ed. Oxford American Desk Dictionary & Thesaurus, 1 vol. 3rd ed. 2010. (ENG.). 928p. 19.95 *(978-0-19-973927-1(7))* Oxford Univ. Pr., Inc.

—Pocket Oxford American Dictionary. 2nd ed. 2008. (ENG., Illus.). 1008p. pap. 12.95 *(978-0-19-530163-2(3))* Oxford Univ. Pr., Inc.

Oxford Staff, ed. Oxford American Dictionary for Learners of English. 2010. (ENG.). 34.38 *(978-0-19-439972-2(9))* Oxford Univ. Pr., Inc.

Ramsay, Robert L. & Emberson, Frances G. Mark Twain Lexicon. 278p. reprint ed. lib. bdg. 98.00 *(978-0-7222-0498-6(1))* Library Reprints, Inc.

Rowse, Arthur E. Amglish in, Like, Ten Easy Lessons: A Celebration of the New World Lingo. 2011. (ENG., Illus.). 236p. pap. 16.95 *(978-1-4422-1167-4(9))* Rowman & Littlefield Publishers, Inc.

Rudanko, Juhani. Changes in Complementation in British & American English: A Corpus-Based Study. 2011. (ENG., Illus.). 256p. 85.00 *(978-0-230-53733-0(2))* Palgrave Macmillan.

Runyan, W. R. Whiffletrees & Goobers: 1,001 Fun & Fabulous Forgotten Words & Phrases. 2007. (Illus.). 168p. per. 12.95 *(978-1-60239-131-4(9))* Skyhorse Publishing Co., Inc.

—1,001 Fun & Fabulous Forgotten Words & Phrases. 2009. (ENG., Illus.). 176p. 9.99 *(978-0-7858-2494-7(4)*, 0785824944, Castle Bks., Inc.) Book Sales, Inc.

Schele De Vere, Maximilian. Americanisms; the English of the New World. 2006. 700p. per. 36.99 *(978-1-4255-6861-0(0))* MPublishing.

Smiley, Jack. Hash House Lingo: The Slang of Soda Jerks, Short-Order Cooks, Bartenders, Waitresses, Carhops & Other Denizens of Yesterday's Roadside. 2012. (ENG.). 192p. pap. 9.95 *(978-0-486-48112-8(3))* Dover Pubns., Inc.

Spears, Richard. Common American Phrases in Everyday Contexts, 3rd Edition. 3rd ed. 2011. (ENG.). 320p. pap. 14.00 ***(978-0-07-177607-3(9)***, 0071776079) McGraw-Hill Cos., The.

Spears, Richard A. American Idioms Dictionary. 3rd ed. 2008. (Essential Ser.). (ENG., Illus.). 288p. pap. 12.95 *(978-0-07-149784-8(6)*, 0071497846) McGraw-Hill Cos., The.

—Common American Phrases in Everyday Contexts: A Detailed Guide to Real-Life Conversation & Small Talk. 3rd ed. 2011. ix, 309p. E-Book ***(978-0-07-177608-0(7))*** McGraw-Hill Cos., The.

—McGraw-Hill's Dictionary of American Idioms Dictionary. 4th rev. ed. 2006. (McGraw-Hill ESL References Ser.). (ENG., Illus.). 544p. pap. 16.95 *(978-0-07-147893-9(0)*, 0071478930) McGraw-Hill Cos., The.

—McGraw-Hill's Essential American Slang. 2nd ed. 2008. (Essential Ser.). (ENG., Illus.). 288p. per. 12.95 *(978-0-07-149785-5(4)*, 0071497854) McGraw-Hill Cos., The.

—McGraw-Hill's Super-Mini American Slang Dictionary. 2nd ed. 2007. (McGraw-Hill ESL References Ser.). (ENG., Illus.). 288p. per. 6.95 *(978-0-07-149228-7(3)*, 0071492283) McGraw-Hill Cos., The.

—Super-Mini American Idioms Dictionary. 2nd ed. 2007. (McGraw-Hill ESL References Ser.). (ENG., Illus.). 288p. per. 6.95 *(978-0-07-149227-0(5)*, 0071492275) McGraw-Hill Cos., The.

Stevenson, Angus & Lindberg, Christine A. New Oxford American Dictionary, 1 vol. 3rd ed. 2010. (ENG., Illus.). 2096p. 60.00 *(978-0-19-539288-3(4))* Oxford Univ. Pr., Inc.

Zhang, Wen-Hwa. Dictionary of Spoken American English. (CHI & ENG.). pap. 19.95 *(978-7-5600-0809-7(7))* China International Bk. Trading Corp. CHN. Dist: Distribooks, Inc.

AMERICANIZATION

Biase, Anita. Su Guía para Ser Ciudadano de los EE. UU: What You Need to Know to Pass Your U. S. Citizenship Test. 2009. (SPA.). 288p. pap. 24.95 *(978-1-60138-136-1(0))* Atlantic Publishing Co.

—Your U. S. Citizenship Guide: What You Need to Know to Pass Your U. S. Citzenship Test. 2009. (ENG., Illus.). 288p. pap. 24.95 *(978-1-60138-135-4(2))* Atlantic Publishing Co.

Breckinridge, S. P. New Homes for Old. 2009. 400p. 38.99 *(978-1-113-85417-9(0))*; 400p. 33.99 *(978-1-113-85416-2(2))*; (ENG.). 399p. pap. 26.99 *(978-1-113-85411-7(1)*, BiblioLife); (ENG.). 399p. pap. 25.99 *(978-1-113-85408-7(1)*, BiblioLife); 400p. pap. 20.99 *(978-1-113-85413-1(8))*; 400p. pap. 34.75 *(978-1-113-85414-8(6))* BiblioBazaar.

—New Homes for Old. 2010. 400p. pap. 27.96 *(978-1-163-91404-5(5))* 2008. 398p. 49.95 *(978-0-548-93708-2(7))* 2007. (ENG.). 400p. per. 34.95 *(978-0-548-58841-3(4))* Kessinger Publishing, LLC.

Chandra, Sarika. Dislocalism: The Crisis of Globalization & the Remobilizing of Americanism. 2011. 312p. 44.95 ***(978-0-8142-1166-3(6))***; cd-rom 14.95 ***(978-0-8142-9269-3(0))*** Ohio State Univ. Pr.

Clark, Ian. The Americanization of Industrial Relations: An International Relations Perspective on Business. 2007. 304p. 140.00 *(978-0-415-38536-7(9))* Routledge.

Comprehensive Immigration Reform: Becoming Americans: U.S. Immigrant Integration (Continued): Hearing Before the Subcommittee on Immigration, Citizenship, Refugees, Border Security, & International Law of the Committee on the Judiciary, House of Representatives, One Hundred Tenth Congress, First Session, May 23, 2007. 2007. iii, 87p. *(978-0-16-079523-7(0)*, 552-070-36501-0) United States Government Printing Office.

Comprehensive Immigration Reform: Becoming Americans, U.S. Immigrant Integration: Hearing Before the Subcommittee on Immigration, Citizenship, Refugees, Border Security, & International Law of the Committee on the Judiciary, House of Representatives, One Hundred Tenth Congress, First Session, May 16, 2007. 2007. (Illus.). iv, 115p. *(978-0-16-079274-8(6)*, 552-070-36359-9) United States Government Printing Office.

Dinnerstein, Leonard, et al. Ethnic Americans: Immigration & American Society. 5th ed. 2009. (ENG.). 256p. (gr. 17). 79.50 *(978-0-231-14336-3(2))*; pap. 27.50 *(978-0-231-14337-0(0))* Columbia Univ. Pr.

Dorsey, Leroy G. We Are All Americans, Pure & Simple: Theodore Roosevelt & the Myth of Americanism. 2nd ed. 2007. (ENG., Illus.). 280p. 32.50 *(978-0-8173-1592-4(6))* Univ. of Alabama Pr.

First, Anat. America in Jerusalem: Globalization, National Identity, & Israeli Advertising. 2009. (ENG.). 156p. 62.99 *(978-0-7391-3325-5(X))* Lexington Bks.

Gutiérrez, David G. & Hondagneu-Sotelo, Pierrette, eds. Nation & Migration: Past & Future. 2009. (Special Issue of American Quarterly Ser.). (ENG., Illus.). 392p. (C). (gr. 13-17). pap. 25.00 *(978-0-8018-9281-3(3))* Johns Hopkins Univ. Pr.

Hartmann, Edward G. Movement to Americanize the Immigrant. (Columbia University, Studies in the Social Sciences: No. 545). reprint ed. 20.00 *(978-0-404-51545-4(2))* AMS Pr., Inc.

Hirschy, Margaret W. & Hirschy, Patricia L. The Way to U. S. Citizenship. rev. ed. 18.95 *(978-1-56270-972-3(0))* Dominie Pr., Inc.

Jain, Anupama. How to Be South Asian in America: Narratives of Ambivalence & Belonging. 2011. (ENG.). 288p. pap. 26.95 *(978-1-4399-0303-2(4))* Temple Univ. Pr.

jain, anupama. How to Be South Asian in America: Narratives of Ambivalence & Belonging. 2011. (ENG.). 288p. 68.50 *(978-1-4399-0302-5(6))* Temple Univ. Pr.

Keogan, Kevin. Immigrants & the Cultural Politics of Place: A Comparative Study of New York & Los Angeles. 2010. (New Americans). 204p. 62.00 *(978-1-59332-232-8(1))* LFB Scholarly Publishing LLC.

Kraut & Cram101 Textbook Reviews Staff. The Huddled Masses: The Immigrant in American Society, 1880-1921. 2007. 68p. per. 10.95 *(978-1-4288-2796-7(X))* Cram101 Inc.

Kraut, Alan & Diner, Hasia R. From Arrival to Incorporation: Migrants to the U. S. in a Global Era. Barkan, Elliott R., ed. 2007. (ENG.). 320p. per. 25.00 *(978-0-8147-9961-1(2))* New York Univ. Pr.

Kraut, Alan M., et al. From Arrival to Incorporation: Migrants to the U. S. in a Global Era. Barkan, Elliott R. & Kraut, Alan M., eds. 2007. (ENG.). 320p. 75.00 *(978-0-8147-9960-4(4))* New York Univ. Pr.

LearningExpress Staff. Guia de Ciudadania/Naturalizacion en U. S. A. 2008. (SPA & ENG., Illus.). 188p. pap. 9.95 *(978-1-57685-617-8(8))* LearningExpress, LLC.

Leiserson, William M. Adjusting Immigrant & Industry. 2008. 372p. pap. *(978-1-4097-7259-0(4))* Read Bks.

—Adjusting Immigrant & Industry. (Criminology, Law Enforcement, & Social Problems Ser.). Smith, Patterson Publishing Corp.

Mazlish, Bruce, et al, eds. The Paradox of a Global USA. 2007. (ENG.). 240p. 50.00 *(978-0-8047-5155-1(2))*; per. 19.95 *(978-0-8047-5156-8(0))* Stanford Univ. Pr.

Mirel, Jeffrey E. Patriotic Pluralism: Americanization Education & European Immigrants. 2010. (Illus.). 378p. 45.00 *(978-0-674-04638-2(2))* Harvard Univ. Pr.

Peterson's. How to Become a U. S. Citizen. 5th ed. 2010. (ENG.). 250p. (YA). pap. 18.95 *(978-0-7689-2905-8(9))* Peterson's.

Pickus, Noah. True Faith & Allegiance: Immigration & American Civic Nationalism. 2007 (ENG.). 272p. (C). per. 27.95 *(978-0-691-13396-6(4))* Princeton Univ. Pr.

Portes, Alejandro & Rumbaut, Ruben G. Immigrant America: A Portrait. 3rd rev. exp. ed. 2006. (Illus.). 460p. pap. 26.95 *(978-0-520-25041-3(9))* Univ. of California Pr.

Richard, Mark Paul. Loyal but French: The Negotiation of Identity by French-Canadian Descendants in the United States. 2008. (ENG.). 388p. pap. 34.95 *(978-0-87013-837-9(5))* Michigan State Univ. Pr.

Rose, Philip M. The Italians in America. 2008. 166p. 36.95 *(978-0-548-97365-3(2))* 2007. (ENG.). 168p. per. 21.95 *(978-0-548-67440-6(X))* Kessinger Publishing, LLC.

Salomone, Rosemary C. True American: Language, Identity, & the Education of Immigrant Children. 2010. 320p. 35.00 *(978-0-674-04652-8(8))* Harvard Univ. Pr.

Schmidt, Ronald, Sr., et al. Newcomers, Outsiders, & Insiders: Immigrants & American Racial Politics in the Early Twenty-first Century. 2009. (Politics of Race & Ethnicity Ser.). (ENG., Illus.). 336p. (C). pap. 25.95 *(978-0-472-03376-8(X))* Univ. of Michigan Pr.

Selznick, Barbara. Global Television: Co-Producing Culture. 2008. (ENG., Illus.). 224p. 76.50 *(978-1-59213-503-5(X))*; pap. 26.95 *(978-1-59213-504-2(8))* Temple Univ. Pr.

Sorokina, Tatiana. The Legal Alien's Guide: Building a Career & Life in Chicago, Illinois. 2007. 120p. (ENG.). 24.95 *(978-0-595-68855-5(1))*; per. 14.95 *(978-0-595-44622-3(1))* iUniverse, Inc.

Streissguth, Tom. Welcome to America? A Pro/con Debate over Immigration. 2008. (Issues in Focus Today Ser.). (Illus.). 112p. (J). (gr. k-6). lib. bdg. 31.93 *(978-0-7660-2912-5(3))* Enslow Pubs., Inc.

Task Force on New Americans (U.S.), compiled by. Building an Americanization Movement for the 21st Century: A Report. 2008. (ENG., Illus.). 77p. pap. 7.00 *(978-0-16-082095-3(2))* United States Government Printing Office.

Van Elteren, Mel. Americanism & Americanization: A Critical History of Domestic & Global Influence. 2006. (ENG.). 259p. per. 35.00 *(978-0-7864-2785-7(X))* McFarland & Co., Inc. Pubs.

Vigdor, Jacob L. From Immigrants to Americans: The Rise & Fall of Fitting In. 2010. (ENG., Illus.). 232p. 40.00 *(978-1-4422-0136-1(3))* Rowman & Littlefield Publishers, Inc.

Vowell, Sarah. Unfamiliar Fishes. (ENG.). 256p. (gr. 12). 2012. 16.00 ***(978-1-59448-564-0(X)***, Riverhead Trade (Paperbacks)) 2011. 25.95 *(978-1-59448-787-3(1)*, Riverhead Bks. (Hardcover)) Penguin Group (USA) Inc.

—Unfamiliar Fishes. l.t. ed. 2011. (Illus.). 313p. 31.99 *(978-1-4104-3825-6(2))* Thorndike Pr.

Wilson, Sarah. Melting-Pot Modernism. 2010. (Illus.). 264p. 45.00 *(978-0-8014-4816-4(6))* Cornell Univ. Pr.

Zhang, Donghui. Between Two Generations: Language Maintenance & Acculturation among Chinese Immigrant Families. 2008. (New Americans). 276p. 70.00 *(978-1-59332-271-7(2))* LFB Scholarly Publishing LLC.

AMERICANS—EMPLOYMENT—FOREIGN COUNTRIES

Ast, Scott Alan. Managing Security Overseas: Protecting Employees & Assets in Volatile Regions. 2009. (ENG., Illus.). 366p. 87.95 *(978-1-4398-0467-4(2))* Auerbach Pubs., Inc.

Lepadatu/Janoski. Diversity at Kaizen Motors: Gender, Race, Age & Insecurity in a Japanese Auto Transplant. 2011. (ENG.). 160p. 65.00 ***(978-0-7618-5594-1(7))***; pap. 26.95 ***(978-0-7618-5593-4(9))*** Univ. Pr. of America, Inc.

Waitzman, Michelle. Moon Living Abroad in New Zealand. 2011. (Living Abroad Ser.). (ENG., Illus.). 384p. pap. 19.99 ***(978-1-59880-887-2(7))*** Avalon Travel Publishing.

AMERICANS—AFRICA

Anderson, Evalyn. Cairo: June 1967. 2007. 104p. per. 11.95 *(978-0-595-42999-8(8))* iUniverse, Inc.

Codrington, Tessa. Spirits of Tangier. 2008. (ENG., Illus.). 360p. pap. 49.95 *(978-1-905147-84-7(8))* Arcadia Bks. Ltd. GBR. Dist: Dufour Editions, Inc.

Frank, Romano. Storm over Morocco. Strozier, M. Stefan & Torke, Kyle, eds. 2010. 362p. 20.00 *(978-1-935444-61-9(1))* World Audience Pubs.

Gatorano, Elizabeth. Waiting for the Sunrise: One Family's Struggle Against Genocide & Racism. 2008. 386p. pap. 19.00 *(978-1-931847-45-2(2))* Baha'i Publishing Trust, U.S.

Hale, Mary M. On Uganda's Terms: A Journal by an American Nurse-Midwife Working for Change in Uganda, East Africa During Idi Amin's Regime. 2nd ed. 2009. (Illus.). 140p. pap. *(978-1-926585-13-0(5)*, CCB Publishing) CCB Publishing.

Hesseltine, William & Wolf, Hazel. The Blue & the Gray on the Nile. 2007. per. 24.99 *(978-0-9791084-0-2(3))* Heiler Publishing.

Hirsch, Susan F. In the Moment of Greatest Calamity: Terrorism, Grief, & a Victim's Quest for Justice. 2006. (ENG., Illus.). 310p. (C). 35.00 *(978-0-691-12136-9(2))* Princeton Univ. Pr.

Klein, Robert. Being First: An informal history of the early Peace Corps. 2010. pap. 19.95 *(978-1-60494-457-0(9))* Wheatmark.

Mathers, Kathryn Frances. Travel, Humanitarianism, & Becoming American in Africa. 2010. (ENG.). 236p. 84.00 *(978-0-230-10806-6(7))* Palgrave Macmillan.

Meldrum, Andrew. Where We Have Hope: A Memoir of Zimbabwe. 2006. (ENG., Illus.). 304p. per. 14.00 *(978-0-8021-4251-1(6)*, Grove Pr.) Grove/Atlantic, Inc.

Robbins, Sarah, et al. Nellie Arnott's Writings on Angola, 1905-1913: Missionary Narratives Linking Africa & America. 2010. *(978-1-60235-142-4(2))*; pap. *(978-1-60235-141-7(4))* Parlor Pr.

Romano, Frank. Storm over Morocco. Strozier, M. Stefan & Torke, Kyle, eds. 2009. 356p. pap. 15.99 *(978-1-935444-25-1(5))* World Audience Pubs.

Sandford, Floyd R. African Odyssey: The Adventurous Journeys of a Peace Corps Volunteer in Africa. 2007. 172p. per. 15.95 *(978-0-595-44017-7(7))* iUniverse, Inc.

Swiller, Josh. The Unheard: A Memoir of Deafness & Africa. 2010. E-Book 9.99 *(978-1-4299-5347-4(0))* 2007. (ENG., Illus.). 288p. pap. 14.00 *(978-0-8050-8210-4(7)*, Holt Paperback) Holt, Henry & Co.

Zachary, G. Pascal. Married to Africa: A Love Story. 2013. (ENG.). 272p. pap. 17.99 *(978-1-4165-3464-8(4)*, Scribner) Scribner.

AMERICANS—ASIA

Bigg, Margot. Moon Living Abroad in India. 2011. (Living Abroad Ser.). (ENG., Illus.). 328p. pap. 19.99 *(978-1-59880-739-4(0))* Avalon Travel Publishing.

Ciceri, Paul. You Have No Rights Here: A True Story about One American's Thirty-Three Months in a Middle East Prison. Gabell, Julia, ed. 2007. (Illus.). 400p. pap. 17.95 *(978-0-9788679-0-4(4))* Conch Republic Pr.

Conley, Susan. The Foremost Good Fortune. 2011. (ENG.). 288p. 25.95 *(978-0-307-59406-8(8)*, Knopf) Knopf Doubleday Publishing Group.

Corrie, Rachel & Corrie, R. Let Me Stand Alone: The Journals of Rachel Corrie. 2009. (ENG.). 256p. pap. 13.95 *(978-0-393-33390-9(6)*, 33390) Norton, W. W. & Co., Inc.

Imady, Elaine Rippey. Road to Damascus. 2009. (ENG., Illus.). 276p. pap. 19.95 *(978-1-933455-13-6(6))* M S I Pr.

Irvine, Liz. Surviving the Rising Sun. 2010. 405p. pap. 32.95 *(978-0-557-68018-4(2))* Lulu Enterprises Inc.

Jenkins, Charles Robert & Frederick, Jim. The Reluctant Communist: My Desertion, Court-Martial, & Forty-Year Imprisonment in North Korea. 2009. (ENG.). 232p. pap. 19.95 *(978-0-520-25999-7(8))* 2007. (Illus.). 192p. 40.00 *(978-0-520-25333-9(7))* Univ. of California Pr.

Kaminski, Theresa. Citizen of Empire: Ethel Thomas Herold, an American in the Philippines. 2011. 304p. 49.00 *(978-1-57233-757-2(5))* Univ. of Tennessee Pr.

Kukis, Mark. My Heart Became Attached: The Strange Journey of John Walker Lindh. 2008. (Illus.). 220p. pap. 16.95 *(978-1-57488-759-4(9))* Potomac Bks., Inc.

Learning, Linda. Married to Bhutan: How One Woman Got Lost, Said 'I Do', & Found Bliss. 2011. (ENG.). 256p. pap. 14.95 (978-1-4019-2846-9(3)) Hay Hse., Inc.

Loyn, David. In Afghanistan: Two Hundred Years of British, Russian & American Occupation. 2009. (ENG.). 288p. 27.95 (978-0-230-61403-1(5)) Palgrave Macmillan.

Macris, Jeffrey R. The Politics & Security of the Gulf: Anglo-American Hegemony & the Shaping of a Region. 2010. (ENG., Illus.). 336p. (C). 140.00 (978-0-415-77870-1(0)) Routledge.

McCallus, Joseph P. The MacArthur Highway & Other Relics of American Empire in the Philippines. 2010. (Illus.). 380p. 29.95 (978-1-59797-497-4(8)) Potomac Bks., Inc.

McClelland, Mac. For Us Surrender Is Out of the Question: A Story from Burma's Never-Ending War. 2010. (ENG.). 304p. pap. 15.95 (978-1-59376-265-0(8), Soft Skull Pr.) Counterpoint LLC.

Nair, Ajay & Balaji, Murali. Desi Rap: Hip-Hop & South Asian America. Nair, Ajay & Balaji, Murali, eds. 2008. (ENG.). 202p. 57.99 (978-0-7391-2721-6(7)) Lexington Bks.

Platt, Stephen R. Autumn in the Heavenly Kingdom: China, the West, & the Epic Story of the Taiping Civil War. 2012. (Vintage Ser.). (ENG., Illus.). 512p. pap. 16.95 (978-0-307-47221-2(3), Vintage); 30.00 (978-0-307-27173-0(0), Knopf) Knopf Doubleday Publishing Group.

Rich, Katherine Russell. Dreaming in Hindi: Coming Awake in Another Language. 2009. (ENG.). 384p. 26.00 (978-0-618-15545-3(7)) Houghton Mifflin Harcourt Trade & Reference Pubs.

Torres, Evangelista Evangelista. The Americanization of Manila, 1898-1921. 2010. (Illus.). viii, 255p. (978-971-542-613-8(1)) Univ. of the Philippines Pr.

Van Sickle, Emily. The Iron Gates of Santo Tomas: The Firsthand Account of an American Couple Interned by the Japanese in Manila, 1942-1945. 2007. (Illus.). 370p. per. 17.95 (978-0-89733-554-6(6)) Academy Chicago Pubs., Ltd.

Welman, Frans. Behind the Glittering Lights of Bordellos & Brothels: The Philippines. 2006. 422p. pap. 29.95 (978-1-4241-1477-1(2)) PublishAmerica, Inc.

Wesling, Meg. Empire's Proxy: American Literature & U. S. Imperialism in the Philippines. 2011. (ENG., Illus.). 248p. 65.00 (978-0-8147-9476-0(9)); pap. 21.00 (978-0-8147-9477-7(7)) New York Univ. Pr.

AMERICANS—AUSTRALIA

Pickering, Sam. A Tramp's Wallet. 2011. 272p. pap. 25.00 (978-0-88146-235-7(7)) Mercer Univ. Pr.

AMERICANS—CANADA

Frutkin, Mark. Erratic North: A Vietnam Draft Resister's Life in the Canadian Bush. 2008. (ENG., Illus.). 238p. pap. 24.99 (978-1-55002-786-0(7), Dundurn Pr.) Dundurn CAN. Dist: Ingram Pub. Services.

Jodoin, Mark. Shadow Soldiers of the American Revolution: Loyalist Tales from New York to Canada. 2009. (Regional Histories Ser.). 160p. pap. 21.99 (978-1-59629-726-5(3)) History Pr., The.

Key, Joshua. The Deserter's Tale: The Story of an Ordinary Soldier Who Walked Away from the War in Iraq. 2007. (ENG., Illus.). 256p. per. 14.00 (978-0-8021-4345-7(8), Grove Pr.) Grove/Atlantic, Inc.

Little, J. I. Loyalties in Conflict: A Canadian Borderland in War & Rebellion, 1812-1840. 2008. (Canadian Social History Ser.). (ENG., Illus.). 192p. (978-0-8020-9773-6(1)) Univ. of Toronto Pr.

Little, John. Loyalties in Conflict: A Canadian Borderland in War & Rebellion, 1812-1840. 2008. (ENG., Illus.). 192p. pap. (978-0-8020-9525-1(9)) Univ. of Toronto Pr.

Moffett, Samuel Erasmus. The Americanization of Canada. 2008. 291p. 24.99 (978-0-554-86643-7(9)); 190p. pap. 20.75 (978-0-554-86646-8(3)) BiblioBazaar.

Todd, Jack. Desertion in the Time of Vietnam: A Memoir. 2012. (ENG.). 312p. pap. 18.95 (978-0-8032-3981-4(5)) Univ. of Nebraska Pr.

AMERICANS—CARIBBEAN AREA

Hansen, Jonathan M. Guantánamo: An American History. 2011. (ENG., Illus.). 448p. 35.00 (978-0-8090-5341-4(1), Hill & Wang) Farrar, Straus & Giroux.

Villarreal, Rene & Martínez, Raúl. Hemingway's Cuban Son: Reflections on the Writer by His Longtime Majordomo. 2009. (Illus.). x, 157p. (978-0-87333-897-4(9)) Kent State Univ. Pr.

Villarreal, Rene & Villarreal, Raul. Hemingway's Cuban Son: Reflections on the Writer by His Longtime Majordomo. 2009. (Illus.). 224p. 24.95 (978-0-87338-977-8(8)) Kent State Univ. Pr.

AMERICANS—CENTRAL AMERICA

Johns, Michael. The Education of a Radical: An American Revolutionary in Sandinista Nicaragua. 2012. (ENG.). 146p. 45.00 (978-0-292-73788-4(2)) 2011. E-Book (978-0-292-73789-1(0)) Univ. of Texas Pr.

McGuinness, Aims. Path of Empire: Panama & the California Gold Rush. 2007. (United States in the World Ser.). (Illus.). 249p. 60.95 (978-0-8014-4521-7(3)) Cornell Univ. Pr.

Volz, Eric. Gringo Nightmare: A Young American Framed for Murder in Nicaragua. 2010. (ENG., Illus.). 304p. 25.99 (978-0-312-55727-0(2)) St. Martin's Pr.

AMERICANS—CHINA

Conley, Susan. The Foremost Good Fortune. 2012. (Vintage Ser.). (ENG., Illus.). 368p. pap. 15.00 (978-0-307-73986-5(4), Vintage) Knopf Doubleday Publishing Group.

Davis, Judith March. Pagoda Dreamer. 2010. 274p. pap. 15.95 (978-1-934938-90-4(4), Langdon Street Pr.) Hillcrest Publishing Group, Inc.

Ford, Stacilee. Troubling American Women: Narratives of Gender & Nation in Hong Kong. 2011. (Illus.). 256p. (978-988-220-763-9(4)); (978-988-220-658-8(1)); (978-988-8053-69-8(8)) Hong Kong Univ. Pr.

—Troubling American Women: Narratives of Gender & Nation in Hong Kong. 2011. (ENG., Illus.). 256p. (gr. 17). 35.00 (978-988-8083-11-4(2)) Hong Kong Univ. Pr. HKG. Dist: Columbia Univ. Pr.

French, Paul. Carl Crow - A Tough Old China Hand: The Life, Times, & Adventures of an American in Shanghai. 2006. (ENG., Illus.). 324p. (gr. 17). 35.00 (978-962-209-802-2(9)) Hong Kong Univ. Pr. HKG. Dist: Columbia Univ. Pr.

Hlavacek, John. Letters Home: An American Reporter in China, 1939-1944. 2009. 272p. pap. 19.95 (978-0-9819034-5-3(2), Hlucky Bks.) Concierge Marketing, Inc.

Kendall, Gillian. Mr. Ding's Chicken Feet: On a Slow Boat from Shanghai to Texas. 2006. 256p. per. 22.95 (978-0-299-21944-4(5)) Univ. of Wisconsin Pr.

Kidd, David. Peking Story. 2009. (ENG.). 164p. pap. 29.95 (978-1-906011-00-0(1)) Eland Bks. GBR. Dist: Dufour Editions, Inc.

King, Marjorie. China's American Daughter: Ida Pruitt, 1888-1985. 2006. (ENG., Illus.). 296p. (gr. 17). 42.00 (978-962-996-057-5(5)) Chinese Univ. of Hong Kong, The HKG. Dist: Columbia Univ. Pr.

—China's American Daughter: Ida Pruitt (1888-1985) 2007. (ENG., Illus.). 296p. (gr. 17). pap. 23.00 (978-962-996-221-0(7)) Chinese Univ. of Hong Kong, The HKG. Dist: Columbia Univ. Pr.

Lamas, Rosmarie W. N. Everything in Style: Harriet Low's Macau. 2006. (ENG., Illus.). 364p. (gr. 17). 59.50 (978-962-209-788-9(X)); pap. 24.95 (978-962-209-789-6(8)) Hong Kong Univ. Pr. HKG. Dist: Columbia Univ. Pr.

Levy, Michael. Kosher Chinese: Living, Teaching, & Eating with China's Other Billion. 2011. (ENG.). 256p. pap. 15.00 (978-0-8050-9196-0(3), Holt Paperback) Holt, Henry & Co.

McCormick, Elsie. The Unexpurgated Diary of a Shanghai Baby. 2007. 114p. pap. 27.50 (978-988-99874-8-0(1)) China Economic Review Publishing HKG. Dist: Trans-Atlantic Pubns., Inc.

McGinniss, Joe. Never Enough. 2008. (ENG.). 384p. mass mkt. 7.99 (978-1-4165-2717-6(6), Pocket Star) Pocket Star.

—Never Enough. l.t. ed. 2008. (Crime Scene Ser.). 501p. 29.95 (978-1-4104-0432-9(3)) Thorndike Pr.

Moreira, Peter. Hemingway on the China Front: His WWII Spy Mission with Martha Gellhorn. 2007. (Illus.). 256p. per. 17.95 (978-1-57488-882-9(X)) Potomac Bks., Inc.

Paul, Alan. Big in China: My Unlikely Adventures Raising a Family, Playing the Blues, & Becoming a Star in Beijing. 2011. (ENG.). 256p. 25.99 (978-0-06-199315-2(8)) HarperCollins Pubs.

Renouf, Alice & Ryan-Maher, Mary Beth. Yin-Yang: American Perspectives on Living in China. 2011. (978-1-4422-1271-8(3)) Rowman & Littlefield Publishers, Inc.

Renouf/Ryan-Maher. China Survival Guide: American Perspectives on Living in China. 2011. (ENG.). 246p. 70.00 (978-1-4422-1269-5(1)) Rowman & Littlefield Publishers, Inc.

—Yin-Yang: American Perspectives on Living in China. 2011. (ENG.). 246p. pap. 22.95 (978-1-4422-1270-1(5)) Rowman & Littlefield Publishers, Inc.

Scocca, Tom. Beijing Welcomes You: Unveiling the Capital City of the Future. 2011. (ENG., Illus.). 384p. (gr. 12). 26.95 (978-1-59448-784-2(7), Riverhead Bks. (Hardcover)) Penguin Group (USA) Inc.

Sherwood, Jack. Fond Memories of a Young Man in Old Chin. 2009. 288p. pap. 17.49 (978-1-4490-0894-9(1)) AuthorHouse.

Spurling, Hilary. Pearl Buck in China: Journey to the Good Earth. (ENG.). 320p. 2011. pap. 15.00 (978-1-4165-4043-4(1)) 2010. (Illus.). 27.00 (978-1-4165-4042-7(3)) Simon & Schuster.

Vernezze, Peter J. Socrates in Sichuan: Chinese Students Search for Truth, Justice, & the (Chinese) Way. 2011. 212p. 26.95 (978-1-59797-672-5(5)) Potomac Bks., Inc.

Yardley, Jim. Brave Dragons: A Chinese Basketball Team, an American Coach, & Two Cultures Clashing. 2012. (ENG., Illus.). 320p. 26.95 (978-0-307-27221-8(4), Knopf) Knopf Doubleday Publishing Group.

AMERICANS—EUROPE

Danish Culture, Past & Present: Proceedings of an International Conference Sponsored by the Danish American Heritage Society: the Last Two Hundred Years. 2007. (978-0-9652961-6-8(4)) Danish American Heritage Society.

Dreiser, Theodore. A Traveler at Forty. 2009. (ENG.). 567p. 44.99 (978-1-117-56465-4(7)); (ENG.). 565p. 44.99 (978-1-116-98589-4(6)); (ENG.). 567p. pap. 42.75 (978-1-117-56466-1(5)); 568p. 30.99 (978-1-103-66084-1(5)); 568p. pap. 24.99 (978-1-103-66081-0(0)) BiblioBazaar.

—A Traveler at Forty. 2009. 352p. pap. (978-0-217-34397-8(X)); 348p. pap. (978-1-4590-2351-2(X)); 348p. pap. (978-0-217-31282-0(9)) Books LLC.

—A Traveler at Forty. 2007. 566p. 58.95 (978-0-548-00861-4(2)) Kessinger Publishing, LLC.

—A Traveler at Forty. 2007. 564p. per. (978-1-4067-7375-0(1)) Read Bks.

Easton-Brooks, Donald. African Americanæs Academic Outcomes. 2008. 152p. pap. (978-3-639-04586-4(6)) VDM Verlag Dr. Mueller e.K.

Feyerick, Ada. The Sixties: An American Family in Europe. 2010. (Illus.). 152p. 25.00 (978-0-9653159-9-9(1)) Academia Bks., Inc.

Gabrial, Jan. Inside the Volcano: My Life with Malcolm Lowry. 2010. (ENG., Illus.). 224p. pap. 31.00 (978-0-230-61978-4(9)) Palgrave Macmillan.

Jackson, David & Jackson, David J. Classrooms & Barrooms. 2009. (ENG.). 140p. pap. 25.50 (978-0-7618-4383-2(3)) Hamilton Bks.

Meckfessel, Shon. Suffled How It Gush: A North American Anarchist in the Balkans. 2009. (ENG., Illus.). 260p. pap. 16.95 (978-1-904859-85-7(2)) AK Pr. GBR. Dist: Consortium Bk. Sales & Distribution.

Oliva, Héctor & Oliva Camps, Héctor. Veinte Historias de la Barcelona Americana: — Y una Pregunta Descarada. 2008. (SPA., Illus.). 180p. (978-84-92437-05-4(7)) Base, Editorial.

Sanchez, Nellie Van de Grift. The Life of Mrs Robert Louis Stevenson. 2008. 272p. pap. (978-1-4099-1642-0(1)) Dodo Pr.

—The Life of Mrs Robert Louis Stevenson. 2008. (Illus.). 184p. pap. (978-1-84830-941-8(4), Wildhern Pr.); 176p. pap. (978-1-4068-9162-1(2)) Echo Library.

—The Life of Mrs Robert Louis Stevenson. 2007. (ENG.). 376p. 48.95 (978-0-548-02248-1(8)) Kessinger Publishing, LLC.

Schaller, Mary W. Deliver Us from Evil: A Southern Belle in Europe at the Outbreak of World War I. 2011. (Women's Diaries & Letters of the South Ser.). 192p. 29.95 (978-1-57003-950-8(X)) Univ. of South Carolina Pr.

Sjoholm, Barbara. Incognito Street: How Travel Made Me a Writer. 2006. (ENG., Illus.). 256p. per. 15.95 (978-1-58005-172-9(3)) Seal Pr.

Smith, Richard K. & Hall, R. Cargill. Five Down, No Glory: Frank G. Tinker, Merenary Ace in the Spanish Civil War. 2011. (Illus.). 385p. 36.95 (978-1-61251-054-5(X)) Naval Institute Pr.

Theros, Xavier. La Sisena Flota a Barcelona: Quan Els Nord-Americans Envàlen la Rambla. 2010. (CAT., Illus.). 454p. (978-84-96735-49-1(4)) La Campana, Edicions, S.L.

Twain, Mark, pseud. The Innocents Abroad. 2009. 728p. 40.99 (978-0-559-13456-2(8)); 36.99 (978-0-559-13465-4(7)); pap. 50.75 (978-0-559-13458-6(4)); pap. 49.75 (978-0-559-13463-0(0)) BiblioBazaar.

—The Innocents Abroad. 2009. 292p. pap. 9.99 (978-1-4209-3211-9(X)) Digireads.com.

—The Innocents Abroad. 2007. (ENG.). 560p. (gr. 12-18). 7.95 (978-0-451-53049-3(7), Signet Classics) Penguin Group (USA) Inc.

—Innocents Abroad. 2006. 378p. pap. (978-1-4068-1298-5(6)) Echo Library.

Vernon, Alex. Hemingway's Second War: Bearing Witness to the Spanish Civil War. 2011. (ENG.). 264p. pap. 29.95 (978-1-58729-981-0(X)) Univ. of Iowa Pr.

AMERICANS—FOREIGN COUNTRIES

Aiding American Businesses Abroad: Government Action to Help Beleaguered American Firms & Investors: Hearing Before the Subcommittee on Terrorism, Nonproliferation, & Trade of the Committee on Foreign Affairs, House of Representatives, One Hundred Tenth Congress, Second Session, July 17, 2008. 2008. (Illus.). iii, 75p. (978-0-16-082146-2(0), 552-070-38283-6) United States Government Printing Office.

Alvah, Donna. Unofficial Ambassadors: American Military Families Overseas & the Cold War, 1946-1965. 2007. (ENG., Illus.). 304p. 49.00 (978-0-8147-0501-8(4)) New York Univ. Pr.

Axtell, Roger E. Do's & Taboos of Using English Around the World. 2009. (ENG., Illus.). 208p. 9.99 (978-0-7858-2528-9(2), 0785825282, Castle Bks., Inc.) Book Sales, Inc.

Barton, H. Arnold. The Old Country & the New: Essays on Swedes & America. 2006. (ENG., Illus.). 320p. 55.00 (978-0-8093-2714-0(7)) Southern Illinois Univ. Pr.

Bendixen, Alfred & Hamera, Judith. The Cambridge Companion to American Travel Writing. Bendixen, Alfred & Hamera, Judith, eds. 2009. (Cambridge Companions to Literature Ser.). (ENG.). 314p. (C). 81.00 (978-0-521-86109-0(8)) Cambridge Univ. Pr.

Bendixen, Alfred & Hamera, Judith, eds. The Cambridge Companion to American Travel Writing. 2009. (Cambridge Companions to Literature Ser.). (ENG.). 314p. (C). pap. 29.99 (978-0-521-67831-5(5)) Cambridge Univ. Pr.

Black, Randy. Randy Blacks Favorite Tales from Siberia. 2007. 196p. pap. 16.49 (978-1-4303-0349-7(2)) Lulu Enterprises Inc.

Blanck, Dag. The Creation of an Ethnic Identity: Being Swedish American in the Augustana Synod, 1860-1917. 2006. (ENG., Illus.). 280p. 55.00 (978-0-8093-2715-7(5)) Southern Illinois Univ. Pr.

Dennett, Tyler. Americans in Eastern Asia. 2009. 576p. pap. (978-0-217-16336-1(X)) Books LLC.

Ehrman, Mark & Nelson, Cletus. Getting Out: Your Guide to Leaving America. rev. ed. 2012. (Process Self-reliance Ser.). (ENG., Illus.). 460p. pap. 19.95 (978-1-934170-29-8(1)) Process Packaging.

Grandin, Greg. Empire's Workshop: Latin America, the United States, & the Rise of the New Imperialism. annot. ed. 2007. (American Empire Project Ser.). (ENG.). 304p. pap. 18.00 (978-0-8050-8323-1(5), Holt Paperback) Holt, Henry & Co.

Guardia, Mike. American Guerrilla: The Forgotten Heroics of Russell W. Volckmann: The Man Who Escaped from Bataan, Raised a Filipino Army Against the Japanese, & Became 'father' of Special Forces. 2010. (Illus.). 264p. 32.95 (978-1-935149-22-4(9)) Casemate Pubs. & Bk. Distributors, LLC.

Hill, Peter P. Joel Barlow, American Diplomat & Nation Builder. 2012. (Illus.). 272p. 34.95 (978-1-59797-682-4(2)) Potomac Bks., Inc.

Kitto, Mark. Chasing China: How I Went to China in Search of a Fortune & Found a Life. 2009. (ENG.). 304p. 22.95 (978-1-60239-657-9(4), 239657) Skyhorse Publishing Co., Inc.

Knorr, Rosanne. The Grown-up's Guide to Running Away from Home: Making a New Life Abroad. 2nd rev. ed. 2008. (ENG.). 208p. pap. 14.95 (978-1-58008-873-2(2)) Ten Speed Pr.

Laderman, Scott. Tours of Vietnam: War, Travel Guides, & Memory. 2009. (American Encounters/Global Interactions Ser.). (ENG.). 312p. 89.95 (978-0-8223-4396-7(7)); pap. 24.95 (978-0-8223-4414-8(9)) Duke Univ. Pr.

Ling, Laura & Ling, Lisa. Somewhere Inside: One Sister's Captivity in North Korea & the Other's Fight to Bring Her Home. l.t. ed. 2010. lib. bdg. 34.95 (978-1-60285-875-6(6)) Ctr. Point Large Print.

—Somewhere Inside: One Sister's Captivity in North Korea & the Other's Fight to Bring Her Home. 2011. (ENG.). 352p. pap. 15.99 (978-0-06-200068-2(3), William Morrow Paperbacks) 2010. 336p. 26.99 (978-0-06-200067-5(5), Morrow, William & Co.) HarperCollins Pubs.

Mann, A. Dudley. My Ever Dearest Friend: The Letters of A. Dudley Mann to Jefferson Davis, 1869-1889. Moore, John Preston & Hoole, William Stanley, eds. 2011. 116p. 39.95 (978-1-258-07892-8(9)) Literary Licensing, LLC.

McGuinness, Aims. Path of Empire: Panama & the California Gold Rush. 2009. (United States in the World Ser.). (Illus.). 264p. pap. 19.95 (978-0-8014-7538-2(4)) Cornell Univ. Pr.

Melton, Jeffrey. Mark Twain, Travel Books, & Tourism: The Tide of a Great Popular Movement. 2008. (Amer Lit Realism & Naturalism Ser.). (ENG., Illus.). 224p. pap. 29.95 (978-0-8173-5519-7(7)) Univ. of Alabama Pr.

Merrill, Dennis. Negotiating Paradise: U. S. Tourism & Empire in Twentieth-Century Latin America. 2009. (ENG., Illus.). 352p. 69.95 (978-0-8078-3288-2(X)); pap. 23.95 (978-0-8078-5904-9(4)) Univ. of North Carolina Pr.

Mort, Terry. Mark Twain on Travel. 2007. (On Ser.). (ENG.). 304p. per. 15.95 (978-1-59921-074-2(6), Lyons Pr.) Globe Pequot Pr., The.

Peddicord, Kathleen. How to Retire Overseas: Everything You Need to Know to Live Well (For Less) Abroad. 2010. (ENG.). 304p. (gr. 12-18). 25.95 (978-1-59463-065-1(8), Hudson Street Pr.) Penguin Group (USA) Inc.

—How to Retire Overseas: Everything You Need to Know to Live Well (for Less) Abroad. 2011. (ENG.). 304p. (gr. 12). 16.00 (978-0-452-29684-8(6), Plume) Penguin Group (USA) Inc.

Saintelo, Yves & Saintelo, Guy. Four Season: The Many Seasons of Life. 2009. 136p. pap. 13.95 (978-0-595-52746-5(9)) iUniverse, Inc.

Snyder, Wayne. Catching the Wave. 2010. 27.95 (978-1-60264-644-5(9)); pap. 18.95 (978-1-60264-643-8(0)) Virtualbookworm.com Publishing, Inc.

Spickard, Paul. Almost All Aliens: Immigration, Race, & Colonialism in American History & Identity. 2007. (Illus.). 721p. per. 44.95 (978-0-415-93593-7(8)) Routledge.

—Almost All Aliens: Race, Colonialism & Immigration in American History & Identity. 2007. (ENG., Illus.). 744p. 130.00 (978-0-415-93592-0(X)) Routledge.

Taylor, Gordon. Fever & Thirst: A Missionary Doctor amid the Christian Tribes of Kurdistan. 2007. (ENG.). 354p. pap. 18.95 (978-0-89733-572-0(4)) Academy Chicago Pubs., Ltd.

Todd, Martha Sue. Never Too Old to Climb Walls. 2007. 456p. per. 27.85 (978-1-4251-0936-3(5)) Trafford Publishing.

Wennersten, John R. Leaving America: The New Expatriate Generation. 1 vol. 2007. 200p. 39.95 (978-0-313-34506-7(6), C34506, Praeger Pubs.) Greenwood Publishing Group, Inc.

Wevodau, Edward N. Lancaster County, PA , Connections: Compiled from Deeds Recorded in Lancaster from 1770 to 1830, 2 vols. 2010. (Illus.). (978-1-55856-517-3(5)); (978-1-55856-519-7(1)) Closson Pr.

Wineapple, Brenda. Sister Brother: Gertrude & Leo Stein. 2008. (ENG., Illus.). 536p. pap. 25.00 (978-0-8032-1753-9(6), Bison Bks.) Univ. of Nebraska Pr.

AMERICANS—FRANCE

Bard, Elizabeth. Lunch in Paris: A Love Story, with Recipes. (ENG.). 2011. 352p. pap. 13.99 (978-0-316-04278-9(1), Back Bay Bks.) 2010. 336p. 23.99 (978-0-316-04279-6(X)) Little Brown & Co.

Beach, Sylvia. The Letters of Sylvia Beach. Walsh, Keri, ed. 2011. (ENG., Illus.). 376p. (gr. 17). pap. 19.95 (978-0-231-14537-4(3)) Columbia Univ. Pr.

Bishop, Janet, et al, intros. The Steins Collect: Matisse, Picasso, & the Parisian Avant-Garde. 2011. (Illus.). 492p. 75.00 (978-0-300-16941-6(8)) Yale Univ. Pr.

Blower, Brooke Lindy. Becoming Americans in Paris: Transatlantic Politics & Culture Between the World Wars. 2011. (ENG., Illus.). 336p. 34.95 (978-0-19-973781-9(9)) Oxford Univ. Pr., Inc.

Brassaï. Henry Miller: The Paris Years. Bent, Timothy, tr. from FRE. 2011. (ENG., Illus.). 240p. pap. 14.95 (978-1-61145-028-6(4), 611028, Arcade Publishing) Skyhorse Publishing Co., Inc.

de Margerie, Caroline. American Lady: The Life of Susan Mary Alsop. 2012. (ENG., Illus.). 256p. 26.95 (978-0-670-02574-9(7), Viking Adult) Penguin Group (USA) Inc.

Downs, Laura Lee & Gerson, Stephane, eds. Why France? American Historians Reflect on an Enduring Fascination. 2009. 256p. pap. 22.95 (978-0-8014-7570-2(8)) Cornell Univ. Pr.

Espinasse, Kristin. Words in a French Life: Lessons in Love & Language from the South of France. 2007. (ENG., Illus.). 304p. pap. 15.00 (978-0-7432-8729-6(0), Touchstone) Touchstone.

Glass, Charles. Americans in Paris: Life & Death under Nazi Occupation. (ENG.). 544p. (gr. 12). 2011. 18.00 (978-0-14-311866-4(8), Penguin (Non-Classics)) 2010. (Illus.). 32.95 (978-1-59420-242-1(7), Penguin Pr. HC, The) Penguin Group (USA) Inc.

Graham, Laurie. In Other Words: Tales of Paris & Language. 2009. (Illus.). 160p. pap. 12.95 (978-1-59571-370-4(0)) Word Association Pubs.

Greenside, Mark. I'll Never Be French (No Matter What I Do) Living in a Small Village in Brittany. 2008. (ENG., Illus.). 256p. 24.00 *(978-1-4165-8687-6(3)*, Free Pr.) Free Pr.

—I'll Never Be French (no matter what I Do) Living in a Small Village in Brittany. 2009. (ENG., Illus.). 256p. pap. 14.99 *(978-1-4165-8695-1(4)*, Free Pr.) Free Pr.

Hamalian, Linda. The Cramoisy Queen: A Life of Caresse Crosby. 2nd ed. 2009. (Illus.). 296p. pap. 17.95 *(978-0-8093-2901-4(8))* Southern Illinois Univ. Pr.

Hemingway, Ernest. A Moveable Feast: The Restored Edition. (ENG.). 256p. 2010. pap. 15.00 *(978-1-4391-8271-0(X))* 2009. (Illus.). 25.00 *(978-1-4165-9131-3(1))* Scribner. (Scribner).

—On Paris. 2010. (On Ser.). (ENG.). 80p. pap. 15.95 *(978-1-84391-604-8(5))* Hesperus Pr. GBR. Dist: Independent Pubs. Group.

James, Eloisa. Paris in Love: A Memoir. 2012. (ENG., Illus.). 272p. 26.00 ***(978-1-4000-6956-9(4)***, Random House) Random House Publishing Group.

Laddon, Judy. Sally: The Older Woman's Illustrated Guide to Self-Improvement. 2008. (Illus.). 250p. 24.95 *(978-1-934738-59-7(X))* Printed Word Inc, The.

Lebovitz, David. The Sweet Life in Paris: Delicious Adventures in the World's Most Glorious - & Perplexing - City. 2011. (ENG., Illus.). 304p. pap. 14.00 *(978-0-7679-2889-2(X))* Broadway Bks.

Lipton, Eunice. French Seduction: An American's Encounter with France, Her Father, & the Holocaust. 2006. (ENG., Illus.). 224p. 23.95 *(978-0-7867-1626-5(6))* Da Capo Pr., Inc.

Lobe, Kirsten. Paris, Baby! 2011. (ENG.). 352p. pap. 14.99 *(978-0-312-60532-2(3)*, St. Martin's Griffin) St. Martin's Pr.

Lucas II, Conrad G. & Norgard, William D. Europe Beyond Your Means: The Paris Edition. 2008. 180p. 26.95 *(978-0-595-71605-0(9))*; pap. 16.95 *(978-0-595-47927-6(8))* iUniverse, Inc.

Malcolm, Janet. Two Lives: Gertrude & Alice. (Illus.). 240p. 2008. (ENG.). pap. 13.00 *(978-0-300-14310-2(9))* 2007. 25.00 *(978-0-300-12551-1(8))* Yale Univ. Pr.

McCullough, David. The Greater Journey: Americans in Paris. (ENG., Illus.). 576p. 2012. pap. 20.00 ***(978-1-4165-7177-3(9))*** 2011. 37.50 *(978-1-4165-7176-6(0))* Simon & Schuster.

—The Greater Journey: Americans in Paris. l.t. ed. 2011. (Illus.). 861p. 35.99 *(978-1-4104-3820-1(1))* Thorndike Pr.

Meier, Leslie. Christmas Cookie Murder. l.t. ed. 2008. (Lucy Stone Mystery Ser.). 330p. 25.95 *(978-1-59722-859-6(1))* Thorndike Pr.

Murrills, Angela. Hot Sun, Cool Shadow: Savoring the Food, History, & Mystery of the Languedoc. 2008. (ENG., Illus.). 264p. per. 16.95 *(978-0-7627-4747-4(1))* Globe Pequot Pr., The.

Nelson, Michael. Americans & the Making of the Riviera. 2007. (ENG., Illus.). 232p. per. 35.00 *(978-0-7864-3160-1(1))* McFarland & Co., Inc. Pubs.

Price, Marjorie. A Gift from Brittany. 2009. (ENG.). 272p. (gr. 12-18). 15.00 *(978-1-59240-434-6(0)*, Gotham) Penguin Group (USA) Inc.

—A Gift from Brittany: A Memoir of Love & Loss in the French Countryside. l.t. ed. 2008. 320p. 31.95 *(978-1-4104-1107-5(9)*, Wheeler Publishing, Inc.) Cengage Gale.

Ramsey, Rebecca S. French by Heart: An American Family's Adventures in la Belle France. 2007. (ENG.). 320p. pap. 12.95 *(978-0-7679-2522-8(X)*, Broadway) Broadway Bks.

Sloboda, Noel. The Making of Americans in Paris: The Autobiographies of Edith Wharton & Gertrude Stein. 2008. (American University Studies XXIV: American Literature Ser.: Vol. 77). 206p. (C). 67.95 *(978-1-4331-0104-5(1))* Lang, Peter Publishing, Inc.

Souhami, Diana. Gertrude & Alice. 2009. (ENG., Illus.). 304p. pap. 20.00 *(978-1-84885-148-1(0))* I. B. Tauris & Co., Ltd. GBR. Dist: Macmillan.

The Greatest Generations Foundation. The Bridge Has Been Crossed: Passing down the Lessons of D-Day. 2010. 160p. pap. 45.00 *(978-1-4520-4401-9(5))* AuthorHouse.

Thomas, Naturi. How to Die in Paris: A Memoir. 2011. (ENG.). 272p. pap. 17.00 *(978-1-58005-364-8(5))* Seal Pr.

United States Army Staff. Instructions for American Servicemen in France during World War II. 2008. (ENG., Illus.). 84p. 12.00 *(978-0-226-84172-4(3))* Univ. of Chicago Pr.

Waddell, Dan. The Blood Detective. l.t. ed. 2008. 380p. 30.95 *(978-1-4104-1092-4(7))* Thorndike Pr.

Weber, Ronald. News of Paris: American Journalists in the City of Light Between the Wars. 2007. (ENG., Illus.). 352p. per. 16.95 *(978-1-56663-732-9(5))* Dee, Ivan R. Pub.

Ziesche, Philipp. Cosmopolitan Patriots: Americans in Paris in the Age of Revolution. 2010. (Jeffersonian America Ser.). (ENG., Illus.). 256p. (gr. 17). 39.50 *(978-0-8139-2891-3(5))* Univ. Pr. of Virginia.

AMERICANS—GERMANY

Adam, Thomas, ed. Two Boston Brahmins in Goethe's Germany: The Travel Journals of Anna & George Ticknor. 2009. (ENG.). 294p. pap. 34.99 *(978-0-7391-2912-8(0))* Lexington Bks.

Adam, Thomas & Mettele, Gisela. Two Boston Brahmins in Goethe's Germany: The Travel Journals of Anna & George Ticknor. 2009. (ENG.). 294p. 83.99 *(978-0-7391-2911-1(2))* Lexington Bks.

Adams, Bianka J. From Crusade to Hazard: The Denazification of Bremen, Germany. 2010. E-Book *(978-0-8108-7502-9(0))* Scarecrow Pr., Inc.

—From Crusade to Hazard: The Denazification of Bremen Germany. 2009. (ENG., Illus.). 198p. pap. 42.00 *(978-0-8108-5992-0(0))* Scarecrow Pr., Inc.

Jentsch, Mary Hunt. Trek: An American Woman, Two Small Children & Survival in World War II Germany. 2008. (ENG., Illus.). 250p. pap. 14.00 *(978-0-9755618-5-0(5))* McWitty Pr., Inc.

Langsten, Armin. Ellis Island & Beyond. 2011. 290p. pap. 17.95 ***(978-0-9830007-7-8(8))*** Fiction Publishing, Inc.

Larson, Erik. In the Garden of Beasts: Love, Terror, & an American Family in Hitler's Berlin. 2011. (ENG., Illus.). 464p. 26.00 *(978-0-307-40884-6(1)*, Crown) Crown Publishing Group.

—In the Garden of Beasts: Love, Terror, & an American Family in Hitler's Berlin. l.t. ed. 2011. (ENG.). 704p. pap. 26.00 *(978-0-7393-7814-4(7))* Random Hse. Large Print.

Nagorski, Andrew. Hitlerland: American Eyewitnesses to the Nazi Rise to Power. 2012. (ENG., Illus.). 400p. 28.00 ***(978-1-4391-9100-2(X))*** Simon & Schuster.

—Hitlerland: Americans in Germany As the Nazis Rise to Power. 2012. pap. ***(978-1-4391-9101-9(8))*** Simon & Schuster.

Plotkin, Abraham. An American in Hitler's Berlin: Abraham Plotkin's Diary, 1932-33. Collomp, Catherine et al, eds. 2009. (ENG., Illus.). 272p. 62.00 *(978-0-252-03361-2(2))* Univ. of Illinois Pr.

—An American in Hitler's Berlin: Abraham Plotkin's Diary 1932-33. Collomp, Catherine & Groppo, Bruno, eds. 2008. (ENG., Illus.). 272p. pap. 26.00 *(978-0-252-07559-9(5))* Univ. of Illinois Pr.

Weiss, Luisa. My Berlin Kitchen: A Love Story (with Recipes) 2012. (ENG.). 320p. 26.95 ***(978-0-670-02538-1(0)***, Viking Adult) Penguin Group (USA) Inc.

AMERICANS—GREAT BRITAIN

Adams Family. Adams Family Correspondence Vol.10: January 1794-June 1795, Volume 10. Hogan, Margaret A. et al, eds. 2011. (Adams Papers). (Illus.). 608p. 105.00 *(978-0-674-05784-5(8)*, Belknap Pr.) Harvard Univ. Pr.

Becker, Jillian. Giving Up: The Last Days of Sylvia Path. Date not set. pap. *(978-0-312-31599-3(6)*, St. Martin's Paperbacks) St. Martin's Pr.

Bodleian Library, The, ed. Instructions for American Servicemen in Australia 1942. 2007. (Illus.). 72p. 9.99 *(978-1-85124-395-2(X))* Bodleian Library GBR. Dist: Chicago Distribution Ctr.

Byrd Sr., James G. My Son the Brat: Bentwaters/Woodbridge 1955-59. 2010. 96p. pap. 12.63 *(978-1-4251-8721-7(8))* Trafford Publishing.

Dana, Richard H. Hospitable England in the Seventies: The Diary of a Young American 1875-1876. 2007. 436p. (ENG.). 39.95 *(978-1-4344-8447-5(5))*; per 22.95 *(978-1-4344-8446-8(7))* Wildside Pr., LLC.

Dietrich Berryman Eric & Hammond, Charlotte. Passport not Required. 2010. (Illus.). 0192p. 27.95 *(978-1-59114-224-9(5))* Naval Institute Pr.

Fabend, Firth Haring. Only a Paper Life. 2008. 284p. pap. 20.50 *(978-0-557-01461-3(1))* Lulu Enterprises Inc.

Flavell, Julie. When London Was Capital of America. (Illus.). 320p. 2011. (ENG.). pap. 20.00 *(978-0-300-17813-5(1))* 2010. 32.50 *(978-0-300-13739-2(7))* Yale Univ. Pr.

Harrison, Rosina. Rose: My Life in Service to Lady Astor. 2011. (ENG.). 368p. (gr. 12). 15.00 ***(978-0-14-312086-5(7)***, Penguin (Non-Classics)) Penguin Group (USA) Inc.

Hawthorne, Nathaniel. Our Old Home: A Series of English Sketches. 2007. (ENG.). 286p. pap. 21.99 *(978-1-4264-2571-4(6))* 2006. 308p. pap. 24.99 *(978-1-4264-2612-4(7))* BiblioBazaar.

Jones, Sylvia. No, I Live Here. 2006. (ENG., Illus.). 96p. pap. 12.95 ***(978-0-86243-858-6(6))*** Y Lolfa GBR. Dist: Dufour Editions, Inc.

Kershaw, Alex. The Few: The American Knights of the Air Who Risked Everything to Save Britain in the Summer Of 1940. 2007. (ENG., Illus.). 360p. per. 15.95 *(978-0-306-81572-0(9))* Da Capo Pr., Inc.

Lyall, Sarah. The Anglo Files: A Field Guide to the British. (ENG.). 304p. 2009. pap. 15.95 *(978-0-393-33476-0(7)*, 33476) 2008. 24.95 *(978-0-393-05846-8(8)*, 5846) Norton, W. W. & Co., Inc.

Meloney, Marie Mattingly, pref. The Log Cabin Lady: An Anonymous Autobiography. 2011. 76p. pap. ***(978-0-9569466-1-4(5))*** Guidemark Publishing Limited.

Millgate, Helen D. Got Any Gum Chum? GIs in Wartime Britain, 1942-1945. 2010. (ENG., Illus.). 128p. pap. 19.95 *(978-0-7524-5023-0(9))* History Pr. Ltd., The GBR. Dist: Independent Pubs. Group.

Mulvey, Christopher. Anglo-American Landscapes: A Study of Nineteenth-Century Anglo-American Travel Literature. 2009. (ENG.). 312p. pap. 46.00 *(978-0-521-11580-3(9))* Cambridge Univ. Pr.

Rosenthal, Jack. Letters from an Airfield: The True Story of a GI Bride of the Mighty Eighth. 2010. (ENG., Illus.). 192p. pap. 24.95 *(978-0-7524-5252-4(5))* History Pr. Ltd., The GBR. Dist: Independent Pubs. Group.

Sebba, Anne. American Jennie: The Remarkable Life of Lady Randolph Churchill. 2007. (ENG., Illus.). 416p. 26.95 *(978-0-393-05772-0(0)*, 5772) Norton, W. W. & Co., Inc.

Seed, David. American Travellers in Liverpool. 2008. (ENG., Illus.). 320p. pap. 39.95 *(978-1-84631-129-1(2))* Liverpool Univ. Pr. GBR. Dist: Chicago Distribution Ctr.

Slavin, Robert E. Damp Yankees: (Another American Gobsmacked by England) 2011. 68p. pap. 9.95 ***(978-1-4620-4085-8(3))*** iUniverse, Inc.

Wake, Jehanne. Sisters of Fortune: America's Caton Sisters at Home & Abroad. 2011. (ENG., Illus.). 416p. 27.00 *(978-1-4516-0761-1(X)*, Touchstone) Touchstone.

Weintraub, Stanley. Victorian Yankees at Queen Victoria's Court: American Encounters with Victoria & Albert. 2011. (ENG.). 272p. 70.00 *(978-1-61149-060-2(X))* Univ. of Delaware Pr.

AMERICANS—IRELAND

Monagan, David. Ireland Unhinged: Encounters with a Wildly Changing Country. 2011. (ENG.). 300p. 28.00 *(978-1-57178-252-6(4)*, Kanbar & Conrad Bks.) Council Oak Bks.

AMERICANS—ISRAEL

Chasnoff, Joel. The 188th Crybaby Brigade: A Skinny Jewish Kid from Chicago Fights Hezbollah - A Memoir. 2010. (ENG., Illus.). 288p. 25.00 *(978-1-4165-4932-1(3)*, Free Pr.) Free Pr.

Miles, William F. S. Zion in the Desert: American Jews in Israel's Reform Kibbutzim. 2008. pap. 29.95 *(978-0-7914-7104-3(7))* State Univ. of New York Pr.

Williams, Emma. It's Easier to Reach Heaven Than the End of the Street: A Jerusalem Memoir. 2009. 256p. pap. 16.00 *(978-1-56656-789-3(0)*, Olive Branch Pr.) Interlink Publishing Group, Inc.

AMERICANS—ITALY

Di Martino, Guerino. Falling in Love at Trevi: Till Death Did Us Part. 2008. 122p. pap. 19.95 *(978-1-60474-672-3(6))* PublishAmerica, Inc.

Dregni, Eric. Never Trust a Thin Cook & Other Lessons from Italy's Culinary Capital. 2009. pap. *(978-0-8166-6746-8(2))*; (Illus.). 240p. 22.95 *(978-0-8166-6745-1(4))* Univ. of Minnesota Pr.

Gyulai, Michael J. Midnight in Rome: A Wandering Mind in a City Eternal. 2009. 240p. pap. 15.95 *(978-1-935278-76-4(2)*, iUniverse Star) iUniverse, Inc.

Laddon, Judy. Sally: The Older Woman's Illustrated Guide to Self-Improvement. 2008. (Illus.). 250p. 24.95 *(978-1-934738-59-7(X))* Printed Word Inc, The.

Mayes, Frances. Every Day in Tuscany: Seasons of an Italian Life. (ENG.). 320p. 2011. pap. 15.00 *(978-0-7679-2983-7(7))* 2010. 25.00 *(978-0-7679-2982-0(9))* Broadway Bks.

—Every Day in Tuscany: Seasons of an Italian Life. l.t. ed. 2010. (ENG.). 410p. 31.95 *(978-1-4104-2646-8(7))* Thorndike Pr.

Pohlman, Susan. Halfway to Each Other: How a Year in Italy Brought Our Family Home. 2009. (ENG.). 272p. 22.00 *(978-0-8249-4780-4(0)*, Guideposts) Ideals Pubns.

van der Leun, Justine. Marcus of Umbria: What an Italian Dog Taught an American Girl about Love. (ENG.). 224p. 2011. pap. 14.99 *(978-1-60961-139-2(X))* 2010. 23.99 *(978-1-60529-960-0(X))* Rodale Pr., Inc.

AMERICANS—JAPAN

Aponte, Wayne/Lionel. The Year of No Money in Tokyo. 2009. 160p. 19.95 *(978-0-9820550-0-7(5))*; 165p. *(978-0-9820550-2-1(1))*; 165p. pap. *(978-0-9820550-1-4(3))* Watkins & McKay, LLC.

Brown, Bill. Fujiyama Honeymoon. 2007. 208p. 32.50 *(978-1-4251-2711-4(8))* Trafford Publishing.

Cook, Lisa Fineberg. Japan Took the J. A. P. Out of Me: The True Story of a Domesticated Princess. 2009. (ENG.). 288p. pap. 15.00 *(978-1-4391-1003-4(4)*, Downtown Press) Downtown Pr.

Hearn, Lafcadio. Glimpses of Unfamiliar Japan, First Series. 2007. 256p. per. *(978-1-4065-4432-9(9))* Dodo Pr.

—Glimpses of Unfamiliar Japan Vol I. 2006. 356p. per. *(978-1-4067-1377-0(5)*, Hesperides Pr.) Read Bks.

Hesse, Benjamin. Memoirs of a Gaijin: Emails from Japan. 2007. 280p. per. 20.95 *(978-0-595-44869-2(0))* iUniverse, Inc.

Keener, Peggy. Potato in a Rice Bowl. 2010. 416p. (ENG.). 36.95 *(978-1-4502-2041-5(X))*; pap. 26.95 *(978-1-4502-2043-9(6))* iUniverse, Inc.

Nathan, John. Living Carelessly in Tokyo & Elsewhere: A Memoir. 2008. (ENG., Illus.). 336p. 26.00 *(978-1-4165-5345-8(2)*, Free Pr.) Free Pr.

Otowa, Rebecca. At Home in Japan: A Foreign Woman's Journey of Discovery. 2010. (ENG., Illus.) 176p. 21.95 *(978-4-8053-1078-6(2))* Tuttle Publishing.

Pond, Karen. Getting Genki in Japan: The Adventures & Misadventures of an American Family in Tokyo. 2012. (ENG., Illus.). 192p. 17.95 ***(978-4-8053-1176-9(2))*** Tuttle Publishing.

Shaffer, Geneve L. A. The Log of the Empire State. 2008. 52p. pap. *(978-1-4099-5081-3(6))* Dodo Pr.

Thomas, Edward. Lafcadio Hearn. 2009. 94p. pap. 18.75 *(978-1-110-68250-8(6))* 2008. 96p. pap. 18.75 *(978-0-559-21056-3(6))* BiblioBazaar.

—Lafcadio Hearn. 2009. 48p. pap. *(978-0-217-01022-1(9))* Books LLC.

—Lafcadio Hearn. 2007. (ENG.). 108p. 33.95 *(978-0-548-42568-8(X))*; 96p. per. 18.95 *(978-0-548-40258-0(2))* Kessinger Publishing, LLC.

—Lafcadio Hearn. 2008. 92p. pap. *(978-1-4097-1687-7(2))* Read Bks.

AMERICANS—MEXICO

Arthur, Anthony. General Jo Shelby's March. 2010. (ENG., Illus.). 288p. 26.00 *(978-1-4000-6830-2(4))* Random Hse., Inc.

—General Jo Shelby's March. 2012. (ENG., Illus.). 296p. pap. 19.95 ***(978-0-8032-4077-3(5)***, Bison Bks.) Univ. of Nebraska Pr.

Berger, Dina & Wood, Andrew Grant, eds. Holiday in Mexico: Critical Reflections on Tourism & Tourist Encounters. 2010. (American Encounters/Global Interactions Ser.). (ENG., Illus.). 408p. 94.95 *(978-0-8223-4554-1(4))*; pap. 26.95 *(978-0-8223-4571-8(4))* Duke Univ. Pr.

Croucher, Sheila. The Other Side of the Fence: American Migrants in Mexico. 2010. (ENG., Illus.). 270p. pap. 25.00 *(978-0-292-72574-4(4))* Univ. of Texas Pr.

Croucher, Sheila L. The Other Side of the Fence: American Migrants in Mexico. 2009. (ENG.). 270p. 55.00 *(978-0-292-71975-0(2))* Univ. of Texas Pr.

Golson, Barry. Gringos in Paradise: An American Couple Builds Their Retirement Dream House in a Seaside Village in Mexico. 2008. (ENG.). 320p. pap. 15.00 *(978-0-7432-7636-8(1)*, Scribner) Scribner.

Gunn, Drewey Wayne. American & British Writers in Mexico, 1556-1973. 2011. (ENG.). 314p. pap. 30.00 *(978-0-292-72943-8(X))* Univ. of Texas Pr.

Schreiber, Rebecca M. Cold War Exiles in Mexico: U. S. Dissidents & the Culture of Critical Resistance. 2008. (Illus.). 320p. 67.50 *(978-0-8166-4307-3(5))*; pap. 22.50 *(978-0-8166-4308-0(3))* Univ. of Minnesota Pr.

AMERICANS—MIDDLE EAST

Butler, Barbara A. A Woman Sent to Saudi Arabia. 2009. pap. 10.99 *(978-1-60791-594-2(4))* Xulon Pr. Inc.

Butler, Grant & Butler, Grant C. Kings & Camels: An American in Saudi Arabia. 2008. (Illus.). 124p. pap. 34.95 *(978-1-85964-200-9(4))* Garnet Publishing, Ltd. GBR. Dist: International Specialized Bk. Services.

Decker, Kristin. The Unveiling: An American Teacher in a Saudi Palace. 2006. 176p. 20.95 *(978-1-58939-911-2(0))*; per. 13.95 *(978-1-58939-912-9(9))* Virtualbookworm.com Publishing, Inc.

Ender, Morten G. American Soldiers in Iraq: McSoldiers or Innovative Professionals? 2009. (Illus.). xx, 199p. (C). 39.95 ***(978-0-203-87937-5(6))***; (ENG., 224p. (C). 39.95 *(978-0-415-77789-6(5))*; (ENG., 224p. 170.00 *(978-0-415-77788-9(7))* Routledge.

Geniesse, Jane. American Priestess: The Extraordinary Story of Anna Spafford & the American Colony in Jerusalem. 2009. (ENG., Illus.). 416p. pap. 17.95 *(978-0-307-27772-5(0)*, Anchor) Knopf Doubleday Publishing Group.

Havreberg, Marjorie & Litoff, Judy Barrett. Dancing with Colonels: A Young Woman's Adventures in Wartime Turkey: Letters. 2011. (Illus.). 206p. 18.95 ***(978-0-9845041-3-8(3)***, South Dakota State Historical Society Pr.) South Dakota State Historical Society.

Johanyak, Debra. Behind the Veil: An American Woman's Memoir of the 1979 Iran Hostage Crisis. 2006. (International, Political, & Economic History Ser.). (Illus.). 251p. 39.95 *(978-1-931963-38-6(1))* Univ. of Akron Pr., The.

Johnson, Dale A. Fire on the Mountain. 2008. 146p. pap. 18.95 *(978-1-4357-3992-5(2))* Lulu Enterprises Inc.

Kauffman, Richard A. An American in Persia: A Pilgrimage to Iran. 2010. *(978-1-931038-75-1(9))* Cascadia Publishing Hse., LLC.

Kerr, van de Ven. One Familys Response to Terror. 2010. (Illus.). 202p. pap. 19.95 *(978-0-8156-0954-4(X))* Syracuse Univ. Pr.

Packer, George. The Assassins' Gate: America in Iraq. 2006. (ENG., Illus.). 512p. per. 16.00 *(978-0-374-53055-6(6)*, Farrar, Straus & Giroux.

Twain, Mark, pseud. The Innocents Abroad. 2009. 728p. 36.99 *(978-0-559-13465-4(7))*; 40.99 *(978-0-559-13456-2(8))*; pap. 50.75 *(978-0-559-13458-6(4))*; pap. 49.75 *(978-0-559-13463-0(0))* BiblioBazaar.

—The Innocents Abroad. 2009. 292p. pap. 9.99 *(978-1-4209-3211-9(X))* Digireads.com.

—The Innocents Abroad. 2007. (ENG.). 560p. (gr. 12-18). 7.95 *(978-0-451-53049-3(7)*, Signet Classics) Penguin Group (USA) Inc.

—Innocents Abroad. 2006. 378p. pap. *(978-1-4068-1298-5(6))* Echo Library.

Wall, Nancy T. Pulled by the Heart: A Woman's Real-Life Story of Living & Escaping the Middle East. 2009. (Illus.). 196p. pap. 18.95 *(978-1-930374-28-7(3))* DeForest Pr.

Wilson, Willow. The Butterfly Mosque: A Young American Woman's Journey to Love & Islam. 2010. (ENG.). 320p. 24.00 *(978-0-8021-1887-5(9)*, Atlantic Monthly Pr.) Grove/Atlantic, Inc.

AMERICANS—RUSSIA (FEDERATION)

Chatterjee, Choi & Holmgren, Beth, eds. Americans Experience Russia: Encountering the Enigma, 1917 to the Present. 2012. (Routledge Studies in Cultural History Ser.). (ENG.). 272p. (C). 125.00 *(978-0-415-89341-1(0))* Routledge.

AMERICANS—SOUTH AMERICA

Erick, June Carolyn. A Gringa in Bogotá: Living Colombia's Invisible War. 2010. (ENG., Illus.). 128p. 40.00 *(978-0-292-72135-7(8))*; pap. 19.95 *(978-0-292-72297-2(4))* Univ. of Texas Pr.

Mora, Frank O. & Cooney, Jerry W. Paraguay & the United States: Distant Allies. 2007. (United States & the Americas Ser.). (ENG.). 352p. 69.95 *(978-0-8203-2467-8(1))*; per. 24.95 *(978-0-8203-2932-1(0))* Univ. of Georgia Pr.

AMERICANS—SOVIET UNION

Meier, Andrew. The Lost Spy: An American in Stalin's Secret Service. (ENG., 416p. 2009. Illus.). pap. 18.95 *(978-0-393-33535-4(6)*, 33535) 2008. 25.95 *(978-0-393-06097-3(7)*, 6097) Norton, W. W. & Co., Inc.

Paul, Lisa C. Swimming in the Daylight: An American Student, a Soviet-Jewish Dissident, & the Gift of Hope. 2011. (ENG., Illus.). 304p. 24.95 *(978-1-61608-203-1(8)*, 608203) Skyhorse Publishing Co., Inc.

Tzouliadis, Tim. The Forsaken: An American Tragedy in Stalin's Russia. 2009. (ENG.). 448p. (gr. 12-18). 17.00 *(978-0-14-311542-7(1)*, Penguin (Non-Classics)) Penguin Group (USA) Inc.

AMERICANS IN FOREIGN COUNTRIES

see Americans—Foreign Countries

AMERICANS IN LITERATURE

Aldama, Frederick Luis. Your Brain on Latino Comics: From Gus Arriola to Los Bros Hernandez. 2009. (ENG., Illus.). 320p. 60.00 *(978-0-292-71934-7(5))*; pap. 24.95 *(978-0-292-71973-6(6))* Univ. of Texas Pr.

Caminero-Santangelo, Marta. On Latinidad: U.S. Latino Literature & the Construction of Ethnicity. 2007. (ENG.). 336p. 59.95 *(978-0-8130-3083-8(8))* Univ. Pr. of Florida.

Hay, John M. The Bread-Winners: A Social Study. (Americans in Fiction Ser.). 319p. reprint ed. lib. bdg. 9.00 *(978-0-8398-0773-5(2))* Irvington Pubs.

Tucker, Nathaniel B. The Partisan Leader: A Tale of the Future. (Muckrakers Ser.). 392p. reprint ed. lib. bdg. 39.00 *(978-0-8398-1975-2(7))* Irvington Pubs.

Walker, Jeffrey. Leather-Stocking Redux, or, Old Tales, New Essays. 2008. pap. *(978-0-404-62643-3(2))* AMS Pr., Inc.

Wetmore, Kevin J., Jr., ed. Portrayals of Americans on the World Stage: Critical Essays. 2009. (ENG.). 250p. pap. 45.00 *(978-0-7864-4419-9(3))* McFarland & Co., Inc. Pubs.

AMERICANS WITH DISABILITIES ACT, 1990
see United States—Americans with Disabilities Act, 1990

AMERICA'S CUP
D'Antonio, Michael. A Full Cup: Sir Thomas Lipton's Extraordinary Life & His Quest for the America's Cup. (ENG., (gr. 12). 2011. Illus.). 400p. 16.00 *(978-1-59448-521-3(6)*, Riverhead Trade (Paperbacks)) 2010. 368p. 26.95 *(978-1-59448-760-6(X)*, Riverhead Bks. (Hardcover)) Penguin Group (USA) Inc.
Fisher, Bob. The Absorbing Interest - the America's Cup - A History 1851-2003. 2007. (ENG.). 544p. 400.00 ***(978-0-470-51612-6(7)***, Wiley) Wiley, John & Sons, Inc.
Rayner, Ranulf. Story Americas Cup. 3rd rev. ed. 2007. (Illus.). 108p. 40.00 *(978-1-894622-87-5(1))* Warwick Publishing CAN. Dist: Perseus Distribution.
Simpson, Richard V. The America's Cup: Trials & Triumphs. 2010. (ENG., Illus.). 160p. pap. 19.99 *(978-1-59629-329-8(2))* History Pr., The.

AMERINDS
see Indians

AMERY, JOHN, 1912-1945
Keene, Judith. Treason on the Airwaves: Three Allied Broadcasters on Axis Radio During World War II. 2008. (Illus.). 256p. 49.95 *(978-0-313-35328-4(X)*, C35328, Praeger Pubs.) Greenwood Publishing Group, Inc.
—Treason on the Airwaves: Three Allied Broadcasters on Axis Radio During World War II. 2010. (ENG., Illus.). 256p. pap. 17.95 *(978-0-8032-3292-1(6)*, Bison Bks.) Univ. of Nebraska Pr.

AMES, FISHER, 1758-1808
Ames, Fisher. Works of Fisher Ames. 2009. 348p. pap. *(978-0-217-66140-9(8))* Books LLC.

AMETROPIA
see Eye—Accommodation and Refraction

AMEX
see American Stock Exchange

AMHARIC LANGUAGE
Ahland, Michael B. Language Death in Mesmes. 2009. 155p. pap. 25.00 *(978-1-55671-227-2(8))* SIL International.
Akineda, Daniel. Roi Framework for Generic Handwritten Amharic Form. 2010. 116p. pap. *(978-3-639-24852-4(X))* VDM Verlag Dr. Mueller e.K.
Alemu, Mellese Gelaneh. Amharic Second Language Teachers' Pedagogical Grammar Approach. 2010. 88p. pap. *(978-3-639-23529-6(0))* VDM Verlag Dr. Mueller e.K.
Appleyard, David. Colloquial Amharic. 2nd rev. ed. 2012. (Colloquial Ser.). (ENG & AMH., Illus.). 400p. 96.95 *(978-0-415-67180-4(9))*; pap. 52.95 *(978-0-415-67179-8(5))* Routledge.
Armbruster, C. H. Initia Amharica: An Introduction to Spoken Amharic. 2010. (Cambridge Library Collection - Linguistics Ser.). 538p. pap. 39.99 *(978-1-108-01328-4(7))*; (ENG.). 428p. pap. 32.99 *(978-1-108-01329-1(5))* Cambridge Univ. Pr.
—Initia Amharica 2 Part Set: Volume 3, Amharic-English Vocabulary with Phrases: An Introduction to Spoken Amharic, 2 vols. 2010. (Cambridge Library Collection - Linguistics Ser.). (ENG.). 1004p. pap. 73.00 *(978-1-108-01648-3(0))* Cambridge Univ. Pr.
Ayalew, Semahegne. Automatic Document Clustering: Amharic News Items. 2010. 88p. pap. *(978-3-639-22610-2(0))* VDM Verlag Dr. Mueller e.K.
Aycheh, Dagmawi Kebede. Automatic Back of Book Indexing. 2010. 124p. pap. *(978-3-639-26777-8(X))* VDM Verlag Dr. Mueller e.K.
Eadie, J. I. An Amharic Reader. 2011. (AMH & ENG.). 288p. pap. 23.99 *(978-1-107-60133-8(9))* Cambridge Univ. Pr.
Euro Talk. Talk Now! Amharic. 2008. 29.99 *(978-1-84352-373-4(6))* TOPICS Entertainment.
Habtewolde, Messele. The Genius Alaqa Gabrahana. 2011. 144p. 24.95 ***(978-1-4620-2589-3(7))***; pap. 14.95 ***(978-1-4620-2587-9(0))*** iUniverse, Inc.
Hagos, Desalegn. Non-Subject Agreement Elements in Amharic Relative Clause. 2010. 132p. pap. *(978-3-639-24335-2(8))* VDM Verlag Dr. Mueller e.K.
Icon Group International, Inc. Staff, compiled by. Webster's Amharic - English Thesaurus Dictionary. 2008. 34p. ring bd. 28.95 incl. audio compact disk *(978-0-497-83424-1(3))* Icon Group International, Inc.
Leslau, Wolf. Concise Amharic Dictionary. (AMH & ENG.). 95.00 *(978-0-8288-1153-8(9)*, F 55180) French & European Pubns., Inc.
Lonely Planet Staff, et al. Ethiopian Amharic. 3rd rev. ed. 2008. (Phrasebook Ser.). (AMH & ENG., Illus.). 292p. pap. 8.99 *(978-1-74059-645-9(5))* Lonely Planet Pubns.
Samuel, Wube. The Grammatical Competence in Amharic of Native English Speakers: The Investigation of the Grammatical Competence of Adult Monolingual American English Speaking Learners of Amharic As a Second Language. 2011. 92p. pap. ***(978-3-639-33918-5(5))*** VDM Verlag Dr. Mueller e.K.
Yassin Hamid, Ibrahim. Automatic Information Extraction Using Hidden Markov Model. 2010. 104p. pap. *(978-3-639-10358-8(0))* VDM Verlag Dr. Mueller e.K.
Zenawi, Endale. Amharic-English, English-Amharic Dictionary. 2nd ed. 2007. (AMH & ENG.). 668p. per. *(978-1-84356-015-9(1))* Wallenberg, Simon Pr.

AMHERST COLLEGE
Aries, Elizabeth. Race & Class Matters at an Elite College. 2008. (ENG., Illus.). 248p. 78.50 *(978-1-59213-725-1(3))*; pap. 26.95 *(978-1-59213-726-8(1))* Temple Univ. Pr.
Cutting, George Rugg. Student Life at Amherst College. 2010. 208p. pap. 15.95 *(978-1-4290-4324-3(5))* Applewood Bks.
McCormick, Lem Atanga & Klein, Nadav. Amherst College 2012: Off the Record. 2011. 188p. pap. 16.95 ***(978-1-4274-0330-8(9))*** College Prowler, Inc.

AMHERST COLLEGE—HISTORY
Adams, David L. & Adams, Lynne E. Massachusetts Memories: UMass Amherst History. 2008. (Illus.). 177p. pap. 18.95 *(978-0-9770454-7-1(1))* Levellers Pr.
Burgess, John William. Reminiscences of an American Scholar. reprint ed. 20.00 *(978-0-404-01236-6(1))* AMS Pr., Inc.
Hitchcock, Edward. Reminiscences of Amherst College: Historical Scientific, Biographical & Autobiographical. 2010. 430p. pap. 26.95 *(978-1-4290-4327-4(X))* Applewood Bks.
Wilson, Douglas. Passages of Time: Narratives in the History of AmherstCollege. Wilson, Douglas, ed. 2007. 312p. 25.00 *(978-0-943184-11-1(8))* Amherst College Pr.

AMIDES
see also Polyamides
Cram101 Textbook Reviews & Cram101 Textbook Reviews. Outlines & Highlights for Metal Amide Chemistry by Michael Lappert, Isbn: 9780470721841 0470721847. 2011. 86p. pap. 27.95 ***(978-1-61461-998-7(0))*** Cram101 Inc.
Kolev, Tsonko. Quantum Chemical, Spectroscopic & Structural Study of Hydrochlorides, Hydrogens Squarates & Ester Amides of Squaric Acid of Amina. 2008. (Illus.). viii, 95p. pap. 39.00 *(978-1-60456-431-0(8))* Nova Science Pubs., Inc.
Lappert, Michael, et al. Metal Amide Chemistry. 2009. (ENG., Illus.). 370p. 155.00 *(978-0-470-72184-1(7)*, Wiley) Wiley, John & Sons, Inc.

AMIEL, HENRI FREDERIC, 1821-1881
Amiel, Henri-Frederic. Amiel's Journal. 2008. 428p. 32.99 *(978-0-554-22792-4(4))*; 30.99 *(978-0-554-32095-3(9))* BiblioBazaar.
—Amiel's Journal: The Journal Intime of Henri-Frédéric Amiel. Ward, Humphrey, tr. 2007. (ENG.). 380p. pap. 25.99 *(978-1-4264-3056-5(6))* BiblioBazaar.
—Amiel's Journal: The Journal Intime of Henri-Frédéric Amiel. HUMPHREY WARD, tr. l.t. ed. 2007. (ENG.). 426p. pap. 28.99 *(978-1-4264-3121-0(X))* BiblioBazaar.

AMIENS (FRANCE)—CATHEDRALE D'AMIENS
see Cathedrale d'Amiens

AMIENS, BATTLE OF, AMIENS, FRANCE, 1918
McCluskey, Alistair. Amiens 1918: The Black Day of the German Army. 2008. (Campaign Ser.). (ENG., Illus.). 96p. pap. 19.95 *(978-1-84603-303-2(9))* Osprey Publishing, Ltd. GBR. Dist: Random Hse., Inc.
Messenger, Charles. The Day We Won the War: Turning Point at Amiens, 8 August 1918. 2010. (ENG., Illus.). 320p. 12.95 *(978-0-7538-2593-8(7)*, Phoenix) Orion Publishing Group, Ltd. GBR. Dist: Sterling Publishing Co., Inc.
—The Day We Won the War: Turning Point at Amiens 8 August 1918. 2009. (ENG., Illus.). 320p. *(978-0-297-85281-0(7)*, Weidenfeld & Nicolson) Orion Publishing Group, Ltd. GBR. Dist: Sterling Publishing Co., Inc.

AMIGA (COMPUTER)
Maher, Jimmy. The Future Was Here: The Commodore Amiga. 2012. (Platform Studies). (ENG., Illus.). 344p. (gr. 17). 26.95 ***(978-0-262-01720-6(2))*** MIT Pr.

AMILLENNIALISM
see Millennialism

AMIN, IDI, 1924-2003
Moghal, Manzoor. Idi Amin: Lion of Africa. 2010. (Illus.). 180p. pap. 15.99 *(978-1-4490-3974-5(X))* AuthorHouse.
Rice, Andrew. The Teeth May Smile but the Heart Does Not Forget: Murder & Memory in Uganda. 2010. (ENG., Illus.). 384p. pap. 17.00 *(978-0-312-42973-7(8))* Picador.

AMINES
see also Histamine; Polyamines; Primaquine
Azuma, Junichi, et al. Taurine 7. 2008. (Advances in Experimental Medicine & Biology Ser.). (Illus.). 500p. 269.00 *(978-0-387-75680-6(9))* Springer.
Chen, Yanwen. Inside the Plasma Amine Oxidase. 2010. 216p. pap. *(978-3-639-25568-3(2))* VDM Verlag Dr. Mueller e.K.
Farooqui, Tahira & Farooqui, Akhlaq A., eds. Biogenic Amines: Pharmacological, Neurochemical & Molecular Aspects in the CNS. 2010. (Pharmacology - Research, Safety Testing & Regulation Ser.). 125.00 *(978-1-60876-625-3(X)*, Nova Biomedical Bks.) Nova Science Pubs., Inc.
Kolev, Tsonko. Quantum Chemical, Spectroscopic & Structural Study of Hydrochlorides, Hydrogens Squarates & Ester Amides of Squaric Acid of Amina. 2008. (Illus.). viii, 95p. pap. 39.00 *(978-1-60456-431-0(8))* Nova Science Pubs., Inc.
Lawrence, Stephen A. Amines: Synthesis, Properties & Applications. 2006. (ENG., Illus.). 384p. (C). pap. 87.00 *(978-0-521-02972-8(4))* Cambridge Univ. Pr.
Liebman, Joel F. & Rappoport, Zvi Z., eds. The Chemistry of Hydroxylamines, Oximes & Hydroxamic Acids, 2 vols., Vol. 2. 2011. (Patai's Chemistry of Functional Groups Ser.). (ENG., Illus.). 1118p. 1115.00 *(978-0-470-68263-0(9)*, Wiley-Blackwell) Wiley, John & Sons, Inc.
Mondovi, Bruno, et al. Copper Amine Oxidases: Structures, Catalytic Mechanisms & Role in Pathophysiology. 2009. (ENG., Illus.). 374p. 154.95 *(978-1-4200-7680-6(9)*, CRC Press) Taylor & Francis Group GBR. Dist: Taylor & Francis Group.
Nugent, Thomas C., ed. Chiral Amine Synthesis: Methods, Developments & Applications. 2010. (ENG., Illus.). 520p. 230.00 *(978-3-527-32509-2(3)*, Wiley-VCH) Wiley, John & Sons, Inc.
O'Byrne, Paul. Red Wine & Health. 2009. (Illus.). xvii, 527p. 89.00 *(978-1-60692-718-2(3))* Nova Science Pubs., Inc.
Oja, Simo S. & Saransaari, Pirjo, eds. Taurine 6. 2010. (Advances in Experimental Medicine & Biology Ser.). (Illus.). xx, 556p. pap. 199.00 *(978-1-4419-4079-7(0)*, 1441940790) Springer.
Rabie, Dr. Mohamed, et al. Biogenic Amines in Food. 2010. 88p. pap. *(978-3-8383-5383-8(8))* Lambert Academic Publishing.
Rappoport, Zvi, ed. Chemistry of Anilines, 2 vols., Set. 2007. (Patai's Chemistry of Functional Groups Ser.: 152). (ENG.). 1180p. 1400.00 *(978-0-470-87171-3(7)*, Wiley) Wiley, John & Sons, Inc.
Rappoport, Zvi & Liebman, Joel F. The Chemistry of Hydroxylamines, Oximes & Hydroxamic Acids, 2 vols. 2009. (Patai's Chemistry of Functional Groups Ser.). (ENG., Illus.). 1078p. 1950.00 *(978-0-470-51261-6(X)*, Wiley) Wiley, John & Sons, Inc.
Ropital, F. Amine Unit Corrosion in Refineries: (efc 46) 24p. *(978-1-84569-237-7(3))* Woodhead Publishing Ltd. GBR. Dist: CRC Pr. LLC.
Ropital F Staff. Amine Unit Corrosion in Refineries (Efc 46) 2007. (ENG.). 37p. pap. 87.95 *(978-1-4200-5495-8(3)*, CRC Press) Taylor & Francis Group GBR. Dist: Taylor & Francis Group.
Sobolev, Victor S., et al, eds. The Peanut Plant & Light: Spermidines from Peanut Flowers. 2010. (Agriculture Issues & Policies Ser.). pap. 43.00 *(978-1-61668-028-2(8))* Nova Science Pubs., Inc.
Tseng, Kuei-Yuan & Atzori, Marco, eds. Monoaminergic Modulation of Cortical Excitability. 2010. (ENG., Illus.). x, 329p. pap. 179.00 *(978-1-4419-4428-3(1)*, 1441944281) Springer.
Yifru, Dawit. Phytoremediation of Perchlorate & N-Nitrosodimethylamine. 2011. 152p. pap. ***(978-3-8443-1262-1(5))*** Lambert Academic Publishing.

AMINO ACID METABOLISM
see Amino Acids—Metabolism

AMINO ACIDS
see also Polyamides
Aftab, Usama & Ashraf, Muhammad. Protein & Amino Acid Responses of Broilers with Low-Energy Diets. 2010. 144p. pap. *(978-3-639-23631-6(9))* VDM Verlag Dr. Mueller e.K.
Alam Mahmood, Zafar. L-Lysine. 2010. 180p. pap. *(978-3-639-23151-9(1))* VDM Verlag Dr. Mueller e.K.
Alterman, Michail A. & Hunziker, Peter, eds. Amino Acid Analysis: Methods & Protocols. 2011. (Methods in Molecular Biology Ser.). (ENG., Illus.). xiv, 363p. 139.00 ***(978-1-61779-444-5(9)***, 1617794449) Humana Pr.
Amir, Muhammad, et al. Amino Acid Production by Utilizing Indigenous Substrates. 2011. 96p. pap. ***(978-3-8443-0095-6(3))*** Lambert Academic Publishing.
Antonio, Jose, et al, eds. Essentials of Creatine in Sports & Health. 2007. (Illus.). 249p. 109.00 *(978-1-58829-690-0(3))* Humana Pr.
Appleton, Jeremy. Creatine. 2008. (Woodland Health Ser.). 30p. pap. 4.95 *(978-1-58054-113-8(5))* Woodland Publishing, Inc.
Ashmead, H. DeWayne. Amini Acid Chelation in Human & Animal Nutrition. 2012. (ENG., Illus.). 269p. 129.95 ***(978-1-4398-9767-6(0)***, CRC Press) Taylor & Francis Group GBR. Dist: Taylor & Francis Group.
Azuma, Junichi, et al. Taurine 7. 2008. (Advances in Experimental Medicine & Biology Ser.). (Illus.). 500p. 269.00 *(978-0-387-75680-6(9))* Springer.
Bendich, Adrianne, et al, eds. Essentials of Sports Nutrition & Supplements. 2008. (Illus.). 875p. (C). 129.00 *(978-1-58829-611-5(3)*, 1588296113) Humana Pr.
Blaskovich, Mark A. Handbook on Syntheses of Amino Acids: General Routes to Amino Acids. 2010. (ENG., Illus.). 1328p. 175.00 *(978-0-8412-7219-4(0))* American Chemical Society.
Boyd, Richard N. Stardust, Supernovae & the Molecules of Life: Might We All Be Aliens? 2011. (Astronomers' Universe Ser.). (ENG., Illus.). xi, 215p. pap. 34.95 ***(978-1-4614-1331-8(1)***, 1461413311) Springer.
Brückner, Hans & Fujii, Noriko, eds. D-Amino Acids in Chemistry, Life Sciences, & Biotechnology. 2011. (ENG., Illus.). 392p. 180.00 *(978-3-906390-65-9(9)*, Wiley-VCH) Wiley, John & Sons, Inc.
Bujnicki, Janusz & Bujnicki, Janusz M. Prediction of Protein Structures, Functions, & Interactions. 2009. (ENG., Illus.). 302p. 170.00 *(978-0-470-51767-3(0)*, Wiley) Wiley, John & Sons, Inc.
Bujnicki, Janusz M., ed. Practical Bioinformatics. 2007. (Nucleic Acids & Molecular Biology Ser.). (Illus.). 265p. pap. 109.00 *(978-3-540-74267-8(0))* Springer.
Cooper, Catherine, ed. Amino Acid Analysis Protocols. 2010. (Methods in Molecular Biology Ser.). (Illus.). 280p. pap. 149.00 *(978-1-61737-117-2(3)*, 1617371173) Humana Pr.
Cortese, Riccardo, ed. Combinatorial Libraries: Synthesis, Screening & Application Potential. (ENG.). XII, 232p. 196.00 ***(978-3-11-185021-4(8))*** De Gruyter, Walter Inc.
D'Elia, Valerio. Synthesis, Characterization & Application of A/ß-Oligopeptides. 2010. 176p. pap. *(978-3-639-25344-3(2))* VDM Verlag Dr. Mueller e.K.
D'Mello, J. P. F., ed. Amino Acids in Human Nutrition & Health. 2012. (Illus.). 584p. 240.00 ***(978-1-84593-798-0(8))*** CABI GBR. Dist: Stylus Publishing, LLC.
Essentials of Amino Acids in Sports. 2009. 99.50 *(978-1-58829-689-4(X))* Humana Pr.
Faurie, Robert & Thommel, Jørgen. Microbial Production of L-Amino Acids. 2010. (Advances in Biochemical Engineering Biotechnology Ser.). (Illus.). xiii, 185p. pap. 159.00 *(978-3-642-07775-3(7)*, 3642077757) Springer.
Florinsky, Igor V., ed. Man & the Geosphere. 2010. (Earth Sciences in the 21st Century Ser.). 399p. 145.00 *(978-1-60876-387-0(0))* Nova Science Pubs., Inc.
Hamano, Yoshimitsu, ed. Amino-Acid Homopolymers Occurring in Nature. 2010. (Microbiology Monographs). (Illus.). vii, 250p. 219.00 *(978-3-642-12452-5(6)*, 3642124526) Springer.
Hayat, Shamsul & Hayat, Qaiser. Role of Proline & Salicylic Acid in Overcoming the Stress of Cadmium. 2011. 184p. pap. ***(978-3-8443-1660-5(4))*** Lambert Academic Publishing.
Hughes, Andrew B., contrib. by. Amino Acids, Peptides & Proteins in Organic Chemistry: Protection Reactions, Medicinal Chemistry, Combinatorial Synthesis, 6 vols., Volume 4. 2011. (Amino Acids, Peptides & Proteins in Organic Chemistry (VCH) Ser.: 2). (ENG., Illus.). 552p. 195.00 *(978-3-527-32103-2(9)*, Wiley-VCH) Wiley, John & Sons, Inc.
—Amino Acids, Peptides & Proteins in Organic Chemistry Vol. 3: Building Blocks, Catalysis & Coupling Chemistry, 6 vols., Volume 3. 2011. (Amino Acids, Peptides & Proteins in Organic Chemistry (VCH) Ser.: 1). (ENG., Illus.). 604p. 200.00 *(978-3-527-32102-5(0)*, Wiley-VCH) Wiley, John & Sons, Inc.
Hughes, Andrew B., contrib. by. Amino Acids, Peptides & Proteins in Organic Chemistry Vol. 5: Analysis & Function of Amino Acids & Peptides, 6 vols., Volume 5. 2011. (Amino Acids, Peptides & Proteins in Organic Chemistry (VCH) Ser.: 3). (ENG., Illus.). 508p. 210.00 ***(978-3-527-32104-9(7)***, Wiley-VCH) Wiley, John & Sons, Inc.
Hughes, William. Origins & Synthesis of Amino Acids, 6 vols., Volume 1. 2009. (Amino Acids, Peptides & Proteins in Organic Chemistry (VCH) Ser.: 6). (ENG., Illus.). 734p. 240.00 *(978-3-527-32096-7(2)*, Wiley-VCH) Wiley, John & Sons, Inc.
Jhoti, Harren & Leach, Andrew R., eds. Structure-based Drug Discovery. 2010. (ENG.). xii, 252p. pap. 219.00 *(978-90-481-7123-1(7)*, 9048171237) Springer.
Jonas, Peter & Monyer, Hannah, eds. Ionotropic Glutamate Receptors in the CNS. 2010. (Handbook of Experimental Pharmacology Ser.). (Illus.). xxii, 535p. pap. 629.00 *(978-3-642-08539-0(3)*, 3642085393) Springer.
Kazmierski, Wieslaw M., ed. Peptidomimetics Protocols. 2010. (Methods in Molecular Medicine Ser.). 576p. pap. 149.00 *(978-1-61737-059-5(2)*, 1617370592) Humana Pr.
Khalid, Sumbul. Growth Hormone of Pakistani Buffalo. 2010. 108p. pap. *(978-3-8383-5098-1(7))* Lambert Academic Publishing.
Kochen, Walter & Steinhart, Hans, eds. L-Tryptophan: Current Prospects in Medicine & Drug Safety. (ENG.). X, 458p. 419.00 ***(978-3-11-180631-0(6))*** De Gruyter, Walter Inc.
Konno, Ryuichi, et al. D-Amino Acids: Practical Methods & Protocols, Volume 1: Analytical Methods for D-Amino Acids. 2009. (D-Amino Acids: Practical Methods & Protocols Ser.). 145.00 *(978-1-60741-376-9(0))* Nova Science Pubs., Inc.
—D-Amino Acids: Practical Methods & Protocols, Volume 2: Free D-Amino Acids. 2009. (D-Amino Acids: Practical Methods & Protocols Ser.). 145.00 *(978-1-60741-377-6(9))* Nova Science Pubs., Inc.
—D-Amino Acids: Practical Methods & Protocols, Volume 3: D-Amino Acids in Peptides & Proteins. 2009. (D-Amino Acids: Practical Methods & Protocols Ser.). 145.00 *(978-1-60741-378-3(7))* Nova Science Pubs., Inc.
—D-Amino Acids: Practical Methods & Protocols, Volume 4: Enzymes Involved in the Metabolism of D-Amino Acids. 2009. (D-Amino Acids: Practical Methods & Protocols Ser.). 145.00 *(978-1-60741-379-0(5))* Nova Science Pubs., Inc.
Kumar, Santosh. Vivrational Spectroscopy. 2010. 208p. pap. *(978-3-639-23870-9(2))* VDM Verlag Dr. Mueller e.K.
LeBlanc, Mark & Dyer, Betsey Dexter. Perl for Exploring DNA. 2007. (ENG., Illus.). 288p. 125.00 *(978-0-19-532757-1(8))* Oxford Univ. Pr., Inc.
Li, Min, ed. NMDA Receptor Protocols. 2010. (Methods in Molecular Biology Ser.). 208p. pap. 139.00 *(978-1-61737-146-2(7)*, 1617371467) Humana Pr.
Lorne Protein Workshop Staff, compiled by. 31st Lorne Proteins Conference 2006. 2007. 149p. pap. 93.00 *(978-1-60423-750-4(3))* Curran Assocs., Inc.
Mayer, Gunter. Nucleic Acid & Peptide Aptamers: Methods & Protocols. Mayer, Ganter, ed. 2009. (Methods in Molecular Biology Ser.). (ENG., Illus.). xi, 408p. 159.00 *(978-1-934115-89-3(4))* Humana Pr.
Muir, Tom W. & Abelson, John N. Non-Natural Amino Acids. 2009. (ENG., Illus.). 350p. 187.00 *(978-0-12-374310-7(9)*, Academic Pr.) Elsevier Science & Technology Bks.
Mun, Hee-Chang. L-Amino Acid Sensing by the Calcium Sensing Receptor. 2009. 196p. pap. *(978-3-639-06192-5(6))* VDM Verlag Dr. Mueller e.K.
Narayanan, Venkatathri. Studies on Mercury Interaction with Dicarboxylic Aminoacids. 2010. 100p. pap. *(978-3-8383-4218-4(6))* Lambert Academic Publishing.
Nguyen, Tri. Total Sulfur Amino Acid Requirement of Tilapi. 2009. 80p. pap. *(978-3-639-13426-1(5))* VDM Verlag Dr. Mueller e.K.
Nur, Hadi & Kheng Wei, Lim. Amino Acids Functionalized Heterogeneous Chiral Catalyst. 2011. 96p. pap. ***(978-3-8454-0758-6(1))*** Lambert Academic Publishing.
Paley, Benjamin F. & Warfield, Tomas E. Amino Acid Receptor Research. 2008. (Illus.). xv, 458p. 129.00 *(978-1-60456-283-5(8)*, Nova Biomedical Bks.) Nova Science Pubs., Inc.
Petersen, John R. & Mohammad, Amin A., eds. Clinical & Forensic Applications of Capillary Electrophoresis. 2010. (Pathology & Laboratory Medicine Ser.). (Illus.). 456p. pap. 169.00 *(978-1-61737-113-4(0)*, 1617371130) Humana Pr.
Pollegioni, Loredano & Servi, Stefano, eds. Unnatural Amino Acids: Methods & Protocols. 2011. (Methods in Molecular Biology Ser.). (ENG., Illus.). xiv, 409p. 139.00 ***(978-1-61779-330-1(2)***, 1617793302) Humana Pr.

Rejsek, Klement, et al. The Soil Amino Acids: Quality, Distribution & Site Ecology. 2010. (Advances in Environmental Research Ser.). 89.00 *(978-1-61668-335-1(X))* Nova Science Pubs., Inc.

Rejsek, Klement, et al. Soil Amino Acids: Quality, Distribution & Site Ecology. 2011. (Environmental Science, Engineering & Technology Ser.). 236p. pap. 59.00 ***(978-1-62100-511-7(9))*** Nova Science Pubs., Inc.

Ricci, Alfredo, ed. Amino Group Chemistry: From Synthesis to the Life Sciences. 2008. (ENG., Illus.). 408p. 235.00 *(978-3-527-31741-7(4),* Wiley-VCH) Wiley, John & Sons, Inc.

Rodriguez-Moreno, Antonio & Sihra, Talvinder S., eds. Kainate Receptors: Novel Signaling Insights. 2011. (Advances in Experimental Medicine & Biology Ser.). (ENG., Illus.). xx, 128p. 139.00 *(978-1-4419-9556-8(0),* 1441995560) Springer.

Royal Society of Chemistry Staff. Amino Acids, Peptides & Proteins, Vol. 35. Davies, J. S., ed. 2006. (Specialist Periodical Reports). (ENG., Illus.). 472p. 448.00 ***(978-0-85404-247-0(4))*** Royal Society of Chemistry, The GBR. Dist: Ingram Pub. Services.

Sahley, Billie Jay & Birkner, Katherine M. Heal with Amino Acids & Nutrients: Survive Stress, Pain, Anxiety, Depression, & More — What to Use & When. 2011. (Illus.). 268p. pap. 18.95 *(978-1-889391-37-3(9))* Pain & Stress Pubns.

Sajjad, Sumera. Role of Eaa in the Regulation of Prolactin in Nonhuman Primates. 2011. 180p. pap. ***(978-3-8443-0989-8(6))*** Lambert Academic Publishing.

Salomons, Gajja S. & Wyss, Markus, eds. Creatine & Creatine Kinase in Health & Disease. (Subcellular Biochemistry Ser.). 2010. xviii, 352p. pap. 319.00 *(978-90-481-7652-6(2),* 9048176522) 2008. (Illus.). 351p. 319.00 *(978-1-4020-6485-2(3))* Springer.

Schäfer, Hanna A. & Wohlber, Lilli M. Diamino Amino Acids. 2008. 256p. 89.00 *(978-1-60456-892-9(5))* Nova Science Pubs., Inc.

Schmidt, Werner & Reith, Maarten E. A., eds. Dopamine & Glutamate in Psychiatric Disorders. 2010. (Illus.). 602p. pap. 225.00 *(978-1-61737-495-1(4),* 1617374954) Humana Pr.

Sharma, Virender K. & Rokita, Steven E. Oxidation of Amino Acids, Peptides, & Proteins: Kinetics & Mechanism. 2012. (Wiley Series of Reactive Intermediates in Chemistry & Biology Ser.: 7). (ENG.). 400p. 125.00 *(978-0-470-62776-1(X),* Wiley) Wiley, John & Sons, Inc.

Shartava, Tsisana. Ligands, Polymers & Amino Acids. 2011. (Biochemistry Research Trends Ser.). 89.00 *(978-1-61122-793-2(3),* Nova Biomedical Bks.) Nova Science Pubs., Inc.

Soloshonok, Vadim A. & Izawa, Kunisuke, eds. Asymmetric Synthesis & Application of Alpha-Amino Acids. 2009. (ACS Symposium Ser.). (ENG., Illus.). 504p. 195.00 *(978-0-8412-6974-3(2))* American Chemical Society.

Stout, Jeffrey R., et al, eds. Essentials of Creatine in Sports & Health. 2010. (Illus.). x, 254p. pap. 109.00 *(978-1-61737-719-8(8),* 1617377198) Humana Pr.

Tate, Suresh. How Amino Acids Create Hemoglobin, Neurotransmitters, DNA, & RNA. 2011. (Colloquium Series on the Cell Biology of Medicine Ser.). 100p. pap. 35.00 *(978-1-61504-294-4(6))* Morgan & Claypool Life Science Publishers.

Uversky, Vladimir N., ed. Methods in Protein Structure & Stability Analysis — Conformational Stability, Size, Shape & Surface of Protein Molecules. 2007. 129.00 *(978-1-60021-704-3(4))* Nova Science Pubs., Inc.

Uversky, Vladimir N. & Permiakov, E. A. Protein Structures: Methods in Protein Structure & Stability Analysis. 2006. 372p. 225.00 *(978-1-60021-404-2(5))* Nova Science Pubs., Inc.

Vollrath, Victoria Marie. Amino Acids Essential for Human Health & Life with Index & Medical Analysis of New Research Information for all Nations. 2006. (Illus.). 160p. 69.95 *(978-0-7883-4388-9(2),* 07883-43882) ABBE Pubs. Assn. of Washington, D.C.

Wendisch, Volker F. Amino Acid Biosynthesis - Pathways, Regulation & Metabolic Engineering. (Microbiology Monographs). (Illus.). x, 413p. 2010. pap. 319.00 *(978-3-642-08018-0(9),* 3642080189) 2007. 319.00 *(978-3-540-48595-7(3))* Springer.

Wexler, Barbara. Tryptophan: Powerful Serotonin Booster. 2007. (Woodland Health Ser.). (Illus.). 30p. pap. 4.95 *(978-1-58054-121-3(6))* Woodland Publishing, Inc.

Whitley, Blake L. & Thornton, Sarah H., eds. Tryptophan: Dietary Sources, Functions & Health Benefits. 2012. ***(978-1-62100-445-5(7))*** Nova Science Pubs., Inc.

World Health Organization. Protein & Amino Acid Requirements in Human Nutrition: Report of a Joint WHO/FAO/UNU Expert Consultation. 2007. (Technical Report Ser.). (ENG.). 276p. pap. 48.00 *(978-92-4-120935-9(6))* World Health Organization.

Wu, Guang & Yan, Shaomin. Lecture Notes on Computational Mutation. 2008. (Illus.). ix, 230p. 98.00 *(978-1-60456-516-4(0))* Nova Science Pubs., Inc.

Zaki, Mohammed & Bystroff, Chris, eds. Protein Structure Prediction. 2nd ed. 2010. (Methods in Molecular Biology Ser.). (Illus.). xii, 337p. pap. 149.00 *(978-1-61737-757-0(0),* 1617377570) Humana Pr.

Zaki, Mohammed J. & Bystroff, Chris, eds. Protein Structure Prediction. 2nd ed. 2007. (Methods in Molecular Biology Ser.). (Illus.). 337p. 149.00 *(978-1-58829-752-5(7))* Humana Pr.

Zhu, Jinge. Characterization of S-Ribosylhomocysteinase. 2009. 224p. pap. *(978-3-639-16515-9(2))* VDM Verlag Dr. Mueller e.K.

AMINO ACIDS—METABOLISM

Carmel, Ralph & Jacobsen, Donald W., eds. Homocysteine in Health & Disease. 2011. (ENG., Illus.). 536p. pap. 95.00 *(978-1-107-40242-3(5))* Cambridge Univ. Pr.

Chikkali, Samir. Catechol Phosphines: Metal Assisted Self-assembly & Application. 2008. 200p. pap. *(978-3-639-07138-2(7))* VDM Verlag Dr. Mueller e.K.

Di Pasquale, Mauro G. Amino Acids & Proteins for the Athlete: The Anabolic Edge. 2nd rev. ed. 2007. (Nutrition in Exercise & Sport Ser.). (ENG., Illus.). 456p. 113.95 *(978-1-4200-4380-8(3),* CRC Press) Taylor & Francis Group GBR. Dist: Taylor & Francis Group.

Handbook of Neurochemistry & Molecular Neurobiology: Sensory Neurochemistry. 3rd rev. ed. 2007. (Springer Reference Ser.). (Illus.). 301p. 249.00 *(978-0-387-30349-9(9))* Springer.

Jones, Patricia M. & Rakheja, Dinesh. Quick Guide to Organic Acid Interpretation. 2011. ***(978-1-59425-126-9(6),*** AACC Pr.) American Assn. for Clinical Chemistry, Inc.

Kochen, Walter & Steinhart, Hans, eds. L-Tryptophan: Current Prospects in Medicine & Drug Safety. (ENG.). X, 458p. 419.00 ***(978-3-11-180631-0(6))*** De Gruyter, Walter Inc.

Masella, Roberta, et al. Glutathione & Sulfur Amino Acids in Human Health & Disease. 2009. (ENG., Illus.). 598p. 163.00 *(978-0-470-17085-4(9),* Wiley) Wiley, John & Sons, Inc.

Wallsgrove, R. M., ed. Amino Acids & their Derivatives in Higher Plants. 2008. (Society for Experimental Biology Seminar Ser.). (ENG., Illus.). 296p. pap. 58.00 *(978-0-521-05051-7(0))* Cambridge Univ. Pr.

AMIS, KINGSLEY, 1922-1995

DePietro, Thomas, ed. Conversations with Kingsley Amis. (Literary Conversations Ser.). (ENG.). 224p. 2010. 50.00 *(978-1-60473-290-0(3))* 2009. pap. 22.00 *(978-1-60473-291-7(1))* Univ. Pr. of Mississippi.

Leader, Zachary. The Life of Kingsley Amis. 2007. (ENG., Illus.). 1008p. 39.95 *(978-0-375-42498-4(9),* Pantheon) Knopf Doubleday Publishing Group.

—The Life of Kingsley Amis. 2011. (ENG.). 1012p. pap. 25.95 *(978-0-8101-2759-3(8))* Northwestern Univ. Pr.

AMIS, MARTIN, 1949-

Adami, Valentina. Trauma Studies & Literature: Martin Amis's Time's Arrow As Trauma Fiction. 2008. (Anglo-amerikanische Studien - Anglo-American Studies). 120p. pap. 35.95 *(978-3-631-57796-7(6))* Lang, Peter GmbH, Europaischer Verlag der Wissenschaften DEU. Dist: Lang, Peter.

Bentley Nicholas. Martin Amis. 2012. (Writers & Their Work Ser.). (ENG.). 128p. (C). pap. 26.00 *(978-0-7463-1178-3(8))* Northcote Hse. Publishers, Ltd. GBR. Dist: Brown, David Bk. Co., The.

Bentley Nick & Bentley, Nicholas. Martin Amis. 2012. (Writers & Their Work Ser.). (ENG.). 128p. (C). 80.00 *(978-0-7463-1173-8(7))* Northcote Hse. Publishers, Ltd. GBR. Dist: Brown, David Bk. Co., The.

Bradley, Arthur & Tate, Andrew. The New Atheist: Fiction, Philosophy & Polemic after 9/11. 2010. (New Directions in Religion & Literature Ser.). (ENG.). 160p. 27.95 *(978-0-8264-4629-9(9));* 90.00 *(978-0-8264-4429-5(6))* Continuum International Publishing Group, Ltd. GBR. Dist: National Bk. Network.

Finney, Brian. Martin Amis. 2008. XII, 180p. 28.95 *(978-0-415-40292-7(1));* 95.00 *(978-0-415-40291-0(3))* Routledge.

Keulks, Gavin. Martin Amis: Postmodernism & Beyond. Keulks, Gavin, ed. 2006. (ENG.). 256p. 84.00 *(978-0-230-00830-4(5))* Palgrave Macmillan.

AMISH

Aurand Jr., Ammon Monroe. Little Known Facts about the Amish & the Mennonites: A Study of the Social Customs & Habits of Pennsylvania's Plain People. 2011. 36p. 35.95 ***(978-1-258-02716-2(X))*** Literary Licensing, LLC.

Bachmann-Geiser, Brigitte. Amish: The Way of Life of the Amish in Berne, Indiana. 2008. (Illus.). 246p. pap. 37.95 *(978-0-89725-850-0(9))* Picton Pr.

Beiler, Jonas. Think No Evil: Inside the Story of the Amish Schoolhouse Shooting... & Beyond. 2009. (ENG., Illus.). 224p. 23.99 *(978-1-4165-6295-6(2),* Howard Bks.) Howard Books.

Black, Marie. Not My Amish Father's Wishes. 2011. 116p. pap. 12.68 ***(978-1-4634-2542-5(2))*** AuthorHouse.

Clark, Mindy Starns. A Pocket Guide to Amish Life. 2010. 144p. pap. 6.99 *(978-0-7369-2864-9(2))* Harvest Hse. Pubs.

Craker, Lorilee. Money Secrets of the Amish: Finding True Abundance in Simplicity, Sharing, & Saving. 2011. 240p. pap. 15.99 *(978-1-59555-341-6(X))* Nelson, Thomas Inc.

Detweiler Malinda. I Was Amish: A personal story of an Amish girl & her Life. 2011. 168p. 29.99 ***(978-1-4568-6990-8(6));*** pap. 19.99 ***(978-1-4568-6989-2(2))*** Xlibris Corp.

Down A Country Road with the Amish. 2009. (Illus.). 81p. lib. bdg. 12.99 *(978-0-615-27716-5(0))* Brush Creek Publishing.

Egenes, Linda. Visits with the Amish: Impressions of the Plain Life. 2009. (Bur Oak Book Ser.). (ENG., Illus.). 126p. pap. 17.95 *(978-1-58729-785-4(X))* Univ. of Iowa Pr.

Eicher, Lovina & Williams, Kevin. The Amish Cook's Baking Book. 2009. (ENG.). 224p. 29.99 *(978-0-7407-8547-4(8))* Andrews McMeel Publishing.

Fisher, Suzanne Woods. Amish Peace: Simple Wisdom for a Complicated World. 2009. (Illus.). 208p. pap. 12.99 *(978-0-8007-3338-4(X))* Revell.

Garrett, Ruth Irene & Morse-Kahn, Deborah. Born Amish. 2008. pap. 14.95 *(978-1-935001-12-6(4))* Acclaim Pr., Inc.

Gingerich, Hugh F. & Kreider, Rachel W., compiled by. Amish & Amish Mennonite Genealogies. 2007. 955p. 90.00 *(978-1-60126-018-5(0))* Masthof Pr.

Gingerich, Orland. The Amish of Canada. (Illus.). 23.85 *(978-1-894710-19-0(3))* Pandora Pr. CAN. Dist: Herald Pr.

Good, Merle. Who Are the Amish? 128p. 29.95 *(978-1-56148-332-7(X))* Good Bks.

Huntington, Gertrude Enders. Amish in Michigan. 2008. (Discovering the Peoples of Michigan Ser.). (ENG., Illus.). 55p. pap. 12.95 *(978-0-87013-597-2(X))* Michigan State Univ. Pr.

Hurst, Charles E. & McConnell, David L. An Amish Paradox: Diversity & Change in the World's Largest Amish Community. 2010. (Young Center Books in Anabaptist & Pietist Studies). (ENG., Illus.). 376p. (gr. 17). 61.00 *(978-0-8018-9398-8(4));* pap. 31.00 *(978-0-8018-9399-5(2))* Johns Hopkins Univ. Pr.

Johnson-Weiner, Karen M. New York Amish: Life in the Plain Communities of the Empire State. 2010. (Illus.). 240p. 24.95 *(978-0-8014-4518-7(3))* Cornell Univ. Pr.

—Train up a Child: Old Order Amish & Mennonite Schools. 2006. (Young Center Books in Anabaptist & Pietist Studies). (ENG., Illus.). 304p. (gr. 17). 51.95 *(978-0-8018-8495-5(0))* Johns Hopkins Univ. Pr.

Kloskowski, Jr. Pedaggy Plain & Fancy: Historical Analysis. 2009. 180p. 24.99 *(978-1-4389-9940-1(2));* pap. 14.49 *(978-1-4389-9939-5(9))* AuthorHouse.

Kraybill, Donald B. The Amish of Lancaster County. 2008. (ENG., Illus.). 96p. pap. 15.95 *(978-0-8117-3478-3(1))* Stackpole Bks.

Kraybill, Donald B., et al. The Amish Way: Patient Faith in a Perilous World. (ENG.). 288p. 2012. pap. 16.95 ***(978-1-118-15276-8(X))*** 2010. 24.95 *(978-0-470-52069-7(8))* Wiley, John & Sons, Inc. (Jossey-Bass).

Lehman, James O. & Nolt, Steven M. Mennonites, Amish, & the American Civil War. 2007. (Young Center Books in Anabaptist & Pietist Studies). (ENG., Illus.) 376p. (gr. 17). 43.00 *(978-0-8018-8672-0(4))* Johns Hopkins Univ. Pr.

Lehman, Martin. Roots & Branches: A Narrative History of the Amish & Mennonites in Southeast United States, 1892-1992, Volume 2, Branches, 2 vols., Vol. 2. 2011. (ENG.). 242p. pap. 21.95 *(978-1-931038-84-3(6))* Cascadia Publishing Hse., LLC.

Lehman, Martin W. Roots & Branches: A Narrative History of the Amish & Mennonites in Southeast United States, 1892-1992, Volume 1, Roots, 2. 2010. (Illus.). 308p. pap. 23.95 *(978-1-931038-69-0(4))* Cascadia Publishing Hse., LLC.

Mackall, Joe. Plain Secrets: An Outsider among the Amish, 1 vol. (ENG.). 2008. 248p. pap. 15.00 *(978-0-8070-1065-5(0))* 2007. 256p. 24.95 *(978-0-8070-1064-8(2))* Beacon Pr.

Monroe, Hochstetler, compiled by. Life & Times in Honduras: Twenty Families Struggle in Honduras. 2007. 406p. 12.95 *(978-0-9797819-0-2(6))* Hochstetler Variety.

Navor, Darlene. Neighbor to the Amish. 2010. 116p. (ENG.). 21.99 *(978-1-4520-4492-7(9));* pap. 11.49 *(978-1-4520-4490-3(2))* AuthorHouse.

Naylor, Phyllis Reynolds. An Amish Family. 20.95 *(978-0-8488-0109-0(1))* Amereon LTD.

Nolt, Steven M. & Meyers, Thomas J. Plain Diversity: Amish Cultures & Identities. 2007. (Young Center Books in Anabaptist & Pietist Studies). (ENG., Illus.). 256p. (gr. 17). 51.00 *(978-0-8018-8605-8(8))* Johns Hopkins Univ. Pr.

Perry, Marta. Naomi's Christmas. 2012. (Pleasant Valley Ser.). (ENG.). (gr. 12). pap. 14.00 ***(978-0-425-25329-8(5),*** Berkley Trade) Penguin Group (USA) Inc.

Puchalla, Kitty. A Double Life. 2009. 120p. 23.99 *(978-1-4343-9248-0(1));* pap. 12.49 *(978-1-4343-9249-7(X))* AuthorHouse.

RAUTER, Timm. No Photographing, 1 vol. 2011. (ENG., Illus.). 156p. 48.00 ***(978-3-86930-322-2(0))*** Steidl, Gerhard Druckerei und Verlag DEU. Dist: Innovative Logistics.

Ruth, John L. Forgiveness: A Legacy of the West Nickel Mines Amish School. 2011. (ENG., Illus.). 157p. pap. 10.99 ***(978-0-8361-9573-6(6))*** 2007. 151p. per. 10.99 *(978-0-8361-9373-2(3))* Herald Pr.

Schlabach, Theron F. Peace, Faith, Nation: Mennonites & Amish in Nineteenth-Century America. 2007. (Dove Ser.). (Illus.). 416p. pap. 46.00 *(978-1-55635-197-6(6),* Wipf and Stock) Wipf & Stock Pubs.

Schrock, Mary. The Greater Inheritance: The tru story of one Amish family's journey to the Truth. 2009. 150p. pap. 13.95 *(978-1-935298-24-3(0))* Truth Pubs.

Schwieder, Elmer & Schwieder, Dorothy. A Peculiar People: Iowa's Old Order Amish. enl. ed. 2009. (Bur Oak Book Ser.). (ENG., Illus.). 204p. pap. 19.95 *(978-1-58729-805-9(8))* Univ. of Iowa Pr.

Scott, Gary. Out of the Ordinary. 2011. pap. 12.95 ***(978-0-7414-6584-9(1))*** Infinity Publishing.

Shachtman, Tom. Rumspringa: To Be or Not to Be Amish. 2009. (ENG.). 286p. 25.00 *(978-1-4379-6296-3(3))* DIANE Publishing Co.

—Rumspringa: To Be or Not to Be Amish. annot. ed. 2007. (ENG.). 304p. per. 16.00 *(978-0-86547-742-1(6),* North Point Pr.) Farrar, Straus & Giroux.

Sheldon, George. What the Amish Know: The Hidden Ways - & Wisdom - of America's Most Secret Community. 2011. (ENG.). 256p. pap. 14.95 *(978-1-4405-2573-5(0))* Adams Media Corp.

Smith, Elmer Lewis. The Amish People: Seventeenth-Century Tradition in Modern America. 2011. 270p. 47.95 ***(978-1-258-10328-6(1))*** Literary Licensing, LLC.

—The Amish Today: An Analysis of Their Beliefs, Behavior & Contemporary Problems. 2011. 406p. 54.95 ***(978-1-258-00697-6(9))*** Literary Licensing, LLC.

Stevick, Pauline. Beyond the Plain & Simple: A Patchwork of Amish Lives. 2006. (Illus.). 159p. 22.95 *(978-0-87338-880-1(1))* Kent State Univ. Pr.

Stevick, Richard A. Growing up Amish: The Teenage Years. 2007. (Young Center Books in Anabaptist & Pietist Studies). (ENG., Illus.). 320p. 28.00 *(978-0-8018-8567-9(1))* Johns Hopkins Univ. Pr.

Tharp, Bruce M. Ascetical Value. 2009. 360p. pap. *(978-3-639-10256-7(6))* VDM Verlag Dr. Mueller e.K.

Trollinger, Susan L. Selling the Amish: The Tourism of Nostalgia. 2012. (Young Center Books in Anabaptist & Pietist Studies). (ENG., Illus.). 216p. (gr. 17). 50.00 ***(978-1-4214-0419-6(2))*** Johns Hopkins Univ. Pr.

Wagler, Ira. Growing up Amish: A Memoir. l.t. ed. 2011. lib. bdg. 34.95 ***(978-1-61173-196-5(8))*** Ctr. Point Large Print.

—Growing up Amish: A Memoir. 2011. (ENG.). 288p. pap. 14.99 *(978-1-4143-3936-8(4))* Tyndale Hse. Pubs.

Waters, Bruce M. Faces of Lancaster County. 2011. (Illus.). 128p. *(978-0-7643-3707-9(6),* Schiffer Publishing Ltd) Schiffer Publishing, Ltd.

Wittmer, Joe. The Gentle People: An Inside View of Amish Life. 3rd exp. ed. 2006. Orig. Title: The Gentle People: Personal Reflections of Amish Life Expanded Edition. (Illus.). 208p. per. 9.95 *(978-0-9715404-1-5(1))* Black Buggy Restaurant & General Store LLC.

AMISH COOKING

Brunstetter, Wanda E. Amish Friends Cookbook. 2007. (ENG., Illus.). 224p. pap. 14.99 *(978-1-59789-644-3(6),* Barbour Bks.) Barbour Publishing, Inc.

—Amish Friends Cookbook Vol. 2: 200 Hearty Recipes from Amish Country. 2009. (ENG.). 224p. pap. 14.99 *(978-1-60260-345-5(6),* Barbour Bks.) Barbour Publishing, Inc.

Byler, Linda. Lizzie's Amish Cookbook: Favorite Recipes from Three Generations of Amish Cooks, 1 vol. 2011. (ENG.). 320p. pap. 13.99 ***(978-1-56148-735-6(X));*** spiral bd. 18.95 ***(978-1-56148-738-7(4))*** Good Bks.

Centenary M.E. Church (Lebanon, contrib. by. The Lebanon Cook Book. 2007. (Illus.). 200p. pap. 29.00 *(978-0-7884-4297-1(X))* Heritage Bks.

Eicher, Lovina. The Amish Cook's Anniversary Book: 20 Years of Food, Family, & Faith. 2010. (ENG.). 304p. 24.99 *(978-0-7407-9765-1(4))* Andrews McMeel Publishing.

Eicher, Lovina & Williams, Kevin. The Amish Cook at Home: Simple Pleasures of Food, Family, & Faith. 2008. (ENG., Illus.). 224p. 29.99 *(978-0-7407-7372-3(0))* Andrews McMeel Publishing.

—The Amish Cook's Baking Book. 2009. (ENG.). 224p. 29.99 *(978-0-7407-8547-4(8))* Andrews McMeel Publishing.

Favorite Brand Name Recipes Editors, ed. All New Amish Cookbook. 2010. 96p. 7.98 *(978-1-4508-0131-7(5))* Publications International, Ltd.

Mennonite Central Committee. Treasured Amish & Mennonite Recipes: 600 Delicious, down-to-Earth Recipes from Authentic Country Kitchens. 2011. (ENG., Illus.). 320p. pap. 19.95 *(978-1-56523-599-1(1))* Fox Chapel Publishing Co., Inc.

Publications International Staff, ed. Amish Cooking. 2010. 160p. spiral bd. 10.98 *(978-1-60553-863-1(9))* Publications International, Ltd.

Publications International Staff, ed. Best Loved Amish Cooking. 2011. 64p. spiral bd. ***(978-1-4508-0799-9(2))*** Publications International, Ltd.

Varozza, Georgia. The Homestyle Amish Kitchen Cookbook: Plainly Delicious Recipes from the Simple Life. 2010. 272p. spiral bd. 14.99 *(978-0-7369-2858-8(8))* Harvest Hse. Pubs.

Yoder, Kathy. The Amish & Mennonite Berry Cookbook. 2007. (Illus.). 176p. 5.95 *(978-1-57166-435-8(1))* Hearts 'N Tummies Cookbook Co.

AMISH COUNTRY (OHIO)

Hurst, Charles E. & McConnell, David L. An Amish Paradox: Diversity & Change in the World's Largest Amish Community. 2010. (Young Center Books in Anabaptist & Pietist Studies). (ENG., Illus.). 376p. (gr. 17). 61.00 *(978-0-8018-9398-8(4));* pap. 31.00 *(978-0-8018-9399-5(2))* Johns Hopkins Univ. Pr.

Stuart & Watson, Norma. Experience Northeast Ohio Amish Country Map. 2009. pap. *(978-1-61584-664-1(6))* Independent Pub.

Trollinger, Susan L. Selling the Amish: The Tourism of Nostalgia. 2012. (Young Center Books in Anabaptist & Pietist Studies). (ENG., Illus.). 216p. (gr. 17). 50.00 ***(978-1-4214-0419-6(2))*** Johns Hopkins Univ. Pr.

AMISH QUILTS

see Quilts, Amish

AMISH WOMEN

Olson, Anna Dee. Growing up Amish: Insider Secrets from One Woman's Inspirational Journey. 2008. (ENG.). 138p. pap. 14.95 *(978-1-60037-334-3(8))* Morgan James Publishing.

Schrock, Mary. The Greater Inheritance: The tru story of one Amish family's journey to the Truth. 2009. 150p. pap. 13.95 *(978-1-935298-24-3(0))* Truth Pubs.

Yoder, Joseph W. Rosanna of the Amish: The Restored Text. Kasdorf, Julie Spicher, ed. 2008. 350p. pap. 15.99 *(978-0-8361-9408-1(X))* Herald Pr.

AMISTAD (SCHOONER)

The Amistad Argument & the State of the Union Addresses. 2007. 208p. 33.95 *(978-0-9793363-6-2(8))* Ellis, Frederick.

Christensen, Matthew J. Rebellious Histories: The Amistad Slave Revolt & the Cultures of Late Twentieth-Century Black Transnationalism. 2012. pap. *(978-1-4384-3970-9(9));* (ENG.). 192p. 65.00 *(978-1-4384-3969-3(5))* State Univ. of New York Pr.

Rediker, Marcus. The Amistad Rebellion: An Atlantic Odyssey of Slavery & Freedom. 2012. (ENG., Illus.). 304p. 27.95 ***(978-0-670-02504-6(6),*** Viking Adult) Penguin Group (USA) Inc.

AMMIANUS MARCELLINUS

Boeft, J. den. Philological & Historical Commentary on Ammianus Marcellinus XXVII. 2009. *(978-90-04-18037-6(0))* BRILL.

Davies, Jason P. Rome's Religious History. 2007. (ENG.). 352p. pap. 45.00 *(978-0-521-04791-3(9))* Cambridge Univ. Pr.

Den Boeft, J., et al, eds. Philological & Historical Commentary on Ammianus Marcellinus 26. 2007. (Philological & Historical Commentary on Ammianus Marcellin Ser.). 356p. (978-90-04-16346-1(8)) BRILL.

Den Boeft, Jan, et al, eds. Ammianus after Julian: The Reign of Valentinian & Valens in Books 26-31 of the Res Gestae. 2007. (Mnemosyne: Bibliotheca Classica Batava Ser.). 326p. (978-90-04-16212-9(7)) BRILL.

Kelly, Gavin. Ammianus Marcellinus: The Allusive Historian. (Cambridge Classical Studies). (ENG.). 2011. 392p. pap. 50.00 (978-0-521-20359-3(7)) 2008. 390p. 103.99 (978-0-521-84299-0(9)) Cambridge Univ. Pr.

Marcellinus, Ammianus & Eyssenhardt, Franciscus. Rerum Gestarum Libri Qui Supersunt. 2008. 620p. 59.95 (978-1-4370-1562-1(X)); pap. 44.95 (978-1-4367-6647-0(8)) Kessinger Publishing, LLC.

Matthews, John. The Roman Empire of Ammianus. 2007. (ENG., Illus.). 608p. (C). 60.00 (978-0-9799713-2-7(2)) Michigan Classical Pr.

Ratti, S., ed. Antiquus Error: Les ultimes feux de la resistance Paienne. 2010. (Bibliotheque de l'antiquite Tardive Ser.). (FRE.). 328p. (C). pap. 58.00 (978-2-503-53261-5(6)) Brepols Pubs. BEL. Dist: Brown, David Bk. Co., The.

Sidwell, Barbara. The Portrayal & Role of Anger in the Res Gestae of Ammianus Marcellinus. 2009. 125.00 (978-1-60724-128-7(5)) Gorgias Pr., LLC.

AMMONIA

see also Liquid Ammonia

Akah, Aaron. The Remediation of Ammonia in Waste Streams. 2010. 188p. pap. (978-3-8383-7546-5(7)) Lambert Academic Publishing.

Cavazzoni, Carlo, et al. Simulation of Water & Ammonia at High Pressure & Temperature. 2010. 112p. pap. (978-3-8383-6715-6(4)) Lambert Academic Publishing.

Fekete, Victoria A. & Molnár, Réka L., eds. Ammonia: Structure, Biosynthesis & Functions. 2012. (Chemical Engineering Methods & Technology Biochemistry Research Trends Ser.). 147p. 95.00 (978-1-62100-502-5(X)) Nova Science Pubs., Inc.

James, G. R. Ammonia. 2nd ed. Date not set. (Illus.). (978-0-8247-9617-4(9)) Dekker, Marcel Inc.

Monteny, Gert-Jan & Hartung, Eberhard, eds. Ammonia emissions in Agriculture. 2007. 404p. 92.00 (978-90-8686-029-6(X)) Wageningen Academic Publishers NLD. Dist: Enfield Publishing & Distribution Co., Inc.

Sahu, J. N., et al. Synthesis of Ammonia from Urea for Flue Gas Conditioning. 2010. 212p. pap. (978-3-639-26206-3(9)) VDM Verlag Dr. Mueller e.K.

Starmans, Dick A. J. & van der Hoek, Klaas W., eds. Ammonia: The case of the Netherlands. 2007. 220p. 69.00 (978-90-8686-028-9(1)) Wageningen Academic Publishers NLD. Dist: Enfield Publishing & Distribution Co., Inc.

Stevens, Carly. The Impact of Atmospheric Nitrogen Deposition on Grasslands. 2009. 148p. pap. (978-3-639-14414-7(7)) VDM Verlag Dr. Mueller e.K.

Sutton, Mark, et al. Atmospheric Ammonia: Detecting Emission Changes & Environmental Impacts: Results of an Expert Workshop under the Convention on Long-Range Transboundary Air Pollution. 2008. (Illus.). 490p. 189.00 (978-1-4020-9120-9(6)) Springer.

Twigg, Martyn V. The Catalyst Handbook. 3rd rev. ed. 2011. (ENG.). 624p. 129.95 (978-1-84076-087-3(7)) Manson Publishing, Ltd. GBR. Dist: Thieme Medical Pubs., Inc.

AMMONIUM COMPOUNDS

Kreysa, Gerhard & Schütze, Michael, eds. Corrosion Handbook - Corrosive Agents & Their Interaction with Materials Vol. 9: Potassium Hydroxide, Ammonium & Ammonium Hydroxide, 13 vols., Volume 9. 2nd ed. 2007. (Kreysa Continuation Ser.: 9). (ENG., Illus.). 568p. 575.00 (978-3-527-31125-5(4), Wiley-VCH) Wiley, John & Sons, Inc.

AMMONOIDEA

Brayard, Arnaud & Bucher, Hugo. Smithian (Early Triassic) Ammonoid Faunas from Northwestern Guangxi (South China) - Taxonomy & Biochronology, Volume 55. 2009. (Fossils & Strata Monograph Ser.: 55). (ENG., Illus.). 184p. pap. 74.95 (978-1-4051-8666-7(6), Wiley-Blackwell) Wiley, John & Sons, Inc.

Schulz, M. G., et al. Coniacian & Santonian Belemnite Faunas from Bornholm/Santonian to Maastrichtian Ammonites from Scania, Number 44. 2006. (Fossils & Strata Monograph Ser.: 44). (ENG.). 128p. pap. 54.95 (978-82-00-37695-8(8), Wiley-Blackwell) Wiley, John & Sons, Inc.

Verma, Harish M. & Westermann, G. E. Ammonoid fauna of the Kimmeridgian-Tithonian boundary beds of Mombasa, Kenya, No. 135. (Illus.). 312p. pap. (978-0-88854-297-7(6)) BRILL.

AMMON'S HORN

see Hippocampus (Brain)

AMMUNITION

see also Bombs; Cartridges; Gunpowder

Adler, Dennis. Winchester Shotguns. 2008. (ENG., Illus.). 372p. 29.99 (978-0-7858-2108-3(2), 0785821082) Book Sales, Inc.

Bussard, Michael. Ammo Encyclopedia. Allen, John B. & Kosowski, David, eds. 2008. (Illus.). 791p. pap. 29.95 (978-1-886768-79-6(X)) Blue Bk. Pubns., Inc.

—Ammo Encyclopedia. Allen, John B. et al, eds. 2nd ed. 2010. (Illus.). 840p. pap. 29.95 (978-1-936120-01-7(1)) Blue Bk. Pubns., Inc.

Bussard, Mike, et al. Ammo Encyclopedia. 3rd ed. 2011. (Illus.). 912p. pap. (978-1-936120-10-9(0)) Blue Bk. Pubns., Inc.

Donnelly, John J. & Donnelly, Judy. The Handloader's Manual of Cartridge Conversions. 2011. (ENG., Illus.). 608p. pap. 29.95 (978-1-61608-238-3(0), 608238) Skyhorse Publishing Co., Inc.

Halstead, Tom. Reduced Load Ballistics Research Manual. 2011. pap. 12.95 (978-0-7414-6516-0(7)) Infinity Publishing.

Hoyem, George A., ed. Cartridge Catalogues. Date not set. (Illus.). 480p. 95.00 (978-0-939683-17-8(2)) Armory Pubns.

James, Rodney. The ABCs of Reloading: The Definitive Guide for Novice to Expert. 9th ed. 2011. (ENG., Illus.). 288p. pap. 26.99 (978-1-4402-1396-0(8)) Krause Pubns.

Jane's Ammunition Handbook: Aim for the Best in Ammunition Reference. 495.00 (978-0-7106-2308-9(9)) Jane's Information Group, Inc.

Smyth Wallace, James. Chemical Analysis of Firearms, Ammunition, & Gunshot Residue. 2008. (International Forensic Science & Investigation Ser.). (ENG., Illus.). 320p. 109.95 (978-1-4200-6966-2(7), CRC Press) Taylor & Francis Group GBR. Dist: Taylor & Francis Group.

AMMUNITION—LAW AND LEGISLATION

see Firearms—Law and Legislation

AMNESIA

see also Aphasia

Bolzan, Scott, et al. My Life, Deleted: A Memoir. 2011. (ENG.). 256p. 25.99 (978-0-06-202547-0(3), HarperOne) HarperCollins Pubs.

Chauncey, James Wilburn. Eyewitness to Heaven: A Glimpse into the Obscure. 2011. (ENG.). 215p. pap. 13.99 (978-1-61346-013-9(9)) Tate Publishing & Enterprises, LLC.

Christianson, Sven A., ed. Offenders' Memories of Violent Crimes. 2007. (Wiley Series in Psychology of Crime, Policing & Law Ser.: 32). (ENG., Illus.). 400p. 155.00 (978-0-470-01507-0(1)); per. 66.95 (978-0-470-01508-7(X)) Wiley, John & Sons, Inc. (Wiley).

Hudetz, Anthony & Pearce, Robert, eds. Suppressing the Mind: Anesthetic Modulation of Memory & Consciousness. 2010. (Contemporary Neuroscience Ser.). (ENG., Illus.). x, 252p. 219.00 (978-1-60761-463-0(4), 1607614634) Humana Pr.

Mary, Theresa. Amnesia of Sin. 2011. pap. 12.99 (978-1-61777-352-5(2)) Tate Publishing & Enterprises, LLC.

AMNESTY

see also Pardon

Baer, Katherine & Le Borgne, Eric. Tax Amnesties: Theory, Trends, & Some Alternatives. 2008. viii, 70p. (978-1-58906-736-3(3)) International Monetary Fund.

Bubenzer, O. Post-TRC Prosecutions in South Africa: Accountability for Political Crimes after the Truth & Reconciliation Commission's Amnesty Process. 2009. 200p. (978-90-04-17703-1(5)) BRILL.

Du Bois-Pedain, Antje. Transitional Amnesty in South Africa. 2007. (ENG., Illus.). 420p. 120.00 (978-0-521-87829-6(2)) Cambridge Univ. Pr.

du Bois-Pedain, Antje. Transitional Amnesty in South Africa. 2011. (ENG.). 422p. pap. 50.00 (978-1-107-40401-4(0)) Cambridge Univ. Pr.

Evans, Derek. Dispatches from the Global Village. 2007. (ENG., Illus.). 192p. per. 19.95 (978-1-55145-553-2(6), Copperhouse) Wood Lake Publishing, Inc. CAN. Dist: Westminster John Knox Pr.

Freeman, Mark. Necessary Evils: Amnesties & the Search for Justice. (ENG.). 2011. 376p. pap. 45.00 (978-1-107-40323-9(5)) 2009. 374p. 93.00 (978-0-521-89525-5(1)) Cambridge Univ. Pr.

Lessa, Francesca & Payne, Leigh A., eds. Amnesty in the Age of Human Rights Accountability: Comparative & International Perspectives. 2012. (ENG.). 375p. pap. 39.99 (978-1-107-61733-9(2)); (Illus.). 110.00 (978-1-107-02500-4(1)) Cambridge Univ. Pr.

Levy, Janey. Illegal Immigration & Amnesty: Open Borders & National Security. 2010. (In the News Ser.). (ENG.). 64p. (YA). pap. 12.95 (978-1-4358-8548-6(1)) Rosen Publishing Group, Inc., The.

Mallinder, Louise. Amnesty, Human Rights & Political Transitions: Bridging the Peace & Justice Divide. 2008. (Studies in International Law Ser.). (ENG., Illus.). 586p. (C). 124.00 (978-1-84113-771-1(5)) Hart Publishing Ltd. GBR. Dist: International Specialized Bk. Services.

McEvoy, Kieran & McGregor, Lorna, eds. Transitional Justice from Below: Grassroots Activism & the Struggle for Change. 2008. (ENG.). 254p. (C). pap. 62.00 (978-1-84113-821-3(5)) Hart Publishing Ltd. GBR. Dist: International Specialized Bk. Services.

Neff, Stephen C. Justice in Blue & Gray: A Legal History of the American Civil War. 2010. 360p. 47.50 (978-0-674-03602-4(6)) Harvard Univ. Pr.

Ntoubandi, Faustin Z. Amnesty for Crimes Against Humanity under International Law. 2007. 252p. (978-90-04-16231-0(3)) BRILL.

Sanders, Mark. Ambiguities of Witnessing: Law & Literature in the Time of a Truth Commission. 2007. (Meridian: Crossing Aesthetics Ser.). (ENG.). 280p. 60.00 (978-0-8047-5615-0(5)) Stanford Univ. Pr.

Smith, Kathleen E. Remembering Stalin's Victims: Popular Memory & the End of the USSR. 2009. (Illus.). 240p. pap. 24.95 (978-0-8014-7596-2(1)) Cornell Univ. Pr.

Verwoerd, Wilhelm & Verwoerd, W. Equity, Mercy, Forgiveness: Interpreting Amnesty within the South African Truth & Reconciliation Commission. 2007. (Morality & the Meaning of Life Ser.). (ENG., Illus.). 210p. (C). pap. 77.00 (978-90-429-1906-8(X)) Peeters Pubs. & Booksellers BEL. Dist: Brown, David Bk. Co., The.

AMOEBIC DYSENTERY

see Amebiasis

AMON (EGYPTIAN DEITY)

Blyth, Elizabeth. Karnak: Evolution of a Temple. 2006. (Illus.). 258p. 145.00 (978-0-415-40486-0(X)); per. 49.95 (978-0-415-40487-7(8)) Routledge.

Lull, Jose. Los Sumos Sacerdotes de Amon Tebanos de la Whm Mswt y Dinastia XXI. 2006. (Bar S Ser.). (ENG & SPA., Illus.). 402p. (C). 95.00 (978-1-84171-905-4(6)) British Archaeological Reports Ltd. GBR. Dist: Brown, David Bk. Co., The.

Rocheleau, Caroline M. Amun Temples in Nubia: A Typological Study of New Kingdom, Napatan & Meroitic Temples. 2008. (Bar S Ser.). (ENG., Illus.). 96p. (C). pap. 65.00 (978-1-4073-0337-6(6)) British Archaeological Reports Ltd. GBR. Dist: Brown, David Bk. Co., The.

AMORAIM

see also Tannaim

Cohen, Barak S. The Legal Methodology of Late Nehardean Sages in Sananian Babylonia. 2011. 212p. (978-90-04-19381-9(2)) BRILL.

Duker, Jonathan. The Spirits Behind the Law: The Talmudic Scholars. 2007. 123p. 21.95 (978-965-7108-97-0(7)) Urim Pubns. ISR. Dist: Lambda Pubs., Inc.

AMORITES

Dunteman, Paul L. The Christian Life & the History of Israel. 2009. 484p. pap. 24.99 (978-1-60791-274-3(0)) Xulon Pr., Inc.

AMORPHOUS SUBSTANCES

Binder, Kurt. Glassy Materials & Disordered Solids: An Introduction to their Statistical Mechanics (Revised Edition) 2011. 564p. 107.00 (978-981-4350-17-4(6)) World Scientific Publishing Co., Inc.

Chu, Virginia, ed. Amorphous & Polycrystalline Thin-film Silicon Science & Technology; Proceedings. International Symposium on [Title] (2007: San Francisco, CA) 2009. 594p. pap. 114.00 (978-1-55899-949-7(3)) Materials Research Society.

Deshpande, Abhijit, et al. Rheology of Complex Fluids. 2010. (ENG., Illus.). x, 290p. 129.00 (978-1-4419-6493-9(2), 1441964932) Springer.

Donth, E. The Glass Transition: Relaxation Dynamics in Liquids & Disordered Materials. 2010. (Springer Series in Materials Science Ser.). (Illus.). xvii, 420p. pap. 269.00 (978-3-642-07519-3(3), 3642075193) Springer.

Ehrentraut, Dirk, et al, eds. Technology of Gallium Nitride Crystal Growth. 2010. (Springer Series in Materials Science Ser.). (Illus.). xx, 334p. 179.00 (978-3-642-04828-9(5), 3642048285) Springer.

Esquinazi, Pablo, ed. Tunneling Systems in Amorphous & Crystalline Solids. 2010. (Illus.). xxiii, 600p. pap. 206.00 (978-3-642-08371-6(4), 3642083714) Springer.

Götze, Wolfgang. Complex Dynamics of Glass-Forming Liquids: A Mode-Coupling Theory. 2009. (International Series of Monographs on Physics Ser.). (ENG., Illus.). 656p. 145.00 (978-0-19-923534-6(1)) Oxford Univ. Pr., Inc.

Gotze, Wolfgang. Complex Dynamics of Glass-Forming Liquids: A Mode-Coupling Theory. 2012. (ENG., Illus.). 656p. pap. 84.99 (978-0-19-965614-1(2)) Oxford Univ. Pr., Inc.

Hou, Thomas Y. Multi-Scale Phenomena in Complex Fluids Vol. 12: Modeling, Analysis & Numerical Simulations. 2009. 380p. 106.00 (978-981-4273-25-1(2)) World Scientific Publishing Co., Inc.

Inoue, A. & Hashimoto, K., eds. Amorphous & Nanocrystalline Materials: Preparation, Properties, & Applications. 2010. (Advances in Materials Research Ser.). (Illus.). x, 206p. pap. 169.00 (978-3-642-08664-9(0), 3642086640) Springer.

Kawazoe, Yoshiyuki & Waseda, Yoshio. Structure & Properties of Aperiodic Materials. 2010. (Advances in Materials Research Ser.). (Illus.). xi, 207p. pap. 129.00 (978-3-642-05672-7(5), 3642056725) Springer.

Leong, Keith. Surface Passivation of Crystalline Silicon Using Amorphous Silicon. 2008. 88p. pap. (978-3-639-02353-4(6)) VDM Verlag Dr. Mueller e.K.

Ligatchev, Valeri. Polycrystalline & Spatially Non-Homogenous Amorphous Semiconductors. Ligatchev, Valeri, ed. 2008. (Illus.). viii, 144p. (C). 39.00 (978-1-60456-371-9(0)) Nova Science Pubs., Inc.

Mikla, Victor I. & Mikla, Victor V. Amorphous Chalcogenides: The Past, Present & Future. 2011. (ENG.). 172p. 140.00 (978-0-12-388429-9(2)) Elsevier Science & Technology Bks.

Mott, Nevill Francis & Davis, Edward A. Electronic Processes in Non-Crystalline Materials. 2012. (ENG., Illus.). 608p. pap. 67.99 (978-0-19-964533-6(7)) Oxford Univ. Pr., Inc.

Ossi, Paolo M. Disordered Materials: An Introduction. 2nd ed. (Illus.). 2012. (ENG.). xii, 329p. pap. 149.00 (978-3-642-06738-9(7), 3642067387) 2006. 329p. 149.00 (978-3-540-29609-6(3), 3540296093) Springer.

Telle, Jason R. & Pearlstine, Norman A. Amorphous Materials: Research, Technology & Applications. 2009. (Illus.). xi, 335p. 129.00 (978-1-60692-235-4(1)) Nova Science Pubs., Inc.

Thorpe, M. F. & Mitkova, M. I., eds. Amorphous Insulators & Semiconductors. 2010. (NATO Science Partnership Sub-Series: 3: Ser.). 536p. pap. 489.00 (978-90-481-4791-5(3), 9048147913) Springer.

Tokuyama, Michio, et al. Complex Systems: 5th International Workshop on Complex Systems, Sendai, Japan, 25-28 September 2007. 2008. (AIP Conference Proceedings / Mathematical & Statistical Phsyics Ser.). (Illus.). xix, 829p. 255.00 (978-0-7354-0501-1(8)) American Institute of Physics.

Torre, Renato, ed. Time-Resolved Spectroscopy in Complex Liquids: An Experimental Perspective. 2010. (ENG., Illus.). xii, 252p. pap. 135.00 (978-1-4419-3803-9(6), 1441938036) Springer.

Tsai, C. C. Amorphous & Polycrystalline Thin-Film Silicon Science & Technology - 2010: Volume 1245. Wang, Q. et al, eds. 2010. (MRS Proceedings Ser.). (C). 115.00 (978-1-60511-222-0(4)) Cambridge Univ. Pr.

Ullah, Imdad & Yousaf Chaudhary, Ahsan. Drone Age & the Law. 2011. 76p. pap. (978-3-8443-8159-7(7)) Lambert Academic Publishing.

Zhukov, Arcady & Zhukova, Valentina. Magnetic Properties & Applications of Ferromagnetic Microwires with Amorphous & Nanocrystalline Structure. 2009. (Nanotechnology Science & Technology Ser.). pap. 43.00 (978-1-60741-770-5(7)) Nova Science Pubs., Inc.

AMORTIZATION

see also Reserves (Accounting); Sinking-Funds

Amortization Book. Date not set. pap. 7.95 (978-0-932453-71-6(6)) Dugan Pubs., Inc.

Pfister, Joel. Critique for What? Cultural Studies, American Studies, Left Studies. 2007. (ENG.). 320p. pap. 45.95 (978-1-59451-226-1(4)) Paradigm Pubs.

AMORTIZATION SCHEDULES

see Loan Amortization Tables

AMORTIZATION TABLES

see Loan Amortization Tables

AMOS (BIBLICAL PROPHET)

Fyall, Bob. Teaching Amos: Unlocking the Prophecy of Amos for the Bible Teacher. 2006. (ENG.). 160p. per. 10.99 (978-1-84550-142-6(X)) Christian Focus Pubns. GBR. Dist: STL Distribution North America.

Hadjiev, Tchavdar S. The Composition & Redaction of the Book of Amos. 2009. (Beihefte zur Zeitschrift für die alttestamentliche Wissenschaft Ser.). (ENG.). XVIII, 247p. 112.00 (978-3-11-021271-6(4)); 168.00 (978-3-11-173597-9(4)) De Gruyter, Walter Inc.

Neusner, Jacob. Amos in Talmud & Midrash: A Source Book. 2006. (Studies in Judaism Ser.). (ENG.). 153p. per. 31.50 (978-0-7618-3593-6(8)) Univ. Pr. of America, Inc.

Radine, Jason. The Book of Amos in Emergent Judah. 2010. (Illus.). 279p. pap. 117.50 (978-3-16-150114-2(4)) Mohr Siebeck GmbH & Co. KG DEU. Dist: Coronet Bks.

AMPHETAMINES

see also Methamphetamine

Biersack, Hans J. & Winkler, Cuno, eds. Amphetamines & pH-shift Agents for Brain Imaging: Basic Research & Clinical Results. (ENG.). VIII, 186p. 210.00 (978-3-11-179301-6(X)) De Gruyter, Walter Inc.

Chhay, Haksym. Road to Recovery. 2011. 108p. pap. (978-3-8443-1311-6(7)) Lambert Academic Publishing.

Farren, Mick. Speed-Speed-Speedfreak: A Fast History of Amphetamine. 2010. (ENG., Illus.). 175p. pap. 12.95 (978-1-932595-82-6(1)) Feral Hse.

Fornai, Francesco, et al, eds. Cellular & Molecular Mechanisms of Drugs of Abuse & Neurotoxicity: Cocaine, GHB, & Substituted Amphetamines. 2006. (Annals of the New York Academy of Sciences Ser.: Vol. 1369). (ENG., Illus.). 552p. per. 159.95 (978-1-57331-629-3(6), Wiley-Blackwell) Wiley, John & Sons, Inc.

Halkitis, Perry N. Methamphetamine Addiction: Biological Foundations, Psychological Factors, & Social Consequences. 2009. (Illus.). 264p. 49.95 (978-1-4338-0423-6(9)) American Psychological Assn.

Heston, Leonard L. The Medical Casebook of Adolf Hitler: His Illnesses, Doctors & Amphetamine Abuse. 2007. 184p. per. 15.95 (978-0-595-42353-8(1)) iUniverse, Inc.

Iversen, Leslie L. Speed, Ecstasy, Ritalin: The Science of Amphetamines. 2008. (ENG., Illus.). 232p. pap. 35.00 (978-0-19-853090-9(0)) Oxford Univ. Pr., Inc.

Ledgard, Jared. A Laboratory History of Narcotics, Amphetamines & Derivatives, Vol. 1. 2007. 266p. pap. 49.95 (978-0-615-15694-1(0)) Ledgard, Jared.

Moore, Elaine A. The Amphetamine Debate: The Use of Adderall, Ritalin & Related Drugs for Behavior Modification, Neuroenhancement & Anti-Aging Purposes. 2010. (McFarland Health Topics Ser.). (ENG., Illus.). 248p. pap. 29.95 (978-0-7864-5873-8(9)) McFarland & Co., Inc. Pubs.

Pates, Richard & Riley, Diane, eds. Interventions for Amphetamine Misuse. 2009. (Addiction Press Ser.: 7). (ENG., Illus.). 256p. pap. 60.99 (978-1-4051-7558-6(3), Wiley-Blackwell) Wiley, John & Sons, Inc.

Rasmussen, Nicholas. On Speed: The Many Lives of Amphetamine. 2009. (ENG.). 400p. pap. 23.00 (978-0-8147-7639-1(6)) New York Univ. Pr.

Rasmussen, Nicolas. On Speed: The Many Lives of Amphetamine. 2008. (ENG., Illus.). 400p. 50.00 (978-0-8147-7601-8(9)) New York Univ. Pr.

Rincón, Antoine. Amphetamines: Neurobiological Mechanisms, Pharmacology & Effects. 2012. (Neuroscience Research Progress Ser.). 207p. 95.00 (978-1-61470-305-1(1)) Nova Science Pubs., Inc.

Silber, Beata Yvonne. The Acute Effects of Amphetamines on Driving Cognition & the SFSTs: Does a Single Therapeutic Dose of Amphetamine Affect Human Performance? 2008. 316p. pap. (978-3-639-09810-5(2)) VDM Verlag Dr. Mueller e.K.

United Nations. Amphetamines & Ecstasy: 2011 Global Ats Assessment. 2011. (ENG.). 120p. pap. 28.00 (978-92-1-148265-2(8)) United Nations Pubns.

Willett, Edward. Speed. 2008. (Incredibly Disgusting Drugs Ser.). (Illus.). 48p. lib. bdg. 26.50 (978-1-4042-1377-7(5), Rosen Central) Rosen Publishing Group, Inc., The.

AMPHIBIAN PLANES

Adcock, Al. U.S. Navy Flying Boats & Amphibians in World War II. 2008. (Illus.). 80p. pap. (978-0-89747-556-3(9)) Squadron Signal Pubns.

Hotson, Fred W. & Rodina, Matthew E., Jr. Grumman Mallard: The Enduring Classic. 2010. (Illus.). 186p. 39.95 (978-1-896941-44-8(3)) Brass, Robin Studio, Inc. CAN. Dist: Midpoint Trade Bks., Inc.

Johnson, E. R. American Flying Boats & Amphibious Aircraft: An Illustrated History. 2009. (ENG., Illus.). 384p. pap. 49.95 (978-0-7864-3974-4(2)) McFarland & Co., Inc. Pubs.

Rottman, Gordon. Landing Craft, Infantry & Fire Support. 2009. (New Vanguard Ser.). (ENG., Illus.). 48p. pap. 17.95 (978-1-84603-435-0(3)) Osprey Publishing, Ltd. GBR. Dist: Random Hse., Inc.

AMPHIBIANS

see also Anura; Frogs; Salamanders; Toads

Akintunde, Oluyinka Akinbanjo. Herpetological Resources of Abeokut. 2010. 292p. pap. (978-3-639-26078-6(3)) VDM Verlag Dr. Mueller e.K.

Alderton, David. Firefly Encyclopedia of the Vivarium: Keeping Amphibians, Reptiles, & Insects, Spiders & Other Invertebrates in Terraria, Aquaterraria, & Aquaria. 2007. (ENG., Illus.). 224p. 39.95 (978-1-55407-300-9(6)) Firefly Bks., Ltd.

Alexander, David. Hop into Action: The Amphibian Curriculum Guide for Grades K4. 2010. (Illus.). xxvi, 132p. **(978-1-936137-07-7(0))** National Science Teachers Assn.

Alvarez-Pellitero, P. Mucosal Intestinal Immunity & Response to Parasite Infections in Ectothermic Vertebrates. 2011. pap. (978-1-61209-571-4(2)) Nova Science Pubs., Inc.

Attenborough, David. Life in Cold Blood. 2008. (ENG., Illus.). 288p. 29.95 (978-0-691-13718-6(8)) Princeton Univ. Pr.

Bartlett, R. D., et al. Reptiles, Amphibians, & Invertebrates: An Identification & Care Guide. 2nd rev. ed. 2010. (ENG., Illus.). 288p. pap. 16.99 (978-0-7641-4356-4(5)) Barron's Educational Series, Inc.

Bartlett, Richard D. & Bartlett, Patricia. Florida's Frogs, Toads, & Other Amphibians: A Guide to Their Identification & Habits. 2011. (ENG., Illus.). 272p. pap. 24.95 (978-0-8130-3669-4(0)) Univ. Pr. of Florida.

Bartlett, Richard D. & Bartlett, Patricia Pope. Guide & Reference to the Amphibians of Western North America (North of Mexico) & Hawaii. 2009. (ENG., Illus.). 288p. pap. 29.95 (978-0-8130-3298-6(9)) Univ. Pr. of Florida.

Bartlett, Richard D., et al. Guide & Reference to the Amphibians of Eastern & Central North America (North of Mexico) 2006. (ENG., Illus.). 312p. pap. 29.95 (978-0-8130-2950-4(3)) Univ. Pr. of Florida.

Beane, Jeffrey C., et al. Amphibians & Reptiles of the Carolinas & Virginia, 2nd Ed. 2nd ed. 2010. (ENG., Illus.). 288p. 55.00 (978-0-8078-3374-2(6)); pap. 25.00 (978-0-8078-7112-6(5)) Univ. of North Carolina Pr.

Bernini, Franco, et al, eds. Atlante degli Anfibi e dei Rettili dItalia / Atlas of Italian Amphibians & Reptiles. 2nd ed. 2010. (ENG & ITA., Illus.). 792p. (C). 135.00 (978-88-596-0629-1(2)) Polistampa ITA. Dist: Brown, David Bk. Co., The.

Carroll, Robert Lynn. The Rise of Amphibians: 365 Million Years of Evolution. 2009. (ENG., Illus.). 392p. (gr. 17). 68.00 (978-0-8018-9140-3(X)) Johns Hopkins Univ. Pr.

Collins & Taggart, Travis William. Amphibians, Reptiles & Turtles in Kansas. 2010. (Illus.). xvi, 312p. (978-0-9720154-5-5(0), Nicholson) Eagle Mountain Publishing, L.C.

Collins, James P. & Crump, Martha L. Extinction in Our Times: Global Amphibian Decline. 2009. (ENG., Illus.). 304p. 29.95 (978-0-19-531694-0(0)) Oxford Univ. Pr., Inc.

Dodd, C. Kenneth, Jr., ed. Amphibian Ecology & Conservation: A Handbook of Techniques. 2009. (Techniques in Ecology & Conservation Ser.). (ENG., Illus.). 464p. pap. 59.95 (978-0-19-954119-5(1)) Oxford Univ. Pr., Inc.

Duellman, William E. Amphibian Species of the World: Additions & Corrections. Trueb, Linda, ed. (Special Publications: No. 21). 372p. pap. 35.00 (978-0-89338-045-8(8)) Univ. of Kansas, Natural History Museum.

Fitzgibbon, Keith. Westland Road Culverts As Amphibian Conduits. 2008. 216p. pap. (978-3-639-04671-7(4)) VDM Verlag Dr. Mueller e.K.

Gibbons, J. Whitfield & Semlitsch, Raymond D. Guide to the Reptiles & Amphibians of the Savannah River Site. 2010. (ENG., Illus.). 144p. pap. 19.95 (978-0-8203-3495-0(2)) Univ. of Georgia Pr.

Gibbs, James P., et al. The Amphibians & Reptiles of New York State: Identification, Natural History, & Conservation. 2007. (ENG., Illus.). 504p. per. 44.99 (978-0-19-530444-2(6)) Oxford Univ. Pr., Inc.

Glaw, Frank & Vences, Miguel. Field Guide to the Amphibians & Reptiles of Madagascar. 2007. (ENG., Illus.). 496p. pap. 129.50 (978-3-929449-03-7(X)) Edition Chimaira DEU. Dist: Serpent's Tale Natural History Bk. Distributors, Inc.

Gunther, Albrecht Carl. Reptiles of British India. 2008. 540p. pap. (978-3-8364-4017-2(2)) VDM Verlag Dr. Mueller e.K.

Hailey, Adrian, et al. Conservation of Caribbean Island Herpetofaunas. 2011. (978-90-04-19408-3(8)); (978-90-04-18395-7(7)); (978-90-04-19410-6(X)) BRILL.

Hellweg, Michael R. Raising Live Foods: A Comprehensive Guide to Culturing Live Foods for Reptiles & Amphibians, 1 vol. 2009. (ENG.). 160p. pap. (978-0-7938-2960-9(0)) TFH Pubns., Inc.

Henderson, Carrol L. Mammals, Amphibians, & Reptiles of Costa Rica: A Field Guide. 2010. (ENG., Illus.). 214p. pap. 29.95 (978-0-292-72274-3(5)) Univ. of Texas Pr.

Henderson, Robert W. & Powell, Robert. Natural History of West Indian Reptiles & Amphibians. 2009. (ENG., Illus.). 576p. 85.00 (978-0-8130-3394-5(2)) Univ. Pr. of Florida.

Holman, J. Alan. The Amphibians & Reptiles of Michigan: A Quaternary & Recent Faunal Adventure. 2012. 50.00 **(978-0-8143-3239-9(0))**; E-Book **(978-0-8143-3713-4(9))** Wayne State Univ. Pr.

Jarvik, Erik. The Devonian Tetrapod Ichthyostega, Number 40. 2006. (Fossils & Strata Monograph Ser.: 40). (ENG.). 212p. pap. 64.95 (978-82-00-37560-6(5), Wiley-Blackwell) Wiley, John & Sons, Inc.

Jensen, John B., et al, eds. Amphibians & Reptiles of Georgia. 2008. (ENG., Illus.). 600p. pap. 39.95 (978-0-8203-3111-9(2)) Univ. of Georgia Pr.

Kavanagh, James. Indiana Wildlife: An Introduction to Familiar Species. 2009. (State Nature Guides). (ENG., Illus.). 1p. 5.95 (978-1-58355-476-0(9)) Waterford Pr., Inc.

—New Jersey Wildlife: An Introduction to Familiar Species. 2009. (State Nature Guides). (ENG., Illus.). 1p. 5.95 (978-1-58355-481-4(5)) Waterford Pr., Inc.

—Ohio Wildlife: An Introduction to Familiar Species. 2009. (State Nature Guides). (ENG., Illus.). 1p. 5.95 (978-1-58355-482-1(3)) Waterford Pr., Inc.

Kraus, Fred. Alien Reptiles & Amphibians: A Scientific Compendium & Analysis. 2008. (Invading Nature - Springer Series in Invasion Ecology Ser.). (Illus.). xii, 563p. 89.95 (978-1-4020-8945-9(7)) Springer.

Lemm, Jeffrey M. Field Guide to Amphibians & Reptiles of the San Diego Region. 2006. (California Natural History Guides Ser.: Vol. 89). (Illus.). 326p. 60.00 (978-0-520-24573-0(3)); pap. 24.95 (978-0-520-24574-7(1)) Univ. of California Pr.

MacCulloch, Ross Douglas & Lathrop, Amy. Herpetofauna of Mount Ayanganna, Guyana: Results of the Royal Ontario Museum Ayanganna Expedition 2000. 2009. (ROM contributions in Science Ser.). (ENG.). 36p. pap. 19.99 (978-0-88854-472-8(3)) Royal Ontario Museum CAN. Dist: Univ. of Toronto Pr.

MacDonald, S. O. & Cook, J. A. Mammals & Amphibians of Southeast Alaska. 2007. pap. 25.00 (978-0-9794517-2-0(8)) Museum of Southwest Biology Pubn. Series.

Matsuda, Brent M., et al. Amphibians & Reptiles of British Columbia, 1 vol. 2007. (Royal BC Museum Handbook Ser.). (ENG., Illus.). 288p. pap. 25.95 (978-0-7726-5448-9(4)) UBC Pr. CAN. Dist: Univ. of Washington Pr.

Mattison, Christopher & Mattison, Chris, eds. Firefly Encyclopedia of Reptiles & Amphibians. 2nd rev. ed. 2008. (ENG., Illus.). 240p. 49.95 (978-1-55407-366-5(9)) Firefly Bks., Ltd.

McCranie, James R. & Castañeda, Franklin E. Guía de Campo de los Anfibios de Honduras. 2006. (Illus.). 320p. 20.00 (978-1-932871-11-1(X)) Bibliomania!

McCranie, James R., et al. The Amphibians & Reptiles of the Honduran Mosquitia. 2006. (Illus.). 302p. (C). 63.50 (978-1-57524-270-5(2)) Krieger Publishing Co.

McKinnell, Robert Gilmore. Cloning: Nuclear Transplantation in Amphibia. 2009. (ENG.). 332p. pap. 60.00 (978-0-8166-5827-5(7)) Univ. of Minnesota Pr.

Means, D. Bruce. Stalking the Plumed Serpent & Other Adventures in Herpetology. 2008. (ENG.). 238p. 19.95 (978-1-56164-433-9(1)) Pineapple Pr., Inc.

Mercurio, Vincenzo. Amphibians of Malawi. 2011. (Illus.). 393p. 95.00 (978-3-89973-495-9(5)) Edition Chimaira DEU. Dist: Serpent's Tale Natural History Bk. Distributors, Inc.

Miller, John. Show-Me Herps. 2010. 152p. pap. 10.99 (978-1-887247-70-2(X)) Missouri Dept. of Conservation.

Mitchell, Joseph C., et al. Urban Herpetology. 2008. (Illus.). xvii, 586p. (978-0-916984-79-3(6)) Society for the Study of Amphibians & Reptiles.

Müller, Hendrik. Developmental Morphological Diversity in Caecilian Amphibians: Amphibians Systematic & Evolutionary Implications. 2007. (LUP Dissertaties Ser.). 266p. pap. (978-90-8728-027-7(0), Leiden Univ. Pr.) Amsterdam Univ. Pr.

Narins, P. M., et al, eds. Hearing & Sound Communication in Amphibians. 2006. (Springer Handbook of Auditory Research Ser.: Vol. 28). (Illus.). xiv, 362p. 159.00 (978-0-387-32521-7(2), 0387325212) Springer.

Narins, Peter M., et al, eds. Hearing & Sound Communication in Amphibians. 2010. (Springer Handbook of Auditory Research Ser.). (Illus.). xiv, 362p. pap. 159.00 (978-1-4419-2187-1(7), 1441921877) Springer.

Nasira, Khatoon & Bilqees, F. M. Acanthocephala of Vertebrates a Word Record. 2011. 576p. pap. **(978-3-639-32875-2(2))** VDM Verlag Dr. Mueller e.K.

Niemiller, Matthew L. & Reynolds, R. Graham. The Amphibians of Tennessee. 2011. (ENG.). pap. 39.95 **(978-1-57233-762-6(1))** Univ. of Tennessee Pr.

Norris, David O. & Lopez, Kristin H., eds. Hormones & Reproduction of Vertebrates - Vol 2: Amphibians, 5 vols. 2010. (ENG., Illus.). 240p. 119.95 (978-0-12-374931-4(X), Academic Pr.) Elsevier Science & Technology Bks.

Ogielska, Maria. Reproduction of Amphibians. 2009. (Biological Systems in Vertebrates Ser.). (ENG., Illus.). 436p. 129.95 (978-1-57808-307-7(9)) BIOS Scientific Publishers Ltd. GBR. Dist: Taylor & Francis Group.

Ouboter, Paul E. & Jairam, Rawien. Amphibians of Suriname. 2012. (ENG., Illus.). **(978-90-04-20799-8(6))**; pap. **(978-90-04-21075-2(X))** BRILL.

Petzold, Hans-Günter & Murphy, James B. The Lives of Captive Reptiles. 2008. (Illus.). xxix, 275p. (978-0-916984-73-1(7)) Society for the Study of Amphibians & Reptiles.

Powell, Robert, et al. A Key to the Herpetofauna of the Continental United States & Canada. 2nd ed. 2012. (Illus.). viii, 152p. pap. **(978-0-7006-1833-0(3))** Univ. Pr. of Kansas.

Prinz zu Wied-Neuwied, Maximilian. Verzeichniss der Reptilien, welche auf einer Reise im nördlichen America. 2007. (GER., Illus.). 152p. 675.00 (978-1-932871-03-6(9)) Bibliomania!

Reichling, Steven B. Reptiles & Amphibians of the Southern Pine Woods. 2008. (ENG., Illus.). 320p. pap. 29.95 (978-0-8130-3250-4(4)) Univ. Pr. of Florida.

Rothschild, Bruce M., et al. Herpetological Osteopathology: Annotated Bibliography of Amphibians & Reptiles. 2012. (ENG., Illus.). xi, 450p. 209.00 **(978-1-4614-0823-9(7)**, 1461408237) Springer.

Sparling, Donald W., et al, eds. Ecotoxicology of Amphibians & Reptiles, Second Edition. 2nd rev. ed. 2010. (ENG., Illus.). 944p. 159.95 (978-1-4200-6416-2(9), CRC Press) Taylor & Francis Group GBR. Dist: Taylor & Francis Group.

Spawls, Stephen, et al. Reptiles & Amphibians of East Africa. 2006. (Princeton Pocket Guides). (ENG., Illus.). 240p. pap. 24.95 (978-0-691-12884-9(7)) Princeton Univ. Pr.

Stebbins, Robert C. & McGinnis, Samuel M. Field Guide to Amphibians & Reptiles of California. rev. ed. 2012. (California Natural History Guides). (ENG., Illus.). 544p. 70.00 (978-0-520-24466-5(4)); pap. 29.95 (978-0-520-27051-0(7)) Univ. of California Pr.

Tipton, Bob L. Texas Amphibians: A Field Guide. 2012. E-Book **(978-0-292-73736-5(X))** Univ. of Texas Pr.

Tipton, Bob L., et al. Texas Amphibians: A Field Guide. 2012. (ENG.). 325p. pap. 24.95 **(978-0-292-73735-8(1))** Univ. of Texas Pr.

Townsend, Josiah H. & Wilson, Larry David. Guide to the Amphibians & Reptiles of Cusuco National Park, Honduras: Guía de Los Anfibios y Reptiles Del Parque Nacional Cusuco, Honduras. 2008. (SPA & ENG., Illus.). xiv, 322p. (978-1-932871-12-8(8)) Bibliomania!

Trauth, Stanley E., et al. The Amphibians & Reptiles of Arkansas. 2006. (Illus.). 421p. pap. 32.50 (978-1-55728-738-0(4)) Univ. of Arkansas Pr.

Walls, Jerry G. Vivaria Designs. 2007. (Advanced Vivarium Systems: Ser.). (ENG., Illus.). 144p. per. 12.95 (978-1-882770-92-2(7)) BowTie Pr.

Wells, Kentwood David. The Ecology & Behavior of Amphibians. 2007. (ENG., Illus.). 1400p. 80.00 (978-0-226-89334-1(0)) Univ. of Chicago Pr.

Werner, J. Kirwin, et al. Amphibians & Reptiles of Montana. (Illus.). 276p. pap. 20.00 (978-0-87842-500-6(4), 445) Mountain Pr. Publishing Co., Inc.

White, James F. & White, Amy Wendt, photos by. Amphibians & Reptiles of Delmarva. 2nd ed. 2007. 14.95 (978-0-87033-596-9(0), Cornell Maritime Pr./Tidewater Pubs.) Schiffer Publishing, Ltd.

Withers, Philip, et al. Ecological & Environmental Physiology of Amphibians. (Ecological & Environmental Physiology Ser.). (ENG., Illus.). 2009. 488p. pap. 65.00 (978-0-19-857032-5(5)) 2008. 464p. 150.00 (978-0-19-857031-8(7)) Oxford Univ. Pr., Inc.

Young, Mary Taylor. The Guide to Colorado Reptiles & Amphibians. 2011. (ENG., Illus.). 176p. pap. 26.95 **(978-1-55591-584-1(1))** Fulcrum Publishing.

AMPHIBIANS—EMBRYOLOGY

see Embryology—Amphibians

AMPHIBIANS—JUVENILE LITERATURE

Rafferty, John P., ed. Reptiles & Amphibians. 2011. (Britannica Guide to Predators & Prey Ser.). (Illus.). 296p. (YA). 103.40 (978-1-61530-457-8(6)) Rosen Publishing Group, Inc., The.

AMPHIBIOUS WARFARE

Here are entered works on the joint operation of air, land, and sea forces to establish troops on shore, as developed in World War II. General works on the landing of waterborne or airborne troops on hostile territory, including tactics of transporting, landing and establishing such troops and their supplies, and combat during the landing phase are entered under Landing Operations.

see also subdivision Amphibious Operations under names of wars, e.g. World War, 1939-1945—Amphibious Operations

Amphibious Operations: Hearing Before the Subcommittee on Seapower & Projection Forces of the Committee on Armed Services, House of Representatives, One Hundred Twelfth Congress, First Session, Hearing Held March 16, 2011. 2011. (Illus.). iii, 47p. **(978-0-16-089509-8(X)**, 552-070-43468-2) United States Government Printing Office.

Boose, Donald W., Jr. Over the Beach: U. S. Army Amphibious Operations in the Korean War: U. S. Army Amphibious Operations in the Korean War. 2008. (ENG., Illus.). 515p. pap. 45.00 (978-0-9801236-7-8(4), Dept. of the Army) United States Government Printing Office.

Button, Robert W. & Gordon, James, 4th. Warfighting & Logistic Support of Joint Forces from the Joint Sea Base. 2007. (Illus.). 140p. pap. 37.00 (978-0-8330-4195-1(9), mg-649) RAND Corp., The.

Daugherty, Leo J. Pioneers of Amphibious Warfare, 1898-1945: Profiles of Fourteen American Military Strategists. 2009. (ENG., Illus.). 456p. pap. 49.95 (978-0-7864-3394-0(9)) McFarland & Co., Inc. Pubs.

Ireland, Bernard. The World Encyclopedia of Amphibious Warfare Vessels: An Illustrated History of Modern Amphibious Warfare. 2011. (ENG., Illus.). 256p. 35.00 (978-0-7548-2090-1(4)) Anness Publishing GBR. Dist: National Bk. Network.

Lavery, Brian. Assault Landing Craft: Design, Construction & Operations. 2009. (Illus.). 120p. 39.99 (978-1-84832-050-5(7), Seaforth) Pen & Sword Bks. Ltd. GBR. Dist: Casemate Pubs. & Bk. Distributors, LLC.

Megee, Vernon E. Memoirs of a Marine - Old Corps - New Corps 1919 To 1959. 2011. 258p. pap. 19.95 **(978-1-933177-28-1(4))** Atriad Pr.

Rottman, Gordon. Landing Craft, Infantry & Fire Support. 2009. (New Vanguard Ser.). (ENG., Illus.). 48p. pap. 17.95 (978-1-84603-435-0(3)) Osprey Publishing Ltd. GBR. Dist: Random Hse., Inc.

AMPHIBOLES

Hawthorne, Frank, et al, eds. Amphiboles: Crystal Chemistry, Occurrences, & Health Issues, 67. 2007. (Reviews in Mineralogy & Geochemistry Ser.: 67). (Illus.). 545p. per. 45.00 (978-0-939950-79-9(0)) Mineralogical Society of America.

AMPHIMIXIS

see Fertilization (Biology); Reproduction

AMPLIFIERS (ELECTRONICS)

see also Amplifiers, Vacuum-Tube

Abrie, Pieter L. D. Design of RF & Microwave Amplifiers & Oscillators. 2nd ed. 2009. (Artech House Microwave Library). (Illus.). 504p. 149.00 (978-1-59693-098-8(5)) Artech Hse., Inc.

Al Tahir, Hibah. Multidimensional Measurements. 2011. 64p. pap. **(978-3-8383-9085-7(7))** Lambert Academic Publishing.

Bahl, Inder & Bahl. Fundamentals of RF & Microwave Transistor Amplifiers. 2009. (ENG., Illus.). 696p. 166.00 (978-0-470-39166-2(9), Wiley-Interscience) Wiley, John & Sons, Inc.

Bilal, Syed Muhammad & M. Zafrullah, Prof. Optical Amplifiers - a Hybrid Approach. 2011. 64p. pap. **(978-3-8443-3356-5(8))** Lambert Academic Publishing.

Broeng, Jes & Headley, Clifford. Fiber Lasers V: Technology, Systems, & Applications: 21-24 January 2008, San Jose, California, USA. 2008. (Proceedings of SPIE Ser.). (Illus.). 500p. pap. 140.00 (978-0-8194-7048-5(1)) SPIE.

Bruccoleri, Federico, et al. Wideband Low Noise Amplifiers Exploiting Thermal Noise Cancellation. 2010. (Springer International Series in Engineering & Computer Science Ser.). ix, 182p. pap. 229.00 (978-1-4419-5266-0(7), 1441952667) Springer.

Celuch, Malgorzata & Yakovlev, Vadim V., eds. Microwave Power Engineering with Advanced Computer Modeling. 2012. (ENG., Illus.). 450p. 149.95 **(978-1-4398-5013-8(5)**, CRC Press) Taylor & Francis Group GBR. Dist: Taylor & Francis Group.

Colantonio, Paolo, et al. High Efficiency RF & Microwave Solid State Power Amplifiers. 2009. (Microwave & Optical Engineering Ser.). (ENG., Illus.). 514p. 150.00 (978-0-470-51300-2(4), Wiley) Wiley, John & Sons, Inc.

Cordell, Bob. Designing Audio Power Amplifiers. 2010. (ENG., Illus.). 640p. pap. 60.00 (978-0-07-164024-X), 007164024X, TAB/Electronics) McGraw-Hill Professional Publishing.

Dailey, Denton J. Electronics for Guitarists. 2011. (ENG., Illus.). xiv, 290p. 129.00 (978-1-4419-9535-3(8), 1441995358) Springer.

Dal Fabbro, Paulo Augusto & Kayal, Maher. Linear CMOS RF Power Amplifiers for Wireless Applications: Efficiency Enhancement & Frequency-Tunable Capability. 2010. (Analog Circuits & Signal Processing Ser.). (Illus.). xiv, 220p. 159.00 (978-90-481-9360-8(5), 9048193605) Springer.

FASA Corporation Staff. Boosters. (Shadowrun Ser.). 107.64 (978-1-55560-333-5(5), 03335F) FASA Corp.

Feucht, D. Designing Amplifier Circuits. 2009. (Analog Circuit Design Ser.). (ENG., Illus.). 207p. 49.00 (978-1-891121-86-9(3)) SciTech Publishing, Inc.

—Designing High Performance Amplifiers. 2009. (Analog Circuit Design Ser.). (ENG., Illus.). 280p. pap. 49.00 (978-1-891121-84-5(7)) SciTech Publishing, Inc.

Fjestad, Zachary R. Blue Book of Guitar Amplifiers. Fjestad, S. P., ed. 3rd ed. 2008. (Blue Book Ser.). (ENG., Illus.). per. 29.95 (978-1-886768-59-8(5)) Blue Bk. Pubns., Inc.

Gapontsev, Denis V. Fiber Lasers VI: Technology, Systems, & Applications: 26-29 January 2009, San Jose, California, United States. 2009. (Proceedings of SPIE Ser.). (Illus.). 652p. pap. 160.00 (978-0-8194-7441-4(X)) SPIE.

Grebennikov, Andrei, et al. Switchmode RF & Microwave Power Amplifiers. 2nd ed. 2012. (ENG., Illus.). 550p. 119.95 **(978-0-12-415907-5(9)**, Academic Pr.) Elsevier Science & Technology Bks.

Grebennikov, Andrei, et al. Switchmode RF Power Amplifiers. 2007. (Communications Engineering Ser.). (ENG., Illus.). 448p. 102.00 (978-0-7506-7962-6(X), Newnes) Elsevier Science & Technology Bks.

Harter, Donald J. Fiber Lasers IV: Technology, Systems, & Applications: 22-25 January, 2007, San Jose, California, USA. 2007. (Proceedings of SPIE Ser.). (Illus.). 570p. pap. 140.00 (978-0-8194-6566-5(6)) SPIE.

Hoang, Le Nam. On the Performance of Two-Way Amplify-and-Forward Relay Networks: Performance Metrics, Relay Networks. 2011. 64p. pap. **(978-3-639-28142-2(X))** VDM Verlag Dr. Mueller e.K.

Huijsing, Johan H., et al, eds. Analog Circuit Design: Volt Electronics; Mixed-Mode Systems; Low-Noise & RF Power Amplifiers for Telecommunication. 2010. (ENG.). 428p. pap. 235.00 (978-1-4419-5071-0(0), 1441950710) Springer.

Isaksson, Magnus. Radio Frequency Power Amplifiers. 2009. 68p. pap. (978-3-639-17021-4(0)) VDM Verlag Dr. Mueller e.K.

Islam, Mohammad Aminul, et al. Design Study & Development of a Scintillation Amplifier. 2011. 68p. pap. **(978-3-8443-1305-5(2))** Lambert Academic Publishing.

Jackson, Lee M. Complete Schematics: Instrument Amplifier & Effects Schematics. 2012. (ENG., Illus.). 650p. pap. 29.99 (978-1-57560-446-6(9), 1575604469) Cherry Lane Music Co.

Kates, James. Digital Hearing Aids. 2008. (Illus.). 464p. pap. 95.00 (978-1-59756-317-8(X)) Plural Publishing, Inc.

Kazimierczuk, Marian K. RF Power Amplifiers. 2008. (ENG., Illus.). 422p. 130.00 (978-0-470-77946-0(2), Wiley) Wiley, John & Sons, Inc.

Koli, Kimmo & Halonen, Kari A. I. CMOS Current Amplifiers: Speed versus Nonlinearity. 2010. (Springer International Series in Engineering & Computer Science Ser.). 300p. pap. 269.00 (978-1-4419-5280-6(2), 1441952802) Springer.

Leach, William. Introduction to Electroacoustics & Audio Amplifier Design. 4th rev. ed. 2009. (ENG.). 312p. pap. 85.44 (978-0-7575-7286-9(3)) Kendall Hunt Publishing Co.

Legarda, Jon. Feedforward Amplifiers for Wideband Communication Systems. (ENG.). xvii, 177p. 2010. pap. 145.00 (978-1-4419-4196-1(7), 1441941967) 2006. (Illus.). 145.00 (978-0-387-35137-7(X), 038735137X) Springer.

Leroux, Paul & Steyaert, Michiel. LNA-ESD Co-Design for Fully Integrated CMOS Wireless Receivers. 2010. (Springer International Series in Engineering & Computer Science Ser.). xv, 187p. pap. 209.00 (978-1-4419-5267-7(5), 1441952675) Springer.

Leyssenne, Laurent, et al. Reconfigurable RF Power Amplifiers on Silicon for Wireless Handsets. 2011. (Analog Circuits & Signal Processing Ser.). (ENG., Illus.). xvi, 166p. 129.00 *(978-94-007-0424-4(0)*, 9400704240) Springer.

Li, Huiyun. Digital Pulse Width Modulator. 2009. 96p. pap. *(978-3-639-17876-0(9))* VDM Verlag Dr. Mueller e.K.

Lin, Changgui, et al. Design of Rf Cmos Low Noise Amplifiers. 2010. 184p. pap. *(978-3-8383-4904-6(0))* Lambert Academic Publishing.

Marx, Wallace, Jr. Gibson Amplifiers 1933-2008: 75 Years of the Gold Tone. 2009. (Blue Book Ser.). (ENG., Illus.). pap. 29.95 *(978-1-886768-90-1(0))* Blue Bk. Pubns., Inc.

Marzuki, Arjuna, et al, eds. Advances in Monolithic Microwave Integrated Circuits for Wireless Systems: Modeling & Design Technologies. 2011. 451p. 195.00 *(978-1-60566-886-4(9)*, Engineering Science Reference) IGI Global.

Marzuki, Arjuna, et al. Advances in Monolithic Microwave Integrated Circuits for Wireless Systems: Modeling & Design Technologies. 2011. ***(978-1-61350-119-1(6))*** IGI Global.

Mustaffa, Mohd Taffir. A Reconfigurable Low Noise Amplifier for a Multi-Standard Receiver. 2010. 256p. pap. *(978-3-8383-8786-4(4))* Lambert Academic Publishing.

Nesimoglu, Tayfun. Rf & Microwave Amplifier Linearization for Wireless Communications. 2009. 196p. pap. *(978-3-639-18361-0(4))* VDM Verlag Dr. Mueller e.K.

Palumbo, Gaetano & Pennisi, Salvatore. Feedback Amplifiers: Theory & Design. 2012. (ENG.). 280p. pap. 239.00 *(978-1-4419-4944-8(5)*, 1441949445) Springer.

Pinksterboer, Hugo & Hal Leonard Corporation Staff. Tipbook: Amplifiers & Effects. 2009. (ENG., Illus.). 296p. pap., instr.'s gde. ed. 14.99 *(978-1-4234-6277-4(7)*, 1423462777) Leonard, Hal Corp.

Puttnam, Ben. Sub-Systems for Dynamic Wavelength-Routed Optical Networks. 2010. 216p. pap. *(978-3-8383-5103-2(7))* Lambert Academic Publishing.

Reynaert, Patrick & Steyaert, Michiel. RF Power Amplifiers for Mobile Communications. (Analog Circuits & Signal Processing Ser.). x, 251p. 2010. pap. 169.00 *(978-90-481-7286-3(1)*, 9048172861) 2006. 169.00 *(978-1-4020-5116-6(6)*, 1402051166) Springer.

Rudiakova, Anna N. & Krizhanovski, Vladimir. Advanced Design Techniques for RF Power Amplifiers. 2010. (Analog Circuits & Signal Processing Ser.). (Illus.). x, 136p. pap. 149.00 *(978-90-481-7160-6(1)*, 9048171601) Springer.

Schaub, Arthur, ed. Digital Hearing Aids. 2008. (ENG.). 188p. pap. 54.99 *(978-1-60406-006-5(9))* Thieme Medical Pubs., Inc.

Sechi, Franco & Bujatti, Marina. Solid-State Microwave High-Power Amplifiers. 2009. (Illus.). 338p. 139.00 *(978-1-59693-319-4(4))* Artech Hse., Inc.

Self, Douglas. Audio Power Amplifier Design Handbook. 5th ed. 2009. (ENG., Illus.). 608p. pap. 67.95 *(978-0-240-52162-6(5)*, Focal Pr.) Elsevier Science & Technology Bks.

Shirvani, Alireza & Wooley, Bruce A. Design & Control of RF Power Amplifiers. 2012. (ENG.). 168p. pap. 159.00 *(978-1-4419-5386-5(8)*, 1441953868) Springer.

Smith, Bill, rev. Electronic Amplifiers & Circuit Design. 2009. 162p. pap. 24.95 *(978-1-934939-61-1(7))* Wexford College Pr.

Soliman, Eman. Design of the Differential Difference Operational Floating Amplifier. 2009. 136p. pap. *(978-3-639-17849-4(1))* VDM Verlag Dr. Mueller e.K.

Srirattana, Nuttapong, et al. Modeling & Design Techniques for RF Power Amplifiers. 2008. (ENG., Illus.). 206p. 104.00 *(978-0-471-71746-1(0)*, Wiley-IEEE Pr.) Wiley, John & Sons, Inc.

Staric, Peter & Margan, Erik. Wideband Amplifiers. 2007. (ENG., Illus.). xiii, 634p. 195.00 *(978-0-387-28340-1(4)*, 0387283404) Springer.

Steyaert, Michiel, et al, eds. Analog Circuit Design: High-Speed Clock & Data Recovery, High-Performance Amplifiers, Power Management. 2008. (ENG., Illus.). xii, 360p. 209.00 *(978-1-4020-8943-5(0)*, 1402089430) Springer London, Ltd. GBR. Dist: Springer.

Swike, Tim. How to make 9 volt portable guitar Amplifiers. 2010. 138p. pap. 14.95 *(978-0-557-58403-1(5))* Lulu Enterprises Inc.

Thanki, Rohit M., et al. Design of Operational Transconductance Amplifier. 2011. 64p. pap. ***(978-3-8433-6146-0(0))*** Lambert Academic Publishing.

Verhoeven, Chris J. M., et al. Structured Electronic Design: Negative-Feedback Amplifiers. 2010. 380p. pap. 199.00 *(978-1-4419-5392-6(2)*, 1441953922) Springer.

Vogel, Burkhard. How to gain Gain: A Reference Book on Triodes in Audio Pre-Amps. 2010. (ENG., Illus.). xii, 312p. 109.00 *(978-3-642-08904-6(6)*, 3642089046) Springer.

—How to Gain Gain: On Triode Driven Audio Pre-Amp Gain Stage Building Blocks. 2008. (ENG., Illus.). xii, 312p. 109.00 *(978-3-540-69502-8(8)*, 3540695028) Springer.

—The Sound of Silence: Lowest-Noise RIAA Phono-Amps: Designer's Guide. (ENG., Illus.). 2010. xii, 352p. pap. 139.00 *(978-3-642-09557-3(7)*, 3642095577) 2nd ed. 2011. xxiii, 752p. 129.00 ***(978-3-642-19773-4(6)***, 3642197736) Springer.

Weber, Gerald. All about Vacuum Tube Guitar Amplifiers. 2009. (ENG.). 520p. pap. 34.95 *(978-0-9641060-3-1(5)*, 0964106035) Leonard, Hal Corp.

Wheeler, Tom. The Soul of Tone: Celebrating 60 Years of Fender Amps. 2007. (ENG., Illus.). 512p. 60.00 incl. audio compact disk *(978-0-634-05613-0(1)*, 0634056131) Leonard, Hal Corp.

Yarman, Binboga Siddik. Design of Ultra Wideband Power Transfer Networks. 2010. (ENG., Illus.). 774p. 145.00 *(978-0-470-31989-5(5)*, Wiley) Wiley, John & Sons, Inc.

Zhong Yuan Chong & Sansen, Willy M. C. Low-Noise Wide-Band Amplifiers in Bipolar & CMOS Technologies. 2010. (Springer International Series in Engineering & Computer Science Ser.). (Illus.). 228p. pap. 279.00 *(978-1-4419-5124-3(5)*, 1441951245) Springer.

Zyskind, John & Srivastava, Atul, eds. Optically Amplified WDM Networks. 2010. (ENG., Illus.). 512p. 130.00 *(978-0-12-374965-9(4)*, Academic Pr.) Elsevier Science & Technology Bks.

AMPLIFIERS, FLUID

see Fluid Amplifiers

AMPLIFIERS, PARAMETRIC

see Parametric Amplifiers

AMPLIFIERS, TRANSISTOR

see Transistor Amplifiers

AMPLIFIERS, VACUUM-TUBE

see also Feedback (Electronics); Traveling-Wave Tubes

Jones, Morgan. Valve Amplifiers. 4th ed. 2011. (ENG., Illus.). 700p. pap. 69.95 ***(978-0-08-096640-3(3)***, Newnes) Elsevier Science & Technology Bks.

Kuehnel, Richard. Guitar Amplifier Power Amps: Vacuum Tube Circuit Design. 2008. (Illus.). 376p. *(978-0-9769822-4-1(2))* Pentode Pr.

Schreurs, Dominique, et al, eds. RF Power Amplifier Behavioral Modeling. 2008. (Cambridge RF & Microwave Engineering Ser.). (ENG., Illus.). 288p. 110.00 *(978-0-521-88173-9(0))* Cambridge Univ. Pr.

Weber, Gerald. All about Vacuum Tube Guitar Amplifiers. 2009. (ENG.). 520p. pap. 34.95 *(978-0-9641060-3-1(5)*, 0964106035) Leonard, Hal Corp.

Whitaker, Jerry. The TAB Guide to Vacuum Tube Audio: Understanding & Building Tube Amps. 2011. (TAB Electronics Ser.). (ENG., Illus.). 368p. pap. 40.00 ***(978-0-07-175321-0(4)***, 0071753214, TAB/Electronics) McGraw-Hill Professional Publishing.

AMPUTATION

see also Amputees

Beach, Chris. Indian Joe Blow: Pishikii-Kigeet-Black Eagle Thunderbird Man. 2011. 244p. pap. 14.99 ***(978-1-4634-2852-5(9))*** AuthorHouse.

Kirkup, John. A History of Limb Amputation. 2006. (ENG., Illus.). viii, 184p. 185.00 *(978-1-84628-443-4(0)*, 1846284430) Springer.

Kirkup, John R. A History of Limb Amputation. 2010. (ENG., Illus.). viii, 184p. pap. 185.00 *(978-1-84996-602-3(8)*, 1849966028) Springer.

Matthijs, Silvia & Sidransky, Raphaël. Amputations: Types, Procedures, & Risks. 2011. ***(978-1-62100-072-3(9))*** Nova Science Pubs., Inc.

May, Bella J. & Lockard, Margery A. Prosthetics & Orthotics in Clinical Practice: A Case Study Approach. 2011. (Illus.). 512p. 84.95 *(978-0-8036-2257-9(0))* Davis, F. A. Co.

Murray, Craig, ed. Amputation, Prosthesis, & Phantom Limb Pain: An Interdisciplinary Perspective. 2009. (ENG., Illus.). ix, 203p. 129.00 *(978-0-387-87461-6(5)*, 0387874615) Springer.

Pinzur, Michael & Myerson, Mark S. Infection, Ischemia, & Amputation, an Issue of Foot & Ankle Clinics. 2010. (Clinics: Orthopedics Ser.: 15-3). (ENG., Illus.). viii, 392p. 101.00 *(978-1-4377-2450-9(7)*, Saunders) Elsevier - Health Sciences Div.

Vasconelos, E. Modern Methods of Amputation. *(978-0-8022-1768-4(0))* Philosophical Library, Inc.

AMPUTEES

Ahmed, Laeeq. 3 Dimensional Scanner. 2011. 56p. pap. ***(978-3-8433-9442-0(3))*** Lambert Academic Publishing.

Anderson, Bryan & Mack, David. No Turning Back: One Man's Inspiring True Story of Courage, Determination, & Hope. 2012. (ENG., Illus.). 272p. (gr. 12). pap. 15.00 ***(978-0-425-25319-9(8)***, Berkley Trade) Penguin Group (USA) Inc.

Borden Institute, Walter Reed Army Medical Center, ed. Care of the Combat Amputee. 2010. (Textbooks of Military Medicine Ser.). (ENG., Illus.). 820p. 98.00 *(978-0-16-084077-7(5)*, Dept. of the Army) United States Government Printing Office.

Devaul, Gary & Thallander, Mark. Champions Plus. 2007. 232p. per. 14.95 *(978-1-59330-501-7(X))* Aventine Pr.

Elguindi, Nader. My Decision to Live. 2007. 155p. per. 13.95 *(978-1-58776-857-6(7))* NetSource Distribution.

Faulder, Liane. The Long Walk Home: Paul Franklin's Journey from Afghanistan - A Soldier's Story, 1 vol. 2007. (ENG., Illus.). 224p. per. *(978-1-897142-25-7(0))* Brindle & Glass Publishing.

Grose, Leanne. Just a Step: The Autobiography of Leanne Grose. 2008. (ENG., Illus.). 360p. pap. 11.99 *(978-1-906229-47-4(3)*, 1906229473) G2 Entertainment Ltd. GBR. Dist: MBI Distribution Services/Quayside Distribution.

Hasegawa, Guy R. Mending Broken Soldiers: The Union & Confederate Programs to Supply Artificial Limbs. 2012. E-Book ***(978-0-8093-3131-4(4))***; (Illus.). 160p. 24.95 ***(978-0-8093-3130-7(6))*** Southern Illinois Univ. Pr.

Hicks, Gill. One Unknown: A Powerful Account of Survival & One Woman's Inspirational Journey to a New Life. 2007. (ENG., Illus.). 244p. 27.95 *(978-1-4050-9989-9(5))* Macmillan Pubs., Ltd. GBR. Dist: Independent Pubs. Group.

—One Unknown: A powerful account of survival & one woman's inspirational journey to a new Life. 2008. (ENG., Illus.). 244p. pap. 15.95 *(978-1-905744-14-5(5))* Macmillan Pubs., Ltd. GBR. Dist: Independent Pubs. Group.

Martin, Paul. Drinking from My Leg: Lessons from a Blistered Optimist. 2010. 236p. pap. 18.95 *(978-1-4502-1755-2(9))* iUniverse, Inc.

May, Bella J. & Lockard, Margery A. Prosthetics & Orthotics in Clinical Practice: A Case Study Approach. 2011. (Illus.). 512p. 84.95 *(978-0-8036-2257-9(0))* Davis, F. A. Co.

Reinertsen, Sarah & Goldsher, Alan. In a Single Bound: Losing My Leg, Finding Myself, & Training for Life. 2010. (ENG., Illus.). 256p. pap. 16.95 *(978-0-7627-6127-2(X)*, Lyons Pr.) Globe Pequot Pr., The.

Rigsby, Scott. Unthinkable: The True Story about the First Double Amputee to Complete the World-Famous Hawaiian Ironman Triathlon. 2009. (ENG.). 288p. pap. 14.99 *(978-1-4143-3314-4(5))* Tyndale Hse. Pubs.

Robson, J. S. How a One-Legged Rebel Lives. 21.95 *(978-0-8488-1141-9(0))* Amereon LTD.

West, Spencer. Standing Tall: My Journey, 1 vol. 2012. (ENG., Illus.). 192p. pap. 19.95 ***(978-1-55365-951-8(1)***, Greystone Bks.) D&M Pubs. Inc. CAN. Dist: Perseus-PGW.

AMPUTEES—REHABILITATION

see also Artificial Limbs

Centre of Excellence Defence Against Terrorism Staff & North Atlantic Treaty Organization, Public Diplomacy Division Staff, contrib. by. Amputee Sports for Victims of Terrorism. 2007. (Illus.). xii, 129p. *(978-1-58603-808-3(7))* IOS Pr., Inc.

Murray, Craig, ed. Amputation, Prosthesis, & Phantom Limb Pain: An Interdisciplinary Perspective. 2009. (ENG., Illus.). ix, 203p. 129.00 *(978-0-387-87461-6(5)*, 0387874615) Springer.

O'Shei, Tim. Shark Attack! Bethany Hamilton's Story of Survival. 2007. (True Tales of Survival Ser.). (ENG., Illus.). 32p. (gr. 3-4). 27.32 *(978-0-7368-6776-4(7)*, Edge Bks.) Capstone Pr., Inc.

Subcommittee Hearing on Ensuring Continuity of Care for Veteran Amputees: The Role of Small Prosthetic Practices. 2008. iii, 90p. *(978-0-16-081686-4(6)*, 552-070-37917-7) United States Government Printing Office.

AMRITSAR (INDIA)

Collett, Nigel & Collett. The Butcher of Amritsar: General Reginald Dyer. 2006. (ENG., Illus.). 576p. 29.95 *(978-1-85285-575-8(4)*, Hambledon Continuum) Continuum International Publishing Group, Ltd. GBR. Dist: National Bk. Network.

Lloyd, Nick. The Amritsar Massacre: The Untold Story of One Fateful Day. 2011. (ENG., Illus.). 288p. 35.00 ***(978-1-84885-723-0(3))*** I. B. Tauris & Co., Ltd. GBR. Dist: Macmillan.

AMSTERDAM (NETHERLANDS)

Barbour, Violet. Capitalism in Amsterdam in the Seventeenth Century. (Johns Hopkins University. Studies in the Social Sciences, Thirtieth Ser.: 1). reprint ed. 39.50 *(978-0-404-61313-6(6))* AMS Pr., Inc.

Hornstra, N. E., et al. The Turkish & Moroccan Second Generation & Their Comparison Group Peers in Amsterdam & Rotterdam: Technical Report & Codebook. 2012. (DANS Publications). (ENG.). 384p. pap. ***(978-90-8555-054-9(8)***, Pallas Publications) Amsterdam Univ. Pr.

Jacobson, Sid & Colon, Ernie. Anne Frank: The Anne Frank House Authorized Graphic Biography. 2010. (ENG., Illus.). 160p. 30.00 *(978-0-8090-2684-5(8)*, Hill & Wang) Farrar, Straus & Giroux.

Jacobson, Sid & Colón, Ernie. Anne Frank: The Anne Frank House Authorized Graphic Biography. 2010. (ENG., Illus.). 160p. pap. 16.95 *(978-0-8090-2685-2(6)*, Hill & Wang) Farrar, Straus & Giroux.

Kaal, Harm. Het Hoofd Van de Stad: Amsterdam en Zijn Burgemeester Tijdens Het Interbellum. 2008. (DUT., Illus.). 341p. 43.25 ***(978-90-5260-282-0(4))*** Aksant Academic Pubs. NLD. Dist: Amsterdam Univ. Pr.

Lesger, Cle. The Rise of the Amsterdam Market & Information Exchange: Merchants, Commercial Expansion & Change in the Spatial Economy of the Low Countries, C. 1550-1630. 2006. (Illus.). 338p. 150.00 *(978-0-7546-5220-5(3))* Ashgate Publishing Co.

Maarsen, Jacqueline Van. Inheriting Anne Frank. Doyle, Brian, tr. from DUT. 2010. (ENG., Illus.). 158p. pap. 24.95 *(978-1-906413-27-9(4))* Arcadia Bks. Ltd. GBR. Dist: Dufour Editions, Inc.

Nell, Liza & Rath, Jan, eds. Ethnic Amsterdam: Immigrants & Urban Change in the Twentieth Century. 2010. (Solidarity & Identity Ser.). (Illus.). 208p. pap. *(978-90-8964-168-7(8))* Amsterdam Univ. Pr.

Phillips, Derek. Well-Being in Amsterdam's Golden Age. 2009. (Illus.). 264p. pap. *(978-90-8555-042-6(4)*, Leiden Univ. Pr.) Amsterdam Univ. Pr.

AMSTERDAM (NETHERLANDS)—DESCRIPTION AND TRAVEL

AA Publishing Staff & Gauldie, Robin. Frommer's 24 Great Walks in Amsterdam. 2009. (Great Walks Ser.). (ENG., Illus.). 176p. pap. 15.99 *(978-0-470-45368-1(0)*, Frommers) Wiley, John & Sons, Inc.

Abrahamse, Jaap Evert & Lebesque, Sabine. Eastern Harbour District Amsterdam: Urbanism & Architecture, 1 vol. 2007. (ENG., Illus.). 240p. pap. 80.00 *(978-90-5662-553-5(5))* NAi Uitgevers / Publishers Stichting NLD. Dist: D.A.P./Distributed Art Pubs.

Awaja, Cirsten. Amsterdam / Netherlands, A City Walking Tour from Centraal Station to Centraal Station. 2008. 61p. pap. 41.95 *(978-0-557-01447-7(6))* Lulu Enterprises Inc.

—Amsterdam / Niederlande Stadtwanderung von CS nach CS. 2008. 61p. pap. 41.95 *(978-0-557-01868-0(4))* Lulu Enterprises Inc.

Baker, Andy, et al. Amsterdam: The Complete Residents' Guide. rev. ed. 2008. (Explorer (Explorer Publishing) Ser.). (ENG., Illus.). 432p. pap. 24.95 *(978-9948-03-379-0(5))* Explorer Publishing UAE. Dist: Globe Pequot Pr., The.

Bendahán, Marcelo. Amsterdam Always. 3rd ed. 2010. (DUT.). 177p. 40.00 *(978-90-809396-7-7(6))* International Publishers Marketing.

Bijkerk, Pia Jane. Amsterdam: Made by Hand. 2010. (ENG., Illus.). 176p. pap. 19.95 *(978-1-892145-84-0(7))* Little Bookroom.

BIS Publishers Staff. Amsterdam Memory Game. 2010. (ENG.). 60p. 17.00 *(978-90-6369-226-1(9))* Bis B.V., Uitgeverij(BIS Publishers) NLD. Dist: Consortium Bk. Sales & Distribution.

Blyth, Derek. Amsterdam Explored. 2nd ed. 2010. (Pallas for Pleasure Ser.). (ENG., Illus.). 336p. pap. 22.99 *(978-1-873429-47-1(9))* Pallas Athene GBR. Dist: Independent Pubs. Group.

Calder, Simon & Mawer, Fred. AAA Spiral Amsterdam, 4th Edition. 4th ed. 2010. (ENG.). 212p. spiral bd. 17.95 *(978-1-59508-384-5(7))* AAA.

Clutterbuck, Paul. Inside Amsterdam. 2008. 94p. pap. 41.50 *(978-0-557-01780-5(7))* Lulu Enterprises Inc.

Colwell, Dara. The Q Guide to Amsterdam: Stuff You Didn't Even Know You Wanted to Know... about Europe's Most Liberated, Notorious City. 2007. (Q Guide To... Ser.). (ENG., Illus.). 160p. per. 12.95 *(978-1-55583-980-2(0))* Alyson Pubns.

Duncan, Fiona & Glass, Leonie. Top 10 Amsterdam. 2012. (Eyewitness top 10 travel Guide Ser.). (ENG.). 160p. pap. 14.00 ***(978-0-7566-9595-8(3))*** Dorling Kindersley Publishing, Inc.

Duncan, Fiona, et al. Amsterdam: Die besten Museen & Sammlungen - Ausflüge an Grachten & Kanälen - Paläste, Türme & Windmühlen - Restaurants & Braune Cafés - Hotels für jeden Geldbeutel - Die beliebtesten Blumenmärkte - Oper, Theater, Ballett & Jazz - Attraktionen für Kinder - Königliches Amsterdam - Praxis-Tipps von Experten. 2011. (Eyewitness top 10 travel Guide Ser.). (ENG.). 160p. 14.00 *(978-0-7566-6747-4(X))* Dorling Kindersley Publishing, Inc.

Dunford, Martin. Rough Guide Pocket Amsterdam. 2011. (Rough Guide Pocket Guides). (ENG., Illus.). 148p. 12.99 *(978-1-84836-235-2(8))* Rough Guides, Ltd. GBR. Dist: Dorling Kindersley Publishing, Inc.

Dunford, Martin, et al. Amsterdam. 10th ed. 2010. (ENG., Illus.). 356p. pap., instr.'s gde. ed. 19.99 *(978-1-84836-515-5(2))* Rough Guides, Ltd. GBR. Dist: Dorling Kindersley Publishing, Inc.

Explorer Publishing & Distribution. Amsterdam Mini Explorer. rev. ed. 2008. (ENG., Illus.). 200p. pap. 11.95 *(978-9948-03-444-5(9))* Explorer Publishing UAE. Dist: Globe Pequot Pr., The.

Fodor's Travel Publications, Inc. Staff. Amsterdam & the Netherlands: With Side Trips Through Belgium. 2nd ed. 2011. (Full-Color Gold Guides). (ENG., Illus.). 464p. pap. 21.99 *(978-1-4000-0509-3(4)*, Fodor's) Fodor's Travel Pubns.

—Fodor's Amsterdam's 25 Best, 8th Edition. 2011. (25 Best Ser.). (ENG.). 128p. pap. 11.99 *(978-1-4000-0537-6(X)*, Fodor's) Fodor's Travel Pubns.

Forgeur, Brigitte. Lebenskunst in Amsterdam. (GER.). *(978-3-8067-2856-9(9))* Gerstenberg DEU. Dist: International Bk. Import Service, Inc.

Gauldie, Robin. The Best of Amsterdam. 2006. (Globetrotter Best of Ser.). (ENG., Illus.). 96p. pap. 8.95 *(978-1-84537-219-4(0))* New Holland Pubs., Ltd. GBR. Dist: Globe Pequot Pr., The.

Gauldie, Robin & Globetrotter. Amsterdam. 3rd ed. 2008. (Globetrotter Travel Packs Ser.). (ENG., Illus.). 128p. 14.95 *(978-1-84773-242-2(9)*, Globetrotter) New Holland Pubs., Ltd. GBR. Dist: Globe Pequot Pr., The.

Golden Book on Amsterdam. 128p. pap. *(978-88-7009-602-6(5))* Casa Editrice Bonechi.

Guides, Damron. Damron Amsterdam Guide. 2nd rev. ed. 2007. 190p. pap. 12.95 *(978-0-929435-53-4(2))* Damron Co.

Haefner, Scott G. & Farquhar, Kelly Yacobucci. Amsterdam. 2006. (Images of America Ser.). (ENG., Illus.). 128p. per. 21.99 *(978-0-7385-4646-9(1))* Arcadia Publishing.

Harvard Student Agencies, Inc. Let's Go Amsterdam & Brussels: The Student Travel Guide. 2011. (Let's Go Ser.). (ENG., Illus.). 272p. pap. 14.95 *(978-1-59880-715-8(3)*, Let's Go) Avalon Travel Publishing.

JPM Publication Staff. This Way Amsterdam. (This Way Guides). (Illus.). 64p. pap. 6.95 *(978-2-88452-148-2(8))* JPM Pubns. CHE. Dist: Hunter Publishing, Inc.

Kesselskramer. The Worst Hotel in the World: The Hans Brinker Budget Hotel, Amsterdam. 2009. (ENG., Illus.). 280p. 35.00 *(978-1-86154-311-0(5))* Booth-Clibborn Editions GBR. Dist: Hachette Bk. Group.

Knopf Guides Staff. Amsterdam. 2011. (Knopf Mapguides Ser.). (ENG., Illus.). 48p. pap. 10.95 *(978-0-375-71056-8(6)*, Knopf) Knopf Doubleday Publishing Group.

Lebesque, Sabine, ed. Around Amsterdam's Waterfront: From Architecture & Art to Green & New Development Areas. 2011. (ENG., Illus.). 192p. pap. 24.95 *(978-90-78088-48-6(6))* Valiz NLD. Dist: D.A.P./Distributed Art Pubs.

Lonely Planet Staff, ed. Amsterdam 1: 17 500. City Flash: Tourist City Guide. Sightseeing. Public Transport. Index. Shopping. (Illus.). pap. *(978-3-8283-0053-8(7))* Hallwag Verlag GmbH DEU. Dist: Rand McNally.

Lonely Planet Staff & O'Neill, Zora. Amsterdam 1: 17 500. City Flash: Tourist City Guide. Sightseeing. Public Transport. Index. Shopping. 2nd rev. ed. 2010. (Encounter Ser.). (ENG., Illus.). 192p. pap. 11.99 *(978-1-74179-706-0(3))* Lonely Planet Pubns.

Marcelis, Ritsaart. Stadspoort Amsterdam. 2010. 148p. pap. *(978-3-8383-7045-3(7))* Lambert Academic Publishing.

Marco Polo. Amsterdam Marco Polo Guide. 2012. (Marco Polo Guides Ser.). (ENG., Illus.). 140p. pap. 9.99 ***(978-3-8297-0651-3(0))*** Marco Polo Travel Publishing GBR. Dist: Innovative Logistics.

Martin, Faith & Thomas Cook Publishing Staff. Amsterdam. 3rd ed. 2010. (Thomas Cook Pocket Guides). (ENG., Illus.). 160p. pap. 9.95 *(978-1-84848-274-6(4))* Cook, Thomas Publishing GBR. Dist: Globe Pequot Pr., The.

McDonald, George. AAA Essential Amsterdam, 6th Edition. 6th ed. 2011. (ENG.). 192p. pap. 11.95 *(978-1-59508-411-8(8))* AAA.

—Frommer's Amsterdam. 16th ed. 2011. (Frommer's Complete Guides: 986). (ENG., Illus.). 320p. pap. 17.99 *(978-0-470-97129-1(0),* Frommers) Wiley, John & Sons, Inc.

Pascoe, Robin, et al. Eyewitness Travel Guides - Amsterdam. 2011. (Eyewitness Travel Guides). (ENG.). 312p. 25.00 *(978-0-7566-6954-6(5))* Dorling Kindersley Publishing, Inc.

Pauker, Joe. Amsterdam. 96p. pap. 13.00 *(978-90-802561-4-9(5))* Get Lost Publishing NLD. Dist: SCB Distributors.

Practical Guide to Visiting Amsterdam. 96p. *(978-88-7009-608-8(4))* Casa Editrice Bonechi.

Snyder, Gerald R. & von Hasseln, Robert. Amsterdam. 2010. (Postcard History Ser.). (ENG., Illus.). 128p. pap. 21.99 *(978-0-7385-7253-6(5))* Arcadia Publishing.

Steves, Rick & Openshaw, Gene. Rick Steves' Amsterdam, Bruges & Brussels. 2011. (Rick Steves Ser.). (ENG., Illus.). 648p. pap. 19.99 *(978-1-59880-768-4(4))* Avalon Travel Publishing.

Sweeney, Sarah. Amsterdam. 2009. (SMART GUIDE Ser.). (Illus.). 144p. 11.95 *(978-981-258-971-2(6))* Insight Guides.

Thomas Cook Publishing. Traveller Guides Amsterdam, 4th. 4th ed. 2011. (Travellers - Thomas Cook Ser.). (ENG., Illus.). 192p. pap. 16.95 *(978-1-84848-422-1(4))* Cook, Thomas Publishing GBR. Dist: Globe Pequot Pr., The.

Thomas Cook Publishing Staff, contrib. by. Out Around Amsterdam: Your Gay Travel Companion. 2nd ed. 2006. (Out Around - Thomas Cook Ser.). (ENG., Illus.). 160p. pap. 12.95 *(978-1-84157-661-9(1))* Cook, Thomas Publishing GBR. Dist: Globe Pequot Pr., The.

Tichar, Sian & Dietrich, Lucas. Stylecity Amsterdam. 2nd rev. ed. 2007. (ENG., Illus.). 192p. pap. 24.95 *(978-0-500-21021-5(7))* Thames & Hudson.

Tiedeke, Thorsten, photos by. Amsterdam. 2007. (Panoramas: Pocket Edition Ser.). (Illus.). 32p. per. *(978-3-938446-58-4(7))* NZVP Bks. & Calendars Ltd.

Time Out Guides Staff. Time Out Shortlist Amsterdam. 2009. (Time Out Shortlist Ser.). (ENG., Illus.). 192p. pap. 12.95 *(978-1-84670-134-4(1))* Time Out Guides Ltd. GBR. Dist: Perseus-PGW.

Time Out Guides Staff, ed. Time Out Amsterdam. 11th ed. 2011. (Time Out Guides). (ENG., Illus.). 336p. pap. 19.95 *(978-1-84670-198-6(8))* Time Out Guides Ltd. GBR. Dist: Perseus-PGW.

—Time Out Selecciones Amsterdam: Time Out Shortlist Amsterdam. 2010. (Selecciones Ser.). (SPA., Illus.). 196p. pap. 12.95 *(978-84-9801-459-4(X))* Time Out Guides Ltd. GBR. Dist: Perseus-PGW.

van Eys, Marjolijn & Robiot, Delphine. Secret Amsterdam: Local Guides by Local People. 2010. (Secret Ser.). (ENG., Illus.). 320p. pap. 17.95 *(978-2-915807-36-3(1))* Jonglez Editions FRA. Dist: Globe Pequot Pr., The.

VV., AA., et al. Guia Popout - Amsterdam. Compass Map, ed. 2008. 15.95 *(978-84-670-2674-0(X))* Espasa Calpe, S.A. ESP. Dist: Planeta Publishing Corp.

Wall, Siobhan. Quiet Amsterdam. 2012. (ENG., Illus.). 144p. pap. 19.95 ***(978-0-7112-3342-3(X))*** Lincoln, Frances Ltd. GBR. Dist: Perseus-PGW.

Wallpaper Magazine Editors, ed. Amsterdam 2012 - Wallpaper City Guide. 2011. (ENG.). 128p. pap. 9.95 ***(978-0-7148-6277-4(0))*** Phaidon Pr., Inc.

Wallpaper Magazine Editors, ed. Wallpaper City Guide - Amsterdam 2011. 2nd ed. 2011. (ENG., Illus.). 128p. pap. 9.95 *(978-0-7148-5938-5(9))* Phaidon Pr., Inc.

Zimmerman, Karla & Chandler, Sarah. Amsterdam, 28 vols. 8th rev. ed. 2012. (City Travel Guide Ser.). (ENG., Illus.). 312p. pap. 19.99 *(978-1-74179-903-3(1))* Lonely Planet Pubns.

AMSTERDAM (NETHERLANDS)—RIJKSMUSEUM

see Rijksmuseum (Netherlands)

AMTRAK

Amtrak Reauthorization: Hearing Before the Subcommittee on Railroads, Pipelines, & Hazardous Materials of the Committee on Transportation & Infrastructure, House of Representatives, One Hundred Tenth Congress, Second Session, May 14, 2008. 2008. (Illus.). xvi, 85p. *(978-0-16-083788-3(X),* 552-070-39490-7) United States Government Printing Office.

Amtrak, The staff of. Amtrak - An American Story: The First Forty Years in Word & Pictures. 2011. (ENG., Illus.). 144p. pap. 19.95 *(978-0-87116-444-5(2))* Kalmbach Publishing Co., Bks. Div.

Amtrak's Capital Needs: Hearing Before the Subcommittee on Railroads, Pipelines, & Hazardous Materials of the Committee on Transportation & Infrastructure, House of Representatives, One Hundred Tenth Congress, First Session, July 11, 2007. 2007. (Illus.). xiv, 78p. *(978-0-16-079696-8(2),* 552-070-36632-6) United States Government Printing Office.

Dorin, Patrick C. American Passenger Trains: WWII to Amtrak. 2009. (ENG., Illus.). 128p. pap. 29.95 *(978-1-58388-232-0(4),* 1583882324) Iconografix, Inc.

—Santa Fe Passenger Trains in California: From the 1940s Thru Amtrak & More. 2007. (ENG., Illus.). 90p. 29.95 *(978-0-9766201-7-4(0),* 0976620170) TLC Publishing, Inc.

Expanding Passenger Rail Service: Field Hearing Before the Subcommittee on Railroads, Pipelines, & Hazardous Materials of the Committee on Transportation & Infrastructure, House of Representatives, One Hundred Eleventh Congress, First Session, June 22, 2009 (Pittsburgh, Pennsylvania) 2009. (Illus.). xi, 148p. *(978-0-16-084520-8(3),* 552-070-40042-7) United States Government Printing Office.

Future of Intercity Passenger Rail Service & Amtrak: Hearing Before the Committee on Commerce, Science, & Transportation, United States Senate, One Hundred Eighth Congress, First Session, April 29, 2003. 2011. (Illus.). iv, 149p. ***(978-0-16-089246-2(5),*** 552-070-43243-4) United States Government Printing Office.

Hanus, Chris & Shaske, John. USA West by Train: The Complete Amtrak Travel Guide. 2009. 320p. pap. 26.95 *(978-0-9730897-6-9(8))* Way Of The Rail Publishing CAN. Dist: AtlasBooks Distribution.

Hecker, JayEtta Z. Commuter Rail: Commuter Rail Issues Should Be Considered in Debate over Amtrak. 2006. (Illus.). 51p. (C). pap. 20.00 *(978-1-4223-0786-1(7))* DIANE Publishing Co.

Hoffman, Eva J. A Guidebook to Amtrak's Southwest Chief: Chicago to Kansas City. 2007. (Illus.). 79p. spiral bd. 8.50 *(978-0-9721683-3-5(8))* Flash Yellow Guidebks.

—A Guidebook to Amtrak's Sunset Limited: New Orleans to San Antonio. 2009. (Illus.). 172p. spiral bd. 15.00 *(978-0-9721683-6-6(2))* Flash Yellow Guidebks.

Nominations to the Amtrak Reform Board, Federal Motor Carrier Safety Administration, National Transportation Safety Board, & the Department of Transportation: Hearing Before the Committee on Commerce, Science, & Transportation, United States Senate, One Hundred Ninth Congress, Second Session, June 8, 2006. 2011. iii, 60p. ***(978-0-16-088450-4(0),*** 552-070-42662-1) United States Government Printing Office.

Nominations to the U.S. Coast Guard, the Department of Commerce, the National Transportation Safety Board, the Marine Mammal Commission, & the Amtrak Board of Directors: Hearing Before the Committee on Commerce, Science, & Transportation, United States Senate, One Hundred Eleventh Congress, Second Session, March 18, 2010. 2011. iv, 109p. ***(978-0-16-088059-9(9),*** 552-070-42481-4) United States Government Printing Office.

Protecting the Mass Transit Critical Infrastructure in New York City & in the Nation: Hearing Before the Subcommittee on Transportation Security & Infrastructure Protection of the Committee on Homeland Security, House of Representatives, One Hundred Tenth Congress, Second Session, April 25, 2008. 2008. iii, 62p. *(978-0-16-081146-3(5),* 552-070-37568-6) United States Government Printing Office.

S. 294: The Passenger Rail Investment & Improvement ACT of 2007: Hearing Before the Subcommittee on Surface Transportation & Merchant Marine Infrastructure, Safety, & Security of the Committee on Commerce, Science, & Transportation, United States Senate, One Hundred Tenth Congress, First Session, February 27, 2007. 2010. (Illus.). iii, 45p. *(978-0-16-086806-1(8),* 552-070-41722-2) United States Government Printing Office.

United States, Congress House Committee on Transportation and Infrastructure Subcommittee on Railroads Staff, contrib. by. New Hands on the Amtrak Throttle: Hearing Before the Subcommittee on Railroads of the Committee on Transportation & Infrastructure, House of Representatives, One Hundred Ninth Congress, Second Session, September 28, 2007 [i.e. 2006]. 2007. v, 40p. *(978-0-16-078106-3(X),* 552-070-35508-1) United States Government Printing Office.

United States, Government Accountability Office Staff, contrib. by. Commuter Rail Issues. 2008. (Illus.). 71p. (C). pap. 50.00 *(978-1-60456-462-4(8))* Nova Science Pubs., Inc.

AMULETS

see also Charms; Scarabs; Talismans

Bannerman-Phillips, E. Ivy A. Amulets & Birthstones: Their Astrological Significance. 2011. 60p. 36.95 ***(978-1-258-00969-4(2))*** Literary Licensing, LLC.

Born, Wolfgang. Fetish, Amulet & Talisman: Ciba Symposia V7, No. 7, October 1945. Caspari-Rosen, Beate, ed. 2011. 34p. 35.95 ***(978-1-258-01994-5(9))*** Literary Licensing, LLC.

Bratley, George H. The Power of Gems & Charms. 2009. 110p. pap. 14.14 *(978-1-150-30189-6(9))* General Bks. LLC.

—The Power of Gems & Charms. 2009. 212p. 39.95 *(978-1-104-34081-0(X));* pap. 24.95 *(978-1-104-32269-4(2))* Kessinger Publishing, LLC.

Brown, Reginald. History & Origin of Horse Brasses. 2006. 68p. per. *(978-1-4067-9629-2(8),* Hesperides Pr.) Read Bks.

Danck, Robert. Amulets & Talismans: Simple Techniques for Creating Meaningful Jewelry. 2009. (ENG., Illus.). 144p. pap. 24.99 *(978-1-60061-161-2(3),* North Light Bks.) F&W Media, Inc.

Farrell, Kim. The Amulet Manual: A Guide to Understanding & Making Your Own Amulets. 2007. (ENG., Illus.). 160p. per. 16.95 *(978-1-84694-006-4(0))* O Bks. John Hunt.

Francis, Doris, ed. Faith & Transformation: Votive Offerings & Amulets from the Alexander Girard Collection. 2007. (ENG., Illus.). 160p. pap. 29.95 *(978-0-89013-504-4(5))* Museum of New Mexico Pr.

Germond, Philippe. The Symbolic World of Egyptian Amulets: From the Jacques-Edouard Berger Collection. 2008. (ENG., Illus.). 164p. 45.00 *(978-88-7439-244-5(3))* 5 Continents ITA. Dist: Hachette Bk. Group.

Kovács, László & Rádóczy, Gyula. Vulvae, Eyes, Snake Heads: Archaeological Finds of Cowrie Amulets. 2008. (Bar S Ser.). (Illus.). 512p. (C). 172.50 *(978-1-4073-0333-8(3))* British Archaeological Reports Ltd. GBR. Dist: Brown, David Bk. Co., The.

Porter, Venetia. Arabic & Persian Seals & Amulets in the British Museum. 2011. (British Museum Research Publication). (ENG., Illus.). 208p. (C). pap. 80.00 *(978-0-86159-160-2(7))* British Museum Pr. GBR. Dist: Brown, David Bk. Co., The.

Reisner, George Andrew. Amulets Par M. G. A. Reisner. 2008. (Illus.). 125.00 *(978-1-57898-718-4(0))* Martino Publishing.

Schaefer, Karl R. Enigmatic Charms: Medieval Arabic Block Printed Amulets in American & European Libraries & Museums. 2006. (Handbook of Oriental Studies). (Illus.). 250p. *(978-90-04-14789-8(6))* BRILL.

Skorupski, Tadeusz. Tibetan Amulets. 2010. (ENG., Illus.). 138p. pap. 25.00 *(978-974-524-120-6(2))* Orchid Pr. THA. Dist: National Bk. Network.

Sousa, Rogerio. The Heart of Wisdom: Studies on the Heart Amulet in Ancient Egypt. 2011. (Bar S Ser.). (ENG., Illus.). 133p. (C). pap. 85.00 ***(978-1-4073-0769-5(X))*** British Archaeological Reports Ltd. GBR. Dist: Brown, David Bk. Co., The.

Varner, Gary R. The History & Use of Amulets, Charms & Talismans. 2008. 192p. 28.50 *(978-0-557-00891-9(3));* pap. 15.95 *(978-1-4357-1988-0(3))* Lulu Enterprises Inc.

AMUNDSEN, ROALD, 1872-1928

Amundsen, Roald. My Life As an Explorer. 2009. (Illus.). 192p. pap. 29.95 *(978-1-84868-059-3(7))* Amberley Publishing GBR. Dist: Casemate Pubs. & Bk. Distributors, LLC.

—Race to the South Pole. 2007. (Great Adventures Ser.). (ENG., Illus.). 256p. 14.95 *(978-88-544-0217-1(6),* White Star) Rizzoli International Pubns., Inc.

—To the South Pole: An Account of the Norwegian Antarctic Expedition in the Fram, 1910-1912. 2008. *(978-1-934941-39-3(5))* Red & Black Pubs.

Amundsen, Roald & Hansen, Godfred. Roald Amundsen's "The North West Passage" Being the Record of a Voyage of Exploration of the Ship Gjoa, 1903-1907. 2007. *(978-1-57898-679-8(6))* Martino Publishing.

Amundsen, Roald E. The South Pole: An Account of the Norwegian Antarctic Expedition in the "Fram", 1910-1912. 2007. (ENG.). 320p. 29.95 *(978-1-4218-3305-7(0));* 296p. 28.95 *(978-1-4218-3304-0(2));* (ENG.). 320p. per. 14.95 *(978-1-4218-3405-4(7));* (ENG.). 296p. per. 13.95 *(978-1-4218-3404-7(9))* 1st World Publishing, Inc. (1st World Library - Literary Society).

—The South Pole: An Account of the Norwegian Antarctic Expedition in the "Fram", 1910-1912. 2007. (Twelve-Point Ser.). lib. bdg. 27.00 *(978-1-58287-436-4(0));* lib. bdg. 30.00 *(978-1-58287-925-3(7))* North Bks.

Bown, Stephen. The Last Viking: The Life of Roald Amundsen. 2012. (Merloyd Lawrence Book Ser.). (ENG., Illus.). 320p. 26.00 ***(978-0-306-82067-0(6))*** Da Capo Pr., Inc.

Cox, Lynne. South with the Sun: Roald Amundsen, His Polar Explorations, & the Quest for Discovery. 2012. (ENG.). 320p. pap. 15.95 ***(978-0-547-90578-5(5),*** Mariner Bks.) Houghton Mifflin Harcourt Trade & Reference Pubs.

—South with the Sun: Roald Amundsen, His Polar Explorations, & the Quest for Discovery. 2011. (ENG., Illus.). 320p. 26.00 *(978-0-307-59340-5(1),* Knopf) Knopf Doubleday Publishing Group.

Herbert, Kari & Lewis-Jones, Huw. In Search of the South Pole. 2012. (ENG., Illus.). 192p. 29.95 *(978-1-84486-137-8(6),* Conway Maritime Pr.) Anova Bks. GBR. Dist: Sterling Publishing Co., Inc.

Huntford Roland. Race for the South Pole: The Expedition Diaries of Scott & Amundsen. 2011. (ENG., Illus.). 352p. pap. 16.95 *(978-1-4411-2667-2(8))* Continuum International Publishing Group, Ltd. GBR. Dist: National Bk. Network.

Langner, Rainer-K. Scott & Amundsen: Duel in the Ice. 2007. (ENG., Illus.). 232p. 24.95 *(978-1-905791-08-8(9))* Haus Publishing GBR. Dist: Consortium Bk. Sales & Distribution.

MacPhee, Ross D. E. Race to the End: Amundsen, Scott, & the Attainment of the South Pole. 2010. (ENG., Illus.). 286p. 27.95 *(978-1-4027-7029-6(4),* Sterling Innovation) Sterling Publishing Co., Inc.

Maynard, Jeff. Wings of Ice: The Mystery of the Polar Air Race. 2010. (ENG., Illus.). 304p. 19.95 *(978-1-74166-934-3(0))* Random Hse. Australia AUS. Dist: Independent Pubs. Group.

Rees, Jasper & Fiennes, Ranulph. Blizzard: Race to the Pole. 2006. (ENG., Illus.). 288p. 29.95 *(978-0-563-49326-6(7))* BBC Worldwide GBR. Dist: Independent Pubs. Group.

AMUR RIVER

Bassin, Mark. Imperial Visions: Nationalist Imagination & Geographical Expansion in the Russian Far East, 1840-1865. 2006. (Cambridge Studies in Historical Geography Ser.). (ENG., Illus.). 348p. pap. 69.00 *(978-0-521-02674-1(1))* Cambridge Univ. Pr.

AMUSEMENT PARKS

see also Amusement Rides; Disneyland (Calif.); Disneyland Paris (Marne-la-Vallee, France); Walt Disney World (Fla.)

Alcorn, Steve & Green, David. Building a Better Mouse: The Story of the Electronic Imagineers Who Designed Epcot. 2007. 142p. 29.99 *(978-0-9729777-3-9(2))* Theme Perks, Inc.

Applegate, Harry & Benton, Thomas. Six Flags Great ADV. 2009. (Images of America Ser.). (ENG., Illus.). 128p. pap. 21.99 *(978-0-7385-6569-9(5))* Arcadia Publishing.

Barrett, Steven. The Hassle-Free Walt Disney World Vacation, 2011 Edition. 10th ed. 2010. (ENG.). 272p. pap. 15.95 *(978-1-887140-91-1(3))* Intrepid Traveler, The.

Bettencourt, David & Chauvin, Stephanie. Rocky Point Park. 2009. (Images of America Ser.). (ENG., Illus.). 128p. pap. 21.99 *(978-0-7385-6236-0(X))* Arcadia Publishing.

Birnbaum Travel Guides. Birnbaum's Walt Disney World Pocket Parks Guide 2010. 2009. (ENG., Illus.). 128p. pap. 11.95 *(978-1-4231-1704-9(2),* Disney Editions) Disney Pr.

Birnbaum Travel Guides Staff. Birnbaum's Disneyland Resort 2011. 2010. (ENG.). 144p. pap. 14.95 *(978-1-4231-2377-4(8),* Disney Editions) Disney Pr.

Burke, Kathryn W. Playland. 2008. (Images of America Ser.). (ENG., Illus.). 128p. pap. 21.99 *(978-0-7385-5470-9(7))* Arcadia Publishing.

Charter, Carla & Washington, Ethel M. Union County's Black Soldiers & Sailors of the Civil War. 2011. 150p. pap. 19.99 *(978-1-59629-446-2(9))* History Pr., The.

Chen, I-Pin. The Responsive Actions in Tourism & Amusement Enterprises in Taiwan. 2009. 56p. pap. *(978-3-639-18733-5(4))* VDM Verlag Dr. Mueller e.K.

Clavé, S. Anton. The Global Theme Park Industry. Clarke, Andrew, tr. 2007. (Illus.). 352p. per. 65.00 *(978-1-84593-208-4(0))* CABI GBR. Dist: Stylus Publishing, LLC.

Daisy, Michael. Detroit's Historic Water Works Park. 2012. (Images of America Ser.). (ENG., Illus.). 128p. pap. 21.99 ***(978-0-7385-9363-0(X))*** Arcadia Publishing.

Davis, Hattie Caldwell & Burke, Janet. The History of Ghost Town 1960 to 2007. 2007. (Illus.). 94p. pap. *(978-0-9670689-6-1(7))* Davis, Hattie C.

DeMello, Julie. Hawaii: Hundreds of Ideas for Day Trips with the Kids. 7th ed. 2009. (Fun with the Family Ser.). (ENG., Illus.). 232p. pap. 13.95 *(978-0-7627-4859-4(1),* Globe Pequot Pr., The.

Disney Institute Staff & Kinni, Theodore. Be Our Guest: Perfecting the Art of Customer Service. Lefkon, Wendy, ed. 10th anniv. rev. ed. 2011. (ENG., Illus.). 224p. 24.95 *(978-1-4231-4584-4(4),* Disney Editions) Disney Pr.

Dunlop, Beth. Building a Dream: The Art of Disney Architecture. 2011. (ENG., Illus.). 208p. 60.00 *(978-1-4231-2918-9(0),* Disney Editions) Disney Pr.

Easdown, Martin. Amusement Park Rides. 2012. (Shire Library). (ENG., Illus.). 64p. pap. 12.95 ***(978-0-7478-1154-1(7))*** Shire Pubns., Ltd. GBR. Dist: Random Hse., Inc.

Faulkner, Debra B. Mary Elitch Long: First Lady of Fun. 2008. (Now You Know Bio Ser.). (J). pap. 8.95 *(978-0-86541-094-7(1))* Filter Pr., LLC.

Fodor's. Fodor's Walt Disney World with Kids 2013: With Universal Orlando, SeaWorld & Aquatica. 2012. (Travel Guide Ser.). (ENG.). 512p. pap. 18.99 ***(978-0-307-92922-8(1),*** Fodor's) Fodor's Travel Pubns.

Fodor's Travel Publications, Inc. Staff. Walt Disney World 2012: With Universal, Seaworld, & the Best of Central Florida. 2011. (Full-Color Travel Guide Ser.). (ENG., Illus.). 608p. pap. 19.99 *(978-0-679-00948-1(5),* Fodor's) Fodor's Travel Pubns.

Fowler, Scott E. LeSourdsville Lake Amusement Park. 2011. (Images of America Ser.). (Illus.). 128p. pap. 21.99 *(978-0-7385-8314-3(6))* Arcadia Publishing.

Futrell, Jim. Amusement Parks of Virginia, Maryland, & Delaware. 2008. (Amusement Parks Ser.). (ENG., Illus.). 224p. per. 19.95 *(978-0-8117-3475-2(7))* Stackpole Bks.

Galda, Ed. Just for Fun! Jimmy Johnson's Playland Park. 2007. (Illus.). 152p. 34.95 *(978-0-9670438-1-4(6))* Galda, Ed.

Garner, Doug. Forest Park Highlands. 2007. (Images of America Ser.). (ENG., Illus.). 128p. per. 21.99 *(978-0-7385-5162-3(7))* Arcadia Publishing.

Greathouse, Lisa. How Things Work: How Amusement Parks Work: Forces & Motion. 2009. (Science Readers Ser.). 32p. (gr. 2-3). pap. 8.99 *(978-1-4333-0308-1(6))* Teacher Created Materials, Inc.

Harris, Richard. Early Amusement Parks of Orange County. 2008. (Images of America Ser.). (ENG., Illus.). 128p. pap. 21.99 *(978-0-7385-5947-6(4))* Arcadia Publishing.

Hench, John & Van Pelt, Peggy. Designing Disney: Imagineering & the Art of the Show. 2009. (ENG.). 160p. pap. 24.99 *(978-1-4231-1915-9(0),* Disney Editions) Disney Pr.

Herlyn, Hendrik G. & Contreras, Alan L. Oaks Park Pentimento: Portland's Lost & Found Carousel Art. 2009. (ENG.). 48p. 25.00 *(978-0-87071-578-5(X))* Oregon State Univ. Pr.

Hirsch, Rose Ann. Western New York Amusement Parks. 2011. (Images of America Ser.). (Illus.). 128p. pap. 21.99 *(978-0-7385-7456-1(2))* Arcadia Publishing.

Hollis, Tim. See Rock City: The History of Rock City Gardens. 2008. *(978-1-59629-577-3(5))* History Pr., The.

Hyde, Andrew. Experience the Point: Unofficial Guidebook to Cedar Point. 3rd Edition. 2007. 108p. pap. 10.95 *(978-0-7414-3893-5(3))* Infinity Publishing.

Imagineers Staff. Walt Disney Imagineering: A Behind the Dreams Look at Making More Magic Real. 2010. (ENG., Illus.). 192p. 60.00 *(978-1-4231-0766-8(7),* Disney Editions) Disney Pr.

Jennings, Jay. Knott's Berry Farm: The Early Years. 2009. (Images of America Ser.). (ENG., Illus.). 128p. pap. 21.99 *(978-0-7385-6921-5(6))* Arcadia Publishing.

Liebowitz, Steve. Steel Pier, Atlantic City: Showplace of the Nation. 2009. (Illus.). 263p. 39.00 *(978-1-59322-036-5(7),* Cormorant Bks.) Down The Shore Publishing.

Livingston, Patrick. Summer Dreams: The Story of Bob-lo Island. 2008. (Great Lakes Bks.). (Illus.). 192p. pap. 24.95 *(978-0-8143-3365-5(6))* Wayne State Univ. Pr.

Lukas, Scott & Lukas, Scott A. Theme Park. 2008. (Reaktion Books - Objekt Ser.). (ENG., Illus.). 256p. pap. 27.00 *(978-1-86189-394-9(9))* Reaktion Bks., Ltd. GBR. Dist: Chicago Distribution Ctr.

Madden, Gloria. Cherished Memories. 2008. 76p. pap. 11.49 *(978-1-4343-9200-8(7))* AuthorHouse.

Mangels, William F. Outdoor Amusement Industry. lib. bdg. 20.95 *(978-0-8488-2002-2(9))* Amereon LTD.

Marx, Jennifer, et al. PassPorter's Walt Disney World 2012: The Unique Travel Guide, Planner, Organizer, Journal, & Keepsake! 2012. (PassPorter Ser.). (ENG., Illus.). 362p. spiral bd. 24.95 ***(978-1-58771-103-9(6),*** PassPorter Travel Pr.) MediaMarx, Inc.

—PassPorter's Walt Disney World 2012 Deluxe: The Unique Travel Guide, Planner, Organizer, Journal, & Keepsake! 2012. (PassPorter Ser.). (ENG.). 362p. ring bd. 47.95 ***(978-1-58771-104-6(4)***, PassPorter Travel Pr.) MediaMarx, Inc.

McDaniel, Brian. Walt Disney World: The Full Report. 2008. 328p. pap. 22.95 *(978-1-4401-0329-2(1))* iUniverse, Inc.

McLaughlin, Robert. Pleasure Island. 2009. (Images of America Ser.). (ENG., Illus.). 128p. pap. 21.99 *(978-0-7385-6460-9(5))* Arcadia Publishing.

Merritt, Christopher & Lynxwiler, J. Eric. Knott's Preserved: From Boysenberry to Theme Park: The History of Knott's Berry Farm. 2010. *(978-1-883318-97-0(1))*; *(978-1-883318-77-2(7))* Angel City Pr.

Miller, Alex. California Theme Parks. 2010. (Illus.). 128p. pap. 19.99 *(978-0-7643-3478-8(6))* Schiffer Publishing, Ltd.

Neal, Julie & Neal, Mike. The Complete Guide to Walt Disney World. 2007. (ENG., Illus.). 320p. pap. 24.95 *(978-0-9709596-4-5(8))* Coconut Pr.

—The Complete Guide to Walt Disney World 2008. 2007. (Illus.). 336p. pap. 24.95 *(978-0-9709596-9-0(9))* Coconut Pr.

—The Complete Walt Disney World 2009. 2008. (Illus.). 336p. pap. 24.95 *(978-0-9709596-8-3(0))* Coconut Pr.

Neal, Julie & Neal, Mike. The Complete Walt Disney World 2012. 2011. (ENG., Illus.). 384p. pap. 24.95 ***(978-0-9709596-6-9(4))*** Coconut Pr.

Newcomb, Chris. Crossing the Berm the Disney Theme Park As Sacralized Space. 2008. 112p. pap. *(978-3-8364-6685-1(6))* VDM Verlag Dr. Mueller e.K.

O'Brien, Tim. Ripley's Believe It or Not! Amusement Park Oddities & Trivia. 2007. pap. *(978-1-893951-25-9(1)*, Gousha, H. M. Maps & Atlases) Ripley Entertainment, Inc.

Rabinovitz, Lauren. Electric Dreamland: Amusement Parks, Movies, & American Modernity. 2012. (Film & Culture Ser.). (ENG., Illus.). 240p. (gr. 17). 82.50 ***(978-0-231-15660-8(X))***; pap. 27.50 ***(978-0-231-15661-5(8))*** Columbia Univ. Pr.

Russell, Lynda J. Lake Compounce. 2008. (Images of America Ser.). (ENG., Illus.). 128p. pap. 19.99 *(978-0-7385-5757-1(9))* Arcadia Publishing.

Santa Cruz Seaside Company. The Santa Cruz Beach Boardwalk: A Century by the Sea. 2007. (ENG., Illus.). 176p. 28.95 *(978-1-58008-815-2(5))*; pap. 19.95 *(978-1-58008-814-5(7))* Ten Speed Pr.

Schlehe, Judith, et al, eds. Staging the Past: Themed Environments in Transcultural Perspectives. 2011. (ENG.). 274p. pap. 41.95 *(978-3-8376-1481-7(6))* Transcript Verlag DEU. Dist: Transaction Pubs.

Sehlinger, Bob, et al. Beyond Disney: The Unofficial Guide to Universal Orlando, SeaWorld & the Best of Central Florida. 7th ed. 2011. (Unofficial Guides: 275). (ENG., Illus.). 384p. pap. 17.99 *(978-0-470-88608-3(0)*, Wiley) Wiley, John & Sons, Inc.

Seiders-Metz, Margaret. The Four Daredevils. 2010. 84p. pap. 9.25 *(978-1-935125-96-9(6))* Robertson Publishing.

Smith, Broc. The Tragic Kingdom or; 'Prisoner in a Chinese Theme Park' 2009. 342p. 18.95 *(978-1-60264-415-1(2))*; pap. 13.95 *(978-1-60264-414-4(4))* Virtualbookworm.com Publishing, Inc.

Smith, James R. San Francisco's Playland at the Beach: The Early Years. 2010. (Illus.). 152p. pap. 21.95 *(978-1-884995-67-5(5))* Linden Publishing Co., Inc.

Tofte, Mavis. Enchanted Forest's Challenge of Mondor. 2007. per. 15.00 *(978-0-9709906-6-2(9))* Creative Quill Publishing, Inc.

Trabucco, Pete. America's Top Roller Coasters & Amusement Parks: A Guide for Those who Ride Them & Tips for Those who Fear Them. 2009. pap. 29.99 *(978-1-60696-645-7(6))* Tate Publishing & Enterprises, LLC.

Vasillu, Michelle. Thrills & Spills. 2007. 32p. pap. 10.95 *(978-0-86431-662-2(3))* ACER Pr. AUS. Dist: International Specialized Bk. Services.

Vickers, Lu. Weeki Wachee, City of Mermaids: A History of One of Florida's Oldest Roadside Attractions. 2007. (Florida History & Culture Ser.). (ENG., Illus.). 320p. 34.95 *(978-0-8130-3041-8(2))* Univ. Pr. of Florida.

Walton, John K. Riding on Rainbows: Blackpool Pleasure Beach & its Place in British Popular Culture. 2007. (Illus.). 162p. per. *(978-0-9544573-6-5(6))* Skelter Publishing LLP.

Wenz, Phillip L. Santa's Village. 2007. (Images of America Ser.). (Illus.). 127p. per. 21.99 *(978-0-7385-4149-5(4))* Arcadia Publishing.

West, Rick & Loika, Mason. Pickled Punks & Girlie Shows: A Life Spent on the Midways of America. 2011. (Illus.). 160p. *(978-0-7643-3703-1(3)*, Schiffer Publishing Ltd) Schiffer Publishing, Ltd.

Wright, Alex. The Imagineering Field Guide to Disney's Hollywood Studios. 2010. (ENG.). 128p. pap. 11.99 *(978-1-4231-1593-9(7)*, Disney Editions) Disney Pr.

—The Imagineering Field Guide to Magic Kingdom at Walt Disney World — Updated! 2009. (ENG.). 128p. pap. 9.95 *(978-1-4231-2468-9(5)*, Disney Editions) Disney Pr.

Wright, Jack. A Wild Ride: The Story of Morey's Piers, Planet Earth's Greatest Seaside Amusement Park. 2009. 192p. pap. 19.95 *(978-0-9799051-5-5(X))* Exit Zero Publishing, Inc.

AMUSEMENT RIDES

see also Amusement Parks; Roller Coasters

Tofte, Mavis. Enchanted Forest's Challenge of Mondor. 2007. per. 15.00 *(978-0-9709906-6-2(9))* Creative Quill Publishing, Inc.

AMUSEMENTS

see also Amateur Theater; Amusement Rides; Carnivals; Casinos; Charades; Children's Parties; Church Entertainments; Circus; Concerts; Creative Activities and Seat Work; Dance; Entertaining; Family Recreation; Fortune-Telling; Games; Hobbies; Juggling; Literary Recreations; Magic Tricks; Mathematical Recreations; Performing Arts; Play; Puzzles; Recreation; Riddles; Scientific Recreations; Sideshows; String Figures; Tableaux; Toys; Vaudeville; Ventriloquism; Wild West Shows

Agnew, Jeremy. Entertainment in the Old West: Theater, Music, Circuses, Medicine Shows, Prizefighting & Other Popular Amusements. 2011. (ENG., Illus.). 241p. pap. 35.00 *(978-0-7864-6280-3(9))* McFarland & Co., Inc. Pubs.

Aist, Jennifer. Babes in the Woods: Hiking, Camping & Boating with Babies & Young Children. 2010. (ENG.). 176p. pap. 16.95 *(978-1-59485-343-2(6))* Mountaineers Bks., The.

Arden, Allison. The Book of Doing: Everyday Activities to Unlock Your Creativity & Joy. 2012. (ENG.). 192p. (gr. 12). 15.00 ***(978-0-399-53734-9(1)***, Perigee Trade) Penguin Group (USA) Inc.

August, Evelyn. The Black-Out Book: 500 Family Games & Puzzles for Wartime Entertainment. 2009. (General Military Ser.). (ENG., Illus.). 224p. 14.95 *(978-1-84603-923-2(1))* Osprey Publishing, Ltd. GBR. Dist: Random Hse., Inc.

Austin, John. Mini Weapons of Mass Destruction: Build Implements of Spitball Warfare. 2009. (Illus.). 256p. pap. 16.95 *(978-1-55652-953-5(8))* Chicago Review Pr., Inc.

—Mini Weapons of Mass Destruction 2: Build a Secret Agent Arsenal. 2011. (ENG.). 256p. pap. 16.95 *(978-1-56976-716-0(5))* Chicago Review Pr., Inc.

Bailey, MaryLou. The Fun Never Stops. 2008. 11.99 *(978-1-59955-153-1(5))* Cedar Fort, Inc./CFI Distribution.

Baldauf, Anette. Entertainment Cities: Stadtentwicklung und Unterhaltungskultur. 2008. (Illus.). 195p. pap. 29.95 *(978-3-211-71572-7(X))* Springer Wien AUT. Dist: Springer.

Beale, Sharon. Office Party Themes. 2008. 141p. pap. 24.95 *(978-1-60441-868-2(0))* PublishAmerica, Inc.

Beard, Daniel C The Fair Weather & Rainy Day Handy Book. 2009. (Dover Children's Activity Bks.). (ENG., Illus.). 336p. pap. 9.95 *(978-0-486-47403-8(8))* Dover Pubns., Inc.

Bellew, Frank. The Art of Amusing. 2009. 122p. pap. *(978-1-150-17925-9(2))* Books LLC.

—Art of Amusing A Collection of Graceful. 2006. pap. 30.95 *(978-1-4286-3874-7(1))* Kessinger Publishing, LLC.

Bellow, Frank. The Art of Amusing. 2008. 332p. pap. 29.95 *(978-1-4437-7393-5(X))* Audubon Pr. & Christian Bk. Service.

Benning, Lee Edwards. The Granny-Nanny Has Fun with Kids! (Ages 3 & Up) Crazy Crafts, Magic Tricks, Giggle Treats, & Fun Facts. 2007. (Granny-Nanny Ser.). (ENG.). pap. 16.95 *(978-1-59624-076-6(8))* Cleveland Clinic Pr.

Berger, Erich, ed. Homo Ludens Ludens. 2008. 555p. pap. *(978-84-612-4141-5(X))* Actar Birkhauser Distribution.

Bertrand, Isabelle, et al. It's All Fun & Games: 230 Activities for the Whole Family! Stout, Mark tr. from FRE. 2009. (ENG., Illus.). 112p. (J). (gr. -1-9). spiral bd. 26.95 *(978-2-89579-210-9(0))* Owlkids Bks. Inc. CAN. Dist: Perseus-PGW.

Bilby, Joseph G. & Ziegler, Harry F. Asbury Park, New Jersey: A Brief History. 2008. 19.99 *(978-1-59629-604-6(6))* History Pr., The.

Brewer, Susan. Classic Playground Games. 2008. (Illus.). 192p. 32.95 *(978-1-84468-025-2(8))* Pen & Sword Bks. Ltd. GBR. Dist: Casemate Pubs. & Bk. Distributors, LLC.

Brooks, Helen. The Rainy Day Book. 2009. (ENG., Illus.). 246p. 23.95 *(978-0-85265-139-1(2))* Random Hse. GBR. Dist: Independent Pubs. Group.

Brown, Suzanne. Summer: A User's Guide. 2007. (ENG., Illus.). 224p. pap. 19.95 *(978-1-57965-316-3(2)*, 1579653162) Artisan.

Carr, Neil. Children's & Families' Holiday Experience. 2011. (Contemporary Geographies of Leisure, Tourism & Mobility Ser.). (ENG., Illus.). 216p. (C). 148.00 *(978-0-415-54543-3(9))* Routledge.

Cavert, Chris & Acosta, Susana. Are You More Like... ?/What Would it Be Like... ? 2007. 140p. per. 14.95 *(978-1-885473-77-6(X))* Wood 'N' Barnes.

Christensen, Madonna Dries. Toys Remembered: Men Recall Their Childhood Toys. 2011. 196p. pap. 16.95 *(978-1-4502-7543-9(5))* iUniverse, Inc.

Cram101 Textbook Reviews Staff. Outlines & Highlights for Entertainment Marketing & Communication: Selling Branded Performance, People, & Places by Shay Sayre, ISBN. 2009. 108p. pap. 28.95 *(978-1-4288-3065-3(0))* Cram101 Inc.

Curran, Josie. The Book of Summer: How to Stretch Out Those Halcyon Days. 2011. (ENG., Illus.). 216p. 24.95 ***(978-0-7535-3992-7(6))*** Virgin Bks. Ltd. GBR. Dist: Independent Pubs. Group.

Cutler, Tom. 211 Things a Bright Boy Can Do. 2007. (ENG., Illus.). 336p. (gr. 12-18). 15.95 *(978-0-399-53415-7(6)*, Perigee Trade) Penguin Group (USA) Inc.

Danks, Fiona & Schofield, Jo. Stick Book: Loads of Things You Can Make or Do with a Stick. 2012. (ENG., Illus.). 128p. pap. 14.95 ***(978-0-7112-3241-9(5))*** Lincoln, Frances Ltd. GBR. Dist: Perseus-PGW.

Daoust, Phil & van der Zee, Bibi, eds. Summer Living: Make Every Day a Festival. 2009. (ENG., Illus.). 240p. pap., instr.'s gde. ed. 27.95 *(978-0-85265-126-1(0))* Random Hse. GBR. Dist: Independent Pubs. Group.

Davis, Heidi. Everyday Food Fun & Fitness. 2nd rev. ed. 2011. (ENG.). 120p. spiral bd. 32.95 *(978-0-7575-8609-5(0))* Kendall Hunt Publishing Co.

De Lafayette, Maximillien. Entertainment Greats from the 1800's to the Present: Volume 6 of World Who's Who in Jazz, Cabaret, Music & Entertainment: Cinema, Music, Divas, Legends. 2007. (Illus.). 400p. per. 69.95 *(978-0-9799750-3-5(4))* Elite Assocs. International-Times Square Pr.

Dec, Robert J. After Dark: A Comprehensive Guide to Dining & Evening Entertainment. 3rd ed. Date not set. (Illus.). pap. 4.95 *(978-0-9671547-0-1(7))* After Dark Pubns.

Denmead, Ken. Geek Dad: Awesomely Geeky Projects & Activities for Dads & Kids to Share. 2010. (ENG.). 240p. (gr. 12). 17.00 *(978-1-59240-552-7(5)*, Gotham) Penguin Group (USA) Inc.

Entertainment Publications, Inc. Staff, compiled by. Albany 2009 Entertainment Book. 2008. pap. 35.00 *(978-1-59878-652-1(0))* Entertainment Pubns., Inc.

—Appleton/Green Bay 2009 Entertainment Book. 2008. pap. 35.00 *(978-1-59878-667-5(9))* Entertainment Pubns., Inc.

—Atlanta 2009 Entertainment Book. 2008. pap. 25.00 *(978-1-59878-621-7(0))* Entertainment Pubns., Inc.

—Augusta 2009 Entertainment Book. 2008. pap. 25.00 *(978-1-59878-742-9(X))* Entertainment Pubns., Inc.

—Austin Passbook 2009 Entertainment Book. 2008. pap. 25.00 *(978-1-59878-722-1(5))* Entertainment Pubns., Inc.

—Bakersfield 2009 Entertainment Book. 2008. pap. 25.00 *(978-1-59878-691-0(1))* Entertainment Pubns., Inc.

—Baltimore 2009 Entertainment Book. 2008. pap. 30.00 *(978-1-59878-617-0(2))* Entertainment Pubns., Inc.

—Baton Rouge 2009 Entertainment Book. 2008. pap. 25.00 *(978-1-59878-743-6(8))* Entertainment Pubns., Inc.

—Binghamton 2009 Entertainment Book. 2008. pap. 25.00 *(978-1-59878-696-5(2))* Entertainment Pubns., Inc.

—Birmingham 2009 Entertainment Book. 2008. pap. 25.00 *(978-1-59878-693-4(8))* Entertainment Pubns., Inc.

—Boise 2009 Entertainment Book. 2008. pap. 25.00 *(978-1-59878-674-3(1))* Entertainment Pubns., Inc.

—Boston 2009 Entertainment Book. 2008. pap. 30.00 *(978-1-59878-623-1(7))* Entertainment Pubns., Inc.

—Brevard County 2009 Entertainment Book. 2008. pap. 30.00 *(978-1-59878-717-7(9))* Entertainment Pubns., Inc.

—Buffalo 2009 Entertainment Book. 2008. pap. 30.00 *(978-1-59878-605-7(9))* Entertainment Pubns., Inc.

—Calgary 2009 Entertainment Book. 2008. pap. 45.00 *(978-1-59878-656-9(3))* Entertainment Pubns., Inc.

—Canton 2009 Entertainment Book. 2008. pap. 35.00 *(978-1-59878-660-6(1))* Entertainment Pubns., Inc.

—Charleston, SC 2009 Entertainment Book. 2008. pap. 25.00 *(978-1-59878-746-7(2))* Entertainment Pubns., Inc.

—Charleston, WV 2009 Entertainment Book. 2008. pap. 30.00 *(978-1-59878-701-6(2))* Entertainment Pubns., Inc.

—Charlotte 2009 Entertainment Book. 2008. pap. 25.00 *(978-1-59878-635-4(0))* Entertainment Pubns., Inc.

—Chicago North 2009 Entertainment Book. 2008. pap. 25.00 *(978-1-59878-603-3(2))* Entertainment Pubns., Inc.

—Chicago South 2009 Entertainment Book. 2008. pap. 25.00 *(978-1-59878-620-0(2))* Entertainment Pubns., Inc.

—Chicago West 2009 Entertainment Book. 2008. pap. 25.00 *(978-1-59878-609-5(1))* Entertainment Pubns., Inc.

—Cincinnati 2009 Entertainment Book. 2008. pap. 25.00 *(978-1-59878-597-5(4))* Entertainment Pubns., Inc.

—Cleveland 2009 Entertainment Book. 2008. pap. 30.00 *(978-1-59878-599-9(0))* Entertainment Pubns., Inc.

—Colorado North 2009 Gold C Book. 2008. pap. 10.00 *(978-1-59878-759-7(4))* Entertainment Pubns., Inc.

—Colorado South 2009 Gold C Book. 2008. pap. 10.00 *(978-1-59878-760-3(8))* Entertainment Pubns., Inc.

—Colorado Springs 2009 Entertainment Book. 2008. pap. 30.00 *(978-1-59878-721-4(7))* Entertainment Pubns., Inc.

—Columbia 2009 Entertainment Book. 2008. pap. 25.00 *(978-1-59878-614-9(8))* Entertainment Pubns., Inc.

—Columbus 2009 Entertainment Book. 2008. pap. 25.00 *(978-1-59878-598-2(2))* Entertainment Pubns., Inc.

—Corpus Christi 2009 Entertainment Book. 2008. pap. 25.00 *(978-1-59878-720-7(9))* Entertainment Pubns., Inc.

—D. C. /Maryland 2009 Entertainment Book. 2008. pap. 30.00 *(978-1-59878-615-6(6))* Entertainment Pubns., Inc.

—D. C. /North Virginia 2009 Entertainment Book. 2008. pap. 30.00 *(978-1-59878-661-3(X))* Entertainment Pubns., Inc.

—Dallas Passbook 2009 Entertainment Book. 2008. pap. 25.00 *(978-1-59878-725-2(X))* Entertainment Pubns., Inc.

—Dayton 2009 Entertainment Book. 2008. pap. 30.00 *(978-1-59878-600-2(8))* Entertainment Pubns., Inc.

—Delaware 2009 Entertainment Book. 2008. pap. 35.00 *(978-1-59878-736-8(5))* Entertainment Pubns., Inc.

—Denver 2009 Entertainment Book. 2008. pap. 30.00 *(978-1-59878-631-6(8))* Entertainment Pubns., Inc.

—Denver 2009 Gold C Book. 2008. pap. 10.00 *(978-1-59878-755-9(1))* Entertainment Pubns., Inc.

—Des Moines 2009 Entertainment Book. 2008. pap. 25.00 *(978-1-59878-645-3(8))* Entertainment Pubns., Inc.

—Detroit 2009 Entertainment Book. 2008. pap. 25.00 *(978-1-59878-596-8(6))* Entertainment Pubns., Inc.

—East Bay 2009 Entertainment Book. 2008. pap. 30.00 *(978-1-59878-647-7(4))* Entertainment Pubns., Inc.

—Edmonton 2009 Entertainment Book. 2008. pap. 45.00 *(978-1-59878-657-6(1))* Entertainment Pubns., Inc.

—Fairfield County 2009 Entertainment Book. 2008. pap. 30.00 *(978-1-59878-670-5(9))* Entertainment Pubns., Inc.

—Fayetteville 2009 Entertainment Book. 2008. pap. 25.00 *(978-1-59878-745-0(4))* Entertainment Pubns., Inc.

—Fresno 2009 Entertainment Book. 2008. pap. 30.00 *(978-1-59878-675-0(X))* Entertainment Pubns., Inc.

—Ft. Lauderdale 2009 Entertainment Book. 2008. pap. 35.00 *(978-1-59878-628-6(8))* Entertainment Pubns., Inc.

—Ft. Myers 2009 Entertainment Book. 2008. pap. 35.00 *(978-1-59878-665-1(2))* Entertainment Pubns., Inc.

—Ft. Wayne 2009 Entertainment Book. 2008. pap. 25.00 *(978-1-59878-668-2(7))* Entertainment Pubns., Inc.

—Ft. Worth Passbook 2009 Entertainment Book. 2008. pap. 25.00 *(978-1-59878-727-6(6))* Entertainment Pubns., Inc.

—Gainesville 2009 Entertainment Book. 2008. pap. 30.00 *(978-1-59878-630-9(X))* Entertainment Pubns., Inc.

—Grand Rapids 2009 Entertainment Book. 2008. pap. 25.00 *(978-1-59878-729-0(2))* Entertainment Pubns., Inc.

—Greensboro 2009 Entertainment Book. 2008. pap. 25.00 *(978-1-59878-700-9(4))* Entertainment Pubns., Inc.

—Halifax 2009 Entertainment Book. 2008. pap. 35.00 *(978-1-59878-713-9(6))* Entertainment Pubns., Inc.

—Hamilton 2009 Entertainment Book. 2008. pap. 40.00 *(978-1-59878-651-4(2))* Entertainment Pubns., Inc.

—Harrisburg 2009 Entertainment Book. 2008. pap. 30.00 *(978-1-59878-741-2(1))* Entertainment Pubns., Inc.

—Hartford 2009 Entertainment Book. 2008. pap. 35.00 *(978-1-59878-638-5(5))* Entertainment Pubns., Inc.

—Hawaii 2009 Entertainment Book. 2008. pap. 35.00 *(978-1-59878-726-9(8))* Entertainment Pubns., Inc.

—Houston 2009 Entertainment Book. 2008. pap. 25.00 *(978-1-59878-613-2(X))* Entertainment Pubns., Inc.

—Houston 2009 Gold C Book. 2008. pap. 10.00 *(978-1-59878-753-5(5))* Entertainment Pubns., Inc.

—Huntington 2009 Entertainment Book. 2008. pap. 25.00 *(978-1-59878-703-0(9))* Entertainment Pubns., Inc.

—Indiana Northwest 2009 Entertainment Book. 2008. pap. 25.00 *(978-1-59878-650-7(4))* Entertainment Pubns., Inc.

—Indianapolis 2009 Gold C Book. 2008. pap. 10.00 *(978-1-59878-756-6(X))* Entertainment Pubns., Inc.

—Indianapolis/Central Indiana 2009 Entertainment Book. 2008. pap. 25.00 *(978-1-59878-632-3(6))* Entertainment Pubns., Inc.

—Inland Empire 2009 Entertainment Book. 2008. pap. 25.00 *(978-1-59878-687-3(3))* Entertainment Pubns., Inc.

—Jackson, MS 2009 Entertainment Book. 2008. pap. 25.00 *(978-1-59878-749-8(7))* Entertainment Pubns., Inc.

—Jacksonville 2009 Entertainment Book. 2008. pap. 25.00 *(978-1-59878-629-3(6))* Entertainment Pubns., Inc.

—Kansas City 2009 Entertainment Book. 2008. pap. 25.00 *(978-1-59878-692-7(X))* Entertainment Pubns., Inc.

—Lafayette, la 2009 Entertainment Book. 2008. pap. 30.00 *(978-1-59878-750-4(0))* Entertainment Pubns., Inc.

—Lake Tahoe/Reno 2009 Entertainment Book. 2008. pap. 30.00 *(978-1-59878-697-2(0))* Entertainment Pubns., Inc.

—Lancaster/York 2009 Entertainment Book. 2008. pap. 30.00 *(978-1-59878-662-0(8))* Entertainment Pubns., Inc.

—Las Vegas 2009 Entertainment Book. 2008. pap. 25.00 *(978-1-59878-728-3(4))* Entertainment Pubns., Inc.

—Lehigh Valley 2009 Entertainment Book. 2008. pap. 25.00 *(978-1-59878-653-8(9))* Entertainment Pubns., Inc.

—Lexington 2009 Entertainment Book. 2008. pap. 25.00 *(978-1-59878-706-1(3))* Entertainment Pubns., Inc.

—Little Rock 2009 Entertainment Book. 2008. pap. 25.00 *(978-1-59878-672-9(5))* Entertainment Pubns., Inc.

—Long Island 2009 Entertainment Book. 2008. pap. 25.00 *(978-1-59878-626-2(1))* Entertainment Pubns., Inc.

—Los Angeles 2009 Entertainment Book. 2008. pap. 30.00 *(978-1-59878-610-1(5))* Entertainment Pubns., Inc.

—Louisville/Southern Indiana 2009 Entertainment Book. 2008. pap. 25.00 *(978-1-59878-648-4(2))* Entertainment Pubns., Inc.

—Madison 2009 Entertainment Book. 2008. pap. 30.00 *(978-1-59878-641-5(5))* Entertainment Pubns., Inc.

—Memphis 2009 Entertainment Book. 2008. pap. 25.00 *(978-1-59878-702-3(0))* Entertainment Pubns., Inc.

—Miami/Florida Keys 2009 Entertainment Book. 2008. pap. 35.00 *(978-1-59878-733-7(0))* Entertainment Pubns., Inc.

—Mid Hudson 2009 Entertainment Book. 2008. pap. 25.00 *(978-1-59878-676-7(8))* Entertainment Pubns., Inc.

—Milwaukee 2009 Entertainment Book. 2008. pap. 40.00 *(978-1-59878-625-5(3))* Entertainment Pubns., Inc.

—Milwaukee 2009 Gold C Book. 2008. pap. 15.00 *(978-1-59878-754-2(3))* Entertainment Pubns., Inc.

—Minneapolis 2009 Gold C Book. 2008. pap. 15.00 *(978-1-59878-758-0(6))* Entertainment Pubns., Inc.

—Monterey Peninsula 2009 Entertainment Book. 2008. pap. 30.00 *(978-1-59878-684-2(9))* Entertainment Pubns., Inc.

—Montreal 2009 Entertainment Book. 2008. pap. 35.00 *(978-1-59878-678-1(4))* Entertainment Pubns., Inc.
—Nashville 2009 Entertainment Book. 2008. pap. 25.00 *(978-1-59878-655-2(5))* Entertainment Pubns., Inc.
—New Hampshire South 2009 Entertainment Book. 2008. pap. 30.00 *(978-1-59878-711-5(X))* Entertainment Pubns., Inc.
—New Haven 2009 Entertainment Book. 2008. pap. 30.00 *(978-1-59878-724-5(1))* Entertainment Pubns., Inc.
—New Jersey Central/Middlesex 2009 Entertainment Book. 2008. pap. 30.00 *(978-1-59878-640-8(7))* Entertainment Pubns., Inc.
—New Jersey Central/Monmouth 2009 Entertainment Book. 2008. pap. 30.00 *(978-1-59878-683-5(0))* Entertainment Pubns., Inc.
—New Jersey North Bergen 2009 Entertainment Book. 2008. pap. 30.00 *(978-1-59878-644-6(X))* Entertainment Pubns., Inc.
—New Jersey North Essex 2009 Entertainment Book. 2008. pap. 30.00 *(978-1-59878-619-4(9))* Entertainment Pubns., Inc.
—New Jersey North Morris 2009 Entertainment Book. 2008. pap. 30.00 *(978-1-59878-682-8(2))* Entertainment Pubns., Inc.
—New Jersey South 2009 Entertainment Book. 2008. pap. 35.00 *(978-1-59878-666-8(0))* Entertainment Pubns., Inc.
—Norfolk 2009 Entertainment Book. 2008. pap. 25.00 *(978-1-59878-654-5(7))* Entertainment Pubns., Inc.
—Okanagan 2009 Entertainment Book. 2008. pap. 35.00 *(978-1-59878-689-7(X))* Entertainment Pubns., Inc.
—Oklahoma City 2009 Entertainment Book. 2008. pap. 25.00 *(978-1-59878-739-9(X))* Entertainment Pubns., Inc.
—Omaha 2009 Entertainment Book. 2008. pap. 30.00 *(978-1-59878-718-4(7))* Entertainment Pubns., Inc.
—Orange County 2009 Entertainment Book. 2008. pap. 40.00 *(978-1-59878-608-8(3))* Entertainment Pubns., Inc.
—Orange County 2009 Values Book. 2008. pap. 20.00 *(978-1-59878-762-7(4))* Entertainment Pubns., Inc.
—Oregon 2009 Entertainment Book. 2008. pap. 25.00 *(978-1-59878-643-9(1))* Entertainment Pubns., Inc.
—Orlando 2009 Entertainment Book. 2008. pap. 30.00 *(978-1-59878-732-0(2))* Entertainment Pubns., Inc.
—Ottawa/Outaouais 2009 Entertainment Book. 2008. pap. 40.00 *(978-1-59878-658-3(X))* Entertainment Pubns., Inc.
—El Paso 2009 Entertainment Book. 2008. pap. 25.00 *(978-1-59878-709-2(8))* Entertainment Pubns., Inc.
—Pennsylvania Northeast 2009 Entertainment Book. 2008. pap. 25.00 *(978-1-59878-735-1(7))* Entertainment Pubns., Inc.
—Philadelphia North 2009 Entertainment Book. 2008. pap. 30.00 *(978-1-59878-624-8(5))* Entertainment Pubns., Inc.
—Philadelphia West 2009 Entertainment Book. 2008. pap. 30.00 *(978-1-59878-669-9(5))* Entertainment Pubns., Inc.
—Phoenix 2009 Entertainment Book. 2008. pap. 30.00 *(978-1-59878-639-2(3))* Entertainment Pubns., Inc.
—Pittsburgh 2009 Entertainment Book. 2008. pap. 25.00 *(978-1-59878-602-6(4))* Entertainment Pubns., Inc.
—Pittsburgh East 2009 Entertainment Book. 2008. pap. 25.00 *(978-1-59878-705-4(5))* Entertainment Pubns., Inc.
—Portland 2009 Entertainment Book. 2008. pap. 25.00 *(978-1-59878-622-4(9))* Entertainment Pubns., Inc.
—Providence, RI 2009 Entertainment Book. 2008. pap. 30.00 *(978-1-59878-734-4(9))* Entertainment Pubns., Inc.
—Puerto Rico 2009 Gold C Book. 2008. pap. 20.00 *(978-1-59878-761-0(6))* Entertainment Pubns., Inc.
—Puget Sound North 2009 Entertainment Book. 2008. pap. 25.00 *(978-1-59878-723-8(3))* Entertainment Pubns., Inc.
—Puget Sound South 2009 Entertainment Book. 2008. pap. 25.00 *(978-1-59878-642-2(3))* Entertainment Pubns., Inc.
—Quad Cities/Davenport 2009 Entertainment Book. 2008. pap. 25.00 *(978-1-59878-747-4(0))* Entertainment Pubns., Inc.
—Raleigh/Durham 2009 Entertainment Book. 2008. pap. 25.00 *(978-1-59878-693-6(7))* Entertainment Pubns., Inc.
—Reading/Pottsville 2009 Entertainment Book. 2008. pap. 30.00 *(978-1-59878-671-2(7))* Entertainment Pubns., Inc.
—Richmond 2009 Entertainment Book. 2008. pap. 30.00 *(978-1-59878-737-5(3))* Entertainment Pubns., Inc.
—Sacramento 2009 Entertainment Book. 2008. pap. 45.00 *(978-1-59878-634-7(2))* Entertainment Pubns., Inc.
—Sacramento 2009 Gold C Book. 2008. pap. 12.00 *(978-1-59878-757-3(8))* Entertainment Pubns., Inc.
—Saginaw/Flint 2009 Entertainment Book. 2008. pap. 25.00 *(978-1-59878-748-1(9))* Entertainment Pubns., Inc.
—San Antonio 2009 Entertainment Book. 2008. pap. 25.00 *(978-1-59878-731-3(4))* Entertainment Pubns., Inc.
—San Diego 2009 Entertainment Book. 2008. pap. 45.00 *(978-1-59878-611-8(3))* Entertainment Pubns., Inc.
—San Diego 2009 Values Book. 2008. pap. 20.00 *(978-1-59878-763-4(2))* Entertainment Pubns., Inc.
—San Fernando 2009 Entertainment Book. 2008. pap. 25.00 *(978-1-59878-606-4(7))* Entertainment Pubns., Inc.
—San Francisco/San Mateo 2009 Entertainment Book. 2008. pap. 30.00 *(978-1-59878-663-7(6))* Entertainment Pubns., Inc.
—San Gabriel 2009 Entertainment Book. 2008. pap. 25.00 *(978-1-59878-686-6(5))* Entertainment Pubns., Inc.
—San Juan 2009 Entertainment Book. 2008. pap. 45.00 *(978-1-59878-688-0(1))* Entertainment Pubns., Inc.
—Sarasota 2009 Entertainment Book. 2008. pap. 35.00 *(978-1-59878-704-7(7))* Entertainment Pubns., Inc.
—Saskatchewan 2009 Entertainment Book. 2008. pap. 35.00 *(978-1-59878-716-0(0))* Entertainment Pubns., Inc.
—Seattle/Eastside 2009 Entertainment Book. 2008. pap. 25.00 *(978-1-59878-616-3(4))* Entertainment Pubns., Inc.
—South Bend 2009 Entertainment Book. 2008. pap. 25.00 *(978-1-59878-738-2(1))* Entertainment Pubns., Inc.
—Spartanburg 2009 Entertainment Book. 2008. pap. 25.00 *(978-1-59878-712-2(8))* Entertainment Pubns., Inc.
—Spokane 2009 Entertainment Book. 2008. pap. 35.00 *(978-1-59878-679-8(2))* Entertainment Pubns., Inc.
—Springfield, MA 2009 Entertainment Book. 2008. pap. 30.00 *(978-1-59878-708-5(X))* Entertainment Pubns., Inc.
—Springfield/Branson 2009 Entertainment Book. 2008. pap. 25.00 *(978-1-59878-715-3(2))* Entertainment Pubns., Inc.
—St. Louis 2009 Entertainment Book. 2008. pap. 30.00 *(978-1-59878-607-1(5))* Entertainment Pubns., Inc.
—St. Louis 2009 Gold C Book. 2008. pap. 10.00 *(978-1-59878-751-1(9))* Entertainment Pubns., Inc.
—St. Petersburg/Clearwater 2009 Entertainment Book. 2008. pap. 25.00 *(978-1-59878-719-1(5))* Entertainment Pubns., Inc.
—Stockton/Modesto 2009 Entertainment Book. 2008. pap. 25.00 *(978-1-59878-690-3(3))* Entertainment Pubns., Inc.
—Syracuse 2009 Entertainment Book. 2008. pap. 25.00 *(978-1-59878-664-4(4))* Entertainment Pubns., Inc.
—Tampa 2009 Entertainment Book. 2008. pap. 25.00 *(978-1-59878-637-8(7))* Entertainment Pubns., Inc.
—Toledo 2009 Entertainment Book. 2008. pap. 35.00 *(978-1-59878-612-5(1))* Entertainment Pubns., Inc.
—Toronto 2009 Entertainment Book. 2008. pap. 30.00 *(978-1-59878-646-0(6))* Entertainment Pubns., Inc.
—Tri-Cities 2009 Entertainment Book. 2008. pap. 25.00 *(978-1-59878-744-3(6))* Entertainment Pubns., Inc.
—Tucson 2009 Entertainment Book. 2008. pap. 40.00 *(978-1-59878-659-0(8))* Entertainment Pubns., Inc.
—Tulsa 2009 Entertainment Book. 2008. pap. 25.00 *(978-1-59878-730-6(6))* Entertainment Pubns., Inc.
—Twin Cities 2009 Entertainment Book. 2008. pap. 35.00 *(978-1-59878-680-4(6))* Entertainment Pubns., Inc.
—Twin Ports 2009 Entertainment Book. 2008. pap. 30.00 *(978-1-59878-707-8(1))* Entertainment Pubns., Inc.
—Utah 2009 Entertainment Book. 2008. pap. 25.00 *(978-1-59878-681-1(4))* Entertainment Pubns., Inc.
—Vancouver 2009 Entertainment Book. 2008. pap. 51.00 *(978-1-59878-618-7(0))* Entertainment Pubns., Inc.
—Vancouver 2009 Values Book. 2008. pap. 20.00 *(978-1-59878-764-1(0))* Entertainment Pubns., Inc.
—Vancouver Island 2009 Entertainment Book. 2008. pap. 35.00 *(978-1-59878-694-1(6))* Entertainment Pubns., Inc.
—Vermont 2009 Entertainment Book. 2008. pap. 35.00 *(978-1-59878-685-9(7))* Entertainment Pubns., Inc.
—Westchester 2009 Entertainment Book. 2008. pap. 25.00 *(978-1-59878-633-0(4))* Entertainment Pubns., Inc.
—Wichita 2009 Entertainment Book. 2008. pap. 25.00 *(978-1-59878-649-1(0))* Entertainment Pubns., Inc.
—Winnipeg 2009 Entertainment Book. 2008. pap. 30.00 *(978-1-59878-740-5(3))* Entertainment Pubns., Inc.
—Worcester County 2009 Entertainment Book. 2008. pap. 30.00 *(978-1-59878-695-8(4))* Entertainment Pubns., Inc.
—Youngstown 2009 Entertainment Book. 2008. pap. 30.00 *(978-1-59878-714-6(4))* Entertainment Pubns., Inc.
Erickson, Holly. Lights! Cameras! Cuisine! Cooking Fabulous Food from the Films You Love. 2010. 240p. 29.95 *(978-1-4269-0524-7(6))*; pap. 19.95 *(978-1-4269-0523-0(8))* Trafford Publishing.
Floor, Willem. Games Persians Play. 2011. 420p. pap. ***(978-1-933823-44-7(5))*** Mage Pubs., Inc.
Fyall, Alan, et al, eds. Managing Visitor Attractions: New Directions. 2nd rev. ed. 2008. (ENG., Illus.). 384p. (C). pap. 48.95 *(978-0-7506-8545-0(X))* Routledge.
Gilman, Caroline Howard. Oracles from the Poets; a Fanciful Diversion for the Drawing-Room by Caroline Gilman. 2006. 244p. per. 20.99 *(978-1-4255-2023-6(5))* MPublishing.
Gilmore, Gayle M. It Can't Be Boring! 104p. pap. 8.95 *(978-1-882185-47-4(1))* Cornerstone Publishing, Inc.
Giustino, Cathleen M., et al. Socialist Escapes: Breaking Away from Ideology & Everyday Routine in Eastern Europe, 1945-1989. 2012. (ENG.). 268p. 90.00 ***(978-0-85745-669-4(5))*** Berghahn Bks., Inc.
Goodson, Steve. Highbrows Hillbillies & Hellfire: Public Entertainment in Atlanta, 1880-1930. 2007. (ENG., Illus.). 272p. per. 24.95 *(978-0-8203-2930-7(4))* Univ. of Georgia Pr.
Gordon, Beverly. The Saturated World: Aesthetic Meaning, Intimate Objects, Women's Lives, 1890-1940. 2006. (Illus.). 240p. 38.00 *(978-1-57233-542-4(4))* Univ. of Tennessee Pr.
Goytia Prat, Ana. Los rostros de Ulysses: Modelo para el analisis de turistas en funcion de la experiencia de ocio. 2008. 288p. pap. *(978-3-639-10680-0(6))* VDM Verlag Dr. Mueller e.K.
Gustwiller, Tom. For Amusement Only. Date not set. (Illus.). 270p. 29.95 *(978-0-9644748-0-2(3))* Taylor Printing.
Gyver, Maddix. A Holiday Every Day. 2009. 159p. pap. 10.98 *(978-0-557-08186-8(6))* Lulu Enterprises Inc.
Hall, Nancy Wilson, et al. 365 Activities You & Your Child Will Love: Fun Ideas for Your Preschooler's Growing Mind! rev. ed. 2007. (ENG., Illus.). 256p. pap. 16.95 *(978-1-55263-881-1(2))* Key Porter Bks. CAN. Dist: Perseus-PGW.
Hanson, Lise & Kempskie, Heather. The Siblings' Busy Book: 200 Fun Activities for Kids of Different Ages. 2008. (Illus.). 448p. pap. *(978-0-88166-530-7(4))* Meadowbrook Pr.
Harris, Jake. What Would You Do for A Fiver?? 2010. (ENG., Illus.). 160p. pap. 9.95 ***(978-1-84953-053-4(9))*** Summerdale Pubs. GBR. Dist: Independent Pubs. Group.
Haupert, Michael J. The Entertainment Industry, 1 vol. 2006. (Emerging Industries in the United States Ser.). 296p. 65.00 *(978-0-313-32173-3(6)*, GR2173, Greenwood Pr.) Greenwood Publishing Group, Inc.
Havig, Alan R. & intro. Filling Leisure Hours: Essays from the Missouri Historical Review, 1906-2006. 2008. (Century of Missouri History Scholarship Ser.: Vol. 3). (Illus.). 278p. 40.00 *(978-0-9622891-9-4(1))*; pap. 30.00 *(978-0-9622891-8-7(3))* State Historical Society of Missouri.
Hewett, Katie. Parlour Games: Indoor Fun for the Whole Family! 2012. (ENG., Illus.). 128p. 9.95 ***(978-1-84340-674-7(8)***, Collins & Brown) Anova Bks. GBR. Dist: Sterling Publishing Co., Inc.
Higgens, Emily Mayer. Holidays at the Grange or A Week's Delight: Games & Stories for Parlor & Fireside. 2007. (ENG.). 244p. pap. 20.99 *(978-1-4264-9491-8(2))*; 274p. pap. 23.99 *(978-1-4264-9872-5(1))* BiblioBazaar.
Hodgkinson, Tom & Kieran, Dan. The Book of Idle Pleasures. 2010. (ENG.). 224p. 12.99 *(978-0-7407-8508-5(7))* Andrews McMeel Publishing.
Hollis, Tim. The Land of the Smokies: Great Mountain Memories. 2007. (ENG., Illus.). 226p. 55.00 *(978-1-57806-943-9(2))* Univ. Pr. of Mississippi.
Iggulden, Conn & Iggulden, Hal. The Dangerous Book for Boys. 2012. 288p. 12.99 ***(978-0-06-220897-2(7)***, Morrow, William & Co.) HarperCollins Pubs.
—The Dangerous Book for Boys: Australian Edition. 2007. (Illus.). 304p. *(978-0-7322-8635-4(2)*, HarperCollins Pubs. Australia.
—Dangerous Book for Boys: Das einzig wahre Handbuch für Väter und ihre Söhne. 2007. (ENG., Illus.). 288p. (gr. 4-7). 26.95 *(978-0-06-124358-5(2)*, Morrow, William & Co.) HarperCollins Pubs.
—The Dangerous Book for Boys: New Zealand Edition. 2008. (Illus.). 304p. *(978-1-86950-709-1(6))* HarperCollins Pubs. Australia.
—The Dangerous Book for Boys: Things to Know. 2008. (ENG.). 224p. 14.95 *(978-0-06-164993-6(7)*, Morrow, William & Co.) HarperCollins Pubs.
—The Pocket Dangerous Book for Boys - Things to Do. 2008. (ENG., Illus.). 224p. 14.95 *(978-0-06-165682-8(8)*, Morrow, William & Co.) HarperCollins Pubs.
Innovation in Entertainment. 2010. 32p. lib. bdg. 189.50 *(978-1-60279-292-0(5)*, 200188) Cherry Lake Publishing.
Ito, Mizuko. Engineering Play: A Cultural History of Children's Software. 2012. (John D. & Catherine T. MacArthur Foundation Series on Digital Media & Learning Ser.). (ENG., Illus.). 248p. (gr. 17). pap. 12.95 ***(978-0-262-51738-6(8))*** MIT Pr.
Jenkins, Steven & Stalder, Erika. 97 Things to Do Before You Finish High School. 2008. (ENG., Illus.). 208p. (YA). (gr. 9-18). pap. 9.99 *(978-0-9790173-0-8(0))* Zest Bks.
King, Bart. The Pocket Guide to Games, 1 vol. 2008. (ENG., Illus.). 248p. pap. 9.99 *(978-1-4236-0469-3(5))* Gibbs Smith, Publisher.
Klutz, Inc Staff, contrib. by. The Encyclopedia of Immaturity. 2009. (Illus.). 201p. ***(978-1-59174-686-7(8))*** Klutz.
Law, John. Diana Ross in Central Park: 25th Anniversary Retrospective. 2008. (Illus.). 145p. mass mkt. 16.95 *(978-0-9665676-7-0(6))* Aplomb Publishing.
Ma, Lizhuang, et al. Entertainment Computing - ICEC 2007: 6th International Conference Shanghai, China, September 15-17, 2007 Proceedings. 2007. (Lecture Notes in Computer Science Ser.). (Illus.). 480p. pap. 139.00 *(978-3-540-74872-4(5))* Springer.
Maines, Rachel P. Hedonizing Technologies: Paths to Pleasure in Hobbies & Leisure. 2009. (ENG., Illus.). 224p. (gr. 17). 55.00 *(978-0-8018-9146-5(9))* Johns Hopkins Univ. Pr.
Mapes, Mary A. Fun with Your Child. 2007. (ENG.). 192p. 37.95 *(978-0-548-06110-7(6))* Kessinger Publishing, LLC.
McGovern, Una. Lost Crafts. 2011. (ENG., Illus.). 352p. pap. 16.95 *(978-0-550-10472-4(0))* Chambers Harrap Pubs., Ltd. GBR. Dist: Houghton Mifflin Harcourt Trade & Reference Pubs.
McLaughlin, Miriam & Peyser, Sandra. The New Encyclopedia of Icebreakers. 2011. (ENG.). 368p. pap. 75.00 ***(978-1-118-15754-1(0)***, Pfeiffer) Wiley, John & Sons, Inc.
Meredith, Susan. Entertaining & Educating Young Children. 2010. (Parent's Guides). 128p. (J). pap. 12.99 *(978-0-7945-1926-1(1)*, Usborne) EDC Publishing.
Monahan, Sherry. Tombstone's Treasure: Silver Mines & Golden Saloons. 2007. (ENG., Illus.). 215p. pap. 17.95 *(978-0-8263-4176-1(4))* Univ. of New Mexico Pr.
Morton Palter, Elisa & Wert, Shari. Help!.. We've Got Kids: GTA's Complete Childrens Resource Directory Covering Oakville Topickering & Newmarket to the Lake. 15th ed. 2008. (Help... We've Got Kids Ser.). (Illus.). 342p. pap. *(978-1-896208-24-4(X))* Help...We've Got Kids.
Moss, Stuart. The Entertainment Industry: An Introduction. 2010. (Cabi Tourism Texts). (Illus.). 400p. pap. 70.00 *(978-1-84593-551-1(9))* CABI GBR. Dist: Stylus Publishing, LLC.
Natkin, Stéphane & Dupire, Jérome. Entertainment Computing: 8th International Conference, ICEC 2009, Paris, France, September 3-5, 2009, Proceedings. 2009. (Lecture Notes in Computer Science / Information Systems & Applications, incl. Internet/Web, & HCI Ser.). xiv, 341p. pap. 109.00 *(978-3-642-04051-1(9)*, 36420405`9) Springer.
Nesbit, E. Wings & the Child: Or the Building of Magic Cities or the Building of Magic Cities. 2009. (ENG., Illus.). 238p. pap. 24.95 *(978-1-59583-348-8(X))* Laughing Elephant.
Northbrooke, John. A Treatise Against Dicing, Dancing, Plays & Interludes with Other Idle Pastimes. 2007. (ENG.). 208p. 39.95 *(978-0-548-03490-3(7))* Kessinger Publishing, LLC.
Oino, Espen & Farameh, Patrice. Luxury Toys Top of the World. 2008. (ENG.). 59.95 *(978-3-8327-9254-1(6))* teNeues Publishing Co.
Party Games & Amusements for Young and. 2006. (Illus.). 156p. per. *(978-1-4067-9694-0(8)*, Hesperides Pr.) Read Bks.
Pashko, Stanley. American Boy's Treasury of Sports, Hobbies & Games. 2011. 398p. 54.95 ***(978-1-258-06533-1(9))*** Literary Licensing, LLC.
Percival, O. Indoor Games & Amusements. 2006. pap. *(978-1-4067-9639-1(5))* Read Bks.
Roberts, Marion. Planning the Night-Time City. 2009. (ENG., Illus.). 256p. 155.00 *(978-0-415-43617-5(6))* Routledge.
Rochefort, Alfred. Healthful Sports for Boys. 2007. 100p. (gr. 4-7). per. *(978-1-4068-3956-2(6))* Echo Library.
—Healthful Sports for Boys: the American Boy's Ultimate Guide to Building Confidence, Strength & Good Moral Character Through Sports, Games, Camping, Boating, Swimming, Cycling, Skating, Sledding, Sleight of Hand Magic & More! 2007. 152p. pap. 11.95 *(978-0-615-17926-1(6))* Betteer Days Bks.
Rose, Frank. The Art of Immersion: How the Digital Generation Is Remaking Hollywood, Madison Avenue, & the Way We Tell Stories. (ENG.). 2012. 368p. pap. 16.95 ***(978-0-393-34125-6(9)***, 34125) 2011. 354p. 26.95 *(978-0-393-07601-1(6)*, 7601) Norton, W. W. & Co., Inc.
Ross, Becki. Burlesque West: Showgirls, Sex, & Sin in Postwar Vancouver. 2009. (Illus.). 368p. *(978-0-8020-9698-2(0))*, Univ. of Toronto Pr.
Sayre, Shay & King, Cynthia. Entertainment & Society: Influences, Impacts, & Innovations. 2nd ed. 2010. (ENG., Illus.). 600p. (C). 195.00 *(978-0-415-99806-2(9))*; pap. 59.95 *(978-0-415-99807-9(7))* Routledge.
Schnitzer, Claudia. Höfische Maskeraden Funktion und Ausstattung Von Verkleidungsdivertissements an Deutschen Höfen der Frühen Neuzeit. (Frahe Neuzeit Ser.). (GER.). VIII, 465p. 314.00 ***(978-3-11-181582-4(X))*** De Gruyter, Walter Inc.
Scott, Foresman and Company Staff. Sing & Dance, Whistles & Dreams. 29.48 *(978-0-673-21374-7(9)*, Scott Foresman) Addison Wesley Schl.
Seeger, Frederica. Entertainments for Home Church & School. 2008. 164p. 22.99 *(978-0-554-36425-4(5))* 2008. 164p. 25.99 *(978-0-554-27122-4(2))* 2007. (ENG.). 146p. pap. 18.99 ***(978-1-4346-2575-5(3))*** 2007. (ENG.). 160p. pap. 21.99 ***(978-1-4346-2605-9(9))*** BiblioBazaar.
Seldman, David & Hemmel, Jeff. The Anti-Pirate Potato Cannon: And 101 Other Things for Young Mariners to Build, Try, & Do on the Water. 2010. (ENG., Illus.). 272p. 24.95 *(978-0-07-162837-2(1)*, 0071628371, International Marine/Ragged Mountain Pr.) McGraw-Hill Professional Publishing.
Silva, Adriana de Souza e. & Sutko, Daniel M. Digital Cityscapes: Merging Digital & Urban Playspaces. 2009. (Digital Formations Ser.). (ENG., Illus.). 384p. (C). 36.95 *(978-1-4331-0532-6(2))* Lang, Peter Publishing, Inc.
Smith, Alison Wilson. Nature's Playthings. 2008. (ENG., Illus.). 192p. 24.95 ***(978-1-906122-00-3(8))*** Unwin, Merlin Bks. GBR. Dist: SCB Distributors.
Smith, Robert Paul. How to Do Nothing with Nobody All Alone by Yourself. 2010. (ENG., Illus.). 130p. (gr. 4). 14.95 *(978-0-9820539-5-9(9))* Tin Hse. Bks., LLC.
Snow, Michelle. Summer Bucket List for Kids. 2012. pap. 12.99 ***(978-1-59955-484-6(4))*** Cedar Fort, Inc./CFI Distribution.
Sole, Mia & Haycock, Jeff. Theatre Games for Elementary School Children Ages 7-12. 2009. pap. 24.95 *(978-0-578-01219-3(7))* Play-Ground Theatre Co.
—Theatre Games for Preschool Children Ages 3-6. 2009. pap. 24.95 *(978-0-578-01175-2(1))* Play-Ground Theatre Co.
Stein, Andi. Why We Love Disney: The Power of the Disney Brand. 2011. (Illus.). 296p. (C). 129.95 *(978-1-4331-0898-3(4))*; pap. 34.95 *(978-1-4331-0897-6(6))* Lang, Peter Publishing, Inc.
Stromberg, Peter G. Caught in Play: How Entertainment Works on You. 2009. (ENG.). 232p. 65.00 *(978-0-8047-6110-9(8))*; pap. 22.95 *(978-0-8047-6111-6(6))* Stanford Univ. Pr.
Sundem, Garth. Brain Candy: Science, Paradoxes, Puzzles, Logic, & Illogic to Nourish Your Neurons. 2010. (ENG., Illus.). 288p. pap. 14.00 *(978-0-307-58803-6(3))*, Three Rivers Pr.) Crown Publishing Group.
teNeues. Luxury Toys for Men. 2010. (Illus.) 59.95 *(978-3-8327-9426-2(3))* teNeues Publishing Co.
Theater of the Mind. 37.00 *(978-0-945296-26-3(6))* Hermetic Pr., Inc.

Villalon, Oscar. The Way of the Thumb: The Semisweet Science of Thumb Wrestling. 2007. (ENG., Illus.). 20p. (J). pap., instr.'s gde. ed. 10.00 *(978-0-9790073-1-6(3))* 826 Valencia.

Wagman, Tracie. Help! . We've Got Kids. 18th ed. 2011. (Help!.. We've Got Kids Ser.). (ENG., Illus.). 278p. pap. ***(978-1-896208-27-5(4))*** Help...We've Got Kids.

Walsh, Mike. Futuretainment: Yesterday the World Changed, Now It's Your Turn. 2009. (ENG., Illus.). 224p. 29.95 *(978-0-7148-4875-4(1))* Phaidon Pr., Inc.

Ward, C. M. Asking No Question for Conscience Sake. 2011. 28p. 35.95 ***(978-1-258-06486-0(3))*** Literary Licensing, LLC.

Ward, Jennifer. I Love Dirt! 52 Activities to Help You & Your Kids Discover the Wonders of Nature. 2008. (ENG., Illus.). 144p. pap. 14.00 *(978-1-59030-535-5(3)*, Trumpeter) Shambhala Pubns., Inc.

Weskott, Aljoscha & Marietta, Kesting, eds. Sun Tropes. 2010. (ENG., Illus.). 292p. pap. 49.95 *(978-3-941360-04-4(3))* Verlag der Buchhandlung Walther Konig DEU. Dist: D.A.P./Distributed Art Pubs.

Who's Buying Entertainment. 3rd ed. 2006. (Who's Buying Ser.). 99p. pap. 59.95 *(978-1-933588-12-4(8))* New Strategist Pubns., Inc.

Wikström, Ingegerd. Leisure Activities in Rheumatoid Arthritis: Associated Factors & Assessment. 2008. 72p. pap. *(978-3-639-09280-6(5))* VDM Verlag Dr. Mueller e.K.

Wilhelmson, Troy. Devil's Gulch: Basic Roleplaying Adventures in the Weird Wild West. 2010. (ENG., Illus.). 88p. pap. 16.95 *(978-1-56882-328-7(2))* Chaosium, Inc.

Worthington, Jennifer. In the Spirit of Las Vegas. 2006. (ENG., Illus.). 160p. 45.00 *(978-2-7594-0125-3(1))* Assouline FRA. Dist: Perseus Distribution.

Young, Mark. Entertainment Marketing. 2011. (ENG.). 300p. (C). 73.33 *(978-0-13-199516-1(2)*, Prentice Hall) Prentice Hall PTR.

Zavatsky, Michele & Zavatsky, George. Kids Love Michigan: A Family Travel Guide to Exploring Kid-Tested Places in Michigan... Year Round! 4th exp. ed. 2008. (Kids Love Ser.). (Illus.). 247p. (J). pap. 14.95 *(978-0-9774434-5-1(0))* Kids Love Pubns.

AMUSEMENTS—LAW AND LEGISLATION

Manchester, Colin, et al. Alcohol & Entertainment Licensing Law. 2nd rev. ed. 2008. (Illus.). 975p. pap. 99.95 *(978-0-415-42290-1(6)*, Routledge Cavendish) Taylor & Francis Group GBR. Dist: Taylor & Francis Group.

Truxal, Andrew G. Outdoor Recreation Legislation & Its Effectiveness. (Columbia University, Studies in the Social Sciences: No. 311). reprint ed. 21.00 *(978-0-404-51311-5(5))* AMS Pr., Inc.

Truxal, Andrew Gehr. Outdoor Recreation Legislation & Its Effectiveness: A Summary of American Legislation for Public Outdoor Recreation, 1915-1927, together with A Stu. 2006. 232p. per. 20.99 *(978-1-4255-1928-5(8))* MPublishing.

AMUSEMENTS—RELIGIOUS ASPECTS

Ankerberg, John, et al. The Facts on Halloween. 2008. (Facts on Ser.). 96p. mass mkt. 5.99 *(978-0-7369-2219-7(9))* Harvest Hse. Pubs.

Crane, Jonathan Townley. Popular Amusements by Rev J T Crane with an Introduction, by Bishop E S Janes. 2006. 212p. per. 20.99 *(978-1-4255-1735-9(8))* MPublishing.

Dardashti, Danielle & Sarig, Roni. The Jewish Family Fun Book: Holiday Projects, Everyday Activities, & Travel Ideas with Jewish Themes. 2nd ed. 2008. (Illus.). 277p. pap. 18.99 *(978-1-58023-333-0(3))* Jewish Lights Publishing.

Hand, Brian R. Upright Downtime: Biblical Wisdom for Entertainment Choices. 2008. *(978-1-59166-856-5(5))* BJU Pr.

Pell, Patty. Hospitality: God's Call to Compassion. 2008. (LifeGuide Bible Studies). (ENG.). 96p. pap. 8.00 *(978-0-8308-3128-9(2)*, IVP Conn.) InterVarsity Pr.

Vincent, Marvin Richardson. Amusement; a Force in Christian Training. 2006. 144p. per. 16.99 *(978-1-4255-1012-1(4))* MPublishing.

AMUSEMENTS—FRANCE

Newcomb, Chris. Crossing the Berm the Disney Theme Park As Sacralized Space. 2008. 112p. pap. *(978-3-8364-6685-1(6))* VDM Verlag Dr. Mueller e.K.

AMUSEMENTS—GREAT BRITAIN

Boulton, William Biggs. The Amusements of Old London: Being a Survey of the Sports & Pastimes, Tea Gardens & Parks, Playhouses & Other Diversions of the People of London from the 17th to the Beginning of the 19th Century. 2011. (Cambridge Library Collection - History Ser.). (ENG.). 288p. pap. 23.99 ***(978-1-108-03628-3(7))***; (Illus.). 306p. pap. 24.99 ***(978-1-108-03627-6(9))*** Cambridge Univ. Pr.

Bradshawe, Joan. When I Were a Lass... Snapshots from a Time that Political Correctness Forgot. 2012. (ENG., Illus.). 144p. 14.95 ***(978-1-907554-58-2(0))*** Anova Bks. GBR. Dist: Independent Pubs. Group.

Coke, David E. & Borg, Alan. Vauxhall Gardens: A History. 2011. (Paul Mellon Centre for Studies in British Art Ser.). (Illus.). 400p. 95.00 *(978-0-300-17382-6(2))* Yale Univ. Pr.

Crone, Rosalind. Violent Victorians. 2012. (ENG., Illus.). 320p. 95.00 ***(978-0-7190-8684-7(1))*** Manchester Univ. Pr. GBR. Dist: Macmillan.

—Violent Victorians: Popular Entertainment in Nineteenth-Century London. 2012. (ENG., Illus.). 320p. pap. 34.95 ***(978-0-7190-8685-4(X))*** Manchester Univ. Pr. GBR. Dist: Macmillan.

Ditchfield, Peter Hampson. Old English Sports. 2008. (Illus.). 104p. per. *(978-1-4065-8753-1(2))* Dodo Pr.

—Old English Sports. 2007. 88p. per. *(978-1-4068-6146-4(4))* Echo Library.

Horn, Pamela. Pleasures & Pastimes in Victorian Britain. 2011. (Illus.). 320p. pap. 24.95 ***(978-1-84868-813-1(X))*** Amberley Publishing GBR. Dist: Casemate Pubs. & Bk. Distributors, LLC.

Laister, Nick. Pennies by the Sea: The Life & Times of Joyland Amusements, Bridlington. 2006. (ENG., Illus.). 128p. per. *(978-0-9544573-5-8(8))* Skelter Publishing LLP.

Manchester, Colin, et al. Alcohol & Entertainment Licensing Law. 2nd rev. ed. 2008. (Illus.). 975p. pap. 99.95 *(978-0-415-42290-1(6)*, Routledge Cavendish) Taylor & Francis Group GBR. Dist: Taylor & Francis Group.

Otto, Peter. Multiplying Worlds: Romanticism, Modernity, & the Emergence of Virtual Reality. 2011. (ENG., Illus.). 376p. 110.00 *(978-0-19-956767-6(0))* Oxford Univ. Pr., Inc.

Phagan, Patricia, et al. Thomas Rowlandson: Pleasures & Pursuits in Georgian England. 2011. (ENG., Illus.). 184p. 59.95 *(978-1-904832-78-2(4))* Giles, D. Ltd. GBR. Dist: Antique Collectors' Club.

—Thomas Rowlandson: Pleasures & Pursuits in Georgian England. 2011. (Illus.). 184p. *(978-0-9820606-1-2(0))* Loeb, Frances Lehman Art Ctr., Vassar Coll., The.

Pullen, David. Britains Toy Model Catalogues, 1970-1979. 2010. (ENG., Illus.). 304p. pap. 49.95 *(978-1-84584-275-8(8)*, 1845842758) Veloce Publishing Ltd. GBR. Dist: MBI Distribution Services/Quayside Distribution.

Roud, Steve. The Lore of the Playground: The Children's World - Then & Now. 2011. (ENG., Illus.). 560p. pap. 16.95 ***(978-0-09-950527-3(4))*** Random Hse. GBR. Dist: Independent Pubs. Group.

Salter, Brian. Building Toys: Bayko & other Systems. 2011. (Shire Library). (ENG., Illus.). 64p. pap. 12.95 *(978-0-7478-0815-2(5))* Shire Pubns., Ltd. GBR. Dist: Random Hse., Inc.

Sim, Alison. Pleasures & Pastimes in Tudor England. 2009. (ENG., Illus.). 224p. pap. 19.95 *(978-0-7524-5031-5(X))* History Pr. Ltd.,The GBR. Dist: Independent Pubs. Group.

AMUSEMENTS—NEW YORK (STATE)

Entertainment Publications, Inc. Staff, compiled by. Cortland/Ithaca 2009 Entertainment Book. 2008. pap. 25.00 *(978-1-59878-698-9(9))* Entertainment Pubns., Inc.

AMUSEMENTS—NEW YORK (STATE)—NEW YORK

Entertainment Publications, Inc. Staff, compiled by. New York City/Westchester 2009 Entertainment Book. 2008. pap. 30.00 *(978-1-59878-627-9(X))* Entertainment Pubns., Inc.

—Rochester 2009 Entertainment Book. 2008. pap. 30.00 *(978-1-59878-636-1(9))* Entertainment Pubns., Inc.

Peiss & Cram101 Textbook Reviews Staff. Cheap Amusements: Working Women & Leisure in Turn-of-the-Century New York. 2007. 60p. per. 9.95 *(978-1-4288-2806-3(0))* Cram101 Inc.

Peretti, Burton W. Nightclub City: Politics & Amusement in Manhattan. (Illus.). 304p. (C). 2011. pap. 24.95 *(978-0-8122-2157-2(5))* 2007. 55.00 *(978-0-8122-3997-3(0))* Univ. of Pennsylvania Pr.

Perrone, Dina. The High Life: Qualitative Studies in Crime & Justice, volume 2. 2009. pap. *(978-1-881798-46-0(1))* Rienner, Lynne Pubs.

AMYLOIDOSIS

Anika. The Functional Fold: Amyloid Structures in Nature. Jarvis, Suzi & Mostaert, Anika, eds. 2012. (ENG.). 300p. 149.95 *(978-981-4267-40-3(6))* Pan Stanford Publishing SGP. Dist: Taylor & Francis Group.

Beyreuther, K., et al, eds. Neurodegenerative Disorders: Loss of Function Through Gain of Function: Loss of Function Through Gain of Function. 2010. (Research & Perspectives in Alzheimer's Disease Ser.). (Illus.). xiv, 190p. pap. 129.00 *(978-3-642-07448-6(0)*, 3642074480) Springer.

Byrne, Adam C. & O'Doherty, Cian B. Protein Misfolding. 2008. 129.00 *(978-1-60456-881-3(X))* Nova Science Pubs., Inc.

Dowler, Brynn C. Endocytosis: Structural Components, Functions & Pathways. 2010. (Cell Biology Research Progress Ser.). (Illus.). 259p. 129.00 *(978-1-61668-189-0(6))* Nova Science Pubs., Inc.

Gertz, Morie A. & Rajkumar, S. Vincent, eds. Amyloidosis: Diagnosis & Treatment. 2010. (Contemporary Hematology Ser.). (ENG., Illus.). x, 238p. 219.00 *(978-1-60761-630-6(0)*, 1607616300) Humana Pr.

Halcheck, Irene P. & Vernon, Nancy R. Amyloids: Composition, Functions, & Pathology. 2012. ***(978-1-62100-538-4(0))*** Nova Science Pubs., Inc.

Herrera, Guillermo A. The Kidney in Plasma Cell Dyscrasias. (Contributions to Nephrology Ser.: Vol. 153). (Illus.). vi, 216p. *(978-3-8055-8178-3(5))* Karger, S. AG.

Jelinek, Raz, ed. Lipids & Cellular Membranes in Amyloid Diseases. 2011. (ENG.). 296p. 180.00 *(978-3-527-32860-4(2)*, Wiley-VCH) Wiley, John & Sons, Inc.

Keller, Steve. Lost in Amyloidosis. 2008. 173p. pap. 65.95 *(978-0-615-19244-4(0))* Keller, Steve.

Martinez, Ana, ed. Emerging Drugs & Targets for Alzheimer's Disease: Volume 1: Beta-Amyloid, Tau Protein & Glucose Metabolism, 2 vols. 2010. (RSC Drug Discovery Ser.). (Illus.). 342p. 232.00 ***(978-1-84973-063-1(6))*** Royal Society of Chemistry, The GBR. Dist: Ingram Pub. Services.

Rahimi, Farid & Bitan, Gal, eds. Non-fibrillar Amyloidogenic Protein Assemblies - Common Cytotoxins Underlying Degenerative Diseases. 2012. (ENG., Illus.). viii, 565p. 209.00 ***(978-94-007-2773-1(9)***, 9400727739) Springer.

Ramirez-Alvarado, Marina, et al, eds. Protein Misfolding Diseases: Current & Emerging Principles & Therapies. 2010. (Wiley Series in Protein & Peptide Science Ser.: 2). (ENG., Illus.). 1069p. 205.00 *(978-0-471-79928-3(9)*, Wiley) Wiley, John & Sons, Inc.

Scheibel, Thomas, ed. Fibrous Proteins. 2008. *(978-1-58706-316-9(6))* Landes Bioscience.

Sigurdsson, Einar M., ed. Amyloid Proteins. 2010. (Methods in Molecular Biology Ser.). (Illus.). 408p. pap. 134.00 *(978-1-61737-502-6(0)*, 1617375020) Humana Pr.

Skinner, Martha, et al, eds. XIth International Symposium on Amyloidosis, Vol. 2. 2007. (ENG., Illus.). 432p. 199.95 *(978-1-4200-4281-8(5)*, CRC Press) Taylor & Francis Group GBR. Dist: Taylor & Francis Group.

Toon, Peter. Foretaste of Heaven Amidst Suffering: Living with the Life-Threatening Disease of Amyloidosis. 2010. 130p. pap. 16.00 *(978-1-60899-790-9(1)*, Wipf and Stock) Wipf & Stock Pubs.

Verbeek, M. M., et al, eds. Cerebral Amyloid Angiopathy in Alzheimer's Disease & Related Disorders. 2010. 384p. pap. 182.00 *(978-90-481-5480-7(4)*, 9048154804) Springer.

Wetzel, Ronald & Kheterpal, Indu. Amyloid, Prions, & Other Protein Aggregates, 3 vols., Pt. C. 2006. (Methods in Enzymology Ser.). (ENG., Illus.). 416p. 187.00 *(978-0-12-182818-9(2)*, Academic Pr.) Elsevier Science & Technology Bks.

—Amyloid, Prions, & Other Protein Aggregates, 3 vols., Pt. B. 2006. (Methods in Enzymology Ser.). (ENG., Illus.). 430p. 187.00 *(978-0-12-182817-2(4)*, Academic Pr.) Elsevier Science & Technology Bks.

AMYOTROPHIC LATERAL SCLEROSIS

Albom, Mitch. Tuesdays with Morrie: An Old Man, a Young Man, & Life's Greatest Lesson. Lt. ed. 2010. (ENG.). 320p. pap. 20.00 *(978-0-7393-7777-2(9))* Random Hse. Large Print.

Ardolf, Joanne. Within My Limits, I Pray: Talking to God about Illness, Disability & Life Changes. 2009. 96p. pap. 16.95 *(978-1-60836-643-9(X))* PublishAmerica, Inc.

Boyd, Jim. A Servant Leader's Journey: Lessons from Life. 2009. 192p. pap. 18.95 *(978-0-8091-4568-3(5))* Paulist Pr.

Boyer, Sue. Als, a Daughter's View. 2009. 80p. pap. 16.95 *(978-1-60749-011-1(0))* PublishAmerica, Inc.

Bradley, Walter G. Gib's Odyssey: A Tale of Faith & Hope on the Intracoastal Waterway. 2011. (ENG.). 224p. 22.95 *(978-0-7627-6416-7(3)*, Lyons Pr.) Globe Pequot Pr., The.

Brock, Nicholle. Principles of ALS Care. 2009. 370p. pap. 60.95 *(978-0-7637-6581-1(3))* Jones & Bartlett Learning, LLC.

Brooks, Rich. Reprise. 2007. 128p. per. 14.95 *(978-1-934246-88-7(3))* Peppertree Pr., The.

Carlo, Philip. The Killer Within: In the Company of Monsters. 2011. (ENG.). 256p. (gr. 12). 25.95 *(978-1-59020-431-3(X))* Overlook Pr., The.

Committee on the Review of the Scientific Literature on Amyotrophic Lateral Sclerosis in Veterans. Amyotrophic Lateral Sclerosis in Veterans: Review of the Scientific Literature. 2006. (ENG.). 62p. pap. 21.00 *(978-0-309-10254-4(5))* National Academies Pr.

Day, Christopher. (My) Dying Is Fun: A Comedy of Disabled Misadventures. 2007. (Illus.). 170p. 19.99 *(978-1-4251-0622-5(6))* Trafford Publishing.

Eisen, Andrew & Krieger, Charles. Amyotrophic Lateral Sclerosis: A Synthesis of Research & Clinical Practice. 2006. (ENG.). 324p. pap. 67.00 *(978-0-521-03426-5(4))* Cambridge Univ. Pr.

Engdahl, Sylvia, ed. Lou Gehrig's Disease. 2012. (Perspectives on Diseases & Disorders Ser.). (ENG., Illus.). 144p. (gr. 10-12). lib. bdg. 38.95 ***(978-0-7377-5776-7(0)***, Greenhaven Pr., Inc.) Cengage Gale.

Farrell, Jason G. New Amyotrophic Lateral Sclerosis Research. 2008. (C). 129.00 *(978-1-60021-623-7(4))* Nova Science Pubs., Inc.

Guion, Lida & Guion, Lee. Respiratory Management of ALS: Amyotrophic Lateral Sclerosis. 2009. (Illus.). 258p. 69.95 *(978-0-7637-5545-4(1))* Jones & Bartlett Learning, LLC.

Hale, Kathy Feagin. Our Journey of Nineteen Month's in Hell with Lou Gehrig's Disease: (Charles Hale's Story) 2008. 188p. pap. 25.99 *(978-1-4389-2094-8(6))* AuthorHouse.

Hawking, Jane. Traveling to Infinity: My Life with Stephen. 2007. (ENG., Illus.). 492p. 27.95 *(978-1-84688-034-6(3))* Alma Bks. GBR. Dist: Independent Pubs. Group.

Hawking, Jane. Travelling to Infinity: My Life with Stephen. 2010. (ENG., Illus.). 450p. pap. 13.95 ***(978-1-84688-115-2(3))*** Alma Bks. GBR. Dist: Independent Pubs. Group.

Horvath/Tortuga Pines Publishing. Irene's Night: N/a. Horvath/Tortuga Pines Publishing, ed. 2008. 600p. pap. *(978-0-9793415-2-6(3))* Tortuga Pines Publishing.

Kertesz, Andrew, frwd. Dementia & Motor Neuron Disease. 2006. (ENG., Illus.). 498p. 209.95 *(978-0-415-39166-5(0))* Taylor & Francis Group.

Langton, Phyllis A. Last Flight Out: Living, Loving & Leaving. 2011. 248p. pap. 20.00 ***(978-0-9827262-2-8(8))*** Wising Up Pr.

Limmer, Daniel. ALS Vital Signs. 2008. (ENG.). (C). cd-rom 33.00 *(978-0-13-222919-7(6)*, Prentice Hall) Prentice Hall PTR.

—ALS Vital Signs: Network Version. 2007. (C). cd-rom *(978-0-13-222920-3(X)*, Prentice Hall) Prentice Hall PTR.

Mancini, Raffaele L., ed. Motor Neuron Disease Research Progress. 2008. (Illus.). 129.00 *(978-1-60456-155-5(6)*, Nova Biomedical Bks.) Nova Science Pubs., Inc.

McDonald, Jeff. ALS Skills Review. 2008. 524p. pap. 68.95 *(978-0-7637-5121-0(9))* Jones & Bartlett Learning, LLC.

Oliver, David, et al, eds. Palliative Care in Amyotrophic Lateral Sclerosis: From Diagnosis to Bereavement. 2nd rev. ed. 2006. (ENG., Illus.). 368p. *(978-0-19-921293-4(7))* Oxford Univ. Pr., Inc.

Oliver, M. J. Motor Neurone Disease. 2nd ed. 2007. (Illus.). 128p. pap. 13.95 *(978-0-85969-977-8(3)*, Sheldon Press) SPCK Publishing GBR. Dist: Westminster John Knox Pr.

Orchard, Jack. Extra Hands: Grasping for a Meaningful Life. 2007. 192p. pap. 17.95 *(978-0-615-16406-9(4))* Orchard, Jack Trust.

Paulson, Robert E. Not in Kansas Anymore: A Memoir of the Farm, New York Citk, & Life with ALS. 2008. (Illus.). 254p. pap. *(978-0-9696477-4-4(3))* Gemma B. Publishing.

Schwartz, Morrie. Morrie - In His Own Words: Life Wisdom from a Remarkable Man. 2008. (ENG., Illus.). 144p. pap. 11.00 *(978-0-8027-1717-7(9))* Walker & Co.

Sinton, William. I Choose to Live: A Journey Through Life with ALS. rev. ed. 2006. 168p. pap. 14.95 *(978-0-9706007-1-4(2))* Banbury Publishing.

Smith, Ginger E. Broken Man, Empty Garden. 2011. 46p. pap. 16.95 ***(978-1-4560-9975-6(2))*** PublishAmerica, Inc.

Strong, Michael J., ed. Amyotrophic Lateral Sclerosis & the Frontotemporal Dementias. 2012. (ENG., Illus.). 438p. 175.00 ***(978-0-19-959067-4(2))*** Oxford Univ. Pr., Inc.

Sturtz, Elaine J. The Final Dance of Life: Our Journey with Judy. 2006. 192p. per. 12.99 *(978-1-59886-669-8(9))* Tate Publishing & Enterprises, LLC.

Talbot, Kevin & Marsden, Rachael. Motor Neuron Disease. 2008. (Facts Ser.). (ENG., Illus.). 160p. pap. 29.95 *(978-0-19-920691-9(0))* Oxford Univ. Pr., Inc.

Talbot, Kevin, et al. Motor Neuron Disease: A Practical Manual. 2010. (Oxford Care Manuals Ser.). (ENG., Illus.). 256p. pap. 42.95 *(978-0-19-954736-4(X))* Oxford Univ. Pr., Inc.

Turner, Bradley James & Atkin, Julie. Motor Neuron Diseases: Causes, Classification & Treatments. 2012. (Neurology - Laboratory & Clinical Research Developments Ser.). 244p. 140.00 ***(978-1-61470-101-9(6))*** Nova Science Pubs., Inc.

Wakefield, Darcy. I Remember Running: The Year I Got Everything I Ever Wanted - & ALS. 2006. (ENG.). 208p. per. 14.95 *(978-1-56924-279-7(8))* Da Capo Pr., Inc.

Wenham, Michael. My Donkey Body: Living with a Body That No Longer Obeys You!, 1 vol. 2009. (ENG.). 160p. pap. 12.99 *(978-0-8254-6295-5(9)*, Monarch Bks.) Lion Hudson PLC GBR. Dist: Kregel Pubns.

Woodard, Bert. Living with It ~ Not Dying of It. 2007. 88p. per. 17.95 *(978-1-933912-64-6(2))* Westview Publishing Co., Inc.

Zimdahl, Robert L. When That Day Comes: A Memoir. 2011. 120p. pap. 10.95 ***(978-1-4357-9356-9(0))*** Lulu Enterprises Inc.

ANA

see Aphorisms and Apothegms; Epigrams; Maxims; Proverbs; Quotations; Table-Talk

ANABAPTISTS

see also Baptists; Mennonites; Peasants' War, 1524-1525

Baker, Sharon L. & Hardin, Michael. Peace Be with You: Christ's Benediction amid Violent Empires. 2010. *(978-1-931038-73-7(2))* Cascadia Publishing Hse., LLC.

Bax, Ernest Belfort. German Culture Past & Present. 2008. 180p. 22.99 *(978-0-554-37973-9(2))* 2008. 180p. 25.99 *(978-0-554-28670-9(X))* 2007. (ENG.). 162p. pap. 19.99 *(978-1-4346-6020-6(6))* 2007. (ENG.). 178p. pap. 21.99 *(978-1-4346-6021-3(4))* BiblioBazaar.

—German Culture Past & Present. 2007. 152p. per. *(978-1-4065-3673-7(3))* Dodo Pr.

Beachy, Kirsten. Tongue Screws & Testimonies: Poems, Stories, & Essays Inspired by the Martyrs Mirror. 2010. pap. *(978-0-8361-9519-4(1))* Herald Pr.

Boers, Arthur, et al, compiled by. Take Our Moments & Our Days: An Anabaptist Prayer Book Advent through Pentecost. 2010. 912p. 34.99 *(978-0-8361-9449-4(7))* Herald Pr.

Boers, Arthur P., et al. Take Our Moments & Our Days: An Anabaptist Prayer Book: A Four-Week Cycle of Morning & Evening Prayers for Ordinary Time. 2007. 240p. 10.00 *(978-0-8361-9334-3(2))* Institute of Mennonite Studies.

Boers, Arthur Paul, et al, eds. Take Our Moments & Our Days: An Anabaptist Prayer Book: Ordinary Time. 2007. 384p. per. 22.99 *(978-0-8361-9374-9(1))* Herald Pr.

Bollinger, Dennis E. First-Generation Anabaptist Ecclesiology, 1525-1561: A study of Swiss, German, & Dutch Sources. 2009. (Illus.). 296p. 109.95 *(978-0-7734-4748-6(2))* Mellen, Edwin Pr., The.

Dyck, Cornelius J. Confessions of Faith in the Anabaptist Tradition, 1527-1660. xii, 366p. 33.00 *(978-1-894710-62-6(2))* Pandora Pr. CAN. Dist: Herald Pr.

Grimsrud, Ted. Embodying the Way of Jesus: Anabaptist Convictions for the Twenty-First Century. 2007. 262p. pap. 27.00 *(978-1-59752-987-7(7)*, Wipf and Stock) Wipf & Stock Pubs.

Halteman, James. The Clashing Worlds of Economics & Faith. annot. ed. 2007. 224p. pap. 24.00 *(978-1-55635-170-9(4)*, Wipf and Stock) Wipf & Stock Pubs.

Kautsky, Karl. Communism in Central Europe in the Time of the Reformation. 2010. 304p. pap. 29.75 *(978-1-143-05419-8(9))* BiblioBazaar.

—Communism in Central Europe in the Time of the Reformation. 2009. 198p. pap. 19.66 *(978-1-151-04675-8(2))* General Bks. LLC.

—Communism in Central Europe in the Time of the Reformation. Mulliken, J. L. & Mulliken, E. G., trs. 2008. 304p. 43.95 *(978-1-4369-5904-9(7))*; pap. 28.95 *(978-1-4368-1100-2(7))* Kessinger Publishing, LLC.

Keith, Kent. Have Faith Anyway: The Vision of Habakkuk for Our Times. 2008. (ENG.). 128p. 16.95 *(978-0-470-28628-9(8)*, Jossey-Bass) Wiley, John & Sons, Inc.

Koop, Karl. Anabaptist-Mennonite Confessions of Faith: The Development of a Tradition. 178p. 19.35 *(978-1-894710-32-9(0))* Pandora Pr. CAN. Dist: Herald Pr.

Krabill, James R. & Murray, Stuart. Forming Christian Habits in Post-Christendom: The Legacy of Alan & Eleanor Kreider. 2011. pap. **(978-0-8361-9602-3(3))** Herald Pr.

Kraus, C. Norman. God Our Savior: Theology in a Christological Mode. annot. ed. 2006. 272p. (Orig.). pap. 29.00 *(978-1-55635-150-1(X)*, Wipf and Stock) Wipf & Stock Pubs.

Kraybill, Donald B. Concise Encyclopedia of Amish, Brethren, Hutterites, & Mennonites. 2010. (ENG., Illus.). 328p. (gr. 17). 35.00 *(978-0-8018-9657-6(6))* Johns Hopkins Univ. Pr.

Levington, John. Scripture Baptism Defended, & Anabaptist Notions Proved to Be Anti-Scriptural Novelties. 2006. 160p. per. 18.99 *(978-1-4255-1180-7(5))* MPublishing.

Mast, Gerald J. & Weaver, J. Denny. Defenseless Christianity: Anabaptism for a Nonviolent Church. 2009. 136p. pap. 12.95 *(978-1-931038-63-8(5))* Cascadia Publishing Hse., LLC.

Missio Dei & Van Steenwyk, Mark. The Missio Dei Breviary. 2008. 159p. pap. 13.99 *(978-0-615-18804-1(4))* Missio Dei.

Murray, Stuart. Anabautismo Al Desnudo: Convicciones Básicas de una Fe Radical. 2011. pap. **(978-0-8361-9614-6(7))** Herald Pr.

Murray, Stuart. The Naked Anabaptist: The Bare Essentials of a Radical Faith. 2010. (ENG.). 300p. pap. 13.99 *(978-0-8361-9517-0(5))* Herald Pr.

Neufeld, Alfred. What We Believe Together, 1 vol. 2007. (ENG.). 160p. pap. 9.95 *(978-1-56148-626-7(4))* Good Bks.

Peters, Galen, ed. The Earliest Hymns of the Ausbund: Some Beautiful Christian Songs Composed & Sung in the Prison at Passau. Riall, Robert, tr. 469p. 40.00 *(978-1-894710-34-3(7))* Pandora Pr. CAN. Dist: Herald Pr.

Riedemann, Peter. Love is Like Fire: The Confession of an Anabaptist Prisoner: Written at Gmunden, Upper Austria, Between 1529 & 1532.Tr. of Glaubenszeugnisse Oberdeutscher Taufgesinnter. iii, 74p. 12.50 *(978-1-894710-72-5(X))* Pandora Pr. CAN. Dist: Herald Pr.

Roth, John D. Practices: Mennonite Worship & Witness. 2009. pap. 12.99 *(978-0-8361-9427-2(5))* Herald Pr.

Showalter, Lester E. Our Heritage of Christian Song. 2010. (Illus.). 228p. 10.60 *(978-0-7399-2407-5(9))* Rod & Staff Pubs., Inc.

Snyder, C. Arnold & Peters, Galen, eds. Reading the Anabaptist Bible: Reflections for Every Day of the Year. 425p. 36.00 *(978-1-894710-25-1(8))* Pandora Pr. CAN. Dist: Herald Pr.

Van Braght, Thieleman J. The Bloody Theater: Or Martyrs Mirror of the Defenseless Christians. Sohm, Joseph F., tr. 2011. 1158p. 87.95 **(978-1-258-04626-2(1))** Literary Licensing, LLC.

Verheyden, A. L. E. Anabaptism in Flanders 1530-1650: A Century of Struggle. 2008. (Illus.). 152p. pap. 17.00 *(978-1-60608-339-0(2))* Wipf & Stock Pubs.

Vogt, Virgil, ed. The Roots of Concern: Writings on Anabaptist Renewal, 1952-1957. 2008. 212p. pap. 23.00 *(978-1-59752-189-5(2))* Wipf & Stock Pubs.

Von Der Lippe, George B. & Reck-Malleczewen, Viktoria M., eds. A History of the Münster Anabaptists: Inner Emigration & the Third Reich - A Critical Edition of Friedrich Reck-Malleczewen's Bockelson - A Tale of Mass Insanity. 2008. (ENG., Illus.). 276p. 95.00 *(978-0-230-60547-3(8))* Palgrave Macmillan.

Weaver, Alain Epp & Mast, Gerald J., eds. The Work of Jesus Christ in Anabaptist Perspective: Essays in Honor of J. Denny Weaver. 2008. 432p. pap. 26.95 *(978-1-931038-49-2(X))* Cascadia Publishing Hse., LLC.

Weis, Frederick L. The Life & Teaching of Ludwig Hesser: Leader & Martyr of the Anabaptists, 1500-1529. reprint ed. 31.50 *(978-0-404-19875-6(9))* AMS Pr., Inc.

ANABAPTISTS—HISTORY

Arnold, Snyder C. From Anabaptist Seed. 2007. 0054p. pap. 8.95 *(978-1-56148-585-7(3))* Good Bks.

Bekgaard, Wm. F. The Non-Protestant Baptists. 2008. 192p. 24.99 *(978-1-4389-1797-9(X))*; pap. 14.99 *(978-1-4389-1796-2(1))* AuthorHouse.

Dosker, Henry E., ed. The Dutch Anabaptists: Stone Lectures Delivered at Princeton Theological Seminary, 1918-1919. reprint ed. 36.50 *(978-0-404-19825-2(7))* AMS Pr., Inc.

Goertz, Hans-Jurgen. The Anabaptists. 2008. 240p. 34.00 *(978-0-415-47910-3(X))*, Routledge.

Heath, Richard. Anabaptism, from Its Rise at Zwickau to Its Fall at Munster. reprint ed. 37.50 *(978-0-404-19833-6(3))* AMS Pr., Inc.

Hutter, Jakob. Brotherly Faithfulness: Epistles from a Time of Persecution. xvi, 233p. 12.50 *(978-1-894710-73-2(8))* Pandora Pr. CAN. Dist: Herald Pr.

Isaak, Helmut. Menno Simons & the New Jerusalem. 158p. 19.00 *(978-1-894710-69-5(X))* Pandora Pr. CAN. Dist: Herald Pr.

Kerssenbrock, Hermann von. Narrative of the Anabaptist Madness: The Overthrow of Münster, the Famous Metropolis of Westphalia. 2007. (Studies in the History of Christian Traditions). *(978-90-04-15721-7(2))* BRILL.

Klaassen, Walter & Klassen, William. Marpeck: A Life of Dissent & Conformity. 2008. (Illus.). 423p. 32.99 *(978-0-8361-9423-4(3))* Herald Pr.

Lehman, James O. & Nolt, Steven M. Mennonites, Amish, & the American Civil War. 2007. (Young Center Books in Anabaptist & Pietist Studies). (ENG., Illus.). 376p. (gr. 17). 43.00 *(978-0-8018-8672-0(4))* Johns Hopkins Univ. Pr.

Loewen, Harry. Through Fire & Water: An Overview of Mennonite History. 2010. (ENG.). 350p. (YA). pap. 16.99 *(978-0-8361-9506-4(X))* Herald Pr.

Packull, Werner O. Commoners & Community: Essays in Honour of Werner O. Packull. Snyder, C. Arnold, ed. 323p. 29.25 *(978-1-894710-27-5(4))* Pandora Pr. CAN. Dist: Herald Pr.

—Mysticism & the Early South German - Austrian Anabaptist Movement 1525 - 1531. 2008. 252p. pap. 28.00 *(978-1-60608-338-3(4)*, Wipf and Stock) Wipf & Stock Pubs.

Roth, John D. Stories: How Mennonites Came to Be. 2006. (Illus.). 245p. per. 9.99 *(978-0-8361-9338-1(5))* Herald Pr.

Schlachta, Astrid von. Gefahr oder Segen? Die Täufer in der politischen Kommunikation. 2009. (Schriften zur politischen Kommunikation Ser.). (GER.). 484p. (C). 84.00 *(978-3-89971-758-7(9))* Vandenhoeck & Ruprecht GmbH & Co. KG DEU. Dist: ISD.

Shenk, Joanna. Widening the Circle: Experiments in Christian Discipleship. 2011. pap. **(978-0-8361-9558-3(2))** Herald Pr.

Stayer, James M. & Roth, John D., eds. A Companion to Anabaptism & Spiritualism, 1521-1700. 2006. (Brill's Companions to the Christian Tradition Ser.: Vol. 6). (Illus.). 574p. *(978-90-04-15402-5(7))* BRILL.

Waite, Gary K. Eradicating the Devil's Minions: Anabaptists & Witches in Reformation Europe, 1525-1600. 2009. (ENG., Illus.). xvi, 319p. pap. *(978-1-4426-1032-3(8))* Univ. of Toronto Pr.

—Eradicating the Devil's Minions: Anabaptists & Witches in Reformation Europe, 1535-1600. 2007. (ENG., Illus.). 384p. *(978-0-8020-9155-0(5))* Univ. of Toronto Pr.

Wenger, John Christian. Even unto Death: The Heroic Witness of the Sixteenth Century Anabaptists. 2011. 126p. 40.95 **(978-1-258-02123-8(4))** Literary Licensing, LLC.

Yoder, John Howard, et al. Anabaptism & Reformation in Switzerland: An Historical & Theological Analysis of the Dialogues Between Anabaptists & Reformers. lxviii, 441p. 41.50 *(978-1-894710-44-2(4))* Pandora Pr. CAN. Dist: Herald Pr.

ANABOLIC STEROIDS

Beamish, Rob. Steroids: A New Look at Performance-Enhancing Drugs, 1 vol. 2011. (Illus.). 211p. 44.95 *(978-0-313-38024-2(4)*, A2196C); E-Book **(978-0-313-38025-9(2)**, Praeger Pubs.) Greenwood Publishing Group, Inc.

"Body Building Products & Hidden Steroids: Enforcement Barriers": Hearing Before the Subcommittee on Crime & Drugs of the Committee on the Judiciary, United States Senate, One Hundred Eleventh Congress, First Session, September 29, 2009. 2010. iii, 207p. **(978-0-16-086426-1(7)**, 552-070-41487-8) United States Government Printing Office.

Clark, Dan. Gladiator: A True Story of 'Roids, Rage, & Redemption. 2011. (ENG., Illus.). 256p. pap. 16.99 *(978-1-4165-9733-9(6)*, Scribner) Scribner.

Conte, Victor. BALCO: The Straight Dope on Steroids, Barry Bonds, Marion Jones, & What We Can Do to Save Sports. 2009. 320p. 24.95 *(978-1-60239-295-3(1)*, 239295) Skyhorse Publishing Co., Inc.

Dimeo, Paul, et al, eds. Elite Sport, Doping & Public Health. 2009. 192p. pap. 44.00 *(978-87-7674-410-6(8))* Univ. Pr. of Southern Denmark DNK. Dist: International Specialized Bk. Services.

Drugs in Sports: Compromising the Health of Athletes & Undermining the Integrity of Competition: Hearing Before the Subcommittee on Commerce, Trade, & Consumer Protection of the Committee on Energy & Commerce, House of Representatives, One Hundred Tenth Congress, Second Session, February 27, 2008. 2008. vi, 181p. *(978-0-16-085256-5(0)*, 552-070-40598-4) United States Government Printing Office.

Encyclopaedia Britannica, Inc., compiled by. Steroids: Make Believe Muscles. 2008. 49.95 *(978-1-59339-619-0(8))* Encyclopaedia Britannica, Inc.

Fainaru-Wada, Mark & Williams, Lance. Game of Shadows: Barry Bonds, Balco, & the Steroids Scandal That Rocked Professional Sports. 2007. (ENG., Illus.). 368p. (gr. 12-18). 15.00 *(978-1-59240-268-7(2)*, Gotham) Penguin Group (USA) Inc.

—Game of Shadows: Barry Bonds, Balco, & the Steroids Scandal That Rocked Professional Sports. l.t. ed. 2006. (Thorndike Nonfiction Ser.). (Illus.). 607p. 30.95 *(978-0-7862-8866-3(3))* Thorndike Pr.

Fett, B. Michael. Beautiful Hardship: My Story. 2009. *(978-1-58982-555-0(1))* American Bk. Publishing Group.

Hamidi, Mehrdad, et al, eds. Drug Abuse in Sport: Doping. 2011. (Sports & Athletics Preparation, Performance, & Psychology Ser.). 140.00 **(978-1-61324-574-3(2))** Nova Science Pubs., Inc.

Harris, Michael. A Culture of Steroid Use among High School Athletes. 2008. 206p. pap. 20.99 *(978-1-4357-4383-0(0))* Lulu Enterprises Inc.

Karch, Steven B. Karch's Pathology of Drug Abuse. 4th rev. ed. (ENG., Illus.). 2012. 832p. 159.95 *(978-1-4398-6146-2(3))* 2008. 736p. 154.95 *(978-0-8493-7880-5(X))* Taylor & Francis Group GBR. (CRC Press). Dist: Taylor & Francis Group.

Kiesbye, Stefan. Steroids. 2007. (Contemporary Issues Companion Ser.). (ENG.). 147p. (gr. 10-12). 27.50 *(978-0-7377-3710-3(7)*, Greenhaven Pr., Inc.); (Illus.). (YA). (gr. 9-12). pap. 39.70 *(978-0-7377-3709-7(3))* Cengage Gale.

Lau, Doretta. Steroids. 2008. (Incredibly Disgusting Drugs Ser.). (Illus.). 48p. lib. bdg. 26.50 *(978-1-4042-1376-0(7))* Rosen Publishing Group, Inc., The.

The Mitchell Report: The Illegal Use of Steroids in Major League Baseball, Day 2: Hearing Before the Committee on Oversight & Government Reform, House of Representatives, One Hundred Tenth Congress, Second Session, February 13, 2008. 2008. (Illus.). iii, 162p. *(978-0-16-081413-6(8)*, 552-070-37787-5) United States Government Printing Office.

The Mitchell Report: The Illegal Use of Steroids in Major League Baseball: Hearing Before the Committee on Oversight & Government Reform, House of Representatives, One Hundred Tenth Congress, Second Session, January 15, 2008. 2010. iii, 155p. *(978-0-16-085840-6(2)*, 552-070-41052-0) United States Government Printing Office.

Piehl, Norah. Performance-Enhancing Drugs. 2010. (Social Issues Firsthand Ser.). (ENG.). 120p. 31.80 *(978-0-7377-5011-9(1)*, Greenhaven Pr., Inc.) Cengage Gale.

Reiter, Martina. Possible New Screening Methods for Anabolic Agents. 2008. 76p. pap. *(978-3-639-08089-6(0))* VDM Verlag Dr. Mueller e.K.

Roach, Randy. Muscle, Smoke & Mirrors, Vol. 2. 2011. 728p. 79.95 **(978-1-4670-3840-9(7))**; pap. 69.95 **(978-1-4670-3841-6(5))** AuthorHouse.

Roberts, Paul K., ed. Steroid Use & Abuse. 2010. (Drug Transit & Distribution, Interception & Control Ser.). 71p. pap. 43.00 *(978-1-60692-324-5(2))* Nova Science Pubs., Inc.

Robson, David. Steroids. 2008. (Compact Research Ser.). (YA). (gr. 7-12). 25.95 *(978-1-60152-067-8(0)*, ReferencePoint Pr., Inc.

Thieme, Detlef & Hemmersbach, Peter, eds. Doping in Sports: Biochemical Principles, Effects & Analysis. 2009. (Handbook of Experimental Pharmacology Ser.). (ENG., Illus.). xiv, 540p. 529.00 *(978-3-540-79087-7(X)*, 354079087X) Springer.

Whitfield, James F. Growing Bone, Second Edition. 2nd ed. 2007. (Illus.). 272p. 159.00 *(978-1-58706-156-1(2))* Landes Bioscience.

Wiley, Warren. Better Than Steroids! 2007. (Illus.). 180p. per. 35.00 *(978-1-4251-0339-2(1))* Trafford Publishing.

ANABOLISM

see Metabolism

ANACHRONISMS, LITERARY

see Errors and Blunders, Literary

ANAEMIA

see Anemia

ANAEROBIC BACTERIA

Amin Saleh, Famaz. Bagasse As a Fuel for Combined Heat & Power. 2011. 132p. pap. **(978-3-8454-1483-6(9))** Lambert Academic Publishing.

Brook, Itzhak. Anaerobic Infections: Diagnosis & Management. 2007. (Infectious Disease & Therapy Ser.: Vol. 46). (ENG., Illus.). 440p. 150.00 *(978-0-8493-8257-4(2)*, Informa Healthcare) Taylor & Francis Group GBR. Dist: Taylor & Francis Group.

Elshahed, Mostafa. Anaerobic Biodegradation of Monoaromatic Compounds. 2008. 180p. pap. *(978-3-639-08264-7(8))* VDM Verlag Dr. Mueller e.K.

Hayworth, James M., ed. Methane Digesters & Biogas Recovery. 2011. (Agriculture Issues & Policies Ser.). (Illus.). 92p. pap. 47.00 *(978-1-61324-594-1(7))* Nova Science Pubs., Inc.

Juergen, Wiegel. Incredible Anaerobes: From Physiology to Genomics to Fuels. Maier, Robert et al, eds. 2008. (Annals of the New York Academy of Sciences Ser.). (ENG., Illus.). 452p. pap. 159.95 *(978-1-57331-705-4(5)*, Wiley-Blackwell) Wiley, John & Sons, Inc.

Khanal, Samir. Anaerobic Biotechnology for Bioenergy Production: Principles & Applications. 2008. (ENG., Illus.). 320p. 237.00 *(978-0-8138-2346-1(3)*, Wiley-Blackwell) Wiley, John & Sons, Inc.

Ljungdahl, Lars G., et al, eds. Biochemistry & Physiology of Anaerobic Bacteria. 2010. (ENG., Illus.). xvii, 270p. pap. 225.00 *(978-1-4419-3068-2(X)*, 144193068X) Springer.

Rockland, Samuel D., ed. Anaerobic Digestion for Energy Generation & Greenhouse Gas Reduction. 2009. (Energy Science, Engineering & Technology Ser.). 115.00 *(978-1-61728-679-7(6))* Nova Science Pubs., Inc.

Speece & Speece, Richard E. Anaerobic Biotechnology & Odor/Corrosion Control for Municipalities & Industries: Corrosion Control. 2008. (Illus.). xxx, 586p. *(978-1-57643-052-9(6))* Fields Publishing, Inc.

ANAEROBIOSIS

Martin, William F. & Müller, Miklós, eds. Origin of Mitochondria & Hydrogenosomes. 2010. (ENG., Illus.). xviii, 306p. pap. 209.00 *(978-3-642-07246-8(1)*, 3642072461) Springer.

ANAESTHESIA

see Anesthesia

ANAESTHETICS

see Anesthetics

ANAGRAMS

Evans, Rod L. Tyrannosaurus Lex: The Gigantic Book of Palindromes, Anagrams, & Other Delightful & OutrageousWordplay. 2012. (ENG.). 288p. (gr. 12). 14.00 **(978-0-399-53749-3(X)**, Perigee Trade) Penguin Group (USA) Inc.

Margoliouth, D. S. The Homer of Aristotle. 2009. 258p. 30.99 *(978-1-110-47513-1(6))*; pap. 25.75 *(978-1-110-47509-4(8))* BiblioBazaar.

Minter, James F. The 2nd Big Pencil Pastimes Book of Word Games: Mazes, Anagrams & Much More. 2007. 224p. pap. *(978-0-88486-398-4(0))* Bristol Park Bks.

—The 2nd Big Pencil Pastimes Book of Word Search. 2007. 224p. pap. *(978-0-88486-397-7(2))* Bristol Park Bks.

ANAHEIM ANGELS (BASEBALL TEAM)

see Los Angeles Angels of Anaheim (Baseball Team)

ANAL EROTICISM

see Anus (Psychology)

ANALGESIA

see also Analgesics

Abadir, Adel R. & Harahap, Marwali, eds. Anesthesia & Analgesia in Dermatologic Surgery. 2008. (Basic & Clinical Dermatology Ser.). (ENG., Illus.). 232p. 200.00 *(978-0-8493-3698-0(8)*, Informa Healthcare) Taylor & Francis Group.

Argoff, Charles E. & McCleane, Gary. Pain Management Secrets. 3rd ed. 2009. (Secrets Ser.). (ENG., Illus.). 408p. pap. 54.95 *(978-0-323-04019-8(5)*, Mosby) Elsevier - Health Sciences Div.

Ballantyne, Jane C., et al, eds. Bonica's Management of Pain. 4th rev. ed. 2009. (ENG., Illus.). 2064p. 329.99 *(978-0-7817-6827-6(6))* Lippincott Williams & Wilkins.

Benedetti, F. & Brune, K., contrib. by. Analgesia. 2007. (Handbook of Experimental Pharmacology Ser.). (Illus.). 435p. 449.00 *(978-3-540-33822-2(5)*, 3540338225) Springer.

Benzon, Honorio T., et al. Practical Management of Pain. Benzon, Honorio T. et al, eds. 4th ed. 2008. (ENG., Illus.). 1344p. 274.00 *(978-0-323-04184-3(1)*, Mosby) Elsevier - Health Sciences Div.

Buckenmaier, Chester, III & Bleckner, Lisa. Military Advanced Regional Anesthesia & Analgesia Handbook: Spiral Book with a DVD. Borden Institute, Walter Reed Army Medical Center, ed. 2009. (ENG.). 154p. 35.00 *(978-0-16-082568-2(7)*, Dept. of the Army) United States Government Printing Office.

Cairns, Brian E. Peripheral Receptor Targets for Analgesia: Novel Approaches to Pain Management. 2009. (ENG., Illus.). 549p. 153.00 *(978-0-470-25131-7(X)*, Wiley) Wiley, John & Sons, Inc.

Carroll, Gwendolyn L., ed. Small Animal Anesthesia & Analgesia. 2008. (ENG., Illus.). 283p. 89.99 *(978-0-8138-0230-5(X)*, Wiley-Blackwell) Wiley, John & Sons, Inc.

Castro-Lopes, José, et al, eds. Pain 2008 - an Updated Review: Refresher Course Syllabus. 2008. pap. 40.00 *(978-0-931092-73-2(6))* International Assn. for the Study of Pain/IASP Pr.

Chaitow, Leon. You Can Conquer Pain: Break the Pain Cycle & Regain Control of Your Life. 2012. (ENG., Illus.). 176p. pap. 14.95 **(978-1-78028-121-6(8)**, Watkins Publishing) Duncan Baird Pubs. GBR. Dist: Sterling Publishing Co., Inc.

Cousins, Michael J., et al, eds. Neural Blockade: In Clinical Anesthesia & Pain Medicine. 4th rev. ed. 2008. (ENG., Illus.). 1360p. 234.99 *(978-0-7817-7388-1(1))* Lippincott Williams & Wilkins.

Cox, Felicia, ed. Perioperative Pain Management. 2008. (ENG., Illus.). 336p. pap., instr.'s hndbk. ed. 83.99 *(978-1-4051-8077-1(3)*, Wiley-Blackwell) Wiley, John & Sons, Inc.

Cram101 Textbook Reviews. Outlines & Highlights for Acute Pain Management: A Practical Guide by Pamela Macintyre, ISBN. 2011. 192p. pap. 30.95 **(978-1-61461-465-4(2))** Cram101 Inc.

—Outlines & Highlights for Bonicas Management of Pain by Scott Fishman, Isbn: 9780781768276. 2011. 542p. pap. 36.95 **(978-1-61461-444-9(X))** Cram101 Inc.

—Outlines & Highlights for Textbook of Regional Anesthesia & Acute Pain Management by Admir Hadzic, Isbn: 9780071449069. 2011. 382p. pap. 34.95 **(978-1-61461-469-2(5))** Cram101 Inc.

Cram101 Textbook Reviews & Cram101 Textbook Reviews. Outlines & Highlights for Acute Pain Management by Raymond S Sinatra, Isbn: 9780521874915 0521874912. 2011. 448p. pap. 36.95 **(978-1-61490-318-5(2))** Cram101 Inc.

D'Arcy, Yvonne. Compact Clinical Guide to Acute Pain Management: An Evidence-Based Approach. 2011. 240p. pap. *(978-0-8261-0549-3(1))*; E-Book *(978-0-8261-0550-9(5))* Springer Publishing Co., Inc.

Deer, Timothy, et al. Diagnosis, Management, & Treatment of Discogenic Pain, Vol. 3. 2011. (Interventional & Neuromodulatory Techniques in Pain Management Ser.). (ENG., Illus.). 176p. 139.00 *(978-1-4377-2218-5(0)*, Saunders) Elsevier - Health Sciences Div.

—Intrathecal Drug Delivery for Pain & Spasticity, Vol. 2. 2011. (Interventional & Neuromodulatory Techniques in Pain Management Ser.). (ENG., Illus.). 224p. 139.00 *(978-1-4377-2217-8(2)*, Saunders) Elsevier - Health Sciences Div.

—Neurostimulation for the Treatment of Chronic Pain: A Volume in the Interventional & Neuromodulatory Techniques for Pain Management Series - Expert Consult Premium Edition — Enhanced Online Features & Print, Vol. 1. 2011. (Interventional & Neuromodulatory Techniques in Pain Management Ser.). (ENG., Illus.). 248p. 139.00 *(978-1-4377-2216-1(4)*, Saunders) Elsevier - Health Sciences Div.

Deer, Timothy R. Interventional & Neuromodulatory Techniques for Pain Management. 2012. (Interventional & Neuromodulatory Techniques in Pain Management Ser.). (ENG., Illus.). 1600p. 549.00 **(978-1-4377-3791-2(9)**, Saunders) Elsevier - Health Sciences Div.

Deer, Timothy R., et al. Reducing Risks & Complications of Interventional Pain Procedures Vol. 5: Interventional & Neuromodulatory Techniques for Pain Management. 2012. (Interventional & Neuromodulatory Techniques in Pain Management Ser.). (ENG., Illus.). 176p. 139.00 **(978-1-4377-2220-8(2)**, Saunders) Elsevier - Health Sciences Div.

Dormandy, Thomas. The Worst of Evils: The Fight Against Pain. 2006. (ENG., Illus.). 560p. 39.00 *(978-0-300-11322-8(6))* Yale Univ. Pr.

Fish. Pain Management Pocketpedia. 2011. (Illus.). 144p. pap. 34.95 *(978-0-7817-7218-1(4))* Lippincott Williams & Wilkins.

Fish, Richard, et al, eds. Anesthesia & Analgesia in Laboratory Animals. 2nd ed. 2008. (American College of Laboratory Animal Medicine Ser.). (ENG., Illus.). 672p. 165.00 *(978-0-12-373898-1(9)*, Academic Pr.) Elsevier Science & Technology Bks.

Ganapathy, Sugantha & Chan, Vincent W. S. Regional Analgesia & Acute Pain Management, an Issue of Anesthesiology Clinics. 2011. (Clinics: Surgery Ser.: 29-2). (ENG., Illus.). 192p. 105.00 *(978-1-4377-2426-4(4)*, Saunders) Elsevier - Health Sciences Div.

Girard-Powell, Valerie. Pain, Analgesia & Anesthesia, an Issue of Perioperative Nursing Clinics. 2009. (Clinics: Nursing Ser.: 4-4). (ENG., Illus.). xiv, 477p. 61.00 (978-1-4377-1749-5(7), Saunders) Elsevier - Health Sciences Div.

Gloth, F. Michael. Handbook of Pain Relief in Older Adults: An Evidence-Based Approach. 2nd ed. 2011. (Illus.). x, 210p. E-Book (978-1-60761-618-4(1)) Humana Pr.

Gloth, III, F. Michael, FMichael, ed. Handbook of Pain Relief in Older Adults: An Evidence-Based Approach. 2nd ed. 2010. (Aging Medicine Ser.). (ENG., Illus.). x, 210p. 109.00 (978-1-60761-617-7(3), 1607616173) Humana Pr.

Grimm, Kurt A., et al, eds. Essentials of Small Animal Anesthesia & Analgesia. 2nd ed. 2011. (ENG., Illus.). 584p. pap. 69.99 (978-0-8138-1236-6(4), Wiley-Blackwell) Wiley, John & Sons, Inc.

Hadzic, Admir. Textbook of Regional Anesthesia & Acute Pain Management. 2006. (ENG., Illus.). 2000p. 259.00 (978-0-07-144906-9(X), 007144906X) McGraw-Hill Professional Publishing.

Harrar, Sari. Your New Pain Prescription: From Migraines to Arthritis, Ulcers to Cancer Pain, Find Relief at Last with Customized Treatment Plans for More Than 60 Common Chronic Pain Conditions. 2011. (978-1-60529-132-1(3)) Rodale Pr., Inc.

Kerr, Dennis. Local Infiltration Analgesia. 2009. pap. 99.95 (978-1-4398-0183-3(5), Informa Healthcare) Taylor & Francis Group.

Knotkova, Helena, et al, eds. Pain. Brain Stimulation in the Treatment of Pain. 2010. (Disability Studies (Joav Merrick - Series Editor - National Institute of Child Health & Human Development, Ministry of Social Affairs, Jerusalem Ser.). 89.00 (978-1-60876-690-1(X)) Nova Science Pubs., Inc.

Macintyre, Pamela & Schug, Stephan A. Acute Pain Management: A Practical Guide. 3rd rev. ed. 2007. (ENG., Illus.). 320p. pap. 64.95 (978-0-7020-2770-3(7), Saunders) Elsevier - Health Sciences Div.

Malviya, Shobha, ed. Sedation & Analgesia for Diagnostic & Therapeutic Procedures. 2010. (Contemporary Clinical Neuroscience Ser.). (Illus.). 310p. pap. 169.00 (978-1-61737-228-5(5), 1617372285) Humana Pr.

Mao, Jianren, ed. Opioid-Induced Hyperalgesia. 2009. (ENG., Illus.). 202p. 150.00 (978-1-4200-8899-1(8), Informa Healthcare) Taylor & Francis Group GBR. Dist: Taylor & Francis Group.

McCleane, Gary J. Pain Management: Expanding the Pharmacological Options. 2008. (ENG., Illus.). 200p. pap. 115.95 (978-1-4051-7823-5(X), Wiley-Blackwell) Wiley, John & Sons, Inc.

McConachie, Ian, ed. Controversies in Obstetric Anesthesia & Analgesia. 2011. (ENG., Illus.). 280p. pap. 75.00 (978-0-521-17183-0(0)) Cambridge Univ. Pr.

Merrick, Joav, ed. Pain Management Yearbook 2008. 2009. 145.00 (978-1-60692-867-7(8)) Nova Science Pubs., Inc.

Oakes, Linda L. Compact Clinical Guide to Infant & Children's Pain Management: An Evidence-Based Approach. 2011. E-Book (978-0-8261-0618-6(8)); (Illus.). 280p. pap. (978-0-8261-0617-9(X)) Springer.

Olivier, Abraham. Being in Pain. 212p. pap. 46.95 (978-3-631-56225-3(X)) Lang, Peter Publishing, Inc.

Pandharipande, Pratik & Ely, E. Wesley. Sedation & Analgesia in the ICU: Pharmacology, Protocolization, & Clinical Consequences, an Issue of Anesthesiology Clinics. 2011. (Clinics: Surgery Ser.: 29-4). (ENG., Illus.). xi, 568p. 110.00 (978-1-4557-3360-6(1), Saunders) Elsevier - Health Sciences Div.

Rathmell. Complication Reg Anes Pain Med Cb. 2nd rev. ed. 2012. (ENG., Illus.). 495p. 149.00 (978-1-4511-0978-8(4)) Lippincott Williams & Wilkins.

Ray, Charles E., Jr., ed. Pain Management in Interventional Radiology. 2008. (ENG., Illus.). 344p. 93.00 (978-0-521-86592-0(1)) Cambridge Univ. Pr.

Sinatra, Raymond S., et al, eds. Acute Pain Management. 2009. (ENG., Illus.). 726p. 125.00 (978-0-521-87491-5(2)) Cambridge Univ. Pr.

Sluka, Kathleen A., ed. Mechanisms & Management of Pain for the Physical Therapist. 2009. pap. 90.00 (978-0-931092-77-0(9)) International Assn. for the Study of Pain/IASP Pr.

Smith, Tim, et al, eds. Fundamentals of Anaesthesia. 3rd rev. ed. 2009. (ENG., Illus.). 956p. pap. 149.00 (978-0-521-69249-6(0)) Cambridge Univ. Pr.

Stanton-Hicks, M. Pain Management. 2008. (Cleveland Clinic Guides). (ENG.). 200p. pap. 14.95 (978-1-59624-017-9(2)) Cleveland Clinic Pr.

Szallasi, Arpad, ed. Analgesia. 2010. (Methods in Molecular Biology Ser.). (Illus.). 528p. 189.00 (978-1-60327-322-0(0), 1603273220) Humana Pr.

Thomas, John & Lerche, Phillip. Anesthesia & Analgesia for Veterinary Technicians. 4th ed. 2010. (ENG., Illus.). 432p. (C). pap. 55.95 (978-0-323-05504-8(4), Mosby) Elsevier - Health Sciences Div.

Thomas, Stephen H., ed. Emergency Department Analgesia: An Evidence-Based Guide. 2008. (Cambridge Pocket Clinicians Ser.). (ENG., Illus.). 430p. pap. 56.00 (978-0-521-69601-2(1)) Cambridge Univ. Pr.

Valani, Rahim, ed. Essential Emergency Procedural Sedation & Pain Management: 2011. (ENG., Illus.). 240p. pap. 74.95 (978-1-4511-1606-9(3)) Lippincott Williams & Wilkins.

Vincent, Mathis L. & Moreau, Theo M. Accidental Falls: Causes, Preventions & Interventions. 2008. (Illus.). 301p. (C). 139.00 (978-1-60456-767-0(8)) Nova Science Pubs., Inc.

Waldman, Steven D. Atlas of Interventional Pain Management with DVD. 3rd ed. 2009. (ENG., Illus.). 720p. 274.00 (978-1-4160-9994-9(8), Saunders) Elsevier - Health Sciences Div.

—Atlas of Pain Management Injection Techniques. 2nd rev. ed. 2007. (ENG., Illus.). 616p. 218.00 (978-1-4160-3855-9(8), Saunders) Elsevier - Health Sciences Div.

Watkins-Pitchford, J. Michael, et al. The Essence of Analgesia & Analgesics. 2010. (ENG., Illus.). 550p. pap. 99.00 (978-0-521-14450-6(7)) Cambridge Univ. Pr.

Willens, Joyce S. & Willens, Joyce. Pain Management. 2014. (Nurse to Nurse Ser.). (ENG., Illus.). 300p. pap. 30.00 (978-0-07-160008-8(6), 0071600086) McGraw-Hill Professional Publishing.

Yentis, Steve, et al, eds. Analgesia, Anaesthesia & Pregnancy: A Practical Guide. 2nd var. ed. 2007. (ENG., Illus.). 414p. 88.00 (978-0-521-69474-2(4)) Cambridge Univ. Pr.

ANALGESICS

Ahmad, Rashidi & Ghazali Ab Rashid, Mohd. Acute Traumatic Pain in the Emergency Department. 2010. 96p. pap. (978-3-8383-4750-9(1)) Lambert Academic Publishing.

Al-Nimer, Marwan S. M., ed. Pharmacological Intervention in Management of Neck Pain Disorders: A Review. 2010. (Pain & its Origins, Diagnosis & Treatments Ser.). pap. 49.00 (978-1-61728-221-8(9), Nova Biomedical Bks.) Nova Science Pubs., Inc.

Aronson, Jeffrey K. Meyler's Side Effects of Analgesics & Anti-inflammatory Drugs. 2009. (ENG.). 702p. 63.95 (978-0-444-53273-2(0), Elsevier Science) Elsevier Science & Technology Bks.

Bailey, Allison & Audette, Joseph F., eds. Integrative Pain Medicine: The Science & Practice of Complementary & Alternative Medicine in Pain Management. 2008. (Contemporary Pain Medicine Ser.). (Illus.). 579p. 179.00 (978-1-58829-786-0(1), 1588297861) Humana Pr.

BCC Research Staff. The Global Market for Pain Management Drugs & Devices. 2007. per. 4250.00 (978-1-59623-297-6(8)) BCC Research.

Beaulieu, Pierre, et al, eds. Pharmacology of Pain. 2010. 100.00 (978-0-931092-78-7(7)) International Assn. for the Study of Pain/IASP Pr.

Bolen, Jennifer E., ed. Handbook of Risk Management in Pain Medicine. 2009. (Contemporary Pain Medicine Ser.). 225p. 99.50 (978-1-58829-820-1(5)) Humana Pr.

Clark, M. R. & Treisman, G. J., eds. Chronic Pain & Addiction. 2011. (Advances in Psychosomatic Medicine Ser.). (Illus.). 166p. (978-3-8055-9725-8(8)) Karger, S. AG.

Clark, M. R & Treisman, Glenn J. Chronic Pain & Addiction. 2011. (Illus.). v, 165p. E-Book (978-3-8055-9726-5(6)) Karger, S. AG.

Cox, Felicia, ed. Perioperative Pain Management. 2008. (ENG., Illus.). 336p. pap., instr.'s hndbk. ed. 83.99 (978-1-4051-8077-1(3), Wiley-Blackwell) Wiley, John & Sons, Inc.

Cram101 Textbook Reviews & Cram101 Textbook Reviews. Outlines & Highlights for Pain Assessment & Pharmacologic Management by Chris Pasero. 2011. 152p. pap. 29.95 (978-1-61830-627-2(8)) Cram101 Inc.

D'Arcy, Yvonne M. Compact Clinical Guide to Chronic Pain Management: Evidence-Based Approach for Primary Care. 2010. (Illus.). 240p. (978-0-8261-0540-0(8)) Springer Publishing Co., Inc.

De Leo, Joyce A., et al, eds. Immune & Glial Regulation of Pain. 2007. (ENG.). 75.00 incl. cd-rom (978-0-931092-67-1(1)) International Assn. for the Study of Pain/IASP Pr.

Fine, P. G. & Davies, Andrew. The Diagnosis & Treatment of Breakthrough Pain. 2008. (Oxford American Pain Library). (ENG., Illus.). 112p. pap. 24.99 (978-0-19-536904-5(1)) Oxford Univ. Pr., Inc.

Forbes, Karen. Opioids in Cancer Pain. Forbes, Karen, ed. 2008. (Oxford Pain Management Library Ser.). (ENG., Illus.). 152p. 26.99 (978-0-19-921880-6(3)) Oxford Univ. Pr., Inc.

Gomtsyan, Arthur & Faltynek, Connie R. Vanilloid Receptor TRPV1 in Drug Discovery: Targeting Pain & Other Pathological Disorders. 2010. (ENG., Illus.) 465p. 139.00 (978-0-470-17557-6(5), Wiley) Wiley, John & Sons, Inc.

Gupta, Anita, ed. Interventional Pain Medicine, 1 vol. 2012. (ENG.). 320p. spiral bd. 98.50 (978-0-19-974060-4(7)) Oxford Univ. Pr., Inc.

Hughes, John. Pain Management: From Basics to Clinical Practice. 2008. (ENG., Illus.). 320p. (C). pap. 54.95 (978-0-443-10336-0(4), Churchill Livingstone) Elsevier - Health Sciences Div.

Jacobs, Vivian & Lang, Alexander. Analgesics: New Research. 2012. (978-1-62100-674-9(3)) Nova Science Pubs., Inc.

Jawale, Bhushan. Best Analgesics for Pain Associated with Separator Placement-A Study. 2011. 124p. pap. (978-3-8433-9130-6(0)) Lambert Academic Publishing.

Kane, Brigid M. Codeine. Triggle, David J., ed. 2007. (Drugs Ser.). (Illus.). 104p. (YA) (gr. 9-12). lib. bdg. 30.00 (978-0-7910-8550-9(3)) Facts On File, Inc.

Katz, Nathaniel. Opioid Prescribing Toolkit. 2010. 80p. pap. 24.95 (978-0-19-539011-7(3)) Oxford Univ. Pr., Inc.

Lyon, Joshua. Pill Head: The Secret Life of a Painkiller Addict. (ENG.). 288p. 2010. pap. 14.99 (978-1-4013-1022-6(2)) 2009. 24.99 (978-1-4013-2298-4(0)) Hyperion Pr.

Marcovitz, Hal. Painkillers. 2009. (Compact Research Ser.). (YA). (gr. 7-12). 25.95 (978-1-60152-100-2(6)) ReferencePoint Pr., Inc.

McCleane, Gary J. Pain Management: Expanding the Pharmacological Options. 2008. (ENG., Illus.). 200p. pap. 115.95 (978-1-4051-7823-5(X), Wiley-Blackwell) Wiley, John & Sons, Inc.

McPherson, Mary Lynn M. Demystifying Opioid Conversion Calculations: A Guide for Effective Dosing. 2009. (978-1-58528-198-5(0)) American Society of Health-System Pharmacists.

McQuay, H. J., et al, eds. Systematic Reviews in Pain Research: Methodology Refined. 2008. (Illus.). 407p. pap. 70.00 (978-0-931092-69-5(8)) International Assn. for the Study of Pain/IASP Pr.

Pain Management Clinics Market. 90p. (Orig.). pap. (978-0-7605-2322-3(3)) Rector Pr., Ltd.

Pain Management Products Market. 198p. (Orig.). pap. (978-0-7605-2321-6(5)) Rector Pr., Ltd.

Phillips, W. James, et al. Pain Management & Procedural Sedation. 2008. (Mobile Medicine Ser.). (ENG., Illus.). 240p. pap., instr.'s hndbk. ed. 49.95 (978-0-323-05333-4(5), Mosby) Elsevier - Health Sciences Div.

Pohl, Mel. A Day Without Pain. rev. ed. 2011. (ENG.). 264p. pap. 15.95 (978-1-936290-62-8(6)) Central Recovery Pr.

Rainsford, Kim D. Ibuprofen - A Critical Bibliographic Review. 2nd ed. 2009. (Illus.). 896p. 199.95 (978-1-4200-4636-6(5)) CRC Pr. LLC.

Rathmell, James P. Atlas of Image-Guided Intervention in Regional Anesthesia & Pain Medicine. 2nd rev. ed. 2011. (ENG., Illus.). 256p. 159.00 (978-1-60831-704-2(8)) Lippincott Williams & Wilkins.

Renner, John A., Jr. & Levounis, Petros. Handbook of Office-Based Buprenorphine Treatment of Opioid Dependence. 2010. (ENG., Illus.). pap. 59.00 (978-1-58562-369-3(5)) American Psychiatric Publishing, Inc.

Richeimer, Steven H., et al, eds. Integrative Pain Medicine: The Science & Practice of Complementary & Alternative Medicine in Pain Management. 2006. (Contemporary Pain Medicine Ser.). 300p. 99.50 (978-1-59745-344-8(7)) Humana Pr.

Roseman, Mark E. & Seppala, Marvin D. Prescription Painkillers: History, Pharmacology, & Treatment. 2010. (ENG.). 272p. pap. 17.95 (978-1-59285-901-6(1)) Hazelden Publishing & Educational Services.

Smith, Howard S. Opioid Therapy in the 21st Century. 2008. (Oxford American Pain Library). (ENG., Illus.). 208p. pap. 24.99 (978-0-19-533949-9(5)) Oxford Univ. Pr., Inc.

Stannard, Cathy, et al. Opioids in Non-Cancer Pain. 2008. (Oxford Pain Management Library Ser.). (ENG., Illus.). 136p. 24.95 (978-0-19-923123-2(0)) Oxford Univ. Pr., Inc.

Stiehl, Chris & DeVries, Henry. Pain Killer Marketing: How to Turn Customer Pain into Market Gain. 2008. (Illus.). 256p. 24.95 (978-0-8329-5016-2(5), WBusiness Bks.) New Win Publishing.

Twycross, Robert. Hospice & Palliative Care Formulary USA. Wilcock, Andrew, ed. 2nd ed. 2008. (Illus.). 600p. pap. (978-0-9552547-2-7(8)) Palliativedrugs.com, Ltd.

Watkins-Pitchford, J. Michael, et al. The Essence of Analgesia & Analgesics. 2010. (ENG., Illus.). 550p. pap. 99.00 (978-0-521-14450-6(7)) Cambridge Univ. Pr.

Webster, Lynn R. & Dove, Beth. Avoiding Opioid Abuse While Managing Pain: A Guide for Practitioners. 2007. (Illus.). 202p. per. (978-0-9624814-8-2(3)) Sunrise River Pr.

White, Robert M. & Black, Matthew L. Pain Management Testing Reference. 2007. (978-1-59425-076-7(6)) American Assn. for Clinical Chemistry, Inc.

ANALOG-DIGITAL CONVERTERS

see Analog-To-Digital Converters

ANALOG ELECTRONIC SYSTEMS

see also Analog-To-Digital Converters; Electronic Analog Computers

Analog & Mixed-Signal Devices. 2007. per. 4250.00 (978-1-59623-271-6(4)) BCC Research.

Brewer, Thomas E. & Robinson, R. Allen. Experiments in Analog & Digital Electronics: Text for Ece 3741. 6th rev. ed. 2011. (ENG.). 170p. spiral bd. 41.95 (978-0-7575-9187-7(6)) Kendall Hunt Publishing Co.

Buzzard. Audience Ratings in a Digital Age: The Changing Business Models for the US Television Industry. 2012. (ENG.). 208p. pap. 49.95 (978-0-08-585852-9(8)) Routledge.

Carrasco, Rolando Antonio & Johnston, Martin. Non-Binary Error Control Coding for Wireless Communication & Data Storage. 2009. (ENG., Illus.). 322p. 140.00 (978-0-470-51819-9(7), Wiley) Wiley, John & Sons, Inc.

Chatterjee, Shouri, et al. Analog Circuit Design Techniques At 0. 5V. 2007. (Analog Circuits & Signal Processing Ser.). (Illus.). 156p. 159.00 (978-0-387-69953-0(8)) Springer.

Cram101 Textbook Reviews & Cram101 Textbook Reviews. Outlines & Highlights for Introduction to Media Production by Gorham Kindem, Isbn: 9780240810829 0240810821. 2011. 120p. pap. 28.95 (978-1-61490-123-5(6)) Cram101 Inc.

Dimopoulos, Hercules G. & Constantinides, Anthony. Analog Electronic Filters: Theory, Design & Synthesis. 2011. (Analog Circuits & Signal Processing Ser.). (ENG., Illus.). xiii, 498p. 119.00 (978-94-007-2189-0(7), 9400721897) Springer.

Dnlger, Fikret & Sßnchez-Sinencio, Edgar. Integrated Rf Building Blocks for Wireless Communication Transceivers. 2008. 280p. pap. (978-3-639-07430-7(0)) VDM Verlag Dr. Mueller e.K.

Ford, Gary E. & Arft, Carl M. Analog Electronic Circuits & Systems Laboratory Manual. 3rd rev. ed. 2010. (ENG.). 134p. pap. 75.62 (978-0-7575-2941-2(0)) Kendall Hunt Publishing Co.

Graeb, Helmut E. Analog Design Centering & Sizing. (ENG.). xxii, 195p. 2010. pap. 119.00 (978-90-481-7499-7(6), 9048174996) 2007. (Illus.). 119.00 (978-1-4020-6003-8(3), 1402060033) Springer.

Gray, Paul R., et al. Analysis & Design of Analog Integrated Circuits. 5th ed. 2009. (ENG., Illus.). 896p. (C). 209.95 (978-0-470-24599-6(9), Wiley) Wiley, John & Sons, Inc.

Hamad, Omar Fakih. Analog, Digital & Multimedia Telecommunications: Basic & Classic Principles. 2011. 382p. pap. 19.99 (978-1-4568-1020-7(0)) Xlibris Corp.

Jenkins, Mark. Analog Synthesizers: Understanding, Performing, Buying - From the Legacy of Moog to Software Synthesis. 2007. (ENG., Illus.). 336p. pap. 45.95 (978-0-240-52072-8(6), Focal Pr.) Elsevier Science & Technology Bks.

Karam, Lina & Mounsef, Naji. Introduction to Engineering I: A Starter's Guide with Hands-on Analog Multimedia Explorations. 2010. (Synthesis Lectures on Engineering Ser.). 64p. pap. 30.00 (978-1-59829-759-1(7)) Morgan & Claypool Pubs.

Kindem, Gorham & Musburger, Robert B. Introduction to Media Production: The Path to Digital Media Production. 4th ed. 2009. (ENG., Illus.). 536p. pap. 51.95 (978-0-240-81082-9(1), Focal Pr.) Elsevier Science & Technology Bks.

McConaghy, Trent, et al. Variation-Aware Analog Structural Synthesis: A Computational Intelligence Approach. 2009. (Analog Circuits & Signal Processing Ser.). (Illus.). xxii, 306p. 179.00 (978-90-481-2905-8(2), 9048129052) Springer.

Northeastern University Staff & University of Hertfordshire Staff. SHARC - International DSP Conference 2001. Date not set. (Illus.). 400p. 200.00 (978-0-916550-25-7(7)) Analog Devices, Inc.

Ochoa, Agustin. Feedback in Analog Circuits. 2010. 105.00 (978-1-4020-7673-2(8), 1402076738) Springer.

Pastre, Marc & Kayal, Maher. Methodology for the Digital Calibration of Analog Circuits & Systems: With Case Studies. 2010. (Springer International Series in Engineering & Computer Science Ser.). xviii, 257p. pap. 239.00 (978-90-481-7087-6(7), 9048170877) Springer.

Popa, Cosmin Radu. Synthesis of Computational Structures for Analog Signal Processing. 2011. (ENG., Illus.). xv, 449p. 179.00 (978-1-4614-0402-6(9), 1461404029) Springer.

Redouté, Jean-Michel & Steyaert, Michiel. EMC of Analog Integrated Circuits. 2009. (Analog Circuits & Signal Processing Ser.). (ENG., Illus.). x, 243p. 159.00 (978-90-481-3229-4(0), 9048132290) Springer.

Schaumann, Rolf, et al. Design of Analog Filters, 1 vol. 2nd ed. 2009. (Oxford Series in Electrical & Computer Engineering Ser.). (ENG.). 848p. (C). 149.95 (978-0-19-537394-3(4)) Oxford Univ. Pr., Inc.

Sen, Taskin. Sensitivity Analysis Tool for Analog Layout Generation. 2010. 84p. pap. (978-3-8383-4613-7(0)) Lambert Academic Publishing.

Su, K. L. Analog Filters. 2nd ed. 2010. (ENG.). 424p. pap. 159.00 (978-1-4419-5277-6(2), 1441952772) Springer.

U Seng Pan, Ben, et al. Design of Very High-Frequency Multirate Switched-Capacitor Circuits: Extending the Boundaries of CMOS Analog Front-End Filtering. 2010. (Springer International Series in Engineering & Computer Science Ser.). xxxii, 227p. pap. 179.00 (978-1-4419-3867-1(2), 1441938672) Springer.

Vanassche, Piet, et al. Systematic Modeling & Analysis of Telecom Frontends & their Building Blocks. 2010. (Springer International Series in Engineering & Computer Science Ser.). xix, 229p. pap. 199.00 (978-1-4419-5265-3(9), 1441952659) Springer.

Vashchenko, V. A. & Shibkov, Andrei. ESD Design for Analog Circuits. 2010. (ENG., Illus.). xx, 457p. 179.00 (978-1-4419-6564-6(5), 1441965645) Springer.

Vogel, Burkhard. The Sound of Silence: Lowest-Noise RIAA Phono-Amps: Designer's Guide. (ENG., Illus.). 2010. xii, 352p. pap. 139.00 (978-3-642-09557-3(7), 3642095577) 2nd ed. 2011. xxiii, 752p. 129.00 (978-3-642-19773-4(6), 3642197736) Springer.

Voldman, Steven H. ESD - Design & Synthesis. 2011. (ENG., Illus.). 290p. 130.00 (978-0-470-68571-6(9), Wiley) Wiley, John & Sons, Inc.

Yarlagadda, R. K. Rao. Analog & Digital Signals & Systems. 2010. (ENG., Illus.). xxviii, 540p. 139.00 (978-1-4419-0033-3(0), 1441900330) Springer.

ANALOG-TO-DIGITAL CONVERTERS

see also MIDI (Standard)

Ahmed, Syed Imran. Pipelined ADC Design & Enhancement Techniques. 2009. (Analog Circuits & Signal Processing Ser.). (ENG., Illus.). 200p. 159.00 (978-90-481-8651-8(X), 904818651X) Springer.

Bajdechi, Ovidiu & Huijsing, Johan H. Systematic Design of Sigma-Delta Analog-to-Digital Converters. 2010. (Springer International Series in Engineering & Computer Science Ser.). 208p. pap. 219.00 (978-1-4419-5456-5(2), 1441954562) Springer.

Bakker, Anton & Huijsing, Johan H. High-Accuracy CMOS Smart Temperature Sensors. 2010. (Springer International Series in Engineering & Computer Science Ser.). 136p. pap. 279.00 (978-1-4419-4862-5(7), 1441948627) Springer.

Breems, Lucien & Huijsing, Johan H. Continuous-Time Sigma-Delta Modulation for A/D Conversion in Radio Receivers. 2010. (Springer International Series in Engineering & Computer Science Ser.). 176p. pap. 259.00 (978-1-4419-4912-7(7), 1441949127) Springer.

Cao, Zhiheng & Yan, Shouli. Low-Power High-Speed ADCs for Nanometer CMOS Integration. (Analog Circuits & Signal Processing Ser.). 2010. xiv, 94p. pap. 159.00 (978-90-481-7885-8(1), 9048178851) 2008. (Illus.). XIV, 98p. 159.00 (978-1-4020-8449-2(8), 1402084498) Springer.

Casier, Herman. Analog Circuit Design: Sensors, Actuators & Power Drivers - Integrated Power Amplifiers from Wireline to RF - Very High Frequency Front Ends. 2008. (ENG.). x, 362p. 189.00 (978-1-4020-8262-7(2), 1402082622) Springer.

Casier, Herman, et al, eds. Analog Circuit Design: Sensors, Actuators & Power Drivers; Integrated Power Amplifiers from Wireline to RF; Very High Frequency Front Ends. 2010. (ENG.). x, 362p. pap. 189.00 (978-90-481-7824-7(X), 904817824X) Springer.

Chen, Sao-Jie & Hsieh, Yong-Hsiang. IQ Calibration Techniques for CMOS Radio Tranceivers. 2006. (Analog Circuits & Signal Processing Ser.). xix, 90p. 199.00 (978-1-4020-5082-4(8), 1402050828) Springer.
Chiu, Yun. Analysis & Design of Pipeline Analog-to-Digital Converters. 2010. 400p. 129.95 (978-0-387-27039-5(6), 0387270396) Springer.
Dallet, Dominique & Machado da Silva, José, eds. Dynamic Characterisation of Analogue-to-Digital Converters. 2010. (Springer International Series in Engineering & Computer Science Ser.). xx, 280p. pap. 159.00 (978-1-4419-3849-7(4), 1441938494) Springer.
El-Chammas, Manar & Murmann, Boris. Background Calibration of Time-Interleaved Data Converters. 2011. (Analog Circuits & Signal Processing Ser.). (ENG., Illus.). xix, 123p. 129.00 **(978-1-4614-1510-7(1),** 1461415101) Springer.
Engelen, Jurgen Van & Plassche, Rudy J. van de. Bandpass Sigma Delta Modulators: Stability Analysis, Performance & Design Aspects. 2010. (ENG.). 208p. pap. 239.00 (978-1-4419-5116-8(4), 1441951164) Springer.
Figueiredo, Pedro M. & Vital, João C. Offset Reduction Techniques in High-Speed Analog-to-Digital Converters: Analysis, Design & Tradeoffs. (Analog Circuits & Signal Processing Ser.). (ENG.). xx, 384p. 2010. pap. 159.00 **(978-90-481-8192-6(5),** 9048181925) 2009. (Illus.). 159.00 (978-1-4020-9715-7(8)) Springer.
Geerts, Yves, et al. Design of Multi-Bit Delta-Sigma A/D Converters. 2010. (Springer International Series in Engineering & Computer Science Ser.). 240p. pap. 219.00 (978-1-4419-5288-2(8), 1441952888) Springer.
Gerfers, Friedel & Ortmanns, Maurits. Continuous-Time Sigma-Delta A/D Conversion: Fundamentals, Performance Limits & Robust Implementations. 2010. (Springer Series in Advanced Microelectronics Ser.). (Illus.). xxii, 241p. pap. 249.00 (978-3-642-06664-1(X), 364206664X) Springer.
Goes, João, et al. Systematic Design for Optimisation of Pipelined ADCs. 2010. (Springer International Series in Engineering & Computer Science Ser.). 176p. pap. 279.00 (978-1-4419-4879-3(1), 1441948791) Springer.
Gustavsson, Mikael, et al. CMOS Data Converters for Communications. 2010. (Springer International Series in Engineering & Computer Science Ser.). 404p. pap. 339.00 (978-1-4419-4968-4(2), 1441949682) Springer.
Haddad, Sandro A. P. & Serdijn, Wouter. Ultra Low-Power Biomedical Signal Processing: An Analog Wavelet Filter Approach for Pacemakers. 2009. (Analog Circuits & Signal Processing Ser.). (Illus.). 250p. 159.00 (978-1-4020-9072-1(2)) Springer.
Harpe, Pieter & Roermund, Arthur H. M. Smart AD & DA Converters. 2010. (Analog Circuits & Signal Processing Ser.). (ENG., Illus.). ix, 190p. 159.00 (978-90-481-9041-6(X), 904819041X) Springer.
Harwood, Emily. Digital CCTV: A Security Professional's Guide. 2007. (ENG., Illus.). 328p. 67.95 (978-0-7506-7745-5(7), Butterworth-Heinemann) Elsevier Science & Technology Bks.
Henzler, Stephan. Time-to-Digital Converters. 2010. (Springer Series in Advanced Microelectronics Ser.). (ENG., Illus.). xii, 124p. 159.00 (978-90-481-8627-3(7), 9048186277) Springer.
Huijsing, Johan H., et al, eds. Analog Circuit Design: Low-Noise, Low-Power, Low-Voltage; Mixed-Mode Design with CAD Tools; Voltage, Current & Time References. 2010. (ENG.). 432p. pap. 139.00 (978-1-4419-5157-1(1), 1441951571) Springer.
—Analog Circuit Design: Operational Amplifiers, Analog to Digital Convertors, Analog Computer Aided Design. 2010. (ENG., Illus.). 464p. pap. 319.00 (978-1-4419-5131-1(8), 1441951318) Springer.
Jonsson, Bengt E. Switched-Current Signal Processing & A/D Conversion Circuits: Design & Implementation. 2010. (Springer International Series in Engineering & Computer Science Ser.). 192p. pap. 259.00 (978-1-4419-4986-8(0), 1441949860) Springer.
Kates, James. Digital Hearing Aids. 2008. (Illus.). 464p. pap. 95.00 (978-1-59756-317-8(X)) Plural Publishing, Inc.
Louwsma, Simon, et al. Time-Interleaved Analog-To-Digital Converters. 2010. (Analog Circuits & Signal Processing Ser.). (Illus.). xvi, 136p. 159.00 (978-90-481-9715-6(5), 9048197155) Springer.
Maloberti, Franco. Data Converters. (ENG., Illus.). xvi, 440p. 2010. pap. 124.00 (978-1-4419-4087-2(1), 1441940871) 2007. 124.00 (978-0-387-32485-2(2), 0387324852) Springer.
Medeiro, Fernando, et al. Top-down Design of High-Performance Sigma-Delta Modulators. 2010. (Springer International Series in Engineering & Computer Science Ser.). 312p. pap. 299.00 (978-1-4419-5067-3(2), 1441950672) Springer.
Murmann, Boris & Boser, Bernhard E. Digitally Assisted Pipeline ADCs: Theory & Implementation. 2010. (ENG.). 175p. pap. 199.00 (978-1-4419-5443-5(0), 1441954430) Springer.
Pace, P. & Ng, W. Photonic Sampling & Analog-to-Digital Conversion. 2008. 224p. per. 89.95 (978-1-934939-14-7(5)) Wexford College Pr.
Pelgrom, Marcel J. M. Analog to Digital Conversion. 2010. (ENG., Illus.). xx, 455p. 179.00 (978-90-481-8887-1(3), 9048188873) Springer.
Peluso, Vincenzo, et al. Design of Low-Voltage Low-Power CMOS DeltaSigma A/D Converters. 2010. (Springer International Series in Engineering & Computer Science Ser.). 192p. pap. 239.00 (978-1-4419-5074-1(5), 1441950745) Springer.
Petrovic, Predrag B. & Stevanovic, Milorad R. Digital Processing & Reconstruction of Complex Signals. 2009. 280p. 159.00 (978-3-642-03842-6(5), 3642038425) Springer.
Philips, Kathleen & Roermund, Arthur H. M. van. Sigma Delta A/D Conversion for Signal Conditioning. 2010. (Springer International Series in Engineering & Computer Science Ser.). x, 227p. pap. 189.00 (978-90-481-7169-9(5), 9048171695) Springer.
Plassche, Rudy J. van de, et al, eds. Analog Circuit Design: High-Speed Analog-to-Digital Converters, Mixed Signal Design; PLLs & Synthesizers. 2010. (ENG.). 408p. pap. 299.00 (978-1-4419-5002-4(8), 1441950028) Springer.
—Analog Circuit Design: Low-Power Low-Voltage, Integrated Filters & Smart Power. 2010. (ENG.). 392p. pap. 349.00 (978-1-4419-5149-6(0), 1441951490) Springer.
Ploeg, Hendrik van der & Nauta, Bram. Calibration Techniques in Nyquist A/D Converters. 2010. (Springer International Series in Engineering & Computer Science Ser.). xviii, 190p. pap. 189.00 (978-90-481-7159-0(8), 9048171598) Springer.
Quinn, Patrick J. & Roermund, Arthur H. M. van. Switched-Capacitor Techniques for High-Accuracy Filter & ADC Design. 2010. (Analog Circuits & Signal Processing Ser.). xvii, 244p. pap. 189.00 (978-90-481-7585-7(2), 9048175852) Springer.
Quinn, Patrick J. & Van Roermund, Arthur H. M. Switched-Capacitor Techniques for High-Accuracy Filter & ADC Design. 2007. (Analog Circuits & Signal Processing Ser.). (Illus.). 244p. 189.00 (978-1-4020-6257-5(5)) Springer.
Rodriguez-Vázquez, Angel, et al, eds. CMOS Telecom Data Converters. 2010. (ENG.). 375p. pap. 185.00 (978-1-4419-5382-7(5), 1441953825) Springer.
Roermund, Arthur H. M. van, et al, eds. Analog Circuit Design: High-Speed A-D Converters, Automotive Electronics & Ultra-Low Power Wireless. 2010. (ENG.). x, 411p. pap. 189.00 (978-90-481-7302-0(7), 9048173027) Springer.
Ruiz-Amaya, Jesús, et al. Device-Level Modeling & Synthesis of High-Performance Pipeline ADCs. 2011. (ENG., Illus.). xiii, 209p. 129.00 (978-1-4419-8845-4(9), 1441988459) Springer.
Sansen, Willy M. C., et al, eds. Analog Circuit Design: Mixed A/D Circuit Design, Sensor Interface Circuits & Communication Circuits. 2010. (ENG.). 332p. pap. 299.00 (978-1-4419-5138-0(5), 1441951385) Springer.
Sauerbrey, Jens. Entwurf analoger CMOS Schaltungen für extrem niedrige Versorgungsspannungen: 108 Abb., 9 Tab. 2007. (Halbleiter-Elektronik Ser.). (GER., Illus.). 164p. 99.00 (978-3-540-40703-4(0)) Springer.
Schaub, Arthur, ed. Digital Hearing Aids. 2008. (ENG.). 188p. pap. 54.99 (978-1-60406-006-5(9)) Thieme Medical Pubs., Inc.
Shoop, Barry L. Photonic Analog-to-Digital Conversion. 2010. (Springer Series in Optical Sciences Ser.). (Illus.). xiii, 330p. pap. 149.00 (978-3-642-07460-8(X), 364207460X) Springer.
Silva, Paulo & Huijsing, Johan H. High-Resolution IF-to-Baseband SigmaDelta ADC for Car Radios. 2010. (Analog Circuits & Signal Processing Ser.). xii, 220p. pap. 159.00 (978-90-481-7788-2(X), 904817788X) Springer.
Sin, Sai-Weng, et al. Generalized Low-Voltage Circuit Techniques for Very High-Speed Time-Interleaved Analog-to-Digital Converters. 2010. (Analog Circuits & Signal Processing Ser.). (Illus.). xvi, 150p. 129.00 (978-90-481-9709-5(0), 9048197090) Springer.
Steyaert, Michiel, et al, eds. Analog Circuit Design: High-speed Clock & Data Recovery, High-performance Amplifiers, Power Management. 2010. (ENG.). xii, 360p. pap. 209.00 (978-90-481-8032-5(5), 9048180325) Springer.
—Analog Circuit Design: Structured Mixed-Mode Design, Multi-Bit Sigma-Delta Converters, Short Range RF Circuits. 2010. (ENG.). 452p. pap. 149.00 (978-1-4419-5308-7(6), 1441953086) Springer.
van de Plassche, Rudy J. CMOS Integrated Analog-to-Digital & Digital-to-Analog Converters. 2nd ed. 2010. (Springer International Series in Engineering & Computer Science Ser.). 640p. pap. 259.00 (978-1-4419-5367-4(1), 1441953671) Springer.
van Roermund, Arthur H. M., et al, eds. Analog Circuit Design: High-Speed A-D Converters, Automotive Electronics & Ultra-Low Power Wireless. 2006. (ENG., Illus.). x, 411p. 189.00 (978-1-4020-5185-2(9), 1402051859) Springer.
van Veldhoven, Robert H. M. & van Roermund, Arthur H. M. Robust Sigma Delta Converters: And their application in low-power highly-digitized flexible Receivers. 2011. (Analog Circuits & Signal Processing Ser.). (ENG.). xxiii, 294p. 129.00 (978-94-007-0643-9(X), 940070643X) Springer.
Waltari, Mikko E. & Halonen, Kari A. I. Circuit Techniques for Low-Voltage & High-Speed A/D Converters. 2010. (Springer International Series in Engineering & Computer Science Ser.). 265p. pap. 205.00 (978-1-4419-5317-9(5), 1441953175) Springer.
Yao, Libin, et al. Low-Power Low-Voltage Sigma-Delta Modulators in Nanometer CMOS. 2010. (Springer International Series in Engineering & Computer Science Ser.). xxiii, 158p. pap. 169.00 (978-90-481-7057-9(5), 9048170575) Springer.
Zjajo, Amir & Pineda de Gyvez, José. Low-Power High-Resolution Analog to Digital Converters: Design, Test & Calibration. 2010. (Analog Circuits & Signal Processing Ser.). (Illus.). xx, 250p. 129.00 (978-90-481-9724-8(4), 9048197244) Springer.

ANALOGIES, ELECTROMECHANICAL
see Electromechanical Analogies

ANALOGIES TEST, MILLER
see Miller Analogies Test

ANALOGY
Aubusson, Peter, et al. Metaphor & analogy in science Education. 2009. (Science & Technology Education Library). 210p. pap. 52.00 (978-1-4020-5707-6(5)) Springer.
Bartha, Paul F. A. By Parallel Reasoning. 2010. (ENG., Illus.). 384p. 74.00 (978-0-19-532553-9(2)) Oxford Univ. Pr., Inc.
Brittain, Patti Tobin. Planetary Powers: The Morin Method. 2011. 126p. pap. 16.95 **(978-0-86690-616-6(9))** American Federation of Astrologers, Inc.
Cajetan, Thomas De Vio. The Analogy of Names & Concept of Being. Bushinski, Edward A., tr. 2011. 104p. 39.95 **(978-1-258-04422-0(6))** Literary Licensing, LLC.
Cajetan, Tommaso de Vio. The Analogy of Names, & the Concept of Being. Bushinski, Edward A. & Koren, Henry J., trs. 2009. 106p. pap. 13.00 (978-1-60608-463-2(1), Wipf and Stock) Wipf & Stock Pubs.
Clement, John J. Creative Model Construction in Scientists & Students: The Role of Imagery, Analogy, & Mental Simulation. 2009. (ENG.). 632p. pap. 89.95 (978-90-481-3023-8(9), 9048130239); (Illus.). 289.00 (978-1-4020-6711-2(9), 1402067119) Springer.
Grothe, Mardy. I Never Metaphor I Didn't Like: A Comprehensive Compilation of History's Greatest Analogies, Metaphors, & Similes. 2008. (ENG.). 336p. 15.99 (978-0-06-135813-5(4)) HarperCollins Pubs.
Hallyn, F., ed. Metaphor & Analogy in the Sciences. 2010. (Origins: Studies in the Sources of Scientific Creativity Ser.). 252p. pap. 189.00 (978-90-481-5559-0(2), 9048155592) Springer.
Harrison, Allan G. & Coll, Richard K., eds. Using Analogies in Middle & Secondary Science Classrooms: The FAR Guide - An Interesting Way to Teach with Analogies. 2007. (Illus.). 288p. 86.95 (978-1-4129-1332-4(2), B13322C) Corwin Pr.
—Using Analogies in Middle & Secondary Science Classrooms: The FAR Guide-An Interesting Way to Teach with Analogies. 2007. (Illus.). 288p. per. 39.95 (978-1-4129-1333-1(0), B13322P) Corwin Pr.
Helman, D. H., ed. Analogical Reasoning: Perspectives of Artificial Intelligence, Cognitive Science, & Philosophy. 2010. (Synthese Library). 440p. pap. 379.00 (978-90-481-8450-7(9), 9048184509) Springer.
Hochschild, Joshua P. The Semantics of Analogy: Rereading Cajetan's de Nominum Analogia. 2010. (ENG., Illus.). 280p. pap. 35.00 (978-0-268-03091-9(X), Univ. of Notre Dame Pr.
Hussain, Shahid. Learnability Results for Elementary Formal Systems. 2009. 80p. pap. (978-3-639-12201-5(1)) VDM Verlag Dr. Mueller e.K.
Indurkhya, B. Metaphor & Cognition: An Interactionist Approach. 2010. (Studies in Cognitive Systems Ser.). (Illus.). 474p. pap. 409.00 (978-90-481-4146-3(X), 904814146X) Springer.
Jantke, K. P. Analogical & Inductive Inference: International Workshop All'86 Wendisch-Rietz, GDR, October 6-10, 1986, Proceedings. 2007. (Lecture Notes in Computer Science Ser.). 240p. per. 34.95 (978-3-540-18081-4(8)) Springer.
Kleinman, Liza. Daily Warm-Ups for Analogies: Level II. 2007. (Daily Warm-Ups Ser.). (ENG.). 191p. per. 18.99 (978-0-8251-6256-5(4)) Walch Education
Musolff, Andreas. Metaphor, Nation & the Holocaust: The Concept of the Body Politic. 2010. (Routledge Critical Studies in Discourse Ser.). (ENG., Illus.). 220p. (C). 128.00 (978-0-415-80119-5(2)) Routledge.
Ross, James F., ed. Portraying Analogy. 2009. (Cambridge Studies in Philosophy Ser.). (ENG.). 260p. pap. 38.99 (978-0-521-11086-0(6)) Cambridge Univ. Pr.
Skousen, R. Analogy & Structure. 2010. 392p. pap. 267.00 (978-90-481-4196-8(6), 9048141966) Springer.
Steinhart, E. C. The Logic of Metaphor: Analogous Parts of Possible Worlds. 2010. (Synthese Library). 264p. pap. 159.00 (978-90-481-5712-9(9), 9048157129) Springer.
Swinburne, Richard. Revelation: From Metaphor to Analogy. 2nd ed. 2007. (ENG.). 364p. 135.00 (978-0-19-921246-0(5)) Oxford Univ. Pr., Inc.
Tatom, Marianne, ed. Unlocking Analogies, Grades 2-3. 2007. (Unlocking Analogies Ser.). (Illus.). 48p. pap. 7.99 (978-1-4190-3390-2(5)) Steck-Vaughn.
—Unlocking Analogies, Grades 4-5. 2007. (Unlocking Analogies Ser.). (Illus.). 48p. pap. 7.99 (978-1-4190-3391-9(3)) Steck-Vaughn.
—Unlocking Analogies, Middle School. 2007. (Unlocking Analogies Ser.). (Illus.). 48p. pap. 7.99 (978-1-4190-3392-6(1)) Steck-Vaughn.
Walch Education, creator. 85 Lesson Launchers Analogies. 2009. (85 Lesson Launchers Ser.). 89p. pap. 11.00 (978-0-8251-6295-4(5)) Walch Education.
—85 More Lesson Launchers Analogies. 2009. (85 More Lesson Launchers Ser.). 89p. pap. 11.00 (978-0-8251-6296-1(3)) Walch Education.
Weiner. Analogies in Physics & Life. 2008. 112.00 (978-981-270-470-2(1)); pap. 73.00 (978-981-270-471-9(X)) World Scientific Publishing Co., Inc.
Zilberman, David B. Analogy in Indian & Western Philosophical Thought. Gourko, Helena & Cohen, Robert S., eds. 2010. (Boston Studies in the Philosophy of Science Ser.). viii, 273p. pap. 299.00 (978-90-481-6839-2(2), 9048168392) Springer.

ANALOGY (LAW)
see Law—Interpretation and Construction

ANALOGY (RELIGION)
see also Anthropomorphism
Bushnell, Horace. Forgiveness & Law, Grounded in Principles Interpreted by Human Analogies. 2009. 144p. pap. (978-0-217-72565-1(1)) Books LLC.
—Forgiveness & Law, Grounded in Principles Interpreted by Human Analogies. 2006. 268p. per. 23.99 (978-1-4255-2391-6(9)) MPublishing.
Butler, J. The Analogy of Religion to the Constitution. 2006. 364p. per. 26.99 (978-1-4255-3802-6(9)) MPublishing.
Butler, Joseph. The Analogy of Religion. 2008. 404p. 30.99 (978-0-559-05027-5(5)); 32.99 (978-0-559-05023-7(2)); pap. 33.75 (978-0-559-05026-8(7)); pap. 34.75 (978-0-559-05024-4(0)) BiblioBazaar.
—The Analogy of Religion. 2009. 254p. pap. (978-0-217-56791-6(6)); 446p. pap. (978-0-217-56794-7(0)) Books LLC.
—The Analogy of Religion. 2007. (ENG.). 300p. per. 19.94 (978-0-615-15872-3(2)) Shenandoah Bible Ministries.
—The Analogy of Religion, etc with an introductory Essay by Albert Barnes. 2006. 336p. per. 23.99 (978-1-4255-3412-7(0)) MPublishing.
—The Analogy of Religion, Natural & Revealed, to the Constitution & Course of Nature by Joseph Butler with an Analysis of the Work by Rev B. 2006. 352p. per. 23.99 (978-1-4255-3570-4(4)) MPublishing.
Johnson, Keith L. Karl Barth & the Analogia Entis. 2011. (T&T Clark Studies in Systematic Theology Ser.). (ENG.). 256p. pap. 44.95 **(978-0-567-34463-2(0),** T&T Clark Int'l) Continuum International Publishing Group, Ltd. GBR. Dist: National Bk. Network.
Klubertanz, SJ, George P. St. Thomas Aquinas on Analogy: A Textual Analysis & Systematic Synthesis. 2009. 328p. pap. 36.00 (978-1-60608-450-2(X), Wipf and Stock) Wipf & Stock Pubs.
Long, Steven A. Analogia Entis: On the Analogy of Being, Metaphysics, & the Act of Faith. 2011. (ENG.). 152p. pap. 25.00 **(978-0-268-03412-2(5))** Univ. of Notre Dame Pr.
Pannenberg, Wolfhart. Analogie und Offenbarung: Eine kritische Untersuchung zur Geschichte des Analogiebegriffs in der Lehre von der Gotteserkenntnis. 2007. (GER.). 215p. (C). 93.00 (978-3-525-56158-4(X)) Vandenhoeck & Ruprecht GmbH & Co. KG DEU. Dist: ISD.
Phelan, Gerald B. St Thomas & Analogy: The Aquinas Lecture 1941. 2011. 70p. 36.95 **(978-1-258-04621-7(0))** Literary Licensing, LLC.
Pickstock, Catherine. In the Names of God: Analogy, Univocity & the Destiny of the West. 2008. 22.95 (978-0-415-18684-1(6)) Routledge.
White, Roger M. Talking about God: The Concept of Analogy & the Problem of Religious Language. 2010. (Transcending Boundaries in Philosophy & Theology Ser.). 220p. 99.95 (978-1-4094-0036-3(0)); pap. 39.95 (978-1-4094-0042-4(5)) Ashgate Publishing Co.
White, Thomas Joseph. The Analogy of Being: Invention of the Antichrist or the Wisdom of God? 2010. 448p. pap. 48.00 (978-0-8028-6533-5(X)) Eerdmans, William B. Publishing Co.

ANALYSIS (MATHEMATICS)
see Calculus; Functions; Harmonic Analysis; Mathematical Analysis

ANALYSIS (PHILOSOPHY)
see also Linguistic Analysis (Linguistics); Logical Positivism; Semantics (Philosophy)
Agosta, Lou. Empathy in the Context of Philosophy. 2010. (Renewing Philosophy Ser.). (ENG., Illus.). 256p. 84.00 (978-0-230-24183-1(2)) Palgrave Macmillan.
Akehurst, Thomas L. The Cultural Politics of Analytic Philosophy: Britishness & the Spectre of Europe. (ENG.). 220p. 2011. pap. 44.95 **(978-1-4411-2657-3(0))** 2010. 130.00 (978-1-84706-450-9(7)) Continuum International Publishing Group, Ltd. GBR. Dist: National Bk. Network.
Beaney, Michael. Frege: Making Sense. (Illus.). 352p. 30.50 (978-0-7156-2712-9(0)) Duckworth Publishers GBR. Dist: International Publishers Marketing.
Beaney, Michael, ed. The Analytic Turn. 2009. 308p. pap. 39.95 (978-0-415-87575-2(7)) Routledge.
—The Analytic Turn: Analysis in Early Analytic Philosophy & Phenomenology. 2007. (Routledge Studies in Twentieth Century Philosophy Ser.). 290p. 156.00 (978-0-415-38167-3(3)) Routledge.
Beards, Andrew. Insight & Analysis: Essays in Applying Lonergan's Thought. 2010. (ENG.). 288p. 130.00 (978-1-4411-5434-7(5)) Continuum International Publishing Group, Ltd. GBR. Dist: National Bk. Network.
—Method in Metaphysics: Lonergan & the Future of Analytical Philosophy. 2008. (Lonergan Studies). (ENG.). 448p. (978-0-8020-9752-1(9)) Univ. of Toronto Pr.
Becker, Edward. The Themes of Quine's Philosophy: Meaning, Reference, & Knowledge. 2012. (ENG.). 344p. 95.00 **(978-1-107-01523-4(5))** Cambridge Univ. Pr.
Birnbacher, Dieter. Analytische Einführung in die Ethik. 2nd ed. 2007. (De Gruyter Studienbuch Ser.). (GER., Illus.). XV, 460p. (C). pap. 35.00 (978-3-11-019442-5(2)) De Gruyter, Walter Inc.
Black, Max, ed. Philosophical Analysis: A Collection of Essays. (Essay Index Reprint Ser.). 405p. reprint ed. lib. bdg. 52.00 (978-0-8290-0796-1(2)) Irvington Pubs.
Bottani, A., et al, eds. Individuals, Essence & Identity: Themes of Analytic Metaphysics. 2010. (Topoi Library). (ENG & ACE.). 516p. pap. 229.00 (978-90-481-5988-8(1), 9048159881) Springer.
Boundas, Constantin V., ed. Columbia Companion to Twentieth-Century Philosophies. (ENG.). 740p. (gr. 17). 2009. pap. 35.00 (978-0-231-14203-8(X)) 2007. 100.00 (978-0-231-14202-1(1)) Columbia Univ. Pr.
Braddon-Mitchell, David & Nola, Robert. Conceptual Analysis & Philosophical Naturalism. Braddon-Mitchell, David & Nola, Robert, eds. 2008. (ENG.). 384p. (gr. 17). 75.00 (978-0-262-01256-0(1)) MIT Pr.
Braddon-Mitchell, David & Nola, Robert, eds. Conceptual Analysis & Philosophical Naturalism. 2008. (ENG., Illus.). 384p. (gr. 17). pap. 40.00 (978-0-262-51228-2(9)) MIT Pr.
BRANDL, Johannes L., et al, eds. Grazer Philosophische Studien: Volume 73 - 2006. 2007. (Grazer Philosophische Studien: 73). (GER & ENG.). 269p. pap. 73.00 (978-90-420-2232-4(9)) Rodopi.
Brandom, Robert. Between Saying & Doing: Towards an Analytic Pragmatism. 2008. (ENG., Illus.). 240p. 45.00 (978-0-19-954287-1(2)) Oxford Univ. Pr., Inc.

Butrick, Richard. Carnap on meaning & Analyticity. (Janua Linguarum. Series Minor Ser.). (ENG.). 77p. 210.00 (978-3-11-213364-4(1)); 135.00 **(978-3-11-129213-7(4))** De Gruyter, Mouton DEU. Dist: de Gruyter, Walter GmbH & Co. KG.
Candlish, Stewart. The Russell/Bradley Dispute & its Significance for Twentieth Century Philosophy. 2009. (ENG.). 240p. pap. 36.00 (978-0-230-23051-4(2)) Palgrave Macmillan.
—The Russell/Bradley Dispute & Its Significance for Twentieth-Century Philosophy. annot. ed. 2007. (ENG.). 256p. 100.00 (978-0-230-50685-5(2)) Palgrave Macmillan.
Capaldi, N. The Enlightenment Project in the Analytic Conversation. 2010. (Philosophical Studies in Contemporary Culture Ser.). 552p. pap. 289.00 (978-90-481-5019-9(1), 9048150191) Springer.
Cappelen, Herman & Hawthorne, John. Relativism & Monadic Truth. 2009. (ENG.). 170p. 45.00 (978-0-19-956055-4(2)) Oxford Univ. Pr., Inc.
Carnap, Rudolph. The Unity of Science (Routledge Revivals) 2011. (Routledge Revivals Ser.). (ENG.). 106p. 80.00 (978-0-415-67939-8(7)) Routledge.
Carrara, Massimiliano & Morato, V. ittorio, eds. Language, Knowledge, & Metaphysics. 2009. (Illus.). 264p. pap. (978-1-904987-79-6(6)) College Pubns.
Carrier, David. Proust/Warhol: Analytical Philosophy of Art. 2008. (American University Studies XX: Fine Arts Ser.). 142p. (C). 58.95 (978-1-4331-0433-6(4)) Lang, Peter Publishing, Inc.
Chase, James & Reynolds, Jack. Analytic versus Continental: Arguments on the Methods & Value of Philosophy. 2011. (ENG.). 304p. pap. (978-0-7735-3808-5(9)); (C). (978-0-7735-3807-8(0)) McGill-Queen's Univ. Pr.
Christensen, Carleton B. Self & World: From Analytic Philosophy to Phenomenology. 2008. (Quellen und Studien Zur Philosophie Ser.). (ENG.). X, 394p. 147.00 (978-3-11-020401-8(0)); 224.00 **(978-3-11-173826-0(4))** De Gruyter, Walter Inc.
Coggins, Geraldine. Could There Have Been Nothing? Against Metaphysical Nihilism. 2011. (ENG., Illus.). 288p. 84.00 (978-0-230-57363-5(0)) Palgrave Macmillan.
Crasnow, Sharon L. & Superson, Anita M., eds. Out from the Shadows: Analytical Feminist Contributions to Traditional Philosophy, 1 vol. 2012. (Studies in Feminist Philosophy Ser.). (ENG.). 560p. 99.00 (978-0-19-985546-9(3)); pap. 39.95 (978-0-19-985547-6(1)) Oxford Univ. Pr., Inc.
Danto, Arthur C. Analytical Philosophy of Action. 2009. (ENG.). 240p. pap. 29.99 (978-0-521-11751-7(8)) Cambridge Univ. Pr.
Doussaud, Valérie. Static & Dynamic Elements in Ted Hughes' River. 2011. 100p. pap. **(978-3-8433-8865-8(2))** Lambert Academic Publishing.
Dzhafarov, Ehtibar N. & Perry, Lacey. Descriptive & Normative Approaches to Human Behavior. 2011. 332p. 108.00 **(978-981-4368-00-1(8))** World Scientific Publishing Co., Inc.
Farrand, Frederick. A New, Objective, Pro-Objectivity Normative Theory: An Objective Basis for Morality, Society, Politics, Law, Education, Etc.- And for Liberty & Peace. 2010. (ENG.). 222p. pap. 31.99 (978-0-7618-5286-5(7)) Univ. Pr. of America, Inc.
Fleming, Richard. Evil & Silence. 2010. (Media & Power Ser.). 168p. pap. 26.95 (978-1-59451-729-7(0)) Paradigm Pubs.
Gallois, Andri. The World Without, the Mind Within: An Essay on First-Person Authority. 2008. (Cambridge Studies in Philosophy Ser.). (ENG.). 228p. pap. 42.00 (978-0-521-05021-0(9)) Cambridge Univ. Pr.
Gibbs, Errol A. & Grey, Philip A. Thoughts to Enlighten & Empower the Mind: 2001 Questions & Philosophical Thoughts to Inspire, Enlighten, & Empower Our World to Limitless Heights. 2011. 268p. pap. 16.95 **(978-1-4567-4071-9(7))** AuthorHouse.
Glock, Hans-Johann. What Is Analytic Philosophy? 2008. (ENG.). 304p. (C). 80.00 (978-0-521-87267-6(7)); (Illus.). pap. 23.99 (978-0-521-69426-1(4)) Cambridge Univ. Pr.
Glock, Hans-Johann & Hyman, John, eds. Wittgenstein & Analytic Philosophy: Essays for P. M. S. Hacker. 2009. (ENG., Illus.). 296p. 95.00 (978-0-19-921323-8(2)) Oxford Univ. Pr., Inc.
Gutting, Gary. What Philosophers Know: Case Studies in Recent Analytic Philosophy. 2009. (ENG.). 264p. 90.00 (978-0-521-85621-8(3)); pap. 31.99 (978-0-521-67222-1(8)) Cambridge Univ. Pr.
Haaparanta, L., ed. Mind, Meaning & Mathematics: Essays on the Philosophical Views of Husserl & Frege. 2010. (Synthese Library). 300p. pap. 239.00 (978-90-481-4366-5(7), 9048143667) Springer.
Hacking, Ian, ed. Exercises in Analysis: Essays by Students of Casimir Lewy. 2009. (ENG.). 220p. pap. 31.99 (978-0-521-10965-9(5)) Cambridge Univ. Pr.
Hallett, Garth. One God of All? Probing Pluralist Identities. 2010. (ENG.). 160p. 100.00 (978-0-8264-4632-9(9)) Continuum International Publishing Group, Ltd. GBR. Dist: National Bk. Network.
Heaton, John. The Talking Cure: Wittgenstein's Therapeutic Method for Psychotherapy. 2010. (ENG., Illus.). 288p. 89.00 (978-0-230-23761-2(4)) Palgrave Macmillan.
Hylton, Peter. Propositions, Functions, & Analysis: Selected Essays on Russell's Philosophy. 2008. (ENG.). 230p. 39.95 (978-0-19-954362-5(3)) Oxford Univ. Pr., Inc.
Jackson, Howell E. & Kaplow, Louis. Analytical Methods for Lawyers, 2d. 2nd rev. ed. 2010. (University Casebook Ser.). (Illus.). 568p. 141.00 (978-1-59941-921-3(1), Foundation Pr.) West.
Jadacki, Jacek & Pacewiczek, Jacek, eds. The Lvov-Warsaw School: The New Generation. 2006. (Poznan Studies in the Philosophy of the Sciences & the Humanities: 89). (ENG.). 512p. 156.00 (978-90-420-2068-9(7)) Rodopi.
Juhl, Cory. Analyticity. 2009. (ENG.). 320p. 35.95 (978-0-415-77333-1(4)); 190.00 (978-0-415-77332-4(6)) Routledge.
Khathchadourian, H. A Critical Study in Method. 2010. 272p. pap. 172.00 (978-90-481-8250-3(6), 9048182506) Springer.
Kimmons, Ronald. An Infinity of Interpretations: A Bit of Social Commentary on & a Philosophical Examination of Life in These Times. 2010. 216p. pap. 17.95 (978-1-4401-7663-0(9)) iUniverse, Inc.
Langkau, Julia & Nimtz, Christian, eds. New Perspectives on Concepts. 2010. (Illus.). 264p. pap. 74.00 (978-90-420-3018-3(6)) Rodopi.
Larrey, Philip. Thinking Logically: A Historical Critique of Trends in Contemporary Philosophy of Logic in the Analytical Tradition. 2006. (ENG.). 118p. pap. 16.00 (978-1-888570-80-9(6)) Davies Group Pubs., The.
Linsky, Bernard. The Evolution of Principia Mathematica: Bertrand Russell's Manuscripts & Notes for the Second Edition. 2011. (ENG., Illus.). 418p. 150.00 (978-1-107-00327-9(X)) Cambridge Univ. Pr.
Livingston, Paul. Analytic Philosophy & the Vision of Language. 2008. (Routledge Studies in Twentieth Century Philosophy Ser.). (ENG.). 304p. 125.00 (978-0-415-96114-1(9)) Routledge.
Mader, Linda. Supremacist Ideology & the American Language of Empire. 2008. 144p. pap. (978-3-639-06158-1(6)) VDM Verlag Dr. Mueller e.K.
Margolis, Joseph. Pragmatism's Advantage: American & European Philosophy at the End of the Twentieth Century. 2010. (ENG.). 192p. 65.00 (978-0-8047-6268-7(6)); pap. 24.95 (978-0-8047-7046-0(8)) Stanford Univ. Pr.
Martinich, A. P. & Sosa, David, eds. Analytic Philosophy: An Anthology. 2nd ed. 2011. (Blackwell Philosophy Anthologies Ser.: 25). (ENG.). 600p. pap. 59.95 (978-1-4443-3570-5(7), Wiley-Blackwell) Wiley, John & Sons, Inc.
McCall, Thomas H. Which Trinity? Whose Monotheism? Philosophical & Systematic Theologians on the Metaphysics of Trinitarian Theology. 2010. vii, 256p. pap. 30.00 (978-0-8028-6270-9(5)) Eerdmans, William B. Publishing Co.
McGinn, Colin. Truth by Analysis: Games, Names, & Philosophy, 1 vol. 2011. (ENG.). 304p. 65.00 **(978-0-19-985614-5(1))** Oxford Univ. Pr., Inc.
Michael George, Kizito. Analytic Philosophy for the Perplexed. 2011. 220p. pap. **(978-3-8443-2837-0(8))** Lambert Academic Publishing.
Milkov, N. A Hundred Years of English Philosophy. 2010. (Philosophical Studies Ser.). 312p. pap. 189.00 (978-90-481-6345-8(5), 9048163455) Springer.
Mittleman, Alan. Hope in a Democratic Age: Philosophy, Religion, & Political Theory. 2009. (ENG.). 272p. 39.95 (978-0-19-929715-3(0)) Oxford Univ. Pr., Inc.
Nielsen, Keld Stehr. The Evolution of the Private Language Argument. 2008. (Ashgate Wittgensteinian Studies Ser.). (Illus.). 220p. 114.95 (978-0-7546-5629-6(2)) Ashgate Publishing Co.
Norris, Christopher. The Deconstructive Turn: Essays in the Rhetoric of Philosophy. 2010. (Routledge Revivals Ser.). (ENG.). 202p. 105.00 (978-0-415-57244-6(4), Routledge) Taylor & Francis Group GBR. Dist: Taylor & Francis Group.
Norris, Christopher & Norris. On Truth & Meaning: Language, Logic & the Grounds of Belief. 2006. (ENG.). 216p. 44.95 (978-0-8264-9128-2(6)) Continuum International Publishing Group, Ltd. GBR. Dist: National Bk. Network.
Nuzzo, Angelica. Hegel & the Analytic Tradition. Nuzzo, Angelica, ed. 2010. (Continuum Studies in Philosophy Ser.). (ENG.). 224p. 120.00 (978-1-4411-3950-4(8)) Continuum International Publishing Group, Ltd. GBR. Dist: National Bk. Network.
Nuzzo, Angelica, ed. Hegel & the Analytic Tradition. 2011. (ENG.). 218p. pap. 44.95 **(978-1-4411-1356-6(8))** Continuum International Publishing Group, Ltd. GBR. Dist: National Bk. Network.
Paterson, Craig & Pugh, Matthew S. Analytical Thomism: Traditions in Dialogue. 2006. 356p. 130.00 (978-0-7546-3438-6(8)) Ashgate Publishing Co.
Patron, Sylvie, ed. Théorie, Analyse, Interprétation des Récits/Theory, Analysis, Interpretation of Narratives. 2011. (ENG & FRE.). 367p. pap. **(978-3-0343-0055-1(7))** Lang, Peter.
Pedhazur, E. & Schmelkin, L. Measurement, Design, & Analysis: An Integrated Approach. 2nd ed. 59.95 (978-0-8058-3244-0(0)) Erlbaum, Lawrence Assocs., Inc.
Preston, Aaron. Analytic Philosophy: The History of an Illusion. 2010. (Continuum Studies in Philosophy Ser.). (ENG.). 208p. 44.95 (978-1-4411-3196-6(5)) Continuum International Publishing Group, Ltd. GBR. Dist: National Bk. Network.
Preston, Aaron & Preston. Analytic Philosophy: The History of an Illusion. 2007. (Continuum Studies in Philosophy). (ENG.). 204p. 120.00 (978-0-8264-9003-2(4)) Continuum International Publishing Group, Ltd. GBR. Dist: National Bk. Network.
Putnam, Hilary. Meaning & the Moral Sciences (Routledge Revivals) 2010. (Routledge Revivals Ser.). (Illus.). 158p. 95.00 (978-0-415-58091-5(9), Routledge) Taylor & Francis Group GBR. Dist: Taylor & Francis Group.
Ramsey, Ian T., ed. Words about God: The Philosophy of Religion. 2011. (Ian T. Ramsey Reprint Ser.). 252p. pap. 28.00 **(978-1-61097-257-4(0),** Wipf and Stock) Wipf & Stock Pubs.
Redding, Paul. Analytic Philosophy & the Return of Hegelian Thought. 2007. (Modern European Philosophy Ser.). (ENG.). 264p. 111.00 (978-0-521-87272-0(3)) Cambridge Univ. Pr.
—Analytic Philosophy & the Return of Hegelian Thought. 2010. (Modern European Philosophy Ser.). (ENG.). 264p. pap. 35.99 (978-0-521-17234-9(9)) Cambridge Univ. Pr.
Reed, Ananya Mukherjee & Reed, Delbert. Origins of Analytic Philosophy: Kant & Frege. 2008. (Continuum Studies in Philosophy Ser.). (ENG.). 224p. 130.00 (978-0-8264-9337-8(8)) Continuum International Publishing Group, Ltd. GBR. Dist: National Bk. Network.
Reed, Delbert. Origins of Analytic Philosophy: Kant & Frege. 2010. (Continuum Studies in Philosophy Ser.). (ENG.). 224p. 44.95 (978-1-4411-2302-2(4)) Continuum International Publishing Group, Ltd. GBR. Dist: National Bk. Network.
Reynolds, Jack, et al, eds. Postanalytic & Metacontinental: Crossing Philosophical Divides. 2011. (ENG.). 272p. pap. 44.95 **(978-1-4411-0999-6(4))** Continuum International Publishing Group, Ltd. GBR. Dist: National Bk. Network.
Ronald E. Kimmons. An Infinity of Interpretations: A Bit of Social Commentary on & a Philosophical Examination of Life in These Times. 2010. 216p. 27.95 (978-1-4401-7665-4(5)) iUniverse, Inc.
Rorty, Richard & Rorty, R. Philosophy & the Mirror of Nature. 30th anniv. ed. 2008. (ENG.). 472p. pap. 35.00 (978-0-691-14132-9(0)) Princeton Univ. Pr.
Ross, James. Thought & World: The Hidden Necessities. 2008. (ENG., Illus.). 280p. 50.00 (978-0-268-04056-7(7)); pap. 28.00 (978-0-268-04057-4(5)) Univ. of Notre Dame Pr.
Russell, Joseph. Analysis & Dialectic: Studies in the Logic of Foundation Problems. Russell, P., ed. 2010. (Nijhoff International Philosophy Ser.). 492p. pap. 419.00 (978-90-481-8281-7(6), 9048182816) Springer.
Saint-Louis, Jose. The Fundamental Principles of a Good Government. 2011. 182p. 27.95 **(978-1-60976-810-2(8),** Eloquent Bks.) AEG Literary Publishing Services, Inc.
Salmon, Nathan. Content, Cognition, & Communication: Philosophical Papers II. 2007. 420p. 150.00 (978-0-19-928272-2(2)) Oxford Univ. Pr., Inc.
Salmon, Nathan U. Content, Cognition, & Communication: Philosophical Papers II. 2007. (ENG.). 384p. per. 60.00 (978-0-19-928472-6(5)) Oxford Univ. Pr., Inc.
Schear, Joseph K., ed. Mind, Reason & Being-in-the-World: The Mcdowell-Dreyfus Debate. 2012. (ENG.). 272p. (C). pap. 39.95 (978-0-415-48587-6(8)) Routledge.
—Mind, Reason & Being-in-the-World: The McDowell-Dreyfus Debate. 2012. (ENG.). 272p. (C). 140.00 (978-0-415-48586-9(X)) Routledge.
Schnieder, Benjamin & Schulz, Moritz, eds. Themes from Early Analytic Philosophy: Essays in Honour of Wolfgang Künne. 2011. (Illus.). 417p. pap. 123.00 **(978-90-420-3362-7(2))** Rodopi.
Schwartz, Stephen P. A Brief History of Analytic Philosophy: From Russell to Rawls. 2012. (ENG.). 368p. pap. 29.95 **(978-0-470-67208-2(0),** Wiley-Blackwell) Wiley, John & Sons, Inc.
—A Brief History of Analytic Philosophy: From Russell to Rawls. 2012. (ENG.). 368p. 99.95 **(978-0-470-67207-5(2),** Wiley-Blackwell) Wiley, John & Sons, Inc.
Siltala, Raimo. Law, Truth, & Reason: A Treatise on Legal Argumentation. 2011. (Law & Philosophy Library). (ENG., Illus.). xv, 290p. 139.00 **(978-94-007-1871-5(3),** 9400718713) Springer.
Sluga, H. Frege-arg Philosophers. 2008. (ENG.). 384p. 45.00 (978-0-415-48772-6(2)) Routledge.
Smith, Peter James. Realism & the Progress of Science. 2009. (Cambridge Studies in Philosophy Ser.). (ENG.). 144p. pap. 28.99 (978-0-521-11034-1(3)) Cambridge Univ. Pr.
Stengel, Kathrin. Das Subjekt Als Grenze: Ein Vergleich der Erkenntnistheoretischen Ansätze Bei Wittgenstein und Merleau-Ponty. (Quellen und Studien zur Philosophie Ser.). (GER.). XI, 152p. 150.00 **(978-3-11-182460-4(8))** De Gruyter, Walter Inc.
Tartaglia, James. Rorty & the Mirror of Nature. 2007. (Routledge Philosophy Guidebooks Ser.). (ENG.). 264p. (C). per. 27.95 (978-0-415-38331-8(5)) Routledge.
—Routledge Philosophy Guidebook to Rorty & the Mirror of Nature. 2007. (Routledge Philosophy Guidebooks Ser.). (ENG.). 264p. (C). 110.00 (978-0-415-38330-1(7)) Routledge.
Textor, Mark. The Astrian Contribution to Analytic Philosophy. annot. ed. 2006. (London Studies in the History of Philosophy). 328p. 130.00 (978-0-415-40405-1(3)) Routledge.
Trakakis, Nick. End of Philosophy of Religion. 2009. (ENG.). 192p. 120.00 (978-1-84706-534-6(1)) Continuum International Publishing Group, Ltd. GBR. Dist: National Bk. Network.
Trakakis, Nick. The End of Philosophy of Religion. 2011. (ENG.). 192p. pap. 44.95 **(978-1-4411-4970-1(8))** Continuum International Publishing Group, Ltd. GBR. Dist: National Bk. Network.
Tugendhat, Ernst. Traditional & Analytical Philosophy: Lectures on the Philosophy of Language. Gorner, P. A., tr. from GER. 2010. (ENG.). 452p. pap. 44.00 (978-0-521-12573-4(1)) Cambridge Univ. Pr.
Vanderbeeken, Robrecht & D'Hooghe, Bart, eds. Worldviews, Science & Us: Studies of Analytical Metaphysics: A Selection of Topics from a Methodological Perspective. 2009. 241p. 85.00 (978-981-4295-81-9(7)) World Scientific Publishing Co., Inc.
Wagner, Pierre. Carnap's Logical Syntax of Language. 2009. (History of Analytic Philosophy Ser.). (ENG., Illus.). 304p. 100.00 (978-0-230-20151-4(2)) Palgrave Macmillan.
Williams, James, et al, eds. Postanalytic & Metacontinental: Crossing Philosophical Divides. 2010. (Continuum Studies in Philosophy Ser.). (ENG., Illus.). 272p. 120.00 (978-0-8264-2441-9(4)) Continuum International Publishing Group, Ltd. GBR. Dist: National Bk. Network.
Wolterstorff, Nicholas & Cuneo, Terence. Inquiring about God: Volume 1, Selected Essays, 2 vols. 2010. (ENG.). 322p. 89.00 (978-0-521-51465-1(7)) Cambridge Univ. Pr.
Zabala, Santiago. The Hermeneutic Nature of Analytic Philosophy: A Study of Ernst Tugendhat. Haskell, Michael, tr. from ITA. 2008. (ENG., Illus.). 264p. (gr. 17). 45.00 (978-0-231-14388-2(5)) Columbia Univ. Pr.

ANALYSIS, CHEMICAL
see Chemistry, Analytic

ANALYSIS, CHROMATOGRAPHIC
see Chromatographic Analysis

ANALYSIS, CONFORMATIONAL
see Conformational Analysis

ANALYSIS, DREAM
see Dream Interpretation

ANALYSIS, ELECTROCHEMICAL
see Electrochemical Analysis

ANALYSIS, FACTORIAL
see Factor Analysis

ANALYSIS, FOURIER
see Fourier Analysis

ANALYSIS, GLOBAL (MATHEMATICS)
see Global Analysis (Mathematics)

ANALYSIS, INTERACTION (EDUCATION)
see Interaction Analysis in Education

ANALYSIS, JOB
see Job Analysis

ANALYSIS, MICROPROBE
see Microprobe Analysis

ANALYSIS, MICROSCOPIC
see Microscopy

ANALYSIS, MUSICAL
see Musical Analysis

ANALYSIS, P-ADIC
see p-Adic Analysis

ANALYSIS, PHILOSOPHICAL
see Analysis (Philosophy)

ANALYSIS, RISK
see Risk Assessment

ANALYSIS, SPATIAL (STATISTICS)
see Spatial Analysis (Statistics)

ANALYSIS, SPECTRUM
see Spectrum Analysis

ANALYSIS, STOCHASTIC
see Stochastic Analysis

ANALYSIS, TRACE
see Trace Analysis

ANALYSIS, VOLUMETRIC
see Volumetric Analysis

ANALYSIS OF BLOOD
see Blood—Analysis

ANALYSIS OF CONTENT (COMMUNICATION)
see Content Analysis (Communication)

ANALYSIS OF CONVERSATION
see Conversation Analysis

ANALYSIS OF ENVIRONMENTAL IMPACT
see Environmental Impact Analysis

ANALYSIS OF FOOD
see Food—Analysis; Food Adulteration and Inspection

ANALYSIS OF SOILS
see Soils—Analysis

ANALYSIS OF TIME SERIES
see Time-Series Analysis

ANALYSIS OF URBAN IMPACT
see Urban Impact Analysis

ANALYSIS OF VARIANCE
see also Experimental Design; Multivariate Analysis; Sampling (Statistics)

Basso, Dario, et al. Permutation Tests for Stochastic Ordering & ANOVA: Theory & Applications with R. 2009. (Lecture Notes in Statistics Ser.). (ENG., Illus.). xiv, 218p. pap. 89.95 (978-0-387-85955-2(1)) Springer.
Box, George E. P. Statistics for Experimenters Set: Design, Innovation, & Discovery. 2nd ed. 2009. (ENG.). 664p. 158.00 (978-0-470-57094-4(6)); 187.00 (978-0-470-57091-3(1)) Wiley, John & Sons, Inc. (Wiley).
Brennan, Robert L. Generalizability Theory. 2010. (Statistics for Social & Behavioral Sciences Ser.). xx, 538p. pap. 109.00 (978-1-4419-2938-9(X), 144192938X) Springer.
Ceyhan, Elvan. Correcting for Covariates. 2009. 68p. pap. (978-3-639-19607-8(4)) VDM Verlag Dr. Mueller e.K.

Christensen, Ronald. Plane Answers to Complex Questions: The Theory of Linear Models. (Springer Texts in Statistics Ser.). (Illus.). 3rd ed. 2010. xix, 473p. pap. 119.00 *(978-1-4419-2971-6(1)*, 1441929711) 4th ed. 2011. (ENG., xxi, 494p. 99.00 ***(978-1-4419-9815-6(2)***, 1441998152) Springer.
Clark, Virginia A., et al. Applied Statistics: Analysis of Variance & Regression. 3rd ed. 2009. (Wiley Series in Probability & Statistics Ser.: 836). (ENG., Illus.). 480p. pap. 102.00 *(978-0-470-57125-5(X)*, Wiley) Wiley, John & Sons, Inc.
Cram101 Textbook Reviews. Outlines & Highlights for Analysis of Variance Designs: A Conceptual & Computational Approach by Glenn Gamst. 2011. 148p. pap. 29 95 ***(978-1-61812-979-6(1))*** Cram101 Inc.
—Outlines & Highlights for Data Analysis for Experimental Design by Richard Gonzalez. 2011. 170p. pap. 29.95 ***(978-1-61905-156-0(7))*** Cram101 Inc.
Cram101 Textbook Reviews Staff. Outlines & Highlights for Applied Linear Statistical Models by Kutner, Isbn: 9780073108742. 2009. 246p. pap. 31.95 *(978-1-4288-6816-8(X))* Cram101 Inc.
Davis, James B. Statistics Using SAS Enterprise Guide. 2006. (SAS Press Ser.). (Illus.). 784p. per. 99.95 *(978-1-59047-566-9(6)*, SAS Pr.) SAS Publishing.
Doncaster, C. Patrick & Davey, Andrew J. H. Analysis of Variance & Covariance: How to Choose & Construct Models for the Life Sciences. 2007. (ENG., Illus.). 304p. 128.00 *(978-0-521-86562-3(X))* Cambridge Univ. Pr.
Doncaster, Patrick & Davey, Andrew. Analysis of Variance & Covariance: How to Choose & Construct Models for the Life Sciences. 2007. (ENG., Illus.). 302p. (C). pap. 56.00 *(978-0-521-68447-7(1))* Cambridge Univ. Pr.
Ellis, Paul D. The Essential Guide to Effect Sizes: Statistical Power, Meta-Analysis, & the Interpretation of Research Results. 2010. (ENG., Illus.). 192p. pap. 36.00 *(978-0-521-14246-5(6))* Cambridge Univ. Pr.
Evans, Myron. Generally Covariant Unified Field Theory - the Geometrization of Physics - Volume III. 2006. (Illus.). 188p. per. *(978-1-84549-131-4(9))* arima publishing.
Fung, Kaiser. Numbers Rule Your World: The Hidden Influence of Probabilities & Statistics on Everything You Do. 2010. (ENG., Illus.). 224p. 22.95 *(978-0-07-162653-8(0)*, 0071626530) McGraw-Hill Cos., The.
Gamst, Glenn, et al. Analysis of Variance Designs: A Conceptual & Computational Approach with SPSS & SAS. 2008. (ENG., Illus.). 594p. (C). 95.00 *(978-0-521-87481-6(5))* Cambridge Univ. Pr.
Gebril, Atta. Score Generalizability in Writing Assessment. 2009. 236p. pap. *(978-3-639-13171-0(1))* VDM Verlag Dr. Mueller e.K.
George, Pradeep. Response Surface Method. 2008. 76p. pap. *(978-3-639-01185-2(6))* VDM Verlag Dr. Mueller e.K.
Giudici, Paolo & Figini, Silvia. Applied Data Mining for Business & Industry. 2nd ed. 2009. (ENG., Illus.). 258p. pap. 75.00 *(978-0-470-05887-9(0)*, Wiley) Wiley, John & Sons, Inc.
Gonzalez, Richard. Data Analysis for Experimental Design. 2008. (ENG., Illus.). 439p. 70.00 *(978-1-60623-017-6(4))* Guilford Pubns., Inc.
Grissom, Robert J. & Kim, John J. Effect Sizes for Research. 2nd rev. ed. 2011. (ENG.). 452p. 135.00 *(978-0-415-87768-8(7))*; pap. 49.95 *(978-0-415-87769-5(5))* Taylor & Francis Group GBR. (Routledge). Dist: Taylor & Francis Group.
Gu, Chong. Smoothing Spline ANOVA Models. 2010. (Springer Series in Statistics Ser.). (Illus.). xiii, 289p. pap. 139.00 *(978-1-4419-2966-2(5)*, 1441929665) Springer.
Hox, Joop. Multilevel Analysis: Techniques & Applications. 2nd rev. ed. 2010. (Quantitative Methodology Ser.). (ENG., Illus.). 392p. (C). 95.00 *(978-1-84872-845-5(X))*; pap. 49.95 *(978-1-84872-846-2(8))* Taylor & Francis Group GBR. (Routledge). Dist: Taylor & Francis Group.
Johnson, Dallas E. & Milliken, George A. Analysis of Messy Data, Vol. 1. 2nd rev. ed. 2009. (ENG., Illus.). 674p. 92.95 *(978-1-58488-334-0(0)*, Chapman & Hall/CRC) CRC Pr. LLC.
Jordan, John. Production Variance Analysis in SAP Controlling. 2nd exp. ed. 2011. (Illus.). 240p. 84.95 *(978-1-59229-381-0(6)*, SAP PR.) Galileo Pr., Inc.
Klemelä, Jussi. Smoothing of Multivariate Data: Density Estimation & Visualization. 2009. (Wiley Series in Probability & Statistics Ser.: 737). (ENG., Illus.). 603p. 137.00 *(978-0-470-29088-0(9)*, Wiley) Wiley, John & Sons, Inc.
Knight, Mike & Mather, Robert. Analysis of Variance: An Integrated Approach to Experimental Design. rev. ed. 2010. (ENG.). 290p. pap. 82.58 *(978-0-7575-5167-3(X))* Kendall Hunt Publishing Co.
Kurz, Ludwik & Benteftifa, M. Hafed. Analysis of Variance in Statistical Image Processing. 2006. (ENG., Illus.). 228p. pap. 48.00 *(978-0-521-03196-7(6))* Cambridge Univ. Pr.
MacFarland, Thomas W. Two-Way Analysis of Variance: Statistical Tests & Graphics Using R. 2011. (SpringerBriefs in Statistics Ser.). (ENG., Illus.). vii, 150p. pap. 39.95 ***(978-1-4614-2133-7(0)***, 1461421330) Springer.
Meijer, Erik & de Leeuw, Jan, eds. Handbook of Multilevel Analysis. 2008. (ENG., Illus.). xiv, 494p. 225.00 *(978-0-387-73183-4(0)*, 0387731830) Springer.
Montgomery, Douglas C. Design & Analysis of Experiments, Student Solutions Manual. 7th ed. 2009. (ENG., Illus.). 256p. (C). pap., stu. ed. 64.95 *(978-0-470-16991-9(5)*, Wiley) Wiley, John & Sons, Inc.
Montgomery, Douglas C. & Kowalski, Scott M. Design & Analysis of Experiments: MINITAB Companion. 7th ed. 2010. (ENG., Illus.). 128p. (C). pap. 51.95 *(978-0-470-16990-2(7)*, Wiley) Wiley, John & Sons, Inc.
Pini, Gianreto. Applied Generalizability Theory. 2009. (Quantitative Methodology Ser.). (ENG., Illus.). 240p. 68.95 *(978-1-84872-828-8(X)*, Routledge) Taylor & Francis Group GBR Dist: Taylor & Francis Group.
Pollock III, Philip H. An SPSS Companion to Political Analysis, 00 vols. 4th rev. ed. 2011. (Illus.). 288p. pap. 49.00 *(978-1-60871-687-6(2))* CQ Pr.
—Stata Companion to Political Analysis, 00 vols. 2nd rev. ed. 2010. (Illus.). 256p. pap. 52.00 *(978-1-60871-671-5(6))* CQ Pr.
Rosenbaum, Paul R. Design of Observational Studies. (Illus.). 2010. xviii, 384p. *(978-1-4419-1213-8(4))* 2009. xviii, 385p. 109.00 *(978-1-4419-1212-1(6)*, 1441912126) Springer.
—Observational Studies. 2nd ed. 2010. (Springer Series in Statistics Ser.). (Illus.). xiv, 375p. pap. 139.00 *(978-1-4419-3191-7(0)*, 1441931910) Springer.
Rutherford, Andrew. ANCVA & ANCOVA: A GLM Approach. 2nd ed. 2011. (ENG., Illus.). 360p. 110.00 *(978-0-470-38555-5(3)*, Wiley) Wiley, John & Sons, Inc.
Walters, Lisa M. & Badley, Jacquelyn K. Carpenter. S3: Simple Six Sigma for Blood Banking, Transfusion, & Cellular Therapy. 2007. *(978-1-56395-249-4(1)*, AABB Pr.) American Assn. of Blood Banks.
Wichura, Michael J. The Coordinate-Free Approach to Linear Models. 2006. (Cambridge Series in Statistical & Probabilistic Mathematics Ser.). (ENG., Illus.). 216p. 63.99 *(978-0-521-86842-6(4))* Cambridge Univ. Pr.
Wolter, Kirk. Introduction to Variance Estimation. 2nd ed. (Statistics for Social & Behavioral Sciences Ser.). (Illus.). 2010. xi, 427p. pap. 119.00 *(978-1-4419-2197-0(4)*, 1441921974) 2006. 447p. 119.00 *(978-0-387-32917-8(X)*, 038732917X) Springer.

ANALYSIS SITUS

see Topology

ANALYTIC CONTINUATION

Langmann, K. & Lntkebohmert, W. Cousinvertellungen und Fortsetzungssätze. 2008. (Lecture Notes in Mathematics Ser.). 160p. pap. 29.95 *(978-3-540-06683-5(7))* Springer.
Mujica, Jorge. Complex Analysis in Banach Spaces. 2010. (Dover Books on Mathematics Ser.). (ENG.). 464p. pap. 17.95 *(978-0-486-47466-3(6))* Dover Pubns., Inc.
Sibuya, Yasutaka. Linear Differential Equations in the Complex Domain: Problems of Analytic Continuation. 2008. (Translations of Mathematical Monographs Ser.). 267p. pap. 94.00 *(978-0-8218-4676-6(0))* American Mathematical Society.

ANALYTIC FUNCTIONS

see also Function Algebras

Agler, Jim, et al. Classical Function Theory, Operator Dilation Theory, & Machine Computation on Multiply-Connected Domains. 2008. (Memoirs of the American Mathematical Society Ser.). 159p. pap. 71.00 *(978-0-8218-4046-7(0))* American Mathematical Society.
Alexander, Daniel S., et al. Early Days in Complex Dynamics. 2011. (History of Mathematics Ser.). (Illus.). 454p. 99.00 ***(978-0-8218-4464-9(4))*** American Mathematical Society.
Ancona, V. & Tomassini, G. Modifications Analytiques. 2008. (Lecture Notes in Mathematics Ser.). 26.00 *(978-3-540-11570-0(6))* Springer.
Andrianov, Anatoli. Introduction to Siegel Modular Forms & Dirichlet Series. 2009. (Universitext Ser.). 184p. spiral bd. 59.95 *(978-0-387-78752-7(6))* Springer.
Bak, Joseph & Newman, Donald J. Complex Analysis. 3rd ed. 2010. (Undergraduate Texts in Mathematics Ser.). Orig. Title: Complex Analysis. (Illus.). xi, 320p. 74 95 *(978-1-4419-7287-3(0)*, 1441972870) Springer.
Blasco, Oscar, et al, eds. Topics in Complex Analysis & Operator Theory. 2012. (Contemporary Mathematics Ser.). (Illus.). 252p. pap. 89.00 ***(978-0-8218-5275-0(2))*** American Mathematical Society.
Castaing, C. & Valadier, M. Convex Analysis & Measurable Multifunctions. 2008. (Lecture Notes in Mathematics Ser.). 296p. pap. 59.95 *(978-3-540-08144-9(5))* Springer.
Chou, C. -C. La Transformation de Fourier Complexe et L'Equation de Convolution. 2008. (Lecture Notes in Mathematics Ser.). 152p. pap. 26.00 *(978-3-540-06301-8(3))* Springer.
Dellacherie, Claude. Ensembles Analytiques, Capacités: Mesures de Hausdorff. 2008. (Lecture Notes in Mathematics Ser.). (FRE.). xii, 123p. 26.00 *(978-3-540-06076-5(6))* Springer.
Dudziak, James J. Vitushkin's Conjecture for Removable Sets. 2010. (Universitext Ser.). xii, 272p. pap. 69.95 *(978-1-4419-6708-4(7)*, 1441967087) Springer.
Einsiedler, Manfred Leopold. Homogeneous Flows, Moduli Spaces, & Arithmetic: Proceedings of the Clay Mathematics Institute Summer School, Centro Di Recerca Matematica Ennio de Giorgi, Pisa, Italy, June 11 — July 6, 2007. 2010. (Clay Mathematics Proceedings Ser.). (Illus.). 438p. pap. 99.00 *(978-0-8218-4742-8(2))* American Mathematical Society.
From Divergent Power Series to Analytic Functions. 2008. (Lecture Notes in Mathematics Ser.). pap. 39.95 *(978-3-540-58268-7(1))* Springer.
Garnett, J. Analytic Capacity & Measure. 2008. (Lecture Notes in Mathematics Ser.). (ENG.). 148p. pap. 39.95 *(978-3-540-06073-4(1)*, 3540060731) Springer.
Garnett, John. Bounded Analytic Functions. 2010. (Graduate Texts in Mathematics Ser.). (Illus.). xiv, 466p. pap. 69.95 *(978-1-4419-2216-8(4)*, 1441922164) Springer.
Garnett, John B. Bounded Analytic Functions. 2nd ed. 2006. (Graduate Texts in Mathematics Ser.). (Illus.). 459p. 69.95 *(978-0-387-33621-3(4)*, 0387336214) Springer.
Generalized Analytic Functions on Riemann Surfaces. 2008. (Lecture Notes in Mathematics Ser.). pap. 39.95 *(978-3-540-18572-7(0))* Springer.
Gonchar, A. A., et al, eds. Complex Analysis I: Entire & Meromorphic Functions. Polyanalytic Functions & Their Generalizations. Rublinetskij, V. I. & Tkachenko, V., trs. 2010. (Encyclopaedia of Mathematical Sciences Ser.). x, 261p. pap. 189.00 *(978-3-642-08127-9(4)*, 3642081274) Springer.
Hayden, T. L. & Suffridge, T. J., eds. Proceedings on Infinite Dimensional Holomorphy. 2008. (Lecture Notes in Mathematics Ser.). 224p. pap. 59.95 *(978-3-540-06619-4(5))* Springer.
Hervier, Y. & Hirschowitz, A., eds. Varietes Analytiques Compactes: Colloque, Nice 19.- 23. Septembre 1977. 2008. (Lecture Notes in Mathematics Ser.). 256p. pap. 46.00 *(978-3-540-08949-0(7))* Springer.
Hough, J. Ben, et al. Zeros of Gaussian Analytic Functions & Determinantal Point Processes. 2009. (University Lecture Ser.). (Illus.). 154p. pap. 39.00 *(978-0-8218-4373-4(7))* American Mathematical Society.
Immink, G. Asymptotics of Analytic Difference Equations. 2008. (Lecture Notes in Mathematics Ser.). pap. 39.95 *(978-3-540-13867-9(6))* Springer.
Kim, Kang-Tae. Schwarz's Lemma from a Differential Geometric Viewpoint. 2010. 100p. 50.00 *(978-981-4324-78-6(7))* World Scientific Publishing Co., Inc.
Kresin, Gershon & Mazia, V. G. Sharp Real-Part Theorems: A Unified Approach. 2007. (Lecture Notes in Mathematics Ser.: Vol. 1903). XVI, 144p. pap. 39.00 *(978-3-540-69573-8(7)*, 3540695737) Springer.
Lawrynowicz, J., ed. Analytic Functions Blazejewko 1982: Proceedings of a Conference held in Blazejewko, Poland, August 19-27, 1982. 2008. (Lecture Notes in Mathematics Ser.). pap. 59.00 *(978-3-540-12712-3(7))* Springer.
—Analytic Functions. Kozubnik 1979: Proceedings of a Conference Held in Kozubnik, Poland, April 19-25, 1979. 2008. (Lecture Notes in Mathematics Ser.). 488p. pap. 59.00 *(978-3-540-09985-7(9))* Springer.
Lin, I-Hsiung. Classical Complex Analysis: A Geometric Approach. 2010. 712p. 150.00 *(978-981-4271-28-8(4))*; pap. 96.00 *(978-981-4271-29-5(2))* World Scientific Publishing Co., Inc.
—Classical Complex Analysis Vol. 1: A Geometric Approach. 2010. 900p. 216.00 *(978-981-4261-22-7(X))* pap. 88.00 *(978-981-4261-23-4(8))* World Scientific Publishing Co., Inc.
MacGregor, Thomas H. Banach Spaces of Analytic Functions. Hibschweiler, Rita A., ed. 2003. (Contemporary Mathematics Ser.). 147p. (C). pap. 61.00 *(978-0-8218-4268-3(4))* American Mathematical Society.
Mashreghi, Javad. Representation Theorems in Hardy Spaces. 2009. (London Mathematical Society Student Texts). (ENG., Illus.). 384p. 133.00 *(978-0-521-51768-3(0))*; pap. 46.99 *(978-0-521-73201-7(8))* Cambridge Univ. Pr.
Mashreghi, Javad, et al, eds. Hilbert Spaces of Analytic Functions. 2010. (CRM Proceedings & Lecture Notes Ser.). 214p. pap. 99.00 *(978-0-8218-4879-1(8))* American Mathematical Society.
Milnor, John Willard. Holomorphic Dynamics & Renormalization: A Volume in Honour of John Milnor's 75th Birthday. Lyubich, Mikhail & Yampolsky, Michael, eds. 2008. (Fields Institute Communications Ser.). (Illus.). 395p. (C). 123.00 *(978-0-8218-4275-1(7))* American Mathematical Society.
Sabadini, Irene & Sommen, F. Hypercomplex Analysis & Applications. 2010. (Trends in Mathematics Ser.). (ENG.). viii, 282p. 124.00 *(978-3-0346-0245-7(6)*, 3034602456) Birkhauser Verlag AG CHE. Dist: Springer.
Schilling, René L., et al. Bernstein Functions: Theory & Applications. 2010. (De Gruyter Studies in Mathematics Ser.). (ENG.). XI, 313p. 168.00 ***(978-3-11-173350-0(5))*** De Gruyter, Walter Inc.
Schilling, Rene L., et al. Bernstein Functions: Theory & Applications. 2010. (De Gruyter Studies in Mathematics Ser.). (ENG., Illus.). XI, 313p. 112.00 *(978-3-11-021530-4(6))* De Gruyter, Walter Inc.
Schilling, René L. et al. Bernstein Functions: Theory & Applications. 2nd ed. 2012. (De Gruyter Studies in Mathematics Ser.: 37). (ENG.). 460p. (gr. 17-17). E-Book 252.00 ***(978-3-11-026900-0(7))*** De Gruyter, Walter Inc.
—Bernstein Functions: Theory & Applications. 2nd ed. 2012. (De Gruyter Studies in Mathematics Ser.: 37). (ENG., Illus.). 460p. (gr. 17-17). 168.00 ***(978-3-11-025229-3(5))*** De Gruyter, Walter Inc.
Shirokov, Nikolai A. Analytic Functions Smooth up to the Boundary. 2008. (Lecture Notes in Mathematics Ser.). pap. 46.00 *(978-3-540-19255-8(7))* Springer.
Silverman, Joseph H. Moduli Spaces & Arithmetic Dynamics. 2012. (CRM Monograph Ser.). (Illus.). 140p. 59.00 ***(978-0-8218-7582-7(5))*** American Mathematical Society.
Siu, Yum-Tong & Trautmann, Gnnther. Gap-Sheaves & Extension of Coherent Analytic Subsheaves. 2008. (Lecture Notes in Mathematics Ser.). 180p. pap. 26.00 *(978-3-540-05294-4(1)*, 3540052941) Springer.
Tognoli, A. Singularities of Analytical Spaces: Lectures given at the Centro Internazionale Matematico Estivo (C. I. M. E.) held in Bressanone (Bolzano), Italy, June 16-25 1974. 2010. (CIME Summer Schools Ser.). 180p. pap. 29.95 *(978-3-642-10942-3(X)*, 364210942X) Springer.
Weissauer, Rainer. Endoscopy for GSp(4) & the Cohomology of Siegel Modular Threefolds. 2009. (Lecture Notes in Mathematics Ser.). (ENG., Illus.). xvii, 368p. pap. 79.95 *(978-3-540-89305-9(9))* Springer.
Wong, Man-Wah. Complex Analysis, Vol. 2. 2008. (Series on Analysis, Applications & Computation). (C). 60.00 *(978-981-281-107-3(9))* World Scientific Publishing Co., Inc.
Zalcman, Lawrence. Analytic Capacity & Rational Approximation. 2007. (Lecture Notes in Mathematics Ser.). 164p. per. 39.95 *(978-3-540-04220-4(2))* Springer.

ANALYTIC PHILOSOPHY

see Analysis (Philosophy)

ANALYTIC PSYCHOLOGY

see Jungian Psychology

ANALYTICAL BIBLIOGRAPHY

see Bibliography, Critical

ANALYTICAL CHEMISTRY

see Chemistry, Analytic

ANALYTICAL GEOMETRY

see Geometry, Analytic

ANALYTICAL MECHANICS

see Mechanics, Analytic

ANALYTICAL PHILOSOPHY

see Analysis (Philosophy)

ANALYTICAL PSYCHOLOGY

see Jungian Psychology

ANAPHYLAXIS

see also Allergy

(ACAAI), Asthma & Immunology, American College of Allergy, Asthma & Immunology & (AAAAI), American Academy of Allergy Asthma & Immunology. Anaphylaxis GUIDELINES Pocketcard 2011. 2011. 14p. spiral bd. 11.95 ***(978-0-9846290-9-1(2))*** International Guidelines Ctr., Inc.
Brown, Simon. Preventing Anaphylaxis to Venom of the Jack Jumper Ant. 2008. 228p. pap. *(978-3-639-04838-4(5))* VDM Verlag Dr. Mueller e.K.
Castells, Mariana C., ed. Anaphylaxis & Hypersensitivity Reactions. 2010. (ENG., Illus.). xiii, 361p. 219.00 *(978-1-60327-950-5(4)*, 1603279504) Humana Pr.
Evennett, Karen. Living with Nut Allergies. 85p. *(978-0-85969-835-1(1)*, Sheldon Press) SPCK Publishing.
Ring, J., ed. & contrib. by. Anaphylaxis. 2010. (Chemical Immunology & Allergy Ser.). (ENG., Illus.). 228p. *(978-3-8055-9441-7(0))* Karger, S. AG.

ANARCHISM

see also Anarchists; Libertarianism; Nihilism; Socialism

Amster, Randall. Anarchism Today, 1 vol. 2012. 230p. 48.00 ***(978-0-313-39872-8(0)***, A3648C); E-Book ***(978-0-313-39873-5(9)***, Praeger Pubs.) Greenwood Publishing Group Inc.
Amster, Randall. Contemporary Anarchist Studies: An Introductory Anthology of Anarchy in the Academy. Amster, Randall et al, eds. 2009. (ENG.). 336p. 148.00 *(978-0-415-47401-6(9))* Routledge.
—Contemporary Anarchist Studies: An Introductory Anthology of Anarchy in the Academy. DeLeon, Abraham et al, eds. 2009. (ENG.). 336p. pap. 49.95 *(978-0-415-47402-3(7))* Routledge.
Anderson, Benedict. Under Three Flags: Anarchism & the Anti-Colonial Imagination. 2007. (ENG., Illus.). 256p. per. 18.95 *(978-1-84467-090-1(2)*, 844090) Verso Bks. GBR. Dist: Norton, W. W. & Co., Inc.
Antonioli, Maurizio & McNab, Nestor. The International Anarchist Congress: Amsterdam (1907) 2009. 29.95 *(978-0-9737827-3-8(0))* Black Cat Pr. CAN. Dist: AK Pr. Distribution.
Azarov, Vyacheslav & Archibald, Malcolm. Kontrrazvedka: The Story of the Makhnovist Secret Service. 2009. 14.00 *(978-0-9737827-2-1(2))* Black Cat Pr. CAN. Dist: AK Pr. Distribution.
Bader, Ralf M. & Meadowcroft, John. Robert Nozick. Meadowcroft, John, ed. 2010. (Major Conservative & Libertarian Thinkers Ser.). (ENG.). 160p. 130.00 *(978-0-8264-2429-7(5))* Continuum International Publishing Group, Ltd. GBR. Dist: National Bk. Network.
Bader, Ralf M. & Meadowcroft, John, eds. The Cambridge Companion to Nozick's Anarchy, State, & Utopia. 2011. (Cambridge Companions to Philosophy Ser.). (ENG.). 332p. (C). 90.00 ***(978-0-521-19776-2(7))***; pap. 29.99 ***(978-0-521-12002-9(0))*** Cambridge Univ. Pr.
Baillargeon, Normand. Les Chiens Ont Soif: Critiques et Propositions Libertaires. 2nd ed. 2010. (FRE.). 301p. *(978-2-89596-108-6(5))* Lux, editeur.
Bakunin, Mikhail. God & the State. 2009. pap. 8.75 *(978-0-9737827-7-6(3))* Black Cat Pr. CAN. Dist: AK Pr. Distribution.
Baldelli, Giovanni. Social Anarchism. 2009. (ENG.). 204p. pap. 24.95 *(978-0-202-36339-4(2))* Aldine Transaction.
Bamyeh, Mohammed & Bamyeh, Mohammed A. Anarchy as Order: The History & Future of Civic Humanity. 2009. (World Social Change Ser.). (ENG.). 250p. 72.00 *(978-0-7425-5673-7(5))* Rowman & Littlefield Publishers, Inc.
Bamyeh, Mohammed A. Anarchy as Order: The History & Future of Civic Humanity. 2010. (World Social Change Ser.). (ENG.). 250p. pap. 37.50 *(978-0-7425-5674-4(3))* Rowman & Littlefield Publishers, Inc.
Barsky, Robert F. The Chomsky Effect: A Radical Works Beyond the Ivory Tower. (ENG., Illus.). 400p. (gr. 17). 2009. pap. 15.95 *(978-0-262-51316-6(1))* 2007. 29.95 *(978-0-262-02624-6(4))* MIT Pr.
Berkman, Alexander. The Abc of Communist Anarchism. 2011. 274p. pap. 14.99 ***(978-1-61001-001-6(9))*** Red & Black Pubs.
Berkman, Alexander. Now & after: the ABC of Anarchist Communism. 2010. 144p. pap. 13.50 *(978-1-4092-9907-3(4))* Lulu Enterprises Inc.
Berry, David. A History of the French Anarchist Movement, 1917-1945. 2009. (ENG.). 348p. pap. 21.95 *(978-1-904859-82-6(8))* AK Pr. GBR. Dist: Consortium Bk. Sales & Distribution.
Bevington, L. S. Collected Essays of Louisa Sarah Bevington (1879-1896) 2010. *(978-0-8201-1563-4(0))* Scholars' Facsimiles & Reprints.
Bey, Hakim. The Temporary Autonomous Zone; Ontological Anarchy; Poetic Terrorism. 2007. 132p. per. 18.99 *(978-1-4346-9431-7(3))* BiblioBazaar.
Bouillon, Hardy & Kliemt, Hartmut, eds. Ordered Anarchy: Jasay & His Surroundings. 2007. (Illus.). 212p. 99.95 *(978-0-7546-6113-9(X))* Ashgate Publishing Co.
Butterworth, Alex. The World That Never Was: A True Story of Dreamers, Schemers, Anarchists, & Secret Agents. (Vintage Ser.). (ENG., Illus.). 2011. 544p. pap. 15.95 *(978-0-307-38575-5(9)*, Vintage) 2010. 528p. 30.00 *(978-0-375-42511-0(X)*, Pantheon) Knopf Doubleday Publishing Group.

Butterworth, Alex & Butterworth, L. The World That Never Was: A True Story of Dreamers, Schemers, Anarchists & Secret Agents. 2010. (ENG., Illus.). 384p. (978-0-224-07807-8(0), Bodley Head) RHCB.

Carroll, John. Break-Out from the Crystal Palace: The Anarcho-Psychological Critique: Stirner, Nietzsche, Dostoevsky. 2010. (Rouledge Library Editions: Friedrich Nietzsche Ser.). (ENG.). 14p. 100.00 (978-0-415-56222-5(8)) Routledge.

Carter, April. The Political Theory of Anarchism. 2009. (ENG.). 124p. 104.00 (978-0-415-55593-7(0)) Routledge.

Casey, Gerard. Libertarian Anarchy: Against the State. 2012. (Think Now Ser.). (ENG.). 208p. 80.00 (978-1-4411-2552-1(3)); pap. 24.95 (978-1-4411-4467-6(6)) Continuum International Publishing Group, Ltd. GBR. Dist: National Bk. Network.

Chartier, Gary & Johnson, Charles W., eds. Markets Not Capitalism: Individualist Anarchism Against Bosses, Inequality, Corporate Power, & Structural Poverty. 2011. (ENG.). 440p. pap. 32.00 (978-1-57027-242-4(5)) Autonomedia.

Christie, Stuart. Granny Made Me an Anarchist: General Franco, the Angry Brigade & Me. 2007. (ENG., Illus.). 400p. per. 19.95 (978-1-904859-65-9(8)) AK Pr. GBR. Dist: Consortium Bk. Sales & Distribution.

—We, the Anarchists! A Study of the Iberian Anarchist Federation (FAI), 1927-1937. 2008. (ENG.). 180p. pap. 17.95 (978-1-904859-75-8(5)) AK Pr. GBR. Dist: Consortium Bk. Sales & Distribution.

Christie, Stuart & Meltzer, Albert. The Floodgates of Anarchy. 2010. (ENG., Illus.). 160p. pap. 15.95 (978-1-60486-105-1(3)) PM Pr.

Christoyannopoulos, Alexandre. Christian Anarchism: A Political Commentary on the Gospel. abr. ed. 2011. (ENG.). 250p. pap. 34.90 (978-1-84540-247-1(2)) Imprint Academic GBR. Dist: Ingram Pub. Services.

Cohn, Jesse. Anarchism & the Crisis of Representation: Hermeneutics, Aesthetics, Politics. 2006. (ENG.). 326p. 60.00 (978-1-57591-105-2(1)) Susquehanna Univ. Pr.

Crimethinc, ed. Expect Resistance: A Crimethink Field Manual. 2008. (Illus.). 339p. pap. 11.95 (978-0-9709101-6-5(9)) CrimethInc. Workers' Collective.

Critchley, Simon. Infinitely Demanding: Ethics of Commitment, Politics of Resistance. 2008. (ENG.). 168p. pap. 16.95 (978-1-84467-296-7(4), 844296) Verso Bks. GBR. Dist: Norton, W. W. & Co., Inc.

Curran, Giorel. 21st Century Dissent: Anarchism, Anti-Globalization & Environmentalism. 2007. (International Political Economy Ser.). (ENG.). 256p. 105.00 (978-1-4039-4881-6(X)) Palgrave Macmillan.

Dame, V. & Archibald, Malcolm. Anarcho-Syndicalism in the 20th Century. 2009. 244p. pap. 21.95 (978-0-9737827-6-9(5)) Black Cat Pr. CAN. Dist: AK Pr. Distribution.

Davis, Laurence & Kinna, Ruth, eds. Anarchism & Utopianism. 2010. (ENG.). 304p. 90.00 (978-0-7190-7934-4(9)) Manchester Univ. Pr. GBR. Dist: Macmillan.

Delf, Hanna & Mattenklott, Gert, eds. Gustav Landauer Im Gespräch: Symposium Zum 125. Geburtstag. (Conditio Judaica Ser.). (GER.). IX, 288p. 210.00 (978-3-11-187365-7(X)) De Gruyter, Walter Inc.

Dolgoff, Sam, ed. The Anarchist Collectives: Workers' Self-management in the Spanish Revolution 1936-1939. 2011. (ENG.). 220p. pap. 16.99 (978-1-55164-344-1(8)) Black Rose Bks. CAN. Dist: Consortium Bk. Sales & Distribution.

Dubovik, Anatoly V. & Rublyov, D, D.I. After Makhno: The Anarchist underground in the Ukraine in the 1920s & 1930s: Outlines of history & The Story of a Leaflet & the Fate of the Anarchist Varshavskiy (From the History of Anarchist Resistance to Totalitarianism) Szarapow, tr. from RUS. 2009. (ENG., Illus.). 22p. 3.00 (978-1-873605-84-4(6)) Sharpley, Kate Library GBR. Dist: AK Pr. Distribution.

Ealham, Chris. Anarchism & the City: Revolution andd Counter Revolution in Barcelona, 1898-1937. 2010. (ENG., Illus.). 284p. pap. 20.00 (978-1-84935-012-9(4)) AK Pr. GBR. Dist: Consortium Bk. Sales & Distribution.

Eckstein, Arthur M. & Eckstein, A. M. Mediterranean Anarchy, Interstate War, & the Rise of Rome. 2009. (Hellenistic Culture & Society Ser.). (Illus.). 389p. pap. 27.95 (978-0-520-25992-8(0)) Univ. of California Pr.

Edmundson, William A. Three Anarchical Fallacies: An Essay on Political Authority. 2007. (Cambridge Studies in Philosophy & Law Ser.). (ENG.). 208p. pap. 50.00 (978-0-521-03751-8(4)) Cambridge Univ. Pr.

Ellul, Jacques. Anarchy & Christianity. Bromiley, Geoffrey W., tr. 2011. (Jacques Ellul Legacy Ser.). 114p. pap. 15.00 (978-1-60608-971-2(4), Wipf and Stock) Wipf & Stock Pubs.

Eltzbacher, Paul. Anarchism. 2010. 358p. pap. 32.75 (978-1-148-08473-2(8)) BiblioBazaar.

—Anarchism. 2009. 242p. pap. (978-1-4588-1239-1(1)); 122p. pap. (978-1-4588-1240-7(5)); 290p. pap. (978-1-4590-3075-6(3)) Books LLC.

—Anarchism. Byington, Steven T., tr. 2007. (ENG.). 344p. 46.95 (978-0-548-36726-1(4)); per. 31.95 (978-0-548-31024-3(6)) Kessinger Publishing, LLC.

—Anarchism. 2008. 356p. pap. (978-1-4097-8011-3(2)) Read Bks.

Eltzbacher, Paul & Byington, Steven T. Anarchism. 2010. (ENG.). 360p. pap. 32.75 (978-1-177-62510-4(5)) BiblioBazaar.

Emma, Goldman. Anarchism & Other Essays. 2007. 188p. pap. 19.99 (978-1-4346-1721-7(1)) BiblioBazaar.

Everett, Martyn. War & Revolution: The Hungarian Anarchist Movement in World War I & the Budapest Commune 1919. 2006. (Illus.). 28p. pap. 3.50 (978-1-873605-38-7(2)) Sharpley, Kate Library GBR. Dist: AK Pr. Distribution.

Falk, Gerhard. An Encyclopedia of Assassinations & Terrorism in World History: Cases of Anarchism from Tutankamen to Wikileaks. 2011. 119.95 (978-0-7734-1478-5(9)) Mellen, Edwin Pr., The.

Fernandez, Frank. El Anarquismo en Cuba. (SPA., Illus.). 204p. (978-84-86864-41-5(0)) Fundación de Estudios Libertarios Anselmo Lorenzo.

Finzi, Paolo. Emilio Canzi: An Anarchist partisan in Italy & Spain. Sharkey, Paul, ed. & tr. by. from ITA. 2006. (Illus.). 32p. 3.50 (978-1-873605-29-5(3)) Sharpley, Kate Library GBR. Dist: AK Pr. Distribution.

For Know-It-Alls Staff. Anarchism for Know-It-Alls. 2008. pap. 9.99 (978-1-59986-218-7(2), For Know-It-Alls) Filiquarian Publishing, LLC.

Foust, Christina R. Transgression as a Mode of Resistance: Rethinking Social Movement in an Era of Corporate Globalization. 2010. (ENG.). 256p. 78.99 (978-0-7391-4335-3(2)) Lexington Bks.

Franks, Benjamin. Rebel Alliances: The Means & Ends of Contemporary British Anarchisms. 2006. (ENG., Illus.). 240p. per. 19.95 (978-1-904859-40-6(2)) AK Pr. GBR. Dist: Consortium Bk. Sales & Distribution.

Franks, Benjamin, et al, eds. Anarchism & Moral Philosophy. 2011. (ENG., Illus.). 272p. 89.00 (978-0-230-58066-4(1)) Palgrave Macmillan.

Galleani, Luigi & Sharkey, Paul. Anarchy Will Be! The Selected Writings of Luigi Galleani. Pateman, Barry, ed. 2007. 500p. pap. 19.95 (978-1-904859-39-0(9)) AK Pr. GBR. Dist: Consortium Bk. Sales & Distribution.

Gans, Chaim. Philosophical Anarchism & Political Disobedience. 2009. (ENG.). 192p. (C). pap. 28.99 (978-0-521-12507-9(3)) Cambridge Univ. Pr.

Goaman, Karen. The Old World Is Behind You: The Situationists & Beyond in Contemporary Anarchism. 2007. 192p. pap. 15.95 (978-1-57027-180-9(1)) Autonomedia.

Goldman, Emma. Anarchism, & Other Essays. 2010. 126p. pap. (978-1-151-88384-1(0)) Books LLC.

—Anarchism & Other Essays. 2008. 168p. pap. 8.99 (978-1-60450-583-2(4), Serenity Pubs.) Arc Manor.

—Anarchism & Other Essays. 2010. 290p. pap. 28.75 (978-1-141-76660-4(4)) 2008. 216p. 27.99 (978-0-554-26773-9(X)) 2008. 216p. 24.99 (978-0-554-36076-8(4)) 2007. 212p. pap. 22.99 (978-1-4346-1890-0(0)) BiblioBazaar.

—Anarchism & Other Essays. 2009. 148p. pap. (978-0-217-77642-4(6)) Books LLC.

—Anarchism & Other Essays. 2008. 116p. pap. 6.99 (978-1-4209-3136-5(9)) Digireads.com.

—Anarchism & Other Essays. 2008. 184p. pap. (978-1-4099-1538-6(7)) Dodo Pr.

—Anarchism & Other Essays. 2007. 136p. per. (978-1-4068-6225-6(8)) Echo Library.

—Anarchism & Other Essays. 2010. (Illus.). 122p. pap. 21.14 (978-1-153-58555-2(3)) General Bks. LLC.

—Anarchism & Other Essays. 2010. 150p. pap. (978-1-4076-2082-4(7)) HardPr.

—Anarchism & Other Essays. 2010. 274p. pap. 22.36 (978-1-163-23624-6(1)) 2010. 274p. 34.36 (978-1-163-51768-0(2)) 2007. 272p. 42.95 (978-0-548-21594-4(4)) 2007. 276p. per. 27.95 (978-1-4325-3593-3(5)) Kessinger Publishing, LLC.

—Anarchism & Other Essays. 2011. 280p. pap. 9.50 (978-1-891396-54-0(4)) Martino Publishing.

—Anarchism & Other Essays. 2011. 196p. pap. 13.99 (978-1-61279-101-2(8)) Publishing in Motion.

Goldman, Emma. Anarchismn & Other Writings. 2007. 288p. 36.95 (978-0-9793363-8-6(4)) Ellis, Frederick.

Goldman, Emma & Havel, Hippolyte. Anarchism, & Other Essays. 2010. 300p. pap. 29.75 (978-1-177-67590-1(0)); 298p. pap. 28.75 (978-1-177-77612-7(X)) BiblioBazaar.

Goldman, Emma & Havel, Hippolyte. Anarchism & Other Essays. 2011. 296p. pap. 28.75 (978-1-246-07328-7(5)) BiblioBazaar.

Goodman, Paul. Drawing the Line Once Again: Paul Goodman's Anarchist Writings. 2010. (ENG.). 128p. pap. 14.95 (978-1-60486-057-3(X)) PM Pr.

Goodway, David & Walter, Nicolas. The Anarchist Past & Other Essays. 2009. 192p. pap. 14.95 (978-1-905512-16-4(3)) Five Leaves Pubns. GBR. Dist: AK Pr. Distribution.

Gordon, Uri. Anarchy Alive! Anti-Authoritarian Politics from Practice to Theory. 2007. (ENG.). 208p. 84.00 (978-0-7453-2684-9(6)); per. 26.95 (978-0-7453-2683-2(8)) Pluto Pr. GBR. Dist: Macmillan.

Goyens, Tom. Beer & Revolution: The German Anarchist Movement in New York City, 1880-1914. 2007. (Illus.). 296p. 42.00 (978-0-252-03175-5(X)) Univ. of Illinois Pr.

Haldeman, Joe & Graham, Robert, eds. Anarchism Vol. 3: A Documentary History of Libertarian Ideas - The New Anarchism, 1974-2008. 2011. (ENG.). 530p. pap. 28.99 (978-1-55164-336-6(7)) Black Rose Bks. CAN. Dist: Consortium Bk. Sales & Distribution.

—Anarchism Vol. 3: The New Anarchism, 1974-2008. 2011. (ENG.). 530p. 48.99 (978-1-55164-337-3(5)) Black Rose Bks. CAN. Dist: Consortium Bk. Sales & Distribution.

—Anarchism, a Documentary History of Libertarian Ideas Vol. 2: The Anarchist Current (1939-2006) 2009. (ENG.). 500p. 57.99 (978-1-55164-311-3(1)) Black Rose Bks. CAN. Dist: Consortium Bk. Sales & Distribution.

—Anarchism, a Documentary History of Libertarian Ideas Vol. 2: The Anarchist Current, 1939-2006. 2009. (ENG.). 500p. pap. 28.99 (978-1-55164-310-6(3)) Black Rose Bks. CAN. Dist: Consortium Bk. Sales & Distribution.

Hapgood, Hutchins. The Spirit of Labor. 2009. 412p. 27.99 (978-0-559-90685-5(4)); pap. 21.99 (978-0-559-90682-4(X)) BiblioBazaar.

—The Spirit of Labor. 2009. 166p. pap. 19.99 (978-0-217-89661-0(8)) General Bks. LLC.

Harrison, Frank. The Modern State: An Anarchist Analysis. (Illus.). 354p. pap. 12.95 (978-0-919619-17-3(7)) Black Rose Bks. CAN. Dist: AK Pr. Distribution.

Haskins, Rob. Anarchic Societies of Sounds. 2009. 280p. pap. (978-3-639-13209-0(2)) VDM Verlag Dr. Mueller e.K.

Haworth, Robert H. & Grubacic, Andrej, eds. Anarchist Pedagogies: Collective Actions, Theories, & Critical Reflections on Education. 2012. (ENG.). 280p. pap. 22.95 (978-1-60486-484-7(2)) PM Pr.

Hebden, Keith. Dalit Theology & Christian Anarchism. 2011. (New Critical Thinking in Religion, Theology & Biblical Studies). 186p. 99.95 (978-1-4094-2439-0(1)) Ashgate Publishing Co.

Heckert, Jamie & Cleminson, Richard, eds. Anarchism & Sexuality: Ethics, Relationships & Power. 2011. (Social Justice Ser.). (ENG.). 256p. 135.00 (978-0-415-59989-4(X)) Routledge.

Herod, James. Getting Free: Creating an Association of Democratic Autonomous Neighborhoods. 2007. 144p. pap. 14.00 (978-0-9794264-0-7(5)) Parsons, Lucy Ctr.

Hirsch, Steven & Van der Walt, Lucien, eds. Anarchism & Syndicalism in the Colonial & Postcolonial World, 1870-1940: The Praxis of National Liberation, Internationalism, & Social Revolution. 2010. (Studies in Global Social History Ser.). (Illus.). 448p. (978-90-04-18849-5(5)) BRILL.

Hoffman, Robert, ed. Anarchism as Political Philosophy. 2010. (ENG.). 165p. pap. 29.95 (978-0-202-36364-6(3)) Aldine Transaction.

Honeywell, Carissa. British Anarchist Tradition: Herbert Read, Alex Comfort, & Colin Ward. 2011. (ENG., Illus.). 224p. 120.00 (978-1-4411-9017-8(1)) Continuum International Publishing Group, Ltd. GBR. Dist: National Bk. Network.

Horrox, James. A Living Revolution: Anarchism in the Kibbutz Movement. 2009. (ENG.). 250p. pap. 17.95 (978-1-904859-92-5(5)) AK Pr. GBR. Dist: Consortium Bk. Sales & Distribution.

Hunter, Robert. Violence & the Labor Movement. 2010. 426p. pap. 35.75 (978-1-142-89770-3(2)); 424p. pap. 35.75 (978-1-142-09328-0(X)) BiblioBazaar.

—Violence & the Labor Movement. 2009. 264p. pap. (978-0-217-14292-2(3)) Books LLC.

Jones, Thai. More Powerful Than Dynamite: Radicals, Plutocrats, Progressives, & New York's Year of Anarchy. 2012. (ENG., Illus.). 416p. 28.00 (978-0-8027-7933-5(6), 226190) Walker & Co.

Jun, Nathan. Anarchism & Political Modernity. 2011. (ENG., Illus.). 272p. 100.00 (978-1-4411-4015-9(8)); pap. 29.95 (978-1-4411-6686-9(6)) Continuum International Publishing Group, Ltd. GBR. Dist: National Bk. Network.

Jun, Nathan J. & Wahl, Shane. New Perspectives on Anarchism. 2009. (ENG.). 456p. 110.50 (978-0-7391-3240-1(7)); pap. 49.50 (978-0-7391-3241-8(5)) Lexington Bks.

Kinna, Ruth. Continuum Companion to Anarchism. 2012. (Continuum Companions Ser.). (ENG.). 480p. 175.00 (978-1-4411-7212-9(2)) Continuum International Publishing Group, Ltd. GBR. Dist: National Bk. Network.

Klausen, Jimmy. How Not to Be Governed: Readings & Interpretations from a Critical Anarchist Left. 2011. (ENG.). 244p. 75.00 (978-0-7391-5034-4(0)); pap. 29.95 (978-0-7391-5035-1(9)) Lexington Bks.

Klausen, Jimmy Casas & Martel, James R. How Not to Be Governed: Readings & Interpretations from a Critical Anarchist Left. 2010. xxviii, 193p. (978-0-7391-5036-8(7)) Lexington Bks.

Kloosterman, Jaap, et al. Rebels with a Cause: Five centuries of social history collected by the International Institute of Social History. 2010. (ENG., Illus.). 240p. 34.95 (978-90-5260-389-6(8)) Aksant Academic Pubs. NLD. Dist: Amsterdam Univ. Pr.

Kropotkin, Peter. Appeal to the Young. 2006. pap. 15.95 (978-1-4286-4664-3(7)) Kessinger Publishing, LLC.

Kropotkin, Petr Alekseevich. The Black Flag: Peter Kropotkin on Anarchism. 2010. 110p. pap. (978-1-934941-81-2(6)) Red & Black Pubs.

—The Conquest of Bread. 2009. 300p. 24.99 (978-1-103-86372-3(X)); pap. 18.99 (978-1-103-86362-4(2)) BiblioBazaar.

—The Conquest of Bread. 2009. 150p. pap. (978-0-217-57913-1(2)) Books LLC.

—The Conquest of Bread. 2011. (ENG.). 304p. pap. 12.95 (978-0-486-47850-0(5)) Dover Pubns., Inc.

Landauer, Gustav. Revolution & Other Writings: A Political Reader. Kuhn, Gabriel, ed. 2010. (ENG.). 360p. pap. 26.95 (978-1-60486-054-2(5)) PM Pr.

Lee, Vernon. Gospels of Anarchy & Other Contemporary Studies. 2009. 212p. pap. (978-1-4099-8204-3(1)) Dodo Pr.

—Gospels of Anarchy & Other Contemporary Studies. 372p. reprint ed. 98.00 (978-0-7222-1623-1(8)) Library Reprints, Inc.

Leier, Mark. Bakunin: The Creative Passion-A Biography. 2009. (ENG.). 384p. pap. 17.95 (978-1-58322-894-4(2)) Seven Stories Pr.

Lucian, Damian Aaron. The Emergence of the Global Union. 2008. 52p. pap. (978-3-639-06683-8(9)) VDM Verlag Dr. Mueller e.K.

Lynd, Staughton. From Here to There: The Staughton Lynd Reader. Grubacic, Andrej, ed. 2010. (ENG.). 304p. pap. 22.00 (978-1-60486-215-7(7)) PM Pr.

Lynd, Staughton & Grubacic, Andrej. Wobblies & Zapatistas: Conversations on Anarchism, Marxism & Radical History. 2008. (PM Press Ser.). (ENG.). 300p. pap. 20.00 (978-1-60486-041-2(3)) PM Pr.

Machan, Tibor R. Anarchism/Minarchism: Is a Government Part of a Free Country? Long, Roderick T., ed. 2008. 208p. 99.95 (978-0-7546-6066-8(4)) Ashgate Publishing Co.

Macphee, Josh & Milstein, Cindy. Paths Toward Utopia: Graphic Explorations of Everyday Anarchism. 2012. (ENG., Illus.). 120p. pap. 14.95 (978-1-60486-502-8(4)) PM Pr.

Manzanera, Elias. The Iron Column: Testament of a Revolutionary. Sharkey, Paul, tr. from SPA. 2006. 30p. pap. 3.00 (978-1-873605-19-6(6)) Sharpley, Kate Library GBR. Dist: AK Pr. Distribution.

Marshall, Peter. Demanding the Impossible: A History of Anarchism. 2010. (ENG.). 800p. pap. 28.95 (978-1-60486-064-1(2)) PM Pr.

Mayer, Marcos. Anarchism for Beginners. 2008. (For Beginners Ser.). (ENG., Illus.). 176p. pap. 14.95 (978-1-934389-32-4(3), For Beginners) Steerforth Pr.

McHarg, Farquhar. Pistoleros!: the Chronicles of Farquhar Mcharg: Volume 1: 1918. 2011. (ENG.). 264p. pap. 18.95 (978-1-60486-401-4(X)) PM Pr.

McKay, Iain. Anarchist FAQ. 2008. (ENG.). 748p. pap. 25.00 (978-1-902593-90-6(1)) AK Pr. GBR. Dist: Consortium Bk. Sales & Distribution.

McKinley, C. Alexander. Illegitimate Children of the Enlightenment: Anarchists & the French Revolution, 1880-1914. 2007. (Francophone Cultures & Literatures Ser.). (Illus.). 250p. (C). 70.95 (978-1-4331-0059-8(2)) Lang, Peter Publishing, Inc.

Mclaughlin, Paul. Anarchism & Authority: A Philosophical Introduction to Classical Anarchism. 2007. (Ashgate New Critical Thinking in Philosophy Ser.). 210p. 99.95 (978-0-7546-6196-2(2)) Ashgate Publishing Co.

Mechoso, Juan C., et al. The Federacion Anarquista Uruguaya (FAU) Crisis, Armed Struggle & Dictatorship, 1967-1985. 2009. 50p. pap. 3.00 (978-1-873605-69-1(2)) Sharpley, Kate Library GBR. Dist: AK Pr. Distribution.

Merriman, John. The Dynamite Club: How a Bombing in Fin-de-Siècle Paris Ignited the Age of Modern Terror. 2009. (ENG., Illus.). 224p. 26.00 (978-0-618-55598-7(6)) Houghton Mifflin Harcourt Trade & Reference Pubs.

Messer-Kruse, Timothy. The Trial of the Haymarket Anarchists: Terrorism & Justice in the Gilded Age. 2011. (ENG., Illus.). 244p. 90.00 (978-0-230-11660-3(4)); pap. 30.00 (978-0-230-12077-8(6)) Palgrave Macmillan.

Miller, Scott. The President & the Assassin: McKinley, Terror, & Empire at the Dawn of the American Century. 2011. (ENG., Illus.). 432p. 28.00 (978-1-4000-6752-7(9)) Random Hse., Inc.

Milstein, Cindy. Anarchism & Its Aspirations. 2010. (Anarchist Interventions Ser.). (ENG., Illus.). 152p. pap. 12.00 (978-1-84935-001-3(9)) AK Pr. GBR. Dist: Consortium Bk. Sales & Distribution.

Mintz, Frank. Anarchism & Workers' Self-Management in Revolutionary Spain. Sharkey, Paul, tr. from SPA. 2012. (ENG., Illus.). 250p. pap. 17.00 (978-1-84935-078-5(7)) AK Pr. GBR. Dist: Consortium Bk. Sales & Distribution.

Muhsam, Erich. Liberating Society from the State & Other Writings: A Political Reader. Kuhn, Gabriel, tr. 2011. (ENG.). 320p. pap. 26.95 (978-1-60486-055-9(3)) PM Pr.

Nematollahy, Ali. Anarchism. 2011. 240p. pap. (978-3-8443-8473-4(1)) Lambert Academic Publishing.

Newman Saul. From Bakunin to Lacan: Anti-Authoritarianism & the Dislocation of Power. 2007. (ENG.). 208p. per. 31.50 (978-0-7391-2455-0(2)) Lexington Bks.

Newman, Saul. The Politics of Postanarchism. 2011. (ENG.). 192p. (gr. 17). pap. 45.00 (978-0-7486-3496-5(7)) Edinburgh Univ. Pr. GBR. Dist: Columbia Univ. Pr.

Newman, Saul. The Politics of Postanarchism. 2010. (ENG.). 192p. (gr. 17). 105.00 (978-0-7486-3495-8(9)) Edinburgh Univ. Pr. GBR. Dist: Columbia Univ. Pr.

Nozick, Robert. Anarchy, State, & Utopia. rev. ed. 2013. (ENG.). 384p. (gr. 9). pap. 19.99 (978-0-465-05100-7(6)) Basic Bks.

Papanikolas, Theresa. Anarchism & the Advent of Paris Dada: Art & Criticism, 1914-1924. 2010. (Illus.). 206p. 99.95 (978-0-7546-6626-4(3)) Ashgate Publishing Co.

Pataud, Emile & Pouget, Emile. How Shall We Bring about the Revolution. 288p. pap. 9.95 (978-1-85305-017-6(2)) Pluto Pr. GBR. Dist: AK Pr. Distribution.

Paz, Abel. Story of the Iron Column: Militant Anarchism in the Spanish Civil War. Sharkey, Paul, tr. from SPA. 2011. (ENG., Illus.). 288p. pap. 18.95 (978-1-84935-064-8(7)) AK Pr. GBR. Dist: Consortium Bk. Sales & Distribution.

Pernicone, Nunzio. Italian Anarchism, 18641892. 2009. (ENG., Illus.). 356p. pap. 21.95 (978-1-904859-97-0(6)) AK Pr. GBR. Dist: Consortium Bk. Sales & Distribution.

Petard, Paul, illus. The Anarchist Quiz Book. 2007. 97p. per. 12.95 (978-1-904491-07-1(3)) Freedom Pr. GBR. Dist: AK Pr. Distribution.

Plechanoff, George. Anarchism & Socialism. Aveling, Eleanor Marx, tr. 2010. 104p. pap. (978-1-4099-9218-9(7)) Dodo Pr.

—Anarchism & Socialism. Aveling, Eleanor Marx, tr. 2010. 72p. pap. (978-1-4068-5519-7(7)) Echo Library.

Pokrovskaya, Elena. IN RESPONSE TO THE AUTONOMY-BASED ANARCHIST CHALLENGE: TO POLITICAL PHILOSOPHY. 2008. 56p. pap. (978-3-639-11275-7(X)) VDM Verlag Dr. Mueller e.K.

Porter, David, ed. Eyes to the South: French Anarchists & Algeria. 2011. (ENG., Illus.). 550p. pap. 25.00 (978-1-84935-076-1(0)) AK Pr. GBR. Dist: Consortium Bk. Sales & Distribution.

Prichard, Alex. The International Political Theory of Pierre-Joseph Proudhon: A World Without Sovereigns. 2012. (New International Relations Ser.). (ENG.). 224p. (C). 125.00 (978-0-415-59688-6(2)) Routledge.

Proudhon, Pierre-Joseph. Property Is Theft! A Pierre-Joseph Proudhon Anthology. 2011. (ENG.). 670p. pap. 26.95 (978-1-84935-024-2(8)) AK Pr. GBR. Dist: Consortium Bk. Sales & Distribution.

Purchase, Graham. Anarchism & Environmental Survival. 2011. (ENG.). 182p. (Orig.). pap. 23.95 ***(978-1-926878-09-6(4))*** Black Cat Pr. CAN. Dist: AK Pr. Distribution.

Purkiss, Richard. Democracy, Trade Unions & Political Violence in Spain: The Valencian Anarchist Movement, 1918-1936. 2011. (ENG.). 340p. 74.95 *(978-1-84519-461-1(6))* Sussex Academic Pr. GBR. Dist: International Specialized Bk. Services.

Radical Politics/The Socialist Tradition, 14 vols., Set E. 2009. 6820p. 1535.49 *(978-0-415-55603-3(1))* Routledge.

Ramnath, Maia. Decolonizing Anarchism: An Antiauthoritarian History of India's Liberation Struggle. 2012. (Anarchist Interventions Ser.). (ENG.). 304p. pap. 16.00 ***(978-1-84935-082-2(5))*** AK Pr. GBR. Dist: Consortium Bk. Sales & Distribution.

Ritter, Alan. Anarchism: A Theoretical Analysis. 2010. (ENG.). 196p. pap. 27.99 *(978-0-521-13570-2(2))* Cambridge Univ. Pr.

Roslak, Robyn. Neo-Impressionism & Anarchism Politics in Fin-de-Siecle France: Painting Politics & Landscape. 2007. (Illus.). 232p. 124.95 *(978-0-7546-5711-8(5))* Ashgate Publishing Co.

Rousselle, Duane & Evren, Sareyyya, eds. Post-Anarchism: A Reader, 1 vol. 2011. (ENG.). 320p. lib. bdg. 100.00 *(978-0-7453-3087-7(8))*; 30.00 *(978-0-7453-3086-0(X))* Pluto Pr. GBR. Dist: Macmillan.

Rudahl, Sharon. A Dangerous Woman: The Graphic Biography of Emma Goldman. Buhle, Paul, ed. 2007. (ENG., Illus.). 115p. per. 17.95 *(978-1-59558-054-1(6))* New Pr., The.

Ruiz, Laura. Free Women: Voices & Memories for a Libertarian Future. 2010. 106p. *(978-94-6091-088-3(2))*; pap. *(978-94-6091-087-6(4))* Sense Pubs.

Russell, Bertrand. Proposed Roads to Freedom. 2008. 168p. 22.99 *(978-0-554-38111-4(7))*; 25.99 *(978-0-554-28808-6(7))* BiblioBazaar.

—Proposed Roads to Freedom. 2009. 124p. pap. *(978-0-217-53726-1(X))* Books LLC.

—Proposed Roads to Freedom. 2008. 132p. pap. *(978-1-4099-0105-1(X))* Dodo Pr.

—Proposed Roads to Freedom: Socialism, Anarchism & Syndicalism. 2009. 240p. 23.99 *(978-1-103-55409-6(3))*; pap. 17.99 *(978-1-103-55406-5(9))* BiblioBazaar.

—Proposed Roads to Freedom: Socialism, Anarchism & Syndicalism. 2009. 164p. pap. 11.99 *(978-1-934941-74-4(3))* Red & Black Pubs.

Sartwell, C. Against the State: An Introduction to Anarchist Political Theory. 2008. 128p. (C). 49.50 *(978-0-7914-7447-1(X))* State Univ. of New York Pr.

Sartwell, Crispin. Against the State: An Introduction to Anarchist Political Theory. 2008. 124p. pap. 19.95 *(978-0-7914-7448-8(8))* State Univ. of New York Pr.

Sartwell, Crispin, ed. The Practical Anarchist: Writings of Josiah Warren. 2nd ed. 2011. (American Philosophy Ser.). (ENG., Illus.). 240p. 55.00 *(978-0-8232-3370-0(7))* Fordham Univ. Pr.

Schmidt, Michael & van der Walt, Lucien. Global Fire: 150 Fighting Years of International Anarchism & Syndicalism (Counter-Power Vol 2) 2008. 500p. pap. 24.95 *(978-1-904859-68-0(2))* AK Pr. GBR. Dist: Consortium Bk. Sales & Distribution.

Shannon, Deric, et al, eds. Accumulation of Freedom: Writings on Anarchist Economics. 2012. (ENG., Illus.). 320p. pap. 21.00 ***(978-1-84935-094-5(9))*** AK Pr. GBR. Dist: Consortium Bk. Sales & Distribution.

Shantz, Jeff. Active Anarchy: Political Practice in Contemporary Movements. 2011. (ENG.). 180p. 60.00 *(978-0-7391-6613-0(1))* Lexington Bks.

Shantz, Jeffery. Living Anarchy: Theory & Practice in Anarchist Movements. 2009. (Illus.). 230p. lib. bdg. *(978-1-933146-53-9(2))* Academica Pr., LLC.

Shantz, Jeffrey. Living Anarchy: Theory & Practice of Anarchist Movements. 2009. 230p. pap. *(978-1-933146-83-6(4))* Academica Pr., LLC.

Shantz, Jeffrey A. Constructive Anarchy: Rebuilding Infrastructures of Resistance. 2010. 214p. 99.95 *(978-1-4094-0402-6(1))* Ashgate Publishing Co.

Sherlin, Keith A. Satan's Strategy to Curse Christ's Congregation: An Analysis of How Anarchy & Apostasy Develop in Christian Congregations & Elderships. 2010. 240p. 25.00 *(978-1-4520-7382-8(1))*; pap. 17.00 *(978-1-4520-7383-5(X))* AuthorHouse.

Shukaitis, Stevphen & Graeber, David, eds. Constituent Imagination: Militant Investigations, Collective Theorization. 2007. (ENG., Illus.). 320p. per. 21.95 *(978-1-904859-35-2(6))* AK Pr. GBR. Dist: Consortium Bk. Sales & Distribution.

Sonn, Richard David. Sex, Violence, & the Avant-Garde: Anarchism in Interwar France. 2010. 232p. 65.00 *(978-0-271-03663-2(X))* Pennsylvania State Univ. Pr.

Sorel, Georges. Syndicalism: Writings on Revolutionary Socialist Unions. 2010. *(978-1-934941-94-2(8))* Red & Black Pubs.

Stringham, Edward. Anarchy & the Law: The Political Economy of Choice. 2007. (Independent Studies in Political Economy). (ENG., Illus.). 712p. pap. 39.95 *(978-1-4128-0579-7(1))* Transaction Pubs.

Suissa, Judith. Anarchism & Education: A Philosophical Perspective. 2nd ed. 2010. (ENG.). 176p. pap. 19.95 *(978-1-60486-114-3(2))* PM Pr.

Suriano, Juan. Paradoxes of Utopia: Anarchist Culture & Politics in Buenos Aires, 1890-1910. 2010. (ENG.). 288p. pap. 18.95 *(978-1-84935-006-8(X))* AK Pr. GBR. Dist: Consortium Bk. Sales & Distribution.

Thomas, Paul. Karl Marx & the Anarchists. 2009. (ENG.). 432p. 157.00 *(978-0-415-55602-6(3))* Routledge.

Tremblay, Francois. Market Anarchy Explained: "but Who Will Build the Roads?" 2007. 304p. per. 22.99 *(978-1-4257-6940-6(3))* Xlibris Corp.

van der Walt, Lucien & Schmidt, Michael. Black Flame: The Revolutionary Class Politics of Anarchism & Syndicalism (Counter-Power Vol 1) 2009. (ENG.). 500p. pap. 22.95 *(978-1-904859-16-1(X))* AK Pr. GBR. Dist: Consortium Bk. Sales & Distribution.

Van Deusen, David & Massot, Xavier, compiled by. The Black Bloc Papers: An Anthology of Primary Texts from the North American Anarchist Black Bloc, 1988-2005. 2006. pap. 19.95 *(978-0-9791671-0-2(8))* Breaking Glass Pr.

Walter, Nicolas. Damned Fools in Utopia: And Other Writings on Anarchism & War Resistance. Goodway, David, ed. 2011. (ENG.). 304p. pap. 22.95 *(978-1-60486-222-5(X))* PM Pr.

Ward, Colin. Autonomy, Solidarity, Possibility: The Colin Ward Reader. White, Damian F. & Wilbert, Chris, eds. 2011. (ENG., Illus.). 375p. pap. 21.95 ***(978-1-84935-020-4(5))*** AK Pr. GBR. Dist: Consortium Bk. Sales & Distribution.

Webster, Nesta H. World Revolution the Plot Against Civilization. 2007. 344p. per. 25.45 *(978-1-59462-744-6(4))*, Book Jungle) Standard Pubns., Inc.

Weinberg, Chaim Leib. Forty Years in the Struggle: The Memoirs of a Jewish Anarchist. Cohen, Naomi, tr. from YID. 2009. pap. 28.00 *(978-0-9802004-3-0(1))* Litwin Bks., LLC.

Wilkin, Peter. The Strange Case of Tory Anarchism. 2010. (ENG.). 240p. pap. 20.00 *(978-1-907471-10-0(3))* Libri Publishing Ltd GBR. Dist: Independent Pubs. Group.

Woodcock, George. Anarchism: A History of Libertarian Ideas & Movements. 2011. 512p. (Orig.). 60.95 ***(978-1-258-00160-5(8))*** Literary Licensing, LLC.

York, Tripp. Living on Hope While Living in Babylon: The Christian Anarchists of the 20th Century. 2009. 138p. pap. 17.00 *(978-1-55635-685-8(4))*, Wipf and Stock) Wipf & Stock Pubs.

Ystehede, Per J°Rgen. In the Twilight of Good & Evil. 2008. 164p. pap. *(978-3-639-07128-3(X))* VDM Verlag Dr. Mueller e.K.

Zenker, E. V. Anarchism. 2008. 344p. pap. 30.45 *(978-1-4097-8012-0(0))* Audubon Pr. & Christian Bk. Service.

Zerzan, John. Future Primitive Revisited. enl. ed. 2012. (ENG., Illus.). 240p. pap. 15.00 ***(978-1-936239-29-0(9))*** Feral Hse.

ANARCHISM—BIBLIOGRAPHY

Longa, Ernesto A. Anarchist Periodicals in English Published in the United States, 1833-1955. annot. ed. 2009. (ENG.). 336p. (gr. 17). 90.00 *(978-0-8108-7254-7(4))* Scarecrow Pr., Inc.

ANARCHISM AND ANARCHISTS

see Anarchism; Anarchists

ANARCHISM IN ART

Antliff, Allan. Anarchist Modernism: Art, Politics, & the First American Avant-Garde. 2007. (Illus.). 314p. per. 45.00 *(978-0-226-02104-1(1))* Univ. of Chicago Pr.

Campbell, Russell. Arena: On Anarchist Cinema. Porton, Richard, ed. 2009. (Arena Journal Ser.). (ENG., Illus.). 280p. pap. 14.00 *(978-1-60486-050-4(2))* PM Pr.

Jacques, David. Por Convencion Ferrer: The Northwest of England, Anarchosyndicalism & Time Travel. 2009. (ENG., Illus.). 128p. 39.95 *(978-1-84631-206-9(X))* Liverpool Univ. Pr. GBR. Dist: Chicago Distribution Ctr.

ANARCHISM IN LITERATURE

Shantz, Jeff. Against All Authority: Anarchism & the Literary Imagination. 2011. (ENG.). 250p. pap. 34.90 *(978-1-84540-237-2(5))* Imprint Academic GBR. Dist: Ingram Pub. Services.

ANARCHISTS

Berkman, Alexander, et al. Prison Blossoms: Anarchist Voices from the American Past. Brody, Miriam & Buettner, Bonnie, eds. 2011. (John Harvard Library). (ENG.). 320p. 26.95 *(978-0-674-05056-3(8))*, Belknap Pr.) Harvard Univ. Pr.

Butterworth, Alex & Butterworth, L. The World That Never Was: A True Story of Dreamers, Schemers, Anarchists & Secret Agents. 2010. (ENG., Illus.). 384p. *(978-0-224-07807-8(0)*, Bodley Head) RHCB.

Carr, Gordon. The Angry Brigade: A History of Britain's First Urban Guerilla Group. 2nd ed. 2010. (ENG., Illus.). 288p. pap. 24.95 *(978-1-60486-049-8(9))* PM Pr.

Dulles, John W. F. Anarchists & Communists in Brazil, 1900-1935. 2012. (ENG., Illus.). 654p. pap. 55.00 ***(978-0-292-74076-1(X))*** Univ. of Texas Pr.

Eltzbacher, Paul. Anarchism. 2008. 356p. pap. *(978-1-4097-8011-3(2))* Read Bks.

Fernandez, Frank. El Anarquismo en Cuba. (SPA., Illus.). 204p. *(978-84-86864-41-5(0))* Fundación de Estudios Libertarios Anselmo Lorenzo.

Goodway, David. Anarchist Seeds Beneath the Snow: Left-Libertarian Thought & British Writers from William Morris to Colin Ward. 2011. (ENG.). 420p. pap. 24.95 ***(978-1-60486-221-8(1))*** PM Pr.

Hahne, Ron & Morea, Ben. Black Mask & up Against the Wall Motherfucker: The Incomplete Works of Ron Hahne, Ben Morea, & the Black Mask Group. 2011. (ENG.). 176p. pap. 15.95 *(978-1-60486-021-4(9))* PM Pr.

Kröger, Marianne. Jüdische Ethik und Anarchismus im Spanischen Bürgerkrieg: Simone Weil - Carl Einstein - Etta Federn. 2010. (Kulturtransfer und Geschlechterforschung. Transcultural & Gender Studies). (GER., Illus.). 208p. 57.95 *(978-3-631-59141-3(1))* Lang, Peter GmbH, Europaischer Verlag der Wissenschaften DEU. Dist: Lang, Peter.

McKinley, C. Alexander. Illegitimate Children of the Enlightenment: Anarchists & the French Revolution 1880-1914. 2007. (Francophone Cultures & Literatures Ser.). (Illus.). 250p. (C). 70.95 *(978-1-4331-0059-8(2))* Lang, Peter Publishing, Inc.

Nomad, Max. Rebels & Renegades. 464p. 2008. 52.95 *(978-1-4366-8829-1(9))* 2007. per. 37.95 *(978-1-4304-9656-4(8))* Kessinger Publishing, LLC.

Parsons, Albert & Spies, August. The Haymarket Trial: Selected Testimony from the Trial of the Chicago Anarchists. Flank, Lenny, ed. 2011. 404p. pap. 16.99 ***(978-1-61001-006-1(X))*** Red & Black Pubs.

Podshuvalov, Igor. Siberian Makhnovschina: Siberian Anarchists in the Russian Civil War (1918-1924) 2011. (ENG.). 52p. 10.00 ***(978-1-926878-08-9(6))*** Black Cat Pr. CAN. Dist: AK Pr. Distribution.

Roulston, Travis. Anarchist Individualism. 2010. 80p. pap. *(978-3-8383-6466-7(X))* Lambert Academic Publishing.

Serge, Victor. Revolution in Danger. 2011. (ENG.). 156p. pap. *(978-1-60846-083-0(5))* Pluto Pr.

Thomas, Paul. Karl Marx & the Anarchists. 2009. (ENG.). 432p. 157.00 *(978-0-415-55602-6(3))* Routledge.

Yelensky, Boris. In the Struggle for Equality: The Story of the Anarchist Red Cross. 2011. 98p. 38.95 ***(978-1-258-02634-9(1))*** Literary Licensing, LLC.

York, Tripp. Living on Hope While Living in Babylon: e Christian Anarchists of the 20th Century. 2009. (ENG.). 136p. pap. 42.50 *(978-0-7188-9202-9(X))* Lutherworth Pr., The GBR. Dist: Brown, David Bk. Co., The.

ANARCHISTS—BIOGRAPHY

Berkman, Alexander. Prison Memoirs of an Anarchist. 2012. (ENG., Illus.). 500p. pap. 21.95 ***(978-1-84935-068-6(X))*** AK Pr. GBR. Dist: Consortium Bk. Sales & Distribution.

—Prison Memoirs of an Anarchist. 2009. (Illus.). 318p. pap. *(978-1-150-58429-9(7))* Books LLC.

—Prison Memoirs of an Anarchist. 2009. 416p. pap. *(978-1-4099-4940-4(0))* Dodo Pr.

Biographiq. Emma Goldman. 2008. pap. 9.99 *(978-1-59986-215-6(8)*, Biographiq) Filiquarian Publishing, LLC.

Chalberg, John C. Emma Goldman: American Individualist. Carnes, Mark C., ed. 2nd ed. 2007. (Library of American Biography Ser.). (ENG., Illus.). 240p. (C). per. 25.20 *(978-0-321-37073-0(2))* Longman Publishing Group.

Christie, Stuart. Granny Made Me an Anarchist: General Franco, the Angry Brigade & Me. 2007. (ENG., Illus.). 400p. per. 19.95 *(978-1-904859-65-9(8))* AK Pr. GBR. Dist: Consortium Bk. Sales & Distribution.

Dalmau, Antoni. El Cas Rull: Viure Del Terror a la Ciutat de les Bombes (1901-1908) 2008. (CAT., Illus.). 411p. *(978-84-664-0897-4(5))* Columna Edicions.

Delf, Hanna & Mattenklott, Gert, eds. Gustav Landauer Im Gespräch: Symposium Zum 125. Geburtstag. (Conditio Judaica Ser.). (GER.). IX, 288p. 210.00 ***(978-3-11-187365-7(X))*** De Gruyter, Walter Inc.

Domaschi, Giovanni. Le Mie Prigioni e le Mie Evasioni: Memorie Di un Anarchio Veronese Dal Carcere a Dal Confino Fascista. 2007. (Illus.). x, 409p. *(978-88-8314-425-7(2))* Cierre Edizioni.

Ferguson, Kathy. Emma Goldman: Political Thinking in the Streets. 2011. (20th Century Political Thinkers Ser.). (ENG., Illus.). 362p. (gr. 17). 65.00 *(978-0-7425-2300-5(4))* Rowman & Littlefield Publishers, Inc.

Finch, R. Parsifal. Correspondence. 2010. 520p. 54.95 *(978-0-9558555-3-5(5))* Laplace Pubns. GBR. Dist: Lulu Enterprises Inc.

Finzi, Paolo. Emilio Canzi: An Anarchist partisan in Italy & Spain. Sharkey, Paul, ed. & tr. by. from ITA. 2006. (Illus.). 32p. 3.50 *(978-1-873605-29-5(3))* Sharpley, Kate Library GBR. Dist: AK Pr. Distribution.

Garcia Oliver, Juan & Gomez, Freddy. My Revolutionary Life: Juan Garcia Oliver Interviewed by Freddy Gomez. Sharkey, Paul, tr. from FRE. 2009. 40p. pap. 3.50 *(978-1-873605-54-7(4))* Sharpley, Kate Library GBR. Dist: AK Pr. Distribution.

Gornick, Vivian. Emma Goldman: Revolution as a Way of Life. 2011. (Jewish Lives Ser.). (Illus.). 160p. 25.00 *(978-0-300-13726-2(5))* Yale Univ. Pr.

Helms, Robert P. George Brown, the Cobbler Anarchist of Philadelphia. rev. ed. 2006. (Illus.). 58p. pap. 5.00 *(978-1-873605-34-9(X))* Sharpley, Kate Library GBR. Dist: AK Pr. Distribution.

Hennacy, Ammon. The Book of Ammon. 2010. (Catholic Worker Reprint Ser.). (Illus.). 512p. (Orig.). pap. 55.00 *(978-1-60899-053-5(2))*, Wipf and Stock) Wipf & Stock Pubs.

Kropotkin, Peter. Memoirs of a Revolutionist. 2010. (ENG.). 608p. pap. 19.95 *(978-0-486-47316-1(3))* Dover Pubns., Inc.

—Memoirs of a Revolutionist. 2007. 544p. 57.95 *(978-0-548-11675-3(X))* Kessinger Publishing, LLC.

Leier, Mark. Bakunin: The Creative Passion-A Biography. 2009. (ENG.). 384p. pap. 17.95 *(978-1-58322-894-4(2))* Seven Stories Pr.

Makhno, Nestor Ivanovich, et al. The Ukrainian Revolution (July - December 1918) 2011. (ENG., Illus.). 232p. pap. 26.95 ***(978-1-926878-05-8(1))*** Black Cat Pr. CAN. Dist: AK Pr. Distribution.

Makhno, Nestor Ivanovich, et al. Under the Blows of the Counterrevolution: April - June 1918. 2009. 24.95 *(978-0-9737827-5-2(7))* Black Cat Pr. CAN. Dist: AK Pr. Distribution.

McHarg, Farquhar. Pistoleros!: the Chronicles of Farquhar Mcharg: Volume 1: 1918. 2011. (ENG.). 264p. pap. 18.95 *(978-1-60486-401-4(X))* PM Pr.

Nicholson, C. Brid. Emma Goldman: Still Dangerous. 2010. (ENG., Illus.). 208p. 48.99 *(978-1-55164-327-4(8))*; pap. 19.99 *(978-1-55164-326-7(X))* Black Rose Bks. CAN. Dist: Consortium Bk. Sales & Distribution.

Paz, Abel. Durruti in the Spanish Revolution. Morse, Chuck, tr. from SPA. 2006. (ENG., Illus.). 800p. per. 27.95 *(978-1-904859-50-5(X))* Consortium Bk. Sales & Distribution.

Pickering, Leslie James, ed. Conspiracy to Riot in Furtherance of Terrorism: The Collective Autobiography of the RNC 8. 2011. (ENG.). 416p. pap. 14.95 *(978-1-936900-18-3(1))* Arissa Media Group.

Shone, Steve J. Lysander Spooner: American Anarchist. 2010. (ENG.). 138p. 57.99 *(978-0-7391-4450-3(2))* Lexington Bks.

Tejada, Susan. In Search of Sacco & Vanzetti: Double Lives, Troubled Times, & the Massachusetts Murder Case That Shook the World. 2012. (ENG., Illus.). 352p. 27.95 ***(978-1-55553-730-2(8))*** Northeastern University Pr.) Univ. Pr. of New England.

Weinberg, Chaim Leib. Forty Years in the Struggle: The Memoirs of a Jewish Anarchist. Cohen, Naomi, tr. from YID. 2009. pap. 28.00 *(978-0-9802004-3-0(1))* Litwin Bks., LLC.

ANARCHY

see Anarchism

ANASARCA

see Edema

ANASAZI CULTURE

see Indians of North America—Southwest, New

ANASTASIIA NIKOLAEVNA, GRAND DUCHESS, DAUGHTER OF NICHOLAS II, EMPEROR OF RUSSIA, 1901-1918

King, Greg & Wilson, Penny. The Resurrection of the Romanovs: Anastasia, Anna Anderson, & the World's Greatest Royal Mystery. 2010. (ENG., Illus.). 432p. 35.00 *(978-0-470-44498-6(3)*, Wiley) Wiley, John & Sons, Inc.

ANASTASIUS I, EMPEROR OF THE EAST, CA. 430-518

Haarer, F K. Anastasius I: Politics & Empire in the Late Roman World. 2006. (ARCA Classical & Medieval Texts, Papers & Monographs). (Illus.). 351p. 130.00 *(978-0-905205-43-4(X))* Cairns, Francis Publications, Limited GBR. Dist: Brown, David Bk. Co., The.

ANASTASIUS, THE LIBRARIAN, CA. 810-CA. 878

Neil, B. Seventh-Century Popes & Martyrs: The Political Hagiography of Anastasius the Librarian. 2007. (Studia Antiqua Australiensia Ser.). (ENG.). 336p. (C). pap. 73.00 *(978-2-503-51887-9(7))* Brepols Pubs. BEL. Dist: ISD.

ANATHEMA

see Excommunication

ANATIDAE

Owen, Myrfyn, et al. Wildfowl in Great Britain. 2nd rev. ed. 2009. (ENG., Illus.). 628p. pap. 84.00 *(978-0-521-11174-4(3))* Cambridge Univ. Pr.

ANATOLIA

see Turkey

ANATOMICAL GIFTS

see Donation of Organs, Tissues, etc.

ANATOMICAL SPECIMENS

Clark, William. Catalogue of the Osteological Portions of Specimens Contained in the Anatomical Museum of the University of Cambridge. 2009. (Cambridge Library Collection - Life Sciences Ser.). (ENG.). 148p. pap. 19.99 *(978-1-108-00467-1(9))* Cambridge Univ. Pr.

Degueurce, Christophe. Fragonard Museum: the Ecorches. 2011. (ENG.). 160p. 50.00 *(978-0-922233-39-7(X))* Blast Bks.

Point-of-Care Testing. (Specialty Collections). ring bd. 200.00 *(978-1-56238-294-0(2)*, SC17-L) NCCLC.

ANATOMICAL SPECIMENS—COLLECTION AND PRESERVATION

Body Fluid & Tissue Specimen Collection. (Specialty Collections). ring bd. 250.00 *(978-1-56238-295-7(0)*, SC18-L) NCCLC.

ANATOMY

see also Body Composition; Dissection; Histology; Human Anatomy; Nervous System; Physiology; Plant Anatomy; Veterinary Anatomy

also specific subjects, with or without the subdivision Anatomy

Allan, Richard, et al. Anatomy & Physiology. 2009. (ENG., Illus.). 232p. (YA). pap. *(978-1-877462-26-9(8))* BIOZONE International, Ltd.

Anatomical Chart Company Staff. Anatomica Visual Guide to Sports Injuries. 2009. (ENG.). 90p. spiral bd. 82.95 *(978-0-7817-7361-4(X))* Lippincott Williams & Wilkins.

Anderson, Bryan E. The Netter Collection of Medical Illustrations - Integumentary System: Volume 4. 2nd ed. 2012. (Netter Green Book Collection). (ENG., Illus.). 272p. 99.00 ***(978-1-4377-5654-8(9)***, Saunders) Elsevier - Health Sciences Div.

Applegate, Edith J., et al. Mosby's Radiography Online: Sectional Anatomy & the Sectional Anatomy Learning System - 2-Vol Set (User Guide, Access Code, & Textbook Package) 3rd ed. 2009. (ENG.). (C). pap. 128.61 *(978-0-323-07120-8(1)*, Mosby) Elsevier - Health Sciences Div.

BarCharts, Inc. Endocrine System. 2010. (ENG.). 6p. 5.95 *(978-1-4232-1500-4(1))* Barcharts, Inc.

Béclard, P. A. Elémens D'Anatomie Générale: Ou, Description de Tous les Genres D'organe. 2009. (FRE.). 741p. pap. 51.75 *(978-1-117-49630-6(9))* BiblioBazaar.

Bertoloni Meli, Domenico. Mechanism, Experiment, Disease: Marcello Malpighi & Seventeenth-Century Anatomy. 2011. (ENG., Illus.). 456p. (gr. 17). 90.00 *(978-0-8018-9903-4(6))* Johns Hopkins Univ. Pr.

—Mechanism, Experiment, Disease: Marcello Malpighi & Seventeenth-Century Anatomy. 2011. (ENG., Illus.). 456p. (gr. 17). pap. 45.00 *(978-0-8018-9904-1(4))* Johns Hopkins Univ. Pr.

Booth, Kathryn, et al. Anatomy, Physiology, & Disease for the Health Professions w/Connect Plus 1 Semester Access Card. 3rd ed. 2012. (ENG.). (C). pap. 69.00 ***(978-0-07-760513-1(6))***, 0077605136) McGraw-Hill Higher Education.

—Anatomy, Physiology, & Disease for the Health Professions with Workbook. 3rd ed. 2012. (ENG.). (C). pap., pap. 99.41 ***(978-0-07-760514-8(4))***, 0077605144) McGraw-Hill Higher Education.

Booth, Kathryn A. & Stoia, J. Virgil. Anatomy, Physiology, & Disease for the Health Professions. 3rd ed. 2012. (ENG., Illus.). 576p. (C). pap. 60.00 ***(978-0-07-340222-2(2)***, 0073402222) McGraw-Hill Cos., The.

Booth, Kathryn A. & Wyman, Terri D. Anatomy, Physiology, & Pathophysiology for Allied Health. 2nd ed. 2008. (ENG., Illus.). 312p. (C). pap. 64.55 *(978-0-07-337395-9(8)*, 0073373958) McGraw-Hill Higher Education.

Borg, Philip & Alvi, Abdul Rahman. Radiological Anatomy for FRCR Part 1. 2010. (Illus.). xiii, 286p. pap. 49.95 *(978-3-642-13750-1(4)*, 3642137504) Springer.

Braude, Stanton, et al. Case Studies for Understanding the Human Body. 2nd ed. 2011. 196p. pap. 34.95 *(978-1-4496-0499-8(4))* Jones & Bartlett Learning, LLC.

Buck, Carol J. CCS Coding Exam Review 2011: The Certification Step. 2010. (ENG., Illus.). 584p. pap. 74.95 *(978-1-4377-1655-9(5)*, Saunders) Elsevier - Health Sciences Div.

Buck, Carol J. CCS Coding Exam Review 2012: The Certification Step. 2011. (ENG., Illus.). 584p. pap. 79.95 ***(978-1-4557-0683-9(3)***, Saunders) Elsevier - Health Sciences Div.

Case, Drew. Essentials of Anatomy & Physiology Workbook Study Guide. rev. ed. 2012. (ENG.). 336p. spiral bd. 58.00 ***(978-0-7575-9518-9(9))*** Kendall Hunt Publishing Co.

Casey. Student Study Guide for Bio-168 Bio-169 & Basic Anatomy Bio-163 Human Anatomy & Physiology I & Ii. 2nd rev. ed. 2011. (ENG.). 402p. spiral bd. 42.20 ***(978-0-7575-9574-5(X))*** Kendall Hunt Publishing Co.

Chitty, Joseph. A Practical Treatise on Medical Jurisprudence, with So Much of Anatomy, Physiology, Pathology, & the Practice of Medicine & Surgery: As Are Essential to Be Known by Members of Parliament, Lawyers, Coroners, Magistrates, Officers in the Army & Navy, & Private Gentlemen an All the Laws Relating to Medical Practioners, with Explanatory Plates. 2006. *(978-1-57588-904-7(8))* Hein, William S. & Co., Inc.

Coastline Learning Systems Staff & Erickson, John L. Anatomy & Physiology: An Introduction. rev. ed. 2010. (ENG.). 558p. pap. 149.95 *(978-0-7575-6016-3(4))* Kendall Hunt Publishing Co.

Cohen, Barbara Janson. Memmlers Human Body in Health & Disease. 12th rev. ed. 2012. (ENG., Illus.). 656p. pap. 54.95 ***(978-1-60913-905-6(4))*** Lippincott Williams & Wilkins.

—Memmler's Structure & Function of the Human Body. 10th rev. ed. 2012. (ENG., Illus.). 512p. 55.95 ***(978-1-60913-902-5(X))***; pap. 53.95 ***(978-1-60913-900-1(3))*** Lippincott Williams & Wilkins.

Colbert, Bruce J. & Ankney, Jeff J. Anatomy & Physiology for Health Professions: An Interactive Journey. 2nd ed. 2010. (ENG.). (C). 6.67 *(978-0-13-509651-2(0)*, Prentice Hall) Prentice Hall PTR.

Cook, Gray, et al. Movement: Functional Movement Systems: Screening, Assessment, Corrective Strategies. 2011. (ENG., Illus.). 408p. pap. 49.95 ***(978-1-931046-30-5(1))*** On Target Pubns.

Cram101 Textbook Reviews. Outlines & Highlights for Essential Clinical Anatomy by Keith L Moore, Anne Mr Agur, Isbn: 9780781762748. 2010. 646p. pap. 41.95 *(978-1-61698-447-2(3))* Cram101 Inc.

Cram101 Textbook Reviews & Cram101 Textbook Reviews. Outlines & Highlights for Animal Structure & Function Volume 5 by Cecie Starr, Isbn: 9780495558026 0495558028. 2011. 636p. pap. 40.95 ***(978-1-61490-556-1(8))*** Cram101 Inc.

—Outlines & Highlights for Fundamental Anatomy by Walter Hartwig, Isbn: 9780781768887 0781768888. 2011. 376p. pap. 42.95 ***(978-1-61490-234-8(8))*** Cram101 Inc.

—Outlines & Highlights for Learning Human Anatomy: Laboratory Text & Workbook by Julia Guy, ISBN. 2011. 470p. pap. 36.95 ***(978-1-61461-543-9(8))*** Cram101 Inc.

Cram101 Textbook Reviews Staff. Outlines & Highlights for Human Anatomy & Physiology by Marieb, Isbn: 0805359095. 2008. 480p. pap. 19.95 *(978-1-4288-6057-5(6))* Cram101 Inc.

Culbertson-Tanner. The Anatomy & Physiology of Speech & Swallowing. rev. ed. 2011. (ENG.). 324p. pap. 170.00 ***(978-0-7575-9422-9(0))*** Kendall Hunt Publishing Co.

Cunningham, Andrew. The Anatomist Anatomis'D: An Experimental Discipline in Enlightenment Europe. 2010. (History of Medicine in Context Ser.). (Illus.). 468p. 134.95 *(978-0-7546-6338-6(8))* Ashgate Publishing Co.

Curtis, John, et al. First FRCR Anatomy: Questions & Answers. 2012. (ENG., Illus.). 226p. pap. 45.00 ***(978-1-107-67949-8(4))*** Cambridge Univ. Pr.

Daniels, A. U. & Wirz, Dieter, eds. Mechanical Properties of Articular Cartilage, Meniscus & Related Materials. 2011. (Orthopedic Biology & Medicine Ser.). (ENG., Illus.). 400p. 179.00 *(978-1-60327-994-9(6)*, 1603279946) Humana Pr.

Deane, Andrew & Richardson, April. Principles of Human Anatomy: Part I. 2011. 151p. spiral bd. 22.50 ***(978-1-935985-57-0(4))*** Preston Publishing.

—Principles of Human Anatomy: Part II. 2011. 171p. spiral bd. 22.50 ***(978-1-935985-58-7(2))*** Preston Publishing.

Delmar Publishers Staff & Delmar Cengage Learning Staff. Fundamentals of Anatomy & Physiology Online Course. 2007. (ENG.). (C). 62.95 *(978-1-4180-0131-5(7))* Delmar Cengage Learning.

Derrickson, Bryan H. Principles of Anatomy & Physiology. Tortora, Gerard J., ed. 12th ed. 2008. (Wiley Plus Products Ser.). pap. 79.95 *(978-0-470-13876-2(9)*, Wiley) Wiley, John & Sons, Inc.

Deslauriers, Jean. Thoracic Anatomy, Part II, an Issue of Thoracic Surgery Clinics, 2 vols. 2011. (Clinics: Surgery Ser.: 21-2). (ENG., Illus.). 200p. 105.00 *(978-1-4377-2269-7(5)*, Saunders) Elsevier - Health Sciences Div.

Dowd, Irene. Taking Root to Fly Ten Articles on Functional Anatomy. pap. *(978-0-937645-02-4(8))* Contact Editions.

Ellis, Harold & Mahadevan, Vishy. Clinical Anatomy: Applied Anatomy for Students & Junior Doctors. 12th ed. 2010. (ENG., Illus.). 488p. pap. 66.95 *(978-1-4051-8617-9(8)*, Wiley-Blackwell) Wiley, John & Sons, Inc.

Esrey, William P. A Treatise on Anatomy & Physiology. 2006. 196p. per. 18.99 *(978-1-4255-1618-5(1))* MPublishing.

Fedorenko, Dmitri N. Evolution of the Beetle Hind Wing,with Special Reference to Folding: Insecta, Coleoptera. Golovatch, Sergei, ed. 2009. 336p. pap. 157.50 *(978-954-642-494-5(3))* Pensoft Pubs. BGR. Dist: Coronet Bks.

Fort, J. A. Compendio de Anatomia Descriptiva. (SPA.). 546p. pap. 19.95 *(978-0-7859-0869-2(2)*, S-50272) French & European Pubns., Inc.

Freudenrich, Craig & Tortora, Gerard J. Visualizing Anatomy & Physiology. 2011. (ENG., Illus.). 569p. (C). pap. 125.95 *(978-0-470-49124-9(8)*, Wiley) Wiley, John & Sons, Inc.

Freudenrich, Craig, et al. Visualizing Anatomy & Physiology, First Edition Binder Ready Version. 2011. 640p. (C). ring bd. 70.95 *(978-0-470-91776-3(8)*, Wiley) Wiley, John & Sons, Inc.

Fritsch, Helga & Kuehnel, Wolfgang. Color Atlas of Human Anatomy. 5th ed. 2007. (ENG.). 456p. pap. 47.99 *(978-1-58890-097-5(5))* Thieme Medical Pubs., Inc.

Gallucci, Massimo, et al. Radiographic Atlas of Skull & Brain Anatomy. 2010. (Illus.). x, 362p. pap. 259.00 *(978-3-642-07059-4(0)*, 3642070590) Springer.

Garrett, Lori K. Get Ready for A & P. 3rd rev. ed. 2012. (ENG.). 272p. (C). pap. 53.40 ***(978-0-321-81336-7(7))*** Benjamin-Cummings Publishing Co.

Gerdin, Judith. Workbook for Health Careers Today. 4th ed. 2007. (ENG., Illus.). 400p. (C). per. 32.95 *(978-0-323-04842-2(0)*, Mosby) Elsevier - Health Sciences Div.

Gilroy, Anne. Anatomy: An Illustrated Review. 2012. (ENG., Illus.). 504p. pap. 39.99 ***(978-1-60406-207-6(X))*** Thieme Medical Pubs., Inc.

Gilroy, Anne M., et al. Atlas of Anatomy. 2nd ed. 2012. (ENG.). 712p. pap. 79.99 ***(978-1-60406-745-3(4))*** Thieme Medical Pubs., Inc.

Gray, Henry. Gray's Anatomy. 2008. (Illus.). 1257p. lib. bdg. 14.97 *(978-1-58173-690-8(8))* Sweetwater Pr.

Gross Anatomy. 2011. (Oklahoma Notes Ser.). pap. *(978-3-540-97295-2(1))* Springer.

Hayes, Bill. The Anatomist: A True Story of Gray's Anatomy. 2009. (ENG.). 250p. pap. 16.95 *(978-1-934137-21-5(9))* Bellevue Literary Pr.

Hofer, Matthias. CT Teaching Manual: A Systematic Approach to CT Reading. 4th ed. 2010. (ENG., Illus.). 224p. pap. 74.99 ***(978-3-13-124354-6(6))*** Thieme Medical Pubs., Inc.

Hogan, Mary Ann, et al. Anatomy & Physiology: Review & Rationales. 2008. (ENG.). 216p. (C). pap. 37.80 *(978-0-13-172051-0(1)*, Prentice Hall) Prentice Hall PTR.

Hollins, Carole. Basic Guide to Anatomy & Physiology for Dental Care Professionals. 2012. (Basic Guide Dentistry Ser.). (ENG.). 208p. pap. 38.99 ***(978-0-470-65611-2(5)***, Wiley) Wiley, John & Sons, Inc.

Homan, Jaque. Student Study Guide Anatomy & Physiology: The Unity of Form & Function. 5th ed. 2009. (ENG.). 288p. (C). spiral bd. 67.00 *(978-0-07-325096-0(1)*, 0073250961, McGraw-Hill Science, Engineering & Mathematics) McGraw-Hill Higher Education.

Howell, L. Daniel. Anatomy & Physiology Lecture Guide: BIOL 212 Spring 2008. 2008. (Illus.). (C). per. 40.00 *(978-0-9796323-2-7(3))* Creation Curriculum, LLC.

Inside Nature's Giants Team Staff & Dugan, David. Inside Nature's Giants. 2012. (ENG., Illus.). 224p. 29.95 ***(978-0-00-743880-8(X))*** HarperCollins Pubs. Ltd. GBR. Dist: Independent Pubs. Group.

Jenkins, Gail W., et al. Anatomy & Physiology: From Science to Life. 2nd ed. 2009. (ENG., Illus.). 1040p. (C). 215.95 *(978-0-470-22758-9(3)*, Wiley) Wiley, John & Sons, Inc.

Johnson, Reuben D. Anatomy Tutor for Surgeons in Training. 2008. 180p. (C). pap. 56.00 *(978-0-521-73474-5(6))* Cambridge Univ. Pr.

Jones, Betty Davis. Comprehensive Medical Terminology (Book Only) 4th ed. 2010. (ENG.). (C). pap. 87.95 *(978-1-111-32029-4(2))* Delmar Cengage Learning.

Jones, Shirley. Pocket Anatomy & Physiology. 2008. (Illus.). 272p. spiral bd. 28.95 *(978-0-8036-1824-4(7))* Davis, F. A. Co.

Jordan, Sue, et al. Vital Notes on Anatomy & Physiology: Applied Anatomy & Physiology. 2006. (Illus.). 496p. pap. 39.95 *(978-1-4051-0875-1(4)*, Wiley-Blackwell) Wiley, John & Sons, Inc.

Kaminoff, Leslie & Matthews, Amy. Yoga Anatomy-2nd Edition. 2nd ed. 2011. (Illus.). 288p. pap. 19.95 ***(978-1-4504-0024-4(8))*** Human Kinetics Pubs.

Kelley, Lorrie L. & Petersen, Connie. Sectional Anatomy. 2nd ed. 2007. (ENG.). (C). stu. ed., wbk. ed. 125.01 *(978-0-323-02005-3(4)*, Mosby) Elsevier - Health Sciences Div.

Kelley, Lorrie L., et al. Mosby's Radiography Online: Sectional Anatomy & Sectional Anatomy for Imaging Professionals (User Guide, Access Code, Textbook, & Workbook Package) 2nd ed. 2009. (ENG.). (C). 167.26 *(978-0-323-07119-2(8)*, Mosby) Elsevier - Health Sciences Div.

Kipp, Brian H. Anatomy & Physiology. 2012. (ENG., Illus.). 216p. pap. 34.95 ***(978-1-60831-212-2(7))*** Lippincott Williams & Wilkins.

Klestinec, Cynthia. Theaters of Anatomy: Students, Teachers, & Traditions of Dissection in Renaissance Venice. 2011. (ENG., Illus.). 280p. (gr. 17). 55.00 *(978-1-4214-0142-3(8))* Johns Hopkins Univ. Pr.

Kooijmans, Luuc. Death Defied: The Anatomy Lessons of Frederik Ruysch. Webb, Diane, tr. from DUT. (History of Science & Medicine Library). (Illus.). 464p. *(978-90-04-18784-9(7))* BRILL.

Lam, Tania & Inglis, J. Timothy. Introduction to Human Musculoskeletal Gross Anatomy. rev. ed. 2011. (ENG.). 102p. spiral bd., wbk. ed., lab manual ed. 34.99 *(978-0-7575-7885-4(3))* Kendall Hunt Publishing Co.

Langley. Principles of Anatomy & Physiology. 8th ed. Date not set. pap., tchr. ed. *(978-0-673-55777-3(4))* Addison-Wesley Educational Pubs., Inc.

Lasko, Casey. Skin. 2010. (Illus.). 16p. ***(978-0-545-24797-9(7))*** Scholastic, Inc.

Liebgott, Bernard. The Anatomical Basis of Dentistry. 3rd ed. 2009. (ENG., Illus.). 523p. (C). pap. 96.95 *(978-0-323-06807-9(3)*, Mosby) Elsevier - Health Sciences Div.

Lippincott Williams & Wilkins Staff, contrib. by. Anatomy & Physiology Made Incredibly Easy! 4th rev. ed. 2012. (ENG.). 384p. pap. 46.95 ***(978-1-4511-4726-1(0))*** Lippincott Williams & Wilkins.

Logan, Bari M. & Hutchings, Ralph T. McMinn's Color Atlas of Foot & Ankle Anatomy. 4th ed. 2011. (ENG., Illus.). 160p. (C). 75.95 ***(978-0-323-05615-1(6)***, Saunders) Elsevier - Health Sciences Div.

Lukacs, Gabor. Kaitai Shinsho: The Single Most Famous Japanese Book of Medicine: And Geka Soden: An Early Very Important Manuscript on Surgery. 2008. (Illus.). 286p. 400.00 *(978-90-6194-499-7(6))* HES & DE GRAAF Pubs. BV NLD. Dist: Oak Knoll Pr.

Lumley, John S. P. Surface Anatomy: The Anatomical Basis of Clinical Examination. 4th ed. 2008. (ENG., Illus.). 136p. (C). pap. 44.95 *(978-0-443-06794-5(5)*, Churchill Livingstone) Elsevier - Health Sciences Div.

Lütjen-Drecoll, Elke, et al. Color Atlas of Anatomy: A Photographic Study of the Human Body. 7th rev. ed. 2010. (ENG., Illus.). 556p. 87.99 *(978-1-58255-856-1(6))* Lippincott Williams & Wilkins.

Manocchia, Pat. Anatomy of Strength Training: The 5 Essential Exercises. 2010. (ENG., Illus.). 160p. pap. 19.95 *(978-1-60710-204-5(8)*, Thunder Bay Pr.) Advantage Pubs. Group.

Marieb, Elaine N. Essentials of Human Anatomy & Physiology, Books a la Carte Plus Essentials of Interactive Physiology CD-ROM. 10th ed. 2011. (ENG.). 640p. (C). ring bd. 89.60 incl. cd-rom *(978-0-321-76235-1(5))* Benjamin-Cummings Publishing Co.

Marieb, Elaine N. & Hoehn, Katja N. Human Anatomy & Physiology. 9th rev. ed. 2012. (ENG.). 1264p. (C). 228.73 ***(978-0-321-74326-8(1))*** Benjamin-Cummings Publishing Co.

Marieb, Elaine N. & Hoehn, Katja N. Human Anatomy & Physiology & Human Anatomy & Physiology. 8th ed. 2011. (ENG.). 1264p. (C). lab manual ed. 179.73 *(978-0-321-77727-0(1))* Benjamin-Cummings Publishing Co.

Marieb, Elaine N., et al. Human Anatomy, Media Update. 6th rev. ed. 2011. (ENG., Illus.). 880p. (C). 216.87 *(978-0-321-75327-4(5))* Benjamin-Cummings Publishing Co.

Marieb, Elaine Nicpon & Hoehn, Katja. Human Anatomy & Physiology. 8th ed. 2010. (Illus.). xxxii, 1114p. *(978-0-321-54312-7(2))* Benjamin-Cummings Publishing Co.

Marieb, Elaine Nicpon, et al. Human Anatomy. 6th ed. 2012. 880p. *(978-0-321-76503-1(6))* Benjamin-Cummings Publishing Co.

Maroto, Miguel & Whittock, Neil V., eds. Somitogenesis. 2010. (Advances in Experimental Medicine & Biology Ser.). (Illus.). viii, 194p. pap. 199.00 *(978-1-4419-1871-0(X)*, 144191871X) Springer.

Martini & Bartholomew. Essentials of Anatomy & Physiology. 4th ed. 648p. tchr. ed. 18.97 *(978-0-8053-7516-9(3))* Addison-Wesley Educational Pubs., Inc.

Martini, Frederic. Fundamentals of Anatomy & Physiology. 7th ed. 1248p. tchr. ed. 18.97 *(978-0-8053-7281-6(4))* Addison-Wesley Educational Pubs., Inc.

—Fundamentals of Anatomy & Physiology. 7th ed. 1248p. stu. ed. 95.47 *(978-0-13-197210-0(3))* Prentice Hall (Schl. Div.).

Martini, Frederic H. & Bartholomew, Edwin F. Essentials of Anatomy & Physiology. 5th ed. 2009. (ENG.). 800p. (C). 163.47 incl. cd-rom *(978-0-321-57554-8(7))* Benjamin-Cummings Publishing Co.

Martini, Frederic H. & Nath, Judi L. Anatomy & Physiology. 2nd ed. 2010. (ENG., Illus.). 1056p. (C). 194.73 *(978-0-321-59713-7(3))* Benjamin-Cummings Publishing Co.

—Anatomy & Physiology P-copy (text Component) 2nd ed. 2008. *(978-0-321-59720-5(6))* Benjamin-Cummings Publishing Co.

—Anatomy & Physiology with IP-10. 2nd ed. 2009. (ENG.). 1056p. (C). 194.73 *(978-0-321-59660-4(9))* Benjamin-Cummings Publishing Co.

Martini, Frederic H. & Welch, Kathleen. A&P Applications Manual. 9th ed. 2011. (ENG.). 272p. (C). pap. 38.00 *(978-0-321-74169-1(2))* Benjamin-Cummings Publishing Co.

Martini, Frederic H., et al. Fundamentals of Anatomy & Physiology. 9th ed. 2011. (ENG.). 1264p. (C). spiral bd. 228.73 *(978-0-321-71979-9(4))*; spiral bd., ring bd. 147.27 *(978-0-321-73745-8(8))*; E-Book 126.67 *(978-0-321-73736-6(9))* Benjamin-Cummings Publishing Co.

—Human Anatomy. 7th ed. 2011. (ENG.). 904p. (C). spiral bd., ring bd. 140.13 *(978-0-321-73236-1(7))* Benjamin-Cummings Publishing Co.

—Mastering A & P: Student Access Code Card for Fundamentals of Anatomy & Physiology. 9th ed. 2011. (ENG.). (C). 64.67 *(978-0-321-74171-4(4))* Benjamin-Cummings Publishing Co.

—Student Worksheets for Visual Anatomy & Physiology. (ENG.). 320p. (C). 2011. pap. 16.87 *(978-0-321-76827-8(2))* 2010. pap. 13.33 *(978-0-321-74199-8(4))* Benjamin-Cummings Publishing Co.

—Visual Anatomy & Physiology. (ENG.). (C). 2011. 979p. spiral bd. 147.27 incl. cd-rom *(978-0-321-78435-3(9))* 2010. 35.00 *(978-0-321-58354-3(X))* 2011. (Illus.). 1128p. 228.73 *(978-0-321-78667-8(X))* 2011. 1128p. spiral bd. 228.73 *(978-0-321-76937-4(6))* Benjamin-Cummings Publishing Co.

—Visual Anatomy & Physiology, Books a la Carte Edition. 2011. (ENG.). 1128p. (C). ring bd. 137.27 *(978-0-321-78765-1(X))* Benjamin-Cummings Publishing Co.

—Visual Essentials of Anatomy & Physiology. rev. ed. 2012. (ENG.). 800p. (C). pap. 159.47 ***(978-0-321-78077-5(9))*** Benjamin-Cummings Publishing Co.

—Visual Essentials of Anatomy & Physiology, Books a la Carte Edition. 2012. (ENG.). 800p. (C). ring bd. 95.73 ***(978-0-321-79272-3(6))*** Benjamin-Cummings Publishing Co.

—Visual Essentials of Anatomy & Physiology, Books a la Carte Plus MasteringA&Preg; 2012. (ENG.). 800p. (C). ring bd. 105.73 incl. cd-rom ***(978-0-321-79302-7(1))*** Benjamin-Cummings Publishing Co.

Medical College of Georgia Staff & University of Tolendo Staff. Anatomy & Physiology Revealed. 2008. (ENG.). (C). cd-rom 28.50 *(978-0-07-337831-2(3)*, 0073378313, McGraw-Hill Science, Engineering & Mathematics) McGraw-Hill Higher Education.

Meyers, Morton A., et al. Meyers' Dynamic Radiology of the Abdomen: Normal & Pathologic Anatomy. 6th ed. 2010. (Illus.). xviii, 800p. 269.00 *(978-1-4419-5938-6(6)*, 1441959386) Springer.

Milady. Anatomy & Physiology: Reference for Beauty & Wellness Professionals. 2nd ed. 2011. (ENG.). (C). 72p. spiral bd. 32.95 ***(978-1-111-64212-9(5))***; 36p. spiral bd. 25.50 *(978-1-111-64211-2(7))* Delmar Cengage Learning. (Milady Publishing Co.).

Moini, Jahangir. Anatomy & Physiology for Health Professionals International Edition. 2011. (Illus.). 424p. pap. 62.95 *(978-1-4496-3229-8(7))* Jones & Bartlett Learning, LLC.

—Anatomy & Physiology for Health Professionals with Companion Web Site. 2011. 424p. pap. 62.95 *(978-1-4496-2214-5(3))* Jones & Bartlett Learning, LLC.

Mosby & Matusiak, Dan. Anatomy & Physiology. 2009. (ENG., Illus.). 320p. (C). 28.95 *(978-0-323-06652-5(6)*, Mosby) Elsevier - Health Sciences Div.

Ohlemiller, Kevin K. & Clark, William W. Anatomy & Physiology of Hearing for Audiologists. 2007. (ENG., Illus.). 480p. (C). 138.95 *(978-1-4018-1444-1(1))* Delmar Cengage Learning.

Otis, Laura. Müller's Lab. 2007. (ENG., Illus.). 336p. 59.99 *(978-0-19-530697-2(X))* Oxford Univ. Pr., Inc.

Ox. Anatomical Terms & Their Derivation. pap. 37.00 *(978-981-270-387-3(X))* World Scientific Publishing Co., Inc.

Oxnard. Ghostly Muscles, Wrinkled Brains, Heresi. . 2008. 300p. pap. 69.00 *(978-981-279-743-8(2))* World Scientific Publishing Co., Inc.

Oxnard, Charles. Ghostly Muscles, Wrinkled Brains, Heresies & Hobbits. 2008. 300p. 112.00 *(978-981-279-742-1(4))* World Scientific Publishing Co., Inc.

Patton, Kevin T. & Thibodeau, Gary A. Anatomy & Physiology. (ENG., Illus.). (C). 7th ed. 2009. 1224p. 155.00 *(978-0-323-05532-1(X))* 8th ed. 2012. 1240p. 175.00 ***(978-0-323-08357-7(9))*** Elsevier - Health Sciences Div. (Mosby).

—Anatomy & Physiology (Binder-Ready Version) 7th ed. 2010. (ENG.). (C). ring bd. 109.00 *(978-0-323-08018-7(9)*, Mosby) Elsevier - Health Sciences Div.

Patton, Kevin T., et al. Essentials of Anatomy & Physiology. 2011. (ENG.). (C). pap., lab manual ed. 145.76 *(978-0-323-09897-7(5))*; pap., lab manual ed., pupil's gde. ed. 188.01 *(978-0-323-09896-0(7))*; pap. 145.76 *(978-0-323-09898-4(3))* Elsevier - Health Sciences Div. (Mosby).

Pegington, John. Multiple Choice Questions in Anatomy. 96p. pap. *(978-0-340-50785-8(3)*, Hodder Arnold) Hodder Education.

Perveen, Farzana. Crane, Its Evolution & Biology. 2010. 152p. pap. *(978-3-639-25456-3(2))* VDM Verlag Dr. Mueller e.K.

Piñal, Francisco del, ed. Arthroscopic Management of Distal Radius Fractures. 2010. (ENG., Illus.). xiv, 264p. 189.00 *(978-3-642-05353-5(X)*, 364205353X) Springer.

Rae-Dupree, Janet & Dupree, Pat. Anatomy & Physiology. 2007. (ENG., Illus.). 312p. pap., wbk. ed. 19.99 *(978-0-470-16932-2(X)*, For Dummies) Wiley, John & Sons, Inc.

Remington, Lee Ann. Clinical Anatomy & Physiology of the Visual System. 3rd ed. 2011. (ENG., Illus.). 588p. (C). 115.00 *(978-1-4377-1926-0(0)*, Butterworth-Heinemann) Elsevier - Health Sciences Div.

Rizzo, Donald C. Fundamentals of Anatomy & Physiology. 3rd ed. 2009. (ENG.). (C). 576p. 94.95 *(978-1-111-03869-4(4))*; 576p. pap. 102.95 *(978-1-4354-3871-2(X))*; 320p. pap., stu. ed. 60.95 *(978-1-4354-3873-6(6))* Delmar Cengage Learning.

Roiger, Deborah. Anatomy & Physiology: Foundations for the Health Professions. 2012. (ENG., Illus.). 688p. (C). pap. 54.93 ***(978-0-07-340212-3(5)***, 0073402125) McGraw-Hill Cos., The.

—Anatomy & Physiology: Foundations for the Health Professions with Connect Plus 1 Semester Access Card. 2012. (ENG.). (C). pap., pap. 63.93 ***(978-0-07-760487-5(3)***, 0077604873) McGraw-Hill Higher Education.

—Anatomy & Physiology: Foundations for the Health Professions with Connect Plus 1 Semester Access Card & Workbook. 2012. (ENG.). (C). pap. 97.92 ***(978-0-07-760511-7(X)***, 007760511X) McGraw-Hill Higher Education.

—Anatomy & Physiology: Foundations for the Health Professions with Workbook. 2012. (ENG.). (C). pap., pap. 91.25 ***(978-0-07-760512-4(8)***, 0077605128) McGraw-Hill Higher Education.

—Workbook for use with Anatomy & Physiology: Foundations for the Health Professions. 2012. (ENG., Illus.). 352p. (C). pap. 33.99 ***(978-0-07-740163-4(8)***, 0077401638) McGraw-Hill Higher Education.

Rudman, Jack. Anatomy & Physiology. (Regents College Proficiency Examination Ser.: Vol. 37). (C). 49.95 *(978-0-8373-5487-3(0)*, Passbooks) National Learning Corp.

—Anatomy, Physiology & Microbiology. (College Level Examination Ser.: Vol. 38). (C). 49.95 *(978-0-8373-5388-3(2)*, Passbooks) National Learning Corp.

Saladin, Kenneth. Anatomy Physiology: The Unity of Form & Function. 6th ed. 2011. (ENG.). 224p. (C). spiral bd. 22.33 *(978-0-07-747213-9(6)*,

0077472136, McGraw-Hill Science, Engineering & Mathematics) McGraw-Hill Higher Education.

—Loose Leaf Version for Anatomy & Physiology: A Unity of Form & Function. 6th ed. 2011. (ENG.). (C). ring bd. 165.67 *(978-0-07-743134-1(0)*, 0077431340, McGraw-Hill Science, Engineering & Mathematics) McGraw-Hill Higher Education.

Santamaria, L. Neuroendocrine Cells & Peptidergic Innervation in Human & Rat Prostrate. 2007. (Advances in Anatomy, Embryology & Cell Biology Ser.). (Illus.). xii, 80p. pap. 159.00 *(978-3-540-69815-9(9))* Springer.

Schuenke, Michael, et al. General Anatomy & Musculoskeletal System Vol. 1: Latin Nomenclature. 2010. (ENG., Illus.). 556p. 99.99 *(978-1-60406-378-3(5))* Thieme Medical Pubs., Inc.

Seeley, Rodney R., et al. Anatomy & Physiology. 8th ed. 2007. *(978-0-07-296557-5(6))* McGraw-Hill Cos., The.

—Anatomy & Physiology. 8th rev. ed. 2007. (Illus.). 1116p. 190.31 *(978-0-07-329368-4(7)*, 9780073293684, McGraw-Hill Science, Engineering & Mathematics) McGraw-Hill Higher Education.

Shier & Martin, Terry. Laboratory Manual for Hole's Essentials of A&P. 11th ed. 2011. (ENG., Illus.). 384p. (C). spiral bd. 120.33 *(978-0-07-733887-9(1)*, 0077338871, McGraw-Hill Science, Engineering & Mathematics) McGraw-Hill Higher Education.

Shier, David, et al. Hole's Essentials of Human Anatomy & Physiology. 11th ed. 2011. (ENG., Illus.). 640p. (C). 165.00 *(978-0-07-337815-2(1)*, 0073378151, McGraw-Hill Science, Engineering & Mathematics) McGraw-Hill Higher Education.

Sinclair, Colleen S. Anatomy & Physiology I & II. rev. ed. 2010. (ENG.). 94p. spiral bd., lab manual ed. 34.86 *(978-0-7575-7878-6(0))* Kendall Hunt Publishing Co.

Slutsky, David J. & Osterman, A. Lee. Fractures & Injuries of the Distal Radius & Carpus: The Cutting Edge. 2008. (ENG., Illus.). 592p. 250.00 *(978-1-4160-4083-5(8)*, Saunders) Elsevier - Health Sciences Div.

Starr, Lisa, et al. Volume 5 - Animal Structure & Function. 13th ed. 2012. (ENG., Illus.). 304p. (C). pap. 72.95 ***(978-1-111-58074-2(X))*** Brooks/Cole.

Staugaard-Jones, Jo Ann. The Vital Psoas Muscle: Connecting Physical, Emotional, & Spiritual Well-Being. 2012. (ENG., Illus.). 128p. pap. 19.95 ***(978-1-58394-458-5(3))*** North Atlantic Bks.

Stephens, Elizabeth. Anatomy as Spectacle: Public Exhibitions of the Body from the Nineteenth Century to the Present. 2011. (Liverpool University Press - Representations: Health, Disability, Culture & So Ser.). (ENG., Illus.). 166p. 95.00 *(978-1-84631-644-9(8))* Liverpool Univ. Pr. GBR. Dist: Chicago Distribution Ctr.

Tank, Patrick W. & Gest, Thomas R. Lippincott Williams & Wilkins Atlas of Anatomy (Canadian Version) 2008. 448p. pap. 72.95 *(978-1-60547-724-4(9))* Lippincott Williams & Wilkins.

Tate, Philip. Loose Leaf Version for Seeley's Principles of Anatomy & Physiology. 2nd ed. 2011. (ENG.). (C). ring bd. 138.33 *(978-0-07-743141-9(3)*, 0077431413, McGraw-Hill Science, Engineering & Mathematics) McGraw-Hill Higher Education.

Thibodeau, Gary A. & Patton, Kevin T. Anatomia y Fisiologia. 6th ed. 2007. (SPA.). 1288p. (C). 155.00 *(978-84-8086-235-6(1)*, Elsevier) Elsevier - Health Sciences Div.

Thomas, A. R. A Practical Guide for Making Post-Mortem Examinations, & for the Study of Morbid Anatomy, with Directions for Embalming the Dead, & for the Preser. 2006. (Illus.). 336p. per. 23.99 *(978-1-4255-3455-4(4))* MPublishing.

Tortora, Gerard J. Introduction to the Human Body Wileyplus Standalone Card. 7th ed. 2006. pap. 59.95 *(978-0-470-10228-2(4))* Wiley, John & Sons, Inc.

—Principles of Anatomy & Physiology (Registration Card) 12th ed. 2008. pap. 12.95 *(978-0-470-38125-0(6)*, Wiley) Wiley, John & Sons, Inc.

Tortora, Gerard J., ed. Principles of Anatomy & Physiology. 2008. (Wiley Plus Products Ser.). pap. 79.95 *(978-0-470-13870-0(X)*, Wiley) Wiley, John & Sons, Inc.

Tortora, Gerard J. & Derrickson, Bryan H. WP Course Principles of Anatomy & Physiology. 13th ed. 2011. (C). 71.95 ***(978-0-470-93079-3(9)***, Wiley) Wiley, John & Sons, Inc.

Toy, Eugene C., et al. Pharmacology. 2nd ed. 2008. (LANGE Case Files Ser.). (ENG., Illus.). 456p. pap. 36.00 *(978-0-07-148858-7(8)*, 0071488588) McGraw-Hill Medical Publishing Div.

University of Toledo Staff & Medical College of Ohio (Cincinnati, Ohio) Staff. Anatomy & Physiology Revealed Version 2. 0 CD. 2007. (ENG., Illus.). (C). cd-rom 48.75 *(978-0-07-337807-7(0)*, 0073378070, McGraw-Hill Science, Engineering & Mathematics) McGraw-Hill Higher Education.

Van De Graaff, Kent M., et al. A Photographic Atlas for the Anatomy & Physiology Laboratory. 7th ed. 2007. (Illus.). (C). spiral bd. 37.95 *(978-0-89582-698-5(4))* Morton Publishing Co.

Vilensky, Joel A., et al. Photographic Anatomy. 2008. (ENG., Illus.). 440p. 44.99 *(978-0-7817-7835-0(2))* Lippincott Williams & Wilkins.

Waller, Pip. Holistic Anatomy: An Integrative Guide to the Human Body. 2010. (ENG., Illus.). 416p. pap. 19.95 *(978-1-55643-865-3(6))* North Atlantic Bks.

Wise, Eric. Principles of Anatomy & Physiology. 2nd ed. 2011. (ENG., Illus.). 576p. (C). spiral bd. 99.00 *(978-0-07-735128-1(2)*, 0077351282, McGraw-Hill Science, Engineering & Mathematics) McGraw-Hill Higher Education.

Wistar, Caspar. A System of Anatomy. 2010. Vol. 1. 542p. pap. 31.95 *(978-1-4290-4366-3(0))* Vol. 2. 648p. pap. 37.95 *(978-1-4290-4364-9(4))* Applewood Bks.

Young, Martin Ferrier. Essential Physics for Manual Medicine. 2009. (ENG., Illus.). 272p. pap. 50.95 *(978-0-443-10342-1(9)*, Churchill Livingstone) Elsevier - Health Sciences Div.

ANATOMY—DICTIONARIES

Drake, Richard, et al. Dorland's/Gray's Pocket Atlas of Anatomy. 2008. (Dorland's Medical Dictionary Ser.). (ENG., Illus.). 608p. (C). pap. 44.95 *(978-0-443-06761-7(5)*, Churchill Livingstone) Elsevier - Health Sciences Div.

Hodgson, Charles. Carnal Knowledge: A Navel Gazer's Dictionary of Anatomy, Etymology, & Trivia. (ENG., Illus.). 2007. 272p. pap. 16.99 *(978-0-312-37121-0(7)*, St. Martin's Griffin) 2006. 288p. pap. 24.95 *(978-0-312-35275-2(1))* St. Martin's Pr.

Shiland, Betsy J. Medical Terminology & Anatomy for ICD-10 Coding. 2011. (ENG., Illus.). 792p. (C). pap. 74.95 ***(978-1-4557-0774-4(0)***, Mosby) Elsevier - Health Sciences Div.

ANATOMY—EARLY WORKS TO 1800

Galen. Galen on Anatomical Procedures: The Later Books. Lyons, M. C. & Towers, B., eds. Duckworth, Wynfrid Laurence Henry, tr. 2010. (Cambridge Library Collection - Cambridge Ser.). 304p. pap. 24.99 *(978-1-108-00944-7(1))* Cambridge Univ. Pr.

ANATOMY—JUVENILE LITERATURE

Canetti, Yanitzia. Amazing Adaptations! 2010. (J). *(978-1-59835-215-3(6))* Cambridge BrickHouse, Inc.

ANATOMY—LABORATORY MANUALS

Allen, Connie & Harper, Valerie. Anatomy & Physiology Laboratory Manual. 4th ed. 2011. 752p. (C). ring bd. 84.95 *(978-0-470-91753-4(9)*, Wiley) Wiley, John & Sons, Inc.

Laboratory Manual T/A Anatomyand Physiology Princ. 2008. (C). pap. 69.95 *(978-1-4180-0615-0(7))* Delmar Cengage Learning.

Lippert, Lynn & Minor, Mary Alice. Laboratory Manual for Clinical Kinesiology & Anatomy. 3rd rev. ed. 2011. (Illus.). 320p. pap. 36.95 *(978-0-8036-2390-3(9))* Davis, F. A. Co.

Marieb, Elaine N. & Hoehn, Katja. Anatomy & Physiology. 4th ed. 2010. (ENG.). (C). ring bd. 123.53 *(978-0-321-72447-2(X))* Benjamin-Cummings Publishing Co.

Martin, Terry R. Human A&P Laboratory Manual, Fetal Pig Dissection. 3rd rev. ed. 2007. (Illus.). 496p. 111.25 *(978-0-07-282734-7(3))* McGraw-Hill Higher Education.

Morton, David A., et al. Human Anatomy. 2nd rev. ed. 2006. (Gray's Anatomy Ser.). (ENG., Illus.). 568p. (C). spiral bd. 54.95 *(978-0-443-06951-2(4)*, Churchill Livingstone) Elsevier - Health Sciences Div.

Patton, Kevin T. & Thibodeau, Gary A. Anatomy & Physiology. 7th ed. 2009. (ENG., Illus.). 1224p. (C). 155.00 *(978-0-323-05532-1(X)*, Mosby) Elsevier - Health Sciences Div.

Peterson, Caryl E. Upper Extremity: Guide to the Prosected Cadaver. rev. ed. 2011. (ENG.). 110p. pap. 40.57 *(978-0-7575-6044-6(X))* Kendall Hunt Publishing Co.

Thibodeau, Gary A. & Patton, Kevin T. Anatomy & Physiology. 6th rev. ed. 2006. (Illus.). 1272p. (C). *(978-0-7234-3448-1(4)*, Mosby) Elsevier - Health Sciences Div.

Wise, Eric. Lab Manual to accompany Seeley's Principles of Anatomy & Physiology. 2008. (ENG., Illus.). 576p. (C). spiral bd. 132.00 *(978-0-07-721690-0(3)*, 0077216903, McGraw-Hill Science, Engineering & Mathematics) McGraw-Hill Higher Education.

—Laboratory Manual to Accompany Seeley's Anatomy & Physiology. 8th ed. 2007. (C). spiral bd. 112.50 *(978-0-07-334725-7(6)*, 9780073347257, McGraw-Hill Science, Engineering & Mathematics) McGraw-Hill Higher Education.

—Laboratory Manual (Wise) to Accompany Anatomy & Physiology. 8th ed. 2007. 560p. (C). spiral bd. 111.25 *(978-0-07-296561-2(4)*, 9780072965612, McGraw-Hill Science, Engineering & Mathematics) McGraw-Hill Higher Education.

Womble, Mark D. Laboratory Guide for Introduction to Human Gross Anatomy. 2nd rev. ed. 2011. (ENG.). 110p. spiral bd. 49.00 *(978-0-7575-7921-9(3))* Kendall Hunt Publishing Co.

Wood, Michael G. Instructor's Review Copy for Laboratory Manuals for Anatomy & Physiology Featuring Martini Art, Main, Cat & Pig. 5th ed. 2011. (ENG.). 944p. spiral bd., instr's lab manual ed. ***(978-0-321-80977-3(7))*** Pearson Bks.

—Laboratory Manual for Anatomy & Physiology featuring Martini Art, Pig Version. 5th rev. ed. 2011. (ENG., Illus.). 848p. (C). spiral bd. 114.73 ***(978-0-321-80412-9(0))*** Benjamin-Cummings Publishing Co.

ANATOMY—PROGRAMMED INSTRUCTION

Broyles, Robert. Workbook A & P Revealed ONLINE. 2007. 512p. pap. 19.50 *(978-0-07-337804-6(6))* McGraw-Hill Professional Publishing.

Chung, Harold M. & Kyung Won, Yoo. Gross Anatomy. 7th rev. ed. 2011. (Board Review Ser.). (ENG.). 504p. pap. 45.99 *(978-1-60547-745-9(1))* Lippincott Williams & Wilkins.

Colbert, Bruce J. & Ankney, Jeff. Anatomy, Physiology, & Disease: An Interactive Journey for Health Professionals. 2008. (ENG.). 336p. (C). pap., wbk. ed. 27.00 *(978-0-13-159006-9(5)*, Prentice Hall) Prentice Hall PTR.

ANATOMY, ARTISTIC

see also Human Figure in Art; Medicine and Art; Proportion (Art)

Barcsay, Jeno. Anatomy for the Artist. 2006. (ENG., Illus.). 342p. 14.95 *(978-1-4027-3542-4(1))* Sterling Publishing Co., Inc.

Blast Books Staff & College of Physicians of Philadelphia Staff. Mutter Museum Historic Medical Photographs: The College of Physicians of Philadelphia. Lindgren, Laura, ed. 2007. (ENG., Illus.). 224p. 50.00 *(978-0-922233-29-1(4))* Blast Bks.

Bleeker, Maaike, ed. Anatomy Live. 2008. (MediaMatters Ser.). (Illus.). 272p. pap. *(978-90-5356-516-2(7)*, Leiden Univ. Pr.) Amsterdam Univ. Pr.

Bradbury, Charles Earl. Anatomy & Construction of the Human Figure. 2007. (Dover Art Instruction Ser.). (ENG., Illus.). 208p. per. 19.95 *(978-0-486-45552-5(1)*, Dover Pubns., Inc.

Bridgman, George. Bridgman's Complete Guide to Drawing from Life. 2009. (ENG., Illus.). 352p. pap. 17.95 *(978-1-4027-6678-7(5))* Sterling Publishing Co., Inc.

Bridgman, George B. Constructive Anatomy. 2010. 216p. pap. 24.75 *(978-1-144-03223-2(7))* BiblioBazaar.

—Constructive Anatomy. 2009. 214p. pap. 7.99 *(978-1-4209-3429-8(5))* Digireads.com.

—Constructive Anatomy. 216p. 2010. 31.96 *(978-1-169-73750-1(1))* 2010. 39.95 *(978-1-161-77593-8(5))* 2008. pap. 24.95 *(978-1-4368-1275-7(5))* Kessinger Publishing, LLC.

Carlson, Charles. Art Anatomy Simplified. 2006. (Dover Anatomy for Artists Ser.). (ENG., Illus.). 48p. per. 5.95 *(978-0-486-45262-3(X))* Dover Pubns., Inc.

Clayton, Martin & Philo, Ronald. Leonardo da Vinci: The Mechanics of Man. 2010. (Illus.). 29.95 *(978-1-60606-020-9(1))* Getty Pubns.

Clayton, Martin & Philo, Ronald. Leonardo da Vinci: Anatomy: Anatomy. 2012. (Illus.). 256p. 25.00 ***(978-1-905686-39-1(0))*** Royal Collection Enterprises Ltd. GBR. Dist: Chicago Distribution Ctr.

Cuir, Raphael. The Development of the Study of Anatomy from the Renaissance to Cartesianism: Da Carpi, Vesalius, Estienne, Bidloo. 2009. (Illus.). 278p. 109.95 *(978-0-7734-4657-1(5))* Mellen, Edwin Pr., The.

Dunlop, James M. Anatomical Diagrams for Art Students. 2007. (Dover Art Instruction Ser.). (ENG., Illus.). 80p. per. 7.95 *(978-0-486-45775-8(3))* Dover Pubns., Inc.

Edwards, Carol F. & Grosenick, Brenda A. Realism: A Study in Human Structural Anatomy. 2nd ed. 2008. (ENG., Illus.). 448p. (C). 93.40 *(978-0-13-612745-9(X)*, Prentice Hall) Prentice Hall PTR.

Ehrlich, Richard. Anatomia Digitale. 2009. (Illus.). *(978-1-59005-263-1(3))* Nazraeli Pr.

Fau, J. Human Anatomy for Artists: A New Edition of the 1849 Classic with CD-ROM. 2009. (Dover Anatomy for Artists Ser.). (ENG., Illus.). 80p. pap. 14.95 *(978-0-486-47024-5(5))* Dover Pubns., Inc.

Feher, Gyorgy, text. Anatomy Drawing School: Human, Animal, Comparative Anatomy. 2008. (Hobbies & Nature Ser.). (Illus.). 603p. 49.95 *(978-0-8416-0164-2(X))* American Map Corp.

—Human Anatomy for Artists. 2008. (Hobbies & Nature Ser.). (Illus.). 496p. 49.95 *(978-0-8416-0178-9(X))* American Map Corp.

Foster, Vivian. Anatomy & Figure Drawing Artistas: A Comprehensive Guide to the Art of Drawing the Human Body. 2009. (ENG.). 224p. spiral bd., instr.'s hndbk. ed. 18.99 *(978-0-7641-6284-8(5))* Barron's Educational Series, Inc.

Goldstein, Nathan. Figure Drawing: The Structural Anatomy & Expressive Design of the Human Form. 7th ed. 2010. (ENG.). 368p. (C). pap. 115.00 *(978-0-13-603191-8(9)*, Prentice Hall) Prentice Hall PTR.

Grafton, Carol Belanger, ed. Great Anatomical Drawings by the Masters CD-ROM & Book. 2008. (Dover Electronic Clip Art Ser.). (ENG., Illus.). 48p. pap. 16.95 *(978-0-486-99367-1(3))* Dover Pubns., Inc.

Harter, Jim, ed. Anatomical & Medical Illustrations: A Pictorial Archive with over 2000 Royalty-Free Images. 2008. (Dover Pictorial Archive Ser.). (ENG., Illus.). 224p. pap. 19.95 *(978-0-486-46752-8(X))* Dover Pubns., Inc.

Hogarth, Burne. Dynamic Anatomy: The Original Edition. 2009. (Dover Art Instruction Ser.). (ENG.). 240p. pap. 19.95 *(978-0-486-47401-4(1))* Dover Pubns., Inc.

Hoggett, Sarah & Milne, Vincent. A Masterclass in Drawing & Painting the Human Figure: Anatomy, the Nude, Portraits & People. 2009. (ENG., Illus.). 256p. 35.00 *(978-0-7548-1845-8(4))* Anness Publishing GBR. Dist: National Bk. Network.

Laurenza, Domenico. Art & Anatomy in Renaissance Italy: Images from a Scientific Revolution. 2012. (ENG., Illus.). 48p. pap. 14.95 ***(978-0-300-17957-6(X))*** Yale Univ. Pr.

Leonardo. Leonardo & Anatomy. Taglialagamba, Sara, ed. 2010. (Leonardo Collection). (ENG., Illus.). 152p. (C). pap. 24.95 ***(978-88-95686-20-2(9))*** Cartei, C.B. & Bianchi Edizioni ITA. Dist: Brown, David Bk. Co., The.

—The Temple of the Soul: The Anatomy of Leonardo Da Vinci Between Mondinus & Berengarius: Twenty-Two Sheets of Manuscripts & Drawings in the Royal Library of Windsor & in Other Collections in Their Chronological Order. Pedretti, Carlo, ed. 2nd ed. 2008. (ENG., Illus.). 240p. (C). pap. 60.00 ***(978-88-95686-08-0(X))*** Cartei, C.B. & Bianchi Edizioni ITA. Dist: Brown, David Bk. Co., The.

Lutz, E. Practical Art Anatomy. 2007. 254p. per. *(978-1-905217-85-4(4))* Mills, Jeremy Publishing.

Muscolino, Joseph E. Musculoskeletal Anatomy Coloring Book. 2nd ed. 2009. (ENG., Illus.). 456p. (C). pap. 30.95 *(978-0-323-05721-9(7)*, Mosby) Elsevier - Health Sciences Div.

—Musculoskeletal Anatomy Coloring Book 2e - Text & Flashcards 2e Package. 2nd ed. 2009. (ENG.). (C). pap. 58.87 *(978-0-323-07164-2(3)*, Mosby) Elsevier - Health Sciences Div.

—Musculoskeletal Anatomy Flashcards. 2nd ed. 2009. (ENG., Illus.). 512p. (C). 35.95 *(978-0-323-05722-5(5)*, Mosby) Elsevier - Health Sciences Div.

Raynes, John. Complete Anatomy & Figure Drawing. 2007. (ENG., Illus.). 144p. 24.95 *(978-0-7134-9036-7(5)*, Batsford, B. T. Ltd.) Anova Bks. GBR. Dist: Sterling Publishing Co., Inc.

Rifkin, Benjamin A. & Ackerman, Michael J. Human Anatomy: A Visual History from the Renaissance to the Digital Age. 2011. (ENG., Illus.). 344p. pap. 16.95 *(978-0-8109-9798-1(3))* Abrams.

Rohlander, Nathan. Drawing: the Figure. Learn the classical approach to drawing the human form-step by Step. 2011. (How to Draw & Paint Ser.). (ENG., Illus.). 32p. pap. 8.95 *(978-1-60058-205-9(2)*, 1600582052) Foster, Walter Publishing, Inc.

—Drawing: the Head: Learn the classical approach to drawing the human head-step by Step. 2011. (How to Draw & Paint Ser.). (ENG., Illus.). 32p. pap. 8.95 *(978-1-60058-206-6(0)*, 1600582060) Foster, Walter Publishing, Inc.

Sanmiguel, David. The Art of Drawing Anatomy. 2008. (ENG., Illus.). 160p. pap. 17.95 *(978-1-4027-5517-0(1))* Sterling Publishing Co., Inc.

Sappol, Michael. Dream Anatomy. 2006. (NIH Publication Ser.). (ENG., Illus.). 190p. pap. 31.50 *(978-0-16-075982-5(X)*, National Institutes of Health) United States Government Printing Office.

Schramm, Helmar, et al. Spuren der Avantgarde: Theatrum Anatomicum: Frühe Neuzeit und Moderne Im Kulturvergleich. 2011. (GER., Illus.). 591p. 168.00 ***(978-3-11-024578-3(7))*** De Gruyter, Walter Inc.

Simpson, Peter M. Practical Anatomy for Artists, 1 vol. 2010. (ENG., Illus.). 224p. 32.95 *(978-1-84797-177-7(6))* Crowood Pr., Ltd. GBR. Dist: Independent Pubs. Group.

Sparkes, John C. L. The Complete Guide to Artistic Anatomy. 2010. (Dover Anatomy for Artists Ser.). (ENG., Illus.). 176p. pap. 12.95 *(978-0-486-47941-5(2))* Dover Pubns., Inc.

Szunyoghy, András, illus. Human Anatomy for Artists. 2011. (ENG.). 496p. pap. 29.99 ***(978-3-8331-6256-5(2))*** h.f.ullmann DEU. Dist: Innovative Logistics.

Szunyoghy, Andras & Feher, Gyorgy. Anatomy Drawing School Animal Anatomy. 2010. 224p. pap. 16.99 *(978-0-8416-7222-2(9))* Langenscheidt Publishing Group.

—Anatomy Drawing School Human Anatomy. 2010. 24p. pap. 16.99 *(978-0-8416-7221-5(0))* Langenscheidt Publishing Group.

—Animal Anatomy, 1 vol. 2010. (GER & ENG., Illus.). 224p. spiral bd. 14.99 *(978-3-8331-5736-3(4))* h.f.ullmann DEU. Dist: Innovative Logistics.

—Human Anatomy, 1 vol. 2010. (GER & ENG., Illus.). 204p. spiral bd. 14.99 *(978-3-8331-5731-8(3))* h.f.ullmann DEU. Dist: Innovative Logistics.

Vesalius, Andreas, et al. Classic Anatomical Illustrations: Vesalius, Albinus, Leonardo, & Others. 2008. (Dover Fine Art, History of Art Ser.). (ENG., Illus.). 96p. pap. 12.95 *(978-0-486-46162-5(9)*, Dover Pubns., Inc.

Warren, Henry. Artistic Anatomy of the Human Figure. 2010. 68p. pap. 17.75 *(978-1-141-78605-3(2))* BiblioBazaar.

—Artistic Anatomy of the Human Figure. 2010. 66p. 25.56 *(978-1-168-80571-3(6))* 2010. 66p. 31.95 *(978-1-161-76933-3(1))* 2008. 68p. pap. 16.95 *(978-1-4367-8196-1(5))* Kessinger Publishing, LLC.

Watson, J. Leonard. Lessons on Figure Drawing. 2007. (Dover Art Instruction Ser.). (ENG., Illus.). 128p. per. 7.95 *(978-0-486-45463-4(0))* Dover Pubns., Inc.

Weller, Alan. Human Anatomy. 2011. (Dover Pictura Electronic Clip Art Ser.). (ENG., Illus.). 128p. pap. 39.95 *(978-0-486-99120-7(2))* Dover Pubns., Inc.

ANATOMY, COMPARATIVE

Here are entered general works on animal anatomy and morphology. Works on the principles of structure in the animal kingdom are entered under Morphology (Animals).

see also Morphology

Ankel-Simons, Friderun. Primate Anatomy: An Introduction. 3rd ed. 2007. (ENG., Illus.). 752p. per. 80.95 *(978-0-12-372576-9(3)*, Academic Pr.) Elsevier Science & Technology Bks.

Cram101 Textbook Reviews & Cram101 Textbook Reviews. Outlines & Highlights for Vertebrates: Comparative Anatomy, Function, Evolution by Kenneth Kardong, ISBN. 2011. 530p. pap. 38.95 ***(978-1-61490-514-1(2))*** Cram101 Inc.

Crile, George. Intelligence, Power & Personality. Crile, Grace, ed. 2007. (ENG.). 352p. 46.95 *(978-0-548-09957-5(X))* Kessinger Publishing, LLC.

Endo, Hideki & Frey, Roland, eds. Anatomical Imaging: Towards a New Morphology. 2010. (Illus.). xvi, 105p. pap. 239.00 *(978-4-431-99842-6(X)*, 443199842X) Springer.

Feher, Gyorgy, text. Anatomy Drawing School: Human, Animal, Comparative Anatomy. 2008. (Hobbies & Nature Ser.). (Illus.). 603p. 49.95 *(978-0-8416-0164-2(X))* American Map Corp.

Fishbeck, Dale W. & Sebastiani, Aurora. Comparative Anatomy: Manual of Vertebrate Dissection. 2nd ed. 2008. (Illus.). 474p. (Orig.). (C). ring bd. 67.95 net. *(978-0-89582-748-7(4))* Morton Publishing Co.

Harrison, D. F. N. The Anatomy & Physiology of the Mammalian Larynx. 2009. (ENG., Illus.). 304p. pap. 55.00 *(978-0-521-10280-3(4))* Cambridge Univ. Pr.

Hickman, et al. Laboratory Studies for Animal Diversity. 6th ed. 2011. (ENG., Illus.). 320p. (C). spiral bd. 95.67 ***(978-0-07-734597-6(5)***, 0077345975, McGraw-Hill Science, Engineering & Mathematics) McGraw-Hill Higher Education.

Hudson, Arthur J. The Evolution of the Eye from Algae & Jellyfish to Humans: How Vision Adapts to Environment. 2010. (Illus.). iv, 154p. *(978-0-7734-3699-2(5))* Mellen, Edwin Pr., The.

Hyde, Kenneth M. Zoology: An Inside View of Animals. 3rd rev. ed. 2010. (ENG.). 612p. pap. 128.34 *(978-0-7575-5073-7(8))* Kendall Hunt Publishing Co.

Jansen, Heiko T., et al. An Atlas of the Sheep Brain. 2012. (ENG., Illus.). 128p. pap. 125.00 (978-0-470-08477-9(4), Wiley) Wiley, John & Sons, Inc.

Kardong. Vertebrates: Comparative Anatomy, Function, Evolution. 6th ed. 2012. (Illus.). xix, 794p. pap. **(978-0-07-108655-4(2))** McGraw-Hill Cos., The.

Kardong, Kenneth. Vertebrates: Comparative Anatomy, Function, Evolution. (ENG., Illus.). (C). 5th ed. 2008. 800p. 195.33 (978-0-07-304058-5(4), 0073040584) 6th ed. 2011. 816p. 195.33 (978-0-07-352423-8(9), 0073524239) McGraw-Hill Higher Education. (McGraw-Hill Science, Engineering & Mathematics).

Larsell, Olof. The Comparative Anatomy & Histology of the Cerebellum: From Monotremes Through Apes. Jansen, Jan, ed. 2009. (ENG.). 280p. pap. 50.00 (978-0-8166-5809-1(9)) Univ. of Minnesota Pr.

Mayer, John J. & Brisbin, I. Lehr. Wild Pigs in the United States: Their History, Comparative Morphology, & Current Status. 2008. (ENG.). 336p. per. 24.95 (978-0-8203-3137-9(6)) Univ. of Georgia Pr.

Novartis Foundation Staff, ed. Vascular Development. 2007. (Novartis Foundation Symposia Ser.). (ENG., Illus.). 260p. 195.00 (978-0-470-03428-6(9), Wiley-Interscience) Wiley, John & Sons, Inc.

Owen, Richard. On the Anatomy of Vertebrates. 2011. (Cambridge Library Collection - Life Sciences Ser.). (ENG.). 610p. pap. 43.00 **(978-1-108-03826-3(3))**; (Illus.). 698p. pap. 48.00 **(978-1-108-03825-6(5))**; 930p. pap. 56.99 **(978-1-108-03827-0(1))** Cambridge Univ. Pr.

Paxinos, George & Watson, Charles. The Rat Brain: In Stereotaxic Coordinates. 6th ed. 2006. (ENG., Illus.). 456p. spiral bd. 210.00 (978-0-12-547612-6(4), Academic Pr.) Elsevier Science & Technology Bks.

Saxena, R. K. & Saxena, Sumitra. Comparative Anatomy of Vertebrates. 2008. (Illus.). 480p. pap. 80.00 (978-1-905740-99-4(9)) Anshan GBR. Dist: Publishers Storage & Shipping.

Schwab, Ivan R. Evolution's Witness: How Eyes Evolved, 1 vol. 2011. (ENG., Illus.). 328p. 75.00 (978-0-19-536974-8(2)) Oxford Univ. Pr., Inc.

Szunyoghy, Andras & Feher, Gyorgy. Anatomy Drawing School Animal Anatomy. 2010. 224p. pap. 16.99 (978-0-8416-7222-2(9)) Langenscheidt Publishing Group.

—Anatomy Drawing School Human Anatomy. 2010. 24p. pap. 16.99 (978-0-8416-7221-5(0)) Langenscheidt Publishing Group.

Thomson, James Stuart. The Anatomy of the Tortoise. 2006. (Illus.). 140p. 35.00 (978-1-932871-10-4(1)) Bibliomania!

Treuting, Piper M. & Dintzis, Suzanne M., eds. Comparative Anatomy & Histology: A Mouse & Human Atlas. 2011. (ENG.). 474p. 149.95 (978-0-12-381361-9(1), Academic Pr.) Elsevier Science & Technology Bks.

Tshambuluka, Noxolo Doris, et al. Cardiovascular Effects of Leonotis Leonurus in Anesthesized Rats. 2011. 124p. pap. **(978-3-8443-2046-6(6))** Lambert Academic Publishing.

ANATOMY, COMPARATIVE—ATLASES

Adams, Bradley J. & Crabtree, Pamela J. Comparative Skeletal Anatomy: A Photographic Atlas for Medical Examiners, Coroners, Forensic Anthropologists, & Archaeologists. 2008. (Illus.). 348p. 169.00 (978-1-58829-844-7(2)) Humana Pr.

Atlas der Anatomie. 4th ed. 2008. (C). (978-3-437-41602-6(2), Churchill Livingstone) Elsevier - Health Sciences Div.

Cram101 Textbook Reviews Staff. Outlines & Highlights for Anatomy: A Regional Atlas of the Human Body by Carmine D Clemente, ISBN. 2009. 592p. pap. 39.95 (978-1-4288-7827-3(0)) Cram101 Inc.

Drake, Richard, et al. Dorland's/Gray's Pocket Atlas of Anatomy. 2008. (Dorland's Medical Dictionary Ser.). (ENG., Illus.). 608p. (C). pap. 44.95 (978-0-443-06761-7(9), Churchill Livingstone) Elsevier - Health Sciences Div.

Dutton, Jonathan J. Atlas of Clinical & Surgical Orbital Anatomy. 2nd ed. 2011. (ENG., Illus.). 280p. 229.00 (978-1-4377-2272-7(5), Saunders) Elsevier - Health Sciences Div.

Evans, Susan A., et al. Color Atlas of Veterinary Anatomy, Volume 3, the Dog & Cat, Vol. 3. 2nd ed. 2009. (ENG., Illus.). 540p. pap. 160.00 (978-0-7234-3415-3(8), Mosby) Elsevier - Health Sciences Div.

Kopf-Maier, P. Wolf-Heidegger's Atlas of Human Anatomy: English Nomenclature: Head & Neck, Thorax, Abdomen, Pelvis, CNS, Eye, Ear, Vol. 2. 6th rev. ed. (Wolf-Heidegger's Atlas of Human Anatomy (English Nomenclature, 6th, Completely Revised & Supplemented Edition 2004, Vol. 1 + 2) Ser.). (Illus.). suppl. ed. (978-3-8055-7668-0(4)) Karger, S. AG.

Krahn, Lois E., et al, eds. Atlas of Sleep & Sleep Medicine. 2009. (Illus.). CLXp. 199.95 (978-0-415-45008-9(X), Informa Healthcare) Taylor & Francis Group.

Le Minor, Jean-Marie, et al. Atlas of Human Anatomy & Surgery: The complete colored Plates of 1831-1854. 25th ed. 2008. (ENG., Illus.). 554p. 69.99 (978-3-8365-0865-0(6)) TASCHEN DEU. Dist: Ingram Pub. Services.

Malinzak, Michael D. Netter's Correlative Imaging - Musculoskeletal Anatomy. 2011. (Netter Clinical Science Ser.). (ENG., Illus.). 639p. 299.00 (978-1-4377-0012-1(8), Saunders) Elsevier - Health Sciences Div.

Moses, et al. Atlas of Clinical Gross Anatomy: With STUDENT CONSULT Online Access. 2nd ed. 2012. (ENG., Illus.). 656p. (C). 79.95 **(978-0-323-07779-8(X)**, Saunders) Elsevier - Health Sciences Div.

Paxinos, George, et al, eds. Chemoarchitectonic Atlas of the Rat Brain. 2nd ed. 2008. (ENG., Illus.). 380p. 285.00 (978-0-12-374237-7(4), Academic Pr.) Elsevier Science & Technology Bks.

Schuenke, Michael, et al. General Anatomy & Musculoskeletal System (THIEME Atlas of Anatomy) 2010. (ENG., Illus.). 560p. 139.99 (978-1-60406-292-2(4)) Thieme Medical Pubs., Inc.

Watson, Charles, et al, eds. The Spinal Cord: A Christopher & Dana Reeve Foundation Text & Atlas. 2008. (ENG., Illus.). 408p. 190.00 (978-0-12-374247-6(1), Academic Pr.) Elsevier Science & Technology Bks.

ANATOMY, COMPARATIVE—EXAMINATIONS, QUESTIONS, ETC.

Bobick, James & Balaban, Naomi. The Handy Anatomy Answer Book. 2008. (Handy Answer Book Ser.). (ENG.). 352p. pap. 21.95 (978-1-57859-190-9(2)) Visible Ink Pr.

Chung, Harold M. & Kyung Won, Yoo. Gross Anatomy. 7th rev. ed. 2011. (Board Review Ser.). (ENG.). 504p. pap. 45.99 (978-1-60547-745-9(1)) Lippincott Williams & Wilkins.

Garrett, Lori K. Get Ready for A & P (text Component) 2nd ed. 2010. (Illus.). 272p. pap. 53.40 (978-0-321-55695-0(X)) Benjamin-Cummings Publishing Co.

Gould, Douglas J. Clinical Anatomy for Your Pocket. 2008. (ENG., Illus.). 224p. spiral bd. 30.99 (978-0-7817-9193-9(6)) Lippincott Williams & Wilkins.

Klein, Robert & Enders, George C. Anatomy, Histology, & Cell Biology. 4th ed. 2010. (PreTest Basic Science Ser.). (ENG., Illus.). 654p. pap. 33.00 (978-0-07-162343-8(4), 007162343) McGraw-Hill Medical Publishing Div.

ANATOMY, COMPARATIVE—LABORATORY MANUALS

see also Dissection

Adams, Bradley & Crabtree, Pam. Comparative Osteology: A Laboratory & Field Guide of Common North American Animals. 2011. (ENG., Illus.). 460p. spiral bd. 59.95 **(978-0-12-388437-4(3)**, Academic Pr.) Elsevier Science & Technology Bks.

Donnersberger, Anne B. A Laboratory Textbook of Anatomy & Physiology: Cat Version. 9th rev. ed. 2009. 544p. spiral bd. 139.95 (978-0-7637-5550-8(8)) Jones & Bartlett Learning, LLC.

Hickman, Cleveland & Kats, Lee. Laboratory Studies in Animal Diversity. 5th ed. 2008. (ENG., Illus.). 288p. (C). spiral bd. 95.67 (978-0-07-334925-1(9), 0073349259, McGraw-Hill Science, Engineering & Mathematics) McGraw-Hill Higher Education.

Kardong, Kenneth & Zalisko, Edward J. Comparative Vertebrate Anatomy: A Laboratory Dissection Guide. 5th ed. 2008. (ENG., Illus.). 400p. (C). pap. 119.33 (978-0-07-297008-1(1), 0072970081, McGraw-Hill Science, Engineering & Mathematics) McGraw-Hill Higher Education.

Kardong, Kenneth V. & Zalisko, Edward J. Comparative Vertebrate Anatomy: A Laboratory Dissection Guide. 6th ed. 2011. (ENG., Illus.). 384p. (C). spiral bd. 119.33 (978-0-07-336943-3(8), 0073369438, McGraw-Hill Science, Engineering & Mathematics) McGraw-Hill Higher Education.

Marieb, Elaine N. & Hoehn, Katja. Anatomy & Physiology. 4th ed. 2010. (ENG.). (C). ring bd. 123.53 (978-0-321-72447-2(X)) Benjamin-Cummings Publishing Co.

Mathew, Saramma T. A lab manual of programmed instruction to dissect a Frog. 2007. 96p. per. 24.95 (978-1-4327-0124-6(X)) Outskirts Pr., Inc.

Walker, Warren F. & Homberger, Dominique G. A Study of the Cat: With Reference to Human Beings. 5th ed. 2007. pap. 12.95 (978-1-4288-1880-4(4)) Cram101 Inc.

ANATOMY, DENTAL

see Teeth

ANATOMY, HUMAN

see Human Anatomy

ANATOMY, MICROSCOPIC

see Histology

ANATOMY, PATHOLOGICAL

see also Autopsy; Pathology

Baehr, Mathias & Frotscher, Michael. Duus' Topical Diagnosis in Neurology: Anatomy, Physiology, Signs, Symptoms. 5th ed. 2012. (ENG., Illus.). 344p. pap. 59.99 **(978-3-13-612805-3(2))** Thieme Medical Pubs., Inc.

Baillie, Matthew. The Morbid Anatomy of Some of the Most Important Parts of the Human Body. 2009. 312p. pap. 29.75 (978-1-115-34406-7(4)); pap. 28.75 (978-1-115-34404-3(8)) BiblioBazaar.

—The Morbid Anatomy of Some of the Most Important Parts of the Human Body. 2007. (ENG.). 516p. 55.95 (978-0-548-35171-0(6)); per. 40.95 (978-0-548-29414-7(3)) Kessinger Publishing, LLC.

Cheng, Liang & Bostwick, David. Essentials of Anatomic Pathology. 3rd ed. 2010. (ENG., Illus.). 1450p. 199.00 (978-1-4419-6042-9(2), 1441960422) Springer.

Cheng, Liang & Bostwick, David G., eds. Essentials of Anatomic Pathology. 3rd ed. 2010. (ENG., Illus.). 1450p. 245.00 (978-1-60327-576-7(2), 1603275762) Humana Pr.

Gould, Douglas J. Clinical Anatomy Flash Cards. 2007. (Illus.). 696p. 39.99 (978-0-7817-6509-1(9)) Lippincott Williams & Wilkins.

Martini, Frederic H. & Welch, Kathleen. A&P Applications Manual. 9th ed. 2011. (ENG.). 272p. (C). pap. 38.00 (978-0-321-74169-1(2)) Benjamin-Cummings Publishing Co.

—Anatomy & Physiology. 8th ed. 2008. (ENG., Illus.). 224p. (C). pap. 38.00 (978-0-321-51227-7(8)) Benjamin-Cummings Publishing Co.

Murg, Stephanie & Terry, Mark, eds. Business Strategies for Anatomic Pathology. 2007. 228p. pap. 895.00 (978-1-58673-242-4(0)) Institute of Management & Administration, IOMA.

Pommerville, Jeffrey. Guide to Infectious Diseases by Body System. 2nd ed. 2010. 33p. pap. 18.95 (978-1-4496-0591-9(5)) Jones & Bartlett Learning, LLC.

Rose, Alan. Atlas of Gross Pathology: With Histologic Correlation. 2008. (ENG., Illus.). 672p. 125.00 (978-0-521-86879-2(3)) Cambridge Univ. Pr.

Seif, Sue. Anatomy & Physiology Handbook. 2009. (Illus.). 104p. pap. 19.95 (978-0-615-18474-6(X)) Seif & Assocs. Inc.

Toy, Eugene C., et al. Anatomy. 2nd ed. 2008. (LANGE Case Files Ser.). (ENG., Illus.). 384p. pap. 36.00 (978-0-07-148980-5(0), 0071489800) McGraw-Hill Medical Publishing Div.

—Pharmacology. 2nd ed. 2008. (LANGE Case Files Ser.). (ENG., Illus.). 456p. pap. 36.00 (978-0-07-148858-7(8), 0071488588) McGraw-Hill Medical Publishing Div.

Vilensky, Joel A., et al. Medical Imaging of Normal & Pathologic Anatomy. 2010. (ENG., Illus.). 192p. pap. 39.95 (978-1-4377-0634-5(7), Saunders) Elsevier - Health Sciences Div.

ANATOMY, PRACTICAL

see Human Dissection

ANATOMY, REGIONAL

see Anatomy, Surgical and Topographical

ANATOMY, SURGICAL AND TOPOGRAPHICAL

see also names of organs and regions of the body

Agur. Grants Atlas of Anatomy (Us Ed) Pb. 13th rev. ed. 2012. (ENG., Illus.). 888p. pap. 84.95 **(978-1-60831-756-1(0))** Lippincott Williams & Wilkins.

Agur, Anne & Dalley, Arthur F. Grant's Atlas of Anatomy, Twelfth Edition (Canadian Version) 2008. (Illus.). 834p. pap. 76.95 (978-0-7817-9612-5(1)) Lippincott Williams & Wilkins.

Applegate, Edith J. & Applegate, Edith Ms. The Sectional Anatomy Learning System: Concepts & Applications 2-Volume Set, 2 vols. 3rd ed. 2009. (ENG., Illus.). 608p. (C). pap. 95.95 (978-1-4160-5013-1(2), Saunders) Elsevier - Health Sciences Div.

Atkins, Elaine, et al. A Practical Approach to Orthopaedic Medicine: Assessment, Diagnosis, Treatment. 3rd ed. 2010. (ENG., Illus.). 480p. (C). pap. 86.95 (978-0-7020-3174-8(7), Churchill Livingstone) Elsevier - Health Sciences Div.

Bercajs, Denis & Turina, Marko, eds. Operative Anatomy of the Heart. 2009. (Illus.). 580p. 199.00 (978-3-540-69227-0(4)) Springer.

Bontrager, Kenneth L. & Lampignano, John. Radiographic Positioning & Related Anatomy Package, 2 vols., Vol 1 & 2. 7th ed. 2009. (ENG., Illus.). (C). pap., wbk. ed. 89.95 (978-0-323-05411-9(0), Mosby) Elsevier - Health Sciences Div.

—Workbook for Textbook for Radiographic Positioning & Related Anatomy: Volume 2. 7th ed. 2009. (ENG., Illus.). 272p. (C). pap. 49.95 (978-0-323-05413-3(7), Mosby) Elsevier - Health Sciences Div.

Campbell, Joan. Acupuncture Channels & Points. 2008. (ENG., Illus.). xxiv, 264p. (C). pap. 79.95 (978-0-7295-3866-4(4), Churchill Livingstone) Elsevier - Health Sciences Div.

Clemente, Carmine D. Anatomy: A Regional Atlas of the Human Body. 6th rev. ed. 2010. (ENG., Illus.). 752p. pap. 80.99 (978-1-58255-889-9(2)) Lippincott Williams & Wilkins.

Cram101 Textbook Reviews. Outlines & Highlights for Clinical Anatomy by Regions by Richard S Snell, Isbn: 9780781764049 0781764041. 2011. 338p. pap. 42.95 **(978-1-61490-417-5(0))** Cram101 Inc.

Cram101 Textbook Reviews & Cram101 Textbook Reviews. Outlines & Highlights for the Sectional Anatomy Learning System: Concepts & Applications 2-Volume Set by Edith J. Applegate; Edith Ms Applegate, IS. 2011. 524p. pap. 38.95 **(978-1-61461-765-5(1))** Cram101 Inc.

Cram101 Textbook Reviews Staff. Outlines & Highlights for Anatomy: A Regional Atlas of the Human Body by Carmine D Clemente, ISBN. 2009. 592p. pap. 39.95 (978-1-4288-7827-3(0)) Cram101 Inc.

Cross, John R. The Concise Book of Acupoints. 2010. (ENG., Illus.). 192p. pap. (978-1-905367-19-1(8)) Lotus Publishing.

DeBoer, Piet, et al. Surgical Exposures in Orthopaedics: The Anatomic Approach. 4th rev. ed. 2009. (ENG., Illus.). 768p. 245.99 (978-0-7817-7623-3(6)) Lippincott Williams & Wilkins.

Dudek, Ronald W. Gross Anatomy. 4th rev. ed. 2010. (High-Yield Ser.). (ENG., Illus.). 320p. pap. 34.99 (978-1-60547-763-3(X)) Lippincott Williams & Wilkins.

Field, Derek & Hutchinson, Jane Owen. Field's Anatomy, Palpation & Surface Markings. 4th rev. ed. 2006. (ENG., Illus.). 392p. (C). pap. 76.95 (978-0-7506-8848-2(3), Butterworth-Heinemann) Elsevier - Health Sciences Div.

—Lower Limb Anatomy, Palpation & Surface Markings. 2008. (ENG., Illus.). 134p. (C). pap. 56.95 (978-0-7020-3018-5(X), Churchill Livingstone) Elsevier - Health Sciences Div.

Finando, Donna. Puntos de Activacion: Manual de Autoayuda. 2009. (ENG.). 1p. pap. 19.95 (978-1-59477-280-1(0)) Inner Traditions International, Ltd.

Hahne, Karl-Heinz. VOXEL-MAN 3D-Navigator: Inner Organs. Regional, Systemic & Radiological Anatomy / Innere Organe. Topographische, Systematische und Radiologische Anatomie. 2009. (GER.). 24p. 119.00 (978-3-642-10495-4(9), 3642104959) Springer.

Hinrichsen. A Synopsis of Regional Anatomy. 2008. 82.00 (978-981-279-012-5(8)); 124.00 (978-981-279-011-8(X)) World Scientific Publishing Co., Inc.

Hurst, Joy. Anatomy & Physiology in a Flash! An Interactive, Flash-Card Approach. 2010. (Illus.). 24.95 (978-0-8036-2430-6(1)); pap. 46.95 (978-0-8036-2361-3(5)) Davis, F. A. Co.

Jarmey, Chris. The Concise Book of Muscles, Revised Edition. rev. ed. 2008. (ENG., Illus.). 192p. pap. 29.95 (978-1-55643-719-9(6)) North Atlantic Bks.

Jordan, David R., et al. Surgical Anatomy of the Ocular Adnexa: A Clinical Approach, 1 vol. 2nd ed. 2012. (American Academy of Ophthalmology Monograph Ser.). (ENG., Illus.). 224p. (Orig.). 175.00 **(978-0-19-974426-8(2))** Oxford Univ. Pr., Inc.

Lee, Ilchi. Meridian Exercise for Self-Healing: Classified by Common Symptoms. 2nd rev. ed. 2010. 336p. pap. 24.95 (978-1-935127-10-9(1)) BEST Life Media.

Lumley, John S. P. Surface Anatomy: The Anatomical Basis of Clinical Examination. 4th ed. 2008. (ENG., Illus.). 136p. (C). pap. 44.95 (978-0-443-06794-5(5), Churchill Livingstone) Elsevier - Health Sciences Div.

Lunsford, L. Dade & Sheehan, Jason P., eds. Intracranial Stereotactic Radiosurgery. 2009. (ENG., Illus.). 200p. 179.99 (978-1-60406-200-7(2)) Thieme Medical Pubs., Inc.

Mann, Douglas, et al. Upper & Lower Extremity Injury Evaluation. 2010. (ENG.). (C). 758.95 (978-1-111-13883-7(4)) Delmar Cengage Learning.

Moeller, T. B. & Reif, E. Pocket Atlas of Sectional Anatomy: Computed Tomography & Magnetic Resonance Imaging. 3rd ed. 2006. (ENG., Illus.). 255p. pap. 47.99 (978-1-58890-577-2(2)) Thieme Medical Pubs., Inc.

Möller, Torsten B. & Reif, Emil. Pocket Atlas of Sectional Anatomy. 3rd ed. 2007. (Illus.). 44.95 (978-3-13-125603-4(6)) Thieme Medical Pubs., Inc.

Muscolino, Joseph E. Flashcards for Palpation, Trigger Points, & Referral Patterns. 2008. (ENG., Illus.). 480p. 35.95 (978-0-323-05169-9(3), Mosby) Elsevier - Health Sciences Div.

—The Muscle & Bone Palpation Manual with Trigger Points, Referral Patterns & Stretching. 2008. (ENG., Illus.). 544p. (C). pap. 61.95 (978-0-323-05171-2(5), Mosby) Elsevier - Health Sciences Div.

Myers, Thomas W. Anatomy Trains: Myofascial Meridians for Manual & Movement Therapists. 2nd ed. 2008. (ENG., Illus.). 440p. pap. 66.95 (978-0-443-10283-7(X), Churchill Livingstone) Elsevier - Health Sciences Div.

Palazzi, Xavier. The Beagle Brain in Stereotaxic Coordinates. 2011. (ENG., Illus.). xvii, 119p. 189.00 (978-1-4419-8371-8(6), 1441983716) Springer.

Raftery, Andrew T. Applied Basic Science for Basic Surgical Training. 2nd ed. 2008. (MRCS Study Guides). (ENG., Illus.). 660p. (C). pap. 115.00 (978-0-08-045140-4(3), Churchill Livingstone) Elsevier - Health Sciences Div.

Reichert, Bernhard. Palpation Techniques: Surface Anatomy for Physical Therapists. 2010. (ENG., Illus.). 416p. 109.99 (978-3-13-146341-8(4)) Thieme Medical Pubs., Inc.

Reif, Emil & Moeller, Torsten Bert. Pocket Atlas of Sectional Anatomy Vol. 3: Computed Tomography & Magnetic Resonance Imaging. 3rd ed. 2006. (Basic Sciences (Thieme) Ser.). (ENG., Illus.). 341p. pap. 47.99 (978-1-58890-566-6(7)) Thieme Medical Pubs., Inc.

Sadry, Forat, et al. Radiological Anatomy: A Multiple Choice Examination in Radiology in English, German & French. 2006. (ENG, FRE & GER., Illus.). VI, 236p. 49.95 (978-3-540-30972-7(1), 3540309721) Springer.

Saleem, Kadharbatcha S. & Logothetis, Nikos K. A Combined MRI & Histology Atlas of the Rhesus Monkey Brain in Stereotaxic Coordinates. 2nd ed. 2012. (ENG., Illus.). 402p. 249.95 **(978-0-12-385087-4(8)**, Academic Pr.) Elsevier Science & Technology Bks.

Schuenke, Michael, et al. General Anatomy & Musculoskeletal System Vol. 1: Latin Nomenclature. 2010. (ENG., Illus.). 556p. 99.99 (978-1-60406-378-3(5)) Thieme Medical Pubs., Inc.

—General Anatomy & Musculoskeletal System (THIEME Atlas of Anatomy) 2010. (ENG., Illus.). 560p. 139.99 (978-1-60406-292-2(4)) Thieme Medical Pubs., Inc.

—Head & Neuroanatomy Vol. 3: Latin Nomenclature. 2010. (ENG., Illus.). 432p. 99.99 (978-1-58890-442-3(3)) Thieme Medical Pubs., Inc.

—Neck & Internal Organs (THIEME Atlas of Anatomy) 2010. (ENG., Illus.). 372p. 139.99 (978-1-60406-294-6(0)) Thieme Medical Pubs., Inc.

Scott-Conner, Carol E. H. & Dawson, David L. Operative Anatomy. 3rd rev. ed. 2008. (ENG., Illus.). 768p. 188.99 (978-0-7817-6539-8(0)) Lippincott Williams & Wilkins.

Sinnatamby, Chummy S. & Last, R. J. Last's Anatomy: Regional & Applied. 12th ed. 2011. (MRCS Study Guides). (ENG., Illus.). 560p. (C). pap. 83.95 (978-0-7020-3395-7(2), Churchill Livingstone) Elsevier - Health Sciences Div.

Skandalakis, John E. Anatomic Basis of Tumor Surgery. Wood, William C. & Staley, Charles, eds. 2nd ed. 2009. (ENG., Illus.). 852p. 199.00 (978-3-540-74176-3(3), 3540741763) Springer.

Snell. Clinical Anatomy Regions (Us Ed) 9th rev. ed. 2011. (ENG.). 768p. pap. 79.99 **(978-1-60913-446-4(X))** Lippincott Williams & Wilkins.

Tortora, Gerard J. A Brief Atlas of the Human Skeleton, Surface Anatomy & Selected Medical Images, 2 vols. 12th ed. 2008. (ENG., Illus.). 80p. (C). pap. 15.95 (978-0-470-14113-7(1), Wiley) Wiley, John & Sons, Inc.

Trelease, Robert. Surgical Anatomy Review P. R. N. 2010. (Netter Clinical Science Ser.). (ENG., Illus.). 432p. pap. 35.95 (978-1-4377-1792-1(6), Saunders) Elsevier - Health Sciences Div.

ANATOMY, VETERINARY

see Veterinary Anatomy

ANAXAGORAS

Anaxagoras & Cleve, Felix. M. Philosophy of Anaxagoras: An Attempt at Reconstruction. 2011. 190p. 42.95 **(978-1-258-03294-4(5))** Literary Licensing, LLC.

Anaxagoras & Curd, Patricia. Anaxagoras of Clazomenae: Fragments & Testimonia. 2007. (Phoenix Presocractic Ser.). (GEC & ENG.). 304p. (978-0-8020-9325-7(6)) Univ. of Toronto Pr.

Anaxagoras & Curd, Patricia. Anaxagoras of Clazomenae: Fragments & Testimonia: A Text & Translation with Notes & Essays. 2010. (GEC & ENG.). xiv, 279p. pap. **(978-1-4426-1163-4(4))** Univ. of Toronto Pr.

Schofield, Malcolm. An Essay on Anaxagoras. 2007. (Cambridge Classical Studies). (ENG.). 200p. pap. 39.99 (978-0-521-04261-1(5)) Cambridge Univ. Pr.

ANAXIMANDER

Couprie, Dirk. Heaven & Earth in Ancient Greek Cosmology: From Thales to Heraclides Ponticus. 2011. (Astrophysics & Space Science Library). (ENG., Illus.). xxxii, 264p. 129.00 *(978-1-4419-8115-8(2)*, 1441981152) Springer.
Hahn, Robert. Archaeology & the Origins of Philosophy. 335p. 2011. pap. 26.95 ***(978-1-4384-3164-2(3)***, Suny Pr.) 2010. (ENG.). 80.00 *(978-1-4384-3165-9(1))* State Univ. of New York Pr.
Kahn, Charles H. Anaximander & the Origins of Greek Cosmology. 2011. 272p. 47.95 ***(978-1-258-00192-6(6))*** Literary Licensing, LLC.
Rovelli, Carlo. First Scientist. 2011. (ENG., Illus.). 256p. 24.95 *(978-1-59416-131-5(3))* Westholme Publishing.

ANCESTOR WORSHIP

see also Apotheosis

Bae, Choon-Sup. Ancestor Worship. 2008. 248p. pap. *(978-3-639-08714-7(3))* VDM Verlag Dr. Mueller e.K.
Bay, Edna. Asen, Ancestors, & Vodun: Tracing Change in African Art. 2008. (Illus.). 208p. 42.00 *(978-0-252-03255-4(1))* Univ. of Illinois Pr.
Brashier, K. E. Ancestral Memory in Early China. 2011. (Harvard-Yenching Institute Monograph Ser.: 72). (ENG., Illus.). 484p. 39.95 *(978-0-674-05607-7(8))* Harvard Univ., Asia Ctr.
Butcher, Beverly J. Chinese & Chinese American Ancestor Veneration in the Catholic Church, 635 A.D. to the Present. 2010. (CHI & ENG., Illus.). viii, 447p. 129.95 *(978-0-7734-3624-4(3))* Mellen, Edwin Pr., The.
Callaway, Henry. The Religious System of the Amazulu Part One: Unkulunkulu or the Tradition of Creation. 2007. pap. 37.95 *(978-1-4304-5240-9(4))* Kessinger Publishing, LLC.
Couderc, Pascal & Sillander, Kenneth. Ancestors in Borneo Societies: Death, Transformation, & Social Immortality. 2012. (Illus.). 432p. ***(978-87-7694-091-1(8))***; pap. ***(978-87-7694-092-8(6))*** Nordic Institute of Asian Studies.
Ephirim-Donkor, Anthony. African Religion Defined: A Systematic Study of Ancestor Worship among the Akan. 2010. (Illus.). 160p. pap. 25.50 *(978-0-7618-5328-2(6))* Univ. Pr. of America, Inc.
—African Spirituality: On Becoming Ancestors. 2011. (ENG.). 200p. pap. 29.50 *(978-0-7618-5467-8(3))* Univ. Pr. of America, Inc.
Frazer, James George. The Fear of the Dead in Primitive Religion. 2011. 214p. 44.95 ***(978-1-258-00723-2(1))*** Literary Licensing, LLC.
Gehman, Richard J. Who Are the Living-Dead? A Theology of Death, Life after Death, & the Living-Dead. 2009. (Illus.). xviii, 350p. 24.99 *(978-9966-20-068-4(6))* Evangel Publishing Hse.
Gose, Peter. Invaders as Ancestors: On the Intercultural Making & Unmaking of Spanish Colonialism in the Andes. 2008. (Anthropological Horizons Ser.). (ENG., Illus.). 404p. *(978-0-8020-9876-4(2))*; pap. *(978-0-8020-9617-3(4))* Univ. of Toronto Pr.
Hozumi, Nobushige. Ancestor-Worship & Japanese Law. 2010. (ENG.). 88p. pap. 18.75 *(978-1-176-31615-7(X))* 2010. (ENG.). 90p. pap. 18.75 *(978-1-176-18802-0(X))* 2010. 90p. pap. 18.75 *(978-1-143-07963-4(9))* 2010. 86p. pap. 18.75 *(978-1-141-35075-9(0))* 2008. 195p. 27.99 *(978-0-554-62528-7(8))* 2008. 235p. 24.99 *(978-0-554-62540-9(7))* 2008. 235p. pap. 25.75 *(978-0-554-62531-7(8))* 2008. 211p. pap. 24.75 *(978-0-554-62537-9(7))* BiblioBazaar.
—Ancestor-Worship & Japanese Law. 2009. 48p. pap. *(978-0-217-17447-3(7))* Books LLC.
—Ancestor-Worship & Japanese Law. 2007. (ENG.). 84p. per. 17.95 *(978-1-4304-7744-0(X))* Kessinger Publishing, LLC.
—Ancestor-Worship & Japanese Law. 2008. 88p. pap. *(978-1-4097-8025-0(2))* Read Bks.
Huan Chie, Niki Leong. Ancestor Worship in Singapore. 2009. 52p. pap. *(978-3-639-12461-3(8))* VDM Verlag Dr. Mueller e.K.
Johnston, Reginald Fleming. Confucianism & Modern China. 2008. (Illus.). 208p. per. 22.95 *(978-0-9680459-4-7(4))* Soul Care Publishing CAN. Dist: Ingram Bk. Co.
Lusteguy, Pierre. The Role of Women in Tonkinese Religion & Property. 2009. 160p. 24.00 *(978-1-59740-733-5(X))*; 158p. pap. 16.00 *(978-1-59740-755-7(0))* ACLS Humanities E-Book.
Moodley, Edley J. Shembe, Ancestors, & Christ: A Christological Inquiry with Missiological Implications. 2008. (American Society of Missiology Monograph Ser.). 272p. pap. 30.00 *(978-1-55635-880-7(6)*, Pickwick Pubns.) Wipf & Stock Pubs.
Ramos, Gabriela. Death & Conversion in the Andes: Lima & Cuzco, 1532-1670. 2010. (History Lang & Cult Spanish Portuguese Ser.). (ENG., Illus.). 368p. pap. 39.00 *(978-0-268-04028-4(1))* Univ. of Notre Dame Pr.
Scott, Janet Lee. For Gods, Ghosts & Ancestors: The Chinese Tradition of Paper Offerings. 2007. 352p. pap. *(978-962-209-827-5(4))*; (ENG., Illus.). pap. *(978-0-295-98718-7(9))* Hong Kong Univ. Pr.
Shoko, Tabona. Karanga Indigenous Religion in Zimbabwe: Health & Wellbeing. 2007. (Vitality of Indigenous Religions Ser.). (Illus.). 172p. 99.95 *(978-0-7546-5881-8(3))* Ashgate Publishing Co.
Stavrakopoulou, Francesca. Land of Our Fathers: The Roles of Ancestor Veneration in Biblical Land Claims. (Library Hebrew Bible/Old Testament Studies). (ENG.). 208p. 2012. pap. 44.95 ***(978-0-567-41188-4(5))*** Vol. 473. 2010. 110.00 *(978-0-567-02881-5(X))* Continuum International Publishing Group, Ltd. GBR. (T&T Clark Int'l). Dist: National Bk. Network.

ANCESTRY

see Genealogy; Heredity

ANCHORAGE (ALASKA)

Alaska: Anchorage & South Central. Date not set. pap. *(978-1-56944-151-0(0))* Terrell Creative.
Arno, Rae. Anchorage Place Names: The Who & Why of Streets, Parks, & Places. 2008. 9.95 net. *(978-1-57833-407-0(1))* Todd Communications.
Bowers, Don. Fond Memories of Anchorage Pioneers. 29.95 *(978-1-57833-184-0(6))* Todd Communications.
Decker, Julie. Expanded View: The New Wing of the Anchorage Museum at Rasmuson Center. 2010. *(978-1-56898-892-4(3))* Princeton Architectural Pr.
Fletcher, Alder Rye. Maria. 2010. 54p. pap. 10.85 *(978-0-557-47663-3(1))* Lulu Enterprises Inc.
Jones, Preston. City for Empire: An Anchorage History, 1914-1941. 2010. (ENG., Illus.). 214p. pap. 26.95 *(978-1-60223-084-2(6))* Univ. of Alaska Pr.
Maloney, Lisa. 50 Hikes Around Anchorage. 2010. (50 Hikes Ser.). (ENG., Illus.). 232p. pap. 18.95 *(978-0-88150-905-2(1)*, 150905) Countryman Pr.
Senkowsky, Sonya & Coyne, Amanda. Alaska Then & Now. 2008. (Then & Now Thunder Bay Ser.). (ENG., Illus.). 144p. 19.95 *(978-1-59223-799-9(1)*, Thunder Bay Pr.) Advantage Pubs. Group.
Tyson, John. Best Easy Day Hikes Anchorage. 2009. (Best Easy Day Hikes Ser.). (ENG., Illus.). 96p. pap. 9.95 *(978-0-7627-5102-0(9)*, Falcon Guides) Globe Pequot Pr., The.
Vanasse, Deb. Anchorage & Southcentral Alaska: Including the Kenai Peninsula, Prince William Sound, & Denali National Park. 2nd ed. 2009. (Insiders' Guide Ser.). (ENG., Illus.). 232p. pap. 18.95 *(978-0-7627-5071-9(5)*, Insiders' Guide) Globe Pequot Pr., The.
Vassilopoulos, Peter. Anchorages & Marine Parks. 2008. (Illus.). pap. *(978-0-919317-24-6(3))* Heritage Hse.

ANCHORAGE

Fagan, Brian M. Staying Put! The Art of Anchoring. 2006. (ENG., Illus.). 112p. (Orig.). pap. 17.95 *(978-0-9634635-2-4(7)*, Wiley) Wiley, John & Sons, Inc.
Lawyer, Anthony B. Sevannah Guide to Lashing: For All Deep Sea Vessels, Vol. III. 2011. 72p. 24.99 ***(978-1-4628-6231-3(4))***; pap. 15.99 ***(978-1-4628-6230-6(6))*** Xlibris Corp.
Nielsen, Peter. Anchoring. 2007. (Captain's Quick Guides). (ENG., Illus.). 16p. 8.95 *(978-0-07-148771-9(9)*, 0071487719, International Marine/Ragged Mountain Pr.) McGraw-Hill Professional Publishing.
Schenk, Bobby. The Adlard Coles Book of Anchoring. 2012. (Adlard Coles Book Of Ser.). (ENG., Illus.). 112p. pap. 22.95 ***(978-1-4081-2944-9(2))*** A & C Black GBR. Dist: Macmillan.
United States. Bureau Of Navigation (Dep. Rules & Regulations Relating to the Anchorage of Vessels in the Port of New York, April 25 1907. 2011. 30p. pap. 11.99 ***(978-1-4181-8668-5(6))*** MPublishing.

ANCHORAGE (STRUCTURAL ENGINEERING)

Aci, ed. Qualification of Post-Installed Anchors in Concrete & Commentary. 2007. per. *(978-0-87031-247-2(2))* American Concrete Institute.
Cook, Ronald A., et al. Adhesive Anchors in Concrete under Sustained Loading Conditions. 2009. (Illus.). *(978-0-309-11788-3(7))* Transportation Research Board.
Das, Braja M. Earth Anchors. 2008. (J. Ross Publishing Classics Ser.). (Illus.). 241p. per. *(978-1-932159-72-1(X))* Ross, J. Publishing, Inc.
Fishman, Kenneth L. & Withiam, James L. LRFD Metal Loss & Service-Life Strength Reduction Factors for Metal-Reinforced Systems. 2011. (Illus.). 105p. pap. ***(978-0-309-15549-6(5))*** Transportation Research Board.
Littlejohn, G. S., ed. Ground Anchorages & Anchored Structures in Service. 2008. (Illus.). xxxvi, 494p. *(978-0-7277-3561-4(6))* Telford, Thomas Ltd.

ANCHORITES

see Hermits

ANCHORMEN

see Television News Anchors

ANCHORPERSONS

see Television News Anchors

ANCHORS

Fagan, Brian M. Staying Put! The Art of Anchoring. 2006. (ENG., Illus.). 112p. (Orig.). pap. 17.95 *(978-0-9634635-2-4(7)*, Wiley) Wiley, John & Sons, Inc.
Poiraud, Alain, et al. The Complete Anchoring Handbook: Stay Put on Any Bottom in Any Weather. 2007. (ENG., Illus.). 256p. per. 25.00 *(978-0-07-147508-2(7)*, 0071475087, International Marine/Ragged Mountain Pr.) McGraw-Hill Professional Publishing.
Schenk, Bobby. The Adlard Coles Book of Anchoring. 2012. (Adlard Coles Book Of Ser.). (ENG., Illus.). 112p. pap. 22.95 ***(978-1-4081-2944-9(2))*** A & C Black GBR. Dist: Macmillan.
Taylor, R. J., et al. Design of Uplift-Resisting Anchors for Ships & Submarines. 2008. 172p. pap. 59.95 *(978-1-934939-51-2(X))* Wexford College Pr.
Upham, N. E. Anchors. 2nd ed. 2008. (Shire Library). (ENG., Illus.). 32p. pap. 11.95 *(978-0-7478-0508-3(3))* Shire Pubns., Ltd. GBR. Dist: Random Hse., Inc.

ANCHORS (TELEVISION JOURNALISM)

see Television News Anchors

ANCIENT AND MYSTICAL ORDER ROSAE CRUCIS

see Society of Rosicrucians

ANCIENT ART

see Art, Ancient

ANCIENT CIVILIZATION

see Civilization, Ancient

ANCIENT EGYPTIAN LITERATURE

see Egyptian Literature

ANCIENT ETHICS

see Ethics, Ancient

ANCIENT GEOGRAPHY

see Geography, Ancient

ANCIENT GREEK EDUCATION

see Education, Greek

ANCIENT HISTORY

see History, Ancient

ANCIENT LAW

see Law, Ancient

ANCIENT POTTERY

see Pottery, Ancient

ANCIENT SCIENCE

see Science, Ancient

ANCIENT TRAVEL

see Travel, Ancient

ANCIENT WEAPONS

see Weapons, Ancient

ANCYLOSTOMIASIS

see Hookworm Disease

ANDALUSIA (SPAIN)

Bardaji, Anna Gil. Traducir A-Andalus: El discurso del Otro en el Arabismo Espanol. de Conde a Garcia Gomez. 2009. (SPA.). 392p. 119.95 *(978-0-7734-3885-9(8))* Mellen, Edwin Pr., The.
Kennedy, Jeffrey. Top 10 Andalucia & Costa Del Sol. 2012. (Eyewitness Top 10 Travel Guide Ser.). (ENG.). 160p. 14.00 ***(978-0-7566-8463-1(3))*** Dorling Kindersley Publishing, Inc.
Monville, Joseph, ed. History as Prelude: Muslims & Jews in the Medieval Mediterranean. 2011. (ENG.). 214p. 60.00 ***(978-0-7391-6814-1(2))*** Lexington Bks.

ANDALUSIA (SPAIN)—DESCRIPTION AND TRAVEL

Chetwode, Penelope. Two Middle-Aged Ladies in Andalusia. 2012. (ENG., Illus.). 154p. pap. 29.95 ***(978-1-906011-68-0(0))*** Eland Bks. GBR. Dist: Dufour Editions, Inc.
Eisenschmid, Rainer, et al. Andalucia Baedeker Guide. 2012. (Baedeker Guides Ser.). (ENG., Illus.). 446p. 20.00 ***(978-3-8297-6485-8(5))*** Marco Polo Travel Publishing GBR. Dist: Innovative Logistics.
Garvey, Geoff & Ellingham, Mark. The Rough Guide to Andalucia. 7th ed. 2012. (Rough Guide To... Ser.). (ENG., Illus.). 616p. 21.99 *(978-1-4053-8990-7(7))* Rough Guides, Ltd. GBR. Dist: Dorling Kindersley Publishing, Inc.
Glassman, Paul. Andalucia. Cannon, Gwen, ed. 3rd rev. ed. 2007. (Michelin Green Guide Andalucia Ser.). (Illus.). 434p. 21.95 *(978-2-06-712333-5(5))* Michelin.
Golden Book on Andalusia. 128p. pap. *(978-88-7009-569-2(X))* Casa Editrice Bonechi.
Head, Jeremy. Frommer's Seville, Granada & the Best of Andalusia. 4th ed. 2011. (Frommer's Complete Guides: 995). (ENG., Illus.). 416p. pap. 19.99 *(978-0-470-57431-5(1)*, Frommers) Wiley, John & Sons, Inc.
Hintzen-Bohlen, Brigitte. Andalusia, 1 vol. 2010. (ENG., Illus.). 536p. pap. 9.99 *(978-3-8331-5280-1(X))* h.f.ullmann DEU. Dist: Innovative Logistics.
Hunter-Watts, Guy. Small Hotels & Inns of Andalusia: Charming Places to Stay in Southern Spain. 3rd ed. 2006. (Illus.). 307p. pap. *(978-84-89954-50-2(X))* Santana Bks.
Konemann Staff. Great Houses of Andalusia. Date not set. (Illus.). 250p. 19.95 *(978-3-8290-4068-6(7)*, 521508) Konemann.
Locken, E. Travel Journal Andalucia. 2010. 192p. pap. 19.99 *(978-0-557-42178-7(0))* Lulu Enterprises Inc.
Maugham, W. Somerset. Andalusia: Sketches & Impressions. reprint ed. lib. bdg. 98.00 *(978-0-7426-3185-4(0))* Classic Bks.
Mead, Rowland. Footprint Andalucia Handbook: The Travel Guide. (Illus.). 336p. *(978-0-900751-94-3(0))* Footprint Handbooks.
Michelin. Michelin Travel Guide Andalucia. 4th ed. 2009. (Green Guide Ser.). (ENG., Illus.). 416p. pap. 21.99 *(978-1-906261-39-9(3))* Michelin Travel & Lifestyle.
Nichols, Fiona. Andalucia. 2nd rev. ed. (Illus.). 128p. pap. 10.95 *(978-1-84330-531-6(3))* New Holland Pubs., Ltd. GBR. Dist: Globe Pequot Pr., The.
—Globetrotter Andalucia Travel Pack. 3rd ed. 2008. (Globetrotter Travel Packs Ser.). (ENG., Illus.). 128p. pap. 14.95 *(978-1-84537-844-8(X))* New Holland Pubs., Ltd. GBR. Dist: Globe Pequot Pr., The.
Oldfield, John & Oldfield, Christine. Landscapes of Andalucia & the Costa Del Sol. 2nd ed. (Illus.). 152p. pap. 14.95 *(978-1-85691-208-2(6))* Sunflower Bks. (UK) GBR. Dist: Hunter Publishing, Inc.
Symington, Andy. Andalucia: Travel Guide to Andalucia Including Detailed Festival Listings. 6th ed. 2009. (ENG., Illus.). 512p. instr.'s hndbk. ed. 24.95 *(978-1-906098-51-3(4))* Footprint Handbooks GBR. Dist: Globe Pequot Pr., The.
Symington, Andy. Andalucia Handbook 7th. 7th ed. 2012. (Footprint - Handbooks Ser.). (ENG., Illus.). 496p. 22.95 ***(978-1-907263-58-3(6))*** Footprint Handbooks GBR. Dist: Globe Pequot Pr., The.
Thomas Cook Publishing Staff. Traveller Guides Andalucia Inc. Seville. 4th ed. 2011. (Travellers - Thomas Cook Ser.). (ENG., Illus.). 192p. pap. 16.95 *(978-1-84848-338-5(4))* Cook, Thomas Publishing GBR. Dist: Globe Pequot Pr., The.

ANDALUSIA (SPAIN)—HISTORY

Baste, Pierre. A Marine of the Imperial Guard: Eyewitness to the French Failure in Spain 1808. Mahon, Timothy, tr. 2009. 82p. pap. 15.38 *(978-1-934840-50-4(5))* Nimble Bks. LLC.
Boone, James L. Lost Civilisation? The Contested Islamic Past in Spain & Portugal. 2009. (Duckworth Debates in Archaeology Ser.). (Illus.). 144p. pap. 24.95 *(978-0-7156-3568-1(9))* Duckworth Publishers GBR. Dist: International Publishers Marketing.
Corfis, Ivy A. Al-Andalus, Sepharad, & Medieval Iberia: Cultural Contact & Diffusion. 2009. pap. *(978-90-04-17919-6(4))* BRILL.
Edwards, Gwynne. A Cultural Journey Through Andalusia: From Granada to Seville. 2009. (ENG., Illus.). 224p. pap. 25.00 *(978-0-7083-2207-9(7))* Univ. of Wales Pr. GBR. Dist: Chicago Distribution Ctr.
Fierra, Maribel. The Almohad Revolution: Politics & Religion in the Islamic West During the Twelfth-Thirteenth Centuries. 2012. (Variorum Collected Studies). 330p. 154.95 ***(978-1-4094-4053-6(2))*** Ashgate Publishing Co.

ANDAMAN AND NICOBAR ISLANDS (INDIA)

Academic Foundation Staff & Planning Commission, Government of India Staff. Andaman & Nicobar Islands Development Report. 2008. (State Development Report Ser.). (ENG., Illus.). 248p. pap. 45.95 *(978-81-7188-652-4(3))* Academic Foundation IND. Dist: Independent Pubs. Group.
Man, Edward H. The Nicobar Islands & Their People. (Royal Anthropological Institute of Great Britain & Ireland, Publication Ser.). reprint ed. 55.00 *(978-0-404-16767-7(5))* AMS Pr., Inc.
Pandya, Vishvajit. In the Forest: Visual & Material Worlds of Andamanese History (1858-2006) 2009. (ENG., Illus.). 540p. pap. 68.50 *(978-0-7618-4153-1(9))* Univ. Pr. of America, Inc.
Sen, Satadru. Savagery & Colonialism in the Indian Ocean: Power, Pleasure & the Andaman Islanders. (ENG., Illus.). 288p. (C). 2012. pap. 42.95 ***(978-0-415-62670-5(6))*** 2010. 130.00 *(978-0-415-49782-4(5))* Routledge.
Sircar, Pronob Kumar. Jarawa: The Struggle Continues- 2011. (Illus.). xiv, 231p. *(978-81-8370-261-4(9)*, Library of Congress — New Delhi Overseas Office) Akansha Publishing House.
Vaidik, Aparna. Imperial Andamans: Colonial Encounter & Island History. 2010. (Cambridge Imperial & Post-Colonial Studies). (ENG., Illus.). 288p. 89.00 *(978-0-230-57605-6(2))* Palgrave Macmillan.

ANDEAN COUNTRIES

see Andes Region

ANDEAN REGION

see Andes Region

ANDERSEN, H. C. (HANS CHRISTIAN), 1805-1875

Andersen, Hans Christian. Hans Christian Andersen's Correspondence 1880. Crawford, Frederick, ed. 2007. (ENG.). 472p. 52.95 *(978-0-548-05461-1(4))* Kessinger Publishing, LLC.
—The True Story of My Life. 2007. (ENG.). 192p. 26.95 *(978-1-4218-4173-1(8))*; per. 11.95 *(978-1-4218-4271-4(8))* 1st World Publishing, Inc. (1st World Library - Literary Society).
—The True Story of My Life. 2008. 184p. 22.99 *(978-0-554-31773-1(7))* 2008. 184p. 25.99 *(978-0-554-22470-1(4))* 2007. (ENG.). 162p. pap. 19.99 *(978-1-4264-2371-0(3))* 2007. (ENG.). 182p. pap. 21.99 *(978-1-4264-2419-9(1))* BiblioBazaar.
Andersen, Hans Christian & Michael, Maurice. The Mermaid Man: The Autobiography of Hans Christian Andersen. 2011. 242p. 46.95 ***(978-1-258-01184-0(0))*** Literary Licensing, LLC.
Auchet, Marc. (Re)lire Andersen: Modernité de L'oeuvre. 2007. (FRE., Illus.). 300p. (C). pap. 39.00 ***(978-2-252-03636-5(2))*** Klincksieck, Editions FRA. Dist: ISD.
de Mylius, Johan, et al, eds. Hans Christian Andersen: Between Children's Literature & Adult Literature. 2008. (Illus.). 639p. (C). 62.00 *(978-87-7674-256-0(3))* Univ. Pr. of Southern Denmark DNK. Dist: International Specialized Bk. Services.
Lurie, Alison. Boys & Girls Forever: Children's Classics from Cinderella to Harry Potter. 2006. 219p. reprint ed. 25.00 *(978-1-4223-5774-3(0))* DIANE Publishing Co.
Rowland, Herbert. More Than Meets the Eye: Hans Christian Andersen & Nineteenth-Century American Criticism. 2006. (Illus.). 274p. 52.50 *(978-0-8386-4092-0(3))* Fairleigh Dickinson Univ. Pr.
Teicher, Hendel. Cut-Outs & Cut-Ups: Hans Christian Andersen & William Seward Burroughs. 2008. (Illus.). 197p. 89.50 *(978-1-903811-81-8(3))* Irish Museum of Modern Art IRL. Dist: Trans-Atlantic Pubns., Inc.

ANDERSON, CLAYTON AND COMPANY

Garwood, Ellen Clayton. Will Clayton: A Short Biography. 2011. 194p. 42.95 ***(978-1-258-09367-9(7))*** Literary Licensing, LLC.

ANDERSON, DOUGLAS, 1943-

Anderson, Doug. Keep Your Head Down: Vietnam, the Sixties, & a Journey of Self-Discovery. 2009. (ENG.). 288p. 25.95 *(978-0-393-06855-9(2)*, 6855) Norton, W. W. & Co., Inc.

A

ANDERSON, JACK, 1922-

Feldstein, Mark. Poisoning the Press: Richard Nixon, Jack Anderson, & the Rise of Washington's Scandal Culture. 2010. (ENG., Illus.). 480p. 30.00 *(978-0-374-23530-7(9))* Farrar, Straus & Giroux.

—Poisoning the Press: Richard Nixon, Jack Anderson, & the Rise of Washington's Scandal Culture. 2011. (ENG., Illus.). 496p. pap. 20.00 *(978-0-312-61070-8(X))* Picador.

ANDERSON, LAURIE, 1947-

Anderson, Laurie. Night Life, 1 vol. 2009. (ENG., Illus.). 96p. 35.00 *(978-3-86521-339-5(1))* Steidl, Gerhard Druckerei und Verlag DEU. Dist: Innovative Logistics.

Sun-Kleinberger, Nathan. The Children of Holden. 2009. 68p. pap. *(978-3-639-16371-1(0))* VDM Verlag Dr. Mueller e.K.

Yee, Lydia, ed. Laurie Anderson, Trisha Brown, Gordon Matta-Clark: Pioneers of the Downtown Scene, New York 1970s. 2011. (Illus.). 240p. 49.95 *(978-3-7913-5122-3(2))* Prestel Publishing.

ANDERSON, MARIAN, 1897-1993

Arsenault, Raymond. The Sound of Freedom: Marian Anderson, the Lincoln Memorial, & the Concert That Awakened America. (ENG., Illus.). 320p. 2010. pap. 18.00 *(978-1-60819-056-0(0))* 2009. 25.00 *(978-1-59691-578-7(1))* Bloomsbury Publishing.

Kaplan, Howard S. Marian Anderson. 2007. (Women Who Dare Ser.). (Illus.). 64p. 12.95 *(978-0-7649-3891-7(6)*, A133) Pomegranate Communications, Inc.

ANDERSON, MAXWELL, 1888-1959

Clark, Barrett H. Maxwell Anderson: The Man & His Plays. 2007. (ENG.). 48p. per. 15.95 *(978-1-4325-6866-5(3))* Kessinger Publishing, LLC.

ANDERSON, SHERWOOD, 1876-1941

Anderson, Sherwood. American Spring Song: The Selected Poems of Sherwood Anderson. 2007. 105p. per. *(978-0-87338-896-2(8))* Kent State Univ. Pr.

Fagin, N. Bryllion. The Phenomenon of Sherwood Anderson: A Study in American Life & Letters. 2011. 170p. 41.95 ***(978-1-258-05346-8(2))*** Literary Licensing, LLC.

Lindsay, Clarence. Such a Rare Thing: The Art of Sherwood Anderson's Winesburg, Ohio. 2009. 192p. pap. 24.95 *(978-0-87338-981-5(6))* Kent State Univ. Pr.

Rideout, Walter B. Sherwood Anderson Vol. 2: A Writer in America, 2 vols. 2006. (ENG., Illus.). 520p. 60.00 *(978-0-299-22020-4(6))* Univ. of Wisconsin Pr.

Taylor, Welford Dunaway, ed. Sherwood Anderson Remembered. 2009. (American Writers Remembered Ser.). (ENG., Illus.). 384p. 42.50 *(978-0-8173-1666-2(3))* Univ. of Alabama Pr.

Whalan, Mark. Race, Manhood, & Modernism in America: The Short Story Cycles of Sherwood Anderson & Jean Toomer. 2007. (ENG.). 304p. 43.00 *(978-1-57233-580-6(7))* Univ. of Tennessee Pr.

ANDERSON ISLAND (WASH.)

Galentine, Elizabeth & Anderson Island Historical Society. Anderson Island. 2006. (Images of America Ser.). (ENG., Illus.). 128p. per. 19.99 *(978-0-7385-4854-8(5))* Arcadia Publishing.

ANDERSONVILLE PRISON

Andersonville Prison & American Prisoners of War. 2007. (Illus.). 52p. (YA). 4.95 *(978-1-888213-31-7(0))* Eastern National.

Davis, Robert Scott. Andersonville Civil War Prison. 2010. (Civil War Sesquicentennial Ser.). (ENG., Illus.). 144p. pap. 19.99 *(978-1-59629-752-3(X))* History Pr., The.

Futch, Ovid L. History of Andersonville Prison. rev. ed. 2011. (ENG., Illus.). 176p. pap. 19.95 *(978-0-8130-3691-5(7))* Univ. Pr. of Florida.

Goss, Warren. The Soldier's Story of His Captivity at Andersonville, Belle Isle, & Other Rebel Prisons. 2008. (Civil War Ser.). (ENG.). 284p. pap. 19.95 *(978-1-4290-1617-9(5))* Applewood Bks.

Goss, Warren Lee. The Soldier's Story of His Captivity at Andersonville, Belle Isle & Other Rebel Prisons. 2007. (ENG.). 402p. 49.95 *(978-0-548-26505-5(4))*; 404p. per. 34.95 *(978-1-4326-6932-4(X))* Kessinger Publishing, LLC.

Hogge, Jeffery A. Norton Parker Chipman: A Biography of the Andersonville War Crimes Prosecutor. 2008. (ENG., Illus.). 249p. pap. 39.95 *(978-0-7864-3449-7(X))* McFarland & Co., Inc. Pubs.

Huffman, Alan. Sultana: Surviving the Civil War, Prison, & the Worst Maritime Disaster in American History. 2010. (ENG.). 320p. pap. 14.99 *(978-0-06-147056-1(2)*, HarperPerennial) HarperCollins Pubs.

Kellogg, Robert. Life & Death in Rebel Prisons. 2008. (Civil War Ser.). (ENG.). 404p. pap. 24.95 *(978-1-4290-1620-9(5))* Applewood Bks.

Kellogg, Robert H. Life & Death in Rebel Prisons. 2008. 400p. 31.99 *(978-0-554-44515-1(8))*; 29.99 *(978-0-554-44523-6(9))*; pap. 33.75 *(978-0-554-44517-5(4))*; pap. 32.75 *(978-0-554-44522-9(0))* BiblioBazaar.

—Life & Death in Rebel Prisons. 2009. 234p. pap. *(978-0-217-50429-4(9))*; 244p. pap. *(978-0-217-23278-4(7))* Books LLC.

—Life & Death in Rebel Prisons. 2007. (ENG.). 398p. 49.95 *(978-0-548-23681-9(X))*; 400p. per. 34.95 *(978-1-4326-3792-7(4))* Kessinger Publishing, LLC.

Maile, John Levi. "Prison Life in Andersonville" Special Reference to the Opening of Providence Spring. 152p. reprint ed. 88.00 *(978-0-7222-8123-9(4))* Library Reprints, Inc.

Marvel, William. Andersonville: The Last Depot. (Civil War America Ser.). (ENG., Illus.). 350p. 2006. per. 23.00 *(978-0-8078-5781-6(5))* 2010. pap. 35.00 *(978-0-8078-6615-3(6))* Univ. of North Carolina Pr.

Mcelroy, John. Andersonville a Story of Rebel Military Prisons. 2010. 456p. 42.36 *(978-1-169-34616-1(2))*; pap. 30.36 *(978-1-162-65312-9(4))* Kessinger Publishing, LLC.

—Andersonville, a Story of Rebel Military Prisons. 2010. 670p. pap. 47.75 *(978-1-175-91337-1(5))* BiblioBazaar.

McElroy, John & Mcelroy, John. Andersonville a Story of Rebel Military Prisons. 2010. 456p. 52.95 *(978-1-161-42177-4(7))* Kessinger Publishing, LLC.

Mowris, James. A History of the One Hundred & Seventeenth Regiment, N. Y. Volunteers (Fourth Oneida) 2008. (Civil War Ser.). (ENG.). 296p. pap. 19.95 *(978-1-4290-1616-2(7))* Applewood Bks.

O'Connor, Bob. The U. S. Colored Troops at Andersonville Prison. 2009. 103p. pap. 10.95 *(978-0-7414-5767-7(9))* Infinity Publishing.

Page, James Madison. The True Story of Andersonville Prison. (Travels in the Confederate States Ser.). 248p. reprint ed. 98.00 *(978-0-7222-8124-6(2))* Library Reprints, Inc.

—The True Story of Andersonville Prison: A Defense of Major Henry Wirz. (Illus.). 248p. reprint ed. lib. bdg. 98.00 *(978-0-7222-0887-8(1))* Library Reprints, Inc.

Roach, Alva C. A Yankee in Rebel Prisons. 2011. 232p. pap. 24.00 ***(978-0-9790443-9-7(1))*** Baughman Literary.

Tyler, Wm. N. The Dispatch Carrier: A Sergeant of the 9th Illinois Cavalry, Union Army on Campaign & in Andersonville Prison During the American Civil War. 2011. 104p. ***(978-0-85706-669-5(2))***; pap. ***(978-0-85706-670-1(6))*** Leonaur Ltd.

ANDES

Avilés, William. Globalization & Military Power in the Andes. 2010. (ENG., Illus.). 208p. 89.00 *(978-0-230-10387-0(1))* Palgrave Macmillan.

Bennett, Wendell C. & D'Harnoncourt, Rene. Ancient Art of the Andes. (Museum of Modern Art Publications in Reprint). (Illus.). reprint ed. 18.00 *(978-0-405-01521-2(6))* Ayer Co. Pubs., Inc.

Bowman, Isaiah. The Andes of Southern Peru. 2010. 212p. pap. 25.14 *(978-1-153-35412-7(8))* General Bks. LLC.

Chamussy, Vincent. Les Débuts de la Guerre Institutionnalisée Dans L'Aire Andine Centrale: Vers la Formation de L'État, Du Formatif a la Période Intermédiaire Ancienne (2000 Av. J.-C-500 Apr. J.-C.) 2009. (Bar S Ser.). (FRE & ENG., Illus.). 383p. (C). pap. 145.00 *(978-1-4073-0592-9(1))* British Archaeological Reports Ltd. GBR. Dist: Brown, David Bk. Co., The.

Franck, Harry A. Vagabonding down the Andes. 612p. reprint ed. 128.00 *(978-0-7222-9553-3(7))* Library Reprints, Inc.

Head, Francis Bond. Rough Notes Taken during some Rapid Journeys across the Pampas & among the Andes. 2009. (Cambridge Library Collection - Life Sciences Ser.). (ENG.). 328p. pap. 19.99 *(978-1-108-00161-8(0))* Cambridge Univ. Pr.

Jacobs, Michael. Andes. 2011. (ENG.). 576p. pap. 24.95 *(978-1-58243-737-8(8)*, Counterpoint) Counterpoint LLC.

—Andes. 2010. (Illus.). 600p. *(978-1-84708-129-2(0))*; xi, 580p. *(978-1-84708-170-4(3))* Granta.

Orton, James. The Andes & the Amazon; or, Across the Continent of South America. 2006. 360p. per. 26.99 *(978-1-4255-3675-6(1))* MPublishing.

Post, Charles Johnso. Across the Andes A Tale of Wandering Day. 2006. pap. 33.95 *(978-1-4286-5708-3(8))* Kessinger Publishing, LLC.

Suarez, Ananda Cohen & George, Jeremy James. Handbook to Life in the Inca World. 2011. (Handbook to Life Ser.). (Illus.). 342p. (C). (gr. 9). 70.00 *(978-0-8160-7449-5(6))* Facts On File, Inc.

Woods, Josephine Hoeppner. High Spots in the Andes: Peruvian Letters of A Mining Engineer's Wife. 2011. 352p. 51.95 ***(978-1-258-02628-8(7))*** Literary Licensing, LLC.

ANDES REGION

Burger, Richard L., et al. Variations in the Expression of Inka Power: A Symposium at Dumbarton Oaks, 18 & 19 October 1997. Burger, Richard L. et al, eds. 2008. (Dumbarton Oaks Other Titles in Pre-Columbian Studies). (Illus.). 640p. 55.00 *(978-0-88402-351-7(6))* Dumbarton Oaks.

Canessa, Andrew. Natives Making Nation: Gender, Indigeneity, & the State in the Andes. 2011. (ENG.). 208p. pap. 22.00 *(978-0-8165-3013-7(0))* Univ. of Arizona Pr.

Carvajal, Paola Gonzalez & Bray, Tamara L., eds. Lenguajes Visuales De Los Incas. 2008. (Bar S Ser.). (ENG & SPA., Illus.). 193p. (C). 87.50 *(978-1-4073-0335-2(X))* British Archaeological Reports Ltd. GBR. Dist: Brown, David Bk. Co., The.

Charles, John. Allies at Odds: The Andean Church & Its Indigenous Agents, 1583-1671. 2010. (ENG., Illus.). 296p. (C). pap. 27.95 *(978-0-8263-4831-9(9))* Univ. of New Mexico Pr.

Damonte, Gerardo H. The Constitution of Political Actors. 2008. (Illus.). 368p. pap. *(978-3-8364-5982-2(5))* VDM Verlag Dr. Mueller e.K.

Davies, Nigel. The Incas. 2007. (ENG., Illus.). 259p. per. 27.95 *(978-0-87081-865-3(1))* Univ. Pr. of Colorado.

Dean, Carolyn. A Culture of Stone: Inka Perspectives on Rock. 2010. (ENG., Illus.). 320p. 84.95 *(978-0-8223-4791-0(1))*; pap. 23.95 *(978-0-8223-4807-8(1))* Duke Univ. Pr.

Diaz Andrade, Antonio Eduardo. Activators of Information in the Peruvian Rural Andes. 2009. 252p. pap. *(978-3-639-17373-4(2))* VDM Verlag Dr. Mueller e.K.

Dillehay, Tom D. From Foraging to Farming in the Andes: New Perspectives on Food Production & Social Organization. 2011. (ENG., Illus.). 350p. 90.00 *(978-1-107-00527-3(2))* Cambridge Univ. Pr.

Dillehay, Tom D., et al. Tombs for the Living: Andean Mortuary Practices. 2011. (Dumbarton Oaks Pre-Columbian Symposia & Colloquia Ser.). (ENG., Illus.). 434p. pap. 40.00 *(978-0-88402-374-6(5))* Dumbarton Oaks.

Dohmmann, Aaron J. The Andean Trade Preference Act (ATPA) 2011. (Series: Trade Issues, Policies & Laws Ser.). 194p. 185.00 *(978-1-61324-386-2(3))* Nova Science Pubs., Inc.

Dransart, Penelope, ed. Kay Pacha: Cultivating Earth & Water in the Andes. 2006. (BAR International Ser.: Vol. 1478). (ENG & SPA., Illus.). 245p. (C). pap. 92.50 *(978-1-84171-913-9(7))* Archaeopress GBR. Dist: Brown, David Bk. Co., The.

Fierro-Carrion, Gustavo, photos by. Retorno a las Alturas. 2006. 22.50 *(978-1-4276-0664-8(1))* Aardvark Global Publishing.

Glidden, Lisa. Mobilizing Ethnic Identities in the Andes: A Study of Ecuador & Peru. 2011. (ENG.). 146p. 55.00 *(978-0-7391-3465-8(5))* Lexington Bks.

Gose, Peter. Invaders as Ancestors: On the Intercultural Making & Unmaking of Spanish Colonialism in the Andes. 2008. (Anthropological Horizons Ser.). (ENG., Illus.). 404p. *(978-0-8020-9876-4(2))*; pap. *(978-0-8020-9617-3(4))* Univ. of Toronto Pr.

Harrison, John. Cloud Road: A Journey Through the Inca Heartland. 2010. (ENG.). 350p. pap. 14.95 *(978-1-906998-12-7(4))* Parthian Bks. GBR. Dist: Independent Pubs. Group.

Hasluck, Lindsay Robert. Urban Continuity in the Andes: A Pre-Historical Planning Tradition. 2009. (ENG., Illus.). 265p. (C). pap. 125.00 *(978-1-4073-0538-7(7))* British Archaeological Reports Ltd. GBR. Dist: Brown, David Bk. Co., The.

Himpele, Jeff D. Circuits of Culture: Media, Politics, & Indigenous Identity in the Andes. 2007. (Visible Evidence Ser.). (Illus.). 240p. 75.00 *(978-0-8166-3918-2(3))* Univ. of Minnesota Pr.

Himpele, Jeffrey D. Circuits of Culture: Media, Politics, & Indigenous Identity in the Andes. 2007. (Visible Evidence Ser.). (Illus.). 240p. per. 25.00 *(978-0-8166-3919-9(1))* Univ. of Minnesota Pr.

Humboldt, Alexander von, et al. Views of the Cordilleras & Monuments of the Indigenous Peoples of the Americas: A Critical Edition. 2012. (Alexander Von Humboldt in English Ser.). 576p. 65.00 ***(978-0-226-86506-5(1))*** Univ. of Chicago Pr.

Hunefeldt, Christine & Kokotovic, Milos, eds. Power, Culture, & Violence in the Andes. 2009. (ENG., Illus.). 202p. 69.95 *(978-1-84519-247-1(8))* Sussex Academic Pr. GBR. Dist: International Specialized Bk. Services.

Hyslop, John. Inka Settlement Planning. 2010. (ENG., Illus.). 393p. pap. 35.00 *(978-0-292-72855-4(7))* Univ. of Texas Pr.

Isbell, William H. Mummies & Mortuary Monuments: A Postprocessual Prehistory of Central Andean Social Organization. 2010. (ENG.). 391p. pap. 35.00 *(978-0-292-71799-2(7))* Univ. of Texas Pr.

Jacobsen, Frode & McNeish, John-Andrew. From Where Life Flows: The Local Knowledge & Politics of Water in the Andes. 2006. 151p. (C). pap. 77.00 *(978-82-519-2144-2(9))* Tapir Forlag NOR. Dist: International Specialized Bk. Services.

Jennings, Justin & Bowser, Brenda J. Drink, Power, & Society in the Andes. Jennings, Justin & Bowser, Brenda J., eds. 2009. (ENG., Illus.). 320p. 75.00 *(978-0-8130-3306-8(3))* Univ. Pr. of Florida.

Jones, David M. The Inca World: Ancient People & Places. 2010. (ENG., Illus.). 256p. 35.00 *(978-0-7548-1726-0(1))* Anness Publishing GBR. Dist: National Bk. Network.

Morelli, Luigi. Spiritual Turning Points of South American History, 1 vol. 2011. (ENG.). 380p. pap. 25.00 ***(978-1-58420-108-3(8)***, Lindisfarne Bks.) SteinerBooks, Inc.

Muller, Karin. Por el Camino del Inca: Odisea de una Mujer en el Corazon de Los Andes. 2007. (Adventure Press Ser.). (SPA., Illus.). 256p. per. 14.00 *(978-1-4262-0159-2(1)*, National Geographic) National Geographic Society.

Pillsbury, Joanne, ed. Guide to Documentary Sources for Andean Studies, 1530-1900, 3 vols. 2008. (ENG., Illus.). (C). 1296p. 195.00 *(978-0-8061-9963-4(6))*; Vol. 1. 464p. 80.00 *(978-0-8061-3817-6(3))*; Vol. 2. 2nd ed. 384p. 80.00 *(978-0-8061-3820-6(3))* Univ. of Oklahoma Pr.

—Guide to Documentary Sources for Andean Studies, 1530-1900 Vol. 3, 3 vols. 3rd ed. 2008. (ENG., Illus.). 448p. (C). 80.00 *(978-0-8061-3821-3(1))* Univ. of Oklahoma Pr.

Ramos, Gabriela. Death & Conversion in the Andes: Lima & Cuzco, 1532-1670. 2010. (History Lang & Cult Spanish Portuguese Ser.). (ENG., Illus.). 368p. pap. 39.00 *(978-0-268-04028-4(1))* Univ. of Notre Dame Pr.

Rivero Romero, Marlene. Vacations in Bonill. 2009. 80p. pap. 27.50 *(978-1-59754-493-1(0))* Editorial Libros en Red.

Roberts, Elizabeth F. S. God's Laboratory: Assisted Reproduction in the Andes. 2012. (ENG.). 298p. 70.00 ***(978-0-520-27082-4(7))***; pap. 29.95 ***(978-0-520-27083-1(5))*** Univ. of California Pr.

Sax, Marieka. An Ethnography of Feeding, Perception, & Place in the Peruvian Andes (Where Hungry Spirits Bring Illness & Wellbeing) 2011. 212p. 119.95 ***(978-0-7734-3916-0(1))*** Mellen, Edwin Pr., The.

Silverman, Helaine & Isbell, W. Andean Archaeology III: North & South. 2008. (ENG., Illus.). xii, 524p. pap. 39.95 *(978-0-387-75730-8(9)*, 0387757309) Springer.

Smyth, William & Lowe, Frederick. Narrative of a Journey from Lima to para, across the Andes & down the Amazon: Undertaken with a View of Ascertaining the Practicability of a Navigable Communication with the Atlantic, by the Rivers Pachitea, Ucayali, & Amazon. 2011. (Cambridge Library Collection - Travel & Exploration Ser.). (ENG., Illus.). 354p. pap. 29.99 ***(978-1-108-03379-4(2))*** Cambridge Univ. Pr.

Stanish, Charles. Ancient Andean Political Economy. 2011. (ENG., Illus.). 208p. pap. 19.95 *(978-0-292-72945-2(6))* Univ. of Texas Pr.

Thompson, Hugh. A Sacred Landscape: The Search for Ancient Peru. 2007. (ENG., Illus.). 376p. (gr. 12). 27.95 *(978-1-58567-901-0(1))* Overlook Pr., The.

Thomson, Hugh. A Sacred Landscape: The Search for Ancient Peru. 2008. (ENG., Illus.). 416p. (gr. 12). pap. 16.95 *(978-1-59020-058-2(6))* Overlook Pr., The.

Van Cott, Donna Lee. Radical Democracy in the Andes. 2008. (ENG.). 278p. pap. 25.99 *(978-0-521-73417-2(7))*; 90.00 *(978-0-521-51558-0(0))* Cambridge Univ. Pr.

Vierci, Pablo. La sociedad de la Nieve. 2009. (SPA.). 338p. pap. 19.95 *(978-0-307-39281-7(3))* Random House Mondadori ESP. Dist: Random Hse., Inc.

Wilson, Jason. Andes, 1 vol. 2009. (Landscapes of Imagination Ser.). (ENG., Illus.). 256p. pap. 16.95 *(978-0-19-538635-6(3))* Oxford Univ. Pr., Inc.

ANDES REGION—ECONOMIC INTEGRATION

Álvarez, Eric Tremolada. El Derecho Andino en Colombia. 2006. (SPA.). 131p. pap. 12.00 ***(978-958-710-177-5(4))*** Universidad Externado de Colombia COL. Dist: Siglo del Hombre.

ANDHRA LANGUAGE

see Telugu Language

ANDO, HIROSHIGE

see Hiroshige, 1797-1858

ANDORRA

Marsh, Rosalie. Chasing Rainbows: With Just Us Two. 2011. (ENG., Illus.). 198p. pap. ***(978-1-908302-00-7(3))*** Christal Publishing.

Robertson, Alf & Meadowcroft, Jane. The Mountains of Andorra: Walks, Scrambles, Via Ferratas & Treks. 2010. (Cicerone Mountain Guide Ser.). (Illus.). 192p. vinyl bd. 19.95 *(978-1-85284-424-0(8))* Cicerone Pr. GBR. Dist: Midpoint Trade Bks., Inc.

ANDOVER (MASS.)

Abbot, Elinor. Our Company Increases Apace: History, Language, & Social Identity in Early Colonial Andover, Massachusetts. 2007. (Publications in Ethnography: 40). 276p. pap. 25.00 *(978-1-55671-169-5(7))* SIL International.

Patrakis, Joan Silva. Andover in the Civil War. 2008. (ENG., Illus.). 128p. pap. 21.99 *(978-1-59629-437-0(X))* History Pr., The.

ANDOVER THEOLOGICAL SEMINARY

Bendroth, Margaret Lamberts. A School of the Church: Andover Newton across Two Centuries. 2008. 240p. 28.00 *(978-0-8028-6370-6(1))* Eerdmans, William B. Publishing Co.

Fehler, Brian M. Calvinist Rhetoric in Nineteenth-Century America: The Bartlet Professors of Sacred Rhetoric of Andover Seminary. 2007. 208p. *(978-0-7734-5430-9(6))* Mellen, Edwin Pr., The.

ANDRAGOGICAL LEARNING

see Adult Learning

ANDRE, JOHN, 1751-1780

Abbatt, William. The Crisis of the Revolution: The Story of Arnold & Andre. 119p. reprint ed. 88.00 *(978-0-7222-9262-4(7))* Library Reprints, Inc.

—The CRISIS of the REVOLUTION; Being the Story of Arnold & Andre, Now for the First Time Collected from All Sources, & illustrated with Views of All Places Identified with It. 2007. (Illus.). 280p. pap. 39.95 *(978-1-60105-130-1(1)*, 6D7E) Scholar's Bookshelf.

Lossing, Benson John. The Two Spies: Nathan Hale & John Andre. 169p. reprint ed. 88.00 *(978-0-7222-7712-6(1))*; 88.00 *(978-0-7222-7771-3(7))* Library Reprints, Inc.

Sargent, Winthrop. Life & Career of Major John Andre Adju. 2006. pap. 38.95 *(978-1-4286-3435-0(5))* Kessinger Publishing, LLC.

ANDRE, LE CHAPELAIN

Weigand, Hermann J. Three Chapters on Courtly Love in Arthurian France & Germany. (North Carolina University, Studies in the Germanic Languages & Literatures: No. 17). reprint ed. 27.00 *(978-0-404-50917-0(7))* AMS Pr., Inc.

ANDREA DORIA (STEAMSHIP)

Simpson, Pierette. Alive on the Andrea Doria! The Greatest Sea Rescue in History. 2008. (ENG.). pap. 18.00 *(978-1-60037-460-9(3))* Morgan James Publishing.

ANDREAS-SALOME, LOU, 1861-1937

Benert, Britta. Une Lecture de 'Im Zwischenland' Le Paradigme de L'AltéRité Au Coeur de la CréAtion Romanesque de Lou Andreas-Salomé. 2012. (Nouvelle poétique comparatiste - New Comparative Poetics Ser.). (FRE & GER.). 127p. pap. 41.95 ***(978-90-5201-801-0(4))*** PIE - Peter Lang BEL. Dist: Lang, Peter.

Cormican, Muriel. Women in the Works of Lou Andreas-Salomé: Negotiating Identity. 2009. (Studies in German Literature Linguistics & Culture Ser.: Volume 52). 194p. 75.00 *(978-1-57113-414-1(X))* Camden Hse.

Vickers, Julia. Lou Von Salomé: A Biography of the Woman Who Inspired Freud, Nietzsche & Rilke. 2008. (ENG., Illus.). 217p. pap. 39.95 *(978-0-7864-3606-4(9))* McFarland & Co., Inc. Pubs.

ANDREE, SALOMON AUGUST, 1854-1897

Wilkinson, Alec. The Ice Balloon: S. A. Andrée & the Heroic Age of Arctic Exploration. 2012. (ENG., Illus.). 256p. 25.95 ***(978-0-307-59480-8(7)***, Knopf) Knopf Doubleday Publishing Group.

ANDREEV, LEONID NIKOLAEVICH, 1871-1919

see Andreyev, Leonid, 1871-1919

ANDRETTI, MARIO, 1940-

O' Leary, Mike. Mario Andretti: The Complete Record. 2007. (Illus.). 155p. reprint ed. pap. 17.00 *(978-1-4223-6640-0(5))* DIANE Publishing Co.

ANDREW, APOSTLE, SAINT

Dvornik, Francis. The Idea of Apostolicity in Byzantium & the Legend of Apostle Andrew. 2011. 352p. 51.95 ***(978-1-258-08369-4(8))*** Literary Licensing, LLC.

ANDREWES, LANCELOT, 1555-1626

Andrewes, Lancelot. Complete Works, 11 vols. Wilson, J. P. & Bliss, J., eds. (BCL Ser.: No. 1). reprint ed. 1275.00 *(978-0-404-52020-5(0))* AMS Pr., Inc.

—Lancelot Andrewes & His Private Devotions. 2009. (ENG.). 24.99 *(978-1-84550-429-8(1),* Christian Heritage) Christian Focus Pubns. GBR. Dist: STL Distribution North America.

Dorman, Marianne. Lancelot Andrewes 1555-1626: Teacher & Preacher in the Post-Reformation English Church. 2006. pap. 28.95 *(978-1-58736-639-0(8))* Wheatmark.

ANDREWS, CHARLES MCLEAN, 1863-1943

Eisenstadt, Abraham S. Charles McLean Andrews: A Study in American Historical Writing. (Columbia University, Studies in the Social Sciences: No. 588). reprint ed. 20.00 *(978-0-404-51588-1(6))* AMS Pr., Inc.

ANDREWS, JOSEPH, 1805-1873

Fielding, Henry. The Adventures of Joseph Andrews. 2007. (ENG.). 548p. 35.00 *(978-1-4344-8877-0(2));* per. 19.95 *(978-1-4344-8876-3(4))* Wildside Pr., LLC.

ANDREWS, JULIE, 1935-

Andrews, Julie. Home: A Memoir of My Early Years. (ENG.). 352p. 2009. pap. 15.99 *(978-0-7868-8475-9(4))* 2008. (Illus.). 26.95 *(978-0-7868-6565-9(2))* Hyperion Pr.

Stirling, Richard. Julie Andrews: An Intimate Biography. 2009. (ENG., Illus.). 384p. pap. 17.95 *(978-0-312-56498-8(8),* St. Martin's Griffin) St. Martin's Pr.

ANDREWS, ROY CHAPMAN, 1884-1960

Andrews, Roy Chapman. The New Conquest of Central Asia: A Narrative of the Explorations of the Central Asiatic Expeditions in Mongolia & China, 1921-1930. 2007. *(978-1-57898-684-2(2))* Martino Publishing.

—Under a Lucky Star. 2008. 280p. 25.00 *(978-0-9768781-8-6(6))* Borderland Bks.

Andrews, Roy Chapman & Yvette Borup Andrews. Camps & Trails in China: A Narrative of Exploration Adventure & Sport I. 2007. (ENG.). 266p. pap. 21.99 *(978-1-4264-5930-6(0));* 292p. pap. 23.99 *(978-1-4264-5998-6(X))* BiblioBazaar.

Bjerke, Carol Chase. Hidden Agenda. 2008. (ENG., Illus.). 96p. 45.00 *(978-0-9815620-0-1(0))* Borderland Bks.

ANDREWS, THOMAS, 1873-1912

Bullock, Shan F. Thomas Andrews, Shipbuilder. 2010. 34p. pap. 9.89 *(978-1-153-64901-8(2))* General Bks. LLC.

ANDREWS' RAID, 1862

see Chattanooga Railroad Expedition, 1862

ANDREYEV, LEONID, 1871-1919

Gamsa, M. The Chinese Translation of Russian Literature: Three Studies. 2008. (Sinica Leidensia Ser.). 450p. *(978-90-04-16844-2(3))* BRILL.

ANDROGENS

see also Antiandrogens; Testosterone

Ardis, L. I. Testosterone Research Trends. 2007. 304p. (C). 129.00 *(978-1-60021-550-6(5))* Nova Science Pubs., Inc.

Azziz, Ricardo, ed. Androgen Excess Disorders in Women. 2010. (Contemporary Endocrinology Ser.). (Illus.). 488p. pap. 209.00 *(978-1-61737-704-4(X),* 161737704X) Humana Pr.

Azziz, Ricardo, et al. Androgen Excess Disorders in Women: Polycystic Ovary Syndrome & Other Disorders. 2nd ed. 2006. (Contemporary Endocrinology Ser.). (Illus.). 466p. 209.00 *(978-1-58829-663-4(6),* 1588296636) Humana Pr.

Bagatell, Carrie & Bremner, William J., eds. Androgens in Health & Disease. 2010. (Contemporary Endocrinology Ser.). (Illus.). 460p. pap. 179.00 *(978-1-61737-314-5(1),* 161737314l) Humana Pr.

Buhner, Stephen Harrod. The Natural Testosterone Plan: For Sexual Health & Energy. 2007. (ENG.). 1p. per. 14.95 *(978-1-59477-168-2(5),* Healing Arts Pr.) Inner Traditions International, Ltd.

Jockenhövel, Friedrich & Schubert, Markus. Male Hypogonadism. 2nd ed. 2007. (UNI-MED Science Ser.). (Illus.). 192p. *(978-3-89599-859-1(1))* UNI-MED Verlag AG.

Saatcioglu, Fahri. Androgen Action: Methods & Protocols. 2011. (Illus.). xi, 386p. E-Book ***(978-1-61779-243-4(8))*** Humana Pr.

Saatcioglu, Fahri, ed. Androgen Action: Methods & Protocols. 2011. (Methods in Molecular Biology Ser.). (ENG., Illus.). xi, 386p. 139.00 *(978-1-61779-242-7(X),* 161779242X) Humana Pr.

The Endocrine Society. Androgen Deficiency Syndromes Guidelines Pocketcard 2010: Testosterone Therapy in Men. 2010. 10p. 9.95 *(978-0-9845778-9-7(0))* International Guidelines Ctr., Inc.

Tindall, Donald & Mohler, James, eds. Androgen Action in Prostate Cancer. 2009. (ENG., Illus.). viii, 800p. 169.00 *(978-0-387-69177-0(4),* 0387691774) Springer.

ANDROGYNY (PSYCHOLOGY)

Goulian, Jon-Jon. The Man in the Gray Flannel Skirt. 2011. (Illus.). 336p. 25.00 *(978-1-4000-6811-1(8),* Random House) Random House Publishing Group.

Hemingway, John. Strange Tribe: A Family Memoir. 2007. (ENG., Illus.). 224p. 24.95 *(978-1-59921-112-1(2),* Lyons Pr.) Globe Pequot Pr., The.

Stone, James W. Crossing Gender in Shakespeare. (Illus.). 2011. (ENG.). 186p. pap. 39.95 ***(978-0-415-89651-1(7))*** 2010. xv, 185p. (C). 95.00 *(978-0-203-85276-1(8))* Routledge.

Waldner, Katharina. Geburt und Hochzeit des Kriegers: Geschlechterdifferenz und Initiation in Mythos und Ritual der griechischen Polis. (Religionsgeschichtliche Versuche und Vorarbeiten Ser.). (GER.). IX, 281p. 210.00 ***(978-3-11-176113-8(4))*** De Gruyter, Walter Inc.

ANDROID (ELECTRONIC RESOURCE)

Absar, Javed. Programming for the Android Dalvik Virtual Machine. 2012. (ENG., Illus.). 200p. 129.00 ***(978-1-4614-2388-1(0),*** 1461423880) Springer.

Burnette, Ed. Hello, Android: Introducing Google's Mobile Development Platform. 3rd ed. 2010. (ENG., Illus.). 300p. pap. 34.95 *(978-1-934356-56-2(5),* Pragmatic Bookshelf, The) Pragmatic Programmers, LLC, The.

Butow, Eric & Ballew, Joli. Droid Companion. 2011. (ENG.). 304p. pap. 19.99 ***(978-1-118-17764-3(9),*** Wiley) Wiley, John & Sons, Inc.

Collins, Charlie, et al. Android in Practice. 2011. (ENG., Illus.). 648p. pap. 49.99 *(978-1-935182-92-4(7))* Manning Pubns. Co.

—Unlocking Android. 2009. (ENG., Illus.). 416p. pap., instr.'s gde. ed. 39.99 *(978-1-933988-67-2(3))* Manning Pubns. Co.

Conder, Shane & Darcey, Lauren. Android Wireless Application Development Vol. II: Advanced Android. 3rd rev. ed. 2012. (Developer's Library). (ENG.). 528p. pap. 49.99 ***(978-0-321-81384-8(7))*** Addison Wesley Professional.

Conder, Shane & Darcey, Lauren. Sams Teach Yourself Android Application Development in 24 Hours. 2nd rev. ed. 2011. (Sams Teach Yourself — Hours Ser.). (ENG., Illus.). 512p. pap. 39.99 *(978-0-672-33569-3(7))* Sams.

Darcey, Lauren & Conder, Shane. Android Wireless Application Development: Android Essentials. 3rd ed. 2012. pap. ***(978-0-321-81496-8(7))*** Addison-Wesley Longman, Inc.

—Learning Android Application Programming for the Kindle Fire: A Hands-on Guide to Building Your First Android Application. 2012. (Learning Ser.). (ENG.). 500p. pap. 39.99 ***(978-0-321-83397-6(X),*** Addison Wesley Professional.

Deitel, Paul & Deitel, Harvey. Android: How to Program. 2012. (ENG., Illus.). 850p. (C). pap. 125.00 ***(978-0-13-299054-7(7),*** Prentice Hall) Prentice Hall PTR.

Gookin, Dan. Droid X2 for Dummies. 2011. (ENG.). 352p. pap. 24.99 ***(978-1-118-14864-8(9),*** For Dummies) Wiley, John & Sons, Inc.

Haseman, Chris, et al. Pro Android. 2009. (ENG., Illus.). 464p. pap. 44.99 *(978-1-4302-1596-7(8))* Apress L. P.

Hashimi, Sayed Y., et al. Pro Android 2. 2010. (Illus.). xvi, 718p. E-Book ***(978-1-4302-2660-4(9))*** Apress L. P.

Johnston, Craig James. My Droid. (My... Ser.). (ENG., Illus.). 2010. 432p. pap. 24.99 *(978-0-7897-4719-8(7))* 2nd rev. ed. 2011. 464p. pap. 24.99 ***(978-0-7897-4939-3(6))*** Que.

Komatineni, Satya, et al. Pro Android 3. 2011. (Illus.). xxii, 1175p. E-Book ***(978-1-4302-3223-0(4))*** Apress L. P.

Lee, We-Meng. Android Application Development Cookbook: 100 Recipes for Building Winning Apps. 2012. (ENG.). 448p. pap. 39.99 ***(978-1-118-17767-9(3),*** Wrox) Wiley, John & Sons, Inc.

—Beginning Android 4 Application Development. 2012. (ENG., Illus.). 560p. pap. 39.99 ***(978-1-118-19954-1(5),*** Wrox) Wiley, John & Sons, Inc.

Lee, Wei-Meng. Beginning Android Application Development. 2011. (Illus.). (ENG.). 448p. pap. 39.99 *(978-1-118-01711-1(0),* Wrox); xx, 428p. E-Book ***(978-1-118-08729-9(1));*** xx, 428p. E-Book ***(978-1-118-08780-0(1));*** xx, 428p. E-Book ***(978-1-118-08749-7(6))*** Wiley, John & Sons, Inc.

Matthews, Robbie. Beginning Android Tablet Programming. 2011. (ENG.). 292p. pap. 39.99 *(978-1-4302-3783-9(X))* Apress L. P.

McGrath, Mike. Building Android Apps in Easy Steps. 2012. (In Easy Steps Ser.). (ENG., Illus.). 192p. pap. 14.99 ***(978-1-84078-528-9(4))*** Computer Step GBR. Dist: Perseus-PGW.

Meier, Reto. Professional Android 2 Application Development. 2nd ed. 2010. (ENG., Illus.). 576p. pap. 44.99 *(978-0-470-56552-0(7),* Wrox) Wiley, John & Sons, Inc.

Monk, Simon. Arduino + Android Projects for the Evil Genius: Control Arduino with Your Smartphone or Tablet. 2011. (Evil Genius Ser.). (ENG., Illus.). 224p. pap. 25.00 ***(978-0-07-177596-0(X),*** 007177596X, TAB/Electronics) McGraw-Hill Professional Publishing.

Murphy, Mark. Beginning Android. 2009. (ENG.). 384p. pap. 44.99 *(978-1-4302-2419-8(3))* Apress L. P.

—Beginning Android 2. 2nd ed. 2010. (ENG.). 416p. pap. 44.99 *(978-1-4302-2629-1(3))* Apress L. P.

O'Dell, Jolie Anne. Android Photography. 2012. (ENG., Illus.). 160p. pap. 19.95 ***(978-1-4547-0346-4(6),*** Pixiq) Sterling Publishing Co., Inc.

O'Grady, Jason D. The Droid Pocket Guide. 2nd rev. ed. 2011. (Pocket Guide Ser.). (ENG., Illus.). 240p. pap. 14.99 *(978-0-321-74742-6(9))* Peachpit Pr.

Rollins, Mark. The Business of Android Apps Development: Making & Marketing Apps That Succeed. 2011. (ENG., Illus.). 244p. pap. 29.99 ***(978-1-4302-3942-0(5))*** Apress L. P.

Semko, Vitaly & Marruchi-Foino, Romain. Game & Graphics Programming for iOS & Android with OpenGL ES 2.0. 2012. (ENG., Illus.). 308p. pap. 44.99 ***(978-1-119-97591-5(3),*** Wrox) Wiley, John & Sons, Inc.

Silva, Vladimir. Pro Android Games. 2009. (ENG.). 300p. pap. 39.99 *(978-1-4302-2647-5(1))* Apress L. P.

Six, Jeff. Application Security for the Android Platform: Processes, Permissions, & Other Safeguards. 2011. (ENG.). 114p. pap. 17.99 ***(978-1-4493-1507-8(0))*** O'Reilly Media, Inc.

Stroud, Adam & Milette, Greg. Professional Android Sensor Programming. 2012. (ENG.). 552p. pap. 49.99 ***(978-1-118-18348-9(7),*** Wrox) Wiley, John & Sons, Inc.

Taylor, Richard & Zechner, Mario. Beginning Android Games. 2011. (ENG., Illus.). 688p. pap. 39.99 *(978-1-4302-3042-7(8))* Apress L. P.

Tyler, Jason. App Inventor for Android: Build Your Own Apps. 2011. (ENG., Illus.). 416p. pap. 34.99 *(978-1-119-99133-5(1),* Wiley) Wiley, John & Sons, Inc.

Wolber, David, et al. App Inventor. 2011. (ENG., Illus.). 384p. pap. 39.99 *(978-1-4493-9748-7(4))* O'Reilly Media, Inc.

Yaghmour, Karim. Embedded Android: Porting, Extending & Customizing. 2012. (ENG.). 200p. pap. 33.99 ***(978-1-4493-0829-2(5))*** O'Reilly Media, Inc.

Zheng, Pei, et al. Windows Phone 7 Programming for Android & iOS Developers. 2011. (ENG., Illus.). 360p. pap. 39.99 *(978-1-118-02197-2(5),* Wrox) Wiley, John & Sons, Inc.

ANDROIDS

Bar-Cohen, Yoseph, et al. The Coming Robot Revolution: Expectations & Fears about Emerging Intelligent, Humanlike Machines. 2009. (Illus.). 250p. 29.95 *(978-0-387-85348-2(3))* Springer.

Crawfis, Roger, et al. Android Game Programming for Dummies. 2012. (ENG.). 504p. pap. 34.99 ***(978-1-118-02774-5(4),*** For Dummies) Wiley, John & Sons, Inc.

Dufty, David F. How to Build an Android: The True Story of Philip K. Dick's Robotic Resurrection. 2012. (ENG., Illus.). 288p. 26.00 ***(978-0-8050-9551-7(9))*** Holt, Henry & Co.

Harada, Kensuke, et al, eds. Motion Planning for Humanoid Robots. 2010. (ENG., Illus.). xvi, 320p. 179.00 *(978-1-84996-219-3(7),* 1849962197) Springer.

Hornyak, Timothy N. Loving the Machine: The Art & Science of Japanese Robots, 1 vol. 2006. (ENG., Illus.). 160p. 26.95 *(978-4-7700-3012-2(6))* Kodansha America, Inc.

Starr, Brigitte. D13. 2010. 59p. pap. 28.95 *(978-0-557-23726-5(2))* Lulu Enterprises Inc.

Vadakkepat, Prahlad, et al, eds. Trends in Intelligent Robotics: 15th Robot World Cup & Congress, FIRA 2010, Bangalore, India, September15-19, 2010, Proceedings. 2010. (Communications in Computer & Information Science Ser.). xii, 370p. pap. 95.00 *(978-3-642-15809-4(9),* 3642158099) Springer.

Zehr, E. Paul. Inventing Iron Man: The Possibility of a Human Machine. 2011. (ENG., Illus.). 224p. 24.95 ***(978-1-4214-0226-0(2))*** Johns Hopkins Univ. Pr.

ANDROLOGY

Björndahl, Lars, et al, eds. A Practical Guide to Basic Laboratory Andrology. 2010. (ENG., Illus.). 348p. pap. 65.00 *(978-0-521-73590-2(4))* Cambridge Univ. Pr.

Callahan, Gerald N. Between XX & XY: Intersexuality & the Myth of Two Sexes. 2009. (ENG., Illus.). 208p. 24.95 *(978-1-55652-785-2(3))* Chicago Review Pr., Inc.

Giwercman, Aleksander, et al, eds. Clinical Andrology: EAU/ESAU Course Guidelines. 2010. (Illus.). 544p. 260.00 *(978-1-84184-650-4(5),* Informa Healthcare) Taylor & Francis Group.

Hauri, D. & Weidner, W., eds. Operative Andrology: Urologia Internationalis, Vol. 70. (Illus.). 62p. *(978-3-8055-7545-4(9))* Karger, S. AG.

Lunenfeld, Bruno, et al, eds. Textbook of Men's Health & Aging. 2nd rev. ed. 2008. (ENG., Illus.). 784p. 289.95 *(978-0-415-42580-3(8),* Informa Healthcare) Taylor & Francis Group GBR. Dist: Taylor & Francis Group.

Nieschlag, Eberhard, et al. Andrology: Male Reproductive Health & Dysfunction. 3rd ed. 2009. (Illus.). 628p. 189.00 *(978-3-540-78354-1(7),* 3540783547) Springer.

Patton, Philip E. & Battaglia, David E., eds. Office Andrology. 2010. (Contemporary Endocrinology Ser.). (Illus.). 320p. pap. 159.00 *(978-1-61737-491-3(1),* 1617374911) Humana Pr.

Schill, Wolf-Bernhard, et al, eds. Andrology for the Clinician. 2010. (Illus.). xxv, 645p. pap. 299.00 *(978-3-642-06218-6(0),* 3642062180) Springer.

Strumia, Renata, et al. Eating Disorder in Males. 2010. (Eating Disorders in the 21st Century Ser.). (Illus.). vi, 202p. 89.00 *(978-1-61668-489-1(5))* Nova Science Pubs., Inc.

ANDROPOGON SORGHUM

see Sorghum

ANDROS, EDMUND, SIR, 1637-1714

Andrews, Charles M., ed. Narratives of the Insurrections 1675 To 1690. 2007. 432p. 51.95 *(978-0-548-03501-5(6))* Kessinger Publishing, LLC.

Andrews, Charles McLean. Narratives of the Insurrections, 1675-1690. 2009. 300p. pap. *(978-1-151-12254-4(8));* 368p. pap. *(978-0-217-51640-2(8))* Books LLC.

—Narratives of the Insurrections, 1675-1690. (Original Narratives of Early American History Ser.). 414p. reprint ed. 98.00 *(978-0-7222-6521-5(2))* Library Reprints, Inc.

Andros Tracts. 2009. 210p. pap. 19.99 *(978-1-150-03520-3(X))* General Bks. LLC.

Ferguson, Henry. Essays in American History. 2009. 88p. pap. *(978-0-217-47227-2(3))* Books LLC.

—Essays in American History. 2009. 214p. 39.95 ***(978-1-104-80057-4(8));*** pap. 24.95 *(978-1-104-74405-2(8))* Kessinger Publishing, LLC.

ANDROSCOGGIN RIVER AND VALLEY

Sargent, David A. Remembering Lewiston-Auburn on the Mighty Androscoggin: River Views. 2010. 128p. pap. 19.99 *(978-1-59629-366-3(7))* History Pr., The.

ANECDOTES

see also Children—Anecdotes and Sayings; Exempla; Homiletical Illustrations; Last Words; Public Speaking—Introductions, Anecdotes, etc.; Table-Talk also subdivision Anecdotes under names of countries, cities, etc., names of individual persons, families, and corporate bodies, uniform titles of sacred works, and under classes of persons, ethnic groups, and topical headings for anecdotes about the subjects

Alworth, Sharon & Birnam, Bonnie. Letters to Fathers from Daughters: A Pathway to Hope & Healing. 2007. per. 16.95 *(978-1-932279-74-0(1))* Wyatt-MacKenzie Publishing.

Aqa Khan Kirmani, Abd al-Husayn & Vahuman, Harun. Rizvan. 2007. (PER., Illus.). 482p. *(978-1-59584-133-9(4))* Ketab Corp.

Barrick, Ken. The First 130 Feet: True Stories from the Dive Deck. 2011. 108p. 22.95 ***(978-1-4620-6304-8(7));*** pap. 12.95 ***(978-1-4620-6302-4(0))*** iUniverse, Inc.

Battles, Louise P. From the Mouths of Babes: Wee Wisdom from Little Ones. Date not set. (Illus.). 95p. pap. 5.95 *(978-1-885055-00-2(5))* Aiken-Argo Publishing Co.

Beem, Edgar Allen. Backyard Maine: Local Essays. 2010. 209p. pap. 15.00 *(978-0-88448-317-5(7))* Tilbury Hse. Pubs.

Burian, Al. Burn Collector: Collected Stories from One through Nine. 2010. (ENG.). 296p. pap. 16.00 *(978-1-60486-220-1(3))* PM Pr.

Burke, J. Bernard. Romantic Records of Distinguished Famili. 2006. pap. 31.95 *(978-1-4286-4234-8(X));* (ENG.). pap. 31.95 *(978-1-4286-4235-5(8))* Kessinger Publishing, LLC.

Cherry, Don. Don Cherry's Hockey Stories, Pt. 2. 2010. (ENG., Illus.). 272p. 25.00 *(978-0-385-67003-6(6))* Doubleday Canada, Ltd. CAN. Dist: Random Hse., Inc.

Clarkson, Jeremy. The World According to Clarkson. 2010. (ENG.). 352p. pap. 14.00 *(978-0-14-101789-1(9),* Penguin Global) Penguin Group (USA) Inc.

Cousens, Barbara. My Alexandria Tales. 2011. (Illus.). 26p. 12.95 *(978-0-615-32623-8(4))* Barbara Cousens Communications, LLC.

Crossley, Jack. Barmy Britain. 2008. (ENG., Illus.). 294p. pap. 15.95 *(978-1-84454-682-4(9))* Blake, John Publishing, Ltd. GBR. Dist: Independent Pubs. Group.

Crowley, Francis Edward. Stories from the Other Side: Thematic Memoirs. 5th ed. 2009. (ENG.). (C). pap. 82.00 *(978-0-558-20907-0(6))* Pearson Learning Solutions.

Droke, Maxwell, ed. The Speaker's Treasury of Anecdotes. 2011. 446p. 56.95 ***(978-1-258-10157-2(2))*** Literary Licensing, LLC.

Farnsworth, Janet Webb. Grandma Needs a Four-Wheel Drive: Adventure Travel for Seniors. 2011. (Illus.). pap. 12.95 *(978-1-60494-557-7(5))* Wheatmark.

Fogg, Walter. One Thousand Sayings of History: Presented As Pictures in Prose. 2011. 926p. 79.95 ***(978-1-258-10143-5(2))*** Literary Licensing, LLC.

Forbes, B. C. Little Bits about Big Men. 2011. 222p. 44.95 ***(978-1-258-08426-4(0))*** Literary Licensing, LLC.

Fromm, Ann McKenna. Steel City Love Song: Extraordinary Moments in Ordinary Lives. 2007. 188p. 30.99 *(978-1-4257-3195-3(3))* Xlibris Corp.

Fuller, Mary, ed. Pick & Mix: An Anthology. 2011. (Illus.). 103p. 22.50 ***(978-1-84624-635-7(0))*** Book Guild, Ltd. GBR. Dist: Trans-Atlantic Pubns., Inc.

Garner, Simon. Taxi! 2006. (Illus.). 160p. 24.95 *(978-0-7112-1544-3(8))* Lincoln, Frances Ltd. GBR. Dist: Perseus-PGW.

Greene, Sam T. Parables for Men of Management. 2011. 128p. 40.95 ***(978-1-258-03467-2(0))*** Literary Licensing, LLC.

Hammack, Aubrey. The Winning Edge: Lessons from Billy Henderson. 2011. pap. *(978-0-9796462-6-3(X))* Stroud & Hall Publishing.

Hanson, Eric. A Book of Ages: An Eccentric Miscellany of Great & Offbeat Moments in the Lives of the Famous & Infamous, Ages 1 To 100. 2008. (ENG., Illus.). 320p. 19.95 *(978-0-307-40894-5(9),* Harmony) Crown Publishing Group.

Harris, Adeline. An Unconventional Love. 2010. (ENG., Illus.). 276p. 11.95 *(978-0-00-735425-2(8))* HarperCollins Pubs. Ltd. GBR. Dist: Independent Pubs. Group.

Hindley, Charles, ed. Tavern Anecdotes & Sayings: Including the Origin of Signs, & Reminiscences Connected with Taverns, Coffee-houses, Clubs, Etc. 2011. (Cambridge Library Collection - History Ser.). (ENG., Illus.). 438p. pap. 32.99 ***(978-1-108-03889-8(1))*** Cambridge Univ. Pr.

Hirschman, Dale. The Cowboy Call: Living for Jesus in the Western World. 2011. pap. 12.99 *(978-1-61739-417-1(3))* Tate Publishing & Enterprises, LLC.

Humayunfar, Izzat Allah & Babauf, Mahdi. Dastanha-Yi Sipid Va Siyah-I Tarikhi. 2008. (PER.). 151p. *(978-1-59584-152-0(0))* Ketab Corp.

Kaplan, Cynthia. Leave the Building Quickly. 2008. (P. S. Ser.). 240p. pap. 13.95 *(978-0-06-054852-0(5),* HarperPerennial) HarperCollins Pubs.

Lang, Gregory E. Why a Son Needs a Dad: 100 Reasons. 2007. (ENG., Illus.). 128p. 14.95 *(978-1-58182-633-3(8),* Cumberland Hse.) Sourcebooks, Inc.

Lebrecht, Norman. Book of Musical Anecdotes. 2010. (ENG.). 384p. pap. 23.99 *(978-1-4391-9994-7(9),* Free Pr.) Free Pr.

Lemon, Mark. The Jest Book, the Choicest Anecdotes & Sayings. 2011. 212p. pap. 14.99 ***(978-1-61203-308-2(3))*** Bottom of the Hill Publishing.

Lewis, Roger. What Am I Still Doing Here? My Years as Me. (ENG.). 2012. 384p. pap. 12.95 ***(978-1-4447-0869-1(4))*** 2011. (Illus.). 368p. 32.95 ***(978-1-4447-0868-4(6))*** Hodder General Publishing Div. GBR. (Hodder & Stoughton). Dist: Independent Pubs. Group.

Lincecum, Jerry B. & Redshaw, Peggy A., eds. First-born, Middle Child, Caboose: Stories about birth order & family Relationships. 2007. (Illus.). 150p. pap. 20.00 *(978-0-9793541-0-6(2))* Big Barn Pr.

Mahony, Patrick. Barbed Wit & Malicious Humor. 2011. 190p. 42.95 ***(978-1-258-06925-4(3))*** Literary Licensing, LLC.

May, James. Car Fever: The Car Bore's Essential Companion. 2010. (ENG.). 304p. pap. 12.95 *(978-0-340-99455-9(X),* Hodder & Stoughton) Hodder General Publishing Div. GBR. Dist: Independent Pubs. Group.

A

[Pell, Robert Conger]. The Companion after-Dinner Table-Talk by Chetwood Evelyn, Esq [Pseud]. 2006. 196p. per. 18.99 *(978-1-4255-1580-5(0))* MPublishing.

Rahimi, Kheirollah. Laugh Your Way to Wisdom. 2010. 118p. pap. 19.99 *(978-1-4500-9946-2(7))* Xlibris Corp.

Schusteff, Arlene, compiled by. Special Gifts: Women Writers on the Heartache, the Happiness & the Hope of Raising a Special Needs Child. 2007. 228p. per. 15.00 *(978-1-932279-59-7(8))* Wyatt-MacKenzie Publishing.

Sedaris, Amy. I Like You: Hospitality under the Influence. 2008. (ENG.). 304p. pap. 15.99 *(978-0-446-69677-7(3))* Grand Central Publishing.

Shapiro, Sidney. Schwartz & the Mega-Super-Ultra-Stupendous Ice Cream Sundae. 2010. 21p. 10.30 *(978-0-557-04722-2(6))* Lulu Enterprises Inc.

Strike, Anna Wafula. In My Dreams I Dance. 2010. (ENG., Illus.). 278p. 11.95 *(978-0-00-735428-3(2))* HarperCollins Pubs. Ltd. GBR. Dist: Independent Pubs. Group.

Stubbs, Les. 2000 Weddings but No Funerals! 2011. 228p. pap. 16.95 ***(978-1-4670-0729-0(3))*** AuthorHouse.

Thomas, John B. Selected Stories, Quotations & Aphorisms. 2011. 312p. 50.95 ***(978-1-258-03944-8(3))*** Literary Licensing, LLC.

Thomas, Lowell. Pageant of Life. 2011. 286p. 48.95 ***(978-1-258-09284-9(0))*** Literary Licensing, LLC.

Thoms, William John, ed. Anecdotes & Traditions, Illustrative of Early English History & Literature, Derived from Manuscript Sources. (Camden Society, London, Publications, First Ser.: No. 5). reprint ed. 47.50 *(978-0-404-50105-1(2))* AMS Pr., Inc.

Thornborrow, Jacqi. Be Forty & Fabulously Naughty. 2011. 64p. pap. 10.00 ***(978-1-60976-302-2(5)***, Eloquent Bks.) AEG Literary Publishing Services, Inc.

Turkish Evening Entertainments. 2006. 392p. per. 26.99 *(978-1-4255-4162-0(3))* MPublishing.

Various. 100 y más historias Reales. 2009. (SPA.). 326p. pap. 19.99 *(978-1-59835-124-8(9)*, CBH Bks.) Cambridge BrickHouse, Inc.

Waddell, Michael & Schoby, Mike. Hunting Booger Bottom: Life Lessons from the Field. 2011. 240p. pap. 14.99 *(978-0-06-173354-3(7)*, Harper Paperbacks) HarperCollins Pubs.

Watkins, John. Memoirs of the Life & Writings of the Right Honourable Lord Byron. 2009. 194p. pap. *(978-0-217-86437-4(6))* Books LLC.

Weil, Steven E. Ask Papa Jack: Wisdom from the World's Oldest CEO. 2009. (ENG.). 15.95 *(978-1-55566-428-2(8))* Johnson Bks.

Wilson, Todd. Don't Believe It! (Illus.). 192p. 15.95 *(978-1-85479-620-2(8))*; pap. 7.95 *(978-1-85479-683-7(6))* O'Mara, Michael Bks., Ltd. GBR. Dist: Trans-Atlantic Pubns., Inc.

Ziglar, Zig. Something to Smile About: Encouragement & Inspiration for Life's Ups & Downs, 0 vols. 2009. 226p. pap. 11.99 *(978-0-7852-9744-4(8))* Nelson, Thomas Inc.

ANELASTICITY

see Internal Friction

ANEMIA

see also Aplastic Anemia; Blood; Hemoglobinopathy; Hemorrhage; Hookworm Disease; Iron Deficiency Anemia; Leukemia; Sickle Cell Anemia; Thalassemia

Aapro, Matti & San Miguel, Jesús, eds. Epoetin Beta (NeoRecormon(r)) Vol. 67, Suppl. 1: Energising Anaemia Management for Patients with Cancer: Highlights from the Proceedings of Roche-Sponsored Symposium Madrid, Spain, May 7-9, 2004. (Illus.). *(978-3-8055-7861-5(X))* Karger, S. AG.

Balducci, Lodovico, et al, eds. Anemia in the Elderly. 2008. pap. 44.95 *(978-0-387-09791-6(0))* Springer.

Bardes, Charles L. Pale Faces: The Masks of Anemia. 2008. (BLP Pathography Ser.). (ENG., Illus.). 192p. 20.00 *(978-1-934137-10-9(3))* Bellevue Literary Pr.

Chan, Joyce Chee Wun. Pernicious Anaemia in Chinese. 2011. 164p. pap. ***(978-3-8443-8434-0(7))*** Lambert Academic Publishing.

Ershler, William B. & Bennett, John M., eds. Anemia in the Elderly. 2007. (Illus.). 145p. 129.00 *(978-0-387-49505-7(3)*, 0387495053) Springer.

Foote, MaryAnn, et al. Erythropoietins, Erythropoietic Factors, & Erythropoiesis: Molecular, Cellular, Preclinical, & Clinical Biology. Elliott, Steven G. & Foote, MaryAnn, eds. Molineux, Graham, ed. 2nd ed. 2009. (Milestones in Drug Therapy Ser.). (ENG., Illus.). xviii, 326p. 219.00 *(978-3-7643-8694-8(0))* Birkhauser Boston.

Garrison, Cheryl. The Iron Disorders Institute Guide to Anemia. 2nd rev. ed. 2009. (ENG., Illus.). 496p. pap. 18.99 *(978-1-58182-692-0(3)*, Cumberland Hse.) Sourcebooks, Inc.

Huch, Renate & Breymann, Christian. Anaemia in pregnancy & the Puerperium. 2006. (UNI-MED Science Ser.). (Illus.). 96p. *(978-3-89599-990-1(3))* UNI-MED Verlag AG.

Ifudu, Onyekachi, ed. Renal Anemia: Conflicts & Controversies: Conflicts & Controversies. 2010. 160p. pap. 84.95 *(978-90-481-6045-7(6)*, 9048160456) Springer.

Mintz, Paul D. Transfusion Therapy: Clinical Principles & Practice. 3rd ed. 2010. *(978-1-56395-307-1(2)*, AABB Pr.) American Assn. of Blood Banks.

Molineux, Graham, et al, eds. Erythropoietins & Erythropoiesis: Molecular, Cellular, Preclinical, & Clinical Biology. 2006. (Milestones in Drug Therapy Ser.). (Illus.). X, 269p. pap. 99.00 *(978-3-7643-7542-3(6)*, 3764375426) Birkhauser Boston.

Nowrousian, Mohammad R., ed. Recombinant Human Erythropoietin (rhEPO) in Clinical Oncology: Scientific & Clinical Aspects of Anemia in Cancer. 2nd ed. 2007. (Illus.). 400p. 159.00 *(978-3-211-25223-9(1)*, 3211252231) Springer.

Sahak, Mohammad Nadir. Anemia & Malaria among Pregnant Women in Laghman, Afghanistan. 2010. 60p. pap. *(978-3-639-23848-8(6))* VDM Verlag Dr. Mueller e.K.

Schindler, Detlev & Hoehn, Holger. Fanconi Anemia: A Paradigmatic Disease for the Understanding of Cancer & Aging. 2007. (Monographs in Human Genetics: Vol. 15). *(978-3-8055-8277-3(3))* Karger, S. AG.

Shinde, Swati D. & Shinde, Ramkrishna L. Anaemia in Pregnancy. 2011. 64p. pap. ***(978-3-8454-1077-7(9))*** Lambert Academic Publishing.

Singh, Ajay K., et al. Anemia & Heart Failure, an Issue of Heart Failure Clinics. 2010. (Clinics Internal Medicine Ser.: 6-3). (ENG., Illus.). xviii, 271p. 94.00 *(978-1-4377-2456-1(6)*, Saunders) Elsevier - Health Sciences Div.

Whitehouse, Beth. The Match: Savior Siblings & One Family's Battle to Heal Their Daughter. 2011. pap. 16.00 *(978-0-8070-0121-9(X))* 2010. (ENG.). 272p. 24.95 *(978-0-8070-7286-8(9))* Beacon Pr.

Wick, Manfred & Pinggera, Germar-Michael. Clinical Aspects & Laboratory. Iron Metabolism, Anemias. 2010. 219p. pap. 49.95 *(978-3-7091-0086-8(0))* Springer.

ANEMIA, DREPANOCYTIC

see Sickle Cell Anemia

ANESTHESIA

see also Analgesia; Anesthesia in Dentistry; Anesthesia in Obstetrics; Anesthesia in Ophthalmology; Anesthesia in Veterinary Surgery; Anesthesiology; Anesthetics; Hypnotism—Therapeutic Use; Local Anesthesia; Muscle Relaxants; Pediatric Anesthesia; Peridural Anesthesia

Abadir, Adel R. & Harahap, Marwali, eds. Anesthesia & Analgesia in Dermatologic Surgery. 2008. (Basic & Clinical Dermatology Ser.). (ENG., Illus.). 232p. 200.00 *(978-0-8493-3698-0(8)*, Informa Healthcare) Taylor & Francis Group.

Agasti, T. K. Textbook of Anesthesia for Postgraduates. 2010. (Illus.). 600p. 105.00 ***(978-93-80704-94-4(1))*** Jaypee Brothers, Medical Pubs. IND. Dist: BookMasters Distribution Services (BDS).

Aitkenhead, Alan R., et al. Textbook of Anaesthesia. 5th rev. ed. 2007. (ENG., Illus.). 868p. per. 148.00 *(978-0-443-10078-9(0)*, Churchill Livingstone) Elsevier - Health Sciences Div.

Al-Shaikh, Baha & Stacey, Simon. Essentials of Anaesthetic Equipment. 3rd rev. ed. 2007. (ENG., Illus.). 240p. pap. 87.95 *(978-0-443-10087-1(X)*, Churchill Livingstone) Elsevier - Health Sciences Div.

Allaria, Biagio, ed. Practical Issues in Anesthesia & Intensive Care. 2012. (ENG., Illus.). xii, 172p. pap. 39.95 ***(978-88-470-2459-5(5)***, 8847024595) Springer.

Allman, Keith, et al, eds. Anaesthesia & Emergencies in Anaesthesia, Pack. 2007. (Oxford Handbooks Ser.). (Illus.). 1088p. pap. 89.95 *(978-0-19-923940-5(1))* Oxford Univ. Pr., Inc.

Allman, Keith & Wilson, Iain, eds. Oxford Handbook of Anaesthesia for PDAs. 2nd ed. 2007. (Oxford Handbooks Ser.). (ENG., Illus.). 1240p. cd-rom 67.50 *(978-0-19-922717-4(9))* Oxford Univ. Pr., Inc.

Allman, Keith, et al. Emergencies in Anaesthesia. Allman, Keith et al, eds. 2nd ed. 2009. (Emergencies in Ser.). (ENG., Illus.). 560p. pap. 42.50 *(978-0-19-956082-0(X))* Oxford Univ. Pr., Inc.

—Oxford Handbook of Anaesthesia. 3rd ed. 2011. (ENG., Illus.). 1344p. (Orig.). 59.95 *(978-0-19-958404-8(4))* Oxford Univ. Pr., Inc.

Anaesthesia, Pain, Intensive Care & Emergency A. P. I. C. E. 2007. (Illus.). 423p. pap. 99.00 *(978-88-470-0772-7(0))* Springer.

Anesthesia Board Review Practice Questions 2007. 2007. spiral bd. 189.95 *(978-1-889344-86-7(9))* MEDTEXT Medical World, Inc.

Anesthesia Cross Coder. 2006. pap. 174.95 *(978-1-56337-889-8(2)*, OP591407CSD) OptumInsight, Inc.

Antognini, Joseph E., ed. Neural Mechanisms of Anesthesia. 2010. (Contemporary Clinical Neuroscience Ser.). (Illus.). 480p. pap. 239.00 *(978-1-61737-294-0(3)*, 1617372943) Humana Pr.

ASPAN, et al. Certification Review for PeriAnesthesia Nursing. 3rd ed. 2012. (ENG.). 272p. pap. 56.95 ***(978-1-4557-0970-0(0)***, Saunders) Elsevier - Health Sciences Div.

Astuto, Marinella, ed. Basics. 2008. (Anaesthesia, Intensive Care & Pain in Neonates & Children Ser.). (Illus.). xix, 257p. pap. 109.00 *(978-88-470-0654-6(6))* Springer.

Atlee, John L. Complications in Anesthesia. 2nd rev. ed. 2006. (ENG., Illus.). 1040p. 164.00 *(978-1-4160-2215-2(5)*, Saunders) Elsevier - Health Sciences Div.

BARASH & Barash. Clinical Anesthesia. Barash, Paul G. et al, eds. 6th rev. ed. 2009. (ENG., Illus.). 1760p. 210.99 *(978-0-7817-8763-5(7))* Lippincott Williams & Wilkins.

—Handbook of Clinical Anesthesia. Barash, Paul G. et al, eds. 6th rev. ed. 2009. (ENG., Illus.). 1146p. pap. 59.99 *(978-0-7817-8948-6(6))* Lippincott Williams & Wilkins.

Barbeito, Atilio & Shaw, Andrew. Thoracic Anesthesia: Ready to Practice Package (Set2) 2012. (ENG., Illus.). 400p. pap. 90.00 *(978-0-07-162568-5(2)*, 0071625682) McGraw-Hill Professional Publishing.

Barbeito, Atilio, et al. Thoracic Anesthesia: Ready to Practice. 2012. ***(978-0-07-162567-8(4))***; (ENG., Illus.). 528p. pap. 75.00 ***(978-0-07-162566-1(6)***, 0071625666) McGraw-Hill Professional Publishing.

Barker, Julian M., et al. The Clinical Anaesthesia Viva Book. 2nd rev. ed. 2009. (ENG., Illus.). 448p. pap. 72.00 *(978-0-521-72018-2(4))* Cambridge Univ. Pr.

Barnard, Matthew & Martin, Bruce. Cardiac Anaesthesia. 2010. (ENG., Illus.). 624p. pap. 75.00 *(978-0-19-920910-1(3))* Oxford Univ. Pr., Inc.

Bigelow, Henry Jacob. Surgical Anaesthesia; Addresses, & Other Papers. 2009. 226p. pap. 20.31 *(978-0-217-56537-0(9))* General Bks. LLC.

Boezaart, André, ed. Anesthesia & Orthopaedic Surgery. 2006. (ENG., Illus.). 544p. 207.00 *(978-0-07-144686-0(9)*, 0071446869) McGraw-Hill Professional Publishing.

Boggs, Steve. Letters to Dinah. 2011. 224p. 24.59 ***(978-1-4634-4287-3(4))*** AuthorHouse.

Borshoff, David. Anaesthetic Crisis Manual. 2011. (ENG.). 60p. spiral bd. 29.99 ***(978-0-521-27986-4(0))*** Cambridge Univ. Pr.

Bowman-Howard, Michelle. Anesthesia Review. 2nd rev. ed. 2006. (ENG., Illus.). 368p. 66.95 *(978-0-7817-9444-2(7))* Lippincott Williams & Wilkins.

Bricker, Simon. The Anaesthesia Science Viva Book. 2nd ed. 2008. (ENG., Illus.). 442p. pap. 81.00 *(978-0-521-72644-3(1))* Cambridge Univ. Pr.

Brown, David L. Atlas of Regional Anesthesia. 4th ed. 2010. (ENG., Illus.). 416p. 195.00 *(978-1-4160-6397-1(8)*, Saunders) Elsevier - Health Sciences Div.

Burch, Thomas M., et al. Conquer the PTE Exam. 2007. (ENG., Illus.). 544p. pap. 98.95 *(978-1-4160-3833-7(7)*, Saunders) Elsevier - Health Sciences Div.

Burkey, Dell. Anesthesia Pocket Consult: Regional Anesthesia PDA: Print + IPod. 2008. (Illus.). cd-rom 69.95 *(978-1-4160-3345-5(9)*, Saunders) Elsevier - Health Sciences Div.

Calder, Ian & Pearce, Adrian, eds. Core Topics in Airway Management. 2nd rev. ed. 2010. (ENG., Illus.). 330p. 88.00 *(978-0-521-11188-1(9))* Cambridge Univ. Pr.

Carroll, Gwendolyn L., ed. Small Animal Anesthesia & Analgesia. 2008. (ENG., Illus.). 283p. 89.99 *(978-0-8138-0230-5(X)*, Wiley-Blackwell) Wiley, John & Sons, Inc.

Cashman, Jeremy & Grounds, Michael, eds. Recent Advances in Anaesthesia & Intensive Care: Volume 24. 2007. (Recent Advances Ser.). (ENG., Illus.). 264p. 82.00 *(978-0-521-70649-0(1))* Cambridge Univ. Pr.

Chestnut, David H. Year Book of Anesthesiology & Pain Management 2010. 2010. (Year Bks.: 2010). (ENG.). 176.00 *(978-0-323-06824-6(3)*, Mosby) Elsevier - Health Sciences Div.

Chestnutt, David. Year Book of Anesthesiology & Pain Management 2011 - E-Book1. 2011. E-Book ***(978-0-323-08728-5(0)***, Mosby Canada) Elsevier - Health Sciences Div.

Chu, Larry F. & Fuller, Andrea. A Visual Guide to Anesthesia Procedures. 2011. (Point of Care Essentials Ser.). (ENG.). 30p. spiral bd. 31.99 ***(978-1-4511-3010-2(4))*** Lippincott Williams & Wilkins.

Chu, Larry F., et al. A Visual Guide to Regional Anesthesia. 2011. (Point of Care Essentials Ser.). (ENG.). 30p. spiral bd. 31.99 ***(978-1-4511-3012-6(0))*** Lippincott Williams & Wilkins.

Clark, Morris S. & Brunick, Ann. Handbook of Nitrous Oxide & Oxygen Sedation. 3rd rev. ed. 2007. (ENG., Illus.). 256p. pap. 55.95 *(978-0-323-04827-9(7)*, Mosby) Elsevier - Health Sciences Div.

Classroom Productions. Procedural Sedation. 2010. (Concept Media: Educational Videos Ser.). (ENG.). (C). 650.00 *(978-1-111-13656-7(4)*, Concept Media) Delmar Cengage Learning.

Cold, Georg E. & Dahl, Bent L. Topics in Neuroanaesthesia & Intensive Care: Experimental & Clinical Studies upon Cerebral Circulation, Metabolism & Intracranial Pressure. 2012. (ENG.). xiv, 416p. pap. 201.00 *(978-3-642-07537-7(1)*, 3642075371) Springer.

Connelly. Review of Clinical Anesthesia. Connelly, Neil Roy & Silverman, David G., eds. 5th rev. ed. 2009. (ENG., Illus.). 320p. pap. 69.99 *(978-0-7817-8951-6(6))* Lippincott Williams & Wilkins.

Contexo Media, creator. Coding & Billing for Anesthesia/Pain Management: A Comprehensive & Illustrative Specialty Guide. 2011. (Illus.). 526p. spiral bd. 199.95 *(978-1-58383-702-3(7))* Contexo Media.

Coursin, Douglas B., et al, eds. Anesthesia & Co-Existing Disease. 2007. (Cambridge Pocket Clinicians Ser.). (ENG.). 396p. per. 55.00 *(978-0-521-70938-5(5))* Cambridge Univ. Pr.

Cousins, Michael J., et al, eds. Neural Blockade: In Clinical Anesthesia & Pain Medicine. 4th rev. ed. 2008. (ENG., Illus.). 1360p. 234.99 *(978-0-7817-7388-1(1))* Lippincott Williams & Wilkins.

Cox, Felicia, ed. Perioperative Pain Management. 2008. (ENG., Illus.). 336p. pap., instr.'s hndbk. ed. 83.99 *(978-1-4051-8077-1(3)*, Wiley-Blackwell) Wiley, John & Sons, Inc.

CPT Easy Link 2007 Anesthesia. 2007. per. 116.96 *(978-1-57066-426-7(9))* Practice Management Information Corp.

Cram101 Textbook Reviews. Outlines & Highlights for Anesthesia & Co-Existing Disease by Roberta L Hines, Isbn: 9781416039983 1416039988. 2011. 446p. pap. 36.95 ***(978-1-61812-193-6(6))*** Cram101 Inc.

—Outlines & Highlights for Benumofs Airway Management by Carin Hagberg, Isbn: 9780323022330. 2011. 224p. pap. 30.95 ***(978-1-61461-439-5(3))*** Cram101 Inc.

—Outlines & Highlights for Trauma Anesthesia by Charles Smith. 2011. 138p. pap. 28.95 ***(978-1-61905-616-9(X))*** Cram101 Inc.

Cram101 Textbook Reviews & Cram101 Textbook Reviews. Outlines & Highlights for Clinical Anesthesia by Paul G Barash, Isbn: 9780781787635 0781787637. 2011. 688p. pap. 42.95 ***(978-1-61490-398-7(0))*** Cram101 Inc.

—Outlines & Highlights for Core Topics in Airway Management by Adrian Pearce Edited by Ian Calder, Isbn: 9780521869102. 2011. 92p. pap. 27.95 ***(978-1-61461-222-3(6))*** Cram101 Inc.

—Outlines & Highlights for Evidence-Based Practice of Anesthesiology: Expert Consult 2nd by Lee A. Fleisher, ISBN. 2011. 202p. pap. 30.95 ***(978-1-61461-620-7(5))*** Cram101 Inc.

—Outlines & Highlights for Nurse Anesthesia by John J Nagelhout, Karen L Plaus, Isbn: 9781416050254. 2011. 520p. pap. 38.95 ***(978-1-61461-722-8(8))*** Cram101 Inc.

—Outlines & Highlights for Yao & Artusios Anesthesiology by Fun-Sun F Yao, Isbn: 9780781765107 0781765102. 2011. 464p. pap. 36.95 ***(978-1-61812-050-2(6))*** Cram101 Inc.

Crozier, Thomas Allen. Anaesthesia for Minimally Invasive Surgery. 2010. (ENG.). 210p. pap. 45.00 *(978-0-521-17977-5(7))* Cambridge Univ. Pr.

Dahaba, Ashraf. Using the Non Depolarizing Neuromuscular Blocking Agent Vecuronium in Patients with Liver Dysfunction. 2008. 124p. pap. *(978-3-8364-9089-4(7))* VDM Verlag Dr. Mueller e.K.

Davis, James B., ed. 2008 Coding Guide Family Practice. 2007. (ENG.). 750p. per. 129.95 *(978-1-57066-508-0(7))* Practice Management Information Corp.

Dodds, Chris, et al. Anaesthesia for the Elderly Patient. 2007. (Oxford Anaesthesia Library). (ENG., Illus.). 160p. per. 24.95 *(978-0-19-923462-2(0))* Oxford Univ. Pr., Inc.

Dormandy, Thomas. The Worst of Evils: The Fight Against Pain. 2006. (ENG., Illus.). 560p. 39.00 *(978-0-300-11322-8(6))* Yale Univ. Pr.

Dorsch, Jerry A. & Dorsch, Susan E. A Practical Approach to Anesthesia Equipment. 2010. (ENG.). 750p. pap. 84.99 *(978-0-7817-9867-9(1))* Lippincott Williams & Wilkins.

Drain, Cecil B. & Odom-Forren, Jan. Perianesthesia Nursing: A Critical Care Approach. 5th ed. 2008. (ENG., Illus.). 888p. 84.95 *(978-1-4160-3474-2(9)*, Saunders) Elsevier - Health Sciences Div.

Duke, James. Anesthesia Secrets. 4th ed. 2010. (Secrets Ser.). (ENG., Illus.). 592p. pap. 54.95 *(978-0-323-06524-5(4)*, Mosby) Elsevier - Health Sciences Div.

Elisha, Sass. Case Studies in Nurse Anesthesia. rev. ed. 2009. 666p. pap. 80.95 *(978-0-7637-6387-9(X))* Jones & Bartlett Learning, LLC.

Ely, E. Wesley & Pandharipande, Pratik. Sedation & Analgesia in the ICU: Pharmacology, Protocolization, & Clinical Consequences. 2009. (Clinics: Internal Medicine Ser.: 25-3). (ENG., Illus.). xvi, 432p. 99.00 *(978-1-4377-1203-2(7)*, Saunders) Elsevier - Health Sciences Div.

Euliano, T. Y. Essential Anesthesia: From Science to Practice. 2nd ed. 2011. (ENG., Illus.). 214p. (C). pap. 49.00 *(978-0-521-14945-7(2))* Cambridge Univ. Pr.

Farag, Ehab, ed. Anesthesia for Spine Surgery. 2012. (ENG., Illus.). 488p. 125.00 ***(978-1-107-00531-0(0))*** Cambridge Univ. Pr.

Flecknell, Paul. Laboratory Animal Anaesthesia. 3rd ed. 2009. (ENG., Illus.). 304p. (C). 131.00 *(978-0-12-369376-1(4)*, Academic Pr.) Elsevier Science & Technology Bks.

Fleisher, Lee A. Evidence-Based Practice of Anesthesiology: Expert Consult - Online & Print. 2nd ed. 2009. (ENG., Illus.). 544p. pap. 99.95 *(978-1-4160-5996-7(2)*, Saunders) Elsevier - Health Sciences Div.

Fleisher, Lee A. & Roizen, Michael F. Essence of Anesthesia Practice: Expert Consult - Online & Print. 3rd ed. 2010. (ENG.). 768p. 86.95 *(978-1-4377-1720-4(9)*, Saunders) Elsevier - Health Sciences Div.

Fontes, Manuel L. & Malhotra, Vinod, eds. Yao & Artusio's Anesthesiology: Problem-Oriented Patient Management. 7th rev. ed. 2011. (ENG., Illus.). 1376p. 119.00 ***(978-1-4511-0265-9(8))*** Lippincott Williams & Wilkins.

Foot, Carole. Examination Intensive Care. 2nd ed. 2011. (ENG.). (C). pap. 110.00 ***(978-0-7295-3962-3(8)***, Churchill Livingstone) Elsevier - Health Sciences Div.

Friedberg, Barry L. Anesthesia in Cosmetic Surgery. 2007. (ENG., Illus.). 284p. 107.00 *(978-0-521-87090-0(9))* Cambridge Univ. Pr.

Fuller, Andrea & Chu, Larry F. Manual of Clinical Anesthesiology. 2011. (Illus.). 1300p. pap. 89.95 *(978-0-7817-7379-9(2))* Lippincott Williams & Wilkins.

Gallagher, Christopher. Anesthesia Unplugged, Second Edition. 2nd ed. 2012. (ENG., Illus.). 480p. pap. 110.00 ***(978-0-07-176717-0(7)***, 0071767177) McGraw-Hill Professional Publishing.

Gallagher, Christopher, et al, eds. Core Clinical Competencies in Anesthesiology. 2010. (ENG.). 486p. (C). pap. 85.00 *(978-0-521-14413-1(2))* Cambridge Univ. Pr.

Gallagher, Christopher, et al. Anesthesia Unplugged: A Step-by-Step Guide to Techniques & Procedures. 2006. (ENG., Illus.). 368p. (C). pap. 110.00 *(978-0-07-145816-0(6)*, 0071458166) McGraw-Hill Professional Publishing.

Gallagher, Christopher J. Board Stiff Three: Preparation for Anesthesia Orals. 3rd ed. 2008. (ENG.). 440p. pap. 87.95 *(978-0-7020-3092-5(9)*, Butterworth-Heinemann) Elsevier - Health Sciences Div.

Gallagher, Christopher J. & Issenberg, S. Barry. Simulation in Anesthesia. 2006. (ENG., Illus.). 512p. 124.00 *(978-1-4160-3135-2(9)*, Saunders) Elsevier - Health Sciences Div.

Galley, Helen F. & Webster, Nigel, eds. Anaesthesia Science. 2006. (ENG., Illus.). 472p. 173.95 *(978-0-7279-1773-7(0))* Wiley, John & Sons, Inc.

Garrioch, Magnus & Murray, Bosseau. Anaesthesia. 2011. (ENG., Illus.). 192p. pap. 39.95 *(978-1-84076-077-4(X))* Manson Publishing, Ltd. GBR. Dist: Thieme Medical Pubs., Inc.

Girard-Powell, Valerie. Pain, Analgesia & Anesthesia, an Issue of Perioperative Nursing Clinics. 2009. (Clinics: Nursing Ser.: 4-4). (ENG., Illus.). xiv, 477p. 61.00 *(978-1-4377-1749-5(7)*, Saunders) Elsevier - Health Sciences Div.

Glass, Peter S. A. Ambulatory Anesthesia, an Issue of Anesthesiology Clinics. 2010. (Clinics: Surgery Ser.: 28-2). (ENG., Illus.). xviii, 185p. 105.00 *(978-1-4377-1796-9(9)*, Saunders) Elsevier - Health Sciences Div.

Gold, Barbara & Gross, Wendy L. Anesthesia Outside the Operating Room, an Issue of Anesthesiology Clinics. 2009. (Clinics: Surgery Ser.: 27-1). (ENG., Illus.). 240p. 99.00 *(978-1-4377-0453-2(0)*, Saunders) Elsevier - Health Sciences Div.

Goldschneider, Kenneth, et al, eds. Clinical Pediatric Anesthesia: A Case-Based Handbook. 2012. (ENG., Illus.). 784p. pap. 79.99 ***(978-0-19-976449-5(2))*** Oxford Univ. Pr., Inc.

Gullo, A., ed. Anaesthesia, Pain, Intensive Care & Emergency Medicine - A. P. I. C. E. Proceedings of the 20th Postgraduate Course in Critical Care Medicine, Trieste, Italy, November 18-21 2005. 2006. xxviii, 867p. pap. 119.00 (978-88-470-0406-1(3), 8847004063) Springer.

Gullo, Antonino, ed. Anaesthesia, Pharmacology, Intensive Care & Emergency A. P. I. C. E. Proceedings of the 23rd Annual Meeting - International Symposium on Critical Care Medicine. 2011. (Illus.). 380p. pap. 99.00 (978-88-470-2013-9(1), 8847020131) Springer.

Gupta, Arun K. & Gelb, Adrian W. Essentials of Neuroanesthesia & Neurointensive Care: A Volume in Essentials of Anesthesia & Critical Care. 2008. (Essentials of Anesthesia & Critical Care Ser.). (ENG., Illus.). 368p. pap. 79.95 (978-1-4160-4653-0(4), Saunders) Elsevier - Health Sciences Div.

Gwinnutt, Carl L. Clinical Anaesthesia. 3rd ed. 2008. (Lecture Notes Ser.). (ENG., Illus.). 184p. pap. 45.95 (978-1-4051-7038-3(7), Wiley-Blackwell) Wiley, John & Sons, Inc.

Gwinnutt, Carl L. & Gwinnutt, Matthew. Lecture Notes Clinical Anaesthesia. 4th ed. 2012. (Lecture Notes Ser.: 39). (ENG.). 208p. pap. 42.95 (978-0-470-65892-5(4), Wiley-Blackwell) Wiley, John & Sons, Inc.

Haller, Guy. Patient Safety Indicators in Anaesthesi. 2010. 252p. pap. (978-3-8383-3883-5(9)) Lambert Academic Publishing.

Hardman, Jonathan G., et al, eds. Consent, benefit, & risk in anaesthetic Practice. 2009. (ENG., Illus.). 352p. pap. 85.00 (978-0-19-929687-3(1)) Oxford Univ. Pr., Inc.

Heitmiller, Eugenie S. & Schwengel, Deborah A. Johns Hopkins Anesthesiology Handbook: Mobile Medicine Series. 2009. (Mobile Medicine Ser.). (ENG., Illus.). 544p. pap. 56.95 (978-1-4160-5916-5(4), Mosby) Elsevier - Health Sciences Div.

Hertzog, Milo & Kuhn, Zelig. General Anesthesia Research Developments. 2010. (Advances in Biology & Medicine (Series Editor - Tsisana Shartava, M. D. - Tbilisi, Georgia) Ser.). 145.00 (978-1-60876-395-5(1), Nova Biomedical Bks.) Nova Science Pubs., Inc.

Hines, Roberta L. & Marschall, Katherine. Stoelting's Anesthesia & Co-Existing Disease: Expert Consult - Online & Print. 6th ed. 2012. (ENG., Illus.). 688p. 169.00 (978-1-4557-0082-0(7), Saunders) Elsevier - Health Sciences Div.

Hines, Roberta L. & Marschall, Katherine E. Anesthesia & Coexisting Disease. 5th ed. 2009. (ENG.). instr.'s hndbk. ed. 182.00 (978-1-4160-3996-9(1), Saunders) Elsevier - Health Sciences Div.

—Handbook for Stoelting's Anesthesia & Co-Existing Disease. 3rd ed. 2009. (ENG., Illus.). 525p. pap. 64.95 (978-1-4160-3997-6(X), Saunders) Elsevier - Health Sciences Div.

Hopkins, Bodenha, et al. Practical Ultrasound in Anesthesia for Critical Care & Pain Management. 2007. (ENG., Illus.). 288p. 250.00 (978-0-8247-2886-1(6), Informa Healthcare) Taylor & Francis Group.

Hopkins, Richard, et al, eds. Radiology for Anaesthesia & Intensive Care. 2nd ed. 2009. (ENG., Illus.). 328p. pap. 65.00 (978-0-521-73563-6(7)) Cambridge Univ. Pr.

Horton, Charles. Anesthesia Crash Course. 2008. (ENG., Illus.). 192p. pap. 19.95 (978-0-19-537187-1(9)) Oxford Univ. Pr., Inc.

Hutt, Axel, ed. Sleep & Anesthesia: Neural Correlates in Theory & Experiment. 2011. (Springer Series in Computational Neuroscience Ser.). (ENG., Illus.). xvi, 200p. 189.00 (978-1-4614-0172-8(0), 1461401720) Springer.

Ingenix, creator. Anesthesia Cross Coder: Essential Links from CPT Codes to ICD-9-CM & HCPCS Codes. 2008. 507p. pap. 174.95 (978-1-60151-180-5(9)); (Illus.). 489p. pap. 174.95 (978-1-60151-064-8(0)) OptumInsight, Inc.

—Coding & Payment Guide for Anesthesia Services: An Essential Coding, Billing, & Reimbursement Resource for Anesthesiology & Pain Management. 2007. 562p. spiral bd. 179.95 (978-1-60151-068-6(3)) OptumInsight, Inc.

Irving, Colm. Anaesthesia, intensive care, & pain management for the cancer Patient. Farquhar-Smith, Paul & Wigmore, Tim, eds. 2011. (ENG., Illus.). 272p. 98.50 (978-0-19-958464-2(8)) Oxford Univ. Pr., Inc.

Jackson, Guy, et al. Practical Procedures in Anaesthesia & Critical Care. 2011. (ENG., Illus.). 272p. pap. 65.00 (978-0-19-957302-8(6)) Oxford Univ. Pr., Inc.

James, Mike, ed. Anaesthesia for Patients with Endocrine Disease. 2010. (ENG., Illus.). 266p. 175.00 (978-0-19-957025-6(6)) Oxford Univ. Pr., Inc.

Kaplan, Joel A., et al. Kaplan's Cardiac Anesthesia: The Echo Era. 6th ed. 2011. (ENG., Illus.). 1120p. 299.00 (978-1-4377-1617-7(2), Saunders) Elsevier - Health Sciences Div.

Keat, Sally, et al. Anaesthesia on the Move. 2012. (ENG.). 208p. 37.95 (978-1-4441-2153-7(7)) Hodder Arnold Pubs.

Kokkinos, Vasileios. Cortical Electrical Stimulation in Epilepsy Surgery. 2010. 132p. pap. (978-3-639-26308-4(1)) VDM Verlag Dr. Mueller e.K.

Kumar, Arun. Step by Step Regional Anesthesia. 2008. (Step by Step Ser.). (Illus.). 216p. pap. 34.95 (978-1-84829-004-4(7)) Anshan GBR. Dist: Publishers Storage & Shipping.

Lake, Carol L. & McLoughlin, Thomas M. Advances in Anesthesia. 2009. (Advances Ser.: 27). (ENG., Illus.). 130.00 (978-1-4160-5728-4(5), Mosby) Elsevier - Health Sciences Div.

Levine, Wilton C., ed. Clinical Anesthesia Procedures of the Massachusetts General Hospital: Department of Anesthesia, Critical Care & Pain Medicine, Massachusetts General Hospital, Harvard Medical School. 8th rev. ed. 2010. (ENG., Illus.). 728p. pap. 56.99 (978-1-60547-460-1(6)) Lippincott Williams & Wilkins.

Lewis, Donald P. & McMullin, Ann Marie. Advanced Protocols for Medical Emergencies: An Action Plan for Office Response. 2nd ed. 2008. (Lexi-Comp's Dental Reference Library). (Illus.). 247p. spiral bd. 50.01 (978-1-59195-219-0(0)) Lexi-Comp, Inc.

Leykin, Yigal & Brodsky, Jay, eds. Controversies in the Anesthetic Management of the Obese Surgical Patient. 2012. (ENG., Illus.). ix, 492p. 129.00 (978-88-470-2633-9(4), 8847026334) Springer.

Longnecker, David E. Anesthesiology. 2nd ed. 2012. (978-0-07-166484-4(X)) McGraw-Hill Professional Publishing.

Lovich-Sapola, Jessica. Anesthesia Oral Board Review: Knocking Out the Boards. 2009. (ENG., Illus.). 366p. (C). pap. 60.00 (978-0-521-75619-8(7)) Cambridge Univ. Pr.

Macksey, Lynn Fitzgerald. Nurse Anesthesia: A Resource for Students & Clinicians. 2nd rev. ed. 2009. 222p. spiral bd. 45.95 (978-0-7637-7302-1(6)) Jones & Bartlett Learning, LLC.

Magee, Patrick & Tooley, Mark. The Physics, Clinical Measurement & Equipment of Anaesthetic Practice for the FRCA. 2nd ed. 2011. (ENG., Illus.). 404p. pap. 79.95 (978-0-19-959515-0(1)) Oxford Univ. Pr., Inc.

Malviya, Shobha, ed. Sedation & Analgesia for Diagnostic & Therapeutic Procedures. 2010. (Contemporary Clinical Neuroscience Ser.). (Illus.). 310p. pap. 169.00 (978-1-61737-228-5(5), 1617372285) Humana Pr.

Marcucci, Catherine, et al, eds. Avoiding Common Anesthesia Errors. 2007. (Lippincott Williams & Wilkins Handbook Ser.). (Illus.). 704p. pap. 65.99 (978-0-7817-8847-2(1)) Lippincott Williams & Wilkins.

Marie, Celia. Emerging from the Cave Surviving Graves' Disease. 2010. 72p. pap. 9.99 (978-0-557-40911-2(X)) Lulu Enterprises Inc.

Marmer, Milton J. Hypnosis in Anesthesiology. 2011. 166p. 41.95 (978-1-258-02595-3(7)) Literary Licensing, LLC.

Mashour, George, ed. Consciousness, Awareness, & Anesthesia. 2010. (ENG., Illus.). 272p. 89.00 (978-0-521-51822-2(9)) Cambridge Univ. Pr.

Mashour, George A. & Lydic, Ralph, eds. Neuroscientific Foundations of Anesthesiology, 1 vol. 2011. (ENG., Illus.). 296p. 125.00 (978-0-19-539824-3(6)) Oxford Univ. Pr., Inc.

Mason, Keira P., ed. Pediatric Sedation Outside of the Operating Room: A Multispecialty International Collaboration. 2011. (ENG., Illus.). xvii, 518p. 99.00 (978-0-387-09713-8(9), 0387097139) Springer.

Mason, Rosemary. Anaesthesia Databook: A Perioperative & Peripartum Manual. 3rd rev. ed. 2009. (ENG.). 640p. pap. 61.00 (978-0-521-11419-6(5)) Cambridge Univ. Pr.

Matta, Basil F., et al, eds. Textbook of Neuroanaesthesia & Critical Care. 2nd rev. ed. 2008. (C). pap. 150.00 (978-1-84110-233-7(4)) Greenwich Medical Media Ltd. GBR. Dist: Cambridge Univ. Pr.

McConachie, Ian. Anesthesia for the High-Risk Patient. McConachie, Ian, ed. 2nd ed. 2009. (Illus.). 318p. pap. 89.00 (978-0-521-71018-3(9)) Cambridge Univ. Pr.

McConachie, Ian, ed. Anaesthesia for the High Risk Patient. 2nd rev. ed. 2008. (C). pap. 55.00 (978-1-84110-226-9(1)) Greenwich Medical Media Ltd. GBR. Dist: Cambridge Univ. Pr.

McConachie, Ian, ed. Controversies in Obstetric Anesthesia & Analgesia. 2011. (ENG., Illus.). 280p. pap. 75.00 (978-0-521-17183-0(0)) Cambridge Univ. Pr.

McLeskey, Charles H., et al, eds. Geriatric Anesthesiology. 2nd rev. ed. 2007. (Illus.). 440p. 154.00 (978-0-387-72526-0(1)) Springer.

McLoughlin, Thomas. Advances in Anesthesia - E-Book1. 2011. (978-0-323-08725-4(6), Mosby Canada) Elsevier - Health Sciences Div.

McLoughlin, Thomas M. Advances in Anesthesia. (Advances Ser.: 2011). (ENG.). 2011. 344p. 156.00 (978-0-323-08404-8(4)) 2010. 171.00 (978-0-323-06820-8(0)) Elsevier - Health Sciences Div. (Mosby).

McQuillan, Patrick M., et al. Oxford American Handbook of Anesthesiology. 2008. (Oxford American Handbooks in Medicine Ser.). (ENG., Illus.). 1110p. vinyl bd. 42.95 (978-0-19-530120-5(X)) Oxford Univ. Pr., Inc.

—Oxford American Handbook of Anesthesiology book & PDA Bundle. 2009. (Oxford American Handbooks in Medicine Ser.). (ENG.). (C). 79.95 (978-0-19-534345-8(X)) Oxford Univ. Pr., Inc.

Mendonca, Cyprian & Balasubramanian, Shyam. The Objective Structured Clinical Examination in Anaesthesia: Practice Papers for Teachers & Trainees. 2007. (Illus.). 384p. pap. 70.00 (978-1-903378-56-4(7)) TFM Publishing Ltd. GBR. Dist: JAMCO Distribution.

Mendonca, Cyprian, et al. Single Best Answer MCQs in Anaesthesia. 2010. 250p. pap. (978-1-903378-75-5(3)) TFM Publishing Ltd.

—The Structured Oral Examination in Clinical Anaesthesia: Practice Examination Papers. 2009. (Illus.). 400p. pap. 70.00 (978-1-903378-68-7(0)) TFM Publishing Ltd. GBR. Dist: JAMCO Distribution.

Miller, Ronald D. Miller's Anesthesia, 2 vols. 7th ed. 2010. (Illus.). xxii, 3084p. (978-0-8089-2413-5(3), Churchill Livingstone) Elsevier Health Sciences.

Miller, Ronald D. & Pardo, Manuel. Basics of Anesthesia: Expert Consult - Online & Print. 6th ed. 2011. (ENG., Illus.). 832p. 84.95 (978-1-4377-1614-6(8), Saunders) Elsevier - Health Sciences Div.

Miller, Ronald D., et al. Miller's Anesthesia, 2 vols. 7th ed. 2009. (ENG., Illus.). 3312p. 349.00 (978-0-443-06959-8(X), Churchill Livingstone) Elsevier - Health Sciences Div.

—Miller's Anesthesia: Expert Consult Premium Edition - Enhanced Online Features & Print, 2-Volume Set, 2 vols., Set. 7th ed. 2009. (ENG., Illus.). 3312p. 449.00 (978-1-4160-6624-8(1), Churchill Livingstone) Elsevier - Health Sciences Div.

Moores, Carl & Nimmo, Alastair, eds. Core Topics in Vascular Anesthesia. 2012. (ENG., Illus.). 224p. 80.00 (978-1-107-00181-7(1)) Cambridge Univ. Pr.

Muir, William W., III, et al. Equine Anesthesia: Monitoring & Emergency Therapy. 2nd ed. 2008. (ENG., Illus.). 504p. 117.00 (978-1-4160-2326-5(7), Saunders) Elsevier - Health Sciences Div.

—Handbook of Veterinary Anesthesia. 4th rev. ed. 2006. (ENG., Illus.). 656p. (C). per. 79.95 (978-0-323-04678-7(9), Mosby) Elsevier - Health Sciences Div.

Mustola, Seppo. Hypnotic, Analgesic, & Eeg Endpoints During Intravenous Anaesthesi. 2008. 100p. pap. (978-3-639-08753-6(4)) VDM Verlag Dr. Mueller e.K.

Mythen, Michael (Monty), et al. Anaesthesiology: Churchill's Ready Reference. 2010. (ENG., Illus.). 200p. (C). pap. 39.95 (978-0-08-045137-4(3), Churchill Livingstone) Elsevier - Health Sciences Div.

Nagelhout, John J. & Plaus, Karen. Handbook of Nurse Anesthesia. 4th ed. 2009. (ENG.). 840p. pap. 64.95 (978-1-4160-5024-7(8), Saunders) Elsevier - Health Sciences Div.

Nagelhout, John J., et al. Nurse Anesthesia. 4th ed. 2009. (ENG., Illus.). 1408p. (C). 117.00 (978-1-4160-5025-4(6), Saunders) Elsevier - Health Sciences Div.

Newfield, Philippa & Cottrell, James E. Handbook of Neuroanesthesia. 5th rev. ed. 2012. (ENG., Illus.). 480p. pap. 69.95 (978-1-60547-965-1(9)) Lippincott Williams & Wilkins.

Ngon, Nguyen Chi. Hypotensive Control During Anaesthesi. 2010. 156p. pap. (978-3-639-26902-4(0)) VDM Verlag Dr. Mueller e.K.

Nickells, James & Walton, Ben. SBA & MTF MCQs for the Primary FRCA. 2012. (ENG., Illus.). 192p. pap. 30.00 (978-1-107-60406-3(0)) Cambridge Univ. Pr.

Nickells, James, et al. SBAs for the Final FRCA. 2010. (ENG., Illus.). 306p. (C). pap. 60.00 (978-0-521-13948-9(1)) Cambridge Univ. Pr.

O'Donnell, Aidan. Anaesthesia: A Very Short Introduction. 2012. (Very Short Introductions Ser.). (ENG., Illus.). 144p. pap. 11.95 (978-0-19-958454-3(0)) Oxford Univ. Pr., Inc.

Omoigui, Sota. Sota Omoigui's Anesthesia Drugs Handbook. 4th ed. 2012. 650p. mass mkt. 69.00 (978-0-9796461-9-5(7)) State-of-the-Art Technologies, Inc.

Orebaugh, Steven L. Understanding Anesthesia: What You Need to Know about Sedation & Pain Control. 2011. (Johns Hopkins Press Health Book Ser.). (ENG., Illus.). 168p. pap. 18.95 (978-1-4214-0317-5(X)); (gr. 17). 45.00 (978-1-4214-0316-8(1)) Johns Hopkins Univ. Pr.

Patel, Harshad, ed. Anaesthesia for Burns, Maxillofacial & Plastic Surgery. (ENG., Illus.). 256p. (978-0-340-55302-2(2), Hodder Arnold) Hodder Education.

Perry, Tristan R. The Certified Registered Nurse Anesthetist. 2007. 172p. per. (978-3-8364-3419-5(9)) VDM Verlag Dr. Mueller e.K.

Phillips, W. James, et al. Pain Management & Procedural Sedation. 2008. (Mobile Medicine Ser.). (ENG., Illus.). 240p. pap., instr.'s hndbk. ed. 49.95 (978-0-323-05333-4(5), Mosby) Elsevier - Health Sciences Div.

Raeder, Johan. Clinical Ambulatory Anesthesia. 2010. (ENG., Illus.). 194p. pap. 49.99 (978-0-521-73781-4(8)) Cambridge Univ. Pr.

Rahimi, F.A.A.D., A. David. Please Don't Die Trying to Become Beautiful A Surgeons' Plea. 2010. 104p. pap. 39.20 (978-0-557-32215-2(4)) Lulu Enterprises Inc.

Reader, Al, et al. Successful Local Anesthesia for Restorative Dentistry & Endodontics. 2011. pap. (978-0-86715-513-6(2)) Quintessence Publishing Co., Inc.

Reich, David L. Monitoring in Anesthesia & Perioperative Care. Kahn, Ronald A. et al, eds. 2011. (ENG., Illus.). 432p. 125.00 (978-0-521-75598-6(0)) Cambridge Univ. Pr.

Roberts, Victoria. International Practice of Anaesthesia. Date not set. 448p. pap. 60.00 (978-0-7506-4216-3(5), Butterworth-Heinemann) Elsevier Science & Technology Bks.

Robinson, Neville, et al. How to Survive in Anaesthesia: A Guide for Trainees. 4th ed. 2012. (ENG., Illus.). 256p. pap. 59.95 (978-0-470-65462-0(7)) Wiley, John & Sons, Inc.

Ruskin, Keith & Rosenbaum, Stanley H. Anesthesia Emergencies, 1 vol. 2010. (ENG., Illus.). 432p. pap. 49.95 (978-0-19-539671-3(5)) Oxford Univ. Pr., Inc.

Sandberg, Warren, et al. The MGH Textbook of Anesthetic Equipment. 2010. (ENG., Illus.). 640p. 142.00 (978-1-4377-0973-5(7), Churchill Livingstone) Elsevier - Health Sciences Div.

Shapiro, Fred E. Manual of Office-Based Anesthesia Procedures. 2007. (Illus.). 240p. per. 58.99 (978-0-7817-6908-2(6)) Lippincott Williams & Wilkins.

Shaw, Ian, et al, eds. Anaesthesia for Oral & Maxillofacial Surgery. 2010. (ENG., Illus.). 360p. 225.00 (978-0-19-956421-7(3)) Oxford Univ. Pr., Inc.

Shorten, George, et al. Case-Based Anesthesia: Clinical Learning Guides. 2009. (ENG., Illus.). 238p. 114.99 (978-0-7817-8955-4(9)) Lippincott Williams & Wilkins.

Shubert, David & Leyba, John. Chemistry & Physics for Nurse Anesthesia: A Student Centered Approach. 2009. (Illus.). xix, 423p. (978-0-8261-1844-8(5)) Springer.

Sieber, Frederick E. Geriatric Anesthesia. 2006. (ENG., Illus.). 600p. 132.00 (978-0-07-146308-9(9), 0071463089) McGraw-Hill Professional Publishing.

Silverstein, Jeffrey H. Problems with Geriatric Anesthesia Patients, an Issue of Anesthesiology Clinics. 2009. (Clinics: Internal Medicine Ser.: 27-3). (ENG., Illus.). 240p. 99.00 (978-1-4377-1288-9(6), Saunders) Elsevier - Health Sciences Div.

Slinger, Peter. Principles & Practice of Anesthesia for Thoracic Surgery. 2011. (ENG., Illus.). xix, 732p. 179.00 (978-1-4419-0183-5(3), 1441901833) Springer.

Smith, Brian, et al, eds. Core Topics in Operating Department Practice: Leadership & Management. 2009. (ENG., Illus.). 196p. pap. 60.00 (978-0-521-71704-5(3)) Cambridge Univ. Pr.

Smith, Charles, ed. Trauma Anesthesia. 2008. (ENG., Illus.). 624p. 99.00 (978-0-521-87058-0(5)) Cambridge Univ. Pr.

Smith, Tim, et al, eds. Fundamentals of Anaesthesia. 3rd rev. ed. 2009. (ENG., Illus.). 956p. pap. 149.00 (978-0-521-69249-6(0)) Cambridge Univ. Pr.

Sonner, James M., ed. Manual of Anesthesia Practice. 2007. (Cambridge Pocket Clinicians Ser.). (ENG.). 1108p. per. 58.00 (978-0-521-70935-4(0)) Cambridge Univ. Pr.

Sood, Jayashree & Jain, Anil Kumar. Anaesthesia in Laparoscopic Surgery. 2009. (ENG., Illus.). 272p. 135.00 (978-0-07-163320-8(0), 0071633200) McGraw-Hill Professional Publishing.

Stone, Juliana. Anaesthesia at a Glance. 2010. (ENG.). 104p. pap. (978-1-4051-8756-5(5), Wiley-Blackwell) Wiley, John & Sons, Ltd.

Stonemetz, Jerry & Ruskin, Keith, eds. Anesthesia Informatics. (Health Informatics Ser.). (Illus.). 2009. (ENG.). xxviii, 504p. pap. 69.95 (978-1-84882-961-9(2), 1848829612) 2008. 358p. 89.95 (978-0-387-76417-7(8)) Springer.

Taimoorazy, Benjamin. Before You Go Under: A Step by Step Guide to Ease Your Mind Before Going under Anesthesia. 2008. 199p. pap. 14.95 (978-0-615-18470-8(7)) Accupress.

Tandon, Rakesh, ed. Structured Oral Examination Practice for the Final FRCA. 2012. (ENG., Illus.). 392p. 79.95 (978-0-19-958401-7(X)) Oxford Univ. Pr., Inc.

Thaler, Malcolm S. The Only EKG Book You'll Ever Need. 7th rev. ed. 2012. (ENG., Illus.). 352p. pap. 63.95 (978-1-4511-1905-3(4)) Lippincott Williams & Wilkins.

Tremper, Kevin K. & Kheterpal, Sachin. Information Technology Applied to Anesthesiology: Anesthesiology Clinics of North America. 2011. (Clinics: Surgery Ser.: 29-3). (ENG., Illus.). xvi, 356p. 110.00 (978-1-4557-1030-0(X), Saunders) Elsevier - Health Sciences Div.

Twersky, Rebecca S. & Philip, Beverly K., eds. Handbook of Ambulatory Anesthesia. 2nd rev. ed. 2008. (Illus.). 576p. pap. 89.95 (978-0-387-73328-9(0)) Springer.

Urman, Richard, et al. Anesthesia Outside of the Operating Room, 1 vol. 2011. (ENG., Illus.). 416p. 110.00 (978-0-19-539667-6(7)) Oxford Univ. Pr., Inc.

Urman, Richard D. & Kaye, Alan D., eds. Moderate & Deep Sedation in Clinical Practice. 2012. (ENG., Illus.). 342p. pap. 49.99 (978-1-107-40045-0(7)) Cambridge Univ. Pr.

Urman, Richard D., et al. Pocket Anesthesia. Urman, Richard D. & Ehrenfeld, Jesse M., eds. 2009. (Pocket Notebook Ser.). (ENG., Illus.). 256p. ring bd. 54.99 (978-0-7817-9584-5(2)) Lippincott Williams & Wilkins.

Vacanti, Charles A., et al, eds. Essential Clinical Anesthesia. 2011. (ENG., Illus.). 1102p. pap. 85.00 (978-0-521-72020-5(6)) Cambridge Univ. Pr.

Varon, Albert J. & Smith, Charles, eds. Essentials of Trauma Anesthesia. 2012. (ENG., Illus.). 326p. pap. 65.00 (978-1-107-60256-4(4)) Cambridge Univ. Pr.

Vuyk, J., et al, eds. On the Study & Practice of Intravenous Anaesthesia. 2010. 210p. pap. 190.00 (978-90-481-5366-4(2), 9048153662) Springer.

Wasnick, John, et al. Cardiac Anesthesia & Transesophageal Echocardiography. 2011. (ENG., Illus.). 332p. pap. 78.00 (978-0-07-171798-4(6), 0071717986) McGraw-Hill Professional Publishing.

Webster, Nigel & Galley, Helen, eds. Landmark Papers in Anaesthesia. 2012. (ENG., Illus.). 528p. 110.00 (978-0-19-958338-6(2)) Oxford Univ. Pr., Inc.

Wijayasiri, Lara, et al. The Primary FRCA Structured Oral Examination Study Guide 1. 2010. (Illus.). 232p. pap. (978-1-84619-270-8(6)) Radcliffe Publishing.

Wilkinson, Jonathan, et al. Thoracic Anaesthesia. 2011. (ENG., Illus.). 786p. pap. 85.00 (978-0-19-956309-8(8)) Oxford Univ. Pr., Inc.

Wilson, William C., et al. Trauma: Resuscitation, Anesthesia & Emergency Surgery, 2 vols. 2007. (ENG., Illus.). 1384p. 330.00 (978-0-8247-2920-2(X), Informa Healthcare) Taylor & Francis Group GBR. Dist: Taylor & Francis Group.

Wong, Cynthia. Spinal & Epidural Anesthesia. 2006. (ENG., Illus.). 384p. 130.00 (978-0-07-143772-1(X), 007143772X) McGraw-Hill Professional Publishing.

Woodworth, Glenn & Kirsch, Jeffrey R. The Anesthesia Technician & Technologist's Manual: All You Need to Know for Study & Reference. 2012. (Illus.). 608p. pap. 94.99 (978-1-4511-4266-2(8)) Lippincott Williams & Wilkins.

Yentis, Steven M., et al. Anaesthesia & Intensive Care A-Z: An Encyclopedia of Principles & Practice. 4th ed. 2009. (ENG., Illus.). 584p. pap. 145.00 (978-0-443-06785-3(6), Churchill Livingstone) Elsevier - Health Sciences Div.

Zuo, Zhiyi. Anesthesi: What You Need to Know. 2011. 114p. pap. 19.95 (978-1-4560-7507-1(1)) PublishAmerica, Inc.

ANESTHESIA—COMPLICATIONS

Bellamy, Mark & Struys, Michel. Anaesthesia for the Overweight & Obese Patient. 2007. (Oxford Anaesthesia Library). (Illus.). 136p. pap. 24.95 (978-0-19-923395-3(0)) Oxford Univ. Pr., Inc.

Bosack, Robert C. Anesthetic Complications in the Dental Office: Prevention, Diagnosis, & Management. (978-0-86715-448-1(9)) Quintessence Publishing Co., Inc.

Brock-Utne, John G. Clinical Anesthesia: Near Misses & Lessons Learned. 2008. (ENG., Illus.). xvi, 164p. per. 64.95 (978-0-387-72519-2(9), 0387725199) Springer.

Brodsky, Jay B. & Lemmens, Hendrikus J. M. Anesthetic Management of the Obese Surgical Patient. 2011. (ENG., Illus.). 146p. pap. 52.00 (978-1-107-60333-2(1)) Cambridge Univ. Pr.

Friedberg, Barry L. Getting over Going Under: 5 Things You Must Know Before Anesthesia. 2010. 116p. pap. 18.95 (978-0-9829169-0-2(6)) Goldilocks Pr.

Gravenstein, Nikolaus, et al, eds. Complications in Anesthesiology. 3rd rev. ed. 2007. (ENG., Illus.). 1136p. 189.99 *(978-0-7817-8263-0(5))* Lippincott Williams & Wilkins.

Hines, Roberta L. & Marschall, Katherine E. Anesthesia & Co-Existing Disease. 5th ed. 2008. (Expert Consult Title: Online + Print Ser.). (ENG., Illus.). 688p. 159.00 *(978-1-4160-3998-3(8),* Saunders) Elsevier - Health Sciences Div.

Ijbara, Manhal. An Assessment of Comprehensive Dental Treatment. 2011. 120p. pap. ***(978-3-8433-9122-1(X))*** Lambert Academic Publishing.

Valchanov, Kamen, et al, eds. Anaesthetic & Perioperative Complications. 2011. (ENG., Illus.). 272p. pap. 79.00 ***(978-1-107-00259-3(1))*** Cambridge Univ. Pr.

Wiener-Kronish, Jeanine & Ortiz, Vilma E., eds. Perioperative Anesthesia for the Obese Patient: Complications & Challenges of the Obese Patient. 2009. (Illus.). 200p. 300.00 *(978-1-4200-9530-2(7),* Informa Healthcare) Taylor & Francis Group.

ANESTHESIA—HISTORY

Shephard, David. From Craft to Specialty. 2009. 464p. 34.99 *(978-1-4415-1173-7(3));* pap. 23.99 *(978-1-4415-1172-0(5))* Xlibris Corp.

Sykes, Keith & Bunker, John. Anesthesia & the Practice of Medicine: Historical Perspectives. 2007. (ENG., Illus.). 320p. per. 29.95 *(978-1-85315-674-8(4))* Hodder Arnold Pubs.

ANESTHESIA, CONDUCTION
see Conduction Anesthesia

ANESTHESIA, LOCAL
see Local Anesthesia

ANESTHESIA, PERIDURAL
see Peridural Anesthesia

ANESTHESIA, SPINAL
see Spinal Anesthesia

ANESTHESIA IN CARDIOLOGY

Barnard, Matthew & Martin, Bruce. Cardiac Anaesthesia. 2010. (ENG., Illus.). 624p. pap. 75.00 *(978-0-19-920910-1(3))* Oxford Univ. Pr., Inc.

Cram101 Textbook Reviews. Outlines & Highlights for a Practical Approach to Cardiac Anesthesia by Frederick a Hensley. 2011. 624p. pap. 40.95 ***(978-1-61905-705-0(0))*** Cram101 Inc.

DiNardo, James A. & Zvara, David A. Anesthesia for Cardiac Surgery. 3rd rev. ed. 2007. (ENG., Illus.). 472p. 217.95 *(978-1-4051-5363-8(6),* Wiley-Blackwell) Wiley, John & Sons, Inc.

Kaplan, Joel A. Essentials of Cardiac Anesthesia: A Volume in Essentials of Anesthesia & Critical Care. 2008. (ENG., Illus.). 768p. pap. 76.95 *(978-1-4160-3786-6(1),* Saunders) Elsevier - Health Sciences Div.

Kaplan, Joel A., et al. Kaplan's Cardiac Anesthesia: The Echo Era. 6th ed. 2011. (ENG., Illus.). 1120p. 299.00 *(978-1-4377-1617-7(2),* Saunders) Elsevier - Health Sciences Div.

Mackay, Jonathan & Arrowsmith, Joseph, eds. Core Topics in Cardiac Anaesthesia. 2nd rev. ed. 2012. (ENG., Illus.). 520p. 99.00 ***(978-0-521-19685-7(X))*** Cambridge Univ. Pr.

Martin, Donald E., et al, eds. A Practical Approach to Cardiac Anesthesia. 4th rev. ed. 2007. (Practical Approach Ser.). (ENG., Illus.). 816p. per. 92.95 *(978-0-7817-9533-3(8))* Lippincott Williams & Wilkins.

Mossad, Emad B., et al, eds. Anesthesia for Congenital Heart Disease. 2nd ed. 2010. (ENG., Illus.). 656p. 248.00 *(978-1-4051-8634-6(8),* Wiley-Blackwell) Wiley, John & Sons, Inc.

Piciché, Marco, ed. Dawn & Evolution of Cardiac Procedures: Research Avenues in Cardiac Surgery & Interventional Cardiology. 2012. (ENG., Illus.). xiv, 459p. 189.00 ***(978-88-470-2399-4(8),*** 8847023998) Springer.

Reves, J. G., et al. Atlas of Cardiothoracic Anesthesia. 2nd ed. 2009. (Illus.). 230p. 319.00 *(978-1-57340-278-1(8))* Current Medicine Group LLC.

Subramaniam, Kathirvel, et al, eds. Anesthesia & Perioperative Care for Aortic Surgery. 2010. (Illus.). 300p. 219.00 *(978-0-387-85921-7(7),* 0387859217) Springer.

Wasnick, John, et al. Cardiac Anesthesia & Transesophageal Echocardiography. 2011. (ENG., Illus.). 332p. pap. 78.00 *(978-0-07-171798-4(6),* 0071717986) McGraw-Hill Professional Publishing.

Wasnick, John D. Cardiac Anesthesia & Transesophageal Echocardiography. 2011. (Illus.). xii, 319p. *(978-0-07-163458-8(4));* pap. *(978-0-07-163457-1(6))* McGraw-Hill Professional Publishing.

Weiss, Stuart & Milas, Bonnie L. Anesthesia Pocket Consult: Cardiac Anesthesia: Print + IPod. 2008. (Illus.). pap. 69.95 *(978-1-4160-4651-6(8),* Saunders) Elsevier - Health Sciences Div.

ANESTHESIA IN CHILDHOOD
see Pediatric Anesthesia

ANESTHESIA IN DENTISTRY
see also Hypnotism in Dentistry

Baart, J. A. & Brand, H. S. Local Anaesthesia in Dentistry. 2008. (ENG., Illus.). 192p. pap. 57.99 *(978-1-4051-8436-6(1),* Wiley-Blackwell) Wiley, John & Sons, Inc.

Bassett, Kathy & DiMarco, Arthur. Local Anesthesia for Dental Professionals. 2009. (ENG.). 464p. (C). pap. 80.33 *(978-0-13-158930-8(X),* Prentice Hall) Prentice Hall PTR.

Cram101 Textbook Reviews. Outlines & Highlights for Sedation: A Guide to Patient Management by Stanley Malamed, ISBN. 2011. 504p. pap. 37.95 ***(978-1-61744-963-5(6))*** Cram101 Inc.

Girdler, N. M., et al. Clinical Sedation in Dentistry. 2009. (ENG., Illus.). 184p. pap. 82.99 *(978-1-4051-8069-6(2),* Wiley-Blackwell) Wiley, John & Sons, Inc.

Ijbara, Manhal. An Assessment of Comprehensive Dental Treatment. 2011. 120p. pap. ***(978-3-8433-9122-1(X))*** Lambert Academic Publishing.

Logothetis, Demetra D. Local Anesthesia for the Dental Hygienist. 2011. (ENG., Illus.). 768p. (C). pap. 69.95 *(978-0-323-07371-4(9),* Mosby) Elsevier - Health Sciences Div.

Malamed, Stanley F. Handbook of Local Anesthesia. 6th ed. 2012. (ENG., Illus.). 432p. (C). pap. 84.95 ***(978-0-323-07413-1(8),*** Mosby) Elsevier - Health Sciences Div.

Moore, Paul, et al. Update of Dental Local Anesthesia: Dental Clinics of North America. 2010. (Clinics: Dentistry Ser.: 54-4). (ENG., Illus.). xiv, 588p. 105.00 *(978-1-4377-2441-7(8),* Saunders) Elsevier - Health Sciences Div.

Rogers, Nicola. Basic Guide to Dental Sedation Nursing. 2011. (Basic Guide Dentistry Ser.). (ENG., Illus.). 192p. pap. 35.99 *(978-1-4443-3470-8(0),* Wiley-Blackwell) Wiley, John & Sons, Inc.

Royer, Royann & Paarmann, Carlene. Pain Control for Dental Practitioners: An Interactive Approach. 2007. (ENG., Illus.). 128p. pap. 63.99 *(978-0-7817-7914-2(6))* Lippincott Williams & Wilkins.

ANESTHESIA IN OBSTETRICS
see also Hypnotism in Obstetrics

Bucklin, Brenda, et al, eds. A Practical Approach to Obstetric Anesthesia. 2008. (Practical Approach to Anesthesia Ser.). (ENG., Illus.). 552p. pap. 92.95 *(978-0-7817-7524-3(8))* Lippincott Williams & Wilkins.

Chestnut, David H., et al. Chestnut's Obstetric Anesthesia: Principles & Practice: Expert Consult - Online & Print. 4th ed. 2009. (ENG., Illus.). 1248p. 229.00 *(978-0-323-05541-3(9),* Mosby) Elsevier - Health Sciences Div.

Clyburn, Paul, et al, eds. Obstetric Anaesthesia. 2008. (Oxford Specialist Handbooks in Anaesthesia Ser.). (ENG., Illus.). 768p. pap. 79.95 *(978-0-19-920832-6(8))* Oxford Univ. Pr., Inc.

—Obstetric Anaesthesia for Developing Countries. 2010. (Oxford Anaesthesia Library). (ENG., Illus.). 208p. pap. 24.95 *(978-0-19-957214-4(3))* Oxford Univ. Pr., Inc.

Collis, Rachel E., et al, eds. Textbook of Obstetric Anaesthesia. 2011. (ENG., Illus.). 346p. pap. 39.99 *(978-0-521-17418-3(X))* Cambridge Univ. Pr.

Cram101 Textbook Reviews & Cram101 Textbook Reviews. Outlines & Highlights for Obstetric Anesthesia & Uncommon Disorders by David R Gambling. 2011. 404p. pap. 35.95 ***(978-1-61830-810-8(6))*** Cram101 Inc.

Datta, Sanjay, ed. Anesthetic & Obstetric Management of High-Risk Pregnancy. 3rd ed. 2012. (ENG., Illus.). xviii, 555p. pap. 249.00 *(978-1-4419-1819-2(1),* 1441918191) Springer.

Datta, Sanjay, et al. Obstetric Anesthesia Handbook. 5th ed. 2010. (ENG., Illus.). vii, 470p. pap. 59.95 *(978-0-387-88601-5(X),* 038788601X) Springer.

Gaiser, Robert R., et al. Obstetric, Thoracic & Cardiac Anesthesia: Handbook & IPod. 2009. (ENG., Illus.). 528p. pap. 79.95 *(978-1-4160-5997-4(0),* Saunders) Elsevier - Health Sciences Div.

Gambling, David R., et al, eds. Obstetric Anesthesia & Uncommon Disorders. 2nd rev. ed. (ENG.). 2011. 460p. pap. 80.00 ***(978-1-107-40303-1(0))*** 2008. (Illus.). 480p. 143.00 *(978-0-521-87082-5(8))* Cambridge Univ. Pr.

Ginosar, Yehuda, et al, eds. Anesthesia & the Fetus. 2013. (ENG.). 324p. 149.95 ***(978-1-4443-3707-5(6),*** Wiley-Blackwell) Wiley, John & Sons, Inc.

Leffler, Lisa, ed. Obstetric Anesthesia. 2007. (Cambridge Pocket Clinicians Ser.). (ENG.). 992p. per. 70.00 *(978-0-521-70939-2(3))* Cambridge Univ. Pr.

Palmer, Craig M., et al. Obstetric Anesthesia, 1 vol. 2011. (ENG., Illus.). 368p. pap. 59.95 *(978-0-19-973380-4(5))* Oxford Univ. Pr., Inc.

Tewari, Vinay & Gautam, P. L., eds. Step by Step Anaesthesia in Obstetrics & Gynaecology. 2007. (Step by Step Ser.). (Illus.). 360p. pap. 29.99 *(978-1-905740-02-4(6))* Anshan GBR. Dist: Publishers Storage & Shipping.

Vasdev, Gurinder. Obstetric Anesthesia, an Issue of Anesthesiology Clinics. 2008. (Clinics: Surgery Ser.: 26-1). (ENG., Illus.). 240p. 99.00 *(978-1-4160-6062-8(6),* Saunders) Elsevier - Health Sciences Div.

Wolf, Jacqueline H. Deliver Me from Pain: Anesthesia & Birth in America. 2012. (ENG., Illus.). 296p. (gr. 17). pap. 30.00 ***(978-1-4214-0572-8(5))*** Johns Hopkins Univ. Pr.

Wolf, Jacqueline H. & Wolf, J. H. Deliver Me from Pain: Anesthesia & Birth in America. 2009. (ENG., Illus.). 296p. (gr. 17). 52.00 *(978-0-8018-9110-6(8))* Johns Hopkins Univ. Pr.

Yentis, Steve, et al, eds. Analgesia, Anaesthesia & Pregnancy: A Practical Guide. 2nd var. ed. 2007. (ENG., Illus.). 414p. 88.00 *(978-0-521-69474-2(4))* Cambridge Univ. Pr.

ANESTHESIA IN ONCOLOGY

Srejic & DeMonte. Neurecipes: The MD Anderson Cancer Center Guide to Anesthesia for Neurosurgical Cases. 2008. 116p. pap. 74.99 *(978-1-4389-0547-1(5))* AuthorHouse.

ANESTHESIA IN OPHTHALMOLOGY

Kumar, Chandra, et al. Ophthalmic Anaesthesia. 2012. (Illus.). 302p. pap. 79.95 ***(978-0-19-959139-8(3))*** Oxford Univ. Pr., Inc.

ANESTHESIA IN VETERINARY SURGERY

Avsaroglu, Harutyun. Genetic Background & the Response to Anaesthetics & Analgesics. 2009. (Illus.). 124p. pap. *(978-3-639-15296-8(4))* VDM Verlag Dr. Mueller e.K.

Bryant, Susan, ed. Anesthesia for Veterinary Technicians. 2010. (ENG., Illus.). 416p. pap. 74.99 *(978-0-8138-0586-3(4),* Wiley-Blackwell) Wiley, John & Sons, Inc.

Carroll, Gwendolyn L., ed. Small Animal Anesthesia & Analgesia. 2008. (ENG., Illus.). 283p. 89.99 *(978-0-8138-0230-5(X),* Wiley-Blackwell) Wiley, John & Sons, Inc.

Cooney, Kathleen, et al. Veterinary Euthanasia Techniques: A Practical Guide. 2012. (ENG.). 204p. pap. 59.99 ***(978-0-470-95918-3(5),*** Wiley-Blackwell) Wiley, John & Sons, Inc.

Dugdale, Alexandra. Veterinary Anaesthesia: Principles to Practice. 2010. (ENG., Illus.). 400p. pap. 72.99 *(978-1-4051-9247-7(X),* Wiley-Blackwell) Wiley, John & Sons, Inc.

Fish, Richard, et al, eds. Anesthesia & Analgesia in Laboratory Animals. 2nd ed. 2008. (American College of Laboratory Animal Medicine Ser.). (ENG., Illus.). 672p. 185.00 *(978-0-12-373898-1(9),* Academic Pr.) Elsevier Science & Technology Bks.

Longley, Lesa. Anaesthesia of Exotic Pets. 2008. (ENG., Illus.). 320p. pap. 89.95 *(978-0-7020-2888-5(6),* Saunders) Elsevier - Health Sciences Div.

Muir, William W., III. Veterinary Clinics of North America: Pain in Horses: Physiology, Pathophysiology & Therapeutic Implications. 2010. (Clinics: Veterinary Medicine Ser.: 26-3). (ENG.). 105.00 *(978-1-4377-2502-5(3),* Saunders) Elsevier - Health Sciences Div.

Muir, William W., III, et al. Equine Anesthesia: Monitoring & Emergency Therapy. 2nd ed. 2008. (ENG., Illus.). 504p. 117.00 *(978-1-4160-2326-5(7),* Saunders) Elsevier - Health Sciences Div.

—Handbook of Veterinary Anesthesia. 4th rev. ed. 2006. (ENG., Illus.). 656p. (C). per. 79.95 *(978-0-323-04678-7(9),* Mosby) Elsevier - Health Sciences Div.

Paul-Murphy, Joanne. Analgesia & Pain Management: Veterinary Clinics of North America - Exotic Animal Practice. 2010. (Clinics: Veterinary Medicine Ser.: 14-1). (ENG., Illus.). 200p. 110.00 *(978-1-4557-0520-7(9),* Saunders) Elsevier - Health Sciences Div.

Seibert, Philip. Be Safe! Manager's Guide to Radiation & Waste Anesthetic Gases. 2008. (ENG., Illus.). 32p. 24.95 *(978-1-58326-099-9(4),* AAHA Pr.) American Animal Hospital Assn. Pr.

Seymour, Chris & Duke, Tanya, eds. BSAVA Manual of Canine & Feline Anaesthesia & Analgesia. 2nd rev. ed. 2007. (BSAVA British Small Animal Veterinary Association Ser.: 3). (ENG., Illus.). 352p. pap. 157.99 *(978-0-905214-98-6(6))* British Small Animal Veterinary Assn. (BSAVA) GBR. Dist: Wiley, John & Sons, Inc.

Taylor, Polly & Clarke, Kathy W. Handbook of Equine Anaesthesia. 2nd rev. ed. 2006. (ENG., Illus.). 228p. (C). pap. 89.95 *(978-0-7020-2835-9(5),* Saunders) Elsevier - Health Sciences Div.

Thomas, John & Lerche, Phillip. Anesthesia & Analgesia for Veterinary Technicians. 4th ed. 2010. (ENG., Illus.). 432p. (C). pap. 55.95 *(978-0-323-05504-8(4),* Mosby) Elsevier - Health Sciences Div.

Tranquilli, William J., et al, eds. Lumb & Jones' Veterinary Anesthesia & Analgesia. 4th rev. ed. 2007. (ENG., Illus.). 1096p. 171.99 *(978-0-7817-5471-2(2),* Wiley-Blackwell) Wiley, John & Sons, Inc.

Valverde, Alexander & Doherty, Tom, eds. Manual of Equine Anesthesia & Analgesia. 2006. (ENG., Illus.). 376p. pap. 131.99 *(978-1-4051-2967-1(0),* Wiley-Blackwell) Wiley, John & Sons, Inc.

Welsh, Elizabeth. Anaesthesia for Veterinary Nurses. Welsh, Liz, ed. 2nd ed. 2009. (ENG., Illus.). 408p. pap. 75.99 *(978-1-4051-8673-5(9),* Wiley-Blackwell) Wiley, John & Sons, Inc.

West, Gary, et al, eds. Zoo Animal & Wildlife: Immobilization & Anesthesia. 2007. (ENG., Illus.). 656p. 173.99 *(978-0-8138-2566-3(0),* Wiley-Blackwell) Wiley, John & Sons, Inc.

ANESTHESIOLOGY
see also Anesthesia; Anesthetics

Adams, Anthony P., et al, eds. Emergency Anaesthesia. (Illus.). 384p. pap. *(978-0-7131-4505-2(6),* Hodder Arnold) Hodder Education.

Al-Shaikh, Baha & Stacey, Simon. Essentials of Anaesthetic Equipment. 3rd rev. ed. 2007. (ENG., Illus.). 240p. pap. 87.95 *(978-0-443-10087-1(X),* Churchill Livingstone) Elsevier - Health Sciences Div.

Antognini, Joseph E., ed. Neural Mechanisms of Anesthesia. 2010. (Contemporary Clinical Neuroscience Ser.). (Illus.). 480p. pap. 239.00 *(978-1-61737-294-0(3),* 1617372943) Humana Pr.

Armstrong, Sarah, et al. Final FRCA. 2011. (ENG.). pap. 49.95 *(978-1-85315-919-0(0))* Hodder Arnold Pubs.

Arthurs, G. & Nicholls, Barry. Ultrasound in Anesthetic Practice. Arthurs, Graham & Nicholls, Barry S., eds. 2008. (ENG., Illus.). 214p. pap. 89.00 *(978-0-521-71623-9(3))* Cambridge Univ. Pr.

Atkins, Joshua H. & Mandel, Jeff E. Current Topics in Anesthesia for Head & Neck Surgery , an Issue of Anesthesiology Clinics. 2010. (Clinics: Surgery Ser.: 28-3). (ENG., Illus.). xvi, 397p. 105.00 *(978-1-4377-2425-7(6),* Saunders) Elsevier - Health Sciences Div.

Bahal, Nawal, et al. Get Through Final FRCA - MCQs. 2010. (ENG.). 384p. pap. 49.95 *(978-1-85315-995-4(6))* Hodder Arnold Pubs.

Baughman, Verna L., et al, eds. Anesthesiology & Critical Care Drug Handbook: Including Select Disease States & Perioperative Management. 9th ed. 2009. (Anesthesiology & Critical Care Drug Handbook Ser.). (Illus.). 1821p. pap. 46.95 *(978-1-59195-275-6(1))* Lexi-Comp, Inc.

Bhatt, Himani, et al. Anesthesiology Boards. 2010. (FIRST AID Specialty Boards Ser.). (ENG., Illus.). 454p. (C). pap. 74.95 *(978-0-07-147178-7(2),* 0071471782) McGraw-Hill Medical Publishing Div.

Bigeleisen, Paul E., ed. Ultrasound-Guided Regional Anesthesia & Pain Medicine. 2009. (ENG., Illus.). 320p. 154.99 *(978-1-58255-849-3(3))* Lippincott Williams & Wilkins.

Bready, Lois L., et al. Decision Making in Anesthesiology. 4th rev. ed. 2007. (Decision Making Ser.). (ENG., Illus.). 656p. 148.00 *(978-0-323-03938-3(3),* Mosby) Elsevier - Health Sciences Div.

Brock-Utne, John G. Clinical Anesthesia: Near Misses & Lessons Learned. 2008. (ENG., Illus.). xvi, 164p. per. 64.95 *(978-0-387-72519-2(9),* 0387725199) Springer.

Burch, Thomas M., et al. Conquer the PTE Exam. 2007. (ENG., Illus.). 544p. pap. 98.95 *(978-1-4160-3833-7(7),* Saunders) Elsevier - Health Sciences Div.

Burkey, Dell. Anesthesia Pocket Consult: Regional Anesthesia PDA: Print + IPod. 2008. (Illus.). cd-rom 69.95 *(978-1-4160-3345-5(9),* Saunders) Elsevier - Health Sciences Div.

—Regional Anesthesia & Pain Management: Handbook & IPod. 2009. (ENG., Illus.). 432p. pap., instr.'s hndbk. ed. 79.95 *(978-1-4160-3344-8(0),* Saunders) Elsevier - Health Sciences Div.

Burton, John & Miner, James. Emergency Sedation & Pain Management. 2008. (ENG., Illus.). 296p. 87.00 *(978-0-521-87086-3(0))* Cambridge Univ. Pr.

Chestnut, David H. Year Book of Anesthesiology & Pain Management 2010. 2010. (Year Bks.: 2010). (ENG.). 176.00 *(978-0-323-06824-6(3),* Mosby) Elsevier - Health Sciences Div.

—Year Book of Anesthesiology & Pain Management 2011. 2011. (Year Bks.: 2011). (ENG.). 440p. 159.00 *(978-0-323-08407-9(9),* Mosby) Elsevier - Health Sciences Div.

Chestnut, David H. Year Book of Anesthesiology & Pain Management 2012. 2012. (Year Bks.: 2012). (ENG.). 448p. 173.00 ***(978-0-323-08873-2(2),*** Mosby) Elsevier - Health Sciences Div.

Chestnutt, David. Year Book of Anesthesiology & Pain Management 2011 - E-Book1. 2011. E-Book ***(978-0-323-08728-5(0),*** Mosby Canada) Elsevier - Health Sciences Div.

Cold, Georg E. & Juul, Niels, eds. Monitoring of Cerebral & Spinal Haemodynamics during Neurosurgery. 2010. (ENG., Illus.). xx, 332p. pap. 149.00 *(978-3-642-09669-3(7),* 3642096697) Springer.

Conlay, Lydia, et al. Case Files Anesthesiology. 2010. (LANGE Case Files Ser.). (ENG., Illus.). 518p. (C). pap. 41.00 *(978-0-07-160639-4(4),* 0071606394) McGraw-Hill Medical Publishing Div.

Connell, Karl, Jr. Biography of an Inventor: Dr. Karl Connell. 2008. (Illus.). ix, 195p. *(978-0-9817104-0-2(9))* Wintoon Waters.

Connelly. Review of Clinical Anesthesia. Connelly, Neil Roy & Silverman, David G., eds. 5th rev. ed. 2009. (ENG., Illus.). 320p. pap. 69.99 *(978-0-7817-8951-6(6))* Lippincott Williams & Wilkins.

Cottrell, James E. & Newfield, Philippa, eds. Handbook of Neuroanesthesia. 4th rev. ed. 2006. (Lippincott Williams & Wilkins Handbook Ser.). (ENG., Illus.). 448p. per. 66.95 *(978-0-7817-6245-8(6))* Lippincott Williams & Wilkins.

Cottrell, James E. & Young, William L. Cottrell & Young's Neuroanesthesia. 5th ed. 2010. (ENG., Illus.). 480p. 218.00 *(978-0-323-05908-4(2),* Mosby) Elsevier - Health Sciences Div.

Cram101 Textbook Reviews & Cram101 Textbook Reviews. Outlines & Highlights for Clinical Anesthesia by Paul G Barash, Isbn: 9780781787635 0781787637. 2011. 688p. pap. 42.95 ***(978-1-61490-398-7(0))*** Cram101 Inc.

—Outlines & Highlights for Evidence-Based Practice of Anesthesiology: Expert Consult 2nd by Lee A. Fleisher, ISBN. 2011. 202p. pap. 30.95 ***(978-1-61461-620-7(5))*** Cram101 Inc.

Cyna, Allan M., et al. Handbook of Communication in Anaesthesia & Critical Care: A Practical Guide to Exploring the Art. 2010. (ENG., Illus.). 288p. pap. 65.00 *(978-0-19-957728-6(5))* Oxford Univ. Pr., Inc.

Deakin, Charles D. Clinical Notes for the FRCA. 3rd ed. 2011. (FRCA Study Guides). (ENG., Illus.). 584p. pap. 49.95 *(978-0-7020-3525-8(4),* Churchill Livingstone) Elsevier - Health Sciences Div.

Dorsch, Jerry A. & Dorsch, Susan E. Understanding Anesthesia Equipment. 5th rev. ed. 2007. (ENG., Illus.). 1056p. 178.99 *(978-0-7817-7603-5(1))* Lippincott Williams & Wilkins.

Duke, James. Anesthesia Secrets. 4th ed. 2010. (Secrets Ser.). (ENG., Illus.). 592p. pap. 54.95 *(978-0-323-06524-5(4),* Mosby) Elsevier - Health Sciences Div.

Elfituri, Khaled, et al. MCQs for the Primary FRCA. 2008. (ENG., Illus.). 442p. pap. 58.00 *(978-0-521-70509-7(6))* Cambridge Univ. Pr.

Euliano, T. Y. Essential Anesthesia: From Science to Practice. 2nd ed. 2011. (ENG., Illus.). 214p. (C). pap. 49.00 *(978-0-521-14945-7(2))* Cambridge Univ. Pr.

Ezekiel, Mark. Handbook of Anesthesiology. 2007. (Current Clinical Strategies Digital Bks.). 246p. cd-rom 28.95 *(978-1-934323-01-4(2))* Current Clinical Strategies Publishing.

Feldman, S. A., et al, eds. Mechanisms of Drugs in Anaesthesia. 2nd rev. ed. (Illus.). 448p. *(978-0-340-55157-8(7),* Hodder Arnold) Hodder Education.

Fleisher, Lee A. Evidence-Based Practice of Anesthesiology: Expert Consult - Online & Print. 2nd ed. 2009. (ENG., Illus.). 544p. pap. 99.95 *(978-1-4160-5996-7(2),* Saunders) Elsevier - Health Sciences Div.

Fleisher, Lee A. & Roizen, Michael F. Essence of Anesthesia Practice: Expert Consult - Online & Print. 3rd ed. 2010. (ENG.). 768p. 86.95 *(978-1-4377-1720-4(9),* Saunders) Elsevier - Health Sciences Div.

Friedberg, Barry L. Getting over Going Under: 5 Things You Must Know Before Anesthesia. 2010. 116p. pap. 18.95 *(978-0-9829169-0-2(6))* Goldilocks Pr.

Gaiser, Robert R., et al. Obstetric, Thoracic & Cardiac Anesthesia: Handbook & IPod. 2009. (ENG., Illus.). 528p. pap. 79.95 *(978-1-4160-5997-4(0),* Saunders) Elsevier - Health Sciences Div.

Gold, Barbara & Gross, Wendy L. Anesthesia Outside the Operating Room, an Issue of Anesthesiology Clinics. 2009. (Clinics: Surgery Ser.: 27-1). (ENG., Illus.). 240p. 99.00 *(978-1-4377-0453-2(0),* Saunders) Elsevier - Health Sciences Div.

Goodwin, Alexander P. L. Dr Podcast Scripts for the Primary FRCA. Leslie, Rebecca A. & Johnson, Emily K., eds. 2011. (ENG., Illus.). 416p. pap. 55.00 *(978-1-107-40101-3(1))* Cambridge Univ. Pr.

Goodwin, Dawn. Acting in Anaesthesia: Ethnographic Encounters with Patients, Practioners & Medical Technologies. 2009. (Learning in Doing: Social, Cognitive & Computational Perspectives Ser.). (ENG.). 204p. 82.00 *(978-0-521-88206-4(0))* Cambridge Univ. Pr.

Grande, Christopher M., et al. Trauma: Resuscitation, Perioperative Management, & Critical Care, 2 vols. 2007. (ENG., Illus.). 2296p. 600.00 *(978-0-8247-5892-9(7))* Taylor & Francis Group.

Greco, Frédéric. Echography in Anesthesiology Intensive Care & Emergency Medicine: A Beginner's Guide. 2010. (ENG., Illus.). 96p. pap. 69.95 *(978-2-8178-0015-8(X)*, 281780015X) Springer.

Griffiths, Andrew, et al. Pre-Hospital Anaesthesia Handbook. 2010. (ENG., Illus.). xiii, 102p. pap. 39.95 *(978-1-84996-158-5(1)*, 1849961581) Springer.

Gwinnutt, Carl L. Clinical Anaesthesia. 3rd ed. 2008. (Lecture Notes Ser.). (ENG., Illus.). 184p. pap. 45.95 *(978-1-4051-7038-3(7)*, Wiley-Blackwell) Wiley, John & Sons, Inc.

Hagberg, Carin A. Benumof's Airway Management. 2nd rev. ed. 2007. (ENG., Illus.). 1344p. 218.00 *(978-0-323-02233-0(2)*, Mosby) Elsevier - Health Sciences Div.

Hall, Brian A. & Chantigian, Robert C. Anesthesia: A Comprehensive Review. 4th ed. 2010. (ENG., Illus.). 448p. pap. 92.95 *(978-0-323-06857-4(X)*, Mosby) Elsevier - Health Sciences Div.

Hall, Deborah C., et al, eds. Coding & Payment Guide for Anesthesia Services: An Essential Coding, Billing, & Reimbursement Resource for Anesthesiology & Pain Management. 2008. (Illus.). 540p. spiral bd. 179.95 *(978-1-60151-184-3(1))* OptumInsight, Inc.

Harrop-Griffiths, William. AAGBI Core Topics in Anaesthesia 2012. Johnston, Ian et al, eds. 2011. (ENG., Illus.). 164p. pap. 49.95 ***(978-0-470-65862-8(2)***, Wiley-Blackwell) Wiley, John & Sons, Inc.

Hartigan, Philip M., ed. Practical Handbook of Thoracic Anesthesia. 2012. (ENG., Illus.). xviii, 628p. pap. 69.95 *(978-0-387-88492-9(0)*, 0387884920) Springer.

Hatfield, Anthea & Tronson, Michael. The Complete Recovery Room Book. 4th ed. 2009. (ENG., Illus.). 500p. (Orig.). pap. 79.95 *(978-0-19-923268-0(7))* Oxford Univ. Pr., Inc.

Hines, Roberta L. & Marschall, Katherine E. Handbook for Stoelting's Anesthesia & Co-Existing Disease. 3rd ed. 2009. (ENG., Illus.). 525p. pap. 64.95 *(978-1-4160-3997-6(X)*, Saunders) Elsevier - Health Sciences Div.

Horton, Charles. Anesthesia Crash Course. 2008. (ENG., Illus.). 192p. pap. 19.95 *(978-0-19-537187-1(9))* Oxford Univ. Pr., Inc.

Hudetz, Anthony & Pearce, Robert, eds. Suppressing the Mind: Anesthetic Modulation of Memory & Consciousness. 2010. (Contemporary Neuroscience Ser.). (ENG., Illus.). x, 252p. 219.00 *(978-1-60761-463-0(4)*, 1607614634) Humana Pr.

Hunter, Jennifer, et al, eds. The Year Anaesthesia & Critical Care, Volume 2. 2008. (Year in Anaesthesia & Critical Care Ser.). (Illus.). 423p. *(978-1-84692-003-5(5))* Clinical Publishing Services.

Jaffe, Richard A., ed. Anesthesiologist's Manual of Surgical Procedures. 4th rev. ed. 2009. (ENG., Illus.). 1408p. 189.99 *(978-0-7817-6670-8(2))* Lippincott Williams & Wilkins.

Jakobsson, Jan. Anaesthesia for Day Case Surgery. 2009. (Oxford Anaesthesia Library). (ENG., Illus.). 118p. pap. 24.95 *(978-0-19-957713-2(7))* Oxford Univ. Pr., Inc.

Jawalekar, Shreeniwas. Open Drops to Open Hearts! Journey of an Anesthesiologist from India to America. 2010. 215p. pap. 13.95 *(978-1-4327-5269-9(3))* Outskirts Pr., Inc.

Kamath, B. S. K. & Turle, Sarah. MCQs for the Primary FRCA. 2010. (ENG., Illus.). 312p. pap. 52.95 *(978-0-19-957577-0(0))* Oxford Univ. Pr., Inc.

Kiff, Kevin & Spoors, Catherine, eds. Training in Anaesthesia. 2010. (Oxford Speciality Training Ser.). (ENG., Illus.). 672p. pap. 115.00 *(978-0-19-922726-6(8))* Oxford Univ. Pr., Inc.

Kobayashi, Ba. Cpt-4 Outpatient Coding Reference & Study Guide. 2010. 444p. pap. 99.00 *(978-1-60844-571-4(2))* Dog Ear Publishing, LLC.

Koht, Antoun, et al, eds. Monitoring the Nervous System for Anesthesiologists & Other Health Care Professionals. 2011. (ENG., Illus.). xxxvi, 810p. pap. 89.95 ***(978-1-4614-0307-4(3)***, 1461403073) Springer.

Kretz, Franz-Josef & Schäffer, Jürgen. Anästhesie, Intensivmedizin, Notfallmedizin, Schmerztherapie. 4th ed. 2007. (Springer-Lehrbuch Ser.). (Illus.). XVI, 455p. pap. 44.95 *(978-3-540-25698-4(9)*, 3540256989) Springer.

Kumar, Arun. Step by Step Regional Anesthesia. 2008. (Step by Step Ser.). (Illus.). 216p. pap. 34.95 *(978-1-84829-004-4(7))* Anshan GBR. Dist: Publishers Storage & Shipping.

Leslie, Rebecca A., et al, eds. Dr Podcast Scripts for the Final FRCA. 2011. (ENG., Illus.). 514p. pap. 60.00 ***(978-1-107-40100-6(3))*** Cambridge Univ. Pr.

Levine, Wilton C., ed. Clinical Anesthesia Procedures of the Massachusetts General Hospital: Department of Anesthesia, Critical Care & Pain Medicine, Massachusetts General Hospital, Harvard Medical School. 8th rev. ed. 2010. (ENG., Illus.). 728p. pap. 56.99 *(978-1-60547-460-1(6))* Lippincott Williams & Wilkins.

Longnecker, David, et al. Anesthesiology, Second Edition. 2nd ed. 2012. (ENG.). 2304p. 275.00 incl. DVD ***(978-0-07-178513-6(2)***, 0071785132) McGraw-Hill Professional Publishing.

Longnecker, David E. Anesthesiology. 2nd ed. 2012. ***(978-0-07-166484-4(X))*** McGraw-Hill Professional Publishing.

Longnecker, David E., et al. Anesthesiology. 2007. (ENG., Illus.). 2304p. 291.00 incl. cd-rom *(978-0-07-145984-6(7)*, 0071459847) McGraw-Hill Professional Publishing.

Lovich-Sapola, Jessica. Anesthesia Oral Board Review: Knocking Out the Boards. 2009. (ENG., Illus.). 366p. (C). pap. 60.00 *(978-0-521-75619-8(7))* Cambridge Univ. Pr.

McCombe, Kate, et al. The Primary FRCA Structured Oral Examination Study Guide 2. 2010. (Illus.). 270p. pap. *(978-1-84619-434-4(2))* Radcliffe Publishing.

McLoughlin, Thomas M. Advances in Anesthesia. 2011. (Advances Ser.: 2011). (ENG.). 344p. 156.00 ***(978-0-323-08404-8(4)***, Mosby) Elsevier - Health Sciences Div.

McMahon, Stephen & Koltzenburg, Martin. Wall y Melzack Tratado del Dolor. 5th ed. 2007. (SPA., Illus.). 1280p. 279.00 *(978-84-8174-949-6(4)*, Elsevier Espana) Elsevier - Health Sciences Div.

McQuillan, Patrick M., et al. Oxford American Handbook of Anesthesiology. 2008. (Oxford American Handbooks in Medicine Ser.). (ENG., Illus.). 1110p. vinyl bd. 42.95 *(978-0-19-530120-5(X))* Oxford Univ. Pr., Inc.

—Oxford American Handbook of Anesthesiology book & PDA Bundle. 2009. (Oxford American Handbooks in Medicine Ser.). (ENG.). (C). 79.95 *(978-0-19-534345-8(X))* Oxford Univ. Pr., Inc.

—Oxford American Handbook of Anesthesiology PDA. 2009. (Oxford American Handbooks in Medicine Ser.). (ENG.). (C). 59.95 *(978-0-19-533932-1(0))* Oxford Univ. Pr., Inc.

Miller, Ronald D., et al. Miller's Anesthesia, 2 vols. 7th ed. 2009. (ENG., Illus.). 3312p. 349.00 *(978-0-443-06959-8(X)*, Churchill Livingstone) Elsevier - Health Sciences Div.

Modak, Raj K. Anesthesiology Keywords Review. 2008. (ENG., Illus.). 576p. pap. 102.00 *(978-0-7817-8387-3(9))* Lippincott Williams & Wilkins.

Monsur, Sinha. Essential Topics & Cases for Anesthesia Oral Boards. 2011. 398p. pap. 50.50 ***(978-1-4357-6764-5(0))*** Lulu Enterprises Inc.

Murray, Michael J. Faust's Anesthesiology Review: Expert Consult - Online & Print. 4th ed. 2013. (ENG., Illus.). 624p. pap. 73.95 ***(978-1-4377-1369-5(6)***, Churchill Livingstone) Elsevier - Health Sciences Div.

Nagelhout, John J. & Plaus, Karen. Handbook of Nurse Anesthesia. 4th ed. 2009. (ENG.). 840p. pap. 64.95 *(978-1-4160-5024-7(8)*, Saunders) Elsevier - Health Sciences Div.

Neuman, Mark & Martinez, Elizabeth. Quality of Anesthesia Care, an Issue of Anesthesiology Clinics. 2011. (Clinics: Surgery Ser.: 29-1). (ENG., Illus.). 200p. 110.00 *(978-1-4557-0419-4(9)*, Saunders) Elsevier - Health Sciences Div.

Nickells, James, et al. SAQs for the Final FRCA. 2009. (ENG., Illus.). 220p. (C). pap. 60.00 *(978-0-521-73903-0(9))* Cambridge Univ. Pr.

Ochroch, E. Andrew. Anesthesia Pocket Consult: Airway Management & Thoracic Anesthesia: Print + IPod. 2008. (Illus.). 320p. pap. 69.95 *(978-1-4160-3133-8(2)*, Saunders) Elsevier - Health Sciences Div.

Orebaugh, Steven L. Understanding Anesthesia: What You Need to Know about Sedation & Pain Control. 2011. (Johns Hopkins Press Health Book Ser.). (ENG., Illus.). 168p. pap. 18.95 ***(978-1-4214-0317-5(X))***; (gr. 17). 45.00 ***(978-1-4214-0316-8(1))*** Johns Hopkins Univ. Pr.

Ouellette, Richard G. & Joyce, Joseph A. Pharmacology for Nurse Anesthesiology. rev. ed. 2010. 544p. pap. 86.95 *(978-0-7637-8607-6(1))* Jones & Bartlett Learning, LLC.

Peck, Tom E., et al. Pharmacology for Anaesthesia & Intensive Care. 3rd rev. ed. 2008. (ENG., Illus.). 390p. pap. 75.00 *(978-0-521-70463-2(4))* Cambridge Univ. Pr.

Pollard, Brian. Handbook of Clinical Anaesthesia. 3rd ed. 2012. (ENG., Illus.). 816p. pap. 125.00 ***(978-1-4441-0862-0(X))*** Hodder Arnold Pubs.

Power, Ian & Kam, Peter. Principles of Physiology for the Anaesthetist. 2nd ed. 2008. (ENG., Illus.). 432p. pap. 69.50 *(978-0-340-88799-8(0))* Hodder Arnold Pubs.

Ranasinghe, Sudharma, et al. Anesthesiology Board Review Pearls of Wisdom 3/E. 3rd ed. 2012. (Pearls of Wisdom Medicine Ser.). (ENG.). 430p. (C). pap. 79.00 ***(978-0-07-176145-1(4)***, 0071761454, McGraw-Hill/Appleton & Lange) McGraw-Hill Professional Publishing.

Rosenbaum, Stanley H. & Kohl, Benjamin A. Anesthesiology for Patients Too Sick for Anesthesia: Anesthesiology Clinics. 2010. (Clinics: Surgery Ser.: 28-1). (ENG., Illus.). xvi, 183p. 105.00 *(978-1-4377-1795-2(0)*, Saunders) Elsevier - Health Sciences Div.

Sandberg, Warren, et al. The MGH Textbook of Anesthetic Equipment. 2010. (ENG., Illus.). 640p. 142.00 *(978-1-4377-0973-5(7)*, Churchill Livingstone) Elsevier - Health Sciences Div.

Schnttler, Jnrgen, ed. 50 Jahre Deutsche Gesellschaft Fnr Anssthesiologie und Intensivmedizin. 2007. 616p. 69.95 *(978-3-540-00057-0(7))* Springer.

Shorten, George, et al. Case-Based Anesthesia: Clinical Learning Guides. 2009. (ENG., Illus.). 238p. 114.99 *(978-0-7817-8955-4(9))* Lippincott Williams & Wilkins.

Shorthouse, James R., et al. SAQs for the Final FRCA Examination. 2011. (ENG., Illus.). 384p. pap. 79.95 *(978-0-19-958328-7(5))* Oxford Univ. Pr., Inc.

Silverstein, Jeffrey, et al, eds. Geriatric Anesthesiology. 2nd ed. 2010. (Illus.). xvi, 440p. pap. 49.95 *(978-1-4419-7087-9(8)*, 1441970878) Springer.

Sladen, Arnold. Postoperative Medical Care: A Society of Cardiovascular Anesthesiologists Monograph. Sladen, Robert N., ed. 2011. (ENG.). cd-rom 99.00 *(978-1-4511-2768-3(5))* Lippincott Williams & Wilkins.

Snow, Stephanie J. Blessed Days of Anaesthesia: How Anaesthetics Changed the World. 2010. (ENG.). 226p. 35.00 *(978-1-4379-7334-1(5))* DIANE Publishing Co.

—Blessed Days of Anaesthesia: How anaesthetics changed the World. 2009. (ENG., Illus.). 256p. 18.95 *(978-0-19-280589-8(4))* Oxford Univ. Pr., Inc.

Sonner, James M., ed. Manual of Anesthesia Practice. 2007. (Cambridge Pocket Clinicians Ser.). (ENG.). 1108p. per. 58.00 *(978-0-521-70935-4(0))* Cambridge Univ. Pr.

Spies, Claudia, et al, eds. Check-up Anesthesiology & Pain Therapy. 2007. 450p. pap. 19.95 *(978-3-540-32996-1(X)*, 354032996X) Springer.

Stone, Juliana. Anaesthesia at a Glance. 2010. (ENG.). 104p. pap. *(978-1-4051-8756-5(5)*, Wiley-Blackwell) Wiley, John & Sons, Ltd.

Thomas, Christopher & Butler, Christopher. Examination Anaesthesia. 2nd rev. ed. 2010. (ENG., Illus.). xxiii, 241p. pap. 89.95 *(978-0-7295-3947-0(4)*, Churchill Livingstone) Elsevier - Health Sciences Div.

Tremper, Kevin K. & Kheterpal, Sachin. Information Technology Applied to Anesthesiology: Anesthesiology Clinics of North America. 2011. (Clinics: Surgery Ser.: 29-3). (ENG., Illus.). xvi, 356p. 110.00 *(978-1-4557-1030-0(X)*, Saunders) Elsevier - Health Sciences Div.

Van Norman, Gail A., et al, eds. Clinical Ethics in Anesthesiology: A Case-Based Textbook. 2010. (ENG., Illus.). 318p. pap. 60.00 *(978-0-521-13064-6(6))* Cambridge Univ. Pr.

Ward, C. S. Ward's Anaesthetic Equipment. Davey, Andrew J. & Diba, Ali, eds. 6th ed. 2012. (ENG., Illus.). 600p. 135.00 ***(978-0-7020-3094-9(5)***, Saunders) Elsevier - Health Sciences Div.

Weiss, Stuart & Milas, Bonnie L. Anesthesia Pocket Consult: Cardiac Anesthesia: Print + IPod. 2008. (Illus.). pap. 69.95 *(978-1-4160-4651-6(8)*, Saunders) Elsevier - Health Sciences Div.

Woodworth, Glenn & Kirsch, Jeffrey R. The Anesthesia Technician & Technologist's Manual: All You Need to Know for Study & Reference. 2012. (Illus.). 608p. pap. 94.99 ***(978-1-4511-4266-2(8))*** Lippincott Williams & Wilkins.

ANESTHESIOLOGY—STUDY AND TEACHING

Davis, James B., ed. 2008 Coding Guide Anesthesia. 2007. per. 129.95 *(978-1-57066-465-6(X))* Practice Management Information Corp.

Robinson, Neville, et al. How to Survive in Anaesthesia: A Guide for Trainees. 4th ed. 2012. (ENG., Illus.). 256p. pap. 59.95 ***(978-0-470-65462-0(7))*** Wiley, John & Sons, Inc.

ANESTHETICS

see also Analgesics; Anesthesia; Chloroform; Curare; Ether (Anesthetic); Sedatives

Allman, Keith, et al, eds. Anaesthesia & Emergencies in Anaesthesia, Pack. 2007. (Oxford Handbooks Ser.). (Illus.). 1088p. pap. 89.95 *(978-0-19-923940-5(1))* Oxford Univ. Pr., Inc.

Aronson, Jeffrey K. Drugs Used in Anesthesia. 2008. (Meyler's Side Effects of Drugs Ser.). (ENG.). 320p. 63.95 *(978-0-444-53270-1(6)*, Elsevier Science) Elsevier Science & Technology Bks.

Atlee, John L. Complications in Anesthesia. 2nd rev. ed. 2006. (ENG., Illus.). 1040p. 164.00 *(978-1-4160-2215-2(5)*, Saunders) Elsevier - Health Sciences Div.

Avsaroglu, Harutyun. Genetic Background & the Response to Anaesthetics & Analgesics. 2009. (Illus.). 124p. pap. *(978-3-639-15296-8(4))* VDM Verlag Dr. Mueller e.K.

Baughman, Verna L., et al, eds. Anesthesiology & Critical Care Drug Handbook: Including Select Disease States & Perioperative Management. 9th ed. 2009. (Anesthesiology & Critical Care Drug Handbook Ser.). (Illus.). 1821p. pap. 46.95 *(978-1-59195-275-6(1))* Lexi-Comp, Inc.

Borshoff, David. Anaesthetic Crisis Manual. 2011. (ENG.). 60p. spiral bd. 29.99 ***(978-0-521-27986-4(0))*** Cambridge Univ. Pr.

Bowman-Howard, Michelle. Anesthesia Review. 2nd rev. ed. 2006. (ENG., Illus.). 388p. 66.95 *(978-0-7817-9444-2(7))* Lippincott Williams & Wilkins.

Burch, Thomas M., et al. Conquer the PTE Exam. 2007. (ENG., Illus.). 544p. pap. 98.95 *(978-1-4160-3833-7(7)*, Saunders) Elsevier - Health Sciences Div.

Burkey, Dell. Regional Anesthesia & Pain Management: Handbook & IPod. 2009. (ENG., Illus.). 432p. pap., instr.'s hndbk. ed. 79.95 *(978-1-4160-3344-8(0)*, Saunders) Elsevier - Health Sciences Div.

Cohen, Neal, ed. Medically Challenging Patients Undergoing Cardiothoracic Surgery: A Society of Cardiovascular Anesthesiologists Monograph. 2009. (ENG.). 360p. 68.00 *(978-1-60831-299-3(2))* Lippincott Williams & Wilkins.

Cox, Felicia, ed. Perioperative Pain Management. 2008. (ENG., Illus.). 336p. pap., instr.'s hndbk. ed. 83.99 *(978-1-4051-8077-1(3)*, Wiley-Blackwell) Wiley, John & Sons, Inc.

Cram101 Textbook Reviews. Outlines & Highlights for Anesthesia & Co-Existing Disease by Roberta L Hines, Isbn: 9781416039983 1416039988. 2011. 446p. pap. 36.95 ***(978-1-61812-193-6(6))*** Cram101 Inc.

Cram101 Textbook Reviews & Cram101 Textbook Reviews. Outlines & Highlights for Clinical Anesthesia by Paul G Barash, Isbn: 9780781787635 0781787637. 2011. 688p. pap. 42.95 ***(978-1-61490-398-7(0))*** Cram101 Inc.

—Outlines & Highlights for Nurse Anesthesia by John J Nagelhout, Karen L Plaus, Isbn: 9781416050254. 2011. 520p. pap. 38.95 ***(978-1-61461-722-8(8))*** Cram101 Inc.

Cross, Matthew & Plunkett, Emma. Physics, Pharmacology & Physiology for Anaesthetists: Key Concepts for the FRCA. 2008. (ENG., Illus.). 268p. pap. 53.00 *(978-0-521-70044-3(2))* Cambridge Univ. Pr.

Dosch, Mathias. Atlas of Neural Therapy with Local Anesthetics. 3rd ed. 2012. (ENG., Illus.). 224p. 129.99 ***(978-3-13-130573-2(8))*** Thieme Medical Pubs., Inc.

Evers, Alex S., et al, eds. Anesthetic Pharmacology: Basic Principles & Clinical Practice. 2nd ed. 2011. (ENG., Illus.). 1210p. 195.00 *(978-0-521-89666-5(5))* Cambridge Univ. Pr.

Fleisher, Lee A. & Roizen, Michael F. Essence of Anesthesia Practice: Expert Consult - Online & Print. 3rd ed. 2010. (ENG.). 768p. 86.95 *(978-1-4377-1720-4(9)*, Saunders) Elsevier - Health Sciences Div.

Griffiths, Andrew, et al. Pre-Hospital Anaesthesia Handbook. 2010. (ENG., Illus.). xiii, 102p. pap. 39.95 *(978-1-84996-158-5(1)*, 1849961581) Springer.

Gwinnutt, Carl L. Clinical Anaesthesia. 3rd ed. 2008. (Lecture Notes Ser.). (ENG., Illus.). 184p. pap. 45.95 *(978-1-4051-7038-3(7)*, Wiley-Blackwell) Wiley, John & Sons, Inc.

Gwinnutt, Carl L. & Gwinnutt, Matthew. Lecture Notes Clinical Anaesthesia. 4th ed. 2012. (Lecture Notes Ser.: 39). (ENG.). 208p. pap. 42.95 ***(978-0-470-65892-5(4)***, Wiley-Blackwell) Wiley, John & Sons, Inc.

Hines, Roberta L. & Marschall, Katherine E. Anesthesia & Co-Existing Disease. 5th ed. 2008. (Expert Consult Title: Online + Print Ser.). (ENG., Illus.). 688p. 159.00 *(978-1-4160-3998-3(8)*, Saunders) Elsevier - Health Sciences Div.

Horton, Charles. Anesthesia Crash Course. 2008. (ENG., Illus.). 192p. pap. 19.95 *(978-0-19-537187-1(9))* Oxford Univ. Pr., Inc.

Kumar, Amit, et al. Effect of Adding Fentanyl & Buprenorphine to L a in Brachial Block. 2011. 92p. pap. ***(978-3-8443-1749-7(X))*** Lambert Academic Publishing.

Mahajan, Ravi & Nathanson, Michael. Anaesthesia. 2007. (Churchill Pocketbooks Ser.). (ENG., Illus.). 400p. vinyl bd. 49.95 *(978-0-443-07026-6(1)*, Churchill Livingstone) Elsevier - Health Sciences Div.

Mashour, George A. & Lydic, Ralph, eds. Neuroscientific Foundations of Anesthesiology, 1 vol. 2011. (ENG., Illus.). 296p. 125.00 *(978-0-19-539824-3(6))* Oxford Univ. Pr., Inc.

McQuillan, Patrick M., et al. Oxford American Handbook of Anesthesiology. 2008. (Oxford American Handbooks in Medicine Ser.). (ENG., Illus.). 1110p. vinyl bd. 42.95 *(978-0-19-530120-5(X))* Oxford Univ. Pr., Inc.

—Oxford American Handbook of Anesthesiology book & PDA Bundle. 2009. (Oxford American Handbooks in Medicine Ser.). (ENG.). (C). 79.95 *(978-0-19-534345-8(X))* Oxford Univ. Pr., Inc.

Metcalfe, Stuart & Reilly, Ian. Foot & Ankle Injection Techniques: A Practical Guide. 2010. (ENG., Illus.). 208p. (C). spiral bd. 75.95 *(978-0-7020-3107-6(0)*, Churchill Livingstone) Elsevier - Health Sciences Div.

Miller, Ronald D., et al. Miller's Anesthesia, 2 vols. 7th ed. 2009. (ENG., Illus.). 3312p. 349.00 *(978-0-443-06959-8(X)*, Churchill Livingstone) Elsevier - Health Sciences Div.

Mythen, Michael (Monty), et al. Anaesthesiology: Churchill's Ready Reference. 2010. (ENG., Illus.). 200p. (C). pap. 39.95 *(978-0-08-045137-4(3)*, Churchill Livingstone) Elsevier - Health Sciences Div.

Nagelhout, John J. & Plaus, Karen. Handbook of Nurse Anesthesia. 4th ed. 2009. (ENG.). 840p. pap. 64.95 *(978-1-4160-5024-7(8)*, Saunders) Elsevier - Health Sciences Div.

Ochroch, E. Andrew. Anesthesia Pocket Consult: Airway Management & Thoracic Anesthesia: Print + IPod. 2008. (Illus.). 320p. pap. 69.95 *(978-1-4160-3133-8(2)*, Saunders) Elsevier - Health Sciences Div.

Schattler, Jargen & Schwilden, Helmut. Modern Anesthetics. 2010. (Handbook of Experimental Pharmacology Ser.). (Illus.). xvi, 498p. pap. 529.00 *(978-3-642-09192-6(X)*, 364209192X) Springer.

Schüttler, Jürgen & Schwilden, Helmut. Modern Anesthetics. 2007. (Handbook of Experimental Pharmacology Ser.). 500p. 529.00 *(978-3-540-72813-9(9)*, 3540728139) Springer.

Shorten, George, et al. Case-Based Anesthesia: Clinical Learning Guides. 2009. (ENG., Illus.). 238p. 114.99 *(978-0-7817-8955-4(9))* Lippincott Williams & Wilkins.

Smith, Susan, et al. Drugs in Anaesthesia & Intensive Care. 4th ed. 2011. (ENG.). 404p. pap. 52.95 *(978-0-19-959938-7(6))* Oxford Univ. Pr., Inc.

Snow, Stephanie J. Blessed Days of Anaesthesia: How Anaesthetics Changed the World. 2008. (ENG., Illus.). 256p. 34.95 *(978-0-19-280586-7(X))* Oxford Univ. Pr., Inc.

Sonner, James M., ed. Manual of Anesthesia Practice. 2007. (Cambridge Pocket Clinicians Ser.). (ENG.). 1108p. per. 58.00 *(978-0-521-70935-4(0))* Cambridge Univ. Pr.

Valchanov, Kamen, et al, eds. Anaesthetic & Perioperative Complications. 2011. (ENG., Illus.). 272p. pap. 79.00 ***(978-1-107-00259-3(1))*** Cambridge Univ. Pr.

ANESTHETICS—ADMINISTRATION

Ferreira, David A., et al, eds. Recent Advances in BIS Guided TCI Anesthesia. 2010. (Advances in Biology & Medicine (Series Editor - Tsisana Shartava, M. D. - Tbilisi, Georgia) Ser.). 77p. pap. 43.00 *(978-1-61668-627-7(8))* Nova Science Pubs., Inc.

Malamed, Stanley F. Sedation: A Guide to Patient Management. 5th ed. 2009. (ENG., Illus.). 624p. (C). pap 83.95 *(978-0-323-05680-9(6)*, Mosby) Elsevier - Health Sciences Div.

ANESTHETICS IN DENTISTRY

see Anesthesia in Dentistry

ANESTHETICS IN OBSTETRICS

see Anesthesia in Obstetrics

ANESTHETICS IN OPHTHALMOLOGY

see Anesthesia in Ophthalmology

ANESTHETICS IN VETERINARY SURGERY

see Anesthesia in Veterinary Surgery

A

ANEUPLOIDY

De Rossi, Salvatore & Bianchi, Filippo. Aneuploidy: Etiology, Disorders, & Risk Factors. 2011. ***(978-1-62100-070-9(2))*** Nova Science Pubs., Inc.

Delhanty, J. D. A. & Pellestor, F., eds. Aneuploidy: Reprint of: 'Cytogenetic & Genome Research 2011, Vol. 133, No. 2-4' 2011. (Illus.). 210p. *(978-3-8055-9736-4(3))* Karger, S. AG.

Rasnick, David. The Chromosomal Imbalance Theory of Cancer. 2011. (ENG., Illus.). 330p. 119.95 ***(978-1-57808-737-2(6))*** BIOS Scientific Publishers Ltd. GBR. Dist: Taylor & Francis Group.

ANEURYSMS

see also Intracranial Aneurysms

Doyle, Barry J., et al. Abdominal Aortic Aneurysms: New Approaches to Rupture Risk Assessment. 2010. (Cardiology Research & Clinical Developments Ser.). (Illus.). xii, 81p. pap. 43.00 *(978-1-61668-312-2(0))* Nova Science Pubs., Inc.

Dupouy, Cathy. It's Not That Bad! My Brain Blew Up! 2011. 132p. 21.23 ***(978-1-4670-3571-2(8))***; pap. 10.68 ***(978-1-4670-3572-9(6))*** AuthorHouse.

Florin, Esther. Implementation of a Magnetic Device to Rotate a Stent. 2008. 100p. pap. *(978-3-8364-7415-3(8))* VDM Verlag Dr. Mueller e.K.

Heitzman, PegE. Throughout These Forty Days. 2011. 56p. pap. 9.95 *(978-1-4497-1445-1(5)*, WestBow Pr.) Author Solutions, Inc.

Laurent, Alain & Morel, Ethan. Aneurysms: Types, Risks, Formation & Treatment. 2009. 129.00 *(978-1-60741-557-2(7)*, Nova Biomedical Bks.) Nova Science Pubs., Inc.

Lu, Jing. Detection of Endoleaks in Ct Data for Monitoring of Aaa Stents. 2008. (Illus.). 108p. pap. *(978-3-639-01367-2(0))* VDM Verlag Dr. Mueller e.K.

Magee, Donna G. Aneurysm: Fire in the Brain. 2009. 136p. pap. 11.95 *(978-1-60594-274-2(X)*, Llumina Pr.) Aeon Publishing Inc.

McGloughlin, Tim, ed. Biomechanics & Mechanobiology of Aneurysms. 2011. (Studies in Mechanobiology, Tissue Engineering & Biomaterials Ser.). (ENG., Illus.). xiv, 424p. 179.00 *(978-3-642-18094-1(9)*, 3642180949) Springer.

McGrath, Rick. Johanna's Journey: A True Story of Love, Loss & Faith. 2006. (Illus.). 211p. pap. 11.95 *(978-0-9773576-1-1(9))* Matilija Pr.

Overton, Margaret. Good in a Crisis: A Memoir. 2012. (ENG.). 256p. 24.00 ***(978-1-60819-764-4(6))*** Bloomsbury Publishing.

Siles, Madonna. Eureka! Memories & Motivations: A Strategy for Creating a Healing Home for the Stroke / Brain Injury Patient & Caregiver. 2010. (ENG., Illus.). 216p. pap. 17.95 *(978-0-9825518-0-6(0))* Third Step Pr.

Strickland, Linda Denise. Aneurysms-Why Me? Why Not Me? 2008. 142p. pap. 24.95 *(978-1-60474-035-6(3))* PublishAmerica, Inc.

Takebayashi, Shigeo, et al. Transcatheter Coil Embolization of Visceral Arterial Aneurysms. 2009. (Cardiology Research & Clinical Developments Ser.). (Illus.). 93p. pap. 43.00 *(978-1-60741-439-1(2))* Nova Science Pubs., Inc.

Upchurch, Gilbert R. & Criado, Enrique. Aortic Aneurysms: Pathogenesis & Treatment. 2009. (Illus.). xvii, 381p. E-Book *(978-1-60327-204-9(6))*; 518p. 219.00 *(978-1-60327-203-2(8))* Humana Pr.

Watkins, Margaret. Fine Line. 2006. pap. 14.95 *(978-1-4327-0250-2(5))* Outskirts Pr., Inc.

ANGAMI NAGAS

see Naga (South Asian People)

ANGELA MERICI, SAINT, 1474-1540

Mazzonis, Querciolo. Spirituality, Gender, & the Self in Renaissance Italy: Angela Merici & the Company of St. Ursula (1474-1540) 2007. 247p. per. 35.95 *(978-0-8132-1490-0(4))* Catholic Univ. of America Pr.

ANGELICO, FRA, CA. 1400-1455

Angelico, et al. Rediscovering Fra Angelico: A Fragmentary History. 2006. (ENG., Illus.). 58p. pap. 10.00 *(978-0-89467-950-6(3))* Yale Univ. Art Gallery.

Bartz, Gabriele. Fra Angelico: Guido Di Piero, Ca. 1395-1455. 2008. (Masters of Italian Art Ser.). (Illus.). 119p. pap. 9.95 *(978-0-8416-0079-9(1))* American Map Corp.

Cole Ahl, Diane. Fra Angelico. 2008. (ENG., Illus.). 240p. 69.95 *(978-0-7148-4830-3(1))* Phaidon Pr. Ltd. GBR. Dist: Hachette Bk. Group.

Kanter, Laurence B. Reconstructing the Renaissance: Saint James Freeing Hermogenes by Fra Angelico. 2008. (Kimbell Masterpiece Ser.). (ENG., Illus.). 84p. pap. 16.95 *(978-0-300-12136-0(9))* Kimbell Art Museum.

ANGELOLOGY

see Angels

ANGELOU, MAYA, 1928-

Angelou, Maya. The Heart of a Woman. 2009. (ENG.). 352p. pap. 15.00 *(978-0-8129-8032-5(8)*, Random Hse. Trade Paperbacks) Random House Publishing Group.

—I Know Why the Caged Bird Sings. 2009. (ENG.). 304p. pap. 17.00 *(978-0-8129-8002-8(6)*, Random Hse. Trade Paperbacks); mass mkt. 6.99 *(978-0-345-51440-0(8)*, Ballantine Bks.) Random House Publishing Group.

—I Know Why the Caged Bird Sings: Novel Test: Prestwick Premium Downloadable Resources. 2007. 6p. 5.99 *(978-1-60843-643-9(8))* Prestwick Hse., Inc.

—Letter to My Daughter. (ENG.). 192p. 2009. pap. 15.00 *(978-0-8129-8003-5(4)*, Random Hse. Trade Paperbacks) 2008. 25.00 *(978-1-4000-6612-4(3)*, Random House) Random House Publishing Group.

Bloom, Harold. I Know Why the Caged Bird Sings. 2nd rev. ed. 2010. (Bloom's Guides). 122p. (C). (gr. 9). 30.00 *(978-1-60413-876-4(9)*, Chelsea Hse.) Facts On File, Inc.

Gillespie, Marcia, et al. Maya Angelou: A Glorious Celebration. l.t. ed. 2008. 250p. 31.95 *(978-1-4104-0983-6(X))* Thorndike Pr.

Johnson, Claudia D. Racism in Maya Angelou's I Know Why the Caged Bird Sings. 2007. (Social Issues in Literature Ser.). (ENG., Illus.). 150p. (YA). (gr. 10-12). 26.50 *(978-0-7377-3905-3(3)*, LML02109-238410); pap. 38.45 *(978-0-7377-3901-5(0)*, LML02109-238371) Cengage Gale. (Greenhaven Pr., Inc.).

Thursby, Jacqueline S. Critical Companion to Maya Angelou. 2011. (Critical Companion to Ser.). (Illus.). 440p. (C). (gr. 9). 75.00 *(978-0-8160-8093-9(3))* Facts On File, Inc.

Wedin, Carolyn. Bloom's How to Write about Maya Angelou. 2011. (Bloom's How to Write about Literature Ser.). 228p. (C). (gr. 9). 45.00 *(978-1-60413-891-7(2)*, Chelsea Hse.) Facts On File, Inc.

ANGELS

see also Ark of the Covenant

Akporeha, Thompson. Angels' Protection. 2010. 54p. pap. 15.99 *(978-1-4500-7917-4(2))* Xlibris Corp.

Aladokun, Oba Ilari. Ancestor Paths; Honoring our Ancestors & Guardian Spirits Through Prayers, Rituals, & Offerings. 2009. 212p. pap. 16.95 *(978-1-935097-27-3(X))* Hillcrest Publishing Group, Inc.

Almstedt, Debbie Z. Zibu the Power of Angelic Symbology. 2nd ed. 2007. (Illus.). 220p. per. 16.95 *(978-0-9798302-0-4(6))* Zibu Publishing.

Amato, Norman. Hidden Angels: An Anthology of Angels. 2008. 108p. pap. 18.00 *(978-1-4251-3853-0(5))* Trafford Publishing.

American Bible Society Staff. ABS Angels & Miracles: The Spiritual Realm & the World You Know. 2009. (ENG.). 128p. 25.95 *(978-1-60320-086-8(X))* Time Home Entertainment, Inc.

Anderson, Joan Wester. An Angel to Watch over Me: True Stories of Children's Encounters with Angels. 2012. (ENG.). 144p. pap. 14.95 ***(978-0-8294-3654-9(5))*** Loyola Pr.

—Guardian Angels: True Stories of Answered Prayers. 2006. (ENG.). 240p. per. 14.95 *(978-0-8294-2169-9(6))* Loyola Pr.

—Where Miracles Happen: True Stories of Heavenly Encounters. 2009. (ENG.). 288p. pap. 14.95 *(978-0-8294-2903-9(4))* Loyola Pr.

Anderson, Ken/Ponder. Angels Are Real: They Are in Our Skies & Before Our Eyes. Anderson, Auburn/Ponder, ed. 2007. pap. 15.95 *(978-0-9793906-6-1(4))* Beam Me Up Lord Publishing Hse.

Andrews, Ted. The Intercession of Spirits: Working with Animals, Angels & Ancestors. 2008. (Illus.). 287p. pap. 14.95 *(978-1-888767-55-1(3))* Dragonhawk Publishing.

Aquilina, Mike. Angels of God: The Bible, the Church & the Heavenly Hosts. 2009. 128p. pap. 12.99 *(978-0-86716-898-3(6)*, Servant Bks.) Franciscan Media.

Aquilina, Mike. A Year with the Angels: Daily Meditations with the Messengers of God. 2011. (ENG.). lthr. 44.95 ***(978-1-935302-52-0(3))*** St. Benedict Pr., LLC.

Arthur, Rosemary. Pseudo-dionysius as Polemicist: The development & purpose of the angelic hierarchy in 6th century Syria. 2008. (New Critical Thinking in Religion, Theology & Biblical Studies). 226p. 99.95 *(978-0-7546-6258-7(6))* Ashgate Publishing Co.

Astell, Christine. Gifts from the Angels: Inspiring Stories of Angelic Intervention. 2011. (ENG.). 256p. pap. 14.95 *(978-1-78028-009-7(2)*, Watkins Publishing) Duncan Baird Pubs. GBR. Dist: Sterling Publishing Co., Inc.

B. Maureen Gaglardi. Angels Are for Us. 2010. 82p. 24.99 *(978-1-4535-2685-9(4))*; pap. 15.99 *(978-1-4535-2684-2(6))* Xlibris Corp.

Baker, H. A. Heaven & Angels. 2009. 160p. pap. *(978-1-905991-33-4(9))* New Wine Pr.

Ballinger, Jean Mills. In the Presence of Angels. 2008. 168p. pap. 17.99 *(978-1-4389-0350-7(2))* AuthorHouse.

Bandstra, Andrew J. In the Company of Angels: What the Bible Teaches, What You Need to Know. *(978-0-08-923922-5(9))* Brassey's, UK Ltd.

Barnard, George. In the Service Of 11:11: A Celestial / Mortal Alliance. 2010. (11.11 Documents Ser.). (Illus.). 244p. pap. 15.00 *(978-0-9577889-5-4(9))* 11.11 Publishers Pty Ltd AUS. Dist: AtlasBooks Distribution.

Barnes, Kathy. Angels Protect Giraffes. 2010. 16p. pap. 7.95 *(978-1-4497-0577-0(4)*, WestBow Pr.) Author Solutions, Inc.

Barnes, Velva. Angels Still Fly. 2010. 60p. pap. 13.95 *(978-1-4497-0492-6(1)*, WestBow Pr.) Author Solutions, Inc.

Bartlett, Sarah. A Brief History of Angels & Demons. 2011. (ENG.). 380p. pap. 13.95 *(978-0-7624-4278-2(6))* Running Pr. Bk. Pubs.

Batten, Robert J. The G Street Chronicles: Our Amazing Journey. 2011. pap. 20.99 *(978-1-61739-153-8(0))* Tate Publishing & Enterprises, LLC.

Berg, Joseph Frederick. Abaddon, & Mahanaim; or, Daemons & Guardian Angels. 2006. 276p. per. 23.99 *(978-1-4255-2522-4(9))* MPublishing.

Berg, Yehuda. Angel Intelligence. 2007. (ENG.). 256p. 17.95 *(978-1-57189-569-1(8))* Research Centre of Kabbalah.

Bowlin, Metaphysician, Reiki Master Teacher Dorie, Spiritual Messenger. Down-to-Earth Angel Messages. 2008. 58p. pap. 14.95 *(978-0-557-00673-1(2))* Lulu Enterprises Inc.

Bowman, Robert M., et al. Sense & Nonsense about Angels & Demons, 1 vol. 2007. (Sense & Nonsense Ser.). (ENG.). 160p. (gr. 13). pap. 9.99 *(978-0-310-25429-4(9))* Zondervan.

Bowyer, Carolyn Gilbody. The Angels of the First Heaven: How to Work with the Seven Archangels. 2007. (ENG., Illus.). 160p. per. 21.95 *(978-1-84694-015-6(X))* O Bks.,John Hunt.

Brown, Eva M. The Employ of Angels. 2009. 92p. pap. 10.49 *(978-1-4343-6589-7(1))* AuthorHouse.

Brown, Francesca. The Voices of Angels. 2012. (ENG.). 272p. pap. 11.95 ***(978-1-4447-3617-5(5)***, Hodder & Stoughton) Hodder General Publishing Div. GBR. Dist: Independent Pubs. Group.

Browne, Sylvia. El Libro de los Ángeles de Sylvia Browne. 2006. (SPA & ENG., Illus.). 192p. per. 14.95 *(978-1-4019-1680-0(5))* Hay Hse., Inc.

Bruce, Marie. Angel Craft & Healing: Tap into This Vital Source of Power & Magickal Help to Enhance Your Life. 2007. (ENG., Illus.). 160p. per. 18.95 *(978-0-572-03317-0(6))* Foulsham, W. Co., Ltd. GBR. Dist: APG Sales & Distribution Services.

Buck, Roland. Angeles en Misiones Especiales: Angels on Assignment. (SPA.). 236p. *(978-84-7228-559-0(6)*, 360023) Clie, Editorial.

Bulgakov, Sergei Nikolaevich. Jacob's Ladder: On Angels. 2010. 183p. pap. 25.00 *(978-0-8028-6516-8(X))* Eerdmans, William B. Publishing Co.

Burge, Stephen. Angels in Islam: Jalal Al-Din Al-Suyuti's Al-Haba'Ik Fi Akhbar Al-Mala'Ik. 2011. (Culture & Civilization in the Middle East Ser.). (ENG., Illus.). 352p. (C). 145.00 *(978-0-415-67292-4(9))* Routledge.

Burnham, Kirstin. Borderlands: Angels I Have Known. 2009. 72p. pap. 15.99 *(978-1-4415-9493-8(0))* Xlibris Corp.

Burnham, Sophy. A Book of Angels: Reflections on Angels Past & Present, & True Stories of How They Touch Our Lives. 2011. (ENG.). 384p. (gr. 12). 16.95 *(978-1-58542-877-9(9)*, Tarcher) Penguin Group (USA) Inc.

Burson, Nancy. Lineage: What If the Universe Gave You a Gift? 3rd ed. 2008. (ENG., Illus.). 1p. pap. *(978-0-615-19546-9(6))* ThankYouVeryMuch Publishing.

Calbaris, Argyris. Nothing Is Ever Lost. 2008. 288p. pap. *(978-960-88940-7-5(7))* Elytron Pubns.

Campo Hernandez, Yanira. Arcangeles: Amor, Amistad y Armonia. 2009. 68p. pap. 12.99 *(978-1-4269-1418-8(0))* Trafford Publishing.

Carpenter, Thomas E. Angel Talks: Unraveling the Mysteries of God. 2010. 275p. per. 14.95 *(978-1-931741-84-2(0))* Reed, Robert D. Pubs.

Catholic Book Publishing Co, creator. Angels Surround Us. 2008. (St. Joseph Rattle Board Bks.). (Illus.). 14p. (gr. -1-k). bds. 4.95 *(978-0-89942-724-9(3))* Catholic Bk. Publishing Corp.

Cec, Gerard. The Looking Angel. 2011. 108p. pap. 15.99 ***(978-1-4628-7669-3(2))*** Xlibris Corp.

Channer, Cecily & Brown, Damon. The Complete Idiot's Guide to Connecting with Your Angels. 2009. (Complete Idiot's Guide Ser.). (ENG.). 272p. (gr. 12-18). pap. 14.95 *(978-1-59257-878-8(0)*, Alpha Bks.) Penguin Group (USA) Inc.

Chapian, Marie. Angels in Our Lives: Everything You've Always Wanted to Know about Angels & How They Affect Your Life. 2006. 271p. per. 15.99 *(978-0-7684-2370-9(8))* Destiny Image Pubs.

—Angels in Our Lives Special Hard Cover Edition. 2008. 276p. 32.99 *(978-0-7684-2807-0(6))* Destiny Image Pubs.

Chapman, George. Bussy DAmbois & the Revenge of Bussy D. 2006. pap. 34.95 *(978-1-4286-3512-8(2))* Kessinger Publishing, LLC.

Choquette, S. Ask Your Guides. 2008. 360p. *(978-1-4019-1615-2(5)*, 514) Hay Hse. UK, Ltd. GBR. Dist: Grantham Bk. Services.

Christian, Loren. Angel Justice. 2008. 156p. pap. 19.95 *(978-0-557-00589-5(2))* Lulu Enterprises Inc.

Clarke, Victoria Mary. Why Did God Make Gucci If Not for Me? 2007. (ENG., Illus.). 344p. pap. 23.95 *(978-1-905172-35-1(4))* Collins Pr., The IRL. Dist: Dufour Editions, Inc.

Clayton, George. Angelology Remarks & Reflections Touching the Agency & Ministration of Holy Angels by George Clayton, Jr. 2006. 268p. per. 23.99 *(978-1-4255-2431-9(1))* MPublishing.

Clivaz, C. L' Ange et la Sueur de Sang (Lc 22,43-44) Ou Comment on Pourrait Bien Encore Ecrire l'Histoire. 2010. (Biblical Tools & Studies). (FRE.). 733p. (C). 124.00 *(978-90-429-2278-5(8))* Peeters Pubs. & Booksellers BEL. Dist: Brown, David Bk. Co., The.

Conrad, Laurie. Visits with Angels & Other Divine Beings. 2011. 212p. pap. 14.95 ***(978-1-4567-5035-0(6))*** AuthorHouse.

Constantine, Orlando. 2008-2010 Notes to the Book Angels, Let's Talk. 2010. 353p. pap. 22.61 *(978-0-557-50076-5(1))* Lulu Enterprises Inc.

Conway, D. J. Guides, Guardians & Angels: Enhance Relationships with Your Spiritual Companions. 2009. (ENG., Illus.). 192p. pap. 17.95 *(978-0-7387-1124-9(1))* Llewellyn Pubns.

Cooper, Diana. Angel Answers: What the Angels Can Teach Us about the World We Live In. 2007. (ENG.). 272p. per. 15.95 *(978-1-84409-120-1(1))* Findhorn Pr. GBR. Dist: Independent Pubs. Group.

—Angel Inspiration: Together, Humans & Angels Have the Power to Change the World. 2007. (ENG.). 224p. per. 15.95 *(978-1-84409-105-8(8))* Findhorn Pr. GBR. Dist: Independent Pubs. Group.

—A New Light on Angels. 2009. (ENG., Illus.). 144p. pap. 15.95 *(978-1-84409-166-9(X))* Findhorn Pr. GBR. Dist: Independent Pubs. Group.

Cooper, Diana & Crosswell, Kathy. Ascension Through Orbs. 2009. (ENG., Illus.). 240p. pap. 24.95 *(978-1-84409-150-8(3))* Findhorn Pr. GBR. Dist: Independent Pubs. Group.

—Enlightenment Through Orbs. 2009. (ENG., Illus.). 168p. pap. 19.95 *(978-1-84409-153-9(8))* Findhorn Pr. GBR. Dist: Independent Pubs. Group.

Cormack, Susan. Do You Believe in Angels? You Should: True life experiences & guidance with never before seen Photographs. 2009. (Illus.). 108p. pap. 30.49 *(978-1-4389-3335-1(5))* AuthorHouse.

Corral, Michelle. Angels Assigned to You: Divinely Directed & Protected by God's Guardians. 2007. (ENG.). 144p. per. 12.95 *(978-0-9774223-5-7(6))* Lifebridge Bks.

Cortens, Theolyn. Working with Archangels: A Path to Transformation & Power. (ENG.). 256p. 2011. pap. 12.95 ***(978-0-7499-4060-7(3))*** 2007. (Illus.). pap. 12.95 *(978-0-7499-2800-1(X))* Piatkus Bks. GBR. Dist: Independent Pubs. Group.

Cortens, Theolyn. Working with Your Guardian Angel: An Inspirational 12-Week Programme for Finding Life's Purpose. 2006. (ENG., Illus.). 230p. per. 12.95 *(978-0-7499-2662-5(7))* Piatkus Bks. GBR. Dist: Independent Pubs. Group.

Cresswell, Julia. The Watkins Dictionary of Angels. 2006. 320p. per. 17.95 *(978-1-84293-205-6(5)*, Watkins Publishing) Duncan Baird Pubs. GBR. Dist: Sterling Publishing Co., Inc.

Curran, Robert. The Handbook of Angels & Fallen Angels: An Essential Guide to Angels & Demons and, More Importantly, How to Spot Them. 2011. (ENG.). 80p. 14.99 *(978-0-7641-6420-0(1))* Barron's Educational Series, Inc.

Dana, Bruce. Prophetic Teachings on Death, Angels, & Heavenly Manifestations. 2011. 160p. pap. 12.99 *(978-1-59955-491-4(7)*, Bonneville Bks.) Cedar Fort, Inc./CFI Distribution.

D'Angelo, Ishvara. Angels in Our Time: Why They're Here, Where to See Them & How to Work with Them. 2006. (ENG., Illus.). 160p. per. 21.95 *(978-1-905047-87-1(8))* O Bks.,John Hunt.

Daniélou, Jean. The Angels & Their Mission. 2009. Orig. Title: Les Anges et Leur Mission. 144p. pap. 13.95 *(978-1-933184-46-3(9))* Sophia Institute Pr.

Danyans, Eugenio. Visitantes del Cielo: Visitors from the Sky. (SPA., Illus.). 284p. *(978-84-7228-202-5(3)*, 220946) Clie, Editorial.

Dapozzo, Erinno. Angeles en el Infierno: Angels in Hell. (SPA.). *(978-84-7228-106-6(X)*, 220037) Clie, Editorial.

Davis, Nancy Ruth. An Angel Named Promise. 2006. (Illus.). 48p. per. 15.00 *(978-1-4120-9357-6(0))* Trafford Publishing.

DeStefano, Anthony. Angels All Around Us: A Sightseeing Guide to the Invisible World. 2012. (ENG.). 208p. pap. 14.99 ***(978-0-385-52222-9(3)***, Image) Doubleday Religious Publishing Group, The.

DeYoung, Gail. Angel Guide To Go. 2008. 180p. pap. 12.95 *(978-1-4199-8039-8(4))* Ellora's Cave Publishing, Inc.

Discover Angels: Who They Are & What They Do. (Discover Your Bible Ser.). pap. 3.35 *(978-1-56212-690-2(3)*, 152480) Faith Alive Christian Resources.

Dolfyn. Angelic Wisdom: Celestial Beings & Their Spiritual Powers. 128p. pap. 7.95 *(978-0-929268-19-4(9))* Earthspirit, Inc.

Drozdowski, Paul, illus. St. Seraphim's Beatitudes: Blessings for Our Path to Heaven Based on the Life of the Wonderworker of Sarov. 2008. 32p. (J). lib. bdg. 19.95 *(978-0-9786543-0-6(7))* St. Innocent Pr.

Eade, Alfred Thompson. The New Panorama Bible Study Course: Panorama Study No. 2 the Study of Angelology, No.2. deluxe ed. 2008. (Illus.). 33p. 24.99 *(978-0-9799734-1-3(4))* Oak Knoll Publishing.

Eason, Cassandra. Angel Magic: A Hands-on Guide to Inviting Divine Help into Your Everyday Life. 2010. (ENG.). 264p. pap. 16.95 *(978-0-7387-2178-1(6))* Llewellyn Pubns.

—Your Angel Is Waiting to Help: Find Her & Let Her Touch You. 2009. (ENG.). 144p. 14.95 *(978-0-572-03492-4(X))* Foulsham, W. Co., Ltd. GBR. Dist: APG Sales & Distribution Services.

Eckersley, Glennyce. Angels to Watch over Us: How Angels Help Us from Our Earliest Years. 2007. (ENG.). 176p. per. 12.50 *(978-1-84604-030-6(2))* Random Hse. GBR. Dist: Independent Pubs. Group.

Eckersley, Glennyce & Quinn, Gary. Angel Wisdom: Bring the Guidance of Angels into Your Life. 2008. (ENG.). 208p. (gr. 12-18). 14.95 *(978-1-58542-702-4(0)*, Tarcher) Penguin Group (USA) Inc.

—Everyday Angels: Bring the Angels into Your Life Each Day of the Year. 2008. (ENG.). 384p. (gr. 12-18). 14.95 *(978-1-58542-703-1(9)*, Tarcher) Penguin Group (USA) Inc.

Eckersley, Glennyce S. An Angel at My Shoulder: True Stories of Angelic Experiences. rev. ed. 2007. (ENG., Illus.). 192p. per. 13.95 *(978-1-84604-065-8(5))* Random Hse. GBR. Dist: Independent Pubs. Group.

—Angel to Guide Me: How Angels Speak to Us from the Beyond. 2009. (ENG.). 246p. pap. 12.95 *(978-1-84604-160-0(0))* Random Hse. GBR. Dist: Independent Pubs. Group.

Eckersley, Glennyce S. & Quinn, Gary. Angels Believe & Receive: Bring the Guidance & Wisdom of Angels into Your Life. 2008. (ENG.). 256p. pap. 15.95 *(978-1-84604-086-3(8))* Random Hse. GBR. Dist: Independent Pubs. Group.

Fairchild, Sophia, ed. Angels: Winged Whispers - True Stories from Angel Experts around the World. 2011. (ENG., Illus.). 168p. pap. 16.95 *(978-0-9845930-1-9(2))* Soul Wings Pr.

Faw, Jenny, illus. Angels Are Forever. 2007. (Petite Plus Kit Ser.). 78p. pap. 7.95 *(978-1-59359-880-8(7))* Peter Pauper Pr. Inc.

Fix, Miranda. Calling All Angels. 2011. 92p. pap. 19.95 ***(978-1-4512-7767-8(9))*** PublishAmerica, Inc.

Flach, Frederic. The Secret Strength of Angels: 7 Virtues to Live By. 2008. (Little Book. Big Idea Ser.). (ENG.). 256p. 15.95 *(978-1-57826-282-3(8))* Hatherleigh Co., Ltd., The.

Follansbee, Eleanor. Heavenly History: An Account of Heavenly Architecture after Dante, Milton, Swedenborg & Blake. 2011. 110p. 39.95 ***(978-1-258-02488-8(8))*** Literary Licensing, LLC.

Forman, Edward. Angel at My Side. 2008. pap. 9.00 *(978-0-8059-8637-2(5))* Dorrance Publishing Co., Inc.

Forster, Annette. Journey: Reminders from A Guardian Angel Memoir. 2011. (Illus.). 144p. pap. 17.23 *(978-1-4520-7923-3(4))* AuthorHouse.

Freese, Thomas Lee. Ghosts, Spirits, & Angels: True Tales from Kentucky & Beyond. 2009. *(978-1-935001-25-6(6))* Acclaim Pr., Inc.

Freese, Thomas Lee. More True Tales of Ghosts, Spirits & Angels. 2011. ***(978-1-935001-70-6(1))*** Acclaim Pr., Inc.

Gabriel, Wendy, et al. Angel on My Shoulder: Divine Life Wisdom from the World's Foremost Angel Experts. Gabriel, Wendy, ed. 2007. 272p. pap. 16.95 *(978-0-9799923-0-8(3))* Malachite Pr.
Garcia, Danielle. Angel Blessings - A Collection of Channeled Messages from the Angelic Realm. 2008. 204p. pap. 14.95 *(978-0-557-02760-6(8))* Lulu Enterprises Inc.
Gardella, Peter. American Angels: Useful Spirits in the Material World. 2007. (Culture America Ser.). (Illus.). 285p. 29.95 *(978-0-7006-1537-7(7))* Univ. Pr. of Kansas.
Garrett, Susan R. No Ordinary Angel: Celestial Spirits & Christian Claims about Jesus. 2008. (Anchor Yale Bible Reference Library). (ENG.). 352p. 30.00 *(978-0-300-14095-8(9))* Yale Univ. Pr.
Goll, Michal Ann & Goll, James W. Angelic Encounters: Engaging Help from Heaven. 2007. (ENG.). 224p. pap. 14.99 *(978-1-59979-065-7(3)*, Charisma Hse.) Charisma Media.
Grace, Sonja. Angels in the 21st Century. 2009. 108p. pap. 14.95 *(978-0-944638-55-2(4))* Educare Pr.
Graham, Billy. Angels. 2011. 192p. pap. 14.99 *(978-0-8499-1059-3(5))* Nelson, Thomas Inc.
Grant, Robert J. Angeles, Arcangeles y Fuerzas Invisibles. 2007. (SPA., Illus.). 251p. per. *(978-0-87604-537-4(9)*, Libros Iluminados) A.R.E. Pr.
Gray-Cobb, Maiya & Gray-Cobb, Geof. Angels: The Guardians of Your Destiny. 2008. 176p. per. 14.00 *(978-1-886940-78-9(9))* Ozark Mountain Publishing, Inc.
Gray, Kyle. The Angel Whisperer: Incredible Stories of Hope & Love from the Angels. 2012. (ENG.). 256p. pap. 17.95 ***(978-1-84850-842-2(5))*** Hay Hse., Inc.
Greenaway, Beleta. Simply Angels. 2009. (Simply Ser.). (ENG., Illus.). 160p. pap. 9.95 *(978-1-4027-4493-8(5)*, Sterling/Zambezi) Sterling Publishing Co., Inc.
Greene. Angels Among Us, Earth Angels. 76p. pap. 12.95 *(978-1-881165-20-0(5))* People Skills International.
Gregg, Susan. The Complete Encyclopedia of Angels: A Guide to 200 Celestial Beings to Help, Heal, & Assist You in Everyday Life. 2011. (ENG., Illus.). 320p. pap. 17.99 *(978-1-59233-466-7(0)*, 1592334660) Quayside.
Guardian Angel Canon. 3.00 *(978-1-879038-88-2(9)*, Oakwood Pubns.) St. Vladimir's Seminary Pr.
Guiley, Rosemary Ellen. I Bring You Glad Tidings. 2010. (ENG.). 224p. pap. 15.99 *(978-1-4516-0604-1(4)*, Beyond Words/Atria Bks.) Atria Bks.
Hall, Ieisha K. M. B. Sprinkles. 2010. 16p. 12.99 *(978-1-4490-6569-0(4))* AuthorHouse.
Halvorsen, Lyn. Everyday Angels. 2007. 40p. 24.50 *(978-1-84753-633-4(6))* Lulu Enterprises Inc.
Harding, Mike. A Little Book of Angels. 2008. (Little Bks.). (ENG.). 96p. 12.95 *(978-1-84513-305-4(6))* Aurum Pr., Ltd. GBR. Dist: Independent Pubs. Group.
Harkness, Deborah. John Dee's Conversations with Angels: Cabala, Alchemy, & the End of Nature. 2006. (ENG., Illus.). 268p. pap. 53.00 *(978-0-521-02748-9(9))* Cambridge Univ. Pr.
Haygood, Elmer M. They Came to Heal Us. 2011. 132p. pap. 11.95 ***(978-1-4620-2133-8(6))*** iUniverse, Inc.
Hayler, Freddy. All about Angels: The Song of Michael. 2006. (Illus.). 171p. 17.99 incl. audio compact disk *(978-0-88368-494-8(2)*, 774942) Whitaker Hse.
Heathcote-James, Emma. Seeing Angels: True Contemporary Accounts of Hundreds of Angelic Experiences. 2009. (ENG., Illus.). 272p. pap. 13.95 *(978-1-84454-786-9(8))* Blake, John Publishing, Ltd. GBR. Dist: Independent Pubs. Group.
Hewitt, Nancy. In Search of My Angel. 2009. (ENG.). 140p. pap. 19.95 *(978-1-58982-507-9(1)*, Millennial Mind Publishing) American Bk. Publishing Group.
Hodge, Charles B. Angels. pap. 4.99 *(978-0-89098-447-5(6))* Twentieth Century Christian Bks.
Hronas, Georgia. Tell Us about the Angels, Grandma. 2006. (ENG., Illus.). 82p. pap. 13.95 *(978-1-933654-04-1(X))* Light & Life Publishing Co.
Huffman, Stephen. Trouble in Paradise. 2009. 143p. pap. 13.95 *(978-0-557-15431-9(6))* Lulu Enterprises Inc.
Hunt. Hang on to me Mary. 2007. (Illus.). pap. 24.95 net. *(978-0-615-20295-2(0))* Hunt, Robin.
Hurnard, Hanna. Vida con Alas (Winged Life) (SPA.). 144p. *(978-84-7228-594-1(4)*, 220941) Clie, Editorial.
Iavoschi, Roxana Ileana. The Archangel Gabriel in History & Tradition - an Analysis of His Role & Function in Judaism, Christianity, & Islam. 2008. 92p. per. *(978-3-8364-6805-3(0))* VDM Verlag Dr. Mueller e.K.
Iribarren, Isabel & Lenz, Martin, eds. Angels in Medieval Philosophical Inquiry: Their Function & Significance. 2008. (Ashgate Studies in Medieval Philosophy Ser.). (Illus.). 250p. 114.95 *(978-0-7546-5803-0(1))* Ashgate Publishing Co.
Jane, Lisa. Angel Kisses: A Book of Comfort & Joy..., 0 vols. 2009. (Illus.). 112p. 17.99 *(978-1-4041-8715-3(4))* Nelson, Thomas Inc.
Jawor, Annee. A Spark in the Night. 2009. 143p. pap. 21.00 *(978-0-578-03536-9(7))* Ascent of an Angel.
Jeremiah, David. Angels: Who They Are & How They Help — What the Bible Reveals. 2009. (ENG.). 240p. pap. 14.99 *(978-1-60142-269-9(5)*, Multnomah) Doubleday Religious Publishing Group, The.
—Angels: Who They Are & How They Help ... What the Bible Reveals. lt. ed. 2010. (ENG.). 365p. pap. 17.99 *(978-1-59415-315-0(9))* Cengage Gale.
Johnston, Grace. Dancing with the Angels: A Light in Times of Darkness. 2009. 84p. pap. 10.95 *(978-1-4401-0683-5(5))* iUniverse, Inc.
Jones, David Albert. Angels: A Very Short Introduction. 2011. (Very Short Introductions Ser.). (ENG., Illus.). 144p. 11.95 ***(978-0-19-954730-2(0))*** Oxford Univ. Pr., Inc.
Jones, Jessica. Ask for the Ancient Paths. 2008. 280p. pap. 15.99 *(978-0-9814548-8-7(7))*; 284p. 26.95 *(978-0-9814548-9-4(5))* Quiddity Pr. & Productions.
Justyn, Daria. Angels Whisper to Us: Decoding the Messages in Daydreams. 2008. 160p. pap. 14.95 *(978-1-4401-0928-7(1))* iUniverse, Inc.
Kallen, Stuart A. Angels: Part of the Mysterious & Unknown. 2008. (Mysterious & Unknown Ser.). (YA). (gr. 7-12). 25.95 *(978-1-60152-055-5(7))* ReferencePoint Pr., Inc.
Kaya & Christiane, Muller. The Book of Angels. 2008. 392p. pap. *(978-2-923097-11-4(4))* Universe/City Mikael (UCM) Publishing, Inc.
Kinnaman, Gary. Angels Dark & Light. 2011. 220p. pap. 14.95 *(978-1-935906-32-2(1))* Intermedia Publishing Group.
La Porta, S. Two Anonymous Sets of Scholia on Dionysius the Areopagite's Heavenly Hierarchy (Scriptores Armeniaci 29) 2008. (Corpus Scriptorum Christianorum Orientalium Ser.). (ENG.). 124p. (C). pap. 76.00 *(978-90-429-1918-1(3))* Peeters Pubs. & Booksellers BEL. Dist: Brown, David Bk. Co., The.
—Two Anonymous Sets of Scholia on Dionysius the Areopagite's Heavenly Hierarchy (Scriptores Armeniaci 30) 2008. (Corpus Scriptorum Christianorum Orientalium Ser.). (ENG.). 157p. (C). pap. 70.00 *(978-90-429-1919-8(1))* Peeters Pubs. & Booksellers BEL. Dist: Brown, David Bk. Co., The.
Lampert, Vanessa. The Angel Book. 2007. (ENG., Illus.). 160p. *(978-1-906094-17-1(9))* Ryland Peters & Small.
—The Angel Book of Days: A Personal Journal with an Angel Message for Every Day of the Year. 2007. (Illus.). 144p. *(978-1-906094-07-2(1))* Ryland Peters & Small.
Langenberg, Kate. Fallen Angels. 2011. (ENG.). 160p. 5.95 *(978-0-7624-4080-1(5))* Running Pr. Bk. Pubs.
Lavey, Sylvia. Angels: A book for self realization through angels & your personal Guides. 2008. 160p. pap. 14.95 *(978-0-595-51864-7(8))* iUniverse, Inc.
Law, T. S. La Verdad Sobre los Angeles.Tr. of Truth about Angels. (SPA.). 9.99 *(978-958-9354-18-6(1)*, 550056) Editorial Unilit.
Leigh, Allana. Angelica Regime. 2006. 219p. per. 19.95 *(978-0-9790254-9-5(4))* LP Inspirations.
Lewis, James R. & Oliver, Evelyn Dorothy. Angels A to Z. 2nd ed. 2008. (ENG., Illus.). 500p. pap. 24.95 *(978-1-57859-212-8(7))* Visible Ink Pr.
Lightner, Robert. Angels, Satan, & Demons. 2010. pap. 17.99 *(978-1-57972-901-1(0))* Insight for Living.
Lofton, Rhonda. Angels Are Real. 2006. pap. 13.99 *(978-1-60034-227-1(2))* Xulon Pr., Inc.
Longstaff, J. M. How to Wage Spiritual Warfare. 2009. 400p. pap. 22.99 *(978-1-60791-846-2(3))* Xulon Pr., Inc.
Love, Barbara. Guardian Angels by My Side: True Stories of Angelic Encounters & Divine Interventions. 2010. 136p. pap. 11.95 *(978-1-4497-0753-8(X)*, WestBow Pr.) Author Solutions, Inc.
Luby, Brenda Delozier. The Stellars. 2009. 220p. pap. 14.95 *(978-1-936107-28-6(7))* Mill City Pr., Inc.
Lucie-Smith, Edward. The Glory of Angels. 2009. (ENG., Illus.). 192p. 35.00 *(978-0-06-178777-5(9)*, Collins Design) HarperCollins Pubs.
Lung, Chick. Angel on His Shoulder. 2011. 184p. pap. 16.99 ***(978-1-4634-5299-5(3))*** AuthorHouse.
Lysette, Chantel. Angel Code: Your Interactive Guide to Angelic Communication. 2010. (ENG.). 288p. pap. 17.95 *(978-0-7387-2123-1(9))* Llewellyn Pubns.
—Azrael Loves Chocolate - Michael's a Jock: An Insider's Guide to What Your Angels Are Really Like. 2008. (ENG., Illus.). 264p. pap. 14.95 *(978-0-7387-1441-7(0))* Llewellyn Pubns.
Macy, Jonathan. In the Shadow of His Wings: The Pastoral Ministry of Angels - Yesterday, Today, & for Heaven. 2011. (ENG.). 172p. pap. 30.25 *(978-0-7188-9250-0(X))* Lutterworth Pr., The GBR. Dist: Printondemand-worldwide.com.
—In the Shadow of His Wings: The Pastoral Ministry of Angels: Yesterday, Today, & for Heaven. 2010. 172p. pap. 20.00 *(978-1-60899-837-1(1)*, Cascade Bks.) Wipf & Stock Pubs.
Madsen, Scott. He Has Risen: The Riveting, Real-Life Story of an Ordinary Man & His Supernatural Encounters with Jesus Christ. 2009. 228p. pap. 15.99 *(978-1-60791-724-3(6))* Xulon Pr., Inc.
Mair, Devan. Angels Watching over You. 2006. pap. 9.99 *(978-1-60034-605-7(7))* Xulon Pr., Inc.
Maldon Sr., Charles & Maldon, Charles. In the Shadow of Angels. 2010. 212p. 27.95 *(978-1-4401-9792-5(X))*; (ENG.). pap. 17.95 *(978-1-4401-9790-1(3))* iUniverse, Inc.
Manitara, Olivier. Essene Gospel of Archangel Gabriel I: Healing Relationships. 2010. 160p. *(978-1-926764-03-0(X))* Essenia Bks. Publishing.
—Essene Gospel of Archangel Raphael I: Breathing with the Angels. 2010. 160p. *(978-1-926764-02-3(1))* Essenia Bks. Publishing.
—Essene Gospel of Archangel Uriel I: Become a Genuine Essene. 2010. 160p. *(978-1-926764-04-7(8))* Essenia Bks. Publishing.
Mark, Barbara & Griswold, Trudy. The Angelspeake Book of Prayer & Healing. 2009. (ENG.). 160p. pap. 11.99 *(978-1-4391-9106-4(9))* Simon & Schuster.
Markell, Jan. Angeles en Campos Concentracion: Angels in the Camp. (SPA.). 176p. *(978-84-7228-785-3(8)*, 220038) Clie, Editorial.
Marooney, Kimberly. The Angel Blessings Kit, Revised Edition: Cards of Sacred Guidance & Inspiration. 2010. (ENG., Illus.). 192p. pap. 19.99 *(978-1-59233-435-3(0)*, 1592334350) Quayside.
Marshall, George J. Angels: An Indexed & Partially Annotated Bibliography of over 4300 Scholarly Books & Articles since the 7th Century B. C. alt. ed. 2008. (ENG.). 485p. pap. 49.95 *(978-0-7864-3749-8(9))* McFarland & Co., Inc. Pubs.
Marshall, Judith. My Conversations with Angels: Inspirational Moments with Guardian Spirits. 2012. (ENG.). 264p. pap. 15.99 ***(978-0-7387-3286-2(9))*** Llewellyn Pubns.
Marshall, Peter & Walsham, Alexandra, eds. Angels in the Early Modern World. 2006. (ENG., Illus.). 340p. 122.99 *(978-0-521-84332-4(4))* Cambridge Univ. Pr.
Martlott, Carla. Mi Experiencia con Los Angeles. 2009. 44p. pap. 10.95 *(978-1-4327-2962-2(4))* Outskirts Pr., Inc.
Mattera, Nicola. Storia di Angeli: il secondo Angelo. 2009. 95p. pap. 14.50 *(978-1-4092-5466-9(6))* Lulu Enterprises Inc.
May, Carol. Working with Angels in Everyday Life. 2007. 88p. per. 11.00 *(978-1-59858-389-2(1))* Dog Ear Publishing, LLC.
McClure, Gerry S. Heaven on Earth's Little Book of Angels. (Illus.). 18p. 10.00 *(978-0-9641174-0-2(1))* Heaven On Earth, Inc.
McGerr, Angela. The Angel Almanac: An Inspirational Guide to Healing & Harmony. 2008. (Illus.). 256p. 19.95 incl. audio compact disk *(978-1-84400-640-3(9))* Quadrille Publishing, Ltd. GBR. Dist: Ingram Pub. Services.
—The Angel Quest of the Heart: A Journey of Spiritual Transformation. 2007. (Illus.). 144p. 29.95 *(978-1-84400-528-4(3))* Quadrille Publishing, Ltd. GBR. Dist: Ingram Pub. Services.
—Angelic Abundance. 2007. (Illus.). 166p. 16.95 *(978-1-84400-466-9(X))* Quadrille Publishing, Ltd. GBR. Dist: Ingram Pub. Services.
—A Harmony of Angels. Rockwood, Richard, tr. & illus. by. (ENG.). 1p. pap. 19.95 *(978-1-84400-633-3(8))* Quadrille Publishing, Ltd. GBR. Dist: Graphic Arts Ctr. Publishing Co.
McMahon, Raymond. Angels365 - an Angel for Everyday. 2009. 412p. pap. 47.50 *(978-1-4092-1646-3(5))*; 424p. pap. 35.95 *(978-1-4092-8676-9(2))* Lulu Enterprises Inc.
—Angelswiki - A Dictionary of Angels. 2009. 432p. pap. 35.95 *(978-0-557-12031-4(4))* Lulu Enterprises Inc.
Medina, Carol-Ann. Angel Whispers: Be Still & Listen. 2010. 152p. (ENG.). 22.49 *(978-1-4520-2755-5(2))*; pap. 14.95 *(978-1-4520-2754-8(4))* AuthorHouse.
Miller, Leslie. Todo Sobre los Angeles.Tr. of All about Angels. (SPA.). 128p. *(978-84-7228-101-1(9)*, 220895) Clie, Editorial.
Mitchel, Samuel. A Boy & His Angel. 2010. 100p. pap. 10.50 *(978-0-557-30648-0(5))* Lulu Enterprises Inc.
Mohamed, Feisal G. In the Anteroom of Divinity: The Reformation of the Angels from Colet to Milton. 2008. (ENG.). 248p. *(978-0-8020-9792-7(8))* Univ. of Toronto Pr.
Montague, Charlotte. Angels: The Complete Mythology of Angels & Their Everyday Presence among Us. 2011. (ENG.). 192p. 14.99 *(978-0-7858-2727-6(7)*, 0785827277, Chartwell) Book Sales, Inc.
Mora, Eva-Maria. Quantum Angel Healing: Energy Therapy & Communication with Angels. 2011. 312p. pap. 16.95 *(978-0-9845040-1-5(X))* Synergy Bks.
More, John Henry. Sky & Ice. 2009. 88p. pap. 16.99 *(978-1-935436-23-2(6))* Rodalan Pr.
Muller, Kaya & Muller, Christiane. How to Read Signs: The Origin of Angels, Signs & Symbols. 2010. 384p. pap. 19.85 *(978-2-923097-61-9(0))* Universe/City Mikael (UCM) Publishing, Inc. CAN. Dist: New Leaf Distributing Co., Inc.
Mullinax, Jackie. When Angels Speak Bk. 1: The Awakening A Pleiadian Endeavor. 2011. 284p. pap. 18.95 ***(978-1-4634-1545-7(1))*** AuthorHouse.
—When Angels Speak: Book One: The Awakening A Pleiadian Endeavor. 2011. 284p. 26.95 ***(978-1-4634-1544-0(3))*** AuthorHouse.
My Guardian Angel. Date not set. 8.95 *(978-0-88271-559-9(3)*, 10523) Regina Pr., Malhame & Co.
Myers, Gary. A Brush with Angels: Compelling Tales of Biblical Proportion. 2011. pap. 14.99 *(978-0-89112-290-6(7)*, Leafwood Pubs.) Abilene Christian Univ. Pr.
Nahmad, Claire. Angel Messages: The Oracle of the Birds. 2010. (ENG.). 224p. pap. 19.95 *(978-1-906787-51-6(4)*, Watkins Publishing) Duncan Baird Pubs. GBR. Dist: Sterling Publishing Co., Inc.
—Make Your Own Angel Blessing Scrolls: Inspiration for Gifts of Healing, Hope, & Joy. 2010. (ENG., Illus.). 208p. pap. 19.95 *(978-1-906787-94-3(8)*, Watkins Publishing) Duncan Baird Pubs. GBR. Dist: Sterling Publishing Co., Inc.
—Your Guardian Angel: Connect, Communicate, & Heal with Your Own Divine Companion. 2007. (ENG.). 256p. per. 14.95 *(978-1-84293-142-4(3)*, Watkins Publishing) Duncan Baird Pubs. GBR. Dist: Sterling Publishing Co., Inc.
Narde, Kimberly Lael & Weled, Nancy Karen. Imagine Angels Everywhere. 2008. (Illus.). 48p. 15.00 *(978-0-8059-7879-7(8))* Dorrance Publishing Co., Inc.
National Museum of Decorative Painting, compiled by. 100 Angels: A Collection of Hand Painted Angels. 2011. (ENG., Illus.). 240p. 49.95 *(978-0-9819762-9-7(8)*, 0981976298) All American Crafts.
Netty. Angels for Life. 2007. 104p. per. *(978-1-84549-188-8(2))* arima publishing.
Newcomb, Jacky. Angel Kids: Die medialen Erfahrungen unserer Kinder. 2008. xvi, 253p. *(978-1-84850-016-7(5)*, 785) Hay Hse. UK, Ltd. GBR. Dist: Grantham Bk. Services.
—Angel Kids: Enchanting Stories of True-Life Guardian Angels & 'Sixth Sense' Abilities in Children. 2009. (ENG.). xvi, 256p. pap. 17.95 *(978-1-4019-2285-6(6))* Hay Hse., Inc.
Nixon, Thomas C. Angelic Encounter. unabr. ed. Date not set. 80p. pap. *(978-0-9650982-2-9(2))* Elmira Pr.
Nowell, Irene. 101 Questions & Answers on Angels & Devils. 2010. xii, 97p. pap. *(978-0-8091-4694-9(0))* Paulist Pr.
Nozedar, Adele. The Magic of Angels: How to Recognise & Harness Your Own Angelic Powers. 2010. (ENG.). 266p. pap. 13.95 *(978-1-84454-899-6(6))* Blake, John Publishing, Ltd. GBR. Dist: Independent Pubs. Group.
Nuestros Amigos, los Angeles.Tr. of Our Friends, the Angels. (SPA.). 112p. pap. 4.95 *(978-980-350-362-8(6))* Sociedad de San Pablo VEN. Dist: St Pauls/Alba Hse. Pubs.
Oluoch, Silvanus. Holy Angels: The Facts - Clear & Specific Information on God's Invisible Agents. 2009. 212p. pap. 13.99 *(978-1-60696-632-7(4))* Tate Publishing & Enterprises, LLC.
O'Riley, Carolyn Ann. Going up! Hold on to Your Angels. 2009. 360p. pap. 27.40 *(978-0-557-07166-1(6))* Lulu Enterprises Inc.
Paolino, Karen. The Everything Guide to Angels: Discover the wisdom & healing power of the Angelic Kingdom. 2009. (ENG.). 304p. pap. 15.95 *(978-1-60550-121-5(2))* Adams Media Corp.
Pasquali, Elena. Prayers for Little Angels, 1 vol. 2009. 32p. 12.95 *(978-0-8254-7850-5(2)*, Lion Children's) Lion Hudson PLC GBR. Dist: Kregel Pubns.
Pearce, Stewart. The Angels of Atlantis: Twelve Mighty Forces to Transform Your Life Forever. 2011. (ENG., Illus.). 176p. pap. 16.95 ***(978-1-84409-569-8(X))*** Findhorn Pr. GBR. Dist: Independent Pubs. Group.
Pedersen, Joy S. Wisdom of the Guardian: Treasures from Archangel Michael to Change Your Life. 2011. 112p. 22.95 *(978-1-4502-9704-2(8))*; pap. 12.95 *(978-1-4502-9703-5(X))* iUniverse, Inc.
Pelletier, Jean. Como Comunicarse con Su Angel de la Guardia.Tr. of How to Communicate with Your Guardian Angel. (SPA.). 10.98 *(978-970-05-1243-3(6))* Grijalbo, Editorial MEX. Dist: Continental Bk. Co., Inc.
Pengelly, Nick. Don't Forget the Angels. 2007. 167p. per. 13.99 *(978-88-89127-30-8(9))* Destiny Image Europe ITA. Dist: Destiny Image Pubs.
Pepper, Kathleen. Hand in Hand with Angels: A Book of Attunement. 2010. (ENG., Illus.). 176p. pap. 19.95 *(978-1-905398-21-8(2))* Polair Publishing GBR. Dist: SCB Distributors.
Phillips, Ron. Our Invisible Allies: The Definitive Guide on Angels & How They Work Behind the Scenes. 2009. (ENG.). 224p. pap. 14.99 *(978-1-59979-523-2(X)*, Charisma Hse.) Charisma Media.
Pierce, Gary. Angels Hear What the Spirit Is Saying to the Seven Churches Revelation 1-3. 2007. 52p. per. 9.99 *(978-1-60034-887-7(4))* Xulon Pr., Inc.
Poirier, John C. The Tongues of Angels: The Concept of Angelic Languages in Classical Jewish & Christian Texts. 2010. (Illus.). XI, 224p. pap. 117.50 *(978-3-16-150569-0(7))* Mohr Siebeck GmbH & Co. KG DEU. Dist: Coronet Bks.
Prophet, Elizabeth Clare. Fallen Angels among Us: What You Need to Know. 2010. (ENG.). 400p. pap. 9.95 *(978-1-932890-55-6(6))* Summit Univ. Pr.
Puhalo, Lazar. Guardian Angel: Contemplations. Date not set. 47p. pap. 6.00 *(978-1-879038-50-9(1)*, 9019) Synaxis Pr.
—On Angels. Date not set. 32p. pap. 3.50 *(978-1-879038-60-8(9)*, 9030) Synaxis Pr.
Pye, Edith M. The Angels Carried Me Between Life & Death for Sixteen Minutes. 2011. 92p. pap. 11.95 ***(978-1-4620-4118-3(3))*** iUniverse, Inc.
Rabast, Jochen. Angels in Luggage. 2010. 98p. pap. *(978-3-8391-2340-9(2))* Books on Demand GmbH.
Radeff, Kathryn. Angel Encounters: Miracle Stories of Hope, Healing, Faith & Love, 1 vol. 2009. (ENG.). 95p. pap. 16.95 *(978-1-60836-237-0(X))* PublishAmerica, Inc.
Raven, Hazel. The Angel Bible: The Definitive Guide to Angel Wisdom. 2006. (ENG., Illus.). 400p. pap. 14.95 *(978-1-4027-4190-6(1))* Sterling Publishing Co., Inc.
—The Angel Experience: Your Complete Angel Workshop in a Book with a CD of Meditations. 2010. (ENG., Illus.). 256p. pap. 14.99 *(978-1-84181-393-6(1)*, Godsfield Press) Octopus Publishing Group GBR. Dist: Hachette Bk. Group.
Raymond, Joad & Kassell, Lauren, eds. Conversations with Angels: Essays Towards a History of Spiritual Communication, 1100-1700. 2011. (ENG., Illus.). 320p. 95.00 *(978-0-230-55203-6(X))* Palgrave Macmillan.
Regan, Patrick & Andrews McMeel Publishing Staff. Of Angels. gif. ed. 2006. (ENG., Illus.). 80p. 5.99 *(978-0-7407-6185-0(4))* Andrews McMeel Publishing.
Reilly, Carmel. True Tales of Angel Encounters. 2009. (ENG.). 312p. pap. 15.95 *(978-0-7387-1494-3(1))* Llewellyn Pubns.
Rhew, Jan. And the Angels Said Welcome to Heaven. 2011. 24p. pap. 12.79 ***(978-1-4634-1349-1(1))*** AuthorHouse.
Ripley, Frances. Visions Unseen: Aspects of the Natural Realm. 2007. (ENG., Illus.). 96p. pap. 27.95 *(978-1-84409-093-8(0))* Findhorn Pr. GBR. Dist: Independent Pubs. Group.
Roberts, Sandye M. & Jones, I. I. I. Divine Intervention: A Guide to Reiki Angels & Archangels. 2009. 108p. 34.99 *(978-1-4490-0509-2(8))*; pap. 24.99 *(978-1-4490-0508-5(X))* AuthorHouse.
Roberts, Scott. The Rise & Fall of the Nephilim: The Untold Story of Fallen Angels, Giants on the Earth, & Their Extraterrestrial Origins. 2012. (ENG., Illus.). 1p. pap. 16.99 *(978-1-60163-197-8(9)*, New Page Bks.) Career Pr., Inc.
Roberts, Scott Alan. The Rise & Fall of the Nephilim: The Untold Story of Fallen Angels, Giants on Earth, & Their Extraterrestrial Origins. 2012. 256p. E-Book ***(978-1-60163-629-4(6)***, New Page Bks.) Career Pr., Inc.
Rodriguez, J. F. Angel de la Bondad: Angel of Kindness. (SPA.). 99p. *(978-84-7228-017-5(9)*, 220035) Clie, Editorial.

Roling, Bernd. Locutio Angelica: Die Diskussion der Engelsprache Als Antizipation Einer Sprechakttheorie in Mittelalter und Fruher Neuzeit. 2008. (Studien und Texte Zur Geistesgeschichte des Mittelalters Ser.). 754p. (978-90-04-16553-3(3)) BRILL.

Ross, David. Angel Inspirations: Essential Wisdom, Insight, & Guidance. 160p. 2010. (ENG.). pap. 10.95 (978-1-84483-908-7(7)) 2006. (Illus.). (978-1-84483-191-3(4)) Duncan Baird Pubs. GBR. Dist: Sterling Publishing Co., Inc.

Sado, Sachiko, tr. Angel Presence Angel Presents A Most Holy Book: Japanese Translation. 2008.Tr. of Angel Presence Angel Presents A Most Holy Book. (JPN.). 104p. pap. 33.30 (978-0-9716590-4-9(4)) Angel Pr.

Salerno, Toni Carmine. Healing Angel Cards: Loving Guidance from the Angels. 2010. (978-1-57281-657-2(0)) Blue Angel Gallery.

Salvana, Hazel Catherine. Angelic Whisper: Words of Wisdom & Inspirations in Today's Troubled World. 2008. 96p. pap. 15.49 (978-1-4389-0726-0(5)) AuthorHouse.

Sandra Lee. Angels & Chicken Wings. 2009. 108p. 25.95 (978-1-4269-1570-3(5)) Trafford Publishing.

Sangha, Laura. Angels & Belief in England, 1480-1700, 1 vol. 2012. (Religious Cultures in the Early Modern World Ser.). (ENG.). 288p. 99.00 (978-1-84893-145-9(X)) Pickering & Chatto Pubs., Ltd. GBR. Dist: Ashgate Publishing Co.

Savastano, D. R. On the Breath of Angels. 2008. 316p. per. 17.99 (978-1-60477-566-2(1)) Xulon Pr., Inc.

Schlink, M. Basilea. Mundo Invisible de los Angeles y Dem: Unseen World of Angels. (SPA.). 144p. (978-84-7645-246-2(2), 223280) Clie, Editorial.

Schneider, Petra & Pieroth, Gerhard. Archangels & Earthangels. 176p. 14.95 (978-0-910261-19-7(9)) Lotus Pr.

Schweitzer. Your Guardian Angels. 2009. 284p. 25.99 (978-1-4490-0701-0(5)); pap. 17.99 (978-1-4490-0700-3(7)) AuthorHouse.

Schweitzer, Sarah A. Your Guardian Angels. 2009. xvii, 265p. E-Book (978-1-4490-0699-0(X)) AuthorHouse.

Seaman, Suzanne Margaret. Messages from Light. 2010. 114p. pap. (978-1-897435-25-0(8)) Agio Publishing Hse.

Seymour, Jane. Among Angels. 2010. (Illus.). 128p. pap. 14.99 (978-0-8249-4850-4(5), Guideposts) Ideals Pubns.

Seymour, Yvonne. The Secret World of Guardian Angels. 2011. 48p. 24.99 (978-1-4628-6680-9(8)); pap. 15.99 (978-1-4628-6679-3(4)) Xlibris Corp.

Shapiro, Rami. The Angelic Way: Angels Through the Ages & Their Meaning for Us. 2009. (ENG.). 240p. pap. 15.95 (978-1-933346-19-9(1)) BlueBridge.

Sheum'un, Basileios. Commentary on the Six Wings of the Seraph as Spoken by the Prophet Isaiah. 2010. (SYR.). pap. 19.00 (978-1-61719-925-7(7)) Gorgias Pr., LLC.

Simkins, Shirl A. There Are Angels among Us. 2008. pap. (978-1-60266-370-1(X)) Xulon Pr., Inc.

Simpson-Hubbart, Mary. Little Lawrence. 2011. 64p. pap. 9.95 (978-1-4627-0659-4(2)) Cross Bks. Publishing.

Skinner, Stephen & Rankine, David. The Practical Angel Magic of Dr. John Dee's Enochian Tables: Tabularum Bonorum Angelorum Invocationes. 2010. (ENG.). 296p. 65.00 (978-0-7387-2351-8(7)) Llewellyn Pubns.

Smedley, Jenny. A Year with the Angels. 2011. (Illus.). 240p. pap. (978-1-84850-370-0(9)) Hay Hse. UK, Ltd.

Smith, Tony. The Rise & Fall of Satan 'the Accuser' 2009. 59p. pap. 14.91 (978-0-557-14593-5(7)) Lulu Enterprises Inc.

Solaris Orisis, Emanuel. The Divinity Within You: Participating in your own evolution now & Beyond 2012. 2009. 140p. 23.95 (978-1-4401-1045-0(X)); pap. 13.95 (978-1-4401-1043-6(3)) iUniverse, Inc.

Spangler, Ann. When You Need a Miracle: Stories to Give You Faith & Bring You Hope. 304p. 2010. pap. 12.99 (978-0-310-27841-2(4)) 2009. (ENG.). 16.99 (978-0-310-27839-9(2)) Zondervan.

Spangler, David. Subtle Worlds: An Explorer's Field Notes. Spangler, Julia & Secrest, Freya, eds. 2010. 226p. pap. 15.95 (978-0-936878-26-3(6)) Lorian Assn., The.

Spendlove, Evelyn. Messages of the Angels: Information on Angels. 2009. 128p. 24.99 (978-1-4389-2709-1(6)); pap. 16.49 (978-1-4389-5397-7(6)) AuthorHouse.

Spezzano, Penny. Angel Messages from Penny. 2008. 244p. pap. 17.76 (978-1-4357-2912-4(9)) Lulu Enterprises Inc.

Spillman, James R. A Conspiracy of Angels. 2nd ed. 2006. (Illus.). 228p. spiral bd. 29.95 (978-0-9767811-2-7(3), True Potential) True Potential Publishing, Inc.

Starr, Morgana. Angel Whispers: A Journey into the World of the Earth's Oldest Guardians. 2011. 248p. pap. 16.95 (978-1-61434-524-4(4)) Booklocker.com, Inc.

Steiger, Brad & Steiger, Sherry Hansen. Angel Miracles: Inspirational True Stories of Heavenly Help. 2008. (ENG.). 272p. pap. 12.95 (978-1-59869-609-7(2)) Adams Media Corp.

Stone, Perry. Angels on Assignment: God's Relentless Protection of You & Your Loved Ones. 2009. (ENG.). 176p. 15.99 (978-1-59979-752-6(6), Charisma Hse.) Charisma Media.

Storm, Sue. Angel First Aid: Remedies for Life, Love, & Prosperity. 2010. (ENG., Illus.). 192p. 17.95 (978-1-4027-7087-6(1)) Sterling Publishing Co., Inc.

—Angel First Aid: Rx for Success. 144p. pap. 17.95 (978-0-9675291-1-0(5)) Angelight Productions.

Struthers, Jane. Angels. 2011. (ENG., Illus.). 96p. pap. 9.95 (978-1-84953-079-8(3)) Summerdale Pubs. GBR. Dist: Independent Pubs. Group.

Swain, Alison Campbell. The Angels'healing Garden. 2011. 44p. pap. 14.99 (978-1-61379-046-5(5)) Xulon Pr., Inc.

Taggart, Ed. Angels Surround Us: The Truth about Angels & Fallen Angels. 256p. pap. 12.99 (978-1-85792-681-1(1), Christian Focus) Christian Focus Pubns. GBR. Dist: Riverside.

Thompson, Sharon. Angel Attributes & How to Use Them in Your Life. 2007. 140p. per. 24.95 (978-1-4241-9278-6(1)) PublishAmerica, Inc.

Tiffen, Gregge. Do the Angels Take a Vacation? 2007. 15p. 13.00 (978-0-9795160-4-7(8)) P Systems.

Till, Nina-Gai. This Is Not A Fairy Tale. 2010. 128p. pap. 12.00 (978-0-557-39769-3(3)) Lulu Enterprises Inc.

Trouvé, Marianne Lorraine, compiled by. Angels: Help from on High. 2010. pap. (978-0-8198-0790-8(7)) Pauline Bks. & Media.

Vallés, Carlos G. Mi Angel y Yo. 128p. 4.95 (978-958-607-968-6(6)) Sociedad de San Pablo COL. Dist: St Pauls/Alba Hse. Pubs.

Van Diest, Milagros Inexplicables.Tr. of Unsolved Miracles. 8.99 (978-0-7899-0468-3(3), 495034) Editorial Unilit.

Van Diest, John. Amazing Miracles: Inspiring True Stories of God at Work. 2012. pap. 12.99 (978-0-7369-3802-0(8)) Harvest Hse. Pubs.

Van Diest, John & Van Diest, David, compiled by. Unsolved Miracles Vol. 2. 2009. (Unsolved Miracles Ser.). (ENG.). 250p. pap. 13.99 (978-0-9816514-2-2(9)) Last Chapter Publishing.

Van Natta, Bruce. Saved by Angels to Share How God Talks to Everyday People. 2008. pap. 16.99 (978-0-7684-2651-9(0)) Destiny Image Pubs.

Vazey, Julia. Speaking in the Language of Angels. 2007. 188p. per. (978-0-7552-1063-3(8)) Authors OnLine, Ltd.

Virtue, D. Daily Guidance from Your Angels. 2007. 367p. (978-1-4019-1578-0(7), 491) Hay Hse. UK, Ltd. GBR. Dist: Grantham Bk. Services.

Virtue, Doreen. Angel Numbers 101: The Meaning of 111, 123, 444, & Other Number Sequences. 2008. (ENG., Illus.). 128p. pap. 9.95 (978-1-4019-2001-2(2)) Hay Hse., Inc.

—The Angel Therapy Handbook. (ENG.). 2012. 272p. pap. 14.95 (978-1-4019-1836-1(0)) 2011. 256p. 19.95 (978-1-4019-1834-7(4)) Hay Hse., Inc.

—Angel Visions Ii. 2006. 198p. (978-1-4019-1065-5(3), 383) Hay Hse. UK, Ltd. GBR. Dist: Grantham Bk. Services.

—Archangels 101: How to Connect Closely with Archangels Michael, Raphael, Gabriel, Uriel, & Others for Healing, Protection, & Guidance. 3rd ed. 2011. (ENG., Illus.). 160p. pap. 11.95 (978-1-4019-2639-7(8)) Hay Hse., Inc.

—Archangels 101: How to Connect Closely with Archangels Michael, Raphael, Uriel, Gabriel & Others for Healing, Protection, & Guidance. 2010. (ENG., Illus.). 160p. 15.95 (978-1-4019-2638-0(X)) Hay Hse., Inc.

—Daily Guidance from Your Angels: 365 Angelic Messages to Soothe, Heal, & Open Your Heart. (ENG.). 2007. 250p. pap. 14.95 (978-1-4019-0774-7(1)) 2006. 400p. 24.95 (978-1-4019-0771-6(7)) 2008. (Illus.). 256p. pap. 25.95 (978-1-4019-1716-6(X)) Hay Hse., Inc.

—Goddesses & Angels. 2006. (Illus.). 260p. (978-1-4019-1079-2(3), 393) Hay Hse. UK, Ltd. GBR. Dist: Grantham Bk. Services.

—Guia Diaria de Sus Angeles: 365 Mensages de Los Angeles Para Aliviar, Sanar y Abrir su Corazon. 2008. (SPA & ENG.). 400p. pap. 14.95 (978-1-4019-1729-6(1)) Hay Hse., Inc.

—The Healing Miracles of Archangel Raphael. (ENG.). 2011. pap. 12.95 (978-1-4019-2473-7(5)) 2010. 216p. 17.95 (978-1-4019-2472-0(7)) Hay Hse., Inc.

—How to Hear Your Angels. 2007. 128p. (978-1-4019-1541-4(8), 460) Hay Hse. UK, Ltd. GBR. Dist: Grantham Bk. Services.

—How to Hear Your Angels. 2007. (ENG.). 128p. per. 12.95 (978-1-4019-1705-0(4)) Hay Hse., Inc.

—Life Purpose Oracle Cards. 2011. (ENG.). 44p. 15.95 (978-1-4019-2475-1(1)) Hay Hse., Inc.

—The Miracles of Archangel Michael. 2008. 256p. (978-1-84850-054-9(8), 804) Hay Hse. UK, Ltd. GBR. Dist: Grantham Bk. Services.

—The Miracles of Archangel Michael. 2009. 226p. pap. (978-1-84850-189-8(7), 1200) 2009. (ENG.). 200p. pap. 13.95 (978-1-4019-2206-1(6)) 2008. (ENG.). 256p. 19.95 (978-1-4019-2205-4(8)) Hay Hse., Inc.

—My Guardian Angel: True Stories of Angelic Encounters from the Readers of Woman's World Magazine. 2008. (ENG.). 160p. pap. 10.95 (978-1-4019-1753-1(4)) Hay Hse., Inc.

—Realms of the Earth Angels: More Information for Incarnated Angels, Elementals, Wizards, & Other Lightworkers. 2007. (ENG.). 176p. per. 7.00 (978-1-4019-1718-0(6)) Hay Hse., Inc.

—Reinos de los Ángeles En la Tierra: Información Acerca de Ángeles Encarnados, Elementales, Magos Y Otros Trabajadores de la Luz. 2008. (SPA & ENG.). 176p. pap. 7.00 (978-1-4019-1890-3(5)) Hay Hse., Inc.

—Saved by an Angel: True Accounts of People Who Have Had Extraordinary Experiences with Angels... & How You Can, Too! 2011. (ENG.). 270p. pap. 15.95 (978-1-4019-3361-6(0)) Hay Hse., Inc.

—Signs from Above: Angelic Messages to Guide Your Life Choices. 2009. 128p. pap. (978-1-84850-026-6(2), 794) Hay Hse. UK, Ltd. GBR. Dist: Grantham Bk. Services.

—Terapia Angélica: Mensajes para Sanar Todas las Áreas de Su Vida. 2008. (SPA & ENG.). 224p. pap. 13.95 (978-1-4019-1895-8(6)) Hay Hse., Inc.

Vivo, Gaetano. Messages from the Angels of Transparency: Powerful Words from Gentle Souls. 2012. (ENG.). 130p. pap. 14.95 (978-1-84694-974-6(2)) Hunt, John Publishing Ltd. GBR. Dist: National Bk. Network.

Von Dornheim, Curt H. Angel Words of Wisdom. Date not set. 64p. 12.95 (978-0-89404-223-2(8)) Aztex Corp.

—Visiting with the Angels. Date not set. 128p. (Orig.). pap. 12.95 (978-0-89404-224-9(6)) Aztex Corp.

Wallace, Karen, et al. Angels at Bedtime: Tales of Love, Guidance & Support for You to Read with Your Child to Comfort, Calm & Heal. 2011. (ENG., Illus.). 144p. pap. 16.95 (978-1-78028-026-4(2), Watkins Publishing) Duncan Baird Pubs. GBR. Dist: Sterling Publishing Co., Inc.

Ware Jr., Michael. The Beginning of the Heavenly Realm & Earth: ... an Intriguing Book that Captures the Mind of the Spiritual Reader. 2008. 68p. pap. 9.95 (978-0-595-52850-9(3)) iUniverse, Inc.

Warner, Sandy. Angels & Demons. 2008. 256p. pap. 16.00 (978-1-4357-2537-9(9)) Lulu Enterprises Inc.

Wauters, Ambika. Angel Blessings for Babies. 2011. (ENG., Illus.). 128p. 19.95 (978-1-904760-82-5(1)) Carroll & Brown Pubs., Ltd. GBR. Dist: Independent Pubs. Group.

—The Healing Power of Angels: How They Guide & Protect Us. 2011. (ENG.). 256p. pap. 14.95 (978-1-907486-42-5(9), Watkins Publishing) Duncan Baird Pubs. GBR. Dist: Sterling Publishing Co., Inc.

We Hear the Christmas Angels: True Stories of Their Presence. 2006. (Illus.). 257p. 14.95 (978-0-8249-4704-0(5)) Ideals Pubns.

Webster, Richard. Encyclopedia of Angels. 2009. (ENG.). 264p. pap. 15.95 (978-0-7387-1462-2(3)) Llewellyn Pubns.

Williams, Guy. The Spirit World in the Letters of Paul the Apostle: A Critical Examination of the Role of Spiritual Beings in the Authentic Pauline Epistles. 2009. (Forschungen Zur Religion und Literatur des Alten & Neuen Testament Ser.). (ENG.). 336p. (C). 110.00 (978-3-525-53095-5(1)) Vandenhoeck & Ruprecht GmbH & Co. KG DEU. Dist: ISD.

Williamson, John. God's Fluttering Servants: The biblical story of Angels. 2011. 158p. pap. 24.95 (978-1-4560-6523-2(8)) PublishAmerica, Inc.

Willoughby, Ro & Willoughby, Robert. Angels: A Journey of Exploration for Individuals, Small Groups or Churches. 2006. (Messenger Ser.). (Illus.). 64p. pap. 16.99 (978-1-84427-223-5(0)) Scripture Union GBR. Dist: STL Distribution North America.

Wilson, Douglas & Morin, Terry. The Forgotten Heavens: Six Essays on Cosmology. 2010. pap. (978-1-59128-071-2(0)) Canon Pr.

Woolmer, John. Angels of Glory & Darkness: Angels of Good & Evil, Angels in Christianity, Angels in History, Angels Today. 2006. 224p. pap. 14.99 (978-0-8254-6122-4(7), Monarch Bks.) Lion Hudson PLC GBR. Dist: Kregel Pubns.

Wright, Vinita Hampton. A Catalogue of Angels: The Heavenly, the Fallen, & the Holy Ones among Us. 2006. (ENG.). 192p. (gr. 13). per. 16.95 (978-1-55725-421-4(4)) Paraclete Pr., Inc.

Wyllie, Timothy. The Return of the Rebel Angels. 2011. (ENG., Illus.). 1p. pap. 22.00 (978-1-59143-125-1(5)) Bear & Co.

—The Return of the Rebel Angels: The Urantia Mysteries & the Coming of the Light. 2011. (Illus.). xvii, 459p. E-Book (978-1-59143-945-5(0)) Bear & Co.

Young, Sherriane R. R. Angels. 2011. 12p. pap. 9.36 (978-1-4634-0143-6(4)) AuthorHouse.

ANGELS—ART

see Angels in Art

ANGELS (JUDAISM)

Berg, Yehuda. Inteligencia Angelical: Angel Intelligence. 2009. (ENG & SPA.). 176p. pap. 14.95 (978-1-57189-621-6(X)) Research Centre of Kabbalah.

ANGELS IN ART

Angelou, Maya. Love's Exquisite Freedom. 2011. (ENG., Illus.). 32p. 19.95 (978-1-59962-103-6(7), Welcome Bks.) Welcome Enterprises, Inc.

Arantza, et al, illus. Angel Lust, Volume 2: A Gallery Girls Collection. 2007. (Gallery Girls Collection). 64p. per. 9.95 (978-0-86562-150-3(0)) S.Q. Productions, Inc.

Baeck, Philippe De. Angels, 1 vol. Diman, Paz, ed. 2009. (DUT, FRE, GER & ENG., Illus.). 480p. pap. 14.95 (978-94-6065-001-7(5)) booQs Publishers bvba BEL. Dist: Innovative Logistics.

Balchin, Judy. Handmade Fairy Cards. 2009. (Simple & Stunning Ser.). (ENG., Illus.). 48p. pap. 13.95 (978-1-84448-305-1(3)) Search Pr., Ltd. GBR. Dist: Independent Pubs. Group.

Bates, Maryann, photos by. Angels over Macon. 2007. (Illus.). 40p. per. 14.95 (978-1-934144-23-7(1)) Sphinx Publishing.

Bertucci, Mary Lou, compiled by. Tiffany's Swedenborgian Angels: Stained Glass Windows Representing the Seven Churches from the Book of Revelation. 2011. (Illus.). 96p. pap. (978-0-87785-339-8(8)) Swedenborg Foundation, Inc.

Buranelli, Francesco. Between God & Man: Angels in Italian Art. Dietrick, Robin C., ed. 2007. (ENG., Illus.). 192p. 34.95 (978-1-887422-15-4(3)) Univ. Pr. of Mississippi.

Bussagli, Marco. Angels. Giammanco, Rosanna, tr. from ITA. 2007. (ENG., Illus.). 780p. 19.95 (978-0-8109-9436-2(4)) Abrams.

Butkus, Michael, et al. How to Draw Fallen Angels: Discover the secrets to drawing, painting, & illustrating beings of the Otherworld. 2011. (Fantasy Underground Ser.). (ENG., Illus.). 128p. pap. 19.95 (978-1-60058-221-9(4), 1600582214) Foster, Walter Publishing, Inc.

Chase, Pat. Angel Companions. 2007. (Illus.). 36p. 17.95 (978-1-932327-25-0(8)) CKE Pubns.

Dillman, Meredith. Fairies & Fantasy: Learn to Paint the Enchanted World of Fairies, Angels, & Mermaids. 2009. (Watercolor Made Easy Ser.). (ENG., Illus.). 64p. pap. 9.95 (978-1-60058-141-0(2), 1600581412) Foster, Walter Publishing, Inc.

Fairy, Sprite & Angel Photos: Actual Photographs of the Elemental Realm. 2007. per. (978-1-934574-44-7(9)) Nature Angel Publishing.

Gorgievski, Sandra. Face to Face with Angels: Images in Medieval Art & in Film. 2010. (ENG., Illus.). 232p. pap. 55.00 (978-0-7864-4220-1(4)) McFarland & Co., Inc. Pubs.

Guilloux, Fabien. Saint François D'Assise et L'ange Musicien: Thème et Varations Iconographiques Dans les Collections du Museo Francescano de Rome. 2010. (FRE., Illus.). 165p. (978-88-88001-73-9(5)) Ist. Storico dei Cappuccini.

Hamer, Elaine. Angels in Watercolour. 2009. (Fantasy Art Ser.). (ENG., Illus.). 48p. pap. 15.95 (978-1-84448-396-9(7)) Search Pr., Ltd. GBR. Dist: Independent Pubs. Group.

Jaritz, Gerhard. Angels, Devils: The Supernatural & Its Visual Representation. 2011. pap. (978-615-5053-22-1(7)) Central European Univ. Pr.

Jaritz, Gerhard, ed. Angels, Devils: The Supernatural & Its Visual Representation. 2011. (ENG.). 205p. (978-615-5053-21-4(9)) Central European Univ. Pr.

Jones, David Albert. Angels: A History. 2010. (ENG., Illus.). 224p. 19.95 (978-0-19-958295-2(5)) Oxford Univ. Pr., Inc.

Langmuir, Erika. Angels. 2010. (ENG., Illus.). 96p. pap. 15.00 (978-1-85709-484-8(0)) Yale Univ. Pr.

Law, Stephanie Pui-Mon. Dreamscapes: Creating Magical Angel, Faery & Mermaid Worlds with Watercolor. 2008. (ENG., Illus.). 176p. pap. 24.99 (978-1-58180-964-0(6), North Light Bks.) F&W Media, Inc.

Locke, Karen B. Angels are Abound. 2011. 72p. pap. 49.99 (978-1-4567-2691-1(9)) AuthorHouse.

McRae Books. Angels. 2010. (Magnet Art Bks.). (ENG.). 24p. 5.95 (978-88-6098-168-4(9)) McRae Bks. Srl ITA. Dist: Independent Pubs. Group.

Publications International Staff, ed. Blessed by an Angel. 2007. 10.98 (978-1-4127-1374-0(9)) Publications International, Ltd.

Rackham, Arthur. Rackham's Fairies, Elves & Goblins: More Than 80 Full-Color Illustrations. Menges, Jeff A., ed. 2007. (Dover Fine Art, History of Art Ser.). (ENG., Illus.). 96p. pap. 14.95 (978-0-486-46023-9(1)) Dover Pubns., Inc.

Richardson, Keith. Doorways to Heaven: A Spiritual Journey Guided by Angels, Miracles & the Art of Andy Lakey. 2010. 256p. pap. 16.95 (978-1-4327-6080-9(7)) Outskirts Pr., Inc.

Russell, Anita M. Hand to Heart: An Easy Guide to Making Angel Pins. 2009. (Illus.). 76p. pap. 8.99 (978-1-60696-427-9(5)) Tate Publishing & Enterprises, LLC.

Sasser, Angela. Angelic Visions: Create Fantasy Art Angels with Watercolor, Ink & Colored Pencil. 2011. (ENG., Illus.). 128p. pap. 22.99 (978-1-60061-953-3(3), North Light Bks.) F&W Media, Inc.

Scott, Laura, ed. Crafting an Angel a Day. 2006. (Illus.). 191p. reprint ed. 22.00 (978-1-4223-5597-8(7)) DIANE Publishing Co.

Vedrenne, Penny. Angels: A Book of Stencils. 2007. 56p. pap. 19.95 (978-1-4303-1140-9(1)) Lulu Enterprises Inc.

—Cherubs: A Book of Stencils. 2007. 64p. pap. 19.95 (978-1-4303-2498-0(8)) Lulu Enterprises Inc.

Virtue, Doreen. Archangel Michael Oracle Cards: A 44-Card Deck & Guidebook. 2009. (ENG.). 44p. instr.'s gde. ed. 15.95 (978-1-4019-2273-3(2), 876) Hay Hse., Inc.

Weller, Alan. Angels. 2009. (Dover Pictura Electronic Clip Art Ser.). (ENG.). 128p. pap. 39.95 (978-0-486-99047-7(8)) Dover Pubns., Inc.

ANGER

Abrams, Mitch. Anger Management in Sport: Understanding & Controlling Violence in Athletes. 2010. (ENG., Illus.). 296p. 54.00 (978-0-7360-6168-1(1)) Human Kinetics Pubs.

Adams, Dennis D. Honest Direct Respectful: Three Simple Words That Will Change Your Life. 2007. (ENG., Illus.). 112p. 12.99 (978-1-933204-29-1(X)) Deep River Bks.

Alei, Ariole K. The Power of Anger: Blasting Through Your Limitations & Transforming the World. 2009. 17.95 (978-1-4357-1818-0(6)) Lulu Enterprises Inc.

Alkon, Amy. I See Rude People: One Woman's Battle to Beat Some Manners into Impolite Society. 2009. (ENG., Illus.). 224p. pap. 16.95 (978-0-07-160021-7(3), 0071600213) McGraw-Hill Cos., The.

Allan, Robert. Getting Control of Your Anger: A Clinically Proven, Three-Step Plan for Getting to the Root of the Problem & Resolving It. 2009. (ENG.). 272p. pap. 16.95 (978-0-07-174244-3(1), 0071742441) McGraw-Hill Cos., The.

Anderson, David A. Sometimes I Get So Angry! Anger Management for Everyone. 2006. 8.70 net. (978-0-9709057-1-0(8)) Pensive Pr., LLC.

Anger Regulation Therapy. 2012. 49.95 (978-0-203-86491-3(3)) Routledge.

ARISE Foundation Staff & Benson, Susan. Life Skills Curriculum: ARISE Rules of the Road (Instructor's Manual) 2011. (Work in Progress Ser.). (ENG.). 134p. (J). pap., tchr. ed. 24.95 (978-1-58614-197-4(X)) Arise Foundation.

Barnes, Elizabeth. A Family Guidebook on Bullies, Self-Esteem & Hidden Hurts! 2008. 108p. pap. 19.95 (978-1-4389-1076-5(2)) AuthorHouse.

Baruch, Rhoda, et al. Creative Anger: Putting That Powerful Emotion to Good Use, 1 vol. 2007. 256p. 44.95 (978-0-275-99874-5(6), C9874, Praeger Pubs.) Greenwood Publishing Group, Inc.

Basset, Lytta. Holy Anger: Jacob, Job, Jesus. 2007. (ENG.). 304p. 34.95 (978-0-8264-8072-9(1)) Continuum International Publishing Group, Ltd. GBR. Dist: National Bk. Network.

—Holy Anger: Jacob, Job, Jesus. 2007. 295p. per. 28.00 (978-0-8028-6237-2(3)) Eerdmans, William B. Publishing Co.

Baumgardner, Frances Garrett. Surviving Illness & Death. 2007. 72p. per. 9.99 (978-1-60266-143-1(X)) Xulon Pr., Inc.

Berry, Diane M. A Peace of My Mind: A Therapist's Guide to Handling Anger & Other Difficult Emotions. 2008. 312p. per. 15.95 *(978-0-9742076-5-8(3))* Blue Waters Pubns.

Bevere, Lisa. Be Angry, but Don't Blow It! Maintaining Your Passion Without Losing Your Cool, 0 vols. 2007. 208p. per. 14.99 *(978-0-7852-8918-0(6))* Nelson, Thomas Inc.

Bhave, Swati Y. & Saini, Sunil. Anger Management. 2009. (Response Bks.). (Illus.). 220p. (C). pap. 19.95 *(978-81-321-0085-0(9),* B00859P) SAGE Pubns., Inc.

Bhave, Swati Y. & Saini, Sunil, eds. AHA Syndrome & Cardiovascular Disease. 2009. (ENG., Illus.). 300p. 120.00 *(978-1-84829-023-5(3))* Anshan GBR. Dist: Publishers Storage & Shipping.

Black, Claudia. Anger Strategies: Practical Tools for Professionals Treating Anger. 2006. ring bd. 59.00 *(978-0-910223-30-0(0))* MAC Publishing.

Braund, Susanna & Most, Glenn W., eds. Ancient Anger: Perspectives from Homer to Galen. 2007. (Yale Classical Studies). (ENG.). 336p. pap. 69.00 *(978-0-521-03642-9(9))* Cambridge Univ. Pr.

Bray, Wendy & Ledger, Christine. Insight into Anger. 2007. 112p. *(978-1-85345-437-0(0))* Crusade for World Revival.

Brennan, Ian. Anger Antidotes: How Not to Lose Your S#&! 2011. (ENG.). 184p. pap. 14.95 *(978-0-393-70705-2(9),* 70705) Norton, W. W. & Co., Inc.

Bretherick, Graham. Healing Life's Hurts: Make Your Anger Work for You, 1 vol. 2008. 224p. pap. 12.99 *(978-0-8254-6279-5(7),* Monarch Bks.) Lion Hudson PLC GBR. Dist: Kregel Pubns.

Brill, Losw. Relationships Without Anger. 2009. 120p. pap. 22.95 *(978-1-4490-2789-6(X))* AuthorHouse.

Brody, Lazer. The Trail to Tranquility. 2007. 280p. 24.95 *(978-0-9797530-2-2(3))* Kalcom Publishing.

Bruce, Timothy J. & Jongsma, Arthur E. Evidence-Based Treatment Planning for Anger Control Problems. 2011. (Evidence-Based Psychotherapy Treatment Planning Video Ser.: 31). (ENG.). 72p. pap. 29.00 *(978-0-470-56844-6(5),* Wiley) Wiley, John & Sons, Inc.

Bunge, Gabriel. Dragon's Wine & Angel's Bread: The Teaching of Evagrius Ponticus on Anger & Meekness. Gythiel, Anthony P., tr. from GER. 2009. pap. 13.00 *(978-0-88141-337-3(2))* St. Vladimir's Seminary Pr.

Caffery, Larry E. Years of Grace, Life of Mercy: The Story of an Angry Man who Finds Happiness. 2010. pap. 11.99 *(978-1-61566-671-3(0))* Tate Publishing & Enterprises, LLC.

Campbell, Jerry. Who? Me! Angry? 2011. 162p. pap. 24.95 ***(978-1-257-77590-3(1))*** Lulu Enterprises Inc.

Canning, Maureen. Lust, Anger, Love: Understanding Sexual Addiction & the Road to Healthy Intimacy. 2008. (ENG.). 320p. per. 16.95 *(978-1-4022-0868-3(5))* Sourcebooks, Inc.

Cannon, Marcia G. The Gift of Anger: Seven Steps to Uncover the Meaning of Anger & Gain Awareness, True Strength, & Peace. 2011. (ENG.). 192p. pap. 17.95 *(978-1-57224-966-0(8))* New Harbinger Pubns.

Carter, Les. Getting the Best of Your Anger: Before It Gets the Best of You. rev. ed. 2007. 176p. pap. 12.99 *(978-0-8007-3175-5(1))* Revell.

Cavell, Timothy A. & Malcolm, Kenya T., eds. Anger, Aggression, & Interventions for Interpersonal Violence. 2006. (ENG.). 472p. 120.95 *(978-0-8058-5554-8(8))*; per. 47.95 *(978-0-8058-6152-5(1))* Routledge.

Chapman, Annie. Letting Go of Anger: How to Get Your Emotions under Control. 2010. 208p. pap. 11.99 *(978-0-7369-2473-3(6))* Harvest Hse. Pubs.

Chapman, Gary D. Anger: Handling a Powerful Emotion in a Healthy Way. rev. ed. 2007. (ENG., Illus.). 240p. per. 14.99 *(978-1-881273-88-2(1))* Northfield Publishing.

Chapman, Mark. Discover the Roots to Your Anger. 2008. 108p. 21.49 *(978-1-4343-8809-4(3))*; pap. 12.99 *(978-1-4343-8808-7(5))* AuthorHouse.

Clausen, Elana I. Psychology of Anger. 2007. 129.00 *(978-1-60021-772-2(9))* Nova Science Pubs., Inc.

Cose, Ellis. The End of Anger: A New Generation's Take on Race & Rage. (ENG.). 2012. 224p. pap. 14.99 ***(978-0-06-199856-0(7))*** 2011. 320p. 24.99 *(978-0-06-199855-3(9))* HarperCollins Pubs. (Ecco).

Davies, William. Overcoming Anger & Irritability: A Self-Help Guide Using Cognitive Behavioral Techniques. 2008. (Overcoming Ser.). (ENG., Illus.). 288p. pap. 14.95 *(978-0-465-00544-4(6))* Basic Bks.

Davis, Teresa, ed. Victory over Anger: Rules of Engagement. 2010. pap. 12.99 *(978-1-61566-818-2(7))* Tate Publishing & Enterprises, LLC.

DiGiuseppe, Raymond & Tafrate, Raymond Chip. Understanding Anger Disorders, 1 vol. 2010. (ENG.). 432p. pap. 35.00 *(978-0-19-977409-8(9))* Oxford Univ. Pr., Inc.

Dobson, James C. Todo Sobre la Ira.Tr. of Dr. Dobson Talks About Anger. (SPA.). 56p. *(978-84-7228-248-3(1),* 220889) Clie, Editorial.

Dryden, Windy. Overcoming Anger. x, 102p. *(978-0-85969-713-2(4),* Sheldon Press) SPCK Publishing.

Earle, David W. Lpc. What to Do While You Count To. 2011. 104p. 24.99 ***(978-1-4568-6270-1(7))***; pap. 15.99 ***(978-1-4568-6269-5(3))*** Xlibris Corp.

Eason, Paulette. Anger Management. 2007. 105p. pap. 19.95 *(978-0-9795180-3-1(7))* Williams, Benjamin Publishing.

Edmiston, Susan & Scheff, Leonard. The Cow in the Parking Lot: A Zen Approach to Overcoming Anger. 2010. (ENG., Illus.). 197p. pap. 12.95 *(978-0-7611-5815-8(4),* 0761158154) Workman Publishing Co., Inc.

Ellis Eastman, Linda, ed. Survival Skills for the African American Woman. 2007. 19.95 *(978-0-9791153-5-6(3))* Professional Woman Publishing.

Ellis, Jimmie A. Coping with Anger. 2007. 48p. per. 9.99 *(978-1-59755-147-2(3),* Advantage Inspirational) Advantage Bks.

Faupel, Adrian, et al. Anger Management. 2nd ed. 2010. (ENG., Illus.). 144p. instr.'s gde. ed. 36.95 *(978-0-415-58071-7(4))* Routledge.

Fauteux, Kevin. Defusing Angry People: Practical Tools for Handling Bullying, Threats, & Violence. 2011. (ENG.). 224p. pap. 14.95 *(978-0-88282-349-2(3),* New Horizon Pr. Pubs., Inc.

Fawcett, John. An Essay on Anger. 2007. (ENG.). 176p. 37.95 *(978-0-548-04267-0(5))* Kessinger Publishing, LLC.

Frances, Dee. Handling Anger in a Christian Way. Koster, Henry, ed. Date not set. 6.00 *(978-1-885519-37-5(0))* DDDD Pubns.

—Three Ways to Handle Anger: One Appropriate. Date not set. pap. 6.00 *(978-1-885519-38-2(9))* DDDD Pubns.

Funches, Venessa. Shoppers Scorned. 2009. 204p. pap. *(978-3-639-09149-6(3))* VDM Verlag Dr. Mueller e.K.

Gardner, Frank & Moore, Zella. Anger Regulation Therapy. 2010. (Practical Clinical Guidebooks Ser.). (ENG.). 240p. 95.00 *(978-0-415-87297-3(9))*; pap. 27.95 *(978-0-415-87298-0(7))* Routledge.

Gentry, W. Doyle. Anger Management for Dummies. 2006. (ENG., Illus.). 384p. per. 19.99 *(978-0-470-03715-7(6),* For Dummies) Wiley, John & Sons, Inc.

George, Mike. Don't Get Mad Get Wise: Why No One Ever Makes You Angry... Ever! 2007. (ENG., Illus.). 160p. per. 14.95 *(978-1-905047-82-6(7))* Hunt, John Publishing Ltd. GBR. Dist: National Bk. Network.

Gillaspie, D. E. Anger, A Biblical Perspective. 2011. 224p. 33.95 ***(978-1-4497-2511-2(2))***; pap. 17.95 ***(978-1-4497-2510-5(4))*** Author Solutions, Inc. (WestBow Pr.).

Gillette, Gertrude. Four Faces of Anger: Seneca, Evagrius Ponticus, Cassian, & Augustine. 2010. (ENG.). 178p. pap. 28.50 *(978-0-7618-5169-1(0))* Univ. Pr. of America, Inc.

Godzich, Leo. Administracion de Ira para Parejas. 2008.Tr. of Anger Management for Couples. (SPA.). 45p. *(978-0-9712847-8-4(4))* National Assn. of Marriage Enhancement.

Goldblatt, Hal. Anger. 2009. 56p. pap. 9.95 *(978-1-60693-936-9(X),* Strategic Bk. Publishing) AEG Literary Publishing Services, Inc.

Gourishanker, Patnaik & Purnamasi, Patnaik. Understanding Anger: Effective Management Techniques. 2011. 132p. pap. ***(978-3-639-32968-1(6))*** VDM Verlag Dr. Mueller e K.

Greene. Anger Management Skills for Women. 108p. pap. 15.95 *(978-1-881165-09-5(4))* People Skills International.

Greene, Ida. Anger Management Skills for Men. 94p. pap. 15.95 *(978-1-881165-10-1(8))* People Skills International.

Heery, Gery. Parental Anger Management: The PAMP Programme. 2007. (Illus.). 187p. pap. 49.95 *(978-1-905541-04-1(X))* Russell Hse. Publishing Ltd. GBR. Dist: International Specialized Bk. Services.

Hoy, Lynette J. & Griffin, Ted. What's Good about Anger? Putting Your Anger to Work for Good. 3rd exp. ed. 2009. Orig. Title: What's Good about Anger? an Anger Management Course with Application Devotionals. (ENG.). 168p. per. 16.95 *(978-0-9717599-1-6(X))* CounselCare Connection.

Huebner, Mary. Deal with It: A 12 Week Study on Teenage Girls' Anger, 1 vol. 2009. (ENG.). 128p. pap. 12.99 *(978-0-310-28510-6(0))* Zondervan.

Hummel, Rand. Turn Away Wrath: Meditations to Control Anger & Bitterness. 2007. 165p. per. *(978-1-59166-734-6(8))* BJU Pr.

Hunt, June. Keeping Your Cool — When Your Anger Is Hot! Practical Steps for Tempering Your Fiery Emotions. 2009. 304p. pap. 13.99 *(978-0-7369-2424-5(8))* Harvest Hse. Pubs.

Jones, Robert D. Freedom from Resentment: Stopping Hurts from Turning Bitter. 2010. 24p. 3.99 *(978-1-935273-66-0(3))* New Growth Pr.

Jongsma, Arthur E. & Bruce, Timothy J. Treatment Planning for Anger Control Problems. 2011. (Evidence-Based Psychotherapy Treatment Planning Video Ser.: 3). (ENG.). mass mkt. 40.00 *(978-0-470-41788-1(9))*; 72p. pap., wbk. ed. 25.00 *(978-0-470-56845-3(3))*; mass mkt. 55.25 *(978-1-118-02891-9(0))* Wiley, John & Sons, Inc. (Wiley).

Joo, Samantha. Provocation & Punishment: The Anger of God in the Book of Jeremiah & Deuteronomistic Theology. (Beihefte zur Zeitschrift fur die alttestamentliche Wissenschaft Ser.). (ENG.). XIV, 320p. 225.00 ***(978-3-11-184527-2(3))***; 2006. 140.00 *(978-3-11-018994-0(1))* De Gruyter, Walter Inc.

Kalimtzis, Kostas. Taming Anger: The Hellenic Approach to the Limitations of Reason. 2012. 224p. 120.00 *(978-0-7156-4079-1(8))* Duckworth Publishers GBR. Dist: International Publishers Marketing.

Krueger, Lisa. Anger Management. 2009. (Current Controversies Ser.). (ENG.). 240p. (gr. 10-12). 27.50 *(978-0-7377-4131-5(7))*; pap. 39.70 *(978-0-7377-4130-8(9))* Cengage Gale. (Greenhaven Pr., Inc.).

Ladd, Karol. Defuse: A Mom's Survival Guide to More Love, Less Anger, 0 vols. 2007. 208p. per. 13.99 *(978-0-8499-0724-1(1))* Nelson, Thomas Inc.

Lee, John R. The Anger Solution: The Proven Method for Achieving Calm & Developing Healthy, Long-Lasting Relationships. 2009. (ENG.). 240p. pap. 15.95 *(978-0-7382-1260-9(1))* Da Capo Pr., Inc.

Leifer, Ron. Vinegar into Honey: Seven Steps to Understanding & Transforming Anger, Agression, & Violence. 2008. (ENG.). 144p. pap. 14.95 *(978-1-55939-293-8(2))* Snow Lion Pubns., Inc.

Lester, Andrew D. Anger: Discovering Your Spiritual Ally. 2007. (ENG.). 126p. per. 15.00 *(978-0-664-22499-8(7))* Westminster John Knox Pr.

Liebmann, Marian, ed. Art Therapy & Anger. 2008. (ENG., Illus.). 256p. (C). pap. *(978-1-84310-425-4(3))* Kingsley, Jessica Ltd.

Mary J. Clark M.A. L.P.C. Managing My Anger: Weekly Meditations & Journal Exercises for Growth. 2009. 132p. 23.95 *(978-1-4401-6718-8(4))*; pap. 13.95 *(978-1-4401-6719-5(2))* iUniverse, Inc.

May, Sharon Morris. How to Argue So Your Spouse Will Listen: 6 Principles for Turning Arguments into Conversations, 0 vols. 2007. 224p. per. 13.99 *(978-0-8499-1868-1(5))* Nelson, Thomas Inc.

McMahon, Gladeana. No More Anger! Be Your Own Anger Management Coach. 2008. (Illus.). 160p. per. 22.95 *(978-1-85575-430-3(4))* Karnac Bks. GBR. Dist: Stylus Publishing, LLC.

McMurray, Ann & Jantz, Gregory L. Every Woman's Guide to Managing Your Anger, 1 vol. 2009. (ENG.). 272p. pap. 12.99 *(978-0-8007-3314-8(2))* Revell.

Messer, Mitchell H. Beyond the Boiling Point: Managing Anger in the Classroom. *(978-1-929305-01-8(X))* Anger Institute, The.

Meyer, Joyce. Do Yourself a Favor... Forgive: Learn How to Take Control of Your Life Through Forgiveness. 2012. (ENG.). 208p. 19.99 ***(978-0-446-54727-7(1))***; 272p. 21.99 ***(978-1-4555-1338-3(5))*** FaithWords.

Moye, Michel & Ave, Anthony. Anger Management Guide Workbook: Boy (B) Model. 2009. pap. *(978-1-61623-421-8(0))* Independent Pub.

Nay, W. Robert. Overcoming Anger in Your Relationship: How to Break the Cycle of Arguments, Put-Downs, & Stony Silences. 2010. (ENG.). 259p. 40.00 *(978-1-60623-642-0(3))*; pap. 16.95 *(978-1-60623-283-5(5))* Guilford Pubns., Inc.

—Taking Charge of Anger: Six Steps to Asserting Yourself Without Losing Control. 2nd rev. ed. 2012. (ENG.). 289p. 45.00 ***(978-1-4625-0380-3(2))*** Guilford Pubns., Inc.

—Taking Charge of Anger, Second Edition: Six Steps to Asserting Yourself Without Losing Control. 2nd rev. ed. 2012. (ENG.). 289p. pap. 16.95 ***(978-1-4625-0242-4(3))*** Guilford Pubns., Inc.

Novaco, Raymond W., et al. Anger Treatment for Offenders. (Wiley Series in Forensic Clinical Psychology Ser.). 350p. pap. 150.00 *(978-0-471-49153-8(5))* Wiley, John & Sons, Inc.

O'Bannon, Kathleen. The Anger Cure: A Step-by-Step Program to Reduce Anger, Rage, Negativity, Violence, & Depression in Your Life, 1 vol. 2007. (ENG., Illus.). 224p. pap. 17.95 *(978-1-59120-199-1(3))* Basic Health Pubns., Inc.

Osho, Osho & Osho. Emotional Wellness: Transforming Fear, Anger, & Jealousy into Creative Energy. 2007. (ENG.). 304p. 22.00 *(978-0-307-33788-7(X),* Harmony) Crown Publishing Group.

Pahlavan, Farzaneh, ed. Multiple Facets of Anger: Getting Mad or Restoring Justice? 2011. 194p. ***(978-1-61761-195-7(6))*** Nova Science Pubs., Inc.

Parker Hall, Sue. Anger, Rage & Relationship: An Empathic Approach to Anger Management. 2008. (ENG., Illus.). 232p. (C). 110.00 *(978-0-415-41347-3(8))*; pap. 34.95 *(978-0-415-41348-0(6))* Routledge.

Perkins, Bill. When Good Men Get Angry. 2009. (ENG.). 192p. 16.99 *(978-1-4143-1141-8(9))* Tyndale Hse. Pubs.

Pfeiffer, Janet. The Secret Side of Anger: The Quickest & Easiest Guide (Ever!) to Managing Anger. 2009. pap. 12.99 *(978-1-60696-530-6(1))* Tate Publishing & Enterprises, LLC.

Potegal, Michael, et al, eds. International Handbook of Anger: Constituent & Concomitant Biological, Psychological, & Social Processes. 2010. (ENG., Illus.). xiv, 590p. 199.00 *(978-0-387-89675-5(9),* 0387896759) Springer.

Potter-Efron, Ronald T. Healing the Angry Brain: How Understanding the Way Your Brain Works Can Help You Control Anger & Aggression. 2012. (ENG.). 184p. pap. 16.95 ***(978-1-60882-133-4(1))***; (Illus.). viii, 172p. ***(978-1-60882-135-8(8))*** New Harbinger Pubns.

Potter-Efron, Ronald T. Rage: A Step-by-Step Guide to Overcoming Explosive Anger. 2007. (ENG.). 176p. per. 16.95 *(978-1-57224-462-7(3))* New Harbinger Pubns.

Potter-Efron, Ronald T. & Potter-Efron, Patricia. Thirty-Minute Therapy for Anger: Everything You Need to Know in the Least Amount of Time. 2011. (New Harbinger Thirty-Minute Therapy Ser.). (ENG.). 120p. pap. 15.95 *(978-1-60882-029-0(7))* New Harbinger Pubns.

Potter-Efron, Ronald T. & Potter-Efron, Patricia S. Letting Go of Anger: The Eleven Most Common Anger Styles & What to Do about Them. 2nd rev. ed. 2006. (ENG.). 200p. pap. 16.95 *(978-1-57224-448-1(8))* New Harbinger Pubns.

Randolph, MoriEl. What to Do When People Get on Your Nerves. 2007. 140p. pap. 14.50 *(978-0-615-15960-7(5))* FreshView.

Richardson, Roy Franklin. Psychology & Pedagogy of Anger. 2006. pap. 19.95 *(978-1-4286-5588-1(3))* Kessinger Publishing, LLC.

Rogne, Carol. Anger & Guilt: Our Foes & Friends. 2011. 198p. pap. 15.95 ***(978-1-4327-7757-9(2))*** Outskirts Pr., Inc.

Rubin, Rhea Joyce. Defusing the Angry Patron: A How-To-Do-It Manual for Librarians. 2nd ed. 2010. xv, 125p. 65.00 *(978-1-55570-731-6(9))* Neal-Schuman Pubs., Inc.

Rusz, Renata. Keyword: Anger. 2008. 64p. pap. *(978-3-639-02064-9(2))* VDM Verlag Dr. Mueller e.K.

Sacco, Peter Andrew. What's Your Anger Type for Christians - Good Anger Versus Bad Anger? 2007. 260p. pap. 15.95 *(978-1-60145-149-1(0))* Booklocker.com, Inc.

Sasseen, Michael. Surviving the Demons, 1 vol. 2009. 211p. pap. 24.95 *(978-1-60610-735-6(6))* PublishAmerica, Inc.

Shaw, C. C. Free Counseling: How to Problem Solve in Daily Life. 2009. pap. 10.99 *(978-1-60799-991-1(9))* Tate Publishing & Enterprises, LLC.

Shelby, Patty. Inside an Anger Management Class. 2006. 136p. per. 9.95 *(978-1-60002-257-9(X),* 4436) Mountain Valley Publishing, LLC.

Sloterdijk, Peter. Rage & Time: A Psychopolitical Investigation. Wenning, Mario, tr. from GER. (Insurrections: Critical Studies in Religion, Politics, & Culture Ser.). (ENG.). 256p. (gr. 17). 2012. pap. 25.00 ***(978-0-231-14523-7(3))*** 2010. (Illus.). 34.50 *(978-0-231-14522-0(5))* Columbia Univ. Pr.

Smalley, Gary & Cunningham, Ted. Del enojo a la Intimidad, 1 vol. 2010. Orig. Title: From Anger to Intimacy. (SPA.). 256p. pap. 12.99 *(978-0-8254-1787-0(2),* Editorial Portavoz) Kregel Pubns.

—From Anger to Intimacy. 2009. (ENG.). 128p. pap., pupil's gde. ed. 12.99 *(978-0-8307-4675-0(7))* Gospel Light Pubns.

—From Anger to Intimacy: How Forgiveness Can Transform Your Marriage. 2009. (ENG.). 256p. 22.99 *(978-0-8307-4676-7(5))* Gospel Light Pubns.

Spencer, Eddie Charles. Put Out the Fire: How to Control Your Anger Before It Destroys Your Life. 2006. (ENG.) 140p. per. 14.99 *(978-1-4141-0858-2(3))* Pleasant Word.

Stauffer, Andrew M. Anger, Revolution, & Romanticism. 2009. (Cambridge Studies in Romanticism Ser.). (ENG.). 240p. pap. 34.99 *(978-0-521-10069-4(0))* Cambridge Univ. Pr.

Stoner, Marcia J., ed. Live It: Dealing with Anger for Tweens: Building Skills for Christian Living. 2006. (Live It! Ser.). (Illus.). 63p. 15.95 *(978-0-687-49534-4(2),* Abingdon Pr.

Swindoll, Charles R. La Ira: El Fusible Candente de la Hostilidad. (Serie Realidades - Realities Ser.).Tr. of Anger. (SPA.). 1.99 *(978-1-56063-276-4(3),* 498115) Editorial Unilit.

Tafrate, Raymond Chip & Kassinove, Howard. Anger Management for Everyone: Seven Proven Ways to Control Anger & Live a Happier Life. 2009. (ENG., Illus.). 240p. pap. 17.95 *(978-1-886230-83-5(8))* Impact Pubs., Inc.

Thomas, Sandra P. Transforming Nurses' Stress & Anger: Steps Toward Healing. 3rd ed. 2008. 800p. *(978-0-8261-2542-2(5))* Springer.

VanNoy, Steven. A Meditation Curriculum on Anger, Hostility, andEgolism for Incarcerated Adults: A Treatment Outcome Study. 2008. 124p. pap. *(978-3-8364-6090-3(4))* VDM Verlag Dr. Mueller e.K.

Washington, Shontel. How Can I Cope & Control Myself When I Am Angry? Anger Management Helpful Guidelines & Workbook. 2010. 16p. 8.49 *(978-1-4520-7069-8(5))* AuthorHouse.

Wasoba, Karen. Lord, Shut Me up! Anger Management for Christians. 2007. 216p. per. 17.95 *(978-1-58736-763-2(7))* Wheatmark.

Welch, Edward T. Living with an Angry Spouse: Help for Victims of Abuse. 2008. (ENG.). 24p. 3.99 *(978-1-934885-35-2(5))* New Growth Pr.

Welty, James P. Psychology of Anger: Symptoms, Causes & Coping. 2011. (Psychology of Emotions, Motivations & Actions Ser.). 319p. 165.00 ***(978-1-61209-615-5(6))*** Nova Science Pubs., Inc.

Williams, Debra Kay. Through the Storms. 2009. 16p. pap. 8.49 *(978-1-4389-9842-8(2))* AuthorHouse.

Williams, Emma E. & Barlow, Rebecca. Anger Control Training, 3 vols. (Illus.). 186p. spiral bd. *(978-0-86388-334-7(6),* 002-3091) Speechmark Publishing Ltd.

Wilson, Amy Lyles, intro. Anger: Minding Your Passion. 2010. 96p. 12.00 *(978-1-935205-07-4(2))* Fresh Air Bks.

Wood, Chester W. Hurt People Hurt People. 2008. 80p. pap. 12.99 *(978-1-60647-835-6(4))* Xulon Pr., Inc.

Wood, Peter. A Bee in the Mouth: Anger in America Now. 2007. (ENG.). 304p. 25.95 *(978-1-59403-053-6(7))* Encounter Bks.

Wright, H. Norman. Respuesta a la Frustracion & a la Ira: Answer to Anger & Frustration. (SPA.). *(978-84-7228-624-5(X),* 220767) Clie, Editorial.

Wynne, Jeremy J. Wrath among the Perfections of God's Life. 2012. (T&T Clark Studies in Systematic Theology Ser.). (ENG.). 242p. pap. ***(978-0-567-10310-9(2),*** T&T Clark Int'l) Continuum International Publishing Group, Ltd.

Zailckas, Koren. Fury: A Memoir. 2010. (ENG.). 336p. (gr. 12). 25.95 *(978-0-670-02230-4(6),* Viking Adult) Penguin Group (USA) Inc.

Zailckas, Koren. Fury: True Tales of a Good Girl Gone Ballistic. 2012. (ENG.). 336p. (gr. 12). 16.00 ***(978-0-14-312037-7(9),*** Penguin (Non-Classics)) Penguin Group (USA) Inc.

ANGER IN ADOLESCENCE

Anderson, Maureen. The Angry Adolescent: The Resiliencies & Forms of Forgiveness That ImpactTeenage Anger Expression. 2008. 220p. pap. *(978-3-639-06902-0(1))* VDM Verlag Dr. Mueller e.K.

Burney, DeAnna McKinnie. The Adolescent Anger Rating Scale: Its Initial Development & Validation. 2008. (Illus.). 244p. 109.95 *(978-0-7734-5076-9(9))* Mellen, Edwin Pr., The.

Diconsiglio, John. Out of Control: How to Handle Anger - Yours & Everyone Else's. 2008. (Scholastic Choices Ser.). (ENG., Illus.). 112p. (YA). (gr. 8-12). pap. 8.95 *(978-0-531-14771-9(1),* Watts, Franklin) Scholastic Library Publishing.

Fitzell, Susan Gingras. Transforming Anger to Personal Power: An Anger Management Curriculum for Grades 6-12. 2007. (ENG.). 136p. pap. 23.95 *(978-0-87822-538-5(2))* Research Pr.

Fleeman, William. Managing Teen Anger & Violence: A Pathways to Peace Program. 2008. (ENG., Illus.). 230p. per. 19.95 *(978-1-57023-276-3(8))* Impact Pubns.

Gibson, Andrew D. Got an Angry Kid? Parenting Spike, a Seriously Difficult Child. 2009. 188p. pap. *(978-1-932590-89-7(1))* Loving Healing Pr., Inc.

Greene. Anger Management Skills for Children Teens. 2008. 56p. pap. 10.95 *(978-1-881165-23-1(X))* People Skills International.

Guild, Kathy. How to Stop Before You Pop: A Six Lesson Anger-Management Program. 2007. 88p. pap. 16.96 *(978-1-57543-146-8(7))* MAR*CO Products, Inc.

Kellner, Millicent M. Being in Control Bingo: A Game for Teaching Anger Management to Young Adolescents. 2006. 39.95 *(978-0-87822-580-4(3),* 5231) Research Pr.

Luxmoore, Nick. Working with Anger & Young People. 2006. (ENG.). 16p. per. *(978-1-84310-466-7(0))* Kingsley, Jessica Ltd.

Quill, Charlie. Anger & Anger Management. 2008. (Teen Mental Health Ser.). (Illus.). 48p. (YA). (gr. 7-12). lib. bdg. 26.50 *(978-1-4042-1800-0(9))* Rosen Publishing Group, Inc., The.

Whitson, Signe & Long, Nicholas. How to be Angry: An Assertive Anger Expression Group Guide for Kids & Teens. 2011. (ENG.). 216p. pap. *(978-1-84905-867-4(9))* Kingsley, Jessica Ltd.

ANGER IN CHILDREN

Blum, Paul. Anger & Conflict Management Pocketbook. 2009. (Illus.). 128p. pap. *(978-1-903776-95-7(3)*, Teachers' Pocketbooks) Management Pocketbooks GBR. Dist: Ware-Pak, Inc.

Crum, Thomas, et al. The New Conflict Cookbook: A Parent/Teacher Guide for Helping Young People Deal with Anger & Conflict. Date not set. 15.00 *(978-1-877803-11-6(1))* Aiki Works, Inc.

Emlet, Michael R. Angry Children: Understanding & Helping Your Child Regain Control. 2008. (ENG.). 24p. 3.99 *(978-1-934885-26-0(6))* New Growth Pr.

Faupel, Adrian, et al. Anger Management: A Practical Guide. 2nd ed. 2010. E-Book 36.95 *(978-0-203-83988-1(9))* Routledge.

Foa, Edna B., et al. Prolonged Exposure Therapy for Adolescents with PTSD: Emotional Processing of Traumatic Experiences. 2008. (Treatments That Work Ser.). (ENG., Illus.). 144p. (C). pap., instr.'s gde. ed. 36.99 *(978-0-19-533174-5(5))* Oxford Univ. Pr., Inc.

Gibson, Andrew D. Got an Angry Kid? Parenting Spike, a Seriously Difficult Child. 2009. 188p. pap. *(978-1-932690-89-7(1))* Loving Healing Pr., Inc.

Greene, Ida. Anger Management Skills for Children Middle School. 2008. pap. 10.95 *(978-1-881165-24-8(8))* People Skills International.

Jacobelli, Frank & Watson, Lynn Ann. SmartHelp for Good 'n' Angry Kids: Teaching Children to Manage Anger. 2009. (ENG., Illus.). 222p. pap. 33.95 *(978-0-470-75802-1(3)*, Wiley) Wiley, John & Sons, Inc.

Mah, Ronald. The One-Minute Temper Tantrum Solution: Strategies for Responding to Children's Challenging Behaviors. 2008. 160p. 71.95 *(978-1-4129-5720-5(6)*, B57206C); pap. 29.95 *(978-1-4129-5721-2(4)*, B57206P) Corwin Pr.

Palomares, Susanna. Anger Control & Conflict Management for Kids. 2011. 134p. pap. 25.95 ***(978-1-56499-078-5(8))*** Innerchoice Publishing.

Pelta-Heller, Zack, et al. I'M Not Bad, I'm Just Mad: A Workbook to Help Kids Control Their Anger. 2008. (Instant Help Ser.). 132p. pap. 16.95 *(978-1-931704-28-1(7))* Play2Grow.

Plummer, Deborah M. Anger Management Games for Children. 2008. (ENG., Illus.). 144p. pap. *(978-1-84310-628-9(0))* Kingsley, Jessica Ltd.

Priolo, Lou. Workbook for the Heart of Anger: Practical Help for the Prevention & Cure of Anger in Children. 2007. 79p. pap. 16.99 *(978-1-879737-51-8(5))* Calvary Pr.

Pudney, Warwick & Whitehouse, Eliane. Little Volcanoes: Helping Young Children & Their Parents to Deal with Anger. 2012. (Illus.). 176p. pap. ***(978-1-84905-217-7(4))*** Kingsley, Jessica Ltd.

Schnoes, Connie J. Show Me Your Mad Face: Teaching Children to Feel Angry without Losing Control. 2012. (ENG.). 229p. pap. 13.95 ***(978-1-934490-31-0(8))*** Boys Town Pr.

Shapiro, Lawerence, et al. I'm Not Bad, I'm Just Mad: A Workbook to Help Kids Control Their Anger. 2008. (Instant Help Ser.). (ENG., Illus.). 152p. (J). pap. 16.95 *(978-1-57224-606-5(5))* Play2Grow.

Sukhodolsky, Denis G. & Scahill, Lawrence. Cognitive-Behavioral Therapy for Anger & Aggression in Children. 2012. (ENG.). 184p. pap. 30.00 ***(978-1-4625-0632-3(1))*** Guilford Pubns., Inc.

Whitson, Signe & Long, Nicholas. How to be Angry: An Assertive Anger Expression Group Guide for Kids & Teens. 2011. (ENG.). 216p. pap. *(978-1-84905-867-4(9))* Kingsley, Jessica Ltd.

Wright, H. Norman. Cómo Ayudar a Sus Hijos a Enfrentar el Enojo, el Miedo y la Tristeza, 1 vol. 2008.Tr. of Helping Your Kids Deal with Anger, Fear, & Sadness. (SPA., Illus.). 192p. pap. 9.99 *(978-0-8254-1878-5(X)*, Editorial Portavoz) Kregel Pubns.

ANGER OF GOD

see God—Wrath

ANGERS (FRANCE)

Kekewich, Margaret L. The Good King: Rene of Anjou & 15th Century Europe. 2008. (ENG., Illus.). 256p. 100.00 *(978-1-4039-8820-1(X))* Palgrave Macmillan.

ANGINA PECTORIS

Camm, A. John & Tendera, Micha, eds. Heart Rate Slowing by IF Current Inhibition. (Advances in Cardiology Ser.: Vol. 43). (Illus.). viii, 116p. *(978-3-8055-8160-8(2))* Karger, S. AG.

Chirkov, Yuliy Y., et al. Beneficial Effects of Perhexiline in Cardiovascular Disease States. 2010. (Cardiology Research & Clinical Developments Ser.). viii, 43p. pap. 43.00 *(978-1-61668-977-3(3)*, Nova Biomedical Bks.) Nova Science Pubs., Inc.

Gallos, Alice P. & Jones, Margaret L. Angina Pectoris: Etiology, Pathogenesis & Treatment. Gallo, Alice, ed. 2008. (C). 185.00 *(978-1-60456-674-1(4))* Nova Science Pubs., Inc.

Jackson, Patrick Thaddeus. Angina. 4th rev. ed. 2008. (ENG., Illus.). 104p. pap. 99.95 *(978-1-84184-669-9(4)*, Informa Healthcare) Taylor & Francis Group GBR. Dist: Taylor & Francis Group.

Jevon, Phil. Angina & Heart Attack. 2012. (ENG., Illus.). 112p. pap. 21.95 ***(978-0-19-959928-8(9))*** Oxford Univ. Pr., Inc.

Pantano, James A. Living with Angina: A Cardiologist's Guide to Dealing with Your Chest Pain & Your Doctor 2nd Edition. 2011. 256p. pap. 22.95 ***(978-1-4670-6023-3(2))*** AuthorHouse.

Smith, Tom. Living with Angina. (Illus.). 117p. *(978-0-85969-749-1(5)*, Sheldon Press) SPCK Publishing.

Wathall, Paul. Cardiac Rehabilitation: Exercise. 2009. 526p. pap. *(978-3-639-17748-0(7))* VDM Verlag Dr. Mueller e.K.

ANGIOCARDIOGRAPHY

Achenbach, Stephan S., et al. Coronary CT Angiography. 2009. *(978-3-642-01730-8(4))* Springer.

Baliga, Ragavendra R. Introductory Guide to Cardiac CT Imaging. 2009. (ENG., Illus.). 168p. pap., instr.'s gde. ed. 36.00 *(978-1-58255-938-4(4))* Lippincott Williams & Wilkins.

Dewey, Marc. Coronary CT Angiography. (Illus.). 262p. 159.00 *(978-3-540-79843-9(9))* Springer.

Lu, Jing. Detection of Endoleaks in Ct Data for Monitoring of Aaa Stents. 2008. (Illus.). 108p. pap. *(978-3-639-01367-2(0))* VDM Verlag Dr. Mueller e.K.

Marwick, Thomas H., et al, eds. Myocardial Imaging: Tissue Doppler & Speckle Tracking. 2007. (ENG., Illus.). 336p. 185.95 *(978-1-4051-6113-8(2)*, Wiley-Blackwell) Wiley, John & Sons, Inc.

Pelberg, Robert & Mazur, Wojciech. Cardiac CT Angiography Manual. 2007. (Illus.). 142p. pap. 69.95 *(978-1-84628-674-2(3))* Springer.

Raman, Subha V., et al. Cardiovascular Multidetector Computed Tomography Angiography. 2007. (ENG., Illus.). 200p. 210.00 *(978-1-84184-645-3(7)*, Informa Healthcare) Taylor & Francis Group GBR. Dist: Taylor & Francis Group.

Serruys, P. W., et al, eds. Quantitative Coronary Angiography in Clinical Practice. 2010. (Developments in Cardiovascular Medicine Ser.). (Illus.). 744p. pap. 749.00 *(978-90-481-4295-8(4)*, 9048142954) Springer.

ANGIOGRAPHY

see also Angiocardiography

Baert, Albert L., frwd. MR Angiography of the Body: Technique & Clinical Applications. 2009. (Medical Radiology / Diagnostic Imaging Ser.). (Illus.). 310p. 239.00 *(978-3-540-79716-6(5))* Springer.

Cademartiri, Filippo, et al, eds. Clinical Applications of Cardiac CT. 2008. xviii, 480p. 9.95 *(978-88-470-0862-5(X))* Springer.

Carr, James C. & Carroll, Timothy J., eds. Magnetic Resonance Angiography: Principles & Applications. 2012. (ENG., Illus.). xvii, 412p. 179.00 ***(978-1-4419-1685-3(7)***, 1441916857) Springer.

Carroll, John D. & Chen, S. James. Advances in Coronary Angiography, an Issue of Cardiology Clinics. 2009. (Clinics: Internal Medicine Ser.: 27-3). (ENG., Illus.). 240p. 99.00 *(978-1-4377-1197-4(9)*, Saunders) Elsevier - Health Sciences Div.

Chenevert, Thomas L. & Weadock, William J. Emerging Concepts in MR Angiography, an Issue of Magnetic Resonance Imaging Clinics. 2009. (Clinics: Radiology Ser.: 17-1). (ENG., Illus.). 240p. 99.00 *(978-1-4377-0497-6(2)*, Saunders) Elsevier - Health Sciences Div.

Cho, Kyung J. & Hawkins, Irvin F., eds. Carbon Dioxide Angiography: Principles, Techniques, & Practices. 2007. (ENG., Illus.). 312p. 300.00 *(978-0-8247-2831-1(9))* CRC Pr. LLC.

Chopdar, Amresh. Fundus Fluorescein & Endocyanine Green Angiography. 2007. (Illus.). 180p. 140.00 *(978-1-905740-57-4(3))* Anshan GBR. Dist: Publishers Storage & Shipping.

Dithmar, Stefan & Holz, Frank Gerhard. Fluoreszenzangiographie in der Augenheilkunde. 2007. (Illus.). X, 226p. 149.00 *(978-3-540-35223-5(6)*, 3540352236) Springer.

Finn, J. Paul & Lohan, Derek G. Cardiovascular MRI & MRA: from Seating Area to Signed Report: Volume 2: Interpretation Atlas. 2010. (Illus.). 450p. 189.00 *(978-1-60761-017-5(5))* Humana Pr.

Foley, W. Dennis. CT Angiography, an Issue of Radiologic Clinics of North America. 2010. (Clinics: Radiology Ser.: 48-2). (ENG., Illus.). xiii, 475p. 105.00 *(978-1-4377-1943-7(0)*, Saunders) Elsevier - Health Sciences Div.

Golzarian, Jafar, et al, eds. Vascular Embolotherapy: A Comprehensive Approach, Volume 1: General Principles, Chest, Abdomen, & Great Vessels. 2012. (Medical Radiology / Diagnostic Imaging Ser.). (ENG., Illus.). xii, 309p. pap. 239.00 *(978-3-642-05972-8(4)*, 3642059724) Springer.

Gould, Jennifer E., et al. Vascular & Interventional Imaging: Case Review Series. 2nd ed. 2009. (Case Review Ser.). (ENG., Illus.). 304p. pap. 54.95 *(978-0-323-05249-8(5)*, Mosby) Elsevier - Health Sciences Div.

Holz, Frank G., et al, eds. Atlas of Fundus Autofluorescence Imaging. 2010. (Illus.). xiv, 342p. pap. 129.00 *(978-3-642-09119-3(9)*, 3642091199) Springer.

Krestin, G. P. Gabriel. Computed Tomography of the Coronary Arteries. De Feyter, Pim J., ed. 2nd rev. ed. 2008. (ENG., Illus.). 304p. 170.00 *(978-1-84184-657-6(0)*, Informa Healthcare) Taylor & Francis Group GBR. Dist: Taylor & Francis Group.

Lasjaunias, P., et al. Surgical Neuroangiography: 1 Clinical Vascular Anatomy & Variations. 2nd ed. 2012. (ENG., Illus.). xxii, 773p. pap. 589.00 *(978-3-642-07443-1(X)*, 364207443X) Springer.

Lemos. Diagnostic Methods in the Catheterization Laboratory. 2009. (ENG., Illus.). 288p. 250.00 *(978-1-84184-658-3(9)*, Informa Healthcare) Taylor & Francis Group.

Mukherjee, Debabrata, et al, eds. CT & MR Angiography of the Peripheral Circulation: Practical Approach with Clinical Protocols. 2007. (ENG., Illus.). 662p. 310.00 *(978-1-84184-606-4(6)*, Informa Healthcare) Taylor & Francis Group GBR. Dist: Taylor & Francis Group.

Neri, Emanuele, et al, eds. MR Angiography of the Body: Technique & Clinical Applications. 2011. (Medical Radiology / Diagnostic Imaging Ser.). (ENG., Illus.). x, 178p. pap. 109.00 ***(978-3-642-23590-0(5)***, 3642235905) Springer.

Pelberg, Robert & Mazur, Wojciech. Vascular CT Angiography Manual. 2010. (ENG., Illus.). xviii, 377p. pap. 59.95 *(978-1-84996-259-9(6)*, 1849962596) Springer.

Pons-Llado, Guillem & Leta-Petracca, Ruben. Atlas of Non-Invasive Coronary Angiography by Multidetector Computed Tomography. 2006. (Developments in Cardiovascular Medicine Ser.). (Illus.). 129p. 159.00 *(978-0-387-33044-0(5)*, 0387330445) Springer.

Ribes, Ramón & Muñoz Ruíz-Canela, J. J. Learning Vascular & Interventional Radiology: A Teaching File. 2010. (Learning Imaging Ser.). (ENG., Illus.). xiv, 252p. pap. 59.95 *(978-3-540-87996-1(X)*, 354087996X) Springer.

Rubin, Geoffrey D. & Rofsky, Neil M., eds. CT & MR Angiography: Comprehensive Vascular Assessment. 2008. (ENG., Illus.). 1316p. 299.99 *(978-0-7817-4525-3(X))* Lippincott Williams & Wilkins.

Saito, Shigeru. Chronic Total Occlusions. Saito, Shigeru & Waksman, Ron, eds. 2009. (ENG., Illus.). 256p. 146.95 *(978-1-4051-5703-2(8)*, Wiley-Blackwell) Wiley, John & Sons, Inc.

Uflacker, Renan. Atlas of Vascular Anatomy: An Angiographic Approach. 2nd rev. ed. 2006. (ENG., Illus.). 928p. 278.99 *(978-0-7817-6081-2(X))* Lippincott Williams & Wilkins.

Venkatesh. Mini Atlas of Fluorescein Angiography. 2009. (Anshan Gold Standard Mini Atlas Ser.). (ENG., Illus.). 350p. pap. 34.95 incl. cd-rom *(978-1-905740-26-0(3))* Anshan GBR. Dist: Publishers Storage & Shipping.

Wolf, Karl-Jurgen, et al. Vascular Imaging. 2009. (Direct Diagnosis in Radiology Ser.). (ENG., Illus.). 303p. pap. 64.99 *(978-3-13-145181-1(5))* Thieme Medical Pubs., Inc.

ANGIOLOGY

see Blood-Vessels; Blood-Vessels—Diseases

ANGIOPLASTY

see also Transluminal Angioplasty

Antoniucci, David. Primary Angioplasty: Mechanical Interventions for Acute Myocardial Infarction. Antoniucci, David, ed. 2nd rev. ed. 2009. (ENG., Illus.). 264p. 300.00 *(978-1-84184-662-0(7)*, Informa Healthcare) Taylor & Francis Group.

Brecker. Essential Concepts of Primary Angioplasty. 2010. 256p. 136.00 *(978-1-84184-673-6(2)*, Informa Healthcare) Taylor & Francis Group.

Fogarty, Thomas J. & White, Rodney A. Peripheral Endovascular Interventions. 3rd ed. 2010. (Illus.). xix, 512p. E-Book *(978-1-4419-1387-6(4))* Springer.

Henry, Michel. The Carotid & Supra-Aortic Trunks: Diagnosis, Angioplasty & Stenting. 2nd ed. 2011. (ENG., Illus.). 520p. 209.95 *(978-1-4051-9854-7(0)*, Wiley-Blackwell) Wiley, John & Sons, Inc.

Hobson, Robert W. Endovascular Surgery Clinical. 2007. 119.95 *(978-0-8493-3995-0(2))* Dekker, Marcel Inc.

Hobson, Robert W., et al. Endovascular Surgery. 2007. 119.95 *(978-0-8493-9894-0(0)*, Informa Healthcare) Taylor & Francis Group.

Layton, Kevin G. & Percelle, Raymond A., eds. Angioplasty Research Progress. 2008. (Illus.). xii, 522p. 215.00 *(978-1-60456-422-8(9))* Nova Science Pubs., Inc.

Mehran, Roxana & Kini, Annapoorna S. Percutaneous Interventions in Women, an Issue of Interventional Cardiology Clinics. 2012. (Clinics: Internal Medicine Ser.: 1-2). (ENG.). 110.00 ***(978-1-4557-3882-3(4)***, Saunders) Elsevier - Health Sciences Div.

Morgan, Robert A. & Walser, Eric. Handbook of Angioplasty & Stenting Procedures. 2010. (Techniques in Interventional Radiology Ser.). (Illus.). 350p. pap. 69.95 *(978-1-84800-398-9(6))* Springer.

Redwood, Simon, et al, eds. Oxford Textbook of Interventional Cardiology. 2010. (ENG., Illus.). 700p. 225.00 *(978-0-19-956908-3(8))* Oxford Univ. Pr., Inc.

Schmilowski, E. Von & Swanton, R. H. Essential Angioplasty. 2012. (ENG., Illus.). 392p. 149.95 ***(978-0-470-65726-3(X)***, Wiley-Blackwell) Wiley, John & Sons, Inc.

Tcheng, James E. Primary Angioplasty in Acute Myocardial Infarction. 2nd ed. 2008. (Contemporary Cardiology Ser.). (Illus.). 270p. 119.00 *(978-1-60327-496-8(0))* Humana Pr.

ANGIOSCOPY

Fogarty, Thomas J. & White, Rodney A. Peripheral Endovascular Interventions. 3rd ed. 2010. (Illus.). xix, 512p. E-Book *(978-1-4419-1387-6(4))* Springer.

Hobson, Robert W., et al. Endovascular Surgery. 2007. 119.95 *(978-0-8493-9894-0(0)*, Informa Healthcare) Taylor & Francis Group.

ANGIOSPERMS

see also Dicotyledons; Monocotyledons

Barrett, Spencer C. H., ed. Major Evolutionary Transitions in Flowering Plant Reproduction. 2008. (ENG., Illus.). 216p. pap. 30.00 *(978-0-226-03816-2(5))* Univ. of Chicago Pr.

Batygina. Embryology Flowering Plants: Vol 3: Terminology & Concepts Vol 3. 2009. (Embryology of Flowering Plants Ser.). (ENG.). 598p. 139.95 *(978-1-57808-265-0(X))* BIOS Scientific Publishers Ltd. GBR. Dist: Taylor & Francis Group.

Bell, Adrian D. & Bryan, Alan. Plant Form: An Illustrated Guide to Flowering Plant Morphology. 2nd ed. 2008. (ENG., Illus.). 432p. 49.95 *(978-0-88192-850-1(X)*, 088192850X) Timber Pr., Inc.

Bhojwani, S. S. & Woong-Young Soh, eds. Current Trends in the Embryology of Angiosperms. 2010. 544p. pap. 329.00 *(978-90-481-5679-5(3)*, 9048156793) Springer.

Bhowmik, Pankaj. Molecular Analysis of Postharvest Changes in Green Asparagus. 2009. 108p. pap. *(978-3-639-18730-4(X))* VDM Verlag Dr. Mueller e.K.

Brown, C. A. Ferns & Flowering Plants of Isle Royale, Michigan. (Illus.). reprint ed. lib. bdg. 125.00 *(978-0-7222-0083-4(8))* Library Reprints, Inc.

Callaway, Dorothy J. The World of Magnolias. 2010. (ENG.). 308p. pap. 44.95 *(978-1-60469-226-6(X)*, 160469226X) Timber Pr., Inc.

Ciancio, A. & Mukerji, K. G., eds. Integrated Management & Biocontrol of Vegetable & Grain Crops Nematodes. 2010. (Integrated Management of Plant Pests & Diseases Ser.). xx, 356p. pap. 229.00 *(978-90-481-7523-9(2)*, 9048175232) Springer.

Darwin, Charles. The Different Forms of Flowers on Plants of the Same Species. 2007. (ENG.). 302p. pap. 23.99 *(978-1-4346-7374-9(X))*; 340p. pap. 24.99 *(978-1-4346-7375-6(8))* BiblioBazaar.

—The Different Forms of Flowers on Plants of the Same Species. 2007. (ENG.). 376p. 48.95 *(978-0-548-10223-7(6))* Kessinger Publishing, LLC.

Fiala, John L. & Vrugtman, Freek. Lilacs: A Gardener's Encyclopedia. 2nd ed. 2008. (ENG., Illus.). 416p. 49.95 *(978-0-88192-795-5(3)*, 0881927953) Timber Pr., Inc.

Flora of North America Editorial Committee, ed. Flora of North American, 1 vol., Vol. 9. 2012. (Flora of North America Ser.). (ENG.). 600p. 95.00 *(978-0-19-534029-7(9))* Oxford Univ. Pr., Inc.

Glover, Beverley. Understanding Flowers & Flowering: An Integrated Approach. 2008. (Illus.). 256p. 180.00 *(978-0-19-856597-0(6))* Oxford Univ. Pr., Inc.

Glover, Beverley J. Understanding Flowers & Flowering: An Intergrated Approach. 2008. (ENG., Illus.). 256p. per. 75.00 *(978-0-19-856596-3(8))* Oxford Univ. Pr., Inc.

Haddis Weldeghebrael, Ezana. Responsibility of the Ethiopian Floriculture Industry to Its Workers. 2010. 128p. pap. *(978-3-639-26146-2(1))* VDM Verlag Dr. Mueller e.K.

Harder, Lawrence D. & Barrett, Spencer C. H., eds. The Ecology & Evolution of Flowers. 2007. (ENG., Illus.). 384p. per. 99.00 *(978-0-19-857086-8(4))* Oxford Univ. Pr., Inc.

Hegi, Gustav. Illustrierte Flora von Mitteleuropa. Pteridophyta - Spermatophyta (Illustrated Flora of Central Europe) Band II: Spermatophyta - Angiospermae - Monocotyledones 2, Tl. 3. Von Conert, Hans et al, eds. 3rd rev. ed. Date not set. (Illus.). *(978-3-8263-3027-8(7)*, Wiley-Blackwell) Wiley, John & Sons, Ltd.

—Illustrierte Flora von Mitteleuropa. Pteridophyta - Spermatophyta (Illustrated Flora of Central Europe) Band IV: Spermatophyta - Angiospermae - Dicotyledones 2, Tl. 2C. Von Conert, Hans et al, eds. 2nd rev. ed. Date not set. *(978-3-8263-3065-0(X)*, Wiley-Blackwell) Wiley, John & Sons, Ltd.

—Illustrierte Flora von Mitteleuropa. Pteridophyta - Spermatophyta (Illustrated Flora of Central Europe) Band VI: Spermatophyta - Angiospermae - Dicotyledones 4. Von Conert, Hans et al, eds. Date not set. (Illus.). Tl. 2, Lfg. 3. 2nd rev. ed. pap. *(978-3-8263-3028-5(5))*Tl. 2, Lfg. 4. rev. ed. pap. *(978-3-8263-3081-0(1))* Wiley, John & Sons, Ltd. (Wiley-Blackwell).

Heywood, V. H., et al. Flowering Plant Families of the World. rev. ed. 2007. (ENG., Illus.). 424p. 59.95 *(978-1-55407-206-4(9))* Firefly Bks., Ltd.

Heywood, Vernon. Flowering Plants: A Pictorial Guide to the World's Flora. Gray, Leon, ed. 2011. (ENG., Illus.). 288p. pap. 24.95 *(978-1-55407-767-0(2))* Firefly Bks., Ltd.

Hickey, Leo J. & Taylor, David W. Leaf Architecture of the Angiosperms. 2007. (Illus.). 512p. 150.00 *(978-0-300-11485-0(0))* Yale Univ. Pr.

Hoblyn, Alison. Green Flowers: Unexpected Beauty for the Garden, Container or Vase. 2009. (ENG., Illus.). 184p. 24.95 *(978-0-88192-919-5(0)*, 0881929190) Timber Pr., Inc.

Jarvis, R. Paul, ed. Chloroplast Research in Arabidopsis: Methods & Protocols, Volume I. 2011. (Methods in Molecular Biology Ser.). (ENG., Illus.). x, 374p. 139.00 *(978-1-61779-233-5(0)*, 1617792330) Humana Pr.

—Chloroplast Research in Arabidopsis: Methods & Protocols, Volume II. 2011. (Methods in Molecular Biology Ser.). (ENG., Illus.). xi, 432p. 139.00 *(978-1-61779-236-6(5)*, 1617792365) Humana Pr.

Judd, Walter S. Revision of Miconia sect. Chaenopleura (Miconieae, Melastomataceae) in the Greater Antilles. Anderson, Christiane, ed. 2007. (Illus.). 235p. 42.00 *(978-0-912861-81-4(9))* American Society of Plant Taxonomists, The.

Kays, Stanley J. & Nottingham, Stephen F. Biology & Chemistry of Jerusalem Artichoke: Helianthus Tuberosus L. 2007. (ENG., Illus.). 496p. 157.95 *(978-1-4200-4495-9(8)*, CRC Press) Taylor & Francis Group GBR. Dist: Taylor & Francis Group.

Krassilov & Rasnitsyn. Plant-Arthropod Interactions in the Early Angiosperm History: Evidence from the Cretaceous of Israel. 2008. 222p. (C). *(978-90-04-17071-1(5))* BRILL.

Krassilov, Valentin. Cercidiphyllum & Fossil Allies: Morphological Interpretation & General Problems of Plant Evolution & Development. 2010. 150p. pap. 108.00 *(978-954-642-524-9(9))* Pensoft Pubs. BGR. Dist: Coronet Bks.

Kubitzki, K. & Jeffrey, C., eds. Flowering Plants: Eudicots: Asterales. 2007. (Families & Genera of Vascular Plants Ser.: Vol. 8). (Illus.). 636p. 449.00 *(978-3-540-31050-1(9)*, 3540310509) Springer.

Kubitzki, Klaus, ed. Flowering Plants. Eudicots: Berberidopsidales, Buxales, Crossosomatales, Fabales P. P. , Geraniales, Gunnerales, Myrtales P. P. , Proteales, Saxifragales, Vitales, Zygophyllales, Clusiaceae Alliance, Passifloraceae Alliance, Dilleniaceae, Huaceae, Picramniaceae, Sabiaceae.

(Families & Genera of Vascular Plants Ser.). (Illus.). xiv, 509p. 2010. pap. 419.00 *(978-3-642-06883-6(9)*, 3642068839) 2007. 419.00 *(978-3-540-32214-6(0)*, 3540322140) Springer.

—Flowering Plants. Monocotyledons: Lilianae (except Orchidaceae) 2010. (Families & Genera of Vascular Plants Ser.). (Illus.). x, 478p. pap. 639.00 *(978-3-642-08377-8(3)*, 3642083773) Springer.

Mohlenbrock, Robert H. Acanthaceae to Myricaceae: Water Willows to Wax Myrtles. 2008. (Aquatic & Standing Water Plants of the Central Midwest Ser.). (ENG., Illus.). 416p. 67.00 *(978-0-8093-2790-4(2))* Southern Illinois Univ. Pr.

—Nelumbonaceae to Vitaceae: Water Lotuses to Grapes. 2010. (Aquatic & Standing Water Plants of the Central Midwest Ser.). (ENG., Illus.). 488p. 67.00 *(978-0-8093-2894-9(1))* Southern Illinois Univ. Pr.

Nettancourt, Dreux de. Incompatibility & Incongruity in Wild & Cultivated Plants. 2nd ed. 2010. (Illus.). xxix, 356p. pap. 229.00 *(978-3-642-08457-7(5)*, 3642084575) Springer.

Olsen, Odd-Arne, ed. Endosperm: Developmental & Molecular Biology. (Plant Cell Monographs). (Illus.). x, 249p. 2010. pap. 189.00 *(978-3-642-09031-8(1)*, 3642090311) 2007. 189.00 *(978-3-540-71234-3(8))* Springer.

Raghavan, Val. Double Fertilization: Embryo & Endosperm Development in Flowering Plants. 2010. (Illus.). xx, 237p. pap. 259.00 *(978-3-642-06616-0(X)*, 364206616X) Springer.

Ronse De Craene, Louis P. Floral Diagrams: An Aid to Understanding Flower Morphology & Evolution. 2010. (ENG., Illus.). 458p. 130.00 *(978-0-521-49346-8(3))*; pap. 59.99 *(978-0-521-72945-1(9))* Cambridge Univ. Pr.

Rudall, Paula. Anatomy of Flowering Plants: An Introduction to Structure & Development. 3rd rev. ed. 2007. (ENG., Illus.). 158p. per. 49.00 *(978-0-521-69245-5(8))* Cambridge Univ. Pr.

Ruksans, Janis. Crocuses: A Complete Guide to the Genus. 2011. (ENG., Illus.). 280p. 45.00 *(978-1-60469-106-1(9)*, 1604691069) Timber Pr., Inc.

Sinha, R. K. Practical Taxonomy of Angiosperms. 2010. 416p. (C). pap. *(978-93-80578-21-7(0))* I.K. International Publishing House Pvt. Ltd.

Small, Ernest. Alfalfa & Relatives: Evolution & Classification of Medicago. 2011. (Illus.). 760p. pap. 210.00 *(978-1-84593-750-8(3))* CABI GBR. Dist: Stylus Publishing, LLC.

Suriyamongkol, Pornpa. Phb Production in Transgenic a Thaliana Seeds. 2010. 212p. pap. *(978-3-8383-7542-7(4))* Lambert Academic Publishing.

Swanevelder, Dirk & Fisher, Roger C. Clivia: Nature & Nurture. 2012. (Illus.). 224p. 44.95 *(978-1-875093-61-8(3))* International Publishers Marketing.

Takhtajan, Armen. Flowering Plants. 2nd ed. 2009. (ENG.). xlvi, 872p. 319.00 *(978-1-4020-9608-2(9)*, 1402096089) Springer.

Tebbitt, Mark C., et al. Bleeding Hearts, Corydalis, & Their Relatives. 2008. (ENG., Illus.). 220p. 34.95 *(978-0-88192-882-2(8)*, 0881928828) Timber Pr., Inc.

Tellstone, Jeremy J. Flowering Plants: Classification, Characteristics & Breeding. 2011. (Botanical Research & Practices Ser.). (Illus.). 200p. 95.00 *(978-1-61324-653-5(6))* Nova Science Pubs., Inc.

Wang, Xin. The Dawn Angiosperms. 2010. (Lecture Notes in Earth Sciences Ser.). (ENG., Illus.). xxi, 236p. 159.00 *(978-3-642-01160-3(8)*, 3642011608) Springer.

Wanntorp, Livia & Ronse De Craene, Louis, eds. Flowers on the Tree of Life. 2011. (Systematics Association Special Volume Ser.). (ENG., Illus.). 326p. 99.00 *(978-0-521-76599-2(4))* Cambridge Univ. Pr.

Wickens, G. E. The Baobabs: Pachycauls of Africa, Madagascar & Australia: Pachycauls of Africa, Madagascar & Australia. 2010. xi, 500p. pap. 289.00 *(978-90-481-7639-7(5)*, 9048176395) Springer.

Zhu, Guangchao. Temperatures & the Growth & Development of Apple Trees. 2010. 56p. pap. *(978-3-8383-5511-5(3))* Lambert Academic Publishing.

Zilis, Mark R. The Hosta Handbook. (C). pap. 34.95 *(978-0-9679440-0-5(7))* Q & Z Nursery, Inc.

ANGKOR (EXTINCT CITY)

Albanese, Marilia. The Treasures of Angkor: Cultural Travel Guide. 2010. (Rizzoli Art Guide Ser.). (ENG., Illus.). 288p. 24.95 *(978-88-544-0117-4(X))* White Star ITA. Dist: Sterling Publishing Co., Inc.

Bracken, Gregory Byrne. Angkor: Sketches of an Ancient City, 1 vol. 2010. (ENG.). 120p. pap. 24.50 *(978-981-261-875-7(9))* Marshall Cavendish Corp.

Brukoff, Barry & Jessup, Helen Ibbitson. The Temples of Cambodia: The Heart of Angkor. 2011. (ENG., Illus.). 256p. 65.00 *(978-0-86565-262-0(7))* Vendome Pr., The.

Candee, Helen Churchill. Angkor the Magnificent: The Wonder City of Ancient Cambodia. Davis, Kent, ed. 2008. (ENG., Illus.). 376p. 49.00 *(978-1-934431-00-9(1))* DatASIA.

Carver, Norman F. Angkor. (Illus.). 224p. 39.95 *(978-0-932076-16-8(5))*; pap. 29.95 *(978-0-932076-17-5(3))* Documan Pr., Ltd.

Chavanat, Damien, et al. Cambodia & Angkor: A Travel Sketchbook. 2007. (ENG., Illus.). 190p. 35.00 *(978-981-4068-72-7(1)*, Didier Millet,Csi) Continental Sales, Inc.

Coe, Michael D. Angkor: The Preah Khan Monastic Complex. 2011. (ENG., Illus.). 88p. pap. 14.95 *(978-1-85759-494-2(0))* Scala, Editions FRA. Dist: National Bk. Network.

De Lopez, Thanakvaro. Where the Stone Flowers - the People of Angkor. 2007. (Illus.). 218p. 55.00 *(978-0-9795620-0-6(7))* Blue Reamker.

Finot, Louis. Le Temple D'Angkor Vat. 2006. (ENG.). 350.00 *(978-1-878529-16-9(1))* Orchid Pr. THA. Dist: National Bk. Network.

Jacq-Hergoualc'h, Michel. The Armies of Angkor: Military Structure & Weaponry of the Khmers. Smithies, Michael, tr. from FRE. 2007. (ENG., Illus.). 200p. 40.00 *(978-974-524-096-4(6))* Orchid Pr. THA. Dist: National Bk. Network.

Jacques, Claude. Angkor: Cities & Temples. 2006. (ENG., Illus.). 319p. 80.00 *(978-974-8225-15-9(1)*, River Bks. Pr. Dist A C) Antique Collectors' Club GBR. Dist: National Bk. Network.

Jacques, Claude & Freeman, Michael. Ancient Angkor. 2009. (ENG., Illus.). 240p. pap. 25.00 *(978-974-9863-81-7(X)*, River Bks. Pr. Dist A C) Antique Collectors' Club GBR. Dist: National Bk. Network.

Loti, Pierre. Siam. 2006. (ENG.). 220p. per. *(978-1-4067-3375-4(X)*, Hesperides Pr.) Read Bks.

Passage to Angkor. 3rd ed. 2008. (Illus.). 144p. 59.95 *(978-0-9653574-3-2(0))* Friends Without a Border.

Ripa, Giuseppe, photos by & suppl. Giuseppe Ripa: Stone Memories, 1 vol. 2007. (ITA & ENG., Illus.). 104p. pap. 39.95 *(978-88-8158-620-2(7))* Charta ITA. Dist: D.A.P./Distributed Art Pubs.

Rooney, Dawn F. Angkor Observed: A Travel Anthology of 'Those There Before' 2006. (Orchid Guides Ser.). (ENG., Illus.). pap. 23.00 *(978-974-8304-79-3(5))* Orchid Pr. THA. Dist: National Bk. Network.

Roveda, Vittorio. Sacred Angkor: The Carved Reliefs of Angkor Wat. 2007. (ENG., Illus.). 290p. per. 30.00 *(978-974-8225-83-8(6))* River Bks. THA. Dist: Antique Collectors' Club.

Smithies, Michael, tr. from FRE. Angkor & Cambodia in the Sixteenth Century: According to Portuguese & Spanish Sources. 2006. (ENG., Illus.). 208p. 35.00 *(978-974-524-053-7(2))* Orchid Pr. THA. Dist: National Bk. Network.

Snellgrove, David L. Khmer Civilization & Angkor. 2006. (Orchid Guides Ser.). (ENG., Illus.). pap. 19.00 *(978-974-8304-95-3(7))* Orchid Pr. THA. Dist: National Bk. Network.

Sobol, Richard. The Mysteries of Angkor Wat. 2011. (Traveling Photographer Ser.). (ENG., Illus.). 48p. (J). (gr. 1-5). 17.99 *(978-0-7636-4166-5(9))* Candlewick Pr.

Spooner, Andrew. Angkor Wat Footprint Focus. 2011. (Footprint Focus Ser.). (ENG., Illus.). 88p. pap. 8.95 *(978-1-908206-14-5(4))* Footprint Handbooks GBR. Dist: Globe Pequot Pr., The.

Stanford, David. Angkor. 2009. (ENG., Illus.). 112p. 29.95 *(978-0-7112-3044-6(7))* Lincoln, Frances Ltd. GBR. Dist: Perseus-PGW.

Vater, Tom. Moon Spotlight Angkor Wat. 2010. (Moon Spotlight Ser.). (ENG.). 72p. pap. 7.95 *(978-1-59880-551-1(4))* Avalon Travel Publishing.

Winter, David. Post-Conflict Heritage, Postcolonial Tourism: Tourism, Politics & Development at Angkor. 2007. (Routledge Studies in Asia's Transformations Ser.). (Illus.). XXVI, 174p. 160.00 *(978-0-415-43095-1(X))* Routledge.

Winter, Tim. Post-Conflict Heritage Postcolonial Tourism. 2011. (ENG.). 200p. pap. 42.95 *(978-0-415-63958-8(9))* Routledge.

ANGLESEY, HENRY WILLIAM PAGET, MARQUIS OF, 1768-1854

Shand, Alexander Innes. Wellington's Lieutenants. 2010. 474p. pap. 37.75 *(978-1-146-54018-6(3))* BiblioBazaar.

—Wellington's Lieutenants. 2009. 72p. pap. *(978-0-217-41962-8(3))* Books LLC.

ANGLICAN CHURCH

see Church of England

ANGLICAN CHURCH OF CANADA

Anglican Church of Canada, Primate's Theological Commission, contrib. by. Longing for God: Anglicans Talk about Revelation, Nature, Culture, & Authority. (Wrestling with God Ser.: Vol. 1). (Illus.). 108p. pap. 12.95 *(978-1-55126-343-4(2)*, 1630) Anglican Bk. Ctr. CAN. Dist: Forward Movement Pubns.

Anglican Church of Canada, Primate's Theological Commission Staff, contrib. by. Meeting God Vol. 3: Anglicans Talk about Creation, the Trinity, & the Church. 177p. pap. 21.95 *(978-1-55126-345-8(9)*, 1802) Anglican Bk. Ctr. CAN. Dist: Forward Movement Pubns.

Bays, Patricia. Anglican Diversity: Challenges for the 21st Century. 128p. pap. 11.95 *(978-1-55126-327-4(0)*, 1673) Anglican Bk. Ctr. CAN. Dist: Forward Movement Pubns.

—Meet the Family: Welcome to the Anglican Church. pap., stu. ed. 12.95 *(978-1-55126-235-2(5))* Forward Movement Pubns.

Church Publishing Staff. The Gospels. rev. ed. 2007. 240p. lthr. 190.00 *(978-0-89869-552-6(X))* Church Publishing, Inc.

—The Gospels: For the Revised Common Lectionary Together with Holy Days & Special Occasions. rev. ed. 2007. 240p. 95.00 *(978-0-89869-553-3(8))* Church Publishing, Inc.

Coleman, Roger, ed. Resolutions of the Twelve Lambeth Conferences 1867-1988. 320p. 32.95 *(978-0-921846-44-4(4)*, 1277) Anglican Bk. Ctr. CAN. Dist: Forward Movement Pubns.

Hill, John W. Making Disciples: Serving Those Who Are Entering the Christian Life. 144p. spiral bd. 14.95 *(978-1-895457-02-5(5)*, 1129) Hoskin Group CAN. Dist: Forward Movement Pubns.

Holeton, David R. Growing in Newness of Life: Christian Initiation in Anglicanism Today. 784p. pap. 13.95 *(978-1-55126-045-7(X)*, 1244) Anglican Bk. Ctr. CAN. Dist: Forward Movement Pubns.

Jones, Nick. All the Days of His Life: A Biography of Archdeacon H. A. Cody. (Illus.). 432p. pap. 11.95 *(978-0-919326-07-1(2))* New Brunswick Museum CAN. Dist: Goose Lane Editions.

MacLean, Paul & Cowling, Douglas. Sharing the Banquet: Liturgical Renewal in Your Parish. 192p. pap. 14.95 *(978-1-55126-058-7(1)*, 1246) Anglican Bk. Ctr. CAN. Dist: Forward Movement Pubns.

Occasional Celebrations: Anglican Church of Canada. 224p. 24.95 *(978-0-921846-51-2(7)*, 1317) Forward Movement Pubns.

Peel, Donald. The Ministry of Listening: Team Visiting in Hospital & Home. 123p. pap. 16.95 *(978-0-919030-57-2(2)*, 1299) Forward Movement Pubns.

Plater, Ormonde. Deacons in the Liturgy. 2nd rev. ed. 2009. 144p. (Org.). pap. 16.00 *(978-0-89869-634-9(8))* Church Publishing, Inc.

Reynolds, Stephen, compiled by. For All the Saints: Prayers & Readings for Saints' Days. 800p. 55.00 *(978-0-921846-50-5(9)*, 1324) Anglican Bk. Ctr. CAN. Dist: Forward Movement Pubns.

Stuchbery, Ian. This Is Our Faith: A Guide to Faith & Belief for Anglicans. 192p. pap. 19.95 *(978-0-921846-21-5(5)*, 1024) Forward Movement Pubns.

Sumner, George R., et al. In Spirit & In Truth: The Challenge of Discernment for Canadian Anglicans Today. 2009. 192p. pap. *(978-1-57383-443-8(2))* Regent College Publishing.

Sykes, Stephen W., ed. Authority in the Anglican Communion: Essays Presented to Bishop John Howe. 286p. pap. 11.95 *(978-0-919891-61-6(6)*, 1292) Anglican Bk. Ctr. CAN. Dist: Forward Movement Pubns.

ANGLICAN COMMUNION

Allen, John. Desmond Tutu: Rabble-Rouser for Peace - The Authorized Biography. 2008. (ENG.). 496p. pap. 16.95 *(978-1-55652-798-2(5)*, Hill, Lawrence Bks.) Chicago Review Pr., Inc.

Andrewes, Lancelot. Ninety-Six Sermons by the Right Honourable & Reverend Father in God, Lancelot Andrewes, Sometime Lord Bishop of Winchester, Vol. IV. 2008. 425p. pap. 36.00 *(978-1-60608-122-8(5)*, Wipf and Stock) Wipf & Stock Pubs.

—Ninety-Six Sermons by the Right Honourable & Reverend Father in God, Lancelot Andrewes, Sometime Lord Bishop of Winchester, Vol. V. 2008. 592p. pap. 50.00 *(978-1-60608-121-1(7)*, Wipf and Stock) Wipf & Stock Pubs.

Anglican Church of Canada, Primate's Theological Commission, contrib. by. Turning to God: Anglicans Talk about Sin, Grace, & the Christian Life, Vol. 2. (Wrestling with God Ser.: Vol. 2). (Illus.). 106p. pap. 12.95 *(978-1-55126-344-1(0)*, 1631) Anglican Bk. Ctr. CAN. Dist: Forward Movement Pubns.

ARCIC II Staff. Mary: Grace & Hope in Christ. Bolen, Donald & Cameron, Gregory, eds. rev. exp. ed. 2006. (ENG., Illus.). 288p. 22.95 *(978-0-8264-8155-9(8))* Continuum International Publishing Group, Ltd. GBR. Dist: National Bk. Network.

Avis. The Identity of Anglicanism: Essentials of Anglican Ecclesiology. 2008. (ENG.). 216p. 34.95 *(978-0-567-03204-1(3))*; 110.00 *(978-0-567-03203-4(5))* Continuum International Publishing Group, Ltd. GBR. (T&T Clark Int'l). Dist: National Bk. Network.

Avis, Paul D. L. The Anglican Understanding of the Church: An Introduction. 104p. 10.00 *(978-0-281-05282-0(4))* SPCK Publishing GBR. Dist: Pilgrim Pr., The/United Church Pr.

Ball, Peter. Anglican Spiritual Direction. 2nd ed. 2007. (Spiritual Directors International Book Ser.). 144p. per. 22.00 *(978-0-8192-2254-1(2))* Church Publishing, Inc.

Barnum, Thaddeus. Never Silent: How Third World Missionaries are Bringing the Gospel to the US. Bubeck, Craig, ed. 2008. 380p. 24.99 *(978-0-615-20694-3(8))* Eleison Publishing.

Barrow, Simon, ed. Fear or Freedom? 2008. 152p. pap. *(978-1-905565-14-6(3))* Shoving Leopard Productions.

Bayer, Oswald & Suggate, Alan, eds. Worship & Ethics: Lutherans & Anglicans in Dialogue. (Theologische Bibliothek Töpelmann Ser.). (ENG.). XV, 293p. 255.00 *(978-3-11-179433-4(4))* De Gruyter, Walter Inc.

Bess, Douglas. Divided We Stand: A History of the Conti. 2006. pap. 20.95 *(978-1-933993-10-2(3))* Apocryphile Pr.

Black, Vicki K. Welcome to Anglican Spiritual Traditions. 2010. E-Book *(978-0-8192-2722-5(6)*, Morehouse Publishing) Church Publishing, Inc.

Blunt, John Henry. Annotated Book of Common Prayer Being an. 2006. pap. 52.95 *(978-1-4286-3633-0(1))* Kessinger Publishing, LLC.

Bonner, Jeremy. Called Out of Darkness into Marvelous Light: A History of the Episcopal Diocese of Pittsburgh, 1750-2006. 2009. 376p. pap. 41.00 *(978-1-60608-163-1(2)*, Wipf and Stock) Wipf & Stock Pubs.

Borsch, Frederick, et al. Introducing the Lessons of the Church Year. 3rd rev. ed. 2009. 288p. pap. 25.00 *(978-0-8192-2346-3(8)*, Morehouse Publishing) Church Publishing, Inc.

Braddock, Andrew. The Role of the Book of Common Prayer in the Formation of Modern Anglican Church Identity: A Study of English Parochial Worship, 1750-1850. 2010. 340p. 119.95 *(978-0-7734-1442-6(8))* Mellen, Edwin Pr., The.

Buchanan, Colin, ed. Anglican Eucharistic Liturgies: From around the World, 1985 To 2010. 2011. 320p. pap. 45.00 *(978-1-84825-087-1(8)*, Canterbury Pr. Norwich) Hymns Ancient & Modern Ltd GBR. Dist: Westminster John Knox Pr.

—The Bishop in Liturgy. 2009. 88.00 *(978-1-60724-361-8(X))* Gorgias Pr., LLC.

—Modern Anglican Ordination Rites. 2009. 88.00 *(978-1-60724-359-5(8))* Gorgias Pr., LLC.

Burt, C. David, ed. The Anglican Use Gradual. 2007. 35.00 *(978-0-9793800-3-7(0))*; lib. bdg. 100.00 *(978-0-9793800-2-0(2))* Partridge Hill Pr.

—The Anglican Use Office. 2007. 40.00 *(978-0-9793800-4-4(9))*; lib. bdg. 125.00 *(978-0-9793800-5-1(7))* Partridge Hill Pr.

Canterbury Press, creator. Anglican Religious Life: A Yearbook of Religious Orders & Communities in the Anglican Communion, & Tertiaries, Oblates, Associates & Companions. 2007. (Illus.). 206p. per. *(978-1-85311-814-2(1))* Norwich Bks. & Music.

Cavanagh, Lorraine. By One Spirit: Reconciliation & Renewal in Anglican Life. 2009. 285p. pap. 54.95 *(978-3-03911-389-7(5))* Lang, Peter AG GBR. Dist: Lang, Peter.

Cavanaugh, Stephen E., ed. Anglicans & the Roman Catholic Church: Reflections on Recent Developments. 2011. 255p. pap. 18.95 *(978-1-58617-499-6(1))* Ignatius Pr.

Chandler, Andrew. The Church & Humanity: The Life & Work of George Bell, 1883-1958. 2012. 240p. 99.95 *(978-1-4094-2557-1(6))*; 99.95 *(978-1-4094-2556-4(8))* Ashgate Publishing Co.

Chapman, Alister. Godly Ambition: John Stott & the Evangelical Movement, 1 vol. 2011. (ENG.). 240p. 55.00 *(978-0-19-977397-8(1))* Oxford Univ. Pr., Inc.

Chapman, Mark. The Anglican Covenant: Unity & Diversity in the Anglican Communion. 2008. (Affirming Catholicism Ser.). (ENG.). 224p. 24.95 *(978-0-567-03253-9(1))* Mowbray, A. R. & Co., Ltd. GBR. Dist: National Bk. Network.

—Anglican Theology. 2012. (Doing Theology Ser.). (ENG.). 288p. 80.00 *(978-0-567-25031-5(8))*; pap. 29.95 *(978-0-567-00802-2(9))* Continuum International Publishing Group, Ltd. GBR. (T&T Clark Int'l). Dist: National Bk. Network.

—Anglicanism. 2006. (Very Short Introductions Ser.). (ENG., Illus.). 168p. per. 11.95 *(978-0-19-280693-2(9))* Oxford Univ. Pr., Inc.

Chapman, Mark, ed. Hope of Things to Come: Anglicanism & the Future. 2010. (Affirming Catholicism Ser.). (ENG.). 192p. 24.95 *(978-0-567-58884-5(X))* Mowbray, A. R. & Co., Ltd. GBR. Dist: National Bk. Network.

Chapman, Mark D. & Chapman, Mark. Bishops, Saints & Politics: Anglican Studies. 2007. (ENG.). 256p. 140.00 *(978-0-567-03179-2(9)*, T&T Clark Int'l) Continuum International Publishing Group, Ltd. GBR. Dist: National Bk. Network.

Chartres, Caroline & Chartres. Why I Am Still an Anglican: Essays & Conversations. 2007. (ENG.). 176p. 27.95 *(978-0-8264-8312-6(7))* Continuum International Publishing Group, Ltd. GBR. Dist: National Bk. Network.

Church, Mary C. Life & Letters of Dean Church. 2009. 382p. 33.99 *(978-1-113-59607-9(4))*; pap. 20.99 *(978-1-113-59606-2(6))*; pap. 33.75 *(978-1-113-60868-0(4))* BiblioBazaar.

—Life & Letters of Dean Church. 2009. 166p. pap. *(978-0-217-01093-1(8))* Books LLC.

Church, Mary C., ed. Life & Letters of Dean Church. 2007. (ENG.). 384p. 48.95 *(978-0-548-09049-7(1))* Kessinger Publishing, LLC.

Cirlot, Felix L. Apostolic Succession & Anglicanism: A Defense of Anglican Orders & Catholicity. 2011. 452p. 57.95 *(978-1-258-01464-3(5))* Literary Licensing, LLC.

Companion to the Alternative Service Book. 4.00 *(978-0-687-85151-5(3))* Abingdon Pr.

Cook, Stephen L. Conversations with Scripture: 2 Isaiah. 2008. (Anglican Association of Biblical Scholars Ser.). 176p. pap. 18.00 *(978-0-8192-2149-0(X)*, Morehouse Publishing) Church Publishing, Inc.

Countryman, Louis William. Calling on the Spirit in Unsettling Times. 2012. E-Book *(978-0-8192-2771-3(4)*, Morehouse Publishing) Church Publishing, Inc.

Cramer, Jared C. Safeguarded by Glory: Michael Ramsey's Ecclesiology & the Struggles of Contemporary Anglicanism. 2010. (ENG.). 172p. 60.00 *(978-0-7391-4271-4(2))* Lexington Bks.

Crumb, Lawrence N. The Oxford Movement & Its Leaders: A Bibliography of Secondary & Lesser Primary Sources. 2nd ed. 2009. (ATLA Bibliography Ser.). (ENG.). 936p. 195.00 *(978-0-8108-6193-0(3))* Scarecrow Pr., Inc.

Dalby, Mark. Anglican Missals & their Canons. 2009. 88.00 *(978-1-60724-392-2(X))* Gorgias Pr., LLC.

Dean, Joanna Elizabeth & Dean, Joanna. Religious Experience & the New Woman: The Life of Lily Dougall. 2007. (ENG., Illus.). 336p. 19.95 *(978-0-253-34814-2(5)*, 0253348145) Indiana Univ. Pr.

Development of the Anglican Liturgy 1662-1980. 5.00 *(978-0-687-85226-0(9))* Abingdon Pr.

Dormor, Duncan. An Acceptable Sacrifice. 2007. pap. *(978-0-281-05851-8(2))* SPCK Publishing.

Douglas, Brian. A Companion to Anglican Eucharistic Theology: Volume 1: the Reformation to the 19th Century. 2012. (ENG.). 690p. *(978-90-04-21930-4(7))* BRILL.

Duckworth, Penelope. Mary's Hours: Daily Prayers with the Mother of God. 2009. 160p. 20.00 *(978-0-8192-2342-5(5)*, Morehouse Publishing) Church Publishing, Inc.

Dunstan, Peta, ed. Anglican Religious Life 2012-13: A Yearbook of Religious Orders & Communities in the Anglican Communion & Tertiaries, Oblates, Associates & Companions. 2011. 208p. pap. 12.99 *(978-1-84825-089-5(4)*, Canterbury Pr. Norwich) Hymns Ancient & Modern Ltd GBR. Dist: Westminster John Knox Pr.

Eames, Robin. Finding Common Ground: The Search for a Way Forward. 2012. (ENG.). 42.95 *(978-1-85607-666-1(0))* Columba Pr. IRL. Dist: Dufour Editions, Inc.

Eaton, Arthur Wentworth Hamilton. The Heart of the Creeds: Historical Religion in the Light of Modern. 2007. (ENG.). 212p. per. 24.95 *(978-1-4304-4347-6(2))* Kessinger Publishing, LLC.

Elliott, Kenneth Ray. Anglican Church Policy, Eighteenth Century Conflict, & the American Episcopate. 2011. 227p. *(978-1-4331-1431-1(3))* Lang, Peter GmbH, Europaischer Verlag der Wissenschaften.

Fitch, John. Anglican Eirenicon: The Concept of Churchmanship in the Quest for Christian Unity. 2009. (Illus.). 284p. pap. 38.00 *(978-0-7188-9212-8(7))* Lutherworth Pr., The GBR. Dist: Brown, David Bk. Co., The.

Foulkes, Richard. Church & Stage in Victorian England. 2006. (ENG.). 280p. pap. 60.00 *(978-0-521-03437-1(X))* Cambridge Univ. Pr.

Frame, Tom. Anglicans in Australia. 2007. (ENG.). 304p. pap. 35.95 *(978-0-86840-830-9(1)*, UNSW Press) NewSouth Publishing AUS. Dist: Independent Pubs. Group.

Garrison, Becky. Ancient Future Disciples: Meeting Jesus in Mission-Shaped Ministries. 2011. E-Book ***(978-1-59627-232-3(5)***, Seabury Bks.) Church Publishing, Inc.

Giles, Richard. Times & Seasons: Creating Transformative Worship Throughout the Year. 2008. 192p. pap. 30.00 *(978-0-89869-613-4(5))* Church Publishing, Inc.

Gitari, David, ed. Anglican Liturgical Inculturation in Africa. 2009. 88.00 *(978-1-60724-380-9(6))* Gorgias Pr., LLC.

Grey, Mary. Anglican Tradition. 640p. 43.00 *(978-0-281-04496-2(1))* SPCK Publishing GBR. Dist: Pilgrim Pr., The/United Church Pr.

Groves, Phil, ed. The Anglican Communion & Homosexuality: The official study guide to enable listening & dialogue. 2008. 288p. pap. *(978-0-281-05963-8(2))* SPCK Publishing.

Harrold, Philip E. & Williams, D. H., eds. The Great TraditionNtilde;A Great Labor: Studies in Ancient-Future Faith. 2011. 124p. pap. 15.00 ***(978-1-60899-814-2(2)***, Cascade Bks.) Wipf & Stock Pubs.

Hassett, Miranda K. Anglican Communion in Crisis: How Episcopal Dissidents & Their African Allies Are Reshaping Anglicanism. 2007. (ENG., Illus.). 320p. (C). 49.95 *(978-0-691-12518-3(X))* Princeton Univ. Pr.

Hawkins, James Barney. Staying One, Remaining Open: Educating Leaders for a 21st Century Church. Jones, Richard J., ed. 2010. 216p. pap. 28.00 *(978-0-8192-2396-8(4)*, Morehouse Publishing) Church Publishing, Inc.

Hebb, Ross N. Samuel Seabury & Charles Inglis: Two Bishops, Two Churches. 2010. 43.50 *(978-0-8386-4257-3(8))*; (ENG.). 164p. 43.50 *(978-1-61147-432-9(9))* Fairleigh Dickinson Univ. Pr.

Hefling, Charles & Shattuck, Cynthia. The Book of Common Prayer: A Worldwide Survey. 2008. (ENG., Illus.). 640p. per. 30.00 *(978-0-19-529762-1(8))* Oxford Univ. Pr., Inc.

Hein, David. Geoffrey Fisher: Archbishop of Canterbury. 2008. (ENG.). 140p. pap. 38.00 *(978-0-227-17295-7(7))* Clarke, James Co., Ltd. GBR. Dist: Brown, David Bk. Co., The.

—Geoffrey Fisher: Archbishop of Canterbury, 1945-1961. 2007. (Princeton Theolgoical Monograph Ser.). 140p. pap. 17.00 *(978-1-59752-824-5(2)*, Pickwick Pubns.) Wipf & Stock Pubs.

Holder, Timothy. The Hip Hop Prayer: The Remix. 2nd rev. ed. 2008. 184p. pap. 17.00 *(978-1-59627-090-9(X)*, Seabury Bks.) Church Publishing, Inc.

Holeton, David, ed. Liturgical Inculturation in the Anglican Communion. 2009. 88.00 *(978-1-60724-369-4(5))* Gorgias Pr., LLC.

Holeton, David & Dowling, Ronald L., eds. Equipping the Saints: Ordination in Anglicanism Today. 2007. (ENG.). 244p. pap. 45.95 *(978-1-85607-543-5(5))* Columba Pr. IRL. Dist: Dufour Editions, Inc.

Hooker, Richard. Of the Laws of Ecclesiastical Polity. 2009. 192p. 22.99 *(978-1-103-56704-1(7))*; pap. 16.99 *(978-1-103-56702-7(0))* BiblioBazaar.

Howe, John W. & Carey, George. Our Anglican Heritage: Can an Ancient Church Be a Church of the Future? 2nd ed. 2010. 258p. pap. 28.00 *(978-1-60899-489-2(9)*, Cascade Bks.) Wipf & Stock Pubs.

Hughes, Philip E. Theology of the English Reformers, Revised & Expanded Edition. 2009. 320p. pap. 35.00 *(978-1-60608-746-6(0)*, Wipf and Stock) Wipf & Stock Pubs.

Iarccum. Anglican-Roman Catholic Dialogue. 2007. 64p. pap. *(978-0-281-05939-3(X))* SPCK Publishing.

Jacob. Making of Anglican Church Worldwde. (Illus.). 352p. 29.00 *(978-0-281-05043-7(0))* SPCK Publishing GBR. Dist: Pilgrim Pr., The/United Church Pr.

James, Rob. Faith, Belief, & Scripture: Anglicanism & Homosexuality. 2011. 192p. pap. ***(978-1-86335-924-5(9))*** Common Ground Publishing Pty, Ltd.

Jewel, John. An Apology of the Church of England. 2009. 226p. 28.99 *(978-1-116-91775-8(0))*; 226p. 32.99 *(978-1-116-91774-1(2))*; 226p. pap. 25.75 *(978-1-116-91776-5(9))*; (ENG.). 225p. pap. 22.99 *(978-1-116-91778-9(5)*, BiblioLife); (ENG.). 225p. pap. 20.99 *(978-1-116-91779-6(3)*, BiblioLife); 226p. pap. 24.75 *(978-1-116-91777-2(7))* BiblioBazaar.

—The Apology of the Church of England. 2008. 128p. 24.99 *(978-0-554-26125-6(1))* 2008. 128p. 21.99 *(978-0-554-35428-6(4))* 2007. 112p. pap. 18.99 *(978-1-4346-0482-8(9))* 2007. (ENG.). 124p. pap. 19.99 *(978-1-4346-0515-3(9))* BiblioBazaar.

—The Apology of the Church of England. Morley, Henry, ed. Bacon, Lady Ann, tr. 2007. 100p. per. *(978-1-4065-3473-3(0))* Dodo Pr.

Johnson, Eleanor & Clark, John, eds. Anglicans in Mission: A Transforming Journey: Report of MISSIO, the Mission Commission of the Anglican Communion, to the Anglican Consultative Council, Meeting in Edinburgh, Scotland, September 1999. 160p. 21.00 *(978-0-281-05322-3(7))* SPCK Publishing GBR. Dist: Pilgrim Pr., The/United Church Pr.

Jones, Rhidian. The Canon Law of the Roman Catholic Church & the Church of England: A Handbook. 2nd ed. 2011. (ENG.). 208p. 80.00 *(978-0-567-61641-8(X)*, T&T Clark Int'l) Continuum International Publishing Group, Ltd. GBR. Dist: National Bk. Network.

Jones, Sarah Rowland, compiled by. Faith in Action: Njongonkulu Ndungane Archbishop for the church & the World. 2011. 256p. pap. 27.95 *(978-0-7963-0763-7(6))* NB Pubs. Ltd. ZAF. Dist: International Publishers Marketing.

Kaye, Bruce. An Introduction to World Anglicanism. 2008. (Introduction to Religion Ser.). (ENG., Illus.). 288p. pap. 30.00 *(978-0-521-61866-3(5))* Cambridge Univ. Pr.

Kaye, Bruce N. Conflict & the Practice of Christian Faith. 2011. (ENG.). 192p. pap. 36.25 *(978-0-7188-9243-2(7))* Lutherworth Pr., The GBR. Dist: Printondemand-worldwide.com.

—Conflict & the Practice of Christian Faith. 2009. 192p. pap. 22.00 *(978-1-55635-970-5(5)*, Cascade Bks.) Wipf & Stock Pubs.

Kennedy, David J. & Kennedy, David. Eucharistic Sacramentality in an Ecumenical Context: The Anglican Epiclesis. 2008. (New Critical Thinking in Religion, Theology & Biblical Studies). 270p. 114.95 *(978-0-7546-6376-8(0))* Ashgate Publishing Co.

Kirkpatrick, Frank G. The Episcopal Church in Crisis: How Sex, the Bible, & Authority Are Dividing the Faithful, 1 vol. 2008. (Religion, Politics, & Public Life under the auspices of the Leonard E. Greenberg Center for the Study of Religion in Public Life, Trinity College, Hartford, CT Ser.). 248p. 44.95 *(978-0-313-34662-0(3)*, C34662, Praeger Pubs.) Greenwood Publishing Group, Inc.

Kisker, Scott Thomas. Foundation for Revival: Anthony Horneck, the Religious Societies, & the Construction of an Anglican Pietism. 2007. (Revitalization: Explorations in World Christian Movements Ser.). (ENG., Illus.). 268p. per. 64.00 *(978-0-8108-5799-5(5))* Scarecrow Pr., Inc.

Loades. Truth-Seeking Heart. 2006. (Canterbury Studies in Spiritual Theology). 192p. 19.99 *(978-1-85311-712-1(9))* Norwich Bks. & Music GBR. Dist: Westminster John Knox Pr.

Marshall, William. Scripture, Tradition & Reason: A Selected View of Anglican Theology Through the Centuries. 2011. (ENG.). 264p. pap. 34.95 *(978-1-85607-700-2(4))* Columba Pr. IRL. Dist: Dufour Editions, Inc.

McGrath, Francis J. & Murray, Dom Placid. John Henry Newman Sermons 1824-1843: Volume III: Sermons & Lectures for Saint's Days & Holy Days & General Theology. 2010. (John Henry Newman Sermons Ser.). (ENG.). 528p. 199.99 *(978-0-19-920090-0(4))* Oxford Univ. Pr., Inc.

Melinsky, M. A. Hugh. The Shape of the Ministry. 2012. xiii, 302p. pap. ***(978-1-85311-047-4(7))*** Church Hse. Publishing.

Meyers, Ruth. Worship-Shaped Life: Liturgical Formation for the People of God. Earey, Mark, ed. 2010. (Canterbury Studies in Agnlicanism Ser.). 160p. pap. 24.00 *(978-0-8192-2398-2(0)*, Morehouse Publishing) Church Publishing, Inc.

Moore, Honor. The Bishop's Daughter: A Memoir. 2008. (ENG., Illus.). 368p. 25.95 *(978-0-393-05984-7(7)*, 5984) Norton, W. W. & Co., Inc.

Moore, Honor & Moore, H. The Bishop's Daughter: A Memoir. 2009. (ENG., Illus.). 384p. pap. 16.95 *(978-0-393-33536-1(4)*, 33536) Norton, W. W. & Co., Inc.

Morgan, Nigel J., ed. English Monastic Liturgies of the Saints after 1100 Vol. 1: Abbotsbury - Peterborough. 2012. (Henry Bradshaw Society Ser.: Volume 119). 214p. 75.00 ***(978-1-907497-26-1(9))*** Bradshaw, Henry Society GBR. Dist: Boydell & Brewer, Inc.

Nelson, Louis P. The Beauty of Holiness: Anglicanism & Architecture in Colonial South Carolina. 2009. (Richard Hampton Jenrette Series in Architecture & the Decorative Arts Ser.). (ENG., Illus.). 516p. 52.95 *(978-0-8078-3233-2(2))* Univ. of North Carolina Pr.

Newton, John. Seafarers' Voices 3 Slaver Captain. 2011. (Illus.). 224p. *(978-1-84832-079-6(5))* Pen & Sword Bks. Ltd.

Nourse, John. A Love of High Places. 2007. pap. 17.95 *(978-988-99937-1-9(6))* Inkstone Bks.

O'Donovan, Oliver. Church in Crisis: The Gay Controversy & the Anglican Communion. 2008. 134p. pap. 17.00 *(978-1-55635-897-5(0)*, Cascade Bks.) Wipf & Stock Pubs.

O'Donovan, Oliver. On the Thirty-Nine Articles: A Conversation with Tudor Christianity. 2011. 180p. pap. 30.00 ***(978-0-334-04398-0(0)***, SCM Pr.) Hymns Ancient & Modern Ltd GBR. Dist: Westminster John Knox Pr.

Oxford, ed. The Book of Common Prayer 1979. 2008. (ENG.). 1056p. 19.99 *(978-0-19-528776-9(2))* Oxford Univ. Pr., Inc.

—1979 Book of Common Prayer Personal Edition, Bonded White. 2008. (ENG.). 1056p. 44.99 *(978-0-19-528783-7(5))* Oxford Univ. Pr., Inc.

—1979 Book of Common Prayer (RCL edition) & the New Revised Standard Version Bible with the Apocrypha. 2009. (ENG.). 65.00 *(978-0-19-528838-4(6))* Oxford Univ. Pr., Inc.

Packer, J. I. & Beckwith, Roger T. The Thirty-Nine Articles: Their Place & Use Today. 2007. (ENG.). 104p. per. *(978-1-57383-413-1(0)*, Regent College Publishing) Regent College Publishing.

Pawley, Margaret. Donald Coggan: Servant of Christ. 24.00 *(978-0-687-85156-0(4))* Abingdon Pr.

Peters, Bosco. The Anglican Eucharist in New Zealand 1814-1989. 2009. 88.00 *(978-1-60724-374-8(1))* Gorgias Pr., LLC.

Philip Sheldrake Staff. George Herbert: Ccsst. 2010. viii, 178p. pap. *(978-1-85311-948-4(2)*, Morehouse Publishing) Church Publishing, Inc.

Pitchford. Abc for the Pcc 5th Ed (p) 5th rev. ed. 2008. (ENG.). 228p. pap. 24.95 *(978-1-906286-07-1(8))* Mowbray, A. R. & Co., Ltd. GBR. Dist: National Bk. Network.

Plater, Ormonde. Deacons in the Liturgy. 2nd rev. ed. 2009. 144p. (Orig.). pap. 16.00 *(978-0-89869-634-9(8))* Church Publishing, Inc.

Porter, Muriel. Sydney Anglicans & the Threat to World Anglicanism: The Sydney Experiment. 2011. (Ashgate Contemporary Ecclesiology Ser.). 190p. 99.95 ***(978-1-4094-2028-6(0))***; pap. 39.95 ***(978-1-4094-2027-9(2))*** Ashgate Publishing Co.

Ramsey, Michael. The Gospel & the Catholic Church, 1 vol. 2009. (ENG.). 249p. 16.95 *(978-1-59856-389-4(0))* Hendrickson Pubs. Marketing, LLC.

—The Gospel & the Catholic Church. 2008. 248p. pap. 27.00 *(978-1-60608-245-4(0)*, Wipf and Stock) Wipf & Stock Pubs.

Redmile, Robert. Apostolic Succession & the Catholic Ep. 2006. (ENG.). 25.99 *(978-1-60034-517-3(4))*; pap. 15.99 *(978-1-60034-516-6(6))* Xulon Pr., Inc.

Rees, Christina & Percy, Martyn, eds. Apostolic Women, Apostolic Authority: Transfiguring Leadership in Today's Church. 2011. (Canterbury Studies in Agnlicanism Ser.). 160p. pap. 18.00 *(978-0-8192-2450-7(2)*, Morehouse Publishing) Church Publishing, Inc.

Robbins, Mandy. Clergywomen in the Church of England: A Psychological Study. 2008. 248p. 109.95 *(978-0-7734-4948-0(5))* Mellen, Edwin Pr., The.

Rose, Margaret, et al, eds. Lifting Women's Voices: Prayers to Change the World. 2009. 416p. 25.00 *(978-0-8192-2323-4(9)*, Morehouse Publishing) Church Publishing, Inc.

Rowell, Geoffrey, ed. The English Religious Tradition & the Genius of Anglicanism. 2009. 256p. pap. 28.00 *(978-1-60608-209-6(4)*, Wipf and Stock) Wipf & Stock Pubs.

Ruth Meyers Staff. Worship-Shaped Life: Liturgical Information for the People of God Canterbury Studies in Agnlicanism Series. 2010. xviii, 138p. pap. ***(978-1-84825-007-9(X)***, Morehouse Publishing) Church Publishing, Inc.

Sachs, William L. Homosexuality & the Crisis of Anglicanism. 2009. (ENG.). 264p. 99.00 *(978-0-521-85120-6(3))* Cambridge Univ. Pr.

Samuel, Vinay, et al. The Way, the Truth & the Life: Theological Resources for a Pilgrimage to a Global Anglican Future. 2008. 104p. pap. *(978-1-57383-429-2(7))* Regent College Publishing.

Schmidt, Richard H. Glorious Companions: Five Centuries of Anglican Spirituality. (Illus.). 360p. pap. 25.00 *(978-0-8028-2222-2(3))* Forward Movement Pubns.

Schnitker, Thaddaeus A. The Church's Worship. 2009. 260p. pap. 29.00 *(978-1-60899-114-3(8)*, Wipf and Stock) Wipf & Stock Pubs.

Schwanke, Johannes. John Henry Newmans Konversion: Sein Weg zur katholischen Kirche aus protestantischer Perspektive. (Theologische Bibliothek Töpelmann Ser.).Tr. of John Henry Newmanâ€(tm)s Conversion. His Way to the Catholic Church Viewed from a Protestant Perspective. 2011. (GER.). XIV, 339p. 196.00 ***(978-3-11-174461-2(2))*** 2010. 340p. 126.00 *(978-3-11-022894-6(7))* De Gruyter, Walter Inc.

Sell, Alan P. F. Four Philosophical Anglicans: W. G. de Burgh W. R. Matthews O. C. Quick H. A. Hodges. 2010. (Illus.). 340p. 124.95 *(978-1-4094-0059-2(X))* Ashgate Publishing Co.

Shortt, Rupert. Rowan's Rule: The Biography of the Archbishop of Canterbury. 2009. 484p. 30.00 *(978-0-8028-6461-1(9))* Eerdmans, William B. Publishing Co.

Smith, James. The Eucharistic Doctrine of the Later Nonjurors. 2009. 88.00 *(978-1-60724-396-0(2))* Gorgias Pr., LLC.

Spencer, Stephen. Anglicanism. 2010. (SCM Studyguides Ser.). (ENG.). 256p. (C). pap. 29.99 *(978-0-334-04337-9(9)*, SCM Pr.) Hymns Ancient & Modern Ltd GBR. Dist: Westminster John Knox Pr.

Stebbing, Nicholas & Taylor, Benjamin F., eds. Walter Frere. 2011. 224p. pap. 28.99 *(978-1-85311-868-5(0)*, Canterbury Pr. Norwich) Hymns Ancient & Modern Ltd GBR. Dist: Westminster John Knox Pr.

Steer, Roger. Basic Christian: The Inside Story of John Stott. 2010. (ENG.). 288p. pap. 19.00 *(978-0-8308-3846-2(5)*, IVP Bks.) InterVarsity Pr.

Stott, John, ed. The Anglican Communion & Scripture: Papers from the First International Consultation of the Evangelical Fellowship in the Anglican Communion, Canterbury, UK, June 1993. 2011. 198p. pap. 23.00 ***(978-1-61097-559-9(6)***, Wipf and Stock) Wipf & Stock Pubs.

Strong, Rowan. Anglicanism & the British Empire, C. 1700-1850. 2007. (ENG.). 320p. 125.00 *(978-0-19-921804-2(8))* Oxford Univ. Pr., Inc.

Taylor, Barbara Brown. An Altar in the World: A Geography of Faith. (Plus Ser.). 240p. 2010. (ENG.). pap. 14.99 *(978-0-06-137047-2(9))* 2009. 24.99 *(978-0-06-137046-5(0))* HarperCollins Pubs. (HarperOne).

—Leaving Church: A Memoir of Faith. 2007. (ENG.). 256p. pap. 14.99 *(978-0-06-087263-2(2)*, HarperOne) HarperCollins Pubs.

Tengatenga, James. The UMCA in Malawi. 446p. pap. *(978-99908-87-65-5(9))* Michigan State Univ. Pr.

Thompson, Roderico Iacobo Marcello. Liber Precum Publicarum: Et Administrationis Sacramentorum Aliorumque Rituum Caerimoniarumque Ecclesiae: Cum Psalterio Davidico: Secundum Usum Ecclesiae Episcopalis in Duobus Voluminibus, 2 vols. 2008. (LAT.). *(978-0-615-21905-9(5))*; *(978-0-615-21906-6(3))* Laud Liturgical Pr.

Tovey, Phillip. The Theory & Practice of Extended Communion. 2009. (Liturgy, Worship & Society Ser.). (Illus.). 210p. 99.95 *(978-0-7546-6684-4(0))* Ashgate Publishing Co.

Turner, Timothy. Welcoming the Baptized. 2009. 88.00 *(978-1-60724-385-4(7))* Gorgias Pr., LLC.

VanNerley, David. The Voice of the Stranger. 2009. 132p. pap. *(978-3-639-12972-4(5))* VDM Verlag Dr. Mueller e.K.

Ward, Kevin. A History of Global Anglicanism. 2006. (ENG., Illus.). 374p. (C). per. 44.99 *(978-0-521-00866-2(2))*; 108.00 *(978-0-521-80395-3(0))* Cambridge Univ. Pr.

Welch, P., ed. Church & Settler in Colonial Zimbabwe: A Study in the History of the Anglican Diocese of Mashonaland/Southern Rhodesia, 1890-1925. 2008. (Studies of Religion in Africa Ser.). (Illus.). 250p. (C). *(978-90-04-16746-9(3))* BRILL.

Weller, John. The Flying Bishop. 2008. (Illus.). 100p. per. *(978-1-84748-225-9(2))* Athena Pr.

Wells And Coakley Staff, et al. Praying for England: Priestly Presence in Contemporary Culture. 2008. (ENG.). 208p. 27.95 *(978-0-567-03230-0(2))* Continuum International Publishing Group, Ltd. GBR. Dist: National Bk. Network.

Wild-Wood, E. Migration & Christian Identity in Congo (DRC) 2008. (Studies of Religion in Africa Ser.). (Illus.). 250p. *(978-90-04-16464-2(2))* BRILL.

Wilkinson, Alan. The Community of the Resurrection. 2011. (Illus.). xvi, 386p. ***(978-0-334-02526-9(5)***, SCM Pr.) Hymns Ancient & Modern Ltd.

Wilson, Todd. John Henry Newman: Prayers, Poems, Meditations. 2007. pap. *(978-0-281-05973-7(X))* SPCK Publishing.

Wright, Christopher J. H., ed. Portraits of a Radical Disciple: Recollections of John Stott's Life & Ministry. 2011. (ENG.). 242p. pap. 16.00 ***(978-0-8308-3810-3(4)***, IVP Bks.) InterVarsity Pr.

ANGLICAN COMMUNION—PASTORAL THEOLOGY

see Pastoral Theology—Anglican Communion

ANGLICAN CONVERTS

Cutie, Albert. Dilemma: A Priest's Struggle with Faith & Love. (ENG.). 336p. (gr. 12). 2012. 16.00 ***(978-0-451-23389-9(1)***, Celebra) 2011. 25.95 *(978-0-451-23201-4(1))* Penguin Group (USA) Inc.

Cutié, Padre Alberto. Dilema: La Lucha de un Sacerdote Entre Su Fe y el Amor. Ochoa, Santiago, tr. from ENG. 2011. (SPA.). 368p. (gr. 12). 25.95 *(978-0-451-23202-1(X))* Penguin Group (USA) Inc.

Cutie, Padre Alberto. Dilema: La Lucha de un Sacerdote Entre Su Fe y el Amor. Ochoa, Santiago, tr. 2012. (SPA.). 368p. (gr. 12). 16.00 ***(978-0-451-23390-5(5)***, Celebra) Penguin Group (USA) Inc.

Hunter, Todd D. The Accidental Anglican: The Surprising Appeal of the Liturgical Church. 2010. (ENG.). 138p. pap. 15.00 *(978-0-8308-3839-4(2)*, IVP Bks.) InterVarsity Pr.

Lewis, C. S. Surprised by Joy: The Shape of My Early Life. 22.95 *(978-0-8488-1078-8(3))* Amereon LTD.

—Surprised by Joy / the Four Loves. 2011. (ENG.). 336p. 22.00 *(978-0-547-59939-7(0))* Houghton Mifflin Harcourt Trade & Reference Pubs.

Mines, Flavel S. (Flavel Scott). A Presbyterian Clergyman Looking for the Church by One of Three Hundred. 2006. 596p. per. 32.99 *(978-1-4255-6394-3(5))* MPublishing.

Ordway, Holly. Not God's Type: A Rational Academic Finds a Radical Faith, 1 vol. 2010. (ENG.). 160p. pap. 13.99 *(978-0-8024-3194-3(1))* Moody Pubs.

Parker, Kenneth & Pahls, Michael J. Oxford Movement Converts & the Infallibility Debates of the Nineteenth Century: 1835 - 1875. 2009. (Illus.). 246p. lib. bdg. *(978-1-933146-44-7(3))* Academica Pr., LLC.

Winner, Lauren F. Still: Notes on a Mid-Faith Crisis. 2012. (ENG.). 256p. 24.99 ***(978-0-06-176811-8(1)***, HarperOne) HarperCollins Pubs.

ANGLICAN MONASTICISM AND RELIGIOUS ORDERS

Canterbury Press, creator. Anglican Religious Life: A Yearbook of Religious Orders & Communities in the Anglican Communion, & Tertiaries, Oblates, Associates & Companions. 2007. (Illus.). 206p. per. *(978-1-85311-814-2(1))* Norwich Bks. & Music.

Canterbury Press Staff. Anglican Religious Communities Year Book, 2000. (Illus.). 208p. pap. 9.95 *(978-1-85311-319-2(0)*, 1566) Norwich Bks. & Music GBR. Dist: Morehouse Publishing.

Kelly, S. E., ed. Charters of Peterborough Abbey. 2009. (ENG., Illus.). 320p. 125.00 *(978-0-19-726438-6(7))* Oxford Univ. Pr., Inc.

Lewis, Harold T. A Church for the Future: South Africa & the Future of Anglicanism. 2007. 176p. pap. 18.00 *(978-0-89869-566-3(X))* Church Publishing, Inc.

Wilkinson, Alan. The Community of the Resurrection. 2011. (Illus.). xvi, 386p. ***(978-0-334-02526-9(5)***, SCM Pr.) Hymns Ancient & Modern Ltd.

ANGLICAN ORDERS

Holeton, David, ed. Anglican Orders & Ordinations. 2009. 88.00 *(978-1-60724-390-8(3))* Gorgias Pr., LLC.

ANGLING

see Fishing

ANGLO-AMERICAN CATALOGUING RULES

Association of College and Research Libraries, Rare Books and Manuscripts Section Bibliographic Standards Committee Staff & Library of Congress, Cataloging Policy and Support Office Staff, contrib. by. Descriptive Cataloging of Rare Materials (Books) 2007. *(978-0-8444-1162-0(0))* Library of Congress.

Genereux, Cecilia & Moeller, Paul, eds. Notes for Serials Cataloging, 1 vol. 3rd rev. ed. 2009. 196p. pap. 55.00 *(978-1-59158-653-1(4)*, LU8653) Libraries Unlimited, Inc.

Mortimer, Mary. Learn Descriptive Cataloging Second North American Edition. 2007. 284p. per. 44.99 *(978-1-59095-803-2(9))* TotalRecall Pubns., Inc.

Olson, Nancy B., et al. Cataloging of Audiovisual Materials & Other Special Materials: A Manual Based on AACR2 & MARC 21, 1 vol. 5th ed. 2008. (Illus.). 332p. pap. 45.00 *(978-1-59158-635-7(6)*, LU5863) Libraries Unlimited, Inc.

Welsh, Anne & Batley, Sue. Practical Cataloguing: AACR, RDA & MARC21. 2012. ***(978-1-55570-743-9(2))*** Neal-Schuman Pubs., Inc.

ANGLO-AMERICAN LAW

see Common Law; Law—Great Britain; Law—United States

ANGLO-CATHOLICISM

see also Catholicity

Connor, Timothy G. The Kenotic Trajectory of the Church in Donald MacKinnon's Theology: From Galilee to Jerusalem to Galilee. 2011. (T&T Clark Studies in Systematic Theology Ser.). (ENG.). 256p. 120.00 *(978-0-567-11449-5(X)*, T&T Clark Int'l) Continuum International Publishing Group, Ltd. GBR. Dist: National Bk. Network.

Copeland, W. J., et al, eds. Library of Anglo-Catholic Theology, 18 titles in 81 vols., Set. reprint ed. *(978-0-404-52010-6(3))* AMS Pr., Inc.

Gunstone, John. Lift High the Cross: Anglo-Catholicism in the Congress Years. 2010. (ENG., Illus.). 384p. pap. 35.00 *(978-1-85311-817-3(6),* Canterbury Pr. Norwich) Hymns Ancient & Modern Ltd GBR. Dist: Westminster John Knox Pr.

Hewson, Helen, ed. Symposium Papers 2007. 2007. (Illus.). 68p. *(978-0-9587512-3-0(4))* Saint Laurence Pr.

Janes, Dominic. Victorian Reformation: The Fight over Idolatry in the Church of England, 1840-1860. 2009. (ENG., Illus.). 272p. 65.00 *(978-0-19-537851-1(2))* Oxford Univ. Pr., Inc.

L'Estrange, Hamon. Alliance of Divine Offices. (Library of Anglo-Catholic Theology: No. 12). reprint ed. 40.00 *(978-0-404-52104-2(5))* AMS Pr., Inc.

Maiden, John. National Religion & the Prayer Book Controversy, 1927-1928. 2009. (Studies in Modern British Religious History Ser.: Volume 21). 226p. 90.00 *(978-1-84383-521-9(5),* Boydell Press) Boydell & Brewer, Ltd. GBR. Dist: Boydell & Brewer, Inc.

Nash, John F. The Sacramental Church: The Story of Anglo-Catholicism. 2011. 306p. pap. 34.00 *(978-1-60899-789-3(8),* Wipf and Stock) Wipf & Stock Pubs.

Spurr, Barry. Anglo-Catholic in Religion: T. S. Eliot & Christianity. 2010. (ENG., Illus.). 340p. pap. 53.00 *(978-0-7188-3073-1(3))* Lutherworth Pr., The GBR. Dist: Brown, David Bk. Co., The.

Staley, Vernon. The Catholic Religion: A Manual of Instruction for Members of the Anglican Communion. 2007. (Illus.). 424p. pap. 47.00 *(978-1-55635-468-7(1),* Wipf and Stock) Wipf & Stock Pubs.

ANGLO-DUTCH WAR, 1672-1674
see Dutch War, 1672-1678

ANGLO-FRENCH INTERVENTION IN EGYPT, 1956
see Egypt—History—Intervention, 1956

ANGLO-FRENCH WAR, 1689-1697
see United States—History—King William's War, 1689-1697

ANGLO-FRENCH WAR, 1755-1763
see also United States—History—King George's War, 1744-1748; United States—History—French and Indian War, 1755-1763

Baugh, D. A. The Global Seven Years War, 1754-1763. 2011. (Modern Wars in Perspective Ser.). (ENG.). 752p. (C). pap. 50.00 *(978-0-582-09239-6(6))* Longman Publishing Group.

Corbett, Julian Stafford. England in the Seven Years' War: A Study in Combined Strategy. 2010. (Cambridge Library Collection - History Ser.). (ENG., Illus.). 512p. pap. 37.99 *(978-1-108-02356-6(8))* Cambridge Univ. Pr.

—England in the Seven Years' War: Volume 2: A Study in Combined Strategy. 2010. (Cambridge Library Collection - History Ser.). (ENG., Illus.). 424p. pap. 32.99 *(978-1-108-02357-3(6))* Cambridge Univ. Pr.

ANGLO-FRENCH WAR, 1778-1783

Cookson, J. E. The Friends of Peace: Anti-War Liberalism in England 1793-1815. 2008. (ENG.). 340p. pap. 46.00 *(978-0-521-07282-3(4))* Cambridge Univ. Pr.

Durey, Michael. William Wickham, Master Spy: The Secret War Against the French Revolution, 1 vol. 2009. (Enlightenment World Ser.). (ENG.). 288p. 99.00 *(978-1-85196-983-8(7))* Pickering & Chatto Pubs., Ltd. GBR. Dist: Ashgate Publishing Co.

Mahan, Alfred Thayer. The Major Operations of the Navies in the War of American Independence. 2008. (ENG.). 286p. per. 28.75 *(978-1-4375-2523-6(7));* 256p. per. 25.75 *(978-1-4375-2387-4(0))* BiblioBazaar.

—The Major Operations of the Navies in the War of American Independence. 2009. 282p. pap. *(978-0-217-12347-1(3))* Books LLC.

—The Major Operations of the Navies in the War of American Independence. 2007. (Illus.). 190p. reprint ed. pap. 30.00 *(978-1-4223-5932-7(8))* DIANE Publishing Co.

—The Major Operations of the Navies in the War of American Independence. 2008. (Illus.). 292p. pap. *(978-1-4065-7032-8(X))* Dodo Pr.

ANGLO-INDIAN LITERATURE—HISTORY AND CRITICISM

Johnson, Alan G. Out of Bounds: Anglo-Indian Literature & the Geography of Displacement. 2011. 320p. 53.00 *(978-0-8248-3483-8(6));* pap. 28.00 *(978-0-8248-3521-7(2))* Univ. of Hawaii Pr.

Kapila, Shuchi. Educating Seeta: The Anglo-Indian Family Romance & the Poetics of Indirect Rule. 2010. (Victorian critical Interventio Ser.). (ENG.). 200p. 39.95 *(978-0-8142-1126-7(7));* cd-rom 14.95 *(978-0-8142-9224-2(0))* Ohio State Univ. Pr.

Malhotra, Ashok. Making British Indian Fictions, 1772-1823. 2012. (Palgrave Studies in Cultural & Intellectual History Ser.). (ENG., Illus.). 288p. 85.00 *(978-0-230-11126-4(2))* Palgrave Macmillan.

Rajamannar, Shefali. Reading the Animal in the Literature of the British Raj. 2012. (ENG., Illus.). 232p. 85.00 *(978-0-230-11449-4(0))* Palgrave Macmillan.

Sharrad, Paul. Postcolonial Literary History & Indian English Fiction. 2008. 109.95 *(978-1-60497-560-4(1))* Cambria Pr.

Towheed, Shafquat & Melikoglu, Koray, eds. New Readings in the Literature of British India, C 1780-1947. 2007. 344p. per. *(978-3-89821-673-9(X))* ibidem-Verlag.

ANGLO-INDIANS

Anthony, Frank. Britain's Betrayal in India: An Anglo Indian Heritage Book: the Story of the Anglo Indian Community (an Anglo Indian Heritage Book) 2nd ed. 2007. 512p. per. *(978-1-84356-010-4(0))* Wallenberg, Simon Pr.

Brown, Warren. Anglo-Indian Race Preservation Course. 2010. 145p. pap. 21.50 *(978-1-4457-3472-9(9))* Lulu Enterprises Inc.

—The Secret Race: Anglo-Indians. 2010. 144p. pap. 24.50 *(978-1-4457-1811-8(1))* Lulu Enterprises Inc.

Cassiopaeiae & Cassiopaeiae. Dolly Dudman. 2009. (Illus.). 164p. pap. 11.99 *(978-1-4389-0225-8(5))* AuthorHouse.

Maher, Reginald James. These Are the Anglo Indians (an anglo indian heritage Book) 2007. 132p. per. *(978-1-84356-012-8(7))* Wallenberg, Simon Pr.

Mizutani, Satoshi. The Meaning of White: Race, Class, & the 'Domiciled Community' in British India 1858-1930. 2012. (ENG., Illus.). 288p. 110.00 *(978-0-19-969770-0(1))* Oxford Univ. Pr., Inc.

White, Bridget. Kolar Gold Fields - down Memory Lane: Paeans to Lost Glory! 2010. (Illus.). 212p. pap. 14.49 *(978-1-4520-4459-0(7))* AuthorHouse.

Women of Anglo-India: Tales & Memoirs. 2010. 250p. lib. bdg. 18.00 *(978-0-9754639-5-6(0))* Calcutta Tiljallah Relief, Inc.

ANGLO-IRANIAN OIL DISPUTE, 1951-1954

Read, Colin. BP & the Macondo Spill: The Complete Story. 2011. (ENG., Illus.). 256p. 40.00 *(978-0-230-29358-8(1))* Palgrave Macmillan.

ANGLO-ISRAELISM
see also Lost Tribes of Israel

Hansen, Vaughn E. Israel's Lost 10 Tribes: Migrations to Britain & USA. 2011. *(978-1-59955-951-3(X))* Cedar Fort, Inc./CFI Distribution.

Smith, Worth. The House of Glory: Prophecies & Allied Messages of the Holy Bible & the Great Pyramid of Gizeh 1948. 2007. (ENG.). 158p. 36.95 *(978-0-548-05400-0(2))* Kessinger Publishing, LLC.

ANGLO-NORMAN DIALECT

Henri D'Arci. Vitas Patrum. O'Connor, Basilides A., ed. (Catholic University of America, Studies in Romance Languages & Literatures: No. 29). reprint ed. 37.50 *(978-0-404-50329-1(2))* AMS Pr., Inc.

Ingham, Richard, ed. The Anglo-Norman Language & Its Context. 2010. (Illus.). 196p. 90.00 *(978-1-903153-30-7(1))* York Medieval Pr. GBR. Dist: Boydell & Brewer, Inc.

Jones, Mari C. The Guernsey Norman French Translations of Thomas Martin. 2008. (Orbis Supplementa Ser.). (ENG., Illus.). 181p. (C). pap. 79.00 *(978-90-429-2113-9(7))* Peeters Pubs. & Booksellers BEL. Dist: Brown, David Bk. Co., The.

Kelham, Robert. A Dictionary of the Norman or Old French Language: Collected from Such Acts of Parliament, Parliament Rolls, Journals, Acts of State, Records, Law Books, Antient Historians, & Manuscripts, as Relate to this Nation. Calculated to Illustrate the Rights & Customs of Former Ages, the Forms of Laws & Jurisprudence, the Names of Dignities & Offices, of Persons & Places; & to Render the Reading of Those Records, More Easy; As Well as Restore. 2007. 95.00 *(978-1-58477-719-9(2))* Lawbook Exchange, Ltd., The.

ANGLO-NORMAN LITERATURE

Gray, Douglas. From the Norman Conquest to the Black Death: An Anthology of Writings from England. 2011. (ENG., Illus.). 608p. 160.00 *(978-0-19-812353-8(1))* Oxford Univ. Pr., Inc.

North, Richard, et al. Longman Anthology of Old English, Old Icelandic, & Anglo-Norman Literatures. rev. ed. 2011. (ANG, ENG & ROA.). 888p. (C). pap. 52.00 *(978-1-4082-4770-9(4))* Longman Publishing Group.

Vincent, Nicholas, ed. Records, Administration & Aristocratic Society in the Anglo-Norman Realm: Papers Commemorating the 800th Anniversary of King John's Loss of Normandy. 2009. (Illus.). 226p. 99.00 *(978-1-84383-485-4(5),* Boydell Press) Boydell & Brewer, Ltd. GBR. Dist: Boydell & Brewer, Inc.

ANGLO-NORMAN LITERATURE—HISTORY AND CRITICISM

North, Richard & Allard, Joe. Beowulf & Other Stories: A New Introduction to Old English, Old Icelandic & Anglo-Norman Literatures. (ENG., Illus.). (C). 2007. 560p. per. 54.67 *(978-1-4058-3572-5(9))* 2nd ed. 2011. 596p. pap. 44.00 *(978-1-4082-8603-6(3))* Longman Publishing Group.

ANGLO-SAXON ARCHITECTURE
see Architecture, Anglo-Saxon

ANGLO-SAXON ART
see Art, Anglo-Saxon

ANGLO-SAXON CHRONICLE

Bergs, Alexander & Skaffari, Janne, eds. The Language of the Peterborough Chronicle. 2007. (Studies in English Medieval Language & Literature Ser.: Vol. 20). 197p. pap. 46.95 *(978-3-631-56454-7(6))* Lang, Peter GmbH, Europaischer Verlag der Wissenschaften DEU. Dist: Lang, Peter Publishing, Inc.

Jorgensen, A., ed. Reading the Anglo-Saxon Chronicle: Language, Literature, History. 2010. (Studies in the Early Middle Ages Ser.). (ENG & ANG., Illus.). 344p. (C). 102.00 *(978-2-503-52394-1(3))* Brepols Pubs. BEL. Dist: ISD.

ANGLO-SAXON CIVILIZATION
see Civilization, Anglo-Saxon

ANGLO-SAXON LANGUAGE
see English Language—Old English, ca. 450-1100

ANGLO-SAXON LAW
see Law, Anglo-Saxon

ANGLO-SAXON LITERATURE (COLLECTIONS)
see English Literature (Collections)—Old English, ca. 450-1100

ANGLO-SAXON MEDICINE
see Medicine, Anglo-Saxon

ANGLO-SAXON MISSIONARIES
see Missionaries, Anglo-Saxon

ANGLO-SAXON POETRY (COLLECTIONS)
see English Poetry (Collections)—Old English, ca. 450-1100

ANGLO-SAXON SCULPTURE
see Sculpture, Anglo-Saxon

ANGLO-SAXONS

Albany F. Early Wars of Wessex: Being Studies from England's School of Arms in the West. Whistler, Charles W., ed. 2010. (Cambridge Library Collection - History Ser.). (Illus.). 282p. pap. 23.99 *(978-1-108-01008-5(3))* Cambridge Univ. Pr.

Albertsson, Alaric. Travels Through Middle Earth: The Path of a Saxon Pagan. 2009. (ENG.). 240p. pap. 16.95 *(978-0-7387-1536-0(0))* Llewellyn Pubns.

Alfred the Great. Whole Works of Alfred the Great, 3 pts. in 2 vols. Giles, J. A., ed. reprint ed. 175.00 *(978-0-404-00380-7(X))* AMS Pr., Inc.

Allen, Grant. Anglo Saxon Britain. 2007. (Illus.). 204p. per. 19.95 *(978-1-934255-04-9(1))* El Paso Norte Pr.

—Early Britain. 2008. 192p. 22.99 *(978-0-554-35465-1(9));* 25.99 *(978-0-554-26162-1(6))* BiblioBazaar.

Allen, T. G. Saved from the Grave: Neolithic to Saxon Discoveries at Spring Road Municipal Cemetery, Abingdon, Oxfordshire, 1990-2000. 2008. (Thames Valley Landscapes Monograph Ser.). (Illus.). xi, 106p. (C). 50.00 *(978-0-9549627-6-0(1))* Oxford Archaeological Unit GBR. Dist: Brown, David Bk. Co., The.

The Anglo-Saxon Chronicle. 2008. 276p. 28.99 *(978-0-554-28375-3(1))* 2008. 276p. 25.99 *(978-0-554-37678-3(4))* 2007. 242p. pap. 22.99 *(978-1-4346-5248-5(3))* BiblioBazaar.

The Anglo-Saxon Chronicle. 2007. 176p. per. *(978-1-4068-1741-6(4))* Echo Library.

Atkins, Rob & Connor, Aileen. Farmers & Ironsmiths: Prehistoric, Roman & Anglo-Saxon Settlement Beside Brandon Road, Thetford, Norfolk. 2010. (East anglian archaeology Monograph Ser.). (ENG., Illus.). 150p. (C). pap. 30.00 *(978-1-907588-00-6(0))* East Anglian Archaeology GBR. Dist: Brown, David Bk. Co., The.

Barrow, Julia, et al. Myth, Rulership, Church & Charters: Essays in Honour of Nicholas Brooks. Barrow, Julia & Wareham, Andrew, eds. 2008. (Illus.). 286p. 124.95 *(978-0-7546-5120-8(7))* Ashgate Publishing Co.

Baxter, Stephen David. The Earls of Mercia: Lordship & Power in Late Anglo-Saxon England. 2008. (Oxford Historical Monographs). (ENG., Illus.). 384p. 150.00 *(978-0-19-923098-3(6))* Oxford Univ. Pr., Inc.

Biddle, Martin, et al. Anglo-Saxon England Volume 10. Clemoes, Peter, ed. 2007. (Anglo-Saxon England Ser.). (ENG.). 344p. pap. 63.00 *(978-0-521-03835-2(7))* Cambridge Univ. Pr.

Bowker, Alfred. Alfred the Great Containing Chapters on. 2008. pap. 28.95 *(978-1-4286-5110-4(1))* Kessinger Publishing, LLC.

Boyle, Angela, et al. The Anglo-Saxon Cemetery at Butler's Field, Lechlade, Gloucestershire Vol. 2: Discussion & Synthesis, 2 vols. 2011. (Thames Valley Landscapes Ser.: 33). (ENG., Illus.). 197p. (C). pap. 40.00 *(978-1-905905-19-5(X))* Oxford Archaeological Unit GBR. Dist: Brown, David Bk. Co., The.

Brookes, Stuart. Economics & Social Change in Anglo-Saxon Kent AD 400-900: Landscapes, Communities & Exchange. 2007. (Bar Ser.). (Illus.). 243p. (C). 90.00 *(978-1-4073-0016-0(4))* British Archaeological Reports Ltd. GBR. Dist: Brown, David Bk. Co., The.

Carver, M. O. H., ed. The Age of Sutton Hoo: The Seventh Century in North-Western Europe. 2012. (Illus.). 456p. reprint ed. pap. 45.00 *(978-0-85115-361-2(5),* Boydell Press) Boydell & Brewer, Ltd. GBR. Dist: Boydell & Brewer, Inc.

Carver, Martin, et al, eds. Signals of Belief in Early England: Anglo-Saxon Paganism Revisited. 2010. (ENG., Illus.). 226p. (C). pap. 60.00 *(978-1-84217-395-4(2))* Oxbow Bks., Ltd. GBR. Dist: Brown, David Bk. Co., The.

Chadwick, H. Munro. The Origin of the English Nation. 2010. (Cambridge Library Collection - History Ser.). (ENG., Illus.). 356p. pap. 29.99 *(978-1-108-01006-1(7))* Cambridge Univ. Pr.

—Studies on Anglo-Saxon Institutions. 2010. (Cambridge Library Collection - History Ser.). (ENG.). 442p. pap. 32.99 *(978-1-108-01005-4(9))* Cambridge Univ. Pr.

Clemoes, Peter, ed. Anglo-Saxon England Volume 9. 2007. (Anglo-Saxon England Ser.). (ENG.). 336p. pap. 63.00 *(978-0-521-03866-9(9))* Cambridge Univ. Pr.

—Anglo-Saxon England Volume 11. 2007. (Anglo-Saxon England Ser.). (ENG.). 360p. (C). pap. 63.00 *(978-0-521-03833-1(2))* Cambridge Univ. Pr.

—Anglo-Saxon England Volume 13. 2007. (Anglo-Saxon England Ser.). (ENG.). 348p. pap. 63.00 *(978-0-521-03837-9(5))* Cambridge Univ. Pr.

—Anglo-Saxon England Volume 14. 2007. (Anglo-Saxon England Ser.). (ENG.). 392p. (C). pap. 63.00 *(978-0-521-03838-6(3))* Cambridge Univ. Pr.

—Anglo-Saxon England Volume 15. 2007. (Anglo-Saxon England Ser.). (ENG.). 300p. (C). pap. 63.00 *(978-0-521-03839-3(1))* Cambridge Univ. Pr.

—Anglo-Saxon England Volume 16. 2007. (Anglo-Saxon England Ser.). (ENG.). 376p. (C). pap. 63.00 *(978-0-521-03840-9(5))* Cambridge Univ. Pr.

Clemoes, Peter, et al, eds. Anglo-Saxon England Volume 1. 2007. (Anglo-Saxon England Ser.). (ENG.). 356p. (C). pap. 63.00 *(978-0-521-03835-5(9))* Cambridge Univ. Pr.

—Anglo-Saxon England Volume 2. 2007. (Anglo-Saxon England Ser.). (ENG.). 348p. (C). pap. 63.00 *(978-0-521-03844-7(8))* Cambridge Univ. Pr.

—Anglo-Saxon England Volume 4. 2007. (Anglo-Saxon England Ser.). (ENG.). 284p. (C). pap. 63.00 *(978-0-521-03861-4(8))* Cambridge Univ. Pr.

—Anglo-Saxon England Volume 5. 2007. (Anglo-Saxon England Ser.). (ENG.). 344p. (C). pap. 63.00 *(978-0-521-03862-1(6))* Cambridge Univ. Pr.

—Anglo-Saxon England Volume 6. 2007. (Anglo-Saxon England Ser.). (ENG.). 336p. (C). pap. 63.00 *(978-0-521-03863-8(4))* Cambridge Univ. Pr.

—Anglo-Saxon England Volume 7. 2007. (Anglo-Saxon England Ser.). (ENG.). 320p. (C). pap. 63.00 *(978-0-521-03864-5(2))* Cambridge Univ. Pr.

—Anglo-Saxon England Volume 8. 2007. (Anglo-Saxon England Ser.). (ENG.). 392p. (C). pap. 63.00 *(978-0-521-03865-2(0))* Cambridge Univ. Pr.

—Anglo-Saxon England Volume 12. 2007. (Anglo-Saxon England Ser.). (ENG.). 348p. pap. 63.00 *(978-0-521-03834-8(0))* Cambridge Univ. Pr.

Costen, Michael. Anglo-Saxon Somerset. 2011. (ENG., Illus.). 264p. (C). pap. 70.00 *(978-1-84217-988-8(8))* Oxbow Bks., Ltd. GBR. Dist: Brown, David Bk. Co., The.

Cramp, Rosemary, et al. Aedificia Nova: Studies in Honor of Rosemary Cramp. 2008. (Illus.). xv, 427p. 80.00 *(978-1-58044-110-0(6))* Medieval Institute Pubns.

Crawford, Sally & Hamerow, Helena, eds. Anglo-Saxon Studies in Archaeology & History 15. 2008. (Anglo-Saxon Studies in Archaeology & History Ser.). (ENG., Illus.). 400p. (C). pap. 100.00 *(978-1-905905-10-2(6))* Oxford Univ. Schl. of Archaeology GBR. Dist: Brown, David Bk. Co., The.

Crick, Julia, ed. Charters of St Albans. 2008. (Anglo-Saxon Charters Ser.). (ENG., Illus.). 240p. 99.00 *(978-0-19-726396-9(8))* Oxford Univ. Pr., Inc.

Crossley-Holland, Kevin, tr. from ANG. The Anglo-Saxon World: An Anthology. 2009. (Oxford World's Classics Ser.). (ENG.). 320p. pap. 12.95 *(978-0-19-953871-3(9))* Oxford Univ. Pr., Inc.

Devlin, Zoe. Remembering the Dead in Anglo-Saxon England. 2007. (Bar Bs Ser.). (ENG., Illus.). 148p. (C). pap. 87.50 *(978-1-4073-0144-0(6))* British Archaeological Reports Ltd. GBR. Dist: Brown, David Bk. Co., The.

Duckett, Eleanor Shipley. Alfred the Great. 2011. 230p. 46.95 *(978-1-258-01619-7(2))* Literary Licensing, LLC.

Dunn, Marilyn. The Christianization of the Anglo-Saxons C. 597-C. 700: Discourses of Life, Death & Afterlife. 2010. (ENG.). 282p. 49.95 *(978-1-4411-1013-8(5))* Continuum International Publishing Group, Ltd. GBR. Dist: National Bk. Network.

Dunn, Roger & Dunn, Marilyn. The Christianization of the Anglo-Saxons C.597-C700: Discources of Life, Death & after Life. 2009. (ENG., Illus.). 288p. 120.00 *(978-1-84725-189-3(7))* Continuum International Publishing Group, Ltd. GBR. Dist: National Bk. Network.

Ennis, Trevor. An Early Saxon Cemetary at Rayleigh, Essex: Excavations at the Former Park School. 2009. (ENG., Illus.). viii, 62p. (C). pap. 25.00 *(978-1-84194-086-1(0))* East Anglian Archaeology GBR. Dist: Brown, David Bk. Co., The.

Evans, D. H. & Loveluck, Christopher. Life & Economy at Early Medieval Flixborough, C. AD 600-1000: The Artefact Evidence. Excavations at Flixborough, Volume 2. 2009. (Excavations at Flixborough Ser.). (ENG., Illus.). 448p. (C). 60.00 *(978-1-84217-310-7(3))* Oxbow Bks., Ltd. GBR. Dist: Brown, David Bk. Co., The.

Evison, Vera I. & Marzinzik, Sonja. Catalogue of Anglo-Saxon Glass in the British Museum. 2008. (Research Paper Ser.). (ENG., Illus.). 184p. (C). pap. 70.00 *(978-0-86159-167-1(4))* British Museum Pr. GBR. Dist: Brown, David Bk. Co., The.

Firth, C. H. Milton. 2006. 156p. per. *(978-1-4067-1646-7(4),* Hesperides Pr.) Read Bks.

Foot, Sarah. Monastic Life in Anglo-Saxon England, C. 600-900. 2006. (ENG., Illus.). 414p. 117.00 *(978-0-521-85946-2(8))* Cambridge Univ. Pr.

Gildas. On the Ruin of Britain. 2009. 140p. pap. 6.99 *(978-1-60450-678-5(4),* Serenity Pubs.) Arc Manor.

—On the Ruin of Britain. Giles, J. A., tr. 2007. 48p. per. *(978-1-4065-2851-0(X))* Dodo Pr.

Godden, Malcolm, et al, eds. Anglo-Saxon England. 2006. (Anglo-Saxon England Ser.). (ENG., Illus.). 376p. 190.00 *(978-0-521-84906-7(3))* Cambridge Univ. Pr.

—Anglo-Saxon England Volume 18. 2007. (Anglo-Saxon England Ser.). (ENG.). 308p. (C). pap. 63.00 *(978-0-521-03842-3(1))* Cambridge Univ. Pr.

Godden, Malcolm & Keynes, Simon, eds. Anglo-Saxon England: Volume 35. 2008. (Anglo-Saxon England Ser.). (ENG.). 408p. 185.00 *(978-0-521-88342-9(3))* Cambridge Univ. Pr.

—Anglo-Saxon England Volume 34. 2007. (Anglo-Saxon England Ser.). (ENG., Illus.). 388p. (C). pap. 63.00 *(978-0-521-03860-7(X))* Cambridge Univ. Pr.

—Anglo-Saxon England Volume 37. 2009. (Anglo-Saxon England Ser.). (ENG.). 376p. (C). 180.00 *(978-0-521-76736-1(9))* Cambridge Univ. Pr.

Godden, Malcolm R., ed. Anglo-Saxon England Volume 27. 2007. (Anglo-Saxon England Ser.). (ENG.). 380p. pap. 63.00 *(978-0-521-03852-2(9))* Cambridge Univ. Pr.

Graham-Campbell, James & Ryan, Michael. Anglo-Saxon: Irish Relations Before the Vikings. Graham-Campbell, James & Ryan, Michael, eds. 2010. (Proceedings of the British Academy Ser.). (ENG., Illus.). 400p. 110.00 *(978-0-19-726450-8(6))* Oxford Univ. Pr., Inc.

Gretsch, Mechthild. The Intellectual Foundations of the English Benedictine Reform. 2006. (Cambridge Studies in Anglo-Saxon England Ser.). (ENG.). 484p. pap. 61.00 *(978-0-521-03052-6(8))* Cambridge Univ. Pr.

Grills, Hubert. The Life & Times of Godwine, Earl of Wessex. 2009. (ENG., Illus.). 272p. (C). pap. 39.95 *(978-1-898281-52-8(1))* Anglo-Saxon Bks. GBR. Dist: Brown, David Bk. Co., The.

Hamerow, Helena, et al. The Oxford Handbook of Anglo-Saxon Archaeology. 2011. (Oxford Handbooks Ser.). (ENG., Illus.). 1104p. 160.00 *(978-0-19-921214-9(7))* Oxford Univ. Pr., Inc.

Hardy, Alan, et al. A Roman Rural Landscape at Kempsford Quarry, Gloucestershire: The Archaeology of a Middle Saxon Estate Centre at Higham Ferrers, Northamptonshire. 2007. (Oxford Archaeology Monograph Ser.). (Illus.). 250p. 40.00 *(978-0-904220-43-8(5))* Oxford Archaeological Unit GBR. Dist: Brown, David Bk. Co., The.

Hart, Cyril. Chronicles of the Reign of Alfred the Great: Part I: Introduction & Commentary: the Early Chronicles of England, Volume IV, 2 vols. 2010. (ANG, LAT & ENG., Illus.). 232p. 109.95 *(978-0-7734-3729-6(0))* Mellen, Edwin Pr., The.

—Chronicles of the Reign of Alfred the Great: Part II: the Texts: the Early chronicles of England, Volume IV, 2 vols. 2010. (ENG, ANG & LAT., Illus.). 416p. 129.95 *(978-0-7734-3731-9(2))* Mellen, Edwin Pr., The.

Hawkes, Sonia Chadwi. The Anglo-Saxon Cemetery at Finglesham, Kent. 2006. (Oxford University School of Archaeology Monograph Ser.). (ENG., Illus.). 436p. (C). 52.00 *(978-0-9549627-1-5(0))* Oxford Univ. Schl. of Archaeology GBR. Dist: Brown, David Bk. Co., The.

Hawkins, Dexter Arnoll. The Anglosaxon Race: Its history, character, & Destiny. 2011. 32p. pap. 11.99 ***(978-1-4181-9370-6(4))*** MPublishing.

Hayward, P. A. Kingship, Childhood & Martyrdom in Anglo-Saxon England. 2012. (Studies in the Early Middle Ages Ser.). (ENG.). 300p. (C). 87.00 *(978-2-503-51420-8(0))* Brepols Pubs. BEL. Dist: Brown, David Bk. Co., The.

Higham, Nicholas J. & Ryan, Martin J., eds. The Landscape Archaeology of Anglo-Saxon England. 2010. (Pubns Manchester Centre for Anglo-Saxon Studies: Volume 9). (Illus.). 244p. 99.00 *(978-1-84383-582-0(7)*, Boydell Press) Boydell & Brewer, Ltd. GBR. Dist: Boydell & Brewer, Inc.

—Place-Names, Language & the Anglo-Saxon Landscape. 2011. (Pubns Manchester Centre for Anglo-Saxon Studies: Volume 10). (Illus.). 258p. 99.00 *(978-1-84383-603-2(3)*, Boydell Press) Boydell & Brewer, Ltd. GBR. Dist: Boydell & Brewer, Inc.

Hyer & Crocker. The Material Culture of Daily Living in the Anglo-Saxon World. 2011. (Illus.). 386p. 115.00 *(978-0-85989-843-0(1))* Univ. of Exeter Pr. GBR. Dist: Chicago Distribution Ctr.

Ingram, J. The Anglo Saxon Chronicle: A History of England from Roman Times to the Norman Conquest. 2009. 224p. pap. *(978-1-934941-50-8(6))* Red & Black Pubs.

Jolly, Karen Louise. The Community of St. Cuthbert in the Late Tenth Century: The Chester-Le-Street Additions to Durham Cathedral Library A.IV.19. 2012. (Text & Context Ser.). 536p. 99.95 ***(978-0-8142-1181-6(X))***; cd-rom 39.95 ***(978-0-8142-9282-2(8))*** Ohio State Univ. Pr.

Karkov, Catherine E. & Howe, Nicholas. Conversion & Colonization in Anglo-Saxon England. 2006. (C). *(978-0-86698-363-1(5))* Arizona State Univ., Arizona Ctr. for Medieval & Renaissance Studies.

Keynes, Simon & Lapidge, Michael. Anglo-Saxon England Volume 17. Clemoes, Peter, ed. 2007. (Anglo-Saxon England Ser.). (ENG.). 356p. (C). pap. 63.00 *(978-0-521-03841-6(3))* Cambridge Univ. Pr.

Lapidge, Michael, ed. Anglo-Saxon England Volume 21. 2007. (Anglo-Saxon England Ser.). (ENG.). 344p. (C). pap. 63.00 *(978-0-521-03846-1(4))* Cambridge Univ. Pr.

—Anglo-Saxon England Volume 22. 2007. (Anglo-Saxon England Ser.). (ENG.). 344p. (C). pap. 63.00 *(978-0-521-03847-8(2))* Cambridge Univ. Pr.

—Anglo-Saxon England Volume 23. 2007. (Anglo-Saxon England Ser.). (ENG.). 352p. (C). pap. 63.00 *(978-0-521-03848-5(0))* Cambridge Univ. Pr.

—Anglo-Saxon England Volume 26. 2007. (Anglo-Saxon England Ser.). (ENG.). 340p. pap. 63.00 *(978-0-521-03851-5(0))* Cambridge Univ. Pr.

—Archbishop Theodore: Commemorative Studies on his Life & Influence. 2006. (Cambridge Studies in Anglo-Saxon England Ser.). (ENG.). 360p. pap. 69.00 *(978-0-521-03210-0(5))* Cambridge Univ. Pr.

Lapidge, Michael, et al, eds. Anglo-Saxon England Volume 19. 2007. (Anglo-Saxon England Ser.). (ENG.). 308p. (C). pap. 63.00 *(978-0-521-03843-0(X))* Cambridge Univ. Pr.

—Anglo-Saxon England Volume 20. 2007. (Anglo-Saxon England Ser.). (ENG.). 324p. pap. 63.00 *(978-0-521-03845-4(6))* Cambridge Univ. Pr.

—Anglo-Saxon England Volume 24. 2007. (Anglo-Saxon England Ser.). (ENG.). 380p. pap. 63.00 *(978-0-521-03849-2(9))* Cambridge Univ. Pr.

—Anglo-Saxon England Volume 25. 2007. (Anglo-Saxon England Ser.). (ENG.). 360p. pap. 63.00 *(978-0-521-03850-8(2))* Cambridge Univ. Pr.

—Anglo-Saxon England Volume 28. 2007. (Anglo-Saxon England Ser.). (ENG., Illus.). 456p. (C). pap. 63.00 *(978-0-521-03853-9(7))* Cambridge Univ. Pr.

—Anglo-Saxon England Volume 29. 2007. (Anglo-Saxon England Ser.). (ENG.). 376p. pap. 63.00 *(978-0-521-03854-6(5))* Cambridge Univ. Pr.

—Anglo-Saxon England Volume 30. 2007. (Anglo-Saxon England Ser.). (ENG.). 384p. (C). pap. 63.00 *(978-0-521-03856-0(1))* Cambridge Univ. Pr.

—Anglo-Saxon England Volume 31. 2007. (Anglo-Saxon England Ser.). (ENG., Illus.). 396p. (C). pap. 63.00 *(978-0-521-03857-7(X))* Cambridge Univ. Pr.

—Anglo-Saxon England Volume 32. 2007. (Anglo-Saxon England Ser.). (ENG.). 432p. (C). pap. 63.00 *(978-0-521-03858-4(8))* Cambridge Univ. Pr.

—Anglo-Saxon England Volume 33. 2007. (Anglo-Saxon England Ser.). (ENG., Illus.). 416p. (C). pap. 63.00 *(978-0-521-03859-1(6))* Cambridge Univ. Pr.

Lavelle, Ryan. Aethelred II: King of the English. 2008. (English Monarchs Ser.). (ENG., Illus.). 240p. pap. 29.95 *(978-0-7524-4678-3(9))* History Pr. Ltd.,The GBR. Dist: Independent Pubs. Group.

Laycock, Stuart. Britannia - The Failed State: Tribal Conflict & the End of Roman Britain. 2008. (ENG., Illus.). 256p. pap. 43.95 *(978-0-7524-4614-1(2))* History Pr. Ltd.,The GBR. Dist: Independent Pubs. Group.

Leahy, Kevin. "Interrupting the Pots" The Excavation of Cleatham Anglo-Saxon Cemetery, North Lincolnshire. 2007. (CBA Research Report). (Illus.). 278p. (C). pap. 60.00 *(978-1-902771-71-7(0))* Council for British Archaeology GBR. Dist: Brown, David Bk. Co., The.

Leahy, Kevin & Bland, Roger. The Staffordshire Hoard. 2009. (ENG., Illus.). 48p. (C). pap. 12.95 *(978-0-7141-2328-8(5))* British Museum Pr. GBR. Dist: Brown, David Bk. Co., The.

Lee, Christina. Feasting the Dead: Food & Drink in Anglo-Saxon Burial Rituals. 2007. (Anglo-Saxon Studies: Volume 9). (Illus.). 202p. 90.00 *(978-1-84383-142-6(2)*, Boydell Press) Boydell & Brewer, Ltd. GBR. Dist: Boydell & Brewer, Inc.

Lewis, C. P., ed. Anglo-Norman Studies 32: Proceedings of the Battle Conference 2009. 2010. (Anglo-Norman Studies: Volume 32). (Illus.). 254p. 80.00 *(978-1-84383-563-9(0)*, Boydell Press) Boydell & Brewer, Ltd. GBR. Dist: Boydell & Brewer, Inc.

—Anglo-Norman Studies 33: Proceedings of the Battle Conference 2010. 2011. (Anglo-Norman Studies: Volume 33). (Illus.). 212p. 80.00 *(978-1-84383-658-2(0)*, Boydell Press) Boydell & Brewer, Ltd. GBR. Dist: Boydell & Brewer, Inc.

—Proceedings of the Battle Conference 2005. 2006. (Anglo-Norman Studies: Volume 28). (Illus.). 198p. 80.00 *(978-1-84383-217-1(8))* Boydell & Brewer, Inc.

Liebermann, Felix. The National Assembly in the Anglo Saxon Period. 2007. (ENG.). 108p. 33.95 *(978-0-548-05292-1(1))* Kessinger Publishing, LLC.

Loveluck, Christopher. Rural Settlement, Lifestyles & Social Change in the Later First Millennium AD. 2007. (Excavations at Flixborough Ser.). (Illus.). 256p. 60.00 *(978-1-84217-256-8(5))* Oxbow Bks., Ltd. GBR. Dist: Brown, David Bk. Co., The.

Mitchell, Bruce. Anglo-Saxon England Volume 3. Clemoes, Peter et al, eds. 2007. (Anglo-Saxon England Ser.). (ENG.). 284p. (C). pap. 63.00 *(978-0-521-03855-3(3))* Cambridge Univ. Pr.

Mortimer, Richard, ed. Edward the Confessor: The Man & the Legend. 2009. (Illus.). 228p. 90.00 *(978-1-84383-436-6(7)*, Boydell Press) Boydell & Brewer, Ltd. GBR. Dist: Boydell & Brewer, Inc.

Myres, J. N. L. A Corpus of Anglo-Saxon Pottery of the Pagan Period 2 Part Set, 2 vols. 2009. (Gulbenkian Archaeological Ser.). (ENG.). 382p. pap. 95.00 *(978-0-521-12610-6(X))* Cambridge Univ. Pr.

Naismith, Rory. Money & Power in Anglo-Saxon England: The Southern English Kingdoms, 757-865. 2011. (Cambridge Studies in Medieval Life & Thought: Fourth Ser.). (ENG., Illus.). 376p. 99.00 ***(978-1-107-00662-1(7))*** Cambridge Univ. Pr.

North, Richard. Heathen Gods in Old English Literature. 2006. (Cambridge Studies in Anglo-Saxon England Ser.). (ENG.). 392p. pap. 74.00 *(978-0-521-03026-7(9))* Cambridge Univ. Pr.

Owen-Crocker. Working with Anglo-Saxon Manuscripts. Owen-Crocker, Gale R., ed. 2009. (UEP - Exeter Medieval Texts & Studies). (Illus.). 320p. 115.00 *(978-0-85989-840-9(7))*; (ENG., pap. 50.00 *(978-0-85989-841-6(5))* Univ. of Exeter Pr. GBR. Dist: Chicago Distribution Ctr.

Owen-Crocker, Gale R. Dress in Anglo-Saxon England. rev. ed. 2010. (Illus.). 428p. pap. 34.95 *(978-1-84383-572-1(X)*, Boydell Press) Boydell & Brewer, Ltd. GBR. Dist: Boydell & Brewer, Inc.

Owen-Crocker, Gale R., ed. King Harold II & the Bayeux Tapestry. 2011. (Pubns Manchester Centre for Anglo-Saxon Studies: Volume 3). (Illus.). 214p. pap. 29.95 *(978-1-84383-615-5(7)*, Boydell Press) Boydell & Brewer, Ltd. GBR. Dist: Boydell & Brewer, Inc.

Palmer, James T. Anglo-Saxons in a Frankish World, 690-900. 2009. (Studies in the Early Middle Ages Ser.). (ENG., Illus.). 324p. (C). 123.00 *(978-2-503-51911-1(3))* Brepols Pubs. BEL. Dist: ISD.

Penn, Kenneth. The Anglo-Saxon Cemetery at Shrubland Hall Quarry, Coddenham, Suffolk. 2011. (East Anglian Archaeology Monograph Ser.: 139). (ENG., Illus.). 146p. (C). pap. 30.00 ***(978-0-9568747-0-2(3))*** East Anglian Archaeology GBR. Dist: Brown, David Bk. Co., The.

Penn, Kenneth, et al. Aspects of Anglo-Saxon Inhumation Burial: Morning Thorpe, Spong Hill, Bergh Apton & Westgarth Gardens. 2007. (East Anglian Archaeology Ser.). (ENG., Illus.). xii, 126p. (C). pap. 33.00 ***(978-0-905594-45-3(2))*** East Anglian Archaeology GBR. Dist: Brown, David Bk. Co., The.

Plunkett, Steven J. Sutton Hoo. 2006. (National Trust Guidebooks Ser.). (ENG., Illus.). 32p. pap. 9.95 *(978-1-84359-009-5(3))* History Pr. Ltd.,The GBR. Dist: Independent Pubs. Group.

Pollington, Stephen. Anglo-Saxon Art, Myth & Material Culture from the 4th to 7th Century: Wayland's Work. 2010. (ENG., Illus.). 542p. (C). 170.00 *(978-1-898281-56-6(4))* Anglo-Saxon Bks. GBR. Dist: Brown, David Bk. Co., The.

—Anglo-Saxon Burial Mounds: Princely Burials in the 6th & 7th Centuries. 2008. (ENG., Illus.). 272p. (C). pap. 30.00 *(978-1-898281-51-1(3))* Anglo-Saxon Bks. GBR. Dist: Brown, David Bk. Co., The.

—Anglo-Saxon FAQs. 2008. (Illus.). 128p. (C). pap. 22.95 *(978-1-898281-50-4(5))* Anglo-Saxon Bks. GBR. Dist: Brown, David Bk. Co., The.

Reno, Frank D. Arthurian Figures of History & Legend: A Biographical Dictionary. 2010. (ENG., Illus.). 272p. pap. 39.95 *(978-0-7864-4420-5(7))* McFarland & Co., Inc. Pubs.

Reuter, Timothy, et al. Cross & Cruciform in the Anglo-Saxon World: Studies to Honor the Memory of Timothy Reuter. 2010. (Wv medieveal european Studies). (ENG.). 400p. pap. 44.95 *(978-1-933202-50-1(5))* West Virginia Univ. Pr.

Robertson, Agnes, ed. Anglo-Saxon Charters: Volume 1. 2009. 588p. pap. 55.00 *(978-0-521-17832-7(0))* Cambridge Univ. Pr.

Seebohm, Frederic. Tribal Custom in Anglo-Saxon Law. 538p. reprint ed. 98.00 *(978-0-7222-1984-3(9))* Library Reprints, Inc.

Soames, Henry. The Anglo-Saxon Church: Its History, Revenues & General Character. 4th ed. reprint ed. 39.50 *(978-0-404-18786-6(2))* AMS Pr., Inc.

Thompson, Susan D. Anglo-Saxon Royal Diplomas: A Palaeography. 2006. (Pubns Manchester Centre for Anglo-Saxon Studies: Volume 6). (Illus.). 198p. 90.00 *(978-1-84383-218-8(6))* Boydell & Brewer, Inc.

Thompson, Victoria. Dying & Death in Later Anglo-Saxon England. 2012. (Anglo-Saxon Studies: Volume 4). (Illus.). 246p. pap. 34.95 ***(978-1-84383-731-2(5)***, Boydell Press) Boydell & Brewer, Ltd. GBR. Dist: Boydell & Brewer, Inc.

Unknown. The Anglo-Saxon Chronicle. 2007. (ENG.). 242p. pap. 20.99 *(978-1-4346-5247-8(5))* BiblioBazaar.

Wallis, Heather. Romano-British & Saxon Occupation at Billingford, Central Norfolk. 2011. (ENG., Illus.). 112p. (C). pap. 25.00 *(978-0-905594-52-1(5))* East Anglian Archaeology GBR. Dist: Brown, David Bk. Co., The.

Whitelock, Dorothy. Anglo-Saxon Wills. 2011. (ENG & ANG.). 302p. pap. 30.99 *(978-1-107-40221-8(2))* Cambridge Univ. Pr.

Williamson, Tom. The Origins of Hertfordshire. 2010. (ENG., Illus.). 256p. pap. 33.95 *(978-1-905313-95-2(0))* Univ. of Hertfordshire Pr. GBR. Dist: Independent Pubs. Group.

—Sutton Hoo & Its Landscape: The Contexts of Monuments. 2008. (Illus.). 220p. (C). pap. 40.00 *(978-1-905119-25-7(9))* Windgather Pr. GBR. Dist: Brown, David Bk. Co., The.

Wood, Harriet Harvey. The Battle of Hastings: The Fall of Anglo-Saxon England. 2009. (ENG., Illus.). 240p. 26.95 *(978-1-84354-807-2(0))*; pap. 15.95 *(978-1-84354-808-9(9))* Atlantic Bks., Ltd. GBR. Dist: Independent Pubs. Group.

—The Battle of Hastings: The Fall of Anglo-Saxon England. 2009. (ENG.). 240p. (gr. 12-18). 26.95 *(978-1-59020-276-0(7))* Overlook Pr., The.

Wright, Thomas. The Celt, the Roman & the Saxon: A History of the Early Inhabitants of Britain 1861. 2007. (ENG.). 542p. 57.95 *(978-0-548-05396-6(0))* Kessinger Publishing, LLC.

ANGOLA

Ravenstein, E. G., ed. The Strange Adventures of Andrew Battell of Leigh, in Angola & the Adjoining Regions. 2010. (Hakluyt Society, Second Ser.). 264p. 69.95 *(978-1-4094-1373-8(X))* Hakluyt Society GBR. Dist: Ashgate Publishing Co.

Shannon, Vere, et al, eds. Benguela: Predicting a Large Marine Ecosystem. 2006. (Large Marine Ecosystems Ser.: 14). (ENG., Illus.). 438p. 155.00 *(978-0-444-52759-2(1)*, Elsevier Science) Elsevier Science & Technology Bks.

Stead, Mike & Rorison, Sean. Angola. 2010. (Bradt Travel Guide Ser.). (ENG., Illus.). 240p. pap. 27.99 *(978-1-84162-304-7(0))* Bradt Travel Guides GBR. Dist: Globe Pequot Pr., The.

ANGOLA—ECONOMIC CONDITIONS

Chabal, Patrick & Vidal, Nuno, eds. Angola: The Weight of History. 2007. (Columbia/Hurst Ser.). (ENG.). 256p. (gr. 17). 55.00 *(978-0-231-70015-3(6))* Columbia Univ. Pr.

Clarence-Smith, W. G. Slaves, Peasants & Capitalists in Southern Angola 1840-1926. 2007. (African Studies). (ENG.). 148p. pap. 30.99 *(978-0-521-04743-2(9))* Cambridge Univ. Pr.

Icon Group International, Inc. Staff, compiled by. The 2006 Economic & Product Market Databook for Benguela, Angola. 2006. 618p. ring bd. 95.00 *(978-0-497-80184-7(1))* Icon Group International, Inc.

—The 2006 Economic & Product Market Databook for Huambo, Angola. 2006. 618p. ring bd. 95.00 *(978-0-497-81910-1(4))* Icon Group International, Inc.

—The 2006 Economic & Product Market Databook for Lobito, Angola. 2006. 618p. ring bd. 95.00 *(978-0-497-80874-7(9))* Icon Group International, Inc.

—The 2006 Economic & Product Market Databook for Luanda, Angola. 2006. 618p. ring bd. 95.00 *(978-0-497-80883-9(8))* Icon Group International, Inc.

—The 2006 Economic & Product Market Databook for Lubango, Angola. 2006. 618p. ring bd. 95.00 *(978-0-497-80886-0(2))* Icon Group International, Inc.

—The 2006 Economic & Product Market Databook for Malanje, Angola. 2006. 618p. ring bd. 95.00 *(978-0-497-80929-4(X))* Icon Group International, Inc.

—The 2006 Economic & Product Market Databook for Namibe, Angola. 2006. 618p. ring bd. 95.00 *(978-0-497-81091-7(3))* Icon Group International, Inc.

—The 2006 Economic & Product Market Databook for Nampo, North Korea. 2006. 618p. ring bd. 95.00 *(978-0-497-82029-9(3))* Icon Group International, Inc.

le Billon, Philippe. Wars of Plunder: Conflicts, Profits & the Politics of Resources. 2012. (Columbia/Hurst Ser.). (ENG.). 240p. (gr. 17). 35.00 ***(978-0-231-70268-3(X))*** Columbia Univ. Pr.

Reed, Kristin. Crude Existence: Environment & the Politics of Oil in Northern Angola. 2009. (Global, Area, & International Archive Ser.). (ENG., Illus.). 344p. pap. 34.95 *(978-0-520-25822-8(3))* Univ. of California Pr.

ANGOLA—HISTORY

Baines, Gary & Vale, Peter, eds. Beyond the Border War: New Perspectives on Southern Africa's Late-Cold War Conflicts. 2008. (Illus.). 362p. pap. 43.00 *(978-1-86888-456-8(2))* Unisa Press / Uitgewers GBR. Dist: International Specialized Bk. Services.

Blake, Cameron. Troepie Snapshots: A Pictorial Recollection of the South African Border War. 2011. (Illus.). 384p. pap. 49.95 *(978-1-920143-46-6(7))* 30° South Pubs. ZAF. Dist: International Publishers Marketing.

Cann, John. Counterinsurgency in Africa. 2012. (Illus.). 240p. pap. 49.95 ***(978-1-907677-73-1(9))*** Helion & Co., Ltd. GBR. Dist: Casemate Pubs. & Bk. Distributors, LLC.

Chabal, Patrick & Vidal, Nuno, eds. Angola: The Weight of History. 2007. (Columbia/Hurst Ser.). (ENG.). 256p. (gr. 17). 55.00 *(978-0-231-70015-3(6))* Columbia Univ. Pr.

Chapman, William & Stassen, Nicol. William Chapman: Reminiscences Including an Account of the Trek Boers into Angola & of Their Sojourn During the Forty-Eight Years They Struggled in That Country under Portuguese Rule. 2012. (Illus.). 476p. 50.00 ***(978-1-86919-192-4(7))*** International Publishers Marketing.

Clarence-Smith, W. G. Slaves, Peasants & Capitalists in Southern Angola 1840-1926. 2007. (African Studies). (ENG.). 148p. pap. 30.99 *(978-0-521-04743-2(9))* Cambridge Univ. Pr.

Davies, Ann. Constructive Engagement? Chester Crocker & American Policy in South Africa, Namibia & Angola. 2007. (Illus.). 256p. pap. 29.95 *(978-1-84701-304-0(X)*, Currey, James) Boydell & Brewer, Ltd. GBR. Dist: Boydell & Brewer, Inc.

—Constructive Engagement? Chester Crocker & American Policy in South Africa, Namibia & Angola. 2007. (Illus.). 256p. 90.00 *(978-1-84701-305-7(8)*, Currey, James) Boydell & Brewer, Ltd. GBR. Dist: Boydell & Brewer, Inc.

Davies, J. E. Constructive Engagement? Chester Crocker & American Policy in South Africa, Namibia & Angola, 1981-8. 2007. (ENG., Illus.). 256p. 59.95 *(978-0-8214-1781-2(9))*; pap. 26.95 *(978-0-8214-1782-9(7))* Ohio Univ. Pr.

Fitzsimmons, Scott. Mercenaries in Asymmetric Conflicts. 2012. (ENG., Illus.). 368p. 99.00 ***(978-1-107-02691-9(1))*** Cambridge Univ. Pr.

Golan, Tamar & Ron, Tamar. Angolan Rendezvous: Man & Nature in the Shadow of War. 2010. (Illus.). 304p. pap. 29.95 *(978-1-920143-42-8(4))* 30° South Pubs. ZAF. Dist: International Publishers Marketing.

Heerden, Roelf van & Hudson, Andrew. Four Ball One Tracer. 2012. (Illus.). 320p. 49.95 ***(978-1-907677-76-2(3))*** Helion & Co., Ltd. GBR. Dist: Casemate Pubs. & Bk. Distributors, LLC.

Holt, Clive. At Thy Call We Did Not Falter. 2006. (Illus.). 194p. pap. 19.95 *(978-1-77007-117-9(2)*, Zebra Pr.) Struik Pubs. ZAF. Dist: International Publishers Marketing.

James, W. Martin. Historical Dictionary of Angola. 2nd ed. 2011. E-Book *(978-0-8108-7458-9(X))*; (ENG.). 400p. 95.00 *(978-0-8108-7193-9(9))* Scarecrow Pr., Inc.

Lord, Brigadier Dick. From Tailhooker to Mudmover: An Aviation Career in the Royal Naval Fleet Air Arm, United States Navy, & South African Air Force. 2010. 360p. pap. 29.95 *(978-0-620-30762-8(5))* 30° South Pubs. ZAF. Dist: International Publishers Marketing.

Maier, Karl. Angola: Promises & Lies. 2nd rev. ed. 2007. (Illus.). 232p. pap. 17.95 *(978-1-897959-52-7(4))* Serif GBR. Dist: Interlink Publishing Group, Inc.

Malaquias, Assis. Rebels & Robbers: Violence in Post-Colonial Angola. 2007. 264p. pap. 39.95 *(978-91-7106-580-3(6))* Nordiska Afrikainstitutet SWE. Dist: Stylus Publishing, LLC.

McWilliams, Mike. Battle for Cassinga: South Africa's Controversial Cross-Border Raid, Angola 1978. 2011. (Africa@war Ser.). (Illus.). 80p. pap. 29.95 ***(978-1-907677-39-7(9))*** Helion & Co., Ltd. GBR. Dist: Casemate Pubs. & Bk. Distributors, LLC.

Moorman, Marissa J. Intonations: A Social History of Music & Nation in Luanda, Angola, from 1945 to Recent Times. 2008. (New African Histories Ser.). (ENG.). 320p. 52.95 *(978-0-8214-1823-9(8))*; (Illus.). pap. 29.95 *(978-0-8214-1824-6(6))* Ohio Univ. Pr.

Nortje, Piet. 32 Battalion: The Inside Story of South Africa's Elite Fighting Unit. 2011. 352p. pap. 23.95 *(978-1-86872-914-2(1)*, Zebra Pr.) Struik Pubs. ZAF. Dist: International Publishers Marketing.

Peters, Christabelle. Cuban Identity & the Angolan Experience. 2012. (New Directions in Latino American Culture Ser.). (ENG., Illus.). 256p. 85.00 ***(978-0-230-34093-0(8))*** Palgrave Macmillan.

Porto, J. Gomes, et al. From soldiers to Citizens: Demilitarisation of conflict & Society. 2007. (Illus.). 208p. 114.95 *(978-0-7546-7210-4(7))* Ashgate Publishing Co.

Robbins, Sarah, et al. Nellie Arnott's Writings on Angola, 1905-1913: Missionary Narratives Linking Africa & America. 2010. *(978-1-60235-142-4(2))*; pap. *(978-1-60235-141-7(4))* Parlor Pr.

Scheepers, Marius. Striking Inside Angola with 32 Battalion. 2012. (Illus.). 176p. pap. 39.95 ***(978-1-907677-77-9(1))*** Helion & Co., Ltd. GBR. Dist: Casemate Pubs. & Bk. Distributors, LLC.

Thompson, J. H. An Unpopular War: From Afkak to Bosbefok: Voices of South African National Servicemen. 2007. 256p. pap. 22.95 *(978-1-77007-301-2(9)*, Zebra Pr.) Struik Pubs. ZAF. Dist: International Publishers Marketing.

Weigert, Stephen L. Angola: A Modern Military History, 1961-2002. 2011. (ENG., Illus.). 272p. 85.00 *(978-0-230-11777-8(5))* Palgrave Macmillan.

Williams, David. On the Border: The White South African Military Experience, 1965-1990. 2010. (Illus.). 160p. pap. 26.95 *(978-0-624-04469-7(6))* NB Pubs. Ltd. ZAF. Dist: International Publishers Marketing.

Wilsworth, Clive. First in, Last Out: The South African Artillery in Action: 1975-1988. 2010. (Illus.). 352p. pap. 29.95 *(978-1-920143-40-4(8))* 30° South Pubs. ZAF. Dist: International Publishers Marketing.

ANGOLA—POLITICS AND GOVERNMENT

Chabal, Patrick & Vidal, Nuno, eds. Angola: The Weight of History. 2007. (Columbia/Hurst Ser.). (ENG.). 256p. (gr. 17). 55.00 *(978-0-231-70015-3(6))* Columbia Univ. Pr.

James, W. Martin. A Political History of the Civil War in Angola, 1974-1990. 2011. (ENG.). 327p. pap. 34.95 *(978-1-4128-1506-2(1))* Transaction Pubs.

le Billon, Philippe. Wars of Plunder: Conflicts, Profits & the Politics of Resources. 2012. (Columbia/Hurst Ser.). (ENG.). 240p. (gr. 17). 35.00 ***(978-0-231-70268-3(X))*** Columbia Univ. Pr.

Mai, Vincent A. & Wisner, Frank G. Toward an Angola Strategy: Prioritizing U. S. -Angola Relations. Nash, William L., ed. 2007. (ENG.). 48p. per. 10.00 *(978-0-87609-370-2(5))* Council on Foreign Relations.

Maier, Karl. Angola: Promises & Lies. 2nd rev. ed. 2007. (Illus.). 232p. pap. 17.95 *(978-1-897959-52-7(4))* Serif GBR. Dist: Interlink Publishing Group, Inc.

ANGOLA—SOCIAL CONDITIONS

Clarence-Smith, W. G. Slaves, Peasants & Capitalists in Southern Angola 1840-1926. 2007. (African Studies). (ENG.). 148p. pap. 30.99 *(978-0-521-04743-2(9))* Cambridge Univ. Pr.

Grassi, Marzia. Forms of Familial, Economic, & Political Association in Angola Today: A Foundational Sociology of an African State. 2010. (Illus.). ix, 251p. 109.95 *(978-0-7734-3677-0(4))* Mellen, Edwin Pr., The.

Porto, J. Gomes, et al. From soldiers to Citizens: Demilitarisation of conflict & Society. 2007. (Illus.). 208p. 114.95 *(978-0-7546-7210-4(7))* Ashgate Publishing Co.

Tetteh, Ruby Saakor. Assessing Citizen Participation in Local Governance. 2011. 96p. pap. ***(978-3-8443-9913-4(5))*** Lambert Academic Publishing.

ANGOLA (IND.)

Sims, Newell LeRoy. A Hoosier Village: A Sociological Study with Special Reference to Social Causation (1912) 2008. 188p. 37.95 *(978-1-4366-2323-2(3))*; pap. 22.95 *(978-0-548-85800-4(4))* Kessinger Publishing, LLC.

ANGORA RABBITS

see Rabbits

ANGUILLA

Casselman, J. M. & Cairns, David Kenneth. Eels at the Edge: Science, Status, & Conservation Concerns. 2009. (Illus.). xxvi, 460p. *(978-1-888569-96-4(4))* American Fisheries Society.

Fodor's Travel Publications, Inc. Staff. St. Maarten, St. Barth & Anguilla. 2nd ed. 2010. (In Focus-Color Ser.). (ENG.). 216p. pap. 11.99 *(978-1-4000-0467-6(5))* Fodor's Travel Pubns.

Webster, J. Ronald. Revolutionary Leader: Relections on Life, Leadership, Politics. 2011. 214p. pap. 29.95 *(978-1-4327-6896-6(4))* Outskirts Pr., Inc.

ANGULAR CORRELATIONS (NUCLEAR PHYSICS)

see also Gamma Rays

Hofer, Lars. Rare Hadronic B Decays. 2011. 148p. pap. ***(978-3-8381-2473-5(1))*** Südwestdeutscher Verlag für Hochschulschriften AG & Co. KG.

ANGULAR MOMENTUM (NUCLEAR PHYSICS)

see also Nuclear Spin; Regge Theory

Balcar, Ewald & Lovesey, Stephen W. Introduction to the Graphical Theory of Angular Momentum: Case Studies. 2009. (Springer Tracts in Modern Physics Ser.). (ENG., Illus.). xii, 227p. 189.00 *(978-3-642-03117-5(X)*, 364203117X) Springer.

Bekshaev, A., et al. Paraxial Light Beams with Angular Momentum. 2008. pap. 39.00 *(978-1-60456-114-2(9))* Nova Science Pubs., Inc.

Biedenharn, L. C., et al. The Racah-Wigner Algebra in Quantum Theory. 2009. (Encyclopedia of Mathematics & its Applications Ser.). (ENG.). 628p. pap. 100.00 *(978-0-521-11617-6(1))* Cambridge Univ. Pr.

Devanathan, V. Angular Momentum Techniques in Quantum Mechanics. 2010. (Fundamental Theories of Physics Ser.). (Illus.). 256p. pap. 269.00 *(978-90-481-5281-0(X)*, 904815281X) Springer.

Gribov, V. N. The Theory of Complex Angular Momenta: Gribov Lectures on Theoretical Physics. 2007. (Cambridge Monographs on Mathematical Physics). (ENG., Illus.). 312p. pap. 73.00 *(978-0-521-03703-7(4))* Cambridge Univ. Pr.

Li, Siao-Jing. The Angular Momentum of Gravitational Fields. 2010. 104p. pap. *(978-3-8383-4345-2(1))* Lambert Academic Publishing.

Nikolaevskiy, Victor N. Angular Momentum in Geophysical Turbulence: Continuum Spatial Averaging Method. 2010. 256p. pap. 105.00 *(978-90-481-6478-3(8)*, 9048164788) Springer.

Torres, Juan P. & Torner, Lluis, eds. Twisted Photons: Applications of Light with Orbital Angular Momentum. 2011. (ENG., Illus.). 288p. 195.00 *(978-3-527-40907-5(6)*, Wiley-VCH) Wiley, John & Sons, Inc.

Tudosa, Ioan. Magnetization Dynamics in Short Magnetic Field Pulses. 2009. 100p. pap. *(978-3-639-11208-5(3))* VDM Verlag Dr. Mueller e.K.

Webb, G. A., ed. NMR, Vol. 36. 2007. (Specialist Periodical Reports). (ENG.). 440p. 448.00 *(978-0-85404-362-0(4))* Royal Society of Chemistry, The GBR. Dist: Ingram Pub. Services.

ANGUS CATTLE

see Aberdeen-Angus Cattle

ANHYDRIDES

World Health Organization. Cyclic Acid Anhydrides: Human Health Aspects. 2009. (Concise International Chemical Assessment Document No 75 Ser.). (ENG.). 70p. pap. 24.00 *(978-92-4-153075-0(8))* World Health Organization.

ANHYDROUS AMMONIA

see Ammonia

ANILINE COLORS

see Coal-Tar Colors

ANIMAL BABIES

see Animals—Infancy

ANIMAL BAITING

see Bullfights

ANIMAL BEHAVIOR

see also Animal Defenses; Animal Intelligence; Animal Migration; Animals—Food; Animals—Infancy; Behavior Genetics; Cannibalism in Animals; Hibernation; Insect Societies; Instinct; Mimicry (Biology); Parental Behavior in Animals; Psychology, Comparative; Social Behavior in Animals

also subdivision Behavior under individual animals and groups of animals, e.g. Birds—Behavior; Cats—Behavior; Primates—Behavior

Abitbol, M. Maurice. The Roots of Human Sexuality: Review of the Stages Between the Animal Condition & Present Human Culture. 2010. vi, 268p. *(978-1-933132-62-4(0))* Spuyten Duyvil.

Agoramoorthy, Govindasamy. Infanticide in Monkeys. 2011. 152p. pap. ***(978-3-8383-4315-0(8))*** Lambert Academic Publishing.

Aitken, Edward Hamilton. Concerning Animals & Other Matters. 2008. 168p. 22.99 *(978-0-554-36254-0(6))* 2008. 168p. 25.99 *(978-0-554-26951-1(1))* 2007. (ENG.). 150p. pap. 18.99 *(978-1-4346-2187-0(1))* 2007. (ENG.). 166p. pap. 21.99 *(978-1-4346-2247-1(9))* BiblioBazaar.

—The Tribes on My Frontier: An Indian Naturalist's Foreign Policy. 2007. (ENG.). 224p. 39.95 *(978-0-548-04244-1(6))* Kessinger Publishing, LLC.

Akeley, Delia J. J T Jr: The Biography of an African Monkey. 2011. 266p. 47.95 ***(978-1-258-08154-8(7))*** Literary Licensing, LLC.

Alcorn, Jo Lynn. Amazing Animal Art Projects: 20 Easy Step-by-Step Paper Projects That Connect to Seasonal & Science Topics. 2008. (ENG., Illus.). 80p. pap. 15.99 *(978-0-439-51786-7(9)*, Teaching Resources) Scholastic, Inc.

Alderton, David. Animal Grief: How Animals Mourn. 2011. (ENG., Illus.). 80p. 19.95 *(978-1-84584-288-8(X)*, 184584288X, Hubble & Hattie) Veloce Publishing Ltd. GBR. Dist: MBI Distribution Services/Quayside Distribution.

Ammen, Amy & Foth-Regner, Kitty. Hip Ideas for Hyper Dogs. 2007. (ENG., Illus.). 240p. per. 16.99 *(978-0-470-04101-7(3)*, Howell Bk. Hse.) Wiley, John & Sons, Inc.

Anderson, Casey. The Story of Brutus: My Life with Brutus the Bear & the Grizzlies of North America. 2011. (ENG., Illus.). 272p. pap. 14.95 *(978-1-60598-253-3(9)*, 605253) Pegasus Bks.

Anderson, Wendy. Animal Adaptations. 2007. 32p. pap. 10.95 *(978-0-86431-526-7(0))* ACER Pr. AUS. Dist: International Specialized Bk. Services.

Andrews, Katherine. Influences on Female Social Networks in Old-World Primates. 2009. 104p. pap. *(978-3-639-13092-8(8))* VDM Verlag Dr. Mueller e.K.

Anthes, Nils, et al. Animal Behaviour: Evolution & Mechanisms: Evolution & Mechanisms. Kappeler, Peter, ed. 2010. (ENG., Illus.). 707p. 69.95 *(978-3-642-02623-2(0)*, 3642026230) Springer.

Anwar, Duaa. I Am Equus: Understanding the Horse's Potential through Everyday Encounters. 2010. 258p. pap. 17.95 *(978-1-4327-5149-4(2))* Outskirts Pr., Inc.

Appleby, David, ed. The Apbc Book of Companion Animal Behaviour. 2nd ed. 2011. (ENG., Illus.). 320p. pap. 24.95 *(978-0-285-63887-7(4))* Souvenir Pr. Ltd. GBR. Dist: Independent Pubs. Group.

Arnold, Oren. Wild Life in the Southwest. 2007. (ENG.). 306p. 43.95 *(978-0-548-07363-6(5))* Kessinger Publishing, LLC.

Asada, Minoru. From Animals to Animats 10: 10th International Conference on Simulation of Adaptive Behavior, SAB 2008, Osaka, Japan, July 7-12 2008, Proceedings. 2008. (Lecture Notes in Computer Science / Lecture Notes in Artificial Intelligence Ser.). (Illus.). xiii, 530p. pap. 99.00 *(978-3-540-69133-4(2)*, 3540691332) Springer.

Baker, Samuel White. Wild Beasts & Their Ways: Reminiscences of Europe Asia Africa & America. 2007. 268p. pap. 21.99 *(978-1-4346-5983-5(6))*; (ENG.). 300p. pap. 23.99 *(978-1-4346-5984-2(4))* BiblioBazaar.

Balcombe, Jonathan. Pleasurable Kingdom: Animals & the Nature of Feeling Good. rev. ed. 2007. (ENG., Illus.). 360p. pap. 14.95 *(978-1-4039-8602-3(9))* Palgrave Macmillan.

—Second Nature: The Inner Lives of Animals. (MacSci Ser.). (ENG.). 256p. 2011. pap. 17.00 *(978-0-230-10781-6(8))* 2010. (Illus.). 27.00 *(978-0-230-61362-1(4))* Palgrave Macmillan.

Balcombe, Jonathan Peter. The Exultant Ark: A Pictorial Tour of Animal Pleasure. 2011. (ENG., Illus.). 225p. 34.95 *(978-0-520-26024-5(4))* Univ. of California Pr.

Barash, David P. & Lipton, Judith Eve. Strange Bedfellows: The Surprising Connection Between Sex, Evolution & Monogamy. 2009. (ENG.). 192p. 25.00 *(978-1-934137-20-8(0))* Bellevue Literary Pr.

Barrows, Edward M. Animal Behavior Desk Reference. 3rd rev. ed. 2011. (ENG., Illus.). 800p. 159.95 *(978-1-4398-3651-4(5)*, CRC Press) Taylor & Francis Group GBR. Dist: Taylor & Francis Group.

Bartkowski, Frances. Kissing Cousins: A New Kinship Bestiary. 2008. (ENG., Illus.). 224p. (gr. 17). 35.00 *(978-0-231-14452-0(0))* Columbia Univ. Pr.

Bastock, Margaret. Courtship: An Ethological Study. 2007. (ENG., Illus.). 228p. pap. 22.95 *(978-0-202-30911-8(8))* Aldine Transaction.

Bearzi, Maddalena & Stanford, Craig B. Beautiful Minds: The Parallel Lives of Great Apes & Dolphins. 2010. 368p. pap. 14.95 *(978-0-674-04627-6(7))* Harvard Univ. Pr.

Bekoff, Marc. The Animal Manifesto: Six Reasons for Expanding Our Compassion Footprint. 2010. (ENG.). 272p. pap. 14.95 *(978-1-57731-649-7(5))* New World Library.

Bekoff, Marc & Pierce, Jessica. Wild Justice: The Moral Lives of Animals. 2010. (ENG., Illus.). 208p. pap. 17.00 *(978-0-226-04163-6(8))* Univ. of Chicago Pr.

Bekoff, Marc, et al. Wild Justice: The Moral Lives of Animals. 2nd ed. 2009. (ENG., Illus.). 204p. 26.00 *(978-0-226-04161-2(1))* Univ. of Chicago Pr.

Berger, Joel. The Better to Eat You With: Fear in the Animal World. 2008. (ENG., Illus.). 360p. 29.00 *(978-0-226-04363-0(0))* Univ. of Chicago Pr.

Bergman, Daniel. Conditions Influencing Aggression. 2009. 152p. pap. *(978-3-639-00152-5(4))* VDM Verlag Dr. Mueller e.K.

Blake, Henry. Talking with Horses: A Study of Communication Between Man & Horse. 2007. (ENG., Illus.). 176p. per. 16.95 *(978-0-285-62998-1(0))* Souvenir Pr. Ltd. GBR. Dist: Independent Pubs. Group.

Blake, Mychelle E., ed. The Dog Trainer's Resource: The APDT Chronicle of the Dog Collection, 1. 2006. (Illus.). 339p. per. 24.95 *(978-1-929242-39-9(5))* Dogwise Publishing.

Blumstein, Daniel T. A Primer of Conservation Biology. 3910. (Illus.). 300p. pap. *(978-0-87893-401-0(4))* Sinauer Assocs., Inc.

Blumstein, Daniel T. & Daniel, Janice C. Quantifying Behavior the JWatcher Way. 2007. (C). pap. *(978-0-87893-047-0(7))* Sinauer Assocs., Inc.

Boesch, Christophe. Real Chimpanzee: Sex Strategies in the Forest. 2009. (ENG., Illus.). 196p. (C). 120.00 *(978-0-521-11008-2(4))*; pap. 52.00 *(978-0-521-12513-0(8))* Cambridge Univ. Pr.

Bolhuis, Johan J. & Giraldeau, Luc-Alain, eds. Animal Behaviour, 4 vols. 2009. (SAGE Library of Cognitive & Experimental Psychology Ser.). 1712p. 995.00 *(978-1-84787-539-6(4)*, B75396C) SAGE Pubns., Ltd. GBR. Dist: SAGE Pubns., Inc.

Bolhuis, Johan J. & Verhulst, Simon M., eds. Evolution, Function, Development & Causation: Tinbergen's Four Questions & Contemporary Behavioural Biology. 2005. 240p. *(978-90-04-14243-5(6))* BRILL.

Boyle, Laura, et al, eds. Applied Ethology: Addressing future challenges in animal Agriculture. 2008. (Illus.). 314p. pap. 45.00 *(978-90-8686-081-4(8))* Wageningen Academic Publishers NLD. Dist: Enfield Publishing & Distribution Co., Inc.

Boysen, Sally & Custance, Deborah. The Smartest Animals on the Planet: Extraordinary Tales of the Natural World's Cleverest Creatures. 2009. (ENG., Illus.). 192p. 35.00 *(978-1-55407-456-3(8))* Firefly Bks., Ltd.

Boysen, Sarah Till, et al. The Smartest Animals on the Planet. enl. ed. 2012. (ENG., Illus.). 192p. pap. 24.95 ***(978-1-55407-965-0(9))*** Firefly Bks., Ltd.

Bradshaw, G. A. Elephants on the Edge: What Animals Teach Us about Humanity. 2010. (Illus.). 352p. pap. 18.00 *(978-0-300-16783-2(0))* Yale Univ. Pr.

Bradshaw, John W. S., et al. Principles of Companion Animal Behaviour Therapy. 2nd rev. ed. 2007. (Illus.). 352p. pap. *(978-0-632-06396-3(3)*, Wiley-Blackwell) Wiley John & Sons, Ltd.

Brakes, Philippa & Simmonds, Mark, eds. Whales & Dolphins: Cognition, Culture, Conservation & Human Perceptions. 2011. (ENG., Illus.). 256p. 140.00 *(978-1-84971-224-8(7))*; pap. 39.95 *(978-1-84971-225-5(5))* Routledge.

Breed, et al. Animal Behavior / Field & Laboratory Exercises in Animal Behavior (SET) 2011. (ENG.). 99.95 ***(978-1-4377-5597-8(6)***, Academic Pr.) Elsevier Science & Technology Bks.

Breed, Michael D. & Moore, Janice. Encyclopedia of Animal Behavior, 3 vols. 2010. (Illus.). 2672p. (ENG.). 900.00 *(978-0-08-045333-0(3))*; 900.00 *(978-0-08-045337-8(6))* Elsevier Science & Technology Bks. (Academic Pr.).

Brockmann, H. Jane, et al, eds. Advances in the Study of Behavior. (ENG.). 2010. 394p. 144.00 *(978-0-12-380892-9(8))* 2009. 362p. 144.00 *(978-0-12-374474-6(1))* 2008. (Illus.). 552p. 144.00 *(978-0-12-004538-9(9))* 2007. 496p. 144.00 *(978-0-12-004537-2(0))* 2006. (Illus.). 488p. 144.00 *(978-0-12-004536-5(2))* Vol. 42. 2010. 352p. 144.00 *(978-0-12-380894-3(4))* Elsevier Science & Technology Bks. (Academic Pr.).

Brookfield, Michael. Dinosaur Sex. 2009. (ENG.). 68p. pap. *(978-1-85756-673-4(4))* Janus Publishing Co.

Brown, Augustus. Why Pandas Do Handstands: And Other Curious Truths about Animals. 2010. (ENG.). 320p. pap. 19.99 *(978-1-4516-2427-4(1)*, Free Pr.) Free Pr.

Buccafusco, Jerry J., ed. Methods of Behavioral Analysis in Neuroscience. 2nd rev. ed. 2008. (Frontiers in Neuroscience Ser.). (ENG., Illus.). 360p. 157.95 *(978-1-4200-5234-3(9)*, CRC Press) Taylor & Francis Group GBR. Dist: Taylor & Francis Group.

Burghardt, Gordon M. The Genesis of Animal Play: Testing the Limits. 2006. (ENG., Illus.). 518p. (gr. 17). per. 32.00 *(978-0-262-52469-8(4))* MIT Pr.

Burroughs, John. Squirrels & Other Fur-Bearers. 2009. 190p. 26.99 *(978-1-110-60737-2(7))*; pap. 21.75 *(978-1-110-60735-8(0))* BiblioBazaar.

—Squirrels & Other Fur-Bearers. 2008. (ENG., Illus.). 112p. per. *(978-1-4065-9246-7(3))* Dodo Pr.

—Squirrels & Other Fur-Bearers. 2007. (ENG.). 188p. 37.95 *(978-0-548-09950-6(2))* Kessinger Publishing, LLC.

—Squirrels & Other Fur-Bearers. 2009. (ENG.). 86p. pap. 8.45 *(978-1-4385-2365-1(3)*, Book Jungle) Standard Pubns., Inc.

Burton, Robert. The Mating Game. (Illus.). 160p. *(978-0-517-52632-3(8))* Crown Publishing Group.

Campbell, Christina J. Spider Monkeys: Behavior, Ecology & Evolution of the Genus Ateles. Campbell, Christine, ed. 2008. (Cambridge Studies in Biological & Evolutionary Anthropology Ser.). (ENG., Illus.). 352p. 139.00 *(978-0-521-86750-4(9))* Cambridge Univ. Pr.

Candolin, Ulrika & Wong, Bob B. M. Behavioural Responses to a Changing World: Mechanisms & Consequences. 2012. (ENG., Illus.). 304p. 130.00 ***(978-0-19-960256-8(5))*** Oxford Univ. Pr., Inc.

Candolin, Ulrika & Wong, Bob B. M., eds. Behavioural Responses to a Changing World: Mechanisms & Consequences. 2012. (ENG., Illus.). 304p. pap. 64.99 ***(978-0-19-960257-5(3))*** Oxford Univ. Pr., Inc.

Carlson, Dan. Trophy Bucks in Any Weather: How to Use Weather to Predict Deer Behavior. 2008. (ENG., Illus.). 272p. pap. 21.99 *(978-0-89689-610-9(2)*, Krause Pubns.

Carolina Biological Staff, compiled by. Behaving Like Animals. 2009. (Inquiries in Science Biology Ser.). *(978-1-4350-0372-9(1))*; tchr. ed., spiral bd. *(978-1-4350-0371-2(3))* Carolina Biological Supply Co.

Casale, Paolo. El Comportamiento de los Animales: Instinto, Aprendizaje, Cooperación. (Coleccion Bravo). (SPA., Illus.). 76p. *(978-84-7131-905-0(5)*, EDI30262) Editex, Editorial S.A. ESP. Dist: Lectorum Pubns., Inc.

Chadwick, W. S. Giants of the Forest: African Hunting Adventures. 2011. 370p. 53.95 ***(978-1-258-06914-8(8))*** Literary Licensing, LLC.

Childs, Jack L. & Childs, Anna Mary. Ambushed on the Jaguar Trail: Hidden Cameras on the Mexican Border. 2008. 96p. pap. 14.95 *(978-1-933855-09-7(6))* Rio Nuevo Pubs.

Cloudsley-Thompson, John L. Ecology & Behaviour of Mesozoic Reptiles. 2010. (ENG., Illus.). xii, 219p. pap. 249.00 *(978-3-642-06124-0(9)*, 3642061249) Springer.

Coombs, Sheryl & New, John G., eds. Multimodal Sensory Guidance of Complex Behaviors: 6th International Congress of Neuroethology Bonn, July 29-August 3, 2001. (Brain, Behavior & Evolution Ser.: Vol. 59, No. 4). (Illus.). 76p *(978-3-8055-7466-2(5))* Karger, S. AG.

Coren, Stanley. Why Does My Dog Act That Way? A Complete Guide to Your Dog's Personality. 2007. (ENG.). 304p. pap. 19.99 *(978-0-7432-7707-5(4)*, Free Pr.) Free Pr.

Cram101 Textbook Reviews. Outlines & Highlights for Advances in the Study of Behavior: 9780123744746. 2011. 76p. pap. 27.95 ***(978-1-61461-706-8(6))*** Cram101 Inc.

—Outlines & Highlights for Advances in the Study of Behavior by H Brockmann, Isbn: 9780120045372 9780120045389. 2011. 84p. pap. 27.95 ***(978-1-61461-886-7(0))*** Cram101 Inc.

—Outlines & Highlights for an Introduction to Behavioural Ecology by J R Krebs, N B Davies, Isbn: 9780632035465 0632035463. 2011. 360p. pap. 34.95 ***(978-1-61812-630-6(X))*** Cram101 Inc.

—Outlines & Highlights for Perspectives on Animal Behavior by Judith Goodenough. 2011. 192p. pap. 30.95 ***(978-1-61905-766-1(2))*** Cram101 Inc.

—Outlines & Highlights for Principles of Animal Behavior: (Second Edition) by Lee Alan Dugatkin. 2011. 310p. pap. 32.95 ***(978-1-61905-697-8(6))*** Cram101 Inc.

Cram101 Textbook Reviews & Cram101 Textbook Reviews. Outlines & Highlights for Advances in the Study of Behavior: 9780123808929. 2011. 56p. pap. 26.95 ***(978-1-61461-916-1(6))*** Cram101 Inc.

Cram101 Textbook Reviews Staff. Outlines & Highlights for Principles of Animal Behavior by Lee Alan Dugatkin, Isbn: 9780393931693. 2009. 82p. pap. 27.95 *(978-1-4288-8440-3(8))* Cram101 Inc.

Crump, Marty. Headless Males Make Great Lovers: And Other Unusual Natural Histories. 2007. (ENG., Illus.). 216p. per. 14.00 *(978-0-226-12202-1(6))* Univ. of Chicago Pr.

—Sexy Orchids Make Lousy Lovers: & Other Unusual Relationships. 2009. (ENG., Illus.). 232p. 25.00 *(978-0-226-12185-7(2))* Univ. of Chicago Pr.

Dagg, Anne Innis. Animal Friendships. 2011. (ENG., Illus.). 246p. 120.00 *(978-1-107-00542-6(6))*; pap. 49.00 ***(978-0-521-18315-4(4))*** Cambridge Univ. Pr.

Danchin, Etienne, et al, eds. Behavioural Ecology: An Evolutionary Perspective on Behaviour. 2008. (ENG., Illus.). 668p. (C). pap. 79.95 *(978-0-19-920629-2(5))* Oxford Univ. Pr., Inc.

Das, Gokul & M.C. Yadav. Bull-Biostimulation in Postpartum Buffaloes. 2011. 116p. pap. ***(978-3-8443-0765-8(6))*** Lambert Academic Publishing.

Dawkins, Marian Stamp. Observing Animal Behaviour: Design & Analysis of Quantitive Controls. 2007. (ENG., Illus.). 176p. 150.00 *(978-0-19-856935-0(1))* Oxford Univ. Pr., Inc.

De Waal, Frans B. M. Our Inner Ape: A Leading Primatologist Explains Why We Are Who We Are. 2006. (ENG., Illus.). 304p. (gr. 12-18). 16.00 *(978-1-59448-196-3(2)*, Riverhead Trade (Paperbacks)) Penguin Group (USA) Inc.

—Primates & Philosophers: How Morality Evolved. Macedo, Stephen & Ober, Josiah, eds. 2009. (Princeton Science Library). (ENG., Illus.). 232p. pap. 15.95 *(978-0-691-14129-9(0))* Princeton Univ. Pr.

Delgado, Magali & Pignon, Frederic. Gallop to Freedom: Training Horses with Our Six Golden Principles. 2009. (ENG.). 160p. 29.95 *(978-1-57076-420-2(4))* Trafalgar Square Bks.

Delmont, Joseph. Catching Wild Beasts Alive. 2008. 252p. pap. 14.95 *(978-1-930585-47-8(0))* Coachwhip Pubns.

Denton, Derek. The Primordial Emotions: The Dawning of Consciousness. 2006. (ENG., Illus.). 296p. (C). 69.95 *(978-0-19-920314-7(8))* Oxford Univ. Pr., Inc.

Dixon, Royal. The Human Side of Animals. 2008. 208p. 24.99 *(978-0-554-36879-5(X))* 2008. 208p. 27.99 *(978-0-554-27576-5(7))* 2007.

(ENG.). 184p. pap. 19.99 (978-1-4346-3518-1(X)) 2007. (ENG.). 204p. pap. 22.99 (978-1-4346-3519-8(8)) BiblioBazaar.

—The Human Side of Animals. 2009. (Illus.). 186p. pap. (978-1-4099-7659-2(9)) Dodo Pr.

—The Human Side of Animals. 2007. (ENG.). 112p. per. (978-1-4068-6154-9(5)) Echo Library.

—The Human Side of Animals. 2007. (ENG.). 156p. 95.99 (978-1-4280-7708-9(1)); per. 89.99 (978-1-4280-7674-7(3)) IndyPublish.com.

—The Human Side of Animals. 2007. (ENG.). 306p. 43.95 (978-0-548-01394-6(2)) Kessinger Publishing, LLC.

Dixson, Alan F. Primate Sexuality: Comparative Studies of the Prosimians, Monkeys, Apes, & Humans. 2nd ed. 2012. (ENG., Illus.). 800p. 135.00 (978-0-19-954464-6(6)) Oxford Univ. Pr., Inc.

Dorling Kindersley Publishing Staff & Uhlenbroek, Charlotte. Animal Life: Secrets of the Animal World Revealed. 2011. (ENG.). 512p. 27.95 (978-0-7566-7221-8(X)) Dorling Kindersley Publishing, Inc.

Drickamer, Lee & Dewsbury, Donald. Leaders in Animal Behaviour: The Second Generation. 2009. (ENG., Illus.). 632p. (C). 126.00 (978-0-521-51758-4(3)); pap. 50.99 (978-0-521-74129-3(7)) Cambridge Univ. Pr.

Drickamer, Lee C., et al. Animal Behavior. 5th ed. 2007. pap. 11.95 (978-1-4288-1936-8(3)) Cram101 Inc.

Dudzinski, Kathleen M. & Frohoff, Toni. Dolphin Mysteries: Unlocking the Secrets of Communication. 2010. (ENG., Illus.). 256p. pap. 20.00 (978-0-300-12114-8(8)) Yale Univ. Pr.

Duff, Beth. When the Red Horse Spoke: Bringing learning with horses from dream to Reality. 2009. 260p. pap. 21.49 (978-1-4389-8654-8(8)) AuthorHouse.

Dugatkin, Lee Alan. Principles of Animal Behavior. 2nd ed. (ENG., Illus.). 642p. (C). 2009. pap. 69.00 net. (978-0-393-93441-0(1), 93441) 2008. 89.00 net. (978-0-393-93169-3(2), 93169) Norton, W. W. & Co., Inc.

Dukas, Reuven & Ratcliffe, John M., eds. Cognitive Ecology II. 2009. (ENG., Illus.). 384p. 100.00 (978-0-226-16935-4(9)); pap. 40.00 (978-0-226-16936-1(7)) Univ. of Chicago Pr.

Durrell, Gerald. Menagerie Manor. 180p. 29.75 (978-0-8446-7314-1(5)) Smith, Peter Pub., Inc.

—Menagerie Manor. 2007. (ENG., Illus.). 192p. (gr. 12-18). 14.00 (978-0-14-303853-5(2), Penguin (Non-Classics)) Penguin Group (USA) Inc.

Einstein, Gillian, ed. Sex & the Brain. 2007. (ENG., Illus.). 856p. (gr. 17). 65.00 (978-0-262-05087-6(0)) MIT Pr.

Ellis, Shaun & Junor, Penny. The Man Who Lives with Wolves. 2010. (ENG.). 288p. pap. 15.00 (978-0-307-46470-5(9), Three Rivers Pr.) Crown Publishing Group.

Ellison, Peter T. & Gray, Peter B., eds. Endocrinology of Social Relationships. 2009. (Illus.). 512p. 54.50 (978-0-674-03117-3(2)) Harvard Univ. Pr.

Ellison, Peter T., et al. Endocrinology of Social Relationships. 2012. (ENG., Illus.). 512p. pap. 22.95 (978-0-674-06399-0(6)) Harvard Univ. Pr.

Engel, Cindy. Wild Health: How Animals Keep Themselves Well & What We Can Learn from Them. 2006. (Illus.). 305p. reprint ed. pap. 22.00 (978-1-4223-5769-9(4)) DIANE Publishing Co.

Estrada, Alejandro. Comportamiento Animal. (Ciencia para Todos Ser.). (SPA.). pap. 6.99 (978-968-16-3041-6(6)) Fondo de Cultura Economica USA.

Evans, Linda. Animal Behaviour in Egyptian Art: Representations of the Natural World in Memphite Tomb Scenes. 2010. (ACE Studies). (ENG., Illus.). 350p. (C). pap. 130.00 (978-0-85668-826-3(6)) Australian Ctr. for Egyptology AUS. Dist: Brown, David Bk. Co., The.

Fernandez, Eduardo. Stereotypies & Foraging. 2010. 164p. pap. (978-3-639-25209-5(8)) VDM Verlag Dr. Mueller e.K.

Fitzmaurice, Sue. Small Animal Neurology. 2010. (ENG., Illus.). 352p. pap. 89.95 (978-0-7020-2911-0(4), Saunders) Elsevier - Health Sciences Div.

Francis Channing Woodworth. Stories about Animals: With Pictures to Match. l.t. ed. 2007. 164p. pap. 21.99 (978-1-4264-9820-6(9)) BiblioBazaar.

Fraser, Andrew Ferguson. The Behaviour & Welfare of the Horse. 2nd ed. 2010. 270p. 145.00 (978-1-84593-629-7(9)); (Illus.). pap. 70.00 (978-1-84593-628-0(0)) CABI GBR. Dist: Stylus Publishing, LLC.

Fullick, Ann. Understanding Health & Behavior. 2008. (Why Science Matters Ser.). (ENG., Illus.). 56p. 33.50 (978-1-4329-1840-8(0)); pap. 9.49 (978-1-4329-1853-8(2)) Heinemann-Raintree. (NA-h).

George, J. Romanes. Animal Intelligence. 2008. 540p. (978-1-4437-2215-5(4), Hesperides Pr.) Read Bks.

Ghuman, Sartaj, et al. A Study of Vigilance Behaviour of Chital. 2010. 80p. pap. (978-3-8383-5803-1(1)) Lambert Academic Publishing.

Gingerich, Ryan & Hendrickson, Ami. Beyond a Whisper: Training Horses with a New Language from the Behaviorist. 2010. (ENG.). 176p. 29.95 (978-1-57076-429-5(8)) Trafalgar Square Bks.

Goodenough, Judith, et al. Perspectives on Animal Behavior. 2nd ed. 2007. pap. 11.95 (978-1-4288-1937-5(1)) Cram101 Inc.

—Perspectives on Animal Behavior. 3rd ed. 2009. (ENG., Illus.). 544p. (C). 161.95 (978-0-470-04517-6(5), Wiley) Wiley, John & Sons, Inc.

Goodwin, Stephen F. & F. Goodwin, Stephen. Genetic Dissection of Neural Circuits & Behavior. 2009. (ENG., Illus.). 216p. 161.00 (978-0-12-374836-2(4), Academic Pr.) Elsevier Science & Technology Bks.

Gordon, I J & Prins, H. H. T., eds. The Ecology of Browsing & Grazing. 2007. (Ecological Studies). (Illus.). 328p. 189.00 (978-3-540-72421-6(4)) Springer.

Gordon, Iain J. & Prins, Herbert H. T. The Ecology of Browsing & Grazing. 2010. (Ecological Studies). (Illus.). xvi, 330p. pap. 189.00 (978-3-642-09148-3(2), 3642091482) Springer.

Gould, Todd D., ed. Mood & Anxiety Related Phenotypes in Mice: Characterization Using Behavioral Tests, 2 vols. 2009. (Neuromethods Ser.). (ENG., Illus.). xii, 330p. 149.00 (978-1-60761-302-2(6), 1607613026) Humana Pr.

Grandin, Temple & Johnson, Catherine. Animals in Translation: Using the Mysteries of Autism to Decode Animal Behavior. 2010. (ENG.). 368p. 28.00 (978-1-4391-8710-4(X), Scribner) Scribner.

—Animals Make Us Human: Creating the Best Life for Animals. (ENG.). 2010. 360p. pap. 15.95 (978-0-547-24823-3(7), Mariner Bks.) 2009. 352p. 26.00 (978-0-15-101489-7(2)) Houghton Mifflin Harcourt Trade & Reference Pubs.

Gromov, Vladimir. Parental Care, Tactile Stimulation, & Sociality Evolution in Rodents. 2011. 112p. pap. (978-3-8443-8250-1(X)) Lambert Academic Publishing.

Groos, Karl. The Play of Animals. 2009. 226p. pap. (978-0-217-10411-1(8)) Books LLC.

Hailman, Jack P. & Strier, Karen B. Planning, Proposing, & Presenting Science Effectively: A Guide for Graduate Students & Researchers in the Behavioral Sciences & Biology. 2nd rev. ed. 2006. (ENG., Illus.). 248p. per. 46.00 (978-0-521-53388-1(0)) Cambridge Univ. Pr.

Hamilton, Allan J. Zen Mind, Zen Horse: The Science & Spirituality of Working with Horses. 2011. (ENG., Illus.). 320p. pap. 24.95 (978-1-60342-565-0(9), 1603425659) Storey Publishing, LLC.

Hamlen, Peggy. Foxy & Her Forest Friends. 2011. 32p. pap. 14.39 (978-1-4567-0109-3(6)) AuthorHouse.

Harada, Sumio, photos by. Mountain Goats of Glacier National Park. 2008. (Illus.). 80p. per. 9.95 (978-1-56037-472-5(1)) Farcountry Pr.

Harman, Oren. The Price of Altruism: George Price & the Search for the Origins of Kindness. 2011. (ENG., Illus.). 451p. pap. 18.95 (978-0-393-33999-4(8), 33999) Norton, W. W. & Co., Inc.

Harris, Gabrielle. Touching Animal Souls - Developing Awareness Through the Animal World. 2011. 274p. pap. (978-0-9869858-3-6(X)) Kima Global Pubs.

Hatkoff, Amy. The Inner World of Farm Animals: Their Amazing Social, Emotional, & Intellectual Capacities. 2009. (ENG., Illus.). 168p. 19.95 (978-1-58479-748-7(7)) Stewart, Tabori & Chang.

Hausberger, M., et al, eds. Horse behaviour & Welfare. 2007. (Eaap Ser.). 152p. 74.00 (978-90-8686-033-3(8)) Wageningen Academic Publishers NLD. Dist: Enfield Publishing & Distribution Co., Inc.

Heinrich, Bernd. Life Everlasting: The Animal Way of Death. 2012. (ENG., Illus.). 256p. 25.00 (978-0-547-75266-2(0)) Houghton Mifflin Harcourt Trade & Reference Pubs.

Hempfling, Klaus Ferdinand. It's Not I Who Seek the Horse, the Horse Seeks Me: My Path to an Understanding of Equine Body Language. 2010. (ENG.). 344p. 49.95 (978-3-86127-975-4(4)) Cadmos Verlag GmbH DEU. Dist: Independent Pubs. Group.

Henderson, Junius. Ethnozoology of the Tewa Indians. 2008. 92p. pap. 18.75 (978-0-559-25337-9(0)) BiblioBazaar.

—Ethnozoology of the Tewa Indians. 2010. 74p. pap. (978-1-152-90196-4(6)); pap. (978-1-152-90194-0(X)) Books LLC.

—Ethnozoology of the Tewa Indians. 2008. (ENG.). 88p. per. (978-1-4086-6306-6(6)) Read Bks.

Henderson, Junius & Harrington, John Peabody. Ethnozoology of the Tewa Indians. 2009. 90p. pap. 18.75 (978-1-116-93981-1(9)); pap. 18.75 (978-1-116-93980-4(0)) BiblioBazaar.

—Ethnozoology of the Tewa Indians. 2007. (ENG.). 88p. per. 18.95 (978-0-548-61883-7(6)) Kessinger Publishing, LLC.

Henry, Thomas R. The Strangest Things in the World. 2007. (ENG.). 212p. 39.95 (978-0-548-08418-2(1)) Kessinger Publishing, LLC.

Henty, G. A. Those Other Animals. 2007. (ENG.). 228p. per. 26.95 (978-0-548-48600-9(X)) Kessinger Publishing, LLC.

Hess, Elizabeth. Nim Chimpsky: The Chimp Who Would Be Human. 2008. (ENG., Illus.). 384p. 15.00 (978-0-553-38277-8(2)) Random House Publishing Group.

Holland, Jennifer. Unlikely Friendships: 50 Remarkable Stories from the Animal Kingdom. 2011. (ENG., Illus.). 160p. pap. 13.95 (978-0-7611-5913-1(4), 0761159134) Workman Publishing Co., Inc.

Holland, Jennifer S. Unlikely Friendships: 47 Remarkable Stories from the Animal Kingdom. 2011. lib. bdg. 25.70 (978-0-606-23503-7(5), Turtleback) Turtleback Bks.

Holmes, Martha, et al. Life: Extraordinary Animals, Extreme Behaviour. 2010. 312p. 39.95 (978-0-520-26537-0(8)) Univ. of California Pr.

Hornaday, William T. The Minds & Manners of Wild Animals. 2008. 284p. 25.99 (978-0-554-31243-9(3)); 28.99 (978-0-554-21940-0(9)) BiblioBazaar.

—The Minds & Manners of Wild Animals: A Book of Personal Observations. 2006. (ENG.). 294p. pap. 21.99 (978-1-4264-1293-6(2)); 280p. pap. 23.99 (978-1-4264-1298-1(3)) BiblioBazaar.

Hosey, Geoff, et al. Zoo Animals: Behaviour, Management & Welfare. 2009. (ENG., Illus.). 480p. 55.00 (978-0-19-923306-9(3)) Oxford Univ. Pr., Inc.

Houpt, Katherine A. Domestic Animal Behavior for Veterinarians & Animal Scientists. 5th ed. 2010. (ENG., Illus.). 416p. 84.99 (978-0-8138-1676-0(9), Wiley-Blackwell) Wiley, John & Sons, Inc.

Hudson, W. H. A Hind in Richmond Park. reprint ed. 64.50 (978-0-404-03413-9(6)) AMS Pr., Inc.

—A Hind in Richmond Park. 2008. 224p. pap. (978-1-4099-0532-5(2)) Dodo Pr.

—A Hind in Richmond Park. 2008. 354p. 46.95 (978-1-4366-5383-1(5)); 356p. pap. 31.95 (978-0-548-85639-0(7)) Kessinger Publishing, LLC.

—A Hind in Richmond Park. 2008. 352p. pap. (978-1-4097-0447-8(5)) Read Bks.

—The Naturalist in la Plata. reprint ed. 64.50 (978-0-404-03393-4(8)) AMS Pr., Inc.

—The Naturalist in la Plata. 2007. (ENG., Illus.). 260p. per. (978-1-4065-6020-6(0)) Dodo Pr.

Ingersoll, Ernest. Wild Life of Orchard & Field. 2007. (ENG.). 406p. 49.95 (978-0-548-02672-4(6)) Kessinger Publishing, LLC.

—Wild Life of Orchard & Field. 2008. (ENG.). 408p. per. (978-1-4086-4109-5(7)) Read Bks.

Inoue-Murayama, Miho, et al, eds. From Genes to Animal Behavior: Social Structures, Personalities, Communication by Color. 2011. (Primatology Monographs). (ENG., Illus.). 290p. 189.00 (978-4-431-53891-2(7), 4431538917) Springer.

Johnson, Jinny. Animal Tracks & Signs: Track over 400 Animals from Big Cats to Garden Birds. 2011. (ENG.). 192p. 12.99 (978-0-7858-2867-9(2), 0785828672, Chartwell) Book Sales, Inc.

Judean W. Etheredge, W. Etheredge & Judean W. Etheredge. Dr Judittle. 2009. 92p. pap. 11.95 (978-1-4401-8416-1(X)) iUniverse, Inc.

Kaiser, Stephan, et al, eds. Creating Balance?! International Perspectives on the Work-Life Integration of Professionals. 2011. (ENG.). vi, 330p. 139.00 (978-3-642-16198-8(7), 3642161987) Springer.

Kalueff, Allan, et al, eds. Neurobiology of Grooming Behaviour. 2010. (ENG., Illus.). 298p. 110.00 (978-0-521-11638-1(4)) Cambridge Univ. Pr.

Kalueff, Allan V. & LaPorte, Justin L. Behavioral Models in Stress Research. 2008. (Illus.). (C). 89.00 (978-1-60456-361-0(3)) Nova Science Pubs., Inc.

Kalueff, Allan V. & Porte, Justin L., eds. Experimental Animal Models in Neurobehavioral Research. 2008. 79.00 (978-1-60692-022-0(7)) Nova Science Pubs., Inc.

Kanwal, Jagmeet & Shanor, Karen. Bats Sing, Mice Giggle: The Surprising Sciences of Animals' Inner Lives. 2011. 304p. pap. (978-1-84831-223-4(7)) Icon Bks., Ltd.

Kaplan, Eugene H. Sensuous Seas: Tales of a Marine Biologist. 2006. (ENG., Illus.). 288p. (C). 29.95 (978-0-691-12560-2(0)) Princeton Univ. Pr.

Kinsey, Mike & Denison, Jennifer. Backcountry Basics: Your Guide to Solving Problems on the Trail. 2009. (ENG.). 216p. pap. 23.95 (978-0-911647-84-6(8)) Western Horseman.

Kirby, William. On the Power, Wisdom & Goodness of God as Manifested in the Creation of Animals & in their History, Habits & Instincts. 2009. (Cambridge Library Collection - Religion Ser.). (ENG.). 536p. pap. 39.99 (978-1-108-00074-1(6)); 576p. pap. 39.99 (978-1-108-00075-8(4)) Cambridge Univ. Pr.

Knottnerus, J. David. Ritual as a Missing Link: Sociology, Structural Ritualization Theory, & Research. 2010. (Sociological Imagination Ser.). 208p. 108.00 (978-1-59451-855-3(6)) Paradigm Pubs.

Krebs, John R., et al. An Introduction to Behavioural Ecology. 4th ed. 2012. (ENG., Illus.). 520p. 149.95 (978-1-4443-3949-9(4), Wiley-Blackwell) Wiley, John & Sons, Inc.

Krutch, Joseph Wood. The Great Chain of Life. 2009. (Sightline Bks.). (ENG., Illus.). 246p. pap. 19.95 (978-1-58729-820-2(1)) Univ. of Iowa Pr.

Kunz, Thomas H. & Parsons, Stuart, eds. Ecological & Behavioral Methods for the Study of Bats. 2nd ed. 2009. (ENG., Illus.). 920p. (gr. 17). 105.00 (978-0-8018-9147-2(7)) Johns Hopkins Univ. Pr.

Laland, Kevin N. & Galef, Bennett G., eds. The Question of Animal Culture. 2009. (Illus.). 360p. 54.50 (978-0-674-03126-5(1)) Harvard Univ. Pr.

Lamoureux, Victor S., ed. Animal Behavior: An Evolutionary Approach. 2011. (ENG.). 320p. 99.95 (978-1-926692-78-4(0)) Apple Academic Pr., Inc. CAN. Dist: Taylor & Francis Group.

Lazareva, Olga F., et al. How Animals See the World: Comparative Behavior, Biology, & Evolution of Vision, 1 vol. 2012. (ENG., Illus.). 560p. 135.00 (978-0-19-533465-4(5)) Oxford Univ. Pr., Inc.

Leavell, Bonita. Studies on the Conditioned Enhancement of Acoustic Startle & Fear. 2009. 116p. pap. (978-3-639-12126-1(0)) VDM Verlag Dr. Mueller e.K.

Lei, Runhua & Engberg, Shannon. Nocturnal Lemur Diversity at Masoala National Park, 53. Baker, R. J. & Bradley, Lisa, eds. 2008. (Special Publications: 53). (Illus.). 44p. pap. (978-1-929330-15-7(4)) Museum of Texas Tech Univ.

Leighton, Gerald R. The Life-History of British Serpents & Their Local Distribution in the British Isles. 2009. 400p. pap. 31.45 (978-1-4446-3091-6(1)) Harrison House Pubs.

Lembke, Janet. Because the Cat Purrs: How We Relate to Other Species & Why It Matters. 2008. (ENG., Illus.). 240p. 22.95 (978-1-60239-235-9(8)) Skyhorse Publishing Co., Inc.

Lerch-Henning, Sara, et al. The Role of Acoustic Communication in African Lions: Which Are the Acoustic Features That Characterize Lion Roars? 2011. 76p. pap. (978-3-639-28477-5(1)) VDM Verlag Dr. Mueller e.K.

LernerClassroom Editors. Animal Traits. 2009. pap., tchr. ed. 7.95 (978-0-8225-1746-7(9)) Lerner Publishing Group.

Lincoln, Micheal J. Animals Their Psycho-Symbolic Meaning. 2007. (ENG.). spiral bd. 79.00 (978-0-9772069-5-7(5)) Talking Hearts.

Lombardi, Linda. Animals Behaving Badly: Boozing Bees, Cheating Chimps, Dogs with Guns, & Other Beastly True Tales. 2011. (ENG., Illus.). 224p. (gr. 12). 13.95 (978-0-399-53697-7(3), Perigee Trade) Penguin Group (USA) Inc.

Long, William J. How Animals Talk. 2009. (ENG., Illus.). 208p. pap. 10.95 (978-0-486-46880-8(1)) Dover Pubns., Inc.

—Wood Folk at School. 2007. (ENG.). 216p. 39.95 (978-0-548-02990-9(3)) Kessinger Publishing, LLC.

Long, William Joseph. Wilderness Ways. 2008. 116p. 24.99 (978-0-554-26213-0(4)) 2008. 116p. 21.99 (978-0-554-35516-0(7)) 2007. (ENG.). 106p. pap. 18.99 (978-1-4346-0720-1(8)) 2007. (ENG.). 114p. pap. 19.99 (978-1-4346-0722-5(4)) BiblioBazaar.

—Wilderness Ways. 2007. (ENG.). 120p. per. (978-1-4065-6675-8(6)) Dodo Pr.

Lonsdorf, Elizabeth V., et al, eds. The Mind of the Chimpanzee: Ecological & Experimental Perspectives. 2010. (ENG., Illus.). 464p. 125.00 (978-0-226-49278-0(8)); pap. 49.00 (978-0-226-49279-7(6)) Univ. of Chicago Pr.

Lorenz, K. The Foundations of Ethology. Lorenz, K. & Kickert, R. W., trs. 2010. (ENG.). 404p. pap. 59.95 (978-3-211-99936-3(1), 3211999361) Springer.

Lu, Cheng-Kuan & Young, Darrin J. Wireless Mems Accelerometer for Small Laboratory Animal Activity Monitoring. 2008. 68p. pap. (978-3-8364-7595-2(2)) VDM Verlag Dr. Mueller e.K.

Magnan, Pierre, et al, eds. Ecology, Behaviour & Conservation of the Charrs, Genus Salvelinus. 2010. (Developments in Environmental Biology of Fishes Ser.). (Illus.). 360p. pap. 219.00 (978-90-481-6088-4(X), 904816088X) Springer.

Malashichev, Yegor B. & Deckel, A. Wallace. Behavioral & Morphological Asymmetries in Vertebrates. 2006. 139.00 (978-1-58706-105-9(8)) Landes Bioscience.

Manning, Aubrey & Stamp Dawkins, Marian. An Introduction to Animal Behaviour. 6th rev. ed. 2012. (ENG., Illus.). 472p. (C). 120.00 (978-1-107-00016-2(5)); pap. 55.00 (978-0-521-16514-3(8)) Cambridge Univ. Pr.

Marks, Kelly. Teach Your Horse Perfect Manners: How You Should Behave So Your Horse Does Too. 2010. (ENG.). 192p. pap. 29.95 (978-1-57076-457-8(3)) Trafalgar Square Bks.

Marlitt, Wendy. How Horses Feel & Think: Understanding behaviour, emotions & Intelligence. 2011. (ENG.). 128p. pap. 29.95 (978-0-85788-000-0(4)) Cadmos Verlag GmbH DEU. Dist: Independent Pubs. Group.

Martinelli, Dario. Of Birds, Whales, & Other Musicians: An Introduction to Zoomusicology. 2009. (University of Scranton Press - Approaches to Postmodernity Ser.). (ENG., Illus.). 100p. 30.00 (978-1-58966-187-5(7)) Univ. of Scranton Pr.

Marty, Sid. The Black Grizzly of Whiskey Creek. 2008. (ENG.). 296p. pap. 19.95 (978-0-7710-5698-7(2), Emblem Edns) McClelland & Stewart CAN. Dist: Random Hse., Inc.

Mason, G. & Rushen, J., eds. Stereotypic Animal Behaviour: Fundamentals & Applications to Welfare. 2nd ed. 2008. (Illus.). 384p. pap. 75.00 (978-1-84593-465-1(2)) CABI GBR. Dist: Stylus Publishing, LLC.

Mason, Georgia & Rushen, Jeffrey, eds. Stereotypic Animal Behaviour: Fundamentals & Applications to Welfare. 2nd ed. 2006. (Illus.). 384p. 145.00 (978-0-85199-004-0(5)) CABI GBR. Dist: Stylus Publishing, LLC.

Matignon, Katrine. Emotional Life of Animals. 2006. 176p. 12.98 (978-1-56852-581-5(8), Konecky & Konecky) Konecky, William S. Assocs., Inc.

Mayer, Charles. Jungle Beasts I Have Captured. 2007. (ENG.). 314p. 45.95 (978-0-548-02950-3(4)) Kessinger Publishing, LLC.

—Trapping Wild Animals in Malay Jungles. 2009. 100p. pap. (978-0-217-30116-9(9)) Books LLC.

Mazet, Ruth. My Horse Rears. 2012. (ENG., Illus.). 160p. pap. 34.95 (978-0-85131-990-2(4), Allen, J. A. & Company, Limited) Hale, Robert Ltd. GBR. Dist: Independent Pubs. Group.

McDougall, Len. Tracking & Reading Sign: A Guide to Mastering the Original Forensic Science. 2010. (ENG., Illus.). 192p. pap. 18.95 (978-1-61608-006-8(X), 608006) Skyhorse Publishing Co., Inc.

McFarland, David. Guilty Robots, Happy Dogs: The Question of Alien Minds. 2009. (ENG.). 256p. pap. 15.95 (978-0-19-921930-8(3)) Oxford Univ. Pr., Inc.

McGregor, Peter K., ed. Playback & Studies of Animal Communication. 2010. (Nato Science Series: A: Ser.). 248p. pap. 279.00 (978-1-4419-3224-2(0), 1441932240) Springer.

Mikesell, Robert & Baker, MeeCee. Animal Science Biology & Technology. 3rd ed. 2010. (ENG.). 64p. (C). pap., lab manual ed. 70.95 (978-1-4354-8639-3(0)) Delmar Cengage Learning.

—Animal Science Biology & Technology. 3rd ed. 2010. (Texas Science Ser.). (ENG., Illus.). 464p. (C). 93.95 (978-1-4354-8637-9(4)) Delmar Cengage Learning.

Miller, Peter. The Smart Swarm: How to Work Efficiently, Communicate Effectively, & Make Better Decisions Using the Secrets of Flocks, Schools, & Colonies. 2011. (ENG.). 304p. (gr. 12). 16.00 (978-1-58333-428-7(9), Avery) Penguin Group (USA) Inc.

—The Smart Swarm: How Understanding Flocks, Schools, & Colonies Can Make Us Better at Communicating, Decision Making, & Getting Things Done. 2010. (ENG.). 304p. (gr. 12). 26.00 (978-1-58333-390-7(8), Avery) Penguin Group (USA) Inc.

Mills, Daniel S. The Encyclopedia of Applied Animal Behaviour & Welfare. 2010. (Illus.). 750p. 370.00 (978-0-85199-724-7(4)) CABI GBR. Dist: Stylus Publishing, LLC.

Mills, Enos A. Watched by Wild Animals. 2007. (ENG.). 276p. 42.95 (978-0-548-08618-6(4)) Kessinger Publishing, LLC.

Moesta, Alexandra. Behaviour of Laying Hens in Aviaries - Special Aspects: Social Structure in Large Groups & Effects of Litter Quality on Dustbathing Behaviour. 2008. 172p. pap. (978-3-639-03839-2(8)) VDM Verlag Dr. Mueller e.K.

Moore, Janice & Breed, Michael D. Animal Behavior. 2011. (ENG., Illus.). 496p. (C). pap. 79.95 (978-0-12-372581-3(X), Academic Pr.) Elsevier Science & Technology Bks.

Morgan, C. Lloyd. Habit & Instinct. 2007. (ENG.). 364p. 46.95 *(978-0-548-05838-8(1))* Kessinger Publishing, LLC.

Moss, Cynthia J., et al, eds. The Amboseli Elephants: A Long-Term Perspective on a Long-Lived Mammal. 2011. (ENG., Illus.). 400p. 65.00 *(978-0-226-54223-2(8))* Univ. of Chicago Pr.

Muller, Martin N. Sexual Coercion in Primates & Humans: An Evolutionary Perspective on Male Aggression Against Females. Wrangham, Richard, ed. 2009. (Illus.). 504p. 58.00 *(978-0-674-03324-5(8))* Harvard Univ. Pr.

Murdoch, Wendy. 50 5-Minute Fixes to Improve Your Riding: Simple Solutions for Better Position & Performance in No Time. 2010. (ENG., Illus.). 160p. 27.95 *(978-1-57076-455-4(7)*, 1310887) Trafalgar Square Bks.

Murray, Craig A., ed. Whales & Dolphins: Behavior, Biology & Distribution. 2010. (Animal Science, Issues & Professions Ser.). 59.00 *(978-1-61668-693-2(6))* Nova Science Pubs., Inc.

Musiani, Marco & Boitani, Luigi. World of Wolves: New Perspectives on Ecology, Behaviour, & Management. Korieh, Chima, ed. 2010. (Energy, Ecology & the Environment Ser.). (Illus.). 432p. pap. 34.95 *(978-1-55238-269-1(9))* Univ. of Calgary Pr. CAN. Dist: Michigan State Univ. Pr.

Naguib, Marc, et al, eds. Vocal Communication in Birds & Mammals. 2009. (ENG.). 350p. 144.00 *(978-0-12-374475-3(X)*, Academic Pr.) Elsevier Science & Technology Bks.

Naldi, Giovanni, et al, eds. Mathematical Modeling of Collective Behavior in Socio-Economic & Life Sciences. 2010. (Modeling & Simulation in Science, Engineering & Technology Ser.). (Illus.). x, 438p. 124.00 *(978-0-8176-4945-6(X)*, 081764945X) Birkhauser Verlag AG CHE. Dist: Springer.

National Geographic Society Staff & Farris, Melissa. Deadly Instinct. 2011. (ENG., Illus.). 192p. 30.00 *(978-1-4262-0725-9(5)*, National Geographic) National Geographic Society.

Nelson & Nelson, Randy Joe. An Introduction to Behavioral Endocrinology. 3rd ed. 3905. (Illus.). pap. *(978-0-87893-576-5(2))* Sinauer Assocs., Inc.

Neubauer, Raymond L. Evolution & the Emergent Self: The Rise of Complexity & Behavioral Versatility in Nature. 2011. (ENG., Illus.). 336p. (gr. 17). 32.50 ***(978-0-231-15070-5(9))*** Columbia Univ. Pr.

Nishida, Toshisada, et al. Chimpanzee Behavior in the Wild: An Audio-Visual Encyclopedia. 2010. (Illus.). 255p. 189.00 *(978-4-431-53894-3(1)*, 4431538941) Springer.

Nolfi, Stefano, et al, eds. From Animals to Animats 9: 9th International Conference on Simulation of Adaptive Behavior, SAB 2006Rome, Italy, September 25-29, 2006Proceedings. 2006. (Lecture Notes in Computer Science Ser.). (Illus.). XV, 869p. pap. 139.00 *(978-3-540-38608-7(4)*, 3540386084) Springer.

O'Heare, James. Empowerment Training: Training for Creativity, Persistence, Industriousness, Resilience & Behavioral Well-Being. 2011. 105p. pap. 23.95 ***(978-0-9738309-7-4(0))*** Dogwise Publishing.

Okrent, Mark. Rational Animals: The Teleological Roots of Intentionality. 2007. (Series in Continental Thought Ser.). 248p. 49.95 *(978-0-8214-1743-0(6))*; per. 26.95 *(978-0-8214-1744-7(4))* Ohio Univ. Pr.

Overall, Karen. Canine Geriatric Behavior: A Clinician's Guide. 2011. (Illus.). 320p. 79.99 *(978-0-8138-2046-0(4)*, Wiley-Blackwell) Wiley, John & Sons, Inc.

Pajor, Edmond A. & Marchant-Forde, Jeremy, eds. Scientific evaluation of behavior, welfare & Enrichment: Proceedings of the 45th congress of the ISAE. 2011. 214p. pap. 44.00 ***(978-90-8686-179-8(2))*** Wageningen Academic Publishers NLD. Dist: Enfield Publishing & Distribution Co., Inc.

Parker, Sue Taylor, et al, eds. The Mentalities of Gorillas & Orangutans: Comparative Perspectives. 2006. (ENG., Illus.). 432p. pap. 83.00 *(978-0-521-03193-6(1))* Cambridge Univ. Pr.

Peterson, Dale. The Moral Lives of Animals. 2011. (ENG., Illus.). 352p. 26.00 *(978-1-59691-424-7(6))* Bloomsbury Publishing.

Pickeral, Tamsin. The Horse Lover's Bible: The Complete Practical Guide to Horse Care & Management. 2009. (ENG., Illus.). 224p. 35.00 *(978-1-55407-391-7(X))* Firefly Bks., Ltd.

Pirk, Wendy. Weird Canadian Animals. 2009. (ENG., Illus.). 216p. pap. *(978-1-897278-52-9(7))* Blue Bike Bks. CAN. Dist: Lone Pine Publishing.

Pitt, Frances. Animal Mind. 2006. 388p. per. *(978-1-4067-9674-2(3)*, Hesperides Pr.) Read Bks.

Poiani, Aldo & Dixson, Alan. Animal Homosexuality: A Biosocial Perspective. 2010. (ENG., Illus.). 576p. 140.00 *(978-0-521-19675-8(2))*; pap. 68.00 *(978-0-521-14514-5(7))* Cambridge Univ. Pr.

Poulsen, Else. Smiling Bears: A Zookeeper Explores the Behaviour & Emotional Life of Bears, 1 vol. 2009. (ENG.). 272p. 25.95 *(978-1-55365-387-5(4)*, Greystone Bks.) D&M Pubs. Inc. CAN. Dist: Perseus-PGW.

Press, Ammonite, ed. Mates for Life: Devoted Couples from the Animal Kingdom. 2011. (ENG., Illus.). 96p. pap. 9.95 *(978-1-907708-02-2(2)*, Ammonite Pr.) AE Pubns. GBR. Dist: BookMasters Distribution Services (BDS).

Pycraft, W. P. The Courtship of Animals. 2007. (ENG.). 408p. 49.95 *(978-0-548-06844-1(5))* Kessinger Publishing, LLC.

Raber, Jacob, ed. Animal Models of Behavioral Analysis. 2010. (Neuromethods Ser.). (Illus.). xv, 354p. 139.00 *(978-1-60761-882-9(6)*, 1607618826) Humana Pr.

Raffaele, Paul. Among the Great Apes: Adventures on the Trail of Our Closest Relatives. 2011. (ENG.). 384p. pap. 15.99 *(978-0-06-167184-5(3)*, Harper Paperbacks) HarperCollins Pubs.

Ranquet, Joan. Communication with All Life. 2008. (Illus.). 160p. *(978-1-4019-1613-8(9)*, 512) Hay Hse. UK, Ltd. GBR. Dist: Grantham Bk. Services.

Rashid, Mark. Considering the Horse: Tales of Problems Solved & Lessons Learned. 2nd ed. 2010. (ENG., Illus.). 224p. (Orig.). 24.95 *(978-1-61608-156-0(2)*, 608156) Skyhorse Publishing Co., Inc.

Rashid, Mark & Lindley, Kathleen. A Life with Horses: Spirit of the Work. 2007. (Illus.). 185p. per. 27.50 *(978-1-55566-407-7(5))* Johnson Bks.

Reed, Tom & Gookin, John. Bear Essentials: Hiking & Camping in Bear Country. 2009. (Nols Ser.). (ENG., Illus.). 112p. pap. 9.95 *(978-0-8117-3549-0(4))* Stackpole Bks.

Richardson, Nan. Wild Love. Umbrage Editors, ed. 2010. (ENG., Illus.). 80p. (gr. k-2). 15.00 *(978-1-884167-95-9(0))* Umbrage Editions.

Ritter, William E. The Natural History of Our Conduct. 2007. (ENG.). 348p. 46.95 *(978-0-548-07048-2(2))* Kessinger Publishing, LLC.

Roberts, Monty. The Man Who Listens to Horses: The Story of a Real-Life Horse Whisperer. 2008. (ENG.). 288p. pap. 16.00 *(978-0-345-51045-7(3)*, Ballantine Bks.) Random House Publishing Group.

Roots, Clive. Animal Parents, 1 vol. 2007. (Greenwood Guides to the Animal World). (Illus.). 232p. 65.00 *(978-0-313-33986-8(4)*, GR3986, Greenwood Pr.) Greenwood Publishing Group, Inc.

Rossellini, Isabella. Green Porno: A Book & Short Films. 2009. 208p. pap. 24.99 *(978-0-06-179106-2(7))* HarperCollins Pubs.

Rothenberg, David. Thousand Mile Song: Whale Music in a Sea of Sound. 2010. (ENG., Illus.). 304p. (gr. 9). pap. 18.00 *(978-0-465-01889-5(0))* Basic Bks.

Roughgarden, Joan. The Genial Gene: Deconstructing Darwinian Selfishness. 2010. (ENG.). 272p. pap. 21.95 *(978-0-520-26593-6(9))* 2009. 252p. 40.00 *(978-0-520-25826-6(5))* Univ. of California Pr.

Rubbert, Tim. Hiking with Grizzlies: Lessons Learned. 2006. (Illus.). 135p. per. 10.95 *(978-1-931832-69-4(2))* Riverbend Publishing.

Ruckstuhl, Kathreen & Neuhaus, Peter, eds. Sexual Segregation in Vertebrates. 2011. (ENG.). 502p. pap. 65.00 *(978-0-521-18421-2(5))* Cambridge Univ. Pr.

Ryan, Michael J. & Wilczynski, Walter. An Introduction to Animal Behavior: An Integrative Approach. 2011. (Illus.). 300p. 81.00 *(978-1-936113-18-7(X))*; pap. 46.00 *(978-0-87969-858-4(6))* Cold Spring Harbor Laboratory Pr.

Sablik, Elisabeth. Macaca sylvanus auf Gibraltar: Verhalten und Physiologie männlicher Berberaffen während der Paarungssaison. 2010. 84p. pap. *(978-3-639-22869-4(3))* VDM Verlag Dr. Mueller e.K.

Schleich, Cristian E., et al, eds. Subterranean Rodents: News from Underground. 2007. (ENG., Illus.). xviii, 398p. 215.00 *(978-3-540-69275-1(4)*, 3540692754) Springer.

Schuster, Gerd, et al. Thinkers of the Jungle: The Orangutan Report. 2008. (Photograpghy Ser.). (Illus.). 319p. 49.95 *(978-0-8416-0285-4(9))* American Map Corp.

—Thinkers of the Jungle: The Orangutan Report, 1 vol. 2012. (ENG., Illus.). 320p. 19.99 ***(978-3-8331-4623-7(0))*** h.f.ullmann DEU. Dist: Innovative Logistics.

Scott-Fox, Penny. And Baby Makes Four: A Trimester-by-Trimester Guide to a Baby-Friendly Dog. 2007. (Illus.). 95p. 9.95 *(978-0-7938-0567-9(8))* TFH Pubns., Inc.

Senson, Pat. Nasty, Brutish, & Short: The Quirks & Quarks Guide to Animal Sex & Other Weird Behaviour. 2010. (ENG.). 296p. pap. 18.95 *(978-0-7710-7968-9(0)*, McClelland & Stewart) McClelland & Stewart CAN. Dist: Random Hse., Inc.

Seton, Ernest Thompson. Wild Animal Ways. 2008. (ENG.). 272p. per. *(978-1-4086-4097-5(X))* Read Bks.

—Wild Animals at Home. 2008. 272p. pap. *(978-1-4086-9727-6(0))*; (ENG.). 288p. per. *(978-1-4086-4096-8(1))* Read Bks.

—Wild Animals at Home. 2010. (ENG.). 296p. pap. 28.75 *(978-1-172-34732-2(8))*; 346p. pap. 32.75 *(978-1-177-55608-8(1))* BiblioBazaar.

—Wild Animals at Home. 2010. (Illus.). 88p. pap. 20.00 *(978-1-153-80817-0(X))*; 84p. pap. 17.50 *(978-1-152-11788-4(2))* General Bks. LLC.

Shanor, Karen & Kanwal, Jagmeet. Bats Sing, Mice Giggle: Revealing the Secret Lives of Animals. 2010. (ENG.). 272p. 17.95 *(978-1-84831-197-8(4))* Totem Bks. GBR. Dist: Consortium Bk. Sales & Distribution.

Shumaker, Robert W., et al. Animal Tool Behavior: The Use & Manufacture of Tools by Animals. 2nd rev. ed. 2011. (ENG., Illus.). 304p. (gr. 17). 65.00 *(978-0-8018-9853-2(6))* Johns Hopkins Univ. Pr.

Sigl, Stefanie & Dbaly, Helena. Playtime for Cats: Activities & Games for Felines. 2010. (ENG., Illus.). 112p. pap. 24.95 *(978-3-86127-970-9(3))* Cadmos Verlag GmbH DEU. Dist: Independent Pubs. Group.

Simmons, Laurence & Armstrong, Philip, eds. Knowing Animals. 2007. (Human-Animal Studies: Vol. 4). (Illus.). 296p. pap. *(978-90-04-15773-6(5))* BRILL.

Simmons, Peter J. & Young, David. Nerve Cells & Animal Behaviour. 3rd rev. ed. 2010. (ENG., Illus.). 292p. (C). 110.00 *(978-0-521-89977-2(X))*; pap. 47.00 *(978-0-521-72848-5(7))* Cambridge Univ. Pr.

Singer, Michael A. Comparative Physiology, Natural Animal Models & Clinical Medicine: Insights into Clinical Medicine from Animal Adaptations. 2007. (Illus.). 271p. 82.00 *(978-1-86094-782-7(4))* Imperial College Pr. GBR. Dist: World Scientific Publishing Co., Inc.

Smith, Howard. In the Company of Wild Bears: A Celebration of Backcountry Grizzlies & Black Bears. 2006. (ENG., Illus.). 248p. 22.95 *(978-1-59228-952-3(5)*, Lyons Pr.) Globe Pequot Pr., The.

Smith, Stevenson. General Psychology in Terms of Behavior. 2009. 154p. pap. *(978-0-217-47909-7(X))* Books LLC.

—General Psychology in Terms of Behavior. 2007. (ENG.). 292p. per. *(978-1-4067-0767-0(8))* Read Bks.

Smith, Stevenson & Guthrie, Edwin R. General Psychology in Terms of Behavior. 2008. 286p. 43.95 *(978-1-4365-2255-7(2))* 2007. (ENG.). 288p. per. 28.95 *(978-0-548-74745-2(8))* Kessinger Publishing, LLC.

Snowdon, Charles T. & Wynne-Edwards, Katherine E., eds. Advances in the Study of Behavior. 2011. (ENG.). 350p. 144.00 *(978-0-12-380896-7(0)*, Academic Pr.) Elsevier Science & Technology Bks.

Solomon, Nancy G. & French, Jeffrey A., eds. Cooperative Breeding in Mammals. 2007. (ENG., Illus.). 408p. pap. 79.00 *(978-0-521-03828-7(6))* Cambridge Univ. Pr.

Sommer, Volker & Vasey, Paul L., eds. Homosexual Behaviour in Animals: An Evolutionary Perspective. 2006. (ENG., Illus.). 392p. 168.00 *(978-0-521-86446-5(1))* Cambridge Univ. Pr.

Sorenson, John. Ape. 2009. (Reaktion Books - Animal Ser.). (ENG., Illus.). 224p. pap. 19.95 *(978-1-86189-422-9(8))* Reaktion Bks., Ltd. GBR. Dist: Chicago Distribution Ctr.

Starr, Lisa, et al. Volume 6 - Ecology & Behavior. 13th ed. 2012. (ENG., Illus.). 160p. (C). pap. 44.95 ***(978-1-111-58069-8(3))*** Brooks/Cole.

Stockman, Catherine & Barnes, Anne. Sheep Exposed to Heat Load Within Intensive Sheep Industries. 2008. 216p. pap. *(978-3-639-04196-5(8))* VDM Verlag Dr. Mueller e.K.

Sumpter, D. Collective Animal Behavior. 2010. (ENG., Illus.). 312p. (C). 80.00 *(978-0-691-12963-1(0))* Princeton Univ. Pr.

Sykes, Barbara. Understanding Your Dog. 2007. (ENG., Illus.). 160p. pap. 32.95 *(978-1-86126-941-6(2))* Crowood Pr., Ltd. GBR. Dist: Independent Pubs. Group.

Tasi, István & Hornyánszky, Balázs. Nature's I.Q: Extraordinary Animal Behaviors That Defy Evolution. 2009. 160p. 24.95 *(978-0-9817273-0-1(1))* Torchlight Publishing.

Taylor, Jeremy. Not a Chimp: The Hunt to Find the Genes That Make Us Human. (ENG., Illus.). 2010. 368p. pap. 14.95 *(978-0-19-922779-2(9))* 2009. 256p. (J). 27.95 *(978-0-19-922778-5(0))* Oxford Univ. Pr., Inc.

Tellington-Jones, Linda & Taylor, Sybil. Getting in TTouch with Your Horse: Understand & Influence Personality. 2009. (ENG., Illus.). 204p. pap. 22.95 *(978-1-57076-415-8(8))* Trafalgar Square Bks.

Terrill, Ceiridwen. Part Wild: One Woman's Journey with a Creature Caught Between the Worlds of Wolves & Dogs. 2011. (ENG.). 288p. 25.00 *(978-1-4516-3481-5(1)*, Scribner) Scribner.

Thierry, Bernard, et al, eds. Macaque Societies: A Model for the Study of Social Organization. 2010. (Cambridge Studies in Biological & Evolutionary Anthropology Ser.). (ENG.). 440p. pap. 58.00 *(978-0-521-52168-0(8))* Cambridge Univ. Pr.

Thomas, Elizabeth Marshall. The Hidden Life of Deer: Lessons from the Natural World. (ENG.). 2010. 256p. pap. 14.99 *(978-0-06-179211-3(X)*, Harper Perennial) 2009. 288p. 24.99 *(978-0-06-179210-6(1))* HarperCollins Pubs.

Thorndike, Edward L. Animal Intelligence: An Experimental Study of the Associative Processes in Animals. (Illus.). 109p. reprint ed. lib. bdg. 38.00 *(978-0-7222-3083-1(4))* Library Reprints, Inc.

Tillberg, Chadwick V., et al. Field & Laboratory Exercises in Animal Behavior. 2007. (ENG., Illus.). 232p. (C). pap. 36.95 *(978-0-12-372582-0(8)*, Academic Pr.) Elsevier Science & Technology Bks.

Travis, Georgia-Rose. C Hectori: Behaviour in Response to Tour-Boat & Yacht Presence. 2008. 124p. pap. *(978-3-639-04394-5(4))* VDM Verlag Dr. Mueller e.K.

—C Hectori: Dolphin Behaviour in Response. 2008. 192p. pap. *(978-3-639-04081-4(3))* VDM Verlag Dr. Mueller e.K.

—Issues Central to Behavioural Studies. 2008. 88p. pap. *(978-3-639-02456-2(7))* VDM Verlag Dr. Mueller e.K.

Turner, Jacky. Animal Breeding, Welfare & Society. 2010. (ENG., Illus.). 336p. 140.00 *(978-1-84407-588-1(5))*; pap. 41.95 *(978-1-84407-589-8(3))* Routledge.

TVH, et al. Principles & Applications of Domestic Animal Behavior. 2008. (Illus.). 352p. pap. 65.00 *(978-1-84593-398-2(2))* CABI GBR. Dist: Stylus Publishing, LLC.

Twain, Mark, pseud. Animals. Fishkin, Shelley Fisher, ed. 2009. (Jumping Frogs: Undiscovered, Rediscovered, & Celebrated Writings of Mark Twain Ser.). (Illus.). 340p. 50.00 *(978-0-520-24855-7(4))* Univ. of California Pr.

—Mark Twain's Book of Animals. Fishkin, Shelley Fisher, ed. 2011. (Jumping Frogs: Undiscovered, Rediscovered, & Celebrated Writings of Mark Twain Ser.). (ENG., Illus.). 344p. pap. 21.95 *(978-0-520-27152-4(1))* Univ. of California Pr.

Tyler, Laura. The Story of Little Beaky Robin: A special story with a happy Ending. 2009. 40p. pap. 19.99 *(978-1-4490-4259-2(7))* AuthorHouse.

Tynes, Valarie V., ed. Behavior of Exotic Pets. 2010. (ENG., Illus.). 248p. pap. 82.99 *(978-0-8138-0078-3(1)*, Wiley-Blackwell) Wiley, John & Sons, Inc.

Uexkull, Marina von. A Foray into the Worlds of Animals & Humans: With a Theory of Meaning. O'Neil, Joseph D., tr. from GER. 2010. (Posthumanities Ser.). (ENG., Illus.). 248p. 75.00 *(978-0-8166-5899-2(4))*; pap. 25.00 *(978-0-8166-5900-5(1))* Univ. of Minnesota Pr.

Velarde, A. & Geers, R. On Farm Monitoring of Pig Welfare: COST Action 846, Working Group 2 - on Farm Monitoring of Welfare, Subworking Group - Pigs. Velarde, A. & Geers, R., eds. 2007. (Illus.). 208p. 77.00 *(978-90-8686-025-8(7))* Wageningen Academic Publishers NLD. Dist: Enfield Publishing & Distribution Co., Inc.

Verhulst, Simon & Bolhuis, Johan J. Tinbergen's Legacy: Function & Mechanism in Behavioral Biology. Bolhuis, Johan, ed. 2009. (ENG., Illus.). 262p. 112.99 *(978-0-521-87478-6(5))*; pap. 52.00 *(978-0-521-69755-2(7))* Cambridge Univ. Pr.

Ward, Madalyn. Horse Harmony: Understanding Horse Types & Temperaments: Are You & Your Horse a Good Match? 2008. per. 19.95 *(978-0-9779714-1-1(4))* Myriah Pr.

Weber, Emilie A. & Krause, Lara H. Animal Behavior: New Research. 2008. (Illus.). 227p. 98.00 *(978-1-60456-782-3(1))* Nova Science Pubs., Inc.

Werre, Jan Lodewijk. The Niger Delta Red Colobus. 2009. 168p. pap. *(978-3-639-16855-6(0))* VDM Verlag Dr. Mueller e.K.

West, Stuart A., et al. An Introduction to Behavioural Ecology. 4th ed. 2012. (ENG., Illus.). 520p. pap. 79.95 ***(978-1-4051-1416-5(9)***, Wiley-Blackwell) Wiley, John & Sons, Inc.

Westneat, David & Fox, Charles, eds. Evolutionary Behavioral Ecology, 1 vol. 2010. (ENG., Illus.). 664p. pap. 49.95 *(978-0-19-533192-9(3))* Oxford Univ. Pr., Inc.

Williams, Peter. Snail. 2009. (Reaktion Books - Animal Ser.). (ENG., Illus.). 224p. pap. 19.95 *(978-1-86189-528-8(3))* Reaktion Bks., Ltd. GBR. Dist: Chicago Distribution Ctr.

Williams, Rachel M., ed. Monkeys: Biology, Behavior & Disorders. 2011. (Animal Science, Issues & Professions Ser.). (Illus.). x, 211p. 129.00 *(978-1-61209-911-8(4))* Nova Science Pubs., Inc.

Woods, Vanessa. Bonobo Handshake: A Memoir of Love & Adventure in the Congo. 2011. (ENG.). 288p. (gr. 12). 16.00 *(978-1-59240-634-0(3)*, Gotham) Penguin Group (USA) Inc.

Yahner, Richard H. Wildlife Behavior & Conservation. 2011. (ENG., Illus.). xxi, 173p. 189.00 ***(978-1-4614-1515-2(2)***, 1461415152) Springer.

Yannella, Philip R. & Bolhuis, Johan J. Development of Animal Behavior: An Introduction. 2010. 176p. pap. *(978-0-631-21955-2(2)*, Wiley-Blackwell) Wiley, John & Sons, Ltd.

Young, Stanley P. Sketches of American Wildlife. 2007. (ENG.). 154p. 36.95 *(978-0-548-06690-4(6))* Kessinger Publishing, LLC.

Zeigler, H. Philip, et al, eds. New Perspectives on Neurobehavioral Evolution. 2011. (Annals of the New York Academy of Sciences Ser.: 80). (ENG., Illus.). 252p. pap. 130.00 ***(978-1-57331-807-5(8)***, Wiley-Blackwell) Wiley, John & Sons, Inc.

Zhang, Wen & Liu, Hong. Behavioral & Chemical Ecology. 2010. (Environmental Research Advances Ser.). 145.00 *(978-1-60741-099-7(0))* Nova Science Pubs., Inc.

Zullo, Allan. Bad Pets: True Tales of Misbehaving Animals. 2010. 112p. pap. ***(978-0-545-20643-3(X))*** Scholastic, Inc.

Zupan, Jakob L. & Mlakar, Sara L., eds. Bats: Biology, Behavior & Conservation. 2011. (Animal Science, Issues & Professions Ser.). (Illus.). 371p. 165.00 *(978-1-61209-749-7(9))* Nova Science Pubs., Inc.

Zupanc, Günther K. H. Behavioral Neurobiology: An Integrative Approach. 2nd ed. 2010. (ENG., Illus.). 400p. pap. 64.95 *(978-0-19-920830-2(1))* Oxford Univ. Pr., Inc.

ANIMAL BEHAVIOR—JUVENILE LITERATURE

Anderson, Sheila. What Can Live in a Grassland? 2010. (First Step Nonfiction - Animal Adaptations Ser.). (Illus.). 24p. (J). (gr. k-2). lib. bdg. 21.27 *(978-0-7613-4574-9(4))* Lerner Publishing Group.

Animals Should Definitely Not Act Like People. *(978-1-59112-825-0(0))*; *(978-1-59112-841-0(2))* Live Oak Media.

Nocturnal Animals. 2011. (Nocturnal Animals Ser.). (ENG.). 24p. (gr. k-1). lib. bdg. 147.90 *(978-1-4296-5290-2(X)*, Pebble Plus) Capstone Pr., Inc.

ANIMAL BREEDING

see also Artificial Insemination

also subdivision Breeding under individual animals and groups of animals, e.g. Birds—Breeding; Livestock—Breeding

Adebambo, Olufunmilayo. Fundamentals of Animal Breeding & Genetics. 2010. 428p. pap. *(978-3-639-11038-8(2)*, VDM Verlag Dr. Mueller e.K.

Benard Aswani Ouna & Aswani, Ouna Benard. Migration & Admixture of Sheep in Africa: Molecular Genetics. 2008. 72p. pap. *(978-3-639-09526-5(X))* VDM Verlag Dr. Mueller e.K.

Bondoc, Orville L. Animal Breeding: Principles & Practice in the Philippine Context. 2010. (Illus.). 386p. pap. 53.00 *(978-971-542-589-6(5))* Univ. of the Philippines Pr. PHL. Dist: Univ. of Hawaii Pr.

Braun, Sebastian Felix. Buffalo Inc: American Indians & Economic Development. 2008. (ENG., Illus.). 280p. (C). 39.95 *(978-0-8061-3904-3(8))* Univ. of Oklahoma Pr.

Ekarius, Carol. Storey's Illustrated Breed Guide to Sheep, Goats, Cattle & Pigs: 163 Breeds, from Common to Rare. 2008. (ENG., Illus.). 320p. pap. 24.95 *(978-1-60342-036-5(3)*, 1603420363) Storey Publishing, LLC.

—Storey's Illustrated Breed Guide to Sheep, Goats, Cattle & Pigs: 194 Breeds, from Common to Rare. 2008. (ENG., Illus.). 320p. 34.95 *(978-1-60342-037-2(1)*, 1603420371) Storey Publishing, LLC.

Frankham, Richard, et al, eds. Adaptation & Fitness in Animal Populations: Evolutionary & Breeding Perspectives on Genetic Resource Management. 2008. (ENG., Illus.). xii, 260p. 189.00 *(978-1-4020-9004-2(8)*, 1402090048) Springer.

Gupta, Lokesh & Murdia, P. C. Improvement of Roughages by Urea & Sulphur Supplementation. 2011. 144p. pap. ***(978-3-8443-2829-5(7))*** Lambert Academic Publishing.

Harris, Carol. A Guide to Traditional Pig Keeping. 2009. (ENG., Illus.). 202p. pap. 32.99 *(978-1-904871-60-6(7)*, 1904871607) Good Life Pr., The GBR. Dist: MBI Distribution Services/Quayside Distribution.

Heim, Susanne. Calories, Caoutchouc, Careers: Plant Breeding & Agrarian Research in Kaiser-Wilhelm-Institutes 1933-1945. 2008. (Boston Studies in the Philosophy of Science Ser.). (Illus.). 300p. 179.00 *(978-1-4020-6717-4(8))* Springer.

Jöchle, W. & Lamond, D. R., eds. Control of Reproductive Functions in Domestic Animals. 2010. (Current Topics in Veterinary Medicine Ser.). 248p. pap. 219.00 *(978-90-481-8263-3(8)*, 9048182638) Springer.

Khan, Sarzamin. Lactation-Reproduction Interaction in Dairy Buffaloes. 2009. 140p. pap. *(978-3-639-14444-4(9))* VDM Verlag Dr. Mueller e.K.

Kinghorn, Brian. Animal Breeding: Use of New Technologies. 80.00 *(978-0-646-38713-0(8))* Wageningen Academic Publishers NLD. Dist: Enfield Publishing & Distribution Co., Inc.

Masum, A. K. M., et al. Utilization of Soymilk As Milk Replacer for Raising Calves. 2011. 108p. pap. ***(978-3-8443-8208-2(9))*** Lambert Academic Publishing.

Mills, Alan. The City of Animals. 2007. *(978-0-7322-8047-5(8))* HarperCollins Pubs. Australia.

Pala, Akin. Three Twice-A-Year Breeding Schedules in Four Breeds of Sheep. 2010. 112p. pap. *(978-3-639-22496-2(5))* VDM Verlag Dr. Mueller e.K.

pandian, soundara & Pandian, Soundara. Seed Production & Fattening of Commercially Important Portunid Crab. 2010. 56p. pap. *(978-3-639-25667-3(0))* VDM Verlag Dr. Mueller e.K.

Pisc. Model Codes of Practice for the Welfare of Animals: Pigs 3rd edition PISC Technical Report 92. 3rd ed. 2008. (Primary Industries Report Ser.). 30p. pap. 22.00 *(978-0-643-09477-2(6))* CSIRO Publishing AUS. Dist: Stylus Publishing, LLC.

Robinson, Holly. The Gerbil Farmer's Daughter: A Memoir. 2010. (ENG., Illus.). 304p. pap. 14.00 *(978-0-307-33746-7(4)*, Three Rivers Pr.) Crown Publishing Group.

Rodriguez-Martinez, Heriberto, ed. Control of Pig Reproduction VIII. 2010. (ENG., Illus.). 344p. 123.95 *(978-1-904761-39-6(9))* Nottingham Univ. Pr. GBR. Dist: Independent Pubs. Group.

Rudy, Guerra. Primer of Stat Genet. 2009. 69.95 *(978-1-58488-516-0(5)*, Chapman & Hall/CRC) CRC Pr. LLC.

Ruechel, Julius. Grass-Fed Cattle: How to Produce & Market Natural Beef. 2006. (ENG., Illus.). 384p. pap. 24.95 *(978-1-58017-605-7(4)*, 1580176054) Storey Publishing, LLC.

Schatten, Heide & Constantinescu, Gheorghe M. Comparative Reproductive Biology. 2007. (ENG., Illus.). 432p. 157.99 *(978-0-8138-1554-1(1)*, Wiley-Blackwell) Wiley, John & Sons, Inc.

Scudamore, Wendy. Small-scale Outdoor Pig Breeding. 2012. (ENG., Illus.). 144p. 24.95 ***(978-1-84797-307-8(8))*** Crowood Pr., Ltd. GBR. Dist: Independent Pubs. Group.

Statistical Genetics. 2009. (Methods in Molecular Biology Ser.). 99.50 *(978-1-58829-728-0(4))* Humana Pr.

Tanveer, Hussain & Masroor, Ellahi Babar. Phylogenetic Analysis Based on Snps & Allelic Variations: Genetic Characterization of Pakistani Buffalo Breeds by Mitochondrial D-Loop & Microsatellite Analyses. 2011. 132p. pap. ***(978-3-639-24433-5(8))*** VDM Verlag Dr. Mueller e.K.

Turner, Jacky. Animal Breeding, Welfare & Society. 2010. (ENG., Illus.). 336p. 140.00 *(978-1-84407-588-1(5))*; pap. 41.95 *(978-1-84407-589-8(3))* Routledge.

ANIMAL CLASSIFICATION

see Animals—Classification

ANIMAL COGNITION

see Cognition in Animals

ANIMAL COLLECTING

see Wild Animal Collecting

ANIMAL COMMUNICATION

see also Animal Sounds; Sound Production by Animals

Bea Lydecker's Naturals, Rose Mary. Explore the fun & Mystery of Talking with Animals. 2008. 304p. pap. *(978-0-9622094-1-3(4)*, Living Free Pubns.) Lydecker's, Bea Naturals.

Blake, Joanna. Routes to Child Language: Evolutionary & Developmental Precursors. 2007. (ENG., Illus.). 296p. per. 42.00 *(978-0-521-03397-8(7))* Cambridge Univ. Pr.

Bradbury, et al. Principles of Animal Communication. 2nd rev. ed. 2011. (Illus.). 600p. ***(978-0-87893-045-6(0))*** Sinauer Assocs., Inc.

Brammer, Ingrid M. Animal Illumination: The Essential Guide to Learning Intuitive Animal Communication. 2011. 112p. pap. 10.95 *(978-1-4502-9327-3(1))* iUniverse, Inc.

Braun, Martina. Chat to Your Cat: Lessons in Cat Conversation. 2009. (ENG.). 80p. pap. 19.95 *(978-3-86127-966-2(5))* Cadmos Verlag GmbH DEU. Dist: Independent Pubs. Group.

Brudzynski, Stefan M., ed. Handbook of Mammalian Vocalization: An Integrative Neuroscience Approach. 2009. (Handbook of Behavioral Neuroscience Ser.: 19). (ENG., Illus.). 546p. 195.00 *(978-0-12-374593-4(4)*, Academic Pr.) Elsevier Science & Technology Bks.

Cointreau, Sandra. Energy Healing for Animals & Their Owners: an Earth Lodge Guide to Pet Wellness. 2009. 164p. pap. 19.95 *(978-0-578-03159-0(0))* Earth Lodge.

Craige, Betty Jean. Conversations with Cosmo: At Home with an African Grey Parrot. 2010. 144p. 19.95 *(978-1-890932-37-4(X))* Sherman Asher Publishing.

Croft, D. P., et al. Exploring Animal Social Networks. 2008. (ENG., Illus.). 208p. (C). 82.50 *(978-0-691-12751-4(4))*; pap. 39.95 *(978-0-691-12752-1(2))* Princeton Univ. Pr.

Davies, Nicola. Talk, Talk, Squawk! A Human's Guide to Animal Communication. 2011. (ENG., Illus.). 64p. (J). (gr. 3). 14.99 *(978-0-7636-5088-9(9))* Candlewick Pr.

Dessalles, Jean-Louis. Why We Talk: The Evolutionary Origins of Language. Grieve, James, tr. from FRE. 2007. (Studies in the Evolution of Language Ser.: Vol. 7). (ENG., Illus.). 400p. 75.00 *(978-0-19-927623-3(4))* Oxford Univ. Pr., Inc.

Dudzinski, Kathleen M. & Frohoff, Toni. Dolphin Mysteries: Unlocking the Secrets of Communication. 2010. (ENG., Illus.). 256p. pap. 20.00 *(978-0-300-12114-8(8))* Yale Univ. Pr.

Frey, Jeffrey W. Assessment of Nutrient Enrichment by Use of Algal-, Invertebrate-, & Fish-Community Attributes in Wadeable Streams in Ecoregions Surrounding the Great Lakes. 2011. (Illus.). vii, 49p. ***(978-1-4113-3103-7(6))*** United States Geological Survey.

Hailman, Jack P. Coding & Redundancy: Man-Made & Animal-Evolved Signals. 2008. (Illus.). 272p. 44.00 *(978-0-674-02795-4(7))* Harvard Univ. Pr.

Halloran, Andrew R. The Song of the Ape: Understanding the Languages of Chimpanzees. 2012. (ENG., Illus.). 288p. 25.99 ***(978-0-312-56311-0(6))*** St. Martin's Pr.

Heine, Bernd & Kuteva, Tania. The Genesis of Grammar: A Reconstruction. 2007. (Studies in the Evolution of Language Ser.). (Illus.). 352p. 215.00 *(978-0-19-922776-1(4))* Oxford Univ. Pr., Inc.

Heinrich, Bernd. Life Everlasting: The Animal Way of Death. 2012. (ENG., Illus.). 256p. 25.00 ***(978-0-547-75266-2(0))*** Houghton Mifflin Harcourt Trade & Reference Pubs.

Herzing, Denise & Herzing, Denise L. Dolphin Diaries: My 25 Years with Spotted Dolphins in the Bahamas. 2011. (ENG., Illus.). 336p. 26.99 *(978-0-312-60896-5(9))* St. Martin's Pr.

Herzing, Denise L. Dolphin Diaries: My 25 Years with Spotted Dolphins in the Bahamas. 2012. (ENG.). 336p. pap. 16.99 ***(978-1-250-00691-2(0)***, St. Martin's Griffin) St. Martin's Pr.

Hill, Peggy S. M. Vibrational Communication in Animals. 2008. (Illus.). 272p. 44.00 *(978-0-674-02798-5(1))* Harvard Univ. Pr.

King, Barbara J., ed. Origins of Language: What Nonhuman Primates Can Tell Us. (Advanced Seminar Ser.). (Illus.). 464p. 29.95 *(978-0-933452-59-6(4))*; pap. 24.95 *(978-0-933452-60-2(8))* School for Advanced Research Pr./SAR Pr.

Lerch-Henning, Sara, et al. The Role of Acoustic Communication in African Lions: Which Are the Acoustic Features That Characterize Lion Roars? 2011. 76p. pap. ***(978-3-639-28477-5(1))*** VDM Verlag Dr. Mueller e.K.

Liebal, Katja, et al. Gestural Communication in Nonhuman & Human Primates. Liebal, Katja et al, eds. 2007. (Illus.). xiv, 245p. (C). *(978-90-272-2240-4(1))* Benjamins, John Publishing Co.

Long, William J. How Animals Talk. 2009. (ENG., Illus.). 208p. pap. 10.95 *(978-0-486-46880-8(1))* Dover Pubns., Inc.

Maran, Timo, et al, eds. Readings in Zoosemiotics. (Semiotics, Communication & Cognition Ser.). (ENG., 2012. Illus.). 752p. (gr. 17). pap. 56.00 ***(978-3-11-025342-9(9))*** 2011. 321.00 ***(978-3-11-026218-6(5))*** 2011. VII, 438p. 210.00 ***(978-3-11-025320-7(8))*** De Gruyter, Mouton DEU. Dist: de Gruyter, Walter GmbH & Co. KG.

Martin, Arthur. Mechanisms That Affect Agonism & Resource Acquisition. 2010. 136p. pap. *(978-3-639-14320-1(5))* VDM Verlag Dr. Mueller e.K.

Martinelli, Dario. A Critical Companion to Zoosemiotics: People, Paths, Ideas. 2010. (Biosemiotics Ser.). (Illus.). xiv, 353p. 219.00 *(978-90-481-9248-9(X)*, 904819248X) Springer.

Masataka, Nobuo, ed. The Origins of Language: Unraveling Evolutionary Forces. (ENG., Illus.). viii, 157p. 2010. pap. 119.00 *(978-4-431-99853-2(5)*, 4431998535) 2008. 119.00 *(978-4-431-79101-0(9)*, 4431791019) Springer.

McGregor, Peter K., ed. Playback & Studies of Animal Communication. 2010. (Nato Science Series A: Ser.). 248p. pap. 279.00 *(978-1-4419-3224-2(0)*, 1441932240) Springer.

Menino, Holly. Calls Beyond Our Hearing: Unlocking the Secrets of Animal Voices. 2012. (ENG.). 272p. 25.99 ***(978-0-312-58757-4(0))*** St. Martin's Pr.

Menzel, Nancy G. Animal Thinking: Contemporary Issues in Comparative Cognition. 2011. (Strüngmann Forum Reports). (ENG., Illus.). 416p. (gr. 17). 40.00 ***(978-0-262-01663-6(X))*** MIT Pr.

Oller, D. Kimbrough & Griebel, Ulrike, eds. Evolution of Communicative Flexibility: Complexity, Creativity, & Adaptability in Human & Animal Communication. 2008. (Vienna Series in Theoretical Biology Ser.). (ENG., Illus.). 368p. (gr. 17). 50.00 *(978-0-262-15121-4(9))* MIT Pr.

Owings, Donald H. & Morton, Eugene S. Animal Vocal Communication: A New Approach. 2006. (ENG., Illus.). 300p. pap. 66.00 *(978-0-521-03129-5(X))* Cambridge Univ. Pr.

Pepperberg, Irene. Alex & Me: How a Scientist & a Parrot Discovered a Hidden World of Animal Intelligence - And Formed a Deep Bond in the Process. l.t. ed. 2008. 240p. pap. 23.95 *(978-0-06-173484-7(5)*, HarperLuxe) HarperCollins Pubs.

Pepperberg, Irene & Lewin, Roger. Alex & Me: How a Scientist & a Parrot Discovered a Hidden World of Animal Intelligence - And Formed a Deep Bond in the Process. 2008. (ENG., Illus.). 256p. 23.95 *(978-0-06-167247-7(5))* HarperCollins Pubs.

Potocki, Emil & Krasinski, Juliusz, eds. Primatology: Theories, Methods & Research. 2009. (Animal Science, Issues & Professions Ser.). 129.00 *(978-1-60741-852-8(5))* Nova Science Pubs., Inc.

Radick, Gregory. The Simian Tongue: The Long Debate about Animal Language. 2008. (Illus.). 578p. 47.50 *(978-0-226-70224-7(3))* Univ. of Chicago Pr.

Shanor, Karen & Kanwal, Jagmeet. Bats Sing, Mice Giggle: Revealing the Secret Lives of Animals. 2010. (ENG.). 272p. 17.95 *(978-1-84831-197-8(4))* Totem Bks. GBR. Dist: Consortium Bk. Sales & Distribution.

Simmons, Andrea & Fay, Richard R., eds. Acoustic Communication. 2010. (Springer Handbook of Auditory Research Ser.). (Illus.). xiv, 404p. pap. 189.00 *(978-1-4419-3148-1(1)*, 1441931481) Springer.

Slobodchikoff, Con. Chasing Doctor Dolittle: Learning the Language of Animals. 2012. (ENG.). 320p. 25.99 ***(978-0-312-61179-8(X))*** St. Martin's Pr.

Slobodchikoff, Con, et al. Prairie Dogs: Communication & Community in an Animal Society. 2009. (Illus.). 280p. 44.00 *(978-0-674-03181-4(4))* Harvard Univ. Pr.

Stadler, Bernhard, et al. Mutualism: Ants & Their Insect Partners. 2008. (ENG., Illus.). 248p. 99.00 *(978-0-521-86035-2(0))* Cambridge Univ. Pr.

Tomasello, Michael. Origins of Human Communication. 2010. (Bradford Bks.). (ENG.). 408p. (gr. 17). pap. 19.00 *(978-0-262-51520-7(2))* MIT Pr.

Tripovich, Joy. Vocal Communication in Australian Fur Seals. 2010. 172p. pap. *(978-3-639-23664-4(5))* VDM Verlag Dr. Mueller e.K.

Williams, Marta. Ask Your Animal: Resolving Animal Behavioral Issues through Intuitive Communication. 2008. (ENG., Illus.). 256p. per. 15.95 *(978-1-57731-609-1(6))* New World Library.

ANIMAL DEFENSES

see also Mimicry (Biology)

Clerici, Carlo Alfredo & Veneroni, Laura. The Impossible Escape: Studies on the Tonic Immobility in Animals from a Comparative Psychology Perspective. 2011. pap. ***(978-1-62100-183-6(0))*** Nova Science Pubs., Inc.

Zaccone, Giacomo. Fish Defences. Zaccone, Giacomo et al, eds. 2009. (ENG., Illus.). 390p. 119.95 *(978-1-57808-327-5(3))* BIOS Scientific Publishers Ltd. GBR. Dist: Taylor & Francis Group.

ANIMAL DISEASES

see Animals—Diseases

ANIMAL DRAWING

see Animal Painting and Illustration

ANIMAL ECOLOGY

see also Animal Populations; Zoogeography

Archer, S., et al, eds. Adaptive Mechanisms in the Ecology of Vision. 2010. 680p. pap. 470.00 *(978-90-481-5124-0(4)*, 9048151244) Springer.

Aubry, Keith Baker. Biology & Conservation of Martens, Sables, & Fishers: A New Synthesis. 2012. ***(978-0-8014-5088-4(8)***, Comstock Publishing Assocs.) Cornell Univ. Pr.

Barboza, Perry S., et al. Integrative Wildlife Nutrition. 2009. (ENG., Illus.). xviii, 342p. 209.00 *(978-3-540-87884-1(X)*, 354087884X) Springer.

Barth, Friedrich G. & Schmid, Axel, eds. Ecology of Sensing. 2010. (Illus.). xiii, 360p. pap. 259.00 *(978-3-642-08619-9(5)*, 3642086195) Springer.

Baskin, Leonid & Danell, Kjell. Ecology of Ungulates: A Handbook of Species in Eastern Europe & Northern & Central Asia. 2010. (ENG., Illus.). xv, 434p. pap. 399.00 *(978-3-642-07852-1(4)*, 3642078524) Springer.

Behnassi, Mohamed, et al, eds. Sustainable Agricultural Development: Recent Approaches in Resources Management & Environmentally -Balanced Production Enhancement. 2011. (ENG., Illus.). xl, 278p. 129.00 *(978-94-007-0518-0(2)*, 9400705182) Springer.

Boitani, Luigi & Powell, Roger A., eds. Carnivore Ecology & Conservation: A Handbook of Techniques. 2012. (ENG., Illus.). 544p. pap. 62.95 ***(978-0-19-955853-7(1))*** Oxford Univ. Pr., Inc.

Boyd, Ian L., et al. Marine Mammal Ecology & Conservation: A Handbook of Techniques. 2010. (Techniques in Ecology & Conservation Ser.). (ENG., Illus.). 499p. pap. 49.95 *(978-0-19-921657-4(6))* Oxford Univ. Pr., Inc.

Bratton, Susan. Wildlife Ecology: Field & Laboratory Exercises. 2011. (ENG.). 154p. spiral bd. 39.99 ***(978-0-7575-9233-1(3))*** Kendall Hunt Publishing Co.

Breneman, Don & Seeley, Mark. Voyageur Skies: Weather & the wilderness in Minnesota's national Park. 2011. (Illus.). 104p. 32.00 *(978-1-890434-82-3(5))* Afton Historical Society Pr.

Briggs, Kay Marano. Proceedings of the U.S. Geological Survey Interdisciplinary Microbiology Workshop, Estes Park, Colorado, October 15-17, 2008. 2010. (Illus.). xii, 49p. ***(978-1-4113-2963-8(5))*** United States Geological Survey.

Bruin, J., et al, eds. Ecology & Evolution of the Acari. 2011. (Series Entomologica Ser.). (Illus.). 692p. pap. 499.00 *(978-90-481-5200-1(3)*, 9048152003) Springer.

Cahler, A. A. & Marsten, J. P. Deer: Habitat, Behavior & Conservation. 2012. ***(978-1-62100-676-3(X))*** Nova Science Pubs., Inc.

Campbell, Christina J. Spider Monkeys: Behavior, Ecology & Evolution of the Genus Ateles. Campbell, Christina, ed. 2008. (Cambridge Studies in Biological & Evolutionary Anthropology Ser.). (ENG., Illus.). 352p. 139.00 *(978-0-521-86750-4(9))* Cambridge Univ. Pr.

Carde', Ring T. & Millar, Jocelyn G., eds. Advances in Insect Chemical Ecology. 2011. (Illus.). 352p. pap. 70.00 *(978-0-521-18893-7(8))* Cambridge Univ. Pr.

Cloudsley-Thompson, John L. Ecology & Behaviour of Mesozoic Reptiles. 2010. (ENG., Illus.). xii, 219p. pap. 249.00 *(978-3-642-06124-0(9)*, 3642061249) Springer.

Cram101 Textbook Reviews. Outlines & Highlights for an Introduction to Behavioural Ecology by J R Krebs, N B Davies, Isbn: 9780632035465 0632035463. 2011. 360p. pap. 34.95 ***(978-1-61812-630-6(X))*** Cram101 Inc.

Cram101 Textbook Reviews & Cram101 Textbook Reviews. Outlines & Highlights for Cognition, Evolution, & Behavior by Sara J Shettleworth. 2011. 154p. pap. 29.95 ***(978-1-61830-480-3(1))*** Cram101 Inc.

—Outlines & Highlights for Introduction to Wildlife & Fisheries by David Willis, Isbn: 9781429204460 142920446x. 2011. 222p. pap. 30.95 ***(978-1-61490-818-0(4))*** Cram101 Inc.

—Outlines & Highlights for Wildlife Ecology, Conservation, & Management by Anthony R E Sinclair, Isbn: 9781405107372. 2011. 98p. pap. 27.95 ***(978-1-61461-377-0(X))*** Cram101 Inc.

Croxall, J. P., ed. Seabirds: Feeding Ecology & Role in Marine Ecosystems. 2009. (ENG.). 420p. pap. 53.00 *(978-0-521-10510-1(2))* Cambridge Univ. Pr.

Crumley, Jim. Brother Nature. 2007. (Illus.). 176p. *(978-1-904445-34-0(9))* Whittles Publishing.

Danchin, Etienne, et al, eds. Behavioural Ecology: An Evolutionary Perspective on Behaviour. 2008. (ENG., Illus.). 688p. (C). pap. 79.95 *(978-0-19-920629-2(5))* Oxford Univ. Pr., Inc.

Darmaraj, Mark Rayan & Anuar, Shahrul. The Ecology of the Common Treeshrew & Other Small Mammals in Malaysi. 2010. 272p. pap. *(978-3-639-23607-1(6))* VDM Verlag Dr. Mueller e.K.

Denny, Mark & McFadzean, Alan. Engineering Animals: How Life Works. 2011. (ENG., Illus.). 400p. 35.00 *(978-0-674-04854-6(7)*, Belknap Pr.) Harvard Univ. Pr.

Dodd, C. Kenneth, Jr., ed. Amphibian Ecology & Conservation: A Handbook of Techniques. 2009. (Techniques in Ecology & Conservation Ser.). (ENG., Illus.). 464p. pap. 59.95 *(978-0-19-954119-5(1))* Oxford Univ. Pr., Inc.

Dukas, Reuven & Ratcliffe, John M., eds. Cognitive Ecology II. 2009. (ENG., Illus.). 384p. 100.00 *(978-0-226-16935-4(9))*; pap. 40.00 *(978-0-226-16936-1(7))* Univ. of Chicago Pr.

Fleming, Theodore H. & Racey, Paul A., eds. Island Bats: Evolution, Ecology, & Conservation. 2010. (ENG., Illus.). 560p. 65.00 *(978-0-226-25330-5(9))* Univ. of Chicago Pr.

Flowers, Seville, et al. Ecological Studies of the Flora & Fauna of Flaming Gorge Reservoir Basin, Utah & Wyoming. (Upper Colorado Ser.: No. 3). reprint ed. 42.00 *(978-0-404-60648-0(2))* AMS Pr., Inc.

Forest Wildlife Ecology & Habitat Management. 2011. 89.95 ***(978-1-4398-3703-0(1)***, CRC Press) Taylor & Francis Group GBR. Dist: Taylor & Francis Group.

Frick-Ruppert, Jennifer. Mountain Nature: A Seasonal Natural History of the Southern Appalachians. 2010. (ENG., Illus.). 256p. 45.00 *(978-0-8078-3386-5(X))*; pap. 20.00 *(978-0-8078-7116-4(8))* Univ. of North Carolina Pr.

Fulbright, Timothy E. & Hewitt, David G., eds. Wildlife Science: Linking Ecological Theory & Management Applications. 2007. (ENG., Illus.). 384p. 124.95 *(978-0-8493-7487-6(1)*, CRC Press) Taylor & Francis Group GBR. Dist: Taylor & Francis Group.

Gehrt, Stanley D., et al, eds. Urban Carnivores: Ecology, Conflict, & Conservation. 2010. (ENG., Illus.). 304p. (gr. 17). 75.00 *(978-0-8018-9389-6(5))* Johns Hopkins Univ. Pr.

Golovatch, S. I., ed. Species & Communities in Extreme Environments. 2009. 530p. 187.50 *(978-954-642-452-5(8))* Pensoft Pubs. BGR. Dist: Coronet Bks.

Gulick, Amy. Salmon in the Trees: Life in Alaska's Tongass Rain Forest. 2010. (ENG., Illus.). 176p. 29.95 *(978-1-59485-091-2(7)*, Braided River) Mountaineers Bks., The.

Heinrich, Bernd. Life Everlasting: The Animal Way of Death. 2012. (ENG., Illus.). 256p. 25.00 ***(978-0-547-75266-2(0))*** Houghton Mifflin Harcourt Trade & Reference Pubs.

Howell, F. Clark, et al, eds. African Ecology & Human Evolution. 2007. (ENG., Illus.). 674p. (gr. 11). pap. 44.95 *(978-0-202-36136-9(5))* Aldine Transaction.

Krebs, John R., et al. An Introduction to Behavioural Ecology. 4th ed. 2012. (ENG., Illus.). 520p. 149.95 *(978-1-4443-3949-9(4)*, Wiley-Blackwell) Wiley, John & Sons, Inc.

Leader-Williams, N. Reindeer on South Georgia: The Ecology of an Introduced Population. 2009. (Studies in Polar Research Ser.). (ENG., Illus.). 336p. pap. 48.00 *(978-0-521-10698-6(2))* Cambridge Univ. Pr.

Lonsdorf, Elizabeth V., et al, eds. The Mind of the Chimpanzee: Ecological & Experimental Perspectives. 2010. (ENG., Illus.). 464p. 125.00 *(978-0-226-49278-0(8))*; pap. 49.00 *(978-0-226-49279-7(6))* Univ. of Chicago Pr.

Magnan, Pierre, et al, eds. Ecology, Behaviour & Conservation of the Charrs, Genus Salvelinus. 2010. (Developments in Environmental Biology of Fishes Ser.). (Illus.). 360p. pap. 219.00 *(978-90-481-6088-4(X)*, 904816088X) Springer.

Mani, M. S. Ecology & Biogeography of High Altitude Insects. 2010. (Series Entomologica Ser.). 548p. pap. 329.00 *(978-90-481-8511-5(4)*, 9048185114) Springer.

McCullough, Dale R., et al, eds. Sika Deer: Biology & Management of Native & Introduced Populations. (ENG., Illus.). xx, 666p. 2010. pap. 379.00 *(978-4-431-99802-0(0)*, 4431998020) 2008. 379.00 *(978-4-431-09428-9(8)*, 4431094288) Springer.

Mercurio, Vincenzo. Amphibians of Malawi. 2011. (Illus.). 393p. 95.00 *(978-3-89973-495-9(5))* Edition Chimaira DEU. Dist: Serpent's Tale Natural History Bk. Distributors, Inc.

Mitani, John, et al, eds. The Evolution of Primate Societies. 2012. 504p. pap. 50.00 ***(978-0-226-53172-4(4))***; (Illus.). 145.00 ***(978-0-226-53171-7(6))*** Univ. of Chicago Pr.

Morrison, Michael, et al. Wildlife-Habitat Relationships: Concepts & Applications. 3rd ed. 2006. (ENG.). 520p. 90.00 *(978-1-59726-094-7(0))* Island Pr.

Morrison, Michael L., et al. Wildlife-Habitat Relationships: Concepts & Applications. 3rd ed. 2006. (ENG., Illus.). 520p. pap. 55.00 *(978-1-59726-095-4(9))* Island Pr.

—Wildlife Study Design. 2nd ed. (Springer Series on Environmental Management Ser.). (Illus.). 2010. xxxiv, 386p. pap. 79.95 (978-1-4419-2594-7(5), 1441925945) 2008. XXXIV, 386p. 79.95 (978-0-387-75527-4(6), 0387755276) Springer.

Mullin, Stephen J. & Seigel, Richard A. Snakes: Ecology & Conservation. 2009. (Illus.). 376p. 62.95 (978-0-8014-4565-1(5), Comstock Publishing Assocs.) Cornell Univ. Pr.

Mulville. Totems & Sacrifices. 2007. (Illus.). 224p. 110.00 (978-0-415-41168-4(8)) Routledge.

Musiani, Marco, et al, eds. New Era for Wolves & People: Wolf Recovery, Human Attitudes, & Policy. 2009. (Energy, Ecology, & the Environment Ser.). (ENG., Illus.). 304p. pap. 34.95 (978-1-55238-270-7(2)) Univ. of Calgary Pr. CAN. Dist: Chicago Distribution Ctr.

Musiani, Marco & Boitani, Luigi. World of Wolves: New Perspectives on Ecology, Behaviour, & Management. Korieh, Chima, ed. 2010. (Energy, Ecology & the Environment Ser.). (Illus.). 432p. pap. 34.95 (978-1-55238-269-1(9)) Univ. of Calgary Pr. CAN. Dist: Michigan State Univ. Pr.

O'Connor, Terry & Sykes, Naomi, eds. Extinctions & Invasions: A Social History of British Fauna. 2010. (ENG., Illus.). 254p. pap. 56.00 (978-1-905119-31-8(3)) Windgather Pr. GBR. Dist: Brown, David Bk. Co., The.

Patterson, I. J. The Shelduck: A Study in Behavioural Ecology. 2009. (ENG., Illus.). 288p. pap. 42.00 (978-0-521-11335-9(0)) Cambridge Univ. Pr.

Patton, David R. Forest Wildlife Ecology & Habitat Management. 2010. (ENG., Illus.). 292p. 94.95 (978-1-4398-3702-3(3), CRC Press) Taylor & Francis Group GBR. Dist: Taylor & Francis Group.

Pekins, Peter. Wildlife Ecology Laboratory Manual (Nr 433) rev. ed. 2011. (ENG.). 118p. spiral bd. 43.99 **(978-0-7575-8820-4(4))** Kendall Hunt Publishing Co.

Powell, Roger A. Carnivore Ecology & Conservation: A Handbook of Techniques. Boitani, Luigi, ed. 2012. (ENG., Illus.). 544p. 135.00 **(978-0-19-955852-0(3))** Oxford Univ. Pr., Inc.

Prioli, Carmine. The Wild Horses of Shackleford Banks. 2007. (Illus.). 120p. per. 16.95 (978-0-89587-334-7(6)) Blair, John F. Pub.

Ranger, Shelagh. The Word of Wisdom & the Creation of Animals in Africa. 2007. (ENG., Illus.). 264p. per. 58.00 (978-0-227-67986-9(5)) Clarke, James Co., Ltd. GBR. Dist: Brown, David Bk. Co., The.

Reichling, Steven B. Reptiles & Amphibians of the Southern Pine Woods. 2008. (ENG., Illus.). 320p. pap. 29.95 (978-0-8130-3250-4(4)) Univ. Pr. of Florida.

Rosalino, Luís M. & Gheler-Costa, Carla. Middle-Sized Carnivores in Agricultural Landscapes. 2011. (978-1-61122-033-9(5)) Nova Science Pubs., Inc.

Rotter, Birgit. Population Ecology of the Edible Dormouse. 2009. 52p. pap. (978-3-639-20445-2(X)) VDM Verlag Dr. Mueller e.K.

Sinclair, A. R. E. Serengeti III: Human Impacts on Ecosystem Dynamics. Sinclair, A. R. E. et al, eds. 2008. (ENG., Illus.). 512p. 125.00 (978-0-226-76033-9(2)) Univ. of Chicago Pr.

Sinclair, A. R. E., et al, eds. Serengeti III: Human Impacts on Ecosystem Dynamics. 2008. (ENG., Illus.). 512p. pap. 45.00 (978-0-226-76034-6(0)) Univ. of Chicago Pr.

Sparling, Fred & Sparling, Joyce. North to Nunavut: An Arctic Love Affair. 2011. (Illus.). 246p. pap. 24.95 **(978-1-59715-080-4(0))** Chapel Hill Pr.

Verhoeven, Jos T. A., et al. Wetlands & Natural Resource Management. 2010. (Ecological Studies). (Illus.). xxii, 347p. pap. 219.00 (978-3-642-06972-7(X), 364206972X) Springer.

Werre, Jan Lodewijk. The Niger Delta Red Colobus. 2009. 168p. pap. (978-3-639-16855-6(0)) VDM Verlag Dr. Mueller e.K.

West, Stuart A., et al. An Introduction to Behavioural Ecology. 4th ed. 2012. (ENG., Illus.). 520p. pap. 79.95 **(978-1-4051-1416-5(9)**, Wiley-Blackwell) Wiley, John & Sons, Inc.

Westneat, David & Fox, Charles, eds. Evolutionary Behavioral Ecology, 1 vol. 2010. (ENG., Illus.). 684p. pap. 49.95 (978-0-19-533192-9(3)) Oxford Univ. Pr., Inc.

Whitlatch, Terryl & Banducci, Gilbert. Animals Real & Imagined: The fantasy of what is & what might Be. 2010. (Illus.). 160p. 49.95 (978-1-933492-91-9(0)) Design Studio Pr.

Williams, Amirtharaj. The Ecology & Population Parameters of Asian Elephants in Nw Indi. 2011. 152p. pap. **(978-3-8383-5431-6(1))** Lambert Academic Publishing.

Wood, Alix. Amazing Animal Partners. 2012. (Wow! Wildlife Ser.). (ENG.). 24p. (gr. k-5). 22.60 **(978-1-4488-8101-7(3))**; (Illus.). pap. 8.25 **(978-1-4488-8164-2(1))** Windmill Bks.

Woodbury, Angus M., et al. Ecological Studies of Flora & Fauna in Glen Canyon. (Glen Canyon Ser.: No. 7). reprint ed. 42.00 (978-0-404-60640-4(7)) AMS Pr., Inc.

—Ecological Studies of the Flora & Fauna of Navajo Reservoir Basin, Colorado & New Mexico. (Upper Colorado Ser.: No. 5). reprint ed. 34.50 (978-0-404-60655-8(5)) AMS Pr., Inc.

—Ecological Studies of the Flora & Fauna of the Curecanti Reservoir Basins, Western Colorado. (Upper Colorado Ser.: No. 8). reprint ed. 42.50 (978-0-404-60659-6(8)) AMS Pr., Inc.

Zhang, Wen & Liu, Hong. Behavioral & Chemical Ecology. 2010. (Environmental Research Advances Ser.). 145.00 (978-1-60741-099-7(0)) Nova Science Pubs., Inc.

ANIMAL ELECTRICITY

see Electrophysiology

ANIMAL EUTHANASIA

see Euthanasia of Animals

ANIMAL EXPERIMENTATION

see also Laboratory Animals; Vivisection

Beauchamp, Tom L., et al. The Human Use of Animals: Case Studies in Ethical Choice. 2nd ed. 2008. (ENG., Illus.). 352p. (C). pap. 39.99 (978-0-19-534019-8(1)) Oxford Univ. Pr., Inc.

Bogdanske, John J., et al. Laboratory Mouse & Laboratory Rat Procedural Techniques: Manuals & DVDs, 2 vols. 2010. (Illus.). 192p. pap. 108.00 (978-1-4398-5050-3(X), CRC Press) Taylor & Francis Group GBR. Dist: Taylor & Francis Group.

Brakebusch, Cord & Pihlajaniemi, Taina, eds. Mouse as a Model Organism: From Animals to Cells. 2011. (ENG., Illus.). xiv, 165p. 189.00 (978-94-007-0749-8(5), 9400707495) Springer.

Burgess, Colin & Dubbs, Chris. Animals in Space: From Research Rockets to the Space Shuttle. 2007. (Springer Praxis Books / Space Exploration Ser.). (Illus.). 406p. per. 39.95 (978-0-387-36053-9(0), 0387360530) Springer.

Conn, P. Michael, et al. The Animal Research War. 2008. (ENG.). 224p. 42.00 (978-0-230-60014-0(X)) Palgrave Macmillan.

Cram101 Textbook Reviews. Outlines & Highlights for Ethical Issues in Behavioral Research by Allan J Kimmel. 2011. 120p. pap. 28.95 **(978-1-61490-933-0(4))** Cram101 Inc.

Dolan, Kevin. Laboratory Animal Law: Legal Control of the Use of Animals in Research. 2nd rev. ed. 2007. (ENG., Illus.). 240p. pap. 99.99 (978-1-4051-6282-1(1), Wiley-Blackwell) Wiley, John & Sons, Inc.

Editorial Staff of Annals of the New York Academy of Sciences, ed. Animal Models. 2012. (Annals of the New York Academy of Sciences Ser.: 98). (ENG., Illus.). 96p. pap. 75.00 **(978-1-57331-875-4(2)**, Wiley-Blackwell) Wiley, John & Sons, Inc.

Fadali, Moneim A. Animal Experimentation: A Harvest of Shame. 288p. pap. 14.95 (978-1-885113-55-9(2)) Hidden Springs Pr.

Fisch, Gene S. & Flint, Jonathan, eds. Transgenic & Knockout Models of Neuropsychiatric Disorders. 2010. (Contemporary Clinical Neuroscience Ser.). (Illus.). 312p. pap. 189.00 (978-1-61737-607-8(8), 1617376078) Humana Pr.

Fried, Bernard & Graczyk, T. K., eds. Echinostomes as Experimental Models for Biological Research. 2010. 284p. pap. 174.00 (978-90-481-5392-3(1), 9048153921) Springer.

Garrett, Jeremy R. The Ethics of Animal Research: Exploring the Controversy. 2012. (Basic Bioethics Ser.). (ENG., Illus.). 352p. 54.00 **(978-0-262-01706-0(7))**; pap. 27.00 **(978-0-262-51691-4(8))** MIT Pr.

Gigliotti, Carol, ed. Leonardo's Choice: Genetic Technologies & Animals. (ENG., Illus.). xxviii, 256p. 2010. pap. 49.95 (978-94-007-0523-4(9), 9400705239) 2009. 139.00 (978-90-481-2478-7(6), 9048124786) Springer.

Harré, Rom. Pavlov's Dogs & Schrödinger's Cat: Scenes from the Living Laboratory. 2010. (ENG., Illus.). 288p. pap. 18.95 (978-0-19-923857-6(X)) Oxford Univ. Pr., Inc.

—Pavlov's Dogs & Schrödinger's Cat: Scenes from the Living Laboratory. 2009. (ENG., Illus.). 288p. 39.95 (978-0-19-923856-9(1)) Oxford Univ. Pr., Inc.

Hart, Lynette A., et al. Why Dissection? Animal Use in Education, 1 vol. 2008. (Illus.). 240p. 49.95 (978-0-313-32390-4(9), GR2390) Greenwood Publishing Group, Inc.

Hau, Jann & Schapiro, Steven, eds. Handbook of Laboratory Animal Science Vol. 2: Animal Models. 3rd rev. ed. 2011. (ENG., Illus.). 480p. 119.95 (978-1-4200-8457-3(7), CRC Press) Taylor & Francis Group GBR. Dist: Taylor & Francis Group.

Haugen, David M. Animal Experimentation. 2006. (Opposing Viewpoints Ser.). (ENG., Illus.). 234p. (J). 27.50 (978-0-7377-3347-1(0)); lib. bdg. 39.70 (978-0-7377-3346-4(2)) Cengage Gale. (Greenhaven Pr., Inc.).

Haynes, Richard P. Animal Welfare: Competing Conceptions & Their Ethical Implications. 2010. (ENG.). xxv, 162p. pap. 49.95 (978-90-481-8787-4(7), 9048187877) Springer.

Helton, William S. Canine Ergonomics: The Science of Working Dogs. 2009. (ENG., Illus.). 366p. 92.95 (978-1-4200-7991-3(3), CRC Press) Taylor & Francis Group GBR. Dist: Taylor & Francis Group.

Knight, Andrew. The Costs & Benefits of Animal Experiments: Evidence & Ethics. 2011. (Palgrave Macmillan Animal Ethics Ser.). (ENG., Illus.). 272p. 85.00 (978-0-230-24392-7(4)) Palgrave Macmillan.

Lankford, Ronnie D. Animal Experimentation, No. 9. 2009. (At Issue Ser.). (ENG.). 128p. (gr. 10-12). pap. 31.80 (978-0-7377-4280-0(1)); (Illus.). pap. 22.50 (978-0-7377-4279-4(8)) Cengage Gale. (Greenhaven Pr., Inc.).

Luo, Z. David, ed. Pain Research: Methods & Protocols. 2010. (Methods in Molecular Medicine Ser.). (Illus.). 320p. pap. 129.00 (978-1-61737-358-9(3), 1617373583) Humana Pr.

Magel, Charles R. Keyguide: Animal Rights. xiv, 267p. (978-0-7201-1984-8(7), Burns & Oates) Continuum International Publishing Group, Ltd.

Maguire, Tim & Novik, Eric. Methods in Bioengineering: Alternatives to Animal Testing. 2010. (Illus.). 295p. 139.00 (978-1-60807-011-4(5)) Artech Hse., Inc.

The Market for In Vitro Toxicology Testing. 2007. per. 4250.00 (978-1-59623-275-4(7)) BCC Research.

McArthur, Robert A. & Borsini, Franco, eds. Animal & Translational Models for CNS Drug Discovery, 3 vols. 2008. (ENG., Illus.). 1376p. 210.00 (978-0-12-373861-5(X), Academic Pr.) Elsevier Science & Technology Bks.

Monamy, Vaughan. Animal Experimentation: A Guide to the Issues. 2nd ed. 2009. (ENG.). 128p. (C). 84.00 (978-0-521-87879-1(9)); pap. 27.99 (978-0-521-70348-2(4)) Cambridge Univ. Pr.

Morrison, Adrian R. An Odyssey with Animals: A Veterinarian's Reflections on the Animal Rights & Welfare Debate. 2009. (ENG., Illus.). 288p. 29.95 (978-0-19-537444-5(4)) Oxford Univ. Pr., Inc.

Rigalli, Alfredo & Di Loreto, Veronica, eds. Experimental Surgical Models in the Laboratory Rat. 2009. (ENG., Illus.). 232p. 139.95 (978-1-4200-9326-1(6), CRC Press) Taylor & Francis Group GBR. Dist: Taylor & Francis Group.

Rollin, Bernard. The Unheeded Cry. 2010. 348p. pap. 24.95 (978-0-557-57821-4(3)) Lulu Enterprises Inc.

Salem, Deborah J. & Rowan, Andrew N. The State of the Animals IV, 2007. 2007. (Illus.). vii, 238p. pap. 29.95 (978-0-9748400-9-3(2)) Humane Society of the United States, The.

Schwabe, Calvin W. Cattle, Priests, & Progress in Medicine. 2009. (ENG.). 292p. pap. 50.00 (978-0-8166-5867-1(6)) Univ. of Minnesota Pr.

Shanks, Niall & Greek, C. Ray. Animal Models in Light of Evolution. 2009. 444p. pap. 64.95 (978-1-59942-502-3(5), Brown Walker Pr.) Universal Pubs.

szumski, bonnie. Is animal experimentation Ethical? 2011. (In Controversy Ser.). (Illus.). 96p. (YA). (gr. 7-12). lib. bdg. 27.95 (978-1-60152-174-3(X)) ReferencePoint Pr., Inc.

Twine, Richard. Animals as Biotechnology: Ethics, Sustainability & Critical Animal Studies. 2010. (Science in Society Ser.). (ENG., Illus.). 232p. 84.95 (978-1-84407-830-1(2)) Routledge.

Ward, Robin. A Manual for Laboratory Animal Mana. . V5. 2008. (Manuals in Biomedical Research Ser.). pap. 61.00 (978-981-277-958-8(2)) World Scientific Publishing Co., Inc.

Warnik, Jason E., ed. Translational Neuroscience & Its Advancement of Animal Research Ethics. 2010. (Neuroscience Research Progress Ser.). 89.00 (978-1-60876-185-2(1)) Nova Science Pubs., Inc.

Wildavsky, Aaron. Regulation of Carcinogens: Are Animal Tests a Sound Foundation? (Illus.). 38p. pap. 5.95 (978-0-945999-57-7(7), 1009) Independent Institute, The.

ANIMAL FIGHTING

see also Bullfights

Alexander, David E. Why Don't Jumbo Jets Flap Their Wings? Flying Animals, Flying Machines, & How They Are Different. 2009. (ENG., Illus.). 296p. 26.95 (978-0-8135-4479-3(3)) Rutgers Univ. Pr.

ANIMAL FLUIDS AND HUMORS

see Body Fluids

ANIMAL FOLKLORE

see Animals—Folklore

ANIMAL FOOD

see Food of Animal Origin

ANIMAL FORMS IN DECORATION AND ORNAMENT

see Decoration and Ornament—Animal Forms

ANIMAL GENETICS

Adebambo, Olufunmilayo. Fundamentals of Animal Breeding & Genetics. 2010. 428p. pap. (978-3-639-11038-8(2)) VDM Verlag Dr. Mueller e.K.

Avise, John C. Genetics in the Wild. 2010. (ENG., Illus.). 270p. pap. 24.95 (978-1-58834-293-5(X)) Smithsonian Institution Pr.

Bailey, E. & Brooks, S. A. Horse Genetics. 2nd ed. 2013. 272p. pap. 75.00 (978-1-84593-675-4(2)) CABI GBR. Dist: Stylus Publishing, LLC.

Boonen, Kurt. Peptidomics of the Mouse. 2010. 156p. pap. (978-3-8383-0459-5(4)) Lambert Academic Publishing.

Çagatay, Ifakat Tülay. The Glycosylation of Dichelobacter Nodosus Fimbriae. 2010. 136p. pap. (978-3-8383-5699-0(3)) Lambert Academic Publishing.

Charmley, E., et al, eds. Redesigning Animal Agriculture: The Challenge of the 21st Century. 2007. (Illus.). 336p. (C). 145.00 (978-1-84593-223-7(4)) CABI GBR. Dist: Stylus Publishing, LLC.

Chowdhary, Bhanu, ed. Animal Genomics. (Illus.). 366p. (978-3-8055-7734-2(6)) Karger, S. AG.

Detrich, H. William, III. Essential Zebrafish Methods: Genetics & Genomics. Westerfield, Monte & Zon, Leonard I., eds. 2009. (Reliable Lab Solutions Ser.). (ENG., Illus.). 400p. pap. 78.95 (978-0-12-375160-7(8), Academic Pr.) Elsevier Science & Technology Bks.

Frankham, Richard, et al, eds. Adaptation & Fitness in Animal Populations: Evolutionary & Breeding Perspectives on Genetic Resource Management. 2008. (ENG., Illus.). xii, 260p. 189.00 (978-1-4020-9004-2(8), 1402090048) Springer.

Gjedrem, Trygve. Selection & Breeding Programs in Aquaculture. 2010. (ENG.). xvii, 364p. pap. 139.00 (978-90-481-6840-8(6), 9048168406) Springer.

Gomase, Virendra & Murti, Madhur. Animal Biotechnology. 2010. 364p. pap. (978-3-639-25031-2(1)) VDM Verlag Dr. Mueller e.K.

Gould, Laura L. Cats Are Not Peas: A Calico History of Genetics. 2nd rev. ed. 2008. (ENG.). 312p. 39.00 (978-1-56881-320-2(1)) AK Peters, Ltd.

Hadlaczky, Gyula. Mammalian Chromosome Engineering: Methods & Protocols. 2011. (Illus.). ix, 257p. E-Book **(978-1-61779-099-7(0))** Humana Pr.

Hartley, James L., ed. Protein Expression in Mammalian Cells: Methods & Protocols. 2011. (Methods in Molecular Biology Ser.). (ENG., Illus.). xi, 276p. 119.00 **(978-1-61779-351-6(5)**, 1617793515) Humana Pr.

Iannuzzi, L., et al, eds. Molecular & Evolutionary Cytogenetics of Domestic Animals. 2009. (Illus.). 226p. (978-3-8055-9346-5(5)) Karger, S. AG.

Jiang, Zhihua & Ott, Troy L., eds. Reproductive Genomics in Domestic Animals. 2010. (ENG., Illus.). 472p. 220.95 (978-0-8138-1784-2(6), Wiley-Blackwell) Wiley, John & Sons, Inc.

Karamichou, Eleni. Genetic Aspects of Carcass Composition & Meat Quality in Sheep. 2011. 196p. pap. **(978-3-8443-0073-4(2))** Lambert Academic Publishing.

Martínez, Paulino & Fernández, Jesús. Estimating Parentage Relationships Using Molecular Markers in Aquaculture. 2008. pap. 89.00 (978-1-60692-140-1(1)) Nova Science Pubs., Inc.

Ndubuisi, Machebe. Poultry Semen: Effects of Season & Genotypes on Quality. 2011. 88p. pap. **(978-3-639-33339-8(X))** VDM Verlag Dr. Mueller e.K.

Ostrander, Elaine A. & Ruvinsky, Anatoly, eds. The Genetics of the Dog. 2nd ed. 2012. (Illus.). 512p. 220.00 **(978-1-84593-940-3(9))** CABI GBR. Dist: Stylus Publishing, LLC.

Pandian, T. J. Sex Determination in Fish. 2011. (ENG., Illus.). 280p. 79.95 (978-1-57808-748-8(1)) BIOS Scientific Publishers Ltd. GBR. Dist: Taylor & Francis Group.

Pease, Shirley & Lois, Carlos, eds. Mammalian & Avian Transgenesis - New Approaches. 2010. (Principles & Practice Ser.). (ENG., Illus.). xx, 281p. pap. 269.00 (978-3-642-06665-8(8), 3642066658) Springer.

Pinard, Marie-Hélène. Animal Genomics for Animal Health: Paris, France, 25-27 October 2007. 2008. (Developments in Biologicals Ser.). (Illus.). 440p. pap. (978-3-8055-8619-1(1)) Karger, S. AG.

Rechi, Leopold J. Animal Genetics. 2009. (Animal Science, Issues & Professions Ser.). 139.00 (978-1-60741-844-3(4)) Nova Science Pubs., Inc.

Scherf, B., et al, eds. Animal Genetic Resources, Volume 48: An International Journal. 2011. (Animal Genetic Resources Ser.). (ENG, FRE & SPA., Illus.). 141p. pap. **(978-92-5-006864-0(6))** Food & Agriculture Organization of the United Nations.

Sehgal, Lalit. Drug Induced Locomotor Alteration in Drosophila Melanogaster. 2010. 76p. pap. (978-3-8383-7740-7(0)) Lambert Academic Publishing

te Pas, Marinus. Systems Biology & Livestock Science. 2011. (ENG.). 324p. 199.95 **(978-0-470-96301-2(8)**, Wiley-Blackwell) Wiley, John & Sons, Inc.

Womack, James, ed. Bovine Genomics. 2012. (ENG.). 284p. 199.95 **(978-0-8138-2122-1(3)**, Wiley-Blackwell) Wiley, John & Sons, Inc.

ANIMAL GUT INDUSTRIES

see also Sutures

Gewertz, Deborah B. & Errington, Frederick Karl. Cheap Meat: Flap Food Nations in the Pacific Islands. 2010. (ENG., Illus.). 224p. 55.00 (978-0-520-26092-4(9)); pap. 24.95 (978-0-520-26093-1(7)) Univ. of California Pr.

ANIMAL HABITAT

see Habitat (Ecology)

ANIMAL HERMAPHRODITISM

see Intersexuality in Animals

ANIMAL INTERSEXUALITY

see Intersexuality in Animals

ANIMAL HOMES, DOMESTIC

see Animal Housing

ANIMAL HOMES, WILD

see Animals—Habitations

ANIMAL HOSPITALS

see Veterinary Hospitals

ANIMAL HOUSING

see also Birdhouses

Barthel, Thomas. Dogscaping: Creating the Perfect Backyard & Garden for You & Your Dog. 2010. (ENG.). 144p. (gr. 6). pap. 16.95 (978-1-933958-33-0(2)) BowTie Pr.

Graves, Robert Edwin. Penn State Housing Plans for Calves & Heifers. 2007. (978-1-933395-17-3(6)) Natural Resource, Agricultural, & Engineering Service.

Griffin, David. Black & Decker 24 Weekend Projects for Pets: Dog Houses, Cat Trees, Rabbit Hutches & More. 2007. (Black & Decker Ser.). (ENG., Illus.). 160p. per. 19.95 (978-1-58923-308-9(5), 1589233085, Creative Publishing International) Quayside.

Harbolt, Tami L. Bridging the Bond: The Cultural Construction of the Shelter Pet. 2009. (ENG.). 166p. pap. 19.95 (978-1-55753-545-0(0)) Purdue Univ. Pr.

Henderson, Carrol L. Woodworking for Wildlife: Homes for Birds & Animals. 2010. (ENG., Illus.). 164p. pap. 19.95 (978-0-9754338-3-6(0)) Minnesota's Bookstore.

Lambton, Lucinda. Palaces for Pigs: Animal Architecture & other Beastly Dwellings. 2011. (ENG., Illus.). 255p. 50.00 (978-1-85074-989-9(2)) English Heritage GBR. Dist: Brown, David Bk. Co., The.

Larkin, David. Farmhouse. 39.95 (978-0-8478-2611-7(2)) Rizzoli International Pubns., Inc.

LaTour, Randy. 101 Different Ways to Build Homes & Pens for Your Animals: A Complete Step-by-Step Guide. 2011. (ENG.). 288p. pap. 24.95 (978-1-60138-371-6(1)) Atlantic Publishing Co.

Pisc. Model Codes of Practice for the Welfare of Animals: Pigs 3rd edition PISC Technical Report 92. 3rd ed. 2008. (Primary Industries Report Ser.). 30p. pap. 22.00 (978-0-643-09477-2(6)) CSIRO Publishing AUS. Dist: Stylus Publishing, LLC.

Sandilands, Victoria & Hocking, Paul M., eds. Alternative Systems for Poultry: Health, Welfare & Productivity. 2012. (Poultry Science Symposium Ser.: Vol. 30). 320p. 160.00 **(978-1-84593-824-6(0))** CABI GBR. Dist: Stylus Publishing, LLC.

Smith, Paul, et al. Perfecting the Pig Environment. 2009. (ENG., Illus.). 90p. 40.00 (978-1-904761-81-5(X)) Nottingham Univ. Pr. GBR. Dist: Independent Pubs. Group.

Szabo, Julia & Szabo. Pretty Pet-Friendly: Easy Ways to Keep Spot's Digs Stylish & Spotless. 2009. (ENG., Illus.). 224p. pap. 16.99 *(978-0-470-37728-4(3),* Howell Bk. Hse.) Wiley, John & Sons, Inc.

Walker, Bob. The Cats' House. 2009. (ENG.). 92p. pap. 14.99 *(978-0-7407-7861-2(7))* Andrews McMeel Publishing.

ANIMAL-HUMAN COMMUNICATION

see Human-Animal Communication

ANIMAL-HUMAN RELATIONSHIPS

see Human-Animal Relationships

ANIMAL HUSBANDRY

see Domestic Animals; Livestock

ANIMAL IMMOBILIZATION

Ross, Lindsay G. & Ross, Barbara. Anaesthetic & Sedative Techniques for Aquatic Animals. 3rd rev. ed. 2008. (ENG., Illus.). 240p. 169.95 *(978-1-4051-4938-9(8),* Wiley-Blackwell) Wiley, John & Sons, Inc.

ANIMAL INDUSTRY

see also Cattle Trade; Dairying; Domestic Animals; Hides and Skins Industry; Livestock; Livestock—Marketing; Poultry Industry; Working Animals

Alberto, P. Di & Costa, C. New Research on Livestock Science & Dairy Farming. 2008. 228p. pap. 98.00 *(978-1-60456-556-0(X))* Nova Science Pubs., Inc.

Andrieu, S., ed. Gaining the edge in ruminant Production: Nutritional strategies for optimal productivity & Efficiency. 2007. 124p. pap. 78.00 *(978-90-8686-044-9(3))* Wageningen Academic Publishers NLD. Dist: Enfield Publishing & Distribution Co., Inc.

Baur, Gene. Farm Sanctuary: Changing Hearts & Minds about Animals & Food. 2008. (ENG.). 320p. pap. 15.00 *(978-0-7432-9159-0(X),* Touchstone) Touchstone.

Boutelle, Veronica & Jorgensen, Rikke. Minding Your Dog Business: A Practical Guide to Business Success for Dog Professionals. 2010. (Illus.). 144p. 19.95 *(978-1-929242-74-0(3))* Dogwise Publishing.

Casady, R. B., et al. Commercial Rabbit Raising. (Lost Arts Ser.). (Illus.). 69p. reprint ed. pap. 10.00 *(978-0-8466-6054-5(7),* U54) Shorey's Bookstore.

Coleman, G. J. & Hemsworth, P. H. Human-Livestock Interactions: The Stockperson & the Productivity of Intensively Farmed Animals. 2nd ed. 2011. (Illus.). 194p. 125.00 *(978-1-84593-673-0(6))* CABI GBR. Dist: Stylus Publishing, LLC.

Committee on the Economic Development and Current Status of the Sheep Industry in the United States. Changes in the Sheep Industry in the United States: Making the Transition from Tradition. National Research Council Staff, ed. 2008. (ENG.). 364p. pap. 75.00 *(978-0-309-12161-3(2))* National Academies Pr.

Continuing Problems in USDA's Enforcement of the Humane Methods of Slaughter ACT: Hearing Before the Subcommittee on Domestic Policy of the Committee on Oversight & Government Reform, House of Representatives, One Hundred Eleventh Congress, Second Session, March 4, 2010. 2010. (Illus.). iii, 120p. ***(978-0-16-089007-9(1),*** 552-070-43039-3) United States Government Printing Office.

Cottle, D. J., ed. International Sheep & Wool Handbook. 2010. (ENG., Illus.). 450p. instr.'s hndbk. ed. 100.00 *(978-1-904761-86-0(0))* Nottingham Univ. Pr. GBR. Dist: Independent Pubs. Group.

Cram101 Textbook Reviews & Cram101 Textbook Reviews. Outlines & Highlights for Introduction to Animal Science by W Stephen Damron. 2011. 100p. pap. 27.95 ***(978-1-61830-890-0(4))*** Cram101 Inc.

Cunningham, Merle, et al. Animal Science & Industry. 8th rev. ed. 2011. (ENG.). 800p. 109.33 *(978-0-13-502527-7(3),* Prentice Hall) Prentice Hall PTR.

Damron, W. Stephen. Introduction to Animal Science. 5th rev. ed. 2012. (ENG., Illus.). 736p. (C). 139.20 ***(978-0-13-262389-6(7),*** Prentice Hall) Prentice Hall PTR.

—Introduction to Animal Science: Global, Biological, Social, & Industry Perspectives. 4th ed. 2008. (ENG.). 864p. (C). 144.80 *(978-0-13-609497-5(X),* Prentice Hall) Prentice Hall PTR.

Damron, W. Stephen. Introduction to Animal Science, Student Value Edition. 5th ed. 2012. (ENG., Illus.). 736p. (C). ring bd. 83.20 ***(978-0-13-262415-2(X),*** Prentice Hall) Prentice Hall PTR.

Egendorf, Laura K. Food. 2006. (Opposing Viewpoints Ser.). (ENG., Illus.). 227p. (gr. 10-12). 27.50 *(978-0-7377-3232-0(6),* Greenhaven Pr., Inc.); (YA). (gr. 9-12). pap. 39.70 *(978-0-7377-3231-3(8))* Cengage Gale.

Encyclopedia of Animal Science. 2011. cd-rom 595.00 ***(978-0-415-80286-4(5),*** CRC Press) Taylor & Francis Group GBR. Dist: Taylor & Francis Group.

Entrepreneur Press Staff. Start Your Own Pet Business & More. 2009. (ENG., Illus.). 220p. 19.95 *(978-1-59918-186-8(X),* 159918186X) Entrepreneur Pr. dba Entrepreneur Media, Inc.

Gillespie, James R. & Flanders, Frank. Modern Livestock & Poultry Production. 8th ed. 2009. (Texas Science Ser.). Orig. Title: Livestock & Poultry Production. (ENG.). 1136p. (C). 111.95 *(978-1-4283-1808-3(9))* Delmar Cengage Learning.

Grandin, Temple. Improving Animal Welfare: A Practical Approach. 2010. (Illus.). 336p. pap. 75.00 *(978-1-84593-541-2(1))* CABI GBR. Dist: Stylus Publishing, LLC.

Hemming, David, ed. Animal Science Reviews 2010. 2011. (CAB Reviews Ser.). 280p. 265.00 *(978-1-84593-880-2(1))* CABI GBR. Dist: Stylus Publishing, LLC.

Imhoff, Daniel, ed. CAFO: The Tragedy of Industrial Animal Factories. 2010. (ENG., Illus.). 400p. 50.00 *(978-1-60109-058-4(7),* Earth Aware Editions) Mandala Publishing.

—The CAFO Reader: The Tragedy of Industrial Animal Factories. 2010. (ENG.). 480p. pap. 21.95 *(978-0-9709500-5-5(5))* Watershed Media Pr.

Impacts of U.S. Consumer Demand on the Illegal & Unsustainable Trade of Wildlife Products: Oversight Hearing Before the Subcommittee on Fisheries, Wildlife, & Oceans of the Committee on Natural Resources, U.S. House of Representatives, One Hundred Tenth Congress, Second Session, Tuesday, September 16, 2008. 2009. iii, 37p. *(978-0-16-082659-7(4),* 552-070-38676-9) United States Government Printing Office.

Kirby, David. Animal Factory: The Looming Threat of Industrial Pig, Dairy, & Poultry Farms to Humans & the Environment. (ENG.). 512p. 2011. pap. 17.99 *(978-0-312-67174-7(1),* St. Martin's Griffin) 2010. 26.99 *(978-0-312-38058-8(5))* St. Martin's Pr.

Kirkpatrick, Jamie. People, Sheep & Nature Conservation: The Tasmanian Experience. 2007. (Illus.). 264p. pap. 35.95 *(978-0-643-09372-0(9))* CSIRO Publishing AUS. Dist: Stylus Publishing, LLC.

Laufer, Peter. Forbidden Creatures: Inside the World of Animal Smuggling & Exotic Pets. (ENG.). 2011. 288p. pap. 16.95 *(978-0-7627-7180-6(1))* 2010. 272p. 19.95 *(978-1-59921-926-4(3))* Globe Pequot Pr., The. (Lyons Pr.).

Matolla, Pascual F. & Miers, Sandy S. Animal Science Research Biographical Sketches & Research Summaries. 2012. ***(978-1-62100-873-6(8))*** Nova Science Pubs., Inc.

McPeak, John G., et al. Risk & Social Change in an African Rural Economy: Livelihoods in Pastoralist Communities. 2011. (Routledge ISS Studies in Rural Livelihoods Ser.). (ENG., Illus.). 224p. (C). 125.00 *(978-0-415-61598-3(4))* Routledge.

Mikesell, Robert & Baker, MeeCee. Animal Science Biology & Technology. 3rd ed. 2010. (ENG.). 64p. (C). pap., lab manual ed. 70.95 *(978-1-4354-8639-3(0))* Delmar Cengage Learning.

—Animal Science Biology & Technology. 3rd ed. 2010. (Texas Science Ser.). (ENG., Illus.). 464p. (C). 93.95 *(978-1-4354-8637-9(4))* Delmar Cengage Learning.

Misginaw, Tamirat. Cattle Commercial off-Take in Pastoral Areas of Hadiya Zone: Constraints & Opportunities of Cattle Commercial off-Take in Pastoral Areas of Hadiya Zone, Snnpr, Ethiopia. 2011. 96p. pap. ***(978-3-639-32787-8(X))*** VDM Verlag Dr. Mueller e.K.

Niemeyer, Darlene. Doggy Business 101: A Practical Guide to Starting & Running Your Own Business, 1 vol. 2009. (ENG., Illus.). 208p. 24.95 *(978-0-7938-0627-0(5))* TFH Pubns., Inc.

Petrov, Krassimir. A Bayesian Vector Autoregresive Model of the U S Dairy Industry. 2010. 176p. pap. *(978-3-8383-1893-6(5))* Lambert Academic Publishing.

Pond, Wilson G., et al, eds. Animal Welfare in Animal Agriculture. 2011. (ENG., Illus.). 333p. 89.95 ***(978-1-4398-4842-5(4),*** CRC Press) Taylor & Francis Group GBR. Dist: Taylor & Francis Group.

Pond, Wilson G., et al, eds. Encyclopedia of Animal Science, 2 vols. 2nd rev. ed. 2011. (ENG., Illus.). 1296p. 595.00 *(978-1-4398-0932-7(1),* CRC Press) Taylor & Francis Group GBR. Dist: Taylor & Francis Group.

Review of the Impact of Feed Costs on the Livestock Industry: Hearing Before the Subcommittee on Livestock, Dairy, & Poultry of the Committee on Agriculture, House of Representatives, One Hundred Tenth Congress, First Session, March 8, 2007. 2007. (Illus.). iii, 154p. *(978-0-16-079604-3(0),* 552-070-36562-1) United States Government Printing Office.

Review of the Market Structure of the Livestock Industry: Hearing Before the Subcommittee on Livestock, Dairy, & Poultry of the Committee on Agriculture, House of Representatives, One Hundred Tenth Congress, First Session, April 17, 2007. 2008. (Illus.). iv, 227p. *(978-0-16-080688-9(7),* 552-070-37284-9) United States Government Printing Office.

Ricke, Steven C., et al, eds. Organic Meat Production & Processing. 2012. (Institute of Food Technologists Ser.: 53). (ENG.). 464p. 199.95 ***(978-0-8138-2126-9(6),*** Wiley-Blackwell) Wiley, John & Sons, Inc.

Rosati, A., et al, eds. Animal production & animal science Worldwide: WAAP book of the Year 2007. 2008. (Illus.). 330p. 154.00 *(978-90-8686-068-5(0))* Wageningen Academic Publishers NLD. Dist: Enfield Publishing & Distribution Co., Inc.

Saunderson, Mont H. Western Stock Ranching. 2009. (ENG.). 264p. pap. 50.00 *(978-0-8166-5865-7(X))* Univ. of Minnesota Pr.

Schaffer, Michael. One Nation under Dog: America's Love Affair with Our Dogs. 2010. (ENG., Illus.). 304p. pap. 15.00 *(978-0-8050-9146-5(7),* Holt Paperback) St. Martin's Pr.

Soliva, Carla Riccarda, et al, eds. Greenhouse Gases & Animal Agriculture: an Update: Proceedings of the 2nd International Conference on Greenhouse Gases & Animal Agriculture, Held in Zurich, Switzerland Between 20 & 24 September 2005. 2006. (International Congress Ser.). (Illus.). 377p. 190.00 *(978-0-444-52248-1(4),* Churchill Livingstone) Elsevier - Health Sciences Div.

Stein, Sarah Abrevaya. Plumes: Ostrich Feathers, Jews, & a Lost World of Global Commerce. 2010. (ENG., Illus.). 256p. pap. 20.00 *(978-0-300-16818-1(7))* Yale Univ. Pr.

Thomsen, Peter M., ed. The U. S. Eu Beef Hormone & Poultry Disputes. 2010. pap. 47.00 *(978-1-61728-985-9(X))* Nova Science Pubs., Inc.

Tolenhoff, Karl B., ed. Animal Agriculture: Research Progress. 2008. 134p. 82.00 *(978-1-60456-058-9(4))* Nova Science Pubs., Inc.

Ullrey, Duane E., et al. Encyclopedia of Animal Science Second Edition - Volume 1, 2 vols. 2nd ed. 2010. (Illus.). xlviii, 1131p. *(978-1-4398-5098-5(4))* CRC Pr. LLC.

—Encyclopedia of Animal Science Second Edition - Volume 2, 2 vols. 2nd ed. 2010. (Illus.). xlviii, 1131p. *(978-1-4398-5100-5(X))* CRC Pr. LLC.

Webster, John, et al, eds. The Meat Crisis: Developing More Sustainable Production & Consumption. 2010. (ENG., Illus.). 328p. 140.00 *(978-1-84407-902-5(3));* pap. 39.95 *(978-1-84407-903-2(1))* Routledge.

Zilberman, David, et al, eds. Health & Animal Agriculture in Developing Countries. 2011. (Natural Resource Management & Policy Ser.). (ENG., Illus.). vii, 424p. 139.00 *(978-1-4419-7076-3(2),* 1441970762) Springer.

ANIMAL INDUSTRY—LAW AND LEGISLATION

Barnett, Stephen W., ed. Manual of Animal Technology. 2007. (ENG., Illus.). 440p. pap. 120.99 *(978-0-632-05593-7(6),* Wiley-Blackwell) Wiley, John & Sons, Inc.

Burnett, D. Graham. Trying Leviathan: The Nineteenth-Century New York Court Case That Put the Whale on Trial & Challenged the Order of Nature. (ENG.). 304p. (C). 2010. pap. 22.95 *(978-0-691-14615-7(2))* 2007. (Illus.). 49.95 *(978-0-691-12950-1(9))* Princeton Univ. Pr.

Dockery, Opal. Animal Cruelty Law in the United States, A Comparative Analysis. 2010. 225p. pap. 25.00 *(978-0-557-57780-4(2))* Lulu Enterprises Inc.

Evans, E. P. Criminal Prosecution & Capital Punishm. 2006. pap. 31.95 *(978-1-4286-4072-6(X))* Kessinger Publishing, LLC.

Favre, David S. Animal Law: Welfare, Interests, & Rights. 2008. (Illus.). xvi, 495p. pap. *(978-0-7355-7313-0(1),* Aspen Pubs.) Wolters Kluwer Law & Business.

Frasch, Pamela & Hessler, Kathy. Animal Law in a Nutshell. 2010. (Nutshell Ser.). 445p. 38.00 *(978-0-314-19597-5(1),* West Legalworks) West.

Kyalo-Willy, Daniel, et al. Spatial Distribution of Livestock Production Systems. 2010. 76p. pap. *(978-3-8383-9275-2(2))* Lambert Academic Publishing.

National Archives and Records Administration, creator. Animals & Animal Products: Parts 1 To 199. 2011. (Code of Federal Regulations Ser.). 1067p. pap. 67.00 ***(978-1-60946-320-5(X))*** National Archives & Records Administration.

ANIMAL INFERTILITY

see Infertility in Animals

ANIMAL INSTINCT

see Instinct

ANIMAL INTELLIGENCE

see also Animal Behavior; Cognition in Animals; Instinct; Learning, Psychology of; Psychology, Comparative

Balcombe, Jonathan. Second Nature: The Inner Lives of Animals. (MacSci Ser.). (ENG.). 256p. 2011. pap. 17.00 *(978-0-230-10781-6(8))* 2010. (Illus.). 27.00 *(978-0-230-61362-1(4))* Palgrave Macmillan.

Barnes, Ronald A. Cat IQ Test: Fun for You, Fun for Your Pet How Smart Is Your CAT? 2006. (Illus.). 24p. per. 19.95 *(978-0-9785609-3-5(0))* New Global Publishing.

—Dog IQ Test: Fun for You, Fun for Your Pet How Smart Is Your Dog? 2006. (Illus.). 24p. per. 19.95 *(978-0-9785609-2-8(2))* New Global Publishing.

Bierens De Haan, J. A. Animal Psychology - Its Nature & Its P. 2006. 164p. per. *(978-1-4067-9566-0(6),* Hesperides Pr.) Read Bks.

Boysen, Sally & Custance, Deborah. The Smartest Animals on the Planet: Extraordinary Tales of the Natural World's Cleverest Creatures. 2009. (ENG., Illus.). 192p. 35.00 *(978-1-55407-456-3(8))* Firefly Bks., Ltd.

Boysen, Sarah Till, et al. The Smartest Animals on the Planet. enl. ed. 2012. (ENG., Illus.). 192p. pap. 24.95 ***(978-1-55407-965-0(9))*** Firefly Bks., Ltd.

Bradshaw, John. Dog Sense: How the New Science of Dog Behavior Can Make You a Better Friend to Your Pet. (ENG.). 352p. (gr. 9). 2012. pap. 15.99 ***(978-0-465-03003-3(3))*** 2011. 25.99 *(978-0-465-01944-1(7))* Basic Bks.

Cram101 Textbook Reviews. Outlines & Highlights for Animal Learning & Cognition: An Introduction by John M. Pearce, ISBN. 2010. 262p. pap. 31.95 *(978-1-61654-095-1(8))* Cram101 Inc.

Del Monte, Laila. Psychic Communication with Animals for Health & Healing. 2010. (ENG.). 1p. pap. 16.00 *(978-1-59143-100-8(X),* 1309792) Bear & Co.

George, J. Romanes. Animal Intelligence. 2008. 540p. *(978-1-4437-2215-5(4),* Hesperides Pr.) Read Bks.

Gould, Carol Grant & Gould, James L. Animal Architects: Building & the Evolution of Intelligence. 2007. (ENG., Illus.). 336p. (gr. 9). 26.95 *(978-0-465-02782-8(2))* Basic Bks.

Gould, James L. & Gould, Carol Grant. Animal Architects: Building & the Evolution of Intelligence. 2012. (ENG.). 336p. (gr. 9). pap. 16.99 ***(978-0-465-02838-2(1))*** Basic Bks.

Hatkoff, Amy. The Inner World of Farm Animals: Their Amazing Social, Emotional, & Intellectual Capacities. 2009. (ENG., Illus.). 168p. 19.95 *(978-1-58479-748-7(7))* Stewart, Tabori & Chang.

Heinrich, Bernd. Mind of the Raven: Investigations & Adventures with Wolf-Birds. 2007. (P. S. Ser.). (ENG., Illus.). 336p. pap. 14.99 *(978-0-06-113605-4(0),* HarperPerennial) HarperCollins Pubs.

Hornaday, William T. The Minds & Manners of Wild Animals: A Book of Personal Observations. 2006. (ENG.). 294p. pap. 21.99 *(978-1-4264-1293-6(2));* 280p. pap. 23.99 *(978-1-4264-1298-1(3))* BiblioBazaar.

Maurice Rowdon. The Ape of Sorrows: From Stranger to Destroyer. 2009. 340p. 33.95 *(978-0-595-49360-9(2));* pap. 23.95 *(978-0-595-49558-0(3))* iUniverse, Inc.

McFarland, David. Guilty Robots, Happy Dogs: The Question of Alien Minds. 2009. (ENG.). 256p. pap. 15.95 *(978-0-19-921930-8(3))* Oxford Univ. Pr., Inc.

Parker, Henry W. Spirit of Beauty Essays Scientific & A. 2006. pap. 26.95 *(978-1-4286-5407-5(0))* Kessinger Publishing, LLC.

Pearce, John M. Animal Learning & Cognition: An Introduction. 3rd rev. ed. 2008. (ENG., Illus.). 432p. (C). 95.00 *(978-1-84169-655-3(2));* 54.50 *(978-1-84169-656-0(0))* Taylor & Francis Group GBR. (Psychology Press). Dist: Taylor & Francis Group.

Pepperberg, Irene. Alex & Me: How a Scientist & a Parrot Discovered a Hidden World of Animal Intelligence - And Formed a Deep Bond in the Process. 2009. (ENG.). 288p. pap. 13.99 *(978-0-06-167398-6(6),* HarperPerennial) HarperCollins Pubs.

Pfungst, Oskar. Clever Hans (The Horse of Mr. Von Osten) Wozniak, Robert H., ed. (Classics in Psychology Ser.). (Illus.). 286p. *(978-1-85506-697-7(1),* Burns & Oates) Continuum International Publishing Group, Ltd.

Pitt, Frances. Animal Mind. 2006. 388p. per. *(978-1-4067-9674-2(3),* Hesperides Pr.) Read Bks.

Pryor, Karen. Reaching the Animal Mind: Clicker Training & What It Teaches Us about All Animals. 2010. (ENG.). 288p. pap. 15.00 *(978-0-7432-9777-6(6),* Scribner) Scribner.

Reiss, Diana. The Dolphin in the Mirror: Exploring Dolphin Minds & Saving Dolphin Lives. 2012. (ENG., Illus.). 288p. pap. 13.95 ***(978-0-547-84461-9(1),*** Mariner Bks.) Houghton Mifflin Harcourt Trade & Reference Pubs.

Reznikova, Zhanna. Animal Intelligence: From Individual to Social Cognition. 2007. (ENG., Illus.). 488p. (C). per. 71.00 *(978-0-521-53202-0(7));* 147.00 *(978-0-521-82504-7(0))* Cambridge Univ. Pr.

Romanes, George J. Mental Evolution in Animals. (Illus.). 411p. reprint ed. lib. bdg. 98.00 *(978-0-7222-3082-4(6))* Library Reprints, Inc.

Romanes, George John. Mental Evolution in Animals. 2009. 296p. pap. *(978-0-217-23556-3(5))* Books LLC.

Romanes, George John. Mental Evolution in Animals: With a Posthumous Essay on Instinct by Charles Darwin. 2011. (Cambridge Library Collection - Life Sciences Ser.). (ENG., Illus.). 426p. pap. 31.99 ***(978-1-108-03787-7(9))*** Cambridge Univ. Pr.

Russon, Anne E. & Begun, David R., eds. The Evolution of Thought: Evolutionary Origins of Great Ape Intelligence. 2007. (ENG., Illus.). 396p. pap. 79.00 *(978-0-521-03992-5(4))* Cambridge Univ. Pr.

Shenk, David. The Genius in All of Us: New Insights into Genetics, Talent, & IQ. 2010. (ENG., Illus.). 320p. 26.95 *(978-0-385-52365-3(3),* Doubleday) Knopf Doubleday Publishing Group.

Thorndike, Edward L. Animal Intelligence: An Experimental Study of the Associative Processes in Animals. (Illus.). 109p. reprint ed. lib. bdg. 88.00 *(978-0-7222-3083-1(4))* Library Reprints, Inc.

Thorndike, Edward Lee. Animal Intelligence. Wozniak, Robert H., ed. (Classics in Psychology Ser.). (Illus.). 311p. *(978-1-85506-698-4(X),* Burns & Oates) Continuum International Publishing Group, Ltd.

Washburn, Margaret F. The Animal Mind. Wozniak, Robert H., ed. (Classics in Psychology Ser.). (Illus.). 402p. *(978-1-85506-695-3(5),* Burns & Oates) Continuum International Publishing Group, Ltd.

Wasserman, Edward A. & Zentall, Thomas R., eds. Comparative Cognition: Experimental Explorations of Animal Intelligence. 2009. (ENG., Illus.). 720p. pap. 65.00 *(978-0-19-537780-4(X))* Oxford Univ. Pr., Inc.

—The Oxford Handbook of Comparative Cognition, 1 vol. 2nd ed. 2012. (Oxford Library of Psychology Ser.). (ENG.). 960p. 175.00 *(978-0-19-539266-1(3))* Oxford Univ. Pr., Inc.

Wood, J. G. Man & Beast, Here & Hereafter, Illustrated by More Than Three Hundred Original Anecdotes by the Rev J G Wood. 2006. (Illus.). 148p. per. 16.99 *(978-1-4255-1108-1(2))* MPublishing.

ANIMAL INTRODUCTION

Animal Invaders. 2010. 32p. lib. bdg. 379.00 *(978-1-60279-288-3(7),* 200088) Cherry Lake Publishing.

Leader-Williams, N. Reindeer on South Georgia: The Ecology of an Introduced Population. 2009. (Studies in Polar Research Ser.). (ENG., Illus.). 336p. pap. 48.00 *(978-0-521-10698-6(2))* Cambridge Univ. Pr.

Newell, Jennifer. Trading Nature: Tahitians, Europeans, & Ecological Exchange. 2010. 336p. (C). 45.00 *(978-0-8248-3281-0(7))* Univ. of Hawaii Pr.

Price, Mark R. Stanley. Animal Reintroductions: The Arabian Oryx in Oman. 2010. (Cambridge Studies in Applied Ecology & Resource Management Ser.). (ENG.). 316p. pap. 33.99 *(978-0-521-13167-4(7))* Cambridge Univ. Pr.

Williams, Gill. 100 Alien Invaders: Animals & Plants That Are Changing Our World. 2011. (ENG., Illus.). 160p. 24.99 *(978-1-84162-359-7(8))* Bradt Travel Guides GBR. Dist: Globe Pequot Pr., The.

ANIMAL KINGDOM

see Zoology

ANIMAL LANGUAGE

see Animal Communication; Animal Sounds; Sound Production by Animals

ANIMAL LIBERATION

see Animal Rights

ANIMAL LOCOMOTION

see also Running; Swimming; Walking

Bertram, Albrecht. Understanding Mammalian Locomotion: Concepts & Applications. 2015. (ENG.). 404p. 99.00 ***(978-0-470-45464-0(4),*** Wiley-Blackwell) Wiley, John & Sons, Inc.

Frampton, Michael. Embodiments of Will: Anatomical & Physiological Theories ofVoluntary Animal Motion from Greek Antiquity to the Latin Middle Ages, 400 B.C-A.D. 1300. 2008. 660p. pap. *(978-3-639-08294-4(X))* VDM Verlag Dr. Mueller e.K.

Graziano, Michael S. A. The Intelligent Movement Machine: An Ethological Perspective on the Primate Motor System. 2008. (ENG., Illus.). 240p. 79.95 *(978-0-19-532670-3(9))* Oxford Univ. Pr., Inc.

Kato, Naomi & Kamimura, Shinji, eds. Bio-mechanisms of Swimming & Flying: Fluid Dynamics, Biomimetic Robots, & Sports Science. 2010. (ENG., Illus.). xiv, 403p. pap. 189.00 *(978-4-431-99829-7(2),* 4431998292) Springer.

Lewis, Mark A. & Moorcroft, Paul R. Mechanistic Home Range Analysis. 2006. (Monographs in Population Biology). (Illus.). 172p. 99.00 *(978-0-691-00927-8(9))* Princeton Univ. Pr.

Maddock, L., et al, eds. The Mechanics & Physiology of Animal Swimming. 2008. (ENG.). 264p. pap. 53.00 *(978-0-521-06495-8(3))* Cambridge Univ. Pr.

Moorcroft, Paul R. & Lewis, Mark A. Mechanistic Home Range Analysis. 2006. (Monographs in Population Biology). (ENG., Illus.). 208p. (C). per. 49.95 *(978-0-691-00928-5(7))* Princeton Univ. Pr.

Muybridge, Eadweard. Muybridge's Animals in Motion CD-ROM & Book. 2007. (Dover Electronic Clip Art Ser.). (ENG., Illus.). 48p. pap. 16.95 *(978-0-486-99767-4(7))* Dover Pubns., Inc.

Pettigrew, James Bell. Animal Locomotion. 2006. 296p. per. 23.99 *(978-1-4255-2778-5(7))* MPublishing.

Taylor, Graham, et al, eds. Animal Locomotion. 2010. (ENG., Illus.). 350p. 169.00 *(978-3-642-11632-2(9),* 3642116329) Springer.

ANIMAL LORE

see Animals—Folklore

ANIMAL LUMINESCENCE

see Bioluminescence

ANIMAL MAGNETISM

see also Hypnotism; Mesmerism

Ashburner, John. Notes & Studies in the Philosophy of Animal Magnetism & Spiritualism. 2007. (ENG.). 468p. 52.95 *(978-0-548-05170-2(4))* Kessinger Publishing, LLC.

Colquhoun, John Campbell. History of Magic Witchcraft & Animal M. 2006. pap. 34.95 *(978-1-4286-4853-1(4));* (ENG.). pap. 30.95 *(978-1-4286-4854-8(2))* Kessinger Publishing, LLC.

Donker, Gerald. Exposing the Secret Law of Attraction. 2008. 88p. pap. 11.95 *(978-1-4092-3614-6(5))* Lulu Enterprises Inc.

Dumont, Theron Q. The Advanced Course in Personal Magnetism (New Edition) 2007. 236p. per. 13.45 *(978-1-59462-600-5(6),* 637, Book Jungle) Standard Pubns., Inc.

—How to Protect Yourself Against Injurious Thought Attraction - 2006. pap. 12.95 *(978-1-4286-8551-2(0))* Kessinger Publishing, LLC.

—How to Use Your Personality to Win the Affection of the Opposite. 2006. pap. 9.95 *(978-1-4286-8545-1(6))* Kessinger Publishing, LLC.

Fine, Catherine G., et al. Despine & the Evolution of Psychology: Historical & Medical Perspectives on Dissociative Disorders. Fine, Catherine G. & McKeown, Joanne M., eds. 2008. (ENG.). 288p. 100.00 *(978-0-230-60867-2(1))* Palgrave Macmillan.

Holland, Charles. Spiritual or Magnetic Forces. 2007. (ENG.). 108p. 33.95 *(978-0-548-08238-6(3))* Kessinger Publishing, LLC.

Lee, Edwin. Animal Magnetism & Magnetic Lucid Somnambulism 1866. 2007. (ENG.). 352p. 46.95 *(978-0-548-05650-9(1))* Kessinger Publishing, LLC.

Poe, Edgar Allan. Philosophy of Animal Magnetism. 2006. pap. 19.95 *(978-1-4286-4736-7(8))* Kessinger Publishing, LLC.

Shaftesbury, Edmund. The Book of Shaftesbury's Secrets. 2011. 446p. 56.95 ***(978-1-258-00714-0(2))*** Literary Licensing, LLC.

Townshend, Chauncy Hare. Facts in Mesmerism, with Reasons for a Dispassionate Inquiry into It. 2011. (Cambridge Library Collection - Magic & the Supernatural Ser.). (Illus.). 598p. pap. 43.00 *(978-1-108-02589-8(7))* Cambridge Univ. Pr.

Tuttle, Hudson. Arcana of Nature; or, the History & Laws of Creation by Hudson Tuttle with an Appendix, by Datus Kelley + 2006. (ENG.). 320p. per. 23.99 *(978-1-4255-3158-4(X));* 268p. per. 23.99 *(978-1-4255-2407-4(9))* MPublishing.

Von Reichenbach, Baron Charles. PhysicoPhysiological Researches on the D. 2006. pap. 37.95 *(978-1-4286-4778-7(3))* Kessinger Publishing, LLC.

ANIMAL-MAN RELATIONSHIPS

see Human-Animal Relationships

ANIMAL MECHANICS

see also Animal Locomotion; Human Mechanics

Ahlborn, Boye K. Zoological Physics: Quantitative Models of Body Design, Actions, & Physical Limitations of Animals. 2010. (ENG., Illus.). xx, 428p. pap. 99.00 *(978-3-642-05877-6(9),* 3642058779) Springer.

Blignault, Karin. Equine Biomechanics for Riders: The Key to Balanced Riding. 2009. (Paca, la macaca Ser.). (ENG., Illus.). 272p. 57.95 *(978-0-85131-953-7(X))* Trafalgar Square Bks.

Corcilius, Klaus. Streben und Bewegen: Aristoteles' Theorie der animalischen Ortsbewegung. 2008. (Quellen und Studien zur Philosophie Ser.).Tr. of Striving & Movement. Aristotle's Theory of Animal Movement. (GER.). X, 410p. 147.00 *(978-3-11-019454-8(6));* 224.00 ***(978-3-11-173700-3(4))*** De Gruyter, Walter Inc.

Graziano, Michael S. A. The Intelligent Movement Machine: An Ethological Perspective on the Primate Motor System. 2008. (ENG., Illus.). 240p. 79.95 *(978-0-19-532670-3(9))* Oxford Univ. Pr., Inc.

Lewis, Mark A. & Moorcroft, Paul R. Mechanistic Home Range Analysis. 2006. (Monographs in Population Biology). (Illus.). 172p. 99.00 *(978-0-691-00927-8(9))* Princeton Univ. Pr.

Moorcroft, Paul R. & Lewis, Mark A. Mechanistic Home Range Analysis. 2006. (Monographs in Population Biology). (ENG., Illus.). 208p. (C). per. 49.95 *(978-0-691-00928-5(7))* Princeton Univ. Pr.

Viswanathan, Gandhimohan. M., et al. The Physics of Foraging: An Introduction to Random Searches & Biological Encounters. 2011. (ENG., Illus.). 178p. 50.00 *(978-1-107-00679-9(1))* Cambridge Univ. Pr.

ANIMAL MIGRATION

see also Birds—Migration

Baker, Robin. Fantastic Journeys, the Marvels of Animal Migration. (Illus.). 240p. 25.00 *(978-1-85391-185-6(2))* Sterling Publishing Co., Inc.

Bass, Karen, ed. Nature's Great Events: The Most Amazing Natural Events on the Planet. 2009. (Illus.). 320p. 39.95 *(978-0-226-47154-9(3))* Univ. of Chicago Pr.

Benard Aswani Ouna & Aswani, Ouna Benard. Migration & Admixture of Sheep in Africa: Molecular Genetics. 2008. 72p. pap. *(978-3-639-09526-5(X))* VDM Verlag Dr. Mueller e.K.

Dean, W. Richard J. Nomadic Desert Birds. 2010. (Adaptations of Desert Organisms Ser.). (Illus.). x, 185p. pap. 219.00 *(978-3-642-07325-0(5),* 3642073255) Springer.

Elewa, Ashraf M. T., ed. Migration of Organisms: Climate. Geography. Ecology. 2010. (ENG., Illus.). xiv, 332p. pap. 139.00 *(978-3-642-06591-0(0),* 3642065910) Springer.

Hoare, Ben. Animal Migration: Remarkable Journeys in the Wild. 2009. (Illus.). 176p. 36.95 *(978-0-520-25823-5(1))* Univ. of California Pr.

Hobson, Keith A. & Wassenaar, Leonard I. Tracking Animal Migration with Stable Isotopes. 2008. (Terrestrial Ecology Ser.: 2). (ENG., Illus.). 160p. 86.95 *(978-0-12-373867-7(9),* Academic Pr.) Elsevier Science & Technology Bks.

Jones, M. B., et al, eds. Migrations & Dispersal of Marine Organisms. 2010. (Developments in Hydrobiology Ser.). 280p. pap. 159.00 *(978-90-481-6480-6(X),* 904816480X) Springer.

Kostyal, Karen M. Great Migrations: Epic Animal Journeys. 2010. (Illus.). 304p. 35.00 *(978-1-4262-0644-3(5),* National Geographic) National Geographic Society.

Milner-Gulland, E. J., et al. Animal Migration: A Synthesis. 2011. (ENG., Illus.). 304p. 135.00 *(978-0-19-956899-4(5));* pap. 67.50 *(978-0-19-956900-7(2))* Oxford Univ. Pr., Inc.

Rozhok, Andrii. Orientation & Navigation in Vertebrates. (ENG., Illus.). vi, 164p. 2010. pap. 189.00 *(978-3-642-09747-8(2),* 3642097472) 2008. 189.00 *(978-3-540-78718-1(6),* 3540787186) Springer.

Stewart, Robyn. Nomads of the Serengeti. 2006. (Illus.). 176p. pap. 32.95 *(978-1-86872-762-9(9))* Struik Pubs. ZAF. Dist: International Publishers Marketing.

Werner, Dietrich, ed. Biological Resources & Migration. 2010. (ENG., Illus.). xxiv, 363p. pap. 339.00 *(978-3-642-05989-6(9),* 3642059899) Springer.

Wilcove, David S. No Way Home: The Decline of the World's Great Animal Migrations. (ENG., Illus.). 256p. 2010. pap. 25.00 *(978-1-59726-823-3(2))* 2007. 40.00 *(978-1-55963-985-9(7))* Island Pr.

ANIMAL MORPHOLOGY

see Morphology (Animals)

ANIMAL MOVEMENTS

see Animal Mechanics

ANIMAL NAMES, LATIN

see Animals—Nomenclature

ANIMAL NAMES, POPULAR

see Animals—Nomenclature (Popular)

ANIMAL NAMES, SCIENTIFIC

see Animals—Nomenclature

ANIMAL NAVIGATION

see also Animal Migration; Bird Navigation

Gould, James L. & Gould, Carol Grant. Nature's Compass: The Mystery of Animal Navigation. 2012. (Science Essentials Ser.). (ENG., Illus.). 320p. 29.95 ***(978-0-691-14045-2(6))*** Princeton Univ. Pr.

Menzel, Nancy G. Animal Thinking: Contemporary Issues in Comparative Cognition. 2011. (Strüngmann Forum Reports). (ENG., Illus.). 416p. (gr. 17). 40.00 ***(978-0-262-01663-6(X))*** MIT Pr.

Rozhok, Andrii. Orientation & Navigation in Vertebrates. 2010. (ENG., Illus.). vi, 164p. pap. 189.00 *(978-3-642-09747-8(2),* 3642097472) Springer.

ANIMAL NUTRITION

see also Feeds

also subdivision Feeding and Feeds under names of animals and groups of animals. e.g. Poultry—Feeding and Feeds

Adams, Clifford A. & Adams, C. A. Nutrition-Based Health: Nutricines & Nutrients, Health Maintenance & Disease Avoidance in Animals. 2008. (Nutricine Concept Ser.). (ENG., Illus.). 170p. pap. 70.00 *(978-1-904761-58-7(5))* Nottingham Univ. Pr. GBR. Dist: Independent Pubs. Group.

Ajibola, Abdulwahid. Nutritional Management of Domestic Animals Amidst Water Shortages. 2011. (Illus.). 96p. pap. ***(978-3-8454-0198-0(2))*** Lambert Academic Publishing.

Alonso-Amelot, Miguel E. Tannins & Phenolics in Animal Nutrition: Chemistry & Challenges. 2011. (Series: Food & Beverage Consumption & Health Ser.). 43.00 *(978-1-61209-220-1(9))* Nova Science Pubs., Inc.

Awad Mahmoud Morsy, Wael. Nutritional & Physiological Studies on Rabbits. 2011. 128p. pap. ***(978-3-8443-9563-1(6))*** Lambert Academic Publishing.

Barboza, Perry S., et al. Integrative Wildlife Nutrition. 2009. (ENG., Illus.). xviii, 342p. pap. 89.95 *(978-3-642-03695-8(3),* 3642036953); 209.00 *(978-3-540-87884-1(X),* 354087884X) Springer.

Bedford, M. R. & Partridge, G. G., eds. Enzymes in Farm Animal Nutrition. 2nd ed. 2011. (Illus.). 330p. 160.00 *(978-1-84593-674-7(4))* CABI GBR. Dist: Stylus Publishing, LLC.

Bels, V., ed. Feeding in Domestic Vertebrates: From Structure to Behaviour. 2006. (Illus.). 384p. (C). 160.00 *(978-1-84593-063-9(0))* CABI GBR. Dist: Stylus Publishing, LLC.

Bernstein, Anna R. Maintaining a Healthy Diet. 2010. (Nutrition & Diet Research Progress Ser.). 115p. pap. 43.00 *(978-1-60741-856-6(8))* Nova Science Pubs., Inc.

Borgearo, Sarah R. Animal Feed: Types, Nutrition & Safety. 2011. (Agriculture Issues & Policies Ser.). (Illus.). 276p. 129.00 *(978-1-61209-346-8(9))* Nova Science Pubs., Inc.

Brown, William, et al. Supplementing Grazing Cows Diet. 2009. 84p. pap. *(978-3-639-09414-5(X))* VDM Verlag Dr. Mueller e.K.

Buczinski, Sebastien. Bovine Ultrasound: Veterinary Clinics of North America - Food Animal Practice. 2009. (Clinics: Veterinary Medicine Ser.: 25-3). (ENG., Illus.). xii, 554p. 99.00 *(978-1-4377-1284-1(3),* Saunders) Elsevier - Health Sciences Div.

Burger, I. H. & Rivers, J. P. W., eds. Nutrition of the Dog & Cat: Waltham Symposium Number 7. 2009. (ENG., Illus.). 432p. pap. 55.00 *(978-0-521-10545-3(5))* Cambridge Univ. Pr.

Cheeke, Peter Robert & Dierenfeld, Ellen S. Comparative Animal Nutrition. 2010. (Illus.). 350p. pap. 75.00 *(978-1-84593-631-0(0))* CABI GBR. Dist: Stylus Publishing, LLC.

Crovetto, G. Matteo, ed. Energy & protein metabolism & Nutrition. 2010. (Eaap Scientific Ser.: 127). (Illus.). 736p. 188.00 *(978-90-8686-153-8(9))* Wageningen Academic Publishers NLD. Dist: Enfield Publishing & Distribution Co., Inc.

Davies, Zoe. Introduction to Horse Nutrition. 2009. (ENG., Illus.). 248p. pap. 49.99 *(978-1-4051-6998-1(2),* Wiley-Blackwell) Wiley, John & Sons, Inc.

Dawo, Mohamed Ishma. Assessment of New Phaseolus Lines As Animal Feed. 2011. 292p. pap. ***(978-3-8433-8945-7(4))*** Lambert Academic Publishing.

Donette, Jack Frank. Feeding Behavior of Non-Human Species with Index & Medical Analysis of New Research Information for All Nations. 2006. (Illus.). 160p. 69.95 *(978-0-7883-4549-4(4),* 07883-45494) ABBE Pubs. Assn. of Washington, D.C.

Doppenberg, Jannes & van der Aar, Piet, eds. Dynamics in Aimal Nutrition. 2010. (Illus.). 206p. pap. 69.00 *(978-90-8686-149-1(0))* Wageningen Academic Publishers NLD. Dist: Enfield Publishing & Distribution Co., Inc.

Dryden, G. & Dryden, Gordon McL. Animal Nutrition Science. 2008. (Illus.). 320p. pap. 75.00 *(978-1-84593-412-5(1))* CABI GBR. Dist: Stylus Publishing, LLC.

El Boushy, A. H. & van der Poel, A. F. B. Handbook of Poultry Feed from Waste: Processing & Use. 2nd ed. 2010. 420p. pap. 359.00 *(978-90-481-5523-1(1),* 9048155231) Springer.

Fascetti, Andrea J. & Delaney, Sean J., eds. Applied Veterinary Clinical Nutrition. 2012. (ENG., Illus.). 400p. 99.99 *(978-0-8138-0657-0(7),* Wiley-Blackwell) Wiley, John & Sons, Inc.

France, J. & Kebreab, E., eds. Mathematical Modelling in Animal Nutrition. 2008. (Illus.). 640p. 230.00 *(978-1-84593-354-8(0))* CABI GBR. Dist: Stylus Publishing, LLC.

Frape, David. Equine Nutrition & Feeding. 4th ed. 2010. (ENG., Illus.). 512p. pap. 77.99 *(978-1-4051-9546-1(0),* Wiley-Blackwell) Wiley, John & Sons, Inc.

Garnsworthy, P. C. & Wiseman, J. Recent Advances in Animal Nutrition 2008. 2009. (Recent Advances in Animal Nutrition Ser.). (ENG., Illus.). 374p. 120.00 *(978-1-904761-04-4(6))* Nottingham Univ. Pr. GBR. Dist: Independent Pubs. Group.

Garnsworthy, P. C. & Wiseman, J., eds. Recent Advances in Animal Nutrition 2006. 2008. (Recent Advances in Animal Nutrition Ser.). (ENG., Illus.). 376p. 130.00 *(978-1-904761-02-0(X))* Nottingham Univ. Pr. GBR. Dist: Independent Pubs. Group.

—Recent Advances in Animal Nutrition 2007. 2008. (Recent Advances in Animal Nutrition Ser.). (ENG., Illus.). 362p. 130.00 *(978-1-904761-03-7(8))* Nottingham Univ. Pr. GBR. Dist: Independent Pubs. Group.

—Recent Advances in Animal Nutrition 2009. 2010. (Recent Advances in Animal Nutrition Ser.). (ENG., Illus.). 365p. 96.00 *(978-1-904761-05-1(4))* Nottingham Univ. Pr. GBR. Dist: Independent Pubs. Group.

Geor, Raymond J. Equine Practice. 2009. (Clinics: Veterinary Medicine Ser.: 25-1). (ENG.). 240p. 99.00 *(978-1-4377-0556-0(1),* Saunders) Elsevier - Health Sciences Div.

Godwyll, Paschal, et al. Feed Supplements on Utilisation of Maize Leaf Strippings by Sheep. 2010. 144p. pap. *(978-3-639-25257-6(8))* VDM Verlag Dr. Mueller e.K.

Islam, Shilpi, et al. Aquatic Plants As Cattle Feed with Special Reference to Water Hyacinth. 2011. 68p. pap. ***(978-3-8443-1709-1(0))*** Lambert Academic Publishing.

Jez, Joseph, ed. Sulfur: A Missing Link between Soils, Crops, & Nutrition. 2008. (Agronomy Ser.: 50). lib. bdg. 90.00 *(978-0-89118-168-2(7))* ASA-CSSA-SSSA.

Jorgensen, Hans-Heinrich. Schussler Tissue Salts for Horses: Healthy & Fit with Minerals. 2008. (Understanding Your Horse Ser.). (ENG., Illus.). 96p. pap. 21.95 *(978-3-86127-926-6(6))* Cadmos Verlag GmbH DEU. Dist: Independent Pubs. Group.

Jurgens, Marshall H. & Bregendahl, Kristjan. Animal Feeding & Nutrition. 10th rev. ed. 2010. (ENG., Illus.). 636p. pap. 94.33 *(978-0-7575-3176-7(8))* Kendall Hunt Publishing Co.

Katunguka-Rwakishaya, Eli, et al. A Handbook on Livestock Nutrition. (Illus.). v, 85p. *(978-9970-02-763-7(8))* Fountain Pubs. Ltd.

Kellems, Richard O. & Church, David C. Livestock Feeds & Feeding. 6th ed. 2009. (ENG., Illus.). 656p. (C). pap. 144.80 *(978-0-13-159475-3(3),* Prentice Hall) Prentice Hall PTR.

Kellon, Eleanor M. Horse Journal Guide to Equine Supplements & Nutraceuticals. 2008. (ENG., Illus.). 304p. 29.95 *(978-1-59921-178-7(5),* Lyons Pr.) Globe Pequot Pr., The.

Laurence, Michael. Maternal Productivity in Beef Cattle. 2011. 328p. pap. ***(978-3-8454-0806-4(5))*** Lambert Academic Publishing.

Lee, Cheng-Sheng, et al. Alternative Protein Sources in Aquaculture Diets. 2008. (ENG.). 626p. (C). 139.95 *(978-1-56022-148-7(8),* CRC Press) Taylor & Francis Group GBR. Dist: Taylor & Francis Group.

Lindner, Arno, ed. Applied equine nutrition & Training: Equine NUtrition & TRAining COnference (ENUTRACO) 2009. 2009. (Illus.). 240p. 80.00 *(978-90-8686-124-8(5))* Wageningen Academic Publishers NLD. Dist: Enfield Publishing & Distribution Co., Inc.

Luckstadt, Christian, ed. Acidifiers in Animal Nutrition: A Guide for Feed Preservation & Acidification to Promote Animal Performance. 2008. (ENG., Illus.). 90p. pap. 50.00 *(978-1-904761-40-2(2))* Nottingham Univ. Pr. GBR. Dist: Independent Pubs. Group.

Makkar, Harinder P. S. Quantification of Tannins in Tree & Shrub Foliage: A Laboratory Manual. 2010. 116p. pap. 139.00 *(978-90-481-6428-8(1),* 9048164281) Springer.

Makkar, Harinder P. S., et al. Plant Secondary Metabolites. (Methods in Molecular Biology Ser.). (Illus.). xii, 130p. 2010. pap. 124.00 *(978-1-61737-872-0(0),* 1617378720) 2007. 124.00 *(978-1-58829-993-2(7))* Humana Pr.

Marta, Terre. Enhanced-Growth Feeding Programs for Dairy Calves - Nutrition, Management. 2008. 156p. pap. *(978-3-8364-7777-2(7))* VDM Verlag Dr. Mueller e.K.

Mavromichalis, Ioannis. Applied Nutrition for Young Pigs. 2006. (Illus.). 272p. 145.00 *(978-1-84593-067-7(3))* CABI GBR. Dist: Stylus Publishing, LLC.

McDonald, Peter, et al. Animal Nutrition. 7th rev. ed. 2011. (ENG., Illus.). 692p. pap. 122.50 ***(978-1-4082-0423-8(1))*** Pearson Education, Ltd. GBR. Dist: Trans-Atlantic Pubns., Inc.

Middle, Clare. Real Food for Dogs & Cats: A Practical Guide to Feeding Your Pet a Balanced, Natural Diet. 2008. (ENG., Illus.). 160p. pap. 14.95 *(978-1-921361-35-7(2))* Fremantle Pr. AUS. Dist: Independent Pubs. Group.

Mindell, Earl & Renaghan, Elizabeth. Dr. Earl Mindell's Nutrition & Health for Dogs. 2nd rev. ed. 2007. (ENG., Illus.). 448p. pap. 19.95 *(978-1-59120-203-5(5),* Basic Health Pubns., Inc.

Miraglia, N. & Martin-Rosset, W. Nutrition & feeding of the Broodmare. 2006. (Eaap Ser.). 416p. 102.00 *(978-90-8686-014-2(1))* Wageningen Academic Publishers NLD. Dist: Enfield Publishing & Distribution Co., Inc.

Moore, Lucile. Rabbit Nutrition & Nutritional Healing. 2011. 188p. pap. 15.95 ***(978-1-60264-785-5(2))*** Virtualbookworm.com Publishing, Inc.

Nash, Leanne T. & Burrows, Anne M. The Evolution of Exudativory in Primates. 2010. (Illus.). xxi, 303p. E-Book ***(978-1-4419-6661-2(7))*** Springer.

National Research Council (U.S.) Staff & Examining the Safety of Dietary Supplements for Horses Committee. Safety of Dietary Supplements for Horses, Dogs, & Cats. 2008. (ENG.). 216p. 295.00 *(978-0-309-12570-3(7))* National Academies Pr.

National Research Council Staff & Nutrient Requirements of Horses Committee. Nutrient Requirements of Horses. 6th rev. ed. 2007. (ENG., Illus.). 360p. 99.95 *(978-0-309-10212-4(X))* National Academies Pr.

Nestle, Marion & Nesheim, Malden. Feed Your Pet Right: The Authoritative Guide to Feeding Your Dog & Cat. 2010. (ENG., Illus.). 384p. pap. 16.99 *(978-1-4391-6642-0(0),* Free Pr.) Free Pr.

Obeda, Godwin. Fish Nutrition. 2010. 72p. pap. *(978-3-639-27794-4(5))* VDM Verlag Dr. Mueller e.K.

Oljaca Halas, Danka & R. Pluske, John. Strategies to Improve the Health & Production of Weaner Pigs. 2011. 208p. pap. ***(978-3-8443-9085-8(5))*** Lambert Academic Publishing.

Olson, Lew. Raw & Natural Nutrition for Dogs: The Definitive Guide to Homemade Meals. 2010. (ENG., Illus.). 240p. pap. 16.95 *(978-1-55643-903-2(2))* North Atlantic Bks.

Pagan, J. D., ed. Advances in Equine Nutrition IV. 2009. (Equine Nutrition Ser.). (ENG., Illus.). 530p. 110.00 *(978-1-904761-87-7(9))* Nottingham Univ. Pr. GBR. Dist: Independent Pubs. Group.

Pavia, Audrey & Gentry-Running, Kate. Horse Health & Nutrition for Dummies. 2008. (ENG., Illus.). 392p. pap. 21.99 *(978-0-470-23952-0(2),* For Dummies) Wiley, John & Sons, Inc.

Purr-Fect Recipes for a Healthy Cat: 101 Natural Cat Food & Treat Recipes to Make Your Cat Happy. 2011. (ENG.). 288p. pap. 24.95 *(978-1-60138-398-3(3))* Atlantic Publishing Co.

Ramirez-Lozano, Roque G. Browse Foliage As Protein Supplement for Sheep Fed Low Quality Diets. 2011. 120p. pap. ***(978-3-8443-3156-1(5))*** Lambert Academic Publishing.

Rayburn, Edward B. & Bamka, William J. Animal Production Systems for Pasture-Based Livestock Production. 2007. pap. *(978-1-933395-04-3(4))* Natural Resource, Agricultural, & Engineering Service.

Reinhardt, Bryan. Put Your Pig on a Diet. 2010. 54p. pap. 16.95 *(978-0-557-58477-2(9))* Lulu Enterprises Inc.

Royal Society of Chemistry Staff. Analyses for Hormonal Substances in Food Producing Animals. Kay, Jack F., ed. 2009. (RSC Food Analysis

A

Monographs). (ENG., Illus.). 236p. 195.00 (978-0-85404-198-5(2)) Royal Society of Chemistry, The GBR. Dist: Ingram Pub. Services.

Saastamoinen, M. & Martin-Rosset, M., eds. Nutrition of the exercising Horse. 2008. (EAAP Publications: 126). (Illus.). 432p. 110.00 (978-90-8686-071-5(0)) Wagenigen Academic Publishers NLD. Dist: Enfield Publishing & Distribution Co., Inc.

Salem, Abdel-Fattah Z. M. Plant-Phytochemicals in Animal Nutrition. 2011. (Animal Science, Issues & Professions Chemistry Research & Applications Ser.). 188p. 89.00 (978-1-61209-555-4(0)) Nova Science Pubs., Inc.

Sauvant, D., et al, eds. Modelling nutrient digestion & utilisation in farm Animals. 2010. (Illus.). 430p. 137.00 (978-90-8686-156-9(3)) Wageningen Academic Publishers NLD. Dist: Enfield Publishing & Distribution Co., Inc.

Shapiro, Jeffrey. Perspectives. 2009. pap. 9.95 (978-1-61623-156-9(4)) Independent Pub.

Simpson, Stephen J. & Raubenheimer, David. The Nature of Nutrition: A Unifying Framework from Animal Adaptation to Human Obesity. 2012. (ENG., Illus.). 260p. (C). 49.50 **(978-0-691-14565-5(2))** Princeton Univ. Pr.

Sithambaram, Shanmugavelu. Enzymes & Phytochemicals in Chicken Diets - the Influence of Enzymes & Phytochemicals in Chicken Diets on Performance, Nutrient Utilisation & Gu. 2008. 264p. pap. (978-3-639-04437-9(1)) VDM Verlag Dr. Mueller e.K.

Steiner, Tobias, ed. Phytogenics in Animal Nutrition: Natural Concepts to Optimize Gut Health & Performance. 2010. (ENG., Illus.). 192p. pap. 57.95 (978-1-904761-71-6(2)) Nottingham Univ. Pr. GBR. Dist: Independent Pubs. Group.

Suttle, Neville F. Mineral Nutrition of Livestock. 4th ed. 2010. (Illus.). 544p. 220.00 (978-1-84593-472-9(5)) CABI GBR. Dist: Stylus Publishing, LLC.

Taylor-Pickard, J. & Spring, P., eds. Gut Efficiency, the Key Ingredient in Pig & Poultry Production: Elevating Animal Performance & Health. 2008. (Illus.). 192p. 140.00 (978-90-8686-060-9(5)) Wageningen Academic Publishers NLD. Dist: Enfield Distribution, Enfield Publishing & Distribution Co., Inc.

Taylor-Pickard, J. A., et al, eds. Formula for the Future: Elevating performance & health in pigs & poultry: nutrition or Pathology? 2008. (Illus.). 280p. 140.00 (978-90-8686-088-3(5)) Wageningen Academic Publishers NLD. Dist: Enfield Publishing & Distribution Co., Inc.

Torrallardona, David & Roura, Eugeni, eds. Voluntary feed intake in Pigs. 2009. (Illus.). 368p. 107.00 (978-90-8686-096-8(6)) Wageningen Academic Publishers NLD. Dist: Enfield Publishing & Distribution Co., Inc.

Vitti, Dorinha M. S. S., et al, contrib. by. Phosphorous & Calcium Utilization & Requirements in Farm Animals. 2010. (Illus.). 208p. 160.00 (978-1-84593-626-6(4)) CABI GBR. Dist: Stylus Publishing, LLC.

Waldorf Gewirtz, Elaine, et al. The Everything Natural Health for Dogs Book: The Healthy, Affordable Way to Ensure a Long, Happy Life for Your Pet. 2009. (ENG.). 304p. pap. 15.95 (978-1-59869-991-3(1)) Adams Media Corp.

Wortinger, Ann. Nutrition for Veterinary Technicians & Nurses. 2007. (ENG., Illus.). 256p. per. 48.99 (978-0-8138-2913-5(5), Wiley-Blackwell) Wiley, John & Sons, Inc.

Xu, Fangsen, et al, eds. Advances in Plant & Animal Boron Nutrition: Proceedings of the 3rd International Symposium on all Aspects of Plant & Animal Boron Nutrition. 2010. xvi, 402p. pap. 259.00 (978-90-481-7356-3(6), 9048173566) Springer.

Young, Malachy, et al. Programs for Developing & Feeding the Breeding Herd. 2010. 236p. pap. (978-3-8383-1730-4(0)) Lambert Academic Publishing.

ANIMAL OILS
see Oils and Fats

ANIMAL-ORIGIN FOOD
see Food of Animal Origin

ANIMAL PAINTING AND ILLUSTRATION
Here are entered works on the art of animal painting and illustration.
see also Animals in Art; Birds in Art

Buford, Bill. Walton Ford Pancha Tantra. 2007. (Illus.). 356p. 7000.00 (978-3-8228-5193-7(0)) TASCHEN DEU. Dist: Ingram Pub. Services.

Buford, Bill & Ford, Walton. Walton Ford Pancha Tantra. 2007. (ENG., Illus.). 354p. 2000.00 (978-3-8228-4386-4(5)) TASCHEN DEU. Dist: Ingram Pub. Services.

Calder, Alexander. Alexander Calder: Animal Sketching. 2009. (ENG., Illus.). 104p. 45.00 (978-2-916275-53-6(3)) Dilecta, Editions FRA. Dist: D.A.P./Distributed Art Pubs.

Campana, D. M. Teacher of Animal Painting. (Illus.). 9.95 (978-0-939608-14-0(6)) Campana Art Co.

Cook, Gladys Emerson. You Can Draw Cats. 2006. (Dover Art Instruction Ser.). (ENG., Illus.). 64p. per. 5.95 (978-0-486-45126-8(7)) Dover Pubns., Inc.

Davidow, Ann H. Lets Draw Animals. 2011. 82p. 37.95 **(978-1-258-10381-1(8))** Literary Licensing, LLC.

Davidson, Jane P. A History of Paleontology Illustration. 2008. (Life of the Past Ser.). (ENG., Illus.). 240p. 39.95 (978-0-253-35175-3(8), 0253351758) Indiana Univ. Pr.

de Crecy, Nicolas & Senges, Pierre. Adventures of Percival. Daniele, Riviere, ed. 2009. (ENG., Illus.). 128p. pap. 30.00 (978-2-914563-47-5(7)) Dis Voir Editions FRA. Dist: D.A.P./Distributed Art Pubs.

Dover, ed. Butterflies. 2007. (Dover Pictura Electronic Clip Art Ser.). (ENG., Illus.). 128p. pap. 39.95 (978-0-486-99808-4(8)) Dover Pubns., Inc.

Drochon, Christophe. Painting Animals. 2006. (ENG., Illus.). 128p. 24.95 (978-1-84537-545-4(9)) New Holland Pubs., Ltd. GBR. Dist: Sterling Publishing Co., Inc.

Gallerani, Paola. The Menagerie of Pieter Boel: Animal Painter in the Age of Louis XIV. 2011. (ENG., Illus.). 88p. 29.95 **(978-88-89854-74-7(X))** Officina Libraria srl ITA. Dist: Antique Collectors' Club.

Gisby, Jane. How to Make Wild Animals. (Illus.). 48p. pap. 9.95 (978-0-85532-629-6(8), 629-8) Search Pr., Ltd. GBR. Dist: Independent Pubs. Group.

Heitman, Danny. A Summer of Birds: John James Audubon at Oakley House. 2008. (Hill Collection: Holdings of the LSU Libraries Ser.). (Illus.). 152p. 26.95 (978-0-8071-3330-9(2)) Louisiana State Univ. Pr.

Lawrence, Rod. Animals / Acrylic: Learn to Paint Step by Step. 2009. (How to Draw & Paint Ser.). (ENG., Illus.). 32p. pap. 8.95 (978-1-60058-123-6(4), 1600581234) Foster, Walter Publishing, Inc.

Longley, Brett, illus. In Love with Labs. 2008. 32p. 15.99 (978-0-7369-2156-5(7)) Harvest Hse. Pubs.

Meena, Madan, contrib. by. Nurturing Walls. 2009. (ENG., Illus.). 64p. 24.95 (978-81-86211-68-7(3)) Tara Publishing IND. Dist: Perseus-PGW.

Michel, Sally. Painting Cats in Watercolour. (Leisure Arts Ser.: No. 26). (Illus.). 32p. pap. 4.95 (978-0-85532-558-9(5), 558-5) Search Pr., Ltd. GBR. Dist: Independent Pubs. Group.

Wellford, Lin. Painted Garden Art: Anyone Can Do. 2009. (ENG., Illus.). 112p. pap. 22.99 (978-0-9777065-1-8(6)) ArtStone Pr.

ANIMAL PARASITES
see Parasites

ANIMAL PHOTOGRAPHY
see Photography of Animals

ANIMAL PICTURES
see Animals—Pictorial Works

ANIMAL PIGMENTS
see also Animals—Color; Chromatophores

Black, Maureen M., et al. Melanins & Melanosomes: Biosynthesis, Biogenesis, Physiological, & Pathological Functions. Borovansky, Jan, ed. 2011. (ENG., Illus.). 429p. 159.95 (978-3-527-32892-5(0), Wiley-VCH) Wiley, John & Sons, Inc.

Delmas, Véronique, et al. The Colors of Mice: A Model Genetic Network. 2010. (ENG., Illus.). 312p. 169.95 (978-1-4051-7954-6(6), Wiley-Blackwell) Wiley, John & Sons, Inc.

Ma, Xiao-Peng & Sun, Xiao-Xiao, eds. Melanin: Biosynthesis, Functions & Health Effects. 2012. **(978-1-62100-991-7(2))** Nova Science Pubs., Inc.

ANIMAL-PLANT RELATIONSHIPS
see also Insect-Plant Relationships

Crump, Marty. Sexy Orchids Make Lousy Lovers: & Other Unusual Relationships. 2009. (ENG., Illus.). 232p. 25.00 (978-0-226-12185-7(2)) Univ. of Chicago Pr.

Dew, J. Lawrence & Boubli, Jean P., eds. Tropical Fruits & Frugivores: The Search for Strong Interactors. 2010. (ENG.). vii, 260p. pap. 149.00 (978-90-481-6976-4(3), 9048169763) Springer.

Gheysen, Godelieve & Fenoll, Carmen, eds. Genomics & Molecular Genetics of Plant-Nematode Interactions. 2011. (ENG., Illus.). xxiv, 557p. 209.00 (978-94-007-0433-6(X), 940070433X) Springer.

Gordon, Iain J. & Prins, Herbert H. T. The Ecology of Browsing & Grazing. 2010. (Ecological Studies). (Illus.). xvi, 330p. pap. 189.00 (978-3-642-09148-3(2), 3642091482) Springer.

Herrera, Carlos M. Multiplicity in Unity: Plant Subindividual Variation & Interactions with Animals. 2009. (Interspecific Interactions Ser.). (ENG., Illus.). 448p. 110.00 (978-0-226-32793-8(0)); pap. 40.00 (978-0-226-32794-5(9)) Univ. of Chicago Pr.

Patiny, Sèbastien, ed. Evolution of Plant-Pollinator Relationships. 2011. (Systematics Association Special Volume Ser.). (ENG., Illus.). 504p. 125.00 **(978-0-521-19892-9(5))** Cambridge Univ. Pr.

Pretty, Jules. The Earth Only Endures: On Reconnecting with Nature & Our Place in It. 2007. (ENG., Illus.). 288p. 99.95 (978-1-84407-432-7(3)) Routledge.

Rafferty, John P., ed. Grazers. 2011. (Britannica Guide to Predators & Prey Ser.). (Illus.). 360p. (YA). 103.40 (978-1-61530-466-0(5)) Rosen Publishing Group, Inc., The.

Schaefer, H. Martin & Ruxton, Graeme D. Plant-Animal Communication. 2011. (Illus.). (ENG.). 296p. 135.00 (978-0-19-956360-9(8)); 320p. pap. 67.50 (978-0-19-956359-3(4)) Oxford Univ. Pr., Inc.

Schaller, Andreas. Induced Plant Resistance to Herbivory. 2008. (ENG.). xvi, 464p. 289.00 (978-1-4020-8181-1(2), 1402081812) Springer.

Seckbach, Joseph & Dubinsky, Z., eds. All Flesh Is Grass: Plant-Animal Interrelationships. 2010. (Cellular Origin, Life in Extreme Habitats & Astrobiology Ser.). (ENG., Illus.). xv, 531p. 209.00 (978-90-481-9315-8(X), 904819315X) Springer.

Tabor, Bob. Horse Whisperings: Portraits by Bob Tabor. 2010. (ENG., Illus.). 168p. (978-1-85149-635-8(1), Antique Collectors Club Dist) Antique Collectors' Club.

Tallamy, Douglas W. Bringing Nature Home: How You Can Sustain Wildlife with Native Plants. 2nd exp. enl. rev. ed. 2009. (ENG., Illus.). 360p. pap. 17.95 (978-0-88192-992-8(1), 0881929921) Timber Pr., Inc.

Talwana, Herbert. Plant-Parasitic Nematodes & Banana Root Systems Interactions. 2010. 188p. pap. (978-3-8383-7011-8(2)) Lambert Academic Publishing.

Ueckermann, Edward A., ed. Eriophyoid Mites: Progress & Prognoses: Progress & Prognoses. 2010. (Illus.). vi, 310p. 209.00 (978-90-481-9561-9(6), 9048195616) Springer.

Wilcock. Plant Animal Interactions. (978-0-412-00961-7(7)) CENGAGE Learning.

ANIMAL POETRY
see Animals—Poetry

ANIMAL POISONS
see Venom

ANIMAL POPULATIONS
see also Bird Populations; Fish Populations; Population Genetics

Borchers, D. L., et al. Estimating Animal Abundance: Closed Populations. 2010. (Statistics for Biology & Health Ser.). (Illus.). xiii, 332p. pap. 119.00 (978-1-84996-885-0(3), 1849968853) Springer.

COLLEGE OF WILLIAM & MARY. Animal Populations: A Study of Physical, Conceptual, & Mathematical Models. 2007. 256p. 49.95 (978-0-7575-4126-1(7)) Kendall Hunt Publishing Co.

—Animal Populations: Student Pak. 2007. 49.95 (978-0-7575-4127-8(5)) Kendall Hunt Publishing Co.

Conroy, Michael J. & Carroll, John P. Quantitative Conservation of Vertebrates. 2009. (ENG., Illus.). 352p. 184.95 (978-1-4051-9098-5(1), Wiley-Blackwell) Wiley, John & Sons, Inc.

Conroy, Michael J., et al. Quantitative Conservation of Vertebrates. 2009. (ENG., Illus.). 352p. pap. 89.95 (978-1-4051-8228-7(8), Wiley-Blackwell) Wiley, John & Sons, Inc.

Cram101 Textbook Reviews. Outlines & Highlights for Conservation of Wildlife Populations: Demography, Genetics, & Management by L. Mills, ISBN. 2011. 468p. pap. 36.95 **(978-1-61461-451-7(2))** Cram101 Inc.

Hone, Jim. Applied Population & Community Ecology: The Case of Feral Pigs in Australia. 2012. (Conservation Science & Practice Ser.). (ENG.). 256p. 129.95 **(978-0-470-65864-2(9)**, Wiley-Blackwell) Wiley, John & Sons, Inc.

Linacre, Adrian. Forensic Science in Wildlife Investigations. 2009. (International Forensic Science & Investigation Ser.). (ENG., Illus.). 178p. 144.95 (978-0-8493-0410-1(5), CRC Press) Taylor & Francis Group GBR. Dist: Taylor & Francis Group.

Lott, Dale F. Intraspecific Variation in the Social Systems of Wild Vertebrates. 2009. (Cambridge Studies in Behavioural Biology Ser.). (ENG.). 256p. pap. 38.99 (978-0-521-11523-0(X)) Cambridge Univ. Pr.

McComb, Brenda C., et al. Monitoring Animal Populations & Their Habitats. 2010. (ENG., Illus.). 296p. 89.95 (978-1-4200-7055-2(X), CRC Press) Taylor & Francis Group GBR. Dist: Taylor & Francis Group.

McLaren, Ian A. & McLaren, Ian. Natural Regulation of Animal Populations. 2006. (ENG., Illus.). 195p. (gr. 11). pap. 24.95 (978-0-202-30876-0(6)) Aldine Transaction.

Planning for a Changing Climate & Its Impacts on Wildlife & Oceans: State & Federal Efforts & Needs: And H.R. 4455, Wildlife Without Borders Authorization ACT: Oversight & Legislative Hearing Before the Subcommittee on Fisheries, Wildlife & Oceans of the Committee on Natural Resources, U.S. House of Representatives, One Hundred Tenth Congress, Second Session, Tuesday, June 24, 2008. 2009. iii, 103p. (978-0-16-082670-2(5), 552-070-38687-4) United States Government Printing Office.

Sukhovolskii, V. G., et al. Optimizatsionnye Modeli Mezhpopuliatsionnykh Vzaimodeistvii. 2008. (RUS., Illus.). 161p. (978-5-02-023260-0(2)) Nauka.

Thomson, David L., et al. Modeling Demographic Processes in Marked Populations. 2009. (Environmental & Ecological Statistics Ser.). (Illus.). 700p. 194.00 (978-0-387-78150-1(1)) Springer.

Turner, Jacky. Animal Breeding, Welfare & Society. 2010. (ENG., Illus.). 336p. 140.00 (978-1-84407-588-1(5)); pap. 41.95 (978-1-84407-589-8(3)) Routledge.

Wilcove, David S. No Way Home: The Decline of the World's Great Animal Migrations. 2010. (ENG., Illus.). 256p. pap. 25.00 (978-1-59726-823-3(2)) Island Pr.

Williams, George, ed. Group Selection. 2008. (ENG.). 210p. pap. 29.95 (978-0-202-36222-9(1)) Aldine Transaction.

ANIMAL PRODUCTS
see also Bee Products; Dairy Products; Food of Animal Origin; Meat; Raw Materials
also names of particular products, e.g. Ivory, Wool, etc.

Arvanitoyannis, Ioannis S. HACCP & ISO 22000 Vol. 1: Application to Foods of Animal Origin. 2009. (Institute of Food Science & Technology Ser.). (ENG., Illus.). 560p. 263.00 (978-1-4051-5366-9(0), Wiley-Blackwell) Wiley, John & Sons, Inc.

Book of Abstracts of the 61st Annual Meeting of the European Association for Animal Production: Heraklion - Crete Island, Greece, 23-27 August 2010. 2010. (EAAP Book of Abstracts: 16). 478p. pap. 72.00 (978-90-8686-152-1(0)) Wageningen Academic Publishers NLD. Dist: Enfield Publishing & Distribution Co., Inc.

Childs, Laura. The Joy of Keeping Farm Animals: Raising Chickens, Goats, Pigs, Sheep, & Cows. 2010. (Joy of Ser.). (ENG., Illus.). 256p. pap. 14.95 (978-1-60239-745-3(7), 239745) Skyhorse Publishing Co., Inc.

Ekarius, Carol & Robson, Deborah. The Fleece & Fiber Sourcebook: More Than 200 Fibers, from Animal to Spun Yarn. 2011. (ENG., Illus.). 448p. 35.00 (978-1-60342-711-1(2), 1603427112) Storey Publishing, LLC.

Faye, Bernard & Sinyavskiy, Yuriy, eds. Impact of Pollution on Animal Products. 2008. (NATO Science for Peace & Security Series C: Environmental Security Ser.). (Illus.). XX, 205p. 219.00 (978-1-4020-8357-0(2), 1402083572); pap. 79.95 (978-1-4020-8358-7(0), 1402083580) Springer.

Goode, G. Brown (George Brown). Classification of the Collection to Illustrate the Animal Resources of the United States; 2006. 136p. per. 16.99 (978-1-4255-0991-0(6)) MPublishing.

Hui, Y. H., et al, eds. Handbook of Animal-Based Fermented Foods & Beverages. 2nd rev. ed. 2012. (ENG., Illus.). 814p. 199.95 **(978-1-4398-5022-0(4)**, CRC Press) Taylor & Francis Group GBR. Dist: Taylor & Francis Group.

Maks, Michele & Ellison, Connie, eds. Itty-Bitty Animals. 2009. (ENG.). 50p. pap. 9.95 (978-1-59635-251-3(5)) Annie's Publishing, LLC.

Müssig, Jörg, ed. Industrial Applications of Natural Fibres: Structure, Properties & Technical Applications. 2010. (Wiley Series in Renewable Resource Ser.). (ENG., Illus.). 560p. 200.00 (978-0-470-69508-1(0), Wiley) Wiley, John & Sons, Inc.

National Archives and Records Administration, creator. Animals & Animal Products: Parts 1 To 199. 2011. (Code of Federal Regulations Ser.). 1067p. pap. 67.00 **(978-1-60946-320-5(X))** National Archives & Records Administration.

Nollet, Leo M. L. Handbook of Analysis of Edible Animal By-Products. 2011. (ENG., Illus.). 471p. 169.95 (978-1-4398-0360-8(9), CRC Press) Taylor & Francis Group GBR. Dist: Taylor & Francis Group.

Office of the Federal Register (U.S.), compiled by. Code of Federal Regulations, Title 9, Animals & Animal Products, Pt. 1-199, Revised as of January 1 2011. rev. ed. 2011. (ENG.). 1077p. pap. 67.00 **(978-0-16-087542-7(0)**, Office of the Federal Register) United States Government Printing Office.

—Code of Federal Regulations, Title 9, Animals & Animal Products, Pt. 200-End, Revised as of January 1 2011. rev. ed. 2011. (ENG., Illus.). 764p. pap. 64.00 **(978-0-16-087543-4(9)**, Office of the Federal Register) United States Government Printing Office.

Pet Foods & Pet Products International Market. 330p. (Orig.). pap. (978-0-7605-2225-7(1)) Rector Pr., Ltd.

Pisc. Australian Standard for Hygienic Rendering of Animal Products. 2nd rev. ed. 2007. (Primary Industries Report Ser.). 20p. pap. 22.00 (978-0-643-09273-0(0)) CSIRO Publishing AUS. Dist: Stylus Publishing, LLC.

ANIMAL PSYCHOLOGY
see Psychology, Comparative

ANIMAL RADIO TRACKING

Almeida, Pedro R., et al. Developments in Fish Telemetry: Proceedings of the 6th Conference on Fish Telemetry Held in Europe. 2007. (Developments in Hydrobiology Ser.). viii, 300p. 169.00 (978-1-4020-6236-0(2), 1402062362) Springer.

—Developments in Fish Telemetry: Proceedings of the Sixt Conference on Fish Telemetry held in Europe. 2010. (Developments in Hydrobiology Ser.). viii, 300p. pap. 169.00 (978-90-481-7578-9(X), 904817578X) Springer.

Benson, Etienne. Wired Wilderness: Technologies of Tracking & the Making of Modern Wildlife. 2010. (Animals, History, Culture Ser.). (ENG., Illus.). 264p. (gr. 17). 55.00 (978-0-8018-9710-8(6)) Johns Hopkins Univ. Pr.

ANIMAL REMAINS (ARCHAEOLOGY)
see also Kitchen-Middens

Albarella, Umberto & Trentacoste, Angela, eds. Ethnozooarchaeology: The Present & Past of Human-Animal Relationships. 2011. (ENG., Illus.). 174p. (C). 90.00 (978-1-84217-997-0(7)) Oxbow Bks., Ltd. GBR. Dist: Brown, David Bk. Co., The.

Allen, Michael J., et al, eds. Land & People: Papers in Memory of John G. Evans. 2009. (Prehistoric Society Research PaperS). (ENG., Illus.). 259p. (C). 70.00 (978-1-84217-373-2(1)) Oxbow Bks., Ltd. GBR. Dist: Brown, David Bk. Co., The.

Badenhorst, Shaw, et al, eds. Animals & People: Archaeozoological Papers in Honour of Ina Plug. 2008. (Bar S Ser.). (ENG., Illus.). 228p. (C). pap. 90.00 (978-1-4073-0336-9(8)) British Archaeological Reports Ltd. GBR. Dist: Brown, David Bk. Co., The.

Bakels, Corrie, et al, eds. Of Plants & Snails: A Collection of Papers Presented to Wim Kuijper in Gratitude for Forty Years of Teaching & Identifying. 2010. (ENG & DUT., Illus.). 279p. (C). pap. 58.00 (978-90-8890-051-8(5)) Sidestone Pr. NLD. Dist: Brown, David Bk. Co., The.

Beck, Charlotte & Jones, George T. The Archaeology of the Eastern Nevada Paleoarchaic, Part 1: The Sunshine Locality. 2009. (University of Utah Anthropological Paper Ser.). (ENG., Illus.). 312p. pap. 40.00 (978-0-87480-939-8(8)) Univ. of Utah Pr.

Bejenaru, Luminita. Archaeozoological Approach to Medieval Moldavia. 2009. (ENG., Illus.). 153p. (C). pap. 85.00 (978-1-4073-0437-3(2)) British Archaeological Reports Ltd. GBR. Dist: Brown, David Bk. Co., The.

Bignon, Olivier. Chasser les Chevaux à la Fin du Paléolitique Dans le Bassin Parisien: Stratégie Cynégétique et Mode de Vie Au Magdalenien et à L'Azilien Ancien. 2008. (Bar S Ser.). (FRE., Illus.). 170p. (C). 85.00 (978-1-4073-0189-1(6)) British Archaeological Reports Ltd. GBR. Dist: Brown, David Bk. Co., The.

Blaise, Emilie. Économie Animale et Gestion des Troupeaux Au Néolithique Final en Provence: Approche Archéozoologique et Contribution des Analyses Isotopiques de L'émail Dentaire. 2010. (Bar S Ser.). (FRE & ENG., Illus.). 400p. (C). pap. 145.00 (978-1-4073-0479-3(8)) British Archaeological Reports Ltd. GBR. Dist: Brown, David Bk. Co., The.

Bökönyi, Sándor & Gál, Erika. The Chora of Metaponto 2: Archaeozoology at Pantanello & Five Other Sites. Bartosiewicz, László, ed. 2010. (ENG., Illus.). 144p. 75.00 (978-0-292-72134-0(X)) Univ. of Texas Pr.

Brinkhuizen, D. C., et al, eds. Birds in Archaeology: Proceedings of the 6th Meeting of the ICAZ Bird Working Group in Groningen (23. 8 - 27. 8. 2008) 2010. (Groningen Archaeological Studies: 12). (ENG.). 284p. (C). pap. 73.00

(978-90-77922-77-4(6)) Barkhuis Publishing NLD. Dist: Brown, David Bk. Co., The.

Burger, Richard L. & Salazar, Lucy C., eds. The/1912 Yale Peruvian Scientific Expedition Collections from Machu Picchu Vol. 91: Metal Artifacts. 2011. (Yale University Publications in Anthropology Ser.). (Illus.). 225p. pap. 69.95 *(978-0-913516-27-0(9))* Yale Univ. Pr.

Çakirlar, Canan. Mollusk Shells in Troia, Yenibademli, & Ulucak: An Archaeomalacological Approach to the Environment & Economy of the Aegean. 2009. (Bar S Ser.). (ENG., Illus.). 210p. (C). pap. 125.00 *(978-1-4073-0469-4(0))* British Archaeological Reports Ltd. GBR. Dist: Brown, David Bk. Co., The.

Cakirlar, Canan, ed. Archaeomalacology Revisited: Non-dietary use of molluscs in archaeological Settings. 2011. (ENG., Illus.). 104p. (C). pap. 60.00 *(978-1-84217-436-4(3))* Oxbow Bks., Ltd. GBR. Dist: Brown, David Bk. Co., The.

Carlson, Jenna K. Culinary Creolization: Subsistence & Cultural Interaction at Fort Michilimackinac, 1730-1761. 2012. pap. ***(978-0-911872-90-3(6))*** Mackinac State Historic Parks.

Corona M, Eduardo & Arroyo-Cabrales, Joaquín. Human & Faunal Relationships Reviewed: An Archaeozoological Approach. 2007. (Bar S Ser.). (SPA & ENG., Illus.). 121p. (C). pap. 75.00 *(978-1-4073-0041-2(5))* British Archaeological Reports Ltd. GBR. Dist: Brown, David Bk. Co., The.

Cram101 Textbook Reviews & Cram101 Textbook Reviews. Outlines & Highlights for Zooarchaeology by Elizabeth Jean Reitz, Isbn: 0521673933 9780521673938. 2011. 304p. pap. 32.95 ***(978-1-4288-8912-5(4))*** Cram101 Inc.

Daujeard, Camille. Exploitation du Milieu Animal Par les Néanderthaliens Dans le Sud-Est de la France. 2008. (FRE & ENG., Illus.). 634p. (C). pap. 200.00 *(978-1-4073-0234-8(5))* British Archaeological Reports Ltd. GBR. Dist: Brown, David Bk. Co., The.

deFrance, S. D., et al, eds. Anthropological Approaches to Zooarchaeology: Colonialism, Complexity & Animal Transformations. 2010. (ENG., Illus.). 286p. (C). 160.00 *(978-1-84217-390-9(1))* Oxbow Bks., Ltd. GBR. Dist: Brown, David Bk. Co., The.

Dixon, Kelly J., et al, eds. Archaeology of Desperation: Exploring the Donner Party's Alder Creek Camp. 2011. (ENG., Illus.). 384p. (C). 34.95 *(978-0-8061-4210-4(3))* Univ. of Oklahoma Pr.

Domínguez-Rodrigo, Manuel, et al. Deconstructing Olduvai: A Taphonomic Study of the Bed I Sites. 2007. (Vertebrate Paleobiology & Paleoanthropology Ser.). xvi, 337p. 129.00 *(978-1-4020-6150-9(1)*, 1402061501) Springer.

Emery, Kitty F. Dietary, Environmental, & Societal Implications of Ancient Maya Animal Use in the Petexbatun: A Zooarchaeological Perspective on the Collapse. 2010. (Vanderbilt Institute of Mesoamerican Archaeology Ser.: VIMA #5). (ENG., Illus.). 240p. lib. bdg. 69.95 *(978-0-8265-1646-6(7))* Vanderbilt Univ. Pr.

Fillios, Melanie A. Measuring Complexity in Early Bronze Age Greece: The Pig As a Proxy Indicator of Socio-Economic Structures. 2007. (ENG., Illus.). viii, 234p. (C). pap. 112.50 *(978-1-4073-0205-8(1))* British Archaeological Reports Ltd. GBR. Dist: Brown, David Bk. Co., The.

Florian, Mary-Lou E. Protein Facts: Fibrous Proteins in Cultural & Natural History Artifacts. 2008. (ENG., Illus.). 160p. pap. 55.00 *(978-1-873132-34-0(4))* Archetype Pubns. GBR. Dist: National Bk. Network.

Fontana, Laure, et al. In Search of Total Animal Exploitation - Case Studies from the Upper Palaeolithic & Mesolithic. 2009. (Bar S Ser.). (FRE & ENG., Illus.). 154p. (C). pap. 102.50 ***(978-1-4073-0467-0(4))*** British Archaeological Reports Ltd. GBR. Dist: Brown, David Bk. Co., The.

Furniss-Roe, Tina Dudley. Incremental Structures & Wear Patterns of Teeth for Age Assessment of Red Deer. 2008. (Bar S Ser.). (ENG., Illus.). 131p. (C). pap. 72.50 *(978-1-4073-0319-2(8))* British Archaeological Reports Ltd. GBR. Dist: Brown, David Bk. Co., The.

Glassow, Michael A. Exploring Methods of Faunal Analysis: Insights from California Archaeology. Joslin, Terry L., ed. 2012. (ENG.). 276p. (C). pap. 34.95 ***(978-1-931745-87-1(0))*** Cotsen Institute of Archaeology at UCLA.

Gutierrez, María A. Taphonomy & Zooarchaeology in Argentina. 2007. (BAR International Ser.: Vol. 1601). (Illus.). 233p. 87.50 *(978-1-4073-0018-4(0))* Archaeopress GBR. Dist: Brown, David Bk. Co., The.

Hill, Matthew G. Paleoindian Subsistence Dynamics on the Northwestern Great Plains. 2008. (Bar S Ser.). (Illus.). 144p. (C). 75.00 *(978-1-4073-0195-2(0))* British Archaeological Reports Ltd. GBR. Dist: Brown, David Bk. Co., The.

Izeta, Andrés D. Zooarqueología Del Sur de Los Valles Calchaquíes (Provincias de Catamarca y Tucumán, República Argentina) Análisis de Conjuntos Faunísticos Del Primer Milenio A.D. 2007. (BAR International Ser.: Vol. 1612). (SPA., Illus.). vi, 164p. pap. 102.50 *(978-1-4073-0054-2(7))* British Archaeological Reports Ltd. GBR. Dist: Brown, David Bk. Co., The.

Knell, Simon J. The Great Fossil Enigma: The Search for the Conodont Animal. 2012. (Life of the Past Ser.). (ENG., Illus.). 416p. 45.00 ***(978-0-253-00604-2(X)***, 025300604X) Indiana Univ. Pr.

Knipper, Corina. Die Raumliche Organisation der Linearbandkeramischen Rinderhaltung. 2011. (Bar S Ser.). (GER & ENG., Illus.). 485p. (C). pap. 187.50 ***(978-1-4073-0882-1(3))*** British Archaeological Reports Ltd. GBR. Dist: Brown, David Bk. Co., The.

Lang, Richard W. & Harris, Arthur. The Faunal Remains from Arroyo Hondo Pueblo, New Mexico: A Study in Short-Term Subsistence Change. (Arroyo Hondo Archaeological Ser.: Vol. 5). (Illus.). 325p. pap. 14.95 *(978-0-933452-09-1(8))* School for Advanced Research Pr./SAR Pr.

Laurie, Eva M. An Investigation of the Common Cockle (Cerastoderma edule (L)) 2008. (Bar S Ser.). (Illus.). 305p. (C). 117.50 *(978-1-4073-0318-5(X))* British Archaeological Reports Ltd. GBR. Dist: Brown, David Bk. Co., The.

Linseele, Veerle. Archaeofaunal Remains from the Past 4000 Years in Sahelian West Africa: Domestic Livestock, Subsistence Strategies & Environmental Changes. 2007. (Bar S Ser.). (ENG., Illus.). 340p. (C). pap. 105.00 *(978-1-4073-0094-8(6))* British Archaeological Reports Ltd. GBR. Dist: Brown, David Bk. Co., The.

Lyman, R. Lee. Quantitative Paleozoology. 2008. (Cambridge Manuals in Archaeology Ser.). (ENG., Illus.). 372p. (C). 85.00 *(978-0-521-88749-6(6))*; pap. 30.99 *(978-0-521-71536-2(9))* Cambridge Univ. Pr.

Marciniak, Arkadiusz. Placing Animals in the Neolithic: Social Zooarchaeology of Prehistoric Farming Communities. 2007. (University College London Institute of Archaeology Publications). (ENG., Illus.). 295p. 99.95 *(978-1-59874-212-1(4))* Left Coast Pr., Inc.

Miklikova, Zora & Thomas, Richard, eds. Current Research in Animal Palaeopathology: Proceedings of the Second ICAZ Animal Palaeopathology Working Group Conference. 2008. (Bar S Ser.). (Illus.). 98p. (C). 65.00 *(978-1-4073-0331-4(7))* British Archaeological Reports Ltd. GBR. Dist: Brown, David Bk. Co., The.

Morin, Eugene. Reassessing Paleolithic Subsistence: The Neandertal & Modern Human Foragers of Saint-Césaire. 2012. (ENG., Illus.). 350p. 99.00 ***(978-1-107-02327-7(0))*** Cambridge Univ. Pr.

Mulville. Totems & Sacrifices. 2007. (Illus.). 224p. 110.00 *(978-0-415-41168-4(8))* Routledge.

O'Connor, Terry. The Archaeology of Animal Bones. 2008. (Texas A&M University Anthropology Ser.). (ENG.). 216p. pap. 29.95 *(978-1-60344-084-4(4))* Texas A&M Univ. Pr.

Oueslati, Tarek. Approche Archeozoologique des Modes d'Acquisition, de Transformation et de Consommation des Ressources Animales dans le Contexte Urbain Gallo-Romain de Lutece. 2006. (Bar S Ser.). (FRE., Illus.). 416p. (C). 112.50 *(978-1-84171-914-6(5))* British Archaeological Reports Ltd. GBR. Dist: Brown, David Bk. Co., The.

Pacher, Martina, et al, eds. Early Pleistocene Bear Remains from Deutsch-Altenburg (Lower Austria)/ Die Altpleistozanen Baren von Deutsch-Altenburg (Niederosterreich) 2010. (MITTEILUNGEN der KOMMISSION FuR QUARTaRFORSCHUNG Ser.). (ENG & GER., Illus.). 139p. (C). 147.00 *(978-3-7001-6827-0(6))* Austrian Academy of Sciences Press AUT. Dist: Brown, David Bk. Co., The.

Pasda, Kerstin. Osteometry & Osteological Age & Sex Determination of the Sisimiut Reindeer Population (Rangifer Tarandus Groenlandicus) 2009. (ENG., Illus.). 283p. (C). pap. 125.00 *(978-1-4073-0453-3(4))* British Archaeological Reports Ltd. GBR. Dist: Brown, David Bk. Co., The.

Pawankar, Seema J. Man & Animal Relationship in Early Farming Communities of Western India, with Special Reference to Inamgaon. 2007. (Bar S Ser.). (Illus.). xi, 296p. 130.00 *(978-1-4073-0062-7(8))* British Archaeological Reports Ltd. GBR. Dist: Brown, David Bk. Co., The.

Pigiere, Fabienne. Evolution de L'economie Alimentaire et des Pratiques D'elevage de L'Antiquite au Haut Moyen Age en Gaule du Nord. 2009. (FRE & ENG., Illus.). 276p. (C). pap. 120.00 *(978-1-4073-0612-4(X))* British Archaeological Reports Ltd. GBR. Dist: Brown, David Bk. Co., The.

Potts, Richard. Early Hominid Activities at Olduvai. 2010. (ENG., Illus.). 407p. pap. 39.95 *(978-0-202-36396-7(1))* Transaction Pubs.

Puputti, Anna-Kaisa. Living with Animals: A Zooarchaeological Study of Urban Human-Animal Relationships in Early Modern Tornio (northern Finland), 1621-1800. 2010. (Bar S Ser.). (ENG., Illus.). 74p. (C). pap. 65.00 *(978-1-4073-0576-9(X))* British Archaeological Reports Ltd. GBR. Dist: Brown, David Bk. Co., The.

Rabinovich, Rivka, et al. The Acheulian Site of Gesher Benot Ya'aqov Vol. III: Mammalian Taphonomy. the Assemblages of Layers V-5 & V-6. 2011. (Vertebrate Paleobiology & Paleoanthropology Ser.). (ENG., Illus.). xii, 269p. 139.00 ***(978-94-007-2158-6(7)***, 9400721587) Springer.

Reitz, Elizabeth J. & Wing, Elizabeth S. Zooarchaeology. 2nd rev. ed. 2008. (Cambridge Manuals in Archaeology Ser.). (ENG., Illus.). 536p. (C). 101.00 *(978-0-521-85726-0(0))* Cambridge Univ. Pr.

Russell, Nerissa. Social Zooarchaeology: Humans & Animals in Prehistory. 2011. (ENG.). (C). 560p. 99.00 ***(978-0-521-76737-8(7))***; (Illus.). 552p. pap. 49.00 ***(978-0-521-14311-0(X))*** Cambridge Univ. Pr.

Sánchez, Eloísa Bernáldez. Bioestratinomía de Macromamíferos Terrestres de Doñana. 2009. (SPA & ENG., Illus.). 211p. (C). pap. 102.50 *(978-1-4073-0510-3(7))* British Archaeological Reports Ltd. GBR. Dist: Brown, David Bk. Co., The.

Sasson, Aharon. Animal Husbandry in Ancient Israel: A Zooarchaeological Perspective on Livestock Exploitation, Herd Management & Economic Strategies. 2010. (Approaches to Anthropological Archaeology Ser.). (ENG., Illus.). 166p. (C). 165.00 *(978-1-84553-179-9(5))* Equinox Publishing Ltd. GBR. Dist: ISD.

Soltysiak, Arkadiusz, ed. Bioarchaeology of the near East 1 (2007) 2010. 110.00 *(978-1-60724-666-4(X))* Gorgias Pr., LLC.

—Bioarchaeology of the near East 2 (2008) 2010. 110.00 *(978-1-60724-667-1(8))* Gorgias Pr., LLC.

Stewart, John R. An Evolutionary Study of Some Archaeologically Significant Avian Taxa in the Quaternary of the Western Palaearctic. 2007. (Bar S Ser.). (ENG., Illus.). 272p. (C). pap. 95.00 *(978-1-4073-0059-4(X))* British Archaeological Reports Ltd. GBR. Dist: Brown, David Bk. Co., The.

Sykes, Naomi Jane. The Norman Conquest: A Zooarchaeological Perspective. 2007. (Bar S Ser.). (ENG., Illus.). 132p. (C). pap. 85.00 *(978-1-4073-0092-4(X))* British Archaeological Reports Ltd. GBR. Dist: Brown, David Bk. Co., The.

Teschler-Nicola, Maria, ed. Early Modern Humans at the Moravian Gate: The Mladec Caves & their Remains. 2010. (Illus.). xvi, 528p. pap. 239.00 *(978-3-211-99875-5(6)*, 3211998756) Springer.

VanDerwarker, Amber M. & Peres, Tanya M., eds. Integrating Zooarchaeology & Paleoethnobotany: A Consideration of Issues, Methods, & Cases. 2010. (ENG., Illus.). xx, 317p. 129.00 *(978-1-4419-0934-3(6)*, 1441909346) Springer.

Wing, Elizabeth S. & Reitz, Elizabeth Jean. Zooarchaeology. 2nd rev. ed. 2008. (Cambridge Manuals in Archaeology Ser.). (ENG., Illus.). 558p. (C). pap. 48.99 *(978-0-521-67393-8(3))* Cambridge Univ. Pr.

ANIMAL RESCUE

Anderson, Allen & Anderson, Linda C. Rescued - Saving Animals from Disaster: Life-Changing Stories & Practical Suggestions. 2006. (ENG., Illus.). 272p. per. 16.95 *(978-1-57731-544-5(8))* New World Library.

Animal, Rescue L. Animal Rescue League for Love of Dogs. 2011. 192p. pap. 24.95 ***(978-1-935726-12-8(9))*** Landauer Publishing, LLC.

—Animal Resuce League for Love of Cats. 2011. 128p. pap. 21.95 ***(978-1-935726-13-5(7))*** Landauer Publishing, LLC.

Animal Welfare Institute Staff & Humane Society of the United States Staff, contrib. by. Basic Guidelines for Operating an Equine Rescue or Retirement Facility. 2nd ed. 2008. (Illus.). 20p. *(978-0-938414-95-7(X))* Animal Welfare Institute.

Arluke, Arnold. Brute Force: Animal Police & the Challenge of Cruelty. 2007. (Illus.). 175p. per. 19.95 *(978-1-55753-450-7(0))* Purdue Univ. Pr.

Bechtel, Stefan. DogTown: Tales of Rescue, Rehabilitation, & Redemption. 2010. (ENG., Illus.). 304p. pap. 15.95 *(978-1-4262-0642-9(9)*, National Geographic) National Geographic Society.

Best Friends Animal Society. Not Left Behind: Rescuing the Pets of New Orleans. 2006. (Illus.). 95p. 19.95 *(978-0-9767442-5-2(2))* Yorkville Pr.

Best Friends Animal Society Staff & Somerville, Bob. Dogtown: A Sanctuary for Rescued Dogs. 2008. (Illus.). 80p. 16.95 *(978-1-4162-0526-5(8))* Sellers Publishing, Inc.

Blood-Horse Publications & Staff and Correspondents of Blood-Horse Publications. Second-Chance Horses: Inspiring Stories of Ex-Racehorses Succeeding in New Careers. 2009. (ENG., Illus.). 222p. 22.95 *(978-1-58150-211-4(7)*, Eclipse Pr.) Blood-Horse, Inc., The.

Boneham, Sheila. Rescue Matters. rev. l.t. ed. 2010. 391p. 30.95 *(978-1-4104-2278-1(X))* Thorndike Pr.

Boneham, Sheila Webster. Rescue Matters: How to Find, Foster, & Rehome Companion Animals: A Guide for Volunteers & Organizers. 2009. (Illus.). xi, 148p. pap. 14.95 *(978-1-57779-101-0(0))* Alpine Pubns., Inc.

Bowles, Melanie Sue. Hoof Prints: More Stories from Proud Spirit. 2008. (ENG., Illus.). 231p. 19.95 *(978-1-56164-412-4(9))* Pineapple Pr., Inc.

Bowlin, Melanie, et al. Real Stories of Big Cat Rescues: Tales from the Exotic Feline Rescue Center. 2010. (ENG., Illus.). 128p. pap. 19.95 *(978-0-253-22234-3(6)*, 0253222346, Quarry Bks.) Indiana Univ. Pr.

Bowyer, Christine. A Life for Lucy: The touching true story of a wild dog's journey to Happiness. 2009. 164p. pap. 19.99 *(978-1-4401-1605-3(7))* iUniverse, Inc.

Buckle, Catherine. Innocent Victims: Rescuing the Stranded Animals of Zimbabwe's Farm Invasions. 2009. (ENG., Illus.). 352p. 24.95 *(978-1-906122-07-2(5))* Unwin, Merlin Bks. GBR. Dist: SCB Distributors.

Christos, Andrea. Healing Our Animal Friends with Eft. 2009. 80p. pap. 15.49 *(978-1-4389-1470-1(9))* AuthorHouse.

Crisp, Terri & Hurn, C. J. No Buddy Left Behind: Bringing U. S. Troop's Dogs & Cats Safely Home from the Combat Zone. 2011. (ENG., Illus.). 264p. 21.95 *(978-0-7627-7386-2(3)*, Lyons Pr.) Globe Pequot Pr., The.

Dmytryk, Rebecca. Wildlife Search & Rescue: A Guide for First Responders. 2012. (ENG., Illus.). 248p. 145.00 ***(978-0-470-65510-8(0)***, Wiley-Blackwell) Wiley, John & Sons, Inc.

—Wildlife Search & Rescue: A Guide for First Responders. 2012. (ENG., Illus.). 248p. pap. 59.99 ***(978-0-470-65511-5(9)***, Wiley-Blackwell) Wiley, John & Sons, Inc.

D'Onofrio, Sister Alice Marie. Rocky's Forever Home. 2010. 20p. 10.95 *(978-1-4490-9896-4(7))* AuthorHouse.

DuGahl, Helene. The Puppies Find a Home. 2011. 28p. 13.54 ***(978-1-4567-2336-1(7))*** AuthorHouse.

Eades, Deborah. EVERY RESCUED DOG HAS A TALE: Stories from the Dog Rescue Railroad. 2007. 110p. pap. 12.95 *(978-1-4303-1738-8(8))* Lulu Enterprises Inc.

Every Life Matters: Inspiring Stories of Wildlife Rescues & Releases. 2007. (YA). *(978-0-9795716-0-2(X))* EarthAg Consulting.

Garner, Sharon K. & Klam, Julie. Love at First Bark: How Saving a Dog Can Sometimes Help You Save Yourself. l.t. ed. 2011. (ENG.). 337p. 31.99 ***(978-1-4104-4356-4(6))*** Thorndike Pr.

Gimenez, Rebecca, et al, eds. Technical Large Animal Emergency Rescue. 2008. (ENG., Illus.). 440p. 146.99 *(978-0-8138-1998-3(9)*, Wiley-Blackwell) Wiley, John & Sons, Inc.

Goodall, Jane. Hope for Animals & Their World: How Endangered Species Are Being Rescued from the Brink. 2009. (ENG., Illus.). 416p. 27.99 *(978-0-446-58177-6(1))*; 720p. pap. 27.99 *(978-0-446-55994-2(6))* Grand Central Publishing.

Gorant, Jim. The Lost Dogs: Michael Vick's Dogs & Their Tale of Rescue & Redemption. (ENG.). 304p. (gr. 12). 2011. 16.00 *(978-1-59240-667-8(X))* 2010. 26.00 *(978-1-59240-550-3(9))* Penguin Group (USA) Inc. (Gotham).

A Happy Ending for Rescued Dogs. 2008. pap. 19.95 *(978-3-8327-9278-7(3))* teNeues Publishing Co.

Harper, Rex. An Eagle in the Airing Cupboard: More True Tales from an Animal Sanctuary. 2009. (ENG., Illus.). 352p. pap. 15.95 *(978-0-7553-1803-2(X))* Headline Bk. Publishing GBR. Dist: Independent Pubs. Group.

Hentz, Peggy Sue & Hentz, Peggy. Rescuing Wildlife: A Guide to Helping Injured & Orphaned Animals. 2009. (ENG., Illus.). 128p. pap. 14.95 *(978-0-8117-3588-9(5))* Stackpole Bks.

Ink, Rescue. Rescue Ink: Tough Guys on a Mission to Keep Our Animals Safe. 2010. (ENG.). 256p. (gr. 12). 16.00 *(978-0-452-29647-3(1)*, Plume) Penguin Group (USA) Inc.

Irvine, Leslie. Filling the Ark: Animal Welfare in Disasters. 2009. (Animals & Ethics Ser.). (ENG.). 176p. 26.50 *(978-1-59213-834-0(9))* Temple Univ. Pr.

Klam, Julie. Love at First Bark: How Saving a Dog Can Sometimes Help You Save Yourself. 2011. (ENG.). 192p. (gr. 12). 22.95 *(978-1-59448-828-3(2)*, Riverhead Bks. (Hardcover)) Penguin Group (USA) Inc.

Kotler, Steven. A Small Furry Prayer: Dog Rescue & the Meaning of Life. 2010. (ENG., Illus.). 320p. 24.00 *(978-1-60819-002-7(1))* Bloomsbury Publishing.

Kuzman, Beverly. Maxi's Story. 2010. 36p. pap. 13.95 *(978-1-936343-27-0(4))* Peppertree Pr., The.

Langford, Sharon. Living with the Rescues. 2010. (Illus.). 128p. 19.95 *(978-1-60832-045-5(6)*, Greenleaf Book Group Pr.) Greenleaf Book Group.

Lewin, Ted & Lewin, Betsy. Puffling Patrol. 2012. (ENG., Illus.). 56p. (J). 19.95 ***(978-1-60060-424-9(2))*** Lee & Low Bks., Inc.

MacLeod, Ray. Hope for Wildlife: True Stories of Animal Rescue, 1 vol. 2011. (ENG., Illus.). 170p. pap. 19.95 ***(978-1-55109-817-3(2))*** Down East Bks.

MacMillan, Brigitta. The Cat Who Sang & Other Stories of Rescued Animals. 2009. *(978-0-9813528-0-0(4))* Insomniac Pr.

Maimon, Romy A. Animal Lovers. 2006. 350p. pap. 18.95 *(978-0-7414-3642-9(6))* Infinity Publishing.

Makris, Katerina Lorenzatos & Frost, Shelley. Your Adopted Dog: Everything You Need to Know about Rescuing & Caring for a Best Friend in Need. 2007. (ENG., Illus.). 256p. per. 16.95 *(978-1-59921-047-6(9)*, Lyons Pr.) Globe Pequot Pr., The.

Markovics, Joyce. Saving Animals after Earthquakes. 2011. (Rescuing Animals from Disasters Ser.). 32p. (YA). (gr. 2-5). lib. bdg. 25.27 *(978-1-61772-289-9(8))* Bearport Publishing Co., Inc.

—Saving Animals after Floods. 2011. (Rescuing Animals from Disasters Ser.). 32p. (YA). (gr. 2-5). lib. bdg. 25.27 *(978-1-61772-292-9(8))* Bearport Publishing Co., Inc.

McLennan, Bardi. Rescue Me! 2007. (Kennel Club Dog Breed Ser.). (ENG., Illus.). 160p. per. 12.95 *(978-1-59378-666-3(2))* Kennel Club Bks.

Meadows, A. J. & Meadows, A. J. Hurricane Katrina Animal Rescue: A Story Buried Deep. 2011. 72p. pap. ***(978-1-77067-528-5(0))*** FriesenPress.

Meeder, Kim. Bridge Called Hope: Stories of Triumph from the Ranch of Rescued Dreams. 2006. (ENG., Illus.). 256p. per. 13.99 *(978-1-59052-655-2(4)*, Multnomah) Doubleday Religious Publishing Group, The.

Mortensen, Ky. Horses of the Storm: The Incredible Rescue of Katrina's Horses. 2008. (ENG., Illus.). 220p. pap. 19.95 *(978-1-58150-185-8(4)*, Eclipse Pr.) Blood-Horse, Inc., The.

National Geographic Society Staff & Bechtel, Stefan. DogTown: Tales of Rescue, Rehabilitation, & Redemption. 2009. (ENG., Illus.). 304p. 26.00 *(978-1-4262-0562-0(7)*, National Geographic) National Geographic Society.

Nice, Brian. Rescue Tails: Portraits of Dogs & Their Celebrities. 2009. (ENG., Illus.). 176p. pap. 19.95 *(978-1-4391-5276-8(4))* Gallery Pr., The IRL. Dist: Simon & Schuster, Inc.

No Voice Unheard, ed. Ninety-Five: Meeting America's Farmed Animals in Stories & Photographs. 2010. (ENG., Illus.). 168p. pap. 19.95 *(978-0-9728387-5-7(9))* No Voice Unheard.

O'Hara, Shelley. Hopeful Tales: Stories of Rescued Pets & Their Forever Families. 2007. 144p. pap. 13.99 *(978-0-470-17067-0(0)*, Howell Bk. Hse.) Wiley, John & Sons, Inc.

Owings, Natalie. The Heart & Soul Animal Sanctuary: To Love & Be Loved. 2009. (ENG., Illus.). 192p. 45.00 *(978-0-86534-708-3(5))* Sunstone Pr.

Paradise for Rescued Animals. 2008. 24.95 *(978-3-8327-9276-3(7))* teNeues Publishing Co.

Parker-Simons, Nancy. The Road to Utopia: How Kinky, Tony, & I Saved More Animals Than Noah. 2006. (ENG., Illus.). 224p. mass mkt. 15.95 *(978-0-292-71488-5(2))* Univ. of Texas Pr.

Person, Stephen. Saving Animals from Fires. 2011. (Rescuing Animals from Disasters Ser.). 32p. (YA). (gr. 2-5). lib. bdg. 25.27 ***(978-1-61772-293-6(6))*** Bearport Publishing Co., Inc.

Quirk, Joe. Call to the Rescue: The Story of the Marine Mammal Center. 2009. (Illus.). 94p. *(978-0-8118-7007-8(3))* Chronicle Bks. LLC.

Rachwitz-Frye, Kyle M. Every Pet Has a Tale: The Story of Merlin's Refuge. 2008. 128p. pap. 19.95 *(978-1-60563-914-7(1))* PublishAmerica, Inc.

Reardon, Lynn. Beyond the Homestretch: What I've Learned from Saving Racehorses. 2009. (ENG.). 304p. 25.95 *(978-1-57731-647-3(9))* New World Library.

—Beyond the Homestretch: What Saving Racehorses Taught Me about Starting over, Facing Fear, & Finding My Inner Cowgirl. 2011. (ENG.). 304p. pap. 15.95 *(978-1-57731-956-6(7))* New World Library.

Rescue, Ink & Flaim, Denise. Rescue Ink. rev. l.t. ed. 2010. (ENG.). 321p. 31.95 *(978-1-4104-2289-7(5))* Thorndike Pr.

Rodi, Robert. Dogged Pursuit: How a Rescue Dog Rescued Me. 2010. (ENG.). 288p. (gr. 12). 15.00 *(978-0-452-29613-8(7)*, Plume) Penguin Group (USA) Inc.

Rude, Bob And Kathy. The Best Little Cat House in Maryland: The True & Mostly Accurate Story of How Rude Ranch Animal Rescue Came to Be. 2009. 256p. 24.99 *(978-1-4490-0884-0(4))*; pap. 14.95 *(978-1-4490-0883-3(6))* AuthorHouse.

Salaks, Tina & Estes, Allison. Paw & Order: Dramatic Investigations by an Animal Cop on the Beat. 2008. (ENG., Illus.). 200p. pap. 12.95 *(978-1-933958-21-7(9))* BowTie Pr.

Schubert, Julie Anne. Rescued! Tales of California Canine Rescue. 2010. 136p. 23.95 *(978-1-4502-6123-4(X))*; pap. 13.95 *(978-1-4502-6121-0(3))* iUniverse, Inc.

Scott, Cathy. Pawprints of Katrina: Pets Saved & Lessons Learned. 2008. (ENG., Illus.). 288p. 19.99 *(978-0-470-22851-7(2)*, Howell Bk. Hse.) Wiley, John & Sons, Inc.

Scott, Traer. Shelter Dogs. 2009. (Illus.). 96p. pap. *(978-1-85894-498-2(8))* Merrell Pubs. Ltd.

—Street Dogs. 2007. (ENG., Illus.). 128p. 22.95 *(978-1-85894-408-1(2))* Merrell Pubs. Ltd. GBR. Dist: Perseus Distribution.

Stevens, Kathy. Animal Camp: My Summer with a Horse, a Pig, a Cow, a Pigeon, a Dog, Two Cats, & One Very Patient Man. 2010. (ENG., Illus.). 208p. 24.95 *(978-1-61608-011-2(6)*, 608011) Skyhorse Publishing Co., Inc.

—Where the Blind Horse Sings: Love & Healing at an Animal Sanctuary. 2009. (ENG., Illus.). 206p. pap. 14.95 *(978-1-60239-669-2(8)*, 239669) Skyhorse Publishing Co., Inc.

Stutz, Birgit & Scanlan, Lawrence. The Rescue of Belle & Sundance: One Town's Incredible Race to Save Two Abandoned Horses. 2012. (Merloyd Lawrence Book Ser.). (ENG.). 240p. 22.00 ***(978-0-306-82097-7(8))*** Da Capo Pr., Inc.

Sullivan, Diane & Vietzke, Holly, eds. Please, Can We Keep the Donkey? A Collection of Animal Rescue Stories by the Massachusetts School of Law Community. 2008. (Illus.). 174p. 19.95 *(978-1-59056-122-5(8))* Lantern Bks.

Summers, Jane & Ritson, Janie. Hoping for a Home: How a Woman with a Big Heart Gave New Lives to Animals in Need. 2011. (ENG.). 240p. 12.95 *(978-0-00-737891-3(2))* HarperCollins Pubs. Ltd. GBR. Dist: Independent Pubs. Group.

Todd, Jackie. Dog Days in Andalucía: Tails from Spain. 2010. (ENG., Illus.). 256p. pap. 14.95 *(978-1-84596-613-3(9))* Mainstream Publishing Co., Ltd. GBR. Dist: Independent Pubs. Group.

Van Frankenhuyzen, Robbyn Smith. Itsy Bitsy & Teeny Weeny. 2009. (Hazel Ridge Farm Stories Ser.). 48p. (J). (gr. k-2). 16.95 *(978-1-58536-417-6(7))* Sleeping Bear Pr.

Weller, Frank. Equine Angels: Stories of Rescue, Love, & Hope. 2008. (ENG., Illus.). 192p. 24.95 *(978-1-59921-444-3(X)*, Lyons Pr.) Globe Pequot Pr., The.

Westoll, Andrew. The Chimps of Fauna Sanctuary: A True Story of Resilience & Recovery. (ENG.). 288p. 2012. pap. 14.95 ***(978-0-547-73738-6(6)***, Mariner Bks.) 2011. (Illus.). 25.00 *(978-0-547-32780-8(3))* Houghton Mifflin Harcourt Trade & Reference Pubs.

Whitney, Kendall. Pick-up Dogs: How Two Rescue Dogs Save the West from Being Won. 2012. (ENG.). 174p. pap. 9.95 ***(978-1-4663-0275-4(5))*** CreateSpace.

Williams, Jennifer. How to Start & Run a Rescue. 2007. *(978-1-929164-36-3(X))* Primedia Enthusiast Pubns.

Winegar, Karin. Saved: Rescued Animals & the Lives They Transform. 2009. (ENG., Illus.). 256p. pap. 18.00 *(978-0-306-81842-4(6))* Da Capo Pr., Inc.

Yeadon, Helen. When Sophie Met Darcy Day: A Neglected Racehorse, a Troubled Child, a Friendship That Would Change Lives Forver. 2011. (ENG.). 320p. 13.95 *(978-0-00-735424-5(X))* HarperCollins Pubs. Ltd. GBR. Dist: Independent Pubs. Group.

ANIMAL RESTRAINT

see Animal Immobilization

ANIMAL RIGHTS

Here are entered works on the inherent rights attributed to animals. Works on the protection and treatment of animals are entered under Animal Welfare.

Adams, Carol J. The Sexual Politics of Meat: A Feminist-Vegetarian Critical Theory. 20th anniv. ed. 2010. (ENG., Illus.). 344p. pap. 22.95 *(978-1-4411-7328-7(5))* Continuum International Publishing Group, Ltd. GBR. Dist: National Bk. Network.

Anderson, Patricia K., et al, eds. Anthrozoös, Vol. 20, Set. 2008. (ENG., Illus.). 1p. pap. 3600.00 *(978-1-84788-226-4(9))* Berg Pubs. GBR. Dist: Macmillan.

Animal's Rights in Islam. 2009. 72p. pap. *(978-3-639-16001-7(0))* VDM Verlag Dr. Mueller e.K.

Armstrong, Susan J. & Botzler, Richard George. The Animal Ethics Reader. Armstrong, Susan & Botzler, Richard G., eds. 2nd rev. ed. 2008. XXX, 650p. 46.95 *(978-0-415-77539-7(6))* Routledge.

Beauchamp, Tom L. & Frey, R. G. The Oxford Handbook of Animal Ethics, 1 vol. 2011. (Oxford Handbooks Ser.). (ENG., Illus.). 984p. 175.00 *(978-0-19-537196-3(8))* Oxford Univ. Pr., Inc.

Beers, Diane L. For the Prevention of Cruelty: The History & Legacy of Animal Rights Activism in the United States. 2006. (Illus.). 368p. 34.95 *(978-0-8040-1086-3(2))*; (ENG., per. 22.95 *(978-0-8040-1087-0(0))* Swallow Pr.

Bekoff, Marc. Encyclopedia of Animal Rights & Animal Welfare, 2 vols. 2nd ed. 2009. (Illus.). xlii, 685p. E-Book *(978-0-313-35256-0(9)*, Greenwood Pr.) Greenwood Publishing Group, Inc.

Bekoff, Marc, ed. Encyclopedia of Animal Rights & Animal Welfare, 2 vols. 2nd rev. ed. 2009. (Illus.). 685p. 165.00 *(978-0-313-35255-3(0)*, GR5255, Greenwood Pr.) Greenwood Publishing Group, Inc.

Boddice, Rob. A History of Attitudes & Behaviours Toward Animals in Eighteenth-and Nineteenth-Century Britain: Anthropocentrism & the Emergence of Animals. 2009. 400p. 119.95 *(978-0-7734-4903-9(5))* Mellen, Edwin Pr., The.

Boddice, Rob, ed. Anthropocentrism: Humans, Animals, Environments. 2011. (Human-Animal Studies). XXII, 348p. pap. ***(978-90-04-18794-8(4))*** BRILL.

Bronner, Simon J. Killing Tradition: Inside Hunting & Animal Rights Controversies. 2008. (ENG., Illus.). 320p. 40.00 *(978-0-8131-2528-2(6))* Univ. Pr. of Kentucky.

Castricano, Jodey, ed. Animal Subjects: An Ethical Reader in a Posthuman World. 2008. (Environmental Humanities Ser.). (ENG., Illus.). 324p. pap. 42.95 *(978-0-88920-512-3(4))* Wilfrid Laurier Univ. Pr. CAN. Dist: Univ. of Toronto Pr.

Cavalieri, Paola. The Death of the Animal: A Dialogue. 2009. (ENG., Illus.). 168p. (gr. 17). 24.95 *(978-0-231-14552-7(7))* Columbia Univ. Pr.

Christiansen, Stine, et al. Ethics of Animal Use. 2008. (ENG., Illus.). 192p. pap. 74.99 *(978-1-4051-5120-7(X)*, Wiley-Blackwell) Wiley, John & Sons, Inc.

Cochrane, Alasdair. Animal Rights without Liberation: Applied Ethics & Human Obligations. 2012. (Critical Perspectives on Animals: Theory, Culture, Science & Law Ser.). (ENG.). 272p. (gr. 17). 89.50 ***(978-0-231-15826-8(2))***; pap. 29.50 ***(978-0-231-15827-5(0))*** Columbia Univ. Pr.

Cochrane, Alasdair. An Introduction to Animals & Political Theory. 2010. (Palgrave Macmillan Animal Ethics Ser.). (ENG.). 208p. 95.00 *(978-0-230-23925-8(0))*; pap. 34.00 *(978-0-230-23926-5(9))* Palgrave Macmillan.

Conn, P. Michael, et al. The Animal Research War. 2008. (ENG.). 224p. 42.00 *(978-0-230-60014-0(X))* Palgrave Macmillan.

Dawn, Karen. Thanking the Monkey: Rethinking the Way We Treat Animals. 2008. (ENG., Illus.). 400p. pap. 19.95 *(978-0-06-135185-3(7)*, William Morrow Paperbacks) HarperCollins Pubs.

DeKoven, Marianne & Lundblad, Michael, eds. Species Matters: Humane Advocacy & Cultural Theory. 2011. (ENG., Illus.). 240p. (gr. 17). 84.50 ***(978-0-231-15282-2(5))***; pap. 27.50 ***(978-0-231-15283-9(3))*** Columbia Univ. Pr.

Dixon, B. A. Animals, Emotion, & Morality: Marking the Boundary. 2008. (ENG.). 240p. pap. 21.98 *(978-1-59102-629-7(6))* Prometheus Bks., Pubs.

Donahue, Jesse & Trump, Erik. The Politics of Zoos: Exotic Animals & Their Protectors. 2006. (Illus.). 236p. 40.00 *(978-0-87580-364-7(4))*; per. 24.00 *(978-0-87580-613-6(9))* Northern Illinois Univ. Pr.

Donaldson, Sue & Kymlicka, Will. Zoopolis: A Political Theory of Animal Rights. 2011. (ENG.). 264p. 29.95 ***(978-0-19-959966-0(1))*** Oxford Univ. Pr., Inc.

Donovan, Josephine, et al, eds. The Feminist Care Tradition in Animal Ethics. 2007. (ENG., Illus.). 400p. (gr. 17). 85.00 *(978-0-231-14038-6(X))* Columbia Univ. Pr.

Donovan, Josephine & Adams, Carol, eds. The Feminist Care Tradition in Animal Ethics. 2007. (ENG.). 400p. (gr. 17). pap. 27.00 *(978-0-231-14039-3(8))* Columbia Univ. Pr.

Dupras, Georges R. Values in Conflict: Reflections of an Animal Advocate. 2011. 324p. 32.95 ***(978-1-4620-5387-2(4))***; pap. 22.95 ***(978-1-4620-5385-8(8))*** iUniverse, Inc.

Engel, Mylan & Jenni, Kathie. The Philosophy of Animal Rights: A Brief Introduction for Students & Teachers. 2010. xxi, 127p. *(978-1-59056-177-5(5))* Lantern Bks.

Evans, E. P. The Criminal Prosecution & Capital Punishment of Animals. 2007. (ENG.). 352p. 46.95 *(978-0-548-13031-5(0))* Kessinger Publishing, LLC.

Favre, David S. Animal Law: Welfare, Interests, & Rights. 2008. (Illus.). xvi, 495p. pap. *(978-0-7355-7313-0(1)*, Aspen Pubs.) Wolters Kluwer Law & Business.

Fellenz, Marc R. The Moral Menagerie: Philosophy & Animal Rights. 2007. 312p. 62.00 *(978-0-252-03118-2(0))*; per. 26.00 *(978-0-252-07360-1(6))* Univ. of Illinois Pr.

Fitzgerald, Amy & Kalof, Linda, eds. The Animals Reader: The Essential Classic & Contemporary Writings. 2007. (ENG., Illus.). 448p. 115.95 *(978-1-84520-469-3(7))* Berg Pubs. GBR. Dist: Macmillan.

Francione, Gary L. Animals as Persons: Essays on the Abolition of Animal Exploitation. (ENG.). 256p. (gr. 17). 2009. pap. 24.50 *(978-0-231-13951-9(9))* 2008. (Illus.). 40.00 *(978-0-231-13950-2(0))* Columbia Univ. Pr.

Francione, Gary L. & Garner, Robert. The Animal Rights Debate: Abolition or Regulation? 2010. (Critical Perspectives on Animals: Theory, Culture, Science & Law Ser.). (ENG.). 288p. (gr. 17). 79.50 *(978-0-231-14954-9(9))*; pap. 24.50 *(978-0-231-14955-6(7))* Columbia Univ. Pr.

Franklin, Julian H. Animal Rights & Moral Philosophy. 2006. (ENG.). 176p. (gr. 17). pap. 26.00 *(978-0-231-13423-1(1))* Columbia Univ. Pr.

Freeman, Carol, et al, eds. Considering Animals: Contemporary Studies in Human-Animal Relations. 2011. (Illus.). 252p. 64.95 *(978-1-4094-0013-4(1))* Ashgate Publishing Co.

French, Thomas. Zoo Story: Life in the Garden of Captives. 2010. (ENG.). 304p. 24.99 *(978-1-4013-2346-2(4))* Hyperion Pr.

Gale Editor, ed. Information Plus Animal Rights. 2011. pap. 58.00 *(978-1-4144-4869-5(4))* Cengage Gale.

Goodale, Greg & Black, J. E. Arguments about Animal Ethics. 2010. (ENG.). 262p. 73.50 *(978-0-7391-4298-1(4))* Lexington Bks.

Granata, Silvia. Take Every Creature In, of Every Kind: Continuity & Change in Eighteenth-Century Representations of Animals. 2011. (Europäische Hochschulschriften. Reihe 14: Angelsächsische Sprache und Literatur Ser.). 200p. pap. *(978-3-0343-0544-0(3))* Lang, Peter.

Grant, Catharine. The No-Nonsense Guide to Animal Rights. 2006. (No-Nonsense Guides). (ENG., Illus.). 144p. per. 11.95 *(978-1-904456-40-7(5))* New Internationalist Pubns., Ltd. GBR. Dist: Consortium Bk. Sales & Distribution.

Gruen, Lori. Ethics & Animals: An Introduction. 2011. (Cambridge Applied Ethics Ser.). (ENG.). 250p. (C). 85.00 *(978-0-521-88899-8(9))*; pap. 27.99 *(978-0-521-71773-1(6))* Cambridge Univ. Pr.

Hall, Lee. Capers in the Churchyard: Animal rights advocacy in the age of Terror. 2006. 14.95 *(978-0-9769159-1-1(X))* Friends of Animals.

Hribal, Jason. Fear of the Animal Planet: The Secret History of Animal Resistance. 2011. (Counterpunch Ser.). (ENG.). 280p. pap. 15.95 ***(978-1-84935-026-6(4))*** AK Pr. GBR. Dist: Consortium Bk. Sales & Distribution.

Hughes, Alan & Brazier, Chris, eds. Political Animals. 2007. (ENG., Illus.). 192p. pap. 8.95 *(978-1-904456-24-7(3))* New Internationalist Pubns., Ltd. GBR. Dist: Consortium Bk. Sales & Distribution.

Irvine, Leslie. Animals & Society Institute: Animals & Society Institute: Animals in Disasters: Responsibility & Action. 2007. 15.00 *(978-0-9788572-2-6(4))* Animals & Society Institute.

Joy, Melanie. Strategic Action for Animals: A Handbook on Strategic Movement Building, Organizing, & Activism for Animal Liberation. 2008. (Flashpoint Ser.: 4). 176p. pap. 20.00 *(978-1-59056-136-2(8))* Lantern Bks.

Kalof, Linda & Fitzgerald, Amy, eds. The Animals Reader: The Essential Classic & Contemporary Writings. 2007. (ENG., Illus.). 448p. pap. 35.95 *(978-1-84520-470-9(0))* Berg Pubs. GBR. Dist: Macmillan.

Karlsson, Fredrik. Weighing Animal Lives: A Critical Assessment of Justification & Prioritization in Animal-Rights Theories. 2009. (Uppsala Studies in Social Ethics Ser.). (Illus.). 340p. pap. 79.50 *(978-91-554-7576-5(0))* Uppsala Universitet/Acta Universitatis Uppsaliensis SWE. Dist: Coronet Bks.

Kazez, Jean. Animalkind: What We Owe to Animals. 2010. (ENG., Illus.). 216p. 94.95 *(978-1-4051-9937-7(7))*; pap. 27.95 *(978-1-4051-9938-4(5))* Wiley, John & Sons, Inc. (Wiley-Blackwell).

Kemmerer, Lisa. In Search of Consistency: Ethics & Animals. 2006. (Human-Animal Studies: Vol. 3). 555p. pap. *(978-90-04-14725-6(X))* BRILL.

Kemmerer, Lisa, ed. Speaking up for Animals: An Anthology of Women's Voices. 2011. 224p. 98.00 ***(978-1-61205-087-4(5))***; pap. 24.95 ***(978-1-61205-088-1(3))*** Paradigm Pubs.

Kemmerer, Lisa A., ed. Sister Species: Women, Animals & Social Justice. 2011. (ENG.). 208p. 65.00 *(978-0-252-03617-0(4))* Univ. of Illinois Pr.

—Sister Species: Women, Animals, & Social Justice. 2011. (ENG.). 208p. pap. 21.95 *(978-0-252-07811-8(X))* Univ. of Illinois Pr.

Kirk, Ronald W., et al, eds. Worship Not the Creature: Animal Rights & the Bible. 2009. (ENG., Illus.). 192p. pap. 19.99 *(978-0-9824929-1-8(X))* Nordskog Publishing, Inc.

Lankford, Ronnie D. Animal Experimentation, No. 9. 2009. (At Issue Ser.). (ENG.). 128p. (gr. 10-12). pap. 31.80 *(978-0-7377-4280-0(1))*; (Illus.). pap. 22.50 *(978-0-7377-4279-4(8))* Cengage Gale. (Greenhaven Pr., Inc.).

Liddick, Donald R. & Liddick, Donald R., Jr. Eco-Terrorism: Radical Environmental & Animal Liberation Movements, 1 vol. 2006. (Illus.). 200p. 39.95 *(978-0-275-98535-6(0)*, C8535, Praeger Pubs.) Greenwood Publishing Group, Inc.

Magel, Charles R. Keyguide: Animal Rights. xiv, 267p. *(978-0-7201-1984-8(7)*, Burns & Oates) Continuum International Publishing Group, Ltd.

Martin, Glen. Game Changer: Animal Rights & the Fate of Africa's Wildlife. 2012. (ENG., Illus.). 244p. 29.95 ***(978-0-520-26626-1(9))*** Univ. of California Pr.

McLean, Lesley. Ethics about Animals. 2010. 144p. pap. *(978-3-8383-5000-4(6))* Lambert Academic Publishing.

Milligan, Tony. Beyond Animal Rights: Food, Pets & Ethics. 2010. (Think Now Ser.). (ENG.). 184p. 19.95 *(978-1-4411-5753-9(0))*; 80.00 *(978-1-4411-9486-2(X))* Continuum International Publishing Group, Ltd. GBR. Dist: National Bk. Network.

Newkirk, Ingrid. The PETA Practical Guide to Animal Rights: Simple Acts of Kindness to Help Animals in Trouble. 2009. (ENG.). 496p. pap. 19.99 *(978-0-312-55994-6(1)*, St. Martin's Griffin) St. Martin's Pr.

Newman DVM, Kenneth. Meet Me at the Rainbow Bridge. 2010. 196p. pap. 17.95 *(978-0-557-50385-8(X))* Lulu Enterprises Inc.

Nussbaum, Martha C. Frontiers of Justice: Disability, Nationality, Species Membership. 2007. (Tanner Lectures on Human Values Ser.). 512p. per. 22.50 *(978-0-674-02410-6(9)*, Belknap Pr.) Harvard Univ. Pr.

Office of the Federal Register (U.S.), compiled by. Code of Federal Regulations, Title 9, Animals & Animal Products, Pt. 1-199, Revised as of January 1 2011. rev. ed. 2011. (ENG.). 1077p. pap. 67.00 ***(978-0-16-087542-7(0)***, Office of the Federal Register) United States Government Printing Office.

—Code of Federal Regulations, Title 9, Animals & Animal Products, Pt. 200-End, Revised as of January 1 2011. rev. ed. 2011. (ENG., Illus.). 764p. pap. 64.00 ***(978-0-16-087543-4(9)***, Office of the Federal Register) United States Government Printing Office.

Owen, Marna A. Animal Rights: Noble Cause or Needless Effort? 2009. (USA TODAY's Debate: Voices & Perspectives Ser.). 160p. (YA). (gr. 9-12). 35.93 *(978-0-7613-4082-9(3))* Lerner Publishing Group.

Palmer, Clare. Animal Ethics in Context. 2010. (ENG.). 216p. (gr. 17). 89.50 *(978-0-231-12904-6(1))*; pap. 27.50 *(978-0-231-12905-3(X))* Columbia Univ. Pr.

Palmer, Clare, ed. Animal Rights. 2008. (International Library of Essays on Rights Ser.). 582p. 325.00 *(978-0-7546-2741-8(1))* Ashgate Publishing Co.

Parker, James V. Animal Minds, Animal Souls, Animal Rights. 2010. (ENG.). 166p. pap. 25.99 *(978-0-7618-5177-6(1))*; (Illus.). viii, 153p. E-Book ***(978-0-7618-5178-3(X))*** Univ. Pr. of America, Inc.

Pearson, Susan J. The Rights of the Defenseless: Protecting Animals & Children in Gilded Age America. 2011. (ENG., Illus.). 280p. 45.00 *(978-0-226-65201-6(7))* Univ. of Chicago Pr.

Perkins, David. Romanticism & Animal Rights. 2007. (Cambridge Studies in Romanticism Ser.). (ENG.). 212p. pap. 48.00 *(978-0-521-04598-8(3))* Cambridge Univ. Pr.

Petrinovich, Lewis. Darwinian Dominion: Animal Welfare & Human Interests. 2008. (ENG.). 431p. pap. 25.00 *(978-1-4379-5870-6(2))* DIANE Publishing Co.

Phelps, Norm. The Longest Struggle: Animal Advocacy from Pythagoras to PETA. 2007. (ENG.). 367p. per. 20.00 *(978-1-59056-106-5(6))* Lantern Bks.

Philips, Allie. Defending the Defenseless: A Guide to Protecting & Advocating for Pets. 2011. (ENG.). 312p. 37.95 *(978-1-4422-0214-6(9))* Rowman & Littlefield Publishers, Inc.

Regan, Tom. Defending Animal Rights. 2006. 200p. per. 21.00 *(978-0-252-07416-5(5))* Univ. of Illinois Pr.

Ritter, Christie. Animal Rights. 2008. (Essential Viewpoints Set 2 Ser.). (Illus.). 112p. (YA). (gr. 7-12). 34.22 *(978-1-60453-054-4(5))* ABDO Publishing Co.

Rollin, Bernard. Animal Rights & Human Morality. 3rd rev. ed. 2006. (ENG.). 360p. per. 24.98 *(978-1-59102-421-7(8))* Prometheus Bks., Pubs.

—The Unheeded Cry. 2010. 348p. pap. 24.95 *(978-0-557-57821-4(3))* Lulu Enterprises Inc.

Rowlands, Mark. Animal Rights: Moral Theory & Practice. 2nd rev. ed. 2009. (ENG.). 240p. 105.00 *(978-0-230-21944-1(6))*; pap. 30.00 *(978-0-230-21945-8(4))* Palgrave Macmillan.

Rudy, Kathy. Loving Animals: Toward a New Animal Advocacy. 2011. (ENG.). 288p. 24.95 ***(978-0-8166-7468-8(X))*** Univ. of Minnesota Pr.

Ryan, Thomas. Animals & Social Work: A Moral Introduction. 2011. (Palgrave Macmillan Animal Ethics Ser.). (ENG.). 240p. 85.00 *(978-0-230-27250-7(9))* Palgrave Macmillan.

Ryder, Richard D. Speciesism, Painism & Happiness: A Morality for the 21st Century. 2011. (Societas Ser.). (ENG.). 128p. pap. 17.90 ***(978-1-84540-235-8(9))*** Imprint Academic GBR. Dist: Ingram Pub. Services.

Salem, Deborah J. & Rowan, Andrew N. The State of the Animals IV, 2007. 2007. (Illus.). vii, 238p. pap. 29.95 *(978-0-9748400-9-3(2))* Humane Society of the United States, The.

Sanbonmatsu, John. Critical Theory & Animal Liberation. 2011. (Nature's Meaning Ser.). (ENG.). 376p. (gr. 17). 40.00 *(978-1-4422-0580-2(6))* Rowman & Littlefield Publishers, Inc.

—On the Animal Question: Animal Liberation & Critical Theory. 2010. *(978-1-4422-0582-6(2))* Rowman & Littlefield Publishers, Inc.

Scruton, Roger. Animal Rights & Wrongs. 3rd ed. 2006. (ENG., Illus.). 224p. 34.95 *(978-0-8264-9404-7(8))* Continuum International Publishing Group, Ltd. GBR. Dist: National Bk. Network.

Sherry, Clifford J. Animal Rights. 2nd rev. ed. 2009. (Contemporary World Issues Ser.). (Illus.). 295p. 55.00 *(978-1-59884-191-6(2)*, ANIRIG2C) ABC-CLIO, LLC.

Singer, Peter. Animal Liberation: The Definitive Classic of the Animal Movement. 2009. (P. S. Ser.). (ENG.). 368p. pap. 14.99 *(978-0-06-171130-5(6)*, HarperPerennial) HarperCollins Pubs.

Smith, Kimberly K. Governing Animals: Animal Welfare & the Liberal State. 2012. (ENG.). 240p. 34.95 ***(978-0-19-989575-5(9))*** Oxford Univ. Pr., Inc.

Smith, Wesley J. A Rat Is a Pig Is a Dog Is a Boy: The Human Cost of the Animal Rights Movement. (ENG.). 2012. 336p. pap. 16.99 ***(978-1-59403-614-9(4))*** 2010. 270p. 25.95 *(978-1-59403-346-9(3))* Encounter Bks.

Smulewicz-Zucker, Gregory R. Strangers to Nature: Animal Lives & Human Ethics. 2011. ***(978-0-7391-4549-4(5))*** Lexington Bks.

Sorenson, John. About Canada: Animal Rights. 2010. (About Canada Ser.). (ENG.). 192p. pap. 17.95 *(978-1-55266-356-1(6))* Fernwood Publishing Co., Ltd. CAN. Dist: Independent Pubs. Group.

Sterba, James. Earth Ethics. 3rd ed. 2009. (ENG.). 363p. (C). pap. 53.33 *(978-0-13-600654-1(X)*, Prentice Hall) Prentice Hall PTR.

Stone, Lora. The Ideology of Progress, World Culture, & Animal Protection. 2006. (ENG., Illus.). 96p. pap. 26.50 *(978-0-7618-3608-7(X))* Univ. Pr. of America, Inc.

Torres, Bob. Making a Killing: The Political Economy of Animal Rights. 2007. (ENG.). 185p. per. 17.95 *(978-1-904859-67-3(4))* AK Pr. GBR. Dist: Consortium Bk. Sales & Distribution.

Twain, Mark, pseud. Animals. Fishkin, Shelley Fisher, ed. 2009. (Jumping Frogs: Undiscovered, Rediscovered, & Celebrated Writings of Mark Twain Ser.). (Illus.). 340p. 50.00 *(978-0-520-24855-7(4))* Univ. of California Pr.

—Mark Twain's Book of Animals. Fishkin, Shelley Fisher, ed. 2011. (Jumping Frogs: Undiscovered, Rediscovered, & Celebrated Writings of Mark Twain Ser.). (ENG., Illus.). 344p. pap. 21.95 *(978-0-520-27152-4(1))* Univ. of California Pr.

Varner, Gary E. Personhood, Ethics, & Animal Cognition: Situating Animals in Hare's Two Level Utilitarianism. 2012. (ENG.). 288p. 74.00 ***(978-0-19-975878-4(6))*** Oxford Univ. Pr., Inc.

Volpe, Tina & Carman, Judy. The Missing Peace: The Hidden Power of our Kinship with Animals: the Hidden Power of Our Kinship with Animals. 2009. 232p. pap. 16.95 *(978-0-9797908-2-9(4))* Dreamriver Pr.

Waldau, Paul. Animal Rights: What Everyone Needs to Know, 1 vol. 2011. (What Everyone Needs to Know Ser.). (ENG.). 272p. pap. 16.95 *(978-0-19-973996-7(X))* Oxford Univ. Pr., Inc.

Wilkie, Rhoda & Inglis, David, eds. Animals & Society, 5 vols., Set. 2006. (Critical Concepts in the Social Sciences Ser.). (ENG., Illus.). 2032p. (C). 1680.00 *(978-0-415-37184-1(8))* Routledge.

Williams, Erin E. Why Animals Matter: The Case for Animal Protection. 2007. (ENG., Illus.). 1p. per. 21.98 *(978-1-59102-523-8(0))* Prometheus Bks., Pubs.

Wise, Steven M. An American Trilogy: Death, Slavery, & Dominion on the Banks of the Cape Fear River. 2009. (ENG.). 304p. 26.00 *(978-0-306-81475-4(7))* Perseus Bks. Group.

Young, Peter, intro. Animal Liberation Front: The First 30 Years. 2010. (ENG.). 74p. pap. 12.95 *(978-0-9842844-0-5(0))* Warcry.

ANIMAL RIGHTS ACTIVISTS

Alemanno, Alberto, ed. Governing Disasters: The Challenges of Emergency Risk Regulation. 2011. 320p. 125.00 ***(978-0-85793-572-4(0))*** Elgar, Edward Publishing, Inc.

Beers, Diane L. For the Prevention of Cruelty: The History & Legacy of Animal Rights Activism in the United States. 2006. (Illus.). 368p. 34.95 *(978-0-8040-1086-3(2))*; (ENG., per. 22.95 *(978-0-8040-1087-0(0))* Swallow Pr.

Eco-Terrorism Specifically Examining Stop Huntingdon Animal Cruelty ("SHAC") Hearing Before the Committee on Environment & Public Works, United States Senate, One Hundred Ninth Congress, First Session, October 26, 2005. 2008. (Illus.). iv, 72p. *(978-0-16-080539-4(2)*, 552-070-37201-6) United States Government Printing Office.

Eisenstein, Yolanda. Careers in Animal Law. 2012. (ENG.). 160p. pap. 54.95 ***(978-1-61632-961-7(0))*** American Bar Assn.

Gaarder, Emily. Women & the Animal Rights Movement. 2011. (ENG., Illus.). 196p. (C). pap. 23.95 *(978-0-8135-4968-2(X))*; 69.00 *(978-0-8135-4967-5(1))* Rutgers Univ. Pr.

Greenwald, Marilyn. Cleveland Amory: Media Curmudgeon & Animal Rights Crusader. 2009. (ENG., Illus.). 276p. 27.95 *(978-1-58465-681-4(6))* Univ. Pr. of New England.

Hawthorne, Mark. Striking at the Roots: A Practical Guide to Animal Activism. 2007. (ENG., Illus.). 304p. per. 19.95 *(978-1-84694-091-0(5))* O Bks., John Hunt.

Joy, Melanie. Strategic Action for Animals: A Handbook on Strategic Movement Building, Organizing, & Activism for Animal Liberation. 2008. (Flashpoint Ser.: 4). 176p. pap. 20.00 *(978-1-59056-136-2(8))* Lantern Bks.

Kuipers, Dean. Operation Bite Back: Rod Coronado's War to Save American Wilderness. 2010. (ENG.). 320p. pap. 17.00 *(978-1-60819-204-5(0))* Bloomsbury Publishing.

Lane, Carla. Someday I'll Find Me - Carla Lane: Her Frank & Captivating Autobiography. 2006. (ENG., Illus.). 260p. 29.95 *(978-1-86105-973-4(6))* Anova Bks. GBR. Dist: Independent Pubs. Group.

Leney, Joy. Such a Nuisance to Die: The Autobiography of Her Serene Highness Princess Elisabeth de Croy. 2010. (Illus.). 256p. 38.50 *(978-1-84624-448-3(X))* Book Guild, Ltd. GBR. Dist: Trans-Atlantic Pubns., Inc.

Lovitz, Dara. Muzzling a Movement: The Effects of Anti-Terrorism Law, Money, & Politics on Animal Activism. 2010. *(978-1-59056-176-8(7))* Lantern Bks.

Martin, Glen. Game Changer: Animal Rights & the Fate of Africa's Wildlife. 2012. (ENG., Illus.). 244p. 29.95 ***(978-0-520-26626-1(9))*** Univ. of California Pr.

Mathews, Dan. Committed: A Rabble-Rouser's Memoir. 2008. (ENG., Illus.). 272p. pap. 17.99 *(978-0-7432-9194-1(8)*, Beyond Words/Atria Bks.) Atria Bks.

Mezzatesta, V. Barking in the Wind: Conflict with Human Apathy. 2011. 104p. pap. 9.95 ***(978-1-4620-3923-4(5))*** iUniverse, Inc.

Philips, Allie. Defending the Defenseless: A Guide to Protecting & Advocating for Pets. 2011. (ENG.). 312p. 37.95 *(978-1-4422-0214-6(9))* Rowman & Littlefield Publishers, Inc.

Rudy, Kathy. Loving Animals: Toward a New Animal Advocacy. 2011. (ENG.). 288p. 24.95 ***(978-0-8166-7468-8(X))*** Univ. of Minnesota Pr.

Song, Hoon. Pigeon Trouble: Bestiary Biopolitics in a Deindustrialized America. 2010. 272p. (C). 49.95 *(978-0-8122-4242-3(4))* Univ. of Pennsylvania Pr.

Young, Peter, intro. Animal Liberation Front: The First 30 Years. 2010. (ENG.). 74p. pap. 12.95 *(978-0-9842844-0-5(0))* Warcry.

ANIMAL RUNNING

see Animal Locomotion

ANIMAL SIGNS

see Animal Tracks

ANIMAL SOCIETIES

Here are entered works on groups of animals which are characterized by specific social patterns due to their proximity, interrelationships and-or similarities.

see also Insect Societies; Social Behavior in Animals

Bearzi, Maddalena & Stanford, Craig B. Beautiful Minds: The Parallel Lives of Great Apes & Dolphins. 368p. 2010. pap. 14.95 *(978-0-674-04627-6(7))* 2008. 24.95 *(978-0-674-02781-7(7))* Harvard Univ. Pr.

Eaton, Barry. Dominance in Dogs: Fact or Fiction? 2011. 11.95 *(978-1-929242-80-1(8))* Dogwise Publishing.

Mitani, John, et al, eds. The Evolution of Primate Societies. 2012. 504p. pap. 50.00 ***(978-0-226-53172-4(4))***; (Illus.). 145.00 ***(978-0-226-53171-7(6))*** Univ. of Chicago Pr.

Sherman, Paul W. & Wolff, Jerry O., eds. Rodent Societies: An Ecological & Evolutionary Perspective. 2007. (Illus.). 610p. per. 52.50 *(978-0-226-90537-2(3))* Univ. of Chicago Pr.

Whitehead, Hal. Analyzing Animal Societies: Quantitative Methods for Vertebrate Social Analysis. 2008. (ENG., Illus.). 320p. 75.00 *(978-0-226-89521-5(1))*; pap. 29.00 *(978-0-226-89523-9(8))* Univ. of Chicago Pr.

Wolff, Jerry. Rodent Societies: An Ecological & Evolutionary Perspective. Sherman, Paul W. et al, eds. 2007. (Illus.). 610p. 135.00 *(978-0-226-90536-5(5))* Univ. of Chicago Pr.

ANIMAL SOUNDS

see also Birdsongs; Insect Sounds

Halloran, Andrew R. The Song of the Ape: Understanding the Languages of Chimpanzees. 2012. (ENG., Illus.). 288p. 25.99 ***(978-0-312-56311-0(6))*** St. Martin's Pr.

Krause, Bernie. The Great Animal Orchestra: Finding the Origins of Music in the World's Wild Places. 2012. (ENG., Illus.). 288p. 26.99 *(978-0-316-08687-5(8))* Little Brown & Co.

McGregor, Peter K., ed. Playback & Studies of Animal Communication. 2010. (Nato Science Series: A: Ser.). 248p. pap. 279.00 *(978-1-4419-3224-2(0)*, 1441932240) Springer.

Menino, Holly. Calls Beyond Our Hearing: Unlocking the Secrets of Animal Voices. 2012. (ENG.). 272p. 25.99 ***(978-0-312-58757-4(0))*** St. Martin's Pr.

Rothenberg, David. Thousand Mile Song: Whale Music in a Sea of Sound. 2010. (ENG., Illus.). 304p. (gr. 9). pap. 18.00 *(978-0-465-01889-5(0))* Basic Bks.

Sample, Geoff. Garden Bird Songs & Calls. 2009. (ENG., Illus.). 32p. 23.95 *(978-0-00-731329-7(2))* HarperCollins Pubs. Ltd. GBR. Dist: Independent Pubs. Group.

ANIMAL STERILITY

see Infertility in Animals

ANIMAL STORIES

see Animals—Folklore; Animals—Legends

ANIMAL SYSTEMATICS

see Animals—Classification

ANIMAL TAXONOMY

see Animals—Classification

ANIMAL TRACKS

see also Tracking and Trailing

Bang, Preben & Dahlstrom, Preben. Animal Tracks & Signs. 2006. (ENG., Illus.). 264p. 35.00 *(978-0-19-929997-3(8))* Oxford Univ. Pr., Inc.

Carss, Bob. The SAS Guide to Tracking. 2008. (ENG., Illus.). 352p. pap., instr.'s gde. ed. 19.95 *(978-1-59921-437-5(7)*, Lyons Pr.) Globe Pequot Pr., The.

Eiseman, Charley, et al. Tracks & Sign of Insects & Other Invertebrates: A Guide to North American Species. 2010. (ENG., Illus.). 576p. pap. 39.95 *(978-0-8117-3624-4(5))* Stackpole Bks.

Elbroch, Mark, et al. Field Guide to Animal Tracks & Scat of California. 2012. (California Natural History Guides). (ENG.). 398p. 75.00 ***(978-0-520-25378-0(7))***; pap. 34.95 ***(978-0-520-27109-8(2))*** Univ. of California Pr.

Elbroch, Mark, et al. Practical Tracking: A Guide to Following Footprints & Finding Animals. 2010. (ENG., Illus.). 352p. pap. 29.95 *(978-0-8117-3627-5(X))* Stackpole Bks.

Gibbons, Diane, et al. Stories Tracks & Sign: Reading the Clues Animals Leave Behind. 2008. (ENG., Illus.). 113p. pap. 21.95 *(978-0-8117-3508-7(7))* Stackpole Bks.

Halfpenny, James. Scats & Tracks of North America: A Field Guide to the Signs of Nearly 150 Wildlife Species. 2008. (Scats & Tracks Ser.). (ENG., Illus.). 336p. pap. 14.95 *(978-0-7627-4842-6(7)*, Falcon Guides) Globe Pequot Pr., The.

Hitchcock, Edward. Ichnology of New England. 2011. (ENG.). 296p. pap. 18.95 ***(978-1-4585-0105-9(1))*** Univ. of Michigan Library.

Holland, Anne. Horses for Courses: An Irish Racing Year. 2007. (ENG., Illus.). 208p. pap. 14.95 *(978-1-84596-299-9(0))* Mainstream Publishing Co., Ltd. GBR. Dist: Independent Pubs. Group.

Johnson, Jinny. Animal Tracks & Signs: Track over 400 Animals from Big Cats to Garden Birds. 2011. (ENG.). 192p. 12.99 ***(978-0-7858-2867-9(2)***, 0785828672, Chartwell) Book Sales, Inc.

Judkins, Aaron. The Global Phenomenon of Human Fossil Footprints in Rock. 2010. 426p. pap. 29.95 *(978-0-557-03507-6(4))* Lulu Enterprises Inc.

Kavanagh, James. Animal Tracking: A Waterproof Pocket Guide to Animal Tracking & Behavior. 2010. (Duraguide Ser.). (ENG.). 2p. 7.95 *(978-1-58355-551-4(X))* Waterford Pr., Inc.

McDougall, Len. The Complete Tracker, 2nd: Tracks, Signs, & Habits of North American Wildlife. 2nd ed. 2012. (ENG., Illus.). 384p. pap. 19.95 *(978-1-59921-858-8(5)*, Lyons Pr.) Globe Pequot Pr., The.

—Tracking & Reading Sign: A Guide to Mastering the Original Forensic Science. 2010. (ENG., Illus.). 192p. pap. 18.95 *(978-1-61608-006-8(X)*, 608006) Skyhorse Publishing Co., Inc.

Morgan, Tiffany & Young, Jon. Animal Tracking Basics. 2007. (ENG., Illus.). 298p. pap. 19.95 *(978-0-8117-3326-7(2))* Stackpole Bks.

Moskowitz, David. Wildlife of the Pacific Northwest: Tracking & Identifying Mammals, Birds, Reptiles, Amphibians, & Invertebrates. 2010. (ENG., Illus.). 364p. pap. 25.95 *(978-0-88192-949-2(2)*, 0881929492) Timber Pr., Inc.

ANIMAL TRAINING

see also Dogs—Training; Domestication; Horses—Training

Bartlett, Patricia. Training Your Pet Rabbit. 2nd rev. ed. 2012. (Training Your Pet Ser.). (ENG., Illus.). 196p. pap. 9.99 ***(978-1-4380-0034-3(0))*** Barron's Educational Series, Inc.

Book, Mandy & Smith, Cheryl S. Quick Clicks: Fast & Fun Behaviors to Teach Your Dog with a Clicker. 2nd ed. 2010. (Illus.). 245p. *(978-1-929242-76-4(X))* Dogwise Publishing.

Court, Alfred. My Life with the Big Cats. 2011. 204p. 44.95 ***(978-1-258-03219-7(8))*** Literary Licensing, LLC.

Delgado, Magali & Pignon, Frederic. Gallop to Freedom: Training Horses with Our Six Golden Principles. 2009. (ENG.). 160p. 29.95 *(978-1-57076-420-2(4))* Trafalgar Square Bks.

Direct, Animal Jobs. Working with Animals. 2010. 198p. pap. 27.50 *(978-1-4452-3890-6(X))* Lulu Enterprises Inc.

Downs, Dan. Training Dolphins in the Classroom, 1 vol. 2009. 93p. pap. 16.95 *(978-1-60749-294-8(6))* PublishAmerica, Inc.

Fisher, Gail Tamases. The Thinking Dog: Crossover to Clicker Training. 2009. 328p. 24.95 *(978-1-929242-62-7(X))* Dogwise Publishing.

Fowler, Murray E. Restraint & Handling of Wild & Domestic Animals. 3rd ed. 2008. (ENG., Illus.). 488p. 136.99 *(978-0-8138-1432-2(4)*, Wiley-Blackwell) Wiley, John & Sons, Inc.

Frank Charles Bostock. The Training of Wild Animals. Ellen Velvin, ed. 2009. 276p. pap. 12.95 *(978-1-60386-190-8(4)*, Watchmaker Publishing) Wexford College Pr.

Hauschild, Christine. Trick Training for Cats: Smart fun with the Clicker. 2011. (ENG.). 96p. pap. 19.95 *(978-0-85788-400-8(X))* Cadmos Verlag GmbH DEU. Dist: Independent Pubs. Group.

Hearne, Vicki. Adam's Task: Calling Animals by Name. 2007. (ENG.). 288p. per. 14.95 *(978-1-60239-002-7(9)*, 239002) Skyhorse Publishing Co., Inc.

Hodges, Meredith. Basic Foundation for Saddle. (Training Mules & Donkeys: A Logical Approach to Longears Ser.: Vol. 4). spiral bd., wbk. ed. 39.95 incl. VHS Lucky 3 Ranch, Inc.

—Equus Revisited: A Complete Approach to Athletic Conditioning. 2009. (Illus.). 246p. pap. 29.95 *(978-1-928624-44-8(8))* Lucky 3 Ranch, Inc.

—Foal Training. (Training Mules & Donkeys: A Logical Approach to Longears Ser.: Vol. 1). spiral bd., wbk. ed. 39.95 incl. VHS Lucky 3 Ranch, Inc.

—Intermediate Saddle Training. (Training Mules & Donkeys: A Logical Approach to Longears Ser.: Vol. 5). spiral bd., wbk. ed. 39.95 incl. VHS Lucky 3 Ranch, Inc.

—Preparing for Performance: Driving. (Training Mules & Donkeys: A Logical Approach to Longears Ser.: Vol. 3). spiral bd., wbk. ed. 39.95 incl. VHS Lucky 3 Ranch, Inc.

MacDonald, Carina. Dog Care & Training: A Complete Illustrated Guide to Adopting, House-Breaking & Raising a Hea. 2009. (Knack: Make It Easy Ser.). (ENG., Illus.). 256p. pap. 19.95 *(978-1-59921-507-5(1)*, Knack) Globe Pequot Pr., The.

Nduckwe, Kingsley. Co-Existing. 2011. 56p. pap. 15.25 *(978-1-4567-7449-3(2))* AuthorHouse.

O'Heare, James. Empowerment Training: Training for Creativity, Persistence, Industriousness, Resilience & Behavioral Well-Being. 2011. 105p. pap. 23.95 ***(978-0-9738369-7-4(0))*** Dogwise Publishing.

Pfungst, Oskar. Clever Hans (The Horse of Mr. Von Osten) Wozniak, Robert H., ed. (Classics in Psychology Ser.). (Illus.). 286p. *(978-1-85506-697-7(1)*, Burns & Oates) Continuum International Publishing Group, Ltd.

Pryor, Karen. Reaching the Animal Mind: Clicker Training & What It Teaches Us about All Animals. (ENG.). 2010. 288p. pap. 15.00 *(978-0-7432-9777-6(6))* 2009. 272p. 25.00 *(978-0-7432-9776-9(8))* Scribner. (Scribner).

Roberts, Cindy K. Answers to Your Mule Questions. 2007. per. *(978-1-59916-268-3(7))* Printing Systems.

Ryals, Rick. Sportsman's Best: Dolphin Book & DVD. Florida Sportsman Staff, ed. 2008. (Sportsman's Best Ser.). (ENG., Illus.). 213p. pap. *(978-1-892947-33-8(1)*, Florida Sportsman) InterMedia Outdoors.

Schlegl-Kofler, Katherine. Clicker Training. 2011. (ENG., Illus.). 64p. pap. 8.99 *(978-0-7641-4577-3(0))* Barron's Educational Series, Inc.

Stafford, Grey. Zoomility: Keeper Tales of Training with Positive Reinforcement. DeWitt, Denise & Nguyen, Kim, eds. 2007. (Illus.). 144p. per. 14.95 *(978-0-9796810-0-4(6))* iReinforce.com.

Stieg, Megan. Pawfect Pet Trainer. 2009. (Illus.). 24p. *(978-0-545-14562-6(7))* Scholastic, Inc.

Sutherland, Amy. Kicked, Bitten, & Scratched: Life & Lessons at the World's Premier School for Exotic Animal Trainers. 2007. (ENG.). 336p. (gr. 12-18). 15.00 *(978-0-14-311194-8(9)*, Penguin (Non-Classics)) Penguin Group (USA) Inc.

—What Shamu Taught Me about Life, Love, & Marriage: Lessons for People from Animals & Their Trainers. 2009. (ENG.). 192p. pap. 13.00 *(978-0-8129-7808-7(0)*, Random Hse. Trade Paperbacks) Random House Publishing Group.

Tellington-Jones, Linda & Taylor, Sybil. The Tellington TTouch: Caring for Animals with Heart & Hands. rev. ed. 2008. (ENG.). 304p. (gr. 12-18). 16.00 *(978-0-14-311456-7(5)*, Penguin (Non-Classics)) Penguin Group (USA) Inc.

Thornton, Kim Campbell. Learn. 2008. (Illus.). 39p. *(978-1-933958-47-7(2))*; *(978-1-933958-46-0(4))*; *(978-1-933958-48-4(0))*; *(978-1-933958-45-3(6))* BowTie Pr.

ANIMAL WALKING

see Animal Locomotion

ANIMAL WASTE

Aland, A. & Madec, F., eds. Sustainable animal Production: The challenges & potential developments for professional Farming. 2009. (Illus.). 496p. 116.00 *(978-90-8686-099-9(0))* Wageningen Academic Publishers NLD. Dist: Enfield Publishing & Distribution Co., Inc.

Daigle, Justin M. Transformation of U. S. Animal Agriculture. 2010. (Agriculture Issues & Policies Ser.). 204p. 115.00 *(978-1-60876-938-4(0))* Nova Science Pubs., Inc.

Gujarathi, Ninad. Phytoremediation of Antibiotics from Wastes of Animal Feedlots. 2009. (Illus.). 152p. pap. *(978-3-639-13576-3(8))* VDM Verlag Dr. Mueller e.K.

Gullick, R., et al. Source Water Protection for Concentrated Animal Feeding Operations: A Guide for Drinking Water Utilities: AwwaRF Report 91159. 2007. 212p. (C). pap. *(978-1-84339-154-8(6))* IWA Publishing.

Gullick, Richard, et al. Source Water Protection for Concentrated Animal Feeding Operations: A Guide for Drinking Water Utilities. 2007. 212p. pap. 269.00 *(978-1-58321-523-4(9))* American Water Works Assn.

Kurup, Rajendra. Constructed Wetlands for High Strength Wastewater Treatment & Nutrient Removal. 2008. (Illus.). 164p. pap. *(978-3-639-01774-8(9))* VDM Verlag Dr. Mueller e.K.

Monteny, Gert-Jan & Hartung, Eberhard, eds. Ammonia emissions in Agriculture. 2007. 404p. 92.00 *(978-90-8686-029-6(X))* Wageningen Academic Publishers NLD. Dist: Enfield Publishing & Distribution Co., Inc.

Niman, Nicolette Hahn. Righteous Porkchop: Finding a Life & Good Food Beyond Factory Farms. (ENG.). 2010. 336p. pap. 14.99 *(978-0-06-199845-4(1)*, Harper Paperbacks) 2009. 256p. 23.99 *(978-0-06-146649-6(2)*, Morrow, William & Co.) HarperCollins Pubs.

Poliafico, Marco. Anaerobic Digestion: Decision Support Software. 2009. 216p. pap. *(978-3-639-13567-1(9))* VDM Verlag Dr. Mueller e.K.

Roberts, Gillian S. Environmental Concerns in Animal Agriculture & Feeding Operations. 2011. (Environmental Science, Engineering & Technology Ser.). 115.00 *(978-1-61209-518-9(6))* Nova Science Pubs., Inc.

Starmans, Dick A. J. & van der Hoek, Klaas W., eds. Ammonia: The case of the Netherlands. 2007. 220p. 69.00 *(978-90-8686-028-9(1))* Wageningen Academic Publishers NLD. Dist: Enfield Publishing & Distribution Co., Inc.

ANIMAL WELFARE

Here are entered works on the protection and treatment of animals. Works on the inherent rights attributed to animals are entered under Animal Rights.

see also Animal Rescue; Vivisection

ABBE Research Division Staff. Abuse of Pets & Domestic Animals with Index & Medical Analysis of New Research Information for All Nations. 2006. (Illus.). 160p. 69.95 *(978-0-7883-4478-7(1)*, 0-7883-4478-1); 69.95 *(978-0-7883-4400-8(5)*, 0-7883-4400-5) ABBE Pubs. Assn. of Washington, D.C.

—Analysis of World-Wide Human Cruelty of Different Animal Species with Index & Medical Analysis of New Research Information for All Nations. 2007. (Illus.). 160p. 6895.00 *(978-0-7883-4621-7(0)*, 0-7883-4621-0) ABBE Pubs. Assn. of Washington, D.C.

—Animal Life with Neglect, Pain, Careless Treatments & loss or absence of emotional bonding with Index & Medical Analysis of new Research Information for All Nations. 2007. (Illus.). 160p. 69.94 *(978-0-7883-4608-8(3)*, 0-7883-4608-3) ABBE Pubs. Assn. of Washington, D.C.

Acharya, Keshav K. Institutional Capability Assessment. 2010. 140p. pap. *(978-3-8383-5169-6(X))* Lambert Academic Publishing.

Adams, Carol J. The Sexual Politics of Meat: A Feminist-Vegetarian Critical Theory. 20th anniv. ed. 2010. (ENG., Illus.). 344p. pap. 22.95 *(978-1-4411-7328-7(5))* Continuum International Publishing Group, Ltd. GBR. Dist: National Bk. Network.

Agoramoorthy, Govindasamy. Wildlife Welfare in Zoos. 2011. 160p. pap. ***(978-3-8433-9382-9(6))*** Lambert Academic Publishing.

Akhtar, Aysha. Animals & Public Health: Why Treating Animals Better Is Critical to Human Welfare. 2012. (Palgrave Macmillan Animal Ethics Ser.). (ENG., Illus.). 264p. 85.00 ***(978-0-230-24973-8(6))*** Palgrave Macmillan.

Al Masri, Hafiz. Animal Welfare in Islam. 2009. (ENG.). 180p. 38.00 *(978-0-86037-411-4(4))*; pap. 20.00 *(978-0-86037-595-1(1))* Kube Publishing Ltd. GBR. Dist: Consortium Bk. Sales & Distribution.

Andrieu, S., ed. Gut efficiency; the key ingredient in ruminant Production: Elevating animal performance & Health. 2008. (Illus.). 150p. pap. 71.00 *(978-90-8686-067-8(2))* Wageningen Academic Publishers NLD. Dist: Enfield Publishing & Distribution Co., Inc.

Animal Welfare Institute Staff & Humane Society of the United States Staff, contrib. by. Basic Guidelines for Operating an Equine Rescue or Retirement Facility. 2nd ed. 2008. (Illus.). 20p. *(978-0-938414-95-7(X))* Animal Welfare Institute.

Appleby, M. C., et al, eds. Animal Welfare. 2nd ed. 2011. (Illus.). 344p. pap. 72.50 *(978-1-84593-659-4(0))* CABI GBR. Dist: Stylus Publishing, LLC.

Appleby, Michael C., et al, eds. Long Distance Transport & Welfare of Farm Animals. 2008. (Illus.). 480p. 145.00 *(978-1-84593-403-3(2))* CABI GBR. Dist: Stylus Publishing, LLC.

Arluke, Arnold. Brute Force: Animal Police & the Challenge of Cruelty. 2007. (Illus.). 175p. per. 19.95 *(978-1-55753-450-7(0))* Purdue Univ. Pr.

Armstrong, Susan J. & Botzler, Richard George. The Animal Ethics Reader. Armstrong, Susan & Botzler, Richard G., eds. 2nd rev. ed. 2008. XXX, 650p. 46.95 *(978-0-415-77539-7(6))* Routledge.

Aronson, Stephen. Animal Control Management: A New Look at A Public Responsibility. 2010. 370p. pap. 39.95 *(978-1-55753-540-5(X))* Purdue Univ. Pr.

Ayaz, Mazhar. The Welafre, Management & Diseases of Laboratory & Zoo Animals. 2011. 200p. pap. ***(978-3-8443-9275-3(0))*** Lambert Academic Publishing.

Ball, Matt & Friedrich, Bruce. The Animal Activists' Handbook: Maximizing Our Positive Impact in Today's World. 2009. *(978-1-59056-120-1(1))* Lantern Bks.

Banks, Ron E., et al. Exotic Small Mammal Care & Husbandry. 2010. (ENG., Illus.). 192p. pap. 54.99 *(978-0-8138-1022-5(1)*, Wiley-Blackwell) Wiley, John & Sons, Inc.

Baur, Gene. Farm Sanctuary: Changing Hearts & Minds about Animals & Food. 2008. (ENG.). 320p. pap. 15.00 *(978-0-7432-9159-0(X)*, Touchstone) Touchstone.

Baxter, S. H., et al, eds. Farm Animal Housing & Welfare. 2010. (Current Topics in Veterinary Medicine Ser.). 364p. pap. 409.00 *(978-90-481-5819-5(2)*, 9048158192) Springer.

Beadshaw, G. A. Animals & Society Institute: Elephants in Circuses: Animals & Society Institute: Elephants in Circuses: Analysis of Practice, Policy, & Future. 2007. 40p. 15.00 *(978-0-9788572-3-3(2))* Animals & Society Institute.

Beauchamp, Tom L. & Frey, R. G. The Oxford Handbook of Animal Ethics, 1 vol. 2011. (Oxford Handbooks Ser.). (ENG., Illus.). 984p. 175.00 *(978-0-19-537196-3(8))* Oxford Univ. Pr., Inc.

Beauchamp, Tom L., et al. The Human Use of Animals: Case Studies in Ethical Choice. 2nd ed. 2008. (ENG., Illus.). 352p. (C). pap. 39.99 *(978-0-19-534019-8(1))* Oxford Univ. Pr., Inc.

Beers, Diane L. For the Prevention of Cruelty: The History & Legacy of Animal Rights Activism in the United States. 2006. (Illus.). 368p. 34.95 *(978-0-8040-1086-3(2))*; (ENG., per. 22.95 *(978-0-8040-1087-0(0))* Swallow Pr.

Beirne, null & Beirne, Piers. Confronting Animal Abuse: Law, Criminology, & Human-Animal Relationships. 2009. (ENG., Illus.). 256p. 90.00 *(978-0-7425-4743-8(4))*; pap. 33.00 *(978-0-7425-4744-5(2))* Rowman & Littlefield Publishers, Inc.

Beirne, Piers & South, Nigel, eds. Issues in Green Criminology: Confronting Harms Against Environments, Other Animals & Humanity & Other Animals. (Illus.). 336p. (C). 2012. (ENG.). pap. 44.95 *(978-1-84392-219-3(3))* 2007. 89.95 *(978-1-84392-220-9(7))* Willan Publishing GBR. Dist: Taylor & Francis Group.

Bekoff, Marc. Animals Matter: A Biologist Explains Why We Should Treat Animals with Compassion & Respect. 2nd rev. ed. 2007. (ENG.). 160p. pap. 14.00 *(978-1-59030-522-5(1))* Shambhala Pubns., Inc.

—Encyclopedia of Animal Rights & Animal Welfare, 2 vols. 2nd ed. 2009. (Illus.). xlii, 685p. E-Book *(978-0-313-35256-0(9)*, Greenwood Pr.) Greenwood Publishing Group, Inc.

Bekoff, Marc, ed. Encyclopedia of Animal Rights & Animal Welfare, 2 vols. 2nd rev. ed. 2009. (Illus.). 685p. 165.00 *(978-0-313-35255-3(0)*, GR5255, Greenwood Pr.) Greenwood Publishing Group, Inc.

Best Friends Animal Society Staff & Somerville, Bob. The Cats of Kittyville: New Lives for Rescued Felines. 2008. (Illus.). 80p. 16.95 *(978-1-4162-0527-2(6))* Sellers Publishing, Inc.

—Dogtown: A Sanctuary for Rescued Dogs. 2008. (Illus.). 80p. 16.95 *(978-1-4162-0526-5(8))* Sellers Publishing, Inc.

Bid, Kimber T. Old Furriends. 2011. 32p. pap. 16.95 ***(978-1-4626-0990-1(2))*** PublishAmerica, Inc.

Boddice, Rob. A History of Attitudes & Behaviours Toward Animals in Eighteenth-and Nineteenth-Century Britain: Anthropocentrism & the Emergence of Animals. 2009. 400p. 119.95 *(978-0-7734-4903-9(5))* Mellen, Edwin Pr., The.

Boneham, Sheila. Rescue Matters. rev. l.t. ed. 2010. 391p. 30.95 *(978-1-4104-2278-1(X))* Thorndike Pr.

Boneham, Sheila Webster. Rescue Matters: How to Find, Foster, & Rehome Companion Animals: A Guide for Volunteers & Organizers. 2009. (Illus.). xi, 148p. pap. 14.95 *(978-1-57779-101-0(0))* Alpine Pubns., Inc.

Bowlin, Melanie, et al. Real Stories of Big Cat Rescues: Tales from the Exotic Feline Rescue Center. 2010. (ENG., Illus.). 128p. pap. 19.95 *(978-0-253-22234-3(6)*, 0253222346, Quarry Bks.) Indiana Univ. Pr.

Broom, D. M. & Fraser, A. F. Domestic Animal Behaviour & Welfare. 4th ed. 2007. (Illus.). 540p. pap. 75.00 *(978-1-84593-287-9(0))* CABI GBR. Dist: Stylus Publishing, LLC.

Brown, Paula. Fur Shui: The Fabulous World of Animal Feng Shui. 2008. (ENG., Illus.). 104p. 12.95 *(978-1-59921-276-0(5)*, Lyons Pr.) Globe Pequot Pr., The.

Buckle, Catherine. Innocent Victims: Rescuing the Stranded Animals of Zimbabwe's Farm Invasions. 2009. (ENG., Illus.). 352p. 24.95 ***(978-1-906122-07-2(5))*** Unwin, Merlin Bks. GBR. Dist: SCB Distributors.

Carlton, Dennis G., ed. Animal Protection: Treatment & Welfare Issues. 2010. (Animal Science, Issues & Professions Ser.). (Illus.). ix, 164p. 130.00 *(978-1-61728-353-6(3))* Nova Science Pubs., Inc.

Cochrane, Alasdair. Animal Rights without Liberation: Applied Ethics & Human Obligations. 2012. (Critical Perspectives on Animals: Theory, Culture, Science & Law Ser.). (ENG.). 272p. (gr. 17). 89.50 ***(978-0-231-15826-8(2))***; pap. 29.50 ***(978-0-231-15827-5(0))*** Columbia Univ. Pr.

Cochrane, Alasdair. An Introduction to Animals & Political Theory. 2010. (Palgrave Macmillan Animal Ethics Ser.). (ENG.). 208p. 95.00 *(978-0-230-23925-8(0))*; pap. 34.00 *(978-0-230-23926-5(9))* Palgrave Macmillan.

Coffrin, Trevor. Dominating Animals- the Logic of Domination. 2008. 60p. pap. *(978-3-639-05045-5(2))* VDM Verlag Dr. Mueller e.K.

Coleman, G. J. & Hemsworth, P. H. Human-Livestock Interactions: The Stockperson & the Productivity of Intensively Farmed Animals. 2nd ed. 2011. (Illus.). 194p. 125.00 *(978-1-84593-673-0(6))* CABI GBR. Dist: Stylus Publishing, LLC.

Conn, P. Michael, et al. The Animal Research War. 2008. (ENG.). 224p. 42.00 *(978-0-230-60014-0(X))* Palgrave Macmillan.

Continuing Problems in USDA's Enforcement of the Humane Methods of Slaughter ACT: Hearing Before the Subcommittee on Domestic Policy of the Committee on Oversight & Government Reform, House of Representatives, One Hundred Eleventh Congress, Second Session, March 4, 2010. 2010. (Illus.). iii, 120p. ***(978-0-16-089007-9(1)***, 552-070-43039-3) United States Government Printing Office.

CT Municipal Animal Control Officers Association, prod. CT Animal Care & Control: Including Fisheries & Game. 2011. (ENG.). 468p. ring bd. 23.95 *(978-0-930137-75-5(2)*, LLP) Looseleaf Law Pubns., Inc.

Cunningham, Alan Blain, compiled by. Silent Voices: Stories & Recognition for War Dogs of Vietnam & Canine Soldiers Today. 2007. (Illus.). 100p. per. 15.95 *(978-0-9777072-5-6(3)*, Agreka) Agreka Bks., LLC.

Dawkins, Marian Stamp. Why Animals Matter: Animal Consciousness, Animal Welfare, & Human Well-being. 2012. (ENG.). 256p. 24.95 ***(978-0-19-974751-1(2))*** Oxford Univ. Pr., Inc.

Dawkins, Marian Stamp & Bonney, Roland, eds. The Future of Animal Farming: Renewing the Ancient Contract. 2008. (ENG., Illus.). 256p. 109.95 *(978-1-4051-8583-7(X))*; pap. 44.95 *(978-1-4051-7782-5(9))* Wiley, John & Sons, Inc. (Wiley-Blackwell).

De Passillé, Anne Maria, ed. The Welfare of Cattle. 2007. (Animal Welfare Ser.). (Illus.). 310p. 199.00 *(978-1-4020-6557-6(4))* Springer.

De Vries, Marielle. Protecting Marine Mammals. 2010. (Wildlife Protection, Destruction & Extinction Ser.). 89p. 69.00 *(978-1-60741-569-5(0))* Nova Science Pubs., Inc.

Deane-Drummond, Celia & Clough, David, eds. Creaturely Theology: On God, Humans & Other Animals. 2011. 288p. pap. ***(978-0-334-04189-4(9)***, SCM Pr.) Hymns Ancient & Modern Ltd.

Deboo, Richard J. Nine Steps to Eden - the Humane Route to Paradise. 2011. 172p. pap. ***(978-0-7552-1347-4(5))*** Authors OnLine, Ltd.

Dijk, Van. Sharing the Load. 2011. (ENG., Illus.). 256p. pap. 29.95 *(978-1-85339-719-6(9))* Practical Action Publishing GBR. Dist: Stylus Publishing, LLC.

Dijkstra, Marjolein Efting. The Animal Substitute: An Ethnological Perspective on the Origin of Image-making & Art. 2011. (Illus.). 304p. 30.00 *(978-90-5972-422-8(4))* Eburon Academic Pubs. NLD. Dist: Chicago Distribution Ctr.

Dixon, B. A. Animals, Emotion, & Morality: Marking the Boundary. 2008. (ENG.). 240p. pap. 21.98 *(978-1-59102-629-7(6))* Prometheus Bks., Pubs.

Dockery, Opal. Animal Cruelty Law in the United States, A Comparative Analysis. 2010. 225p. pap. 25.00 *(978-0-557-57780-4(2))* Lulu Enterprises Inc.

Donahue, Jesse & Trump, Erik. The Politics of Zoos: Exotic Animals & Their Protectors. 2006. (Illus.). 236p. 40.00 *(978-0-87580-364-7(4))*; per. 24.00 *(978-0-87580-613-6(9))* Northern Illinois Univ. Pr.

Dwyer, Cathy. The Welfare of Sheep. 2008. (Animal Welfare Ser.). (Illus.). 432p. 199.00 *(978-1-4020-8552-9(4))* Springer.

Dwyer, Cathy, ed. The Welfare of Sheep. 2010. (Animal Welfare Ser.). xiv, 366p. pap. 199.00 *(978-90-481-7909-1(2)*, 9048179092) Springer.

Eadie, Edward, ed. Education for Animal Welfare. 2011. (Animal Welfare Ser.). xiv, 88p. 139.00 *(978-3-642-16813-0(2)*, 3642168132) Springer.

Eddy, Sarah J. Friends & Helpers. 2007. (ENG.). 188p. per. *(978-1-4065-1639-5(2))* Dodo Pr.

Eisenstein, Yolanda. Careers in Animal Law. 2012. (ENG.). 160p. pap. 54.95 ***(978-1-61632-961-7(0))*** American Bar Assn.

Eisnitz, Gail A. Slaughterhouse: The Shocking Story of Greed, Neglect, & Inhumane Treatment Inside the U. S. Meat Industry. 2006. (ENG., Illus.). 1p. per. 19.98 *(978-1-59102-450-7(1))* Prometheus Bks., Pubs.

Ekesbo, Ingvar. Farm Animal Behaviour: Characteristics for Assessment of Health & Welfare. 2011. (Illus.). 248p. pap. 72.50 *(978-1-84593-770-6(8))* CABI GBR. Dist: Stylus Publishing, LLC.

Elizabeth, Charlotte. Kindness to Animals or the Sin of Cruelt. 2006. pap. *(978-1-4065-1409-4(8))* Dodo Pr.

Engel, Mylan & Jenni, Kathie. The Philosophy of Animal Rights: A Brief Introduction for Students & Teachers. 2010. xxi, 127p. *(978-1-59056-177-5(5))* Lantern Bks.

Epps, Tracey. International Trade & Health Protection: A Critical Assessment of the WTO's SPS Agreement. 2008. (Elgar International Economic Law Ser.). (Illus.). 368p. 157.00 *(978-1-84720-657-2(3))* Elgar, Edward Publishing, Inc.

Evans, E. P. The Criminal Prosecution & Capital Punishment of Animals. 2007. (ENG.). 352p. 46.95 *(978-0-548-13031-5(0))* Kessinger Publishing, LLC.

Favre, David S. Animal Law: Welfare, Interests, & Rights. 2008. (Illus.). xvi, 495p. pap. *(978-0-7355-7313-0(1)*, Aspen Pubs.) 2nd ed. 2011. ***(978-1-4548-0266-2(9))*** Wolters Kluwer Law & Business.

Fennell, David A. Tourism & Animal Ethics. 2011. (Contemporary Geographies of Leisure, Tourism & Mobility Ser.). (ENG., Illus.). 328p. (C). 153.00 *(978-0-415-58171-4(0))* Routledge.

Finkelstein, J. J. The Ox That Gored: A Reprint of Transaction of the American Philosophical Society, vol. 71, No. 2. 2007. 89p. reprint ed. pap. 25.00 *(978-1-4223-7478-8(5))* DIANE Publishing Co.

Flynn, Clifton P. Understanding Animal Abuse: A Sociological Analysis. 2012. ***(978-1-59056-339-7(5))***; E-Book ***(978-1-59056-340-3(9))*** Lantern Bks.

Francione, Gary L. Animals as Persons: Essays on the Abolition of Animal Exploitation. (ENG.). 256p. (gr. 17). 2009. pap. 24.50 *(978-0-231-13951-9(9))* 2008. (Illus.). 40.00 *(978-0-231-13950-2(0))* Columbia Univ. Pr.

Francione, Gary L. & Garner, Robert. The Animal Rights Debate: Abolition or Regulation? 2010. (Critical Perspectives on Animals: Theory, Culture, Science & Law Ser.). (ENG.). 288p. (gr. 17). 79.50 *(978-0-231-14954-9(9))*; pap. 24.50 *(978-0-231-14955-6(7))* Columbia Univ. Pr.

Fraser, Andrew Ferguson. The Behaviour & Welfare of the Horse. 2nd ed. 2010. 270p. 145.00 *(978-1-84593-629-7(9))*; (Illus.). pap. 70.00 *(978-1-84593-628-0(0))* CABI GBR. Dist: Stylus Publishing, LLC.

Fraser, David. Understanding Animal Welfare: The Science in Its Cultural Context. 4th ed. 2008. (UFAW Animal Welfare Ser.: 4). (ENG., Illus.). 336p. pap. 82.99 *(978-1-4051-3695-2(2)*, Wiley-Blackwell) Wiley, John & Sons, Inc.

Freeman, Carol, et al, eds. Considering Animals: Contemporary Studies in Human-Animal Relations. 2011. (Illus.). 252p. 64.95 *(978-1-4094-0013-4(1))* Ashgate Publishing Co.

Friend, Catherine. The Compassionate Carnivore: Or, How to Keep Animals Happy, Save Old MacDonald's Farm, Reduce Your Hoofprint & Still Eat Meat. 2008. (ENG.). 256p. 24.00 *(978-1-60094-007-1(2))* Da Capo Pr., Inc.

—The Compassionate Carnivore: Or, How to Keep Animals Happy, Save Old Macdonald's Farm, Reduce Your Hoofprint, & Still Eat Meat. 2009. (ENG.). 304p. pap. 14.95 *(978-0-7382-1309-5(8))* Da Capo Pr., Inc.

Gale Editor, ed. Information Plus Animal Rights. 2011. pap. 58.00 *(978-1-4144-4869-5(4))* Cengage Gale.

GAO. National Animal Identification System. 2008. pap. 39.00 *(978-1-60692-046-6(4))* Nova Science Pubs., Inc.

Glatz, Phil, et al, eds. The Welfare of Farmed Ratites. 2011. (Animal Welfare Ser.). (Illus.). xvii, 263p. 189.00 *(978-3-642-19296-8(3)*, 3642192963) Springer.

Gogerly, Liz. Caring for Animals. 2012. (Charities in Action Ser.). (ENG.). 64p. (gr. 6-10). pap. 9.99 ***(978-1-4329-6391-0(0))***; lib. bdg. 35.00 ***(978-1-4329-6384-2(8))*** Heinemann-Raintree. (NA-h).

Goodale, Greg & Black, J. E. Arguments about Animal Ethics. 2010. (ENG.). 262p. 73.50 *(978-0-7391-4298-1(4))* Lexington Bks.

Gorant, Jim. The Lost Dogs: Michael Vick's Dogs & Their Tale of Rescue & Redemption. (ENG.). 304p. (gr. 12). 2011. 16.00 *(978-1-59240-667-8(X))* 2010. 26.00 *(978-1-59240-550-3(9))* Penguin Group (USA) Inc. (Gotham).

Granata, Silvia. Take Every Creature In, of Every Kind: Continuity & Change in Eighteenth-Century Representations of Animals. 2011. (Europäische Hochschulschriften. Reihe 14: Angelsächsische Sprache und Literatur Ser.). 200p. pap. *(978-3-0343-0544-0(3))* Lang, Peter.

Grandin, Temple. Humane Livestock Handling: Understanding Livestock Behavior & Building Facilities for Healthier Animals. 2008. (ENG., Illus.). 227p. pap. 24.95 *(978-1-60342-028-0(2)*, 1603420282) Storey Publishing, LLC.

—Improving Animal Welfare: A Practical Approach. 2010. (Illus.). 336p. pap. 75.00 *(978-1-84593-541-2(1))* CABI GBR. Dist: Stylus Publishing, LLC.

Greenberg, Linda C. No Fleas on Us: Animal Shelter Tales. 2007. (ENG.). 264p. per. 27.95 *(978-1-4241-8135-3(6))* PublishAmerica, Inc.

Gregory, Neville G. & Grandin, Temple. Animal Welfare & Meat Production. 2nd ed. 2007. (Illus.). 400p. per. 75.00 *(978-1-84593-215-2(3))* CABI GBR. Dist: Stylus Publishing, LLC.

Gross, Aaron & Vallely, Anne. Animals & the Human Imagination: A Companion to Animal Studies. 2012. (ENG., Illus.). 392p. (gr. 17). 89.50 ***(978-0-231-15296-9(5))***; pap. 29.50 ***(978-0-231-15297-6(3))*** Columbia Univ. Pr.

Gruen, Lori. Ethics & Animals: An Introduction. 2011. (Cambridge Applied Ethics Ser.). (ENG.). 250p. (C). 85.00 *(978-0-521-88899-8(9))*; pap. 27.99 *(978-0-521-71773-1(6))* Cambridge Univ. Pr.

Hamilton, J. P. The Adventures of Barney Hello World! 2010. 64p. pap. 15.50 *(978-1-935125-78-5(8))* Robertson Publishing.

Harbolt, Tami L. Bridging the Bond: The Cultural Construction of the Shelter Pet. 2009. (ENG.). 166p. pap. 19.95 *(978-1-55753-545-0(0))* Purdue Univ. Pr.

Harper, Rex. An Eagle in the Airing Cupboard: More True Tales from an Animal Sanctuary. 2008. (ENG., Illus.). 304p. 34.95 *(978-0-7553-1802-5(1))* Headline Bk. Publishing GBR. Dist: Independent Pubs. Group.

Haskins, Norma. Unleashed, Memories from a Career in Animal Control. 2009. 192p. 25.50 *(978-1-60860-431-9(4)*, Eloquent Bks.) AEG Literary Publishing Services, Inc.

Hau, Jann & Schapiro, Steven, eds. Handbook of Laboratory Animal Science Vol. 2: Animal Models. 3rd rev. ed. 2011. (ENG., Illus.). 480p. 119.95 *(978-1-4200-8457-3(7)*, CRC Press) Taylor & Francis Group GBR. Dist: Taylor & Francis Group.

Hausberger, M., et al, eds. Horse behaviour & Welfare. 2007. (Eaap Ser.). 152p. 74.00 *(978-90-8686-033-3(8))* Wageningen Academic Publishers NLD. Dist: Enfield Publishing & Distribution Co., Inc.

Hawthorne, Mark. Striking at the Roots: A Practical Guide to Animal Activism. 2007. (ENG., Illus.). 304p. per. 19.95 *(978-1-84694-091-0(5))* O Bks.,John Hunt.

Haynes, Richard P. Animal Welfare: Competing Conceptions & Their Ethical Implications. (ENG.). xxv, 162p. 2010. pap. 99.00 *(978-90-481-7934-3(3)*, 9048179343) 2010. pap. 49.95 *(978-90-481-8787-4(7)*, 9048187877) 2008. 99.00 *(978-1-4020-8618-2(0)*, 1402086180) Springer.

Heppermann, Christine. City Chickens. 2012. (ENG., Illus.). 64p. (J). (gr. 1-4). 16.99 ***(978-0-547-51830-5(7))*** Houghton Mifflin Harcourt Publishing Co.

Hobgood-Oster, Laura. The Friends We Keep: Unleashing Christianity's Compassion for Animals. 2010. (ENG., Illus.). 230p. pap. 19.95 *(978-1-60258-264-4(5))* Baylor Univ. Pr.

Hollow, Michele C. & Rives, William P. The Everything Guide to Working with Animals: From dog groomer to wildlife rescuer - tons of great jobs for animal Lovers. 2009. (ENG.). 304p. pap. 14.95 *(978-1-59869-786-5(2))* Adams Media Corp.

Hosey, Geoff, et al. Zoo Animals: Behaviour, Management & Welfare. 2009. (ENG., Illus.). 480p. 55.00 *(978-0-19-923306-9(3))* Oxford Univ. Pr., Inc.

Huettner, Klim. Barefoot Veterinarians in the Tropics. 2010. 132p. pap. *(978-3-639-22106-0(0))* VDM Verlag Dr. Mueller e.K.

Huijser, Marcel P. Animal-Vehicle Collision Data Collection. 2007. (Illus.). 107p. pap. 47.00 *(978-0-309-09787-1(8))* Transportation Research Board.

Humane Society of the United States Staff. Wild Neighbors: The Humane Approach to Living with Wildlife. 2nd rev. ed. 2007. per. *(978-0-9748400-8-6(4)*, Humane Society Pr.) Humane Society of the United States, The.

Ijaz, Muhammad. Epidemiology, Diagnosis & Chemotherapy. 2011. 184p. pap. ***(978-3-8443-8936-4(9))*** Lambert Academic Publishing.

Inglis, Ian, et al. Wildlife Management & Welfare. 2007. (Illus.). 272p. pap. 79.99 *(978-1-4051-1211-6(5)*, Wiley-Blackwell) Wiley, John & Sons, Inc.

Irvine, Leslie. Animals & Society Institute: Animals & Society Institute: Animals in Disasters: Responsibility & Action. 2007. 15.00 *(978-0-9788572-2-6(4))* Animals & Society Institute.

—Filling the Ark: Animal Welfare in Disasters. 2009. (Animals & Ethics Ser.). (ENG.). 176p. 26.50 *(978-1-59213-834-0(9))* Temple Univ. Pr.

Itoh, Mayumi. Japanese Wartime Zoo Policy: The Silent Victims of World War II. 2010. (ENG.). 266p. 89.00 *(978-0-230-10894-3(6))* Palgrave Macmillan.

Jenkins, Garry. A Home of Their Own: The Heart-Warming 150-Year History of Battersea Dogs & Cats Home. 2011. (ENG., Illus.). 288p. pap. 14.95 *(978-0-553-82001-0(X))* Transworld Publishers Ltd. GBR. Dist: Independent Pubs. Group.

Joy, Melanie. Strategic Action for Animals: A Handbook on Strategic Movement Building, Organizing, & Activism for Animal Liberation. 2008. (Flashpoint Ser.: 4). 176p. pap. 20.00 *(978-1-59056-136-2(8))* Lantern Bks.

Judah, Vicki & Nuttall, Kathy. Exotic Animal Care & Management. 2008. (ENG.). 64p. (C). pap., wbk. ed. 29.95 *(978-1-4180-4200-4(5))* Delmar Cengage Learning.

Jung, Claudia. Caring for the Older Horse: How to Keep Your Veteran Fit & Healthy. 2009. (ENG., Illus.). 128p. pap. 26.95 *(978-3-86127-965-5(7))* Cadmos Verlag GmbH DEU. Dist: Independent Pubs. Group.

Kaliste, Eila. The Welfare of Laboratory Animals. 2007. (Animal Welfare Ser.). (ENG., Illus.). 360p. per. 79.95 *(978-1-4020-6136-3(6))* Springer.

Karlekar, Hiranmay. Savage Humans & Stray Dogs: A study in Aggression. 2008. (Illus.). 296p. (C). pap. 29.95 *(978-81-7829-879-5(1)*, B98795P) SAGE Pubns., Inc.

Kazez, Jean. Animalkind: What We Owe to Animals. 2010. (ENG., Illus.). 216p. 94.95 *(978-1-4051-9937-7(7))*; pap. 27.95 *(978-1-4051-9938-4(5))* Wiley, John & Sons, Inc. (Wiley-Blackwell).

Kemmerer, Lisa. In Search of Consistency: Ethics & Animals. 2006. (Human-Animal Studies: Vol. 3). 555p. pap. *(978-90-04-14725-6(X))* BRILL.

Kemmerer, Lisa, ed. Speaking up for Animals: An Anthology of Women's Voices. 2011. 224p. 98.00 ***(978-1-61205-087-4(5))***; pap. 24.95 ***(978-1-61205-088-1(3))*** Paradigm Pubs.

Kemmerer, Lisa & Nocella, Anthony J. Call to Compassion: Reflections on Animal Advocacy from the World's Religions. 2010. *(978-1-59056-182-9(1))* Lantern Bks.

Kemmerer, Lisa A., ed. Sister Species: Women, Animals & Social Justice. 2011. (ENG.). 208p. 65.00 *(978-0-252-03617-0(4))* Univ. of Illinois Pr.

—Sister Species: Women, Animals, & Social Justice. 2011. (ENG.). 208p. pap. 21.95 *(978-0-252-07811-8(X))* Univ. of Illinois Pr.

Kheel, Marti. Nature Ethics: An Ecofeminist Perspective. 2007. (Studies in Social, Political, & Legal Philosophy Ser.). (ENG.). 354p. 85.00 *(978-0-7425-5200-5(4))*; per. 32.95 *(978-0-7425-5201-2(2))* Rowman & Littlefield Publishers, Inc.

Kimberling, Cleon V. & Parsons, Gerilyn. Raising Healthy Sheep. 2nd ed. 2008. (Raising Healthy Animals Ser.). *(978-1-886532-18-2(4))* Christian Veterinary Mission.

Kirk, Ronald W., et al, eds. Worship Not the Creature: Animal Rights & the Bible. 2009. (ENG., Illus.). 192p. pap. 19.99 *(978-0-9824929-1-8(X))* Nordskog Publishing, Inc.

Kirkwood, James & Hubrecht, Robert, eds. The UFAW Handbook on the Care & Management of Laboratory & Other Research Animals. 8th rev. ed. 2010. (ENG., Illus.). 848p. 374.99 *(978-1-4051-7523-4(0)*, Wiley-Blackwell) Wiley, John & Sons, Inc.

Kleiman, Devra G., et al, eds. Wild Mammals in Captivity: Principles & Techniques for Zoo Management. 2nd ed. 2010. (ENG., Illus.). 548p. 85.00 *(978-0-226-44009-5(5))* Univ. of Chicago Pr.

Köpernik, Kristin. Die Rechtsprechung zum Tierschutzrecht: 1972 Bis 2008: Unter besonderer Berücksichtigung der Staatszielbestimmung des Art. 20a GG. 2010. (GER.). 288p. 79.95 *(978-3-631-60855-5(1))* Lang, Peter GmbH, Europaischer Verlag der Wissenschaften DEU. Dist: Lang, Peter.

Lane, Marion S. & Zawistowski, Stephen L. Heritage of Care: The American Society for the Prevention of Cruelty to Animals, 1 vol. 2007. (Illus.). 216p. 39.95 *(978-0-275-99021-3(4)*, C9021, Praeger Pubs.) Greenwood Publishing Group, Inc.

Lea, Suzanne R. Goodney. Delinquency & Animal Cruelty: Myths & Realities about Social Pathology. 2007. (Criminal Justice). 176p. 58.00 *(978-1-59332-197-0(X))* LFB Scholarly Publishing LLC.

Lemieux, Leah. Rekindling the Waters: The Truth about Swimming with Dolphins. 2009. (ENG., Illus.). 272p. pap. *(978-1-84876-057-8(4))* Troubadour Publishing Ltd.

Levin, Larry. Oogy: The Dog Only a Family Could Love. (ENG., Illus.). 2011. 240p. pap. 13.99 *(978-0-446-54630-0(5))* 2010. 224p. 19.99 *(978-0-446-54631-7(3))* Grand Central Publishing.

—Oogy: The Dog Only a Family Could Love. l.t. ed. 2010. (ENG.). 233p. 32.99 *(978-1-4104-3235-3(1))* Thorndike Pr.

Li, Hon-Lam. New Essays on Applied Ethics: Animal Rights, Personhood & the Ethics of Killing. Li, Hon-Lam & Yeung, Anthony, eds. 2007. (ENG., Illus.). 256p. 100.00 *(978-0-230-00650-8(7))* Palgrave Macmillan.

Linzey, Andrew. Creatures of the Same God: Explorations in Animal Theology. 2009. *(978-1-59056-142-3(2))* Lantern Bks.

—Why Animal Suffering Matters: Philosophy, Theology, & Practical Ethics. 2009. (ENG.). 224p. 29.95 *(978-0-19-537977-8(2))* Oxford Univ. Pr., Inc.

Linzey, Andrew, ed. Link Between Animal Abuse & Human Violence. 2009. (ENG.). 346p. 84.95 *(978-1-84519-324-9(5))* Sussex Academic Pr. GBR. Dist: International Specialized Bk. Services.

—The Link Between Animal Abuse & Human Violence. 2009. (ENG.). 346p. pap. 44.95 *(978-1-84519-325-6(3))* Sussex Academic Pr. GBR. Dist: International Specialized Bk. Services.

Loring, Marti T., et al, eds. Animal Abuse & Family Violence: Linkages, Research, & Implications for Professional Practice. 2008. 132p. pap. 41.95 *(978-0-7890-3819-7(6))* Routledge.

Loring, Marti Tamm, et al. Animal Abuse & Family Violence: Linkages, Research, & Implications for Professional Practice. 2008. 160p. 110.00 *(978-0-7890-3818-0(8))* Routledge.

Luke, Brian. Brutal: Manhood & the Exploitation of Animals. 2007. (Illus.). 296p. 50.00 *(978-0-252-03176-2(8))*; per. 26.00 *(978-0-252-07424-0(6))* Univ. of Illinois Pr.

Magel, Charles R. Keyguide: Animal Rights. xiv, 267p. *(978-0-7201-1984-8(7))*, Burns & Oates) Continuum International Publishing Group, Ltd.

Mahoney, James. From Elephants to Mice: Animals Who Have Touched My Soul. 2010. (ENG., Illus.). 256p. 22.95 *(978-0-470-50158-0(8)*, Howell Bk. Hse.) Wiley, John & Sons, Inc.

Marchant-Forde, Jeremy N. The Welfare of Pigs. 2009. (Animal Welfare Ser.). (ENG., Illus.). xiv, 350p. 179.00 *(978-1-4020-8908-4(2)*, 1402089082) Springer.

Marchant-Forde, Jeremy N., ed. The Welfare of Pigs. 2010. (Animal Welfare Ser.). (ENG.). xiv, 350p. pap. 179.00 *(978-90-481-8024-0(4)*, 9048180244) Springer.

Markovics, Joyce. Saving Animals after Earthquakes. 2011. (Rescuing Animals from Disasters Ser.). 32p. (YA). (gr. 2-5). lib. bdg. 25.27 *(978-1-61772-289-9(8))* Bearport Publishing Co., Inc.

Martin, Glen. Game Changer: Animal Rights & the Fate of Africa's Wildlife. 2012. (ENG., Illus.). 244p. 29.95 ***(978-0-520-26626-1(9))*** Univ. of California Pr.

Mason, G. & Rushen, J., eds. Stereotypic Animal Behaviour: Fundamentals & Applications to Welfare. 2nd ed. 2008. (Illus.). 384p. pap. 75.00 *(978-1-84593-465-1(2))* CABI GBR. Dist: Stylus Publishing, LLC.

McCloskey, Erin. Bear Attacks in Canada. 2008. (ENG., Illus.). 224p. pap. *(978-1-55105-562-6(7))* Lone Pine Publishing.

McEldowney, John, et al. The Regulation of Animal Health & Welfare. 2012. (Law, Science & Society Ser.). (ENG.). 224p. 120.00 ***(978-0-415-50474-4(0))*** Routledge.

McFarland, Sarah E. & Hediger, Ryan. Animals & Agency: An Interdisciplinary Exploration. 2009. (Illus.). 416p. pap. *(978-90-04-17580-8(6))* BRILL.

McGowan, Katherine A. Coalition Building for Animal-Care Organizations. 2008. pap. *(978-1-934785-02-7(4)*, Humane Society Pr.) Humane Society of the United States, The.

McLean, Lesley. Ethics about Animals. 2010. 144p. pap. *(978-3-8383-5000-4(6))* Lambert Academic Publishing.

Mead, Marie. Rabbits: Gentle Hearts, Valiant Spirits: Inspirational Stories of Rescue, Triumph, & Joy. 2007. (Illus.). 152p. pap. 18.95 *(978-0-9786226-0-2(X))* Nova Maris Pr.

Mellor, David, et al. The Sciences of Animal Welfare. 2009. (UFAW Animal Welfare Ser.: 5). (ENG., Illus.). 224p. pap. 72.99 *(978-1-4051-3495-8(X)*, Wiley-Blackwell) Wiley, John & Sons, Inc.

Merck, Melinda D., ed. Veterinary Forensics: Animal Cruelty Investigations. 2007. (ENG., Illus.). 368p. pap. 115.99 *(978-0-8138-1501-5(0)*, Wiley-Blackwell) Wiley, John & Sons, Inc.

Mezzatesta, V. Barking in the Wind: Conflict with Human Apathy. 2011. 104p. pap. 9.95 ***(978-1-4620-3923-4(5))*** iUniverse, Inc.

Miller, Daniel. Animal Ethics & Theology: The Lens of the Good Samaritan. 2011. (Routledge Studies in Religion Ser.). (ENG., Illus.). 250p. (C). 125.00 ***(978-0-415-80875-0(8))*** Routledge.

Miller, Lila & Hurley, Kate F., eds. Infectious Disease Management in Animal Shelters. 2009. (ENG., Illus.). 400p. pap. 94.99 *(978-0-8138-1379-0(4)*, Wiley-Blackwell) Wiley, John & Sons, Inc.

Miller, Rose. The Horse That Wouldn't Trot: A Life with Tennessee Walking Horses. 2009. 240p. pap. 14.95 *(978-1-60844-264-5(0))* Dog Ear Publishing LLC.

Mills, Daniel S. The Encyclopedia of Applied Animal Behaviour & Welfare. 2010. (Illus.). 750p. 370.00 *(978-0-85199-724-7(4))* CABI GBR. Dist: Stylus Publishing, LLC.

Mol, Annemarie, et al, eds. Care in Practice: On Tinkering in Clinics, Homes & Farms. 2010. (ENG., Illus.). 300p. pap. 49.95 *(978-3-8376-1447-3(6))* Transcript Verlag DEU. Dist: Transaction Pubs.

Monahan, Casey J., ed. Equine Welfare Concerns: Horse Slaughter, Wild & Unwanted Horses. 2012. ***(978-1-62100-427-1(9))*** Nova Science Pubs., Inc.

Moran, Victoria & Moran, Adair. Main Street Vegan: Everything You Need to Know to Eat Healthfully & Live Compassionately in the Real World. 2012. (ENG.). 384p. (gr. 12). pap. 16.95 ***(978-1-58542-933-2(3)***, Tarcher) Penguin Group (USA) Inc.

Morrison, Adrian R. An Odyssey with Animals: A Veterinarian's Reflections on the Animal Rights & Welfare Debate. 2009. (ENG., Illus.). 288p. 29.95 *(978-0-19-537444-5(4))* Oxford Univ. Pr., Inc.

National Academies Press, creator. Recognition & Alleviation of Distress in Laboratory Animals. 2008. (ENG., Illus.). 136p. pap. 37.95 *(978-0-309-10817-1(9))* National Academies Pr.

National Research Council (U.S.) Staff & Guidelines for the Humane Transportation of Laboratory Animals Committee. Guidelines for the Humane Transportation of Research Animals. 2006. (ENG., Illus.). 164p. per. 34.95 *(978-0-309-10110-3(7))* National Academies Pr.

National Research Council Staff & Committee on Recognition and Alleviation of Pain in Laboratory Animals. Recognition & Alleviation of Pain in Laboratory Animals. 2009. (ENG., Illus.). 196p. pap. 37.95 *(978-0-309-12834-6(X))* National Academies Pr.

Newkirk, Ingrid. The PETA Practical Guide to Animal Rights: Simple Acts of Kindness to Help Animals in Trouble. 2009. (ENG.). 496p. pap. 19.99 *(978-0-312-55994-6(1)*, St. Martin's Griffin) St. Martin's Pr.

Niman, Nicolette Hahn. Righteous Porkchop: Finding a Life & Good Food Beyond Factory Farms. (ENG.). 2010. 336p. pap. 14.99 *(978-0-06-199845-4(1)*, Harper Paperbacks) 2009. 256p. 23.99 *(978-0-06-146649-6(2)*, Morrow, William & Co.) HarperCollins Pubs.

Nocella, Giuseppe. Farm Animal Welfare in Europe. 2009. 256p. pap. *(978-3-639-14956-2(4))* VDM Verlag Dr. Mueller e.K.

Nordenfelt, Lennart. Animal & Human Health & Welfare: A Comparative Philosophical Analysis. 2006. 208p. (C). per. 65.00 *(978-1-84593-059-2(2))* CABI GBR. Dist: Stylus Publishing, LLC.

Norwood, F. Bailey & Lusk, Jayson L. Compassion, by the Pound: The Economics of Farm Animal Welfare. 2011. (ENG., Illus.). 416p. 45.00 *(978-0-19-955116-3(2))* Oxford Univ. Pr., Inc.

O'Barry, Richard & Coulbourn, Keith. Behind the Dolphin Smile: One Man's Campaign to Protect the World's Dolphins. 2012. (ENG., Illus.). 285p. pap. 15.99 ***(978-1-60887-105-6(3)***, Insight Editions) Palace Publishing Group, LP.

Office of the Federal Register (U.S.), compiled by. Code of Federal Regulations, Title 9, Animals & Animal Products, Pt. 1-199, Revised as of January 1 2011. rev. ed. 2011. (ENG.). 1077p. pap. 67.00 ***(978-0-16-087542-7(0)***, Office of the Federal Register) United States Government Printing Office.

—Code of Federal Regulations, Title 9, Animals & Animal Products, Pt. 200-End, Revised as of January 1 2011. rev. ed. 2011. (ENG., Illus.). 764p. pap. 64.00 ***(978-0-16-087543-4(9)***, Office of the Federal Register) United States Government Printing Office.

Oliver, Gary. Cinemazoo: My Urban Safari. 2011. (ENG., Illus.). 208p. pap. ***(978-1-894694-62-9(7))*** Granville Island Publishing.

Osborne, Catherine. Dumb Beasts & Dead Philosophers: Humanity & the Humane in Ancient Philosophy & Literature. (ENG.). 2009. 274p. pap. 49.95 *(978-0-19-956827-7(8))* 2007. 288p. 85.00 *(978-0-19-928206-7(4))* Oxford Univ. Pr., Inc.

O'Sullivan, Siobhan & Office for National Statistics Staff. Animals, Equality & Democracy. 2011. (Palgrave Macmillan Animal Ethics Ser.). (ENG., Illus.). 224p. 80.00 ***(978-0-230-24387-3(8))*** Palgrave Macmillan.

Owen, Marna A. Animal Rights: Noble Cause or Needless Effort? 2009. (USA TODAY's Debate: Voices & Perspectives Ser.). 160p. (YA). (gr. 9-12). 35.93 *(978-0-7613-4082-9(3))* Lerner Publishing Group.

Pacelle, Wayne. The Bond: Our Kinship with Animals, Our Call to Defend Them. 2012. (ENG.). 320p. pap. 16.99 *(978-0-06-196980-5(X)*, William Morrow Paperbacks) 2011. 24.99 *(978-0-06-204715-1(9)*, Morrow, William & Co.) 2011. (ENG.). 320p. 26.99 *(978-0-06-196978-2(8)*, Morrow, William & Co.) 2011. (ENG.). 658p. pap. 26.99 *(978-0-06-201786-4(1)*, HarperLuxe) HarperCollins Pubs.

Pachirat, Timothy. Every Twelve Seconds: Industrialized Slaughter & the Politics of Sight. 2011. (Yale Agrarian Studies Ser.). (ENG., Illus.). 320p. 30.00 *(978-0-300-15267-8(1))* Yale Univ. Pr.

Palmer, Clare. Animal Ethics in Context. 2010. (ENG.). 216p. (gr. 17). 89.50 *(978-0-231-12904-6(1))*; pap. 27.50 *(978-0-231-12905-3(X))* Columbia Univ. Pr.

Palmeri, Frank, ed. Humans & Other Animals in Eighteenth-Century British Culture: Representation, Hybridity, Ethics. 2006. (Illus.). 244p. 110.00 *(978-0-7546-5475-9(3))* Ashgate Publishing Co.

Parker, James V. Animal Minds, Animal Souls, Animal Rights. 2010. (ENG.). 166p. pap. 25.99 *(978-0-7618-5177-6(1))*; (Illus.). viii, 153p. E-Book ***(978-0-7618-5178-3(X))*** Univ. Pr. of America, Inc.

Pederson, Helena. Animals in Schools: Processes & Strategies in Human-Animal Education. 2009. (ENG.). 146p. pap. 22.95 *(978-1-55753-523-8(X))* Purdue Univ. Pr.

Perkins, David. Romanticism & Animal Rights. 2007. (Cambridge Studies in Romanticism Ser.). (ENG.). 212p. pap. 48.00 *(978-0-521-04598-8(3))* Cambridge Univ. Pr.

Petrinovich, Lewis. Darwinian Dominion: Animal Welfare & Human Interests. 2008. (ENG.). 431p. pap. 25.00 *(978-1-4379-5870-6(2))* DIANE Publishing Co.

Phelps, Norm. The Longest Struggle: Animal Advocacy from Pythagoras to PETA. 2007. (ENG.). 357p. per. 20.00 *(978-1-59056-106-5(6))* Lantern Bks.

Phillips, Allie. Defending the Defenseless: A Guide to Protecting & Advocating for Pets. 2011. (ENG.). 312p. 37.95 *(978-1-4422-0214-6(9))* Rowman & Littlefield Publishers, Inc.

—How Shelter Pets are Brokered for Experimentation: Understanding Pound Seizure. 2010. (ENG.). 248p. 37.50 *(978-1-4422-0211-5(4))* Rowman & Littlefield Publishers, Inc.

Phillips, Allie. How Shelter Pets Are Brokered for Experimentation: Understanding Pound Seizure. 2010. x, 238p. *(978-1-4422-0213-9(0))* Rowman & Littlefield Publishers, Inc.

Phillips, Clive. The Welfare of Animals: The Silent Majority. 2008. (Animal Welfare Ser.). (Illus.). xx, 220p. 129.00 *(978-1-4020-9218-3(0))* Springer London, Ltd. GBR. Dist: Springer.

Pinches, Charles & McDaniel, Jay B., eds. Good News for Animals? Christian Approaches to Animal Well-Being. 2008. 270p. pap. 31.00 *(978-1-59244-601-8(9))* Wipf & Stock Pubs.

Pond, Wilson G., et al, eds. Animal Welfare in Animal Agriculture. 2011. (ENG., Illus.). 333p. 89.95 ***(978-1-4398-4842-5(4)***, CRC Press) Taylor & Francis Group GBR. Dist: Taylor & Francis Group.

Prevention of Equine Cruelty ACT of 2008 & the Animal Cruelty Statistics ACT of 2008: Hearing Before the Subcommittee on Crime, Terrorism, & Homeland Security of the Committee on the Judiciary, House of Representatives, One Hundred Tenth Congress, Second Session, on H.R. 6598 & H.R. 6597, July 31, 2008. 2009. (Illus.). iv, 397p. *(978-0-16-082757-0(4)*, 552-070-38762-5) United States Government Printing Office.

Primary Industries Standing Committee. Model Code of Practice for the Welfare of Animals: PISC Report 90. 2nd ed. 2006. (Primary Industries Report Ser.). 18p. pap. 22.00 *(978-0-643-09358-4(3))* CSIRO Publishing AUS. Dist: Stylus Publishing, LLC.

—Model Code of Practice for the Welfare of Animals: PISC Report 91. 2nd rev. ed. 2006. (Primary Industries Report Ser.). 20p. pap. 22.00 *(978-0-643-09360-7(5))* CSIRO Publishing AUS. Dist: Stylus Publishing, LLC.

—Model Code of Practice for the Welfare of Animals: The Sheep. 2nd rev. ed. 2006. (Primary Industries Report Ser.). (Illus.). 30p. pap. 22.00 *(978-0-643-09356-0(7))* CSIRO Publishing AUS. Dist: Stylus Publishing, LLC.

Prohibiting Obscene Animal Crush Videos in the Wake of United States V. Stevens: Hearing Before the Committee on the Judiciary, United States Senate, One Hundred Eleventh Congress, Second Session, September 15, 2010. 2011. iii, 102p. ***(978-0-16-088477-1(2)***, 552-070-42683-3) United States Government Printing Office.

The Protein Myth: Significantly Reducing the Risk of Cancer, Heart Disease, Stoke & Diabetes while Saving the Animals & the Planet. 2011. (ENG.). 444p. pap. 19.95 *(978-1-84694-673-8(5)*, Earth Books) Hunt, John Publishing Ltd. GBR. Dist: National Bk. Network.

Rao, Chilkuri Vasantha. Ecological & Theological Apsects of Some Animal Laws in the Pentateuch. 2011. 380p. 129.95 ***(978-0-7734-3918-4(8))*** Mellen, Edwin Pr., The.

Regan, Tom. Defending Animal Rights. 2006. 200p. per. 21.00 *(978-0-252-07416-5(5))* Univ. of Illinois Pr.

Requejo Conde, Carmen. La Protección Penal de la Fauna: Especial Consideración Del Delito de Maltrato a Los Animales. 2010. (SPA.). xv, 146p. *(978-84-9836-695-2(X))* Comares, Editorial SL.

Review of the Welfare of Animals in Agriculture: Hearing Before the Subcommittee on Livestock, Dairy, & Poultry of the Committee on Agriculture, House of Representatives, One Hundred Tenth Congress, First Session, May 8, 2007. 2008. (Illus.). iv, 441p. *(978-0-16-080335-2(7)*, 552-070-37036-6) United States Government Printing Office.

Reyes, Cassandra. Of Fists & Fangs. 2010. 132p. pap. *(978-3-639-24781-7(7))* VDM Verlag Dr. Mueller e.K.

Ritter, Christie. Animal Rights. 2008. (Essential Viewpoints Set 2 Ser.). (Illus.). 112p. (YA). (gr. 7-12). 34.22 *(978-1-60453-054-4(5))* ABDO Publishing Co.

Ritter, Erika. The Dog by the Cradle, the Serpent Beneath: And Other Paradoxes of Human-Animal Relationships. 2009. (ENG.). 320p. 24.95 *(978-1-55470-076-9(0))* Key Porter Bks. CAN. Dist: Perseus-PGW.

—The Dog by the Cradle, the Serpent Beneath: Some Paradoxes of Human-Animal Relationships. 2010. (ENG.). 320p. pap. 16.95 *(978-1-55470-295-4(X))* Key Porter Bks. CAN. Dist: Perseus-PGW.

Ritvo, Harriet. Noble Cows & Hybrid Zebras: Essays on Animals & History. 2010. (ENG., Illus.). 256p. (gr. 17). 39.50 *(978-0-8139-3060-2(X))* Univ. Pr. of Virginia.

Rochlitz, Irene. The Welfare of Cats. 2007. (Animal Welfare Ser.). (ENG., Illus.). 308p. per. 79.95 *(978-1-4020-6143-1(9))* Springer.

Roeder, Larry, ed. Diplomacy, Funding & Animal Welfare. 2011. (Animal Welfare Ser.). (ENG., Illus.). xx, 230p. 189.00 *(978-3-642-21273-4(5)*, 3642212735) Springer.

Rogers, Tom. A Working Guide to Animal Control & Enforcement, 1 vol. 2009. 91p. pap. 16.95 *(978-1-60813-741-1(4))* PublishAmerica, Inc.

Rollin, Bernard. Putting the Horse Before Descartes: A Memoir. 2011. (Animals & Ethics Ser.). (ENG.). 304p. 35.00 *(978-1-59213-825-8(X))* Temple Univ. Pr.

—The Unheeded Cry. 2010. 348p. pap. 24.95 *(978-0-557-57821-4(3))* Lulu Enterprises Inc.

Rollin, Bernard E. & McIlwraith, C. Wayne, eds. Equine Welfare. 2011. (UFAW Animal Welfare Ser.: 6). (ENG., Illus.). 504p. pap. 72.99 *(978-1-4051-8763-3(8)*, Wiley-Blackwell) Wiley, John & Sons, Inc.

Rudy, Kathy. Loving Animals: Toward a New Animal Advocacy. 2011. (ENG.). 288p. 24.95 ***(978-0-8166-7468-8(X))*** Univ. of Minnesota Pr.

Rushen, Jeffrey, et al. The Welfare of Cattle. 2010. (Animal Welfare Ser.). x, 310p. pap. 199.00 *(978-90-481-7669-4(7)*, 9048176697) Springer.

Ryan, Thomas. Animals & Social Work: A Moral Introduction. 2011. (Palgrave Macmillan Animal Ethics Ser.). (ENG.). 240p. 85.00 *(978-0-230-27250-7(9))* Palgrave Macmillan.

Salem, Deborah J. & Rowan, Andrew N. The State of the Animals IV, 2007. 2007. (Illus.). vii, 238p. pap. 29.95 *(978-0-9748400-9-3(2))* Humane Society of the United States, The.

Sawyer, Jacqui. We Are All Special. 2011. 20p. pap. 12.00 ***(978-1-4634-3054-2(X))*** AuthorHouse.

Schaffner, Joan. An Introduction to Animals & the Law. 2010. (Palgrave Macmillan Animal Ethics Ser.). (ENG.). 240p. 95.00 *(978-0-230-23563-2(8))*; pap. 33.00 *(978-0-230-23564-9(6))* Palgrave Macmillan.

Scientific and Humane Issues in the Use of Random Source Dogs and Cats for Research Committee. Scientific & Humane Issues in the Use of Random Source Dogs & Cats in Research. National Research Council Staff, ed. 2009. (ENG.). 118p. pap. 35.00 *(978-0-309-13807-9(8))* National Academies Pr.

Scruton, Roger. Animal Rights & Wrongs. 3rd ed. 2006. (ENG., Illus.). 224p. 34.95 *(978-0-8264-9404-7(8))* Continuum International Publishing Group, Ltd. GBR. Dist: National Bk. Network.

Shapiro, Leland S. Applied Animal Ethics. 2nd ed. 2007. (Illus.). 547p. (C). pap. *(978-0-9797288-0-8(0))* Ari Farms.

Sharp, Patrick E. & Villano, Jason. The Laboratory Rat. 2nd rev. ed. 2012. (Laboratory Animal Pocket Reference Ser.). (ENG., Illus.). 288p. pap. 59.95 *(978-1-4398-2986-8(1)*, CRC Press) Taylor & Francis Group GBR. Dist: Taylor & Francis Group.

Sherman, Sheryl L. Primate Enrichment Diary. 2009. 92p. pap. 22.00 *(978-0-9741608-9-4(X))* Phoenix Exotics Wildlife Assn.

Sherry, Clifford J. Animal Rights. 2nd rev. ed. 2009. (Contemporary World Issues Ser.). (Illus.). 295p. 55.00 *(978-1-59884-191-6(2)*, ANIRIG2C) ABC-CLIO, LLC.

Shevelow, Kathryn. For the Love of Animals: The Rise of the Animal Protection Movement. 2009. (ENG., Illus.). 368p. pap. 19.00 *(978-0-8050-9024-6(X)*, Holt Paperback) Holt, Henry & Co.

Shimozako, Helio Junji & de Barros Couto Junior, Euro. Photographic Capture-Recapture for Estimation of Stray Dog Population. 2010. 92p. pap. *(978-3-639-24061-0(8))* VDM Verlag Dr. Mueller e.K.

Shultz, William J. Humane Movement in the United States, 1910-1922. (Columbia University, Studies in the Social Sciences: No. 252). reprint ed. 21.00 *(978-0-404-51252-1(8))* AMS Pr., Inc.

Silverman, Jerald, et al, eds. The IACUC Handbook. 2nd rev. ed. 2006. (ENG., Illus.). 680p. 89.95 *(978-0-8493-4010-9(1)*, CRC Press) Taylor & Francis Group GBR. Dist: Taylor & Francis Group.

Sinclair, Leslie, et al. Forensic Investigation of Animal Cruelty: A Guide for Veterinary & Law Enforcement Professionals. 2006. (Illus.). ix, 262p. *(978-0-9748400-6-2(8))* Humane Society of the United States, The.

Singer, Peter. Animal Liberation: The Definitive Classic of the Animal Movement. 2009. (P. S. Ser.). (ENG.). 368p. pap. 14.99 *(978-0-06-171130-5(6)*, HarperPerennial) HarperCollins Pubs.

Sirois, Margi. Principles & Practice of Veterinary Technology - Text & Workbook Package. 3rd ed. 2010. (ENG.). (C). pap. 98.01 *(978-0-323-07792-7(7)*, Mosby) Elsevier - Health Sciences Div.

Smith, Ethan. Building an Ark: 101 Solutions to Animal Suffering. 2007. (Solutions Ser.). (ENG., Illus.). 288p. pap. 24.95 *(978-0-86571-566-0(1)*, 9780865715660) New Society Pubs., Ltd. CAN. Dist: Consortium Bk. Sales & Distribution.

Smith, Kimberly K. Governing Animals: Animal Welfare & the Liberal State. 2012. (ENG.). 240p. 34.95 ***(978-0-19-989575-5(9))*** Oxford Univ. Pr., Inc.

Smith, Wesley J. A Rat Is a Pig Is a Dog Is a Boy: The Human Cost of the Animal Rights Movement. (ENG.). 2012. 336p. pap. 16.99 ***(978-1-59403-614-9(4))*** 2010. 270p. 25.95 *(978-1-59403-346-9(3))* Encounter Bks.

Smulders, Frans J. & Algers, Bo, eds. Welfare of production Animals: Assessment & management of Risks. 2009. (Illus.). 588p. 153.00 *(978-90-8686-122-4(9))* Wageningen Academic Publishers NLD. Dist: Enfield Publishing & Distribution Co., Inc.

Smulewicz-Zucker, Gregory R. Strangers to Nature: Animal Lives & Human Ethics. 2011. ***(978-0-7391-4549-4(5))*** Lexington Bks.

Sollund, Ragnhild. Global Harms: Ecological Crime & Speciesism. 2011. (Environmental Science, Engineering & Technology Ser.). 228p. pap. 69.00 ***(978-1-61324-680-1(3))*** Nova Science Pubs., Inc.

Sollund, Ragnhild Aslaug. Global Harms: Ecological Crime & Speciesism. 2011. (Environmental Science, Engineering & Technology Ser.). 228p. 69.00 *(978-1-60456-770-0(8))* Nova Science Pubs., Inc.

Sorenson, John. About Canada: Animal Rights. 2010. (About Canada Ser.). (ENG.). 192p. pap. 17.95 *(978-1-55266-356-1(6))* Fernwood Publishing Co., Ltd. CAN. Dist: Independent Pubs. Group.

South, Nigel & Beirne, Piers, eds. Green Criminology. 2nd ed. 2006. (International Library of Criminology, Criminal Justice & Penology - Second Ser.). (Illus.). 614p. 350.00 *(978-0-7546-2592-6(3))* Ashgate Publishing Co.

Stafford, Kevin. The Welfare of Dogs. 2007. (Animal Welfare Ser.). 300p. per. 79.95 *(978-1-4020-6144-8(7))* Springer.

Steel, Karl. How to Make a Human: Animals & Violence in the Middle Ages. 2011. (Interventions: New Studies Medieval Cult Ser.). 328p. 49.95 *(978-0-8142-1157-1(7))*; cd-rom 14.95 *(978-0-8142-9256-3(9))* Ohio State Univ. Pr.

Steiner, Gary. Animals & the Moral Community: Mental Life, Moral Status, & Kinship. 2008. (ENG., Illus.). 232p. (gr. 17). 45.00 *(978-0-231-14234-2(X))* Columbia Univ. Pr.

—Anthropocentrism Its Discontents. 2010. (ENG.). 344p. pap. 27.95 *(978-0-8229-6119-2(9))* Univ. of Pittsburgh Pr.

A

Stevens, Kathy. Where the Blind Horse Sings: Love & Healing at an Animal Sanctuary. 2007. (ENG., Illus.). 206p. 22.95 *(978-1-60239-055-3(X)*, 239055) Skyhorse Publishing Co., Inc.

Stibbe, Arran. Animals Erased: Discourse, Ecology, & Reconnection with the Natural World. 2012. (ENG., Illus.). 232p. (C). 70.00 ***(978-0-8195-7231-8(4))***; pap. 24.95 ***(978-0-8195-7232-5(2))*** Wesleyan Univ. Pr.

Stone, Lora. The Ideology of Progress, World Culture, & Animal Protection. 2006. (ENG., Illus.). 96p. pap. 26.50 *(978-0-7618-3608-7(X))* Univ. Pr. of America, Inc.

Stratton, Cameron L. Thoroughbred Horseracing & the Welfare of the Thoroughbred. 2009. (Sports & Athletics Preparation, Performance, & Psychology Ser.). 79.00 *(978-1-60692-724-3(8))* Nova Science Pubs., Inc.

Sullivan, Diane & Vietzke, Holly, eds. Please, Can We Keep the Donkey? A Collection of Animal Rescue Stories by the Massachusetts School of Law Community. 2008. (Illus.). 174p. 19.95 *(978-1-59056-122-5(8))* Lantern Bks.

Sybesma, W., ed. The Welfare of Pigs. 2010. (Current Topics in Veterinary Medicine Ser.). 348p. pap. 259.00 *(978-90-481-8267-1(0)*, 9048182670) Springer.

Thomas. Animals, International Law, International Trade, & Morality. 2011. xiv, 500p. *(978-90-411-3338-0(0))* Kluwer Law International.

Thorpe LLB (Hons), Laceyn & Ruscitto, Antonella. You, your dog & the Law. A dog owners guide in England & Wales. 2009. 89p. pap. 15.01 *(978-0-557-09662-6(6))* Lulu Enterprises Inc.

Toft, Amir A. The Islamic Laws of Animal Slaughter: A Discussion on the Islamic Laws for Slaughtering Animals & a Survey of Modern-Day Slaughtering Methods. 2006. Orig. Title: Ahkam Al-Dhaba'ih. 160p. pap. 12.95 *(978-1-933764-01-6(5))* White Thread Pr.

Torres, Bob & Torres, Jenna. Vegan Freak: Being Vegan in a Non-Vegan World. 2nd rev. ed. 2010. (Tofu Hound Press Ser.). (ENG.). 196p. pap. 14.95 *(978-1-60486-015-3(4))* PM Pr.

Trine, Ralph. Every Living Creature. 2006. pap. 12.50 *(978-1-59605-984-9(2)*, Cosimo Classics) Cosimo, Inc.

Turner, Jacky. Animal Breeding, Welfare & Society. 2010. (ENG., Illus.). 336p. 140.00 *(978-1-84407-588-1(5))*; pap. 41.95 *(978-1-84407-589-8(3))* Routledge.

Van Tuyl, Christine. Zoos & Animal Welfare. 2007. (Issues that Concern You Ser.). (ENG., Illus.). 112p. (YA). (gr. 7-12). lib. bdg. 35.75 *(978-0-7377-3818-6(9)*, Greenhaven Pr., Inc.) Cengage Gale.

Velarde, A. & Geers, R. On Farm Monitoring of Pig Welfare: COST Action 846, Working Group 2 - on Farm Monitoring of Welfare, Subworking Group - Pigs. Velarde, A. & Geers, R., eds. 2007. (Illus.). 208p. 77.00 *(978-90-8686-025-8(7))* Wageningen Academic Publishers NLD. Dist: Enfield Publishing & Distribution Co., Inc.

Volpe, Tina & Carman, Judy. The Missing Peace: The Hidden Power of our Kinship with Animals: the Hidden Power of Our Kinship with Animals. 2009. 232p. pap. 16.95 *(978-0-9797908-2-9(4))* Dreamriver Pr.

Wagman, Bruce A. & Liebman, Matthew. A Worldview of Animal Law. 2011. 358p. pap. 50.00 *(978-1-59460-462-1(2))* Carolina Academic Pr.

Waran, N., ed. The Welfare of Horses. 2007. (Animal Welfare Ser.). (Illus.). 248p. per. 79.95 *(978-1-4020-6142-4(0))* Springer.

Wemmer, Christen & Christen, Catherine A., eds. Elephants & Ethics: Toward a Morality of Coexistence. 2008. (ENG., Illus.). 512p. (gr. 17). 79.00 *(978-0-8018-8818-2(2))* Johns Hopkins Univ. Pr.

White, Betty. Betty & Friends: My Life at the Zoo. 2011. (ENG.). 304p. (gr. 12). 26.95 ***(978-0-399-15754-7(9)***, Putnam Adult) Penguin Group (USA) Inc.

White, Rob. Crimes Against Nature: Environmental Criminology & Ecological Justice. (ENG.). 328p. 2011. pap. 37.95 *(978-1-84392-361-9(0))* 2008. 89.95 *(978-1-84392-362-6(9))* Willan Publishing GBR. Dist: Taylor & Francis Group.

White, Thomas I. In Defense of Dolphins: The New Moral Frontier. 2007. (Blackwell Public Philosophy Ser.). (ENG., Illus.). 248p. 93.95 *(978-1-4051-5778-0(X)*, Wiley-Blackwell) Wiley, John & Sons, Inc.

—In Defense of Dolphins: The New Moral Frontier. 2007. (Blackwell Public Philosophy Ser.: 6). (ENG., Illus.). 248p. pap. 29.95 *(978-1-4051-5779-7(8)*, Wiley-Blackwell) Wiley, John & Sons, Inc.

Widowski, Tina, et al, eds. Proceedings of the 5th International Conference on the Assessment of Animal Welfare at the Farm & Group Level. 2011. pap. 44.00 ***(978-90-8686-182-8(2))*** Wageningen Academic Publishers NLD. Dist: Enfield Publishing & Distribution Co., Inc.

Williams, Erin E. Why Animals Matter: The Case for Animal Protection. 2007. (ENG., Illus.). 1p. per. 21.98 *(978-1-59102-523-8(0))* Prometheus Bks., Pubs.

Williams, Jennifer. How to Start & Run a Rescue. 2007. *(978-1-929164-36-3(X))* Primedia Enthusiast Pubns.

Winegar, Karin. Saved: Rescued Animals & the Lives They Transform. 2009. (ENG., Illus.). 256p. pap. 18.00 *(978-0-306-81842-4(6))* Da Capo Pr., Inc.

Wise, Steven M. An American Trilogy: Death, Slavery, & Dominion on the Banks of the Cape Fear River. 2009. (ENG.). 304p. 26.00 *(978-0-306-81475-4(7))* Perseus Bks. Group.

Wooster, Chuck. Living with Pigs: Everything You Need to Know to Raise Your Own Porkers. Hansen, Geoff, ed. & photos by by. 2008. (Living With Ser.). (ENG., Illus.). 208p. 24.95 *(978-1-59228-877-9(4)*, Lyons Pr.) Globe Pequot Pr., The.

Zamir, Tzachi. Ethics & the Beast: A Speciesist Argument for Animal Liberation. 2007. (ENG.). 158p. (C). 42.00 *(978-0-691-13328-7(X))* Princeton Univ. Pr.

Zilney, Lisa Anne. Linking Animal Cruelty & Family Violence. 2007. (ENG.). 248p. (C). 99.95 *(978-1-934043-67-7(2))* Cambria Pr.

ANIMAL WELFARE—JUVENILE LITERATURE

Mack, Gail. Animal Rights. 2011. (Debating the Issues Ser.). 64p. (gr. 6). 32.79 *(978-0-7614-4967-6(1))* Marshall Cavendish Corp.

ANIMAL WORSHIP

see also Serpent Worship

Farbridge, Maurice H. Studies in Biblical & Semitic Symbolism. 2007. 304p. pap. 26.00 *(978-1-55635-701-5(X))* Wipf & Stock Pubs.

Irimoto, Takashi. Ainu No Kumamatsuri. 2010. (JPN., Illus.). ii, 277p. *(978-4-639-02131-5(3))* Yuzankaku Shuppan.

Waterbury, Florence. Bird Deities in China. 2007. *(978-1-57898-678-1(8))* Martino Publishing.

ANIMAL YOUNG

see Animals—Infancy

ANIMALS

Here are entered general works on animals. Works on animals of specific places are entered under Zoology subdivided by place.

see also Aquatic Animals; Cave Animals; Dangerous Animals; Domestic Animals; Euthanasia of Animals; Extinct Animals; Forest Animals; Herbivores; Human-Animal Relationships; Intersexuality in Animals; Invertebrates; Island Animals; Mammals; Mountain Animals; Photography of Animals; Rare Animals; Soil Animals; Transgenic Animals; Vertebrates; Wildlife Attracting; Working Animals; Zoology

Adams, Charles Christopher. Guide to the Study of Animal Ecology. 2009. 104p. pap. 19.99 *(978-1-151-70199-2(8))* General Bks. LLC.

Agassiz, Louis. Methods of Study in Natural History. 332p. 2009. 25.99 *(978-1-103-36652-1(1))* 2009. 25.99 *(978-1-103-27874-9(6))* 2009. pap. 19.99 *(978-1-103-36650-7(5))* 2009. pap. 19.99 *(978-1-103-27870-1(3))* 2008. 25.99 *(978-0-559-23765-2(0))* 2008. pap. 19.99 *(978-0-559-23762-1(6))* BiblioBazaar.

—Methods of Study in Natural History. 2009. 140p. pap. *(978-0-217-02350-4(9))*; pap. *(978-0-217-51431-6(6))* Books LLC.

—Methods of Study in Natural History. 2007. (ENG.). 328p. 45.95 *(978-0-548-00814-0(0))* Kessinger Publishing, LLC.

Alberti, Samuel J. M. M. The Afterlives of Animals: A Museum Menagerie. 2011. E-Book ***(978-0-8139-3208-8(4))*** Univ. Pr. of Virginia.

Alberti, Samuel J. M. M., ed. The Afterlives of Animals: A Museum Menagerie. 2011. (ENG., Illus.). 256p. (gr. 17). 35.00 *(978-0-8139-3167-8(3))* Univ. Pr. of Virginia.

Altschiller, Donald. Animal-Assisted Therapy, 1 vol. 2011. (Health & Medical Issues Today Ser.). (Illus.). 179p. 35.00 *(978-0-313-35720-6(X)*, GR5720); E-Book *(978-0-313-35721-3(8)*, Greenwood Pr.) Greenwood Publishing Group, Inc.

Ament, Rob. Safe Passages: Highways, Wildlife, & Habitat Connectivity. Beckmann, Jon P. et al, eds. 2010. (ENG., Illus.). 424p. 70.00 *(978-1-59726-653-6(1))*; pap. 40.00 *(978-1-59726-654-3(X))* Island Pr.

Animal Library, 6 bks. & 6 cass., Set. 39.95 incl. audio *(978-0-86545-166-7(4))*; 39.95 *(978-0-86545-167-4(2))* Spizzirri Pr., Inc.

Animals & Birds. 96p. *(978-0-86388-510-5(1)*, 001-2215) Speechmark Publishing Ltd.

Arment, Chad. Varmints: Mystery Carnivores of North America. 2010. 686p. pap. 29.95 *(978-1-61646-019-8(9))* Coachwhip Pubns.

Atkins, Peter. Animated Cities: Urban Historical Insights into Human-Animal Interaction. 2012. 270p. 124.95 ***(978-1-4094-4655-2(7))*** Ashgate Publishing Co.

Beard, Peter. The Last Word from Paradise. *(978-0-679-40846-8(0))* Knopf, Alfred A. Inc.

Beers, Terry & Elrod, Emily. Califauna: A Literary Field Guide. 2007. (California Legacy Ser.). (Illus.). 293p. per. *(978-1-59714-049-2(X))* Santa Clara Univ., de Saisset Museum.

Bellows, Melina Gerosa. Mother's Love: Inspiring True Stories from the Animal Kingdom. 2012. (ENG., Illus.). 96p. 9.95 ***(978-1-4262-0922-2(3)***, National Geographic) National Geographic Society.

Beyer, W. Nelson & Meador, James, eds. Environmental Contaminants in Wildlife: Interpreting Tissue Concentrations. 2nd rev. ed. 2011. (ENG., Illus.). 768p. 129.95 *(978-1-4200-8405-4(4)*, CRC Press) Taylor & Francis Group GBR. Dist: Taylor & Francis Group.

Blake, Charlie, et al, eds. Beyond Human: From Animality to Transhumanism. 2012. (ENG., Illus.). 312p. 120.00 *(978-1-4411-0742-8(8))*; pap. 34.95 *(978-1-4411-5011-0(0))* Continuum International Publishing Group, Ltd. GBR. Dist: National Bk. Network.

Bonavia, Duccio. South American Camelids. 2008. (Monograph Ser.). pap. 75.00 *(978-1-931745-40-6(4))* Cotsen Institute of Archaeology at UCLA.

—South American Camelids. Marcus, Joyce, tr. from SPA. 2008. (Monograph Ser.). (ENG.). 110.00 *(978-1-931745-41-3(2))* Cotsen Institute of Archaeology at UCLA.

Brightwen, Elizabeth. Wild Nature Won by Kindness. 2009. 148p. 21.99 *(978-0-559-11064-1(2))*; 24.99 *(978-0-559-11049-8(9))*; pap. 15.99 *(978-0-559-11059-7(6))*; pap. 21.75 *(978-0-559-11053-5(7))* BiblioBazaar.

Brooker, Robert J., et al. Plants & Animals Volume II: Selected Material from Brooker, Widmaier, Graham, Stiling, Vol. 2. 2007. (ENG., Illus.). 522p. (C). per. 87.67 *(978-0-07-335331-9(0)*, 0073353310, McGraw-Hill Science, Engineering & Mathematics) McGraw-Hill Higher Education.

Burgat. Liberté et Inquiétude de la Vie Animale. (FRE.). 311p. *(978-2-84174-381-0(0))* Kime Editions.

Burton, John A. Wild Animals: A Spotter's Guide to Britain & Europe's Most Common Species. 2009. (Collins Gem Ser.). (ENG., Illus.). 192p. pap. 7.95 *(978-0-00-728410-8(1))* HarperCollins Pubs. Ltd. GBR. Dist: Independent Pubs. Group.

Butchart, Duncan. Wildlife of South Africa. 2010. (Illus.). 168p. pap. 23.95 *(978-1-77007-632-7(8))* Struik Pubs. ZAF. Dist: International Publishers Marketing.

Byrne, John H. Learning & Memory Set: A Comprehensive Reference, 4 vols. 2008. (ENG., Illus.). 3400p. 1830.00 *(978-0-12-370504-4(5)*, Academic Pr.) Elsevier Science & Technology Bks.

Caesar, Terry. Speaking of Animals: Essays on Dogs & Others. 2009. pap. *(978-90-04-17406-1(0))* BRILL.

Calarco, Matthew. Zoographies: The Question of the Animal from Heidegger to Derrida. 2008. (ENG.). 184p. (gr. 17). pap. 26.50 *(978-0-231-14023-2(1))*; (Illus.). 89.50 *(978-0-231-14022-5(3))* Columbia Univ. Pr.

Cardoza, Zartiphin & Martin, Leilani E. A B C Animal Safari. 2011. 44p. pap. 19.99 *(978-1-4520-4668-6(9))* AuthorHouse.

Carruthers, Vincent. The Wildlife of Southern Africa: The Larger Illustrated Guide to the Animals & Plants of the Region. 2008. (Illus.). 320p. pap. 31.00 *(978-1-77007-199-5(7))* Struik Pubs. ZAF. Dist: International Publishers Marketing.

Carson, David. Find Your Spirit Animals: Nurture, Guidance & Healing from Your Inner Self. 2011. (ENG., Illus.). 160p. pap. 14.95 *(978-1-907486-74-6(7)*, Watkins Publishing) Duncan Baird Pubs. GBR. Dist: Sterling Publishing Co., Inc.

Carwardine, Mark. Extreme Nature. 2008. 320p. pap. 19.95 *(978-0-06-137389-3(3)*, HarperPerennial) HarperCollins Pubs.

Cary, Kate. Il Animal Alphabet. 2010. 32p. 12.99 *(978-1-4520-2730-2(7))* AuthorHouse.

Cavell, Stanley, et al. Philosophy & Animal Life. 2008. (ENG., Illus.). 184p. (gr. 17). 24.50 *(978-0-231-14514-5(4))* Columbia Univ. Pr.

Center for Gifted Education Staff. Survive & Thrive: A Life Science Unit for Grades K-1. 2010. (ENG.). 148p. (gr. k-1). pap. 39.95 *(978-1-59363-393-6(9))* Prufrock Pr.

Childs, James E., et al. Wildlife & Emerging Zoonotic Diseases: the Biology, Circumstances & Consequences of Cross-Species Transmission: The Biology, Circumstances & Consequences of Cross-Species Transmission. 2010. (Current Topics in Microbiology & Immunology Ser.). (Illus.). viii, 524p. pap. 279.00 *(978-3-642-08996-1(8)*, 3642089968) Springer.

Cochrane, Marjorie. Three Dogs, Two Mules, & a Reindeer: True Animal Adventures on the Alaska Frontier. 2009. (J). pap. *(978-0-87842-564-8(0))* Mountain Pr. Publishing Co., Inc.

Colette, Martine. A Tiger in My Salad. Date not set. 224p. pap. 12.50 *(978-0-06-093064-6(0))* HarperCollins Pubs.

Cooper, Ross Gordon. African Giant Rats - an Essay. 2010. 32p. pap. 28.50 *(978-0-557-41884-8(4))* Lulu Enterprises Inc.

Cussons, Eugene. Saving Chimpanzees: A Man on A Rescue Mission. 2012. (ENG.). 256p. (gr. 12). pap. 35.00 ***(978-0-14-352813-5(0)***, Penguin Global) Penguin Group (USA) Inc.

Da Silva, Nicholas. Dread & Alive: Welcome to the Jungle, Vol. 3. Lin, Maria, ed. Date not set. (Illus.). 50p. (Orig.). pap. 4.95 *(978-0-9656228-2-0(7))* Zoolook.

DeMello, Margo. Teaching the Animal: Human/Animal Studies Across the Disciplines. 2010. (Illus.). xix, 429p. *(978-1-59056-168-3(6))* Lantern Bks.

Denny, Mark & McFadzean, Alan. Engineering Animals: How Life Works. 2011. (ENG., Illus.). 400p. 35.00 *(978-0-674-04854-6(7)*, Belknap Pr.) Harvard Univ. Pr.

Derrida, Jacques. The Animal That Therefore I Am. Mallet, Marie-Louise & Wills, David, eds. 3rd ed. 2008. (Perspectives in Continental Philosophy Ser.). (ENG.). 192p. 60.00 *(978-0-8232-2790-7(1))* Fordham Univ. Pr.

—The Animal That Therefore I Am. Mallet, Marie-Louise, ed. Wills, David, tr. from FRE. 3rd ed. 2008. (Perspectives in Continental Philosophy Ser.). (ENG.). 192p. pap. 23.00 *(978-0-8232-2791-4(X))* Fordham Univ. Pr.

Diaz, Julio Enrique. Pasatiempos. 128p. 5.95 *(978-958-607-839-9(6))* Sociedad de San Pablo COL. Dist: St Pauls/Alba Hse. Pubs.

Dillard-Wright, David B. Ark of the Possible: The Animal World in Merleau-Ponty. 2009. (ENG.). 130p. 57.99 *(978-0-7391-2937-1(6))* Lexington Bks.

Diski, Jenny. What I Don't Know about Animals. 2011. 320p. 26.00 *(978-0-300-17684-1(8))* Yale Univ. Pr.

Domm, Jeffrey C. Formac Pocketguide to Nature: Animals, plants & birds in New Brunswick, Nova Scotia & Prince Edward Island. 2nd ed. 2012. (ENG., Illus.). 128p. (gr. 3-8). pap. 9.95 ***(978-1-4595-0061-7(X))*** Formac Publishing Co., Ltd. CAN. Dist: Casemate Pubs. & Bk. Distributors, LLC.

Dorling Kindersley Publishing Staff. Animals. tchr. ed. 41.95 *(978-0-382-40655-3(9))* Cobblestone Publishing Co.

Du Toit, Johan. Wild Rangelands: Conserving Wildlife While Maintaining Livestock in Semi-Arid Ecosystems. Deutsch, James & Kock, Richard, eds. 2010. (Conservation Science & Practice Ser.). (ENG., Illus.). 448p. 159.95 *(978-1-4051-9488-4(X)*, Wiley-Blackwell) Wiley, John & Sons, Inc.

du Toit, Johan, et al, eds. Wild Rangelands: Conserving Wildlife While Maintaining Livestock in Semi-Arid Ecosystems. 2010. (Conservation Science & Practice Ser.: 6). (ENG., Illus.). 448p. pap. 99.95 *(978-1-4051-7785-6(3)*, Wiley-Blackwell) Wiley, John & Sons, Inc.

Emmett, et al. Game Ranger in Your Backpack: All-in-one interpretive Guide to the Lowveld. 2012. (Illus.). 352p. pap. 37.95 ***(978-1-920217-06-8(1))*** International Publishers Marketing.

Ernst, Tim. Arkansas Wildlife: Intimate Portraits of Wild Species That Roam the Natural State. 2010. (Illus.). 144p. 34.95 *(978-1-882906-66-6(7))* Cloudland.net Publishing.

Exploring the World of Animals Set, 3-Titles; 18-Volumes. 2009. (Exploring the World of Animals Ser.). (gr. 5-8). 630.00 *(978-1-60413-860-3(2)*, Chelsea Hse.) Facts On File, Inc.

Faraone, Christopher A. & Naiden, F. S., eds. Greek & Roman Animal Sacrifice: Ancient Victims, Modern Observers. 2012. (ENG., Illus.). 224p. 95.00 ***(978-1-107-01112-0(4))*** Cambridge Univ. Pr.

Farmer, Steven D. Power Animals: How to Connect with Your Animal Spirit Guide. 2009. (ENG.). 128p. pap. 17.95 *(978-1-4019-2553-6(7)*, 1069) Hay Hse., Inc.

Faye, Bernard & Sinyavskiy, Yuriy, eds. Impact of Pollution on Animal Products. 2008. (NATO Science for Peace & Security Series C: Environmental Security Ser.). (Illus.). XX, 205p. 219.00 *(978-1-4020-8357-0(2)*, 1402083572); pap. 79.95 *(978-1-4020-8358-7(0)*, 1402083580) Springer.

Feinstein, Julie. Field Guide to Urban Wildlife. 2011. (ENG., Illus.). 496p. pap. 34.95 *(978-0-8117-0585-1(4))* Stackpole Bks.

Ffolliott, Peter F. & Davis, Owen K., eds. Natural Environments of Arizona: From Desert to Mountains. 2008. (ENG., Illus.). 208p. 40.00 *(978-0-8165-2696-3(6))*; pap. 19.95 *(978-0-8165-2697-0(4))* Univ. of Arizona Pr.

Fine, Aubrey H., ed. Handbook on Animal-Assisted Therapy: Theoretical Foundations & Guidelines for Practice. 3rd ed. 2010. (ENG.). 552p. 69.95 *(978-0-12-381453-1(7)*, Academic Pr.) Elsevier Science & Technology Bks.

Flanders, Frank. Exploring Animal Science. 2012. (ENG.). 320p. pap. ***(978-1-111-31091-2(2))*** Delmar Cengage Learning.

Flanders, Frank (Frank Flanders). Exploring Animal Science. 2011. (ENG.). 928p. (C). 101.95 *(978-1-4354-3952-8(X))* Delmar Cengage Learning.

Fothergill, Alastair & Berlowitz, Vanessa. Frozen Planet: A World Beyond Imagination. 2011. (ENG., Illus.). 312p. 39.95 ***(978-1-55407-991-9(8))*** Firefly Bks., Ltd.

Francione, Gary L. Animals as Persons: Essays on the Abolition of Animal Exploitation. 2009. (ENG.). 256p. (gr. 17). pap. 24.50 *(978-0-231-13951-9(9))* Columbia Univ. Pr.

Francis Channing Woodworth. Stories about Animals: With Pictures to Match. l.t. ed. 2007. 164p. pap. 21.99 *(978-1-4264-9820-6(9))* BiblioBazaar.

Freeman, Dan. Mangroves & Man-Eaters: And Other Wildlife Encounters. 2010. (Illus.). 224p. pap. *(978-1-84995-009-1(1))* Whittles Publishing.

Global Warming & Wildlife: Hearing Before the Subcommittee on Private Sector & Consumer Solutions to Global Warming & Wildlife [Protection] of the Committee on Environment & Public Works, United States Senate, One Hundred Tenth Congress, First Session, February 7, 2007. 2010. (Illus.). iii, 318p. *(978-0-16-085325-8(7)*, 552-070-40655-7) United States Government Printing Office.

Glover, Tim. Mating Males: An Evolutionary Perspective on Mammalian Reproduction. 2012. (ENG., Illus.). 200p. (C). 110.00 ***(978-1-107-00001-8(7))***; pap. 44.99 ***(978-0-521-15957-9(1))*** Cambridge Univ. Pr.

Gould, Donna. Our Trail. 2007. *(978-1-929830-20-6(3))* Innovations Pr.

Gould, Edwin. Encyclopedia of Animals: Mammals, Birds, Reptiles, Amphibians. (Illus.). 240p. 25.00 *(978-1-85391-126-2(7))* Sterling Publishing Co., Inc.

Gould, Francesca & Haviland, David. Why Dogs Eat Poop: And Other Useless or Gross Information about the Animal Kingdom. 2010. (ENG.). 272p. (gr. 12). 12.95 *(978-1-58542-799-4(3)*, Tarcher) Penguin Group (USA) Inc.

Greive, Bradley Trevor. Every Day Is Christmas. 2011. (ENG.). 120p. pap. 4.99 ***(978-1-4494-1409-2(5))*** Andrews McMeel Publishing.

Grice, Gordon. Deadly Kingdom: The Book of Dangerous Animals. 2010. (Illus.). 352p. 27.00 *(978-0-385-33562-1(8)*, Dial Pr.) Random House Publishing Group.

Grogan, John. Bad Dogs Have More Fun: Selected Writings on Family, Animals, & Life from the Philadelphia Inquirer. 2008. 128p. pap. 4.95 *(978-0-7624-3533-3(X))* Running Pr. Bk. Pubs.

—Bad Dogs Have More Fun: Selected Writings on Family, Animals, & Life from the Philadelphia Inquirer. 2008. (ENG., Illus.). 256p. pap. 12.95 *(978-1-59315-490-5(9))* Vanguard Pr.

Grzimeks Enzyklopaedie Saugetiere, 6 Bands, Set. (Bibliothek Ser.). (GER.). *(978-3-7653-8000-6(8))* Brockhaus, F. A., GmbH DEU. Dist: International Bk. Import Service, Inc.

Gutteridge, Lee. The Bushveld: A South African Field Guide. 2011. 704p. pap. 49.95 *(978-1-920143-53-4(X))* 30° South Pubs. ZAF. Dist: International Publishers Marketing.

Haas, Timothy C. Improving Natural Resource Management: Ecological & Political Models. 2011. (Statistics in Practice Ser.). (ENG., Illus.). 272p. 88.00 *(978-0-470-66113-0(5)*, Wiley) Wiley, John & Sons, Inc.

Harmer, Lucy. Discovering Your Spirit Animal: The Wisdom of the Shamans. 2009. (ENG., Illus.). 120p. pap. 12.95 *(978-1-55643-796-0(X))* North Atlantic Bks.

Hearne, Vicki. Animal Happiness: A Moving Exploration of Animals & Their Emotions. 2007. (ENG.). 256p. per. 14.95 *(978-1-60239-167-3(X))* Skyhorse Publishing Co., Inc.

Heinrich, Bernd. Summer World: A Season of Bounty. 2010. (ENG.). 288p. pap. 14.99 *(978-0-06-074218-8(6)*, Ecco) HarperCollins Pubs.

Hoffman, Anita. Animales Desconocidos. (Ciencia para Todos Ser.). (SPA.). pap. 6.99 *(978-968-16-2860-4(8))* Fondo de Cultura Economica USA.

Holland, Peter. The Animal Kingdom: A Very Short Introduction. 2012. (Very Short Introductions Ser.). (ENG., Illus.). 144p. pap. 11.95 ***(978-0-19-959321-7(3))*** Oxford Univ. Pr., Inc.

Horwell. Galapagos Wildlife/3 Bradt. 3rd rev. ed. 2011. (ENG., Illus.). 152p. pap. 22.99 *(978-1-84162-360-3(1))* Bradt Travel Guides GBR. Dist: Globe Pequot Pr., The.

Hunt, Victoria. Animal Omens. 2008. (ENG., Illus.). 192p. pap. 15.95 (978-0-7387-1377-9(5)) Llewellyn Pubns.

Jackson, Donald C. Life in a Shell: A Physiologist's View of a Turtle. 2011. (Illus.). 192p. 29.95 (978-0-674-05034-1(7)) Harvard Univ. Pr.

Jackson, Tom. The Illustrated Encyclopedia of Animals, Birds & Fish of North America: A Natural History & Identification Guide with More Than 420 Native Species from the United States of America & Canada. 2012. (ENG., Illus.). 256p. 35.00 (978-0-7548-1987-5(6)) Anness Publishing GBR. Dist: National Bk. Network.

—The Illustrated Encyclopedia of Animals of the World: An Expert Reference Guide to 840 Amphibians, Reptiles & Mammals from Every Continent. 2009. (ENG., Illus.). 512p. 35.00 (978-0-7548-1778-9(4)) Anness Publishing GBR. Dist: National Bk. Network.

Jackson, Tom. The Illustrated Encyclopedia of Animals of the World: An expert reference guide to 840 amphibians, reptiles & mammals from every Continent. 2012. (ENG., Illus.). 512p. pap. 18.99 **(978-1-78019-108-9(1))** Anness Publishing GBR. Dist: National Bk. Network.

Josipovic, Stanislas & Ludwig, Elias. Heat Stress: Causes, Treatment & Prevention. 2012. (Environmental Health - Physical, Chemical & Biological Factors Ser.). 258p. 140.00 **(978-1-62100-187-4(3))** Nova Science Pubs., Inc.

Kalof, Linda & Montgomery, Georgina M., eds. Making Animal Meaning. 2011. (Animal Turn Ser.). (ENG., Illus.). 212p. 44.95 **(978-1-61186-016-0(4))** Michigan State Univ. Pr.

Kavanagh, James. Acadia National Park Wildlife: An Introduction to Familiar Species. 2008. (Pocket Naturalist - Waterford Press Ser.). (ENG., Illus.). 1p. 5.95 (978-1-58355-355-8(X)) Waterford Pr., Inc.

—Louisiana Wildlife: An Introduction to Familiar Species. 2008. (Pocket Naturalist - Waterford Press Ser.). (ENG., Illus.). 1p. 5.95 (978-1-58355-410-4(6)) Waterford Pr., Inc.

—Middle East Wildlife: An Introduction to Familiar & Dangerous Species in Iraq, Iran, Afghanistan & the Middle East. 2010. (Duraguide Ser.). (ENG.). 2p. 7.95 (978-1-58355-555-2(2)) Waterford Pr., Inc.

—New England Beachcomber: A Waterproof Reference to Beach Habitats, Plants & Animals. 2010. (Duraguide Ser.). (ENG.). 2p. 7.95 (978-1-58355-556-9(0)) Waterford Pr., Inc.

—Pacific Northwest Beachcomber: A Waterproof Reference to Beach Habitats, Plants & Animals. 2010. (Duraguide Ser.). 2p. 7.95 (978-1-58355-557-6(9)) Waterford Pr., Inc.

Kitchell, Kenneth. Animals in the Ancient World from A to Z. 2009. (978-0-415-39244-0(6), Routledge) Taylor & Francis Group.

Knutson, Roger M. Flattened Fauna, Revised: A Field Guide to Common Animals of Roads, Streets, & Highways. rev. ed. 2006. (ENG., Illus.). 96p. pap. 9.95 (978-1-58008-755-1(8)) Ten Speed Pr.

Laland, Stephanie. Random Acts of Kindness by Animals. 2nd rev. ed. 2008. (ENG., Illus.). 224p. pap. 12.95 (978-1-57324-350-6(7), Conari Pr.) Red Wheel/Weiser.

Laufer, Peter. Forbidden Creatures: Inside the World of Animal Smuggling & Exotic Pets. 2011. (ENG.). 288p. pap. 16.95 (978-0-7627-7180-6(1), Lyons Pr.) Globe Pequot Pr., The.

Lawlor, Leonard. This Is Not Sufficient: An Essay on Animality & Human Nature in Derrida. 2007. (ENG.). 192p. (gr. 17). 40.00 (978-0-231-14312-7(5)) Columbia Univ. Pr.

Lawrence, Debbie & Lawrence, Richard. The Animal Kingdom. 2006. (God's Design for Life Ser.). (Illus.). 118p. per. 22.99 (978-1-893345-82-9(3)) Answers in Genesis Ministries.

Lindo, David. The Urban Birder. 2012. (ENG., Illus.). 224p. 14.95 **(978-1-84773-950-6(4))** New Holland Pubs., Ltd. GBR. Dist: Sterling Publishing Co., Inc.

López-Larrea, Carlos, ed. Sensing in Nature. 2012. (Advances in Experimental Medicine & Biology Ser.). (ENG., Illus.). xxii, 314p. 209.00 **(978-1-4614-1703-3(1)**, 1461417031) Springer.

Lowen, James. Pantanal Wildlife: A Visitor's Guide to Brazil's Great Wetland. 2010. (ENG., Illus.). 176p. pap. 25.99 (978-1-84162-305-4(9)) Bradt Travel Guides GBR. Dist: Globe Pequot Pr., The.

Lupa. A Field Guide to Otherkin. 2007. 316p. per. (978-1-905713-07-3(X)) Megalithica Bks.

Lurz, Robert W., ed. The Philosophy of Animal Minds. 2009. (ENG., Illus.). 320p. 85.00 (978-0-521-88502-7(7)) Cambridge Univ. Pr.

Lydekker, R. Phases of Animal Life: Past & Present. 2007. (ENG.). 284p. 43.95 (978-0-548-09129-6(3)) Kessinger Publishing, LLC.

Maher, Patrick T., et al. Polar Tourism: Human, Environmental, & Governanace Dimensions. 2010. (978-1-882345-55-7(X)) Cognizant Communication Corp.

Marín, Lluvia & Kovac, Dimos. Native Species: Identification, Conservation & Restoration. 2011. (Animal Science, Issues & Professions Ser.). 95.00 **(978-1-61470-613-7(1))** Nova Science Pubs., Inc.

Markovics, Joyce. Saving Animals after Floods. 2011. (Rescuing Animals from Disasters Ser.). 32p. (YA). (gr. 2-5). lib. bdg. 25.27 (978-1-61772-292-9(8)) Bearport Publishing Co., Inc.

Mars, F. St. The Way of the Wild. 2007. (ENG.). 246p. pap. 20.99 (978-1-4346-1165-9(5)); 272p. pap. 23.99 (978-1-4346-1236-6(8)) BiblioBazaar.

Martin, Edward C., III. The Peaceable Kingdom in Hartsdale - America's First Pet Cemetery. 2010. 112p. pap. 14.95 (978-0-557-46810-2(8)) Lulu Enterprises Inc.

Martin, Stella. Australian Wildlife: Wildlife Explorer. 2010. (ENG., Illus.). 200p. pap. 26.99 (978-1-84162-324-5(5)) Bradt Travel Guides GBR. Dist: Globe Pequot Pr., The.

Martins, Cesar, et al. Animal Genomes under the Focus of Cytogenetics. 2011. (Genetics - Research & Issues Ser.). (Illus.). vi, 160p. 69.00 (978-1-61209-390-1(6)) Nova Science Pubs., Inc.

Masson, Jeffrey Moussaieff & Masson, J. Moussaieff. Altruistic Armadillos, Zenlike Zebras: Understanding the World's Most Intriguing Animals. 2010. (ENG., Illus.). 368p. pap. 14.95 (978-1-60239-738-5(4), 239738) Skyhorse Publishing Co., Inc.

Matisoff, James A. English-Lahu Lexicon. 2006. (University of California Publications in Linguistics: Vol. 139). (SIT & ENG.). 472p. 45.00 (978-0-520-09855-8(2)) Univ. of California Pr.

Mazis, Glen A. Humans, Animals, Machines: Blurring Boundaries. 2008. (Illus.). 304p. 83.50 (978-0-7914-7555-3(7)); pap. 29.95 (978-0-7914-7556-0(5)) State Univ. of New York Pr.

McCardle, Peggy, et al, eds. Animals in Our Lives: Human-Animal Interaction in Family, Community, & Therapeutic Settings. 2010. 264p. pap. 44.95 (978-1-59857-157-8(5)) Brookes, Paul H. Publishing Co.

McCloskey, Erin. Southern California Nature Guide. 2009. (ENG.). 224p. pap. 19.95 (978-976-8200-55-6(3)) Lone Pine Publishing USA.

McCuaig, Carol Bennett. Encountering the Wild. 2011. (ENG., Illus.). 230p. pap. 25.00 (978-1-55488-858-0(1), Dundurn Pr.) Dundurn CAN. Dist: Ingram Pub. Services.

Mcisaac, Gerald. Bird from Hell: And Other Mega Fauna. 2010. 108p. 21.59 (978-1-4269-2306-7(6)) Trafford Publishing.

McShane, Clay & Tarr, Joel. The Horse in the City: Living Machines in the Nineteenth Century. 2011. (Animals, History, Culture Ser.). (ENG., Illus.). 280p. (gr. 17). pap. 30.00 (978-1-4214-0043-3(X)) Johns Hopkins Univ. Pr.

Meyer, Karl, text. Wild Animals of North America. 2006. (ENG., Illus.). 64p. (J). pap. 9.95 (978-1-58017-643-9(7), 1580176437) Storey Publishing, LLC.

Milam, Erika L. Looking for a Few Good Males: Female Choice in Evolutionary Biology. 2011. (Animals, History, Culture Ser.). (ENG., Illus.). 248p. (gr. 17). pap. 30.00 **(978-1-4214-0402-8(8))** Johns Hopkins Univ. Pr.

Mirarchi, Ralph E., ed. Alabama Wildlife, 4 vols., Set. 2nd ed. 2009. (ENG.). 896p. pap. 75.00 (978-0-8173-9906-1(2)) Univ. of Alabama Pr.

Mitchell, Joseph C., et al. Urban Herpetology. 2008. (Illus.). xvii, 586p. (978-0-916984-79-3(6)) Society for the Study of Amphibians & Reptiles.

Mitchinson, John & Lloyd, John. The Book of Animal Ignorance: Everything You Think You Know Is Wrong. 2008. (ENG., Illus.). 256p. 19.95 (978-0-307-39493-4(X), Harmony) Crown Publishing Group.

Molloy, Claire, et al, eds. Beyond Human: From Animality to Transhumanism. 2012. (Illus.). 224p. E-Book **(978-1-4411-7399-7(4))**; E-Book **(978-1-4411-7124-5(X))** Continuum International Publishing Group, Ltd.

Montroll, John. Mythological Creatures & the Chinese Zodiac Origami. 2010. (Dover Origami Papercraft Ser.). (ENG., Illus.). 120p. pap. 14.95 (978-0-486-47951-4(X)) Dover Pubns., Inc.

Moyes, Christopher D. & Schulte, Patricia M. Principles of Animal Physiology. 2nd ed. 2007. (ENG., Illus.). 784p. (C). 166.87 (978-0-321-50155-4(1)) Benjamin-Cummings Publishing Co.

Myers, Nancy Clopton. Never kiss a Turtle: The Joys & Sorrows of Pet Ownership. 2010. 160p. pap. 14.95 (978-1-4502-4838-9(1)) iUniverse, Inc.

Nationalnyckeln till Sveriges Flora Och Fauna. (SWE., Illus.). 60.00 (978-91-88506-51-1(7)) Apollo Bks. DNK. Dist: International Specialized Bk. Services.

Nicotext. Animalisticus Fantasticus: 600 Amazing & True Facts about Animals. 2010. (ENG., Illus.). 200p. pap. 9.95 (978-91-86283-05-6(7)) Nicotext, Ltd. SWE. Dist: SCB Distributors.

Novotny, George M. Wild Times on the Course: Animal Encounters in My Golfing Life. 2011. 48p. pap. 9.95 **(978-1-4269-7387-1(X))** Trafford Publishing.

Ober, Lynne. Benson's Wild Animal Farm. 2010. pap. 17.95 (978-0-578-05785-9(9)) GoJo Venture.

O'Donnell, Elliot. Animal Ghosts: Or, Animal Hauntings & the Hereafter. 2007. (ENG.). 188p. pap. 19.99 (978-1-4264-5140-9(7)); 208p. pap. 22.99 (978-1-4264-5441-7(4)) BiblioBazaar.

Office of the Federal Register (U.S.), compiled by. Code of Federal Regulations, Title 50, Wildlife & Fisheries, (Sec. 17. 95(c) to End of Section 17. 95), Revised as of October 1 2010. rev. ed. 2011. (ENG., Illus.). 986p. pap. 37.00 (978-0-16-086510-7(7), Office of the Federal Register) United States Government Printing Office.

—Code of Federal Regulations, Title 50, Wildlife & Fisheries, (Sec. 17. 96-17. 99(i)), Revised as of October 1 2010. rev. ed. 2011. (ENG., Illus.). 1379p. pap. 64.00 (978-0-16-086511-4(5), Office of the Federal Register) United States Government Printing Office.

Office of the Federal Register (U.S.), ed. Code of Federal Regulations, Title 50, Wildlife & Fisheries, Pt. 17 (Sec. 17. 1-17. 95(b)), Revised as of October 1 2010. rev. ed. 2011. (ENG., Illus.). 1397p. pap. 37.00 (978-0-16-086509-1(3), Office of the Federal Register) United States Government Printing Office.

—Code of Federal Regulations, Title 50, Wildlife & Fisheries, Pt. 18-199, Revised as of October 1 2010. 2011. (ENG.). 787p. pap. 56.00 (978-0-16-086513-8(1), Office of the Federal Register) United States Government Printing Office.

—Code of Federal Regulations, Title 50, Wildlife & Fisheries, Pt. 200-599, Revised as of October 1 2010. rev. ed. 2011. (ENG.). 1212p. pap. 51.00 (978-0-16-086514-5(X), Office of the Federal Register) United States Government Printing Office.

—Code of Federal Regulations, Title 50, Wildlife & Fisheries, Pt. 600-659, Revised as of October 1 2010. 2011. (ENG.). 819p. pap. 36.00 (978-0-16-086515-2(8), Office of the Federal Register) United States Government Printing Office.

—Code of Federal Regulations, Title 50, Wildlife & Fisheries, Pt. 660-End, Revised as of October 1 2010. rev. ed. 2011. (ENG.). 923p. pap. 36.00 (978-0-16-086516-9(6), Office of the Federal Register) United States Government Printing Office.

Oliver, Kelly. Animal Lessons: How They Teach Us to Be Human. 2009. (Illus.). 416p. E-Book (978-0-231-52049-2(2)); (ENG., 376p. (gr. 17). 89.50 (978-0-231-14726-2(0)); (ENG., 376p. (gr. 17). pap. 29.50 (978-0-231-14727-9(9)) Columbia Univ. Pr.

Ouchley, Kelby. Flora & Fauna of the Civil War: An Environmental Reference Guide. 2010. (Illus.). 272p. 29.95 (978-0-8071-3688-1(3)) Louisiana State Univ. Pr.

Pearson, David L. & Beletsky, Les. Thailand. 2008. (Travellers' Wildlife Guides). (Illus.). 472p. pap. 29.95 (978-1-56656-694-0(0), Interlink Bks.) Interlink Publishing Group, Inc.

Pee, H. M. Law of the Wild. lt. ed. 2010. 224p. 23.99 (978-1-84262-759-4(7)) Dales Large Print Bks. GBR. Dist: Ulverscroft Large Print Bks., Ltd.

Person, Stephen. Saving Animals from Fires. 2011. (Rescuing Animals from Disasters Ser.). 32p. (YA). (gr. 2-5). lib. bdg. 25.27 (978-1-61772-293-6(6)) Bearport Publishing Co., Inc.

Piedmont Trail Guide Staff, contrib. by. North Carolina Birding Trail: Piedmont Trail Guide. 2008. (Illus.). 176p. spiral bd. 19.95 (978-0-8078-5917-9(6)) Univ. of North Carolina Pr.

Pierson, Clara Dillingham. Dooryard Stories. 2008. 164p. pap. 8.95 (978-1-59915-297-4(5)) Yesterday's Classics.

Piper, Ross. Extraordinary Animals: An Encyclopedia of Curious & Unusual Animals, 1 vol. 2007. (Illus.). 320p. 85.00 (978-0-313-33922-6(8), GR3922, Greenwood Pr.) Greenwood Publishing Group, Inc.

Polaszek, Andrew. Systema Naturae 250 - the Linnaean Ark. 2010. (ENG., Illus.). 300p. 99.95 (978-1-4200-9501-2(3), CRC Press) Taylor & Francis Group GBR. Dist: Taylor & Francis Group.

Prasad, Kathleen. Newsletter 2004-2005. 2008. 128p. pap. 14.95 (978-1-4357-0529-6(7)) Lulu Enterprises Inc.

Press, Search. Cute Creatures to Knit & Crochet. 2011. (ENG., Illus.). 128p. pap. 19.95 (978-1-84448-607-6(9)) Search Pr., Ltd. GBR. Dist: Independent Pubs. Group.

Priddy Books Staff. Wild Animals. (Illus.). bds. 8.95 (978-0-312-49331-8(2), Priddy Bks.) St. Martin's Pr.

Proctor, Noble S. & Lynch, Patrick J. A Field Guide to the Southeast Coast & Gulf of Mexico: Coastal Habitats, Seabirds, Marine Mammals, Fish, & Other Wildlife. 2012. (ENG., Illus.). 386p. pap. 24.00 (978-0-300-11328-0(5)) Yale Univ. Pr.

Ptak, Roderich. Birds & Beasts in Chinese Texts & Trade: Lectures Related to South China & the Overseas World. 2011. (Maritime Asia Ser.). (ENG., Illus.). 140p. (C). 57.00 **(978-3-447-06449-1(8))** Harrassowitz, Otto Verlag DEU. Dist: ISD.

Quillet Staff. Encyclopedie Illustree du Monde Animal. (FRE., Illus.). 600p. 29.95 (978-0-7859-0395-6(X), M6218) French & European Pubns., Inc.

Rappole, John H. Wildlife of the Mid-Atlantic: A Complete Reference Manual. 2007. (ENG., Illus.). 384p. 49.95 (978-0-8122-3982-9(2)) Univ. of Pennsylvania Pr.

Redfern, Nick. Man-Monkey - in Search of the British Bigfoot. 2007. 164p. per. (978-1-905723-16-4(4)) CFZ Pr.

Redfield, James W. Comparative Physiognomy; or, Resemblances Between Men & Animals by James W Redfield Illustrated by 330 Engravings. 2006. (Illus.). 336p. per. 23.99 (978-1-4255-3345-8(0)) MPublishing.

Regan, Lisa. Bloodsucking Beasts. 2011. (Monsters & Myths Ser.). (Illus.). 48p. (J). (gr. 4-6). pap. 14.05 (978-1-4339-4992-0(X), Stevens, Gareth Learning Library) Stevens, Gareth Publishing LLLP.

Rial, Anabel, et al, eds. Rapid Assessment of the Biodiversity & Socio-Ecosystem Aspects of the Ramal de Calderas, Venezuelan Andes. 2011. (Conservation International - RAP Bulletin of Biological Assessment Ser.). 183p. pap. 19.95 (978-1-934151-37-2(8)) Conservation International.

Richert, Katelyn. Where's the Point? 2010. 28p. 12.49 (978-1-4520-2562-9(2)) AuthorHouse.

Roberts, Mark S. The Mark of the Beast: Animality & Human Oppression. 2008. (New Directions in the Human-Animal Bond Ser.). 217p. pap. 29.95 (978-1-55753-474-3(8)) Purdue Univ. Pr.

Robinson, Chris & Robinson, Christine. Scottish Wildlife. 2008. (ENG., Illus.). 128p. pap. 9.95 (978-1-84502-195-5(9)) Black & White Publishing Ltd. GBR. Dist: Interlink Publishing Group, Inc.

Robleda, Maria. Como los Animales (Like the Animals) (SPA.). 4.95 (978-970-629-120-2(2)) Sistemas Tecnicos de Edicion, S.A. de C.V. MEX. Dist: AIMS International Bks., Inc.

Roper, Matt. World's Weirdest Animals. 2011. (ENG., Illus.). 96p. 9.95 **(978-1-84024-749-7(5))** Summersdale Pubs. GBR. Dist: Independent Pubs. Group.

Rose, Rebecca & Smith, Carin A. Career Choices for Veterinary Technicians: Opportunities for Animal Lovers. 2009. xvi, 179p. pap. (978-1-58326-105-7(2), American Animal Hospital Assn. Pr.

Rowlands, Mark. Can Animals Be Moral? 2012. 288p. 29.95 **(978-0-19-984200-1(0))** Oxford Univ. Pr., Inc.

Rozelle, Jane. Creatures of the Creator: A Maine Grandmother's Memories. 2007. 148p. per. 24.95 (978-1-4241-9453-7(9)) PublishAmerica, Inc.

Ruf, Thomas, et al, eds. Living in a Seasonal World: Thermoregulatory & Metabolic Adaptations. 2012. (ENG., Illus.). xiv, 563p. 239.00 **(978-3-642-28677-3(1)**, 3642286771) Springer.

Ryan, James M. Adirondack Wildlife: A Field Guide. 2009. (ENG., Illus.). 296p. pap. 24.95 (978-1-58465-749-1(9)) Univ. Pr. of New England.

Sanborn, Kate. My Literary Zoo. 2009. 160p. 22.99 (978-1-103-93863-6(0)); pap. 16.99 (978-1-103-93855-1(X)) BiblioBazaar.

—My Literary Zoo. 2008. 160p. 36.95 (978-1-4371-9067-0(7)); pap. 21.95 (978-1-4370-5988-5(0)) Kessinger Publishing, LLC.

Satris, Stephen. Taking Sides: Clashing Views on Moral Issues. 13th ed. 2011. (Taking Sides Ser.). (ENG.). 352p. (C). pap. 48.00 (978-0-07-805009-1(X), 007805009X, McGraw-Hill/Dushkin) McGraw-Hill Higher Education.

Schaller, George B. A Naturalist & Other Beasts: Tales from a Life in the Field. (ENG., Illus.). 272p. 2010. pap. 16.95 (978-1-57805-170-0(3)) 2007. 24.95 (978-1-57805-129-8(0)) Sierra Club Bks.

Schmidt, Dennis & Schmidt, Esther. Wildlife of Western Canada. 96p. (978-1-55153-814-3(8)) Altitude Publishing Canada Ltd.

Schutt, Bill. Dark Banquet: Blood & the Curious Lives of Blood-Feeding Creatures. 2009. (ENG., Illus.). 336p. pap. 15.00 (978-0-307-38113-2(7), Three Rivers Pr.) Crown Publishing Group.

Scott, Joanne. The WTO Agreement on Sanitary & Phytosanitary Measures: A Commentary. 2007. (ENG.). 360p. 195.00 (978-0-19-927112-2(7)) Oxford Univ. Pr., Inc.

Scott, M. Douglas & Scott, Suvi A. Wildlife of Yellowstone & Grand Teton National Parks. (Illus.). pap. 6.95 (978-0-9702067-1-8(2)) Wheelwright Publishing.

Semper, Karl. Animal Life As Affected by the Natural Conditions of Existence. 2010. 498p. pap. 38.75 (978-1-177-77439-0(9)) BiblioBazaar.

Serjeantson, Dale, ed. Animals in the Neolithic of Britain & Europe. 2006. (Neolithic Studies Group Seminar Papers: Vol. 7). (ENG., Illus.). 192p. (C). per. 60.00 (978-1-84217-214-8(X)) Oxbow Bks., Ltd. GBR. Dist: Brown, David Bk. Co., The.

Seton, Ernest Thompson. Lobo, Rag & Vixen. 2008. (Illus.). 96p. pap. (978-1-4065-9176-7(9)) Dodo Pr.

—Wild Animals I Have Known. 2008. 156p. 22.99 (978-0-554-38729-1(8)) 2008. 156p. 25.99 (978-0-554-29426-1(5)) 2007. (ENG.). 136p. per. 18.99 (978-1-4346-7614-6(5)) BiblioBazaar.

—Wild Animals I Have Known. 2008. (ENG.). 136p. per. (978-1-4065-9179-8(3)) Dodo Pr.

—Wild Animals I Have Known. 2006. pap. (978-1-84702-462-6(9)) Echo Library.

—Wild Animals I Have Known. 2009. (Illus.). 272p. pap. 15.95 (978-0-7710-9380-7(2), New Can Library) McClelland & Stewart CAN. Dist: Random Hse., Inc.

—Wild Animals I Have Known. 2008. (ENG.). 136p. pap. 10.95 (978-1-60597-720-1(9)); pap. 3.95 (978-1-4385-1065-1(9)) Standard Pubns., Inc. (Book Jungle).

—Wild Animals I Have Known. 2009. 86p. pap. (978-0-217-90710-1(5)) Books LLC.

—Wild Animals I Have Known. 2010. (Illus.). 88p. pap. 20.00 (978-1-153-74071-5(0)) General Bks. LLC.

—Wild Animals I Have Known. lt. ed. 2007. (ENG.). 152p. per. 21.99 (978-1-4346-7615-3(3)) BiblioBazaar.

—Wild Animals I Have Known. (Illus.). 357p. reprint ed. lib. bdg. 98.00 (978-0-7222-3084-8(2)) Library Reprints, Inc.

Shugart, H. H. How the Earthquake Bird Got Its Name & Other Tales of an Unbalanced Nature. 2007. (ENG., Illus.). 240p. per. 18.00 (978-0-300-12270-1(5)) Yale Univ. Pr.

Shuker, Karl. Extraordinary Animals Revisited. 2007. 328p. per. (978-1-905723-17-1(2)) CFZ Pr.

Smith, C. U. M., et al. The Animal Spirit Doctrine: A Physiological Odyssey. 2012. (ENG.). 304p. 120.00 **(978-0-19-976649-9(5))** Oxford Univ. Pr., Inc.

Smith, Chris. Determination of Animal & Plant Species in Foodstuffs. Bonwick, Graham, ed. 2008. (Institute of Food Science & Technology Ser.). (Illus.). 256p. (978-1-4051-1907-8(1), Wiley-Blackwell) Wiley, John & Sons, Ltd.

Smith, Lewis. Why the Cheetah Cheats: And Other Mysteries of the Animal World. 2009. (ENG., Illus.). 240p. pap. 29.95 (978-1-55407-534-8(3)) Firefly Bks., Ltd.

Snopek, Roxanne Willems. Inspiring Animal Tales: Heartwarming Stories of Courage & Devotion, 1 vol. 2009. (Amazing Stories Ser.). (ENG., Illus.). 136p. pap. (978-1-894974-77-6(8)) Heritage Hse.

Speart, Jessica. Winged Obsession: The Pursuit of the World's Most Notorious Butterfly Smuggler. (ENG.). 320p. 2012. pap. 15.99 **(978-0-06-177244-3(5)**, William Morrow Paperbacks) 2011. 25.99 (978-0-06-177243-6(7), Morrow, William & Co.) HarperCollins Pubs.

Stang, Debra. Hospice Tails: The Animal Companions Who Journey with Hospice Patients & Their Families. 2011. 108p. pap. 12.95 **(978-1-61434-261-8(X))** Booklocker.com, Inc.

Sterry, Paul. Collins Complete British Animals: A Photographic Guide to Every Common Species. 2010. (Collins Complete Guide Ser.). (ENG., Illus.). 224p. pap. 24.95 (978-0-00-734950-0(5)) HarperCollins Pubs. Ltd. GBR. Dist: Independent Pubs. Group.

—Collins Complete Irish Wildlife. 2010. (Collins Complete Guide Ser.). (ENG., Illus.). 320p. pap. 24.95 (978-0-00-734951-7(3)) HarperCollins Pubs. Ltd. GBR. Dist: Independent Pubs. Group.

Stevenson-Hamilton, James. Animal Life in Africa. 2010. 82p. pap. (978-1-151-88739-9(0)); 82p. pap. (978-1-151-88735-1(8)); 72p. pap. (978-1-151-88742-9(0)) Books LLC.

Stuart, Chris & Mathilde. Dangerous Creatures of Africa: Understand-Identify-Avoid-Survive. 2009. (Illus.). 300p. 33.50 *(978-1-77007-355-5(8))* Struik Pubs. ZAF. Dist: International Publishers Marketing.

Tait, Malcolm. Animal Tragic: Popular Misconceptions of Wildlife Through the Centuries. 2006. (Mammoth Mistakes Ser.). (ENG., Illus.). 160p. 9.95 *(978-1-84525-015-7(X))* Sterling Publishing Co., Inc.

—The Wildlife Pocket Companion. 2008. (Pocket Companion Ser.). (ENG.). 160p. 13.95 *(978-1-86205-825-5(3),* Pavilion Bks., Ltd.) Anova Bks. GBR. Dist: Independent Pubs. Group.

Ted, Andrews. Animal-Wise: Understanding the Language of Animal Messengers & Companions. 2nd rev. ed. 2010. 416p. pap. 22.95 *(978-1-888767-63-6(4))* Dragonhawk Publishing.

Thomas. Animals, International Law, International Trade, & Morality. 2011. xiv, 500p. *(978-90-411-3338-0(0))* Kluwer Law International.

Thomas, E. Donnall, Jr. Have Bow, Will Travel: Around the World Adventure with Longbow & Recurve. 2011. (ENG., Illus.). 302p. pap. 22.00 *(978-0-9816584-6-9(6))* Raven's Eye Pr., LLC.

Thompson, Jean M. Wild Kindred of Fur, Feather & Fin. 2007. (ENG.). 344p. 46.95 *(978-0-548-04008-9(7))* Kessinger Publishing, LLC.

Die Tiere (Animals) (Schulerduden Ser.). (ENG & GER.). 392p. 27.95 *(978-3-411-02216-8(7),* B2216) Bibliographisches Institut & F. A. Brockhaus AG DEU. Dist: Continental Bk. Co., Inc.

Togashi, Tatsuya & Cox, Paul Alan, eds. The Evolution of Anisogamy: A Fundamental Phenomenon Underlying Sexual Selection. 2011. (ENG., Illus.). 262p. 75.00 *(978-0-521-88095-4(5))* Cambridge Univ. Pr.

Toldrá, Fidel, ed. Meat Biotechnology. 2010. (ENG., Illus.). xiv, 502p. pap. 169.00 *(978-1-4419-2721-7(2),* 1441927212) Springer.

Tompkins, Ptolemy. The Divine Life of Animals: One Man's Quest to Discover Whether the Souls of Animals Live On. 2011. (ENG.). 256p. pap. 13.00 *(978-0-307-45133-0(X),* Three Rivers Pr.) Crown Publishing Group.

True Facts. (Children's Reference Ser.). 224p. *(978-1-4054-9546-2(4))* Parragon, Inc.

Tyler, Tom. Ciferae: A Bestiary in Five Fingers. 2012. (Posthumanities Ser.). (Illus.). 376p. 90.00 ***(978-0-8166-6543-3(5))***; pap. 30.00 ***(978-0-8166-6544-0(3))*** Univ. of Minnesota Pr.

Tymieniecka, Anna-Teresa, ed. Phenomenology of Life - from the Animal Soul to the Human Mind: Book I. In Search of Experience. 2010. (Analecta Husserliana Ser.). xlii, 452p. pap. 169.00 *(978-90-481-7305-1(1),* 9048173051) Springer.

van Lill, Dawid. African Wildlife Trivia. 2008. 128p. pap. 12.95 *(978-1-77007-523-8(2))* Struik Pubs. ZAF. Dist: International Publishers Marketing.

Vermeer, Jan & Essen, Frieda van. Arctic. 2009. (ENG., Illus.). 300p. *(978-90-78964-21-6(9),* Thieme Art (Acc)) Antique Collectors' Club.

La Vida de los Animales Salvajes. (SPA.). 9.95 *(978-84-241-5407-3(X))* Torres, Eliseo & Sons.

Vines. Plant & Animal Biology. 4th ed. Date not set. (Illus.). Vol. 1. x, 1345p. pap. 11.25 *(978-0-582-35598-9(2))* Vol. 2. x, 1092p. pap. 11.25 *(978-0-582-35599-6(0))* Addison-Wesley Longman, Ltd. GBR. Dist: Trans-Atlantic Pubns., Inc.

Wagman, Bruce A., et al. Animal Law: Cases & Materials. 4th ed. 2009. 768p. 85.00 *(978-1-59460-672-4(2))* Carolina Academic Pr.

Wall, Aimee N. North Carolina Guide for Animal Control Law. 2008. pap. *(978-1-56011-577-9(7))* Schl. of Government.

Waring, Rob. Wild Animal Trackers (US) 2008. (ENG.). 24p. (C). pap. 10.95 *(978-1-4240-4424-5(3))* Cengage Heinle.

Warner, Darren E. Whitetail Dreams: Hunting Deer the Right Way in Northern Michigan. 2008. 80p. pap. 16.95 *(978-1-60474-898-7(2))* PublishAmerica, Inc.

Way, Twigs. Crocodile in the Fernery. 2008. (ENG., Illus.). 192p. 29.95 *(978-0-7509-4872-2(8))* History Pr. Ltd., The GBR. Dist: Independent Pubs. Group.

Webster, Richard. Spirit & Dream Animals: Decipher Their Messages, Discover Your Totem. 2011. (ENG.). 264p. pap. 14.95 *(978-0-7387-2770-7(9))* Llewellyn Pubns.

Weiss, Flo & Alstadt, LeAnn. What Animals Say Around the World. 2011. 40p. pap. 19.57 ***(978-1-4269-6532-6(X))*** Trafford Publishing.

Weiss, Stefanie Iris. Spirit Animals: Unlocking the Secrets of Our Animal Companions. 2009. (ENG., Illus.). 108p. pap. 14.95 *(978-0-8118-6843-3(5))* Chronicle Bks. LLC.

Wheeler, David. Wild New Jersey: Nature Adventures in the Garden State. 2011. (ENG., Illus.). 256p. pap. 19.95 *(978-0-8135-4921-7(3),* Rivergate Bks.) Rutgers Univ. Pr.

Wheeler, Joe L. Amelia, the Flying Squirrel: And Other Stories of God's Smallest Creatures. 2009. pap. 13.99 *(978-0-8163-2366-1(6))* Pacific Pr. Publishing Assn.

—Dick, the Babysitting Bear: And Other Great Wild Animal Stories. 2007. 13.99 *(978-0-8163-2221-3(X))* Pacific Pr. Publishing Assn.

Wheeler, Joe L. Tawny the Magnificent Jaguar & Other Jungle Stories. 2011. pap. ***(978-0-8163-2533-7(2))*** Pacific Pr. Publishing Assn.

Wheeler, Ward. Dynamic Homology & Phylogenetic Systematics: A Unified Approach Using POY. 2006. (Illus.). vi, 365p. *(978-0-913424-58-2(7))* American Museum of Natural History.

White, Kathy. Animal Heroes. 2008. (Connectors Ser.). (gr. 5). pap. 7.50 *(978-1-877453-46-5(3))* Pacific Learning, Inc.

Wild Animals I Have Known (Yesterday's Classics) 2007. (J). per. 11.95 *(978-1-59915-181-6(2))* Yesterday's Classics.

Wind River. The Animals' Appeal: Have Mercy! 2009. 112p. pap. 12.49 *(978-1-4490-2600-4(1))* AuthorHouse.

Wood, Ingrid. The Leprosy of Stormwind Farm. 2011. 192p. 24.95 ***(978-1-4634-2394-0(2))***; pap. 14.95 ***(978-1-4634-2392-6(6))*** AuthorHouse.

Wood, J. G. Man & Beast, Here & Hereafter, Illustrated by More Than Three Hundred Original Anecdotes by the Rev J G Wood. 2006. (Illus.). 148p. per. 16.99 *(978-1-4255-1108-1(2))* MPublishing.

ANIMALS—ABNORMALITIES

see also Dislocations; Monsters

Jay, Ricky. Celebrations of Curious Characters. 2011. (ENG., Illus.). 112p. 26.00 *(978-1-936365-03-6(0))* McSweeney's Publishing.

Lannoo, Michael J. Malformed Frogs: The Collapse of Aquatic Ecosystems. 2008. (Illus.). 288p. 65.00 *(978-0-520-25588-3(7))* Univ. of California Pr.

Russell, E. S. Form & Function: A Contribution to the History of Animal Morphology. 2007. (Illus.). 384p. per. *(978-1-4065-5047-4(7))* Dodo Pr.

Wilson, James G. & Fraser, F. Clark, eds. Handbook of Teratology: General Principles & Etiology. 488p. 65.00 *(978-0-306-36241-5(4))* Springer.

ANIMALS—ABUSE OF

see Animal Welfare

ANIMALS—BEHAVIOR

see Animal Behavior

ANIMALS—CLASSIFICATION

see also subdivision Classification under individual animals and groups of animals, e.g. Fishes—Classification

Ax, Peter. Multicellular Animals: Order in Nature - System Made by Man. Dunmur, Richard, tr. from GER. 2010. Orig. Title: Das System der Metazoa III. ein Lehrbuch der phylogenetischen Systematik. (ENG., Illus.). xii, 317p. pap. 229.00 *(978-3-642-05515-7(X),* 364205515X) Springer.

Bahls, Loren L., ed. Northwest Diatoms: A Photographic Catalogue of Species in the Montana Diatom Collection with Ecological Optima, Associates & Distribution Records for the 9 Northwestern United States, 3. 2007. (Illus.). 472p. ring bd. 150.00 *(978-0-945345-83-1(6))* Lubrecht & Cramer, Ltd.

Hickman, et al. Laboratory Studies for Animal Diversity. 6th ed. 2011. (ENG., Illus.). 320p. (C). spiral bd. 95.67 ***(978-0-07-734597-6(5)***, 0077345975, McGraw-Hill Science, Engineering & Mathematics) McGraw-Hill Higher Education.

Johnson, Jinny. Animal Tracks & Signs: Track over 400 Animals from Big Cats to Garden Birds. 2011. (ENG.). 192p. 12.99 ***(978-0-7858-2867-9(2)***, 0785828672, Chartwell) Book Sales, Inc.

Khan, Muhammad Akbar. Middle Siwalik Ruminants in Northern Pakistan. 2010. 244p. pap. *(978-3-639-27567-4(5))* VDM Verlag Dr. Mueller e.K.

Owen, Richard. On the Classification & Geographical Distribution of the Mammalia. 2009. (Cambridge Library Collection - Life Sciences Ser.). (ENG., Illus.). 112p. pap. 19.99 *(978-1-108-00198-4(X))* Cambridge Univ. Pr.

Pohl, Gregory R. Annotated List of the Lepidoptera of Alberta, Canada. 2010. (ZooKeys Ser.). 549p. pap. 192.50 *(978-954-642-534-8(6))* Pensoft Pubs. BGR. Dist: Coronet Bks.

Rix, Michael G. & Harvey, Mark S. Australian Assassins: A Review of the Assassin Spiders (Araneae, Archaeidae) of Mid-Eastern Australia. 2011. (ZooKeys Ser.). (Illus.). 100p. pap. 67.50 ***(978-954-642-601-7(6))*** Pensoft Pubs. BGR. Dist: Coronet Bks.

Schmidt, B. Christian & Lafontaine, J. Donald, eds. Annotated Check List of the Noctuoidea (Insecta, Lepidoptera) of North America North of Mexico. 2010. (ZooKeys Ser.). 239p. pap. 108.00 *(978-954-642-535-5(4))* Pensoft Pubs. BGR. Dist: Coronet Bks.

—Contributions to the Systematics of New World Macro-Moths II. 2010. (ZooKeys Ser.). 272p. pap. 117.50 *(978-954-642-536-2(2))* Pensoft Pubs. BGR. Dist: Coronet Bks.

ANIMALS—COLOR

see also Animal Pigments; Birds—Color

Archer, S., et al, eds. Adaptive Mechanisms in the Ecology of Vision. 2010. 680p. pap. 470.00 *(978-90-481-5124-0(4),* 9048151244) Springer.

Inoue-Murayama, Miho, et al, eds. From Genes to Animal Behavior: Social Structures, Personalities, Communication by Color. 2011. (Primatology Monographs). (ENG., Illus.). 290p. 189.00 *(978-4-431-53891-2(7),* 4431538917) Springer.

Parker, George Howard. Animal Colour Changes & their Neurohumours: A Survey of Investigations 1910-1943. 2012. (ENG.). 388p. pap. 39.99 ***(978-1-107-61325-6(6))*** Cambridge Univ. Pr.

Sponenberg, D. Phillip & Sponenberg. Equine Color Genetics. 3rd ed. 2009. (ENG., Illus.). 296p. 94.99 *(978-0-8138-1364-6(6),* Wiley-Blackwell) Wiley, John & Sons, Inc.

Stebbins, Robert, et al. Animal Coloration: Activities on the Evolution of Concealment. 2008. (ENG., Illus.). 174p. pap. 21.95 *(978-1-933531-29-8(0))* National Science Teachers Assn.

ANIMALS—DEFORMITIES

see Animals—Abnormalities

ANIMALS—DISEASES

see also Communicable Diseases in Animals; Veterinary Medicine; Veterinary Parasitology; Wildlife Diseases

also subdivision Diseases under individual animals and groups of animals, e.g. Cattle—Diseases; Fishes—Diseases; Livestock—Diseases; and individual animal diseases, e.g. Foot-and-Mouth Disease

Adams, Clifford A. & Adams, C. A. Nutrition-Based Health: Nutricines & Nutrients, Health Maintenance & Disease Avoidance in Animals. 2008. (Nutricine Concept Ser.). (ENG., Illus.). 170p. pap. 70.00 *(978-1-904761-58-7(5))* Nottingham Univ. Pr. GBR. Dist: Independent Pubs. Group.

Afshan, Kiran. Fasciolosis & Snail Fauna of Potohar Region, Pakistan. 2010. 140p. pap. *(978-3-639-25201-9(2))* VDM Verlag Dr. Mueller e.K.

Anderson, David E. & Rings, Michael. Food Animal Practice. 5th ed. 2008. (Current Veterinary Therapy Ser.). (ENG., Illus.). 736p. 185.00 *(978-1-4160-3591-6(5),* Saunders) Elsevier - Health Sciences Div.

Aspinall, Victoria. The Complete Textbook of Veterinary Nursing. 2nd ed. 2011. (ENG., Illus.). 748p. (C). pap. 99.95 *(978-0-7020-4050-4(9),* Butterworth-Heinemann) Elsevier - Health Sciences Div.

Ayaz, Mazhar. The Welafre, Management & Diseases of Laboratory & Zoo Animals. 2011. 200p. pap. ***(978-3-8443-9275-3(0))*** Lambert Academic Publishing.

Ayers, Susie. Small Animal Radiographic Techniques & Positioning. 2012. (ENG., Illus.). 340p. 54.99 ***(978-0-8138-1152-9(X)***, Wiley-Blackwell) Wiley, John & Sons, Inc.

Ballard, Bonnie M. & Cheek, Ryan, eds. Exotic Animal Medicine for the Veterinary Technician. 2nd ed. 2010. (ENG., Illus.). 520p. pap. 74.99 *(978-0-8138-2206-8(8),* Wiley-Blackwell) Wiley, John & Sons, Inc.

Bassert, Joanna M. & McCurnin, Dennis M. Clinical Textbook for Veterinary Technicians. 7th ed. 2009. (ENG., Illus.). 432p. (C). pap., wbk. ed. 26.95 *(978-1-4160-5702-4(1),* Saunders) Elsevier - Health Sciences Div.

—McCurnin's Clinical Textbook for Veterinary Technicians. 7th ed. 2009. (ENG., Illus.). 1456p. (C). 96.95 *(978-1-4160-5700-0(5),* Saunders) Elsevier - Health Sciences Div.

B.C., Khem Raj. Tick Fauna in Bovine, Caprine & Canine of Kathmandu Valley, Nepal. 2011. 96p. pap. ***(978-3-8454-0648-0(8))*** Lambert Academic Publishing.

Bonagura, John D. & Twedt, David C. Current Veterinary Therapy, No. XIV. 14th rev. ed. 2008. (Current Veterinary Therapy Ser.). (ENG., Illus.). 1440p. 139.00 *(978-0-7216-9497-9(7),* Saunders) Elsevier - Health Sciences Div.

Brooks, Harriet. General Pathology for Veterinary Nurses. 2010. (ENG., Illus.). 256p. pap. 54.99 *(978-1-4051-5590-8(6),* Wiley-Blackwell) Wiley, John & Sons, Inc.

Brown, F. & Roth, J. A., eds. Vaccines for OIE List A & Emerging Animal Diseases Vol. 114: International Symposium, Ames, Iowa, September 2002: Proceedings. (Developments in Biologicals Ser.: Vol. 114). (Illus.). *(978-3-8055-7577-5(7))* Karger, S. AG.

Busia, Gianluca & Mazzette, Rina. Shiga-Like Toxin-Producing E Coli in Sarda Slaughtered Sheep. 2011. 308p. pap. ***(978-3-8443-9840-3(6))*** Lambert Academic Publishing.

Campbell, Terry W. & Grant, Krystan. Clinical Cases in Avian & Exotic Animal Hematology & Cytology. 2010. (ENG., Illus.). 392p. 136.99 *(978-0-8138-1661-6(0),* Wiley-Blackwell) Wiley, John & Sons, Inc.

Collins, Michael T. Johne's Disease, an Issue of Veterinary Clinics: Food Animal Practice. 2011. (Clinics: Veterinary Medicine Ser.: 27-3). (ENG.). 110.00 ***(978-1-4557-1041-6(5)***, Saunders) Elsevier - Health Sciences Div.

Constantine, Denny G. Bat Rabies & Other Lyssavirus Infections. 2008. *(978-1-4113-2259-2(2))* United States Geological Survey.

Cram101 Textbook Reviews & Cram101 Textbook Reviews. Outlines & Highlights for Exotic Animal Care & Management by Vicki Judah, Isbn: 9781418041984. 2011. 118p. pap. 28.95 ***(978-1-61461-411-1(3))*** Cram101 Inc.

Crump, Kenneth & Thamm, Douglas H., eds. Cancer Chemotherapy for the Veterinary Health Team. 2011. (ENG., Illus.). 156p. pap. 49.99 ***(978-0-8138-2116-0(9)***, Wiley-Blackwell) Wiley, John & Sons, Inc.

Denoix, Jean-Marie & Pailloux, Jean-Pierre. Physical Therapy & Massage for the Horse: Biomechanics - Excercise - Treatment. 2nd ed. 2012. (ENG., Illus.). 224p. pap. 34.95 ***(978-1-84076-161-0(X))*** Manson Publishing, Ltd. GBR. Dist: Thieme Medical Pubs., Inc.

Divers, Stephen J. Endoscopy & Endosurgery: Veterinary Clinics of North America - Exotic Animal Practice. 2010. (Clinics: Veterinary Medicine Ser.: 13-2). (ENG.). 105.00 *(978-1-4377-1884-3(1),* Saunders) Elsevier - Health Sciences Div.

Duncanson, Graham R. Veterinary Treatment of Llamas & Alpacas. 2012. (Illus.). 224p. 145.00 ***(978-1-78064-006-8(4))*** CABI GBR. Dist: Stylus Publishing, LLC.

—Veterinary Treatment of Sheep & Goats. 2012. (Illus.). 296p. 145.00 ***(978-1-78064-003-7(X))***; pap. 85.00 ***(978-1-78064-004-4(8))*** CABI GBR. Dist: Stylus Publishing, LLC.

El Behiry, Ayman. Clinical & Laboratory Studies on Some Camel Affections. 2009. 112p. pap. *(978-3-639-15996-7(9))* VDM Verlag Dr. Mueller e.K.

Ellis, Steve. Conference of Research Workers in Animal Diseases: Proceedings of the 87th Annual Meeting, December 3, 4 & 5 2006. Ellis, Robert P., ed. 2007. (ENG.). 179p. pap. 39.99 *(978-0-8138-2033-0(2),* Wiley-Blackwell) Wiley, John & Sons, Inc.

Eshetu, Mekonnen. Bacterial Mastitis of Cattle & Antibiotic Resistance Patterns: The Case of Dairy Farms Around Harar Town, Eastern Ethiopia. 2011. 88p. pap. ***(978-3-639-34258-1(5))*** VDM Verlag Dr. Mueller e.K.

Faillace, Linda. Mad Sheep: The True Story Behind the USDA's War on a Family Farm. 2007. (ENG.). 336p. pap. 17.95 *(978-1-933392-76-9(2))* Chelsea Green Publishing.

Feil, Robert & Metzger, Daniel. Conditional Mutagenesis: an Approach to Disease Models: An Approach to Disease Models. 2010. (Handbook of Experimental Pharmacology Ser.). (Illus.). xi, 500p. pap. 529.00 *(978-3-642-07121-8(X),* 364207121X) Springer.

Fm, Prof Dr Bilqees, et al. Paramphistomum Cervi Infection & Liver Tissue Damage in Buffaloes: Trematode Infection & Liver Tissue Damage in Buffaloes. 2011. 112p. pap. ***(978-3-639-32554-6(0))*** VDM Verlag Dr. Mueller e.K.

Foale, Rob & Demetriou, Jackie. Small Animal Oncology. 2010. (Saunders Solutions in Veterinary Practice Ser.). (ENG., Illus.). 224p. pap. 79.95 *(978-0-7020-2869-4(X),* Saunders) Elsevier - Health Sciences Div.

Fowler, Murray E. & Bravo, P. Walter. Medicine & Surgery of Camelids. 3rd ed. 2010. (ENG., Illus.). 636p. 164.99 *(978-0-8138-0616-7(X),* Wiley-Blackwell) Wiley, John & Sons, Inc.

Fraser, Mary A., et al. Rabbit Medicine & Surgery for Veterinary Nurses. 2009. (ENG., Illus.). 240p. pap. 72.99 *(978-1-4051-4706-4(7),* Wiley-Blackwell) Wiley, John & Sons, Inc.

Friend, Milton. Tularemia. 2006. (Illus.). xi, 67p. *(978-1-4113-1045-2(4))* United States Geological Survey.

Graham, Jerry, et al. A Guide to Traffic Control of Rural Roads in an Agricultural Emergency: Surface Transportation Security. 2008. (Illus.). 45p. pap. *(978-0-309-11749-4(6))* Transportation Research Board.

Grist, A. Ovine Meat Inspection: Anatomy, Physiology & Disease Conditions. 2nd ed. 2011. (Illus.). 335p. pap. 70.00 *(978-1-907284-76-2(1))* Nottingham Univ. Pr. GBR. Dist: Independent Pubs. Group.

Hess, Laurie & Antinoff, Natalie. Nutrition & Behavior of Uncommon Species: Veterinary Clinics of North America - Exotic Animal Practice. 2009. (Clinics: Veterinary Medicine Ser.: 12-2). (ENG., Illus.). 240p. 99.00 *(978-1-4377-0558-4(8),* Saunders) Elsevier - Health Sciences Div.

Hoppes, Sharman M. & Gray, Patricia. Geriatrics, an Issue of Veterinary Clinics: Exotic Animal Practice. 2010. (Clinics: Veterinary Medicine Ser.: 13-1). (ENG., Illus.). x, 169p. 105.00 *(978-1-4377-1883-6(3),* Saunders) Elsevier - Health Sciences Div.

Hrapkiewicz, Karen & Medina, Leticia, eds. Clinical Laboratory Animal Medicine: An Introduction. 3rd rev. ed. 2006. (ENG., Illus.). 384p. pap. 64.99 *(978-0-8138-2966-1(6),* Wiley-Blackwell) Wiley, John & Sons, Inc.

Jepson, Lance. Exotic Animal Medicine: A Quick Reference Guide. 2009. (ENG., Illus.). 592p. pap. 95.95 *(978-0-7020-2873-1(8),* Saunders) Elsevier - Health Sciences Div.

Johnson-Delaney, Cathy A. & Meredith, Anna, eds. Exotic Pets. 5th ed. 2010. (BSAVA British Small Animal Veterinary Association Ser.). (ENG., Illus.). 424p. pap. 135.00 *(978-1-905319-16-9(9))* British Small Animal Veterinary Assn. (BSAVA) GBR. Dist: Wiley, John & Sons, Inc.

Johnson-Delaney, Cathy A. & Orosz, Susan E. The Exotic Animal Respiratory System: Veterinary Clinics of North America - Exotic Animal Practice. 2011. (Clinics: Veterinary Medicine Ser.: 14-2). (ENG., Illus.). 256p. 110.00 *(978-1-4557-0521-4(7),* Saunders) Elsevier - Health Sciences Div.

Kaufman, Julie Ann. JointYoga for Animals. 2007. 39.95 *(978-0-9672085-2-7(1))* Xenophon Pubns.

Kimberling, Cleon V. & Parsons, Gerilyn. Raising Healthy Sheep. 2nd ed. 2008. (Raising Healthy Animals Ser.). *(978-1-886532-18-2(4))* Christian Veterinary Mission.

Kyung-Tai, Min & Chang, Karen. Animal Models of Human Disease. 2011. (ENG., Illus.). 550p. 161.00 *(978-0-12-384878-9(4),* Academic Pr.) Elsevier Science & Technology Bks.

Ladds, Philip William. Pathology of Australian Native Wildlife. 2009. 648p. 172.00 *(978-0-643-09444-4(X))* CSIRO Publishing AUS. Dist: Stylus Publishing, LLC.

Lamour, Kurt, et al. Oomycete Genetics & Genomics: Diversity, Interactions & Research Tools. 2009. (ENG., Illus.). 582p. 179.95 *(978-0-470-25567-4(6),* Wiley-Blackwell) Wiley, John & Sons, Inc.

Lane, Denis Richard, et al. Dictionary of Veterinary Nursing. 3rd ed. 2007. (ENG., Illus.). 316p. vinyl bd. 56.95 *(978-0-08-045265-4(5),* Butterworth-Heinemann) Elsevier - Health Sciences Div.

Larson, Martha M. & Daniel, Gregory B. New Concepts in Diagnostic Imaging - Small Animal Practice. 2009. (Clinics: Veterinary Medicine Ser.: 39-4). (ENG.). 76.00 *(978-1-4377-1285-8(1),* Saunders) Elsevier - Health Sciences Div.

Lewington, John Henry, ed. Ferret Husbandry, Medicine & Surgery. 2nd rev. ed. 2007. (ENG., Illus.). 536p. (C). pap. 122.00 *(978-0-7020-2827-4(4),* Saunders) Elsevier - Health Sciences Div.

Lombard, Michel & Dodet, Betty. OIE Reference Laboratories & Collaborating Centres: 1st International Conference, Florianopolis, December 2006: Proceedings. 2007. (Developments in Biologicals Ser.: Vol. 128). (Illus.). 196p. pap. *(978-3-8055-8321-3(4))* Karger, S. AG.

Longley, Lesa. Small Animal Exotic Pet Medicine. 2010. (Saunders Solutions in Veterinary Practice Ser.). (ENG., Illus.). 272p. pap. 89.95 *(978-0-7020-2985-1(8),* Saunders) Elsevier - Health Sciences Div.

Lorenz, Michael D., et al. Handbook of Veterinary Neurology. 5th ed. 2010. (ENG., Illus.). 560p. (C). 99.95 *(978-1-4377-0651-2(7),* Saunders) Elsevier - Health Sciences Div.

Mani, Sarathi. Rna Interference: An antiviral therapy for White spot syndrome Virus. 2010. 244p. pap. *(978-3-8383-6551-0(8))* Lambert Academic Publishing.

Mansooryar, Morteza. Metabolic Disorders of Transition Dairy Cows. 2011. 324p. pap. ***(978-3-8454-1246-7(1))*** Lambert Academic Publishing.

Marshall, Kemba. Advances & Updates in Internal Medicine: Veterinary Clinics of North America - Exotic Animal Practice. 2010. (Clinics: Veterinary Medicine Ser.: 13-3). (ENG., Illus.). xiv, 334p. 105.00 *(978-1-4377-2503-2(1),* Saunders) Elsevier - Health Sciences Div.

Matthews, John G. Diseases of the Goat. 3rd ed. 2009. (ENG., Illus.). 448p. pap. 94.99 *(978-1-4051-6136-7(1)*, Wiley-Blackwell) Wiley, John & Sons, Inc.

Mayer, Joerg & Donnelly, Thomas M. Clinical Veterinary Advisor: Birds & Exotic Pets. 2010. 800p. 99.00 *(978-1-4160-3969-3(4)*, Saunders) Elsevier - Health Sciences Div.

McAnulty, Peter A., et al, eds. The Minipig in Biomedical Research. 2011. (ENG., Illus.). 662p. 189.95 *(978-1-4398-1118-4(0)*, CRC Press) Taylor & Francis Group GBR. Dist: Taylor & Francis Group.

McInnes, Elizabeth F. Background Lesions in Laboratory Animals: A Color Atlas. 2011. (ENG., Illus.). 256p. 235.00 ***(978-0-7020-3519-7(X)***, Saunders) Elsevier - Health Sciences Div.

Meredith, Anna & Flecknell, Paul, eds. BSAVA Manual of Rabbit Medicine & Surgery. 2nd rev. ed. 2007. (BSAVA British Small Animal Veterinary Association Ser.: 2). (ENG., Illus.). 200p. pap. 125.99 *(978-0-905214-96-2(X))* British Small Animal Veterinary Assn. (BSAVA) GBR. Dist: Wiley, John & Sons, Inc.

Meredith, Anna & Keeble, Emma. Wildlife Medicine & Rehabilitation: Self-Assessment Colour Review. 2011. (ENG., Illus.). 240p. pap. 149.00 *(978-1-84076-146-7(6))* Thieme Medical Pubs., Inc.

Mettenleiter, Thomas C. & Sobrino, Francisco, eds. Animal Viruses: Molecular Biology. 2008. (Illus.). 544p. 319.00 *(978-1-904455-22-6(0))* Caister Academic Pr. GBR. Dist: International Specialized Bk. Services.

Miller, Lila & Hurley, Kate F., eds. Infectious Disease Management in Animal Shelters. 2009. (ENG., Illus.). 400p. pap. 94.99 *(978-0-8138-1379-0(4)*, Wiley-Blackwell) Wiley, John & Sons, Inc.

Mohr, Ulrich, ed. International Classification of Rodent Tumors. the Mouse. 2012. (ENG., Illus.). xx, 476p. pap. 679.00 *(978-3-642-08422-5(2)*, 3642084222) Springer.

Moore, Alasdair Hotston & Rudd, Suzanne. Manual of Canine & Feline Advanced Veterinary Nursing. 2nd ed. 2008. (BSAVA British Small Animal Veterinary Association Ser.: 6). (ENG., Illus.). 352p. pap. 157.99 *(978-0-905214-92-4(7))* British Small Animal Veterinary Assn. (BSAVA) GBR. Dist: Wiley, John & Sons, Inc.

Neumann, Leon & Meier, Sophie, eds. Veterinary Immunology & Immunopathology. 2010. (Veterinary Sciences & Medicine Ser.). 145.00 *(978-1-60876-342-9(0))* Nova Science Pubs., Inc.

Njaa, Bradley L., ed. Kirkbride's Diagnosis of Abortion & Neonatal Loss in Animals. 4th ed. 2012. (ENG., Illus.). 256p. 124.99 ***(978-0-470-95852-0(9)***, Wiley-Blackwell) Wiley, John & Sons, Inc.

Nuotio, Lasse. Control & Eradication of Viral Diseases of Ruminants. 2008. 92p. pap. *(978-3-639-09160-1(4))* VDM Verlag Dr. Mueller e.K.

Oglesbee, Barbara L., ed. Blackwell's Five-Minute Veterinary Consult: Small Mammal. 2nd ed. 2011. (ENG.). 712p. 99.99 *(978-0-8138-2018-7(9)*, Wiley-Blackwell) Wiley, John & Sons, Inc.

Petersen, Christine A., et al. Maddie's(r) Infection Control Manual for Animal Shelters. Petersen, Christine A. et al, eds. 2008. 144p. spiral bd. 30.00 *(978-0-9745525-7-6(7))* Center for Food Security & Public Health.

Peterson, Michael E. & Kutzler, Michelle. Small Animal Pediatrics: The First 12 Months of Life. 2010. (ENG., Illus.). 544p. (C). pap. 93.95 *(978-1-4160-4889-3(8)*, Saunders) Elsevier - Health Sciences Div.

Pfeiffer, Dirk. Veterinary Epidemiology: An Introduction. 2010. (ENG., Illus.). 152p. pap. 48.99 *(978-1-4051-7694-1(6)*, Wiley-Blackwell) Wiley, John & Sons, Inc.

Pinard, Marie-Hélène. Animal Genomics for Animal Health: Paris, France, 25-27 October 2007. 2008. (Developments in Biologicals Ser.). (Illus.). 440p. pap. *(978-3-8055-8619-1(1))* Karger, S. AG.

Prymak, Caroline, et al. Small Animal Oncology: An Introduction. 2009. (ENG., Illus.). 304p. 118.00 *(978-0-7020-2800-7(2)*, Saunders) Elsevier - Health Sciences Div.

Purdey, Mark. Animal Pharm: One Man's Struggle to Discover the Truth about Mad Cow Disease & Variant CJD. Purdey, Nigel, ed. 2008. (Illus.). 276p. per. *(978-1-905570-11-9(2))* Clairview Bks.

Quesenberry, Katherine & Carpenter, James W. Ferrets, Rabbits, & Rodents: Clinical Medicine & Surgery. 3rd ed. 2011. (ENG., Illus.). 608p. pap. 79.95 ***(978-1-4160-6621-7(7)***, Saunders) Elsevier - Health Sciences Div.

Rhodes, Karen Helton & Werner, Alexander H., eds. Blackwell's Five-Minute Veterinary Consult Clinical Companion: Small Animal Dermatology. 2nd ed. 2011. (ENG., Illus.). 768p. pap. 99.99 *(978-0-8138-1596-1(7)*, Wiley-Blackwell) Wiley, John & Sons, Inc.

Root Kustritz, Margaret. Clinical Canine & Feline Reproduction: Evidence-Based Answers. 2009. (ENG., Illus.). 332p. pap. 84.99 *(978-0-8138-1584-8(3)*, Wiley-Blackwell) Wiley, John & Sons, Inc.

Rosenthal, Karen L., et al, eds. Rapid Review of Small Exotic Animal Medicine & Husbandry. 2008. (ENG., Illus.). 320p. pap. *(978-1-84076-055-2(9))* Manson Publishing Ltd.

Rovid Spickler, Anna & Roth, James A., eds. Emerging & Exotic Diseases of Animal, 3rd Edition, 3rd Printing. 3rd ed. 2008. (Illus.). 297p. spiral bd. 65.00 *(978-0-9745525-5-2(0))* Center for Food Security & Public Health.

Rushton, Jonathan A., ed. The Economics of Animal Health & Production. 2011. 376p. pap. 72.50 ***(978-1-84593-875-8(5))*** CABI GBR. Dist: Stylus Publishing, LLC.

Sargison, Neil. Sheep Flock Health: A Planned Approach. 2008. (ENG., Illus.). 480p. 115.99 *(978-1-4051-6044-5(6)*, Wiley-Blackwell) Wiley, John & Sons, Inc.

Schudel, Alejandro & Lombard, Michel. Control of Infectious Animal Diseases by Vaccination: Buenos Aires, Argentina, 13-16 April, 2005, Vol. 119. (Developments in Biologicals Ser.). (Illus.). 12;5*6p. pap. *(978-3-8055-7874-5(1))* Karger, S. AG.

Scott, Philip R. Cattle & Sheep Medicine. 2010. (ENG., Illus.). 192p. pap. 44.95 *(978-1-84076-126-9(1))* Manson Publishing, Ltd. GBR. Dist: Thieme Medical Pubs., Inc.

—Sheep Medicine. 2007. (ENG., Illus.). 336p. pap. 69.95 *(978-1-84076-149-8(0))* Manson Publishing, Ltd. GBR. Dist: Thieme Medical Pubs., Inc.

Sehgal, Lalit. Drug Induced Locomotor Alteration in Drosophila Melanogaster. 2010. 76p. pap. *(978-3-8383-7740-7(0))* Lambert Academic Publishing.

Shahzad, Waseem, et al. Small Ruminant Mycoplasmas in Pakistan & Its Immunosuppression Study. 2011. 136p. pap. ***(978-3-8443-8697-4(1))*** Lambert Academic Publishing.

Shapiro, Leland S. Pathology & Parasitology for Veterinary Technicians. 2nd ed. 2009. (Veterinary Technology Ser.). (ENG.). 320p. (C). pap. 102.95 *(978-1-4354-3855-2(8))* Delmar Cengage Learning.

Shrestha, Birodhan. Seroprevalence of Brucellosis in Different Species of Animals in Nepal. 2011. 88p. pap. ***(978-3-8443-9957-8(7))*** Lambert Academic Publishing.

Slaten, Les. Sadie: A Hunters Story - My Best Friend. 2010. 76p. pap. 10.99 *(978-1-4490-8555-1(5))* AuthorHouse.

Smith, Bradford P. Large Animal Internal Medicine. 4th ed. 2008. (ENG., Illus.). 1872p. 215.00 *(978-0-323-04297-0(X)*, Mosby) Elsevier - Health Sciences Div.

Smith, Mary C., et al. Goat Medicine. 2nd ed. 2009. (ENG., Illus.). 888p. 199.99 *(978-0-7817-9643-9(1)*, Wiley-Blackwell) Wiley, John & Sons, Inc.

Stevenson, Mark, et al. Spatial Analysis in Epidemiology. Pfeiffer, Dirk U. & Robinson, Timothy P., eds. 2008. (ENG., Illus.). 208p. (C). 135.00 *(978-0-19-850988-2(X))*; pap. 70.00 *(978-0-19-850989-9(8))* Oxford Univ. Pr., Inc.

Sugiyama, Taketoshi. Experimental Leukemia: History, Biology & Genetics. 2009. 98.00 *(978-1-60021-497-4(5))* Nova Science Pubs., Inc.

Sun, Maic-Kun. Research Progress in Alzheimer's Disease & Dementia, Volume 3. 2007. 185.00 *(978-1-60021-960-3(8))* Nova Science Pubs., Inc.

Tadele, Tolosa. Bovine Brucellosis: Introduction Literature Review Materials & Methods Results Discussion Conclusions & Recommendations References. 2011. 88p. pap. ***(978-3-639-33008-3(0))*** VDM Verlag Dr. Mueller e.K.

Tizard, Ian R. Veterinary Immunology. 9th ed. 2012. (ENG.). 568p. (C). pap. 87.95 ***(978-1-4557-0362-3(1)***, Saunders) Elsevier - Health Sciences Div.

Tizard, Ian R. Veterinary Immunology - Text & VETERINARY CONSULT Package: An Introduction. 8th ed. 2008. (ENG., Illus.). xiv, 574p. (C). pap. 127.43 *(978-1-4160-6927-0(5)*, Saunders) Elsevier - Health Sciences Div.

Trevejo, Rosalie. Veterinary Public Health: Veterinary Clinics of North America - Small Animal Practice. 2009. (Clinics: Veterinary Medicine Ser.: 39-2). (ENG., Illus.). 240p. 76.00 *(978-1-4377-0561-4(8)*, Saunders) Elsevier - Health Sciences Div.

Tynes, Valarie V., ed. Behavior of Exotic Pets. 2010. (ENG., Illus.). 248p. pap. 82.99 *(978-0-8138-0078-3(1)*, Wiley-Blackwell) Wiley, John & Sons, Inc.

Vaden, Shelly L., et al, eds. Laboratory Tests & Diagnostic Procedures: Canine & Feline. 5th ed. 2009. (ENG., Illus.). 808p. 99.99 *(978-0-8138-1748-4(X)*, Wiley-Blackwell) Wiley, John & Sons, Inc.

Vannier, Philippe & Espeseth, David. New Diagnostic Technology: Applications in Animal Health & Biologics Controls: Saint-Malo, France, October 3-5, 2005. (Developments in Biologicals Ser.: Vol. 126). (Illus.). x, 336p. *(978-3-8055-8116-5(5))* Karger, S. AG.

Williams, Rachel M., ed. Monkeys: Biology, Behavior & Disorders. 2011. (Animal Science, Issues & Professions Ser.). (Illus.). x, 211p. 129.00 *(978-1-61209-911-8(4))* Nova Science Pubs., Inc.

Williams, Ralph E. Veterinary Entomology: Livestock & Companion Animals. 2009. (ENG., Illus.). 375p. (C). 104.95 *(978-1-4200-6849-8(0)*, CRC Press) Taylor & Francis Group GBR. Dist: Taylor & Francis Group.

Winter, Agnes C. & Clarkson, M.J. A Handbook for the Sheep Clinician. 7th ed. 2012. 208p. pap. 70.00 ***(978-1-84593-974-8(3))***; (Illus.). 145.00 ***(978-1-84593-973-1(5))*** CABI GBR. Dist: Stylus Publishing, LLC.

with Amir Maurer, and Tal Saarony, Esther van Praag, Ph.D., DVM. Skin Diseases of Rabbits. 2010. 408p. pap. 85.00 *(978-0-557-53307-7(4))* Lulu Enterprises Inc.

World Animal Health in 2000. *(978-92-9044-530-2(0))* Office International des Epizooties.

Wuestenberg, Kimm. Clinical Small Animal Care: Promoting Patient Health Through Preventative Nursing. 2012. (ENG.). 284p. pap. 54.99 ***(978-0-8138-0514-6(7)***, Wiley-Blackwell) Wiley, John & Sons, Inc.

Xie, Huisheng. Xie's TCVM Clinic Chart - Heart. 2007. 15.00 *(978-0-9720045-3-4(X))* Chi Institute of Chinese Medicine.

Zeb, Muhammad Tariq, et al. Udder Health of Camels under Pastoralist Management Conditions. 2011. 88p. pap. ***(978-3-8443-1662-9(0))*** Lambert Academic Publishing.

ANIMALS—EXTINCTION

see Extinction (Biology)

ANIMALS—FOLKLORE

see also Animals—Legends; Animals, Mythical; Bestiaries; Monsters

Atkinson, Eleanor. Greyfriar's Bobby. 2007. 304p. 43.95 *(978-0-548-54078-7(0))*; (ENG.). per. 28.95 *(978-0-548-49112-6(7))* Kessinger Publishing, LLC.

—Greyfriar's Bobby. 2007. 300p. 29.95 *(978-1-4344-8373-7(8))*; per. 17.95 *(978-1-4344-8372-0(X))* Wildside Pr., LLC.

Barber, Richard. Bestiary: Being an English Verison of the Bodleian Library, Oxford, MS Bodley 764. fac. ed. 2010. (Illus.). 206p. pap. 24.95 *(978-0-85115-753-5(X))* Boydell & Brewer, Inc.

Beauquier, C. Faune et Flore Populaires de Franche-Comte, 2 vols., 1 bk. (Collection de Contes et de Chansons Populaires: Vols. 32-33). reprint ed. 43.00 *(978-0-404-60382-3(3))* AMS Pr., Inc.

Cheatham, Carolyn. Sleep with the Wolf — Walk with the Bear. 168p. pap. 12.95 *(978-0-9651232-4-2(3)*, AC503) Ammons Communications, Ltd.

Dupre, Kelly, illus. The Lion's Share: A Somali Folktale = Qayb Libaax. 2007. (SOM & ENG.). (J). *(978-1-931016-12-4(7))* Minnesota Humanities Ctr.

Eason, Cassandra. Fabulous Creatures, Mythical Monsters, & Animal Power Symbols: A Handbook, 1 vol. 2007. (Illus.). 200p. 45.00 *(978-0-275-99425-9(2)*, C9425, Greenwood Pr.) Greenwood Publishing Group, Inc.

Farrier, Monica. Mysterious Beasties of the Northwoods: Creatures from North American Folklore. 2011. (Illus.). 80p. pap. 19.95 ***(978-0-9711111-1-0(1))*** Farrier & Farrier, LLC.

Gillespie, Angus K. & Mechling, Jay, eds. American Wildlife in Symbol & Story. (Illus.). 262p. 22.50 *(978-1-57233-259-1(X))* Univ. of Tennessee Pr.

Grambo, Rebecca. Wolf: Legend, Enemy, Icon. 2008. (ENG., Illus.). 176p. pap. 24.95 *(978-1-55407-388-7(X))* Firefly Bks., Ltd.

Harris, Joel Chandler. Told by Uncle Remus: New Stories of the Old Plantation. 2007. (ENG.). 340p. 46.95 *(978-0-548-09384-9(9))* Kessinger Publishing, LLC.

—Told by Uncle Remus: New Stories of the Old Plantation. 295p. reprint ed. lib. bdg. 98.00 *(978-0-7222-0878-6(2))* Library Reprints, Inc.

—Uncle Remus: His Songs & His Sayings. 2007. (ENG.). 196p. pap. 19.99 *(978-1-4346-1752-1(1))* BiblioBazaar.

—Uncle Remus: His Songs & His Sayings. 2007. 156p. (gr. -1-3). per. *(978-1-4065-3271-5(1))* Dodo Pr.

—Uncle Remus: His Songs & His Sayings. 2010. 262p. pap. 26.75 *(978-1-145-61994-4(0))* BiblioBazaar.

—Uncle Remus: His Songs & His Sayings. 2010. 320p. pap. 30.75 *(978-1-146-39109-2(9))* BiblioBazaar.

—Uncle Remus: His Songs & His Sayings. lt. ed. 2007. (ENG.). 214p. pap. 22.99 *(978-1-4346-1921-1(4))* BiblioBazaar.

—Uncle Remus & His Friends: Old Plantation Stories, Songs & Ballads with Sketches of Negro Character. 2007. (ENG.). 376p. 48.95 *(978-0-548-17157-8(2))* Kessinger Publishing, LLC.

—Uncle Remus, His Songs & His Sayings. 2008. (ENG.). 336p. per. *(978-1-4086-5088-2(6))* Read Bks.

—Uncle Remus, His Songs & His Sayings. 2011. 292p. pap. 28.75 ***(978-1-245-54650-8(3))*** 2010. (ENG.). 312p. pap. 29.75 *(978-1-171-05158-9(1))* 2010. 322p. pap. 30.75 *(978-1-172-32007-3(1))* 2010. 316p. pap. 30.75 *(978-1-178-23146-5(1))* 2009. 314p. 36.99 *(978-1-117-58910-7(2))* 2009. (ENG.). 312p. pap. 28.75 *(978-1-117-58911-4(0))* 2009. (ENG.). 312p. pap. 23.99 *(978-1-117-58912-1(9)*, BiblioLife) BiblioBazaar.

—Uncle Remus, His Songs & His Sayings. 2010. 96p. pap. *(978-1-152-09161-0(1))* Books LLC.

—Uncle Remus, His Songs & His Sayings. 2010. (Illus.). 98p. pap. 20.00 ***(978-1-153-74327-3(2))*** General Bks. LLC.

Harris, Joel Chandler. Uncle Remus His Songs & His Sayings. 2010. 294p. 35.16 *(978-1-163-21012-3(9))*; pap. 23.16 *(978-1-162-77323-0(5))* Kessinger Publishing, LLC.

Harris, Joel Chandler, creator. Uncle Remus: His Songs & His Sayings. 2010. 266p. pap. 27.75 ***(978-1-171-93261-1(8))*** BiblioBazaar.

Harris, Joel Chandler & Frost, A. b. 1851-1928. Uncle Remus, His Songs & His Sayings. 2011. 342p. pap. 32.75 ***(978-1-245-53108-5(5))*** BiblioBazaar.

Harris, Joel Chandler & Frost, A. B. 1851-1928. illus. Uncle Remus, His Songs & His Sayings. 2010. (ENG.). 320p. pap. 30.75 *(978-1-171-56905-3(X))* BiblioBazaar.

Harris, Joel Chandler & Frost, Arthur Burdett. Uncle Remus, His Songs & His Sayings. 2009. 318p. (gr. 4-7). 36.99 *(978-1-116-85168-7(7))*; 32.99 *(978-1-116-85169-4(5))*; pap. 29.75 *(978-1-116-85171-7(7))*; pap. 30.75 *(978-1-116-85170-0(9))* BiblioBazaar.

Holbrook, Florence. The Book of Nature Myths. 2008. (ENG.). 156p. per. 20.75 *(978-1-4375-2779-7(5))*; 162p. per. 21.75 *(978-1-4375-2929-6(1))* BiblioBazaar.

—The Book of Nature Myths. 2008. (Illus.). 152p. pap. *(978-1-4099-0317-8(6))* Dodo Pr.

—The Book of Nature Myths. 2009. 224p. 39.95 *(978-1-104-55449-1(6))*; 222p. pap. 24.95 *(978-1-104-48122-3(7))* Kessinger Publishing, LLC.

—The Book of Nature Myths. 2009. (Illus.). 188p. pap. 9.95 *(978-1-59915-313-1(0))* Yesterday's Classics.

Jauss, Anne Marie. Legends of Saints & Beasts. 2011. 50p. 35.95 ***(978-1-258-02944-9(8))*** Literary Licensing, LLC.

Jones, Charles Colcock. Negro Myths from the Georgia Coast Told in the Vernacular. 171p. reprint ed. lib. bdg. 88.00 *(978-0-7222-0870-0(7))* Library Reprints, Inc.

Krutch, Joseph, ed. The World of Animals: An Anthology of Lore, Legend, & Literature. 2010. (ENG., Illus.). 541p. pap. 39.95 *(978-1-4128-1440-9(5))* Transaction Pubs.

MacCoitir, Niall. Ireland's Animals: Myths, Legends & Folklore. 2011. (ENG., Illus.). 264p. 52.95 *(978-1-84889-060-2(5))* Collins Pr., The IRL. Dist: Dufour Editions, Inc.

Marchand, Barbara, illus. Kou-Skelowh: We Are the People - A Trilogy of Okanagan Legends. 2008. (ENG.). 88p. pap. 14.95 *(978-1-894778-66-4(9))* Theytus Bks., Ltd. CAN. Dist: Univ. of Toronto Pr.

Mould, Paul, ed. The Hedgedog, The Fox & the Owl: And Other Animal Fables. 2009. 54p. pap. 16.00 *(978-1-58690-088-5(9))* Mould, Paul Publishing GBR. Dist: Gazelle Bk.Services Ltd.

Newall, Venetia. Discovering the Folklore of Birds & Beasts. 2008. (Shire Discovering Ser.). (ENG., Illus.). 72p. pap. 11.95 *(978-0-85263-126-3(X))* Shire Pubns., Ltd. GBR. Dist: Random Hse., Inc.

Pepper, Elizabeth & Stacy, Barbara. The Little Book of Magical Creatures: A Revised & Expanded Edition, 1 vol. 2009. (ENG., Illus.). 160p. pap. 12.95 *(978-0-9773703-9-9(9))* Witches Almanac Ltd., The.

Phipson, Emma. The Animal-Lore of Shakespeare's Time. 2010. 498p. pap. 38.75 *(978-1-149-10594-8(1))*; pap. 38.75 *(978-1-146-09141-1(9))* BiblioBazaar.

—The Animal-Lore of Shakespeare's Time. 2009. 346p. pap. *(978-1-150-62053-9(6))* Books LLC.

Taylor, L. B. Monsters of Virginia: Mysterious Creatures in the Old Dominion. 2012. (Monsters Ser.). (ENG.). 128p. pap. 12.95 ***(978-0-8117-0856-2(X))*** Stackpole Bks.

Trout, Paul A. Deadly Powers: Animal Predators & the Mythic Imagination. 2011. (ENG., Illus.). 300p. 26.00 ***(978-1-61614-501-9(3))*** Prometheus Bks., Pubs.

Tucker, Linda. Mystery of the White Lions: Children of the Sun God. 2010. (ENG., Illus.). 350p. pap. 19.95 *(978-1-4019-2721-9(1))* Hay Hse., Inc.

Vaudrey, Glen. The Mystery Animals of the British Isles: The Northern Isles. 2011. 212p. pap. ***(978-1-905723-74-4(1))*** CFZ Pr.

Villasenor, Victor. Frog & His Friends Save Humanity la Rana y Sus Amigos Salvan a la Humanidad. 2009. 32p. pap. 7.95 *(978-1-55885-556-4(4)*, Piñata Books) Arte Publico Pr.

ANIMALS—FOOD

Here are entered works on the nutritional substances animals find or provide for themselves as well as works on their food habits. Works on the nutritional preparations provided for animals by humans are entered under Feeds.

see also Food Chains (Ecology)

also subdivision Feeding and Feeds or subdivision Food under kinds of animals, e.g. Poultry—Feeding and Feeds; Dogs—Food

Barboza, Perry S., et al. Integrative Wildlife Nutrition. 2009. (ENG., Illus.). xviii, 342p. pap. 89.95 *(978-3-642-03695-8(3)*, 3642036953) Springer.

Brussow, Harald. The Quest for Food: A Natural History of Eating. 2007. (Illus.). 866p. 148.00 *(978-0-387-30334-5(0)*, 0387303340) Springer.

Geor, Raymond J. Equine Practice. 2009. (Clinics: Veterinary Medicine Ser.: 25-1). (ENG.). 240p. 99.00 *(978-1-4377-0556-0(1)*, Saunders) Elsevier - Health Sciences Div.

Gibbs, Dee. Recipes for Your Four-Legged & Feathered Friends! 2007. 244p. per. 24.95 *(978-1-4241-8066-0(X))* PublishAmerica, Inc.

Godwyll, Paschal, et al. Feed Supplements on Utilisation of Maize Leaf Strippings by Sheep. 2010. 144p. pap. *(978-3-639-25257-6(8))* VDM Verlag Dr. Mueller e.K.

Gonzalez, L. M. R. Gifts Lucy. Doggie Treats-Woof! 2008. 52p. pap. 19.95 *(978-0-557-00737-0(2))* Lulu Enterprises Inc.

Goodijk, Dorieke. Feed Strategies for Sheep & Goats. 2011. 124p. pap. ***(978-3-8443-0223-3(9))*** Lambert Academic Publishing.

Hellweg, Michael R. Raising Live Foods: A Comprehensive Guide to Culturing Live Foods for Reptiles & Amphibians, 1 vol. 2009. (ENG.). 160p. pap. *(978-0-7938-2860-9(0))* TFH Pubns., Inc.

Hope, A. G. & Parmenter, R. R. Food Habits of Rodents Inhabiting Arid & Semi-arid Ecosystems of Centeral New Mexico. 2007. pap. 20.00 *(978-0-9794517-3-7(6))* Museum of Southwest Biology Pubn. Series.

Manly, B. F., et al. Resource Selection by Animals: Statistical Design & Analysis for Field Studies. 2nd ed. 2010. (Illus.). 240p. pap. 119.00 *(978-90-481-6044-0(8)*, 9048160448) Springer.

Palika, Liz. The Ultimate Pet Food Guide: Everything You Need to Know about Feeding Your Dog or Cat. 2003. (ENG., Illus.). 256p. pap. 15.95 *(978-1-60094-071-2(4))* Da Capo Pr., Inc.

Patton, R. The Paradox of Animal Nutrition: Perfected by Lack, Beset by Excess. 2011. (ENG., Illus.). 278p. pap. 24.00 *(978-1-904761-72-3(0))* Nottingham Univ. Pr. GBR. Dist: Independent Pubs. Group.

Puripunpinyoo, Anucha. High-Plains States. 2008. 168p. pap. *(978-3-639-05394-4(X))* VDM Verlag Dr. Mueller e.K.

Small, Ernest. Alfalfa & Relatives: Evolution & Classification of Medicago. 2011. (Illus.). 760p. pap. 210.00 *(978-1-84593-750-8(3))* CABI GBR. Dist: Stylus Publishing, LLC.

Smith, Gary & Kelly, Alan M., eds. Food Security in a Global Economy: Veterinary Medicine & Public Health. 2008. 208p. (C). pap. 24.95 *(978-0-8122-2044-5(7))* Univ. of Pennsylvania Pr.

Stephens, David W. & Ydenberg, Ronald C., eds. Foraging: Behavior & Ecology. 2007. (Illus.). 576p. 107.50 *(978-0-226-77263-9(2))*; per. 47.50 *(978-0-226-77264-6(0))* Univ. of Chicago Pr.

Tayo, Tilling, et al. Feeding of Canola Meal on Lactating Cows. 2011. 72p. pap. ***(978-3-8443-9065-0(0))*** Lambert Academic Publishing.

ANIMALS—GEOGRAPHICAL DISTRIBUTION

see Zoogeography

ANIMALS—HABITAT

see Habitat (Ecology)

ANIMALS—HABITATIONS

Bahamón, Alejandro & Pérez, Patricia. Animals. 2009. (Building/Biology Connection Ser.). (ENG., Illus.). 192p. pap. 35.00 *(978-0-393-73271-9(1),* 73271) Norton, W. W. & Co., Inc.

Carpenter, James W. Exotic Animal Formulary. 4th ed. 2012. (ENG., Illus.). 744p. 59.95 ***(978-1-4377-2264-2(4),*** Saunders) Elsevier - Health Sciences Div.

Flannery, Tim. Chasing Kangaroos: A Continent, a Scientist, & a Search for the World's Most Extraordinary Creature. 2008. (ENG.). 272p. pap. 14.00 *(978-0-8021-4371-6(7),* Grove Pr.) Grove/Atlantic, Inc.

Gould, Carol Grant & Gould, James L. Animal Architects: Building & the Evolution of Intelligence. 2007. (ENG., Illus.). 336p. (gr. 9). 26.95 *(978-0-465-02782-8(2))* Basic Bks.

Gould, James L. & Gould, Carol Grant. Animal Architects: Building & the Evolution of Intelligence. 2012. (ENG.). 336p. (gr. 9). pap. 16.99 ***(978-0-465-02838-2(1))*** Basic Bks.

Hansell, Mike. Built by Animals: The Natural History of Animal Architecture. (Illus.). 256p. 2009. (ENG.). (YA). pap. 18.95 *(978-0-19-920557-8(4))* 2008. 29.95 *(978-0-19-920556-1(6))* Oxford Univ. Pr., Inc.

Haviland, Maud D. Forest, Steppe & Tundra: Studies in the Animal Environment. reprint ed. 24.00 *(978-0-404-15933-7(8))* AMS Pr., Inc.

Heinrich, Bernd. Winter World: The Ingenuity of Animal Survival. 2009. (P. S. Ser.). (ENG.). 384p. pap. 14.99 *(978-0-06-112907-0(0),* HarperPerennial) HarperCollins Pubs.

Price, Mark R. Stanley. Animal Reintroductions: The Arabian Oryx in Oman. 2010. (Cambridge Studies in Applied Ecology & Resource Management Ser.). (ENG.). 316p. pap. 33.99 *(978-0-521-13167-4(7))* Cambridge Univ. Pr.

Puttker, Thomas. Effects of Habitat Fragmentation on Small Mammals of the Atlantic Forest, Brazil. 2008. 124p. pap. *(978-3-639-01820-2(6))* VDM Verlag Dr. Mueller e.K.

Wood, J. G. Homes Without Hands Being a Description of the Habitations of Animals, Classed According to Their Principle of Construction by the Rev J G Wood. 2006. 696p. per. 36.99 *(978-1-4255-6852-8(1))* MPublishing.

—Strange Dwellings; Being a Description of the Habitations of Animals [Abridged from 'Homes Without Hands'] by the Rev J G Wood with Designs By. 2006. 424p. per. 26.99 *(978-1-4255-4595-6(5))* MPublishing.

—Wonderful Nests from Homes Without Hands. 2007. 254p. 42.95 *(978-0-548-07384-1(8))* Kessinger Publishing, LLC.

ANIMALS—INFANCY

Bleiman, Andrew & Eastland, Chris. ZooBorns. 2010. (ENG., Illus.). 160p. 11.99 *(978-1-4391-9531-4(5))* Simon & Schuster.

Finn, Roderick Nigel & Kapoor, B.G. Fish Larval Physiology. 2008. (ENG., Illus.). 742p. 139.95 *(978-1-57808-388-6(5))* BIOS Scientific Publishers Ltd. GBR. Dist: Taylor & Francis Group.

Henriksen, Sr. Tom's Journey: The Cat That God Sent to Look after Me. 2009. 98p. pap. 26.50 *(978-1-60860-221-6(4),* Eloquent Bks.) AEG Literary Publishing Services, Inc.

Marlier, Elaine. Think Adoption First! the Feline Series: Heartfelt tales of why you should think adoption First! 2006. (Illus.). 116p. 19.95 *(978-1-59879-180-8(X));* per. 16.95 *(978-1-59879-179-2(6))* Lifevest Publishing, Inc.

McKenna, Rachael Hale. Best Friends Forever. 2011. (ENG., Illus.). 176p. 14.95 *(978-1-4521-0102-6(7))* Chronicle Bks. LLC.

McNally, Georgia M. Baby Animals. 2007. (ENG.). 280p. 42.95 *(978-0-548-05814-5(8))* Kessinger Publishing, LLC.

Palika, Liz, et al. Puppy Love. 2009. (ENG., Illus.). 312p. 24.99 *(978-0-470-39317-8(3),* Howell Bk. Hse.) Wiley, John & Sons, Inc.

Richardson, Nan. Wild Babies. Umbrage Editions, ed. 2010. (ENG., Illus.). 80p. (gr. k-2). 15.00 *(978-1-884167-97-3(7))* Umbrage Editions.

Shattil, Wendy & Rozinski, Bob, photos by. Born Wild in Colorado. 2007. (Illus.). 80p. (J). (gr. -1-3). pap. 12.95 *(978-1-56037-412-1(8))* Farcountry Pr.

Spaulding, C. E. & Clay, Jackie. The Complete Care of Baby Animals: Expert Advice on Raising Orphaned, Adopted, or Newly Bought Kittens, Puppies, Foals, Lambs, Chicks, & More. 2nd ed. 2011. (ENG., Illus.). 304p. pap. 14.95 *(978-1-61608-288-8(7),* 608288) Skyhorse Publishing Co., Inc.

Tallack, Peter, et al. In the Womb: Animals. 2009. (ENG., Illus.). 160p. 26.00 *(978-1-4262-0175-2(3),* National Geographic) National Geographic Society.

ANIMALS—INFANCY—JUVENILE LITERATURE

Dorling Kindersley Publishing Staff. Roar! Roar! 2010. (ENG.). 12p. (J). (gr. -1-k). 12.99 *(978-0-7566-5866-3(7))* Dorling Kindersley Publishing, Inc.

Northcott, Richard. Baby Animals. Wright, Craig, ed. 2010. (ENG.). 20p. 4.81 *(978-0-19-440081-7(6))* Oxford Univ. Pr., Inc.

Rizzi, Kathleen. Are You My Baby? (Arabic/English) 2012. (ARA & ENG., Illus.). 24p. (J). bds. 5.95 ***(978-1-59572-360-4(9))*** Star Bright Bks., Inc.

Schmidt, Dennis & Schmidt, Esther. Baby Wild Animals, 1 vol. 2009. (ENG., Illus.). 48p. (J). pap. *(978-1-894974-66-0(2))* Heritage Hse.

ANIMALS—JUVENILE LITERATURE

see also Animal Behavior—Juvenile Literature

Algor, Marie. Save Earth's Animals!, 7 vols., Set. Incl. Endangered Animals of Africa. lib. bdg. 21.25 *(978-1-4488-2528-8(8));* Endangered Animals of Antarctica & the Arctic. lib. bdg. 21.25 *(978-1-4488-2534-9(2));* Endangered Animals of Asia. lib. bdg. 21.25 *(978-1-4488-2529-5(6));* Endangered Animals of Australia. lib. bdg. 21.25 *(978-1-4488-2530-1(X));* Endangered Animals of Europe. 21.25 *(978-1-4488-2531-8(8));* Endangered Animals of North America. 21.25 *(978-1-4488-2532-5(6));* Endangered Animals of South America. lib. bdg. 21.25 *(978-1-4488-2533-2(4));* (J). (gr. 3-4). (Save Earth's Animals! Ser.). (Illus.). 24p. 2011. Set lib. bdg. 148.75 *(978-1-4488-2778-7(7),* PowerKids Pr.) Rosen Publishing Group, Inc., The.

Animals on the Edge. 2011. (Animals on the Edge Ser.). (ENG.). 32p. (gr. 3-4). lib. bdg. 53.30 *(978-1-4296-5403-6(1),* Fact Finders) Capstone Pr., Inc.

Baby Animals. (Disney Jigsaw Book Ser.). 6p. bds. *(978-1-4054-8483-1(7))* Parragon, Inc.

Bicknell, Joanna & Phillips, Sarah. Phonics. 2011. (Illus.). 12p. (J). 7.99 *(978-1-84610-091-8(7))* Make Believe Ideas GBR. Dist: Nelson, Thomas Inc.

Bloom, Steve. Big Cats: In Search of Lions, Leopards, Cheetahs, & Tigers. 2012. (ENG., Illus.). 48p. (J). (gr. k-4). 15.95 ***(978-0-500-65004-2(7),*** 565004) Thames & Hudson.

Canetti, Yanitzia. Amazing Adaptations! 2010. (J). *(978-1-59835-215-3(6))* Cambridge BrickHouse, Inc.

Coster, Patience. The Debate about Animal Testing. 2010. (Ethical Debates Ser.). (ENG.). 48p. (YA). lib. bdg. 26.50 *(978-1-4358-9648-2(3),* Rosen Central) Rosen Publishing Group, Inc., The.

Harasymiw, Therese. Hedgehogs in the Dark. 2012. (Creatures of the Night Ser.). 24p. (J). (gr. 1-3). lib. bdg. 22.60 ***(978-1-4339-6372-8(8))*** Stevens, Gareth Publishing LLLP.

Hudak, Heather C. Omnivores. 2011. (Food Chains Ser.). (Illus.). 24p. (J). (gr. 2-5). 27.13 *(978-1-61690-709-9(6))* Weigl Pubs., Inc.

Jenkins, Steve. Living Color. 2012. (ENG.). 32p. (J). (gr. 1-4). pap. 7.99 *(978-0-547-57682-4(X),* Sandpiper) Houghton Mifflin Harcourt Trade & Reference Pubs.

—Living Color. 2012. lib. bdg. 18.40 ***(978-0-606-23393-4(8),*** Turtleback) Turtleback Bks.

Jungle Animals. (My First Book About... Ser.). 32p. *(978-1-4054-4557-3(2))* Parragon, Inc.

Kavanagh, James. Rocky Mountain Wildlife Nature Activity Book. 2011. (Children's Nature Activity Bks.). (ENG.). 32p. (J). (gr. 4-7). pap. 6.95 *(978-1-58355-583-5(8))* Waterford Pr., Inc.

Kudlinski, Kathleen. Horse Indian Wolf: The Hidden Pictures of Judy Larson. 2010. (ENG., Illus.). 48p. (J). 16.95 *(978-0-86713-150-5(0),* 0867131500) Greenwich Workshop Pr.

McCauley, Jane R. Animals That Live in Trees. National Geographic Society.

Page, Robin. Sisters & Brothers: Sibling Relationships in the Animal World. 2012. (ENG., Illus.). 32p. (J). (gr. k-3). pap. 6.99 ***(978-0-547-72738-7(0),*** Sandpiper) Houghton Mifflin Harcourt Trade & Reference Pubs.

Richardson, Alex. Phoenix. 2010. pap. 15.00 *(978-0-578-04965-6(1))* Miller Beach Publishing.

Rodrigue, George. Are You Blue Dog's Friend? 2009. (ENG., Illus.). 40p. (J). (gr. -1-3). 18.95 *(978-0-8109-4069-7(8),* Abrams Bks. for Young Readers) Abrams.

Salzmann, Mary Elizabeth. Home Sweet Burrow. 2011. (Animal Homes Ser.). (ENG., Illus.). 24p. (J). (gr. k-3). 21.35 *(978-1-61714-815-6(6))* ABDO Publishing Co.

—Home Sweet Cave. 2011. (Animal Homes Ser.). (ENG., Illus.). 24p. (J). (gr. k-3). 21.35 *(978-1-61714-816-3(4))* ABDO Publishing Co.

—Home Sweet Den. 2011. (Animal Homes Ser.). (ENG., Illus.). 24p. (J). (gr. k-3). 21.35 *(978-1-61714-817-0(2))* ABDO Publishing Co.

—Home Sweet Nest. 2011. (Animal Homes Ser.). (ENG., Illus.). 24p. (J). (gr. k-3). 21.35 *(978-1-61714-818-7(0))* ABDO Publishing Co.

—Home Sweet Tree. 2011. (Animal Homes Ser.). (ENG., Illus.). 24p. (J). (gr. k-3). 21.35 *(978-1-61714-819-4(9))* ABDO Publishing Co.

—Home Sweet Web. 2011. (Animal Homes Ser.). (ENG., Illus.). 24p. (J). (gr. k-3). 21.35 *(978-1-61714-820-0(2))* ABDO Publishing Co.

ANIMALS—LEGENDS

see also Animals—Folklore

Barnum, P. T. Animal Stories. reprint ed. lib. bdg. 22.95 *(978-0-89190-447-2(6),* Rivercity Pr.) Amereon LTD.

Bromfield, Louis. Animals & Other People. Date not set. lib. bdg. 23.95 *(978-0-8488-1758-9(3))* Amereon LTD.

—Animals & Other People. 2008. (ENG., Illus.). 256p. pap. 14.00 *(978-1-59098-106-1(5))* Wooster Bk. Co., The.

Brooks, Walter R. Wiggins for President. Date not set. lib. bdg. 22.95 *(978-0-8488-1707-7(9))* Amereon LTD.

Cheatham, Carolyn. Sleep with the Wolf — Walk with the Bear. 168p. pap. 12.95 *(978-0-9651232-4-2(3),* AC503) Ammons Communications, Ltd.

Jones, Michael P. Songs of the Animals & Other Tales: A Selection of Little-Told Myths & Legends from the Pacific Northwest & Northern Regions. (Illus.). 100p. 18.95 *(978-0-89904-302-9(X));* pap. 10.95 *(978-0-89904-303-6(8))* Crumb Elbow Publishing.

Lee, Henry. Sea Monsters Unmasked. 2007. per. 11.95 *(978-1-930585-37-9(3))* Coachwhip Pubns.

Lee, R. Anecdotes of the Habits & Instinct of Animals. 2008. 280p. 28.99 *(978-0-554-27999-2(1))* 2008. 280p. 25.99 *(978-0-554-37302-7(5))* 2007. (ENG.). 252p. per. 21.99 *(978-1-4346-4483-1(9))* 2007. (ENG.). 276p. per. 23.99 *(978-1-4346-4484-8(7))* BiblioBazaar.

—Anecdotes of the Habits & Instinct of Animals. 2007. 264p. per. *(978-1-4065-5157-0(0))* Dodo Pr.

Seton, Ernest Thompson. Wild Animal Ways. 2008. (ENG.). 272p. per. *(978-1-4086-4097-5(X))* Read Bks.

ANIMALS—NAMES

see Animals—Nomenclature

ANIMALS—NOMENCLATURE

see also subdivision Nomenclature under individual animals and groups of animals, e.g. Fishes—Nomenclature

Andrews, Ted. Animal-Speak Runes. 2009. 128p. pap. 24.95 *(978-1-888767-58-2(8))* Dragonhawk Publishing.

ANIMALS—NOMENCLATURE (POPULAR)

Moffett, Rodney. Sesotho Plant & Animal Names & Plants Used by the Basotho. 2010. (AFR & ENG.). xi, 306p. *(978-1-920383-08-4(5))* Sun Media.

ANIMALS—PICTORIAL WORKS

Here are entered popular works containing chiefly pictures and photographs of animals. Scientific works consisting exclusively or predominantly of pictures without a significant amount of text are entered under Zoology—Pictorial Works.

Amelchenko, Paul. The Da Vinci Dog: The Passion, Paintings & Slobber of Brinks the Dog. 2007. (ENG., Illus.). 96p. 14.95 *(978-1-59543-631-3(6))* Willow Creek Pr., Inc.

Angel, Heather. Heather Angel's Wild Kew. 2010. (Illus.). 128p. pap. 18.00 *(978-1-84246-402-1(7))* Kew Publishing GBR. Dist: Chicago Distribution Ctr.

Ayers, Chris. The Daily Zoo: Keeping the Doctor at Bay with a Drawing a Day. 2008. (ENG., Illus.). 159p. 29.95 *(978-1-933492-32-2(5))* Design Studio Pr.

Barnes, Richard, et al. Animal Logic. 2009. (ENG., Illus.). 160p. 65.00 *(978-1-56898-861-0(3))* Princeton Architectural Pr.

Bernasconi, Alex. Wild Africa. 2010. (ENG., Illus.). 270p. 49.95 *(978-1-55407-772-4(9))* Firefly Bks., Ltd.

Blocksma, Mary. Whats in the Woods. 2008. pap. 12.50 *(978-0-9708575-7-6(8))* Beaver Island Arts.

Bloom, Steve. Spirit of the Wild. 2007. (ENG., Illus.). 128p. 34.95 *(978-0-500-51320-0(1))* Thames & Hudson.

Bochet, Laurent, photos by. 1000 Degrees C Deyrolle. 2010. (Illus.). *(978-2-7594-0558-9(3))* Assouline.

Bowker, John. An an Alphabet of Animals. 2010. (Illus.). 142p. pap. 29.99 *(978-0-9782526-7-0(5))* Key Publishing Hse., Inc., The CAN. Dist: AtlasBooks Distribution.

Branzuela, Lorna J. A Day Without Shadows: Pictures, Poems & True Encounters with Wild Critters of Alaska. 2006. per. 21.95 *(978-0-9777216-0-3(4))* Barnhart Productions.

Breakey, Kate, photos by. Las Sombras/the Shadows. 2012. (ENG., Illus.). 168p. 75.00 ***(978-0-292-74420-2(X))*** Univ. of Texas Pr.

Brown, Milly. Animals in Love. 2012. (ENG., Illus.). 96p. 9.95 ***(978-1-84024-714-5(2))*** Summerdale Pubs. GBR. Dist: Independent Pubs. Group.

Brunelli, Giacomo, photos by. The Animals. 2009. (ENG., Illus.). 72p. 45.00 *(978-1-904587-71-2(2))* Lewis, Dewi Publishing GBR. Dist: Consortium Bk. Sales & Distribution.

Cairns, Peter & Hamblin, Mark. Tooth & Claw: Living Alongside Britain's Predators. 2007. (Illus.). 240p. *(978-1-904445-46-3(2))* Whittles Publishing.

Christo, Cyril & Wilkinson, Marie. Walking Thunder: In the Footsteps of the African Elephant. 2009. (Illus.). 160p. *(978-1-85894-505-7(4))* Merrell Pubs. Ltd.

Colbert, Gregory, photos by. Ashes & Snow Feather to Fire. 2008. (Ashes & Snow Bks.). (ENG & JPN., Illus.). 60p. pap. 30.00 *(978-1-933632-34-6(8))* Flying Elephants Pr.

Cox, Rosamund Kidman. Wildlife Photographer of the Year. 2010. (ENG., Illus.). 160p. 45.00 *(978-1-84607-760-9(5))* BBC Worldwide GBR. Dist: Independent Pubs. Group.

Cox, Rosamund Kidman, ed. Portfolio, Vol. 18. 2009. (Wildlife Photographer of the Year Ser.). (ENG., Illus.). 160p. 45.00 *(978-1-84607-581-0(5))* BBC Worldwide GBR. Dist: Independent Pubs. Group.

De Fabianis, Valeria Manferto, ed. WildLife. 2010. (MiniCube Ser.). (ENG., Illus.). 768p. 6.95 *(978-88-544-0418-2(7))* White Star ITA. Dist: Sterling Publishing Co., Inc.

De Vosjoli, Philippe. Crested Geckos: From the Experts at Advanced Vivarium Systems. 2007. (ENG., Illus.). 92p. pap. 8.95 *(978-1-882770-80-9(3))* BowTie Pr.

Dearing, Charles. Wildlife Portraits in Wood: 30 Patterns to Capture the Beauty of Nature. 2008. (Scroll Saw, Woodworking & Crafts Book Ser.). (ENG., Illus.). 67p. pap. 14.95 *(978-1-56523-338-6(7))* Fox Chapel Publishing Co., Inc.

Dorling Kindersley Publishing Staff. Animal. 2011. (ENG., Illus.). 672p. 50.00 *(978-0-7566-8677-2(6))* Dorling Kindersley Publishing, Inc.

Dorling Kindersley Publishing Staff & Scubazoo Staff. Reef. 2009. (ENG.). 360p. (gr. 12). pap. 24.95 *(978-0-7566-5575-4(7))* Dorling Kindersley Publishing, Inc.

Dover Publications Inc. Staff. Dover Digital Design Source #5: Grandville's Animals. Appelbaum, Stanley, tr. 2010. (Dover Electronic Clip Art Ser.). (ENG., Illus.). 128p. pap. 19.95 *(978-0-486-99069-9(9))* Dover Pubns., Inc.

Dresser, Eric. Wildlife Images of the Adirondacks. 2010. (Illus.). 144p. 24.95 *(978-1-59531-026-2(6))* North Country Bks., Inc.

Eckstrom, Christine, ed. Eye to Eye: Frans Lanting. 25th ed. 2009. (ENG., Illus.). 253p. 19.99 *(978-3-8365-0894-0(X))* TASCHEN DEU. Dist: Ingram Pub. Services.

Ehrich, Joanne. Klassic Koalas: Mr. Douglas' Koalas & the Stars of Qantas. gif. ed. 2007. 80p. pap. 31.99 *(978-0-9764698-4-1(7))* Koala Jo Publishing.

—Koalas: Zen in Fur. 2007. pap. 37.99 *(978-0-9764698-5-8(5))* Koala Jo Publishing.

—Koalas: Zen in Fur, BW Educational Edition. 2007. (Illus.). 96p. (C). pap., tchr. ed. 24.99 *(978-0-9764698-7-2(1))* Koala Jo Publishing.

Endo, Hideki & Frey, Roland. Anatomical Imaging: Towards a New Morphology. (Illus.). 105p. 239.00 *(978-4-431-76932-3(3))* Springer.

Erikson, Nelson. A Pictorial Souvenir of Yellowstone: With German, Spanish, Mandarin & Japanese Translations, 1 vol. 2007. (ENG., Illus.). 112p. pap. 14.95 *(978-1-4236-0151-7(3))* Gibbs Smith, Publisher.

Eskildsen, Ute, ed. The Photographed Animal: Useful, Cute & Collected, 1 vol. 2008. (ENG., Illus.). 336p. 50.00 *(978-3-86521-209-2(3))* Steidl, Gerhard Druckerei und Verlag DEU. Dist: Innovative Logistics.

Franco, Barbara, et al. Vanishing Animals. 2008. (ENG., Illus.). 304p. 29.95 *(978-88-544-0397-0(0))* White Star ITA. Dist: Random Hse., Inc.

Freeman, Barry J. Never Pull a Lion's Tail: A Collection of Poetry & Photographs about Animals of Africa. 2006. (ENG., Illus.). 180p. (J). (gr. 4-7). 25.00 *(978-1-904722-24-3(5))* Camerapix GBR. Dist: Interlink Publishing Group, Inc.

Frees, Harry Whittier, photos by. Cats, Dogs & Other Rabbits: The Extraordinary World of Harry Whittier Frees. 2006. (ENG., Illus.). 80p. 20.00 *(978-1-904587-24-8(0))* Lewis, Dewi Publishing GBR. Dist: Consortium Bk. Sales & Distribution.

Gallerani, Paola. The Menagerie of Pieter Boel: Animal Painter in the Age of Louis XIV. 2011. (ENG., Illus.). 88p. 29.95 ***(978-88-89854-74-7(X))*** Officina Libraria srl ITA. Dist: Antique Collectors' Club.

Gilpin, Daniel. The Illustrated Guide to Freshwater Fish & River Creatures: A visual guide to aquatic life featuring more than 450 fabulous species accompanied by 500 colour illustrations, photographs & distribution Maps. 2011. (ENG., Illus.). 160p. pap. 19.99 *(978-1-84476-791-5(4))* Anness Publishing GBR. Dist: National Bk. Network.

Gopal, Rajesh. Land of the Striped Stalker: Wildlife of Madhya Pradesh. 2010. (ENG., Illus.). 96p. 34.95 *(978-81-8328-153-9(2))* Wisdom Tree IND. Dist: SCB Distributors.

Greenberg, Jill. Monkey Portraits. rev. ed. 2007. (ENG., Illus.). 128p. pap. 17.99 *(978-0-316-00512-8(6))* Little Brown & Co.

Greive, Bradley Trevor. Dear Mom: Thank You for Everything. 2011. (ENG.). 80p. 9.99 *(978-1-4494-0113-9(9))* Andrews McMeel Publishing.

—Friends to the End: The True Value of Friendship. 2011. (ENG.). 120p. 9.99 *(978-1-4494-0317-1(4))* Andrews McMeel Publishing.

—Querido Papá: Padre, Amigo y Heroe. 2008. (ENG., Illus.). 96p. 9.99 *(978-0-7407-7246-7(5))* Andrews McMeel Publishing.

Grobler, Sabrina, photos by. The Canadian Rockies: A Complete Photographic Portrait, 1 vol. 2009. (KOR.). 64p. pap. *(978-1-55153-250-9(6))* Rocky Mountain Bks.

Hagey, Thomas. Cowsmopolitan. (Illus.). reprint ed. pap. 9.95 *(978-0-9628198-3-4(2))* Kent, William Inc.

—Playboar. (Illus.). reprint ed. pap. 9.95 *(978-0-9628198-2-7(4))* Kent, William Inc.

Hanaor, Cigalle & Hérem, Thibaud. Know Your Rodent. 2010. (ENG., Illus.). 48p. 13.99 *(978-0-9562053-1-5(3))* Cicada Bks. GBR. Dist: D.A.P./Distributed Art Pubs.

Hankey, Wilbur & Hankey, Megan. A B C Animal Book. 2009. 32p. pap. 14.00 *(978-1-4389-9978-4(X))* AuthorHouse.

Hess, John. The Galápagos: Exploring Darwin's Tapestry. 2009. (ENG., Illus.). 208p. (gr. 9). 49.95 *(978-0-8262-1837-7(7))* Univ. of Missouri Pr.

Hirschi, Ron & Mangelsen, Thomas D. Our Three Bears. 2008. (ENG., Illus.). 32p. (J). (gr. 4-7). 16.95 *(978-1-59078-015-2(9))* Boyds Mills Pr.

Horenstein, Henry, photos by. Animalia. 2008. (ENG., Illus.). 80p. 40.00 *(978-0-9761955-2-8(6))* Pond Pr.

Ildos, Angela Serena. Baby Animals: Supercube. 2006. (Supercubes Ser.). (ENG., Illus.). 736p. 39.95 *(978-88-544-0174-7(9),* White Star) Rizzoli International Pubns., Inc.

Ildos, Angela Serena, text. Baby Animals. 2010. (MiniCube Ser.). (ENG., Illus.). 768p. 6.95 *(978-88-544-0199-0(4))* White Star ITA. Dist: Sterling Publishing Co., Inc.

Joubert, Dereck & Joubert, Beverly. Relentless Enemies: Lions & Buffalo. 2006. (ENG., Illus.). 176p. 40.00 *(978-1-4262-0004-5(8),* National Geographic) National Geographic Society.

Kagii, Yasuaki. Deep Blue: Diving to Inner Space. 2010. (ENG., Illus.). 256p. 39.95 *(978-1-84796-002-3(2),* Goodman Pubs.) Carlton Bks., Ltd. GBR. Dist: Sterling Publishing Co., Inc.

Koch, Heidi Jurgen & Koch, Hans Jurgen, photos by. Animal Life. 2008. 240p. 49.95 *(978-0-8416-0347-9(2))* American Map Corp.

Kostyal, Karen M. Great Migrations: Epic Animal Journeys. 2010. (Illus.). 304p. 35.00 *(978-1-4262-0644-3(5),* National Geographic) National Geographic Society.

Krueger, Kurt L. A Wildlife Collection: Celebrating Wisconsin's Conservation Ethic. 2011. 144p. 39.95 ***(978-0-615-50539-8(2))*** Krueger Northwoods Photography.

Laidler, Keith. Animals: A Visual Guide to the Animal Kingdom. 2011. (ENG., Illus.). 208p. 39.95 *(978-1-84916-004-9(X))* Quercus GBR. Dist: Independent Pubs. Group.

Laita, Mark. Sea. 2011. (ENG., Illus.). 200p. 50.00 *(978-1-4197-0087-3(1))* Abrams.

Lark Books, ed. Wildlife Photographer of the Year, Portfolio 21. 2011. (ENG., Illus.). 160p. 29.95 ***(978-1-4547-0405-8(5),*** Pixiq) Sterling Publishing Co., Inc.

Ledner, Catherine & Fried, Katrina. Animal House. 2007. (ENG., Illus.). 96p. 24.95 *(978-1-59962-039-8(1),* Welcome Bks.) Welcome Enterprises, Inc.

Loon, Rael. Hidden Wonders: The Small 5005 of Southern Africa Insects, Spiders, Frogs & Reptiles. 2008. (ENG.). 272p. pap. 38.95 *(978-1-77009-309-6(5))* Jacana Media ZAF. Dist: Independent Pubs. Group.

Lynch, Wayne. Planet Arctic: Life at the Top of the World. 2010. (ENG., Illus.). 240p. 40.00 *(978-1-55407-632-1(3))* Firefly Bks., Ltd.

Macarro, Liberto, et al. Between Sky & Earth. 2008. (ENG., Illus.). 128p. 35.00 *(978-88-7439-267-4(2))* 5 Continents ITA. Dist: Hachette Bk. Group.
Magliaro, Joseph & Hung, Shiu Shiang. Dead Animals. 2007. (Illus.). 64p. 26.00 *(978-0-9791774-0-6(5))* Historical Fiction Pr.
Manferto de Fabianis, Valeria. Fur & Feathers: An Unusual Farm. 2010. (Illus.). 240p. 35.00 *(978-88-544-0478-6(0))* White Star ITA. Dist: Random Hse., Inc.
Marchand, Peter. Nature Guide to the Northern Forest: Exploring the Ecology of the Forests of New York, New Hampshire, Vermont, & Maine. 2010. (ENG., Illus.). 192p. pap. 19.95 *(978-1-934028-42-1(8))* Appalachian Mountain Club Bks.
Mauris, Elisabeth & Baccega, Eric. Bears: The Solitary Rulers. 2010. (ENG., Illus.). 220p. 35.00 *(978-88-544-0227-0(3))* White Star ITA. Dist: Random Hse., Inc.
Meyers, Mark S., photos by. Peaceful Valley Candids: Photographs by Mark S. Meyers Quotes by Real People. 2007. 48p. ring bd. 19.99 *(978-0-9771471-2-0(6))* Peaceful Valley Donkey Rescue.
Moyal, Ann Mozley. Koala: A Historical Biography. 2009. (Illus.). 248p. 34.95 *(978-0-643-09401-7(6))* CSIRO Publishing AUS. Dist: Stylus Publishing, LLC.
Naskrecki, Piotr. The Smaller Majority. 2007. (Illus.). 288p. per. 29.00 *(978-0-674-02562-2(8))*, Belknap Pr.) Harvard Univ. Pr.
Nice, Brian. Rescue Tails: Portraits of Dogs & Their Celebrities. 2009. (ENG., Illus.). 176p. pap. 19.95 *(978-1-4391-5276-8(4))* Gallery Pr., The IRL. Dist: Simon & Schuster, Inc.
O'Hara, Shelley. Pet Tails: Heartwarming Photos. 2006. 12.99 *(978-0-470-03764-5(4))* Wiley, John & Sons, Inc.
Parry, James. Global Safari. 2009. (ENG., Illus.). 256p. *(978-1-84732-175-6(5))* Carlton Bks., Ltd. GBR. Dist: Sterling Publishing Co., Inc.
Perry, George. Perry's Arcana. Petit, Richard E., ed. fac. ed. 2009. (ENG., Illus.). 576p. 102.00 *(978-1-4399-0195-3(3))* Temple Univ. Pr.
Peschak, Thomas P. Wild Seas, Secret Shores of Africa. 2008. (Illus.). 184p. 20.95 *(978-1-77007-590-0(9))* Struik Pubs. ZAF. Dist: International Publishers Marketing.
Plytkevich, S. Dikaia Zhizn V Tsentre Evropy: Fotoalbom = Wildlife in the Centre of Europe: Photoalbum. 2009. (RUS & ENG., Illus.). 235p. *(978-985-6919-11-7(8))* Riftur, Ryklamnae pryvatnae unitarnae pradpryemstva.
Poliza, Michael, photos by. Animals of Africa. 2008. 288p. 85.00 *(978-3-8327-9260-2(0))* teNeues Publishing Co.
Poliza, Michael, photos by. AntArctic. 2011. (ENG, GER, FRE, SPA & ITA., Illus.). 240p. pap. 39.95 ***(978-3-8327-9590-0(1))*** teNeues Publishing Co.
Prahms, Wendy. Animals in Newcastle: An Illustrated History. 2008. (ENG., Illus.). 96p. pap. 22.95 *(978-0-7524-4726-1(2))* History Pr. Ltd., The GBR. Dist: Independent Pubs. Group.
Quillet Staff. Encyclopédie Illustree du Monde Animal. 175.00 *(978-0-8288-8147-0(2)*, M6210) French & European Pubns., Inc.
Richards, Dave. The Best of East African Wildlife. 2009. 128p. 25.00 *(978-1-77007-518-4(6))* Struik Pubs. ZAF. Dist: International Publishers Marketing.
Richardson, Nan. Wild Love. Umbrage Editors, ed. 2010. (ENG., Illus.). 80p. (gr. k-2). 15.00 *(978-1-884167-95-9(0))* Umbrage Editions.
Ross, Mark & Reesor, David. Predator: Life & Death in the African Bush. 2007. (ENG., Illus.). 208p. 35.00 *(978-0-8109-9301-3(5))* Abrams.
Russell, Geoff. Mini Encyclopedia of Rabbit Breeds & Care: A Color Directory of the Most Popular Breeds & Their Care. 2009. (ENG., Illus.). 208p. pap. 19.95 *(978-1-55407-474-7(6))* Firefly Bks., Ltd.
Schuster, Gerd, et al. Thinkers of the Jungle: The Orangutan Report, 1 vol. 2012. (ENG., Illus.). 320p. 19.99 ***(978-3-8331-4623-7(0))*** h.f.ullmann DEU. Dist: Innovative Logistics.
Segal, Julia. Feel Better, Little Buddy: Animals with Casts. 2011. (ENG., Illus.). 160p. pap. 12.95 *(978-0-8118-7760-2(4))* Chronicle Bks. LLC.
Shay, Don. Endangered Liaisons. 2008. (Illus.). 320p. 60.00 *(978-0-615-21345-3(6))* Alarus Pr.
Skinner, Catherine Eaton. Unleashed. 2009. (ENG., Illus.). 92p. 49.95 *(978-0-295-98876-4(2))* Univ. of Washington Pr.
Solnit, Rebecca & Caron, Mona. A California Bestiary. 2010. *(978-1-59714-125-3(9))* Heyday.
Starosta, Paul & Teddy, Moncuit. Frogs: And Other Amphibians. 2006. (ENG., Illus.). 192p. *(978-1-905377-05-3(3)*, Antique Collectors Club Dist) Antique Collectors' Club.
Stevenson, Andrew. Whale Song: Journeys into the Secret Lives of the North Atlantic Humpbacks. 2011. (ENG., Illus.). 176p. 27.50 ***(978-0-7627-7971-0(3)***, Lyons Pr.) Globe Pequot Pr., The.
Stewart, Robyn. Nomads of the Serengeti. 2006. (Illus.). 176p. pap. 32.95 *(978-1-86872-762-9(9))* Struik Pubs. ZAF. Dist: International Publishers Marketing.
Stirling, Ian. Polar Bears: The Natural History of a Threatened Species, 1 vol. 2011. (ENG.). 300p. pap. 40.00 *(978-1-55455-155-2(2))* Fitzhenry & Whiteside, Ltd. CAN. Dist: Ingram Pub. Services.
Summers, Jennie. So Cute You Could Die! Puppies, Kitties, Bunnies Galore! 2007. (ENG., Illus.). 256p. 9.95 *(978-1-59474-150-0(6))* Quirk Bks.
Sutherland, Peter, photos by. Buck Shots. 2007. (ENG., Illus.). 100p. pap. 29.95 *(978-1-57687-401-1(X))* powerHouse Cultural Entertainment, Inc.
Thapar, Valmik. The Tiger: Soul of India. 2011. (ENG., Illus.). 184p. 49.95 *(978-0-19-806969-0(3))* Oxford Univ. Pr., Inc.
Thunder Bay Press Staff, ed. Photo Fun Picture Puzzles: Animals. 2011. (ENG., Illus.). 192p. pap. 11.95 *(978-1-60710-225-0(0)*, Thunder Bay Pr.) Advantage Pubs. Group.
Timmy the Turtle & Cinnabun. Buddy Up! 2010. (ENG.). 96p. 12.99 *(978-1-4391-7332-9(X))* Gallery Pr., The IRL. Dist: Simon & Schuster, Inc.
Tögel, Conni. Sheep Incognito. 2008. 164p. pap. 69.50 *(978-0-615-25562-0(0))* Charisma Art Gallery, LLC.
Tromp, Janyre. All about God's Animals-Colors, 1 vol. 2009. 24p. bds. 6.99 *(978-0-8254-3878-3(0))* Kregel Pubns.
—Around the Water, 1 vol. 2009. 24p. bds. 6.99 *(978-0-8254-3876-9(4))* Kregel Pubns.
Unwin, Mike. 100 Bizarre Animals. 2010. (ENG., Illus.). 160p. 24.99 *(978-1-84162-300-9(8))* Bradt Travel Guides GBR. Dist: Globe Pequot Pr., The.
Weitz, Paul. Monkey Portraits. 2006. (ENG., Illus.). 112p. 24.99 *(978-0-8212-5755-5(2))* Bulfinch.
White, Betty. Betty & Friends: My Life at the Zoo. 2012. (ENG.). (gr. 12). pap. 16.00 ***(978-0-425-25301-4(5)***, Berkley Trade) Penguin Group (USA) Inc.
—Betty & Friends: My Life at the Zoo. Lt. ed. 2011. (ENG.). 286p. 32.99 ***(978-1-4104-4525-4(9))*** Thorndike Pr.
Widstrand, Staffan, et al. Wild Wonders of Europe. 2010. (ENG., Illus.). 288p. 50.00 *(978-0-8109-9614-4(6))* Abrams.
Wildlife: Screen Saver. cd-rom *(978-1-55153-121-2(6))* Altitude Publishing Canada Ltd.
Wurtz, Maurizio & Repetto, Nadia. Dolphins & Whales: Revised & Updated. 2010. (White Star Guides). (ENG., Illus.). 168p. 22.95 *(978-88-544-0452-6(7))* White Star ITA. Dist: Sterling Publishing Co., Inc.
Zuckerman, Andrew, photos by. Creature. 2008. (ENG.). 300p. 60.00 *(978-0-8118-6963-6(7))* Chronicle Bks. LLC.

ANIMALS—POETRY

Apollinaire, Guillaume. The Bestiary, or Procession of Orpheus. Kennedy, X. J., tr. from FRE. 2011. (ENG & FRE., Illus.). 96p. pap. 19.95 *(978-1-4214-0007-5(3))*; (gr. 17). 45.00 *(978-1-4214-0006-8(5))* Johns Hopkins Univ. Pr.
Appleman, Philip & Pozzatti, Rudy. Darwin's Ark. 2009. (ENG., Illus.). 112p. pap. 19.95 *(978-0-253-22092-9(0)*, 0253220920) Indiana Univ. Pr.
Bolster, Stephanie, et al, eds. Penned: Zoo Poems. 2010. (ENG., Illus.). 154p. pap. 21.95 *(978-1-55065-263-5(X))* Vehicule Pr. CAN. Dist: Independent Pubs. Group.
Ciuraru, Carmela, ed. Poems about Horses. 2009. (Everyman's Library Pocket Poets). (ENG.). 256p. 13.50 *(978-0-307-26925-6(6)*, Everyman's Library) Knopf Doubleday Publishing Group.
Hayley, William. The Eulogies of Howard. 2007. (ENG.). 48p. per. *(978-1-4065-4410-7(8))* Dodo Pr.
Jussaume, Christina R. Amazing Pets & Animals. 2008. 167p. pap. 18.50 *(978-0-615-18026-1(0))* P.F.P. Pubs.
Lawrence, D. H. Birds, Beasts & Flowers. 2011. 178p. pap. ***(978-1-84861-157-3(9))*** Shearsman Bks.
Loydell, Rupert M. Wildlife. 2011. 80p. pap. ***(978-1-84861-152-8(8))*** Shearsman Bks.
Momaday, N. Scott. In the Bear's House. 2010. (ENG., Illus.). 112p. 24.95 *(978-0-8263-4839-5(4))* Univ. of New Mexico Pr.
Oliver, Mary. The Truro Bear & Other Adventures: Poems & Essays. (ENG.). 96p. 2010. pap. 14.00 *(978-0-8070-6885-4(3))* 2008. 23.00 *(978-0-8070-6884-7(5))* Beacon Pr.

ANIMALS—READERS

see Readers—Animals

ANIMALS—RELIGIOUS ASPECTS

see also Animal Worship

Anderson, Allen & Anderson, Linda C. Angel Animals: Divine Messengers of Miracles. 2nd ed. 2007. (ENG., Illus.). 288p. per. 14.95 *(978-1-57731-610-7(6))* New World Library.
Anderson, Allen, et al. A Writer's Book of Days: A Spirited Companion & Lively Muse for the Writing Life. rev. ed. 2010. (ENG.). 272p. pap. 16.95 *(978-1-57731-935-8(2))* New World Library.
Andrews, Ted. The Intercession of Spirits: Working with Animals, Angels & Ancestors. 2008. (Illus.). 287p. pap. 14.95 *(978-1-888767-55-1(3))* Dragonhawk Publishing.
Animal's Rights in Islam. 2009. 72p. pap. *(978-3-639-16001-7(0))* VDM Verlag Dr. Mueller e.K.
Bai, Durga. SSSS: Snake Art & Allegory. 2010. (ENG., Illus.). 48p. 24.95 *(978-81-906756-6-6(4))* Tara Publishing IND. Dist: Perseus-PGW.
Bauer, Judith. For God's Creatures Great & Small: Prayers for Our Pets & Other Animals. 2006. 56p. pap. 6.95 *(978-0-88271-226-0(8))* Regina Pr., Malhame & Co.
Benson, Kristina. Animal Totem Guide: The Spiritual & Magickal Powers of Mammals, Birds, Insects, & Fish. 2008. 136p. pap. 18.00 *(978-1-60332-017-7(2))* Equity Pr.
Bickerstaff, Marcella. Dog Is God Spelled Backwards. 2011. 192p. pap. 14.99 ***(978-1-61379-157-8(7))*** Xulon Pr., Inc.
Bloomer V.N.D., Kim. Animals Taught Me That: Memoirs of my life from cradle to present on the life lessons learned through the animals who've graced it. 2009. 228p. pap. *(978-1-61507-047-3(8))* Cross Bks. Publishing.
Boehrer, Bruce. A Cultural History of Animals in the Renaissance, 6 vols. Boehrer, Bruce, ed. 2011. (ENG., Illus.). 272p. pap. 34.95 *(978-1-84788-819-8(4))* Berg Pubs. GBR. Dist: Macmillan.
Booth, Bradley. The Seventh-Day Ox, & Other Miracle Stories from Russia. 2011. (ENG., Illus.). 192p. pap. 14.99 *(978-0-8280-2517-1(7))* Review & Herald Publishing Assn.
Bostwick, Miriam. Animal News from Heaven. 2008. 360p. pap. 17.95 *(978-0-9798828-2-1(6)*, Epigraph Bks.) Monkfish Bk. Publishing Co.
Browne, Sylvia. All Pets Go to Heaven: The Spiritual Lives of the Animals We Love. 2009. (ENG.). 224p. pap. 14.00 *(978-1-4165-9125-2(7)*, Touchstone) Touchstone.
Brunke, Dawn Baumann. Shapeshifting with Our Animal Companions. 2008. (ENG., Illus.). 1p. pap. 16.00 *(978-1-59143-083-4(6))* Bear & Co.
Bulanda, Susan. God's Creatures: A Biblical View of Animals. 2008. (Illus.). 127p. pap. 11.49 *(978-0-9759619-8-8(5))* CLADACH Publishing.
Canham, Elizabeth. Ask the Animals: Spiritual Wisdom from All God's Creatures. 2006. (Illus.). 160p. per. 16.00 *(978-0-8192-2232-9(1)*, Morehouse Publishing) Church Publishing, Inc.
Caruso, Lynn L., ed. Blessing the Animals: Prayers & Ceremonies to Celebrate God's Creatures, Wild & Tame. 2008. 256p. pap. 15.99 *(978-1-59473-253-9(1))* SkyLight Paths Publishing.
Celesta, Sophia. The book of the Beasts. 2010. 188p. pap. 12.99 *(978-0-557-23775-3(0))* Lulu Enterprises Inc.
Chancellor, Edward. Animal Spirits. Date not set. 26.00 *(978-0-374-10513-6(8))* Farrar, Straus & Giroux.
Cico Books Staff & Luttichau, Chris. Animal Spirit Guides. 2009. (ENG., Illus.). 160p. 16.95 *(978-1-906525-54-5(4))* CICO Bks. GBR. Dist: Ryland Peters & Small.
Collinson, Dixie M. Precepts from the Pig: Spiritual Concepts Captured by the Cavy. 2008. pap. 9.99 *(978-1-60477-930-1(6))* Xulon Pr., Inc.
Deane-Drummond, Celia & Clough, David, eds. Creaturely Theology: On God, Humans & Other Animals. 2011. 288p. pap. ***(978-0-334-04189-4(9)***, SCM Pr.) Hymns Ancient & Modern Ltd.
Farrington, Debra K. All God's Creatures: The Blessing of Animal Companions. 2006. (ENG.). 160p. (gr. 13). per. 15.99 *(978-1-55725-472-6(9))* Paraclete Pr., Inc.
Gunn, Celia M. Simply Totem Animals. 2010. (Simply Ser.). (ENG., Illus.). 160p. pap. 9.95 *(978-1-4027-5459-3(0)*, Sterling/Zambezi) Sterling Publishing Co., Inc.
Hamilton, Katie F. Snails, Sex & Sermons in 1744. 5.00 *(978-1-889023-09-0(4))* Metheglin Pr.
Healy, Marti. The God-Dog Connection: Things I've Learned about God & Faith from the Dogs & Cats in My Life. 2007. 72p. *(978-0-9791277-0-0(X))* Design Group Pr., The.
—The God-Dog Connection Pet Ministry. 2008. 28p. pap. 9.95 *(978-0-9791277-2-4(6))* Design Group Pr., The.
—The God-Dog Connection Study Guide. 2008. 56p. pap. 9.95 *(978-0-9791277-1-7(8))* Design Group Pr., The.
Hobe, Phyllis. Angels in Disguise: When God Sends Animals to Comfort Us. 2009. (ENG.). 224p. 14.99 *(978-0-8249-4782-8(7)*, Guideposts) Ideals Pubns.
Hobgood-Oster, Laura. The Friends We Keep: Unleashing Christianity's Compassion for Animals. 2010. (ENG., Illus.). 230p. pap. 19.95 *(978-1-60258-264-4(5))* Baylor Univ. Pr.
—Holy Dogs & Asses: Animals in the Christian Tradition. 2008. (Illus.). 192p. 37.00 *(978-0-252-03213-4(6))* Univ. of Illinois Pr.
Jones, David, ed. Buddha Nature & Animality. 2007. 236p. per. 35.00 *(978-0-89581-860-7(4))* Jain Publishing Company, Inc.
Kalof, Linda. A Cultural History of Animals in Antiquity, 6 vols. Kalof, Linda, ed. 2011. (ENG., Illus.). 272p. pap. 34.95 *(978-1-84788-817-4(8))* Berg Pubs. GBR. Dist: Macmillan.
Kemmerer, Lisa. Animals & World Religions: Rightful Relations, 1 vol. 2011. (ENG.). 360p. 99.00 *(978-0-19-979067-8(1))*; pap. 35.00 *(978-0-19-979068-5(X))* Oxford Univ. Pr., Inc.
Kete, Kathleen. A Cultural History of Animals in the Age of Empire, 6 vols. Kete, Kathleen, ed. 2011. (ENG., Illus.). 272p. pap. 34.95 *(978-1-84788-821-1(6))* Berg Pubs. GBR. Dist: Macmillan.
Kirk, Ronald W., et al. eds. Worship Not the Creature: Animal Rights & the Bible. 2009. (ENG., Illus.). 192p. pap. 19.99 *(978-0-9824929-1-8(X))* Nordskog Publishing, Inc.
Kit, Sandy. Pups, Kittens, Birds Will Heaven Be Their Home? 2009. 394p. pap. 19.99 *(978-1-4363-3264-4(8))* Xlibris Corp.
Lee, Constance. All of the Animals Are Talking about It. 2010. 76p. pap. 27.49 *(978-1-4490-6750-2(6))* AuthorHouse.
Liang, Liling. Han Yi Fo Dian Dong Wu Gu Shi Zhi Yan Jiu. 2010. (CHI., Illus.). vi, 370p. *(978-957-668-916-1(3))* Wen Chin Publishing Co, Ltd.
Linzey, Andrew. Creatures of the Same God: Explorations in Animal Theology. 2009. *(978-1-59056-142-3(2))* Lantern Bks.
Linzey, Andrew & Regan, Tom, eds. Animals & Christianity: A Book of Readings. 2007. 228p. pap. 25.00 *(978-1-55635-688-9(9))* Wipf & Stock Pubs.
Malamud, Randy. A Cultural History of Animals in the Modern Age, 6 vols. Malamud, Randy, ed. 2011. (ENG., Illus.). 272p. pap. 34.95 *(978-1-84788-822-8(4))* Berg Pubs. GBR. Dist: Macmillan.
Malone, Sam. Native British Totem Animals. 2008. 84p. pap. 12.95 *(978-1-4092-4808-8(9))* Lulu Enterprises Inc.
Messenger, The. Here Comes the King: Who Is Jesus Christ Our Lord. 2009. 64p. pap. 15.99 *(978-1-4500-0844-0(5))* Xlibris Corp.
Murray, Michael. Nature Red in Tooth & Claw: Theism & the Problem of Animal Suffering. 2008. (ENG.). 208p. 74.00 *(978-0-19-923727-2(1))* Oxford Univ. Pr., Inc.
Patton, Kimberley & Waldau, Paul, eds. A Communion of Subjects: Animals in Religion, Science, & Ethics. 2006. (ENG., Illus.). 720p. (gr. 17). 90.00 *(978-0-231-13642-6(0))* Columbia Univ. Pr.
Perlo, Katherine Wills. Kinship & Killing: The Animal in World Religions. 2009. (ENG.). 292p. (gr. 17). 79.50 *(978-0-231-14622-7(1))*; pap. 27.50 *(978-0-231-14623-4(X))* Columbia Univ. Pr.
Petropoulou, Maria-Zoe. Animal Sacrifice in Ancient Greek Religion, Judaism, & Christianity, 100 BC to AD 200. 2012. (Oxford Classical Monographs). 352p. pap. 55.00 ***(978-0-19-963935-9(3))*** Oxford Univ. Pr., Inc.
Pinches, Charles & McDaniel, Jay B., eds. Good News for Animals? Christian Approaches to Animal Well-Being. 2008. 270p. pap. 31.00 *(978-1-59244-601-8(9))* Wipf & Stock Pubs.
Pittman, Allison K. Saturdays with Stella: How My Dog Taught Me to Sit, Stay, & Come When God Calls. 2008. (ENG., Illus.). 176p. pap. 13.99 *(978-1-60142-139-5(7)*, Multnomah) Doubleday Religious Publishing Group, The.
Resl, Brigitte. A Cultural History of Animals in the Medieval Age, 6 vols. Resl, Brigitte, ed. 2011. (ENG., Illus.). 272p. pap. 34.95 *(978-1-84788-818-1(6))* Berg Pubs. GBR. Dist: Macmillan.
—Understanding Animals 1150-1350. 2012. (ENG.). 256p. 69.95 *(978-1-4039-3818-3(0))* Palgrave Macmillan.
Sandsmark, Joanna. 10 Spiritual Lessons You Can Learn from Your Cat. 2007. (ENG., Illus.). 96p. 9.95 *(978-1-84181-240-3(4)*, Godsfield Press) Octopus Publishing Group GBR. Dist: Hachette Bk. Group.
Scott, Peter M. Anti-Human Theology: Nature, Technology & the Post-Natural. Deane-Drummond, Celia, ed. 2010. (SCM Revisioning Ethics Ser.). (ENG.). 256p. pap. 90.00 *(978-0-334-04354-6(9)*, SCM Pr.) Hymns Ancient & Modern Ltd GBR. Dist: Westminster John Knox Pr.
Searl, Edward. In Praise of Animals: A Treasury of Poems, Quotations & Readings. 2007. (ENG.). 1p. per. 14.00 *(978-1-55896-511-9(4)*, Skinner Hse. Bks.) Unitarian Universalist Assn.
Senior, Matthew. A Cultural History of Animals in the Age of Enlightenment, 6 vols. Senior, Matthew, ed. 2011. (ENG., Illus.). 272p. pap. 34.95 *(978-1-84788-820-4(8))* Berg Pubs. GBR. Dist: Macmillan.
Shanahan, Niki Behrikis. Who Says Animals Go to Heaven? A Collection of Prominent Christian Leaders' Beliefs in Life after Death for Animals. 2008. 96p. pap. 13.99 *(978-0-9720301-5-1(8))* Pete Publishing.
Skinner, Susan. Symbols of the Soul: Sacred Beasts. 2012. (ENG.). 84p. pap. 14.95 ***(978-1-84694-670-7(0))*** Hunt, John Publishing Ltd. GBR. Dist: National Bk. Network.
Smith, David. Bible Lessons from Our Pets. 2011. (ENG.). 144p. mass mkt. 12.95 ***(978-1-936417-25-4(1))*** Pilot Communications Group, Inc.
Storle, Frank. Animal Totem Guides: Messages for the World: Communicating with Your Power Animal Guides. 2011. 108p. 22.95 ***(978-1-4620-2071-3(2))***; pap. 12.95 ***(978-1-4620-2069-3(0))*** iUniverse, Inc.
Susi Pittman. Animals in Heaven? Catholics Want to Know! 2009. 168p. 25.95 *(978-1-4401-7727-9(9))* iUniverse, Inc.
Taylor, Lynda. A Journey into the Soulful Garden: Connecting Spirit with Nature. 2010. 120p. 22.95 *(978-1-4502-0290-9(X))*; pap. 12.95 *(978-1-4502-0292-3(6))* iUniverse, Inc.
Vantassel, Stephen M. Dominion over Wildlife? An Environmental Theology of Human-Wildlife Relations. 2009. 232p. pap. 26.00 *(978-1-60608-343-7(0)*, Resource Pubns.) Wipf & Stock Pubs.
Vincent, Tina Pauline. Moolajig & Harry the Pig. 2011. 24p. pap. 13.95 ***(978-1-61507-710-6(3))*** Cross Bks. Publishing.
Waldau, Paul & Patton, Kimberley, eds. A Communion of Subjects: Animals in Religion, Science, & Ethics. 2009. (ENG., Illus.). 720p. (gr. 17). pap. 29.50 *(978-0-231-13643-3(9))* Columbia Univ. Pr.
Way, Kenneth. Donkeys in the Biblical World: A Ceremonial & Symbolic Study. 2011. ***(978-1-57506-213-6(5))*** Eisenbrauns, Inc.
Wintz, Jack. Will I See My Dog in Heaven? 2009. (ENG.). 153p. (gr. 13). pap. 14.99 *(978-1-55725-568-6(7))*, Paraclete Pr., Inc.

ANIMALS—SOCIAL ASPECTS

see also Animal Welfare

Anderson, Allen, et al. Angel Animals Book of Inspiration: Divine Messengers of Wisdom & Compassion. 2nd ed. 2009. (ENG.). 256p. pap. 14.95 *(978-1-57731-666-4(5))* New World Library.
Bauer, Radhika. Animals in Social Life. 2007. 336p. per. *(978-3-8364-2614-5(5))* VDM Verlag Dr. Mueller e.K.
Baur, Gene. Farm Sanctuary: Changing Hearts & Minds about Animals & Food. 2008. (ENG.). 320p. pap. 15.00 *(978-0-7432-9159-0(X)*, Touchstone) Touchstone.
Boehrer, Bruce. A Cultural History of Animals in the Renaissance, 6 vols. Boehrer, Bruce, ed. 2011. (ENG., Illus.). 272p. pap. 34.95 *(978-1-84788-819-8(4))* Berg Pubs. GBR. Dist: Macmillan.
Boesch, Christophe. Real Chimpanzee: Sex Strategies in the Forest. 2009. (ENG., Illus.). 196p. (C). 120.00 *(978-0-521-11008-2(4))* Cambridge Univ. Pr.
Brantz, Dorothee, ed. Beastly Natures: Animals, Humans, & the Study of History. 2010. (ENG., Illus.). 304p. (gr. 17). 39.50 *(978-0-8139-2947-7(4))*, Univ. Pr. of Virginia.
Burnett, D. Graham. Trying Leviathan: The Nineteenth-Century New York Court Case That Put the Whale on Trial & Challenged the Order of Nature. (ENG.).

304p. (C). 2010. pap. 22.95 (978-0-691-14615-7(2)) 2007. (Illus.). 49.95 (978-0-691-12950-1(9)) Princeton Univ. Pr.

Carter, Bob & Charles, Nickie, eds. Human & Other Animals: Critical Perspectives. 2011. (ENG., Illus.). 256p. 85.00 (978-0-230-24659-1(1)) Palgrave Macmillan.

Castricano, Jodey, ed. Animal Subjects: An Ethical Reader in a Posthuman World. 2008. (Environmental Humanities Ser.). (ENG., Illus.). 324p. pap. 42.95 (978-0-88920-512-3(4)) Wilfrid Laurier Univ. Pr. CAN. Dist: Univ. of Toronto Pr.

Cudworth, Erika. Social Lives with Other Animals: Tales of Sex, Death & Love. 2011. (ENG., Illus.). 224p. 85.00 (978-0-230-24151-0(4)) Palgrave Macmillan.

Donald, Diana. Picturing Animals in Britain. 2008. (ENG., Illus.). 256p. 65.00 (978-0-300-12679-2(4)) Yale Univ. Pr.

Edwards, Peter, et al, eds. The Horse As Cultural Icon: The Real & the Symbolic Horse in the Early Modern World. 2011. (Intersections Ser.). (ENG., Illus.). XVIII, 410p. (978-90-04-21206-0(X)) BRILL.

Hribal, Jason. Fear of the Animal Planet: The Secret History of Animal Resistance. 2011. (Counterpunch Ser.). (ENG.). 280p. pap. 15.95 (978-1-84935-026-6(4)) AK Pr. GBR. Dist: Consortium Bk. Sales & Distribution.

Hyde, Walter Woodburn. The Prosecution of Lifeless Things & Animals in Greek Law. 2010. 85.16 (978-1-61143-453-8(X)); 85.16 (978-1-61143-489-7(0)) Gorgias Pr., LLC.

Inglis. Animals & Society, 5 vols. 2006. (Critical Concepts in the Social Sciences Ser.). (Illus.). 416p. (978-0-415-38172-7(X)); (978-0-415-38170-3(3)) Routledge.

—Animals & Society V2, 5 vols. 2006. (Critical Concepts in the Social Sciences Ser.). (Illus.). (978-0-415-38171-0(1)) Routledge.

—Animals & Society V4, 5 vols. 2006. (Critical Concepts in the Social Sciences Ser.). (Illus.). 424p. (978-0-415-38173-4(8)) Routledge.

Inglis, David, ed. Animals & Society, 5 vols. 2006. (Critical Concepts in the Social Sciences Ser.). (Illus.). 416p. (978-0-415-39646-2(8)) Routledge.

Irwin, Robert. Camel. 2010. (Reaktion Books - Animal Ser.). (ENG., Illus.). 224p. pap. 19.95 (978-1-86189-649-0(2)) Reaktion Bks., Ltd. GBR. Dist: Chicago Distribution Ctr.

Joy, Melanie. Why We Love Dogs, Eat Pigs, & Wear Cows: An Introduction to Carnism. 2009. (ENG.). 208p. 19.95 (978-1-57324-461-9(9)), Conari Pr.) Red Wheel/Weiser.

Kalof, Linda. A Cultural History of Animals in Antiquity, 6 vols. Kalof, Linda, ed. 2011. (ENG., Illus.). 272p. pap. 34.95 (978-1-84788-817-4(8)) Berg Pubs. GBR. Dist: Macmillan.

Kete, Kathleen. A Cultural History of Animals in the Age of Empire, 6 vols. Kete, Kathleen, ed. 2011. (ENG., Illus.). 272p. pap. 34.95 (978-1-84788-821-1(6)) Berg Pubs. GBR. Dist: Macmillan.

Malamud, Randy. A Cultural History of Animals in the Modern Age, 6 vols. Malamud, Randy, ed. 2011. (ENG., Illus.). 272p. pap. 34.95 (978-1-84788-822-8(4)) Berg Pubs. GBR. Dist: Macmillan.

Nicholls, Henry. The Way of the Panda: The Curious History of China's Political Animal. 2011. (ENG., Illus.). 304p. 25.00 (978-1-60598-188-8(5), 605188) Pegasus Bks.

Peggs, Kay. Animals & Sociology. 2012. (Palgrave Macmillan Animal Ethics Ser.). (ENG., Illus.). 192p. (C). 95.00 (978-0-230-29257-4(7)); pap. 33.00 (978-0-230-29258-1(5)) Palgrave Macmillan.

Resl, Brigitte. A Cultural History of Animals in the Medieval Age, 6 vols. Resl, Brigitte, ed. 2011. (ENG., Illus.). 272p. pap. 34.95 (978-1-84788-818-1(6)) Berg Pubs. GBR. Dist: Macmillan.

—Understanding Animals 1150-1350. 2012. (ENG.). 256p. 69.95 (978-1-4039-3818-3(0)) Palgrave Macmillan.

Scott-Fox, Penny. And Baby Makes Four: A Trimester-by-Trimester Guide to a Baby-Friendly Dog. 2007. (Illus.). 95p. 9.95 (978-0-7938-0567-9(8)) TFH Pubns., Inc.

Senior, Matthew. A Cultural History of Animals in the Age of Enlightenment, 6 vols. Senior, Matthew, ed. 2011. (ENG., Illus.). 272p. pap. 34.95 (978-1-84788-820-4(8)) Berg Pubs. GBR. Dist: Macmillan.

Shapiro, Robert. The Explorer Race Series (Book 13) Each animal brings a wondrous gift to share with humanity - enjoy it!, 17 vols., Vol. 13. 2007. (Explorer Race Ser.). (Illus.). 570p. pap. 29.95 (978-1-891824-50-0(3)) Light Technology Publishing, LLC.

Steel, Karl. How to Make a Human: Animals & Violence in the Middle Ages. 2011. (Interventions: New Studies Medieval Cult Ser.). 328p. 49.95 (978-0-8142-1157-1(7)); cd-rom 14.95 (978-0-8142-9256-3(9)) Ohio State Univ. Pr.

Stibbe, Arran. Animals Erased: Discourse, Ecology, & Reconnection with the Natural World. 2012. (ENG., Illus.). 232p. (C). 70.00 (978-0-8195-7231-8(4)); pap. 24.95 (978-0-8195-7232-5(2)) Wesleyan Univ. Pr.

Zawistowski, Stephen. Companion Animals in Society. 2008. (ENG., Illus.). 304p. (C). 130.95 (978-1-4180-1370-7(6)) Delmar Cengage Learning.

ANIMALS—SYMBOLIC ASPECTS

Benjamin, Andrew. Of Jews & Animals. 2011. (Frontiers of Theory Ser.). (ENG., Illus.). 224p. (gr. 17). pap. 32.00 (978-0-7486-4317-2(6)) Edinburgh Univ. Pr. GBR. Dist: Columbia Univ. Pr.

Bough, Jill. Donkey. 2011. (Reaktion Books - Animal Ser.). (ENG., Illus.). 198p. pap. 19.95 (978-1-86189-803-6(7)) Reaktion Bks., Ltd. GBR. Dist: Chicago Distribution Ctr.

Cohen, Simona. Animals as Disguised Symbols in Renaissance Art. 2008. 352p. (C). (978-90-04-17101-5(0)) BRILL.

Eason, Cassandra. Fabulous Creatures, Mythical Monsters, & Animal Power Symbols: A Handbook, 1 vol. 2007. (Illus.). 200p. 45.00 (978-0-275-99425-9(2), C9425, Greenwood Pr.) Greenwood Publishing Group, Inc.

Gillespie, Angus K. & Mechling, Jay, eds. American Wildlife in Symbol & Story. (Illus.). 262p. 22.50 (978-1-57233-259-1(X)) Univ. of Tennessee Pr.

Granata, Silvia. Take Every Creature In, of Every Kind: Continuity & Change in Eighteenth-Century Representations of Animals. 2011. (Europäische Hochschulschriften. Reihe 14: Angelsächsische Sprache und Literatur Ser.). 200p. pap. (978-3-0343-0544-0(3)) Lang, Peter.

Milne, Anne. Lactilla Tends Her Fav'rite Cow: Ecocritical Readings of Animals & Women in Eighteenth-Century British Labouring-Class Women's Poetry. 2008. (Illus.). 176p. (C). 45.50 (978-0-8387-5692-8(1)) Bucknell Univ. Pr.

Obermaier, Sabine. Tiere und Fabelwesen Im Mittelalter: Zu Ihrer Bedeutung in Wissenschaft, Religion, Geschichte, Bildender Kunst und Literatur. Obermaier, Sabine, ed. 2009.Tr. of Animals & Mythical Creatures in the Middle Ages. (GER., Illus.). VIII, 342p. 140.00 (978-3-11-020137-6(2)) De Gruyter, Walter Inc.

Obermaier, Sabine, ed. Tiere und Fabelwesen im Mittelalter. 2009.Tr. of Animals & Mythical Creatures in the Middle Ages. (GER.). VIII, 342p. 210.00 (978-3-11-173736-2(5)) De Gruyter, Walter Inc.

Pepper, Elizabeth & Stacy, Barbara. The Little Book of Magical Creatures: A Revised & Expanded Edition, 1 vol. 2009. (ENG., Illus.). 160p. pap. 12.95 (978-0-9773703-9-9(9)) Witches Almanac Ltd., The.

Shukin, Nicole. Animal Capital: Rendering Life in Biopolitical Times. 2009. (Posthumanities Ser.). (ENG., Illus.). 288p. 67.50 (978-0-8166-5341-6(0)); pap. 22.50 (978-0-8166-5342-3(9)) Univ. of Minnesota Pr.

Skinner, Susan. Symbols of the Soul: Sacred Beasts. 2012. (ENG.). 84p. pap. 14.95 (978-1-84694-670-7(0)) Hunt, John Publishing Ltd. GBR. Dist: National Bk. Network.

Tsurumoto, Masahiro. Charanavi: Explore Your Personality & Improve Your Relationships. Saito, Chikako, tr. from JPN. 2007. (Illus.). 184p. per. 14.95 (978-1-934140-00-0(7)) Natural Spirit Internation Inc.

ANIMALS—TRAINING

see Animal Training

ANIMALS—WAR USE

DiMarco, Louis. War Horse: A History of the Military Horse & Rider. 2008. (Illus.). 432p. 29.95 (978-1-59416-034-9(1)) Westholme Publishing.

Ensminger, John. Police & Military Dogs. 2011. (ENG., Illus.). 304p. 79.95 (978-1-4398-7239-0(2), CRC Press) Taylor & Francis Group GBR. Dist: Taylor & Francis Group.

George, Isabel. Beyond the Call of Duty: Heart-Warming Stories of Canine Devotion & Wartime Bravery. 2010. (ENG.). 296p. 11.95 (978-0-00-737151-8(9)) HarperCollins Pubs. Ltd. GBR. Dist: Independent Pubs. Group.

Goodavage, Maria. Soldier Dogs: The Untold Story of America's Canine Heroes. 2012. (ENG.). 304p. (gr. 12). 26.95 (978-0-525-95278-7(0), Dutton Adult) Penguin Group (USA) Inc.

Jarymowycz, Roman. Cavalry from Hoof to Track. 2009. (Military History Ser.). (ENG., Illus.). 320p. pap. 21.95 (978-0-8117-3577-3(X)) Stackpole Bks.

Johnson, Paul Louis. Horses of the German Army in World War II. 2007. (Schiffer Military History Book Ser.). (Illus.). 352p. 59.95 (978-0-7643-2421-5(7)) Schiffer Publishing, Ltd.

Kistler, John M. Animals in the Military: From Hannibal's Elephants to the Dolphins of the U. S. Navy, 1 vol. 2011. (Illus.). 393p. 65.00 (978-1-59884-346-0(X), A2617C) ABC-CLIO, LLC.

Kistler, John M. & Kistler, John. War Elephants. 2007. (ENG., Illus.). 352p. pap. 19.95 (978-0-8032-6004-7(0), Bison Bks.) Univ. of Nebraska Pr.

Le Chene, Evelyn. Silent Heroes: The Bravery & Devotion of Animals in War. 2010. (ENG., Illus.). 240p. pap. 16.95 (978-0-285-63861-7(0)) Souvenir Pr. Ltd. GBR. Dist: Independent Pubs. Group.

Merritt, Susan. Seek On! 2011. 214p. pap. 14.50 (978-1-60911-337-7(3), Strategic Bk. Publishing) AEG Literary Publishing Services, Inc.

Nossov, Konstantin & Nossov, K. War Elephants. 2008. (New Vanguard Ser.). (ENG., Illus.). 48p. pap. 17.95 (978-1-84603-268-4(7)) Osprey Publishing, Ltd. GBR. Dist: Random Hse., Inc.

Rogak, Lisa. The Dogs of War: The Courage, Love, & Loyalty of Military Working Dogs. l.t. ed. 2012. (ENG.). 351p. 31.99 (978-1-4104-4558-2(5)) Thorndike Pr.

Ronson, Jon. The Men Who Stare at Goats. 2009. (ENG.). 272p. pap. 15.00 (978-1-4391-8177-5(2)) Simon & Schuster.

Rosenkrans, Robert. U. S. Military War Dogs in World War II. 2011. (Illus.). 144p. 49.99 (978-0-7643-3949-3(4), Schiffer Publishing Ltd) Schiffer Publishing, Ltd.

ANIMALS (IN RELIGION, FOLK-LORE, ETC.)

see Animals—Folklore; Animals—Religious Aspects

ANIMALS, ABNORMALITIES OF

see Animals—Abnormalities

ANIMALS, AQUATIC

see Aquatic Animals

ANIMALS, CRUELTY TO

see Animal Welfare

ANIMALS, DISEASES OF

see Animals—Diseases

ANIMALS, DOMESTIC

see Domestic Animals

ANIMALS, DOMESTICATION OF

see Domestication

ANIMALS, EDIBLE

see Food of Animal Origin

ANIMALS, EXPERIMENTAL

see Laboratory Animals

ANIMALS, EXTINCT

see Extinct Animals

ANIMALS, FICTITIOUS

see Animals, Mythical

ANIMALS, FOOD HABITS OF

see Animals—Food

ANIMALS, FOSSIL

see also Conodonts; Invertebrates, Fossil; Vertebrates, Fossil

Bartels, Christoph, et al. The Fossils of the Hunsrück Slate: Marine Life in the Devonian. 2009. (Cambridge Paleobiology Ser.). (ENG., Illus.). 324p. pap. 46.00 (978-0-521-11707-4(0)) Cambridge Univ. Pr.

Boyd, Brian. People & Animals in Levantine Prehistory. 2008. 225p. (C). 58.00 (978-0-521-80714-2(X)) Cambridge Univ. Pr.

Clarke, Ronald, et al. Caves of the Ape-Men: South Africa's Cradle of Humankind World Heritage Site. 2011. (ENG., Illus.). 160p. pap. 60.00 (978-1-86814-510-2(7)) Witwatersrand Univ. Pr. Pubns. ZAF. Dist: Transaction Pubs.

Cranfield, Ingrid, ed. Illustrated Directory of Dinosaurs & Other Prehistoric Creatures. 2007. (Illus.). 360p. pap. 20.00 (978-1-4223-9023-8(3)) DIANE Publishing Co.

Dixon, Dougal & Dixon, Dougal. The World Encyclopedia of Dinosaurs & Prehistoric Creatures/= The Ultimate Illustrated Reference Guide to More Than 1000 Dinosaurs & Prehistoric Creatures, with 2000 Specially Commisioned Watercolours, Maps & Photographs. 2011. (ENG., Illus.). 512p. 29.99 (978-0-7548-1730-7(X)) Anness Publishing GBR. Dist: National Bk. Network.

DK Publishing. Prehistoric Life: The Definitive Visual History of Life on Earth. 2012. (ENG.). 512p. pap. 27.95 (978-0-7566-9910-9(X)) Dorling Kindersley Publishing, Inc.

Dominguez-Rodrigo, Manuel, et al. Deconstructing Olduvai: A Taphonomic Study of the Bed I Sites. 2007. (Vertebrate Paleobiology & Paleoanthropology Ser.). xvi, 337p. 129.00 (978-1-4020-6150-9(1), 1402061501) Springer.

Everhart, Mike. Sea Monsters: Prehistoric Creatures of the Deep. 2007. (ENG., Illus.). 192p. 30.00 (978-1-4262-0085-4(4), National Geographic) National Geographic Society.

Fleminger, David. Cradle of Humankind. 2008. (World Heritage Sites of South Africa Travel Guides). 144p. pap. 10.95 (978-0-9584891-3-3(0)) 30° South Pubs. ZAF. Dist: International Publishers Marketing.

Gunnell, Gregg F. & Simmons, Nancy B., eds. Evolutionary History of Bats: Fossils, Molecules & Morphology. 2012. (Cambridge Studies in Morphology & Molecules: New Paradigms in Evolutionary Bio Ser.). (ENG., Illus.). 572p. 135.00 (978-0-521-76824-5(1)); pap. 65.00 (978-0-521-74526-0(8)) Cambridge Univ. Pr.

Haines, Tim & Chambers, Paul. The Complete Guide to Prehistoric Life. 2007. (ENG., Illus.). 216p. (gr. 8-12). pap. 24.95 (978-1-55407-181-4(X)) Firefly Bks., Ltd.

Harrison, Terry, ed. Neogene, Paleontology of the Manonga Valley, Tanzania: A Window into the Evolutionary History of East Africa. 2011. (Topics in Geobiology Ser.). (ENG.). pap. 195.00 (978-1-4419-3265-5(8), 1441932658) Springer.

Holman, J. Alan. The Amphibians & Reptiles of Michigan: A Quaternary & Recent Faunal Adventure. 2012. 50.00 (978-0-8143-3239-9(0)); E-Book (978-0-8143-3713-4(9)) Wayne State Univ. Pr.

Hou, Xian-guang, et al. The Cambrian Fossils of Chengjiang, China: The Flowering of Early Animal Life. 2007. (ENG.). 248p. pap. 69.95 (978-1-4051-6719-2(X), Wiley-Blackwell) Wiley, John & Sons, Inc.

Janis, Christine M., et al, eds. Evolution of Tertiary Mammals of North America: Small Mammals, Xenarthrans, & Marine Mammals, 2 vols., Vol. 2. 2008. (ENG., Illus.). 802p. 290.00 (978-0-521-78117-6(5)) Cambridge Univ. Pr.

Kaesler, Roger L. & Lieberman, Bruce S. Prehistoric Life: Evolution & the Fossil Record. 2010. (ENG., Illus.). 400p. pap. 109.95 (978-0-632-04472-6(1), Wiley-Blackwell) Wiley, John & Sons, Inc.

Kitchell, Kenneth. Animals in the Ancient World from A to Z. 2008. (Ancient World from A to Z Ser.). 110.00 (978-0-415-39243-3(8)) Routledge.

Landgraf, Kelly. No Bones about It: The Truth about Fossils & Other Science Myths. 2011. pap. 12.99 (978-1-61346-120-4(8)) Tate Publishing & Enterprises, LLC.

Lieberman, Bruce S. & Kaesler, Roger L. Prehistoric Life: Evolution & the Fossil Record. 2010. (ENG.). 400p. 159.95 (978-1-4443-3408-1(5), Wiley-Blackwell) Wiley, John & Sons, Inc.

Lister, Adrian & Bahn, Paul. Mammoths: Giants of the Ice Age. rev. ed. 2009. (ENG.). 192p. pap. 21.95 (978-0-520-26160-0(7)) Univ. of California Pr.

McNamara, Kenneth J. The Star-Crossed Stone: The Secret Life, Myths, & History of a Fascinating Fossil. 2010. (Illus.). 280p. 27.50 (978-0-226-51469-7(2)) Univ. of Chicago Pr.

Naples, Virginia L., et al, eds. The Other Saber-Tooths: Scimitar-Tooth Cats of the Western Hemisphere. 2011. (ENG., Illus.). 252p. (gr. 17). 110.00 (978-0-8018-9664-4(9)) Johns Hopkins Univ. Pr.

Polsky, Richard. Boneheads: My Search for T. Rex. 2011. 208p. E-Book (978-1-57178-308-0(3)); (ENG.). pap. 25.00 (978-1-57178-253-3(2)) Council Oak Bks.

Rand McNally Staff. El Gran Libro de Animales Prehistoricos.Tr. of Great Book of Prehistoric Animals. (SPA.). (978-968-416-609-7(5), 1010) Fernandez USA Publishing.

Tudge, Colin. The Link: Uncovering Our Earliest Ancestor. 2010. (ENG., Illus.). 272p. pap. 15.99 (978-0-316-07009-6(2), Back Bay Bks.) Little Brown & Co.

Wang, Xiaoming & Tedford, Richard H. Dogs: Their Fossil Relatives & Evolutionary History. 2010. (ENG., Illus.). 232p. (gr. 17). pap. 22.95 (978-0-231-13529-0(7)) Columbia Univ. Pr.

Winker, Kevin. On the Origin of Species Through Heteropatric Differentiation: A Review & a Model of Speciation in Migratory Animals. 2010. (Ornithological Monographs). 40p. pap. 19.95 (978-0-943610-88-7(5)) Univ. of California Pr.

ANIMALS, HABITATIONS OF

see Animals—Habitations

ANIMALS, HABITS AND BEHAVIOR OF

see Animal Behavior

ANIMALS, IMAGINARY

see Animals, Mythical

ANIMALS, INFANCY OF

see Animals—Infancy

ANIMALS, INJURIOUS AND BENEFICIAL

see Zoology, Economic

ANIMALS, LEGENDS AND STORIES OF

see Animals—Folklore; Animals—Legends

ANIMALS, MIGRATION OF

see Animal Migration

ANIMALS, MOVEMENTS OF

see Animal Mechanics

ANIMALS, MYTHICAL

see also Dragons; Sea Monsters; Unicorns; Vampires; Werewolves; Zoology—Pre-Linnean Works

Alterman, Steve & Ibelli, Tricia. Outer Banks Wild: A Winged Horse Extravaganza Pictorial. 2006. (Outer Banks Wild Ser.). (Illus.). 80p. pap. (978-0-9713890-9-0(8)) Outer Banks Pr.

Barber, Richard. Bestiary: Being an English Verison of the Bodleian Library, Oxford, MS Bodley 764. fac. ed. 2010. (Illus.). 206p. pap. 24.95 (978-0-85115-753-5(X)) Boydell & Brewer, Inc.

Black, Kathryn A. & Black, Ann N. More Readers Theatre for Middle School Boys: Adventures with Mythical Creatures, 1 vol. 2009. (Readers Theatre Ser.). 153p. pap. 28.00 (978-1-59158-757-6(3), TIP8757) Libraries Unlimited, Inc.

Borges, Jorge Luis. The Book of Imaginary Beings. Hurley, Andrew, tr. deluxe ed. 2006. (Penguin Classics Deluxe Edition Ser.). (ENG., Illus.). 256p. (gr. 12-18). 17.00 (978-0-14-303993-8(8), Penguin Classics) Penguin Group (USA) Inc.

Bright, Michael. Beasts of the Field: The Revealing Natural History of Animals in the Bible. 2006. (ENG., Illus.). 320p. 24.95 (978-1-86105-831-7(4), Robson Bks. Ltd.) Anova Bks. GBR. Dist: Independent Pubs. Group.

Campos, Cristian. Magical Creatures Design Handbook, 1 vol. 2009. (MUL & ENG., Illus.). 559p. pap. 19.95 (978-94-6065-006-2(6)) booQs Publishers bvba BEL. Dist: Innovative Logistics.

Cipa, Shawn. Carving Gargoyles: Grotesques, & Other Creatures of Myth. 2009. (ENG., Illus.). 159p. pap. 19.95 (978-1-56523-329-4(8)) Fox Chapel Publishing Co., Inc.

Coleman, Loren & Hallenbeck, Bruce G. Monsters of New Jersey: Mysterious Creatures in the Garden State. 2010. (ENG.). 144p. pap. 12.95 (978-0-8117-3596-4(6)) Stackpole Bks.

Cryptozoological Society Staff. Natural History of the Unnatural World. Date not set. pap. (978-0-312-28865-5(4), St. Martin's Griffin) St. Martin's Pr.

Cunningham, Gary & Coghlan, Ronan. The Mystery Animals of Ireland. 2010. (Illus.). 188p. pap. (978-1-905723-59-1(8)) CFZ Pr.

Foster, Michael Dylan. Pandemonium & Parade: Japanese Monsters & the Culture of Yokai. 2008. (Illus.). 290p. 55.00 (978-0-520-25361-2(2)); pap. 25.95 (978-0-520-25362-9(0)) Univ. of California Pr.

Freeman, Richard. The Great Yokai Encyclopaedi. 2010. 418p. pap. (978-1-905723-54-6(7)) CFZ Pr.

Geer, Alexandra van der. Animals in Stone: Indian Mammals Sculptured Through Time. 2008. (Handbook of Oriental Studies. Section 2 South Asia, 18/2 Ser.). (Illus.). 770p. (C). (978-90-04-16819-0(2)) BRILL.

Gerhard, Ken. Big Bird Modern Sightings of Flying Mon. 2007. 108p. per. (978-1-905723-08-9(3)) CFZ Pr.

Gilmore, David D. Monsters: Evil Beings, Mythical Beasts, & All Manner of Imaginary Terrors. 2009. (Illus.). 224p. (C). pap. 22.50 (978-0-8122-2088-9(9)) Univ. of Pennsylvania Pr.

Godfrey, Linda S. Monsters of Wisconsin: Mysterious Creatures in the Badger State. 2011. (Monsters Ser.). (ENG.). 128p. pap. 12.95 (978-0-8117-0748-0(2)) Stackpole Bks.

Gould, Charles. Mythical Monsters. 2009. 416p. 30.99 (978-0-559-10836-5(2)); 32.99 (978-0-559-10822-8(2)); pap. 33.75 (978-0-559-10833-4(8)); pap. 34.75 (978-0-559-10826-6(5)) BiblioBazaar.

Gray, Rachel. What to Do When You Meet Cthulhu: A Guide to Surviving the Cthulhu Mythos. Jones, William, ed. 2010. (ENG.). 256p. pap. 14.95 (978-1-934501-18-4(2)) Elder Signs Pr., Inc.

Guiley, Rosemary Ellen. Monsters of West Virginia: Mysterious Creatures in the Mountain State. 2012. (ENG.). 128p. pap. 12.95 ***(978-0-8117-1028-2(9))*** Stackpole Bks.

Hamel, Frank. Werewolves, Bird-Women, Tiger-Men & Other Human Animals. 2007. (Dover Occult Ser.). (ENG., Illus.). 320p. per. 12.95 *(978-0-486-46054-3(1))* Dover Pubns., Inc.

Harpur, James. Fantasmagoria: An Atlas of Fabulous Creatures, Magical Monsters & Enchanged Beings. 2009. (ENG.). 224p. 12.99 *(978-0-7858-2577-7(0),* 0785825770, Chartwell) Book Sales, Inc.

Hinds, Kathryn. Griffins & Phoenixes. 2012. (J). 32.79 ***(978-0-7614-4923-2(X))*** Marshall Cavendish Corp.

Ho, Kyun. Sibiji Ui Munhwasa. 2010. (KOR., Illus.). 176p. *(978-89-7199-372-9(3))* Dolbegae Publishing Co.

McCall, Gerrie & Regan, Lisa. Ancient Legends. 2011. (Monsters & Myths Ser.). (Illus.). 48p. (J). (gr. 4-6). pap. 14.05 *(978-1-4339-4989-0(X),* Stevens, Gareth Learning Library) Stevens, Gareth Publishing LLLP.

—Classical Myths. 2011. (Monsters & Myths Ser.). (Illus.). 48p. (J). (gr. 4-6). pap. 14.05 *(978-1-4339-4995-1(4),* Stevens, Gareth Learning Library) Stevens, Gareth Publishing LLLP.

—Ferocious Giants. 2011. (Monsters & Myths Ser.). (Illus.). 48p. (J). (gr. 4-6). pap. 14.05 *(978-1-4339-5001-8(4),* Stevens, Gareth Learning Library) Stevens, Gareth Publishing LLLP.

Mortensen, Lori. Basilisks. 2006. (Monsters Ser.). (ENG., Illus.). 48p. (YA). (gr. 4-7). lib. bdg. 27.50 *(978-0-7377-3529-1(5))* Cengage Gale.

Moseley, Jane. How to Live with a Unicorn: The Fantastic Guide to Keeping Mythical Pets. 2009. (ENG.). 128p. pap. 13.00 *(978-1-4379-7008-1(7))* DIANE Publishing Co.

Newton, Michael. Florida's Unexpected Wildlife: Exotic Species, Living Fossils, & Mythical Beasts in the Sunshine State. 2007. (ENG., Illus.). 208p. per. 21.00 *(978-0-8130-3156-9(7))* Univ. Pr. of Florida.

—Strange Kentucky Monsters. 2010. (Illus.). 160p. pap. 14.99 *(978-0-7643-3440-5(9))* Schiffer Publishing, Ltd.

Nickell, Joe. Tracking the Man-Beasts: Sasquatch, Vampires, Zombies, & More. 2011. (ENG.). 220p. pap. 19.00 *(978-1-61614-415-9(7))* Prometheus Bks., Pubs.

Parnell, Fran. Terrible Chenoo Chapter: A Story from North America. 2011. (ENG., Illus.). 30p. (J). pap. 7.99 *(978-1-84686-556-5(5))* Barefoot Bks., Inc.

Pepper, Elizabeth & Stacy, Barbara. The Little Book of Magical Creatures: A Revised & Expanded Edition, 1 vol. 2009. (ENG., Illus.). 160p. pap. 12.95 *(978-0-9773703-9-9(9))* Witches Almanac Ltd., The.

Petty, Anne C. Dragons of Fantasy. 2nd rev. ed. 2008. 310p. pap. 13.00 *(978-0-9792700-9-3(X))* Kitsune Bks.

Poole, W. Scott. Monsters in America: Our Historical Obsession with the Hideous & the Haunting. 2011. (ENG., Illus.). 295p. 29.95 *(978-1-60258-314-6(5))* Baylor Univ. Pr.

Reece, Gregory L. Creatures of the Night: In Search of Ghosts, Vampires, Werewolves & Demons. 2012. (ENG., Illus.). 256p. pap. 17.00 ***(978-1-84885-385-0(3))*** I. B. Tauris & Co., Ltd. GBR. Dist: Macmillan.

Regan, Lisa & McNab, Chris. Urban Myths & Legendary Creatures. 2011. (Monsters & Myths Ser.). (Illus.). 48p. (J). (gr. 4-6). pap. 14.05 *(978-1-4339-5010-0(3),* Stevens, Gareth Learning Library) Stevens, Gareth Publishing LLLP.

Roling, Bernd. Drachen und Sirenen: Die Rationalisierung und Abwicklung der Mythologie an Den Europäischen Universitäten. 2010. (Mittellateinische Studien und Texte Ser.). (GER.). 832p. *(978-90-04-18520-3(8))* BRILL.

Rosen, Brenda. Mythical Creatures Bible: The Definitive Guide to Legendary Beings. 2009. (ENG., Illus.). 400p. pap. 14.95 *(978-1-4027-6536-0(3))* Sterling Publishing Co., Inc.

Smith, Jaclyn. Fantasy Escape: Mythical Creatures. 2011. 48p. pap. 18.99 ***(978-1-4567-6953-6(7))*** AuthorHouse.

Storm, Rory. Monster Hunt: The Guide to Cryptozoology. 2008. (ENG., Illus.). 208p. 9.95 *(978-1-4027-6314-4(X))* Sterling Publishing Co., Inc.

Tilov, Dinko & Tilov, Boris. Sculpting Mythical Creatures Out of Polymer Clay: Making a Gnome, Pixie, Halfling, Fairy, Mermaid, Gorgon Vampire, Griffin, Sphinx, Unicorn, Centaur, Leviathan, & Dragon! 2009. (ENG., Illus.). 136p. pap. 22.99 *(978-1-59253-514-9(3),* 1592535143, Quarry Books) Quayside.

Trout, Paul A. Deadly Powers: Animal Predators & the Mythic Imagination. 2011. (ENG., Illus.). 300p. 26.00 ***(978-1-61614-501-9(3))*** Prometheus Bks., Pubs.

van Dinter, M. Hesselt. Fabulous Creatures: Demons, Unicorns, Dragons, Griffin. 2008. (Illus.). 250p. pap. *(978-90-78900-06-1(7))* Mundurucu Pubs.

Ward, Peter L. Eric & the Mystical Bear. 2011. 152p. 23.14 *(978-1-4269-5500-6(6));* pap. 13.14 *(978-1-4269-5501-3(4))* Trafford Publishing.

Watier, Matt. The Secret Magicks of Maine. 2009. (Illus.). *(978-1-4415-0269-8(6))* Xlibris Corp.

White, Julia C. Fantasy Flight. Date not set. 125p. pap. 19.95 *(978-1-888059-02-1(6))* White, Julia C.

Whitlatch, Terryl & Banducci, Gilbert. Animals Real & Imagined: The fantasy of what Is & what might Be. 2010. (Illus.). 160p. 49.95 *(978-1-933492-91-9(0))* Design Studio Pr.

Winter, Galen. Legendary Northwoods Animals: A Fabricated Field Guide. 2007. (ENG., Illus.). 128p. per. 14.95 *(978-1-59543-601-6(4))* Willow Creek Pr., Inc.

ANIMALS, NOCTURNAL
see Nocturnal Animals

ANIMALS, ORIENTATION OF
see Orientation

ANIMALS, PARTHENOGENESIS IN
see Parthenogenesis (Animals)

ANIMALS, PHOTOGRAPHY OF
see Photography of Animals

ANIMALS, POISONOUS
see Poisonous Animals

ANIMALS, PREDATORY
see Predatory Animals

ANIMALS, PREHISTORIC
see Animals, Fossil

ANIMALS, PROTECTION OF
see Animal Welfare; Wildlife Conservation

ANIMALS, RARE
see Rare Animals

ANIMALS, RESPIRATION OF
see Respiration

ANIMALS, SOUND PRODUCTION BY
see Sound Production by Animals

ANIMALS, TRAINING OF
see Animal Training

ANIMALS, TREATMENT OF
see Animal Welfare

ANIMALS, USEFUL AND HARMFUL
see Zoology, Economic

ANIMALS, WAR USE OF
see Animals—War Use

ANIMALS, WORKING
see Working Animals

ANIMALS AND CIVILIZATION
see also Zoology, Economic

Aftandilian, Dave, et al, eds. What Are the Animals to Us? Approaches from Science, Religion, Folklore, Literature, & Art. 2006. (Illus.). 400p. 45.00 *(978-1-57233-472-4(X))* Univ. of Tennessee Pr.

Alberti, Samuel J. M. M. The Afterlives of Animals: A Museum Menagerie. 2011. E-Book ***(978-0-8139-3208-8(4))*** Univ. Pr. of Virginia.

Alberti, Samuel J. M. M., ed. The Afterlives of Animals: A Museum Menagerie. 2011. (ENG., Illus.). 256p. (gr. 17). 35.00 *(978-0-8139-3167-8(3))* Univ. Pr. of Virginia.

Anthony, David W. The Horse, the Wheel & Language: How Bronze-Age Riders from the Eurasian Steppes Shaped the Modern World. 2007. (ENG., Illus.). 568p. (C). 45.00 *(978-0-691-05887-0(3))* Princeton Univ. Pr.

—Horse, the Wheel & Language: How Bronze-Age Riders from the Eurasian Steppes Shaped the Modern World. 2010. (ENG., Illus.). 568p. (C). pap. 22.95 *(978-0-691-14818-2(X))* Princeton Univ. Pr.

Bignon, Olivier. Chasser les Chevaux à la Fin du Paléolitique Dans le Bassin Parisien: Stratégie Cynégétique et Mode de Vie Au Magdalenien et à L'Azilien Ancien. 2008. (Bar S Ser.). (FRE., Illus.). 170p. (C). 85.00 *(978-1-4073-0189-1(6))* British Archaeological Reports Ltd. GBR. Dist: Brown, David Bk. Co., The.

Calder, Louise. Cruelty & Sentimentality: Greek Attitudes to Animals, 600-300 BC. 2011. (Studies in Classical Archaeology Ser.). (ENG.). 227p. (C). 80.00 ***(978-1-903767-14-6(8))*** Archaeopress GBR. Dist: Brown, David Bk. Co., The.

Chaline, Eric. Fifty Animals That Changed the Course of History. 2011. (ENG., Illus.). 224p. 29.95 *(978-1-55407-897-4(0))* Firefly Bks., Ltd.

Chamberlin, J. Edward. Horse: How the Horse Has Shaped Civilizations. 2008. (ENG., Illus.). 288p. pap. 13.95 *(978-1-933346-13-7(2))* BlueBridge.

Clutton-Brock, Juliet. Animals As Domesticates: A World View Through History. 2012. pap. ***(978-1-61186-064-1(4))***; (ENG., Illus.). 200p. 44.95 ***(978-1-61186-028-3(8))*** Michigan State Univ. Pr.

Crawford, Dean. Shark. 2008. (Reaktion Books - Animal Ser.). (ENG., Illus.). 224p. pap. 19.95 *(978-1-86189-325-3(6))* Reaktion Bks., Ltd. GBR. Dist: Chicago Distribution Ctr.

De Rijke, V. Duck. 2008. (Reaktion Books - Animal Ser.). (ENG., Illus.). 224p. pap. 19.95 *(978-1-86189-350-5(7))* Reaktion Bks., Ltd. GBR. Dist: Chicago Distribution Ctr.

Donald, Diana. Picturing Animals in Britain. 2008. (ENG., Illus.). 256p. 65.00 *(978-0-300-12679-2(4))* Yale Univ. Pr.

Enright, Kelly. Rhinoceros. 2008. (Reaktion Books - Animal Ser.). (ENG., Illus.). 224p. pap. 19.95 *(978-1-86189-374-1(4))* Reaktion Bks., Ltd. GBR. Dist: Chicago Distribution Ctr.

Groot, Maaike. Animals in Ritual & Economy in a Roman Frontier Community: Excavations in Tiel-Passewaaij. 2009. (Amsterdam University Press - Amsterdam Archaeological Studies). (Illus.). 288p. 69.95 *(978-90-8964-022-2(3),* Leiden Univ. Pr.) Amsterdam Univ. Pr. NLD. Dist: Chicago Distribution Ctr.

Gross, Aaron & Vallely, Anne. Animals & the Human Imagination: A Companion to Animal Studies. 2012. (ENG., Illus.). 392p. (gr. 17). 89.50 ***(978-0-231-15296-9(5))***; pap. 29.50 ***(978-0-231-15297-6(3))*** Columbia Univ. Pr.

Kalof, Linda, ed. A Cultural History of Animals in Antiquity. 2009. (ENG., Illus.). 1p. 120.00 *(978-1-84520-361-0(5))* Berg Pubs. GBR. Dist: Macmillan.

Kelekna, Pita. The Horse in Human History. 2009. (ENG., Illus.). (C). 476p. 99.99 *(978-0-521-51659-4(5))*; 474p. pap. 28.99 *(978-0-521-73629-9(3))* Cambridge Univ. Pr.

Martin, Stephen. Penguin. 2009. (Reaktion Books - Animal Ser.). (ENG., Illus.). 224p. pap. 19.95 *(978-1-86189-376-5(0))* Reaktion Bks., Ltd. GBR. Dist: Chicago Distribution Ctr.

Nicholls, Henry. The Way of the Panda: The Curious History of China's Political Animal. 2011. (ENG., Illus.). 304p. 25.00 *(978-1-60598-188-8(5),* 605188) Pegasus Bks.

Obermaier, Sabine. Tiere und Fabelwesen Im Mittelalter: Zu Ihrer Bedeutung in Wissenschaft, Religion, Geschichte, Bildender Kunst und Literatur. Obermaier, Sabine, ed. 2009.Tr. of Animals & Mythical Creatures in the Middle Ages. (GER., Illus.). VIII, 342p. 140.00 *(978-3-11-020137-6(2))* De Gruyter, Walter Inc.

Obermaier, Sabine, ed. Tiere und Fabelwesen Im Mittelalter. 2009.Tr. of Animals & Mythical Creatures in the Middle Ages. (GER.). VIII, 342p. 210.00 ***(978-3-11-173736-2(3))*** De Gruyter, Walter Inc.

Pastoureau, Michel. The Bear: History of a Fallen King. Holoch, George, tr. from FRE. 2011. Orig. Title: L' ours: Histoire d'un roi Déchu. (ENG., Illus.). 384p. 29.95 *(978-0-674-04782-2(6),* Belknap Pr.) Harvard Univ. Pr.

Pundyk, Grace. The Honey Spinner. 2008. (Illus.). 336p. pap. *(978-1-74196-088-4(6))* Murdoch Bks. Pty Ltd.

Ranger, Sheilagh. The Word of Wisdom & the Creation of Animals in Africa. 2007. (ENG., Illus.). 264p. per. 58.00 *(978-0-227-67986-9(5))* Clarke, James Co., Ltd. GBR. Dist: Brown, David Bk. Co., The.

Resl, Brigitte & Malamud, Randy, eds. A Cultural History of Animals in the Medieval Age. 2009. (ENG., Illus.). 1p. 120.00 *(978-1-84520-369-6(0))* Berg Pubs. GBR. Dist: Macmillan.

Salisbury, Joyce. The Beast Within. 2nd rev. ed. 2010. (ENG., Illus.). 224p. (C). 130.00 *(978-0-415-78094-0(2))*; pap. 34.95 *(978-0-415-78095-7(0))* Routledge.

Schiesari, Juliana. Beasts & Beauties: Animals, Gender, & Domestication in the Italian Renaissance. 2010. (Toronto Italian Studies). (Illus.). 176p. *(978-0-8020-9922-8(X))* Univ. of Toronto Pr.

Stibbe, Arran. Animals Erased: Discourse, Ecology, & Reconnection with the Natural World. 2012. (ENG., Illus.). 232p. (C). 70.00 ***(978-0-8195-7231-8(4))***; pap. 24.95 ***(978-0-8195-7232-5(2))*** Wesleyan Univ. Pr.

Velten, Hannah. Cow. 2007. (Reaktion Books - Animal Ser.). (ENG., Illus.). 224p. pap. 19.95 *(978-1-86189-326-0(4))* Reaktion Bks., Ltd. GBR. Dist: Chicago Distribution Ctr.

Wilson, Bee. The Hive: The Story of the Honeybee & Us. 2008. 308p. 25.00 *(978-1-4379-5844-7(3))* DIANE Publishing Co.

—Hive: The Story of the Honeybee & Us. 2007. (ENG., Illus.). 320p. pap. 14.95 *(978-0-312-37124-1(1),* St. Martin's Griffin) St. Martin's Pr.

Wolloch, Nathaniel. Subjugated Animals: Animals & Anthropocentrism in Early Modern European Culture. 2007. (Illus.). 280p. per. 39.98 *(978-1-59102-494-1(3),* Humanity Bks.) Prometheus Bks., Pubs.

Young, Peter. Swan. 2008. (Reaktion Books - Animal Ser.). (ENG., Illus.). 224p. per. 19.95 *(978-1-86189-349-9(3))* Reaktion Bks., Ltd. GBR. Dist: Chicago Distribution Ctr.

ANIMALS AND HUMANS
see Human-Animal Relationships

ANIMALS AND PLANTS
see Animal-Plant Relationships

ANIMALS AS CARRIERS OF DISEASE
see also Insects As Carriers of Disease; Rodents As Carriers of Disease; Snails As Carriers of Disease

Committee on Achieving Sustainable Global Capacity for Surveillance and Response to Emerging Diseases of Zoonotic Origin Staff & National Research Council. Achieving Sustainable Global Capacity for Surveillance & Response to Emerging Diseases of Zoonotic Origin: Workshop Summary. Beatty, Alexandra et al, eds. 2008. (ENG.). 152p. pap. 36.50 *(978-0-309-12818-6(8))* National Academies Pr.

Lemon, Stanley M. Vector-Borne Diseases: Understanding the Environmental, Human Health, & Ecological Connections, Workshop Summary (Forum on Microbial Threats) 2008. (ENG., Illus.). 350p. pap. 70.00 *(978-0-309-10897-3(7))* National Academies Pr.

Macpherson, Calum N. L., et al, eds. Dogs, Zoonoses & Public Health. 2nd ed. 2012. 400p. 180.00 ***(978-1-84593-835-2(6))*** CABI GBR. Dist: Stylus Publishing, LLC.

Mehlhorn, Heinz, ed. Arthropods as Vectors of Emerging Diseases. 2012. (Parasitology Research Monographs). (ENG., Illus.). xiv, 466p. 209.00 ***(978-3-642-28841-8(3),*** 3642288413) Springer.

Romich, Janet Amundson. Understanding Zoonotic Diseases. 2007. (Veterinary Technology Ser.). (ENG., Illus.). 720p. (C). 112.95 *(978-1-4180-2103-0(2))* Delmar Cengage Learning.

Takken, Willem & Knols, Bart G. J., eds. Olfaction in vector-host interactions. 2010. (Illus.). 360p. 146.00 *(978-90-8686-091-3(5))* Wageningen Academic Publishers NLD. Dist: Enfield Publishing & Distribution Co., Inc.

Viroj Wiwanitkit. Swine Flu & Pig Borne Diseases. 2009. (Public Health in the 21st Century Ser.). pap. 43.00 *(978-1-60876-291-0(2),* Nova Biomedical Bks.) Nova Science Pubs., Inc.

Waltner-Toews, David. The Chickens Fight Back: Pandemic Panics & Deadly Diseases That Jump from Animals to Humans, 1 vol. 2007. (ENG.). 256p. pap. 17.95 *(978-1-55365-270-0(3),* Greystone Bks.) D&M Pubs. Inc. CAN. Dist: Perseus-PGW.

ANIMALS AS FOOD
see Food of Animal Origin

ANIMALS IN ART
see also Animal Painting and Illustration; Decoration and Ornament—Animal Forms
also Birds in Art, Horses in Art, and similar headings

Adel, Jean. Knitted Critters for Kids to Wear: More Than 40 Animal-Themed Accessories. 2008. (ENG., Illus.). 96p. pap. 19.95 *(978-0-307-39466-8(2),* Potter Craft) Crown Publishing Group.

Alexandridis, Annetta, et al, eds. Mensch und Tier in der Antike: Grenzziehung und Grenzüberschreitung. 2009. (GER., Illus.). 588p. (C). 99.00 *(978-3-89500-583-1(5))* Reichert, Ludwig Dr. DEU. Dist: Brown, David Bk. Co., The.

Aloi, Giovanni. Art & Animals. 2011. (Art and... Ser.). (ENG., Illus.). 192p. 75.00 ***(978-1-84885-524-3(9))***; pap. 27.50 ***(978-1-84885-525-0(7))*** I. B. Tauris & Co., Ltd. GBR. Dist: Macmillan.

Anderson, Lynette. It's Quilting Cats & Dogs. 2010. (ENG., Illus.). 128p. pap. 24.99 *(978-0-7153-3757-8(2))* David & Charles Pubs. GBR. Dist: F&W Media, Inc.

Archbold, Rick. An Artist in Nature. 2010. (ENG., Illus.). 175p. 40.00 *(978-1-897330-46-3(4))* Madison Pr. Bks. CAN. Dist: Independent Pubs. Group.

Armstrong, Carol. Best in Show: 24 Applique Quilts for Dog Lovers. 2009. (ENG., Illus.). 64p. pap. 26.95 *(978-1-57120-610-7(8))* C & T Publishing.

Aruz, Joan, et al. The Golden Deer of Eurasia: Perspectives on the Steppe Nomads of the Ancient World. 2006. 25.00 *(978-1-58839-205-3(8))* Metropolitan Museum of Art, The.

Atac, Mehmet Ali. The Mythology of Kingship in Neo-Assyrian Art. 2010. (ENG., Illus.). 300p. (C). 99.00 *(978-0-521-51790-4(7))* Cambridge Univ. Pr.

Ayers, Chris, illus. The Daily Zoo Year 2: Keeping the Doctor at Bay with a Drawing a Day. 2009. (ENG.). 160p. 29.95 *(978-1-933492-47-6(3))* Design Studio Pr.

Banjo, Brett. Let Sleeping Dogs Lie. Date not set. (Illus.). 32p. 17.95 ***(978-0-9846853-0-1(8))*** Banjo Pr.

Barnet, Peter & Dandridge, Pete. Lions, Dragons, & Other Beasts: Aquamanilia of the Middle Ages - Vessels for Church & Table. 2006. (ENG., Illus.). 256p. 55.00 *(978-0-300-11684-7(5))* Yale Univ. Pr.

Benjamin, Andrew. Of Jews & Animals. (Frontiers of Theory Ser.). (ENG., Illus.). 224p. (gr. 17). 2011. pap. 32.00 ***(978-0-7486-4317-2(6))*** 2010. 115.00 *(978-0-7486-4053-9(3))* Edinburgh Univ. Pr. GBR. Dist: Columbia Univ. Pr.

Blue Lantern Studio, creator. Animals at Christmas Postcard Book. 2010. (ENG., Illus.). 60p. pap. 9.95 *(978-1-59583-394-5(3),* Darling & Co.) Laughing Elephant.

Boehrer, Bruce Thomas. Animal Characters: Nonhuman Beings in Early Modern Literature. 2010. (Haney Foundation Ser.). (Illus.). 256p. (C). 49.95 *(978-0-8122-4249-2(1))* Univ. of Pennsylvania Pr.

Bosteels, Linda Millier. Spirit of the Buffalo: Oklahoma's Past & Future. 2006. (Oklahoma Horizons Ser.). (Illus.). 157p. 29.95 *(978-1-885596-58-1(8))* Oklahoma Heritage Assn.

Bowker, John. An an Alphabet of Animals. 2010. (Illus.). 142p. pap. 29.99 *(978-0-9782526-7-0(5))* Key Publishing Hse., Inc., The CAN. Dist: AtlasBooks Distribution.

Broglio, Ron. Surface Encounters: Thinking with Animals & Art. 2011. (Posthumanities Ser.). (ENG., Illus.). 176p. 75.00 ***(978-0-8166-7296-7(2))***; pap. 25.00 ***(978-0-8166-7297-4(0))*** Univ. of Minnesota Pr.

Bryan, Debra Jordan. Whimsical Dogs & Cats to Paint. 2006. (ENG.). 96p. pap. 19.95 *(978-1-60140-122-9(1))* Leisure Arts, Inc.

Buford, Bill. Walton Ford Pancha Tantra. 2009. (FRE, GER & ENG., Illus.). 320p. 69.99 *(978-3-8228-5237-8(5))* TASCHEN DEU. Dist: Ingram Pub. Services.

Bugler, Caroline. The Cat: 3500 Years of the Cat in Art. 2011. (ENG., Illus.). 288p. 49.95 *(978-1-85894-530-9(5))* Merrell Pubs. Ltd. GBR. Dist: Perseus Distribution.

Caines, Michael. Revelations & Dog. 2011. (Revelations And ... Ser.). (ENG., Illus.). 96p. 28.95 *(978-1-935613-08-4(1))* Batty, Mark Pub., LLC.

Calder, Alexander. Animal Sketching. 2010. 66p. 25.56 *(978-1-168-80325-2(X))* 2010. 64p. pap. 13.56 *(978-1-163-16975-9(7))* 2010. 66p. 31.95 *(978-1-161-63739-7(7))* 2007. (ENG.). 64p. (gr. 3-7). per. 16.95 *(978-1-4325-6990-7(2))* Kessinger Publishing, LLC.

Calder, Louise. Cruelty & Sentimentality: Greek Attitudes to Animals, 600-300 BC. 2011. (Studies in Classical Archaeology Ser.). (ENG.). 227p. (C). 80.00 ***(978-1-903767-14-6(8))*** Archaeopress GBR. Dist: Brown, David Bk. Co., The.

Campos, Cristian. Magical Creatures Design Handbook, 1 vol. 2009. (MUL & ENG., Illus.). 559p. pap. 19.95 *(978-94-6065-006-2(6))* booQs Publishers bvba BEL. Dist: Innovative Logistics.

Christine M., Unwin. The Artistic Touch 5. 2012. (Artistic Touch Ser.). 172p. 35.00 *(978-0-9642712-6-5(5))* Creative Art Pr.

Cibos, Lindsay & Hodges, Jared. Draw Furries: How to Create Anthropomorphic & Fantasy Animals. 2009. (ENG., Illus.). 128p. pap. 22.99 *(978-1-60061-417-0(5),* Impact) F&W Media, Inc.

Civardi, Giovanni. The Art of Drawing: Drawing Pets. 2012. (Art of Drawing Ser.). (ENG., Illus.). 64p. pap. 17.95 ***(978-1-84448-784-4(9))*** Search Pr., Ltd. GBR. Dist: Independent Pubs. Group.

Cloutier, Re/*al. Carving Whales. 2007. (Illus.). 64p. pap. 16.95 *(978-0-7643-2767-4(4))* Schiffer Publishing, Ltd.

Cohen, Simona. Animals as Disguised Symbols in Renaissance Art. 2008. 352p. (C). *(978-90-04-17101-5(0))* BRILL.

Colman, David. The Art of Animal Character Design with David Colman, First Edition, English. 2007. 40.00 *(978-0-9790686-0-7(6)*, 2500) David's Doodles.

Conal, Robbie. Not Your Typical Political Animal: Animal Drawings & Paintings by Guerrilla Poster Artist Robbie Conal. 2009. (Illus.). 80p. (YA). pap. 24.95 *(978-0-615-32667-2(6))* ArtAttack Pr.

Cook, Jill. The Swimming Reindeer. 2010. (Objects in Focus Ser.). (ENG., Illus.). 55p. (C). pap. 10.00 *(978-0-7141-2821-4(X))* British Museum Pr. GBR. Dist: Brown, David Bk. Co., The.

Cormack, Malcolm. Country Pursuits: British, American, & French Sporting Art from the Mellon Collections in the Virginia Museum of Fine Arts. 2007. (ENG., Illus.). 480p. (gr. 17). 75.00 *(978-0-8139-2601-8(7))* Univ. Pr. of Virginia.

CowParade Wisconsin. 2006. (Illus.). 127p. 24.95 *(978-1-933197-23-4(4))* Orange Frazer Pr.

Crisante, Cristina D. & Gransingh, Vania, eds. Giambattista Tiepolo: Tra Scherzo e Capriccio. 2010. (ITA.). 112p. pap. 45.00 *(978-88-370-7725-9(4))* Electa ITA. Dist: Trans-Atlantic Pubns., Inc.

Dahl, Anja. Draw Animals with Expression & Personality. 2012. (Drawing Workshop Ser.). (ENG., Illus.). 64p. pap. 17.95 ***(978-1-84448-695-3(8))*** Search Pr., Ltd. GBR. Dist: Independent Pubs. Group.

Daly, Jim. Our Furry Friends: Delighting in the Pets We Love. 2007. 48p. 15.99 *(978-0-7369-1913-5(9))* Harvest Hse. Pubs.

Davies, Dawn. My Art Has Heart. 2009. (Illus.). 56p. pap. 25.49 *(978-1-4490-3585-3(X))* AuthorHouse.

Davies, Paul Bryn. Dragons in Watercolour. 2008. (Fantasy Art Ser.). (ENG., Illus.). 48p. pap. 15.95 *(978-1-84448-382-2(7))* Search Pr., Ltd. GBR. Dist: Independent Pubs. Group.

Dearing, Charles. Wildlife Portraits in Wood: 30 Patterns to Capture the Beauty of Nature. 2008. (Scroll Saw, Woodworking & Crafts Book Ser.). (ENG., Illus.). 67p. pap. 14.95 *(978-1-56523-338-6(7))* Fox Chapel Publishing Co., Inc.

DeMello, Margo. Teaching the Animal. 2010. *(978-1-59056-178-2(3))*; *(978-1-59056-179-9(1))* Lantern Bks.

Denk, Margaret. The Christmas Cat Book. 2006. (Celebration (Red Rock Press) Ser.). (ENG., Illus.). 64p. 9.95 *(978-1-933176-07-9(5))* Red Rock Pr., Inc.

—The Christmas Dog Book. 2006. (Celebration (Red Rock Press) Ser.). (ENG., Illus.). 64p. 9.95 *(978-1-933176-08-6(3))* Red Rock Pr., Inc.

d'Errico, Camilla. Femina & Fauna: the Art of Camilla D'Errico: The Art of Camilla D'Errico. 2011. (Illus.). 112p. 22.99 *(978-1-59582-583-4(5))* Dark Horse Comics.

Derry, Ramsay. The World of Robert Bateman. 2010. (Illus.). 180p. 40.00 *(978-1-897330-45-6(6))* Madison Pr. Bks. CAN. Dist: Independent Pubs. Group.

Detmold, Maurice & Detmold, Edward J. An Edwardian Bestiary: 87 Color Plates. Menges, Jeff A., ed. & intro. by. 2009. (Dover Fine Art, History of Art Ser.). (ENG., Illus.). 96p. pap. 12.95 *(978-0-486-46877-8(1))* Dover Pubns., Inc.

Dgph. The Ark Project: Illustrated Animal Bible by Artists from All over the World. 2010. (ENG., Illus.). 240p. pap. 34.00 *(978-988-18470-1-0(X))* Systems Design, Ltd. HKG. Dist: D.A.P./Distributed Art Pubs.

Donald, Diana. Picturing Animals in Britain. 2008. (ENG., Illus.). 256p. 65.00 *(978-0-300-12679-2(4))* Yale Univ. Pr.

Donga-Durach, Thomas & Edel, Andrea, texts. Frank Herzog: Back to Art History. 2010. (ENG., Illus.). 88p. pap. 25.00 *(978-3-86678-255-6(1))* Kerber Verlag DEU. Dist: D.A.P./Distributed Art Pubs.

Doust, Len A. Animal Sketching for Beginners. 2006. (Dover Art Instruction Ser.). (ENG., Illus.). 64p. per. 4.95 *(978-0-486-45130-5(5))* Dover Pubns., Inc.

Eichhorn, Virginia M. & Harris, Adam Duncan. George McLean: The Living Landscape. 2010. (Illus.). 60.00 ***(978-0-86492-625-8(1))*** Goose Lane Editions CAN. Dist: Univ. of Toronto Pr.

Eliens, Titus M. Pablo Picasso: Keramiek/Ceramics. 2007. (DUT & ENG., Illus.). 96p. 30.00 *(978-90-400-8315-0(0))* Waanders B.V., Uitgeverij NLD. Dist: National Bk. Network.

Ellis, Bud & Hoeckley, Rhonda. Carousel Animal Carving: Patterns & Techniques. 2008. (ENG., Illus.). 160p. per. 17.95 *(978-1-4027-4362-7(9))* Sterling Publishing Co., Inc.

Ellis, Steve. Scream: Draw Classic Vampires, Werewolves, Zombies, Monsters & More. 2009. (ENG., Illus.). 128p. pap. 22.99 *(978-1-60061-179-7(6)*, Impact) F&W Media, Inc.

Evans, E. p. & Evans, E. P. Animal Symbolism in Ecclesiastical Architecture. 2010. 390p. 48.95 *(978-1-161-38110-8(4))* Kessinger Publishing, LLC.

Evans, Linda. Animal Behaviour in Egyptian Art: Representations of the Natural World in Memphite Tomb Scenes. 2010. (ACE Studies). (ENG., Illus.). 350p. (C). pap. 130.00 *(978-0-85668-826-3(6))* Australian Ctr. for Egyptology AUS. Dist: Brown, David Bk. Co., The.

Ewers, John C. Plains Indian Art: The Pioneering Work of John C. Ewers. Robinson, Jane Ewers, ed. 2011. (Charles M. Russell Center Ser. on Art & Photography of the American West Ser.). (ENG., Illus.). 224p. 39.95 *(978-0-8061-3061-3(X))* Univ. of Oklahoma Pr.

Flynn, Ron. The Audubon Price Guide Book. 2008. 252p. pap. 59.95 *(978-1-4357-0809-9(1))* Lulu Enterprises Inc.

Fox, Ron. Cow Parade West Hartford: Around the World & Home Again. 2007. pap. 22.00 *(978-1-933197-42-5(0))* Orange Frazer Pr.

Fox, Ronald A., text. CowParade Boston. 2006. (Illus.). 128p. *(978-1-933197-21-0(8))* Orange Frazer Pr.

Freeman, Carol, et al, eds. Considering Animals: Contemporary Studies in Human-Animal Relations. 2011. (Illus.). 252p. 64.95 *(978-1-4094-0013-4(1))* Ashgate Publishing Co.

Gaffney, Peggy. The Crafty Golden Retriever - Knits: Knitting Projects for Dog Lovers. 2007. (Illus.). 110p. per. 35.00 *(978-0-9770412-2-0(0))* Kanine Knits.

Garland, Claire. Knit & Purl Pets. 2010. (ENG., Illus.). 128p. pap. 22.99 *(978-0-7153-3667-0(3))* David & Charles Pubs. GBR. Dist: F&W Media, Inc.

Getha, Patricia. The Art of Drawing Animals. 2012. ***(978-1-936309-54-2(8))*** Foster, Walter Publishing, Inc.

Gibson, Graeme. The Bedside Book of Beasts: A Wildlife Miscellany. 2009. (Illus.). 384p. 20.00 *(978-0-385-66915-3(1))* Doubleday Canada, Ltd. CAN. Dist: Random Hse., Inc.

—The Bedside Book of Beasts: A Wildlife Miscellany. 2009. (ENG., Illus.). 384p. 35.00 *(978-0-385-52459-9(5)*, Talese, Nan A.) Knopf Doubleday Publishing Group.

Good, Jonni. Make Animal Sculptures with Paper Mache Clay: How to Create Stunning Wildlife Art Using Patterns & My Easy-to-Make, No-Mess Paper Mache Recipe - the New Way to Papier Mache. 2010. (ENG., Illus.). 98p. pap. 22.95 *(978-0-9741065-1-9(8))* Wet Cat Bks.

Gordon, Sophie. Noble Hounds & Dear Companions: The Royal Photograph Collection. 2010. (ENG., Illus.). 120p. 15.00 *(978-1-902163-85-7(0))* Royal Collection Enterprises Ltd. GBR. Dist: Chicago Distribution Ctr.

Grabowska-Konwent, Anna. Zoografika: Gnieznienskie Spotkania Z Plakatem: Spotkanie 8: Plakat, Grafika, Druki Ze Zbiorów Muzeum Narodowego W Poznaniu. 2009. (POL., Illus.). 189p. *(978-83-61391-16-6(9))* Muzeum Poczatkow Panstwa Polskiego w Gnieznie.

Gray, Peter. Everyone Can Draw Animals. 2012. (Everyone Can Draw Ser.). (ENG., Illus.). 32p. (gr. 3-6). lib. bdg. 26.50 ***(978-1-61533-504-6(8))*** Windmill Bks.

Greenlaw, Cybelle. The Representation of Monkeys in the Art & Thought of Mediterranean Cultures: A New Perspective on Ancient Primates. 2011. (Bar S Ser.). (Illus.). 89p. (C). pap. 70.00 *(978-1-4073-0747-3(9))* British Archaeological Reports Ltd. GBR. Dist: Brown, David Bk. Co., The.

Hamernik, Harry. Cartoonimals: How to Draw Amazing Cartoon Animals. 2008. (ENG., Illus.). 128p. pap. 19.99 *(978-1-60061-114-8(1)*, Impact) F&W Media, Inc.

Hammond, Lee. Paint Realistic Animals in Acrylic with Lee Hammond. 2007. (ENG., Illus.). 128p. pap. 24.99 *(978-1-58180-912-1(3)*, North Light Bks.) F&W Media, Inc.

Hart, Christopher. Cartoon Cute Animals: How to Draw the Most Irresistible Creatures on the Planet. 2010. (ENG., Illus.). 160p. pap. 21.99 *(978-0-8230-8556-9(2))* Watson-Guptill Pubns., Inc.

—Drawing Animals Made Amazingly Easy. 2007. (Made Amazingly Easy Ser.). (ENG., Illus.). 144p. pap. 19.95 *(978-0-8230-1390-6(1))* Watson-Guptill Pubns., Inc.

Hastie, F. Bowman, III & Sasquatch Books Staff. Portrait of the Dog As a Young Artist: Art from Scratch, by the World's Preeminent Canine Painter. 2006. (ENG., Illus.). 80p. pap. 14.95 *(978-1-57061-464-4(4))* Sasquatch Bks.

Hayakawa, Hiroshi. Kirigami Menagerie: 38 Paper Animals to Copy, Cut & Fold. 2009. (ENG., Illus.). 128p. pap. 17.95 *(978-1-60059-318-5(6))* Lark Bks.

Heywood, Birdy. Polymer Clay Bears. 2010. (Twenty to Make Ser.). (ENG., Illus.). 48p. pap. 9.95 *(978-1-84448-504-8(6))* Search Pr., Ltd. GBR. Dist: Independent Pubs. Group.

Ho, Kyun. Sibiji Ui Munhwasa. 2010. (KOR., Illus.). 176p. *(978-89-7199-372-9(3))* Dolbegae Publishing Co.

Hoggett, Sarah. A Masterclass in Drawing & Painting Animals. Hoggett, Sarah, ed. 2011. (ENG., Illus.). 256p. 35.00 *(978-0-7548-2059-8(9))* Anness Publishing GBR. Dist: National Bk. Network.

Hoshi, Mitsuki. Ami Ami Dogs: Seriously Cute Crochet. 2011. (ENG., Illus.). 72p. pap. 14.99 *(978-0-06-202570-8(8)*, Collins Design) HarperCollins Pubs.

Huneck, Stephen. Even Bad Dogs Go to Heaven: More from the Dog Chapel. 2010. (ENG., Illus.). 80p. 19.95 *(978-0-8109-9629-8(4))* Abrams.

Hurlbut, Joan L. Pristine's Beaded Beauties: Wolves, Bats & Other Critters of Travel, 1. 2006. (Illus.). 131p. per. 24.95 *(978-0-9760005-1-8(2))* Pristine's Publishing.

Impact Books Editors. DragonWorld: Amazing dragons, advice & inspiration from the artists of DeviantART. Wissman, Pamela & Laichas, Sarah, eds. 2011. (ENG., Illus.). 144p. pap. 26.99 *(978-1-4403-0873-4(X)*, Impact) F&W Media, Inc.

Irwin, Robert. Camel. 2010. (Reaktion Books - Animal Ser.). (ENG., Illus.). 224p. pap. 19.95 *(978-1-86189-649-0(2))* Reaktion Bks., Ltd. GBR. Dist: Chicago Distribution Ctr.

Joeseter Loria Group, concept. Care Bears Sketchbook. 2006. 5.95 *(978-1-60140-110-6(8))* Leisure Arts, Inc.

Journi, David. Animals in a World of Wild Words. 2009. 28p. pap. 13.00 *(978-1-4389-4198-1(6))* AuthorHouse.

Kauffman Yaun, Debra & Yaun, Debra K. Animals: Learn to Draw Step by Step. 2009. (How to Draw & Paint Series: Drawing Ser.). (ENG., Illus.). 32p. pap. 8.95 *(978-1-60058-137-3(4)*, 1600581374) Foster, Walter Publishing, Inc.

Kerr, Kavar, selected by. The Heart of a Collection: National Museum of Wildlife Art: Highlights of the NMWA Collection. 2012. ***(978-1-57864-707-1(X))*** Donning Co. Pubs.

Kowalski, Karla. Monster und Andere Wahrheiten/Monsters & Other Truths: Bildergeschichten/Picture Stories, 1 vol. 2006. (ENG & GER., Illus.). 208p. 65.00 *(978-3-936314-62-5(4))* Jovis Verlag GmbH DEU. Dist: D.A.P./Distributed Art Pubs.

Kurzmayer, Roman. Schlangen Linien / Serpentine Lines: Max von Moos, André Thomkins, Aldo Walker, Max Ernst. 2011. (GER.). 96p. pap. 29.95 ***(978-3-7091-0703-4(2))*** Springer Wien AUT. Dist: Actar Birkhauser Distribution.

Lark Books Staff, creator. 500 Animals in Clay: Contemporary Expressions of the Animal Form. 2006. (Lark Ceramics Book Ser.). (ENG., Illus.). 424p. pap. 24.95 *(978-1-57990-757-0(1))* Lark Bks.

Law, Stephanie Pui-Mon. DreamScapes Myth & Magic: Create Legendary Creatures & Characters in Watercolor. 2010. (ENG., Illus.). 176p. pap. 24.99 *(978-1-60061-817-8(0)*, Impact) F&W Media, Inc.

Leisure Arts, creator. Dogs & Cats to Paint. 2006. (ENG.). 48p. pap. 11.95 *(978-1-60140-325-4(9))* Leisure Arts, Inc.

Lied, Charles. How to Draw Animals. 2007. (Dover Art Instruction Ser.). (ENG., Illus.). 64p. per. 4.95 *(978-0-486-45606-5(4))* Dover Pubns., Inc.

Lindstrand, Doug. The Artist's Guide to Drawing Realistic Animals. 2006. (ENG., Illus.). 144p. pap. 19.99 *(978-1-58180-728-8(7)*, North Light Bks.) F&W Media, Inc.

Link, Mary. Fast Fun & Easy Fabric Critter Bags: From Stuff Stashers to Beach Bags to Pillowcases. 2007. (ENG., Illus.). 48p. pap. 17.95 *(978-1-57120-422-6(9))* C &T Publishing.

Locke, Harvey. Yellowstone to Yukon: The Journey of Wildlife & Art. 2012. ***(978-1-56373-192-1(4))*** Fulcrum Publishing.

Maday, Jane. Draw Baby Animals. 2009. (ENG., Illus.). 112p. pap. 18.99 *(978-1-60061-195-7(8)*, North Light Bks.) F&W Media, Inc.

Magee, Judith. Art & Nature: Three Centuries of Natural History Art from Around the World, 1 vol. 2010. (ENG., Illus.). 256p. 45.00 *(978-1-55365-517-6(6)*, Greystone Bks.) D&M Pubs. Inc. CAN. Dist: Perseus-PGW.

Marchant, Deborah DeWit. Painting Cats. 2008. (Illus.). 106p. 35.00 *(978-1-59028-228-1(0)*, William, James & Co.) Franklin, Beedle & Assocs., Inc.

Marchant, Deborah DeWit & Piercy, Marge. Painting Cats. 2008. *(978-1-59028-208-3(6)*, William, James & Co.) Franklin, Beedle & Assocs., Inc.

Mason, Peter. Before Disenchantment: Images of Exotic Animals & Plants in the Early Modern World. 2009. (ENG., Illus.). 248p. 49.00 *(978-1-86189-437-3(6))* Reaktion Bks., Ltd. GBR. Dist: Chicago Distribution Ctr.

Mattesi, Mike. Force: Animal Drawing: Animal locomotion & design concepts for Animators. 2011. (ENG., Illus.). 224p. pap. 29.95 *(978-0-240-81435-3(5)*, Focal Pr.) Elsevier Science & Technology Bks.

McGarry, Susan Hallsten & Palmore, Thomas. Earthlings: The Paintings of Tom Palmore. 2008. (ENG., Illus.). 120p. (C). 45.00 *(978-1-934397-05-3(9))* Quaid Publishing.

McMurdo, Glenn. Green-Winged Teal Pair. 2008. (Workbench Projects Ser.). (ENG., Illus.). 85p. spiral bd. 24.95 *(978-1-881982-60-9(2))* Stackpole Bks.

McOnie, Tessa. Dog Designs: Patterns for Craftspeople & Artisans. 2008. (ENG., Illus.). 56p. per. 19.95 *(978-0-9581988-5-1(3))* Glass Bks. Pty, Ltd. AUS. Dist: Independent Pubs. Group.

McRae Books. Cats. 2010. (Magnet Art Bks.). (ENG.). 24p. 5.95 *(978-88-6098-165-3(4))* McRae Bks. Srl ITA. Dist: Independent Pubs. Group.

—Dogs. 2010. (Magnet Art Bks.). (ENG.). 24p. 5.95 *(978-88-6098-166-0(2))* McRae Bks. Srl ITA. Dist: Independent Pubs. Group.

Mizelle, Brett. Pig. 2011. (Reaktion Books - Animal Ser.). (ENG., Illus.). 224p. pap. 19.95 *(978-1-86189-805-0(3))* Reaktion Bks., Ltd. GBR. Dist: Chicago Distribution Ctr.

Moore, Neal. Animal Portraits in Wood: Crafting 16 Artistic Mosaics with Your Scroll Saw. 2006. (ENG., Illus.). 128p. pap. 17.95 *(978-1-56523-293-8(3))* Fox Chapel Publishing Co., Inc.

Morita, Yoneo. Kittens in 3-D. 2011. (ENG., Illus.). 96p. 16.99 *(978-0-06-203957-6(1)*, Collins Design) HarperCollins Pubs.

—Puppies in 3-D. 2011. (ENG., Illus.). 96p. 16.99 *(978-0-06-203958-3(X)*, Collins Design) HarperCollins Pubs.

Morrison, Elizabeth. Beasts: Factual & Fantastic. 2007. (Illus.). 112p. 19.95 *(978-0-89236-888-4(8))* Oxford Univ. Pr., Inc.

Murdock Publishing Company, creator. Animal Illustrations: Murdock Art Achive. 2007. per. *(978-1-934102-05-3(9))* Murdock Publishing Co.

Musgrove, Scott. The Late Fauna of Early North America: The Art of Scott Musgrove. 2009. (Illus.). 160p. 34.95 *(978-0-86719-710-5(2))* Last Gasp of San Francisco.

Muybridge, Eadweard. Muybridge's Animals in Motion CD-ROM & Book. 2007. (Dover Electronic Clip Art Ser.). (ENG., Illus.). 48p. pap. 16.95 *(978-0-486-99767-4(7))* Dover Pubns., Inc.

Nagakubo, Nobuko. Fleece Dog: A Little Bit of Magic Created with Raw Wool & a Special Needle. 2006. (ENG., Illus.). 96p. pap. 22.95 *(978-1-57120-433-2(4))* C & T Publishing.

Nelson, Christine. Drawing Babar: Early Drafts & Watercolors. 2008. (Illus.). xi, 150p. *(978-0-87598-151-2(8))*; pap. *(978-0-87598-152-9(6))* Pierpont Morgan Library.

Nesi, Antonella, ed. Il Porcellino di Pietro Tacca: Le sue basi, la sua Storia. 2011. (ITA., Illus.). 80p. (C). pap. 20.00 ***(978-88-596-0913-1(5))*** Polistampa ITA. Dist: Brown, David Bk. Co., The.

Newey, Jonathan. How to Draw Wild Animals In Simple Steps. 2011. (How to Draw Ser.). (ENG., Illus.). 32p. pap. 9.95 *(978-1-84448-573-4(0))* Search Pr., Ltd. GBR. Dist: Independent Pubs. Group.

Nice, Claudia. Painting Your Favorite Animals in Pen, Ink & Watercolor. 2006. (ENG., Illus.). 144p. 26.99 *(978-1-58180-776-9(7)*, North Light Bks.) F&W Media, Inc.

Noever, Peter, ed. & text. Furniture as Trophy. 2010. (ENG., Illus.). 120p. pap. 45.00 *(978-3-941185-59-3(4))* Verlag fur Moderne Kunst DEU. Dist: D.A.P./Distributed Art Pubs.

North Light Books Staff. Drawing & Painting Animals: The Essential Guide. 2008. (ENG.). 192p. pap. 19.99 *(978-1-60061-110-0(9)*, North Light Bks.) F&W Media, Inc.

Obermaier, Sabine. Tiere und Fabelwesen Im Mittelalter: Zu Ihrer Bedeutung in Wissenschaft, Religion, Geschichte, Bildender Kunst und Literatur. Obermaier, Sabine, ed. 2009.Tr. of Animals & Mythical Creatures in the Middle Ages. (GER., Illus.). VIII, 342p. 140.00 *(978-3-11-020137-6(2))* De Gruyter, Walter Inc.

Obermaier, Sabine, ed. Tiere und Fabelwesen im Mittelalter. 2009.Tr. of Animals & Mythical Creatures in the Middle Ages. (GER.). VIII, 342p. 210.00 ***(978-3-11-173736-2(5))*** De Gruyter, Walter Inc.

O'Connor, William. Dracopedia the Great Dragons: An Artist's Field Guide & Drawing Journal. 2012. (ENG., Illus.). 160p. 26.99 ***(978-1-4403-1067-6(X)***, Impact) F&W Media, Inc.

Ogden Museum of Southern Art Staff. One World, Two Artists: John Alexander & Walter Anderson. Strachan, Sue, ed. 2011. (ENG., Illus.). 90p. 55.00 *(978-0-9833707-0-3(2)*, Univ. Pr. of Mississippi/Ogden Museum of Southern Art) Univ. Pr. of Mississippi.

Okeefe, Raven. Raven's L'il Critters. 2008. 60p. pap. 12.95 *(978-1-934543-62-7(4))* HollywoodComics.com, LLC.

Oliver, Gary. Cinemazoo: My Urban Safari. 2011. (ENG., Illus.). 208p. pap. ***(978-1-894694-62-9(7))*** Granville Island Publishing.

Os, Gerard van. Cowlection. 2007. 320p. *(978-90-808666-3-8(6))* Stockmans NV.

Otsuka, Ayako. Stitchy Kitty Fuzzy Puppy: 60 Motifs to Stitch Everywhere. 2009. (ENG.). 120p. pap. 19.95 *(978-1-59668-183-5(7))* Interweave Pr., LLC.

Palamar, Todd. Maya Feature Creature Creations. 2nd ed. 2008. (ENG., Illus.). 320p. pap. 49.99 *(978-1-58450-547-1(8))* Charles River Media.

Park, Carrie Stuart & Parks, Rick. The Big Book of Realistic Drawing Secrets: Easy Techniques for drawing people, animals, flowers & Nature. 2009. (ENG., Illus.). 224p. pap. 24.99 *(978-1-60061-458-3(2)*, North Light Bks.) F&W Media, Inc.

Parkstone Press Staff. Beauty of the Beast. 2012. (Mega Square Ser.). (ENG., Illus.). 256p. 12.95 ***(978-1-906981-45-7(0))*** Parkstone Pr. USA, Ltd.

Patterson, Gary, illus. Cat Laughs. 2010. 64p. 9.99 *(978-0-7369-2657-7(7))* Harvest Hse. Pubs.

Peffer, J. "NeonDragon". DragonArt: Explore New Coloring Techniques. 2012. (ENG., Illus.). 112p. pap., wbk. ed. 16.99 ***(978-1-4403-1864-1(6)***, Impact) F&W Media, Inc.

Perard, Victor. Drawing Animals. 2007. (Dover Art Instruction Ser.). (ENG., Illus.). 48p. per. 5.95 *(978-0-486-46031-4(2))* Dover Pubns., Inc.

Phelps, Earl R. How to Draw Magnificent Mammals. 2006. (ENG., Illus.). 80p. per. 14.95 *(978-1-887627-06-1(5))* Phelps Publishing.

Pickeral, Tamsin. The Dog: 5000 Years of the Dog in Art. (Illus.). 288p. 2010. (ENG.). pap. 29.95 *(978-1-85894-532-3(1))* 2008. 49.95 *(978-1-85894-420-3(1))* Merrell Pubs. Ltd. GBR. Dist: Perseus Distribution.

Pinder, Polly. Cats. 2009. (How to Draw Ser.). (ENG., Illus.). 32p. pap. 9.95 *(978-1-84448-369-3(X))* Search Pr., Ltd. GBR. Dist: Independent Pubs. Group.

Pinder, Polly, et al. How to Draw Animals: In Simple Steps. 2011. (How to Draw Ser.). (ENG., Illus.). 144p. pap. 19.95 *(978-1-84448-664-9(8))* Search Pr., Ltd. GBR. Dist: Independent Pubs. Group.

Pinkney, Jerry. Jerry Pinkney: Aesop's Fables & Other Tails. 2007. (Illus.). 17p. pap. *(978-0-9795872-1-4(2))* Brandywine River Museum.

Piwocka, Magdalena. Arrasy Króla Zygmunta Augusta Zwierzeta. 2009. (POL., Illus.). *(978-83-88476-89-1(0))* Zamek Krolewski na Wawelu, Panstwowe Zbiory Sztuki, Dzial Wydawnictw.

Poliquin, Rachel. The Breathless Zoo: Taxidermy & the Cultures of Longing. 2012. (ENG.). 240p. ***(978-0-271-05372-1(0))*** Pennsylvania State Univ. Pr.

Prod'Hom, Chantel. Animal Style. 2006. *(978-88-7439-346-6(6))* 5 Continents.

Ram, Vikramajit. Elephant Kingdom: Sculptures from Indian Architecture. 2007. (ENG., Illus.). 128p. pap. 35.00 *(978-1-890206-96-3(2))* Mapin Publishing Pvt. Ltd IND. Dist: National Bk. Network.

Rebora, Ballo. Carving a Bull Fighter & the Bull. 2008. (Illus.). 64p. pap. 14.95 *(978-0-7643-2910-4(3))* Schiffer Publishing, Ltd.

Recklies, Adele Rogers. Bead Crochet Snakes: History & Technique. 2007. (Illus.). 112p. pap. 22.95 *(978-0-9791649-0-3(7))* Reckless Beading Pr.

Resl, Brigitte. Understanding Animals 1150-1350. 2012. (ENG.). 256p. 69.95 *(978-1-4039-3818-3(0))* Palgrave Macmillan.

ricorico. Marine Animals: Make Thousands of Customized Graphics from 100 Image Templates. 2011. (Ready-Made Art-Book & CD Ser.). (ENG., Illus.). 144p. 19.99 *(978-1-59253-659-7(X)*, 159253659X) Quayside.

Ross, Elliot. Animal. 2010. (ENG., Illus.). 112p. 70.00 *(978-90-5330-730-4(3))* Mets en Schilt Uitgevers NLD. Dist: Ingram Pub. Services.

Russell, Ben. Woodcarving: 10 Step-by-Step Animal Projects. 2012. (ENG., Illus.). 128p. (C). pap. 32.00 *(978-0-85442-176-3(9))* Stobart Davies, Ltd. GBR. Dist: Brown, David Bk. Co., The.

Ruthven, Ianthe. Animal London. 2011. (ENG., Illus.). 174p. pap. 19.95 ***(978-0-224-08704-9(5))*** Random Hse. GBR. Dist: Independent Pubs. Group.

Salmony, Alfred. Sino-Siberian Art in the Collection of C. T. Loo. 2006. (ENG., Illus.). 119p. 70.00 *(978-1-878529-36-7(6))* Orchid Pr. THA. Dist: National Bk. Network.

Schimmel, Schim. Our Home Too. (Illus.). 295p. 69.00 *(978-0-9650972-0-8(X))*; 2nd ed. 69.00 *(978-0-9650972-1-5(8))* Art Impressions, Inc.

Secord, William. Dog Painting: A History of the Dog in Art. 2nd ed. 2009. (ENG., Illus.). 456p. 85.00 (978-1-85149-576-4(2)) Antique Collectors' Club.

Semelka, Richard. Clyde Jones Penguins, Giraffes & Other Critters His Joyous Vision. 2010. 93p. pap. 33.81 (978-0-557-18317-3(0)) Lulu Enterprises Inc.

Sergio Guinot Studio Staff & Diman, Paz. Tiere zeichnen -Schritt für Schritt, 1 vol. 2010. (DUT, ENG, FRE & GER., Illus.). 352p. pap. 22.95 (978-94-6065-028-4(7)) booQs Publishers bvba BEL. Dist: Innovative Logistics.

Shannon, Lindsay, ed. Kate Javens: American Beasts, 1 vol. 2008. (ENG., Illus.). 156p. 45.00 (978-0-911883-10-7(X)) Blanden Memorial Art Museum.

Smith, Cindy. Baby Animals: Learn to Draw Step by Step. 2009. (How to Draw & Paint Series: Drawing Ser.). (ENG., Illus.). 32p. pap. 8.95 (978-1-60058-135-9(8), 1600581358) Foster, Walter Publishing, Inc.

Spencer, Neal. The Gayer-Anderson Cat. 2007. (British Museum Objects in Focus Ser.). (Illus.). 64p. pap. 12.50 (978-0-7141-1973-1(3)) British Museum Pr. GBR. Dist: Brown, David Bk. Co., The.

Spurlock, J. David. How to Draw Chiller Monsters, Werewolves, Vampires, & Zombies. 2011. (ENG., Illus.). 144p. pap. 19.99 (978-0-8230-9532-2(0)) Watson-Guptill Pubns., Inc.

Staatsgemäldesammlungen, Bayersche & Rott, Herbert W., eds. George Stubbs. 2011. (Illus.). 224p. 49.95 (978-3-7913-5170-4(2)) Prestel Publishing.

Stacey, Nolon. Dogs & Cats: Learn to Draw Step by Step. 2009. (How to Draw & Paint Series: Drawing Ser.). (ENG., Illus.). 32p. pap. 8.95 (978-1-60058-136-5(6), 1600581366) Foster, Walter Publishing, Inc.

—Drawing Made Easy: Dogs & Puppies - Discover Your "Inner Artist" As You Explore the Basic Theories & Techniques of Pencil Drawing. 2007. (Drawing Made Easy Ser.). (ENG., Illus.). 64p. pap. 9.95 (978-1-60058-027-7(0), 1600580270) Foster, Walter Publishing, Inc.

Stronge, Susan. Tipu's Tigers. 2009. (ENG., Illus.). 96p. 19.95 (978-1-85177-575-0(7)) V & A Pubns. GBR. Dist: Hachette Bk. Group.

Suera, Vincenzo. Character Styling Vol. 2: The Bear. 2010. (ENG., Illus.). 72p. 75.00 incl. DVD (978-88-88766-13-3(8)) Arkivia Bks. ITA. Dist: National Bk. Network.

—Character Styling - The Cat, Vol. 1. 2010. (ENG., Illus.). 72p. 75.00 incl. DVD (978-88-88766-09-6(X)) Arkivia Bks. ITA. Dist: National Bk. Network.

Suera, Vincenzo & Moricci, Michele. Natural Pop Graphics, Vol. 1. 2010. (ENG., Illus.). 144p. 135.00 incl. DVD (978-88-88766-12-6(X)) Arkivia Bks. ITA. Dist: National Bk. Network.

Sung, Hou-Mei. Decoded Messages: The Symbolic Language of Chinese Animal Painting. 2009. (Illus.). xv, 271p. (978-0-931537-35-6(5)); (ENG., 256p. 75.00 (978-0-300-14152-8(1)) Yale Univ. Pr.

Szunyoghy, Andras & Feher, Gyorgy. Anatomy Drawing School Animal Anatomy. 2010. 224p. pap. 16.99 (978-0-8416-7222-2(9)) Langenscheidt Publishing Group.

—Anatomy Drawing School Human Anatomy. 2010. 24p. pap. 16.99 (978-0-8416-7221-5(0)) Langenscheidt Publishing Group.

—Animal Anatomy, 1 vol. 2010. (GER & ENG., Illus.). 224p. spiral bd. 14.99 (978-3-8331-5736-3(4)) h.f.ullmann DEU. Dist: Innovative Logistics.

Tanimoto, Ichiro, ed. Animals, Birds & Butterflies. 2008. (Shikosha Design Library). (Illus.). 120p. pap. 16.95 (978-1-933330-77-8(5)) Stone Bridge Pr.

Thapar, Valmik. The Tiger: Soul of India. 2011. (ENG., Illus.). 184p. 49.95 (978-0-19-806969-0(3)) Oxford Univ. Pr., Inc.

Thurstan, Meriel & Martin, Rosie. Natural History Painting: With the Eden Project. 2009. (ENG., Illus.). 144p. 27.95 (978-1-906388-49-2(0), Batsford, B. T. Ltd.) Anova Bks. GBR. Dist: Sterling Publishing Co., Inc.

Tilov, Dinko & Tilov, Boris. Sculpting Mythical Creatures Out of Polymer Clay: Making a Gnome, Pixie, Halfling, Fairy, Mermaid, Gorgon Vampire, Griffin, Sphinx, Unicorn, Centaur, Leviathan, & Dragon! 2009. (ENG., Illus.). 136p. pap. 22.99 (978-1-59253-514-9(3), 1592535143, Quarry Books) Quayside.

Trifonov (Nasmio), Stanislav. A Graffiti of Cats. 2011. (ENG., Illus.). 27p. 14.00 (978-1-897476-73-4(6)) Simply Read Bks. CAN. Dist: Perseus-PGW.

TvBoy, et al. Animal Collective. 2008. (ENG., Illus.). 96p. pap. 29.00 (978-88-88493-23-7(9)) Drago Arts & Communication ITA. Dist: SCB Distributors.

Vacation from Reality: The Art of Anthony Ausgang. 2007. (Illus.). 139p. pap. 34.95 (978-0-9766325-0-4(0)) 9mm Bks.

Vähämäki, Amanda. Souvlaki Circus. 2008. (Illus.). 80p. 13.95 (978-0-9800039-1-8(1)) Buenaventura Pr.

van Dinter, M. Hesselt. Fabulous Creatures: Demons, Unicorns, Dragons, Griffin. 2008. (Illus.). 250p. pap. (978-90-78900-06-1(7)) Mundurucu Pubs.

Van Zyle, Jon. Jon Van Zyle's Alaska Sketchbook: Four Season in the Far North. 2nd ed. 2009. (ENG., Illus.). 64p. (gr. 6). pap. 9.95 (978-0-9800825-1-7(X)) Epicenter Pr., Inc.

Van Zyle, Jon, illus. Iditarod Memories: 30 Years of Poster Art from the Last Great Race. 2009. (ENG.). 64p. (gr. 9). pap. 9.95 (978-0-9800825-2-4(8)) Epicenter Pr., Inc.

Vedrenne, Penny. Red-Eyed Tree Frogs - A Book of Stencils. 2007. 68p. pap. 19.95 (978-1-4303-2267-2(5)) Lulu Enterprises Inc.

Viebrock, Clint. The Christmas Animal Book. 2007. (Celebration (Red Rock Press) Ser.). (ENG., Illus.). 64p. 9.95 (978-1-933176-11-6(3)) Red Rock Pr., Inc.

Webb, Spider. Flash Dragons: The Art of Spider Webb. 2006. (Illus.). 80p. pap. 19.95 (978-0-7643-2559-5(0)) Schiffer Publishing, Ltd.

Weil, Linda. Lifelike Animals: Discover Your Inner Artist as You Learn to Draw Animals in Graphite. 2008. (Drawing Made Easy Ser.). (ENG., Illus.). 64p. pap. 9.95 (978-1-60058-067-3(X), 160058067X) Foster, Walter Publishing, Inc.

Weller, Alan & Clip Art Staff. Fantasy Vector Motifs. 2012. (Dover Electronic Clip Art Ser.). (ENG., Illus.). 48p. pap. 19.95 (978-0-486-99200-6(4)) Dover Pubns., Inc.

Wernhard, Hannelore & Messent, Jan. The Knitted Farmyard. Messent, Jan, ed. Simpson, Hilary, tr. from GER. 2007. (Search Press Classics Ser.). (ENG., Illus.). 32p. spiral bd. 9.95 (978-1-84448-217-7(0)) Search Pr., Ltd. GBR. Dist: Independent Pubs. Group.

Witt, David L. & Seton, Ernest Thompson. Ernest Thompson Seton: The Life & Legacy of an Artist & Conservationist, 1 vol. 2010. (ENG., Illus.). 192p. 40.00 (978-1-4236-0391-7(5)) Gibbs Smith, Publisher.

Wr, David Gilmore. Catalogue of Prints by Peter Moran (1841-1914), 2 vols., Vol. 2. 2010. 60.00 net. (978-0-9789779-7-9(1)) Creo Pr.

Wright, David Gilmore. Domestic & Wild: Peter Moran's Images of America, 2 vols., Vols. 1 & 2. 2010. 120.00 net. (978-0-9789779-5-5(5)) Creo Pr.

—The Life & Art of Peter Moran, Painter-Etcher, 2 vols., Vol. 1. 1000th ed. 2010. (Illus.). 280p. 60.00 net. (978-0-9789779-6-2(3)) Creo Pr.

Wyeth, Jamie. Dog Days. 2007. (Illus.). 108p. (978-0-9795872-0-7(4)) Brandywine River Museum.

Yow, John & Wyland Foundation Staff. Wyland: Twenty-Five Years at Sea. 2006. (ENG., Illus.). 180p. 39.95 (978-0-7407-6080-8(7)) Andrews McMeel Publishing.

Yu, Peng & Yuan, Sun. Sun Yuan & Peng Yu: Can't Have it All. 2010. (ENG., Illus.). 250p. pap. 50.00 (978-988-18033-8-2(1)) Timezone 8 Ltd. HKG. Dist: D.A.P./Distributed Art Pubs.

Zaidenberg, Arthur. Dynamic Animal Drawing. 2009. (Dover Art Instruction Ser.). (ENG., Illus.). 176p. pap. 12.95 (978-0-486-47008-5(3)) Dover Pubns., Inc.

Zolan, Donald, illus. Puppy Love: Wiggles & Wags to Warm Your Heart. 2007. 32p. 14.99 (978-0-7369-1802-2(7)) Harvest Hse. Pubs.

ANIMALS IN LITERATURE

Alexandridis, Annetta, et al, eds. Mensch und Tier in der Antike: Grenzziehung und Grenzuberschreitung. 2009. (GER., Illus.). 588p. (C). 99.00 (978-3-89500-583-1(5)) Reichert, Ludwig Dr. DEU. Dist: Brown, David Bk. Co., The.

Armstrong, Philip. What Animals Mean in the Fiction of Modernity. 2008. 256p. 110.00 (978-0-415-35838-5(8)) 2007. VIII, 256p. 36.95 (978-0-415-35839-2(6)) Routledge.

Blackwell, Mark. The Secert Life of Things: Animals, Objects, & It-Narratives in Eighteenth-Century England. 2007. (Bucknell Studies in Eighteenth-Century Literature & Culture). (Illus.). 365p. (978-0-8387-5666-9(2)) Bucknell Univ. Pr.

Blackwell, Mark. British It-Narratives, 1750-1830, 4 vols. 2012. (ENG.). 1696p. 625.00 (978-1-84893-120-6(4)) Pickering & Chatto Pubs., Ltd. GBR. Dist: Ashgate Publishing Co.

Boehrer, Bruce Thomas. Animal Characters: Nonhuman Beings in Early Modern Literature. 2010. (Haney Foundation Ser.). (Illus.). 256p. (C). 49.95 (978-0-8122-4249-2(1)) Univ. of Pennsylvania Pr.

Bowker, John. An an Alphabet of Animals. 2010. (Illus.). 142p. pap. 29.99 (978-0-9782526-7-0(5)) Key Publishing Hse., Inc., The CAN. Dist: AtlasBooks Distribution.

Brown, Laura. Homeless Dogs & Melancholy Apes: Humans & Other Animals in the Modern Literary Imagination. 2010. (Illus.). 176p. 35.00 (978-0-8014-4828-7(X)) Cornell Univ. Pr.

Casson, Caryl. A Brontë Bestiary. 2010. 92p. pap. (978-3-8383-5105-6(3)) Lambert Academic Publishing.

de Crécy, Nicolas & Senges, Pierre. Adventures of Percival. Daniele, Riviere, ed. 2009. (ENG., Illus.). 128p. pap. 30.00 (978-2-914563-47-5(7)) Dis Voir Editions FRA. Dist: D.A.P./Distributed Art Pubs.

Debus, Allen A. Dinosaurs in Fantastic Fiction: A Thematic Survey. 2006. (ENG., Illus.). 230p. 45.00 (978-0-7864-2672-0(1)) McFarland & Co., Inc. Pubs.

Fiamengo, Janice, ed. Other Selves: Animals in the Canadian Literary Imagination. 2007. (Reappraisals: Canadian Writers Ser.). (ENG., Illus.). 368p. (gr. 14). pap. (978-0-7766-0645-3(X)) Univ. of Ottawa Pr./Presses de l'Universite d'Ottawa.

Gibson, Graeme. The Bedside Book of Beasts: A Wildlife Miscellany. 2009. (Illus.). 384p. 20.00 (978-0-385-66915-3(1)) Doubleday Canada, Ltd. CAN. Dist: Random Hse., Inc.

—The Bedside Book of Beasts: A Wildlife Miscellany. 2009. (ENG., Illus.). 384p. 35.00 (978-0-385-52459-9(5), Talese, Nan A.) Knopf Doubleday Publishing Group.

Gleim, William S. The Meaning of Moby Dick. 2007. (ENG.). 156p. 36.95 (978-0-548-10333-3(X)) Kessinger Publishing, LLC.

Granata, Silvia. Take Every Creature In, of Every Kind: Continuity & Change in Eighteenth-Century Representations of Animals. 2011. (Europäische Hochschulschriften, Reihe 14: Angelsächsische Sprache und Literatur Ser.). 200p. pap. (978-3-0343-0544-0(3)) Lang, Peter.

Hartmann, Sieglinde, ed. Fauna & Flora in the Middle Ages: Studies of the Medieval Environment & its Impact on the Human Mind Papers Delivered at the International Medieval Congress, Leeds, in 2000, 2001 & 2002. 2007. (Beihefte Zur Mediaevistik. Monographien, Editionen, Sammelbände. Ser.: Vol. 8). 323p. (C). pap. 59.95 (978-3-631-56302-1(7)) Lang, Peter Publishing, Inc.

Heymans, Peter. Animality in British Romanticism. 2012. (Routledge Studies in Romanticism Ser.). (ENG.). 234p. (C). 125.00 (978-0-415-50730-1(8)) Routledge.

Hoare, Philip. The Whale: In Search of the Giants of the Sea. 2010. (ENG., Illus.). 464p. 27.99 (978-0-06-197621-6(0), Ecco) HarperCollins Pubs.

Hogan, Walter. Animals in Young Adult Fiction. 2009. (Scarecrow Studies in Young Adult Literature Ser.). (ENG.). 268p. 50.00 (978-0-8108-5994-4(7)) Scarecrow Pr., Inc.

Horne, Jackie C. & White, Donna R. The Wind in the Willows: A Children's Classic at 100. 2009. (Children's Literature Association Centennial Studies). (ENG.). 302p. 60.00 (978-0-8108-7258-5(7)) Scarecrow Pr., Inc.

Irwin, Robert. Camel. 2010. (Reaktion Books - Animal Ser.). (ENG., Illus.). 224p. pap. 19.95 (978-1-86189-649-0(2)) Reaktion Bks., Ltd. GBR. Dist: Chicago Distribution Ctr.

Jackson, Dierdre & Jackson, Deirdre. Lion. 2010. (Reaktion Books - Animal Ser.). (ENG., Illus.). 224p. pap. 19.95 (978-1-86189-655-1(7)) Reaktion Bks., Ltd. GBR. Dist: Chicago Distribution Ctr.

Kordecki, Lesley. Ecofeminist Subjectivities: Chaucer's Talking Birds. 2011. (New Middle Ages Ser.). (ENG., Illus.). 224p. 85.00 (978-0-230-11527-9(6)) Palgrave Macmillan.

Lucht, Marc. Kafka's Creatures: Animals, Hybrids, & Other Fantastic Beings. 2010. (ENG., Illus.). 306p. 78.99 (978-0-7391-4394-0(8)) Lexington Bks.

Lucht, Marc & Yarri, Donna, eds. Kafka's Creatures: Animals, Hybrids, & Other Fantastic Beings. 2012. (ENG.). 316p. pap. 36.99 (978-0-7391-4395-7(6)) Lexington Bks.

MacKenzie-Bowie, Ewen. The Wolf in Children's Literature. 2011. 104p. pap. (978-3-8443-9235-7(1)) Lambert Academic Publishing.

Mann, Jill. From Aesop to Reynard: Beast Literature in Medieval Britain. 2010. (ENG., Illus.). 448p. 110.00 (978-0-19-921768-7(8)) Oxford Univ. Pr., Inc.

McDonald, William E. Encountering Disgrace: Reading & Teaching Coetzee's Novel. McDonald, Bill, ed. 2009. 372p. 75.00 (978-1-57113-403-5(4)) Camden Hse.

McHugh, Susan. Animal Stories: Narrating Across Species Lines. 2011. (Posthumanities Ser.). (Illus.). 336p. 75.00 (978-0-8166-7032-1(3)); pap. 25.00 (978-0-8166-7033-8(1)) Univ. of Minnesota Pr.

Milne, Anne. Lactilla Tends Her Fav'rite Cow: Ecocritical Readings of Animals & Women in Eighteenth-Century British Labouring-Class Women's Poetry. 2008. (Illus.). 176p. (C). 45.50 (978-0-8387-5692-8(1)) Bucknell Univ. Pr.

Mitts-smith, Debra. Picturing the Wolf in Children's Literature. 2010. (Children's Literature & Culture Ser.). (ENG., Illus.). 218p. (C). 125.00 (978-0-415-80117-1(6)) Routledge.

Morse, Deborah Denenholz & Danahay, Martin A., eds. Victorian Animal Dreams: Representations of Animals in Nineteenth-Century Literature & Culture. 2007. (Nineteenth Century Ser.). (Illus.). 322p. 124.95 (978-0-7546-5511-4(3)) Ashgate Publishing Co.

Nelson, Christine. Drawing Babar: Early Drafts & Watercolors. 2008. (Illus.). xi, 150p. (978-0-87598-151-2(8)) Pierpont Morgan Library.

Obermaier, Sabine. Tiere und Fabelwesen im Mittelalter: Zu Ihrer Bedeutung in Wissenschaft, Religion, Geschichte, Bildender Kunst und Literatur. Obermaier, Sabine, ed. 2009.Tr. of Animals & Mythical Creatures in the Middle Ages. (GER., Illus.). VIII, 342p. 140.00 (978-3-11-020137-6(2)) De Gruyter, Walter Inc.

Obermaier, Sabine, ed. Tiere und Fabelwesen im Mittelalter. 2009.Tr. of Animals & Mythical Creatures in the Middle Ages. (GER.). VIII, 342p. 210.00 (978-3-11-173736-2(5)) De Gruyter, Walter Inc.

Palmeri, Frank, ed. Humans & Other Animals in Eighteenth-Century British Culture: Representation, Hybridity, Ethics. 2006. (Illus.). 244p. 110.00 (978-0-7546-5475-9(3)) Ashgate Publishing Co.

Payne, Mark. The Animal Part: Human & Other Animals in the Poetic Imagination. 2010. (ENG.). 160p. 35.00 (978-0-226-65084-5(7)) Univ. of Chicago Pr.

Perkins, David. Romanticism & Animal Rights. 2007. (Cambridge Studies in Romanticism Ser.). (ENG.). 212p. pap. 48.00 (978-0-521-04598-8(3)) Cambridge Univ. Pr.

Pick, Anat. Creaturely Poetics: Animality & Vulnerability in Literature & Film. 2011. (ENG.). 264p. (gr. 17). 79.50 (978-0-231-14786-6(4)); pap. 26.50 (978-0-231-14787-3(2)) Columbia Univ. Pr.

Pluskowski, Aleksander. Wolves & the Wilderness in the Middle Ages. 2006. (Illus.). 248p. 90.00 (978-1-84383-236-2(4)) Boydell & Brewer, Inc.

Poirier, Jacques. L'animal Littéraire: Des Animaux et des Mots. 2010. (FRE.). 236p. (978-2-915611-63-2(7)) Editions universitaires de Dijon.

Poliquin, Rachel. The Breathless Zoo: Taxidermy & the Cultures of Longing. 2012. (ENG.). 240p. (978-0-271-05372-1(0)) Pennsylvania State Univ. Pr.

Ptak, Roderich. Birds & Beasts in Chinese Texts & Trade: Lectures Related to South China & the Overseas World. 2011. (Maritime Asia Ser.). (ENG., Illus.). 140p. (C). 57.00 (978-3-447-06449-1(8)) Harrassowitz, Otto Verlag DEU. Dist: ISD.

Rajamannar, Shefali. Reading the Animal in the Literature of the British Raj. 2012. (ENG., Illus.). 232p. 85.00 (978-0-230-11449-4(0)) Palgrave Macmillan.

Robisch, S. K. Wolves & the Wolf Myth in American Literature. 2009. (ENG.). 512p. pap. 29.95 (978-0-87417-773-2(1)); 49.95 (978-0-87417-772-5(3)) Univ. of Nevada Pr.

Rohman, Carrie. Stalking the Subject: Modernism & the Animal. 2008. (ENG.). 208p. (gr. 17). 90.00 (978-0-231-14506-0(3)); pap. 29.50 (978-0-231-14507-7(1)) Columbia Univ. Pr.

Rothwell, Jr, Kenneth S., Kenneth S. Nature, Culture, & the Origins of Greek Comedy: A Study of Animal Choruses. 2010. (ENG.). 340p. (C). pap. 36.99 (978-0-521-17193-9(8)) Cambridge Univ. Pr.

Schiesari, Juliana. Polymorphous Domesticities: Pets, Bodies, & Desire in Four Modern Writers. 2012. (FlashPoints Ser.). (ENG.). 152p. pap. 39.95 (978-0-520-27084-8(3)) Univ. of California Pr.

Shaw, Bruce. The Animal Fable in Science Fiction & Fantasy. 2010. (Critical Explorations in Science Fiction & Fantasy Ser.). (ENG., Illus.). 268p. pap. 35.00 (978-0-7864-4783-1(4)) McFarland & Co., Inc. Pubs.

Stephen Newmyer Staff. Animals in Greek & Roman Thought. 2010. (Routledge Sourcebooks for the Ancient World Ser.). (ENG.). 160p. 100.00 (978-0-415-77334-8(2)); pap. 38.95 (978-0-415-77335-5(0)) Routledge.

Train, John & Kelly, Linda. Animals & Us: A Very Special Relationship. 2011. (ENG., Illus.). 120p. 16.95 (978-1-905377-52-7(5), Maria Teresa Train Mtt Scala) Antique Collectors' Club GBR. Dist: National Bk. Network.

Unglaub, Erich. Panther und Aschanti: Rilke-Gedichte in Kulturwissenschaftlicher Sicht. (GER., Illus.). 184p. 36.95 (978-3-631-53791-6(3)) Lang, Peter GmbH, Europaischer Verlag der Wissenschaften DEU. Dist: Lang, Peter Publishing, Inc.

Vint, Sherryl. Animal Alterity: Science Fiction & the Question of the Animal. 2010. (Liverpool University Press - Liverpool Science Fiction Texts & Studies). (ENG.). 256p. 95.00 (978-1-84631-234-2(5)) Liverpool Univ. Pr. GBR. Dist: Chicago Distribution Ctr.

Weil, Kari. Thinking Animals: Why Animal Studies Now? 2012. (ENG.). 216p. (gr. 17). 89.50 (978-0-231-14808-5(9)); pap. 27.50 (978-0-231-14809-2(7)) Columbia Univ. Pr.

Winslow, Helen M. Concerning Cats: My Own & Some Others. 2007. (ENG.). 144p. pap. 18.99 (978-1-4264-3574-4(6)) 2006. 158p. pap. 19.99 (978-1-4264-3625-3(4)) BiblioBazaar.

Woodward, Wendy. The Animal Gaze: Animal Subjectivities in Southern African Narratives. 2009. (ENG.). 200p. pap. 34.95 (978-1-86814-462-4(3)) Witwatersrand Univ. Pr. Pubns. ZAF. Dist: Transaction Pubs.

Yarbrough, Wynn William. Masculinity in Children's Animal Stories, 1888-1928: A Critical Study of Anthropomorphic Tales by Wilde, Kipling, Potter, Grahame & Milne. 2011. (ENG., Illus.). 195p. pap. 40.00 (978-0-7864-5943-8(3)) McFarland & Co., Inc. Pubs.

ANIMALS IN MOTION PICTURES

Bubbles. My Secret Diary: From Swaziland to Neverland. 2010. (ENG., Illus.). 228p. pap. 13.95 (978-1-84454-913-9(5)) Blake, John Publishing, Ltd. GBR. Dist: Independent Pubs. Group.

Camino, Mercedes Maroto. Film, Memory & the Legacy of the Spanish Civil War: Resistance & Guerrilla, 1936-2010. 2011. (ENG., Illus.). 232p. 85.00 (978-0-230-24055-1(0)) Palgrave Macmillan.

Freeman, Carol, et al, eds. Considering Animals: Contemporary Studies in Human-Animal Relations. 2011. (Illus.). 252p. 64.95 (978-1-4094-0013-4(1)) Ashgate Publishing Co.

Helfer, Ralph. The Beauty of the Beasts: Tales of Hollywood's Wild Animal Stars. 2007. (ENG., Illus.). 256p. pap. 13.95 (978-0-06-113678-8(6), HarperPerennial) HarperCollins Pubs.

Mitman, Gregg. Reel Nature: America's Romance with Wildlife on Film. 2nd ed. 2009. (ENG., Illus.). 320p. pap. 22.50 (978-0-295-98886-3(X)) Univ. of Washington Pr.

Orlean, Susan. Rin Tin Tin: The Life & the Legend. (ENG., Illus.). 336p. 2012. pap. 16.00 (978-1-4391-9014-2(3)) 2011. 26.99 (978-1-4391-9013-5(5)) Simon & Schuster.

—Rin Tin Tin: The Life & the Legend. lt. ed. 2012. (ENG.). 509p. pap. 16.99 (978-1-59413-561-3(4), Large Print Pr.) Thorndike Pr.

Orlean, Susan & Horton, Robert J. Rin Tin Tin: The Life & the Legend. lt. ed. 2011. (ENG.). 496p. 31.99 (978-1-4104-4344-1(2)) Thorndike Pr.

Painter, Deborah. Hollywood's Top Dogs: The Dog Hero in Film. 2008. (Illus.). 227p. pap. (978-1-887664-84-4(X)) Midnight Marquee Pr., Inc.

Pick, Anat. Creaturely Poetics: Animality & Vulnerability in Literature & Film. 2011. (ENG.). 264p. (gr. 17). 79.50 (978-0-231-14786-6(4)); pap. 26.50 (978-0-231-14787-3(2)) Columbia Univ. Pr.

Rossellini, Isabella. Green Porno: A Book & Short Films. 2009. 208p. pap. 24.99 (978-0-06-179106-2(7)) HarperCollins Pubs.

Wells, Paul. The Animated Bestiary: Animals, Cartoons, & Culture. 2008. (Na Ser.). (ENG., Illus.). 236p. 65.00 (978-0-8135-4414-4(9)); pap. 23.95 (978-0-8135-4415-1(7)) Rutgers Univ. Pr.

ANIMALS IN RESEARCH

see Laboratory Animals

ANIMALS' RIGHTS

see Animal Rights

ANIMATED CARTOONS

see Animated Films

ANIMATED FILMS

Abraham, Adam. When Magoo Flew: The Rise & Fall of Animation Studio UPA. 2012. (ENG., Illus.). 332p. 29.95 (978-0-8195-6914-1(3)) Wesleyan Univ. Pr.

Amidi, Amid. The Art of Pixar: The Complete Color Scripts & Select Art from 25 Years of Animation. 25th anniv. ed. 2011. (ENG., Illus.). 320p. 50.00 (978-0-8118-7963-7(1)) Chronicle Bks. LLC.

—Cartoon Modern: Style & Design in Fifties Animation. 2006. (ENG., Illus.). 192p. 40.00 (978-0-8118-4731-5(4)) Chronicle Bks. LLC.

Andersson, Lars Gustaf, et al. A History of Swedish Experimental Film Culture: From Early Animation to Video Art. 2010. (ENG., Illus.). 190p. pap. 29.95 (978-0-86196-699-8(6), 0861966996) Indiana Univ. Pr.

Bacher, Hans P. Dream Worlds: Production Design for Animation. 2007. (ENG., Illus.). 216p. 39.95 (978-0-240-52093-3(9), Focal Pr.) Elsevier Science & Technology Bks.

Beck, Jerry. The Art of Madagascar: Escape 2 Africa. 2008. (ENG., Illus.). 160p. 45.00 (978-1-933784-70-0(9), Insight Editions) Palace Publishing Group, LP.

Beck, Jerry, ed. The 100 Greatest Looney Tunes Cartoons. 2010. (ENG., Illus.). 256p. 24.95 (978-1-60887-003-5(0)) Palace Pr. International.

Beiman, Nancy. Prepare to Board! Creating Story & Characters for Animation Features & Shorts. 2nd ed. 2007. (ENG., Illus.). 336p. pap. 39.95 (978-0-240-80820-8(7), Focal Pr.) Elsevier Science & Technology Bks.

Berninger, Mark. Comics as a Nexus of Cultures: Essays on the Interplay of Media, Disciplines & International Perspectives. Ecke, Jochen et al, eds. 2010. (Critical Explorations in Science Fiction & Fantasy Ser.). (ENG., Illus.). 308p. pap. 39.95 (978-0-7864-3987-4(4)) McFarland & Co., Inc. Pubs.

Besen, Ellen. Animation Unleashed: 100 Principles Every Animator, Comic Book Writer, Filmmaker, Video Artist, & Game Developer Should Know. 2008. (ENG., Illus.). 245p. pap. 26.95 (978-1-932907-49-0(1)) Wiese, Michael Productions.

Booker, M. Keith. Disney, Pixar, & the Hidden Messages of Children's Films, 1 vol. 2009. 214p. 44.95 (978-0-313-37672-6(7), C37672, Praeger Pubs.) Greenwood Publishing Group, Inc.

Browning, John Edgar & Picart, Caroline Joan. Dracula in Visual Media: Film, Television, Comic Book & Electronic Game Appearances, 1921-2010. 2010. (ENG., Illus.). 312p. pap. 45.00 (978-0-7864-3365-0(5)) McFarland & Co., Inc. Pubs.

Buchan, Suzanne. The Quay Brothers: Into a Metaphysical Playroom. 2011. (ENG., Illus.). 296p. 75.00 (978-0-8166-4658-6(9)); pap. 25.00 (978-0-8166-4659-3(7)) Univ. of Minnesota Pr.

Buchan, Suzanne, ed. Animation. 2013. (AFI Film Readers Ser.). (ENG., Illus.). 320p. (C). 135.00 **(978-0-415-80723-4(9))**; pap. 39.95 **(978-0-415-80724-1(7))** Routledge.

Bukatman, Scott. The Poetics of Slumberland: Animated Spirits & the Animating Spirit. 2012. (ENG., Illus.). 276p. 70.00 **(978-0-520-26571-4(8))**; pap. 29.95 **(978-0-520-26572-1(6))** Univ. of California Pr.

Canemaker, John. Storytelling in Animation Vol. 2: The Art of the Animated Image. pap. 9.95 (978-0-573-60697-7(8)) French, Samuel Inc.

Carlton Books, ed. The World of Ice Age. 2012. (ENG., Illus.). 32p. (J). (gr. 1). 14.95 **(978-1-78097-038-7(2))** Carlton Bks., Ltd. GBR. Dist: Sterling Publishing Co., Inc.

Cavallaro, Dani. Anime & the Art of Adaptation: Eight Famous Works from Page to Screen. 2010. (ENG., Illus.). 220p. pap. 35.00 (978-0-7864-5860-8(7)) McFarland & Co., Inc. Pubs.

—The Art of Studio Gainax: Experimentation, Style & Innovation at the Leading Edge of Anime. 2008. (ENG.). 240p. pap. 35.00 (978-0-7864-3376-6(0)) McFarland & Co., Inc. Pubs.

—Magic As Metaphor in Anime: A Critical Study. 2009. (ENG.). 220p. pap. 35.00 (978-0-7864-4744-2(3)) McFarland & Co., Inc. Pubs.

Chronicle Books Staff & Solomon, Charles. Art of Toy Story 3. 2010. (ENG., Illus.). 176p. 40.00 (978-0-8118-7434-2(6)) Chronicle Bks. LLC.

Clarke, James. Animated Films. 2007. (Virgin Film Ser.). (ENG., Illus.). 208p. pap. 12.95 (978-0-7535-1258-6(0)) Virgin Bks. Ltd. GBR. Dist: Independent Pubs. Group.

Cohen, Sheldon. This Sweater Is for You! Celebrating the Creative Process in Film & Art with the Animator & Illustrator of the Hockey Sweater. 2012. (ENG., Illus.). 224p. pap. 29.95 (978-1-55022-960-8(5)) ECW Pr. CAN. Dist: Independent Pubs. Group.

Coyle, Rebecca. Drawn to Sound: Animation Film Music & Sonicity. 2010. (Genre, music & Sound Ser.). (ENG., Illus.). 269p. (C). pap. 29.95 (978-1-84553-352-6(6)) Equinox Publishing Ltd. GBR. Dist: ISD.

Coyle, Rebecca, ed. Drawn to Sound. Animation Film Music & Sonicity. 2009. (Genre, music & Sound Ser.). 256p. (C). 95.00 (978-1-84553-353-3(4)) Equinox Publishing Ltd. GBR. Dist: Brown, David Bk. Co., The.

Crafton, Donald. Shadow of a Mouse: Performance, Belief, & World-Making in Animation. 2012. (ENG.). 443p. 75.00 **(978-0-520-26103-7(8))**; pap. 34.95 **(978-0-520-26104-4(6))** Univ. of California Pr.

Dacosta, Charles. Framing Invisibility. 2010. 212p. pap. (978-3-8383-4683-0(1)) Lambert Academic Publishing.

Deneulin, Luc & Swinnen, Johan. Raoul Servais: The Wizard of Ostend: Commitment, Challenge, Recognition. 2009. (ENG, DUT & FRE., Illus.). 320p. pap. 54.00 (978-90-5487-480-5(5)) VUB Univ. Pr. BEL. Dist: Independent Pubs. Group.

Disney Book Group. The Art of the Disney Princess. 2009. (ENG., Illus.). 176p. 40.00 (978-1-4231-2371-2(9), Disney Editions) Disney Pr.

Disney Book Group Staff. Design. 2010. (ENG., Illus.). 256p. 60.00 (978-1-4231-3420-6(6), Disney Editions) Disney Pr.

Dobbs, G. Escape. 2007. 272p. per. 19.95 (978-1-59393-110-0(7)) BearManor Media.

Dobson, Nichola. Historical Dictionary of Animation & Cartoons. 2009. (Historical Dictionaries of Literature & the Arts Ser.). (ENG., Illus.). 304p. 90.00 (978-0-8108-5830-5(4)) Scarecrow Pr., Inc.

Dodge, Brent. From Screen to Theme: A Guide to Disney Animated Film References Found Throughout the Walt Disney World(r) Resort. 2010. 256p. pap. 14.95 (978-1-60844-408-3(2)) Dog Ear Publishing, LLC.

Dong, Lan. Mulan's Legend & Legacy in China & the United States. 2010. (ENG., Illus.). 280p. 70.50 (978-1-59213-970-5(1)); pap. 27.95 (978-1-59213-971-2(X)) Temple Univ. Pr.

Ebihara, Isao. All the World Is Anime: Religions, Myths & Spiritual Metaphors in the World of Japanimation & Manga. 2010. (Illus.). 200p. **(978-1-935434-05-4(5))** Global Education Advance.

Encyclopaedia Britannica, Inc., compiled by. Beauty & the Beast. 2008. 49.95 (978-1-59339-685-5(6)) Encyclopaedia Britannica, Inc.

—Debts. 2008. 49.95 (978-1-59339-659-6(7)) Encyclopaedia Britannica, Inc.

Farnell, Andy. Designing Sound. 2010. (ENG., Illus.). 688p. 53.00 (978-0-262-01441-0(6)) MIT Pr.

Furniss, Maureen. The Animation Bible: A Practical Guide to the Art of Animating from Flipbooks to Flash. 2008. (ENG., Illus.). 340p. pap. 29.95 (978-0-8109-9545-1(X)) Abrams.

Gasser, Christian. Animation. Ch: Vision & Versatility in Contemporary Swiss Animated Film. 2012. (ENG & GER., Illus.). 320p. 55.00 **(978-3-7165-1693-5(7))** Benteli Verlag CHE. Dist: National Bk. Network.

Ghazala, Mohamed. Animation in the Arab World. 2011. 56p. pap. **(978-3-8443-8548-9(7))** Lambert Academic Publishing.

Gilland, Joseph. Elemental Magic Vol. 1: The Art of Special Effects Animation. 2009. (ENG., Illus.). 328p. pap. 49.95 (978-0-240-81163-5(1), Focal Pr.) Elsevier Science & Technology Bks.

Goldberg, Eric. Character Animation Crash Course! 2008. (ENG., Illus.). 218p. pap. 35.00 (978-1-879505-97-1(5)) Silman-James Pr.

Goldmark, Daniel. Tunes For 'Toons: Music & the Hollywood Cartoon. 2007. (Illus.). 225p. per. 21.95 (978-0-520-25311-7(6)) Univ. of California Pr.

Goldmark, Daniel & Keil, Charlie. Funny Pictures: Animation & Comedy in Studio-Era Hollywood. 2011. (ENG., Illus.). 344p. 65.00 (978-0-520-26723-7(0)) Univ. of California Pr.

Goldmark, Daniel & Keil, Charlie, eds. Funny Pictures: Animation & Comedy in Studio-Era Hollywood. 2011. (ENG., Illus.). 344p. pap. 26.95 (978-0-520-26724-4(9)) Univ. of California Pr.

Graber, Sheila. Animation: A Handy Guide. 2011. (ENG., Illus.). 144p. pap. 29.95 (978-1-4081-0283-1(8)) A & C Black GBR. Dist: Macmillan.

Grant, John. Animated Movies Facts, Figures & Fun. 2006. (Illus.). 96p. 5.95 (978-1-904332-52-7(8)) AAPPL Artists & Photographers Pr., Ltd. GBR. Dist: Sterling Publishing Co., Inc.

Graydon, Danny. The Art of Planet 51. 2009. (ENG., Illus.). 144p. 39.95 (978-1-933784-97-7(0), Insight Editions) Palace Publishing Group, LP.

Hal Leonard Corporation Staff, creator. The Squeakuel: Music from the Motion Picture Soundtrack. 2010. (ENG.). 108p. pap. 16.99 (978-1-4234-9174-3(2), 1423491742) Leonard, Hal Corp.

Halas, Vivien & Wells, Paul. Halas & Batchelor Cartoons: An Animated History. 2007. (ENG., Illus.). 224p. pap. 35.00 (978-1-904915-17-1(5)) No Exit Pr. GBR. Dist: Independent Pubs. Group.

Hauser, Tim. The Art of Wall. E. 2008. (ENG., Illus.). 160p. 40.00 (978-0-8118-6235-6(6)) Chronicle Bks. LLC.

—The Pixar Treasures. 2010. (ENG.). 64p. 60.00 (978-1-4231-1653-0(4), Disney Editions) Disney Pr.

Haynes Editors. Wallace & Gromit: Cracking Contraptions Manual. 2010. (ENG., Illus.). 128p. 22.95 (978-1-84425-958-6(7), 1844259587) Haynes Publishing PLC GBR. Dist: MBI Distribution Services/Quayside Distribution.

Hench, John & Van Pelt, Peggy. Designing Disney: Imagineering & the Art of the Show. 2009. (ENG.). 160p. pap. 24.99 (978-1-4231-1915-9(0), Disney Editions) Disney Pr.

Hieronimus, Robert R. Inside the Yellow Submarine: The Making of the Beatles' Animated Classic. 2006. (Illus.). 430p. reprint ed. pap. 25.00 (978-1-4223-5269-4(2)) DIANE Publishing Co.

Hilty, Greg, ed. Watch Me Move: The Animation Show. 2011. (ENG., Illus.). 224p. pap. 39.95 (978-1-85894-558-3(5)) Merrell Pubs. Ltd. GBR. Dist: Perseus Distribution.

Irving, Christopher. From Four Color to Silver Screen: the First Movie Superheroes: The First Movie Superheroes. 2009. (Illus.). 208p. pap. 39.99 (978-1-932563-04-7(0)) Hermes Pr.

Jenewein, Henri - Paul. Stop Motion: Von Willis H. O'Brien und Ray Harryhausen zu Tim Burton. 2009. 96p. pap. (978-3-639-20172-7(8)) VDM Verlag Dr. Mueller e.K.

Johnson, Tim & Wright, Will. Krazy! The Delirious World of Anime - Comics - Video Games - Art. Grenville, Bruce & Wilson, Charles Reagan, eds. 2008. (Illus.). 276p. pap. 36.95 (978-0-520-25784-9(7)) Univ. of California Pr.

Kozlowski, Andrzej. Evolution von Machinima: Untersuchung zukünftiger Entwicklungen auf Basis vergangener und aktueller Tendenzen. 2010. 104p. pap. (978-3-639-22201-2(6)) VDM Verlag Dr. Mueller e.K.

Kricfalusi, John & Amidi, Amid. The Art of John Kricfalusi & Spümco. 2010. (Illus.). 272p. (978-0-8109-9583-3(2)) Abrams.

Kriger, Judith. Animated Realism: A Behind the Scenes Look at the Animated Documentary Genre. 2011. (ENG., Illus.). 224p. pap. 34.95 **(978-0-240-81439-1(8)**, Focal Pr.) Elsevier Science & Technology Bks.

Kurtti, Jeff. Art of the Princess & the Frog. 2009. (ENG.). 160p. 40.00 (978-0-8118-6635-4(1)) Chronicle Bks. LLC.

Lamarre, Thomas. The Anime Machine: A Media Theory of Animation. 2009. (ENG., Illus.). 408p. 75.00 (978-0-8166-5154-2(X)); pap. 24.95 (978-0-8166-5155-9(8)) Univ. of Minnesota Pr.

Lasseter, et al, comments. Animation Magazine: 20-Year Collection. 2007. 320p. 34.95 (978-1-4243-3851-1(4)) Animation Magazine.

Lasseter, John & Daly, Steve. Toy Story the Art & Making of the Animated Film. 2009. (ENG., Illus.). 128p. 40.00 (978-1-4231-2967-7(9), Disney Editions) Disney Pr.

Lee, Newton & Madej, Krystina. Disney Stories: Getting to Digital. 2012. (ENG., Illus.). xv, 196p. 99.00 **(978-1-4614-2100-9(4)**, 1461421004) Springer.

Lehman, Christopher P. American Animated Cartoons of the Vietnam Era: A Study of Social Commentary in Films & Television Programs, 1961-1973. 2006. (ENG., Illus.). 231p. per. 39.95 (978-0-7864-2818-2(X)) McFarland & Co., Inc. Pubs.

—The Colored Cartoon: Black Representation in American Animated Short Films, 1907-1954. 2007. 137p. 29.95 net. (978-1-55849-613-2(0)) Univ. of Massachusetts Pr.

Lenburg, Jeff. The Encyclopedia of Animated Cartoons. 3rd rev. ed. 2008. 784p. (gr. 6-12). 85.00 (978-0-8160-6599-8(3)) Facts On File, Inc.

Lent, John A. Cartooning in Africa. 2008. (Illus.). 304p. (C). (978-1-57273-553-8(8)); pap. (978-1-57273-554-5(6)) Hampton Pr., Inc.

Lord, Peter & Sibley, Brian. Cracking Animation: The Aardman Book of 3-D Animation. 3rd rev. ed. 2010. (ENG., Illus.). 240p. pap. 31.95 (978-0-500-28906-8(9), 528906) Thames & Hudson.

Lowood, Henry & Nitsche, Michael. The Machinima Reader. 2011. (ENG., Illus.). 360p. (gr. 17). 40.00 (978-0-262-01533-2(1)) MIT Pr.

MacLean, Fraser. Setting the Scene: The Art & Evolution of Animation Layout. 2011. (ENG., Illus.). 270p. 60.00 (978-0-8118-6987-4(3)) Chronicle Bks. LLC.

Mangels, Andy. Lou Scheimer: Creating the Filmation Generation. 2012. 160p. pap. 21.95 (978-1-893905-96-2(9)) TwoMorrows Publishing.

Merritt, Russell. Walt Disney's Silly Symphonies: A Companion to the Classic Cartoon Series. 2007. (Illus.). 256p. 44.95 (978-88-86155-27-4(1)) La Cineteca del Friuli - Le Giornate del Cinema Muto ITA. Dist: Indiana Univ. Pr.

Miller-Zarneke, Tracey. The Art & Making of Cloudy with a Chance of Meatballs. 2009. (ENG.). 156p. 50.00 (978-1-933784-89-2(X), Insight Editions) Palace Publishing Group, LP.

Miller-Zarneke, Tracey, text. The Art of How to Train Your Dragon. 2010. (ENG., Illus.). 160p. 40.00 (978-1-55704-863-9(0)) Newmarket Pr.

Mul, Ati & De Vries, Tjitte. They Thought It Was a Marvel: Arthur Melbourne-Cooper (1874-1961), Pioneer of Puppet Animation. 2010. (Illus.). 576p. (978-90-8555-016-7(5), Pallas Publications) Amsterdam Univ. Pr.

Mundi, Anima. Animation Now! 25th ed. 2007. (FRE, GER & ENG., Illus.). 351p. 14.99 (978-3-8228-3789-4(X)) TASCHEN DEU. Dist: Ingram Pub. Services.

Murphy, Kevin, et al. Three Fragments of a Lost Tale - Sculpture & Story by John Frame. 2011. (ENG.). 112p. pap. 24.95 (978-0-87328-245-1(0)) Huntington Library Pr.

Murray, Robin L. & Heumann, Joseph K. That's All Folks? Ecocritical Readings of American Animated Features. 2011. (ENG., Illus.). 296p. 50.00 (978-0-8032-3512-0(7)) Univ. of Nebraska Pr.

Narged, Sid. Anything I Ever Really Needed to Know I Learned from Anime. 2008. (Illus.). 112p. (YA). pap. 12.95 (978-0-9793080-3-1(8)) Narged, Sid.

Neupert, Richard. French Animation History. 2011. (ENG., Illus.). 216p. 115.95 (978-1-4443-3836-2(6), Wiley-Blackwell) Wiley, John & Sons, Inc.

Newman, Randy. Toy Story 3, 1 vol. 2010. (ENG.). 32p. pap. 14.99 (978-1-4234-9640-3(X), 142349640X) Leonard, Hal Corp.

Norman, Floyd. Animated Life: A Lifetime of tips, tricks, techniques & stories from a Disney Legend. 2012. (ENG., Illus.). 224p. pap. 34.95 **(978-0-240-81805-4(9)**, Focal Pr.) Elsevier Science & Technology Bks.

Osmond, Andrew. 100 Animated Feature Films. 2011. (Screen Guides). (ENG., Illus.). 256p. 30.00 (978-1-84457-340-0(0)) BFI Publishing GBR. Dist: Macmillan.

Paik, Karen. To Infinity & Beyond! The Story of Pixar Animation Studios. 2007. (ENG., Illus.). 320p. 75.00 (978-0-8118-5012-4(9)) Chronicle Bks. LLC.

Paik, Karen & Queen, Ben. The Art of Cars 2. 2011. (ENG., Illus.). 160p. 40.00 (978-0-8118-7891-3(0)) Chronicle Bks. LLC.

Paik, Karen M. Art of Ratatouille. 2007. (ENG., 160p. Illus.). 40.00 (978-0-8118-5834-2(0)); 400.00 (978-0-8118-6130-4(9)) Chronicle Bks. LLC.

Pallant, Chris. Demystifying Disney: A History of Disney Feature Animation. 2011. (ENG., Illus.). 184p. 110.00 (978-1-4411-7421-5(4)) Continuum International Publishing Group, Ltd. GBR. Dist: National Bk. Network.

Papp, Zilia. Anime & Its Roots in Early Japanese Monster Art, 1 vol. 2010. (ENG., Illus.). 240p. (978-1-906876-18-0(5)) BRILL.

Perumal, Vimala. Indian Classical Dance in 3d Animation. 2010. 76p. pap. (978-3-639-23789-4(7)) VDM Verlag Dr. Mueller e.K.

Pilling, Jayne, ed. Animating the Unconscious: Desire, Sexuality & Animation. 2012. (ENG.). 244p. (gr. 17). 75.00 **(978-0-231-16198-5(0))** Wallflower Pr. GBR. Dist: Columbia Univ. Pr.

—Animating the Unconscious - Desire, Sexuality & Animation. 2012. (ENG.). 244p. (gr. 17). pap. 25.00 **(978-0-231-16199-2(9))** Wallflower Pr. GBR. Dist: Columbia Univ. Pr.

Plympton, Bill. Make Toons That Sell Without Selling Out. 2012. (ENG., Illus.). 292p. pap. 39.95 **(978-0-240-81779-8(6)**, Focal Pr.) Elsevier Science & Technology Bks.

Pollmiller, Britta & Sercombe, Martin. The Teachers' Animation Toolkit. 2011. (ENG., Illus.). 192p. pap. 44.95 (978-1-4411-4525-3(7)) Continuum International Publishing Group, Ltd. GBR. Dist: National Bk. Network.

Pollmüller, Britta & Sercombe, Martin. The Teachers' Animation Toolkit. 2011. (Illus.). x, 170p. (978-1-4411-3107-2(8)); (978-1-4411-4796-7(9)) Continuum International Publishing Group, Ltd.

Pontieri, Laura. Soviet Animation & the Thaw of The 1960s: Not Only for Children. 2012. (ENG., Illus.). 256p. pap. 28.00 **(978-0-253-00784-1(4)**, 0253007844) Libbey, John & Co., Ltd. AUS. Dist: Indiana Univ. Pr.

Price, David A. The Pixar Touch. 2009. (Vintage Ser.). (ENG., Illus.). 320p. pap. 16.00 (978-0-307-27829-6(8), Vintage) Knopf Doubleday Publishing Group.

Rall, Hans-Martin. Tradigital Mythmaking. 2011. (Illus.). 204p. pap. **(978-3-8433-7323-4(X))** Lambert Academic Publishing.

Reinke, Steve & Gehman, Chris, eds. The Sharpest Point: Animation at the End of Cinema. 2006. (ENG., Illus.). 288p. per. 20.95 (978-0-920397-32-9(8)) Y Y Z Artists Outlet CAN. Dist: LitDistCo.

Robinson, Amanda & Robinson, Chris. Animators Unearthed: A Guide to the Best of Contemporary Animation. 2010. (ENG., Illus.). 256p. pap. 27.95 (978-0-8264-2956-8(4)) Continuum International Publishing Group, Ltd. GBR. Dist: National Bk. Network.

Robinson, Chris. Estonian Animation: Between Genius & Utter Illiteracy. 2007. (ENG., Illus.). 224p. pap. 24.95 (978-0-86196-667-7(8), 0861966678) Libbey, John & Co., Ltd. AUS. Dist: Indiana Univ. Pr.

Saito, Kaori, ed. Girl, Illustrated: Japanese Manga, Anime & Video Game Characters. 2010. (JPN & ENG., Illus.). 208p. pap. 29.95 (978-4-7562-4008-8(9), PIE Bks.) Rizzoli International Pubns., Inc.

Santucci, Walter & Santucci. The Guerrilla Guide to Animation: Making Animated Films Outside the Mainstream. 2009. (ENG., Illus.). 304p. pap. 32.95 (978-0-8264-2985-8(8)) Continuum International Publishing Group, Ltd. GBR. Dist: National Bk. Network.

Schmitz, Jerry. The Art of Shrek Forever After. 2010. (ENG., Illus.). 144p. 24.95 (978-1-60887-002-8(2)) Palace Pr. International.

Slade, Kathy, ed. Kota Ezawa: Odessa Staircase Redux. 2010. (ENG., Illus.). 168p. pap. 35.00 (978-3-03764-083-8(9)) JRP Ringier Kunstverlag AG CHE. Dist: D.A.P./Distributed Art Pubs.

Smith, Derek. Wallace & Gromit: From the Bun Vac 6000 to the Mind Manipulation-o-Matic. 2011. (ENG., Illus.). 104p. 22.95 **(978-0-85733-147-2(7)**, 0857331477) Haynes Publishing PLC GBR. Dist: MBI Distribution Services/Quayside Distribution.

Telotte, J. P. Animating Space: From Mickey to WALL-E. 2010. (ENG., Illus.). 296p. 40.00 (978-0-8131-2586-2(3)) Univ. Pr. of Kentucky.

The Blackheart Gang, compiled by. The Tale of How, 2 vols. 2011. (ENG.). 40p. 50.00 (978-0-620-43496-6(1)) Pictoplasma Publishing DEU. Dist: Innovative Logistics.

Thompson, Frank & Burton, Tim. Tim Burton's the Nightmare Before Christmas: The Film - The Art - The Vision. 2009. (ENG., Illus.). 192p. pap. 21.95 (978-1-4231-2541-9(X), Disney Editions) Disney Pr.

Thomsen, Jane Elisabeth. Translation Strategies in Animated Films. 2011. 76p. pap. **(978-3-8383-9861-7(0))** Lambert Academic Publishing.

Trowell, Melody. Linguistic Stereotypes in Children's Animated Film: A Language Attitude Study. 2008. 60p. pap. (978-3-639-11002-9(1)) VDM Verlag Dr. Mueller e.K.

Tumbusch, Tom E. Tomart's Disneyana Guide to Pin Trading. Henry, Amber, ed. 6th ed. 2007. (Tomart's Illustrated Disneyana Catalog & Price Guide Ser.). (Illus.). 176p. per. 29.95 (978-0-914293-62-0(1)) Tomart Pubns.

Valley, Robert. Massive Swerve, Book One. 2008. (Illus.). 96p. pap. 19.95 (978-0-9814895-3-7(2)) Heavy Metal Magazine.

Van Riper, A. Bowdoin, ed. Learning from Mickey, Donald & Walt: Essays on Disney's Edutainment Films. 2011. (ENG., Illus.). 274p. pap. 40.00 (978-0-7864-5957-5(3)) McFarland & Co., Inc. Pubs.

Velarde, Robert. The Wisdom of Pixar: An Animated Look at Virtue. 2010. (ENG.). 174p. pap. 15.00 (978-0-8308-3297-2(1), IVP Bks.) InterVarsity Pr.

Walt Disney Animation Studios (Firm) Staff, contrib. by. Animation. 2009. (ENG., Illus.). 272p. 50.00 (978-1-4231-1716-2(6), Disney Editions) Disney Pr.

Webb, Graham. The Animated Film Encyclopedia: A Complete Guide to American Shorts, Features, & Sequences, 1900-1979, 2 vols. alt. ed. 2006. (ENG.). 648p. pap. 75.00 (978-0-7864-2859-5(7)) McFarland & Co., Inc. Pubs.

—The Animated Film Encyclopedia: A Complete Guide to American Shorts, Features & Sequences, 1900-1999, 2d Ed. 2nd rev. ed. 2011. (ENG., Illus.). 515p. pap. 125.00 (978-0-7864-4985-9(3)) McFarland & Co., Inc. Pubs.

Wells, Paul. The Animated Bestiary: Animals, Cartoons, & Culture. 2008. (Na Ser.). (ENG., Illus.). 236p. 65.00 (978-0-8135-4414-4(9)); pap. 23.95 (978-0-8135-4415-1(7)) Rutgers Univ. Pr.

—Scriptwriting. 2007. (Basics Animation Ser.). (ENG., Illus.). 183p. pap. 29.95 (978-2-940373-16-1(7)) AVA Publishing GBR. Dist: Ingram Pub. Services.

—Understanding Animation. 2nd rev. ed. 2012. (ENG., Illus.). 304p. (C). 120.00 (978-0-415-39729-2(4)); pap. 33.95 (978-0-415-39730-8(8)) Routledge.

White, Tony. How to Make Animated Films: Tony White's Complete Masterclass on the Traditional Principles of Animation. 2009. (ENG., Illus.). 510p. pap. 49.95 (978-0-240-81033-1(3), Focal Pr.) Elsevier Science & Technology Bks.

Whitley, David. The Idea of Nature in Disney Animation. 2008. (Ashgate Studies in Childhood, 1700 to the Present Ser.). 162p. 89.95 (978-0-7546-6085-9(0)) Ashgate Publishing Co.

—The Idea of Nature in Disney Animation: From Snow White to Wall-E. 2nd rev. ed. 2012. (Ashgate Studies in Childhood, 1700 to the Present Ser.). 190p. 104.95 **(978-1-4094-3748-2(5))** Ashgate Publishing Co.

—The Idea of Nature in Disney Animation: From Snow White to Wall-E:Second Edition. 2nd rev. ed. 2012. (Ashgate Studies in Childhood, 1700 to the Present Ser.). 190p. pap. 39.95 **(978-1-4094-3749-9(3))** Ashgate Publishing Co.

Willardson, David. The Disney Art of David Willardson. 2008. (ENG., Illus.). 128p. 39.95 (978-1-933784-58-8(X), Insight Editions) Palace Publishing Group, LP.

Wolfgram Evans, Noell K. Animators of Film & Television: Nineteen Artists, Writers, Producers & Others. 2011. (ENG., Illus.). 228p. pap. 35.00 (978-0-7864-4832-6(6)) McFarland & Co., Inc. Pubs.

Yune, Tommy. The Art of Robotech: The Shadow Chronicles. 2007. (ENG., Illus.). 144p. per. 19.95 (978-1-933330-29-7(5)) Stone Bridge Pr.

Zahed, Ramin. The Art of Puss in Boots. 2011. (ENG.). 144p. 39.95 **(978-1-60887-034-9(0)**, Insight Editions) Palace Publishing Group, LP.

Zahl, David & Brewer, Todd. The Gospel According to Pixar. 2010. 74p. pap. 12.50 (978-0-557-58448-2(5)) Lulu Enterprises Inc.

ANIMATED FILMS—JAPAN

Brenner, Robin E. Understanding Manga & Anime, 1 vol. 2007. (Illus.). 356p. per. 40.00 *(978-1-59158-332-5(2),* LU3322) Libraries Unlimited, Inc.

Brown, Steven T. Cinema Anime. 2008. (ENG., Illus.). 256p. pap. 31.00 *(978-0-230-60621-0(0))* Palgrave Macmillan.

—Tokyo Cyberpunk: Posthumanism in Japanese Visual Culture. 2010. (ENG., Illus.). 272p. 95.00 *(978-0-230-10359-7(6));* pap. 28.00 *(978-0-230-10360-3(X))* Palgrave Macmillan.

Camp, Brian & Davis, Julie. Anime Classics Zetta! 100 Must-See Japanese Animation Masterpieces. 2007. (ENG., Illus.). 408p. per. 18.95 *(978-1-933330-22-8(8))* Stone Bridge Pr.

Cavallaro, Dani. Anime & Memory: Aesthetic, Cultural & Thematic Perspectives. 2009. (ENG.). 204p. pap. 35.00 *(978-0-7864-4112-9(7))* McFarland & Co., Inc. Pubs.

—Anime & the Visual Novel: Narrative Structure, Design & Play at the Crossroads of Animation & Computer Games. 2009. (ENG.). 268p. pap. 35.00 *(978-0-7864-4427-4(4))* McFarland & Co., Inc. Pubs.

—Anime Intersections: Tradition & Innovation in Theme & Technique. 2007. (ENG.). 218p. per. 35.00 *(978-0-7864-3234-9(9))* McFarland & Co., Inc. Pubs.

Cavallaro, Dani. Art in Anime: The Creative Quest as Theme & Metaphor. 2011. (ENG.). 242p. pap. 35.00 ***(978-0-7864-6561-3(1))*** McFarland & Co., Inc. Pubs.

Clements, Jonathan & McCarthy, Helen. The Anime Encyclopedia: A Guide to Japanese Animation Since 1917. 2nd rev. exp. ed. 2006. (ENG., Illus.). 867p. per. 29.95 *(978-1-933330-10-5(4))* Stone Bridge Pr.

Cocoro Books Staff. Hayao Miyazaki. 2008. 192p. pap. 11.95 *(978-1-932897-47-0(X),* cocoro bks.) DH Publishing, Inc.

Cornog, Martha & Perper, Timothy, eds. Mangatopia: Essays on Manga & Anime in the Modern World, 1 vol. (Illus.). 254p. pap. 50.00 *(978-1-59158-908-2(8),* A2247P) Pearson Education GBR. Dist: ABC-CLIO, LLC.

de Weck, Ziba Ardalan. Tabaimo: Boundary Layer. 2011. (ENG., Illus.). 80p. pap. 45.00 *(978-3-86560-828-4(0))* Verlag der Buchhandlung Walther Konig DEU. Dist: D.A.P./Distributed Art Pubs.

Hissey, Ivan, et al. The Complete Step-by-Step Guide to Drawing Cartoons, Manga & Anime: Expert Techniques & Projects, Shown in More Than 2000 Illustrations. 2012. (ENG., Illus.). 512p. 29.99 ***(978-0-7548-2373-5(3))*** Anness Publishing GBR. Dist: National Bk. Network.

Hu, Tze-yue G. Frames of Anime: Culture & Image-Building. 2010. (CHI., Illus.). 256p. ***(978-988-220-772-1(3))*** Hong Kong Univ. Pr.

—Frames of Anime: Culture & Image-Building. 2010. (ENG., Illus.). 256p. (gr. 17). 55.00 *(978-962-209-097-2(4));* pap. 28.00 *(978-962-209-098-9(2))* Hong Kong Univ. Pr. HKG. Dist: Columbia Univ. Pr.

Kalen, Elizabeth. Mostly Manga: A Genre Guide to Popular Manga, Manwha, Manhua, & Anime, 1 vol. (Genreflecting Advisory Ser.). (Illus.). 150p. 55.00 ***(978-1-59884-938-7(7),*** A3585C) Pearson Education GBR. Dist: ABC-CLIO, LLC.

Koyama-Richard, Brigette. Japanese Animation: From Painted Scrolls to Pokémon. 2010. (ENG., Illus.). 248p. 49.95 *(978-2-08-030153-6(5))* Flammarion et Cie FRA. Dist: Random Hse., Inc.

Lunning, Frenchy, ed. Fanthropologies, No. 5. 2010. (Mechademia Ser.: No. 5). (ENG., Illus.). 352p. pap. 24.95 *(978-0-8166-7387-2(X))* Univ. of Minnesota Pr.

—Mechademia 3: Limits of the Human. 2008. (Illus.). 296p. pap. 19.95 *(978-0-8166-5482-6(4))* Univ. of Minnesota Pr.

MacWilliams, Mark W., ed. Japanese Visual Culture: Explorations in the World of Manga & Anime. 2008. (ENG., Illus.). 368p. 95.95 *(978-0-7656-1601-2(7));* pap. 34.95 *(978-0-7656-1602-9(5))* Sharpe, M.E. Inc. (East Gate Bk.).

Mccarthy, Helen. 500 Essential Anime Movies. 2009. 528p. pap. 24.95 *(978-0-06-147450-7(9),* Collins Design) HarperCollins Pubs.

Odell, Colin & Le Blanc, Michelle. Studio Ghibli: The Films of Hayao Miyazaki & Isao Takahata. 2009. (ENG., Illus.). 160p. pap. 24.95 *(978-1-84243-279-2(6))* Oldcastle Bks., Ltd. GBR. Dist: Independent Pubs. Group.

Osmond, Andrew. Satoshi Kon: The Illusionist. 2009. (ENG., Illus.). 128p. pap. 18.95 *(978-1-933330-74-7(0))* Stone Bridge Pr.

Perper, Timothy & Cornog, Martha. Mangatopia: Essays on Manga & Anime in the Modern World. 2011. (Illus.). xx, 254p. E-Book ***(978-1-59158-909-9(6))*** Libraries Unlimited, Inc.

Robinson, Chris. Japanese Animation: Time Out of Mind. 2010. (ENG., Illus.). 160p. pap. 29.95 *(978-0-86196-692-9(9),* 0861966929) Indiana Univ. Pr.

Robinson, Jeremy Mark. The Cinema of Hayao Miyazaki. 2011. (Illus.). 496p. pap. ***(978-1-86171-305-6(3))*** Crescent Moon Publishing.

Schodt, Frederik L. The Astro Boy Essays: Osamu Tezuka, Mighty Atom, & the Manga/Anime Revolution. 2007. (ENG., Illus.). 248p. per. 16.95 *(978-1-933330-54-9(6))* Stone Bridge Pr.

Steiff, Josef & Tamplin, Tristan D., eds. Anime & Philosophy: Wide Eyed Wonder. 2010. (Popular Culture & Philosophy Ser.). (ENG.). 288p. pap. 19.95 *(978-0-8126-9670-7(0))* Open Court Publishing Co.

Steinberg, Marc. Anime's Media Mix: Franchising Toys & Characters in Japan. 2012. 304p. pap. 25.00 ***(978-0-8166-7550-0(3));*** (Illus.). 75.00 ***(978-0-8166-7549-4(X))*** Univ. of Minnesota Pr.

Tamaki, Saito & Azuma, Hiroki. Beautiful Fighting Girl. Vincent, J. Keith & Lawson, Dawn, trs. from JPN. 2011. (Illus.). 248p. pap. 19.95 *(978-0-8166-5451-2(4))* Univ. of Minnesota Pr.

Tamaki, Saito & Vincent, J. Keith. Beautiful Fighting Girl. Lawson, Dawn, tr. from JPN. 2011. (Illus.). 248p. 60.00 *(978-0-8166-5450-5(6))* Univ. of Minnesota Pr.

von Feigenblatt, Otto, MA. Understanding Japanese Animation: the Hidden Meaning Revealed. 2008. 93p. pap. 9.22 *(978-0-557-02422-3(6))* Lulu Enterprises Inc.

Yonebayashi, Hiromasa & Miyazaki, Hayao. The Art of the Secret World of Arrietty. 2012. (Art of Arrietty Ser.). (ENG., Illus.). 200p. pap. 34.99 ***(978-1-4215-4118-1(1))*** Viz Media.

ANIMATION (CINEMATOGRAPHY)

see also Computer Animation

Albee, Timothy. Fundamentals of Character Animation. 2008. 400p. pap. 49.95 incl. cd-rom *(978-1-55622-248-1(3))* Wordware Publishing, Inc.

Animated Illusions: Level T, Group 1, 6 vols. (Sunshine Ser.). 48p. 44.95 *(978-0-7802-6093-1(7))* Wright Group, The.

Animation World Network Staff. On Animation-the Director's Perspective. 2012. (ENG.). 304p. pap. 39.99 *(978-1-59863-407-5(0))* Course Technology.

Arakawa, Hiromu. The Anime. Searleman, Eric, ed. 2006. (Fullmetal Alchemist Ser.). (ENG., Illus.). 96p. 19.99 *(978-1-4215-0766-8(8))* Viz Media.

Belman, Nancy. Animated Performance: Bringing Imaginary Animal, Human & Fantasy Characters to Life. 2010. (Required Reading Range Ser.). (ENG., Illus.). 232p. pap. 49.95 *(978-2-940373-81-9(7))* Ava Publishing SA CHE. Dist: Ingram Pub. Services.

Besen, Ellen. Animation Unleashed: 100 Principles Every Animator, Comic Book Writer, Filmmaker, Video Artist, & Game Developer Should Know. 2008. (ENG., Illus.). 245p. pap. 26.95 *(978-1-932907-49-0(1))* Wiese, Michael Productions.

Block, Alexis, ed. Animatrix 19 - A Journal of the UCLA Animation Workshop. 2011. (Animatrix Ser.). (ENG.). 100p. pap. 19.95 ***(978-0-9828354-8-7(5))*** UCLA Graduate Students Assn. Pubns.

Book Industry Services Publishers Staff & Hoogerbrugge, Han. Modern Living. 2006. (ENG., Illus.). 200p. 49.00 *(978-90-6369-187-5(4))* Bis B.V., Uitgeverij(BIS Publishers) NLD. Dist: Consortium Bk. Sales & Distribution.

Bratt, Benjamin. Rotoscoping: Techniques & Tools for the Aspiring Artist. 2011. (ENG., Illus.). 304p. pap. 39.95 *(978-0-240-81704-0(4),* Focal Pr.) Elsevier Science & Technology Bks.

Brown, Steven T. Cinema Anime. 2008. (ENG., Illus.). 256p. pap. 31.00 *(978-0-230-60621-0(0))* Palgrave Macmillan.

Buchan, Suzanne. Animated Worlds. Buchan, Suzanne, ed. 2007. (ENG., Illus.). 256p. pap. 27.95 *(978-0-86196-661-5(9),* 0861966619) Libbey, John & Co., Ltd. AUS. Dist: Indiana Univ. Pr.

—The Quay Brothers: Into a Metaphysical Playroom. 2011. (ENG., Illus.). 296p. 75.00 *(978-0-8166-4658-6(9));* pap. 25.00 *(978-0-8166-4659-3(7))* Univ. of Minnesota Pr.

Buchan, Suzanne, ed. Animation. 2013. (AFI Film Readers Ser.). (ENG., Illus.). 320p. (C). 135.00 ***(978-0-415-80723-4(9));*** pap. 39.95 ***(978-0-415-80724-1(7))*** Routledge.

Canemaker, John. Storytelling in Animation Vol. 2: The Art of the Animated Image. pap. 9.95 *(978-0-573-60697-7(8))* French, Samuel Inc.

Cavalier, Stephen. The World History of Animation. 2011. 416p. 39.95 *(978-0-520-26112-9(7))* Univ. of California Pr.

Cook, Benjamin & Thompson, Kirsten Moana. The Animatel Book. Thomas, Gary, ed. 2007. (ENG., Illus.). 250p. (gr. 17). pap. 30.00 *(978-0-9548569-2-2(9))* WallFlower Pr. GBR. Dist: Columbia Univ. Pr.

Cotte, Olivier. Secrets of Oscar-Winning Animation: Behind the Scenes of 13 Classic Short Animations. 2007. (ENG., Illus.). 288p. per. 37.95 *(978-0-240-52070-4(X),* Focal Pr.) Elsevier Science & Technology Bks.

Disney Book Group Staff. Story. 2008. (Walt Disney Classics Ser.). (ENG.). 224p. 50.00 *(978-1-4231-0723-1(3),* Disney Editions) Disney Pr.

Drate, Spencer & Salavetz, Judith. Pure Animation: Steps to Creation with 57 Cutting-Edge Animators. 2007. (Illus.). 175p. pap. *(978-1-85894-365-7(5))* Merrell Pubs. Ltd.

Fischer, Stuart. The Hanna-Barbera Story: The Life & Times of TV's Greatest Animation Studio. 2011. 534p. pap. 34.95 ***(978-1-4626-3354-8(4))*** PublishAmerica, Inc.

Furniss, Maureen. Art in Motion: Animation Aesthetics. 2nd rev. ed. 2008. (ENG., Illus.). 288p. pap. 24.95 *(978-0-86196-663-9(5),* 0861966635) Libbey, John & Co., Ltd. AUS. Dist: Indiana Univ. Pr.

Furniss, Maureen, ed. Animation: Art & Industry. 2009. (ENG., Illus.). 256p. pap. 27.95 *(978-0-86196-680-6(5),* 0861966805) Libbey, John & Co., Ltd. AUS. Dist: Indiana Univ. Pr.

Gasek, Tom. Frame-by-Frame Stop Motion: The Guide to Non-Traditional Animation Techniques. 2011. (ENG., Illus.). 216p. pap. 39.95 ***(978-0-240-81728-6(1),*** Focal Pr.) Elsevier Science & Technology Bks.

Georgenes, Chris. Pushing Pixels: Secret Weapons for the Modern Flash Animator. 2012. (ENG., Illus.). 280p. pap. 39.95 ***(978-0-240-81843-6(1),*** Focal Pr.) Elsevier Science & Technology Bks.

Ghazala, Mohamed. Animation in the Arab World. 2011. 56p. pap. ***(978-3-8443-8548-9(7))*** Lambert Academic Publishing.

Ghertner, Ed. Layout & Composition for Animation. 2010. (ENG., Illus.). 216p. pap. 34.95 *(978-0-240-81441-4(X),* Focal Pr.) Elsevier Science & Technology Bks.

Gilland, Joseph. Elemental Magic, Volume II: The Technique of Special Effects Animation. 2011. (ENG., Illus.). 360p. pap. 49.95 ***(978-0-240-81479-7(7),*** Focal Pr.) Elsevier Science & Technology Bks.

Goldman, Michael, ed. Imageworks: Where Imagination Meets Technology - Inside the Award-Winning Sony Production Studio. 2008. (ENG., Illus.). 50.00 *(978-1-933784-54-0(7),* Insight Editions) Palace Publishing Group, LP.

Graber, Sheila. Animation: A Handy Guide. 2011. (ENG., Illus.). 144p. pap. 29.95 *(978-1-4081-0283-1(8))* A & C Black GBR. Dist: Macmillan.

Hal Leonard Corporation Staff, creator. Alvin & the Chipmunks. 2008. (ENG., Illus.). 80p. pap. 14.95 *(978-1-4234-5522-6(3),* 1423455223) Leonard, Hal Corp.

Hardman, Paul. Animation. 2007. (ENG., Illus.). 96p. pap. 14.95 *(978-1-84537-674-1(9))* New Holland Pubs., Ltd. GBR. Dist: Sterling Publishing Co., Inc.

Hayes, Derek & Webster, Chris. Acting & Performance for Animation. 2012. (ENG.). 250p. pap. 39.95 ***(978-0-240-81239-7(5),*** Focal Pr.) Elsevier Science & Technology Bks.

Hess, Roland & Hess, D. Roland. Animating with Blender: How to Create Short Animations from Start to Finish. 2008. (ENG., Illus.). 368p. pap. 44.95 *(978-0-240-81079-9(1),* Focal Pr.) Elsevier Science & Technology Bks.

Hooks, Ed. Acting for Animators. 3rd ed. 2011. (ENG., Illus.). 192p. 100.00 *(978-0-415-58023-6(4));* pap. 31.95 *(978-0-415-58024-3(2))* Routledge.

Huang, He. Journey to the East. 2010. 124p. pap. *(978-3-8383-7813-8(X))* Lambert Academic Publishing.

Jenewein, Henri - Paul. Stop Motion: Von Willis H. O'Brien und Ray Harryhausen zu Tim Burton. 2009. 96p. pap. *(978-3-639-20172-7(8))* VDM Verlag Dr. Mueller e.K.

Johnson, Phylis & Pettit, Donald. Machinima: The Art & Practice of Virtual Filmmaking. 2012. (ENG.). 327p. pap. 38.00 ***(978-0-7864-6171-4(3))*** McFarland & Co., Inc. Pubs.

King, Sarah, ed. The Dissolve. 2010. (ENG., Illus.). 240p. 50.00 *(978-0-9764492-3-4(3))* Site Santa Fe.

Kozlowski, Andrzej. Evolution von Machinima: Untersuchung zukünftiger Entwicklungen auf Basis vergangener und aktueller Tendenzen. 2010. 104p. pap. *(978-3-639-22201-2(6))* VDM Verlag Dr. Mueller e.K.

Krasner, Jon S. Motion Graphic Design: Applied History & Aesthetics. 2nd ed. 2008. (ENG., Illus.). 432p. pap. 49.95 *(978-0-240-80989-2(0),* Focal Pr.) Elsevier Science & Technology Bks.

Kundert-Gibbs, John & Kundert-Gibbs, Kristin. Action! Acting Lessons for CG Animators. 2009. (ENG., Illus.). 352p. pap. 49.99 *(978-0-470-22743-5(5),* Sybex) Wiley, John & Sons, Inc.

Lab-Volt Staff. Animation: Tech-Design ESeries. 2010. 43p. 5.00 *(978-1-60533-269-0(2));* 52p. ring bd. 7.00 *(978-1-60533-157-7(0))* Lab-Volt Systems, Inc.

Lallo, M. J. & Wright, Jean Ann. Voice-Over for Animation. 2009. (ENG., Illus.). 288p. pap. 29.95 *(978-0-240-81015-7(5),* Focal Pr.) Elsevier Science & Technology Bks.

Lasseter, et al, comments. Animation Magazine: 20-Year Collection. 2007. 320p. 34.95 *(978-1-4243-3851-1(4))* Animation Magazine.

Laybourne, Kit. Mediapedia: Creative Tools & Techniques for Camera, Computer, & Beyond. 2008. (ENG., Illus.). 304p. pap. 24.95 *(978-1-59921-401-6(6),* Knack) Globe Pequot Pr., The.

Lee, Newton & Madej, Krystina. Disney Stories: Getting to Digital. 2012. (ENG., Illus.). xv, 196p. 99.00 ***(978-1-4614-2100-9(4),*** 1461421004) Springer.

Levy, David. Directing Animation. 2010. (ENG., Illus.). 256p. pap. 24.95 *(978-1-58115-746-8(0),* 115746, Allworth Pr.) Skyhorse Publishing Co., Inc.

Lord, Peter & Sibley, Brian. Cracking Animation: The Aardman Book of 3-D Animation. 3rd rev. ed. 2010. (ENG., Illus.). 240p. pap. 31.95 *(978-0-500-28906-8(9),* 528906) Thames & Hudson.

Lowe, Richard, ed. Learning with Animation: Research Implications for Design. 2007. (ENG., Illus.). 402p. per. 32.99 *(978-0-521-61739-0(1))* Cambridge Univ. Pr.

Maloney, Tim. Get Animated! Creating Professional Cartoon Animation on Your Home Computer. 2009. (ENG., Illus.). 160p. pap. 24.95 *(978-0-8230-9921-4(0))* Watson-Guptill Pubns., Inc.

Marx, Christy, ed. Write Your Way into Animation & Games: Create a Writing Career in Animation & Games. 2010. (ENG., Illus.). 424p. pap. 39.95 *(978-0-240-81343-1(X),* Focal Pr.) Elsevier Science & Technology Bks.

Mazany, Ondrej & Svoboda, Tomas. Articulated 3d Human Model & its Animation. 2010. 72p. pap. *(978-3-8383-1560-7(X))* Lambert Academic Publishing.

McCarthy, Helen. Art of Osamu Tezuka: God of Manga. 2009. (ENG., Illus.). 272p. 40.00 *(978-0-8109-8249-9(8))* Abrams.

Miyazaki, Hayao. Starting Point: 1979-1996. 2009. (ENG.). 500p. pap. 29.99 *(978-1-4215-0594-7(0))* Viz Media.

Montgomery, Lee. Tradigital Maya: A CG Animator's Guide to Applying the Classical Principles of Animation. 2011. (ENG., Illus.). 568p. pap. 49.95 *(978-0-12-385222-9(6),* Focal Pr.) Elsevier Science & Technology Bks.

Muir, Shannon. Gardner's Guide to Writing & Producing Animation. 2007. (Gardner's Guide Ser.). (ENG., Illus.). 288p. per. 34.95 *(978-1-58965-027-5(1))* Gardner, Garth Co., Inc. (GGC).

Murdock, Kelly L. Anime Studio: The Official Guide. 2008. (ENG., Illus.). 512p. pap. 39.99 *(978-1-59863-432-7(1))* Course Technology.

Murphy, Mary. Animation: Everything You Need to Know to Get Started. 2008. (ENG., Illus.). 128p. pap. 22.95 *(978-0-8230-9922-1(9))* Watson-Guptill Pubns., Inc.

Newman, Victor, intro. IdN Extra 02: New York. 2011. (ENG., Illus.). 132p. pap. 25.00 *(978-988-18470-3-4(6))* Systems Design, Ltd. HKG. Dist: D.A.P./Distributed Art Pubs.

Osipa, Jason. Stop Staring: Facial Modeling & Animation Done Right. 3rd ed. 2010. (ENG., Illus.). 432p. pap. 49.99 *(978-0-470-60990-3(7),* Sybex) Wiley, John & Sons, Inc.

Papapetros, Spyros. On the Animation of the Inorganic: Art, Architecture, & the Extension of Life. 2012. (ENG., Illus.). 440p. 45.00 ***(978-0-226-64568-1(1))*** Univ. of Chicago Pr.

Pardew, Les. Character Emotion in 2D & 3D Animation. 2007. (ENG., Illus.). 264p. pap. 34.99 *(978-1-59863-381-8(3))* Course Technology.

Parisi, Frank & Scheppke, Gary. The Art of Star Wars: The Clone Wars. 2009. (ENG., Illus.). 272p. 50.00 *(978-0-8118-6889-1(3))* Chronicle Bks. LLC.

Pettigrew, Neil. The Stop-Motion Filmography: A Critical Guide to 297 Features Using Puppet Animation, 2 vols., 2 vol set. alt. ed. 2007. (ENG., Illus.). 878p. pap. 75.00 *(978-0-7864-3107-6(5))* McFarland & Co., Inc. Pubs.

Plunkett, Kilian, et al, illus. Battle Milk 2: Tangents & Transitions in Concept Art. 2010. (ENG.). 128p. pap. 24.95 *(978-1-933492-53-7(8))* Design Studio Pr.

Plympton, Bill. Make Toons That Sell Without Selling Out. 2012. (ENG., Illus.). 292p. pap. 39.95 ***(978-0-240-81779-8(6),*** Focal Pr.) Elsevier Science & Technology Bks.

Pollmiler, Britta & Sercombe, Martin. The Teachers' Animation Toolkit. 2011. (ENG., Illus.). 192p. pap. 44.95 *(978-1-4411-4525-3(7))* Continuum International Publishing Group, Ltd. GBR. Dist: National Bk. Network.

Pollmüller, Britta & Sercombe, Martin. The Teachers' Animation Toolkit. 2011. (Illus.). x, 170p. *(978-1-4411-4795-7(9));* *(978-1-4411-3107-2(8))* Continuum International Publishing Group, Ltd.

Purves, Barry. Stop-Motion. 2010. (Basics Animation Ser.). (ENG., Illus.). 200p. pap. 29.95 *(978-2-940373-73-4(6))* AVA Publishing GBR. Dist: Ingram Pub. Services.

Purves, Barry J. C. Stop Motion: Passion, Process & Performance. 2007. (ENG., Illus.). 372p. pap. 49.95 *(978-0-240-52060-5(2),* Focal Pr.) Elsevier Science & Technology Bks.

Rall, Hans-Martin. Tradigital Mythmaking. 2011. (Illus.). 204p. pap. ***(978-3-8433-7323-4(X))*** Lambert Academic Publishing.

Ratner, Peter & Ratner. 3-D Human Modeling & Animation. 3rd ed. 2009. (ENG., Illus.). 400p. pap. 55.00 *(978-0-470-39667-4(9),* Wiley) Wiley, John & Sons, Inc.

Reinke, Steve & Gehman, Chris, eds. The Sharpest Point: Animation at the End of Cinema. 2006. (ENG., Illus.). 288p. per. 20.95 *(978-0-920397-32-9(8))* Y Y Z Artists Outlet CAN. Dist: LitDistCo.

Roberts, Steve. Character Animation Fundamentals: Developing Skills for 2D & 3D Character Animation. 2011. (ENG., Illus.). 456p. pap. 41.95 *(978-0-240-52227-2(3),* Focal Pr.) Elsevier Science & Technology Bks.

Robinson, Chris J. & Robinson, Chris. Canadian Animation: Looking for a Place to Happen. 2008. (ENG., Illus.). 300p. pap. 27.95 *(978-0-86196-688-2(0),* 0861966880) Libbey, John & Co., Ltd. AUS. Dist: Indiana Univ. Pr.

Sacks, Terence J. Opportunities in Cartooning & Animation Careers. 2007. (ENG.). 160p. per. 14.95 *(978-0-07-148206-6(7),* 0071482067) McGraw-Hill Cos., The.

Sawicki, Mark. Animating with Stop Motion Pro. 2010. (ENG., Illus.). 239p. pap. 44.95 *(978-0-240-81219-9(0),* Focal Pr.) Elsevier Science & Technology Bks.

Scheppke, Gary & Parisi, Frank. The Art of Star Wars: The Clone Wars. ltd. ed. 2009. (ENG.). 192p. 120.00 *(978-0-8118-7102-0(9))* Chronicle Bks. LLC.

Schnotz, Wolfgang & Lowe, Richard, eds. Learning with Animation: Research Implications for Design. 2007. (ENG., Illus.). 402p. 88.99 *(978-0-521-85189-3(0))* Cambridge Univ. Pr.

Selby, Andrew. Animation in Process. 2009. (ENG., Illus.). 192p. pap. 40.00 *(978-1-85669-587-9(5))* King, Laurence Publishing GBR. Dist: Hachette Bk. Group.

Shapurjee, Shanaz. South African Animation. 2009. 108p. pap. *(978-3-639-21683-7(0))* VDM Verlag Dr. Mueller e.K.

Shaver, Buy. Moving the Eye Through 2-D Design: A Visual Primer. 2010. (ENG., Illus.). 157p. pap. 40.00 *(978-1-84150-363-9(0))* Intellect, Ltd. GBR. Dist: Chicago Distribution Ctr.

Shaw, Susannah. Stop Motion: Craft Skills for Model Animation. 2nd ed. 2008. (Focal Press Visual Effects & Animation Ser.). (ENG., Illus.). 264p. per. 34.95 *(978-0-240-52055-1(6),* Focal Pr.) Elsevier Science & Technology Bks.

Shiau, Hong-Chi. Animating the Cute, the Mean & the Beautiful: The Production & Consumption of Animation: Taiwan's Struggles in the Age of Globalization. 2008. (Illus.). 216p. pap. *(978-3-639-09397-1(6))* VDM Verlag Dr. Mueller e.K.

Simon, Mark A. Storyboards - Motion in Art. 3rd ed. 2006. (ENG., Illus.). 448p. per. 46.95 *(978-0-240-80805-5(3),* Focal Pr.) Elsevier Science & Technology Bks.

Svitil, Torene. So You Want to Work in Animation & Special Effects? 2007. (Careers in Film & Television Ser.). (Illus.). 128p. (J). (gr. 6-9). lib. bdg. 31.93 *(978-0-7660-2737-4(6))* Enslow Pubs., Inc.

Takamoto, Iwao. Iwao Takamoto: My Life with a Thousand Characters. 2009. (ENG., Illus.). 240p. 50.00 *(978-1-60473-193-4(1))* Univ. Pr. of Mississippi.

Takamoto, Iwao & Mallory, Michael. Iwao Takamoto: My Life with a Thousand Characters. 2009. (ENG., Illus.). 240p. pap. 22.00 *(978-1-60473-194-1(X))* Univ. Pr. of Mississippi.

Taylor, Angie. Design Essentials for the Motion Media Artist: A Practical Guide to Principles & Techniques. 2010. (ENG., Illus.). 400p. pap. 44.95 *(978-0-240-81181-9(X),* Focal Pr.) Elsevier Science & Technology Bks.

Theme Ament, Vanessa. The Foley Grail: The Art of Performing Sound for Film, Games, & Animation. 2009. (ENG., Illus.). 216p. pap. 44.95 *(978-0-240-81125-3(9),* Focal Pr.) Elsevier Science & Technology Bks.

Tillman, Bryan. Creative Character Design. 2011. (ENG., Illus.). 256p. pap. 29.95 *(978-0-240-81495-7(9),* Focal Pr.) Elsevier Science & Technology Bks.

Voltron: Defender of the Universe. 2011. (Illus.). 192p. 29.95 *(978-1-933076-87-4(9))* Moonstone.

A

von Busack, Richard. Art of Megamind. 2010. (ENG., Illus.). 156p. 39.95 *(978-1-60887-004-2(9),* Insight Editions) Palace Publishing Group, LP.

von Feigenblatt, Otto, MA. Understanding Japanese Animation: the Hidden Meaning Revealed. 2008. 93p. pap. 9.22 *(978-0-557-02422-3(6))* Lulu Enterprises Inc.

Walt Disney Animation Studios (Firm) Staff, contrib. by. Animation. 2009. (ENG., Illus.). 272p. 50.00 *(978-1-4231-1716-2(6),* Disney Editions) Disney Pr.

Webster, Chris. Action Analysis for Animators. 2012. (ENG.). 424p. pap. 39.95 *(978-0-240-81218-2(2),* Focal Pr.) Elsevier Science & Technology Bks.

Wells, Paul. The Fundamentals of Animation. 2006. (Fundamentals Ser.). (JPN & ENG., Illus.). 196p. pap. 29.95 *(978-2-940373-02-4(7))* AVA Publishing GBR. Dist: Ingram Pub. Services.

Wells, Paul, et al. Re-Imagining Animation: The Changing Face of the Moving Image. 2008. (Required Reading Range Ser.). (ENG., Illus.). 192p. pap. 49.95 *(978-2-940373-69-7(8))* Ava Publishing SA CHE. Dist: Ingram Pub. Services.

Weston Woods Staff, creator. What's the Big Idea, Ben Franklin? 2011. 18.95 ***(978-0-439-77905-0(7));*** 38.75 ***(978-0-439-77907-4(3));*** 29.95 ***(978-0-439-77910-4(3))*** Weston Woods Studios, Inc.

Whitaker, Harold & Halas, John. Timing for Animation. Sito, Tom, ed. 2nd ed. 2009. (ENG., Illus.). 176p. pap. 30.95 *(978-0-240-52160-2(9),* Focal Pr.) Elsevier Science & Technology Bks.

White, Tony. Animation from Pencils to Pixels: Classical Techniques for the Digital Animator. 2006. (ENG., Illus.). 528p. pap. 49.95 *(978-0-240-80670-9(0),* Focal Pr.) Elsevier Science & Technology Bks.

—How to Make Animated Films: Tony White's Complete Masterclass on the Traditional Principles of Animation. 2009. (ENG., Illus.). 510p. pap. 49.95 *(978-0-240-81033-1(3),* Focal Pr.) Elsevier Science & Technology Bks.

Williams, Richard E. The Animator's Survival Kit Kit: A Manual of Methods, Principles & Formulas for Classical, Computer, Games, Stop Motion & Internet Animators. 2nd rev. exp. ed. 2009. (ENG., Illus.). 392p. pap. 35.00 *(978-0-571-23834-7(3))* Faber & Faber, Inc.

Wilson, Rowland B. Rowland B. Wilson's Trade Secrets: Notes for Cartooning & Animation. Lemieux-Wilson, Suzanne, ed. 2012. (ENG., Illus.). 320p. pap. 39.95 ***(978-0-240-81734-7(6),*** Focal Pr.) Elsevier Science & Technology Bks.

Winder, Catherine & Dowlatabadi, Zahra. Producing Animation. Miller-Zarneke, Tracey, ed. 2nd ed. 2011. (ENG., Illus.). 368p. 45.95 *(978-0-240-81535-0(1),* Focal Pr.) Elsevier Science & Technology Bks.

Zahl, David & Brewer, Todd. The Gospel According to Pixar. 2010. 74p. pap. 12.50 *(978-0-557-58448-2(5))* Lulu Enterprises Inc.

ANIMATORS

The Art of Disney. 2008. 240p. pap. 24.95 *(978-1-4231-1914-2(2),* Disney Editions) Disney Pr.

Barrier, Michael. The Animated Man: A Life of Walt Disney. 2007. (Illus.). 393p. 39.95 *(978-0-520-24117-6(7))* Univ. of California Pr.

Barrier, Michael & Barrier, J. Michael. The Animated Man: A Life of Walt Disney. 2008. (Illus.). 393p. pap. 22.95 *(978-0-520-25619-4(0))* Univ. of California Pr.

Botero, Silvio. Esquemas de Trabajo para un Animador de Grupos. (SPA.). 152p. 6.95 *(978-958-607-290-8(8))* Sociedad de San Pablo COL. Dist: St Pauls/Alba Hse. Pubs.

Canemaker, John. Two Guys Named Joe: Master Animation Storytellers Joe Grant & Joe Ranft. 2010. (ENG., Illus.). 192p. 40.00 *(978-1-4231-1067-5(6),* Disney Editions) Disney Pr.

Cook, Benjamin & Thompson, Kirsten Moana. The Animate! Book. Thomas, Gary, ed. 2007. (ENG., Illus.). 250p. (gr. 17). pap. 30.00 *(978-0-9548569-2-2(9))* Wallflower Pr. GBR. Dist: Columbia Univ. Pr.

Fleischer, Richard. Out of the Inkwell: Max Fleischer & the Animation Revolution. 2011. (ENG., Illus.). 232p. pap. 21.95 *(978-0-8131-3464-2(1))* Univ. Pr. of Kentucky.

Ghez, Didier. Walt's People - 2011. 328p. pap. 19.99 ***(978-1-4568-5150-7(0))*** Xlibris Corp.

Grandinetti, Fred. Jack Mercer, the Voice of Popeye. 2007. 208p. per. 19.95 *(978-1-59393-096-7(8))* BearManor Media.

Harryhausen, Ray & Dalton, Tony. Ray Harryhausen's Fantasy Scrapbook: Models, Artwork & Memories from 65 Years of Filmmaking. 2012. (ENG., Illus.). 192p. 55.00 ***(978-1-84513-557-7(1))*** Aurum Pr., Ltd. GBR. Dist: Independent Pubs. Group.

Jones, Marian & Clough, Linda Jones, intros. Stroke of Genius: A Collection of Paintings & Musings on Life, Love & Art by Chuck Jones. deluxe ed. 2007. 75.00 *(978-0-615-13746-9(6))* Jones, Linda Enterprises, Inc.

Krasniewicz, Louise & Blitz, Michael. Walt Disney Vol. 1: A Biography, 1 vol. 2010. (Greenwood Biographies Ser.). (Illus.). 155p. 35.00 *(978-0-313-35830-2(3),* GR5830, Greenwood Pr.) Greenwood Publishing Group, Inc.

Lallo, M. J. & Wright, Jean Ann. Voice-Over for Animation. 2009. (ENG., Illus.). 288p. pap. 29.95 *(978-0-240-81015-7(5),* Focal Pr.) Elsevier Science & Technology Bks.

Lenburg, Jeff. Legends of Animation. 2011. (Legends of Animation Ser.). (gr. 6-12). 279.60 ***(978-0-7910-9976-6(8));*** 139.80 ***(978-0-7910-9962-9(8))*** Facts On File, Inc. (Chelsea Hse.).

McCarthy, Helen. Art of Osamu Tezuka: God of Manga. 2009. (ENG., Illus.). 272p. 40.00 *(978-0-8109-8249-9(8))* Abrams.

McKinnon, Robert J. Stepping into the Picture: Cartoon Designer Maurice Noble. 2008. (ENG., Illus.). 177p. 50.00 *(978-1-934110-43-0(4));* per. 22.00 *(978-1-934110-44-7(2))* Univ. Pr. of Mississippi.

Mundi, Anima. Animation Now! 25th ed. 2007. (FRE, GER & ENG., Illus.). 351p. 14.99 *(978-3-8228-3789-4(X))* TASCHEN DEU. Dist: Ingram Pub. Services.

Newman, Victor, intro. IdN Extra 02: New York. 2011. (ENG., Illus.). 132p. pap. 25.00 *(978-988-18470-3-4(6))* Systems Design, Ltd. HKG. Dist: D.A.P./Distributed Art Pubs.

Osmond, Andrew. Satoshi Kon: The Illusionist. 2009. (ENG., Illus.). 128p. pap. 18.95 *(978-1-933330-74-7(0))* Stone Bridge Pr.

Peri, Don. Working with Disney: Interviews with Animators, Producers, & Artists. 2011. (ENG.). 192p. 55.00 *(978-1-60473-939-8(8));* pap. 25.00 *(978-1-60473-940-4(1))* Univ. Pr. of Mississippi.

—Working with Walt: Interviews with Disney Artists. 2008. (ENG.). 256p. 50.00 *(978-1-934110-67-6(1));* per. 22.00 *(978-1-60473-023-4(4))* Univ. Pr. of Mississippi.

Plympton, Bill. Independently Animated, Bill Plympton: The Life & Art of the King of Indie Animation. 2011. (Illus.). 264p. 39.95 *(978-0-7893-2209-8(9))* Universe Publishing.

Robinson, Amanda & Robinson, Chris. Animators Unearthed: A Guide to the Best of Contemporary Animation. 2010. (ENG., Illus.). 256p. pap. 27.95 *(978-0-8264-2956-8(4))* Continuum International Publishing Group, Ltd. GBR. Dist: National Bk. Network.

Russett, Robert. Hyperanimation: Digital Images & Virtual Worlds. 2009. (ENG., Illus.). 300p. pap. 35.00 *(978-0-86196-654-7(6),* 0861966546) Libbey, John & Co., Ltd. AUS. Dist: Indiana Univ. Pr.

Russett, Robert & Russett, Robert. Hyperanimation: Digital Images & Virtual Worlds. 2009. (ENG., Illus.). 300p. 95.00 *(978-0-86196-693-6(7),* 0861966937) Libbey, John & Co., Ltd. AUS. Dist: Indiana Univ. Pr.

Sito, Tom. Drawing the Line: The Untold Story of the Animation Unions from Bosko to Bart Simpson. 2006. (ENG., Illus.). 440p. 35.00 *(978-0-8131-2407-0(7))* Univ. Pr. of Kentucky.

Susanin, Timothy S. Walt Before Mickey: Disney's Early Years, 1919-1928. 2011. (ENG., Illus.). 384p. 35.00 *(978-1-60473-960-2(6))* Univ. Pr. of Mississippi.

Takamoto, Iwao. Iwao Takamoto: My Life with a Thousand Characters. 2009. (ENG., Illus.). 240p. 50.00 *(978-1-60473-193-4(1))* Univ. Pr. of Mississippi.

Takamoto, Iwao & Mallory, Michael. Iwao Takamoto: My Life with a Thousand Characters. 2009. (ENG., Illus.). 240p. pap. 22.00 *(978-1-60473-194-1(X))* Univ. Pr. of Mississippi.

Tumbusch, Tom E. Walt Disney the American Dreamer. 2008. (Illus.). 176p. 22.95 *(978-0-914293-61-3(3))* Tomart Pubns.

Vischer, Phil. Me, Myself & Bob: A True Story about Dreams, God, & Talking Vegetables, 0 vols. 2008. 272p. per. 14.99 *(978-1-59555-122-1(0))* Nelson, Thomas Inc.

Wolfgram Evans, Noell K. Animators of Film & Television: Nineteen Artists, Writers, Producers & Others. 2011. (ENG., Illus.). 228p. pap. 35.00 *(978-0-7864-4832-6(6))* McFarland & Co., Inc. Pubs.

ANIME

see Animated Films—Japan

ANIMISM

see also Idealism; Idols and Images; Materialism; Soul; Spiritualism

Bailey, Keith. Strange Gods: Responding to the Rise of Spirit Worship in America. 2nd ed. 2009. 256p. pap. 14.99 *(978-1-934233-09-2(9))* Evangel Publishing Hse.

Clodd, Edward. Animism & Malevolent Spirits. 2006. pap. 9.95 *(978-1-4286-7867-5(0))* Kessinger Publishing, LLC.

—Animism, the Seed of Religion. 2009. 60p. pap. *(978-1-4590-3309-2(4))* Books LLC.

—Naturalism or Conception of Power Everywhere. 2006. pap. 9.95 *(978-1-4286-7859-0(X))* Kessinger Publishing, LLC.

—Prehuman Elements in Religion. 2006. pap. 9.95 *(978-1-4286-7858-3(1))* Kessinger Publishing, LLC.

—Spirits in Inanimate Things. 2006. pap. 9.95 *(978-1-4286-7860-6(3))* Kessinger Publishing, LLC.

—Stone Worship. 2006. pap. 9.95 *(978-1-4286-7863-7(8))* Kessinger Publishing, LLC.

De Quincey, Christian. Radical Nature: The Soul of Matter. 2010. (ENG.). 1p. pap. *(978-1-59477-340-2(8),* Park Street Pr.) Inner Traditions International, Ltd.

Jok, Kuel M. & Arfman, William R. Animism of the Nilotics & Discourses of Islamic Fundamentalism in Sudan. 2011. (ENG., Illus.). 142p. (C). pap. 56.00 *(978-90-8890-054-9(X))* Sidestone Pr. NLD. Dist: Brown, David Bk. Co., The.

Mcdougall, William. Body & Mind - A History & A Defense of Animism. 2007. pap. *(978-1-4067-5540-4(0))* McDougall Trust.

Roheim, Geza. Animism & Religion: The Psychoanalytic Quarterly, V1 1932. 2011. 58p. 36.95 ***(978-1-258-03880-9(3))*** Literary Licensing, LLC.

Segy, Ladislas. African Art & Animism: The Journal of Human Relations, V2, No. 1, November 1953. 2011. 16p. pap. 35.95 ***(978-1-258-09775-2(3))*** Literary Licensing, LLC.

Tylor, Edward B. Primitive Culture V1 Researches into the. 2006. pap. 40.95 *(978-1-4286-3829-7(6))* Kessinger Publishing, LLC.

—Primitive Culture V2 Researches into the. 2006. pap. 38.95 *(978-1-4286-3830-3(X))* Kessinger Publishing, LLC.

Tylor, Edward Burnett. Primitive Culture: Researches into the Development of Mythology, Philosophy, Religion, Art, & Custom. 2010. (Cambridge Library Collection - Anthropology Ser.). (ENG.). 440p. pap. 32.99 *(978-1-108-01751-0(7));* 468p. pap. 34.99 *(978-1-108-01750-3(9))* Cambridge Univ. Pr.

Vater, Tom. Sacred Skin: Thailand's Spirit Tattoos. 2011. (Illus.). 200p. pap. 32.95 *(978-962-85637-9-1(3))* Visionary World, Ltd. HKG. Dist: AtlasBooks Distribution.

Willerslev, Rane. Soul Hunters: Hunting, Animism, & Personhood among the Siberian Yukaghirs. 2007. (Illus.). 229p. 65.00 *(978-0-520-25216-5(0));* per. 26.95 *(978-0-520-25217-2(9))* Univ. of California Pr.

ANIONIC POLYMERIZATION

see Addition Polymerization

ANIONS

Blondeau, Pascal. Anion Receptors Based on Ion Pairing & Hydrogen Bonding. 2011. 196p. pap. ***(978-3-8443-8424-6(3))*** Lambert Academic Publishing.

Bowman-James, Kristin, et al, eds. Anion Coordination Chemistry. 2012. (ENG., Illus.). 574p. 215.00 ***(978-3-527-32370-8(8),*** Wiley-VCH) Wiley, John & Sons, Inc.

Gale, Philip A. & Dehaen, Wim, eds. Anion Recognition in Supramolecular Chemistry. 2010. (Topics in Heterocyclic Chemistry Ser.). (Illus.). x, 365p. 409.00 *(978-3-642-15443-0(3),* 3642154433) Springer.

Jia, Beike. Negative Ions Made by Collisional Ionization. 2009. 104p. pap. *(978-3-639-15325-5(1))* VDM Verlag Dr. Mueller e.K.

Massey, Harrie. Negative Ions. 3rd ed. 2011. (Cambridge Monographs on Physics Ser.). (ENG.). 760p. pap. 70.00 *(978-0-521-28317-5(5))* Cambridge Univ. Pr.

Novartis Foundation Staff. Epithelial Anion Transport in Health & Disease: The Role of the SLC26 Transporters Family. 2006. (Novartis Foundation Symposia Ser.: 150). (ENG., Illus.). 284p. 195.00 *(978-0-470-01624-4(8),* Wiley) Wiley, John & Sons, Inc.

Stockli, Martin. Production & Neutralization of Negative Ions & Beams. 2007. (AIP Conference Proceedings / Accelerators, Beams, & Instrumentations Ser.). 137.00 *(978-0-7354-0435-9(6))* American Institute of Physics.

Surrey, Elizabeth & Simonin, Alain, eds. Negative Ions, Beams & Sources: Proceedings of the 1st International Symposium on Negative Ions, Beams & Sources. 2009. (AIP Conference Proceedings Ser.). (ENG.). 512p. 229.00 *(978-0-7354-0630-8(8))* American Institute of Physics.

Takeiri, Yasuhiko & Tsumori, Katsuyoshi, eds. Second International Symposium on Negative Ions, Beams & Sources. 2012. (AIP Conference Proceedings / Accelerators, Beams, & Instrumentations Ser.). (ENG., Illus.). 718p. pap. 231.00 ***(978-0-7354-0955-2(2),*** 0735409552, AIP Pr.) Springer.

Vilar, Ramon. Recognition of Anions. 2010. (Structure & Bonding Ser.). (Illus.). xii, 252p. pap. 349.00 *(978-3-642-09796-6(0),* 3642097960) Springer.

—Recognition of Anions. 2008. (Structure & Bonding Ser.). 252p. 349.00 *(978-3-540-79091-4(8),* 3540790918) Springer.

ANISOPTERA

see Dragonflies

ANISOTROPY

al-khayat, Omar & Al-Khayat, Omar. An Introduction to the Theory of the Cosmic Microwave Background. 2010. 184p. pap. *(978-3-8383-5014-1(6))* Lambert Academic Publishing.

Arash, A. Samimi. Magnetic Exchange Interactions in Terbium Manganese Oxide. 2009. 72p. pap. *(978-3-639-20089-8(6))* VDM Verlag Dr. Mueller e.K.

Burnell, E. E. & Lange, C. A. de, eds. NMR of Ordered Liquids. 2012. (ENG.). 488p. pap. 215.00 *(978-90-481-6305-2(6),* 9048163056) Springer.

Elboth, Thomas. Vector Field Visualization Using Anisotropic Diffusion. 2009. 112p. pap. *(978-3-639-15554-9(8))* VDM Verlag Dr. Mueller e.K.

Esling, Claude, et al, eds. French-German Texture & Anisotropy Meeting. 2008. 52p. pap. 10.00 *(978-977-454-046-2(8))* Hindawi Publishing Corp.

Freger, Garry Efimovich, et al. Spirally Anisotropic Composites. 2010. (Springer Series in Materials Science Ser.). (Illus.). xii, 310p. pap. 179.00 *(978-3-642-05945-2(7),* 3642059457) Springer.

Gambin, W. Plasticity & Textures. 2010. (Illus.). 250p. pap. 179.00 *(978-90-481-5912-3(1),* 9048159121) Springer.

Golfman, Yosif. Hybrid Anisotropic Composites for Wind Power Turbine Blades. 2012. (ENG., Illus.). 253p. 129.95 *(978-1-4398-6858-4(1),* CRC Press) Taylor & Francis Group GBR. Dist: Taylor & Francis Group.

Golfman, Yosif, ed. Hybrid Anisotropic Materials for Structural Aviation Parts. 2010. (ENG., Illus.). 339p. 139.95 *(978-1-4398-3680-4(9),* CRC Press) Taylor & Francis Group GBR. Dist: Taylor & Francis Group.

Gopalakrishnan, S., et al. Spectral Finite Element Method: Wave Propagation, Diagnostics & Control in Anisotropic & Inhomogeneous Structures. 2008. (Computational Fluid & Solid Mechanics Ser.). (Illus.). 440p. 199.00 *(978-1-84628-355-0(8),* 1846283558) Springer.

Gopalakrishnan, Srinivasan, et al. Spectral Finite Element Method: Wave Propagation, Diagnostics & Control in Anisotropic & Inhomogeneous Structures. 2010. (Computational Fluid & Solid Mechanics Ser.). (Illus.), xiv, 440p. pap. 199.00 *(978-1-84996-587-3(0),* 1849965870) Springer.

Gorbatsevich, Feliks. Acoustopolariscopy of Minerals & Rocks. 2009. 148p. pap. *(978-3-639-13637-1(3))* VDM Verlag Dr. Mueller e.K.

Hwu, Chyanbin. Anisotropic Elastic Plates. 2010. (ENG., Illus.). xxv, 500p. 179.00 *(978-1-4419-5914-0(9),* 1441959149) Springer.

Igbokoyi, Alpheus. Well Analysis in Naturally Fractured Reservoir Using Elliptical Flow. 2009. 268p. pap. *(978-3-639-14964-7(5))* VDM Verlag Dr. Mueller e.K.

Ke, Chien-Chung & Chen, Chao-Shi. Boundary Element Analysis of Crack Propagation on Anisotropic Rocks: Stress Intensity Factor, Fracture Toughness, Crack Propagation Path. 2008. 132p. pap. *(978-3-639-10809-5(4))* VDM Verlag Dr. Mueller e.K.

Klein, H. & Schwarzer, R. A., eds. Texture & Anisotrophy of Polycrystals III. 2010. (Solid State Phenomena: 159-160). (Illus.). 340p. pap. 246.00 *(978-3-908451-78-5(7))* Translatons for Technology.

Mackay, Tom G. Electromagnetic Anisotropy Bianisotropy. 2009. 236p. 79.00 *(978-981-4289-61-0(2))* World Scientific Publishing Co., Inc.

Saraf, Gaurav. Anisotropy in A-Plane Magnesium Zinc Oxide Thin Films. 2009. 124p. pap. *(978-3-639-14022-4(2))* VDM Verlag Dr. Mueller e.K.

Siparov, Sergey. Introduction to the Anisotropic Geometrodynamics. 2011. 320p. 110.00 ***(978-981-4340-83-0(9))*** World Scientific Publishing Co., Inc.

Skrzypek, Jacek J. & Ganczarski, Artur W., eds. Anisotropic Behaviour of Damaged Materials. 2012. (Lecture Notes in Applied & Computational Mechanics Ser.). (ENG., Illus.). xii, 366p. pap. 149.00 *(978-3-642-05587-4(7),* 3642055877) Springer.

Terentiev, Leonid. The Turbulence Closure Model Based on Linear Anisotropy Invariant Analysis. 2008. 196p. per. *(978-3-8364-6605-9(8))* VDM Verlag Dr. Mueller e.K.

Truszkowski, Wojciech. The Plastic Anisotropy in Single Crystals & Polycrystalline Metals. 2010. 168p. pap. 91.00 *(978-90-481-5662-7(9),* 9048156629) Springer.

TSvankin, I. D. & Grechka, V. IU. Seismology of Azimuthally Anisotropic Media & Seismic Fracture Characterization. 2011. *(978-1-56080-228-0(6))* Society of Exploration Geophysicists.

Upadhyay, S. K. Seismic Reflection Processing: With Special Reference to Anisotropy. 2010. (ENG., Illus.). xv, 636p. pap. 189.00 *(978-3-642-07414-1(6),* 3642074146) Springer.

Uzunoglu, Nikolaos & Tarkhanyan, Roland. Radiowaves & Polaritons in Anisotropic Media: Uniaxial Semiconductors. 2006. (ENG.). 224p. 200.00 *(978-3-527-40615-9(8),* Wiley-VCH) Wiley, John & Sons, Inc.

Vashakmadze, T. S. The Theory of Anisotropic Elastic Plates. 2010. (Mathematics & Its Applications Ser.). (Illus.). 256p. pap. 199.00 *(978-90-481-5215-5(1),* 9048152151) Springer.

Weinberger, Peter & Weinberger, P. Magnetic Anisotropies in Nanostructured Matter. 2008. (Condensed Matter Physics Ser.). (ENG., Illus.). 310p. 129.95 *(978-1-4200-7265-5(X),* Chapman & Hall/CRC) CRC Pr. LLC.

ANJOU, MARGARET OF, 1430-1482

see Margaret, of Anjou, Queen, Consort of Henry VI, King of England, 1430-1482

ANJOU (FRANCE)

Peltzer, Jörg & Peltzer, Jörg Henning. Canon Law, Careers & Conquest: Episcopal Elections in Normandy & Greater Anjou, C.1140-C.1230. 2007. (Cambridge Studies in Medieval Life & Thought). (ENG., Illus.). 352p. 130.00 *(978-0-521-88062-6(9))* Cambridge Univ. Pr.

ANJOU, HOUSE OF

Everard, J. A. Brittany & the Angevins: Province & Empire 1158-1203. 2006. (Cambridge Studies in Medieval Life & Thought). (ENG., Illus.). 264p. pap. 53.00 *(978-0-521-02692-5(X))* Cambridge Univ. Pr.

Hookham, Mary Ann. The Life & Times of Margaret of Anjou, Queen of England & France. 2009. 274p. pap. 22.35 *(978-1-4589-2410-0(6))* General Bks. LLC.

—The Life & Times of Margaret of Anjou, Queen of England & France; & of Her Father, Rene the Good V1. 2007. 448p. (ENG.). 51.95 *(978-0-548-27790-4(7));* per. 36.95 *(978-1-4326-8311-5(X))* Kessinger Publishing, LLC.

Kekewich, Margaret L. The Good King: Rene of Anjou & 15th Century Europe. 2008. (ENG., Illus.). 256p. 100.00 *(978-1-4039-8820-1(X))* Palgrave Macmillan.

ANKARA (TURKEY)

Cosan-Eke, Deniz. The Changing Gender Roles in the Perception of Two Cohorts. 2009. 124p. pap. *(978-3-639-16378-0(8))* VDM Verlag Dr. Mueller e.K.

Saner, Mehmet. Urban Transformations & Political Actors. 2009. 104p. pap. *(978-3-639-13262-5(9))* VDM Verlag Dr. Mueller e.K.

ANKHESENAMEN, QUEEN OF EGYPT

Bois, Yvon. The Ankh Is the Key: Volume 1: Theory of a Self-Programmed Universe, 1 vol. 2009. 496p. pap. 29.95 *(978-1-4489-8264-6(2))* PublishAmerica, Inc.

—The Ankh Is the Key: Volume 2: Theory of a Self-Programmed Universe, 1 vol. 2009. 484p. pap. 29.95 *(978-1-4489-7860-1(2))* PublishAmerica, Inc.

ANKLE

Amendola, Ned & Stone, James W. AANA Advanced Arthroscopy: the Foot & Ankle: Expert Consult: Online, Print & DVD. 2010. (AANA Advanced Arthroscopy Ser.). (ENG., Illus.). 224p. 250.00 *(978-1-4377-0662-8(2),* Saunders) Elsevier - Health Sciences Div.

Baravarian, Babek & Baravarian, Bob. Foot & Ankle Athletic Injuries, an Issue of Clinics in Podiatric Medicine & Surgery. 2011. (Clinics: Orthopedics Ser.: 28-1). (ENG., Illus.). 248p. 110.00 *(978-1-4557-0494-1(6),* Saunders) Elsevier - Health Sciences Div.

Chiodo, Chris & Bluman, Eric M. Tendon Transfers in the Foot & Ankle, an Issue of Foot & Ankle Clinics. 2011. (Clinics: Orthopedics Ser.: 16-3). (ENG., Illus.). xi, 376p. 106.00 *(978-1-4557-0448-4(2),* Saunders) Elsevier - Health Sciences Div.

Crim, Julia, et al. Knee, Ankle, Foot. 2007. (Diagnostic & Surgical Imaging Anatomy Ser.). (ENG., Illus.). 650p. 229.00 *(978-1-931884-42-6(0))* Lippincott Williams & Wilkins.

Deboer, et al. Surg Exposures Foor & Ankle Surgery. 2012. (Illus.). 192p. 149.95 ***(978-1-4511-4450-5(4))*** Lippincott Williams & Wilkins.

Easley, Mark E. Operative Techniques in Foot & Ankle Surgery. 2010. (ENG., Illus.). 1184p. 295.99 *(978-1-60831-904-6(0))* Lippincott Williams & Wilkins.

Ficke, James R. & Bluman, Eric M. Traumatic Foot & Ankle Injuries Related to Recent International Conflicts, an Issue of Foot & Ankle Clinics. 2010. (Clinics: Orthopedics Ser.: 15-1). (ENG., Illus.). xiv, 233p. 101.00 *(978-1-4377-1820-1(5),* Saunders) Elsevier - Health Sciences Div.

Hintermann, Beat. Current & New Techniques for Primary & Revision Arthrodesis, an Issue of Foot & Ankle Clinics. 2011. (Clinics: Orthopedics Ser.: 16-1). (ENG., Illus.). 232p. 106.00 *(978-1-4557-0447-7(4),* Saunders) Elsevier - Health Sciences Div.

Judge, Molly S. Recent Advances in Hallux Rigidus Surgery, an Issue of Clinics in Podiatric Medicine & Surgery. 2011. (Clinics: Orthopedics Ser.: 28-2). (ENG., Illus.). 232p. 110.00 *(978-1-4557-0495-8(4),* Saunders) Elsevier - Health Sciences Div.

Kelikian, Armen S. & Sarrafian, Shahan, eds. Sarrafian's Anatomy of the Foot & Ankle: Descriptive, Topographic, Functional. 3rd rev. ed. 2011. (ENG., Illus.). 736p. 259.99 *(978-0-7817-9750-4(0))* Lippincott Williams & Wilkins.

Logan, Bari M. & Hutchings, Ralph T. McMinn's Color Atlas of Foot & Ankle Anatomy. 4th ed. 2011. (ENG., Illus.). 160p. (C). 75.95 ***(978-0-323-05615-1(6),*** Saunders) Elsevier - Health Sciences Div.

Maffulli, Nicola & Easley, Mark, eds. Minimally Invasive Surgery of the Foot & Ankle. 2010. (ENG., Illus.). viii, 448p. 219.00 *(978-1-84996-416-6(5),* 1849964165) Springer.

Manaster. Knee, Ankle, Foot. 2007. (ENG., Illus.). 650p. 129.00 *(978-1-931884-36-5(6))* Lippincott Williams & Wilkins.

Manaster, B. J., et al. Diagnostic & Surgical Imaging Anatomy. 2007. (ENG.). 650p. 129.00 *(978-1-931884-43-3(9))* Lippincott Williams & Wilkins.

—Diagnostic & Surgical Imaging Anatomy: Knee, Ankle, Foot. 2007. (Diagnostic & Surgical Imaging Anatomy Ser.). (Illus.). 650p. 329.00 *(978-1-931884-01-3(3))* Amirsys, Inc.

Miller, Stuart D. Orthobiologic Concepts in Foot & Ankle, an Issue of Foot & Ankle Clinics. 2010. (Clinics: Orthopedics Ser.: 15-4). (ENG., Illus.). x, 544p. 101.00 *(978-1-4377-2451-6(5),* Saunders) Elsevier - Health Sciences Div.

Murphy, G. Andrew. Achilles Tendon, an Issue of Foot & Ankle Clinics. 2009. (Clinics: Orthopedics Ser.: 14-4). (ENG., Illus.). xiv, 618p. 99.00 *(978-1-4377-1218-6(5),* Saunders) Elsevier - Health Sciences Div.

Muscarella, Vincent J. & Boc, Steven F. Arthrodesis of the Foot & Ankle, an Issue of Clinics in Podiatric Medicine & Surgery. 2012. (Clinics: Orthopedics Ser.: 29-1). (ENG., Illus.). xvi, 154p. 115.00 ***(978-1-4557-3921-9(9),*** Saunders) Elsevier - Health Sciences Div.

Pfeffer, Glenn B., et al. Operative Techniques: Foot & Ankle Surgery: Book, Website & DVD. 2009. (Operative Techniques Ser.). (ENG., Illus.). 704p. 249.00 *(978-1-4160-3280-9(0),* Saunders) Elsevier - Health Sciences Div.

Rubin, Lawrence G. Foot & Ankle Arthroscopy: Clinics in Podiatric Medicine & Surgery. 2011. (Clinics: Orthopedics Ser.: 28-3). (ENG., Illus.). 183p. 110.00 *(978-1-4557-1050-8(4),* Saunders) Elsevier - Health Sciences Div.

Saxena, Amol, ed. International Advances in Foot & Ankle Surgery. 2011. (ENG., Illus.). xvi, 548p. 239.00 ***(978-0-85729-608-5(6),*** 0857296086) Springer.

Scuderi, Giles R. & Tria, Alfred J., eds. Minimally Invasive Surgery in Orthopedics: Foot & Ankle Handbook. 2011. (ENG., Illus.). ix, 227p. pap. 79.95 ***(978-1-4614-0892-5(X),*** 146140892X) Springer.

Zgonis, Thomas. Foot & Ankle Surgery, an Issue of Perioperative Nursing Clinics. 2011. (Clinics: Nursing Ser.: 6-1). (ENG.). 112p. 65.00 *(978-1-4557-0487-3(3),* Saunders) Elsevier - Health Sciences Div.

ANKLE—DISEASES

Berquist, Thomas H. Imaging of the Foot & Ankle. 3rd rev. ed. 2010. (ENG., Illus.). 720p. 204.95 *(978-1-60547-572-1(6))* Lippincott Williams & Wilkins.

Catanzariti, Alan, et al. Update on Ankle Arthritis, an Issue of Clinics in Podiatric Medicine & Surgery. 2009. (Clinics: Orthopedics Ser.: 26-2). (ENG., Illus.). 240p. 99.00 *(978-1-4377-0531-7(6),* Saunders) Elsevier - Health Sciences Div.

Coetzee, Christian & Hurwitz, Shepard R. The Foot & Ankle. 2009. (Arthritis & Arthroplasty Ser.). (ENG., Illus.). 360p. 250.00 *(978-1-4160-4972-2(X),* Saunders) Elsevier - Health Sciences Div.

Coughlin, Michael J., et al. Surgery of the Foot & Ankle, 2 vols., Set. 8th rev. ed. 2006. (ENG., Illus.). 2400p. 490.00 *(978-0-323-03305-3(9),* Mosby) Elsevier - Health Sciences Div.

—Surgery of the Foot & Ankle E-dition: Text with Continually Updated Online Reference. 8th rev. ed. 2006. (ENG., Illus.). 1511p. 599.00 *(978-0-323-04029-7(2),* Mosby) Elsevier - Health Sciences Div.

Deluane, Valerie. Trigger Point Therapy for Foot, Ankle, Knee, & Leg Pain: A Self-Treatment Workbook. 2010. (ENG., Illus.). 192p. pap. 19.95 *(978-1-57224-842-7(4))* New Harbinger Pubns.

DiDomenico, Lawrence A. The Rheumatoid Foot & Ankle, an Issue of Clinics in Podiatric Medicine & Surgery. 2010. (Clinics: Orthopedics Ser.: 27-2). (ENG., Illus.). xx, 184p. 105.00 *(978-1-4377-1864-5(7),* Saunders) Elsevier - Health Sciences Div.

Foster, Alethea V. M. & Edmonds, Michael E. A Colour Atlas of Foot & Ankle Disorders. 2007. (ENG., Illus.). 196p. 106.00 *(978-0-443-10207-3(4),* Churchill Livingstone) Elsevier - Health Sciences Div.

Gould, John. Nerve Problems of the Lower Extremity, an Issue of Foot & Ankle Clinics. 2011. (Clinics: Orthopedics Ser.: 16-2). (ENG., Illus.). 184p. 106.00 *(978-1-4557-0446-0(6),* Saunders) Elsevier - Health Sciences Div.

Harris, Gerald F. Foot & Ankle Motion Analysis. 2007. (Biomedical Engineering Ser.). (ENG., Illus.). 704p. 199.95 *(978-0-8493-3971-4(5),* CRC Press) Taylor & Francis Group GBR. Dist: Taylor & Francis Group.

Hartzell, Dick & Shimmel, Michael. Don't Ice that Ankle Sprain! The F. A. S. T. Approach to Preventing & Treating Sprained Ankles. LaRosa, Sherri, ed. 2007. per. 59.95 *(978-0-9790941-0-1(0))* Jump Stretch, Inc.

Holmes, George B., Jr. & Lee, Simon, eds. Curbside Consultation of the Foot & Ankle: 49 Clinical Questions. 2012. (Curbside Consultation Ser.). (ENG.). 288p. pap. 83.95 *(978-1-55642-939-2(8))* SLACK, Inc.

Hurwitz, Shepard R. & Parekh, Selene. Musculoskeletal Examination of the Foot & Ankle: Making the Complex Simple. 2011. (ENG.). 256p. pap. 44.95 *(978-1-55642-919-4(3))* SLACK, Inc.

Kadakia, Anish R. & Kadakia, Arpita. Correction of Multiplanar Deformity of the Foot & Ankle, an Issue of Foot & Ankle Clinics. 2009. (Clinics: Orthopedics Ser.: 14-3). (ENG., Illus.). viii, 370p. 99.00 *(978-1-4377-1217-9(7),* Saunders) Elsevier - Health Sciences Div.

McCarthy, James. The Child's Foot & Ankle. Drennan, James C., ed. 2nd rev. ed. 2009. (ENG., Illus.). 576p. 248.99 *(978-0-7817-7847-3(6))* Lippincott Williams & Wilkins.

Metcalfe, Stuart & Reilly, Ian. Foot & Ankle Injection Techniques: A Practical Guide. 2010. (ENG., Illus.). 208p. (C). spiral bd. 75.95 *(978-0-7020-3107-6(0),* Churchill Livingstone) Elsevier - Health Sciences Div.

Myerson, Mark S. Reconstructive Foot & Ankle Surgery: Management of Complications. 2nd ed. 2010. (ENG., Illus.). 576p. 250.00 *(978-1-4377-0923-0(0),* Saunders) Elsevier - Health Sciences Div.

Pinzur, Michael & Myerson, Mark S. Infection, Ischemia, & Amputation, an Issue of Foot & Ankle Clinics. 2010. (Clinics: Orthopedics Ser.: 15-3). (ENG., Illus.). viii, 392p. 101.00 *(978-1-4377-2450-9(7),* Saunders) Elsevier - Health Sciences Div.

Steck, Jerome K. Revisional Foot & Ankle Surgery, an Issue of Clinics in Podiatric Medicine & Surgery. 2009. (Clinics: Orthopedics Ser.: 26-1). (ENG., Illus.). 240p. 99.00 *(978-1-4377-0530-0(8),* Saunders) Elsevier - Health Sciences Div.

Stretch away ankle pain, second Edition. 2006. cd-rom 17.95 *(978-0-9789455-8-9(1))* Stretch Away Pain, LLC.

Sullivan, Raymond J. The Pediatric Foot & Ankle, an Issue of Foot & Ankle Clinics. 2010. (Clinics: Orthopedics Ser.: 15-2). (ENG., Illus.). viii, 236p. 101.00 *(978-1-4377-1821-8(3),* Saunders) Elsevier - Health Sciences Div.

Trepman, Elly. Instructional Course Lectures Foot & Ankle. Trepman, Elly & Arangio, George A., eds. E-Book 419.00 *(978-0-89203-632-5(X))* American Academy of Orthopaedic Surgeons.

Umans, Hilary. Foot & Ankle Imaging, an Issue of Radiologic Clinics. 2009. (Clinics: Radiology Ser.: 46-6). (ENG., Illus.). x, 958p. 89.00 *(978-1-4160-6601-9(2),* Saunders) Elsevier - Health Sciences Div.

Zgonis, Thomas. Surgical Reconstruction of the Diabetic Foot & Ankle. Zgonis, Thomas, ed. 2009. (ENG.). 448p. 248.99 *(978-0-7817-8458-0(1))* Lippincott Williams & Wilkins.

ANKYLOSIS

see also Arthrodesis

Khan, Muhammad Asim. Ankylosing Spondylitis. 2009. (Oxford American Rheumatology Library). (ENG., Illus.). 150p. pap. 24.95 *(978-0-19-536807-9(X))* Oxford Univ. Pr., Inc.

Shrivastava, Anshul. Use of Hla-B27pcr Technique for Detection of Ankylosing Spondylitis. 2011. 76p. pap. ***(978-3-8443-3064-9(X))*** Lambert Academic Publishing.

Sieper, Joachim & Braun, Jürgen. Ankylosing Spondylitis: In Clinical Practice. 2010. (ENG., Illus.). xi, 83p. pap. 39.95 *(978-0-85729-179-0(3),* 0857291793) Springer.

Weisman, Michael H. Ankylosing Spondylitis, 1 vol. 2011. (ENG., Illus.). 248p. 24.95 *(978-0-19-539910-3(2))* Oxford Univ. Pr., Inc.

ANKYLOSTOMIASIS

see Hookworm Disease

ANN, CAPE (MASS.)

East, Elyssa. Dogtown: Death & Enchantment in a New England Ghost Town. 2009. (ENG., Illus.). 304p. 26.00 *(978-1-4165-8704-0(7),* Free Pr.) Free Pr.

ANN ARBOR (MICH.)

Bidlack, Russell E. Letters Home: The Story of Ann Arbor's Forty-Niners. 2011. 66p. 36.95 ***(978-1-258-03345-3(3))*** Literary Licensing, LLC.

Goff, Alice & Cooney, Megan. Historic Photos of Ann Arbor. 2007. (Historic Photos Ser.). (ENG., Illus.). 205p. 39.95 *(978-1-59652-389-0(1))* Turner Publishing Co.

Hildebrand, Grant. Frank Lloyd Wright's Palmer House. 2007. (ENG., Illus.). 120p. pap. 30.00 *(978-0-295-98640-1(9))* Univ. of Washington Pr.

Jones, Lola M. & Gibson, Carol. Another Ann Arbor. 2006. (Black America Ser.). (ENG., Illus.). 128p. per. 21.99 *(978-0-7385-4052-8(8))* Arcadia Publishing.

Lee K. Sanford. It's Over. 2010. 216p. pap. 15.95 *(978-1-4269-2738-6(X))* Trafford Publishing.

Mann, James Thomas. Wicked Ann Arbor. 2011. 128p. pap. 19.99 ***(978-1-60949-343-1(5))*** History Pr., The.

PinPointer: Ann Arbor. 163p. pap. *(978-1-58461-115-8(4))* Techni Graphic Systems, Inc.

Rand McNally, creator. Rand Mcnally Detroit & Ann Arbor Street Guide. 6th ed. 2007. (Rand Mcnally Detroit & Ann Arbor Street Guide Ser.). (Illus.). pap. 19.95 *(978-0-528-86704-0(0))* Rand McNally.

Shackman, Grace. Ann Arbor Observed: Selections from Then & Now. 2006. (ENG., Illus.). 280p. pap. 19.95 *(978-0-472-03175-7(9))* Univ. of Michigan Pr.

Warrick, Robert I. The Ann Arbor Railroad in Color: History & Operations, 1869 to 1976. 2008. (Illus.). 128p. ***(978-1-58248-235-4(7))*** Morning Sun Bks., Inc.

ANNALS

see Chronology, Historical; History

ANNAPOLIS (MD.)

Durston, Tammy. Annapolis & the Gualala River. 2010. (Images of America Ser.). (Illus.). 128p. pap. 21.99 *(978-0-7385-8114-9(3))* Arcadia Publishing.

Martin, Mary & Wolfgang-Price, Nathaniel. Greetings from Annapolis. 2007. (Schiffer Book for Collectors Ser.). (Illus.). 128p. pap. 19.95 *(978-0-7643-2600-4(7))* Schiffer Publishing, Ltd.

McWilliams, Jane Wilson. Annapolis, City on the Severn: A History. 2011. (ENG., Illus.). 512p. (gr. 17). 44.95 *(978-0-8018-9659-0(2))* Johns Hopkins Univ. Pr.

Norris, Walter B. Annapolis: Its Colonial & Naval Story with Selections from Diaries & Private Letters. 2008. (Illus.). 336p. reprint ed. pap. 32.00 *(978-1-55613-223-0(9))* Heritage Bks.

Okonowicz, Ed, photos by. Annapolis Ghosts: History, Mystery, Legends & Lore. 2007. (Illus.). 120p. pap. *(978-1-890690-19-9(8))* Myst & Lace Pubs., Inc.

Seylor, Deborah. A Year in Annapolis. (Illus.). 24p. pap. 5.00 *(978-0-942720-04-4(0))* Fishergate Publishing Co., Inc.

Tigner, Jr. & Tigner, James. Annapolis Reflections. 2009. (Illus.). 128p. bds. 29.99 *(978-0-7643-3157-2(4))* Schiffer Publishing, Ltd.

ANNAPURNA (NEPAL)

Herzog, Maurice. Annapurna: The First Conquest of an 8,000-Meter Peak. 2nd ed. 2010. (ENG., Illus.). 240p. pap. 16.95 *(978-1-59921-893-9(3),* Lyons Pr.) Globe Pequot Pr., The.

ANNAPURNA (NEPAL)—DESCRIPTION AND TRAVEL

Viesturs, Ed. The Will to Climb: Obsession & Commitment & the Quest to Climb Annapurna — the World's Deadliest Peak. 2012. (ENG., Illus.). 304p. pap. 15.00 ***(978-0-307-72043-6(8))*** Broadway Bks.

Viesturs, Ed & Roberts, David. The Will to Climb: Obsession & Commitment & the Quest to Climb Annapurna - The World's Most Deadly Peak. 2011. (ENG., Illus.). 304p. 26.00 *(978-0-307-72042-9(X))* Broadway Bks.

ANNATES

see also Church Finance; Tithes

Lunt, William E. Financial Relations of the Papacy with England, To 1327. 2011. 776p. 72.95 ***(978-1-258-02912-8(X))*** Literary Licensing, LLC.

ANNE, QUEEN, CONSORT OF JAMES I, KING OF ENGLAND, 1574-1619

Craig, J. T. Gibson. Papers Relative to the Marriage of King James VI of Scotland with the Princess Anna of Denmark. 2007. 64p. per. 16.95 *(978-1-4325-3579-7(X))* Kessinger Publishing, LLC.

Gibson Craig, James T. Papers Relative to the Marriage of King James the Sixth of Scotland with the Princess Anna of Denmark. (Bannatyne Club, Edinburgh Publications: No. 26). reprint ed. 37.50 *(978-0-404-52732-7(9))* AMS Pr., Inc.

ANNE, QUEEN, CONSORT OF RICHARD III, KING OF ENGLAND, 1456-1485

Hicks, Michael. Anne Neville: Queen to Richard III. 2007. (England's Forgotten Queens Ser.). (ENG., Illus.). 256p. per. 19.95 *(978-0-7524-4129-0(9))* History Pr. Ltd., The GBR. Dist: Independent Pubs. Group.

ANNE, QUEEN OF GREAT BRITAIN, 1665-1714

Beem, Charles W. The Lioness Roared: The Problems of Female Rule in English History. 2008. (Queenship & Power Ser.). (ENG.). 280p. pap. 34.00 *(978-0-230-60634-0(2))* Palgrave Macmillan.

Grin, Francois. The Economics of the Multilingual Workplace. 2010. (Routledge Studies in Sociolinguistics Ser.). (ENG., Illus.). 242p. (C). 128.00 *(978-0-415-80018-1(8),* Routledge) Taylor & Francis Group GBR. Dist: Taylor & Francis Group.

Jones, Nick. British Politics in the Age of Holmes: Geoffrey Holmes's British Politics in the Age of Anne 40 Years On. Jones, Clyve, ed. 2009. (Parliamentary History Book Ser.: 5). (ENG., Illus.). 220p. pap. 39.95 *(978-1-4051-9334-4(4),* Wiley-Blackwell) Wiley, John & Sons, Inc.

McCarthy, Justin. The Reign of Queen Anne. 2009. (ENG.). 397p. 33.99 *(978-1-116-95966-6(6));* 398p. 38.99 *(978-1-116-95965-9(8));* (ENG.). 397p. pap. 34.75 *(978-1-116-95967-3(4));* (ENG.). 397p. pap. 33.75 *(978-1-116-95968-0(2))* BiblioBazaar.

—The Reign of Queen Anne. 2009. 226p. pap. *(978-1-4589-8278-0(5))* Books LLC.

—The Reign of Queen Anne. 2009. 232p. pap. 20.21 *(978-0-217-76538-1(6))* General Bks. LLC.

—The Reign of Queen Anne. 2009. 608p. 59.95 *(978-1-104-98182-2(3));* pap. 44.95 *(978-1-104-92077-7(8))* Kessinger Publishing, LLC.

—The Reign of Queen Anne, 2 Vols. reprint ed. 250.00 *(978-0-7222-1884-5(2))* Library Reprints, Inc.

Oliphant, M. O. W. Historical Characters of the Reign of Qu. 2006. pap. 28.95 *(978-1-4286-5759-5(2))* Kessinger Publishing, LLC.

Parsons, Nicola. Reading Gossip in Early Eighteenth-Century England. 2009. (Palgrave Studies in the Enlightenment, Romanticism & the Cultures of Print Ser.). (ENG., Illus.). 256p. 84.00 *(978-0-230-54671-4(4))* Palgrave Macmillan.

Paul, Herbert W. Queen Anne. 2009. (ENG.). 322p. 36.99 *(978-1-117-36962-4(5))* pap. 29.75 *(978-1-117-36963-1(3))* BiblioBazaar.

—Queen Anne. 315p. reprint ed. 98.00 *(978-0-7222-1886-0(9))* Library Reprints, Inc.

Ryan, William. Queen Anne & Her Court, 2 Vols. reprint ed. 250.00 *(978-0-7222-1887-7(7))* Library Reprints, Inc.

Waller, Maureen. Ungrateful Daughters: The Stuart Princesses Who Stole Their Father's Crown. mass mkt. *(978-0-312-98577-6(0),* St. Martin's Paperbacks) St. Martin's Pr.

ANNE, OF BRITTANY, CONSORT OF LOUIS XII, KING OF FRANCE, 1476-1514

Brown, Cynthia J., ed. The Cultural & Political Legacy of Anne de Bretagne: Negotiating Convention in Books & Documents. 2010. (Gallica Ser.: Volume 16). (Illus.). 240p. 95.00 *(978-1-84384-223-1(8),* D. S. Brewer) Boydell & Brewer, Ltd. GBR. Dist: Boydell & Brewer, Inc.

Brown, Cynthia Jane. The Queen's Library: Image-Making at the Court of Anne of Brittany, 1477-1514. 2010. (Material Texts). (Illus.). 416p. (C). 79.95 *(978-0-8122-4282-9(3),* Univ. of Pennsylvania Pr.

Ryley, M. Beresford. Queens of the Renaissance. 2009. 372p. 33.99 *(978-1-116-80851-3(X));* 38.99 *(978-1-116-80850-6(1));* pap. 32.75 *(978-1-116-80852-0(8));* pap. 31.75 *(978-1-116-80853-7(6))* BiblioBazaar.

—Queens of the Renaissance. 2007. (ENG.). 412p. per. 34.95 *(978-0-548-78699-4(2))* Kessinger Publishing, LLC.

ANNE, OF CLEVES, QUEEN, CONSORT OF HENRY VIII, KING OF ENGLAND, 1515-1557

Norton, Elizabeth. Anne of Cleves. 2010. (Illus.). 224p. pap. 19.95 *(978-1-4456-0183-0(4))* Amberley Publishing GBR. Dist: Casemate Pubs. & Bk. Distributors, LLC.

Warnicke, Retha M. The Marrying of Anne of Cleves: Royal Protocol in Early Modern England. 2011. (ENG., Illus.). 377p. pap. 36.99 *(978-0-521-17969-0(6))* Cambridge Univ. Pr.

ANNE ARUNDEL COUNTY (MD.)

ADC, the Map People Staff, creator. Anne Arundel County, Maryland Street Map Book. 27th ed. 2006. (Street Map Bks.). (Illus.). 64p. 12.95 *(978-0-87530-806-7(6))* ADC The Map People.

Blackpool, Stephen. Maryland Historical Markers Anne Arundel & Howard Counties. 2008. (ENG.). per. 49.95 *(978-0-9742554-1-5(6))* Blackpool, Stephen Inc.

Ross, Joseph. Arundel Burning: The Maryland Oyster Roast Fire Of 1956. 2008. (Illus.). 208p. pap. 18.00 *(978-0-9635159-7-1(7))* Chesapeake Bk. Co.

ANNE BOLEYN, QUEEN, CONSORT OF HENRY VIII, KING OF ENGLAND, 1507-1536

Bernard, G. W. Anne Boleyn: Fatal Attractions. 2010. (Illus.). 256p. 30.00 *(978-0-300-16245-5(6))* Yale Univ. Pr.

Denny, Joanna. Anne Boleyn: A New Life of England's Tragic Queen. 2007. (ENG., Illus.). 400p. per. 16.95 *(978-0-306-81540-9(0))* Da Capo Pr., Inc.

Fraser, Antonia, intro. & selected by. Agnes Strickland's Lives of the Queens of England. 2011. (Continuum Histories Ser.). (ENG.). 160p. 14.95 *(978-1-4411-0947-7(1))* Continuum International Publishing Group, Ltd. GBR. Dist: National Bk. Network.

Friedmann, Paul. Anne Boleyn. 2010. (ENG., Illus.). 352p. 29.95 *(978-1-84868-827-8(X))* Amberley Publishing GBR. Dist: Casemate Pubs. & Bk. Distributors, LLC.

—Anne Boleyn: A Chapter of English History, 1527-1536. 2010. 408p. pap. 34.75 *(978-1-143-26188-6(7))* BiblioBazaar.

Hamer, Colin. Anne Boleyn: One Short Life That Changed the English-Speaking World. 2007. (History Today Ser.). 141p. pap. 13.00 *(978-1-84625-083-5(8))* DayOne Pubns. GBR. Dist: STL Distribution North America.

Henry VIII. Love Letters of Henry VII to Anne Boleyn. 2010. 72p. pap. 3.49 *(978-1-60386-357-5(5),* Merchant Bks.) Rough Draft Printing.

—Love Letters of Henry VII to Anne Boleyn. 2009. 72p. pap. 7.95 *(978-1-60386-189-2(2),* Watchmaker Publishing) Wexford College Pr.

Henry VIII & Ellis, Henry. The Love Letters of Henry VIII to Anne Boleyn & Other Correspondence & Documents Concerning the King & His Wives. 2011. 124p. ***(978-0-85706-609-1(9));*** pap. ***(978-0-85706-610-7(2))*** Leonaur Ltd.

Lipscomb, Suzannah. 1536: The Year That Changed Henry VIII. (ENG., Illus.). 2010. 240p. pap. 14.95 *(978-0-7459-5332-8(8))* 2009. 256p. 24.95 *(978-0-7459-5365-6(4))* Lion Hudson PLC GBR. Dist: Independent Pubs. Group.

Norton, Elizabeth. Anne Boleyn. 2010. (Illus.). 32p. pap. 9.95 *(978-1-84868-918-3(7))* Amberley Publishing GBR. Dist: Casemate Pubs. & Bk. Distributors, LLC.

—Anne Boleyn: Henry VII's Obsession. 2009. (Illus.). 240p. 29.95 *(978-1-84868-084-5(8))* Amberley Publishing GBR. Dist: Casemate Pubs. & Bk. Distributors, LLC.

Norton, Elizabeth. The Anne Boleyn Companion. 2011. (Illus.). 344p. 34.95 ***(978-1-4456-0043-7(9))*** Amberley Publishing GBR. Dist: Casemate Pubs. & Bk. Distributors, LLC.

Pakenham-Walsh, W. S. A Tudor Story: The Return of Anne Boleyn, 1. 2006. (ENG.). 200p. reprint ed. pap. 34.00 *(978-0-7188-9166-4(X))* Lutherworth Pr., The GBR. Dist: Brown, David Bk. Co., The.

Trovillion, Violet & Trovillion, Hal W. eds. Love Letters of Henry the VIII: Being Some of the Letters That Passed Between Henry VIII, When He Wooed & Won Anne Boleyn. 2011. 46p. 35.95 ***(978-1-258-10508-2(X))*** Literary Licensing, LLC.

Weir, Alison. The Lady in the Tower: The Fall of Anne Boleyn. 2010. (ENG., Illus.). 464p. pap. 17.00 *(978-0-345-45322-8(0),* Ballantine Bks.) Random House Publishing Group.

Wilkinson, Josephine. Anne Boleyn: the Young Queen to Be. 2011. (Illus.). 224p. pap. 19.95 ***(978-1-4456-0395-7(0))*** Amberley Publishing GBR. Dist: Casemate Pubs. & Bk. Distributors, LLC.

ANNE BOLEYN, QUEEN, CONSORT OF HENRY VIII, KING OF ENGLAND, 1507-1536—DRAMA
Boker, George H. Anne Boleyn: A Tragedy. by George H. Boker. 2006. 224p. per. 20.99 *(978-1-4255-1846-2(X))* MPublishing.

ANNEALING OF METALS
Berhe, Temesgen Yirdaw & Tessema (), Genene. Variation of Population in Silicon with P-111cd Annealing Temperature. 2010. 60p. pap. *(978-3-639-25645-1(X))* VDM Verlag Dr. Mueller e.K.

Prangnell, P. B. & Bate, P. S., eds. Fundamentals of Deformation & Annealing. 2007. (Illus.). 670p. *(978-0-87849-434-7(0))* Trans Tech Pubns., Ltd.

Technology Research Editors, ed. Annealing & Lubricants for the Cold Rolling of Steels, 2007 Ed. 2007. pap. 128.50 *(978-1-60030-465-1(6)*, Search-In-Print) CSA Journal Division.

ANNELIDA
see also Earthworms; Leeches; Oligochaeta; Polychaeta

Dorresteijn, Adriaan W. C. & Westheide, Wilfried, eds. Reproductive Strategies & Developmental Patterns in Annelids. 2010. (Developments in Hydrobiology Ser.). 328p. pap. 259.00 *(978-90-481-5340-4(9)*, 9048153409) Springer.

Shain, Daniel H. & Shain. Annelids in Modern Biology. 2009. (ENG., Illus.). 367p. 149.95 *(978-0-470-34421-7(0)*, Wiley-Blackwell) Wiley, John & Sons, Inc.

ANNENBERG, WALTER H., 1908-2002
De Long, David G., ed. Sunnylands: Art & Architecture of the Annenberg Estate in Rancho Mirage, California. 2009. (Illus.). 200p. 34.95 *(978-0-8122-4161-7(4))* Univ. of Pennsylvania Pr.

Stein, Susan Alyson, et al. The Annenberg Collection: Masterpieces of Impressionism & Post-Impressionism. 2009. (Illus.). xiv, 338p. 65.00 *(978-1-58839-341-8(0))*; pap. 39.95 *(978-1-58839-342-5(9))* Metropolitan Museum of Art, The.

ANNEXATION (MUNICIPAL GOVERNMENT)
Archibald, Rae W. & Sleeper, Sally. Government Consolidation & Economic Development in Allegheny County & the City of Pittsburgh. 2008. 62p. pap. 23.00 *(978-0-8330-4463-1(X)*, tr-569) RAND Corp., The.

Faulk, Dagney Gail & Hicks, Michael J. Local Government Consolidation in the United States. 2011. *(978-1-60497-748-6(5))* Cambria Pr.

Lawrence, David M. Annexation Law in North Carolina: Volume OneiGeneral Topics, 3 vols., Vol. 1. 2nd ed. 2007. ring bd. 55.00 net. *(978-1-56011-555-7(6))* Schl. of Government.

—Annexation Law in North Carolina Vol. 3: Involuntary Annexation. 2006. ring bd. *(978-1-56011-477-2(0)*, 2005.15) Schl. of Government.

Rocha, Roberto Rezende, et al. Annuities & Other Retirement Products: Designing the Payout Phase. 2011. (Directions in Development Ser.). (ENG.). 372p. pap. 40.00 *(978-0-8213-8573-9(9)*, 9780821385739) World Bank Pubns.

Schaffer, Albert. Woodruff: A Study of Community Decision Making. 2011. (ENG.). 336p. pap. 40.00 *(978-0-8078-9772-0(8))* Univ. of North Carolina Pr.

ANNIHILATION, POSITRON
see Positron Annihilation

ANNIVERSARIES
see also Days; Festivals; Holidays

also subdivision Anniversaries, etc. under names of individuals, e.g. Lincoln, Abraham, 1809-1865—Anniversaries, etc.

Chase's Calendar of Events Editors. The Teachers Calendar 2011-2012. 2011. (ENG.). 1125p. (C). pap. 25.00 *(978-0-07-176108-6(X)*, 007176108X) McGraw-Hill Cos., The.

Dhondt, Pieter. National, Nordic or European? Nineteenth-Century University Jubilees & Nordic Cooperation. 2011. 320p. ***(978-90-04-21694-5(4))*** BRILL.

Gvsu News & Invormation. Grand Valley State University 50th Anniversary: 1960-2010. 2009. *(978-1-61623-896-4(8))* Independent Pub.

Johnston, William M. Celebrations: The Cult of Anniversaries in Europe & the United States Today. 2011. (ENG.). 199p. pap. 24.95 *(978-1-4128-4233-4(6))* Transaction Pubs.

Kimura, Gregory W., ed. Alaska At 50: The Past, Present, & Future of Alaska Statehood. 2010. (Illus.). 285p. pap. 24.95 *(978-1-60223-081-1(1))* Univ. of Alaska Pr.

Poltarnees, Welleran. Happy Anniversary. 2007. (ENG., Illus.). 19.95 *(978-1-59583-136-1(3))* Laughing Elephant.

Twigg, Nancy. Celebrate Simply: Your Guide to Simpler, More Meaningful Holidays & Special Occasions. 2006. 224p. pap. 10.99 *(978-0-8254-3890-5(X))* Kregel Pubns.

United Nations Staff. Soixante réalisations de l'ONU qui ont changé le Monde. 2010. (FRE.). 48p. pap. 10.00 *(978-92-1-200297-2(8))* United Nations Pubns.

World Health Organization: Regional Office for Europe. Mass Gatherings & Public Health: The Experience of the Athens 2004 Olympic Games. Tsouros, Agis D. et al, eds. 2007. (Euro Nonserial Publication). (ENG., Illus.). 396p. pap. 84.00 *(978-92-890-7288-5(1))* World Health Organization.

ANNOTATIONS AND CITATIONS (LAW)
Here are entered compilations of legal citations such as citation books. Works on the method of citing legal authorities are entered under Citation of Legal Authorities.

see also Citation of Legal Authorities; Law Reports, Digests, Etc.

Barger. ALWD Citation Workbook. 2010. pap. 24.50 *(978-0-7355-8929-2(1))* Wolters Kluwer Law & Business.

Barger, Coleen M. & Bowman, Brooke J. ALWD Companion: A Citation Practice Book. 2010. xxii, 379p. *(978-0-7355-9175-2(X)*, Aspen Pubs.) Wolters Kluwer Law & Business.

Barris, Linda J. Understanding & Mastering the Bluebook: A Guide for Students & Practitioners. 2007. (ENG.). 136p. (C). spiral bd. 25.00 *(978-1-59460-365-5(0))* 2nd ed. 2010. 180p. spiral bd. 28.00 *(978-1-59460-733-2(8))* Carolina Academic Pr.

Dickerson. ALWD Citation Manual: A Professional System of Citation. 4th ed. 2010. pap. 33.95 *(978-0-7355-8930-8(5))* Wolters Kluwer Law & Business.

Excess Surplus Lines and Reinsurance Committee. Annotations to Surplus Lines Statutes, 2010 Edition. 2010th ed. 2011. (ENG.). 210p. pap. 79.95 *(978-1-60442-941-1(0))* American Bar Assn.

Immigration & Naturalization Citations. cd-rom 640.00 *(978-0-7698-1117-8(5))* Shepard's.

Lahore, J. & Rothnie, W. Butterworths Annotated Acts: Copyright Act. *(978-0-409-31001-6(8)*, Austral, MICHIE) LEXIS Publishing.

Shepard Broad Law Center (Nova Southeastern University) Staff, contrib. by. Manual of International & Foreign Legal Citation: The Greenbook. 2007. *(978-0-8377-3830-7(X))* Hein, William S. & Co., Inc.

ANNOTATIONS AND CITATIONS (LAW)—DELAWARE
Michie Company Editorial Staff. Delaware Code Annotated, Revised 1974, 21 vols., Set. *(978-0-87215-247-2(2)*, MICHIE) LEXIS Publishing.

ANNOTATIONS AND CITATIONS (LAW)—NORTH DAKOTA
Michie Butterworth Editorial Staff. North Dakota Court Rules Annotated, 1994-95 Edition. 55.00 *(978-0-87473-870-4(9)*, MICHIE) LEXIS Publishing.

ANNOTATIONS AND CITATIONS (LAW)—RHODE ISLAND
Michie Butterworth Editorial Staff. Rhode Island Court Rules, 1994 Edition. annot. ed. 45.00 *(978-1-55834-089-3(0)*, MICHIE) LEXIS Publishing.

Michie Company Editorial Staff. Rhode Island Court Rules Annotated, 1991-92. 1216p. pap. 45.00 *(978-0-87473-729-5(X)*, MICHIE) LEXIS Publishing.

ANNOTATIONS AND CITATIONS (LAW)—SOUTH DAKOTA
Michie Butterworth Editorial Staff. South Dakota Court Rules, 1994 Edition. pap. 52.50 *(978-1-55834-144-9(7)*, MICHIE) LEXIS Publishing.

ANNOTATIONS AND CITATIONS (LAW)—WASHINGTON (STATE)
Michie Butterworth Editorial Staff. Washington Rules of Court Annotated, 1994 Edition. 50.00 *(978-1-55834-178-4(1)*, MICHIE) LEXIS Publishing.

ANNOUNCING FOR RADIO
see Radio Announcing

ANNOUNCING FOR TELEVISION
see Television Announcing

ANNUAL (PLANTS)
see Annuals (Plants)

ANNUAL GIFT BOOKS
see Gift Books

ANNUAL INCOME GUARANTEE
see Guaranteed Annual Income

ANNUAL REPORTS, CORPORATION
see Corporation Reports

ANNUAL WAGE PLANS
see Guaranteed Annual Wage

ANNUALS
see Almanacs; Calendars; Yearbooks

ANNUALS (GIFT BOOKS)
see Gift Books

ANNUALS (PLANTS)
Bird, Richard. Making the Most of Annuals in the Garden: A Comprehensive Visual Directory & Practical Encyclopedia of Annual Plants to Suit All Styles & Every Kind of Outdoor Space. 2007. (ENG., Illus.). 96p. pap. 14.99 *(978-1-84476-379-5(X))* Anness Publishing GBR. Dist: National Bk. Network.

Bryant, Geoff & Rodd, Tony. Annuals & Perennials: A Gardener's Encyclopedia. 2011. (ENG., Illus.). 304p. pap. 19.95 *(978-1-55407-837-0(7))* Firefly Bks., Ltd.

Cheifetz, Anna, et al, eds. Annuals & Perennials. 2008. (Botanica's Pocket Ser.). (Illus.). 1008p. pap. 19.95 *(978-0-8416-0262-5(X))* American Map Corp.

Creative Homeowner Press Editors, ed. Smart Guide. annuals 2008. (Smart Guide Ser.). (ENG., Illus.). 96p. (gr. 5). pap. 10.95 *(978-1-58011-419-6(9))* Creative Homeowner.

Denver Botanic Gardens Staff & Plant Select Staff. Durable Plants for the Garden: A Plant Select Guide. Denver Water and Botanic Garden, ed. 2009. (ENG., Illus.). 216p. pap. 24.95 *(978-1-55591-590-2(6))* Fulcrum Publishing.

Smith, Gideon & van Wyk, Ben-Erik. The Garden Succulents Primer. 2008. (ENG., Illus.). 320p. 34.95 *(978-0-88192-954-6(9)*, 0881929549) Timber Pr., Inc.

ANNUITIES
see also Pensions

also subdivisions Pensions or Salaries, Pensions, etc. under classes of persons

Alliance, Nat'L. Life & Benefits Essentials: Life & Health Insurance Financial Planning. 2009. xviii, 191p. pap. *(978-1-878204-33-2(5))* Academy of Producer Insurance Studies, Inc., The.

Cannon, Edmund, et al. Annuity Markets. 2008. (ENG.). 200p. 99.00 *(978-0-19-921699-4(1))* Oxford Univ. Pr., Inc.

Conant, Susan. Financial Aspects of Annuities: AAPA 313 Text 2007. 2nd ed. 2007. per. *(978-1-57974-307-9(2))* Life Office Management Assn.

Conners, C. Brian & Eckel, James W. Planning for the Golden Years with Variable Annuities. (Illus.). 75p. pap. 24.95 *(978-0-910882-20-0(7))* Lexington Hse., Inc.

Dellinger, Jeffrey K. The Handbook of Variable Income Annuities. 2006. (Wiley Finance Ser.: 311). (ENG., Illus.). 776p. 185.00 *(978-0-471-73382-9(2)*, Wiley) Wiley, John & Sons, Inc.

Desoutter, Nicholas L. Intro to Annuities Instructor's Kit. (Step One Ser.). 57p. ring bd. 55.00 *(978-0-939921-93-5(6))* Life Office Management Assn.

Edwards, James Matthew. The Financial Insider's Annuity Guide: Understanding Annuities & Your Financial Portfolio. 2010. (Illus.). 166p. pap. ***(978-0-9843763-0-8(5))*** First American Financial Pr.

G Young, Matthew. The Complete Guide to Investing in Annuities: How to Earn High Rates of Return Safely. 2011. (ENG.). 288p. pap. 24.95 *(978-1-60138-291-7(X))* Atlantic Publishing Co.

Gantenbein, Marco & Mata, Mario A. Swiss Annuities & Life Insurance: Secure Returns, Asset Protection, & Privacy. 2008. (Wiley Finance Ser.: 400). (ENG., Illus.). 332p. 75.00 *(978-0-470-11811-5(3)*, Wiley) Wiley, John & Sons, Inc.

Gilley, Sean Schaeffer & Hartley, Robert H. Test Preparation Guide for AAPA 313: Financial Aspects of Annuities (2007) 2nd ed. 2007. per. *(978-1-57974-308-6(0))* Life Office Management Assn.

Kaminsky, Kenneth. Financial Literacy: Introduction to the Mathematics of Interest, Annuities, & Insurance. 2nd ed. 2010. (ENG.). 388p. pap. 50.00 *(978-0-7618-5309-1(X))* Univ. Pr. of America, Inc.

Levy, Donald R. 403B. 7th ed. 2008. 290.00 *(978-0-7355-7433-5(2))* Wolters Kluwer Law & Business.

Lovelady, Michael. Profiting with Synthetic Annuities: Option Strategies to Increase Yield & Control Portfolio Risk. 2012. (ENG.). 270p. 49.99 ***(978-0-13-292911-0(2))*** FT Press.

Lowder, Ellie. Section 403(b) Compliance Guide for Public Education Employers: The Final 403(b) Regulations & Related Guidance. 3rd ed. 2009. (ENG.). 104p. 40.00 *(978-1-60709-229-2(8))* Rowman & Littlefield Education.

Mackenzie, George A. (Sandy). Annuity Markets & Pension Reform. 2006. (ENG., Illus.). 258p. (C). 70.00 *(978-0-521-84632-5(3))* Cambridge Univ. Pr.

Marketing, Distribution, & Uses of Annuities: AAPA 283 Text 2008. 2nd ed. 2007. per. *(978-1-57974-310-9(2))* Life Office Management Assn.

Mars-Proietti, Laura, ed. TheStreet. com Ratings Consumer Box Set: 2007. 2007. pap. 359.00 *(978-1-59237-347-5(X))* Grey Hse. Publishing.

—TheStreet. com Ratings Consumer Box Set: 2008. 2008. pap. 359.00 *(978-1-59237-346-8(1))*; pap. 359.00 *(978-1-59237-345-1(3))* Grey Hse. Publishing.

Matthews, Gregory E. 403b: Forms & Worksheets. 2009. pap. 229.00 *(978-0-7355-8504-1(0))* Wolters Kluwer Law & Business.

Mooney, F. Bentley. An Advisor's Guide to Private Annuities. 2011. 292p. pap. 29.99 *(978-1-4520-1997-0(5))* AuthorHouse.

Pechter, Kerry & Pechter, Kerry H. Annuities for Dummies. 2008. (ENG., Illus.). 364p. per. 21.99 *(978-0-470-17889-8(2)*, For Dummies) Wiley, John & Sons, Inc.

Reindel, David J. Don't Die Broke: How Annuities Can Guarantee Your Income & Keep Your Retirement from Going Belly-Up. 2010. (ENG.). 191p. pap. 15.00 *(978-1-932841-53-4(9))* Agate Publishing, Inc.

Rocha, Roberto Rezende, et al. Annuities & Other Retirement Products: Designing the Payout Phase. (Directions in Development Ser.). 2011. (ENG.). 372p. pap. 40.00 *(978-0-8213-8573-9(9)*, 9780821385739) 2010. *(978-0-8213-8574-6(7))* World Bank Pubns.

Ruggerio, FIC, CWC, J. Marc, CRC. The Truth about Variable Annuities. 2010. (ENG & ABK.). 151p. 29.99 *(978-0-557-44824-1(7))* Lulu Enterprises Inc.

Ruggerio, J. Marc. The Truth about Variable Annuities. 2010. 151p. pap. 15.99 *(978-0-557-45188-3(4))* Lulu Enterprises Inc.

Seymon-Hirsch, Barbara N. & Anderson, Janet M. 403(B) Answer Book. 8th ed. 2011. ***(978-0-7355-0879-8(8))*** Kluwer Law International.

Sheshinski, Eytan. The Economic Theory of Annuities. 2007. (ENG., Illus.). 184p. (C). 42.00 *(978-0-691-13305-8(0))* Princeton Univ. Pr.

Shestopaloff, Yuri K. Mortgages & Annuities: Mathematical Foundations & Computational Algorithms. 2010. (ENG., Illus.). 287p. pap. 59.95 *(978-0-9809667-7-0(9))* AKVY Pr. CAN. Dist: Lightning Source, Inc.

—Mortgages & Annuities. an Introduction: An Introduction. 2010. (Illus.). 205p. 59.95 *(978-0-9809667-8-7(7))* AKVY Pr. CAN. Dist: Lightning Source, Inc.

Spurgeon, E. F. Life Contingencies. 3rd rev. ed. 2011. 510p. pap. 37.99 ***(978-1-107-64809-8(2))*** Cambridge Univ. Pr.

Test Preparation Guide for AAPA 283: Marketing, Distribution, & Uses of Annuities (2008) 2007. per. *(978-1-57974-311-6(0))* Life Office Management Assn.

TheStreet. com Ratings Consumer Guide to Variable Annuities. 2007. pap. 49.00 *(978-1-58773-391-8(9))* TheStreet.com Ratings, Inc.

TheStreet.com Ratings, ed. Thestreet. Com Ratings Consumer Box Set: Fall 2009. 2009. pap. 249.00 *(978-1-59237-476-2(X))* Grey Hse. Publishing.

—TheStreet. com Ratings Consumer Box Set: Spring 2009. 2009. pap. 359.00 *(978-1-59237-475-5(1))* Grey Hse. Publishing.

Thorburn, Craig & Rocha, Roberto Rezende. Developing Annuities Markets: The Experience of Chile. 2006. (Directions in Development Ser.). (ENG., Illus.). 288p. per. 30.00 *(978-0-8213-6666-0(1)*, 9780821366660) World Bank Pubns.

Turner, John A. Pension Policy: The Search for Better Solutions. 2009. 40.00 *(978-0-88099-355-5(3))*; 240p. pap. 20.00 *(978-0-88099-354-8(5))* Upjohn, W.E. Institute for Employment Research.

Weisman, Steve. The Truth about Buying Annuities. 2008. (Truth About Ser.). (ENG.). 208p. pap. 20.99 *(978-0-13-235308-3(3))* FT Press.

Weiss Ratings, ed. Weiss Ratings Consumer Box Set. 2011. pap. 359.00 *(978-1-59237-811-1(0))*; pap. 359.00 *(978-1-59237-810-4(2))* Grey Hse. Publishing.

Zimmerman, Robert. The Annuity from Mystery to Mastery. 2006. 108p. per. 19.95 *(978-1-59858-238-3(0))* Dog Ear Publishing, LLC.

ANNULENES
Fray, G. I. & Saxton, R. G. The Chemistry of Cyclo-Octatetraene & its Derivatives. 2009. (ENG., Illus.). 504p. pap. 61.00 *(978-0-521-10565-1(X))* Cambridge Univ. Pr.

ANNULMENT OF MARRIAGE
see Marriage—Annulment

ANODYNES
see Analgesics

ANOINTINGS
see Unction

ANOMALIES, CONGENITAL
see Abnormalities, Human

ANOMY
Robinson, Matthew, et al. Greed Is Good: Maximization & Elite Deviance in America. 2008. (ENG.). 150p. 75.00 *(978-0-7425-6070-3(8))*; pap. 26.95 *(978-0-7425-6071-0(6))* Rowman & Littlefield Publishers, Inc.

ANONYMS AND PSEUDONYMS
see also Anagrams

Browne, William H. Famous Women of History: Containing Nearly Three Thousand Brief Biographies & Over One Thousand Female Pseudonyms. 434p. reprint ed. 98.00 *(978-0-7222-1691-0(2))* Library Reprints, Inc.

Ciuraru, Carmela. Nom de Plume: A (Secret) History of Pseudonyms. (P. S. Ser.). (ENG.). 2012. 288p. pap. 15.99 ***(978-0-06-173527-1(2)***, HarperPerennial) 2011. 368p. 24.99 *(978-0-06-173526-4(4))* HarperCollins Pubs.

Davis, Joyce. Dictionary of Pseudonyms & Alternative Names of Women Writers. *(978-0-7201-2103-2(5)*, Burns & Oates) Continuum International Publishing Group, Ltd.

Drone, Jeanette Marie. Musical AKAs: Assumed Names & Sobriquets of Composers, Songwriters, Librettists, Lyricists, Hymnists & Writers on Music. Drone, Jeanette Marie, ed. 2006. (ENG.). 544p. 116.00 *(978-0-8108-5739-1(1))* Scarecrow Pr., Inc.

Gaines, Pierce Welch, ed. Political Works of Concealed Authorship During the Administrations of Washington, Adams, & Jefferson, 1789-1809. 2011. 150p. 40.95 ***(978-1-258-08521-6(6))*** Literary Licensing, LLC.

North, Marcy L. The Anonymous Renaissance: Cultures of Discretion in Tudor-Stuart England. Date not set. pap. 22.00 *(978-0-226-59438-5(6))* Univ. of Chicago Pr.

Room, Adrian. Dictionary of Pseudonyms: 13,000 Assumed Names & Their Origins. 5th rev. ed. 2010. (ENG., Illus.). 536p. 95.00 *(978-0-7864-4373-4(1))* McFarland & Co., Inc. Pubs.

Starner, Janet Wright & Traister, Barbara. Anonymity in Early Modern England: What's in a Name? 2011. 198p. 99.95 *(978-0-7546-6949-4(1))* Ashgate Publishing Co.

ANORECTIC DRUGS
see Appetite Depressants

ANOREXIA
Here are entered works on diminished appetite in general. Works on a psychiatric disorder manifested by severe weight loss and extreme aversion to food are entered under Anorexia Nervosa.

Amarteifio, Ebsen William. What Has Food Got to Do with It, Anyway? (A Battle Between Miss Positive & Miss Timid) 2011. 140p. pap. 15.60 ***(978-1-4567-8394-5(7))*** AuthorHouse.

Arnold, Carrie. Decoding Anorexia: How Breakthroughs in Science Offer Hope for Eating Disorders. 2012. (ENG., Illus.). 240p. 94.95 *(978-0-415-89866-9(8))*; pap. 29.95 *(978-0-415-89867-6(6))* Routledge.

Brisbin, Leigh-Ann. My True Reflection: Freedom from Eating Disorders. 2009. 232p. pap. 14.99 *(978-0-88270-588-0(1))* Bridge-Logos Foundation.

Brown, Harriet. Brave Girl Eating: A Family's Struggle with Anorexia. (ENG.). 2011. 288p. pap. 14.99 *(978-0-06-172548-7(X)*, Harper Paperbacks) 2010. 320p. 25.99 *(978-0-06-172547-0(1)*, Morrow, William & Co.) HarperCollins Pubs.

Carlton, Pamela & Ashin, Deborah. Take Charge of Your Child's Eating Disorder: A Physician's Step-by-Step Guide to Defeating Anorexia & Bulimia. 2007. (ENG.). 256p. per. 15.95 *(978-1-56924-263-6(1))* Da Capo Pr., Inc.

Chase, Stephen, ed. Eating Disorder: Complete Handbook. 2011. 136p. pap. 14.95 ***(978-1-937354-05-3(9))*** Rapid Publishing LLC.

Christie, Sheryl. Red Tears & Rib Bones: A True Story of Anorexia, Sexual Abuse, & Self-Mutilation. 2008. 112p. pap. 19.95 *(978-1-60563-251-3(1))* PublishAmerica, Inc.

Fortier, Marian Rae. The Perfect Size: An Eating Disordered Tale of Winning the Anorexic War One Battle at a Time. 2008. 59p. pap. 16.95 *(978-1-60563-806-5(4))* PublishAmerica, Inc.

Gilhar, Linie. Voiceless, in a Starving Inner World. 2009. 564p. pap. *(978-3-639-17218-8(3))* VDM Verlag Dr. Mueller e.K.

Giordano, Simona. Understanding Eating Disorders: Conceptual & Ethical Issues in the Treatment of Anorexia & Bulimia Nervosa. 2008. (ENG.). 320p. per. 49.95 *(978-0-19-923295-6(4))* Oxford Univ. Pr., Inc.

Grahl, Gary A. Skinny Boy: A Young Man's Battle & Triumph over Anorexia. 2007. (ENG.). 240p. pap. 17.95 *(978-0-9761547-4-7(9))* American Legacy Media.

Halse, Christine, et al. Inside Anorexia: The Experiences of Girls & Their Families. 2007. (ENG.). 224p. per. (978-1-84310-597-8(7)) Kingsley, Jessica Ltd.
Johnson, Lynn. Anorexia - a Parent's Guide - How to Help Your Child Overcome Anorexi. 2011. 64p. pap. 12.00 **(978-0-557-59373-6(5))** Lulu Enterprises Inc.
Kingsley, Jo & Kingsley, Alice. Alice in the Looking Glass: A Mother & Daughter's Experience of Anorexia. 2006. 208p. 14.95 (978-0-7499-2637-3(6)) Piatkus Bks. GBR. Dist: National Bk. Network.
Moore-Groarke, Gillian, ed. In Search of Thinness: Treating Anorexia & Bulimia. 2008. (ENG., Illus.). 191p. pap. 28.95 (978-1-85607-963-1(5)) Currach Pr. IRL. Dist: Dufour Editions, Inc.
Myers, Michelle. The Look That Kills: An Anorexic's Addiction to Control. 2010. 128p. pap. 11.95 (978-1-61507-224-8(1)) Cross Bks. Publishing.
Nelson, Tammy. Whats Eating You: A Workbook for Teens with Anorexia, Bulimia, & Other Eating Disorders. 2008. (Instant Help Ser.). 110p. pap. 14.95 (978-1-931704-44-1(9)) Play2Grow.
Otto, Jennifer. Never Drink Calories: Theories of an Anorexic. 2011. 178p. pap. 14.95 **(978-1-936400-59-1(6))** Mill City Pr., Inc.
Rowell, Shannon. Chains Be Broken: Finding Freedom from Cutting, Anxiety, Depression, Anorexia, & Suicide. 2010. (ENG.). 224p. pap. 12.99 (978-1-935245-22-3(8)) HigherLife Development Services, Inc.
Shaw, Ashley. Journey: Recovering from Anorexia. 2008. 112p. pap. 11.95 (978-1-60126-149-6(7)) Masthof Pr.
Sheldon, Tanya J. A Mind Less Ordinary: My Experience of Living with Anorexia & Schizoaffective Disorder. 2011. 134p. pap. **(978-1-84991-527-4(X))** Chipmunkapublishing.
Taylor, Kate M. Going Hungry: Writers on Desire, Self-Denial, & Overcoming Anorexia. 2008. (ENG.). 352p. pap. 15.95 (978-0-307-27834-0(4), Anchor) Knopf Doubleday Publishing Group.

ANOREXIA NERVOSA

Here are entered works on a psychiatric disorder manifested by severe weight loss and extreme aversion to food. Works on diminished appetite in general are entered under Anorexia.

Alexander, June & Le Grange, Daniel. My Kid Is Back. 2010. (ENG.). 272p. pap. 17.95 (978-0-415-58115-8(X)) Routledge.
Allison, Mandy. Dying to Live. 2009. 280p. pap. (978-1-84991-031-6(6)) Chipmunkapublishing.
Baratta, Maria. "Skinny" Revisited: Women, Beauty, & Anorexia. 2011. **(978-0-87101-407-8(6)**, NASW Pr.) National Assn. of Social Workers/NASW Pr.
Binstock, Melissa. Nourishment: Feeding My Starving Soul When My Mind & Body Betrayed Me. 2011. (ENG.). 288p. pap. 14.95 (978-0-7573-1542-8(9)) Health Communications, Inc.
Bowman, Grace. Thin. 2008. (ENG.). 304p. (gr. 12-18). 15.00 (978-0-14-102284-0(1), Penguin Global) Penguin Group (USA) Inc.
Breen, Carol. Anorexia Nervosa - Hidden Meanings & Agendas. 2010. 64p. pap. (978-3-639-27619-0(1)) VDM Verlag Dr. Mueller e.K.
Brown, Harriet. Brave Girl Eating: A Family's Struggle with Anorexia. 2011. (ENG.). 288p. pap. 14.99 (978-0-06-172548-7(X), Harper Paperbacks) HarperCollins Pubs.
Bryant-Waugh, Rachel, ed. Eating Disorders in Childhood & Adolescence. 3rd rev. ed. 2007. (ENG., Illus.). 424p. per. 42.50 (978-0-415-42589-6(1)) Routledge.
Camatta, Silvia. Lo Sciopero Della Fame Di Lore Berger: Narrare L'anoressia Nervosa Nella Svizzera Della Geistige Landesverteidigung. 2009. (ITA.). 208p. (978-88-8098-268-5(0)) Unipress.
Christou, Theodore. Poetic Ekphonesis. 2010. 156p. pap. (978-3-639-22576-1(7)) VDM Verlag Dr. Mueller e.K.
de Rossi, Portia. Unbearable Lightness: A Story of Loss & Gain. (ENG., Illus.). 320p. 2011. pap. 16.00 (978-1-4391-7779-2(1)) 2010. 25.99 (978-1-4391-7778-5(3)) Atria Bks. (Beyond Words/Atria Bks.).
Dignon, Andreé. All of Me: A Fuller Picture of Anorexia. 2007. 267p. pap. 64.95 (978-3-03911-075-9(6)) Lang, Peter Publishing, Inc.
Feigenbaum, Naomi. One Life: Hope, Healing & Inspiration on the Path to Recovery from Eating Disorders. 2009. (ENG.). 160p. pap. (978-1-84310-912-9(3)) Kingsley, Jessica Ltd.
Ferraro, Lisa. The Peer Culture of Adolescent Girls with Anorexia Nervosa. 2009. 160p. pap. (978-3-639-20450-6(6)) VDM Verlag Dr. Mueller e.K.
Flashback, Part II: Argentina, Three parts so far, Part II. 2007. (Illus.). 229p. pap. 15.95 (978-0-9791074-1-2(5)) Zeoli, A. Jorgelina.
Gottlieb, Lori. Stick Figure: A Diary of My Former Self. 2009. (ENG., Illus.). 224p. pap. 14.00 (978-1-4391-4890-7(2)) Simon & Schuster.
Grahame, Nikki. Dying to Be Thin: The True Story of My Lifelong Battle Against Anorexia. 2009. (ENG., Illus.). 316p. 26.95 (978-1-84454-743-2(4)) Blake, John Publishing, Ltd. GBR. Dist: Independent Pubs. Group.
Grahl, Gary A. Skinny Boy: A Young Man's Battle & Triumph over Anorexia. 2007. 243p. 30.55 (978-1-4178-0824-3(1), Turtleback) Turtleback Bks.
Greenblatt, James. Answers to Anorexia: A New Breakthrough Nutritional Treatment That Is Saving Lives. 2010. 224p. pap. 16.95 (978-1-934716-07-6(3)) Sunrise River Pr.
Greenfield, Lauren. Thin. 2006. (ENG., Illus.). 224p. 35.00 (978-0-8118-5633-1(X)) Chronicle Bks. LLC.
Halban, Emily. Anorexia & Me. 2009. (ENG.). 336p. pap. 14.95 (978-0-09-191749-4(2)) Random Hse. GBR. Dist: Independent Pubs. Group.
Hale-Seubert, Barbara. Riptide: Struggling with & Resurfacing from a Daughter's Eating Disorder. 2011. (ENG.). 234p. pap. 17.95 (978-1-55022-995-0(8)) ECW Pr. CAN. Dist: Independent Pubs. Group.
Hay, Vicky. Wounded: Fighting my Demons. 2010. (Illus.). 132p. pap. 10.99 (978-1-4520-1905-5(3)) AuthorHouse.
Hosin, Amer A. Autism, ADHD, & Anorexia Nervosa: Essays on Three Childhood Disorders. (Illus.). 120p. 89.95 (978-0-7734-5163-6(3)) Mellen, Edwin Pr., The.
Howard-Taylor, Lucy. Biting Anorexia: A Firsthand Account of an Internal War. 2009. (ENG.). 192p. pap. 19.95 (978-1-57224-702-4(9)) New Harbinger Pubns.
Kiesbye, Stefan. Anorexia. 2010. (At Issue Ser.). (ENG.). 104p. 31.80 (978-0-7377-4866-6(4)); pap. 22.50 (978-0-7377-4867-3(2)) Cengage Gale. (Greenhaven Pr., Inc.).
Knapp, Caroline. Appetites. rev. ed. 2011. (ENG.). 224p. pap. 14.95 **(978-1-58243-808-5(0)**, Counterpoint) Counterpoint LLC.
Lask, Bryan & Bryant-Waugh, Rachel. Eating Disorders in Childhood & Adolescence. 3rd rev. ed. 2007. (ENG., Illus.). 424p. 120.00 (978-0-415-39457-4(0)) Routledge.
Lawrence, Marilyn. The Anorexic Mind. 2008. (Tavistock Clinic Ser.). 143p. pap. (978-1-85575-383-9(9)) Karnac Bks.
Lucas, Alexander R. Demystifying Anorexia Nervosa: An Optimistic Guide to Understanding & Healing. 2008. (ENG., Illus.). 192p. pap. 14.95 (978-0-19-534080-8(9)) Oxford Univ. Pr., Inc.
Ma, Joyce L. C. Anorexia Nervosa & Family Therapy in a Chinese Context. 2011. (ENG.). 250p. (gr. 17). pap. 30.00 (978-962-996-460-3(0)) Chinese Univ. of Hong Kong, The HKG. Dist: Columbia Univ. Pr.
Mancini, Antonio, et al. Anorexia Nervosa: A Multi-disciplinary Approach: from Biology to Philosophy. 2009. (Eating Disorders in the 21st Century Ser.). 98.00 (978-1-60876-200-2(9), Nova Biomedical Bks.) Nova Science Pubs., Inc.
Metcalfe, Katie. Anorexia: A Stranger in the Family. 2006. (ENG., Illus.). 252p. per. 11.95 (978-1-905170-35-7(1)) Accent Pr. Ltd. GBR. Dist: SCB Distributors.
Moisin, Laura. Kid Rex: The Inspiring True Account of a Life Salvaged from Despair, Anorexia & Dark Days in New York City. 2008. (ENG.). 300p. pap. 19.95 (978-1-55022-838-0(2)) ECW Pr. CAN. Dist: Independent Pubs. Group.
Pettit, Christie. Empty: A Story of Anorexia. 2006. (Illus.). 208p. (YA). (gr. 8-12). pap. 16.00 (978-0-8007-3135-9(2)) Revell.
Pieters, Guido. Psychomotor Functioning in Anorexia Nervosa: Neuropsychological & Electrophysiological Studies. 2006. (Acta Biomedica Lovaniensia Ser.: Vol. 359). (Illus.). pap. 99.50 (978-90-5867-539-2(4)) Leuven Univ. Pr. BEL. Dist: Cornell Univ. Pr.
Raviv, Shani. Being Ana: A Memoir of Anorexia Nervosa. 2010. 264p. pap. 18.95 (978-1-4502-3777-2(0)) iUniverse, Inc.
Rio, Linda M. & Rio, Tara M. The Anorexia Diaries: A Mother & Daughter's Triumph over Teenage Eating Disorders. 2006. 260p. reprint ed. 22.00 (978-1-4223-5471-1(7)) DIANE Publishing Co.
Rivera, Erica. Insatiable: A Young Mother's Struggle with Anorexia. 2010. (ENG.). 368p. (gr. 12). 15.00 (978-0-425-23663-5(3), Berkley Trade) Penguin Group (USA) Inc.
Robinson, Paul H. Severe & Enduring Eating Disorder (SEED) Management of Complex Presentations of Anorexia & Bulimia Nervosa. 2009. (ENG., Illus.). 184p. pap. 55.95 (978-0-470-06207-4(X), Wiley) Wiley, John & Sons, Inc.
Robinson, Paul H., et al. Severe & Enduring Eating Disorder (SEED) Management of Complex Presentations of Anorexia & Bulimia Nervosa. 2009. (ENG., Illus.). 184p. 144.95 (978-0-470-06206-7(1), Wiley) Wiley, John & Sons, Inc.
Rumney, Avis. Dying to Please: Anorexia, Treatment & Recovery. 2nd rev. ed. 2009. (ENG.). 198p. pap. 35.00 (978-0-7864-4378-9(2)) McFarland & Co., Inc. Pubs.
Samelson, Doreen & Samelson, Doreen A. Feeding the Starving Mind: A Personalized, Comprehensive Approach to Overcoming Anorexia & Other Starvation Eating Disorders. 2009. (Workbook Ser.). (ENG., Illus.). 256p. pap. 21.95 (978-1-57224-584-6(0)) New Harbinger Pubns.
Saukko, Paula. The Anorexic Self: A Personal, Political Analysis of a Diagnostic Discourse. 2008. 134p. 59.50 (978-0-7914-7461-7(5)); pap. 24.95 (978-0-7914-7462-4(3)) State Univ. of New York Pr.
Schleenstein, Dorothé. Frauenspezifische Suchtproblematik aus theologischer Perspektive am Beispiel der Ess-Störungen. 2010. (Europäische Hochschulschriften. Reihe 23: Theologie Ser.). (GER.). 264p. pap. 67.95 (978-3-631-59870-2(X)) Lang, Peter GmbH, Europaischer Verlag der Wissenschaften DEU. Dist: Lang, Peter.
Shepphird, Sari Fine. 100 Questions & Answers about Anorexia Nervosa. 2009. (ENG.). 180p. pap. 22.95 (978-0-7637-5450-1(1)) Jones & Bartlett Learning, LLC.
Stryer, Stacy Beller. Anorexia, 1 vol. 2009. (Biographies of Disease Ser.). (Illus.). 192p. 45.00 (978-0-313-35975-0(X), GR5975) Greenwood Publishing Group, Inc.
Warin, Megan. Abject Relations: Everyday Worlds of Anorexia. rev. ed. 2009. (Studies in Medical Anthropology Ser.). (ENG.). 248p. (C). pap. 25.95 (978-0-8135-4690-2(7)); 72.00 (978-0-8135-4689-6(3)) Rutgers Univ. Pr.
Weaver, Kathryn. Women's Recovering from Anorexia Nervosa. 2010. 204p. pap. (978-3-639-23970-6(9)) VDM Verlag Dr. Mueller e.K.
Wilson, C. Philip. The Fear of Being Fat. 384p. reprint ed. pap. (978-1-56821-012-4(4), Aronson, Jason) Rowman & Littlefield Publishers, Inc.
Wilson, Kelly G., et al. Acceptance & Commitment Therapy for Eating Disorders: A Process-Focused Guide to Treating Anorexia & Bulimia. 2011. (Professional Ser.). (ENG., Illus.). 312p. 59.95 (978-1-57224-733-8(9)) New Harbinger Pubns.
Zemba, William. David & the Old Man. 2010. 152p. 30.95 (978-1-4497-0572-5(3)); pap. 13.95 (978-1-4497-0571-8(5)) Author Solutions, Inc. (WestBow Pr.).

ANOREXIGENIC DRUGS

see Appetite Depressants

ANOXEMIA

see also Oxygen in the Body

Aldashev, Almaz & Naeije, Robert, eds. Problems of High Altitude Medicine & Biology. 2007. (NATO Science for Peace & Security Series / NATO Science for Peace & Security Series A: Chemistry & Biology Ser.). (ENG., Illus.). viii, 306p. per. 99.00 (978-1-4020-6299-5(0), 1402062990); 316p. 219.00 (978-1-4020-6298-8(2)) Springer.
Antony, Manju. Hypoxia on Rat Brain & Therapeutic Use of Superoxide Dismutase. 2011. 184p. pap. **(978-3-8454-1441-6(3))** Lambert Academic Publishing.
Brauner, Colin J., et al. Hypoxia. Richards, Jeffrey G. et al, eds. 2009. (Fish Physiology Ser.: 27). (ENG., Illus.). 517p. 114.00 (978-0-12-374632-0(9), Academic Pr.) Elsevier Science & Technology Bks.
Brüne, Bernhard, ed. Oxygen Biology & Hypoxia. 2007. (Methods in Enzymology Ser.). (ENG., Illus.). 592p. 187.00 (978-0-12-373970-4(5), Academic Pr.) Elsevier Science & Technology Bks.
Chandel, Navdeep S., et al, eds. Hypoxia & Consequences. 2009. (Annals of the New York Academy of Sciences Ser.: 35). (ENG., Illus.). 352p. pap. 134.95 (978-1-57331-773-3(X), Wiley-Blackwell) Wiley, John & Sons, Inc.
Dale, Virginia H., ed. Hypoxia in the Northern Gulf of Mexico. 2010. (Springer Series on Environmental Management Ser.). (ENG., Illus.). 340p. 149.00 (978-0-387-89685-4(6), 0387896856) Springer.
Gauge, Susan. CTG Made Easy. 4th ed. 2012. (ENG., Illus.). 208p. pap. 35.95 **(978-0-7020-5214-9(0)**, Churchill Livingstone) Elsevier - Health Sciences Div.
Haddad, Gabriel G. & Yu, Shan Ping. Brain Hypoxia & Ischemia. 2009. (Contemporary Clinical Neuroscience Ser.). (ENG., Illus.). xii, 268p. 189.00 (978-1-60327-578-1(9)) Humana Pr.
Harmful Algal Blooms & Hypoxia: Formulating an Action Plan: Hearing Before the Subcommittee on Energy & Environment, Committee on Science & Technology, House of Representatives, One Hundred Eleventh Congress, First Session, September 17, 2009. 2009. (Illus.). iv, 87p. (978-0-16-084953-4(5), 552-070-40343-4) United States Government Printing Office.
Lutz, P. L., et al. The Brain Without Oxygen: Causes of Failure - Physiological & Molecular Mechanisms for Survival. 3rd ed. 2010. 260p. pap. 159.00 (978-90-481-6237-6(8), 9048162378) Springer.
Machulla, H. J., ed. Imaging of Hypoxia: Tracer Developments. 2010. (Developments in Nuclear Medicine Ser.). 184p. pap. 139.00 (978-90-481-5157-8(0), 9048151570) Springer.
Mishra, Om P. Mechanisms of Hypoxic Brain Injury in the Newborn & Potential Strategies for Neuroprotection. 2007. (Illus.). 218p. (978-81-7895-263-5(7)) Transworld Research Network.
Roach, Robert, et al, eds. Hypoxia & Exercise. 2010. (Advances in Experimental Medicine & Biology Ser.). (Illus.). xv, 354p. pap. 259.00 (978-1-4419-4192-3(4), 1441941924) Springer.
—Hypoxia & the Circulation. (Advances in Experimental Medicine & Biology Ser.). 2010. (Illus.). xii, 348p. pap. 189.00 (978-1-4419-4527-3(X), 144194527X) 2007. 360p. 189.00 (978-0-387-75433-8(4)) Springer.
Roach, Robert C., et al, eds. Hypoxia: From Genes to the Bedside. 2010. (Advances in Experimental Medicine & Biology Ser.). 462p. pap. 179.00 (978-1-4419-3374-4(3), 1441933743) Springer.
Roux, Océane M. Brain Hypoxia-Ischemia Research Progress. 2008. (C). 129.00 (978-1-60456-139-5(4)) Nova Science Pubs., Inc.
Salas, Benjamin M. Hypoxia in the Northern Gulf of Mexico. 2011. (Environmental Science, Engineering & Technology Ser.). 195.00 (978-1-61209-318-5(3)) Nova Science Pubs., Inc.
Schaller, Bernhard J. Endogenous Neuroprotection. 2008. (Illus.). 100p. 89.00 (978-1-60456-228-6(5), Nova Biomedical Bks.) Nova Science Pubs., Inc.
Simon, M. Celeste, ed. Diverse Effects of Hypoxia on Tumor Progression. 2010. (Current Topics in Microbiology & Immunology Ser.). (Illus.). x, 143p. 219.00 (978-3-642-13328-2(2), 3642133282) Springer.
Swenson / Barts. Hypoxia: Human Adaptation to High Altitude, Second Edition. 2nd rev. ed. 2011. (Lung Biology in Health & Disease Ser.). (ENG., Illus.). 500p. (978-1-4200-9535-7(8)) Informa Healthcare.
Tichauer, Kenneth. Near-Infrared Spectroscopy: Diagnosis of neonatal Hypoxia-ischemia. 2010. 116p. pap. (978-3-639-24307-9(2)) VDM Verlag Dr. Mueller e.K.
Wagner, Peter D., et al, eds. Hypoxia & Exercise. 2006. (Advances in Experimental Medicine & Biology Ser.: Vol. 588). (Illus.). 353p. 259.00 (978-0-387-34816-2(6), 0387348166) Springer.
Xi, Lei, ed. Intermittent Hypoxia: from Molecular Mechanisms to Clinical Applications. 2009. (Physiology - Laboratory & Clinical Research Ser.). (Illus.). xxxi, 615p. 89.00 (978-1-60876-127-2(4)) Nova Science Pubs., Inc.

ANOXYBIOSIS

see Anaerobiosis

ANSARII

see Nosairians

ANSCHLUSS MOVEMENT, 1918-1938

Weizig, Werner, ed. 'Anschluss' - März/April 1938 in Österreich. 2010. (Kulturforschungen Ser.). (GER.). 180p. (C). pap. 59.00 (978-3-7001-6768-6(7)) Austrian Academy of Sciences Press AUT. Dist: Brown, David Bk. Co., The.

ANSELM, SAINT, ARCHBISHOP OF CANTERBURY, 1033-1109

Anselm, Saint. Anselm of Canterbury: The Major Works. Davies, Brian & Evans, G. R., eds. 2008. (Oxford World's Classics Ser.). (ENG.). 544p. pap. 14.95 (978-0-19-954008-2(X)) Oxford Univ. Pr., Inc.
Boschung, Peter. From a Topical Point of View: Dialectic in Anselm of Canterbury's de Grammatico. 2006. (Studien und Texte Zur Geistesgeschichte des Mittelalters Ser.: Vol. 90). 346p. (978-90-04-15431-5(0)) BRILL.
Clayton, Joseph. Saint Anselm: A Critical Biography. 2007. (Gorgias Theological Library: 24). 69.00 (978-1-59333-722-3(1)) Gorgias Pr., LLC.
—Saint Anselm: A Critical Biography. 192p. 2008. 37.95 (978-1-4366-9035-5(8)) 2007. (ENG.). per. 22.95 (978-1-4325-4308-2(3)) Kessinger Publishing, LLC.
Hick, John & McGill, Arthur C., eds. The Many-Faced Argument: Studies on the Ontological Argument for the Existence of God. 2009. 384p. pap. 41.00 (978-1-60608-695-7(2), Wipf and Stock) Wipf & Stock Pubs.
Logan, Ian. Reading Anselm's Proslogion: The History of Anselm's Argument & Its Significance Today. 2009. (New Critical Thinking in Religion, Theology & Biblical Studies). 230p. 99.95 (978-0-7546-6123-8(7)) Ashgate Publishing Co.
Ngien, Dennis. Gifted Response: The Triune God as the Causative Agency of our Responsive Worship. 2008. (ENG.). 200p. 29.99 (978-1-84227-610-5(7), Paternoster) Authentic Media.
Rogers, Katherin. Anselm on Freedom. 2008. (ENG.). 256p. 99.00 (978-0-19-923167-6(2)) Oxford Univ. Pr., Inc.
Southern, R. W. Saint Anselm & His Biographer: A Study of Monastic Life & Thought, 1059-C. 1130. 2009. (ENG.). 408p. pap. 42.00 (978-0-521-10331-2(2)) Cambridge Univ. Pr.
St. Anselm. St. Anselm: Opera Omni (SGML) Schmitt, F. S., ed. (Past Masters Ser.). (C). (978-1-57085-153-7(0)) Intelex Corp.
—St. Anselm: Opera Omnia. Schmitt, F. S., ed. (Past Masters Ser.). (C). (978-1-57085-200-8(6)) Intelex Corp.
Sweeney, Eileen C. Anselm of Canterbury & the Desire for the Word. 2012. (ENG.). 416p. 74.95 **(978-0-8132-1958-5(2))** Catholic Univ. of America Pr.
Vaughn, Sally N. Archbishop Anselm: Archiepiscopal Saint & Primate of All Britain, 1093-1109. 2012. (Archbishops of Canterbury Ser.). (Illus.). 200p. 99.95 **(978-1-4094-0121-6(9))**; pap. 39.95 **(978-1-4094-0122-3(7))** Ashgate Publishing Co.
Visser, Sandra & Williams, Thomas. Anselm. 2008. (ENG.). 384p. 99.00 (978-0-19-530938-6(3)); pap. 29.95 (978-0-19-530939-3(1)) Oxford Univ. Pr., Inc.
Welch, A. C. Anselm & His Work. 2008. 268p. 42.95 (978-1-4365-5865-5(4)) 2007. (ENG.). 272p. per. 27.95 (978-0-548-77362-8(9)) Kessinger Publishing, LLC.

ANSON, GEORGE ANSON, BARON, 1697-1762

Walter, Richard. Anson's Voyage Round the World. 2008. 216p. 27.99 (978-0-554-27240-5(7)); 24.99 (978-0-554-36543-5(X)) BiblioBazaar.
—Anson's Voyage Round the World. Household, H. W., ed. 2009. 192p. pap. (978-1-4099-8014-8(6)) Dodo Pr.

ANSWERS TO QUESTIONS

see Questions and Answers

ANT

see Ants

ANTAGONISTS ENZYME

see Enzyme Inhibitors

ANTARCTIC FLORA

see Botany—Antarctica

ANTARCTIC OCEAN

Here are entered works on the southern parts of the Atlantic, Indian, and Pacific oceans that surround Antarctica.

Best, Peter. Whales & Dolphins of the Southern African Subregion. 2008. (ENG., Illus.). 352p. 199.00 (978-0-521-89710-5(6)) Cambridge Univ. Pr.
Heller, Peter. The Whale Warriors: On Board a Pirate Ship in the Battle to Save the World's Largest Mammals. 2008. 320p. (978-0-7322-8732-0(4)) HarperCollins Pubs. Australia.
Morozov, Eugene G., et al. Abyssal Channels in the Atlantic Ocean: Water Structure & Flows. 2010. (ENG., Illus.). xxii, 266p. 129.00 (978-90-481-9357-8(5), 9048193575) Springer.

ANTARCTIC REGIONS

see Antarctica

ANTARCTICA

Here are entered works on the continent of Antarctica and the associated region adjacent to it.

see also South Pole

Anschntz, Helgard. On the Snow Accumulation Pattern in Coastal East Antarctic. 2008. 92p. pap. (978-3-639-03374-3(4)) VDM Verlag Dr. Mueller e.K.
Barell, John F. Quest for Antarctica: A Journey of Wonder & Discovery. 2011. 204p. pap. 17.95 **(978-1-4620-2121-5(2))** iUniverse, Inc.
Bergstrom, Dana M., et al, eds. Trends in Antarctic Terrestrial & Limnetic Ecosystems: Antarctica as a Global Indicator. 2007. (ENG., Illus.). xiv, 369p. 159.00 (978-1-4020-5276-7(6), 1402052766) Springer.

Brady, Anne-Marie, ed. The Emerging Politics of Antarctica. 2012. (Routledge Advances in International Relations & Global Politics Ser.). (ENG.). 240p. (C). 135.00 **(978-0-415-53139-9(X))** Routledge.

Bull, Henrik Johan. The Cruise of the Antarctic to the South Polar Regions. 2011. (Cambridge Library Collection - Travel & Exploration Ser.). (ENG., Illus.). 282p. pap. 23.99 **(978-1-108-04186-7(8))** Cambridge Univ. Pr.

Capra, Alessandro & Dietrich, Reinhard, eds. Geodetic & Geophysical Observations in Antarctica: An Overview in the IPY Perspective. 2010. (ENG., Illus.). xx, 356p. pap. 199.00 *(978-3-642-09428-6(7)*, 3642094287) Springer.

Carey, Peter & Franklin, Craig. Antarctica Cruising Guide: Includes Falkland Islands, South Georgia & Ross Sea. 2nd ed. 2009. (ENG., Illus.). 240p. pap. 25.95 *(978-0-9582916-3-7(2))* Awa Pr. NZL. Dist: Independent Pubs. Group.

Cassidy, William A. Meteorites, Ice, & Antarctica: A Personal Account. 2012. (ENG., Illus.). 364p. pap. 35.99 **(978-1-107-40391-8(X))** Cambridge Univ. Pr.

Committee on Future Science Opportunities in Antarctica and the Southern Ocean & National Research Council. Future Science Opportunities in Antarctica & the Southern Ocean. 2011. (ENG.). 230p. pap. 50.00 **(978-0-309-21469-8(6))** National Academies Pr.

Cook, James. A Voyage Towards the South Pole & Round the World. 2008. 340p. 29.99 *(978-0-554-25453-1(0))* 2008. 356p. 31.99 *(978-0-554-25424-1(7))* 2008. 340p. 28.99 *(978-0-554-34756-1(3))* 2008. 356p. 29.99 *(978-0-554-34727-1(X))* Vol. 2. 2007. (ENG.). 336p. pap. 24.99 *(978-1-4264-9142-9(5))* BiblioBazaar.

—A Voyage Towards the South Pole & Round the World. 2007. (ENG.). 292p. per. *(978-1-4065-1520-6(5))*; 280p. per. *(978-1-4065-1521-3(3))* Dodo Pr.

—A Voyage Towards the South Pole & Round the World. 2007. (ENG.). 232p. per. *(978-1-4068-6381-9(5))*; 220p. per. *(978-1-4068-6382-6(3))* Echo Library.

—A Voyage Towards the South Pole & Round the World Volume 2. 2007. (ENG.). 298p. pap. 21.99 *(978-1-4264-9088-0(7))* BiblioBazaar.

Cowcher, Helen. Antarctica. (VIE & ENG.). 16.95 Milet Publishing.

—Antarctica. 2009. (ENG., Illus.). 40p. (J). (gr. -1-3). pap. 7.99 *(978-0-312-58979-0(4))* Square Fish.

Debenham, Frank. The Voyage of Captain Bellingshausen to the Antarctic Seas 1819-1821 Translated from the Russian. 2010. (Hakluyt Society, Second Ser.). 222p. 69.95 *(978-1-4094-1458-2(2))* Hakluyt Society GBR. Dist: Ashgate Publishing Co.

Debenham, Frank, ed. The Voyage of Captain Bellingshausen to the Antarctic Seas 1819-1821 Translated from the Russian. 2010. (Hakluyt Society, Second Ser.). 298p. 69.95 *(978-1-4094-1457-5(4))* Hakluyt Society GBR. Dist: Ashgate Publishing Co.

—The Voyages of Captain Bellingshausen to the Antarctic Seas 1819-1821: Translated from the Russian. 2010. (Hakluyt Society, Second Ser.). 520p. 120.00 *(978-1-4094-2488-8(X))* Hakluyt Society GBR. Dist: Ashgate Publishing Co.

Dodds, Klaus. The Antarctic: A Very Short Introduction. 2012. (ENG., Illus.). 144p. pap. 11.95 **(978-0-19-969768-7(X))** Oxford Univ. Pr., Inc.

Edwards, Robert F. Antarctica: My Journey North from Antarctica. 2010. 23.65 *(978-1-4269-2075-2(X))* Trafford Publishing.

Ferranti, Helene Smith. Sailing to Antarctica. 2008. (Illus.). ix, 182p. pap. *(978-1-934582-06-0(9))* Back Channel Pr.

Flem-Ath, Rand & Flem-Ath, Rose. Atlantis Beneath the Ice: The Fate of the Lost Continent. 2012. (ENG.). 240p. pap. **(978-1-59143-137-4(9))** Bear & Co.

Fox, William L. Terra Antarctica: Looking into the Emptiest Continent. 2007. (ENG., Illus.). 328p. per. 19.95 *(978-1-59376-148-6(1))* Counterpoint LLC.

Glasberg, Elena. Antarctica as Cultural Critique: The Gendered Politics of Scientific Exploration & Climate Change. 2012. (Critical Studies in Gender, Sexuality, & Culture Ser.). (ENG., Illus.). 208p. 85.00 **(978-0-230-11687-0(6))** Palgrave Macmillan.

Golemansky, V. & Metcheva, R., eds. Bulgarian Antarctic Research: Life Science, Vol. 5. 2006. (Illus.). pap. 69.50 *(978-954-642-263-7(0))* Pensoft Pubs. BGR. Dist: Coronet Bks.

Hooper, Meredith. The Ferocious Summer: Adelie Penguins & the Warming of Antarctica, 1 vol. 2008. (ENG., Illus.). 336p. 26.95 *(978-1-55365-369-1(6)*, Greystone Bks.) D&M Pubs. Inc. CAN. Dist: Perseus-PGW.

James Cook. A Voyage Towards the South Pole & Round the World. l.t. ed. 2007. (ENG.). 352p. pap. 26.99 *(978-1-4264-8968-6(4))* BiblioBazaar.

Kernahan, Amy. Orion Is Upside Down: To the Antarctic in search of Shackleton. 2011. (Illus.). 160p. pap. 20.99 **(978-1-906791-75-9(9))** Arena Bks. GBR. Dist: Lightning Source UK, Ltd.

King, J. C. & Turner, J. Antarctic Meteorology & Climatology. 2007. (Cambridge Atmospheric & Space Science Ser.). (ENG.). 424p. pap. 79.00 *(978-0-521-03984-0(3))* Cambridge Univ. Pr.

Krupnik, Igor, et al. Smithsonian at the Poles: Contributions to International Polar Year Science. 2009. pap. *(978-0-9788460-1-5(X))* Smithsonian Institution Scholarly Pr.

Locken, E. Travel Journal Antarctica. 2009. 192p. pap. 20.95 *(978-0-557-07865-3(2))* Lulu Enterprises Inc.

Lovecraft, Amy Lauren & Eicken, Hajo, eds. North By 2020: Perspectives on Alaska's Changing Social-Ecological Systems. 2011. (ENG., Illus.). 736p. pap. 70.00 *(978-1-60223-142-9(7))* Univ. of Alaska Pr.

Lucas, Mike. Antarctica. 2009. (ENG.). 160p. 60.00 *(978-1-84537-700-7(1))* New Holland Pubs., Ltd. GBR. Dist: National Bk. Network.

McClintock, James. Goodbye Antarctica. 2012. (MacSci Ser.). (ENG., Illus.). 256p. 26.00 **(978-0-230-11245-2(5))** Palgrave Macmillan.

McGregor, Alasdair. Mawson's Huts: An Antarctic Expedition Journal. (Illus.). 194p. pap. *(978-0-86806-653-0(2)*, Hale & Iremonger) GHR Pr., The.

Mulder, Thomas J., ed. Antarctica: Global, Environmental & Economic Issues. 2010. (Series:Arctic Region & Antarctica Issues & Research Ser.). 160.00 *(978-1-60876-014-5(6))* Nova Science Pubs., Inc.

Munz-Krines, Marion. Expeditionen ins Eis: Historische Polarreisen in der Literatur. 2008. (Helicon - Beiträge zur deutschen Literatur Ser.). 240p. pap. 61.95 *(978-3-631-58202-2(1))* Lang, Peter GmbH, Europaischer Verlag der Wissenschaften DEU. Dist: Lang, Peter.

Nicoll, Alastair Vere. Riding the Ice Wind: By Kite & Sledge across Antarctica. 2010. (ENG., Illus.). 272p. 26.00 *(978-1-84885-306-5(8))* I. B. Tauris & Co., Ltd. GBR. Dist: Macmillan.

Ommanney, F. D. South Latitude. 2008. (Illus.). 332p. *(978-1-4437-2596-5(X))* 2006. 328p. per. *(978-1-4067-3758-5(5))* Read Bks. (Hesperides Pr.).

Plenitz, Reinhard, et al, eds. Long-term Environmental Change in Arctic & Antarctic Lakes. 2010. (Developments in Paleoenvironmental Research Ser.). xxx, 562p. pap. 129.00 *(978-90-481-6595-7(4)*, 9048165954) Springer.

Pinnock, Don. Blue Ice: Travels in Antarctica. 2008. (Illus.). 176p. pap. 36.00 *(978-1-77013-013-5(6))* Double Storey Bks. ZAF. Dist: International Publishers Marketing.

Proceedings of the 10th International Symposium on Antarctic Earth Sciences, et al. Antarctica: A Keystone in a Changing World. Cooper, Alan K. et al, eds. 2008. (ENG.). 164p. 38.00 *(978-0-309-11854-5(9))* National Academies Pr.

Riddell, Anna & Triggs, Gillian, eds. Antarctica: Legal & Environmental Challenges for the Future. 2007. (Illus.). 457p. (C). pap. 110.00 *(978-1-905221-09-7(6))* British Institute of International & Comparative Law GBR. Dist: International Specialized Bk. Services.

Riffenburgh, Beau, ed. Encyclopedia of the Antarctic, 2 vols., Set. 2006. (Illus.). 1272p. 445.00 *(978-0-415-97024-2(5))* Routledge.

Rogers, Alex D., et al, eds. Antarctic Ecosystems: An Extreme Environment in a Changing World. 2012. (ENG., Illus.). 564p. 159.95 **(978-1-4051-9840-0(0)**, Wiley-Blackwell) Wiley, John & Sons, Inc.

Rogers, Susan Fox, ed. Antarctica: Life on the Ice. 2007. (Travelers' Tales Guides). (ENG.). 264p. per. 17.95 *(978-1-932361-53-7(7))* Travelers' Tales, Inc.

Rubin, Jeff & Lonely Planet Staff. Antarctica. 4th rev. ed. 2008. (Country Guide Ser.). (ENG., Illus.). 380p. pap. 27.99 *(978-1-74104-549-9(5))* Lonely Planet Pubns.

Steger, Will & Bowermaster, Jon. Crossing Antarctica. 2010. (ENG.). 312p. pap. 15.95 *(978-0-89732-896-8(5))* Menasha Ridge Pr., Inc.

Stewart, John. Antarctica: An Encyclopedia, 2 vols. 2nd rev. ed. 2011. (ENG.). 1771p. 495.00 **(978-0-7864-3590-6(9))** McFarland & Co., Inc. Pubs.

Suparta, Wayan. Remote Sensing of Solar Influence on Antarctic Terrestrial Climate from a GPS Perspective. 2011. (Environmental Science, Engineering & Technology Ser.). 98p. pap. 43.00 *(978-1-61761-317-3(7))* Nova Science Pubs., Inc.

Swan, Robert & Reavill, Gil. The Earth's Last Wilderness: A Quest to Save Antarctica. 2010. (Illus.). 304p. pap. 14.99 *(978-0-7679-3176-2(9))* Broadway Bks.

Thomas, Charles Ward. Ice Is Where You Find It. 2011. 404p. 54.95 **(978-1-258-07960-4(7))** Literary Licensing, LLC.

Torrissen, Bjo Christian. One for the Road. 2008. 400p. pap. 19.00 *(978-1-84799-453-0(9))* Lulu Enterprises Inc.

Triggs, Gillian D., ed. The Antarctic Treaty Regime: Law, Environment & Resources. 2009. (Studies in Polar Research Ser.). (ENG., Illus.). 268p. pap. 36.99 *(978-0-521-10008-3(9))* Cambridge Univ. Pr.

Turley, Charles. The Voyages of Captain Scott. 2009. 448p. 34.99 *(978-1-113-49437-5(9))*; pap. 35.75 *(978-1-113-49436-8(0))* BiblioBazaar.

Walsh, Quentin R. The Whaling Expedition of the Ulysses, 1937-38. Capelotti, P. J., ed. 2010. (New Perspectives on Maritime History & Nautical Archaeology Ser.). (ENG., Illus.). 400p. 34.95 *(978-0-8130-3479-9(5))* Univ. Pr. of Florida.

Weddell, James. A Voyage Towards the South Pole: Performed in the Years 1822-24: Containing an Examination of the Antarctic Sea, & a Visit to Tierra del Fuego. 2011. (Cambridge Library Collection - Travel & Exploration Ser.). (ENG., Illus.). 316p. pap. 28.99 **(978-1-108-04158-4(2))** Cambridge Univ. Pr.

ANTARCTICA—DISCOVERY AND EXPLORATION

see also names of individual exploring expeditions

Amundsen, Roald. Race to the South Pole. 2007. (Great Adventures Ser.). (ENG., Illus.). 256p. 14.95 *(978-88-544-0217-1(6)*, White Star) Rizzoli International Pubns., Inc.

—To the South Pole: An Account of the Norwegian Antarctic Expedition in the Fram, 1910-1912. 2008. *(978-1-934941-39-3(5))* Red & Black Pubs.

Amundsen, Roald E. The South Pole: An Account of the Norwegian Antarctic Expedition in the "Fram", 1910-1912. 2007. 296p. 28.95 *(978-1-4218-3304-0(2))*; (ENG.). 320p. 29.95 *(978-1-4218-3305-7(0))*; (ENG.). 320p. per. 14.95 *(978-1-4218-3405-4(7))*; (ENG.). 296p. per. 13.95 *(978-1-4218-3404-7(9))* 1st World Publishing, Inc. (1st World Library - Literary Society).

—The South Pole: An Account of the Norwegian Antarctic Expedition in the "Fram", 1910-1912. 2007. (Large Print Ser.). lib. bdg. 30.00 *(978-1-58287-925-3(7))*; lib. bdg. 27.00 *(978-1-58287-436-4(0))* North Bks.

Aston, Felicity. Call of the White: Taking the World to the South Pole. 2012. (ENG., Illus.). 320p. pap. 13.95 **(978-1-84953-134-4(X))** Summerdale Pubs. GBR. Dist: Independent Pubs. Group.

Baughman, T. H. Pilgrims on the Ice: Robert Falcon Scott's First Antarctic Expedition. 2008. (ENG., Illus.). 352p. pap. 18.95 *(978-0-8032-1639-6(4)*, Bison Bks.) Univ. of Nebraska Pr.

—Shackleton of the Antarctic. 2009. (ENG., Illus.). 136p. pap. 12.95 *(978-0-8032-1944-1(X)*, Bison Bks.) Univ. of Nebraska Pr.

Beals, Herbert K., et al, eds. Four Travel Journals: The Americas, Antarctica & Africa, 1775-1874. 2008. (Hakluyt Society, Third Series: 18 Ser.). (Illus.). 414p. 99.95 *(978-0-904180-90-9(5))* Hakluyt Society GBR. Dist: Ashgate Publishing Co.

Bergstrom, D. M., et al, eds. Trends in Antarctic Terrestrial & Limnetic Ecosystems: Antarctica as a Global Indicator. 2010. (ENG.). xiv, 369p. pap. 159.00 *(978-90-481-7327-3(2)*, 9048173272) Springer.

Blackhall, Sue. Scott of the Antarctic: We Shall Die Like Gentlemen. 2012. (Illus.). 224p. 39.95 **(978-1-84884-664-7(9))** Pen & Sword Bks. Ltd. GBR. Dist: Casemate Pubs. & Bk. Distributors, LLC.

Books. A Voyage of Discovery & Research in the Southern & Antarctic Regions During the Years 1839-1843. 2010. (Illus.). 176p. pap. 19.99 *(978-1-154-17676-6(2))* General Bks. LLC.

Boothe, Joan N. The Storied Ice: Exploration, Discovery, & Adventure in Antarctica's Peninsula Region. 2011. (ENG., Illus.). 372p. pap. 24.95 **(978-1-58790-218-5(4))** Regent Pr.

Bown, Stephen. The Last Viking: The Life of Roald Amundsen. 2012. (Merloyd Lawrence Book Ser.). (ENG., Illus.). 320p. 26.00 **(978-0-306-82067-0(6))** Da Capo Pr., Inc.

Bryan, Rorke. Ordeal by Ice: Ships of the Antarctic, 1 vol. 2011. (ENG.). 554p. 45.00 **(978-1-57409-312-4(6))** Sheridan Hse., Inc.

Bull, Colin. Innocents in the Dry Valleys: An Account of the Victoria University of Wellington Antarctic Expedition, 1958-59. 2010. (Illus.). 267p. pap. 25.00 *(978-1-60223-071-2(4))* Univ. of Alaska Pr.

Cherry-Garrard, Apsley. The Worst Journey in the World. 2009. 712p. 36.99 *(978-0-559-08653-3(9))*; 40.99 *(978-0-559-08642-7(3))*; pap. 48.75 *(978-0-559-08651-9(2))*; pap. 49.75 *(978-0-559-08645-8(8))* BiblioBazaar.

—The Worst Journey in the World. 2008. (Twelve-Point Ser.). lib. bdg. 30.00 *(978-1-58287-471-5(9))* North Bks.

—The Worst Journey in the World: Antarctic 1910-1913. 2007. (ENG.). 436p. per. *(978-1-4068-4534-1(5))* Echo Library.

—The Worst Journey in the World: With Scott in Antarctica 1910-1913. 2010. (ENG.). 528p. pap. 16.95 *(978-0-486-47732-9(0))* Dover Pubns., Inc.

Cox, Lynne. South with the Sun: Roald Amundsen, His Polar Explorations, & the Quest for Discovery. 2012. (ENG.). 320p. pap. 15.95 **(978-0-547-90578-5(5)**, Mariner Bks.) Houghton Mifflin Harcourt Trade & Reference Pubs.

—South with the Sun: Roald Amundsen, His Polar Explorations, & the Quest for Discovery. 2011. (ENG., Illus.). 320p. 26.00 *(978-0-307-59340-5(1)*, Knopf) Knopf Doubleday Publishing Group.

Crane, David. Scott of the Antarctic: A Biography. 2007. (Vintage Ser.). (ENG., Illus.). 608p. pap. 16.95 *(978-1-4000-3141-2(9)*, Vintage) Knopf Doubleday Publishing Group.

Encyclopaedia Britannica, Inc., compiled by. Science on Ice. 2008. 49.95 *(978-1-59339-651-0(1))* Encyclopaedia Britannica, Inc.

Evans, Edward R. G. R. South with Scott. 2008. 264p. 25.99 *(978-0-554-33179-9(9))* 2008. 264p. 28.99 *(978-0-554-23876-0(4))* 2007. 236p. pap. 20.99 *(978-1-4264-5111-9(3))* 2007. 262p. pap. 23.99 *(978-1-4264-5412-7(0))* BiblioBazaar.

—South with Scott. 2009. 232p. pap. *(978-1-4099-6291-5(1))* Dodo Pr.

Evans, Rear-Admiral E. South with Scott. 2006. pap. *(978-1-4068-0123-1(2))* Echo Library.

Faure, Gunter & Mensing, Teresa M. The Transantarctic Mountains: Rocks, Ice, Meteorites & Water. 2010. (Illus.). xxvi, 804p. 229.00 *(978-1-4020-8406-5(4)*, 1402084064) Springer.

Florindo, Fabio & Siegert, Martin, eds. Antarctic Climate Evolution. 2008. (Developments in Earth & Environmental Sciences Ser.: 8). (ENG., Illus.). 606p. 155.00 *(978-0-444-52847-6(4)*, Elsevier Science) Elsevier Science & Technology Bks.

Green, Bill. Water, Ice & Stone: Science & Memory on the Antarctic Lakes. 2008. (ENG., Illus.). 300p. reprint ed. pap. 15.95 *(978-1-934137-08-6(1))* Bellevue Literary Pr.

Griffiths, Tom. Slicing the Silence: Voyaging to Antarctica. 2010. (Illus.). 408p. pap. 20.00 *(978-0-674-03470-9(8))* Harvard Univ. Pr.

Gurney, Alan. Below the Convergence: Voyages Toward Antarctica, 1699-1839. 2007. (ENG., Illus.). 336p. per. 15.95 *(978-0-393-32904-9(6)*, 32904) Norton, W. W. & Co., Inc.

Haddelsey, Stephen. Ice Captain: The Life of the Endurance Expedition's Other Hero, Joseph Russell Stenhouse. 2008. (ENG., Illus.). 256p. 46.95 *(978-0-7509-4348-2(3))* History Pr. Ltd., The GBR. Dist: Independent Pubs. Group.

Hempleman-Adams, David, et al. The Heart of the Great Alone: Scott, Shackleton & Antarctic Photography. 2009. (ENG., Illus.). 240p. 47.50 *(978-1-60819-007-2(2))* Bloomsbury Publishing.

Hooper, Meredith. The Longest Winter: Scott's Other Heroes. 2011. (ENG., Illus.). 320p. 26.00 *(978-1-58243-762-0(9)*, Counterpoint) Counterpoint LLC.

—The Longest Winter: Scott's Other Heroes. 2010. (ENG.). 320p. 19.95 *(978-1-84854-306-5(9))*; (Illus.). 358p. 29.95 *(978-0-7195-9580-6(0))* Murray, John GBR. Dist: Independent Pubs. Group.

Huntford, Roland. Race for the South Pole: The Expedition Diaries of Scott & Amundsen. 2010. (ENG., Illus.). 352p. 27.95 *(978-1-4411-6982-2(2))* Continuum International Publishing Group, Ltd. GBR. Dist: National Bk. Network.

Huntford Roland. Race for the South Pole: The Expedition Diaries of Scott & Amundsen. 2011. (ENG., Illus.). 352p. pap. 16.95 *(978-1-4411-2667-2(8))* Continuum International Publishing Group, Ltd. GBR. Dist: National Bk. Network.

Klink, Amyr & Norton, Thomas H. Endless Sea: Alone Around Antarctica — As Far South As a Boat Can Sail. Norton, Thomas H., tr. from POR. 2008. (ENG., Illus.). 272p. pap. 19.95 *(978-1-57409-259-2(6))* Sheridan Hse., Inc.

Langner, Rainer-K. Scott & Amundsen: Duel in the Ice. 2007. (ENG., Illus.). 232p. 24.95 *(978-1-905791-08-8(9))* Haus Publishing GBR. Dist: Consortium Bk. Sales & Distribution.

Larson, Edward J. An Empire of Ice: Scott, Shackleton, & the Heroic Age of Antarctic Science. 2011. (Illus.). 326p. 28.00 *(978-0-300-15408-5(9))* Yale Univ. Pr.

Liggett, Daniela Haase. Tourism in the Antarctic. 2009. 244p. pap. *(978-3-639-12797-3(8))* VDM Verlag Dr. Mueller e.K.

Limb, Sue. Captain Oates. Cordingley, Patrick, ed. 2009. (Illus.). 256p. pap. 25.99 *(978-1-84884-088-1(8))* Pen & Sword Bks. Ltd. GBR. Dist: Casemate Pubs. & Bk. Distributors, LLC.

Lipton, David L. A World Ethnohistory of the Antarctic Region During the Early Modern Era. 2010. pap. 9.95 *(978-0-7414-5831-5(4))* Infinity Publishing.

MacPhee, Ross D. E. Race to the End: Amundsen, Scott, & the Attainment of the South Pole. 2010. (ENG., Illus.). 286p. 27.95 *(978-1-4027-7029-6(4)*, Sterling Innovation) Sterling Publishing Co., Inc.

Mawson, Douglas & Fiennes, Ranulph. The Home of the Blizzard: A True Story of Antarctic Survival. 2007. (Illus.). 484p. pap. 14.95 *(978-1-60239-144-4(0))* Skyhorse Publishing Co., Inc.

Maynard, Jeff. Wings of Ice: The Mystery of the Polar Air Race. 2010. (ENG., Illus.). 304p. 19.95 *(978-1-74166-934-3(0))* Random Hse. Australia AUS. Dist: Independent Pubs. Group.

Paine, M L, ed. Footsteps on the Ice: The Antarctic Diaries of Stuart D. Paine, Second Byrd Expedition. 2007. (ENG., Illus.). 400p. (gr. 9). 34.95 *(978-0-8262-1741-7(9))* Univ. of Missouri Pr.

Pennington, Rochelle & Pennington, Nicholas. The Endurance. 2007. (Illus.). 63p. 16.95 *(978-0-9740810-3-8(5))* Pathways Pr.

Ponting, Jess. Consuming Nirvan. 2009. 230p. pap. *(978-3-639-12602-0(5))* VDM Verlag Dr. Mueller e.K.

Principles of Environmental Stewardship for the Exploration and Study of Subglacial Environments Committee, et al, contrib. by. Exploration of Antarctic Subglacial Aquatic Environments: Environmental & Scientific Stewardship. 2007. (ENG., Illus.). 162p. pap. 38.25 *(978-0-309-10635-1(4))* National Academies Pr.

Rabassa, Jorge & Borla, Maria Laura, eds. Antarctic Peninsula & Tierra del Fuego: 100 Years of Swedish-Argentine Scientific Cooperation at the End of the World. 2006. (ENG., Illus.). 214p. 135.95 *(978-0-415-41379-4(6)*, Taylor & Francis) Taylor & Francis Group GBR. Dist: Taylor & Francis Group.

Raeside, Adrian. Return to Antarctica: The Amazing Adventure of Sir Charles Wright on Robert Scott's Journey to the South Pole. 2011. (ENG., Illus.). 336p. pap. 22.95 *(978-0-470-93215-5(5)*, Wiley) Wiley, John & Sons, Inc.

Rees, Jasper & Fiennes, Ranulph. Blizzard: Race to the Pole. 2006. (ENG., Illus.). 288p. 29.95 *(978-0-563-49326-6(7))* BBC Worldwide GBR. Dist: Independent Pubs. Group.

Robert, Headland. A Chronology of Antarctic Exploration. 2nd rev. ed. 2008. (Illus.). 608p. 140.00 *(978-0-521-82852-9(X))* Cambridge Univ. Pr.

Roberts, Leslie Carol. The Entire Earth & Sky: Views on Antarctica. 2008. (ENG., Illus.). 322p. 24.95 *(978-0-8032-1617-4(3))* Univ. of Nebraska Pr.

Roberts, Peder. The European Antarctic: Science & Strategy in Scandinavia & the British Empire. 2011. (Palgrave Studies in Cultural & Intellectual History Ser.). (ENG., Illus.). 284p. 85.00 *(978-0-230-11591-0(8))* Palgrave Macmillan.

Ross, James Clark. A Voyage of Discovery & Research in the Southern & Antarctic Regions During the Years 1839-1843. 2010. (Illus.). 184p. pap. 19.99 *(978-1-154-13926-6(3))* 2009. 204p. pap. 28.85 *(978-1-150-05934-6(6))* General Bks. LLC.

—A Voyage of Discovery & Research in the Southern & Antarctic Regions, During the Years 1839-43. 2010. 496p. pap. 38.75 *(978-1-177-79766-5(6))*; 504p. pap. 38.75 *(978-1-146-74679-3(2))*; 464p. pap. 37.75 *(978-1-146-04981-8(1))*; 430p. pap. 35.75 *(978-1-144-78736-1(X))*; 432p. pap. 35.75 *(978-1-142-21829-4(5))* BiblioBazaar.

—A Voyage of Discovery & Research in the Southern & Antarctic Regions, During the Years 1839-43. 2011. (Cambridge Library Collection - Travel & Exploration Ser.). (ENG.). 478p. pap. 35.99 *(978-1-108-03085-4(8))*; 504p. pap. 37.99 *(978-1-108-03086-1(6))* Cambridge Univ. Pr.

—A Voyage of Discovery & Research in the Southern & Antarctic Regions, During the Years 1839-43. 2010. 178p. pap. 26.44 *(978-1-152-10785-4(2))* General Bks. LLC.

—A Voyage of Discovery & Research in the Southern & Antarctic Regions V1: During the Years 1839-43 (1847) 424p. 2010. 41.56 **(978-1-164-79657-2(7))** 2010. pap. 29.56 **(978-1-164-55633-6(9))** 2008. 51.95 *(978-1-4369-9770-6(4))* 2008. pap. 36.95 *(978-1-4367-5745-4(2))* Kessinger Publishing, LLC.

Ross, Sir James Clark. A Voyage of Discovery & Research in the Southern & Antarctic Regions, During the Years 1839-43. 2010. 186p. pap. 27.09 *(978-1-154-24919-4(0))* 2009. 208p. pap. 29.22 *(978-1-150-13842-3(4))* General Bks. LLC.

Sanderson, Marie. Griffith Taylor: Antarctic Scientist & Pioneer Geographer, No. 145. 218p. *(978-0-88629-068-9(6))* McGill-Queen's Univ. Pr.

Scott, Angela & Scott, Jonathan. Antarctica: Exploring a Fragile Eden. 2008. (ENG., Illus.). 256p. 39.95 *(978-0-00-718345-6(3))* HarperCollins Pubs. Ltd. GBR. Dist: Independent Pubs. Group.

Scott, Robert Falcon. Journals: Captain Scott's Last Expedition. Jones, Max, ed. 2008. (Oxford World's Classics Ser.). (ENG., Illus.). 592p. pap. 17.95 *(978-0-19-953680-1(5))* Oxford Univ. Pr., Inc.

Sever, George. Edward Wilson of the Antarctic. 2008. 396p. *(978-1-4437-2329-9(0))* 2006. 392p. per. *(978-1-4067-2083-9(6))* Read Bks. (Hesperides Pr.).

Shackleton, E. H. & David, T. W. Edgeworth. The Heart of the Antarctic: Being the Story of the British Antarctic. 2007. (ENG.). 544p. per. 42.95 *(978-1-4304-4235-6(2))* Kessinger Publishing, LLC.

Shackleton, Ernest. South: The Last Antarctic Expedition of Shackleton & the Endurance. 2nd ed. 2008. (Explorers Club Classics Ser.). (ENG., Illus.). 488p. pap. 19.95 *(978-1-59921-323-1(0)*, Lyons Pr.) Globe Pequot Pr., The.

—South! The Story of Shackleton's Last Expedition, 1914-1917. 2009. (Stanfords Travel Classics Ser.). 336p. pap. 14.95 *(978-1-906780-04-3(8))* Beaufoy, John Publishing GBR. Dist: Midpoint Trade Bks., Inc.

Siegert, Martin J., et al. Antarctic Subglacial Aquatic Enviroments. 2011. *(978-0-87590-482-5(3))* American Geophysical Union.

Smith, Michael. Great Endeavour: Ireland's Antarctic Explorers. 2010. (ENG., Illus.). 258p. 54.95 *(978-1-84889-023-7(0))* Collins Pr., The IRL. Dist: Dufour Editions, Inc.

—I Am Just Going Outside: Captain Oates, Antarctic Tragedy. 2006. (ENG., Illus.). 320p. pap. 32.50 *(978-1-86227-355-9(3))* History Pr. Ltd.,The GBR. Dist: Independent Pubs. Group.

—Tom Crean: An Illustrated Life - Unsung Hero of the Scott & Shackleton Expeditions. 2011. (ENG., Illus.). 176p. pap. 22.95 *(978-1-84889-119-7(9))* Collins Pr., The IRL. Dist: Dufour Editions, Inc.

—Tom Crean an Illustrated Life: Unsung Hero of the Scott & Shackleton Expeditions. 2007. (ENG., Illus.). 200p. 55.95 *(978-1-905172-18-4(4))* Collins Pr., The IRL. Dist: Dufour Editions, Inc.

Stephenson, Jon. Crevasse Roulette: The First Trans-Antarctic Crossing 1957-58. 2009. (Illus.). 192p. 49.95 *(978-1-877058-66-0(1))* Rosenberg Publishing Pty, Ltd. AUS. Dist: International Specialized Bk. Services.

Tait, Stephen. Shambles. 2009. 204p. 25.50 *(978-1-60860-044-1(0)*, Strategic Bk. Publishing) AEG Literary Publishing Services, Inc.

Tyler-Lewis, Kelly. The Lost Men: The Harrowing Saga of Shackleton's Ross Sea Party. 2007. (ENG., Illus.). 384p. (gr. 12-18). 15.00 *(978-0-14-303851-1(6)*, Penguin (Non-Classics)) Penguin Group (USA) Inc.

Watson, Nigel. Still Life: Inside the Antarctic Huts of Scott & Shackleton. 2012. (ENG., Illus.). 224p. 50.00 ***(978-1-74196-739-5(2))*** Murdoch Bks. Pty Ltd. AUS. Dist: Independent Pubs. Group.

Waxman, Malcolm & Porter, Malcolm. Atlas of South America & Antarctica. 2010. (Illus.). 48p. (YA). pap. 11.75 *(978-1-4358-9116-6(3)*, Rosen Central) Rosen Publishing Group, Inc., The.

Wilson, David M. The Lost Photographs of Captain Scott: Unseen Images from the Legendary Antarctic Expedition. 2011. (ENG., Illus.). 192p. 35.00 *(978-0-316-17350-1(0))* Little Brown & Co.

Worsley, Frank Arthur. Shackletons Expedition in die Antarktis. (GER.). *(978-3-548-35988-5(4))* Ullstein-Taschenbuch-Verlag DEU. Dist: International Bk. Import Service, Inc.

Worsley, Henry. In Shackleton's Footsteps: A Return to the Heart of the Antarctic. 2011. (Illus.). 256p. 24.95 *(978-0-7627-7763-1(X)*, Lyons Pr.) Globe Pequot Pr., The.

ANTARCTICA—INTERNATIONAL STATUS

Berkman, Paul Arthur. Science Diplomacy: Science, Antarctica, & the Governance of International Spaces. 2011. *(978-1-935623-06-9(0))* Smithsonian Institution Scholarly Pr.

Caporaso Gottlieb, Giovanni. Antarcticland, una Nazione un Pianeta. 2009. (ITA.). 102p. pap. 42.95 *(978-0-557-04423-8(5))* Lulu Enterprises Inc.

Hemmings, Alan D., et al. Antarctic Security in the Twenty-First Century: Legal & Policy Perspectives. 2012. E-Book ***(978-0-203-12100-9(7))*** Routledge.

Krüger, Niels. Anwendbarkeit von Umweltschutzverträgen in der Antarktis: The Applicability of Environmental Treaties in the Antarctic. 2011. (GER.). xxii, 360p. ***(978-3-540-67058-2(0))*** Springer Singapore Pte. Ltd.

Orrego-Vicuna, Francisco, ed. Antarctic Resources Policy: Scientific, Legal & Political Issues. 2009. (ENG., Illus.). 344p. pap. 46.00 *(978-0-521-10550-7(1))* Cambridge Univ. Pr.

Parsons, Anthony, ed. Antarctica: the Next Decade: Report of a Group Study Chaired by Sir Anthony Parsons. 2009. (Studies in Polar Research Ser.). (ENG.). 180p. pap. 39.99 *(978-0-521-10403-6(3))* Cambridge Univ. Pr.

Resources for the Future Staff, contrib. by. The Seventh Continent: Antarctica in a Resource Age, 7 vols. 2011. (RFF Global Environment & Development Set Ser.). (ENG.). 315p. 99.95 *(978-1-61726-048-3(7)*, RFF Pr.) Earthscan LLC.

Vicuna, Francisco Orrego. Antarctic Mineral Exploitation: The Emerging Legal Framework. 2009. (Studies in Polar Research Ser.). (ENG.). 636p. pap. 79.00 *(978-0-521-10007-6(0))* Cambridge Univ. Pr.

ANTARCTICA—PICTORIAL WORKS

Copeland, Sebastian. Antarctica: The Global Warning. 2007. (ENG., Illus.). 160p. 55.00 *(978-1-933784-19-9(9)*, Earth Aware Editions) Mandala Publishing.

Dick, Laurent. Antarctica: The Last Continent. 2009. (ENG., Illus.). 264p. *(978-90-209-7977-0(9)*, Lannoo Pubs. (Acc)) Antique Collectors' Club.

Faber. Infinite Ice Traversing the Arctic & the Alps from 1860 to the Present. 2009. (ENG.). 112p. 45.00 *(978-3-7757-2253-7(X))* Hatje Cantz Verlag GmbH & Co KG DEU. Dist: D.A.P./Distributed Art Pubs.

Finlay, Colin, photos by. 12° N x 23° E, 64° S x 60° E: Sudan, Antarctica. 2007. 22p. 75.00 *(978-0-9801747-0-0(8))*; (ENG.). pap. 10.00 *(978-0-9801747-1-7(6))* Definitive Stories.

Hempleman-Adams, David, et al. The Heart of the Great Alone: Scott, Shackleton & Antarctic Photography. 2009. (ENG., Illus.). 240p. 47.50 *(978-1-60819-007-2(2))* Bloomsbury Publishing.

Klipper, Stuart & Chronicle Books Staff. Antarctic: From the Circle to the Pole. 2008. (ENG., Illus.). 175p. 40.00 *(978-0-8118-6229-5(1))* Chronicle Bks. LLC.

Martin, James, photos by. Planet Ice: A Climate for Change. 2009. (ENG., Illus.). 176p. 39.95 *(978-1-59485-085-1(2)*, Braided River) Mountaineers Bks., The.

Masó, Mireya. Antarctica: Time of Change. 2010. (Illus.). 128p. pap. *(978-84-92861-26-2(6))* Actar Birkhauser Distribution.

McGonigal, David, ed. Antarctica: Secrets of the Southern Continent. 2008. (ENG., Illus.). 400p. 59.95 *(978-1-55407-398-6(7))* Firefly Bks., Ltd.

Miller, Paul D. The Book of Ice. 2011. (ENG., Illus.). 128p. 29.95 *(978-1-935613-14-5(6))* Batty, Mark Pub., LLC.

Monteath, Colin & White Star Publishing Staff. Vanishing Wilderness of Antarctica. 2011. (ENG., Illus.). 272p. 24.95 *(978-88-544-0487-8(X))* White Star ITA. Dist: Sterling Publishing Co., Inc.

Pietromarchi, Bartolomeo, ed. Antarctica: [in English & Italian]. 2008. 176p. 57.50 *(978-88-370-6337-5(7))* Electa ITA. Dist: Trans-Atlantic Pubns., Inc.

Vermeer, Jan & Essen, Frieda van. Antarctica. 2009. (ENG., Illus.). 300p. *(978-90-78964-10-0(3)*, Thieme Art (Acc)) Antique Collectors' Club.

Watson, Nigel. Still Life: Inside the Antarctic Huts of Scott & Shackleton. 2012. (ENG., Illus.). 224p. 50.00 ***(978-1-74196-739-5(2))*** Murdoch Bks. Pty Ltd. AUS. Dist: Independent Pubs. Group.

ANTEDILUVIAN ANIMALS

see Animals, Fossil

ANTELOPES

see also Pronghorn Antelope

Shah, Anup & Shah, Manoj. African Odyssey: 365 Days. 2007. (ENG., Illus.). 744p. 32.50 *(978-0-8109-9396-9(1))* Abrams.

ANTENNAS (ELECTRONICS)

see also Microwave Antennas; Radio—Antennas; Radio Telescopes

Abayneh, Esuballew. Dual Band Patch Antennas for Mobile Phone. 2009. 124p. pap. *(978-3-639-18690-1(7))* VDM Verlag Dr. Mueller e.K.

Abdul Aziz, Muhammad Ezanuddin, et al. Development of a Complementary Split Ring Resonator Antenn. 2011. 144p. pap. ***(978-3-8443-2832-5(7))*** Lambert Academic Publishing.

Aberle, James T. & Loepsinger-Romak, Robert. Antennas with Non-Foster Matching Networks. 2007. (Synthesis Lectures on Antennas & Propagation Ser.). (Illus.). 100p. per. 35.00 *(978-1-59829-102-5(5))* Morgan & Claypool Pubs.

Abumazwed, Ahmed. Half Cylindrical Dielectric Resonator Antenn. 2010. 100p. pap. *(978-3-8383-7418-5(5))* Lambert Academic Publishing.

Al-Ka&apos, et al. Wireless Communication Systems. 2010. 200p. pap. *(978-3-8383-1085-5(3))* Lambert Academic Publishing.

Alexiou, Angeliki, et al, eds. Smart Antennas for Next Generation Wireless Systems. 2007. 192p. pap. 29.00 *(978-977-454-019-6(0))* Hindawi Publishing Corp.

Anderson, Theodore. Plasma Antennas. 2011. 220p. 139.00 ***(978-1-60807-143-2(X))*** Artech Hse., Inc.

Angell, Thomas S. & Kirsch, Andreas. Optimization Methods in Electromagnetic Radiation. 2012. (Springer Monographs in Mathematics Ser.). (ENG., Illus.). 331p. pap. 109.00 *(978-1-4419-1914-4(7)*, 1441919147) Springer.

Antenna Measurement Techniques Association (AMTA) Staff, compiled by. Annual Meeting & Symposium of the Antenna Measurement Techniques Association. 2007. 459p. pap. 156.00 *(978-1-60423-724-5(4))* Curran Assocs., Inc.

—Antenna Measurement Techniques Association 24th Annual Meeting & Symposium 2002. 2007. 544p. pap. 156.00 *(978-1-60423-725-2(2))* Curran Assocs., Inc.

—Antenna Measurement Techniques Association 25th Annual Meeting & Symposium 2003. 2007. 567p. pap. 156.00 *(978-1-60423-657-6(4))* Curran Assocs., Inc.

—26th Annual Meeting & Symposium of the Antenna Measurement Techniques Association 2004 (AMTA 2004) 2007. 556p. pap. 156.00 *(978-1-60423-497-8(0))* Curran Assocs., Inc.

—27th Annual Meeting & Symposium of the Antenna Measurement Techniques Association (AMTA 2005) 2007. 501p. pap. 156.00 *(978-1-60423-498-5(9))* Curran Assocs., Inc.

Antolovic, Danko. Radiolocation in Ubiquitous Wireless Communication. 2010. (Illus.). xi, 183p. 129.00 *(978-1-4419-1631-0(8)*, 1441916318) Springer.

Araque Quijano, Javier Leonardo. Design of Compact Reconfigurable Antennas for Mobile Terminals. 2010. 72p. pap. *(978-3-8383-6341-7(8))* Lambert Academic Publishing.

Baars, Jacob W. M. The Paraboloidal Reflector Antenna in Radio Astronomy & Communication: Theory & Practice. 2007. (Astrophysics & Space Science Library: Vol. 348). (Illus.). 253p. 199.00 incl. cd-rom *(978-0-387-69733-8(0))* Springer.

Balanis, Constantine. Mmic Transmission Lines, Circuits & Antennas. 2008. 164p. per. 44.95 *(978-1-934939-99-4(4))* Wexford College Pr.

Balanis, Constantine A. Modern Antenna Handbook. 2007. 950p. 185.00 *(978-0-470-03638-9(9))*; 185.00 *(978-0-470-03635-8(4))* Wiley, John & Sons, Inc. (Wiley-Interscience).

Balanis, Constantine A., ed. Modern Antenna Handbook. 2008. (ENG., Illus.). 1680p. 216.00 *(978-0-470-03634-1(6)*, Wiley-Interscience) Wiley, John & Sons, Inc.

Balanis, Constantine A. & Ioannides, Panayiotis I. Introduction to Smart Antennas. 2007. (Synthesis Lectures on Antennas Ser.). (Illus.). 100p. per. 40.00 *(978-1-59829-176-6(9))* Morgan & Claypool Pubs.

Bancroft, Randy. Microstrip & Printed Antenna Design. 2nd ed. 2008. (Illus.). 320p. *(978-1-891121-73-9(1))* SciTech Publishing, Inc.

Barbagallo, Sebastiano. Synthesis of Novel Metamaterials. 2008. 92p. per. *(978-3-8364-5804-7(7))* VDM Verlag Dr. Mueller e.K.

Bashir, Saiid & Ismail Shah, Syed. Enabling High Data Rate Communication. 2011. 124p. pap. ***(978-3-8443-1183-9(1))*** Lambert Academic Publishing.

Baumann, Carl E., et al, eds. Ultra-Wideband, Short-Pulse Electromagnetics 3. 2011. (ENG.). 532p. pap. 242.00 *(978-1-4419-3276-1(3)*, 1441932763) Springer.

Bégaud, Xavier. Ultra Wide Band Antennas. 2011. (Iste Ser.: 508). (ENG., Illus.). xii, 273p. 132.00 *(978-1-84821-232-9(1)*, Wiley-ISTE) Wiley, John & Sons, Inc.

Bernhard, Jennifer T. Reconfigurable Antennas. 2007. (Synthesis Lectures on Antennas & Propagation Ser.). 100p. pap. 35.00 *(978-1-59829-026-4(6))* Morgan & Claypool Pubs.

Best, Richard. Antennas for Wireless Communication. 2010. 350p. 74.95 *(978-0-471-35674-5(3)*, Wiley-Interscience) Wiley, John & Sons, Inc.

Best, Richard & Best, Steven R. Advances in Electrically Small Antennas. 2014. (ENG., Illus.). 416p. 79.95 *(978-0-471-68158-8(X)*, Wiley-IEEE Pr.) Wiley, John & Sons, Inc.

Blake, Lamont V. Antennas. 3rd ed. 2009. (Illus.). 650p. *(978-1-891121-78-4(2))* SciTech Publishing, Inc.

Blake, Lamont V. & Long, Maurice W. Antennas: Fundamentals, Design, Measurement. 2009. *(978-1-891121-79-1(0))* SciTech Publishing, Inc.

Boardman, Allan, et al. Metamaterials: Fundamentals & Applications IV. 2011. (Proceedings of SPIE Ser.). 306p. pap. 160.00 ***(978-0-8194-8703-2(1))*** SPIE.

Booth, Nigel, M0cvo. Beyond the Dipole. 2008. 65p. pap. 28.50 *(978-1-4092-2459-4(7))* Lulu Enterprises Inc.

Chandran, Sathish, ed. Adaptive Antenna Arrays: Trends & Applications. 2012. (Signals & Communication Technology Ser.). (ENG., Illus.). xii, 660p. pap. 319.00 *(978-3-642-05775-5(6)*, 3642057756) Springer.

Chen, Xiaodong. Ultrawideband Antennas: Design & Applications. 2010. (Illus.). 212p. 90.00 *(978-1-84816-491-8(2))* World Scientific Publishing Co., Inc.

Chen, Zhi Ning, ed. Antennas for Portable Devices. 2007. (ENG., Illus.). 304p. 130.00 *(978-0-470-03073-8(9)*, Wiley) Wiley, John & Sons, Inc.

Chen, Zhi Ning, et al. Antennas for Base Stations: In Wireless Communications. 2009. (ENG., Illus.). 412p. 99.95 *(978-0-07-161288-3(2)*, 0071612882) McGraw-Hill Professional Publishing.

Choi, Jinho. Optimal Combining & Detection: Statistical Signal Processing for Communications. 2010. (ENG., Illus.). 348p. 99.00 *(978-0-521-51760-7(5))* Cambridge Univ. Pr.

Christodoulou, Christos & Blaunstein, Nathan. Radio Propagation & Adaptive Antennas for Wireless Communication Links: Terrestrial, Atmospheric & Ionospheric. 2006. (Wiley Series in Microwave & Optical Engineering Ser.: 193). (ENG., Illus.). 614p. 168.00 *(978-0-471-25121-7(6)*, Wiley-Interscience) Wiley, John & Sons, Inc.

Christodoulou, Christos & Martinez Ramon, Manuel. Support Vector Machines for Antenna Array Processing & Electromagnetics. 2006. (Synthesis Lectures on Computational Electromagnetics Ser.). 120p. pap. 40.00 *(978-1-59829-024-0(X))* Morgan & Claypool Pubs.

Christodoulou, Christos G. Reconfigurable Antennas & Their Applications. 2013. (Wiley Series in Microwave & Optical Engineering Ser.: 228). (ENG.). 450p. 130.00 *(978-0-470-63343-4(3)*, Wiley) Wiley, John & Sons, Inc.

Costa, Nelson & Haykin, Simon. Multiple-Input Multiple-Output Channel Models: Theory & Practice. 2010. (Adaptive & Learning Systems for Signal Processing, Communications & Control Ser.: 65). (ENG., Illus.). 229p. 104.00 *(978-0-470-39983-5(X)*, Wiley-Interscience) Wiley, John & Sons, Inc.

Cram101 Textbook Reviews. Outlines & Highlights for Antenna Theory Analysis & Design by Balanis, Isbn: 0471592684. 2011. 200p. pap. 30.95 ***(978-1-61830-007-2(5))*** Cram101 Inc.

Daso, Don. Antenna Towers for Radio Amateurs: A Guide for Design, Installation & Construction. 2010. (Illus.). ***(978-0-87259-094-6(1))*** American Radio Relay League, Inc.

de Schweinitz, David & De Schweinitz, David. Design of a Switched-Beam Scanning Parasitic Array. 2011. 96p. pap. ***(978-3-8433-7937-3(8))*** Lambert Academic Publishing.

DeFlavlis, Franco, et al. Multi-Antenna Systems for MIMO Communications. Balanis, Constantine, ed. 2008. (Synthesis Lectures on Antennas & Propagation Ser.). (Illus.). 100p. pap. 50.00 *(978-1-59829-088-2(6))* Morgan & Claypool Pubs.

Drabowitch, S., et al. Modern Antennas. 2nd ed. 2010. (ENG.). xx, 689p. pap. 139.00 *(978-1-4419-5271-4(3)*, 1441952713) Springer.

Dybdal, Robert. Communication Satellite Antennas: System Architecture, Technology, & Evaluation. 2009. (ENG., Illus.). 340p. 99.95 *(978-0-07-160918-0(0)*, 0071609180) McGraw-Hill Professional Publishing.

Elmezughi, Abdurrezagh S. & S. T. Rowe, Wayne. Broadband Microstrip Patch Antennas. 2010. 120p. pap. *(978-3-639-27214-7(5))* VDM Verlag Dr. Mueller e.K.

Elsherbeni, Atef Z. & Demir, Veysel. The Finite-Difference Time-Domain Method for Electromagnetics with MATLAB Simulations. 2008. (Illus.). xxvii, 425p. *(978-1-891121-71-5(5))* SciTech Publishing, Inc.

Feng, Zhenghe & Sun, Jiawen. 2007 International Conference on Microwave & Millimeter Wave Technology. 2007. pap. 340.00 *(978-1-4244-1048-4(7)*, 07EX1705) IEEE.

Fenn, Alan J. Adaptive Antennas & Phased Arrays for Radar & Communications. 2007. (Artech House Radar Library). (Illus.). 394p. 159.00 *(978-1-59693-273-9(2))* Artech Hse., Inc.

Ferrero, Albert I., ed. Antennas: Parameters, Models & Applications. 2009. (Illus.). xiii, 320p. 139.00 *(978-1-60692-463-1(X))* Nova Science Pubs., Inc.

Fikioris, George J. Mellin-Transform for Integral Evaluation: Introduction & Applications for Electromagnetics. 2007. (Synthesis Lectures on Computational Electromagnetics Ser.). (Illus.). 100p. pap. 40.00 *(978-1-59829-184-1(X))* Morgan & Claypool Pubs.

Forzati, Marco. A Genetic Algorithm for Satellite Antennas. 2008. 120p. pap. *(978-3-639-08424-5(1))* VDM Verlag Dr. Mueller e.K.

Foti, Stephen. Practical Antennas for Mobile Telecommunications Networks: A Guide to Understanding Base Station Antennas. 2013. (ENG.). 320p. 90.00 *(978-0-470-87058-7(3)*, Wiley) Wiley, John & Sons, Inc.

Foutz, Jeff & Spanias, Andreas. Narrowband Direction of Arrival Estimation for Antenna Arrays. 2008. (Synthesis Lectures on Antennas Ser.). (Illus.). 100p. pap. 35.00 *(978-1-59829-650-1(7))* Morgan & Claypool Pubs.

Fujimoto, Kyohei & James, J. R. Mobile Antenna Systems Handbook. 3rd ed. 2008. (Artech House Antennas & Propagation Library). (Illus.). 950p. 209.00 *(978-1-59693-126-8(4))* Artech Hse., Inc.

Gawronski, Wodek. Modeling & Control of Antennas & Telescopes. (Mechanical Engineering Ser.). (Illus.). 2010. xvi, 225p. pap. 149.00 *(978-1-4419-4624-9(1)*, 1441946241) 2008. 244p. 149.00 *(978-0-387-78792-3(5))* Springer.

Gross, Frank. Frontiers in Antennas: Next Generation Design & Engineering. 2011. (ENG., Illus.). 544p. 120.00 *(978-0-07-163793-0(1)*, 0071637931) McGraw-Hill Professional Publishing.

Gucluoglu, Tansal. Low Complexity Space-Time Coded Systems. 2010. 156p. pap. *(978-3-8383-7280-8(8))* Lambert Academic Publishing.

Guo, Y. Jay & Barton, Stephen K. Fresnel Zone Antennas. 2010. (ENG.). 132p. pap. 139.00 *(978-1-4419-5294-3(2)*, 1441952942) Springer.

Hall, Peter S. & Hao, Yang, eds. Antennas & Propagation for Body-Centric Wireless Communications. 2006. (Artech House Antennas & Propagation Library). (Illus.). 291p. 139.00 *(978-1-58053-493-2(7))* Artech Hse., Inc.

Hansen, Robert C. & Collin, Robert E. Small Antenna Handbook. 2011. (ENG., Illus.). 360p. 125.00 *(978-0-470-89083-7(5)*, Wiley) Wiley, John & Sons, Inc.

Harish, A. R. & Sachidananda, M. Antennas & Wave Propagation. 2007. (ENG., Illus.). 448p. 65.00 *(978-0-19-568666-1(7))* Oxford Univ. Pr., Inc.

Haroon, Ahsan. Wireless Imaging Using Cooperative Diversity of Relay Networks. 2010. 68p. pap. *(978-3-8383-6853-5(3))* Lambert Academic Publishing.

Haupt, Randy L. Antenna Arrays: A Computational Approach. 2010. (ENG., Illus.). 534p. 139.00 *(978-0-470-40775-2(1)*, Wiley-IEEE Pr.) Wiley, John & Sons, Inc.

Hopengarten, Fred. Antenna Zoning: Broadcast, Cellular & Mobile Radio, Wireless Internet-Laws, Permits & Leases. 2009. (ENG., Illus.). 448p. 134.00 *(978-0-240-81112-3(7)*, Focal Pr.) Elsevier Science & Technology Bks.

Hu, Honglin, et al, eds. Distributed Antenna Systems: Open Architecture for Future Wireless Communications. 2007. (Wireless Networks & Mobile Communications Ser.). (ENG., Illus.). 496p. 113.95 *(978-1-4200-4288-7(2))* Auerbach Pubs., Inc.

Huang, John, et al. Reflectarray Antennas. 2007. (ENG., Illus.). 216p. 134.00 *(978-0-470-08491-5(X)*, Wiley-IEEE Pr.) Wiley, John & Sons, Inc.

Huang, Kao-Cheng & Edwards, David J. Millimetre Wave Antennas for Gigabit Wireless Communications: A Practical Guide to Design & Analysis in a System Context. 2008. 384p. *(978-0-470-69949-2(3)*, Wiley-Blackwell) Wiley, John & Sons, Ltd.

Huang, Yi & Boyle, Kevin. Antennas: From Theory to Practice. 2008. (ENG., Illus.). 378p. 130.00 *(978-0-470-51028-5(5)*, Wiley) Wiley, John & Sons, Inc.

IEEE Staff. 2007 6th International Conference on Antenna Theory & Techniques. 2007. pap. 308.00 *(978-1-4244-1584-7(5))* IEEE.

—2008 International ITG Workshop on Smart Antennas. 2008. pap. 214.00 *(978-1-4244-1756-8(2))* IEEE.

—2008 International Workshop on Antenna Technology. 2008. pap. 268.00 *(978-1-4244-1522-9(5))* IEEE.

—2009 Loughborough Antennas & Propagation Conference. 2009. pap. 280.00 *(978-1-4244-2720-8(7))* IEEE.

Imbriale, William A., et al. Space Antenna Handbook. 2012. (ENG.). 776p. 200.00 ***(978-1-119-99319-3(9)***, Wiley) Wiley, John & Sons, Inc.

International Symposium on Space Terahertz Technology (ISSTT) Staff, compiled by. 17th International Symposium on Space Terahertz Technology 2006. 2007. 264p. pap. 125.00 *(978-1-60423-975-1(1))* Curran Assocs., Inc.

Kannan Ramachandran, Srividya. Distributed Antenna Systems. 2009. 68p. pap. *(978-3-639-16883-9(6))* VDM Verlag Dr. Mueller e.K.

Karmakar, Nemai Chandra, ed. Handbook of Smart Antennas for RFID Systems. 2010. (ENG., Illus.). 620p. 148.00 *(978-0-470-38764-1(5)*, Wiley-Interscience) Wiley, John & Sons, Inc.

Kasapi, Athos. Smart Antennas & Adaptive Arrays: Multi-Antenna Techniques for Wireless Communications. 2011. (ENG.). 424p. pap. 69.95 *(978-0-7506-7809-4(7)*, Newnes) Elsevier Science & Technology Bks.

King, R. W. P. Arrays of Cylindrical Dipoles. 2009. (ENG., Illus.). 512p. pap. 100.00 *(978-0-521-11485-1(3))* Cambridge Univ. Pr.

A

Kirk, Mustafa Sancay. Microstrip Patch Antenna for Leo Satellite Communications. 2010. 92p. pap. *(978-3-8383-5665-5(9))* Lambert Academic Publishing.
Kishk, A. Dielectric Resonator Antennas: Theory, Design, & Applications. 2013. (Wiley Series in Microwave & Optical Engineering Ser.). (ENG.). 350p. 125.00 ***(978-0-470-28714-9(4)***, Wiley-Interscience) Wiley, John & Sons, Inc.
Kogure, Hiroaki, et al. Introduction to Antenna Analysis Using EM Simulators. 2011. (Illus.). 300p. 119.00 *(978-1-60807-157-9(X))* Artech Hse., Inc.
Kozakoff, Dennis J. Analysis of Radome Enclosed Antennas, Second Edition. 2nd rev. ed. 2009. (Illus.). 300p. 139.00 *(978-1-59693-441-2(7))* Artech Hse., Inc.
Kralovec. Reflector Antennas. 2007. (Synthesis Lectures on Antennas Ser.). 40.00 *(978-1-59829-252-7(8))* Morgan & Claypool Pubs.
Kshetrimayum, R. S. Ebg Assisted Micromachined Patch Antenn. 2009. 96p. pap. *(978-3-639-18066-4(6))* VDM Verlag Dr. Mueller e.K.
Kumar, Rajneesh. Plasma Antenn. 2011. 140p. pap. ***(978-3-8443-0530-2(0))*** Lambert Academic Publishing.
Lager, I. E. & Simeoni, M., eds. Antennas for Ubiquitous Radio Services in a Wireless Information Society: Proceedings of the Symposium Concluding the Wide Band Sparse Element Array Antennas - WISE Project. 2010. 180p. 104.00 *(978-1-60750-486-3(3))* IOS Pr., Inc.
Laheurte, J. Compact Antennas for Wireless Communications & Terminals: Theory & Design. 2011. (Iste Ser.: 575). (ENG., Illus.). 272p. 125.00 ***(978-1-84821-307-4(7)***, Wiley-ISTE) Wiley, John & Sons, Inc.
Lauriston, Andy. Bilingual Dictionary of International Telecommunications Vol. 4: Telecommunications Services. (ENG & FRE.). 547p. 225.00 *(978-0-8288-9451-7(5))* French & European Pubns., Inc.
Le Chevalier, François, et al. Non-standard Antennas. 2011. (Iste Ser.: 543). (ENG., Illus.). 480p. 205.00 *(978-1-84821-274-9(7)*, Wiley-ISTE) Wiley, John & Sons, Inc.
Lee, Kwan-Ho. Development of Four Novel Uwb Antennas Assisted by Fdtd Method. 2009. 184p. pap. *(978-3-639-15872-4(5))* VDM Verlag Dr. Mueller e.K.
Lim, Eng Hock & Leung, Kwok Wa. Multifunctional Antennas for Microwave Wireless Systems. 2012. (Wiley Series in Microwave & Optical Engineering Ser.: 215). (ENG.). 248p. 99.95 ***(978-0-470-40732-5(8)***, Wiley) Wiley, John & Sons, Inc.
Lin, Chi Chang. Research of Planar Printed Antennas for Wlan & Uwb Communication Systems. 2008. 124p. pap. *(978-3-639-01562-1(2))* VDM Verlag Dr. Mueller e.K.
Loughborough University Staff, contrib. by. 2007 Loughborough Antennas & Propagation Conference. 2007. pap. 260.00 *(978-1-4244-0775-0(3)*, 07EX1605) IEEE.
MacLeod, Heather. Adaptive Antenna Array Configuration for Hybrid Diversity. 2008. 112p. pap. *(978-3-639-04336-5(7))* VDM Verlag Dr. Mueller e.K.
Macnamara, Thereza. Introduction to Antenna Placement & Installation. 2010. (Aerospace Ser.: 11). (ENG., Illus.). 424p. 136.00 *(978-0-470-01981-8(6)*, Wiley) Wiley, John & Sons, Inc.
Mailloux, Robert. Electronically Scanned Arrays. 2007. (Synthesis Lectures on Antennas Ser.). 100p. pap. 40.00 *(978-1-59829-182-7(3))* Morgan & Claypool Pubs.
Marasini, Cecilia. A New Approach for Wire Antennas Design. 2010. 272p. pap. *(978-3-8383-4153-8(8))* Lambert Academic Publishing.
Minin, Igor V. & Minin, Oleg V. Basic Principles of Fresnel Antenna Arrays. 2010. (Lecture Notes in Electrical Engineering Ser.). (Illus.). xviii, 199p. pap. 139.00 *(978-3-642-09850-5(9)*, 3642098509) Springer.
Monzingo, Robert A., et al. Introduction to Adaptive Arrays. 2nd rev. ed. 2010. 530p. 129.00 *(978-1-891121-57-9(X))* SciTech Publishing, Inc.
Moradi Shahrbabak, Shahla. Hand's Effect. 2009. 84p. pap. *(978-3-639-17542-4(5))* VDM Verlag Dr. Mueller e.K.
Munk, Benedikt A., et al. Metamaterials: Critique & Alternatives. 2009. (ENG., Illus.). 189p. 99.95 *(978-0-470-37704-8(6)*, Wiley-Interscience) Wiley, John & Sons, Inc.
Nesterenko, Mikhail V., et al. Thin Impedance Vibrators: Theory & Applications. 2011. (Lecture Notes in Electrical Engineering Ser.). (ENG., Illus.). xiii, 223p. 129.00 *(978-1-4419-7849-3(6)*, 1441978496) Springer.
Noginov, Mikhail A. Metamaterials: Fundamentals & Applications: 10-13 August 2008, San Diego, California, USA. 2008. (Proceedings of SPIE Ser.). (Illus.). 200p. pap. 105.00 *(978-0-8194-7249-6(2))* SPIE.
Okon, Ernest, et al, eds. Ultra Wideband Antennas & Propagation for Communications, Radar & Imaging. 2006. (ENG., Illus.). 508p. 150.00 *(978-0-470-03255-8(3)*, Wiley) Wiley, John & Sons, Inc.
Otoshi, Tom Y. Noise Temperature Theory & Applications for Deep Space Communications Antenna Systems. 2008. (Illus.). 300p. 145.00 *(978-1-59693-377-4(1))* Artech Hse., Inc.
Parthasarathy V, Krishnan. Mutual Coupling in Patch Antennas. 2011. 84p. pap. ***(978-3-8443-0932-4(2))*** Lambert Academic Publishing.
Petosa, Aldo. Dielectric Resonator Antenna Handbook. 2007. (Artech House Antennas & Propagation Library). (Illus.). 308p. 139.00 *(978-1-59693-206-7(6))* Artech Hse., Inc.
Pitzer, T. L. Antenna Design Optimization. 2007. 128p. per. 74.95 *(978-1-4276-1949-5(2))* Wexford College Pr.
Poisel, Richard. Principles of Electronic Warfare Antenna Systems. 2011. (Illus.). 740p. 159.00 ***(978-1-60807-484-6(6))*** Artech Hse., Inc.
Poljak, D., et al. Computer Aided Design of Wire Structures: Frequency & Time Domain Analysis. 2007. (Advances in Fluid Mechanics Ser.: 3). (Illus.). 160p. 139.00 incl. cd-rom *(978-1-85312-884-4(8))* WIT Pr GBR. Dist: WIT Pr.
Primak, Serguei & Kontorovich, Valeri. Wireless Multi-Antenna Channels: Modeling & Simulation. 2011. (Wireless Communications & Mobile Computing Ser.). (ENG., Illus.). 272p. 130.00 ***(978-0-470-69720-7(2)***, Wiley) Wiley, John & Sons, Inc.
Queen Mary, University of London Staff & Institute of Electrical and Electronics Engineers Staff, contrib. by. 2007 International Workshop on Antenna Technology. 2007. pap. 276.00 *(978-1-4244-1087-3(8)*, 07EX1729) IEEE.
Rabinovich, Victor, et al. Automative Antenna Design & Applications. 2010. (ENG., Illus.). 330p. 129.95 *(978-1-4398-0407-0(9)*, CRC Press) Taylor & Francis Group GBR. Dist: Taylor & Francis Group.
Rahmat-Samii, Yahya & Kim, Jaehoon. Implanted Antennas in Medical Wireless Communications. 2006. (Synthesis Lectures on Antennas & Propagation Ser.). 82p. pap. 40.00 *(978-1-59829-054-7(1))* Morgan & Claypool Pubs.
Rehman, Masood Ur, et al. Antennas for Global Navigation Satellite Systems. 2nd ed. 2012. (ENG., Illus.). 232p. 115.00 ***(978-1-119-99367-4(9)***, Wiley) Wiley, John & Sons, Inc.
Rizvi, Syed Ahsaan Panjtan. Reconfigurable Rf Front-End for Multi-Standard Communication. 2011. 96p. pap. ***(978-3-8443-0426-8(6))*** Lambert Academic Publishing.
Rodenbeck, Christopher. LOW-COST PHASED ARRAYS AND SCANNING ANTENNAS: NOVEL TECHNOLOGIES AND TECHNIQUES. 2008. 180p. pap. *(978-3-639-10593-3(1))* VDM Verlag Dr. Mueller e.K.
Rooyen, Pieter Van, et al. Space-Time Processing for CDMA Mobile Communications. 2010. (Springer International Series in Engineering & Computer Science Ser.). 336p. pap. 149.00 *(978-1-4419-4966-0(6)*, 1441949666) Springer.
Royal Institute of Technology (KTH) Staff, compiled by. 4th European Workshop on Conformal Antennas 2005. 2007. 121p. pap. 106.00 *(978-1-60423-395-7(8))* Curran Assocs., Inc.
Rößler, Mario. Antenna Coupling Effects in Handheld & Mobile Applications. 2009. 152p. pap. *(978-3-639-15608-9(0))* VDM Verlag Dr. Mueller e.K.
Sahalos, John & Kyriacou, George. Tuneable Materials for Antennas & Microwaves. Balanis, Constantine, ed. 2007. (Synthesis Lectures on Antennas & Propagation Ser.). 100p. pap. 40.00 *(978-1-59829-086-8(X))* Morgan & Claypool Pubs.
Sánchez-Hernández, David, ed. Multiband Integrated Antennas for 4G Terminals. 2008. (Illus.). 336p. 139.00 *(978-1-59693-331-6(3))* Artech Hse., Inc.
Sandhu, Waseem Hussain, et al. Multiple Antenna Techniques. 2010. 72p. pap. *(978-3-8383-6571-8(2))* Lambert Academic Publishing.
Saunders, Simon R. & Aragón-Zavala, Alejandro. Antennas & Propagation for Wireless Communication Systems. 2nd rev. ed. 2007. (ENG., Illus.). 546p. 90.00 *(978-0-470-84879-1(0)*, Wiley) Wiley, John & Sons, Inc.
Savazzi, Stefano & Spagnolini, Umberto. Cooperative Networks in Fading Channels. 2010. 200p. pap. *(978-3-639-23396-4(4))* VDM Verlag Dr. Mueller e.K.
Schellander, David. Iterative Receiver Design for Lte Downlink. 2010. 108p. pap. *(978-3-639-24681-0(0))* VDM Verlag Dr. Mueller e.K.
Scholz, Peter. Inductively Coupled Antenna Systems. 2011. 216p. pap. ***(978-3-8381-2325-7(5))*** Südwestdeutscher Verlag für Hochschulschriften AG & Co. KG.
Sengupta, Suranjana. Characterization of Terahertz Emission from High Resistivity Fe-doped Bulk Ga0. 69In0. 31As Based Photoconducting Antennas. 2011. (Springer Theses Ser.). (ENG., Illus.). x, 74p. 99.00 *(978-1-4419-8197-4(7)*, 1441981977) Springer.
Sikdar, Manik Wasek Ali. Design, Simulation, Fabrication & Testing of Wimax Antenn. 2010. 108p. pap. *(978-3-8383-7208-2(5))* Lambert Academic Publishing.
Simeone, Osvaldo & Spagnolini, Umberto. Linear Processing for Mimo Systems over Frequency-Selective Channels. 2010. 200p. pap. *(978-3-639-23360-5(3))* VDM Verlag Dr. Mueller e.K.
Siwiak, Kazimierz & Bahreini, Yasaman. Radiowave Propagation & Antennas for Personal Communications. 3rd ed. 2007. (Illus.). 464p. 159.00 incl. cd-rom *(978-1-59693-073-5(X))* Artech Hse., Inc.
Smith, B. Communication Structures. 2007. (Illus.). 352p. *(978-0-7277-3400-6(8))* Telford, Thomas Ltd.
Stelzried, Charles T., et al. LONRS: Low Noise Receiving Systems Measurement & Analysis Toolkit. 2010. 100p. spiral bd. 199.00 *(978-1-59693-997-4(4))* Artech Hse., Inc.
Stutzman, Warren L. & Thiele, Gary A. Antenna Theory & Design. 3rd ed. 2012. (ENG.). 848p. (C). 208.95 ***(978-0-470-57664-9(2)***, Wiley) Wiley, John & Sons, Inc.
Sun, Chen, et al, eds. Handbook on Advancements in Smart Antenna Technologies for Wireless Networks. 2008. (Illus.). 584p. 195.00 *(978-1-59904-988-5(0))* IGI Global.
Taneja, Pankhuri. Full-¿ & Half-¿ Patch Antennas for Dual Band Wlan Applications. 2011. 100p. pap. ***(978-3-8443-9096-4(0))*** Lambert Academic Publishing.
Thornton, John & Huang, Kao-Cheng. Lens Antennas for Communications. 2012. (IEEE Press Series on Electromagnetic Wave Theory Ser.: 39). (ENG., Illus.). 310p. 125.00 ***(978-1-118-01065-5(5)***, Wiley-IEEE Pr.) Wiley, John & Sons, Inc.
Tsiboukis, Theodoros & Kantartzis, Nikolaos. Higher-Order FDTD Schemes for Waveguide & Antenna Structures. 2006. (Synthesis Lectures on Computational Electromagnetics Ser.). 226p. pap. 40.00 *(978-1-59829-028-8(2))* Morgan & Claypool Pubs.
Uysal, Murat, ed. Cooperative Communications for Improved Wireless Network Transmission: Framework for Virtual Antenna Array Applications. 2009. 632p. 180.00 *(978-1-60566-665-5(3))* IGI Global.
Vidémé Bossou, Olivier. Wood Antenn. 2009. 100p. pap. *(978-3-639-19912-3(X))* VDM Verlag Dr. Mueller e.K.
Visser, Hubregt J. Antenna Theory & Applications. 2012. (ENG., Illus.). 280p. 79.95 ***(978-1-119-99025-3(4)***, Wiley) Wiley, John & Sons, Inc.
Volakis, John. Antenna Engineering. Johnson, Richard C. et al, eds. 4th rev. ed. 2007. (ENG., Illus.). 1800p. instr.'s hndbk. ed. 175.00 *(978-0-07-147574-7(5)*, 0071475745) McGraw-Hill Professional Publishing.
Volakis, John, et al. Small Antennas: Miniaturization Techniques & Applications. 2010. (ENG., Illus.). 448p. 99.95 *(978-0-07-162553-1(4)*, 0071625534) McGraw-Hill Professional Publishing.
Walker, C., ed. 14th International Symposium on Space Terahertz Technology 2003. 2007. 566p. pap. 118.00 *(978-1-60423-187-8(4))* Curran Assocs., Inc.
Warnick, Karl F. & Russer, Peter. Problem Solving in Electromagnetics, Microwave Circuit, & Antenna Design for Communications Engineering. 2006. (Artech House Antennas & Propagation Library). (Illus.). 360p. 119.00 *(978-1-59693-096-4(9))* Artech Hse., Inc.
Waterhouse, Rod. Microstrip Patch Antennas: A Designer's Guide. 2010. (ENG.). 432p. pap. 179.00 *(978-1-4419-5338-4(8)*, 1441953388) Springer.
Waterhouse, Rod, ed. Printed Antennas for Wireless Communications. 2008. (Rsp Ser.). (ENG., Illus.). 472p. 145.00 *(978-0-470-51069-8(2)*, Wiley) Wiley, John & Sons, Inc.
Weng, Wei-Chung, et al. Electromagnetics & Antenna Optimization Using Taguchi's Method. 2007. (Synthesis Lectures on Computational Electromagnetics Ser.). (Illus.). 100p. per. 40.00 *(978-1-59829-538-2(1))* Morgan & Claypool Pubs.
Wrulich, Martin. Capacity Analysis of Mimo Systems. 2008. (Illus.). 112p. pap. *(978-3-639-01710-6(2))* VDM Verlag Dr. Mueller e.K.
Wu, Xuan Hui, et al. Generalized Transmission Line Method to Study the Far-zone Radiation of Antennas under a Multilayer Structure. 2008. (Synthesis Lectures on Antennas Ser.). 100p. pap. 35.00 *(978-1-59829-813-0(5))* Morgan & Claypool Pubs.
Wymeersch, Henk. Iterative Receiver Design. 2007. (ENG., Illus.). 272p. 99.00 *(978-0-521-87315-4(0))* Cambridge Univ. Pr.
Yang, Fan & Rahmat-Samii, Yahya. Electromagnetic Band Gap Structures in Antenna Engineering. 2008. (Cambridge RF & Microwave Engineering Ser.). (ENG., Illus.). 280p. 102.00 *(978-0-521-88991-9(X))* Cambridge Univ. Pr.
Yarman, Binboga Siddik. Design of Ultra Wideband Power Transfer Networks. 2010. (ENG., Illus.). 774p. 145.00 *(978-0-470-31989-5(5)*, Wiley) Wiley, John & Sons, Inc.
Zhou, Yijun, et al. Polymer-Ceramic Composites for Conformal Multilayer Antenna/Rf Systems. 2010. 184p. pap. *(978-3-8383-7979-1(9))* Lambert Academic Publishing.
2007 IEEE Antennas & Propagation Society International Symposium. 2007. pap. 1052.00 *(978-1-4244-0877-1(6)*, 07CH37860) IEEE.
2007 International Kharkov Symposium Physics & Engineering of Millimeter & Sub-Millimeter Waves. 2007. 384.00 *(978-1-4244-1237-2(4)*, 07EX1786) IEEE.
2007 International Symposium on Microwave, Antenna, Propagation & EMC Technologies for Wireless Communications. 2007. pap. 366.00 *(978-1-4244-1044-6(4)*, 07EX1718) IEEE.
2008 Mosharaka International Conference on Communications, Propagation & Electronics: Amman, Jordan, 6-8, March 2008. 2008. (Illus.). xiii, 87p. *(978-9957-486-02-0(0))* IEEE.

ANTENUPTIAL CONTRACTS

Calif. Marital Settlement & Other Family Law Agreements: April 2007 Update, 2 vols. 3rd ed. 2007. 500p. ring bd. 79.00 *(978-0-7626-1256-7(8)*, FA-35512) Continuing Education of the Bar-California.
Cochrane, Michael G. Do You Need a Marriage Contract: Understanding How a Legal Agreement Can Strengthen Your Life Together. 2010. (ENG.). 208p. pap. 26.95 *(978-0-470-73751-4(4)*, Wiley) Wiley, John & Sons, Inc.
Davis, Akeela. Divorce Dollars: Get Your Fair Share. 3rd ed. 2009. (ENG.). 152p. pap. 14.95 *(978-1-55180-851-2(X))* Self-Counsel Pr., Inc. CAN. Dist: Midpoint Trade Bks., Inc.
Florida Bar, Continuing Legal Education Staff, contrib. by. Drafting Marriage Contracts in Florida. 8th ed. 2008. (Illus.). *(978-1-4224-5135-9(6))* Florida Bar Continuing Legal Education Pubns., The.
Haman, Edward A. The Complete Prenuptial Agreement Kit. 2006. (ENG., Illus.). 222p. pap. 26.99 *(978-1-57248-534-1(5)*, 1254649, Sphinx Publishing) Sourcebooks, Inc.
Harris, Iain. Prenuptial Agreements: A Practical Guide. 2008. 133p. pap. *(978-1-85811-601-3(5))* EMIS Professional Publishing.
Kent, Richard G. Prenup /Postnup: How They Work & Why You Might Need One. 2009. (ENG.). 144p. pap. 14.95 *(978-1-58182-694-4(X)*, Cumberland Hse.) Sourcebooks, Inc.
Luhn, Christopher. Privatautonomie und Inhaltskontrolle von Eheverträgen: Ein kritischer Vergleich des deutschen und des australischen Rechts mit Bezügen zum Internationalen Privatrecht. 2008. (Studien zum vergleichenden und internationalen Recht. Comparative & International Law Studies). 326p. pap. 81.95 *(978-3-631-57708-0(7))* Lang, Peter GmbH, Europaischer Verlag der Wissenschaften DEU. Dist: Lang, Peter.
Nachshin, Robert J. & Weston, Scott N. I Do, You Do... but Just Sign Here: A Quick & Easy Guide to Cohabitation, Postnuptial & Prenuptial Agreements. 2nd ed. 2006. pap. 14.95 *(978-0-9765970-2-5(0))* ExecuProv.
Quraishi, Asifa & Vogel, Frank E., eds. The Islamic Marraige Contract: Case Studies in Islamic Family Law. 2009. (Harvard Series in Islamic Law Ser.: 6). (Illus.). 389p. 29.95 *(978-0-674-02821-0(X))* Harvard Univ. Pr.
Salter, David, et al. International Pre-Nuptial & Post-Nuptial Agreements. 2011. (ENG.). 544p. pap. *(978-1-84661-231-2(4))* Jordan Publishing, Ltd.
Smith, Lona. Help! He Wants Me to Sign a Prenup. 2007. per. 19.99 *(978-0-9796309-0-3(8))* Help Publishing, Inc.
Stoner, Katherine E. & Irving, Shae. Prenuptial Agreements: How to Write a Fair & Lasting Contract, 2 vols. 3rd rev. ed. 2008. (ENG., Illus.). 320p. pap. 34.99 *(978-1-4133-0715-3(9))* NOLO.

ANTERIOR SPINAL PARALYSIS

see Poliomyelitis

ANTHELMINTICS

Kumsa, Bersissa. Small Ruminant Haemonchosis. 2009. 108p. pap. *(978-3-639-20527-5(8))* VDM Verlag Dr. Mueller e.K.
World Health Organization. Preventive Chemotherapy in Human Helminthiasis: Coordinated Use of Anthelminthic Drugs in Control Interventions- A Manual for Health Professionals & Programme Manager. 2006. (Nonserial Publication). (ENG.). 71p. pap. 24.00 *(978-92-4-154710-9(3))* World Health Organization.

ANTHEMS

Here are entered works composed in the form of the anthem.
see also Sacred Vocal Music

Anthems Cassette Abingdon December 1996. *(978-0-687-90280-4(0))* Abingdon Pr.
Are You Ready, Little Town Anthem. 1.50 *(978-0-687-07791-5(5))* Abingdon Pr.
The Bells of Christmas Anthem. 2008. 1.80 *(978-0-687-49257-2(2))* Abingdon Pr.
Blended Worship 2: 12 Praise & Worship Songs with 12 Praise & Worship Hymns Arranged in 12 Medleys. 2007. (ENG.). 128p. pap. 6.99 *(978-0-8341-7592-1(4)*, 0834175924) Lillenas Publishing Co.
Brown, Timothy, ed. Choral Works with Orchestra. 2009. (William Walton Edition Ser.). 328p. pap. 195.00 *(978-0-19-368307-5(5))* Oxford Univ. Pr., Inc.
Chilcott, Bob. Bob Chilcott Anthems 2. 2009. (ENG.). 64p. pap. 12.95 *(978-0-19-336493-6(X))* Oxford Univ. Pr., Inc.
The Earth Belongs to the Lord Anthem. 1.75 *(978-0-687-04378-1(6))* Abingdon Pr.
Endicott, Stan & Barron, Chris. The Risen One: Resurrection Songs for Choir-Led Worship. 2006. (ENG.). 136p. pap. 8.99 *(978-0-8341-7544-0(4)*, 0834175444) Lillenas Publishing Co.
Fettke, Tom, et al. Southern Gospel Favorites: 15 Outstanding Arrangements for Choir. 2006. (ENG.). 96p. pap. 6.99 *(978-0-8341-7541-9(X)*, 083417541X) Lillenas Publishing Co.
Goss, Lari & Stone, Regi, contrib. by. Make a Joyful Noise: A Worship Choir Collection. 2007. audio compact disk 10.00 *(978-5-557-49690-2(4)*, Word Music) Word Entertainment.
—Make a Joyful Noise: A Worship Choir Collection: SATB. 2007. 119p. pap. 8.95 *(978-5-557-49727-5(7)*, Word Music) Word Entertainment.
Hal Leonard Corporation Staff, creator. One Rehearsal Wonders Vol. 2: Almost Instant Anthems for Any Occasion. 2007. (ENG.). 80p. pap. 7.99 *(978-1-59235-183-1(2)*, 1592351832, Glory Sound) Shawnee Pr., Inc.
Hayes, Mark. Mark Hayes' Sing Praise Project: An Anthology of His Most Popular Anthems for SATB (Preview Pack), Book & CD. 2009. (ENG.). pap. 16.95 *(978-0-7390-6487-0(8))* Alfred Publishing Co., Inc.
—Mark Hayes' Sing Praise Project: An Anthology of His Most Popular Anthems for SATB (Songbook) 2009. (ENG.). 128p. pap. 8.95 *(978-0-7390-6409-2(6))* Alfred Publishing Co., Inc.
I Praise You, Lord Anthem. 1.50 *(978-0-687-04467-2(7))* Abingdon Pr.
Labenske, Victor. My Jesus, I Love Thee: Devotional Hymns for the Journey of Faith. 2007. (ENG., Illus.). 56p. pap. 15.99 *(978-0-8341-7583-9(5)*, 0834175835) Lillenas Publishing Co.
Lift up Your Head Anthem. 1.50 *(978-0-687-32480-4(7))* Abingdon Pr.
Little Lamb Online Vocal Solo. 3.00 *(978-0-687-00222-1(2))* Abingdon Pr.
Look Toward Christmas Anthem. 1.50 *(978-0-687-04298-2(4))* Abingdon Pr.
Lullaby in Bethlehem Online Anthem. 1.35 *(978-0-687-04319-4(0))* Abingdon Pr.
Mauldin, Russell, contrib. by. We Will Stand: 10 Timeless Songs of Faith & Inspiration. 2007. audio compact disk 10.00 *(978-5-557-49268-3(2)*, Word Music) Word Entertainment.
—We Will Stand: 10 Timeless Songs of Faith & Inspiration: SATB. 2007. 143p. pap. 8.95 *(978-5-557-49273-7(9)*, Word Music) Word Entertainment.
The New Oxford Easy Anthem Book. 2006. 256p. spiral bd. 26.95 *(978-0-19-335578-1(7))* Oxford Univ. Pr., Inc.
Parable of the Sower Anthem. 1.00 *(978-0-687-02892-4(2))* Abingdon Pr.
Parks, Marty. O for a Dozen Tongues to Sing - Gospel Hymns: Six Ready-to-Sing Anthems for Two-part Mixed Voices. 2009. spiral bd. 29.95 *(978-1-4267-0016-3(4))* Abingdon Pr.
—Songs of Hope & Restoration: Arranged for Any Choir. 2006. (ENG.). 120p. pap. 8.99 *(978-0-8341-7540-2(1)*, 083-417-5401) Lillenas Publishing Co.
Pearsall, Robert. Let Your Light So Shine. 2009. pap., pap. 2.00 *(978-0-19-395388-8(9))* Oxford Univ. Pr., Inc.
Reverence: Music for Choir-Led Worship. 2007. (ENG., Illus.). 152p. pap. 8.99 *(978-0-8341-7579-2(7)*, 0834175797) Lillenas Publishing Co.
Robertson, Barny & Robertson, Carter, contrib. by. Ready for Worship: 12 Complete Worship Sets with No Transposition or Transitions Required. 2007. (ENG.). 176p. pap. 9.99 *(978-0-8341-7596-9(7)*, 0834175967) Lillenas Publishing Co.

Robertson, Carter & Robertson, Barney, contrib. by. Ready for Worship: 12 Complete Worship Sets with No Transpositions or Transitions Required. 2007. (ENG.). 158p. pap. 19.99 **(978-0-8341-7601-0(7)**, 0834176017) Lillenas Publishing Co.

Schram, Scott. The Last Noel: A Christmas Musical for Children. 2007. (ENG.). pap. 16.95 *(978-0-7390-4486-5(9))*; pap. 22.50 *(978-0-7390-4483-4(4))* Alfred Publishing Co., Inc.

Sheperd Psalm Anthem. 1.75 *(978-0-687-07831-8(8))* Abingdon Pr.

Southern Gospel Favorites: 15 Outstanding Arrangements for Choir. 2006. (ENG.). 132p. pap. 19.99 *(978-0-8341-7548-8(7)*, 0834175487) Nazarene Publishing Hse.

Speck, Mike & Whitmire, Stan. Everlasting Praise 2: A Timeless Resource for Congregation & Choir. 2008. (ENG.). 180p. spiral bd. 9.99 *(978-0-8341-7666-9(1)*, 9780834176669) Lillenas Publishing Co.

Speck, Mike & Whitmire, Stan. Everlasting Praise 3: A Timeless Resource for Congregation & Choir. 2012. (ENG.). 192p. pap. 9.99 **(978-0-8341-8119-9(3)**, 0834181193) Lillenas Publishing Co.

Speck, Mike, et al. Redeemed: Songs for the Soul-Winning Church. 2006. (ENG.). 168p. pap. 8.99 *(978-0-8341-7547-1(9)*, 0834175479) Lillenas Publishing Co.

Sterling, Robert, et al, contrib. by. Simply... the Best Easter, Volume 3: Satb. 2007. 39p. pap. 3.50 *(978-5-557-53116-0(5)*, Word Music) Word Entertainment.

Walton, William & Lloyd-Jones, David. Coronation Anthems: Crown Imperial & Orb & Sceptre. 2010. (William Walton Edition Ser.). (ENG.). 96p. pap. 24.95 *(978-0-19-336613-8(4))* Oxford Univ. Pr., Inc.

WILBERG, Mack. Rest in Me(Suo-Gân) 2009. 8p. pap. 1.85 *(978-0-19-386989-9(6))* Oxford Univ. Pr., Inc.

ANTHEMS, NATIONAL
see National Songs

ANTHOLOGIA GRAECA
see Greek Anthology

ANTHOLOGIES
Here are entered collections of general interest, too broad to use more specific headings, such as Literature—Collections; Quotations; Sports Stories; etc.
see also Gift Books; Literature—Collections; Readers
also names of literatures, e.g. English Literature; and subdivision Literary Collections under subjects for literary anthologies involving two or more literary forms, e.g. Agriculture—Literary Collections

Brito, Manuel. Market Fructification of Innovative American Poetry in the Late 20th Century. 2010. 182p. pap. 50.95 *(978-3-0343-0444-3(7))* Lang, Peter Publishing, Inc.

Derleth, August, ed. The Arkham Sampler (1948-1949). 2 vols. fac. ed. 2010. 149.95 *(978-1-55246-927-9(1))* Battered Silicon Dispatch Box, The.

Dobson, Austin. A Bookman's Budget. 2009. 232p. 23.99 *(978-1-103-33265-6(1))*; pap. 17.99 *(979-1-103-33263-2(5))* BiblioBazaar.

Dobson, Austin, ed. A Bookman's Budget. 2009. 236p. 41.95 *(978-1-104-00904-5(8))*; pap. 26.95 *(978-1-4374-4714-9(7))* Kessinger Publishing, LLC.

Edwards-Jones, Imogen, et al, eds. In Bed with Anthology. 2010. (ENG.). 336p. (gr. 12). 15.00 *(978-0-425-23425-9(8)*, Berkley Trade) Penguin Group (USA) Inc.

Fraser, John Forbes. Thoughts: Occurrences That Interrupted A Rambling Life. 2011. 344p. 28.28 **(978-1-4634-3856-2(7))**; pap. 17.72 **(978-1-4634-3857-9(5))** AuthorHouse.

Fuller, Mary, ed. Pick & Mix: An Anthology. 2011. (Illus.). 103p. 22.50 **(978-1-84624-635-7(0))** Book Guild, Ltd. GBR. Dist: Trans-Atlantic Pubns., Inc.

Henry, Tom. The Ideal Dog: And Other Delusions. unabr. ed. (ENG., Illus.). 192p. *(978-1-55017-450-1(X))* Harbour Publishing Co., Ltd.

Kostelanetz, Richard, et al, eds. Reassembling Assembling. 2000p. lib. bdg. 2500.00 *(978-0-915066-26-1(2))* Assembling Pr.

Lange, Henrik. 90 Classic Books for People in a Hurry. 2009. (Illus.). 150p. pap. 9.95 *(978-91-85869-29-9(5))* Nicotext, Ltd. SWE. Dist: SCB Distributors.

Pu-Chu, Chao. A Message from the Chinese Buddhists. 2011. 26p. 35.95 **(978-1-258-01291-5(X))** Literary Licensing, LLC.

Roberts, Andy. Strangely Strange but Oddly Normal. 2010. 202p. pap. *(978-1-905723-44-7(X))* CFZ Pr.

Tomlinson, H. M. Anthology of Modern Travel Writing. 2006. 272p. per. *(978-1-4067-3257-3(5)*, Hesperides Pr.) Read Bks.

Urban, Martina. Aesthetics of Renewal: Martin Buber's Early Representation of Hasidism as Kulturkritik. 2008. (ENG.). 240p. 32.00 *(978-0-226-84270-7(3))* Univ. of Chicago Pr.

Yost, Paula Stallings & McNees, Pat, eds. My Words Are Gonna Linger: The Art of Personal History. 2009. (Illus.). 320p. pap. 19.95 *(978-0-9820134-0-3(X))* Personal History Pr.

ANTHOLOGIES—HISTORY AND CRITICISM

Braddock, Jeremy. Collecting as Modernist Practice. 2011. (Hopkins Studies in Modernism Ser.). (ENG., Illus.). 336p. (gr. 17). 39.95 **(978-1-4214-0364-9(1))** Johns Hopkins Univ. Pr.

Lavoie, Chantel M. Collecting Women: Poetry & Lives, 1700-1780. 2009. 215p. 53.00 *(978-0-8387-5749-9(9))*; (ENG.). 60.00 *(978-1-61148-341-3(7))* Bucknell Univ. Pr.

Mohr, Richard, ed. One Book, the Whole Universe: Plato's Timaeus Today: Plato's Timaeus Today 2010. (ENG., Illus.). 416p. (C). (gr. 13). pap. 87.00 *(978-1-930972-32-2(6))* Parmenides Publishing.

Odber de Baubeta, Patricia Anne. The Anthology in Portugal: A New Approach to the History of Portuguese Literature in the Twentieth Century. 2007. (Illus.). 286p. pap. 73.95 *(978-3-03910-919-7(7))* Lang, Peter Publishing, Inc.

ANTHOLOGY SOCIETY (BOSTON, MASS.)

Simon, Sternly K. This Black-Ideology: Anthology of Poems by a Black Child. 2011. 100p. pap. 12.10 **(978-1-4567-8214-6(2))** AuthorHouse.

ANTHONY, OF EGYPT, SAINT, CA. 250-355 OR 6

Budge, E. A. Wallis, intro. The Paradise or Garden of the Holy Fathers. 2010. 259.60 *(978-1-61143-101-8(8))*; 259.60 *(978-1-61143-100-1(X))* Gorgias Pr., LLC.

Daughters of St. Paul Staff. Devotion to St. Anthony. 46p. pap. 1.75 *(978-0-8198-1848-5(8)*, 332-064) Pauline Bks. & Media.

Gorg, Peter & Görg, Peter H. The Desert Fathers: Anthony & the Beginnings of Monasticism. 2011. (Illus.). xiii, 131p. **(978-1-58617-445-3(2))** Ignatius Pr.

Harter, Ursula. Die Versuchung des Heiligen Antonius: Zwischen Religion & Wissenschaft: Flaubert, Moreau, Redon. (GER., Illus.). 266p. *(978-3-496-01133-5(1))* Reimer, Dietrich.

Westheider, Ortrud & Philipp, Michael, eds. Schrecken und Lust: Die Versuchung des heiligen Augustinus von Hieronymus Bosch bis Max Ernst. 2008. (GER., Illus.). 215p. (C). pap. 60.00 *(978-3-7774-3945-7(2))* Hirmer Verlag GmbH DEU. Dist: Brown, David Bk. Co., The.

ANTHONY, OF PADUA, SAINT, 1195-1231

Arnaud. Gleanings from the Life of St. Anthony of Padua. 116p. pap. 12.95 *(978-2-89420-142-8(7))* Mediaspaul CAN. Dist: St Pauls/Alba Hse. Pubs.

Ernest, Brother. The Boy Who Worked Wonders: A Story of St. Anthony of Padua. 2011. 92p. 38.95 **(978-1-258-06306-1(9))** Literary Licensing, LLC.

St. Anthony of Padua. 19.95 *(978-1-58617-527-6(0))* Ignatius Pr.

St. Anthony of Padua. 2008. (ENG.). pap. 19.95 *(978-1-58002-471-6(8))* Journeys of Faith.

Stoddard, Charles Warren. The Wonder-Worker of Padua. 172p. 2008. 37.95 *(978-0-548-91555-5(X))* 2007. (ENG.). per. 22.95 *(978-0-548-60560-8(2))* Kessinger Publishing, LLC.

Ward-Ling, Sheilah. Saint Anthony of Padua: Friend of All the World. 158p. pap. 15.95 *(978-0-8189-9503-3(3))* St Pauls/Alba Hse. Pubs.

ANTHONY, THE GREAT, SAINT, CA. 250-355 OR 6
see Anthony, of Egypt, Saint, ca. 250-355 or 6

ANTHONY, THE HERMIT, SAINT, CA. 250-355 OR 6
see Anthony, of Egypt, Saint, ca. 250-355 or 6

ANTHONY, MARK, 83?-30 B.C.
see Antonius, Marcus, 83?-30 B.C.

ANTHONY, SUSAN B. (SUSAN BROWNELL), 1820-1906

An Account of the Proceedings on the Trial of Susan B. Anthony. 2006. 210p. pap. 20.99 *(978-1-4264-5152-2(0))* BiblioBazaar.

Anonymous. An Account of the Proceedings on the Trial of Susan B. Anthony. l.t. ed. 2007. (ENG.). 242p. pap. 22.99 *(978-1-4264-5453-0(8))* BiblioBazaar.

Anthony, Susan B. (Susan Brownell). An Account of the Proceedings on the Trial of Susan B Anthony at the Presidential Election in Nov 1872. 2006. 224p. per. 20.99 *(978-1-4255-1828-8(1))* MPublishing.

DeGezelle, Terri. Susan B. Anthony & the Women's Movement. 1 vol. 2007. (Life in the Time Of Ser.). (ENG., Illus.). 32p. (gr. -1-3). pap. 7.99 *(978-1-4034-9677-5(3))*; (gr. 1-3). 26.65 *(978-1-4034-9669-0(2))* Heinemann-Raintree. (Heinemann First Library).

Gordon, Ann D., ed. The Selected Papers of Elizabeth Cady Stanton & Susan B. Anthony Vol. V: Their Place Inside the Body-Politic, 1887 to 1895. 2009. (ENG., Illus.). 736p. 70.00 *(978-0-8135-2321-7(4))* Rutgers Univ. Pr.

Hull, N. E. H. The Woman Who Dared to Vote: The Trial of Susan B. Anthony. 2012. 232p. **(978-0-7006-1848-4(1))**; pap. **(978-0-7006-1849-1(X))** Univ. Pr. of Kansas.

Ida Husted Harper. The Life & Work of Susan B. Anthony. l.t. ed. 2007. 480p. pap. 34.99 *(978-1-4264-8530-5(1))* BiblioBazaar.

Lutz, Alma. Susan B Anthony. 2008. 424p. 30.99 *(978-0-554-38617-1(8))*; 32.99 *(978-0-554-29314-1(5))* BiblioBazaar.

Newell, Terry. Statesmanship, Character & Leadership in America: Lessons from History for Forging a Good Society. 2012. (ENG., Illus.). 300p. 90.00 **(978-0-230-34108-1(X))** Palgrave Macmillan.

Schechter, Patricia A. Exploring the Decolonial Imaginary: Four Transnational Lives. 2011. (Palgrave Macmillan Transnational History Ser.). (ENG., Illus.). 284p. 85.00 **(978-0-230-33877-7(1))** Palgrave Macmillan.

ANTHOZOA
see also Corals; Sea-Anemones

Hubmann, Bernhard & Piller, Werner, eds. Fossil Corals & Sponges: Proceedings of the 9th International Symposium on Fossil Cnidaria & Porifera, Graz 2003. 2007. (Schriftenreihe der erdwissenschaftlichen Kommission Ser.). (Illus.). 532p. (C). pap. 111.00 *(978-3-7001-3826-6(1))* Austrian Academy of Sciences Press AUT. Dist: Brown, David Bk. Co., The.

ANTHRACITE COAL

Ardan, Brian. The Anthracite Coal Region's Slavic Community. 2008. (Images of America Ser.). (ENG., Illus.). 128p. pap. 21.99 *(978-0-7385-6277-3(7))* Arcadia Publishing.

Curra, Thomas M. & Matkosky, Greg. Stories from the Mines. 2006. (Illus.). 82p. 25.00 *(978-1-58965-051-9(X))* Univ. of Scranton Pr.

Hosey, G. ed. Anthracite One. mass mkt. 7.95 *(978-0-9719456-0-9(8))* Anthracite.

Nearing, Scott. Anthracite: An Instance of Natural Resource Monopoly. 2009. 256p. 24.99 *(978-1-103-79283-2(0))*; pap. 18.99 *(978-1-103-79276-4(8))* BiblioBazaar.

Roberts, Peter. Anthracite Coal Communities: A Study of the Demography, the Social, Educational & Moral Life of the Anthracite Regions. 2010. 450p. pap. 36.75 *(978-1-143-50241-5(8))* BiblioBazaar.

Wolensky, Robert P. & Keating, Joseph M. Tragedy at Avondale: The Causes, Consequences, & Legacy of the Pennsylvania Anthracite Coal Industry's Most Deadly Mining Disaster, September 6 1869. 2008. (Illus.). 208p. per. 19.95 *(978-0-930973-40-7(2)*, Canal History & Technology Pr.) Moore, Hugh Historical Park & Museums, Inc.

ANTHRACOSIS
see Lungs—Dust Diseases

ANTHRAX

Bergman, Nicholas H., ed. Bacillus Anthracis & Anthrax. 2010. (ENG., Illus.). 337p. 129.95 *(978-0-470-41011-0(6)*, Wiley-Blackwell) Wiley, John & Sons, Inc.

Bradburne, Chris. Of Mice & Monocytes: Anthrax & the Host Genomic Response: Inhalational Anthrax Disease Pathogenesis & Progression, from Initial Mucosal Interactions to Organ System Functional Genomic Response. 2008. 124p. pap. *(978-3-639-08297-5(4))* VDM Verlag Dr. Mueller e.K.

Coen, Bob & Nadler, Eric. Anthrax War: Dead Silence... Fear & Terror on the Anthrax Trail. 2010. (ENG.). 272p. pap. 15.95 *(978-1-58243-587-9(1)*, Counterpoint Pr.) Basic Bks. GBR. Dist: Perseus-PGW.

—Dead Silence: Fear & Terror on the Anthrax Trail. 2009. (ENG.). 256p. 25.00 *(978-1-58243-509-1(X)*, Counterpoint Pr.) Basic Bks. GBR. Dist: Perseus-PGW.

Cole, Leonard A. The Anthrax Letters: A Leading Expert on Bioterrorism Explains the Science Behind the Anthrax Attacks. 2009. (ENG.). 304p. pap. 14.95 *(978-1-60239-715-6(5)*, 239715) Skyhorse Publishing Co., Inc.

Committee on Effectiveness of National Biosurveillance Systems: BioWatch and the Public Health System & National Research Council. BioWatch & Public Health Surveillance: Evaluating Systems for the Early Detection of Biological Threats: Abbreviated Version. 2011. (ENG.). 252p. pap. 50.50 *(978-0-309-13971-7(6))* National Academies Pr.

Committee on Review of the Scientific Approaches Used During the FBI's Investigation of the 2001 Bacillus Anthracis Mailings & National Research Council. Review of the Scientific Approaches Used During the FBI's Investigation of the 2001 Anthrax Letters. 2011. (ENG.). 250p. pap. 49.00 *(978-0-309-18719-0(2))* National Academies Pr.

Guillemin, Jeanne. American Anthrax: Fear, Crime, & the Investigation of the Nation's Deadliest Bioterror Attack. 2011. (ENG.). 336p. 27.00 *(978-0-8050-9104-5(1)*, Times Bks.) Holt, Henry & Co.

Johnstone, R. William. Bioterror: Anthrax, Influenza, & the Future of Public Health Security. 1 vol. 2008. (Praeger Security International Ser.). (Illus.). 232p. 49.95 *(978-0-275-99326-9(4)*, C9326, Praeger Security International) Greenwood Publishing Group, Inc.

Jones, Susan D. Death in a Small Package: A Short History of Anthrax. 2010. (Johns Hopkins Biographies of Disease Ser.). (ENG., Illus.). 352p. (gr. 17). 24.95 *(978-0-8018-9696-5(7))* Johns Hopkins Univ. Pr.

King, Leslie. A Clinical Laboratories Response to a Terrorist Assault with Anthrax. 2009. 172p. pap. *(978-3-639-19724-2(0))* VDM Verlag Dr. Mueller e.K.

Koehler, T. M., ed. Anthrax. 2010. (Current Topics in Microbiology & Immunology Ser.). (Illus.). ix, 169p. pap. 219.00 *(978-3-642-07799-9(4)*, 3642077994) Springer.

Matsumoto, Gary. Vaccine A: The Covert Government Experiment That's Killing Our Soldiers - And Why GI's Are Only the First Victims. 2010. (ENG.). 384p. (gr. 9). pap. 18.95 *(978-0-465-02182-6(4))* Basic Bks.

Rhodes, Keith. Anthrax Detection: DHS Cannot Ensure That Sampling Activities Will be Validated. 2007. (Illus.). 14p. (C). pap. 15.00 *(978-1-4223-1558-3(4))* DIANE Publishing Co.

Sarasin, Philipp. Anthrax: Bioterror as Fact & Fantasy. Weiss, Giselle, tr. from GER. 2006. (Illus.). 336p. 24.95 *(978-0-674-02346-8(3))* Harvard Univ. Pr.

Stroud, Clare, et al, eds. Prepositioning Antibiotics for Anthrax. 2012. (ENG.). 358p. pap. 64.00 **(978-0-309-21808-5(X))** National Academies Pr.

United States, Congress House Committee on Government Reform Subcommittee on National Security, Emerging Threats, and International Relations Staff, contrib. by. Anthrax Protection: Progress or Problems?: Hearing Before the Subcommittee on National Security, Emerging Threats, & International Relations of the Committee on Government Reform, House of Representatives, One Hundred Ninth Congress, Second Session, May 9, 2006. 2007. (Illus.). iv, 171p. *(978-0-16-078653-2(3)*, 552-070-35895-1) United States Government Printing Office.

Ust, ün T. B., et al. Anthrax in Humans & Animals. 4th rev. ed. 2009. (Nonserial Publication Ser.). (ENG.). 215p. pap. 48.00 *(978-92-4-154753-6(7))* World Health Organization.

Wan, Xiang. Microwave & Millimeter Characterization & Radiation. 2010. 240p. pap. *(978-3-639-14885-5(1))* VDM Verlag Dr. Mueller e.K.

Willman, David. The Mirage Man: Bruce Ivins, the Anthrax Attacks, & America's Rush to War. 2011. (Illus.). 464p. (ENG.). E-Book *(978-0-345-53021-9(7))*; 27.00 *(978-0-553-80775-2(7))* Random House Publishing Group.

ANTHROPO-LINGUISTICS
see Anthropological Linguistics

ANTHROPOGEOGRAPHY
see Human Geography

ANTHROPOLOGICAL ETHICS

Albro, Robert, et al, eds. Anthropologists in the SecurityScape: Ethics, Practice, & Professional Identity. 2011. (ENG.). 277p. 89.00 *(978-1-61132-012-1(7))*; pap. 34.95 *(978-1-61132-013-8(5))* Left Coast Pr., Inc.

Armbruster, Heidi & Lærke, Anna, eds. Taking Sides: Ethics, Politics, & Fieldwork in Anthropology. 2008. 272p. (C). 90.00 *(978-1-84545-421-0(9))* Berghahn Bks., Inc.

Fassin, Didier, ed. A Companion to Moral Anthropology. 2012. (Wiley-Blackwell Companions to Anthropology Ser.: 7). (ENG.). 664p. 195.00 **(978-0-470-65645-7(X)**, Wiley-Blackwell) Wiley, John & Sons, Inc.

Gewald, Jan-Bart, et al, eds. Strength Beyond Structure: Social & Historical Trajectories of Agency in Africa. 2007. (African Dynamics Ser.). (Illus.). 344p. pap. *(978-90-04-15696-8(8))* BRILL.

Goodale, Mark. Human Rights: An Anthropological Reader. 2008. (Wiley-Blackwell Readers in Anthropology Ser.). (ENG., Illus.). 416p. 104.95 *(978-1-4051-8335-2(7))*; pap. 46.95 *(978-1-4051-8334-5(9))* Wiley, John & Sons, Inc. (Wiley-Blackwell).

Hemley, Robin. Invented Eden: The Elusive, Disputed History of the Tasaday. 2007. (ENG., Illus.). 346p. pap. 23.95 *(978-0-8032-7363-4(0)*, Bison Bks.) Univ. of Nebraska Pr.

Katz, Adam, ed. The Originary Hypothesis: A Minimal Proposal for Humanistic Inquiry. 2007. (ENG.). 382p. pap. 28.00 *(978-1-888570-36-6(9))* Davies Group Pubs., The.

Lambek, Michael, ed. Ordinary Ethics: Anthropology, Language, & Action. 3rd ed. 2010. (ENG.). 480p. 100.00 *(978-0-8232-3316-8(2))*; pap. 32.00 *(978-0-8232-3317-5(0))* Fordham Univ. Pr.

Lucas, George R., Jr. Anthropologists in Arms: The Ethics of Military Anthropology. 2009. (Critical Issues in Anthropology Ser.). (ENG.). 246p. 75.00 *(978-0-7591-1212-4(6))*; pap. 27.50 *(978-0-7591-1213-1(4))* AltaMira Pr.

Lærke, Anna. Taking Sides: Ethics, Politics, & Fieldwork in Anthropology. Armbruster, Heidi, ed. 2010. 272p. 29.95 *(978-1-84545-701-3(3))* Berghahn Bks., Inc.

Madison, D. Soyini. Critical Ethnography: Method, Ethics, & Performance. 2nd ed. 2011. (Illus.). 304p. (C). pap. 45.00 *(978-1-4129-8024-1(0)*, B80234P) SAGE Pubns., Inc.

Robertson, Jennifer. Politics & Pitfalls of Japan Ethnography: Reflexivity, Responsibility, & Anthropological Ethics. 2009. (Illus.). 110p. 125.00 *(978-0-415-48649-1(1))* Routledge.

Salzano, Hurtado & Cram101 Textbook Reviews Staff. Lost Paradises & the Ethics of Research & Publication. 2007. 112p. per. 11.95 *(978-1-4288-2686-1(6))* Cram101 Inc.

Sanford, Victoria, ed. Engaged Observer: Anthropology, Advocacy, & Activism. 2006. (ENG.). 272p. (C). 68.00 *(978-0-8135-3891-4(2))* Rutgers Univ. Pr.

Turner & Cram101 Textbook Reviews Staff. Biological Anthropology & Ethics. 2007. 128p. per. 11.95 *(978-1-4288-2684-7(X))* Cram101 Inc.

Whiteford, Linda M. & Trotter, Robert T., 2nd. Ethics for Anthropological Research & Practice. 2008. 130p. (C). pap. 16.50 *(978-1-57766-535-9(X))* Waveland Pr., Inc.

ANTHROPOLOGICAL LINGUISTICS

Abe, Hideko. Queer Japanese: Gender & Sexual Identities Through Linguistic Practices. 2010. (ENG.). 212p. 79.00 *(978-0-230-62236-4(4))* Palgrave Macmillan.

Adelaar, Alexander. Siraya: Retrieving the Phonology, Grammar & Lexicon of a Dormant Formosan Language. (Trends in Linguistics. Documentation [TILDOC] Ser.). (ENG., 2012. Illus., XVI, 413p. (gr. 17). E-Book 280.00 **(978-3-11-219171-2(4))** 2011. 320p. 182.00 **(978-3-11-025295-8(3))** De Gruyter, Mouton DEU. Dist: de Gruyter, Walter GmbH & Co. KG.

Ahearn, Laura M. Living Language: An Introduction to Linguistic Anthropology. 2011. (Primers in Anthropology Ser.: 4). (ENG., Illus.). 368p. pap. 40.95 *(978-1-4051-2441-6(5))*; 94.95 *(978-1-4051-2440-9(7))* Wiley, John & Sons, Inc. (Wiley-Blackwell).

Anchimbe, Eric A. & Mforteh, Stephen A., eds. Postcolonial Linguistic Voices: Identity Choices & Representations. 2011. (Contributions to the Sociology of Language [CSL] Ser.). (ENG., Illus.). 210.00 **(978-3-11-026199-8(5))**; XIII, 365p. 140.00 **(978-3-11-026066-3(2))** De Gruyter, Mouton DEU. Dist: de Gruyter, Walter GmbH & Co. KG.

Ardener. The Voice of Prophesy & Other Essays. 2006. 326p. 27.50 **(978-1-84545-331-2(X))** Berghahn Bks., Inc.

Barriga Villanueva, Rebeca & Martín Butragueño, Pedro. Historia Sociolingüística de México, 2 vols. 2010. (Estudios Lingüísticos y Literarios Ser.). (SPA., Illus.). 634p. pap. 78.99 *(978-607-462-081-8(4))*; 694p. pap. 78.99 *(978-607-462-080-1(6))* El Colegio de México, A.C., Biblioteca Miguel Cosío Villegas MEX. Dist: Fondo de Cultura Economica USA.

Bartminski, Jerzy. Aspects of Cognitive Ethnolinguistics. Zinken, Jorg, ed. (Advances in Cognitive Linguistics Ser.). (ENG., Illus.). (C). 2012. 272p. pap. 34.95 *(978-1-84553-970-2(2))* 2009. 256p. 120.00 *(978-1-84553-342-7(9))* Equinox Publishing Ltd. GBR. Dist: ISD.

Bartminski, Jerzy & Lühr, Rosemarie, eds. Europa und seine Werte: Akten der internationalen Arbeitstagung Normen- und Wertbegriffe in der Verständigung zwischen Ost- und Westeuropa, 3./4. April 2008 in Lublin, Polen. 2009. (GER.). 298p. pap. 76.95 *(978-3-631-59057-7(1))* Lang, Peter GmbH, Europaischer Verlag der Wissenschaften DEU. Dist: Lang, Peter.

Blommaert, Jan. Grassroots Literacy: Writing, Identity & Voice in Central Africa. 2008. (Literacies Ser.). (ENG.). 240p. pap. 45.95 *(978-0-415-42630-5(8))*; XVI, 224p. 145.00 *(978-0-415-42631-2(6))* Routledge.

Botha, Rudolf & Knight, Chris, eds. The Cradle of Language. 2009. (Studies in the Evolution of Language Ser.). (ENG., Illus.). 408p. pap. 45.00 *(978-0-19-954586-5(3))* Oxford Univ. Pr., Inc.

—The Prehistory of Language. 2009. (Studies in the Evolution of Language Ser.). (ENG., Illus.). 368p. 150.00 *(978-0-19-954587-2(1))*; pap. 50.00 *(978-0-19-954588-9(X))* Oxford Univ. Pr., Inc.

Brenzinger, Matthias, ed. Language Death: Factual & Theoretical Explorations with Special Reference to East Africa. (Contributions to the Sociology of Language [CSL] Ser.). (ENG.). VIII, 445p. 105.00 ***(978-3-11-179261-3(7))*** De Gruyter, Mouton DEU. Dist: de Gruyter, Walter GmbH & Co. KG.

Briscoe, Ted, ed. Linguistic Evolution through Language Acquisition. 2008. (ENG., Illus.). 360p. pap. 48.00 *(978-0-521-07893-1(8))* Cambridge Univ. Pr.

Cleuziou, Serge, et al. Origin & Evolution of Languages: Approaches, Models, Paradigms. Laks, Bernard, ed. 2009. (ENG., Illus.). 352p. (C). pap. 35.00 *(978-1-84553-553-7(7))* Equinox Publishing Ltd. GBR. Dist: ISD.

Csergo, Zsuzsa. Talk of the Nation: Language & Conflict in Romania & Slovakia. 2007. (Illus.). 228p. 55.00 *(978-0-8014-4537-8(X))* Cornell Univ. Pr.

Davies, Catherine. English & Ethnicity. Janina, Brutt-Griffler, ed. 2006. (Signs of Race Ser.). (ENG.). 320p. 100.00 *(978-0-312-29599-8(5))* Palgrave Macmillan.

—English & Ethnicity. Brutt-Griffler, Janina, ed. 2006. (Signs of Race Ser.). (ENG.). 320p. pap. 32.00 *(978-0-312-29600-1(2))* Palgrave Macmillan.

D'Errico, Francesco & Hombert, Jean-Marie. Becoming Eloquent: Advances in the Emergence of Language, Human Cognition, & Modern Cultures. 2009. (Illus.). vi, 289p. *(978-90-272-3269-4(5))* Benjamins, John Publishing Co.

Duranti, Alessandro, ed. Linguistic Anthropology: A Reader. 2nd ed. 2009. (Wiley-Blackwell Anthologies in Social & Cultural Anthropology Ser.). (ENG., Illus.). 536p. 116.95 *(978-1-4051-2633-5(7))*; pap. 56.95 *(978-1-4051-2632-8(9))* Wiley, John & Sons, Inc. (Wiley-Blackwell).

Ehret, Christopher. History & the Testimony of Language. 2010. (California World History Library). (ENG., Illus.). 304p. 65.00 *(978-0-520-26204-1(2))*; pap. 29.95 *(978-0-520-26205-8(0))* Univ. of California Pr.

Farr, Marcia. Rancheros in Chicagoacán: Language & Identity in a Transnational Community. 2006. (ENG., Illus.). 342p. mass mkt. 30.00 *(978-0-292-71483-0(1))* Univ. of Texas Pr.

Fishman, Joshua & Garcia, Ofelia, eds. Handbook of Language & Ethnic Identity Vol. 2: The Success-Failure Continuum in Language & Ethnic Identity Efforts. 2011. (ENG., Illus.). 512p. 99.00 *(978-0-19-539245-6(0))* Oxford Univ. Pr., Inc.

Fought, Carmen. Language & Ethnicity. 2006. (Key Topics in Sociolinguistics Ser.). (ENG.). 264p. 116.00 *(978-0-521-84843-5(1))*; (C). per. 47.00 *(978-0-521-61291-3(8))* Cambridge Univ. Pr.

French, Brigittine M. Maya Ethnolinguistic Identity: Violence, Cultural Rights, & Modernity in Highland Guatemala. 2010. (ENG., Illus.). 192p. 50.00 *(978-0-8165-2767-0(9))* Univ. of Arizona Pr.

Goebel, Zane. Language, Migration, & Identity: Neighborhood Talk in Indonesia. 2010. (ENG., Illus.). 240p. 95.00 *(978-0-521-51991-5(8))* Cambridge Univ. Pr.

Granadillo, Tania & Orcutt-Gachiri, Heidi A. Ethnographic Contributions to the Study of Endangered Languages. 2011. (ENG., Illus.). 248p. 55.00 *(978-0-8165-2699-4(0))* Univ. of Arizona Pr.

Granberry, Julian. The Calusa: Linguistic & Cultural Origins & Relationships. 2011. (Illus.). 104p. *(978-0-8173-8579-8(7))*; (ENG., pap. 30.00 *(978-0-8173-1751-5(1))* Univ. of Alabama Pr.

Gregory, David A. Zuni Origins: Toward a New Synthesis of Southwestern Archaeology. Wilcox, David R., ed. 2007. (ENG., Illus.). 624p. 75.00 *(978-0-8165-2486-0(6))* Univ. of Arizona Pr.

Gregory, David A. & Wilcox, David R., eds. Zuni Origins: Toward a New Synthesis of Southwestern Archaeology. 2010. (ENG., Illus.). 544p. pap. 45.00 *(978-0-8165-2893-6(4))* Univ. of Arizona Pr.

Haarmann, Harald. Language in Ethnicity: A View of Basic Ecological Relations. (Contributions to the Sociology of Language [CSL] Ser.). (ENG.). IX, 287p. 90.00 ***(978-3-11-188406-6(6))*** De Gruyter, Mouton DEU. Dist: de Gruyter, Walter GmbH & Co. KG.

Harris, Roxy. New Ethnicities & Language Use. (Language & Globalization Ser.). (ENG.). 2009. 210p. pap. 37.00 *(978-0-230-58007-7(6))* 2006. (Illus.). 224p. 100.00 *(978-1-4039-9894-1(9))* Palgrave Macmillan.

Hintz, Daniel. Crossing Aspectual Frontiers: Emergence, Evolution, & Interwoven Semantic Domains in South Conchucos Quechua Discourse. 2011. (UC Publications in Linguistics Ser.). 372p. 44.95 ***(978-0-520-09885-5(4))*** Univ. of California Pr.

Homborg, Alf & Hill, Jonathan D., eds. Ethnicity in Ancient Amazonia: Reconstructing Past Identities form Archaeology, Linguistics, & Ethnohistory. 2011. (ENG., Illus.). 408p. 75.00 *(978-1-60732-094-4(0))* Univ. Pr. of Colorado.

Homborg, Alf & Hill, Jonathan David. Ethnicity in Ancient Amazonia: Reconstructing Past Identities from Archaeology, Linguistics, & Ethnohistory. 2011. (Illus.). xviii, 380p. E-Book ***(978-1-60732-095-1(9))*** Univ. Pr. of Colorado.

Householder, Fred W. & Lotfi, Mansour. Basic course in Azerbaijani. (Uralic & Altaic Ser.). (ENG.). XIII, 275p. 210.00 ***(978-3-11-207672-9(9))***; 135.00 ***(978-3-11-102434-9(2))*** De Gruyter, Mouton DEU. Dist: de Gruyter, Walter GmbH & Co. KG.

Jacobson, Rodolfo. The Pulse of a Malaysian University: Ethno- & Sociolinguistic Issues & the TESOL Dimension at Universiti Putra Malaysia. 2006. (Berkeley Insights in Linguistics & Semiotics Ser.: Vol. 60). (C). 69.95 *(978-0-8204-6393-3(0))* Lang, Peter Publishing, Inc.

Jones, Doug & Milicic, Bojka, eds. Kinship, Language, & Prehistory: Per Hage & the Renaissance in Kinship Studies. 2010. (ENG., Illus.). 350p. 70.00 *(978-1-60781-005-6(0))* Univ. of Utah Pr.

Kasi, Eswarappa & Malik, Ramesh, eds. Theory & Practice of Ethnography: Readings from the Periphery. 2009. 366p. 60.00 *(978-81-316-0306-2(7))* Rawat Pubns. IND. Dist: International Specialized Bk. Services.

Kroskrity, Paul V., ed. Telling Stories in the Face of Danger: Language Renewal in Native American Communities. 2012. (ENG., Illus.). 288p. (C). pap. 24.95 ***(978-0-8061-4227-2(8))*** Univ. of Oklahoma Pr.

Kroskrity, Paul V. & Field, Margaret C. Native American Language Ideologies: Beliefs, Practices, & Struggles in Indian Country. 2009. (ENG., Illus.). 336p. pap. 26.95 *(978-0-8165-2916-2(7))* Univ. of Arizona Pr.

—Native American Language Ideologies: Beliefs, Practices, & Struggles in Indian Country. Kroskrity, Paul V. & Field, Margaret C., eds. 2009. (ENG., Illus.). 336p. 49.95 *(978-0-8165-2719-9(9))* Univ. of Arizona Pr.

Kuipers, Joel & McDermott, Raymond, eds. Fine Description: Ethnographic & Linguistic Essays by Hal Conklin. 2007. (Monograph Series, Yale Southeast Asia Studies: 56). 535p. lib. bdg. 38.00 *(978-0-938692-84-3(4))* Yale Univ. Southeast Asia Studies.

Kuipers, Joel C. & McDermott, Raymond, eds. Fine Description: Ethnographic & Linguistic Essays by Hal Conklin. 2007. (Monograph Series, Yale Southeast Asia Studies: 56). 535p. pap. 27.00 *(978-0-938692-85-0(2))* Yale Univ. Southeast Asia Studies.

Labrum, Marian B., ed. The Changing Scene in World Languages: Issues & Challenges. (ATA Scholarly Monographs: Vol. IX). 160p. 126.00 *(978-1-55619-628-7(8))* Benjamins, John Publishing Co.

Laks, Bernard, ed. Origin & Evolution of Languages: Approaches, Models, Paradigms. 2008. (ENG., Illus.). 352p. (C). 95.00 *(978-1-84553-204-8(X))* Equinox Publishing Ltd. GBR. Dist: ISD.

Manning, Paul. The Semiotics of Drink & Drinking. 2012. (ENG.). 256p. 140.00 ***(978-1-4411-6018-8(3))***; pap. 44.95 ***(978-1-4411-3774-6(2))*** Continuum International Publishing Group, Ltd. GBR. Dist: National Bk. Network.

Masataka, Nobuo, ed. The Origins of Language: Unraveling Evolutionary Forces. (ENG., Illus.). viii, 157p. 2010. pap. 119.00 *(978-4-431-99853-2(5)*, 4431998535) 2008. 119.00 *(978-4-431-79101-0(9)*, 4431791019) Springer.

McCarty, Teresa L., ed. Ethnography & Language Policy. 2010. (ENG., Illus.). 328p. 49.95 *(978-0-415-80140-9(0))* Routledge.

Meyer, Christian & Girke, Felix, eds. The Rhetorical Emergence of Culture. 2011. (SRC Ser.). (Illus.). 342p. 95.00 *(978-0-85745-112-5(X))* Berghahn Bks., Inc.

O'Neill, Sean. Cultural Contact & Linguistic Relativity among the Indians of Northwestern California. 2008. (ENG., Illus.). 356p. (C). 50.00 *(978-0-8061-3922-7(6))* Univ. of Oklahoma Pr.

Patrick, Donna. Language, Politics, & Social Interaction in an Inuit Community. (Language, Power & Social Process [LPSP] Ser.). (ENG.). XII, 269p. 210.00 ***(978-3-11-180625-9(1))*** De Gruyter, Mouton DEU. Dist: de Gruyter, Walter GmbH & Co. KG.

Pelkey, Jamin R. Dialectology As Dialectic: Interpreting Phula Variation. 2011. (Trends in Linguistics. Studies & Monographs [TiLSM] Ser.). *(978-3-11-024584-4(1))* de Gruyter, Walter GmbH & Co. KG.

Pelkey, Jamin R. Dialectology as Dialectic: Interpreting Phula Variation. 2011. (Trends in Linguistics. Studies & Monographs [TiLSM] Ser.). (ENG., Illus.). XXXIV, 498p. 210.00 ***(978-3-11-187130-1(4))*** De Gruyter, Mouton DEU. Dist: de Gruyter, Walter GmbH & Co. KG.

Pepin, Nicolas. Identités Fragmentees: Elements Pour une Grammaire de l'identite. (FRE.). 326p. pap. 44.95 *(978-3-03911-299-9(6))* Lang, Peter Publishing, Inc.

Potowski, Kim. Language & Identity in a Dual Immersion School. 2007. (Bilingual Education & Bilingualism Ser.: 63). (ENG., Illus.). 240p. 99.95 *(978-1-85359-944-6(1))* Multilingual Matters GBR. Dist: Univ. of Toronto Pr.

—Language & Identity in a Dual Immersion School. 2007. (ENG., Illus.). 200p. pap. 39.95 *(978-1-85359-943-9(3))* Multilingual Matters GBR. Dist: Univ. of Toronto Pr.

Prasad, Ravi. Language, Caste & Ethnicity. 2010. 180p. pap. *(978-3-639-25458-7(9))* VDM Verlag Dr. Mueller e.K.

Reyes, Angela. Language, Identity, & Stereotype among Southeast Asian American Youth: The Other Asian. 2006. (ENG., Illus.). 192p. 95.00 *(978-0-8058-5539-5(4))* Routledge.

Roesch, Karen A. Language Maintenance & Language Death: The Decline of Texas Alsatian. 2012. (Culture & Language Use Ser.: Vol. 6). 149.00 ***(978-90-272-0288-8(5))*** Benjamins, John Publishing Co.

Rojas-Primus, Constanza. Lengua Ritual y Sincretismo. 2009. 228p. pap. *(978-3-639-17482-3(8))* VDM Verlag Dr. Mueller e.K.

Salzmann, Zdenek, et al. Language, Culture, & Society: An Introduction to Linguistic Anthropology. 5th ed. 2011. (ENG.). 448p. pap. 48.00 *(978-0-8133-4540-6(5))* Westview Pr.

Simpson, Andrew, ed. Language & National Identity in Africa. 2008. (ENG., Illus.). 448p. 165.00 *(978-0-19-928674-4(4))* Oxford Univ. Pr., Inc.

Singer, Milton B. Semiotics of Cities, Selves, & Cultures: Explorations in Semiotic Anthropology. (Approaches to Semiotics [AS] Ser.). (ENG.). XIII, 380p. 196.00 ***(978-3-11-178774-9(5))*** De Gruyter, Mouton DEU. Dist: de Gruyter, Walter GmbH & Co. KG.

Sodikoff, Genese Marie, ed. The Anthropology of Extinction: Essays on Culture & Species Death. 2011. (ENG., Illus.). 256p. 70.00 *(978-0-253-35713-7(6)*, 0253357136); pap. 24.95 *(978-0-253-22364-7(4)*, 0253223644) Indiana Univ. Pr.

Suleiman, Yasir. Arabic, Self & Identity: A Study in Conflict & Displacement, 1 vol. 2011. (ENG., Illus.). 288p. pap. 39.95 *(978-0-19-974700-9(8))* Oxford Univ. Pr., Inc.

Tallerman, Maggie & Gibson, Kathleen, eds. The Oxford Handbook of Language Evolution. 2012. (Oxford Handbooks Ser.). (ENG., Illus.). 752p. 175.00 ***(978-0-19-954111-9(6))*** Oxford Univ. Pr., Inc.

Underhill, James W. Ethnolinguistics & Cultural Concepts: Truth, Love, Hate & War. 2012. (ENG., Illus.). 264p. 99.00 ***(978-1-107-01064-2(0))*** Cambridge Univ. Pr.

Van Broekhoven, Laura N. K., ed. The Social & Linguistic Heritage of Native Peoples in the Americas: The Struggle to Maintain Cultural Particularity. 2006. 308p. *(978-0-7734-5639-6(2))* Mellen, Edwin Pr., The.

Whiteside, Anne. 'We Are the Explorers' Transnational Yucatec Maya-speakers NegotiatingMultilingual California. 2008. 204p. pap. *(978-3-639-04616-8(1))* VDM Verlag Dr. Mueller e.K.

Whorf, Benjamin Lee, et al. Language, Thought, & Reality: Selected Writings of Benjamin Lee Whorf. 2nd ed. 2012. pap. ***(978-0-262-51775-1(2))*** MIT Pr.

ANTHROPOLOGISTS

see also Women Anthropologists

Adams, William Y. The Road from Frijoles Canyon: Anthropological Adventures on Four Continents. 2009. (ENG., Illus.). 371p. 45.00 *(978-0-8263-4787-9(8))* Univ. of New Mexico Pr.

Amit, Vered. Biographical Dictionary of Social & Cultural Anthropology. 2008. (ENG.). 640p. (C). pap. 64.00 *(978-0-415-47553-2(8))* Routledge.

Bal, Özgür. Memory, Identity, Home. 2011. 360p. pap. ***(978-3-8443-9253-1(X))*** Lambert Academic Publishing.

Barnhart, Terry A. Ephraim George Squier & the Development of American Anthropology. 2009. (Critical Studies in the History of Anthropology Ser.). (ENG., Illus.). 444p. pap. 29.95 *(978-0-8032-2784-2(1))* Univ. of Nebraska Pr.

Blair, Mary Ellen. A Life Well Led: The Biography of Barbara Freire-Marreco Aitken, British Anthropologist. 2008. pap. 24.95 *(978-0-86534-496-9(5))* Sunstone Pr.

Bowman-Kruhm, Mary. The Leakeys: A Biography. 2009. (ENG., Illus.). 164p. pap. 17.00 *(978-1-59102-761-4(6))* Prometheus Bks., Pubs.

Britten, Marion Hale & Chadwick, Ida S. General Index: American Anthropologist, Current Anthropological Literature & Memoirs of the American Anthropological Association, 1888-1928. Kidder, Alfred Vincent, ed. 2011. 200p. 44.95 ***(978-1-258-06501-0(0))*** Literary Licensing, LLC.

Carrasco, David, et al. Breaking Through Mexico's Past: Digging the Aztecs with Eduardo Matos Moctezuma. 2007. (ENG., Illus.). 195p. 34.95 *(978-0-8263-3831-0(3))* Univ. of New Mexico Pr.

Caton, Steven C. Yemen Chronicle: An Anthropology of War & Mediation. 2006. (ENG., Illus.). 352p. per. 17.00 *(978-0-8090-9882-8(2)*, Hill & Wang) Farrar, Straus & Giroux.

Cei, José M. & Cei, Marcos. Faccetta Nera e la Regina Di Saba: Africa Orientale: Il Diario Di un Antropologo Alle Soglie Della Seconda Guerra Mondiale. 2007. (ITA., Illus.). 133p. (C). 20.00 *(978-88-596-0168-5(1))* Edizioni Polistampa ITA. Dist: Brown, David Bk. Co., The.

Chapman, Janet & Barrie, Karen. Kenneth Milton Chapman: A Life Dedicated to Indian Arts & Artists. 2008. (ENG., Illus.). 384p. 34.95 *(978-0-8263-4424-3(0))* Univ. of New Mexico Pr.

Chapman, Kenneth Milton. Kenneth Chapman's Santa Fe: Artists & Archaeologists, 1907-1931. 2008. (School for Advanced Research Resident Scholar Ser.). (ENG., Illus.). 200p. pap. 34.95 *(978-1-930618-92-3(1))* School for Advanced Research Pr./SAR Pr.

Cole, Sally. Ruth Landes: A Life in Anthropology. 2007. (Critical Studies in the History of Anthropology). (ENG.). 315p. pap. 29.95 *(978-0-8032-2245-8(9))* Univ. of Nebraska Pr.

Colwell-Chanthaphonh, Chip. Inheriting the Past: The Making of Arthur C. Parker & Indigenous Archaeology. 2009. (ENG., Illus.). 288p. 49.95 *(978-0-8165-2655-0(9))*; 296p. pap. 24.95 *(978-0-8165-2656-7(7))* Univ. of Arizona Pr.

Cram101 Textbook Reviews. Outlines & Highlights for Visions of Culture: An Introduction to Anthropological Theories & Theorists by Jerry Moore. 2011. 166p. pap. 29.95 ***(978-1-61490-597-4(5))*** Cram101 Inc.

Crook, Paul. Grafton Elliot Smith, Egyptology & the Diffusion of Culture: A Biographical Perspective. 2012. (Illus.). 168p. pap. 29.95 *(978-1-84519-481-9(0))* Sussex Academic Pr. GBR. Dist: International Specialized Bk. Services.

Dalby, Liza. East Wind Melts the Ice: A Memoir Through the Seasons. 2007. (Illus.). 318p. 40.00 *(978-0-520-25053-6(2))* Univ. of California Pr.

—East Wind Melts the Ice: A Memoir through the Seasons. 2009. (ENG.). 352p. pap. 21.95 *(978-0-520-25991-1(2))* Univ. of California Pr.

Davies, Peter J. Myth, Matriarchy & Modernity: Johann Jacob Bachofen in German Culture, 1860-1945. 2010. (Interdisciplinary German Cultural Studies). (ENG.). X, 462p. 99.95 *(978-3-11-022708-6(8))* De Gruyter, Walter Inc.

de Castro, Eduardo Viveiros, et al. The Turn of the Native. 2009. (ENG.). 100p. pap. 12.95 *(978-0-9761475-4-1(8))* Prickly Paradigm Pr., LLC.

De Neve, Geert & Unnithan-Kumar, Maya. Critical Journeys: The Making of Anthropologists. 2006. 220p. 120.00 *(978-0-7546-4809-3(5))* Ashgate Publishing Co.

Dube, Saurabh. Historias Esparcidas. 2007. (Estudios de Asia y África Ser.). (SPA., Illus.). 286p. pap. 57.99 *(978-968-12-1272-8(X))* El Colegio de México, A.C., Biblioteca Miguel Cosio Villegas MEX. Dist: Fondo de Cultura Economica USA.

Durrenberger, E. Paul & Erem, Suzan. Paradigms for Anthropology: An Ethnographic Reader. 2010. 352p. pap. 39.95 *(978-1-59451-781-5(9))* Paradigm Pubs.

Fenton, William N. Iroquois Journey: An Anthropologist Remembers. Campisi, Jack & Starna, William A., eds. 2009. (Iroquoians & Their World Ser.). (ENG., Illus.). 224p. pap. 24.95 *(978-0-8032-2789-7(2))* Univ. of Nebraska Pr.

Fenton, William Nelson & Fenton, William. Iroquois Journey: An Anthropologist Remembers. Campisi, Jack et al, eds. 2007. (Iroquoians & Their World Ser.). (ENG., Illus.). 223p. 55.00 *(978-0-8032-2021-8(9))* Univ. of Nebraska Pr.

Fratkin, Elliot M. Laibon: An Anthropologist's Journey with Samburu Diviners in Kenya. 2011. ***(978-0-7591-2069-3(2))***; (ENG.). 202p. 65.00 ***(978-0-7591-2067-9(6))***; (ENG.). 202p. pap. 24.95 ***(978-0-7591-2068-6(4))*** AltaMira Pr.

Friedlaender, Jonathan S. From Anthropometry to Genomics: Reflections of a Pacific Fieldworker. 2009. 264p. 29.95 *(978-1-4401-8288-4(4))*; pap. 19.95 *(978-1-4401-7672-2(8))* iUniverse, Inc.

Glenn, Anita. Nobody's Daughter: A Cherokee Story. 2008. 202p. pap. 16.51 *(978-1-4357-4479-0(9))* Lulu Enterprises Inc.

Gordon, Rob. Going Abroad: How to Travel Like an Anthropologist. 2010. (ENG.). 208p. 100.00 *(978-1-59451-770-9(3))* Paradigm Pubs.

Gordon, Robert. Fifty Key Anthropologists. 2010. (Routledge Key Guides). (ENG.). 320p. (C). 110.00 *(978-0-415-46104-7(9))*; pap. 27.95 *(978-0-415-46105-4(7))* Routledge.

—Going Abroad: How to Travel Like an Anthropologist, 1 vol. 2010. (ENG.). 208p. pap. 19.95 *(978-1-59451-771-6(1))* Paradigm Pubs.

Henderson, Harry. The Leakey Family. 2012. (Trailblazers in Science & Technology Ser.). 152p. (gr. 6-12). 35.00 *(978-1-60413-674-6(X)*, Chelsea Hse.) Facts On File, Inc.

Highland, Genevieve A. General Index: American Anthropologist & Memoirs of American Anthropological Association, 1939-1948, V53, No. 4, Part 2, October 1951. 2011. 78p. 37.95 ***(978-1-258-06625-3(4))*** Literary Licensing, LLC.

Hingston Quiggin, A. C. Haddon the Head Hunter: A Short Sketch of the Life of A. C. Haddon. 2011. (ENG.). 194p. pap. 12.99 *(978-0-521-16632-4(2))* Cambridge Univ. Pr.

Howe, James. Chiefs, Scribes, & Ethnographers: Kuna Culture from Inside & Out. 2009. (ENG., Illus.). 360p. 55.00 *(978-0-292-72110-4(2))* Univ. of Texas Pr.

Johnson, Thomas Hoevet & Johnson, Helen S. Two Toms: Lessons from a Shoshone Doctor. 2011. (ENG., Illus.). 104p. (gr. 13). pap. 15.95 *(978-1-60781-090-2(5))* Univ. of Utah Pr.

Kan, Sergei A. Lev Shternberg: Anthropologist, Russian Socialist, Jewish Activist. 2009. (Critical Studies in the History of Anthropology Ser.). (ENG., Illus.). 574p. 65.00 *(978-0-8032-1603-7(3))* Univ. of Nebraska Pr.

Kane, Eileen. Trickster: An Anthropological Memoir. 2010. (CAI & ENG., Illus.). 248p. ***(978-1-4426-0177-2(9))***; pap. ***(978-1-4426-0178-9(7))*** Univ. of Toronto Pr.

Kehoe, Alice Beck & Doughty, Paul L., eds. Expanding American Anthropology, 1945-1980: A Generation Reflects. 2012. (ENG., Illus.). 312p. pap. 40.00 ***(978-0-8173-5688-0(6))*** Univ. of Alabama Pr.

Kehoe, Alice Beck, et al. Expanding American Anthropology, 19451980: A Generation Reflects. 2011. ***(978-0-8173-8589-7(4))*** Univ. of Alabama Pr.

Kennedy, Roger G. Hidden Cities: The Discovery & Loss of Ancient North American Cities. 2011. (ENG.). 384p. pap. 23.99 ***(978-1-4516-5875-0(3)***, Free Pr.) Free Pr.

Kerns, Virginia. Journeys West: Jane & Julian Steward & Their Guides. 2010. (ENG., Illus.). 444p. 55.00 *(978-0-8032-2508-4(3))* Univ. of Nebraska Pr.

—Scenes from the High Desert: Julian Steward's Life & Theory. 2009. (ENG., Illus.). 448p. pap. 26.00 *(978-0-252-07635-0(4))* Univ. of Illinois Pr.

Koerner, E. F. K., ed. Edward Sapir: Critical Assessments of Leading Linguists, 3 vols. 2007. (Critical Assessments of Leading Linguists Ser.). (ENG.). 1200p. (C). 835.00 *(978-0-415-25507-3(4))* Routledge.

Koerner K Staff. Edward Sapir Vol. 1: Critical Assessments. 2007. 384p. *(978-0-415-25508-0(2))* Routledge.

—Edward Sapir Vol. 2: Critical Assessments. 2007. 400p. *(978-0-415-25509-7(0))* Routledge.

—Edward Sapir Vol. 3: Critical Assessments. 2007. 416p. *(978-0-415-25510-3(4))* Routledge.

Lamothe, Daphne. Inventing the New Negro: Narrative, Culture, & Ethnography. 2008. 240p. (C). 59.95 *(978-0-8122-4093-1(6))* Univ. of Pennsylvania Pr.

Latourette, K. s. & Laufer, Berthold. Biographical Memoir of Berthold Laufer, 1874-1934: National Academy of Sciences Biographical Memoirs, V18, Third Memoir. 2011. 34p. 35.95 ***(978-1-258-06839-4(7))*** Literary Licensing, LLC.

Malaurie, Jean. Hummocks: Journeys & Inquiries among the Canadian Inuit. 2007. (ENG., Illus.). 424p. (C). *(978-0-7735-3200-7(5))* McGill-Queen's Univ. Pr.

Malinowski, Bronislaw. A Diary in the Strict Sense of the Term. Guterman, N., tr. from POL. 2nd ed. (Illus.). 315p. *(978-0-485-11354-9(6))* Continuum International Publishing Group, Ltd.

Marcos. Notes from the Jungle. 2008. 244p. (ENG.). 31.99 *(978-1-4257-5186-9(5))*; per. 21.99 *(978-1-4257-5184-5(9))* Xlibris Corp.

Moore, Jerry D. Visions of Culture: An Introduction to Anthropological Theories & Theorists. 3rd ed. 2008. (ENG.). 416p. 90.00 *(978-0-7591-1145-5(6))*; pap. 39.95 *(978-0-7591-1146-2(4))* AltaMira Pr.

Nabudere, W. Archie Mafeje: Scholar, Activist & Thinker. 2011. 118p. pap. ***(978-0-7983-0286-9(0))*** Africa Institute of South Africa.

Nielsen, Kenneth Bo. Imagining & Encountering the Indian State. 2011. 152p. pap. ***(978-3-8454-2463-7(X))*** Lambert Academic Publishing.

Nixon, Joseph M. The Left Handed Cannibal: The Life & Writings of Myron Stanley Nixon, 1919-2000. 2009. 152p. 22.95 (978-1-4490-2472-7(6)); pap. 11.99 (978-1-4490-2471-0(8)) AuthorHouse.

Norcini, Marilyn. Edward P. Dozier: The Paradox of the American Indian Anthropologist. 2007. (ENG., Illus.). 208p. 45.00 (978-0-8165-1790-9(8)) Univ. of Arizona Pr.

Panwar, Jayprakash. New Media Society. 2010. 68p. pap. (978-3-639-11402-7(7)) VDM Verlag Dr. Mueller e.K.

Patterson, Thomas C. & Patterson, Thomas Carl. Karl Marx, Anthropologist. 2009. (ENG.). 256p. pap. 34.95 (978-1-84520-511-9(1)); (Illus.). 1p. 109.95 (978-1-84520-509-6(X)) Berg Pubs. GBR. Dist: Macmillan.

Patterson, Wm Patrick, et al. The Life & Teachings of Carlos Castaneda. 2008. (978-1-879514-97-3(4)) Arete Communications.

Peace, William J. Leslie A. White: Evolution & Revolution in Anthropology. 2007. (Critical Studies in the History of Anthropology). (ENG.). 312p. pap. 29.95 (978-0-8032-2254-0(8)) Univ. of Nebraska Pr.

Price, David H. Anthropological Intelligence: The Deployment & Neglect of American Anthropology in the Second World War. 2008. (ENG.). 400p. (C). 94.95 (978-0-8223-4219-9(7)); pap. 26.95 (978-0-8223-4237-3(5)) Duke Univ. Pr.

Price, David H. Weaponizing Anthropology: Social Science in Service of the Militarized State. 2011. (Counterpunch Ser.). (ENG., Illus.). 208p. pap. 15.95 **(978-1-84935-063-1(9))** AK Pr. GBR. Dist: Consortium Bk. Sales & Distribution.

Rivière, Peter. A History of Oxford Anthropology. 2007. (Methodology & History in Anthropology Ser.). (Illus.). 230p. 90.00 (978-1-84545-348-0(4)) Berghahn Bks., Inc.

Rivière, Peter, ed. A History of Oxford Anthropology. 2009. 230p. 24.50 (978-1-84545-599-3(8)) Berghahn Bks., Inc.

Robert Anderson. The Back Door to Medicine: An Embedded Anthropologist Tells All. 2009. 276p. pap. 20.95 (978-1-4401-7289-2(7)) iUniverse, Inc.

Rolston, Scott L. The Big Picture Man: Reflections on the Life & Thought of Alfred Louis Kroeber. 2011. 224p. pap. 18.95 (978-1-4502-5953-8(7)) iUniverse, Inc.

Sackman, Douglas C. Wild Men: Ishi & Kroeber in the Wilderness of Modern America. 7th ed. 2010. (New Narratives in American History Ser.). (ENG., Illus.). 352p. 24.95 (978-0-19-517852-4(1)) Oxford Univ. Pr., Inc.

Sackman, Douglas Cazaux. Wild Men: Ishi & Kroeber in the Wilderness of Modern America. 7th ed. 2010. (New Narratives in American History Ser.). (ENG., Illus.). 384p. (C). pap. 14.95 (978-0-19-517853-1(X)) Oxford Univ. Pr., Inc.

Sanderson, Stephen K. & Kuznar, Lawrence A. Studying Societies & Cultures: Marvin Harris's Cultural Materialism & Its Legacy. 2008. (ENG., Illus.). 344p. per. 50.95 (978-1-59451-288-9(4)) Paradigm Pubs.

—Studying Societies & Cultures: Marvin Harris's Cultural Materialism & Its Legacy. Sanderson, Stephen K., ed. 2006. (Studies in Comparative Social Science). (ENG., Illus.). 344p. 125.00 (978-1-59451-287-2(6)) Paradigm Pubs.

Seifert, Mark. Feeding the Mouth of the Bull: Provisioning native Caribbean foragers within the new economy of Bocas del Toro, Panama. 2008. 220p. pap. (978-3-639-06648-7(0)) VDM Verlag Dr. Mueller e.K.

Shankland, David, ed. Archaeology, Anthropology & Heritage in the Balkans & Anatolia. 2010. 208.00 (978-1-61719-087-2(X)); 208.00 (978-1-61719-088-9(8)) Gorgias Pr., LLC.

Stewart, William. Biographical Dictionary of Anthropologists. 2009. (ENG.). 245p. pap. 55.00 (978-0-7864-3671-2(9)) McFarland & Co., Inc. Pubs.

Stocking, George W. Glimpses into My Own Black Box: An Exercise in Self-Deconstruction. 2010. (History of Anthropology Ser.). (ENG., Illus.). 168p. pap. 24.95 (978-0-299-24984-7(0)) Univ. of Wisconsin Pr.

Strother, Ruth. Margaret Mead: Cultural Anthropologist. 2009. (Essential Lives Set 3 Ser.). (Illus.). 112p. (YA). (gr. 7-12). 34.22 (978-1-60453-525-9(3)) ABDO Publishing Co.

Swanton, John Reed & Holmes, William Henry. Biographical Memoir of William Henry Holmes, 1846-1933: National Academy of Sciences Biographical Memoirs, V17, Tenth Memoir. 2011. 38p. 35.95 **(978-1-258-06848-6(6))** Literary Licensing, LLC.

Swindler, Daris R. New Britain Diary 1954: An Anthropologist's Journal. 2007. (ENG., Illus.). 150p. per. 18.95 (978-0-9791921-1-1(0)) Ravenna Pr.

Thomas, Vicky. The Naga Queen: Ursula Graham Bowers & Her Jungle Warriors, 1939-45. 2012. (ENG., Illus.). 240p. 35.00 **(978-0-7524-6401-5(9))** History Pr. Ltd.,The GBR. Dist: Independent Pubs. Group.

Van Bremen, Jan, et al, eds. Asian Anthropology. 2009. 12p. pap. 39.95 (978-0-415-54667-6(2)) Routledge.

Waterston, Alisse & Vesperi, Maria D., eds. Anthropology off the Shelf: Anthropologists on Writing. 2009. (ENG.). 232p. 94.95 (978-1-4051-8920-0(7), Wiley-Blackwell) Wiley, John & Sons, Inc.

Wilcken, Patrick. Claude Lévi-Strauss: The Father of Modern Anthropology. 2012. (ENG., Illus.). 432p. (gr. 12). 18.00 **(978-0-14-312062-9(X)**, Penguin (Non-Classics)) Penguin Group (USA) Inc.

Wilcken, Patrick. Claude Levi-Strauss: The Poet in the Laboratory. 2010. (ENG., Illus.). 416p. (gr. 12). 29.95 (978-1-59420-273-5(7), Penguin Pr. HC, The) Penguin Group (USA) Inc.

Wilcox, Clifford. Robert Redfield & the Development of American Anthropology. 2006. (ENG., Illus.). 246p. per. 29.50 (978-0-7391-1777-4(7)) Lexington Bks.

Willerslev, Rane. On the Run in Siberia. OhAlseadha, Collin, tr. from DAN. 2012. (Illus.). 216p. 60.00 **(978-0-8166-7626-2(7))**; pap. 19.95 **(978-0-8166-7627-9(5))** Univ. of Minnesota Pr.

Wuletaw, Mekuria. Adoption of Trapezoidal Water Harvesting Ponds in Northern Ethiopia: Determinants & Alternative Measures of Floodwater Harvesting Techniques at Household Level. 2011. 72p. pap. **(978-3-639-33666-5(6))** VDM Verlag Dr. Mueller e.K.

ANTHROPOLOGY

see also Acculturation; Anthropological Linguistics; Applied Anthropology; Archaeology; Art and Anthropology; Assimilation (Sociology); Business Anthropology; Educational Anthropology; Ethnology; Extraterrestrial Anthropology; Historical Sociology; Human Geography; Language and Languages; Law and Anthropology; Literature and Anthropology; Medical Anthropology; National Characteristics; Physical Anthropology

also individual races, tribes, etc., e.g. Caucasian Race; Indians of North America; Shona (African People); also subdivisions Ethnic Relations and Race Relations under names of countries, cities, etc.

Aaslid, Flore Singer. Facing the Dragon. 2010. 268p. pap. (978-3-639-12155-1(4)) VDM Verlag Dr. Mueller e.K.

Aberi, George. Critical Perspectives on Language & Girl Education. 2010. 100p. pap. (978-3-639-24249-2(1)) VDM Verlag Dr. Mueller e.K.

Adams, Bradley J. & Byrd, John E., eds. Recovery, Analysis, & Identification of Commingled Human Remains. 2010. (ENG., Illus.). xv, 374p. pap. 149.00 (978-1-61737-765-5(1), 1617377651) Humana Pr.

Agosta, Diana. Naming the Future. 2009. 256p. pap. (978-3-639-14689-9(1)) VDM Verlag Dr. Mueller e.K.

Alcock, Susan E. & Osborne, Robin, eds. Classical Archaeology. 2nd ed. 2012. (Wiley-Blackwell Studies in Global Archaeology Ser.: 14). (ENG.). 548p. pap. 44.95 **(978-1-4443-3691-7(6)**, Wiley-Blackwell) Wiley, John & Sons, Inc.

Allgayer-Kaufmann, Regine & Weber, Michael, eds. African Perspectives: Pre-colonial History, Anthropology, & Ethnomusicology. 2008. (Vergleichende Musikwissenschaft Ser.). (Illus.). 370p. pap. 81.95 (978-3-631-56503-2(8)) Lang, Peter GmbH, Europaischer Verlag der Wissenschaften DEU. Dist: Lang, Peter.

Alves, Joao Pedro Galhano. The Artificial Simulacrum World the Geopolitical Elimination of Communitary Land Use & Its Effects on Our Present Global Condition. 2009. 76p. pap. 9.95 (978-1-60860-701-3(1), Eloquent Bks.) AEG Literary Publishing Services, Inc.

Amare, Hanna Getachew. Tourism in South Omo: The Case of the Mursi of Southern Ethiopia. 2010. 92p. pap. (978-3-639-28517-8(4)) VDM Verlag Dr. Mueller e.K.

Amit, Vered & Dyck, Noel, eds. Claiming Individuality: The Cultural Politics of Distinction. 2006. (Anthropology, Culture & Society Ser.). (ENG.). 240p. 100.00 (978-0-7453-2459-3(2)); per. 31.00 (978-0-7453-2458-6(4)) Pluto Pr. GBR. Dist: Macmillan.

AMS Studies in Anthropology, 11 vols. (978-0-404-62600-6(9)) AMS Pr., Inc.

Anemone, Robert L. Anthropology 1500: Race, Biology, & Culture. 2nd rev. ed. 2009. (ENG.). 166p. spiral bd. 72.07 (978-0-7575-6089-7(X)) Kendall Hunt Publishing Co.

—Race & Human Diversity: A Biocultural Approach. rev. ed. 2010. (ENG.). 216p. (C). pap. 45.60 (978-0-13-183876-5(8), Prentice Hall) Prentice Hall PTR.

Angeloni, Elvio. Annual Editions: Anthropology 12/13. 35th ed. 2011. (Annual Editions Ser.). (ENG., Illus.). 256p. (C). pap. 44.00 **(978-0-07-805101-2(0)**, 0078051010, McGraw-Hill/Dushkin) McGraw-Hill Higher Education.

—Anthropology. 2007. (Classic Edition Sources Ser.). (ENG.). 272p. (C). per. 45.63 (978-0-07-337969-2(7), 0073379697, McGraw-Hill/Dushkin) McGraw-Hill Higher Education.

—Anthropology 09/10. annuals 32nd ed. 2008. (Annual Editions Ser.). (ENG.). 256p. (C). pap. 44.00 (978-0-07-339783-2(0), 0073397830, McGraw-Hill/Dushkin) McGraw-Hill Higher Education.

—Anthropology 11/12. 34th ed. 2010. (Annual Editions Ser.). (ENG., Illus.). 256p. (C). pap. 44.00 (978-0-07-805070-1(7), 0078050707, McGraw-Hill/Dushkin) McGraw-Hill Higher Education.

Angst, Linda Isako. In a Dark Time: Memory, Community, & Gendered Nationalism in Postwar Okinawa. 2009. (Harvard East Asian Monographs). (Illus.). 250p. 39.95 (978-0-674-02869-2(4)) Harvard Univ., Asia Ctr.

Annual Review of Anthropology. 2006. 75.00 (978-0-8243-1935-9(4)) Annual Reviews, Inc.

Anthro 5 Lab Manual. 2nd ed. 2007. (C). spiral bd. 15.00 net. (978-0-9724419-1-9(3)) Birkdale Pubs.

Anthropological Essays Presented o Edward Burnett Tylor in Honour of His 75th Birthday, Oct. 2, 1907. 416p. reprint ed. 98.00 (978-0-7222-1948-5(2)) Library Reprints, Inc.

Anthropology. 2011. (ENG.). VI, 166p. pap. 84.00 **(978-3-11-023653-8(2))** De Gruyter, Walter Inc.

Anthropology: [Print + Online]. 2011. (ENG.). 320p. 105.00 **(978-3-11-023655-2(9))** De Gruyter, Walter Inc.

Apoh, Wazi. Concise Anthropology: The Five-Field Approach. rev. ed. 2010. (ENG.). 266p. pap. 78.00 (978-0-7575-7245-6(6)) Kendall Hunt Publishing Co.

Apolon, Leon. Comprehension: The World's Reality. 2009. 120p. pap. 30.95 (978-1-4389-9845-9(7)) AuthorHouse.

Arno & Arno, Andrew. Alarming Reports: Communicating Conflict in the Daily News. 2009. (Illus.). 216p. 75.00 (978-1-84545-579-8(7)) Berghahn Bks., Inc.

Ash, Patricia J. & Robinson, David J. The Emergence of Humans: An Exploration of the Evolutionary Timeline. 2010. (ENG., Illus.). 338p. pap. 73.95 (978-0-470-01315-1(X), Wiley) Wiley, John & Sons, Inc.

Ashby, Muata. Comparative Mythology, Cultural & Social Studies & the Cultural Category- Factor Correlation Method: A New Approach to Comparative Cultural, Relig. 2007. 308p. per. 21.95 (978-1-884564-72-7(0)) Sema Institute of Yoga.

Atran, Scott. Talking to the Enemy: Faith, Brotherhood, & the (Un) Making of Terrorists. 2010. 384p. 27.99 (978-0-06-134490-9(7), Ecco) HarperCollins Pubs.

Axelsson, Per & Sköld, Peter, eds. Indigenous Peoples & Demography: The Complex Relation Between Identity & Statistics. 2011. (ENG., Illus.). 354p. 120.00 (978-0-85745-000-5(X)) Berghahn Bks., Inc.

Baca, George, et al, eds. Empirical Futures: Anthropologists & Historians Engage the Work of Sidney W. Mintz. 2009. (ENG.). 272p. 62.95 (978-0-8078-3345-2(2)); pap. 26.95 (978-0-8078-5988-9(5)) Univ. of North Carolina Pr.

Baker, Lee D. Anthropology & the Racial Politics of Culture. 2010. (ENG.). 296p. pap. 23.95 (978-0-8223-4698-2(2)); (Illus.). 84.95 (978-0-8223-4686-9(9)) Duke Univ. Pr.

Baldwin, Neil. Leyendas de la Serpiente Emplumada: Biografia de un Dios Mexicano.Tr. of Legends of the Plumed Serpent: Biography of a Mexican God. (SPA.). 224p. 36.95 (978-84-01-01289-1(9), PJ11254) Plaza & Janes Editores, S.A. ESP. Dist: Lectorum Pubns., Inc.

Balkansky. The Human Experience: A Recitation Manual for Anthropology. 2nd rev. ed. 2011. (ENG.). 120p. spiral bd. 47.02 (978-0-7575-6652-3(9)) Kendall Hunt Publishing Co.

Bancel, Nicolas, et al, eds. Human Zoos: From the Hottentot Venus to Reality Shows. Bridgeman, Teresa, tr. 2009. (ENG., Illus.). 352p. pap. 39.95 (978-1-84631-174-1(8)) Liverpool Univ. Pr. GBR. Dist: Chicago Distribution Ctr.

—Human Zoos: Science & Spectacle in the Age of Colonial Empires. Bridgeman, Teresa, tr. 2009. (ENG., Illus.). 352p. 85.00 (978-1-84631-123-9(3)) Liverpool Univ. Pr. GBR. Dist: Chicago Distribution Ctr.

Bank, Leslie J. Home Spaces, Street Styles: Contesting Power & Identity in a South African City, 1 vol. 2011. (ENG., Illus.). 272p. 96.00 (978-0-7453-2328-2(6)); pap. 33.00 (978-0-7453-2327-5(8)) Pluto Pr. GBR. Dist: Macmillan.

Barnard, Alan. Genesis of Symbolic Thought. 2012. (ENG.). 216p. pap. **(978-1-107-65109-8(3))**; (Illus.). **(978-1-107-02569-1(9))** Cambridge Univ. Pr.

Barnard, Alan & Spencer, Jonathan, eds. Encyclopedia of Social & Cultural Anthropology. 2nd rev. ed. 2011. (ENG., Illus.). 896p. (C). pap. 65.00 **(978-0-415-80936-8(3))** Routledge.

Barnouw. Introduction to Anthropology, 1. 4th ed. Date not set. (Anthropology Ser.). mass mkt. 21.75 (978-0-534-10473-3(8)) Wadsworth.

Baronov, David. The African Transformation of Western Medicine & the Dynamics of Global Cultural Exchange. 2008. (ENG.). 264p. (C). 61.50 (978-1-59213-915-6(9)) Temple Univ. Pr.

Bashkow, Ira. An Anthropological Theory of the Corporation. 2012. 94p. pap. 12.95 (978-0-9794057-9-2(3)) Prickly Paradigm Pr., LLC.

Beddoe, John. The Anthropological History of Europe. 2009. 92p. pap. (978-1-151-60562-7(X)) Books LLC.

—The Anthropological History of Europe. 2009. 132p. 35.95 (978-1-104-79097-4(1)); pap. 20.95 (978-1-104-78305-1(3)) Kessinger Publishing, LLC.

Belting, Hans & Dunlap, Thomas. An Anthropology of Images - Picture, Medium, Body. 2011. (ENG., Illus.). 208p. (C). 39.95 (978-0-691-14500-6(8)) Princeton Univ. Pr.

Bengtsson, Tommy. Kinship & Demographic Behavior in the Past. 2008. (International Studies in Population Ser.). (Illus.). X, 284p. (C). 129.00 (978-1-4020-6732-7(1), 1402067321) Springer.

Bille, Mikkel, et al. The Anthropology of Absence. 2010. (Illus.). xi, 221p. E-Book (978-1-4419-5529-6(1)) Springer.

Binda, Judy. The Renaissance of Native Spirituality: The Journey of the Spiritual Seeker & Traditional Healing Practices. 2011. 180p. 26.95 **(978-1-4620-2783-5(0))**; pap. 16.95 **(978-1-4620-2782-8(2))** iUniverse, Inc.

Bird, S. Elizabeth, ed. The Anthropology of News & Journalism: Global Perspectives. 2009. (ENG., Illus.). 344p. pap. 25.00 (978-0-253-22126-1(9), 0253221269) Indiana Univ. Pr.

Birx, H. James, ed. 21st Century Anthropology, 2 vols. 2010. (Illus.). 1144p. 345.00 (978-1-4129-5738-0(9), B57389C) SAGE Pubns., Inc.

Black, S. M., et al. Disaster Victim Identification: Experience & Practice. 2011. (ENG., Illus.). 272p. 129.95 (978-1-4200-9412-1(2), CRC Press) Taylor & Francis Group GBR. Dist: Taylor & Francis Group.

Blau, Soren & Ubelaker, Douglas, eds. Handbook of Forensic Anthropology & Archaeology. 2011. (World Archaeological Congress Research Ser.). (ENG., Illus.). 534p. pap. 49.95 (978-1-61132-793-9(8)) Left Coast Pr., Inc.

Bloch, Maurice. In & Out of Each Others' Bodies: Theory of Mind, Evolution, Truth, & the Nature of the Social, 1 vol. 2011. 160p. 91.00 **(978-1-61205-101-7(4))** Paradigm Pubs.

Boas, Frank. Anthropology in North America. 378p. reprint ed. 98.00 (978-0-7222-9651-6(7)) Library Reprints, Inc.

Boas, Franz, et al. Anthropology in North America. 2007. (ENG.). 384p. per. 33.95 (978-0-548-63882-8(9)) Kessinger Publishing, LLC.

Boivin, Michel. Sindh through History & Representations: French Contributions to Sindhi Studies. 2007. (Illus.). 146p. 24.95 (978-0-19-547503-6(8)) Oxford Univ. Pr., Inc.

Bollnow, Otto Friedrich. Human Space. Kohlmaier, Joseph, ed. Shuttleworth, Christine, tr. from GER. 2011. (ENG.). 320p. pap. 35.00 (978-0-907259-35-0(9)) Princeton Architectural Pr.

Boogaarts-de Bruin, Simone. Something for Everyone? Changes & Choices in the Ethno-Party Scene in Urban Nightlife. 2011. (UvA Proefschriften Ser.). 224p. pap. (978-90-5629-669-3(8), Vossiupers UvA) Amsterdam Univ. Pr.

Bosk, Charles L. What Would You Do? Juggling Bioethics & Ethnography. 2008. 288p. 50.00 (978-0-226-06676-9(2)); (ENG.). pap. 20.00 (978-0-226-06677-6(0)) Univ. of Chicago Pr.

Bowen, John Richard & Bowen, Jack. Religions in Practice: An Approach to the Anthropology of Religion. 5th ed. 2010. (ENG., Illus.). 272p. (C). pap. 42.60 (978-0-205-79525-3(0), Prentice Hall) Prentice Hall PTR.

Braha, Dan, et al, eds. Complex Engineered Systems: Science Meets Technology. 2010. (Understanding Complex Systems Ser.). x, 385p. pap. 149.00 (978-3-642-06937-6(1), 3642069371) Springer.

Brear, Holly Beachley. Inherit the Alamo: Myth & Ritual at an American Shrine. 2008. (ENG.). 192p. pap. 24.95 (978-0-292-71874-6(8)) Univ. of Texas Pr.

Brenner, Joni, et al. Life of Bone: Art Meets Science. 2011. (ENG., Illus.). 160p. 50.00 **(978-1-86814-539-3(5))** Witwatersrand Univ. Pr. Pubns. ZAF. Dist: Transaction Pubs.

Brickley, Megan B. & Ferllini, Roxana. Forensic Anthropology: Case Studies from Europe. 2007. (Illus.). 268p. 68.95 (978-0-398-07703-7(7)); pap. 48.95 (978-0-398-07704-4(5)) Thomas, Charles C. Pub., Ltd.

Britten, Marion Hale & Chadwick, Ida S. General Index: American Anthropologist, Current Anthropological Literature & Memoirs of the American Anthropological Association, 1888-1928. Kidder, Alfred Vincent, ed. 2011. 200p. 44.95 **(978-1-258-06501-0(0))** Literary Licensing, LLC.

Brody, Hugh & Brody, H. Maps & Dreams, 1 vol. (ENG., Illus.). 320p. pap. 22.95 (978-0-88894-593-8(0)) D&M Pubs. Inc. CAN. Dist: Perseus-PGW.

Brooks, James, et al. Small Worlds: Method, Meaning, & Narrative in Microhistory. 2008. (School for Advanced Research Advanced Seminar Ser.). (C). pap. 29.95 (978-1-930618-94-7(8)) School for Advanced Research Pr./SAR Pr.

Burger, Joachim, et al, eds. Population Dynamics in Pre- And Early History: New Approaches by Using Stable Isotopes & Genetics. 2012. (Topoi Ser.: 5). (ENG., Illus.). X, 353p. (gr. 17-17). 140.00 **(978-3-11-026629-0(6))** De Gruyter, Walter Inc.

Burns, Karen Ramey. Forensic Anthropology Training Manual. 3rd rev. ed. 2012. (ENG.). 384p. (C). spiral bd. 70.60 **(978-0-205-02259-5(6)**, Prentice Hall) Prentice Hall PTR.

Calabrese, John Anthony. The Emergence of Social & Political Complexity in the Shashi-Limpopo Valley of Southern Africa, AD 900 to 1300: Ethnicity, Class, & Polity. 2007. (Bar S Ser.). (Illus.). xv, 384p. (C). pap. 120.00 (978-1-4073-0029-0(6)) British Archaeological Reports Ltd. GBR. Dist: Brown, David Bk. Co., The.

Carlson, David. Shared Diversity: People & Culture in Our Global Village. 350p. pap. 49.95 (978-1-57879-027-2(1)) Bowers, Eddie Publishing Company, Inc.

Carlson, Elwood. The Lucky Few: Between the Greatest Generation & the Baby Boom. 2008. (ENG., Illus.). xx, 216p. pap. 34.95 (978-1-4020-8850-6(7), 1402088507) Springer.

Carpenter, Carol. Environmental Anthropology: A Historical Reader. Dove, Michael R. & Carpenter, Carol, eds. Dove, Michael, ed. 2007. (Wiley-Blackwell Anthologies in Social & Cultural Anthropology Ser.). (ENG., Illus.). 504p. 120.95 (978-1-4051-1125-6(9), Wiley-Blackwell) Wiley, John & Sons, Inc.

Carrere, Ernest Daniel. Creating a Human World: A New Psychological & Religious Anthropology in Dialogue with Freud, Heidegger, & Kierkegaard. 2006. 281p. 30.00 (978-1-58966-116-5(8)); per. 20.00 (978-1-58966-122-6(2)) Univ. of Scranton Pr.

Carver, Martin, et al. Wasperton: A Roman, British & Anglo-Saxon Community in Central England. 2009. (Anglo-Saxon Studies: Volume 11). (Illus.). 384p. 99.00 (978-1-84383-427-4(8), Boydell Press) Boydell & Brewer, Ltd. GBR. Dist: Boydell & Brewer, Inc.

Casper, Monica & Moore, Lisa Jean. Missing Bodies: The Politics of Visibility. 2009. (ENG., Illus.). 240p. 70.00 (978-0-8147-1677-9(6)); pap. 21.00 (978-0-8147-1678-6(4)) New York Univ. Pr.

Chacon, Richard J. & Mendoza, Rubén G., eds. The Ethics of Anthropology & Amerindian Research: Reporting on Environmental Degradation & Warfare. 2011. (ENG., Illus.). xvi, 521p. 179.00 **(978-1-4614-1064-5(9)**, 1461410649) Springer.

Chazan, Michael. World Prehistory & Archaeology. 2nd ed. 2010. (ENG.). 480p. (C). 82.67 (978-0-205-78754-8(1)); 46.67 (978-0-205-79731-8(8)) Prentice Hall PTR. (Prentice Hall).

—World Prehistory & Archaeology: Pathways Through Time. 2nd ed. 2010. (ENG., Illus.). 480p. (C). pap. 123.33 (978-0-205-78623-7(5), Prentice Hall) Prentice Hall PTR.

—World Prehistory & Archaeology, Books a la Carte Edition. 2nd ed. 2010. (ENG.). 480p. (C). ring bd. 80.67 (978-0-205-00353-2(2), Prentice Hall) Prentice Hall PTR.

—World Prehistory & Archaeology, Books a la Carte Plus MyAnthroLab. 2nd ed. 2010. (ENG.). (C). ring bd. 87.33 (978-0-205-00354-9(0), Prentice Hall) Prentice Hall PTR.

Chua, Liana. The Christianity of Culture: Conversion, Ethnic Citizenship, & the Matter of Religion in Malaysian Borneo. 2011. (Contemporary Anthropology of Religion Ser.). (ENG., Illus.). 274p. 90.00 **(978-0-230-12046-4(6))** Palgrave Macmillan.

Churchward, Albert. Ancient Implements & How to Distinguish Them. 2006. pap. 12.95 (978-1-4286-7792-0(5)) Kessinger Publishing, LLC.

—The People of the British Isles, the Druids, & the Lunar Cult. 2006. pap. 9.95 (978-1-4286-7773-9(9)) Kessinger Publishing, LLC.

Clark-Decès, Isabelle. A Companion to the Anthropology of India. 2011. (Wiley-Blackwell Companions to Anthropology Ser.: 14). (ENG.). 568p. 199.95 (978-1-4051-9892-9(3), Wiley-Blackwell) Wiley, John & Sons, Inc.

Cochrane, Ethan E. The Evolutionary Archaeology of Ceramic Diversity in Ancient Fiji. 2009. (Bar S Ser.). (Illus.). 167p. (C). bds. 90.00 *(978-1-4073-0395-6(3))* British Archaeological Reports Ltd. GBR. Dist: Brown, David Bk. Co., The.

Coffman, Candace. Accessing Anthropology: A Workbook/Reader Introducing the Field of Cultural Anthropology. rev. ed. 2010. (ENG.). 470p. pap. 74.88 *(978-0-7575-7221-0(9))* Kendall Hunt Publishing Co.

Cohen, Alix. Kant & the Human Sciences: Biology, Anthropology & History. 2009. (ENG., Illus.). 256p. 95.00 *(978-0-230-22432-2(6))* Palgrave Macmillan.

Cohen, Yehudi, ed. Human Adaptation: The Biosocial Background. 2010. (ENG., Illus.). 533p. pap. 39.95 *(978-0-202-36384-4(8))* Transaction Pubs.

Coleman, Simon & Collins, Peter. Locating the Field: Space, Place & Context in Anthropology. Collins, Peter, ed. 2007. (ASA Monographs). (ENG., Illus.). 256p. pap. 36.95 *(978-1-84520-403-7(4))* Berg Pubs. GBR. Dist: Macmillan.

—Locating the Field: Space, Place & Context in Anthropology. 2006. (ASA Monographs). (ENG., Illus.). 1p. 120.95 *(978-1-84520-402-0(6))* Berg Pubs. GBR. Dist: Macmillan.

Colleyn, Jean-Paul. The Horses of Satire: The Kcrdugaw of Mali. 2011. 160p. 40.00 *(978-2-35340-093-5(0))* Gourcuff Gradenigo FRA. Dist: National Bk. Network.

Colleyn, Jean-Paul, et al. The World of the Anthropologist. Howe, John, tr. from FRE. rev. ed. 2006. (ENG.). 192p. pap. 25.95 *(978-1-84520-448-8(4))* Berg Pubs. GBR. Dist: Macmillan.

Compiled by the British Library of Political and Economic Science, ed. IBSS: Anthropology: 2010 Vol. 56: International Bibliography of the Social Sciences. 2012. (ENG.). 752p. (C). 570.00 ***(978-0-415-69286-1(5))*** Routledge.

Compiled by the British Library of Political and Economic Science, ed. International Bibliography of the Social Sciences 2008 Vol. 54: Anthropology. 2009. 522p. 490.00 *(978-0-415-55466-4(7))* Routledge.

Cooper, Eugene & Simic, Andrei. Readings in Anthropology. 2nd rev. ed. 2007. (ENG.). 324p. pap. 80.30 *(978-0-7575-2087-7(1))* Kendall Hunt Publishing Co.

Copeland, Nick & Labuski, Christine. Walmart & the American Dream. 2013. (Routledge Series for Creative Teaching & Learning in Anthropology Ser.). (ENG.). 128p. 110.00 *(978-0-415-89487-6(5))*; pap. 25.95 *(978-0-415-89488-3(3))* Routledge.

Cox, Margaret, et al, eds. Scientific Investigation of Mass Graves: Towards Protocols & Standard Operating Procedures. 2007. (ENG., Illus.). 592p. 203.00 *(978-0-521-86587-6(5))* Cambridge Univ. Pr.

Cram101 Textbook Reviews. Outlines & Highlights for the Anthropology of Globalization by Ind. 2011. 138p. pap. 28.95 ***(978-1-61905-192-8(3))*** Cram101 Inc.

Cram101 Textbook Reviews & Cram101 Textbook Reviews. Outlines & Highlights for Anthropology: Appreciating Human Diversity by Conrad Kottak, ISBN. 2011. 474p. pap. 37.95 ***(978-1-61461-906-2(9))*** Cram101 Inc.

—Outlines & Highlights for Anthropology: The Human Challenge by William Haviland, ISBN. 2011. 620p. pap. 41.95 ***(978-1-61461-910-9(7))*** Cram101 Inc.

—Outlines & Highlights for Culture & Health: Applying Medical Anthropology by Michael Winkelman, ISBN. 2011. 272p. pap. 32.95 ***(978-1-61744-892-8(3))*** Cram101 Inc.

—Outlines & Highlights for Introducing Anthropology: An Integrated Approach by Michael Park, ISBN. 2011. 266p. pap. 31.95 ***(978-1-61461-875-1(5))*** Cram101 Inc.

—Outlines & Highlights for the Subject of Anthropology: Gender, Symbolism & Psychoanalysis by Henrietta L. Moore (William Wyse Chair of Social Anthro. 2011. 188p. pap. 30.95 ***(978-1-4288-6496-2(2))*** Cram101 Inc.

Cram101 Textbook Reviews Staff. Outlines & Highlights for Anthropology: The Exploration of Human Diversity with Living Anthropology Student by Conrad Kottak, ISBN. 2009. 70p. pap. 27.95 *(978-1-4288-8499-1(8))* Cram101 Inc.

—Outlines & Highlights for Anthropology by Conrad Phillip Kottak, Isbn: 9780073405360. 2009. 178p. pap. 29.95 *(978-1-4288-9640-6(6))* Cram101 Inc.

Crate, Susan A. & Nuttall, Mark, eds. Anthropology & Climate Change: From Encounters to Actions. 2009. (ENG., Illus.). 416p. lib. bdg. 89.00 *(978-1-59874-333-3(3))* Left Coast Pr., Inc.

Cremo, Michael A. The Forbidden Archeologist: The Atlantis Rising Columns of Michael Cremo. 2010. 248p. 21.95 *(978-0-89213-337-6(6))* Torchlight Publishing.

Cultural Research Services Staff. Modern Primitives: The Recurrent Ritual of Adornment. (ICR Monographs: No. 37). 21p. 8.00 *(978-0-904674-29-3(0)*, MOPR1) Institute for Cultural Research, The GBR. Dist: I S H K.

Cunnane, Stephen & Stewart, Kathlyn, eds. Human Brain Evolution: The Influence of Freshwater & Marine Food Resources. 2010. (ENG., Illus.). 217p. 144.95 *(978-0-470-45268-4(4)*, Wiley-Blackwell) Wiley, John & Sons, Inc.

Davies, James. The Making of Psychotherapists: An Anthropological Analysis. 2009. 340p. pap. 53.00 *(978-1-85575-656-4(0))* Karnac Bks. GBR. Dist: Stylus Publishing, LLC.

Davis, Dorothy. A Study Guide for Contemporary Non-Western Cultures. 6th rev. ed. 2011. (ENG.). 116p. spiral bd. 40.11 *(978-0-7575-8584-5(1))* Kendall Hunt Publishing Co.

Davis, Dorothy I. A Study Guide for Contemporary Non-Western Cultures. 5th rev. ed. 2010. (ENG.). 118p. spiral bd. 38.21 *(978-0-7575-5501-5(2))* Kendall Hunt Publishing Co.

Davis, Merryl. Introducing Anthropology. 2010. (Introducing Ser.). (ENG., Illus.). 176p. 9.95 ***(978-1-84831-168-8(0))*** Totem Bks. GBR. Dist: Consortium Bk. Sales & Distribution.

Davis-Palmer, Yvonne. Cultural Identity & Creolized Religion in Sligoville. 2010. 456p. pap. *(978-3-8383-4994-7(6))* Lambert Academic Publishing.

De Quatrefages, A. The Natural History of Man: a Course of Elementary Lectures. Youmans, Eliza A., tr. 2007. (ENG.). 156p. per. 21.95 *(978-1-4304-4364-3(2))* Kessinger Publishing, LLC.

Dean, Bartholomew & Homan, Joshua E. Anthropological Illuminations of the Varieties of Human Experience. rev. ed. 2010. (ENG.). 418p. pap. 83.62 *(978-0-7575-7923-3(X))* Kendall Hunt Publishing Co.

Delaney, Carol. Investigating Culture: An Experiential Introduction to Anthropology. 2nd ed. 2011. (ENG., Illus.). 424p. pap. 61.95 *(978-1-4051-5424-6(1)*, Wiley-Blackwell) Wiley, John & Sons, Inc.

Denega, Danielle M. & Denega, Danielle. Have You Seen This Face? The Work of Forensic Artists. 2007. (24/7: Science Behind the Scenes Ser.). (ENG., Illus.). 64p. (YA). (gr. 9-12). 29.00 *(978-0-531-11823-8(1)*, Watts, Franklin) Scholastic Library Publishing.

DeSalle, Rob & Tattersall, Ian. Human Origins: What Bones & Genomes Tell Us about Ourselves. 2012. (Texas A&M University Anthropology Ser.). (Illus.). 216p. pap. 29.95 ***(978-1-60344-518-4(8))*** Texas A&M Univ. Pr.

Dove, Michael R. & Carpenter, Carol, eds. Environmental Anthropology: A Historical Reader. 2007. (Wiley-Blackwell Anthologies in Social & Cultural Anthropology Ser.). (ENG., Illus.). 504p. pap. 64.95 *(978-1-4051-1137-9(2)*, Wiley-Blackwell) Wiley, John & Sons, Inc.

Downey, Gary L. & Dumit, Joseph, eds. Cyborgs & Citadels: Anthropological Interventions in Emerging Sciences & Technologies. (Advanced Seminar Ser.). 328p. 29.95 *(978-0-933452-96-1(9))*; pap. 24.95 *(978-0-933452-97-8(7))* School for Advanced Research Pr./SAR Pr.

Dudgeon, Roy C. The Pattern Which Connects: Batesonian Holism & Postmodern Science. 2008. 168p. pap. 19.95 *(978-1-4357-4299-4(0))* Lulu Enterprises Inc.

Dunbar, Robin, et al. Social Brain, Distributed Mind. 2010. (Proceedings of the British Academy Ser.). (ENG., Illus.). 400p. 95.00 *(978-0-19-726452-2(2))* Oxford Univ. Pr., Inc.

Dupret, Badouin & Pinto, Paulo. Ethnographies of Islam: Ritual Performances & Everyday Practices. Pierret, Thomas & Spellman-Poots, Kathryn, eds. 2012. (ENG., Illus.). 192p. (gr. 17). 95.00 ***(978-0-7486-4550-3(0))*** Edinburgh Univ. Pr. GBR. Dist: Columbia Univ. Pr.

Durham, William H., ed. Annual Review of Anthropology, Vol. 36. 2007th ed. 2007. 422p. pap. 181.00 *(978-0-8243-1936-6(2))* Annual Reviews, Inc.

Edwards, Jeanette & PetroviAuml;Dagger;-Aring; teger, Maja, eds. Recasting Anthropological Knowledge: Inspiration & Social Science. 2011. (ENG., Illus.). 218p. 95.00 ***(978-1-107-00968-4(5))*** Cambridge Univ. Pr.

Ember, et al. Anthropology, Books a la Carte Edition. 13th ed. 2010. (ENG.). 624p. (C). ring bd. 94.00 *(978-0-205-82857-9(4)*, Prentice Hall) Prentice Hall PTR.

—Anthropology, Books a la Carte Plus MyAnthroLab. 13th ed. 2010. (ENG.). (C). ring bd. 100.67 *(978-0-205-84210-0(0)*, Prentice Hall) Prentice Hall PTR.

Ember, Carol R., et al. Anthropology. 12th ed. 2006. pap. *(978-0-13-240561-4(X))* Pearson Education Canada.

—Anthropology. 13th ed. 2011. (Illus.). xviii, 606p. *(978-0-205-73885-4(0))* 2010. (ENG.). 656p. (C). pap. 143.67 *(978-0-205-73882-3(6)*, Prentice Hall) Prentice Hall PTR.

—eText Student Access Code Card for Anthropology. 13th ed. 2010. (ENG.). 656p. (C). 109.33 *(978-0-205-79733-2(4)*, Prentice Hall) Prentice Hall PTR.

Ember, Melvin R., et al. Human Evolution & Culture. 7th rev. ed. 2011. (ENG., Illus.). 528p. (C). pap. 99.33 ***(978-0-205-23239-0(6)***, Prentice Hall) Prentice Hall PTR.

Endicott, Kirk & Welsch, Robert. Anthropology: Clashing Views in Anthropology. 4th ed. 2008. (Taking Sides Ser.). (ENG., Illus.). 432p. (C). pap. 48.00 *(978-0-07-351522-9(1)*, 0073515221, McGraw-Hill/Dushkin) McGraw-Hill Higher Education.

Erickson & University of Toronto Press. Anthropological Theory (Set) 2009. (ENG.). pap. *(978-1-55402-805-4(1))* Univ. of Toronto Pr.

Eriksen, Thomas Hylland. Globalization: The Key Concepts. 2007. (Key Concepts Ser.). (ENG.). 1p. 88.95 *(978-1-84520-523-2(5))*; 192p. pap. 20.95 *(978-1-84520-524-9(3))* Berg Pubs. GBR. Dist: Macmillan.

Fagan, Brian. Cro-Magnon: How the Ice Age Gave Birth to the First Modern Humans. 2010. (ENG., Illus.). 320p. 28.00 *(978-1-59691-582-4(X))* Bloomsbury Publishing.

Fagan, Brian M. World Prehistory: A Brief Introduction. 8th ed. 2010. (ENG.). 432p. (C). pap. 105.67 *(978-0-205-01791-1(6)*, Prentice Hall) Prentice Hall PTR.

Fassin, Didier, ed. A Companion to Moral Anthropology. 2012. (Wiley-Blackwell Companions to Anthropology Ser.: 7). (ENG.). 664p. 195.00 ***(978-0-470-65645-7(X)***, Wiley-Blackwell) Wiley, John & Sons, Inc.

Faubion, James D. & Marcus, George E., eds. Fieldwork Is Not What It Used to Be: Learning Anthropology's Method in a Time of Transition. 2009. 248p. pap. 21.95 *(978-0-8014-7511-5(2))*; (Illus.). 71.95 *(978-0-8014-4776-1(3))* Cornell Univ. Pr.

Fedorak, Shirley. Anthropology Matters! 2007. (Illus.). 234p. pap. *(978-1-55111-761-4(4))* Univ. of Toronto Pr.

Ferraro, Gary & Andreatta, Susan. Cultural Anthropology: An Applied Perspective. 9th ed. 2011. (ENG.). 480p. (C). pap. 184.95 *(978-1-111-30151-4(4))*; ring bd. 114.95 *(978-1-111-63319-6(3))* Wadsworth.

Fikes, Jay. Unknown Huichol: Shamans & Immortals, Allies against Chaos. 2010. (ENG., Illus.). 65.00 *(978-0-7591-2026-6(9))* AltaMira Pr.

Fikes, Jay C. Unknown Huichol: Shamans & Immortals, Allies Against Chaos. 2010. *(978-0-7591-2028-0(5))* Rowman & Littlefield Publishers, Inc.

Firth, Raymond. Social Organization & Peasant Societies: Festschrift in Honor of Raymond Firth. Freedman, Maurice, ed. 2008. (ENG.). 309p. pap. 39.95 *(978-0-202-36216-8(7))* Transaction Pubs.

Fischer, Michael. Anthropological Futures. 2009. (Experimental Futures Ser.). (ENG., Illus.). 424p. pap. 27.95 *(978-0-8223-4476-6(9))* Duke Univ. Pr.

Fischer, Michael M. J. Anthropological Futures. 2009. (Experimental Futures Ser.). (ENG., Illus.). 424p. 99.95 *(978-0-8223-4461-2(0))* Duke Univ. Pr.

Fisher, Jennifer & Shay, Anthony, eds. When Men Dance: Choreographing Masculinities Across Borders. 2009. (ENG., Illus.). 432p. pap. 29.95 *(978-0-19-538670-7(1))* Oxford Univ. Pr., Inc.

Flannery, Kent & Marcus, Joyce. The Creation of Inequality: How Our Prehistoric Ancestors Set the Stage for Monarchy, Slavery, & Empire. 2012. (ENG., Illus.). 544p. 39.95 ***(978-0-674-06469-0(0))*** Harvard Univ. Pr.

Fontana, Bernard L., et al. The Kiva V25, No 3, February 1960. Fontana, Bernard L., ed. 2011. 48p. 35.95 ***(978-1-258-01499-5(8))*** Literary Licensing, LLC.

Fox, Richard G., ed. Recapturing Anthropology: Working in the Present. (Advanced Seminar Ser.). 264p. 34.95 *(978-0-933452-77-0(2))*; (ENG.). 1p. pap. 29.95 *(978-0-933452-78-7(0))* School for Advanced Research Pr./SAR Pr.

Fox, Richard G. & Field, Les W., eds. Anthropology Put to Work. 2007. (Wenner-Gren International Symposium Ser.). (ENG.). 256p. pap. 31.95 *(978-1-84520-601-7(0))* Berg Pubs. GBR. Dist: Macmillan.

Freeman, Leslie. Anthropology without Informants: Collected Works in Paleoanthropology by L. G. Freeman. 2009. (ENG., Illus.). 352p. 60.00 *(978-0-87081-947-6(X))* Univ. Pr. of Colorado.

Friedman, Kajsa. The Anthropology of Global Systems, 2 Vols. 2007. (ENG.). 144.95 *(978-0-7591-1161-5(8))* AltaMira Pr.

Fuchs, Stephen. The Origin of Man & His Culture. 2nd ed. 300p. 20.00 *(978-0-89563-291-3(8))* Coronet Bks.

Gardiner Barber, Pauline, et al, eds. Confronting Capital: Critique & Engagement in Anthropology. 2012. (Routledge Studies in Anthropology Ser.). (ENG.). 256p. (C). 125.00 *(978-0-415-89629-0(0))* Routledge.

Geller, Pamela L. & Stockett, Miranda K., eds. Feminist Anthropology: Past, Present, & Future. 2007. 248p. (C). per. 24.95 *(978-0-8122-2005-6(6))* Univ. of Pennsylvania Pr.

Gezon, Lisa & Kottak, Conrad Phillip. Culture. 2011. (ENG., Illus.). 352p. (C). pap. 94.33 *(978-0-07-803502-9(3)*, 0078035023) McGraw-Hill Cos., The.

Gibbon, Sahra, et al, eds. Racial Identities, Genetic Ancestry, & Health in South America: Argentina, Brazil, Colombia, & Uruguay. 2011. (ENG., Illus.). 272p. 85.00 *(978-0-230-11061-8(4))* Palgrave Macmillan.

Gibson, Lois. Forensic Art Essentials: A Manual for Law Enforcement Artists. 2007. (ENG., Illus.). 432p. per. 108.00 *(978-0-12-370898-4(2)*, Academic Pr.) Elsevier Science & Technology Bks.

Girard, René. To Double Business Bound: Essays on Literature, Mimesis & Anthropology. 248p. *(978-0-485-11343-3(0))* Continuum International Publishing Group, Ltd.

Glazer, Ilsa M. We're the Bipeds: An Introduction to Anthropology. 5th ed. 2008. 330p. spiral bd. 40.00 *(978-0-9753247-3-8(X))* New Life Publishing Co.

Glorstad, Hakon & Prescott, Christopher, eds. Becoming European: The Transformation of Third Millennium Northern & Western Europe. 2011. (ENG., Illus.). 181p. (C). pap. 70.00 ***(978-1-84217-450-0(9))*** Oxbow Bks., Ltd. GBR. Dist: Brown, David Bk. Co., The.

Gluckman, Max. Closed Systems & Open Minds: The Limits of Naivety in Social Anthropolgy. Gluckman, Max, ed. 2006. (ENG.). 284p. (gr. 11). pap. 29.95 *(978-0-202-30859-3(6))* Aldine Transaction.

Goode, Joshua. Impurity of Blood: Defining Race in Spain, 1870-1930. 2009. 288p. 39.95 *(978-0-8071-3516-7(X))* Louisiana State Univ. Pr.

Goodman, Jane E. & Silverstein, Paul A., eds. Bourdieu in Algeria: Colonial Politics, Ethnographic Practices, Theoretical Developments. Fogarty, Patricia, tr. 2009. (France Overseas: Studies in Empire & D Ser.). (ENG., Illus.). 290p. pap. 35.00 *(978-0-8032-1362-3(X))* Univ. of Nebraska Pr.

Gordon, Robert. Fifty Key Anthropologists. 2010. (Routledge Key Guides). (ENG.). 320p. (C). pap. 27.95 *(978-0-415-46105-4(7))* Routledge.

Gottlieb, Alma. The Restless Anthropologist: New Fieldsites, New Visions. 2012. (ENG.). 208p. 67.50 ***(978-0-226-30489-2(2))***; pap. 22.50 ***(978-0-226-30490-8(6))*** Univ. of Chicago Pr.

Goudineau, Yves & Lorrillard, Michel. Recherches Nouvelles Sur le Laos: New Research on Laos. 2009. (FRE & ENG., Illus.). 678p. pap. 90.00 *(978-2-85539-654-5(9))* Silkworm Bks. THA. Dist: Univ. of Washington Pr.

Goulet, Jean-Guy A. & Miller, Bruce Granville, eds. Extraordinary Anthropology: Transformations in the Field. 2007. (ENG., Illus.). 472p. pap. 34.95 *(978-0-8032-5992-8(1))* Univ. of Nebraska Pr.

Graslund, Bo. The Birth of Prehistoric Chronology: Dating Methods & Dating Systems in Nineteenth-Century Scandinavian Archaeology. 2008. (New Studies in Archaeology Ser.). (ENG.). 144p. pap. 33.99 *(978-0-521-10388-6(6))* Cambridge Univ. Pr.

Gray, Gordon. Cinema: A Visual Anthropology. 2010. (ENG., Illus.). 1p. 99.95 *(978-1-84520-793-9(9))*; 224p. pap. 29.95 *(978-1-84520-794-6(7))* Berg Pubs. GBR. Dist: Macmillan.

Greenhouse, Carol J. The Paradox of Relevance: Ethnography & Citizenship in the United States. 2011. 328p. (C). 59.95 *(978-0-8122-4312-3(9))* Univ. of Pennsylvania Pr.

Gullette, Gregory, et al. The Essence of Anthropology. 2006. (ENG.). 240p. (C). stu. ed., per. 59.95 *(978-0-534-62374-6(3))* Wadsworth.

Haddon, Alfred C. The Study of Man. 2010. 482p. pap. 37.75 *(978-1-149-55497-5(5))* BiblioBazaar.

—The Study of Man. 460p. 2010. 42.36 *(978-1-163-40064-7(5))* 2010. pap. 30.36 *(978-1-162-92730-5(5))* 2007. (ENG.). 52.95 *(978-0-548-09258-3(3))* Kessinger Publishing, LLC.

Hafez, Sherine & Slyomovics, Susan, eds. Anthropology of the Middle East & North Africa: Into the New Millennium. 2012. (Public Cultures of the Middle East & North Africa Ser.). (ENG.). 368p. 85.00 ***(978-0-253-00746-9(1)***, 0253007461); pap. 30.00 ***(978-0-253-00753-7(4)***, 0253007534) Indiana Univ. Pr.

Hanlon, Michael. Eternity: Our Next Billion Years. 2008. (MacSci Ser.). (ENG., Illus.). 280p. 24.95 *(978-0-230-21931-1(4))* Palgrave Macmillan.

Hannerz, Ulf. Anthropology's World: Life in a Twenty-First Century, 1 vol. 2010. (ENG.). 216p. 30.00 *(978-0-7453-3047-1(9))*; lib. bdg. 95.00 *(978-0-7453-3048-8(7))* Pluto Pr. GBR. Dist: Macmillan.

Harrison, Julia & Darnell, Regna, eds. Historicizing Canadian Anthropology. 2007. (ENG.). 352p. pap. *(978-0-7748-1273-3(7))* Univ. of British Columbia Pr.

Harvard University, Peabody Museum of Archaeology Staff. Russian Translation Series, 4 vols. in 10 pts. reprint ed. lib. bdg. 544.50 *(978-0-404-52640-5(3))* AMS Pr., Inc.

Harvey. Text & Context: The Social Anthropology of Tradition. Date not set. (C). pap. *(978-0-312-04807-5(6))* Bedford/Saint Martin's.

Haviland & Cram101 Textbook Reviews Staff. Anthropology. 2007. 180p. per. 12.95 *(978-1-4288-2584-0(3))* Cram101 Inc.

Haviland, Prins & Cram101 Textbook Reviews Staff. Anthropology the Human Challenge. 2007. 364p. per. 17.95 *(978-1-4288-2676-2(9))* Cram101 Inc.

Haviland, William A., et al. Anthropology: The Human Challenge. 13th ed. 2010. (ENG.). 784p. (C). pap. 177.95 *(978-0-495-81084-1(3))*; ring bd. 123.95 *(978-0-8400-3331-4(1))* Wadsworth.

—The Essence of Anthropology. (ENG., (C). 2006. Illus.). 432p. per. 117.95 *(978-0-534-62371-5(9))* 2nd ed. 2009. 408p. pap. 131.95 *(978-0-495-59981-4(6))* Wadsworth.

Hedgepeth, Jessica Dianne. The Domestic Economy of Early Postclassic Rio Viejo, Oaxac. 2010. 212p. pap. *(978-3-639-23169-4(4))* VDM Verlag Dr. Mueller e.K.

Hertzog, Esther, et al, eds. Perspectives on Israeli Anthropology. 2013. (Illus.). 732p. pap. 45.00 *(978-0-8143-3050-0(9))* Wayne State Univ. Pr.

Heuberger, Barbara. Cultural Diversity: Building Skills for Awareness, Understanding & Application. 3rd rev. ed. 2007. (ENG.). 246p. pap. 50.61 *(978-0-7575-1375-6(1)*, 0757513751) Kendall Hunt Publishing Co.

Highland, Genevieve A. General Index: American Anthropologist & Memoirs of American Anthropological Association, 1939-1948, V53, No. 4, Part 2, October 1951. 2011. 78p. 37.95 ***(978-1-258-06625-3(4))*** Literary Licensing, LLC.

Highmore, Ben. Ordinary Lives. 2010. (ENG., Illus.). 208p. (C). pap. 31.95 *(978-0-415-46187-0(1))* Routledge.

—Ordinary Lives. 2010. (ENG., Illus.). 208p. (C). 115.00 *(978-0-415-46186-3(3))* Routledge.

Hochwald, Eve, ed. Visionary Observers: Anthropological Inquiry & Education. Cherneff, Jill B. R., tr. 2006. (Critical Studies in the History of Anthropology). (ENG., Illus.). 262p. pap. 29.95 *(978-0-8032-6464-9(X))* Univ. of Nebraska Pr.

Hodder, Ian, et al, eds. Pattern of the Past: Studies in the Honour of David Clarke. 2009. (ENG., Illus.). 456p. pap. 58.00 *(978-0-521-10843-0(8))* Cambridge Univ. Pr.

Hsu, Elisabeth & Low, Chris. Wind, Life, Health: Anthropological & Historical Perspectives. 2008. (Journal of the Royal Anthropological Institute Special Issue Book Ser.). (ENG., Illus.). 192p. pap. 34.95 *(978-1-4051-7893-8(0)*, Wiley-Blackwell) Wiley, John & Sons, Inc.

Inda, Jonathan Xavier & Rosaldo, Renato, eds. The Anthropology of Globalization: A Reader. 2nd rev. ed. 2007. (Wiley-Blackwell Readers in Anthropology Ser.: 6). (ENG.). 496p. 116.95 *(978-1-4051-3613-6(8))*; pap. 51.95 *(978-1-4051-3612-9(X))* Wiley, John & Sons, Inc. (Wiley-Blackwell).

Ingold, Tim. Archaeology Anthropology Art & Architecture. 2012. (ENG.). 288p. pap. 39.95 *(978-0-415-56723-7(8))* Routledge.

—Archaeology Anthropology Art & Architecture. 2010. 288p. 120.00 *(978-0-415-56722-0(X)*, Routledge) Taylor & Francis Group GBR. Dist: Taylor & Francis Group.

Jalais, Annu. Forest of Tigers: People, Politics & Environment in the Sundarbans. 2009. (ENG., Illus.). 268p. (C). 110.00 *(978-0-415-54461-0(0)*, Routledge India) Taylor & Francis Group GBR. Dist: Taylor & Francis Group.

Jebens, Holger & Kohl, Karl-Heinz, eds. The End of Anthropology? 2011. (Illus.). 264p. 110.00 ***(978-1-907774-05-8(X))*** Kingston, Sean Publishing GBR. Dist: Lightning Source, Inc.

Jencson, Linda. Cultures Emerging: Anthropology for a New Millennium. rev. ed. 2011. (ENG.). 316p. pap. 79.91 *(978-0-7575-6476-5(3))* Kendall Hunt Publishing Co.

Johler, Reinhard, et al, eds. Doing Anthropology in Wartime & War Zones: World War I & the Cultural Sciences in Europe. 2010. (ENG., Illus.). 332p. pap. 54.95 *(978-3-8376-1422-0(0))* Transcript Verlag DEU. Dist: Transaction Pubs.

Jordan-Bychkov, Terry G., et al. The Human Mosaic. 11th ed. 2009. (ENG.). 496p. (C). pap. 139.95 *(978-1-4292-1426-1(0))* Freeman, W. H. & Co.

Jurmain, Robert, et al. Physical Anthropology Lab Manual. 12th ed. 2009. (ENG.). 176p. (C). spiral bd. 61.95 *(978-0-8400-3283-6(8))* Wadsworth.

Kalland, Arne. Shingu: A Study of a Japanese Fishing Community. 2010. (ENG., Illus.). 212p. 115.00 *(978-0-415-58805-8(7))* Routledge.

Kalra, Virinder S., ed. Pakistani Diasporas: Culture, Conflict, & Change. 2009. (ENG.). 350p. 49.95 *(978-0-19-547625-5(5))* Oxford Univ. Pr., Inc.

Kants Gesammelte Schriften, Vols. 24-28. De Gruyter, Walter Inc.

Kapferer, Bruce. Intellectual Complicity: The State & Its Destructions. 2007. (ENG.). 100p. pap. 12.95 *(978-0-9728196-6-4(5))* Prickly Paradigm Pr., LLC.

Kapitan, Gerhard. Records of Traditional Watercraft from South & West Sri Lanka. 2009. (Illus.). 191p. (C). 112.50 *(978-1-4073-0413-7(5))* British Archaeological Reports Ltd. GBR. Dist: Brown, David Bk. Co., The.

Kaul, Adam R. Turning the Tune: Traditional Music, Tourism, & Social Change in an Irish Village. 2009. (Illus.). 200p. 80.00 *(978-1-84545-623-8(8))* Berghahn Bks., Inc.

Kehoe, Alice Beck & Doughty, Paul L., eds. Expanding American Anthropology, 1945-1980: A Generation Reflects. 2012. (ENG., Illus.). 312p. pap. 40.00 ***(978-0-8173-5688-0(6))*** Univ. of Alabama Pr.

Kehoe, Alice Beck, et al. Expanding American Anthropology, 19451980: A Generation Reflects. 2011. ***(978-0-8173-8589-7(4))*** Univ. of Alabama Pr.

Khittl, Christopher. <Die Musik fangt im Menschen An> Anthropologische Musikdidaktik. (GER., Illus.). 373p. pap. 77.95 *(978-3-03910-992-0(8))* Lang, Peter Publishing, Inc.

Kirsh, Marvin. Uniqueness, Self Belonging & Intercourse in Nature. 2010. 128p. pap. *(978-3-8383-6737-8(5))* Lambert Academic Publishing.

Klakegg, Ole Jonny. Early Warning Signs in Complex Projects. 2010. *(978-1-935589-18-1(0))* Project Management Institute.

K'Meyer, Tracy Elaine & Hart, Joy L. I Saw It Coming: Worker Narratives of Plant Closings & Job Loss. 2009. (Palgrave Studies in Oral History Ser.). (ENG.). 208p. 89.00 *(978-1-4039-7745-8(3))* Palgrave Macmillan.

Knudson, Kelly J. & Stojanowski, Christopher M., eds. Bioarchaeology & Identity in the Americas. 2010. (Bioarchaeological Interpretations of the Human Past: Local, Regional, & Global Ser.). (ENG., Illus.). 272p. pap. 34.95 *(978-0-8130-3678-6(X))* Univ. Pr. of Florida.

Kockel, Ullrich, et al, eds. A Companion to the Anthropology of Europe. 2012. (Wiley-Blackwell Companions to Anthropology Ser.: 25). (ENG.). 624p. 199.95 ***(978-1-4051-9073-2(6)***, Wiley-Blackwell) Wiley, John & Sons, Inc.

Konner, Melvin. The Evolution of Childhood: Relationships, Emotion, Mind. 2010. (Illus.). 960p. 39.95 *(978-0-674-04566-8(1)*, Belknap Pr.) Harvard Univ. Pr.

Kottak & Cram101 Textbook Reviews Staff. Anthropology: The Exploration of Human Diversity. 2007. 96p. per. 10.95 *(978-1-4288-2580-2(0))* Cram101 Inc.

Kottak, Conrad. Window on Humanity: A Concise Introduction to Anthropology. 5th ed. 2011. (ENG., Illus.). 560p. (C). pap. 112.00 ***(978-0-07-803489-3(2)***, 0078034892) McGraw-Hill Cos., The.

Kottak, Conrad. Window on Humanity: A Concise Introduction to General Anthropology. 4th ed. 2009. (ENG., Illus.). 544p. (C). pap. 112.00 *(978-0-07-353103-8(0)*, 0073531030) McGraw-Hill Cos., The.

Kottak, Conrad Phillip. Anthropology: Appreciating Human Diversity. 14th ed. 2010. (ENG., Illus.). 720p. (C). pap. 162.67 *(978-0-07-811699-5(6)*, 0078116996) McGraw-Hill Cos., The.

—Anthropology: The Exploration of Human Diversity. 13th ed. 2008. (ENG., Illus.). 704p. (C). pap. 162.67 *(978-0-07-340536-0(1)*, 0073405361) McGraw-Hill Cos., The.

Kowalczyk, Marlena Mroslawa & Cudak, Henryk, eds. Otherness in varoius social Contexts. 2011. pap. 10.00 *(978-1-4276-5184-6(1))* Aardvark Global Publishing.

Kroefges, Peter C. En Tierras Desconocidas. 2010. 160p. pap. *(978-3-8383-2205-6(3))* Lambert Academic Publishing.

Kronenfeld, David B., et al, eds. A Companion to Cognitive Anthropology. 2011. (Wiley-Blackwell Companions to Anthropology Ser.: 16). (ENG., Illus.). 624p. 199.95 *(978-1-4051-8778-7(6)*, Wiley-Blackwell) Wiley, John & Sons, Inc.

Lahire, Bernard. The Plural Actor. 2011. (ENG.). 280p. 69.95 *(978-0-7456-4684-3(0))*; pap. 26.95 *(978-0-7456-4685-5(9))* Polity Pr. GBR. Dist: Wiley, John & Sons, Inc.

Lancy, David F. The Anthropology of Childhood: Cherubs, Chattel, Changelings. 2008. (ENG., Illus.). 480p. 109.00 *(978-0-521-88773-1(9))* Cambridge Univ. Pr.

Language, Man & Society, 23 titles in 31 vols., Set. reprint ed. 1137.50 *(978-0-404-08490-5(7))* AMS Pr., Inc.

Langwick, Stacey A. Bodies, Politics, & African Healing: The Matter of Maladies in Tanzania. 2011. (ENG., Illus.). 320p. 70.00 *(978-0-253-35527-0(3)*, 0253355273); pap. 24.95 *(978-0-253-22245-9(1)*, 0253222451) Indiana Univ. Pr.

Lannoo International. The Exotic Human: Other cultures as Entertainment. 2009. (ENG., Illus.). 176p. pap. *(978-90-209-8289-3(3)*, Lannoo Pubs. (Acc)) Antique Collectors' Club.

Lassiter, Luke E. Invitation to Anthropology. 3rd ed. (ENG.). 248p. 2009. 75.00 *(978-0-7591-1152-3(9))* 2008. pap. 29.95 *(978-0-7591-1153-0(7))* Rowman & Littlefield Publishers, Inc.

Latham, Krista/E & Finnegan, Michael, eds. Age Estimation of the Human Skeleton. 2010. 310p. *(978-0-398-07949-9(8))*; pap. *(978-0-398-07950-5(1))* Thomas, Charles C. Pub., Ltd.

Lavenda, Robert H. & Schultz, Emily A. Anthropology: What Does It Mean to Be Human? 2nd ed. 2011. (ENG.). 528p. (C). pap. 89.95 ***(978-0-19-539287-6(6))*** Oxford Univ. Pr., Inc.

Layton, Robert, et al, eds. Time & Change: Archaeological & Anthropological Perspectives on the Long Term in Hunter-Gatherer Societies. 2008. (ENG., Illus.). 168p. (C). pap. 60.00 *(978-1-84217-320-6(0))* Oxbow Bks., Ltd. GBR. Dist: Brown, David Bk. Co., The.

Leblic, I. Molène: Une île tournée vers la Mer. 2007. (Société d'Études Linguistiques et Anthropologiques de France Ser.). (ENG.). 542p. (C). pap. 90.00 *(978-90-429-1925-9(5))* Peeters Pubs. & Booksellers BEL. Dist: Brown, David Bk. Co., The.

Linke, Uli & Smith, Danielle Taana, eds. Cultures of Fear: A Critical Reader, 1 vol. 2009. (Anthropology, Culture & Society Ser.). (ENG.). 320p. pap. 34.95 *(978-0-7453-2965-9(9))*; 95.00 *(978-0-7453-2966-6(7))* Pluto Pr. GBR. Dist: Macmillan.

Linton, Ralph. The Science of Man in the World Crisis. 2007. (ENG.). 544p. per. *(978-1-4067-6865-7(0))* Read Bks.

Macclancy, Jeremy M. Consuming the Inedible: Neglected Dimensions of Food Choice. Henry, Jeya & Macbeth, Helen, eds. 2007. (Anthropology of Food & Nutrition Ser.: Vol. 6). (Illus.). 258p. (C). 90.00 *(978-1-84545-353-4(0))* Berghahn Bks., Inc.

Macclancy, Jeremy M., et al, eds. Consuming the Inedible: Neglected Dimensions of Food Choice. 2009. (Illus.). 258p. 29.95 *(978-1-84545-684-9(X))* Berghahn Bks., Inc.

Macdonald, Gaynor & Heil, Daniela. The Anthropology Companion. 2013. (Palgrave Student Companions Ser.). (ENG.). 320p. (C). pap. 29.95 *(978-0-230-00822-9(4))* Palgrave Macmillan.

MacDonald, Margaret E. At Work in the Field of Birth: Midwfery Narratives of Nature, Tradition, & Home. 2008. (ENG.). 196p. (C). per. 24.95 *(978-0-8265-1577-3(0))* Vanderbilt Univ. Pr.

—At Work in the Field of Birth: Midwifery Narratives of Nature, Tradition, & Home. 2008. (ENG.). 196p. 59.95 *(978-0-8265-1576-6(2))* Vanderbilt Univ. Pr.

Macek, Ivana. Sarajevo under Siege: Anthropology in Wartime. 2009. (Ethnography of Political Violence Ser.). (Illus.). 272p. (C). 55.00 *(978-0-8122-4126-6(6))* Univ. of Pennsylvania Pr.

Malefyt, Timothy de Waal & Morais, Robert J. Advertising & Anthropology: Ethnographic Practice & Cultural Perspectives. 2012. (ENG.). 192p. (C). 99.95 ***(978-0-85785-201-4(9)***, 134595); pap. 29.95 ***(978-0-85785-202-1(7)***, 134742) Berg Pubs. GBR. Dist: Macmillan.

Manners, Robert A. & Kaplan, David, eds. Anthropological Theory. 2007. (ENG., Illus.). 590p. (gr. 11). pap. 39.95 *(978-0-202-36133-8(0))* Aldine Transaction.

Marcus, George E., ed. Critical Anthropology Now: Unexpected Contexts, Shifting Constituencies, Changing Agendas. (Advanced Seminar Ser.). 456p. 29.95 *(978-0-933452-50-3(0))*; pap. 24.95 *(978-0-933452-51-0(9))* School for Advanced Research Pr./SAR Pr.

Marcus, Jean. Introduction to Anthropology. rev. ed. 2011. (ENG.). 232p. spiral bd. 52.88 *(978-0-7575-7748-2(2))* Kendall Hunt Publishing Co.

Marett, R. R. Anthropology. 2009. 148p. pap. *(978-1-4099-6348-6(9))* Dodo Pr.

—Anthropology. 2008. 260p. pap. *(978-1-4097-8174-5(7)*, Home Farm Bks.) Read Bks.

Marett, Robert Ranulph. Anthropology. 2008. 164p. 25.99 *(978-0-554-26285-7(1))* 2008. 164p. 22.99 *(978-0-554-35588-7(4))* 2007. (ENG.). 146p. pap. 18.99 *(978-1-4346-0817-3(4))* 2007. (ENG.). 162p. pap. 21.99 *(978-1-4346-0891-3(3))* BiblioBazaar.

Marston, A. T. The Swanscombe Skull. reprint ed. 27.50 *(978-0-404-18271-7(2))* AMS Pr., Inc.

Marston, John, ed. Anthropology & Community in Cambodia: Reflections on the Work of May Ebihara. 2011. 258p. pap. 29.95 *(978-1-876924-74-4(8)*, Monash Univ. Pr.) Monash Univ. Publishing AUS. Dist: International Specialized Bk. Services.

Maryanski, Alexandra & Turner, Jonathan H. On the Origin of Societies by Natural Selection. (Studies in Comparative Social Science Ser.). 376p. 2009. pap. 40.95 *(978-1-59451-517-0(4))* 2008. (Illus.). (C). 125.00 *(978-1-59451-516-3(6))* Paradigm Pubs.

Mascia-Lees, Frances E. Gender & Difference in a Globalizing World: Twenty-First Century Anthropology. 2009. 299p. (C). pap. 45.95 *(978-1-57766-598-4(8))* Waveland Pr., Inc.

McClelland, Bruce. Slayers & Their Vampires: A Cultural History of Killing the Dead. 2006. (ENG., Illus.). 280p. 80.00 *(978-0-472-09923-8(X))*; pap. 21.95 *(978-0-472-06923-1(3))* Univ. of Michigan Pr.

Menicocci, Marco & Tiziani, Moreno. Antrocom: Online Journal of Anthropology. 2011. pap. 56.45 ***(978-1-4632-0051-0(X))*** Gorgias Pr., LLC.

Mierek, Joanne. Interrelating with Animal Selves. 2011. 68p. pap. ***(978-3-8433-8543-5(2))*** Lambert Academic Publishing.

Miller & Miller, Barbara. Anthropology, Books a la Carte Plus MyAnthroLab. 2nd ed. 2010. (ENG.). (C). ring bd. 106.67 *(978-0-205-80526-6(4)*, Prentice Hall) Prentice Hall PTR.

Miller, Barbara. MyAnthroLab with Pearson eText Student Access Code Card for Anthropology. 2nd ed. 2010. (ENG.). 736p. (C). 109.33 *(978-0-205-79738-7(5)*, Prentice Hall) Prentice Hall PTR.

Miller, Barbara D. Anthropology. 2nd ed. 2010. (ENG.). 736p. (C). ring bd. 100.00 *(978-0-205-80517-4(5)*, Prentice Hall) Prentice Hall PTR.

Miller, Barbara D. & Wood, Bernard. Anthropology. 2006. (Books a la Carte Ser.). (Illus.). ring bd. 72.00 *(978-0-205-50958-4(4))* Allyn & Bacon, Inc.

Miller, Daniel, ed. Anthropology & the Individual: A Material Culture Perspective. 2009. (Materializing Culture Ser.). (ENG., Illus.). 1p. 89.95 *(978-1-84788-495-4(4))* Berg Pubs. GBR. Dist: Macmillan.

Miller, David Philip & Reill, Peter Hanns, eds. Visions of Empire: Voyages, Botany, & Representations of Nature. 2010. (ENG., Illus.). 394p. pap. 36.99 *(978-0-521-17261-5(6))* Cambridge Univ. Pr.

Miller, Jason E. & Schmid, Oona. How to Get Published in Anthropology: A Guide for Students & Young Professionals. 2011. ***(978-0-7591-2109-6(5))*** AltaMira Pr.

Minta, Anna & Nicolai, Bernd, eds. Modernity & Early Cultures: Reconsidering Non Western References for Modern Architecture in a Cross-Cultural Perspective. 2011. (Neue Berner Schriften zur Kunst Ser.). (Illus.). 236p. pap. *(978-3-0343-0508-2(7))* Lang, Peter.

Mitchell, William E. The Bamboo Fire: Field Work with the New Guinea Wape. 2nd ed. 2012. (ENG.). 304p. pap. 29.95 ***(978-1-4128-4255-6(7))*** Transaction Pubs.

Mittermaier, Amira. Dreams That Matter: Egyptian Landscapes of the Imagination. 2010. (ENG., Illus.). 278p. 55.00 *(978-0-520-25850-1(9))* Univ. of California Pr.

Molloy, Maureen A. On Creating a Usable Culture: Margaret Mead & the Emergence of American Cosmopolitanism. 2008. (Illus.). 200p. 39.00 *(978-0-8248-3116-5(0))* Univ. of Hawaii Pr.

Moore, Henrietta L. The Subject of Anthropology: Gender, Symbolism & Psychoanalysis. 2007. (ENG.). 288p. 69.95 *(978-0-7456-0808-2(6))*; pap. 24.95 *(978-0-7456-0809-9(4))* Polity Pr. GBR. Dist: Wiley, John & Sons, Inc.

Moore, Jerry & Moore, Jerry D. Visions of Culture: An Annotated Reader. 2009. (ENG.). 516p. pap. 49.95 *(978-0-7591-1855-3(8))*; (Illus.). 99.00 *(978-0-7591-1854-6(X))* AltaMira Pr.

Moore, Jerry D. Visions of Culture: An Annotated Reader. 2009. pap. *(978-0-7591-1162-2(6))* AltaMira Pr.

Moran, Emilio F. Human Adaptability: An Introduction to Ecological Anthropology. 3rd rev. ed. 2007. (ENG., Illus.). 496p. pap. 45.00 *(978-0-8133-4367-9(4))* Westview Pr.

Morgan, Lewis H. Systems of Consanguinity & Affinity of the Human Family. 590p. reprint ed. 98.00 *(978-0-7222-1809-9(5))*; 98.00 *(978-0-7222-1978-2(4))* Library Reprints, Inc.

Morgan, Rhian. Culture, Anthropology & Cross-Cultural Training. 2010. 176p. pap. *(978-3-639-27957-3(3))* VDM Verlag Dr. Mueller e.K.

Morley, Iain. Becoming Human: Innovation in Prehistoric Material & Spiritual Culture. Renfrew, Colin, ed. 2009. (ENG., Illus.). 324p. (C). 85.00 *(978-0-521-87654-4(0))*; pap. 31.00 *(978-0-521-73466-0(5))* Cambridge Univ. Pr.

Morton, Christopher & Edwards, Elizabeth. Photography, Anthropology & History: Expanding the Frame. 2009. (Illus.). 310p. 114.95 *(978-0-7546-7909-7(8))* Ashgate Publishing Co.

Moses, Daniel Noah. The Promise of Progress: The Life & Work of Lewis Henry Morgan. 2009. (ENG., Illus.). 344p. (C). 47.50 *(978-0-8262-1818-6(0))* Univ. of Missouri Pr.

Mottin Sylla, Marie Hélène & Palmieri, Joëlle. Confronting Female Genital Mutilation: The Role of Youth & ICTs in Changing Africa. 2011. (ENG., Illus.). 136p. pap. ***(978-0-85749-031-5(1))*** Pambuzuka Pr.

Moutu, Andrew. Names are Thicker than Blood: Kinship & Ownership amongst the Iatmul. 2010. (British Academy Ser.). (ENG., Illus.). 220p. 70.00 *(978-0-19-726445-4(X))* Oxford Univ. Pr., Inc.

Murray, Gilbert. Tradition & Progress. 2010. 226p. pap. 25.75 *(978-1-178-33918-5(1))* 2010. (ENG.). 226p. pap. 25.75 *(978-1-177-64217-0(4))* 2010. 226p. pap. 25.75 *(978-1-177-79731-3(3))* 2009. 224p. 23.99 *(978-1-103-75985-9(X))* 2009. 224p. pap. 17.99 *(978-1-103-75982-8(5))* BiblioBazaar.

—Tradition & Progress. 2009. 152p. pap. 19.99 *(978-1-4589-4548-8(0))* General Bks. LLC.

—Tradition & Progress. (Essay Index Reprint Ser.). 221p. reprint ed. lib. bdg. 19.00 *(978-0-8290-0490-8(4))* Irvington Pubs.

—Tradition & Progress. 2008. 218p. 39.95 *(978-1-4365-1322-7(7))* 2007. (ENG.). 220p. per. 24.95 *(978-0-548-70275-8(6))* Kessinger Publishing, LLC.

Nadjmabadi, Shahnaz R. Conceptualizing Iranian Anthropology: Past & Present Perspectives. 2010. 288p. 90.00 *(978-1-84545-626-9(2))* Berghahn Bks., Inc.

Nanda. Sg Anthro a Holistic Appr. 2007. (C). pap. 19.95 *(978-0-534-61471-3(X))* Wadsworth.

Neis, Cordula. Anthropologie im Sprachdenken des 18. Jahrhunderts: Die Berliner Preisfrage nach dem Ursprung der Sprache (1771) (Studia Linguistica Germanica Ser.). (GER.). XIII, 656p. 344.00 ***(978-3-11-180068-4(7))*** De Gruyter, Walter Inc.

Ntarangwi, Mwenda. Reversed Gaze: An African Ethnography of American Anthropology. 2010. (ENG., Illus.). 200p. 65.00 *(978-0-252-03579-1(8))*; 176p. pap. 20.00 *(978-0-252-07769-2(5))* Univ. of Illinois Pr.

Nuttall, Mark & Crate, Susan Alexandra. Anthropology & Climate Change: From Encounters to Actions. Crate, Susan A. & Nuttall, Mark, eds. 2009. (ENG., Illus.). 416p. pap. 34.95 *(978-1-59874-334-0(1))* Left Coast Pr., Inc.

Ohtsuka, Ryutaro & Ulijaszek, Stanley J., eds. Health Change in the Asia-Pacific Region: Biocultural & Epidemiological Approaches. 2007. (Cambridge Studies in Biological & Evolutionary Anthropology Ser.: Vol. 52). (ENG., Illus.). 324p. 157.99 *(978-0-521-83792-7(8))* Cambridge Univ. Pr.

Otto, Ton, et al, eds. Warfare & Society: Archaeological & Social Anthropological Perspectives. 2006. (ENG., Illus.). 557p. (C). 84.00 *(978-87-7934-110-4(1))* Aarhus Universitetsforlag DNK. Dist: ISD.

Park, Michael. Introducing Anthropology: an Integrated Approach. 5th ed. 2010. (ENG., Illus.). 448p. (C). pap. 120.67 *(978-0-07-811695-7(3)*, 0078116953) McGraw-Hill Cos., The.

Parkin, David J. & Ulijaszek, Stanley J., eds. Holistic Anthropology: Emergence & Convergence. 2011. (MHA Ser.). 224p. 29.95 *(978-0-85745-152-1(9))* Berghahn Bks., Inc.

Parkins, David, et al, eds. Holistic Anthropology: Emergence & Convergence. 2007. (Methodology & History in Anthropology Ser.). 224p. 90.00 *(978-1-84545-354-1(9))* Berghahn Bks., Inc.

Peake, Harold J. & Fleure, Herbert J. Apes & Men, Vol. 1. *(978-0-404-18251-9(8))* AMS Pr., Inc.

Pearce, J. E. Tales That Dead Men Tell. 2010. 130p. pap. 16.76 *(978-1-162-98716-3(2))* 2007. (ENG.). 128p. 35.95 *(978-0-548-14809-9(0))* 2006. (ENG.). pap. 20.95 *(978-1-4236-6292-6(8))* Kessinger Publishing, LLC.

Peck, Pamela J. Coming of Age in Anthropology: Commentaries on Growing up in the Global Village. 2011. 176p. pap. 14.95 ***(978-1-4269-4820-6(4))*** Trafford Publishing.

Pellizzi, Francesco. Absconding, Vol. 55/56. 2010. (Res: Anthropology & Aesthetics Ser.). (Illus.). 360p. pap. 50.00 *(978-0-87365-854-6(X))* Peabody Museum of Archaeology & Ethnology, Harvard Univ., Pubns. Dept.

—Spring/Autumn 2006. 2006. (Res: Anthropology & Aesthetics Ser.). (Illus.). 272p. pap. 50.00 *(978-0-87365-767-9(5))* Peabody Museum of Archaeology & Ethnology, Harvard Univ., Pubns. Dept.

Pellizzi, Francesco, ed. Res Vol. 52: Museums — Crossing Boundaries. 2008. (Res: Anthropology & Aesthetics Ser.). (Illus.). 240p. per. 50.00 *(978-0-87365-790-7(X))* Peabody Museum of Archaeology & Ethnology, Harvard Univ., Pubns. Dept.

—Res 53/54 Spring/Autumn 2008: Anthropology & Aesthetics, Vol. 53. 2008. (Res: Anthropology & Aesthetics Ser.). (Illus.). 350p. pap. 50.00 *(978-0-87365-840-9(X))* Peabody Museum of Archaeology & Ethnology, Harvard Univ., Pubns. Dept.

—Res, Volume 51: Anthropology & Aesthetics, Spring 2007. 2007. (Res: Anthropology & Aesthetics Ser.). (Illus.). 272p. per. 50.00 *(978-0-87365-775-4(6))* Peabody Museum of Archaeology & Ethnology, Harvard Univ., Pubns. Dept.

Peoples & Jurmain, Robert. Anthropology for College of Misercordia. Date not set. (Adaptable Courseware-Softside Ser.) pap. 44.00 *(978-0-534-15956-6(7))* Wadsworth.

Peralta, Elsa & Anico, Marta. Heritage & Identity: Engagement & Demission in the Contemporary World. Peralta, Elsa & Anico, Marta, eds. 2009. (Museum Meanings Ser.). (ENG., Illus.). 208p. (C). 125.00 *(978-0-415-45335-6(6))* Routledge.

—Heritage & Identity: Engagement & Demission in the Contemporary World. Anico, Marta, ed. 2009. (Museum Meanings Ser.). (ENG., Illus.). 208p. (C). pap. 41.95 *(978-0-415-45336-3(4))* Routledge.

Phiri, George Allan. Social-Cultural Anthropology: Communication with the African Society. 2009. 208p. pap. 23.00 *(978-1-60608-736-7(3)*, Resource Pubns.) Wipf & Stock Pubs.

Pine. On the Margins of Religion. 2008. 296p. (C). 90.00 *(978-1-84545-409-8(X))* Berghahn Bks., Inc.

Pinney, Christopher. Photography & Anthropology. 2011. (Reaktion Books - Exposures Ser.). (ENG., Illus.) 192p. pap. 29.95 *(978-1-86189-804-3(5))* Reaktion Bks., Ltd. GBR. Dist: Chicago Distribution Ctr.

Podolefsky, Aaron, et al. Applying Anthropology: An Introductory Reader. 10th ed. 2011. (ENG., Illus.). 432p. (C). pap. 67.67 ***(978-0-07-811704-6(6)***, 0078117046) McGraw-Hill Cos., The.

Polizzi, Kristina. Dragons Behind Glasses. 2008. 92p. pap. *(978-3-8364-7108-4(6))* VDM Verlag Dr. Mueller e.K.

Porter, Leila M. The Behavioral Ecology of Callimicos & Tamarins in Northwestern Bolivia. 2006. (Primate Field Studies). (ENG., Illus.). 192p. (C). per. 28.40 *(978-0-13-191470-4(7)*, Prentice Hall) Prentice Hall PTR.

Price, David H. Weaponizing Anthropology: Social Science in Service of the Militarized State. 2011. (Counterpunch Ser.). (ENG., Illus.). 208p. pap. 15.95 ***(978-1-84935-063-1(9))*** AK Pr. GBR. Dist: Consortium Bk. Sales & Distribution.

Quiggin, E. C., ed. Essays & Studies Presented to William Ridgeway: On his Sixtieth Birthday - 6th August 1913. 2012. (ENG.). 722p. pap. 73.00 ***(978-1-107-60556-5(3))*** Cambridge Univ. Pr.

Quinones, John. Everyday Heroes: My Conversation with America. 2008. 208p. 21.95 *(978-1-4013-2345-5(6))* Hyperion Pr.

Raab, L. Mark, et al. California Maritime Archaeology: A San Clemente Island Perspective. 2009. (ENG.). 290p. 75.00 *(978-0-7591-1316-9(5))* AltaMira Pr.

Rafferty, Kevin & Ukaegbu, Dorothy C. Faces of Anthropology. 6th ed. 2010. (ENG.). 432p. (C). pap. 71.20 *(978-0-205-64532-9(1)*, Prentice Hall) Prentice Hall PTR.

Ralph, Sarah, ed. Past Violence: Indeterdisciplinary Approaches. 2012. (Institute for European & Mediterranean Archaeology Distinguished Monograph Ser.). (ENG.). 368p. 95.00 ***(978-1-4384-4441-3(9))*** State Univ. of New York Pr.

Ramaswamy, Sumathi. The Goddess & the Nation: Mapping Mother India. 2010. (ENG., Illus.). 400p. 99.95 *(978-0-8223-4592-3(7))*; pap. 27.95 *(978-0-8223-4610-4(9))* Duke Univ. Pr.

Ratzel, Friedrich. The History of Mankind, 3 vols., Set Butler, A. J., tr. from GER. 2nd ed. reprint ed. 375.00 *(978-0-7222-2635-3(7))* Library Reprints, Inc.

Reclus, Elisee. The Earth & Its Inhabitants. 2010. 364p. pap. *(978-1-152-89153-1(7))*; 374p. pap. *(978-1-152-89152-4(9))*; 334p. pap. *(978-1-152-89154-8(5))*; 390p. pap. *(978-1-152-89155-5(3))* Books LLC.

—The Earth & Its Inhabitants. 2010. 402p. pap. 47.24 *(978-1-152-88969-9(9))*; 344p. pap. 41.76 *(978-1-152-63884-6(X))*; 372p. pap. 44.36 *(978-1-152-89157-9(X))*; 402p. pap. 47.24 *(978-1-152-88975-0(3))*; 372p. pap. 44.45 *(978-1-152-88985-9(0))*; 346p. pap. 41.94 *(978-1-153-34335-0(5))*; 366p. pap. 43.89 *(978-1-152-88967-5(2))*; 400p. pap. 46.96 *(978-1-152-88958-3(3))*; 374p. pap. 44.64 *(978-1-152-88979-8(6))*; 358p. pap. 43.15 *(978-1-152-88966-8(4))*; 386p. pap. 45.75 *(978-1-152-88960-6(5))*; 372p. pap. 44.45 *(978-1-152-88977-4(X))*; 368p. pap. 44.08 *(978-1-152-88956-9(7))*; 376p. pap. 44.73 *(978-1-152-88983-5(4))*; 352p. pap. 42.59 *(978-1-152-88973-6(7))*; 370p. pap. 44.26 *(978-1-152-88971-2(0))*; 380p. pap. 45.10 *(978-1-152-88962-0(1))*; 372p. pap. 44.45

(978-1-152-88964-4(8)); 376p. pap. 44.73 (978-1-152-88981-1(8)) General Bks. LLC.

Renfrew, Colin. Prehistory: The Making of the Human Mind. 2009. (Modern Library Chronicles Ser.). (ENG., Illus.). 240p. pap. 15.00 (978-0-8129-7661-8(4), Modern Library) Random House Publishing Group.

Ricarda, Motschilnig. Indigenous Knowledge & Localised Curriculum in Zambia: ... the Road to Sustainable Development? 2011. 100p. pap. **(978-3-639-33161-5(3))** VDM Verlag Dr. Mueller e.K.

Rice, Patricia. Writings in Anthropology. 2007. (ENG.). 156p. (C). pap. 27.67 (978-0-07-338791-8(6), 0073387916) McGraw-Hill Cos., The.

Robinson, David J. & Ash, Patricia J. The Emergence of Humans: An Exploration of the Evolutionary Timeline. 2010. (ENG., Illus.). 338p. 190.00 (978-0-470-01313-7(3), Wiley) Wiley, John & Sons, Inc.

Rose, Deidre. Bouyon Kultur: Creolization & Culture in Dominica. rev. ed. 2009. (ENG.). 118p. pap. 21.88 (978-0-7575-6037-8(7)) Kendall Hunt Publishing Co.

Roth, Silke. Encounters with Melanie Klein: Selected Papers of Elizabeth Spillius. 2007. (New Library of Psychoanalysis Ser.). (ENG., Illus.). 264p. (C). 125.00 (978-0-415-41998-7(0)) Routledge.

Rubenstein, Steven L. Border Crossings: Transnational Americanist Anthropology. Fine-Dare, Kathleen S., ed. 2009. (ENG., Illus.). 404p. pap. 35.00 (978-0-8032-1086-8(8)) Univ. of Nebraska Pr.

Ruggles, D. Fairchild & Silverman, Helaine, eds. Intangible Heritage Embodied. 2009. (ENG., Illus.). viii, 210p. 109.00 (978-1-4419-0071-5(3), 1441900713) Springer.

Saka, Erkan. Blaming Others. 2010. 92p. pap. (978-3-8383-4673-1(4)) Lambert Academic Publishing.

Sale, et al. Understanding Our World, Bk. 1. Date not set. (Illus.). 192p. pap. 59.50 (978-0-582-87246-2(4)) Addison-Wesley Longman, Ltd. GBR. Dist: Trans-Atlantic Pubns., Inc.

Saltzman, Rachelle H. A Lark for the Sake of Their Country: The 1926 General Strike Volunteers in Folklore & Memory. 2012. (ENG., Illus.). 304p. 100.00 **(978-0-7190-7977-1(2))** Manchester Univ. Pr. GBR. Dist: Macmillan.

Sapiezinskas, Aline. Cultural Heritage in Brazil: The Anthropological Perspective & the Local Point of View. 2011. 144p. pap. 19.99 **(978-1-4568-8960-9(5))** Xlibris Corp.

Saran, Prem. Yoga, Bhoga & Ardhanariswara: Individuality, Wellbeing & Gender in Tantra. 2008. (ENG., Illus.). 284p. 110.00 (978-0-415-48001-7(9), Routledge India) Taylor & Francis Group GBR. Dist: Taylor & Francis Group.

Sasaki, Masamichi, ed. Elites: New Comparative Perspectives. 2007. (International Studies in Sociology & Social Anthropology Ser.). 222p. per. (978-90-04-16402-4(2)) BRILL.

Saunders, Barry F. CT Suite: The Work of Diagnosis in the Age of Noninvasive Cutting. 2008. (Body, Commodity, Text Ser.). (ENG., Illus.). 416p. 94.95 (978-0-8223-4104-8(2)); pap. 26.95 (978-0-8223-4123-9(9)) Duke Univ. Pr.

Schiffer, Michael Brian, ed. Anthropological Perspectives on Technology. 2011. (Amerind Foundation New World Studies Ser.). (ENG., Illus.). 256p. pap. 45.00 **(978-0-8263-5039-8(9))** Univ. of New Mexico Pr.

Schmalzer, Sigrid. The People's Peking Man: Popular Science & Human Identity in Twentieth-Century China. 2008. (Illus.). 368p. 85.00 (978-0-226-73859-8(0)) Univ. of Chicago Pr.

Schmid, Oona & Miller, Jason. How to Get Published in Anthropology: A Guide for Students & Young Professionals. 2011. (ENG.). 184p. pap. 25.00 **(978-0-7591-2108-9(7))** AltaMira Pr.

Schmitt, Aurore, ed. Forensic Anthropology & Medicine: Complementary Sciences from Recovery to Cause of Death. 2010. (Illus.). 480p. pap. 179.00 (978-1-61737-792-1(9), 1617377929) Humana Pr.

Schmuhl, Hans-Walter. Crossing Boundaries: The Kaiser-Wilhelm-Institute for Anthropology, Human Heredity & Eugenics, 1927-1945. 2008. (Boston Studies in the Philosophy of Science Ser.). 367p. 219.00 (978-1-4020-6599-6(X), 140206599X) Springer.

A Scientific Theory of Culture & Other Essays: [1944]. 2009. 272p. 39.95 (978-0-415-48837-2(0)) Routledge.

Scott, Gini Graham. The Researcher's Bible: An Overview of Key Concepts & Methods in Social Science Research. 2011. 72p. pap. 12.95 **(978-1-4620-3777-3(1))** iUniverse, Inc.

Scupin & Cram101 Textbook Reviews Staff. Race & Ethnicity. 2007. 272p. per. 14.95 (978-1-4288-2678-6(5)) Cram101 Inc.

Scupin, et al. Anthropology: A Global Perspective, Books a la Carte Plus MyAnthroLab. 7th ed. 2011. (ENG.). (C). ring bd. 100.00 **(978-0-205-18212-1(7)**, Prentice Hall) Prentice Hall PTR.

Scupin, Ph.D., Raymond R & DeCorse, Christopher R. Anthropology. 7th rev. ed. 2011. (ENG.). (C). 46.67 **(978-0-205-18327-2(1)**, Prentice Hall) Prentice Hall PTR.

—Anthropology: A Global Perspective. 7th rev. ed. 2011. (ENG., Illus.). 672p. (C). pap. 142.67 **(978-0-205-18102-5(3)**, Prentice Hall) Prentice Hall PTR.

Scupin, Raymond & DeCorse, Christopher R. Anthropology. 7th rev. ed. 2011. (ENG.). 672p. (C). 82.67 (978-0-205-22784-6(8), Prentice Hall) Prentice Hall PTR.

Scupin, Raymond & DeCorse, Christopher R. Anthropology: A Global Perspective, Books a la Carte Edition. 7th ed. 2011. (ENG.). 672p. (C). ring bd. 93.33 **(978-0-205-18211-4(9)**, Prentice Hall) Prentice Hall PTR.

Senders, Stefan & Truitt, Allison. Money: Ethnographic Encounters. Senders, Stefan & Truitt, Allison, eds. 2007. (ENG.). 160p. pap. 26.95 (978-1-84520-751-9(3)) Berg Pubs. GBR. Dist: Macmillan.

Shankland, David, ed. Archaeology, Anthropology & Heritage in the Balkans & Anatolia. 2010. 208.00 (978-1-61719-087-2(X)); 208.00 (978-1-61719-088-9(8)) Gorgias Pr., LLC.

Shapiro, Sherry. Dance in a World of Change: Reflections on Globalization & Cultural Difference. 2008. (ENG., Illus.). 328p. (gr. 9-17). pap. 37.00 (978-0-7360-6943-4(7)) Human Kinetics Pubs.

Shaw, Susan J. Governing How We Care: Contesting Community & Defining Difference in U. S. Public Health Programs. 2012. E-Book 27.95 **(978-1-4399-0684-2(X))**; (ENG., Illus.). 214p. 84.50 **(978-1-4399-0682-8(3))**; (ENG., Illus.). 214p. pap. 27.95 **(978-1-4399-0683-5(1))** Temple Univ. Pr.

Shelach, Gideon. Leadership Strategies, Economic Activity, & Interregional Interaction: Social Complexity in Northeast China. 2010. (Fundamental Issues in Archaeology Ser.). 278p. pap. 129.00 (978-1-4419-3314-0(X), 144193314X) Springer.

Shennan, Stephen. Pattern & Process in Cultural Evolution. 2009. (Origins of Human Behavior & Culture Ser.). (ENG., Illus.). 336p. 60.00 (978-0-520-25599-9(2)) Univ. of California Pr.

Siliotti, Alberto. Archaeology Treasures. 2008. 432p. 29.99 (978-88-540-0857-1(5)) White Star ITA. Dist: Book Sales, Inc.

Simpkins, Karen Li & Freidin, Nicholas. Cultural Mosaic: Readings in Introductory Anthropology. 4th rev. ed. 2010. (ENG.). 248p. pap. 68.14 (978-0-7575-2353-3(6), 0757523536) Kendall Hunt Publishing Co.

Slyomovics, Susan, ed. Clifford Geertz in Morocco. 2012. (ENG., Illus.). 248p. (C). pap. 45.95 **(978-0-415-51816-1(4))** Routledge.

—Clifford Geertz in Morocco. 2010. (ENG., Illus.). 256p. (C). 125.00 (978-0-415-55907-2(3), Routledge) Taylor & Francis Group GBR. Dist: Taylor & Francis Group.

Smith, Cameron M & Dummies Press Staff. Anthropology for Dummies. 2008. (ENG., Illus.). 384p. pap. 19.99 (978-0-470-27966-3(4), For Dummies) Wiley, John & Sons, Inc.

Smith, Dianne, ed. Transformations: Readings in Evolution, Hominids, & the Environment. 4th ed. 2007. (Illus.). 132p. per. 31.00 (978-0-07-338673-7(1)) McGraw-Hill Cos., The.

Sobo, Elisa J. & Loustaunau, Martha Oehmke. The Cultural Context of Health, Illness, & Medicine, 1 vol. 2nd rev. ed. 268p. pap. 19.95 (978-0-313-37785-3(5), B37785, Praeger Pubs.) Greenwood Publishing Group, Inc.

Spencer, Jonathan. Anthropology, Politics, & the State: Democracy & Violence in South Asia. 2007. (New Departures in Anthropology Ser.). (ENG.). 208p. 104.00 (978-0-521-77177-1(3)); (Illus.). 218p. per. 36.99 (978-0-521-77746-9(1)) Cambridge Univ. Pr.

Spencer, Robert F. Method & Perspective in Anthropology: Papers in Honor of Wilson D. Wallis. 2009. (ENG.). 342p. pap. 60.00 (978-0-8166-6003-2(4)) Univ. of Minnesota Pr.

Spier, Leslie, ed. Southwestern Journal of Anthropology, V12, No 4, Winter 1956. 2011. 140p. 40.95 **(978-1-258-01712-5(1))** Literary Licensing, LLC.

Spillius, Elizabeth Bott. Encounters with Melanie Klein. Roth, Priscilla & Rusbridger, Richard, eds. 2007. (New Library of Psychoanalysis Ser.). (ENG., Illus.). 264p. (C). per. 42.50 (978-0-415-41999-4(9)) Routledge.

Spradley, James & McCurdy, David W. Conformity & Conflict: Readings in Cultural Anthropology. 14th rev. ed. 2011. (ENG., 480p. (C). Illus.). pap. 73.60 **(978-0-205-23410-3(0))**; 49.33 (978-0-205-06579-0(1)) Prentice Hall PTR. (Prentice Hall).

—Conformity & Conflict: Readings in Cultural Anthropology, Books a la Carte Edition. 14th ed. 2011. (ENG.). 432p. (C). ring bd. 48.00 **(978-0-205-25043-1(2)**, Prentice Hall) Prentice Hall PTR.

—Conformity & Conflict: Readings in Cultural Anthropology, Books a la Carte Plus MyAnthroLab. 14th ed. 2011. (ENG.). (C). ring bd. 54.67 **(978-0-205-06461-8(2)**, Prentice Hall) Prentice Hall PTR.

Steenberg, M. C. & Steenberg. Of God & Man: Theology as Anthropology from Irenaeus to Athanasius. 2009. (ENG.). 224p. 39.95 (978-0-567-03370-3(8)); 140.00 (978-0-567-03369-7(4)) Continuum International Publishing Group, Ltd. GBR. (T&T Clark Int'l). Dist: National Bk. Network.

Steiner, Rudolf. The Essential Steiner: Basic Writings of Rudolf Steiner. McDermott, Robert A., ed. & intro. by. (Illus.). 464p. pap. 19.95 (978-0-86315-225-2(2)) Floris Bks. GBR. Dist: SteinerBooks, Inc.

Stevens, Phillips, ed. Anthropology of Religion, 4 vols. 2011. (ENG., Illus.). 1352p. 1140.00 (978-0-415-49423-6(0)) Routledge.

Stout, Adam. Creating Prehistory: Druids, Ley Hunters & Archaeologists in Pre-War Britain. 2008. (ENG., Illus.). 336p. 116.95 (978-1-4051-5504-5(3)); pap. 62.95 (978-1-4051-5505-2(1)) Wiley, John & Sons, Inc. (Wiley-Blackwell).

Stringer, M. D. & Stringer. Contemporary Western Ethnography & the Definition of Religion. 2008. (Continuum Advances in Religious Studies). (ENG.). 142p. 110.00 (978-0-8264-9978-3(3)) Continuum International Publishing Group, Ltd. GBR. Dist: National Bk. Network.

Subramanyam, V., ed. Indigenous Science & Technology for Sustainable Development. 2008. 368p. (C). 40.00 (978-81-316-0131-0(5)) Rawat Pubns. IND. Dist: International Specialized Bk. Services.

Sullivan, Alan P., III, ed. Archaeological Concepts for the Study of the Cultural Past. 2008. (Foundations of Archaeological Inquiry Ser.). (ENG., Illus.). 288p. 25.00 (978-0-87480-922-0(3)); pap. 25.00 (978-0-87480-916-9(9)) Univ. of Utah Pr.

Sumiala, Johanna. Media & Ritual. 2012. (Media, Religion & Culture Ser.). (ENG., Illus.). 176p. 115.00 (978-0-415-68432-3(3)); pap. 36.95 (978-0-415-68433-0(1)) Routledge.

Sutton, Mark Q., et al. Paleonutrition. 2010. (ENG., Illus.). 384p. 75.00 (978-0-8165-2794-6(6)) Univ. of Arizona Pr.

Taussig, Michael. Walter Benjamin's Grave. 2006. (Illus.). 258p. 60.00 (978-0-226-79003-9(7)); (ENG., per. 24.00 (978-0-226-79004-6(5)) Univ. of Chicago Pr.

Tax, Sol, ed. Horizons of Anthropology. 2007. (ENG.). 288p. (gr. 11). pap. 24.95 (978-0-202-36140-6(3)) Aldine Transaction.

Tersigni-Tarrant, MariaTeresa & Shirley, Natalie, eds. Forensic Anthropology: An Introduction. 2012. (ENG., Illus.). 512p. 99.95 (978-1-4398-1646-2(8), CRC Press) Taylor & Francis Group GBR. Dist: Taylor & Francis Group.

Thomas, David Hurst & Kelly, Robert L. Archaeology: Down to Earth. 4th ed. 2010. (ENG.). (C). 304p. pap. 122.95 (978-0-495-81409-2(1)); 1p. ring bd. 63.95 (978-0-495-81412-2(1)) Wadsworth.

Thornton, Robert J. Unimagined Community: Sex, Networks, & AIDS in Uganda & South Africa. 2008. (California Series in Public Anthropology: Vol. 20). (Illus.). 304p. pap. 26.95 (978-0-520-25553-1(4)); 60.00 (978-0-520-25552-4(6)) Univ. of California Pr.

Tsitsishvili, Nino. Cultural Paradigms & Political Change in the Caucasus. 2010. 316p. pap. (978-3-8383-8856-4(9)) Lambert Academic Publishing.

Uberoi, Patricia. Anthropology in the East: Founders of Indian Sociology & Anthropology. Sundar, Nandini & Deshpande, Satish, eds. 2008. (ENG., Illus.). 568p. pap. 39.95 (978-1-905422-78-4(4)); 109.95 (978-1-905422-77-7(6)) Seagull Bks. GBR. Dist: Chicago Distribution Ctr.

Valentine, David. Imagining Transgender: An Ethnography of a Category. 2007. (ENG., Illus.). 320p. (C). 89.95 (978-0-8223-3853-6(X)); per. 24.95 (978-0-8223-3869-7(6)) Duke Univ. Pr.

Valsiner, Jaan, ed. The Oxford Handbook of Culture & Psychology, 1 vol. 2012. (Oxford Library of Psychology Ser.). (ENG.). 1152p. 250.00 (978-0-19-539643-0(X)) Oxford Univ. Pr., Inc.

van der Grijp, Paul. Passion & Profit: Towards an Anthropology of Collecting. Stadler, Friedrich, ed. 2007. (ENG.). 336p. (gr. 11). pap. 49.95 (978-3-8258-9258-6(1)) Lit Verlag DEU. Dist: Transaction Pubs.

Van der Hoorn, Mélanie. Indispensable Eyesores: An Anthropology of Undesired Buildings. 2009. (Illus.). 272p. 90.00 (978-1-84545-530-9(4)) Berghahn Bks., Inc.

van Ginkel, Rob. Coastal Cultures: An Anthropology of Fishing & Whaling. 2008. (ENG., Illus.). 240p. pap. 49.95 (978-90-5589-294-5(7)) Het Spinhuis NLD. Dist: Transaction Pubs.

Van Vleet, Krista E. Performing Kinship: Narrative, Gender, & the Intimacies of Power in the Andes. 2008. (ENG., Illus.). 288p. pap. 24.95 (978-0-292-71708-4(3)) Univ. of Texas Pr.

Vanderwal, Ron, ed. John Bulmer's Recollections of Victorian Aboriginal Life, 1855-1980. 2006. (ENG., Illus.). 106p. (J). pap. 19.95 (978-0-9577471-2-8(8)) Museum Victoria Publishing AUS. Dist: National Bk. Network.

Vargas-Ramos, Carlos. Migration & Political Behavior. 2010. 456p. pap. (978-3-8383-4509-3(6)) Lambert Academic Publishing.

Vijver, Fons J. R. van de. Fundamental Questions in Cross-Cultural Psychology. Chasiotis, Athanasios & Breugelmans, Seger M., eds. 2011. (ENG., Illus.). 602p. 130.00 (978-0-521-76015-7(1)); pap. 49.00 (978-0-521-75751-5(7)) Cambridge Univ. Pr.

Visweswaran, Kamala. Un Common Cultures: Racism & the Rearticulation of Cultural Difference. 2010. (ENG.). 360p. pap. 25.95 (978-0-8223-4635-7(4)); (Illus.). 94.95 (978-0-8223-4621-0(4)) Duke Univ. Pr.

Vivian, Lauraine Margaret Helen. Psychiatric Disorder in Amaxhosa Men Following Circumcision. 2011. 280p. pap. **(978-3-8454-2205-3(X))** Lambert Academic Publishing.

vom Bruck, Gabriele & Bodenhorn, Barbara, eds. An Anthropology of Names & Naming. 2009. (ENG.). 304p. pap. 42.00 (978-0-521-12171-2(X)) Cambridge Univ. Pr.

Wadsworth. Careers in Anthropology Module. 2011. (ENG.). 16p. (C). pap. 7.95 (978-1-111-77067-9(0)) Wadsworth.

Waitz, Theodor. Introduction to Anthropology. Collingwood, J. Frederick, ed. 2008. 440p. 51.95 (978-1-4372-6967-3(2)); 438p. pap. 36.95 (978-1-4371-4352-2(0)) Kessinger Publishing, LLC.

Wallace, Alfred Russel. Studies - Scientific & Social - 2009. 544p. pap. 33.95 (978-1-4446-4614-6(1), Kent Pr.) Kent Communications, Ltd.

Wallman, Sandra. The Capability of Places: Methods for Modelling Community Response to Change, 1 vol. 2011. (Anthropology, Culture & Society Ser.). (ENG., Illus.). 240p. lib. bdg. 110.00 **(978-0-7453-3146-1(7))** Pluto Pr. GBR. Dist: Macmillan.

—The Capability of Places: Methods for Modelling Community Response to Intrusion & Change, 1 vol. 2011. (Anthropology, Culture & Society Ser.). (ENG., Illus.). 240p. 35.00 **(978-0-7453-3145-4(9))** Pluto Pr. GBR. Dist: Macmillan.

Warren, Michael W., et al, eds. The Forensic Anthropology Laboratory. 2008. (ENG., Illus.). 240p. 129.95 (978-0-8493-2320-1(7), CRC Press) Taylor & Francis Group GBR. Dist: Taylor & Francis Group.

Waters, Donald J. Strange Ways & Sweet Dreams: Afro-American Folklore from the Hampton Institute. 460p. 2009. 69.00 (978-1-59740-287-3(7)) 2008. pap. 46.00 (978-1-59740-695-6(3)) ACLS Humanities E-Book.

Waterston, Alisse & Vesperi, Maria D., eds. Anthropology off the Shelf: Anthropologists on Writing. 2011. (ENG.). 232p. pap. 34.95 (978-1-4443-3879-9(X), Wiley-Blackwell) Wiley, John & Sons, Inc.

Waterton, Emma & Watson, Steve. Culture Heritage & Representations: Perspectives on Visuality & the Past. 2010. (Heritage, Culture & Identity Ser.). (Illus.). 296p. 124.95 (978-0-7546-7598-3(X)) Ashgate Publishing Co.

Weidenreich, Franz. Selected Anthropological Papers, 1928-1949. reprint ed. 57.50 (978-0-404-18279-3(8)) AMS Pr., Inc.

Weinstein, Roni. Nisuin Nusah Italyah: Al Yehude Italyah Be-Reshit Ha-Et Ha-Hadashah. 2007. (HEB.). 365p. (978-965-235-116-6(4)) Ben-Zi Inst.

Wells, Peter S. Image & Response in Early Europe. 2008. (Duckworth Debates in Archaeology Ser.). (Illus.). 208p. (C). pap. 24.95 (978-0-7156-3682-4(0)) Duckworth Publishers GBR. Dist: International Publishers Marketing.

Welsch, Wolfgang, et al, eds. Interdisciplinary Anthropology: Continuing Evolution of Man. 2011. (ENG.). 250p. 189.00 (978-3-642-11667-4(1), 3642116671) Springer.

Werbner, Pnina. Anthropology & the New Cosmopolitanism: Rooted, Feminist & Vernacular Perspectives. Werbner, Pnina, ed. 2008. (ASA Monographs). (ENG.). 1p. 109.95 (978-1-84788-197-7(1)) Berg Pubs. GBR. Dist: Macmillan.

Werbner, Pnina, ed. Anthropology & the New Cosmopolitanism: Rooted, Feminist & Vernacular Perspectives. 2009. (ASA Monographs). (ENG.). 1p. pap. 39.95 (978-1-84788-198-4(X)) Berg Pubs. GBR. Dist: Macmillan.

Wesson, Cameron B. Introduction to Anthropology: Human Cultures. 2010. (ENG.). 360p. pap. 99.52 (978-0-7575-6820-6(3)) Kendall Hunt Publishing Co.

West, Michael. An Intact Chest from the 1686 French Shipwreck la Belle. 2011. 284p. pap. **(978-3-8443-0650-7(1))** Lambert Academic Publishing.

White, Leslie A., , Leslie A & White, Leslie A. Modern Capitalist Culture. 2008. (ENG.). 700p. 79.95 (978-1-59874-157-5(8)) Left Coast Pr., Inc.

Wieczkowski & Wieczkowski, Julie. The Human Journey: A Workbook on Human Origins. rev. ed. 2011. (ENG.). 94p. spiral bd. 49.70 (978-0-7575-7674-4(5)) Kendall Hunt Publishing Co.

Wikan, Unni. Resonance: Beyond the Words. 2012. 344p. 90.00 **(978-0-226-92446-5(7))**; pap. 30.00 **(978-0-226-92447-2(5))** Univ. of Chicago Pr.

Wiseman, Boris. Levi-Strauss, Anthropology, & Aesthetics. 2009. (Ideas in Context Ser.). 264p. pap. 38.99 (978-0-521-12301-3(1)) Cambridge Univ. Pr.

Wood, Bernard A., et al, eds. Major Topics in Primate & Human Evolution. 2009. (ENG.). 376p. (C). pap. 69.00 (978-0-521-11338-0(5)) Cambridge Univ. Pr.

Woolfson, Charles. Labour Theory of Culture, Vol. 42. 2009. 140p. 104.00 (978-0-415-55583-8(3)) Routledge.

Zakir, Majumder. Beyond Blurred Genres: Literature, Anthropology, & Ethnography. 2011. 176p. pap. **(978-3-639-32984-1(8))** VDM Verlag Dr. Mueller e.K.

Zigon, Jarrett. Morality: An Anthropological Perspective. 2008. (ENG.). 224p. pap. 29.95 (978-1-84520-659-8(2)) Berg Pubs. GBR. Dist: Macmillan.

Zimmer-Tamakoshi, Laura & Dickerson-Putman, Jeanette, eds. Pulling the Right Threads: The Ethnographic Life & Legacy of Jane C. Goodale. 2008. (Illus.). 272p. per. 26.00 (978-0-252-07484-4(X)) Univ. of Illinois Pr.

ANTHROPOLOGY—BIBLIOGRAPHY

British Library of Political and Economic Science Staff, ed. IBSS: Anthropology: 2005, Vol. 51. 2006. 598p. (C). 625.00 (978-0-415-41720-4(1)) Routledge.

Kibbee, Josephine & Jacoby, JoAnn. Cultural Anthropology: A Guide to Reference & Information Sources, 1 vol. 2nd rev. ed. 2007. (Reference Sources in the Social Sciences Ser.). 300p. per. 65.00 (978-1-59158-357-8(8), LU3578) Libraries Unlimited, Inc.

Price, T. Douglas & Feinman, Gary M., eds. Archaeology at the Millennium: A Sourcebook. 2008. (ENG., Illus.). xvi, 512p. per. 74.95 (978-0-387-72610-6(1), 0387726101) Springer.

ANTHROPOLOGY—DATA PROCESSING

Weber, Gerhard W. & Bookstein, Fred L. Virtual Anthropology. 2009. (Illus.). 250p. 99.00 (978-3-211-48647-4(X)) Springer.

ANTHROPOLOGY—DICTIONARIES

Barnard, Alan & Spencer, Jonathan, eds. Encyclopedia of Social & Cultural Anthropology. 2nd rev. ed. 2010. (ENG., Illus.). 896p. (C). 350.00 (978-0-415-40978-0(0)) Routledge.

Stewart, William. Biographical Dictionary of Anthropologists. 2009. (ENG.). 245p. pap. 55.00 (978-0-7864-3671-2(9)) McFarland & Co., Inc. Pubs.

ANTHROPOLOGY—HISTORY

Berliner, David & Sarró, Ramon, eds. Learning Religion: Anthropological Approaches. 2007. (Methodology & History in Anthropology Ser.). 248p. 90.00 (978-1-84545-374-9(3)) Berghahn Bks., Inc.

Buschmann, Rainer F. Anthropology's Global Histories: The Ethnographic Frontier in German New Guinea, 1870-1935. 2009. (Illus.). 280p. (C). 57.00 (978-0-8248-3184-4(5)) Univ. of Hawaii Pr.

Clark, Grahame. Prehistory at Cambridge & Beyond. 2009. (ENG.). 188p. pap. 31.99 (978-0-521-10194-3(8)) Cambridge Univ. Pr.

Davidson, Iain & McDougall, Russell, eds. The Roth Family, Anthropology, & Colonial Administration. 2008. (Univ Col London Inst Arch Pub Ser.). (ENG., Illus.). 304p. 94.00 (978-1-59874-228-2(0)) Left Coast Pr., Inc.

Denega, Danielle. Dead Men Floating: A Small Town Is Awash in Skeletons. 2011. (978-0-545-32802-9(0)) Scholastic, Inc.

Dube, Saurabh. Historical Anthropology. 2007. (ENG.). 464p. 65.00 (978-0-19-569071-2(0)) Oxford Univ. Pr., Inc.

Erickson, Paul & Murphy, Liam D. A History of Anthropological Theory. 3rd ed. 2008. (ENG., Illus.). 300p. pap. (978-1-55111-871-0(8)) Univ. of Toronto Pr.

Erickson, Paul A. & Murphy, Liam D. A History of Anthropological Theory. 4th ed. 2008. (ENG.). 300p. pap. (978-1-4426-0110-9(8)) Univ. of Toronto Pr.

Erickson, Paul A. & Murphy, P. A. E. Liam D. History of Anthropological Theory. 3rd ed. 2010. (Illus.). 625p. pap. (978-1-4426-0069-0(1)) Univ. of Toronto Pr.

Evans, Andrew D. Anthropology at War: World War I & the Science of Race in Germany. 2010. (ENG., Illus.). 312p. 85.00 (978-0-226-22267-7(5)); pap. 29.00 (978-0-226-22268-4(3)) Univ. of Chicago Pr.

Fienieg, Anouk. Sejarah Sintang - the History of Sintang: A Collection of Books, Manuscripts, Archives & Articles. Sagita, Novia, tr. from ENG. 2007. (Bulletins of the Royal Tropical Institute Ser.). (Illus.). 112p. pap. 35.00 (978-90-6832-449-5(7)) Royal Tropical Institute Pr. (KIT (Koninklijk Instituut voor de Tropen) NLD. Dist: Stylus Publishing, LLC.

Fowler, Don. Laboratory for Anthropology: Science & Romanticism in the American Southwest, 1846-1930. 2010. (ENG.). 502p. (gr. 13). pap. 34.95 (978-1-60781-035-3(2)) Univ. of Utah Pr.

Gable, Eric. Anthropology & Egalitarianism: Ethnographic Encounters from Monticello to Guinea-Bissau. 2010. (ENG., Illus.). 246p. pap. 24.95 (978-0-253-22275-6(3), 0253222753) Indiana Univ. Pr.

Gewald, Jan-Bart, et al, eds. Strength Beyond Structure: Social & Historical Trajectories of Agency in Africa. 2007. (African Dynamics Ser.). (Illus.). 344p. pap. (978-90-04-15696-8(8)) BRILL.

Gisi, Lucas Marco. Einbildungskraft und Mythologie: Die Verschränkung von Anthropologie und Geschichte im 18. Jahrhundert. 2007. (Spectrum Literaturwissenschaft / Spectrum Literature Ser.). (GER., Illus.). X, 482p. 168.00 (978-3-11-019942-0(4)) De Gruyter, Walter Inc.

Godelier, Maurice. In & Out of the West: Reconstructing Anthropology. Scott, Nora, tr. 2009. (Page#45;Barbour Lectures). (ENG.). 256p. (gr. 17). 45.00 (978-0-8139-2707-7(2)) Univ. Pr. of Virginia.

Handler, Richard, ed. Central Sites, Peripheral Visions: Cultural & Institutional Crossings in the History of Anthropology. 2006. (History of Anthropology Ser.: Vol. 11). (Illus.). 288p. 24.95 (978-0-299-21920-8(8)) Univ. of Wisconsin Pr.

Harrison, Faye V. Outsider Within: Reworking Anthropology in the Global Age. 2008. 376p. 73.00 (978-0-252-03261-5(6)); per. 26.00 (978-0-252-07490-5(4)) Univ. of Illinois Pr.

Herle, Anita & Rouse, Sandra, eds. Cambridge & the Torres Strait: Centenary Essays on the 1898 Anthropological Expedition. 2008. (ENG., Illus.). 272p. pap. 37.99 (978-0-521-10386-2(X)) Cambridge Univ. Pr.

Kerns, Virginia. Journeys West: Jane & Julian Steward & Their Guides. 2010. (ENG., Illus.). 444p. 55.00 (978-0-8032-2508-4(3)) Univ. of Nebraska Pr.

Kuklick, Henrika, ed. A New History of Anthropology. 2007. (ENG., Illus.). 416p. pap. 50.95 (978-0-631-22600-0(1)); 111.95 (978-0-631-22599-7(4)) Wiley, John & Sons, Inc. (Wiley-Blackwell).

Launay, Robert, ed. Foundations of Anthropological Theory: From Classical Antiquity to Early Modern Europe. 2010. (Wiley-Blackwell Anthologies in Social & Cultural Anthropology Ser.). (ENG., Illus.). 312p. 104.95 (978-1-4051-8776-3(X)); pap. 49.95 (978-1-4051-8775-6(1)) Wiley, John & Sons, Inc. (Wiley-Blackwell).

McDougall, Russell & Davidson, Iain, eds. The Roth Family, Anthropology, & Colonial Administration. 2009. (University College London Institute of Archaeology Publications). (ENG.). 304p. pap. 34.95 (978-1-59874-352-4(X)) Left Coast Pr., Inc.

Moberg, Mark. Engaging Anthropological Theory. 2012. (ENG., Illus.). 440p. (C). 130.00 **(978-0-415-69999-0(1))**; pap. 39.95 **(978-0-415-80916-0(9))** Routledge.

Patterson, Thomas C. & Patterson, Thomas Carl. Karl Marx, Anthropologist. 2009. (ENG.). 256p. pap. 34.95 (978-1-84520-511-9(1)); (Illus.). 1p. 109.95 (978-1-84520-509-6(X)) Berg Pubs. GBR. Dist: Macmillan.

Price, David H. Anthropological Intelligence: The Deployment & Neglect of American Anthropology in the Second World War. 2008. (ENG.). 400p. (C). 94.95 (978-0-8223-4219-9(7)); pap. 26.95 (978-0-8223-4237-3(5)) Duke Univ. Pr.

Rivière, Peter. A History of Oxford Anthropology. 2007. (Methodology & History in Anthropology Ser.). (Illus.). 230p. 90.00 (978-1-84545-348-0(4)) Berghahn Bks., Inc.

Rivière, Peter, ed. A History of Oxford Anthropology. 2009. 230p. 24.50 (978-1-84545-699-3(8)) Berghahn Bks., Inc.

Robbins, Joel & Friedman, Jonathan, eds. Anthropological Theory. 2013. 1664p. 995.00 (978-1-84787-488-7(6), B74887C) SAGE Pubns., Ltd. GBR. Dist: SAGE Pubns., Inc.

Schafft, Gretchen E. From Racism to Genocide: Anthropology in the Third Reich. 2007. (Illus.). 320p. per. 25.00 (978-0-252-07453-0(X)) Univ. of Illinois Pr.

Schmidt, Peter R. & Patterson, Thomas C., eds. Making Alternative Histories. (Advanced Seminar Ser.). (Illus.). 312p. 29.95 (978-0-933452-92-3(6)) School for Advanced Research Pr./SAR Pr.

Schmuhl, Hans-Walter. The Kaiser Wilhelm Institute for Anthropology, Human Heredity & Eugenics, 1927-1945: Crossing Boundaries. 2010. (Boston Studies in the Philosophy of Science Ser.). xiv, 468p. pap. 219.00 (978-90-481-7678-6(6), 9048176786) Springer.

Sevelius, Gunnar. The Nine Pillars of History: An Anthropological Review of History, Five Religions, Sexuality & Modern Economics, All as a Guide for Peace. 2010. 368p. (ENG.). 36.49 (978-1-4520-2351-9(4)); pap. 22.99 (978-1-4520-0061-9(1)) AuthorHouse.

Stocking, George W. After Tylor: British Social Anthropology, 1888-1951. (Illus.). 592p. pap. (978-0-485-30089-5(3)) Continuum International Publishing Group, Ltd.

Tilley, Gordon & Gordon, Robert J. Ordering Africa: Anthropology, European Imperialism & the Politics of Knowledge. Tilley, Helen L., ed. 2011. (Studies in Imperialism Ser.). (ENG.). 404p. pap. 50.00 (978-0-7190-8212-2(9)) Manchester Univ. Pr. GBR. Dist: Macmillan.

Trautmann, Thomas R. Lewis Henry Morgan & the Invention of Kinship. 2nd ed. 2008. (ENG., Illus.). 312p. pap. 24.95 (978-0-8032-6006-1(7)) Univ. of Nebraska Pr.

Wang, Mingming. Empire & Local Worlds: A Chinese Model for Long-Term Historical Anthropology. 2009. (Critical Cultural Heritage Series, University College London Institute of Archaeology Publications). (ENG., Illus.). 344p. pap. 36.95 (978-1-59874-405-7(4)); lib. bdg. 89.00 (978-1-59874-404-0(6)) Left Coast Pr., Inc.

Wax, Dustin M. Anthropology at the Dawn of the Cold War. 2008. (Anthropology, Culture & Society Ser.). (ENG.). 192p. 100.00 (978-0-7453-2587-3(4)) Pluto Pr. GBR. Dist: Macmillan.

—Anthropology at the Dawn of the Cold War: The Influence of Foundations, Mccarthyism, & the CIA. 2008. (Anthropology, Culture & Society Ser.). (ENG.). 192p. per. 34.00 (978-0-7453-2586-6(6)) Pluto Pr. GBR. Dist: Macmillan.

Whitehead, Neil L. & Alemán, Stephanie W., eds. Anthropologies of Guayana: Cultural Spaces in Northeastern Amazonia. 2009. (Native Peoples of the Americas Ser.). (ENG., Illus.). 320p. 70.00 (978-0-8165-2607-9(9)) Univ. of Arizona Pr.

Wilcox, Clifford. Robert Redfield & the Development of American Anthropology. 2006. (ENG., Illus.). 246p. per. 29.50 (978-0-7391-1777-4(7)) Lexington Bks.

Wilford, Andrew C. & Tagliacozzo, Eric, eds. Clio/Anthropos: Exploring the Boundaries Between History & Anthropology. 2009. (ENG., Illus.). 312p. 65.00 (978-0-8047-6020-1(9)) Stanford Univ. Pr.

Wolff, Larry & Cipolloni, Marco, eds. The Anthropology of the Enlightenment. 2007. (ENG.). 432p. 70.00 (978-0-8047-5202-2(8)); per. 29.95 (978-0-8047-5203-9(6)) Stanford Univ. Pr.

ANTHROPOLOGY—METHODOLOGY

Ahamer, Julia & Lechleitner, Gerda. Um-Feld-Forschung: Erfahrungen, Erlebnisse, Ergebnisse. 2007. (Mitteilungen des Phonogrammarchivs Ser.). (GER & ENG., Illus.). 350p. (C). 89.00 (978-3-7001-3820-4(2)) Austrian Academy of Sciences Press AUT. Dist: Brown, David Bk. Co., The.

Aronoff, Myron Joel & Kubík, Jan. Anthropology & Political Science: A Convergent Approach. 2012. 332p. 95.00 **(978-0-85745-725-7(X))** Berghahn Bks., Inc.

Barrett, Stanley. Anthropology. 2nd ed. 2009. 280p. (ENG.). pupil's gde. ed. (978-0-8020-9916-7(5)); pap., stu. ed., pupil's gde. ed. (978-0-8020-9612-8(3)) Univ. of Toronto Pr.

Berliner, David & Sarró, Ramon, eds. Learning Religion: Anthropological Approaches. 2007. (Methodology & History in Anthropology Ser.). 248p. 90.00 (978-1-84545-374-9(3)) Berghahn Bks., Inc.

Cram101 Textbook Reviews. Outlines & Highlights for Visions of Culture: An Introduction to Anthropological Theories & Theorists by Jerry Moore. 2011. 166p. pap. 29.95 **(978-1-61490-597-4(5))** Cram101 Inc.

Cram101 Textbook Reviews & Cram101 Textbook Reviews. Outlines & Highlights for Reclaiming a Scientific Anthropology by Lawrence Kuznar, isbn: 9780759111080. 2011. 190p. pap. 30.95 **(978-1-61461-855-3(0))** Cram101 Inc.

Engelke, Matthew, ed. The Objects of Evidence. 2009. (Journal of the Royal Anthropological Institute Special Issue Book Ser.: 1). (ENG., Illus.). 168p. pap. 39.95 (978-1-4051-9296-5(8), Wiley-Blackwell) Wiley, John & Sons, Inc.

Epstein, A. L. The Craft of Social Anthropology. 2012. (ENG.). 298p. pap. 34.95 (978-1-4128-4587-8(4)) Transaction Pubs.

Fabian, Johannes. Memory Against Culture: Arguments & Reminders. 2007. (ENG., Illus.). 208p. 79.95 (978-0-8223-4056-0(9)); per. 22.95 (978-0-8223-4077-5(1)) Duke Univ. Pr.

Harris. Ways of Knowing: New Approaches in the Anthropology of Knowledge & Learning. 2007. (Methodology & History in Anthropology Ser.: Vol. 18). 354p. 90.00 (978-1-84545-364-0(6)) Berghahn Bks., Inc.

James, Deborah, et al, eds. Culture Wars: Context, Models & Anthropologists' Accounts. 2010. (EASA Ser.). 228p. 80.00 (978-1-84545-641-2(6)) Berghahn Bks., Inc.

Katz, Adam, ed. The Originary Hypothesis: A Minimal Proposal for Humanistic Inquiry. 2007. (ENG.). 382p. pap. 28.00 (978-1-888570-36-6(9)) Davies Group Pubs., The.

Kuznar, Lawrence A. Reclaiming a Scientific Anthropology. 2nd ed. 2008. (ENG., Illus.). 266p. 85.00 (978-0-7591-1108-0(1)); pap. 29.95 (978-0-7591-1109-7(X)) AltaMira Pr.

McGee & Warms & Cram101 Textbook Reviews Staff. Anthropological Theory: An Introductory History. 2007. 192p. per. 12.95 (978-1-4288-2602-1(5)) Cram101 Inc.

McGee, R. Jon & Warms, Richard. Anthropological Theory: An Introductory History. 5th ed. 2011. (ENG., Illus.). 672p. (C). pap. 125.33 (978-0-07-803488-6(4), 0078034884) McGraw-Hill Cos., The.

McGee, R. Jon & Warms, Richard L. Anthropological Theory: An Introductory History. 4th ed. 2007. (ENG., Illus.). 684p. (C). per. 125.33 (978-0-07-340522-3(1), 0073405221) McGraw-Hill Cos., The.

Moberg, Mark. Engaging Anthropological Theory. 2012. (ENG., Illus.). 440p. (C). 130.00 **(978-0-415-69999-0(1))**; pap. 39.95 **(978-0-415-80916-0(9))** Routledge.

Moore, Jerry D. Visions of Culture: An Introduction to Anthropological Theories & Theorists. 3rd ed. 2008. (ENG.). 416p. 90.00 (978-0-7591-1145-5(6)); pap. 39.95 (978-0-7591-1146-2(4)) AltaMira Pr.

Parkin, Robert & de Sales, Anne, eds. Out of the Study & into the Field: Ethnographic Theory & Practice in French Anthropology. 2010. (MHA Ser.). (Illus.). 300p. 90.00 (978-1-84545-695-5(5)) Berghahn Bks., Inc.

Pitt, David C. Using Historical Sources in Anthropology & Sociology. (George & Louise Spindler Case Studies in Cultural Anthropology). 92p. (C). reprint ed. pap. (978-0-8290-0587-5(0)) Irvington Pubs.

Rabinow, Paul. Reflections on Fieldwork in Morocco. 30th ed. 2007. (Illus.). 172p. per. 21.95 (978-0-520-25177-9(6)) Univ. of California Pr.

Salzman, Philip C. & Rice, Patricia C. Thinking Anthropologically: A Practical Guide for Students. 3rd ed. 2010. (ENG.). 160p. (C). pap. 24.40 (978-0-205-79271-9(5), Prentice Hall) Prentice Hall PTR.

Sarana, Gopala. Explorations in Method & Theory in Anthropology. 2008. 470p. 60.00 (978-81-316-0163-1(3)) Rawat Pubns. IND. Dist: International Specialized Bk. Services.

Shankland, David. Archaeology & Anthropology: Past, Present & Future. 2012. (Association of Social Anthropologists Monographs). (ENG.). 256p. 99.95 **(978-1-84788-966-9(2))** Berg Pubs. GBR. Dist: Macmillan.

Strang, Veronica. What Anthropologists Do. 2009. (ENG.). 1p. pap. 29.95 (978-1-84520-355-9(0)); (Illus.). 99.95 (978-1-84520-354-2(2)) Berg Pubs. GBR. Dist: Macmillan.

Taussig, Michael. I Swear I Saw This: Drawings in Fieldwork Notebooks, Namely My Own. 2011. (ENG., Illus.). 192p. 48.00 (978-0-226-78982-8(9)); pap. 16.00 (978-0-226-78983-5(7)) Univ. of Chicago Pr.

Taussig, Michael. Michael Taussig: Feldforschungsnotizbücher. 2011. (ENG., Illus.). 36p. pap. 10.00 **(978-3-7757-2850-8(3))** Hatje Cantz Verlag GmbH & Co KG DEU. Dist: D.A.P./Distributed Art Pubs.

Ukaegbu & Ukaegbu, Dorothy C. Writing in Anthropology: The Summary & the Critique Paper. 2nd ed. 2011. (ENG.). 348p. (C). pap. 90.67 **(978-1-256-29279-1(6))** Pearson Learning Solutions.

Unterberger, Alayne. Invisible Anthropologists No. 31: Engaged Anthropology in Immigrant Communities, Number 31. 2009. (NAPA Bulletin Ser.: 6). (ENG., Illus.). 200p. pap. 26.95 (978-1-4443-3203-2(1), Wiley-Blackwell) Wiley, John & Sons, Inc.

ANTHROPOLOGY—OUTLINES, SYLLABI, ETC.

Cram101 Textbook Reviews. Outlines & Highlights for Anthropology: A Global Perspective by Raymond Scupin, Christopher R. Decorse, ISBN. 2010. 96p. pap. 27.95 (978-1-61698-533-2(X)) Cram101 Inc.

—Outlines & Highlights for Anthropology & Contemporary Human Problems by John H Bodley, Isbn: 9780759111387 0759111383. 2011. 224p. pap. 30.95 **(978-1-4288-7638-5(3))** Cram101 Inc.

—Outlines & Highlights for Anthropology by Barbara D Miller, Isbn: 9780205583539. 2010. 210p. pap. 30.95 (978-1-61698-541-7(0)) Cram101 Inc.

—Outlines & Highlights for Anthropology by Carol R Ember, Melvin Ember, Peter N Peregrine, Melvin R Ember, Isbn: 9780132277532. 2010. 74p. pap. 27.95 (978-1-61698-540-0(2)) Cram101 Inc.

—Outlines & Highlights for Anthropology of Religion by Fiona Bowie. 2011. 182p. pap. 30.95 **(978-1-4288-6457-3(1))** Cram101 Inc.

—Outlines & Highlights for Core Concepts in Biological Anthropology by Fuentes, Agustin, Isbn: 9780767424264 0767424263. 2011. 328p. pap. 33.95 **(978-1-4288-6760-4(0))** Cram101 Inc.

—Outlines & Highlights for Cultural Anthropology: A Global Perspective by Raymond Scupin, ISBN. 2010. 80p. pap. 27.95 (978-1-61698-534-9(8)) Cram101 Inc.

—Outlines & Highlights for Cultural Anthropology by Carol R Ember, Isbn: 9780205711208 9780205828586 9780205797356. 2011. 518p. pap. 37.95 **(978-1-4288-8539-4(0))** Cram101 Inc.

—Outlines & Highlights for Culture Sketches: Case Studies in Anthropology by Holly Peters-Golden, ISBN. 2010. 76p. pap. 27.95 (978-1-61698-122-8(9)) Cram101 Inc.

—Outlines & Highlights for Medical Anthropology: A Biocultural Approach by Andrea S. Wiley; John S. Allen. 2011. 286p. pap. 32.95 **(978-1-4288-8069-6(0))** Cram101 Inc.

—Outlines & Highlights for Understanding Physical Anthropology & Archaeology by Barry Lewis, Robert Jurmain, Lynn Kilgore, Isbn: 9780534623968. 2011. 320p. pap. 33.95 **(978-1-4288-7629-3(4))** Cram101 Inc.

—Outlines & Highlights for Visions of Culture: An Introduction to Anthropological Theories & Theorists by Jerry Moore. 2011. 166p. pap. 29.95 **(978-1-61490-597-4(5))** Cram101 Inc.

Cram101 Textbook Reviews & Cram101 Textbook Reviews. Outlines & Highlights for Introducing Anthropology: An Integrated Approach by Park, Michael A. Park, Michael A. , ISBN. 2011. 618p. pap. 40.95 **(978-1-61744-958-1(X))** Cram101 Inc.

Cram101 Textbook Reviews Staff. Outlines & Highlights for Conformity & Conflict, Web Edition by James & Spradley, Isbn: 9780205619269. 2009. 88p. pap. 27.95 (978-1-4288-9625-3(2)) Cram101 Inc.

—Outlines & Highlights for Essence of Anthropology by William a Haviland, Isbn: 9780534623715. 2009. 100p. pap. 27.95 (978-1-4288-9709-0(7)) Cram101 Inc.

—Outlines & Highlights for the Essence of Anthropology by William a Haviland, Isbn: 9780495599814. 2009. 120p. pap. 28.95 (978-1-4288-8800-5(4)) Cram101 Inc.

McGee & Warms & Cram101 Textbook Reviews Staff. Anthropological Theory: An Introductory History. 2007. 192p. per. 12.95 (978-1-4288-2602-1(5)) Cram101 Inc.

ANTHROPOLOGY—PHILOSOPHY

Abram, David. Becoming Animal: An Earthly Cosmology. (Vintage Ser.). (ENG.). 336p. 2011. pap. 16.95 (978-0-375-71369-9(7), Vintage) 2010. 26.95 (978-0-375-42171-6(8), Pantheon) Knopf Doubleday Publishing Group.

Angelis, Simone de. Anthropologien: Genesis & Configuration of a 'Science of Man' in the Early Modern Age. 2010. (Historia Hermeneutica. Series Studia Ser.). (GER.). XI, 479p. 137.00 (978-3-11-020225-0(5)) De Gruyter, Walter Inc.

Barrett, Stanley. Anthropology. 2nd ed. 2009. 280p. (ENG.). pupil's gde. ed. (978-0-8020-9916-7(5)); pap., stu. ed., pupil's gde. ed. (978-0-8020-9612-8(3)) Univ. of Toronto Pr.

Collins, Samuel Gerald. All Tomorrow's Cultures: Anthropological Engagements with the Future. 2007. 150p. (C). 29.95 (978-1-84545-406-1(1)) Berghahn Bks., Inc.

Desjarlais, Robert R. Counterplay: An Anthropologist at the Chessboard. (ENG., Illus.). 2012. 266p. pap. 19.95 **(978-0-520-27260-6(9))** 2011. 276p. 50.00 (978-0-520-26739-8(7)) Univ. of California Pr.

Durrenberger, E. Paul & Erem, Suzan. Anthropology Unbound: A Field Guide to the 21st Century. 2007. (ENG., Illus.). 310p. per. 28.95 (978-1-59451-262-9(0)) 2nd ed. 2010. (ENG.). 352p. pap., instr.'s gde. ed. 32.95 (978-1-59451-773-0(8)) 2nd ed. 2009. (Illus.). 352p. 125.00 (978-1-59451-772-3(X)) Paradigm Pubs.

—Paradigms for Anthropology: An Ethnographic Reader. 352p. 2010. pap. 39.95 (978-1-59451-781-5(9)) 2009. (ENG.). 113.00 (978-1-59451-780-8(0)) Paradigm Pubs.

Erickson, Paul & Murphy, Liam D. A History of Anthropological Theory. 3rd ed. 2008. (ENG., Illus.). 300p. pap. (978-1-55111-871-0(8)) Univ. of Toronto Pr.

Erickson, Paul A. & Murphy, P. A. E. Liam D. History of Anthropological Theory. 3rd ed. 2010. (Illus.). 625p. pap. (978-1-4426-0069-0(1)) Univ. of Toronto Pr.

Evens. Anthropology As Ethics: Non-Dualism & the Conduct of Sacrifice. 2007. 248p. (C). 95.00 (978-1-84545-224-7(0)) Berghahn Bks., Inc.

Evens, T. M. S. Anthropology As Ethics: Nondualism & the Conduct of Sacrifice. 2009. 418p. 34.95 (978-1-84545-629-0(7)) Berghahn Bks., Inc.

Fabian, Johannes. Memory Against Culture: Arguments & Reminders. 2007. (ENG., Illus.). 208p. 79.95 (978-0-8223-4056-0(9)); per. 22.95 (978-0-8223-4077-5(1)) Duke Univ. Pr.

Fillitz, Thomas & Saris, A. Jamie, eds. Debating Authenticity: Concepts of Modernity in Anthropological Perspective. 2012. (ENG.). 276p. 85.00 **(978-0-85745-496-6(X))** Berghahn Bks., Inc.

Gans, Eric & Gans, Eric Lawrence. The Scenic Imagination: Originary Thinking from Hobbes to the Present Day. 2007. (ENG.). 232p. 55.00 (978-0-8047-5700-3(3)) Stanford Univ. Pr.

Geertz, Clifford. Life among the Anthros & Other Essays. Inglis, Fred, ed. 2010. (ENG.). 280p. (C). 29.95 (978-0-691-14358-3(7)) Princeton Univ. Pr.

Gordon, Robert. Going Abroad: How to Travel Like an Anthropologist, 1 vol. 2010. (ENG.). 208p. pap. 19.95 (978-1-59451-771-6(1)) Paradigm Pubs.

Handler, Richard, ed. Central Sites, Peripheral Visions: Cultural & Institutional Crossings in the History of Anthropology. 2006. (History of Anthropology Ser.: Vol. 11). (Illus.). 288p. 24.95 (978-0-299-21920-8(8)) Univ. of Wisconsin Pr.

Harvey, Penelope. Anthropology & Science: Epistemologies in Practice. Edwards, Jeanette et al, eds. 2008. (ASA Monographs). (ENG., Illus.). 256p. pap. 39.95 (978-1-84520-500-3(6)) Berg Pubs. GBR. Dist: Macmillan.

Ingold, Tim. Being Alive: Essays on Movement, Knowledge & Description. 2011. (ENG., Illus.). 288p. 39.95 (978-0-415-57684-0(9)); 125.00 (978-0-415-57683-3(0)) Routledge.

—The Perception of the Environment: Essays on Livelihood, Dwelling & Skill. 2011. (ENG., Illus.). 488p. (C). pap. 54.95 (978-0-415-61747-5(2)) Routledge.

Ingold, Tim. Redrawing Anthropology: Materials Movements Lines. 2011. (Anthropological Studies of Creativity & Perception Ser.). (Illus.). 216p. 99.95 **(978-1-4094-1774-3(3))** Ashgate Publishing Co.

Jackson, Michael. Lifeworlds: Essays in Existential Anthropology. 2012. 320p. 90.00 **(978-0-226-92364-2(9))**; pap. 30.00 **(978-0-226-92365-9(7))** Univ. of Chicago Pr.

Johnson, David E. & Michaelsen, Scott. Anthropology's Wake: Attending to the End of Culture. 2nd ed. 2008. (ENG.). 224p. 70.00 (978-0-8232-2877-5(0)); pap. 28.00 (978-0-8232-2878-2(9)) Fordham Univ. Pr.

Katz, Adam, ed. The Originary Hypothesis: A Minimal Proposal for Humanistic Inquiry. 2007. (ENG.). 382p. pap. 28.00 (978-1-888570-36-6(9)) Davies Group Pubs., The.

Klein, Rebekka A. & Sitling, Martina. Sociality As the Human Condition: Anthropology in Economic, Philosophical & Theological Perspective. 2011. XVI, 324p. **(978-90-04-19199-0(2))** BRILL.

Launay, Robert, ed. Foundations of Anthropological Theory: From Classical Antiquity to Early Modern Europe. 2010. (Wiley-Blackwell Anthologies in Social & Cultural Anthropology Ser.). (ENG., Illus.). 312p. 104.95 (978-1-4051-8776-3(X), Wiley-Blackwell) Wiley, John & Sons, Inc.

Liebersohn, Harry. The Return of the Gift: European History of a Global Idea. 2010. (ENG.). 224p. 80.00 (978-1-107-00218-0(4)) Cambridge Univ. Pr.

Loewen, Gregory V. Evaluating the Scholarly Achievement of Professor Elvi Whittaker: Essays in Philosophical Anthropology. 2010. 308p. 119.95 (978-0-7734-1308-5(1)) Mellen, Edwin Pr., The.

Marcus, George. Ethnographica Moralia: Experiments in Interpretive Anthropology. Panourgia, Neni, ed. 2008. (ENG.). 224p. 70.00 (978-0-8232-2886-7(X)); 2nd ed. pap. 28.00 (978-0-8232-2887-4(8)) Fordham Univ. Pr.

Marks, Jonathan & Marks, J. Why I Am Not a Scientist: Anthropology & Modern Knowledge. 2009. (ENG.). 304p. 55.00 (978-0-520-25959-1(9)); 344p. pap. 25.95 (978-0-520-25960-7(2)) Univ. of California Pr.

Mathews, Gordon & Izquierdo, Carolina, eds. Pursuits of Happiness: Well-Being in Anthropological Perspective. 290p. 2009. 32.50 (978-1-84545-708-2(0)) 2008. (Illus.). 90.00 (978-1-84545-448-7(0)) Berghahn Bks., Inc.

McGee & Warms & Cram101 Textbook Reviews Staff. Anthropological Theory: An Introductory History. 2007. 192p. per. 12.95 *(978-1-4288-2602-1(5))* Cram101 Inc.

McGee, R. Jon & Warms, Richard. Anthropological Theory: An Introductory History. 5th ed. 2011. (ENG., Illus.). 672p. (C). pap. 125.33 *(978-0-07-803488-6(4)*, 0078034884) McGraw-Hill Cos., The.

McGee, R. Jon & Warms, Richard L. Anthropological Theory: An Introductory History. 4th ed. 2007. (ENG., Illus.). 684p. (C). per. 125.33 *(978-0-07-340522-3(1)*, 0073405221) McGraw-Hill Cos., The.

Moberg, Mark. Engaging Anthropological Theory. 2012. (ENG., Illus.). 440p. (C). 130.00 ***(978-0-415-69999-0(1))***; pap. 39.95 ***(978-0-415-80916-0(9))*** Routledge.

Otto, Ton & Bubandt, Nils, eds. Experiments in Holism: Theory & Practice in Contemporary Anthropology. 2010. (ENG., Illus.) 336p. 125.95 *(978-1-4443-3323-7(2)*, Wiley-Blackwell) Wiley, John & Sons, Inc.

Parkin, Robert & de Sales, Anne, eds. Out of the Study & into the Field: Ethnographic Theory & Practice in French Anthropology. 2010. (MHA Ser.). (Illus.). 300p. 90.00 *(978-1-84545-695-5(5))* Berghahn Bks., Inc.

Patterson, Thomas C. & Patterson, Thomas Carl. Karl Marx, Anthropologist. 2009. (ENG.). 256p. pap. 34.95 *(978-1-84520-511-9(1))*; (Illus.). 1p. 109.95 *(978-1-84520-509-6(X))* Berg Pubs. GBR. Dist: Macmillan.

Rabinow, Paul. Marking Time: On the Anthropology of the Contemporary. 2007. (ENG.). 176p. (C). per. 24.95 *(978-0-691-13363-8(8))*; 149p. 55.00 *(978-0-691-13362-1(X))* Princeton Univ. Pr.

Rapport, Nigel. Human Nature As Capacity: An Ethnographic Approach. 2010. (MHA Ser.). 224p. 80.00 *(978-1-84545-637-5(8))* Berghahn Bks., Inc.

Salzman, Philip C. & Rice, Patricia C. Thinking Anthropologically: A Practical Guide for Students. 3rd ed. 2010. (ENG.). 160p. (C). pap. 24.40 *(978-0-205-79271-9(5)*, Prentice Hall) Prentice Hall PTR.

Sanford, Victoria, ed. Engaged Observer: Anthropology, Advocacy, & Activism. 2006. (ENG.). 272p. (C). 68.00 *(978-0-8135-3891-4(2))* Rutgers Univ. Pr.

—Engaged Observer: Anthropology, Advocacy, & Activism. 2006. (ENG.). 272p. per. 25.95 *(978-0-8135-3892-1(0))* Rutgers Univ. Pr.

Sarana, Gopala. Explorations in Method & Theory in Anthropology. 2008. 470p. 60.00 *(978-81-316-0163-1(3))* Rawat Pubns. IND. Dist: International Specialized Bk. Services.

Sodikoff, Genese Marie, ed. The Anthropology of Extinction: Essays on Culture & Species Death. 2011. (ENG., Illus.). 256p. 70.00 *(978-0-253-35713-7(6)*, 0253357136); pap. 24.95 *(978-0-253-22364-7(4)*, 0253223644) Indiana Univ. Pr.

Stafford, Charles, et al. Questions of Anthropology. 2007. (London School of Economics Monographs on Social Anthropology Ser.). (ENG., Illus.). 384p. pap. 29.95 *(978-1-84520-748-9(3))* Berg Pubs. GBR. Dist: Macmillan.

Tilley, Gordon & Gordon, Robert J. Ordering Africa: Anthropology, European Imperialism & the Politics of Knowledge. Tilley, Helen L., ed. 2011. (Studies in Imperialism Ser.). (ENG.). 404p. pap. 50.00 *(978-0-7190-8212-2(9))* Manchester Univ. Pr. GBR. Dist: Macmillan.

Turner, Stephen P. & Risjord, Mark W. Philosophy of Anthropology & Sociology. 2006. (Handbook of the Philosophy of Science Ser.). (ENG.). 900p. 250.00 *(978-0-444-51542-1(9)*, North Holland) Elsevier Science & Technology Bks.

Van Oort, Richard. The End of Literature: Essays in Originary Aesthetics. 2009. 248p. pap. 24.00 *(978-1-934542-05-7(9))* Davies Group Pubs., The.

Wagner, Roy. Coyote Anthropology. 2010. (ENG., Illus.). 216p. 40.00 *(978-0-8032-1082-0(5))* Univ. of Nebraska Pr.

Wolff, Larry & Cipolloni, Marco, eds. The Anthropology of the Enlightenment. 2007. (ENG.). 432p. 70.00 *(978-0-8047-5202-2(8))*; per. 29.95 *(978-0-8047-5203-9(6))* Stanford Univ. Pr.

Yengoyan, Aram, ed. Modes of Comparison: Theory & Practice. 2006. (Comparative Studies in Society & History Book Ser.). (ENG., Illus.). 496p. per. 42.50 *(978-0-472-06918-7(7))* Univ. of Michigan Pr.

Yengoyan, Aram A., ed. Modes of Comparison: Theory & Practice. 2006. (Comparative Studies in Society & History Book Ser.). (ENG., Illus.). 496p. 95.00 *(978-0-472-09918-4(3))* Univ. of Michigan Pr.

ANTHROPOLOGY—RESEARCH

Ahamer, Julia & Lechleitner, Gerda. Um-Feld-Forschung: Erfahrungen, Erlebnisse, Ergebnisse. 2007. (Mitteilungen des Phonogrammarchivs Ser.). (GER & ENG., Illus.). 350p. (C). 89.00 *(978-3-7001-3820-4(2))* Austrian Academy of Sciences Press AUT. Dist: Brown, David Bk. Co., The.

Albro, Robert, et al, eds. Anthropologists in the SecurityScape: Ethics, Practice, & Professional Identity. 2011. (ENG.). 277p. 89.00 *(978-1-61132-012-1(7))*; pap. 34.95 *(978-1-61132-013-8(5))* Left Coast Pr., Inc.

Alexander, Jeffrey C. Interpreting Clifford Geertz: Cultural Investigation in the Social Sciences. 2011. (Cultural Sociology Ser.). (ENG.). 230p. 85.00 *(978-0-230-11171-4(8))* Palgrave Macmillan.

Alexander, Jeffrey C., et al, eds. Interpreting Clifford Geertz: Cultural Investigation in the Social Sciences. 2011. (Cultural Sociology Ser.). (ENG.). 230p. pap. 28.00 *(978-0-230-11172-1(6))* Palgrave Macmillan.

Biolsi, Thomas, ed. Companion to the Anthropology of American Indians. 2008. (Wiley-Blackwell Companions to Anthropology Ser.). (ENG.). 592p. pap. 57.95 *(978-1-4051-8288-1(1)*, Wiley-Blackwell) Wiley, John & Sons, Inc.

Cram101 Textbook Reviews & Cram101 Textbook Reviews. Outlines & Highlights for Clausewitzs Puzzle: The Political Theory of War by Andreas Herberg-Rothe, ISBN. 2011. 88p. pap. 27.95 ***(978-1-4288-8039-9(9))*** Cram101 Inc.

—Outlines & Highlights for Companion to the Anthropology of American Indians by Thomas Biolsi, Isbn: 9781405182881. 2011. 420p. pap. 36.95 ***(978-1-4288-8068-9(2))*** Cram101 Inc.

—Outlines & Highlights for Reclaiming a Scientific Anthropology by Lawrence Kuznar, Isbn: 9780759111080. 2011. 190p. pap. 30.95 ***(978-1-61461-855-3(0))*** Cram101 Inc.

Fedorak, Shirley. Anthropology Matters! 2nd ed. 2007. (ENG.). 234p. pap. *(978-1-4426-0108-6(6))* Univ. of Toronto Pr.

Foner, Nancy, ed. American Arrivals: Anthropology Engages the New Immigration. (School of American Research Advanced Seminar Ser.). (Illus.). 360p. 34.95 *(978-1-930618-33-6(6))*; pap. 19.95 *(978-1-930618-34-3(4))* School for Advanced Research Pr/SAR Pr.

Geertz, Clifford. Life among the Anthros & Other Essays. Inglis, Fred, ed. 2010. (ENG.). 280p. (C). 29.95 *(978-0-691-14358-3(7))* Princeton Univ. Pr.

Guest, Greg & MacQueen, Kathleen M., eds. Handbook for Team-Based Qualitative Research. 2007. (ENG., Illus.). 300p. pap. 44.95 *(978-0-7591-0911-7(7))* AltaMira Pr.

Guest/Macqueen. Handbook for Team-Based Qualitative Research. 2007. (ENG., Illus.). 300p. 95.00 *(978-0-7591-0910-0(9))* AltaMira Pr.

Hendry, Joy & Fitznor, Laara, eds. Anthropologists, Indigenous Scholars & the Research Endeavour: Seeking Bridges Towards Mutual Respect. 2012. (Routledge Studies in Anthropology Ser.). (ENG., Illus.). 312p. (C). 125.00 ***(978-0-415-51833-8(4))*** Routledge.

Howell, Signe & Talle, Aud, eds. Returns to the Field: Multitemporal Research & Contemporary Anthropology. 2011. (ENG., Illus.). 286p. 70.00 *(978-0-253-35676-5(8)*, 0253356768); pap. 24.95 *(978-0-253-22348-7(2)*, 0253223482) Indiana Univ. Pr.

James, Deborah, et al, eds. Culture Wars: Context, Models & Anthropologists' Accounts. 2010. (EASA Ser.). 228p. 80.00 *(978-1-84545-641-2(6))* Berghahn Bks., Inc.

Konrad, Monica. Collaborators Collaborating: Counterparts in Anthropological Knowledge & International Research Relations. 2012. E-Book ***(978-0-85745-481-2(1))*** Berghahn Bks., Inc.

Konrad, Monica, ed. Collaborators Collaborating: Counterparts in Anthropological Knowledge & International Research Relations. 2012. (ENG.). 308p. 90.00 ***(978-0-85745-480-5(3))*** Berghahn Bks., Inc.

Kuznar, Lawrence A. Reclaiming a Scientific Anthropology. 2nd ed. 2008. (ENG., Illus.). 266p. 85.00 *(978-0-7591-1108-0(1))*; pap. 29.95 *(978-0-7591-1109-7(X))* AltaMira Pr.

Lee, Sandra Soo-. Race, Justice, & the New Genetic Sciences: Issues & Implications. 2008. pap. 36.95 *(978-0-415-98941-1(8))* Routledge.

Lærke, Anna. Taking Sides: Ethics, Politics, & Fieldwork in Anthropology. Armbruster, Heidi, ed. 2010. 272p. 29.95 *(978-1-84545-701-3(3))* Berghahn Bks., Inc.

Moore, Jerry D. Visions of Culture: An Introduction to Anthropological Theories & Theorists. 3rd ed. 2008. (ENG.). 416p. 90.00 *(978-0-7591-1145-5(6))*; pap. 39.95 *(978-0-7591-1146-2(4))* AltaMira Pr.

Rabinow, Paul & Foucault, Michel. The Accompaniment: Assembling the Contemporary. 2011. (ENG.). 248p. 63.00 *(978-0-226-70169-1(7))*; pap. 21.00 *(978-0-226-70170-7(0))* Univ. of Chicago Pr.

Strang, Veronica. What Anthropologists Do. 2009. (ENG.). 1p. pap. 29.95 *(978-1-84520-355-9(0))*; (Illus.). 99.95 *(978-1-84520-354-2(2))* Berg Pubs. GBR. Dist: Macmillan.

Ukaegbu & Ukaegbu, Dorothy C. Writing in Anthropology: The Summary & the Critique Paper. 2nd ed. 2011. (ENG.). 348p. (C). pap. 90.67 ***(978-1-256-29279-1(6))*** Pearson Learning Solutions.

Wallace, et al. Anthropology & Fisheries Management in the United States: Methodology for Research, Number 28. 2007. (NAPA Bulletin Ser.). (ENG., Illus.). 168p. pap. 31.95 *(978-1-931303-35-4(5)*, Wiley-Blackwell) Wiley, John & Sons, Inc.

Whiteford, Linda M. & Trotter, Robert T., 2nd. Ethics for Anthropological Research & Practice. 2008. 130p. (C). pap. 16.50 *(978-1-57766-535-9(X))* Waveland Pr., Inc.

ANTHROPOLOGY—STATISTICAL METHODS

Madrigal, Lorena. Statistics for Anthropology. 2nd ed. 2012. (ENG., Illus.). 278p. (C). pap. 45.00 ***(978-0-521-14708-8(5))*** Cambridge Univ. Pr.

ANTHROPOLOGY—STUDY AND TEACHING

Browman, David L. & Williams, Stephen. Anthropology at Harvard: A Biographical History, 1790-1940. 2012. (Peabody Museum Monographs: 11). (ENG., Illus.). 640p. 65.00 ***(978-0-87365-913-0(9))*** Peabody Museum of Archaeology & Ethnology, Harvard Univ., Pubns. Dept.

Durrenberger, E. Paul & Erem, Suzan. Paradigms for Anthropology: An Ethnographic Reader. 2010. 352p. pap. 39.95 *(978-1-59451-781-5(9))* Paradigm Pubs.

Ellick, Carol J. & Watkins, Joe E. The Anthropology Graduate's Guide: From Student to a Career. 2010. (ENG.). 160p. (C). 79.00 *(978-1-59874-568-9(9))*; pap. 24.95 *(978-1-59874-569-6(7))* Left Coast Pr., Inc.

Rice, Patricia C. & McCurdy, David W. Strategies in Teaching Anthropology. (ENG.). (C). 5th ed. 2007. 170p. pap. 48.60 *(978-0-13-603466-7(7))* 6th ed. 2010. 204p. pap. 30.80 *(978-0-205-71123-9(5))* Prentice Hall PTR. (Prentice Hall).

Rudman, Jack. General Anthropology. (Dantes Subject Standardized Tests Ser.: DANTES-66). (C). pap. 29.95 *(978-0-8373-6666-1(6)*, Passbooks) National Learning Corp.

Stark, Rebecca. Anthropology, No. 4. Date not set. tchr. ed. 10.95 *(978-1-56644-959-5(6)*, 959-6APT); tchr. ed., stu. ed. 5.95 *(978-0-910857-36-9(9))* Educational Impressions.

ANTHROPOLOGY—VOCATIONAL GUIDANCE

Briller, Sherylyn H. Designing an Anthropology Career: Professional Development Exercises. 2008. (ENG.). 166p. 65.00 *(978-0-7591-0942-1(7))*; pap. 26.95 *(978-0-7591-0943-8(5))* AltaMira Pr.

Ellick, Carol J. & Watkins, Joe E. The Anthropology Graduate's Guide: From Student to a Career. 2010. (ENG.). 160p. (C). 79.00 *(978-1-59874-568-9(9))*; pap. 24.95 *(978-1-59874-569-6(7))* Left Coast Pr., Inc.

Guerron-Montero, Carla. Careers in Applied Anthropology in the 21st Century: Perspectives from Academics & Practitioners, Number 29. 2009. (NAPA Bulletin Ser.). (ENG., Illus.). 160p. pap. 28.95 *(978-1-4051-9015-2(9)*, Wiley-Blackwell) Wiley, John & Sons, Inc.

Okely, Judith. Anthropological Practice: Fieldwork & the Ethnographic Method. 2011. (ENG.). 224p. (C). 99.95 ***(978-1-84520-602-4(9))***; pap. 29.95 ***(978-1-84520-603-1(7))*** Berg Pubs. GBR. Dist: Macmillan.

Sabloff, Paula L. W. Careers in Anthropology: Profiles of Practitioner Anthropologists, Number 20. 2008. (NAPA Bulletin Ser.). (ENG.). 112p. pap. 31.95 *(978-0-913167-98-4(3)*, Wiley-Blackwell) Wiley, John & Sons, Inc.

Strang, Veronica. What Anthropologists Do. 2009. (ENG.). 1p. pap. 29.95 *(978-1-84520-355-9(0))*; (Illus.). 99.95 *(978-1-84520-354-2(2))* Berg Pubs. GBR. Dist: Macmillan.

Wasson, Christina, et al. Making History at the Frontier: Women Creating Careers As Practicing Anthropologists, Number 26. 2006. (NAPA Bulletin Ser.: Vol. 26). (ENG., Illus.). 232p. pap. 31.95 *(978-1-931303-29-3(0)*, Wiley-Blackwell) Wiley, John & Sons, Inc.

ANTHROPOLOGY, CRIMINAL

see Criminal Anthropology

ANTHROPOLOGY, DOCTRINAL

see Theological Anthropology

ANTHROPOLOGY, PHILOSOPHICAL

see Philosophical Anthropology

ANTHROPOLOGY, PHYSICAL

see Physical Anthropology

ANTHROPOLOGY, POLITICAL

see Political Anthropology

ANTHROPOLOGY, THEOLOGICAL

see Theological Anthropology

ANTHROPOLOGY, URBAN

see Urban Anthropology

ANTHROPOLOGY AS A PROFESSION

see Anthropology—Vocational Guidance

ANTHROPOLOGY IN LITERATURE

Bertschik, Julia. Maulwurfsarchäologie: Zum Verhältnis Von Geschichte und Anthropologie in Wilhelm Raabes Historischen Erzähltexten. (Untersuchungen zur deutschen Literaturgeschichte Ser.). (GER.). XIII, 270p. 120.00 ***(978-3-11-184732-0(2))*** De Gruyter, Walter Inc.

Hart, Anne. Ethno-Playography: How to Create Salable Ethnographic Plays, Monologues, & Skits from Life Stories, Social Issues, & Current Events for all Ages with Samples for Performance. 2007. 652p. per. 33.95 *(978-0-595-46066-3(6)*, ASJA Pr.) iUniverse, Inc.

Literary & Anthropological Studies: Collected Essay's Volume II. 2008. per. *(978-0-9765508-7-7(3))* Manitou Communications, Inc.

Molloy, Maureen A. On Creating a Usable Culture: Margaret Mead & the Emergence of American Cosmopolitanism. 2008. (Illus.). 200p. 39.00 *(978-0-8248-3116-5(0))* Univ. of Hawaii Pr.

Streim, Gregor. Das Ende des Anthropozentrismus: Anthropologie und Geschichtskritik in der deutschen Literatur zwischen 1930 und 1950. 2008. (Quellen und Forschungen zur Literatur- und Kulturgeschichte Ser.). (GER.). IX, 431p. 147.00 *(978-3-11-020103-1(8))* De Gruyter, Walter Inc.

ANTHROPOMETRY

see also Body Size; Criminal Anthropology; Fingerprints; Physical Fitness—Testing

Abidi, Besma R., ed. Face Biometrics for Personal Identification: Multi-Sensory Multi-Modal Systems. 2007. (Signals & Communication Technology Ser.). (Illus.). 275p. 159.00 *(978-3-540-49344-0(1)*, 3540493441) Springer.

Abrahams, Peter H., et al. The Human Skeleton. 2nd rev. ed. 2007. (ENG., Illus.). 60p. (C). spiral bd. 99.95 *(978-0-323-04793-7(9)*, Mosby) Elsevier - Health Sciences Div.

Applied Body Composition Assessment. 2nd ed. (C). instr.'s gde. ed. 24.00 *(978-0-7360-5170-5(8))* Human Kinetics Pubs.

Bhanu, Bir & Govindaraju, Venu, eds. Multibiometrics for Human Identification. 2011. (ENG., Illus.). 408p. (C). 90.00 *(978-0-521-11596-4(5))* Cambridge Univ. Pr.

Birket-Smith, Kaj. Anthropological Observations on the Central Eskimos. Calvert, W. E., tr. (Thule Expedition, 1921-24 Ser.: Vol. 3, No. 2). (Illus.). reprint ed. 42.50 *(978-0-404-58312-5(1))* AMS Pr., Inc.

Bolle, Ruud M., et al. Guide to Biometrics. 2010. (Springer Professional Computing Ser.). (Illus.). xxix, 364p. pap. 129.00 *(978-1-4419-2305-9(5)*, 1441923055) Springer.

Davies, P. S. W. & Cole, T. J., eds. Body Composition Techniques in Health & Disease. 2006. (Society for the Study of Human Biology Symposium Ser.: Vol. 36). (ENG., Illus.). 296p. pap. 58.00 *(978-0-521-03192-9(3))* Cambridge Univ. Pr.

Duterloo, Herman S. & Planché, Pierre-Georges. Handbook of Cephalometric Superimposition. 2011. ***(978-0-86715-508-2(6))*** Quintessence Publishing Co., Inc.

Eston, Roger. Kinanthropometry & Exercise Physiology Vol. 1: Tests, Procedures & Data, 2 vols. Reilly, Thomas, ed. 3rd rev. ed. 2008. (ENG., Illus.). 352p. (C). 200.00 *(978-0-415-43721-9(0))*; pap., lab manual ed. 71.95 *(978-0-415-43720-2(2))* Routledge.

—Kinanthropometry & Exercise Physiology Vol. 2: Tests, Procedures & Data, 2 vols. Reilly, Thomas, ed. 3rd rev. ed. 2008. (Illus.). (ENG.). 376p. (C). pap., lab manual ed. 71.95 *(978-0-415-43723-3(7))*; Vol. 2. XXVIII, 348p. lab manual ed. 200.00 *(978-0-415-43722-6(9))* Routledge.

—Kinanthropometry Lab Manual: Anthropometry & Exercise Physiology, 2 vols. Reilly, Tom, ed. 3rd ed. 2008. (Illus.). 110.00 *(978-0-415-46671-4(7))* Routledge.

Fabian, Ann. The Skull Collectors: Race, Science, & America's Unburied Dead. 2010. (Illus.). 288p. 27.50 *(978-0-226-23348-2(0))* Univ. of Chicago Pr.

Farrús, Mireia. Prosody in Automatic Speaker Recognition. 2010. 216p. pap. *(978-3-639-08991-2(X))* VDM Verlag Dr. Mueller e.K.

Floud, Roderick, et al. The Changing Body: Health, Nutrition, & Human Development in the Western World since 1700. 2011. (New Approaches to Economic & Social History Ser.). (Illus.). 456p. 90.00 *(978-0-521-87975-0(2))*; pap. 32.99 *(978-0-521-70561-5(4))* Cambridge Univ. Pr.

Fok, T F, et al. Neonatal Anthropometry for the Chinese. 2008. (ENG., Illus.). 80p. (gr. 17). pap. 22.00 *(978-962-996-335-4(3))* Chinese Univ. of Hong Kong, The HKG. Dist: Columbia Univ. Pr.

Frisancho, Andres Roberto. Anthropometric Standards: An Interactive Nutritional Reference of Body Size & Body Composition for Children & Adults. 2008. (ENG., Illus.). 352p. 95.00 *(978-0-472-11591-4(X))* Univ. of Michigan Pr.

Gates, Kelly. Our Biometric Future: Facial Recognition Technology & the Culture of Surveillance. 2011. (ENG., Illus.). 288p. 75.00 *(978-0-8147-3209-0(7))*; pap. 24.00 *(978-0-8147-3210-6(0))* New York Univ. Pr.

Gripp, Karen, et al. Handbook of Physical Measurements. 2nd ed. 2006. (ENG., Illus.). 520p. 65.00 *(978-0-19-530149-6(8))* Oxford Univ. Pr., Inc.

Hauff, Krystal Rae. Body Mass Index among Seventh-Day Adventists in North Texas. 2008. 56p. pap. *(978-3-639-01268-2(2))* VDM Verlag Dr. Mueller e.K.

Herskovits, Melville Jean. Anthropometry of the American Negro. (Columbia University, Contributions to Anthropology Ser.: No. 11). reprint ed. 32.50 *(978-0-404-50561-5(9))* AMS Pr., Inc.

Heyberger, Laurent. L' histoire Anthropométrique. 2011. (Population, Famille et Société - Population, Family, & Society Ser.). (Illus.). 181p. pap. *(978-3-0343-0586-0(9))* Lang, Peter.

Houghton, Philip. People of the Great Ocean: Aspects of Human Biology of the Early Pacific. 2009. (ENG., Illus.). 304p. (C). pap. 46.00 *(978-0-521-11930-6(8))* Cambridge Univ. Pr.

Human Kinetics Staff. Assessing Body Composition. 78p. stu. ed. 99.00 *(978-0-7360-0145-8(X))* Human Kinetics Pubs.

IEEE Staff. 2009 IEEE Workshop on Computational Intelligence in Biometrics: Theory, Algorithms, & Applications. 2009. pap. 182.00 *(978-1-4244-2773-4(8))* IEEE.

Jain, Anil K., et al, eds. Handbook of Biometrics. 2010. (ENG., Illus.). x, 556p. pap. 79.95 *(978-1-4419-4375-0(7)*, 1441943757) Springer.

Jakob, Tina. Prevalence & Patterns of Disease in Early Medieval Populations: A Comparison of Skeletal Samples of the 5th-8th Centuries A.D. from Britain & Southwestern Germany. 2009. (Bar S Ser.). (ENG., Illus.). 220p. (C). pap. 115.00 *(978-1-4073-0456-4(9))* British Archaeological Reports Ltd. GBR. Dist: Brown, David Bk. Co., The.

King, Christopher A. Stable Isotopic Analysis of Carbon & Nitrogen As an Indicator of Paleodietary Change among Pre-State Metal Age Societies in Northeast Thailand. 2008. (Bar S Ser.). (Illus.). 132p. (C). 72.50 *(978-1-4073-0276-8(0))* British Archaeological Reports Ltd. GBR. Dist: Brown, David Bk. Co., The.

Kues, Arne Benjamin. Essays in Anthropometric History - Four Papers on the Anthropometric Past & Presence of the United States & Switzerland. 2007. 148p. per. *(978-3-8364-4597-9(2))* VDM Verlag Dr. Mueller e.K.

Kumar, Ajay & Zhang, David, eds. Ethics & Policy of Biometrics: Third International Conference on Ethics & Policy of Biometrics & International Data Sharing, Hong Kong, January 4-5 2010. 2010. (Lecture Notes in Computer Science / Security & Cryptology Ser.). viii, 169p. pap. 72.00 *(978-3-642-12594-2(8)*, 3642125948) Springer.

Kung, S. Y., et al. Biometric Authentication: A Machine Learning Approach. 2010. (Prentice Hall Information & System Sciences Ser.). (ENG.). 496p. pap. 150.00 *(978-0-13-707483-9(2)*, Prentice Hall) Prentice Hall PTR.

Mangion, Ramon. Are Biometric Passports the Way Forward? 2011. 92p. pap. ***(978-3-8443-3254-4(5))*** Lambert Academic Publishing.

Marfell-Jones, Michael, et al, eds. Kinanthropometry IX: Proceedings of the 9th International Conference of the International Society for the Advancement of Kinanthropometry. 2008. 168p. 49.95 *(978-0-415-48493-0(6))* Routledge.

Marfell-Jones, Mike & Olds, Tim, eds. Kinanthropometry X: Proceedings of the 10th International Society for Advancement of Kinanthropometry Conference, Held in Conjunction with the 13th Commonwealth International Sport Conference. 2007. (ENG.). 272p. (C). 190.00 *(978-0-415-43470-6(X))* Routledge.

Mars-Proietti, Laura, ed. Grey House Biometric Information Directory: 2009. 2nd rev. ed. 2009. 500p. pap. 225.00 *(978-1-59237-419-9(0))* Grey Hse. Publishing.

Mays, Simon. The Archaeology of Human Bones. 2nd rev. ed. 2010. (ENG., Illus.). 432p. (C). 145.00 *(978-0-415-48090-1(6))*; pap. 49.95 *(978-0-415-48091-8(4))* Routledge.

McDowell, Margaret A., et al. Anthropometric Reference Data for Children & Adults: United States, 1988-1994. 2009. *(978-0-8406-0631-0(1))* National Ctr. for Health Statistics.

Melin, Patricia, et al, eds. Soft Computing for Recognition based on Biometrics. 2010. (Studies in Computational Intelligence Ser.). (Illus.). 510p. 269.00 *(978-3-642-15110-1(8)*, 3642151108) Springer.

Mironov, Boris Nikolaevich. The Standard of Living & Revolutions in Russia, 1700-1917. 2012. ***(978-0-203-11944-0(4))*** Routledge.

Modi, Shimon K. Biometric Technologies & Applications. 2011. (Illus.). 250p. 109.00 ***(978-1-60807-017-6(4))*** Artech Hse., Inc.

Mordini, Emilio & Tzovaras, Dimitros, eds. Second Generation Biometrics: The Ethical, Legal & Social Context. 2012. (International Library of Ethics, Law & Technology Ser.: 11). (ENG., Illus.). x, 353p. 139.00 ***(978-94-007-3891-1(9)***, 9400738919) Springer.

Muller, Benjamin. Security, Risk & the Biometric State: Governing Borders & Bodies. 2010. (PRIO New Security Studies). (ENG., Illus.). 160p. (C). 130.00 *(978-0-415-43440-4(5))* Routledge.

Nelson, Lisa S. America Identified: Biometric Technology & Society. 2010. (ENG., Illus.). 272p. (gr. 17). 34.00 *(978-0-262-01477-9(7))* MIT Pr.

Nichols, Ellen R., ed. Biometrics: Theory, Applications, & Issues. 2010. (Biotechnology in Agriculture, Industry & Medicine Ser.). 89.00 *(978-1-61728-765-7(2)*, Nova Biomedical Bks.) Nova Science Pubs., Inc.

NIOSH Head-and-Face Anthropometric Survey of U.S. Respirator Users Committee. Assessment of the NIOSH Head-and-Face Anthropometric Survey of U. S. Respirator Users. Bailar, John C. et al, eds. 2007. (ENG., Illus.) 122p. pap. 31.25 *(978-0-309-10398-5(3))* National Academies Pr.

Nixon, Mark S., et al. Human Identification Based on Gait. 2010. (International Series on Biometrics Ser.). (Illus.). x, 187p. pap. 149.00 *(978-1-4419-3742-1(0)*, 1441937420) Springer.

Oladipo, Gabriel. Craniofacial Anthropometrya Reliable Method for Classifying Population. 2010. 116p. pap. *(978-3-8383-8842-7(9))* Lambert Academic Publishing.

Organizational & Policy Proposals for the Fiscal Year 2008 Department of Homeland Security Authorization: [positioning US-VISIT for Success & Establishing a Quadrennial Homeland Security Review Process]: Full Hearing of the Committee on Homeland Security, House of Representatives, One Hundred Tenth Congress, First Session, March 20, 2007. 2009. iv, 66p. *(978-0-16-083340-3(X)*, 552-070-39164-9) United States Government Printing Office.

Osborne, Richard H. & De George, Frances V. Genetic Basis of Morphological Variation: An Evaluation & Application of the Twin Study Method. 2011. 232p. 46.95 ***(978-1-258-06502-7(9))*** Literary Licensing, LLC.

Petrovska-Delacrétaz, Dijana, et al. Guide to Biometric Reference Systems & Performance Evaluation. 2009. (Illus.). 403p. 119.00 *(978-1-84800-291-3(2))* Springer.

Preedy, Victor R., ed. Handbook of Anthropometry: Physical Measures of Human Form in Health & Disease. 4 vols. 2012. (ENG., Illus.). l, 3107p. 1100.00 ***(978-1-4419-1787-4(X)***, 144191787X) Springer.

Pugliese, Joseph. Biometrics: Bodies, Technologies, Biopolitics. 2010. (Routledge Studies in Science, Technology & Society Ser.). (ENG., Illus.). 192p. 125.00 *(978-0-415-87487-8(4))* Routledge.

Reed, Matthew P. & Klinich, Kathleen D. Child Anthropometry for Improved Vehicle Occupant Safety. 2010. (Illus.). vii, 416p. pap. *(978-0-7680-2172-1(3))* SAE Intl.

Robinette, Kathleen. Computer Aided Anthropometry for Research & Design. 2011. 300p. 89.95 *(978-0-8058-5789-4(3))* Erlbaum, Lawrence Assocs., Inc.

Rodgers, Waymond. E-Commerce Issues Addressed in a Throughput Model. 2010. (Internet Policies & Issues Ser.). 219p. 89.00 *(978-1-61668-244-6(2))* Nova Science Pubs., Inc.

Ross, Arun A., et al. Handbook of Multibiometrics. 2010. (International Series on Biometrics Ser.). (Illus.). xxii, 202p. pap. 109.00 *(978-1-4419-3547-2(9)*, 1441935479) Springer.

Slice, Dennis E., ed. Modern Morphometrics in Physical Anthropology. 2010. (Developments in Primatology: Progress & Prospects Ser.). (Illus.). xxii, 384p. pap. 162.00 *(978-1-4419-3467-3(7)*, 1441934677) Springer.

Soni, Puneet. Biometrics for Security in Bluetooth Environment. 2009. 76p. pap. *(978-3-639-17185-3(3))* VDM Verlag Dr. Mueller e.K.

Sun, Zhenan, et al, eds. Biometric Recognition: 6th Chinese Conference, CCBR 2011, Beijing, China, December 3-4, 2011. Proceedings. 2011. (Lecture Notes in Computer Science / Image Processing, Computer Vision, Pattern Recognition, & Graphics Ser.). (ENG., Illus.). xiv, 290p. pap. 83.00 ***(978-3-642-25448-2(9)***, 3642254489) Springer.

Tanner, James Mourilyan. A History of the Study of Human Growth. 2010. (ENG.). 512p. pap. 39.99 *(978-0-521-13402-6(1))* Cambridge Univ. Pr.

Test Package for Applied Body Composition Assessment. 2nd ed. 24.00 *(978-0-7360-5230-6(5))* Human Kinetics Pubs.

US-VISIT Exit: Closing Gaps in Our Security: Hearing Before the Subcommittee on Border, Maritime, & Global Counterterrorism of the Committee on Homeland Security, House of Representatives, One Hundred Tenth Congress, First Session, June 28, 2007. 2009. iv, 54p. *(978-0-16-083813-2(4)*, 552-070-39511-3) United States Government Printing Office.

Wechsler, Harry. Reliable Face Recognition Methods: System Design, Implementation & Evaluation. 2010. (Illus.). xiii, 329p. pap. 99.00 *(978-1-4419-3548-9(7)*, 1441935487) Springer.

Whither Biometrics Committee & National Research Council. Biometric Recognition: Challenges & Opportunities. 2010. (ENG.). 182p. pap. 41.50 *(978-0-309-14207-6(5))* National Academies Pr.

Wilkinson, Caroline & Rynn, Christopher. Craniofacial Identification. 2012. (ENG., Illus.). 272p. (C). 110.00 ***(978-0-521-76862-7(4))*** Cambridge Univ. Pr.

Willey, P. & Lowry, Thomas P. Mystery of the Bones. 2008. 194p. pap. 14.95 *(978-0-615-19033-4(2))* Vallombrosa Pr.

World Health Organization. WHO Child Growth Standards: Growth Velocity Based on Weight, Length & Head Circumference - Methods & Development. 2009. (Nonserial Publication Ser.). (ENG., Illus.). 261p. pap. 60.00 *(978-92-4-154763-5(4))* World Health Organization.

World Health Organization Staff & World Health Organization, Nutrition for Health and Development Staff, contrib. by. Who Child Growth Standards: Head Circumference-for-Age, Arm Circumference-For Age, Triceps Skinfold-for-Age & Subscapular Skinfold-For Age. 2007. (Nonserial Publication). (ENG.). 234p. pap. 48.00 *(978-92-4-154718-5(9))* World Health Organization.

Yampolskiy, Roman. Game strategy: a novel behavioral Biometric. 2009. 204p. 99.99 *(978-0-578-03685-4(1))* Independent Univ. Pr.

Yordanov, Yordan, ed. Anthropology of the Bulgarian Population at the End of the 20th Century: (30-40 Years Old Persons) in English & Bulgarian. 2006. (Illus.). 431p. 167.50 *(978-954-322-080-9(8))* Drinov, Marin Akadem izdatelstvo BGR. Dist: Coronet Bks.

Young, Harvey. Embodying Black Experience: Stillness, Critical Memory, & the Black Body. 2010. (Theater: Theory/Text/Performance Ser.). (ENG., Illus.). 272p. 80.00 *(978-0-472-07111-1(4))*; pap. 32.50 *(978-0-472-05111-3(3))* Univ. of Michigan Pr.

Zhang, David, et al. Advanced Pattern Recognition Technologies with Applications to Biometrics. 2009. (Illus.). 384p. 225.00 *(978-1-60566-200-8(3))* IGI Global.

ANTHROPOMORPHISM

DeMello, Margo, ed. Speaking for Animals: Animal Autobiographical Writing. 2012. (Routledge Advances in Sociology Ser.). (ENG., Illus.). 272p. (C). 125.00 ***(978-0-415-80899-6(5))*** Routledge.

Drake, Scott. A Well-Composed Body - Anthropomorphism in Architecture. 2008. 268p. pap. *(978-3-639-06652-4(9))* VDM Verlag Dr. Mueller e.K.

Gheorghiu, Dragos & Cyphers, Ann, eds. Anthropomorphic & Zoomorphic Miniature Figures in Eurasia, Africa & Meso-America. 2010. (Bar S Ser.). (Illus.). 158p. (C). pap. 87.50 *(978-1-4073-0679-7(0))* British Archaeological Reports Ltd. GBR. Dist: Brown, David Bk. Co., The.

Hamori, Esther J. When Gods Were Men: The Embodied God in Biblical & near Eastern Literature. 2008. (Beihefte zur Zeitschrift für die alttestamentliche Wissenschaft Ser.). (ENG.). XVI, 185p. 91.00 *(978-3-11-020345-6(0))* De Gruyter, Walter Inc.

Herles, Michael. Gotterdarstellungen Mesopotamiens in der 2. Halfte des 2. Jahrtausends v. Chr. Das Anthropomorphe Bild Im Verhaltnis zum Symbol. 2006. (Alter Orient und Altes Testament Ser.: 329). (GER., Illus.). 394p. (C). 140.00 *(978-3-934628-76-2(1))* Ugarit-Verlag DEU. Dist: Eisenbrauns, Inc.

Hight, Christopher. Architectural Principles in the Age of Cybernetics. 2008. (ENG., Illus.). 248p. (C). 165.00 *(978-0-415-38481-0(8))* Routledge.

—Architectural Principles in the Age of Cybernetics. 2007. (Illus.). 239p. per. 54.95 *(978-0-415-38482-7(6))* Taylor & Francis Group.

Mitman, Gregg & Daston, Lorraine, eds. Thinking with Animals: New Perspectives on Anthropomorphism. 2006. (ENG., Illus.). 240p. (gr. 17). pap. 28.00 *(978-0-231-13039-4(2))* Columbia Univ. Pr.

Rossini, Manuela S. & Tyler, Tom, eds. Animal Encounters. 2009. (Human-Animal Studies). (Illus.). 280p. pap. *(978-90-04-16867-1(2))* BRILL.

Simmons, Laurence & Armstrong, Philip, eds. Knowing Animals. 2007. (Human-Animal Studies: Vol. 4). (Illus.). 296p. pap. *(978-90-04-15773-6(5))* BRILL.

ANTHROPONOMY

see Names, Personal

ANTHROPOPHAGY

see Cannibalism

ANTHROPOSOPHY

see also Karma; Reincarnation; Theosophy; Waldorf Method of Education

Ahern, Geoffrey. Sun at Midnight: The Rudolf Steiner Movement & Gnosis in the West. 2009. (ENG.). 279p. pap. 42.50 *(978-0-227-17293-3(0))* Clarke, James Co., Ltd. GBR. Dist: Brown, David Bk. Co., The.

Barfield, Owen. Romanticism Comes of Age. 2006. 256p. (ENG.). *(978-1-59731-115-1(4))*; per. *(978-1-59731-114-4(6)*, Harwood Academic Pubs.) Perennis, Sophia.

Blunt, Richard. Waldorf Education: Theory & Practice. (Illus.). xi, 239p. pap. 21.95 *(978-0-9583885-4-2(7)*, 2006) Novalis Trust ZAF. Dist: SteinerBooks, Inc.

Bock, Emil. Apocalypse of Saint John. 3rd rev. ed. 208p. pap. 30.00 *(978-0-86315-539-0(1))* Floris Bks. GBR. Dist: SteinerBooks, Inc.

Burkhard, Gudrun. Biographical Work: The Anthroposophical Basis. 2007. (Illus.). 206p. per. *(978-0-86315-598-7(7))* Floris Bks.

Christin, Olivier, et al. Dictionnaire des Concepts Nomades des Sciences Humaines. 2010. (FRE.). 461p. *(978-2-86424-754-8(2))* Metailie, Editions.

Cotterell, Mabel. Cosmic Rhythms in the Life of Man. 2011. 16p. pap. 35.95 ***(978-1-258-01476-6(9))*** Literary Licensing, LLC.

Down, Reg. Color & Gesture: The Inner Life of Color. 2007. (Illus.). 532p. per. 68.50 *(978-0-9794452-1-7(3))* Lightly Pr.

Dunlop, D. N., ed. Anthroposophy V8, No 2, Midsummer 1933. 2011. 112p. 39.95 ***(978-1-258-01477-3(7))*** Literary Licensing, LLC.

Emoto, Masaru. The Secret Life of Water. 2011. (ENG., Illus.). 224p. pap. 16.99 *(978-0-7432-9032-6(1)*, Beyond Words/Atria Bks.) Atria Bks.

Finser, Siegfried E. Money Can Heal: Evolving Our Consciousness: the Story of RSF & Its Innovations in Social Finance. annot. ed. 2007. (Illus.). 225p. per. 25.00 *(978-0-88010-573-6(9))* SteinerBooks, Inc.

Hemmerich, Fritz Helmut. Handbook of Anthroposophic Gynecology. Luborsky, Peter, tr. 2007. 129p. ring bd. 20.00 *(978-0-936132-30-3(2))* Mercury Pr.

Hutchins, Eileen. Introduction to the Mystery Plays. pap. 14.95 *(978-0-85440-408-7(2)*, 1001) Steiner, Rudolf Pr. GBR. Dist: Steiner, Rudolf Pr.

Jachens, Lueder. Healing the Skin: Holistic Approaches to Treating Skin Conditions: A Practical Guide Based on Anthroposophic Medicine. Meuss, Anna R., tr. from GER. 2008. (Illus.). 179p. pap. *(978-1-902636-91-7(0))* Temple Lodge Publishing.

Jones, T. Gordon. The Formation of Price. 2011. 26p. 35.95 ***(978-1-258-01475-9(0))*** Literary Licensing, LLC.

Kiersch, Johannes. A History of the School of Spiritual Science: The First Class. 2007. (Illus.). 271p. *(978-1-902636-80-1(5))* Temple Lodge Publishing.

Lachman, Gary. Rudolf Steiner: An Introduction to His Life & Work. annot. ed. 2007. (ENG.). 304p. (gr. 12-18). 16.95 *(978-1-58542-543-3(5)*, Tarcher) Penguin Group (USA) Inc.

Lehrs, Ernst. Man or Matter. 2008. 444p. 32.99 *(978-0-554-22267-7(1))* 2008. 444p. 30.99 *(978-0-554-31570-6(X))* 2006. 408p. pap. 26.99 *(978-1-4264-1948-5(1))* 2007. (ENG.). 488p. pap. 30.99 *(978-1-4264-2059-7(5))* BiblioBazaar.

—Man or Matter. 2nd ed. 544p. pap. 24.00 *(978-0-85440-430-8(9)*, 1027) Steiner, Rudolf Pr. GBR. Dist: Steiner, Rudolf Pr.

McCausland, Bruce H. Coping with Evil. 2006. (Illus.). 190p. pap. 20.00 *(978-1-58420-044-4(8)*, Lindisfarne Bks.) SteinerBooks, Inc.

McDermott, Robert & Steiner, Rudolf. The New Essential Steiner: An Introduction to Rudolf Steiner for the 21st Century. McDermott, Robert, ed. 2009. 344p. pap. 40.00 *(978-1-58420-056-7(1)*, Lindisfarne Bks.) SteinerBooks, Inc.

Merry, E. c. The Healing Plant. 2011. 24p. 35.95 ***(978-1-258-01473-5(4))*** Literary Licensing, LLC.

Meyer, T. H. Rudolf Steiner's Core Mission: The Birth & Development of Spiritual-Scientific Karma Research. 2010. (Illus.). 207p. pap. *(978-1-906999-10-0(4))* Temple Lodge Publishing.

Nesfield-Cookson, Bernard. At the Dawn of a New Consciousness: Art, Philosophy & the Birth of the Modern World. 2010. (Illus.). 129p. pap. *(978-1-906999-11-7(2))* Temple Lodge Publishing.

Oberman, Ida. The Waldorf Movement in Education from European Cradle to American Crucible, 1919-2008. 2008. (Illus.). 396p. *(978-0-7734-4970-1(1))* Mellen, Edwin Pr., The.

Oberski, Iddo. Key to Life: An Introductory Sketch to Rudolf Steiner's Philosophy of Freedom. 2010. 64p. pap. 10.95 *(978-1-60911-865-5(0)*, Eloquent Bks.) AEG Literary Publishing Services, Inc.

O'Meara, John. The Thinking Spirit: Rudolf Steiner & Romantic Theory. 2007. 152p. per. 14.95 *(978-0-595-45714-4(2))* iUniverse, Inc.

Pailin, David A. The Anthropological Character of Theology: Conditioning Theological Understanding. 2009. (ENG.). 304p. pap. 42.00 *(978-0-521-09328-6(7))* Cambridge Univ. Pr.

Pooler, Russell. A Rosicrucian Soul: The Life Journey of Paul Marshall Allen, 1 vol. 2009. (ENG., Illus.). 328p. pap. 35.00 *(978-1-58420-067-3(7)*, Lindisfarne Bks.) SteinerBooks, Inc.

Powell, Robert. Cultivating Inner Radiance & the Body of Immortality: Awakening the Soul through Modern Etheric Movement, 1 vol. 2012. (ENG., Illus.). 244p. pap. 25.00 ***(978-1-58420-117-5(7)***, Lindisfarne Bks.) SteinerBooks, Inc.

Prokofieff, Sergei O. The Esoteric Significance of Spiritual Work in Anthroposophical Groups: And the Future of the Anthroposophical Society. 2007. 56p. per. *(978-1-902636-83-2(X))* Temple Lodge Publishing.

—The Guardian of the Threshold & the Philosophy of Freedom: On the Relationship of the Philosophy of Freedom to the Fifth Gospel. 2011. (ENG., Illus.). 114p. pap. ***(978-1-906999-24-7(4))*** Temple Lodge Publishing.

Prokofieff, Sergei O. The Mystery of the Resurrection in the Light of Anthroposophy. 2010. (Illus.). 214p. pap. *(978-1-906999-12-4(0))* Temple Lodge Publishing.

Prokofieff, Sergei O. & Selg, Peter. The Creative Power of Anthroposophical Christology. 2011.Tr. of Die Christologie des Buches Die Geheimwissenschaft im Umriss. 272p. pap. 25.00 ***(978-0-88010-733-4(2))*** SteinerBooks, Inc.

Richter, Gottfried. Art & Human Consciousness. 272p. pap. 35.00 *(978-0-88010-478-4(3))* SteinerBooks, Inc.

Sardello, Robert. Acts of the Heart: Culture-Building, Soul-Researching: Introductions by Robert Sardello. 2011. (ENG.). 380p. pap. 25.00 ***(978-1-58420-112-0(6)***, Lindisfarne Bks.) SteinerBooks, Inc.

Sardello, Robert, ed. Mani & Service - Classics from the Journal for Anthroposophy. 2007. 128p. per. 15.00 *(978-0-9674562-4-9(X))* Anthroposophical Society in America, The.

Scala, Patsy & Steiner, Rudolf. Weekly Meditations: Rudolf Steiner's the Calendar of the Soul with Accompanying Reflections. 2008. 128p. pap. 12.00 *(978-0-88010-589-7(5))* SteinerBooks, Inc.

Schillebeeckx, Edward. Jesus in Our Western Culture: Mysticism, Ethics & Politics. 2012. viii, 84p. pap. ***(978-0-334-02098-1(0)***, SCM Pr.) Hymns Ancient & Modern Ltd.

Schilthuis, Willy. Biodynamic Agriculture. 2nd rev. ed. (Illus.). 128p. (Orig.). pap. 14.95 *(978-0-86315-397-6(6))* Floris Bks. GBR. Dist: SteinerBooks, Inc.

Schindler, Maria. Pure Color. 270p. pap. 29.95 *(978-0-85440-916-7(5)*, 1487) Steiner, Rudolf Pr. GBR. Dist: Steiner, Rudolf Pr.

Seddon, Richard. Mystery of Arthur at Tintagel. (Illus.). 200p. pap. 22.95 *(978-0-85440-436-0(8)*, 432) Steiner, Rudolf Pr. GBR. Dist: Steiner, Rudolf Pr.

Seiler-Hugova, Ueli. Colour: Seeing, Experiencing, Understanding. 2011. (ENG., Illus.). 134p. ***(978-1-906999-23-0(6))*** Temple Lodge Publishing.

Selg, Peter. Christ & the Disciples: The Destiny of an Inner Community. Creeger, Catherine E., tr. from GER. 2011.Tr. of Christus und die Jünger: Vom Schicksal der inneren Gemeinschaft. 128p. ***(978-0-88010-745-7(6))*** SteinerBooks, Inc.

—I Am for Going Forward: Ita Wegman & the Medical Section. 2012. ***(978-1-62148-002-0(X))*** SteinerBooks, Inc.

—Rudolf Steiner & the Fifth Gospel: Insights into a New Understanding of the Christ Mystery. Creeger, Catherine E., tr. from GER. 2009. 144p. pap. 20.00 *(978-0-88010-707-5(3))* SteinerBooks, Inc.

—Rudolf Steiner & the Fundamental Social Law: The Work of the Individual & the Spirit of Community. 2011. 128p. pap. 15.00 ***(978-0-88010-654-2(9))*** SteinerBooks, Inc.

—Rudolf Steiner¿s Intentions for the Anthroposophical Society: The Executive Council, the School of Spiritual Science, & the Sections. von Arnim, Christian, tr. from GER. 2011.Tr. of Vorstand, die Sektionen und die Gesellschaft. Welche Hochschule wollte Rudolf Steiner? (Illus.). 96p. pap. 15.00 ***(978-0-88010-738-9(3))*** SteinerBooks, Inc.

Selg, Peter. Unbornness: Human Pre-existence & the Journey Toward Birth. Saar, Margot, tr. from GER. 2010. (Illus.). 88p. pap. 15.00 *(978-0-88010-718-1(9))* SteinerBooks, Inc.

Shepherd, Arthur Pearce. Anthroposophy & the Christian Churches. 2011. 20p. 35.95 ***(978-1-258-00124-7(1))*** Literary Licensing, LLC.

Sloan, Douglas, ed. Reimagining Society & Culture: Classic Articles from the Journal for Anthroposophy, 77. 2007. per. 15.00 *(978-0-9674562-6-3(6))* Anthroposophical Society in America, The.

Smith, Edward Reaugh. The Temple Sleep of the Rich Young Ruler: How Lazarus Became the Evangelist John. 2011. 366p. pap. 29.95 *(978-0-88010-732-7(4))* SteinerBooks, Inc.

Stebbing, Peter, tr. & compiled by. Conversations about Painting with Rudolf Steiner: Recollections of Five Pioneers of the New Art Impulse. 2008. (Illus.). 208p. 35.00 *(978-0-88010-590-3(9))* SteinerBooks, Inc.

Stein, Walter Johannes. The Death of Merlin: Arthurian Myth & Alchemy, 1 vol. 2008. (ENG.). 240p. pap. *(978-0-86315-641-0(X))* Floris Bks.

Steiner, Rudolf. Anthroposophy & the Social Question. 2006. 54p. pap. 16.95 *(978-1-4286-4639-1(6))* Kessinger Publishing, LLC.

—Art in the Light of Mystery Wisdom. 2011. 206p. 44.95 ***(978-1-258-00161-2(6))*** Literary Licensing, LLC.

—Balance in Teaching: Stuttgart September 15-22, 1920 & October 15-16, 1923. 2007. (Foundations of Waldorf Education Ser.: 11).Tr. of Erziehung und Unterricht aus Menschenerkenntnis. (Illus.). 116p. (Orig.). per. 24.95 *(978-0-88010-551-4(8))* SteinerBooks, Inc.

—Becoming the Archangel Michael's Companions: Rudolf Steiner's Challenge to the Younger Generation. 2007. (Collected Works of Rudolf Steiner: 217). (Illus.). 201p. per. 19.95 *(978-0-88010-609-2(3))* SteinerBooks, Inc.

—The Bhagavad Gita & the West: The Esoteric Significance of the Bhagavad Gita & Its Relation to the Letters of St. Paul. Easwaran, Eknath, tr. from GER. 2009. (Collected Works of Rudolf Steiner: 142).Tr. of Die Bhagavad Gita und die Paulusbriefe — Die okkulten Grundlagen der Bhagavad Gita. 464p. pap. 35.00 *(978-0-88010-604-7(2))* SteinerBooks, Inc.

—The Bible Begins with Reference to Foregoing Conditions of Old. 2006. pap. 12.95 *(978-1-4304-2535-9(0))* Kessinger Publishing, LLC.

—Calendar of the Soul: The Year Participated. Barfield, Owen, tr. from GER. 2006. (Illus.). 60p. per. *(978-1-85584-188-8(6))* Steiner, Rudolf Pr.

—Christ & the Spiritual World: And the Search for the Holy Grail. Davy, C. & Osmond, D., trs. 2008. 141p. pap. *(978-1-85584-202-1(5))* Steiner, Rudolf Pr.

—Christianity As Mystical Fact. Welburn, Andrew J., tr. from GER. & pref. by. 5th ed. 2006. (Classics in Anthroposophy Ser.: 8). 256p. pap. 17.95 *(978-0-88010-436-4(8))* SteinerBooks, Inc.

—Cosmic & Human Metamorphoses A Course. 2006. pap. 19.95 *(978-1-4286-3836-5(9))* Kessinger Publishing, LLC.

—Cosmic Forces in Man: Three Lectures Given in Christiania, November 24, 27, & December 4 1921. 2011. 68p. 36.95 ***(978-1-258-00230-5(2))*** Literary Licensing, LLC.

—Cosmic New Year A Course of Lectures by. 2006. pap. 19.95 *(978-1-4286-4494-6(6))* Kessinger Publishing, LLC.

—The Dead Are with Us. 2006. 47p. per. *(978-1-85584-104-8(5))* Steiner, Rudolf Pr.

—Death As Metamorphosis of Life: Seven Lectures Held in Various Cities November 29, 1917-October 16, 1918. Seiler, Sabine, tr. from GER. 2008. (Collected Works of Rudolf Steiner: No. 182). 216p. pap. 20.00 *(978-0-88010-507-8(7))* SteinerBooks, Inc.

—Descent of the Spirit. 2006. (ENG.). pap. 16.95 *(978-1-4304-5152-5(1))*; pap. 15.95 *(978-1-4304-4198-4(4))* Kessinger Publishing, LLC.

—Effects of Substances in the Cosmos & in the Human Body: Iron, Sodium, Carbon, Chlorine. Evans, V. E., tr. 2011. 16p. pap. 35.95 ***(978-1-258-00310-4(4))*** Literary Licensing, LLC.

—The Essential Rudolf Steiner. 2008. 508p. pap. 19.99 *(978-1-60459-384-6(9))* Wilder Pubns., Ltd.

—Essential Steiner. McDermott, Robert A., ed. 2007. 468p. pap. 29.95 (978-1-58420-051-2(0), Lindisfarne Bks.) SteinerBooks, Inc.

—The Evolution of Consciousness: As Revealed Through Initiation Knowledge. 2007. (Illus.). 297p. per. (978-1-85584-129-1(0)) Steiner, Rudolf Pr.

—From the History & Contents of the First Section of the Esoteric School 1904-1914: Letters, Documents, & Lectures. Wiesberger, Hella, ed. Wood, John, tr. from GER. 2nd ed. 2010. (Collected Works of Rudolf Steiner: 264). (Illus.). 464p. pap. 35.00 (978-0-88010-640-5(9)) SteinerBooks, Inc.

—The Gospel of St. Luke. 203p. 22.00 (978-0-88010-218-6(7)) SteinerBooks, Inc.

—The Healing Process: Spirit, Nature & Our Bodies. Creeger, Catherine, ed. 2nd ed. 2009. (Foundations of Anthroposophical Medicine Ser.: No. 319).Tr. of Anthroposophische Menschenerkenntnis und Medizin. (Illus.). 320p. pap. 25.00 (978-0-88010-474-6(0)) SteinerBooks, Inc.

—How Do I Find the Christ? 2006. 58p. per. (978-1-85584-193-2(2)) Steiner, Rudolf Pr.

—How Genesis Describes the Preparation for Lemuria until Moon. 2006. pap. 12.95 (978-1-4304-2539-7(3)) Kessinger Publishing, LLC.

—How the Spiritual World Interpenetrates the Physical. 2011. 26p. 35.95 (978-1-258-00605-1(7)) Literary Licensing, LLC.

—How to Know Higher Worlds. 2011. 280p. pap. 11.85 (978-1-61427-121-5(6)); pap. 11.95 (978-1-61427-003-4(1)) Martino Publishing.

—The Incarnation of Ahriman: The Embodiment of Evil on Earth: Seven Lectures Given Between October & December 1919. 2006. 115p. per. (978-1-85584-178-9(9)) Steiner, Rudolf Pr.

—The Influence of Spiritual Beings upon Man. 2011. 202p. 44.95 (978-1-258-00824-6(6)) Literary Licensing, LLC.

—The Influence of the Dead on Destiny. 2007. (Collected Works of Rudolf Steiner: 179). (Illus.). 162p. per. 25.00 (978-0-88010-614-6(X)) SteinerBooks, Inc.

—Inner Reading & Inner Hearing: And, How to Achieve Existence in the World of Ideas: Two Lecture Cycles, Followed by Two Christmas Lectures, Dornach, October 3-7 & December 12-20, 1914 & Basel, December 27, 1914. Miller, Michael, tr. from GER. 2008. (Collected Works of Rudolf Steiner: 156).Tr. of Okkultes Lesen und okkultes Hören. (Illus.). 248p. pap. 20.00 (978-0-88010-619-1(0)) SteinerBooks, Inc.

—The Interior of the Earth: An Esoteric Study of the Subterranean Spheres. O'Leary, Paul V., ed. 2007. 130p. per. (978-1-85584-119-2(3)) Steiner, Rudolf Pr.

—Karmic Relationships: Esoteric Studies. Osmond, D. S., tr. from GER. 2nd ed. Vol. 6. 184p. 16.95 (978-0-85440-242-7(X), 614) Vol. 8. (Illus.). 102p. 16.95 (978-0-85440-018-8(4), 79) Steiner, Rudolf Pr. GBR. Dist: Steiner, Rudolf Pr.

—Karmic Relationships, Vol. V: Esoteric Studies, 8 vols. Osmond, D. S., tr. from GER. 2011. (Karmic Relationships Ser.). 111p. pap. (978-1-85584-257-1(2)) Steiner, Rudolf Pr.

—Learning to See into the Spiritual World. Stuber, Walter & Gardner, Mark, trs. from GER. 2009.Tr. of Rhythmen im Kosmos und im Menschenwesen; Wie Kommt man zum Schauen der Geistigen Welt. 88p. pap. 15.00 (978-0-88010-281-0(0)) SteinerBooks, Inc.

—Lecture on Eurythmy. 36p. 5.95 (978-0-85440-189-5(X), 51) Steiner, Rudolf Pr. GBR. Dist: Steiner, Rudolf Pr.

—Man's Being, His Destiny, & World Evolution. McArthur, Erna, tr. 2011. 122p. 39.95 (978-1-258-00542-9(5)) Literary Licensing, LLC.

—Metamorphoses of the Soul. 2008. 228p. (978-1-4437-3897-2(2), Home Farm Bks.) Read Bks.

—The Mission of the Archangel Michael. 2011. 162p. 41.95 (978-1-258-00794-2(0)) Literary Licensing, LLC.

—Mystery Centers: A Series of Fourteen Lectures Given in Dornach 1923. 2011. 124p. 40.95 (978-1-258-00524-5(7)) Literary Licensing, LLC.

—Old & New Methods of Initiation. (Illus.). 188p. pap. 24.95 (978-0-85440-446-9(5), 1454) Steiner, Rudolf Pr. GBR. Dist: Steiner, Rudolf Pr.

—Our Dead: Memorial, Funeral, & Cremation Addresses 1906-1924. Seiler, Sabine, tr. from GER. 2011. 372p. 30.00 (978-0-88010-650-4(6)) SteinerBooks, Inc.

—Outline of Occult Science. Gysi, Max, ed. 2011. (Cambridge Library Collection - Spiritualism & Esoteric Knowlege Ser.). (ENG., Illus.). 492p. pap. 35.99 (978-1-108-07267-0(4)) Cambridge Univ. Pr.

—An Outline of Occult Science. 2007. 448p. per. 33.45 (978-1-59462-796-5(7), Book Jungle) Standard Pubns., Inc.

—Paths of Experience. 2008. 244p. (978-1-4437-3598-8(1), Hesperides Pr.) Read Bks.

—The Philosophy of Freedom. 2011. 170p. pap. 9.80 (978-1-257-83512-6(2)) Lulu Enterprises Inc.

—Renewing Christian Religious Work: Courses for Priests, 1. Post, Marsha, tr. from GER. 2010. (Collected Works of Rudolf Steiner: 342). (Illus.). 328p. pap. 30.00 (978-0-88010-622-1(0)) SteinerBooks, Inc.

—Road to Self Knowledge & the Threshold. 2006. 220p. per. (978-1-4067-9699-5(9), Hesperides Pr.) Read Bks.

—Some Deeper Secrets of Human Development in the Light of the Gospel of St Matthew. 2011. 70p. 36.95 (978-1-258-00532-0(8)) Literary Licensing, LLC.

—The Spiritual Hierarchies & the Physical World: Zodiac, Planets, & Cosmos. Querido, René & Gates, Jan, trs. from GER. 2008. (Collected Works of Rudolf Steiner: No. 110).Tr. of Geistige Hiearchien und ihre Wiederspiegelung in der physischen Welt. Tierkreis, Planeten, Kosmos. (Illus.). 240p. pap. 25.00 (978-0-88010-440-1(6)) SteinerBooks, Inc.

—The Spiritual Hierarchies & the Physical World: Zodiac, Planets & Cosmos. Querido, R. M., tr. from GER. 2008. 256p. pap. (978-0-88010-601-6(8)) SteinerBooks, Inc.

—St John's: An Introductory Reader. 2007. (Pocket Library of Spiritual Wisdom Ser.). 102p. per. (978-1-85584-174-1(6)) Sophia Bks.

—The Stages of Higher Knowledge: Imagination, Inspiration, Intuition. rev. ed. 2009. 72p. pap. 12.00 (978-0-910142-37-3(8)) SteinerBooks, Inc.

—The Sun Mystery & the Mystery of Death & Resurrection: Exoteric & Esoteric Christianity: Twelve Lectures Held in Various Cities in 1922. Creeger, Catherine E., tr. from GER. 2006. (Collected Works of Rudolf Steiner: 211).Tr. of Sonnenmysterium und das Mysterium von Tod und Auferstehung. Exoterisches und esoterisches Christentum. 204p. per. 24.95 (978-0-88010-608-5(5)) SteinerBooks, Inc.

—Theosophy: An Introduction to the Supersensible Knowledge of the World & the Destination of Man. Shields, Elizabeth Douglas, tr. 2011. (Cambridge Library Collection - Spiritualism & Esoteric Knowlege Ser.).Tr. of Theosophie: Einfuehrung in uebersinnliche Welterkenntnis und Menschenbestimmung. (ENG.). 234p. pap. 22.99 (978-1-108-07266-3(6)) Cambridge Univ. Pr.

—Theosophy: An Introduction to the Supersensible Knowledge of the World & the Destination of Man. Cotterell, M. & Shepherd, A. P., trs. 2011.Tr. of Theosophie: Einfuehrung in uebersinnliche Welterkenntnis und Menschenbestimmung. (ENG.). (978-1-85584-254-0(8)) Steiner, Rudolf Pr.

—The Threefold State. 2009. 68p. pap. (978-0-217-30046-9(4)); pap. (978-0-217-64317-7(5)) Books LLC.

—The Threshold of the Spiritual World. 2007. (ENG.). 104p. per. 12.45 (978-1-60206-052-4(5)) Cosimo, Inc.

—Turning Points in Spiritual History: Zarathustra, Hermes, Buddha, Moses, Elijah, Christ. 2007. 220p. pap. 25.00 (978-0-88010-525-5(9)) SteinerBooks, Inc.

—What Is Necessary in These Urgent Times. Bradley, Rory, tr. from GER. 2010. (Collected Works of Rudolf Steiner: 196). (Illus.). 376p. pap. 35.00 (978-0-88010-631-3(X)) SteinerBooks, Inc.

—Why Material Concepts Are Insufficient to Understand the Spiritual - 2006. pap. 9.95 (978-1-4304-2525-0(3)) Kessinger Publishing, LLC.

—Youth & the Etheric Heart: Rudolf Steiner Speaks to the Younger Generation: Addresses, Essays, Discussions, & Reports, 1920-1924. Creeger, Catherine E., tr. from GER. 2007. (Collected Works of Rudolf Steiner: 217a). (Illus.). 246p. per. (978-0-88010-616-0(6)) SteinerBooks, Inc.

Steiner, Rudolf & Parker, A. H. True & False Paths in Spiritual Investigation. 2010.Tr. of Initiaten-Bewusstsein. Die wahren und die falschen Wege der geistigen Forschung. 224p. 31.96 (978-1-169-73968-0(7)); 39.95 (978-1-161-37581-7(3)) Kessinger Publishing, LLC.

Steiner, Rudolph. Knowledge of the Higher Worlds & its Attainment. 2007. pap. 14.99 (978-1-59986-902-5(0), FQ Classics) Filiquarian Publishing, LLC.

—Stages of Higher Knowledge. 2006. 100p. per. (978-1-4067-9693-3(X), Hesperides Pr.) Read Bks.

Steiner, Rudulf. Theosophy: An Introduction to the Supersensible Knowledge of the World & the Destination of Man. 2011. 162p. pap. 6.85 (978-1-61427-050-8(3)) Martino Publishing.

Tradowsky, Peter. The Stigmata: Destiny as a Question of Knowledge. Barton, Matthew, tr. from GER. 2010. (Illus.). 62p. pap. (978-1-906999-13-1(9)) Temple Lodge Publishing.

Turner, Bryan S. The Body & Society: Explorations in Social Theory. 3rd ed. 2008. (Published in Association with Theory, Culture & Society Ser.). 296p. (C). 116.00 (978-1-4129-2986-8(5), B29865C); pap. 51.00 (978-1-4129-2987-5(3), B29865P) SAGE Pubns., Ltd. GBR. Dist: SAGE Pubns., Inc.

Ullrich, Heiner. Rudolf Steiner: Leben und Lehre. 2008. (Continuum Library of Educational Thought Ser.). (ENG.). 280p. 140.00 (978-0-8264-8419-2(0)) Continuum International Publishing Group, Ltd. GBR. Dist: National Bk. Network.

Van Dijk, Danielle. Christ Consciousness: A Path of Inner Development. 2010. (Illus.). 174p. pap. (978-1-906999-09-4(0)) Temple Lodge Publishing.

Von Halle, Judith. Descent into the Depths of the Earth: On the Anthroposophic Path of Schooling. 2011. (ENG., Illus.). 144p. (978-1-906999-22-3(8)) Temple Lodge Publishing.

Von Halle, Judith. Secrets of the Stations of the Cross & the Grail Blood: The Mystery of Transformation. 2008. (Illus.). 152p. (978-1-902636-89-4(9)) Temple Lodge Publishing.

Wannamaker, Olin D. What Is Anthroposophy: An Answer in Outline to This Question. 2011. 38p. 35.95 (978-1-258-01941-9(8)) Literary Licensing, LLC.

Whicher, Olive. Sunspace. (Illus.). 140p. 24.95 (978-0-85440-726-2(X), 1488) Steiner, Rudolf Pr. GBR. Dist: Steiner, Rudolf Pr.

Zander, Helmut. Anthroposophie in Deutschland. 2 Bände: Theosophische Weltanschauung und gesellschaftliche Praxis 1884-1945, 2 vols. 2nd ed. 2008. (GER., Illus.). 1884p. (C). 224.00 (978-3-525-55452-4(4)) Vandenhoeck & Ruprecht GmbH & Co. KG DEU. Dist: ISD.

ANTI-ABORTION MOVEMENT

see Pro-Life Movement

ANTI-ACCELERATION SUITS

see Pressure Suits

ANTI-AGING

see Aging—Prevention

ANTI-AIRCRAFT ARTILLERY

see Antiaircraft Artillery

ANTI-AIRCRAFT GUNS

see Antiaircraft Guns

ANTI-AMERICANISM

Alexander Stephan Staff. Americanization & Anti-Americanism: The German Encounter with American Culture after 1945. 2008. 256p. 34.95 (978-1-84545-487-6(1)) Berghahn Bks., Inc.

—The Americanization of Europe: Culture, Diplomacy & Anti-Americanism after 1945. 2007. 444p. 34.95 (978-1-84545-486-9(3)) Berghahn Bks., Inc.

Anholt, Simon & Hildreth, Jeremy. Brand America: The Making, Unmaking & Remaking of the Greatest National Image of All Time. 2010. 192p. pap. 15.95 (978-1-905736-56-0(8)) Marshall Cavendish GBR. Dist: Midpoint Trade Bks., Inc.

Arab Opinion on American Policies, Values & People: Joint Hearing Before the Subcommittee on International Organizations, Human Rights, & Oversight & the Subcommittee on the Middle East & South Asia of the Committee on Foreign Affairs, House of Representatives, One Hundred Tenth Congress, First Session, May 3, 2007. 2007. v, 58p. (978-0-16-078911-3(7), 552-070-36037-9) United States Government Printing Office.

Armenta, Amira. En el Patio de Atrás. 2008. (SPA.). 140p. per. 9.50 (978-1-84799-330-4(3)) Lulu Enterprises Inc.

Armus, Seth. French Anti-Americanism, 1930-1948: Critical Moments in a Complex History. 2010. (ENG.). 190p. pap. 29.50 (978-0-7391-1269-4(4)) Lexington Bks.

Armus, Seth D. French Anti-Americanism (1930-1948) Critical Moments in a Complex History. 2007. (ENG.). 190p. 62.99 (978-0-7391-1268-7(6)) Lexington Bks.

Berman, Russell A. Anti-Americanism in Europe: A Cultural Problem. 2008. (Hoover Classics Ser.). (ENG.). 128p. 14.95 (978-0-8179-4511-4(3)) Hoover Institution Pr.

Brogi, Alessandro. Confronting America: The Cold War between the United States & the Communists in France & Italy. 2011. (New Cold War History Ser.). (ENG., Illus.). 560p. 55.00 (978-0-8078-3473-2(4)) Univ. of North Carolina Pr.

Chiozza, Giacomo. Anti-Americanism & the American World Order. 2009. (ENG., Illus.). 256p. (C). (gr. 13-17). 62.00 (978-0-8018-9206-6(6)); pap. 27.00 (978-0-8018-9208-0(2)) Johns Hopkins Univ. Pr.

Declining Approval for American Foreign Policy in Muslim Countries: Does It Make It More Difficult to Fight Al-Qaeda?: Hearing Before the Subcommittee on International Organizations, Human Rights, & Oversight of the Committee on Foreign Affairs, House of Representatives, One Hundred Tenth Congress, First Session, May 17, 2007. 2007. (Illus.). iii, 56p. (978-0-16-078932-8(X), 552-070-36059-0) United States Government Printing Office.

D'Souza, Dinesh. The Enemy at Home: The Cultural Left & Its Responsibility For 9/11. 2008. (ENG.). 384p. pap. 15.95 (978-0-7679-1561-8(5), Broadway) Broadway Bks.

Efforts to Deal with America's Image Abroad: Are They Working?: Hearing Before the Subcommittee on International Organizations, Human Rights, & Oversight of the Committee on Foreign Affairs, House of Representatives, One Hundred Tenth Congress, First Session, April 26, 2007. 2007. (Illus.). iii, 56p. (978-0-16-078912-0(5), 552-070-36038-7) United States Government Printing Office.

El-Bendary, Mohamed. The Ugly American in the Arab Mind: Why Do Arabs Resent America? 2011. (Illus.). 220p. 27.50 (978-1-59797-673-2(3)) Potomac Bks., Inc.

Faath, Sigrid. Anti-Americanism in the Islamic World. 2006. xii, 305p. 88.95 (978-1-55876-396-8(1)); pap. 28.95 (978-1-55876-397-5(X)) Wiener, Markus Pubs., Inc.

Fabbrini, Sergio, ed. The United States Contested: American Unilateralism & European Discontent. 2007. (Illus.). 234p. 160.00 (978-0-415-39090-3(7), RU0907X) Routledge.

Farber, David R., ed. What They Think of Us: International Perceptions of the United States Since 9/11. annot. ed. 2007. (ENG.). 206p. (C). 29.95 (978-0-691-13025-5(6)) Princeton Univ. Pr.

Gould, Carol. Don't Tread on Me: Anti-Americanism Abroad. 2009. (ENG.). 250p. 25.95 (978-1-59403-239-4(4)) Encounter Bks.

Graham, Carol Madison. Coping with Anti-Americanism: A Guide to Getting the Most Out of Studying Abroad. 2011. 234p. pap. 17.95 (978-1-59797-409-7(9)) Potomac Bks., Inc.

Gulddal, Jesper. Anti-Americanism in European Literature. 2011. (Studies in European Culture & History Ser.). (ENG., Illus.). 252p. 85.00 (978-0-230-12082-2(2)) Palgrave Macmillan.

Higgott, Richard, et al. The Political Consequences of Anti-Americanism. Malbasic, Ivona, ed. 2008. (Illus.). 256p. 140.00 (978-0-415-46391-1(2)) Routledge.

Hollander, Paul. The Only Super Power: Reflections on Strength, Weakness, & Anti-Americanism. 2008. (ENG.). 302p. 41.99 (978-0-7391-2543-4(5)) Lexington Bks.

Holmes, Stephen. The Matador's Cape: America's Reckless Response to Terror. 2007. (ENG.). 378p. 34.00 (978-0-521-87516-5(1)) Cambridge Univ. Pr.

Holsti, Ole Rudolf. To See Ourselves as Others See Us: How Publics Abroad View the United States After 9/11. 2008. (ENG.). 248p. 90.00 (978-0-472-07036-7(3)); (Illus.). pap. 27.95 (978-0-472-05036-9(2)) Univ. of Michigan Pr.

Horne. Blows Against the Empire: U. S. Imperialism in Crisis. 2008. 160p. pap. 10.00 (978-0-7178-0746-8(0)) International Publishers Co., Inc.

Kahan, Alan. Mind vs. Money: The War between Intellectuals & Capitalism. 2010. (ENG.). 311p. 39.95 (978-1-4128-1063-0(9)) Transaction Pubs.

Katzenstein, Peter J. & Keohane, Robert O., eds. Anti-Americanisms in World Politics. 2006. (Cornell Studies in Political Economy). (Illus.). 351p. 68.95 (978-0-8014-4517-0(5)); per. 24.95 (978-0-8014-7351-7(9)) Cornell Univ. Pr. (Comstock Publishing Assocs.).

Krastev, Ivan & McPherson, Alan L. The Anti-American Century. Krastev, Ivan & McPherson, Allen, eds. 2007. (ENG., Illus.). 220p. 39.95 (978-963-7326-80-6(4)) Central European Univ. Pr.

Kuisel, Richard. French Fascination with America. 2011. (ENG., Illus.). 544p. (C). 49.50 (978-0-691-15181-6(4)) Princeton Univ. Pr.

Kull, Steven. Feeling Betrayed: The Roots of Muslim Anger at America. 2011. (ENG., Illus.). 275p. pap. 27.95 (978-0-8157-0559-8(X)) Brookings Institution Pr.

Lacey, Jim. The Canons of Jihad: Terrorists' Strategy for Defeating America. 2008. (Illus.). 186p. per. 18.00 (978-1-59114-461-8(2)) Naval Institute Pr.

Lacorne, Denis & Judt, Tony. With Us or Against Us: Studies in Global Anti-Americanism. 2007. (Sciences Po Series in International Relations & Political Economy Ser.). (ENG.). 256p. pap. 32.00 (978-0-230-60226-7(6)) Palgrave Macmillan.

Markovits, Andrei S. Uncouth Nation: Why Europe Dislikes America. 2007. (Public Square Ser.). (ENG.). 302p. (C). 24.95 (978-0-691-12287-8(3)) Princeton Univ. Pr.

Martin, Dick. Rebuilding Brand America: What We Must Do to Restore Our Reputation & Safeguard the Future of American Business Abroad. 2007. (ENG., Illus.). 304p. 27.95 (978-0-8144-7333-7(4)) Amacom.

Medved, Michael. The 10 Big Lies about America: Combating Destructive Distortions about Our Nation. 2009. (ENG.). 288p. pap. 15.00 (978-0-307-39407-1(7), Three Rivers Pr.) Crown Publishing Group.

Miler, Christoph Hendrik. West Germans Against the West, 1949-1968: Anti-Americanism in Media & Public Opinion in the Federal Republic of Germany. 2010. (Palgrave Studies in the History of the Media Ser.). (ENG.). 272p. 95.00 (978-0-230-23155-9(1)) Palgrave Macmillan.

O'connor, Brendon. Beyond Anti-Americanism. 2011. 208p. 150.00 (978-0-415-47428-3(0)); pap. 41.95 (978-0-415-47429-0(9)) Routledge.

O'Connor, Brendon, ed. Anti-Americanism: History, Causes, Themes, 4 vols. 2007. 1407p. 300.00 (978-1-84645-004-4(7), GWP004) Greenwood Publishing Group, Inc.

Pilon, Juliana Geran. Why America Is Such a Hard Sell: Beyond Pride & Prejudice. 2007. (ENG.). 280p. 84.00 (978-0-7425-5148-0(2)) Rowman & Littlefield Publishers, Inc.

Public Diplomacy in the Middle East & South Asia: Is the Message Getting Through?: Hearing Before the Subcommittee on the Middle East & South Asia of the Committee on Foreign Affairs, House of Representatives, One Hundred Tenth Congress, First Session, May 16, 2007. 2007. ii, 78p. (978-0-16-079129-1(4), 552-070-36224-0) United States Government Printing Office.

Release & Review of the Subcommittee Report: "The Decline in America's Reputation: Why?": Markup & Hearing Before the Subcommittee on International Organizations, Human Rights, & Oversight of the Committee on Foreign Affairs, House of Representatives, One Hundred Tenth Congress, Second Session, June 11, 2008. 2008. iii, 59p. (978-0-16-081334-4(4), 552-070-37714-0) United States Government Printing Office.

Roger, Philippe. The American Enemy: The History of French Anti-Americanism. Bowman, Sharon, tr. from FRE. 2006. (ENG.). 536p. pap. 25.00 (978-0-226-72369-3(0)) Univ. of Chicago Pr.

Sanders, Barry A. American Avatar: The United States in the Global Imagination. 2011. (Illus.). 240p. 29.95 (978-1-59797-681-7(4)) Potomac Bks., Inc.

Schweitzer, Glenn E. & Schweitzer, Carole D. America on Notice: Stemming the Tide of Anti-Americanism. 2006. (ENG.). 325p. 28.98 (978-1-59102-428-6(5)) Prometheus Bks., Pubs.

Sciutto, Jim. Against Us: The New Face of America's Enemies in the Muslim World. 2009. (ENG.). 288p. pap. 15.00 (978-0-307-40689-7(X), Three Rivers Pr.) Crown Publishing Group.

Shohat, Ella & Stam, Robert. Flagging Patriotism: The Dilemma of Patriotism in Transnational Perspective. 2006. (ENG.). 408p. 95.00 (978-0-415-97921-4(8)) Routledge.

Singh, Robert. Anti-Americanisms: Power, Principle & the End of American Foreign Policy. 2007. 208p. 34.95 (978-0-415-41882-9(8)); 135.00 (978-0-415-41881-2(X)) Routledge.

Smucker, Philip. My Brother, My Enemy: America & the Battle of Ideas Across the Islamic World. 2010. (ENG.). 345p. 26.00 (978-1-61614-184-4(0)) Prometheus Bks., Pubs.

Snow, Nancy. The Arrogance of American Power: What U. S. Leaders Are Doing Wrong & Why It's Our Duty to Dissent. 2006. (ENG.). 224p. per. 28.95 (978-0-7425-5374-3(4)) Rowman & Littlefield Publishers, Inc.

South America & the United States: How to Fix a Broken Relationship: Hearing Before the Committee on Foreign Affairs, House of Representatives, One Hundred Tenth Congress, First Session, June 19, 2007. 2007. (Illus.). iii, 69p. (978-0-16-079304-2(1), 552-070-36382-3) United States Government Printing Office.

Stam, Robert & Shohat, Ella. Flagging Patriotism: Crises of Narcissism & Anti-Americanism. 2006. (ENG.). 408p. per. 34.95 (978-0-415-97922-1(6)) Routledge.

Stefanidis, Ioannis. Stirring the Greek Nation: Political Culture Irredentism & Anti-Americanism in Post-War Greece 1945-1967. 2007. (Illus.). 318p. 134.95 (978-0-7546-6059-0(1)) Ashgate Publishing Co.

Sweig, Julia E. Friendly Fire: Losing Friends & Making Enemies in the Anti-American Century. 2007. (ENG.). 272p. per. 16.95 (978-1-58648-520-7(2)) PublicAffairs.

United States, Congress House Committee on Foreign Affairs Subcommittee on International Organizations, Human Rights, and Oversight Staff, contrib. by. Global Polling Data on Opinion of American Policies, Values & People: Hearing Before the Subcommittee on International Organizations, Human Rights, & Oversight of the Committee on Foreign Affairs, House of Representatives, One Hundred Tenth Congress, First Session, March 14, 2007. 2007. (Illus.). iii, 28p. *(978-0-16-078500-9(6),* 552-070-35781-5) United States Government Printing Office.

—Global Polling Data on Opinion of American Policies, Values & People: Hearing Before the Subcommittee on International Organizations, Human Rights, & Oversight of the Committee on Foreign Affairs, House of Representatives, One Hundred Tenth Congress, First Session, March 6, 2007. 2007. (Illus.). iii, 29p *(978-0-16-078481-1(6),* 552-070-35762-9) United States Government Printing Office.

—Welcome to America? Hearing Before the Subcommittee on International Organizations, Human Rights, & Oversight of the Committee on Foreign Affairs, House of Representatives, One Hundred Tenth Congress, First Session, March 20, 2007. 2007. iii, 45p. *(978-0-16-078485-9(9),* 552-070-35766-1) United States Government Printing Office.

United States, Congress House Committee on Foreign Affairs Subcommittee on International Organizations, Human Rights, and Oversight Staff & United States, Congress House Committee on Foreign Affairs Subcommittee on Europe (2007-) Staff, contrib. by. Polling Data on European Opinion of American Policies, Values & People: Joint Hearing Before the Subcommittee on International Organizations, Human Rights, & Oversight & the Subcommittee on Europe of the Committee on Foreign Affairs, House of Representatives, One Hundred Tenth Congress, First Session, March 22, 2007. 2007. (Illus.) v, 76p. *(978-0-16-078622-8(3),* 552-070-35865-0) United States Government Printing Office.

United States, Congress House Committee on Foreign Affairs Subcommittee on International Organizations, Human Rights, and Oversight Staff & United States, Congress House Committee on Foreign Affairs Subcommittee on the Western Hemisphere Staff, contrib. by. Polling Data on Latin American Opinion of United States Policies, Values & People: Joint Hearing Before the Subcommittee on International Organizations, Human Rights, & Oversight & the Subcommittee on the Western Hemisphere of the Committee on Foreign Affairs, House of Representatives, One Hundred Tenth Congress, First Session, March 8, 2007. 2007. v, 39p. *(978-0-16-078710-2(6),* 552-070-35934-6) United States Government Printing Office.

Waiman, Misha. 17 Vorurteile, die wir Deutschen gegen Amerika und die Amerikaner haben und die so nicht ganz stimmen Können. 2008.Tr. of 17 Prejudices That We Germans Have Against America & Americans & That Can't be Right: a Post-Pisan Polemic Addressed to the German Nation. (GER.). 74p. pap. 14.95 *(978-0-9795829-3-6(8))* Upper West Side Philosophers, Inc.

ANTI-APARTHEID MOVEMENTS

see also Apartheid; South Africa—History—Soweto Uprising, 1976

Alexander, Amanda & Mngxitama, Andile. Biko Lives! Contesting the Legacies of Steve Biko. Gibson, Nigel, ed. 2008. (Contemporary Black History Ser.). (ENG.). 304p. pap. 31.00 *(978-0-230-60649-4(0))* Palgrave Macmillan.

Badran, Amneh & Badran, Amneh Daoud. Zionist Israel & Apartheid South Africa: Civil society & peace building in ethnic-national States. 2009. (ENG., Illus.). 272p. 130.00 *(978-0-415-48981-2(4))* Routledge.

Callinicos, Luli. Oliver Tambo: Beyond the Engeni Mountains. 2nd ed. 2012. (Illus.). 608p. pap. 41.95 ***(978-0-86486-666-0(6))*** International Publishers Marketing.

Conway, Daniel. Masculinities, Militarisation & the End Conscription Campaign: War Resistance in Apartheid South Africa. 2012. (ENG., Illus.). 176p. 100.00 ***(978-0-7190-8320-4(6))*** Manchester Univ. Pr. GBR. Dist: Macmillan.

Everatt, David. The Origins of Non-Racialism: White Opposition to Apartheid in The 1950s. 2010. (ENG., Illus.). 280p. pap. 34.95 *(978-1-86814-500-3(X))* Witwatersrand Univ. Pr. Pubns. ZAF. Dist: Transaction Pubs.

Feinberg, Barry. Time to Tell: An Activist's Story. 2011. (ENG., Illus.). 180p. pap. 22.95 *(978-1-920222-34-5(0))* STE Pubs. ZAF. Dist: Independent Pubs. Group.

Limb, Peter. The ANC's Early Years: Nation, Class & Place in South Africa Before 1940. 2010. 602p. pap. 48.95 *(978-1-86888-529-9(1))* Unisa Press / Uitgewers GBR. Dist: International Specialized Bk. Services.

Lindfors, Bernth, ed. The Dennis Brutus Tapes: Essays at Autobiography. 2011. (Illus.). 224p. 70.00 *(978-1-84701-034-6(2),* Currey, James) Boydell & Brewer, Ltd. GBR. Dist: Boydell & Brewer, Inc.

Magaziner, Daniel R. The Law & the Prophets: Black Consciousness in South Africa, 1968-1977. 2010. (New African Histories Ser.). (ENG., Illus.). 280p. 59.95 *(978-0-8214-1917-5(X))* Ohio Univ. Pr.

—The Law & the Prophets: Faith, Hope, & Politics in South Africa, 1968-1977. 2010. (New African Histories Ser.). (ENG., Illus.). 280p. pap. 26.95 *(978-0-8214-1918-2(8))* Ohio Univ. Pr.

Mandela, Nelson. Let Freedom Reign: The Words of Nelson Mandela. Russell, Henry, ed. 2010. (ENG.). 144p. 14.95 *(978-1-56656-800-5(5),* Interlink Bks.) Interlink Publishing Group, Inc.

—Selected Speeches & Writings of Nelson Mandela: The End of Apartheid in South Africa. 2010. 290p. pap. *(978-1-934941-78-2(6))* Red & Black Pubs.

Mngxitama, Andile, et al. Biko Lives! Contesting the Legacies of Steve Biko. Alexander, Amanda et al, eds. 2008. (Contemporary Black History Ser.). (ENG.). 304p. 95.00 *(978-0-230-60519-0(2))* Palgrave Macmillan.

Ntantala, Phyllis. Life's Mosaic: The Autobiography of Phyllis Ntantala. 2nd ed. 2010. (ENG.). 256p. pap. 24.00 *(978-1-77009-670-7(1))* Jacana Media ZAF. Dist: Independent Pubs. Group.

O'Malley, Padraig. Shades of Difference: Mac Maharaj & the Struggle for South Africa. 2007. (Illus.). xix, 648p. *(978-0-670-08523-1(5),* Viking Adult) Penguin Group (USA) Inc.

Pinnock, Don. Writing Left: The Radical Journalism of Ruth First. 2007. (Illus.). 284p. pap. 26.75 *(978-1-86888-365-3(5))* Unisa Press / Uitgewers GBR. Dist: International Specialized Bk. Services.

Sachs, Albie. The Strange Alchemy of Life & Law. (ENG.). 320p. 2011. pap. 25.00 *(978-0-19-960577-4(7))* 2009. (Illus.). 25.00 *(978-0-19-957179-6(1))* Oxford Univ. Pr., Inc.

Sadet (South African Democracy Education Trust), ed. The Road to Democracy in South Africa: Volume 1 (1960-1970) (Revised Edition) 2010. 735p. 52.00 *(978-1-86888-563-3(1))* Unisa Press / Uitgewers GBR. Dist: International Specialized Bk. Services.

Sisulu, Elinor Batezat. Walter & Albertina Sisulu: In Our Lifetime. 2011. 688p. pap. 42.95 *(978-0-86486-639-4(9))* International Publishers Marketing.

Skinner, Rob. The Foundations of Anti-Apartheid: Liberal Humanitarians & Transnational Activists in Britain & the United States, C. 1919-64. 2010. (ENG.). 280p. 84.00 *(978-0-230-20366-2(3))* Palgrave Macmillan.

Spivey, Kirby. The Cola Wars in South Afric. 2011. 68p. pap. ***(978-3-8443-2057-2(1))*** Lambert Academic Publishing

Thörn, Håkan. Anti-Apartheid & the Emergence of a Global Civil Society. 2009. (St. Antony's Ser.) (ENG.). 272p. pap. 31.00 *(978-0-230-23496-3(8))* Palgrave Macmillan.

ANTI-BLACKOUT SUITS

see Pressure Suits

ANTI-CATHOLICISM

see also Catholic Church—Controversial Literature; Nativism

Alvarez Recio, Leticia. Fighting the Antichrist: A Cultural History of Anti-Catholicism in Tudor England. 2011. (ENG., Illus.). 238p. 69.95 *(978-1-84519-427-7(6))* Sussex Academic Pr. GBR. Dist: International Specialized Bk. Services.

Borutta, Manuel. Antikatholizismus: Deutschland und Italien im Zeitalter der europäischen Kulturkämpfe. 2010. (Burgertum Neue Folge Ser.). (GER.). 488p. (C). 84.00 *(978-3-525-36849-7(6))* Vandenhoeck & Ruprecht GmbH & Co. KG DEU. Dist: ISD.

Davies, Sharon. Rising Road: A True Tale of Love, Race, & Religion in America. 1 vol. (ENG., Illus.). 352p. 2011. pap. 18.95 *(978-0-19-979445-4(5))* 2010. 27.95 *(978-0-19-537979-2(9))* Oxford Univ. Pr., Inc.

Fenton, Elizabeth. Religious Liberties: Anti-Catholicism & Liberal Democracy in Nineteenth-Century U. S. Literature & Culture. 1 vol. 2011. (Imagining the Americas Ser.). 192p. 65.00 *(978-0-19-538409-3(1))* Oxford Univ. Pr., Inc.

Fowler, Franklin S. When "The" Church Rides the Beast: Unfolding a Rome-Centered Mystery!: (Revelation Chapters 17, 13 & 13:1-8) 2009. (Illus.). x, 185p. ***(978-0-9789263-1-1(5))*** Christian Heritage Foundation.

Issel, William. For Both Cross & Flag: Catholic Action, Anti-Catholicism, & National Security Politics in World War II San Francisco. 2009. (Urban Life, Landscape & Policy Ser.). (ENG., Illus.). 216p. 42.00 *(978-1-4399-0028-4(0))* Temple Univ. Pr.

LaMonaca, Maria. Masked Atheism: Catholicism & the Secular Victorian Home. 2008. (ENG., Illus.). 69.95 *(978-0-8142-1084-0(8))* Ohio State Univ. Pr.

Menendez, Albert J. The Religious Factor in the 1960 Presidential Election: An Analysis of the Kennedy Victory over Anti-Catholic Prejudice. 2011. (ENG., Illus.). 271p. pap. 45.00 *(978-0-7864-6037-3(7))* McFarland & Co., Inc. Pubs.

Monk, Maria. Awful Disclosures: Containing, Also, Many Incidents Never before Published. 2007. (ENG.). 286p. pap. 21.99 *(978-1-4264-2573-8(2))* BiblioBazaar.

—Awful Disclosures: Containing, Also, Many Incidents Never Before Published. Lt. ed. 2007. (ENG.). 304p. pap. 24.99 *(978-1-4264-2614-8(3))* BiblioBazaar.

Neuheiser, Jö, et al. Krone, Kirche und Verfassung: Konservatismus in den englischen Unterschichten 1815 - 1867. 2010. (Kritische Studien Zur Geschichtswissenschaft Ser.). (GER.). 349p. (C). 77.00 *(978-3-525-37009-4(1))* Vandenhoeck & Ruprecht GmbH & Co. KG DEU. Dist: ISD.

Nordstrom, Justin. Danger on the Doorstep: Anti-Catholicism & American Print Culture in the Progressive Era. 2006. (Illus.). 312p. per. 30.00 *(978-0-268-03605-8(5))* Univ. of Notre Dame Pr.

Paz, Denis. Dickens & Barnaby Rudge: Anti-Catholicism & Chartism. 2007. 256p. 50.00 *(978-0-85036-575-7(9))* Merlin Pr. Ltd. GBR. Dist: Independent Pubs. Group.

Purves, Maria. The Gothic & Catholicism: Religion, Cultural Exchange & the Popular Novel, 1785-1829. 2010. (University of Wales Press - Gothic Literary Studies). (ENG., Illus.). 192p. 85.00 *(978-0-7083-2091-4(0))* Univ of Wales Pr. GBR. Dist: Chicago Distribution Ctr.

—Gothic & Catholicism: Religion, Exchange & the Popular Novel, 1785-1829. 2010. (University of Wales Press - Gothic Literary Studies). (ENG., Illus.). 192p. 85.00 *(978-0-7083-2090-7(2))* Univ. of Wales Pr. GBR. Dist: Chicago Distribution Ctr.

Ramsay, Jacob. Mandarins & Martyrs: The Church & the Nguyen Dynasty in Early Nineteenth-Century Vietnam. 2008. (ENG., Illus.). 224p. 50.00 *(978-0-8047-5651-8(1))* Stanford Univ. Pr.

Rule, William Harris. The Brand of Dominic; or, Inquisition; 2006. 312p. per. 23.99 *(978-1-4255-3039-6(7))* MPublishing.

Shogimen, Takashi. Ockham & Political Discourse in the Late Middle Ages. 2007. (Cambridge Studies in Medieval Life & Thought). (ENG.). 322p. 116.00 *(978-0-521-84581-6(5))* Cambridge Univ. Pr.

Verhoeven, Timothy. Transatlantic Anti-Catholicism: France & the United States in the Nineteenth Century. 2010. (Palgrave Macmillan Transnational History Ser.). (ENG.). 240p. 84.00 *(978-0-230-10287-3(5))* Palgrave Macmillan.

ANTI-CLERICALISM

Frede, Victoria. Doubt, Atheism, & the Nineteenth-Century Russian Intelligentsia. 2011. (ENG., Illus.). 314p. pap. 26.95 ***(978-0-299-28444-2(1))*** Univ. of Wisconsin Pr.

Martínez Fiol, David & Martínez Fiol, David. La Setmana Tràgica. 2009. (CAT., Illus.). 165p. *(978-84-9809-068-0(7))* Portic Editorial.

Radcliffe, Timothy. Take the Plunge: Living Baptism & Confirmation. 2012. (ENG.). 320p. pap. 16.95 ***(978-1-4411-1848-6(9)),*** Burns & Oates) Continuum International Publishing Group, Ltd. GBR. Dist: National Bk. Network.

Sanabria, Enrique. Republicanism & Anticlerical Nationalism in Spain. 2009. (ENG., Illus.). 272p. 95.00 *(978-0-230-61371-7(4))* Palgrave Macmillan.

Scase, Wendy. Piers Plowman & the New Anticlericalism. 2007. (Cambridge Studies in Medieval Literature Ser.). (ENG.). 268p. pap. 56.00 *(978-0-521-04454-7(5))* Cambridge Univ. Pr.

ANTI-COLONIALISM

see Colonies

ANTI-COMMUNIST MOVEMENTS

see also Propaganda, Anticommunist

Alwood, Edward. Dark Days in the Newsroom: McCarthyism Aimed at the Press. 2007. 208p. 70.50 *(978-1-59213-341-3(X))* Temple Univ. Pr.

Blauner, Bob. Resisting McCarthyism: To Sign or Not to Sign California's Loyalty Oath. 2009. (ENG., Illus.). 328p. 34.95 *(978-0-8047-5922-9(7))* Stanford Univ. Pr.

Ceplair, Larry. Anti-Communism in Twentieth-Century America. 2011. E-Book ***(978-1-4408-0048-1(0),*** Praeger Pubs.) Greenwood Publishing Group, Inc.

Ceplair, Larry. Anti-Communism in Twentieth-Century America: A Critical History. 1 vol. 2011. (Illus.). 372p. 48.00 *(978-1-4408-0047-4(2),* A3738C) Greenwood Publishing Group, Inc.

Chapman, Michael E. Arguing Americanism: Pro-Franco Lobbyists, Roosevelt's Foreign Policy, & the Spanish Civil War. 2011. (New Studies in U.S. Foreign Relations Ser.). (Illus.). 288p. 60.00 *(978-1-60635-078-2(1))* Kent State Univ. Pr.

Conant, Jennet. A Covert Affair: Julia Child & Paul Child in the OSS. 2011. (ENG., Illus.). 416p. 28.00 *(978-1-4391-6352-8(9))* Simon & Schuster.

—A Covert Affair: Julia Child & Paul Child in the OSS. Lt. ed. 2011. 31.99 *(978-1-4104-3745-7(0))* Thorndike Pr.

Conant, Jennet. A Covert Affair: When Julia Child & Paul Child in the OSS They Had No Way of Knowing That Their Adventures with the Spy Service Would Lead Them into a World of Intrigue and, Because of one Idealistic but Reckless Colleague, a Terrifying FBI Investigation. 2011. (ENG., Illus.). 416p. pap. 16.00 ***(978-1-4391-6353-5(7))*** Simon & Schuster.

Corsellis, John & Ferrar, Marcus. Slovenia 1945: Memories of Death & Survival after World War II. 2010. (ENG., Illus.). 288p. pap. 25.00 *(978-1-84885-534-2(6))* I. B. Tauris & Co., Ltd. GBR. Dist: Macmillan.

Cox, Terry. Challenging Communism in Eastern Europe: 1956 & its Legacy. 2008. pap. 40.00 *(978-0-415-49567-7(9))* Routledge.

Crouse, Eric R. American Stand: Senator Margaret Chase Smith & the Communist Menace, 1948-1972. 2010. (ENG.). 204p. 65.00 *(978-0-7391-4442-8(1))* Lexington Bks.

Crouse, Eric Robert. An American Stand: Senator Margaret Chase Smith & the Communist Menace, 1948-1972. 2010. *(978-0-7391-4444-2(8))* Lexington Bks.

Emmons, Caroline S. Cold War & McCarthy ERA: People & Perspectives. 2010. (Illus.). xliv, 227p. E-Book *(978-1-59884-104-6(1))* ABC-CLIO, LLC.

Evans, M. Stanton. Blacklisted by History: The Untold Story of Senator Joe McCarthy & His Fight Against America's Enemies. 2009. (ENG.). 672p. pap. 18.00 *(978-1-4000-8106-6(8),* Three Rivers Pr.) Crown Publishing Group.

Everitt, David. A Shadow of Red: Communism & the Blacklist in Radio & Television. 2007. (ENG., Illus.). 432p. 27.50 *(978-1-56663-575-2(6))* Dee, Ivan R. Pub.

Fleming, John V. The Anti-Communist Manifestos: Four Books That Shaped the Cold War, 4 bks. 2009. (ENG., Illus.). 368p. 27.95 *(978-0-393-06925-9(7),* 6925) Norton, W. W. & Co., Inc.

Francis, Daniel. Seeing Reds: The Red Scare of 1918-1919, Canada's First War on Terror. 2011. (ENG., Illus.). 220p. 26.95 *(978-1-55152-373-6(6))* Arsenal Pulp Pr. CAN. Dist: Consortium Bk. Sales & Distribution.

Greenhaven Editor, ed. The Red Scare. 2011. (World History Ser.). (Illus.). 128p. (YA). (gr. 9-12). 33.45 *(978-1-4205-0680-8(3))* Cengage Gale.

Hughes, Quenby Olmsted. In the Interest of Democracy: The Rise & Fall of the Early Cold War Alliance Between the American Federation of Labor & the Central Intelligence Agency. 2011. (Trade Unions Past, Present & Future Ser.). 204p. pap. 55.95 *(978-3-0343-0212-8(6))* Lang, Peter AG GBR. Dist: Lang, Peter.

Johnson, Haynes. The Age of Anxiety: McCarthyism to Terrorism. 2006. (ENG., Illus.). 672p. pap. 35.95 *(978-0-15-603039-7(X),* Mariner Bks.) Houghton Mifflin Harcourt Trade & Reference Pubs.

Joiner, Lynne. Honorable Survivor: Mao's China, McCarthy's America, & the Persecution of John S. Service. 2009. (Illus.). 450p. 37.95 *(978-1-59114-423-6(X))* Naval Institute Pr.

Kellogg, Michael. The Russian Roots of Nazism: White Emigres & the Making of National Socialism, 1917-1945. 2008. (New Studies in European History Ser.). (ENG.). 344p. pap. 48.00 *(978-0-521-07005-8(8))* Cambridge Univ. Pr.

Kurkowska-Budzan, Marta. Antykomunistyczne Podziemie Zbrojne Na Bialostocczyznie: Analiza Wspóczesnej Symbolizacji Przeszosci. 2009. (POL., Illus.). 256p. *(978-83-88737-24-4(4))* Historia Iagellonica, Towarzystwo Wydawnicze.

Lazarski, Christophe. The Lost Opportunity: Attempts at Unification of the Anti-Bolsheviks, 1917-1919. 2008. (ENG.). 190p. 66.50 *(978-0-7618-4119-7(9))* Univ. Pr. of America, Inc.

Lazarski, Christopher. Lost Opportunity: Attempts at Unification of the Anti-Bolsheviks - 1917-1919. 2008. (ENG.). 190p. pap. 34.99 *(978-0-7618-4120-3(2))* Univ. Pr. of America, Inc.

Leab, Daniel J. 'I Was a Communist for the FbiApos. 2008. pap. 22.95 *(978-0-271-02812-5(2))* Pennsylvania State Univ. Pr.

Levi, Steven C. The Great Red Scare in World War One Alaska: Elite Panic, Government Hysteria,Supression of Civil Liberties,Unio-Breaking,and Germanophobia, 1915 - 1920. 2010. (Illus.). 264p. pap. *(978-1-933146-96-6(6))* Academica Pr., LLC.

Lichtman, Robert M. Deadly Farce: Harvey Matusow & the Informer System in the Mccarthy Era. Cohen, Ronald D., ed. 2008. (ENG., Illus.). 248p. pap. 17.95 *(978-0-252-07516-2(1))* Univ. of Illinois Pr.

Lieberman, Robbie. The Strangest Dream Communism, Anticommunism, & the U S Peace Movement, 1945-1963. 2010. 266p. pap. 45.99 *(978-1-61735-054-2(0))* Information Age Publishing, Inc.

Luff, Jennifer. Commonsense Anticommunism: Labor & Civil Liberties between the World Wars. 2012. (ENG., Illus.). 272p. 39.95 ***(978-0-8078-3541-8(2))*** Univ. of North Carolina Pr.

Malaspina, Ann. The McCarthy Era: Communists in America. 2011. (Milestones in American History Ser.). (Illus.). 134p. (gr. 6-12). 35.00 *(978-1-60413-765-1(7),* Chelsea Hse.) Facts On File, Inc.

Masin, Barbara. Gauntlet: Five Friends, 20,000 Enemy Troops, & the Secret That Could Have Changed the Course of the Cold War. 2006. (Illus.). 382p. 29.95 *(978-1-59114-515-8(5))* Naval Institute Pr.

Milne, David. America's Rasputin: Walt Rostow & the Vietnam War. 2009. (ENG., Illus.). 336p. pap. 16.00 *(978-0-374-53162-1(5),* Hill & Wang) Farrar, Straus & Giroux.

Pleshakov, Constantine. There Is No Freedom Without Bread! 1989 & the Civil War That Brought down Communism. 2010. (ENG.). 304p. pap. 18.00 *(978-0-312-65533-4(9))* Picador.

Redish, Martin H. The Logic of Persecution: Free Expression & the Mccarthy Era. 2006. (ENG.). 320p. per. 23.95 *(978-0-8047-5593-1(0))* Stanford Univ. Pr.

Richter, Michael. Die Friedliche Revolution: Aufbruch Zur Demokratie in Sachsen 1989-90, 2 vols. 2009. (Schriften des Hannah-Arendt-Instituts fur Totalitarismusforschung Ser.). (GER., Illus.). 1612p. (C). 137.00 *(978-3-525-36914-2(X))* Vandenhoeck & Ruprecht GmbH & Co. KG DEU. Dist: ISD.

Schrecker & Cram101 Textbook Reviews Staff. The Age of Mccarthyism. 2007. 148p. per. 12.95 *(978-1-4288-2392-1(1))* Cram101 Inc.

Singer, Margaret Fuchs. Legacy of a False Promise: A Daughter's Reckoning. 2009. (ENG., Illus.). 264p. 39.95 *(978-0-8173-1674-7(4))* Univ. of Alabama Pr.

Spear, Sheldon. Daniel J. Flood: A Biography: The Congressional Career of an Economic Savior & Cold War Nationalist. 2008. (Illus.). 190p. 44.50 *(978-0-9801496-0-9(6))* Lehigh Univ. Pr.

Stromquist, Shelton, ed. Labor's Cold War: Local Politics in a Global Context. 2008. (Working Class in American History Ser.). 320p. 73.00 *(978-0-252-03222-6(5));* per. 26.00 *(978-0-252-07469-1(6))* Univ. of Illinois Pr.

Thompson, Nicholas. The Hawk & the Dove: Paul Nitze, George Kennan, & the History of the Cold War. 2010. (ENG., Illus.). 432p. pap. 17.00 *(978-0-312-65886-1(9))* Picador.

Walker, William T. McCarthyism & the Red Scare: A Reference Guide. 2011. (Illus.). xxviii, 210p. E-Book *(978-1-59884-438-2(5));* 210p. 55.00 *(978-1-59884-437-5(7),* A2879C) ABC-CLIO, LLC.

Zake, Ieva. American Latvians: Politics of a Refugee Community. 2010. (ENG., Illus.). 225p. 49.95 *(978-1-4128-1451-5(0))* Transaction Pubs.

—Anti-Communist Minorities in the U. S. Political Activism of Ethnic Refugees. Zake, Ieva, ed. 2009. (ENG., Illus.). 292p. 95.00 *(978-0-230-60681-4(4))* Palgrave Macmillan.

ANTI-COMMUNIST PROPAGANDA

see Propaganda, Anticommunist

ANTI-CORN-LAW LEAGUE

Anonymous. History of the Anti-Corn-Law League. 2010. 448p. pap. 36.75 *(978-1-143-48801-6(6))* BiblioBazaar.

—History of the Anti-Corn-Law League. 2010. 448p. pap. 36.75 *(978-1-142-32726-2(4))* BiblioBazaar.

Ashworth, Henry. Recollections of Richard Cobden, M P , & the Anti-Corn-Law League. 2010. 196p. pap. *(978-1-152-79373-6(X))* Books LLC.

—Recollections of Richard Cobden M P & the Anti-Corn-Law League. 2009. 310p. 32.99 *(978-1-116-10454-7(7));* 36.99 *(978-1-116-10453-0(9));* pap. 29.75 *(978-1-116-10455-4(5))* BiblioBazaar.

—Recollections of Richard Cobden, M P & the Anti-Corn-Law League. 2009. 434p. 41.99 *(978-1-116-52408-6(2));* pap. 35.75 *(978-1-116-52410-9(4));* pap. 34.75 *(978-1-116-52411-6(2))* BiblioBazaar.

—Recollections of Richard Cobden, M P & the Anti-Corn-Law League. 2010. 190p. pap. 18.69 *(978-1-152-79371-2(3))* General Bks. LLC.

A

—Recollections of Richard Cobden M. P & the Anti-corn-law League. 2009. 308p. (ENG.). pap. 23.99 *(978-1-116-10458-5(X))*; pap. 24.99 *(978-1-116-10457-8(1))* BiblioBazaar. (BiblioLife).

—Recollections of Richard Cobden, M. P. & the Anti-corn-law League. 2009. 432p. (ENG.). pap. 26.99 *(978-1-116-52413-0(9))*; pap. 28.99 *(978-1-116-52412-3(0))* BiblioBazaar. (BiblioLife).

Prentice, Archibald. History of the Anti-Corn-Law League. 2010. 458p. pap. 36.75 *(978-1-142-58313-2(9))* BiblioBazaar.

—History of the Anti-Corn-Law League. 2010. 322p. pap. 24.95 *(978-1-150-85195-7(3))*; 282p. pap. 24.75 *(978-1-152-65871-4(9))*; 262p. pap. 24.75 *(978-1-152-65869-1(7))* General Bks. LLC.

—History of the Anti-Corn-Law League V1. 2007. 448p. 51.95 *(978-0-548-33089-0(1))*; (ENG.). per. 36.95 *(978-1-4326-8965-0(7))* Kessinger Publishing, LLC.

ANTI-CORROSIVE PAINT

see Corrosion and Anti-Corrosives

ANTI-DISCRIMINATION LAWS

see Discrimination—Law and Legislation

ANTI-GAY BIAS

see Homophobia

ANTI-HOMOSEXUAL BIAS

see Homophobia

ANTI-INFECTIVE AGENTS

see also Anthelmintics; Antibiotics; Antiviral Agents; Chemotherapy

Abatih, Emmanuel & Kjær Ersboll, Annette. Assessment of the Impact of the Non-Human Use of Antimicrobial Agents. 2011. 112p. pap. ***(978-3-8383-3513-1(9))*** Lambert Academic Publishing.

Aktories, K. & Wilkins, T. D., eds. Clostridium Difficile. 2010. (Current Topics in Microbiology & Immunology Ser.). (Illus.). x, 143p. pap. 179.00 *(978-3-642-08668-7(3)*, 3642086683) Springer.

Amyes, Sebastian. Antibacterial Chemotherapy: Theory, Problems, & Practice. 2010. (ENG., Illus.). 100p. pap. 24.95 *(978-0-19-958136-8(3))* Oxford Univ. Pr., Inc.

Anderson, Rosaleen, et al. Antibacterial Agents: Chemistry, Mode of Action, Mechanisms of Resistance & Clinical Applications. 2012. (ENG.). 288p. 160.00 ***(978-0-470-97244-1(0))***; pap. 60.00 ***(978-0-470-97245-8(9))*** Wiley, John & Sons, Inc. (Wiley).

Aronson, Jeffrey K. Meyler's Side Effects of Antimicrobial Drugs. 2009. (ENG.). 1160p. 63.95 *(978-0-444-53272-5(2)*, Elsevier Science) Elsevier Science & Technology Bks.

Bergogne-Bérézin, Eugénie. Acinetobacter Biology & Pathogenesis. 2008. (Infectious Agents & Pathogenesis Ser.). 179.00 *(978-0-387-77943-0(4))* Springer.

Bonilla, Adriel R. & Muniz, Kaden P. Antibiotic Resistance: Causes & Risk Factors, Mechanisms & Alternatives. 2009. (Pharmacology - Research, Safety Testing & Regulation Ser.). 129.00 *(978-1-60741-623-4(9)*, Nova Biomedical Bks.) Nova Science Pubs., Inc.

Bradley, John S. & Nelson, John D. 2010-2011 Nelson's Pocket Book of Pediatric Antimicrobial Therapy. 18th ed. 2010. (Nelson's Pocket Book of Pediatric Antimicrobial Therapy Ser.). (ENG., Illus.). 168p. pap. 34.95 *(978-1-58110-373-1(5))* American Academy of Pediatrics.

Brusch, John L. Endocarditis Essentials. rev. ed. 2010. 264p. pap. 28.95 *(978-0-7637-8166-8(5))* Jones & Bartlett Learning, LLC.

Bush, Karen, ed. Antimicrobial Therapeutics Reviews. 2011. (Annals of the New York Academy of Sciences Ser.: 69). (ENG., Illus.). 252p. pap. 130.00 *(978-1-57331-788-7(8)*, Wiley-Blackwell) Wiley, John & Sons, Inc.

Bush, Karen, ed. Antimicrobial Therapeutics Reviews: Antibiotics That Target the Ribosome. 2012. (Annals of the New York Academy of Sciences Ser.: 94). (ENG.). 252p. pap. 130.00 ***(978-1-57331-848-8(5)***, Wiley-Blackwell) Wiley, John & Sons, Inc.

Cavalieri, Stephen J. Manual de Pruebas de Susceptibilidad Antimicrobiano. 2009. (SPA.). *(978-1-55581-347-5(X))* ASM Pr.

Champney, W. Scott. New Antibiotic Targets. 2008. (Methods in Molecular Medicine Ser.: Vol. 142). (Illus.). xi, 274p. *(978-1-59745-246-5(7))* Humana Pr.

Champney, W. Scott, ed. New Antibiotic Targets. (Methods in Molecular Medicine Ser.). (Illus.). 2010. xii, 274p. pap. 99.00 *(978-1-61737-843-0(7)*, 1617378437) 2007. 274p. 99.00 *(978-1-58829-915-4(5))* Humana Pr.

Cioffi, Nicola & Rai, Mahendra, eds. Nano-Antimicrobials: Progress & Prospects. 2012. (ENG., Illus.). xvi, 556p. 259.00 ***(978-3-642-24427-8(0)***, 3642244270) Springer.

Ck, Venil. Antimicrobial Properties of Acorus Calamus. 2011. 60p. pap. ***(978-3-8443-8063-7(9))*** Lambert Academic Publishing.

Committee on the Methodological Challenges in HIV Prevention Trials. Methodological Challenges in Biomedical HIV Prevention Trials. Lagakos, Stephen W. & Gable, Alicia R., eds. 2008. (ENG.). 270p. pap. 56.50 *(978-0-309-11430-1(6))* National Academies Pr.

Cram101 Textbook Reviews. Outlines & Highlights for Antibacterial Therapy & Newer Agents, an Issue of Infectious Disease Clinics by Keith S Kaye, Isbn: 9781437712322. 2011. 174p. pap. 29.95 ***(978-1-61461-911-6(5))*** Cram101 Inc.

Csizmadia, Emanuel & Kalnoky, Istvan. Antimalarial Drugs: Costs, Safety & Efficacy. 2009. (Tropical Diseases - Etiology, Pathogenesis & Treatments Ser.). 129.00 *(978-1-60741-432-2(5)*, Nova Biomedical Bks.) Nova Science Pubs., Inc.

Cunha, Burke A. Antibiotic Essentials 2009. 7th rev. ed. 2008. pap. 21.95 *(978-0-7637-6118-9(4))* Jones & Bartlett Learning, LLC.

De Costa, Paul & Bezerra, Peter. Fungicides: Chemistry, Environmental Impact & Health Effects. 2008. 89.00 *(978-1-60692-631-4(4))* Nova Science Pubs., Inc.

Drider, D., ed. Antimicrobial Peptides: Food, Veterinary & Medical Applications [Bibliography & Price not definite.]: Special Issue: Journal of Molecular Microbiology & Biotechnology 2007, Vol. 13, No. 4. 2007. (Illus.). 78p. pap. *(978-3-8055-8355-8(9))* Karger, S. AG.

Emami, Saeed, ed. New Quinolones with Potential Anti-MRSA Activity. 2010. (Cancer Etiology, Diagnosis & Treatments Ser.). pap. 43.00 *(978-1-60876-736-6(1)*, Nova Biomedical Bks.) Nova Science Pubs., Inc.

Emergence of the Superbug: Antimicrobial Resistance in the United States: Hearing of the Committee on Health, Education, Labor, & Pensions, United States Senate, One Hundred Tenth Congress, Second Session, on Examining the Public Health Impacts of Antimicrobial Resistant Bacterial Infections in the United States, Focusing on Current Antimicrobials & Continued Development of New Solutions for the Future Protection Agains. 2010. iv, 113p. *(978-0-16-085123-0(8)*, 552-070-40479-1) United States Government Printing Office.

Ernst, Erika J., ed. Antifungal Agents. 2010. (Methods in Molecular Medicine Ser.). (Illus.). 224p. pap. 119.00 *(978-1-61737-467-8(9)*, 1617374679) Humana Pr.

Evans, Onyancha, et al. Phytochemical & Antimicrobial Analysis of Kenyan Teclea Nobilis: Phytochemical & Antimicrobial Analysis of Teclea Nobilis Del. Used in Ethnomedicine in Kenya. 2011. 72p. pap. ***(978-3-639-32761-8(6))*** VDM Verlag Dr. Mueller e.K.

Extending the Cure: Policy Responses to the Growing Threat of Antibiotic Resistance. 2007. (ENG., Illus.). 192p. pap. 29.95 *(978-1-933115-57-3(2))* Routledge.

Finberg, Robert W. & Guharoy, Roy. Clinical Use of Anti-Infective Agents: A Guide to How to Prescribe Drugs Used to Treat Infections. 2012. (ENG., Illus.). xi, 181p. 139.00 ***(978-1-4614-1067-6(3)***, 1461410673) Springer.

Finch, Roger, et al. Antimicrobial Chemotherapy. 6th ed. 2012. (ENG., Illus.). 416p. pap. 77.95 ***(978-0-19-969765-6(5))*** Oxford Univ. Pr., Inc.

Finch, Roger G., et al. Antibiotic & Chemotherapy: Expert Consult. 9th ed. 2010. (ENG., Illus.). 916p. 218.00 *(978-0-7020-4064-1(9)*, Saunders) Elsevier - Health Sciences Div.

Fong, I. W. & Drlica, Karl, eds. Antimicrobial Resistance & Implications for the 21st Century. (Emerging Infectious Diseases of the 21st Century Ser.). (Illus.). 2010. xii, 408p. pap. 179.00 *(978-1-4419-4437-5(0)*, 1441944370) 2007. 420p. (C). 179.00 *(978-0-387-72417-1(6))* Springer.

Fouad, Ashraf F. & Fouad. Endodontic Microbiology. 2009. (ENG., Illus.). 368p. 199.99 *(978-0-8138-2646-2(2)*, Wiley-Blackwell) Wiley, John & Sons, Inc.

Franklin, Trevor J. & Snow, George Alan. Biochemistry & Molecular Biology of Antimicrobial Drug Action. 6th ed. 2010. (ENG., Illus.). x, 182p. pap. 134.00 *(978-1-4419-3549-6(5)*, 1441935495) Springer.

Gallagher, Jason C. Antibiotics Simplified. 2nd ed. 2011. 258p. pap. 31.95 *(978-1-4496-1459-1(0))* Jones & Bartlett Learning, LLC.

Giguere, Steeve, et al, eds. Antimicrobial Therapy in Veterinary Medicine. 4th rev. ed. 2007. (ENG., Illus.). 626p. 157.99 *(978-0-8138-0656-3(9)*, Wiley-Blackwell) Wiley, John & Sons, Inc.

Gilbert, David N., et al, eds. The Sanford Guide to Antimicrobial Therapy. (Guide to Antimicrobial Therapy (Sanford) Ser.). 38th ed. 2008. 216p. pap. 13.45 *(978-1-930808-45-4(3))* 38th ed. 2008. (Illus.). 216p. pap. 39.95 *(978-1-930808-47-8(X))* 39th ed. 2009. (Illus.). 212p. pap. 39.95 *(978-1-930808-54-6(2))* Antimicrobial Therapy, Inc.

Gilbert, David N., et al. The Sanford Guide to Antimicrobial Therapy. (Guide to Antimicrobial Therapy (Sanford) Ser.). 37th ed. 2007. 202p. per. 12.95 *(978-1-930808-38-6(0))* 41st ed. 2011. (Illus.). 220p. pap. 44.95 ***(978-1-930808-67-6(4))*** Antimicrobial Therapy, Inc.

Gillespie, Stephen H., ed. Management of Multiple Drug-Resistant Infections. 2010. (Infectious Disease Ser.). (Illus.). 428p. pap. 149.00 *(978-1-61737-438-8(5)*, 1617374385) Humana Pr.

Gould, Ian M. & Meer, Jos W. M., eds. Antibiotic Policies: Controlling Hospital Acquired Infection. 2011. (ENG., Illus.). 300p. 189.00 *(978-1-4419-1733-1(0)*, 1441917330) Springer.

Greenwood, David. Antimicrobial Drugs: Chronicle of a twentieth century medical Triumph. 2008. (ENG., Illus.). 408p. 125.00 *(978-0-19-953484-5(5))* Oxford Univ. Pr., Inc.

Gulfraz, Muhammad, et al. Antimicrobial Activities of Plant Materials. 2011. 116p. pap. ***(978-3-8443-8336-2(0))*** Lambert Academic Publishing.

Gyang, Kofi Oteng. Ocular Drugs Handbook: An Easy Reference Guide to Eye Medications. 2008. 212p. pap. 25.49 *(978-1-4343-4533-2(5))* AuthorHouse.

Hager, Thomas. The Demon under the Microscope: From Battlefield Hospitals to Nazi Labs, One Doctor's Heroic Search for the World's First Miracle Drug. 2007. (ENG.). 352p. pap. 15.00 *(978-1-4000-8214-8(5)*, Three Rivers Pr.) Crown Publishing Group.

Hamid, Rabia, et al. Antimicrobial Plant Lectins. 2011. 96p. pap. ***(978-3-8443-2828-8(9))*** Lambert Academic Publishing.

Hauser, Alan R. Antibiotic Basics for Clinicians: Choosing the Right Antibacterial Agent. 2nd rev. ed. 2012. 336p. pap. 47.95 ***(978-1-4511-1221-4(1))*** Lippincott Williams & Wilkins.

Henriques, Ana. The Antibacterial Activity of Honey. 2011. 196p. pap. ***(978-3-8443-9968-4(2))*** Lambert Academic Publishing.

Hettiarachchi, Dhanushka. Antibacterial Compounds of Conkerberry. 2010. 88p. pap. *(978-3-8383-8079-7(7))* Lambert Academic Publishing.

Hipler, U. -C & Elsner, Peter. Biofunctional Textiles & the Skin. (Current Problems in Dermatology Ser.: Vol. 33). (Illus.). *(978-3-8055-8121-9(1))* Karger, S. AG.

Jensen, Lars Bogo, et al, eds. Guide to Antimicrobial Use in Animals. 2008. (ENG., Illus.). 240p. 138.99 *(978-1-4051-5079-8(3)*, Wiley-Blackwell) Wiley, John & Sons, Inc.

Jenssen, Havard. Antimicrobial Activity of Lactoferrin & Lactoferrin Derived Peptides. 2009. pap. 37.00 *(978-1-60692-518-8(0))* Nova Science Pubs., Inc.

Johns Hopkins Hospital, et al. Harriet Lane Handbook & Harriet Lane Handbook of Pediatric Antimicrobial Therapy Package. 2nd ed. 2011. (Mobile Medicine Ser.). (ENG.). pap. 79.95 ***(978-0-323-08723-0(X)***, Mosby) Elsevier - Health Sciences Div.

Kathurima, Morris. Antimicrobial Activity & Phytochemical Evaluation. 2010. 52p. pap. *(978-3-639-24686-5(1))* VDM Verlag Dr. Mueller e.K.

Kato, Hideaki & Kato, Haru. Clostridum Difficile-Associated Diarrhea. 2010. (Public Health in the 21st Century Ser.). pap. 43.00 *(978-1-61728-278-2(2)*, Nova Novinka) Nova Science Pubs., Inc.

Kaye, Donald & Kaye, Keith S. Antibacterial Therapy & Newer Agents, an Issue of Infectious Disease Clinics. 2009. (Clinics: Internal Medicine Ser.: 23-4). (ENG., Illus.). xiv, 758p. 99.00 *(978-1-4377-1232-2(0)*, Saunders) Elsevier - Health Sciences Div.

Kaye, Keith & Kaye, Donald. Antibacterial Therapy & Newer Agents , an Issue of Medical Clinics of North America. 2011. (Clinics: Internal Medicine Ser.: 95-4). (ENG., Illus.). 224p. 83.00 ***(978-1-4557-2291-4(X)***, Saunders) Elsevier - Health Sciences Div.

Kelland, Lloyd R. & Farrell, Nicholas P., eds. Platinum-Based Drugs in Cancer Therapy. 2010. (Cancer Drug Discovery & Development Ser.). (Illus.). 360p. pap. 160.00 *(978-1-61737-091-5(6)*, 1617370916) Humana Pr.

Kleinberg, Michael E., ed. Managing Infections in Patients with Hematological Malignancies. 2009. (Contemporary Hematology Ser.). 300p. 219.00 *(978-1-58829-986-4(4))* Humana Pr.

Lacroix, Christophe, ed. Protective Cultures, Antimicrobial Metabolites & Bacteriophages for Food & Beverage Biopreservation. 2011. (Woodhead Publishing Series in Food Science, Technology & Nutrition Ser.). (ENG., Illus.). 544p. 265.00 *(978-1-84569-669-6(7))* Woodhead Publishing Ltd. GBR. Dist: Ingram Pub. Services.

Lee, Moses. Heterocyclic Antitumor Antibiotics. 2010. (Topics in Heterocyclic Chemistry Ser.). xiv, 252p. pap. 199.00 *(978-3-642-06814-0(6)*, 3642068146) Springer.

Lerner, S. A. & Kaatz, G. W. Bacterial Resistance to Antimicrobial Agents. Date not set. (Infectious Disease & Therapy Ser.). *(978-0-8247-9404-0(4))* Dekker, Marcel Inc.

Lesch, John E., ed. The First Miracle Drugs: How the Sulfa Drugs Transformed Medicine. 2006. (ENG., Illus.). 376p. 29.95 *(978-0-19-518775-5(X))* Oxford Univ. Pr., Inc.

Letter, Medical. Drugs for Parasitic Infections. 2007. 83p. pap. 199.00 *(978-0-9719093-6-6(9))* Medical Letter, Inc., The.

Li, Qigui & Weina, Peter J. Antimalarial Drugs: Age of the Artemisinins. 2011. (Pharmacology - Research, Safety Testing & Regulation Ser.). (Illus.). xiv, 645p. 195.00 *(978-1-61761-851-2(9)*, Nova Biomedical Bks.) Nova Science Pubs., Inc.

Mainous, Arch G. & Schreiner, Schreiner, eds. MGMT of Antimicrobials in Infectious Diseases: Impact of Antibiotic Resistance. 2nd ed. 2009. (Infectious Disease Ser.). (Illus.). 400p. 209.00 *(978-1-60327-238-4(0))* Humana Pr.

Majumder, Hemanta K. Drug Targets in Kinetoplastid Parasites. 2008. (Advances in Experimental Medicine & Biology Ser.: Vol. 625). (Illus.). XX, 158p. 199.00 *(978-0-387-77569-2(2)*, 0387775692) Springer.

Majumder, Hemanta K., ed. Drug Targets in Kinetoplastid Parasites. 2010. (Advances in Experimental Medicine & Biology Ser.). (Illus.). xx, 158p. pap. 199.00 *(978-1-4419-2656-2(9)*, 1441926569) Springer.

Maurio, Don J. A Practical Guide to Antibacterial Agents. Date not set. 40p. (Orig.). pap. 15.95 *(978-0-9657721-1-2(X))* Group Technology, Ltd.

Mayers, Douglas. Antimicrobial Drug Resistance Handbook, 2 vols. 2009. (Infectious Disease Ser.). (Illus.). (ENG.). xxvi, 678p. 209.00 *(978-1-60327-592-7(4)*, 1603275924); 533p. 209.00 *(978-1-60327-594-1(0))* Humana Pr.

Mayers, Douglas L. Antimicrobial Drug Resistance: Principles & Practice for the Clinic & Bench. 2008. (Infectious Disease Ser.). 800p. 309.00 *(978-1-58829-405-0(6))* Springer.

McMillan, Julia A., et al. Pediatric Antimicrobial Therapy. 2008. (Mobile Medicine Ser.). (ENG., Illus.). 544p. pap. 27.95 *(978-0-323-05334-1(3)*, Mosby) Elsevier - Health Sciences Div.

Medical Letter Staff, intro. Handbook of Antimicrobial Therapy. 2008. 476p. pap. 35.00 net. *(978-0-9719093-8-0(5))* Medical Letter, Inc., The.

Mendez-Vilas, A., ed. Science & Technology Against Microbial Pathogens: Research, Development & Evaluation: Proceedings of the International Conference on Antimicrobial Research (ICAR2010), Valladolid, Spain, 3-5 November 2010. 2011. (ENG., Illus.). 432p. 130.00 ***(978-981-4354-85-1(6))*** World Scientific Publishing Co., Inc.

Miller, Alita A. & Miller, Paul F., eds. Emerging Trends in Antibacterial Discovery: Answering the Call to Arms. 2011. (Illus.). 468p. 360.00 *(978-1-904455-89-9(1))* Caister Academic Pr. GBR. Dist: International Specialized Bk. Services.

Moellering, Robert C., Jr., ed. The Sanford Guide to Antimicrobial Therapy. 37th ed. 2007. (Guide to Antimicrobial Therapy (Sanford) Ser.). 202p. spiral bd. 29.95 *(978-1-930808-39-3(9))* Antimicrobial Therapy, Inc.

Mossialos, E., et al. Policies & Incentives for Promoting Innovation in Antibiotic Research. 2010. (Euro Non Serial Publications). 220p. pap. 60.00 *(978-92-890-4213-0(3))* World Health Organization.

Munich, Lutz Gürtler, et al, eds. Evolution of Anti-HIV Drug Resistance - Interpretation & Its Therapeutic Progress Vol. 55, No. 2: Special Topic Issue - 'Intervirology 2012. 2012. (ENG., Illus.). 112p. pap. ***(978-3-8055-9902-3(1))*** Karger, S. AG.

Musallam, Imadidden. Studies on Antimicrobial Residues in Table Egg. 2011. 144p. pap. ***(978-3-8443-1851-7(8))*** Lambert Academic Publishing.

Owens, Robert C., et al, eds. Antimicrobial Resistance: Problem Pathogens & Clinical Countermeasures. 2007. (Infectious Disease & Therapy Ser.: Vol. 48). (ENG., Illus.). 520p. 300.00 *(978-0-8247-2941-7(2)*, Informa Healthcare) Taylor & Francis Group GBR. Dist: Taylor & Francis Group.

Paulson, Daryl S., ed. Topical Antimicrobial Testing & Evaluation. 2nd rev. ed. 2013. (ENG., Illus.). 376p. 149.95 *(978-1-4398-1322-5(1)*, CRC Press) Taylor & Francis Group GBR. Dist: Taylor & Francis Group.

Pirsch, John, et al. Transplantation Drug Manual. 5th ed. 2007. (ENG.). 192p. spiral bd. 45.00 *(978-1-57059-698-8(0))* Landes Bioscience.

Piscitelli, Stephen C., et al, eds. Drug Interactions in Infectious Diseases. 3rd ed. 2011. (Infectious Disease Ser.). (ENG., Illus.). xiii, 692p. 99.00 *(978-1-61779-212-0(8)*, 1617792128) Humana Pr.

Rai, Mahendra & Chikindas, Michael L., eds. Natural Antimicrobials in Food Safety & Quality. 2011. 500p. 220.00 ***(978-1-84593-769-0(4))*** CABI GBR. Dist: Stylus Publishing, LLC.

Riley, Margaret A. & Chavan, Milind, eds. Bacteriocins: Ecology & Evolution. 2006. (ENG., Illus.). x, 150p. 109.00 *(978-3-540-36603-4(2)*, 3540366032) Springer.

Riley, Margaret A. & Chavan, Milind A., eds. Bacteriocins: Ecology & Evolution. 2010. (ENG., Illus.). x, 150p. pap. 109.00 *(978-3-642-07170-6(8)*, 3642071708) Springer.

Riley, Margaret A. & Gillor, Osnat, eds. Research & Applications in Bacteriocins. rev. ed. 2006. (Illus.). 218p. 220.00 *(978-1-904933-23-6(8))* Horizon Bioscience GBR. Dist: Taylor & Francis Group.

Ritchason, Jack. Olive Leaf Extract. 2nd ed. 2007. (Woodland Health Ser.). 24p. pap. 4.95 *(978-1-58054-441-2(X))* Woodland Publishing, Inc.

Ronco, C. & Mishkin, Gary J. Disinfection by Sodium Hypochlorite: Dialysis Applications. (Contributions to Nephrology Ser.: Vol. 154). (Illus.). 157p. *(978-3-8055-8193-6(9))* Karger, S. AG.

Rosenthal, Philip J., ed. Antimalarial Chemotherapy: Mechanisms of Action, Resistance, & New Directions in Drug Discovery. 2010. (Infectious Disease Ser.). (Illus.). 400p. pap. 179.00 *(978-1-61737-124-0(6)*, 1617371246) Humana Pr.

Sachs, Jessica Snyder. Good Germs, Bad Germs: Health & Survival in a Bacterial World. 2008. (ENG., Illus.). 304p. pap. 15.00 *(978-0-8090-1642-6(7)*, Hill & Wang) Farrar, Straus & Giroux.

Sanford. Sanford Guide to Antimicrobial Therapy, 1997: Medical Book System. 27th ed. 47.95 *(978-1-56712-422-4(4))* Franklin Electronics Pubs., Inc.

Scarpignato, C. Rifaximin, a Poorly Absorbed Antibiotic Vol. 51: Pharmacology & Clinical Use. (Illus.). *(978-3-8055-7917-9(9))* Karger, S. AG.

Scarpignato, C. & Lanas, A. Bacterial Flora in Digestive Disease: Focus on Rifaximin, Vol. 73. (Illus.). 156p. *(978-3-8055-8083-0(5))* Karger, S. AG.

Scarpignato, Carmelo & Lanas, Ángel, eds. Bacterial Flora in Digestive Disease: Focus on Rifaximin, Vol. 73. (Digestion Ser.). (Illus.). 152p. pap. *(978-3-8055-8078-6(9))* Karger, S. AG.

Schlossberg, David & Samuel, Rafik. Antibiotics Manual. 2011. 500p. pap. *(978-1-60795-084-4(7))* PMPH-USA. Ltd.

Sköld, Ola. Antibiotics & Antibiotic Resistance. 2011. (ENG.). 224p. pap. 49.95 *(978-0-470-43850-3(9)*, Wiley) Wiley, John & Sons, Inc.

Slonczewski, Joan L. & Foster, John W. Microbiology: An Evolving Science. 2nd ed. 2010. (ENG., Illus.). 1097p. (C). 142.00 net. *(978-0-393-93447-2(0)*, 93447) Norton, W. W. & Co., Inc.

Springhouse Publishing Company Staff & Lippincott Williams and Wilkins Staff, eds. Nursing Anti-Infective Drug Handbook 2011. 2010. (ENG.). 288p. pap. 25.99 *(978-1-4511-0309-0(3))* Lippincott Williams & Wilkins.

STAT - Steps to Antimicrobial Therapy, Bovine. 2007. spiral bd. *(978-1-889750-89-7(1))* North American Compendiums, Inc.

Tegos, George & Mylonakis, Eleftherios, eds. Antimicrobial Drug Discovery: Emerging Strategies. 2012. (Advances in Molecular & Cellular Biology Ser.). (Illus.). 416p. 180.00 ***(978-1-84593-943-4(3))*** CABI GBR. Dist: Stylus Publishing, LLC.

Thormar, Halldor, ed. Lipids & Essential Oils as Antimicrobial Agents. 2011. (ENG., Illus.). 334p. 160.00 *(978-0-470-74178-8(3)*, Wiley) Wiley, John & Sons, Inc.

UNAIDS. Guidelines for the Treatment of Malaria. 2nd rev. ed. 2010. (Nonseral Publication). (ENG.). 194p. pap. 24.00 *(978-92-4-154792-5(8))* World Health Organization.

Valgimigli, Luca. Essential Oils As Natural Food Additives: Composition, Applications, Antioxidant & Antimicrobial Properties. 2012. (Advances in Food Safety & Food Microbiology Ser.). 476p. 215.00 ***(978-1-62100-241-3(1))*** Nova Science Pubs., Inc.

Vekshin, N. L. Biophysics of DNA-Antibiotic Complexes. 2010. 75.00 *(978-1-61761-199-5(9))* Nova Science Pubs., Inc.

Villa, Tomas G. & Crespo, Patricia Veiga, eds. Enzybiotics: Antibiotic Enzymes as Drugs & Therapeutics. 2010. (ENG., Illus.). 284p. 111.00 *(978-0-470-37655-3(4)*, Wiley) Wiley, John & Sons, Inc.

Vinšová, Jarmila & Krátký, Martin, eds. Development of New MDR-Tuberculosis Drugs. 2010. (Pharmacology - Research, Safety Testing & Regulation Ser.). pap. 43.00 *(978-1-61668-233-0(7))* Nova Science Pubs., Inc.

Wang, Jian, et al, eds. Chemical Analysis of Antibiotic Residues in Food. 2011. (Wiley - Interscience Series on Mass Spectrometry Ser.: 38). (ENG., Illus.). 384p. 110.00 (978-0-470-49042-6(X), Wiley) Wiley, John & Sons, Inc.

Wax, Richard G., et al, eds. Bacterial Resistance to Antimicrobials. 2nd rev. ed. 2007. (ENG., Illus.). 448p. 209.95 (978-0-8493-9190-3(3), CRC Press) Taylor & Francis Group GBR. Dist: Taylor & Francis Group.

Webb, Jr., James L. A., James LA. Humanity's Burden: A Global History of Malaria. 2008. (Studies in Environment & History Ser.). (ENG., Illus.). 248p. (C). 90.00 (978-0-521-85418-4(0)); pap. 23.99 (978-0-521-67012-8(8)) Cambridge Univ. Pr.

Wilson, James W. & Estes, Lynn, eds. Mayo Clinic Antimicrobial Therapy Quick Reference Guide. 2008. 352p. pap. 29.95 (978-1-4200-6713-2(3), Informa Healthcare) Taylor & Francis Group GBR. Dist: Taylor & Francis Group.

Wilson, John W. & Estes, Lynn, eds. Mayo Clinic Antimicrobial Therapy: Quick Guide. 2008. (ENG.). 352p. pap. 50.00 (978-1-4200-8518-1(2), Informa Healthcare) Taylor & Francis Group GBR. Dist: Taylor & Francis Group.

Wilson, John W. & Estes, Lynn L. Mayo Clinic Antimicrobial Therapy: Quick Guide, 1 vol. 2nd ed. 2011. (Mayo Clinic Scientific Press Ser.). (ENG.). 392p. pap. 34.95 **(978-0-19-979778-3(1))** Oxford Univ. Pr., Inc.

World Health Organization. Malaria Rapid Diagnostic Test Performance 2008: Results of WHO Product Testing of RDTs. 2009. (DOCUMENTS for SALE Ser.). (ENG.). 104p. pap. 30.00 (978-92-4-159807-1(7)) World Health Organization.

—Management of MDR-TB: A Field Guide: A Companion Document to Guidelines for Programmatic Management of Drug-resistant Tuberculosis. 2010. (Nonserial Publications Ser.). 56p. pap. 24.00 (978-92-4-154776-5(6)) World Health Organization.

—A Practical Handbook on the Pharmacovigilance of Antimalarial Medicines. 2009. (Nonserial Publication Ser.). (ENG., Illus.). 116p. pap. 36.00 (978-92-4-154749-9(9)) World Health Organization.

Zaas, Aimee, et al. Oxford American Handbook of Infectious Diseases, 1 vol. 2011. (Oxford American Handbooks in Medicine Ser.). (ENG.). 800p. pap. 55.00 (978-0-19-538013-2(4)) Oxford Univ. Pr., Inc.

Zhu, Peter C. New Biocides Development: The Combined Approach of Chemistry & Microbiology. 2007. (ACS Symposium Ser.). (ENG., Illus.). 520p. 165.00 (978-0-8412-7405-1(3)) American Chemical Society.

ANTI-INFLAMMATORY AGENTS

see also Antipyrine

Alabdullah, Ebtehal, et al. Synthesis & Biological Testing of 1-Adamantyl Derivatives. 2010. 176p. pap. (978-3-639-24670-4(5)) VDM Verlag Dr. Mueller e.K.

Aronson, Jeffrey K. Meyler's Side Effects of Analgesics & Anti-inflammatory Drugs. 2009. (ENG.). 702p. 63.95 (978-0-444-53273-2(0), Elsevier Science) Elsevier Science & Technology Bks.

Baier, Gottfried, et al. Sparking Signals: Kinases as Molecular Signaltransducers & Pharmacological Drug Targets in Inflammation. 2010. (Ernst Schering Foundation Symposium Proceedings Ser.). (Illus.). xiv, 187p. pap. 99.00 (978-3-642-09262-6(4), 3642092624) Springer.

Baier, Gottfried, et al, eds. Sparking Signals: Kinases as Molecular Signaltransducers & Pharmacological Drug Targets in Inflammation. 2008. (Ernst Schering Foundation Symposium Proceedings Ser.). (Illus.). 185p. 99.00 (978-3-540-73500-7(3)) Springer.

Consumer Dummies Staff, et al. Anti-Inflammation Diet for Dummies. 2011. (ENG.). 384p. pap. 19.99 (978-1-118-02381-5(1), For Dummies) Wiley, John & Sons, Inc.

Cooper, Keith E. Fever & Antipyresis: The Role of the Nervous System. 2008. (Illus.). 200p. pap. 42.00 (978-0-521-07203-8(4)) Cambridge Univ. Pr.

Davis, Lisa M. & Rowe, Barbara. Anti-Inflammatory Foods for Health: Hundreds of Ways to Incorporate Omega-3 Rich Foods into Your Diet to Fight Arthritis, Cancer, Heart Disease, & More. 2008. (ENG., Illus.). 192p. per. 19.95 (978-1-59233-274-8(9), 1592332749) Quayside.

Dkhil, Mohamed. Non-Steroidal Anti-Inflammatory Drug: Piroxicam. 2011. 72p. pap. **(978-3-8443-1976-7(X))** Lambert Academic Publishing.

Eisert, Wolfgang, et al, eds. Innate Inflammation & Stroke. 2010. (Annals of the New York Academy of Sciences Ser.: 61). (ENG., Illus.). 300p. pap. 150.00 (978-1-57331-813-6(2), Wiley-Blackwell) Wiley, John & Sons, Inc.

Elmegeed, Gamal, et al. Non-Ulcerogenic New Anti-Inflammatory Drugs. 2011. 96p. pap. **(978-3-8443-2544-7(1))** Lambert Academic Publishing.

Gabor, Miklos. Experimentally-Induced Paw Oedemas in Mice. 2007. 272p. (C). (978-963-05-8541-5(3)) Akademiai Kiado.

Garg, Ashok, et al. Clinical Applications of Antibiotics & Anti-Inflammatory Drugs in Ophthalmology. Co-Published by Jaypee Brothers & Lippincott Williams & Wilkins. 2007. (Illus.). 618p. 129.00 (978-0-7817-9123-6(5)) Lippincott Williams & Wilkins.

Gratieri, Tais. Pharmacological Treatment of Ocular Inflammatory Diseases. 2010. (Eye & Vision Research Developments Ser.). pap. 49.00 (978-1-61668-772-4(X), Nova Novinka) Nova Science Pubs., Inc.

Gutierrez, Rosa Martha Perez. Handbook of Compounds with Anti-Inflammatory & Anti-Platelet Aggregation Activities Isolated from Plants. 2008. (Illus.). 296p. 98.00 (978-1-60456-607-9(8)) Nova Science Pubs., Inc.

Gyang, Kofi Oteng. Ocular Drugs Handbook: An Easy Reference Guide to Eye Medications. 2008. 212p. pap. 25.49 (978-1-4343-4533-2(5)) AuthorHouse.

Hämäläinen, Mari. Inducible Nitric Oxide Synthase as a Target of Anti-Inflammatory Treatment Modalities. 2009. (Acta Universitatis Tamperensis Ser.). 144p. pap. 72.50 (978-951-44-7421-7(X)) Tampere Univ. Pr. FIN. Dist: Coronet Bks.

Harris, Randall E. Inflammation in the Pathogenesis of Chronic Diseases: The COX-2 Controversy. 2007. (Subcellular Biochemistry Ser.). (Illus.). 340p. 229.00 (978-1-4020-5687-1(7)) Springer.

Harris, Randall E., ed. COX-2 Blockade in Cancer Prevention & Therapy. 2010. (Cancer Drug Discovery & Development Ser.). (Illus.). 384p. pap. 179.00 (978-1-61737-304-6(4), 1617373044) Humana Pr.

—Inflammation in the Pathogenesis of Chronic Diseases: The COX-2 Controversy. 2010. (Subcellular Biochemistry Ser.). xiii, 323p. pap. 229.00 (978-90-481-7429-4(5), 9048174295) Springer.

Holgate, Stephen T., et al, eds. Inflammation & Allergy Drug Design. 2011. (ENG., Illus.). 344p. 144.95 (978-1-4443-3014-4(4), Wiley-Blackwell) Wiley, John & Sons, Inc.

Hörmannsperger, Gabriele. Structure-related anti-inflammatory mechanisms of probiotic Bacteria. 2010. 110p. pap. (978-3-8325-2581-1(5)) Logos Verlag Berlin.

Hussein, Mohammed Abdalla. Hussein's Designed Book in Novel Non Steroidal Anti-Inflammatory Drugs. 2011. 248p. pap. **(978-3-8443-0000-0(7))** Lambert Academic Publishing.

Pelt, Annemarie C., ed. Glucocorticoids: Effects, Action Mechanisms, & Therapeutic Uses. 2010. (Biochemistry Research Trends Ser.). 129.00 (978-1-61728-758-9(X), Nova Biomedical Bks.) Nova Science Pubs., Inc.

Suk, Kyoungho. Research Focus on Natural Products & the Body's Immune & Inflammatory Systems. 2007. 89.00 (978-1-60021-751-7(6)) Nova Science Pubs., Inc.

Thakurdesai, Prasad, et al. Benzimidazole-2-Carboxylic Acids. 2011. 124p. pap. **(978-3-8433-7236-7(5))** Lambert Academic Publishing

Tsagareli, Merab G. & Tisklauri, Nana. Behavioral Study of 'Non-Opioid' Tolerance. 2011. (Pain & its Origins, Diagnosis & Treatments Ser.). (Illus.). i, 107p. pap. 47.00 **(978-1-62100-033-4(8)**, Nova Biomedical Bks.) Nova Science Pubs., Inc.

Vijayamani, Priya & S. Gayahtri Devi. Antioxidant Properties of the Leaves & Stems of Aristolochia Indic. 2011. 88p. pap. **(978-3-8443-0816-7(4))** Lambert Academic Publishing.

Winyard, Paul G. & Willoughby, Derek A., eds. Inflammation Protocols. 2010. (Methods in Molecular Biology Ser.). (Illus.). 380p. pap. 149.00 (978-1-61737-282-7(X), 161737282X) Humana Pr.

ANTI-INFLATIONARY POLICIES

see also Price Regulation; Wage-Price Policy

Ashraf, Mohammad. Inflation Control & Government Intervention. 2011. 76p. pap. **(978-3-8443-2215-6(9))** Lambert Academic Publishing.

Cobham, David & Boughzala, Mongi, eds. Inflation Targeting in MENA Countries: An Unfinished Journey. 2011. (ENG., Illus.). 256p. 105.00 (978-0-230-29021-1(3)) Palgrave Macmillan.

Epstein, Gerald A. & Yeldan, A. Erinc, eds. Beyond Inflation Targeting: Assessing the Impacts & Policy Alternatives. 2010. (Illus.). 336p. 155.00 (978-1-84720-938-2(6)) Elgar, Edward Publishing, Inc.

Hejazi, Jamal. Three Essays on Inflation Targeting. 2009. 140p. pap. (978-3-639-17278-2(7)) VDM Verlag Dr. Mueller e.K.

Impact of Monetary Policy on the Economy: A Regional Fed Perspective on Inflation, Unemployment, & QE3: Hearing Before the Subcommittee on Domestic Monetary Policy & Technology of the Committee on Financial Services, U.S. House of Representatives, One Hundred Twelfth Congress, First Session, July 26, 2011. 2011. iv, 62p. **(978-0-16-089771-9(8)**, 552-070-43623-5) United States Government Printing Office.

ANTI-INJUNCTION LAW

see Injunctions

ANTI-JEWISH PROPAGANDA

Marsden, Victor E. The Protocols of the Elders of Zion (Protocols of the Wise Men of Zion, Protocols of the Learned Elders of Zion, Protocols of the Meetings of the Learned Elders of Zion, Protocols of the Sages of Zion, Protocols of Zion) 2006. 24.99 (978-1-59986-944-5(6)); pap. 9.99 (978-1-59986-952-0(7)) Filquarian Publishing, LLC.

Perry, Marvin B., et al, eds. Antisemitic Myths: A Historical & Contemporary Anthology. 2008. (ENG.). 384p. pap. 27.00 (978-0-253-21950-3(7), 0253219507) Indiana Univ. Pr.

Ruault, Franco. Tödliche Maskeraden: Julius Streicher und die Lösung der Judenfrage. 2009. (GER.). 412p. pap. 72.95 (978-3-631-55174-5(6)) Lang, Peter GmbH, Europaischer Verlag der Wissenschaften DEU. Dist: Lang, Peter.

Van Arkel, Dik. The Drawing of the Mark of Cain: A Social-Historical Analysis of the Growth of Anti-Jewish Stereotypes. 2010. (ENG.). 592p. pap. (978-90-8964-041-3(X), Leiden Univ. Pr.) Amsterdam Univ. Pr.

Woeste, Victoria. Henry Ford's War on Jews & the Legal Battle Against Hate Speech. 2012. (ENG.). 424p. 55.00 **(978-0-8047-7234-1(7))** Stanford Univ. Pr.

ANTI-NAZI MOVEMENT

Adenbauer, Herbert, et al. 70 Jahre Verfolgung und Vertreibung Von Bischof Joannes Baptista Sproll. 2009. (GER., Illus.). 144p. (978-3-7966-1448-4(5)) Schwabenverlag Aktiengesellschaft.

Almond, Gabriel A., ed. The Struggle for Democracy in Germany. 2011. (ENG.). 368p. pap. 50.00 **(978-0-8078-7813-2(8))** Univ. of North Carolina Pr.

Axelrod, Toby. Hans & Sophie Scholl: German Resisters of the White Rose. 2009. (Holocaust Biographies Ser.). 112p. (gr. 7-12). 63.90 (978-1-61513-385-7(2)) Rosen Publishing Group, Inc., The.

Baigent, Michael & Leigh, Richard. Secret Germany: Stauffenberg & the True Story of Operation Valkyrie. 2008. (ENG., Illus.). 432p. pap. 14.95 (978-1-60239-269-4(2), 239269) Skyhorse Publishing Co., Inc.

Beutin, Heidi & Beutin, Wolfgang, eds. Widerstand - gestern und Heute: Beiträge der Konferenz vom 18.-20. April 2008 im Dokumentationszentrum Prora / Rügen. 2009. (Bremer Beiträge zur Literatur- und Ideengeschichte Ser.). (GER.). 220p. pap. 43.95 (978-3-631-58850-5(X)) Lang, Peter GmbH, Europaischer Verlag der Wissenschaften DEU. Dist: Lang, Peter.

Boehm, Eric H. We Survived: The Stories of Fourteen of the Hidden & the Hunted of Nazi Germany. 2011. 326p. 50.95 **(978-1-258-01456-8(4))** Literary Licensing, LLC.

Bonart, Paul. But We Said NO. 2007. 200p. pap. 14.00 (978-0-615-15957-7(5)) Backman, Mark.

Deutsch, Harold C. The Conspiracy Against Hitler in the Twilight War. 2009. (ENG.). 416p. pap. 60.00 (978-0-8166-5743-8(2)) Univ. of Minnesota Pr.

Deutschkron, Inge. Sie blieben im Schatten: Ein Denkmal für 'stille Helden' (GER., Illus.). 159p. (978-3-89468-223-1(X)) Hentrich, Edition, Druck & Verlag Gebr. Hentrich und Tank GmbH & Co.

Dramm, Sabine. Dietrich Bonhoeffer & the Resistance. 2009. 304p. (C). 29.00 (978-0-8006-6322-3(5), Fortress Pr.) Augsburg Fortress, Pubs.

Dumbach, Annette & Newborn, Jud. Sophie Scholl & the White Rose. 2007. (ENG., Illus.). 224p. per. 15.95 (978-1-85168-536-3(7)) Oneworld Pubns. GBR. Dist: National Bk. Network.

Form, Wolfgang & Schiller, Theo, eds. Widerstand und Verfolgung in Hessen 1933-1945: ErschlieUngsband Zur Mikrofiche-Edition; (Index to the Microfiche Edition) 2008. (GER., Illus.). 436p. (978-3-598-35678-0(1)) Saur, K. G. Verlag GmbH & Co.

Fuegner, Richard. Dawn of Courage. 2009. (Illus.). 248p. pap. 24.95 (978-0-9778209-7-9(1)) Soulo Communications.

Gailus, Manfred. Mir aber zerriss es das Herz: Der stille Widerstand der Elisabeth Schmitz. 2nd ed. 2011. (GER., Illus.). 320p. (C). 35.00 (978-3-525-55008-3(1)) Vandenhoeck & Ruprecht GmbH & Co. KG DEU. Dist: ISD.

Gallin, Mary Alice. German Resistance to Hitler: Ethical & Religious Factors. 2011. 270p. 47.95 **(978-1-258-02392-8(X))** Literary Licensing, LLC.

Gollwitzer, Helmut, et al, eds. Dying We Live. 2009. 306p. pap. 35.00 (978-1-60608-366-6(X), Wipf and Stock) Wipf & Stock Pubs.

Hassell, Ulrich von. The Ulrich von Hassell Diaries, 1938-1944: The Story of the Forces Against Hitler Inside Germany. 2010. (Illus.). 576p. 60.00 (978-1-84832-553-1(3), Frontline) Pen & Sword Bks. Ltd. GBR. Dist: Casemate Pubs. & Bk. Distributors, LLC.

Hoffmann, Charles W. Opposition Poetry in Nazi Germany: University of California Publications in Modern Philology, V67. 2011. 206p. 44.95 **(978-1-258-08086-0(9))** Literary Licensing, LLC.

Hoffmann, Peter. Behind Valkyrie: German Resistance to Hitler, Related Documents. 2011. (ENG.). 384p. (C). (978-0-7735-3769-9(4)) McGill-Queen's Univ. Pr.

—Carl Goerdeler & the Jewish Question, 1933-1942. 2011. (ENG., Illus.). 216p. 80.00 (978-1-107-00798-7(4)) Cambridge Univ. Pr.

Jahnke, Karl Heinz. Gegen das Vergessen! Biographische Notizen: Forschungen Zum Widerstand Gegen Die NS-Diktatur in Deutschland. 2008. (GER.). 213p. (978-3-938686-83-6(9)) Koch, Ingo, Verlag & Co. KG.

Kidder, Annemarie S., ed. Ultimate Price: Testimonies of Christians Who Resisted the Third Reich. 2012. (ENG., Illus.). 208p. pap. 22.00 **(978-1-57075-955-0(3))** Orbis Bks.

Krispyn, Egbert. Anti-Nazi Writers in Exile. 2010. (ENG.). 216p. pap. 24.95 (978-0-8203-3490-5(1)) Univ. of Georgia Pr.

Langbein, Hermann. Against all Hope: Resistance in the Nazi Concentration Camps. 2009. Tr. of Nicht Wie Die Schafe Zur Schlachtbank. (ENG.). 502p. pap. 24.95 (978-1-55778-882-5(0)) Paragon Hse. Pubs.

Leisner, Barbara. Sophie Scholl. 2nd ed. (GER., Illus.). 278p. (978-3-612-65059-7(9)) Econ-Verlag GmbH DEU. Dist: International Bk. Import Service, Inc.

Lucas, Peter. The OSS in World War II Albania: Covert Operations & Collaboration with Communist Partisans. 2007. (ENG., Illus.). 220p. per. 35.00 (978-0-7864-2967-7(4)) McFarland & Co., Inc. Pubs.

MacRae, Sigrid, et al. Alliance of Enemies: The Untold Story of the Secret American & German Collaboration to End World War II. 2008. (ENG., Illus.). 416p. pap. 19.99 (978-0-312-37482-2(8), St. Martin's Griffin) St. Martin's Pr.

Manvell, Roger & Fraenkel, Heinrich. The Men Who Tried to Kill Hitler. 2008. (ENG.). 272p. pap. 14.95 (978-1-60239-358-5(3), 239358) Skyhorse Publishing Co., Inc.

McDonough, Frank. Sophie Scholl: The Real Story Behind German's Resistance Heroine. 2009. (ENG., Illus.). 224p. 34.95 (978-0-7524-4675-2(4)) History Pr. Ltd.,The GBR. Dist: Independent Pubs. Group.

—Sophie Scholl: The Real Story of the Woman who Defied Hitler. 2010. (ENG., Illus.). 224p. pap. 17.95 (978-0-7524-5511-2(7)) History Pr. Ltd.,The GBR. Dist: Independent Pubs. Group.

Melon, Ruth Bernadette. Journey to the White Rose in Germany. 2007. 248p. per. 17.95 (978-1-59858-249-9(6)) Dog Ear Publishing, LLC.

Millard, Frank. The Palace & the Bunker: Royal Resistance to Hitler. 2012. (ENG., Illus.). 192p. 29.95 **(978-0-7524-6569-2(4))** History Pr. Ltd.,The GBR. Dist: Independent Pubs. Group.

Mommsen, Hans. Germans Against Hitler: The Stauffenberg Plot & Resistance under the Third Reich. McGeoch, Angus, tr. from GER. 2008. (ENG.). 320p. pap. 24.00 (978-1-84511-852-5(9)) I. B. Tauris & Co., Ltd. GBR. Dist: Macmillan.

Mueller, Michael. Canaris: The Life & Death of Hitler's Spymaster. Brooks, Geoffrey, tr. from GER. 2007. (Illus.). 368p. 34.95 (978-1-59114-101-3(X)) Naval Institute Pr.

Ortner, Helmut. Lone Assassin: The Epic True Story of the Man Who Almost Killed Hilter. Benjamin, Ross, tr. from GER. 2012. (ENG.). 192p. 24.95 **(978-1-61608-383-0(2)**, 608383) Skyhorse Publishing Co., Inc.

Rein. The Kings & the Pawns: Collaboration in Byelorussia During World War II. 2011. (WG Ser.). 458p. 110.00 (978-1-84545-776-1(5)) Berghahn Bks., Inc.

Robbins, Christopher. Courage Beyond Words: The Many Lives & Languages of Michel Thomas. 2007. (ENG., Illus.). 432p. per. 18.95 (978-0-07-149911-8(3), 0071499113) McGraw-Hill Cos., The.

Schad, Martha. Frauen gegen Hitler: Vergessene Widerstandskämpferinnen im Nationalsozialismus. pap. 28.95 (978-3-453-86138-1(8)) Verlag Wilhelm Heyne DEU. Dist: Distribooks, Inc.

Strasser, Otto. Free Germany Against Hitler. 2011. 20p. pap. 35.95 **(978-1-258-02275-4(3))** Literary Licensing, LLC.

Thomsett, Michael C. The German Opposition to Hitler: The Resistance, the Underground, & Assassination Plots, 1938-1945. alt. ed. 2007. (ENG., Illus.). 286p. per. 39.95 (978-0-7864-3027-7(3)) McFarland & Co., Inc. Pubs.

Von Boeselager, Philip Freiherr, et al. Valkyrie: The Story of the Plot to Kill Hitler by Its Last Member. Rendall, Steven, tr. from FRE. 2009. (ENG., Illus.). 224p. 24.95 (978-0-307-27075-7(0), Knopf) Knopf Doubleday Publishing Group.

Wachtel, Gretel & Strachan, Claudia. Gretel's Story. 2011. (ENG.). 288p. 24.95 (978-0-7627-6413-6(9), Lyons Pr.) Globe Pequot Pr., The.

Wentorf, Rudolf & Bloesch, Daniel W. Paul Schneider: Witness of Buchenwald. 2008. (978-1-57383-417-9(3)) Regent College Publishing.

Wyllie, James. Goering & Goering: Hitler's Henchman & His Anti-Nazi Brother. 2010. (ENG., Illus.). 252p. pap. 16.95 (978-0-7524-5648-5(2)) History Pr. Ltd.,The GBR. Dist: Independent Pubs. Group.

ANTI-NAZI MOVEMENT—HISTORY

Bruhns, Wibke. My Father's Country: The Story of a German Family. 2009. (Vintage Ser.). (ENG., Illus.). 384p. pap. 16.95 (978-1-4000-9670-1(7), Vintage) Knopf Doubleday Publishing Group.

Hoffmann, Peter. Behind Valkyrie: German Resistance to Hitler. 2011. (ENG.). 384p. (C). pap. (978-0-7735-3770-5(8)) McGill-Queen's Univ. Pr.

Moorhouse, Roger. Killing Hitler: The Plots, the Assassins, & the Dictator Who Cheated Death. 2007. (ENG., Illus.). 384p. pap. 16.00 (978-0-553-38255-6(1), Bantam) Random House Publishing Group.

O'Donnell, Patrick K. They Dared Return: The True Story of Jewish Spies Behind the Lines in Nazi Germany. 2010. (ENG.). 264p. pap. 15.95 (978-0-306-81923-0(6)) Da Capo Pr., Inc.

Petrescu, Corina L. Against All Odds: Models of Subersive Spaces in National Socialist Germany. 2009. 284p. pap. 60.95 (978-3-03911-845-8(5)) Lang, Peter AG GBR. Dist: Lang, Peter.

Schrader, Helena. Codename 'Valkyrie' General Friedrich Olbricht & the Plot Against Hitler. 2009. (ENG., Illus.). 288p. 39.95 (978-1-84425-533-7(6), 1844255336) Haynes Publishing PLC GBR. Dist: MBI Distribution Services/Quayside Distribution.

Ueberschär, Gerd R. & Steinkamp, Peter. Handbuch zum Widerstand gegen Nationalsozialismus und Faschismus in Europa 1933/39 bis 1945. 2011. (GER.). 383p. **(978-3-598-11767-1(1))** Saur, K. G. Verlag GmbH & Co.

ANTI-NUCLEAR MOVEMENT

see Antinuclear Movement

ANTI-POVERTY PROGRAMS

see Economic Assistance, Domestic

ANTI-REFORMATION

see Counter-Reformation

ANTI-RENT TROUBLES, NEW YORK, 1839-1846

see Antirent War, N.Y. 1839-1846

ANTI-SLAVERY MOVEMENTS

see Antislavery Movements

ANTI-SUBMARINE WARFARE

see also Sonar; Submarine Warfare

Althoff, William. Forgotten Weapons. 2009. (Illus.). 432p. 49.95 (978-1-59114-010-8(2)) Naval Institute Pr.

Button, Robert W., et al. A Survey of Missions for Unmanned Undersea Vehicles. 2009. 220p. pap. 59.50 (978-0-8330-4688-8(8), MG-808) RAND Corp., The.

Cote, Owen R. The Third Battle: Innovation in the U. S. Navy's Silent Cold War Struggle with Soviet Submarines. 2006. 115p. per. 9.00 (978-0-16-076910-8(8), Defense Dept.) United States Government Printing Office.

Friedman, Norman. British Destroyers & Frigates. 2010. (Illus.). 352p. 90.00 (978-1-84832-015-4(9)) Pen & Sword Bks. Ltd. GBR. Dist: Casemate Pubs. & Bk. Distributors, LLC.

Genualdi, Anthony. Four Years in the Donald Duck Navy: A True Story. 2010. 67p. pap. 12.95 (978-1-4327-5553-9(6)) Outskirts Pr., Inc.

Huygen, Michelle Lee. Submarine Warfare in the 20th & 21st Centuries - a Bibliography. 2010. 378p. pap. 22.58 (978-1-60888-025-6(7)) Nimble Bks. LLC.

Jones, H. G. The Sonarman's War: A Memoir of Submarine Chasing & Mine Sweeping in World War II. 2010. (ENG., Illus.). 260p. pap. 35.00 (978-0-7864-5884-4(4)) McFarland & Co., Inc. Pubs.

Lake, Deborah. Smoke & Mirrors: Q-Ships Against the U-Boats in the First World War. 2009. (ENG., Illus.). 256p. pap. 32.95 *(978-0-7524-5055-1(7))* History Pr. Ltd., The GBR. Dist: Independent Pubs. Group.

—Smoke & Mirrors: Q-Ships Against the U-Boats in the First World War. 2007. (ENG., Illus.). 224p. 36.95 *(978-0-7509-4605-6(9))* Sutton Publishing.

National Research Council (U.S.), Committee on Distributed Remote Sensing for Naval Undersea Warfare Staff, contrib. by. Distributed Remote Sensing for Naval Undersea Warfare. 2007. (ENG.). 42p. pap. 21.00 *(978-0-309-10180-6(8))* National Academies Pr.

Owen, David. Anti-Submarine Warfare: An Illustrated History. 2007. (Illus.). 224p. 42.95 *(978-1-59114-014-6(5))* Naval Institute Pr.

Syrett, David. The Defeat of the German U-Boats: The Battle of the Atlantic. 2010. (Studies in Maritime History Ser.). pap. 24.95 *(978-1-57003-952-2(6))* Univ. of South Carolina Pr.

Winfield, Rif. British Warships in the Age of Sail 1714-1795: Design, Construction, Careers & Fates. 2007. (Illus.). 420p. 85.00 *(978-1-86176-291-7(7)*, Chatham Publishing) Duckworth Publishers GBR. Dist: MBI Distribution Services/Quayside Distribution.

ANTI-WAR MOVEMENTS

see Peace Movements

ANTIAIRCRAFT ARTILLERY

see also Antiaircraft Guns

Bright, Christopher J. Continental Defense in the Eisenhower Era: Nuclear Antiaircraft Arms & the Cold War. (Palgrave Studies in the History of Science & Technology Ser.). (ENG., Illus.). 290p. 2012. pap. 28.00 ***(978-1-137-02238-7(8))*** 2010. 84.00 *(978-0-230-62340-8(9))* Palgrave Macmillan.

Hamilton, John A. Blazing Skies: Air Defense Artillery on Fort Bliss, Texas, 1940-2009. 2009. (ENG., Illus.). 388p. pap. 74.00 *(978-0-16-082210-0(6)*, Dept. of the Army) United States Government Printing Office.

Zaloga, Steven J. Red SAM: The SA-2 Guideline Anti-Aircraft Missile. 2007. (New VanGuard Ser.). (ENG., Illus.). 48p. pap. 17.95 *(978-1-84603-062-8(5))* Osprey Publishing, Ltd. GBR. Dist: Random Hse., Inc.

ANTIAIRCRAFT GUNS

Gander, Terry. German 88: The Most Famous Gun of the Second World War. 2009. (Illus.). 176p. 39.99 *(978-1-84884-040-9(3))* Pen & Sword Bks. Ltd. GBR. Dist: Casemate Pubs. & Bk. Distributors, LLC.

ANTIAMERICANISM

see Anti-Americanism

ANTIANDROGENS

see also Androgens

Justman, Stewart. Do No Harm: How a Magic Bullet for Prostate Cancer Became a Medical Quandary. 2008. (ENG., Illus.). 256p. 26.00 *(978-1-56663-627-8(2))* Dee, Ivan R. Pub.

ANTIBACTERIAL AGENTS

see Anti-Infective Agents

ANTIBALLISTIC MISSILES

see Antimissile Missiles

ANTIBIOSIS

Gould, Ian M. & Meer, Jos W. M van der. Antibiotic Policies: Theory & Practice. 2010. (Illus.). xiv, 766p. pap. 179.00 *(978-1-4419-3455-0(3)*, 1441934553) Springer.

Koch, Arthur L. The Bacteria: Their Origin, Structure, Function & Antibiosis. 2007. (Illus.). 224p. pap. 69.95 *(978-1-4020-6625-2(2))* Springer.

ANTIBIOTICS

see also Actinomycin; Penicillin

Ambrose, Paul G., et al, eds. Antimicrobial Pharmacodynamics in Theory & Clinical Practice. 2nd rev. ed. 2007. (Infectious Disease & Therapy Ser.: Vol. 44). (ENG., Illus.). 536p. 300.00 *(978-0-8247-2925-7(0))* Taylor & Francis Group.

Arya, Dev P. Aminoglycoside Antibiotics: From Chemical Biology to Drug Discovery. 2nd ed. 2007. (Wiley Series in Drug Discovery & Development Ser.: 5). (ENG., Illus.). 327p. 156.00 *(978-0-471-74302-6(X)*, Wiley-Interscience) Wiley, John & Sons, Inc.

Aulakh, Virender & Marco A. Ciufolini, Prof. Thiocillin I. 2011. 172p. pap. ***(978-3-8443-9100-8(2))*** Lambert Academic Publishing.

Banik, Bimal K., ed. Heterocyclic Scaffolds I: ß-Lactams, 2 vols. 2010. (Topics in Heterocyclic Chemistry Ser.). (Illus.). xi, 379p. 469.00 *(978-3-642-12844-8(0)*, 3642128440) Springer.

Bartone, John C., ed. Drinking Water & Its Contents of Antibiotics with Index & Medical Analysis of New Research Information for All Nations. 2006. (Illus.). 160p. 69.95 *(978-0-7883-4738-2(1)*, 0-7883-4738-1) ABBE Pubs. Assn. of Washington, D.C.

Beam, Thomas R., ed. Antibiotics, Hosts & Host Defences in Nosocomial Infections. 35.00 *(978-0-915340-07-1(0))* PJD Pubns., Ltd.

Berlatsky, Noah. Antibiotics. 2011. (Opposing Viewpoints Ser.). (ENG.). 240p. 39.70 *(978-0-7377-5209-0(2))*; pap. 26.50 *(978-0-7377-5210-6(6))* Cengage Gale. (Greenhaven Pr., Inc.).

Brakhage, Axel A. Molecular Biotechnology of Fungal beta-Lactam Antibiotics & Related Peptide Synthetases. 2010. (Advances in Biochemical Engineering Biotechnology Ser.). (Illus.). xi, 284p. pap. 239.00 *(978-3-642-06035-9(8)*, 3642060358) Springer.

Bud, Robert. Penicillin: Triumph & Tragedy. 2009. (ENG., Illus.). 340p. pap. 39.95 *(978-0-19-954161-4(2))* Oxford Univ. Pr., Inc.

Calam, C. T. Process Development in Antibiotic Fermentations. 2008. (Cambridge Studies in Biotechnology Ser.). (ENG.). 228p. pap. 53.00 *(978-0-521-06552-8(6))* Cambridge Univ. Pr.

Ck, Venil. Antimicrobial Properties of Acorus Calamus. 2011. 60p. pap. ***(978-3-8443-8063-7(9))*** Lambert Academic Publishing.

Cunha, Burke A. Antibiotic Essentials. 10th ed. 2011. 778p. pap. 24.95 *(978-1-4496-2431-6(6))* Jones & Bartlett Learning, LLC.

—Antibiotic Essentials 2009. 7th rev. ed. 2008. pap. 21.95 *(978-0-7637-6118-9(4))* Jones & Bartlett Learning, LLC.

—Antibiotics Essentials 2010. 9th rev. ed. 2010. 732p. pap. 28.95 *(978-0-7637-9214-5(4))* Jones & Bartlett Learning, LLC.

Del Rosso, James Q. Antibiotic Use in Dermatology, an Issue of Dermatologic Clinics. 2008. (Clinics: Dermatology Ser.: 27-1). (ENG., Illus.). 240p. 99.00 *(978-1-4377-0468-6(9)*, Saunders) Elsevier - Health Sciences Div.

Drider, Djamel & Rebuffat, Sylvie, eds. Prokaryotic Antimicrobial Peptides: From Genes to Applications. 2011. (ENG., Illus.). xiii, 451p. 239.00 *(978-1-4419-7691-8(4)*, 1441976914) Springer.

Ecker, Gerhard & Chiba, Peter. Transporters as Drug Carriers: Structure, Function, Substrates. Ecker, Gerhard & Chiba, Peter, eds. 2009. (Methods & Principles in Medicinal Chemistry Ser.: 112). (ENG., Illus.). 449p. 230.00 *(978-3-527-31661-8(2)*, Wiley-VCH) Wiley, John & Sons, Inc.

Ely, Adrian, et al. Regulating Technology: International Harmonization & Local Realities. 2011. (Pathways to Sustainability Ser.). (ENG., Illus.). 160p. 125.00 *(978-1-84971-246-0(8))*; pap. 36.95 *(978-1-84971-247-7(6))* Routledge.

Feld, Louise. The Role of Lactic Acid Bacteria in Spread of Antibiotic Resistance. 2010. 100p. pap. *(978-3-8383-8664-5(7))* Lambert Academic Publishing.

Finch, Roger G., et al. Antibiotic & Chemotherapy: Expert Consult. 9th ed. 2010. (ENG., Illus.). 916p. 218.00 *(978-0-7020-4064-1(9)*, Saunders) Elsevier - Health Sciences Div.

Forum on Microbial Threats & Institute of Medicine. Antibiotic Resistance: Implications for Global Health & Novel Intervention Strategies: Workshop Summary. 2010. (ENG.). 496p. pap. 95.00 *(978-0-309-15611-0(4))* National Academies Pr.

Frank, Uwe & Tacconelli, Evelina. The Daschner Guide to in-Hospital Antibiotic Therapy: European Standards. 2nd ed. 2011. (ENG., Illus.). 300p. pap. 39.95 *(978-3-642-18401-7(4)*, 3642184014) Springer.

Gallagher, Jason C. Antibiotics Simplified. 2nd ed. 2011. 258p. pap. 31.95 *(978-1-4496-1459-1(0))* Jones & Bartlett Learning, LLC.

Garg, Ashok, et al. Clinical Applications of Antibiotics & Anti-Inflammatory Drugs in Ophthalmology: Co-Published by Jaypee Brothers & Lippincott Williams & Wilkins. 2007. (Illus.). 618p. 129.00 *(978-0-7817-9123-6(5))* Lippincott Williams & Wilkins.

Gilbert, David N., et al, eds. The Sanford Guide to Antimicrobial Therapy. (Guide to Antimicrobial Therapy (Sanford) Ser.). 38th ed. 2008. 216p. pap. 13.45 *(978-1-930808-45-4(3))* 38th ed. 2008. (Illus.). 216p. pap. 39.95 *(978-1-930808-47-8(X))* 39th ed. 2009. (Illus.). 212p. pap. 39.95 *(978-1-930808-54-6(2))* Antimicrobial Therapy, Inc.

—The Sanford Guide to Antimicrobial Therapy 2008. 38th ed. 2008. (Guide to Antimicrobial Therapy (Sanford) Ser.). (Illus.). 216p. spiral bd. 29.95 *(978-1-930808-46-1(1))* Antimicrobial Therapy, Inc.

Gilbert, David N., et al. The Sanford Guide to Antimicrobial Therapy. 41st ed. 2011. (Sanford Guide to Animicrobial Therapy Ser.). (Illus.). 220p. pap. 44.95 ***(978-1-930808-67-6(4))*** Antimicrobial Therapy, Inc.

Gillespie, Steven H. & McHugh, Timothy D., eds. Antibiotic Resistance Protocols: Second Edition. 2nd ed. 2010. (Methods in Molecular Biology Ser.). (ENG., Illus.). xii, 236p. 139.00 *(978-1-60327-278-0(X)*, 160327278X) Humana Pr.

Gould, Ian M. & Meer, Jos W. M van der, eds. Antibiotic Policies: Fighting Resistance: Fighting Resistance. 2010. (ENG., Illus.). xv, 286p. pap. 159.00 *(978-1-4419-4361-3(7)*, 1441943617) Springer.

Gribble, Gordon W., ed. Heterocyclic Scaffolds II: Indoles: Synthesis, Properties & Applications, 2 vols. 2010. (Topics in Heterocyclic Chemistry Ser.). (Illus.). x, 455p. 409.00 *(978-3-642-15732-5(7)*, 3642157327) Springer.

Hearing to Review the Advances of Animal Health Within the Livestock Industry: Hearing Before the Subcommittee on Livestock, Dairy, & Poultry of the Committee on Agriculture, House of Representatives, One Hundred Tenth Congress, Second Session, Thursday, September 25, 2008. 2009. (Illus.). iv, 155p. *(978-0-16-083922-1(X)*, 552-070-39611-0) United States Government Printing Office.

Hof, Herbert. Antibiotics Pocketcard Set. 2009. pap. 6.95 *(978-1-59103-056-0(0))* Bruckmeier, Borm Publishing, LLC.

Karthaus, M. & Ganser, Arnold, eds. Supportive Care in Cancer Patients: Recent Developments, Vol. 50. (Antibiotics & Chemotherapy Ser.: Vol. 50). (Illus.). *(978-3-8055-6910-1(6))* Karger, S. AG.

Kathurima, Morris. Antimicrobial Activity & Phytochemical Evaluation. 2010. 52p. pap. *(978-3-639-24686-5(1))* VDM Verlag Dr. Mueller e.K.

Katz, S. E. & Ragheb, H. S. Analytical Microbiology of Antibiotics: Design, Analysis & Applications. Date not set. *(978-0-8247-9537-5(7))* Dekker, Marcel Inc.

Kaushik, Atul, et al. Aaa's Quinolones & Fluoroquinolones. 2011. 108p. pap. ***(978-3-8443-8940-1(7))*** Lambert Academic Publishing.

Keen, Patricia L. & Montforts, Mark H. M. M. Antimicrobial Resistance in the Environment. 2012. (ENG., Illus.). 632p. 129.95 ***(978-0-470-90542-5(5)***, Wiley-Blackwell) Wiley, John & Sons, Inc.

Lee, Moses. Heterocyclic Antitumor Antibiotics. 2010. (Topics in Heterocyclic Chemistry Ser.). xiv, 252p. pap. 199.00 *(978-3-642-06814-0(6)*, 3642068146) Springer.

Meer, Jos W. M van der. Antibiotic Policies: Fighting Resistance. Gould, Ian M., ed. 2007. (ENG., Illus.). xiv, 286p. 159.00 *(978-0-387-70840-9(5)*, 0387708405) Springer.

Nanjwade, Prof. Basavaraj & S., Chandrashekara. Antibiotic Production from Soil Isolates by Fermentation. 2011. 220p. pap. ***(978-3-8383-8444-3(X))*** Lambert Academic Publishing.

Neumayer, Petra. Naturliche Antibiotika. (GER.). *(978-3-612-20615-2(X))* Econ-Verlag GmbH DEU. Dist: International Bk. Import Service, Inc.

Onyango, David. Drug Susceptibilities & Mechanisms in Salmonella Typhimurium. 2010. 192p. pap. *(978-3-8383-9249-3(3))* Lambert Academic Publishing.

Perry, G., ed. Avian Gut Function in Health & Disease. 2006. (Poultry Science Symposium Ser.). (Illus.). 384p. 160.00 *(978-1-84593-180-3(7))* CABI GBR. Dist: Stylus Publishing, LLC.

Pucci, Michael J. & Dougherty, Thomas J., eds. Antibiotic Discovery & Development. 2011. (ENG., Illus.). xvii, 1127p. 499.00 ***(978-1-4614-1399-8(0)***, 1461413990) Springer.

Rohde, Rodney E. Methicillin Resistant Staphylococcus Aureus. 2011. 132p. pap. ***(978-3-8433-8225-0(5))*** Lambert Academic Publishing.

Rushford, Jaime Salas & Benno DVM, Yoshimi. Morinaga BB536: Japan's Leading Clinically Proven Probiotic. 2011. (Woodland Health Ser.). 52p. pap. 4.95 ***(978-1-58054-206-7(9))*** Woodland Publishing, Inc.

Schlossberg, David & Samuel, Rafik. Antibiotics Manual. 2011. 500p. pap. *(978-1-60795-084-4(7))* PMPH-USA. Ltd.

Schmidt, Michael. Beyond Antibiotics: Strategies for Living in a World of Emerging Infections & Antibiotic-Resistant Bacteria. 3rd rev. ed. 2009. (ENG., Illus.). 456p. pap. 19.95 *(978-1-55643-777-9(3))* North Atlantic Bks.

Shafer, William M. Antimicrobial Peptides & Human Disease. 2010. (Current Topics in Microbiology & Immunology Ser.). (Illus.). xii, 266p. pap. 179.00 *(978-3-642-06756-3(5)*, 3642067565) Springer.

Shafer, William M., ed. Antibacterial Peptide Protocols. 2010. (Methods in Molecular Biology Ser.). 269p. pap. 139.00 *(978-1-61737-027-4(4)*, 1617370274) Humana Pr.

Shahzad, Naveed & Haq Nawaz. Efficacy of Feed Additive Probiotic on Broiler Performance. 2011. 96p. pap. ***(978-3-8443-1314-7(1))*** Lambert Academic Publishing.

Shlaes, David. Antibiotics: The Perfect Storm. 2010. (ENG.). cvi, 8p. 189.00 *(978-90-481-9056-0(8)*, 9048190568) Springer.

Sköld, Ola. Antibiotics & Antibiotic Resistance. 2011. (ENG.). 224p. pap. 49.95 *(978-0-470-43850-3(9)*, Wiley) Wiley, John & Sons, Inc.

Stivers, Tanya. Prescribing under Pressure: Parent-Physician Conversations & Antibiotics, 1 vol. 2007. (Oxford Studies in Sociolinguistics Ser.). (ENG.). 232p. 65.00 *(978-0-19-531115-0(9))* Oxford Univ. Pr., Inc.

Stroud, Clare, et al, eds. Prepositioning Antibiotics for Anthrax. 2012. (ENG.). 358p. pap. 64.00 ***(978-0-309-21808-5(X))*** National Academies Pr.

Tenney, Louise. Grapefruit Seed Extract. 3rd ed. 2011. (Woodland Health Ser.). 36p. pap. 4.95 ***(978-1-58054-202-9(6))*** Woodland Publishing, Inc.

Usman, Muhammad, et al. Comparative Pharmacokinetics of Levofloxacin. 2010. 92p. pap. *(978-3-639-24818-0(X))* VDM Verlag Dr. Mueller e.K.

Vahdat, Laleh. Kinetics of Amoxycillin & Clavulanate Degradation. 2009. 208p. pap. *(978-3-639-20109-3(4))* VDM Verlag Dr. Mueller e.K.

Vekshin, N. L. Biophysics of DNA-Antibiotic Complexes. 2010. 75.00 *(978-1-61761-199-5(9))* Nova Science Pubs., Inc.

Vimala, Yapadinna. Antimicrobial Activity of Decalepsis Hamiltoni. 2011. 84p. pap. ***(978-3-8443-0701-6(X))*** Lambert Academic Publishing.

Walenkamp, G. H. I M. Local Antibiotics in Arthroplasty. 2007. 170p. pap. 99.95 *(978-1-58890-607-6(8))* Thieme Medical Pubs., Inc.

Wang, Guangshun. Antimicrobial Peptides: Discovery, Design, & Novel Therapeutic Strategies. 2010. (Advances in Molecular & Cellular Biology Ser.). (Illus.). 256p. 160.00 *(978-1-84593-657-0(4))* CABI GBR. Dist: Stylus Publishing, LLC.

ANTIBIOTICS IN AGRICULTURE

Cox, Louis Anthony. Quantitative Health Risk Analysis Methods: Modeling the Human Health Impacts of Antibiotics Used in Food Animals. 2010. (International Series in Operations Research & Management Science Ser.). (Illus.). xviii, 354p. pap. 169.00 *(978-1-4419-3850-3(8)*, 1441938508) Springer.

Gujarathi, Ninad. Phytoremediation of Antibiotics from Wastes of Animal Feedlots. 2009. (Illus.). 152p. pap. *(978-3-639-13576-3(8))* VDM Verlag Dr. Mueller e.K.

H.R. 1549: Preservation of Antibiotics for Medical Treatment ACT (PAMTA): Hearing Before the Committee on Rules, U.S. House of Representatives, One Hundred Eleventh Congress, First Session, Monday, July 13, 2009. 2010. (Illus.). iv, 154p. *(978-0-16-085249-7(8)*, 552-070-40591-7) United States Government Printing Office.

ANTIBIOTICS RESISTANCE IN MICROORGANISMS

see Drug Resistance in Microorganisms

ANTIBODIES

see Immunoglobulins

ANTIBODIES, MONOCLONAL

see Monoclonal Antibodies

ANTIBODY-ANTIGEN REACTIONS

see Antigen-Antibody Reactions

ANTICANCER AGENTS

see also Antineoplastic Agents

Avendano, Carmen & Menendez, J. Carlos. Medicinal Chemistry of Anticancer Drugs. 2008. (ENG., Illus.). 400p. 195.00 *(978-0-444-52824-7(5)*, Elsevier Science) Elsevier Science & Technology Bks.

Cho, William C. S., ed. Materia Medica for Various Cancers. 2011. (Evidence-based Anticancer Complementary & Alternative Medicine Ser.). (ENG., Illus.). xii, 406p. 209.00 ***(978-94-007-1982-8(5)***, 9400719825) Springer.

Gastl, G., et al, eds. Standard Operating Procedures for Clinical Trials of the Central European Society for Anticancer Drug Research, Vol. 26. (GER.). *(978-3-8055-7665-9(X))* Karger, S. AG.

Gielen, M., ed. Metal-Based Anti-Tumour Drugs. 1988. *(978-965-294-046-9(1))* Freund Publishing Hse., Ltd.

Joshi, Ms. Dipti, et al. Oroxylum Indicum. 2011. 72p. pap. ***(978-3-8443-2807-3(6))*** Lambert Academic Publishing.

Maurice, Hildebert. Compounds with Antimalarial & Anticancer Activities. 2010. 168p. pap. *(978-3-8383-8199-2(8))* Lambert Academic Publishing.

Nicholson, Allen W., ed. Ribonucleases. 2011. (Nucleic Acids & Molecular Biology Ser.). (ENG., Illus.). xiii, 403p. 209.00 *(978-3-642-21077-8(5)*, 3642210775) Springer.

Sallum, Christine. Production of Radiolabeled E-Peptide. 2010. 76p. pap. *(978-3-8383-7490-1(8))* Lambert Academic Publishing.

Yu, Yu & Richardson, Des. Thiosemicarbazone Iron Chelator. 2011. 220p. pap. ***(978-3-8443-8676-9(9))*** Lambert Academic Publishing.

ANTICHOLESTEREMIC AGENTS

Barake, Roula. Effects of Plant Sterols & Glucomannan on Hyperlipidemi. 2008. 84p. pap. *(978-3-639-06732-3(0))* VDM Verlag Dr. Mueller e.K.

Mason, Roger. Lower Cholesterol Without Drugs, New Edition. 2nd ed. 2012. (ENG.). 128p. pap. ***(978-0-7570-0367-7(2))*** Square One Pubs.

ANTICHRIST

Anderson, Robert. The Coming Prince: The Marvelous Prophecy of Daniel's Seventy Weeks Concerning the Antichrist. 2007. 312p. per. 10.75 *(978-1-60206-230-6(7))* Cosimo, Inc.

Anderson, Sonya T. Even the Very Elect. 2007. 108p. pap. 15.95 *(978-1-4116-8988-6(7))* Lulu Enterprises Inc.

Anonymous. I , the Antichrist. 2009. 192p. 26.95 *(978-1-4401-3789-1(7))*; pap. 16.95 *(978-1-4401-3792-1(7))* iUniverse, Inc.

The Antichrist. pap. 0.95 *(978-0-937408-09-4(3))* GMI Pubns.

Awodeyi, Jonah. Abyss Beast not the Antichrist. 2010. 83p. pap. 8.45 *(978-1-4452-6957-3(0))* Lulu Enterprises Inc.

Blake, John W. The Magnitude of the Word: The Hidden Revelation. 2011. 100p. pap. 11.95 ***(978-1-4497-2752-9(2)***, WestBow Pr.) Author Solutions, Inc.

Bowers, Gary. Out of the Abyss: Can the number of the beast be Solved? 666. 2011. 304p. 37.95 *(978-1-4497-1039-2(5))*; pap. 22.95 *(978-1-4497-1038-5(7))* WestBow Pr. A Div. of Thomas Nelson.

Chi, Thomas. Marilyn Manson Trilogy: Creating an Antichrist. 2007. (ENG, FRE, TUR, SPA & GER., Illus.). 60p. mass mkt. *(978-0-9800862-1-8(3))* LA Portfolio.

Church, J. R. Daniel Reveals the Blood Line of the Antichrist. 2010. (Illus.). 330p. pap. 19.95 *(978-0-941241-22-9(X))* Prophecy Pubns.

Confessions of the Antichrist: Blasphemes, mortifications, incantations, small cosmology of Earth. 2008. pap. 50.00 *(978-0-615-20126-9(1))* Thule Foundation Pubs.

Deakins, John R. From Tabloids to Apocalypse Christianized Myths in a Doomed Modern World. 2011. 154p. pap. 14.99 ***(978-1-61720-283-4(5))*** Wilder Pubns., Ltd.

Desmond Ford. The Coming Worldwide Calvary: Christ Versus Antichrist. 2009. 168p. pap. 15.95 *(978-1-4401-7284-7(6))* iUniverse, Inc.

Diedricks, Louis. The Day of the Lord. 2010. 76p. pap. 13.95 *(978-1-936198-05-4(3))* Hillcrest Publishing Group, Inc.

Eubanks, Miriam R. You Have Been Id'ed: Something You Need to Know about Tattos, the Implantation of Radio Frequency Identification Microchips, & the Mark of the Beast. 2011. 152p. 29.99 ***(978-1-4568-6104-9(2))***; pap. 19.99 ***(978-1-4568-6103-2(4))*** Xlibris Corp.

Froese, Arno. How Democracy Will Elect the Antichrist. 2nd rev. ed. 2008. (Illus.). 349p. 17.95 *(978-0-937422-64-9(9)*, Olive Pr., The) Midnight Call.

Gallagher, Steve. Intoxicated with Babylon: The Seduction of God's People in the Last Days. annot. ed. 2007. (ENG.). 240p. per. 13.99 *(978-0-9758832-4-2(0))* Pure Life Ministries.

GOrDon, Gregory. Ronald Reagan Anti-Christ. 2007. 185p. pap. 14.98 *(978-0-615-15341-4(0))* Light of the World.

Govan, Glenda L. Deception: The Deceptive Work of the Adversary. 2010. 63p. pap. 12.95 *(978-1-4327-4286-7(8))* Outskirts Pr., Inc.

Gyarmati, Attila D'Hun. The Anti-Christ at the Gates of Purgatory. 2011. 184p. pap. 11.95 ***(978-1-60844-775-6(8))*** Dog Ear Publishing, LLC.

Hickman, Bob. Visions of the Beast with Seven Heads & Ten Horns: N. W. O., Reign of the Antichrist. 2010. 88p. pap. 15.49 *(978-1-4520-3508-6(3))* AuthorHouse.

Hitchcock, Mark. Who Is the Antichrist? Answering the Question Everyone Is Asking. 2011. 208p. pap. 13.99 *(978-0-7369-3995-9(4))* Harvest Hse. Pubs.

Hrubik, Vladimir. When They Say Peace Seek Shelter: The Road to Evade the Antichrist. 2009. 384p. pap. 19.99 *(978-1-4389-3342-9(8))* AuthorHouse.

Kingdom Quotes Staff. The Beast of the Revelation: The Antichrist Network. pap. *(978-0-930179-22-9(6))* Johns Enterprises.

Kramer, W. P. Revelation Exposed Plain & Simple: The Rapture or the Tribulation: Is There Really A Choice. 2010. 400p. pap. 21.95 *(978-1-4327-5017-6(8))* Outskirts Pr., Inc.

Lang, Dean. Is This the End? 2011. 294p. 29.99 **(978-1-4568-7447-6(0))**; pap. 19.99 **(978-1-4568-7446-9(2))** Xlibris Corp.
LaVey, Anton. Letters from the Devil: the Lost Writing of Anton Szandor Lavey. 2010. 72p. pap. 16.66 *(978-0-557-43173-1(5))* Lulu Enterprises Inc.
Maman, Federico. Erakion. 2009. (ITA.). 69p. pap. 30.50 *(978-1-4452-4681-9(3))* Lulu Enterprises Inc.
Manty, Jeffrey A. Prophecy Code II: A Last Days Revelation of Allah in Scripture & What It Means to the World. 2006. 160p. pap. 14.95 *(978-1-58736-675-8(4))* Wheatmark.
Massegee, Charles. The Rise & Fall of the Antichrist: Islam, Allah, & the Antichrist in Prophecy. 2011. 450p. pap. 29.95 **(978-1-4327-7335-9(6))** Outskirts Pr., Inc.
McKenzie, Duncan W. The Antichrist & the Second Coming Vol. 1: A Preterist Examination. 2009. 488p. 36.99 *(978-1-61579-038-8(1))*; pap. 24.99 *(978-1-61579-037-1(3))* Xulon Pr., Inc.
McShea, Thomas. The Anti-Christ Is Here. 2008. 256p. 25.99 *(978-1-60266-506-4(0))*; pap. 15.99 *(978-1-60266-334-3(3))* Xulon Pr., Inc.
Morelli, Michael. Let the Church Rise: How to be an Ambassador of Action in Your Local Church & Beyond. 2010. 130p. pap. 9.95 *(978-0-88144-491-9(X))* Yorkshire Publishing Group.
Nietzsche, Friedrich Wilhelm. The Antichrist. 2010. 140p. pap. 4.99 *(978-1-60450-811-6(6))* 2009. 120p. pap. 4.99 *(978-1-60450-648-8(2))* Arc Manor. (Serenity Pubs.).
—The Antichrist. 2009. 66p. pap. 29.95 *(978-1-151-64680-4(6))* Books LLC.
—The Antichrist. Mencken, H. L., tr. 2007. 104p. per. 14.95 *(978-1-934255-09-4(2))* El Paso Norte Pr.
—The Antichrist. 2009. 106p. pap. 5.90 *(978-85-62022-89-0(6))* Endeavor Bks./Mountain States Litho.
—The Antichrist. 2010. (Illus.). 62p. pap. 6.40 *(978-1-77045-151-3(X))* General Bks. LLC.
—The Antichrist. Mencken, H. L., tr. 2008. 80p. pap. 5.95 *(978-1-60355-079-6(8))* Juniper Grove.
—The Antichrist. 2010. 64p. pap. 13.56 *(978-1-162-68795-7(9))*; 25.56 **(978-1-169-21696-9(X))**; 31.95 *(978-1-161-45660-8(0))* Kessinger Publishing, LLC.
—The Antichrist. 2007. (ENG.). 64p. per. 11.99 *(978-1-59547-928-0(7))* NuVision Pubns., LLC.
—The Antichrist. 2007. (ENG.). 112p. per. 10.45 *(978-1-59462-791-0(6))*, Book Jungle) Standard Pubns., Inc.
—The Antichrist. 2011. 96p. pap. **(978-3-8424-4332-7(3))** Tredition GmbH.
Nietzsche, Friedrich Wilhelm. The Antichrist: + Fragments from a Shattering Mind. Falls, Domino, tr. from GER. 2007. (Solar Books - Solar Visionaries Ser.). (Illus.). 154p. per. 13.95 *(978-0-9714578-5-0(9))* Solar Bks.
Nietzsche, Friedrich Wilhelm & Mencken, H. L. The Antichrist. 2007. (ENG.). 88p. per. *(978-1-4065-4956-0(8))* Dodo Pr.
Nietzsche, Friedrich Wilhelm & Nietzsche, Daniel Paul. Der Antichrist. 2012. 88p. pap. **(978-3-8424-1504-1(4))** Tredition GmbH.
Palfrey, Bernard. The Anti-Christ. 2009. 217p. pap. 23.50 *(978-1-4092-3983-3(7))* Lulu Enterprises Inc.
Peckney. Eternal Life in Heaven. 2011. 128p. pap. 10.68 **(978-1-4567-3760-3(0))** AuthorHouse.
Pink, Arthur W. The Antichrist. 2011. 160p. pap. 16.99 **(978-1-61203-332-7(6))** Bottom of the Hill Publishing.
—The Antichrist. 2009. 200p. pap. 9.99 *(978-1-60459-682-3(1))* Wilder Pubns., Ltd.
—El Anticristo: The Antichrist. (SPA.). 264p. *(978-84-7228-835-5(8)*, 220039) Clie, Editorial.
Pink, Arthur Walkington. The Antichrist. 2011. 312p. pap. 9.50 **(978-1-61427-014-0(7))** Martino Publishing.
Powell, Robert & Dann, Kevin. Christ & the Maya Calendar: 2012 & the Coming of the Antichrist, 1 vol. 2009. (ENG., Illus.). 280p. pap. 25.00 *(978-1-58420-071-0(5)*, Lindisfarne Bks.) SteinerBooks, Inc.
Pugh, Joye Jeffries. Eden: The Knowledge of Good & Evil 666. 2006. 482p. per. 29.99 *(978-1-59886-253-9(7))* Tate Publishing & Enterprises, LLC.
Reading, Mario. Nostradamus & the Third Antichrist: Napoleon, Hitler & 'the One Still to Come' 2011. (ENG.). 368p. 16.95 *(978-1-907486-67-8(4)*, Watkins Publishing) Duncan Baird Pubs. GBR. Dist: Sterling Publishing Co., Inc.
Regesh, J. D. Saint Paul, the First Antichrist. 2011. 180p. pap. 12.95 **(978-1-61204-706-5(8)**, Strategic Bk. Publishing) AEG Literary Publishing Services, Inc.
Regesh, John Ben. Saint Paul, the First Antichrist. 2009. 180p. 24.50 *(978-1-60860-266-7(4)*, Eloquent Bks.) AEG Literary Publishing Services, Inc.
Rhodes, James. The Beginning of Sorrows. 2010. 80p. pap. 10.49 *(978-1-4520-1902-4(9))* AuthorHouse.
Rhodes, Ron. Unmasking the Antichrist: Dispelling the Myths, Discovering the Truth. 2012. 256p. pap. 13.99 **(978-0-7369-2850-2(2))** Harvest Hse. Pubs.
Sansano, Ricardo. Voz del Anticristo: Voice of the Antichrist. (SPA.). *(978-84-7645-457-1(8)*, 223564) Clie, Editorial.
Schultz, Eleanor. Before the Rapture: The Four Stages we Must Live Through. 2011. 236p. 33.95 *(978-1-4497-1130-6(8))*; pap. 17.95 *(978-1-4497-1128-3(6))* Author Solutions, Inc. (WestBow Pr.).
Van Zleer, Raymond. The Antichrist Whom Christ Declared: A Biblical Study of Whom Jesus Christ Considered the Antichrist to Be, & Its Implications for Today's World. 2008. (ENG.). 140p. per. 12.95 *(978-1-4251-0346-0(4))* Trafford Publishing.
Vanover, S. T. Holocaust # 2. 2007. 144p. pap. 15.00 *(978-0-8059-7528-4(4))* Dorrance Publishing Co., Inc.
Varner, Steve C. Reading, Writing, & a Roux Addict: Rhymes, Recipes, & Reason for Hope Within. 2007. 269p. pap. 27.95 *(978-1-60441-157-7(0))* PublishAmerica, Inc.
Vicchio, Stephen J. The Legend of the Anti-Christ. 2009. 396p. pap. 44.00 *(978-1-55635-680-3(3)*, Wipf and Stock) Wipf & Stock Pubs.
Ward, Chris. Star Code. 2010. 156p. 29.95 *(978-1-4490-7093-9(0))*; pap. 19.95 *(978-1-4490-3303-3(2))* AuthorHouse.
Wells, David R. Where'd Everybody Go? A Post-Rapture & Great Tribulation Survival Manual. 2011. 126p. 22.99 **(978-1-61215-854-9(4))**; pap. 14.99 **(978-1-61215-853-2(6))** Xulon Pr., Inc.
Wheeler, Cisco. Behold a White Horse. 2009. 444p. pap. 25.99 *(978-1-60791-356-9(0))* Xulon Pr., Inc.
White, Randy. The Antichrist: What You Can Know! What You Need to Know! 2010. 202p. pap. 15.99 *(978-1-61579-920-6(6))* Xulon Pr., Inc.
Willis, D. C. Subtle Deceit: A Layman Perspective. 2011. 172p. 23.89 **(978-1-4567-5546-1(3))**; pap. 13.73 **(978-1-4567-5547-8(1))** AuthorHouse.
Winfrey, Melvin. The Beast That Was, & Is Not, & yet Is. 2009. 136p. *(978-1-4389-9879-4(1))* AuthorHouse.
Wright, Randolph. Mikhail Gorbachev Is Gog & Magog, the Biblical Antichrist. 2010. 228p. (ENG.). 24.99 *(978-1-4520-0520-1(6))*; pap. 15.99 *(978-1-4520-0519-5(2))* AuthorHouse.

ANTICOAGULANTS (MEDICINE)

Agnelli, Giancarlo & Buller, Harry, eds. Anticoagulation Management - Time to Change? ICT Ximelagatran Satellite Symposium, Ljubljana, June 2004, Vol. 34. (Illus.). *(978-3-8055-7913-1(6))* Karger, S. AG.
Crowther, Mark & Donadini, Marco. Hypercoagulable States & New Anticoagulants, an Issue of Hematology/Oncology Clinics of North America. 2010. (Clinics: Internal Medicine Ser.: 24-4). (ENG., Illus.). xiv, 670p. 99.00 *(978-1-4377-2529-2(5)*, Saunders) Elsevier - Health Sciences Div.
Edardes, Joseph P., ed. Coumarin Anticoagulant Research Progress. 2008. (Illus.). 160p. 185.00 *(978-1-60021-990-0(X))* Nova Science Pubs., Inc.
Facts and Comparisons Staff, et al. Managing Oral Anticoagulation Therapy: Clinical & Operational Guidelines. 3rd rev. ed. 2009. (ENG.). 432p. pap. 266.95 *(978-1-57439-287-6(5))* Lippincott Williams & Wilkins.
Fang, Margaret C. Inpatient Anticoagulation. 2011. (Hospital Medicine: Current Concepts Ser.: 4). (ENG., Illus.). 448p. pap. 69.95 *(978-0-470-60211-9(2)*, Wiley-Blackwell) Wiley, John & Sons, Inc.
Gutierrez, Rosa Martha Perez. Handbook of Compounds with Anti-Inflammatory & Anti-Platelet Aggregation Activities Isolated from Plants. 2008. (Illus.). 296p. 98.00 *(978-1-60456-607-9(8))* Nova Science Pubs., Inc.
Horsti, Juha. The Progress of Prothrombin Time to a New Generation Method for Inr. 2008. 108p. pap. *(978-3-639-01167-8(8))* VDM Verlag Dr. Mueller e.K.
Jawahar, Jubie. Novel Indane-1,3-Dione Analogues & Their Biological Evaluation. 2011. 72p. pap. **(978-3-8454-0650-3(X))** Lambert Academic Publishing.
Joint Commission Resources, Inc Staff, contrib. by. Anticoagulation Therapy: Toolkit for Implementing the National Patient Safety Goal. 2008. (Illus.). x, 120p. pap. *(978-1-59940-216-1(5))* Joint Commission Resources.
Khorana, Alok A. & Francis, Charles W., eds. Cancer-Associated Thrombosis New Findings in Translational Science, Prevention, & Treatment. 2007. (ENG., Illus.). 296p. pap. 110.00 *(978-1-4200-7704-9(X)*, Informa Healthcare) Taylor & Francis Group GBR. Dist: Taylor & Francis Group.
Moore, Gary, et al. Warfarin Monitoring: Standard Practice & Beyond. 2012. pap. **(978-1-62100-189-8(X))** Nova Science Pubs., Inc.
Mousa, Shaker A., ed. Anticoagulants, Antiplatelets, & Thrombolytics. 2nd ed. 2010. (Methods in Molecular Biology Ser.). (Illus.). xi, 316p. 159.00 *(978-1-60761-802-7(8)*, 1607618028) Humana Pr.
Patton, Kurt A., et al. Anticoagulant Therapy FAQs: A Guide to Compliance with National Patient Safety Goal 3E. 2008. vii, 94p. *(978-1-60146-246-6(8))* Opus Communications.
Schneider, Diana M. The Coumadin (Warfarin) Help Book: Anticoagulation Therapy to Prevent & Manage Strokes, Heart Attacks, & Other Vascular Conditions. 2008. (ENG., Illus.). 112p. pap. 16.95 *(978-0-9793564-2-1(3))* DiaMed, LLC.
Waksman, Ron & Ajani, Andrew A. E., eds. Pharmacology in the Catheterization Laboratory. 2009. (ENG., Illus.). 400p. 165.95 *(978-1-4051-5704-9(6)*, Wiley-Blackwell) Wiley, John & Sons, Inc.
Warkentin, Theodore & Greinacher, Andreas, eds. Heparin-Induced Thrombocytopenia, Fourth Edition: Abridged, Special Edition. 4th ed. 2007. 112p. 11.50 *(978-1-4200-6897-9(0)*, Informa Healthcare) Taylor & Francis Group GBR. Dist: Taylor & Francis Group.
—Heparin-Induced Thrombocytopenia, Fourth Edition: (Special Edition for GSK) 4th rev. ed. 2007. (ENG., Illus.). 592p. pap. 99.95 *(978-1-4200-8675-1(8)*, Informa Healthcare) Taylor & Francis Group GBR. Dist: Taylor & Francis Group.
Warkentin, Theodore E. & Greinacher, Andreas, eds. Heparin-Induced Thrombocytopenia. 4th rev. ed. 2007. (Fundamental & Clinical Cardiology Ser.: Vol. 62). (ENG., Illus.). 592p. 230.00 *(978-1-4200-4508-6(3)*, Informa Healthcare) Taylor & Francis Group GBR. Dist: Taylor & Francis Group.

ANTICONVULSANTS

Akiskal, Hagop S. & Tohen, Mauricio, eds. Bipolar Psychopharmacotherapy: Caring for the Patient. 2nd ed. 2011. (ENG., Illus.). 544p. 130.95 *(978-0-470-74721-6(8)*, Wiley) Wiley, John & Sons, Inc.
Asadi-Pooya, Ali A. & Sperling, Michael R. Antiepileptic Drugs: A Clinician's Manual. 2009. (ENG., Illus.). 264p. pap. 24.95 *(978-0-19-536821-3(5))* 2008. *(978-0-19-534340-3(9))* Oxford Univ. Pr., Inc.
Bienvenu, Emile. Evaluation of the Antiepileptic Activity. 2009. 52p. pap. *(978-3-639-14635-6(2))* VDM Verlag Dr. Mueller e.K.
de Leon, Jose, ed. A Practitioner's Guide to Prescribing Antiepileptics & Mood Stabilizers for Adults with Intellectual Disabilities. 2012. (ENG.). 540p. pap. 69.95 **(978-1-4614-2011-8(3)**, 1461420113) Springer.
Hamed, Sherifa A., ed. Cognitive Aspects in Idiopathic Epilepsy. 2011. pap. *(978-1-61209-777-0(4))* Nova Science Pubs., Inc.
Keck, Paul E., et al, eds. Antiepileptic Drugs to Treat Psychiatric Disorders. 2008. (Medical Psychiatry Ser.: Vol. 39). (ENG., Illus.). 440p. 180.00 *(978-0-8493-8259-8(9)*, Informa Healthcare) Taylor & Francis Group GBR. Dist: Taylor & Francis Group.
Kossoff, Eric. Ketogenic Diets: Treatments for Epilepsy & Other Disorders. 5th ed. 2011. E-Book **(978-1-61705-064-0(4))** Demos Medical Publishing, LLC.
Kossoff, Eric, et al. Ketogenic Diets: Treatments for Epilepsy & Other Disorders. 5th ed. 2011. (ENG., Illus.). 300p. pap. 29.95 *(978-1-936303-10-6(8))* Demos Medical Publishing, LLC.
McElroy, Susan L., et al, eds. Antiepileptic Drugs to Treat Psychiatric Disorders, Abridged. 2008. 240p. *(978-1-4200-9296-7(0)*, Informa Healthcare) Taylor & Francis Group.
Panayiotopoulos, C. P. Antiepileptic Drugs, Pharmacopoeia. 2010. (ENG.). xi, 108p. pap. 24.95 *(978-0-85729-011-3(8)*, 0857290118) Springer.
Patsalos, Philip N. & Bourgeois, Blaise F. D. The Epilepsy Prescriber's Guide to Antiepileptic Drugs. 2010. (ENG., Illus.). 332p. pap. 65.00 *(978-0-521-68716-4(0))* Cambridge Univ. Pr.
Shorvon, Simon D. Handbook of Epilepsy Treatment. 3rd ed. 2010. (ENG., Illus.). 436p. pap. 83.95 *(978-1-4051-9818-9(4)*, Wiley-Blackwell) Wiley, John & Sons, Inc.
Shorvon, Simon D., et al, eds. The Treatment of Epilepsy. 3rd ed. 2009. (ENG., Illus.). 1116p. 330.95 *(978-1-4051-8383-3(7)*, Wiley-Blackwell) Wiley, John & Sons, Inc.
Stahl, Stephen & Stahl, Stephen M. Mood Stabilizers. 2009. (Stahl's Illustrated Ser.). (ENG., Illus.). 176p. pap. 41.99 *(978-0-521-75849-9(1))* Cambridge Univ. Pr.
Tatum, William O., et al. Epilepsy A to Z: A Concise Encyclopedia. 2nd ed. 2009. pap. 129.00 *(978-1-933864-41-9(9))* Demos Medical Publishing, LLC.

ANTIDEPRESSANTS

see also Fluoxetine

Bennett, Shoshana. Pregnant on Prozac: The Essential Guide to Making the Best Decision for You & Your Baby. 2009. (ENG.). 264p. pap. 16.95 *(978-0-7627-4940-9(7))* Globe Pequot Pr., The.
Beyer, Chad & Stahl, Stephen, eds. Next Generation Antidepressants: Moving Beyond Monoamines to Discover Novel Treatment Strategies for Mood Disorders. 2010. (ENG., Illus.). 150p. 94.00 *(978-0-521-76058-4(5))* Cambridge Univ. Pr.
Biegler, Paul. The Ethical Treatment of Depression: Autonomy Through Psychotherapy. 2011. (Philosophical Psychopathology Ser.). (ENG., Illus.). 232p. (gr. 17). 35.00 *(978-0-262-01549-3(8))* MIT Pr.
Buschmann, Helmut, et al, eds. Antidepressants, Antipsychotics, Anxiolytics: From Chemistry & Pharmacology to Clinical Application. 2007. (ENG.). 1260p. 490.00 *(978-3-527-31058-6(4)*, Wiley-VCH) Wiley, John & Sons, Inc.
Butzer, Bethany. The Antidepressant Antidote: Five Steps to Get off Antidepressants Safely & Effectively. 2010. 188p. pap. 13.95 *(978-1-4525-0038-6(X))* Get Published.
Ciraulo, Domenic A. & Shader, Richard Irwin. Pharmacotherapy of Depression. 2nd ed. 2010. (Illus.). 520p. 149.00 *(978-1-60327-434-0(0)*, 1603274340) Humana Pr.
Code, Bill. Point of Return: Your Personal Guide to Taper off Anti-Anxiety & Anti-Depressant Drugs, 1. I.t. ed. 2007. (Illus.). 170p. 39.00 *(978-0-9778040-1-6(1))* Label Me Sane, Inc.
Cram101 Textbook Reviews & Cram101 Textbook Reviews. Outlines & Highlights for Depression & Bipolar Disorder by Stephen M Stahl, Isbn: 9780521714129 0521714125. 2011. 104p. pap. 28.95 **(978-1-61654-724-0(3))** Cram101 Inc.
Cryan, J. F. & Leonard, B. E., eds. Depression: from Psychopathology to Pharmacotherapy. 2010. (Modern Trends in Pharmacopsychiatry Ser.). (ENG., Illus.). 274p. *(978-3-8055-9605-3(7))* Karger, S. AG.
Exploring the Relationship Between Medication & Veteran Suicide: Hearing Before the Committee on Veterans' Affairs, U.S. House of Representatives, One Hundred Eleventh Congress, Second Session, February 24, 2010. 2010. iii, 97p. *(978-0-16-086194-9(2)*, 552-070-41292-1) United States Government Printing Office.
Ford, Jean. Antidepressants & the Critics: Cure-Alls or Unnatural Poisons? 2007. (Antidepressants Ser.). (Illus.). 112p. (YA). (gr. 7). pap. 14.95 *(978-1-4222-0408-5(1))* Mason Crest Pubs.
Galarraga, Omar & Salkever, David S. Antidepressants & Labor Market Outcomes of Persons Living with HIV: An Analysis of Users of Highly-Active Antiretroviral Therapy in the United States: 1996-2004. 2008. 148p. pap. *(978-3-639-09493-0(X))* VDM Verlag Dr. Mueller e.K.
Greenberg, Gary. Manufacturing Depression: The Secret History of a Modern Disease. (ENG.). 2011. 464p. pap. 16.00 *(978-1-4165-6980-0(4))* 2010. 448p. 27.00 *(978-1-4165-6979-4(0))* Simon & Schuster.
Hirschfeld, Robert M.A. Advanced Mood Disorder Questionnaire (HA-MDQ) 2008. 48p. pap. 30.95 *(978-0-7637-6307-7(1))* Jones & Bartlett Learning, LLC.
Karp, David A. Is It Me or My Meds? Living with Antidepressants. 2007. 304p. per. 20.00 *(978-0-674-02551-6(2))* Harvard Univ. Pr.
Khan, Zaved. Nitric Oxide-Dependent Stress Modulation by Withania Somnifer. 2010. 84p. pap. *(978-3-8383-7778-0(8))* Lambert Academic Publishing.
Kirsch, Irving. The Emperor's New Drugs: Exploding the Antidepressant Myth. 2011. (ENG.). 240p. (gr. 9). pap. 15.99 *(978-0-465-02200-7(6))* Basic Bks.
Leeuwen, Jayden T. Van, ed. Antidepressants: Types, Efficiency & Possible Side Effects. 2010. (Pharmacology - Research, Safety Testing & Regulation Ser.). 248p. 129.00 *(978-1-61668-581-2(6))* Nova Science Pubs., Inc.
Licinio, Julio & Wong, Ma-Li. Antidepressants & Suicide: A Balanced Overview. 2007. 576p. 99.95 *(978-0-470-04260-1(5)*, Wiley-Liss) Wiley, John & Sons, Inc.
Mau, et al. Pharmacotherapy for Depression & Treatment-Resistant Depression. 2010. (Illus.). 726p. 167.00 *(978-981-4287-58-6(X))* World Scientific Publishing Co., Inc.
Michael, Banov. Taking Antidepressants: Your Comprehensive Guide to Starting, Staying on, & When & How to Safely Quit. 2010. (Illus.). 304p. pap. 16.95 *(978-1-934716-06-9(5))* Sunrise River Pr.
Miravalle, John-Mark. The Drug, the Soul, & God: A Catholic Moral Perspective on Antidepressants. 2010. (ENG.). 150p. pap. 28.00 *(978-1-58966-192-9(3))* Univ. of Scranton Pr.
Peters, Eric. The Pharmacogenetics of Antidepressant Response. 2008. pap. *(978-3-8364-7055-1(1))* VDM Verlag Dr. Mueller e.K.
Pompili, Maurizio, et al. Antidepressants Therapy & Risk of Suicide among Patients with Major Depressive Disorders. 2011. (Series: Psychiatry - Theory, Applications & Treatments Ser.). pap. 43.00 *(978-1-61728-378-9(9))* Nova Science Pubs., Inc.
Pritchard, Jenette S. Anti-Depressants in America - Therapeutic Use & Effects: Index of New Information. Date not set. 160p. 57.50 *(978-0-7883-1884-9(5))*; pap. 47.50 *(978-0-7883-1885-6(3))* ABBE Pubs. Assn. of Washington, D.C.
Rush, A. John, ed. Mood Disorders Vol. 25: Systematic Medication Management. (Modern Problems of Pharmacopsychiatry Ser.: Vol. 25, 1996). (Illus.). *(978-3-8055-6223-2(3))* Karger, S. AG.
Sharpe, Katherine. Coming of Age on Zoloft: How Antidepressants Cheered Us up, Let Us down, & Changed Who We Are. 2012. (P. S. Ser.). (ENG.). 336p. pap. 14.99 **(978-0-06-205973-4(4)**, HarperPerennial) HarperCollins Pubs.
Skolnick, Phil, ed. Antidepressants: New Pharmacological Strategies. 2010. (Contemporary Neuroscience Ser.). 272p. pap. 179.00 *(978-1-61737-048-9(7)*, 1617370487) Humana Pr.
Stahl, Stephen. Antidepressants. 2009. (Stahl's Illustrated Ser.). (ENG., Illus.). 200p. pap. 41.99 *(978-0-521-75852-9(1))* Cambridge Univ. Pr.
Stahl, Stephen. Stahl's Essential Psychopharmacology: The Prescriber's Guide: Antidepressants. 4th rev. ed. 2011. (ENG., Illus.). 288p. pap. 39.99 **(978-1-107-66796-9(8))** Cambridge Univ. Pr.
Stahl, Stephen M. Depression & Bipolar Disorder: Stahl's Essential Psychopharmacology. 3rd ed. 2008. (Essential Psychopharmacology Ser.). (ENG., Illus.). 312p. (C). pap. 57.00 *(978-0-521-71412-9(5))* Cambridge Univ. Pr.
Wimmer, Diane C. Effectiveness of Second-Generation Antidepressants in Adult Depression Treatment. 2011. (Public Health in the 21st Century Ser.). 475p. 225.00 *(978-1-61209-613-1(1))* Nova Science Pubs., Inc.

ANTIDEPRESSIVE AGENTS

see Antidepressants

ANTIDOTES

see also Antitoxins

Cantu, Robert P. Flipped: A Drug-Induced Journey to the Event Horizon of Insanity. 2011. 108p. 21.25 **(978-1-4634-4829-5(5))**; pap. 10.75 **(978-1-4634-4830-1(9))** AuthorHouse.
Cram101 Textbook Reviews & Cram101 Textbook Reviews. Outlines & Highlights for Poisoning & Drug Overdose by Kent Olson, Isbn: 9780071443333. 2011. 134p. pap. 28.95 **(978-1-61461-341-1(9))** Cram101 Inc.
Flora, S. J. S., et al, eds. Pharmacological Perspectives of Toxic Chemicals & Their Antidotes. 2012. (ENG., Illus.). xx, 484p. pap. 289.00 *(978-3-642-06117-2(6)*, 3642061176) Springer.
Maimonides, Moses. On Poisons & the Protection against Lethal Drugs: A parallel English-Arabic Edition. Bos, Gerrit, ed. McVaugn, Michael R., tr. from ARA. 2009. (ARA & ENG.). 494p. 49.95 *(978-0-8425-2730-9(3))* Brigham Young Univ.
Matovi?, Vesna, et al, eds. Zinc, Copper, or Magnesium Supplementation Against Cadmium Toxicity. 2010. (Environmental Science, Engineering & Technology Ser.). xiv, 58p. pap. 43.00 *(978-1-61668-332-0(5))* Nova Science Pubs., Inc.
Maynard, Robert L., et al, eds. Chemical Warfare Agents: Toxicology & Treatment. 2nd rev. ed. 2007. (ENG., Illus.). 750p. 389.95 *(978-0-470-01359-5(1)*, Wiley) Wiley, John & Sons, Inc.
Saathoff, Gregory B. Crisis Guide to Psychotropic Drugs & Poisons. 2007. 162p. spiral bd. 42.95 *(978-0-7637-5559-1(1))* Jones & Bartlett Learning, LLC.
Swearingen, Rodger. Why Bad Things Happen to Good People. Swearingen, Rodger et al, eds. 2009. 150p. pap. 20.00 *(978-1-935444-18-3(2))* World Audience Pubs.
Swiderski, Richard. Poison Eaters: Snakes, Opium, Arsenic, & the Lethal Show. 2010. 288p. pap. 25.95 *(978-1-59942-834-5(2))* Universal Pubs.
Turkington, Carol, et al. The Encyclopedia of Poisons & Antidotes. 3rd rev. ed. 2009. (Library of Health & Living). 336p. (C). (gr. 9-18). 75.00 *(978-0-8160-6401-4(6))* Facts On File, Inc.
—Poisons & Antidotes. 3rd rev. ed. 2009. (Library of Health & Living). 336p. pap. 19.95 *(978-0-8160-6402-1(4)*, Checkmark Bks.) Facts On File, Inc.

ANTIDUMPING

see Dumping (International Trade)

ANTIDUMPING DUTIES

Bael. Antidumping & Other Trade Protection Laws of the EC. 5th ed. 2011. xxv, 1368p. 330.00 *(978-90-411-3117-1(5))* Wolters Kluwer Law & Business.

Bentley QC, Philip & Silberston CBE, Aubrey. Anti-Dumping & Countervailing Action: Limits Imposed by Economic & Legal Theory. 2007. (Illus.). 232p. 119.00 *(978-1-84720-344-1(2))* Elgar, Edward Publishing, Inc.

Bermann, George A., et al. Law & Economics of Contingent Protection in International Trade. Bermann, George A. et al, eds. 2009. (ENG., Illus.). 432p. 98.00 *(978-0-521-76907-5(8))* Cambridge Univ. Pr.

Bowman, Gregory. Trade Remedies in North America: Laws, EConomic Analysis Practice. 2010. (Illus.). xxxviii, 700p. 189.00 *(978-90-411-2840-9(9))* Wolters Kluwer Law & Business.

Duc, Nguyen Minh. Effects of Us Antidumping in Perfect & Imperfect Competition. 2009. 76p. pap. *(978-3-639-11692-2(5))* VDM Verlag Dr. Mueller e.K.

Giannakopoulos, Themistoklis K. A Concise Guide to the EU Anti-Dumping/Anti-Subsidies Procedures. 2006. (International Competition Law Ser.: Vol. 23). (Illus.). 231p. *(978-90-411-2464-7(0))* Kluwer Law International.

Haberl, Christiane. Antidumping As a Form of Protectionism. 2009. 80p. pap. *(978-3-639-14670-7(0))* VDM Verlag Dr. Mueller e.K.

Hearing on H.R. 1229: The Nonmarket Economy Trade Remedy ACT of 2007: Hearing Before the Subcommittee on Trade of the Committee on Ways & Means, U.S. House of Representatives, U.S. House of Representatives, One Hundred Tenth Congress, First Session, March 15, 2007. 2009. iii, 77p. ***(978-0-16-087456-7(4)***, 552-070-42148-3) United States Government Printing Office.

Jones, Vivian C. Trade Remedies: New Shipper Reviews. 2008. 79.00 *(978-1-60456-433-4(4))* Nova Science Pubs., Inc.

Jones, Vivian Catherine, et al. Trade Remedies. 2008. 82.00 *(978-1-60456-453-2(9))* Nova Science Pubs., Inc.

Legislation Related to Trade with China: Hearing Before the Subcommittee on Trade of the Committee on Ways & Means, U.S. House of Representatives, One Hundred Tenth Congress, First Session, August 2, 2007. 2009. (Illus.). iv, 181p. *(978-0-16-083844-6(4)*, 552-070-39541-5) United States Government Printing Office.

Luo, Yan. Rise of Legalization in Anti-Dumping Regime: The Wto, EU, China. 2010. (Illus.). xiii, 224p. *(978-90-411-3207-9(4))* Kluwer Law International.

Mueller, Wolfgang, et al. EC & WTO Anti-Dumping Law: A Handbook. 2nd ed. 2009. (ENG.). 960p. 434.50 *(978-0-19-956531-3(7))* Oxford Univ. Pr., Inc.

Raju, K. D. World Trade Organization Agreement on Anti-Dumping: A GATT/WTO & Indian Jurisprudence. 2008. (Illus.). xlvii, 467p. 185.00 *(978-90-411-2780-8(1))* Wolters Kluwer Law & Business.

Raslan, Reem. Antidumping: A Developing World Perspective. 2009. (Illus.). xx, 205p. 158.00 *(978-90-411-3128-7(0))* Wolters Kluwer Law & Business.

Rothgeb, John M. & Chinapandhu, Benjamas. Trade & Development in a Globalized World: The Unfair Trade Problem in U. S. -Thai Trade Relations. 2008. (ENG.). 132p. pap. 24.50 *(978-0-7391-1656-2(8))* Lexington Bks.

Rothgeb, John M. & Chinapandhu, Benjamas, eds. Trade & Development in a Globalized World: The Unfair Trade Problem in U. S. -Thai Trade Relations. 2006. (ENG.). 132p. 57.99 *(978-0-7391-1655-5(X))* Lexington Bks.

Russian Suspension Agreement: Hearing Before the Committee on Energy & Natural Resources, United States Senate, One Hundred Tenth Congress, Second Session, to Receive Testimony to Understand the Impacts of the Capability of the United States to Maintain a Domestic Enrichment Capability As a Result of the Recently Initiated Amendment Between the United States & the Russian Federation on the Agreement Suspending the Antidump. 2008. iii, 63p. *(978-0-16-081342-9(5)*, 552-070-37722-1) United States Government Printing Office.

United Nations. Business Guide to Trade Remdies in Canada: Anti-dumping, Contervailing & Safeguards Legislation, Practices & Procedures. 2007. (Business & Multilateral Trading Systems Ser.). (ENG.). 200p. pap. 50.00 *(978-92-9137-334-5(6))* United Nations Pubns.

Wu, Xiaochen. Anti-Dumping Law & Practice of China. 2008. xxxvi, 430p. 185.00 *(978-90-411-2790-7(9))* Wolters Kluwer Law & Business.

Yanning, Yu & Yu, Yanning. Circumvention & Anti-Circumvention Measures: The Impact on Anti-Dumping Practice in International Trade. 2008. (Global Trade Law Ser.). 185.00 *(978-90-411-2686-3(4))* Wolters Kluwer Law & Business.

ANTIDUMPING TARIFFS

see Antidumping Duties

ANTIEPILEPTICS

see Anticonvulsants

ANTIETAM, BATTLE OF, MD., 1862

Alexander, Charles. Battle of Antietam: The Bloodiest Day. 2011. 160p. pap. 19.99 ***(978-1-60949-179-6(3))*** History Pr., The.

Armstrong, Marion V., Jr. & Armstrong, Marion V. Unfurl Those Colors! McClellan, Sumner, & the Second Army Corps in the Antietam Campaign. 3rd ed. 2008. (ENG., Illus.). 424p. 39.95 ***(978-0-8173-1600-6(0))*** Univ. of Alabama Pr.

Ballard, Ted. Battle of Antietam Staff Ride Guide. 2009. (ENG., Illus.). 119p. pap. 13.00 *(978-0-16-081702-1(1)*, Dept. of the Army) United States Government Printing Office.

Carman, Ezra Ayers & Clemens, Thomas G. The Maryland Campaign of September 1862. 2010. (Illus.). 624p. *(978-1-932714-81-4(2))* Savas Beatie.

Davis, William C. The Battle of Antietam: A Civil War Times Illustrated Special, August 1962. Davis, William C., ed. 2011. 38p. 35.95 ***(978-1-258-00493-4(3))*** Literary Licensing, LLC.

Gindlesperger, James & Gindlesperger, Suzanne. So You Think You Know Antietam? The Stories Behind America's Bloodiest Day. 2012. (Illus.). 224p. pap. 19.95 ***(978-0-89587-579-2(9))*** Blair, John F. Pub.

Gottfried, Bradley. The Maps of Antietam: An Atlas of the Antietam (Sharpsburg) Campaign, including the Battle of South Mountain, September 2 - 20 1862. 2011. (Savas Beatie Military Atlas Ser.). (Illus.). 320p. 39.95 ***(978-1-61121-086-6(0))*** Savas Beatie.

Hartwig, D. Scott. To Antietam Creek: The Maryland Campaign of September 1862. 2012. ***(978-1-4214-0631-2(4))*** Johns Hopkins Univ. Pr.

Heysinger, Isaac W. Antietam & the Maryland & Virginia Campaigns of 1862: The Government Records. 322p. reprint ed. 98.00 *(978-0-7222-8041-6(6))* Library Reprints, Inc.

Kalasky, Robert J. Shadows of Antietam. 2011. 224p. 49.00 *(978-1-60635-088-1(9))* Kent State Univ. Pr.

Palfrey, Francis Winthrop. The Antietam & Fredericksburg. 2009. (ENG.). 243p. 32.99 *(978-1-117-19810-1(3))* 2009. (ENG.). 243p. pap. 25.75 *(978-1-117-19811-8(1))* 2008. 244p. 24.99 *(978-0-559-26307-1(4))* 2008. 244p. pap. 25.75 *(978-0-559-26305-7(8))* BiblioBazaar.

—The Antietam & Fredericksburg. 2010. 136p. pap. *(978-1-151-89368-0(4))* Books LLC.

—The Antietam & Fredericksburg. 2007. (ENG.). 238p. 41.95 *(978-0-548-23487-7(6))*; 240p. per. 26.95 *(978-1-4326-3567-1(0))* Kessinger Publishing, LLC.

—The Antietam & Fredericksburg. (Campaigns of the Civil War Ser.). 228p. reprint ed. 98.00 *(978-0-7222-8036-2(X))* Library Reprints, Inc.

Pierro, Joseph, ed. The Maryland Campaign of September 1862: Ezra A. Carman's Definitive Study of the Union & Confederate Armies at Antietam. 2008. (ENG., Illus.). 512p. 95.00 *(978-0-415-95628-4(5))* Routledge.

Rafuse, Ethan Sepp. Antietam, South Mountain, & Harpers Ferry: A Battlefield Guide. 2008. (This Hallowed Ground: Guides to Civil Wa Ser.). (ENG., Illus.). 282p. pap. 21.95 *(978-0-8032-3970-8(X)*, Bison Bks.) Univ. of Nebraska Pr.

Schildt, John W. The Ninth Corps at Antietam. 203p. (Orig.). 25.00 *(978-1-56013-010-9(5))* Olde Soldier Bks., Inc.

Sheppard, Eric William. The Campaign in Virginia & Maryland, June 26th to Sept. 20th, 1862, Cedar Run, Manassas, & Sharpsburg. (Special Campaign Ser.). 306p. reprint ed. 98.00 *(978-0-7222-8038-6(6))*; 98.00 *(978-0-7222-8042-3(4))* Library Reprints, Inc.

Slotkin, Richard. The Long Road to Antietam: How the Civil War Became a Revolution. 2012. (ENG., Illus.). 480p. 32.95 ***(978-0-87140-411-4(7)***, 40411) Liveright Publishing Corp.

Tilberg, Frederick. Antietam - Naional Battlefield Site. 2010. 72p. pap. 8.95 ***(978-1-58218-782-2(7))*** Digital Scanning, Inc.

—Antietam National Battlefield, Maryland. 60p. pap. 95.00 *(978-0-16-003408-4(6)*, Interior Dept.) United States Government Printing Office.

Tucker, Phillip & Tucker, Phillip Thomas. Burnside's Bridge: The Climactic Struggle of the 2nd & 20th Georgia at Antietam Creek. 2011. (ENG., Illus.). 256p. pap. 19.95 ***(978-0-8117-2816-4(1))*** Stackpole Bks.

Wheeler, Richard. Lee's Terrible Swift Sword: From Antietam to Chancellorsville: an Eyewitness History. 2008. (ENG., Illus.). 430p. 9.99 *(978-0-7858-1712-3(3)*, 0785817123) Book Sales, Inc.

Whitman, T. Stephen. Antietam 1862. 2012. (Battles & Leaders of the American Civil War Ser.). 208p. 48.00 ***(978-0-313-39733-2(3)***, A3553C) Greenwood Publishing Group, Inc.

ANTIETAM CAMPAIGN, 1862

see Maryland Campaign, 1862

ANTIGEN-ANTIBODY REACTIONS

see also Hemolysis and Hemolysins

Levine, Beth, et al. Autophagy in Infection & Immunity. 2009. (Current Topics in Microbiology & Immunology Ser.). (ENG., Illus.). xiv, 339p. 239.00 *(978-3-642-00301-1(X)*, 364200301X) Springer.

Marone, G., ed. Superantigens & Superallergens [Bibliography & Price not Definite.]. 2007. (Chemical Immunology & Allergy Ser.). (Illus.). 242p. *(978-3-8055-8266-7(8))* Karger, S. AG.

Schonewille, H. Red Blood Cell Alloimmunization after Blood Transfusion. 2008. (LUP Dissertaties Ser.). 180p. per. *(978-90-8728-031-4(9)*, Leiden Univ. Pr.) Amsterdam Univ. Pr.

ANTIGENS

see also Antigen-Antibody Reactions; Hepatitis Associated Antigen; Immunoblotting; Immunoglobulins; Toxins

Aktories, K. & Just, I., eds. Bacterial Protein Toxins. 2010. (Handbook of Experimental Pharmacology Ser.). (Illus.). xxxii, 700p. pap. 749.00 *(978-3-642-08540-6(7)*, 3642085407) Springer.

Alvarez, Matt. Treating Algal Toxins Using Oxidation, Adsorption, & Membrane Technologies. 2010. (Illus.). 218p. pap. *(978-1-60573-082-0(3))* Water Research Foundation.

Boltz, Agnes. Mimotope Vaccines Against Tumor Antigenes. 2008. 60p. pap. *(978-3-639-04375-4(8))* VDM Verlag Dr. Mueller e.K.

Cavenaugh, James. Quantitative Studies in T & B Cell Epitope Mimicry. 2010. 152p. pap. *(978-3-8383-1791-5(2))* Lambert Academic Publishing.

Chen, Lieping, ed. The B7-CD28 Family Molecules. 2010. (Molecular Biology Intelligence Unit Ser.). 154p. pap. 149.00 *(978-1-4419-3412-3(X)*, 144193412X) Springer.

Cram101 Textbook Reviews Staff. Outlines & Highlights for Janeways Immunobiology by Kenneth Murphy, Paul Travers, Mark Walport, Isbn: 9780815341239. 2009. 374p. pap. 34.95 *(978-1-4288-8280-5(4))* Cram101 Inc.

Dranoff, Glenn. Cancer Immunology & Immunotherapy. 2011. (Current Topics in Microbiology & Immunology Ser.). (ENG., Illus.). xiii, 304p. 189.00 *(978-3-642-14135-5(8)*, 3642141358) Springer.

Dunn, Louise. Melanotransferrin. 2009. 236p. pap. *(978-3-639-14083-5(4))* VDM Verlag Dr. Mueller e.K.

Gires, Olivier & Seliger, Barbara, eds. Tumor-Associated Antigens: Identification, Characterization, & Clinical Applications. 2009. (ENG., Illus.). 383p. 219.95 *(978-3-527-32084-4(9)*, Wiley-VCH) Wiley, John & Sons, Inc.

Hu, Jiancheng. Regulation of B Cell Migration & Antigen Receptor Signaling by Lsc. 2010. 136p. pap. *(978-3-639-27472-1(5))* VDM Verlag Dr. Mueller e.K.

Keren, David, et al. Flow Cytometry in Clinical Diagnosis. 4th ed. 2007. (Illus.). 384p. 179.25 incl. cd-rom *(978-0-89189-548-0(5))* American Society for Clinical Pathology.

Kiselevsky, Mikhail V. Atlas Effectors of Anti-Tumor Immunity. 2008. (Illus.). 270p. 159.00 *(978-1-4020-6930-7(8))* Springer.

Leong, Anthony S. Y. & Wong, Tommy S. W. Kinematic-Wave Rainfall-Runoff Formulas. 2009. 79.00 *(978-1-60692-705-2(1))* Nova Science Pubs., Inc.

Locht, Camille, ed. Bordetella: Molecular Microbiology. 2007. (ENG., Illus.). 315p. (C). 252.00 *(978-1-904933-31-1(9)*, Taylor & Francis) Taylor & Francis Group GBR. Dist: Taylor & Francis Group.

Lomas-Francis, Christine & Reid, Marion E. Blood Group Antigens & Antibodies: A Guide to Clinical Relevance & Technical Tips. 2007. (Illus.). 214p. pec. 25.00 *(978-1-59572-103-7(7))* Star Bright Bks., Inc.

Mantis, Nicholas, ed. Ricin & Shiga Toxins: Pathogenesis, Immunity, Vaccines & Therapeutics. 2012. (Current Topics in Microbiology & Immunology Ser.: 357). (ENG., Illus.). xi, 276p. 189.00 ***(978-3-642-27469-5(2)***, 3642274692) Springer.

Marone, G., ed. Superantigens & Superallergens [Bibliography & Price not Definite.]. 2007. (Chemical Immunology & Allergy Ser.). (Illus.). 242p. *(978-3-8055-8266-7(8))* Karger, S. AG.

Moody, Branch D., ed. T Cell Activation by CD1 & Lipid Antigens. 2010. (Current Topics in Microbiology & Immunology Ser.). (Illus.). viii, 348p. pap. 169.00 *(978-3-642-08906-0(2)*, 3642089062) Springer.

Morteau, Olivier. Oral Tolerance: The Response of the Intestinal Mucosa to Dietary Antigens. (Medical Intelligence Unit Ser.). 200p. 119.00 *(978-1-58706-054-0(X))* Landes Bioscience.

Rahmanto, Yohan Suryo & Richardson, Des. The Physiological & Pathophysiological Roles of Melanotransferrin. 2008. 216p. pap. *(978-3-639-04600-7(5))* VDM Verlag Dr. Mueller e.K.

Rammensee, Hans & Dawkins, Roger. Antigen Processing. 2007. 460p. 160.00 *(978-3-527-30986-3(1))* Wiley, John & Sons, Inc.

Reid, Marion E. & Shine, Ian. The Discovery & Significance of the Blood Groups. 2012. (Illus.). 214p. 36.00 ***(978-1-59572-422-9(2))*** Star Bright Bks., Inc.

Reineke, Ulrich, ed. Epitope Mapping Protocols: Second Edition. 2nd ed. 2009. (Methods in Molecular Biology Ser.). (ENG., Illus.). xiv, 450p. 129.00 *(978-1-934115-17-6(7))* Humana Pr.

Sasakawa, Chihiro. Molecular Mechanisms of Bacterial Infection via the Gut. 2009. (Current Topics in Microbiology & Immunology Ser.). (ENG., Illus.). xi, 260p. 189.00 *(978-3-642-01845-9(9)*, 3642018459) Springer.

Saylor, Jake A. & Michaels, Lionel B., eds. PSA & Prostate Cancer. 2010. (Cancer Etiology, Diagnosis & Treatments Ser.). (Illus.). xiv, 241p. 145.00 *(978-1-60876-895-0(3)*, Nova Biomedical Bks.) Nova Science Pubs., Inc.

Shi, Shan-Rong, et al. Antigen Retrieval Immunohistochemistry Based Research & Diagnostics. 2010. (Wiley Series in Biomedical Engineering & Multi-Disciplinary Integrated Systems Ser.: 1). (ENG., Illus.). 450p. 153.00 *(978-0-470-62452-4(3)*, Wiley) Wiley, John & Sons, Inc.

Singh, Pratap. Novel Therapeutic Agents for the Treatment ofProstate Cancer: Design & Development of Novel Anti-androgens, Thapsigargin Analogs & Inhibitors of Prostate Specific Antigen. 2008. 196p. pap. *(978-3-639-09050-5(0))* VDM Verlag Dr. Mueller e.K.

Solheim, Joyce C., ed. Antigen Processing & Presentation Protocols. 2010. (Methods in Molecular Biology Ser.). (Illus.). 294p. pap. 119.00 *(978-1-61737-166-0(1)*, 1617371661) Humana Pr.

Stulik, Jiri, et al, eds. BSL3 & BSL4 Agents: Proteomics, Glycomics, & Antigenicity. 2011. (ENG., Illus.). 256p. 139.95 ***(978-3-527-32780-5(0)***, Wiley-VCH) Wiley, John & Sons, Inc.

Sundmacher, R., ed. Adequate HLA Matching in Keratoplasty, Vol. 36. (Developments in Ophthalmology Ser.: Vol. 36). (Illus.). *(978-3-8055-7487-7(8))* Karger, S. AG.

Wajant, Harald, ed. Fas Signaling. 2010. (Medical Intelligence Unit Ser.). (Illus.). viii, 160p. pap. 189.00 *(978-1-4419-4074-2(X)*, 144194074X) Springer.

Yadav, Savita, et al. PSA & Prostate Cancer Research. 2010. (Cancer Etiology, Diagnosis & Treatments Ser.). 64p. pap. 43.00 *(978-1-61668-685-7(5)*, Nova Biomedical Bks.) Nova Science Pubs., Inc.

Yona, Simon & Stacey, Martin, eds. Adhesion-GPCRs: Structure to Function. 2011. (Advances in Experimental Medicine & Biology Ser.). (ENG., Illus.). xxii, 200p. 189.00 *(978-1-4419-7912-4(3)*, 1441979123) Springer.

Yousif, Ashraf & Elagib, Atif. Urinary Circulating Antigens of Schistosomes in Gezira-Sudan. 2010. 76p. pap. *(978-3-8383-7992-0(6))* Lambert Academic Publishing.

Zierhut, Manfred, et al, eds. Antigen-Presenting Cells & the Eye. 2007. (ENG., Illus.). 256p. 200.00 *(978-0-8493-9020-3(6)*, Informa Healthcare) Taylor & Francis Group.

ANTIGUA

Thome, James A. & Kimball, J. Horace. Emancipation in the West Indies: A Six Months' Tour in Antigua, Barbados, & Jamaica, in the Year 1837. 2010. (Cambridge Library Collection - History Ser.). (Illus.). 498p. pap. 35.99 *(978-1-108-01670-4(7))* Cambridge Univ. Pr.

ANTIGUA—DESCRIPTION AND TRAVEL

Anderson, Brian & Anderson, Ellen. Antigua & Barbuda. 2nd rev. ed. (Illus.). 96p. pap. 11.95 *(978-1-84306-061-1(2))* Hunter Publishing, Inc.

Antigua & the Antiguans: A Full Account of the Colony & its Inhabitants. 2011. (Cambridge Library Collection - Slavery & Abolition Ser.). 364p. pap. 29.99 *(978-1-108-02776-2(8))*; (ENG.). 368p. pap. 29.99 *(978-1-108-02777-9(6))* Cambridge Univ. Pr.

Argueta, Al. Moon Guatemala City & Antigua. 2009. (Moon Outdoors Ser.). (ENG.). 80p. pap. 7.95 *(978-1-59880-265-8(8))* Avalon Travel Publishing.

Locken, E. Travel Journal Antigua. 2009. 192p. pap. 20.95 *(978-0-557-08012-0(6))* Lulu Enterprises Inc.

Philpott, Don & Landmarks Staff. Antigua. 2nd rev. ed. 2008. (Illus.). 96p. 11.99 *(978-1-84306-368-1(9))* Landmark Publishing Ltd. GBR. Dist: Hunter Publishing, Inc.

Thomas Cook Publishing. Antigua Pocket Guide, 2nd: Compact & practical pocket guides for sun seekers & city Breakers. 2nd ed. 2011. (Thomas Cook Pocket Guides). (ENG., Illus.). 128p. pap. 9.95 *(978-1-84848-450-4(X))* Cook, Thomas Publishing GBR. Dist: Globe Pequot Pr., The.

ANTIGUA—ECONOMIC CONDITIONS

Icon Group International, Inc. Staff, compiled by. The 2006 Economic & Product Market Databook for Codrington, Antigua & Barbuda. 2006. 618p. ring bd. 95.00 *(978-0-497-80388-9(7))* Icon Group International, Inc.

ANTIGUA—HISTORY

Antigua & the Antiguans: A Full Account of the Colony & its Inhabitants. 2011. (Cambridge Library Collection - Slavery & Abolition Ser.). 364p. pap. 29.99 *(978-1-108-02776-2(8))*; (ENG.). 368p. pap. 29.99 *(978-1-108-02777-9(6))* Cambridge Univ. Pr.

Buhle, Paul. Tim Hector: A Caribbean Radical's Story. 2006. (ENG., Illus.). 272p. 32.00 *(978-1-57806-851-7(7))* Univ. Pr. of Mississippi.

Knight, Emily Vanessa Spencer. Growing up in All Saints Village, Antigu. 2009. 160p. 29.99 *(978-1-4415-3067-7(3))*; pap. 19.99 *(978-1-4415-3066-0(5))* Xlibris Corp.

ANTIHISTAMINES

see also Histamine

Shmaefsky, Brian R. Antihistamines & Other Allergy Drugs. 2011. (Understanding Drugs Ser.). (YA). (gr. 9-12). 34.95 ***(978-1-60413-533-6(6))*** Facts On File, Inc.

Thurmond, Robin L., ed. Histamine in Inflammation. 2011. (Advances in Experimental Medicine & Biology Ser.). (Illus.). xviii, 144p. 189.00 *(978-1-4419-8055-7(5)*, 1441980555) Springer.

ANTIINFLATIONARY POLICIES

see Anti-Inflationary Policies

ANTILLES

see West Indies

ANTILLES, FRENCH

see West Indies, French

ANTILLES, LESSER

see also Barbados; Leeward Islands (West Indies); Netherlands Antilles; Trinidad and Tobago; West Indies, French; Windward Islands

Cameron, Sarah. Caribbean - Insight Guides. 6th ed. 2012. (Insight Guides). (Illus.). 368p. pap. 24.99 ***(978-1-78005-037-9(2))*** APA Publications Services SGP. Dist: Ingram Pub. Services.

Luntta, Karl. The Caribbean: Lesser Antilles. 2nd ed. pap. 22.95 *(978-962-217-690-4(9))* Airphoto International/Odyssey HKG. Dist: Norton, W. W. & Co., Inc.

Rojer, Olga E. Founding Fictions of the Dutch Caribbean: Carel de Haseth's Slave & Master (Katibu Di Shon) 2011. (ENG.). 70p. (C). 35.95 ***(978-1-4331-1605-6(7))*** Lang, Peter Publishing, Inc.

Showker, Kay. Caribbean Ports of Call: A Guide for Today's Cruise Passengers. 2010. (ENG., Illus.). 592p. pap. 18.95 *(978-0-7627-6035-0(4))* Globe Pequot Pr., The.

Sturm, Philip. West Indian Antique Furniture: Of the Lesser Antilles, 1740-1940. 2007. (ENG., Illus.). 224p. 89.50 *(978-1-85149-537-5(1))* Antique Collectors' Club.

Waterton, Charles. Wanderings in South America. I.t. ed. 2007. (ENG.). 240p. pap. 22.99 *(978-1-4264-2641-4(0))* BiblioBazaar.

ANTIMASONIC PARTY

Anonymous & Anonymous. A Narrative of the Facts & Circumstances Relating to the Kidnaping & Murder of William Morgan. 2010. 98p. 33.95 *(978-1-161-48886-9(3))* Kessinger Publishing, LLC.

Brown, Henry. A Narrative of the Anti-Masonick Excitement, in the Western Part of the State of New York, During the Years 1826, '7, '8, & a Part Of 1829. 2010. 268p. pap. 27.75 *(978-1-149-48122-6(6))* BiblioBazaar.

—A Narrative of the Anti-Masonick Excitement, in the Western Part of the State of New York, During the Years 1826, '7, '8, & a Part Of 1829. 2010. 132p. pap. *(978-1-153-05114-9(1))* Books LLC.

Dafoe, Stephen. Morgan: The Scandal That Shook Freemasonry. 2009. 484p. pap. 26.95 *(978-1-934935-54-5(9)*, Cornerstone Bk. Publishers) Poll, Michael Publishing.

Green, Samuel D. The Broken Seal; or, Personal Reminiscences of the Morgan Abduction & Murder. 2009. 307p. 36.99 *(978-1-117-45527-3(0))*; 308p. pap.

28.75 *(978-1-117-45528-0(9))*; (ENG.). 307p. pap. 23.99 *(978-1-117-45529-7(7)*, BiblioLife) BiblioBazaar.

Green, Samuel D. B. The Broken Seal: Or Personal Reminiscences of the Morgan Abduction & Murder (1870) 2008. 306p. 43.95 *(978-1-4372-3876-1(9))*; pap. 28.95 *(978-1-4371-1075-3(4))* Kessinger Publishing, LLC.

Greene, Samuel D. The Broken Seal: Or, Personal Reminiscenses of the Morgan Abduction & Murder. 2010. 314p. pap. 29.75 *(978-1-143-92441-5(X))* BiblioBazaar.

—The Broken Seal: Or, Personal Reminiscenses of the Morgan Abduction & Murder, Volume 44;andnbsp;volume 982. 2010. 310p. pap. 29.75 *(978-1-142-55201-5(2))* BiblioBazaar.

—The Broken Seal; or, Personal Reminiscenses of the Morgan Abduction & Murder. 2009. 132p. pap. 19.99 *(978-1-150-60437-9(9))*; pap. 19.99 *(978-1-150-38531-5(6))* General Bks. LLC.

Mock, Stanley Upton. The Morgan Episode in American Free Masonry. 2011. 156p. 41.95 ***(978-1-258-05405-2(1))*** Literary Licensing, LLC.

A Narrative of the Facts & Circumstances Relating to the Kidnaping & Murder of William Morgan. 2007. 108p. 33.95 *(978-0-548-03692-1(6))* Kessinger Publishing, LLC.

Odiorne, James Creighton. Opinions on Speculative Masonry, Relative to Its Origin, Nature & Tendency. 2006. 292p. per. 23.99 *(978-1-4255-2701-3(5)*, MPublishing.

Palmer, John C. The Morgan Affair & Anti-Masonry. 2010. 128p. 35.95 *(978-1-161-35042-5(X))* Kessinger Publishing, LLC.

Stone. Letters on Masonry & Anti-Masonry, Addressed to the Hon John Quincy Adams. 2010. 330p. pap. 40.46 *(978-1-151-50684-9(2))* General Bks. LLC.

Stone, William L. Letters on Masonry & Anti-Masonry, Addressed to the Hon John Quincy Adams. 2010. 592p. pap. 44.75 *(978-1-177-84778-0(7))* BiblioBazaar.

Stone, William Leete. Letters on Masonry & Anti-Masonry: Addressed to the Hon. John Quincy Adams. 2010. 594p. pap. 44.75 *(978-1-142-46398-4(2))* BiblioBazaar.

—Letters on Masonry & Anti-Masonry; Addressed to the Hon John Quincy Adams. 2009. (Illus.). 342p. pap. 27.09 *(978-1-150-35630-8(8))* General Bks. LLC.

ANTIMATTER

Close, Frank. Antimatter. 2010. (ENG., Illus.). 176p. pap. 12.95 *(978-0-19-957887-0(7))* Oxford Univ. Pr., Inc.

Hasanuddin. The Dominium: Sequencing antimatter & gravity effects: Big Bang to black hole; & implications for a manmade near-future doomsday: End-of-All-Life on Earth. deluxe ed. 2007. 200p. lib. bdg. 28.50 *(978-0-9800963-2-3(4))* Clano Design.

Kanai, Yasuyuki. Proceedings of the Workshop on Cold Antimatter Plasmas & Application to Fundamental Physics: Okinawa, Japan, 20-22 February 2008. 2008. (AIP Conference Proceedings / Atomic, Molecular, Chemical Physics Ser.). (Illus.). 380p. 199.00 *(978-0-7354-0561-5(1))* American Institute of Physics.

Leonardo, Nuno. Matter Antimatter Fluctuations. 2011. 364p. pap. ***(978-3-8433-7693-8(X))*** Lambert Academic Publishing.

Surko, Clifford M. & Gianturco, Franco A., eds. New Directions in Antimatter Chemistry & Physics. 2010. 520p. pap. 207.00 *(978-90-481-5760-0(9)*, 9048157609) Springer.

ANTIMETABOLITES

Asadujjaman, Mohammad, et al. Pharmacological & Phytochemical Evaluation of Brassica Olerace. 2011. 76p. pap. ***(978-3-8443-3413-5(0))*** Lambert Academic Publishing.

Awang, A. Faris, et al. Metabolic Syndrome among Nurses. 2011. 104p. pap. ***(978-3-8443-3266-7(9))*** Lambert Academic Publishing.

Rustum, Youcef M., ed. Fluoropyrimidines in Cancer Therapy. 2010. (Cancer Drug Discovery & Development Ser.). (Illus.). 336p. pap. 199.00 *(978-1-61737-274-2(9)*, 1617372749) Humana Pr.

ANTIMICROBIAL AGENTS

see Anti-Infective Agents

ANTIMILITARISM

see Militarism

ANTIMISSILE MISSILES

Samson, Victoria A. American Missile Defense: A Guide to the Issues. 2010. (Contemporary Military, Strategic & Security Issues Ser.). 242p. instr.'s gde. ed., instr.'s hndbk. ed. 44.95 *(978-0-313-35326-0(3)*, C35326, Praeger Pubs.) Greenwood Publishing Group, Inc.

ANTIMONY

Razeghi, M. Antimony: Characteristics, Compounds, & Applications. 2012. ***(978-1-62100-598-8(4))*** Nova Science Pubs., Inc.

Sun, Hongzhe, ed. Biological Chemistry of Arsenic, Antimony & Bismuth. 2011. (ENG., Illus.). 400p. 175.00 *(978-0-470-71390-7(9)*, Wiley) Wiley, John & Sons, Inc.

ANTIN, MARY, 1881-1949

Antin, Mary. The Promised Land. 2010. 434p. pap. 35.75 *(978-1-142-14570-5(0))* 2010. 430p. pap. 35.75 *(978-1-142-50094-8(2))* 2010. 434p. pap. 35.75 *(978-1-142-14982-6(X))* 2009. 340p. 29.99 *(978-0-559-06814-0(X))* 2009. 340p. 28.99 *(978-0-559-06830-0(1))* 2009. 340p. pap. 31.75 *(978-0-559-06818-8(2))* 2009. 340p. pap. 30.75 *(978-0-559-06825-6(5))* BiblioBazaar.

—The Promised Land. 2009. 196p. pap. *(978-0-217-63364-2(1))* Books LLC.

—The Promised Land. (Best Nonfiction Sellers of 1912 Ser.). reprint ed. lib. bdg 48.00 *(978-0-7426-1224-2(4))* Classic Bks.

—The Promised Land. 2008. (Illus.). 312p. pap. *(978-1-4099-1733-5(9))* Dodo Pr.

—The Promised Land. 2012. (ENG., Illus.). 416p. (gr. 12). pap. 16.00 ***(978-0-14-310677-7(5)***, Penguin Classics) Penguin Group (USA) Inc.

—The Promised Land. 2008. (ENG.). 432p. pap. 19.45 *(978-1-4385-1029-3(2)*, Book Jungle) Standard Pubns., Inc.

Mary, Antin. Promised Land 1912. 2006. pap. 22.45 *(978-1-59462-380-6(5)*, Book Jungle) Standard Pubns., Inc.

ANTINEOPLASTIC AGENTS

see also Antimetabolites; Interferon

Abel, Emily & Subramanian, Saskia. After the Cure: The Untold Stories of Breast Cancer Survivors. 2010. (ENG.). 208p. pap. 20.00 *(978-0-8147-0735-7(1)*, New York Univ. Pr.

Abel, Emily K. & Subramanian, Saskia K. After the Cure: The Untold Stories of Breast Cancer Survivors. 2008. (ENG.). 208p. 50.00 *(978-0-8147-0725-8(4))* New York Univ. Pr.

Adachi, Randy. Novel Drug Delivery Systems for Gene-Targeted Rna Interference. 2010. 136p. pap. *(978-3-8383-4091-3(4))* Lambert Academic Publishing.

Adjei, Alex A., ed. Lung Cancer Therapies. 2009. (Cancer Drug Discovery & Development Ser.). 135.00 *(978-1-60327-010-6(8))* Humana Pr.

Anderson, Kenneth C., et al. Bortezomib in the Treatment of Multiple Myeloma. 2010. (Milestones in Drug Therapy Ser.). (ENG., Illus.). 10p. 189.00 *(978-3-7643-8947-5(8)*, 3764389478) Birkhauser Verlag AG CHE. Dist: Springer.

Anshul, Agarwal. Nanoformulation & Controlled Delivery of Low Solubility Cancer Drugs: A Nanotechnology Based Approach for Formulation of Toxic Therapeutic & Imaging Agents. 2011. 144p. pap. ***(978-3-639-32555-3(9))*** VDM Verlag Dr. Mueller e.K.

Beckerman, Martin. Cellular Signaling in Health & Disease. 2009. (Biological & Medical Physics, Biomedical Engineering Ser.). (ENG., Illus.). x, 486p. 189.00 *(978-0-387-98172-7(1))* Springer.

Berdel, Wolfgang E., et al. Angiogenesis Inhibition. 2009. (Recent Results in Cancer Research Ser.). (ENG., Illus.). xvii, 231p. 189.00 *(978-3-540-78280-3(X)*, 354078280X) Springer.

Blumenthal, Rosalyn D., ed. Chemosensitivity: Volume I: in Vitro Assays. 2010. (Methods in Molecular Medicine Ser.). (Illus.). xiii, 231p. pap. 104.00 *(978-1-61737-508-8(X)*, 161737508X) Humana Pr.

—Chemosensitivity: Volume II: in Vivo Models, Imaging, & Molecular Regulators. 2010. (Methods in Molecular Medicine Ser.). (Illus.). 464p. pap. 169.00 *(978-1-61737-660-3(4)*, 1617376604) Humana Pr.

Bonavida, Benjamin. Nitric Oxide (NO) & Cancer: Prognosis, Prevention, & Therapy. 2010. (Illus.). xx, 513p. E-Book *(978-1-4419-1432-3(3))* Springer.

Bonavida, Benjamin, ed. Nitric Oxide (NO) & Cancer. 2010. (Cancer Drug Discovery & Development Ser.). (ENG., Illus.). x, 250p. 259.00 *(978-1-4419-1431-6(5)*, 1441914315) Springer.

—Sensitization of Cancer Cells for Chemo/Immuno/Radio-therapy. 2010. (Cancer Drug Discovery & Development Ser.). (Illus.). xxi, 419p. pap. 209.00 *(978-1-61737-928-4(X)*, 161737928X) Humana Pr.

—Sensitization of Cancer Cells for Chemo/Immuno/Radio-Therapy. 2008. (Illus.). 479p. (C). 209.00 *(978-1-934115-29-9(0)*, 1934115290) Humana Pr.

Bragalone, Diedra L., ed. Drug Information Handbook for Oncology: A Complete Guide to Combination Chemotherapy Regimens. 9th ed. 2011. (Lex-Comp's Drug Reference Handbooks Ser.). (Illus.). 1707p. pap. 49.95 *(978-1-59195-290-9(5))* Lexi-Comp, Inc.

Brahmer, Julie R., et al, eds. Lung Cancer: Translational & Emerging Therapies. 2007. (Translational Medicine Ser.: Vol. 3). (ENG., Illus.). 280p. 100.00 *(978-0-8493-9021-0(4)*, Informa Healthcare) Taylor & Francis Group GBR. Dist: Taylor & Francis Group.

Brown, Dennis M., ed. Drug Delivery Systems in Cancer Therapy. 2010. (Cancer Drug Discovery & Development Ser.). (Illus.). 400p. pap. 209.00 *(978-1-61737-238-4(2)*, 1617372382) Humana Pr.

Brown, Martin J., et al. Multimodal Concepts for Integration of Cytotoxic Drugs. 2010. (Medical Radiology / Radiation Oncology Ser.). (Illus.). x, 352p. pap. 209.00 *(978-3-642-06505-7(8)*, 3642065058) Springer.

Butler, Sara Aston & Govindan, Ramaswamy. Essential Cancer Pharmacology: The Prescriber's Guide. 2010. (ENG.). 544p. pap. 74.99 *(978-1-60913-704-5(3))* Lippincott Williams & Wilkins.

Carmen Mejia Vazquez, Dra Ma Del & Navarro, Samuel. New Approaches in the Treatment of Cancer. 2011. (Cancer Etiology, Diagnosis & Treatments Ser.). 223p. pap. 79.00 ***(978-1-62100-067-9(2))*** Nova Science Pubs., Inc.

Carr, Daniel J. J., ed. Interferon Methods & Protocols. 2010. (Methods in Molecular Medicine Ser.). (Illus.). 240p. pap. 119.00 *(978-1-61737-554-5(3)*, 1617375543) Humana Pr.

Chabner, Bruce, et al. Harrison's Manual of Oncology. 2008. (Illus.). xxi, 624p. *(978-0-07-150811-7(2))*; *(978-0-07-150812-4(0))* McGraw-Hill Medical Publishing Div.

Chabner, Bruce A. & Longo, Dan L., eds. Cancer Chemotherapy & Biotherapy: Principles & Practice. 5th rev. ed. 2010. (ENG., Illus.). 848p. 238.99 *(978-1-60547-431-1(2))* Lippincott Williams & Wilkins.

Chen, Jin. Tumor-Targeting Taxane-Based Anticancer Agents. 2010. 336p. pap. *(978-3-639-24224-9(6))* VDM Verlag Dr. Mueller e.K.

Chian, Ri-Cheng & Quinn, Patrick, eds. Fertility Cryopreservation. 2010. (ENG., Illus.). 288p. 125.00 *(978-0-521-51778-2(8))* Cambridge Univ. Pr.

Chu, Edward. Physicians' Cancer Chemotherapy Drug Manual. 10th rev. ed. 2009. 559p. spiral bd. 108.95 *(978-0-7637-6176-7(2))* Jones & Bartlett Learning, LLC.

—Physician's Cancer Chemotherapy Drug Manual 2011. 11th ed. 2010. 591p. spiral bd. 99.95 *(978-1-4496-0197-3(9))* Jones & Bartlett Learning, LLC.

—Physician's Cancer Chemotherapy Drug Manual 2012. 12th ed. 2011. 600p. spiral bd. 93.95 ***(978-1-4496-4683-7(2))*** Jones & Bartlett Learning, LLC.

—Pocket Guide to Chemotherapy Protocols. 7th ed. 2011. 234p. spiral bd. 44.95 ***(978-1-4496-4681-3(6))*** Jones & Bartlett Learning, LLC.

—Pocket Guide to Hematologic Cancer Chemotherapy Protocols. rev. ed. 2012. 170p. spiral bd. 31.95 *(978-0-7637-8520-8(2))* Jones & Bartlett Learning, LLC.

—Pocket Guide to Targeted Therapies in Cancer. rev. ed. 2012. 80p. spiral bd. 31.95 *(978-0-7637-8535-2(0)*, Jones & Bartlett Learning, LLC.

Chu, Edward & DeVita, Vincent T. Physicians' Cancer Chemotherapy Drug Manual 2008. 2007. 552p. pap., spiral bd. 89.95 *(978-0-7637-5562-1(1))* Jones & Bartlett Learning, LLC.

Chu, Edward, et al. Physicians' Cancer Chemotherapy Drug Manual. 2007. (Physicians' Cancer Chemotherapy Drug Manual Ser.). (Illus.). 542p. spiral bd. 77.95 incl. cd-rom *(978-0-7637-4308-6(9))* Jones & Bartlett Learning, LLC.

Colotta, Francesco & Mantovani, Alberto, eds. Targeted Therapies in Cancer: Myth or Reality? 2008. (Advances in Experimental Medicine & Biology Ser.: Vol. 610). (Illus.). 222p. 179.00 *(978-0-387-73897-0(5))* Springer.

Cragg, Gordon M., et al, eds. Anticancer Agents from Natural Products Second Edition. 2nd rev. ed. 2011. (ENG., Illus.). 767p. 189.95 *(978-1-4398-1382-9(5)*, CRC Press) Taylor & Francis Group GBR. Dist: Taylor & Francis Group.

Cram101 Textbook Reviews. Outlines & Highlights for Emerging Cancer Therapy: Microbial Approaches & Biotechnological Tools by A. Fialho. 2011. 116p. pap. 28.95 ***(978-1-61905-346-5(2))*** Cram101 Inc.

Cram101 Textbook Reviews & Cram101 Textbook Reviews. Outlines & Highlights for Targeting Protein Kinases for Cancer Therapy by David Matthews, Isbn: 9780470229651. 2011. 158p. pap. 29.95 ***(978-1-61461-142-4(4))*** Cram101 Inc.

Dai, Wei, ed. Checkpoint Responses in Cancer Therapy. (Cancer Drug Discovery & Development Ser.). (Illus.). 2010. xiv, 314p. pap. 219.00 *(978-1-61737-847-8(X)*, 161737847X) 2008. 300p. 219.00 *(978-1-58829-930-7(9))* Humana Pr.

Daoud, Sayed S., ed. Cancer Proteomics: From Bench to Bedside. (Cancer Drug Discovery & Development Ser.). (Illus.). 2010. xii, 264p. pap. 149.00 *(978-1-61737-807-2(0)*, 1617378070) 2007. 264p. 149.00 *(978-1-58829-858-4(2))* Humana Pr.

Diederich, Marc, ed. Natural Compounds & Their Role in Apoptotic Cell Signaling Pathways. 2009. (Annals of the New York Academy of Sciences Ser.: 29). (ENG., Illus.). 400p. pap. 154.95 *(978-1-57331-737-5(3)*, Wiley-Blackwell) Wiley, John & Sons, Inc.

Dietel, Manfred. Targeted Therapies in Cancer. 2007. (Recent Results in Cancer Research Ser.). (Illus.). xiv, 262p. 189.00 *(978-3-540-46090-9(X))* Springer.

Disis, Mary L., ed. Immunotherapy of Cancer. 2010. (Cancer Drug Discovery & Development Ser.). (Illus.). 528p. pap. 229.00 *(978-1-61737-645-0(0)*, 1617376450) Humana Pr.

Edardes, Joseph P., ed. Coumarin Anticoagulant Research Progress. 2008. (Illus.). 160p. 185.00 *(978-1-60021-990-0(X))* Nova Science Pubs., Inc.

Figgins, Herold C. Trends in Cell Apoptosis Research. 2006. 293p. (C). 225.00 *(978-1-60021-424-0(X))* Nova Science Pubs., Inc.

Garrett-Mayer, Elizabeth, ed. Principles of Anticancer Drug Development. 2010. (Cancer Drug Discovery & Development Ser.). (Illus.). xvii, 250p. 189.00 *(978-1-4419-7357-3(5)*, 1441973575) Springer.

Gerber, David E. Targeted Therapy in Non-small Cell Lung Cancer, 1 vol. 2011. (Oxford American Pocket Notes Ser.). (ENG.). 88p. pap. 14.95 ***(978-0-19-974308-7(8))*** Oxford Univ. Pr., Inc.

Gioeli, Daniel, ed. Targeted Therapies: Mechanisms of Resistance. 2011. (Molecular & Translational Medicine Ser.). (ENG., Illus.). xiv, 201p. 139.00 ***(978-1-60761-477-7(4)***, 1607614774) Humana Pr.

Govindan, Ramaswamy, ed. The Washington Manual of Oncology: Department of Medicine, Division of Oncology, Washington University School of Medicine, St. Louis, Missouri. 2nd rev. ed. 2007. (Lippincott Manual Series (Formerly Known As the Spiral Manual Series) Ser.). (ENG., Illus.). 576p. per. 67.99 *(978-0-7817-8402-3(6))* Lippincott Williams & Wilkins.

Gullatte, Mary Magee, ed. Clinical Guide to Antineoplastic Therapy: A Chemotherapy Handbook. 2nd ed. 2007. (AFA., Illus.). 668p. per. *(978-1-890504-68-7(8))* Oncology Nursing Society.

Haas, Marilyn & McBride, Deborah L. Managing the Oral Effects of Cancer Treatment: Diagnosis to Survivorship. 2011. 544p. *(978-1-935864-03-5(3))* Oncology Nursing Society.

Hadjiliadis, Nick D. & Sletten, Einar, eds. Metal Complex - DNA Interactions. 2009. (ENG., Illus.). 544p. 199.99 *(978-1-4051-7629-3(6)*, Wiley-Blackwell) Wiley, John & Sons, Inc.

Hoffman Edward J Staff. Cancer & the Search for Selective Biochemical Inhibitors Second. 2nd rev. ed. 2007. (ENG., Illus.). 480p. 162.95 *(978-1-4200-4593-2(8)*, CRC Press) Taylor & Francis Group GBR. Dist: Taylor & Francis Group.

Idrees, Mohd., et al. Anticancerous Alkaloids of Catharanthus Roseus. 2011. 84p. pap. ***(978-3-8454-0904-7(5))*** Lambert Academic Publishing.

Immunotherapy of Cancer. 2007. per. 4250.00 *(978-1-59623-276-1(5))* BCC Research.

Innocenti, Federico, ed. Genomics & Pharmacogenomics in Anticancer Drug Development & Clinical Response. (Cancer Drug Discovery & Development Ser.). (Illus.). 2010. xiv, 378p. pap. 189.00 *(978-1-61737-694-8(9)*, 1617376949) 2008. 730p. 189.00 *(978-1-58829-646-7(6))* Humana Pr.

Jackman, Ann L. & Leamon, Christopher P., eds. Targeted Drug Strategies for Cancer & Inflammation. 2011. (ENG., Illus.). xi, 221p. 189.00 *(978-1-4419-8416-6(X)*, 144198416X) Springer.

Kelvin, Joanne Frankel & Tyson, Leslie. 100 Questions & Answers about Cancer Symptoms & Cancer Treatment Side Effects. 2nd rev. ed. 2010. 240p. pap. 22.95 *(978-0-7637-7760-9(9))* Jones & Bartlett Learning, LLC.

Krohn, Karsten. Anthracycline Chemistry & Biology. 2008. (Topics in Current Chemistry Ser.). 389.00 *(978-3-540-75814-3(3)*, 3540758143) Springer.

Krueger, Gretchen. Hope & Suffering: Children, Cancer, & the Paradox of Experimental Medicine. 2008. (ENG., Illus.). 232p. (gr. 17). 35.00 *(978-0-8018-8831-1(X))* Johns Hopkins Univ. Pr.

Kurzrock, Razelle & Markman, Maurie, eds. Targeted Cancer Therapy. 2010. (Current Clinical Oncology Ser.). (ENG., Illus.). xii, 452p. pap. 79.95 *(978-1-60761-598-9(3)*, 1607615983) Humana Pr.

Lacroix, Marc. Molecular Therapy of Breast Cancer: Classicism Meets Modernity. 2009. (Cancer Etiology, Diagnosis & Treatments Ser.). 291p. pap. 79.00 *(978-1-60741-593-0(3)*, Nova Biomedical Bks.) Nova Science Pubs., Inc.

Lee, Moses. Heterocyclic Antitumor Antibiotics. 2010. (Topics in Heterocyclic Chemistry Ser.). xiv, 252p. pap. 199.00 *(978-3-642-06814-0(6)*, 3642068146) Springer.

Leong, Stanley P. L. Cancer Clinical Trials: Proactive Strategies. 2006. (Cancer Treatment & Research Ser.). (Illus.). 318p. 149.00 *(978-0-387-33224-6(3)*, 0387332243) Springer.

Lewis, Thomas J. & Robinson, James, eds. Angiogenesis Research Progress. 2008. (Illus.). x, 218p. pap. 39.00 *(978-1-60456-620-8(5))* Nova Science Pubs., Inc.

Lexi-Comp, creator. Drug Information Handbook for Oncology: A Complete Guide to Combination Chemotherapy Regimens. 8th ed. 2010. (Lexi-Comp's Drug Reference Handbooks Ser.). 1560p. pap. 46.95 *(978-1-59195-277-0(8))* Lexi-Comp, Inc.

Li, Rongshi & Stafford, Jeffrey A. Kinase Inhibitor Drugs. 2009. (Wiley Series in Drug Discovery & Development Ser.: 11). (ENG., Illus.). 526p. 139.00 *(978-0-470-27829-1(3)*, Wiley) Wiley, John & Sons, Inc.

Mader, Ines, et al. Extravasation of Cytotoxic Agents: Compendium for Prevention & Management. Twisselmann, B., tr. from GER. 2nd ed. 2009. (Illus.). xiii, 392p. 139.00 *(978-3-211-88889-6(6)*, 3211888896) Springer.

Mahato, Ram I. & Lu, Yi, eds. Pharmaceutical Perspectives of Cancer Therapeutics. 2009. (ENG., Illus.). vi, 596p. 240.00 *(978-1-4419-0130-9(2)*, 1441901302) Springer.

Missailidis, Sotiris. Anticancer Therapeutics. 2008. (ENG., Illus.). 424p. 188.95 *(978-0-470-72303-6(3)*, Wiley) Wiley, John & Sons, Inc.

Moss, Ralph W. Customized Cancer Treatment: How a Powerful Lab Test Predicts Which Drugs Will Work for You — And Which to Avoid. 2010. (ENG.). 271p. pap. 19.95 *(978-1-881025-01-6(2))* Equinox Pr.

Mulzer, J. The Epothilones: An Outstanding Family of Anti-Tumour Agents: From Soil to the Clinic. 2008. (Fortschritte der Chemie organischer Naturstoffe / Progress in the Chemistry of Organic Natural Products Ser.). (Illus.). 340p. 249.00 *(978-3-211-78206-4(0))* Springer.

Murff, Samuel J. Safety & Health Handbook for Cytotoxic Drugs. 2012. (ENG.). 366p. 125.00 *(978-1-60590-704-8(9))* 2011. E-Book ***(978-1-60590-705-5(7))*** Government Institutes.

Neidle, Stephen, ed. Cancer Drug Design & Discovery. 2007. (ENG., Illus.). 496p. 102.00 *(978-0-12-369448-5(5)*, Academic Pr.) Elsevier Science & Technology Bks.

Newman, William G., ed. Pharmacogenetics - Making Cancer Treatment Safer & More Effective. 2010. (ENG., Illus.). vi, 245p. 179.00 *(978-90-481-8617-4(X)*, 904818617X) Springer.

Parsons, Robert A., ed. Progress in Cancer Drug Resistance Research. 2008. 129.00 *(978-1-60021-822-4(9)*, Nova Biomedical Bks.) Nova Science Pubs., Inc.

Penn, John, ed. Retinal & Choroidal Angiogenesis. 2010. xxiv, 568p. pap. 179.00 *(978-90-481-7724-0(3)*, 9048177243) Springer.

Perry, Michael C., ed. The Chemotherapy Source Book. 4th rev. ed. 2007. (ENG., Illus.). 800p. pap. 99.95 *(978-0-7817-7328-7(8))* Lippincott Williams & Wilkins.

Peters, Godefridus J., ed. Deoxynucleoside Analogs in Cancer Therapy. 2010. (Cancer Drug Discovery & Development Ser.). (Illus.). 496p. pap. 209.00 *(978-1-61737-497-5(0)*, 1617374970) Humana Pr.

Pitha, Paula M. Interferon: the 50th Anniversary: The 50th Anniversary. 2010. (Current Topics in Microbiology & Immunology Ser.). (Illus.). viii, 392p. pap. 169.00 *(978-3-642-09044-8(3)*, 3642090443) Springer.

Prendergast, George C. & Jaffee, Elizabeth M., eds. Cancer Immunotherapy: Immune Suppression & Tumor Growth. 2007. (ENG., Illus.). 428p. 114.00 *(978-0-12-372551-6(8)*, Academic Pr.) Elsevier Science & Technology Bks.

Prescher-Hughes, Debra S. Nurse's Chemotherapy Quick Pocket Reference. 2008. (ENG.). 208p. pap. 41.95 *(978-0-7637-5824-0(8))* Jones & Bartlett Learning, LLC.

Pui, Ching-Hon, ed. Treatment of Acute Leukemias: New Directions for Clinical Research. 2010. (Current Clinical Oncology Ser.). (Illus.). 584p. pap. 269.00 *(978-1-61737-212-4(9)*, 1617372129) Humana Pr.

Raffa, Robert B. & Tallarida, Ronald J., eds. Chemo Fog: Cancer Chemotherapy-Related Cognitive Impairment. 2010. (Advances in Experimental Medicine & Biology Ser.). (ENG., Illus.). xx, 212p. 219.00 *(978-1-4419-6305-5(7)*, 1441963057) Springer.

Rhomberg, Walter & Hellmann, Kurt, eds. Razoxane & Dexrazoxane - Two Multifunctional Agents: Experimental & Clinical Results. 2010. (ENG., Illus.). xiii, 243p. 189.00 (978-90-481-9167-3(X), 904819167X) Springer.

Ribatti, Domenico. History of Research on Tumor Angiogenesis. 2009. (ENG., Illus.). x, 126p. 159.00 (978-1-4020-9559-7(7), 1402095597) Springer.

Roboz John Staff. Mass Spectrometry in Cancer Research Second Edition. 2nd ed. 2009. (Illus.). 640p. 199.95 (978-0-8493-7390-9(5)) CRC Pr. LLC.

Salvador, Jorge A. R., ed. Pentacyclic Triterpenes as Promising Agents in Cancer. 2010. (Cancer Etiology, Diagnosis & Treatments Ser.). 135.00 (978-1-60876-973-5(9), Nova Biomedical Bks.) Nova Science Pubs., Inc.

Saria, Marlon Garzo. Chemotherapy & Biotherapy Scenarios. 2010. 88p. (978-1-890504-92-2(0)) Oncology Nursing Society.

Schlag, Peter M. & Stein, Ulrike, eds. Regional Cancer Therapy. 2007. (Cancer Drug Discovery & Development Ser.). (Illus.). 455p. 219.00 (978-1-58829-672-6(5), 1588296725) Humana Pr.

Schlag, Peter M. & Stein, Ulrike S., eds. Regional Cancer Therapy. 2010. (Cancer Drug Discovery & Development Ser.). (Illus.). xiv, 462p. pap. 219.00 (978-1-61737-711-2(2), 1617377112) Humana Pr.

Segal, Jodi B. Hydroxyurea for the Treatment of Sickle Cell Disease. 2008. (AHRQ Publication Ser.: No. 165). (Illus.). ix, 95p. (978-1-58763-343-0(4)) Agency for Healthcare Research & Quality.

Sioud, Mouldy. Target Discovery & Validation: Reviews & Protocols: Volume 1: Emerging Strategies for Targets & Biomarker Discovery, 2 vols. 2006. (Methods in Molecular Biology Ser.: Vol. 360). (Illus.). 354p. 179.00 (978-1-58829-656-6(3), 1588296563) Humana Pr.

—Target Discovery & Validation: Reviews & Protocols: Volume 2: Emerging Molecular Targets & Treatment Options, 2 vols., Vol. 2. 2006. (Methods in Molecular Biology Ser.: Vol. 361). (Illus.). 345p. 149.00 (978-1-58829-890-4(6), 1588298906) Humana Pr.

Skeel, Roland T. & Khleif, Samir. Handbook of Cancer Chemotherapy. 8th rev. ed. 2011. (Lippincott Williams & Wilkins Handbook Ser.). (ENG., Illus.). 832p. pap. 79.99 (978-1-60831-782-0(X)) Lippincott Williams & Wilkins.

Slevin, Mark, ed. Therapeutic Angiogenesis for Vascular Diseases: Molecular Mechanisms & Targeted Clinical Approaches for the Treatment of Angiogenic Disease. 2010. (ENG., Illus.). xvi, 430p. 239.00 (978-90-481-9494-0(6), 9048194946) Springer.

Sluyser, Mels. Application of Apoptosis to Cancer Treatment. 2010. (ENG.). vii, 370p. pap. 159.00 (978-90-481-6833-0(3), 9048168333) Springer.

Small, William. Combining Targeted Biological Agents with Radiotherapy: Current Status & Future Directions. 2008. (Illus.). 139.00 (978-1-933864-34-1(6)) Demos Medical Publishing, LLC.

Solimando, Dominic A., ed. Drug Information Handbook for Oncology: A Complete Guide to Combination Chemotherapy Regimens. 6th rev. ed. 2007. (Lexi-Comp's Drug Reference Handbooks Ser.). 1335p. pap. 42.95 (978-1-59195-175-9(5)) Lexi-Comp, Inc.

Spencer, Peter & Holt, Walter. Anticancer Drugs: Design, Delivery & Pharmacology. 2009. 129.00 (978-1-60741-004-1(4)) Nova Science Pubs., Inc.

Springhouse Publishing Company Staff & Lippincott Williams and Wilkins Staff, eds. Nursing Antineoplastic Drug Handbook 2011. 2010. (ENG.). 180p. pap. 25.99 (978-1-4511-0310-6(7)) Lippincott Williams & Wilkins.

Teicher, Beverly A., ed. Cancer Drug Resistance. 2010. (Cancer Drug Discovery & Development Ser.). (Illus.). 640p. pap. 259.00 (978-1-61737-622-1(1), 1617376221) Humana Pr.

—Cancer Therapeutics: Experimental & Clinical Agents. 2010. (Cancer Drug Discovery & Development Ser.). 464p. pap. 219.00 (978-1-61737-046-5(0), 1617370460) Humana Pr.

Thurston, David E. Chemistry & Pharmacology of Anticancer Drugs. 2006. (ENG., Illus.). 312p. 189.95 (978-0-8493-9219-1(5), CRC Press) Taylor & Francis Group GBR. Dist: Taylor & Francis Group.

Toeh, Gerrard K. H. Towards Individualized Therapy for Multiple Myeloma: A Guide for Choosing Treatment That Best Fits Patients. 2009. 200p. pap. 58.00 (978-981-283-579-6(2)) World Scientific Publishing Co., Inc.

Torres, Liman S. Cancer Drug Resistance Research Perspectives. 2007. 223p. 129.00 (978-1-60021-572-8(6)) Nova Science Pubs., Inc.

Vazquez, Dra. Ma. Del Carmen Mejia & Navarro, Samuel, eds. New Approaches in the Treatment of Cancer. 2011. (Cancer Etiology, Diagnosis & Treatments Ser.). (Illus.). 223p. 79.00 (978-1-61728-304-8(5)) Nova Science Pubs., Inc.

Vereecken, Pierre & Awada, Ahmad. Handbook of Skin Care in Cancer Patients. 2012. (Cancer Etiology, Diagnosis & Treatments Ser.). 217p. 59.00 (978-1-61668-419-8(4)) Nova Science Pubs., Inc.

Wallace, W. H. B. & Kelnar, C. J. H., eds. Endocrinopathy after Childhood Cancer Treatment. 2009. (Endocrine Development Ser.). (ENG., Illus.). 186p. (978-3-8055-9037-2(7)) Karger, S. AG.

Wilkes, Gail & Barton-Burke, Margaret. 2010 Oncology Nursing Drug Handbook. 14th rev. ed. 2009. 1360p. pap. 102.95 (978-0-7637-8124-8(X)) Jones & Bartlett Learning, LLC.

—2011 Oncology Nursing Drug Handbook. 15th ed. 2010. (Illus.). 1368p. pap. 96.95 (978-1-4496-0013-6(1)) Jones & Bartlett Learning, LLC.

Wilkes, Gail M. & Barton-Burke, Margaret. Oncology Nursing Drug Handbook. 2006. (Oncology Nursing Drug Handbook Ser.). 1217p. per. 93.95 (978-0-7637-4306-2(2)) Jones & Bartlett Learning, LLC.

—2008 Oncology Nursing Drug Handbook. 2007. 1220p. pap. 88.95 (978-0-7637-5563-8(X)) Jones & Bartlett Learning, LLC.

Wilkes, Gail M. & Burke, Margaret Barton. 2012 Oncology Nursing Drug Handbook. 16th ed. 2011. 1418p. pap. 93.95 ***(978-1-4496-4462-8(7))*** Jones & Bartlett Learning, LLC.

Wilkes, Gail M., et al. 2009 Oncology Nursing Drug Handbook. 13th ed. 2008. 1298p. pap. 104.95 (978-0-7637-6585-9(6)) Jones & Bartlett Learning, LLC.

Woodruff, Teresa K. & Snyder, Karrie Ann, eds. Oncofertility: Fertility Preservation for Cancer Survivors. 2007. (Cancer Treatment & Research Ser.). (Illus.). 262p. 169.00 (978-0-387-72292-4(0)) Springer.

Yu, Dihua & Hung, Mien-Chie, eds. Breast Cancer Chemosensitivity. 2007. (Advances in Experimental Medicine & Biology Ser.: Vol. 608). 190p. 189.00 (978-0-387-74037-9(6)) Springer.

Zhou, Chunxu & Ling, Xia. DNA Binding & DNA Extraction: Methods, Applications & Limitations. 2012. (DNA & RNA: Properties & Modifications Ser.). 252p. 140.00 ***(978-1-61470-958-9(0))*** Nova Science Pubs., Inc.

Zibaseresht, Ramin. Approaches to Photo Activated Cytotoxins. 2011. 328p. pap. ***(978-3-8443-8236-5(4))*** Lambert Academic Publishing.

ANTINOMIANISM

see also Law and Gospel

Adams, Charles Francis, Jr. Three Episodes of Massachusetts History Set: The Settlement of Boston Bay; The Antinomian Controversy; A Study of Church & Town Government, 2 vols. (Illus.). reprint ed. lib. bdg. 250.00 (978-0-7222-0647-8(X)) Library Reprints, Inc.

Battis, Emery. Saints & Sectaries: Anne Hutchinson & the Antinomian Controversy in the Massachusetts Bay Colony. 2011. (Published for the Omohundro Institute of Early American History & Culture, Williamsburg, Virginia Ser.). (ENG.). 416p. pap. 50.00 ***(978-0-8078-9616-7(0))*** Univ. of North Carolina Pr.

Battis, Emery John. Saints & Sectaries: Anne Hutchinson & the Antinomian Controversy in the Massachusetts Bay Colony. 2011. 398p. 54.95 ***(978-1-258-10287-6(0))*** Literary Licensing, LLC.

Bolton, Samuel. Christian Freedom: Chiefly Taken from Bolton's True Bounds. Martin, Selina, ed. 2007. (ENG.). 192p. per. 22.95 (978-1-4304-4548-7(3)) Kessinger Publishing, LLC.

Curtis, Edith. Anne Hutchinson: A Biography. 2011. 136p. 40.95 ***(978-1-258-06824-0(9))*** Literary Licensing, LLC.

Luther, Martin. Solus Decalogus est Aeternus: Martin Luther's Complete Antinomian Theses & Disputations. 2008.Tr. of Only the Decalogue Is Eternal. (LAT & ENG.). 416p. pap. 21.99 (978-0-9748529-5-9(3), Cygnus Series) Lutheran Pr., Inc.

Nuttall, Geoffrey F. Studies in Christian Enthusiasm: Illustrated from Early Quakerism. 2011. 90p. 38.95 ***(978-1-258-04298-1(3))*** Literary Licensing, LLC.

ANTINUCLEAR MOVEMENT

Beck, Sanderson. Peace or Bust: My Nonviolent Action Campaigns. 2008. x, 619p. (978-0-9792532-9-4(2)) World Peace Communications.

Fairhall, David. Common Ground: The Story of Greenham. 2006. (ENG., Illus.). 256p. 58.00 (978-1-84511-286-8(5)) I. B. Tauris & Co., Ltd. GBR. Dist: Macmillan.

Kolsbun, Ken. Peace: The Biography of a Symbol. 2008. (ENG., Illus.). 176p. 25.00 (978-1-4262-0294-0(6)) National Geographic Society.

Laffin, Arthur J., ed. Swords into Plowshares, Volume Two: A Chronology of Plowshares Disarmament Actions, 1980-2003. 2010. (Catholic Worker Reprint Ser.). 110p. pap. 15.00 (978-1-60899-051-1(6), Wipf and Stock) Wipf & Stock Pubs.

Laffin, Arthur J. & Montgomery, Anne, eds. Swords into Plowshares, Volume One: Nonviolent Direct Action for Disarmament, Peace & Social Justice. 2010. (Catholic Worker Reprint Ser.). 364p. pap. 40.00 (978-1-60899-059-7(1), Wipf and Stock) Wipf & Stock Pubs.

Nepstad, Sharon Erickson. Religion & War Resistance in the Plowshares Movement. 2008. (Cambridge Studies in Contentious Politics Ser.). (ENG., Illus.). 204p. 80.00 (978-0-521-88892-9(1)); 284p. pap. 25.99 (978-0-521-71767-0(1)) Cambridge Univ. Pr.

O'Neill, Dan. The Firecracker Boys: H-Bombs, Inupiat Eskimos, & the Roots of the Environmental Movement. 2007. (ENG., Illus.). 448p. pap. 16.95 (978-0-465-00348-8(6)) Basic Bks.

Roche, Douglas. How We Stopped Loving the Bomb: An Insider's Account of the World on the Brink of Banning Nuclear Arms. 2011. (ENG.). 208p. pap. 22.95 (978-1-55277-652-0(2)) Lorimer, James & Co., Ltd., Pubs. CAN. Dist: Casemate Pubs. & Bk. Distributors, LLC.

Scalmer, Sean. Gandhi in the West: The Mahatma & the Rise of Radical Protest. 2011. 254p. 90.00 (978-0-521-76091-1(7)); pap. 32.99 (978-0-521-13958-8(9)) Cambridge Univ. Pr.

Surbrug, Robert. Beyond Vietnam: The Politics of Protest in Massachusetts, 1974-1990. 2009. 320p. 80.00 net. (978-1-55849-711-5(0)); pap. 29.95 net. (978-1-55849-712-2(9)) Univ. of Massachusetts Pr.

Wills, John. Conservation Fallout: Nuclear Protest at Diablo Canyon. 2006. (ENG., Illus.). 256p. 34.95 (978-0-87417-680-3(8)) Univ. of Nevada Pr.

Wittner, Lawrence S. Confronting the Bomb: A Short History of the World Nuclear Disarmament Movement. 2009. (Stanford Nuclear Age Ser.). (ENG.). 272p. 55.00 (978-0-8047-5631-0(7)); pap. 21.95 (978-0-8047-5632-7(5)) Stanford Univ. Pr.

Zelter, Angie. Faslane 365: A Year of Anti-Nuclear Blockades. 2008. (ENG., Illus.). 278p. pap. 20.00 (978-1-906307-61-5(X)) Luath Pr. Ltd. GBR. Dist: Ingram Pub. Services.

ANTIOCH (TURKEY)

Backrach, Bernard S. & Backrach, David S. The Gesta Tancredi of Ralph of Caen: A History of the Normans on the First Crusades. 2010. (Crusade Texts in Translation Ser.). (Illus.). 196p. pap. 29.95 (978-1-4094-0032-5(8)) Ashgate Publishing Co.

Clayton, Mary & Magennis, Hugh. The Old English Lives of St. Margaret. 2006. (Cambridge Studies in Anglo-Saxon England Ser.). (ENG.). 252p. pap. 53.00 (978-0-521-03267-4(9)) Cambridge Univ. Pr.

Downey, Glanville. A History of Antioch in Syria: From Seleucus to the Arab Conquest. 2009. 110.00 (978-1-57898-800-6(4)) Martino Publishing.

Elias, Ignatius. Select Writings of Mor Ignatius Elias III. 2010. (SYR.). 85.64 (978-1-61143-226-8(X)) Gorgias Pr., LLC.

Robinson, Thomas A. Ignatius of Antioch & the Parting of the Ways: Early Jewish-Christian Relations. 2009. xiv, 285p. (978-1-59856-323-8(8)) Hendrickson Pubs. Marketing, LLC.

ANTIOCH COLLEGE

Allen, Ira Wilder. A Collection of Facts History of the Rise, Difficulties & Suspension of Antioch College Containing Letters & Statements from Professors Horace M. 2006. 316p. per. 23.99 (978-1-4255-3088-4(5)) MPublishing.

Antioch College. Dedication of Antioch College, & Inaugural Address of Its President, Hon Horace Mann; with Other Proceedings. 2006. 136p. per. 16.99 (978-1-4255-0943-9(6)) MPublishing.

Fay, Eli. Rejoinder to I W Allen's Pseudo History of Antioch College. 2006. 228p. per. 20.99 (978-1-4255-1906-3(7)) MPublishing.

ANTIOCH IN PISIDIA (EXTINCT CITY)

Gazda, Elaine K. & Ng, Diana Y., eds. Building a New Rome: The Roman Colony of Pisidian Antioch (25 BC-300 AD) 2011. (Kelsey Museum Publications). (ENG., Illus.). 220p. (C). pap. 35.00 ***(978-0-9741873-4-1(8))*** Kelsey Museum of Archaeology.

ANTIOCHIAN SCHOOL

Here are entered works on the theology of the early Christian church of Antioch which was sometimes complementary and sometimes opposed to that of Alexandria.

see also Alexandrian School, Christian

Barsoum, Aphram I. The Theological School of Antioch 290-430 A. D. 2010. (ARA.). pap. 17.92 (978-1-61719-457-3(3)) Gorgias Pr., LLC.

Behr, John. The Case Against Diodore & Theodore. 2011. (Oxford Early Christian Studies). (ENG.). 544p. 265.00 (978-0-19-956987-8(8)) Oxford Univ. Pr., Inc.

Schor, Adam M. Theodoret's People: Social Networks & Religious Conflict in Late Roman Syria. 2011. (Transformation of the Classical Heritage Ser.). (ENG., Illus.). 320p. 49.95 (978-0-520-26862-3(8)) Univ. of California Pr.

Sellers, Robert V. Two Ancient Christologies: A Study in the Christological Thought of the Schools of Alexandria & Antioch in the Early History of Christian Doctrine. (Orthodoxies & Heresies in the Early Church Ser.). reprint ed. 39.50 (978-0-404-62394-4(8)) AMS Pr., Inc.

ANTIOQUIA (COLOMBIA: DEPT.)

Twinam, Ann. Miners, Merchants, & Farmers in Colonial Colombia. 2011. (ENG.). 206p. pap. 19.95 (978-0-292-73561-3(8)) Univ. of Texas Pr.

ANTIOXIDANTS

Aldini, Giancarlo, et al. Biomarkers for Antioxidant Defense & Oxidative Damage: Principles & Practical Applications. 2010. (ENG., Illus.). 380p. 220.95 (978-0-8138-1535-0(5), Wiley-Blackwell) Wiley, John & Sons, Inc.

Andreescu, Silvana & Hepel, Maria, eds. Oxidative Stress: Diagnostics, Prevention, & Therapy. 2012. (ACS Symposium Ser.). (ENG.). 438p. 175.00 ***(978-0-8412-2683-8(0))*** American Chemical Society.

Armstrong, Donald, ed. Oxidants & Antioxidants: Ultrastructure & Molecular Biology Protocols. 2010. (Methods in Molecular Biology Ser.). (Illus.). 356p. pap. 119.00 (978-1-61737-223-0(4), 1617372234) Humana Pr.

—Oxidative Stress Biomarkers & Antioxidant Protocols. 2010. (Methods in Molecular Biology Ser.). (Illus.). 336p. pap. 149.00 (978-1-61737-222-3(6), 1617372226) Humana Pr.

Asadujjaman, Mohammad, et al. Pharmacological & Phytochemical Evaluation of Brassica Olerace. 2011. 76p. pap. ***(978-3-8443-3413-5(0))*** Lambert Academic Publishing.

Aydogan, Müfide & Korkmaz, Asli. Does Vitamin C Act as an Antioxidant or Prooxidant? 2010. pap. 49.00 (978-1-61761-096-7(8)) Nova Science Pubs., Inc.

Özben, Tomris, ed. Free Radicals, Oxidative Stress, & Antioxidants: Pathological & Physiological Significance. 2010. (Nato Science Series: A: Ser.). 406p. pap. 289.00 (978-1-4419-3292-1(5), 1441932925) Springer.

Bello, Isaac, et al. An Antioxidant from Nature. 2010. 76p. pap. (978-3-8383-7794-0(X)) Lambert Academic Publishing.

Bhutkar, Mangesh & S .B. Bhise. Studies on Antioxidant Properties of Some Indigenous Plants. 2011. 68p. pap. ***(978-3-8443-9107-7(X))*** Lambert Academic Publishing.

Cooper, Kenneth. Revolucion Antioxidantes (Antioxidant Revolution) 19.95 (978-950-08-1386-0(6)) Atlantida ARG. Dist: AIMS International Bks., Inc.

Crohns, Marika. Antioxidants, Cytokines & Markers of Oxidative Stress in Lung Cancer: Associations with adverse events, response & Survival. 2010. (Acta Universitatis Tamperensis Ser.). 198p. pap. 77.50 (978-951-44-7997-7(1)) Tampere Univ. Pr. FIN. Dist: Coronet Bks.

Das, Kusal K. Garlic & Its Effect on Nickel & Chromium VI Toxicities. 2010. 156p. pap. (978-3-639-25925-4(4)) VDM Verlag Dr. Mueller e.K.

Decker, E., et al, eds. Oxidation in foods & beverages & antioxidant Applications: Management in different industry Sectors, 2 vols., Vol. 2. 2010. (Woodhead Publishing Series in Food Science, Technology & Nutrition Ser.). (ENG., Illus.). 560p. 255.00 (978-1-84569-983-3(1)) Woodhead Publishing Ltd. GBR. Dist: Ingram Pub. Services.

—Oxidation in Foods & Beverages & Antioxidant Applications: Understanding Mechanisms of Oxidation & Antioxidant Activity, 2 vols. 2010. (Woodhead Publishing Series in Food Science, Technology & Nutrition Ser.). (ENG., Illus.). 432p. 245.00 (978-1-84569-648-1(4)) Woodhead Publishing Ltd. GBR. Dist: Ingram Pub. Services.

Dubouch, George. Science or Miracle? The Metabolic Glyconutritional Discovery. (Illus.). pap. 12.95 (978-0-9747947-0-9(8)) InnerLife Foundation.

Evans, Mark D. & Cooke, Marcus S. Oxidative Damage to Nucleic Acids. 2007. (Molecular Biology Intelligence Unit Ser.). (Illus.). 246p. 175.00 (978-0-387-72973-2(9)) Springer.

Fahmy, Sohair. Anti-Oxidative Stress of Two Egyptian Crustacean Extracts in Rat. 2011. 100p. pap. ***(978-3-8433-8566-4(1))*** Lambert Academic Publishing.

Flohé, Leopold & Harris, J. Robin, eds. Peroxiredoxin Systems: Structures & Functions. (Subcellular Biochemistry Ser.). 2010. xiv, 407p. pap. 239.00 (978-90-481-7517-8(8), 9048175178) 2007. (Illus.). 389p. 239.00 (978-1-4020-6050-2(5)) Springer.

Foyer, Christine, et al, eds. Redox Metabolism, Vol. 62. 2009. (Experimental Biology Reviews Ser.). (Illus.). 280p. pap. 223.00 (978-0-415-41954-3(9)) Taylor & Francis Group.

Francisco, Ngiambudulu Mbandu. Modulation of Oxidative Stress by Rooibos in Normo Individuals. 2010. 164p. pap. (978-3-8383-6622-7(0)) Lambert Academic Publishing.

Frankel, Edwin Nessim. Antioxidants in Food & Biology: Facts & Fiction. 2007. (Illus.). 272p. 220.00 ***(978-0-9552512-0-7(6))*** Woodhead Publishing Ltd. GBR. Dist: Ingram Pub. Services.

Ghoniem, Gehan. Could Fruits & Vegetables Prevent Cancer? 2010. 176p. pap. (978-3-639-25606-2(9)) VDM Verlag Dr. Mueller e.K.

Glassman, Keri & Mahoney, Sarah. The O2 Diet: The Cutting Edge Antioxidant-Based Program That Will Make You Healthy, Thin, & Beautiful. 2010. (ENG., Illus.). 240p. pap. 15.99 (978-1-60529-167-3(6)) Rodale Pr., Inc.

Grune, Tilman. Oxidants & Antioxidant Defense Systems. 2010. (Handbook of Environmental Chemistry / Reactions & Processes Ser.). (Illus.). xiii, 239p. pap. 189.00 (978-3-642-06125-7(7), 3642061257) Springer.

Gulfraz, Muhammad, et al. Antimicrobial Activities of Plant Materials. 2011. 116p. pap. ***(978-3-8443-8336-2(0))*** Lambert Academic Publishing.

Gupta, S. Dutta. Reactive Oxygen Species & Antioxidants in Higher Plants. 2010. (ENG.). 380p. 149.95 (978-1-57808-686-3(8)) BIOS Scientific Publishers Ltd. GBR. Dist: Taylor & Francis Group.

Habila, James, et al. Beneficial Antioxidant Agent from Nature. 2011. 72p. pap. ***(978-3-8433-9035-4(5))*** Lambert Academic Publishing.

Hamid, Rehana, et al. Antioxidative Efficiency of Brassica Juncea Exposed to Chromium Stress. 2011. 68p. pap. ***(978-3-8454-1939-8(3))*** Lambert Academic Publishing.

Haugen, Leiv & Bjornson, Terje. Beta Carotene: Dietary Sources, Cancer & Cognition. 2009. (Nutrition & Diet Research Progress Ser.). 129.00 (978-1-60741-611-1(5), Nova Biomedical Bks.) Nova Science Pubs., Inc.

Hosseinian, Farah. Flaxseed Lignans: Properties & Health Benefits. 2010. 72p. pap. (978-3-8383-4358-7(1)) Lambert Academic Publishing.

Howes, Randolph M. Death in Small Doses?: BOOKS 1 And 2: Antioxidant Vitamins A, C & E in the Twenty-first Century: Book One Also contains: Antioxidant Vitamins Are Making A Killing: Book Two: A Health Impact Statement for Medical Scientists. 2010. 348p. 29.92 (978-1-4269-3799-6(7)) Trafford Publishing.

Howes Randolph M. Death in Small Doses?: BOOKS 1 And 2: Antioxidant Vitamins A, C & E in the Twenty-first Century: Book One Also contains: Antioxidant Vitamins Are Making A Killing: Book Two: A Health Impact Statement for Medical Scientists. 2010. 348p. pap. 19.92 (978-1-4269-3798-9(9)) Trafford Publishing.

Jeep, Robin & Couey, Richard. The Super Antioxidant Diet & Nutrition Guide: A Health Plan for the Body, Mind, & Spirit. 2008. (ENG., Illus.). 264p. per. 19.95 (978-1-57174-557-6(2)) Hampton Roads Publishing Co., Inc.

Johnson, Ben & Trivieri, Larry, Jr. Healing Waters: The Powerful Benefits of Ionized H2O. 2011. 104p. pap. 14.95 (978-0-7570-0328-8(1)) Square One Pubs.

Joshi, Ms. Dipti, et al. Oroxylum Indicum. 2011. 72p. pap. ***(978-3-8443-2807-3(6))*** Lambert Academic Publishing.

Jyoti, Jeevan, et al. Antioxidants. 2011. 112p. pap. ***(978-3-8443-1666-7(3))*** Lambert Academic Publishing.

Kaithwas, Gaurav, et al. Aloe Vera Gel: Antioxidant with Cholinergic Innervations. 2011. 76p. pap. ***(978-3-639-31723-7(8))*** VDM Verlag Dr. Mueller e.K.

Kandalkar, Ashish, et al. Isolation & Antioxidant Potential of Euphorbia Hirta Linn. 2011. 104p. pap. ***(978-3-8443-1066-5(5))*** Lambert Academic Publishing.

Kinderlehrer, Jane & Kinderlehrer, Daniel A. The Antioxidant Save-Your-Life Cookbook: 150 Nutritious, High-Fiber, Low-Fat Recipes to Protect You Against the Damaging Effects of Free Radicals. 2007. (ENG.). 208p. per. 16.95 (978-1-55704-760-1(X), William Morrow Paperbacks) HarperCollins Pubs.

Kung, Fu-Chen. Effect of Antioxidants Grafting on the Hemocompatibility of Hd. 2009. 108p. pap. (978-3-639-15904-2(7)) VDM Verlag Dr. Mueller e.K.

Kuriakose, Anila. Antioxidative Activity of Green Tea Polyphenols. 2011. 60p. pap. ***(978-3-8443-2140-1(3))*** Lambert Academic Publishing.

Kuznetsov, Yury V. Ambiol As Base of New Effective Drugs. 2008. 129.00 (978-1-60692-006-0(5)) Nova Science Pubs., Inc.

Lea, Wendy. An Antioxidant Capacity Assay & Its Application in Food Samples. 2008. 240p. pap. (978-3-639-04594-9(7)) VDM Verlag Dr. Mueller e.K.

Leon, Terry. Health-promoting Properties of. 2010. 400p. pap. 170.00 (978-1-84593-528-3(4)) CAB International GBR. Dist: Stylus Publishing, LLC.

Li, Yunbo. Antioxidants in Biology & Medicine: Essentials, Advances, & Clinical Applications. 2011. (Medicine & Biology Research Developments (Series Editor - Tsisana Shartava, M. D. - Tbilisi, Georgia) Ser.). 195.00 (978-1-61122-502-0(7), Nova Novinka) Nova Science Pubs., Inc.

Littarru, P. G., ed. The Fifth Conference of the International CoQ10 Association BioFactors: Kobe 2007 - 50th Anniversary of CoQ10 Discovery - Book Edition Of. 2008. 197p. pap. 348.00 (978-1-58603-963-9(5)) IOS Pr., Inc.

Maier, Romana Maria. Antioxidants in Seasoning Herbs During Drought, Storage & Processing. 2011. 152p. pap. **(978-3-8381-2703-3(X))** Südwestdeutscher Verlag für Hochschulschriften AG & Co. KG.

Majumdar, Anuradha. Antioxidant Activity of Eclipta Alba L. 2011. 228p. pap. **(978-3-8443-9716-1(7))** Lambert Academic Publishing.

Makhmoor, Talat. Antioxidants from Medicinal Plants & of Synthetic Origin. 2011. 196p. pap. **(978-3-8433-7559-7(3))** Lambert Academic Publishing.

Maqsood, Sajid, et al. Plant Polyphenolic Compounds. 2011. 132p. pap. **(978-3-8443-8429-1(4))** Lambert Academic Publishing.

Marin, Diego & Garcia, Pablo, eds. New Research on Antioxidants. 2008. (Illus.). x, 300p. 185.00 (978-1-60456-621-5(3)) Nova Science Pubs., Inc.

Milbury, Paul E. & Richer, Alice C. Understanding the Antioxidant Controversy: Scrutinizing the Fountain of Youth, 1 vol. 2007. (Praeger Series on Contemporary Health & Living Ser.). (Illus.). 192p. 49.95 (978-0-275-99376-4(0), C9376, Praeger Pubs.) Greenwood Publishing Group, Inc.

O'Byrne, Paul. Red Wine & Health. 2009. (Illus.). xvii, 527p. 89.00 (978-1-60692-718-2(3)) Nova Science Pubs., Inc.

Oliva. Antioxidants & Stem Cells for Coronary Heart Disease. 2011. 144.00 (978-981-4293-44-0(X)) World Scientific Publishing Co., Inc.

Oxidative Stress, Antioxidative Defence. 24.50 (978-91-554-4960-5(3)) Almqvist & Wiksell International SWE. Dist: Coronet Bks.

Pandi-Perumal, S. R. Melatonin: From Molecules to Therapy. 2006. 195.00 (978-1-60021-121-8(6)) Nova Science Pubs., Inc.

Panglossi, Harold V. Frontiers in Antioxidants Research. 2006. (Nova Biomedical Ser.). (Illus.). 216p. 129.00 (978-1-60021-273-4(5)) Nova Science Pubs., Inc.

—Leading Edge Antioxidants Research. 2006. (Illus.). 266p. (C). 129.00 (978-1-60021-274-1(3)) Nova Science Pubs., Inc.

Pappas, A. C., et al, eds. Cadmium Toxicity & the Antioxidant System. 2010. (Environmental Health - Physical, Chemical & Biological Factors Ser.). pap. 43.00 (978-1-61668-172-2(1)) Nova Science Pubs., Inc.

Parente, Matilde. Resveratrol. 2009. (Woodland Health Ser.). 40p. pap. 4.95 (978-1-58054-187-9(9)) Woodland Publishing, Inc.

Passwater, Richard A. Live Better, Longer: The Science Behind the Amazing Health Benefits of Opc. 2007. (ENG.). 96p. pap. 12.95 (978-1-59120-209-7(4)) Basic Health Pubns., Inc.

Patel, Mulchand S. & Packer, Lester, eds. Lipoic Acid: Energy Production, Antioxidant Activity & Health Effects. 2008. (Oxidative Stress & Disease Ser.: Vol. 24). (ENG., Illus.). 556p. 185.95 (978-1-4200-4537-6(7), CRC Press) Taylor & Francis Group GBR. Dist: Taylor & Francis Group.

Poljsak, Borut, ed. Decreasing Oxidative Stress & Retarding the Aging Process. 2009. (Aging Issues, Health & Financial Alternatives Ser.). 89.00 (978-1-61728-345-1(2), Nova Biomedical Bks.) Nova Science Pubs., Inc.

—Skin Aging, Free Radicals & Antioxidants. 2012. (Series: Aging Issues, Health & Financial Alternatives Ser.). 419p. 215.00 (978-1-61324-718-1(4)) Nova Science Pubs., Inc.

Prasad, Kedar N. Bio-Shield, Antioxidants Against Radiological, Chemical & Biological Weapons. 2008. 204p. 25.50 (978-1-60693-489-0(9), Strategic Bk. Publishing) AEG Literary Publishing Services, Inc.

—Micronutrients in Health & Disease. 2010. (ENG., Illus.). 391p. 129.95 (978-1-4398-2106-0(2), CRC Press) Taylor & Francis Group GBR. Dist: Taylor & Francis Group.

Preedy, Victor R. & Watson, Ronald R., eds. Tocotrienols: Vitamin e Beyond Tocopherols. 2008. (ENG., Illus.). 424p. 162.95 (978-1-4200-8037-7(7), CRC Press) Taylor & Francis Group GBR. Dist: Taylor & Francis Group.

Rodrigo, Ramon. Oxidative Stress & Antioxidants: Their Role in Human Disease. 2009. (Illus.). xiii, 358p. 79.00 (978-1-60741-554-1(2)) Nova Science Pubs., Inc.

Savalas, Constantinos A. & Nicolau, Soussana M. Olive Consumption & Health. 2012. **(978-1-62100-774-6(X))** Nova Science Pubs., Inc.

Snyder, Mariza & Clum, Lauren. The Antioxidant Counter: A Pocket Guide to the Revolutionary ORAC Scale for Choosing Healthy Foods. 2011. (ENG.). 112p. pap. 7.95 (978-1-56975-866-3(2)) Ulysses Pr.

Tenney, Louise. Grapefruit Seed Extract. 3rd ed. 2011. (Woodland Health Ser.). 36p. pap. 4.95 **(978-1-58054-202-9(6))** Woodland Publishing, Inc.

Uppu, Rao M. Free Radicals & Antioxidant Protocols. 2nd ed. 2009. (Methods in Molecular Biology Ser.). (Illus.). xvi, 480p. 139.00 (978-1-58829-710-5(1)) Humana Pr.

Vassallo, Neville, ed. Polyphenols & Health: New & Recent Advances. 2008. (Illus.). xii, 394p. 89.00 (978-1-60456-349-8(4), Nova Biomedical Bks.) Nova Science Pubs., Inc.

Veurink, Gerald. A Radical Approach to Treating Degenerative Diseases. 2009. 304p. pap. (978-3-639-19736-5(4)) VDM Verlag Dr. Mueller e.K.

Vijayamani, Priya & S. Gayathri Devi. Antioxidant Properties of the Leaves & Stems of Aristolochia Indic. 2011. 88p. pap. **(978-3-8443-0816-7(4))** Lambert Academic Publishing.

Wylde, Bryce. The Antioxidant Prescription: How to Use the Power of Antioxidants to Prevent Disease & Stay Healthy for Life. 2009. (ENG., Illus.). 336p. pap. 17.95 (978-0-307-35586-7(1), Random Hse CAN) Random Hse. of Canada, Ltd. CAN. Dist: Random Hse., Inc.

Xu, Zhimin & Howard, Luke R. Analysis of Antioxidant-Rich Phytochemicals. 2012. (ENG.). 408p. 199.95 **(978-0-8138-2391-1(9)**, Wiley-Blackwell) Wiley, John & Sons, Inc.

Yu, Liangli L., ed. Wheat Antioxidants. 2007. (ENG., Illus.). 276p. 111.00 (978-0-470-04259-5(1), Wiley-Interscience) Wiley, John & Sons, Inc.

Zaikov, Gennadii Efremovich, ed. Chemical & Biochemical Physics, Kinetics & Thermodynamics: New Perspectives. 2008. (Illus.). (C). 205.00 (978-1-60456-024-4(X)) Nova Science Pubs., Inc.

—Progress in Chemical & Biochemical Physics, Kinetics & Thermodynamics. 2008. (C). 185.00 (978-1-60456-079-4(7)) Nova Science Pubs., Inc.

Zhang, Jingli. Evaluation of Natural Antioxidants. 2009. 228p. pap. (978-3-639-13519-0(9)) VDM Verlag Dr. Mueller e.K.

ANTIPAPISM

see Anti-Catholicism

ANTIPASTO

see Appetizers

ANTIPATHIES

see Prejudices

ANTIPHLOGISTICS

see Anti-Inflammatory Agents

ANTIPHON, ORATOR, 480-411 B.C.

Antiphon. Antiphon the Sophist: The Fragments. 2010. (Cambridge Classical Texts & Commentaries Ser.). (ENG & GRE.). 488p. pap. 50.00 (978-0-521-12512-0(6)) Cambridge Univ. Pr.

ANTIPODES ISLANDS (N.Z.)

Hiatt, Alfred. Terra Incognita: Mapping the Antipodes Before 1600. 2008. (ENG., Illus.). 224p. 60.00 (978-0-226-33303-8(5)) Univ. of Chicago Pr.

ANTIPOISINOUS AGENTS

see Antidotes

ANTIPSYCHIATRY

Breeding, J. Eyes Wide Open. 2007. 84p. per. (978-1-84747-114-7(5)) Chipmunkapublishing.

Breggin & Breggin, Ginger Ross. Talking Back to Prozac. 2010. 352p. pap. 19.95 (978-0-7592-9572-8(7)) E-Reads.

Ellerby, M. On Anti-Psychiatry. 2007. 76p. per. (978-1-84747-446-9(2)) Chipmunkapublishing.

Szasz, Thomas Stephen. Antipsychiatry: Quackery Squared. 2009. (978-0-8156-0943-8(4)) Syracuse Univ. Pr.

ANTIPYRINE

Cooper, Keith E. Fever & Antipyresis: The Role of the Nervous System. 2008. (Illus.). 200p. pap. 42.00 (978-0-521-07203-8(4)) Cambridge Univ. Pr.

ANTIQUARIAN BOOKSELLERS

see also Book Collecting; Bookstores; Out-of-Print Books

Edwards, Harold W. From Newbury with Love: Letters of Friendship Across the Iron Curtain. Horsbrugh-Porter, Anna & Aldova, Marina, eds. 2007. (ENG., Illus.). 258p. pap. 20.00 (978-1-933633-22-0(0)) Melville Hse. Publishing.

Markham, Sheila. A Book of Booksellers: Conversations with the Antiquarian Book Trade, 1991-2003. 2007. pap. 29.95 (978-1-58456-207-8(2)) Oak Knoll Pr.

McKitterick, David. A Changing View from Amsterdam: Where Next with Book History? 2011. (Frederik Mullerlezing Ser.). 32p. pap. (978-90-5629-645-2(0)) Amsterdam Univ. Pr.

McMurtry, Larry. Books: A Memoir. 2009. (ENG.). 272p. pap. 14.00 (978-1-4165-8335-6(1)) Simon & Schuster.

Rees, Bill. The Loneliness of the Long Distance Book Runner: Sturtevant, Andro, Wekua, Kerstin, Brätsch, Paul, Chan. 2012. 300p. pap. 14.95 **(978-1-906998-92-9(2))** Parthian Bks. GBR. Dist: Independent Pubs. Group.

ANTIQUE AND CLASSIC CARS

Albert, Ken. For the Love of Old Cars: The Jack Passey Story. 2007. (Illus.). 192p. lib. bdg. 39.95 (978-1-932439-99-1(4)) M.T. Publishing Co., Inc.

Benford, Tom. Weekend Projects for Your Classic Corvette 1953-1982. 2010. (Motorbooks Workshop Ser.). (ENG., Illus.). 224p. pap. 29.99 (978-0-7603-3758-5(6), 0760337586, Motorbooks) MBI Publishing Co. LLC.

Bertolino, Jon. Vintage Snowmobiles: The Golden Years 1968-1982. 2007. (Photo Gallery Ser.). (ENG., Illus.). 128p. pap. 37.95 (978-1-58388-193-4(X), 158388193X) Iconografix, Inc.

Brooks, Jackson. Cars I Could've, Should've, Kept: Memoir of a Life Restoring Classic Sports Cars. 2007. (ENG., Illus.). 263p. per. 25.00 (978-0-7864-2810-6(4)) McFarland & Co., Inc. Pubs.

Buckley, Martin. The Illustrated Encyclopedia of Classic Cars: A Celebration of the Classic Car from 1945 to 1985. 2009. (ENG., Illus.). 256p. 35.00 (978-0-7548-1874-8(8)) Anness Publishing GBR. Dist: National Bk. Network.

Buckley, Martin & Rees, Chris. The Complete Illustrated Encyclopedia of Classic Cars: The World's Most Famous & Fabulous Cars from 1945 to 2000 Shown in 1500 Photographs. 2010. (ENG., Illus.). 512p. 35.00 (978-0-7548-1917-2(5)) Anness Publishing GBR. Dist: National Bk. Network.

Burgess-Wise, David. Brighton Belles: A Celebration of Veteran Cars. 2007. (ENG., Illus.). 208p. (978-1-86126-764-1(9), 1861267649) Crowood Pr., Ltd. GBR. Dist: MBI Distribution Services/Quayside Distribution.

Carney, P. & Mertens, J. The Last Eleven. 2009. pap. (978-1-61623-623-6(X)) Independent Pub.

Cotter, Tom. The Cobra in the Barn: Great Stories of Automotive Archaeology. 2010. (ENG., Illus.). 256p. pap. 19.99 (978-0-7603-3661-8(X), 076033661X, Motorbooks) MBI Publishing Co. LLC.

Cotter, Tom. The Hemi in the Barn: More Great Stories of Automotive Archaeology. (ENG., Illus.). 256p. 2012. pap. 19.99 **(978-0-7603-4298-5(9)**, 0760342989) 2007. 25.95 (978-0-7603-2721-0(1), 0760327211) MBI Publishing Co. LLC. (Motorbooks).

Cussler, Clive. Built for Adventure: The Classic Automobiles of Clive Cussler & Dirk Pitt. 2011. (ENG.). 240p. (gr. 12). 50.00 (978-0-399-15810-0(3), Putnam Adult) Penguin Group (USA) Inc.

Demars, Duane. Classic Cars of Montana & Wyoming. 2006. (Illus.). per. 28.99 (978-0-9791647-0-5(2)) Classic Cars of Montana LLC.

Design Museum Staff. Fifty Cars That Changed the World. 2010. (ENG., Illus.). 110p. 20.00 (978-1-84091-536-5(6), Conran Octopus) Octopus Publishing Group GBR. Dist: Hachette Bk. Group.

Garvey, Scott. The Tractor in the Haystack: Great Stories of Tractor Archaeology. 2008. (ENG., Illus.). 256p. 22.00 (978-0-7603-3295-5(9), 0760332959, Voyageur Pr) MBI Publishing Co. LLC.

Genat, Robert. Deuce: 75 Years of the '32 Ford. 2006. (ENG., Illus.). 192p. 39.95 (978-1-932494-13-6(8)) CarTech, Inc.

Haddon, Chris. My Cool Classic Car: An inspirational guide to classic Cars. 2012. (ENG., Illus.). 160p. 24.95 **(978-1-86205-939-9(X))** Chrysalis Children's Bks. GBR. Dist: Independent Pubs. Group.

Heasley, Jerry. Jerry Heasley's Rare Finds. 2011. (Illus.). 144p. (978-1-934709-52-8(2)) CarTech, Inc.

Heimann, Jim, ed. Cars of the 50s. 25th ed. 2009. (ENG., Illus.). 192p. 7.99 (978-3-8365-1427-9(3)) TASCHEN DEU. Dist: Ingram Pub. Services.

Herfel, George E. Wheel'in & Deal'in: Make BIG PROFITS buying & selling Classic Cars & MORE. 2009. 56p. pap. 11.95 (978-1-4327-3663-7(9)) Outskirts Pr., Inc.

Holloway, Hilton & Buckley, Martin. The A-Z of Cars: The Century's Classic Automobiles. 2009. (ENG., Illus.). 400p. 39.95 (978-1-84732-150-3(X)) Carlton Bks., Ltd. GBR. Dist: Sterling Publishing Co., Inc.

Holmes, Mark. Ultimate Classic Cars: The World's Greatest Automobiles. 2007. (Illus.). 160p. 12.99 (978-0-7858-2302-5(6), Chartwell) Book Sales, Inc.

—Ultimate Convertibles: Roofless Beauty. 2007. (Illus.). 160p. 12.99 (978-0-7858-2286-8(0), Chartwell) Book Sales, Inc.

Keister, Douglas, photos by. Teardrops & Tiny Trailers, 1 vol. 2008. (ENG., Illus.). 160p. 19.99 (978-1-4236-0274-3(9)) Gibbs Smith, Publisher.

Kowalke, Ron. 2011 Collector Car Price Guide. 5th ed. 2010. (ENG., Illus.). 760p. pap. 19.99 (978-1-4402-1285-7(6)) Krause Pubns.

Long, Brian. Daimler SP250. 2nd ed. 2008. (Classic Reprint Ser.). (ENG., Illus.). 208p. 34.95 (978-1-904788-77-5(7), 1904788777) Veloce Publishing Ltd. GBR. Dist: MBI Distribution Services/Quayside Distribution.

Long, David. Classic Cars: How Choose Your Dream Car. 2009. 176p. 39.99 (978-1-84468-052-8(5)) Pen & Sword Bks. Ltd. GBR. Dist: Casemate Pubs. & Bk. Distributors, LLC.

Lorenzo, Matt De & DeLorenzo, Matt. Legendary American Cars: Past to Present. 2007. (ENG., Illus.). 300p. 39.95 (978-88-544-0246-1(X), White Star) Rizzoli International Pubns., Inc.

Lyles, Larry. Project Street Rod: The Step-by-Step Restoration of a Popular Vintage Car. 2008. (ENG., Illus.). 184p. pap. 24.95 (978-1-933958-39-2(1)) BowTie Pr.

Lyon, David O. The Gilmore Car Museum: Miles from the Ordinary. 2010. (978-1-57864-630-2(8)) Donning Co. Pubs.

Marek, Bjoern. Sleeping Beauties USA: Abandoned Classic Cars & Trucks. 2011. (ENG., Illus.). 96p. 24.95 (978-1-84584-346-5(0), 1845843460) Veloce Publishing Ltd. GBR. Dist: MBI Distribution Services/Quayside Distribution.

Mark, Savitski. How to Make Your Muscle Car Handle. 2011. (Illus.). 144p. pap. 24.95 (978-1-934709-07-8(7), S-A Design) CarTech, Inc.

Michell, Richard. Which Oil? Choosing the Right Oil & Grease for Your Antique, Vintage, Veteran, Classic or Collector Car. 2011. (ENG., Illus.). 128p. pap. 24.95 (978-1-84584-365-6(7), 1845843657) Veloce Publishing Ltd. GBR. Dist: MBI Distribution Services/Quayside Distribution.

Overstake, T. J. For Love of the Car: Memories of a True Car Guy. 2009. 159p. pap. 11.95 (978-1-4327-3594-4(2)) Outskirts Pr., Inc.

Paxton, Mark. Mini: The Essential Buyer's Guide. 2009. (Essential Buyer's Guide Ser.). (ENG., Illus.). 64p. pap. 19.95 (978-1-84584-204-8(9), 1845842049) Veloce Publishing Ltd. GBR. Dist: MBI Distribution Services/Quayside Distribution.

Peck, Colin. British Woodies: From the 1920's to the 1950's. 2008. (Those Were the Days Ser.). (ENG., Illus.). 96p. pap. 25.95 (978-1-84584-169-0(7), 1845841697) Veloce Publishing Ltd. GBR. Dist: MBI Distribution Services/Quayside Distribution.

Peters, Eric. Road Hogs: Detroit's Big, Beautiful Luxury Performance Cars of the 1960s & 1970s. 2011. (ENG., Illus.). 160p. 35.00 (978-0-7603-3764-6(0), 0760337640, Motorbooks); (978-0-7603-3388-4(2)) MBI Publishing Co. LLC.

Polidori, Robert. Heroes of the Revolution: American Cars & Cuban Beats. 2006. (ENG.). 14.95 incl. lp (978-3-937406-53-4(0)) Edel Classica Gmbh.

Powell, Sinclair. Vintage Franklin: A History of the Car in its Time. Chaplin, Mark, ed. 2007. (Illus.). (978-0-9795841-0-7(8)) Chaplin, Mark.

Publications International Staff. Chevy Classics. 2008. 128p. 10.98 (978-1-4127-1524-9(5)) Publications International, Ltd.

Reddle, John. Cars I Loved & Lost. 2011. 128p. pap. 13.95 **(978-1-4620-4517-4(0))** iUniverse, Inc.

Romanick, Colin. Muscle Cars. 2012. (Shire Library). (ENG., Illus.). 64p. pap. 9.95 **(978-0-7478-1096-4(6))** Shire Pubns., Ltd. GBR. Dist: Random Hse., Inc.

Sen, Gautam. The Maharajas & Their Magnificent Motor Cars. 2011. (ENG., Illus.). 384p. 59.95 (978-0-85733-063-5(2), 0857330632) Haynes Publishing PLC GBR. Dist: MBI Distribution Services/Quayside Distribution.

Stapleton, Daniel. How to Modify your Retro or Classic Car for High Performance. 2012. (SpeedPro Ser.). (ENG., Illus.). 144p. pap. 49.95 (978-1-84584-289-5(8), 1845842898) Veloce Publishing Ltd. GBR. Dist: MBI Distribution Services/Quayside Distribution.

Stein, Jonathan A. The Performing Art of the American Automobile: The Hendricks Collection on Exhibit at the Gateway Colorado Auto Museum. 2011. (ENG., Illus.). 272p. 60.00 (978-0-9779809-0-1(1), 977980) Coachbuilt Pr.

Thaddeus, Martin. Classic Car Electrics: Tips, Techniques & Step-by-Step Repair, Restoration & Maintenance Procedures. 2007. (Enthusiast's Restoration Manual Ser.). (ENG., Illus.). 96p. pap. 39.95 (978-1-903706-64-0(5), 1903706645) Veloce Publishing Ltd. GBR. Dist: MBI Distribution Services/Quayside Distribution.

—How to Restore Classic Car Bodywork. 2012. (Enthusiast's Restoration Manual Ser.). (ENG., Illus.). 128p. pap. 39.95 (978-1-84584-411-0(4), 1845844114) Veloce Publishing Ltd. GBR. Dist: MBI Distribution Services/Quayside Distribution.

the Publisher of Old Cars Weekly. Lost & Found: More Great Barn Finds & Other Automotive Discoveries. 2nd ed. 2011. (ENG.). 144p. pap. 12.99 **(978-1-4402-3070-7(6))** Krause Pubns.

Tony, Huntimer. How to Restore Your Camaro 1967-1969. 2010. 160p. pap. 29.95 (978-1-934709-10-8(7), S-A Design) CarTech, Inc.

Van Bogart, Angelo. Automobile Digest. 2010. (ENG.). 352p. pap. 24.99 (978-1-4402-1665-7(7)) Krause Pubns.

Van Boggart, Angelo. Just 30s. 2011. (ENG.). 144p. pap. 12.99 (978-1-4402-1428-8(X)) Krause Pubns.

—Just Packards. 2010. (ENG.). 144p. pap. 12.99 (978-1-4402-1427-1(1)) Krause Pubns.

Walker, Mick. Sammy Miller: Motorcycle Legend. 2010. (ENG., Illus.). 240p. 34.95 (978-1-85983-763-4(8), 1859837638) DB Publishing GBR. Dist: MBI Distribution Services/Quayside Distribution.

Ware, Michael. Automobiles Lost & Found: Extraordinary Stories of Long-Lost Cars Rediscovered. 2008. (ENG., Illus.). 256p. 39.95 (978-1-84425-438-5(0), 1844254380) Haynes Publishing PLC GBR. Dist: MBI Distribution Services/Quayside Distribution.

Ware, Michael E. Veteran Motor Cars. 2008. (Shire Library). (ENG., Illus.). 32p. pap. 11.95 (978-0-85263-658-9(X)) Shire Pubns., Ltd. GBR. Dist: Random Hse., Inc.

Wilmarth, Charles R., III. Practical Car Restoration: A Guidebook with Lessons from a 1930 Franklin Rebuild. 2006. (ENG., Illus.). 216p. per. 25.00 (978-0-7864-2511-2(3)) McFarland & Co., Inc. Pubs.

Zuehlke, Jeffrey. Classic Cars. 2007. (Motor Mania Ser.). (Illus.). 48p. (YA). (gr. 3-6). lib. bdg. 26.60 (978-0-8225-5926-9(9)) Lerner Publishing Group.

ANTIQUE AUTOMOBILES

see Antique and Classic Cars

ANTIQUE CARS

see Antique and Classic Cars

ANTIQUE CLOTHING

see Vintage Clothing

ANTIQUE COLLECTING

see Antiques

ANTIQUE DEALERS

Cassidy, Brendan. Gavin Hamilton (1723-1798) Artist, Antiquarian & Art Dealer in Eighteenth-Century Rome. with an Edition of his Letters, 2 vols. 2011. (Collectors & Dealers Ser.). (ENG., Illus.). 750p. (C). 196.00 (978-1-905375-59-2(X)) Brepols Pubs. BEL. Dist: Brown, David Bk. Co., The.

Dummer, John. Son of Serge Bastarde: Mayhem in the Antiques Markets of Rural France. 2012. (ENG.). 320p. pap. 13.95 **(978-1-84953-150-4(1))** Summerdale Pubs. GBR. Dist: Independent Pubs. Group.

Fales, Dean, ed. Antiqueman's Diary: The Memoirs of Fred B. Tuck. 2010. (Illus.). 160p. pap. 15.00 (978-0-88448-227-7(8), Harpswell Pr.) Tilbury Hse. Pubs.

Leech, Michael. Essential Guide to London's Antique Shops, Auction Houses & Markets. 2006. (ENG., Illus.). 208p. pap. 24.95 (978-1-84537-256-9(5)) New Holland Pubs., Ltd. GBR. Dist: National Bk. Network.

Newman, Bruce. Don't Come Back until You Find It: Tales from an Antiques Dealer. 2010. (Illus.). 288p. 24.95 (978-0-8253-0536-8(5)) Beaufort Bks., Inc.

Pauly, Edith. The Best Vintage, Antique & Collectible Shops in Paris. 2009. (ENG., Illus.). 240p. pap. 18.95 (978-1-892145-73-4(1)) Little Bookroom.

Peterson, Cleo Ann. Antique Malls: An Antique Dealer's Friend or Foe? pap. (978-0-9709354-0-3(4)) Peterson, Cleo Ann.

Purcell, Rosamond. Owls Head: On the Nature of Lost Things. 2007. (ENG., Illus.). 224p. pap. 14.95 (978-1-59372-033-9(5)) Quantuck Lane Pr. & The Mill Road Collaborative, The.

Rosenstein, Leon. Antiques: The History of an Idea. 2008. 280p. 36.95 (978-0-8014-4734-1(8)) Cornell Univ. Pr.

Shoop, Fiona. How to Deal in Antiques. 5th rev. ed. 2011. (ENG., Illus.). 313p. pap. 34.00 (978-1-84528-456-5(9)) How To Books GBR. Dist: Parkwest Pubns., Inc.

Stanton, Maureen. Killer Stuff & Tons of Money: An Insider's Look at the World of Antiques, Flea Markets, & Collecting. 2012. (ENG.). 336p. (gr. 12). pap. 16.00 ***(978-0-14-312105-3(7)***, Penguin (Non-Classics)) Penguin Group (USA) Inc.

—Killer Stuff & Tons of Money: Seeking History & Hidden Gems in Flea-Market America. l.t. ed. 2011. 483p. 31.99 ***(978-1-4104-4124-9(5))*** Thorndike Pr.

Verchere, Laure. Antiquaires: Flea Markets of Paris. 2010. (ENG., Illus.). 220p. 75.00 *(978-2-7594-0460-5(9))* Assouline FRA. Dist: Perseus Distribution.

Wynter, Harriet. The Price of Every Thinge. 2010. (Illus.). 336p. pap. *(978-1-84530-066-1(1))* Grimsay Pr.

Wyss, Bob. Brimfield Rush: The Thrill of Collecting & the Hunt for the Big Score. 2007. (ENG.). 320p. per. 14.95 *(978-1-933212-52-4(7))* Commonwealth Editions.

Yorke, Louisa, ed. Guide to the Antique Shops of Britain 2008-2009. 2008. (ENG., Illus.). 584p. *(978-1-85149-554-2(1)*, Antique Collectors Club Dist) Antique Collectors' Club.

ANTIQUES

Here are entered works on old decorative or utilitarian objects having aesthetic, historic and financial value. Works on decorative art objects are entered under Art Objects.

see also Americana; Antiquarian Booksellers; Art Objects

also particular kinds of antique objects, especially the subdivisions Catalogs, Collectors and Collecting or Exhibitions when they occur under such objects, e.g. Kitchen Utensils; Firearms—Catalogs; Glassware—Collectors and Collecting; Furniture—Exhibitions

Ahern, Jerry. Armed for Personal Defense. 2010. (ENG.). 240p. pap. 19.99 *(978-1-4402-1408-0(5))* Krause Pubns.

Alcorn, Ellenor. Beyond the Maker's Mark: Paul de Lamerie Silver in the Cahn Collection. 2007. (ENG., Illus.). 128p. 35.00 *(978-0-9524322-6-5(9))* John Adamson Publishing Consultants GBR. Dist: National Bk. Network.

Andrews, John. Antique Furniture. 2007. (Starting to Collect Ser.). (ENG., Illus.). 192p. *(978-1-85149-449-1(9)*, Antique Collectors Club Dist) Antique Collectors' Club.

Arnold, Peter. Card Games. 2007. (ENG., Illus.). 400p. pap. 16.95 *(978-0-550-10336-9(8))* Chambers Harrap Pubs., Ltd. GBR. Dist: Independent Pubs. Group.

Ashworth, Gregory, et al. Pluralising Pasts: Heritage, Identity & Place in Multicultural Societies. 2007. (ENG., Illus.). 248p. 100.00 *(978-0-7453-2286-5(7))*; per. 36.00 *(978-0-7453-2285-8(9))* Pluto Pr. GBR. Dist: Macmillan.

Assouline. Piaget. 2010. (ENG.). 80p. 25.00 *(978-2-7594-0461-2(7))* Assouline FRA. Dist: Perseus Distribution.

Atkins, John Hildreth & Rundy, Jonathan G. The common man's guide to uncommon Riches. 2007. 171p. pap. 14.95 *(978-1-4303-1096-9(0))* Lulu Enterprises Inc.

Attard, Robert & Azzopardi, Romina. Antique Collecting in Malta. 2008. 189p. (C). 70.00 *(978-99932-7-233-5(7))* Midsea Bks. Ltd. MLT. Dist: Brown, David Bk. Co., The.

Baughman, Daren & Baughman, Nancy. Buy It, Sell It, Make Money: Your Guide to Finding & Reselling Luxury Goods Online. 2009. 228p. pap. 19.95 *(978-1-935278-61-0(4)*, iUniverse Star) iUniverse, Inc.

Bemko, Marsha. Antiques Roadshow Behind the Scenes: An Insider's Guide to PBS's #1 Weekly Show. 2009. (ENG., Illus.). 192p. pap. 16.99 *(978-1-4391-0330-2(5)*, Touchstone) Touchstone.

Bissonnette, Zac. Warman's Antiques & Collectibles 2013 Price Guide. 46th ed. 2012. (ENG., Illus.). 800p. pap. 29.99 ***(978-1-4402-2943-5(0))*** Krause Pubns.

Bleichmar, Daniela & Mancall, Peter C., eds. Collecting Across Cultures: Material Exchanges in the Early Modern Atlantic World. 2011. (Early Modern Americas Ser.). (Illus.). 392p. (C). 49.95 *(978-0-8122-4305-5(6))* Univ. of Pennsylvania Pr.

Bradley, Eric. Fantastic Finds. 2011. (ENG.). 176p. pap. 14.99 ***(978-1-4402-3056-1(0))*** Krause Pubns.

Brodie, Neil, et al, eds. Archaeology, Cultural Heritage, & the Antiquities Trade. 2008. (Cultural Heritage Studies). (ENG.). 368p. pap. 29.95 *(978-0-8130-3339-6(X))* Univ. Pr. of Florida.

Brooke, Bob. How to Start a Home-Based Antiques Business. 2011. (Home-Based Business Ser.). (ENG.). 272p. pap. 18.95 *(978-0-7627-6361-0(2))* Globe Pequot Pr., The.

Brownell, Dan. Antique Trader Antiques & Collectibles 2012 Price Guide. 28th ed. 2011. (ENG., Illus.). 816p. pap. 21.99 *(978-1-4402-1695-4(9))* Krause Pubns.

Bruner, Mike. Signs of Our Past: Porcelain Enamel Advertising in America. 2008. (Illus.). 256p. bds. 59.99 *(978-0-7643-3042-1(X))* Schiffer Publishing, Ltd.

Bruno, Guido. Adventures in American Bookshops, Antique Stores & Auction Rooms. 2009. 130p. 24.99 *(978-1-116-77686-7(3))* 2009. 130p. 28.99 *(978-1-116-77685-0(5))* 2009. 130p. pap. 20.75 *(978-1-116-77687-4(1))* 2009. 130p. pap. 19.75 *(978-1-116-77688-1(X))* 2008. 132p. 21.99 *(978-0-559-42179-2(6))* 2008. 132p. pap. 19.75 *(978-0-559-42178-5(8))* BiblioBazaar.

—Adventures in American Bookshops, Antique Stores & Auction Rooms. 2009. 92p. pap. *(978-0-217-67621-2(9))* Books LLC.

—Adventures in American Bookshops, Antique Stores & Auction Rooms. 2008. 132p. 35.95 *(978-1-4368-9403-6(4))*; pap. 20.95 *(978-1-4367-6143-7(3))* Kessinger Publishing, LLC.

Buchanan, S. K. Vietnam Zippos: American Soldiers' Engravings & Stories (1965-1973) 2007. (Illus.). 176p. 25.00 *(978-0-226-07828-1(0))* Univ. of Chicago Pr.

Callaway, Libby, et al. American Pickers Guide to Picking. 2011. (ENG., Illus.). 224p. 24.99 *(978-1-4013-2448-3(7))* Hyperion Pr.

Castner, Leon & Kathenes, Brian. Betcha Didn't Know That: 101 Antique & Collectibles Tips That Can Make You Rich, Famous, & the Hit of the Party. 2007. (Illus.). 168p. pap. 14.95 *(978-1-60097-002-3(8))* Progressive Business Concepts, Inc.

Chaplin, Julia. Gypset Style. 2009. (ENG.). 180p. 45.00 *(978-2-7594-0396-7(3))* Assouline FRA. Dist: Perseus Distribution.

Chinese Arts Auction Records 2000: Antiques 1/1/99 - 12/31/99. (Illus.). 500p. pap. 59.95 *(978-957-99189-8-5(8))* Chinese Art Bks. Cultural Enterprise Co., Ltd. TWN. Dist: Art Media Resources, Inc.

Churchill, John & Turner, Dwight. The Little Armageddon: The Great Controversy Within the Seventh-day Adventist Church. 2010. 220p. pap. 16.00 *(978-1-4269-3241-0(3))* Trafford Publishing.

Collings, Jim & Collings, Merlyn. Character & Novelty Clocks & Watches. 2010. (ENG., Illus.). 192p. 29.95 *(978-1-57432-690-1(2)*, 1574326902) Collector Bks.

Corcoran, Frank & Rabinovitch, Victor. Treasures from the Canadian Museum of Civilization & the Canadian War Museum. 2011. (ENG., Illus.). 200p. (C). pap. 49.95 *(978-0-660-19915-3(7))* Canadian Museum of Civilization/Musee Canadien des Civilisations CAN. Dist: Univ. of Washington Pr.

De Burton, Simon & Negretti, Giampiero. Panerai. 2008. (ENG., Illus.). 192p. 175.00 *(978-2-08-030541-1(7))* Flammarion et Cie FRA. Dist: Random Hse., Inc.

Deasy, Warren R. The Merry-Go-Round Is Worn. 2009. 164p. pap. 19.95 *(978-1-59393-456-9(4))* BearManor Media.

Demuth, Anne. Selling Antiques, Then, Now & the Future: How to Make It in the Antique Business by Really Trying! 2007. 56p. per. 16.95 *(978-1-60441-227-7(5))* PublishAmerica, Inc.

Dorling Kindersley Publishing Staff. Antiques Detective. 2007. 76p. (C). 33.33 *(978-0-13-208131-3(8))* Prentice Hall Higher Education.

Dunlap, Freddie Watson. The Incredible Gourd. 2011. 100p. pap. 51.99 ***(978-1-4568-7571-8(X))*** Xlibris Corp.

Eiland, Murray, III & Eiland, Murray. Oriental Rugs. 2007. (Starting to Collect Ser.). (ENG., Illus.). 192p. *(978-1-85149-406-4(5)*, Antique Collectors Club Dist) Antique Collectors' Club.

Fairall, Nick & Hughes, David. The Guide to Guinness Collectables. 2009. (ENG.). 288p. 54.95 *(978-1-905483-54-9(6))* Liberties Pr. IRL. Dist: Dufour Editions, Inc.

Fjestad, S. P., ed. Blue Book of Electric Guitars. 11th ed. 2008. (Blue Book of Electric Guitars Ser.). (ENG., Illus.). per. 34.95 *(978-1-886768-73-4(0))* Blue Bk. Pubns., Inc.

Flood, Kathy. Warman's Jewelry Field Guide. 2nd ed. 2011. (ENG., Illus.). 512p. pap. 14.99 *(978-1-4402-1438-7(7))* Krause Pubns.

Franklin, M. J. Biscuit Tins, 1868-1939: The Art of Decorative Packaging. 2006. (ENG., Illus.). 168p. *(978-1-872727-93-6(X)*, New Cavendish Bks. Dist) Antique Collectors' Club.

Golden Apple Collect. 24.95 *(978-0-9621662-0-4(0))* White Plains Auxiliary of the White Plains Hospital Medical Ctr.

Greenfield, Briann G. Out of the Attic: Inventing Antiques in Twentieth-Century New England. 2009. (Illus.). 256p. 80.00 net. *(978-1-55849-709-2(9))*; pap. 26.95 net. *(978-1-55849-710-8(2))* Univ. of Massachusetts Pr.

Gross, Leslie. Housewives' Guide to Antiques: How to Get the Most for Your Money When Furnishing Your Home with Antiques. 2009. 186p. 37.95 *(978-1-104-84132-4(0))* 2007. (ENG.). 184p. per. 22.95 *(978-0-548-43832-9(3))* Kessinger Publishing, LLC.

Hammond, Dorothy. Pictorial Price Guide to American Antiques 2006-2007: Objects Made for the American Market. 2007. (Pictorial Price Guide to American Antiques Ser.). (ENG., Illus.). 288p. pap. *(978-1-85149-513-9(4)*, Antique Collectors Club Dist) Antique Collectors' Club.

HarperCollins Publishers Ltd. Staff. Review of Season. (Illus.). 320p. pap. 65.00 *(978-0-903432-42-9(0))* Antique Collectors' Club.

Hearnden, Jonty. Flea Market Secrets: Your Guide to the Hidden Treasures. 2006. (ENG., Illus.). 300p. pap. 19.95 *(978-1-84533-428-4(0)*, Mitchell Beazley) Octopus Publishing Group GBR. Dist: Hachette Bk. Group.

Hey, Denise. My True Ghostly Experiences. 2011. 48p. pap. 9.99 *(978-1-4567-3098-7(3))* AuthorHouse.

Higgins, Katherine & Hearnden, Jonty. Miller's Collectibles Price Guide 2008: Over 5,000 Items Valued. 2007. (ENG., Illus.). 160p. per. 24.95 *(978-1-84533-346-1(2)*, Mitchell Beazley) Octopus Publishing Group GBR. Dist: Hachette Bk. Group.

Hogben, Michael & Abrams, Linda. Collecting under the Radar: Tomorrow's Antiques. (ENG.). 2010. 172p. pap. 24.95 *(978-1-933176-30-7(X))* 2009. 160p. (J). (gr. -1-12). 26.95 *(978-1-933176-23-9(7))* Red Rock Pr., Inc.

Huggins, Maryalice. Aesop's Mirror. 2010. (ENG., Illus.). 288p. pap. 15.00 *(978-0-312-65532-7(0))* Picador.

James, Hillary Shilkitus. It's All About Accessories for the World's Most Fashionable Dolls, 1959-1972. 2011. (Illus.). 352p. 49.99 *(978-0-7643-3669-0(X))* Schiffer Publishing, Ltd.

Jordan, Derek H. Victorian China Fairings: The Collector's Guide. collector's ed. 2007. (ENG., Illus.). *(978-1-85149-446-0(4)*, Antique Collectors Club Dist) Antique Collectors' Club.

Jordan, Scott James. Past Objects. 2010. (ENG., Illus.). 128p. 27.95 *(978-0-9820754-3-2(X))* Batty, Mark Pub., LLC.

Kagan, Julia. Gem Engraving in Britain from Antiquity to the Present: With a Catalogue of the British Engraved Gems in the State Hermitage Musuem. 2010. (Beazley archive: studies in gems & Jewellery Ser.). (ENG., Illus.). 495p. (C). 160.00 *(978-1-903767-12-2(1))* Archaeopress GBR. Dist: Brown, David Bk. Co., The.

Klingshim, William. Divination in Late Antiquity. 2007. 35.95 *(978-0-415-33154-8(4))*; 110.00 *(978-0-415-33153-1(6))* Routledge.

Kovel, Terry & Kovel, Kim. Kovels' Antiques & Colectibles Price Guide 2012: America's Bestselling Antiques Annual. 44th ed. 2011. (ENG., Illus.). 752p. pap. 27.95 *(978-1-57912-883-8(1)*, 1579128831) Black Dog & Leventhal Pubs., Inc.

Lambert, Daryle S. 31 Steps to your Millions with Antiques & Collectibles: The Best Kept Secrets Revealed. 2007. per. 19.95 *(978-0-9796423-0-2(2))* 31 Inc.

Lapedis, Aaron & LaPedis, Aaron. The Garage Sale Millionaire: Make Money in a down Economy with Hidden Finds from Estate Auctions to Garage Sales & Everything In-Between! 2010. 216p. pap. 21.95 *(978-0-9755398-4-2(1))* Beautiful Media LLC.

Lawrence, Edward. Complete Antique Shop Directory for Eastern Michigan, 1994-95. (Illus.). 260p. (Orig.). pap. 10.95 *(978-0-9634597-2-5(4))* Complete Antique Shop Directories.

—Complete Antique Shop Directory for Illinois South of Chicago 96. Date not set. pap. 7.95 *(978-0-9634597-4-9(0))* Complete Antique Shop Directories.

—Complete Antique Shop Directory for Indiana 96. Date not set. pap. 7.95 *(978-0-9634597-5-6(9))* Complete Antique Shop Directories.

Lomax, James & Rothwell, James. Country House Silver: From Dunham Massey. 2007. (ENG.). 220p. 75.00 *(978-1-905400-44-7(6))* Anova Bks. GBR. Dist: Independent Pubs. Group.

MacDonald, S. B. Absinthe Antiques: A Collection from la Belle Epoque. 2011. 46.95 ***(978-0-7414-6375-3(X))*** Infinity Publishing.

Martin, Paul. Britain. 2009. (ENG., Illus.). 248p. pap. 29.95 *(978-0-7524-5030-8(1))* History Pr. Ltd.,The GBR. Dist: Independent Pubs. Group.

—Paul Martin's Britain. 2009. (ENG., Illus.). 256p. pap. 30.95 *(978-0-7509-4726-8(8))* History Pr. Ltd.,The GBR. Dist: Independent Pubs. Group.

Martin, Steven. Opium Fiend: A 21st Century Slave to a 19th Century Addiction. 2012. (ENG., Illus.). 416p. 26.00 ***(978-0-345-51783-8(0)***, Villard Bks.) Random House Publishing Group.

McCormick, Andrea & McCormick, Lynde. Old China/New Style: Antique Furniture & Accessories, 1780-1930. 2007. (Schiffer Book for Collectors Ser.). (Illus.). 254p. 49.95 *(978-0-7643-2148-1(X))* Schiffer Publishing, Ltd.

McKenzie, James W. Comprar, Conservar y Vender Antiguedades. (SPA.). 312p. *(978-84-7927-361-3(5))* Robinbk., Ediciones S.L. ESP. Dist: Lectorum Pubns., Inc.

Mendelsohn, Michael. Life Is Short Art Is Long: Maximizing Estate Planning Strategies for Collectors of Art, Antiques & Collectibles. 2007. pap. 24.95 *(978-1-59969-109-1(4))* Wealth Management Pr.

Mesmer, Philippe. Fan Tales. 2008. (ENG.). 91p. 22.00 *(978-1-4379-6326-7(9))* DIANE Publishing Co.

Mihalick, Roseanna. Collecting Handkerchiefs. 2nd rev. ed. 2007. (Illus.). 144p. pap. 24.95 *(978-0-7643-2517-5(5))* Schiffer Publishing, Ltd.

Miller, James. Hidden Treasure Houses. 2006. (ENG., Illus.). 288p. 49.50 *(978-1-4050-9127-5(4))* Macmillan Pubs., Ltd. GBR. Dist: Trans-Atlantic Pubns., Inc.

Miller, Judith. Antiques Encyclopedia. 2006. (ENG., Illus.). 208p. 50.00 *(978-1-84533-470-3(1)*, Mitchell Beazley) Octopus Publishing Group GBR. Dist: Hachette Bk. Group.

—Miller's Antiques Handbook & Price Guide 2010-2011. 2010. (ENG., Illus.). 648p. instr.'s gde. ed., instr.'s hndbk. ed. 45.00 *(978-1-84533-440-6(X))* Millers Pubns. GBR. Dist: Hachette Bk. Group.

—Miller's Antiques Handbook & Price Guide 2012-2013. 2011. (ENG.). 648p. 45.00 *(978-1-84533-638-7(0)*, Mitchell Beazley) Octopus Publishing Group GBR. Dist: Hachette Bk. Group.

—Miller's Antiques Price Guide 2009: 30th Edition. 2008. (ENG., Illus.). 704p. 45.00 *(978-1-84533-455-0(8)*, Mitchell Beazley) Octopus Publishing Group GBR. Dist: Sterling Publishing Co., Inc.

Miller, Judith & Hill, Mark. Miller's Collectibles Price Guide 2009. 2008. (ENG., Illus.). 512p. pap. 27.95 *(978-1-84533-454-3(X)*, Mitchell Beazley) Octopus Publishing Group GBR. Dist: Sterling Publishing Co., Inc.

Mobil Travel Guide Staff, creator. Antiques & Collectibles. 2008. (MOBIL TRAVEL GUIDE Ser.). 192p. 17.95 *(978-0-8416-0744-6(3))* American Map Corp.

Moore, N. Hudson. The Collector's Manual. 2010. 516p. pap. 39.75 *(978-1-148-51236-5(5))* BiblioBazaar.

—The Collector's Manual. 2010. 504p. 43.16 *(978-1-163-33667-0(X))* 2010. 504p. pap. 31.16 *(978-1-162-64653-4(5))* 2007. (ENG.). 502p. 53.95 *(978-0-548-02500-0(2))* Kessinger Publishing, LLC.

Moran, Mark F. Warman's Antiques & Collectibles 2011 Price Guide. 44th ed. 2010. (ENG., Illus.). 800p. pap. 26.99 *(978-1-4402-0408-1(X))* Krause Pubns.

—Warman's Antiques & Collectibles 2012 Price Guide. 45th ed. 2011. (ENG., Illus.). 800p. pap. 27.99 *(978-1-4402-1404-2(2))* Krause Pubns.

Morley, Iain & Renfrew, Colin, eds. The Archaeology of Measurement: Comprehending Heaven, Earth & Time in Ancient Societies. 2010. (ENG., Illus.). 284p. (C). 95.00 *(978-0-521-11990-0(1))* Cambridge Univ. Pr.

Pauwels, Wim. Architectural Antiques. Watkinson, Laura, tr. 2008. (ENG., Illus.). 256p. *(978-90-77213-94-0(5)*, Beta-Plus (Acc)) Antique Collectors' Club.

—Contemporary Living with Antiques. 2010. (ENG., Illus.). 204p. 125.00 *(978-90-8944-069-3(0))* Beta-Plus Pubs. BEL. Dist: Antique Collectors' Club.

Payne, Stephen. How to Purchase Archaic Jade: On the Internet. 2009. 338p. pap. 88.33 *(978-1-4251-9102-3(9))* Trafford Publishing.

Pickford, Ian. Antique Silver. 2007. (Starting to Collect Ser.). (ENG., Illus.). 192p. *(978-1-85149-450-7(2)*, Antique Collectors Club Dist) Antique Collectors' Club.

Pinhas, Ora. Goldscheider: A Catalogue of Selected Models. 2006. (ENG., Illus.). 200p. 99.50 *(978-0-903685-96-2(5)*, Richard Dennis Pubns. Di) Antique Collectors' Club GBR. Dist: National Bk. Network.

Reed, Ira. The Jamestown Exposition 1907. 2008. 240p. per. 49.95 *(978-1-4327-1946-3(7))* Outskirts Pr., Inc.

Rosenstein, Leon. Antiques: The History of an Idea. 2008. 280p. 36.95 *(978-0-8014-4734-1(8))* Cornell Univ. Pr.

Ryder, Susannah. Don't Call the Thrift Shop: What to Do with a Lifetime of Well-Loved Possessions. 2007. (ENG., Illus.). 264p. per. 19.95 *(978-1-59077-111-2(7))* Evans, M. & Co., Inc.

Sadagursky, Stephanie. The Road to Happy Days: A Memoir of Life on the Road as an Antique Toy Dealer. 2009. 188p. 26.95 *(978-1-4401-0455-8(7))*; pap. 16.95 *(978-1-4401-0453-4(0))* iUniverse, Inc.

Sandon, John. Antique Porcelain. 2007. (Starting to Collect Ser.). (ENG., Illus.). 192p. *(978-1-85149-451-4(0)*, Antique Collectors Club Dist) Antique Collectors' Club.

Saunders, David. British Museum Technical Research Bulletin. 2009. (ENG., Illus.). 96p. pap. 40.00 *(978-1-904982-35-7(2))* Archetype Pubns. GBR. Dist: National Bk. Network.

Seton, Alistair. Collecting Japanese Antiques. 2010. (ENG., Illus.). 304p. pap. 34.95 *(978-4-8053-1122-6(3))* Tuttle Publishing.

Shoop, Fiona. How to Buy & Sell Antiques. 3rd rev. ed. 2006. 306p. pap. 30.00 *(978-1-84528-093-2(8))* Parkwest Pubns., Inc.

—How to Deal in Antiques. 4th ed. 2009. 320p. pap. 30.00 *(978-1-84528-300-1(7))* How To Books GBR. Dist: Parkwest Pubns., Inc.

Siebel, Catherine. A PRODUCT UNRAVELED: AMERICAN NEWSPAPERS AND THE FRAMING OF TOBACCO AS A CROP, A HABIT, AND A POLICY 2008. 232p. pap. *(978-3-639-08955-4(3))* VDM Verlag Dr. Mueller e.K.

Simon, Francios. Artisans of Paradise. 2009. (Illus.). 144p. *(978-2-7594-0398-1(X))* Assouline.

Siraudeau, Sebastien. French Flair: Modern Vintage Interiors. 2012. (ENG., Illus.). 736p. 45.00 ***(978-2-08-020094-5(1))*** Flammarion et Cie FRA. Dist: Random Hse., Inc.

Sorrell, Katherine. Old & New. 2007. (ENG., Illus.). 128p. pap. *(978-1-84597-547-0(2))* Ryland Peters & Small.

Stokes, Gerry. Today's Flea Markets: Antiques & Collectibles. Date not set. (Illus.). 36p. pap. 3.95 *(978-1-883103-08-8(8))* United, Inc.

Swindell, Deane F. Antics of Antiquers. 2011. 190p. 42.95 ***(978-1-258-06654-3(8))*** Literary Licensing, LLC.

Valeriani, Roberto. Antiques in Italian Interiors, Vol.II. 2010. (ENG., Illus.). 318p. 95.00 *(978-1-905216-18-5(1))* Verba Volant, Ltd. GBR. Dist: Ingram Pub. Services.

Victor-Howe, Anne-Marie. Feeding the Ancestors: Tlingit Carved Horn Spoons. Watson, Rubie, ed. 2007. (Peabody Museum Collections Ser.). (Illus.). 128p. pap. 21.95 *(978-0-87365-403-6(X))* Peabody Museum of Archaeology & Ethnology, Harvard Univ., Pubns. Dept.

Wang, Audrey. Chinese Antiquities: An Introduction to the Art Market. 2012. (Illus.). 240p. 60.00 ***(978-1-84822-065-2(0)***, Lund Humphries Pubs.) Ashgate Publishing, Ltd. GBR. Dist: Ashgate Publishing Co.

Warman's. National Parks Quarters Deluxe: 50 States + District of Columbia & Territories: Collector's Deluxe Quarters Folder 2010-2021. 2010. (ENG.). 4p. 7.99 *(978-1-4402-1394-6(1))* Krause Pubns.

Webster, Polly. Antique Collectors Guide to New England: Antique Shops, Auction Houses, Museums & Historic Homes. 2011. 182p. 42.95 ***(978-1-258-06763-2(3))*** Literary Licensing, LLC.

Wilder, Frank Van, ed. Artist's Signatures & Monograms of the 19th & 20th Centuries. (FRE., Illus.). 484p. 59.00 *(978-2-85299-023-4(7))* Editions Van Wilder FRA. Dist: Antique Collectors' Club.

Williams, Stan. The Find: The Housing Works Book of Decorating with Thrift Shop Treasures, Flea Market Objects, & Vintage Details. 2009. (ENG., Illus.). 240p. 27.50 *(978-0-307-40625-5(3))* Crown Publishing Group.

Williard, Joe. Picker's Bible: How to Pick Antiques Like the Pros. 2011. (ENG.). 176p. pap. 14.99 ***(978-1-4402-3039-4(0))*** Krause Pubns.

Yours Sincerely: Essays on Antiques & Country Life. 2006. per. 12.95 *(978-0-9754569-1-0(1))* Belmont Pr., The.

ANTIQUES—COLLECTORS AND COLLECTING

see Antiques

ANTIQUES—CONSERVATION AND RESTORATION

Caraway, Georgia Kemp. Tips, Tools, & Techniques on Caring for Antiques, Collectibles, & Other Treasures. 2012. E-Book ***(978-1-57441-462-2(3))*** Univ. of North Texas Pr.

—Tips, Tools, & Techniques to Care for Antiques, Collectibles, & Other Treasures. 2012. (Practical Guide Ser.: Vol. 5). (Illus.). 144p. pap. 14.95 ***(978-1-57441-451-6(8))*** Univ. of North Texas Pr.

Jackson, Albert & Day, David. Care & Repair of Antiques & Collectables. 2006. (ENG., Illus.). 160p. pap. 16.95 *(978-0-06-113732-7(4)*, HarperPerennial) HarperCollins Pubs.

Jones, M. Conservation Science: Heritage Materials. May, Eric, ed. 2006. (Rsc Paperbacks Ser.). (ENG., Illus.). 390p. (C). 56.00 *(978-0-85404-659-1(3)*, 0854046593) Royal Society of Chemistry, The GBR. Dist: Ingram Pub. Services.

Miller, Judith. Care & Repair of Antiques & Collectables. 2006. (ENG., Illus.). 288p. 29.95 (978-1-84533-426-0(4), Mitchell Beazley) Octopus Publishing Group GBR. Dist: Hachette Bk. Group.

Peterson, Cleo Ann. Antique Malls: An Antique Dealer's Friend or Foe? pap. (978-0-9709354-0-3(4)) Peterson, Cleo Ann.

ANTIQUES—DICTIONARIES

Brulet, R., et al. La ceramique romaine en Gaule du Nord: Dictionnaire des ceramiques. la vaisselle a large Diffusion. 2010. (FRE., Illus.). 464p. (C). 115.00 (978-2-503-53509-8(7)) Brepols Pubs. BEL. Dist: Brown, David Bk. Co., The.

Darvill, Timothy. Concise Oxford Dictionary of Archaeology. 2nd ed. 2010. (Oxford Paperback Reference Ser.). (ENG., Illus.). 544p. pap. 18.95 (978-0-19-953404-3(7)) Oxford Univ. Pr., Inc.

Feder, Kenneth L. Encyclopedia of Dubious Archaeology: From Atlantis to the Walam Olum. 2010. E-Book (978-0-313-37919-2(X), Greenwood Pr.); (Illus.). 292p. 85.00 (978-0-313-37918-5(1), GR7918) Greenwood Publishing Group, Inc.

Hoops, Johannes. Reallexikon der Germanischen Altertumskunde. 2011. 714p. pap. 49.75 **(978-1-172-76553-9(7))**; 630p. pap. 45.75 **(978-1-172-78729-6(8))**; 608p. pap. 45.75 **(978-1-172-81018-5(4))** BiblioBazaar.

—Reallexikon der Germanischen Altertumskunde. (GER.). 630p. 358.00 **(978-3-11-190289-0(7))**; 236.00 **(978-3-11-108780-1(8))** De Gruyter, Walter Inc.

Miller, Judith, ed. Miller's Antiques Encyclopedia. 2008. (ENG., Illus.). 592p. 50.00 (978-1-84533-433-8(7), Mitchell Beazley) Octopus Publishing Group GBR. Dist: Sterling Publishing Co., Inc.

Mobil Travel Guide. Antiques & Collectibles. 2008. (ENG.). 216p. pap. 17.95 (978-1-936010-13-4(5)) Five Star Travel Corp., The.

Reed, Robert & Reed, Claudette. Antique & Collectible Dictionary. 2008. (ENG., Illus.). 240p. 24.95 (978-1-57432-580-5(9), 1574325809) Collector Bks.

Smith, William. A School Dictionary of Greek & Roman Antiquities Abridged from the Larger Dictionary by William Smith, with Corrections, by Charles Anthon. 2006. 368p. per. 26.99 (978-1-4255-3821-7(5)) MPublishing.

ANTIQUITIES

see also Antiques; Archaeology; Christian Antiquities; Classical Antiquities; Forgery of Antiquities

also subdivision Antiquities under names of countries, cities, etc

Aczel, Amir D. The Cave & the Cathedral: How a Real-Life Indiana Jones & a Renegade Scholar Decoded the Ancient Art of Man. 2009. (ENG., Illus.). 264p. 25.95 (978-0-470-37353-8(9), Wiley) Wiley, John & Sons, Inc.

Adams, William Yewdale & Adams, Ernest W. Archaeological Typology & Practical Reality: A Dialectical Approach to Artifact Classification & Sorting. 2007. (ENG., Illus.). 452p. pap. 56.00 (978-0-521-04867-5(2)) Cambridge Univ. Pr.

Adovasio, J. M. Basketry Technology: A Guide to Identification & Analysis, Updated Edition. 2010. (ENG., Illus.). 200p. pap. 34.95 (978-1-59874-557-3(3)) Left Coast Pr., Inc.

Albanese, Marilia, et al, texts. Archaeology from Above: The World from the Air. 2010. (ENG., Illus.). 192p. 39.95 (978-88-544-0493-9(4)) White Star ITA. Dist: Sterling Publishing Co., Inc.

Baca, Murtha, et al. Cataloging Cultural Objects: A Guide to Describing Cultural Works & Their Images. 2006. (Illus.). 396p. per. 75.00 (978-0-8389-3564-4(8)) American Library Assn.

Bahn, Paul. Exploring the Ancient World: A Guide to the Most Outstanding Historical Wonders Ever Built. 2008. (Illus.). 256p. (978-0-7495-5864-2(4)) Automobile Assn.

Ballin Smith, Beverly, et al, eds. West over Sea: Studies in Scandinavian Sea-Borne Expansion & Settlement Before 1300. 2007. (Northern World Ser.). (Illus.). 581p. (978-90-04-15893-1(6)) BRILL.

Barnard, H. & Eerkens, Jelmer W. Theory & Practice of Archaeological Residue Analysis. 2007. (Bar S Ser.). (ENG., Illus.). 274p. (C). pap. 90.00 (978-1-4073-0084-9(9)) British Archaeological Reports Ltd. GBR. Dist: Brown, David Bk. Co., The.

Bradley, Pamela. Cultural Treasures of the Ancient World. 2009. (ENG.). 304p. 39.95 (978-1-74110-495-0(5)) New Holland Pubs. Pty, Ltd. AUS. Dist: Tuttle Publishing.

Brizemeure, Daniel & Lacoudre, Noël. Le Rouleau de cuivre de la grotte 3 de Qumrân (3Q15) Expertise - Restauration - Epigraphie, 2 vols. 2006. (FRE & ENG., Illus.). (978-90-04-14030-1(1)) BRILL.

Carver, Martin Oswald Hugh. Making Archaeology Happen. 2011. (ENG., Illus.). 184p. (C). pap. 29.95 (978-1-61132-025-1(9)) Left Coast Pr., Inc.

—Making Archaeology Happen: Design Versus Dogma. 2011. (ENG., Illus.). 184p. (C). 89.00 (978-1-61132-024-4(0)) Left Coast Pr., Inc.

Colwell-Chanthaphonh, Chip & Ferguson, T. J., eds. Collaboration in Archaeological Practice: Engaging Descendant Communities. 2007. (Archaeology in Society Ser.). (ENG., Illus.). 300p. 85.00 (978-0-7591-1053-3(0)); per. 39.95 (978-0-7591-1054-0(9)) AltaMira Pr.

Cook, Jill. The Discovery of Human Antiquity. 2nd ed. 2012. (Illus.). 300p. 75.00 (978-0-9817736-9-8(9)) KWS Pubs.

Cram101 Textbook Reviews Staff. Outlines & Highlights for Ancient Lives: An Introduction to Archaeology & Prehistory by Fagan, ISBN. 2008. 188p. pap. 12.95 (978-1-4289-6553-2(5)) Cram101 Inc.

Cuno, James. Who Owns Antiquity? Museums & the Battle over Our Ancient Heritage. 2008. (ENG., Illus.). 272p. 24.95 (978-0-691-13712-4(9)) Princeton Univ. Pr.

Cuno, James, et al. Whose Culture? The Promise of Museums & the Debate over Antiquities. Cuno, James, ed. 2009. (ENG., Illus.). 232p. (C). 24.95 (978-0-691-13333-1(6)) Princeton Univ. Pr.

Cuomo, S. Technology & Culture in Greek & Roman Antiquity. 2007. (Key Themes in Ancient History Ser.). (ENG., Illus.). 224p. (C). per. 34.00 (978-0-521-00903-4(0)); 99.00 (978-0-521-81073-9(6)) Cambridge Univ. Pr.

Darvill, Timothy. Concise Oxford Dictionary of Archaeology. 2nd ed. 2008. (ENG., Illus.). 544p. 50.00 (978-0-19-953405-0(5)) Oxford Univ. Pr., Inc.

Dine, Jim & contrib. by. Poet Singing, 1 vol. 2008. (ENG., Illus.). 114p. 35.00 (978-3-86521-828-5(8)) Steidl, Gerhard Druckerei und Verlag DEU. Dist: Innovative Logistics.

Duke, Philip & Hamilakis, Yannis, eds. Archaeology & Capitalism: From Ethics to Politics. 2007. (One World Archaeology Ser.). (ENG., Illus.). 298p. 89.00 (978-1-59874-270-1(1)) Left Coast Pr., Inc.

Dumont-Le Cornec, Elisabeth. Wonders of the World: Natural & Man-Made Majesties. 2007. (Illus.). 150p. (gr. 4-7). 24.95 (978-0-8109-9417-1(8), Abrams Bks. for Young Readers) Abrams.

Elizabeth Pye Staff. Power of Touch: Handling Objects in Museum & Heritage Context. Pye, Elizabeth, ed. 2008. (Univ Col London Inst Arch Pub Ser.). (ENG.). 262p. 94.00 (978-1-59874-303-6(1)) Left Coast Pr., Inc.

Englert, Anton & Trakadas, Athena. Wulfstan's Voyage: The Baltic Sea Region in the Early Viking Age as Seen from Shipboard. 2009. (Maritime Culture of the North Ser.). (ENG., Illus.). 374p. (C). 106.00 (978-87-85180-56-8(4)) Vikingeskibsmuseet DNK. Dist: Brown, David Bk. Co., The.

Fagan & Cram101 Textbook Reviews Staff. Ancient Lives. 2007. 232p. per. 13.95 (978-1-4286-2622-9(X)) Cram101 Inc.

Fagan, Brian M. Ancient Lives: An Introduction to Archaeology & Prehistory. 5th rev. ed. 2011. (ENG., Illus.). 528p. (C). pap. 136.80 **(978-0-205-17807-0(3)**, Prentice Hall) Prentice Hall PTR.

—Ancient Lives: An Introduction to Archaeology & Prehistory, Books a la Carte Edition. 5th ed. 2011. (ENG.). 528p. (C). ring bd. 89.33 **(978-0-205-17883-4(9)**, Prentice Hall) Prentice Hall PTR.

Fagan, Brian M. Discovery! Unearthing the New Treasures of Archaeology. Fagan, Brian M., ed. 2007. (ENG., Illus.). 256p. 40.00 (978-0-500-05149-8(6)) Thames & Hudson.

Funari, Pedro Paulo A., et al, eds. New Perspectives on the Ancient World. 2008. (Bar S Ser.). (Illus.). 248p. (C). 100.00 (978-1-4073-0270-6(1)) British Archaeological Reports Ltd. GBR. Dist: Brown, David Bk. Co., The.

Gisler-Huwiler, Madeleine & Schutze, Sebastian, eds. Antiquities: The Complete Collection. 2007. (ENG., Illus.). 550p. 69.99 (978-3-8365-0086-9(8)) TASCHEN DEU. Dist: Ingram Pub. Services.

Goodburn-Brown, Dana & Jones, Julie, eds. Look after the Pennies: Numismatics & Conservation in The 1990s. 2007. (ENG., Illus.). 92p. pap. 60.00 (978-1-873132-81-4(6)) Archetype Pubns. GBR. Dist: National Bk. Network.

Grana, Costantino & Cucchiara, Rita, eds. Multimedia for Cultural Heritage: First International Workshop, MM4CH 2011, Modena, Italy, May 3, 2011, Revised Selected Papers. 2012. (Communications in Computer & Information Science Ser.). (ENG., Illus.). viii, 217p. pap. 84.00 **(978-3-642-27977-5(5)**, 3642279775) Springer.

Green, Penny & Mackenzie, Simon, eds. Criminology & Archaeology: Studies in Looted Antiquities. 2009. (ENG., Illus.). 182p. pap. 46.00 (978-1-84113-992-0(0)) Hart Publishing Ltd. GBR. Dist: International Specialized Bk. Services.

Hather, Jon G. The Identification of the Northern European Woods: A Guide for Archaeologists & Conservators. 2007. (University College London Institute of Archaeology Publications). (ENG., Illus.). 188p. 90.00 (978-1-873132-47-0(6)) Archetype Pubns. GBR. Dist: National Bk. Network.

Hunt, Patrick. Ten Discoveries That Rewrote History. 2007. (ENG.). 240p. (gr. 12-18). 15.00 (978-0-452-28877-5(0), Plume) Penguin Group (USA) Inc.

Kehoe, Alice Beck. Controversies in Archaeology. 2008. (ENG., Illus.). 256p. (C). 89.00 (978-1-59874-061-5(X)); pap. 36.95 (978-1-59874-062-2(8)) Left Coast Pr., Inc.

Klimczuk, Stephen & Warner, Gerald. Secret Places, Hidden Sanctuaries: Uncovering Mysterious Sights & Societies. 2009. (ENG., Illus.). 272p. 19.95 (978-1-4027-6207-9(0)) Sterling Publishing Co., Inc.

Lucas, Gavin. Understanding the Archaeological Record. 2012. (ENG., Illus.). (C). 320p. 99.00 **(978-1-107-01026-0(8))**; 314p. pap. 32.99 **(978-0-521-27969-7(0))** Cambridge Univ. Pr.

Lugli, Francesca & Stoppiello, Alessandra Assunta, eds. Atti Del 3O Convegno Nazionale Di Etnoarcheologia, Mondaino, 17-19 Marzo 2004 / Proceedings of the 3Rd Italian Congress of Ethnoarchaeology, Mondaino (Italy), 17-19 March, 2004. 2008. (Bar S Ser.). (ITA & ENG., Illus.). 221p. (C). 95.00 (978-1-4073-0326-0(0)) British Archaeological Reports Ltd. GBR. Dist: Brown, David Bk. Co., The.

Martinón-Torres, Marcos & Rehren, Thilo, eds. Archaeology, History & Science: Integrating Approaches to Ancient Materials. 2008. (Univ Col London Inst Arch Pub Ser.). (ENG., Illus.). 218p. 94.00 (978-1-59874-340-1(6)) Left Coast Pr., Inc.

McCallum, Donald F. The Four Great Temples: Buddhist Archaeology, Architecture, & Icons of Seventh-Century Japan. 2008. (Illus.). 360p. (C). 40.00 (978-0-8248-3114-1(4)) Univ. of Hawaii Pr.

Michell, John & Sweetman, John. The Dambusters. 2013. (ENG., Illus.). 288p. pap. 15.95 (978-0-349-12323-3(3)) Little, Brown Bk. Group Ltd. GBR. Dist: Independent Pubs. Group.

Morley, Iain & Renfrew, Colin, eds. The Archaeology of Measurement: Comprehending Heaven, Earth & Time in Ancient Societies. 2010. (ENG., Illus.). 296p. (C). pap. 36.99 (978-0-521-13588-7(5)) Cambridge Univ. Pr.

O'Keefe, Patrick J. Trade in Antiquities: Reducing Destruction & Theft. 2007. (ENG.). 134p. pap. 50.00 (978-1-873132-31-9(X)) Archetype Pubns. GBR. Dist: National Bk. Network.

Parcak, Sarah H. Satellite Remote Sensing for Archaeology. 2009. (ENG., Illus.). 320p. 155.00 (978-0-415-44877-2(8)); pap. 44.95 (978-0-415-44878-9(6)) Routledge.

Pearce, Susan, ed. Visions of Antiquity: The Society of Antiquaries of London 1707-2007. 2007. (Archaeologia Ser.). (Illus.). 488p. (C). 150.00 (978-0-85431-287-0(0)) Society of Antiquaries of London GBR. Dist: Brown, David Bk. Co., The.

Pearsall, Deborah M. Encyclopedia of Archaeology, 3 vols. 2008. (Illus.). (978-0-12-548031-4(8)); (978-0-12-548032-1(6)); (978-0-12-373643-7(9)) Elsevier Science & Technology Bks. (Academic Pr.).

Pescarin, Sofia. Reconstructing Ancient Landscape. 2009. (Series Minor Ser.). (ENG., Illus.). 264p. (C). pap. 50.00 (978-963-9911-09-3(7)) Archaeolingua Alapitvany HUN. Dist: Brown, David Bk. Co., The.

Poffet, Jean-Michel, et al. Le Rouleau de Cuivre de la Grotte 3 de Qumrân (3Q15) Expertise, Restauration, Epigraphie, 2 vols. 2006. (FRE & ENG., Illus.). (978-90-04-15469-8(8)); (978-90-04-15468-1(X)) BRILL.

Pollard, Justin. Wonders of the Ancient World: Antiquity's Greatest Feats of Design & Engineering. 2009. (ENG., Illus.). 256p. 14.99 (978-1-84724-256-3(1), 1847242561) Quercus GBR. Dist: Book Sales, Inc.

Price, T. Douglas & Feinman, Gary M., eds. Archaeology at the Millennium: A Sourcebook. 2008. (ENG., Illus.). xvi, 512p. per. 74.95 (978-0-387-72610-6(1), 0387726101) Springer.

Prisant, Carol. Good, Better, Best: Trade Secrets for Spotting a Find. 2009. (ENG.). 176p. (gr. 12-18). 27.50 (978-0-14-200527-9(4), Studio) Penguin Group (USA) Inc.

Pye, Elizabeth, ed. The Power of Touch: Handling Objects in Museum & Heritage Context. 2008. (Publications of the Institute of Archaeology Ser.). (ENG., Illus.). 262p. pap. 34.95 (978-1-59874-304-3(X)) Left Coast Pr., Inc.

Read, Dwight W. Artifact Classification: A Conceptual & Methodological Approach. (ENG., Illus.). 363p. 2009. pap. 34.95 (978-1-59874-103-2(9)) 2007. 89.00 (978-1-59874-102-5(0)) Left Coast Pr., Inc.

Rebay-Salisbury, Katharina & Sorensen, Marie L. S. Embodied Knowledge: Historical Perspectives on Belief & Technology. 2012. (ENG., Illus.). 176p. (C). 60.00 **(978-1-84217-490-6(8))** Oxbow Bks., Ltd. GBR. Dist: Brown, David Bk. Co., The.

Reedy, Chandra L. Thin-Section Petrography of Stone & Ceramic Cultural Materials. 2008. (ENG., Illus.). 260p. pap. 160.00 (978-1-904982-33-3(6)) Archetype Pubns. GBR. Dist: National Bk. Network.

Renfrew, Colin. Loot, Legitimacy & Ownership: The Ethical Crisis in Archaeology. 2009. (Duckworth Debates in Archaeology). (Illus.). 160p. pap. 24.95 (978-0-7156-3034-1(2)) Duckworth Publishers GBR. Dist: International Publishers Marketing.

Rhodes, Robin F., ed. The Acquisition & Exhibition of Classical Antiquities: Professional, Legal, & Ethical Perspectives. 2008. (ENG., Illus.). 192p. pap. 25.00 (978-0-268-04027-7(3)) Univ. of Notre Dame Pr.

Robinson, Wendy, et al, contrib. by. First Aid for Underwater Finds. (Illus.). 128p. (978-1-873132-66-1(2)) Archetype Pubns.

Robson, Eleanor, et al, eds. Who Owns Objects? The Ethics & Politics of Collecting Cultural Artefacts. 2006. (ENG., Illus.). 156p. (C). per. 48.00 (978-1-84217-233-9(6)) Oxbow Bks., Ltd. GBR. Dist: Brown, David Bk. Co., The.

Ruggles, D. Fairchild, ed. On Location: Heritage Cities & Sites. 2011. (ENG., Illus.). viii, 244p. 129.00 **(978-1-4614-1107-9(6)**, 1461411076) Springer.

Sabloff, Jeremy A. Archaeology Matters: Action Archaeology in the Modern World. 2008. (Key Questions in Anthropology Ser.). (ENG., Illus.). 152p. (C). 79.00 (978-1-59874-088-2(1)); pap. 22.95 (978-1-59874-089-9(X)) Left Coast Pr., Inc.

Schiffer, Michael Brian. Behavioral Archaeology: Principles & Practice. 2010. (Equinox handbooks in anthro Arch Ser.). (ENG., Illus.). 230p. (C). 150.00 (978-1-84553-287-1(2)) Equinox Publishing Ltd. GBR. Dist: ISD.

—Behavioral Archaeology: Principles & Practice. 2010. (Equinox handbooks in anthro Arch Ser.). (ENG., Illus.). 230p. (C). pap. 45.00 (978-1-84553-288-8(0)) Equinox Publishing Ltd. GBR. Dist: ISD.

Schofield, John. Defining Moments: Dramatic Archaeologies of the Twentieth-Century. 2009. (Bar S Ser.). (ENG., Illus.). 164p. (C). pap. 87.50 (978-1-4073-0581-3(6)) British Archaeological Reports Ltd. GBR. Dist: Brown, David Bk. Co., The.

Scourfield, J. H. D. & Chahoud, Anna. Texts & Culture in Late Antiquity: Inheritance, Authority, & Change. Scourfield, J. H. D., ed. 2007. 350p. (C). 89.50 (978-1-905125-17-3(8)) Classical Pr. of Wales, The GBR. Dist: Brown, David Bk. Co., The.

Sereno, Kenneth K. Skeletons in the Sand. (978-0-374-26572-4(0)) Farrar, Straus & Giroux.

Sillotti, Alberto. Archaeology Treasures. 2008. 432p. 29.95 (978-88-540-0857-1(5)) White Star ITA. Dist: Book Sales, Inc.

Sitchin, Zecharia. The Cosmic Code, Bk. 6. 2007. (Earth Chronicles Ser.: Bk. 6). (ENG., Illus.). 320p. mass mkt. 7.99 (978-0-06-137924-6(7)) HarperCollins Pubs.

Skeates, Robin. Debating the Archaeological Heritage. 2009. (Duckworth Debates in Archaeology Ser.). 160p. pap. 24.95 (978-0-7156-2956-7(5)) Duckworth Publishers GBR. Dist: International Publishers Marketng.

Skilling, Peter, et al. Past Lives of the Buddha: Wat Si Chum-Art, Architecture & Inscriptions. 2008. (ENG., Illus.). 296p. 75.00 (978-974-9863-45-9(3)) River Bks. THA. Dist: Antique Collectors' Club.

Steiner, Rudolf. Christianity As Mystical Fact & the Mysteries of Antiquity. Collison, H., ed. 2009. 126p. pap. (978-1-4099-7235-8(6)) Dodo Pr.

—Christianity As Mystical Fact & the Mysteries of Antiquity. 2007. (ENG.). 260p. 42.95 (978-0-548-00395-4(5)) Kessinger Publishing, LLC.

Stout, Andrew, et al, eds. Managing Archaeological Resources: Global Context, National Programs, Local Actions. 2008. (One World Archaeology Ser.). (ENG., Illus.). 300p. 89.00 (978-1-59874-311-1(2)) Left Coast Pr., Inc.

Weidmann, Frederick W. Polycarp & John: The Harris Fragments & Their Challenge to the Literary Traditions. 2010. (ND Christianity & Judaism Anitqui Ser.). (ENG.). 206p. pap. 25.00 (978-0-268-03826-7(0)) Univ. of Notre Dame Pr.

Weiner, Stephen. Microarchaeology: Beyond the Visible Archaeological Record. 2010. (ENG., Illus.). 414p. (C). 95.00 (978-0-521-88003-9(3)); pap. 36.99 (978-0-521-70584-4(3)) Cambridge Univ. Pr.

Xenos Staff. Das Grosse Lexikon der Antiquitaten. (GER.). 576p. 59.95 (978-0-7859-8504-4(2), 3821210761) French & European Pubns., Inc.

1997 Antiquities. (Auction Records Ser.). (Illus.). 500p. pap. 59.95 (978-957-99189-1-6(0)) Chinese Art Bks. Cultural Enterprise Co., Ltd. TWN. Dist: Art Media Resources, Inc.

1998 Antiquities. (Auction Records Ser.). (Illus.). 500p. pap. 59.95 (978-957-99189-3-0(7)) Chinese Art Bks. Cultural Enterprise Co., Ltd. TWN. Dist: Art Media Resources, Inc.

1999 Antiquities. (Auction Records Ser.). (Illus.). 500p. pap. 59.95 (978-957-99189-7-8(X)) Chinese Art Bks. Cultural Enterprise Co., Ltd. TWN. Dist: Art Media Resources, Inc.

ANTIQUITIES—COLLECTION AND PRESERVATION

Ambers, Janet. Holding it All Together. 2010. (ENG., Illus.). 225p. pap. 90.00 (978-1-904982-47-0(6)) Archetype Pubns. GBR. Dist: National Bk. Network.

Bennett, Jim. Ancient Indian Artifacts Volume 2. 2010. (ENG., Illus.). 240p. 29.95 (978-1-57432-624-6(4), 1574326244) Collector Bks.

Bilsel, Can. Antiquity on Display: Regimes of the Authentic in Berlin's Pergamon Museum. 2012. (Classical Presences Ser.). (ENG., Illus.). 328p. 150.00 **(978-0-19-957055-3(8))** Oxford Univ. Pr., Inc.

Boone, Elizabeth Hill, et al. Collecting the Pre-Columbian Past. 2011. (Dumbarton Oaks Pre-Columbian Symposia & Colloquia Ser.). (ENG., Illus.). 366p. pap. 40.00 (978-0-88402-373-9(7)) Dumbarton Oaks.

Boytner, Ran, et al, eds. Controlling the Past, Owning the Future: The Political Uses of Archaeology in the Middle East. 2010. (ENG., Illus.). 320p. 60.00 (978-0-8165-2795-3(4)) Univ. of Arizona Pr.

Buck Sutton, Susan & Stroulia, Anna. Archaeology in Situ: Sites, Archaeology, & Communities in Greece. 2010. (Greek Studies: Interdisciplinary Approaches Ser.). (ENG., Illus.). 532p. 115.50 (978-0-7391-3234-0(2)); pap. 51.50 (978-0-7391-3235-7(0)) Lexington Bks.

Carver, Martin Professor. Archaeological Investigation. 2010. (ENG., Illus.). 480p. (C). 48.95 (978-0-415-48919-5(9)); 140.00 (978-0-415-48918-8(0)) Routledge.

Chatterjee, Helen. Touch in Museums: Policy & Practice in Object Handling. 2008. (ENG., Illus.). 348p. 119.95 (978-1-84788-239-4(0)); pap. 39.95 (978-1-84788-238-7(2)) Berg Pubs. GBR. Dist: Macmillan.

Clark, John. Metal Detecting: An Essential Guide to Detecting Inland, on Beaches & under Water, 1 vol. 2010. (ENG., Illus.). 174p. 44.95 (978-1-84797-149-4(0)) Crowood Pr., Ltd. GBR. Dist: Independent Pubs. Group.

Cuno, J. Who Owns Antiquity - Museums & the Battle over Our Ancient. 2010. (ENG., Illus.). 272p. pap. 18.95 (978-0-691-14810-6(4)) Princeton Univ. Pr.

Cuno, James. Whose Culture? - the Promise of Museums & the Debate over Antiquities. 2012. (ENG., Illus.). 232p. (C). pap. 17.95 **(978-0-691-15443-5(0))** Princeton Univ. Pr.

Endere, Maria Luz. Management of Archaeological Sites & the Public in Argentina. 2007. (Bar S Ser.). (Illus.). 187p. (C). 85.00 (978-1-4073-0152-5(7)) British Archaeological Reports Ltd. GBR. Dist: Brown, David Bk. Co., The.

Florian, Mary-Lou E. Fungal Facts: Solving Fungal Problems in Heritage Collections. 2007. (ENG., Illus.). 146p. pap. 60.00 (978-1-873132-63-0(8)) Archetype Pubns. GBR. Dist: National Bk. Network.

Frederiksen, Rune & Marchand, Eckart, eds. Plaster Casts: Making, Collecting & Displaying from Classical Antiquity to the Present. (Transformationen der Antike Ser.). (ENG., Illus.). XII, 752p. 2011. 280.00 **(978-3-11-173105-6(7))** 2010. 182.00 (978-3-11-020856-6(3)) De Gruyter, Walter Inc.

Gibson, Lisanne & Pendlebury, John, eds. Valuing Historic Environments. 2009. (Heritage, Culture & Identity Ser.). (Illus.). 234p. 99.95 (978-0-7546-7424-5(X)) Ashgate Publishing Co.

Gillman, Derek. The Idea of Cultural Heritage: Revised Edition. rev. ed. 2010. (ENG., Illus.). 216p. (C). 90.00 (978-0-521-19255-2(2)); pap. 27.99 (978-0-521-12257-3(0)) Cambridge Univ. Pr.

Grove, Brian. The Treasure Hunter's Handbook: Britain's Buried Treasure - And How to Find It. 2010. (ENG.). 288p. 15.95 (978-0-7499-4136-9(7)) Piatkus Bks. GBR. Dist: Independent Pubs. Group.

Hamilakis, Yannis & Duke, Philip, eds. Archaeology & Capitalism: From Ethics to Politics. 2009. (One World Archaeology, Vol. 54 Ser.). (ENG.). 298p. pap. 36.95 (978-1-59874-271-8(X)) Left Coast Pr., Inc.

Jones, Andy M. & Kirkham, Graeme. Beyond the Core: Reflections on Regionality in Prehistory. 2011. (ENG., Illus.). 114p. (C). pap. 80.00

(978-1-84217-989-5(6)) Oxbow Bks., Ltd. GBR. Dist: Brown, David Bk. Co., The.

Kik, H. & Willemsen, A., eds. Dorestad in an International Framework: New Research on Centres of Trade & Coinage in Carolingian Times. 2010. (ENG., Illus.). 214p. (C). pap. 102.00 (978-2-503-53401-5(5)) Brepols Pubs. BEL. Dist: ISD.

Kim, Kennis & Symons, Scott. Conserving, Preserving, & Restoring Your Heritage: A Professional's Advice. 2010. (Genealogist's Reference Shelf Ser.). (ENG., Illus.). 174p. pap. 19.99 (978-1-55488-462-9(4), Dundurn Pr.) Dundurn CAN. Dist: Ingram Pub. Services.

Kottaride, Angelike. Makedonikoi Thesauroi: MIA Periegese Sto Mouseio Ton Vasilikon Taphon Ton Aigon. 2011. (GRE & ENG., Illus.). 144p. (C). pap. 27.00 **(978-960-6878-39-8(2))** Kapon, Ekdoseis GRC. Dist: ISD.

Marchetti, Nicolo & Thuesen, Ingolf, eds. Archaia: Case Studies on Research Planning, Characterisation, Conservation & Management of Archaeological Sites. 2008. (Bar S Ser.). (Illus.). 470p. (C). 162.50 (978-1-4073-0357-4(0)) British Archaeological Reports Ltd. GBR. Dist: Brown, David Bk. Co., The.

Martinon-Torres, Marcos & Rehren, Thilo, eds. Archaeology, History, & Science: Integrating Approaches to Ancient Materials. 2009. (University College London Institute of Archaeology Publications). (ENG.). 218p. pap. 36.95 (978-1-59874-350-0(3)) Left Coast Pr., Inc.

McManamon, Francis P. & Stout, Andrew, eds. Managing Archaeological Resources: Global Context, National Programs, Local Actions. 2010. (One World Archaeology Ser.). (ENG., Illus.). 300p. pap. 34.95 (978-1-59874-312-8(0)) Left Coast Pr., Inc.

Messenger, Phyllis Mauch & Smith, George S., eds. Cultural Heritage Management: A Global Perspective. 2010. (Cultural Heritage Studies). (ENG., Illus.). 512p. 85.00 (978-0-8130-3460-7(4)) Univ. Pr. of Florida.

Minzenmayer, Donald. The Ring Bit: History, Form, & Function. 2011. (Illus.). 208p. 49.99 **(978-0-7643-3887-8(0))** Schiffer Publishing, Ltd.

Sánchez Nava, Pedro Francisco & López Wario, Luis Alberto. Coleccionismo, Saqueo y Peritajes Arquelógicos. 2010. (SPA.). 119p. (978-607-484-082-7(2)) Instituto Nacional de Antropologia e Historia.

Saunders, David. British Museum Technical Research Bulletin. 2007. (ENG., Illus.). 80p. pap. 40.00 (978-1-904982-27-2(1)) Archetype Pubns. GBR. Dist: National Bk. Network.

—British Museum Technical Research Bulletin, Volume 3. 2010. (ENG., Illus.). 96p. pap. 40.00 (978-1-904982-48-7(4)) Archetype Pubns. GBR. Dist: National Bk. Network.

Saunders, David. The British Museum Technical Research Bulletin, Volume 5. 2012. (ENG., Illus.). 150p. pap. 40.00 **(978-1-904982-67-8(0))** Archetype Pubns. GBR. Dist: National Bk. Network.

Schut, Peter A. C., ed. Listing Archaeological Sites, Protecting the Historical Landscape. 2009. (EAC Occasional Paper Ser.). (ENG & FRE., Illus.). 169p. (C). 50.00 (978-90-5799-144-8(6)) Archaeolingua Alapitvany HUN. Dist: Brown, David Bk. Co., The.

Shanks, Michael. The Archaeological Imagination. 2012. E-Book **(978-1-61132-784-7(9))** Left Coast Pr., Inc.

Swain, Hedley. An Introduction to Museum Archaeology. 2007. (ENG., Illus.). 392p. (C). 85.00 (978-0-521-86076-5(8)); per. 31.99 (978-0-521-67796-7(3)) Cambridge Univ. Pr.

Unger, A., et al. Conservation of Wood Artifacts: A Handbook. 2010. (Natural Science in Archaeology Ser.). (Illus.). xvii, 578p. pap. 439.00 (978-3-642-07480-6(4), 3642074804) Springer.

Williams, Emily & Peachey, Claire, eds. The Conservation of Archaeological Materials. 2011. (Bar S Ser.). (ENG., Illus.). 244p. (C). pap. 110.00 (978-1-4073-0657-5(X)) British Archaeological Reports Ltd. GBR. Dist: Brown, David Bk. Co., The.

Willink, Robert Joost. Stages in Civilisation: Dutch Museums in Quest of West Central African Collections (1856-1889) 2011. (CNWS Publications). (Illus.). xiii, 389p. pap. (978-90-5789-113-7(1), Leiden Univ. Pr.) Amsterdam Univ. Pr.

ANTIQUITIES—CONSERVATION AND RESTORTAION
see Antiquities—Collection and Preservation

ANTIQUITIES, BIBLICAL
see Bible—Antiquities

ANTIQUITIES, BYZANTINE
see Byzantine Antiquities

ANTIQUITIES, CHRISTIAN
see Christian Antiquities

ANTIQUITIES, CLASSICAL
see Classical Antiquities

ANTIQUITIES, ECCLESIASTICAL
see Christian Antiquities

ANTIQUITIES, GRECIAN
see Classical Antiquities; Greece—Antiquities

ANTIQUITIES, INDO-EUROPEAN
see Indo-European Antiquities

ANTIQUITIES, INDUSTRIAL
see Industrial Archaeology

ANTIQUITIES, PREHISTORIC
see also Art, Prehistoric; Copper Age; Indians—Antiquities; Megalithic Monuments; Prehistoric Peoples; Tools, Prehistoric
also subdivision Antiquities under names of countries, cities, etc. and headings qualified by the word Prehistoric, e.g. Art, Prehistoric

Aikens, C. Melvin, et al. Oregon Archaeology. 2011. (ENG.). 512p. pap. 29.95 **(978-0-87071-606-5(9))** Oregon State Univ. Pr.

Alperson-Afil, Nira & Goren-Inbar, Naama. The Acheulian Site of Gesher Benot Ya´agov: Ancient Flames & Controlled Use of Fire, Vol. III. 2010. (Vertebrate Paleobiology & Paleoanthropology Ser.). (Illus.). 300p. 129.00 (978-90-481-3764-0(0), 9048137640) Springer.

Alusik, Tomas. Defensive Architecture of Prehistoric Crete. 2007. (Bar S Ser.). (ENG., Illus.). 230p. (C). pap. 90.00 (978-1-4073-0076-4(8)) British Archaeological Reports Ltd. GBR. Dist: Brown, David Bk. Co., The.

Arkush, Elizabeth N. & Allen, Mark W., eds. The Archaeology of Warfare: Prehistories of Raiding & Conquest. 2008. (ENG.). 560p. pap. 34.95 (978-0-8130-3284-9(9)) Univ. Pr. of Florida.

Bacvarov, Krum, ed. Babies Reborn: Infant/Child Burials in Pre- & Protohistory, Vol. 24. 2008. (Bar S Ser.). (FRE & ENG., Illus.). 213p. (C). pap. 95.00 (978-1-4073-0316-1(3)) British Archaeological Reports Ltd. GBR. Dist: Brown, David Bk. Co., The.

Bahn, Paul. Legendary Sites of the Ancient World: An Illustrated Guide to over 80 Major Archaeological Discoveries, with Expert Commentary & More Than 350 Stunning Photographs. 2009. (ENG., Illus.). 160p. pap. 19.99 (978-1-84476-701-4(9)) Anness Publishing GBR. Dist: National Bk. Network.

Ballin, Torben Bjarke. Archaeological Pitchstone in Northern Britain: Characterization & Interpretation of an Important Prehistoric Source. 2009. (Bar Ser.). (Illus.). 108p. (C). 87.50 (978-1-4073-0386-4(4)) British Archaeological Reports Ltd. GBR. Dist: Brown, David Bk. Co., The.

Bar-Yosef, Ofer & K. Kozlowski, Janusz, eds. Eurasian Prehistory 5: 1. 2007. (Eurasian Prehistory Ser.). (ENG., Illus.). 165p. (C). pap. 25.00 (978-83-923259-0-1(7)) Instytut Archeologii, UJ POL. Dist: Brown, David Bk. Co., The.

—Eurasian Preshistory 5: 2 (2007) 2007. (Eurasian Prehistory Ser.). (ENG., Illus.). 165p. (C). pap. 25.00 (978-83-923259-1-8(5)) Instytut Archeologii, UJ POL. Dist: Brown, David Bk. Co., The.

Barham, Lawrence & Mitchell, Peter J. The First Africans: African Archaeology from the Earliest Toolmakers to Most Recent Foragers. 2008. (Cambridge World Archaeology Ser.). (ENG., Illus.). 602p. (C). 103.99 (978-0-521-84796-4(6)) Cambridge Univ. Pr.

Bernal, Marcos Terradillos. El Paleolítico inferior en la Meseta Norte, Espana. 2010. (Bar S Ser.). (SPA & ENG., Illus.). 435p. (C). pap. 160.00 (978-1-4073-0697-1(9)) British Archaeological Reports Ltd. GBR. Dist: Brown, David Bk. Co., The.

Berrocal, María Cruz, et al, eds. The Prehistory of Iberia: Debating Early Social Stratification & the State. 2012. (Routledge Studies in Archaeology Ser.). (ENG.). 328p. (C). 125.00 (978-0-415-88592-8(2)) Routledge.

Betts, A. V. G., et al. Later Prehistory of the Badia: Excavation & Surveys in Eastern Jordan, Volume 2. 2012. (Levant Supplementary Ser.). (ENG.). 240p. (C). 96.00 **(978-1-84217-473-9(8))** Oxbow Bks., Ltd. GBR. Dist: Brown, David Bk. Co., The.

Blaise, Emilie. Économie Animale et Gestion des Troupeaux Au Néolithique Final en Provence: Approche Archéozoologique et Contribution des Analyses Isotopiques de L'émail Dentaire. 2010. (Bar S Ser.). (FRE & ENG., Illus.). 400p. (C). pap. 145.00 (978-1-4073-0479-3(8)) British Archaeological Reports Ltd. GBR. Dist: Brown, David Bk. Co., The.

Bougard, Estelle J. Use of Clay in the Upper Paleolithic of Europe. 2010. (Bar S Ser.). (ENG.). 289p. (C). pap. 125.00 (978-1-4073-0476-2(3)) British Archaeological Reports Ltd. GBR. Dist: Brown, David Bk. Co., The.

Bradley, Philipa & Egging Dinwiddy, Kirsten. Prehistoric Activity & a Romano-British Settlement at Poundbury Farm, Dorchester, Dorset. 2011. (Wessex Archaeology Reports). (ENG., Illus.). 192p. (C). 50.00 **(978-1-874350-56-9(6))** Trust for Wessex Archaeology Ltd. GBR. Dist: Brown, David Bk. Co., The.

Bradley, Richard. The Prehistory of Britain & Ireland. 2007. (Cambridge World Archaeology Ser.). (ENG., Illus.). 340p. (C). 90.99 (978-0-521-84811-4(3)); per. 35.00 (978-0-521-61270-8(5)) Cambridge Univ. Pr.

Brandherm, Dirk & Trachsel, Martin, eds. A New Dawn for the Dark Age? Shifting Paradigms In Mediterranean Iron Age Chronology / L'ge Obscur Se Fait-Il Jour De Nouveau? Les Paradigmes Changeants De La Chronologie De L'Age Du Fer en Mediterranee. 2008. (Bar S Ser.). (Illus.). 176p. (C). 85.00 (978-1-4073-0351-2(1)) British Archaeological Reports Ltd. GBR. Dist: Brown, David Bk. Co., The.

Broadbent, Noel. Lapps & Labyrinths: Saami Prehistory, Colonization, & Cultural Resilience. 2010. (ENG.). 304p. 34.95 (978-0-9788460-6-0(0)) Smithsonian Institution Scholarly Pr.

Brooke, Beatrice D. & Magalhães, Roberto Carvalho de. Art & Culture of the Prehistoric World. 2010. (Ancient Art & Cultures Ser.). (ENG., Illus.). 40p. (YA). pap. 11.75 (978-1-61532-879-6(3)) Rosen Publishing Group, Inc., The.

Broughton, Jack M. & Cannon, Michael D., eds. Evolutionary Ecology & Archaeology: Applications to Problems in Human Evolution & Prehistory. 2009. (ENG., Illus.). 456p. pap. 50.00 (978-0-87480-935-0(5)) Univ. of Utah Pr.

Buchvaldek, Miroslav, et al, eds. Archeologicky atlas Evropy. 2009. (Illus.). 724p. 125.00 (978-80-246-0774-0(3)) Karolinum, nakladatelstvi Univerzity Karlovy CZE. Dist: Chicago Distribution Ctr.

Butler, Alan. How to Read Prehistoric Monuments: Understanding Our Ancient Heritage. 2011. (ENG., Illus.). 272p. 24.95 (978-1-907486-44-9(5), Watkins Publishing) Duncan Baird Pubs. GBR. Dist: Sterling Publishing Co., Inc.

Calado, David, et al, eds. Session C68 (Part I) Monumental Questions, 2 vols. 2010. (Bar S Ser.). (FRE, SPA & ENG., Illus.). 167p. (C). pap. 87.50 (978-1-4073-0663-6(4)) British Archaeological Reports Ltd. GBR. Dist: Brown, David Bk. Co., The.

—Session C68 (Part II) Monumental Questions, 2 vols. 2010. (Bar S Ser.). (FRE, SPA & ENG., Illus.). 173p. (C). pap. 90.00 (978-1-4073-0664-3(2)) British Archaeological Reports Ltd. GBR. Dist: Brown, David Bk. Co., The.

Casal, Anton A. Rodriguez, ed. Le Megalithisme Atlantique: Acts of the XIVth UISPP Congress, University of Liege, Belgium, 2-8 September 2001, Colloque / Symposium 9. 4. 2006. (Bar S Ser.).Tr. of Atlantic Megaliths. (ENG, FRE & SPA., Illus.). 65p. (C). 62.50 (978-1-84171-958-0(7)) British Archaeological Reports Ltd. GBR. Dist: Brown, David Bk. Co., The.

Chapman, John & Gaydarska, Bisserka. From Surface Collection to Prehistoric Lifeways: Making Sense of the Multi-Period Site of Orlovo, South East Bulgaria. 2010. (ENG., Illus.). 191p. (C). 110.00 (978-1-84217-391-6(X)) Oxbow Bks., Ltd. GBR. Dist: Brown, David Bk. Co., The.

Chapman, John, et al. Parts & Wholes: Fragmentation in Prehistoric Context. 2006. (ENG., Illus.). 264p. (C). pap. 60.00 (978-1-84217-222-3(0)) Oxbow Bks., Ltd. GBR. Dist: Brown, David Bk. Co., The.

Charlin, Judith E. Estrategias de Aprovisionamiento y Utilizacion de las Materias Primas Liticas en el Campo Volcanico Pali Aike (Prov. Santa Cruz, Argentina) 2009. (Bar S Ser.). (ITA., Illus.). 240p. (C). 100.00 (978-1-4073-0383-3(X)) British Archaeological Reports Ltd. GBR. Dist: Brown, David Bk. Co., The.

Chase, Philip G., et al. The Cave of Fontéchevade: A New Investigation of the Site & its Paleoanthropological Implications. 2008. (ENG., Illus.). 288p. 99.00 (978-0-521-89844-7(7)) Cambridge Univ. Pr.

Cholidis, Nadja, et al. Im Krieg zerstörte Denkmäler und ihre Restaurierung, 5 vols. 2010. (GER., Illus.). XXI, 500p. 182.00 **(978-3-11-022935-6(8))** De Gruyter, Walter Inc.

Clarke, Bob. Prehistoric & Roman Wiltshire an Archaeological Guide. 2012. (ENG., Illus.). 96p. pap. 22.95 **(978-1-84868-877-3(6))** Amberley Publishing GBR. Dist: Casemate Pubs. & Bk. Distributors, LLC.

Cram101 Textbook Reviews. Outlines & Highlights for Images of the Past by Price & Feinman. 2011. 68p. pap. 27.95 **(978-1-61812-853-9(1))** Cram101 Inc.

Cram101 Textbook Reviews Staff. Outlines & Highlights for Evolution & Prehistory: Human Challenge by William A. Haviland, Bunny Mcbride, Dana Walrath, Harald E. Prins, ISBN. 2009. 78p. pap. 27.95 (978-1-4288-9037-4(8)) Cram101 Inc.

Crawford, Sally, et al. Form & Order in the Anglo-Saxon World, AD 600-1100. 2009. (Anglo-Saxon Studies in Archaeology & History Ser.). (Illus.). 128p. (C). pap. 70.00 (978-1-905905-13-3(0)) Oxford Univ. Pr. GBR. Dist: Brown, David Bk. Co., The.

Crevecoeur, I., et al. Recherches a la grotte Walou a Trooz (Belgique) Dewez, M., ed. 2008. (Bar S Ser.). (FRE & ENG., Illus.). 88p. (C). 60.00 (978-1-4073-0277-5(9)) British Archaeological Reports Ltd. GBR. Dist: Brown, David Bk. Co., The.

Darvill, Timothy C. Prehistoric Britain. 2nd rev. ed. 2010. (Routledge World Archaeology Ser.). (ENG., Illus.). 416p. 125.00 (978-0-415-49026-9(X)); pap. 44.95 (978-0-415-49027-6(8)) Routledge.

Davidson, George. The Tracks & Landfalls of Bering & Chirikof on the Northwest Coast of America. 2009. (ENG.). 50p. pap. 16.99 (978-1-110-62306-8(2)); pap. 18.99 (978-1-110-62307-5(0)) BiblioBazaar. (BiblioLife).

Davies, John. Land of Boudica Prehistoric & Roman Norf. 2009. (Illus.). 269p. (C). pap. 39.95 (978-1-905223-33-6(1)) Heritage Marketing & Publications, Ltd. GBR. Dist: Brown, David Bk. Co., The.

Davis, O., et al. Changing Perspectives on the First Millennium BC: Proceedings of the Iron Age Research Student Seminar 2006. 2008. (Cardiff Studies in Archaeology Ser.). (Illus.). (C). pap. 70.00 (978-1-84217-326-8(X)) Oxbow Bks., Ltd. GBR. Dist: Brown, David Bk. Co., The.

Dennell, Robin. The Palaeolithic Settlement of Asia. 2008. (Cambridge World Archaeology Ser.). (ENG., Illus.). 572p. 95.00 (978-0-521-84866-4(0)); pap. 52.99 (978-0-521-61310-1(8)) Cambridge Univ. Pr.

Düring, Bleda. The Prehistory of Asia Minor: From Complex Hunter-Gatherers to Early Urban Socieities. 2010. (ENG., Illus.). 374p. 95.00 (978-0-521-76313-4(4)) Cambridge Univ. Pr.

Elder, Emma. A Comparison of the Late Pleistocene & Early Holocene Burials of North Africa & Western Europe. Grim Investigations: Reaping the Dead. 2010. (Bar S Ser.). (ENG., Illus.). 268p. (C). pap. 120.00 (978-1-4073-0684-1(7)) British Archaeological Reports Ltd. GBR. Dist: Brown, David Bk. Co., The.

Fagan, Brian M. World Prehistory: A Brief Introduction. 8th ed. 2010. (ENG.). 432p. (C). pap. 105.67 (978-0-205-01791-1(6), Prentice Hall) Prentice Hall PTR.

Feinman, Gary & Price, T. Douglas. Images of the Past. 6th ed. 2009. (ENG., Illus.). 640p. (C). pap. 129.67 (978-0-07-353105-2(7), 0073531057) McGraw-Hill Cos., The.

Fernández, E. Muñoz & Cobo, J. Ruiz, eds. De Pesues a Pejanda: Arqueologia de la Cuenca del Nansa. 2010. (Bar S Ser.). (SPA & ENG., Illus.). 361p. (C). pap. 137.50 (978-1-4073-0675-9(8)) British Archaeological Reports Ltd. GBR. Dist: Brown, David Bk. Co., The.

Frachetti, Michael David. Pastoralist Landscapes & Social Interaction in Bronze Age Eurasia. 2009. (ENG., Illus.). 232p. 50.00 (978-0-520-25689-7(1)) Univ. of California Pr.

Furmánek, Václav & Novotná, Mária. Die Sicheln in der Slowakei. 2006. (Prahistorische Bronzefunde (PBF) Ser.). (GER., Illus.). 124p. (C). 97.00 (978-3-515-08981-4(0)) Steiner, Franz Verlag Wiesbaden GmbH DEU. Dist: Brown, David Bk. Co., The.

Galanidou, Nena & Dommasnes, Liv Helga, eds. Telling Children about the Past: An Interdisciplinary Perspective. 2007. (Illus.). 335p. pap. 25.00 (978-1-879621-40-4(1)) International Monographs in Prehistory.

Galor, Katharina & Avni, Gideon. Unearthing Jerusalem: 150 Years of Archaeological Research in the Holy City. 2011. (Illus.). xix, 490p. **(978-1-57506-223-5(2))** Eisenbrauns, Inc.

Garwood, Paul. The Undiscovered Country: The Earlier Prehistory of the West Midlands. 2007. (Illus.). 224p. (C). 110.00 (978-1-84217-282-7(4)) Oxbow Bks., Ltd. GBR. Dist: Brown, David Bk. Co., The.

Gaydarska, Bisserka. Landscape, Material Culture & Society in Prehistoric South East Bulgaria. 2007. (Bar S Ser.). (Illus.). xix, 279p. (C). pap. 112.50 (978-1-4073-0030-6(X)) British Archaeological Reports Ltd. GBR. Dist: Brown, David Bk. Co., The.

Glorstad, Hakon & Prescott, Christopher, eds. Becoming European: The Transformation of Third Millennium Northern & Western Europe. 2011. (ENG., Illus.). 181p. (C). pap. 70.00 **(978-1-84217-450-0(9))** Oxbow Bks., Ltd. GBR. Dist: Brown, David Bk. Co., The.

Goebel, Ted & Buvit, Ian, eds. From the Yenisei to the Yukon: Interpreting Lithic Assemblage Variability in Late Pleistocene/Early Holocene Beringia. 2011. (Peopling of the Americas Publications). (ENG., Illus.). 408p. 80.00 (978-1-60344-321-0(5)) Texas A&M Univ. Pr.

Goren-Inbar, N. & Sharon, Gonen. Axe Age: Acheulian Toolmaking - from Quarry to Discard. 2006. (Approaches to Anthropological Archaeology Ser.). (ENG., Illus.). 608p. (C). 95.00 (978-1-84553-138-6(8)) Equinox Publishing Ltd. GBR. Dist: ISD.

Gray, Jonathan. The Corpse Came Back: Post-Flood Evidence Revealed, 3 vols., Vol. 3. 2008. (Illus.). 320p. pap. 25.95 (978-1-57258-555-3(2)) TEACH Services, Inc.

—The Killing of Paradise Planet: Lost history from the pre-Flood World, 3 bks., Bk. 1. 2008. (Illus.). 200p. pap. 13.95 (978-1-57258-553-9(6)) TEACH Services, Inc.

Grimaldi, Stefano, et al. Mountain Environments in Prehistoric Europe, Vol. 26. 2009. (Bar S Ser.). (FRE & ENG., Illus.). 169p. (C). pap. 82.50 (978-1-4073-0365-9(1)) British Archaeological Reports Ltd. GBR. Dist: Brown, David Bk. Co., The.

Guarducci, Guido. Facing an Empire: Hirbemerdon Tepe & the Upper Tigris Region During the Early Iron Age & Neo-Assyrian Period. 2012. 133.00 **(978-1-4632-0146-3(X))** Gorgias Pr., LLC.

Guerrero Ayuso, Víctor M. Prehistoria de Las Islas Baleares: Registro Arqueológico y Evolución Social Antes de la Edad de Hierro = Prehistory of the Balearic Islands: Archaeological Record & Social Evolution Before the Iron Age. 2007. (Bar S Ser.). (SPA., Illus.). iv, 441p. (C). pap. 117.50 (978-1-4073-0128-0(4)) British Archaeological Reports Ltd. GBR. Dist: Brown, David Bk. Co., The.

Guilaine, J. & van Berg, P. L., eds. La Neolithisation / the Neolithisation Process: Acts of the XIVth UISPP Congress, University of Liege, Belgium, 2-8 September 2001, Colloque / Symposium 9. 2. 2006. (Bar S Ser.). (ENG & FRE., Illus.). i,85p. (C). 70.00 (978-1-84171-957-3(9)) British Archaeological Reports Ltd. GBR. Dist: Brown, David Bk. Co., The.

Harding, Anthony, et al, eds. Enclosing the Past: Inside & Outside in Prehistory. 2006. (Sheffield Archaeological Monographs). (GER & ENG., Illus.). 177p. (C). 65.00 (978-0-906090-53-4(9)) Equinox Publishing Ltd. GBR. Dist: ISD.

Haviland, William A., et al. Evolution & Prehistory: The Human Challenge. (ENG., (C). 8th rev. ed. 2007. Illus.). 384p. per. 145.95 (978-0-495-38190-7(X)) 9th ed. 2010. 400p. pap. 162.95 (978-0-495-81219-7(6)) 9th ed. 2010. 400p. ring bd. 113.95 (978-0-8400-3332-1(X)) Wadsworth.

Heckendorf, Renate. Bubalin und Bovidien in Sudmarokko: Kontext, Klassifikation und Chronologie der Felsbilder Im Mittleren Draa-Tal. 2008. (Forschungen zur Archaologie Aussereuropaischer Kulturen Ser.). (GER., Illus.). 332p. (C). 118.00 (978-3-89500-646-3(7)) Reichert, Ludwig Dr. DEU. Dist: Brown, David Bk. Co., The.

Henry, Donald O. Prehistoric Cultural Ecology & Evolution: Insights from Southern Jordan. 2010. (Interdisciplinary Contributions to Archaeology Ser.). 492p. pap. 179.00 (978-1-4419-3246-4(1), 1441932461) Springer.

Higham, C. F. W. The Origins of the Civilization of Angkor, Volume 3: The Excavation of Ban Non Wat, Introduction. 2009. (ENG., Illus.). 280p. (C). 100.00 (978-974-417-997-5(X)) Fine Arts Dept., The THA. Dist: Brown, David Bk. Co., The.

Hodder, Ian & Doughty, Louise, eds. Mediterranean Prehistoric Heritage: Training, Education & Management. 2007. (McDonald Institute Monographs). (Illus.). 152p. pap. 70.00 incl. cd-rom (978-1-902937-38-0(4)) McDonald Institute for Archaeological Research GBR. Dist: Brown, David Bk. Co., The.

Homsey, Lara K. The Hunter-Gatherer Use of Caves & Rockshelters in the American Midsouth. 2010. (Bar S Ser.). (Illus.). 101p. (C). pap. 87.50 (978-1-4073-0670-4(7)) British Archaeological Reports Ltd. GBR. Dist: Brown, David Bk. Co., The.

Hopp, Nancy P. S. Amber: Jewelry, Art, & Science. 2009. (Illus.). 160p. pap. 29.99 (978-0-7643-3168-8(X)) Schiffer Publishing, Ltd.

Jerem, Erzsebet, et al. Oskori Emlékek és Gyujtemények Magyarországon. 2010. (Itinerarium Hungaricum Ser.). (HUN & ENG., Illus.). 264p. (C). pap. 40.00 (978-963-8046-91-8(0)) Archaeolingua Alapitvany HUN. Dist: Brown, David Bk. Co., The.

Jones, Andrew. Memory & Material Culture. 2007. (Topics in Contemporary Archaeology Ser.). (ENG., 272p. Illus.). per. 27.99 (978-0-521-54551-8(X)); (C). 92.00 (978-0-521-83708-8(1)) Cambridge Univ. Pr.

Jones, Andrew, ed. Prehistoric Europe: Theory & Practice. 2008. (Wiley-Blackwell Studies in Global Archaeology Ser.). (ENG., Illus.). 400p. 108.95

(978-1-4051-2597-0(7)); pap. 51.95 *(978-1-4051-2596-3(9))* Wiley, John & Sons, Inc. (Wiley-Blackwell).

Jones, Andrew Meirion. Prehistoric Materialities: Becoming Material in Prehistoric Britain & Ireland. 2012. (ENG., Illus.). 256p. 110.00 ***(978-0-19-955642-7(3))*** Oxford Univ. Pr., Inc.

Joseph, Frank. Unearthing Ancient America. 2008. (ENG.). 1p. pap. 15.99 *(978-1-60163-031-5(X))* Career Pr., Inc.

Kemble, James. Prehistoric & Roman Essex. 2009. (ENG., Illus.). 224p. pap. 32.95 *(978-0-7524-5032-2(8))* History Pr. Ltd.,The GBR. Dist: Independent Pubs. Group.

Kirch, Patrick Vinton, ed. Island Societies: Archaeological Approaches to Evolution & Transformation. 2009. (New Directions in Archaeology Ser.). (ENG., Illus.). 103p. pap. 29.99 *(978-0-521-10543-9(9))* Cambridge Univ. Pr.

Knapp, A. Bernard. The Archaeology of Cyprus: From Earliest Prehistory through the Bronze Age. 2012. (Cambridge World Archaeology Ser.). (ENG., Illus.). 400p. 99.00 ***(978-0-521-89782-2(3))*** Cambridge Univ. Pr.

Knapp, A. Bernard. Prehistoric & Protohistoric Cyprus: Identity, Insularity, & Connectivity. 2008. (ENG., Illus.). 480p. 175.00 *(978-0-19-923737-1(9))* Oxford Univ. Pr., Inc.

Kontogiorgos, Dimitris. Geoarchaeological & Microartifact Analysis of Archaeological Sediments: A Case Study from a Neolithic Tell Site in Greece. 2008. (Illus.). 243p. (C). 89.00 *(978-1-60456-821-9(6))* Nova Science Pubs., Inc.

Kornfeld, Marcel. On Shelter's Ledge: Histories, Theories & Methods of Rockshelter Research. 2007. (Bar S Ser.). (FRE & ENG., Illus.). 199p. (C). pap. 87.50 *(978-1-4073-0091-7(1))* British Archaeological Reports Ltd. GBR. Dist: Brown, David Bk. Co., The.

Lewis-Williams, David & Pearce, David. Inside the Neolithic Mind: Consciousness, Cosmos & the Realm of the Gods. 2009. (ENG., Illus.). 320p. pap. 22.95 *(978-0-500-28827-6(5)*, 528827) Thames & Hudson.

Lieberman, Daniel E. & Shea, John J., Jr., eds. Transitions in Prehistory: Essays in Honor of Ofer Bar-Yosef. 2009. (ENG., Illus.). 512p. (C). 35.00 *(978-1-84217-340-4(5))* Oxbow Bks., Ltd. GBR. Dist: Brown, David Bk. Co., The.

Longo, Laura M., et al, eds. 'Prehistoric Technology' 40 Years Later: Functional Studies & the Russian Legacy. 2008. (Bar S Ser.). (Illus.). 557p. (C). 182.50 *(978-1-4073-0271-3(X))* British Archaeological Reports Ltd. GBR. Dist: Brown, David Bk. Co., The.

Mac Sweeney, Naoise. Community Identity & Archaeology: Dynamic Communities at Aphrodisias & Beycesultan. 2011. E-Book ***(978-0-472-02765-1(4))***; (ENG., Illus.). 276p. 75.00 ***(978-0-472-11786-4(6))*** Univ. of Michigan Pr.

MacGregor, Neil. A History of the World in 100 Objects. 2011. (ENG., Illus.). 736p (gr. 12). 45.00 *(978-0-670-02270-0(5)*, Viking Adult) Penguin Group (USA) Inc.

Makepeace, Graham A. The Prehistoric Archaeology of Settlement in Southeast Wales & the Borders. 2007. (Bar S Ser.). (ENG., Illus.). 216p. (C). pap. 90.00 *(978-1-4073-0004-7(0))* British Archaeological Reports Ltd. GBR. Dist: Brown, David Bk. Co., The.

McIntosh, Jane. Life in Prehistoric Europe. 2009. (ENG., Illus.). 410p. pap., instr.'s hndbk. ed. 24.95 *(978-0-19-538476-5(8))* Oxford Univ. Pr., Inc.

Milisauskas, Sarunas, ed. European Prehistory: A Survey. 2nd ed. 2011. (Interdisciplinary Contributions to Archaeology Ser.). (ENG., Illus.). xv, 493p. 210.00 ***(978-1-4419-6632-2(3)***, 1441966323) Springer.

Ming Jia, Wei. Transition from Foraging to Farming in Northeast China. 2007. (Bar S Ser.). (Illus.). 211p. (C). pap. 90.00 *(978-1-4073-0043-6(1))* Archaeopress GBR. Dist: Brown, David Bk. Co., The.

Mitchell, Peter J. The First Africans: African Archaeology from the Earliest Toolmakers to Most Recent Foragers. 2008. (Cambridge World Archaeology Ser.). (ENG., Illus.). 602p. (C). pap. 37.99 *(978-0-521-61265-4(9))* Cambridge Univ. Pr.

Moser, Johannes & Nami, Mustapha. La Grotte d'Ifri N'Ammar: Tome 2. le Paleolithique Moyen. 2010. (Forschungen zur Archaologie Aussereuropaischer Kulturen Ser.). (FRE., Illus.). 338p. (C). 168.00 *(978-3-89500-684-5(X))* Reichert, Ludwig Dr. DEU. Dist: Brown, David Bk. Co., The.

Moss, Madonna. Northwest Coast: Archaeology As Deep History. 2011. *(978-0-932839-42-8(8))* Society for American Archaeology.

Murphy, Joanne M., ed. & contrib. by. Prehistoric Crete: Regional & Diachronic Studies on Mortuary Systems. 2011. (ENG., Illus.). 150p. (C). pap. 36.00 *(978-1-931534-61-1(6))* Institute for Aegean Prehistory Pr.

Mussi, Margherita, ed. Il Tardiglaciale in Italia - Lavori in Corso. 2008. (Bar S Ser.). (FRE & ITA., Illus.). 155p. (C). 87.50 *(978-1-4073-0342-0(2))* British Archaeological Reports Ltd. GBR. Dist: Brown, David Bk. Co., The.

Niles, John D. Beowulf & Lejre. 2006. (Illus.). xiv, 495p. (C). *(978-0-86698-368-6(6))* ACMRS.

Nys, Karin, ed. Journal of Prehistoric Religion, Vol. XXII. 2010. 62p. pap. 39.50 *(978-91-7081-242-2(X))* Astroms, Paul Forlag SWE. Dist: Coronet Bks.

O'Connor, Anne. Finding Time for the Old Stone Age: A History of Palaeolithic Archaeology & Quaternary Geology in Britain, 1860-1960. 2007. (ENG., Illus.). 480p. 185.00 *(978-0-19-921547-8(2))* Oxford Univ. Pr., Inc.

Owsley, Douglas W., et al. Arch Lake Woman: Physical Anthropology & Geoarchaeology. 2010. (Peopling of the Americas Publications). (Illus.). 128p. 30.00 *(978-1-60344-208-4(1))* Texas A&M Univ. Pr.

Papadopoulos, John & Urton, Gary, eds. The Construction of Value in the Ancient World. 2012. (ENG., Illus.). 568p. (C). pap. 42.95 ***(978-1-931745-91-8(9))*** Cotsen Institute of Archaeology at UCLA.

Pawankar, Seema J. Man & Animal Relationship in Early Farming Communities of Western India, with Special Reference to Inamgaon. 2007. (Bar S Ser.). (Illus.). xi, 296p. 130.00 *(978-1-4073-0062-7(8))* British Archaeological Reports Ltd. GBR. Dist: Brown, David Bk. Co., The.

Pinhasi, Ron & Stock, Jay T., eds. Human Bioarchaeology of the Transition to Agriculture. 2011. (ENG., Illus.). 500p. 159.95 *(978-0-470-74730-8(7)*, Wiley) Wiley, John & Sons, Inc.

Pollard, Joshua. Lodge Hill Camp, Caerleon, & the Hillforts of Gwent. 2006. (Bar S Ser.). (Illus.). vi,71p. (C). 67.50 *(978-1-84171-935-1(8))* British Archaeological Reports Ltd. GBR. Dist: Brown, David Bk. Co., The.

Pollard, Joshua, ed. Prehistoric Britain. 2008. (Wiley-Blackwell Studies in Global Archaeology Ser.). (ENG., Illus.). 384p. 116.95 *(978-1-4051-2545-1(4))*; pap. 51.95 *(978-1-4051-2546-8(2))* Wiley, John & Sons, Inc. (Wiley-Blackwell).

Prehistoric Library, 6 bks. & 6 cass., Set. 39.95 incl. audio *(978-0-86545-088-2(9))* Spizzirri Pr., Inc.

Prentiss, Anna, et al, eds. Macroevolution in Human Prehistory: Evolutionary Theory & Processual Archaeology. 2009. (ENG., Illus.). x, 326p. 159.00 *(978-1-4419-0681-6(9)*, 1441906819) Springer.

Price & Feinman & Cram101 Textbook Reviews Staff. Images of the Past. 2007. 108p. per. 11.95 *(978-1-4288-2638-0(6))* Cram101 Inc.

Price, T. Douglas. Europe Before Rome: A Site-By-Site Tour of the Stone, Bronze, & Iron Ages. 2012. 464p. 45.00 ***(978-0-19-991470-8(2))*** Oxford Univ. Pr., Inc.

Price, T. Douglas & Feinman, Gary M. Images of the Past. 5th ed. 2006. (Illus.). 656p. (C). pap. 104.55 *(978-0-07-340520-9(5)*, 9780073405209) McGraw-Hill Cos., The.

Pritchard, Erin E. & Ahlman, Todd M., eds. TVA Archaeology: Seventy-Five Years of Prehistoric Site Research. 2009. (ENG., Illus.). 344p. 45.00 *(978-1-57233-650-6(1))* Univ. of Tennessee Pr.

Pryor, Francis. Britain BC: Life in Britain & Ireland Before the Romans. 2006. (ENG., Illus.). 488p. pap. 17.95 *(978-0-00-712693-4(X))* HarperCollins Pubs. Ltd. GBR. Dist: Independent Pubs. Group.

Rabinovich, Rivka, et al. The Acheulian Site of Gesher Benot Ya'aqov Vol. III: Mammalian Taphonomy. the Assemblages of Layers V-5 & V-6. 2011. (Vertebrate Paleobiology & Paleoanthropology Ser.). (ENG., Illus.). xlii, 269p. 139.00 ***(978-94-007-2158-6(7)***, 9400721587) Springer.

Ralph, Sarah. Feasting & Social Complexity in Later Iron Age East Anglia. 2007. (Bar Bs Ser.). (ENG., Illus.). 171p. (C). pap. 105.00 *(978-1-4073-0163-1(2))* British Archaeological Reports Ltd. GBR. Dist: Brown, David Bk. Co., The.

Randall, Margaret. Stones Witness. 2007. (ENG.). 176p. pap. 25.00 *(978-0-8165-2643-7(5))* Univ. of Arizona Pr.

Ray, Ranjana & Jayaswal, Vidula, eds. Status of Prehistoric Studies in the Twenty First Century in India. 2009. (Illus.). 76p. (C). 67.50 *(978-1-4073-0406-9(2))* British Archaeological Reports Ltd. GBR. Dist: Brown, David Bk. Co., The.

Renfrew, Colin. Prehistory: The Making of the Human Mind. 2009. (Modern Library Chronicles Ser.). (ENG., Illus.). 240p. pap. 15.00 *(978-0-8129-7661-8(4)*, Modern Library) Random House Publishing Group.

Robb, John. The Early Mediterranean Village: Agency, Material Culture, & Social Change in Neolithic Italy. 2007. (Cambridge Studies in Archaeology Ser.). (ENG., Illus.). 406p. 110.00 *(978-0-521-84241-9(7))* Cambridge Univ. Pr.

Robinson, Gary. The Prehistoric Island Landscape of Scilly. 2007. (Bar Bs Ser.). (ENG., Illus.). 231p. (C). pap. 90.00 *(978-1-4073-0145-7(4))* British Archaeological Reports Ltd. GBR. Dist: Brown, David Bk. Co., The.

Rosen, Steven A. An Investigation into Early Desert Pastoralism: Excavations at the Camel Site, Negev. 2011. (Monograph Ser.). (ENG., Illus.). 215p. (C). 69.95 *(978-1-931745-83-3(8))*; pap. 39.95 *(978-1-931745-84-0(6))* Cotsen Institute of Archaeology at UCLA.

Rowley-Conwy, Peter. From Genesis to Prehistory: The Archaeological Three Age System & its Contested Reception in Denmark, Britain, & Ireland. 2007. (ENG., Illus.). 360p. 150.00 *(978-0-19-922774-7(8))* Oxford Univ. Pr., Inc.

Runge, Mads. Norre Hedegård: En Nordjysk Byhoj Fra ældre Jernalder. 2009. (DAN., Illus.). 459p. *(978-87-88415-56-8(2))* Jsyk Arkaeologisk Selskab (Jutland Archaeological).

Sanders, Karin. Bodies in the Bog & the Archaeological Imagination. 2012. (ENG., Illus.). 344p. pap. 24.00 ***(978-0-226-73405-7(6))*** Univ. of Chicago Pr.

Scarborough, Vernon L. A Catalyst for Ideas: Anthropological Archaeology & the Legacy of Douglas Schwartz. Scarborough, Vernon L., ed. (School of American Research Advanced Seminar Ser.). (Illus.). 430p. pap. 29.95 *(978-1-930618-71-8(9))* School for Advanced Research Pr./SAR Pr.

Schwartz, Jean Michel. Nouvelles Recherches Sur L'Ile de Paques: Transport des statues Dechiffrment de l'ecriture Rongo-Rongo. 2011.Tr. of Mysteries of Easter Island. (Illus.). 234p. pap. 25.95 ***(978-4-87187-319-2(6))*** Ishi Pr. International.

Shang, Hong & Trinkaus, Erik. The Early Modern Human from Tianyuan Cave, China. 2010. (Texas A&M University Anthropology Ser.). (ENG., Illus.). 272p. 45.00 *(978-1-60344-177-3(8))* Texas A&M Univ. Pr.

Sharma, Sukanya. Celts, Flakes, & Bifaces: The Garo Hills Story. 2007. (Bar S Ser.). (Illus.). x, 91p. (C). 87.50 *(978-1-4073-0068-9(7))* British Archaeological Reports Ltd. GBR. Dist: Brown, David Bk. Co., The.

Sharples, Niall. Social Relations in Later Prehistory: Wessex in the First Millennium BC. 2010. (ENG., Illus.). 360p. 130.00 *(978-0-19-957771-2(4))* Oxford Univ. Pr., Inc.

Sharples, Niall, ed. A Late Iron Age farmstead in the Outer Hebrides: Excavations at Mound 1, Bornais, South Uist. 2012. (Cardiff Studies in Archaeology Ser.). (ENG., Illus.). 280p. (C). 96.00 ***(978-1-84217-469-2(X))*** Oxbow Bks., Ltd. GBR. Dist: Brown, David Bk. Co., The.

Simonet, Aurelien. Typologie Des Armatures Lithiques Gravettiennes de la Grotte D'Isturitz (Pyrenees-Atlantiques, France) 2010. (Bar S Ser.). (FRE & ENG., Illus.). 131p. (C). pap. 105.00 *(978-1-4073-0698-8(7))* British Archaeological Reports Ltd. GBR. Dist: Brown, David Bk. Co., The.

Simpson, D. D. A., et al. Excavations at Northton, Isle of Harris. 2006. (Bar S Ser.). (Illus.). xii,282p. (C). 95.00 *(978-1-84171-936-8(6))* British Archaeological Reports Ltd. GBR. Dist: Brown, David Bk. Co., The.

Smith, Monica L. A Prehistory of Ordinary People. 2010. (ENG., Illus.). 240p. pap. 35.00 *(978-0-8165-2695-6(8))* Univ. of Arizona Pr.

Sommer, Marianne. Bones & Ochre: The Curious Afterlife of the Red Lady of Paviland. 2008. (Illus.). 416p. 46.00 *(978-0-674-02499-1(0))* Harvard Univ. Pr.

Steel, Louise. Cyprus Before History: From the Earliest Settlers to the End of the Bronze Age. 2010. (Duckworth Archaeology Ser.). (Illus.). 192p. pap. 34.95 *(978-0-7156-3164-5(0))* Duckworth Publishers GBR. Dist: International Publishers Marketing.

Sternke, Farina, et al. Non-Flint Raw Material Use in Prehistory: Old Prejudices & New Directions. Sternke, Farina et al, eds. 2009. (FRE & ENG., Illus.). 248p. (C). pap. 112.50 *(978-1-4073-0419-9(4))* British Archaeological Reports Ltd. GBR. Dist: Brown, David Bk. Co., The.

Stout, Adam. Creating Prehistory: Druids, Ley Hunters & Archaeologists in Pre-War Britain. 2008. (ENG., Illus.). 336p. 116.95 *(978-1-4051-5504-5(3))*; pap. 62.95 *(978-1-4051-5505-2(1))* Wiley, John & Sons, Inc. (Wiley-Blackwell).

Teeter, Emily, ed. Before the Pyramids: The Origins of Egyptian Civilization. 2011. (Oriental Institute Museum Publications). (ENG., Illus.). 284p. (C). pap. 39.95 *(978-1-885923-82-0(1))* Oriental Institute of the Univ. of Chicago, The.

Teyssandier, Nicolas. En Route Vers L'Ouest: Les Débuts de L'Aurignacien en Europe. 2007. (Bar S Ser.). (FRE & ENG., Illus.). 312p. (C). 130.00 *(978-1-4073-0061-0(X))* British Archaeological Reports Ltd. GBR. Dist: Brown, David Bk. Co., The.

Twohig, Elizabeth Shee & Ronayne, Margaret, eds. Past Perceptions. (Illus.). 256p. pap. *(978-0-902561-89-2(8))* Cork Univ. Pr.

Van de Noort, Robert. North Sea Archaeologies: A Maritime Biography, 10,000 BC - AD 1500. 2012. (ENG., Illus.). 296p. pap. 45.00 ***(978-0-19-965708-7(4))*** Oxford Univ. Pr., Inc.

Vermeersch, Pierre M., ed. A Holocene Prehistoric Sequence in the Egyptian Red Sea Area: The Tree Shelter. 2008. (Egyptian Prehistory Monographs Ser.). (Illus.). 105p. pap. 45.00 *(978-90-5867-663-4(3))* Leuven Univ. Pr. BEL. Dist: Cornell Univ. Pr.

Vianello, Andrea, ed. Exotica in the Prehistoric Mediterranean. 2011. (ENG.). 216p. (C). pap. 50.00 *(978-1-84217-424-1(X))* Oxbow Bks., Ltd. GBR. Dist: Brown, David Bk. Co., The.

Waters, Michael R., et al. Clovis Lithic Technology: Investigation of a Stratified Workshop at the Gault Site, Texas. 2011. (Peopling of the Americas Publications). (Illus.). 256p. 45.00 ***(978-1-60344-278-7(2))*** Texas A&M Univ. Pr.

Webb, Simon. Unearthing London: The Ancient World Beneath the Metropolis. 2011. (ENG., Illus.). 176p. pap. 24.95 ***(978-0-7524-6274-5(1))*** History Pr. Ltd.,The GBR. Dist: Independent Pubs. Group.

Wells, Peter S. How the Ancients Saw the World - Vision, Art & the Shaping Of. 2012. (ENG.). 304p. (C). 35.00 ***(978-0-691-14338-5(2))*** Princeton Univ. Pr.

Wickstead, Helen. Theorising Tenure: Land Division & Identity in Later Prehistoric Dartmoor, South-West Britain. 2008. (Bar Ser.). (Illus.). 242p. (C). pap. 107.50 *(978-1-4073-0311-6(2))* British Archaeological Reports Ltd. GBR. Dist: Brown, David Bk. Co., The.

ANTIQUITIES, ROMAN

see Classical Antiquities; Rome—Antiquities; Rome (Italy)—Antiquities

ANTIQUITY OF HUMAN BEINGS

see Human Beings—Origin

ANTIRENT WAR, N.Y. 1839-1846

Cheyney, Edward Potts. The Anti-Rent Agitation in the State of New York, 1839-1846. 2009. 68p. pap. 16.95 *(978-1-120-72479-3(1))* Kessinger Publishing, LLC.

Ellis, David Maldwyn. Landlords & Farmers in the Hudson-Mohawk Region, 1790-1850. 2010. 362p. pap. 29.95 *(978-0-8014-7614-3(3)*, Fall Creek Bks.) Cornell Univ. Pr.

Langdon, Grant Dinehart. Rebels of the North: How Land Policy Caused the Civil War. 2009. 100p. pap. 10.89 *(978-0-9790860-1-4(9))* Langdon, Grant Dinehart.

ANTISEMITIC PROPAGANDA

see Anti-Jewish Propaganda

ANTISEMITISM

see also Anti-Jewish Propaganda; Jews—Persecutions

Aberbach, David. European Jews, Patriotism & Antisemitism: Social Psychology & the Liberal State, 1739-1939. 2012. (Routledge Jewish Studies Ser.). (ENG.). 224p. (C). 125.00 ***(978-0-415-54013-1(5))*** Routledge

Achcar, Gilbert. The Arabs & the Holocaust: The Arab-Israeli War of Narratives. 2010. (ENG.). 400p. 30.00 *(978-0-8050-8954-7(3)*, Metropolitan Bks.) Holt, Henry & Co.

—The Arabs & the Holocaust: The Arab-Israeli War of Narratives. 2011. (ENG.). 400p. pap. 20.00 *(978-0-312-56920-4(3))* Picador.

Alexander, Edward. The Jewish Wars. 2010. (ENG.). 228p. pap. 29.95 *(978-1-4128-1132-3(5))* Transaction Pubs.

Ancel, Jean. The History of the Holocaust in Romania. Murciano, Yaffah, tr. from HEB. 2012. (Comprehensive History of the Holocaust Ser.). (ENG., Illus.). 720p. 50.00 *(978-0-8032-2064-5(2))* Univ. of Nebraska Pr.

Anonymous. The Jewish Peril: Protocols of the Learned Elders of Zion. 2010. 106p. pap. 7.95 *(978-1-57898-881-5(0))* Martino Publishing.

Arad, Yitzhak. The Holocaust in the Soviet Union. Cummings, Ora, tr. 2009. (Comprehensive History of the Holocaust Ser.). (ENG., Illus.). 720p. 50.00 *(978-0-8032-2059-1(6))* Univ. of Nebraska Pr.

Arendt, Hannah. The Jewish Writings. Kohn, Jerome & Feldman, Ron H., eds. 2008. (ENG.). 640p. pap. 22.50 *(978-0-8052-1194-8(2)*, Schocken) Knopf Doubleday Publishing Group.

Argast, Regula. Staatsbürgerschaft und Nation: Ausschliessung und Integration in der Schweiz 1848-1933. 2007. (Kritische Studien Zur Geschichtswissenschaft Ser.). (GER.). 379p. (C). pap. 63.00 *(978-3-525-35155-0(0))* Vandenhoeck & Ruprecht GmbH & Co. KG DEU. Dist: ISD.

Aron-Beller, Katherine. Jews on Trial: The Papal Inquisition in Modena, 1598-1638. 2011. (Studies in Early Modern European History Ser.). (ENG., Illus.). 336p. 100.00 ***(978-0-7190-8519-2(5))*** Manchester Univ. Pr. GBR. Dist: Macmillan.

Ascher, Abraham. A Community under Siege: The Jews of Breslau under Nazism. 2007. (Stanford Studies in Jewish History & C Ser.). (ENG., Illus.). 336p. 55.00 *(978-0-8047-5518-4(3))* Stanford Univ. Pr.

Asquith, Nicole. Text & Context of Malediction. 2008. 388p. pap. *(978-3-639-08935-6(9))* VDM Verlag Dr. Mueller e.K.

Badiou, Alain, et al. Reflections on Anti-Semitism. 2012. (ENG.). 256p. pap. 29.95 ***(978-1-84467-877-8(6)***, 844877) Verso Bks. GBR. Dist: Norton, W. W. & Co., Inc.

Bale, Anthony. The Jew in the Medieval Book: English Antisemitisms, 1350-1500. 2007. (Cambridge Studies in Medieval Literature Ser.). (ENG., Illus.). 284p. 104.00 *(978-0-521-86354-4(6))* Cambridge Univ. Pr.

Baum, Steven K. & Samuels, Shimon. Antisemitism Explained. 2011. (ENG., Illus.). 258p. pap. 29.95 ***(978-0-7618-5578-1(5))*** Univ. Pr. of America, Inc

Baumgarten, Murray, et al, eds. Varieties of Antisemitism: History, Ideology, Discourse. 2009. *(978-0-87413-039-3(5))* Univ. of Delaware Pr.

Begley, Louis. Why the Dreyfus Affair Matters. (Why X Matters Ser.). (Illus.). 272p. 2010. (ENG.). pap. 16.00 *(978-0-300-16814-3(4))* 2009. 24.00 *(978-0-300-12532-0(1))* Yale Univ. Pr.

Begriffe, Theorien, Ideologien. 2010.Tr. of Vol. 3. Terms, Theories, Ideologies. 527p. *(978-3-598-24074-4(0))* Saur, K. G. Verlag GmbH & Co.

Beker, Avi. The Chosen: The History of an Idea, & the Anatomy of an Obsession. 2008. (ENG.). 256p. 42.00 *(978-0-230-60048-5(4))* Palgrave Macmillan.

Beller, Steven. Antisemitism. 2007. (Very Short Introductions Ser.). (ENG., Illus.). 144p. per. 11.95 *(978-0-19-289277-5(0))* Oxford Univ. Pr., Inc.

Bendavid-Val, Avrom. The Heavens Are Empty: Discovering the Lost Town of Trochenbrod. 2011. (ENG.). 256p. pap. 15.95 *(978-1-60598-291-5(1)*, 605291) Pegasus Bks.

Benz, Wolfgang. Ereignisse, Dekrete, Kontroversen. 2011. (GER., Illus.). ***(978-3-598-24076-8(7))*** Saur, K. G. Verlag GmbH & Co.

Benzio, Allswang. The Anti-Jewish Phenomenon. 2008. 305p. 25.99 *(978-1-59826-205-6(X))* Feldheim Pubs.

Berenbaum, Michael, ed. Not Your Father's Antisemitism: Hatred of the Jews in the Twenty-First Century. 2008. (ENG.). 450p. pap. 21.95 *(978-1-55778-874-0(X))* Paragon Hse. Pubs.

Bergen, Doris L. The Holocaust: A Concise History. 2nd ed. 2009. (Critical Issues World /Int'l Hist Ser.). (ENG., Illus.). 296p. 26.95 *(978-0-7425-5714-7(6))* Rowman & Littlefield Publishers, Inc.

—War & Genocide: A Concise History of the Holocaust. 2nd ed. 2009. (Critical Issues in World & International History Ser.). (ENG., Illus.). 296p. pap. 27.50 *(978-0-7425-5715-4(4))* Rowman & Littlefield Publishers, Inc.

Berger, David. Persecution, Polemic, & Dialogue: Essays in Jewish-Christian Relations. 2010. (Judaism & Jewish Life Ser.). (ENG.). 450p. 45.00 *(978-1-934843-76-5(8))* Academic Studies Pr.

Berglund, Krista. The Vexing Case of Igor Shafarevich, a Russian Political Thinker. 2012. (ENG.). xiii, 539p. 129.00 ***(978-3-0348-0214-7(5)***, 3034802145) Birkhauser Verlag AG CHE. Dist: Springer.

Bergmann, Birgit. Transcending Tradition: Jewish Mathematicians in German Speaking Academic Culture. Epple, Moritz & Ungar, Ruti, eds. 2011. (ENG., Illus.). xi, 270p. 49.95 ***(978-3-642-22463-8(6)***, 3642224636) Springer.

Berkowitz, Michael. The Crime of My Very Existence: Nazism & the Myth of Jewish Criminality. 2007. (Illus.). 322p. 60.00 *(978-0-520-25112-0(1))* Univ. of California Pr.

Bernstein, Peretz & Bernstein, Perez. The Social Roots of Discrimination: The Case of the Jews. 2008. (ENG.). 339p. pap. 34.95 *(978-1-4128-0866-8(9))* Transaction Pubs.

Biale, David. Blood & Belief: The Circulation of a Symbol Between Jews & Christians. 2008. (Illus.). 316p. pap. 25.95 *(978-0-520-25798-6(7))* Univ. of California Pr.

Birnbaum, Pierre. The Anti-Semitic Moment: A Tour of France in 1898. Todd, Jane Marie, tr. from FRE. 2011.Tr. of Moment Antisemite. (ENG.). 400p. pap. 22.50 *(978-0-226-05206-9(0))* Univ. of Chicago Pr.

Birnbaum, Pierre & Goldhammer, Arthur. A Tale of Ritual Murder in the Age of Louis XIV: The Trial of Raphaël Lévy, 1669. 2012. (Stanford Studies in Jewish History & C Ser.). (ENG.). 192p. 60.00 ***(978-0-8047-7404-8(8))*** Stanford Univ. Pr.

Blech, Arthur. The Causes of Anti-Semitism: A Critique of the Bible. rev. ed. 2006. (ENG.). 1p. per. 21.98 *(978-1-59102-446-0(3))* Prometheus Bks., Pubs.

—The Causes of Anti-Semitism: A Critique of the Bible. 2010. 512p. 29.95 *(978-1-59079-068-7(5))* Select Bks.

Bonnell, Andrew G. & Bonnell, Andrew. Shylock in Germany: Antisemitism & the German Theatre from the Enlightenment to the Nazis. 2008. (ENG., Illus.). 272p. 89.00 *(978-1-84511-557-9(0)*, Tauris Academic Studies) I. B. Tauris & Co., Ltd. GBR. Dist: Macmillan.

Bostom, Andrew G., ed. The Legacy of Islamic Antisemitism: From Sacred Texts to Solemn History. 2008. (ENG., Illus.). 768p. 39.98 *(978-1-59102-554-2(0))* Prometheus Bks., Pubs.

Botsch, Gideon, et al. Politik des Hasses-Antisemitismus und Radikale Rechte in Europa. 2010. (GER.). 348p. lib. bdg. 75.00 *(978-3-487-14438-2(7))* Olms, Georg Verlag AG DEU. Dist: Lubrecht & Cramer, Ltd.

Braham, Randolph, ed. Bibliography of the Holocaust in Hungary. 2012. (ENG., Illus.). 925p. (gr. 17). 95.00 ***(978-0-88033-687-1(0))*** Eastern European Monographs.

Breitman, Richard, et al, eds. Advocate for the Doomed: The Diaries & Papers of James G. Mcdonald, 1932-1935. 2007. (ENG., Illus.). 864p. 39.95 *(978-0-253-34862-3(5)*, 0253348625) Indiana Univ. Pr.

Browning, William H. Sins of the Fathers: Facing Today's Global Challenges. 2008. xxii, 287p. pap. *(978-0-615-24516-4(1))* Wilson, Anne B.

Bunzl, Matti. Anti-Semitism & Islamophobia: Hatreds Old & New in Europe. 2007. 128p. per. 12.95 *(978-0-9761475-8-9(0))* Prickly Paradigm Pr., LLC.

Byford, Jovan. Denial & Repression of Anti-Semitism: Post-Communist Remembrance of the Serbian Bishop Nikolaj Velimirovic. 2009. (ENG.). 280p. pap. *(978-963-9776-31-9(9))* Central European Univ. Pr.

Callil, Carmen. Bad Faith: A Forgotten History of Family, Fatherland & Vichy France. 2007. (Vintage Ser.). (ENG., Illus.). 672p. pap. 16.95 *(978-0-307-27925-5(1)*, Vintage) Knopf Doubleday Publishing Group.

Canfield, John G. Good & Evil Figs. 2011. 398p. 54.95 ***(978-1-258-02444-4(6))*** Literary Licensing, LLC.

Cohen, Yehuda. Germans: Absent Nationality & the Holocaust. 2011. 205p. pap. 34.95 *(978-1-84519-445-1(4))* Sussex Academic Pr. GBR. Dist: International Specialized Bk. Services.

Cohn-Sherbok, Dan. Anti-Semitism. 2009. (ENG., Illus.). 368p. pap. 32.95 *(978-0-7524-5038-4(7))* History Pr. Ltd.,The GBR. Dist: Independent Pubs. Group.

Cohn-Sherbok, Dan & Cohn-Sherbok. The Paradox of Anti-Semitism. 2007. (ENG.). 240p. 19.95 *(978-0-8264-9403-0(X))* Continuum International Publishing Group, Ltd. GBR. Dist: National Bk. Network.

Combating Anti-Semitism: Protecting Human Rights: Hearing Before the Subcommittee on International Organizations, Human Rights, & Oversight of the Committee on Foreign Affairs, House of Representatives, One Hundred Eleventh Congress, Second Session, April 14, 2010. 2010. (Illus.). iii, 102p. *(978-0-16-085935-9(2)*, 552-070-41131-3) United States Government Printing Office.

Confino, Alon. Foundational Pasts: The Holocaust & Historical Understanding. 2011. (ENG., Illus.). 192p. (C). 85.00 ***(978-0-521-51665-5(X))***; pap. 24.99 ***(978-0-521-73632-9(3))*** Cambridge Univ. Pr.

Cram101 Textbook Reviews Staff. Outlines & Highlights for Violence of Hate: Confronting Racism, Anti-Semitism, & Other Forms of Bigotry by Levin, ISBN. 2008. 60p. pap. 9.95 *(978-1-4288-6356-9(7))* Cram101 Inc.

Crane, Richard Francis. Passion of Israel: Jacques Maritain, Catholic Conscience, & the Holocaust. 2010. (ENG.). 180p. pap. 25.00 *(978-1-58966-193-6(1))* Univ. of Scranton Pr.

Dahm, Annkatrin. Der Topos der Juden: Studien zur Geschichte des Antisemitismus im deutschsprachigen Musikschrifttum. 2007. (Judische Religion, Geschichte und Kultur (JRGK) Ser.). (GER.). 388p. (C). 99.00 *(978-3-525-56996-2(3))* Vandenhoeck & Ruprecht GmbH & Co. KG DEU. Dist: ISD.

Davis, Christian. Colonialism, Antisemitism, & Germans of Jewish Descent in Imperial Germany. 2012. (Social History, Popular Culture, & Politics in Germany Ser.). (ENG., Illus.). 296p. (C). 70.00 ***(978-0-472-11797-0(1))*** Univ. of Michigan Pr.

Davis, Christian S. Colonialism, Antisemitism, & Germans of Jewish Descent in Imperial Germany. 2012. (Illus.). viii, 281p. E-Book ***(978-0-472-02780-4(8))*** Univ. of Michigan Pr.

De Cruz, Miguel P. A Nazi Lie Revived: The Target Is You. 2011. 22p. 35.95 ***(978-1-258-00999-1(4))*** Literary Licensing, LLC.

Dinnerstein, Leonard. The Leo Frank Case. rev. ed. 2008. (ENG., Illus.). 280p. pap. 22.95 *(978-0-8203-3179-9(1))* Univ. of Georgia Pr.

Döscher, Hans-Jürgen. „Kampf gegen das Judenthum": Gustav Stille (1845-1920) Antisemit im deutschen Kaiserreich. 2008. (Illus.). 173p. pap. *(978-3-938690-90-1(9))* Veitl, Friedrich Metropol Friedrich Veitl-Verlag.

Falk, Avner. Anti-Semitism: A History & Psychoanalysis of Contemporary Hatred, 1 vol. 2008. (Illus.). 312p. 49.95 *(978-0-313-35384-0(0)*, C35384, Praeger Pubs.) Greenwood Publishing Group, Inc.

Farmer, Alan. Anti-Semitism & the Holocaust. 2nd ed. 2010. (ENG., Illus.). 192p. pap. 14.99 *(978-0-340-98496-3(1))* Hodder Education GBR. Dist: Oxford Univ. Pr., Inc.

Fatah, Tarek. The Jew Is Not My Enemy: Unveiling the Myths That Fuel Muslim Anti-Semitism. 2010. (ENG.). 272p. 24.95 *(978-0-7710-4783-1(5)*, McClelland & Stewart) McClelland & Stewart CAN. Dist: Random Hse., Inc.

—The Jew Is Not My Enemy: Unveiling the Myths that Fuel Muslim Anti-Semitism. 2011. (ENG., Illus.). 272p. pap. 16.95 *(978-0-7710-4784-8(3)*, Emblem Edns) McClelland & Stewart CAN. Dist: Random Hse., Inc.

Fineberg, Michael, et al, eds. Antisemitism. 2007. (Illus.). 329p. (C). pap. 35.00 *(978-0-85303-746-0(9))* Vallentine Mitchell Pubs. GBR. Dist: International Specialized Bk. Services.

—Antisemitism: Essays in Memory of Simon Wiesenthal. 2007. (Illus.). 329p. (C). 75.00 *(978-0-85303-745-3(0))* Vallentine Mitchell Pubs. GBR. Dist: International Specialized Bk. Services.

Fischel, Jack. Historical Dictionary of the Holocaust. 2nd ed. 2010. (Historical Dictionaries of War, Revolution, & Civil Unrest Ser.). (ENG., Illus.). 410p. 95.00 *(978-0-8108-6774-1(5))* Scarecrow Pr., Inc.

Fischer, Lars. The Socialist Response to Antisemitism in Imperial Germany. (ENG.). 2010. 276p. pap. 36.99 *(978-0-521-15324-9(7))* 2007. 272p. 95.00 *(978-0-521-87552-3(8))* Cambridge Univ. Pr.

Ford, Henry. The International Jew. 2010. 162p. pap. 7.95 *(978-1-57898-928-7(0))* Martino Publishing.

Foxman, Abraham H. The Deadliest Lies: The Israel Lobby & the Myth of Jewish Control. (ENG.). 256p. 2009. pap. 14.95 *(978-0-230-60404-9(8))* 2007. 24.95 *(978-1-4039-8492-0(1))* Palgrave Macmillan.

—Jews & Money: The Story of a Stereotype. (ENG., 256p. 2012. Illus.). pap. 17.00 ***(978-0-230-12064-8(4))*** 2010. 26.00 *(978-0-230-62385-9(9))* Palgrave Macmillan.

Frassetto, Michael. Christian Attitudes Toward the Jews in the Middle Ages: A Casebook. 2012. (ENG.). 304p. pap. 42.95 ***(978-0-415-54262-3(6))*** 2006. 222p. 126.00 *(978-0-415-97827-9(0))* Routledge.

Friedländer, Saul. The Years of Extermination: Nazi Germany & the Jews, 1939-1945. 2008. (ENG.). 896p. pap. 19.99 *(978-0-06-093048-6(9)*, HarperPerennial) HarperCollins Pubs.

Frosh, Stephen. Hate & the Jewish Science: Anti-Semitism, Nazism & Psychoanalysis. rev. ed. 2009. (ENG.). 240p. pap. 37.00 *(978-0-230-22952-5(2))* Palgrave Macmillan.

Gabris, Andras. Cognitive Model of the Causal Explanation of Anti-Semitism. 2008. 64p. pap. *(978-3-639-07143-6(3))* VDM Verlag Dr. Mueller e.K.

Garfinkle, Adam. Jewcentricity: Why the Jews Are Praised, Blamed, & Used to Explain Just about Everything. 2009. (ENG.). 320p. 25.95 *(978-0-470-19856-8(7)*, Wiley) Wiley, John & Sons, Inc.

Geller, Jay. The Other Jewish Question: Identifying the Jew & Making Sense of Modernity. 2011. (ENG., Illus.). 448p. 99.00 ***(978-0-8232-3361-8(8))***; pap. 35.00 ***(978-0-8232-3362-5(6))*** Fordham Univ. Pr.

Gerdmar, Anders. Roots of Theological Anti-Semitism: German Biblical Interpretation & the Jews, from Herder & Semler to Kittel & Bultmann. 2010. (Illus.). 678p. pap. *(978-90-04-18621-7(2))* BRILL.

Ghazarian, Vatche. History of the ADL. 2008. (ARM.). *(978-1-931834-22-3(9)*, Mayreni) Mayreni Publishing.

Gilbert, Martin & Gilbert, Martin. Kristallnacht: Prelude to Destruction. 2007. (Making History Ser.). (ENG., Illus.). 336p. pap. 14.99 *(978-0-06-112135-7(5)*, HarperPerennial) HarperCollins Pubs.

Glanninger, Peter. Rassismus und Rechtsextremismus: Rassistische Argumentationsmuster und ihre historischen Entwicklungslinien. 2009. (Mensch und Gesellschaft. Schriftenreihe für Sozialmedizin, Sozialpsychiatrie, medizinische Anthropologie und philosophische Reflexionen Ser.). (GER.). 248p. pap. 65.95 *(978-3-631-57501-7(7))* Lang, Peter GmbH, Europaischer Verlag der Wissenschaften DEU. Dist: Lang, Peter.

Glowacka, Dorota & Zylinska, Joanna, eds. Imaginary Neighbors: Mediating Polish-Jewish Relations after the Holocaust. 2007. (ENG.). 342p. 29.95 *(978-0-8032-2217-5(3))* Univ. of Nebraska Pr.

Goldstein, Phyllis. A Convenient Hatred: The History of Antisemitism. 2011. 432p. pap. 17.95 ***(978-0-9819543-8-7(3))*** Facing History & Ourselves National Foundation, Inc.

Göllner, Renate. Schule und Verbrechen: Die Vertreibung jüdischer Schülerinnen und Schüler von Wiens Mittelschulen. 2009. (GRE.). 108p. pap. 28.95 *(978-3-631-58391-3(5))* Lang, Peter GmbH, Europaischer Verlag der Wissenschaften DEU. Dist: Lang, Peter.

Goska, Danusha. Bieganski: The Brute Polak Stereotype in Polish-Jewish Relations & American Popular Culture. 2010. (Jews of Poland Ser.). (ENG.). 344p. 65.00 *(978-1-936235-15-5(3))* Academic Studies Pr.

Gotzmann, Andreas & Wiese, Christian. Modern Judaism & Historical Consciousness: Identities, Encounters, Perspectives. 2007. 658p. *(978-90-04-15289-2(X))* BRILL.

Greene, Melissa Fay. The Temple Bombing. 2006. (ENG., Illus.). 514p. per. 21.00 *(978-0-306-81518-8(4))* Da Capo Pr., Inc.

Grobman, Alex. Nations United: How the United Nations Is Undermining Israel & the West. 2009. (Illus.). 208p. 19.99 *(978-0-89221-674-1(3)*, Icon Publishing Group) Midpoint Trade Bks., Inc.

Gross, Jan T. Fear: Anti-Semitism in Poland after Auschwitz - An Essay in Historical Interpretation. 2007. (ENG., Illus.). 336p. pap. 15.95 *(978-0-8129-6746-3(1)*, Random Hse. Trade Paperbacks) Random House Publishing Group.

—Fear - Anti-Semitism in Poland after Auschwitz an Essay in Historical Interpretation. 2006. (ENG., Illus.). 336p. 29.95 *(978-0-691-12878-8(2))* Princeton Univ. Pr.

Gross, Jan Tomasz. Strach: Antysemityzm W Polsce Tuz Po Wojnie: Historia Moralnej Zapasci. 2008. (POL & ENG., Illus.). 343p. *(978-83-240-0950-3(7))* Znak, Spoeczny Instytut Wydawniczy, Spokazoo.

Gross, Raphael. Carl Schmitt & the Jews: The Jewish Question, the Holocaust, & German Legal Theory. Golb, Joel, tr. from GER. 2007. (George L. Mosse Ser.). (ENG.). 344p. 45.00 *(978-0-299-22240-6(3))* Univ. of Wisconsin Pr.

Grosvald, Sara, ed. Antisemitism: An Annotated Bibliography. 2009. XXII, 322p. *(978-3-598-23721-8(9))* Saur, K. G. Verlag GmbH & Co.

—2006. 2010. 200p. *(978-3-598-23722-5(7))* Saur, K. G. Verlag GmbH & Co.

Hallman, Diana R. Opera, Liberalism, & Antisemitism in Nineteenth-Century France: The Politics of Halévy's la Juive. 2007. (Cambridge Studies in Opera Ser.). (ENG.). 412p. pap. 82.00 *(978-0-521-03881-2(2))* Cambridge Univ. Pr.

Hamerow, Theodore S. Why We Watched: How Anti-Semitism in the Allied Nations Allowed Hitler to Exterminate European Jewry. 2008. (ENG., Illus.). 544p. 35.00 *(978-0-393-06462-9(X)*, 6462) Norton, W. W. & Co., Inc.

Handbuch des Antisemitismus Band 1. Judenfeindschaft in Geschichte und Gegenwart: Länder und Regionen. 2008.Tr. of Vol. 1. Countries & Regions. (Illus.). 444p. *(978-3-11-023510-4(2))* Saur, K. G. Verlag GmbH & Co.

Hanebrink, Paul A. In Defense of Christian Hungary: Religion, Nationalism, & Antisemitism, 1890-1944. 2009. (Illus.). 272p. pap. 25.95 *(978-0-8014-7530-6(9))* Cornell Univ. Pr.

Harrington, Daniel J. The Synoptic Gospels Set Free: Preaching without Anti-Semitism. 2009. (Stimulus Bks.). (Illus.). 256p. pap. 19.95 *(978-0-8091-4583-6(9))* Paulist Pr.

Harris, Ruth. Dreyfus: Politics, Emotion, & the Scandal of the Century. rev. ed. 2010. (ENG., Illus.). 560p. 35.00 *(978-0-8050-7471-0(6)*, Metropolitan Bks.) Holt, Henry & Co.

—Dreyfus: Politics, Emotion, & the Scandal of the Century. 2011. (ENG.). 572p. pap. 28.00 *(978-0-312-57298-3(0))* Picador.

Harrison, Bernard. The Resurgence of Anti-Semitism: Jews, Israel, & Liberal Opinion. 2006. (Philosophy & the Global Context Ser.). (ENG.). 240p. 74.00 *(978-0-7425-5226-5(8))*; per. 28.95 *(978-0-7425-5227-2(6))* Rowman & Littlefield Publishers, Inc.

Hate Crime 2007 Survey. 2007. pap. 10.00 *(978-0-9753150-9-5(9))* Human Rights First.

Heinz, Daniel, ed. Freikirchen und Juden im »Dritten Reich«: Instrumentalisierte Heilsgeschichte, antisemitische Vorurteile und verdrängte Schuld. 2011. (Kirche, Konfession, Religion Ser.). (GER.). 343p. (C). 68.00 ***(978-3-89971-690-0(6))*** Vandenhoeck & Ruprecht GmbH & Co. KG DEU. Dist: ISD.

Helfer, Martha B. The Word Unheard: Legacies of Anti-Semitism in German Literature & Culture. 2011. (ENG.). 264p. 34.95 *(978-0-8101-2794-4(6))* Northwestern Univ. Pr.

Herf, Jeffrey. The Jewish Enemy: Nazi Propaganda during World War II & the Holocaust. 2008. (Illus.). 400p. pap. 21.00 *(978-0-674-02738-1(8)*, Belknap Pr.) Harvard Univ. Pr.

—Nazi Propaganda for the Arab World: With a New Preface. 2010. 368p. pap. 20.00 *(978-0-300-16805-1(5))* Yale Univ. Pr.

Herf, Jeffrey, ed. Anti-Semitism & Anti-Zionism in Historical Perspective: Convergence & Divergence. 2006. 275p. 150.00 *(978-0-415-40069-5(4))* Routledge.

Herman, Didi. An Unfortunate Coincidence: Jews, Jewishness, & English Law. 2010. (ENG.). 224p. 70.00 *(978-0-19-922976-5(7))* Oxford Univ. Pr., Inc.

Hoffmann, Peter. Carl Goerdeler & the Jewish Question, 1933-1942. 2011. (ENG., Illus.). 216p. 80.00 *(978-1-107-00798-7(4))* Cambridge Univ. Pr.

Idinopulos, Thomas A. Betrayal of Spirit: Jew-hatred, the Holocaust, & Christianity. 2008. (ENG.). 244p. pap. 24.00 *(978-1-888570-96-0(2))* Davies Group Pubs., The.

Israeli, Raphael. Blood Libel & Its Derivatives: The Scourge of Anti-Semitism. 2011. (ENG.). 298p. 39.95 ***(978-1-4128-4271-6(9))*** Transaction Pubs.

—Muslim Anti-Semitism in Christian Europe: Elemental & Residual Anti-Semitism. 2009. (ENG.). 284p. 39.95 *(978-1-4128-1035-7(3))* Transaction Pubs.

Israeli, Raphael. Peace Is in the Eye of the Beholder. (New Babylon Ser.). (ENG.). XXIV, 389p. 210.00 ***(978-3-11-185838-8(3))*** De Gruyter, Mouton DEU. Dist: de Gruyter, Walter GmbH & Co. KG.

Johnson, Hannah. Blood Libel: The Ritual Murder Accusation at the Limit of Jewish History. 2012. (ENG.). 250p. (C). 70.00 ***(978-0-472-11835-9(8))*** Univ. of Michigan Pr.

Julius, Anthony. Trials of the Diaspora: A History of Anti-Semitism in England. (ENG.). 2012. 912p. pap. 27.95 ***(978-0-19-960072-4(4))*** 2010. (Illus.). 889p. 45.00 *(978-0-19-929705-4(3))* Oxford Univ. Pr., Inc.

Kalman, Julie. Rethinking Antisemitism in Nineteenth-Century France. 2009. (ENG., Illus.). 246p. 88.00 *(978-0-521-89732-7(7))* Cambridge Univ. Pr.

Karp, Jonathan & Sutcliffe, Adam, eds. Philosemitism in History. 2011. (ENG.). 344p. (C). 85.00 *(978-0-521-87377-2(0))*; pap. 26.99 *(978-0-521-69547-3(3))* Cambridge Univ. Pr.

Katz, Steven. The Paranoid Apocalypse: A Hundred-Year Retrospective on the Protocols of the Elders of Zion. Landes, Richard, ed. 2011. (ENG.). 264p. 35.00 ***(978-0-8147-4892-3(9))*** New York Univ. Pr.

Kellogg, Michael. The Russian Roots of Nazism: White Emigres & the Making of National Socialism, 1917-1945. 2008. (New Studies in European History Ser.). (ENG.). 344p. pap. 48.00 *(978-0-521-07005-8(8))* Cambridge Univ. Pr.

Kenvin, Helene Schwartz. Silk Road Adventures: Among the Jews of the Caucasus & Central Asia. 2010. 428p. pap. 24.95 *(978-1-935125-89-1(3))* Robertson Publishing.

Klein, L. Ruth. Nazi Germany, Canadian Responses: Confronting Antisemitism in the Shadow of War. 2012. (ENG.). 336p. (C). ***(978-0-7735-4017-0(2))*** McGill-Queen's Univ. Pr.

Kleiner, Edward. The Indestructible Jew: The Real Truth about Anti-Semitism. 2006. *(978-0-9779189-5-9(5))* Waldenhouse Pubs., Inc.

KLIER, John. Russia gathers her Jews: The origins of the jewish question in Russia, 1772-1825. 2011. (ENG., Illus.). 260p. pap. 24.00 ***(978-0-87580-983-0(9))*** Northern Illinois Univ. Pr.

Knittel, Kay M. Seeing Mahler: Music & the Language of Antisemitism in Fin-de-Siècle Vienna. 2010. (Illus.). 218p. 99.95 *(978-0-7546-6372-0(8))* Ashgate Publishing Co.

Koch, Edward I. The Koch Papers: My Fight Against Anti-Semitism. (ENG.). 256p. 2009. pap. 14.95 *(978-0-230-61097-2(8))* 2008. 24.95 *(978-0-230-60102-4(2))* Palgrave Macmillan.

Kovács, András. The Stranger at Hand: Antisemitic Prejudices in Post-Communist Hungary. 2010. (ENG., Illus.). 224p. ***(978-90-04-19194-5(1))*** BRILL.

Kremer, Arndt. Deutsche Juden - deutsche Sprache: Jüdische und judenfeindliche Sprachkonzepte und -konflikte 1893 - 1933. 2007. (Studia Linguistica Germanica Ser.). (GER.). XIV, 450p. 154.00 *(978-3-11-019603-0(4))* De Gruyter, Walter Inc.

Kuentzel, Matthias. Jihad & Jew-Hatred: Islamism, Nazism & the Roots Of 9/11. Meade, Colin, tr. 2009. (ENG.). 180p. pap. 19.95 *(978-0-914386-39-1(5))* Telos Pr., Ltd.

—Jihad & Jew-Hatred: Islamism, Nazism & the Roots Of 9/11. 2007. 200p. 29.95 *(978-0-914386-36-0(0))* Telos Pr., Ltd.

Kühne, Thomas. Belonging & Genocide: Hitler's Community, 1918-1945. 2010. (ENG.). 224p. 40.00 *(978-0-300-12186-5(5))* Yale Univ. Pr.

Kulka, Otto Dov & Jackel, Eberhard, eds. The Jews in the Secret Nazi Reports on Popular Opinion in Germany, 1933-1945. Templer, William, tr. from GER. 2010. (ENG., Illus.). 1064p. 150.00 *(978-0-300-11803-2(1))* Yale Univ. Pr.

Landes, Richard Allen & Katz, Steven T. The Paranoid Apocalypse: A Hundred-Year Retrospective on the Protocols of the Elders of Zion. 2011. E-Book ***(978-0-8147-4945-6(3))***; E-Book ***(978-0-8147-4893-0(7))*** New York Univ. Pr.

Lang, Berel. Heidegger's Silence. 144p. *(978-0-485-30080-2(X))* Continuum International Publishing Group, Ltd.

Lange, Matthew. Antisemitic Elements in the Critique of Capitalism in German Culture, 1850-1933. 348p. pap. 83.95 *(978-3-03911-040-7(3))* Lang, Peter Publishing, Inc.

Laqueur, Walter. The Changing Face of Anti-Semitism: From Ancient Times to the Present Day. 2008. (ENG.). 240p. pap. 15.95 *(978-0-19-534121-8(X))* Oxford Univ. Pr., Inc.

Lassner, Phyllis & Trubowitz, Laura. Antisemitism & Philosemitism in the Twentieth & Twenty-First Centuries: Representing Jews, Jewishness, & Modern Culture. 2008. 248p. (C). 58.50 *(978-0-87413-029-4(8))* Univ. of Delaware Pr.

Lazare, Bernard. Antisemitism, Its History & Causes. 2010. 392p. pap. 33.75 *(978-1-142-07528-6(1))* BiblioBazaar.

Lefkowitz, Mary. History Lesson: A Race Odyssey. 2008. (ENG.). 208p. 25.00 *(978-0-300-12659-4(X))* Yale Univ. Pr.

Lehrer, Steven. Wannsee House & the Holocaust. alt. ed. 2008. (ENG., Illus.). 208p. pap. 29.95 *(978-0-7864-4092-4(9))* McFarland & Co., Inc. Pubs.

Lenarcik, Miroslawa. Jewish Community in Transition: Breslau Before & after 1945. 2010. 272p. pap. 36.95 *(978-3-86649-262-2(6))* Budrich-Esser, Barbara DEU. Dist: International Specialized Bk. Services.

Leroy-Beaulieu, Anatole. Israel among the Nations: A Study of the Jews & Antisemitism. Hellman, Frances, tr. 2007. (ENG.). 408p. 49.95 *(978-0-548-25685-5(3))*; per. 34.95 *(978-1-4326-6041-3(1))* Kessinger Publishing, LLC.

Levin, Jack & Nolan, Jim. Violence of Hate: Confronting Racism, Anti-Semitism, & Other Forms of Bigotry. 3rd ed. 2010. (ENG.). 224p. (C). pap. 44.60 *(978-0-205-71084-3(0)*, Prentice Hall) Prentice Hall PTR.

Levy, Rene H. Baseless Hatred: What It Is & What You Can Do about It. 2011. ***(978-965-229-530-9(2))*** 2nd ed. 2012. ***(978-965-229-588-0(4))*** Gefen Bks.

Likhachev, Vyacheslav. Political Anti-Semitism in Post-Soviet Russia: Actors & Ideas In 1991-2003. Umland, Andreas, ed. 2006. (ENG.). 244p. per. *(978-3-89821-529-9(6))* ibidem-Verlag.

Lindemann, Albert S. & Levy, Richard S. Antisemitism: A History. 2010. (ENG., Illus.). 336p. pap. 31.95 *(978-0-19-923502-5(3))* Oxford Univ. Pr., Inc.

Litvak, Joseph. The Un-Americans: Jews, the Blacklist, & Stoolpigeon Culture. 2009. (Series Q Ser.). (ENG., Illus.). 304p. 89.95 *(978-0-8223-4467-4(X))*; pap. 24.95 *(978-0-8223-4484-1(X))* Duke Univ. Pr.

Litvak, Meir & Webman, Ester. From Empathy to Denial: Arab Responses to the Holocaust. 2009. (Columbia/Hurst Ser.). (ENG.). 416p. (gr. 17). 30.00 *(978-0-231-70074-0(1))* Columbia Univ. Pr.

Luhrssen, David. Hammer of the Gods: The Thule Society & the Birth of Nazism. 2012. (Illus.). 312p. 35.00 ***(978-1-59797-857-6(4))*** Potomac Bks., Inc.

Maccoby, Hyam. Antisemitism & Modernity: Innovation & Continuity. 2009. 196p. pap. 39.95 *(978-0-415-55388-9(1))* 2006. 191p. 180.00 *(978-0-415-31173-1(X)*, RU53117) Routledge.

MacShane, Denis. Globalising Hatred: The New Antisemitism. 2009. (ENG.). 208p. *(978-0-297-84473-0(3)*, Weidenfeld & Nicolson) Orion Publishing Group, Ltd. GBR. Dist: Sterling Publishing Co., Inc.

Mamet, David. The Wicked Son: Anti-Semitism, Self-Hatred, & the Jews. 2009. (ENG.). 224p. pap. 12.95 *(978-0-8052-1157-3(8)*, Schocken) Knopf Doubleday Publishing Group.

Ma'oz, Moshe, ed. Muslim Attitudes to Jews & Israel: The Ambivalences of Contempt, Antagonism, Tolerance & Cooperation. 2010. (ENG.). 338p. 65.00 *(978-1-84519-322-5(9))* Sussex Academic Pr. GBR. Dist: International Specialized Bk. Services.

Marcus, Kenneth L. Jewish Identity & Civil Rights in America. 2010. (ENG.). 224p. 85.00 *(978-0-521-76673-9(7))*; pap. 29.99 *(978-0-521-12745-5(9))* Cambridge Univ. Pr.

Maryks. The Jesuit Order as a Synagogue of Jews: Jesuits of Jewish Ancestry & Purity-of-Blood Laws in the Early Society of Jesus. 2009. (Studies in Medieval

& Reformation Traditions: History, Culture, Religion, Ideas). (Illus.). 314p. (978-90-04-17981-3(X)) BRILL.

Matthaus, Jurgen & Roseman, Mark. Jewish Responses to Persecution, 1933-1938. 2010. (Documenting Life & Destruction: Holocaust Sources in Context Ser.: Volume 1). (ENG., Illus.). 508p. 39.95 (978-0-7591-1908-6(2)) AltaMira Pr.

Mazzenga, Maria, ed. American Religious Responses to Kristallnacht. 2009. (ENG.). 224p. 89.00 (978-0-230-61806-0(5)) Palgrave Macmillan.

McDonald, James G., et al. Refugees & Rescue: The Diaries & Papers of James G. McDonald, 1935-1945. Breitman, Richard et al., eds. 2009. (ENG., Illus.). 376p. 29.95 (978-0-253-35307-8(6), 0253353076) Indiana Univ. Pr.

Melman, Nell. Just the Facts: Anti-Semitism. 2011. 156p. pap. 24.95 (978-1-4560-9412-6(2)) PublishAmerica, Inc.

Melnick, Olivier/J. They Have Conspired Against You: Responding to the New Anti-Semitism. 2007. (ENG.). 240p. per. 18.00 (978-0-9765252-1-9(6)) Prinjinski, Joan.

Mendelsohn, John & Detwiler, Donald S. The Wannsee Protocol: And a 1944 Report on Auschwitz by the Office of Strategic Services. 2009. (978-1-61619-011-8(6)) Lawbook Exchange, Ltd., The.

Mendelson, Alan. Exiles from Nowhere: The Jews & the Canadian Elite. 2008. 432p. pap. 34.95 (978-1-896941-55-4(9)) Brass, Robin Studio, Inc. CAN. Dist: Midpoint Trade Bks., Inc.

Michael, Robert. A History of Catholic Antisemitism: The Dark Side of the Church. 2008. (ENG.). 292p. 100.00 (978-0-230-60388-2(2)) Palgrave Macmillan.

Michael, Robert & Rosen, Philip. Dictionary of Antisemitism: From the Earliest Times to the Present. (ENG.). 520p. 2007. 116.00 (978-0-8108-5862-6(2)) 2006. per. 58.00 (978-0-8108-5868-8(1)) Scarecrow Pr., Inc.

Michaelson, Jay. Antilawyerism & Antisemitism. (978-0-8047-4005-0(4)); pap. (978-0-8047-4006-7(2)) Stanford Univ. Pr.

Michlic, Joanna Beata. Poland's Threatening Other: The Image of the Jew from 1880 to the Present. 2008. (ENG.). 388p. pap. 24.95 (978-0-8032-2079-9(0)) Univ. of Nebraska Pr.

Millman, Richard. La Question Juive Entre les Deux Guerres: Ligues de Droite et Antisémitisme en France. (FRE.). 338p. (978-2-200-21166-0(X)) Armand, Colin.

Mitchell, Harvey. Voltaire's Jews & Modern Jewish Identity: Rethinking the Enlightenment. 2008. (Routledge Jewish Studies Ser.). CCLXII, 34p. 140.00 (978-0-415-77617-2(1)) Routledge.

Moradiellos, Enrique. La Semilla de la Barbarie: Antisemitismo y Holocausto. 2009. (SPA., Illus.). 287p. (978-84-8307-854-9(6)) Peninsula, Ediciones S.A.

Müller, Hans-Harald & Nottscheid, Mirko. Wissenschaft ohne Universität, Forschung ohne Staat: Die Berliner Gesellschaft für deutsche Literatur (1888-1938) 2011. (Quellen und Forschungen zur Literatur- und Kulturgeschichte Ser.).Tr. of Science Without University, Research Without Government. (GER., VII, 563p. Illus.). 252.00 (978-3-11-916575-4(1)); 168.00 (978-3-11-026210-0(X)) De Gruyter, Walter Inc.

Nicosia, Francis R. Zionism & Anti-Semitism in Nazi Germany. (ENG.). 2010. 340p. pap. 29.99 (978-0-521-17298-1(5)) 2008. (Illus.). 344p. 92.99 (978-0-521-88392-4(X)) Cambridge Univ. Pr.

Nilus, Sergiei. The Jewish Peril: Protocols of the Learned Elders of Zion. 2009. (978-1-57898-741-2(5)); pap. (978-1-57898-740-5(7)) Martino Publishing.

Nordau, Max & Gottheil, Gustav. Zionism & Anti-Semitism. 2011. 46p. pap. 7.99 (978-1-61203-170-5(6)) Bottom of the Hill Publishing.

Oisteanu, Andrei. Inventing the Jew: Antisemitic Stereotypes in Romanian & Other Central-East European Cultures. Adascalitei, Mirela, tr. from RUM. 2009. (Studies in Antisemitism Ser.). (ENG.). 480p. 60.00 (978-0-8032-2098-0(7)) Univ. of Nebraska Pr.

Oppeln-Bronikowski, Friedrich-Wilhelm von. Friedrich Von Oppeln-Bronikowski (1873-1936) Offizer, Übersetzer, Schriftsteller, Journalist und Streiter Gegen Den Antisemitismus in der Weimarer Republik: Sein Leben und Wirken. 2009. (GER., Illus.). 219p. (978-3-7980-0581-5(8)) Starke & Dormi Publications.

Parkes, James William. The Conflict of the Church & the Synagogue: A Study in the Origins of Antisemitism. 2008. 456p. pap. 45.00 (978-1-59740-504-1(3)) ACLS Humanities E-Book.

Patterson, David. A Genealogy of Evil: Anti-Semitism from Nazism to Islamic Jihad. 2010. (ENG.). 312p. (C). 85.00 (978-0-521-19747-2(3)); pap. 27.99 (978-0-521-13261-9(4)) Cambridge Univ. Pr.

Pegelow Kaplan, Thomas. The Language of Nazi Genocide: Linguistic Violence & the Struggle of Germans of Jewish Ancestry. 2011. (ENG., Illus.). 320p. pap. 27.99 (978-1-107-65057-2(7)) Cambridge Univ. Pr.

Perry, Marvin B., et al, eds. Antisemitic Myths: A Historical & Contemporary Anthology. 2008. (ENG.). 384p. pap. 27.00 (978-0-253-21950-3(7), 0253219507) Indiana Univ. Pr.

Personen. 2009.Tr. of Vol. 2. Persons. (GER., XLII, 934p. Illus.). (978-3-598-24072-0(4)); (978-3-11-173640-2(7)) Saur, K. G. Verlag GmbH & Co.

Petersen, Hans-Christian & Salzborn, Samuel, eds. Antisemitism in Eastern Europe: History & Present in Comparison. 2010. (Politische Kulturforschung Ser.). 246p. 57.95 (978-3-631-59828-3(9)) Lang, Peter GmbH, Europaischer Verlag der Wissenschaften DEU. Dist: Lang, Peter.

Pietila, Antero. Not in My Neighborhood. 2010. (ENG.). 336p. 28.95 (978-1-56663-843-2(7)) Dee, Ivan R. Pub.

—Not in My Neighborhood: How Bigotry Shaped a Great American City. 2011. (ENG.). 336p. pap. 17.95 (978-1-56663-899-9(2)) Dee, Ivan R. Pub.

Pinkus, Benjamin. The Soviet Government & the Jews 1948-1967: A Documented Study. 2008. (ENG.). 632p. pap. 79.00 (978-0-521-09046-9(6)) Cambridge Univ. Pr.

Pizer, Donald. American Naturalism & the Jews: Garland, Norris, Dreiser, Wharton, & Cather. 2008. (ENG.). 112p. 31.00 (978-0-252-03343-8(4)) Univ. of Illinois Pr.

Propaganda & Aryanization, 1938-1944. 2009. (978-1-61619-004-0(3)) Lawbook Exchange, Ltd., The.

Quarles, Chester L. The Ku Klux Klan & Related American Racialist & Antisemitic Organizations: A History & Analysis. alt. ed. 2008. (ENG.). 324p. pap. 35.00 (978-0-7864-3887-7(8)) McFarland & Co., Inc. Pubs.

Razmolodin, M. L. Russkii Vopros V Ideologii Cherno Sotni. 2010. (RUS.). 333p. (978-5-88610-117-1(9)) Njuans.

Read, Piers Paul. The Dreyfus Affair: The Scandal That Tore France in Two. 2012. (ENG.). 416p. 30.00 (978-1-60819-432-2(9)) Bloomsbury Publishing.

Reale, Luigi. Mussolini's Concentration Camps for Civilians: An Insight into the Nature of Fascist Racism. 2011. (Illus.). 204p. 79.95 (978-0-85303-884-9(8)) Vallentine Mitchell Pubs. GBR. Dist: International Specialized Bk. Services.

Ribuffo, Leo P. The Old Christian Right: The Protestant Far Right from the Great Depression to the Cold War. 2008. 400p. pap. 39.00 (978-1-59740-418-1(7)) ACLS Humanities E-Book.

Rickman, Gregg. Hating the Jews: The Rise of Anti-Semitism in the 21st Century. (Anti-Semitism in America Ser.). (ENG.). 250p. 2012. 49.00 (978-1-936235-25-4(0)) 2011. pap. 24.95 (978-1-936235-43-8(9)) Academic Studies Pr.

Rohr, Isabelle. Spanish Right & the Jews, 1898-1945: Antisemitism & Opportunism. (ENG., 2008. Illus.). 211p. pap. 35.00 (978-1-84519-182-5(X)) 2007. 228p. (C). 62.50 (978-1-84519-181-8(1)) Sussex Academic Pr. GBR. Dist: International Specialized Bk. Services.

Ruault, Franco. Tödliche Maskeraden: Julius Streicher und die Lösung der Judenfrage. 2009. (GER.). 412p. pap. 72.95 (978-3-631-55174-5(6)) Lang, Peter GmbH, Europaischer Verlag der Wissenschaften DEU. Dist: Lang, Peter.

Rubin, Theodore Isaac. Anti-Semitism: A Desease of the Mind. 2011. (Illus.). 184p. pap. 12.95 (978-1-56980-446-9(X)) Barricade Bks., Inc.

Saikia, Robin. The Red Book - the Membership List of the Right Club - 1939. 2010. (Illus.). 160p. pap. (978-1-905742-02-8(9)) Foxley Books.

Schenker, Hillel & Abu Zayyad, Ziad, eds. Islamophobia & Anti-Semitism. 2006. 208p. 68.95 (978-1-55876-402-6(X)) Wiener, Markus Pubs., Inc.

Schenker, Hillel & Abu-Zayyad, Ziad, eds. Islamophobia & Anti-Semitism. 2006. viii, 199p. per. 24.95 (978-1-55876-403-3(8)) Wiener, Markus Pubs., Inc.

Schleicher, Regina. Antisemitismus in der Karikatur: Zur Bildpublizistik in der französischen Dritten Republik und im deutschen Kaiserreich (1871-1914) 2009. (GER., Illus.). 204p. pap. 56.95 (978-3-631-58020-2(7)) Lang, Peter GmbH, Europaischer Verlag der Wissenschaften DEU. Dist: Lang, Peter.

Schoell-Glass, Charlotte. Aby Warburg & Anti-Semitism: Political Perspectives on Images & Culture. Willcocks, Samuel Pakucs, tr. from GER. 2008. (Kritik Ser.). (Illus.). 250p. 54.95 (978-0-8143-3255-9(2)) Wayne State Univ. Pr.

Schoeps, Julius H. & Glöckner, Olaf. A Road to Nowhere? Jewish Experiences in the Unifying Europe. 2011. (Illus.). 372p. (978-90-04-20158-3(0), BRILL.

Schor, Ralph. L'antisémitisme en France Pendant les Années Trente: Prelude à Vichy (FRE.). 380p. (978-2-87027-428-5(9)) Complexe, Editions.

Schwartz, Guri. After Mussolini: Jewish Life & Jewish Memories in Post-Fascist Italy. 2012. 280p. 79.95 (978-0-85303-855-9(4)) Vallentine Mitchell Pubs. GBR. Dist: International Specialized Bk. Services.

Seymour, David. Law, Antisemitism & the Holocaust. 2007. XXII, 136p. 140.00 (978-1-904385-43-1(5), Routledge Cavendish) Taylor & Francis Group GBR. Dist: Taylor & Francis Group.

Seymour, David M. Law, Antisemitism & the Holocaust. 2007. 138p. per. 45.95 (978-0-415-42040-2(7), Routledge Cavendish) Taylor & Francis Group GBR. Dist: Taylor & Francis Group.

Sharan, Shlomo & Bukay, David. Crossovers: Anti-Zionism & Anti-Semitism. 2009. (ENG.). 205p. 39.95 (978-1-4128-1155-2(4)) Transaction Pubs.

Sieg, Ulrich. Germany's Prophet: Paul de Lagarde & the Origins of Modern Antisemitism. 2012. (Tauber Institute Series for the Study of European Jewry Ser.). (ENG.). 368p. 39.95 (978-1-58465-755-2(3), Brandeis University Press) Univ. Pr. of New England.

Silverman, Lisa. Becoming Austrians: Jews & Culture Between the World Wars, 1 vol. 2012. (ENG., Illus.). 336p. 55.00 (978-0-19-979484-3(7)) Oxford Univ. Pr., Inc.

Simms, Norman. Alfred Dreyfus: Man, Milieu, Mentality & Midrash. 2012. (Reference Library of Jewish Intellectual History Ser.). (ENG.). 330p. 55.00 (978-1-936235-39-1(0)) Academic Studies Pr.

Spicer, Kevin P. Hitler's Priests: Catholic Clergy & National Socialism. 2008. (Illus.). 385p. 34.95 (978-0-87580-384-5(9)) Northern Illinois Univ. Pr.

Stanton, Greta W. Still Alive in the Shadow of Shoah. 2009. 396p. 29.99 (978-1-4363-2184-6(0)); pap. 19.99 (978-1-4363-2183-9(2)) Xlibris Corp.

Stein, Leon. The Racial Thinking of Richard Wagner. (978-0-8022-1638-0(2)) Philosophical Library, Inc.

Steinweis, Alan E. Kristallnacht 1938: Ein deutscher Pogrom. 2009. 224p. 23.95 (978-0-674-03623-9(9), Belknap Pr.) Harvard Univ. Pr.

—Studying the Jew: Scholarly Antisemitism in Nazi Germany. 2008. (Illus.). 214p. per. 19.50 (978-0-674-02761-9(2)) Harvard Univ. Pr.

Stoetzler, Marcel. The State, the Nation, & the Jews: Liberalism & the Antisemitism Dispute in Bismarck's Germany. 2009. (ENG.). 540p. 55.00 (978-0-8032-1625-9(4)) Univ. of Nebraska Pr.

Tegel, Susan. The Jew Suss: Life Legend Fiction Film. 2011. (ENG., Illus.). 304p. 44.95 (978-1-84725-017-9(3)) Continuum International Publishing Group, Ltd. GBR. Dist: National Bk. Network.

That Which Is Not Obligatory Is Prohibited: Censorship & Incitement in the Arab World: Hearing Before the Subcommittee on the Middle East & South Asia of the Committee on Foreign Affairs, House of Representatives, One Hundred Tenth Congress, Second Session, January 22, 2008. 2008. iii, 43p. (978-0-16-080858-6(8), 552-070-37411-6) United States Government Printing Office.

Tibebu, Teshale. Hegel & Anti-Semitism. 2008. 196p. pap. 29.00 (978-1-86888-377-6(9)) Unisa Press / Litgewers GBR. Dist: International Specialized Bk. Services.

Tilles, Garau. Fascism & the Jews: Italy & Britain. Tilles, Daniel & Garau, Salvatore, eds. 2011. 219p. 79.95 (978-0-85303-864-1(3)) Vallentine Mitchell Pubs. GBR. Dist: International Specialized Bk. Services.

Tobin, Gary A., et al. The Uncivil University: Intolerance on College Campuses. 2009. (ENG.). 336p. 41.99 (978-0-7391-3266-1(0)) Lexington Bks.

—The Uncivil University: Politics & Propaganda in American Education. 2009. (ENG.). 336p. pap. 26.50 (978-0-7391-3267-8(9)) Lexington Bks.

Tolchin, Martin & Tolchin, Susan. A World Ignited: How Apostles of Ethnic, Religious, & Racial Hatred Torch the Globe. 2007. (ENG., Illus.). 256p. per. 19.95 (978-0-7425-3657-9(2)) Rowman & Littlefield Publishers, Inc.

Tolchin, Martin & Tolchin, Susan J. A World Ignited: How Apostles of Ethnic, Religious, & Racial Hatred Torch the Globe. 2006. (ENG., Illus.). 272p. 26.95 (978-0-7425-3656-2(4)) Rowman & Littlefield Publishers, Inc.

Torrance, David W. & Taylor, George. Israel, God's Servant: God's Key to the Redemption of the World. 2008. (ENG.). 224p. per. 19.99 (978-1-84227-554-2(2), Paternoster) Authentic Media.

Torres, Aramis. Foundational Studies: Establishing Foundations. 2010. 156p. pap. 11.99 (978-1-4490-8345-8(5)) AuthorHouse.

Troy, Gil. Moynihan's Moment: The Fight Against Zionism as Racism. 2012. 384p. 29.95 (978-0-19-992030-3(3)) Oxford Univ. Pr., Inc.

Van Arkel, Dik. The Drawing of the Mark of Cain: A Social-Historical Analysis of the Growth of Anti-Jewish Stereotypes. 2010. (ENG.). 592p. pap. (978-90-8964-041-3(X), Leiden Univ. Pr.) Amsterdam Univ. Pr.

Veidlinger, Jeffrey. The Moscow State Yiddish Theater: Jewish Culture on the Soviet Stage. 2006. (Jewish Literature & Culture Ser.). (ENG., Illus.) 376p. pap. 27.00 (978-0-253-21892-6(6), 0253218926) Indiana Univ. Pr.

Vidal Sassoon International Center for the Study of Antisemitism Staff & Cohen, Susan Sarah, eds. Antisemitism Bibliography, Vol. 19. 2007. (ENG.). 470p. (978-3-598-23719-5(7)) Saur, K. G. Verlag GmbH & Co.

Volkov, Shulamit. Germans, Jews, & Antisemites: Trials in Emancipation. 2006. (ENG.). 326p. per. 30.99 (978-0-521-60959-3(3)); (C). 84.99 (978-0-521-84688-2(9)) Cambridge Univ. Pr.

Wasserstein, Bernard. On the Eve: The Jews of Europe Before the Second World War. 2012. (ENG., Illus.). 576p. 32.50 (978-1-4165-9427-7(2)); pap. (978-1-4165-9428-4(0)) Simon & Schuster.

Webman, Esther, ed. The Global Impact of the Protocols of the Elders of Zion: A Century-Old Myth. 2011. (Routledge Jewish Studies Ser.). (ENG., Illus.). 336p. (C). 135.00 (978-0-415-59892-7(3)) Routledge.

Weinberg, Paul. My Word Is My Bond: A Memoir. 2008. 168p. 24.95 (978-0-595-69579-9(5)); pap. 14.95 (978-0-595-44625-4(6)) iUniverse, Inc.

Weinberg, Sonja. Pogroms & Riots: German Press Responses to Anti-Jewish Violence in Germany & Russia (1881-1882. 2010. 244p. 64.95 (978-3-631-60214-0(6)) Lang, Peter GmbH, Europaischer Verlag der Wissenschaften DEU. Dist: Lang, Peter.

Weinreich, Max. Hitler's Professors: The Part of Scholarship in Germany's Crimes Against the Jewish People. 2011. 294p. 48.95 (978-1-258-03088-9(8)) Literary Licensing, LLC.

Weiss, Jonathan M. Irene Nemirovsky: Her Life & Works. 2006. (Stanford Studies in Jewish History & C Ser.). (ENG., Illus.). 224p. 28.95 (978-0-8047-5481-1(3)) Stanford Univ. Pr.

Whyte, George. The Dreyfus Affair: A Chronological History. 2008. (ENG., Illus.). 560p. pap. 39.00 (978-0-230-20285-6(3)) Palgrave Macmillan.

Wieviorka, Michel. The Lure of Anti-Semitism: Hatred of Jews in Present-Day France. Lobel, Couper, Kristin, tr. from FRE. 2007. (Jewish Identities in a Changing World Ser.). 448p. (978-90-04-16337-9(9)) BRILL.

Wildt, Michael. Hitler's Volksgemeinschaft & the Dynamics of Racial Exclusion: Violence Against Jews in Provincial Germany, 1919-1939. 2012. 328p. 95.00 (978-0-85745-322-8(X)) Berghahn Bks., Inc.

Wilson, Nelly. Bernard-Lazare: Antisemitism & the Problems of Jewish Identity in Late Nineteenth-Century France. 2010. (ENG.). 366p. pap. 35.99 (978-0-521-15791-9(3)) Cambridge Univ. Pr.

Wilson, Todd & Wilson, Stephen. Ideology & Experience: Antisemitism in France at the Time of the Dreyfus Affair. 2007. 828p. pap. 45.00 (978-1-904113-59-1(1)) Littman Library of Jewish Civilization, The GBR. Dist: International Specialized Bk. Services.

Winock, Michel & Baal, Gérard, L'Affaire Dreyfus. (FRE.). 314p. (978-2-02-032848-7(8)) Editions du Seuil.

Wistrich, Robert S. From Ambivalence to Betrayal: The Left, the Jews, & Israel. 2012. (Studies in Antisemitism Ser.). (ENG.). 648p. 55.00 (978-0-8032-4076-6(7)) Univ. of Nebraska Pr.

Wistrich, Robert S. Laboratory for World Destruction: Germans & Jews in Central Europe. 2007. (Studies in Antisemitism Ser.). (ENG., Illus.). 410p. 55.00 (978-0-8032-1134-6(1)) Univ. of Nebraska Pr.

Woeste, Victoria. Henry Ford's War on Jews & the Legal Battle Against Hate Speech. 2012. (ENG.). 424p. 55.00 (978-0-8047-7234-1(7)) Stanford Univ. Pr.

Worrell, Mark. Dialectic of Solidarity: Labor, Antisemitism, & the Frankfurt School. 2008. (C). (978-90-04-16886-2(9)) BRILL.

Worrell, Mark P. Dialectic of Solidarity: Labor, Antisemitism & the Frankfurt School. 2009. (Studies in Critical Social Sciences Ser.). (ENG.). 350p. pap. 28.00 (978-1-60846-036-6(3)) Haymarket Bks.

ANTISEMITISM AND CHRISTIANITY

see Christianity and Antisemitism

ANTISEPTICS

see also Asepsis and Antisepsis; Disinfection and Disinfectants; Phenols

Assadian, Ojan, et al. Antiseptics: Therapy & Prophylaxis in the Healthcare Setting. 2011. 149.95 (978-1-4398-2558-7(0), CRC Press) Taylor & Francis Group GBR. Dist: Taylor & Francis Group.

Ermini, M. & Kobayashi, H., eds. Asian Pacific Congress on Antisepsis Vol. 212: 5th Congress, Cairns, July 2005: Proceedings, (Illus.). 148p. pap. (978-3-8055-8059-5(2)) Karger, S. AG.

Hill, Robert L. R., ed. Second Meeting of the European Infection Control Advisory Panel. 2007. (Round Table Ser.). (Illus.). 110p. per. (978-1-85315-639-7(6), Royal Society of Medicine) Hodder Education.

Zhu, Peter C. New Biocides Development: The Combined Approach of Chemistry & Microbiology. 2007. (ACS Symposium Ser.). (ENG., Illus.). 520p. 165.00 (978-0-8412-7405-1(3)) American Chemical Society.

ANTISLAVERY

see Slavery

ANTISLAVERY MOVEMENTS

Adams, Alice Dana. The Neglected Period of Anti-Slavery in America 1808-1831. 2007. (ENG.). 320p. 45.95 (978-0-548-17171-4(8)); pap. 30.95 (978-1-4304-6979-7(X)) Kessinger Publishing, LLC.

—The Neglected Period of Anti-Slavery in America 1808-1831. (Radcliffe College Monographs Ser.). 307p. reprint ed. 98.00 (978-0-7222-7780-5(6)) Library Reprints, Inc.

Alston, Richard, et al, eds. Ancient Slavery & Abolition: From Hobbes to Hollywood. 2011. (Classical Presences Ser.). (Illus.). 528p. 150.00 (978-0-19-957467-4(7)) Oxford Univ. Pr., Inc.

Bales, Kevin. Ending Slavery: How We Free Today's Slaves. (Illus.). 2008. 274p. pap. 19.95 (978-0-520-25796-2(0)) 2007. 261p. 40.00 (978-0-520-25470-1(8)) Univ. of California Pr.

Bales, Kevin, et al. Modern Slavery: A Beginner's Guide. 2011. (ENG., Illus.). 240p. 14.95 (978-1-85168-815-9(3)) Oneworld Pubns. GBR. Dist: National Bk. Network.

Carton, Evan. Patriotic Treason: John Brown & the Soul of America. 2009. (ENG., Illus.). 400p. pap. 19.95 (978-0-8032-1946-5(6), Bison Bks.) Univ. of Nebraska Pr.

DeCaro, Louis A., Jr. John Brown: The Cost of Freedom. 2007. (Illus.). 192p. pap. 14.00 (978-0-7178-0742-0(8)) International Publishers Co., Inc.

Drescher, Seymour. Abolition: A History of Slavery & Antislavery. 2009. (ENG.). 484p. pap. 26.99 (978-0-521-60085-9(5)); 95.00 (978-0-521-84102-3(X)) Cambridge Univ. Pr.

Fremont-Barnes, Gregory. Encyclopedia of the Age of Political Revolutions & New Ideologies, 1760-1815, Vol. 2. 2007. (Illus.). 952p. 225.00 (978-0-313-33445-0(5), GR3445, Greenwood Pr.) Greenwood Publishing Group, Inc.

Frost, Karolyn Smardz. I've Got a Home in Glory Land: A Lost Tale of the Underground Railroad. 2008. (ENG., Illus.). 480p. pap. 18.00 (978-0-374-53125-6(0)) Farrar, Straus & Giroux.

Gellman, David N. Emancipating New York: The Politics of Slavery & Freedom, 1777-1827. 2006. (Antislavery, Abolition, & the Atlantic World Ser.). (Illus.). 297p. 50.00 (978-0-8071-3174-9(1)) Louisiana State Univ. Pr.

Goff, Robert K. Finding Karishma: Modern-Day Slavery & the New Abolition Movement. 2006. (Illus.). 208p. pap. (978-1-929862-63-4(6)) Pascoe Publishing.

Greenidge, Kerri & Allison, Robert. Boston's Abolitionists. 2006. (NE Remembers Ser.). (ENG., Illus.). 96p. per. 12.95 (978-1-933212-19-7(5)) Commonwealth Editions.

Hinks, Peter P. & McKivigan, John, eds. Encyclopedia of Antislavery & Abolition: Greenwood Milestones in African American History, Set. 2006. (Greenwood Milestones in African American History Ser.). (Illus.). 856p. 199.95 (978-0-313-33142-8(1), GR3142, Greenwood Pr.) Greenwood Publishing Group, Inc.

Knepp, Gary L. Freedom's Struggle: A Response to Slavery from the Ohio Borderlands. (Illus.). 2009. (ENG.). 260p. pap. 22.50 (978-1-932250-71-8(9)) 2008. 272p. 32.50 (978-1-932250-60-2(3)) Little Miami Publishing Co.

Murphy, Angela F. American Slavery, Irish Freedom: Abolition, Immigrant Citizenship, & the Transatlantic Movement for Irish Repeal. 2010. (Antislavery, Abolition, & the Atlantic World Ser.). 304p. 45.00 (978-0-8071-3639-3(5)) Louisiana State Univ. Pr.

Quirk, Joel. The Anti-Slavery Project: From the Slave Trade to Human Trafficking. 2011. (Pennsylvania Studies in Human Rights Ser.). 344p. (C). 65.00 (978-0-8122-4333-8(1)) Univ. of Pennsylvania Pr.

Rodgers, Nini & Rodgers, Nini. Ireland, Slavery & Anti-Slavery, 1612-1865. 2009. (ENG.). 416p. pap. 39.00 (978-0-230-57477-9(7)) Palgrave Macmillan.

Ruggiero, Vincenzo. Penal Abolitionism. 2010. (ENG., Illus.). 256p. 125.00 (978-0-19-957844-3(3)) Oxford Univ. Pr., Inc.

Schmidt-Nowara, Christopher. Slavery, Freedom, & Abolition in Latin America & the Atlantic World. 2011. (Diálogos Ser.). (ENG., Illus.). 222p. (C). pap. 28.95 (978-0-8263-3904-1(2)) Univ. of New Mexico Pr.

Van Der Linden, Marcel, ed. Humanitarian Intervention & Changing Labor Relations: The Long-term Consequences of the Abolition of the Slave Trade. 2010. (Studies in Global Social History Ser.). (Illus.). 496p. *(978-90-04-18853-2(3))* BRILL.

Whyte, Iain. Zachary Macaulay 1768-1838: The Steadfast Scot in the British Anti-Slavery Movement. 2011. (ENG., Illus.). 263p. 95.00 *(978-1-84631-696-8(0))* Liverpool Univ. Pr. GBR. Dist: Chicago Distribution Ctr.

Wilberforce, William. A Letter on the Abolition of the Slave Trade: Addressed to the Freeholders & Other Inhabitants of Yorkshire. 2011. (Cambridge Library Collection - Slavery & Abolition Ser.). 498p. pap. 35.99 *(978-1-108-02499-0(8))* Cambridge Univ. Pr.

Willey, Austin. The History of the Anti-Slavery Cause in State & Nation. 503p. reprint ed. 98.00 *(978-0-7222-9778-0(5))* Library Reprints, Inc.

ANTISLAVERY MOVEMENTS—GREAT BRITAIN

Bethell, Leslie. The Abolition of the Brazilian Slave Trade: Britain, Brazil & the Slave Trade Question. 2009. (Cambridge Latin American Studies). (ENG., Illus.). 444p. pap. 55.00 *(978-0-521-10113-4(1))* Cambridge Univ. Pr.

Bethell, Leslie & Murilo de Carvalho, José, eds. Joaquim Nabuco, British Abolitionists & the End of Slavery in Brazil: Correspondence, 1880-1905. 2009. (ENG.). 202p. pap. 30.00 *(978-1-900039-95-6(8))* Institute of Latin American Studies GBR. Dist: Brookings Institution Pr.

Clapp, Elizabeth J. & Jeffrey, Julie Roy. Women, Dissent & Anti-Slavery in Britain & America, 1790-1865. 2011. (ENG.). 272p. 110.00 *(978-0-19-958548-9(2))* Oxford Univ. Pr., Inc.

Drescher, Seymour. Econocide: British Slavery in the Era of Abolition, 2nd Ed. 2nd ed. 2010. (ENG., Illus.). 320p. 59.95 *(978-0-8078-3446-6(7))*; pap. 24.95 *(978-0-8078-7179-9(6))* Univ. of North Carolina Pr.

Howman, Brian. For Capital, for God, or for Liberty. 2009. 268p. pap. *(978-3-639-10731-9(4))* VDM Verlag Dr. Mueller e.K.

McInnis, Maurie D. Slaves Waiting for Sale: Abolitionist Art & the American Slave Trade. 2011. (ENG., Illus.). 280p. 40.00 *(978-0-226-55933-9(5))* Univ. of Chicago Pr.

Nowatzki, Robert. Representing African Americans in Transatlantic Abolitionism & Blackface Minstrelsy. 2010. (Illus.). 240p. 38.50 *(978-0-8071-3640-9(9))* Louisiana State Univ. Pr.

Oldfield, J. R. & Oldfield, John. Chords of Freedom: Commemoration, Ritual & British Transatlantic Slavery. 2008. (ENG., Illus.). 208p. pap. 26.00 *(978-0-7190-6665-8(4))* Manchester Univ. Pr. GBR. Dist: Macmillan.

Oldfield, John. Chords of Freedom: Commemoration, Ritual & British Transatlantic Slavery. 2008. (ENG., Illus.). 256p. 79.00 *(978-0-7190-6664-1(6))* Manchester Univ. Pr. GBR. Dist: Macmillan.

Peterson, Derek R., ed. Abolitionism & Imperialism in Britain, Africa, & the Atlantic. 2010. (Cambridge Centre of African Studies). (ENG.). 280p. pap. 28.95 *(978-0-8214-1902-1(1))*; (Illus.). 64.95 *(978-0-8214-1901-4(3))* Ohio Univ. Pr.

Piper, John. Amazing Grace in the Life of William Wilberforce. 2007. 80p. pap. 7.99 *(978-1-58134-875-0(4))* Crossway.

Rodgers, Nini. Ireland, Slavery & Anti-Slavery, 1612-1865. 2007. (ENG., Illus.). 440p. 173.00 *(978-0-333-77099-3(4))* Palgrave Macmillan.

Ryden, David Beck. West Indian Slavery & British Abolition, 1783-1807. (ENG., Illus.). 2010. 350p. pap. 27.99 *(978-0-521-14804-7(9))* 2009. 352p. 84.00 *(978-0-521-48659-0(9))* Cambridge Univ. Pr.

Sadler, Nigel. The Slave Trade. 2009. (Shire Library). (ENG., Illus.). 64p. pap. 12.95 *(978-0-7478-0708-7(6))* Shire Pubns., Ltd. GBR. Dist: Random Hse., Inc.

Stanton, Henry B. Sketches of Reforms & Reformers of Great Britain & Ireland. 2007. (ENG.). 390p. 48.95 *(978-0-548-19553-6(6))*; 392p. per. 33.95 *(978-1-4325-0265-2(4))* Kessinger Publishing, LLC.

Swaminathan, Srividhya. Debating the Slave Trade, 1753-1815: Rhetoric of British National Identity. 2009. (Ashgate Ser. in Nineteenth-Century Transatlantic Studies). (Illus.). 262p. 114.95 *(978-0-7546-6767-4(7))* Ashgate Publishing Co.

Tomkins, Stephen. The Clapham Sect: How Wilberforce's Circle Transformed Britain. 2010. (ENG.). 272p. pap. 16.95 *(978-0-7459-5306-9(9))* Lion Hudson PLC GBR. Dist: Independent Pubs. Group.

Walvin, James. The British Slave Trade: Abolition, Parliament & People. Farrell, Stephen & Unwin, Melanie, eds. 2008. (ENG., Illus.). 360p. (gr. 17). pap. 50.00 *(978-0-7486-3314-2(6))* Edinburgh Univ. Pr. GBR. Dist: Columbia Univ. Pr.

Yerxa, Donald A., ed. British Abolitionism & the Question of Moral Progress in History. 2012. (ENG.). 320p. 49.95 ***(978-1-61117-015-3(X))*** Univ. of South Carolina Pr.

ANTISLAVERY MOVEMENTS—UNITED STATES

see also Underground Railroad

Abbott, Richard H. Cotton & Capital. 2009. 306p. pap. 29.95 *(978-1-55849-745-0(5))* Univ. of Massachusetts Pr.

Abruzzo, Margaret Nicola. Polemical Pain: Slavery, Cruelty, & the Rise of Humanitarianism. 2011. (New Studies in American Intellectual & Cultural History Ser.). (ENG., Illus.). 344p. (gr. 17). 55.00 *(978-0-8018-9852-5(8))* Johns Hopkins Univ. Pr.

Adams, Alice Dana. The Neglected Period of Anti-Slavery in America, 1808-1831. 307p. reprint ed. 98.00 *(978-0-7222-9757-5(2))* Library Reprints, Inc.

Adams, Charles Francis. Richard Henry Dana. 2009. 214p. pap. *(978-0-217-78999-8(4))*; 216p. pap. *(978-0-217-78995-0(1))*; 278p. pap. *(978-0-217-86741-2(3))*; 214p. pap. *(978-0-217-27777-8(2))* Books LLC.

—Richard Henry Dana. 2009. 308p. pap. 22.72 *(978-0-217-86750-4(2))*; 210p. pap. 19.99 *(978-0-217-86745-0(6))* General Bks. LLC.

—Richard Henry Dana. 2006. Vol. 1. pap. 33.95 *(978-1-4286-3779-5(6))* Vol. 2. pap. 36.95 *(978-1-4286-3780-1(X))* Kessinger Publishing, LLC.

American Anti-Slavery Society Staff. The Anti-Slavery Examiner, Part 2 Of. 2007. 584p. per. *(978-1-4068-1607-5(8))* Echo Library.

Aymer, Margaret & Aymer. First Pure, Then Peaceable: Frederick Douglass Reads James. 2008. (Library of New Testament Studies, the Ser.). (ENG.). 164p. 130.00 *(978-0-567-03307-9(4)*, T&T Clark Int'l) Continuum International Publishing Group, Ltd. GBR. Dist: National Bk. Network.

Bacon, Margaret Hope. But One Race: The Life of Robert Purvis. 2010. (Excelsior Editions Ser.). (Illus.). 293p. pap. 24.95 *(978-0-7914-7008-4(3)*, Suny Pr.) State Univ. of New York Pr.

Bacon, Margaret Hope & Lapsansky-Werner, Emma, eds. Back to Africa: Benjamin Coates & the Colonization Movement in America, 1848-1880. 2007. (ENG.). 368p. pap. 27.00 *(978-0-271-02763-0(0))* Pennsylvania State Univ. Pr.

Barker, Gordon S. The Imperfect Revolution: Anthony Burns & the Landscape of Race in Antebellum America. 2011. xix, 169p. 39.95 *(978-1-60635-069-0(2))* Kent State Univ. Pr.

Barnes, L. Diane. Frederick Douglass: In Bondage & Freedom. 2012. (Routledge Historical Americans Ser.). (ENG., Illus.). 224p. (C). 150.00 *(978-0-415-89111-0(6))*; pap. 26.95 *(978-0-415-89112-7(4))* Routledge.

Bassett, John S. Anti-Slavery Leaders of North Carolina. (Johns Hopkins University. Studies in the Social Sciences, Thirtieth Ser.: 6). reprint ed. 37.50 *(978-0-404-61120-0(6))* AMS Pr., Inc.

Benezet, Anthony, et al. Early American Abolitionists: A Collection of Anti-Slavery Writings, 1760-1820. Basker, James G. & Ahlstrom, Justine, eds. 2007. (Illus.). 372p. pap. 0.00 *(978-1-932821-06-2(6))* Gilder Lehrman Institute of American History, The.

Blackburn, Robin. The Overthrow of Colonial Slavery, 1776-1848. 2nd ed. 2011. (Verso World History Ser.). (ENG., Illus.). 560p. pap. 29.95 *(978-1-84467-475-6(4)*, 844475) Verso Bks. GBR. Dist: Norton, W. W. & Co., Inc.

Blue, Frederick J. No Taint of Compromise: Crusaders in Antislavery Politics. 2006. (Antislavery, Abolition, & the Atlantic World Ser.). (Illus.). 301p. per. 22.95 *(978-0-8071-3205-0(5))* Louisiana State Univ. Pr.

Bradley, Patricia. Slavery, Propaganda, & the American Revolution. 2007. (ENG.). 184p. pap. 25.00 *(978-1-57806-211-9(X))* Univ. Pr. of Mississippi.

Brendlinger, Irv A. To Be Silent... Would Be Criminal: The Antislavery Influence & Writings of Anthony Benezet. 2006. (Revitalization: Explorations in World Christian Movements Ser.: No. 20). (ENG., Illus.). 246p. per. 45.00 *(978-0-8108-5765-0(0))* Scarecrow Pr., Inc.

Bush, Bryan S. Lincoln & the Speeds: The Untold Story of a Devoted & Enduring Friendsho[. 2008. 24.95 *(978-0-9798802-6-1(2))* Acclaim Pr., Inc.

Calarco, Tom. People of the Underground Railroad: A Biographical Dictionary, 1 vol. 2008. (Illus.). 408p. 75.00 *(978-0-313-33924-0(4)*, GR3924) Greenwood Publishing Group, Inc.

—The Underground Railroad in the Adirondack Region. alt. ed. 2011. (ENG., Illus.). 303p. pap. 29.95 *(978-0-7864-6416-6(X))* McFarland & Co., Inc. Pubs.

Canney, Donald L. Africa Squadron: The U. S. Navy & the Slave Trade, 1842-1861. 2006. (Illus.). 272p. 27.50 *(978-1-57488-606-1(1))* Potomac Bks., Inc.

Carlson, Julie. Uncle Tom's Cabin & the Abolitionist Movement. 2009. (Looking at Literature Through Primary Sources Ser.). 64p. (gr. 5-8). 58.50 *(978-1-61514-309-2(2))* Rosen Publishing Group, Inc., The.

Chesnutt, Charles Waddell. Frederick Douglass. (Beacon Biographies of Eminent Americans Ser.). 141p. reprint ed. 88.00 *(978-0-7222-9064-4(0))* Library Reprints, Inc.

—Frederick Douglass. 141p. reprint ed. 48.00 *(978-0-7950-1413-0(9))* New Library Press LLC.

Child, Lydia, abr. An Appeal in Favor of That Class of Americans Called Africans. 2008. (Civil War Ser.). (ENG.). 244p. pap. 16.95 *(978-1-4290-1495-3(4))* Applewood Bks.

Child, Lydia Maria. An Appeal in Favor of That Class of Americans Called Africans. 2009. 168p. pap. *(978-1-4068-5034-5(9))* Echo Library.

—An Appeal in Favor of That Class of Americans Called Africans. 2008. 216p. 39.95 *(978-0-548-95286-3(8))* 2007. 220p. per. 24.95 *(978-0-548-62789-1(4))* Kessinger Publishing, LLC.

Child, Lydia Maria Francis. An Appeal in Favor of That Class of Americans Called Africans. 2009. 68p. pap. *(978-0-217-17024-6(2))* Books LLC.

Christensen, Matthew J. Rebellious Histories: The Amistad Slave Revolt & the Cultures of Late Twentieth-Century Black Transnationalism. 2012. pap. *(978-1-4384-3970-9(9))*; (ENG.). 192p. 65.00 *(978-1-4384-3969-3(5))* State Univ. of New York Pr.

Christianson, Scott. Freeing Charles: The Struggle to Free a Slave on the Eve of the Civil War. 2010. (New Black Studies Ser.). (ENG., Illus.). 240p. 65.00 *(978-0-252-03439-8(2))*; pap. 24.95 *(978-0-252-07688-6(5))* Univ. of Illinois Pr.

Clarke, James F. Anti-Slavery Days. 223p. reprint ed. 98.00 *(978-0-7222-9761-2(0))* Library Reprints, Inc.

Clarke, James Freeman. James Freeman Clarke: Autobiography, Diary & Correspondence. Hale, Edward Everett, ed. 2006. (ENG.). 444p. per. 36.95 *(978-1-4286-3540-1(8))* Kessinger Publishing, LLC.

Clavin, Matthew J. Toussaint Louverture & the American Civil War: The Promise & Peril of a Second Haitian Revolution. 2011. (Illus.). 248p. (C). pap. 22.50 ***(978-0-8122-2184-8(2))*** Univ. of Pennsylvania Pr.

Cleves, Rachel Hope. The Reign of Terror in America: Visions of Violence from Anti-Jacobinism to Antislavery. (ENG., Illus.). 2012. 314p. pap. 29.99 ***(978-1-107-40398-7(7))*** 2009. 312p. 82.00 *(978-0-521-88435-8(7))* Cambridge Univ. Pr.

Colaiaco, James A. Frederick Douglass & the Fourth of July. 2007. (ENG.). 256p. pap. 16.95 *(978-1-4039-8072-4(1))* Palgrave Macmillan.

Conway, Moncure Daniel. Autobiography Memories & Experiences O. 2006. pap. 38.95 *(978-1-4286-4245-4(5))* Kessinger Publishing, LLC.

Countryman, Edward. Enjoy the Same Liberty: Black Americans & the Revolutionary ERA. 2011. ***(978-1-4422-0029-6(4))*** Rowman & Littlefield Publishers, Inc.

Crawford, Michael J. The Having of Negroes Is Become a Burden: The Quaker Struggle to Free Slaves in Revolutionary North Carolina. 2010. (ENG., Illus.). 224p. 69.95 *(978-0-8130-3470-6(1))* Univ. Pr. of Florida.

Crothers, A. Glenn. Quakers Living in the Lion's Mouth: The Society of Friends in Northern Virginia, 1730-1865. 2012. (Southern Dissent Ser.). (ENG., Illus.). 380p. 69.95 ***(978-0-8130-3973-2(8))*** Univ. Pr. of Florida.

Davis, David Brion. Inhuman Bondage: The Rise & Fall of Slavery in the New World. 2008. (ENG., Illus.). 464p. pap. 18.95 *(978-0-19-533944-4(4))* Oxford Univ. Pr., Inc.

Delbanco, Andrew. The Abolitionist Imagination. 2012. (Alexis de Tocqueville Lectures on American Politics Ser.). (ENG.). 224p. 24.95 ***(978-0-674-06444-7(5))*** Harvard Univ. Pr.

Dodd, William Edward. The Cotton Kingdom. 2009. 84p. pap. 14.14 *(978-1-151-46489-7(9))* General Bks. LLC.

—The Cotton Kingdom. (Chronicles of America Ser.). 161p. reprint ed. 88.00 *(978-0-7222-7100-1(X))* Library Reprints, Inc.

—The Days of the Cotton Kingdom. (Chronicles of America Ser.). 245p. reprint ed. 98.00 *(978-0-7222-7101-8(8))* Library Reprints, Inc.

Dorsey, Peter A. Common Bondage: Slavery as Metaphor in Revolutionary America. 2009. (ENG.). 43.95 *(978-1-57233-671-1(4))* Univ. of Tennessee Pr.

Douglass, Frederick. In the Words of Frederick Douglass: Quotations from Liberty's Champion. McKivigan, John R. & Kaufman, Heather L., eds. 2011. (Illus.). 288p. 22.95 ***(978-0-8014-4790-7(9))*** Cornell Univ. Pr.

—My Bondage & My Freedom. 2008. 388p. 31.99 *(978-0-554-24476-1(4))* 2008. 388p. 29.99 *(978-0-554-33779-1(7))* 2007. (ENG.). 352p. pap. 25.99 *(978-1-4264-6569-7(6))* BiblioBazaar.

—My Bondage & My Freedom. 2009. 268p. pap. *(978-1-150-57694-2(4))* Books LLC.

—My Bondage & My Freedom. 2008. 204p. pap. 7.99 *(978-1-4209-3060-3(5))* Digireads.com.

—My Bondage & My Freedom. 2007. 468p. 52.95 *(978-0-548-21690-3(8))*; 472p. per. 37.95 *(978-1-4325-3712-8(1))* Kessinger Publishing, LLC.

—My Bondage & My Freedom (an African American Heritage Book) 2008. 272p. 24.95 *(978-1-60459-229-0(X))*; (ENG.). per. 8.99 *(978-1-60459-228-3(1))* Wilder Pubns., Ltd.

—My Bondage & My Freedom by Frederick Douglass with an Introduction by Dr James M'Cune Smith. 2006. 468p. per. 29.99 *(978-1-4255-5165-0(3))* MPublishing.

—Narrative of the Life of an American Slave. 2009. (ENG.). 143p. pap. 24.95 *(978-1-4128-1285-6(2))* Transaction Pubs.

Douglass, Frederick & Smith, James McCune. My Bondage & My Freedom. 2009. (ENG.). 469p. pap. 36.75 *(978-1-117-61826-5(9))* BiblioBazaar.

Du Bois, W. E. B. The Suppression of the African Slave-Tra. 2006. pap. *(978-1-4065-1123-9(4))* Dodo Pr.

—The Suppression of the African Slave Trade to the United States of America 1638-1870. 2008. 412p. 30.99 *(978-0-554-35351-7(2))* 2008. 412p. 32.99 *(978-0-554-26048-8(4))*1. 2007. (ENG.). 408p. pap. 28.99 *(978-1-4346-0398-2(9))* BiblioBazaar.

—The Suppression of the African Slave Trade to the United States of America 1638-1870. 2007. 352p. per. 16.95 *(978-1-60206-819-3(4))* Cosimo, Inc.

—The Suppression of the African Slave Trade to the United States of America 1638-1870 Volume I. 2007. (ENG.). 354p. pap. 25.99 *(978-1-4346-0325-8(3))* BiblioBazaar.

Dunphy, John J. Abolitionism & the Civil War in Southwestern Illinois. 2011. ***(978-1-60949-328-8(1))*** History Pr., The.

Dyer, Justin Buckley. Natural Law & the Antislavery Constitutional Tradition. 2012. (ENG.). 216p. 90.00 ***(978-1-107-01363-6(1))*** Cambridge Univ. Pr.

Ellis, Robert P. Northborough in the Civil War: Citizen Soldiering & Sacrifice. 2007. (Illus.). 126p. pap., per. 19.99 *(978-1-59629-220-8(2))* History Pr., The.

Filler, Louis. The Crusade Against Slavery, 1830-1860. 2011. (ENG., Illus.). 335p. pap. 29.95 *(978-1-4128-4219-8(0))* Transaction Pubs.

Frederick Douglass. My Bondage & My Freedom. l.t. ed. 2007. (ENG.). 384p. pap. 26.99 *(978-1-4264-6628-1(5))* BiblioBazaar.

Gac, Scott. Singing for Freedom: The Hutchinson Family Singers & the Nineteenth-Century Culture of Reform. 2007. (ENG., Illus.). 328p. 50.00 *(978-0-300-11198-9(3))* Yale Univ. Pr.

Gellman, David. Emancipating New York. 2008. 312p. pap. 22.95 *(978-0-8071-3368-2(X))* Louisiana State Univ. Pr.

Gerteis, Louis S. Morality & Utility in American Antislavery Reform. 2011. (ENG.). 280p. pap. 40.00 ***(978-0-8078-5732-8(7))*** Univ. of North Carolina Pr.

Gilbert, Alan. Black Patriots & Loyalists: Fighting for Emancipation in the War for Independence. 2012. (ENG.). 392p. 30.00 ***(978-0-226-29307-3(6))*** Univ. of Chicago Pr.

Goodell, William. Slavery & Anti-Slavery. 2009. 430p. pap. 30.06 *(978-0-217-87243-0(3))* General Bks. LLC.

—Slavery & Anti-Slavery: A History of the Great Struggle in Both Hemispheres. 2010. 628p. pap. 45.75 *(978-1-146-76940-2(7))* BiblioBazaar.

Gougeon, Len. Virtue's Hero: Emerson, Antislavery, & Reform. 2010. (ENG.). 424p. pap. 29.95 *(978-0-8203-3469-1(3))* Univ. of Georgia Pr.

Hammond, John Craig & Mason, Matthew, eds. Contesting Slavery: The Politics of Bondage & Freedom in the New American Nation. 2011. (Jeffersonian America Ser.). (ENG., Illus.). 344p. (gr. 17). 49.50 *(978-0-8139-3105-0(3))* Univ. Pr. of Virginia.

Harrold, Stanley. Border War: Fighting over Slavery before the Civil War. 2010. (Civil War America Ser.). (ENG., Illus.). 312p. 30.00 *(978-0-8078-3431-2(9))*; 500p. pap. 35.00 ***(978-0-8078-9969-4(0))*** Univ. of North Carolina Pr.

Herbert, Hilary A. Abolition Crusade & Its Consequences. reprint ed. 37.50 *(978-0-404-00062-2(2))* AMS Pr., Inc.

—Abolition Crusade & Its Consequences F. 2006. pap. 27.95 *(978-1-4286-3564-7(5))* Kessinger Publishing, LLC.

Hillis, Newell Dwight. The Battle of Principles: A Study of the Heroism & Eloquence of the Anti-Slavery Conflict. 2007. (ENG.). 168p. pap. 19.99 *(978-1-4264-9354-6(1))*; 184p. pap. 21.99 *(978-1-4264-9735-3(0))* BiblioBazaar.

—The Battle of Principles: A Study of the Heroism & Eloquence of the Anti-Slavery Conflict. 2007. (ENG.). 336p. 45.95 *(978-0-548-10468-2(9))* Kessinger Publishing, LLC.

Holley, Sallie. A Life for Liberty: Anti-Slavery & Other Letters of Sallie Holley. 2008. 340p. 28.99 *(978-0-559-46922-0(5))*; pap. 30.75 *(978-0-559-46920-6(9))* BiblioBazaar.

—A Life for Liberty: Anti-Slavery & Other Letters of Sallie Holley. Chadwick, John White, ed. 2007. (ENG.). 334p. 45.95 *(978-0-548-23468-6(X))*; 336p. per. 30.95 *(978-1-4326-3545-9(X))* Kessinger Publishing, LLC.

Honeck, Mischa. We Are the Revolutionists: German-Speaking Immigrants & American Abolitionists after 1848. 2011. (Race in the Atlantic World, 1700-1900 Ser.). (ENG & ACE., Illus.). 256p. 59.95 *(978-0-8203-3800-2(1))*; pap. 24.95 *(978-0-8203-3823-1(0))* Univ. of Georgia Pr.

Hudson, J. Blaine. Fugitive Slaves & the Underground Railroad in the Kentucky Borderland. alt. ed. 2011. (ENG., Illus.). 215p. pap. 45.00 *(978-0-7864-4685-8(4))* McFarland & Co., Inc. Pubs.

Hume, John F. The Abolitionists: Together with Personal Memories of the Struggle Fo. 2006. (ENG.). 162p. pap. 19.99 *(978-1-4264-6788-2(5))*; 178p. pap. 21.99 *(978-1-4264-6851-3(2))* BiblioBazaar.

—The Abolitionists, with Personal Memories, 1830-64. 224p. reprint ed. 98.00 *(978-0-7222-9833-6(1))* Library Reprints, Inc.

Husband, Julie. Antislavery Discourse & Nineteenth-Century American Literature: Incendiary Pictures. 2010. (ENG., Illus.). 192p. 84.00 *(978-0-230-62148-0(1))* Palgrave Macmillan.

Jackson, Maurice. Let This Voice Be Heard: Anthony Benezet, Father of Atlantic Abolitionism. (Illus.). 400p. (C). 2010. pap. 24.95 *(978-0-8122-2126-8(5))* 2009. 55.00 *(978-0-8122-4129-7(0))* Univ. of Pennsylvania Pr.

Jackson, Ruby West & McDonald, Walter T. Finding Freedom: The Untold Story of Joshua Glover, Runaway Slave. 2007. (ENG., Illus.). 176p. 18.95 *(978-0-87020-382-4(7))* Wisconsin Historical Society.

Jeffrey, Julie Roy. Abolitionists Remember: Antislavery Autobiographies & the Unfinished Work of Emancipation. 2008. (ENG., Illus.). 352p. 66.50 *(978-0-8078-3208-0(1))*; pap. 27.95 *(978-0-8078-5885-1(4))* Univ. of North Carolina Pr.

Johnson, Reinhard O. The Liberty Party, 1840-1848: Antislavery Third-Party Politics in the United States. 2009. (Antislavery, Abolition, & the Atlantic World Ser.). 616p. 75.00 *(978-0-8071-3393-4(0))* Louisiana State Univ. Pr.

Johnson, Samuel A. The Battle Cry of Freedom: The New England Emigrant Aid Company in the Kansas Crusade. 2011. 372p. 53.95 ***(978-1-258-04543-2(5))*** Literary Licensing, LLC.

Jordan, Ryan P. Slavery & the Meetinghouse: The Quakers & the Abolitionist Dilemma, 1820-1865. 2007. (ENG., Illus.). 200p. 29.95 *(978-0-253-34860-9(9)*, 0253348609) Indiana Univ. Pr.

Joseph, Sturge. A Visit to the United States In 1841. 2008. 328p. 29.99 *(978-0-554-23578-3(1))* 2008. 328p. 28.99 *(978-0-554-32881-2(X))* 2007. (ENG.). 292p. pap. 21.99 *(978-1-4264-4695-5(0))* 2007. (ENG.). 324p. pap. 24.99 *(978-1-4264-4726-6(4))* BiblioBazaar.

Kenny, Gale L. Contentious Liberties: American Abolitionists in Post-Emancipation Jamaica, 1834-1866. (Race in the Atlantic World, 1700-1900 Ser.). (ENG.). 212p. 2011. pap. 24.95 ***(978-0-8203-4045-6(6))*** 2010. 44.95 *(978-0-8203-3399-1(9))* Univ. of Georgia Pr.

Kinealy, Christine. Daniel O'Connell & the Anti-Slavery Movement: The Saddest People the Sun Sees, 1 vol. 2010. (ENG.). 240p. 99.00 *(978-1-85196-633-2(1))* Pickering & Chatto Pubs., Ltd. GBR. Dist: Ashgate Publishing Co.

Kirkpatrick, Jennet. Uncivil Disobedience: Studies in Violence & Democratic Politics. 2008. (ENG.). 152p. (C). pap. 24.95 *(978-0-691-13877-0(X))*; 45.00 *(978-0-691-13709-4(9))* Princeton Univ. Pr.

Lee, Maurice S., ed. The Cambridge Companion to Frederick Douglass. 2009. (Cambridge Companions to Literature Ser.). (ENG.). 212p. (C). 88.00 *(978-0-521-88923-0(5))*; pap. 27.99 *(978-0-521-71787-8(6))* Cambridge Univ. Pr.

Lightner, David L. Slavery & the Commerce Power: How the Struggle Against the Interstate Slave Trade Led to the Civil War. 2006. (ENG., Illus.). 240p. 48.00 *(978-0-300-11470-6(2))* Yale Univ. Pr.

Loguen, Jermain Wesley. The Rev J W Loguen, As a Slave & As a Freeman a Narrative of Real Life. 2006. 456p. per. 29.99 *(978-1-4255-5023-3(1))* MPublishing.

Lowry, Beverly. Harriet Tubman: Imagining a Life. 2008. (ENG., Illus.). 432p. pap. 15.95 *(978-0-385-72177-6(3),* Anchor) Knopf Doubleday Publishing Group.

—Harriet Tubman: Imagining a Life:A Biography. 2007. (ENG., Illus.). 432p. 26.00 *(978-0-385-50291-7(5),* Doubleday) Doubleday Religious Publishing Group, The.

Lubet, Steven. Fugitive Justice: Runaways, Rescuers, & Slavery on Trial. 2010. (ENG.). 384p. 29.95 *(978-0-674-04704-4(4),* Belknap Pr.) Harvard Univ. Pr.

Macy, Jesse. The Anti-Slavery Crusade. 2009. 96p. pap. *(978-1-4068-8115-8(5))* Echo Library.

—The Anti-Slavery Crusade: A Chronicle of the Gathering Storm. 2009. 252p. 32.99 *(978-1-116-15618-8(0));* 252p. 28.99 *(978-1-116-15619-5(9));* 252p. pap. 26.75 *(978-1-116-15620-1(2));* 252p. pap. 25.75 *(978-1-116-15621-8(0));* 260p. 24.99 *(978-1-103-56929-8(5));* 260p. pap. 18.99 *(978-1-103-56927-4(9))* BiblioBazaar.

—The Anti-Slavery Crusade: A Chronicle of the Gathering Storm. (Chronicles of America Ser.). 245p. reprint ed. 98.00 *(978-0-7222-7116-2(6))* Library Reprints, Inc.

Mandel, Bernard. Labor, Free & Slave: Workingmen & the Anti-Slavery Movement in the United States. 2007. 256p. per. 25.00 *(978-0-252-07428-8(9))* Univ. of Illinois Pr.

Martin, Zachary. Martyr to Freedom: The Life & Death of CA. 2nd ed. 2011. (ENG.). 130p. pap. 21.99 ***(978-0-7618-5422-7(3))*** Hamilton Bks.

Martinez, J. Michael. Coming for to Carry Me Home: Race in America from Abolitionism to Jim Crow. 2011. ***(978-1-4422-1500-9(3))*** Rowman & Littlefield Publishers, Inc.

Martinez, Michael J. Coming for to Carry Me Home: Race in America from Abolitionism to Jim Crow. 2011. (American Crisis Series: Books on the Civil War Era Ser.). (ENG.). 334p. 45.00 ***(978-1-4422-1498-9(8))*** Rowman & Littlefield Publishers, Inc.

Matthews, Harry Bradshaw. African American Journey to Freedom in New York & Related Sites, 1823-1870: Freedom Knows No Color. 2008. (Illus.). 480p. 45.00 *(978-0-9799537-4-3(X))* Africana Homestead Legacy Pubs., Inc.

May, Samuel. Some Recollections of Our Antislavery Conflict. 2008. (Civil War Ser.). (ENG.). 420p. pap. 25.95 *(978-1-4290-1655-1(8))* Applewood Bks.

May, Samuel J. (Samuel Joseph). Some Recollections of Our Antislavery Conflict by Samuel J May. 2006. 420p. per. 26.99 *(978-1-4255-4488-1(6))* MPublishing.

McDonald, Anthony. A Catalog of Music Written in Honor of Martin Luther King Jr. 2012. E-Book ***(978-0-8108-8219-5(1))*** 2011. (ENG.). 198p. 65.00 ***(978-0-8108-8198-3(5))*** Scarecrow Pr., Inc.

McGlone, Robert E. John Brown's War Against Slavery. 2009. (ENG., Illus.). 462p. 35.00 *(978-0-521-51443-9(6))* Cambridge Univ. Pr.

McInnis, Maurie D. Slaves Waiting for Sale: Abolitionist Art & the American Slave Trade. 2011. (ENG., Illus.). 280p. 40.00 *(978-0-226-55933-9(5))* Univ. of Chicago Pr.

McKivigan, John R. The War Against Proslavery Religion: Abolitionism & the Northern Churches, 1830-1865. 2009. (Illus.). 328p. pap. 31.50 *(978-0-8014-7576-4(7))* Cornell Univ. Pr.

McNeese, Tim. The Abolitionist Movement: Ending Slavery. 2007. (Reform Movements in American History Ser.). (Illus.). 144p. (YA). (gr. 7-12). lib. bdg. 32.50 *(978-0-7910-9502-7(9))* Facts On File, Inc.

Mealy, Todd. Biography of an Antislavery City: Antislavery Advocates, Abolitionists, & Underground Railroad Activists in Harrisburg, PA. 2007. 264p. per. 27.95 *(978-1-4241-9792-7(9))* PublishAmerica, Inc.

Minardi, Margot. Making Slavery History: Abolitionism & the Politics of Memory in Massachusetts. (ENG., Illus.). 240p. 2012. pap. 24.95 ***(978-0-19-992286-4(1))*** 2010. 49.95 *(978-0-19-537937-2(3))* Oxford Univ. Pr., Inc.

Mitchell, Thomas G. Antislavery Politics in Antebellum & Civil War America, 1 vol. 2007. 296p. 49.95 *(978-0-275-99168-5(7),* C9168, Praeger Pubs.) Greenwood Publishing Group, Inc.

Moody, F. Kennon. Slavery, Antislavery & the Underground Railroad: A Dutchess County Guide. 2010. (Illus.). 59p. pap. ***(978-1-58776-908-5(5),*** Hudson House Publishing) NetPub Corp.

Morgans, James Patrick. John Todd & the Underground Railroad: Biography of an Iowa Abolitionist. 2006. (ENG., Illus.). 224p. per. 35.00 *(978-0-7864-2783-3(3))* McFarland & Co., Inc. Pubs.

—The Underground Railroad on the Western Frontier: Escapes from Missouri, Arkansas, Iowa & the Territories of Kansas, Nebraska & the Indian Nations, 1840-1865. 2010. (ENG., Illus.). 231p. 55.00 *(978-0-7864-3791-7(X))* McFarland & Co., Inc. Pubs.

Morris, Benjamin Franklin. The Life of Thomas Morris: Pioneer & Long A Legislator of Ohio, & U. S. Senator from 1833 to 1839. Ed. by His Son, B. F. Morris. 2006. 412p. per. 26.99 *(978-1-4255-4423-2(1))* MPublishing.

Mueller, Owen W. Theodore Dwight Weld & the American Anti-Slavery Society. 2011. (ENG.). 236p. pap. 45.00 ***(978-0-7864-6396-1(1))*** McFarland & Co., Inc. Pubs.

Mueller, Owen W. The Underground Railroad in Western Illinois. 2007. (ENG., Illus.). 199p. 45.00 *(978-0-7864-3141-0(5))* McFarland & Co., Inc. Pubs.

Mull, Carol E. The Underground Railroad in Michigan. 2010. (ENG., Illus.). 223p. 55.00 *(978-0-7864-4638-4(2))* McFarland & Co., Inc. Pubs.

Nabers, Deak. Victory of Law: The Fourteenth Amendment, the Civil War, & American Literature, 1852-1867. 2006. (ENG.). 256p. (gr. 17). 51.95 *(978-0-8018-8350-7(4))* Johns Hopkins Univ. Pr.

Newman, Richard & Mueller, James, eds. Antislavery & Abolition in Philadelphia: Emancipation & the Long Struggle for Racial Justice in the City of Brotherly Love. 2011. (Antislavery, Abolition, & the Atlantic World Ser.). 264p. 39.95 ***(978-0-8071-3991-2(2))*** Louisiana State Univ. Pr.

Nowatzki, Robert. Representing African Americans in Transatlantic Abolitionism & Blackface Minstrelsy. 2010. (Illus.). 240p. 38.50 *(978-0-8071-3640-9(9))* Louisiana State Univ. Pr.

Pelster, Mae. Abolitionists, Copperheads & Colonizers in Hudson & the Western Reserve. 2011. 128p. pap. 21.99 ***(978-1-60949-253-3(6))*** History Pr., The.

Pferdehirt, Julia. Freedom Train North: Stories of the Underground Railroad in Wisconsin. 2nd ed. 2011. (ENG., Illus.). 136p. (J). pap. 15.95 *(978-0-87020-474-6(2))* Wisconsin Historical Society.

Phillips, Wendell. Speeches, Lectures, & Letters by Wendell Phillips. 2006. 572p. per. 32.99 *(978-1-4255-6220-5(5))* MPublishing.

Pillsbury, Parker. Acts of the Anti-Slavery Apostles. 2010. (ENG.). 514p. pap. 39.75 *(978-1-171-61904-8(9))* 2010. 520p. pap. 39.75 *(978-1-149-26867-4(0))* 2010. 510p. pap. 39.75 *(978-1-144-71819-8(8))* 2010. 512p. pap. 39.75 *(978-1-146-10479-1(0))* 2010. 514p. pap. 39.75 *(978-1-143-99692-4(5))* 2010. 516p. pap. 39.75 *(978-1-142-21286-5(6))* 2009. (ENG.). 506p. 43.99 *(978-1-117-41562-8(7))* 2009. (ENG.). 506p. pap. 38.75 *(978-1-117-41563-5(5))* 2009. 508p. 43.99 *(978-1-117-12367-7(7))* 2009. 508p. pap. 38.75 *(978-1-117-12368-4(5))* 2009. (ENG.). 506p. pap. 30.99 *(978-1-117-12369-1(3),* BiblioLife) BiblioBazaar.

—Acts of the Anti-Slavery Apostles. 2009. 286p. pap. 23.46 *(978-0-217-67479-9(8))* General Bks. LLC.

—Acts of the Anti Slavery Apostles. 2007. (ENG.). 504p. 53.95 *(978-0-548-00736-5(5))* Kessinger Publishing, LLC.

—Acts of the Anti-Slavery Apostles. 503p. reprint ed. 98.00 *(978-0-7222-9772-8(6))* Library Reprints, Inc.

Plank, Geoffrey Gilbert. John Woolman's Path to the Peaceable Kingdom: A Quaker in the British Empire. 2012. (Early American Studies). (Illus.). 320p. (C). 39.95 ***(978-0-8122-4405-2(2))*** Univ. of Pennsylvania Pr.

Poole, William Frederick. Anti-Slavery Opinions Before the Year 1800. 2008. (Civil War Ser.). (ENG.). 108p. pap. 9.95 *(978-1-4290-1641-4(8))* Applewood Bks.

—Anti-Slavery Opinions Before the Year 1800. 2009. 66p. pap. *(978-0-217-33691-8(4))* Books LLC.

—Anti-Slavery Opinions Before the Year 1800. 2007. (ENG.). 108p. 34.95 *(978-0-548-11739-2(X))* Kessinger Publishing, LLC.

Powell, Aaron M. Personal Reminiscences of the Anti Slavery & Other Reforms & Reformers. 2007. (ENG.). 298p. 43.95 *(978-0-548-04698-2(0))* Kessinger Publishing, LLC.

Rediker, Marcus. The Amistad Rebellion: An Atlantic Odyssey of Slavery & Freedom. 2012. (ENG., Illus.). 304p. 27.95 ***(978-0-670-02504-6(6),*** Viking Adult) Penguin Group (USA) Inc.

Reynolds, David S. John Brown, Abolitionist: The Man Who Killed Slavery, Sparked the Civil War, & Seeded Civil Rights. 2006. (Vintage Ser.). (ENG., Illus.). 592p. per. 18.00 *(978-0-375-72615-6(2),* Vintage) Knopf Doubleday Publishing Group.

Reynolds, Donald E. Texas Terror: The Slave Insurrection Panic of 1860 & the Secession of the Lower South. 2007. (Conflicting Worlds: New Dimensions of the American Civil War Ser.). (Illus.). 237p. 45.00 *(978-0-8071-3283-8(7))* Louisiana State Univ. Pr.

Risley, Ford. Abolition & the Press: The Moral Struggle Against Slavery. 2008. (Medill Visions of the American Press Ser.). (ENG.). 248p. pap. 24.95 *(978-0-8101-2507-0(2))* Northwestern Univ. Pr.

Robertson, Stacey M. Hearts Beating for Liberty: Women Abolitionists in the Old Northwest. 2010. (ENG., Illus.). 336p. 39.95 *(978-0-8078-3408-4(4))* Univ. of North Carolina Pr.

Sachsman, David. Seeking a Voice: Images of Race & Gender in the 19th Century. Rushing, S. Kitrell et al, eds. 2009. (ENG.). 347p. 64.95 *(978-1-55753-505-4(1));* 330p. pap. 32.95 *(978-1-55753-508-5(6))* Purdue Univ. Pr.

Salerno, Beth A. Sister Societies: Women's Antislavery Organizations in Antebellum America. 2008. 243p. pap. 24.00 *(978-0-87580-619-8(8))* Northern Illinois Univ. Pr.

Sanborn, Franklin Benjamin. Recollections of Seventy Years. 2009. 124p. pap. *(978-1-151-27703-9(7))* Books LLC.

—Recollections of Seventy Years. 2009. 246p. pap. 19.99 *(978-0-217-98129-3(1))* General Bks. LLC.

—Recollections of Seventy Years, 2 vol., set. reprint ed. 250.00 *(978-0-7222-9004-0(7))* Library Reprints, Inc.

Sanders, Nancy. Black Abolitionists. 2011. (Perspectives on History Ser.). (ENG.). 120p. (gr. 9-14). pap. 7.95 *(978-1-932663-26-6(6))* History Compass, LLC.

Scriven, Darryl. A Dealer of Old Clothes: Philosophical Conversations with David Walker. 2007. (ENG.). 204p. 62.99 *(978-0-7391-2066-8(2))* Lexington Bks.

Smith, David G. On the Edge of Freedom: The Fugitive Slave Issue in South Central Pennsylvania, 1820-1870. 2012. (ENG.). 260p. 45.00 ***(978-0-8232-4032-6(0))*** Fordham Univ. Pr.

Smith, Theodore Clark. The Liberty & Free Soil Parties in the Northwest. 2007. 363p. reprint ed. pap. 34.95 *(978-1-60105-126-4(3),* 6D7A) Scholar's Bookshelf.

Snodgrass, Mary Ellen. The Underground Railroad: An Encyclopedia of People, Places, & Operations, 2 vols., Set. 2007. (ENG., Illus.). 872p. 199.00 *(978-0-7656-8093-8(9),* Sharpe Reference) Sharpe, M.E. Inc.

Stewart, James Brewer. Abolitionist Politics & the Coming of the Civil War. 2008. 256p. pap. 24.95 net. *(978-1-55849-634-7(3));* 236p. per. 80.00 net. *(978-1-55849-635-4(1))* Univ. of Massachusetts Pr.

Stewart, James Brewer, ed. William Lloyd Garrison at Two Hundred. 2008. (David Brion Davis (Gilder Lehrman) Ser.). (ENG.). 160p. pap. 35.00 *(978-0-300-13658-6(7))* Yale Univ. Pr.

Still, William. The Underground Railroad. 2007. 424p. per. *(978-1-4068-2428-5(3));* (ENG.). 432p. per. *(978-1-4068-2429-2(1))* Echo Library.

—The Underground Railroad: Authentic Narratives & First-Hand Accounts. Finseth, Ian Frederick, ed. 2007. (African American Ser.). (ENG., Illus.). 304p. per. 14.95 *(978-0-486-45553-2(X))* Dover Pubns., Inc.

Stoneham, Michae. John Brown & the Era of Literary Confrontation. 2009. (Studies in American Popular History & Culture Ser.). (ENG.). 240p. 125.00 *(978-0-415-99682-2(1))* Routledge.

Swisshelm, Jane Grey. Half a Century. the Memoirs of the Fir. 2006. pap. *(978-1-4068-0894-0(6))* Echo Library.

Swisshelm, Jane Grey Cannon. Half a Century. 2007. (ENG.). 308p. pap. 23.99 *(978-1-4264-5780-7(4));* 332p. pap. 24.99 *(978-1-4264-5840-8(1))* BiblioBazaar.

—Half a Century. 2007. (ENG.). 300p. per. *(978-1-4065-6464-8(8))* Dodo Pr.

Thoreau, Henry David. Anti-Slavery & Reform Papers. 2009. 80p. pap. *(978-1-151-31052-1(2))* Books LLC.

Tomek, Beverly C. Colonization & Its Discontents: Emancipation, Emigration, & Antislavery in Antebellum Pennsylvania. 2011. (ENG.). 304p. 39.00 *(978-0-8147-8348-1(1));* E-Book *(978-0-8147-8349-8(X))* New York Univ. Pr.

Tuckerman, Bayard. William Jay & the Constitutional Movement for the Abolition of Slavery. 2009. 96p. pap. *(978-1-151-69150-7(X))* Books LLC.

—William Jay & the Constitutional Movement for the Abolition of Slavery. 2007. (ENG.). 222p. 39.95 *(978-0-548-04810-8(X))* Kessinger Publishing, LLC.

—William Jay & the Constitutional Movement for the Abolition of Slavery. 185p. reprint ed. 88.00 *(978-0-7222-9844-2(7))* Library Reprints, Inc.

—William Jay & the Constitutional Movement for the Abolition of Slavery. 185p. reprint ed. 48.00 *(978-0-7950-2407-8(X))* New Library Press LLC.

Upchurch, T. Adams. Abolition Movement, 1 vol. 2011. (Landmarks of the American Mosaic Ser.). 195p. 35.00 *(978-0-313-38606-0(4),* A3C45C) Greenwood Publishing Group, Inc.

Upchurch, Thomas Adams. Abolition Movement. 2011. E-Book *(978-0-313-38607-7(2),* Greenwood Pr.) Greenwood Publishing Group, Inc.

Varon, Elizabeth R. Disunion! The Coming of the American Civil War, 1789-1859. (Littlefield History of the Civil War Era Ser.). (ENG., Illus.). 2008. 416p. (C). 34.00 *(978-0-8078-3232-5(4))* 2010. 472p. pap. 36.00 *(978-0-8078-6607-8(5))* Univ. of North Carolina Pr.

Walters, Kerry. The Underground Railroad: A Reference Guide, 1 vol. 2012. (Guides to Historic Events in America Ser.). (Illus.). 226p. 58.00 ***(978-1-59884-647-8(7),*** A3206C) ABC-CLIO, LLC.

Walters, Kerry S. The Underground Railroad: A Reference Guide. 2012. (Illus.). x, 223p. E-Book ***(978-1-59884-648-5(5))*** ABC-CLIO, LLC.

Ward, Samuel Ringgold. Autobiography of a Fugitive Negro; His Anti-Slavery Labours in the United States, Canad. 2010. 152p. pap. 23.85 *(978-1-153-29480-5(X))* General Bks. LLC.

White, Barbara. Visits with Lincoln: Abolitionists Meet the President at the White House. 2011. (ENG.). 180p. 65.00 ***(978-0-7391-6416-7(3));*** pap. 27.95 ***(978-0-7391-6417-4(1))*** Lexington Bks.

White, Barbara A. Visits with Lincoln: Abolitionists Meet the President at the White House. 2011. E-Book ***(978-0-7391-6418-1(X))*** Lexington Bks.

Wong, Edlie L. Neither Fugitive nor Free: Atlantic Slavery, Freedom Suits, & the Legal Culture of Travel. 2009. (ENG., Illus.). 368p. 75.00 *(978-0-8147-9455-5(6))* New York Univ. Pr.

Young, Neely. Ripe for Emancipation. 2011. 236p. pap. 19.95 ***(978-0-9841128-9-0(8))*** Mariner Media, Inc.

ANTISOCIAL PERSONALITY DISORDERS

Here are entered works on a group of personality disorders which have in common antisocial behavior.

Barker, Carole. Crush: VERB 1) to press or squeeze with a force that deforms or Destroys. 2008. 172p. pap. 15.95 *(978-0-595-52225-3(4))* iUniverse, Inc.

Bliesener, Thomas, et al, eds. Antisocial Behavior & Crime: Contributions of Developmental & Education Research to Prevention & Intervention. 2012. (Illus.). 382p. 74.00 ***(978-0-88937-424-9(4))*** Hogrefe Publishing.

Brown, Sandra Lee & Leedom, Liane J. Women Who Love Psychopaths. 2008. 240p. per. 24.95 *(978-0-9778013-2-9(2))* Health & Well-Being Pubns., LLC.

Buttafuoco, Mary Jo. Getting It Through My Thick Skull: Why I Stayed, What I Learned, & What Millions of People Involved with Sociopaths Need to Know. 2009. (ENG., Illus.). 256p. 24.95 *(978-0-7573-1372-1(8))* Health Communications, Inc.

Clarke, Rebecca M. Antisocial Behavior: Causes, Correlations & Treatments. 2011. (Psychology of Emotions, Motivations & Actions Ser.). 201p. 129.00 *(978-1-61122-890-8(5))* Nova Science Pubs., Inc.

Cleckley, Hervey. The Mask of Sanity: An Attempt to Clarify Some Issues about the So-Called Psychopathic Personality. 2011. 596p. 64.95 ***(978-1-258-05891-3(X))*** Literary Licensing, LLC.

Corsello, Lily. The Judas Personality: Dealing with Antisocial Personality Disorder & Its Victims from the Christian Perspective. 2007. 140p. per. 15.99 *(978-1-60477-085-8(5))* Xulon Pr., Inc.

Cram101 Textbook Reviews & Cram101 Textbook Reviews. Outlines & Highlights for the Cambridge Handbook of Violent Behavior & Aggression by Daniel Flannery, Isbn: 9780521607858. 2011. 490p. pap. 37.95 ***(978-1-61461-038-0(X))*** Cram101 Inc.

Dubeski, Norman. Parasitic People & Other Daily Hazards. 2009. pap. *(978-1-890109-58-5(4),* Fenris Brothers) Crossquarter Publishing Group.

Farrington, David P. & Coid, Jeremy W., eds. Early Prevention of Adult Antisocial Behaviour. 2007. (Cambridge Studies in Criminology Ser.). (ENG., Illus.). 396p. pap. 53.00 *(978-0-521-03079-3(X))* Cambridge Univ. Pr.

Fitzgerald, Michael, ed. Young, Violent, & Dangerous to Know. 2010. (Psychiatry - Theory, Applications & Treatments Ser.). 89.00 *(978-1-60876-952-0(6))* Nova Science Pubs., Inc.

Flannery, Daniel, et al, eds. The Cambridge Handbook of Violent Behavior & Aggression. 2007. (Cambridge Handbooks in Psychology Ser.). (ENG., Illus.). 838p. 148.99 *(978-0-521-84567-0(X))* Cambridge Univ. Pr.

Flannery, Daniel J., et al, eds. The Cambridge Handbook of Violent Behavior & Aggression. 2007. (Cambridge Handbooks in Psychology Ser.). (ENG., Illus.). 840p. per. 68.99 *(978-0-521-60785-8(X))* Cambridge Univ. Pr.

Häkkänen-Nyholm, Helinä. Psychopathy & Law: A Practitioner's Guide. Nyholm, Jan-Olof, ed. 2012. (ENG.). 314p. 119.95 ***(978-0-470-97238-0(6));*** pap. 52.95 ***(978-0-470-97237-3(3))*** Wiley, John & Sons, Inc. (Wiley-Blackwell).

Henggeler, Scott W., et al. Multisystemic Therapy for Antisocial Behavior in Children & Adolescents. 2nd ed. 2009. (ENG., Illus.). 324p. 45.00 *(978-1-60623-071-8(3))* Guilford Pubns., Inc.

Leedom, Liane J. Driven to Do Evil: A Guide for Victims, Friends, Families & Lovers of Sociopaths. 2008. 240p. per. 24.95 *(978-0-9778013-3-6(0))* Health & Well-Being Pubns., LLC.

—Just Like His Father? A Guide to Overcoming Your Child's Genetic Connection to Antisocial Behavior, Addiction & ADHD. 2006. per. 14.95 *(978-0-9778013-0-5(6))* Health & Well-Being Pubns., LLC.

McCloskey, George, et al. Essentials of Executive Function Assessment. 2012. (Essentials of Psychological Assessment Ser.: 68). (ENG.). 304p. pap. 48.95 *(978-0-470-42202-1(5),* Wiley) Wiley, John & Sons, Inc.

Patrick, Christopher J., ed. Handbook of Psychopathy. 2007. (ENG., Illus.). 651p. pap. 55.00 *(978-1-59385-591-8(5))* Guilford Pubns., Inc.

Robinson, Matthew B. & Beaver, Kevin M. Why Crime? An Interdisciplinary Approach to Explaining Criminal Behavior. 2009. pap. 50.00 *(978-1-59460-707-3(9))* Carolina Academic Pr.

Rubitel, Reiss. Containment in the Community: Supportive Frameworks for Thinking about Antisocial Behaviour & Mental. 2011. (Portman Papers Ser.). 286p. pap. 37.95 *(978-1-85575-848-3(2))* Karnac Bks. GBR. Dist: Stylus Publishing, LLC.

Spalding, Frank. Antisocial Behavior. 2011. (Teen Mental Health Ser.). (YA). (gr. 7-12). lib. bdg. 27.95 *(978-1-4488-4585-9(8))* Rosen Publishing Group, Inc., The.

Stone, Michael H. The Anatomy of Evil. 2009. (ENG., Illus.). 384p. 26.98 *(978-1-59102-726-3(8))* Prometheus Bks., Pubs.

Thomas, Christopher R. & Pope, Kayla. The Origins of Antisocial Behavior: A Developmental Perspective. 2012. (ENG.). 304p. 65.00 ***(978-0-19-975347-5(4))*** Oxford Univ. Pr., Inc.

Winnicott, D. W. Deprivation & Delinquency. Winnicott, Clare et al, eds. 2011. (Routledge Classics Ser.). (ENG., Illus.). 288p. pap. 26.95 *(978-0-415-67373-0(9))* Routledge.

Yakima, Cheyenne Valentino. The Iceman Speaks. 2010. 196p. pap. 19.99 *(978-1-4535-3263-8(3))* Xlibris Corp.

Yuille, John C. & Herve, Hugues, eds. The Psychopath: Theory, Research, & Practice. 2006. (ENG., Illus.). 598p. per. 70.95 *(978-0-8058-6079-5(7))* Routledge.

ANTISTALKING LAWS

see Stalking

ANTISTATIC COMPOUNDS

see Petroleum Products—Antistatic Additives

ANTITANK GUNS

Rifle, 5. 56, M16, M16E1 & Launcher Grenade 40-MM. 2007. per. 16.95 *(978-1-60170-017-9(2))* Pentagon Publishing.

Rottman, Gordon & Takizawa, Akira. World War II Japanese Tank Tactics. 2008. (Elite Ser.). (ENG., Illus.). 64p. pap. 18.95 *(978-1-84603-234-9(2))* Osprey Publishing, Ltd. GBR. Dist: Random Hse., Inc.

Seidler, Hans. Hitler's Tank Killer: Sturmgeschuumi;tz at War 1940 - 1945. 2010. (Illus.). 160p. pap. 24.95 *(978-1-84884-174-1(4))* Pen & Sword Bks. Ltd. GBR. Dist: Casemate Pubs. & Bk. Distributors, LLC.

Spielberger, Walter J., et al. Heavy Jagdpanzer: Development - Production - Operations. 2007. (Illus.). 200p. 49.95 *(978-0-7643-2625-7(2))* Schiffer Publishing, Ltd.

—Light Jagdpanzer: Development - Production - Operations. 2007. (Illus.). 200p. 49.95 *(978-0-7643-2623-3(6))* Schiffer Publishing, Ltd.

ANTITANK WARFARE

see Tank Warfare

ANTITHESIS

see Polarity

ANTITHROMBOTIC AGENTS

see Fibrinolytic Agents

ANTITOXINS

see also Toxins

Wiley, Ronald G. & Lappi, Douglas A., eds. Molecular Neurosurgery with Targeted Toxins. 2010. (Illus.). 328p. pap. 165.00 *(978-1-61737-420-3(2)*, 1617374202) Humana Pr.

ANTITRUST LAW

see also Corporation Law

ABA Publishing, creator. Antitrust Law & Economics of Product Distribution. 2006. (ENG.). 429p. per. 149.00 *(978-1-59031-697-9(5))* American Bar Assn.

—Criminal Antitrust Litigation Handbook. 2nd ed. 2006. (ENG., Illus.). 565p. per. 114.00 *(978-1-59031-369-5(0))* American Bar Assn.

—Insurance Antitrust Handbook. 2nd ed. 2006. (ENG.). 170p. per. 124.00 *(978-1-59031-701-3(7))* American Bar Assn.

ABA Section of Antitrust Law Staff. Issues in Competition Law & Policy, 3 vols., Set. 2009. (ENG.). 2450p. 550.00 *(978-1-60442-044-9(8))* American Bar Assn.

Akman, Pinar. The Concept of Abuse in Eu Competition Law: Law & Economic Approaches, 0 vols. 2012. (ENG.). 366p. 120.00 ***(978-1-84946-109-2(0))*** Hart Publishing Ltd. GBR. Dist: International Specialized Bk. Services.

Alese, Femi. Federal Antitrust & Ec Competition Law Analysis. 2008. (Illus.). 558p. 190.00 *(978-0-7546-7010-0(4))* Ashgate Publishing Co.

Amato, Guiliano, et al, eds. A Manual of EU Competition Law. 2007. 836p. (C). 164.00 *(978-1-84113-675-2(1))* Hart Publishing Ltd. GBR. Dist: International Specialized Bk. Services.

American Bar Association. 2009 Annual Review of Antitrust Law Developments. 2011. (ENG.). 458p. pap. 169.00 *(978-1-60442-886-5(4))* American Bar Assn.

American Bar Association, Section of Antitrust Law Staff, contrib. by. Antitrust & Associations Handbook. 12th ed. 2010. (ENG.). 266p. pap. 159.00 *(978-1-60442-392-1(7))* American Bar Assn.

—Antitrust Compliance: Perspectives & Resources for Corporate Counselors. 2nd ed. 2010. (Illus.). xi, 357p. pap. ***(978-1-60442-896-4(1))*** American Bar Assn.

—Antitrust Counterattack in Intellectual Property Litigation Handbook. 2010. xiii, 249p. pap. *(978-1-60442-898-8(8))* American Bar Assn.

—The Federal Antitrust Guidelines for the Licensing of Intellectual Property: Origins & Applications. 3rd ed. 2010. viii, 240p. pap. *(978-1-60442-872-8(4))* American Bar Assn.

—FTC Practice & Procedure Manual. 2007. xvi, 240p. *(978-1-59031-869-0(2))* American Bar Assn.

—Handbook on Antitrust Aspects of Standard Setting. 2nd ed. 2011. xi, 288p. pap. ***(978-1-60442-870-4(8))*** American Bar Assn.

—Indirect Purchaser Litigation Handbook. 2007. (Illus.). xvi, 399p. *(978-1-59031-868-3(4))* American Bar Assn.

—Intellectual Property & Antitrust Handbook. 2007. xvi, 602p. (YA). *(978-1-59031-866-9(8))* American Bar Assn.

—Interlocking Directorates: Handbook on Section 8 of the Clayton ACT. 2011. ix, 102p. pap. ***(978-1-60442-876-6(7))*** American Bar Assn.

—Messenger Model Handbook. 2008. ix, 366p. pap. *(978-1-60442-049-4(9))* American Bar Assn.

—Model Jury Instructions in Criminal Antitrust Cases. 12th ed. 2010. (ENG.). 178p. pap. 159.00 *(978-1-59031-865-2(X))* American Bar Assn.

—The Noerr-Pennington Doctrine. 2009. v, 118p. pap. *(978-1-60442-558-1(X))* American Bar Assn.

American Bar Association Staff, contrib. by. Antitrust Law Developments. 6th ed. 2007. 1959p. 390.00 *(978-1-59031-867-6(6))* American Bar Assn.

American Health Lawyers Association. AHLA PDF Antitrust Paths & Pitfalls: What's Really the Deal with the Messenger Model? (AHLA Members) 2007. pap. 25.00 *(978-1-4224-4409-2(0))* American Health Lawyers Assn.

—AHLA PDF Antitrust Year in Review (Non-Members) 2007. pap. 40.00 *(978-92-77-46110-3(1))* American Health Lawyers Assn.

Ameringer, Carl F. The Health Care Revolution: From Medical Monopoly to Market Competition. 2008. (California/Milbank Books on Health & the Public: Vol. 19). (Illus.). 253p. 60.00 *(978-0-520-25480-0(5))* Univ. of California Pr.

Anderman, Steven D., ed. The Interface Between Intellectual Property Rights & Competition Policy. 2009. (ENG.). 588p. pap. 57.00 *(978-0-521-12698-4(3))* Cambridge Univ. Pr.

Anderson, John. Spark Law Antitrust. 2008. per. 17.95 *(978-0-9801482-1-3(9))* Mclaren Legal Pubs. LLC.

Antitrust Agencies: Department of Justice Antitrust Division & Federal Trade Commission Bureau of Competition: Hearing Before the Task Force on Antitrust & Competition Policy of the Committee on the Judiciary, House of Representatives, One Hundred Tenth Congress, First Session, September 25, 2007. 2009. iii, 100p. *(978-0-16-082961-1(5)*, 552-070-38872-9) United States Government Printing Office.

Antitrust Counseling & Litigation. 3rd rev. ed. 1203.00 *(978-0-8205-2596-9(0))* LexisNexis.

Antitrust Enforcement & Intellectual Property Rights: Promoting Innovation & Competition. 2008. (Hein's Electronic Documents Reprint Ser.: Vol. 28). vi, 210p. *(978-0-8377-1683-1(7))* Hein, William S. & Co., Inc.

Antitrust Implications of American Needle V. NFL: Hearing Before the Subcommittee on Courts & Competition Policy of the Committee on the Judiciary, House of Representatives, One Hundred Eleventh Congress, Second Session, January 20, 2010. 2010. iii, 90p. ***(978-0-16-087171-9(9)***, 552-070-42013-4) United States Government Printing Office.

Areeda, Philip E. Antitrust Law. 3rd ed. 2006. (C). Vol. 1. *(978-0-7355-6079-6(X))* Vol. 1A. *(978-0-7355-6080-2(3))* Wolters Kluwer Law & Business. (Aspen Pubs.).

Aspatore Books Staff, compiled by. Antitrust Litigation Best Practices: Leading Lawyers on Developing a Defense Strategy, Evaluating Settlement Opportunities, & Avoiding Common Client Mistakes. 2008. 192p. pap. 110.00 *(978-0-314-19475-6(4))* Aspatore Bks.

—Understanding Antitrust Issues in Health Care: Leading Lawyers on Analyzing the Impact of Health Care Reform, Managing Antitrust Enforcement Concerns, & Preparing Clients for Change (Inside the Minds) 2010. (Illus.). 300p. pap. 100.00 *(978-0-314-26827-3(8))* Aspatore Bks.

—Working with Government Agencies in Antitrust Law: Leading Lawyers on Responding to Investigations, Managing Interactions with Agencies, & Understanding Enforcement Trends. 2008. 268p. 90.00 *(978-0-314-20236-9(6))* Aspatore Bks.

Bael. Competition Law of the EUropean Community 5e. 5th ed. 2009. xlii, 1674p. 356.00 *(978-90-411-2876-8(X))* Wolters Kluwer Law & Business.

—Due Process in Eu Competition Proceedings. 2011. xxvii, 546p. *(978-90-411-3272-7(4))* Kluwer Law International.

Barents. Directory on EC Case Law on Competition. 2007. *(978-90-411-2656-6(2))* Kluwer Law International.

Barents, Rene. Directory of EU Case Law: Direct Taxation. 2009. xiv, 222p. 198.00 *(978-90-411-2797-6(6))* Wolters Kluwer Law & Business.

Barents, Rene & Barents, R. Directory of EC Case Law on State AIDS. 2008. xxiv, 552p. 264.00 *(978-90-411-2732-7(1))* Wolters Kluwer Law & Business.

Barona, Alfredo. Soft Law in Practice - Assessing Technology Pools According to American & European Antitrust Law. 2007. 140p. (C). pap. 36.00 *(978-3-8329-3140-7(6))* Nomos Verlagsgesellschaft DEU. Dist: International Specialized Bk. Services.

Basedow. Structure & Effects in EU Competition Law. 2011. xv, 343p. *(978-90-411-3174-4(4))* Wolters Kluwer Law & Business.

Basedow, Jürgen. International Antitrust Litigation: Conflict of Laws & Coordination, 0 vols. Francq, Stéphanie & Idot, Laurence, eds. 2012. (ENG.). 468p. 190.00 ***(978-1-84946-039-2(6))*** Hart Publishing Ltd. GBR. Dist: International Specialized Bk. Services.

Basedow, Jürgen. Private Enforcement of EC Competition Law. 2007. (International Competition Law Ser.: Vol. 25). (Illus.). ix, 349p. *(978-90-411-2613-9(9))* Kluwer Law International.

Basedow, Jürgen, et al. Private Enforcement of Competition Law. 2011. 252p. 86.00 *(978-3-8329-5651-6(4))* Nomos Verlagsgesellschaft DEU. Dist: International Specialized Bk. Services.

Baskoy, Tuna. The Political Economy of European Union Competition Policy: A Case Study of the Telecommunications Industry. 2008. (New Political Economy Ser.). (ENG., Illus.). 262p. 125.00 *(978-0-415-96525-5(X))* Routledge.

Beck, Arne. Competition for Public Transport Services: Institutional Framework & Empirical Evidence of Bus Services in Germany. 2012. (Contributions to Economics Ser.). (ENG., Illus.). xxvi, 235p. 139.00 ***(978-3-7908-2801-6(7)***, 3790828017) Physica-Verlag DEU. Dist: Springer.

Bektashi, Farid. Collective Dominance in EC Competition Law: Role ofStructural Links: Case Law Analysis under the EC Merger Regulation. 2008. 68p. pap. *(978-3-639-11020-3(X))* VDM Verlag Dr. Mueller e.K.

Bellodi, Leonardo & Tosato, Gian Luigi, eds. Eu Competition Law: Procedure - Antitrust - Merger - State Aid. 2nd ed. 2011. 850p. 385.00 *(978-90-77644-19-5(9))* Claeys & Casteels Publishing BEL. Dist: International Specialized Bk. Services.

Berk, Gerald. Louis Brandeis & the Making of Regulated Competition, 1900-1932. 2009. (ENG., Illus.). 296p. 92.00 *(978-0-521-42596-4(4))* Cambridge Univ. Pr.

Bernitz, Ulf & Ringe, Wolf-Georg, eds. Company Law & Economic Protectionism: New Challenges to European Integration. 2011. (ENG., Illus.). 368p. 150.00 *(978-0-19-959145-9(8))* Oxford Univ. Pr., Inc.

Bhansali, Asim. Current Trends & Issues in Antitrust Litigation. 2010. (Illus.). 134p. pap. *(978-1-4024-1450-3(1))* Practising Law Institute.

Black, Oliver. Conceptual Foundations of Antitrust. 2010. (ENG.). 232p. pap. 29.00 *(978-0-521-14207-6(5))* Cambridge Univ. Pr.

Blair, Roger D. & Harrison, Jeffrey L. Monopsony in Law & Economics. 2nd rev. ed. 2010. (ENG., Illus.). 264p. pap. 29.99 *(978-0-521-74608-3(6))* Cambridge Univ. Pr.

—Monopsony in Law & Economics. 2nd rev. ed. 2010. (ENG., Illus.). 264p. 90.00 *(978-0-521-76230-4(8))* Cambridge Univ. Pr.

Blair, Roger D., et al. Antitrust Economics. 2nd ed. 2008. (ENG., Illus.). 496p. (C). 84.95 *(978-0-19-513535-0(0))* Oxford Univ. Pr., Inc.

Blanke, Gordon. Treatment of US Antitrust Law & EC Comp Law Intl Arb: Hndbk Pra, 2 vols. 2010. xvi, 2252p. 330.00 *(978-90-411-2760-0(7))* Wolters Kluwer Law & Business.

Bogart, John H. Circuit Conflicts in Antitrust Litigation. 2009. *(978-1-60442-544-4(X))* American Bar Assn.

Bork, Robert H. A Time to Speak: Selected Writings & Arguments. 2008. (American Ideals & Institutions Ser.). (ENG.). 750p. (C). 30.00 *(978-1-933859-68-2(7))* ISI Bks.

Brammer, Silke. Co-Operation Between National Competition Agencies in the Enforcement of Ec Competition Law. 2009. 548p. 228.00 *(978-1-84113-931-9(9))* Hart Publishing Ltd. GBR. Dist: International Specialized Bk. Services.

Broder, Douglas. U. S. Antitrust Law & Enforcement: A Practice Introduction, 1 vol. 2nd ed. 2011. (ENG.). 364p. pap. 185.00 ***(978-0-19-979567-3(3))*** Oxford Univ. Pr., Inc.

Brown, Christopher, et al. EU Competition Law: Procedures & Remedies. 2006. (ENG.). 344p. 242.00 *(978-1-904501-64-0(8))* Oxford Univ. Pr., Inc.

Buccirossi, Paolo, ed. Handbook of Antitrust Economics. 2008. (ENG., Illus.). 712p. (gr. 17). pap. 49.00 *(978-0-262-52477-3(5))* MIT Pr.

Budzinski, Oliver. The Governance of Global Competition: Competence Allocation in International Competition Policy. 2008. (Illus.). 320p. 137.00 *(978-1-84720-630-5(1))* Elgar, Edward Publishing, Inc.

Bush. Antitrust Trends in Asia. 2011. *(978-90-411-2693-1(7))* Wolters Kluwer Law & Business.

Buttigieg, Eugene. Competition Law: Safeguarding the Consumer Interest. 2009. xii, 423p. 145.00 *(978-90-411-3119-5(1))* Wolters Kluwer Law & Business.

Capobianco, Antonio, et al. Competition Law Remedies in Europe. 2013. (ENG.). 492p. 190.00 *(978-1-84113-914-2(9))* Hart Publishing Ltd. GBR. Dist: International Specialized Bk. Services.

Carfagna, Peter A. Carfagna's Sports & the Law: Examining the Legal Evolution of America & Three Major Leagues. 2nd rev. ed. 2011. (American Casebook Ser.). 329p. pap. 79.00 ***(978-0-314-27586-8(X))*** West.

—Sports & the Law: Examining the Legal Evolution of America's Three Major Leagues. 2009. (American Casebook Ser.). 270p. 77.00 *(978-0-314-90758-5(0)*, West Legalworks) West.

Carfagna, Peter A. Sports & the Law: Examining the Legal Evolution of America's Three "Major Leagues" 2nd ed. 2011. (Illus.). xiii, 311p. ***(978-0-314-27867-8(2))*** West Publishing Co., College & Schl. Div.

Carrier, Michael A. Innovation for the 21st Century, 1 vol. 2011. 416p. pap. 29.95 *(978-0-19-979428-7(6))* Oxford Univ. Pr., Inc.

—Innovation for the 21st Century: Harnessing the Power of Intellectual Property & Antitrust Law. 2009. (ENG.). 352p. 68.00 *(978-0-19-534258-1(5))* Oxford Univ. Pr., Inc.

Carte, Milton V., ed. Advanced Business Issues: Taxation, Executive Compensation & Antitrust Laws. 2009. 82.00 *(978-1-60456-512-6(8))* Nova Science Pubs., Inc.

Carvalho, Nuno Pires de. The Trips Regime of Antitrust & Undisclosed Information. 2007. *(978-90-411-2643-6(0))* Kluwer Law International.

Casenotes. Antitrust: Pitofsky Goldschmid & Wood 6E. 2010. pap., stu. ed. *(978-0-7355-9768-6(5)*, Aspen Pubs.) Wolters Kluwer Law & Business.

Cengiz, Firat. Antitrust Federalism in the Eu & the Us. 2012. (Routledge Research in Competition Law Ser.). (ENG.). 256p. (C). 145.00 *(978-0-415-67463-8(8))* Routledge.

Cengiz, Firat. Antitrust Federalism in the EU & the US. 2012. xix, 234p. E-Book ***(978-0-203-12518-2(5))*** Routledge.

Cho, Jung Wook. Innovation & Competition in the Digital Network EConomy: Legal. 2007. *(978-90-411-2574-3(4))* Kluwer Law International.

Choi, Jay Pil, ed. Recent Developments in Antitrust: Theory & Evidence. 2006. (CESifo Seminar Ser.). (ENG., Illus.). 352p. (gr. 17). 38.00 *(978-0-262-03356-5(9))* MIT Pr.

Choné, Anne-Sophie. Les Abus de Domination: Essai en Droit des Contrats et en Droit de la Concurrence. 2010. (FRE.). xiv, 444p. *(978-2-7178-5890-7(3))* Economica, Editions.

Clarke. New Developments in UK & EU Competition Policy. 2007. 320p. (C). 137.00 *(978-1-84542-122-9(1))* Elgar, Edward Publishing, Inc.

Clarke, Philip, et al. Competition Law & Policy: Cases & Materials. 3rd rev. ed. 2011. (ENG.). xxxvi, 747p. pap. 125.00 ***(978-0-19-556289-7(5))*** Oxford Univ. Pr., Inc.

Coates, Kevin. Competition Law & Regulation of Technology Markets. 2011. (ENG.). 489p. 290.00 *(978-0-19-957521-3(5))* Oxford Univ. Pr., Inc.

Colino, Sandra Marco & Furse, Mark. Competition Law of the EU & UK. 7th ed. 2011. (ENG., Illus.). 544p. pap. 60.00 *(978-0-19-958732-2(9))* Oxford Univ. Pr., Inc.

Collins, Sara, et al. International Trust Disputes. 2012. (ENG.). 544p. 350.00 ***(978-0-19-959470-2(8))*** Oxford Univ. Pr., Inc.

Competition in the Airline Industry: Hearing Before the Committee on the Judiciary, House of Representatives, One Hundred Eleventh Congress, Second Session, June 16, 2010. 2010. (Illus.). iii, 221p. *(978-0-16-086906-8(4)*, 552-070-41816-4) United States Government Printing Office.

Competition in the Package Delivery Industry: Hearing Before the Committee on the Judiciary, House of Representatives, One Hundred Tenth Congress, Second Session, September 9, 2008. 2009. (Illus.). iv, 144p. *(978-0-16-083229-1(2)*, 552-070-39057-0) United States Government Printing Office.

Concentration in Agriculture & an Examination of the JBS/Swift Acquisitions: Hearing Before the Subcommittee on Antitrust, Competition Policy, & Consumer Rights of the Committee on the Judiciary, United States Senate, One Hundred Tenth Congress, Second Session, May 7, 2008. 2008. (Illus.). iv, 228p. *(978-0-16-082087-8(1)*, 552-070-38243-7) United States Government Printing Office.

Constantine, Lloyd. Priceless: The Case that Brought down the Visa/MasterCard Bank Cartel. 2012. (ENG.). 272p. pap. 14.95 ***(978-1-61608-375-5(1)***, 608375) Skyhorse Publishing Co., Inc.

Crane, Daniel A. The Institutional Structure of Antitrust Enforcement, 1 vol. 2011. (ENG., Illus.). 268p. 75.00 *(978-0-19-537265-6(4))* Oxford Univ. Pr., Inc.

Credit Card Fair Fee ACT of 2009: Hearing Before the Committee on the Judiciary, House of Representatives, One Hundred Eleventh Congress, Second Session, on H.R. 2695, April 28, 2010. 2010. (Illus.). iii, 157p. *(978-0-16-086743-9(6)*, 552-070-41665-0) United States Government Printing Office.

Cuneo, Jonathan W. The International Handbook on Private Enforcement of Competition Law. Foer, Albert A., ed. 2012. (Elgar Original Reference Ser.). (Illus.). 656p. pap. 65.00 ***(978-1-78100-528-6(1))*** Elgar, Edward Publishing, Inc.

Czapracka, Katarzyna. Intellectual Property & the Limits of Antitrust: A Comparative Study of US & EU Approaches. 2010. (New Horizons in Competition Law & Economics Ser.). 168p. 112.00 *(978-1-84720-925-2(4))* Elgar, Edward Publishing, Inc.

Dabbah, Maher M. Competition Law & Policy in the Middle East. 2007. (ENG., Illus.). 366p. 99.00 *(978-0-521-86908-9(0))* Cambridge Univ. Pr.

—International & Comparative Competition Law. 2010. (Antitrust & Competition Law Ser.). (ENG., Illus.). 714p. 150.00 *(978-0-521-51641-9(2))*; pap. 80.00 *(978-0-521-73624-4(2))* Cambridge Univ. Pr.

—The Internationalisation of Antitrust Policy. Ning, Ding, tr. 2009. (ENG.). 348p. pap. 46.00 *(978-0-521-10699-3(0))* Cambridge Univ. Pr.

Dabbah, Maher M. & Hawk, Barry E. Anti-Cartel Enforcement Worldwide 3 Volume Set, 3 vols. 2009. (Antitrust & Competition Law Ser.). (ENG., Illus.). 3000p. 895.00 *(978-0-521-89721-1(1))* Cambridge Univ. Pr.

Danov, Mihail. Jurisdiction & Judgments in Relation to EU Competition Law Claims. 2011. (ENG.). 331p. 110.00 *(978-1-84113-659-2(X))* Hart Publishing Ltd. GBR. Dist: International Specialized Bk. Services.

Davis, Peter J. & Garcés, Eliana. Quantitative Techniques for Competition & Antitrust Analysis. 2009. (ENG., Illus.). 560p. (C). 100.00 *(978-0-691-14257-9(2))* Princeton Univ. Pr.

de Visser, Maartje. Network-Based Governance in EC Law: The Example of EC Competition & EC Communications Law. 2009. (ENG., Illus.). 440p. 176.00 *(978-1-84113-256-3(X))* Hart Publishing Ltd. GBR. Dist: International Specialized Bk. Services.

Decker, Christopher. Economics & the Enforcement of European Competition Law. 2009. (Illus.). 320p. 137.00 *(978-1-84844-307-5(2))* Elgar, Edward Publishing, Inc.

Design Patents & Auto Replacement Parts: Hearing Before the Committee on the Judiciary, House of Representatives, One Hundred Eleventh Congress, Second Session, March 22, 2010. 2010. (Illus.). iii, 139p. *(978-0-16-087075-0(5)*, 552-070-41932-2) United States Government Printing Office.

Dhall, Vinod, ed. Competition Law: Concepts & Practices Relevant for India. 2007. (ENG.). 586p. 85.00 *(978-0-19-568802-3(3))* Oxford Univ. Pr., Inc.

Disner, Eliot G. Antitrust: Questions, Answers, Law, & Commentary. 3rd ed. 2007. 365p. *(978-0-8318-0006-2(2)*, BK51) American Law Institute.

Drauz, Götz & Jones, Christopher, eds. EU Competition Law Vol. II: Mergers & Acquisitions. 2nd ed. 2012. 1690p. 490.00 *(978-90-77644-18-8(0))* Claeys & Casteels Publishing BEL. Dist: International Specialized Bk. Services.

Drexl, Josef. Research Handbook on Intellectual Property & Competition Law. Drexl, Josef, ed. 2008. (Elgar Original Reference Ser.). 512p. 255.00 *(978-1-84542-047-5(0))* Elgar, Edward Publishing, Inc.

Drexl, Josef, ed. Research Handbook on Intellectual Property & Competition Law. 2010. (Elgar Original Reference Ser.). (Illus.). 512p. pap. 69.00 *(978-1-84980-077-8(4))* Elgar, Edward Publishing, Inc.

Drexl, Josef, et al, eds. Economic Theory & Competition Law. 2009. (ASCOLA Competition Law Ser.). 288p. 137.00 *(978-1-84720-631-2(X))* Elgar, Edward Publishing, Inc.

Drexl, Josef, et al, eds. More Common Ground for International Competition Law? 2011. (ASCOLA Competition Law Ser.). (Illus.). 320p. 125.00 ***(978-1-84980-394-6(3))*** Elgar, Edward Publishing, Inc.

Ebsen, Ingwer, ed. Vergaberecht und Vertragswettbewerb in der Gesetzlichen Krankenversicherung. 2009. (Frankfurter Schriften zur Gesundheitspolitik und zum Gesundheitsrecht. Schriftenreihe des Instituts für Europäische Gesundheitspolitik und Sozialrecht an der Johann Wolfgang Goethe-Universität Frankfurt Ser.). (GER.). 214p. 50.95 *(978-3-631-58997-7(2))* Lang, Peter GmbH, Europaischer Verlag der Wissenschaften DEU. Dist: Lang, Peter.

Effects of the Proposed Arrangement Between DHL & UPS on Competition, Customer Service, & Employment: Hearing Before the Committee on Transportation & Infrastructure, House of Representatives, One Hundred Tenth Congress, Second Session, September 16, 2008. 2008. (Illus.). xi, 255p. *(978-0-16-083399-1(X)*, 552-070-39212-2) United States Government Printing Office.

Ehlermann, Claus-Dieter. European Competition Law Annual 2005: The Interaction Between Competition Law & Intellectual Property Law. Atanasiu, Isabela, ed. 2005th ed. 2007. (ENG.). 691p. 218.00 *(978-1-84113-645-5(X))* Hart Publishing Ltd. GBR. Dist: International Specialized Bk. Services.

Ehlermann, Claus-Dieter & Atanasiu, Isabela, eds. European Competition Law Annual 2006: Enforcement of Prohibition of Cartels. 2007. (ENG.). 685p. 218.00 *(978-1-84113-751-3(0))* Hart Publishing Ltd. GBR. Dist: International Specialized Bk. Services.

Ehlermann, Claus-Dieter & Marquis, Mel, eds. European Competition Law Annual 2007: A Reformed Approach to Article 82 EC. 2007th rev. ed. 2008. (ENG., Illus.). 882p. 208.00 *(978-1-84113-838-1(X))* Hart Publishing Ltd. GBR. Dist: International Specialized Bk. Services.

—European Competition Law Annual 2008: Antitrust Settlements under EC Competition Law. 2010. (European Competition Law Annual Ser.). (ENG.). 723p. 250.00 *(978-1-84113-958-6(0))* Hart Publishing Ltd. GBR. Dist: International Specialized Bk. Services.

—European Competition Law Annual 2009: The Evaluation of Evidence & Its Judicial Review in Competition Cases. 2011. (ENG., Illus.). 886p. 250.00 *(978-1-84946-073-6(6))* Hart Publishing Ltd. GBR. Dist: International Specialized Bk. Services.

A

Elhauge. Research Handbook on the Economics of Antitrust Law. 2012. (Research Handbooks in Law & Economics Ser.). 424p. 210.00 **(978-1-84844-080-7(4))** Elgar, Edward Publishing, Inc.

Elhauge & Elhauge, Einer R. United States Antitrust Law & Economics. 2nd rev. ed. 2011. (University Casebook Ser.). 729p. 150.00 **(978-1-59941-880-3(0),** Foundation Pr.) West.

Elhauge, Einer. United States Antitrust Law & Economics. 2008. (University Casebook Ser.). (Illus.). xxi, 708p. (978-1-59941-520-8(8), Foundation Pr.) West.

Elhauge, Einer, et al. Global Competition Law & Economics. 2nd rev. ed. 2011. (ENG., Illus.). 1326p. pap. 80.00 (978-1-84946-044-6(2)) Hart Publishing Ltd. GBR. Dist: International Specialized Bk. Services.

Elhauge, Einer R. & Geradin, Damien. Global Antitrust Law & Economics. 2nd rev. ed. 2011. (University Casebook Ser.). 1327p. 168.00 **(978-1-59941-747-9(2),** Foundation Pr.) West.

Epstein, Richard A. Antitrust Consent Decrees in Theory & Practice: Why Less Is More. 2007. (ENG.). 156p. pap. 20.00 (978-0-8447-4250-2(3), AEI Pr.) American Enterprise Institute for Public Policy Research.

Etro, Federico. Competition, Innovation, & Antitrust: A Theory of Market Leaders & Its Policy Implications. (ENG.). xx, 283p. 2010. pap. 139.00 (978-3-642-08052-4(9), 3642080529) 2007. (Illus.). 139.00 (978-3-540-49600-7(9), 3540496009) Springer.

Evans, David H. Electronic Commerce: Antitrust & Consumer Protection in the Information Age. 2011. x, 266p. pap. **(978-1-60442-868-1(6))** American Bar Assn.

Evrard, Sébastien, et al. Anti-Monopoly Law & Practice in China, 1 vol. 2011. 592p. pap. 295.00 (978-0-19-539478-8(X)) Oxford Univ. Pr., Inc.

Ewing, Ky. Competition Rules for the 21st Century: Principles from America's Experience. 2nd ed. 2006. (International Competition Law Series Set Ser.). (Illus.). xxix, 728p. (978-90-411-2477-7(2)) Kluwer Law International.

An Examination of S. 772: The Railroad Antitrust Enforcement ACT: Hearing Before the Subcommittee on Antitrust, Competition Policy, & Consumer Rights of the Committee on the Judiciary, United States Senate, One Hundred Tenth Congress, First Session, October 3, 2007. 2007. (Illus.). iii, 174p. (978-0-16-080062-7(5), 552-070-36828-1) United States Government Printing Office.

Ezrachi, Ariel. Eu Competition Law: An Analytical Guide to the Leading Cases. 2nd ed. 2010. (ENG.). 542p. pap. 70.00 (978-1-84946-047-7(7)) Hart Publishing Ltd. GBR. Dist: International Specialized Bk. Services.

Farmer, Susan Beth & Carstensen, Peter C. Competition Policy & Merger Analysis in Deregulated & Newly Competitive Industries. Carstensen, Peter & Farmer, Susan Beth, eds. 2008. (Illus.). 264p. 127.00 (978-1-84542-313-1(5)) Elgar, Edward Publishing, Inc.

Faull, Jonathan & Nikpay, Ali, eds. The EC Law of Competition. 2nd rev. ed. 2007. (ENG., Illus.). 2016p. 577.50 (978-0-19-926929-7(7)) Oxford Univ. Pr., Inc.

The Federal Role in National Rail Policy: Hearing Before the Committee on Commerce, Science, & Transportation, United States Senate, One Hundred Eleventh Congress, Second Session, September 15, 2010. 2011. (Illus.). iii, 70p. **(978-0-16-089551-7(0),** 552-070-43502-6) United States Government Printing Office.

Federal Statutory Exemptions from Antitrust Law. 2007. xiv, 426p. (978-1-59031-864-5(1)) American Bar Assn.

Feinstein, Richard. Competition in the Evolving Digital Marketplace: Hearing Before the Subcommittee on Courts & Competition Policy of the Committee on the Judiciary, House of Representatives, One Hundred Eleventh Congress, Second Session, September 16, 2010. 2011. (Illus.). iv, 183p. **(978-0-16-088326-2(1),** 552-070-42631-1) United States Government Printing Office.

Feinstein, Richard A. Antitrust Laws & Their Effects on Healthcare Providers, Insurers & Patients: Hearing Before the Subcommittee on Courts & Competition Policy of the Committee on the Judiciary, House of Representatives, One Hundred Eleventh Congress, Second Session, December 1, 2010. 2011. iv, 139p. **(978-0-16-088318-7(0),** 552-070-42623-0) United States Government Printing Office.

Ferrigno, Luigi, ed. Antitrust Modernization. 2010. (Laws & Legislation Ser.). 195.00 (978-1-60741-805-4(3)) Nova Science Pubs., Inc.

Findings & Recommendations of the Antitrust Modernization Commission: Hearing Before Antitrust Task Force of the Committee on the Judiciary, House of Representatives, One Hundred Tenth Congress, First Session, May 8, 2007. 2007. iii, 114p. (978-0-16-079223-6(1), 552-070-36292-4) United States Government Printing Office.

Flynn, John J. & First, Harry. Antitrust: Statutes, Treaties, Regulations, Guidelines & Policies, 2009-2010 Ed. 2009. (Academic Statutes Ser.). 662p. 35.00 (978-1-59941-636-6(0), Foundation Pr.) West.

—Antitrust: Statutes, Treaties, Regulations, Guidelines, & Policies, 2011-2012. 2011. (Academic Statutes Ser.). 768p. 35.00 (978-1-60930-018-0(1), Foundation Pr.) West.

Flynn, John J., et al. Antitrust: Statutes, Treaties, Regulations, Guidelines, Policies. 2006. 652p. per. 31.00 (978-1-59941-226-9(8), Foundation Pr.) West.

Foer, Albert A. & Cuneo, J. W. The International Handbook on Private Enforcement of Competition Law. Foer, Albert A. & Cuneo, Jonathan W., eds. 2011. (Illus.). 656p. 299.95 (978-1-84844-877-3(5)) Elgar, Edward Publishing, Inc.

Fott, Martin. Trade Marks vs Free Competition & Free Movement of Goods in Ec Law. 2009. 68p. pap. (978-3-639-12973-1(3)) VDM Verlag Dr. Mueller e.K.

Fox, Eleanor M. Cases & Materials on U. S. Antitrust in Global Context, 2d, 2010 Supplement. 2nd rev. ed. 2010. (American Casebook Ser.). 140p. 21.00 (978-0-314-26202-8(4), West Legalworks) West.

Fox, Eleanor M. & Crane, Daniel A. Global Issues in Antitrust & Competition Law. 2010. (Global Issues Ser.). 659p. pap. 30.00 (978-0-314-18362-0(0), West Legalworks) West.

Fox, Eleanor M. & Mateus, Abel Moreira. Economic Development: The Critical Role of Competition Law & Policy. Fox, Eleanor M. & Mateus, Abel Moreira, eds. 2011. 1136p. 599.95 (978-1-84980-046-4(4)) Elgar, Edward Publishing, Inc.

Freyer, Tony. Regulating Big Business: Antitrust in Great Britain & America, 1880-1990. 2008. (ENG.). 416p. pap. 79.00 (978-0-521-05974-9(7)) Cambridge Univ. Pr.

Freyer, Tony A. Antitrust & Global Capitalism, 1930-2004. 2009. (Cambridge Historical Studies in American Law & Society Ser.). (ENG.). 452p. pap. 35.99 (978-0-521-74727-1(9)) Cambridge Univ. Pr.

Furse, Mark. Antitrust Law in China, Korea & Vietnam. 2009. (ENG.). 456p. 374.10 (978-0-19-928586-0(1)) Oxford Univ. Pr., Inc.

Gavil, Andrew I., et al. Antitrust Law in Perspective: Cases, Concepts, & Problems in Competition Policy. 2nd ed. 2008. (Illus.). xlii, 1267p. (978-0-314-16262-5(3)) West Publishing Co., College & Schl. Div.

Geradin, Damien. Global Antitrust Law & Economics. 2007. (University Casebook Ser.). xxxv, 1231p. (978-1-59941-426-3(0)) West.

Geradin, Damien & Elhauge, Einer. Global Antitrust Law & Economics. 2007. (University Casebook Ser.). 1231p. 168.00 (978-1-58778-931-1(0), Foundation Pr.) West.

—Global Antitrust Law & Economics Supplement. 2007. (University Casebook Ser.). (Illus.). 108p. 25.00 (978-1-59941-325-9(6), Foundation Pr.) West.

Geradin, Damien, et al. EC Competition Law & Economics. 2010. (ENG., Illus.). 552p. 275.00 (978-0-19-956656-3(9)) Oxford Univ. Pr., Inc.

Gerber, David J. Global Competition: Law, Markets, & Globalization. 2012. (ENG.). 416p. pap. 40.00 **(978-0-19-965200-6(7),** Oxford Univ. Pr., Inc.

Ghosal, Vivek & Stennek, Johan, eds. The Political Economy of Antitrust. 2007. (Contributions to Economic Analysis Ser.). 489p. 179.95 (978-0-444-53093-6(2)) Emerald Group Publishing Ltd. GBR. Dist: Turpin Distribution Services Ltd.

Giannakopoulos, Themistoklis K. A Concise Guide to the EU Anti-Dumping/Anti-Subsidies Procedures. 2006. (International Competition Law Ser.: Vol. 23). (Illus.). 231p. (978-90-411-2464-7(0)) Kluwer Law International.

Gidley. Worldwide Merger Notification Requirements. 2009. (978-90-411-3203-1(1)) Kluwer Law International.

Goetz, Charles J. & McChesney, Fred S. Antitrust Law: Interpretation & Implementation. 4th ed. 2009. (Illus.). xxxiv, 926p. pap. (978-1-59941-579-6(8), Foundation Pr.) West.

Goldman, Robert M. One Man Out: Curt Flood Versus Baseball. 2008. 200p. (C). 35.00 (978-0-7006-1602-2(0)); pap. 16.95 (978-0-7006-1603-9(9)) Univ. Pr. of Kansas.

Gotts, Ilene K., ed. The Merger Review Process: A Step-by-Step Guide to U. S. & Foreign Merger Review. 3rd ed. 2006. (ENG.). 901p. per. 169.00 (978-1-59031-652-8(5)) American Bar Assn.

Govaere, Inge, et al, eds. Trade & Competition Law in the EU & Beyond. 2011. 512p. 199.95 **(978-0-85793-566-3(6))** Elgar, Edward Publishing, Inc.

Goyder, Joanna & Albors-Llorens, Albertina. EC Competition Law. 5th ed. 2009. (Oxford European Community Law Library). (ENG.). 660p. (C). pap. 99.00 (978-0-19-923230-7(X)) Oxford Univ. Pr., Inc.

—Goyder's EC Competition Law. 5th ed. 2009. (Oxford European Union Law Library). (ENG.). 660p. 235.00 (978-0-19-953531-6(0)) Oxford Univ. Pr., Inc.

Graham, Cosmo. EU & UK Competition Law. 2010. (Illus.). 570p. pap. 87.50 (978-1-4058-5950-9(4), Longman) Pearson Education, Ltd. GBR. Dist: Trans-Atlantic Pubns., Inc.

Green, N. & Brealey, M. Contentious Competition Law. 2009. 350.00 (978-1-84661-137-7(7)) Jordan Publishing, Ltd. GBR. Dist: International Specialized Bk. Services.

Green QC, Nicholas & Brealey QC, Mark, eds. Competition Litigation Practice 2009/2010. 2010. (ENG.). 480p. 406.25 (978-0-19-957333-2(6)) Oxford Univ. Pr., Inc.

Guzmán, Andrew T. Cooperation, Comity, & Competition Policy. 2010. (ENG., Illus.). 336p. 95.00 (978-0-19-538770-4(3)) Oxford Univ. Pr., Inc.

Hahn, Robert William. Antitrust Policy & Vertical Restraints. 2006. (ENG., Illus.). 94p. per. 17.95 (978-0-8157-3391-1(7)) Brookings Institution Pr.

Hammer, Ulf & Roggenkamp, Martha, eds. European Energy Law Report V. 2008. 238p. pap. 119.00 (978-90-5095-786-1(2)) Intersentia Uitgevers N.V. BEL. Dist: International Specialized Bk. Services.

—European Energy Law Report VI. 2009. 294p. pap. 133.00 (978-90-5095-895-0(8)) Intersentia Uitgevers N.V. BEL. Dist: International Specialized Bk. Services.

Hancock, William A. Antitrust Compliance Programs, 3 vols., Set, No. 139. 2nd ed. 2007. (Illus.). 235.00 (978-1-56789-013-6(X)) Business Laws, Inc.

Harlan, John Maynard & McCandless, Lewis W. The Federal Trade Commission: Its Nature & Powers: an Interpretation of the Trade Law & Related Statutes. 2007. 189p. 75.00 (978-1-58477-832-5(6)) Lawbook Exchange, Ltd., The.

Harris, Steven, et al. Regulating Competition in the EU. 2008. 751p. pap. 141.00 (978-87-574-1697-8(4)) Djof Publishing DNK. Dist: International Specialized Bk. Services.

Hartog, Johanna. Der Zusammenschlusstatbestand des wettbewerblich erheblichen Einflusses. 2010. (Deutsches und Europäisches Wirtschaftsrecht Ser.). (GER.). 178p. 60.95 (978-3-631-60147-1(6)) Lang, Peter GmbH, Europaischer Verlag der Wissenschaften DEU. Dist: Lang, Peter.

Hawk, Barry, ed. International Antitrust Law & Policy: Fordham Competition Law - Index & Table of Cases 1981-2006. 2007. 85.00 (978-1-57823-225-3(2)) Juris Publishing, Inc.

—International Antitrust Law & Policy: Fordham Competition Law 2006. 2007. 600p. 125.00 (978-1-57823-223-9(6)) Juris Publishing, Inc.

Health Insurance Industry Enforcement ACT of 2009: Hearing Before the Subcommittee on Courts & Competition Policy of the Committee on the Judiciary, House of Representatives, One Hundred Eleventh Congress, First Session, on H.R. 3596, October 8, 2009. 2010. (Illus.). iii, 153p. (978-0-16-087152-8(2), 552-070-41995-1) United States Government Printing Office.

Heidenhain, Martin & Schneider, Hannes. German Antitrust Law. 4th ed. 416p. 75.00 (978-3-7819-2840-4(3)) Knapp, Fritz GmbH Verlag DEU. Dist: Juris Publishing, Inc.

Heinemann, Andreas & Möllers, Thomas M. J., eds. The Enforcement of Competition Law in Europe. 2008. (Common Core of European Private Law Ser.). (ENG.). 740p. 175.00 (978-0-521-88110-4(2)) Cambridge Univ. Pr.

Helwig, Richard. Die Kompetenz der Europäischen Gemeinschaft zur Schaffung eines europäischen Medienkonzentrationsrechts: Notwendigkeit, Voraussetzungen und Reichweite einer möglichen Regulierung zur Sicherung von Medien- und Meinungsvielfalt in Europa. 2009. (Schriften zum Medien-, Urheber- und Wirtschaftsrecht Ser.). (GER.). 336p. 86.95 (978-3-631-59720-0(7)) Lang, Peter GmbH, Europaischer Verlag der Wissenschaften DEU. Dist: Lang, Peter.

Holmes, et al. A Practical Guide to National Competetion Rules Across Europe. 2nd ed. 2007. (978-90-411-2607-8(4)) Kluwer Law International.

Holmes, Marjorie C., ed. Competition Law & Practice: A Review of Major Jurisdictions, 1 vol. 2008. iv, 425p. 225.00 (978-1-905017-95-9(2)) Cameron May, Ltd. GBR. Dist: Gaunt, Inc.

Hovenkamp, Herbert. The Antitrust Enterprise: Principle & Execution. 2008. (Illus.). 376p. per. 27.50 (978-0-674-02741-1(8)) Harvard Univ. Pr.

—Black Letter Outline on Antitrust, 5th. 5th rev. ed. 2011. (Black Letter Outline Ser.). 464p. 35.00 (978-0-314-27448-9(0), West Legalworks) West.

—Federal Antitrust Policy, the Law of Competition & Its Practice. 4th rev. ed. 2011. 944p. 95.00 **(978-0-314-21005-0(9))** West Publishing Co., College & Schl. Div.

Hovenkamp, Herbert. IP & Antitrust: An Analysis of Antitrust Principles Applied to Intellectual Property Law. 2nd ed. 2009. ring bd. 420.00 (978-0-7355-7548-6(7)) Wolters Kluwer Law & Business.

H.R. 2382, the Credit Card Interchange Fees ACT of 2009; & H.R. 3639, the Expedited Card Reform for Consumers ACT of 2009: Hearing Before the Committee on Financial Services, House of Representatives, One Hundred Eleventh Congress, First Session, October 8, 2009. 2010. (Illus.). iv 282p. (978-0-16-085864-2(X), 552-070-41076-7) United States Government Printing Office.

Hutchings, Michael, et al, eds. Current Competition Law: Volume V. 2007. 713p. pap. 170.00 (978-1-905221-06-6(1)) British Institute of International & Comparative Law GBR. Dist: International Specialized Bk. Services.

Hylton, Keith N. Antitrust Law & Economics. Hylton, Keith N., ed. 2nd ed. 2010. (Encyclopedia of Law & Economics, Second Edition Ser.). (Illus.). 320p. 198.00 (978-1-84720-731-9(6)) Elgar, Edward Publishing, Inc.

Impact of China's Antitrust Law & Other Competition Policies on U.S. Companies: Hearing Before the Subcommittee on Courts & Competition Policy of the Committee on the Judiciary, House of Representatives, One Hundred Eleventh Congress, Second Session, July 13, 2010. 2010. iii, 107p. (978-0-16-087089-7(5), 552-070-41945-4) United States Government Printing Office.

Inoue, Akira. Japanese Antitrust Manual. 2007. xviii, 346p. (978-90-411-2627-6(9)) Kluwer Law International.

Joekes, Susan & Evans, Phil. Competition & Development. 2008. (In Focus Ser.). 104p. pap. 20.00 (978-1-55250-401-7(8)); pap. 20.00 (978-1-55250-404-8(2)) IDRC/CRDI CAN. Dist: Stylus Publishing, LLC.

Joelson, Mark R. An International Antitrust Primer: A Guide to the Operation of United States, European Union, & Other Key Competition Laws in the Global Economy. 3rd ed. 2006. (International Competition Law Series Set Ser.). 717p. (978-90-411-2468-5(3)) Kluwer Law International.

Johnson, Cheryl L. California State Antitrust & Unfair Competition Law. 2009. (978-1-4224-7554-6(9)) LexisNexis Matthew Bender.

Jones, Alison & Sufrin, Brenda. EC Competition Law: Text, Cases & Materials. 4th ed. 2010. (ENG., Illus.). 1352p. 85.00 (978-0-19-957273-1(9)) Oxford Univ. Pr., Inc.

Kamperman. EUropean Intellectual Property Competition Law. 2010. (978-90-411-3149-2(3)) Wolters Kluwer Law & Business.

Kanai, Takaji, et al. Kesubukku Dokusen Kinshiho. 2nd ed. 2010. (JPN.). xv, 598p. (978-4-335-30501-6(X)) Kobundo.

Kanninen, Heikki, et al, eds. EU Competition Law in Context: Essays in Honour of Virpi Tiili. 2009. (ENG.). 340p. 124.00 (978-1-84946-034-7(5)) Hart Publishing Ltd. GBR. Dist: International Specialized Bk. Services.

Karbaum, Christian. Kartellrechtliche Compliance - Rechtsgrundlagen und Umsetzung. 2010. (Osnabrücker Schriften zum Unternehmens- und Wirtschaftsrecht Ser.). (GER.). 432p. 108.95 (978-3-631-61236-1(2)) Lang, Peter GmbH, Europaischer Verlag der Wissenschaften DEU. Dist: Lang, Peter.

Karollus, Margit & Koeck, Heribert, eds. The Modernisation of the European Competition Law: Initial Experiences with Regulation 1/2003: FIDE XXIII Congress Linz 2008 i Congress Publications Vol. 2. 2008. 521p. pap. 138.00 (978-3-8329-3345-6(X)) Nomos Verlagsgesellschaft DEU. Dist: International Specialized Bk. Services.

Kaseberg, Thorsten. Intellectual Property, Antitrust & Cumulative Innovation in the EU & the US. 2012. (ENG.). 327p. 150.00 **(978-1-84946-306-5(9))** Hart Publishing Ltd. GBR. Dist: International Specialized Bk. Services.

Kawagoe, Kenji. Dokusen Kinshiho: Kyoso Shakai No Feanesu. 4th ed. 2010. (JPN., Illus.). 20p. (978-4-322-11016-6(9)) Kinzai.

Kéllezi, Pranvera. Les Mesures Correctives Dans les Cas de Concentrations D Enterprises et D Abus de Position Dominante. 2010. (FRE.). xl, 602p. (978-2-8027-2932-7(2)); (978-3-7272-0667-2(5)) Librairie Generale de droit et de Jurisprudence.

Kingston, Suzanne. Greening EU Competition Law & Policy. 2011. (Antitrust & Competition Law Ser.). (ENG., Illus.). 490p. 110.00 (978-1-107-00302-6(4)) Cambridge Univ. Pr.

Klein, Benjamin & Lerner, Andres V., eds. Economics of Antitrust Law, 2 vols. 2008. (Economic Approaches to Law Ser.). 1312p. 615.00 (978-1-84542-513-5(5)) Elgar, Edward Publishing, Inc.

Kneisz, Stefanie. Motor Vehicle Block Exemption Regulation 1400/2002: Economic Impact on the European Automobile Industry. 2008. 132p. pap. (978-3-639-11207-8(5)) VDM Verlag Dr. Mueller e.K.

Kokkoris. The Reform of EC Competition Law. 2009. (Illus.). xl, 578p. 195.00 (978-90-411-2692-4(9)) Wolters Kluwer Law & Business.

Kokkoris, Ioannis. Competition Law & the Enforcement of Article 102. Etro, Federico, ed. 2011. (ENG., Illus.). 272p. 195.00 (978-0-19-958618-9(7)) Oxford Univ. Pr., Inc.

Komninos, Assimakis & Komninos, Assimakis P. EC Private Antitrust Enforcement: Decentralised Application of EC Competition Law by National Courts. 2008. 314p. 228.00 (978-1-84113-744-5(8)) Hart Publishing Ltd. GBR. Dist: International Specialized Bk. Services.

Komninos, Assimakis & Radicati Di Brozolo, Luca. International Commercial Arbitration & Eu Competition Law. 2013. 354p. 190.00 **(978-1-84113-862-6(2))** Hart Publishing Ltd. GBR. Dist: International Specialized Bk. Services.

Korah, Valentine & Lianos, Ioannis. Competition Law: Text, Cases & Materials. 4th ed. 2013. (ENG.). 896p. pap. 70.00 (978-1-84946-079-8(5)) Hart Publishing Ltd. GBR. Dist: International Specialized Bk. Services.

Kovacic. The Evolution of Us Antitrust Enforcement. 2012. 256p. 99.95 **(978-1-84720-735-7(9))** Elgar, Edward Publishing, Inc.

Kroll, Daniela. Toward Multilateral Competition Law? After Cancun: Reevaluating the Case for Additinal International Competition Rules under Special Consideration of the WTO Agreement. 2007. 217p. pap. 46.95 (978-0-8204-8779-3(1)) Lang, Peter Publishing, Inc.

Kunzlik, Peter F. Antitrust in the Global Era. 2010. (ENG.). 320p. 95.00 (978-0-19-925574-0(1)) Oxford Univ. Pr., Inc.

Kwoka, John E. & White, Lawrence J. The Antitrust Revolution: Economics, Competition, & Policy. 5th ed. 2008. (ENG., Illus.). 544p (978-0-19-532296-5(7)); 608p. (C). pap. 64.95 (978-0-19-532297-2(5)) Oxford Univ. Pr., Inc.

Laing, David J. Global Merger Control Manual, 1 vol. Gomez, Luis A., ed. 8th ed. 2008. 425.00 (978-1-905017-82-9(0)) Cameron May, Ltd. GBR. Dist: Gaunt, Inc.

Laing, David J. & Gomez, Luis A., eds. Global Merger Control Manual. 7th ed. 2007. 628p. 390.00 (978-1-905017-50-8(2)) Cameron May, Ltd. GBR. Dist: Gaunt, Inc.

Langer. Bundling As a Leveraging Concern under Ec Competition Law. 2007. (978-90-411-2575-0(2)) Kluwer Law International.

LeClair, Mark S. Cartelization Antitrust & Globalization in the Us & Europe. 2010. (Routledge Studies in the Modern World Economy Ser.). (ENG., Illus.). 196p. (C). 145.00 (978-0-415-57343-6(2), Routledge) Taylor & Francis Group GBR. Dist: Taylor & Francis Group.

Lee, Sarah, et al. General Principles. 2006. 323p. 242.00 (978-1-904501-63-3(X)) Oxford Univ. Pr., Inc.

Leibowitz, Jon & Varney, Christine Anne. Federal Trade Commission's Bureau of Competition & the U.S. Department of Justice's Antitrust Division: Hearing Before the Subcommittee on Courts & Competition Policy of the Committee on the Judiciary, House of Representatives, One Hundred Eleventh Congress, Second Session, July 27, 2010. 2010. (Illus.). iii, 209p. **(978-0-16-087184-9(0),** 552-070-42026-6) United States Government Printing Office.

Lemley, Mark A. Gilbert Law Summaries on Antitrust, 11th. 11th rev. ed. 2010. (Gilbert Law Summaries Ser.). 330p. 38.00 (978-0-314-27179-2(1)) West.

Leon, Ignacio De. Latin American Competition Law & Policy: A Policy in Search of Identity. 2nd rev. ed. 2009. (Illus.). xxxiii, 647p. (978-90-411-2478-4(0)) Kluwer Law International.

Leoni, Bruno & Lottieri, Carlo. Law, Liberty, & the Competitive Market. Lottieri, Carlo, ed. Turci, Gian & MacDiarmid, Anne, trs. 2008. (ENG.). 241p. 49.95 (978-1-4128-0842-2(1)) Transaction Pubs.

Leslie, Christopher R. Antitrust Law & Intellectual Property Rights: Cases & Materials, 1 vol. 2010. (ENG., Illus.). 688p. (C). 115.00 (978-0-19-533719-8(0)) Oxford Univ. Pr., Inc.

Leveque, Francois & Shelanski, Howard, eds. Antitrust & Regulation in the EU & US: Legal & Economic Perspectives. 2010. (New Horizons in Competition Law & Economics Ser.). (Illus.). 224p. 112.00 (978-1-84720-761-6(8)) Elgar, Edward Publishing, Inc.

Liakopoulos, Demetres I. & Romani, Mauro. The Regulation of Transnational Mergers in International & European Law. 2009. 254p. *(978-90-04-17771-0(X))* BRILL.

Lifland, William T. State Antitrust Law. rev. ed. 530p. *(978-1-58852-022-7(6),* Law Journal Pr.) Incisive Media.

Lorenzon. Shipping Pools & EC Competition Law. 2011. 152.00 *(978-90-411-2743-3(7))* Wolters Kluwer Law & Business.

Lovdahl Gormsen, Liza. A Principled Approach to Abuse of Dominance in European Competition Law. 2010. (Antitrust & Competition Law Ser.). (ENG., Illus.). 226p. 115.00 *(978-0-521-76714-9(8))* Cambridge Univ. Pr.

Lugard, Paul, ed. The International Competition Network at Ten: Origins, Accomplishments & Aspirations. 2011. 440p. pap. 114.00 ***(978-94-000-0192-3(4))*** Intersentia Uitgevers N.V. BEL. Dist: International Specialized Bk. Services.

MacCulloch, Angus & Rodger, Barry. Competition Law & Policy in the EC & UK. 4th rev. ed. 2008. (ENG., Illus.). 488p. (C). pap. 54.95 *(978-0-415-45847-4(1),* Routledge Cavendish) Taylor & Francis Group GBR. Dist: Taylor & Francis Group.

—Competition Law & Policy in the EC & UK. 4th rev. ed. 2008. (ENG., Illus.). 488p. (C). 190.00 *(978-0-415-45848-1(X),* Routledge Cavendish) Taylor & Francis Group GBR. Dist: Taylor & Francis Group.

Mackenrodt, Mark-Oliver, et al, eds. Abuse of Dominant Position: New Interpretation, New Enforcement Mechanisms? New Interpretation, New Enforcement Mechanisms? 2010. (MPI Studies on Intellectual Property, Competition & Tax Law Ser.). (ABK., Illus.). xii, 204p. pap. 139.00 *(978-3-642-08941-1(0),* 3642089410) Springer.

Macnab, Andrew. Bellamy & Child: Materials on European Community Law of Competition: 2011 Edition. 2011. (ENG.). 1984p. pap. 150.00 *(978-0-19-959477-1(5))* Oxford Univ. Pr., Inc.

Macnab, Andrew, ed. Bellamy & Child Materials on European Community Law of Competition, 2 vols. 2008. (Illus.). 1,000p. per. 120.00 *(978-0-19-928652-2(3))* Oxford Univ. Pr., Inc.

—Bellamy & Child: Materials on European Community Law of Competition: 2009 Edition, 2 vols. 2009. (ENG.). 2,016p. pap. 195.00 *(978-0-19-955934-3(1))* Oxford Univ. Pr., Inc.

—Bellamy & Child: Materials on European Community Law of Competition: 2010 Edition. 2010. 2,024p. pap. 175.50 *(978-0-19-957519-0(3))* Oxford Univ. Pr., Inc.

Maggiolino, Mariateresa. Intellectual Property & Antitrust: A Comparative Economic Analysis of US & EU Law. 2011. (New Horizons in Competition Law & Economics Ser.). 288p. 110.00 *(978-1-84844-340-2(4))* Elgar, Edward Publishing, Inc.

Marco Colino, Sandra. Vertical Agreements & Competition Law: A Comparative Study of the EU & US Regimes. 2010. (ENG.). 199p. 100.00 *(978-1-84113-871-8(1))* Hart Publishing Ltd. GBR. Dist: International Specialized Bk. Services.

Markovits, Richard. Economics & the Interpretation & Application of U. S. & E. U. Antitrust Law: Basic Concepts & Economics-Based Analyses of the Legality of Oligopolistic & Predatory Conduct. 2012. (ENG., Illus.). x, 700p. 89.95 ***(978-3-642-24306-6(1),*** 3642243061) Springer.

—Economics & the Interpretation & Application of U. S. & E. U. Antitrust Law Vol. II: Economics-Based Legal Analyses of Mergers, Vertical Practices, & Joint Ventures. 2012. (ENG., Illus.). x, 700p. 79.95 ***(978-3-642-24312-7(6),*** 3642243126) Springer.

Marsden. Handbook of Research in Trans-Atlantic Antitrust. 2007. (Elgar Original Reference Ser.). 800p. (C). 314.00 *(978-1-84542-181-6(7))* Elgar, Edward Publishing, Inc.

Marsden, Philip. A Competition Policy for the WTO. 464p. 185.00 *(978-1-874698-58-6(9))* Cameron May, Ltd. GBR. Dist: Gaunt, Inc.

Marsden, Philip, ed. Handbook of Research in Trans-Atlantic Antitrust. 2008. (Elgar Original Reference Ser.). 800p. pap. 85.00 *(978-1-84720-945-0(9))* Elgar, Edward Publishing, Inc.

Marshall, Kevin Scott & Kalos, Stephen H. The Economics of Antitrust Injury & Firm-Specific Damages. 2007. pap. *(978-1-933264-45-5(4))* Lawyers & Judges Publishing Co., Inc.

Masters, Brooke A. Spoiling for a Fight: The Rise of Eliot Spitzer. 2007. (ENG., Illus.). 384p. pap. 18.00 *(978-0-8050-8302-6(2),* Holt Paperback) Holt, Henry & Co.

McCarthy, Eric. State Indirect Purchaser Lawsuits: A Practice Guide. 2010. *(978-1-59031-800-3(5))* American Bar Assn.

McEwin, Ian, ed. Intellectual Property, Competition Law & Economics in Asia, 0 vols. 2011. (ENG.). 368p. 150.00 *(978-1-84946-087-3(6))* Hart Publishing Ltd. GBR. Dist: International Specialized Bk. Services.

McGowan, Lee. The Anti-Trust Revolution in Europe: The European Commission. S Cartel Policy. 2010. (Illus.). 240p. 112.00 *(978-1-84720-146-1(6))* Elgar, Edward Publishing, Inc.

McNeese, Tim. The Robber Barons & the Sherman Anti-Trust ACT: Reshaping American Business. 2008. (Milestones in American History Ser.). (Illus.). 128p. (YA). (gr. 7-12). 35.00 *(978-1-60413-008-9(3))* Facts On File, Inc.

Mcnutt. Law, Economics & Antitrust Towards a New Perspective. 2007. (Illus.). 432p. pap. 66.00 ***(978-1-84720-090-7(7))*** Elgar, Edward Publishing, Inc.

Medalla. Competition Policy in East Asia. 2007. (Illus.). XVIII, 270p. 39.95 *(978-0-415-43599-4(4))* Routledge.

Mederer, Wolfgang, et al. EU Competition Law: Volume IV, State Aid. 2008. 1596p. 350.00 *(978-90-77644-09-6(1))* Claeys & Casteels Publishing BEL. Dist: International Specialized Bk. Services.

Mehta, Pradeep S. Evolution of Competition Laws & Their Enforcement: A Political Economy Perspective. 2011. (Routledge Studies in Global Competition Ser.). (ENG., Illus.). 240p. (C). 130.00 *(978-0-415-67213-9(9))* Routledge.

Mehta, Pradeep S. The Evolution of Competition Laws & Their Enforcement: A Political Economy Perspective. 2011. (Illus.). xviii, 221p. E-Book ***(978-0-203-35737-8(X))*** Routledge.

Mehta, Pradeep S. & Evenett, Simon J., eds. Politics Triumphs Economics? Political Economy & the Implementation of Competition Law & Economic Regulation in Developing Countries. 2009. (ENG.). 468p. 69.95 *(978-81-7188-725-5(2))* Academic Foundation IND. Dist: Independent Pubs. Group.

Middleton, Kirsty. Blackstone's UK & EU Competition Documents. 7th ed. 2011. (Illus.). 624p. pap. 40.00 ***(978-0-19-958243-3(2))*** Oxford Univ. Pr., Inc.

Middleton, Kirsty, et al. Cases & Materials on UK & EC Competition Law. 2nd ed. 2009. (ENG., Illus.). 644p. (C). pap. 75.00 *(978-0-19-929039-0(3))* Oxford Univ. Pr., Inc.

Mobley, Samantha & Denton, Ross, eds. Global Cartels Handbook: Leniency - Policies & Procedure. 2012. (ENG.). 816p. pap. 190.00 ***(978-0-19-964100-0(5))*** Oxford Univ. Pr., Inc.

Möllers, Thomas M. J. & Heinemann, Andreas, eds. The Enforcement of Competition Law in Europe. 2010. (Common Core of European Private Law Ser.). (ENG.). 740p. pap. 85.00 *(978-0-521-18156-3(9))* Cambridge Univ. Pr.

Monti, Giorgio. EC Competition Law. 2007. (Law in Context Ser.). (ENG., Illus.). 568p. per. 79.00 *(978-0-521-70075-7(2))* Cambridge Univ. Pr.

Monti, Mario, et al, eds. Economic Law & Justice in Times of Globalisation: Festschrift fur Carl Baudenbacher. 2007. 916p. 199.00 *(978-3-8329-2875-9(8))* Nomos Verlagsgesellschaft DEU. Dist: International Specialized Bk. Services.

Morais, Luís. Joint Ventures & EC Competition Law. 2013. (ENG.). 504p. 190.00 *(978-1-84113-793-3(6))* Hart Publishing Ltd. GBR. Dist: International Specialized Bk. Services.

Moreira, et al. Competition Law & Economics: Advances in Competition Policy & Antitrust Enforcement. 2007. (Illus.). *(978-90-411-2632-0(5))* Kluwer Law International.

Moser. China Competition Law & Practice. 2011. *(978-90-411-2598-9(1))* Kluwer Law International.

Negishi, Akira & Funada, Masayuki. Dokusen Kinshiho Gaisetsu. 4th ed. 2010. (JPN.). xviii, 448p. *(978-4-641-14416-3(8))* Yuhikaku.

Nguyen, Tú Thanh. Competition Law, Technology Transfer & the TRIPS Agreement: Implications for Developing Countries. 2010. (Illus.). 360p. 147.00 *(978-1-84980-125-6(8))* Elgar, Edward Publishing, Inc.

Niels, Gunnar, et al. Economics for Competition Lawyers. 2011. (ENG., Illus.). 744p. pap. 110.00 *(978-0-19-958851-0(1))* Oxford Univ. Pr., Inc.

Noonan, Chris. Emerging Principles of International Competition Law. 2008. (International Economic Law Ser.). (ENG.). 600p. 198.00 *(978-0-19-920752-7(6))* Oxford Univ. Pr., Inc.

O'Connor, Edward F. Intellectual Property Law & Litigation: Practical & Irreverent Insights. 12th ed. 2010. (ENG.). 333p. pap. 119.95 *(978-1-60442-527-7(X))* American Bar Assn.

O'Kane, Michael. The Law of Criminal Cartels: Practice & Procedure. 2009. (ENG.). 400p. 291.50 *(978-0-19-956120-9(6))* Oxford Univ. Pr., Inc.

Oller, Jeremy. The Economics of Sales below Cost Laws. 2008. 112p. pap. *(978-3-639-08584-6(1))* VDM Verlag Dr. Mueller e.K.

Ortiz Blanco, Luis. Market Power in EU Antitrust Law. 2012. (ENG., Illus.). 368p. 150.00 *(978-1-84113-528-1(3))* Hart Publishing Ltd. GBR. Dist: International Specialized Bk. Services.

—Shipping Conferences under EC Antitrust Law: Criticism of a Legal Paradox. 2007. (ENG.). 654p. 300.00 *(978-1-84113-527-4(5))* Hart Publishing Ltd. GBR. Dist: International Specialized Bk. Services.

Osterud. Exclusionary Abuses under Article 82: The Spectrum of Tests. 2011. 368p. *(978-90-411-3271-0(6))* Kluwer Law International.

Pace, Lorenzo Federico. European Antitrust Law: Prohibitions, Merger Control & Procedures. 2007. 424p. (C). 163.00 *(978-1-84542-695-8(9))* Elgar, Edward Publishing, Inc.

Pace, Lorenzo Federico, ed. European Competition Law: The Impact of the Commission's Guidance on Article 102. 2011. (Illus.). 192p. 110.00 *(978-1-84844-773-8(6))* Elgar, Edward Publishing, Inc.

Page, William H. Proving Antitrust Damages: Legal & Economic Issues. 2nd ed. 2010. (Illus.). xii, 308p. pap. *(978-1-60442-878-0(3))* American Bar Assn.

Page, William H. & Lopatka, John E. The Microsoft Case: Antitrust, High Technology, & Consumer Welfare. (ENG., Illus.). 2009. 368p. pap. 22.50 *(978-0-226-64464-6(2))* 2007. 317p. 47.50 *(978-0-226-64463-9(4))* Univ. of Chicago Pr.

Papadopoulos, Anestis S. The International Dimension of EU Competition Law & Policy. 2010. (Antitrust & Competition Law Ser.). (ENG., Illus.). 362p. 110.00 *(978-0-521-19646-8(9))* Cambridge Univ. Pr.

Parret, Laura, ed. Side Effects of the Modernisationo of EU Competition Law. 2011. 309p. pap. ***(978-90-5850-619-1(3))*** Wolf Legal Pubs., W.L.P.

Peifer, Karl-Nikolaus. Lauterkeitsrecht: Das UWG in Systematik und Fallbearbeitung. 2011. (De Gruyter Studium Ser.).Tr. of Law of Fair Trading. (GER., Illus.). XXII, 230p. (C). pap. 35.00 ***(978-3-11-025915-5(X))*** De Gruyter, Walter Inc.

Philipp, Marc. Intellectual Property Related Generic Defense Strategies in the European Pharmaceutical Market: Implications of the EU Commission's Sector Inquiry from an IP, Competition Law & Economic Perspective. 2011. 92p. pap. 34.00 ***(978-3-8329-6707-9(9))*** Nomos Verlagsgesellschaft DEU. Dist: International Specialized Bk. Services.

Pitofsky, Robert. How the Chicago School Overshot the Mark: The Effect of Conservative Economic Analysis on U.S. Antitrust. Pitofsky, Robert, ed. 2008. (ENG., Illus.). 328p. 99.00 *(978-0-19-537282-3(4))* Oxford Univ. Pr., Inc.

Pitofsky, Robert, ed. How the Chicago School Overshot the Mark: The Effect of Conservative Economic Analysis on U. S. Antitrust. 2008. (ENG., Illus.). 328p. pap. 45.00 *(978-0-19-533976-5(2))* Oxford Univ. Pr., Inc.

Pitofsky, Robert & Goldschmid, Harvey J. Pitofsky, Goldschmid & Wood's Trade Regulation, Cases & Materials, 5th Edition, 2008 Supplement. 5th rev. ed. 2009. (University Casebook Ser.). 208p. pap. 23.00 *(978-1-59941-483-6(X),* Foundation Pr.) West.

Pitofsky, Robert & Goldschmid, Harvey J. Trade Regulation: Cases & Materials. 6th rev. ed. 2011. 64p. pap. 19.00 ***(978-1-60930-023-4(8),*** Foundation Pr.) West.

Pitofsky, Robert, et al. Trade Regulation Supplement: Cases & Materials. 5th rev. ed. 2007. (University Casebook Ser.). 190p. per. 19.00 *(978-1-59941-303-7(5),* Foundation Pr.) West.

Pitzer, Frank. Interessen im Wettbewerb: Grundlagen und frühe Entwicklung der europäischen Wettbewerbspolitik 1955-1966. Vierteljahrschrift für Sozial- und Wirtschaftsgeschichte - Beihefte 195. 2009. (Vierteljahrschrift für Sozial- und Wirtschaftsgeschichte - Beihefte (VSWG-B) Ser.). (GER.). 482p. (C). pap. 112.00 *(978-3-515-09120-6(3))* Steiner, Franz Verlag Wiesbaden GmbH DEU. Dist: Brown, David Bk. Co., The.

Porto, Brian. The Supreme Court & the NCAA: The Case for Less Commercialism & More Due Process in College Sports. 2012. (ENG.). 264p. (C). 50.00 ***(978-0-472-11804-5(8))*** Univ. of Michigan Pr.

Porto, Brian L. The Supreme Court & the NCAA: The Case for Less Commercialism & More Due Process in College Sports. 2012. E-Book ***(978-0-472-02809-2(X))*** Univ. of Michigan Pr.

Power, Vincent & McCarthy, Alan W. J. Irish Competition Law: The Competition Act 2002. 2nd rev. ed. 2013. (ENG.). 600p. pap. 200.00 *(978-1-84766-550-8(0),* Bloomsbury Professional) Bloomsbury Publishing Plc GBR. Dist: International Specialized Bk. Services.

Pozdnakova, Alla. Liner Shipping & EU Competition Law. 2008. (Illus.). 165.00 *(978-90-411-2717-4(8))* Wolters Kluwer Law & Business.

Prohibiting Price Fixing & Other Anticonpetitive Conduct in the Health Insurance Industry: Hearing Before the Committee on the Judiciary, United States Senate, One Hundred Eleventh Congress, First Session, October 14, 2009. 2010. (Illus.). iv, 186p. *(978-0-16-086346-2(5),* 552-070-41430-4) United States Government Printing Office.

Railroad Antitrust Enforcement ACT of 2007: Hearing Before the Task Force on Antitrust & Competition Policy of the Committee on the Judiciary, House of Representatives, One Hundred Tenth Congress, Second Session, on H.R. 1650, February 25, 2008. 2009. iii, 165p. *(978-0-16-083106-5(7),* 552-070-38989-0) United States Government Printing Office.

Ramsey, David. Antitrust & the Supreme Court. 2012. (ENG.). 282p. 75.00 ***(978-1-59332-495-7(2))*** LFB Scholarly Publishing LLC.

Rees, Martin, ed. Cartel Enforcement Worldwide. 2010. x, 1082p. 330.00 ***(978-1-907174-07-0(9))*** Gaunt, Inc.

Reiber, Oliver. Wettbewerbsverhalten der deutschen Mineralölindustrie im Kraftstoffeinzelhandel, insbesondere Preisverhalten: Zur Bestimmung von Kollusion und kollektiver Marktbeherrschung im Kartellrecht. 2009. (Wettbewerbsrechtliche Studien: Technologierecht - Kartellrecht - Vergaberecht Ser.). (GER.). 326p. 86.95 *(978-3-631-59379-0(1))* Lang, Peter GmbH, Europaischer Verlag der Wissenschaften DEU. Dist: Lang, Peter.

Robert Pitofsky, et al. 2006 Supplement to Cases & Materials on Trade Regulation. 5th rev. ed. 2006. 141p. pap. 15.00 *(978-1-59941-106-4(7))* West.

Rockefeller, Edwin S. The Antitrust Religion. 2007. (ENG.). 124p. 9.95 *(978-1-933995-09-0(2))* Cato Institute.

Rodriguez. Limits to Antitrust Competition Policy in Developing Countries. 2010. (Illus.). xxii, 199p. 149.00 *(978-90-411-3177-5(9))* Wolters Kluwer Law & Business.

Rogers, C. Paul & Andersen, William R. Antitrust Law: Policy & Practice. 4th ed. 2008. xxxv, 1289p. *(978-1-4224-2570-1(3))* LexisNexis Matthew Bender.

Roggenkamp, Martha M. & Hammer, Ulf, eds. European Energy Law Report IV, Vol. 1. 2007. 319p. pap. 119.00 *(978-90-5095-678-9(5))* Intersentia Uitgevers N.V. BEL. Dist: International Specialized Bk. Services.

Rose, Vivien. Bellamy & Child: European Community Law of Competition: Supplement to the Sixth Edition. Roth, Peter, ed. 2010. (ENG.). 200p. 245.00 *(978-0-19-958667-7(5))* Oxford Univ. Pr., Inc.

Rosæg, Erik. Competition & Regulation in Shipping & Shipping Related Industries. Antapassis & Athanassiou, Lia, eds. 2009. 410p. *(978-90-04-17395-8(1))* BRILL.

Roth, QC, Peter & Rose, Vivien. Bellamy & Child: European Community Law of Competition: 2010 Pack. 2010. 3863p. 1012.50 *(978-0-19-958720-9(5))* Oxford Univ. Pr., Inc.

Round, D. K., ed. The Australian Trade Practices Act 1974: Proscriptions & Prescriptions for a More Competitive Economy. 2010. (Studies in Industrial Organization Ser.). 228p. pap. 169.00 *(978-90-481-4491-4(4),* 9048144914) Springer.

Rousseva, Ekaterina. Rethinking Exclusionary Abuses in EU Competition Law: Rethinking Article 82 of the EU Treaty. 2010. (ENG.). 577p. 150.00 *(978-1-84113-926-5(2))* Hart Publishing Ltd. GBR. Dist: International Specialized Bk. Services.

Rubini, Luca, ed. Microsoft on Trial: Legal & Economic Analysis of a Transatlantic Antitrust Case. 2010. (New Horizons in Competition Law & Economics Ser.). 560p. 224.00 *(978-1-84844-244-3(0))* Elgar, Edward Publishing, Inc.

Rudolph, Daniel. Erhalt von Vielfalt im Pressewesen: Unter besonderer Berücksichtigung des publizistischen Wettbewerbs. 2009. (Studien zum deutschen und europäischen Medienrecht Ser.). (GER.). 484p. pap. 107.95 *(978-3-631-58115-5(7))* Lang, Peter GmbH, Europaischer Verlag der Wissenschaften DEU. Dist: Lang, Peter.

Russo, Francesco, et al. European Commission Decisions on Competition: Economic Perspectives on Landmark Antitrust & Merger Cases. (ENG.). 450p. 2011. pap. 75.00 *(978-0-521-29564-2(5))* 2010. (Illus.). 125.00 *(978-0-521-11719-7(4))* Cambridge Univ. Pr.

Rusu. Mergers Acq Takeovers Challenges Ec Merger Control System. 2010. (Illus.). 304p. *(978-90-411-3259-8(7))* Kluwer Law International.

Ryngaert, Cedric. Jurisdiction over Antitrust Violations in International Law. 2008. 230p. (C). 133.00 *(978-90-5095-743-4(9))* Intersentia Uitgevers N.V. BEL. Dist: International Specialized Bk. Services.

Sagers, Christopher L. Antitrust: Examples & Explanations. 2011. ***(978-1-4548-0000-2(3))*** Kluwer Law International.

Sauter, Wolf & Schepel, Harm. State & Market in European Union Law: The Public & Private Spheres of the Internal Market before the EU Courts. 2009. (Cambridge Studies in European Law & Policy Ser.). (ENG.). 270p. 121.00 *(978-0-521-85775-8(9))* Cambridge Univ. Pr.

—State & Market in European Union Law: The Public & Private Spheres of the Internal Market Before the EU Courts. 2009. (Cambridge Studies in European Law & Policy Ser.). (ENG.). 270p. pap. 48.99 *(978-0-521-67447-8(6))* Cambridge Univ. Pr.

Schlossberg, Robert S. Mergers & Acquisitions: Understanding the Antitrust Issues. 3rd ed. 2008. xvi, 1201p. pap. *(978-1-60442-046-3(4))* American Bar Assn.

Schmidt, H. Competition Law, Innovation & Antitrust: An Analysis of Tying & Technological Integration. 2009. (New Horizons in Competition Law & Economics Ser.). (Illus.). 304p. 137.00 *(978-1-84844-632-8(2))* Elgar, Edward Publishing, Inc.

Schwalbe, Ulrich & Zimmer, Daniel. Law & Economics in European Merger Control. 2009. (ENG., Illus.). 400p. 250.00 *(978-0-19-957181-9(3))* Oxford Univ. Pr., Inc.

Section members from the ABA Section of Antitrust. Joint Ventures: Antitrust Analysis of Collaborations among Competitors. 2006. (ENG.). 130p. per. 89.00 *(978-1-59031-700-6(9))* American Bar Assn.

Semmelmann, Constanze. Social Policy Goals in the Interpretation of Article 81 EC. 2008. 231p. pap. 65.00 *(978-3-8329-3876-5(1))* Nomos Verlagsgesellschaft DEU. Dist: International Specialized Bk. Services.

Shelanski, Howard. Is There Life after Trinko & Credit Suisse: The Role of Antitrust in Regulated Industries: Hearing Before the Subcommittee on Courts & Competition Policy of the Committee on the Judiciary, House of Representatives, One Hundred Eleventh Congress, Second Session, June 15, 2010. 2010. iii, 135p. *(978-0-16-087148-1(4),* 552-070-41991-8) United States Government Printing Office.

Sherman, Roger. Market Regulation. 2007. (ENG.). 960p. (C). pap. 206.67 *(978-0-321-32232-6(0))* Addison Wesley.

Simonsson, Ingeborg. Legitimacy in EU Cartel Control. 2010. (ENG.). 439p. 170.00 *(978-1-84946-005-7(1))* Hart Publishing Ltd. GBR. Dist: International Specialized Bk. Services.

Singleton, Susan. Competition Act 1998 2006. 2007. 100p. spiral bd. 290.00 *(978-1-85418-205-0(6))* Thorogood GBR. Dist: Stylus Publishing, LLC.

—Competition Law Compliance 2008. 2008. (Thorogood Reports). 136p. spiral bd. 245.00 *(978-1-85418-378-1(8))* Thorogood GBR. Dist: Stylus Publishing, LLC.

Smitherman, Charles. Transatlantic Merger Cases: United States - European Community Merger Reveiw Co-operation, 1 vol. 2007. 238.00 *(978-1-905017-45-4(6))* Cameron May, Ltd. GBR. Dist: Gaunt, Inc.

Sokol, D. & Lianos, Ioannis, eds. The Global Limits of Competition Law. 2012. (Studies in International Security & Ar Ser.). (ENG.). 312p. 50.00 ***(978-0-8047-7490-1(0))*** Stanford Univ. Pr.

Spitz, Brad, et al. Civil Procedure Used for Enforcement of EC Competition Law by the English, French & German Civil Courts. 2007. (International Competition Law Series Set Ser.). 304p. *(978-90-411-2471-5(3))* Kluwer Law International.

The State of the Airline Industry: The Potential Impact of Airline Mergers & Industry Consolidation: Hearing Before the Committee on Commerce, Science, & Transportation, United States Senate, One Hundred Tenth Congress, First Session, January 24, 2007. 2010. (Illus.). iv, 113p. ***(978-0-16-086802-3(5),*** 552-070-41718-4) United States Government Printing Office.

Steiner, Mark. Economics in Antitrust Policy: Freedom to Compete vs. Freedom to Contract. 2007. 200p. per. 19.95 *(978-1-58112-370-8(1),* Dissertation.com) Universal Pubs.

Stern, Robert M. Systemic Implications of Transatlantic Regulatory Cooperation & Competition. 2011. 352p. 115.00 *(978-981-283-848-3(1))* World Scientific Publishing Co., Inc.

Stroux. US & EC Oligopoly Control. 2nd rev. ed. 2011. *(978-90-411-2563-7(9))* Kluwer Law International.

Subiotto & Snelders, Robert. Antitrust Developments in EUrope 2006. 2007. xviii, 246p. *(978-90-411-2652-8(X))* Kluwer Law International.

Subiotto, Romano. Antitrust Developments in Europe 2005. 2006. xvi, 217p. *(978-90-411-2568-2(X))* Kluwer Law International.

—Antitrust Developments in Europe 2007. 2008. xviii, 250p. 132.00 *(978-90-411-2778-5(X))* Wolters Kluwer Law & Business.

Sullivan, E. Thomas & Harrison, Jeffrey L. Understanding Antitrust & Its Economic Implications. 5th rev. ed. 2008. (C). pap. 41.00 *(978-1-4224-2261-8(5))* LexisNexis Matthew Bender.

Sullivan, Peter. Antitrust Report. 2nd rev. ed. pap. 583.00 *(978-0-8205-2986-8(9))* LexisNexis Matthew Bender.

Taft, William Howard. Popular Government. 283p. reprint ed. 98.00 *(978-0-7222-7349-4(5))* Library Reprints, Inc.

Tamm, Elo. Beer Supply Agreements in Ec Competition Law. 2008. 76p. pap. *(978-3-639-04775-2(3))* VDM Verlag Dr. Mueller e.K.

Taylor, Martyn D. International Competition Law: A New Dimension for the WTO? 2009. (ENG., Illus.). 520p. pap. 61.00 *(978-0-521-10227-8(8))* Cambridge Univ. Pr.

Terhechte, Jörg Philipp. International Competition Enforcement Law Between Cooperation & Convergence. 2011. (ENG.). xiii, 96p. 119.00 *(978-3-642-17166-6(4)*, 3642171664) Springer.

Too Big to Fail: The Role for Bankruptcy & Antitrust Law in Financial Regulation Reform. 2010. iii, 139p. *(978-0-16-086867-2(X)*, 552-070-41779-6) United States Government Printing Office.

Too Big to Fail? The Role of Antitrust Law in Government-Funded Consolidation in the Banking Industry: Hearing Before the Subcommittee on Courts & Competition Policy of the Committee on the Judiciary, House of Representatives, One Hundred Eleventh Congress, First Session, March 17, 2009. 2009. (Illus.). iii, 87p. *(978-0-16-084890-2(3)*, 552-070-40286-1) United States Government Printing Office.

Townley, Christopher. Article 81 EC & Public Policy. 2009. (ENG.). 363p. 134.00 *(978-1-84113-968-5(8))* Hart Publishing Ltd. GBR. Dist: International Specialized Bk. Services.

Turner, Jonathan D. C. Intellectual Property & EU Competition Law. 2010. (ENG.). 384p. 391.50 *(978-1-904501-45-9(1))* Oxford Univ. Pr., Inc.

Uk & Eu Competition Law. 2010. 130.00 *(978-0-415-35578-7(4)*, Routledge) Taylor & Francis Group GBR. Dist: Taylor & Francis Group.

United Nations. Model Law on Competition: Substantive Possible Elements for a Competition Law, Commentaries & Alternative Approaches in Existing Legislations. 2007. (UNCTAD Ser. on Issues in Competition Law & Policy Ser.). (RUS.). 146p. pap. 25.00 *(978-92-1-411022-4(0))* United Nations Pubns.

The United/Continental Airlines Merger: How Will Consumers Fare?: Hearing Before the Subcommittee on Antitrust, Competition Policy, & Consumer Rights of the Committee on the Judiciary, United States Senate, One Hundred Eleventh Congress, Second Session, May 27, 2010. 2010. (Illus.). iii, 121p. *(978-0-16-086983-9(8)*, 552-070-41842-3) United States Government Printing Office.

U.S. Department of Justice and The federal Trade C. Antitrust enforcement & intellectual property Rights: Promoting Innovation & Competition. 2007. (ENG.). 220p. pap. 20.99 *(978-1-4346-5275-1(0))* BiblioBazaar.

U.S. Department of Justice and The Federal Trade C. Antitrust enforcement & intellectual property Rights: Promoting Innovation & Competition. l.t. ed. 2007. (ENG.). 220p. pap. 22.99 *(978-1-4346-5276-8(9))* BiblioBazaar.

VälsäNen, Tuire Anniina. Enforcement of Frand Commitments under Article 102 Tfeu: The Nature of Frand Defence in Patent Litigation. 2011. 82p. pap. 33.00 *(978-3-8329-5837-4(1))* Nomos Verlagsgesellschaft DEU. Dist: International Specialized Bk. Services.

Van Rooijen, Sascha. The Software Interface Between Copyright & Competition Law. 2010. xii, 291p. *(978-90-411-3193-5(0))* Kluwer Law International.

Vigdor, William R. Premerger Coordination: The Emerging Law of Gun Jumping & Information Exchange. Vigdor, William R., ed. 2006. (ENG.). 400p. per. 124.00 *(978-1-59031-525-5(1))* American Bar Assn.

Vogelaar, F. O. W. The Eu Competition Rules: Landmark Cases of the Eu Courts & the European Commission. 3rd ed. 2010. 452p. pap. 60.00 *(978-90-8952-091-3(0))* Europa Law Publishing, Netherlands NLD. Dist: International Specialized Bk. Services.

Voigt, Stefan & Schmidt, André. Making European Merger Policy More Predictable. 2010. (ENG.). xii, 194p. pap. 109.00 *(978-1-4419-5263-9(2)*, 1441952632) Springer.

Wales, David. Impact of Our Antitrust Laws on Community Pharmacies & Their Patients: Hearing Before the Task Force on Antitrust & Competition Policy of the Committee on the Judiciary, House of Representatives, One Hundred Tenth Congress, First Session, October 18, 2007. 2008. iii, 132p. *(978-0-16-081300-9(X)*, 552-070-37689-5) United States Government Printing Office.

Wareham, Philip, ed. Competition Law & Shipping: The EMLO Guide to EU Competition Law in the Shipping & Port Industries. 2010. xxxiv, 330p. 200.00 *(978-1-907174-02-5(8))* Gaunt, Inc.

Whinston, Michael D. Lectures on Antitrust Economics. 2008. (Cairoli Lectures). (ENG., Illus.). 264p. (gr. 17). per. 19.00 *(978-0-262-73187-4(8))* MIT Pr.

Whish, Richard & Bailey, David. Competition Law. 7th ed. 2012. (ENG.). 1052p. pap. 70.00 *(978-0-19-958655-4(1))* Oxford Univ. Pr., Inc.

White. Worldwide Merger Notification Requirements. 2008. ring bd. 420.00 *(978-0-7355-6480-0(9)*, Aspen Pubs.) Wolters Kluwer Law & Business.

Wijckmans, Frank & Tuytschaever, Filip. Vertical Agreements in EU Competition Law. 2nd ed. 2012. (ENG.). 512p. 310.00 ***(978-0-19-969641-3(1))*** Oxford Univ. Pr., Inc.

Wils, Wouter. Efficiency & Justice in European Antitrust Enforcement. 2008. 206p. (C). 124.00 *(978-1-84113-017-0(6))* Hart Publishing Ltd. GBR. Dist: International Specialized Bk. Services.

Wu, Lawrence, ed. Economics of Antitrust: Complex Issues in a Dynamic Economy. 2007. (Illus.). per. 29.95 *(978-0-9748788-3-6(9))* National Economic Research Assocs., Inc.

Zäch, Roger, et al, eds. The Development of Competition Law: Global Perspectives. 2010. (ASCOLA Competition Law Ser.). (Illus.). 352p. 160.00 *(978-1-84844-446-1(X))* Elgar, Edward Publishing, Inc.

Zekos, Georgios I. Economics & Law on Competition in Globalisation. 2008. 278p. (C). 89.00 *(978-1-60456-876-9(3))* Nova Science Pubs., Inc.

Ziegler. New German Antitrust Law in EC & UK Context. 2011. *(978-90-411-2487-6(X))* Kluwer Law International.

Zimmer, Daniel, ed. The Goals of Competition Law. 2012. (ASCOLA Competition Law Ser.). 520p. 199.95 ***(978-0-85793-660-8(3))*** Elgar, Edward Publishing, Inc.

ANTIVIRAL AGENTS

see also Acyclovir; Interferon

Adu, Daniel Y. Modulation of Hiv Co-Receptor Expression on Cells by Anti-Virals. 2011. 92p. pap. ***(978-3-8443-3424-1(6))*** Lambert Academic Publishing.

Barbaro, Giuseppe. Cardiovascular Disease in Aids. 2nd ed. 2008. (Illus.). 246p. spiral bd. 199.00 *(978-88-470-0760-4(7))* Springer.

Bartlett, John A. A Decade of HAART: The Development & Global Impact of Highly Active Antiretroviral Therapy. 2008. (ENG., Illus.). 464p. 130.00 *(978-0-19-922585-9(0))* Oxford Univ. Pr., Inc.

Biehl, João. Will to Live: AIDS Therapies & the Politics of Survival. 2009. (In-Formation Ser.). (ENG., Illus.). 480p. (C). pap. 39.95 *(978-0-691-14385-9(4))* Princeton Univ. Pr.

Bodasing, Uvani. Adherence to Haart for Management of Kaposi's Sarcom. 2011. 280p. pap. ***(978-3-8433-8727-9(3))*** Lambert Academic Publishing.

Bogner, Elke & Holzenburg, Andreas, eds. New Concepts of Antiviral Therapy. 2010. (ENG.). xiv, 538p. pap. 169.00 *(978-1-4419-4049-0(9)*, 1441940499) Springer.

Committee on Implementation of Antiviral Medication Strategies for an Influenza Pandemic & Institute of Medicine. Antivirals for Pandemic Influenza: Guidance on Developing a Distribution & Dispensing Program. 2008. (ENG.). 132p. pap. 31.75 *(978-0-309-11866-8(2))* National Academies Pr.

Committee on the Methodological Challenges in HIV Prevention Trials. Methodological Challenges in Biomedical HIV Prevention Trials. Lagakos, Stephen W. & Gable, Alicia R., eds. 2008. (ENG.). 270p. pap. 56.50 *(978-0-309-11430-1(6))* National Academies Pr.

De Clercq, E., ed. Advances in Antiviral Drug Design. 2007. (Advances in Antiviral Drug Design Ser.: 5). (ENG., Illus.). 264p. 142.00 *(978-0-444-52173-6(9)*, Elsevier Science) Elsevier Science & Technology Bks.

De Clercq, Erik, ed. Antiviral Drug Strategies. 2011. (Methods & Principles in Medicinal Chemistry Ser.: 127). (ENG., Illus.). 426p. 195.00 *(978-3-527-32696-9(0)*, Wiley-VCH) Wiley, John & Sons, Inc.

Gallant, Joel. Antiretroviral Agents in HIV-1 FLASHcard (2011) 2011. 2p. 6.95 ***(978-0-9846423-6-6(6))*** International Guidelines Ctr., Inc.

Harper, David R. Viruses: Biology/Applications/Control. 2011. (ENG., Illus.). 346p. (C). 95.00 *(978-0-8153-4150-5(4)*, Garland Science) Taylor & Francis Group.

Influenza Pandemic & Steps to Counter It. 2008. 71p. 39.00 *(978-1-60456-842-4(9))* Nova Science Pubs., Inc.

Kazmierski, Wieslaw M. Antiviral Drugs: From Basic Discovery Through Clinical Trials. 2011. (ENG., Illus.). 480p. 149.95 *(978-0-470-45563-0(2)*, Wiley) Wiley, John & Sons, Inc.

Kinchington, Derek & Schinazi, Raymond F., eds. Antiviral Methods & Protocols. 2010. (Methods in Molecular Medicine Ser.). (Illus.). 420p. pap. 149.00 *(978-1-61737-073-1(8)*, 1617370738) Humana Pr.

Kräusslich, Hans-Georg & Bartenschlager, Ralf. Antiviral Strategies. 2008. (Handbook of Experimental Pharmacology Ser.: Vol. 1). (Illus.). 360p. 419.00 *(978-3-540-79085-3(3))* Springer.

Maurice, Hildebert. Compounds with Antimalarial & Anticancer Activities. 2010. 168p. pap. *(978-3-8383-8199-2(8))* Lambert Academic Publishing.

McHutchinson, John, et al, eds. Advanced Therapy for Hepatitis C. 2012. (ENG., Illus.). 232p. 116.95 ***(978-1-4051-8745-9(X)***, Wiley-Blackwell) Wiley, John & Sons, Inc.

Neamati, Nouri, ed. HIV-1 Integrase: Mechanism & Inhibitor Design. 2011. (Wiley Series in Drug Discovery & Development Ser.: 9). (ENG.). 528p. 149.95 *(978-0-470-18474-5(4)*, Wiley) Wiley, John & Sons, Inc.

Perni, Robert B. Antivirals. 2010. (Topics in Medicinal Chemistry Ser.). (ENG.). 400p. 199.00 *(978-3-540-88239-8(1))* Springer.

Rij, Ronald P. van, ed. Antiviral RNAi: Concepts, Methods, & Applications. 2011. (Methods in Molecular Biology Ser.). (ENG., Illus.). xi, 355p. 139.00 *(978-1-61779-036-2(2)*, 1617790362) Humana Pr.

Skowron, Gail & Ogden, Richard, eds. Reverse Transcriptase Inhibitors in HIV/AIDS Therapy. 2010. (Infectious Disease Ser.). (Illus.). 544p. pap. 159.00 *(978-1-61737-695-5(7)*, 1617376957) Humana Pr.

Sloshower, Jordan. Negotiating Pharmaceutical Politics & Ethics. 2010. 64p. pap. *(978-3-8383-8396-5(6))* Lambert Academic Publishing.

Song, Baoan, et al. Environment-Friendly Antiviral Agents for Plants. 2010. (Illus.). 305p. 179.00 *(978-3-642-03691-0(0)*, 3642036910) Springer.

Southern California Evidence-Based Practice Center/RAND Staff, contrib. by. Antiretroviral (ARV) Drug Resistance in the Developing World. 2007. (AHRQ Publication Ser.: No. 156). viii, 74p. *(978-1-58763-267-9(5))* Agency for Healthcare Research & Quality.

Tan, Seng-Lai & He, Yupeng, eds. Hepatitis C: Antiviral Drug Discovery & Development. 2011. (Illus.). 406p. 360.00 *(978-1-904455-78-3(6))* Caister Academic Pr. GBR. Dist: International Specialized Bk. Services.

Tenney, Louise. Grapefruit Seed Extract. 3rd ed. 2011. (Woodland Health Ser.). 36p. pap. 4.95 ***(978-1-58054-202-9(6))*** Woodland Publishing, Inc.

Torrence, Paul F., ed. Combating the Threat of Pandemic Influenza: Drug Discovery Approaches. 2007. (ENG., Illus.). 308p. 153.00 *(978-0-470-11879-5(2)*, Wiley-Interscience) Wiley, John & Sons, Inc.

World Health Organization. Practical Handbook on the Pharmacovigilance of Antiretroviral Medicines. 2010. (Nonserial Publication). 146p. pap. 36.00 *(978-92-4-154794-9(4))* World Health Organization.

ANTIVIRALS

see Antiviral Agents

ANTIVIVISECTION

see Vivisection

ANTIWAR MOVEMENTS

see Peace Movements

ANTLIATA

see Diptera

ANTOINE, ANDRE LEONARD, 1858-1943

Chothia, Jean. André Antoine. (Directors in Perspective Ser.). 230p. pap. 36.99 *(978-0-521-27228-5(9))* Cambridge Univ. Pr.

ANTONIO DA PADOVA, SAINT, 1195-1231

see Anthony, of Padua, Saint, 1195-1231

ANTONIONI, MICHELANGELO, 1912-2007

Chatman, Seymour. Michelangelo Antonioni: The Investigation 1912-2007. Duncan, Paul, ed. 2008. (Basic Film Ser.). (ENG., Illus.). 96p. pap. 9.99 *(978-3-8228-3030-7(5))* TASCHEN DEU. Dist: Ingram Pub. Services.

Garner, Philippe. Antonioni's Blow-Up, 1 vol. 2011. (ENG., Illus.). 144p. 49.00 *(978-3-86930-023-8(X))* Steidl, Gerhard Druckerei und Verlag DEU. Dist: Innovative Logistics.

Pomerance, Murray. Michelangelo Red Antonioni Blue: Eight Reflections on Cinema. 2011. (ENG., Illus.). 304p. 65.00 *(978-0-520-25870-9(3))*; pap. 29.95 *(978-0-520-26686-5(2))* Univ. of California Pr.

Rhodes, John David & Rascaroli, Laura, eds. Antonioni: Centenary Essays. 2011. (ENG., Illus.). 344p. (C). 95.00 *(978-1-84457-385-1(0))* Palgrave Macmillan.

ANTONIUS, MARCUS, 83?-30 B.C.

Bloom, Harold. Antony & Cleopatra - William Shakespeare. 2nd ed. 2011. (Bloom's Modern Critical Interpretations Ser.). 224p. (C). (gr. 9). 45.00 *(978-1-60413-359-2(7)*, Chelsea Hse.) Facts On File, Inc.

Goldsworthy, Adrian. Antony & Cleopatra. (Illus.). 480p. 2011. pap. 20.00 *(978-0-300-17745-9(3))* 2010. 35.00 *(978-0-300-16534-0(X))* Yale Univ. Pr.

Preston, Diana. Cleopatra & Antony: Power, Love, & Politics in the Ancient World. (ENG., Illus.). 352p. 2010. pap. 16.00 *(978-0-8027-1059-8(X))* 2009. 26.00 *(978-0-8027-1738-2(1))* Walker & Co.

Southern, Pat. Antony & Cleopatra: The Doomed Love Affair That United Ancient Rome & Egypt. (Illus.). 2012. 224p. pap. 19.95 ***(978-1-4456-0576-0(7))*** 2009. 208p. pap. 24.95 *(978-1-84868-324-2(3))* Amberley Publishing GBR. Dist: Casemate Pubs. & Bk. Distributors, LLC.

Southern, Patricia. Antony & Cleopatra. 2008. (ENG., Illus.). 288p. 34.95 *(978-0-7524-4383-6(6))* History Pr. Ltd.,The GBR. Dist: Independent Pubs. Group.

Southern, Patricia & Norton, Elizabeth. Mark Antony: A Life. 2010. (ENG., Illus.). 320p. 40.00 *(978-1-84868-330-3(8))* Amberley Publishing GBR. Dist: Casemate Pubs. & Bk. Distributors, LLC.

Wooten, Cecil W. & Wooten III, Cecil W. Cicero's Philippics & Their Demosthenic Model: The Rhetoric of Crisis. 2011. (ENG.). 216p. pap. 40.00 ***(978-0-8078-6642-9(3))*** Univ. of North Carolina Pr.

ANTONIUS, MARCUS, 83?-30 B.C.—DRAMA

Dryden, John. All for Love & the Spanish Fryar. Strunk, William, Jr., ed. 2008. 388p. 48.95 *(978-1-4369-8981-7(7))*; pap. 33.95 *(978-1-4367-6410-0(6))* Kessinger Publishing, LLC.

ANTONIUS, THE GREAT, SAINT, CA. 250-355 OR 6

see Anthony, of Egypt, Saint, ca. 250-355 or 6

ANTONY, OF PADUA, SAINT, 1195-1231

see Anthony, of Padua, Saint, 1195-1231

ANTONY, THE GREAT, SAINT, CA. 250-355 OR 6

see Anthony, of Egypt, Saint, ca. 250-355 or 6

ANTONY, MARK, 83?-30 B.C.

see Antonius, Marcus, 83?-30 B.C.

ANTS

Agosti, Donat, ed. Ants: Standard Methods for Measuring & Monitoring Biodiversity. 2008. (ENG.). 80p. pap. 27.00 *(978-1-4379-5147-9(3))* DIANE Publishing Co.

Bolton, Barry, et al. Bolton's Catalogue of Ants of the World: 1758-2005. 2007. cd-rom 60.50 *(978-0-674-02151-8(7))* Harvard Univ. Pr.

Brian, Michael Vaughan, ed. Production Ecology of Ants & Termites. 2009. (International Biological Programme Synthesis Ser.). (ENG., Illus.). 428p. pap. 58.00 *(978-0-521-10714-3(8))* Cambridge Univ. Pr.

Brown, Simon. Preventing Anaphylaxis to Venom of the Jack Jumper Ant. 2008. 228p. pap. *(978-3-639-04838-4(5))* VDM Verlag Dr. Mueller e.K.

Choe, Jae C. Secret Lives of Ants. 2012. (ENG., Illus.). 184p. (gr. 17). 34.95 ***(978-1-4214-0428-8(1))*** Johns Hopkins Univ. Pr.

Don, Warwick. Ants of New Zealand. 2008. (Illus.). 239p. 59.95 *(978-1-877372-47-6(1))* Otago University Pr. NZL. Dist: International Specialized Bk. Services.

Fisher, Brian L. & Cover, Stefan P. Ants of North America: A Guide to the Genera. 2007. *(978-0-520-25349-0(3))*; (Illus.). 194p. pap. 36.95 *(978-0-520-25422-0(8))* Univ. of California Pr.

Gorb, Elena & Gorb, Stanislav S. N. Seed Dispersal by Ants in a Deciduous Forest Ecosystem: Mechanisms, Strategies, Adaptations. 2010. 242p. pap. 219.00 *(978-90-481-6317-5(X)*, 904816317X) Springer.

Gordon, Deborah. Ant Encounters: Interaction Networks & Colony Behavior. 2010. (Primers in Complex Systems Ser.). (ENG., Illus.). 184p. (C). pap. 22.95 *(978-0-691-13879-4(6))* Princeton Univ. Pr.

Gordon, Deborah. Ants at Work: How an Insect Society Is Organized. 2011. (ENG.). 192p. pap. 13.99 ***(978-1-4516-6570-3(9))***, Free Pr.) Free Pr.

Grissell, Eric. Bees, Wasps, & Ants: The Indispensable Role of Hymenoptera in Gardens. 2010. (ENG., Illus.). 336p. 27.95 *(978-0-88192-988-1(3)*, 0881929883) Timber Pr., Inc.

Hedges, Stoy A. PCT Field Guide for the Management of Structure-Infesting Ants. Moreland, Daniel, ed. 3rd ed. 2010. (Illus.). 300p. pap. 9.95 *(978-1-883751-09-8(8))* GIE Media, Inc.

Hölldobler, Bert & Wilson, E. O. The Leafcutter Ants: Civilization by Instinct. 2010. (ENG., Illus.). 160p. pap. 19.95 *(978-0-393-33868-3(1)*, 33868) Norton, W. W. & Co., Inc.

Keller, Laurent & Gordon, Elisabeth. The Lives of Ants. 2010. (ENG., Illus.). 272p. pap. 15.95 *(978-0-19-954187-4(6))* Oxford Univ. Pr., Inc.

Klotz, John, et al. Urban Ants of North America & Europe: Identification, Biology, & Management. 2008. (Cornell Paperbacks Ser.). (Illus.). 212p. pap. 27.95 *(978-0-8014-7473-6(6)*, Comstock Publishing Assocs.) Cornell Univ. Pr.

Lach, Lori, et al, eds. Ant Ecology. 2010. (ENG., Illus.). 424p. pap. 62.95 *(978-0-19-959261-6(6))* Oxford Univ. Pr., Inc.

Mackay, William & Mackay, Emma. The Systematics & Biology of the New World Ants of the Genus Pachycondyla (Hymenoptera: Formicidae) 2010. (Illus.). xii, 642p. 149.95 *(978-0-7734-1305-4(7))* Mellen, Edwin Pr., The.

Moffett, Mark W. Adventures among Ants: A Global Safari with a Cast of Trillions. (Illus.). 288p. 2011. (ENG.). pap. 24.95 *(978-0-520-27128-9(9))* 2010. 60.00 *(978-0-520-26199-0(2))* Univ. of California Pr.

Rico-Gray, Victor & Oliveira, Paulo S. The Ecology & Evolution of Ant-Plant Interactions. 2007. (Interspecific Interactions Ser.). (Illus.). 320p. 75.00 *(978-0-226-71347-2(4))*; per. 30.00 *(978-0-226-71348-9(2))* Univ. of Chicago Pr.

Science and Life Consultants Association Staff. Fire Ants & Harmful-to-Deadly Bites & Stings with Medical Treatment & Control of Territory with Index & Medical Analysis of New Research Information for All Nations. 2006. (Illus.). 160p. 69.95 *(978-0-7883-4572-2(9)*, 0-7883-43254) ABBE Pubs. Assn. of Washington, D.C.

Sleigh, Charlotte. Six Legs Better: A Cultural History of Myrmecology. 2007. (Animals, History, Culture Ser.). (ENG., Illus.). 320p. (gr. 17). 58.00 *(978-0-8018-8445-0(4))* Johns Hopkins Univ. Pr.

Sun, Emily C. Ant Colonies: Behavior in Insects & Computer Applications. 2011. (Computer Science, Technology & Applications Ser.). (Illus.). x, 274p. 89.00 *(978-1-61122-023-0(8))* Nova Science Pubs., Inc.

Technical Learning College, compiled by. ANt Control CEU Training Course: Ant Control. 2007. (Illus.). 100p. (C). *(978-0-9799928-0-3(X))* Technical Learning College.

Verman, D. I. Overwintering & Cold-Hardiness of Ants in the Northeast of Asia. 2010. 294p. pap. 110.00 *(978-954-642-549-2(4))* Pensoft Pubs. BGR. Dist: Coronet Bks.

Wheeler, William M. Ants: Their Structure, Development & Behavior. (Illus.). reprint ed. lib. bdg. 128.00 *(978-0-7222-3081-7(8))* Library Reprints, Inc.

Wiese, Michael. An Characterisation of Jack Jumper Ant Venom - Definition of the Allergic Components & Pharmaceutical Development of Myrmecia Pilosula. 2008. 192p. pap. *(978-3-639-05169-8(6))* VDM Verlag Dr. Mueller e.K.

Wilson, Edward O. & Durán, José María Gómez. Kingdom of Ants: José Celestino Mutis & the Dawn of Natural History in the New World. 2010. (ENG., Illus.). 120p. 24.95 *(978-0-8018-9785-6(8))* Johns Hopkins Univ. Pr.

ANTWERP (BELGIUM)

Dillen, Jean. Antwerp B-70 1944-45. (DUT., Illus.). 192p. 34.95 *(978-90-72547-19-4(5))* De Krijger BEL. Dist: Casemate Pubs. & Bk. Distributors, LLC.

DK Publishing. DK Eyewitness Travel Guide: Brussels, Bruges, Ghent & Antwerp: Brussels, Bruges, Ghent & Antwerp. 2012. (Eyewitness travel Guide Ser.). (ENG.). 208p. pap. 20.00 ***(978-0-7566-9472-2(8))*** Dorling Kindersley Publishing, Inc.

Dorling Kindersley Publishing Staff. Eyewitness Travel Guides - Brussels Bruges Ghent Antwerp. 2011. (Eyewitness Travel Guides). (ENG., Illus.). 208p. 20.00 *(978-0-7566-6958-4(8))* Dorling Kindersley Publishing, Inc.

Lombaerde. Innovation & Experience in Early Baroque in the Southern Netherlands the Case of the Jesuit Church in Antwerp. 2008. (Architectura Moderna Ser.). (ENG., Illus.). 266p. (C). pap. 138.00 *(978-2-503-52388-0(9))* Brepols Pubs. BEL. Dist: ISD.

Thomson, Clare. Antwerp & Ghent. 2006. (Pocket Guides). (ENG., Illus.). 256p. pap. 12.95 *(978-1-904777-75-5(9))* Footprint Handbooks GBR. Dist: Globe Pequot Pr., The.

Van Mieghem, Eugeen. One Foot in America: The Jewish Emigrants of the Red Star Line, 1 vol. 2010. (ENG.). 160p. pap. 39.50 *(978-90-8586-529-2(8))* Exhibitions International BEL. Dist: Innovative Logistics.

Van Reck, Werner. CityLovers: People of Antwerp. 2010. (ENG., Illus.). 320p. pap. *(978-90-209-8479-8(9),* Lannoo Pubs. (Acc)) Antique Collectors' Club.

Wallpaper Magazine Editors, ed. Wallpaper* City Guide Antwerp. 2008. (ENG., Illus.). 128p. pap. 9.95 *(978-0-7148-4893-8(X))* Phaidon Pr., Inc.

Wissens, Marie-Anne. 365 Days - Antwerp. 2009. (DUT & ENG., Illus.). 744p. 65.00 *(978-90-209-7747-9(4))* Lannoo Pubs./Racine.

ANURA

see also Toads

Hagman, Mattias. Control Methods for Unwanted Anurans. 2011. (Animal Science, Issues & Professions Ser.). pap. 43.00 *(978-1-61209-240-9(3))* Nova Science Pubs., Inc.

Liu, X. Johné, ed. Xenopus Protocols: Cell Biology & Signal Transduction. 2010. (Methods in Molecular Biology Ser.). (Illus.). 512p. pap. 159.00 *(978-1-61737-520-0(9),* 1617375209) Humana Pr.

Seidman, Shlomo & Soreq, Hermona. Transgenic Xenopus: Microinjection Methods & Developmental Neurobiology. 2010. (Neuromethods Ser.). 216p. pap. 119.00 *(978-1-61737-045-8(2),* 1617370452) Humana Pr.

ANUS

Ehrenpreis, Eli D., et al, eds. Anal & Rectal Diseases: A Concise Manual. 2011. (ENG., Illus.). xiii, 277p. pap. 49.95 ***(978-1-4614-1101-7(7),*** 1461411017) Springer.

Gupta, Pravin Jaiprakash. A Practitioner's Guide to Common Ano-Rectal Diseases. 2009. (Practitioner's Guides to Diseases Ser.). 69.00 *(978-1-60876-072-5(3),* Nova Biomedical Bks.) Nova Science Pubs., Inc.

Panarelli, Nicole C. & Yantiss, Rhonda K. Frozen Section Library: Appendix, Colon, & Anus: Appendix, Colon, & Anus. 2010. (Frozen Section Library). (Illus.). ix, 136p. pap. 89.95 *(978-1-4419-6583-7(1),* 1441965831) Springer.

Roger, Jean-Claude & Mortensen, Givel Neil J., eds. Anorectal & Colonic Diseases. 3rd ed. 2008. (Illus.). 750p. 339.00 *(978-3-540-69418-2(8))* Springer.

Schiessel, Rudolf & Metzger, Peter, eds. Intersphincteric Resection for Low Rectal Tumors. 2012. (ENG., Illus.). 200p. 189.00 ***(978-3-7091-0928-1(0),*** 3709109280) Springer.

Sileri, Pierpaolo & Lucio Gaspari, Achille, eds. Anal Fissure: Symptoms, Diagnosis & Treatment. 2011. pap. ***(978-1-61209-716-9(2))*** Nova Science Pubs., Inc.

Steele, Scott R. Anorecatal Disease: Surgical Clinics of North America. 2010. (Clinics: Surgery Ser.: 90-1). (ENG., Illus.). xvi, 217p. 99.00 *(978-1-4377-1875-1(2),* Saunders) Elsevier - Health Sciences Div.

Sultan, Abdul H, et al. Perineal & Anal Sphincter Trauma: Diagnosis & Clinical Management. 2008. (ENG., Illus.). xii, 196p. pap. 49.95 *(978-1-84800-996-7(8),* 1848009968) Springer.

Zbar, Andrew P. & Madoff, Robert D., eds. Reconstructive Colorectal & Anal Surgery. 2011. (Illus.). 256p. 240.00 *(978-1-84882-412-6(2),* 1848824122) Springer.

ANUS (PSYCHOLOGY)

see also Scatology

Morin, Jack. Anal Pleasure & Health: A Guide for Men, Women & Couples. 4th rev. ed. 2010. (ENG.). 256p. pap. 17.95 *(978-0-940208-37-7(7))* Down There Pr.

Stockton, Will. Playing Dirty: Sexuality & Waste in Early Modern Comedy. 2011. (Illus.). 192p. 67.50 *(978-0-8166-7459-6(0));* pap. 22.50 *(978-0-8166-6607-2(5))* Univ. of Minnesota Pr.

ANUS PRETERNATURAL

see Colostomy

ANXIETY

see also Fear; Obsessive-Compulsive Disorder; Peace of Mind; Post-Traumatic Stress Disorder; Separation Anxiety; Shame; Worry

Abramowitz, Jonathan S., et al. Exposure Therapy for Anxiety: Principles & Practice. 2010. (ENG.). 398p. 50.00 *(978-1-60918-016-4(X))* Guilford Pubns., Inc.

Aisbett, Bev. The Book of IT: 10 Steps to Conquering Anxiety. 2008. (Illus.). *(978-0-7322-8700-9(6))* HarperCollins Pubs. Australia.

Alfano, Candice A. & Beidel, Deborah C. Social Anxiety in Adolescents & Young Adults: Translating Developmental Science into Practice. 2011. *(978-1-4338-0949-1(4));* (Illus.). 296p. 69.95 *(978-1-4338-0948-4(6))* American Psychological Assn.

Andrews, Gavin, et al. Stress-Induced & Fear Circuitry Disorders: Refining the Research Agenda for DSM-V. 2009. (Illus.). 352p. pap. 70.00 *(978-0-89042-344-8(X))* American Psychiatric Publishing, Inc.

Antony, Martin M. & Norton, Peter J. The Anti-Anxiety Workbook: Proven Strategies to Overcome Worry, Phobias, Panic, & Obsessions. 2008. (Guilford Self-Help Workbook Ser.). (ENG., Illus.). 262p. pap. 21.95 *(978-1-59385-993-0(7))* Guilford Pubns., Inc.

Antony, Martin M. & Stein, Murray B., eds. Anxiety & Related Disorders. 2008. (Oxford Library of Psychology Ser.). (ENG., Illus.). 800p. (C). instr.'s hndbk. ed. 115.00 *(978-0-19-530703-0(8))* Oxford Univ. Pr., Inc.

Appleton, Peter. Children's Anxiety: A Contextual Approach. 2008. (ENG., Illus.). 200p. (C). 120.00 *(978-0-415-41248-3(X))* Routledge.

—Children's Anxiety: A Contextual Approach. Appleton, Peter A., ed. 2008. (ENG., Illus.). 200p. (C). 47.50 *(978-0-415-45944-0(3))* Routledge.

Arden, John B. Heal Your Anxiety: New Technique for Moving from Panic to Inner Peace. 2009. (ENG.). 176p. wbk. ed. 18.99 *(978-1-59233-351-6(6),* 1592333516, Fair Winds Press) Quayside.

Atcheson, Lucy. Free Yourself from Fear. 2007. 256p. *(978-1-4019-1581-0(7),* 493) Hay Hse. UK, Ltd. GBR. Dist: Grantham Bk. Services.

Auriana, Julie. Silently Suffering with Anxiety, Depression, & Agoraphobi. 2008. 164p. per. 11.95 *(978-1-4327-1836-7(3))* Outskirts Pr., Inc.

Ayres, Benjamin & Bristow, Michelle, eds. Anxiety in College Students. 2009. 89.00 *(978-1-60692-282-8(3))* Nova Science Pubs., Inc.

Baker, Amy. Social Anxiety: Being Comfortable in Your Own Skin. 2011. (ENG.). 24p. 3.99 ***(978-1-936768-37-0(2))*** New Growth Pr.

Ballentine, Clay. Why Am I Anxious? One man's story of how not to handle lifelong Disease. 2010. pap. 18.99 *(978-1-61566-571-6(4))* Tate Publishing & Enterprises, LLC.

Baloglu, Mustafa. The Measurement of Mathematics Anxiety. 2009. 174p. pap. *(978-3-639-18165-4(4))* VDM Verlag Dr. Mueller e.K.

Bar, Julia. Healing My Anxiety. 2011. 114p. pap. 19.50 ***(978-1-4452-0166-5(6))*** Lulu Enterprises Inc.

Barlow, David H. & Craske, Michelle G. Mastery of Your Anxiety & Panic: Workbook. 4th ed. 2006. (Treatments That Work Ser.). (ENG.). 224p. per., wbk. ed. 31.95 *(978-0-19-531135-8(3))* Oxford Univ. Pr., Inc.

Barlow, David H. & Craske, Michelle Genevieve. Mastery of Your Anxiety & Panic: Therapist Guide. 4th rev. ed. 2006. (Treatments That Work Ser.). (ENG., Illus.). 209p. (C). per. 47.95 *(978-0-19-531140-2(X))* Oxford Univ. Pr., Inc.

Barry, Harry. Flagging the Therapy: Pathways Out of Depression & Anxiety. 2011. (ENG., Illus.). 352p. pap. 29.95 ***(978-1-907593-14-7(4))*** Liberties Pr. IRL. Dist: Dufour Editions, Inc.

Bartlett, Robert Allen & Bloch, Douglas. Healing from Depression: 12 Weeks to a Better Mood. 2009. (ENG.). 1p. pap. 19.95 *(978-0-89254-155-3(5))* Nicolas-Hays, Inc.

Bassett, Lucinda. The Solution: Conquer Your Fear, Control Your Future. 2011. (ENG.). 288p. 22.95 *(978-1-4027-7988-6(7))* Sterling Publishing Co., Inc.

Bedford/St. Martin's. Insider's Guide to Beating Test Anxiety. 2010. (ENG.). 16p. (C). pap. 3.95 *(978-0-312-61435-5(7))* Bedford/Saint Martin's.

Beidel, Deborah C. & Alfano, Candice. Child Anxiety Disorders: Research & Treatment. 2nd rev. ed. 2011. (ENG., Illus.). 544p. instr.'s gde. ed. 52.95 *(978-0-415-87373-4(8))* Routledge.

Belen, Lourdes. Purring Cat Inside My Chest, My Journey with Generalized Anxiety Disorder. 2009. 184p. 23.99 *(978-1-60860-464-7(0),* Eloquent Bks.) AEG Literary Publishing Services, Inc.

Bell, Jeff. When in Doubt, Make Belief: An OCD-Inspired Approach to Living with Uncertainty. 2009. (ENG.). 224p. pap. 14.95 *(978-1-57731-670-1(3))* New World Library.

Bell, Taunjah P. Vagus Nerve Stimulation & Anxiety. 2010. 108p. 22.95 *(978-1-4502-4286-8(3));* pap. 12.95 *(978-1-4502-4285-1(5))* iUniverse, Inc.

Benor, Daniel J. Seven Minutes to Natural Pain Release. 2009. 251p. pap. 17.95 *(978-0-9819729-0-9(X))* Wholistic Healing Pubns.

Berent, Jonathan & Lemley, Amy. Work Makes Me Nervous: Overcome Anxiety & Build the Confidence to Succeed. 2010. (ENG., Illus.). 272p. 24.95 *(978-0-470-58805-5(5),* Wiley) Wiley, John & Sons, Inc.

Berg, Yehuda. El Monstruo Es Real! Cómo Enfrentarte a Tus Miedos y Eliminarlos para Siempre. 2007. (Technology for the Soul Ser.). (SPA.). 140p. 9.95 *(978-1-57189-561-5(2))* Research Centre of Kabbalah.

Bingaman, Kirk. Treating the New Anxiety: A Cognitive-Theological Approach. 2007. (ENG.). 160p. 78.99 *(978-0-7657-0462-7(5),* Aronson, Jason) Rowman & Littlefield Publishers, Inc.

Bingaman, Kirk A. Treating the New Anxiety: A Cognitive-Theological Approach. 2007. (ENG.). 160p. per. 32.50 *(978-0-7657-0463-4(3),* Aronson, Jason) Rowman & Littlefield Publishers, Inc.

Blair, Linda. Straight Talking: Learn How to Overcome Insomnia, Anxiety, Negative Thinking & Other Modern Day Stresses. 2011. (ENG.). 208p. pap. 13.95 *(978-0-7499-2955-8(3))* Piatkus Bks. GBR. Dist: Independent Pubs. Group.

Blake, Chris & Ledger, Christine. Insight into Anxiety. 2007. 112p. *(978-1-85345-436-3(2))* Crusade for World Revival.

Blanchard, Robert J. Handbook of Anxiety & Fear. Blanchard, Robert J. et al, eds. 2008. (Handbook of Behavioral Neuroscience Ser.: 17). (ENG., Illus.). 450p. 145.00 *(978-0-444-53065-3(7),* Elsevier Science) Elsevier Science & Technology Bks.

Borchard, Therese J. Beyond Blue: Surviving Depression & Anxiety & Making the Most of Bad Genes. 2010. (ENG.). 288p. 21.99 *(978-1-59995-156-0(8))* Center St.

Brantley, Jeffrey. Calming Your Anxious Mind: How Mindfulness & Compassion Can Free You from Anxiety, Fear, & Panic. 2nd rev. ed. 2007. (ENG.). 248p. pap. 16.95 *(978-1-57224-487-0(9))* New Harbinger Pubns.

Brittain, Angela K. The Don't Forget to Look up Workbook: Uncovering the Root of Anxiety, Panic & Fear. 2008. 64p. pap. 8.95 *(978-0-9662003-1-7(4))* Brittain Communications.

Buchwald, Petra, et al, eds. Stress & Anxiety: Application to Education & Health: Application to Education & Health. 2011. 142p. pap. ***(978-3-8325-2886-7(5))*** Logos Verlag Berlin.

Buchwald, Petra, et al. Stress & Anxiety: Application to Life Span Development & Health Promotion. 2008. (Illus.). 171p. pap. *(978-3-8325-1690-1(5))* Logos Verlag Berlin.

Burijon, Barry N. Biological Bases of Clinical Anxiety. 2007. (ENG.). 368p. 47.50 *(978-0-393-70469-3(6),* 70469) Norton, W. W. & Co., Inc.

Butler, Gillian, et al. Cognitive-Behavioral Therapy for Anxiety Disorders: Mastering Clinical Challenges. 2008. (Guides to Individualized Evidence-Based Treatment Ser.). (ENG., Illus.). 224p. 55.00 *(978-1-59385-830-8(2))* Guilford Pubns., Inc.

Cairns, Warwick. How to Live Dangerously: The Hazards of Helmets, the Benefits of Bacteria, & the Risks of Living Too Safe. 2009. (ENG., Illus.). 176p. pap. 14.99 *(978-0-312-53389-2(6),* St. Martin's Griffin) St. Martin's Pr.

Carney, Colleen E. & Edinger, Jack D. Insomnia & Anxiety. 2010. (Series in Anxiety & Related Disorders Ser.). (ENG., Illus.). xi, 300p. 149.00 *(978-1-4419-1433-0(1),* 1441914331) Springer.

Carter, Nicolas. The Bridge to Your Future. 2011. 74p. pap. 19.90 ***(978-3-8423-6529-2(2))*** Bks. on Demand.

Cartwright-Hatton, Sam. Coping with an Anxious or Depressed Child: A Guide for Parents & Carers. 2007. (Coping With (Oneworld) Ser.). (ENG.). 208p. per. 14.95 *(978-1-85168-482-3(4))* Oneworld Pubns. GBR. Dist: National Bk. Network.

Cartwright-Hatton, Samantha. From Timid to Tiger: A Treatment Manual for Parenting the Anxious Child. 2010. (ENG., Illus.). 186p. pap. 41.95 *(978-0-470-68310-1(4),* Wiley) Wiley, John & Sons, Inc.

Chandra, Anita, et al. Views from the Homefront: The Experiences of Youth & Spouses from Military Families. 2011. 122p. pap. 28.00 *(978-0-8330-5127-1(X),* tr-913) RAND Corp., The.

Chansky, Tamar E. Freeing Yourself from Anxiety: The 4-Step Plan to Overcome Worry & Create the Life You Want. 2012. (ENG., Illus.). 336p. pap. 16.00 *(978-0-7382-1483-2(3))* Da Capo Pr., Inc.

Chapman, Alexander, et al. The Dialectical Behavior Therapy Skills Workbook for Anxiety: Breaking Free from Worry, Panic, PTSD, & Other Anxiety Symptoms. 2011. (ENG., Illus.). 240p. pap. 24.95 *(978-1-57224-954-7(4))* New Harbinger Pubns.

Chapman, Christopher C. Freud, Religion, & Anxiety. 2007. 113p. pap. 14.00 *(978-1-4357-0571-5(8))* Lulu Enterprises Inc.

Chesner, Jonathan. ADHD in HD: Brains Gone Wild. 2012. (ENG.). 160p. (YA). pap. 14.99 ***(978-1-57542-386-9(3))*** Free Spirit Publishing, Inc.

Chorpita, Bruce F. Modular Cognitive-Behavioral Therapy for Childhood Anxiety Disorders. 2006. (Guides to Individualized Evidence-Based Treatment Ser.). (ENG., Illus.). 335p. (gr. 1-13). pap. 45.00 *(978-1-59385-363-1(7))* Guilford Pubns., Inc.

Chrestman, Kelly R., et al. Prolonged Exposure Theraphy for PTSD. 2008. (Treatments That Work Ser.). (ENG.). 144p. pap., wbk. ed. 23.00 *(978-0-19-533173-8(7))* Oxford Univ. Pr., Inc.

Cihak, John, Balthasar & Anxiety. 2011. (ENG.). 304p. pap. 49.95 ***(978-0-567-00047-7(8),*** T&T Clark Int'l) Continuum International Publishing Group, Ltd. GBR. Dist: National Bk. Network.

Cihak, John & Cihak. Balthasar & Anxiety. 2009. (ENG.). 304p. 140.00 *(978-0-567-03407-6(0),* T&T Clark Int'l) Continuum International Publishing Group, Ltd. GBR. Dist: National Bk. Network.

Clark, David A. & Beck, Aaron T. The Anxiety & Worry Workbook: The Cognitive Behavioral Solution. 2011. (ENG., Illus.). 294p. pap. 21.95 *(978-1-60623-918-6(X))* Guilford Pubns., Inc.

Clark, David A. & Beck, Aaron T. Cognitive Therapy of Anxiety Disorders: Science & Practice. (ENG., Illus.). 628p. 2011. pap. 35.00 ***(978-1-60918-992-1(2))*** 2009. 70.00 *(978-1-60623-434-1(X))* Guilford Pubns., Inc.

Clark, Taylor. Nerve: Poise under Pressure, Serenity under Stress, & the Brave New Science of Fear & Cool. 2011. (ENG.). 320p. 25.99 *(978-0-316-04289-5(7))* Little Brown & Co.

Coetzer, Rudi. Anxiety & Mood Disorders Following Traumatic Brain Injury: Clinical Assessment & Psychotherapy. 2010. 180p. pap. 30.95 *(978-1-85575-647-2(1))* Karnac Bks. GBR. Dist: Stylus Publishing, LLC.

Colbert, Don. Depression & Anxiety. 2009. (ENG.). 128p. pap. 8.99 *(978-1-59979-760-1(7),* Siloam Pr.) Charisma Media.

Cole, Allan Hugh, Jr. Be Not Anxious: Pastoral Care of Disquieted Souls. 2008. 224p. pap. 20.00 *(978-0-8028-6310-2(8))* Eerdmans, William B. Publishing Co.

Conrad, Cheryl D., ed. Handbook of Stress: Neuropsychological Effects on the Brain. 2011. (Blackwell Handbooks of Behavioral Neuroscience Ser.: 3). (ENG., Illus.). 720p. 199.95 *(978-1-4443-3023-6(3),* Wiley-Blackwell) Wiley, John & Sons, Inc.

Conrod, Patricia. Anxiety & Substance Use Disorders: The Vicious Cycle of Comorbidity. Stewart, Sherry H., ed. 2007. (Series in Anxiety & Related Disorders Ser.). 300p. 89.95 *(978-0-387-74289-2(1),* 0387742891) Springer.

Copper, Derrick & Maslo, Laurel. Stress Reduction & Anxiety Coping Style. 2008. 120p. pap. *(978-3-639-05223-7(4))* VDM Verlag Dr. Mueller e.K.

Cram101 Textbook Reviews & Cram101 Textbook Reviews. Outlines & Highlights for Normal & Abnormal Fear & Anxiety in Children & Adolescents by Peter Muris, Isbn: 9780080450735 0080450733. 2011. 74p. pap. 27.95 ***(978-1-61654-043-2(5))*** Cram101 Inc.

Craske, Michelle G. & Barlow, David H. Mastery of Your Anxiety & Panic: Workbook for Primary Care Settings. 4th rev. ed. 2007. (Treatments That Work Ser.). (ENG.). 136p. pap. 27.95 *(978-0-19-531134-1(5))* Oxford Univ. Pr., Inc.

Crompton, Peg. Journey to Peace: A 12 Step Program for Anxiety, Panic, & Life. 2008. 108p. pap. 13.95 *(978-1-4389-2365-9(1))* AuthorHouse.

Crozier, Ray. Coping with Shyness & Social Phobias: A Step-by-Step Guide Using CBT. 2009. (ENG.). 192p. pap. 14.95 *(978-1-85168-516-5(2))* Oneworld Pubns. GBR. Dist: National Bk. Network.

Curtis, Guy & Locke, Vance. Anxiety, Stereotyping, & Impression Formation. 2010. 180p. pap. *(978-3-639-27344-1(3))* VDM Verlag Dr. Mueller e.K.

Daitch, Carolyn. Affect Regulation Toolbox: Practical & Effective Hypnotic Interventions for the Over-Reactive Client. 2007. (ENG.). 320p. 32.00 *(978-0-393-70495-2(5),* 70495) Norton, W. W. & Co., Inc.

Davis, Edmund, compiled by. Anxiety Management Techniques. 2009. 158p. pap. 19.95 *(978-0-9822136-1-2(1))* Rapid Publishing LLC.

Denkmire, Heather, et al. Anxiety & Depression. 2nd rev. ed. 2010. (Truth about Ser.). (Illus.). 208p. (C). (gr. 9). 35.00 *(978-0-8160-7643-7(X))* Facts On File, Inc.

Dobson, Keith S. & Dozois, David J. A., eds. Risk Factors in Depression. 2008. (ENG.). 510p. 109.00 *(978-0-08-045078-0(4),* Academic Pr.) Elsevier Science & Technology Bks.

Doctor, Ronald M., et al. The A-Z of Phobias, Fears, & Anxieties. 2008. (Library of Health & Living). 592p. (C). (gr. 9). per. 19.95 *(978-0-8160-7558-4(1),* Checkmark Bks.) Facts On File, Inc.

—The Encyclopedia of Phobias, Fears, & Anxieties. 3rd rev. ed. 2008. (Library of Health & Living). (Illus.). 592p. (C). (gr. 9). 75.00 *(978-0-8160-6453-3(9))* Facts On File, Inc.

Dryden, Windy. Letting Go of Anxiety & Depression. 112p. *(978-0-85969-893-1(9),* Sheldon Press) SPCK Publishing.

—Overcoming Anxiety. xii, 132p. *(978-0-85969-816-0(5),* Sheldon Press) SPCK Publishing.

Dubin, Nick. Asperger Syndrome & Anxiety: A Guide to Successful Stress Management. 2009. (ENG.). 224p. pap. *(978-1-84310-895-5(X))* Kingsley, Jessica Ltd.

Dynes, Robin. Anxiety Management: In 10 Groupwork Sessions. 256p. spiral bd. *(978-0-86388-222-7(6),* 002-4178) Speechmark Publishing Ltd.

Eckersely, Jill. Helping Children Cope with Anxiety. 2007. 128p. pap. 13.95 *(978-0-85969-951-8(X),* Sheldon Press) SPCK Publishing GBR. Dist: Westminster John Knox Pr.

Elkholy, Sharin N. Heidegger & a Metaphysics of Feeling: Angst & the Finitude of Being. (ENG.). 2011. 162p. pap. 34.95 ***(978-1-4411-0152-5(7))*** 2008. 176p. 130.00 *(978-0-8264-9875-5(2))* Continuum International Publishing Group, Ltd. GBR. Dist: National Bk. Network.

Elliott, Charles H. & Smith, Laura L. Overcoming Anxiety for Dummies. 2nd ed. 2010. (ENG., Illus.). 360p. pap. 21.99 *(978-0-470-57441-6(0),* For Dummies) Wiley, John & Sons, Inc.

Elwins, Dannie. How to Get Rid of Stress & Live A Worrisome Lifestyle at All Times. 2010. 40p. pap. 16.99 *(978-0-557-25939-7(8))* Lulu Enterprises Inc.

Emanuel, Ricky. Anxiety: Ideas in Psychoanalysis. 2006. 80p. reprint ed. pap. 8.00 *(978-1-4223-5787-3(2))* DIANE Publishing Co.

Emily A. Smith. Anxiety Sucks! 2009. 100p. pap. 14.95 *(978-1-4389-8042-3(6))* AuthorHouse.

Emmons, Henry. The Chemistry of Calm: A Powerful, Drug-Free Plan to Quiet Your Fears & Overcome Your Anxiety. 2010. (ENG.). 288p. pap. 15.00 *(978-1-4391-2906-7(1),* Touchstone) Touchstone.

Ferri, Laura. Te deseo lo mejor/ I wish you the Best. 2008. 48p. 9.95 *(978-987-9201-39-8(6))* Vergara & Riba ARG. Dist: Baker & Taylor Bks.

Field, Andy P. & Hadwin, Julie A., eds. Information Processing Biases & Anxiety: A Developmental Perspective. 2010. (ENG., Illus.). 342p. 110.95 *(978-0-470-99819-9(9),* Wiley) Wiley, John & Sons, Inc.

Fisher, Peter & Wells, Adrian. Metacognitive Therapy: Distinctive Features. 2009. (CBT Distinctive Features Ser.). (ENG., Illus.). 152p. (C). pap. 17.95 *(978-0-415-43499-7(8))* Routledge.

Fletcher, Emma & Langley, Martha. Free Yourself from Anxiety. 2009. 176p. pap. 20.00 *(978-1-84528-311-7(2))* How To Books GBR. Dist: Parkwest Pubns., Inc.

Forbes, Bo. Yoga for Emotional Balance: Simple Practices to Help Relieve Anxiety & Depression. 2011. (ENG., Illus.). 256p. pap. 19.95 *(978-1-59030-760-1(7))* Shambhala Pubns., Inc.

Forsyth, John P., et al. The Mindfulness & Acceptance Workbook for Anxiety: A Guide to Breaking Free from Anxiety, Phobias, & Worry Using Acceptance & Commitment Therapy. 2008. (Workbook Ser.). (ENG., Illus.). 288p. pap. 24.95 *(978-1-57224-499-3(2))* New Harbinger Pubns.

Foxman, Paul. Dancing with Fear: Controlling Stress & Creating a Life Beyond Panic & Anxiety. 2nd ed. 2006. (ENG., Illus.). 320p. per. 17.95 *(978-0-89793-476-3(8))* Hunter Hse., Inc.

Frances, Dee. Healing Fear & Anxiety. Date not set. 20p. pap. 6.00 *(978-1-885519-52-8(4))* DDDD Pubns.

Freedman, Norbert, et al. Another Kind of Evidence: Studies in Internalization, Annihilation Anxiety & Progressive Symbolization in the Psychoanalytic Process. 2011. (CIPS Series on the Boundaries of Psychoanalysis Ser.). 380p. pap. 49.95 *(978-1-85575-852-0(0))* Karnac Bks. GBR. Dist: Stylus Publishing, LLC.

Freeman, Daniel & Freeman, Jason. Anxiety: A Very Short Introduction. 2012. (Very Short Introductions Ser.). (ENG., Illus.). 152p. pap. 11.95 ***(978-0-19-956715-7(8))*** Oxford Univ. Pr., Inc.

Freeston, Mark & Meares, Kevin. Overcoming Worry: A Self-Help Guide Using Cognitive Behavioral Techniques. 2008. (Overcoming Ser.). (ENG., Illus.). 288p. pap. 14.95 *(978-0-465-00538-3(1))* Basic Bks.

Freud, Sigmund. The Problem of Anxiety. Bunker, Henry Alden, tr. 2011. 126p. 40.95 ***(978-1-258-00675-4(8))*** Literary Licensing, LLC.

Fricchione, Gregory L. Compassion & Healing in Medicine & Society: On the Nature & Use of Attachment Solutions to Separation Challenges. 2011. (ENG., Illus.). 552p. (gr. 17). 65.00 *(978-1-4214-0220-8(3))* Johns Hopkins Univ. Pr.

Furer, Patricia, et al. Treating Health Anxiety & Fear of Death: A Practitioner's Guide. (Series in Anxiety & Related Disorders Ser.). (Illus.). 2010. xvi, 272p.

pap. 69.95 (978-1-4419-2248-9(2), 1441922482) 2006. 268p. 69.95 (978-0-387-35144-5(2), 0387351442) Springer.

Gallo, Fred P. & Vincenzi, Harry. Energy Tapping: How to Rapidly Eliminate Anxiety, Depression, Cravings, & More Using Energy Psychology. 2nd rev. ed. 2008. (ENG., Illus.). 320p. pap. 21.95 (978-1-57224-555-6(7)) New Harbinger Pubns.

Gao, Zhiwen. How Tertiary Students Use Music to Manage Stress. 2010. 196p. pap. (978-3-8383-8991-2(3)) Lambert Academic Publishing.

Garnham, L. The Sun Has Got His Hat On: A Self Help Guide to Anxiety. 2008. 128p. pap. (978-1-84747-657-9(0)) Chipmunkapublishing.

Garrett, Jazz. Devotions for Those with Anxiety Disorders: Including Post Traumatic Stress Disorder (PTSD) 2010. 120p. 22.95 (978-1-4502-0575-7(5)) iUniverse, Inc.

Gazelle, Heidi & Rubin, Kenneth H., eds. Social Anxiety in Childhood: Bridging Developmental & Clinical Perspectives. 2010. (J-B CAD Single Issue Child & Adolescent Development Ser.: 98). (ENG.). 120p. pap. 29.00 (978-0-470-61805-9(1), Jossey-Bass) Wiley, John & Sons, Inc.

Gerald, Kevin. Mind Monsters: Conquering Fear, Worry, Guilt & Other Negative Thoughts That Work Against You. 2012. (ENG.). 128p. pap. 9.99 **(978-1-61638-738-9(6)**, Charisma Hse.) Charisma Media.

Ghinassi, Cheryl Winning. Anxiety, 1 vol. 2010. (Biographies of Disease Ser.). (Illus.). 156p. 45.00 (978-0-313-36242-2(4), GR6242) Greenwood Publishing Group, Inc.

Glassner, Barry. Culture of Fear: Why Americans Are Afraid of the Wrong Things - Crime, Drugs, Minorities, Teen Moms, Killer Kids, Mutant Microbes, Plane Crashes, Road Rage, & So Much More. rev. ed. 2010. (ENG.). 360p. (gr. 9). pap. 16.95 (978-0-465-00336-5(2)) Basic Bks.

Goewey, Don Joseph. Mystic Cool: A Proven Approach to Transcend Stress, Achieve Optimal Brain Function, & Maximize Your Creative Intelligence. 2009. (ENG.). 240p. 23.00 (978-1-58270-227-8(6), Beyond Words/Atria Bks.) Atria Bks.

Goldstein, Niles Elliot. Craving the Divine: A Spiritual Guide for Today's Perplexed. 2007. 199p. per. 18.00 (978-1-58768-043-4(2), 043-4, HiddenSpring) Paulist Pr.

Gould, Todd D., ed. Mood & Anxiety Related Phenotypes in Mice: Characterization Using Behavioral Tests, Volume II, 2 vols. 2011. (Neuromethods Ser.). (ENG., Illus.). xiii, 382p. 139.00 **(978-1-61779-312-7(4)**, 1617793124) Humana Pr.

Grand, David & Goldberg, Alan. This Is Your Brain on Sports: Beating Blocks, Slumps & Performance Anxiety for Good! 2011. 226p. pap. 24.95 **(978-1-60844-864-7(9))** Dog Ear Publishing, LLC.

Green, Sherri. A Family Affear. 2011. 84p. pap. **(978-3-8443-0108-3(9))** Lambert Academic Publishing.

Green, Wendy. 50 Things You Can Do Today to Manage Anxiety. 2011. (Personal Health Guides). (ENG.). 128p. pap. 9.95 **(978-1-84953-039-2(4))** Summersdale Pubs. GBR. Dist: Independent Pubs. Group.

Grey, Harrison. Living in the Golden Circle: Where Anxiety & Greed No Longer Bind You. 2008. 284p. pap. 20.95 (978-0-595-50578-4(3)) iUniverse, Inc.

Gron, Arne. The Concept of Anxiety in Soren Kierkegaard. Knox, Jeanette / B. L., tr. from DAN. 2008. 160p. 30.00 (978-0-88146-126-5(1)) Mercer Univ. Pr.

Gross, Esther. You Are Not Alone: A Three-Dimensional Torah Approach to Overcoming Anxiety. 200p. 21.99 (978-1-58330-533-1(5)) Feldheim Pubs.

Hall, Kirsty. The Stuff of Dreams: Fantasy, Anxiety, & Psychoanalysis. 2007. 188p. per. 38.95 (978-1-85575-496-6(7)) Karnac Bks. GBR. Dist: Stylus Publishing, LLC.

Hall, Sharon-Marie. No Worries Managing anxiety with the daily program Method. 2009. pap. 30.00 (978-1-61623-860-5(7)) Independent Pub.

Hammond, Phil. This Has All Been Said Before. 2011. 208p. 24.95 (978-1-4567-1967-8(X)); pap. 14.95 (978-1-4567-1966-1(1)) AuthorHouse.

Hansen, Mark Victor, et al. Stress. 2006. (Chicken Soup for the Soul Healthy Living Ser.). (ENG.). 142p. mass mkt. 4.99 (978-0-7573-0411-8(7)) Health Communications, Inc.

Hargate, Ian. Three Days to Freedom; How to Beat Depression & Anxiety Without Drugs or Therapies. 2009. 56p. pap. 12.95 (978-1-60693-697-9(2), Strategic Bk. Publishing) AEG Literary Publishing Services, Inc.

Hartley, Dustin. The Sky Is Falling. 2009. 162p. 26.96 (978-0-578-00337-5(6)) Hartley Bks.

Hathaway, Richard. Conquering Panic Attacks & Anxiety. 2010. (Illus.). 284p. pap. (978-1-907211-93-5(4), Grosvenor Hse. Publishing Ltd.

Hawkins, David B. When Your Anxiety Makes You Nervous. Date not set. (Illus.). pap. (978-1-930195-09-7(5)) Your Pocket Therapist.

Hazlett-Stevens, Holly. Psychological Approaches to Generalized Anxiety Disorder: A Clinician's Guide to Assessment & Treatment. 2008. (Series in Anxiety & Related Disorders Ser.). xiv, 190p. 69.95 (978-0-387-76869-4(6)) Springer.

Heitler, Susan M. Anxiety: Friend or Foe. pap. (978-1-884998-03-4(8)) Listen-to-Learn Audiotapes.

Hibbs, Stanley. Anxiety Gone: The Three C's of Anxiety Recovery. 2007. 132p. pap. 14.95 (978-0-9779589-3-0(6)) Dare2Dream Books.

HIER, Sean, ed. Moral Panic & the Politics of Anxiety. 2011. (ENG., Illus.). 264p. (C). 154.00 (978-0-415-55555-5(8)); pap. 58.95 (978-0-415-55556-2(6)) Routledge.

Hofmann, Stefan & Otto, Michael. Cognitive-Behavior Therapy of Social Phobia: Evidence-Based & Disorder-Specific Treatment Techniques. 2008. (Practical Clinical Guidebooks). (ENG., Illus.). 216p. 90.95 (978-0-415-95402-0(9)) Routledge.

Hofmann, Stefan G. Psychobiological Approaches for Anxiety Disorders: Treatment Combination Strategies. 2012. (Wiley Series in Clinical Psychology Ser.). (ENG.). 216p. pap. 49.95 **(978-0-470-97180-2(0)**, Wiley-Blackwell) Wiley, John & Sons, Inc.

Hofmann, Stefan G., ed. Psychobiological Approaches for Anxiety Disorders: Treatment Combination Strategies. 2012. (Wiley Series in Clinical Psychology Ser.). (ENG.). 216p. 99.95 **(978-0-470-97181-9(9)**, Wiley-Blackwell) Wiley, John & Sons, Inc.

Holmes, Paul. A Man Derailed: An Autobiography on Depression. 2009. 174p. pap. (978-1-84747-953-2(7)) Chipmunkapublishing.

Holsboer, Florian & Ströhle, Andreas. Anxiety & Anxiolytic Drugs. 2010. (Handbook of Experimental Pharmacology Ser.). xiv, 566p. pap. 499.00 (978-3-642-06143-1(5), 3642061435) Springer.

Hood, Vanassa. Overcoming Grief/Lonliness/Fear/Worry. 2007. per. (978-1-59581-352-7(7), Brentwood Christian Pr.) Brentwood Communications Group.

Hope, Debra A., et al. Managing Social Anxiety: A Cognitive-Behavioral Therapy Approach, 1 vol. 2nd ed. 2010. (Treatments That Work Ser.). (ENG., Illus.). 256p. wbk. ed. 27.95 (978-0-19-533669-6(0)) Oxford Univ. Pr., Inc.

—Managing Social Anxiety: A Cognitive-behavioral Therapy Approach, Therapist Guide, 1 vol. 2nd ed. 2010. (Treatments That Work Ser.). (ENG., Illus.). 240p. 39.95 (978-0-19-533668-9(2)) Oxford Univ. Pr., Inc.

Horwitz, Allan V. & Wakefield, Jerome C. All We Have to Fear: Psychiatry's Transformation of Natural Anxieties into Mental Disorders. 2012. (ENG.). 320p. 29.95 **(978-0-19-979375-4(1))** Oxford Univ. Pr., Inc.

Howell, Davina. Social Anxiety. 2010. 104p. pap. (978-3-639-22760-4(3)) VDM Verlag Dr. Mueller e.K.

Huang, Jinyan, ed. Overcoming Anxiety in Foreign Language Classrooms. 2012. (Series: Psychology Research Progress Ser.). 188p. 75.00 (978-1-61324-775-4(3)) Nova Science Pubs., Inc.

Hummel, Rand. Fear Not! Meditations to Overcome Fear, Worry, & Discouragement. 2008. (978-1-59166-870-1(0)) BJU Pr.

Hunter, R. Lanny & Hunter, Victor L. Living Free in an Anxious World: What Your Doctor & Pastor Want You to Know about Worry. 2010. 160p. pap. 15.99 (978-0-89112-680-5(5), Leafwood Pubs.) Abilene Christian Univ. Pr.

Institute of Psycho-Analysis Staff, contrib. by. Psychoanalytic Study of the Child. viii, 544p. (978-0-7012-0401-3(X), Hogarth Pr.) Random Hse.

Jablonski, Jennifer. Construct-Worded vs. ed-Item Formats. 2008. 100p. pap. (978-3-639-07776-6(8)) VDM Verlag Dr. Mueller e.K.

Jazz Garrett. Devotions for Those with Anxiety Disorders: Including Post Traumatic Stress Disorder (PTSD) 2010. 120p. pap. 12.95 (978-1-4502-0573-3(9)) iUniverse, Inc.

Johnson, Laurie Ruth. Aesthetic Anxiety: Uncanny Symptoms in German Literature & Culture. 2010. (Illus.). 267p. pap. 69.00 (978-90-420-3113-5(1)) Rodopi.

Johnston, Joni E. & Johnston, Joni E., PsyD. The Complete Idiot's Guide to Controlling Anxiety. 2006. (Complete Idiot's Guide Ser.). (ENG., Illus.). 336p. (gr. 12-18). 16.95 (978-1-59257-525-1(0), Alpha Bks.) Penguin Group (USA) Inc.

Jones, Barry. The Instruction Manual for the Mind. 2010. 226p. pap. (978-1-84549-423-0(7)) arima publishing.

Jones, Darryl, et al, eds. It Came from The 1950s! Popular Culture, Popular Anxieties. 2011. (ENG., Illus.). 284p. 85.00 (978-0-230-27221-7(5)) Palgrave Macmillan.

Jongsma, Arthur E. Treatment Planning for Social Anxiety Disorder, Set. 2010. (Evidence-Based Psychotherapy Treatment Planning Video Ser.: 28). (ENG.). mass mkt., wbk. ed. 55.25 (978-0-470-62160-8(5), Wiley) Wiley, John & Sons, Inc.

Jongsma, Arthur E. & Bruce, Timothy J. Evidence-Based Treatment Planning for General Anxiety Disorder. 2012. (Evidence-Based Psychotherapy Treatment Planning Video Ser.: 47). (ENG.). 80p. pap., wbk. ed. 25.00 **(978-0-470-56849-1(6)**, Wiley) Wiley, John & Sons, Inc.

—Evidence-Based Treatment Planning for Generalized Anxiety Disorder. 2012. (Evidence-Based Psychotherapy Treatment Planning Video Ser.: 46). (ENG.). 80p. pap. 29.00 **(978-0-470-56848-4(8)**, Wiley) Wiley, John & Sons, Inc.

Jongsma, Arthur E. & Bruce, Timothy J. Treatment Planning for Social Anxiety Disorder, Set. 2010. (Evidence-Based Psychotherapy Treatment Planning Video Ser.: 24). (ENG.). mass mkt., wbk. ed. 79.90 (978-0-470-62156-1(7), Wiley) Wiley, John & Sons, Inc.

Kaechele, Horst, et al. From Psychoanalytic Narrative to Empirical Single Case Research: Implications for Psychoanalytic Practice. 2008. (Psychoanalytic Inquiry Book Ser.: Vol. 30). (ENG., Illus.). 496p. (C). 140.00 (978-0-88163-488-4(3)) Routledge.

Kahn, Jeffrey P. Angst: Origins of Anxiety & Depression. 2012. (ENG., Illus.). 304p. 34.95 **(978-0-19-979644-1(0))** Oxford Univ. Pr., Inc.

Kase, Larina. Anxious 9 To 5: How to Beat Worry, Stop Second-Guessing Yourself, & Work with Confidence. 2006. (ENG.). 232p. pap. 20.95 (978-1-57224-464-1(X)) New Harbinger Pubns.

Kemp, Andrew H. Emotional Processing in Humans. 2009. 224p. pap. (978-3-639-21105-4(7)) VDM Verlag Dr. Mueller e.K.

Kennedy, Brian. Anxiety Disorders. 2010. (Issues that Concern You Ser.). (Illus.). 144p. 34.70 (978-0-7377-4743-0(9), Greenhaven Pr., Inc.) Cengage Gale.

Kennerley, Helen. Overcoming Anxiety: A Self-Help Guide Using Cognitive Behavioral Techniques. 2009. (ENG., Illus.). 288p. pap. 14.95 (978-0-465-01265-7(5)) Basic Bks.

Kenny, Dianna. The Psychology of Music Performance Anxiety. 2011. (ENG., Illus.). 400p. pap. 65.00 (978-0-19-958614-1(4)) Oxford Univ. Pr., Inc.

Khalid, Faiza & Ahmad Hashmi, Hina. Resilience, Social Support & Anxiety among Drug Addicts. 2011. 88p. pap. **(978-3-8433-8463-6(0))** Lambert Academic Publishing.

King, Rita S. & Chapman, Carolyn. Test Success in the Brain-Compatible Classroom. 2nd ed. 2008. (Illus.). 248p. 82.95 (978-1-4129-6998-7(0), B69987C); pap. 36.95 (978-1-4129-6999-4(9), B69987P) Corwin Pr.

King, Thomas, ed. Anxiety Disorders: Complete Handbook. 2011. 138p. pap. 14.95 **(978-1-937354-07-7(5))** Rapid Publishing LLC.

Knaus, William. The Cognitive Behavioral Workbook for Anxiety: A Step-by-Step Program. 2008. (Workbook Ser.). (ENG., Illus.). 264p. pap. 21.95 (978-1-57224-572-3(7)) New Harbinger Pubns.

Kovitz, Benjamin. Humanity Against Itself: The Retreat from Reason. 2007. (ENG.). 175p. (C). 27.98 (978-1-59102-573-3(7)) Prometheus Bks., Pubs.

Kumar, Sumeet & Kumar, Sameet M. The Mindful Path Through Worry & Rumination: Letting Go of Anxious & Depressive Thoughts. 2010. (ENG.). 184p. pap. 16.95 (978-1-57224-687-4(1)) New Harbinger Pubns.

Laker, Michael A. The Tourguide. 2011. 266p. pap. 16.99 **(978-1-61379-199-8(2))** Xulon Pr., Inc.

—The Tourguide: How God Guided Me from Psychosis to Life in Christ. 2011. 266p. 26.99 **(978-1-61379-050-2(3))** Xulon Pr., Inc.

Landau, Abraham. Intelligence, Anxiety & Pleasure. 2011. 218p. 44.95 **(978-1-258-07627-6(6))** Literary Licensing, LLC.

Langley, Martha. Beat Panic: The Answers You Need — Now. 2012. (Bulle: Guides). (ENG.). 128p. pap. 6.95 **(978-1-4441-5768-0(X)**, Hodder & Stoughton) Hodder General Publishing Div. GBR. Dist: Independent Pubs. Group.

Lawlis, Frank. Retraining the Brain: A 45-Day Plan to Conquer Stress & Anxiety. 2009. (ENG.). 304p. (gr. 12-18). pap. 16.00 (978-0-452-29562-9(9), Plume) Penguin Group (USA) Inc.

Leahy, Robert L. Anxiety Free: Unravel Your Fears Before They Unravel You. 2009. (ENG.). 360p. 25.95 (978-1-4019-2163-7(9)) Hay Hse., Inc.

—Anxiety Free: Unravel Your Fears Before They Unravel You. 2010. (ENG., Illus.). 360p. pap. 16.95 (978-1-4019-2164-4(7)) Hay Hse., Inc.

—The Worry Cure: Seven Steps to Stop Worry from Stopping You. 2006. (ENG., Illus.). 336p. per. 15.00 (978-1-4000-9766-1(5), Three Rivers Pr.) Crown Publishing Group.

Leahy, Robert L., et al. Treatment Plans & Interventions for Depression & Anxiety Disorders. 2nd rev. ed. 2011. (Treatment Plans & Interventions for Evidence-Based Psychotherapy Ser.). (ENG., Illus.). 490p. pap. 75.00 (978-1-60918-649-4(4)) Guilford Pubns., Inc.

Leavell, Bonita. Studies on the Conditioned Enhancement of Acoustic Startle & Fear. 2009. 116p. pap. (978-3-639-12126-1(0)) VDM Verlag Dr. Mueller e.K.

Lejeune, Chad. The Worry Trap: How to Free Yourself from Worry & Anxiety Using Acceptance & Commitment Therapy. 2007. (ENG.). 208p. per. 16.95 (978-1-57224-480-1(1)) New Harbinger Pubns.

Lewis-Fernandez, Roberto. Anxiety Disorders: Theory, Research & Clinical Perspectives. Simpson, Helen Blair et al, eds. 2010. (ENG., Illus.). 394p. 99.00 (978-0-521-51557-3(2)) Cambridge Univ. Pr.

Loiko, Muffy. Just Hold On: A Journey Through Depression with Faith & Hope. 2011. 56p. pap. 9.99 **(978-1-4634-7460-7(1))** AuthorHouse.

Luciani, Joseph J. Self-Coaching: The Powerful Program to Beat Anxiety & Depression. 2nd rev. ed. 2006. (ENG., Illus.). 272p. pap. 14.95 (978-0-471-76828-9(6), Wiley) Wiley, John & Sons, Inc.

Ludgate, John W. Cognitive-Behavioral Therapy & Relapse Prevention for Depression & Anxiety. 2009. (ENG.). 96p. pap. 14.95 (978-1-56887-122-6(8)) Professional Resource Exchange, Inc.

Magrs, Mark. Too Much Information. 2008. 184p. pap. (978-1-84747-684-5(8)) Chipmunkapublishing.

Maisel, Eric. Mastering Creative Anxiety: 24 Lessons for Writers, Painters, Musicians, & Actors from America's Foremost Creativity Coach. 2011. (ENG.). 272p. pap. 14.95 (978-1-57731-932-0(X)) New World Library.

Malvasi, Martina, et al. Library Rx: Measuring & Treating Library Anxiety, a Research Study. 2009. pap. (978-0-8389-8499-4(1)) Assn. of College & Research Libraries.

Manassis, Katharina. Keys to Parenting Your Anxious Child. 2nd rev. ed. 2008. (Barron's Parenting Keys Ser.). (ENG.). 192p. pap. 8.99 (978-0-7641-3916-1(9)) Barron's Educational Series, Inc.

Mander, Gabrielle. Distraction: 150 Cunning Conundrums & Strategies to Beat Angst. 2006. (ENG., Illus.). 256p. per. 12.95 (978-0-7535-1173-2(8)) Virgin Bks. Ltd. GBR. Dist: Independent Pubs. Group.

Mansell, Warren. Coping with Fears & Phobias: A Step-by-Step Guide to Understanding & Facing Your Anxieties. 2007. (Coping With (Oneworld) Ser.). (ENG., Illus.). 192p. per. 14.95 (978-1-85168-514-1(6)) Oneworld Pubns. GBR. Dist: National Bk. Network.

Maurer, Kristin. Architectural Anxiety. 2010. 88p. pap. 8.43 (978-0-557-35898-4(1)) Lulu Enterprises Inc.

May, Rollo. The Meaning of Anxiety [1950. 2011. 396p. pap. 11.95 (978-1-61427-075-1(9)) Martino Publishing.

McCurry, Christopher. Parenting Your Anxious Child with Mindfulness & Acceptance: A Powerful New Approach to Overcoming Fear, Panic, & Worry Using Acceptance & Commitment Therapy. 2009. (ENG.). 248p. pap. 17.95 (978-1-57224-579-2(4)) New Harbinger Pubns.

McKay, Dean & Storch, Eric A., eds. Handbook of Child & Adolescent Anxiety Disorders. 2011. (ENG., Illus.). xx, 532p. 349.00 (978-1-4419-7782-3(1), 1441977821) Springer.

McKay, Matthew & DuFrene, Troy. Thirty-Minute Therapy for Anxiety: Everything You Need to Know in the Least Amount of Time. 2011. (New Harbinger Thirty-Minute Therapy Ser.). (ENG.). 136p. pap. 15.95 (978-1-57224-981-3(1)) New Harbinger Pubns.

Melemis, Steven M. I Want to Change My Life: How to Overcome Anxiety, Depression, & Addiction. 2010. **(978-1-897572-23-8(9))** Modern Therapies.

Mellalieu, Stephen D., et al. A Competitive Anxiety Review: Recent Directions in Sport Psychology Research. 2008. pap. 35.00 (978-1-60692-243-4(3)) Nova Science Pubs., Inc.

Merrell, Kenneth W. Helping Students Overcome Depression & Anxiety. 2nd rev. ed. 2008. (Practical Intervention in the Schools Ser.). (ENG., Illus.). 265p. (gr. k-12). pap., instr.'s gde. ed. 40.00 (978-1-59385-648-9(2)) Guilford Pubns., Inc.

Middleton, Kate. First Steps out of Anxiety. 2010. (First Steps Ser.). (ENG., Illus.). 96p. pap. 9.95 (978-0-7459-5519-3(3)) Lion Hudson PLC GBR. Dist: Independent Pubs. Group.

Miller, Allen R. Living with Anxiety Disorders. 2008. (Teen's Guides). 208p. (gr. 6-12). per. 14.95 (978-0-8160-7559-1(X), Checkmark Bks.) Facts On File, Inc.

Miller, Douglas. Don't Worry: Elimina la Ansiedad de Tu Vida. 2007. (SPA., Illus.). 250p. per. (978-84-7953-653-4(5)) Ediciones Urano S. A.

—Don't Worry: How to Beat the Seven Anxieties of Life. 2007. (ENG., Illus.). 192p. pap. 37.50 (978-0-273-71269-5(1), Prentice Hall) Pearson Education, Ltd. GBR. Dist: Trans-Atlantic Pubns., Inc.

Miller, J. R. A Cure for Care. 2011. 28p. pap. 7.99 **(978-1-61203-155-2(2))** Bottom of the Hill Publishing.

Miller, Jeffrey A. The Anxious Organization: Why Smart Companies Do Dumb Things. 2nd rev. ed. 2008. (ENG.). 240p. per. 19.95 (978-1-889150-52-9(5)) Facts on Demand Pr.

Moore, Michele. Variations in Test Anxiety & Locus of Control Orientation - in Achieving & Underachieving Gifted Middle School Students. 2008. 92p. pap. (978-3-639-05777-5(5)) VDM Verlag Dr. Mueller e.K.

Morales, Anna S., ed. Trait Anxiety. 2011. (Psychology of Emotions, Motivations & Actions Ser.). (Illus.). xiii, 235p. 95.00 (978-1-61324-551-4(3), Nova Science Pubs., Inc.

Morgan, Tammi L. Emerging Butterfly: Finding Life Beyond Anxiety Disorders. 2008. 231p. pap. 24.95 (978-1-60563-980-2(X)) PublishAmerica, Inc.

Munroe, Erin A. The Anxiety Workbook for Girls. 2010. (ENG.). 208p. (J). (gr. 4-7). pap. 14.95 (978-1-57749-232-0(3)) Taylor Trade Publishing.

Murchison, Marc. If You Can Identify It You Can Hogtie It. 2010. 108p. pap. 12.49 (978-1-4520-5577-0(7)) AuthorHouse.

Muris, Peter. Normal & Abnormal Fear & Anxiety in Children & Adolescents. 2007. (BRAT Series in Clinical Psychology Ser.). (ENG., Illus.). 400p. 109.00 (978-0-08-045073-5(3), Elsevier Science) Elsevier Science & Technology Bks.

Nadelberg, David. Mortified: Love Is a Battlefield. 2008. (ENG.). 304p. pap. 14.95 (978-1-4169-5479-8(1)) Gallery Pr., The IRL. Dist: Simon & Schuster, Inc.

Nagaich, Upendra, et al. Formulation & Evaluation of Buspirone Hydrochloride Buccal Films. 2011. 148p. pap. **(978-3-8443-1585-1(3))** Lambert Academic Publishing.

Nejad, Lillian & Volny, Katerina. Treating Stress & Anxiety: A Practitioner's Guide to Evidence-Based Approaches. 2008. (Illus.). 200p. pap. incl. cd-rom (978-1-84590-077-9(4)) Crown Hse. Publishing.

Netsanet, Shiferaw, et al. Emotional Distress: Anxiety & Depression among Clients Prior to Hiv-Vct & Pre Initiation of Art in South Ethiopia. 2011. 72p. pap. **(978-3-639-25622-2(0))** VDM Verlag Dr. Mueller e.K.

Newton, Julie. The Mind & Overcoming Exam Stress. 2009. 45p. pap. 16.50 (978-0-557-09976-4(5)) Lulu Enterprises Inc.

Nik Hussain, Nik Hazlina, et al. Anxiety, Depression & Female Sexual Dysfunction. 2011. 84p. pap. **(978-3-639-26677-1(3))** VDM Verlag Dr. Mueller e.K.

Norton, Peter J. Group Cognitive-Behavioral Therapy of Anxiety: A Transdiagnostic Treatment Manual. 2012. (ENG.). 222p. 35.00 **(978-1-4625-0480-0(9))** Guilford Pubns., Inc.

Noyes, Russell, Jr. & Hoehn-Saric, Rudolf. The Anxiety Disorders. 2006. (ENG., Illus.). 356p. pap. 81.00 (978-0-521-03048-9(X)) Cambridge Univ. Pr.

NurrieStearns, May & NurrieStearns, Rick. Yoga for Anxiety: Meditations & Practices for Calming the Body & Mind. 2010. (ENG., Illus.). 232p. pap. 17.95 (978-1-57224-651-5(0)) New Harbinger Pubns.

Nydegger, Rudy V. Dealing with Anxiety & Related Disorders: Understanding, Coping, & Prevention, 1 vol. 2011. 230p. 48.00 (978-0-313-38422-6(3), A2887C) Greenwood Publishing Group, Inc.

O'Connor, Richard. Undoing Perpetual Stress: The Missing Connection between Depression, Anxiety, & 21st Century Illness. 2006. 534p. reprint ed. 23.00 (978-1-4223-5213-7(7)) DIANE Publishing Co.

Orsillo, Susan M. & Roemer, Lizabeth. The Mindful Way Through Anxiety: Break Free from Chronic Worry & Reclaim Your Life. 2011. (ENG.). 307p. 40.00 (978-1-60623-982-7(1)); pap. 16.95 (978-1-60623-464-8(1)) Guilford Pubns., Inc.

Orsillo, Susan M. & Roemer, Lizabeth, eds. Acceptance- & Mindfulness-Based Approaches to Anxiety: Conceptualization & Treatment. 2010. (Series in Anxiety & Related Disorders Ser.). xviii, 378p. pap. 89.95 (978-1-4419-3855-8(9), 1441938559) Springer.

Otto, Michael & Hofmann, Stefan, eds. Avoiding Treatment Failures in the Anxiety Disorders. (Series in Anxiety & Related Disorders Ser.). (Illus.). xiv, 405p.

2010. pap. 59.95 *(978-1-4419-8169-1(1),* 1441981691) 2009. (ENG., 149.00 *(978-1-4419-0611-3(8),* 1441906118) Springer.

Otto, Michael & Smits, Jasper A. J. Exercise for Mood & Anxiety: Proven Strategies for Overcoming Depression & Enhancing Well-Being, 1 vol. 2011. (ENG.). 136p. pap. 17.99 *(978-0-19-979100-2(7))* Oxford Univ. Pr., Inc.

Paterson, Cal. Great Expectations. 2010. 156p. pap. *(978-3-8383-5143-8(6))* Lambert Academic Publishing.

Patkin, Todd. Finding Happiness: One Man's Quest to Beat Depression & Anxiety and-Finally-Let the Sunshine In. 2011. 392p. pap. 19.95 ***(978-0-9658261-9-8(8))*** Stepwise Pr.

Patnaik, Gourishankar. Understanding Stress. 2010. 80p. pap. *(978-3-639-27735-7(X))* VDM Verlag Dr. Mueller e.K.

Pearson, Patricia. A Brief History of Anxiety (Yours & Mine) 2009. (ENG.). 208p. pap. *(978-0-679-31499-8(7),* Vintage Canada) Random Hse. of Canada, Ltd. CAN. Dist: Random Hse., Inc.

—A Brief History of Anxiety?Yours & Mine. 2009. (ENG.). 208p. pap. 13.00 *(978-1-59691-595-4(1))* Bloomsbury Publishing.

Peden, Andrew. Managing Performance Anxiety in Tennis. 2007. 100p. per. 19.33 *(978-1-4251-2080-1(6))* Trafford Publishing.

Peters, Fiona. Anxiety & Evil in the Writings of Patricia Highsmith. 2011. 210p. 99.95 *(978-1-4094-2334-8(4))* Ashgate Publishing Co.

Phillips, Bob. Overcoming Anxiety & Depression: Practical Tools to Help You Deal with Negative Emotions. 2007. 240p. pap. 12.99 *(978-0-7369-1996-8(1))* Harvest Hse. Pubs.

Pickens, Henry. The Fear Cure: In Four Miraculous Steps. 2009. 161p. pap. 14.95 *(978-0-9761596-1-2(9))* Flying Enigma Pr.

Picus, Donna B., et al. Mastery of Anxiety & Panic for Adolescents Riding the Wave. 2008. (Treatments That Work Ser.). (ENG., Illus.). 176p. pap. 37.95 *(978-0-19-533580-4(5))* Oxford Univ. Pr., Inc.

Pillay, Srinivasan S. Life Unlocked: 7 Revolutionary Lessons to Overcome Fear. (ENG., Illus.). 304p. 2011. pap. 15.99 *(978-1-60961-146-0(2))* 2010. 25.99 *(978-1-60529-852-8(2))* Rodale Pr., Inc.

Pincus, Donna B. Growing up Brave: Expert Strategies for Helping Your Child Overcome Fear, Stress, & Anxiety. 2012. (ENG.). 288p. 25.99 ***(978-0-316-12560-4(1))*** Little Brown & Co.

Plant, Jane & Stephenson, Janet. Beating Stress, Anxiety & Depression: Groundbreaking Ways to Help You Feel Better. 2011. (ENG., Illus.). 352p. pap. 15.95 *(978-0-7499-3991-5(5))* Piatkus Bks. GBR. Dist: Independent Pubs. Group.

Portman, Michael E. Generalized Anxiety Disorder Across the Lifespan: An Integrative Approach. 2009. (ENG., Illus.). xvi, 182p. 79.95 *(978-0-387-89242-9(7),* 0387892427) Springer.

Potter, Beverly. The Worrywart's Companion: Twenty-One Ways to Soothe Yourself & Worry Smart. 2008. (ENG.). 192p. pap. 15.95 *(978-0-07-160213-6(5),* 0071602135) McGraw-Hill Cos., The.

Powell, Mark. Stress Relief: The Ultimate Teen Guide. 2007. (It Happened to Me Ser.). (ENG., Illus.). 112p. (gr. 8-12). per. 20.00 *(978-0-8108-5806-0(1))* Scarecrow Pr., Inc.

Prinz, Steven M. & Wehrenberg, Margaret. The Anxious Brain: The Neurobiological Basis of Anxiety Disorders & How to Effectively Treat Them. 2007. (ENG., Illus.). 288p. 32.00 *(978-0-393-70512-6(9),* 70512) Norton, W. W. & Co., Inc.

Rapee, Ronald M., et al. Helping Your Anxious Child: A Step-by-Step Guide for Parents. 2nd rev. ed. 2008. (ENG., Illus.). 296p. pap. 17.95 *(978-1-57224-575-4(1))* New Harbinger Pubns.

Reaven, Judy, et al. Facing Your Fears Facilitator's Manual: Group Therapy for Managing Anxiety in Children with High-Functioning Autism Spectrum Disorders. 2011. (Illus.). xiii, 169p. 89.95 *(978-1-59857-178-3(8))* Brookes, Paul H. Publishing Co.

Redshaw, Nick & Bethan. 3. 3 PSYA4 Workbook - Anxiety Disorder, Anomalistic Psychology, & Research Methods. 2010. 120p. pap. 27.50 *(978-1-4461-4241-7(8))* Lulu Enterprises Inc.

Reinecke, Andrea. Information Processing in Anxiety. 2008. 248p. pap. *(978-3-639-04304-4(9))* VDM Verlag Dr. Mueller e.K.

Reinecke, Mark. Little Ways to Keep Calm & Carry On: Twenty Lessons for Managing Worry, Anxiety, & Fear. 2010. (ENG., Illus.). 136p. pap. 14.95 *(978-1-57224-881-6(5))* New Harbinger Pubns.

Reznick, Charlotte. The Power of Your Child's Imagination: How to Transform Stress & Anxiety into Joy & Success. 2009. (ENG.). 320p. (gr. 12-18). 14.95 *(978-0-399-53507-9(1),* Perigee Trade) Penguin Group (USA) Inc.

Ricketts, Max & Bien, Edwin. The Great Anxiety Escape: A Revolutionary Program to Escape Anxiety, Insomnia, Depression & Drug Dependency. Date not set. (Illus.). 192p. (Orig.). pap. 9.95 *(978-0-9626205-0-8(5))* Matulungin Publishing.

Riemann, Fritz. Anxiety: Using Depth Psychology to Find a Balance in Your Life. Dunn, Greta, tr. from GER. 2009. 220p. (C). pap. 19.90 *(978-3-86649-218-9(9))* Budrich-Esser, Barbara DEU. Dist: International Specialized Bk. Services.

Rinpoche, Lama Zopa & McDonald, Kathleen. Wholesome Fear: Transforming Your Anxiety about Impermanence & Death. 2010. (ENG.). 168p. pap. 14.95 *(978-0-86171-630-2(2))* Wisdom Pubns.

Ronen, Ruth. Aesthetics of Anxiety. (SUNY series, Insinuations: Philosophy, Psychoanalysis, Literature Ser.). (Illus.). 2010. 195p. pap. 23.95 *(978-0-7914-7668-0(5),* Suny Pr.) 2009. 208p. 65.00 *(978-0-7914-7667-3(7))* State Univ. of New York Pr.

Rosenau, Jeff. Transfer of Trust. 2008. 112p. pap. *(978-1-55452-304-7(4),* Guardian Bks.) Essence Publishing.

Ross, Jerilyn & Cantor-Cooke, Robin. One Less Thing to Worry About: Uncommon Wisdom for Coping with Common Anxieties. 2009. (ENG.). 288p. 25.00 *(978-0-345-50306-0(6),* Ballantine Bks.) Random House Publishing Group.

Roy, Rajnish. Rewiring the Brain: Living without Stress & Anxiety through the Power of Consciousness. 2007. 260p. (ENG.). 31.99 *(978-1-4257-5975-9(0));* per. 21.99 *(978-1-4257-5969-8(6))* Xlibris Corp.

Sandas, Ilyne & Siegel, Christine. The Everything Parent's Guide to Children with Anxiety: Professional Advice to Help Your Child Feel Confident, Happy, & Secure. 2008. (ENG.). 304p. pap. 14.95 *(978-1-59869-686-8(6))* Adams Media Corp.

Schab, Lisa. Anxiety Workbook for Teens: Activities to Help You Deal with Anxiety & Worry. 2008. (Instant Help Ser.). 156p. pap. 14.95 *(978-1-931704-41-0(4))* Play2Grow.

—The Anxiety Workbook for Teens: Activities to Help You Deal with Anxiety & Worry. 2008. (Instant Help Ser.). (ENG.). 192p. (J). pap. 32.95 *(978-1-57224-661-4(8))* Play2Grow.

Schab, Lisa M. The Anxiety Workbook for Teens: Activities to Help You Deal with Anxiety & Worry. 2008. (Instant Help Ser.). (ENG., Illus.). 192p. (J). per. 14.95 *(978-1-57224-603-4(0))* Play2Grow.

Schwartz-Salant, Nathan. The Black Nightgown: The Fusional Complex & the Unlived Life. 2007. (Illus.). 251p. per. 28.95 *(978-1-888602-41-8(4))* Chiron Pubns.

Scott, Trudy. The Antianxiety Food Solution: How the Foods You Eat Can Help You Calm Your Anxious Mind, Improve Your Mood, & End Cravings. 2011. (ENG.). 208p. pap. 17.95 *(978-1-57224-925-7(0))* New Harbinger Pubns.

Seitz Jr., Charles. Freedom in Christ Treatment Methodology. 2010. 144p. pap. *(978-3-639-24567-7(9))* VDM Verlag Dr. Mueller e.K.

Semple, Randye J. & Lee, Jennifer. Mindfulness-Based Cognitive Therapy for Anxious Children: A Manual for Treating Childhood Anxiety. 2011. (Professional Ser.). (ENG.). 394p. 59.95 *(978-1-57224-719-2(3))* New Harbinger Pubns.

Shapiro, Francine. Getting Past Your Past: Take Control of Your Life with Self-Help Techniques from EMDR Therapy. 2012. (ENG.). 352p. 26.99 ***(978-1-59486-425-4(X))*** Rodale Pr., Inc.

Shapiro, Lawrence. The Relaxation & Stress Reduction Workbook for Kids: Help for Children to Cope with Stress, Anxiety, & Transitions. 2009. (Instant Help Ser.). (ENG., Illus.). 144p. (J). pap. 24.95 *(978-1-57224-655-3(3))* Play2Grow.

Shockley, Talmer. The Love-Shy Survival Guide. 2009. (ENG.). 256p. pap. *(978-1-84310-897-6(6))* Kingsley, Jessica Ltd.

Shoji, Kotaro. Factors Affecting the Use of Coping Activities in Anxiety-Provoking Situations. 2008. 52p. pap. *(978-3-639-02433-3(8))* VDM Verlag Dr. Mueller e.K.

Silove, Derrick & Manicavasagar, Vijaya, texts. Overcoming Panic: A Self-Help Guide Using Cognitive Behavioral Techniques. 2009. (Overcoming Ser.). (ENG., Illus.). 256p. pap. 14.95 *(978-0-465-01107-0(1))* Basic Bks.

Simos, Gregoris & Hofmann, Stefan G. CBT for Anxiety Disorders: A Practitioner Book. 2012. (ENG.). 288p. 115.95 ***(978-0-470-97552-7(0));*** pap. 54.95 ***(978-0-470-97553-4(9))*** Wiley, John & Sons, Inc. (Wiley-Blackwell).

Simpson, Terry & Speelman, Craig. Anxiety & Skill Acquisition. 2010. 248p. pap. *(978-3-8383-6524-4(0))* Lambert Academic Publishing.

Sisemore, Timothy. I Bet I Wont Fret: A Workbook to Help Children with Generalized Anxiety Disorder. 2008. (Instant Help Ser.). 138p. pap. 16.95 *(978-1-931704-35-9(X))* Play2Grow.

—I Bet I Won't Fret: A Workbook to Help Children with Generalized Anxiety Disorder. 2008. (Instant Help Ser.). (ENG.). 152p. (J). pap. 32.95 *(978-1-57224-658-4(8))* Play2Grow.

Sisemore, Timothy A. & Sisemore, Timothy. I Bet I Won't Fret: A Workbook to Help Children with Generalized Anxiety Disorder. 2008. (Instant Help Ser.). (ENG.). 152p. (J). (gr. 4-7). pap. 16.95 *(978-1-57224-600-3(6))* Play2Grow.

Slayton, Jake, ed. Insomnia Solutions: Complete Handbook. 2011. 106p. pap. 14.95 ***(978-1-937354-11-4(3))*** Rapid Publishing LLC.

Sookman, Deborah. Treatment Resistant Anxiety Disorders: Resolving Impasses to Symptom Remission. 2009. (ENG., Illus.). 387p. 55.95 *(978-0-415-98891-9(8))* Routledge.

Stahl, Stephen M. & Grady, Meghan M. Stahl's Illustrated Anxiety, Stress, & PTSD. 2010. (Stahl's Illustrated Ser.). (ENG., Illus.). 200p. pap. 44.00 *(978-0-521-15399-7(9))* Cambridge Univ. Pr.

STALLARD. Anxiety. 2009. (CBT with Children, Adolescents & Families Ser.). (ENG., Illus.). 224p. (C). 110.00 *(978-0-415-37256-5(9))* Routledge.

STALLARD & Stallard, Paul. Anxiety: Cognitive Behavioural Therapy with Children & Young People. 2009. (CBT with Children, Adolescents & Families Ser.). (ENG., Illus.). 224p. (C). pap. 34.95 *(978-0-415-37255-8(0))* Routledge.

Starcevic, Vladan. Anxiety Disorders in Adults. 2nd ed. 2009. (ENG., Illus.). 480p. 59.95 *(978-0-19-536925-0(4))* Oxford Univ. Pr. GBR. Dist: Oxford Univ. Pr., Inc.

Stein, Dan J., et al, eds. Textbook of Anxiety Disorders. 2nd ed. 2009. (ENG., Illus.). 822p. 125.00 *(978-1-58562-254-2(0))* American Psychiatric Publishing, Inc.

Stewart, Sherry H. & Conrod, Patricia, eds. Anxiety & Substance Use Disorders: The Vicious Cycle of Comorbidity. 2010. (Series in Anxiety & Related Disorders Ser.). xxii, 282p. pap. 89.95 *(978-1-4419-4492-4(3),* 1441944923) Springer.

Stinson, Angela. Anxiety & Stress: How Poor Performance & Absenteeism Affect the Workplace. 2010. 98p. pap. 25.95 *(978-1-59942-302-9(2),* Dissertation.com) Universal Pubs.

Stone, Tom. Vaporize Your Anxiety. 2010. 238p. pap. 14.95 *(978-0-9825391-0-1(X))* Great Life Technologies, Inc.

Summers, Mark Wahlgren. A Dangerous Stir: Fear, Paranoia, & the Making of Reconstruction. 2009. (Civil War America Ser.). (ENG., Illus.). 344p. 41.95 *(978-0-8078-3304-9(5))* Univ. of North Carolina Pr.

Sun-Kleinberger, Nathan. The Children of Holden. 2009. 68p. pap. *(978-3-639-16371-1(0))* VDM Verlag Dr. Mueller e.K.

Taylor, D. J. Bright Young People: The Lost Generation of London's Jazz Age. 2010. (ENG., Illus.). 384p. pap. 17.00 *(978-0-374-53211-6(7))* Farrar, Straus & Giroux.

Thomas, Brennan. Writing Teacher Anxiety- a Pilot Study. 2007. 276p. per. *(978-3-8364-1731-0(6))* VDM Verlag Dr. Mueller e.K.

Thomas, Gail L. The Struggle Is Over: The Kingdom of Heaven Has Come! 2010. pap. 10.99 *(978-1-61566-100-8(X))* Tate Publishing & Enterprises, LLC.

Thompson, Tina. Released: Setting Your Spirit Free from Depression & Anxiety. 2009. pap. 9.99 *(978-1-60799-653-8(7))* Tate Publishing & Enterprises, LLC.

Tirch, Dennis D. The Compassionate-Mind Guide to Overcoming Anxiety: Using Compassion-Focused Therapy to Calm Worry, Panic, & Fear. 2012. (New Harbinger Compassion-Focused Therapy Ser.). (ENG.). 232p. pap. 16.95 ***(978-1-60882-036-8(X))*** New Harbinger Pubns.

Tone, Andrea. The Age of Anxiety: A History of America's Turbulent Affair with Tranquilizers. (ENG.). 320p. (gr. 9). 2012. pap. 18.99 *(978-0-465-02520-6(X))* 2008. 26.95 *(978-0-465-08658-0(6))* Basic Bks.

Tóth, Zsuzsa. Foreign Language Anxiety & the Advanced Language Learner. 2010. 240p. *(978-1-4438-2377-7(5))* Cambridge Scholars Pub.

Tristan, Kathryn. Anxiety Rescue: Simple Strategies to Stop Fear from Ruling Your World. 2007. (Illus.). 191p. per. 14.95 *(978-0-9790013-0-7(7))* Dancing Eagle Pr.

Twohig, Michael P. & Hayes, Steven C. ACT Verbatim for Depression & Anxiety: Annotated Transcripts for Learning Acceptance & Commitment Therapy. 2008. (Professional Ser.). (ENG., Illus.). 248p. pap. 39.95 *(978-1-57224-523-5(9))* New Harbinger Pubns.

Ty-Wharton, Mark. Mastering the Impossible. 2009. 42p. pap. 9.95 *(978-1-4092-7470-4(5))* Lulu Enterprises Inc.

Van Ameringen, Michael & Pollack, Mark H. Generalized Anxiety Disorders. 2010. (Oxford Psychiatry Ser.). (ENG., Illus.). 120p. pap. 24.95 *(978-0-19-955783-7(7))* Oxford Univ. Pr., Inc.

Vanin, John R. & Helsley, James D. Anxiety Disorders: A Pocket Guide for Primary Care. 2007. (Current Clinical Practice Ser.). (Illus.). 266p. per. 59.95 *(978-1-58829-923-9(6))* Humana Pr.

Venault, Patrice & Chapouthier, Georges, eds. Plasticity & Anxiety. 2007. 188p. per. 28.00 *(978-977-5945-99-0(2))* Hindawi Publishing Corp.

Vye, Christopher, et al. Under Pressure & Overwhelmed: Coping with Anxiety in College, 1 vol. 2007. (Illus.). 232p. 49.95 *(978-0-275-99089-3(3),* C9089, Praeger Pubs.) Greenwood Publishing Group, Inc.

Wagemaker, Herbert. The Surprising Truth about Panic, Phobia & Anxiety Disorders. Date not set. (Illus.). 175p. pap. 12.00 *(978-0-9654996-3-7(4))* Ponte Vedra Publishing.

Warner, Priscilla. Learning to Breathe: My Yearlong Quest to Bring Calm to My Life. (ENG.). 288p. 2012. pap. 15.00 ***(978-1-4391-8108-9(X))*** 2011. lib. bdg. 23.00 *(978-1-4391-8107-2(1))* Free Pr. (Free Pr.).

Warren, Bernie. Suffering the Slings & Arrows of Outra. 2006. 248p. (C). per. *(978-90-420-2148-8(9))* Rodopi B.V. Editions.

Waska, Robert. Treating Severe Depressive & Persecutory: Anxiety States. 2010. 270p. pap. 34.95 *(978-1-85575-720-2(6))* Karnac Bks. GBR. Dist: Stylus Publishing, LLC.

Watt, Margo C. & Stewart, Sherry H. Overcoming the Fear of Fear: How to Reduce Anxiety Sensitivity. 2009. (ENG.). 216p. pap. 16.95 *(978-1-57224-558-7(1))* New Harbinger Pubns.

Wehrenberg, Margaret. The 10 Best-Ever Anxiety Management Techniques. 2012. (ENG., Illus.). 224p. pap., wbk. ed. 19.95 ***(978-0-393-70743-4(1),*** 70743) Norton, W. W. & Co., Inc.

Wehrenberg, Margaret. The 10 Best-Ever Anxiety Management Techniques: Understanding How Your Brain Makes You Anxious & What You Can Do to Change It. 2008. (ENG., Illus.). 256p. pap. 19.95 *(978-0-393-70556-0(0),* 70556) Norton, W. W. & Co., Inc.

Wellman, Lee. My Quarter-Life Crisis: How an Anxiety Disorder Knocked Me down, & How I Got Back Up. 2007. 205p. per. 14.99 *(978-0-9787515-7-9(4))* Adibooks.com.

Wells, Adrian. Metacognitive Therapy for Anxiety & Depression. 2008. (ENG., Illus.). 316p. 55.00 *(978-1-59385-994-7(5))* Guilford Pubns., Inc.

Wenzel, Amy. Anxiety in Childbearing Women: Diagnosis & Treatment. 2010. (Illus.). viii, 273p. E-Book *(978-1-4338-0901-9(X));* 264p. 59.95 *(978-1-4338-0900-2(1))* American Psychological Assn.

Westra, Henny A. Motivational Interviewing in the Treatment of Anxiety. 2012. (Applications of Motivational Interviewin Ser.). (ENG.). 274p. 40.00 ***(978-1-4625-0481-7(7))*** Guilford Pubns., Inc.

Wever, Chris. The School Wobbles. 2011. (Illus.). 22p. (YA). ***(978-0-9808348-2-6(1))*** Shrink-Rap Pr.

Wiegartz, Pamela & Gyoerkoe, Kevin. The Worrier's Guide to Overcoming Procrastination: Breaking Free from the Anxiety That Holds You Back. 2011. (ENG.). 176p. pap. 19.95 *(978-1-57224-871-7(8))* New Harbinger Pubns.

Wiegartz, Pamela & Gyoerkoe, Kevin L. The Pregnancy & Postpartum Anxiety Workbook: Practical Skills to Help You Overcome Anxiety, Worry, Panic Attacks, Obsessions & Compulsions. 2009. (Workbook Ser.). (ENG.). 200p. pap. 21.95 *(978-1-57224-589-1(1))* New Harbinger Pubns.

Wilkinson, David. The Fear Course Handbook of How to do a Job Interview without Nerves or Anxiety. 2010. 58p. pap. 27.50 *(978-1-4461-5838-8(1))* Lulu Enterprises Inc.

Williams, Chris. Overcoming Stress, Worry, Panic & Phobias: A Five Areas Approach. 2nd ed. 2010. (ENG., Illus.). 352p. pap. 39.95 *(978-0-340-98655-4(7),* Hodder Arnold) Hodder Education GBR. Dist: Oxford Univ. Pr., Inc.

Williams, Christopher. Overcoming Anxiety, Stress & Panic: A Five Areas Approac. 3rd rev. ed. 2012. (ENG., Illus.). 432p. pap. 45.00 ***(978-1-4441-6314-8(0))*** Hodder Arnold Pubns.

Wilson, Kelly & DuFrene, Troy. Things Might Go Terribly, Horribly Wrong: A Guide to Life Liberated from Anxiety. 2010. (10 Simple Solutions Ser.). (ENG.). 184p. pap. 16.95 *(978-1-57224-711-6(8))* New Harbinger Pubns.

Wilson, Reid & Wilson, R. R. Don't Panic: Taking Control of Anxiety Attacks. 3rd ed. 2009. (ENG.). 333p. pap. 17.99 *(978-0-06-158244-8(1),* Harper Paperbacks) HarperCollins Pubs.

Wise, David. Paradoxical Relaxation: The Theory & Practice of Dissolving Anxiety by Accepting It. 2010. 304p. pap. 19.95 *(978-0-9727755-8-8(7))* National Ctr. for Pelvic Pain Research.

Wise, Janet. Free from Worry. 2010. (Women of the Word Bible Study Ser.). (ENG.). 112p. pap. 9.99 *(978-0-8307-5232-4(3))* Gospel Light Pubns.

Wittchen, Hans-Ulrich & Gloster, Andrew. Anxiety Disorders, an Issue of Psychiatric Clinics. 2009. (Clinics: Internal Medicine Ser.: 32-3). (ENG.). 99.00 *(978-1-4377-1270-4(3),* Saunders) Elsevier - Health Sciences Div.

Wood, Jeffrey J. & McLeod, Bryce D. Child Anxiety Disorders: A Family-Based Treatment Manual for Practitioners. 2008. (ENG., Illus.). 272p. 32.00 *(978-0-393-70540-9(4),* 70540) Norton, W. W. & Co., Inc.

Wright, H. Norman. Respuesta a la Preocupacion: Answer to Worry & Anxiety. (SPA.). 64p. *(978-84-7228-723-5(8),* 220778) Clie, Editorial.

Zeidner, Moshe. Anxiety 101. 2010. 180p. pap. *(978-0-8261-0488-5(6))* Springer Publishing Co., Inc.

Zondervan Publishing Staff & Stanley, Charles F. Como Manejar el Temor: Confident Living in Anxious Times, 1 vol. 2006. (Guided Growth Booklets Spanish Ser.). (SPA.). 24p. pap. 1.99 *(978-0-8297-4651-8(X))* Vida Pubs.

Zucker, Bonnie. Anxiety-Free Kids: An Interactive Guide for Parents & Children. 2008. (ENG.). 250p. pap. 16.95 *(978-1-59363-343-1(2))* Prufrock Pr.

ANZA, JUAN BAUTISTA DE, 1735-1788

Egert, Nina. Tracing Anza's Trail: A Photographer's Journey: Images Accompanying Journal Entries by the First Spaniards to Travel Overland from Arizona to the San Francisco Bay Area. 2008. (SPA & ENG., Illus.). 98p. pap. *(978-1-60725-700-4(9))* Independent Pub.

Font, Pedro. With Anza to California, 1775-1776: The Journal of Pedro Font, O. F. M. Brown, Alan K., tr. 2011. (Early California Commentaries Ser.). (ENG.). 472p. (C). 55.00 *(978-0-87062-375-2(3),* Clark, Arthur H. Co., The) Univ. of Oklahoma Pr.

ANZA-BORREGO DESERT STATE PARK

Cowan, Ernie. Anza-Borrego: A Photographic Journey. 2008. (Adventures in the Natural History & Cultural Heritage of the Californias Ser.). (Illus.). 80p. 19.95 *(978-0-932653-88-8(X))* Sunbelt Pubns., Inc.

Cunningham, Bill & Cunningham, Polly. Hiking Anza-Borrego Desert State Park: 25 Day & Overnight Hikes. 2007. (Hiking Ser.). (ENG., Illus.). 96p. per. 12.95 *(978-0-7627-4462-6(6),* Falcon Guides) Globe Pequot Pr., The.

ANZIO BEACHHEAD, 1944

Blackwell, Ian. Anzio. 2007. (Battleground Europe Ser.). (Illus.). 192p. per. 19.99 *(978-1-84415-473-9(4))* Pen & Sword Bks. Ltd. GBR. Dist: Casemate Pubs. & Bk. Distributors, LLC.

Clark, Lloyd. Anzio: Italy & the Battle for Rome - 1944. 2007. (ENG., Illus.). 416p. per. 16.00 *(978-0-8021-4326-6(1),* Grove Pr.) Grove/Atlantic, Inc.

D'Este, Carlo. Fatal Decision: Anzio & the Battle for Rome. 2008. (ENG.). 608p. pap. 16.95 *(978-0-06-057649-3(9),* HarperPerennial) HarperCollins Pubs.

Eisenhower, John S. D. They Fought at Anzio. 2007. (ENG., Illus.). 320p. (gr. 9). 34.95 *(978-0-8262-1738-7(9))* Univ. of Missouri Pr.

Morison, Samuel Eliot. Sicily Salerno Anzio Jun 1943 - Jun 1944-V09. rev. ed. 2011. (Illus.). 413p. pap. 24.95 *(978-1-59114-575-2(9))* Naval Institute Pr.

AOL (ONLINE SERVICE)

see America Online (Online Service)

A-ONE SKYRAIDER

see Skyraider (Fighter Planes)

AORTA

Aranda, Pedro J., ed. Disasters in Open & Endovascular Aortic Procedures: Learning from Complications. 2013. (ENG., Illus.). 250p. 139.00 ***(978-3-642-25025-5(4),*** 3642250254) Springer.

Boudoulas. The Aorta. 2008. (ENG., Illus.). 374p. 250.00 *(978-1-84184-591-3(4),* Informa Healthcare) Taylor & Francis Group GBR. Dist: Taylor & Francis Group.

Coselli, Joseph S. & LeMaire, Scott A., eds. Aortic Arch Surgery: Principles, Strategies & Outcomes. 2008. (ENG., Illus.). 400p. 207.95 *(978-1-4051-3361-6(9),* Wiley-Blackwell) Wiley, John & Sons, Inc.

Elefteriades, John A. Controversies in Diseases of the Aorta, an Issue of Cardiology Clinics. 2010. (Clinics: Internal Medicine Ser.: 28-2). (ENG., Illus.). xvii, 191p. 105.00 *(978-1-4377-1801-0(9),* Saunders) Elsevier - Health Sciences Div.

Elefteriades, John A., ed. Acute Aortic Disease. 2007. (Fundamental & Clinical Cardiology Ser.). (ENG., Illus.). 400p. 280.00 *(978-0-8493-7023-6(X),* Informa Healthcare) Taylor & Francis Group GBR. Dist: Taylor & Francis Group.
Eskandari, Mark K., et al. Modern Trends in Vascular Surgery: Surgery of the Aorta & its Body Branches. 2009. 600p. *(978-1-60795-054-7(5))* PMPH-USA, Ltd.
Hutchison, Stuart J. Aortic Diseases: Clinical Diagnostic Imaging Atlas. 2008. (Cardiovascular Emergencies: Atlas & Multimedia Ser.). (ENG., Illus.). 374p. 194.00 *(978-1-4160-5270-8(4),* Saunders) Elsevier - Health Sciences Div.
Kazui, Teruhisa & Takamoto, Shinichi, eds. Advances in Understanding Aortic Disease. 2009. (ENG., Illus.). 312p. pap. 189.00 *(978-4-431-99236-3(7),* 4431992367) Springer.
Koulouri, Alexandra & Maria Petrou, Prof. Automatic Segmentation of the Abdominal Aorta from Ct Images. 2011. (Illus.). 72p. pap. ***(978-3-8443-9720-8(5))*** Lambert Academic Publishing.
Kpodonu, Jacques. Manual of Thoracic Endoaortic Surgery. 2010. (Illus.). x, 350p. pap. 69.95 *(978-1-84996-295-7(2),* 1849962952) Springer.
Kpodonu, Jacques, et al. Endovascular & Hybrid Management of the Thoracic Aorta: A Case-Based Approach. 2008. (ENG., Illus.). 320p. 199.95 *(978-1-4051-7535-7(4),* Wiley-Blackwell) Wiley, John & Sons, Inc.
Subramaniam, Kathirvel, et al, eds. Anesthesia & Perioperative Care for Aortic Surgery. 2010. (Illus.). 300p. 219.00 *(978-0-387-85921-7(7),* 0387859217) Springer.
Torigian, Drew A. & Alavi, Abass. PET Imaging of Thoracic Disease, an Issue of PET Clinics. 2011. (Clinics: Radiology Ser.: 6-3). (ENG., Illus.). 168p. 83.00 *(978-1-4557-1049-2(0),* Saunders) Elsevier - Health Sciences Div.
Upchurch, Gilbert R. & Criado, Enrique. Aortic Aneurysms: Pathogenesis & Treatment. 2009. (Contemporary Cardiology Ser.). (Illus.). 518p. 219.00 *(978-1-60327-203-2(8))* Humana Pr.
Verhoye, Jean-Philippe, et al, eds. Thoracic Aortic Diseases. 2006. (Illus.). 387p. 359.00 *(978-3-540-25734-9(9),* 3540257349) Springer.
Yankah, Abraham Charles, et al, eds. Aortic Root Surgery: The Biological Solution. 2009. (ENG., Illus.). xxiv, 616p. 129.00 *(978-3-7985-1868-1(8),* 3798518688) Steinkopff, Dietrich DEU. Dist: Springer.

AORTIC REGURGITATION
see Heart—Diseases

AORTIC VALVE
Borer, J. S. & Isom, O. W., eds. Pathophysiology, Evaluation & Management of Valvular Heart Diseases: Developed from "Valves in the Heart of the Big Apple: Evaluation & Management of Valvular Heart Diseases", New York, NY, May 2001, Vol. 39. (Advances in Cardiology Ser.: Vol. 39). (Illus.). *(978-3-8055-7402-0(9))* Karger, S. AG.

AORTIC VALVE—DISEASES
Cram101 Textbook Reviews. Outlines & Highlights for Aortic Diseases: Clinical Diagnostic Imaging Atlas by Stuart J. Hutchison, ISBN. 2011. 162p. pap. 29.95 ***(978-1-4288-7644-6(8))*** Cram101 Inc.
Eagle, Kim A., et al, eds. Aortic Dissection & Related Syndromes. 2006. (Developments in Cardiovascular Medicine Ser.). (Illus.). 364p. 229.00 *(978-0-387-36000-3(X),* 038736000X) Springer.
Fuchs, Christina. Gender & Aortic Stenosis. 2008. 60p. pap. *(978-3-639-06449-0(6))* VDM Verlag Dr. Mueller e.K.
Hetzer, Roland, et al, eds. Mitral Valve Repair: The Biologic Solution. 2009. (Illus.). 300p. 99.00 *(978-3-7985-1866-7(1))* Steinkopff, Dietrich DEU. Dist: Springer.
Huber, Christoph. Transcatheter Valve Therapies. 2009. (ENG.). 272p. 250.00 *(978-1-4398-1078-1(8),* Informa Healthcare) Taylor & Francis Group.
Kpodonu, Jacques, et al. Endovascular & Hybrid Management of the Thoracic Aorta: A Case-Based Approach. 2008. (ENG., Illus.). 320p. 199.95 *(978-1-4051-7535-7(4),* Wiley-Blackwell) Wiley, John & Sons, Inc.
Lumsden, Alan B., et al, eds. Advanced Endovascular Therapy of Aortic Disease. 2007. (ENG., Illus.). 240p. 162.95 *(978-1-4051-5570-0(1),* Wiley-Blackwell) Wiley, John & Sons, Inc.

AORTOCORONARY BYPASS
see Coronary Artery Bypass

APACHE (COMPUTER PROGRAM)
Boronczyk, Timothy, et al. Beginning PHP 6, Apache, MySQL 6 Web Development. 2009. (ENG., Illus.). 840p. pap. 49.99 *(978-0-470-39114-3(6),* Wrox) Wiley, John & Sons, Inc.
Bowen, Rich, et al. Apache Cookbook: Solutions & Examples for Apache Administrators. 2nd rev. ed. 2007. (Cookbooks (o'Reilly) Ser.). (ENG., Illus.). 310p. per. 34.99 *(978-0-596-52994-9(5))* O'Reilly Media, Inc.
Carnell, John & Harrop, Rob. Pro Apache Struts with Ajax. Mittal, Kunal, ed. 2006. (Expert's Voice in Java Ser.). (ENG., Illus.). 528p. per. 44.99 *(978-1-59059-738-5(9))* Apress L. P.
Chopra, Vivek, et al. Professional Apache Tomcat 6. 2007. (ENG., Illus.). 672p. pap. 39.99 *(978-0-471-75361-2(0),* Wrox) Wiley, John & Sons, Inc.
DeLisle, Marc. Dominar PhpMyAdmin para una Administracion Efectiva de MySQL. 2007. (SPA.). 288p. per. *(978-1-904811-98-5(1))* Packt Publishing, Ltd.
Ford, Andrew. Apache: For Apache Programmers & Administrators. 2nd rev. ed. 2008. (Pocket Reference (o'Reilly) Ser.). (ENG.). 212p. pap. 14.99 *(978-0-596-51888-2(9))* O'Reilly Media, Inc.
Galbraith, Patrick. Developing Web Applications with Apache, Mysql, Memcached, & Perl. 2009. (ENG., Illus.). 888p. pap. 49.99 *(978-0-470-41464-4(2),* Wrox) Wiley, John & Sons, Inc.
Genender, Jeff, et al. Professional Apache Geronimo. 2006. (ENG., Illus.). 468p. pap. 39.99 *(978-0-471-78543-9(1),* Wrox) Wiley, John & Sons, Inc.
Heather, Cooley, et al. Future Water Requirements for Electricity Generation in the Intermountain West. 2011. (Illus.). 62p. 0.00 ***(978-1-893790-36-0(3))*** Pacific Institute for Studies in Development, Environment & Security.
Holmes, James. Struts, Vol. 2. 2008. (Complete Reference Ser.). 520p. pap. 49.99 *(978-0-07-148990-4(8),* 9780071489904) McGraw-Hill Osborne.
Ibsen, Claus, et al. Camel in Action. rev. ed. 2011. (ENG., Illus.). 552p. pap. 49.99 *(978-1-935182-36-8(6))* Manning Pubns. Co.
Jayasinghe, Deepal. Quickstart Apache Axis2. 2008. 180p. pap. *(978-1-84719-286-8(6))* Packt Publishing, Ltd.
Kew, Nick. The Apache Modules Book: Application Development with Apache. 2007. (Prentice Hall Open Source Software Development Ser.). (ENG., Illus.). 592p. per. 59.99 *(978-0-13-240967-4(4),* Prentice Hall) Prentice Hall PTR.
Marinschek, Martin, et al. The Definitive Guide to Apache Myfaces & Facelets. 2008. (ENG.). 400p. pap. 44.99 *(978-1-59059-737-8(0))* Apress L. P.
Mattmann, Chris & Zitting, Jukka. Tika in Action. 2011. (ENG.). 256p. pap. 44.99 ***(978-1-935182-85-6(4))*** Manning Pubns. Co.
Meloni, Julie C. PHP, MySQL & Apache All in One. 4th ed. 2008. (Sams Teach Yourself Ser.). (ENG., Illus.). 648p. pap. 39.99 *(978-0-672-32976-0(X))* Sams.
—Sams Teach Yourself PHP, MySQL & Apache All in One. 5th rev. ed. 2012. (Sams Teach Yourself Ser.). (ENG., Illus.). 672p. pap. 39.99 incl. cd-rom *(978-0-672-33543-3(3))* Sams.
Moodie, Matthew. Pro Apache Ant. 2012. (ENG.). 360p. pap. 44.99 ***(978-1-4302-4311-3(2))*** Apress L. P.
Moodie, Matthew. Pro Apache Tomcat 6. Mittal, Kunal, ed. 2007. (Expert's Voice in Java Ser.). (ENG., Illus.). 325p. per. 39.99 *(978-1-59059-785-9(0))* Apress L. P.
Newton, Dave. Apache Struts 2 Web Application Development. 2008. (Illus.). 300p. pap. *(978-1-84719-339-1(0))* Packt Publishing, Ltd.
Roughley, Ian. Practical Apache Struts2 Web 2. 0 Projects. 2007. (Expert's Voice in Java Technology Ser.). (ENG., Illus.). 338p. per. 39.99 *(978-1-59059-903-7(9))* Apress L. P.
Sams Publishing Staff & Meloni, Julie. Sams Teach Yourself PHP & MySQL: Video Learning Starter Kit Bundle. 4th ed. 2009. (Sams Teach Yourself Video Ser.). (ENG.). pap. 49.99 *(978-0-672-33089-6(X))* Sams.
The Apache Software Foundation. Apache Tomcat 7 User Guide. 2011. 254p. pap. 29.99 ***(978-1-59682-271-9(6))*** Fultus Corp.
Tong, Kent Ka Iok. Developing Web Services with Apache CXF & Axis2 (3rd Edition) 2010. 259p. pap. 39.95 *(978-0-557-25432-3(9))* Lulu Enterprises Inc.
White, Tom. Hadoop. 2nd ed. 2010. (ENG., Illus.). 628p. pap. 49.99 *(978-1-4493-8973-4(2),* Yahoo Pr.) O'Reilly Media, Inc.
White, Tom. Hadoop: The Definitive Guide. 3rd ed. 2012. (ENG.). 684p. pap. 49.99 ***(978-1-4493-1152-0(0),*** Yahoo Pr.) O'Reilly Media, Inc.

APACHE INDIANS
see Indians of North America—Southwest, New

APARTHEID
Here are entered works on the political, economic and social policies of the government of South Africa designed to keep racial groups in South Africa and Namibia separated.
see also Anti-Apartheid Movements; South Africa—Race Relations
Abingdon. Faces on Faith: Desmond Tutu, Parker Palmer, Adele Gonzales: Classic Interviews with 20th-Century Leaders. 2008. cd-rom 25.00 *(978-0-687-65402-4(5))* Abingdon Pr.
Abramson, Lorraine Lotzof. My Race: A Jewish Girl Growing up under Apartheid in South Africa. 2010. (ENG., Illus.). 352p. 27.95 *(978-0-9816102-3-6(4))* DBM Pr., LLC.
Alegi, Peter & Bolsmann, Chris, eds. South Africa & the Global Game: Football, Apartheid & Beyond. 2012. (ENG., Illus.). 186p. (C). pap. 45.95 ***(978-0-415-51859-8(8))*** Routledge.
Anthonissen, Christine & Blommaert, Jan. Discourse & Human Rights Violations. 2007. (C). 96.00 *(978-90-272-2235-0(5))* Benjamins, John Publishing Co.
Bank, Leslie J. Home Spaces, Street Styles: Contesting Power & Identity in a South African City, 1 vol. 2011. (ENG., Illus.). 272p. 96.00 *(978-0-7453-2328-2(6));* pap. 33.00 *(978-0-7453-2327-5(8))* Pluto Pr. GBR. Dist: Macmillan.
Beningfield, Jennifer. Frightened Land. 2006. (ENG., Illus.). 352p. 59.95 *(978-0-415-36555-0(4))* Routledge.
—The Frightened Land: Land, Landscape & Politics in South Africa in the Twentieth Century. 2007. (ENG., Illus.). 352p. 185.00 *(978-0-415-36593-2(7))* Routledge.
Bray, Rachel, et al. Growing up in the New South Africa: Childhood & Adolescence in Post-Apartheid Cape Town. 2010. (ENG.). 448p. pap. 34.95 *(978-0-7969-2313-4(2))* Human Sciences Research Council ZAF. Dist: Independent Pubs. Group.
Callinicos, Luli. Oliver Tambo: His Life & Legacy, 1917-1993. 2011. (ENG.). 36p. pap. 8.95 *(978-1-919855-85-1(8))* STE Pubs. ZAF. Dist: Independent Pubs. Group.
Canary, Jacintha J. Peppermint Bon Bons. 2011. 128p. 29.99 ***(978-1-4568-8909-8(5))***; pap. 19.99 ***(978-1-4568-8908-1(7))*** Xlibris Corp.
Clark, Nancy L. & Worger, William H. South Africa: The Rise & Fall of Apartheid. 2nd rev. ed. 2011. (Seminar Studies in History Ser.). (ENG., Illus.). 232p. (C). pap. 27.33 *(978-1-4082-4564-4(7))* Longman Publishing Group.
Clingman, Stephen. Bram Fischer: Afrikaner Revolutionary. 2011. 304p. pap. 35.95 *(978-0-86486-677-6(1))* International Publishers Marketing.
Cohen, David Elliot. Nelson Mandela: A Life in Photographs. 2009. (ENG., Illus.). 224p. 24.95 *(978-1-4027-7707-3(8))* Sterling Publishing Co., Inc.
Cole, Catherine M. & Roach, Joseph. Performing South Africa's Truth Commission: Stages of Transition. 2009. (African Expressive Cultures Ser.). (ENG., Illus.). 264p. 65.00 *(978-0-253-35390-0(4),* 0253353904); pap. 24.95 *(978-0-253-22145-2(5),* 0253221455) Indiana Univ. Pr.
Connell, Dan. Old Wrongs, New Rights: Student Views of the New South Africa. 2008. *(978-1-59221-628-4(5));* 168p. pap. *(978-1-59221-629-1(3))* Africa World Pr.
Cram101 Textbook Reviews. Outlines & Highlights for Making of Modern South Afric: Conquest, Apartheid, Democracy by Nigel Worden, ISBN. 2011. 30p. pap. 26.95 ***(978-1-61812-495-1(1))*** Cram101 Inc.
Davies, Ann. Constructive Engagement? Chester Crocker & American Policy in South Africa, Namibia & Angola. 2007. (Illus.). 256p. pap. 29.95 *(978-1-84701-304-0(X),* Currey, James) Boydell & Brewer, Ltd. GBR. Dist: Boydell & Brewer, Inc.
—Constructive Engagement? Chester Crocker & American Policy in South Africa, Namibia & Angola. 2007. (Illus.). 256p. 90.00 *(978-1-84701-305-7(8),* Currey, James) Boydell & Brewer, Ltd. GBR. Dist: Boydell & Brewer, Inc.
Davis, Alexander. The Native Problem in South Africa. 242p. reprint ed. 98.00 *(978-0-7222-9815-2(3))* Library Reprints, Inc.
Daymond, M. J. & Sandwith, Corinne, eds. Africa South: Viewpoints, 1956-1961. 2011. 431p. pap., pap. 55.00 *(978-1-86914-195-0(4))* University of Kwazulu-Natal Press ZAF. Dist: International Specialized Bk. Services.
Deegan, Heather. Politics South Africa. 2nd ed. 2011. (ENG., Illus.). 344p. (C). pap. 43.80 *(978-1-4082-5824-8(2))* Longman Publishing Group.
Dlamini, Jacob. Native Nostalgia. 2010. (ENG.). 200p. pap. 23.00 *(978-1-77009-755-1(4))* Jacana Media ZAF. Dist: Independent Pubs. Group.
Doxtader, Erik. With Faith in the Works of Words: The Beginnings of Reconciliation in South Africa, 1985-1995. 2009. (Rhetoric & Public Affairs Ser.). (ENG.). 368p. pap. 34.95 *(978-0-87013-851-5(0))* Michigan State Univ. Pr.
du Bois-Pedain, Antje. Transitional Amnesty in South Africa. 2011. (ENG.). 422p. pap. 50.00 ***(978-1-107-40401-4(0))*** Cambridge Univ. Pr.
Eno, Mohamed A. The Bantu - Jareer Somali: Unearthing Apartheid in the Horn of Africa. 2008. 320p. pap. *(978-1-905068-95-1(6))* Adonis & Abbey Publishers Ltd.
Fisher, Ryland. Race. 2008. (ENG., Illus.). 252p. pap. 25.95 *(978-1-77009-373-7(7))* Jacana Media ZAF. Dist: Independent Pubs. Group.
Gevisser, Mark. A Legacy of Liberation: Thabo Mbeki & the Future of the South African Dream. 2009. (ENG., Illus.). 400p. 29.95 *(978-0-230-61100-9(1),* Palgrave Macmillan.
Ginsburg, Rebecca. At Home with Apartheid: The Hidden Landscapes of Domestic Service in Johannesburg. 2011. (Illus.). xi, 229p. E-Book *(978-0-8139-3164-7(9));* (ENG., 248p. (gr. 17). 35.00 *(978-0-8139-2888-3(5))* Univ. Pr. of Virginia.
Goodman, Tanya. Staging Solidarity: Truth & Reconciliation in a New South Africa. Eyerman, Ron & Alexander, Jeffrey, eds. 2010. (Yale Cultural Sociology Ser.). (ENG., Illus.). 194p. pap. 33.95 *(978-1-59451-286-5(8))* Paradigm Pubs.
Goodman, Tanya & Sykes, Tanya Goodman. Staging Solidarity: Truth & Reconciliation in a New South Africa. 2009. (Yale Cultural Sociology Ser.). (ENG., Illus.). 194p. 125.00 *(978-1-59451-285-8(X))* Paradigm Pubs.
Grunebaum, Heidi. Memorializing the Past: Everyday Life in South Africa after the Truth & Reconciliation Commission. 2011. (ENG.). 185p. 49.95 *(978-1-4128-1473-7(1))* Transaction Pubs.
Haron, Muhammed. South Africa's Truth & Reconciliation Commission: An Annotated Bibliography [circa 1993-2008]. 2009. (African Political, Economic, & Security Issues Ser.). 69.00 *(978-1-60741-229-8(2))* Nova Science Pubs., Inc.
Holden, Paul & Segal, Lauren. Great Lives: Pivotal Moments. 2009. (ENG., Illus.). 224p. pap. 28.95 *(978-1-77009-592-2(6))* Jacana Media ZAF. Dist: Independent Pubs. Group.
Hook, Derek. A Critical Psychology of the Post-Colonial. 2012. (ENG., Illus.). 264p. 95.00 ***(978-0-415-58756-3(5))*** Routledge.
Hummel, Philip. My Life Growing up White during Apartheid in South Africa. 2011. 100p. pap. 9.99 *(978-1-4567-1800-8(2))* AuthorHouse.
Hysmith-Jones, Annielaurie. Women,Coping Strategies, & Social Change: Eastern Cape South Africa. 2008. 172p. pap. *(978-3-639-08624-9(4))* VDM Verlag Dr. Mueller e.K.
Irwin, Ryan M. Gordian Knot: Apartheid & the Unmaking of the Liberal World Order, 1 vol. 2012. (Oxford Studies in International History Ser.). (ENG.). 288p. 45.00 ***(978-0-19-985561-2(7))*** Oxford Univ. Pr., Inc.
Jacklin, Heather & Vale, Peter, eds. Re-imagining the Social in South Africa: Critique, Theory & Post-Apartheid Society. 2009. 308p. pap. 49.00 *(978-1-86914-179-0(2))* Univ. of Natal Pr. ZAF. Dist: International Specialized Bk. Services.
Kearney, Patrick & Kearney. Guardian of the Light: Archbishop Denis Hurley, a Life Against Apartheid. 2009. (ENG., Illus.). 400p. 34.95 *(978-0-8264-1875-3(9))* Continuum International Publishing Group, Ltd. GBR. Dist: National Bk. Network.
Kepe, Thembela & Ntsebeza, Lungisile, eds. Rural Resistance in South Africa: The Mpondo Revolts after Fifty Years. 2011. (Afrika-Studiecentrum Ser.). (Illus.). vi, 282p. pap. ***(978-90-04-21446-0(1))*** BRILL.
Korr, Chuck & Close, Marvin. More Than Just a Game: Soccer vs. Apartheid: the Most Important Soccer Story Ever Told. (ENG., Illus.). 336p. 2011. pap. 15.99 *(978-0-312-60716-6(4),* St. Martin's Griffin) 2010. 25.99 *(978-0-312-59617-0(0),* Dunne, Thomas Bks.) St. Martin's Pr.
Kros, Cynthia. The Seeds of Separate Development: Origins of Bantu Education. 2010. 213p. pap. 27.50 *(978-1-86888-522-0(4))* Unisa Press / Uitgewers GBR. Dist: International Specialized Bk. Services.
Kumalo, Alf. Through My Lens: A Photographic Memoir. 2011. (Illus.). 224p. 49.95 *(978-0-624-04467-3(X))* NB Pubs. Ltd. ZAF. Dist: International Publishers Marketing.
Lalu, Premesh. The Deaths of Hintsa: Post-Apartheid South Africa & the Shape of Recurring Pasts. 2009. (ENG., Illus.). 352p. pap. 34.95 *(978-0-7969-2233-5(0))* Human Sciences Research Council ZAF. Dist: Independent Pubs. Group.
Lapierre, Dominique. A Rainbow in the Night: The Tumultuous Birth of South Africa. 2013. (ENG.). 336p. pap. 16.00 *(978-0-306-81924-7(4))* Da Capo Pr., Inc.
—A Rainbow in the Night: The Tumultuous Birth of South Africa. 2010. (Playaway Adult Nonfiction Ser.). 59.99 *(978-1-4332-9162-3(2))* Findaway World, LLC.
Le Roux, Wessel & Van Marle, Karin. Post-Apartheid Fragments: Law, Politics & Critique. 2007. (Imagined South Africa Ser.). (Illus.). xiv, 188p. 49.00 *(978-1-86888-405-6(8))* Univ. of South Africa ZAF. Dist: Brill Academic Pubs., Inc.
Lee, Rebekah. African Women & Apartheid: Migration & Settlement in South Africa. 2009. (International Library of African Studies). (ENG., Illus.). 304p. 92.50 *(978-1-84511-819-8(7),* Tauris Academic Studies) I. B. Tauris & Co., Ltd. GBR. Dist: Macmillan.
Lipton, Merle. Liberals, Marxists, & Nationalists: Competing Interpretations of South African History. 2007. (ENG.). 240p. 89.00 *(978-0-230-60059-1(X))* Palgrave Macmillan.
Lollini, Andrea. Constitutionalism & Transitional Justice in South Africa. 2010. (HRC Ser.). 238p. 80.00 *(978-1-84545-764-8(1))* Berghahn Bks., Inc.
Madden, Mike. Planting the Seeds of a Non-Racial Society. 2010. 124p. pap. *(978-3-8383-5430-9(3))* Lambert Academic Publishing.
Mager, Anne Kelk. Beer, Sociability, & Masculinity in South Africa. 2010. (African Systems of Thought Ser.). (ENG.). 248p. pap. 24.95 *(978-0-253-22180-3(3),* 0253221803) Indiana Univ. Pr.
—Beer, Sociability, & Masculinity in South Africa: Drinking, Sociability, & Masculinity. 2010. (African Systems of Thought Ser.). (ENG.). 248p. 65.00 *(978-0-253-35449-5(8),* 0253354498) Indiana Univ. Pr.
Mandela, Nelson. Conversations with Myself. 2010. (ENG., Illus.). 480p. 28.00 *(978-0-374-12895-1(2))* Farrar, Straus & Giroux.
—Conversations with Myself. 2011. (ENG., Illus.). 480p. pap. 18.00 *(978-0-312-61168-2(4))* Picador.
—Conversations with Myself. lt. ed. 2011. 499p. 32.99 *(978-1-4104-3421-0(4))* Thorndike Pr.
—Let Freedom Reign: The Words of Nelson Mandela. Russell, Henry, ed. 2010. (ENG.). 144p. 14.95 *(978-1-56656-800-5(5),* Interlink Bks.) Interlink Publishing Group, Inc.
—Selected Speeches & Writings of Nelson Mandela: The End of Apartheid in South Africa. 2010. 290p. pap. *(978-1-934941-78-2(6))* Red & Black Pubs.
Manson, Andrew & Mbenga, Bernard, eds. People of the Dew: A History of the Bafokeng of Rustenburg District, South Africa, from Early Times to 2000. 2011. (ENG.). 256p. pap. 39.00 *(978-1-77009-825-1(9))* Jacana Media ZAF. Dist: Independent Pubs. Group.
Masilela, Elias. Number 43 Trelawney Park KwaMagogo. 2011. (Illus.). 256p. pap. 30.95 *(978-0-86486-706-3(9))* International Publishers Marketing.
Massey, Daniel. Under Protest: The Rise of Student Resistance at the University of Fort Hare. 2010. 334p. pap. 36.50 *(978-1-86888-542-8(9))* Unisa Press / Uitgewers GBR. Dist: International Specialized Bk. Services.
Matsinhe, David M. Apartheid Vertigo: South African & African Outsiders. 2011. (Interdisciplinary Research Ser. in Ethnic, Gender & Class Relations Ser.). (Illus.). 230p. 99.95 ***(978-1-4094-2619-6(X))*** Ashgate Publishing Co.
McDonald, Peter D. The Literature Police: Apartheid Censorship & Its Cultural Consequences. 2010. (Illus.). 432p. pap. 27.95 *(978-0-19-959111-4(3))* Oxford Univ. Pr., Inc.
McGregor, Liz & Nuttall, Sarah, eds. At Risk: Writing on & over the Edge of South Africa. 2009. 248p. pap. 17.00 *(978-1-86842-271-5(2))* International Publishers Marketing.
Meierhenrich, Jens. The Legacies of Law: Long-Run Consequences of Legal Development in South Africa, 1652-2000. (ENG., Illus.). 406p. 2010. pap. 36.00 *(978-0-521-15699-8(8))* 2008. 95.00 *(978-0-521-89873-7(0))* Cambridge Univ. Pr.
Mojapelo, John Seakalala. The Corner People of Lady Selborne. 2009. 295p. pap. 59.00 *(978-1-86888-560-2(7))* Unisa Press / Uitgewers GBR. Dist: International Specialized Bk. Services.
Moon, Claire. Narrating Political Reconciliation: South Africa's Truth & Reconciliation Commission. (ENG.). 188p. 2009. pap. 26.50 *(978-0-7391-4045-1(0))* 2007. 62.99 *(978-0-7391-2127-6(8))* Lexington Bks.
Mcsegomi, Mosala & Mosupyoe, Boatamo. Soweto Explodes. 2nd rev. ed. 2010. (ENG., Illus.). 350p. pap. 74.35 *(978-0-7575-6344-7(9))* Kendall Hunt Publishing Co.
Noonan, Patrick. They're Burning the Churches. 2011. (ENG.). 288p. pap. 20.95 ***(978-1-77009-986-9(7))*** Jacana Media ZAF. Dist: Independent Pubs. Group.
Orgeret, Kristin Skare. Television News: The South African Post-apartheid Experience. 2009. 364p. pap. *(978-3-639-04279-5(4))* VDM Verlag Dr. Mueller e.K.

Pappé, Ilan. Peoples Apart: Israel, South Africa & the Apartheid Question. 2013. (ENG.). 272p. pap. 19.95 (978-1-84511-721-4(2)) I. B. Tauris & Co., Ltd. GBR. Dist: Macmillan.

Paul, Samuel A. The Ubuntu God: Deconstructing a South African Narrative of Oppression. 2008. (Princeton Theological Monographs). 194p. pap. 22.00 (978-1-55635-510-3(6), Pickwick Pubns.) Wipf & Stock Pubs.

Peclard, et al. Swiss Churches, Apartheid & South Africa. 2011. 400p. pap. 49.95 **(978-3-8258-9796-3(6))** Lit Verlag DEU. Dist: Transaction Pubs.

Plangesis, Esmeralda. In Search of Liberation. 2009. 380p. pap. 19.99 (978-1-4389-9717-9(5)) AuthorHouse.

Postel, Gitte. Unheimlich Moederland: (Anti-)pastorale letteren in Zuid-Afrika. 2007. (LUP Dissertaties Ser.). (DUT.). 300p. per. (978-90-8728-003-1(3), Leiden Univ. Pr.) Amsterdam Univ. Pr.

Potgieter, De Wet. Total Onslaught: Apartheid's Dirty Tricks Exposed. 2008. (Illus.). 344p. pap. 29.00 (978-1-77007-328-9(0)) Struik Pubs. ZAF. Dist: International Publishers Marketing.

Saks, Lucia. Cinema in a Democratic South Africa: The Race for Representation. 2010. (New Directions in National Cinemas Ser.). (ENG., Illus.). 272p. 65.00 (978-0-253-35457-0(9), 0253354579); pap. 24.95 (978-0-253-22186-5(2), 0253221862) Indiana Univ. Pr.

Saul, John S. Revolutionary Traveller: Freeze-Frames from a Life. 2010. (ENG., Illus.). 436p. pap. 26.95 (978-1-894037-37-2(5)) Arbeiter Ring Publishing CAN. Dist: AK Pr. Distribution.

Sawyer, Kem Knapp. Champion of Freedom: Nelson Mandela. 2011. E-Book **(978-1-59935-312-8(1))** Reynolds, Morgan Inc.

Scheub, Harold. The Uncoiling Python: South African Storytellers & Resistance. 2010. (ENG., Illus.). 288p. 46.95 (978-0-8214-1921-2(8)); pap. 24.95 (978-0-8214-1922-9(6)) Ohio Univ. Pr.

Seavers, Corbin. Apartheid: The Untold Story. 59p. (Orig.). pap. 5.95 (978-1-56411-029-9(X)) UBUS Communications Systems.

Shapiro, Ian & Tebeau, Kahreen, eds. After Apartheid: Reinventing South Africa? 2011. (ENG., Illus.). 384p. (gr. 17). 40.00 (978-0-8139-3097-8(9)) Univ. Pr. of Virginia.

Sikakane, Ebenezer M. Wrestling with Apartheid: An Autobiography. 2010. (978-1-77069-009-7(3)) Word Alive Pr.

Skinner, Rob. The Foundations of Anti-Apartheid: Liberal Humanitarians & Transnational Activists in Britain & the United States, C. 1919-64. 2010. (ENG.). 280p. 84.00 (978-0-230-20366-2(3)) Palgrave Macmillan.

Smith, David James. Young Mandela: The Revolutionary Years. 2010. (ENG., Illus.). 416p. 27.99 (978-0-316-03548-4(3)) Little Brown & Co.

Spivey, Kirby. The Cola Wars in South Afric. 2011. 68p. pap. **(978-3-8443-2057-2(1))** Lambert Academic Publishing.

Stone, Judith. When She Was White: The True Story of a Family Divided by Race. 2008. 352p. pap. 14.95 (978-1-4013-0937-4(2)) Miramax Bks.

Thörn, Håkan. Anti-Apartheid & the Emergence of a Global Civil Society. 2009. (St. Antony's Ser.). (ENG.). 272p. pap. 31.00 (978-0-230-23496-3(8)) Palgrave Macmillan.

Totem Media for the Research and Planning Department of the Royal Bafokeng, ed. Mining the Future: The Bafokeng Story. 2011. (ENG.). 128p. pap. 12.00 (978-1-77009-824-4(0)) Jacana Media ZAF. Dist: Independent Pubs. Group.

Tsolo, Donald A. The Promise: Black Youth Confront the Cauldron of Apartheid. 2009. 208p. 27.95 (978-1-4401-4542-1(3)); pap. 17.95 (978-1-4401-4540-7(7)) iUniverse, Inc.

Urbsaitis, Bryan Mark. Wounded Healers. 2009. 276p. pap. (978-3-639-16504-3(7)) VDM Verlag Dr. Mueller e.K.

Van Wyk, Barry. The Balance of Power & the Transition to Democracy in South Afric. 2009. 208p. pap. (978-3-639-17939-2(0)) VDM Verlag Dr. Mueller e.K.

Welsh, David John. The Rise & Fall of Apartheid. 2010. (Reconsiderations in Southern African History Ser.). (ENG., Illus.). 660p. (gr. 17). pap. 35.00 (978-0-8139-3056-5(1)) Univ. Pr. of Virginia.

Weskott, Aljoscha & Marietta, Kesting, eds. Sun Tropes. 2010. (ENG., Illus.). 292p. pap. 49.95 (978-3-941360-04-4(3)) Verlag der Buchhandlung Walther Konig DEU. Dist: D.A.P./Distributed Art Pubs.

White, Ben. Israeli Apartheid: A Beginner's Guide. 2009. (ENG., Illus.). 144p. 60.00 (978-0-7453-2888-1(1)); pap. 15.95 (978-0-7453-2887-4(3)) Pluto Pr. GBR. Dist: Macmillan.

Wilderson, Frank B., III. Incognegro: A Memoir of Exile & Apartheid. 2008. (ENG.). 500p. pap. 18.00 (978-0-89608-783-5(2)) South End Pr.

—Incognegro: From Black Power to Apartheid & Back. 2007. 272p. 24.95 (978-0-8070-7268-4(0)) Beacon Pr.

Worden, Nigel. The Making of Modern South Africa. 5th ed. 2012. (Historical Association Studies). (ENG., Illus.). 224p. pap. 34.95 **(978-0-470-65633-4(6)**, Wiley-Blackwell) Wiley, John & Sons, Inc.

APARTMENT HOUSES

see also Condominiums; Housing Management; Landlord and Tenant; Real Estate Management

Benitez, Cristina Paredes. 200 Small Apartment Ideas. 2012. (ENG., Illus.). 800p. 49.95 **(978-1-77085-045-3(7))** Firefly Bks., Ltd.

Beta-Plus Publishing. Apartments: Home Series 6. 2009. (Home Ser.). (ENG., Illus.). 128p. pap. (978-90-8944-037-2(2), Beta-Plus (Acc)) Antique Collectors' Club.

BETA-PLUS Publishing, creator. Lofts & Apartments. 2008. (ENG., Illus.). 208p. 95.00 (978-90-77213-86-5(4)) Beta-Plus Pubs. BEL. Dist: Antique Collectors' Club.

Broto, Carles. Apartment Buildings. 2012. (Plan Atlas Ser.). (ENG.). 600p. 75.00 (978-84-15123-21-7(3)) Links International (Leading International Key Services Barcelona, S.A.) ESP. Dist: National Bk. Network.

—Apartment Buildings Today. 2011. (ENG., Illus.). 300p. 49.00 (978-84-92796-84-7(7)) Links International (Leading International Key Services Barcelona, S.A.) ESP. Dist: National Bk. Network.

—Apartment Interiors. (ENG., Illus.). 240p. 2009. pap. 29.99 (978-84-96969-91-9(6)) 2007. 45.00 (978-84-96263-71-0(1)) Links International (Leading International Key Services Barcelona, S.A.) ESP. Dist: National Bk. Network.

—Innovative Apartment Buildings. 2008. (ENG., Illus.). 240p. 55.00 (978-84-96263-85-7(1)) Links International (Leading International Key Services Barcelona, S.A.) ESP. Dist: National Bk. Network.

—Urban Apartment Blocks. 2008. (ENG., Illus.). 240p. 39.95 (978-84-96263-90-1(8)) Links International (Leading International Key Services Barcelona, S.A.) ESP. Dist: National Bk. Network.

Browne, Beth, ed. 21st Century Architecture: Apartment Living. 2011. (ENG., Illus.). 224p. 50.00 (978-1-86470-445-7(4)) Images Publishing Group AUS. Dist: National Bk. Network.

Butler-Bowdon, Caroline & Pickett, Charles. Homes in the Sky: Apartment Living in Australia. 2007. (ENG., Illus.). 256p. 53.00 (978-0-522-85316-2(1)) Melbourne Univ. Publishing AUS. Dist: Independent Pubs. Group.

Byers, Ann. First Apartment Smarts. 2009. (Get Smart with Your Money Ser.). (Illus.). 64p. (J). (gr. 7-12). 29.25 (978-1-4358-5272-3(9)) Rosen Publishing Group, Inc., The.

Calicchio, Denise. High Rise Low Down: Who's Who & What's What in New York's Most Coveted Apartment Houses. 2009. (ENG.). 288p. pap. 12.95 (978-1-56980-357-8(9)) Barricade Bks., Inc.

Canizares, Ana G. 150 Best Apartment Ideas. 2007. (ENG., Illus.). 600p. 29.99 (978-0-06-113973-4(4), Collins Design) HarperCollins Pubs.

Canizares, Ana G. & Mola, Francesc Zamora. 150 Best New Apartment Ideas. 2011. (ENG., Illus.). 600p. 29.99 (978-0-06-206723-4(0), Collins Design) HarperCollins Pubs.

Corcuera Aranguiz, Antonio & Minguet, Josep Maria. Remodelling City Apartments. 2007. (POR., Illus.). 192p. 69.50 (978-84-96429-70-3(9)) Instituto Monsa de Ediciones, S.A. ESP. Dist: Trans-Atlantic Pubns., Inc.

Costa Duran, Sergi, ed. High Density Housing. 2009. (Illus.). 256p. (978-84-92463-35-0(X)) Loft Pubns.

De Baeck, Philippe. Mini Apartment Bible, 1 vol. 2009. (ENG., Illus.). 384p. 24.95 (978-90-79761-08-1(7)) Tectum B.V.B.A. BEL. Dist: Innovative Logistics.

de Haro, Fernando & Fuentes, Omar. Ideas: +Apartments. 2012. (Ideas Ser.). (ENG., Illus.). 264p. pap. 24.95 **(978-607-437-086-7(9))** AM Editores MEX. Dist: Perseus-PGW.

Designers Apartments in Japan Low-Rise: Architect-Designed Low Rise Condominiums. 2007. 49.95 (978-4-7661-1712-7(3)) Graphic-Sha JPN. Dist: Gingko Pr., Inc.

Dubois, Martin. Architecture et Habitat Collectif Au Québec: 65 Immeubles Résidentiels. 2010. (FRE., Illus.). xv, 240p. (978-2-551-19863-4(1)) Publications du Quebec, Les.

Ebner, Peter, et al. Typologie+ Innovativer Wohnungsbau. 2009. (Illus.). 431p. (978-3-0346-0086-6(0)) Birkhauser Verlag AG.

Fajardo, Julio. Designer Apartments. 2011. (ENG.). 480p. 29.99 (978-3-8331-6010-3(1)) h.f.ullmann DEU. Dist: Innovative Logistics.

Forner, Johannes. Wohn- & Bürgerhäuser Im Leipziger Musikviertel. 2007. (GER., Illus.). 95p. pap. (978-3-86729-010-4(5)) Heydick, Erika Sax-Verlag Beucha.

Freedman, Philip, et al. Service Charges: Law & Practice. 5th rev. ed. 2012. (ENG.). 450p. pap. (978-1-84661-247-3(0)) Jordan Publishing, Ltd.

Gafsou, Matthieu. Ce Rêve étrange: Le Corbusier à Firminy. 2009. (FRE., Illus.). 106p. (978-2-7424-2695-9(7)) Gallimard, Editions.

Gillingham-Ryan, Maxwell. Apartment Therapy Presents: Real Homes, Real People, Hundreds of Real Design Solutions. 2008. (ENG., Illus.). 264p. 27.50 (978-0-8118-5982-0(7)) Chronicle Bks. LLC.

Gomez, Mariette Himes & Pittel, Christine. Apartments: Defining Style. 2010. (ENG., Illus.). 240p. 39.99 (978-0-06-167236-1(X), Collins Design) HarperCollins Pubs.

Government Printing Office Staff. Current Housing Reports H-130, Market Absorption of Apartments. pap. 18.00 (978-0-16-009570-2(0)) United States Government Printing Office.

Graham, Laurie. In Other Words: Tales of Paris & Language. 2009. (Illus.). 160p. pap. 12.95 (978-1-59571-370-4(0)) Word Association Pubs.

Gregory, Jamee. New York Parties: Private Views. 2010. (ENG., Illus.). 208p. 55.00 (978-0-8478-3403-7(4)) Rizzoli International Pubns., Inc.

Gross, Michael. 740 Park: The Story of the World's Richest Apartment Building. 2006. (ENG., Illus.). 576p. pap. 16.95 (978-0-7679-1744-5(8), Broadway) Broadway Bks.

H. F. Ullmann Staff, creator. Designer Apartments. 2008. (Art & Architecture Ser.). (Illus.). 800p. 69.95 (978-0-8416-0064-5(3)) American Map Corp.

Hicks, Tyler G. How to Build Riches in Real Estate with Multifamily Homes. 2007. ring bd. 150.00 (978-1-56150-813-6(6)) International Wealth Success, Inc.

Hodgkinson, Liz. How to Buy a Flat: All You Need to Know about Apartment Living & Letting. 2006. 214p. per. 22.00 (978-1-84528-115-1(2)) How To Books GBR. Dist: Parkwest Pubns., Inc.

Images Publishing Group. 50 of the World's Best Apartments. 2006. (ENG., Illus.). 344p. 60.00 (978-1-920744-49-6(5)) Images Publishing Group AUS. Dist: National Bk. Network.

Inions, Cynthia. Open-Plan Living: Creating a Stylish & Practical Open-Plan Home. 2007. (ENG., Illus.). 144p. pap. (978-1-84597-557-9(X)) Ryland Peters & Small.

James, Diana E. Shared Walls: Seattle Apartment Buildings, 1900-1939. 2011. (ENG.). 281p. pap. 55.00 **(978-0-7864-6596-5(4))** McFarland & Co., Inc. Pubs.

Kelley, Edward N. Practical Apartment Management. 6th ed. 2009. (978-1-57203-141-8(7)) Institute of Real Estate Management.

Klaffke, Julius. Living Streets - Laubengänge: Living Streets in Residential Building. Ebner, Peter, ed. 2009. (GER & ENG., Illus.). 188p. pap. (978-3-211-79177-6(9), 3211791779) Actar Birkhauser Distribution.

Klag, Robert. Happy about Apartment Management: 30 Years of Expert Tips & Advice on Multifamily Property Management. 2006. pap. (978-1-60005-031-2(X)) Happy About.

Lindahl, David. Multi-Family Millions: How Anyone Can Reposition Apartments for Big Profits. 2008. (ENG., Illus.). 272p. 27.95 (978-0-470-26760-8(7), Wiley) Wiley, John & Sons, Inc.

Martinez, Matthew A. Investing in Apartment Buildings: Create a Reliable Stream of Income & Build Long-Term Wealth. 2008. (ENG., Illus.). 240p. pap. 24.95 (978-0-07-149886-9(9), 0071498869) McGraw-Hill Cos., The.

Meier, Richard. Richard Meier Houses & Apartments. 2007. (ENG., Illus.). 296p. 85.00 (978-0-8478-2994-1(4)) Rizzoli International Pubns., Inc.

Messana, Paola. Soviet Communal Living: An Oral History of the Kommunalka. 2011. (Palgrave Studies in Oral History Ser.). (ENG., Illus.). 184p. 84.00 (978-0-230-11016-8(9)) Palgrave Macmillan.

Mills, Arlen C., et al. The Valuation of Apartment Properties. 2nd ed. 2007. (978-0-922154-95-1(3)) Appraisal Institute, The.

Mostaedi, Arian. New Apartment. 2009. (ENG.). 168p. pap. 24.99 (978-84-96969-99-5(1)) Links International (Leading International Key Services Barcelona, S.A.) ESP. Dist: National Bk. Network.

Pauwels, Wim. Contemporary Apartments. 2011. (ENG., Illus.). 200p. 80.00 (978-90-8944-090-7(9)) Beta-Plus Pubs. BEL. Dist: Antique Collectors' Club.

Penn, Ame. Apartment Renting Basics: Apartment renting for the Novice. 2009. 80p. pap. 14.95 (978-1-4401-2887-5(1)) iUniverse, Inc.

Perks, Sydney. Residential Flats. 2007. 360p. per. (978-1-905217-76-2(5)) Mills, Jeremy Publishing.

Quartino, Daniela Santos. 200 Outstanding Apartment Ideas. 2009. (200 Home Ideas Ser.). (ENG., Illus.). 800p. 39.95 (978-1-55407-394-8(4)) Firefly Bks., Ltd.

Quenby, Richard. Sale & Management of Flats. 3rd rev. ed. 2010. 330p. pap. 215.00 incl. cd-rom (978-1-84766-244-6(7), Bloomsbury Professional) Bloomsbury Publishing Plc GBR. Dist: International Specialized Bk. Services.

Rizzoli Staff, et al. The New Apartment: Smart Living in Small Spaces. 2007. (ENG., Illus.). 420p. pap. 35.00 (978-0-7893-1529-8(7)) Universe Publishing.

Schuneman, Kyle & Summerville, Heather. The First Apartment Book: Cool Design for Small Spaces. 2012. (ENG., Illus.). 256p. pap. 24.99 **(978-0-307-95290-5(8)**, Clarkson Potter) Crown Publishing Group.

Spier, Carol. The Apartment Book: Smart Decorating for Spaces Large & Small. 2007. (House Beautiful Ser.). (ENG., Illus.). 272p. 19.95 (978-1-58816-598-5(1)) Hearst Communications, Inc.

Taschen, Angelika, ed. New Paris Interiors: Nouveaux interieurs parisiens. 2008. (FRE, GER & ENG., Illus.). 300p. 39.99 (978-3-8365-0250-4(X)) TASCHEN DEU. Dist: Ingram Pub. Services.

Treberspurg, Mar, ed. SolarCity Linz-Pichling. Blaschke, Beverly, tr. from GER. 2008. (Illus.). 216p. 69.95 (978-3-211-30562-1(9), 3211305629) Springer Wien AUT. Dist: Actar Birkhauser Distribution.

Trent, Roger J. Don't Show Me the Model: The Secret Guide for Finding an Apartment. 2011. 80p. pap. 9.99 **(978-1-4634-1534-1(6))** AuthorHouse.

Trulove, James Grayson. 25 Apartments & Lofts under 1000 Square Feet. 2008. (Illus.). 224p. pap. 39.95 (978-0-06-134020-8(0)) HarperCollins Pubs.

—25 Apartments & Lofts under 2500 Square Feet. 2007. (Illus.). 224p. pap. 39.95 (978-0-06-114989-4(6), Collins Design) HarperCollins Pubs.

Wietzorrek, Ulrike. Housing+ Threshold, Access & Transparency in Residential Buildings. 2011. (ENG., Illus.). 424p. 99.95 (978-3-0346-0614-1(1)) Birkhauser Verlag AG CHE. Dist: Actar Birkhauser Distribution.

APARTMENT HOUSES, COOPERATIVE

Calicchio, Denise. High Rise Low Down: Who's Who & What's What in New York's Most Coveted Apartment Houses. 2009. (ENG.). 288p. pap. 12.95 (978-1-56980-357-8(9)) Barricade Bks., Inc.

Grimm, Beth A. The Condo Owner's Answer Book. 2008. (ENG.). 256p. per. 16.95 (978-1-57248-633-1(3), Sphinx Publishing) Sourcebooks, Inc.

Irwin, Robert. Tips & Traps When Buying a Condo, CO-Op, or Townhouse: Includes The Latest Info on Shared Ownership Properties. 2nd rev. ed. 2006. (Tips & Traps Ser.). (ENG., Illus.). 208p. per. 16.95 (978-0-07-146795-7(5), 0071467955) McGraw-Hill Cos., The.

Reed, David. Financing Your Condo, Co-Op, or Townhouse, 1 vol. 2009. (ENG.). 240p. pap. 18.95 (978-0-8144-8062-5(4)) Amacom.

APERTURE CARD SYSTEMS

see Microfilm Aperture Card Systems

APES

see also Bonobo; Chimpanzees; Gibbons; Gorilla; Orangutan

Ankel-Simons, Friderun. Primate Anatomy: An Introduction. 3rd ed. 2007. (ENG., Illus.). 752p. per. 80.95 (978-0-12-372576-9(3), Academic Pr.) Elsevier Science & Technology Bks.

Arndt, Ingo. Monkeys & Apes in the Wild. 2009. (ENG.). 224p. 45.00 (978-1-901092-91-2(7)) Papadakis Dist A/C.

Bearzi, Maddalena & Stanford, Craig B. Beautiful Minds: The Parallel Lives of Great Apes & Dolphins. 368p. 2010. pap. 14.95 (978-0-674-04627-6(7)) 2008. 24.95 (978-0-674-02781-7(7)) Harvard Univ. Pr.

Benchley, Belle J. My Friends the Apes. 2007. (ENG.). 338p. 46.95 (978-0-548-06436-8(9)) Kessinger Publishing, LLC.

De la Bédoyère, Camilla. Monkeys & Apes. 2010. (Discovery of Life Ser.). 48p. (YA). lib. bdg. 19.95 (978-1-4222-1522-7(9)) Mason Crest Pubs.

Greenberg, Jill. Monkey Portraits. rev. ed. 2007. (ENG., Illus.). 128p. pap. 17.99 (978-0-316-00512-8(6)) Little Brown & Co.

Guldberg, Helene. Just Another Ape? 2010. (Societas Ser.). (ENG.). 128p. pap. 17.90 (978-1-84540-163-4(8)) Imprint Academic GBR. Dist: Ingram Pub. Services.

Hassan, Rich & Azzara, Mike. The Great Apes Go to Charm School: Notes on Modern Man. 116p. (978-0-9642902-0-4(0)) Hassan, Richard.

Hillix, W. A. & Rumbaugh, Duane. Animal Bodies, Human Minds: Ape, Dolphin, & Parrot Language Skills. 2010. (Developments in Primatology: Progress & Prospects Ser.). 224p. pap. 199.00 (978-1-4419-3400-0(6), 1441934006) Springer.

Hohmann, Gottfried, et al, eds. Feeding Ecology in Apes & Other Primates: Ecological, Physical, & Behavioral Aspects. 2006. (Cambridge Studies in Biological & Evolutionary Anthropology Ser.). (ENG., Illus.). 540p. 165.99 (978-0-521-85837-3(2)) Cambridge Univ. Pr.

Huxley, Thomas Henry. Man's Place in Nature & Other Essays. 2008. 390p. 48.95 (978-1-4365-6619-3(3)) 2007. 392p. per. 33.95 (978-0-548-76241-7(4)) Kessinger Publishing, LLC.

King, Barbara J. Information Continuum: Evolution of Social Information Transfer in Monkeys, Apes, & Hominids. (Illus.). 166p. pap. 19.95 (978-0-933452-40-4(3)) School for Advanced Research Pr./SAR Pr.

Morris, Desmond & Parker, Steve. Planet Ape. 2009. (ENG., Illus.). 288p. 49.95 (978-1-55407-566-9(1)) Firefly Bks., Ltd.

Owen, Richard. On the Classification & Geographical Distribution of the Mammalia. 2009. (Cambridge Library Collection - Life Sciences Ser.). (ENG., Illus.). 112p. pap. 19.99 (978-1-108-00198-4(X)) Cambridge Univ. Pr.

Raffaele, Paul. Among the Great Apes: Adventures on the Trail of Our Closest Relatives. 2011. (ENG.). 384p. pap. 15.99 (978-0-06-167184-5(3), Harper Paperbacks) HarperCollins Pubs.

—Among the Great Apes: Adventures on the Trail of Our Closest Relatives. 2010. 384p. 26.99 (978-0-06-167183-8(5)) Smithsonian Institution Pr.

Rich, Jeremy. Missing Links: The African & American Worlds of R. L. Garner, Primate Collector. 2012. (Race in the Atlantic World, 1700-1900 Ser.). (ENG., Illus.). 200p. 59.95 **(978-0-8203-4059-3(6))**; pap. 24.95 **(978-0-8203-4060-9(X))** Univ. of Georgia Pr.

Robbins, Martha M. & Boesch, Christophe, eds. Among African Apes: Stories & Photos from the Field. 2011. (ENG., Illus.). 196p. 29.95 (978-0-520-26710-7(9)) Univ. of California Pr.

Rumbaugh, Duane M., ed. Gibbon & Siamang: A Series of Volumes on the Lesser Apes, 4 vols., Set. Incl. Vol. 1. Evolution, Ecology, Behavior & Captive Maintenance. 1972. (978-3-8055-1362-3(3)); Vol. 3. Natural History, Social Behavior, Reproduction, Vocalizations, Prehension. 1974. (978-3-8055-1602-0(9)); Vol. 4. Suspensory Behavior, Locomotion & Other Behaviors of Captive Gibbons; Cognition. 1975. (978-3-8055-1658-7(4)); (Illus.). (978-3-8055-2308-0(4)) Karger, S. AG.

Russon, Anne E. & Begun, David R., eds. The Evolution of Thought: Evolutionary Origins of Great Ape Intelligence. 2007. (ENG., Illus.). 396p. pap. 79.00 (978-0-521-03992-5(4)) Cambridge Univ. Pr.

Sorenson, John. Ape. 2009. (Reaktion Books - Animal Ser.). (ENG., Illus.). 224p. pap. 19.95 (978-1-86189-422-9(8)) Reaktion Bks., Ltd. GBR. Dist: Chicago Distribution Ctr.

Washburn, David A., ed. Primate Perspectives on Behavior & Cognition. 2006. (Decade of Behavior Ser.). (Illus.). 319p. 29.95 (978-1-59147-422-7(1)) American Psychological Assn.

Weitz, Paul. Monkey Portraits. 2006. (ENG., Illus.). 112p. 24.99 (978-0-8212-5755-5(2)) Bulfinch.

APHAKIA

Olson, Randall J., et al. Cataract Surgery from Routine to Complex: A Practical Guide. 2011. (ENG., Illus.). 272p. 169.95 (978-1-55642-947-7(9)) SLACK, Inc.

APHASIA

see also Amnesia

Ackerman, Diane. One Hundred Names for Love: A Memoir. 2012. (ENG.). 336p. pap. 15.95 **(978-0-393-34174-4(7)**, 34174) Norton, W. W. & Co., Inc.

Armstrong, Beth. 37th Clinical Aphasiology Conference: A Special Issue of Aphasiology. 2009. (Special Issues of Aphasiology Ser.). (ENG.). 248p. pap. 64.50 (978-1-84169-859-5(8), Psychology Press) Taylor & Francis Group GBR. Dist: Taylor & Francis Group.

—38th Clinical Aphasiology Conference. 2009. (Special Issues of Aphasiology Ser.). (ENG.). 296p. pap. 59.95 (978-1-84872-719-9(4), Psychology Press) Taylor & Francis Group GBR. Dist: Taylor & Francis Group.

Armstrong, Beth, ed. 39th Clinical Aphasiology Conference: A Special Issue of Aphasiology. 2010. (Special Issues of Aphasiology Ser.). (ENG.). 304p. pap. 61.95 (978-1-84872-738-0(0), Psychology Press) Taylor & Francis Group GBR. Dist: Taylor & Francis Group.

—40th Clinical Aphasiology Conference: A Special Issue of 40th Clinical Aphasiology Conference. 2011. (Special Issues of Aphasiology Ser.). (ENG.). 180p. pap. 60.00 (978-1-84872-746-5(1), Psychology Press) Taylor & Francis Group GBR. Dist: Taylor & Francis Group.

Bastiaanse, Roelien & Thompson, Cynthia K., eds. Perspectives on Agrammatism. 2012. (Brain, Behaviour & Cognition Ser.). (ENG., Illus.). 256p. (C). 72.00 *(978-1-84872-055-8(6)*, Psychology Press) Taylor & Francis Group GBR. Dist: Taylor & Francis Group.

Berger Morse, Margaret. Laugh a Lot Cry a Lot: When Tragedy Strikes - A journey through stroke/s & Healing. 2009. 264p. 24.99 *(978-1-4389-7301-2(2))*; pap. 14.49 *(978-1-4389-7300-5(4))* AuthorHouse.

Blumstein, Sheila A. A Phonological Investigation of Aphasic Speech. (Janua Linguarum. Series Minor Ser.). (ENG.). 118p. 210.00 ***(978-3-11-186899-8(0))*** De Gruyter, Mouton DEU. Dist: de Gruyter, Walter GmbH & Co. KG.

Brady & Armstrong. Disordered Communicative Interaction: Current & Future Approach. 2007. (Special Issues of Aphasiology Ser.). 160p. 74.50 *(978-1-84169-822-9(9)*, Psychology Press) Taylor & Francis Group GBR. Dist: Taylor & Francis Group.

Brubaker, Susan. Basic Level Workbook for Aphasia. 2009. pap. 69.95 *(978-0-8143-3316-7(8))* Wayne State Univ. Pr.

Butt, Pamela & Bucks, Romola. Bnvr: The Butt Non-Verbal Reasoning Test. (Illus.). 56p. spiral bd. *(978-0-86388-472-6(5)*, 002-5161) Speechmark Publishing Ltd.

Cacace, Anthony & McFarland, Dennis, eds. Controversies in Central Auditory Processing Disorder. 2008. (Illus.). 371p. 98.95 *(978-1-59756-260-7(2))* Plural Publishing, Inc.

Chapey, Roberta, ed. Language Intervention Strategies in Aphasia & Related Neurogenic Communication Disorders. 5th rev. ed. 2008. (ENG., Illus.). 1091p. 97.99 *(978-0-7817-6981-5(7))* Lippincott Williams & Wilkins.

Code, Chris & Tesak, Juergen. Milestones in the History of Aphasia: Theories & Protagonists. 2nd ed. 2008. (Brain Damage, Behaviour & Cognition Ser.). (ENG., Illus.). 312p. 79.95 *(978-1-84169-513-6(0)*, Psychology Press) Taylor & Francis Group GBR. Dist: Taylor & Francis Group.

Cram101 Textbook Reviews & Cram101 Textbook Reviews. Outlines & Highlights for Language Intervention Strategies in Aphasia & Related Neurogenic Communication Disorders by Roberta Chapey, Isbn: 97807817. 2011. 124p. pap. 28.95 ***(978-1-61654-157-6(1))*** Cram101 Inc.

Cruice, Madeline. Access & Inclusion Issues with Aphasia. 2008. (Special Issues of Aphasiology Ser.). (ENG.). 136p. 74.50 *(978-1-84169-821-2(0)*, Psychology Press) Taylor & Francis Group GBR. Dist: Taylor & Francis Group.

Davis, G. Albyn. Aphasiology: Disorders & Clinical Practice. 2nd rev. ed. 2006. (ENG., Illus.). 400p. (C). pap. 133.33 *(978-0-205-48099-9(3))* Allyn & Bacon, Inc.

Drummond, Sakina S. Neurogenic Communication Disorders: Aphasia & Cognitive-Communication Disorders. 2006. (Illus.). 246p. 55.95 *(978-0-398-07650-4(2))*; pap. 35.95 *(978-0-398-07651-1(0))* Thomas, Charles C. Pub., Ltd.

Duchan, Judith, et al, eds. The Aphasia Therapy File, Volume 2, Vol. 2. 2007. (ENG., Illus.). 296p. 67.95 *(978-1-84169-270-8(0)*, Psychology Press) Taylor & Francis Group GBR. Dist: Taylor & Francis Group.

Edwards, Susan. Fluent Aphasia. 2009. (Cambridge Studies in Linguistics Ser.). (ENG.). 244p. pap. 34.99 *(978-0-521-10749-5(0))* Cambridge Univ. Pr.

Elman, Roberta J. Group Treatment for Neurogenic Communication Disorders: The Expert Clinician's Approach. 2nd rev. ed. 2006. (Illus.). 383p. per. 69.95 *(978-1-59756-070-2(7))* Plural Publishing, Inc.

Fawcus, Margaret, et al. Aphasia Therapy in Practice: Comprehension. 2nd ed. (Illus.). 204p. spiral bd. *(978-0-86388-424-5(5)*, 002-0756) Speechmark Publishing Ltd.

—Aphasia Therapy in Practice: Reading. (Illus.). 152p. spiral bd. *(978-0-86388-086-5(X)*, 002-1312) Speechmark Publishing Ltd.

—Aphasia Therapy in Practice: Writing. (Illus.). 224p. spiral bd. *(978-0-86388-427-6(X)*, 002-1730) Speechmark Publishing Ltd.

Freud, Sigmund. Psychopathology of Everyday Life: Introduction by A. A. Brill. 2011. 352p. pap. 10.50 ***(978-1-891396-57-1(9))*** Martino Publishing.

Gitterman, Martin R., et al, eds. Aspects of Multilingual Aphasia. 2012. (Communication Disorders Across Languages Ser.). (ENG.). 336p. 139.95 ***(978-1-84769-754-7(2))*** Multilingual Matters GBR. Dist: Univ. of Toronto Pr.

Hale, Sheila. The Man Who Lost His Language: A Case of Aphasia. 2007. (ENG., Illus.). 256p. per. *(978-1-84310-564-0(0))* Kingsley, Jessica Ltd.

Holland, Audrey, ed. 35th Clinical Aphasiology Conference. 2008. (Special Issues of Aphasiology Ser.). (ENG.). 288p. 79.95 *(978-1-84169-809-0(1)*, Psychology Press) Taylor & Francis Group GBR. Dist: Taylor & Francis Group.

Icon Health Publications Staff. Official Parents Sourcebook on LandauKle. 2006. 112p. per. 28.95 *(978-0-497-11191-5(8))* Icon Group International, Inc.

Jakobson, Roman. Child Language, Aphasia & Phonological Universals. Keiler, Allan R., tr. (Janua Linguarum. Series Minor Ser.). (ENG.). 101p. 60.00 ***(978-3-11-179541-6(1))*** De Gruyter, Mouton DEU. Dist: de Gruyter, Walter GmbH & Co. KG.

—Child language, aphasia & phonological Universals. Keiler, Allan R., ed. (Janua Linguarum. Series Minor Ser.). (ENG.). 101p. 210.00 ***(978-3-11-219353-2(9))***; 135.00 ***(978-3-11-099831-3(9))*** De Gruyter, Mouton DEU. Dist: de Gruyter, Walter GmbH & Co. KG.

Jakobson, Roman & Halle, Morris. Fundamentals of Language. 2011. 106p. pap. 18.75 ***(978-1-178-71814-0(X))*** BiblioBazaar.

Janet Ling, Ma Ed. All for Chris. 2009. (Illus.). 80p. pap. 32.49 *(978-1-4389-7608-2(9))* AuthorHouse.

Keith, Robin & Croot, Elise. Scoring Software for the Comprehensive Aphasia Test. 2010. (ENG.). cd-rom 175.00 *(978-1-84872-064-0(5)*, Psychology Press) Taylor & Francis Group GBR. Dist: Taylor & Francis Group.

Klein, Evelyn R. & Mancinelli, James M. Acquired Language Disorders: A Case-Based Approach. 2009. (Illus.). 350p. pap. 69.95 *(978-1-59756-055-9(3))* Plural Publishing, Inc.

Koul, Rajinder, ed. Augmentative & Alternative Communication for Adults with Aphasia: Science & Clinical Practice. 2011. (Augmentative & Alternative Communications Perspectives Ser.). 180p. ***(978-1-84855-220-3(3))*** Emerald Group Publishing Ltd.

LaPointe, Leonard L. Aphasia & Related Neurogenic Language Disorders. 4th ed. 2010. 64.95 *(978-1-60406-262-5(2))* Thieme Medical Pubs., Inc.

LaPointe, Leonard L., ed. Aphasia & Related Neurogenic Language Disorders. 4th ed. 2011. (ENG., Illus.). 288p. 64.99 *(978-1-60406-261-8(4))* Thieme Medical Pubs., Inc.

Lees, Janet. Children with Acquired Aphasias. 2nd rev. ed. 2008. (ENG., Illus.). 192p. pap. 72.99 *(978-1-86156-490-0(2)*, Wiley) Wiley, John & Sons, Inc.

Longoni, Francesca. Satzverarbeitung bei Aphasie. 2010. (Europäische Hochschulschriften. Reihe 21: Linguistik Ser.). (GER.). 376p. pap. 86.95 *(978-3-631-60138-9(7))* Lang, Peter GmbH, Europäischer Verlag der Wissenschaften DEU. Dist: Lang, Peter.

Marshall, Jane, et al. The Sentence Processing Resource Pack, 3 vols. (Illus.). 294p. *(978-0-86388-446-7(6)*, 002-4220) Speechmark Publishing Ltd.

Martin, Nadine. Aphasia Rehabilitation: The Impairment & Its Consequences. Thompson, Cynthia K. & Worrall, Linda, eds. 2007. (Illus.). pap. 55.00 *(978-1-59756-162-4(2))* Plural Publishing, Inc.

Morrison, Sarah. Phonology Resource Pack for Adult Aphasia, 5 vols. (Illus.). 380p. spiral bd. *(978-0-86388-228-9(5)*, 002-4210) Speechmark Publishing Ltd.

Nickels, Lyndsey. Progressive Language Impairments: Intervention & Management: A Special Issue of Aphasiology. 2009. (Macquarie Monographs in Cognitive Science Ser.). (ENG.). 208p. 85.00 *(978-1-84872-701-4(1)*, Psychology Press) Taylor & Francis Group GBR. Dist: Taylor & Francis Group.

Papathanasiou. Aphasia & Related Neurogenic Communication Disorders. rev. ed. 2011. 512p. pap. 79.95 *(978-0-7637-7100-3(7))* Jones & Bartlett Learning, LLC.

Pescariu, Serafim. Aphasia: Symptoms, Diagnosis & Treatment. Ibanescu, Grigore, ed. 2010. (Languages & Linguistics Ser.). (Illus.). 200p. 79.00 *(978-1-60741-288-5(8)*, Nova Biomedical Bks.) Nova Science Pubs., Inc.

Quinting, Gerd. Hesitation phenomena in adult aphasic & normal Speech. (Janua Linguarum. Series Minor Ser.). (ENG.). 73p. 210.00 ***(978-3-11-192629-2(X))***; 135.00 ***(978-3-11-099637-1(5))*** De Gruyter, Mouton DEU. Dist: de Gruyter, Walter GmbH & Co. KG.

Sheridan, Sue & Pitts, Bill. Coping with Aphasia. 2009. 106p. pap. 22.99 *(978-0-557-08520-0(9))* Lulu Enterprises Inc.

Stark, Jacqueline Ann, ed. Verbal Perseveration. 2008. (Special Issues of Aphasiology Ser.). (ENG.). 436p. pap. 54.50 *(978-1-84169-834-2(2)*, Psychology Press) Taylor & Francis Group GBR. Dist: Taylor & Francis Group.

Stryker, Stephanie. Speech Illustrated Cards- Set 2: Sentence Stimulation. 2008. (Illus.). 48p. 24.95 net. *(978-0-9821038-1-4(6))* Stryker Illustrations.

—Speech Illustrated Cards- Set 3: Conversation Cards. 2008. (Illus.). 48p. 24.95 net. *(978-0-9821038-2-1(4))* Stryker Illustrations.

—Speech Illustrated Cards- Set 4: Who Is Doing What? 2008. (Illus.). 48p. 24.95 net. *(978-0-9821038-3-8(2))* Stryker Illustrations.

A Tribute to the Quintessential Researcher Clinician & Mentor: Audrey Holland. 2010. (Special Issues of Aphasiology Ser.). (ENG.). 124p. pap. 47.95 *(978-1-84872-733-5(X)*, Psychology Press) Taylor & Francis Group GBR. Dist: Taylor & Francis Group.

Weekes, Brendan, ed. Issues in Bilingual Aphasia. 2010. (Special Issues of Aphasiology Ser.). (ENG.). 208p. pap. 48.95 *(978-1-84872-732-8(1)*, Psychology Press) Taylor & Francis Group GBR. Dist: Taylor & Francis Group.

Zanetti, Dario, et al, eds. The Effects of Drugs on Verbal Fluency. 2010. (Languages & Linguistics Ser.). (Illus.). 70p. pap. 49.00 *(978-1-61668-759-5(2))* Nova Science Pubs., Inc.

Ziegler, Wolfram & Aichert, Ingrid, eds. The Syllable & Beyond: New Evidence from Disordered Speech, A Special Issue of Aphasiology. 2009. (Special Issues of Aphasiology Ser.). (ENG.). 128p. 49.95 *(978-1-84169-862-5(8)*, Psychology Press) Taylor & Francis Group GBR. Dist: Taylor & Francis Group.

APHIDS

Blackman, Roger L. & Eastop, Victor F. Aphids on the World's Herbaceous Plants & Shrubs, 2 vols. 2007. (ENG., Illus.). 1460p. 510.00 *(978-0-471-48973-3(5)*, Wiley) Wiley, John & Sons, Inc.

Dept. Agriculture and Agri-Food Canada Staff. Atlas of Aphids Trapped in Agricultural Crops. (Illus.). 66p. pap. *(978-0-660-15551-7(6)*, Canadian Government Publishing.

Dixon, A. F. G. Insect Herbivore-Host Dynamics: Tree-Dwelling Aphids. 2011. (ENG., Illus.). 208p. pap. 45.00 *(978-1-107-40263-8(8))* Cambridge Univ. Pr.

Holman, Jaroslav. Host Plant Catalog of Aphids. 1200p. 2009. pap. 849.00 *(978-1-4020-8287-0(8)*, 1402082878) 2008. 679.00 *(978-1-4020-8265-6(1))* Springer.

—Host Plant Catalog of Aphids: Palaearctic Region. 2009. 1216p. 679.00 *(978-1-4020-8286-3(X))* Springer.

Kindlmann, Pavel, et al, eds. Aphid Biodiversity under Environmental Change: Patterns & Processes. 2010. (ENG., Illus.). x, 191p. 189.00 *(978-90-481-8600-6(5)*, 9048186005) Springer.

Nyabuga, Franklin. Sustainable Management of Cabbage Aphid & Bagrada Bugs. 2008. 68p. pap. *(978-3-639-08710-9(0))* VDM Verlag Dr. Mueller e.K.

Van Emden, H. F. & Harrington, R., eds. Aphids as Crop Pests. 2007. (Illus.). 752p. 295.00 *(978-0-85199-819-0(4))* CABI GBR. Dist: Stylus Publishing, LLC.

APHORISMS AND APOTHEGMS

see also Epigrams; Maxims; Medicine—Aphorisms; Proverbs; Quotations; Table-Talk

Anderson, Karl. Astrological Aphorisms. 2006. pap. 9.95 *(978-1-4286-6565-9(4))* Kessinger Publishing, LLC.

Anonymous, Unnamed, contrib. by. Everything Is Going to Be OK. 2011. (ENG., Illus.). 96p. 12.95 *(978-0-8118-7877-7(5))* Chronicle Bks. LLC.

Athenaeus. The Learned Banqueters, 10 bks. (Loeb Classical Library: 274). (GEC & ENG.). Volume V. 420th ed. 2009. 528p. 24.00 *(978-0-674-99632-8(1))*Volume VI. 2010. 464p. 24.00 *(978-0-674-99639-7(9))*Volume VII. 2011. 416p. 24.00 *(978-0-674-99673-1(9))* Harvard Univ. Pr.

—The Learned Banqueters Bks. 6-7, Vol. 3, 2 vols., Volume III. 2008. (Loeb Classical Library: 224). (GEC & ENG.). 592p. 24.00 *(978-0-674-99624-3(0))* Harvard Univ. Pr.

Athenaeus. The Learned Banqueters, Volume VIII: Book 15. General Indexes, Volume VIII. 2012. (Loeb Classical Library). Orig. Title: Deipnosophistae. (ENG & GEC.). 392p. 24.00 ***(978-0-674-99676-2(3))*** Harvard Univ. Pr.

Athenaeus & Athenaeus. The Learned Banqueters Bks. 8-10, Vol. 4, 2 vols., Volume IV. 420th ed. 2008. (Loeb Classical Library: 235). (GEC & ENG., Illus.). 512p. 24.00 *(978-0-674-99626-7(7))* Harvard Univ. Pr.

Bacon, Francis. Apophthegmes New & Old. reprint ed. lib. bdg. 98.00 *(978-0-7426-2036-0(0))* Classic Bks.

—The Essayes or Counsels, Civil & Moral of Francis Bacon, 1 Vol. 2007. 90.00 *(978-1-56169-922-3(5))* Gaunt, Inc.

Ball, Marshall S. A Good Kiss: The Wisdom of a Listening Child. 2007. (ENG.). 224p. pap. 16.95 *(978-1-4165-7365-4(8)*, Beyond Words/Atria Bks.) Atria Bks.

Bean, William Bennett, ed. Aphorisms from Latham. 2011. 104p. 39.95 ***(978-1-258-06765-6(X))*** Literary Licensing, LLC.

Blackie, John Stuart. The Day Book of John Stuart Blackie. 2007. (ENG.). 210p. 39.95 *(978-0-548-04121-5(0))* Kessinger Publishing, LLC.

Bourgeois, Louis E. Hosanna: Affirmations & Blasphemies. 2010. 131p. pap. 15.00 *(978-1-879378-58-2(2))* Xenos Bks.

Bowen, Jack. If You Can Read This: The Philosophy of Bumper Stickers. 2010. (ENG., Illus.). 240p. pap. 14.00 *(978-0-8129-8105-6(7)*, Random Hse. Trade Paperbacks) Random House Publishing Group.

Bradley, Mary C. Aphorisms from A to Z. 2007. pap. 8.95 *(978-1-59571-185-4(6))* Word Association Pubs.

Carter, null & Carter, Steven. New Aphorisms & Reflections. 2009. (ENG.). 134p. pap. 21.99 *(978-0-7618-4582-9(8))* Hamilton Bks.

—New Aphorisms & Reflections: Second Series. 2009. (ENG.). 114p. pap. 21.99 *(978-0-7618-4584-3(4))* Hamilton Bks.

Carter, Steven. New Aphorisms & Reflections. 3rd ed. 2010. (ENG.). 102p. pap. 18.99 *(978-0-7618-5061-8(9))* Hamilton Bks.

—222: Aphorisms & Reflections. 2008. (ENG.). 126p. pap. 27.99 *(978-0-7618-4050-3(8))* Hamilton Bks.

—222 Vol. 2: Aphorisms & Reflections. 2008. (ENG.). 154p. pap. 29.99 *(978-0-7618-4140-1(7))* Hamilton Bks.

—222 Vol. 3: Aphorisms & Reflections. 2008. (ENG.). 164p. pap. 28.99 *(978-0-7618-4159-3(8))* Hamilton Bks.

Changing One's Conceptions: Awaji's Aphorisms. 2008.Tr. of Hasso wo Kaeru Awaji Goroku. 262p. pap. *(978-0-9788874-5-2(X))* Hinoki Pr.

Costello, Stephen. 18 Reasons Why Mothers Hate Their Babies. 2009. 126p. 22.50 *(978-1-60860-687-0(2)*, Eloquent Bks.) AEG Literary Publishing Services, Inc.

Dalton, Martin L., compiled by. Aphorisms for Surgeons. 2007. 91p. pap. 12.00 *(978-0-9748320-2-9(2))* Aequanimitas Medical Bks.

Doumon, Jean-Yves. Dictionnaires des Proverbes et Dictons de France. (FRE.). 75.00 *(978-0-8288-7714-5(9))* French & European Pubns., Inc.

Einstein, Albert. Einstein on Cosmic Religion & Other Opinions & Aphorisms. 2009. (ENG.). 112p. pap. 6.95 *(978-0-486-47010-8(5))* Dover Pubns., Inc.

The Erotic Fire of the Unattainable: Aphorisms on Love, Art & the Vicissitudes of Life. 2007. 22.00 *(978-0-9795600-1-9(2))*; pap. 16.00 *(978-0-9795600-0-2(4))* IML Pubns.

Ferreira, Keith. The Masses Should Think for Themselves. 2010. 152p. pap. 14.95 *(978-1-4502-1811-5(3))* iUniverse, Inc.

Ferreira, Keith N. A New Breed of Philosophers. 2007. 140p. per. 13.95 *(978-0-595-45435-8(6))* iUniverse, Inc.

Ferreira, Keith N. Teacup & Saucer. 2011. 116p. pap. 12.95 ***(978-1-4620-1305-0(8))*** iUniverse, Inc.

Figna, Rosanna. Morsels of Reflection. 2011. 60p. (gr. -1). pap. 12.10 ***(978-1-4567-8428-7(5))*** AuthorHouse.

Franklin, Benjamin. The Sayings of Poor Richard: The Prefaces, Proverbs & Poems of Benjamin Franklin. (Knickerbocker Nuggets Ser.). 288p. reprint ed. 98.00 *(978-0-7222-9078-1(0))* Library Reprints, Inc.

Geary, James. Geary's Guide to the World's Great Aphorists. 2007. (ENG., Illus.). 448p. 19.95 *(978-1-59691-252-6(9))* Bloomsbury Publishing.

—The World in a Phrase: A History of Aphorisms. 2006. (ENG.). 240p. per. 9.95 *(978-1-58234-616-8(X))* Bloomsbury Publishing.

Gil, Ruben. DICCIONARIO de ANECDOTAS, DICHOS, ilustraciones, LOCUCIONES Y REFRANES, 1 vol. 2009. (SPA.). 800p. 39.99 *(978-84-8267-465-0(X))* Clie, Editorial ESP. Dist: Zondervan.

Gracián y Morales, Baltasar. Pocket Oracle & Art of Prudence. Robbins, Jeremy, tr. from SPA. & intro. by. 2011. (ENG.). 176p. (gr. 12). 13.00 *(978-0-14-144245-7(X)*, Penguin Classics) Penguin Group (USA) Inc.

Grothe, Mardy. Ifferisms: An Anthology of Aphorisms That Begin with the Word If. 2009. (ENG.). 336p. 15.99 *(978-0-06-167230-9(0))* HarperCollins Pubs.

—Neverisms: A Quotation Lover's Guide to Things You Should Never Do, Never Say, or Never Forget. 2011. (ENG.). 256p. 15.99 *(978-0-06-197065-8(4))* HarperCollins Pubs.

Hale, Rachael. Smitten: A Kitten's Guide to Happiness. 2006. (ENG., Illus.). 160p. 21.99 *(978-0-8212-5848-4(6))* Bulfinch.

Hall, John H. Seed Thoughts & Alliterative Aphorisms: A Thousand Themes for Thorough Thinkers. 2011. 98p. 38.95 ***(978-1-258-03940-0(0))*** Literary Licensing, LLC.

Hall, Samuel Carter. Rhymes in Council. 2010. 74p. pap. 26.45 *(978-1-4455-7051-8(3))* Research Pr.

Herakleitos & Diogenes. Herakleitos & Diogenes: Translated from the Greek by Guy Davenport. Davenport, Guy, tr. 2011. 62p. pap. 9.00 ***(978-1-61097-088-4(8)***, Wipf and Stock) Wipf & Stock Pubs.

Hoffer, Eric. Reflections on the Human Condition. 2006. 88p. per. 13.95 *(978-1-933435-14-5(3))* Hopewell Pubns., LLC.

Holshouser, Michael. The Stillness Before Time. 2010. 56p. pap. 14.49 *(978-0-557-35736-9(5))* Lulu Enterprises Inc.

Howe, E. W. Country Town Sayings: A Collection of Paragraphs from the Atchison Globe. 298p. reprint ed. lib. bdg. 98.00 *(978-0-7222-4904-8(7))* Library Reprints, Inc.

Hughes, David Bruce. Here Be Wisdom. 2010. 173p. pap. 11.95 *(978-0-557-25923-6(1))* Lulu Enterprises Inc.

Kolda, Eugene. Transparent Thoughts: The Message of Love & Truth. 2011. 92p. pap. 13.95 *(978-1-4502-9416-4(2))* iUniverse, Inc.

Kumar, Srini. Sticker Nation Vol. 2. 2009. (ENG.). 64p. pap. 19.95 *(978-1-934708-08-8(9))* Disinformation Co. Ltd., The.

Larousse Staff. Larousse Dictionnaire des Proverbs, Sentences et Maximes. (FRE.). 37.50 *(978-0-8288-7852-4(8))* French & European Pubns., Inc.

MacHin, Joseph. Accents & Aphorisms. Davis, Lincoln K., ed. 2011. 62p. 36.95 ***(978-1-258-01303-5(7))*** Literary Licensing, LLC.

Manlowe, Jennifer. Loving Life As It Is. 2008. 191p. pap. 21.95 *(978-0-615-16862-3(0))* Life Design Inc.

Martin, Fred. Lessons from the Masters. 2009. (ENG.). 36p. pap. 20.00 *(978-0-557-09456-1(9))* Lulu Enterprises Inc.

Mertens, Dieter, et al, eds. Apophthegmata Teutsch: Erläuterungen, Aoebersetzungen und Verifizierungen Mit Einer Einleitung Von Theodor Verweyen und Dieter Me. 2011. (Neudrucke deutscher Literaturwerke Ser.). (GER & LAT., Illus.). XX, 1598p. *(978-3-484-17048-3(4))* Verlag Max Niemeyer.

Mohr, Jan-Steffen. Epigramm und Aphorismus Im Verbund: Kompositionen Aus Kleinen Textformen Im 17. und 18. Jahrhundert. (GER.). 417p. 82.95 *(978-3-631-57365-5(0))* Lang, Peter GmbH, Europäischer Verlag der Wissenschaften DEU. Dist: Lang, Peter Publishing, Inc.

Morgenstern, Christian. Stufen. 2006. (GER.). pap. *(978-1-4068-0826-1(1))* Echo Library.

Morson, Gary Saul. The Long & Short of It: From Aphorism to Novel. 2012. (ENG.). 296p. 80.00 ***(978-0-8047-8051-3(X))***; pap. 24.95 ***(978-0-8047-8169-5(9))*** Stanford Univ. Pr.

Oliver, Harry. Black Cats & April Fools: Origins of Old Wives Tales & Superstitions in Our Daily Lives. 2007. (ENG., Illus.). 258p. 14.95 *(978-1-84358-162-8(0)*, Metro Publishing, Limited) Blake, John Publishing, Ltd. GBR. Dist: Independent Pubs. Group.

Pauper, Peter. Peter Pauper's Epigrams & Aphorisms. 2011. 112p. 39.95 ***(978-1-258-03480-1(8))*** Literary Licensing, LLC.

Ratcliffe, Susan, ed. Oxford Dictionary of Phrase, Saying, & Quotation. 3rd rev. ed. 2006. (ENG.). 720p. 45.00 *(978-0-19-280650-5(5))* Oxford Univ. Pr., Inc.

Rees, Nigel. Don't You Know There's a War On? Wartime Slogans & Sayings. 2011. (ENG.). 256p. 14.95 *(978-1-906388-99-7(7)*, Batsford, B. T. Ltd.) Anova Bks. GBR. Dist: Sterling Publishing Co., Inc.

—More Tea Vicar? An Embarrassment of Domestic Catchphrases. 2009. (ENG.). 272p. 14.95 *(978-1-905400-74-4(8))* National Trust, Aylesbury GBR. Dist: Independent Pubs. Group.

Rev Run. Words of Wisdom: Daily Affirmations of Faith from Run's House to Yours. 2008. (ENG.). 240p. pap. 11.99 *(978-0-06-166015-3(9)*, Harper Paperbacks) HarperCollins Pubs.

Rolls, Geoff & Moore, Edwin. Taking the Proverbial: The Psychology of Proverbs & Sayings. 2008. (ENG., Illus.). 214p. pap. 14.95 *(978-0-550-10335-2(X))* Chambers Harrap Pubs., Ltd. GBR. Dist: Houghton Mifflin Harcourt Trade & Reference Pubs.

Schwartz, Bernard & Flowers, John V. Thoughts for Therapists: Reflections on the Art of Healing. 2008. (Practical Therapist Ser.). 137p. per. 22.95 *(978-1-886230-74-3(9))* Impact Pubs., Inc.

Searby, Denis M., tr. from GEC. The Corpus Parisinum: A Critical Edition of the Greek Text with Commentary & English Translation (A Medieval Anthology of Greek Texts from the Pre-Socratics to the Church Fathers, 600 B. C. - 700 A. D.), 2 vols. 2007. 1036p. 199.95 *(978-0-7734-5300-5(8))* Mellen, Edwin Pr., The.

Searby, Denis Michael, intro. The Corpus Parisinum: A Critical Edition of the Greek Text, with Commentary & English Translation: A Medieval Anthology of Greek Texts from the Pre-Socratics to the Church Fathers, 600 B.C.-700 A.D, 2 vols. 2007. (978-0-7734-5298-5(2)); (978-0-7734-5296-1(6)) Mellen, Edwin Pr., The.

Smarandache, Florentin. 601 Paradoxist Distiches (Chinese language; translated by Yuhua) Yuhua, tr. 2008. (CHI & ENG.). pap. 9.95 (978-1-59973-071-4(5)) Multimedia Larga.

Sternbach, Ludwik. Canakya's Aphorisms in the Hitopadesa V1-4. 2011. 56p. 36.95 (978-1-258-01605-0(2)) Literary Licensing, LLC.

Szczepaniak, Jacek. Zu Sprachlichen Realisierungsmitteln der Komik in Ausgewahlten Aphoristischen Texten aus Pragmalinguistischer Sicht. (Danziger Beitrage zur Germanistik Ser.: Vol. 1). (GER., Illus.). 177p. 30.95 (978-3-631-39606-3(6)) Lang, Peter Publishing, Inc.

Taleb, Nassim Nicholas. The Bed of Procrustes: Philosophical & Practical Aphorisms. 2010. (ENG.). 128p. 18.00 (978-1-4000-6997-2(1), Random House) Random House Publishing Group.

Tuntel, Yunus. Complete Fragments: Notebook A. 2008. 92p. pap. 20.00 (978-1-4389-0975-2(6)) AuthorHouse.

Watson, Burton. The Analects of Confucius. 2009. (Translations from the Asian Classics Ser.). (ENG.). 176p. (gr. 17). pap. 15.95 (978-0-231-14165-9(3)) Columbia Univ. Pr.

White, William M. Great Truths by Great Authors. 2006. 572p. per. 32.99 (978-1-4255-6248-9(5)) MPublishing.

Wintle, Christopher. Metapoetics: Aphorisms, Thoughts & Maxims on Life, Art & Music. 2010. (Illus.). 160p. 45.00 (978-0-9566007-0-7(0)); pap. 26.95 (978-0-9566007-1-4(9)) Plumbago Bks. GBR. Dist: Boydell & Brewer, Inc.

Wolf, Manfred. Almost a Foreign Country: A Personal Geography in Columns & Aphorisms. 2008. 376p. pap. 24.95 (978-0-595-52423-5(0)) iUniverse, Inc.

Wortabet, John. Arabian Wisdom. 2010. 30p. pap. 14.14 (978-1-153-65532-3(2)) General Bks. LLC.

—Arabian Wisdom. 2009. pap. 37.70 (978-1-60724-295-6(8)) Gorgias Pr., LLC.

Zaghi, Nasser. Love Is the Solution: Peace Is Possible. 2007. (ENG., Illus.). 240p. 34.95 (978-1-60109-011-9(0)) Mandala Publishing.

Zobell Jr., Albert L., ed. Moments with the Prophets. 2011. 218p. 44.95 (978-1-258-07231-5(9)) Literary Licensing, LLC.

APHRAATES, THE PERSIAN SAGE, FL. 337-345

Duncan, Edward J. Baptism in the Demonstrations of Aphraat. 2006. pap. 22.95 (978-1-4286-5880-6(7)) Kessinger Publishing, LLC.

Gavin, Frank. Aphraates & the Jews: A Study of the Controversial Homilies of the Persian Sage in their Relation to Jewish Thought. 2007. (Analecta Gorgiana Ser.: 29). per. 29.00 (978-1-59333-620-2(9)) Gorgias Pr., LLC.

Gavin, Frank S. Aphraates & the Jews. (Columbia University, Contributions to Oriental History & Philology Ser.: No. 9). reprint ed. 20.00 (978-0-404-50539-4(2)) AMS Pr., Inc.

Hallock, Frank, tr. Aphrahat's Demonstrations 2 And 7. 2010. pap. 20.32 (978-1-60724-952-8(9)) Gorgias Pr., LLC.

Jarkins, Stephanie K. Skoyles. Aphrahat the Persian Sage & the Temple of God: A Study of Early Syriac Theological Anthropology. 2008. (Gorgias Dissertations in Early Christian Studies: 8). 115.00 (978-1-59333-679-0(9)) Gorgias Pr., LLC.

Schaff, Philip, ed. Nicene & Post-Nicene Fathers: Second Series, Volume XIII Gregory the Great, Ephraim Syrus, Aphrahat. 2007. 440p. 31.95 (978-1-60206-532-1(2)); (ENG.). per. 21.95 (978-1-60206-531-4(4)) Cosimo, Inc.

Wright, William, intro. The Homilies of Aphraates, the Persian Sage. 2010. (SYR.). 151.76 (978-1-60724-897-2(2)) Gorgias Pr., LLC.

APHRAHAT, THE PERSIAN SAGE, FL. 337-345

see Aphraates, The Persian Sage, Fl. 337-345

APHRENIA

see Dementia

APHRODISIACS

Caston, Victor, tr. Alexander of Aphrodisias: on Aristotle on the Soul. 2012. 80.00 (978-0-7156-3923-8(4)) Duckworth Publishers GBR. Dist: International Publishers Marketing.

Grau, María Mercedes, ed. Afrodisiaca. Sabores latin-asiáticos (y otros tantos) con un toque de Pasión. 2007.Tr. of Afrodisiaca. Latin-Asian Cuisine (and other Flavors) with a Touch of Heat. (SPA.). 144p. per. (978-0-9774653-1-6(4)) ISDG Graphic Design.

Hopkins, Martha & Lockridge, Randall. The New Intercourses: An Aphrodisiac Cookbook. 10th anniv. ed. 2007. (ENG., Illus.). 208p. 29.95 (978-0-9653275-2-7(3)) Terrace Publishing.

Leary, Timothy. Search for the True Aphrodisiac. 2009. (ENG., Illus.). 192p. pap. 12.95 (978-1-57951-088-6(4)) Ronin Publishing.

Mitchell, Deborah. Sexual Vigor for Life: The Natural Way. 2007. (ENG., Illus.). 224p. pap. 9.95 (978-1-59687-125-0(3)) IBks., Inc.

Niemoeller, A. F. & Haldeman-Julius, E., eds. The Nature, History, & Uses of Aphrodisiacs: An Account of the Medicaments & Agents Held to Be Provocative of Sexual Desire. 2011. 34p. 35.95 (978-1-258-05608-7(9)) Literary Licensing, LLC.

Ratsch, Christian. The Encyclopedia of Aphrodisiacs. 2012. (Illus.). 784p. 125.00 (978-1-59477-169-9(3)) Inner Traditions International, Ltd.

Walton, Alan Hull. Aphrodisiacs, from Legend to Prescription: A Study of Aphrodisiacs Throughout the Ages. 2011. 292p. 48.95 (978-1-258-00970-0(6)) Literary Licensing, LLC.

Wedeck, Harry Ezekiel. Dictionary of Aphrodisiacs. 2011. 272p. 47.95 (978-1-258-07300-8(5)) Literary Licensing, LLC.

APHRODITE (GREEK DEITY)

Breitenberger, Barbara. Aphrodite & Eros: The Development of Erotic Mythology in Early Greek Poetry & Cult. 2007. (Studies in Classics Ser.: Vol. 4). (ENG., Illus.). 306p. 125.00 (978-0-415-96823-2(2)) Routledge.

Cyrino, Aphrodite. 2010. (Gods & Heroes of the Ancient World Ser.). (ENG., Illus.). 176p. 30.95 (978-0-415-77523-6(X), Routledge) Taylor & Francis Group GBR. Dist: Taylor & Francis Group.

Cyrino, Monica S. Aphrodite. 2010. (Gods & Heroes of the Ancient World Ser.). (ENG., Illus.). 176p. 120.00 (978-0-415-77522-9(1)) Routledge.

Haggard, H. Rider. The World's Desire. 2009. 218p. pap. (978-0-217-89826-3(2)) Books LLC.

Haggard, H. Rider & Lang, Andrew. The World's Desire. 2007. 204p. per. 13.95 (978-1-60312-270-2(2)) Aegypan.

—The World's Desire. 2008. 272p. 25.99 (978-0-554-36433-9(6)); 28.99 (978-0-554-27130-9(3)) BiblioBazaar.

—The World's Desire. 2008. (ENG.). 228p. per. (978-1-4065-6956-8(9)) Dodo Pr.

—The World's Desire. 2008. 304p. pap. 16.95 (978-1-4341-0149-5(5)); 260p. pap. 14.95 (978-1-60096-367-4(6)) Editorium, The.

—The World's Desire. 2008. 394p. 49.95 (978-1-4365-9154-6(6)) 2007. (ENG.). 396p. per. 34.95 (978-0-548-79705-1(6)) Kessinger Publishing, LLC.

—The World's Desire. 2010. (ENG.). 207p. pap. 6.95 (978-1-61600-197-1(6)) Mizzou Media - Univ. BookStores.

Havelock, Christine Mitchell. The Aphrodite of Knidos & Her Successors: A Historical Review of the Female Nude in Greek Art. 2008. (ENG., Illus.). 200p. pap. 37.50 (978-0-472-03277-8(1)) Univ. of Michigan Pr.

Kondoleon, Christine, text. Aphrodite & the Gods of Love. 2011. (ENG., Illus.). 256p. 55.00 (978-0-87846-756-3(4)) Museum of Fine Arts, Boston.

Seifert, Martina. Aphrodite: Herrin des Krieges, Göttin der Liebe. Seifert, Martina, ed. 2009. (GER., Illus.). 141p. (C). 45.00 (978-3-8053-3942-1(9)) Zabern, Philipp von Verlag, GmbH DEU. Dist: Brown, David Bk. Co., The.

Smith, Amy Claire. Brill's Companion to Aphrodite. 2010. (Brill's Companions in Classical Studies). 460p. (978-90-04-18003-1(6)) BRILL.

APHRONESIA

see Dementia

APICOMPLEXA

Becker, Katja, ed. Apicomplexan Parasites: Molecular Approaches Toward Targeted Drug Development. 2011. (Drug Discovery in Infectious Diseases Ser.). (ENG., Illus.). 550p. 159.95 (978-3-527-32731-7(2), Wiley-VCH) Wiley, John & Sons, Inc.

Burleigh, Barbara A. & Soldati, Dominique. Molecular Mechanisms of Parasite Invasion. 2008. (Subcellular Biochemistry Ser.). (ENG., Illus.). 257p. (C). 219.00 (978-0-387-78266-9(4), 0387782664) Springer.

Faye, Farba Balle Khodia. Malaria Resistance or Susceptibility in Red Cells Disorders. 2009. pap. 37.00 (978-1-60692-943-8(7)) Nova Science Pubs., Inc.

Freymond, Céline. Analysis of Expression of Pdcp & Mal13p1 308 of Plasmodium Falciparum. 2010. 80p. pap. (978-3-8383-5735-5(3)) Lambert Academic Publishing.

Prajapati, Surendra Kumar & Moshahid Alam Rizvi, M. Evolution & Genomic Diversity of Plasmodium Vivax. 2011. 212p. pap. (978-3-8443-0318-6(9)) Lambert Academic Publishing.

APICULTURE

see Bee Culture

APL (COMPUTER PROGRAM LANGUAGE)

APL 96: International Conference on APL. Date not set. pap. 34.00 (978-0-89791-806-0(1), 554960) Assn. for Computing Machinery.

Askoolum, Ajay. System Building with APL + WIN. 2006. (Rsp Ser.: 6). (ENG., Illus.). 524p. per. 85.00 (978-0-470-03020-2(8), Wiley) Wiley, John & Sons, Inc.

Dalois. Introduction to APL*PLUS PC. (Illus.). iv, 307p. (978-2-9803472-0-7(5)) EducAPL.

APLASTIC ANEMIA

McMahon, Asa J. Blood Counts: My Triumphant Battle over Aplastic Anemia. 2011. 152p. 21.99 (978-1-4567-4860-9(2)); pap. 11.99 (978-1-4567-4858-6(0)) AuthorHouse.

Strongin, Laurie. Saving Henry: A Mother's Journey. 2010. (ENG.). 288p. 22.99 (978-1-4013-2356-1(1)) Hyperion Pr.

APOCALYPTIC ART

Bastian, M. S. & L, Isabelle. Bastokalypse. 2010. (Illus.). 128p. pap. 59.00 (978-3-85881-296-4(X)) Scheidegger und Spiess AG, Verlag CHE. Dist: Antique Collectors' Club.

Front Forty Press Staff. Signs of the Apocalypse or Rapture. 2008. (Illus.). 284p. 65.00 (978-0-9778689-6-4(6)) Front Forty Pr.

Parkstone Press Staff. Apocalypse. 2012. (Mega Square Ser.). (ENG., Illus.). 256p. 12.95 (978-1-906981-46-4(9)) Parkstone Pr. USA, Ltd.

Uelsberg, Gabriele & Holthuis, Gabriele. Christoph Loos: Nann-Paradox. 2007. 148p. 49.95 (978-3-87909-891-0(3)) Wienand GmbH, Druck- & Verlagshaus DEU. Dist: Independent Pubs. Group.

APOCALYPTIC LITERATURE

Aberth, John. From the Brink of the Apocalypse: Confronting Famine, War, Plague & Death in the Later Middle Ages. 2nd rev. ed. 2009. (ENG., Illus.). 352p. 35.95 (978-0-415-77797-1(6)); 115.00 (978-0-415-77796-4(8)) Routledge.

Alexander, Joseph Addison. Notes on New Testament Literature & Ecclesiastical History. 2007. 340p. 46.95 (978-0-548-54684-0(3)); (ENG.). per. 31.95 (978-0-548-47314-6(5)) Kessinger Publishing, LLC.

—Notes on New Testament Literature & Ecclesiastical History. 2006. 340p. per. 23.99 (978-1-4255-3446-2(5)) MPublishing.

Angel. Chaos & the Son of Man: The Hebrew Chaoskampf Tradition in the Period 515 BCE to 200 CE. 2006. (Library of Second Temple Studies, the Ser.). (ENG.). 256p. 170.00 (978-0-567-03098-6(9), T&T Clark Int'l) Continuum International Publishing Group, Ltd. GBR. Dist: National Bk. Network.

Arbel, Daphna V. & Orlov, Andrei A., eds. With Letters of Light: Studies in the Dead Sea Scrolls, Early Jewish Apocalypticism, Magic & Mysticism. 2010. (Ekstasis: Religious Experience from Antiquity to the Middle Ages Ser.). 640p. 182.00 (978-3-11-022201-2(9)) De Gruyter, Walter Inc.

Arbel, Daphna V. & Orlov, Andrei A., eds. With Letters of Light: Studies in the Dead Sea Scrolls, Early Jewish Apocalypticism, Magic, & Mysticism in Honor of Rachel Elior. 2011. (Ekstasis: Religious Experience from Antiquity to the Middle Ages Ser.). (ENG., Illus.). VII, 456p. 280.00 (978-3-11-219037-1(8)) De Gruyter, Walter Inc.

Assefa, Daniel. L' Apocalypse des animaux (1 Hen 85-90): une propagande Militaire? Approches narrative, historico-critique, perspectives Théologiques. 2007. (Supplements to the Journal for the Study of Judaism Ser.). 280p. (978-90-04-16267-9(4)) BRILL.

Aune, David E. Apocalypticism, Prophecy & Magic in Early Christianity: Collected Essays. 2006. (Wissenshaftliche Untersuchungen zum Neuen Testament Ser.: No. 199). 482p. 215.00 (978-3-16-149020-0(7)) Mohr Siebeck GmbH & Co. KG DEU. Dist: Coronet Bks.

—Apocalypticism, Prophecy, & Magic in Early Christianity: Collected Essays. 2008. 496p. (C). pap. 50.00 (978-0-8010-3594-4(5)) Baker Academic.

Baker Publishing Group Staff. Apocalyptic Thought in Early Christianity, 1 vol. Daly, Robert S. J., ed. 2009. (Holy Cross Studies in Patristic Theology & History Ser.). 304p. (C). pap. 33.00 (978-0-8010-3627-9(5)) Baker Academic.

Baynes, Leslie. The Heavenly Book Motif in Judeo-Christian Apocalypses 200 BCE-200 CE. 2011. (Supplements to the Journal for the Study of Judaism Ser.). (Illus.). ix, 233p. (978-90-04-20726-4(0)) BRILL.

Beale, G. K. The Use of Daniel in Jewish Apocalyptic Literature & in the Revelation of St. John. 2010. 364p. pap. 40.00 (978-1-60899-530-1(5), Wipf and Stock) Wipf & Stock Pubs.

Black, Samuel B. The Tribulation Strategy: Faith in the Coming Storm. 2010. 112p. pap. 11.95 (978-1-4497-0298-4(8), WestBow Pr.) Author Solutions, Inc.

The Book of Enoch. 2008. pap. 6.99 (978-1-4209-3045-0(1)) Digireads.com.

btmi.org, www. & E. Wolfe, Evangelist Larry. The People of the Apocalypse. 2007. 317p. pap. 17.50 (978-0-615-17103-6(6)) Wolfe, Larry E.

Burkitt, F. C. Jewish & Christian Apocalypses: The Schweich Lectures 1913. 2007. (Analecta Gorgiana Ser.: 35). per. 29.00 (978-1-59333-664-6(0)) Gorgias Pr., LLC.

Burkitt, F. Crawford. Jewish & Christian Apocalypses. 2008. (ENG.). 88p. per. (978-1-4086-3471-4(6)) Read Bks.

—Jewish & Christian Apocalypses. 2007. (Schweich Lectures). (Illus.). 90p. pap. 14.00 (978-1-55635-062-7(7), Wipf and Stock) Wipf & Stock Pubs.

Camp, Claudia V. & Berquist, Jon L. Constructions of Space II: The Biblical City & Other Imagined Spaces. Camp, Claudia V., ed. 2008. (Library of Hebrew Bible/Old Testament Studies, the Ser.). (ENG., Illus.). 176p. 120.00 (978-0-567-02708-5(2), T&T Clark Int'l) Continuum International Publishing Group, Ltd. GBR. Dist: National Bk. Network.

Charles, R. H. The Book of Enoch. 2007. (ENG.). 136p. per. 9.95 (978-1-60206-568-0(3)) Cosimo, Inc.

Charles, R. H., ed. The Book of the Secrets of Enoch. Morfill, W.R., tr. 2006. pap. 9.99 (978-1-59986-936-0(5)) Filiquarian Publishing, LLC.

Charles, R. H., tr. The Book of Enoch. 2007. (Dover Occult Ser.). (ENG., Illus.). 160p. per. 7.95 (978-0-486-45466-5(5)) Dover Pubns., Inc.

Chi, Thomas. Marilyn Manson Trilogy: Creating an Antichrist. 2007. (ENG, FRE, TUR, SPA & GER., Illus.). 60p. mass mkt. (978-0-9800862-1-8(3)) LA Portfolio.

Ciuba, Gary M. Walker Percy: Books of Revelations. 2010. (ENG.). 346p. pap. 24.95 (978-0-8203-3793-7(5)) Univ. of Georgia Pr.

Collins, John Joseph & Harlow, Daniel C. The "Other" in Second Temple Judaism: Essays in Honor of John J. Collins. 2011. (Illus.). 528p. 65.00 (978-0-8028-6625-7(5)) Eerdmans, William B. Publishing Co.

Cook, David. Contemporary Muslim Apocalyptic LIT. 2008. 288p. spiral bd. 19.95 (978-0-8156-3195-8(2)) Syracuse Univ. Pr.

Court, John M. Approaching the Apocalypse: A Short History of Christian Millenarianism. 2008. (ENG.). 232p. 89.00 (978-1-84511-758-0(1)); pap. 29.00 (978-1-84511-759-7(X)) I. B. Tauris & Co., Ltd. GBR. Dist: Macmillan.

Croteau, Melissa & Jess-Cooke, Carolyn, eds. Apocalyptic Shakespeare: Essays on Visions of Destruction & Revelation in Recent Film Adaptations. 2009. (ENG., Illus.). 244p. pap. 39.95 (978-0-7864-3392-6(2)) McFarland & Co., Inc. Pubs.

Daschke, Derek. City of Ruins: Mourning the Destruction of Jerusalem Through Jewish Apocalypse. (Illus.). 222p. (978-90-04-18181-6(4)) BRILL.

Davis, D. Mark. Left Behind & Loving It: A Cheeky Look at the End Times. 2011. 130p. pap. 16.00 (978-1-60899-826-5(6), Cascade Bks.) Wipf & Stock Pubs.

DeVun, Leah. Prophecy, Alchemy, & the End of Time: John of Rupecissa in the Late Middle Ages. 2009. (ENG., Illus.). 272p. (gr. 17). 50.00 (978-0-231-14538-1(1)) Columbia Univ. Pr.

Fleenor, Virgil. Revelation Is History Foretold. 2010. 647p. pap. 38.96 (978-0-557-24375-4(0)) Lulu Enterprises Inc.

Flegg, Columba Graham. An Introduction to Reading the Apocalypse. 111p. pap. 11.00 (978-0-88141-186-7(8)) St. Vladimir's Seminary Pr.

Franke, William. Poetry & Apocalypse: Theological Disclosures of Poetic Language. 2008. (ENG.). 232p. 60.00 (978-0-8047-5910-6(3)) Stanford Univ. Pr.

Funk, Wolf-Peter, et al. L' interpretation de la Gnose (NH XI, 1) 2010. (Bibliotheque copte de nag hammadi. section Textes Ser.). (FRE.). 186p. (C). pap. 87.00 (978-90-429-2190-0(0)) Peeters Pubs. & Booksellers BEL. Dist: Brown, David Bk. Co., The.

García Martínez, Florentino & Tigchelaar, Eibert J. C. Qumranica Minora. 2007. (Studies on the Texts of the Desert of Judah: Vols. 63-64). 306p. (978-90-04-15683-8(6)); 326p. (978-90-04-15569-5(4)) BRILL.

Gashler, S. Ted. Opening the Seventh Seal. 2009. pap. 15.99 (978-1-59955-265-1(5)) Cedar Fort, Inc./CFI Distribution.

Gottheil, Richard J. H. A Christian Bahira Legend. 2010. (ARA.). pap. 30.88 (978-1-61143-334-0(7)) Gorgias Pr., LLC.

Greer, John Michael. Apocalypse Not: Everything You Know about 2012, Nostradamus & the Rapture Is Wrong. 2011. (ENG.). 272p. pap. 15.95 (978-1-936740-00-0(1), Viva Editions) Cleis Pr.

Hahne. Corruption & Redemption of Creation: Nature in Romans 8. 19-22 & Jewish Apocalyptic Literature. 2007. (Library of New Testament Studies, the Ser.). (ENG., Illus.). 286p. 170.00 (978-0-567-03055-9(5), T&T Clark Int'l) Continuum International Publishing Group, Ltd. GBR. Dist: National Bk. Network.

Han, Jin Hee. Daniel's Spiel: Apocalyptic Literacy in the Book of Daniel. 2007. (ENG.). 134p. per. 29.50 (978-0-7618-3913-2(5)) Univ. Pr. of America, Inc.

Hanneken, Todd Russell. The Subversion of the Apocalypses in the Book of Jubilees. 2012. pap. (978-1-58983-642-6(1)) Society of Biblical Literature.

Harris, J. Rendel. The Gospel of the Twelve Apostles: Together with the Apocalypses of Each One of Them, Edited from the Syriac MS. with a Translation & Introduction. 2008. 60p. pap. 5.00 (978-1-60608-351-2(1), Wipf and Stock) Wipf & Stock Pubs.

Hassan, Farzana. Prophecy & the Fundamentalist Quest: An Integrative Study of Christian & Muslim Apocalyptic Religion. 2008. (ENG., Illus.). 196p. per. 35.00 (978-0-7864-3300-1(0)) McFarland & Co., Inc. Pubs.

Hays, Richard B. & Alkier, Stefan, eds. Revelation & the Politics of Apocalyptic Interpretation. 2012. (ENG.). 230p. 49.95 (978-1-60258-561-4(X)) Baylor Univ. Pr.

Henze, Matthias. Jewish Apocalypticism in Late First Century Israel: Reading 'Second Baruch' in Context. 2011. (Texts & Studies in Ancient Judaism Ser.). 448p. 247.50 (978-3-16-150859-2(9)) Mohr Siebeck GmbH & Co. KG DEU. Dist: Coronet Bks.

Himmelfarb, Martha. The Apocalypse: A Brief History. 2010. (Blackwell Brief Histories of Religion Ser.). (ENG.). 192p. pap. 33.95 (978-1-4051-1347-2(2), Wiley-Blackwell) Wiley, John & Sons, Inc.

—Apocalypse: A Brief History. 2010. (Blackwell Brief Histories of Religion Ser.: 31). (ENG.). 192p. 94.95 (978-1-4051-1346-5(4), Wiley-Blackwell) Wiley, John & Sons, Inc.

Hogeterp, A. & Hogeterp, Albert L. A. Expectations of the End: A Comparative Traditio-Historical Study of Eschatological, Apocalyptic, & Messianic Ideas in the Dead Sea Scrolls & the New Testament. 2009. (Studies on the Texts of the Desert of Judah). 544p. (978-90-04-17177-0(0)) BRILL.

Horsley, Richard A. Revolt of the Scribes: Resistance & Apocalyptic Origins. 2009. 240p. (C). pap. 21.00 (978-0-8006-6296-7(2), Fortress Pr.) Augsburg Fortress, Pubs.

Howard, Robert Glenn, ed. Network Apocalypse: Visions of the End in an Age of Internet Media. 2011. 248p. (978-1-907534-13-3(X)) Sheffield Phoenix Pr.

Johnson, Timothy Jay. Now My Eye Sees You: Unveiling an Apocalyptic Job. 2009. 212p. (978-1-906055-73-8(4)) Sheffield Phoenix Pr.

Jones, Arthur. Channeling the Apocalypse: From the Eighteenth Dynasty to the Current Incarnations. 2007. (ENG., Illus.). 258p. pap. 29.95 (978-0-615-16204-1(5)) In God We Trust.

Jones, Arthur Earl. Channeling the Apocalypse: From the Eighteenth Dynasty to the Current Incarnations. 2007. (Illus.). 150p. pap. (978-0-9794139-2-6(3)) In God We Trust.

Jones, Ken. Jewish Reactions to the Destruction of Jerusalem in A. D. 70: Apocalypses & Related Pseudepigrapha. 2011. (Supplements to the Journal for the Study of Judaism Ser.). x, 305p. (978-90-04-21027-1(X)) BRILL.

Kaler, Michael. Flora Tells a Story: The Apocalypse of Paul & Its Contexts. Kaler, Michael, ed. 2008. (Studies in Christianity & Judaism Ser.). (ENG., Illus.). 276p. 85.00 (978-1-55458-044-6(7)) Wilfrid Laurier Univ. Pr. CAN. Dist: Univ. of Toronto Pr.

Leigh, S.J., David J. Apocalyptic Patterns in Twentieth-Century Fiction. 2008. (ENG.). 288p. pap. 28.00 (978-0-268-03380-4(3)) Univ. of Notre Dame Pr.

Morgan, David T. The New Brothers Grimm & Their Left Behind Fairy Tales. 2006. (Illus.). 222p. per. 20.00 (978-0-88146-036-0(2)) Mercer Univ. Pr.

Mtetwa, Archieford Kurauone. Old Testament Apocalypticism. 2011. 68p. pap. (978-3-8454-0602-2(X)) Lambert Academic Publishing.

Nash, Susan Smith. Apocalypse in Twentieth-Century Literature, Film, & Cultural Texts. 2011. 200p. pap. (978-3-8433-8542-8(4)) Lambert Academic Publishing.

Newport, Kenneth G. C. & Walliss, John, eds. The End All Around Us: The Apocalyptic Texts & Popular Culture. 2009. (Millennialism & Society Ser.). (ENG., Illus.). 240p. (C). 99.95 (978-1-84553-261-1(9)); pap. 29.95 (978-1-84553-262-8(7)) Equinox Publishing Ltd. GBR. Dist: ISD.

Nicholas, William C. & Nicholas, William C., Jr. I Saw the World End: An Introduction to the Bible's Apocalyptic Literature. 2007. (Illus.). 158p. per. 18.95 *(978-0-8091-4450-1(6)*, 4450-1) Paulist Pr.

O'Regan, Cyril. Theology & the Spaces of Apocalyptic. 2009. *(978-0-87462-589-9(0))* Marquette Univ. Pr.

Orlov, Andrei A. From Apocalypticism to Merkabah Mysticism: Studies in the Slavonic Pseudepigrapha. 2006. (Supplements to the Journal for the Study of Judaism Ser.: Vol. 114). 500p. *(978-90-04-15439-1(6))* BRILL.

Powell, Stephen Ma Lpcc. Apocalyptic Grace: The evolution of culture & Consciousness. 2011. 274p. 29.99 ***(978-1-4628-7829-1(6))***; pap. 19.99 ***(978-1-4628-7219-0(0))*** Xlibris Corp.

Price, Robert M. The Paperback Apocalypse: How the Christian Church Was Left Behind. 2007. (ENG.). 340p. per. 18.98 *(978-1-59102-583-2(4))* Prometheus Bks., Pubs.

Pseudo-Methodius. Apocalypse of Pseudo-Methodius. an Alexandrian World Chronicle. 2012. (Dumbarton Oaks Medieval Library). Orig. Title: Excerpta Latina Barbari. (LAT & ENG.). 464p. 29.95 ***(978-0-674-05307-6(9))*** Harvard Univ. Pr.

Reed, Randall W. A Clash of Ideologies: Marxism, Liberation Theology, & Apocalypticism in New Testament Studies. 2010. (Princeton Theological Monographs). 194p. pap. 22.00 *(978-1-55635-514-1(9)*, Pickwick Pubns.) Wipf & Stock Pubs.

Rosen, Elizabeth K. Apocalyptic Transformation: Apocalypse & the Postmodern Imagination. 2008. (ENG.). 240p. 83.99 *(978-0-7391-1790-3(4))*; per. 36.99 *(978-0-7391-1791-0(2))* Lexington Bks.

Rowland, C. C. & Morray-Jones, C. R. A. Compendia Rerum Iudaicarum ad Novum Testamentum, The Mystery of God: Early Jewish Mysticism & the New Testament, Vol. 12. 2009. 694p. *(978-90-04-17532-7(6))* BRILL.

Sandy, D. Brent, et al. Prophecy & Apocalyptic: An Annotated Bibliography. 2007. (IBR Bibliographies Ser.). 240p. (C). pap. 28.00 *(978-0-8010-2601-0(6))* Baker Academic.

Schipper, Bernd U. & Plasger, George. Apokalyptik und Kein Ende? 2007. (Biblisch-Theologische Schwerpunkte Ser.). (GER.). 302p. (C). pap. 29.00 *(978-3-525-61594-2(9))* Vandenhoeck & Ruprecht GmbH & Co. KG DEU. Dist: ISD.

Silverman, Jason M. Persepolis & Jerusalem: Iranian Influence on the Apocalyptic Hermeneutic. 2012. (ENG., Illus.). 320p. 140.00 ***(978-0-567-20551-3(7)***, T&T Clark) Continuum International Publishing Group, Ltd. GBR. Dist: National Bk. Network.

St John the Evangelist. Revelation & Other Prophetic Books of the Bible. 2007. (Thrift Edition Ser.). (ENG., Illus.). 256p. pap. 3.95 *(978-0-486-45644-7(7))* Dover Pubns., Inc.

Stramara, Daniel F. God's Timetable: The Book of Revelation & the Feast of Seven Weeks. 2011. 202p. pap. 22.00 *(978-1-60899-638-4(7)*, Pickwick Pubns.) Wipf & Stock Pubs.

Swedenborg, Emanuel. Apocalypse Explained. 2009. 724p. pap. *(978-0-217-17499-2(X))* Books LLC.

—Apocalypse Revealed. 2009. 70p. pap. *(978-0-217-17506-7(6))* Books LLC.

Szulakowska, Urszula. The Sacrificial Body & the Day of Doom: Alchemy & Apocalyptic Discourse in the Protestant Reformation. 2006. (Aries Book Ser.: Vol. 1). (Illus.). 180p. *(978-90-04-15025-6(0))* BRILL.

van Donzel, E. J. & Schmidt, A. B. Gog & Magog in Early Syriac & Islamic Sources: Sallam's Quest for Alexander's Wall. 2009. (Brill's Inner Asian Library). (Illus.). 264p. *(978-90-04-17416-0(8))* BRILL.

VanderKam, James C. Enoch: A Man for All Generations. 2008. (ENG.). 324p. pap. 29.95 *(978-1-57003-796-2(5))* Univ. of South Carolina Pr.

Waterman, Leroy. The Historical Jesus: Hope of Mankind. 2011. 148p. 40.95 ***(978-1-258-04743-6(8))*** Literary Licensing, LLC.

Wicks, Henry J. The Doctrine of God in the Jewish Apocryphal & Apocalyptic Literature. 2010. 178p. pap. *(978-1-152-05350-2(7))* Books LLC.

—The Doctrine of God in the Jewish Apocryphal & Apocalyptic Literature. 2008. 385p. pap. 33.00 *(978-1-60608-255-3(8)*, Wipf and Stock) Wipf & Stock Pubs.

APOLLINAIRE, GUILLAUME, 1880-1918

Apollinaire, Guillaume. Alcools Guillaume. pap. 13.95 *(978-2-7616-1366-8(X))* Beauchemin Editions CAN. Dist: Distribooks, Inc.

Apollinaire, Guillaume & Frisch, Max. An Answer from the Silence: A Story from the Mountains. 2011. (SB-the German List Ser.). 118p. 19.00 *(978-1-906497-92-7(3))* Seagull Bks. London Ltd GBR. Dist: Chicago Distribution Ctr.

Bohn, Willard. Apollinaire on the Edge: Modern Art, Popular Culture, & the Avant-Garde. 2010. (Illus.). 143p. pap. 38.00 *(978-90-420-3108-1(5))* Rodopi.

Loffredo, Eugenia & Perteghella, Manuela, eds. One Poem in Search of a Translator: Re-Writing "Les Fenêtres" by Apollinaire. 2008. (Illus.). 284p. pap. 70.95 *(978-3-03911-408-5(5))* Lang, Peter AG GBR. Dist: Lang, Peter.

Read, Peter. Picasso & Apollinaire: The Persistence of Memory. (Illus.). 2010. (ENG.). 336p. pap. 34.95 *(978-0-520-26592-9(0))* 2008. 317p. 55.00 *(978-0-520-24361-3(7))* Univ. of California Pr.

APOLLO (GREEK DEITY)

Frothingham, Arthur. Medusa, Apollo, & the Great Mother. 2009. pap. 19.48 *(978-1-60724-525-4(6))* Gorgias Pr., LLC.

Miller, John F. Apollo, Augustus, & the Poets. 2011. (ENG., Illus.). 422p. pap. 50.00 ***(978-1-107-40358-1(8))*** Cambridge Univ. Pr.

APOLLO PROJECT

see Project Apollo (U.S.)

APOLLONIUS, OF TYANA

Baur, Ferdinand C. Apollonius von Tyana und Christus. 2009. 227p. pap. 20.00 *(978-1-60608-511-0(5)*, Wipf and Stock) Wipf & Stock Pubs.

Blavatsky, H. P. Apollonius of Tyana the Mysterious Teacher. 2006. pap. 12.95 *(978-1-4286-7263-5(X))* Kessinger Publishing, LLC.

Livingston, Marjorie. The New Nuctemeron: The Twelve Hours of Apollonius of Tyana. 2007. (ENG.). 144p. 35.95 *(978-0-548-28082-9(7))* Kessinger Publishing, LLC.

Mead, G. R. S. Apollonius of Tyana: The Philosopher, Explorer & Social Reformer of the First Century A. D. 2007. 176p. per. 16.95 *(978-1-60206-232-0(3))* Cosimo, Inc.

—The Religious Associations & Communities of the First Century - 2006. pap. 12.95 *(978-1-4304-1263-2(1))* Kessinger Publishing, LLC.

Mead, George Robert Stowe. Apollonius of Tyan. 2008. 80p. pap. 9.99 *(978-1-60459-539-0(6))* Wilder Pubns., Ltd.

Newman, John Henry. Historical Sketches: The Turks in Their Relation to Europe; Marcus Tullius Cicero; Apollonius of Tyana; Primitive Christianity. 2007. (ENG.). 372p. pap. 25.99 *(978-1-4346-4537-1(1))*; 414p. pap. 28.99 *(978-1-4346-4538-8(X))* BiblioBazaar.

—Historical Sketches V1. 2008. 468p. 52.95 *(978-1-4365-6975-0(3))* 2007. 472p. per. 37.95 *(978-0-548-75480-1(2))* Kessinger Publishing, LLC.

—The Life of Apollonius Tyanaeus. 2009. 66p. pap. 16.75 *(978-1-110-39399-2(7))* BiblioBazaar.

—The Life of Apollonius Tyanaeus, with a Comparison Between the Miracles of Scripture & Those Elsewhere Related, As Regards Their Respective Object. 2007. 64p. per. 16.95 *(978-0-548-78406-8(X))* Kessinger Publishing, LLC.

Siegmeister, Walter. Apollonius the Nazarene: The Life & Teachings of the Unknown World Teacher of the First Century. 2011. 68p. 36.95 ***(978-1-258-00195-7(0))*** Literary Licensing, LLC.

APOLLONIUS, RHODIUS

Clare, R. J. The Path of the Argo: Language, Imagery & Narrative in the Argonautica of Apollonius Rhodius. 2009. (Cambridge Classical Studies). (ENG.). 312p. (C). pap. 42.00 *(978-0-521-10292-6(8))* Cambridge Univ. Pr.

Lachenaud, Guy. Scholies à Apollonios de Rhodes. 2010. (Fragments Ser.). (FRE & GEC.). 578p. (C). pap. 68.00 ***(978-2-251-74208-3(5))*** Societe d'edition Les Belles lettres FRA. Dist: ISD.

Mori, Anatole. The Politics of Apollonius Rhodius' Argonautica. 2008. (ENG., Illus.). 272p. 99.00 *(978-0-521-88225-5(7))* Cambridge Univ. Pr.

Papanghelis, Theodore D., ed. Brill's Companion to Apollonius Rhodius. 2011. 479p. pap. ***(978-90-04-20588-8(8))*** BRILL.

Schelske, Oliver. Orpheus in der Spätantike: Studien und Kommentar zu den Argonautika des Orpheus: Ein literarisches, religiöses und philosophisches Zeugnis. 2011. (Beiträge zur Altertumskunde Ser.).Tr. of Orpheus in the Antiquity. (GER.). X, 442p. 182.00 ***(978-3-11-025971-1(0))*** De Gruyter, Walter Inc.

Scherer, Burkhard. Mythos, Katalog und Prophezeiung: Studien zu den Argonautika des Apollonios Rhodios. 2006. (Palingenesia. Schriftenreihe fur Klassische Altertumswissenschaft Ser.). (GER., Illus.). 232p. (C). 72.00 *(978-3-515-08808-4(3))* Steiner, Franz Verlag Wiesbaden GmbH DEU. Dist: Brown, David Bk. Co., The.

Thalmann, William G. Apollonius of Rhodes & the Spaces of Hellenism, 1 vol. 2011. (Classical Culture & Society Ser.). (ENG., Illus.). 288p. 65.00 *(978-0-19-973157-2(8))* Oxford Univ. Pr., Inc.

APOLLONIUS OF TYRE (FICTITIOUS CHARACTER)

Commentary on the Historia Apollonii Regis Tyri. 2006. (Mnemosyne: Bibliotheca Classica Batava Ser.). 935p. *(978-90-04-15594-7(5))* BRILL.

Grismer, Raymond L. The Book of Apollonius. Grismer, Raymond L. & Atkins, Elizabeth, trs. 2011. 132p. 40.95 ***(978-1-258-00207-7(8))*** Literary Licensing, LLC.

Libro de Apolonio (Book of Apolonio) (SPA.). 176p. *(978-84-320-6970-3(1))* GeoPlaneta, Editorial, S. A.

Panayotakis, Stelios. The Story of Apollonius, King of Tyre: A Commentary. 2012. (Texte und Kommentare Ser.: 38). (ENG.). 600p. (gr. 17-17). 182.00 *(978-3-11-021412-3(1))*; E-Book 280.00 ***(978-3-11-173885-7(X))*** De Gruyter, Walter Inc.

APOLOGETICS

see also Bible—Evidences, Authority, etc.; Natural Theology; Witness Bearing (Christianity)

also subdivisions Apologetic Works and Controversial Literature under individual religions and denominations; e.g. Catholic Church—Apologetic Works; Society of Friends—Controversial Literature

Abanes, Richard. Religions of the Stars: What Hollywood Believes & How It Affects You. 2009. 224p. pap. 13.99 *(978-0-7642-0648-1(6))* Bethany Hse. Pubs.

Abell, Dave. Common Sense Apologetics: One God, One Book, One Way. 2010. 224p. 33.95 *(978-1-4497-0422-3(0))*; pap. 17.95 *(978-1-4497-0424-7(7))* Author Solutions, Inc. (WestBow Pr.).

Al-Jawzi, Abd Al-Rahman Ibn. The Attributes of God: Daf' Shubah Al-Tashbih Bi-Akaff Al-Tanzih. Hamid Ali, Abdullah Bin, tr. 2006. (ENG.). 176p. pap. 24.95 *(978-0-9552359-0-0(1))* Amal Pr. GBR. Dist: Independent Pubs. Group.

Alexis, Jonas E. Christianity's Dangerous Idea: How the Christian Principle & Spirit Offer the Best Explanation for Life & Why Other Alternatives Fail. 2010. (Illus.). *(978-1-4520-0613-0(X))* AuthorHouse.

Ali, Hull, ed. The Church in the Power of the Spirit: Keswick Yearbook. 2006. (ENG., Illus.). 240p. per. 12.99 *(978-1-85078-720-4(4))* Authentic Media.

Anderson, Robert. A Doubter's Doubts about Science & Religion: By a Criminal Lawyer. 2009. (Cambridge Library Collection - Religion Ser.). (ENG.). 140p. pap. 19.99 *(978-1-108-00014-7(2))* Cambridge Univ. Pr.

Ankerberg, John & Burroughs, Dillon. What's the Big Deal about Jesus? "Why All the Controversy? "Is He Relevant? "Does It Matter to Me? 2007. 240p. pap. 12.99 *(978-0-7369-2120-6(6))* Harvest Hse. Pubs.

Ankerberg, John & Caner, Emir. The Truth about Islam & Women. 2009. (Truth about Islam Ser.). 80p. pap. 7.99 *(978-0-7369-2503-7(1))* Harvest Hse. Pubs.

Ankerberg, John & Weldon, John. Handbook of Biblical Evidences. 2008. (Illus.). 404p. per. 16.99 *(978-0-7369-2199-2(0))* Harvest Hse. Pubs.

Armstrong, Karen. The Case for God: What Religion Really Means. (ENG.). 432p. 2010. pap. 16.95 *(978-0-307-38980-0(4)*, Anchor) 2009. 27.95 *(978-0-307-26918-8(3)*, Knopf) Knopf Doubleday Publishing Group.

Augustine, Saint. De Civitate Dei. Walsh, P. G., ed. 2009. (Classical Texts). (LAT, ENG & EGY.). 160p. (C). pap. 35.00 *(978-0-85668-793-8(6))* Aris & Phillips GBR. Dist: Brown, David Bk. Co., The.

—De Civitate Dei. Walsh, P. G., ed. & tr. by. from LAT. 2009. (Classical Texts). (LAT, ENG & EGY.). 160p. (C). 85.00 *(978-0-85668-798-3(7))* Aris & Phillips GBR. Dist: Brown, David Bk. Co., The.

—De Civitate Dei. 2007. (Classical Texts). (LAT & ENG.). 200p. (C). pap. 36.00 *(978-0-85668-758-7(8))* Aris & Phillips GBR. Dist: Brown, David Bk. Co., The.

Auser, Wallace. Dissing God: The Myth of Religious Neutrality in a Secular Progressive Culture. 2007. 147p. per. 14.99 *(978-0-89957-110-2(7))* AMG Pubs.

Avant, John. If God Were Real: A Journey into a Faith That Matters. 2009. (ENG.). 224p. pap. 14.99 *(978-1-4165-8779-8(6)*, Howard Bks.) Howard Books.

Balabat, Janina. Conversations with an Atheist: The Good News of God's Plan of Salvation for Mankind. 2007. (ENG.). 400p. per. 16.99 *(978-1-59979-266-8(4)*, Creation Hse.) Charisma Media.

Barnes, Albert. Inquiries & Suggestions in Regard to the Foundation of Faith In. 2007. pap. 22.95 *(978-1-4304-5175-4(0))* Kessinger Publishing, LLC.

—Inquiries & Suggestions in Regard to the Foundation of Faith in the Word of God. 2008. 176p. 22.99 *(978-0-559-16951-9(5))*; pap. 16.99 *(978-0-559-16949-6(3))* BiblioBazaar.

—Inquiries & Suggestions in Regard to the Foundation of Faith in the Word of God. 2007. (ENG.). 178p. 37.95 *(978-0-548-15697-1(2))* Kessinger Publishing, LLC.

—Inquiries & Suggestions in Regard to the Foundation of Faith in the Word of God. 2006. 180p. per. 18.99 *(978-1-4255-1392-4(1))* MPublishing.

Bataineh, Rula F. Apologies. 2009. 160p. pap. 59.00 *(978-3-639-14686-8(7))* VDM Verlag Dr. Mueller e.K.

Beck, Richard. The Authenticity of Faith: The Varieties & Illusions of Religious Experience. 2012. (ENG.). 272p. pap. 24.99 ***(978-0-89112-350-7(4)***, ACU Pr.) Abilene Christian Univ. Pr.

Bednar, Lawrence. Evidence of the Divine Hand on the Traditional Texts of Holy Scripture. 2006. (ENG.). 446p. (C). per. 18.95 *(978-0-9760563-7-9(2))* Mechling Bookbindery.

Beigh, William S. The Bamberg Affair: In the ALL. 2008. 308p. 24.95 *(978-0-615-17259-0(8))* Alleron Publishing.

Beilby, James K. Thinking about Christian Apologetics: What It Is & Why We Do It. 2011. (ENG.). 214p. pap. 17.00 ***(978-0-8308-3945-2(3)***, IVP Acad.) InterVarsity Pr.

Benson, Clarence H. & Morgan, Robert J. Exploring Theology: A Guide for Systematic Theology & Apologetics. 2007. 336p. pap. 19.99 *(978-1-58134-962-7(9))* Crossway.

Berdiaev, Nikolai. Freedom & the Spirit. 5th ed. 2009. pap. *(978-1-59731-260-8(6))* Perennis, Sophia.

Berry, Alvin F. So What If the God of the Bible Exists Does It Really Matter at the End of Day? 2011. 68p. pap. 6.99 ***(978-1-4575-0020-6(5))*** Dog Ear Publishing, LLC.

Bertrand, J. Mark, et al. Rethinking Worldview: Learning to Think, Live, & Speak in This World. 2007. 256p. pap. 16.99 *(978-1-58134-934-4(3))* Crossway.

Blair, Robert. The Great Omission: Amazing Ways the Church Muddles the Message: How to Get It Right & Tell It Right. 2007. 303p. per. *(978-0-7880-2442-9(6))* CSS Publishing Co.

Blaise, Pascal. Pensees. (FRE.). pap. 19.95 *(978-2-253-16069-4(5))* Librairie Generale Francaise, LGF FRA. Dist: Distribooks, Inc.

Boomsma, Clarence. Why I Still Believe the Gospel. 2007. 108p. per. 12.00 *(978-0-8028-2736-4(5))* Eerdmans, William B. Publishing Co.

Bowker. Is God a Virus. 288p. 19.00 *(978-0-281-04812-0(6))* SPCK Publishing GBR. Dist: Pilgrim Pr., The/United Church Pr.

Boyd, Edward K. & Boyd, Gregory A. Letters from a Skeptic: A Son Wrestles with His Father's Questions about Christianity. 2008. (ENG.). 256p. pap. 14.99 *(978-1-4347-9980-7(8))* Cook, David C.

Braaten, Carl E. Who Is Jesus? Disputed Questions & Answers. 2011. pap. 20.00 ***(978-0-8028-6668-4(9))*** Eerdmans, William B. Publishing Co.

Brantley M Div, T. Charles. Even Christians Use the Bathroom - Reality Christianity: Simul Iustus et Pecator (Both Jusified & Sinner) 2008. 244p. pap. 14.95 *(978-1-4327-2516-7(5))* Outskirts Pr., Inc.

Brantley, T. Charles. Dissertation: the Spiritual Faust in the Twenty-First Century Church: Apologetics. 2011. 210p. pap. 20.95 *(978-1-4327-6978-9(2)*, Outskirts Pr., Inc.

Broadman and Holman Publishers Staff. Is Jesus Alive Today? The Evidence & Why It Matters to You Holman Bible Editorial Staff, ed. 2009. (ENG.). 64p. pap. 0.99 *(978-1-58640-496-3(2)*, Holman Pubs.) B&H Publishing Group.

Brooks, Ronald M. & Geisler, Norman L. When Skeptics Ask: A Handbook on Christian Evidences. 2008. (Illus.). 352p. pap. 19.99 *(978-0-8010-7164-5(X))* Baker Bks.

Broughton, William P. The Historical Development of Legal Apologetics with an Emphasis on the Resurrection. 2009. 168p. pap. 14.99 *(978-1-60791-968-1(0))* Xulon Pr., Inc.

Brown, Arthur I. Footprints of God. 2007. (ENG.). 248p. 41.95 *(978-0-548-10805-5(6))* Kessinger Publishing, LLC.

Brown, Michael L. Answering Jewish Objections to Jesus: New Testament Objections, 4 vols. 2006. (Answering Jewish Objections to Jesus Ser.). 384p. pap. 27.00 *(978-0-8010-6426-5(0))* Baker Bks.

Brown, Nathan. Seven Reasons Life Is Better with God. 2007. 159p. per. 12.99 *(978-0-8127-0436-5(3))* Autumn Hse. Publishing Co.

Bulfinch, S. G. (Stephen Greenleaf). Manual of the Evidences of Christianity, for Classes & Private Reading by Stephen G Bulfinch, D D. 2006. 160p. per. 18.99 *(978-1-4255-1184-5(8))* MPublishing.

Burns, M. P. Orthodoxy: Pushing at the Boundaries of Faith. 2009. 181p. pap. 16.95 *(978-1-4092-7224-3(9))* Lulu Enterprises Inc.

Busenitz, Nathan. Reasons We Believe: 50 Lines of Evidence That Confirm the Christian Faith. 2008. 224p. pap. 14.99 *(978-1-4335-0146-3(5))* Crossway.

Bushnell, Horace. Nature & the Supernatural, as Together Constituting the One System of God. 2011. (Cambridge Library Collection - Spiritualism & Esoteric Knowlege Ser.). (ENG.). 390p. pap. 31.99 *(978-1-108-07307-3(7))* Cambridge Univ. Pr.

—Nature & the Supernatural, As Together Constituting the One System of God, by Horace Bushnell. 2006. 532p. per. 29.99 *(978-1-4255-5865-9(8))* MPublishing.

Butler, J. The Analogy of Religion to the Constitution. 2006. 364p. per. 26.99 *(978-1-4255-3802-6(9))* MPublishing.

Butler, Joseph. The Analogy of Religion. 2008. 404p. 30.99 *(978-0-559-05027-5(5))*; 32.99 *(978-0-559-05023-7(2))*; pap. 33.75 *(978-0-559-05026-8(7))*; pap. 34.75 *(978-0-559-05024-4(0))* BiblioBazaar.

—The Analogy of Religion. 2009. 254p. pap. *(978-0-217-56791-6(6))*; 446p. pap. *(978-0-217-56794-7(0))* Books LLC.

—The Analogy of Religion. 2007. (ENG.). 300p. per. 19.94 *(978-0-615-15872-3(2))* Shenandoah Bible Ministries.

—The Analogy of Religion, etc with an Introductory Essay by Albert Barnes. 2006. 336p. per. 23.99 *(978-1-4255-3412-7(0))* MPublishing.

—The Analogy of Religion, Natural & Revealed, to the Constitution & Course of Nature by Joseph Butler with an Analysis of the Work by Rev B. 2006. 352p. per. 23.99 *(978-1-4255-3570-4(4))* MPublishing.

Cahill, Mark. One Heartbeat Away: Your Journey into Eternity. 2006. (ENG.). pap. 14.99 *(978-0-9643665-7-2(6))* Biblical Discipleship Pubs.

—A un Solo Latido de Distancia: Tu Viaje a la Eternidad. 2007. (SPA., Illus.). pap. 16.99 *(978-0-9643665-5-8(X))* Biblical Discipleship Pubs.

Campbell, Antony F. The Whisper of Spirit: A Believable God Today. 2008. 167p. per. 16.00 *(978-0-8028-4042-4(6))* Eerdmans, William B. Publishing Co.

Campbell, Charlie H. One-Minute Answers to Skeptics: Concise Responses to the Top 40 Questions. 2010. 128p. pap. 10.99 *(978-0-7369-2918-9(5))* Harvest Hse. Pubs.

Carnell, Edward J., ed. Christian Commitment: An Apologetic. 2007. (Edward Carnell Library). 330p. pap. 36.00 *(978-1-55635-620-9(X))* Wipf & Stock Pubs.

—The Kingdom of Love & the Pride of Life. 2007. (Edward Carnell Library). 164p. pap. 19.00 *(978-1-55635-574-5(2))* Wipf & Stock Pubs.

Carnell, Edward John & Carnell, Edward J. An Introduction to Christian Apologetics: A Philosophic Defense of the Trinitarian-Theistic Faith. 2007. (Edward Carnell Library). 344p. pap. 38.00 *(978-1-55635-266-9(2))* Wipf & Stock Pubs.

Carswell, Roger. Things God Wants Us to Know: Find Purpose in Your Life. 2007. (ENG.). 64p. 7.99 *(978-1-84550-242-3(6))* Christian Focus Pubns. GBR. Dist: STL Distribution North America.

The Case for Christ: A Six-Session Investigation of the Evidence for Jesus, 1 vol. 2009. 19.99 *(978-0-310-82800-6(7))* Zondervan.

The Case for Christ, Session 1: A Six-Session Investigation of the Evidence for Jesus, 1 vol. 2009. 2.99 *(978-0-310-82801-3(5))*; (ENG.). 2.99 *(978-0-310-82815-0(5))*; 2.99 *(978-0-310-82808-2(2))* Zondervan.

The Case for Christ, Session 2: A Six-Session Investigation of the Evidence for Jesus, 1 vol. 2009. 2.99 *(978-0-310-82802-0(3))*; (ENG.). 2.99 *(978-0-310-82809-9(0))*; (ENG.). 2.99 *(978-0-310-82816-7(3))* Zondervan.

The Case for Christ, Session 3: A Six-Session Investigation of the Evidence for Jesus, 1 vol. 2009. (ENG.). 2.99 *(978-0-310-82810-5(4))*; (ENG.). 2.99 *(978-0-310-82817-4(1))*; 2.99 *(978-0-310-82803-7(1))* Zondervan.

The Case for Christ, Session 4: A Six-Session Investigation of the Evidence for Jesus, 1 vol. 2009. 2.99 *(978-0-310-82804-4(X))*; (ENG.). 2.99 *(978-0-310-82818-1(X))*; (ENG.). 2.99 *(978-0-310-82811-2(2))* Zondervan.

The Case for Christ, Session 5: A Six-Session Investigation of the Evidence for Jesus, 1 vol. 2009. (ENG.). 2.99 *(978-0-310-82819-8(8))*; 2.99 *(978-0-310-82805-1(8))*; (ENG.). 2.99 *(978-0-310-82812-9(0))* Zondervan.

The Case for Christ, Session 6: A Six-Session Investigation of the Evidence for Jesus, 1 vol. 2009. (ENG.). 2.99 *(978-0-310-82820-4(1))*; (ENG.). 2.99 *(978-0-310-82813-6(9))*; 2.99 *(978-0-310-82806-8(6))* Zondervan.

The Case for Faith: A Six-Session Investigation of the Toughest Objections to Christianity, 1 vol. 2009. 19.99 *(978-0-310-82768-9(X))* Zondervan.

The Case for Faith, Session 1: A Six-Session Investigation of the Toughest Objections to Christianity, 1 vol. 2009. (ENG.). 2.99 *(978-0-310-82783-2(3))*;

(ENG.). 2.99 *(978-0-310-82776-4(0))*; 2.99 *(978-0-310-82769-6(8))* Zondervan.

The Case for Faith, Session 2: A Six-Session Investigation of the Toughest Objections to Christianity, 1 vol. 2009. 2.99 *(978-0-310-82770-2(1))*; (ENG.). 2.99 *(978-0-310-82784-9(1))*; (ENG.). 2.99 *(978-0-310-82777-1(9))* Zondervan.

The Case for Faith, Session 3: A Six-Session Investigation of the Toughest Objections to Christianity, 1 vol. 2009. 2.99 *(978-0-310-82771-9(X))*; 2.99 *(978-0-310-82778-8(7))*; 2.99 *(978-0-310-82785-6(X))* Zondervan.

The Case for Faith, Session 4: A Six-Session Investigation of the Toughest Objections to Christianity, 1 vol. 2009. 2.99 *(978-0-310-82772-6(8))*; (ENG.). 2.99 *(978-0-310-82779-5(5))*; (ENG.). 2.99 *(978-0-310-82786-3(8))* Zondervan.

The Case for Faith, Session 5: A Six-Session Investigation of the Toughest Objections to Christianity, 1 vol. 2009. 2.99 *(978-0-310-82787-0(6))*; 2.99 *(978-0-310-82780-1(9))*; 2.99 *(978-0-310-82773-3(6))* Zondervan.

The Case for Faith, Session 6: A Six-Session Investigation of the Toughest Objections to Christianity, 1 vol. 2009. 2.99 *(978-0-310-82774-0(4))*; (ENG.). 2.99 *(978-0-310-82781-8(7))*; (ENG.). 2.99 *(978-0-310-82788-7(4))* Zondervan.

Casserley, J. V. Langmead. Apologetics & Evangelism. Cully, Kendig Brubaker, ed. 2011. 186p. 42.95 ***(978-1-258-07254-4(8))*** Literary Licensing, LLC.

Cavey, Bruxy. The End of Religion: Encountering the Subversive Spirituality of Jesus. 2007. (Exploring the Great Ideas Ser.). (ENG.). 272p. pap. 14.99 *(978-1-60006-067-0(6))* NavPress Publishing Group.

Chamberlain, Paul. Why People Don't Believe: Confronting Seven Challenges to Christian Faith. 2011. 176p. pap. 14.99 *(978-0-8010-1377-5(1))* Baker Bks.

Chesteron, G. K. Orthodoxy. 2008. 288p. pap. *(978-1-4097-6940-8(2))* Read Bks.

Chesterson, Gilbert K. Heretics. 2009. 140p. 29.99 *(978-1-59547-535-0(4))* NuVision Pubns., LLC.

Chesterton & Chesterton, G. K. Orthodoxy. 2007. (B&N Library of Essential Reading Ser.). (ENG.). 176p. pap. 8.95 *(978-0-7607-8631-4(3))* Barnes & Noble, Inc.

Chesterton, G. K. Heretics. 2009. 152p. pap. 8.99 *(978-1-60450-616-7(4)*, Serenity Pubs.) Arc Manor.

—Heretics. 2008. 172p. 22.99 *(978-0-554-30780-0(4))* 2008. 172p. 25.99 *(978-0-554-21477-1(6))* 2006. (ENG.). 176p. pap. 19.99 *(978-1-4264-0088-9(8))* 2006. (ENG.). 170p. pap. 21.99 *(978-1-4264-0217-3(1))* BiblioBazaar.

—Heretics. 2007. (ENG.). 176p. per. 10.95 *(978-1-60206-845-2(3))* Cosimo, Inc.

—Heretics. 2006. (ENG.). pap. *(978-1-4065-1003-4(3))* Dodo Pr.

—Heretics. 2007. 216p. pap. 9.99 *(978-1-59986-898-1(9))* Filiquarian Publishing, LLC.

—Heretics. 2007. (Hendrickson Christian Classics Ser.). 179p. 7.97 *(978-1-59856-305-4(X))*; 10.95 *(978-1-59856-015-2(8))* Hendrickson Pubs. Marketing, LLC.

—Heretics. 2008. 120p. 19.99 *(978-1-60459-163-7(3))*; (ENG.). per. 7.49 *(978-1-60459-164-4(1))* Wilder Pubns., Ltd.

—Orthodoxy. 2008. 196p. 22.95 *(978-1-4218-9480-5(7))*; pap. 15.95 *(978-1-4218-9380-8(0))* 1st World Publishing, Inc. (1st World Library - Literary Society).

—Orthodoxy. 2008. 140p. pap. 8.99 *(978-1-60450-585-6(0)*, Serenity Pubs.) Arc Manor.

—Orthodoxy. 2008. 176p. 22.99 *(978-0-554-33475-2(5))* 2008. 176p. 25.99 *(978-0-554-24172-2(2))* 2007. (ENG.). 156p. pap. 19.99 *(978-1-4264-5897-2(5))* BiblioBazaar.

—Orthodoxy. 2011. 142p. pap. 12.99 ***(978-1-61203-253-5(2))*** Bottom of the Hill Publishing.

—Orthodoxy. 2007. 168p. per. 11.95 *(978-1-60206-757-8(0))* Cosimo, Inc.

—Orthodoxy. 2006. (ENG.). pap. *(978-1-4065-1002-7(5))* Dodo Pr.

—Orthodoxy. l.t. ed. 2006. pap. *(978-1-4068-2223-6(X))* Echo Library.

—Orthodoxy. 2008. 172p. pap. 11.95 *(978-1-60096-675-0(6))*; 168p. pap. 11.95 *(978-1-60096-527-2(X))* Editorium, The.

—Orthodoxy. 2007. 200p. pap. 9.99 *(978-1-59986-821-9(0))* Filiquarian Publishing, LLC.

—Orthodoxy, 1 vol. 2009. (Moody Classics Ser.). (ENG.). 240p. pap. 7.99 *(978-0-8024-5657-1(X))* Moody Pubs.

—Orthodoxy. 2007. (ENG.). 152p. pap. 10.45 *(978-1-60424-866-1(1))*; 184p. per. 9.95 *(978-1-59462-817-7(3))* Standard Pubns., Inc. (Book Jungle).

—Orthodoxy. 2011. 128p. pap. 14.99 ***(978-1-61720-237-7(1))*** 2008. 232p. pap. 12.99 *(978-1-60459-292-4(3))* 2008. 108p. 19.99 *(978-1-60459-161-3(7))* 2008. 108p. per. 8.99 *(978-1-60459-162-0(5))* Wilder Pubns., Ltd.

Chesterton, G. K. Orthodoxy: The classic of Christian Apologetics. 2010. 172p. pap. 14.95 *(978-1-60444-082-9(1))* IndoEuropeanPublishing.com.

Choung, James. True Story: A Christianity Worth Believing In. 2008. (ENG., Illus.). 233p. pap. 15.00 *(978-0-8308-3609-3(8)*, IVP Bks.) InterVarsity Pr.

Chris Sandoval. Can Christians Prove the Resurrection? A Reply to the Apologists. 2010. 364p. pap. 21.99 *(978-1-4269-2382-1(1))* Trafford Publishing.

City on a Hill Productions. Storm: Tough Questions about the Christian Faith Kit. 2007. 99.99 *(978-0-7847-1998-5(5))* Standard Publishing.

Clarke, James Freeman. Steps of Belief; or, Rational Christianity Maintained Against Atheism, Free Religion, & Romanism by James Freeman Clarke. 2006. 324p. per. 23.99 *(978-1-4255-3155-3(5))* MPublishing.

Cochran, Matthew E. As Though It Were Actually True. 2009. 256p. pap. 28.00 *(978-1-60608-820-3(3)*, Resource Pubns.) Wipf & Stock Pubs.

Collins, Francis S. The Language of God: A Scientist Presents Evidence for Belief. 2007. (Walker Large Print Ser.). (ENG., Illus.). 388p. per. 17.95 *(978-1-59415-186-6(5)*, Walker Large Print) Cengage Gale.

—The Language of God: A Scientist Presents Evidence for Belief. 2007. (ENG., Illus.). 320p. pap. 15.99 *(978-1-4165-4274-2(4)*, Free Pr.) Free Pr.

Colson, Charles W. The Faith. 2008. (ENG.). 96p. pap., instr.'s gde. ed. 8.99 *(978-0-310-27607-4(1))* Zondervan.

Comfort, Ray. Nothing Created Everything: The Scientific Impossibility of Atheistic Evolution. 2009. 224p. 25.95 *(978-1-935071-23-5(8))* WND Bks, Inc.

Copan, Paul. When God Goes to Starbucks: A Guide to Everyday Apologetics. 2008. 224p. pap. 14.99 *(978-0-8010-6743-3(X))* Baker Bks.

Copan, Paul, ed. True for You, but Not for Me: Overcoming Objections to Christian Faith, 1 vol. rev. ed. 2009. (ENG.). 240p. pap. 14.99 *(978-0-7642-0650-4(8))* Bethany Hse. Pubs.

Copan, Paul & Craig, William Lane, eds. Contending with Christianity's Critics: Anwering New Atheists & Other Objectors. 2009. (ENG.). 304p. pap. 19.99 *(978-0-8054-4936-5(1)*, B&H Academic) B&H Publishing Group.

—Passionate Conviction: Modern Discourses on Christian Apologetics. 2007. (ENG.). 288p. pap. 19.99 *(978-0-8054-4538-1(2)*, B&H Academic) B&H Publishing Group.

Corduan, Winfried. A Tapestry of Faiths: The Common Threads Between Christianity & World Religions. 2009. 248p. pap. 27.00 *(978-1-60608-841-8(6)*, Wipf and Stock) Wipf & Stock Pubs.

Craig, William Lane. On Guard: Defending Your Faith with Reason & Precision. 2010. (Illus.). 286p. *(978-1-4347-0188-6(3))* Kingsway Pubns.

Craig, William Lane & Meister, Chad, eds. God Is Great, God Is Good: Why Believing in God Is Reasonable & Responsible. 2009. (ENG., Illus.). 265p. pap. 19.00 *(978-0-8308-3726-7(4)*, IVP Bks.) InterVarsity Pr.

Crean, Thomas. God Is No Delusion: A Refutation of Richard Dawkins. 2007. 160p. pap. 12.95 *(978-1-58617-231-2(X))* Ignatius Pr.

Cummings, Owen F. & Cummings, Andrew C. Thinking God. 2011. 132p. pap. 16.00 ***(978-1-61097-682-4(7)***, Wipf and Stock) Wipf & Stock Pubs.

Cunningham, Richard B. C. S. Lewis: Defender of the Faith. 2008. (C. S. Lewis Secondary Studies Ser.). 226p. pap. 25.00 *(978-1-55635-922-4(5)*, Wipf and Stock) Wipf & Stock Pubs.

Daniels, Graham. My Mate's Gone Mad: Isn't Christianity Weird, Irrelevant & Untrue? 2008. (ENG.). 28p. 5.99 *(978-1-85078-764-8(6))* Authentic Media.

Dark, David. The Sacredness of Questioning Everything, 1 vol. 2009. (ENG.). 256p. pap. 15.99 *(978-0-310-28618-9(2))* Zondervan.

David, Andrew, et al, eds. 'God Is Dead' & I Don't Feel So Good Myself. 2009. 208p. pap. 23.00 *(978-1-60608-531-8(X)*, Cascade Bks.) Wipf & Stock Pubs.

Davidson, D. The Egyptian King Lists. 2006. pap. 9.95 *(978-1-4286-8299-3(6))* Kessinger Publishing, LLC.

Davis, Stephen T. Disputed Issues: Contending for Christian Faith in Today's Academic Setting. 2008. (ENG.). 260p. (C). pap. 34.95 *(978-1-60258-151-7(7))* Baylor Univ. Pr.

Davison, Andrew, ed. Imaginative Apologetics: Theology, Philosophy & the Catholic Tradition. 2011. (ENG.). 256p. pap. 29.99 *(978-0-334-04352-2(2)*, SCM Pr.) Hymns Ancient & Modern Ltd GBR. Dist: Westminster John Knox Pr.

Dembski, William. The End of Christianity: Finding a Good God in an Evil World, 1 vol. 2009. (ENG.). 254p. 22.99 *(978-0-8054-2743-1(0)*, B&H Academic) B&H Publishing Group.

Demy, Timothy J. & Stewart, Gary P. 101 Most Puzzling Bible Verses: Insight into Frequently Misunderstood Scriptures. 2006. 217p. per. 11.99 *(978-0-7369-1775-9(6))* Harvest Hse. Pubs.

Denison, James. Wrestling with God: How Can I Love a God I'm Not Sure I Trust? 2008. (ENG.). 240p. pap. 14.99 *(978-1-4143-1616-1(X)*, SaltRiver) Tyndale Hse. Pubs.

Dewick, E. C. The Christian Attitude to Other Religions. 2011. (ENG.). 232p. pap. 22.99 ***(978-0-521-24260-8(6))*** Cambridge Univ. Pr.

DiCello, Carmen. Truth in Balance: Doing Apologetics in a Postmodern Culture. 2009. 168p. pap. 19.00 *(978-1-60608-778-7(9)*, Wipf and Stock) Wipf & Stock Pubs.

Dods, John Bovee. Immortality Triumphant: The Existence of a God & Human Immortality Practically Considered & the Truth of Divine Revelation Substantiated 1853. 2007. (ENG.). 216p. 39.95 *(978-0-548-05470-3(3))* Kessinger Publishing, LLC.

Dods, Marcus, tr. from LAT. The City of God: St. Augustine of Hippo. 2009. 900p. pap. 18.95 *(978-1-59856-337-5(8))* Hendrickson Pubs. Marketing, LLC.

Dollar, Jason & Pinkerton, Bradley. Contend: A Survey of Christian Apologetics on a High School Level. 2009. 300p. pap. 16.95 *(978-1-59330-583-3(4))* Aventine Pr.

Douglas, Mark. Believing Aloud: Reflections on Being Religious in the Public Square. 2010. 198p. pap. 23.00 *(978-1-60899-247-8(0)*, Cascade Bks.) Wipf & Stock Pubs.

Eagleton, Terry. Reason, Faith, & Revolution: Reflections on the God Debate. (Terry Lectures Ser.). (ENG.). 200p. 2010. pap. 16.00 *(978-0-300-16453-4(X))* 2009. 25.00 *(978-0-300-15179-4(9))* Yale Univ. Pr.

Egan, Joe. The Godless Delusion: Dawkins & the Limits of Human Sight. 2009. 213p. pap. 44.95 *(978-3-03911-899-1(4))* Lang, Peter AG GBR. Dist: Lang, Peter.

The End of Reason: A Response to the New Atheists, 1 vol. 2009. 144p. pap. 3.49 *(978-0-310-32670-0(2))* Zondervan.

The Evidences of Christianity in their External Division. 2010. pap. 19.00 *(978-1-61143-177-3(8))* Gorgias Pr., LLC.

Faith under Fire 4: A New Kind of Faith, Session 1: Four Sessions on the Relevance of Christianity, 1 vol. 2009. (Zondervangroupware Small Group Edition Ser.). 4.99 *(978-0-310-79884-2(1))* Zondervan.

Faith under Fire 4: A New Kind of Faith, Session 2: Four Sessions on the Relevance of Christianity, 1 vol. 2009. (Zondervangroupware Small Group Edition Ser.). 2.99 *(978-0-310-79885-9(X))*; 4.99 *(978-0-310-79880-4(9))* Zondervan.

Faith under Fire 4: A New Kind of Faith, Session 3: Four Sessions on the Relevance of Christianity, 1 vol. 2009. (Zondervangroupware Small Group Edition Ser.). 4.99 *(978-0-310-79886-6(8))*; 4.99 *(978-0-310-79881-1(7))* Zondervan.

Faith under Fire 4: A New Kind of Faith, Session 4: Four Sessions on the Relevance of Christianity, 1 vol. 2009. (Zondervangroupware Small Group Edition Ser.). 2.99 *(978-0-310-79882-8(5))*; 2.99 *(978-0-310-79887-3(6))* Zondervan.

Faith under Fire#8482; 4: A New Kind of Faith: Four Sessions on the Relevance of Christianity, 1 vol. 2009. (Zondervangroupware Small Group Edition Ser.). 15.99 *(978-0-310-79873-6(6))* Zondervan.

Faith under Fire#8482; 4: A New Kind of Faith, Session 1: Four Sessions on the Relevance of Christianity, 1 vol. 2009. (Zondervangroupware Small Group Edition Ser.). (ENG.). 4.99 *(978-0-310-79879-8(5))*; 2.99 *(978-0-310-79874-3(4))* Zondervan.

Faith under Fire#8482; 4: A New Kind of Faith, Session 2: Four Sessions on the Relevance of Christianity, 1 vol. 2009. (Zondervangroupware Small Group Edition Ser.). 2.99 *(978-0-310-79875-0(2))* Zondervan.

Faith under Fire#8482; 4: A New Kind of Faith, Session 3: Four Sessions on the Relevance of Christianity, 1 vol. 2009. (Zondervangroupware Small Group Edition Ser.). 4.99 *(978-0-310-79876-7(0))* Zondervan.

Faith under Fire#8482; 4: A New Kind of Faith, Session 4: Four Sessions on the Relevance of Christianity, 1 vol. 2009. (Zondervangroupware Small Group Edition Ser.). 4.99 *(978-0-310-79877-4(9))* Zondervan.

Fant, Jr., Gene C., Gene C. God as Author: A Biblical Approach to Narrative, 1 vol. 2010. (ENG.). 224p. pap. 19.99 *(978-0-8054-4790-3(3)*, B&H Academic) B&H Publishing Group.

Fergusson, David. Faith & Its Critics: A Conversation. (ENG.). 208p. 2011. pap. 18.85 *(978-0-19-958568-7(7))* 2009. 35.00 *(978-0-19-956938-0(X))* Oxford Univ. Pr., Inc.

Fernandes, Phil. Contend Earnestly for the Faith: A Survey of Christian Apologetics. 2008. 457p. pap. 29.95 *(978-1-60474-024-0(8))* PublishAmerica, Inc.

Fichter, Joseph H. Textbook in Apologetics. 2011. 336p. 50.95 ***(978-1-258-04147-2(2))*** Literary Licensing, LLC.

Folkemer, Lawrence D. Christianity & Modern Paganism. 2011. 136p. 40.95 ***(978-1-258-01645-6(1))*** Literary Licensing, LLC.

Francisco, Adam S. & Francisco, Adam. Martin Luther & Islam: A Study in Sixteenth-Century Polemics & Apologetics. 2007. (History of Christian-Muslim Relations Ser.). 262p. *(978-90-04-16043-9(4))* BRILL.

Fred, DeRuvo. Raised for His Glory. Hannah, Richards, ed. 2011. 190p. pap. 12.99 ***(978-0-9837006-2-3(1))*** Study-Grow-Know.

Furtak, Rick Anthony, ed. Kierkegaard's 'Concluding Unscientific Postscript' A Critical Guide. 2010. (Cambridge Critical Guides). (ENG.). 272p. 85.00 *(978-0-521-89798-3(X))* Cambridge Univ. Pr.

Galli, Mark. God Wins: Heaven, Hell, & Why the Good News Is Better Than Love Wins. 2011. (ENG.). 224p. pap. 12.99 ***(978-1-4143-6666-1(3))*** Tyndale Hse. Pubs.

Garrison, Becky. The New Atheist Crusaders & Their Unholy Grail: The Misguided Quest to Destroy Your Faith, 0 vols. 2008. 256p. pap. 14.99 *(978-0-8499-1972-5(X))* Nelson, Thomas Inc.

Geisler, Norman L. & Hoffman, Paul K., eds. Why I Am a Christian: Leading Thinkers Explain Why They Believe. expurg. rev. ed. 2006. 368p. pap. 16.99 *(978-0-8010-6712-9(X))* Baker Bks.

Geisler, Norman L. & Howe, Thomas. The Big Book of Bible Difficulties: Clear & Concise Answers from Genesis to Revelation. 2008. 624p. pap. 29.99 *(978-0-8010-7158-4(5))* Baker Bks.

Geisler, Norman L. & Meister, Chad V., eds. Reasons for Faith: Making a Case for the Christian Faith. 2007. (Illus.). 416p. pap. 17.99 *(978-1-58134-787-6(1))* Crossway.

Geisler, Norman L. & Zukeran, Patrick. The Apologetics of Jesus: A Caring Approach to Dealing with Doubters. 2009. 208p. pap. 16.99 *(978-0-8010-7186-7(0))* Baker Bks.

Ghattas, Raouf, et al. A Christian Guide to the Qur'an: Building Bridges in Muslim Evangelism, 1 vol. 2009. 448p. pap. 24.99 *(978-0-8254-2688-9(X))* Kregel Pubns.

Gibson, Scott M. & Koukl, Gregory. Tactics: A Game Plan for Discussing Your Christian Convictions, 1 vol. 2009. (ENG.). 160p. pap. 14.99 *(978-0-310-28292-1(6))* Zondervan.

Glenn, Paul J. Apologetics: A Class Manual in the Philosophy of the Catholic Religion. 2011. 326p. 50.95 ***(978-1-258-06655-0(6))*** Literary Licensing, LLC.

Goetz, Stewart & Taliafero, Charles. Naturalism. 2008. (Interventions Ser.). 132p. pap. 16.00 *(978-0-8028-0768-7(2))* Eerdmans, William B. Publishing Co.

Gomes, Peter J. The Scandalous Gospel of Jesus: What's So Good about the Good News? 2008. (ENG.). 272p. pap. 14.95 *(978-0-06-000074-5(0)*, HarperOne) HarperCollins Pubs.

Gomez, Jose. 50 Preguntas y Respuestas Acerca de Dios. 2009. 148p. 22.49 *(978-1-4490-0137-7(8))*; pap. 11.99 *(978-1-4490-0138-4(6))* AuthorHouse.

Good News Publishers Staff. Only One Way? Reaffirming the Exclusive Truth Claims of Christianity. Phillips, Richard D., ed. & contrib. by by. Wells, David F. et al, contrib. by. 2007. 160p. pap. 12.99 *(978-1-58134-801-9(0))* Crossway.

—The Supremacy of Christ in a Postmodern World. Piper, John & Taylor, Justin, eds. 2007. 192p. pap. 14.99 *(978-1-58134-922-1(X))* Crossway.

Grampa Ed. Afraid to Read the Bible?, 1 vol. 2010. 48p. pap. 16.95 *(978-1-4489-6222-8(6))* PublishAmerica, Inc.

Gregory & Drobner, Hubertus R. Opera exegetica in Genesim: Gregorii Nysseni in Hexaemeron, Vol. 1. 2009. (GER & GEC., Illus.). 224p. *(978-90-04-13315-0(1))* BRILL.

Griffith, Leonard. Barriers to Christian Belief. 2011. 192p. 42.95 ***(978-1-258-09601-4(3))*** Literary Licensing, LLC.

Griffiths, Paul J. An Apology for Apologetics: A Study in the Logic of Interreligious Dialogue. 2007. 126p. (Orig.). pap. 16.00 *(978-1-55635-731-2(1))* Wipf & Stock Pubs.

Groothuis, Doug. Confronting the New Age: How to Resist a Growing Religious Movement. 2010. 226p. pap. 25.00 *(978-1-60899-342-0(6)*, Wipf and Stock) Wipf & Stock Pubs.

Grotius, Hugo. The Truth of the Christian Religion, with Jean le Clerc's Additions. 2012. (Natural Law Paper Ser.). (ENG.). (C). (gr. 12). pap. 14.50 *(978-0-86597-515-6(9))* Liberty Fund, Inc.

Habermas, Gary R. The Secret of the Talpiot Tomb: Unravelling the Mystery of the Jesus Family Tomb. 2008. (ENG., Illus.). 96p. (C). per. 7.99 *(978-0-8054-9506-5(1)*, Holman Reference) B&H Publishing Group.

Hackett, Stuart C. The Reconstruction of the Christian Revelation Claim: A Philosophical & Critical Apologetic. 2009. 350p. pap. 39.00 *(978-1-60608-367-3(8)*, Wipf and Stock) Wipf & Stock Pubs.

Haddad, Jonah F. Leaving Dirt Place: Love as an Apologetic for Christianity. 2011. 156p. pap. 18.00 *(978-1-61097-217-8(1)*, Wipf and Stock) Wipf & Stock Pubs.

Hahn, Scott & Wiker, Benjamin. Answering the New Atheism: Dismantling Dawkins' Case Against God. 2008. 151p. pap. 12.95 *(978-1-931018-48-7(0))* Emmaus Road Publishing.

Haldane. Reasonable Faith. 2010. (ENG.). 224p. (C). 133.00 *(978-0-415-43024-1(0))*; pap. 43.95 *(978-0-415-43025-8(9))* Routledge.

Halton, Thomas P. Hermias, Gentilium Philosophorum Irrisio. 2009. 46p. pap. 6.00 *(978-1-60608-632-2(4)*, Wipf and Stock) Wipf & Stock Pubs.

Ham, Ken & Hodge, Bodie. How Do We Know the Bible Is True? 2011. pap. 14.99 *(978-0-89051-633-1(2))* Master Bks.

Hamilton, Adam. When Christians Get It Wrong. 2010. 144p. pap. 14.00 *(978-1-4267-0914-2(5))* Abingdon Pr.

Hamilton, William Ennis. Studies in Moral Science. 2008. 304p. 28.99 *(978-0-559-35521-9(1))*; pap. 28.75 *(978-0-559-35520-2(3))* BiblioBazaar.

—Studies in Moral Science. 2009. 260p. pap. 19.99 *(978-1-4588-5192-5(3))* General Bks. LLC.

—Studies in Moral Science. 2007. (ENG.). 298p. 43.95 *(978-0-548-15246-1(2))*; 300p. per. 28.95 *(978-1-4304-4616-3(1))* Kessinger Publishing, LLC.

Hanft, Frank. You Can Believe: A Lawyer's Brief on Christianity. 2011. 186p. 42.95 ***(978-1-258-08479-0(1))*** Literary Licensing, LLC.

Hannay, Alastair. Kierkegaard: Concluding Unscientific Postscript. 2009. (Cambridge Texts in the History of Philosophy Ser.). (ENG.). 582p. (C). 108.00 *(978-0-521-88247-7(8))*; pap. 42.00 *(978-0-521-70910-1(5))* Cambridge Univ. Pr.

Harding & Harding, Brian. Augustine & Roman Virtue. 2008. (Continuum Studies in Philosophy Ser.). (ENG.). 220p. 130.00 *(978-1-84706-285-7(7))* Continuum International Publishing Group, Ltd. GBR. Dist: National Bk. Network.

Harding, Brian. Augustine & Roman Virtue. 2011. (ENG.). 220p. pap. 44.95 ***(978-1-4411-7527-4(X))*** Continuum International Publishing Group, Ltd. GBR. Dist: National Bk. Network.

Hardy, Dean. Stand Your Ground: An Introductory Text for Apologetics Students. 2007. (Illus.). 182p. pap. 21.00 *(978-1-55635-104-4(6)*, Wipf and Stock) Wipf & Stock Pubs.

Heimgartner, M. Timotheos I. , Ostsyrischer Patriarch: Disputation mit dem Kalifen Al-Mahdi. 2011. (Corpus Scriptorum Christianorum Orientalium Ser.). (C). (GER.). 123p. pap. 95.00 *(978-90-429-2337-9(7))*; 165p. pap. 102.00 *(978-90-429-2336-2(9))* Peeters Pubs. & Booksellers BEL. Dist: Brown, David Bk. Co., The.

Hill, Stephen. Defying Ignorance: Exposing Christianity's Most Popular Myths. 2007. 152p. per. 24.95 *(978-1-60441-554-4(1))* PublishAmerica, Inc.

Hindson, Ed, et al, eds. The Popular Encyclopedia of Apologetics: Surveying the Evidence for the Truth of Christianity. 2008. 502p. 24.99 *(978-0-7369-2084-1(6))* Harvest Hse. Pubs.

Hogsette, David S. Emails to a Young Seeker: Exchanges in Mere Christianity. 2011. 184p. pap. 21.00 *(978-1-60899-549-3(6)*, Wipf and Stock) Wipf & Stock Pubs.

Holding, James Patrick. Shattering the Christ Myth. 2008. 388p. pap. 22.99 *(978-1-60647-271-2(2))* Xulon Pr., Inc.

Holman Bible Editorial Staff. The Apologetics Study Bible. 2009. (Apologetics Bible Ser.). (ENG.). 2048p. im. lthr. 49.99 *(978-1-58640-510-6(1)*, Holman Pubs.) B&H Publishing Group.

—The Apologetics Study Bible. 2009. (Apologetics Bible Ser.). (ENG.). 2048p. im. lthr. 49.99 *(978-1-58640-509-0(8)*, Holman Pubs.) B&H Publishing Group.

Hopkins, Mark. Evidences of Christianity: Lectures Before the Lowell Institute January. 2007. pap. 31.95 *(978-1-4304-4955-3(1))* Kessinger Publishing, LLC.

—Lectures on the Evidences of Christianity. 2009. (Amer Philosophy, Religion Ser.). (ENG.). 388p. pap. 24.95 *(978-1-4290-1781-7(3))* Applewood Bks.

—Lectures on the Evidences of Christianity, Before the Lowell Institute, January, 1844 by Mark Hopkins. 2006. 384p. per. 26.99 *(978-1-4255-4070-8(8))* MPublishing.

House, H. Wayne, et al. Apologetics & Christian Evidences, 1 vol. 2006. (ZondervanCharts Ser.). (ENG., Illus.). 144p. pap. 18.99 *(978-0-310-21937-8(X))* Zondervan.

Howard, Jeremy Royal & Broadman and Holman Publishers Staff. Holman Quicksource Guide to Understanding Jesus 2009. (Perspectives Ser.). (ENG., Illus.). 400p. pap. 14.99 *(978-0-8054-9521-8(5),* Holman Reference) B&H Publishing Group.

Hutchings, Noah W. The Dark Side of the Purpose Driven Church. 2007. 192p. pap. 13.95 *(978-1-933641-00-3(2))* Bible Belt Pubns.

Hyde, Daniel R. Why Believe in God? 2011. pap. *(978-1-59638-212-1(0))* P & R Publishing.

Illingworth, J. R. Reason & Revelation: An Essay in Christian Apology. 2007. (ENG.). 292p. 43.95 *(978-0-548-12017-0(X))* Kessinger Publishing, LLC.

Inman, Anne E. Evidence & Transcendence: Religious Epistemology & the God-World Relationship. 2008. (ENG.). 216p. pap. 35.00 *(978-0-268-03177-0(0))* Univ. of Notre Dame Pr.

Jabbour, Nabeel T. The Crescent Through the Eyes of the Cross: Insights from an Arab Christian. 2008. (Experiencing God Ser.). (ENG.). 272p. per. 14.99 *(978-1-60006-195-0(8))* NavPress Publishing Group.

Jacobsen, Anders-Christian & Ulrich, Jorg, eds. Critique & Apologetics: Jews, Christians & Pagans in Antiquity. 2009. (Early Christianity in the Context of Antiquity Ser.). 304p. 64.95 *(978-3-631-58011-0(8))* Lang, Peter GmbH, Europaischer Verlag der Wissenschaften DEU. Dist: Lang, Peter.

Jacoby, Douglas A. Why Believe in God? Finding Truth in an Age of Doubt. 2010. 272p. pap. 13.99 *(978-0-7369-2708-6(5))* Harvest Hse. Pubs.

Jeffery, Steve, et al. Pierced for Our Transgressions: Rediscovering the Glory of Penal Substitution. 2007. 384p. pap. 25.00 *(978-1-4335-0108-1(2))* Crossway.

Jenkins, Philip. Laying down the Sword: Why We Can't Ignore the Bible's Violent Verses. (ENG.). 256p. 2012. pap. 15.99 ***(978-0-06-199072-4(8))*** 2011. 26.99 *(978-0-06-199071-7(X))* HarperCollins Pubs. (HarperOne).

Jenyns, Soame. View of the Internal Evidence of the Christian Religion. 2007. (ENG.). 194p. 37.95 *(978-0-548-03656-3(X))* Kessinger Publishing, LLC.

Jeremiah, David. I Never Thought I'd See the Day! Culture at the Crossroads. 2011. 44.99 ***(978-1-61113-275-5(4),*** Sound Library) AudioGO.

—I Never Thought I'd See the Day! Culture at the Crossroads. 2012. (ENG.). 352p. pap. 14.99 ***(978-0-446-56596-7(2))*** 2012. (SPA.). 352p. pap. 12.99 *(978-1-4555-0431-2(9))* 2011. (ENG.). 352p. 24.99 *(978-0-446-56595-0(4))* 2011. (ENG.). 480p. 26.99 *(978-1-4555-0734-4(2))* FaithWords.

Johnson, Jan. Storm Leader's Guide. 2007. per. 6.99 *(978-0-7847-1999-2(3))* Standard Publishing.

Johnson, John J. Currents in Twenty-First-Century Christian Apologetics: Challenges Confronting the Faith. 2008. 210p. pap. 23.00 *(978-1-55635-539-4(4))* Wipf & Stock Pubs.

Jones, Peter. True or False? Thinking Correctly about New Spirituality. 2007. (Wise Choices Ser.). (Illus.). 64p. pap. 3.00 *(978-1-84625-049-1(8))* DayOne Pubns. GBR. Dist: STL Distribution North America.

Kahn, Paul W. Political Theology: Four New Chapters on the Concept of Sovereignty. 2011. (Columbia Studies in Political Thought / Political History Ser.). (ENG.). 224p. (gr. 17). 32.50 *(978-0-231-15340-9(6))* Columbia Univ. Pr.

Kamecke, Fred von. Busted, 1 vol. 2009. (ENG.). 208p. pap. 16.99 *(978-0-310-28320-1(5))* Zondervan.

Keith, Alexander. Evidence of the Truth of the Christian Religion Derived from the Literal Fulfillment of Prophecy. 2009. 286p. 34.99 *(978-1-113-99889-7(X))* BiblioBazaar.

Keller, Timothy. The Reason for God: Belief in an Age of Scepticism. 2009. (ENG.). 336p. (gr. 12-18). 16.00 *(978-1-59448-349-3(3),* Riverhead Trade (Paperbacks)) Penguin Group (USA) Inc.

—The Reason for God: Belief in an Age of Skepticism. l.t. ed. 2009. (ENG.). 446p. pap. 17.99 *(978-1-59415-295-5(0))* Cengage Gale.

—The Reason for God: Belief in an Age of Skepticism. 2008. (ENG.). 320p. (gr. 12-18). 24.95 *(978-0-525-95049-3(4),* Dutton Adult) Penguin Group (USA) Inc.

—The Reason for God: Conversations on Faith & Life, 1 vol. 2010. (ENG.). 24.99 *(978-0-310-33046-2(7));* 128p. pap. 9.99 *(978-0-310-33047-9(5))* Zondervan.

—The Reason for God Pack: Conversations on Faith & Life, 1 vol. 2010. (ENG.). pap., pap. 31.99 inc. DVD *(978-0-310-67142-8(6))* Zondervan.

Kennedy, D. James. Understanding the Trinity: Evidence for God in Three Persons. 2nd rev. ed. 2006. 6.00 *(978-1-929626-26-7(6))* Coral Ridge Ministries Media, Inc.

Kern, Steve. No Other Gods - the Biblical Creation Worldview. 2007. pap. 24.99 *(978-0-9778065-7-1(2))* Amerisearch, Inc.

Kimball, Dan. They Like Jesus but Not the Church Participants Guide: Six Sessions Responding to Culture's Objections to Christianity, 1 vol. 2008. (ENG., Illus.). 144p. (gr. 13). pap., pupil's gde. ed. 8.99 *(978-0-310-27794-1(9))* Zondervan.

Kimpel, Ben F. Religious Faith, Language, & Knowledge: A Philosophical Preface to Theology. 2011. 172p. 42.95 ***(978-1-258-07340-4(4))*** Literary Licensing, LLC.

Kissinger, Thomas / Mark. The Noble Berean: And they searched the scriptures daily, whether those things were So..., 5 volumes, Volume 1. 2007. 104p. pap. 12.95 *(978-0-9785134-1-2(X))* Straightway Publishing Co.

Kluck, Ted & DeYoung, Kevin. Why We Love the Church: In Praise of Institutions & Organized Religion. 2009. (ENG.). 240p. pap. 14.99 *(978-0-8024-5837-7(8))* Moody Pubs.

Kroll, Woodrow. Taking Back the Good Book: How America Forgot the Bible & Why It Matters to You. 2007. 224p. 19.99 *(978-1-58134-826-2(6))* Crossway.

KüNg. On Being a Christian. 2008. (ENG.). 720p. 32.95 *(978-1-84706-406-6(X))* Continuum International Publishing Group, Ltd. GBR. Dist: National Bk. Network.

Lactantius, et al. Divinarum Institutionum Libri Septem. 2007. (Bibliotheca scriptorum Graecorum et Romanorum Teubneriana (BT) Ser.). (LAT.). XII, 232p. pap. 84.00 *(978-3-11-019506-4(2))* De Gruyter, Walter Inc.

Lactantius, Lucius Caecilius Firmianus. Epitome divinarum Institutionum. Heck, Eberhard & Wlosok, Antonie, eds. (Bibliotheca scriptorum Graecorum et Romanorum Teubneriana (BT) Ser.). (LAT.). XLVIII, 128p. 42.00 ***(978-3-11-181354-7(1))*** De Gruyter, Walter Inc.

LaHaye, Tim. Mind Siege Leader's Guide: The Battle for the Truth, 0 vols. 2008. 100p. pap. 11.99 *(978-1-4185-3211-6(8))* Nelson, Thomas Inc.

Lamb, David T. God Behaving Badly: Is the God of the Old Testament Angry, Sexist & Racist? 2011. (ENG.). 205p. pap. 15.00 *(978-0-8308-3826-4(0),* IVP Bks.) InterVarsity Pr.

Lampe, Peter & Brawley, Robert L. New Testament Theology in a Secular World: A Constructivist Work in Christian Apologetics. Lampe, Peter & Brawley, Robert L., trs. from GER. 2012. (ENG.). 224p. 130.00 *(978-0-567-32417-7(6));* pap. 39.95 *(978-0-567-38888-9(3))* Continuum International Publishing Group, Ltd. GBR. (T&T Clark Int'l). Dist: National Bk. Network.

Lander, Jesse M. Inventing Polemic: Religion, Print, & Literary Culture in Early Modern England. 2009. (ENG., Illus.). 336p. pap. 44.00 *(978-0-521-12024-1(1))* Cambridge Univ. Pr.

Lane, Craig William & Craig, William Lane. Reasonable Faith: Christian Truth & Apologetics. 3rd rev. ed. 2008. (Illus.). 416p. pap. 26.00 *(978-1-4335-0115-9(5))* Crossway.

Lash, Nicholas. Theology for Pilgrims. 2008. (ENG.). 200p. pap. 25.00 *(978-0-268-03409-2(5))* Univ. of Notre Dame Pr.

Lawrenz, Mel. I Want to Believe: Finding Your Way in an Age of Many Faiths. 2008. (ENG., Illus.). 256p. 16.99 *(978-0-8307-4452-7(5))* Gospel Light Pubns.

Leitch, Ian. Life Before Death: A Restored, Regenerated, & Renewed Life. 2008. (ENG., Illus.). 134p. per. 14.95 *(978-1-60265-007-7(1))* Grace Acres Pr.

Lewis, C. S. Mere Christianity; The Screwtape Letters; The Great Divorce, Set. 2009. 59.99 *(978-0-06-186489-6(7),* HarperOne) HarperCollins Pubs.

Liber VII: Appendix. Indices. 2011. (Bibliotheca scriptorum Graecorum et Romanorum Teubneriana Ser.). (LAT.). XVIII, 210p. pap. 84.00 ***(978-3-11-022467-2(4))*** De Gruyter, Walter Inc.

Linden, James V. & Costello, William T. The Fundamentals of Religion. 2011. 352p. 51.95 ***(978-1-258-08364-9(7))*** Literary Licensing, LLC.

Lindsley, Art. Love, the Ultimate Apologetic: The Heart of Christian Witness. 2008. (ENG.). 174p. pap. 15.00 *(978-0-8308-3427-3(3),* IVP Bks.) InterVarsity Pr.

Little, Paul E. Know Who You Believe. 2008. (ENG.). 144p. pap. 0.00 *(978-1-59328-218-9(4))* Graham, Billy Evangelistic Assn.

—Know Who You Believe. 2008. (ENG.). 144p. per. 13.00 *(978-0-8308-3424-2(9),* IVP Bks.) InterVarsity Pr.

—Know Why You Believe. 4th ed. 2008. (ENG., Illus.). 231p. per. 15.00 *(978-0-8308-3422-8(2),* IVP Bks.) InterVarsity Pr.

Lose, David J. Making Sense of the Christian Faith. 2010. 238p. pap. 12.99 *(978-0-8066-9848-9(9),* Fortress Pr.) Augsburg Fortress, Pubs.

MacArthur, John. The Jesus You Can't Ignore: What You Must Learn from the Bold Confrontations of Christ. l.t. ed. 2010. (ENG.). 416p. pap. 17.99 *(978-1-59415-336-5(1))* Cengage Gale.

—The Jesus You Can't Ignore: What You Must Learn from the Bold Confrontations of Christ. 2010. 272p. pap. 15.99 *(978-1-4002-0297-3(3))* Nelson, Thomas Inc.

—The Jesus You Can't Ignore: What You Must Learn from the Bold Confrontations of Christ. l.t. ed. 2009. 421p. 30.50 *(978-1-4104-1958-3(4))* Thorndike Pr.

MacKinnon, Donald. Borderlands of Theology: And Other Essays. Roberts, George W. & Smucker, Donovan E., eds. 2011. 256p. pap. 28.00 ***(978-1-61097-581-0(2),*** Wipf and Stock) Wipf & Stock Pubs.

Major Religions of the World ... . Revisited. 2008. 247p. 28.95 *(978-1-934927-02-1(3))* W R F Publishing Co.

Malczewski, Dan. God's Plan: What Every Christian Should Know. 2010. 232p. 33.95 *(978-1-4497-0341-7(0));* pap. 17.95 *(978-1-4497-0340-0(2))* Author Solutions, Inc. (WestBow Pr.).

Malet, Diego. Religión y Ciencia en Armonía. 2009. (SPA.). 103p. 7.99 *(978-980-369-043-4(4))* Giluz, Ediciones VEN. Dist: LD Bks., Inc.

Maltz, Steve. The Truth Is Out There: The Ultimate World Conspiracy - Who Really Is Pulling the Strings? 2006. (ENG.). 128p. per. 12.99 *(978-1-86024-573-2(0))* Authentic Media.

Mann, Gerald. Common Sense Religion: Renewing Your Christian Values. 166p. (Orig.). reprint ed. pap. 9.95 *(978-0-9647272-0-5(X))* Riverbend Pr.

Marcellino, Dennis. The Proof: That God Exists & the Bible Is True. 2009. *(978-0-945272-33-5(2))* Lighthouse Pubns., Inc.

—Why Are We Here Workbook. 2007. 152p. per. 19.95 *(978-0-945272-12-0(X))* Lighthouse Publishing.

Markham, Ian S. Against Atheism: Why Dawkins, Hitchens, & Harris Are Fundamentally Wrong. 2010. (ENG., Illus.). 176p. 94.95 *(978-1-4051-8964-4(9));* pap. 27.95 *(978-1-4051-8963-7(0))* Wiley, John & Sons, Inc. (Wiley-Blackwell).

Marshall, David. The Truth about Jesus & the Lost Gospels: A Reasoned Look at Thomas, Judas, & the Gnostic Gospels. 2007. 181p. per. 9.99 *(978-0-7369-2055-1(2))* Harvest Hse. Pubs.

Martyr, Justin. The Writings of Justin Martyr. Roberts, Alexander & Donaldson, James, eds. 2007. 152p. per. 14.95 *(978-1-933993-46-1(4))* Apocryphile Pr.

Mascord, Keith. Alvin Plantinga & Christian Apologetics. 2007. (Paternoster Theological Monographs). 270p. pap. 30.00 *(978-1-55635-156-3(9),* Wipf and Stock) Wipf & Stock Pubs.

Matt, Evangelist James. Evidence of God: No Subtitle. 2008. pap. 14.99 *(978-1-60647-487-7(1))* Xulon Pr., Inc.

May, J. Lewis. God & the Universe the Christian Posit. 2006. pap. 24.95 *(978-1-4286-5605-5(7))* Kessinger Publishing, LLC.

McCosh, James. Christianity & Positivism A Series of. 2006. pap. 33.95 *(978-1-4286-5956-8(0))* Kessinger Publishing, LLC.

McDowell, Josh & Johnson, Kevin. The Awesome Book of Bible Answers for Kids. 2011. 160p. pap. 11.99 *(978-0-7369-2872-4(3))* Harvest Hse. Pubs.

McDowell, Josh & McDowell, Sean. Evidence for the Resurrection. 2009. (ENG.). 224p. 22.99 *(978-0-8307-4785-6(0))* Gospel Light Pubns.

—Truthwalk Kit #1. 2011. 59.99 *(978-0-7369-4451-9(6))* Harvest Hse. Pubs.

—Truthwalk Kit #2. 2011. 59.99 *(978-0-7369-4455-7(9))* Harvest Hse. Pubs.

McDowell, Sean. Apologetics for a New Generation: A Biblical & Culturally Relevant Approach to Talking about God. 2009. (ConversantLife.com Ser.). 256p. pap. 13.99 *(978-0-7369-2520-4(1))* Harvest Hse. Pubs.

McFarland, Alex. The 10 Most Common Objections to Christianity. 2007. (ENG.). 256p. per. 14.99 *(978-0-8307-4298-1(0),* REL070000) Gospel Light Pubns.

McGrath, Alister. Heresy: A History of Defending the Truth. 2010. (ENG.). 238p. pap. 13.99 *(978-0-06-199899-7(0),* HarperOne) HarperCollins Pubs.

McGrath, Alister & McGrath, Joanna Collicutt. The Dawkins Delusion? Atheist Fundamentalism & the Denial of the Divine. 2010. (Veritas Bks.). (ENG.). 119p. pap. 13.00 *(978-0-8308-3721-2(3),* IVP Bks.) InterVarsity Pr.

McGrath, Alister E. & McGrath, Joanna Collicutt. The Dawkins Delusion? Atheist Fundamentalism & the Denial of the Divine. annot. ed. 2007. (Veritas Bks.). (ENG.). 118p. 16.00 *(978-0-8308-3446-4(X),* IVP Bks.) InterVarsity Pr.

McLaren, Brian D. A Search for What Is Real, 1 vol. 2007. (Finding Faith Ser.). (ENG.). 192p. pap. 12.99 *(978-0-310-27267-0(X))* Zondervan.

—A Search for What Makes Sense, 1 vol. 2007. (Finding Faith Ser.). (ENG., Illus.). 192p. pap. 12.99 *(978-0-310-27266-3(1))* Zondervan.

McLeod-Harrison, Mark S. & Smith, Philip. Being at Home in the World: A New Christian Apologetic. 2011. 150p. pap. 19.00 *(978-1-61097-071-6(3),* Wipf and Stock) Wipf & Stock Pubs.

Meister, Chad V. Building Belief. 2009. 228p. pap. 25.00 *(978-1-60608-799-2(1),* Wipf and Stock) Wipf & Stock Pubs.

Metz, Johann Baptist. Faith in History & Society: Toward a Practical Fundamental Theology. Ashley, J. Matthew, ed. & tr. by. from GER. 2007. (ENG.). 304p. pap. 34.00 *(978-0-8245-2554-5(X),* Herder & Herder) Crossroad Publishing Co., The.

Meynell, Hugo Anthony. The Epistemological Argument Against Atheism: Why a Knowledge of God Is Implied in Everything We Know. 2012. i, 248p. 139.95 ***(978-0-7734-1566-9(1))*** Mellen, Edwin Pr., The.

Middleton, Eric. The New Flatlanders: A Seeker's Guide to the Theory of Everything. 2007. (ENG., Illus.). 176p. (C). per. 16.95 *(978-1-59947-123-5(X))* Templeton Pr.

Minucius Felix, Marcus. Octavius. Kytzler, Bernhard, ed. 2nd ed. (Bibliotheca scriptorum Graecorum et Romanorum Teubneriana (BT) Ser.). (LAT.). XIV, 41p. 42.00 ***(978-3-11-181655-5(9))*** De Gruyter, Walter Inc.

Minucius Felix, Marcus & Fahy, T. Octavius. 2011. 212p. pap. 24.75 ***(978-1-179-73746-1(6))*** BiblioBazaar.

Minucius Felix, Marcus & Freese, John Henry. Octavius. 2010. (ENG.). 108p. pap. 19.75 *(978-1-172-36357-5(9));* pap. 19.75 *(978-1-176-89042-8(5))* BiblioBazaar.

Minucius Felix, Marcus & Holden, Hubert Ashton. Octavius. 2010. (ENG.). 310p. pap. 29.75 *(978-1-178-02654-2(X))* BiblioBazaar.

Mittelberg, Mark. Eligiendo Tu Fe: En un Mundo de Opciones Espirituales. 2008.Tr. of Choosing Your Faith: In a World of Spiritual Options. (SPA.). 320p. pap. 12.99 *(978-1-4143-2063-2(9),* Tyndale Espanol) Tyndale Hse. Pubs.

Mittelberg, Mark, et al. Choosing Your Faith: In a World of Spiritual Options. 2009. 180p. pap. 14.99 *(978-1-4143-1580-5(5))* Tyndale Hse. Pubs.

—Choosing Your Faith Study Guide. 2009. 180p. pap. 7.99 *(978-1-4143-2387-9(5))* Tyndale Hse. Pubs.

Moltmann, Jurgen. Sun of Righteousness, Arise! God's Future for Humanity & the Earth. 2010. 256p. (C). pap. 25.00 *(978-0-8006-9658-0(1),* Fortress Pr.) Augsburg Fortress, Pubs.

Moreland, J. P. The God Question: An Invitation to a Life of Meaning. 2009. (ConversantLife.com Ser.). 272p. pap. 13.99 *(978-0-7369-2488-7(4))* Harvest Hse. Pubs.

Moreland, J. P. & Muehlhoff, Tim. The God Conversation: Using Stories & Illustrations to Explain Your Faith. 2007. (ENG.). 160p. pap. 15.00 *(978-0-8308-3489-1(3),* IVP Bks.) InterVarsity Pr.

Moreland, James Porter & Moreland, J. P. Kingdom Triangle: Recover the Christian Mind, Renovate the Soul, Restore the Spirit's Power, 1 vol. 2007. (ENG.). 240p. 19.99 *(978-0-310-27432-2(X))* Zondervan.

Morrow, Jonathan & McDowell, Sean. Is God Just a Human Invention? And Seventeen Other Questions Raised by the New Atheists, 1 vol. 2010. 304p. pap. 16.99 *(978-0-8254-3654-3(0))* Kregel Pubns.

Muir, Sir William K. C. S. I. Ll. D. D. C. L. The Apology of Al Kindy, Written at the Court of Al Mâmûn. 2011. 224p. pap. 19.99 ***(978-1-4568-2188-3(1))*** Xlibris Corp.

Murphy, Gannon. Reasons for the Christian Hope. 2009. (ENG., Illus.). 144p. pap. 15.99 *(978-1-84550-466-3(6),* Mentor) Christian Focus Pubns. GBR. Dist: STL Distribution North America.

—Voices of Reason in Christian History: Their Lives & Legacies. 2009. 240p. pap. 20.00 *(978-1-60608-489-2(5),* Wipf and Stock) Wipf & Stock Pubs.

Myers, David G. A Friendly Letter to Skeptics & Atheists: Musings on Why God Is Good & Faith Isn't Evil. 2008. (ENG., Illus.). 160p. 16.95 *(978-0-470-29027-9(7),* Jossey-Bass) Wiley, John & Sons, Inc.

Myth-Busters. 2009. pap. *(978-1-59636-345-8(2))* Rose Publishing.

Nichols, Terence L. The Sacred Cosmos: Christian Faith & the Challenge of Naturalism. 2009. 240p. pap. 26.00 *(978-1-60608-413-7(5),* Wipf and Stock) Wipf & Stock Pubs.

Noebel, David A. Worldviews in Collision. 2008. 560p. pap. 17.99 *(978-0-7369-2198-5(2))* Harvest Hse. Pubs.

Noll, James. Where Did the Prophets Go? Proof That Prophets Exist Today. 2009. 88p. pap. 10.95 *(978-1-4327-3769-6(4))* Outskirts Pr., Inc.

Nuels, Jaime. There's No Mystery to the Bible. 2007. 42p. per. *(978-0-9788283-1-8(3))* Acacia Publishing, Inc.

Nuovo, Victor, ed. John Locke: Vindications of the Reasonableness of Christianity. 2011. (Clarendon Edition of the Works of John Locke Ser.). (ENG., Illus.). 448p. 125.00 *(978-0-19-928655-3(8))* Oxford Univ. Pr., Inc.

Oakland, Roger. Let There Be Light: From Evolutionist to Creationist How One Man Left His Canadian Farm to Spread the Gospel Throughout the World. 2011. pap. ***(978-0-9846366-9-3(2))*** Lighthouse Trails Publishing Co.

O'Brien, John A. Truths Men Live By: A Philosophy of Religions & Life. 2007. (ENG.). 442p. 51.95 *(978-0-548-07287-5(6))* Kessinger Publishing, LLC.

O'Leary, Daniel. Unmasking God: Revealing the Divine in the Ordinary. 2011. (ENG.). 144p. pap. 22.95 *(978-1-85607-726-2(8))* Columba Pr. IRL. Dist: Dufour Editions, Inc.

Oliphint, K. Scott & Tipton, Lane G., eds. Revelation & Reason: New Essays in Reformed Apologetics. 2007. 336p. per. 24.99 *(978-0-87552-596-9(2),* P & R Publishing.

Olson, Roger E. Questions to All Your Answers: The Journey from Folk Religion to Examined Faith, 1 vol. 2008. (ENG., Illus.). 192p. pap. 12.99 *(978-0-310-28758-2(8))* Zondervan.

O'Malley, William J. Help My Unbelief. 2008. 160p. 15.00 *(978-1-57075-803-4(4))* Orbis Bks.

Orosius. Orosius: Seven Books of History Against the Pagans. Fear, A. T., ed. 2010. (Liverpool University Press - Translated Texts for Historians Ser.). (ENG.). 456p. pap. 39.95 *(978-1-84631-239-7(6))* Liverpool Univ. Pr. GBR. Dist: Chicago Distribution Ctr.

Orosius, Paulus. Orosius: Seven Books of History Against the Pagans. Fear, A. T., ed. 2010. (Liverpool University Press - Translated Texts for Historians Ser.). (ENG.). 456p. 95.00 *(978-1-84631-473-5(9))* Liverpool Univ. Pr. GBR. Dist: Chicago Distribution Ctr.

Orr-Ewing, Amy. Is Believing in God Irrational? 2008. (ENG.). 142p. pap. 15.00 *(978-0-8308-3353-5(6),* IVP Bks.) InterVarsity Pr.

Paley, William. Evidences of Christianity. 2008. 396p. 31.99 *(978-0-554-27100-2(1))* 2008. 396p. 29.99 *(978-0-554-36403-2(4))* 2007. (ENG.). 358p. pap. 25.99 *(978-1-4346-2500-7(1))* 2007. 392p. pap. 26.99 *(978-1-4346-2542-7(7))* BiblioBazaar.

—Evidences of Christianity. 2009. 364p. pap. *(978-1-4590-7176-6(X))* Books LLC.

—Evidences of Christianity. 2007. (ENG.). 328p. per. *(978-1-4065-4174-8(5))* Dodo Pr.

—Evidences of Christianity. 2007. (ENG.). 256p. per. *(978-1-4068-2316-5(3))* Echo Library.

—A View of the Evidences of Christianity. 2009. (Cambridge Library Collection - Religion Ser.). (ENG.). 408p. pap. 31.99 *(978-1-108-00095-6(9));* 376p. pap. 29.99 *(978-1-108-00094-9(0))* Cambridge Univ. Pr.

Paley, William & Whately, Richard. A View of the Evidences of Christianity: In Three Parts. 2007. (ENG.). 420p. per. 34.95 *(978-1-4304-4989-8(6))* Kessinger Publishing, LLC.

Pantana, Sr. America-A Purpose-Driven Nation. 2007. 484p. (ENG.). 35.99 *(978-1-60266-632-0(6));* per. 23.99 *(978-1-60266-631-3(8))* Xulon Pr., Inc.

Parris, Peter. The Truth of the Gospel. 2008. 192p. 21.99 *(978-1-60477-769-7(9));* per. 13.99 *(978-1-60477-768-0(0))* Xulon Pr., Inc.

Parton, Craig A. Religion on Trial. 2008. (ENG.). 114p. (C). pap. 33.00 *(978-0-7188-9220-3(8))* Lutterworth Pr., The GBR. Dist: Brown, David Bk. Co., The.

—Religion on Trial. 2008. 114p. pap. 14.00 *(978-1-55635-715-2(X),* Wipf and Stock) Wipf & Stock Pubs.

Pascal, Blaise. Thoughts on Religion & Other Subjects. 2007. (ENG.). 366p. 48.95 *(978-0-548-14983-6(6));* 368p. per. 33.95 *(978-1-4304-4309-4(X))* Kessinger Publishing, LLC.

Payton, James R. Irenaeus on the Christian Faith: A Condensation of Against Heresies. 2012. (ENG.). 234p. pap. 39.00 ***(978-0-227-68018-6(9))*** Clarke, James Co., Ltd. GBR. Dist: Brown, David Bk. Co., The.

Pearcey, Nancy. Total Truth: Liberating Christianity from Its Cultural Captivity. 2008. (Illus.). 512p. pap. 20.99 *(978-1-4335-0220-0(8))* Crossway.

Pera, Marcello. Why We Should Call Ourselves Christians: The Religious Roots of Free Societies. 2011. (ENG.). 220p. 23.95 *(978-1-59403-564-7(4))* Encounter Bks.

Peterson, Eugene H. The Jesus Way: A Conversation on the Ways That Jesus Is the Way. 2011. 304p. pap. 17.00 ***(978-0-8028-6703-2(0))*** 2007. 289p. 22.00 *(978-0-8028-2949-8(X))* Eerdmans, William B. Publishing Co.

Peterson, Eugene H. & Santucci, Peter. The Jesus Way Study Guide. 2007. 63p. per. 6.00 *(978-0-8028-4566-5(5))* Eerdmans, William B. Publishing Co.

Petrus, Alfonsi. Petrus Alfonsi: Dialogue Against the Jews. Resnick, Irven M., tr. from LAT. 2006. (Fathers of the Church Ser.: No. 8). (Illus.). 290p. 39.95 *(978-0-8132-1390-3(8))* Catholic Univ. of America Pr.

Pfefferkorn, Johannes, et al. The Jews' Mirror. 2011. (GER & ENG.). ***(978-0-86698-438-6(0))*** ACMRS.

Pickard, Donald L. Apologetics for the Working Christian: Understanding the Great Commission of Jesus Christ. 2009. 192p. pap. 14.99 *(978-1-61579-626-7(6))* Xulon Pr., Inc.

Polkinghorne, John. Exploring Reality: The Intertwining of Science & Religion. 2007. (ENG., Illus.). 208p. per. 16.00 *(978-0-300-12267-1(5))* Yale Univ. Pr.

—Way the World Is: Christian Perspective of a Scientist. 2nd ed. 144p. 8.00 *(978-0-281-04597-6(6))* SPCK Publishing GBR. Dist: Pilgrim Pr., The/United Church Pr.

Potter, Douglas E. Developing A Christian Apologetics Educational Program: In the Secondary School. 2010. 224p. pap. 25.00 *(978-1-55635-503-5(3)*, Wipf and Stock) Wipf & Stock Pubs.

Powell, Doug. Holman QuickSource Guide to Christian Apologetics. 2006. (Holman Quicksource Guides). (ENG., Illus.). 400p. per. 14.99 *(978-0-8054-9460-0(X)*, B&H Academic) B&H Publishing Group.

Priestley, Joseph. Discourses Relating to the Evidences, Vol. 1. 2009. (Amer Philosophy, Religion Ser.). (ENG.). 452p. pap. 27.95 *(978-1-4290-1926-2(3))* Applewood Bks.

—Discourses Relating to the Evidences of Revealed Religion. 2009. (Amer Philosophy, Religion Ser.). (ENG.). 492p. pap. 29.95 *(978-1-4290-1878-4(X))* Applewood Bks.

Pritchard, John. How to Explain Your Faith. 2007. 128p. per. 11.95 *(978-0-8146-3178-2(9))* Liturgical Pr.

Quist, Allen. Many Convincing Proofs: A Biblical Approach to Christian Apologetics. 2008. (Illus.). 81p. pap. 12.95 *(978-0-931057-00-7(0))* Lutheran Synod Bk. Co.

Ramm, Bernard. The Witness of the Spirit: An Essay on the Contemporary Relevance of the Internal Witness of the Holy Spirit. 2011. 140p. pap. 12.00 ***(978-1-61097-585-8(5)***, Wipf and Stock) Wipf & Stock Pubs.

Ramsay, Richard B. The Certainty of the Faith: Apologetics in an Uncertain World. 2008. (Illus.). 280p. pap. 13.99 *(978-1-59638-065-3(9))* P & R Publishing.

Reeb, Charles D. Seven Wonders of the Faith: Answers to Our Most Troubling Questions. 2006. 50p. per. *(978-0-7880-2418-4(3))* CSS Publishing Co.

Reitan, Eric. Is God a Delusion? A Reply to Religion's Cultured Despisers. 2008. (ENG.). 256p. 104.95 *(978-1-4051-8362-8(4))*; pap. 28.95 *(978-1-4051-8361-1(6))* Wiley, John & Sons, Inc. (Wiley-Blackwell).

Reymond, Robert L. Faith's Reasons for Believing: An Apologetic Antidote to Mindless Christianity. 2008. (ENG.). 480p. pap. 19.99 *(978-1-84550-337-6(6)*, Mentor) Christian Focus Pubns. GBR. Dist: STL Distribution North America.

Reynolds, Alan. A Troubled Faith. 2006. 192p. per. *(978-1-894928-98-4(9))* Word Alive Pr.

Rhodes, Ron. 5-Minute Apologetics for Today: 365 Quick Answers to Key Questions. 2010. pap. 14.99 *(978-0-7369-2457-3(4))* Harvest Hse. Pubs.

Robertson, David. The Dawkins Letters Revised Edition. 2010. (ENG.). 160p. mass mkt. 8.99 *(978-1-84550-597-4(2))* Christian Focus Pubns. GBR. Dist: STL Distribution North America.

Robinson, Michael. Presuppositional Apologetics Examines Mormonism: How Van Til's Apologetic Refutes Mormon Theology. 2007. 120p. per. 14.95 *(978-1-4327-0289-2(0))* Outskirts Pr., Inc.

—There Are Moral Absolutes How to Be Abs. 2006. 160p. pap. 10.95 *(978-1-59800-766-4(1))* Outskirts Pr., Inc.

Rogers, John Thomas. Communicating Christ in a Religious World. 2009. 244p. pap. 15.99 *(978-1-61579-306-8(2))* Xulon Pr., Inc.

Roggema, B. The Legend of Sergius Ba??r? Eastern Christian Apologetics & Apocalyptic in Response to Islam. 2008. (History of Christian-Muslim Relations Ser.). 608p. *(978-90-04-16730-8(7))* BRILL.

Ryken, Philip Graham. What Is the Christian Worldview? 2006. (Basics of the Reformed Faith Ser.). 48p. pap. 4.99 *(978-1-59638-008-0(X))* P & R Publishing.

Satta, Ronald F. True & Reasonable: In Defense of the Christian Faith. 2009. 96p. pap. 13.00 *(978-1-60608-486-1(0)*, Wipf and Stock) Wipf & Stock Pubs.

Saunders, Michael. What's Your Excuse? 2007. 16.95 *(978-1-934363-09-6(X))* Zoe Life Publishing.

Schwirzer, Jennifer Jill. Finding My Way in Milwaukee. 2007. 110p. per. 9.99 *(978-0-8280-1913-2(4))* Review & Herald Publishing Assn.

Sell, Alan P. F. Confessing & Commending the Faith: Historic Witness & Apologetic Method. 2006. (Prolegomena to Christian Apologetics: Ser.). 550p. pap. 50.00 *(978-1-59752-872-6(2)*, Wipf and Stock) Wipf & Stock Pubs.

—John Locke & the Eighteenth-Century Divines. 2006. (Prolegomena to Christian Apologetics: Ser.). 442p. pap. 42.00 *(978-1-59752-871-9(4)*, Wipf and Stock) Wipf & Stock Pubs.

Serge, Joe & Nederhood, Joel. Two Men from Malt: Passionate Appeal to Roman Catholics. 2007. 160p. per. 15.99 *(978-1-59925-124-0(8))* Solid Ground Christian Bks.

Siegel, Bob. I'd Like to Believe in Jesus, But... The Harder, Less Frequently Discussed Questions. 2007. 190p. per. 14.95 *(978-1-59352-308-4(4))* Christian Services Publishing.

Sims, Bryan. Christianity & Worldview Analysis. 2009. 152p. pap. *(978-3-639-13358-5(7))* VDM Verlag Dr. Mueller e.K.

Sire, James W. A Little Primer on Humble Apologetics. 2006. (ENG.). 112p. per. 13.00 *(978-0-8308-3382-5(X)*, IVP Bks.) InterVarsity Pr.

—The Universe Next Door: A Basic Worldview Catalog. 5th rev. ed. 2009. (ENG.). 293p. pap. 22.00 *(978-0-8308-3850-9(3)*, IVP Acad.) InterVarsity Pr.

Sloat, John W. A Handbook for Heretics: From Religion to the Kingdom of God. 2nd ed. 2009. 170p. pap. 10.95 *(978-1-926585-56-7(9)*, CCB Publishing) CCB Publishing CAN. Dist: Gardners Bks. Ltd.

Smith, A. E. Wilder. Let us Reason: Insights on creation, Suffer. . 2007. pap. 12.99 *(978-1-59751-037-0(8))* Word For Today, The.

Smith, Timothy. Pensees: Philosopher's Palate Vol. 4. 2009. 261p. mass mkt. 29.95 *(978-0-9823301-5-9(4))* Revelation Insight Publishing Co.

Smith, Wilbur Moorehead. Therefore Stand: A Plea for A Vigorous Apologetic in the Present Crisis of Evangelical Christianity. 2011. 640p. 65.95 ***(978-1-258-05760-2(3))*** Literary Licensing, LLC.

Spencer, Robert R. Religion of Peace? Why Christianity Is & Islam Isn't. 2007. (ENG.). 264p. 27.95 *(978-1-59698-515-5(1))* Regnery Publishing, Inc., An Eagle Publishing Co.

Sproul, R. c. & Sproul, R. C. Defending Your Faith: An Introduction to Apologetics. 2009. 208p. pap. 15.99 *(978-1-4335-0315-3(8))* Crossway.

Stackhouse, John G. & Stackhouse, John G., Jr. Humble Apologetics: Defending the Faith Today. 2006. (ENG.). 288p. per. 14.95 *(978-0-19-530717-7(8))* Oxford Univ. Pr., Inc.

Staneart, Mark. Messianic Apologetics: What's a Nice Baptist Kid Like You... 2009. 46p. pap. 14.84 *(978-0-557-23968-9(0))* Lulu Enterprises Inc.

Stauffer, Douglas. The Da Vinci Con: The Great Deception. 2006. pap. 9.99 *(978-0-9771964-8-7(8))* 21st Century Pr.

Steele, Mark. Christianish: What If We're Not Really Following Jesus at All?, 1 vol. 2009. (ENG.). 272p. pap. 14.99 *(978-1-4347-6692-2(6))* Cook, David C.

Stefanick Chris. Absolute Relativism: The New Dictatorship & What to Do about It. 2011. (ENG.). 59p. pap. 2.95 ***(978-1-933919-46-1(9))*** Catholic Answers, Inc.

Steinberg, Joseph. The Book of Y. 2008. (ENG.). 176p. 15.99 *(978-1-86024-568-8(4))* Authentic Media.

Stephens, Rachel Ford. Divinely Designed: A Scientific Approach to Apologetics for Teens, Young Adults, & Others Who Want to Know. 2011. 96p. pap. 29.98 *(978-1-4567-3091-8(6))* AuthorHouse.

Story, Dan. The Christian Combat Manual: Helps for Defending Your Faith: A Handbook for Practical Apologetics. 2007. (ENG.). 416p. per. 17.99 *(978-0-89957-037-2(2))* AMG Pubs.

Strand, Clark. How to Believe in God: Whether You Believe in Religion or Not. 2009. (ENG.). 256p. 24.95 *(978-0-7679-2069-8(4))* Knopf Doubleday Publishing Group.

Strobel, Lee & Poole, Garry. The Case for Christ. 2008. (ENG.). 112p. instr.'s gde. ed. 24.99 *(978-0-310-28280-8(2))* Zondervan.

Suttles, Virgil. The Poultice. 2009. 196p. pap. 14.99 *(978-1-60791-937-7(0))* Xulon Pr., Inc.

Taizé, Brother Emmanuel. Love, Imperfectly Known: Beyond Spontaneous Representations of God. Taizé, Brother Emmanuel & Livingstone, Dinah, trs. from FRE. 2011. (ENG.). 192p. 24.95 *(978-1-4411-1637-6(0))* Continuum International Publishing Group, Ltd. GBR. Dist: National Bk. Network.

Terrell, Richard. Christ, Faith, & the Holocaust. 2011. 184p. pap. 13.95 *(978-1-4497-0912-9(5)*, WestBow Pr.) Author Solutions, Inc.

Thomas, D. L. Defending Christ: The Latin Apologists before Augustine. 2011. (Studia Traditionis Theologiae Ser.). (ENG.). 230p. (C). pap. 94.00 ***(978-2-503-53669-9(7))*** Brepols Pubs. BEL. Dist: ISD.

Tofflemire, T. J. Evidences for God & His Creations: Nature, the Flood, & the Bible: A Summary Apologetics Book Assembling a Puzzle. 2011. 220p. 24.59 ***(978-1-4634-2700-9(X))***; pap. 14.03 ***(978-1-4634-2701-6(8))*** AuthorHouse.

Toren, Benno van den. Christian Apologetics: Religious Witness as Cross-Cultural Dialogue. 2011. (ENG.). 288p. 110.00 *(978-0-567-05276-6(1))*; pap. 39.95 *(978-0-567-16916-7(2))* Continuum International Publishing Group, Ltd. GBR. (T&T Clark Int'l). Dist: National Bk. Network.

Twoey, Emery. Deconstructing the Big Book of Stories: Is God Really Dead This Time? 2011. (Religion & Spirituality Ser.). 69.00 *(978-1-61209-339-0(6))* Nova Science Pubs., Inc.

Ungar, Paul. The Mystery of Christian Faith: A Tangible Union with the Invisible God - An Apologetic on the Borderline of Theology, Medicine, & Philosophy. 2007. (ENG., Illus.). 424p. per. 59.99 *(978-0-7618-3957-6(7))* Univ. Pr. of America, Inc.

Urquhart, George R. Reasons to Believe. 2010. pap. 12.99 *(978-1-61566-874-8(8))* Tate Publishing & Enterprises, LLC.

Van Hagen, John. Rescuing Religion: How Faith Can Survive Its Encounter with Science. 2012. (ENG.). 288p. pap. 25.00 ***(978-1-59815-037-7(5))*** Polebridge Pr.

Van Til, Cornelius & Oliphint, K. Scott. The Defense of the Faith. 4th ed. 2008. pap. *(978-0-87552-644-7(6))* P & R Publishing.

Velarde, Robert. Conversations with C. S. Lewis: Imaginative Discussions about Life, Christianity & God. 2008. (ENG.). 187p. pap. 15.00 *(978-0-8308-3483-9(4)*, IVP Bks.) InterVarsity Pr.

Vemuri, Raj. From Hinduism to Christ: A Former Hindu Brahmin Looks at World Religions & the Powerful Truths of the Christian Faith. 2009. 292p. pap. 18.99 *(978-1-4141-1493-4(1))* Pleasant Word.

Vickers, Douglas. The Immediacy of God. 2009. 180p. pap. 21.00 *(978-1-60608-625-4(1)*, Wipf and Stock) Wipf & Stock Pubs.

Vidal, César. Las raices de la nueva Era, 0 vols. 2009. (SPA.). 192p. 14.99 *(978-1-60255-278-4(9))* Grupo Nelson.

Vila, Samuel. Manual de Teologia Apologetica: Handbook of Christian Apologetics. (SPA.). 384p. *(978-84-7228-793-8(9)*, 220564) Clie, Editorial.

Waddell, Peter Hately. Christianity As an Ideal. 2007. (ENG.). 216p. 39.95 *(978-0-548-15533-2(X))*; pap. 24.95 *(978-1-4304-4967-6(5))* Kessinger Publishing, LLC.

Waggoner, Robert L. Christianity or Humanism: BLURB: Which Will You Choose? 2007. *(978-0-929540-67-2(0))* Publishing Designs, Inc.

Waite, Th. D. Pastor D. A. A Critical Answer to Michael Sproul's God's Word Preserved. 2008. pap. 15.00 *(978-1-56848-058-9(X))* Old Paths Pubns., Inc., The.

—Dean Burgon Society Deserves Its Name, Ten Reasons Why. 2008. pap. 10.00 *(978-1-888328-08-0(8))* Old Paths Pubns., Inc., The.

Walsh, P. G. Augustine: De Civitate Dei X. 2012. (Classical Texts). (ENG & LAT.). 240p. (C). 80.00 *(978-0-85668-849-2(5))*; pap. 36.00 *(978-0-85668-848-5(7))* Aris & Phillips GBR. Dist: Brown, David Bk. Co., The.

Walsh, P. G., ed. Augustine: De Civitate Dei VIII & IX. (ENG & LAT.). 280p. (C). 2012. pap. 36.00 *(978-0-85668-853-9(3))* 2011. 80.00 *(978-0-85668-854-6(1))* Aris & Phillips GBR. Dist: Brown, David Bk. Co., The.

Walsh, P. G. & intro. Augustine Bks. 6 & 7: De Civitate Dei. 2010. (Classical Texts). (LAT & ENG.). 220p. (C). pap. 35.00 *(978-0-85668-879-9(7))* Aris & Phillips GBR. Dist: Brown, David Bk. Co., The.

Ward, Keith. Divine Action: Examining God's Role in an Open & Emergent Universe. 2007. (ENG.). 288p. per. 19.95 *(978-1-59947-130-3(2))* Templeton Pr.

Webber, Robert E. Who Gets to Narrate the World? Contending for the Christian Story in an Age of Rivals. 2008. (ENG.). 137p. pap. 15.00 *(978-0-8308-3481-5(8)*, IVP Bks.) InterVarsity Pr.

Webster, Douglas D. Second Thoughts for Skeptics. 2010. *(978-1-57383-450-6(5))* Regent College Publishing.

West, Steve. Philosophical Dialogues on the Christian Faith: Discussions on the Arguments, Evidence, & Truth of Christianity. 2007. 118p. pap. 15.00 *(978-1-55635-142-6(9))* Wipf & Stock Pubs.

Whately, Richard. Introductory Lessons on Morals & Christian Evidences. 2007. (ENG.). 348p. 46.95 *(978-0-548-15219-5(5))*; 352p. per. 31.95 *(978-1-4304-4580-7(7))* Kessinger Publishing, LLC.

—Introductory Lessons on Morals, & Christian Evidences. 2009. 352p. 25.99 *(978-1-103-63095-0(4))*; pap. 19.99 *(978-1-103-63091-2(1))* BiblioBazaar.

—Introductory Lessons on Morals, & Christian Evidences. 2009. 244p. pap. *(978-0-217-93537-1(0))* Books LLC.

—Introductory Lessons on Morals, & Christian Evidences. 2006. 352p. per. 26.99 *(978-1-4255-3595-7(X))* MPublishing.

—Introductory Lessons on Morals, & Christian Evidences. 2007. (ENG.). 348p. per. *(978-1-4086-2546-0(6))* Read Bks.

Wilson, Donald R. Because I think I Believe. 2011. 224p. pap. 19.95 *(978-1-58982-754-7(6)*, Millennial Mind Publishing) American Bk. Publishing Group.

Wooddell, Joseph D. The Beauty of the Faith: Using Aesthetics for Christian Apologetics. 2010. 130p. pap. 16.00 *(978-1-60608-195-2(0)*, Wipf and Stock) Wipf & Stock Pubs.

Young, Ben. Why Mike's Not a Christian: Honest Questions about Evolution, Relativism, Hypocrisy, & More. 2006. 141p. per. 10.99 *(978-0-7369-1865-7(5))* Harvest Hse. Pubs.

Zacharias, Ravi. Beyond Opinion: Living the Faith We Defend, 0 vols. 2010. 384p. pap. 15.99 *(978-0-8499-4653-0(0))* Nelson, Thomas Inc.

—Has Christianity Failed You?, 1 vol. 2010. (ENG.). 208p. 19.99 *(978-0-310-26955-7(5))* Zondervan.

Zacharias, Ravi & Geisler, Norman L., eds. Quien Creo A Dios? Y Respuestas A Mas de 100 Preguntas Acerca de Cuestiones de Fe, 1 vol. 2007. (SPA.). 301p. per. 12.99 *(978-0-8297-4890-1(3))* Zondervan.

Zacharias, Ravi K. & Zacharias, Ravi. The End of Reason: A Response to the New Atheists. 2008. (ENG.). 112p. 12.99 *(978-0-310-28251-8(9))* Zondervan.

Zizek, Slavoj. The Essential Zizek, 4 vols., Set. 2009. (Essential Zizek Ser.). (ENG.). 1248p. pap. 75.00 *(978-1-84467-327-8(8)*, 844327) Verso Bks. GBR. Dist: Norton, W. W. & Co., Inc.

—The Fragile Absolute: Or Why Is the Christian Legacy Worth Fighting For? 2nd ed. 2009. (Essential Zizek Ser.). (ENG.). 157p. pap. 22.95 *(978-1-84467-302-5(2)*, 844302) Verso Bks. GBR. Dist: Norton, W. W. & Co., Inc.

APOLOGETICS—HISTORY

Anderson, Owen. The Clarity of God's Existence: The Ethics of Belief after the Enlightenment. 2008. 224p. pap. 25.00 *(978-1-55635-695-7(1))* Wipf & Stock Pubs.

—Reason & Worldviews: Warfield, Kuyper, Van Til & Plantinga on the Clarity of General Revelation & Function of Apologetics. 2008. (ENG.). 152p. pap. 31.50 *(978-0-7618-4038-1(9))* Univ. Pr. of America, Inc.

Barnes, Albert. Lectures on the Evidences of Christianity in the Nineteenth Century Delivered in the Mercer Street Church, New York, January 21 to February 21 1867. 2006. 456p. per. 29.99 *(978-1-4255-4999-2(3))* MPublishing.

Bouter, Chris. Ieder Zijn Eigen God? 2011. 110p. 27.50 ***(978-1-4092-9492-4(7))*** Lulu Enterprises Inc.

Bruce, Alexander Balm. Apologetics or Christianity Defensively. 2006. pap. 42.95 *(978-1-4286-4177-8(7))* Kessinger Publishing, LLC.

Brunton, Lauder. Truth & Delusion. 2006. pap. 15.95 *(978-1-4286-3914-0(4))* Kessinger Publishing, LLC.

Burgess, Richard. The Lectures on the Insufficiency of Unrevealed Religion, & On. 2007. (ENG.). 352p. per. 31.95 *(978-1-4304-4329-2(4))* Kessinger Publishing, LLC.

Butler, Joseph. Hobart's Analysis of Bishop Butler's Analogy of Religion, Natural & Revealed, to the Constitution & Course of Nature with Notes Also, Craufurd's. 2006. 236p. per. 20.99 *(978-1-4255-2041-0(3))* MPublishing.

Campion, Edmund. Ten Reasons Proposed to His Adversaries for Disputation in the Name. 2007. 96p. per. *(978-1-4068-4189-3(7))* Echo Library.

Chang, Curtis. Engaging Unbelief: A Captivating Strategy from Augustine & Aquinas. 2007. 188p. pap. 22.00 *(978-1-55635-520-2(3))* Wipf & Stock Pubs.

Christian Evidence Society Staff. Modern Scepticism a Course of Lectures Delivered at the Request of the Christian Evidence Society, with an Explanatory Paper by the Right Reverend C. 2006. 556p. per. 32.99 *(978-1-4255-6089-8(X))* MPublishing.

Christlieb, Theodor. Modern Doubt & Christian Belief. 2006. 568p. per. 32.99 *(978-1-4255-6226-7(4))* MPublishing.

Croslegh, Charles. Christianity Judged by Its Fruits. 2009. 204p. 23.99 *(978-1-103-34661-5(X))*; pap. 17.99 *(978-1-103-34659-2(8))* BiblioBazaar.

—Christianity Judged by Its Fruits. 2007. (ENG.). 196p. 37.95 *(978-0-548-15545-5(3))*; pap. 22.95 *(978-1-4304-4984-3(5))* Kessinger Publishing, LLC.

Cuffel, Alexandra. Gendering Disgust in Medieval Religious Polemic. 2007. (ENG., Illus.). 448p. pap. 45.00 *(978-0-268-02367-6(0))* Univ. of Notre Dame Pr.

Di Santo, Emanuele. L'apologetica Dell'Ambrosiaster: Cristiani, Pagani e Giudei Nella Roma Tardoantica. 2008. (ITA.). 607p. *(978-88-7961-121-3(6))* Ist. Patristico Augustinianum.

Dodge, Ebenezer. The Evidences of Christianity. 2009. 178p. pap. *(978-0-217-38467-4(6))* Books LLC.

—The Evidences of Christianity. 2007. (ENG.). 244p. 41.95 *(978-0-548-01448-6(5))* Kessinger Publishing, LLC.

Dunn, Geoffrey D. Tertullian's Aduersus Iudaeos: A Rhetorical Analysis. 2008. 224p. (C). pap. 44.95 *(978-0-8132-1526-6(9))* Catholic Univ. of America Pr.

Edgar, William & Oliphint, K. Scott. Christian Apologetics Past & Present: A Primary Source Reader. Edgar, William & Oliphint, K. Scott, eds. 2009. 512p. 39.00 *(978-1-58134-906-1(8))* Crossway.

Edgar, William & Oliphint, K. Scott, eds. Christian Apologetics Past & Present: A Primary Source Reader. 2011. 752p. 55.00 *(978-1-58134-907-8(6))* Crossway.

Fisher, George Park. Essays on the Supernatural Origin of Chr. 2006. pap. 49.95 *(978-1-4286-4464-9(4))* Kessinger Publishing, LLC.

—Essays on the Supernatural Origin of Christianity, with Special Reference to the Theories of Renan, Strauss, & the Tnbingen School by Rev George P. 2006. 604p. per. 32.99 *(978-1-4255-6436-0(4))* MPublishing.

Follis, Bryan A. Truth with Love: The Apologetics of Francis Schaeffer. 2006. 208p. pap. 15.99 *(978-1-58134-774-6(X))* Crossway.

Gebhard, Dorte. Glauben kommt vom Horensagen: Studien zu den Renaissancen von Mission und Apologetik. 2010. (Arbeiten zur Pastoraltheologie, Liturgik und Hymnologie Ser.). (ENG.). 350p. (C). pap. 87.00 *(978-3-525-62442-5(5))* Vandenhoeck & Ruprecht GmbH & Co. KG DEU. Dist: ISD.

Guizot, M. (Frantois). Meditations on the Actual State of Christianity, & on the Attacks Which Are Now Being Made upon It by M Guizot Tr under the Superintendence of T. 2006. 392p. per. 26.99 *(978-1-4255-4206-1(9))* MPublishing.

Haddad, Robert M. The Case for Christianity: St Justin Martyr's Arguments for Religious Liberty. 2010. (ENG.). 210p. pap. 14.95 *(978-1-58979-575-4(X))* Taylor Trade Publishing.

Hartzel, Jonas. A Defense of the Bible Against the Charges of Modern Infidelity; Consisting of the Speeches of Elder Jonas Hartzel, Made During a Debate Conducted By. 2006. 332p. per. 23.99 *(978-1-4255-3297-0(7))* MPublishing.

Kaftan, Julius. The Truth of the Christian Religion V2. 2007. (ENG.). 456p. 52.95 *(978-0-548-09342-9(3))* Kessinger Publishing, LLC.

Kahlos, Maijastina. Debate & Dialogue: Christian & Pagan Cultures C. 360-430. 2007. (New Critical Thinking in Religion, Theology & Biblical Studies). 224p. 99.95 *(978-0-7546-5713-2(2))* Ashgate Publishing Co.

Libri V et VI. 2009. (Bibliotheca scriptorum Graecorum et Romanorum Teubneriana (BT) Ser.). (LAT.). XVIII, 206p. pap. 84.00 *(978-3-11-021466-6(0))* De Gruyter, Walter Inc.

Lightfoot, Joseph Barber. Essays on the work entitled Supernatural Religion. 2007. (ENG.). 308p. pap. 23.99 *(978-1-4264-5132-4(6))*; 348p. pap. 24.99 *(978-1-4264-5433-2(3))* BiblioBazaar.

Little, Bruce A. Francis Schaeffer: A Mind & Heart for God. 2010. pap. *(978-1-59638-161-2(2))* P & R Publishing.

Lukas, Volker. Rhetorik und literarischer Kampf: Tertullians Streitschrift gegen Marcion als Paradigma der Selbstvergewisserung der Orthodoxie gegenüber der Häresie. 2008. (Europäische Hochschulschriften. Reihe 23: Theologie Ser.). (GER.). 560p. pap. 124.95 *(978-3-631-56698-5(0))* Lang, Peter GmbH, Europaischer Verlag der Wissenschaften DEU. Dist: Lang, Peter.

Maitland, Brownlow. The Argument from Prophecy. 2008. 126p. 27.99 *(978-0-554-73570-2(9))*; 109p. 24.99 *(978-0-554-73575-7(X))*; 109p. pap. 24.75 *(978-0-554-73572-6(5))*; 109p. pap. 23.75 *(978-0-554-73574-0(1))* BiblioBazaar.

—The Argument from Prophecy. 2009. 96p. pap. *(978-0-217-29520-8(7))* Books LLC.

Malone, George K. The True Church: A Study in the Apologetics of Orestes Augustus Brownson. 2011. 122p. 39.95 ***(978-1-258-06187-6(2))*** Literary Licensing, LLC.

Molinier, M. Auguste. The Thoughts of Blaise Pascal. Paul, C. Kegan, tr. 2007. (ENG.). 372p. 48.95 *(978-0-548-09920-9(0))* Kessinger Publishing, LLC.

Muir, Pearson M'Adam. Modern Substitutes for Christianity. 2007. (ENG.). 272p. 42.95 *(978-0-548-11918-1(X))* Kessinger Publishing, LLC.

Palmer, Ray. Hints on the Formation of Religious Opinions Addressed Especially to Young Men & Women of Christian Education by Rev Ray Palmer. 2006. 272p. per. 23.99 *(978-1-4255-2405-0(2))* MPublishing.

Ramm, Bernard. Varieties of Christian Apologetics. 2011. 198p. 44.95 ***(978-1-258-06557-7(6))*** Literary Licensing, LLC.

Row, C. A. A Manual of Christian Evidences. 2007. (ENG.). 216p. 39.95 *(978-0-548-08497-7(1))* Kessinger Publishing, LLC.

Staples, Tim. Nuts & Bolts: A Practical, How to Guide for explaining & defending the Catholic Faith. 2007. 128p. pap. *(978-0-9642610-2-0(2))* Basilica Pr.

Teselle, Eugene. Augustine's Strategy as an Apologist: The Saint Augustine Lecture 1973. 2010. 94p. pap. 12.00 *(978-1-60899-871-5(1),* Wipf and Stock) Wipf & Stock Pubs.

Thomson, William. Aids to Faith; a Series of Theological Essays by Several Writers Being a Reply to Essays & Reviews Ed by William Thomson. 2006. 544p. per. 29.99 *(978-1-4255-6025-6(3));* (ENG.). per. 29.99 *(978-1-4255-6026-3(1))* MPublishing.

Trench, Richard Chenevix. The Fitness of Holy Scripture for Unfolding the Spiritual Life of Men II Christ the Desire of All Nations, or, the Unconscious Prophecies of Heathen. 2006. 268p. per. 23.99 *(978-1-4255-2370-1(6))* MPublishing.

Ulrich, Jorg & Jacobsen, Anders-Christian, eds. Continuity & Discontinuity in Early Christian Apologetics. 2009. (Early Christianity in the Context of Antiquity Ser.). 130p. 33.95 *(978-3-631-57976-3(4))* Lang, Peter GmbH, Europaischer Verlag der Wissenschaften DEU. Dist: Lang, Peter.

Walker, James Barr. The Living Questions of the Age by an American Citizen. 2006. 304p. per. 23.99 *(978-1-4255-2846-1(5))* MPublishing.

—Philosophy of Skepticism & Ultraism, Wherein the Opinions of Rev Theodore Parker, & Other Writers Are Shown to Be Inconsistent with Sound Reason. 2006. 288p. per. 23.99 *(978-1-4255-2668-9(3))* MPublishing.

Walsh, Chad. C. S. Lewis: Apostle to the Skeptics. 2008. (C. S. Lewis Secondary Studies Ser.). 192p. pap. 22.00 *(978-1-55635-883-8(0),* Wipf and Stock) Wipf & Stock Pubs.

APOLOGETICS—EARLY CHURCH, CA. 30-600

see also Alexandrian School, Christian

Augustine, Saint. Answer to Faustus, a Manichean. Ramsey, Boniface, ed. Teske, Roland, tr. from LAT. 2007. 454p. 49.00 *(978-1-56548-264-7(6))* New City Pr.

—The City of God. Dods, Marcus, tr. 2009. 644p. pap. 16.99 *(978-1-4209-3372-7(8))* Digireads.com.

Bolton, William Jay. The Evidences of Christianity. 2006. 320p. per. 23.99 *(978-1-4255-3108-9(3))* MPublishing.

Dodge, Ebenezer. The Evidences of Christianity. 2009. 178p. pap. *(978-0-217-38467-4(6))* Books LLC.

—The Evidences of Christianity. 2007. (ENG.). 244p. 41.95 *(978-0-548-01448-6(5))* Kessinger Publishing, LLC.

Gifford, Edwin Hamilton. Preparation for the Gospel. 2010. pap. 134.56 *(978-1-61143-314-2(2))* Gorgias Pr., LLC.

Harris, J. Rendel. Testimonies, Part II. 2009. 150p. pap. 13.00 *(978-1-60608-508-0(5),* Wipf and Stock) Wipf & Stock Pubs.

—Testimonies: Volume 1. 2011. (Cambridge Library Collection - Religion Ser.). (ENG.). 150p. pap. 19.99 ***(978-1-108-03969-7(3))*** Cambridge Univ. Pr.

—Testimonies: Volume 2. 2011. (Cambridge Library Collection - Religion Ser.). (ENG.). 162p. pap. 19.99 ***(978-1-108-03970-3(7))*** Cambridge Univ. Pr.

Henderson, Timothy P. The Gospel of Peter & Early Christian Apologetics: Rewriting the Story of Jesus' Death, Burial, & Resurrection. 2011. (Wissenschaftliche Untersuchungen zum Neuen Testament Ser.). 258p. pap. 127.50 ***(978-3-16-150709-0(6))*** Mohr Siebeck GmbH & Co. KG DEU. Dist: Coronet Bks.

Kahlos, Maijastina. Debate & Dialogue: Christian & Pagan Cultures C. 360-430. 2007. (New Critical Thinking in Religion, Theology & Biblical Studies). 224p. 99.95 *(978-0-7546-5713-2(2))* Ashgate Publishing Co.

Lukas, Volker. Rhetorik und literarischer Kampf: Tertullians Streitschrift gegen Marcion als Paradigma der Selbstvergewisserung der Orthodoxie gegenüber der Häresie. 2008. (Europäische Hochschulschriften. Reihe 23: Theologie Ser.). (GER.). 560p. pap. 124.95 *(978-3-631-56698-5(0))* Lang, Peter GmbH, Europaischer Verlag der Wissenschaften DEU. Dist: Lang, Peter.

Rankin, David. Athenagoras: Philosopher & Theologian. 2009. 202p. 99.95 *(978-0-7546-6604-2(2))* Ashgate Publishing Co.

St. Augustin. City of God. 2007. 528p. 55.95 *(978-0-548-07841-9(6))* Kessinger Publishing, LLC.

Ulrich, Jorg & Jacobsen, Anders-Christian, eds. Continuity & Discontinuity in Early Christian Apologetics. 2009. (Early Christianity in the Context of Antiquity Ser.). 130p. 33.95 *(978-3-631-57976-3(4))* Lang, Peter GmbH, Europaischer Verlag der Wissenschaften DEU. Dist: Lang, Peter.

APOLOGETICS—MIDDLE AGES, 600-1500

Gottheil, Richard J. H. A Christian Bahira Legend. 2010. (ARA.). pap. 30.88 *(978-1-61143-334-0(7))* Gorgias Pr., LLC.

APOLOGETICS—17TH CENTURY

Molinier, M. Auguste. The Thoughts of Blaise Pascal. Paul, C. Kegan, tr. 2007. (ENG.). 372p. 48.95 *(978-0-548-09920-9(0))* Kessinger Publishing, LLC.

Pascal, Blaise. Pascal's Pensees. 2008. 400p. 31.99 *(978-0-554-27310-5(1));* 29.99 *(978-0-554-36613-5(4))* BiblioBazaar.

—Pensees. 2007. (ENG.). 256p. per. 16.99 *(978-1-59547-915-0(5))* NuVision Pubns., LLC.

—Pensees. (FRE.). pap. 9.95 *(978-2-266-05452-2(X))* Presses Pocket FRA. Dist: Distribooks, Inc.

APOLOGETICS—18TH CENTURY

Butler, Joseph. Hobart's Analysis of Bishop Butler's Analogy of Religion, Natural & Revealed, to the Constitution & Course of Nature with Notes Also, Craufurd's. 2006. 236p. per. 20.99 *(978-1-4255-2041-0(3))* MPublishing.

Payton, James R. Irenaeus on the Christian Faith: A Condensation of Against Heresies. 2011. 234p. pap. 26.00 *(978-1-60899-624-7(7),* Pickwick Pubns.) Wipf & Stock Pubs.

APOLOGETICS—19TH CENTURY

Alexander, Archibald. Evidences of the Authenticity, Inspiration, & Canonical Authority of the Holy Scriptures. 2009. 192p. pap. 19.99 *(978-1-150-14392-2(4))* General Bks. LLC.

Baker, David Bristow. The Nature of the Proof of the Christian Religion: with a Statement. 2007. (ENG.). 156p. per. 21.95 *(978-1-4304-4324-7(3))* Kessinger Publishing, LLC.

Barnes, Albert. Lectures on the Evidences of Christianity in the Nineteenth Century Delivered in the Mercer Street Church, New York, January 21 to February 21 1867. 2006. 456p. per. 29.99 *(978-1-4255-4999-2(3))* MPublishing.

Bowen, Francis. Lowell Lectures on the Application of Metaphysical & Ethical Science to the Evidence of Religion. 2009. (Amer Philosophy, Religion Ser.). (ENG.). 488p. pap. 29.95 *(978-1-4290-1861-6(5))* Applewood Bks.

Bruce, Alexander Balm. Apologetics or Christianity Defensively. 2006. pap. 42.95 *(978-1-4286-4177-8(7))* Kessinger Publishing, LLC.

Brunton, Lauder. Truth & Delusion. 2006. pap. 15.95 *(978-1-4286-3914-0(4))* Kessinger Publishing, LLC.

Burgess, Richard. The Lectures on the Insufficiency of Unrevealed Religion, & On. 2007. (ENG.). 352p. per. 31.95 *(978-1-4304-4329-2(4))* Kessinger Publishing, LLC.

Bushnell, Horace. Nature & the Supernatural As Together Constituting the One System of God. 2009. (ENG.). 531p. 43.99 *(978-1-117-60679-8(1));* pap. 39.75 *(978-1-117-60680-4(5))* BiblioBazaar.

—Nature & the Supernatural As Together Constituting the One System of God. 2009. 276p. pap. 23.37 *(978-1-150-36385-6(1))* General Bks. LLC.

Croslegh, Charles. Christianity Judged by Its Fruits. 2009. 204p. 23.99 *(978-1-103-34661-5(X));* pap. 17.99 *(978-1-103-34659-2(8))* BiblioBazaar.

—Christianity Judged by Its Fruits. 2007. (ENG.). 196p. 37.95 *(978-0-548-15545-5(3));* pap. 22.95 *(978-1-4304-4984-3(5)),* Kessinger Publishing, LLC.

Fisher, George Park. Essays on the Supernatural Origin of Chr. 2006. pap. 49.95 *(978-1-4286-4464-9(4))* Kessinger Publishing, LLC.

Guizot, M. (Frantois). Meditations on the Actual State of Christianity, & on the Attacks Which Are Now Being Made upon It by M Guizot Tr under the Superintendence of T. 2006. 392p. per. 26.99 *(978-1-4255-4206-1(9))* MPublishing.

Hartzel, Jonas. A Defense of the Bible Against the Charges of Modern Infidelity; Consisting of the Speeches of Elder Jonas Hartzel, Made During a Debate Conducted By. 2006. 332p. per. 23.99 *(978-1-4255-3297-0(7))* MPublishing.

Hettinger, Franz. Natural Religion: from the Apologie des Christenthums of Franz. 2007. (ENG.). 352p. per. 31.95 *(978-1-4304-4277-6(8))* Kessinger Publishing, LLC.

Jorgenson, Jorgen. The Religion of Christ Is the Religion of Nature. 2007. (ENG.). 430p. 51.95 *(978-0-548-14994-2(1));* 432p. per. 36.95 *(978-1-4304-4320-9(0))* Kessinger Publishing, LLC.

Kaftan, Julius. The Truth of the Christian Religion V2. 2007. (ENG.). 456p. 52.95 *(978-0-548-09342-9(3))* Kessinger Publishing, LLC.

Lightfoot, Joseph Barber. Essays on the work entitled Supernatural Religion. 2007. (ENG.). 308p. pap. 23.99 *(978-1-4264-5132-4(6));* 348p. pap. 24.99 *(978-1-4264-5433-2(3))* BiblioBazaar.

Mcllvaine, Charles Pettit. The Evidences of Christianity; in Their External, or Historical, Division: Exhibited in A Course of Lectures, by Charles Pettit Mcilvaine ... Revised. 2006. 416p. per. 26.99 *(978-1-4255-4475-1(4))* MPublishing.

Patterson, Robert. Fables of Infidelity & Facts of Faith. 2009. 484p. 31.99 *(978-0-559-05575-1(7));* 33.99 *(978-0-559-05563-8(3));* pap. 37.75 *(978-0-559-05568-3(4));* pap. 36.75 *(978-0-559-05572-0(2))* BiblioBazaar.

—Fables of Infidelity & Facts of Faith. 2009. 360p. pap. *(978-0-217-71729-8(2))* Books LLC.

—Fables of Infidelity & Facts of Faith. 2006. 544p. per. 29.99 *(978-1-4255-6006-5(7))* MPublishing.

Row, C. A. A Manual of Christian Evidences. 2007. (ENG.). 216p. 39.95 *(978-0-548-08497-7(1))* Kessinger Publishing, LLC.

Ruble, William. Letters to the Literal Children of Abrah. 2006. pap. 42.95 *(978-1-4286-3632-3(3))* Kessinger Publishing, LLC.

Thomson, William. Aids to Faith; a Series of Theological Essays by Several Writers Being a Reply to Essays & Reviews Ed by William Thomson. 2006. 544p. (ENG.). per. 29.99 *(978-1-4255-6026-3(1));* per. 29.99 *(978-1-4255-6025-6(3))* MPublishing.

Trench, Richard Chenevix. The Fitness of Holy Scripture for Unfolding the Spiritual Life of Men II Christ the Desire of All Nations, or, the Unconscious Prophecies of Heathen. 2006. 268p. per. 23.99 *(978-1-4255-2370-1(6))* MPublishing.

Williams, William George. The Ingham Lectures a Course of Lectures on the Evidences of Natural & Revealed Religion Delivered Before the Ohio Wesleyan University, Delaware. 2006. 380p. per. 26.99 *(978-1-4255-4008-1(2))* MPublishing.

Wilson, Daniel. The Evidences of Christianity V2: Stated in a Popular & Practical. 2007. pap. 48.95 *(978-1-4304-4954-6(3))* Kessinger Publishing, LLC.

APOLOGETICS—20TH CENTURY

Broadman and Holman Publishers Staff. Tough-Minded Christianity: Legacy of John Warwick Montgomery, 1 vol. Dembski, William & Schirrmacher, Thomas, eds. 2009. (ENG.). 800p. pap. 31.99 *(978-0-8054-4783-5(0),* B&H Academic) B&H Publishing Group.

Chesterton, G. K. Orthodoxy. Date not set. 160p. 160.00 *(978-0-8488-2648-2(5))* Amereon LTD.

—Orthodoxy. reprint ed. lib. bdg. 98.00 *(978-0-7426-3013-0(7))* Classic Bks.

Muir, Pearson M'Adam. Modern Substitutes for Christianity. 2007. (ENG.). 272p. 42.95 *(978-0-548-11918-1(X))* Kessinger Publishing, LLC.

Piper, John. Why We Believe the Bible: A Study Guide to the DVD Featuring John Piper. 2009. (John Piper Small Group Ser.). 192p. pap. 11.99 *(978-1-4335-0771-7(4))* Crossway.

Polkinghorne, John. The Way the World Is: The Christian Perspective of a Scientist. 2007. (ENG.). 130p. per. 17.00 *(978-0-664-23214-6(0))* Westminster John Knox Pr.

Smith, David P. B. B. WarfieldÕs Scientifically Constructive Theological Scholarship. 2011. (Evangelical Theological Society Monograph Ser.). 342p. pap. 38.00 ***(978-1-61097-185-0(X),*** Pickwick Pubns.) Wipf & Stock Pubs.

Van Til, Cornelius. Apologetics. 2011. 104p. 39.95 ***(978-1-258-06705-2(6))*** Literary Licensing, LLC.

Walsh, Milton. Ronald Knox as Apologist. 2007. 250p. pap. 14.95 *(978-1-58617-121-6(6))* Ignatius Pr.

APOLOGETICS, JEWISH

see Judaism—Apologetic Works

APOLOGETICS, MISSIONARY

Here are entered works on methods of presenting Christianity in the foreign mission fields, as well as works on Christianity which are prepared for the foreign missions fields.

Pinegar, Ed. Teaching by the Spirit with the Power of God. Date not set. (Especially for Missionaries Ser.: No. 3). pap. 3.95 *(978-1-57734-141-3(4),* 01113127) Covenant Communications, Inc.

APOPLEXY

see Cerebrovascular Disease

APOPTOSIS

Alonso, Covadonga, ed. Viruses & Apoptosis. 2008. (Progress in Molecular & Subcellular Biology Ser.). (Illus.). 340p. pap. 99.00 *(978-3-540-74263-0(8))* Springer.

Bähr, Mathias, ed. Brain Repair. 2010. (Advances in Experimental Medicine & Biology Ser.). (Illus.). xii, 252p. pap. 189.00 *(978-1-4419-3417-8(0),* 1441934170) Springer.

Banfalvi, Gaspar. Apoptotic Chromatin Changes. 2009. (ENG., Illus.). xii, 412p. 209.00 *(978-1-4020-9560-3(0))* Springer.

Bettuzzi, Saverio & Pucci, Sabina. Clusterin, 2 vols. 2009. (Advances in Cancer Research Ser.). (ENG., Illus.). 350p. 161.00 *(978-0-12-374772-3(4),* Academic Pr.) Elsevier Science & Technology Bks.

Boole, Daniel D. Focus on Apoptosis Research. 2006. 267p. 225.00 *(978-1-60021-433-2(9))* Nova Science Pubs., Inc.

Brown, J. Martin, et al, eds. Beyond Apoptosis: Cellular Outcomes of Cancer Therapy. 2008. (ENG., Illus.). 376p. 230.00 *(978-0-8493-9192-7(X),* Informa Healthcare) Taylor & Francis Group GBR. Dist: Taylor & Francis Group.

Calvin V. Burnside. Cell Apoptosis Research Progress. Fenton, Robert H., ed. 2008. (Illus.). xii, 329p. 129.00 *(978-1-60456-066-4(5),* Nova Biomedical Bks.) Nova Science Pubs., Inc.

Cecconi, Francesco & D'Amelio, Marcello, eds. Apoptosome: An up-and-coming therapeutical Tool. 2009. (ENG., Illus.). x, 322p. 179.00 *(978-90-481-3414-4(5),* 9048134145) Springer.

Chen, George G. & Lai, Paul B. S., eds. Apoptosis in Carcinogenesis & Chemotherapy: Apoptosis in Cancer. 2009. (ENG., Illus.). xxii, 386p. 229.00 *(978-1-4020-9596-2(1),* 1402095961) Springer.

Corvin, Alan J. New Developments in Cell Apoptosis Research. 2006. 306p. 225.00 *(978-1-60021-453-0(3))* Nova Science Pubs., Inc.

Davis, Myrtle A., ed. Apoptosis Methods in Pharmacology & Toxicology: Approaches to Measurement & Quantification. 2010. (Methods in Pharmacology & Toxicology Ser.). (Illus.). 176p. pap. 94.50 *(978-1-61737-239-1(0),* 1617372390) Humana Pr.

Demasi, Alex R., ed. Cellular Signaling & Apoptosis Research. 2007. (C). 129.00 *(978-1-60021-565-0(3))* Nova Science Pubs., Inc.

Diederich, Marc, ed. Natural Compounds & Their Role in Apoptotic Cell Signaling Pathways. 2009. (Annals of the New York Academy of Sciences Ser. 29). (ENG., Illus.). 400p. pap. 154.95 *(978-1-57331-737-5(3),* Wiley-Blackwell) Wiley, John & Sons, Inc.

El-Deiry, Wafik S., ed. Death Receptors in Cancer Therapy. 2010. (Cancer Drug Discovery & Development Ser.). (Illus.). 384p. pap. 209.00 *(978-1-61737-401-2(6),* 1617374016) Humana Pr.

Elkon, Keith B. Apoptosis & Its Relevance to Autoimmunity, Vol. 9. (Current Directions in Autoimmunity Ser.: Vol. 9). (Illus.). 210p. *(978-3-8055-8036-6(3))* Karger, S. AG.

Erhardt, Peter & Toth, Ambrus, eds. Apoptosis: Methods & Protocols, Second Edition. 2nd ed. 2009. (Methods in Molecular Biology Ser.). (ENG., Illus.). 360p. 159.00 *(978-1-60327-016-8(7),* 1603270167) Humana Pr.

Erlich, Scott R. Frontiers in Cell Apoptosis Research. 2006. 225.00 *(978-1-60021-450-9(9))* Nova Science Pubs., Inc.

Figgins, Herold C. Trends in Cell Apoptosis Research. 2006. 293p. (C). 225.00 *(978-1-60021-424-0(X))* Nova Science Pubs., Inc.

Gewirtz, David A., et al, eds. Apoptosis, Senescence & Cancer. 2nd ed. 2010. (Cancer Drug Discovery & Development Ser.). (Illus.). xvii, 599p. pap. 199.00 *(978-1-61737-621-4(3),* 1617376213) Humana Pr.

Gottlieb, R. A., ed. Apoptosis in the Hematopoietic System, Vol. 111. (Illus.). 124p. *(978-3-8055-7700-7(1))* Karger, S. AG.

Green, Douglas R. Apoptosis: Physiology & Pathology. Reed, John C., ed. 2011. (ENG., Illus.). 472p. 125.00 *(978-0-521-88656-7(2))* Cambridge Univ. Pr.

—Means to an End: Apoptosis & Other Cell Death Mechanisms. 2010. (Illus.). 250p. 81.00 *(978-0-87969-887-4(X));* pap. 46.00 *(978-0-87969-888-1(8))* Cold Spring Harbor Laboratory Pr.

Griffin, Diane E. Role of Apoptosis in Infection. 2010. (Current Topics in Microbiology & Immunology Ser.). (Illus.). ix, 294p. pap. 189.00 *(978-3-642-06192-9(3),* 3642061923) Springer.

Harry, Jean & Tilson, Hugh A., eds. Neurodegeneration Methods & Protocols. 2010. (Methods in Molecular Medicine Ser.). 328p. pap. 119.00 *(978-1-61737-098-4(3),* 1617370983) Humana Pr.

Henderson, C. E., et al, eds. Neuronal Death by Accident or by Design. 2010. (Research & Perspectives in Neurosciences Ser.). (Illus.). xi, 154p. pap. 129.00 *(978-3-642-07517-9(7),* 3642075177) Springer.

Hetz, Claudio. BCL-2 Protein Family: Essential Regulators of Cell Death. 2010. (Advances in Experimental Medicine & Biology Ser.). 219.00 *(978-1-4419-6705-3(2))* Springer.

Hickman, John A. & Dive, Caroline, eds. Apoptosis & Cancer Chemotherapy. 2010. (Cancer Drug Discovery & Development Ser.). (Illus.). 360p. pap. 139.00 *(978-1-61737-165-3(3),* 1617371653) Humana Pr.

Holcik, Martin, et al, eds. Apoptosis in Health & Disease: Clinical & Therapeutic Aspects. 2010. (ENG.). 264p. pap. 35.99 *(978-0-521-15944-9(X))* Cambridge Univ. Pr.

Imre, Gabriele. Anti-Apoptotic & Pro-Inflammatory Signaling in Cancer Cells - Status & Modulation by Chemotherapeutic Drugs. 2008. 132p. pap. *(978-3-639-00750-3(6))* VDM Verlag Dr. Mueller e.K.

Kaiser, Hans E. & Nasir, Aejaz, eds. Selected Aspects of Cancer Progression: Metastasis, Apoptosis & Immune Response. 2008. (Cancer Growth & Progression Ser.). (Illus.). 249p. 199.00 *(978-1-4020-6728-0(3))* Springer.

—Selected Aspects of Cancer Progression: Metastasis, Apoptosis & Immune Response: Metastasis, Apoptosis & Immune Response. 2010. (Cancer Growth & Progression Ser.). vi, 250p. pap. 199.00 *(978-90-481-7706-6(5),* 9048177065) Springer.

Kalthoff, Holger, ed. Death Receptors & Cognate Ligands in Cancer. 2009. (Results & Problems in Cell Differentiation Ser.). (ENG., Illus.). xiv, 280p. 199.00 *(978-3-642-03044-0(0),* 3642030440) Springer.

Kettleworth, Carter R. Cell Apoptosis Research Advances. 2007. 358p. 129.00 *(978-1-60021-509-4(2))* Nova Science Pubs., Inc.

Khosravi-Far, Roya, et al, eds. Programmed Cell Death Part A, 2 vols. 2008. (ENG., Illus.). 544p. 187.00 *(978-0-12-374312-1(5),* Academic Pr.) Elsevier Science & Technology Bks.

—Programmed Cell Death Part B, 2 vols. 2008. (ENG., Illus.). 504p. 187.00 *(978-0-12-374464-7(4),* Academic Pr.) Elsevier Science & Technology Bks.

Khosravi-Far, Roya & White, Eileen, eds. Programmed Cell Death in Cancer Progression & Therapy. (Advances in Experimental Medicine & Biology Ser.). 2010. xiv, 356p. pap. 219.00 *(978-90-481-7668-7(9),* 9048176689) 2008. 480p. 219.00 *(978-1-4020-6553-8(1))* Springer.

Klausen, Martina P. Neurogenesis Research Advances. 2007. (C). 129.00 *(978-1-60021-676-3(5))* Nova Science Pubs., Inc.

Klionsky, Daniel. Autophagy Pt. A: Lower Eukaryotes & Non-Mammalian Systems, 3 vols. 2008. (ENG., Illus.). 808p. 187.00 *(978-0-12-374548-4(9),* Academic Pr.) Elsevier Science & Technology Bks.

Klionsky, Daniel J. Autophagy in Mammalian Systems, 3 vols., Pt. B. Klionsky, Daniel, ed. 2009. (ENG., Illus.). 560p. 187.00 *(978-0-12-374547-7(0),* Academic Pr.) Elsevier Science & Technology Bks.

Kyprianou. Molecular Exploitation of Apoptosis Pathways in Prostate Cancer. 2010. 400p. 88.00 *(978-1-84816-449-9(1))* World Scientific Publishing Co., Inc.

LeBlanc, Andréa C., ed. Apoptosis Techniques & Protocols. 2nd ed. 2010. (Neuromethods Ser.). (Illus.). 272p. pap. 139.00 *(978-1-61737-306-0(0),* 1617373060) Humana Pr.

Linton, Steven D. & O'Brien, Tom, eds. Design of Caspase Inhibitors as Potential Clinical Agents. 2008. (CRC Enzyme Inhibitors Ser.). (ENG., Illus.). 312p. 185.95 *(978-1-4200-4540-6(7),* CRC Press) Taylor & Francis Group GBR. Dist: Taylor & Francis Group.

Macieira-Coelho, Alvaro, ed. Cell Immortalization. 2010. (Progress in Molecular & Subcellular Biology Ser.). (Illus.). vii, 207p. pap. 269.00 *(978-3-642-08491-1(5),* 3642084915) Springer.

Mattson, Mark P., ed. Membrane Microdomain Signaling: Lipid Rafts in Biology & Medicine. 2010. (Illus.). x, 214p. pap. 115.00 *(978-1-61737-515-6(2), 1617375152)* Humana Pr.

Merchant PhD, Kendra, et al. Novel Molecular Targets for Genistein in Prostate Cancer Cells. 2010. 100p. pap. *(978-3-8383-3884-2(7))* Lambert Academic Publishing.

Miura, Souta & Nakano, Shouta. Progress in DNA Damage Research. 2008. (Illus.). xiii, 408p. 185.00 *(978-1-60456-582-9(9))* Nova Science Pubs., Inc.

Mor, Gil & Alvero, Ayesha, eds. Apoptosis & Cancer: Methods & Protocols. 2010. (Methods in Molecular Biology Ser.). (Illus.). xi, 266p. pap. 119.00 *(978-1-61737-582-8(9), 1617375829)* Humana Pr.

Murphy, Diarmaid. Intracellular Delivery of Peptide Carriers, Substrates & Inhibitors. 2010. 304p. pap. *(978-3-8383-4418-8(9))* Lambert Academic Publishing.

Nafissi, Nafiseh. An Obese Genotype Affects the Apoptosis Related Gene Expressions. 2009. 108p. pap. *(978-3-639-16246-2(3))* VDM Verlag Dr. Mueller e.K.

Oberdanner, Christian. ROS & Antioxidant Systems in Apoptosis: Oxidant Balance in Cell Death & Cancer Therapy. 2008. 132p. pap. *(978-3-8364-8211-0(8))* VDM Verlag Dr. Mueller e.K.

Perez-Martin, Jose, ed. Programmed Cell Death in Protozoa. 2010. (Molecular Biology Intelligence Unit Ser.). xvii, 163p. pap. 189.00 *(978-1-4419-2635-7(6), 1441926356)* Springer.

Perez Martin, Jose Manuel. Programmed Cell Death in Protozoa. 2007. (Molecular Biology Intelligence Unit Ser.). (Illus.). 163p. 189.00 *(978-0-387-76716-1(9))* Springer.

Pickens, Charles O. Cell Apoptotic Signaling Pathways. 2007. 222p. 129.00 *(978-1-60021-507-0(6))* Nova Science Pubs., Inc.

Preedy, Victor R. Apoptosis. 2010. (ENG., Illus.). 650p. 129.95 *(978-1-57808-583-5(7))* BIOS Scientific Publishers Ltd. GBR. Dist: Taylor & Francis Group.

Ray. Apoptosis Cont & Reg Dis. 2010. 400p. 139.95 *(978-0-8247-2976-9(5), Informa Healthcare)* Taylor & Francis Group GBR. Dist: Taylor & Francis Group.

Rhoads, Robert E., ed. Signaling Pathways for Translation: Stress, Calcium, & Rapamycin. 2010. (Progress in Molecular & Subcellular Biology Ser.). (Illus.). x, 176p. pap. 149.00 *(978-3-642-07505-6(3), 3642075053)* Springer.

Salido, Gines Maria & Rosado, Juan Antonio, eds. Apoptosis: Involvement of Oxidative Stress & Intracellular Ca2+ Homeostasis: Involvement of Oxidative Stress & Intracellular Ca2+ Homeostasis. 2009. (ENG., Illus.). x, 238p. 169.00 *(978-1-4020-9872-7(3), 1402098723)* Springer.

Schmid, Carl J. & Wolfe, Jason L. Neuronal Cell Apoptosis. 2011. (Cell Biology Research Progress Ser.). (Illus.). 259p. 140.00 *(978-1-61324-633-7(1))* Nova Science Pubs., Inc.

Shandling, Relif J. Neuronal Cell Apoptosis Research. 2006. (Illus.). 208p. 225.00 *(978-1-60021-456-1(8))* Nova Science Pubs., Inc.

Shultz, Lawrence B. Cell Apoptosis: Regulation & Environmental Factors. 2007. 211p. 129.00 *(978-1-60021-508-7(4))* Nova Science Pubs., Inc.

Sluyser, Mels. Application of Apoptosis to Cancer Treatment. 2010. (ENG.). vii, 370p. pap. 159.00 *(978-90-481-6833-0(3), 9048168333)* Springer.

Snyder, Solomon H. Science & Psychiatry: Groundbreaking Discoveries in Molecular Neuroscience. 2008. (Illus.). 477p. 80.00 *(978-1-58562-273-3(7))* American Psychiatric Publishing, Inc.

Srivastava, Rakesh. Apoptosis, Cell Signaling, & Human Diseases: Molecular Mechanisms, 2 vols., Vol. 2. 2007. (ENG., Illus.). 384p. 159.00 *(978-1-58829-677-1(6), 1588296776)* Humana Pr.

Srivastava, Rakesh, ed. Apoptosis, Cell Signaling, & Human Diseases. 2010. (ENG., Illus.). 384p. pap. 159.00 *(978-1-61737-713-6(9), 1617377139)* Humana Pr.

—Apoptosis, Cell Signaling, & Human Diseases: Molecular Mechanisms, Volume 2. (ENG., Illus.). xvi, 402p. 2010. pap. 179.00 *(978-1-61737-823-2(2), 1617378232)* Vol. 2. 2007. 179.00 *(978-1-58829-882-9(5), 1588298825)* Humana Pr.

Stillman, Bruce, et al, eds. Evolution: The Molecular Landscape, Vol. LXXIV. 2010. (ENG., Illus.). 512p. 310.00 *(978-0-87969-870-6(5))* Cold Spring Harbor Laboratory Pr.

Taylor, Albina W. Cell Apoptosis & Cancer. 2007. (Illus.). 225.00 *(978-1-60021-506-3(8))* Nova Science Pubs., Inc.

Teicher, Beverly A., et al, eds. Apoptosis & Cancer: Methods & Protocols. 2007. (Methods in Molecular Biology Ser.). (Illus.). 350p. 119.00 *(978-1-58829-457-9(9), 1588294579)* Humana Pr.

Tulin, Alexei, ed. Poly(ADP-ribose) Polymerase: Methods & Protocols. 2011. (Methods in Molecular Biology Ser.). (ENG., Illus.). xv, 521p. 139.00 *(978-1-61779-269-4(1), 1617792691)* Humana Pr.

Valentino, Rafe G. New Cell Apoptosis Research. 2006. 242p. 225.00 *(978-1-60021-430-1(4))* Nova Science Pubs., Inc.

Wyllie, A. H. Apoptosis. (British Medical Bulletin Ser.: Vol. 53, No. 3). pap. *(978-1-85315-317-4(6), Royal Society of Medicine)* Hodder Education.

Yin, Xiao-Ming & Dong, Zheng, eds. Essentials of Apoptosis: A Guide for Basic & Clinical Research. 2nd ed. 2009. (ENG., Illus.). xxiii, 707p. 149.00 *(978-1-60327-380-0(8), 1603273808)* Humana Pr.

Yufang Shi, et al, eds. Molecular Mechanisms of Programmed Cell Death. 2010. (ENG.). 220p. pap. 159.00 *(978-1-4419-3404-8(9), 1441934049)* Springer.

APOSTASY

see also Heresy; Schism

BeDuhn, Jason David. Augustine's Manichaean Dilemma Vol. 1: Conversion & Apostasy, 373-388 C. E. 2009. (Divinations: Rereading Late Ancient Religion Ser.). 408p. (C). 69.95 *(978-0-8122-4210-2(6))* Univ. of Pennsylvania Pr.

Brown, L. Duane. What Is the Apostasy? 2010. 232p. pap. 15.99 *(978-0-9845208-1-7(3))* Faithful Life Pubs.

C. Paul Puckett. Liberalization & Apostasy of Americ. 2009. 72p. pap. 10.49 *(978-1-4389-9887-9(2))* AuthorHouse.

Deringil, Selim. The Politics of Conversion & Apostasy in the Late Ottoman Empire. 2012. (ENG., Illus.). 250p. 99.00 ***(978-1-107-00455-9(1))*** Cambridge Univ. Pr.

Houchen, Hoyt H. & Tatum, Ray. The Houchen-Tatum Debate, Four Subjects: Establishment of the Church, Baptism, Apostasy, Pre-Millennialism. 2011. 218p. 44.95 ***(978-1-258-04858-7(2))*** Literary Licensing, LLC.

Isaac Publishing Staff & Sookhdeo, Patrick. Freedom to Believe: Challenging Islam's Apostasy Law. 2009. (ENG.). 176p. pap. 14.99 *(978-0-9787141-9-2(9))* Isaac Publishing.

Marshall, Paul & Shea, Nina. Silenced: How Apostasy & Blasphemy Codes Are Choking Freedom Worldwide. 2011. (ENG., Illus.). 544p. pap. 35.00 *(978-0-19-981228-8(4))* Oxford Univ. Pr., Inc.

McKnight, Scot & Ondrey, Hauna. Finding Faith, Losing Faith: Stories of Conversion & Apostasy. 2008. (ENG.). 260p. pap. 24.95 *(978-1-60258-162-3(2))* Baylor Univ. Pr.

Moody, Dale. Apostasy. 7.00 *(978-0-687-82119-8(3))* Abingdon Pr.

Moore, Richard G. Strange Roads & Forbidden Paths: Avoiding Apostasy in the Latter Days. 2008. pap. 13.99 *(978-1-59955-211-8(6))* Cedar Fort, Inc./CFI Distribution.

Murphy, Richard J. & Murphy, Karen L. The Christian Faith Uninformed by the Culture. 2008. 172p. pap. 13.99 *(978-1-60647-072-5(8))* Xulon Pr., Inc.

Murphy, Richard James. The Christian Faith Informed by the Word of God. 2009. 220p. pap. 15.99 *(978-1-61579-188-0(4))* Xulon Pr., Inc.

Oropeza, B. J. Paul & Apostasy: Eschatology, Perseverance, & Falling Away in the Corinthian Congregation. 2007. 324p. pap. 36.00 *(978-1-55635-333-8(2), Wipf and Stock)* Wipf & Stock Pubs.

Peterson, Robert A. Our Secure Salvation: Preservation & Apostasy. 2009. pap. *(978-1-59638-043-1(8))* P & R Publishing.

Seymour, Susan. Apostasy: The Deceived Generation - Rescuing Our Youth from Satan's Influence. 2008. (ENG.). 368p. pap. 14.99 *(978-1-59979-456-3(X), Creation Hse.)* Charisma Media.

Simmons, Brian. Falling Away: Why Christians Lose Their Faith & What Can Be Done about It. 2008. 272p. pap. 12.99 *(978-0-89112-571-6(X), Leafwood Pubs.)* Abilene Christian Univ. Pr.

Staudacher, Anna L. ... meldet den Austritt aus dem mosaischen Glauben: 18000 Austritte aus dem Judentum in Wien, 1868 - 1914: Namen - Quellen - Daten. 2009. (GER.). 826p. pap. 141.95 *(978-3-631-55832-4(5))* Lang, Peter GmbH, Europaischer Verlag der Wissenschaften DEU. Dist: Lang, Peter.

Vanover, S. T. Religious Bastards versus Men of God. 2007. pap. 15.00 *(978-0-8059-7378-5(8))* Dorrance Publishing Co., Inc.

Zuckerman, Phil. Faith No More: Why People Reject Religion, 1 vol. 2011. (ENG., Illus.). 224p. 24.95 *(978-0-19-974001-7(1))* Oxford Univ. Pr., Inc.

APOSTLES

see also Evangelists (Bible)

The Acts of the Apostles. 2009. 350p. 28.99 *(978-1-116-46263-0(X))*; pap. 31.75 *(978-1-116-46265-4(6))*; pap. 32.75 *(978-1-116-46264-7(8))* BiblioBazaar.

Ajibola, Babatunde Ezekiel. A call to honour, a biography of apostle joseph ayo Babalola. 2008. 212p. 55.95 *(978-1-4092-1304-8(8))* Lulu Enterprises Inc.

Benedict & Coelho, Senra. Os Doze Apóstolos: E Os Primeiros Discípulos de Jesus Nas Origens Da Igreja. 2008. (POR.). 174p. *(978-972-30-1334-4(7))* Paulus.

Benedict XVI, pseud. The Apostles. 2008. (Illus.). 174p. 29.95 *(978-1-59276-538-6(6))* Our Sunday Visitor, Publishing Div.

—The Apostles: The Origin of the Church & Their Co-Workers. 2007. (Illus.). 174p. 14.95 *(978-1-59276-405-1(3))* Our Sunday Visitor, Publishing Div.

—Jesus, the Apostles & the Early Church. 2007. 163p. 19.95 *(978-1-58617-220-6(4))* Ignatius Pr.

Blackmore, Michael. Wonderful Acts: The Acts in 1000 Rhyming Verses. 2008. 308p. pap. 17.99 *(978-1-60477-748-2(6))* Xulon Pr., Inc.

Boadt, Lawrence. The Life of St. Paul. 2008. (Illus.). 128p. 16.95 *(978-0-8091-0519-9(5))* Paulist Pr.

Brackett, Charlie. In the Steps of the Apostles: Devotional Messages from Acts of the Apostles. 2007. (Illus.). 368p. per. 16.95 *(978-0-9779577-7-4(2))* Clarion Word Publishing.

Bruce, Alexander B. The Training of The. 2007. 572p. per. 19.95 *(978-1-60206-539-0(X))* Cosimo, Inc.

Clark, Jonas. Effective Ministries & Believers: Introducing Apostolic Ministry & What It Means to You. 2008. 315p. per. 14.99 *(978-1-886885-25-7(7))* Spirit of Life.

Clark, Jonas A. Advanced Apostolic Studies: Transitioning every believer into apostolic Ministry. 2008. (ENG.). 198p. mass mkt., wbk. ed. 24.99 *(978-1-886885-17-2(6))* Spirit of Life.

Claypool, John R. The First to Follow: The Apostles of Jesus. 2008. 160p. 18.00 *(978-0-8192-2296-1(8))* Church Publishing, Inc.

de Taize, Roger. Amor de Todo Amor.Tr. of Love of all Loves. (SPA.). 144p. pap. 3.25 *(978-958-607-609-8(1))* Sociedad de San Pablo COL. Dist: St Pauls/Alba Hse. Pubs.

Dent, Don. The Ongoing Role of Apostles in Missions: The Forgotten Foundation. 2011. 208p. pap. 17.95 ***(978-1-61507-348-1(5))*** Cross Bks. Publishing.

Devenish, David. Fathering Leaders, Motivating Mission: Restoring the role of the Apostle in todays Church. 2011. (ENG.). 320p. 14.99 ***(978-1-86024-837-5(3))*** Authentic Media.

Div, Israel Prince D. University School of the Apostles / Prophets Certification Manual: Ushering in Present day truth of the Prophetic Movement. 2010. 112p. pap. 12.95 *(978-1-4401-6383-8(9))* iUniverse, Inc.

Dowdy, Naomi. Commissioning: The Process, Protocol, & Importance of Commissioning Modern-Day Apostles. 2006. (SPA.). pap. 10.00 *(978-1-934201-04-6(9))*; pap. 10.00 *(978-1-934201-03-9(0))* Dowdy, Naomi Pubns.

Evans, Roderick L. The Apostle Question: Examining the Role of Apostles in the New Testament Church. 2011. 126p. pap. 12.95 *(978-1-60141-007-8(7), 203754)* Kingdom Builders Publishing.

Farelly, Nicolas. The Disciples in the Fourth Gospel: A Narrative Analysis of Their Faith & Understanding. 2010. (Illus.). 273p. pap. 127.50 *(978-3-16-150583-6(2))* Mohr Siebeck GmbH & Co. KG DEU. Dist: Coronet Bks.

Fisher, Norman A. The Genesis & Growth of the Apostolic Church: An Analysis of the Acts of the Apostles. 2011. 232p. pap. 17.95 ***(978-1-61507-732-8(4))*** Cross Bks. Publishing.

Garcia, Marc. He Said Follow Me. 2010. 42p. pap. 9.95 *(978-0-557-42286-9(8))* Lulu Enterprises Inc.

Geldenhuys, J. Norval. Supreme Authority: The Authority of the Lord, His Apostles & the New Testament. 2008. 126p. pap. 11.00 *(978-1-55635-768-8(0))* Wipf & Stock Pubs.

Hafen, Bruce. A Disciple's Life: The Biography of Neal A. Maxwell. 2010. 656p. pap. 34.99 *(978-1-60641-250-3(7))* Deseret Bk. Co.

Hansen, Kenneth. The Blood Kin of Jesus. 2009. (Illus.). 264p. 25.00 *(978-1-57178-216-8(8))* Council Oak Bks.

Harris, Gordon. Apostol Extraterrestre: Apostle from Space. (SPA.). 248p. *(978-84-7228-474-6(3), 360025)* Clie, Editorial.

Hayes, Kate. A Journey of Discovery: On the Road with Jesus' Followers. 2006. 64p. pap. 8.00 *(978-1-84427-180-1(3))* Scripture Union GBR. Dist: STL Distribution North America.

Higginbotham, Blake. Apostles, Elders & Other Ministries. 2007. 96p. per. 9.99 *(978-1-60266-527-9(3))* Xulon Pr., Inc.

Hinzie, W. C. Secrets of the Apostles: The Stories You Do Not Hear in Sunday School. 2011. 144p. 28.95 ***(978-1-4497-2219-7(9))***; pap. 11.95 ***(978-1-4497-2186-2(9))*** Author Solutions, Inc. (WestBow Pr.).

Hofeldt, Fred D. Restoring Our Christian Foundations: Restoring the Ancient Biblical Foundations of the Christian Faith, 1 vol. 2010. 308p. pap. 29.95 *(978-1-4489-2621-3(1))* PublishAmerica, Inc.

Holzapfel, Richard Neitzel & Wayment, Thomas A. The Life & Teachings of the New Testament Apostles: From the Day of Pentecost to the Apocalypse. 2010. x, 358p. 34.99 *(978-1-60641-824-6(6))* Deseret Bk. Co.

Huba, Al. The Apostle's Heart. 2007. 164p. per. 13.99 *(978-1-60266-285-8(1))* Xulon Pr., Inc.

Lightfoot, J. B. Padres Apostolicos: Apostolics Fathers. (SPA.). *(978-84-7645-442-8(2), 223461)* Clie, Editorial.

Maasen, Janis. Peter the Leader: How an Imperfect Man Became the Leader of the Church. 2009. (ENG.). 160p. pap. 12.99 *(978-1-59979-776-2(3), Creation Hse.)* Charisma Media.

MacKey, Sandra. The Spirit of Truth: God's Unwordly Eternal Presence. 2011. 108p. 28.95 ***(978-1-61507-699-4(9))*** Cross Bks. Publishing.

—The Spirit of Truth: God's Unworldly Eternal Presence. 2011. 108p. pap. 11.95 ***(978-1-61507-698-7(0))*** Cross Bks. Publishing.

Maldonado, Guillermo. The Ministry of the Apostle: Discover the Truth about Apostolic Ministry. 2007. 186p. per. 13.99 *(978-1-59272-236-5(9))* GM Ministries.

McBirnie, William Steuart. En Busca de los Doce Apóstoles. 2009. Orig. Title: The Search for the Twelve Apostles. (SPA.). 304p. pap. 13.99 *(978-1-4143-2398-5(0), Tyndale Espanol)* Tyndale Hse. Pubs.

McCarthy, Dave. Called unto Liberty: A Commentary on the Apostle. 2007. 183p. per. *(978-0-9800096-5-1(0))* Calvary Publishing.

McKeating, Michael. O Timothy! Guard the Deposit of Faith. 2007. 176p. per. 13.99 *(978-1-60266-426-5(9))* Xulon Pr., Inc.

Melbourne, Bertram L. Called to Discipleship. 2007. pap. 1.97 *(978-0-8163-2224-4(4))* Pacific Pr. Publishing Assn.

Mortimer, M. The Story of the Apostles: Or the Acts for Teenagers. 2011. 122p. 39.95 ***(978-1-258-08106-5(7))*** Literary Licensing, LLC.

Nelson, Deborah Harrell. The Successful Ambassador. 2007. 128p. per. 20.99 *(978-1-4257-3532-6(0))* Xlibris Corp.

On the Proper Time for the Admission of Recent Converts to the Full Communion of the Church. 2010. pap. 18.04 *(978-1-61143-185-8(9))* Gorgias Pr., LLC.

Packer, Boyd K. The Earth Shall Teach Thee. 2011. (Illus.). 200p. ***(978-0-8425-2806-1(7)***, Brigham Young Univ. Religious Studies Ctr.) Brigham Young Univ.

Pederson, Rena. The Lost Apostle: Searching for the Truth about Junia. 2008. (ENG., Illus.). 288p. reprint ed. pap. 14.95 *(978-0-470-18462-2(0), Jossey-Bass)* Wiley, John & Sons, Inc.

Peters, Rob. Evangel-Lies. 2007. 180p. per. 13.99 *(978-1-60266-051-9(4))* Xulon Pr., Inc.

Renan, Ernest. Apostles. 2006. pap. 31.95 *(978-1-4286-3945-4(4))* Kessinger Publishing, LLC.

—Apostles. 2006. (ENG.). pap. 26.99 *(978-1-4255-3744-9(8))* MPublishing.

Rose, Els & Rose, E. Ritual Memory: The Apocryphal Acts & Liturgical Commemoration in the Early Medieval West (C. 500-1215) 2009. xii, 334p. *(978-90-04-17171-8(1))* BRILL.

Schnabel, Eckhard J. Paul the Missionary: Realities, Strategies, & Methods. 2008. (ENG.). 518p. pap. 32.00 *(978-0-8308-2887-6(7), IVP Acad.)* InterVarsity Pr.

Selg, Peter. Christ & the Disciples: The Destiny of an Inner Community. Creeger, Catherine E., tr. from GER. 2011.Tr. of Christus und die Jünger: Vom Schicksal der inneren Gemeinschaft. 128p. ***(978-0-88010-745-7(6))*** SteinerBooks, Inc.

Study Guide for the Apostles by Pope Bendict XVI. 2007. 62p. pap. 4.95 *(978-1-59276-409-9(6))* Our Sunday Visitor, Publishing Div.

Taylor, Apostle Jenette. Prisoner of Warfare: P. O. W. 2008. 50p. pap. 9.00 *(978-0-8059-7683-0(3))* Dorrance Publishing Co., Inc.

Taylor, J. Lives of the Holy Evangelists & Apostl. 2006. pap. 20.95 *(978-1-4286-4681-0(7))* Kessinger Publishing, LLC.

Vidal, César. Pablo, el Judío de Tarso: IV Premio Algaba 2006. 2007. (Biografía (Algaba Ediciones) Ser.). 408p. pap. *(978-84-96107-77-9(9))* Algaba Ediciones.

Weiss, Dennis D. Acts: An in-Depth Study. 2011. 120p. 28.95 ***(978-1-4627-0526-9(X))***; pap. 11.95 ***(978-1-4627-0525-2(1))*** Cross Bks. Publishing.

APOSTLES—LEGENDS

McBirnie, William Steuart. The Search for the Twelve Apostles. 2008. (ENG., Illus.). 288p. pap. 14.99 *(978-1-4143-2004-5(3))* Tyndale Hse. Pubs.

APOSTLES' CREED

see also Communion of Saints

The Apostles' Creed. (Foundations in Faith Ser.). 80p. stu. ed. 6.50 *(978-0-570-06866-2(5), 20-2776)* Concordia Publishing Hse.

Ashwin-Siejkowski, Piotr & Ashwin-Siejkowski. The Apostles' Creed: And Its Early Christian Context. 2009. (ENG.). 208p. 24.95 *(978-0-567-32821-2(X), T&T Clark Int'l)* Continuum International Publishing Group, Ltd. GBR. Dist: National Bk. Network.

—The Apostles' Creed: And Its Early Christian Context. 2009. (ENG.). 208p. 120.00 *(978-0-567-00175-7(X), T&T Clark Int'l)* Continuum International Publishing Group, Ltd. GBR. Dist: National Bk. Network.

Barth, Karl. The Faith of the Church: A Commentary on the Apostles' Creed According to Calvin's Catechism. Leuba, Jean-Louis, ed. Vahanian, Gabriel, tr. 2006. 188p. pap. 22.00 *(978-1-59752-800-9(5), Wipf and Stock)* Wipf & Stock Pubs.

Bayes, Jonathan F. The ApostlesÔ Creed: Truth with Passion. 2010. 290p. pap. 32.00 *(978-1-60899-539-4(9), Wipf and Stock)* Wipf & Stock Pubs.

Bevins, Winfield H. Creed: Connect to the Basic Essentials of Historic Christian Faith. 2011. (First Book Challenge Ser.). 144p. pap. 8.99 *(978-1-61747-147-6(X))* NavPress Publishing Group.

Briere, Emile. I Believe: Living the Apostles' Creed. 136p. *(978-0-921440-79-6(0))* Madonna Hse. Pubns.

Burgess, Harold William. The Framework of Our Faith. 2011. x, 81p. pap. ***(978-1-59317-551-1(5))*** Zondervan.

Chester, Tim. The Apostles' Creed: Ten Studies for Individuals or Groups. 2010. (Good Book Guides). 100p. pap. *(978-1-905564-41-5(4))* Good Bk. Co.

Chesterton, G. K. Orthodoxy. Essays on the Apostles' Creed. 2008. pap. *(978-1-84830-108-5(1), Wildhern Pr.)* Echo Library.

Chittister, Joan. In Search of Belief. 2006. 216p. per. 16.95 *(978-0-7648-1484-6(2))* Liguori Pubns.

Cross, Timothy. I Believe... The Apostles' Creed Simply Explained. 2011. (Truth for All Time Ser.). 91p. pap. *(978-1-84625-201-3(6))* DayOne Pubns.

Dodds, James. Exposition of the Apostles Creed. 2008. 132p. 24.99 *(978-0-554-24728-1(3))* 2008. 132p. 21.99 *(978-0-554-34031-9(3))* 2006. (ENG.). 120p. pap. 18.99 *(978-1-4264-7296-1(X))* 2006. (ENG.). 128p. pap. 19.99 *(978-1-4264-7369-2(9))* BiblioBazaar.

Ellens, J. Harold. Honest Faith for Our Time: Truth-Telling about the Bible, the Creed, & the Church. 2010. 194p. pap. 22.00 *(978-1-60899-708-4(1), Pickwick Pubns.)* Wipf & Stock Pubs.

Forte, Bruno. A Short Introduction to the Apostles Creed. pap. 11.50 *(978-0-8189-9464-7(9))* St Pauls/Alba Hse. Pubs.

González, Justo L. The Apostles' Creed for Today. annot. ed. 2007. (For Today Ser.). (ENG.). 100p. per. 13.00 *(978-0-664-22933-7(6))* Westminster John Knox Pr.

Groseclose, Win. Credo, Ergo Confiteor: I Believe; Therefore, I Confess. 2008. 121p. pap. 8.72 *(978-0-557-00174-3(9))* Lulu Enterprises Inc.

Hughey, Donna. The Apostles' Creed: An Advanced Study for the Everyday Believer. 2009. pap. 9.99 *(978-1-60799-809-9(2))* Tate Publishing & Enterprises, LLC.

Jenson, Robert W. Canon & Creed: Resources for the Use of Scripture in the Church. 2010. (Interpretation Ser.). (ENG.). 160p. 25.00 *(978-0-664-23054-8(7))* Westminster John Knox Pr.

John Ogden Staff. Creed & Context. 2010. xviii, 202p. pap. *(978-0-7162-0657-6(9))* Epworth Pr., The.

Johnson, Marshall D. The Apostles' Creed: A User's Guide. 2008. (Exploring Christian Faith Ser.). 128p. pap. 11.99 *(978-0-8066-8051-4(2), Augsburg Bks.)* Augsburg Fortress, Pubs.

Kropf, Richard W. Breaking Open the Creeds: What Can They Mean for Christians Today? 2011. 112p. pap. *(978-0-8091-4550-8(2))* Paulist Pr.

Leininger, David E. As We Believe, So We Behave: Living the Apostles' Creed. 2008. *(978-0-7880-2588-4(0))* CSS Publishing Co.

McNeill, Leon A. & Aaron, Madeleine. The Words of Truth. 2011. 222p. 44.95 (978-1-258-05219-5(9)) Literary Licensing, LLC.

Olevianus, Caspar. An Exposition of the Apostles' Creed: The Articles of the Faith, in which the main points of the gracious eternal covenant between God & believers are briefly & clearly Treated. Bierma, Lyle D., tr. from LAT. 2009.Tr. of Expositio symboli Apostolici. (978-1-60178-074-4(5)) Reformation Heritage Bks.

Packer, J. I. Affirming the Apostles' Creed. 2008. 160p. pap. 9.99 (978-1-4335-0210-1(0)) Crossway.

Phipps, William E. The Apostles' Creed Critically Examined: The Struggle in the Early Church to Define Its Basic Beliefs. 2010. 286p. 109.95 (978-0-7734-3600-8(6)) Mellen, Edwin Pr., The.

Rausch, Thomas P. I Believe in God: A Reflection on the Apostles' Creed. 2008. 167p. per. 18.95 (978-0-8146-5260-2(3), Liturgical Pr. Bks.) Liturgical Pr.

Robbins, Stephen W. Transforming Beliefs: Spiritual Guidance Through the Apostles' Creed. 2006. 138p. pap. 17.00 (978-1-59752-631-9(2), Wipf and Stock) Wipf & Stock Pubs.

Steindl-Rast, David. Deeper Than Words: Living the Apostles' Creed. 2010. 176p. pap. 12.00 (978-0-307-58961-3(7), Image) Doubleday Religious Publishing Group, The.

Swan, Billy. Creed of Love: Reflections on the Apostles' Creed. 2006. (ENG.). 172p. pap. 16.95 (978-1-85390-977-1(7)) Veritas Pubns. IRL. Dist: Dufour Editions, Inc.

Swete, H. B. The Apostles' Creed: Its Relation to Primitive Christianity. 2010. (ENG.). 112p. pap. 19.99 (978-0-521-17071-0(0)) Cambridge Univ. Pr.

Vaghi, Peter J. The Faith We Profess: A Catholic Guide to the Apostles' Creed. 2008. 160p. pap. 13.95 (978-1-59471-177-0(1)) Ave Maria Pr.

Van Deventer, Brian. I Believe in. 2006. 132p. per. 14.95 (978-1-931178-33-4(X)) Vision Publishing.

Vila, Samuel. Como Explicar el Credo: The Apostle's Creed Made Easy. (SPA.). 128p. (978-84-7228-789-1(0), 222315) Clie, Editorial.

Vinzent, Markus. Der Ursprung des Apostolikums Im Urteil der Kritischen Forschung. 2006. (Forschungen Zur Kirchen- und Dogmengeschichte Ser.). (GER.). 480p. (C). 114.00 (978-3-525-55197-4(5)) Vandenhoeck & Ruprecht GmbH & Co. KG DEU. Dist: ISD.

APOSTLES' CREED—EARLY WORKS TO 1800

Cupitt, Don. The Old Creed & the New. 2006. 151p. per. (978-0-334-04053-8(1)) Hymns Ancient & Modern Ltd.

APOSTLES' CREED—SERMONS

Knox, Ronald & Knox, Richard. Creed in Slow Motion. 2009. 256p. pap. 14.95 (978-0-87061-250-3(6), Christian Classic) Ave Maria Pr.

APOSTOLATE, LAY

see Catholic Action

APOSTOLATE, LITURGICAL

see Liturgical Movement—Catholic Church

APOSTOLIC CHRISTIAN CHURCH

Dayhoff, Ruth Ann. My Dad, the Preacher. 2007. 268p. per. 27.95 (978-1-4241-7766-0(9)) PublishAmerica, Inc.

Kusema, Wellingtone Garati. The Believers' Companion: A Concise Topical Handbook on Doctrine in the African Apostolic Church. 2011. 410p. pap. 14.99 (978-0-9557546-1-6(5)) Heritage Pr.

Magaracha, Tendai Joseph & Masengwe, Gift. Power Struggles & Cultural Identity Crises in Aics. 2011. 88p. pap. (978-3-8383-3994-8(0)) Lambert Academic Publishing.

Montier, Gerald & Montier, Carolyn. Remembering the Past Apostolic Faith Mission Celebrating the Present Apostolic Faith Church of God. 2011. 116p. 30.00 (978-1-4567-4023-8(7)); pap. 25.00 (978-1-4567-4022-1(9)) AuthorHouse.

Simpson, A. B. La Iglesia Apostolica: The Apostolic Church. (SPA.). 160p. (978-84-7228-954-3(0), 223018) Clie, Editorial.

APOSTOLIC CHURCH

see Church History—Primitive and Early Church, ca. 30-600

APOSTOLIC FATHERS

Decker, Rodney J. & Decker, Rodney. Koine Greek Reader: Selections from the New Testament, Septuagint, & Early Christian Writers, 1 vol. 2007. 312p. pap. 25.99 (978-0-8254-2442-7(9)) Kregel Pubns.

Foster, Paul & Foster. The Writings of the Apostolic Fathers. 2007. (ENG.). 178p. 35.95 (978-0-567-03106-8(3), T&T Clark Int'l) Continuum International Publishing Group, Ltd. GBR. Dist: National Bk. Network.

Foster, Russell J. The Writings of the Apostolic Fathers. 2007. (ENG.). 184p. 130.00 (978-0-567-03105-1(5), T&T Clark Int'l) Continuum International Publishing Group, Ltd. GBR. Dist: National Bk. Network.

Gregory, Andrew & Tuckett, Christopher, eds. The New Testament & the Apostolic Fathers, 2 vols., Set. 2007. (ENG.). 928p. pap. 99.00 (978-0-19-923006-8(4)) Oxford Univ. Pr., Inc.

Holmes, Michael W., ed. & tr. from GEC. The Apostolic Fathers in English. 3rd ed. 2006. (ENG & GEC., Illus.). 336p. (C). per. 28.00 (978-0-8010-3108-3(7)) Baker Academic.

Howell, Kenneth J. Ignatius of Antioch & Polycarp of Smyrna: A New Translation & Theological Commentary. exp. ed. 2009. pap. (978-0-9800066-5-0(1)) CHResources.

Ignatius of Antioch: A New Translation & Theological Commentary. 2008. 160p. pap. 10.95 (978-0-9800066-0-5(0)) CHResources.

Jefford, Clayton N. The Apostolic Fathers & the New Testament. 2006. 267p. per. 19.95 (978-1-56563-425-1(X)) Hendrickson Pubs. Marketing, LLC.

Lightfoot, J. B. The Apostolic Fathers. 2007. (ENG.). 584p. per. 28.95 (978-1-4209-2948-5(8)) Digireads.com.

Lightfoot, J. B. & Harmer, J. R. The Apostolic Fathers. 2009. 586p. 33.99 (978-1-116-30962-1(9)); pap. 44.75 (978-1-116-30963-8(7)); 44.99 (978-1-116-30961-4(0)); pap. 43.75 (978-1-116-30964-5(5)) BiblioBazaar.

Lightfoot, J. b. & Lightfoot, J. B. The Apostolic Fathers. Harmer, J. R., ed. 2010. 288p. 43.95 (978-1-161-39395-8(1)) Kessinger Publishing, LLC.

Moody Publishing Staff & Moody Publishing. The Apostolic Fathers, 1 vol. 2009. (Moody Classics Ser.). (ENG.). 320p. pap. 8.99 (978-0-8024-5659-5(6)) Moody Pubs.

Oxford Society of Historical Theology Staff. The New Testament in the Apostolic Fathers. 2008. 160p. 22.99 (978-0-559-49252-5(9)); pap. 20.75 (978-0-559-49248-8(0)) BiblioBazaar.

Pratscher, Wilhelm, ed. The Apostolic Fathers: An Introduction. 2010. (ENG., Illus.). 315p. (C). pap. 39.95 (978-1-60258-308-5(0)) Baylor Univ. Pr.

Roberts, Alexander, ed. The Ante-Nicene Fathers: The Writings of the Fathers down to A. D. 325 Volume I - the Apostolic Fathers with Justin Martyr & Irenaeus. 2007. 616p. 35.95 (978-1-60206-470-6(9)); per. 24.95 (978-1-60206-469-0(5)) Cosimo, Inc.

Roberts, Alexander & Donaldson, James, eds. The Writings of the Apostolic Fathers. 2007. 160p. per. 14.95 (978-1-933993-45-4(6)) Apocryphile Pr.

Young, Stephen E. Jesus Tradition in the Apostolic Fathers: Their Explicit Appeals to the Words of Jesus in Light of Orality Studies. 2011. (Wissenschaftliche Untersuchungen zum Neuen Testament Ser.). (Illus.). 386p. pap. 162.50 (978-3-16-151010-6(0)) Mohr Siebeck GmbH & Co. KG DEU. Dist: Coronet Bks.

APOSTOLIC SUCCESSION

see also Anglican Orders; Bishops; Catholic Church—Clergy; Church of England—Clergy; Episcopacy; Popes

Bradshaw, Gordon. The Technology of Apostolic Succession. 2010. 24.95 (978-0-615-38709-3(8)) Kingdom Hse. Publishing.

Bradshaw, Gordon E. Resuscitation Technology. 2008. 460p. pap. 24.99 (978-1-60647-996-4(2)) Xulon Pr., Inc.

Cirlot, Felix L. Apostolic Succession & Anglicanism: A Defense of Anglican Orders & Catholicity. 2011. 452p. 57.95 (978-1-258-01464-3(5)) Literary Licensing, LLC.

Ehrhardt, Arnold. The Apostolic Succession: In the First Two Centuries of the Church. 2009. 168p. pap. 19.00 (978-1-60608-769-5(X), Wipf and Stock) Wipf & Stock Pubs.

Fitch, Chauncey W. James the Lord's Brother: Whose Son Was He? 2006. 112p. per. 16.99 (978-1-4255-0724-4(7)) MPublishing.

Garcia, Joel. The Apostolic Canopy. 2007. 192p. (ENG.). 21.99 (978-1-60266-684-9(9)); per. 13.99 (978-1-60266-683-2(0)) Xulon Pr., Inc.

Joyner, Rick. The Apostolic Ministry. 2006. (ENG.). 203p. mass mkt. 9.99 (978-1-929371-99-0(3)) MorningStar Pubns., Inc.

Ramsey, Michael. The Gospel & the Catholic Church, 1 vol. 2009. (ENG.). 249p. 16.95 (978-1-59856-389-4(0)) Hendrickson Pubs. Marketing, LLC.

—The Gospel & the Catholic Church. 2008. 248p. pap. 27.00 (978-1-60608-245-4(0), Wipf and Stock) Wipf & Stock Pubs.

Redmile, Robert. Apostolic Succession & the Catholic Ep. 2006. (ENG.). 25.99 (978-1-60034-517-3(4)); pap. 15.99 (978-1-60034-516-6(6)) Xulon Pr., Inc.

Schneider, Theodor & Wenz, Gunther. Das Kirchliche Amt in Apostolischer Nachfolge. (Dialog der Kirchen Ser.). (GER.). (C). 2008. 310p. pap. 48.00 (978-3-525-56936-8(X)) 2006. 423p. pap. 48.00 (978-3-525-56934-4(3)) Vandenhoeck & Ruprecht GmbH & Co. KG DEU. Dist: ISD.

Whately, Richard. Apostolical Succession Considered or the Constitution of a Christian Church Its Powers & Ministry. 2007. (ENG.). 160p. 36.95 (978-0-548-01969-6(X)) Kessinger Publishing, LLC.

APOTHECARIES

see Pharmacists

APOTHEGMS

see Aphorisms and Apothegms

APOTHEOSIS

Here are entered works dealing with the deification of rulers, heroes, and others either at death or during life.

see also Emperor Worship; Heroes; Kings and Rulers—Mythology; Kings and Rulers—Religious Aspects; Superman (Philosophical Concept)

Bartos, Emil. Deification in Eastern Orthodox Theology. 2007. (Paternoster Theological Monographs: Ser.). 398p. pap. 40.00 (978-1-59752-792-7(0), Wipf and Stock) Wipf & Stock Pubs.

Blackwell, Ben C. Christosis: Pauline Soteriology in Light of Deification in Irenaeus & Cyril of Alexandria. 2011. (Wissenschaftliche Untersuchungen zum Neuen Testament 2 Ser.). 326p. pap. 157.50 (978-3-16-151672-6(9)) Mohr Siebeck GmbH & Co. KG DEU. Dist: Coronet Bks.

Christensen, Michael J. & Wittung, Jeffery. Partakers of the Divine Nature: The History & Development of Deification in the Christian Traditions. 2007. 325p. (C). (978-0-8386-4111-8(3)) Fairleigh Dickinson Univ. Pr.

Christensen, Michael J. & Wittung, Jeffery A., eds. Partakers of the Divine Nature: The History & Development of Deification in the Christian Traditions. 2008. 336p. (C). pap. 30.00 (978-0-8010-3440-4(X)) Baker Academic.

Frieders, Larry J. The Undruggist: Book One: A Tale of Modern Apothecary & Wellness. 2010. 112p. pap. 11.95 (978-1-4525-0087-4(8)) Get Published.

Habets, Myk. Theosis in the Theology of Thomas Torrance. 2009. (New Critical Thinking in Religion, Theology & Biblical Studies). 222p. 99.95 (978-0-7546-6799-5(5)) Ashgate Publishing Co.

Hudson, Nancy J. Becoming God: The Doctrine of Theosis in Nicholas of Cusa. 2007. 218p. 64.95 (978-0-8132-1472-6(6)) Catholic Univ. of America Pr.

Kezbere, Ilze. Umstrittener Monotheismus: Wahre und Falsche Apotheose im Lukanischen Doppelwerk. 2006. (Novum Testamentum et Orbis Antiquus (Ntoa) Ser.: 60). (GER.). 231p. (C). 59.00 (978-3-525-53960-6(6)) Vandenhoeck & Ruprecht GmbH & Co. KG DEU. Dist: ISD.

Kharlamov, Vladimir. The Beauty of the Unity & the Harmony of the Whole: The Concept of Theosis in the Theology of Pseudo-Dionysius the Areopagite. 2008. 270p. pap. 30.00 (978-1-60608-164-8(0), Wipf and Stock) Wipf & Stock Pubs.

—Theosis: Deification in Christian Theology. Finlan, Stephen, ed. 2006. (ENG.). 194p. pap. 42.50 (978-0-227-17329-9(5)) Clarke, James Co., Ltd. GBR. Dist: Brown, David Bk. Co., The.

Kharlamov, Vladimir, ed. Theosis: Deification in Christian Theology. 2011. (Princeton Theological Monographs). 296p. pap. 33.00 (978-1-61097-070-9(5), Pickwick Pubns.) Wipf & Stock Pubs.

Russell, Norman. The Doctrine of Deification in the Greek Patristic Tradition. 2006. (Oxford Early Christian Studies). (ENG.). 432p. pap. 85.00 (978-0-19-920597-4(3)) Oxford Univ. Pr., Inc.

Wilson, Daniel E. Deification & the Rule of Faith: The Communication of the Gospel in Hellenistic Culture. 2010. 292p. pap. 19.99 (978-1-61507-042-8(7)) Cross Bks. Publishing.

APPALACHIA

see Appalachian Region

APPALACHIAN DULCIMER

see Dulcimer

APPALACHIAN MOUNTAINS

see also Blue Ridge Mountains

Adkins, Leonard M. & Appalachian Trail Conservancy. Along Virginia's Appalachian Trail. 2009. (Images of America Ser.). (ENG., Illus.). 128p. pap. 21.99 (978-0-7385-6630-6(6)) Arcadia Publishing.

Baker, John Bryant. Thoughts along the Way: A Journey on the Appalachian Trail. 2011. 78p. pap. 19.95 (978-1-4626-4315-8(9)) PublishAmerica, Inc.

Bauer, Jennifer A. Wildlife, Wildflowers, & Wild Activities: Exploring Southern Appalachia. 2007. (Illus.). 197p. per. 17.95 (978-1-57072-317-9(5)) Overmountain Pr.

Brunner, Warren. Mountain Moments. 2010. 168p. 34.95 (978-1-935001-42-3(6)) Acclaim Pr., Inc.

Burns, Shirley Stewart, et al, eds. Coal Country: Rising up Against Mountaintop Removal Mining. 2009. (ENG.). 272p. pap. 25.95 (978-1-57805-166-3(5)) Sierra Club Bks.

Butler, Tom, ed. Plundering Appalachia: The Tragedy of Mountaintop Removal Coal Mining. 2009. (ENG.). 228p. 49.95 (978-1-60109-054-6(4), Earth Aware Editions) Mandala Publishing.

Chase, Ron & Chase, Nancy. New England: Scenic Summits for Hikers. 2008. (Mountains for Mortals Ser.). (ENG., Illus.). 224p. pap. 19.95 (978-0-89732-621-6(0)) Menasha Ridge Pr., Inc.

Coyner, Dale. Motorcycle Journeys Through the Appalachians. 3rd ed. 2011. (Motorcycle Journeys Ser.). (ENG., Illus.). 200p. pap. 27.95 (978-1-884313-91-2(4), 1884313914) Whitehorse Pr.

Friends of the Appalachian Trail Staff, photos by. On the Appalachian Trail. 2010. (ENG., Illus.). 32p. pap. 9.95 (978-0-89732-712-1(8)) Menasha Ridge Pr., Inc.

Hanel, Selma I. Carderock Past & Present: A Climber's Guide. Rebellato Annette & Penosa, Vincent, eds. 2nd ed. 2008. (Illus.). 132p. pap. 7.00 (978-0-915746-40-8(9)) Potomac Appalachian Trail Club.

Harvey, Adell Farley. Tales of the Endless Mountains: A True Story of Midwest City Slickers Learning Love & Patience in a Mountain Hamlet. 2011. 212p. 33.95 (978-1-4497-1767-4(5)); pap. 17.95 (978-1-4497-1766-7(7)) Author Solutions, Inc. (WestBow Pr.).

Katz, Gene, ed. Seasons & Colors of the Appalachian Mountains. 2007. 64p. per. 9.95 (978-0-9767745-1-8(8)) Misty Mountain Pr.

McNulty, Jeanne. Voice for the Hollers: A Journey into Solitude & Solidarity in Appalachia. 2009. (Illus.). 154p. pap. 9.95 (978-1-4327-4534-9(4)) Outskirts Pr., Inc.

Miller, David. AWOL on the Appalachian Trail. 2011. (ENG., Illus.). 352p. pap. 14.95 (978-0-547-74552-7(4), Mariner Bks.) Houghton Mifflin Harcourt Trade & Reference Pubs.

Morley, Margaret Warner. The Carolina Mountains. 2008. 464p. 31.99 (978-0-559-78062-2(1)); pap. 35.75 (978-0-559-78058-5(3)) BiblioBazaar.

—The Carolina Mountains. 2009. 254p. pap. (978-0-217-06962-5(2)) Books LLC.

—The Carolina Mountains. 2006. (Southern Appalachian Classics Ser.). (Illus.). 384p. pap. 24.00 (978-0-914875-11-6(6), Historical Images) Bright Mountain Bks., Inc.

—The Carolina Mountains. 2009. 452p. 52.95 (978-1-104-58315-6(1)); pap. 37.95 (978-1-104-48200-8(2)) Kessinger Publishing, LLC.

O'Haynes, Delilah F., et al, eds. Appalachia's Last Stand. 2009. 212p. pap. 16.00 (978-1-893239-97-5(7)) Wind Pubns.

Sherman, Steve & Older, Julia. Appalachian Odyssey: Walking the Trail from Georgia to Maine. 2009. 268p. pap. 19.95 (978-1-4401-1530-1(3)) iUniverse, Inc.

Thacker, Larry D., Jr. Mountain Mysteries: Investigating the Mystic Traditions of Appalachia. 2007. (Illus.). 226p. per. 14.95 (978-1-57072-316-2(8)) Overmountain Pr.

Williams, Jack. East 40 Degrees: An Interpretive Atlas. 2007. (ENG., Illus.) 320p. (gr. 17). 50.00 (978-0-8139-2524-0(X)); pap. 30.00 (978-0-8139-2585-1(1)) Univ. Pr. of Virginia.

APPALACHIAN REGION

Asfar, Dan & Smitten, Susan. Ghost Stories of the Appalachians. 2009. (ENG.). 208p. pap. 12.95 (978-1-894877-20-6(9)) Lone Pine Publishing USA.

Barnwell, Tim. On Earth's Furrowed Brow. 2007. 35.00 (978-0-7930-6267-6(5)) Norton, W. W. & Co., Inc.

—On Earth's Furrowed Brow: The Appalachian Farm in Photographs. 2007. (ENG., Illus.). 224p. 35.00 (978-0-393-06267-0(8), 6267) Norton, W. W. & Co., Inc.

Barnwell, Tim, et al. Hands in Harmony: Traditional Crafts & Music in Appalachia. 2009. (ENG., Illus.). 192p. 49.95 (978-0-393-06815-3(3), 6815) Norton W. W. & Co., Inc.

Baswell, Evans & Evans, Baswell. Alternative Forages for Grazing Beef Cattle: Annuals Forages for Beef in Appalachia. 2011. 124p. pap. (978-3-639-31710-7(6)) VDM Verlag Dr. Mueller e.K.

Bevins, James. The Westport Haunting: A True Story. 2008. 48p. pap. 16.95 (978-1-60703-894-8(3)) PublishAmerica, Inc.

Burch, John R., compiled by. The Bibliography of Appalachia: More Than 4,700 Books, Articles, Monographs & Dissertations, Topically Arranged & Indexed. 2009. (Contributions to Southern Appalachian Studies). (ENG.). 232p. pap. 55.00 (978-0-7864-4133-4(X)) McFarland & Co., Inc. Pubs.

Burdette, Dick. The Waterloo Wonders. 2008. pap. (978-1-4389-0849-6(0)) AuthorHouse.

Burns, Shirley Stewart, et al, eds. Coal Country: Rising up Against Mountaintop Removal Mining. 2009. (ENG.). 272p. 40.00 (978-1-57805-168-7(1)) Sierra Club Bks.

Butler, Tom, ed. Plundering Appalachia: The Tragedy of Mountaintop Removal Coal Mining. 2009. (ENG.). 228p. pap. 39.95 (978-1-60109-050-8(1), Earth Aware Editions) Mandala Publishing.

Cannon, James. In Walking Distance. 2011. 236p. pap. 15.99 (978-0-557-80555-6(4)) Lulu Enterprises Inc.

Caruso, John Anthony. The Appalachian Frontier: America's First Surge Westward. 2011. 410p. 54.95 (978-1-258-08769-2(3)) Literary Licensing, LLC.

Caudill, Harry M. Night Comes to the Cumberlands: A Biography of A Depressed Area. 2011. 412p. 54.95 (978-1-258-09626-7(9)) Literary Licensing, LLC.

Cheek, Angie, et al, eds. The Foxfire 40th Anniversary Book: Faith, Family, & the Land. anniv. ed. 2006. (ENG., Illus.). 560p. pap. 19.95 (978-0-307-27551-6(5), Anchor) Knopf Doubleday Publishing Group.

Clabough, Casey. The Warrior's Path: Reflections along an Ancient Route. 2007. (ENG., Illus.). 200p. per. 24.95 (978-1-57233-602-5(1)) Univ. of Tennessee Pr.

Coonfield, Ted. The Varmits: Living with Appalachian Outlaws. 2011. 196p. 27.00 (978-1-4567-3355-1(9)); pap. 18.00 (978-1-4567-3354-4(0)) AuthorHouse.

Covington, Dennis. Salvation on Sand Mountain: Snake Handling & Redemption in Southern Appalachia. 15th ed. 2009. (ENG.). 288p. pap. 14.95 (978-0-306-81836-3(1)) Da Capo Pr., Inc.

Dabney, Joseph. Smoke Ham, Spoon Bread, & Scuppernong Wine. 2010. (ENG.). 528p. pap. 19.99 (978-1-4022-3913-7(0)) Sourcebooks, Inc.

Dabney, Joseph E. Smokehouse Ham, Spoon Bread & Scuppernong Wine: The Folklore & Art of Southern Appalachian Cooking. 10th anniv. ed. 2008. (ENG., Illus.). 528p. 29.99 (978-1-58182-667-8(2), Cumberland Hse.) Sourcebooks, Inc.

Davis, Adda Leah. Lucinda's Mountain. 2007. ix, 315p. pap. (978-0-941092-51-7(8)) Mountain State Pr.

Davis, Jennifer Pharr. Becoming Odyssa: Epic Adventures on the Appalachian Trail. 2010. 320p. 24.95 (978-0-8253-0649-5(3)) Beaufort Bks., Inc.

DeRosier, Linda Scott. Songs of Life & Grace: A Memoir. 2008. (ENG., Illus.). 280p. pap. 19.95 (978-0-8131-9197-3(1)) Univ. Pr. of Kentucky.

EGOLF, Jennifer, et al. Culture, class, & politics in modern Appalachia: Essays in honor of ronald L. Lewis. 2009. (WEST VIRIGINIA & APPALACHIA Ser.). 384p. 83.95 (978-1-933202-40-2(8)) West Virginia Univ. Pr.

Elkins, Robert. Watchin' the Bluegrass Grow: Appalachian Spirits, Stories, & Tales. 2006. 90p. per. 9.95 (978-1-57072-305-6(2)) Overmountain Pr.

Eller, Ronald D. Uneven Ground: Appalachia Since 1945. 2008. (ENG., Illus.). 376p. 29.95 (978-0-8131-2523-7(5)) Univ. Pr. of Kentucky.

Field Hearing on Veterans' Access to Benefits & Services in Appalachia: Hearing Before the Committee on Veterans' Affairs, United States Senate, One Hundred Eleventh Congress, Second Session, April 5, 2010. 2011. iii, 42p. (978-0-16-088470-2(5), 552-070-42676-1) United States Government Printing Office.

Fisher, Stephen L. & Smith, Barbara Ellen. Transforming Places: Lessons from Appalachia. 2012. E-Book (978-0-252-09376-0(3)) Univ. of Illinois Pr.

Fones-Wolf, Ken. Glass Towns: Industry, Labor, & Political Economy in Appalachia, 1890-1930s. 2006. (Working Class in American History Ser.). (Illus.). 272p. 67.00 (978-0-252-03131-1(8)); per. 26.00 (978-0-252-07371-7(1)) Univ. of Illinois Pr.

Foxfire Fund, Inc. The Foxfire 45th Anniversary Book: Singin', Praisin', Raisin' Green, Joyce & Best, Casi, eds. 2011. (Illus.). 528p. pap. 18.95 (978-0-307-74259-9(8), Anchor) Knopf Doubleday Publishing Group.

Francis, Mitzi Hall. Child of Appalachi. 2011. 254p. pap. 14.95 (978-1-935271-94-9(6)) Published by Westview, Inc.

Frazier, Thomas D. Come Sit A Spell. 2010. pap. 14.95 *(978-0-7414-5782-0(2))* Infinity Publishing.

Goan, Melanie Beals. Mary Breckinridge: The Frontier Nursing Service & Rural Health in Appalachia. 2008. (ENG., Illus.). 360p. 49.95 *(978-0-8078-3211-0(1))* Univ. of North Carolina Pr.

Gregg, Sara M. Managing the Mountains: Land Use Planning, the New Deal, & the Creation of a Federal Landscape in Appalachia. 2010. (Yale Agrarian Studies Ser.). (ENG., Illus.). 304p. 40.00 *(978-0-300-14219-8(6))* Yale Univ. Pr.

Griliches, Diane Asseo. An Appalachian Farmer's Story: Portrait of an Extraordinary Common Man. 2007. (Illus.). 144p. 40.00 *(978-0-88146-062-9(1))* Mercer Univ. Pr.

Harvey, Douglas S. The Theatre of Empire: Frontier Performances in America, 1750-1860, 1 vol. 2010. (Empires in Perspective Ser.). (ENG.). 256p. 99.00 *(978-1-84893-027-8(5))* Pickering & Chatto Pubs., Ltd. GBR. Dist: Ashgate Publishing Co.

Hiscoe, Helen B. Appalachian Passage. 2008. (ENG.). 344p. pap. 24.95 *(978-0-8203-3217-8(8))* Univ. of Georgia Pr.

House, Silas & Howard, Jason. Something's Rising: Appalachians Fighting Mountaintop Removal. 2009. (ENG., Illus.). 320p. 27.95 *(978-0-8131-2546-6(4))* Univ. Pr. of Kentucky.

Inscoe, John C. Race, War, & Remembrance in the Appalachian South. 2009. (ENG.). 412p. pap. 30.00 *(978-0-8131-9300-7(1))* Univ. Pr. of Kentucky.

Jabbour, Alan & Jabbour, Karen. Decoration Day in the Mountains: Traditions of Cemetery Decoration in the Southern Appalachians. 2010. (ENG., Illus.). 256p. 35.00 *(978-0-8078-3397-1(5))* Univ. of North Carolina Pr.

Jacobs, Jimmy & Jacobs, J. Trout Streams of Southern Appalachia: Fly-Casting in Georgia, Kentucky, North Carolina, South Carolina & Tennessee. 3rd ed. 2009. (ENG.). 336p. (Orig.). pap. 21.95 *(978-0-88150-858-1(6)*, 150858) Countryman Pr.

Jobe, Abraham. A Mountaineer in Motion: The Memoir of Dr. Abraham Jobe, 1817-1906. Hsiung, David C., ed. 2009. (ENG.). 37.95 *(978-1-57233-489-2(4))* Univ. of Tennessee Pr.

Joy, David. Growing Gills: A Fly Fisherman's Journey. 2011. pap. 16.00 ***(978-0-914875-60-4(4))*** Bright Mountain Bks., Inc.

Kephart, Horace. Our Southern Highlanders: A Narrative of Adventure in the Southern Appalachians & a Study of Life Among the Mountaineers. (Illus.). 395p. reprint ed. lib. bdg. 98.00 *(978-0-7222-0780-2(8))* Library Reprints, Inc.

Lang, John, ed. Appalachia & Beyond: Conversations with Writers from the Mountain South. 2006. (Illus.). 352p. per. 24.95 *(978-1-57233-535-6(1))* Univ. of Tennessee Pr.

Lemaster, Phil. Philosophically Speaking: The Stories & Musings of an Appalachian Preacher, Teacher, & Psychologist. 2009. (Illus.). 340p. pap. 18.99 *(978-1-61579-407-2(7))* Xulon Pr., Inc.

Lewis, Ronald L., et al. Culture, Class, & Politics in Modern Appalachia: Essays in Honor of Ronald L. Lewis. 2009. (WEST VIRIGINIA & APPALACHIA Ser.). 384p. pap. 27.95 *(978-1-933202-39-6(4))* West Virginia Univ. Pr.

Lorence, James J. A Hard Journey: The Life of Don West. (Illus.). 344p. 2010. (ENG.). pap. 25.00 *(978-0-252-07733-3(4))* 2007. 39.95 *(978-0-252-03231-8(4))* Univ. of Illinois Pr.

Lovingood, Paul, et al. Emerging Patterns in the Southern Highlands: Business Patterns, Vol. IV. (Illus.). 326p. (Orig.). pap. 11.95 *(978-0-913239-54-4(2))* Appalachian Consortium Pr.

Martin, C. Brenden. Tourism in the Mountain South: A Double-Edged Sword. 2007. (Illus.). 264p. 32.00 *(978-1-57233-575-2(0))* Univ. of Tennessee Pr.

McFee, Michael. The Napkin Manuscripts: Selected Essays & an Interview. 2006. 200p. 29.95 *(978-1-57233-540-0(8))* Univ. of Tennessee Pr.

McNeil, Bryan T. Combating Mountaintop Removal: New Directions in the Fight Against Big Coal. 2011. (ENG., Illus.). 216p. 45.00 *(978-0-252-03643-9(3))* Univ. of Illinois Pr.

Miller, Zell. Purt Nigh Gone: The Old Mountain Ways. 2009. pap. *(978-0-9796462-3-2(5))* Stroud & Hall Publishing.

Molloy, Johnny. The Southern Appalachian & Smoky Mountains: A Guide for Car Campers Who Hate RVs, Concrete Slabs, & Loud Portable Stereos. 4th ed. 2007. (Best in Tent Camping Ser.). (ENG., Illus.). 192p. per. 14.95 *(978-0-89732-960-6(0))* Menasha Ridge Pr., Inc.

Morrone, Michele & Buckley, Geoffrey L., eds. Mountains of Injustice: Social & Environmental Justice in Appalachia. 2011. (ENG.). 216p. 49.95 ***(978-0-8214-1980-9(3))*** Ohio Univ. Pr.

Murray, Kenneth M. Appalachia, A Day Before Yesterday. 2008. (Illus.). 152p. pap. 12.95 *(978-0-9665895-2-8(1))* Ctr. for Appalachian Studies & Services.

Obermiller, Phillip J. & Maloney, Mike E. Appalachia: Social Context Past & Present. 5th rev. ed. 2010. (ENG., Illus.). 434p. pap. 91.94 *(978-0-7575-3905-3(X))* Kendall Hunt Publishing Co.

O'Donnell, Kevin. Historic Photos of Appalachia. 2010. (Historic Photos Ser.). (ENG.). 205p. 39.95 *(978-1-59652-540-5(1))* Turner Publishing Co.

—Remembering Appalachia. 2011. 144p. pap. 16.95 *(978-1-59652-729-4(3))* Turner Publishing Co.

Olson, Ted & Olson, Kathy H., eds. James Still: Critical Essays on the Dean of Appalachian Literature. 2007. (Contributions to Southern Appalachian Studies: 17). (ENG., Illus.). 260p. pap. 39.95 *(978-0-7864-3076-5(1))* McFarland & Co., Inc. Pubs.

Oxford-Tolliver, Geraldine. The Way It Was in Appalachi. 2009. 204p. pap. 21.49 *(978-1-4389-0846-5(6))* AuthorHouse.

Parkansky, Steven. Concise Version of Appalachia: Social Context Past & Present. 5th rev. ed. 2011. (ENG.). 76p. pap. 30.00 ***(978-0-7575-9015-3(2))*** Kendall Hunt Publishing Co.

Perrier, Dianne. Interstate 81: The Great Warriors Trace. 2010. (ENG., Illus.). 272p. pap. 24.95 *(978-0-8130-3481-2(7))* Univ. Pr. of Florida.

Podber, Jacob J. The Electronic Front Porch: An Oral History of the Arrival of Modern Media in Rural Appalachia & the Melungeon Community. 2007. (Melungeons Ser.). 166p. 35.00 *(978-0-88146-089-6(3))* Mercer Univ. Pr.

Powell, Scott. Appalachian Educational Realization. 2008. 212p. pap. *(978-3-639-04378-5(2))* VDM Verlag Dr. Mueller e.K.

—Overcoming Stereotypes about Poor Appalachian Single Mothers. 2008. 112p. per. *(978-3-8364-6213-6(3))* VDM Verlag Dr. Mueller e.K.

Reeves, Jr. & McNamara, Billie R. Photographs from the Appalachian & National Conservation Expositions. 2008. 96p. pap. 15.00 *(978-0-9800984-6-4(7))* Reeves, Charles A.

Reichert Powell, Douglas. Critical Regionalism: Connecting Politics & Culture in the American Landscape. 2007. (ENG., Illus.). 280p. 69.95 *(978-0-8078-3091-8(7))* Univ. of North Carolina Pr.

Rohrbough, Malcolm J. Trans-Appalachian Frontier: People, Societies, & Institutions, 1775-1850. 3rd rev. ed. 2008. (History of the Trans-Appalachian Frontier Ser.). (ENG., Illus.). 696p. pap. 27.95 *(978-0-253-21932-9(9)*, 0253219329) Indiana Univ. Pr.

Rowland, Tim. Maryland's Appalachian Highlands: Massacres, Moonshine, & Mountaineering. 2009. 19.99 *(978-1-59629-668-8(2))* History Pr., The.

Rubin, Robert Alden & Alden Rubin, Robert. On the Beaten Path: An Appalachian Pilgrimage. 2nd ed. 2009. (ENG., Illus.). 256p. pap. 16.95 *(978-1-59921-497-9(0)*, Lyons Pr.) Globe Pequot Pr., The.

Sammons, Michael. Backwood Protasis: Appalachian Oral History-Southern Lewis County, Kentucky. 2006. (Illus.). 200p. (YA). spiral bd. 20.00 *(978-1-4276-0183-4(6))* Aardvark Global Publishing.

Saunders, Janice. Cricket's Child, 1945-1955: How I Never Learned to Love the Bomb. 2008. (ENG.). 120p. pap. 26.50 *(978-0-7618-3994-1(1))* Hamilton Bks.

Saunders, Richard. Never Been Rich: The Life & Work of a Southern Ruralist Writer, Harry Harrison Kroll. 2011. (ENG.). 264p. 42.00 ***(978-1-57233-825-8(3))*** Univ. of Tennessee Pr.

Schraff, Marilyn Thornton. Appalachian Childhood: Memories of Growing up in Rural Southern Ohio During the Mid 20th Century. 2010. (ENG., Illus.). 237p. pap. 19.00 *(978-0-9827983-0-0(X))* Schraff, Marilyn Thornton.

Scott, Rebecca R. Removing Mountains: Extracting Nature & Identity in the Appalachian Coalfields. 2010. (Quadrant Book Ser.). (ENG., Illus.). 296p. 75.00 *(978-0-8166-6599-0(0))*; pap. 25.00 *(978-0-8166-6600-3(8))* Univ. of Minnesota Pr.

Shelton, Jeanette. In My Brother's Shadow: The Appalachian Way. 2010. 56p. pap. 10.16 *(978-1-4269-3129-1(8))* Trafford Publishing.

Shrader, Charles A. Dreaming Small. 2010. pap. 17.95 *(978-0-7414-5951-0(5))* Infinity Publishing.

Simmons, Gina. Discovering Lavalette. 2009. 160p. pap. 40.49 *(978-1-4389-8707-1(2))* AuthorHouse.

Slap, Andrew L., ed. Reconstructing Appalachia: The Civil War's Aftermath. 2010. (New Directions in Southern History Ser.). (ENG., Illus.). 390p. 40.00 *(978-0-8131-2581-7(2))* Univ. Pr. of Kentucky.

Smith, Barbara Ellen. Transforming Places: Lessons from Appalachia. Fisher, Stephen L., ed. 2012. (ENG., Illus.). 336p. 85.00 ***(978-0-252-03666-8(2))***; pap. 30.00 ***(978-0-252-07838-5(1))*** Univ. of Illinois Pr.

Stewart, Bruce E., ed. Blood in the Hills: A History of Violence in Appalachia. 2011. (New Directions in Southern History Ser.). (ENG., Illus.). 422p. 55.00 *(978-0-8131-3427-7(7))* Univ. Pr. of Kentucky.

Still, James. The Wolfpen Notebooks: A Record of Appalachian Life. 2009. (ENG.). 192p. pap. 22.00 *(978-0-8131-9344-1(3))* Univ. Pr. of Kentucky.

Tate, Linda. Power in the Blood: A Family Narrative. 2009. (Ethnicity & Gender in Appalach Ser.). (ENG., Illus.). 256p. 46.95 *(978-0-8214-1871-0(8))*; pap. 24.95 *(978-0-8214-1872-7(6))* Ohio Univ. Pr.

Testimony on the Impact of the Last Reauthorization of the Appalachian Regional Commission & Issues Regarding the Upcoming Reauthorization: Hearing Before the Committee on Environment & Public Works, United States Senate, One Hundred Ninth Congress, Second Session, April 20, 2006, Marietta, OH. 2009. (Illus.). iii, 95p. *(978-0-16-082773-0(6)*, 552-070-38773-1) United States Government Printing Office.

Thompson, Samuel H. Hills & Hollows: Southern Appalachian Life. Wallace, David B., ed. Date not set. (Illus.). 38p. reprint ed. pap. 4.75 *(978-1-889074-03-0(9))* Elkhorn Pr.

Valentine, James. Southern Appalachian Celebration: In Praise of Ancient Mountains, Old-Growth Forests, & Wilderness. 2011. (ENG., Illus.). 152p. 35.00 *(978-0-8078-3514-2(5))* Univ. of North Carolina Pr.

Vande Brake, Katherine. Through the Back Door: Melungeon Literacies & Twenty-First Century Technologies. 2009. (Illus.). 224p. pap. 22.00 *(978-0-88146-150-3(4))* Mercer Univ. Pr.

Waples, David A. The Natural Gas Industry in Appalachia: A History from the First Discovery to the Maturity of the Industry. 2011. (Illus.). 286p. pap. 40.00 *(978-0-7864-6632-0(4))* McFarland & Co., Inc. Pubs.

Whisnant, David. All That Is Native & Fine: The Politics of Culture in an American Region. 2009. (ENG., Illus.). 360p. pap. 26.95 *(978-0-8078-5964-3(8))* Univ. of North Carolina Pr.

APPALACHIAN TRAIL

Adkins, Leonard M. Wildflowers of the Appalachian Trail. 2nd ed. 2006. (ENG., Illus.). 214p. pap. 18.95 *(978-0-89732-974-3(0))* Menasha Ridge Pr., Inc.

Adsmond, Lou. The Appalachian Trail Food Planner: Recipes & Menus for a 2,000-Mile Hike. 2nd rev. ed. 2009. 134p. spiral bd. 18.95 *(978-1-889386-61-4(8))* Appalachian Trail Conservancy.

Alt, Jeff. A Walk for Sunshine: A 2,160 Mile Expedition for Charity on the Appalachian Trail. 2nd ed. 2007. 288p. per. 15.95 *(978-0-9679482-2-5(3))* Dreams Shared Pubns., LLC.

Anderson, Larry. Benton MacKaye: Conservationist, Planner, & Creator of the Appalachian Trail. 2008. (Creating the North American Landscape Ser.). (ENG., Illus.). 468p. (gr. 17). pap. 32.00 *(978-0-8018-9094-9(2))* Johns Hopkins Univ. Pr.

Bernstein, Danny. Hiking the Carolina Mountains. 2007. (Illus.). 360p. pap. 19.95 *(978-1-889596-19-8(1))* Milestone Pr., Inc.

Bratton, Susan Power. The Spirit of the Appalachian Trail: Community, Environment, & Belief on a Long-Distance Hiking Path. 2012. (ENG., Illus.). 304p. 49.95 ***(978-1-57233-877-7(6))*** Univ. of Tennessee Pr.

Brill, David. As Far as the Eye Can See: Reflections of an Appalachian Trail Hiker. 3rd ed. 2010. 192p. per. 12.95 *(978-1-889386-44-7(8))* Appalachian Trail Conservancy.

Bryson, Bill. A Walk in the Woods: Rediscovering America on the Appalachian Trail. 2006. (ENG.). 416p. mass mkt. 7.99 *(978-0-307-27946-0(4)*, Anchor) Knopf Doubleday Publishing Group.

Buras, Thom. The Wayfarer's Journal: Episode One: Journey to Katahdin, 3 Episodes, Episode One. 2007. (Illus.). 398p. (YA). per. 24.95 *(978-0-9786169-3-9(6))*; spiral bd. 29.95 *(978-0-9786169-2-2(8))* NorthWest Services.

Chazin, Daniel, ed. Appalachian Trail Guide to New York-New Jersey. 17th rev. ed. 2011. 280p. pap. 22.95 *(978-1-889386-70-6(7))* Appalachian Trail Conservancy.

Chazin, Daniel D., ed. Appalachian Trail Data Book. 29th rev. ed. 2006. (Illus.). 86p. per. 5.95 *(978-1-889386-49-2(9))* Appalachian Trail Conservancy.

Chenowith, Lon. Five Million Steps: Adventure along the Appalachian Trail. 2009. (J). pap. 14.99 *(978-1-60799-416-9(X))* Tate Publishing & Enterprises, LLC.

Chew, V. Collins, ed. Appalachian Trail Guide to Tennessee-North Carolina. 13th rev. ed. 2009. 276p. pap. 27.95 *(978-1-889386-63-8(4))* Appalachian Trail Conservancy.

Davis, Jennifer Pharr. Becoming Odyssa: Adventures on the Appalachian Trail. 2011. 320p. pap. 15.95 *(978-0-8253-0568-9(3))* Beaufort Bks., Inc.

Dillon, Tom, ed. Appalachian Trail Guide to Southwest Virginia. 5th ed. 2011. (Official Appalachian Trail Guides). 232p. pap. 22.95 *(978-1-889386-72-0(3))* Appalachian Trail Conservancy.

Gilbertson, Eric & Gilbertson, Matthew. Mountain Adventures: Whites, West, & the Appalachian Trail. 2009. 244p. pap. 19.49 *(978-1-4389-8144-4(9))* AuthorHouse.

Graf, Irma, ed. Appalachian Trail Guide to Central Virginia. 2nd ed. 2010. 300p. pap. 22.95 *(978-1-889386-57-7(X))* Appalachian Trail Conservancy.

Gross, Wayne E., ed. Appalachian Trail Guide to Pennsylvania. 11th ed. 2009. (ENG.). 205p. pap. 9.00 *(978-0-9717445-5-4(6))* Keystone Trails Assn.

Hammaker, Ben "Stretch". Northbound: The Daily Account of an Appalachian Trail Thru-Hike, 1 vol. 2009. 150p. pap. 24.95 *(978-1-4489-2914-6(8))* PublishAmerica, Inc.

Hedrick, John. Appalachian Trail Guide to Shenandoah National Park: With Side Trails. 2012. ***(978-0-915746-64-4(6))*** Potomac Appalachian Trail Club.

Hedrick, John, ed. Appalachian Trail Guide to Shenandoah National Park: With Side Trails. 13th rev. ed. 2009. (Illus.). 384p. pap. 34.95 *(978-0-915746-54-5(9))* Appalachian Trail Conservancy.

—Appalachian Trail Guide to Shenandoah National Park: With Side Trails. 14th ed. 2012. (Illus.). 344p. pap. 12.00 *(978-0-915746-84-2(0))* Potomac Appalachian Trail Club.

Jensen, Jamie. Road Trip USA Appalachian Trail. 2010. (Road Trip USA Ser.). (ENG.). 128p. pap. 9.95 *(978-1-59880-579-6(7))* Avalon Travel Publishing.

Krentzel, Jarrett. Walking with Pacence: -A True Journey- 2007. 200p. per. 16.95 *(978-0-595-39547-7(3))* iUniverse, Inc.

Lupp, Thomas. The Tuscarora Trail: A Guide to the North Half in Maryland & Pennsylvania. Palatini, Glenn & Thorsen, John, eds. 4th ed. 2011. (Illus.). 108p. pap. 11.00 *(978-0-915746-80-4(8))* Potomac Appalachian Trail Club.

Mass, Leslie. In Beauty May She Walk: Hiking the Appalachian Trail At 60. 2009. 430p. pap. 19.95 *(978-1-889386-62-1(6))* Appalachian Trail Conservancy.

McCullough, Robert L. A Path for Kindred Spirits: The Friendship of Clarence Stein & Benton MacKaye. 2012. (ENG., Illus.). 160p. 39.95 ***(978-1-930066-93-9(7))*** Ctr. for American Places, Inc.

Miller, David. Awol on the Appalachian Trail. 2006. 256p. per. 15.95 *(978-1-59594-109-1(6)*, Wingspan Pr.) WingSpan Publishing.

Miller, David. AWOL on the Appalachian Trail. 2011. (ENG., Illus.). 352p. pap. 14.95 ***(978-0-547-74552-7(4)***, Mariner Bks.) Houghton Mifflin Harcourt Trade & Reference Pubs.

Morgan, Jeff. Lost Then Found. 2010. 148p. (ENG.). 24.99 *(978-1-4520-0981-0(3))*; pap. 14.99 *(978-1-4520-0980-3(5))* AuthorHouse.

Myers, Janet, ed. Appalachian Trail Guide to Maryland & Northern Virginia: With Side Trails. 17th ed. 2008. (Official Guides to the Appalachian Trail Ser.). (Illus.). 272p. pap. 10.00 *(978-0-915746-89-7(1))* Potomac Appalachian Trail Club.

—Appalachian Trail Guide to Maryland-Northern Virginia. 17th rev. ed. 2008. 272p. pap. 34.95 *(978-0-915746-53-8(0))* Appalachian Trail Conservancy.

O'Neal, Don & Williams, Lisa. Appalachian Trail Guide to North Carolina-Georgia. 14th ed. 2011. (Official Appalachian Trail Guides). 204p. pap. 27.95 ***(978-1-889386-76-8(6))*** Appalachian Trail Conservancy.

Otis, Stephen Michael & Roberts, Colin Daniel. A Road More or Less Traveled: Madcap Adventures along the Appalachian Trail. 2008. 400p. pap. *(978-0-615-20305-8(1))* Sunnygold Bks.

Porter, Winton. Just Passin' Thru: A Vintage Store, the Appalachian Trail, & a Cast of Unforgettable Characters. 2009. (ENG., Illus.). 272p. pap. 14.95 *(978-0-89732-849-4(3))* Menasha Ridge Pr., Inc.

Ray, Michelle. How to Hike the A. T: The Nitty-Gritty of a Long-Distance Trek. 2008. (ENG., Illus.). 272p. pap. 16.95 *(978-0-8117-3542-1(7))* Stackpole Bks.

Roberts, Colin. Road More or Less Traveled. 2009. pap. 17.95 *(978-0-692-00044-1(5))* Sunnygold Bks.

Ronan, Roy, ed. Appalachian Trail Guide to Maine. 15th ed. 2009. 172p. pap. 27.95 *(978-1-889386-66-9(9))* Appalachian Trail Conservancy.

Ross, Cindy. A Woman's Journey. 2009. Orig. Title: A Women's Journey on the Appalachian Trail. 128p. pap. 11.95 *(978-1-889386-64-5(2))* Appalachian Trail Conservancy.

Rubin, Robert Alden & Alden Rubin, Robert. On the Beaten Path: An Appalachian Pilgrimage. 2nd ed. 2009. (ENG., Illus.). 256p. pap. 16.95 *(978-1-59921-497-9(0)*, Lyons Pr.) Globe Pequot Pr., The.

Runolfson, Kevin. The Things You Find on the Appalachian Trail: A Memoir of Discovery, Endurance, & a Lazy Dog. 2010. (ENG., Illus.). 228p. pap. 30.00 *(978-0-7864-4767-1(2))* McFarland & Co., Inc. Pubs.

Sherman, Steve & Older, Julia. Appalachian Odyssey: Walking the Trail from Georgia to Maine. 2009. 268p. pap. 19.95 *(978-1-4401-1530-1(3))* iUniverse, Inc.

Smith, Debra, ed. Great Stories of Hiking the Appalachian Trail. 2010. (ENG., Illus.). 256p. pap. 19.95 *(978-0-8117-0598-1(6))* Stackpole Bks.

Spring, Sue, ed. Appalachian Trail Guide to Massachusetts-Connecticut. 12th ed. 2010. (Official Appalachian Trail Guides). 224p. pap. 27.95 *(978-1-889386-67-6(7))* Appalachian Trail Conservancy.

Taylor-Miller, Cynthia, ed. Appalachian Trail Thru-Hikers' Companion. rev. ed. 2006. (Illus.). 265p. per. 13.95 *(978-1-889386-50-8(2))* Appalachian Trail Conservancy.

Thomas, Vaugh H., ed. Appalachian Trail Guide to Southwest Virginia. 4th ed. 2007. (Official Appalachian Trail Guides). (Illus.). 232p. pap. 22.95 *(978-1-889386-52-2(9))* Appalachian Trail Conservancy.

APPALACHIANS (PEOPLE)

Alderman Sterste, LeAnna. The Old Man of the Mountain: Eldridge Mccomb. 2008. (Illus.). 53p. 12.00 *(978-0-615-23219-5(1))* Pocahontas Communications Cooperative.

Anderson, Bridget L. Migration Accomodation & Language Change: Language at the Intersection of Regional & Ethnic Identity. 2008. (ENG., Illus.). 242p. 89.00 *(978-0-230-00886-1(0))* Palgrave Macmillan.

Banker, Mark T. Appalachians All: East Tennesseans & the Elusive History of an American Region. 2011. (ENG.). pap. 25.95 *(978-1-57233-786-2(9))* Univ. of Tennessee Pr.

Biggers, Jeff. The United States of Appalachia: How Southern Mountaineers Brought Independence, Culture, & Enlightenment to America. 2007. (ENG.). 256p. per. 17.95 *(978-1-59376-151-6(1))* Counterpoint LLC.

Blackwell, Joshua Beau. Used to Be a Rough Place in Them Hills: Moonshine, the dark corner, & the new South. 2009. 180p. pap. 14.99 *(978-1-4389-3470-9(X))* AuthorHouse.

Burton, Thomas G. Beech Mountain Man: The Memoirs of Ronda Lee Hicks. 2009. (ENG., Illus.). 176p. 32.95 *(978-1-57233-665-0(X))* Univ. of Tennessee Pr.

Campbell, John C. The Southern Highlander & His Homeland. 2010. 514p. pap. 39.75 *(978-1-144-25465-8(5))* 2009. 448p. 41.99 *(978-1-117-51262-4(2))* 2009. (ENG.). 446p. pap. 35.75 *(978-1-117-51263-1(0))* BiblioBazaar.

—The Southern Highlander & His Homeland. 2010. 288p. pap. 26.75 *(978-1-153-39733-9(1))* General Bks. LLC.

—The Southern Highlander & His Homeland. 2008. 498p. 53.95 *(978-1-4365-7085-5(9))* 2007. (ENG.). 500p. per. 38.95 *(978-0-548-76274-5(0))* Kessinger Publishing, LLC.

—The Southern Highlander & His Homeland. 405p. reprint ed. lib. bdg. 98.00 *(978-0-7222-4866-9(0))* Library Reprints, Inc.

DeRosier, Linda Scott. Songs of Life & Grace: A Memoir. 2008. (ENG., Illus.). 280p. pap. 19.95 *(978-0-8131-9197-3(1))* Univ. Pr. of Kentucky.

French, Laurence Armand. An Oral History of Southern Appalachia. 2008. 212p. (C). 109.95 *(978-0-7734-5106-3(4))* Mellen, Edwin Pr., The.

Gainer, Patrick. Witches, Ghost & Signs: Folklore of the Southern Appalachians. 2nd ed. 2008. (ENG., Illus.). 220p. pap. 18.95 *(978-1-933202-20-4(3))* West Virginia Univ. Pr.

Garduño, Meg. Immaculate Immigrant: The Virgin of Guadalupe in Los Angeles: Reflections & Meditations. 2010. 136p. pap. 28.72 *(978-1-4269-1660-1(4))* Trafford Publishing.

Goodrich, Frances Louisa. Mountain Homespun. 2010. (ENG.). 208p. pap. 24.95 *(978-1-57233-718-3(4))* Univ. of Tennessee Pr.

Griliches, Diane Asseo. An Appalachian Farmer's Story: Portrait of an Extraordinary Common Man. 2007. (Illus.). 144p. 40.00 *(978-0-88146-062-9(1))* Mercer Univ. Pr.

Hesperides. Biographical Memoirs - National Academy of Science. 2007. 292p. per. *(978-1-4067-5508-4(7)*, Hesperides Pr.) Read Bks.

Kendrick, Betty Owsley. Appalachian Memories. 2007. 20.00 *(978-1-60416-025-3(X))*; per. 13.00 *(978-1-60416-024-6(1))* Reformation Pubs. (Williams Printing Co.).

Kiffmeyer, Thomas. Reformers to Radicals: The Appalachian Volunteers & the War on Poverty. 2008. (ENG., Illus.). 320p. 40.00 *(978-0-8131-2509-1(X))* Univ. Pr. of Kentucky.

Lyon, Marguerite. And Green Grass Grows All Around. 2011. 306p. 48.95 ***(978-1-258-06733-5(1))*** Literary Licensing, LLC.

Miller, Zell. Purt Nigh Gone: The Old Mountain Ways. 2009. pap. *(978-0-9796462-3-2(5))* Stroud & Hall Publishing.

Powell, Katrina M. The Anguish of Displacement: The Politics of Literacy in the Letters of Mountain Families in Shenandoah National Park. 2007. (ENG., Illus.). 224p. (gr. 17). 35.00 *(978-0-8139-2628-5(9))* Univ. Pr. of Virginia.

Robbins, Edward E. & Robbins, Flora J. Moonshiner Goes West. 2011. *(978-1-58982-806-3(2)*, Millennial Mind Publishing) American Bk. Publishing Group.

Salsi, Lynn. Voices from the North Carolina Mountains: Appalachian Oral Histories. 2007. pap. 19.99 *(978-1-59629-230-7(X))* History Pr., The.

Samuel Kinkade Cowan. Sergeant York & His People. 2007. (ENG.). 120p. per. 18.99 *(978-1-4346-3944-8(4))*; 128p. per. 19.99 *(978-1-4346-3945-5(2))* BiblioBazaar.

Sandow, Robert M. Deserter Country: Civil War Opposition in the Pennsylvania Appalachians. (North's Civil War Ser.). (ENG., Illus.). 288p. 2011. pap. 25.00 ***(978-0-8232-3052-5(X))*** 3rd ed. 2009. 60.00 *(978-0-8232-3051-8(1))* Fordham Univ. Pr.

Scott, Rebecca R. Removing Mountains: Extracting Nature & Identity in the Appalachian Coalfields. 2010. (Quadrant Book Ser.). (ENG., Illus.). 296p. 75.00 *(978-0-8166-6599-0(0))*; pap. 25.00 *(978-0-8166-6600-3(8))* Univ. of Minnesota Pr.

Sentz, Brandi & Glass, Kelli. How to Eat Fried Chicken, & Be Thin Too. 2009. 108p. pap. 11.95 *(978-1-60860-089-2(0)*, Strategic Bk. Publishing) AEG Literary Publishing Services, Inc.

Sheppard, Muriel E. Cabins in the Laurel. 313p. reprint ed. lib. bdg. 98.00 *(978-0-7222-0511-2(2))* Library Reprints, Inc.

Stackhouses of Appalachia: Even to Our Own Times. 2006. (Illus.). 421p. pap. 29.95 net. *(978-0-9789548-1-9(5))* Grateful Steps.

Thomas, Jean. Big Sandy. 2007. 324p. per. *(978-1-4067-5500-8(1))* Read Bks.

—Blue Ridge Country. 2007. 348p. per. *(978-1-4067-5537-4(0))* Read Bks.

Wallin, Phyllis D. Phillips. Appalachian Woman/Child. 2007. 123p. 14.99 *(978-1-59879-081-8(1))* Lifevest Publishing, Inc.

Whitaker, Fess. History of Corporal Fess Whitaker. 2009. 158p. 36.95 *(978-1-104-79351-7(2))*; pap. 21.95 *(978-1-104-76653-5(1))* Kessinger Publishing, LLC.

Wilson, Samuel Tyndale. The Southern Mountaineers. 202p. reprint ed. lib. bdg. 98.00 *(978-0-7222-4860-7(1))* Library Reprints, Inc.

APPALOOSA HORSE

Dudley, Cheryl. The Legendary Appaloosa: A Tribute in Words & Photos. 2007. (ENG., Illus.). 208p. 29.95 *(978-1-59921-048-3(7)*, Lyons Pr.) Globe Pequot Pr., The.

Sands, Kim & Woolion, Stephanie. Appaloosa Horse. 2009. (Allen Guides to Horse & Pony Breeds Ser.). (ENG., Illus.). 24p. pap. 13.95 *(978-0-85131-889-9(4))* Trafalgar Square Bks.

APPARATUS, CHEMICAL

see Chemical Apparatus

APPARATUS, ELECTRICAL

see Electric Apparatus and Appliances

APPARATUS, MEDICAL

see Medical Instruments and Apparatus

APPARATUS, ORTHOPEDIC

see Orthopedic Apparatus

APPARATUS, PHYSIOLOGICAL

see Physiological Apparatus

APPARATUS, SCIENTIFIC

see Scientific Apparatus and Instruments

APPARATUS, SURGICAL

see Surgical Instruments and Apparatus

APPAREL

see Clothing and Dress

APPAREL, VINTAGE

see Vintage Clothing

APPARITIONS

see also Ghosts; Hallucinations and Illusions; Mary, Blessed Virgin, Saint—Apparitions and Miracles; Poltergeists

Belanger, Jeff. Our Haunted Lives: True Life Ghost Encounters. 2006. (ENG., Illus.). 1p. per. 14.99 *(978-1-56414-856-8(4)*, New Page Bks.) Career Pr., Inc.

Bromley, Carole. The Living Spirit: One Woman's Battle Amongst Ghosts, Spirits & the Living. 2009. 240p. pap. 14.49 *(978-1-4490-0847-5(X))* AuthorHouse.

Calmet, Augustin. The Phantom World. 2009. 212p. pap. *(978-0-217-94480-9(9))*; 234p. pap. *(978-0-217-39579-3(1))*; 214p. pap. *(978-0-217-94475-5(2))* Books LLC.

De Aragon, Ray John. Enchanted Legends & Lore of New Mexico: Witches, Ghosts & Spirits. 2012. 112p. pap. 16.99 ***(978-1-60949-572-5(1))*** History Pr., The.

Defoe, Daniel & Kincade, Kt. An Essay on the History & Reality of Apparitions. 2006. (Illus.). i, 463p. (C). *(978-0-404-64856-5(8))* AMS Pr., Inc.

Hibbert, Samuel. Sketches of the Philosophy of Apparitions: Or, an Attempt to Trace Such Illusions to Their Physical Causes. 2010. 500p. pap. 38.75 *(978-1-142-46343-4(5))* BiblioBazaar.

—Sketches of the Philosophy of Apparitions: Or, an Attempt to Trace Such Illusions to their Physical Causes. 2011. (Cambridge Library Collection - Magic & the Supernatural Ser.). (Illus.). 502p. pap. 35.99 *(978-1-108-02772-4(5))* Cambridge Univ. Pr.

Jenkins, Arlene. Oregon Hauntings & Encounters. 2007. 175p. pap. 15.95 *(978-0-9718781-2-9(9))* Jenkins, Arlene.

Lewis, Isabella. Terrific Tales. 2006. 108p. 39.95 *(978-0-9777841-5-8(0))* Valancourt Bks.

Mayo, Herbert. Popular Superstitions, & the Truth Contained Therein, with an Account of Mesmerism by Herbert Mayo from the 3d London Edition. 2006. 264p. per. 23.99 *(978-1-4255-2325-1(0))* MPublishing.

Notzing, Baron Von Schrenck. Phenomena of Materialisation. 2008. pap. *(978-1-84830-055-2(7)*, Wildhem Pr.) Echo Library.

Offut, Jason. Paranormal Missouri: Show Me Your Monsters. 2010. (Illus.). 160p. pap. 14.99 *(978-0-7643-3577-8(4))* Schiffer Publishing, Ltd.

Okonowicz, Ed, photos by. Annapolis Ghosts: History, Mystery, Legends & Lore. 2007. (Illus.). 120p. pap. *(978-1-890690-19-9(8))* Myst & Lace Pubs., Inc.

Owen, Robert Dale. The Debatable Land between this World & the Next: With Illustrative Narrations. 2011. (Cambridge Library Collection - Spiritualism & Esoteric Knowlege Ser.). (ENG., Illus.). 466p. pap. 34.99 *(978-1-108-07311-0(5))* Cambridge Univ. Pr.

—The Debatable Land Between This World & the Next, with Illustrative Narrations; by Robert Dale Owen. 2006. 560p. per. 32.99 *(978-1-4255-6153-6(5))* MPublishing.

—Footfalls on the Boundary of Another World. 2011. (Cambridge Library Collection - Spiritualism & Esoteric Knowlege Ser.). (ENG.). 422p. pap. 31.99 *(978-1-108-02742-7(3))* Cambridge Univ. Pr.

Podmore, Frank. Apparitions & Thought-Transference: An Examination of the Evidence for Telepathy. 2011. (Cambridge Library Collection - Spiritualism & Esoteric Knowlege Ser.). (ENG., Illus.). 422p. pap. 31.99 *(978-1-108-02805-9(5))* Cambridge Univ. Pr.

Pye, Michael & Dalley, Kirsten, eds. Exposed, Uncovered & Declassified: Ghosts, Spirits, & Hauntings: Am I Being Haunted? 2011. (Exposed, Uncovered, & Declassified Ser.). (ENG.). 1p. mass mkt. 15.99 *(978-1-60163-174-9(X)*, New Page Bks.) Career Pr., Inc.

Reed, William. The Phantom of the Poles. 2008. (ENG.). 142p. pap. 20.75 *(978-1-4375-3273-9(X))*; 164p. pap. 21.75 *(978-1-4375-3274-6(8))* BiblioBazaar.

—The Phantom of the Poles. 2009. 94p. pap. 14.14 *(978-1-4589-3325-6(3))* General Bks. LLC.

—The Phantom of the Poles. 2008. 284p. 43.95 *(978-1-4372-3150-2(0))*; pap. 28.95 *(978-1-4371-0306-9(5))* Kessinger Publishing, LLC.

Righi, Brian. Ghosts, Apparitions & Poltergeists: An Exploration of the Supernatural Through History. 2008. (ENG., Illus.). 240p. pap. 15.95 *(978-0-7387-1363-2(5))* Llewellyn Pubns.

Waters, Colin. The Pregnant Ghost & Other Sexual Hauntings. 2010. (ENG., Illus.). 176p. pap. 12.95 *(978-0-7090-8990-2(2))* Hale, Robert Ltd. GBR. Dist: Independent Pubs. Group.

Webb, Stuart. Ghosts. 2012. (Paranormal Files Ser.). (ENG., Illus.). 80p. (YA). (gr. 7-12). lib. bdg. 33.25 ***(978-1-4488-7175-9(1))*** Rosen Publishing Group, Inc., The.

APPEAL

see Appellate Procedure

APPEALS, ADMINISTRATIVE

see Administrative Remedies

APPEL, KAREL, 1921-2006

Jager, Hans den Hartog & Kuspit, Donald. Karel Appel & Van Gogh, 1 vol. 2011. (ENG.). 96p. 34.50 ***(978-90-5594-791-1(1))*** Exhibitions International BEL. Dist: Innovative Logistics.

Lyotard, Jean-Francois. Karel Appel, A Gesture of Colour / Karel Appel, un geste de Couleur. 2009. (Jean-François Lyotard: Writings on Contemporary Art & Artists Ser.). (ENG & FRE., Illus.). 49.50 *(978-90-5867-756-3(7))* Leuven Univ. Pr. BEL. Dist: Cornell Univ. Pr.

APPELLATE COURTS

see also Appellate Procedure

Abramson, Bruce D. The Secret Circuit: The Little-Known Court Where the Rules of the Information Age Unfold. 2007. (ENG.). 416p. 100.00 *(978-0-7425-5280-7(2))*; per. 37.95 *(978-0-7425-5281-4(0))* Rowman & Littlefield Publishers, Inc.

Blake, Charles, et al. The Court of Appeal. 2007. 196p. 66.00 *(978-1-84113-387-4(6))* Hart Publishing Ltd. GBR. Dist: International Specialized Bk. Services.

Cross, Frank. Decision Making in the U. S. Courts of Appeals. 2007. (ENG.). 264p. 60.00 *(978-0-8047-5366-1(0))*; (Illus.). per. 23.95 *(978-0-8047-5713-3(5))* Stanford Univ. Pr.

Edwards, Harry T. & Elliott, Linda A. Federal Standards of Review: Review of District Court Decisions & Agency Actions. 2007. xix, 237p. pap. *(978-0-314-18809-0(6))* West.

Executive Office for Immigration Review: Hearing Before the Subcommittee on Immigration, Citizenship, Refugees, Border Security, & International Law of the Committee on the Judiciary, House of Representatives, One Hundred Eleventh Congress, Second Session, June 17, 2010. 2010. iii, 91p. *(978-0-16-086960-0(9)*, 552-070-41826-1) United States Government Printing Office.

Flanders, Steven. The Federal Circuit: A Judicial Innovation: Establishing a U.S. Court of Appeals. 2010. (Illus.). xvi, 289p. pap. ***(978-0-9747286-6-7(7))*** Twelve Tables Pr.

Friedenthal, Jack H. 2007 Civil Procedure Supplement. 2007. (Illus.). vii, 699p. pap. *(978-0-314-17984-5(4))* West Publishing Co., College & Schl. Div.

Gonzalez, Yamilet, ed. Reglamento de la Rama Judicial. 2007. pap. *(978-1-59608-362-2(X))* Biblio Services, Inc.

Hettinger, Virginia A., et al. Judging on a Collegial Court: Influences on Federal Appellate Decision Making. 2007. (Constitutionalism & Democracy Ser.). (ENG., Illus.). 168p. (gr. 17). per. 18.50 *(978-0-8139-2697-1(1))* Univ. Pr. of Virginia.

Hume, Robert. How Courts Impact Federal Administrative Behavior. 2009. (Routledge Studies in North American Politics Ser.). (ENG., Illus.). 174p. 125.00 *(978-0-415-99927-4(8))* Routledge.

Hume, Robert J. How Courts Impact Federal Administrative Behavior. 2012. (ENG., Illus.). 164p. pap. 39.95 ***(978-0-415-80741-8(7))*** Routledge.

KöCkritz, Moritz Von. Die Deutschen OberlandesgerichtspräSidenten Im Nationalsozialismus (1933-1945) 2011. (Rechtshistorische Reihe Ser.). (GER., Illus.). 580p. 137.95 ***(978-3-631-61791-5(7))*** Lang, Peter GmbH, Europaischer Verlag der Wissenschaften DEU. Dist: Lang, Peter.

Morris, Jeffrey Brandon. Establishing Justice in Middle America: A History of the United States Court of Appeals for the Eighth Circuit. 2007. (Illus.). 456p. 39.95 *(978-0-8166-4816-0(6))* Univ. of Minnesota Pr.

O'Connor, Kathleen M., et al. Florida's Third District Court of Appeal: Balancing Justice: 50 Years, 1957-2007. 2007. (Illus.). vii, 183p. *(978-0-9741589-7-6(6))* Centennial Pr.

Ogden, Ralph. Colorado Appellate Advocacy Deskbook. 2006. *(978-1-932779-35-6(3))* Bradford Publishing Co.

Responding to the Growing Need for Federal Judgeships: The Federal Judgeship ACT of 2008: Hearing Before the Committee on the Judiciary, United States Senate, One Hundred Tenth Congress, Second Session, June 17, 2008. 2008. (Illus.). iii, 157p. *(978-0-16-081502-7(9)*, 552-070-37861-8) United States Government Printing Office.

Responding to the Growing Need for Federal Judgeships: The Federal Judgeships ACT of 2009: Hearing Before the Subcommittee on Administrative Oversight & the Courts of the Committee on the Judiciary, United States Senate, One Hundred Eleventh Congress, First Session, September 30, 2009. 2010. (Illus.). iii, 203p. ***(978-0-16-086394-3(5)***, 552-070-41473-8) United States Government Printing Office.

Taylor, Matthew M. Judging Policy: Courts & Policy Reform in Democratic Brazil. 2008. (ENG., Illus.). 248p. 55.00 *(978-0-8047-5811-6(5))* Stanford Univ. Pr.

United States, Congress Senate Committee on Veterans' Affairs Staff, contrib. by. Battling the Backlog Part II: Challenges Facing the U.S. Court of Appeals for Veterans Claims: Hearing Before the Committee on Veterans' Affairs, United States Senate, One Hundred Ninth Congress, Second Session, July 13, 2006. 2007. (Illus.). iii, 94p. *(978-0-16-078017-2(9)*, 552-070-35438-7) United States Government Printing Office.

USGPO Staff. Cases Decided in United States Court of Appeals for the Federal Circuit, 3 vols. Date not set. reprint ed. spiral bd. 525.00 *(978-1-57588-481-3(X)*, 201760) Hein, William S. & Co., Inc.

APPELLATE PROCEDURE

see also Administrative Remedies; Appellate Courts; Briefs; Civil Procedure; Pleading; Tax Protests and Appeals; Trial Practice

Arthur, Stephen E. The Attorney's Guide to the Seventh Circuit Court of Appeals. 4th ed. 2009. *(978-1-57862-256-6(5))* State Bar of Wisconsin.

Chinnici, Daniela. Giudizio Penale Di Seconda Istanza e Giusto Processo. 2nd ed. 2009. (ITA.). viii, 303p. *(978-88-348-9854-3(0))* Giappichelli.

Dikarev, I. S. Predvaritelnoe Proizvodstvo V Sude Nadzornoi Instantsii. 2010. (RUS.). 173p. *(978-5-93295-719-6(0))* Juritinform, Izdatel'stvo.

Edler, Franziska. Die Aufhebung von Schiedssprüchen und der Erlass einstweiliger Maßnahmen in Deutschland und Schweden: Ein Rechtsvergleich vor dem Hintergrund der Investitionsschiedsgerichtsbarkeit. 2008. (Studien zum Europäischen und Internationalen Wirtschaftsrecht. Studies in European & International Economic Law Ser.). (GRE.). 338p. pap. 81.95 *(978-3-631-58322-7(2))* Lang, Peter GmbH, Europaischer Verlag der Wissenschaften DEU. Dist: Lang, Peter.

Fezer, Gerhard, et al. Festschrift für Gerhard Fezer zum 70. Geburtstag am 29. Oktober 2008. 2008. (GER., Illus.). XIV, 616p. 245.00 *(978-3-89949-439-6(3))* De Gruyter, Walter Inc.

Greene, Richard, ed. 2008 Kansas Annual Survey, Vol. 19. annuals 2008. (ENG.). ring bd. 80.00 *(978-1-890452-20-9(3))* Kansas Bar Assn.

Haley, Rick. How to Process a Legal Appeal Successfully. 2009. 156p. 29.99 *(978-1-4415-3922-9(0))*; pap. 19.99 *(978-1-4415-3921-2(2))* Xlibris Corp.

Heffernan, Michael S. Appellate Practice & Procedure in Wisconsin. 4th ed. 2006. *(978-1-57862-179-8(8))* State Bar of Wisconsin.

Ingenix, Inc. Staff. Appeals Made Easy 2001. spiral bd. 99.95 *(978-1-56337-384-8(X))* OptumInsight, Inc.

Jacobson, M. H. Sam. Appellate Advocacy: Persuasive Writing & Oral Argument, 1. 2007. (Illus.). 181p. *(978-0-9772740-3-1(9))* Lex Judicata.

Kemp, G., et al. Criminal Procedure Casebook: Strafprosesreg Vonnisbundel. 2010. 368p. pap. 50.00 *(978-0-7021-8226-6(5))* Gaunt, Inc.

Legal Intelligence Staff, ed. Commonwealth of Pennsylvania Court Rules: 2010 Edition. 2011. (ENG., Illus.). 1315p. pap. 83.00 *(978-1-57786-301-4(1))* Incisive Media.

Legal Intelligencer Staff. Commonwealth of Pennsylvania Court Rules: 2011 Edition. 2010. (ENG.). 1014p. pap. 79.00 *(978-1-57786-303-8(8))* Incisive Media.

Liberti, Lahra, et al, eds. Investment Treaty Law: Current Issues Volume II: Nationality & Investment Treaty Claims & Fair & Equitable Treatment in Investment Treaty Law. 2007. 279p. pap. 120.00 *(978-1-905221-08-0(8))* British Institute of International & Comparative Law GBR. Dist: International Specialized Bk. Services.

Prikhodko, I. A., et al. Kommentarii K Postanovleniiu Plenuma Vysshego Arbitrazhnogo Suda Rossiiskoi Federatsii Ot 12 Marta 2007 G. No. 17 "O Primenenii Arbitrazhnogo Protsessualnogo Kodeksa Rossiiskoi Federatsii Pri Peresmotre Vstupivshikh V Zakonnuiu Silu Sudebnykh Aktov Po Vnov Otkryvshimsia Obstoiatelstvam" 2010. (RUS.). 730p. *(978-5-7133-1386-2(9))* Mezdunarodnye Otnosheniya.

Ross, Alison. The Agamben Effect. 2008. (ENG., Illus.). 220p. per. 14.00 *(978-0-8223-6684-3(3))* Duke Univ. Pr.

Sarstedt, Werner. Die Revision in Strafsachen. 7th ed. 2010. (De Gruyter Handbuch Ser.). (GER.). XLIX, 612p. 140.00 *(978-3-89949-021-3(5))* De Gruyter, Walter Inc.

Zhen, Zhen. Min Shi Xing Zheng Jian Cha You Xiu Kang Su an Li Xuan Bian. 2009. (CHI.). *(978-7-5036-9662-6(1))* Law Publishing Hse., The.

APPELLATE PROCEDURE—GREAT BRITAIN

Burton, Michael, ed. Civil Appeals. 2nd rev. ed. 2011. 600p. *(978-1-85811-379-1(2))* EMIS Professional Publishing.

—Civil Appeals: Company & Commercial Cases. 2nd rev. ed. 2011. (Civil Appeals Ser.). 350p. pap. *(978-1-85811-381-4(4))* EMIS Professional Publishing.

—Civil Appeals: Family & Social Welfare. 2nd rev. ed. 2011. (Civil Appeals Ser.). 350p. pap. *(978-1-85811-383-8(0))* EMIS Professional Publishing.

—Civil Appeals: Property Cases. 2nd rev. ed. 2011. (Civil Appeals Ser.). 350p. pap. *(978-1-85811-380-7(6))* EMIS Professional Publishing.

—Employment. 2nd rev. ed. 2011. (Civil Appeals Ser.). 350p. pap. *(978-1-85811-382-1(2))* EMIS Professional Publishing.

Taylor, Paul, ed. Taylor on Criminal Appeals. 2nd ed. 2012. (ENG.). 832p. 290.00 ***(978-0-19-957625-8(4))*** Oxford Univ. Pr., Inc.

APPELLATE PROCEDURE—SOVIET UNION

Alekseevskaia, E. I. Otsenka Zakonnosti Sudebnykh Reshenii: Nauchno-Prakticheskoe Posobie. 2010. (RUS.). 207p. *(978-5-7205-1053-4(2))* Juridiceskij Dom Justicinform.

APPELLATE PROCEDURE—UNITED STATES

American Bar Association Staff. The 2011 Federal Rules Book. 2012. (ENG.). 272p. pap. 49.95 ***(978-1-61632-848-1(7))*** American Bar Assn.

Axelrad, David M. Appellate Practice in State & Federal Courts. 2011. ***(978-1-58852-174-3(5)***, Law Journal Pr.) Incisive Media.

Beazley. A Practical Guide to Appellate Advocacy. 3rd ed. 2010. pap. 77.00 *(978-0-7355-8510-2(5))* Wolters Kluwer Law & Business.

Beazley, Mary Beth. A Practical Guide to Appellate Advocacy. 3rd ed. 2010. (Illus.). xxvii, 404p. *(978-0-7355-8511-9(3))* Kluwer Law International.

Bonneau, Charles M. & Ruddy, Sara H. Appeals & Writs in Criminal Cases. 3rd ed. 2007. (Illus.). *(978-0-7626-1199-7(5))* Continuing Education of the Bar-California.

Childress, Steven Alan & Davis, Martha S. Federal Standards of Review, 3 vols. 4th ed. 2010. *(978-1-4224-7900-1(5))* LexisNexis Matthew Bender.

Clary, Bradley G., et al. Advocacy on Appeal. 3rd ed. 2008. xiv, 254p. *(978-0-314-18407-8(4))* West Publishing Co., College & Schl. Div.

Clermont, Kevin M. Federal Rules of Civil Procedure & Selected Other Procedural Provisions 2010. 2010th rev. ed. 2010. 904p. 44.00 *(978-1-59941-843-8(6)*, Foundation Pr.) West.

—Federal Rules of Civil Procedure & Selected Other Procedural Provisions 2011. 2011. (Academic Statutes Ser.). 928p. 44.00 *(978-1-59941-953-4(X)*, Foundation Pr.) West.

Continuing Education of the Bar. Appeals & Writs in Criminal Cases: April 2008 Update, 2 vols. 3rd ed. 2008. 700p. ring bd. 109.00 *(978-0-7626-1371-7(6))* Continuing Education of the Bar-California.

Coyne, Randall & Entzeroth, Lyn. Capital Punishment & the Judicial Process, Third Edition, 2007 Supplement. 2007. 142p. per. 15.00 *(978-1-59460-327-3(8))* Carolina Academic Pr.

Cram101 Textbook Reviews. Outlines & Highlights for Criminal Procedure: From First Contact to Appeal by John L. Worrall, ISBN. 2011. 142p. pap. 28.95 ***(978-1-61490-342-0(5))*** Cram101 Inc.

Curry, Alan & McConnell, Gail Kikawa, eds. State's Appellate Manual 2007-2009. 2007. 364p. ring bd. 200.00 *(978-0-9796993-9-9(8))* Texas District & County Attorneys Assn.

Dorsaneo, William V. Texas Civil Procedure: Trial & Appellate Practice. 2010. *(978-1-4224-7769-4(X))* 2009. *(978-1-4224-7364-1(3))* 2008. *(978-1-4224-2553-4(3))* LexisNexis Matthew Bender.

Edwards, Harry T. & Elliott, Linda A. Federal Standards of Review: Review of District Court Decisions & Agency Actions. 2007. xix, 237p. pap. *(978-0-314-18809-0(6))* West.

Fontham, Michael R., et al. Persuasive Written & Oral Advocacy in Trial & Appellate Courts. 2nd ed. 2007. xxvii, 460p. *(978-0-7355-6394-0(2))* Lippincott Williams & Wilkins.

—Persuasive Written & Oral Advocacy in Trial & Appellate Courts. 2nd ed. 2007. xxvii, 460p. pap. 75.00 *(978-0-7355-6230-1(X)*, Aspen Pubs.) Wolters Kluwer Law & Business.

Frederick, David C. The Art of Oral Advocacy, 2d. 2nd rev. ed. 2010. (American Casebook Ser.). 340p. 62.00 *(978-0-314-19501-2(7),* West Legalworks) West.

—Supreme Court & Appellate Advocacy: Mastering Oral Argument. 2nd ed. 2010. xxiii, 435p. *(978-0-314-19441-1(X))* West Publishing Co., College & Schl. Div.

Gressman, Eugene. Supreme Court Practice: For Practice in the Supreme Court of the United States. 9th ed. 2007. (Illus.). *(978-1-57018-554-0(9))* Bureau of National Affairs, Inc., (BNA), The.

Heaven, Lewis, Jr. & Andersen, Mark. Kansas Real Estate Practice & Procedure. Heaven, Lewis, Jr. & Andersen, Mark, eds. 5th ed. 2009. ring bd. 200.00 *(978-1-890452-10-0(6))* Kansas Bar Assn.

Heffernan, Michael S. Appellate Practice & Procedure in Wisconsin. 5th ed. 2011. *(978-1-57862-297-9(2))* State Bar of Wisconsin.

House (U S) Committee on the Judiciary, compiled by. Federal Rules of Appellate Procedure, with Forms, December 31 2006. 2007. (ENG.). 52p. pap. 5.50 *(978-0-16-077832-2(8),* Committee on the Judiciary) United States Government Printing Office.

House (U.S.), Committee on the Judiciary, compiled by. Federal Rules of Appellate Procedure, with Forms, December 1 2009. 2010. (ENG.). 66p. pap. 8.00 *(978-0-16-084819-3(9),* Committee on the Judiciary) United States Government Printing Office.

House (U.S.), Committee on the Judiciary Staff, compiled by. Federal Rules of Appellate Procedure, with Forms, December 1 2010. 2011. (ENG.). 66p. pap. 8.00 ***(978-0-16-088519-8(1),*** Committee on the Judiciary) United States Government Printing Office.

Ides. Civil Procedure: Rules Statutes & Cases 2010. 2010. pap. 38.50 *(978-0-7355-9058-8(3),* Aspen Pubs.) Wolters Kluwer Law & Business.

Impact of Federal Habeas Corpus Limitations on Death Penalty Appeals: Hearing Before the Subcommittee on the Constitution, Civil Rights, & Civil Liberties of the Committee on the Judiciary, House of Representatives, One Hundred Eleventh Congress, First Session, December 8, 2009. 2010. iv, 69p. *(978-0-16-085512-2(8),* 552-070-40775-8) United States Government Printing Office.

Lacovara, Philip Allen & Barz, James E. Federal Appellate Practice. 2008. (Illus.). xlii, 955p. *(978-1-57018-669-1(3))* Bureau of National Affairs, Inc., (BNA), The.

Lemon, Joseph L. Run Away & Join the Circuits: Federal Appellate Court Law Clerk's Survival Guide. 2007. *(978-1-59031-888-1(9))* American Bar Assn.

Lofaso, Anne Marie. The Practitioner's Guide to Appellate Advocacy. 2011. (ENG.). 512p. pap. 89.95 *(978-1-60442-914-5(3))* American Bar Assn.

Looper, Donna C. & Kuney, George W. Mastering Appellate Advocacy & Process. 2011. 376p. pap. 32.00 *(978-1-59460-801-8(6))* Carolina Academic Pr.

Rabiej, John K. Proposed Amendments to Federal Rules. 2010. (Illus.). v, 233p. pap. ***(978-1-4224-8253-7(7))*** LexisNexis Matthew Bender.

Reducing the Growing Backlog of Contested Mine Safety Cases: Hearing Before the Committee on Education & Labor, U.S. House of Representatives, One Hundred Eleventh Congress, Second Session, Hearing Held in Washington, DC, February 23, 2010. 2010. (Illus.). iii, 114p. *(978-0-16-086648-7(0),* 552-070-41626-9) United States Government Printing Office.

Removal Clarification ACT of 2010: Hearing Before the Subcommittee on Courts & Competition Policy of the Committee on the Judiciary, House of Representatives, One Hundred Eleventh Congress, Second Session, on H.R. 5281, May 25, 2010. 2010. iii, 85p. ***(978-0-16-087173-3(5),*** 552-070-42015-1) United States Government Printing Office.

Shotsberger, Amanda, ed. 2009 Pennsylvania State Court Rules. 2008. (Court Rules Book Ser.). (ENG., Illus.). 1014p. pap. 77.80 *(978-1-57786-300-7(3))* Incisive Media.

Strazzella, James A. Criminal Appellate Procedure, Cases & Materials. 2011. 400p. pap. 135.00 ***(978-0-314-26757-3(3))*** West Publishing Co., College & Schl. Div.

Texas Trial & Appellate Procedure. 2007. (C). *(978-1-934563-01-4(3))* Flood Publishing.

West. Federal Criminal Code & Rules 2009. 2009th rev. ed. 2009. 1964p. pap. 89.00 *(978-0-314-99092-1(5),* West Legalworks) West.

Williams, Pamela Newell. North Carolina Appellate Law: A Guide to the North Carolina Appellate Rules. 2009. (ENG.). 184p. pap. 22.95 *(978-1-4401-4490-5(7))* iUniverse, Inc.

Wisotsky, Steven. Professional Judgment on Appeal: Bringing & Opposing Appeals. 2nd ed. 2009. 436p. 75.00 *(978-1-59460-651-9(X))* Carolina Academic Pr.

Worrall, John L. Criminal Procedure: A Brief Introduction. 2012. (Justice Ser.). (ENG.). 304p. (C). pap. 91.33 ***(978-0-13-281781-3(0),*** Prentice Hall) Prentice Hall PTR.

Worrall, John L. Criminal Procedure: From First Contact to Appeal. 3rd ed. 2009. (ENG.). 528p. (C). 130.40 *(978-0-13-504319-6(0))* Allyn & Bacon, Inc.

—Criminal Procedure: From First Contact to Appeal. 4th rev. ed. 2011. (ENG., Illus.). 552p. (C). 145.60 ***(978-0-13-270586-8(9),*** Prentice Hall) Prentice Hall PTR.

APPENDICITIS

Augustin, Goran & Majerovic, Mate. Acute Appendicitis in Pregnancy. 2011. (Pregnancy & Infants: Medical, Psychological & Social Issues Ser.). (Illus.). 44p. pap. 43.00 *(978-1-61122-581-5(7))* Nova Science Pubs., Inc.

Keyzer, Caroline & Gevenois, Pierre, eds. Imaging of Acute Appendicitis in Adults & Children. 2011. (Medical Radiology / Diagnostic Imaging Ser.). (ENG., Illus.). ix, 256p. 239.00 *(978-3-642-17871-9(5),* 3642178715) Springer.

Kraehenbuehl, L., et al, eds. Acute Appendicitis: Standard Treatment or Laparoscopic Surgery? International Meeting, Bern, May 1997. (Progress in Surgery Ser.: Vol. 25, 1998). (Illus.). *(978-3-8055-6641-4(7))* Karger, S. AG.

Ryan, William L. Appendicitis: Symptoms, Diagnosis, & Treatments. 2011. (Digestive Diseases - Research & Clinical Developments Ser.). 89.00 *(978-1-61761-737-9(7))* Nova Science Pubs., Inc.

(SIS), Surgical Infection Society. Appendicitis FLASHcard 2011. 2011. 2p. 6.95 ***(978-0-9846290-6-0(8))*** International Guidelines Ctr., Inc.

Tilden, Dr John H. & Tilden, John H. Appendicitis: The Etiology, Hygienic & Dietetic Treatment. 2010. 184p. 37.95 *(978-1-161-35433-1(6))* Kessinger Publishing, LLC.

APPENDIX (ANATOMY)

Keyzer, Caroline & Gevenois, Pierre, eds. Imaging of Acute Appendicitis in Adults & Children. 2011. (Medical Radiology / Diagnostic Imaging Ser.). (ENG., Illus.). ix, 256p. 239.00 *(978-3-642-17871-9(5),* 3642178715) Springer.

Panarelli, Nicole C. & Yantiss, Rhonda K. Frozen Section Library: Appendix, Colon, & Anus: Appendix, Colon, & Anus. 2010. (Frozen Section Library). (Illus.). ix, 136p. pap. 89.95 *(978-1-4419-6583-7(1,* 1441965831) Springer.

APPERCEPTION

see also Attention; Comprehension; Consciousness; Knowledge, Theory Of; Number Concept; Perception

Giovanelli, Marco. Reality & Negation - Kant's Principle of Anticipation of Perception: An Investigation of its Impact on the Post-Kantian Debate. 2010. (Studies in German Idealism Ser.). x, 230p. 139.00 *(978-94-007-0064-2(4),* 9400700644) Springer.

Lange, Karl. Apperception: A Monograph on Psychology & Pedagogy. 2009. 294p. 30.99 *(978-1-110-16231-4(6));* 294p. pap. 27.75 *(978-1-110-16229-1(4));* 292p. 24.99 *(978-1-103-38225-5(X));* 292p. pap. 18.99 *(978-1-103-38224-8(1))* BiblioBazaar.

Winthrop, Simon. How to Be a Mentalist: Master the Secrets Behind the Hit TV Show. 2011. (ENG.). 256p. (gr. 12). 15.00 *(978-0-425-23651-2(X),* Berkley Trade) Penguin Group (USA) Inc.

APPETENCY

see Desire

APPETITE

see also Diet; Hunger

Cooper, Steven J. & Kirkham, Tim, eds. Appetite & Body Weight: Integrative Systems & the Development of Anti-Obesity Drugs. 2006. (ENG., Illus.). 384p. 131.00 *(978-0-12-370633-1(5),* Academic Pr.) Elsevier Science & Technology Bks.

Ellsworth, Shane J. & Schuster, Reece C. Appetite & Nutritional Assessment. 2009. (Series: Nutrition & Diet Research Progress Ser.). 129.00 *(978-1-60741-085-0(0))* Nova Science Pubs., Inc.

Harris, Ruth B. S. & Mattes, Richard D., eds. Appetite & Food Intake: Behavioral & Physiological Considerations. 2008. (ENG., Illus.). 376p. 139.95 *(978-1-4200-4783-7(3),* CRC Press) Taylor & Francis Group GBR. Dist: Taylor & Francis Group.

Kanzler, Isabella. The Role of PYY in Regulating Appetite: PYY 1-36 versus PYY 3-36. 2008. 80p. pap. *(978-3-639-10779-1(9))* VDM Verlag Dr. Mueller e.K.

Katherine, Anne. Lick It! Fix Her Appetite Switch. 2009. 180p. pap. 14.95 *(978-1-59858-713-5(7))* Dog Ear Publishing, LLC.

Knapp, Caroline. Appetites. rev. ed. 2011. (ENG.). 224p. pap. 14.95 ***(978-1-58243-808-5(0),*** Counterpoint) Counterpoint LLC.

Langhans, W. & Geary, N., eds. Frontiers in Eating & Weight Regulation. 2009. (Forum of Nutrition Ser.). (Illus.). 208p. *(978-3-8055-9300-7(7))* Karger, S. AG.

Mitchell, Steven R. Appetite: Regulation, Role in Disease & Control. 2011. (Nutrition & Diet Research Progress Ser.). (Illus.). 285p. 129.00 *(978-1-61209-842-5(8))* Nova Science Pubs., Inc.

Morrison, Jane L., ed. Food Intake: Regulation, Assessing & Controlling. 2012. (Food Science & Technology Nutrition & Diet Research Progress Ser.). 181p. 95.00 ***(978-1-61324-183-7(6))*** Nova Science Pubs., Inc.

Murray, Michael T. & Lyon, Michael R. Hunger Free Forever: The New Science of Appetite Control. 2008. (ENG., Illus.). 304p. pap. 14.00 *(978-1-4165-4905-5(6),* Beyond Words/Atria Bks.) Atria Bks.

Parker, Brooke. Love Your Body: A Diet-Free Approach to Balanced Eating. 2009. (Illus.). 158p. pap. 14.95 *(978-1-935217-37-4(2),* Walnut Springs Press) Leatherwood Pr.

Tribote, Evelyn. Intuitive Eating. rev. ed. Date not set. *(978-0-312-32122-2(8))* St. Martin's Pr.

Virtue, Doreen. The Yo-Yo Diet Syndrome: How to Heal & Stabilize Your Appetite & Weight. 2010. (ENG.). 256p. pap. 15.95 *(978-1-4019-2323-5(2))* Hay Hse., Inc.

APPETITE—EFFECT OF DRUGS ON

Joost, Hans-Georg, ed. Appetite Control. 2012. (Handbook of Experimental Pharmacology Ser.). (ENG., Illus.). x, 474p. 459.00 ***(978-3-642-24715-6(6),*** 3642247156) Springer.

Mitchell, Steven R. Appetite: Regulation, Role in Disease & Control. 2011. (Nutrition & Diet Research Progress Ser.). (Illus.). 285p. 129.00 *(978-1-61209-842-5(8))* Nova Science Pubs., Inc.

APPETITE—LOSS

see Anorexia

APPETITE DEPRESSANTS

see also Amphetamines

May, Suellen. Weight-Loss Drugs. 2009. (Drugs: the Straight Facts Ser.). (Illus.). 112p. (C). (gr. 9-18). 30.00 *(978-1-60413-204-5(3),* Chelsea Hse.) Facts On File, Inc.

Preuss, Harry G. & Gottlieb, Bill. The Natural Fat Loss Pharmacy: Drug-Free Remedies to Help You Safely Lose Weight, Shed Fat, Firm up, & Feel Great. 2007. *(978-1-59486-706-4(2))* Rodale Pr., Inc.

Tucci, ed. Phytochemicals for the Control of Human Appetite & Body Weight. 2010. (Nutrition & Diet Research Progress Ser.). 93p. pap. 43.00 *(978-1-61668-676-5(6))* Nova Science Pubs., Inc.

APPETITE DISORDERS

Here are entered works on appetite disturbances as symptoms of organic, psychological or psychosocial disorders. Works on gross disturbances in eating behavior as a subclass of mental disorders are entered under Eating Disorders.

see also Anorexia; Eating Disorders

Cilley, Marla & Ely, Leanne. Body Clutter: Love Your Body, Love Yourself. 2007. (ENG., Illus.). 256p. pap. 15.99 *(978-1-4165-3462-4(8),* Touchstone) Touchstone.

Guislain, Museum. The Weighty Body: About Thick, Thin, Perfect or Deranged. 2011. (FRE, DUT & ENG., Illus.). 192p. pap. *(978-90-209-9215-1(5),* Lannoo Pubs. (Acc)) Antique Collectors' Club.

Isaacs, Scott. Beat Overeating Now! Take Control of Your Hunger Hormones to Lose Weight Fast. 2012. (ENG., Illus.). 256p. pap. 16.99 ***(978-1-59233-504-6(7),*** 1592335047) Quayside.

Mitchell, Steven R. Appetite: Regulation, Role in Disease & Control. 2011. (Nutrition & Diet Research Progress Ser.). (Illus.). 285p. 129.00 *(978-1-61209-842-5(8))* Nova Science Pubs., Inc.

Ogden, Jane. The Psychology of Eating: From Healthy to Disordered Behavior. 2nd ed. 2010. (ENG., Illus.). 392p. 110.95 *(978-1-4051-9121-0(X));* 312p. pap. 36.95 *(978-1-4051-9120-3(1))* Wiley, John & Sons, Inc. (Wiley-Blackwell).

Owen, J. B., et al, eds. Animal Models - Disorders of Eating Behaviour & Body Composition. 2010. 268p. pap. 169.00 *(978-90-481-5743-3(9),* 9048157439) Springer.

APPETITE LOSS

see Anorexia

APPETIZERS

Adam, Cornelia. Tapas (Appetizers) 6.95 *(978-84-89675-18-6(X))* Zendrera Zariquiey, Editorial ESP. Dist: AIMS International Bks., Inc.

Akis, Eric. Everyone Can Cook Appetizers: Over 100 Tasty Bites. 2010. (Everyone Can Cook Ser.). (ENG., Illus.). 198p. pap. 22.95 *(978-1-55285-793-9(X))* Whitecap Bks., Ltd. CAN. Dist: Midpoint Trade Bks., Inc.

Annie Rigg. Small Plates: Tapas, Meze & Other B. 2011. (ENG., Illus.). 64p. *(978-1-84975-134-6(X))* Ryland Peters & Small.

Aris, Pepita. Tapas & Traditional Spanish Cooking: The Authentic Taste of Spain: 130 Sun-Drenched Classic Recipes Shown in 230 Stunning Photographs. 2008. (ENG., Illus.). 224p. 29.99 *(978-0-7548-1797-0(0))* Anness Publishing GBR. Dist: National Bk. Network.

Armendariz, Matt. On a Stick! 80 Party-Perfect Recipes. 2011. (ENG., Illus.). 184p. pap. 16.95 *(978-1-59474-489-1(0))* Quirk Bks.

Australian Women's Weekly Staff. Finger Food. Blacker, Maryanne, ed. (Illus.). 128p. pap. 12.95 *(978-0-949128-26-3(0))* ACP Publishing Pty, Ltd. AUS. Dist: Graphic Arts Ctr. Publishing Co.

—Finger Food. Coleman, Mary, ed. (Illus.). 64p. pap. 5.95 *(978-1-86396-181-3(X))* ACP Publishing Pty, Ltd. AUS. Dist: Graphic Arts Ctr. Publishing Co.

—Potatoes. Coleman, Mary, ed. (Illus.). 64p. pap. 5.95 *(978-1-86396-250-6(6))* ACP Publishing Pty, Ltd. AUS. Dist: Graphic Arts Ctr. Publishing Co.

Australian Women's Weekly Staff, contrib. by. New Finger Food. (Illus.). 120p. pap. 12.95 *(978-1-86396-282-7(4))* ACP Publishing Pty, Ltd. AUS. Dist: Graphic Arts Ctr. Publishing Co.

Bardi, Carla. Appetizers: Just Great Recipes. 2008. (Treats Ser.). (ENG.). 64p. pap. 5.95 *(978-88-89272-90-9(2))* McRae Bks. Srl ITA. Dist: Independent Pubs. Group.

—Focaccia: Just Great Recipes. 2008. (Treats Ser.). (ENG.). 64p. pap. 5.95 *(978-88-89272-92-3(9))* McRae Bks. Srl ITA. Dist: Independent Pubs. Group.

Bardi, Carla, et al. Antipasti! Appetizers the Italian Way. 2007. (Pane & Vino Ser.). (ENG., Illus.). 120p. pap. 14.95 *(978-88-89272-43-5(0))* McRae Bks. Srl ITA. Dist: Independent Pubs. Group.

Basan, Ghillie. Turkish Meze: The Little Dishes of the Eastern Mediterranean. 2009. (ENG., Illus.). 96p. pap. 16.99 *(978-1-84476-709-0(4))* Anness Publishing GBR. Dist: National Bk. Network.

Better Homes and Gardens Editors. The Ultimate Appetizers Book: More Than 450 No-Fuss Nibbles & Drinks, Plus Simple Party Planning Tips. 2010. (Better Homes & Gardens Ultimate Ser.: 33). (ENG., Illus.). 480p. pap. 19.95 *(978-0-470-63414-1(6),* Wiley) Wiley, John & Sons, Inc.

Betty Crocker Editors. Betty Crocker Small Bites: 100 Recipes for the Way You Really Cook. 2008. (ENG., Illus.). 160p. 14.95 *(978-0-470-32933-7(5),* Wiley) Wiley, John & Sons, Inc.

Bird, Jane. As We Like Them. 2011. 78p. 37.95 ***(978-1-258-06442-6(1))*** Literary Licensing, LLC.

Blake, Susannah. 500 Appetizers: The Only Appetizer Cookbook You'll Ever Need. 2007. (Illus.). 288p. lib. bdg. 15.95 *(978-1-56906-976-9(X),* BTC976) Sellers Publishing, Inc.

Briggs, Janet. The New Appetizer: The Best Recipes for Today's Party Starters. 2007. (Illus.). 256p. *(978-0-89821-526-7(9))* Reiman Pubns., L.P.

Brown, Abigail & Webb, Melissa. Antpasti: Made Easy. 2007. (Made Easy (New Holland) Ser.). (ENG., Illus.). 80p. pap. 12.95 *(978-1-84537-827-1(X))* New Holland Pubs., Ltd. GBR. Dist: Sterling Publishing Co., Inc.

Callahan, Peter & Pelzel, Raquel. Bite by Bite: 100 Stylish Little Plates You Can Make for Any Party. 2011. (ENG., Illus.). 256p. 35.00 *(978-0-307-71879-2(4),* Clarkson Potter) Crown Publishing Group.

Callizo, Gloria Rossi. Las Mejores Tapas, Cenas Frias y Platos Combinados.Tr. of Best Lids, Cold Dinners & Combine dishes. (SPA., Illus.). 224p. 19.95 *(978-84-315-2912-3(1),* VE7003) De Vecchi, Editorial, S.A. ESP. Dist: Continental Bk. Co., Inc.

Casey, Kathy. Sips & Apps. 2009. (ENG., Illus.). 204p. 19.95 *(978-0-8118-6406-0(5))* Chronicle Bks. LLC.

Cassidy, Catherine. Easy Appetizers. 2009. (Illus.). 112p. *(978-0-89821-754-4(7))* Reiman Pubns., L.P.

Cooking Club of America Staff, contrib. by. Appetizer Appeal: Member Recipes. 2010. (Illus.). 176p. ***(978-1-58159-479-9(8))*** North American Media Group.

Culinary Institute of America Staff. Hors d'Oeuvre at Home with the Culinary Institute of America. 2007. (ENG., Illus.). 224p. 29.95 *(978-0-7645-9562-2(8),* Wiley) Wiley, John & Sons, Inc.

Darling, Shari. Orgasmic Appetizers & Matching Wines: Tiny Bites with the MOAN FACTOR. 2010. (Illus.). 192p. pap. 29.95 *(978-1-55285-923-0(1))* Whitecap Bks., Ltd. CAN. Dist: Midpoint Trade Bks., Inc.

Delicious Bite-size. 2007. 96p. *(978-1-4054-9559-2(6))* Parragon, Inc.

Fallon, Peggy. Great Party Dips. 2008. (ENG., Illus.). 128p. 16.95 *(978-0-470-23978-0(6),* Wiley) Wiley, John & Sons, Inc.

Farrow, Joanna. Tapas. 2009. 128p. 14.99 *(978-0-600-61867-6(6),* Mitchell Beazley) Octopus Publishing Group GBR. Dist: Hachette Bk. Group.

Favorite Brand Name Recipes Editors, ed. The Appetizer Bible. 2010. 256p. 14.98 *(978-1-60553-721-4(7))* Publications International, Ltd.

—3 Books in 1: All New Diabetic Cooking: Appetizers, Entrees, Sweet Treats. 2010. 288p. 14.98 *(978-1-60553-699-6(7))* Publications International, Ltd.

Fine Cooking Magazine. Fine Cooking Appetizers: 200 Recipes for Small Bites with Big Flavor. 2010. (ENG., Illus.). 256p. pap. 19.95 *(978-1-60085-330-2(7))* Taunton Pr., Inc.

Finlayson, Judith & Wagman, Jordan. 750 Best Appetizers: From Dips & Salsas to Spreads & Shooters. 2011. (ENG., Illus.). 576p. pap. 24.95 *(978-0-7788-0272-3(8))* Rose, Robert Inc. CAN. Dist: Firefly Bks., Ltd.

Foley, Ray. Best Summer Drinks: 500 Incredible Cocktail & Appetizer Recipes. 2009. (Bartender Magazine Ser.). (ENG.). 240p. mass mkt. 8.99 *(978-1-4022-1843-9(5))* Sourcebooks, Inc.

France, Christine. Sauces, Salsas, Dressings & Dips: The Art of Sauce Making Transform Your Cooking with 150 Delicious Ideas for Every Kind of Dish. 2011. (ENG., Illus.). 224p. 29.99 *(978-0-7548-2336-0(9))* Anness Publishing GBR. Dist: National Bk. Network.

France, Lydia. Party Bites. 2008. (ENG., Illus.). 96p. *(978-1-84597-710-8(6))* Ryland Peters & Small.

Frieberg, Carol. Swirl, Sip & Savor: Northwest Wine & Small Plate Pairings. 2010. (ENG., Illus.). 224p. pap. 21.95 *(978-1-57061-562-7(4))* Sasquatch Bks.

Gee, Denise & Chronicle Books Staff. Porch Parties: Cocktail Recipes & Easy Ideas for Outdoor Entertaining. 2010. (ENG., Illus.). 144p. 16.95 *(978-0-8118-6580-7(0))* Chronicle Bks. LLC.

Gooseberry Patch. Our Favorite Appetizer Recipes Cookbook. 2007. (ENG., Illus.). 126p. spiral bd. 7.95 *(978-1-931890-86-1(2))* Gooseberry Patch.

Harron, Hallie. Cheese Hors D'Oeuvres: 50 Recipes for Crispy Canapes, Delectable Dips, Marinated Morsels, & Other Tasty Tidbits. 2008. (50 Ser.). (ENG., Illus.). 96p. 12.95 *(978-1-55832-371-1(6))* Harvard Common Pr.

Harte-Ross, Debbie. Appetizers Made Easy. 2011. 214p. pap. 24.95 ***(978-1-4626-0486-9(2))*** PublishAmerica, Inc.

Hartley, Julia. The Big Book of World Tapas: 365 Delicious Light Bites for All Occasions. 2009. (ENG., Illus.). 216p. spiral bd. 19.95 *(978-1-84483-803-5(X))* Duncan Baird Pubs. GBR. Dist: Sterling Publishing Co., Inc.

Hendrickson, Kim. Tastefully Small - Dessert Canapés: Bite - Size Sweets for Easy Entertaining. 2008. (Illus.). 120p. per. 16.95 *(978-1-60138-267-2(7))* Atlantic Publishing Co.

—Tastefully Small - Finger Sandwiches: Easy Party Sandwiches for All Occasions. 2008. (Illus.). 120p. per. 16.95 *(978-1-60138-266-5(9))* Atlantic Publishing Co.

—Tastefully Small Finger Sandwiches: Easy Party Sandwiches for All Occasions. 2008. (ENG.). pap. 16.95 *(978-0-9844315-2-6(7))* Atlantic Publishing Co.

Herbenick, Fran. Appetizing Appetizers from the Florida Keys. 2008. 148p. pap. 11.99 *(978-1-4389-2335-2(X))* AuthorHouse.

Heyhoe, Kate. Great Bar Food at Home. 2007. (ENG., Illus.). 128p. 17.95 *(978-0-471-78183-7(5),* Wiley) Wiley, John & Sons, Inc.

Hildyard, Anne. Appetizers: 500 Best-Ever Recipes. 2009. (ENG., Illus.). 256p. 35.00 *(978-0-7548-1948-6(5))* Anness Publishing GBR. Dist: National Bk. Network.

Hildyard, Anne. 325 Appetizers for Special Occasions: Recipes for easy appetizers, fabulous finger foods & scrumptious salads, shown in over 325 Photographs. 2012. (ENG., Illus.). 160p. pap. 19.99 ***(978-1-78019-029-7(8))*** Anness Publishing GBR. Dist: National Bk. Network.

Holland America Line & Sodamin, Rudi. Appetizers: Culinary Signature Collection, Volume IV. 2012. (ENG., Illus.). 192p. 29.95 ***(978-0-8478-3819-6(6))*** Universe Publishing.

Hood, Karen Jean Matsko. Hood & Matsko Family Appetizers Cookbook: A. K. a O'Hood & Macko Family: Our Favorite Appetizer Recipes. l.t. ed. 2007. 320p. per. 22.95 *(978-1-59434-082-6(X))* Whispering Pine Pr. International, Inc.

—Hood & Matsko Family Favorite Christmas Sweets: Our Favorite Christmas Sweets Recipes. braille ed. 2007. pap. 22.95 *(978-1-59649-672-9(X))* Whispering Pine Pr. International, Inc.

Horrilo, Carlos & Morcas, Patrick. Tapas: Simple Combinations, Striking Flavours. 2010. (ENG., Illus.). 176p. pap. 22.95 *(978-1-85626-950-6(7))* Cathie, Kyle Ltd. GBR. Dist: National Bk. Network.

Hough, Jill Silverman. 100 Perfect Pairings: Small Plates to Enjoy with Wines You Love. 2010. (ENG., Illus.). 192p. 16.95 *(978-0-470-44631-7(5),* Wiley) Wiley, John & Sons, Inc.

Ingram, Christine. Appetizers, Starters & Finger Food: 200 Great Ways to Start a Meal or Serve a Buffet with Style. 2011. (ENG., Illus.). 256p. pap. 19.99 ***(978-1-78019-046-4(8))*** Anness Publishing GBR. Dist: National Bk. Network.

Ingram, Christine. 100 Appetizers & Starters: Elegant & Delicious Recipes to Start the Meal, Shown Step By Step in over 300 Mouthwatering Photographs. 2010. (ENG., Illus.). 128p. pap. 17.99 *(978-1-84475-794-6(9))* Anness Publishing GBR. Dist: National Bk. Network.

Johns, Pamela Sheldon. 50 Great Appetizers. 2008. (ENG., Illus.). 112p. 14.99 *(978-0-7407-7650-2(9))* Andrews McMeel Publishing.

Johnson, Mary B. 365 Party Food Recipes. 2007. *(978-1-4027-4792-2(6),* Sterling Innovation) Sterling Publishing Co., Inc.

Jones, Bridget. The Complete Illustrated Book of Appetizers, Buffets, Finger Food & Party Food: How to Plan the Perfect Celebration with over 400 Inspiring First Course, Nibbles, Finger Foods, Buffet & Party Dishes. 2006. (ENG., Illus.). 512p. 29.99 *(978-0-7548-1688-1(5))* Anness Publishing GBR. Dist: National Bk. Network.

Joyce, Jennifer. Plates to Share: Simple Delicious Meals to Enjoy with Friends. 2008. (ENG., Illus.). 64p. *(978-1-84597-630-9(4))* C CO Bks.

King, Jonathan, et al. Appetizers: Finger Foods & Small Plates. 2010. (ENG., Illus.). 160p. 19.95 *(978-0-8118-6869-3(9))* Chronicle Bks. LLC.

Kurella, Laura. Fabulous! Food That Makes You Feel Good: Tiny Bites... & Beverages. 2011. 210p. pap. 24.95 ***(978-1-60920-031-2(4))*** Ajoyin Publishing, Inc.

Liley, Vicki. Dim Sum. 2006. (Tuttle Mini Cookbook Ser.). (ENG., Illus.). 96p. 12.95 *(978-0-8048-3844-3(5))* Tuttle Publishing.

Lillien, Lisa. Hungry Girl Happy Hour: 75 Recipes for Amazingly Fantastic Guilt-Free Cocktails & Party Foods. 2010. (ENG., Illus.). 176p. pap. 14.99 *(978-0-312-62103-2(5),* St. Martin's Griffin) St. Martin's Pr.

MacDougall, James. Delicious Small Dishes: Recipes from Canada's Best Chefs. 2007. (Flavours Cookbook Ser.). (ENG., Illus.). 128p. pap. 24.95 *(978-0-88780-730-5(5))* Formac Publishing Co., Ltd. CAN. Dist: Casemate Pubs. & Bk. Distributors, LLC.

Mahr-Batuz, Sasa, et al. The Barcelona Cookbook: A Celebration of Food, Wine, & Life. 2009. (ENG., Illus.). 224p. 29.99 *(978-0-7407-7394-5(1))* Andrews McMeel Publishing.

McKee, Gwen & Moseley, Barbara. Best of the Best Fast & Fabulous Party Foods & Appetizers. 2008. *(978-1-934193-20-4(8)); (978-1-934193-10-5(0))* Quail Ridge Pr., Inc.

Megel, Christophe & Kilayko, Anton. Asian Tapas: Small Bites, Big Flavors. 2010. (ENG., Illus.). 128p. pap. 17.95 *(978-0-8048-4157-3(8))* Tuttle Publishing.

Miyoshi, Hideaki. Izakaya Hawai'i: Tokkuri Tei Cooking. 2009. pap. *(978-1-56647-908-0(8))* Mutual Publishing LLC.

Montalva, Lisa. The Gourmet Mom: Appetizers, 1 vol. 2010. 382p. pap. 29.95 *(978-1-4489-4275-6(6))* PublishAmerica, Inc.

Moore, Megan. Divinely Decadent Martinis & Appetizers. 2008. 92p. pap. 29.95 *(978-1-4327-1503-8(8))* Outskirts Pr., Inc.

Morgan, Diane. Skinny Dips. 2010. (ENG.). 144p. 18.95 *(978-0-8118-7142-6(8))* Chronicle Bks. LLC.

Murdoch Books, prod. Step by Step Finger Food: More than 250 Recipes. 2011. (ENG., Illus.). 256p. pap. 8.99 ***(978-1-74266-265-7(X),*** 174266265X, Bay Bks.) Murdoch Bks. Pty Ltd. AUS. Dist: Book Sales, Inc.

Murdoch Books Staff. Tapas. Perez, Clara E. Serrano, tr. 2008. (Seleccion Culinaria Ser.). (SPA., Illus.). 80p. pap. 4.95 *(978-84-8076-536-7(4))* Blume ESP. Dist: Independent Pubs. Group.

Nims, Cynthia. Gourmet Game Night: Bite-Sized, Mess-Free Eating for Board-Game Parties, Bridge Clubs, Poker Nights, Book Groups, & More. 2010. (ENG., Illus.). 160p. pap. 17.99 *(978-1-58008-058-0(X))* Ten Speed Pr.

Nunez, David G. The Appetizer Is the Meal. 2011. 84p. pap. 28.99 *(978-1-4520-7574-7(3))* AuthorHouse.

O'Neill, Eve & Biederbeck, Doug "Bix". Bixology: Cocktails, Culture, & a Guide to the Good Life. 2009. (ENG., Illus.). 160p. 16.95 *(978-0-8118-6707-8(2))* Chronicle Bks. LLC.

Ortega, Simone & Ortega, Inés. The Book of Tapas. 2010. (ENG., Illus.). 432p. 39.95 *(978-0-7148-5613-1(4))* Phaidon Pr., Inc.

Osborn, Shane. Appetizers: Recipes for First Course or Main Event. 2008. (ENG., Illus.). 1p. pap. 17.95 *(978-1-84400-639-7(5))* Quadrille Publishing, Ltd. GBR. Dist: Ingram Pub. Services.

Passion for Tapas. 224p. *(978-1-4054-9447-2(6))* Parragon, Inc.

Pawlcyn, Cindy. Appetizers. 2009. (ENG., Illus.). 104p. spiral bd. 15.95 *(978-1-58008-979-1(8))* Ten Speed Pr.

Pawlcyn, Cindy & Jacinto, Pablo. Big Small Plates. 2006. (ENG., Illus.). 384p. 35.00 *(978-1-58008-523-6(7))* Ten Speed Pr.

Payard, Francois. Bite Size: Elegant Recipes for Entertaining. 2006. (ENG., Illus.). 144p. 19.99 *(978-0-06-088722-3(2),* Morrow, William Cookbooks) HarperCollins Pubs.

Price, Jessie. EatingWell Comfort Foods Made Healthy: The Classic Makeover CookbookThe Classic Makeover Cookbook. EatingWell Magazine Editors, ed. 2009. (EatingWell Ser.). (ENG., Illus.). 256p. pap. 19.95 *(978-0-88150-887-1(X),* 150887) Countryman Pr.

Publications International Staff. Best Loved Philadelphia. 2009. 256p. 14.98 *(978-1-4127-9578-4(8),* PIL Kids) Publications International, Ltd.

—Cocktails: 40 Amazing Party-Food Recipes. Favorite Brand Name Recipes Editors, ed. 2010. 144p. spiral bd. 10.98 *(978-1-60553-704-7(7),* PIL Kids) Publications International, Ltd.

—Recipes to Share Appetizers. 2009. 144p. spiral bd. 10.98 *(978-1-4127-9798-6(5),* PIL Kids) Publications International, Ltd.

—Simple 1-2-3 Appetizers Recipes. Favorite Brand Name Recipes Editors, ed. 2010. 160p. spiral bc. 10.98 *(978-1-4127-9582-1(6),* PIL Kids) Publications International, Ltd.

—3 in 1 Holiday Appetizers, Dinner, Cookies. 2009. 156p. spiral bd. 14.98 *(978-1-4127-9827-3(2),* PIL Kids) Publications International, Ltd.

—3 in 1 Nabisco, Velveeta, Kraft. 2009. 288p. spiral bd. 14.98 *(978-1-4127-7786-5(0),* PIL Kids) Publications International, Ltd.

Publications International Staff, creator. Simple 1-2-3 Appetizers. 2007. (Favorite Brand Name Recipes Ser.). (Illus.). 160p. 12.98 *(978-1-4127-2987-1(4))* Publications International, Ltd.

—100 Best Appetizer Recipes. 2007. (100 Best Ser.). (Illus.). 160p. 9.98 *(978-1-4127-2871-3(1))* Publications International, Ltd.

Publications International Staff, ed. Kitchenaid Best-Loved Recipes. 2009. 256p. 14.98 *(978-1-4127-7876-3(X),* PIL Kids) Publications International, Ltd.

Rathbun, A. J. Party Snacks! 50 Simple, Stylish Recipes to Make You a Popular Party Host. 2008. (50 Ser.). (ENG.). 96p. 12.95 *(978-1-55832-347-6(3))* Harvard Common Pr.

RPS Staff. Tapas & Other Spanish Plates to Share. 2006. 144p. *(978-1-84975-056-1(4))* Ryland Peters & Small.

Ryland Peters & Small Staff, creator. Simple Appetizers. 2010. (ENG., Illus.). 64p. *(978-1-84597-989-8(3))* Ryland Peters & Small.

—Tapas: Delicious Little Dishes from Spain. 2007. (ENG., Illus.). 64p. *(978-1-84597-395-7(X))* Ryland Peters & Small.

Schneider, Deborah. Amor y Tacos: Modern Mexican Tacos, Margaritas, & Antojitos. 2010. (ENG., Illus.). 152p. 18.95 *(978-1-58479-824-8(6))* Stewart, Tabori & Chang.

Sibley, Barbara, et al. Antojitos: Festive & Flavorful Mexican Appetizers. 2009. (ENG., Illus.). 160p. 22.99 *(978-1-58008-929-6(1))* Ten Speed Pr.

Stempfle, Laurie. Small Plates for Sharing. 2008. (Illus.). 224p. *(978-1-897069-74-5(X))* Company's Coming Publishing, Ltd.

Sunset Books Staff, et al. Williams-Sonoma New Flavors for Appetizers: Classic Recipes Redefined. 2008. (New Flavors for Ser.). (ENG.). 160p. 22.95 *(978-0-8487-3257-8(X))* Oxmoor Hse., Inc.

Table, Sur La. Everyday Grilling: 50 Recipes from Appetizers to Desserts. 2011. (ENG.). 144p. 15.00 *(978-1-4494-0058-3(2))* Andrews McMeel Publishing.

Taste of Home. Appetizers: 410 Party Favorites. 2010. (ENG.). 256p. (gr. 12). 15.95 *(978-0-89821-801-5(2))* Reader's Digest Assn., Inc., The.

Taste of Home Staff. The New Appetizer: 250 Recipes for Today's Party Starters. 2009. (ENG.). 256p. (gr. 12-18). 24.95 *(978-0-89821-728-5(8))* Reader's Digest Assn., Inc., The.

Tastefully Small Savory Bites: Easy Sophisticated Hors D'oeuvres for Every Occasion. 2010. pap. 18.95 *(978-1-60138-444-7(0))* Atlantic Publishing Co.

Treuille, Eric & Blashford-Snell, Victoria. Hors D'Oeuvres. 2007. (ENG., Illus.). 168p. pap. 14.95 *(978-0-7566-1888-9(6))* Dorling Kindersley Publishing, Inc.

Van Rosendaal, Julie. Grazing: A Healthier Approach to Snacks & Finger Foods. 2nd rev. ed. 2011. (ENG.). 208p. pap. 24.95 *(978-1-55285-965-0(7))* Whitecap Bks., Ltd. CAN. Dist: Midpoint Trade Bks., Inc.

Voltz, Jim. Hors Doeuvres on the Porch. 2011. pap. 17.95 *(978-0-578-07352-1(8))* Elliott, Marjorie.

Warde, Fran. Party! Easy Recipes for Fingerfood & Party Drinks. 2007. (ENG., Illus.). 64p. *(978-1-84597-551-7(0))* Ryland Peters & Small.

Williams, Chuck & Oxmoor House Staff. Appetizers. rev. ed. 2007. (Best of the Lifestyles Ser.). (ENG.). 304p. 24.95 *(978-0-8487-3194-6(8))* Oxmoor Hse., Inc.

Williams, Zac, photos by. French Fries, 1 vol. 2011. (ENG., Illus.). 128p. 16.99 *(978-1-4236-0744-1(9))* Gibbs Smith, Publisher.

Wohl, Kit. New Orleans Classic Appetizers, 1 vol. rev. ed. 2008. (Classics Ser.). (ENG., Illus.). 96p. 16.95 *(978-1-58980-512-2(3))* Pelican Publishing Co., Inc.

Zinngrebe, Rainer & Contreras, Rodrigo Torres. Small Bites Big Taste: Innovative Recipes for Entertaining, 1 vol. 2009. (ENG., Illus.). 192p. 36.00 *(978-981-261-526-8(1))* Marshall Cavendish International (Asia) Private Ltd. SGP. Dist: Marshall Cavendish Corp.

APPIANUS OF ALEXANDRIA

Rathbone, Dominic. Economic Rationalism & Rural Society in Third-Century AD Egypt: The Heroninos Archive & the Appianus Estate. 2007. (Cambridge Classical Studies). (ENG., Illus.). 512p. pap. 67.00 *(978-0-521-03763-1(8))* Cambridge Univ. Pr.

Vollgraff, Johann Christoph. Greek Writers of Roman History - Some Reflections upon the Authorities Used by Plutarch & Appianus. 2010. 116p. pap. 26.95 *(978-1-4460-0576-7(3))* Research Pr.

APPLE

see Apples

APPLE COMPUTER, INC.

Arthur, Charles. Digital Wars: Apple, Google, Microsoft & the Battle for the Internet. 2012. (ENG.). 272p. pap. 19.95 ***(978-0-7494-6413-4(5))*** Kogan Page, Ltd. GBR. Dist: Ingram Pub. Services.

Beahm, George, ed. I, Steve: Steve Jobs in His Own Words. 2011. (In Their Own Words Ser.). (ENG.). 160p. pap. 10.95 ***(978-1-932841-66-4(0))*** Agate Publishing, Inc.

Chen, Brian X. Always On: How the iPhone Unlocked the Anything-Anytime-Anywhere Future — and Locked Us In. 2011. (ENG.) 256p. 25.00 *(978-0-306-81960-5(0))* Da Capo Pr., Inc.

Chen, Brian X. Always On: How the iPhone Unlocked the Anything-Anytime-Anywhere Future — and Locked Us In. 2012. (ENG.) 256p. pap. 15.00 ***(978-0-306-82076-2(5))*** Da Capo Pr., Inc.

Elliot, Jay & Simon, William L. The Steve Jobs Way: ILeadership for a New Generation. 2012. (ENG.). 256p. pap. 15.99 ***(978-1-59315-710-4(X))*** Vanguard Pr.

Elliot, Jay, et al. The Steve Jobs Way: Ileadership for a New Generation. 2011. (ENG., Illus.). 256p. 25.99 *(978-1-59315-639-8(1))* Vanguard Pr.

Groupe, Livres, ed. Steve Jobs: Histoire D'apple. 2010. 38p. pap. 14.14 *(978-1-159-97628-6(7))* General Bks. LLC.

Hertzfeld, Andy. Revolution in the Valley: The Insanely Great Story of How the Mac Was Made. 2011. (ENG., Illus.). 328p. pap. 24.99 ***(978-1-4493-1624-2(7))*** O'Reilly Media, Inc.

Isaacson, Walter. Steve Jobs. 2011. (Vintage Espanol Ser.). (SPA., Illus.). 752p. pap. 17.95 ***(978-0-307-95028-4(X),*** Vintage) Knopf Doubleday Publishing Group.

—Steve Jobs. 2011. (SPA.). pap. ***(978-1-4516-4854-6(5));*** (ENG., Illus.). 656p. 35.00 ***(978-1-4516-4853-9(7))*** Simon & Schuster.

—Steve Jobs. Lt. ed. 2011. (ENG.). 630p. 35.99 ***(978-1-4104-4522-3(4))*** Thorndike Pr.

Kahney, Leander. Inside Steve's Brain. exp. ed. (ENG.). 320p. (gr. 12-18). 2009. 24.95 *(978-1-59184-297-2(2),* Portfolio (Hardcover)) 2012. pap. 16.00 ***(978-1-59184-551-5(3),*** Portfolio Trade) Penguin Group (USA) Inc.

Lashinsky, Adam. Inside Apple: How America's Most Admired — and Secretive — Company Really Works. 2012. (ENG.). 240p. 26.99 ***(978-1-4555-1215-7(X),*** Business Plus) Grand Central Publishing.

O'Grady, Jason & O'Grady, Jason D. Apple Inc, 1 vol. 2008. (Corporations That Changed the World Ser.). (Illus.). 200p. 45.00 *(978-0-313-36244-6(0),* GR6244, Greenwood Pr.) Greenwood Publishing Group, Inc.

Sander, Peter. What Would Steve Jobs Do? How the Steve Jobs Way Can Inspire Anyone to Think Differently & Win. 2011. (ENG.). 240p. 22.00 ***(978-0-07-179274-5(0),*** 0071792740) McGraw-Hill Cos., The.

Seba, Jaime. Steve Jobs: From Apples to Apps. 2012. ***(978-1-4222-2299-7(3)) (978-1-4222-2310-9(8))*** Mason Crest Pubs.

Segall, Ken. Insanely Simple: The Obsession That Drives Apple's Success. 2012. (ENG.). 240p. (gr. 12). 25.95 ***(978-1-59184-483-9(5),*** Portfolio (Hardcover)) Penguin Group (USA) Inc.

Surhone, Lambert M., et al, eds. Steve Jobs. 2010. 128p. pap. ***(978-613-2-12222-3(2))*** VDM Verlag Dr. Mueller e.K.

Sutherland, Adam. The Story of Apple. 2012. (Business of High Tech Ser.). (ENG.). 48p. (YA). (gr. 5-8). pap. 10.00 ***(978-1-4488-7090-5(9),*** Rosen Central); (Illus.). lib. bdg. 23.95 ***(978-1-4488-7040-0(2))*** Rosen Publishing Group, Inc., The.

Wozniak, Steve. IWoz: Computer Geek to Cult Icon: How I Invented the Personal Computer, Co-Founded Apple, & Had Fun Doing It. 2006. (ENG., Illus.). 288p. 25.95 *(978-0-393-06143-7(4))* Norton, W. W. & Co., Inc.

—iWoz: How I Invented the Personal Computer, Co-founded Apple, & Had Fun Doing It. 2007. (ENG., Illus.). 336p. per. 15.95 *(978-0-393-33043-4(5),* 33043) Norton, W. W. & Co., Inc.

APPLE COMPUTERS

see also Apple II (Computer); Apple IIe (Computer); Macintosh (Computer)

Anker, Kevin & Merton, Orren. Logic Pro 9 Power! 2010. (ENG.). 688p. pap., instr.'s gde. ed. 44.99 *(978-1-4354-5612-9(2))* Course Technology.

Cone, Matthew. Master Your Mac: Simple Ways to Tweak, Customize, & Secure OS X. 2012. (ENG.). 352p. pap. 29.95 ***(978-1-59327-406-1(8))*** No Starch Pr., Inc.

Fischer, Volker. Der i-Kosmos. Macht, Mythos und Magie einer Marke / The i-Cosmos. Might, Myth & Magic a Brand. 2011. (ENG & GER., Illus.). 144p. 68.00 *(978-3-936681-48-2(1))* Edition Axel Menges GmbH DEU. Dist: National Bk. Network.

Floegel, Ekkehard. The Apple in Your Hand. 220p. 12.95 *(978-3-88963-178-7(9))* Blue Cat.

Gary, Brian. Apple Pro Training Series: Compressor Quick-Reference Guide. 2006. (Apple Pro Training Ser.). (ENG., Illus.). 160p. pap. 29.99 *(978-0-321-47408-7(2))* Peachpit Pr.

Grover, Chris. Office 2011 for Macintosh: The Missing Manual. 2010. (ENG., Illus.). 816p. pap. 34.99 *(978-1-4493-9335-9(7),* Pogue Pr.) O'Reilly Media, Inc.

McFedries, Paul. MacBook Air Portable Genius. 3rd ed. 2011. (Portable Genius Ser.: 117). (ENG., Illus.). 288p. pap. 25.00 ***(978-1-118-18618-3(4),*** Wiley) Wiley, John & Sons, Inc.

McFedries, Paul. Macs Portable Genius. 2nd ed. 2010. (Portable Genius Ser.: 41). (ENG., Illus.). 352p. pap. 25.00 *(978-0-470-87402-8(3),* Wiley) Wiley, John & Sons, Inc.

McNulty, Scott & Negrino, Tom. ICloud: Visual QuickStart Guide. 2012. (Visual QuickStart Guide Ser.). (ENG.). 192p. pap. 24.99 ***(978-0-321-81410-4(X))*** Peachpit Pr.

Miser, Brad. Teach Yourself VISUALLY MacBook. 2nd ed. 2010. (Teach Yourself VISUALLY Consumer Ser.: 23). (ENG., Illus.). 400p. pap. 29.99 *(978-0-470-56519-3(5),* Visual) Wiley, John & Sons, Inc.

Moritz, Michael. Return to the Little Kingdom: How Apple & Steve Jobs Changed the World. 2009. (ENG.). 352p. (gr. 12-18). 27.95 *(978-1-59020-281-4(3))* Overlook Pr., The.

Nozzi, Joshua. Mastering Xcode 4: Develop & Design. 2011. (Develop & Design Ser.). (ENG., Illus.). 400p. pap. 49.99 ***(978-0-321-76752-3(7))*** Peachpit Pr.

Peachpit Press Staff & Carlson, Jeff. The iPad. 2010. (Pocket Guide Ser.). (ENG., Illus.). 240p. pap. 14.99 *(978-0-321-71758-0(9))* Peachpit Pr.

Peachpit Press Staff, et al. Xsan 2 Administration: A Guide to Designing, Deploying, & Maintaining Xsan. 2008. (Apple Training Ser.). (ENG., Illus.). 312p. pap. 59.99 *(978-0-321-61322-6(8))* Peachpit Pr.

Pilone, Tracey & Pilone, Dan. Head First iPhone & iPad Development: A Learner's Guide to Creating Objective-C Applications for the iPhone & iPad. 2nd ed. 2011. (ENG., Illus.). 674p. pap. 49.99 *(978-1-4493-8782-2(9))* O'Reilly Media, Inc.

Ray, John. My MacBook. 2nd rev. ed. 2011. (My... Ser.). (ENG., Illus.). 384p. pap. 24.99 ***(978-0-7897-4832-4(0))*** Que.

Rich, Jason R. How to Do Everything ICloud. 2012. (How to Do Everything Ser.). (ENG., Illus.). 272p. pap. 25.00 ***(978-0-07-179017-8(9),*** 0071790179) McGraw-Hill Osborne.

Rosenzweig, Gary. My iPad. 2010. (My... Ser.). (ENG., Illus.). 352p. pap. 24.99 *(978-0-7897-4471-5(6))* Que.

Sadun, Erica. Taking Your iPhone to the Max. 2007. (ENG.). 182p. pap. 24.99 *(978-1-59059-926-6(8))* Apress L. P.

Seibold, Chris. Big Book of Apple Hacks: Tips & Tools for Unlocking the Power of Your Apple Devices. rev. ed. 2008. (Hacks Ser.). (ENG., Illus.). 640p. pap. 34.99 *(978-0-596-52982-6(1))* O'Reilly Media, Inc.

Smith, Bud E. Sams Teach Yourself iPad 2 in 10 Minutes. 2nd rev. ed. 2011. (Sams Teach Yourself -- Minutes Ser.). (ENG., Illus.). 288p. pap. 14.99 *(978-0-672-33572-3(7))* Sams.

APPLE II (COMPUTER)

Chinese American Literature, Grades 6-12. (Illus.). pap., tchr. ed. 10.50 *(978-0-8359-0538-1(1))* Globe Fearon Educational Publishing.

APPLE IIE (COMPUTER)

Chinese American Literature, Grades 6-12. (Illus.). pap., tchr. ed. 10.50 *(978-0-8359-0538-1(1))* Globe Fearon Educational Publishing.

APPLE POWERBOOK NOTEBOOK COMPUTERS

see Macintosh Powerbook Notebook Computers

APPLES

see also Cooking (Apples)

Calhoun, Creighton Lee, Jr. Old Southern Apples: A Comprehensive History & Description of Varieties for Collectors, Growers, & Fruit Enthusiasts. 2nd rev. exp. ed. 2011. (ENG., Illus.). 384p. 75.00 *(978-1-60358-294-0(0))* Chelsea Green Publishing.

California. State Commission of Horticulture Staff & Weldon, George. Apple Growing in California. 2009. (Gardening in America Ser.). (ENG.). 128p. pap. 11.95 *(978-1-4290-1481-6(4))* Applewood Bks.

Clayton, Carolyn. It Started with the Apple: The Role of Food in the Faith Journey. 2009. 126p. pap. 19.95 *(978-1-60813-618-6(3))* PublishAmerica, Inc.

Clifford, Sue & King, Angela. Apple Source Book. 2007. (ENG., Illus.). 304p. 32.95 *(978-0-340-95189-7(3),* Hodder & Stoughton) Hodder General Publishing Div. GBR. Dist: Independent Pubs. Group.

Cordoba, Sancho J. & Delgado, Fernando A., eds. Apples: Nutrition, Consumption & Health. 2012. ***(978-1-61942-709-9(5))*** Nova Science Pubs., Inc.

Fm, Prof Dr Bilqees, et al. Nematodes Associated with Apple. 2010. 108p. pap. *(978-3-639-25991-9(2))* VDM Verlag Dr. Mueller e.K.

Hogg, Robert. The British Pomology: The History, Description, Classification, & Synonymes, of the Fruits & Fruit Trees of Great Britain. 2011. (Cambridge Library Collection - Life Sciences Ser.). (ENG., Illus.). 328p. pap. 28.99 ***(978-1-108-03944-4(8))*** Cambridge Univ. Pr.

Heckermann, Johanna. Integrated Control of Cydia Species in Apple Orchards - Evaluation of the Potential of Hyssopus Pallidus As Biological Control Agent. 2008. 104p. pap. *(978-3-639-04329-7(4))* VDM Verlag Dr. Mueller e.K.

Janik, Erika. Apple: A Global History. 2011. (Reaktion Books - Edible Ser.). (Illus.). 132p. 17.00 *(978-1-86189-848-7(7))* Reaktion Bks., Ltd. GBR. Dist: Chicago Distribution Ctr.

Juniper, Barrie E. & Mabberley, David J. The Story of the Apple. 2009. (ENG.). 240p. pap. 29.95 *(978-1-60469-172-6(7),* 1604691727) Timber Pr., Inc.

Knoop, Johann H. & Knoop, Johann Hermann. Pomologia: Nei Paesi Bassi / Germania / Francia / Inghilterra ed altre Regioni. 2012. (ENG, ITA, FRE & GER., Illus.). 188p. 55.00 ***(978-88-96483-02-2(6))*** Congedo Publishing ITA. Dist: National Bk. Network.

Lea, Andrew. Craft Cider Making. 2011. (ENG., Illus.). 144p. pap. 15.95 *(978-1-904871-98-9(4),* 1904871984) Good Life Pr., The GBR. Dist: MBI Distribution Services/Quayside Distribution.

Mikolajski, Andrew. The Illustrated World Encyclopedia of Apples: A Comprehensive Identification Guide to over 400 Varieties Accompanied by 60 Scrumptious Recipes. 2012. (ENG., Illus.). 256p. 35.00 *(978-0-7548-2066-6(1))* Anness Publishing GBR. Dist: National Bk. Network.

Organisation for Economic Co-Operation and Development. International Standardisation of Fruit & Vegetables: Apples. 2011. (Illus.). 120p. pap. ***(978-92-64-08878-8(4))*** Organization for Economic Cooperation & Development.

Sanders, Rosie. The Apple Book. rev. ed. 2010. (ENG., Illus.). 168p. 35.00 *(978-0-7112-3141-2(9))* Lincoln, Frances Ltd. GBR. Dist: Perseus-PGW.

A

Sears, Fred. Productive Orcharding. 2008. (Gardening in America Ser.). (ENG.). 332p. pap. 21.95 *(978-1-4290-1336-9(2))* Applewood Bks.

Stanway, Penny. The Miracle of Apple Cider Vinegar: Practical Tips for Health, Home, & Beauty. 2010. (ENG.). 144p. pap. 12.95 *(978-1-907486-07-4(0),* Watkins Publishing) Duncan Baird Pubs. GBR. Dist: Sterling Publishing Co., Inc.

Thoreau, Henry David. Wild Apples. 2009. (ENG.). 48p. pap. 8.45 *(978-1-4385-2665-2(2),* Book Jungle) Standard Pubns., Inc.

Western Sonoma County Historical Society. Sebastopol's Gravenstein Apple Industry. 2011. (Images of America Ser.). (Illus.). 128p. pap. 21.99 *(978-0-7385-8173-6(9))* Arcadia Publishing.

Zhu, Guangchao. Temperatures & the Growth & Development of Apple Trees. 2010. 56p. pap. *(978-3-8383-5511-5(3))* Lambert Academic Publishing.

APPLES—JUVENILE LITERATURE

Apples in a Box. (Early Intervention Levels Ser.). 21.30 *(978-0-7362-0386-9(9))* Hampton-Brown Bks.

Murphy, Patricia J. The Apple Orchard. 2007. (Visit To... Ser.). (ENG.). 24p. (gr. k-1). lib. bdg. 246.50 *(978-1-4296-0883-1(8),* Pebble Plus) Capstone Pr., Inc.

—La Huerta de Manzanas. 2007. (visita A... / A Visit To... Ser.).Tr. of Apple Orchard. (MUL.). 24p. (gr. k-1). pap. 41.70 *(978-1-4296-0573-1(1),* Pebble Plus Bilingue/Bilingual) Capstone Pr., Inc.

APPLESCRIPT (COMPUTER PROGRAM LANGUAGE)

Ford, Jerry Lee, Jr. AppleScript Programming for the Absolute Beginner. 2007. (ENG., Illus.). 368p. per. 29.99 *(978-1-59863-384-9(8))* Course Technology.

—AppleScript Studio Programming for the Absolute Beginner. 2006. (ENG., Illus.). 384p. pap. 29.99 *(978-1-59863-303-0(1))* Course Technology.

Hart-Davis, Guy. AppleScript. 2009. (ENG., Illus.). 448p. pap. 39.99 *(978-0-07-163954-5(3),* 0071639543) McGraw-Hill Osborne.

Munro, Mark Conway. AppleScript. 2010. (Developer Reference Ser.: 6). (ENG., Illus.). 624p. pap. 49.99 *(978-0-470-56229-1(3),* Wiley) Wiley, John & Sons, Inc.

Rosenthal, Hanaan. AppleScript: The Comprehensive Guide to Scripting & Automation on Mac OS X. 2nd ed. 2006. (ENG., Illus.). 808p. per. 59.99 *(978-1-59059-653-1(6))* Apress L. P.

Soghoian, Sal & Cheeseman, Bill. AppleScript 1-2-3. 2008. (Voices Ser.). (ENG., Illus.). 896p. pap. 49.99 *(978-0-321-14931-2(9))* New Riders Publishing.

APPLESEED, JOHNNY, 1774-1845

Chapin, Henry. The Adventures of Johnny Appleseed. 2011. 254p. 46.95 *(978-1-258-09867-4(9))* Literary Licensing, LLC.

Means, Howard. Johnny Appleseed: The Man, the Myth & the American Story. 2011. (ENG., Illus.). 336p. 26.00 *(978-1-4391-7825-6(9))* Simon & Schuster.

APPLESOFT (COMPUTER PROGRAM)

Biersdorfer, J. D. Best iPhone Apps. 2nd ed. 2010. (ENG., Illus.). 240p. pap. 19.99 *(978-1-4493-9414-1(0))* O'Reilly Media, Inc.

APPLETALK

Pages 2 Essential Training. 2006. cd-rom 49.95 *(978-1-59671-270-6(8))* Lynda.com, LLC.

APPLETON, NATHAN, 1779-1861

Winthrop, Robert C. Memoir of the Hon Nathan Appleton, Ll D. 2011. 88p. pap. 14.99 *(978-1-4255-0415-1(9))* MPublishing.

APPLEWORKS (COMPUTER PROGRAM)

Merritt, Cathleen & Bernhard, Keith, eds. Getting Started with AppleWorks Spread Sheet. Date not set. 128p. pap. 19.95 *(978-0-9620807-8-4(0))* National AppleWorks Users Group.

Zellers, Carolyn M. Computer Activities: Making Slide Shows & Simple Web Pages. 2009. (Illus.). 106p. pap. 15.95 *(978-1-58683-035-9(X))* Linworth Publishing, Inc.

APPLIANCES, ELECTRIC

see Electric Apparatus and Appliances

APPLICATION SOFTWARE

see also Computer Games; Presentation Graphics Software; Web Services

Ahmed, Tariq, et al. Flex3 in Action. 2009. (ENG., Illus.). 576p. pap. 49.99 *(978-1-933988-74-0(6))* Manning Pubns. Co.

Ainsworth, Allison & Patterson, Rob. Essential Guide to Presentation Software. 2009. (ENG.). 80p. (C). pap. 9.95 *(978-0-312-53819-4(7))* Bedford/Saint Martin's.

Alameda, Eldon. Foundation Rails 2. 2008. (ENG.). 480p. pap. 42.99 *(978-1-4302-1039-9(7),* Friends of Ed) Apress L. P.

Alencar, Paulo & Cowan, Donald, eds. Handbook of Research on Mobile Software Engineering: Design Implementation & Emergent Applications (2 Volumes) 2011. 900p. 475.00 *(978-1-61520-655-1(8),* Engineering Science Reference) IGI Global.

Allan, Alasdair. Augmented Reality in iOS: Building Apps with Sensors & Computer Vision. 2012. (ENG.). 50p. pap. 19.99 ***(978-1-4493-0850-6(3))*** O'Reilly Media, Inc.

Allen, Grant. Beginning Android 4. 2011. (ENG., Illus.). 604p. pap. 39.99 *(978-1-4302-3984-0(0))* Apress L. P.

Allen, Rob, et al. Zend Framework in Action. 2009. (ENG., Illus.). 425p. pap. 44.99 *(978-1-933988-32-0(0))* Manning Pubns. Co.

Arab Computer Society Staff & IEEE Computer Society Staff, contrib. by. 2007 IEEE/ACS International Conference on Computer Systems & Applications (AICCSA) Amman, Jordan, 13-16 May 2007, 2 vols. 2007. (Illus.). *(978-1-4244-1031-6(2))* IEEE Computer Society Pr.

Aschwanden, Bernard. JustSystems XMetaL Author: A Hands-on Guide to Creating DITA Compliant Documents. 2008. per. 49.95 *(978-0-9771222-5-7(5))* Above & Beyond Language Learning, Inc.

Aurum, Aybake & Wohlin, Claes, eds. Engineering & Managing Software Requirements. 2010. (ENG., Illus.). xviii, 478p. pap. 139.00 *(978-3-642-06407-4(8),* 3642064078) Springer.

Bajaj, Geetesh & Swinford, Echo. Microsoft Office PowerPoint 2007: Complete Makeover Kit. 2007. (ENG., Illus.). 256p. pap. 34.99 *(978-0-7897-3681-9(0))* Que.

Baker, Barry. Z/TPF & Websphere Application Server in a Service Oriented Architecture. 2007. (Illus.). xiv, 266p. *(978-0-7384-8619-2(1))* IBM.

Begun, Daniel A. Amazing Android Apps for Dummies. 2011. (ENG., Illus.). 256p. pap. 18.99 *(978-0-470-93629-0(0),* For Dummies) Wiley, John & Sons, Inc.

Bergerud, Marly & Busche, Don. Understanding Microcomputers & Applications Software. (DF - Computer Applications Ser.). (C). 15.95 *(978-0-538-70653-7(8));* 15.95 *(978-0-538-70654-4(6))* Cengage South-Western.

Bou Nassif, Ali. Measuring Saas Applications Based on Utilized Features. 2011. 116p. pap. ***(978-3-8443-2813-4(0))*** Lambert Academic Publishing.

Chapman, Barbara, et al. A Practical Programming Model for the Multi-Core Era: International Workshop on OpenMP, IWOMP 2007 Beijing, China, June 3-7, 2007, Proceedings. 2008. (Lecture Notes in Computer Science / Theoretical Computer Science & General Issues Ser.). xii, 207p. pap. 69.95 *(978-3-540-69302-4(5))* Springer.

Chen, Brian X. Always On: How the iPhone Unlocked the Anything-Anytime-Anywhere Future — and Locked Us In. 2011. (ENG.). 256p. 25.00 *(978-0-306-81960-5(0))* Da Capo Pr., Inc.

Chen, Brian X. Always On: How the iPhone Unlocked the Anything-Anytime-Anywhere Future — and Locked Us In. 2012. (ENG.). 256p. pap. 15.00 ***(978-0-306-82076-2(5))*** Da Capo Pr., Inc.

Chris, Carey, et al. An Educator's Guide To: Google Apps for Education. 2007. 29.95 *(978-0-9798787-1-8(3))* FTC Publishing.

Churches, Andrew & Dickens, Harry. Apps for Learning: 40 Best iPad/iPod Touch/iPhone Apps for High School Classrooms. 2011. (21st Century Fluency Ser.). 224p. pap. 24.95 ***(978-1-4522-2532-6(X),*** B25326P) Corwin Pr.

CLEP Exam Secrets Test Prep Staff, ed. CLEP Information Systems & Computer Applications Exam Secrets Study Guide: CLEP Test Review for the College Level Examination Program. 2011. 62.99 *(978-1-61403-500-8(8))* Mometrix Media LLC.

Course Technology. Google Applications CourseNotes. 2009. (CourseNotes Ser.). (ENG.). 6p. (C). 8.95 *(978-0-538-74429-4(4))* Course Technology.

—Google Apps Recharged Coursenotes. 2011. (CourseNotes Ser.). (ENG.). (C). 7.95 ***(978-1-133-18926-8(1))*** Course Technology.

Course Technology. Hot Topics in Technology CourseNotes. 2009. (CourseNotes Ser.). (ENG.). 6p. (C). 8.95 *(978-0-538-74430-0(8))* Course Technology.

Darbyshire, Paul & Darbyshire, Adam. Getting Started with Google Apps. 2010. (Illus.). xxx, 638p. E-Book ***(978-1-4302-2666-6(8),*** Friends of Ed) Apress L. P.

Darmawan, Budi, et al. Deployment Guide Series. 2008. (Illus.). xii, 132p. *(978-0-7384-8664-2(7))* IBM.

Desbien, Frederic, et al. Oracle WebCenter 11g: Build Rich, Customizable Enterprise 2.0 Applications. 2009. (Oracle Press Ser.). (ENG., Illus.). 528p. pap., instr.'s hndbk. ed. 59.99 *(978-0-07-162932-4(7),* 0071629327) McGraw-Hill Osborne.

Desch, Steven & Terndrup, Donald. Starry Night Workbook with Starry Night College Software: For Understanding Our Universe. 2012. (ENG.). 104p. (C). pap. 33.00 net. ***(978-0-393-91868-7(8),*** 91868) Norton, W. W. & Co., Inc.

DeVries, Derek. IOS SDK Development. 2012. (ENG.). 300p. pap. 35.00 *(978-1-934356-94-4(8),* Pragmatic Bookshelf, The) Pragmatic Programmers, LLC, The.

Ditzel, Maarten, et al. Power-Aware Architecting: For data-dominated Applications. 2007. (ENG.). x, 118p. 129.00 *(978-1-4020-6419-7(5),* 1402064195) Springer.

Draheim, Dirk. Trends in Enterprise Application Architecture. 2007. (Lecture Notes in Computer Science / Information Systems & Applications, incl. Internet/Web, & HCI Ser.). spiral bd. 79.95 *(978-3-540-75911-9(5))* Springer.

Draheim, Dirk & Weber, Gerald. Form-Oriented Analysis: A New Methodology to Model Form-Based Applications. 2010. (ENG., Illus.). xvii, 372p. pap. 109.00 *(978-3-642-05822-6(1),* 3642058221) Springer.

Eigenmann, Rudi. OpenMP in a New Era of Parallelism. 2008. (Lecture Notes in Computer Science / Programming & Software Engineering Ser.). spiral bd. 69.95 *(978-3-540-79560-5(X),* 354079560X) Springer.

Eisenberg, Robert & Bennage, Christopher. Sams Teach Yourself WPF in 24 Hours. 2008. (Sams Teach Yourself — Hours Ser.). (ENG., Illus.). 480p. pap. 44.99 *(978-0-672-32985-2(9))* Sams.

Eisenla, Markus. Discovery & Invocation of Environmental Models. 2010. 104p. pap. *(978-3-639-22450-4(7))* VDM Verlag Dr. Mueller e.K.

Eliassen, Frank & Kapitza, Rudiger, eds. Distributed Applications & Interoperable Systems: 10th IFIP WG 6. 1 International Conference, DAIS 2010, Amsterdam, the Netherlands, June 7-9, 2010, Proceedings. 2010. (Lecture Notes in Computer Science / Computer Communication Networks & Telecommunications Ser.). xiv, 243p. pap. 99.00 *(978-3-642-13644-3(3),* 3642136443) Springer.

Eliassen, Frank & Montresor, Alberto. Distributed Applications & Interoperable Systems: 6th IFIP WG 6. 1 International Conference, DAIS 2006, Athens, Greece, June 14-16 2006. 2006. (Lecture Notes in Computer Science Ser.: Vol. 4025). (Illus.). XI, 355p. pap. 109.00 *(978-3-540-35126-9(4),* 3540351264) Springer.

Felber, Pascal & Rouvoy, Romain, eds. Distributed Applications & Interoperable Systems: 11th IFIP WG 6. 1 International Conference, DAIS 2011, Reykjavik, Iceland, June 6-9, 2011, Proceedings. 2011. (Lecture Notes in Computer Science / Computer Communication Networks & Telecommunications Ser.). (Illus.). xii, 301p. pap. 108.00 *(978-3-642-21386-1(3),* 3642213863) Springer.

Fernandez, Obie. The Rails 3 Way. 2nd ed. 2010. (Addison-Wesley Professional Ruby Ser.). (ENG., Illus.). 768p. pap. 49.99 *(978-0-321-60166-7(1))* Addison Wesley Professional.

Fleishman, Glenn. Five-Star Apps: The Best iPhone & iPad Apps for Work & Play. 2010. (ENG., Illus.). 240p. pap. 19.99 *(978-0-321-75143-0(4))* Peachpit Pr.

Ford, Rob. The App & Mobile Case Study Book. Wiedermann, Julius, ed. 2011. (ENG., Illus.). 384p. 39.99 ***(978-3-8365-2880-1(0))*** TASCHEN DEU. Dist: Ingram Pub. Services.

Forta, Ben. Adobe ColdFusion 9 Web Application Construction Vol. 1, Set, 3 vols. 2010. (Construction Kit Ser.). (Illus.). 600p. pap. 59.99 *(978-0-321-66034-3(X))* Adobe Pr.

—Coldfusion 9 Application Development, 3 vols. 2010. (Construction Kit Ser.). (ENG., Illus.). Vol. 2, Kit. 600p. pap. 59.99 *(978-0-321-67919-2(9))* Vol. 3. 640p. pap. 59.99 *(978-0-321-67920-8(2))* Adobe Pr.

Gaskin, Shelley & Ferrett, Robert L. GO! with Microsoft Office Web Apps Getting Started. 2011. (ENG.). 72p. (C). pap. 31.00 *(978-0-13-254484-9(9),* Prentice Hall) Prentice Hall PTR.

Gaskin, Shelley, et al. Go! All in One: Computer Concepts & Applications. 2012. (ENG.). 864p. (C). spiral bd. 133.27 ***(978-0-13-284412-3(5),*** Prentice Hall) Prentice Hall PTR.

—Student CD for Go! All in One: Computer Concepts & Applications. 2012. (ENG.). (C). cd-rom 50.00 ***(978-0-13-284425-3(7),*** Prentice Hall) Prentice Hall PTR.

Gibson, Robert A., et al. WebSphere Application Server Administration Using Jython. 2009. (ENG.). 504p. 54.99 *(978-0-13-700952-7(6))* Pearson Education.

Godara, Varuna, ed. Strategic Pervasive Computing Applications: Emerging Trends. 2010. (Illus.). 403p. 180.00 *(978-1-61520-753-4(8))* IGI Global.

Goer, Evan. YUI 3 Cookbook. 2012. (ENG.). 406p. pap. 39.99 ***(978-1-4493-0419-5(2),*** Yahoo Pr.) O'Reilly Media, Inc.

Gucer, Vasfi. Implementing IBM Tivoli Service Request Manager V7.1 Service Catalog. 2008. (Illus.). x, 214p. *(978-0-7384-3177-2(X))* IBM.

Hailes, Stephen, et al. Sensor Systems & Software: First International ICST Conference, S-CUBE 2009, Pisa, Italy, September 7-9, 2009, Revised Selected Papers. 2010. (Lecture Notes of the Institute for Computer Sciences, Social-Informatics & Telecommunications Engineering Ser.). x, 289p. pap. 72.00 *(978-3-642-11527-1(6),* 3642115276) Springer.

Harty, Julian. A Practical Guide to Testing Wireless Smartphone Applications. Satyanarayanan, Mahadev, ed. 2009. (Synthesis Lectures on Mobile & Pervasive Computing Ser.). 99p. pap. 35.00 *(978-1-60845-253-8(0))* Morgan & Claypool Pubs.

Hendrickson, Mike & Sawyer, Brian. Best Android Apps: The Guide for Discriminating Downloaders. 2010. (ENG., Illus.). 240p. pap. 19.99 *(978-1-4493-8255-1(X))* O'Reilly Media, Inc.

Hoffman, Kevin & Dudek, Nathan. Essential Windows Azure: Architecting & Developing Applications for the Cloud. 2010. (Developer's Library). (ENG.). 432p. pap. 49.99 *(978-0-672-33310-1(4))* Sams.

Holland, Charlie. Microsoft SharePoint 2010 Web Applications the Complete Reference. 2010. (Complete Reference Ser.). (ENG., Illus.). 560p. pap. 45.00 *(978-0-07-174456-0(8),* 0071744568) McGraw-Hill Osborne.

Hooks, Joel, et al. ActionScript Developer's Guide to Robotlegs. 2011. (ENG.). 138p. pap. 19.99 ***(978-1-4493-0890-2(2))*** O'Reilly Media, Inc.

Hughes, Jeffrey. Android Apps Marketing: Secrets to Selling Your Android App. 2010. (Que Biz-Tech Ser.). (ENG., Illus.). 304p. pap. 24.99 *(978-0-7897-4633-7(6))* Que.

—iPhone & iPad Apps Marketing: Secrets to Selling Your iPhone & iPad Apps. 2010. (Que Biz-Tech Ser.). (ENG., Illus.). 312p. pap. 24.99 *(978-0-7897-4427-2(9))* Que.

Hughes, Jeffrey. IPhone & iPad Apps Marketing: Secrets to Selling Your iPhone & iPad Apps. 2nd rev. ed. 2011. (Que Biz-Tech Ser.). (ENG., Illus.). 336p. pap. 24.99 ***(978-0-7897-4833-1(9))*** Que.

Human-Computer Interaction; HCI Applications & Services: 12th International Conference, HCI International 2007 Beijing, China, July 22-27, 2007 Proceedings, Part IV. 2007. (Lecture Notes in Computer Science Ser.). (Illus.). 1225p. pap. 189.00 *(978-3-540-73109-2(1))* Springer.

IEEE Computer Society Press Staff, ed. Interoperability for Enterprise Software & Applications China Proceedings. 2009. 350p. 248.00 *(978-0-7695-3652-1(2))* IEEE Computer Society Pr.

IEEE Computer Society Staff, contrib. by. Proceedings of the 2008 Advanced Software Engineering & Its Applications: 13-15 December 2008, Hainan, China. 2008. (Illus.). xii, 277p. *(978-0-7695-3432-9(5))* IEEE Computer Society Pr.

IEEE Staff. 11th International Database Engineering & Applications Symposium (IDEAS 2007) 6-8 September / Banff, Alberta, Canada. 2007. (Illus.). 330p. pap. 194.00 *(978-0-7695-2947-9(X))* IEEE Computer Society Pr.

Iliescu, Ovidiu. Pro Java ME Apps: Building Commercial Quality Java ME Apps. 2011. (ENG.). 364p. pap. 49.99 *(978-1-4302-3327-5(3))* Apress L. P.

Indulska, Jadwiga & Raymond, Kerry. Distributed Applications & Interoperable Systems: 7th IFIP WG 6. 1 International Conference, DAIS 2007, Paphos, Cyprus, June 6-8, 2007, Proceedings. 2007. (Lecture Notes in Computer Science Ser.). (Illus.). 336p. pap. 109.00 *(978-3-540-72881-8(3))* Springer.

International Business Machines Corporation, International Technical Support Organization Staff, contrib. by. Enabling the on Demand Store with IBM Store Integration Framework. 3rd ed. 2007. (Illus.). xxii, 676p. pap. *(978-0-7384-8989-6(1))* IBM.

International Society for Computers and their Applications (ISCA) Staff, compiled by. 20th International Conference on Computer Applications in Industry & Engineering 2007. 2007. 312p. pap. 125.00 *(978-1-60423-986-7(7))* Curran Assocs., Inc.

—22nd International Conference on Computers & Their Applications 2007. 2007. 424p. pap. 125.00 *(978-1-60423-755-9(4))* Curran Assocs., Inc.

Jackson, Jeffrey C. Web Technologies: A Computer Science Perspective. 2006. (ENG., Illus.). 592p. (C). per. 123.00 *(978-0-13-185603-5(0),* Prentice Hall) Prentice Hall PTR.

Jackson, Philip. Selected Works. 2010. (Illus.). 156p. pap. 24.50 *(978-1-4452-7964-0(9))* Lulu Enterprises Inc.

Jackson, Wallace. Android Apps for Absolute Beginners. 2011. (ENG.). 344p. pap. 29.99 *(978-1-4302-3446-3(6))* Apress L. P.

Janowski, Tomasz, et al. Distributed Computing & Internet Technology: 6th International Conference, ICDCIT 2010, Bhubaneswar, India, February 15-17, 2010, Proceedings. 2010. (Lecture Notes in Computer Science / Information Systems & Applications, incl. Internet/Web, & HCI Ser.). xv, 283p. pap. 72.00 *(978-3-642-11658-2(2),* 3642116582) Springer.

Johnson, Bruce, et al. MCTS Self-Paced Training Kit (Exam 70-503) Microsoft .NET Framework 3.5 Windows Communication Foundation. 2008. (ENG.). 640p. pap. 69.99 *(978-0-7356-2565-5(4))* Microsoft Pr.

Johnston, Craig James. My Droid. 2nd rev. ed. 2011. (My... Ser.). (ENG., Illus.). 464p. pap. 24.99 ***(978-0-7897-4938-3(6))*** Que.

—My Motorola Atrix 4G. rev. ed. 2011. (My... Ser.). (ENG., Illus.). 336p. pap. 24.99 ***(978-0-7897-4888-1(6))*** Que.

Jones, Allen, et al. WPF Recipes in C# 2008: A Problem-Solution Approach. 2008. (ENG., Illus.). 700p. pap. 54.99 *(978-1-4302-1084-9(2))* Apress L. P.

Kanalakis, John. Complete Guide to Torque X. 2008. (ENG.). 393p. pap. 59.00 *(978-1-56881-421-6(6))* AK Peters, Ltd.

Keller, Debra. Multimedia Projects Binder Basics. 2012. (ENG.). 175p. (C). ring bd. 701.95 incl. cd-rom *(978-1-111-53225-3(7))* Course Technology.

Kereki, Federico. Essential GWT Kit: Building for the Web with Google Web. 2010. (Developer's Library). (ENG., Illus.). 352p. pap. 44.99 *(978-0-321-70514-3(9))* Addison Wesley Professional.

Knudsen, Jonathan. Kicking Butt with MIDP & MSA: Creating Great Mobile Applications. 2007. (Java Ser.). (ENG., Illus.). 432p. per. 59.99 *(978-0-321-46342-5(0))* Addison Wesley Professional.

Kodali, Raghu R., et al. EJB 3 Application Development. 2006. (Beginning: from Novice to Professional Ser.). (ENG., Illus.). 512p. pap. 44.99 *(978-1-59059-671-5(4))* Apress L. P.

Komatineni, Satya, et al. Pro Android 3. 2011. (Illus.). xxii, 1175p. E-Book ***(978-1-4302-3223-0(4))*** Apress L. P.

Koning, Sidney de. Automating ActionScript Projects with Eclipse & Ant. 2011. (ENG.). 98p. pap. 19.99 ***(978-1-4493-0773-8(6))*** O'Reilly Media, Inc.

Kooijmans, Alex Louwe. Performance Monitoring & Best Practices for WebSphere on Z/OS. 2007. (Illus.). xvi, 410p. *(978-0-7384-8600-0(0))* IBM.

Kreibich, Jay A. Using SQLite. 2010. (ENG., Illus.). 530p. pap. 49.99 *(978-0-596-52118-9(9))* O'Reilly Media, Inc.

Lal, Rajesh. Silverlight 2. 2010. (How-to Ser.). 400p. pap. 39.99 *(978-0-672-33062-9(8))* Sams.

Lee, Wei-Meng. Building Applications for the Mac App Store. 2011. 28p. pap. 17.99 ***(978-1-118-14535-7(6))*** Wiley, John & Sons, Inc.

Liu, Zhiming & Jifeng, He, eds. Mathematical Frameworks for Component Software: Models for Analysis & Synthesis. 2006. (Series on Component-Based Software Development Ser.). (Illus.). 354p. 142.00 *(978-981-270-017-9(X))* World Scientific Publishing Co., Inc.

MacDonald, Matthew. Pro WPF in C# 2010: Windows Presentation Foundation in . NET 4. 3rd ed. 2010. (ENG.). 1216p. pap. 54.99 *(978-1-4302-7205-2(8))* Apress L. P.

—Pro WPF in VB 2010: Windows Presentation Foundation in . NET 4. 2010. (ENG.). 1216p. pap. 54.99 *(978-1-4302-7240-3(6))* Apress L. P.

Magoules, Frederic & Venet, Cedric. Asynchronous Parallel Algorithms for for Petaflop & Exaflop Computation. 2013. (Chapman & Hall/CRC Numerical Analysis & Scientific Computation Ser.). (ENG., Illus.). 306p. 89.95 ***(978-1-4398-6941-3(3),*** Chapman & Hall/CRC) CRC Pr. LLC.

Makice, Kevin. Twitter API: Up & Running. 2009. (ENG., Illus.). 416p. pap. 34.99 *(978-0-596-15461-5(5))* O'Reilly Media, Inc.

Marinacci, Joshua. Building Mobile Applications with Java: Using the Google Web Toolkit & PhoneGap. 2012. (ENG.). 86p. pap. 19.99 ***(978-1-4493-0823-0(6))*** O'Reilly Media, Inc.

McFedries, Paul. Microsoft Office Web Apps. 2010. (Using Ser.). (ENG., Illus.). 272p. pap. 24.99 *(978-0-7897-4486-9(4))* Que.

Mehner, Paul. Developing Cloud Applications with Windows Azuretrade; Storage. 2012. (ENG.). 256p. pap. 29.99 ***(978-0-7356-6798-3(5))*** Microsoft Pr.

Meier, Rene. Distributed Applications & Interoperable Systems. 2008. (Lecture Notes in Computer Science / Image Processing, Computer Vision, Pattern Recognition, & Graphics Ser.). (Illus.). xi, 301p. pap. 109.00 *(978-3-540-68639-2(8))* Springer.

Ménard, Laurent. Application Integration: EAI, B2B, BPM & SOA. 2008. (Iste Ser.: 368). (ENG., Illus.). 256p. 105.00 (978-1-84821-088-2(4), Wiley-ISTE) Wiley, John & Sons, Inc.

Mermet, Jean, ed. UML-B Specification for Proven Embedded Systems Design. 2010. (ENG., Illus.). ix, 300p. pap. 189.00 (978-1-4419-5256-1(X), 144195256X) Springer.

Mertic, John. The Definitive Guide to SugarCRM: Better Business Applications. 2009. (ENG.). 280p. pap., instr.'s gde. ed. 59.99 (978-1-4302-2439-6(8)) Apress L. P.

Meyers, Peter. Best iPad Apps: The Guide for Discriminating Downloaders. 2010. (ENG., Illus.). 240p. pap. 21.99 (978-1-4493-9247-5(4)) O'Reilly Media, Inc.

Mighell, Tom. Ipad Apps in One Hour for Lawyers. 2012. (978-1-61438-360-4(X)) American Bar Assn.

Miller, Michael. Introduction to Google Apps. 2009. (ENG.). 240p. (C). pap. 78.67 (978-0-13-245747-7(4), Prentice Hall) Prentice Hall PTR.

—Introduction to Google Apps, Personal Apps. 2011. (ENG.). 384p. (C). pap. 78.67 (978-0-13-255212-7(4), Prentice Hall) Prentice Hall PTR.

Monson, Philip. IBM WebSphere Application Server V6.1 on the Solaris 10 Operating System. 2008. (Illus.). xiv, 472p. (978-0-7384-8599-7(3)) IBM.

Morana, Marco & UcedaVelez, Tony. Application Threat Modeling. 2013. (ENG.). 450p. 99.95 (978-0-470-50096-5(4), Wiley) Wiley John & Sons, Inc.

Morel, Médéric, et al. Google Apps: Mastering Integration & Customization. 2011. 249p. pap. (978-1-84969-216-8(5)) Packt Publishing, Ltd.

Müller, Matthias S., et al. Evolving OpenMP in an Age of Extreme Parallelism: 5th International Workshop on OpenMP, IWOMP 2009 Dresden, Germany, June 3-5, 2009 Proceedings. 2009. (Lecture Notes in Computer Science / Programming & Software Engineering Ser.). x, 183p. pap. 69.95 (978-3-642-02284-5(7), 3642022847) Springer.

Munshi, Aaftab, et al. ES 2.0 Programming Guide. 2008. (OpenGL Ser.). (ENG., Illus.). 480p. pap. 59.99 (978-0-321-50279-7(5)) Addison Wesley Professional.

Murphy, Austin. SIA User's Guide. Bloomquist, Don/Lee, Jr., ed. (C). 2006. 371p. pap. 49.00 net. (978-0-9787344-1-1(6)) 2nd ed. 2007. (ENG.). 359p. pap. 49.00 net. (978-0-9787344-3-5(2)) SIA Publishing, LLC.

Murphy, Mark. Beginning Android. 2009. (ENG.). 384p. pap. 44.99 (978-1-4302-2419-8(3)) Apress L. P.

—Beginning Android 2. 2nd ed. 2010. (ENG.). 416p. pap. 44.99 (978-1-4302-2629-1(3)) Apress L. P.

—Beginning Android 3. 2011. (ENG., Illus.). 612p. pap. 39.99 (978-1-4302-3297-1(8)) Apress L. P.

Murphy, Mark L. Beginning Android 3. 2011. (Illus.). xix, 589p. E-Book (978-1-4302-3298-8(6)) Apress L. P.

Nathan, Adam. WPF 4.0. 2010. (Unleashed Ser.). (ENG., Illus.). 848p. pap. 59.99 (978-0-672-33119-0(5)) Sams.

Nathan, Adam & Lehenbauer, Daniel. Windows Presentation Foundation Unleashed. annot. ed. 2006. (Unleashed Ser.). (ENG., Illus.). 656p. per. 59.99 (978-0-672-32891-6(7)) Sams.

Nikolov, George I. Cloud Computing & Government: Background, Benefits, Risks. 2011. (978-1-61761-784-3(9)) Nova Science Pubs., Inc.

Nimphius, Frank & Munsinger, Lynn. Oracle Fusion Developer Guide: Building Rich Internet Applications with Oracle Adf Business Components & Adf Faces. 2009. (Osborne ORACLE Press Ser.). (ENG., Illus.). 768p. pap. 59.99 (978-0-07-162254-7(3), 0071622543) McGraw-Hill Osborne.

O'Connor, Brett. Del. Icio. Us Mashups. 2007. (ENG., Illus.). 381p. per. 29.99 (978-0-470-09776-2(0), Wrox) Wiley, John & Sons, Inc.

Olejniczak, Stephen P. & Kirby, Brady. Asterisk for Dummies. 2007. (ENG., Illus.). 334p. per. 29.99 (978-0-470-09854-7(6), For Dummies) Wiley, John & Sons, Inc.

Pace, Eugenio, et al. Moving Applications to the Cloud on the Microsoft Azure Platform. 2010. (ENG., Illus.). 176p. pap. 29.99 (978-0-7356-4967-5(7)) Microsoft Pr.

Palmer, Steven H., et al. Web Application Vulnerabilities: Detect, Exploit, Prevent. 2007. (ENG., Illus.). 480p. per. 62.95 (978-1-59749-209-6(4), Syngress Press) Elsevier Science & Technology Bks.

Pandian, C. Ravindranath. Applied Software Risk Management: A Guide for Software Project Managers. 2006. (ENG., Illus.). 264p. 99.95 (978-0-8493-0524-5(1)) Auerbach Pubs., Inc.

Parashar, Manish & Aggarwal, Sanjeev K. Distributed Computing & Internet Technology: 5th International Conference, ICDCIT 2008 New Delhi, India, December 10 - 12, 2008 Proceedings. 2008. (Lecture Notes in Computer Science / Information Systems & Applications, incl. Internet/Web, & HCI Ser.). xii, 197p. pap. 69.95 (978-3-540-89736-1(4)) Springer.

Placeholder, Placeholder & Lawson, Rebecca. Skills for Success with Office 2010 Web Applications Getting Started. rev. ed. 2012. (ENG.). 80p. (C). pap. 31.00 (978-0-13-255004-8(0), Prentice Hall) Prentice Hall PTR.

Prima Games. IPhone App Book Vol. 2. 2010. 240p. pap. 12.99 (978-0-307-46955-7(7), Prima Games) Random Hse. Information Group.

Redkar, Tejaswi & Guidici, Tony. Windows Azure Platform. 2nd ed. 2011. (ENG.). 602p. pap. 49.99 (978-1-4302-3563-7(2)) Apress L. P.

Sanchez-Clark, Terry. Ibm« Mq Series« & Websphere Mq« Interview Questions, Answers, & Explanations: Unofficial MQ Series« Certification Review. 2007. 212p. per. 54.95 (978-1-60332-042-9(3)) Equity Pr.

Sarma, Bijon B. & Mira Rani Sarma Paral. Sus , the Latest Unified Script. 2010. 64p. pap. (978-3-8383-7411-6(8)) Lambert Academic Publishing.

Schmidt, Cheryl. MyITcertificationlabs: A+ Lab with Pearson eText — Standalone Access Card — for the Complete A+ Guide to PC Repair. 5th rev. ed. 2011. (ENG.). 6p. (C). E-Book 65.00 (978-0-13-277076-7(8)) Addison Wesley.

Schmidt, Daniel. Manipulation von Multimedia-Daten in Java: Übertragung, Speicherung und Manipulation von Multimedia-Daten in einer Java-Webanwendung. 2010. 96p. pap. (978-3-639-27602-2(7)) VDM Verlag Dr. Mueller e.K.

Seils, Zach, et al. Deploying Cisco Wide Area Application Services: Design & Deploy Cisco WAN Optimization, Application Acceleration, & Branch Virtualization Solutions for the Enterprise WAN. 2nd ed. 2010. (Networking Technology Ser.). (ENG., Illus.). 648p. 70.00 (978-1-58705-912-4(6)) Cisco Pr.

Serrao, Carlos, et al, eds. Web Application Security: Iberic Web Application Security Conference, IBWAS 2009, Madrid, Spain, December 10-11, 2009. Revised Selected Papers. 2010. (Communications in Computer & Information Science Ser.). (ENG., Illus.). x, 83p. pap. 84.00 (978-3-642-16119-3(7), 3642161197) Springer.

Severance, Charles & Severance, C. Using Google App Engine. 2009. (ENG., Illus.). 272p. pap. 29.99 (978-0-596-80069-7(X)) O'Reilly Media, Inc.

Snickars, Pelle & Vonderau, Patrick, eds. Moving Data: The iPhone & the Future of Media. 2012. (ENG., Illus.). 352p. (gr. 17). 89.50 (978-0-231-15738-4(X)); pap. 29.50 (978-0-231-15739-1(8)) Columbia Univ. Pr.

Solis, Daniel. Illustrated WPF. 2009. (ENG.). 550p. pap. 44.99 (978-1-4302-1910-1(5)) Apress L. P.

Soman, A. K., ed. Cloud-Based Solutions for Healthcare IT. 2011. (ENG., Illus.). 290p. 79.95 (978-1-57808-702-0(3)) BIOS Scientific Publishers Ltd. GBR. Dist: Taylor & Francis Group.

Spaanenburg, Lambert & Spaanenburg, Hendrik. Cloud Connectivity & Embedded Sensory Systems. 2010. (ENG., Illus.). xxiii, 285p. 129.00 (978-1-4419-7544-7(6), 1441975446) Springer.

Stanlick, Scott, et al. Struts 2 in Action. 2008. (ENG., Illus.). 432p. pap. 44.99 (978-1-933988-07-8(X)) Manning Pubns. Co.

Stein, Johannes & Kyaw, Aung Sithu. Irrlicht 1. 7 Realtime 3D Engine Beginner's Guide. 2011. 245p. pap. (978-1-84951-398-2(8)) Packt Publishing, Ltd.

Stoecker, Matthew A. MCTS Self-Paced Training Kit (Exam 70-502) Microsoft . NET Framework 3. 5-Windows Presentation Foundation. 2008. (ENG., Illus.). 560p. pap. 69.99 (978-0-7356-2566-2(2)) Microsoft Pr.

Studio Visual Steps Staff. Google for Seniors: Get Acquainted with Free Google Applications - Google Earth, Maps, Reader, Docs, Sites, Chrome. 2010. (Computer Books for Seniors Ser.). (ENG.). 244p. pap. 22.95 (978-90-5905-236-9(6)) Visual Steps B.V. NLD. Dist: Independent Pubs. Group.

Tabin, Herbert & Agranoff, Craig. Checked-in: How to Use Gowalla, Foursquare & Other Geo-Location Applications for Fun & Profit. 2010. pap. 19.95 (978-0-578-06348-5(4)) Pendant Publishing.

Thewlis, Paul. WordPress for Business Bloggers. 2008. (Illus.). 300p. pap. (978-1-84719-532-6(6)) Packt Publishing, Ltd.

Travassos, Willer. A Practical Face Recognition System Using a Game with a Purpose. 2010. 64p. pap. (978-3-8383-9447-3(X)) Lambert Academic Publishing.

Van Sinderen, Marten, ed. Dependable & Adaptable Networks & Services: 13th Open European Summer School & IFIP TC6. 6 Workshop, EUNICE 2007 Enschede, the Netherlands, July 18-20, 2007 Proceedings. 2007. (Lecture Notes in Computer Science Ser.). (Illus.). 148p. per. 59.95 (978-3-540-73529-8(1)) Springer.

Vinh, Khoi. Ordering Disorder: Grid Principles for Web Design. 2010. (Voices That Matter Ser.). (ENG.). 192p. pap. 29.99 (978-0-321-70353-8(7)) New Riders Publishing.

Warden, Pete. Big Data Glossary. 2011. (ENG.). 62p. pap. 19.99 (978-1-4493-1459-0(7)) O'Reilly Media, Inc.

Whitbeck, Ralph & Corebeck, Ralph. What's New with jQuery: Mobile & UI. 2012. (ENG.). 40p. pap. 29.99 (978-1-4493-0672-4(1)) O'Reilly Media, Inc.

Wilcox, Mark. Porting to the Symbian Platform: Open Mobile Development in C/C++ 2009. (Symbian Press Ser.: 31). (ENG., Illus.). 442p. pap. 65.00 (978-0-470-74419-2(7), Wiley) Wiley, John & Sons, Inc.

Winder, Russel & Roberts, Graham. Developing Java Software. 3rd rev. ed. 2006. (ENG., Illus.). 912p. pap. 79.95 (978-0-470-09025-1(1), Wiley) Wiley, John & Sons, Inc.

Zavoral, Filip, et al, eds. Networked Digital Technologies, Part I: Second International Conference, NDT 2010, Prague, Czech Republic, 2010. (Communications in Computer & Information Science Ser.). xxiii, 580p. pap. 139.00 (978-3-642-14291-8(5), 3642142915) Springer.

—Networked Digital Technologies, Part II: Second International Conference, NDT 2010, Prague, Czech Republic, July 7-9, 2010 Proceedings. 2010. (Communications in Computer & Information Science Ser.). xxiii, 730p. pap. 149.00 (978-3-642-14305-2(9), 3642143059) Springer.

Zhang, Du & Tsai, Jeffrey J. P. Advances in Machine Learning Applications in Software Engineering. 2006. (Illus.). 480p. 94.95 (978-1-59140-941-0(1)) IGI Global.

Zhou, Qihai. Proceedings: 2009 International Forum on Computer Science-Technology & Applications: IFCSTA 2009: 25-27 December 2009, Chongqing, China, 3 vols. 2009. (Illus.). (978-0-7695-3930-0(0)) IEEE Computer Society Pr.

2007 ACS/IEEE International Conference on Computer Systems & Applications. 2007. pap. 296.00 (978-1-4244-1030-9(4), EX1688) IEEE.

2007 International Symposium on Industrial Embedded Systems. 2007. pap. 216.00 (978-1-4244-0839-9(3), 07EX1633) IEEE.

APPLICATION SOFTWARE—DEVELOPMENT

see also Cocoa (Application Development Environment)

Abu-Eid, Valery. Designing Dynamic Java Applications with OSGi. 2012. (Developer's Library). (ENG.). 352p. pap. 44.99 (978-0-321-71433-6(4)) Addison Wesley Professional.

Abzaltynova, Zhanna & Williams, Janice. Business Intelligence Software. 2010. 104p. pap. (978-3-8383-6779-8(0)) Lambert Academic Publishing.

Ahson, Syed A. Mobile Web 2. 0: Developing & Delivering Services to Mobile Phones. 2010. (ENG., Illus.). 617p. 119.95 (978-1-4398-0082-9(0)) Auerbach Pubs., Inc.

Alessi, Patrick. Professional iPhone & iPad Database Application Programming. 2010. (ENG., Illus.). 408p. pap. 44.99 (978-0-470-63617-6(3), Wrox) Wiley, John & Sons, Inc.

Alexander, Brandon, et al. Pro iOS 5 Tools: Xcode Instruments & Build Tools. 2011. (ENG.). 392p. pap. 49.99 (978-1-4302-3608-5(6)) Apress L. P.

Ali, Maher. Advanced iOS 4 Programming: Developing Mobile Applications for Apple, iPhone, iPad, & iPod Touch. 2010. (ENG., Illus.). 720p. pap. 49.99 (978-0-470-97123-9(1), Wiley) Wiley, John & Sons, Inc.

—iPhone SDK Programming: Developing Mobile Applications for Apple iPhone & iPod Touch. 2009. (ENG., Illus.). 396p. pap. 44.99 (978-0-470-74282-2(8), Wiley) Wiley, John & Sons, Inc.

Alkhatib, Ghazi & Rine, David, eds. Integrated Approaches in Information Technology & Web Engineering: Advancing Organizational Knowledge Sharing. 2008. (Advances in Information Technology & Web Engineering Book Ser.). (Illus.). 392p. 195.00 (978-1-60566-418-7(9)) IGI Global.

Allan, Alasdair. Geolocation in iOS: Mobile Positioning & Mapping on iPhone & iPad. 2012. (ENG.). 50p. pap. 19.99 (978-1-4493-0844-5(9)) O'Reilly Media, Inc.

—iOS Sensor Apps with Arduino: Wiring the iPhone & iPad into the Internet of Things. 2011. (ENG.). 128p. pap. 19.99 (978-1-4493-0848-3(1)) O'Reilly Media, Inc.

—Learning iOS Programming: From Xcode to App Store. 2nd ed. 2012. (ENG.). 430p. pap. 34.99 (978-1-4493-0377-8(3)) O'Reilly Media, Inc.

Allen, Christopher & Appelcline, Shannon. iPhone in Action: Introduction to Web & SDK Development. 2009. (ENG., Illus.). 472p. pap. 39.99 (978-1-933988-86-3(X)) Manning Pubns. Co.

Allen, Dan. Seam in Action. 2008. (ENG., Illus.). 624p. pap. 44.99 (978-1-933988-40-5(1)) Manning Pubns. Co.

Allen, K. Programming Windows Workflow Foundation. 2006. pap. (978-1-904811-21-3(3)) Packt Publishing, Ltd.

Allen, Kevin. Wsdl 100 Success Secrets Essentials of Understanding & Applying Web Services Description Language - the Xml Based Protocol for Information Exchange. 2008. 144p. pap. (978-1-921523-22-9(0)) Emereo Pty Ltd.

Allen, Sarah, et al. Pro Smartphone Cross-Platform Development: iPhone, Blackberry, Windows Mobile & Android Development & Distribution. 2010. (ENG.). 288p. pap. 49.99 (978-1-4302-2868-4(7)) Apress L. P.

Altun, Tuncay. Sip Phone Application on Single Board Computer with Arm Microprocessor. 2011. 88p. pap. (978-3-8443-9177-0(0)) Lambert Academic Publishing.

Anderson, Chris. Pro Business Applications with Silverlight 5. 2nd ed. 2012. (ENG.). 708p. pap. 49.99 (978-1-4302-3500-2(4)) Apress L. P

Anderson, Frederic F. Xcode 4 Unleashed. 2nd ed. 2012. (Unleashed Ser.). (ENG.). 768p. pap. 44.99 (978-0-672-33327-9(9)) Sams.

Anderson, Jermaine G. Beginning Flash, Flex, & Air Development for Mobile Devices. 2011. (ENG.). 400p. pap. 39.99 (978-0-470-94815-6(9), Wrox) Wiley, John & Sons, Inc.

Anderson, Todd. Building a Photo Gallery with Adobe AIR. 2007. (Wrox Briefs Ser.). 47p. 6.99 (978-0-470-26023-4(8), Wrox) Wiley, John & Sons, Inc.

Andreu, Andres. Professional Pen Testing for Web Applications. 2006. (ENG., Illus.). 522p. pap. 39.99 (978-0-471-78966-6(6), Wrox) Wiley, John & Sons, Inc.

Angelides, Marios C. & Agius, Harry. Intersectionality, Sexuality & Psychological Therapies: Working with Lesbian, Gay & Bisexual Diversity. Butler, Catherine & Nair, Roshan das, eds. 2012. (ENG.). 296p. 119.95 (978-0-470-97500-8(8), Wiley-Blackwell) Wiley, John & Sons, Inc.

Apers, Chris & Paterson, Daniel. Beginning iPhone & iPad Web Apps: Scripting with HTML5, CSS3, & JavaScript. 2010. (ENG.). 512p. pap. 39.99 (978-1-4302-3045-8(2)) Apress L. P.

Architectural Design Patterns in C# 2011. 69.95 (978-1-4398-1658-5(1)) Auerbach Pubs., Inc.

Arevalo, Abraham. Programming the Cell Broadband Engine Architecture: Examples & Best Practices. 2008. (Illus.). xviii, 642p. (978-0-7384-8594-2(2)) IBM.

Armstrong, Peter & Berastau, Dima. Hello! Flex 4. 2009. (ENG., Illus.). 232p. pap. 34.99 (978-1-933988-76-4(2)) Manning Pubns. Co.

Arnold, Tom, et al. Professional Software Testing with Visual Studio 2005 Team System: Tools for Software Developers & Test Engineers. 2007. (ENG., Illus.). 408p. per. 49.99 (978-0-470-14978-2(7), Wrox) Wiley, John & Sons, Inc.

Arval, Peter. Developing the Business Case for a New Mobile Service. 2008. 52p. pap. (978-3-639-04815-5(6)) VDM Verlag Dr. Mueller e.K.

Backlin, Gene & Mishra, Abhishek. iPhone & iPad App 24-Hour Trainer. 2012. (ENG.). 504p. pap. 39.99 (978-1-118-13081-0(2), Wrox) Wiley, John & Sons, Inc.

Baker, Dane & McCann, Tyson. The Art of the App Store: The Business of Apple Development. 2011. (ENG.). 304p. pap. 29.99 (978-0-470-95278-8(4), Wrox) Wiley, John & Sons, Inc.

Ballad, Tricia & Ballad, William. Securing PHP Web Applications. 2008. (For Mere Mortals Ser.). (ENG., Illus.). 336p. pap. 44.99 (978-0-321-53434-7(4)) Addison Wesley Professional.

Ballard, Chuck. Customizing the Informix Dynamic Server for Your Environment. 2008. (Illus.). xx, 508p. (978-0-7384-8589-8(6)) IBM.

Barcia, Roland, et al. IBM(R) WebSphere(R) Deployment & Advanced Configuration. 2010. (ENG.). 720p. pap. 64.99 (978-0-13-248555-5(9)) Pearson Education.

Barney, Lee S. & Barney, Lee. Developing Hybrid Applications for the iPhone: Using HTML, CSS, & JavaScript to Build Dynamic Apps for the iPhone. 2009. (Developer's Library). (ENG., Illus.). 216p. pap. 39.99 (978-0-321-60416-3(4)) Addison Wesley Professional.

Bauer, Christian & King, Gavin. Java Persistence with Hibernate. 2nd ed. 2006. (ENG., Illus.). 904p. per. 59.99 (978-1-932394-88-7(5)) Manning Pubns. Co.

Beadle, Phillip & Krishnan, Mahesh. Microsoft Silverlight 4 for Dummies. 2010. (ENG., Illus.). 384p. pap. 29.99 (978-0-470-52465-7(0), For Dummies) Wiley, John & Sons, Inc.

Beckner, Mark, et al. Pro RFID in BizTalk Server 2009. 2009. (ENG.). 336p. pap. 49.99 (978-1-4302-1837-1(1)) Apress L. P.

Bell, Gavin. Building Social Web Applications: Establishing Community at the Heart of Your Site. 2009. (ENG., Illus.). 448p. pap. 34.99 (978-0-596-51875-2(7)) O'Reilly Media, Inc.

Bell, Kris, et al. Learn to Tango with D. 2008. (ENG.). 208p. pap. 19.99 (978-1-59059-960-0(8)) Apress L. P.

Beres, Jason, et al. Professional Silverlight, No. 4. 2010. (ENG., Illus.). 840p. pap. 44.99 (978-0-470-65092-9(3), Wrox) Wiley, John & Sons, Inc.

Bergmann, Sebastian & Priebsch, Stefan. Real-World Solutions for Developing High-Quality PHP Frameworks & Applications. 2011. (ENG.). 408p. pap. 44.99 (978-0-470-87249-9(7), Wrox) Wiley, John & Sons, Inc.

Bingham, Richard. Managing Oracle Fusion Applications. 2011. (Oracle Press Ser.). (ENG., Illus.). 350p. pap. 50.00 (978-0-07-175033-2(9), 0071750339) McGraw-Hill Osborne.

Binkley-Jones, Timothy, et al. Windows Phone 7 in Action. 2012. (ENG.). 375p. pap. 39.99 (978-1-61729-009-1(2)) Manning Pubns. Co.

Blank, R. AdvancED Flex Application Development: Building Rich Media X. 2008. (Friends of ED Adobe Learning Library). (Illus.). xx, 491p. (978-1-4302-0441-1(9), Friends of Ed) Apress L. P.

Böck, Heiko. The Definitive Guide to NetBeans Platform 7. 2011. (ENG.). 592p. pap. 59.99 (978-1-4302-4101-0(2)) Apress L. P.

Boehm, Anne. Murach's ADO. NET 3. 5, LINQ, & the Entity Framework with VB 2008. 2009. (Illus.). 707p. pap. 52.50 (978-1-890774-52-3(9)) Murach, Mike & Assocs., Inc.

Boehm, Anne & Mead, Ged. Murach's ADO. NET 4 Database Programming with VB 2010. 4th ed. 2011. (Illus.). 756p. pap. 54.50 (978-1-890774-62-2(6)) Murach, Mike & Assocs., Inc.

Boehm, Anne & Murach, Joel. Murach's ASP. NET 4 Web Programming with C# 2010. 4th ed. 2011. (ENG., Illus.). 834p. pap. 54.50 (978-1-890774-61-5(8)) Murach, Mike & Assocs., Inc.

Bowley, David. Portal Application Development Using WebSphere Portlet Factory. 2008. (Illus.). xviii, 708p. pap. (978-0-7384-8865-3(8)) IBM.

Boyd, Ryan. Getting Started with OAuth 2.0 No. 2. 2012. (ENG.). 82p. pap. 22.99 (978-1-4493-1160-5(1)) O'Reilly Media, Inc.

Brandon, Dan. Software Engineering for Modern Web Applications: Methodologies & Technologies. 2008. 300+p. 180.00 (978-1-59904-492-7(7)) IGI Global.

Brannan, James & Ward, Blake D. IOS SDK Programming A Beginners Guide. 2011. (Beginner's Guide Ser.). (ENG., Illus.). 528p. pap. 40.00 (978-0-07-175908-3(5), 0071759085) McGraw-Hill Osborne.

Braswell, Byron. Designing & Coding Applications for Performance & Scalability in Websphere Application Server. 2008. (Illus.). xviii, 668p. (978-0-7384-8864-6(X)) IBM.

Brinkmann, Peter. Making Musical Apps: Real-Time Audio Synthesis on Android & iOS. 2012. (ENG., Illus.). 124p. pap. 24.99 (978-1-4493-1490-3(2)) O'Reilly Media, Inc.

Brossier, Veronique. Developing Android Applications with Adobe AIR. 2011. (ENG., Illus.). 318p. pap. 39.99 (978-1-4493-9482-0(5)) O'Reilly Media, Inc.

Broulik, Brad. Pro jQuery Mobile. 2011. (ENG.). 268p. pap. 39.99 (978-1-4302-3966-6(2)) Apress L. P.

Brown, Charles P. Experience J2EE! Using Websphere Application Server V6.1. 2007. (Illus.). xvi, 444p. (978-0-7384-9451-7(8)) IBM.

Brown, Pete. Silverlight 5 in Action. 2012. (ENG.). 925p. pap. 59.99 (978-1-61729-031-2(9)) Manning Pubns. Co.

Brown, Pete, et al. Silverlight 4. rev. ed. 2010. (In Action Ser.). (ENG., Illus.). 800p. pap. 49.99 (978-1-935182-37-5(4)) Manning Pubns. Co.

Brunetti, Roberto. Windows Azure. 2011. (ENG., Illus.). 344p. pap. 34.99 (978-0-7356-4972-9(3)) Microsoft Pr.

Bücker, Axel. Understanding SOA Security: Design & Implementation. 2007. (Illus.). xiv, 408p. (978-0-7384-8967-4(0)) IBM.

—Understanding SOA Security: Design & Implementation. 2nd ed. 2007. (Illus.). xviii, 478p. (978-0-7384-8665-9(5)) IBM.

Bugnion, Laurent. Silverlight 4 Unleashed. 2010. (Unleashed Ser.). (ENG., Illus.). 736p. pap. 49.99 (978-0-672-33336-1(8)) Sams.

Bukovics, Bruce. Pro WF: Windows Workflow in NET 3. 5. 2008. (Expert's Voice in .NET Ser.). (ENG.). 852p. pap. 52.99 (978-1-4302-0975-1(5)) Apress L. P.

—Pro WF: Windows Workflow in .NET 3.0. 2007. (Expert's Voice In . Net Ser.). (ENG., Illus.). 744p. pap. 49.99 *(978-1-59059-778-1(8))* Apress L. P.

Burke, Bill. RESTful Java with JAX-RS. 2009. (Animal Guide Ser.). (ENG.). 314p. pap. 39.99 *(978-0-596-15804-0(1))* O'Reilly Media, Inc.

Burnette, Ed. Hello, Android: Introducing Google's Mobile Development Platform. 3rd ed. 2010. (ENG., Illus.). 300p. pap. 34.95 *(978-1-934356-56-2(5),* Pragmatic Bookshelf, The) Pragmatic Programmers, LLC, The.

Burrus, Colette & Parkin, Stephanie. Building Applications with IBM Rational Application Developer & JavaBeans: A Guided Tour. 2nd ed. 2008. (ENG., Illus.). 650p. pap. 59.95 *(978-1-931182-27-0(2))* MC Pr., LLC.

Cabrera, P. J., et al. IPhone Games Projects. 2009. (ENG., Illus.). 280p. pap. 39.99 *(978-1-4302-1968-2(8))* Apress L. P.

Calcote, John. Autotools: A Practioner's Guide to GNU Autoconf, Automake, & Libtool. 2010. (ENG.). 360p. pap. 44.95 *(978-1-59327-206-7(5))* No Starch Pr., Inc.

Cameron, Rob. Pro Windows Phone App Development. 2nd ed. 2011. (ENG., Illus.). 664p. pap. 44.99 ***(978-1-4302-3936-9(0))*** Apress L. P.

Cameron, Rob & Ghosh, Jit. Silverlight Recipes: A Problem-Solution Approach. 2nd ed. 2010. (ENG.). 1056p. pap. 49.99 *(978-1-4302-3033-5(9))* Apress L. P.

Cartman, Joseph & Ting, Richard. Strategic Mobile Design: Creating Engaging Experiences. 2008. (Voices That Matter Ser.). (ENG., Illus.). 224p. pap. 34.99 *(978-0-321-58007-8(9))* New Riders Publishing.

Casario, Marco. Flex Solutions: Essential Techniques for Flex 2 & 3 Developers. 2007. (ENG., Illus.). 904p. per. 54.99 *(978-1-59059-876-4(8),* Friends of Ed) Apress L. P.

Casteleyn, Sven, et al. Engineering Web Applications. 2009. (Data-Centric Systems & Applications Ser.). (ENG., Illus.). xiii, 349p. 69.95 *(978-3-540-92200-1(8),* 3540922008) Springer.

Castledine, Earle. Build Mobile: Websites & Apps for Smart Devices. 2011. (ENG., Illus.). 300p. pap. 39.95 *(978-0-9870908-4-3(4))* SitePoint Pty, Ltd. AUS. Dist: Ingram Pub. Services.

Castro Souto, Laura M. On the Development Life Cycle of Distributed Functional Applications. 2011. 264p. pap. ***(978-3-8383-9952-2(8))*** Lambert Academic Publishing.

Chak, Dan. Enterprise Rails. 2008. (ENG., Illus.). 352p. pap. 44.99 *(978-0-596-51520-1(0))* O'Reilly Media, Inc.

Chambers, Mike, et al. Air for Javascript Developers. 2008. (Pocket Guide Ser.). (ENG., Illus.). 208p. pap. 19.99 *(978-0-596-51837-0(4))* O'Reilly Media, Inc.

Chang, Kevin C., et al. Advances in Web & Network Technologies, & Information Management: APWeb/WAIM 2007 International Workshops: DBMAN 2007, WebETrends 2007, PAIS 2007 & ASWAN 2007, Huang Shan, China, June 16-18, 2007, Proceedings. 2007. (Lecture Notes in Computer Science / Information Systems & Applications, incl. Internet/Web, & HCI Ser.). xxiii, 707p. pap. 129.00 *(978-3-540-72908-2(9))* Springer.

Chen, Lei, et al. Advances in Web & Network Technologies & Information Management: AP Web/WAIM 2009 International Workshops: WCMT 2009, RTBI 2009, DBIR-ENQOIR 2009, & PAIS 2009. 2009. (Lecture Notes in Computer Science / Information Systems & Applications, incl. Internet/Web, & HCI Ser.). xvii, 245p. pap. 72.00 *(978-3-642-03995-9(2),* 3642039952) Springer.

Chong, Jan. Knowledge Sharing in Software Development: Comparing XP & Waterfall Methods. 2008. 104p. pap. *(978-3-639-10084-6(0))* VDM Verlag Dr. Mueller e.K.

Chu-Carroll, Mark C. Code in the Cloud. 2011. (ENG., Illus.). 320p. pap. 32.95 *(978-1-934356-63-0(8),* Pragmatic Bookshelf, The) Pragmatic Programmers, LLC, The.

Cimolini, Patrick & Cannell, Karen. Agile Oracle Application Express. 2012. (ENG., Illus.). 200p. pap. 39.99 *(978-1-4302-3759-4(7))* Apress L. P.

Ciurana, Eugene. Beginning Google App Engine. 2009. (ENG.). 350p. pap. 44.99 *(978-1-4302-2411-2(8))* Apress L. P.

Claeys, Kurt, et al. Professional WCF 4: Windows Communication Foundation with . NET 4. 2010. (ENG., Illus.). 480p. pap. 49.99 *(978-0-470-56314-4(1),* Wrox) Wiley, John & Sons, Inc.

Clark, Josh. Tapworthy: Designing Great iPhone Apps. 2010. (ENG., Illus.). 320p. pap. 39.99 *(978-1-4493-8165-3(0))* O'Reilly Media, Inc.

Clark, Terry. Ibm Rational Application Developer Interview Questions: Unofficial IBM RAD Certification Review. 2008. 152p. pap. 54.95 *(978-1-60332-029-0(6))* Equity Pr.

—Ibm«As400« Rpg Interview Questions, Answers, & Explanations: Unofficial RPG IBM AS/400 Certification Review. 2008. 200p. pap. 64.95 *(978-1-60332-049-8(0))* Equity Pr.

Cleeren, Gill & Dockx, Kevin. Microsoft Silverlight 4 Data & Services Cookbook: LITE Edition. 2011. 116p. pap. ***(978-1-84968-384-5(0))*** Packt Publishing, Ltd.

Clevenger, Nathan. Ipad in the Enterprise: Developing & Deploying Business Applications. 2011. (ENG., Illus.). 408p. pap. 44.99 *(978-1-118-02235-1(1),* Wiley) Wiley, John & Sons, Inc.

Cochran, Joel. Expression Blend in Action. 2012. (ENG.). 425p. pap. 44.99 ***(978-1-61729-029-9(7))*** Manning Pubns. Co.

Coffey, Michael. Beginning iPhone 2 Application Development: From Novice to Professional. Anglin, Steve, ed. 2008. (Beginning Ser.). 350p. E-Book 39.99 *(978-1-4302-1052-8(4))* Apress L. P.

Cogoluegnes, Arnaud, et al. Spring Batch in Action. 2011. (ENG.). 504p. pap. 59.99 *(978-1-935182-95-5(1))* Manning Pubns. Co.

Cole, Alaric. Learning Flex 3: Getting up to Speed with Rich Internet Applications. 2008. (Adobe Developer Library). (ENG., Illus.). 304p. pap. 39.99 *(978-0-596-51732-8(7))* O'Reilly Media, Inc.

Collins, Charlie, et al. Android in Practice. 2011. (ENG., Illus.). 648p. pap. 49.99 *(978-1-935182-92-4(7))* Manning Pubns. Co.

—Unlocking Android. 2009. (ENG., Illus.). 416p. pap., instr.'s gde. ed. 39.99 *(978-1-933988-67-2(3))* Manning Pubns. Co.

Collins, Mark. Beginning WF: Windows Workflow in . NET 4. 0. 2010. (ENG.). 500p. pap. 49.99 *(978-1-4302-2485-3(1))* Apress L. P.

Collins, Mark J. & Mayberry, Michael. Pro Office 365 Development. 2012. (ENG.). 676p. pap. 44.99 ***(978-1-4302-4074-7(1))*** Apress L. P.

Conder, Shane & Darcey, Lauren. Android Wireless Application Development. 2nd ed. 2010. (Developer's Library). (ENG., Illus.). 792p. pap. 49.99 *(978-0-321-74301-5(6))* Addison Wesley Professional.

—Android Wireless Application Development Vol. II: Advanced Android. 3rd rev. ed. 2012. (Developer's Library). (ENG.). 528p. pap. 49.99 ***(978-0-321-81384-8(7))*** Addison Wesley Professional.

—Android Wireless Application Development Volume I: Android Essentials. 3rd rev. ed. 2012. (Developer's Library). (ENG., Illus.). 544p. pap. 44.99 ***(978-0-321-81383-1(9))*** Addison Wesley Professional.

Conder, Shane & Darcey, Lauren. Sams Teach Yourself Android Application Development in 24 Hours. 2nd rev. ed. 2011. (Sams Teach Yourself — Hours Ser.). (ENG., Illus.). 512p. pap. 39.99 *(978-0-672-33569-3(7))* Sams.

Conner, Nancy. Quick Base. 2007. (Missing Manual Ser.). (ENG.). 554p. per. 49.99 *(978-0-596-52960-4(0),* Pogue Pr.) O'Reilly Media, Inc.

Constantine, Larry L. Software for Use: A Practical Guide to the Models & Methods of Usage-Centered Design. rev. ed. 2011. (ENG.). 608p. pap. 69.99 *(978-0-321-77372-2(1))* Addison Wesley Professional.

Conway, Joe & Hillegass, Aaron. IOS Programming: The Big Nerd Ranch Guide. 3rd ed. 2012. (Big Nerd Ranch Guides). (ENG.). 590p. pap. 49.99 ***(978-0-321-82152-2(1))*** Addison Wesley Professional.

Cook, Shane. CUDA Programming: A Developer's Guide to Parallel Computing with GPUs. 2012. (Applications of GPU Computing Ser.). (ENG.). 560p. pap. 49.95 ***(978-0-12-415933-4(8)***, Morgan Kaufmann) Elsevier Science & Technology Bks.

Cram101 Textbook Reviews & Cram101 Textbook Reviews. Outlines & Highlights for Web Application Architecture: Principles, Protocols & Practices by Leon Shklar, ISBN. 2011. 342p. pap. 33.95 ***(978-1-61461-667-2(1))*** Cram101 Inc.

Cram101 Textbook Reviews Staff. Outlines & Highlights for Database Design, Application Development, & Administration by Mannino, Isbn: 9780072942200. 2008. 104p. pap. 10.95 *(978-1-4288-6031-5(2))* Cram101 Inc.

Crawfis, Roger, et al. Android Game Programming for Dummies. 2012. (ENG.). 504p. pap. 34.99 ***(978-1-118-02774-5(4)***, For Dummies) Wiley, John & Sons, Inc.

Credle, Rufus. Migrating from WebSphere Application Server Community Edition to WebSphere Application Server. 2007. (Illus.). xvi, 506p. *(978-0-7384-8947-6(6))* IBM.

Crenna, Daniel. Professional Twitter Development: With Examples in .Net 3.5. 2009. (ENG., Illus.). 456p. pap. 39.99 *(978-0-470-53132-7(0),* Wrox) Wiley, John & Sons, Inc.

Crowther, Rob. Quick & Easy Html5 & Css3: A User Friendly Reference Guide. 2012. (ENG.). 325p. pap. 34.99 ***(978-1-935182-89-4(7))*** Manning Pubns. Co.

Cummins, Holly & Ward, Timothy. Enterprise OSGi in Action: With examples using Apache Aries. 2012. (ENG.). 350p. pap. 70.00 ***(978-1-61729-013-8(0))*** Manning Pubns. Co.

Czapski, Michael, et al. Java CAPS Basics: Implementing Common EAI Patterns. 2008. (ENG., Illus.). 496p. 74.99 *(978-0-13-713071-9(6))* Prentice Hall PTR.

Czernicki, Bart. Silverlight 4 Business Intelligence Software. 2nd ed. 2010. (ENG.). 576p. pap. 59.99 *(978-1-4302-3060-1(6))* Apress L. P.

Daigneau, Robert. Service Design Patterns: Fundamental Design Solutions for SOAP/WSDL & RESTful Web Services. 2011. (Addison-Wesley Signature Series (Fowler) Ser.). (ENG., Illus.). 352p. 54.99 *(978-0-321-54420-9(X))* Addison Wesley Professional.

Dalal, Mamta & Ghoda, Ashish. XAML Developer Reference. 2011. (ENG & ABK., Illus.). 342p. pap. 39.99 ***(978-0-7356-5896-7(X))*** Microsoft Pr.

Dannen, Chris. iPhone Design Award-Winning Projects. 2010. (ENG.). 216p. pap. 39.99 *(978-1-4302-7235-9(X))* Apress L. P.

Darcey, Lauren & Conder, Shane. Android: Wireless Application Development. 2nd ed. 2011. (Illus.). 782p. pap. incl. audio compact disk *(978-0-321-74967-3(7))* Pearson Educación.

—Android Application Development. 2010. (Sams Teach Yourself — Hours Ser.). (ENG., Illus.). 480p. pap. 39.99 *(978-0-321-67335-0(2))* Sams.

—Android Wireless Application Development: Android Essentials. 3rd ed. 2012. pap. ***(978-0-321-81496-8(7))*** Addison-Wesley Longman, Inc.

—Learning Android Application Programming for the Kindle Fire: A Hands-on Guide to Building Your First Android Application. 2012. (Learning Ser.). (ENG.). 500p. pap. 39.99 ***(978-0-321-83397-6(X))*** Addison Wesley Professional.

Darmawan, Budi. IBM Tivoli Composite Application Manager Family: Installation, Configuration, & Basic Usage. 3rd ed. 2008. (Illus.). xx, 662p. pap. *(978-0-7384-8659-8(0))* IBM.

Darwin, Ian F. Android Cookbook. 2012. (ENG.). 688p. pap. 54.99 *(978-1-4493-8841-6(8))* O'Reilly Media, Inc.

David, Matthew. Flash Mobile: Developing Android & iOS Applications. 2011. (Visualizing the Web Ser.). (ENG., Illus.). 308p. pap. 44.95 *(978-0-240-81568-8(8),* Focal Pr.) Elsevier Science & Technology Bks.

De Florio, Vincenzo. Application-Layer Fault-Tolerance Protocols. 2009. (Illus.). 378p. 165.00 *(978-1-60566-182-7(1))* IGI Global.

de Jonge, Adriaan. Essential App Engine: Building High-Performance Java Apps with Google App Engine. rev. ed. 2011. (Developer's Library). (ENG., Illus.). 352p. pap. 39.99 ***(978-0-321-74263-6(X))*** Addison Wesley Professional.

—JQuery, jQuery UI, & jQuery Mobile: Recipes & Examples. 2012. (Developer's Library). (ENG.). 400p. pap. 39.99 ***(978-0-321-82208-6(0))*** Addison Wesley Professional.

De Nardis, Amintore. IBM Application Development & Problem Determination Tools V7 for System Z: Application Performance Analyzer, Debug Tool Utilities & Advanced Functions, Fault Analyzer, File Export, File Manager, & Workload Simulator. 2007. (Illus.). xxii, 1270p. *(978-0-7384-8630-7(2))* IBM.

Deitel, Paul. Android App Development Fundamentals. 2012. (ENG.). 512p. pap. 69.99 ***(978-0-13-293180-9(X)***, Prentice Hall) Prentice Hall PTR.

Deitel, Paul & Deitel, Harvey. Android: How to Program. 2012. (ENG., Illus.). 850p. (C). pap. 125.00 ***(978-0-13-299054-7(7)***, Prentice Hall) Prentice Hall PTR.

Deitel, Paul J., et al. Android for Programmers: An App-Driven Approach. 2011. (Deitel Developer Ser.). (ENG.). 512p. pap. 44.99 *(978-0-13-212136-1(0),* Prentice Hall) Prentice Hall PTR.

Delessio, Carmen. Sams Teach Yourself Google TV App Development in 24 Hours. 2012. (ENG.). 400p. pap. 39.99 ***(978-0-672-33603-4(0))*** Sams.

DeVoe, Jiva, et al. Cocoa. 2010. (Developer Reference Ser.: 5). (ENG., Illus.). 624p. pap. 49.99 *(978-0-470-49589-6(8),* Wiley) Wiley, John & Sons, Inc.

Dewey, Ben. Getting Started with Metro Apps: A Guide to the Windows Runtime. 2012. (ENG.). 100p. pap. 14.99 ***(978-1-4493-2055-3(4))*** O'Reilly Media, Inc.

Di Benedetto, Paolo. A Framework for Context Aware Adaptable Software Services. 2011. 180p. pap. ***(978-3-8433-5383-0(2))*** Lambert Academic Publishing.

DiMarzio, J. F. Practical Android 4 Games Development. 2011. (ENG.). 320p. pap. 39.99 ***(978-1-4302-4029-7(6))*** Apress L. P.

Diment, Kieren & Trout, Matt. The Definitive Guide to Catalyst: Writing Extensible, Scalable & Maintainable Perl-Based Web Applications. 2009. (Definitive Guide To Ser.). (ENG.). 362p. pap. 49.99 *(978-1-4302-2365-8(0))* Apress L. P.

Dolce, Julian. Android Development with Flash: Your Visual Blueprint for Developing Mobile Apps. 2010. (Visual Blueprint Ser.: 35). (ENG., Illus.). 352p. pap. 34.99 *(978-0-470-90432-9(1),* Visual) Wiley, John & Sons, Inc.

—Ios Development with Flash: Your Visual Blueprint for Developing Apple Apps. 2010. (Visual Blueprint Ser.: 33). (ENG., Illus.). 352p. pap. 34.99 *(978-0-470-62204-9(0),* Visual) Wiley, John & Sons, Inc.

Donnelly, Martin, et al. Mastering XPages: A Step-by-Step Guide to XPages Application Development & the XSP Language. 2011. (ENG., Illus.). 784p. pap. 64.99 *(978-0-13-248631-6(8))* Pearson Education.

Donnelly, Martin, et al. XPages Portable Command Guide: A Compact Resource to XPages Application Development & the XSP Language. rev. ed. 2012. (Portable Command Guide Ser.). (ENG., Illus.). 320p. pap. 34.99 ***(978-0-13-294305-5(0))*** Pearson Education.

Drance, Matt & Warren, Paul. iOS Recipes: Tips & Tricks for Awesome iphone & ipad Apps. 2011. (ENG., Illus.). 224p. pap. 33.00 *(978-1-934356-74-6(3),* Pragmatic Bookshelf, The) Pragmatic Programmers, LLC, The.

Du, Xiaoyong, et al, eds. Web Technologies & Applications: 13th Asia-Pacific Web Conference, APWeb 2011, Beijing, Chiina, April 18-20, 2011. Proceedings. 2011. (Lecture Notes in Computer Science / Information Systems & Applications, incl. Internet/Web, & HCI Ser.). (Illus.). xix, 486p. pap. 107.00 *(978-3-642-20290-2(X),* 364220290X) Springer.

Dutson, Phillip. Sams Teach Yourself jQuery Mobile in 24 Hours. 2012. (Sams Teach Yourself — Hours Ser.). (ENG.). 450p. pap. 39.99 ***(978-0-672-33594-5(8))*** Sams.

Dwyer, Jeff. Pro Web 2. 0 Application Development with GWT. 2008. (Expert's Voice in Web Development Ser.). (ENG., Illus.). 480p. pap. 44.99 *(978-1-59059-985-3(3))* Apress L. P.

Edelson, Justin & Liu, Henry. JRuby. rev. ed. 2008. (ENG., Illus.). 224p. pap. 34.99 *(978-0-596-51980-3(X))* O'Reilly Media, Inc.

Edge, Charles, et al. Enterprise Mac Administrator's Guide. 2009. (ENG.). 500p. pap. 49.99 *(978-1-4302-2443-3(6))* Apress L. P.

Eisenberg, Robert & Eisenberg, Rob. Windows Workflow Foundation. 2009. (Sams Teach Yourself Ser.). (ENG., Illus.). 624p. pap. 34.99 *(978-0-321-48699-8(4))* Addison Wesley Professional.

Elst, Peter, et al. AdvancED AIR Applications. 2011. (ENG.). 400p. pap. 49.99 *(978-1-4302-0985-0(2),* Friends of Ed) Apress L. P.

Esposito, Dino & Saltarello, Andrea. Microsoft .NET: Architecting Applications for the Enterprise. 2010. (ENG., Illus.). 462p. pap. 44.99 *(978-0-7356-2609-6(X))* Microsoft Pr.

Evjen, Bill, et al. ASP.NET 4 in C# & VB. 2010. (ENG., Illus.). 1536p. pap. 59.99 *(978-0-470-50220-4(7),* Wrox) Wiley, John & Sons, Inc.

—Real World .NET, C#, & Silverlight: Indispensible Experiences from 15 MVPs. 2011. (ENG.). 648p. pap. 54.99 *(978-1-118-02196-5(7),* Wrox) Wiley, John & Sons, Inc.

Fain, Yakov, et al. Enterprise Development with Flex: Best Practices for RIA Developers. 2010. (Adobe Dev Lib Ser.). (ENG., Illus.). 688p. pap. 54.99 *(978-0-596-15416-5(X))* O'Reilly Media, Inc.

—Rich Internet Applications with Adobe Flex & Java: Secrets of the Masters. 2006. per. 119.00 *(978-0-9777622-2-4(X))* SYS-CON Media.

Farley, Jim. Practical JBoss Seam Projects. 2007. (Expert's Voice Ser.). (ENG., Illus.). 229p. per. 39.99 *(978-1-59059-863-4(6))* Apress L. P.

Faucher, Brian. Windows Phone 7 Application Development 24 Hour Trainer. 2011. (ENG.). 288p. pap. 39.99 *(978-0-470-93907-9(9),* Wrox) Wiley, John & Sons, Inc.

Febvre, L. & Burd, Barry. Android Application Development All-in-One for Dummies. 2011. (ENG., Illus.). 648p. pap. 39.99 ***(978-1-118-02770-7(1)***, For Dummies) Wiley, John & Sons, Inc.

Feiler, Jesse. Data-Driven iOS Apps for iPad & iPhone with FileMaker Pro, Bento by FileMaker, & FileMaker Go. rev. ed. 2011. (ENG., Illus.). 400p. pap. 39.99 *(978-0-7897-4786-0(3))* Que.

—Get Rich with Apps! Your Guide to Reaching More Customers & Making Money Now. 2010. (ENG., Illus.). 240p. pap. 19.95 *(978-0-07-170029-0(3),* 0071700293) McGraw-Hill Cos., The.

Feiler, Jesse. Sams Teach Yourself Core Data for Mac & iOS in 24 Hours. 2011. (Sams Teach Yourself — Hours Ser.). (ENG.). 480p. pap. 39.99 ***(978-0-672-33577-8(8))*** Sams.

Felker, Donn. Android Tablet Application Development for Dummies. 2011. (ENG.). 384p. pap. 29.99 *(978-1-118-09623-9(1),* For Dummies) Wiley, John & Sons, Inc.

Fernandez, Obie. The Rails Way. 2007. (Addison-Wesley Professional Ruby Ser.). (Illus.). 912p. per. 54.99 *(978-0-321-44561-2(9))* Addison Wesley Professional.

Ferracchiati, Fabio Claudio & Garofalo, Emanuele. Windows Phone Recipes: A Problem Solution Approach. 2nd ed. 2011. (ENG.). 492p. pap. 39.99 ***(978-1-4302-4137-9(3))*** Apress L. P.

Ferraro, Richard & Aktihanoglu, Murat. Location Aware Applications. 2011. (ENG., Illus.). 320p. pap. 44.99 *(978-1-935182-33-7(1))* Manning Pubns. Co.

Ferrill, Paul. Pro Android Python with SL4A. 2011. (ENG.). 296p. pap. 44.99 *(978-1-4302-3569-9(1))* Apress L. P.

Firtman, Maximiliano. JQuery Mobile: Up & Running. 2012. (ENG., Illus.). 272p. pap. 29.99 *(978-1-4493-9765-4(4))* O'Reilly Media, Inc.

—Programming the Mobile Web. 2010. (ENG., Illus.). 512p. pap. 49.99 *(978-0-596-80778-8(3))* O'Reilly Media, Inc.

Fisher, Mark, et al. Spring Persistence: A Running Start. 2009. (ENG.). 236p. pap. 19.99 *(978-1-4302-1877-7(0))* Apress L. P.

Fitzek, Frank H. P., et al. Qt for Symbian. 2010. (ENG., Illus.). 208p. pap. 45.00 *(978-0-470-75010-0(3),* Wiley) Wiley, John & Sons, Inc.

Flex 2 Beyond the Basics. 2006. cd-rom 149.95 *(978-1-59671-284-3(8))* Lynda.com, LLC.

Ford, Sara. Microsoft Visual Studio Tips: 251 Ways to Improve Your Productivity. 2008. (Visual Studio Tips Ser.). (ENG.). 272p. pap. 34.99 *(978-0-7356-2640-9(5))* Microsoft Pr.

Forta, Ben & Camden, Raymond. Adobe Coldfusion 8 Application Development: Web Application Construction Kit, 3 vols., Vol. 2. 2007. (ENG., Illus.). 552p. per. 59.99 *(978-0-321-51546-9(3))* Adobe Pr.

—Adobe Coldfusion 8 Getting Started Volume 1: Getting Started, 3 vols. 2007. (ENG., Illus.). 600p. per. 50.00 *(978-0-321-51548-3(X))* Adobe Pr.

Forta, Ben & Swaroop, Prayank. Adobe Flex 3 in 24 Hours. 2010. (Sams Teach Yourself — Hours Ser.). (ENG.). 400p. pap. 39.99 *(978-0-672-32987-6(5))* Sams.

Forta, Ben, et al. Adobe Coldfusion 8: Advanced Application Development, 3 vols. 2007. (ENG., Illus.). 696p. per. 59.99 *(978-0-321-51547-6(1))* Adobe Pr.

Fox, Steve. Developing Microsoft Sharepoint Applications Using Windows Azure. 2011. (ENG., Illus.). 336p. pap. 34.99 *(978-0-7356-5662-8(2))* Microsoft Pr.

Fox, Steve & Sheldon, Bill. Professional Office Business Application Development: Using Microsoft Office SharePoint Server 2007 & VSTO. 2008. (ENG., Illus.). 336p. pap. 49.99 *(978-0-470-37731-4(3),* Wrox) Wiley, John & Sons, Inc.

Frederick, Gail & Lal, Rajesh. Smartphone Web Development: Building JavaScript, CSS, HTML & Ajax-Based Applications for iPhone, Android, Palm Pre, BlackBerry, Windows Mobile & Nokia S60. 2010. (ENG., Illus.). 368p. pap. 39.99 *(978-1-4302-2620-8(X))* Apress L. P.

Freeman, Steve & Pryce, Nat. Growing Object-Oriented Software, Guided by Tests. 2009. (Beck Signature Ser.). (ENG., Illus.). 384p. pap. 49.99 *(978-0-321-50362-6(7))* Addison Wesley Professional.

Friesen, Jeff. Beginning Java 7. 2011. (ENG., Illus.). 920p. pap. 39.99 ***(978-1-4302-3909-3(3))*** Apress L. P.

Friesen, Jeff & Smith, Dave. Android Recipes: A Problem-Solution Approach. 2011. (ENG.). 456p. pap. 39.99 *(978-1-4302-3413-5(X))* Apress L. P.

Froehlich, Christopher. The Complete Idiot's Guide to Android App Development. 2011. (Complete Idiot's Guide Ser.). (ENG., Illus.). 416p. (gr. 12). 24.95 *(978-1-61564-106-2(8),* Alpha Bks.) Penguin Group (USA) Inc.

Fuchs, Susanne. Organizational Adoption Models for Early ASP Technology Stages: Adoption & Diffusion of Application Service Providing (ASP) in the Electric Utility Sector. 2008. 252p. pap. *(978-3-8364-7301-9(1))* VDM Verlag Dr. Mueller e.K.

Galbraith, Patrick. Developing Web Applications with Apache, Mysql, Memcached, & Perl. 2009. (ENG., Illus.). 888p. pap. 49.99 *(978-0-470-41464-4(2),* Wrox) Wiley, John & Sons, Inc.

Ganguly, Debashis. Network & Application Security. Lahiri, Shibamauli, ed. 2011. (ENG., Illus.). 160p. pap. 79.95 ***(978-1-57808-755-6(4))*** BIOS Scientific Publishers Ltd. GBR. Dist: Taylor & Francis Group.

Gao, X. Z., et al, eds. Soft Computing in Industrial Applications: Algorithms, Integration, & Success Stories. 2010. (Advances in Intelligent & Soft Computing Ser.). (ENG., Illus.). 300p. pap. 219.00 *(978-3-642-11281-2(1),* 3642112811) Springer.

Garofalo, Raffaele. Building Enterprise Applications with Windows Presentation Foundation & the Model View Viewmodel (Mvmm) Pattern. 2011. (ENG., Illus.). 226p. pap. 19.99 *(978-0-7356-5092-3(6))* Microsoft Pr.

Garrett, Rob. Pro SharePoint 2010 Administration. 2011. (ENG.). 412p. pap. 49.99 ***(978-1-4302-3792-1(9))*** Apress L. P.

Gates, Alan. Programming Pig. 2011. (ENG.). 224p. pap. 39.99 ***(978-1-4493-0264-1(5))*** O'Reilly Media, Inc.

Gaudioso, Victor. Foundation Expression Blend 2: Building Applications in WPF & Silverlight. 2008. (ENG., Illus.). 350p. pap. 39.99 *(978-1-59059-976-1(4)*, Friends of Ed) Apress L. P.

—Foundation Expression Blend 4 with Silverlight. 2013. (ENG., Illus.). 440p. pap. 39.99 *(978-1-4302-2973-5(X)*, Friends of Ed) Apress L. P.

Georgakopoulos, Dimitrios, et al. Event-based Systems. 2011. (Synthesis Lectures on Data Management Ser.). 100p. pap. 35.00 *(978-1-60845-414-3(2))* Morgan & Claypool Pubs.

Gerakines, Nick. Facebook Application Development. 2008. (ENG., Illus.). 330p. pap. 39.99 *(978-0-470-24666-5(9)*, Wrox) Wiley, John & Sons, Inc.

Gerakines, Nick, et al. Erlang Web Applications: Problem-Design-Solution. 2010. (ENG.). 400p. pap. 49.99 *(978-0-470-74384-3(0))* Wiley, John & Sons, Inc.

Ghatol, Rohit & Patel, Yogesh. Beginning PhoneGap: Mobile Web Framework for JavaScript & HTML5. 2012. (ENG., Illus.). 344p. pap. 39.99 ***(978-1-4302-3903-1(4))*** Apress L. P.

Ghoda, Ashish. Introducing Silverlight 4. 2010. (ENG.). 744p. pap. 39.99 *(978-1-4302-2991-9(8))* Apress L. P.

—Pro Silverlight for the Enterprise. 2009. (ENG.). 312p. pap. 49.99 *(978-1-4302-1867-8(3))* Apress L. P.

Ghosh, Jit & Cameron, Rob. Silverlight 2 Recipes, Vol. 2. 2008. (ENG., Illus.). 616p. pap. 44.99 *(978-1-59059-977-8(2))* Apress L. P.

—Silverlight Recipes: A Problem-Solution Approach. 2009. (Problem-Solution Approach Ser.). (ENG.). 992p. pap. 49.99 *(978-1-4302-2435-8(5))* Apress L. P.

Gibbs, Matt & Wahlin, Dan. Professional ASP.NET 2.0 AJAX. 2007. (ENG., Illus.). 336p. per. 39.99 *(978-0-470-10962-5(9)*, Wrox) Wiley, John & Sons, Inc.

Givens, Michael. Adobe Air Programming in 24 Hours. 2008. (Sams Teach Yourself — Hours Ser.). (ENG., Illus.). 432p. pap. 29.99 *(978-0-672-33030-8(X))* Sams.

Givens, Michael, et al. Adobe AIR Programming Unleashed. 2008. (Unleashed Ser.). (ENG., Illus.). 504p. pap. 44.99 *(978-0-672-32971-5(9))* Sams.

Goldman, Jay. Facebook Cookbook: Building Applications to Grow Your Facebook Empire. 2008. (ENG., Illus.). 434p. pap. 39.99 *(978-0-596-51817-2(X))* O'Reilly Media, Inc.

Goldstein, Neal. iPhone Application Development for Dummies. 4th ed. 2012. (ENG.). 464p. pap. 29.99 *(978-1-118-09134-0(5)*, For Dummies) Wiley, John & Sons, Inc.

Goldstein, Neal & Maniyam, Sujee. iOS Cloud Development for Dummies. 2012. (ENG.). 408p. pap. 29.99 *(978-1-118-02623-6(3)*, For Dummies) Wiley, John & Sons, Inc.

Goncalves, Antonio. Beginning Java EE 6 with GlassFish 3. 2nd ed. 2010. (ENG.). 536p. pap. 49.99 *(978-1-4302-2889-9(X))* Apress L. P.

Goodson, John & Steward, Robert A. The Data Access Handbook. 2009. (ENG., Illus.). 360p. pap. 49.99 *(978-0-13-714393-1(1))* Prentice Hall PTR.

Gousset, Mickey, et al. Professional Application Lifecycle Management with Visual Studio 2010. 2010. (ENG., Illus.). 696p. pap. 54.99 *(978-0-470-48426-5(8)*, Wrox) Wiley, John & Sons, Inc.

Gove, Darryl. Solaris Application Programming. 2007. (Solaris Ser.). (ENG., Illus.). 496p. 64.99 *(978-0-13-813455-6(3))* Prentice Hall PTR.

Gralla, Preston. Droid X2. 2nd ed. 2011. (ENG.). 424p. pap. 19.99 ***(978-1-4493-9686-2(0)***, Pogue Pr.) O'Reilly Media, Inc.

Gralla, Preston & Huddleston, Rob. Android Fully Loaded. 2010. (ENG., Illus.). 240p. pap. 24.99 *(978-0-470-93002-1(0)*, Wiley) Wiley, John & Sons, Inc.

Gray, Marion, et al. Pro Spring Integration. 2011. (ENG.). 664p. pap. 54.99 *(978-1-4302-3345-9(1))* Apress L. P.

Grenning, James W. Test-Driven Development for Embedded C: Building High Quality Embedded Software. 2011. (ENG., Illus.). 352p. pap. 34.95 *(978-1-934356-62-3(X)*, Pragmatic Bookshelf, The) Pragmatic Programmers, LLC, The.

Griffin, Marilyn. Business Application Development with Excel 2007. rev. ed. 2007. (ENG.). 580p. spiral bd. 113.49 *(978-0-7575-4619-3(6))* Kendall Hunt Publishing Co.

Grove, Ralph F. Web Based Application Development. 2009. (ENG.). 329p. pap. 73.95 *(978-0-7637-5940-7(6))* Jones & Bartlett Learning, LLC.

Gruman, Galen. InDesign CS5 for Dummies. 2010. (ENG., Illus.). 460p. pap. 26.99 *(978-0-470-61449-5(8)*, For Dummies) Wiley, John & Sons, Inc.

Gucer, Vasfi. Certification Study Guide Series: IBM Tivoli Monitoring V6.2. 2008. (Illus.). xiv, 300p. *(978-0-7384-8520-1(9))* IBM.

Guihot, Hervé. Pro Android Apps Performance Optimization. 2012. (ENG.). 284p. pap. 44.99 ***(978-1-4302-3999-4(9))*** Apress L. P.

Hall, Jonathan & Perry, Phoenix. Meet the Kinect: An Introduction to Programming Natural User Interfaces. 2011. (ENG.). 220p. pap. 29.99 ***(978-1-4302-3888-1(7))*** Apress L. P.

Hamilton, Eric. Tech Empowerment: Android App Inventor. 2011. 222p. pap. 69.99 ***(978-1-4583-7979-5(5))*** Lulu Enterprises Inc.

Han, Wook-Shin. APWEB 2010: 12th Asia Pacific Web Conference: Proceedings, 6-8 April 2010, Busan, Korea. 2010. (Illus.). xviii, 475p. pap. ***(978-0-7695-4012-2(0))*** IEEE Computer Society Pr.

Hannan, Paul, et al. XPages Extension Library: A Step-by-Step Guide to the Next Generation of XPages Components. 2012. (ENG.). 576p. pap. 54.99 ***(978-0-13-290181-9(1))*** Pearson Education.

Hannemann, Alethea, et al. Birt: A Field Guide to Reporting. 2nd ed. 2008. (Eclipse Ser.). (ENG., Illus.). 794p. pap. 54.99 *(978-0-321-58027-6(3))* Addison Wesley Professional.

Harbour, Jonathan S. Sams Teach Yourself Android Game Programming in 24 Hours. 2012. (Sams Teach Yourself — Hours Ser.). (ENG.). 450p. pap. 34.99 ***(978-0-672-33604-1(9))*** Sams.

Hardy, Brian & Phillips, Bill. Android Programming: The Big Nerd Ranch Guide. 2012. (Big Nerd Ranch Guides). (ENG.). 580p. pap. 49.99 ***(978-0-321-80433-4(3))*** Addison Wesley Professional.

Harrington, Lin. IOS 4 in Action: Examples & Solutions for iPhone & iPad. 2011. (ENG., Illus.). 504p. pap. 44.99 *(978-1-61729-001-5(7))* Manning Pubns. Co.

Harris, Alan & Haase, Konstantin. Sinatra - Up & Running. 2011. (ENG.). 122p. pap. 19.99 *(978-1-4493-0423-2(0))* O'Reilly Media, Inc.

Harrison, Guy. Oracle Performance Survival Guide: A Systematic Approach to Database Optimization. 2009. (Prentice Hall Professional Oracle Ser.). (ENG., Illus.). 768p. pap. 59.99 *(978-0-13-701195-7(4))* Prentice Hall PTR.

Harrop, Rob, et al. Pro Spring 2. 5. 2008. (ENG.). 920p. pap. 49.99 *(978-1-59059-921-1(7))* Apress L. P.

Haseman, Chris. Creating Android Applications: Develop & Design. 2011. (Develop & Design Ser.). (ENG., Illus.). 320p. pap. 39.99 ***(978-0-321-78409-4(X))*** Peachpit Pr.

Haseman, Chris, et al. Pro Android. 2009. (ENG., Illus.). 464p. pap. 44.99 *(978-1-4302-1596-7(8))* Apress L. P.

Hashimi, Sayed, et al. Pro Android, No. 2. 2010. (ENG., Illus.). 736p. pap. 49.99 *(978-1-4302-2659-8(5))* Apress L. P.

Hashimi, Sayed Ibrahim & Bartholomew, William. Inside the Microsoft Build Engine: Using MSBuild & Team Foundation Build. (ENG.). 2009. 432p. pap. 49.99 *(978-0-7356-2628-7(6))* 2nd ed. 2011. (Illus.). 618p. pap. 59.99 *(978-0-7356-4524-0(8))* Microsoft Pr.

Hashimi, Sayed Y., et al. Pro Android 2. 2010. (Illus.). xvi, 718p. E-Book ***(978-1-4302-2660-4(9))*** Apress L. P.

Haydar, May. A Formal Framework for Run-Time Verification of Web Applications. 2009. 188p. pap. *(978-3-639-18943-8(4))* VDM Verlag Dr. Mueller e.K.

Hayes, Patrick & Menzel, Christopher. Common Logic. Hendler, James & van Harmelen, Frank, eds. 2011. (Synthesis Lectures on Web Engineering Ser.). 100p. pap. 35.00 *(978-1-60845-396-2(0))* Morgan & Claypool Pubs.

Heath, Robert A. Creating Windows Applications with HTML. 2012. (ENG.). 120p. pap. 19.99 ***(978-1-4493-1622-8(0))*** O'Reilly Media, Inc.

Heffelfinger, David. Java Ee 5 Development Using Glassfish Application Server. 2007. (Illus.). 424p. per. *(978-1-84719-260-8(2))* Packt Publishing, Ltd.

Hejlsberg, Anders, et al. The C# Programming Language. 3rd annot. ed. 2008. (Microsoft . NET Development Ser.). (ENG.). 784p. pap. 44.99 *(978-0-321-56299-9(2))* Addison Wesley Professional.

Hellegouarch, Sylvain. CherryPy Essentials: Design, develop, test, & deploy robust, simple Python web applications with ease. 2007. 250p. per. *(978-1-904811-84-8(1))* Packt Publishing, Ltd.

Hermann, Ben & Mniler, Conrad. Searchbrowser - an Efficient Source Code Search Platform. 2008. 128p. pap. *(978-3-639-06276-2(0))* VDM Verlag Dr. Mueller e.K.

Hernández, Francisco. Developing Workflow Applications for Grid Computing. 2009. 136p. pap. *(978-3-639-12855-0(9))* VDM Verlag Dr. Mueller e.K.

Hiestand, James. Numerical Methods with VBA Programming. 2008. 304p. pap. 91.95 *(978-0-7637-4964-4(8))* Jones & Bartlett Learning, LLC.

Hinze, Annika & Buchmann, Alejandro P. Principles & Applications of Distributed Event-Based Systems. Buchmann, Alejandro, ed. 2010. (Illus.). 390p. 180.00 *(978-1-60566-697-6(1))* IGI Global.

Hockenberry, Craig. iPhone App Development: The Book That Should Have Been in the Box. 2010. (ENG., Illus.). 352p. pap. 39.99 *(978-0-596-80977-5(8)*, Pogue Pr.) O'Reilly Media, Inc.

Hoffman, Kevin. Windows Phone 7 for iPhone Developers. 2011. (Developer's Library). (ENG., Illus.). 336p. pap. 39.99 *(978-0-672-33434-4(8))* Addison Wesley Professional.

Hoffman, Kevin & Podila, Pavan. WPF Control Development: Building Advanced User Experiences. 2009. (Unleashed Ser.). (ENG., Illus.). 364p. pap. 49.99 *(978-0-672-33033-9(4))* Sams.

Hoffman, Kevin Scott. Mac OS X Lion App Development in 24 Hours. 2012. (Sams Teach Yourself — Hours Ser.). (ENG.). 368p. pap. 34.99 ***(978-0-672-33581-5(6))*** Sams.

Hofmeister, Christine, et al. Applied Software Architecture. 2009. (ENG.). 432p. pap. 59.99 *(978-0-321-64334-6(8))* Addison Wesley Professional.

Hofstader, Christian & Lipner, Mia. Building Accessible Applications for OS X & IOS. rev. ed. 2012. (Developer's Library). (ENG.). 375p. pap. 54.99 ***(978-0-321-77695-2(X))*** Addison Wesley Professional.

Holcomb, Robert & Wilcox, Ryan. Objective-C, Cocoa, & XCode. 2010. (ENG.). 864p. pap. 39.99 *(978-0-470-62366-4(7)*, For Dummies) Wiley, John & Sons, Inc.

Holzner, Steven. Sams Teach Yourself jQuery Mobile in 10 Minutes. 2012. (Sams Teach Yourself — Minutes Ser.). (ENG.). 240p. pap. 24.99 ***(978-0-672-33557-0(3))*** Sams.

Holzner, Steven & Felker, Donn. Android Application Development für Dummies. 2010. (ENG., Illus.). 384p. pap. 29.99 *(978-0-470-77018-4(X)*, For Dummies) Wiley, John & Sons, Inc.

Hoog, Andrew. Android Forensics: Investigation, Analysis & Mobile Security for Google Android. 2011. (ENG., Illus.). 432p. pap. 69.95 *(978-1-59749-651-3(0)*, Syngress Press) Elsevier Science & Technology Bks.

Horn, Shannon. Microsoft Silverlight 3.0. 2009. (ENG., Illus.). 288p. pap. 39.99 *(978-0-07-159043-3(9)*, 0071590439) McGraw-Hill Osborne.

Hotka, Dan & Scalzo, Bert. TOAD Handbook. 2nd ed. 2009. (Developer's Library). (ENG., Illus.). 312p. pap. 44.99 *(978-0-321-64910-2(9))* Addison Wesley Professional.

Hughes, Bill & Chakrabarty, Indrajit. Windows Phone 7 Application Development for Dummies. 2011. (ENG., Illus.). 288p. pap. 29.99 *(978-1-118-02175-0(4)*, For Dummies) Wiley, John & Sons, Inc.

Hughes, Roland. The Minimum You Need to Know about Service Oriented Architecture. 2008. (ENG.). 375p. pap. 45.00 *(978-0-9770866-6-5(6))* Logikal Solutions.

—The Minimum You Need to Know to Be an OpenVMS Application Developer. 2006. (ENG.). 800p. pap. 90.00 incl. cd-rom *(978-0-9770866-0-3(7))* Logikal Solutions.

—The Minimum You Need to Know to Be an OpenVMS Application Developer: Second Edition. 2014. 1200p. 90.00 *(978-0-9823580-0-9(8))* Logikal Solutions.

Hurwitz, Judith, et al. Cloud Computing for Dummies. (ENG., 2009. Illus.). 336p. pap. 29.99 *(978-0-470-48470-8(5))* 2nd ed. 2012. 360p. pap. 29.99 ***(978-1-118-12719-3(6))*** Wiley, John & Sons, Inc. (For Dummies).

Ibsen, Claus, et al. Camel in Action. rev. ed. 2011. (ENG., Illus.). 552p. pap. 49.99 *(978-1-935182-36-8(6))* Manning Pubns. Co.

IEEE Computer Society Staff. 32nd Euromicro Conference on Software Engineering & Advanced Applications (EUROMICRO SEAA 2006) 28 August - 01 September 2006/Cavtat, Dubrovnik, Croatia. 2006. (Illus.). 508p. pap. 224.00 *(978-0-7695-2594-5(6)*, P2594) IEEE Computer Society Pr.

Ihnatko, Andy & Hess, Alan. iPad Fully Loaded. 2010. (ENG., Illus.). 304p. pap. 19.99 *(978-0-470-87824-8(X)*, Wiley) Wiley, John & Sons, Inc.

Ingram, Dave. Design - Build - Run: Applied Practices & Principles for Production Ready Software Development. 2009. (ENG., Illus.). 720p. pap. 49.99 *(978-0-470-25763-0(6)*, Wrox) Wiley, John & Sons, Inc.

International Business Machines Corporation, International Technical Support Organization Staff, contrib. by. Using Rational Performance Tester Version 7. 2008. (Illus.). xviii, 548p. pap. *(978-0-7384-8567-6(5))* IBM.

Isted, Tim & Harrington, Tom F. Core Data for iOS: Developing Data-Driven Applications for the iPad, iPhone, & iPod Touch. 2011. (Core Frameworks Ser.). (ENG., Illus.). 304p. pap. 39.99 *(978-0-321-67042-7(6))* Addison Wesley Professional.

Jablonski, Stefan, et al. Guide to Web Application & Platform Architectures. 2010. (Illus.). xi, 245p. pap. 129.00 *(978-3-642-05668-0(7)*, 3642056687) Springer.

Jacob, Bart. Deployment Guide Series. 2008. (Illus.). xxiv, 400p. *(978-0-7384-8526-3(8))* IBM.

—IBM Tivoli Application Dependency Discovery Manager: Capabilities & Best Practices. 2008. (Illus.). xvi, 492p. pap. *(978-0-7384-8862-2(3))* IBM.

Jacobs, Sas. Foundation Flex for Developers: Data-Driven Applications with PHP, ASP. Net, ColdFusion, & LCDs. 2007. (ENG., Illus.). 600p. pap. 46.99 *(978-1-59059-894-8(6)*, Friends of Ed) Apress L. P.

Jawad, Bashar. Groovy & Grails Recipes. 2008. (ENG., Illus.). 424p. pap. 44.99 *(978-1-4302-1600-1(X))* Apress L. P.

Jennings, Roger. Cloud Computing with the Windows Azure Platform. 2009. (ENG., Illus.). 360p. pap. 39.99 *(978-0-470-50638-7(5)*, Wrox) Wiley, John & Sons, Inc.

Jha, Shantenu, Sr. & Katz, Daniel S. Abstractions for Distributed Applications & Systems: A Computational Science Perspective. 2012. (Wiley Series on Parallel & Distributed Computing Ser.: 79). (ENG.). 200p. 110.00 *(978-0-470-56706-7(6)*, Wiley) Wiley, John & Sons, Inc.

Johnston, Craig James. My BlackBerry Torch. 2013. (My... Ser.). (ENG., Illus.). 432p. pap. 24.99 *(978-0-7897-4118-9(0))* Que.

Jones, Bradley L. Windows Live Essentials & Services: Using Free Microsoft Applications for Windows 7. 2009. (ENG., Illus.). 336p. pap. 34.99 *(978-0-470-52687-3(4)*, Wiley) Wiley, John & Sons, Inc.

Jones, Don. Windows PowerShell: In a Month of Lunches. 2011. (ENG.). 600p. pap. 49.99 *(978-1-4302-3321-3(4))* Apress L. P.

Jones, Peter. Applied SAP BI 7.0 Web Reports: Using BEx Web Analyzer & Web Application Designer. 2010. (ENG., Illus.). 512p. (C). pap. 59.99 *(978-0-07-164026-8(6)*, 0071640266) McGraw-Hill Osborne.

Jordan, Lucas. Beginning iOS 5 Games Development: Using the iOS SDK for iPad, iPhone & iPod Touch. 2011. (ENG., Illus.). 344p. pap. 39.99 ***(978-1-4302-3710-5(4))*** Apress L. P.

Judd, Christopher M., et al. Beginning Groovy & Grails: From Novice to Professional. 2008. (ENG.). 440p. (C). pap. 42.99 *(978-1-4302-1045-0(1))* Apress L. P.

Kanjilal, Joydip. Architectural Design Patterns in C# 2010. 350p. 69.95 *(978-1-4398-1656-1(5))* Auerbach Pubs., Inc.

Kaplan, Dean. Android Application Sketch Book. 2011. (ENG.). 160p. pap. 14.99 ***(978-1-4302-4230-7(2))*** Apress L. P.

—BlackBerry Application Sketch Book. 2011. (ENG.). 160p. pap. 14.99 ***(978-1-4302-4239-0(6))*** Apress L. P.

—IOS 5 Application Sketch Book. 2011. (ENG.). 160p. pap. 14.99 ***(978-1-4302-4224-6(8))*** Apress L. P.

—Kindle Fire Application Sketch Book. 2011. (ENG.). 160p. pap. 14.99 ***(978-1-4302-4242-0(6))*** Apress L. P.

Karch, Marziah. Android Tablets Made Simple: For Motorola XOOM, Samsung Galaxy Tab, Asus, Toshiba & Other Tablets. 2011. (ENG., Illus.). 384p. pap. 29.99 *(978-1-4302-3671-9(X))* Apress L. P.

Katz, Yehuda & Bigg, Ryan. Rails 3 in Action. 2011. (ENG.). 592p. pap. 49.99 ***(978-1-935182-27-6(7))*** Manning Pubns. Co.

Keen, Martin. Z/Os Getting Started: Websphere Process Server & Websphere Enterprise Service Bus V6. 2007. (Illus.). xviii, 578p. *(978-0-7384-8959-9(X))* IBM.

Kessin, Zachary. Programming Html5 Applications: Building Powerful Cross-Platform Environments in JavaScript. 2011. (ENG.). 144p. pap. 24.99 ***(978-1-4493-9908-5(8))*** O'Reilly Media, Inc.

Kessler, Carl & Sweitzer, John. Outside-in Software Development: A Practical Approach to Building Successful Stakeholder-based Products. 2007. (ENG.). 240p. pap. 44.99 *(978-0-13-157551-6(1))* Pearson Education.

Keuler, Thorsten. An Aspect-Oriented Approach for Improving Architecture Design Efficiency. Univ. of Kaiserslautern, Computer Science Department, AG Software Engineering; et al, eds. 2011. (PhD Theses in Experimental Software Engineering Ser.). (ENG., Illus.). 205p. pap. 63.20 ***(978-3-8396-0225-6(4))*** Fraunhofer IRB Verlag DEU. Dist: Silvermine International Bks., LLC.

Kew, Nick. The Apache Modules Book: Application Development with Apache. 2007. (Prentice Hall Open Source Software Development Ser.). (ENG., Illus.). 592p. per. 59.99 *(978-0-13-240967-4(4)*, Prentice Hall) Prentice Hall PTR.

Kifer, Michael & Smolka, Scott A. Introduction to Operating System Design & Implementation: The OSP 2 Approach. 2007. (Undergraduate Topics in Computer Science Ser.). (Illus.). 172p. pap. 44.95 *(978-1-84628-842-5(8))* Springer.

King, Chris. Advanced BlackBerry 6 Development. 2nd ed. 2011. (ENG.). 528p. pap. 49.99 *(978-1-4302-3210-0(2))* Apress L. P.

—Advanced BlackBerry Development. 2009. (ENG.). 350p. pap. 39.99 *(978-1-4302-2656-7(0))* Apress L. P.

Kitta, Todd. Professional Windows Workflow Foundation. 2007. (ENG., Illus.). 410p. per. 49.99 *(978-0-470-05386-7(0)*, Wrox) Wiley, John & Sons, Inc.

Kloss, Jörg H. Android Apps with App Inventor: The Fast & Easy Way to Build Android Apps. 2012. (ENG., Illus.). 600p. pap. 44.99 ***(978-0-321-81270-4(0))*** Addison Wesley Professional.

Komatineni, Satya, et al. Pro Android 3. 2011. (Illus.). xxii, 1175p. E-Book ***(978-1-4302-3223-0(4))*** Apress L. P.

Konda, Madhusudhan. Just Spring Integration. 2012. (ENG.). 100p. pap. 19.99 ***(978-1-4493-1608-2(5))*** O'Reilly Media, Inc.

Korhonen, Chris, et al. Creating Mashups with Adobe Flex & AIR. 2008. (Friends of Ed Adobe Learning Library). (ENG., Illus.). 368p. pap. 42.99 *(978-1-59059-936-5(5)*, Friends of Ed) Apress L. P.

Kosmaczewski, Adrian, et al. Pro iOS Table Views: For iPhone, iPad, & iPod Touch. 2012. (ENG.). 340p. pap. 49.99 *(978-1-4302-3348-0(6))* Apress L. P.

Kramer, Jeff, et al. Hacking the Kinect. 2012. (ENG.). 268p. pap. 39.99 ***(978-1-4302-3867-6(4))*** Apress L. P.

Kumar, Mugunth & Napier, Rob. iOS 5 Programming Pushing the Limits: Advanced Application Development for Apple iPhone, iPad, & iPod Touch. 2nd ed. 2011. (Pushing the Limits Ser.). (ENG.). 432p. pap. 44.99 ***(978-1-119-96132-1(7)***, Wiley) Wiley, John & Sons, Inc.

Kusnetzky, Dan. Virtualization: A Manager's Guide. 2011. (ENG.). 74p. pap. 19.99 ***(978-1-4493-0645-8(4))*** O'Reilly Media, Inc.

Kyrnin, Jennifer. Sams Teach Yourself HTML5 Mobile Application Development in 24 Hours. 2011. (Sams Teach Yourself — Hours Ser.). (ENG., Illus.). 496p. pap. 39.99 ***(978-0-672-33440-5(2))*** Sams.

La Counte, Scott. Going Mobile: How to Put Libraries in the Palm of Patrons Hands. 2011. 64p. ***(978-0-8389-1129-7(3))*** American Library Assn.

Labriola, Michael & Tapper, Jeff. Breaking Out of the Web Browser with Adobe AIR. 2008. (ENG., Illus.). 432p. pap. 49.99 *(978-0-321-50356-5(2))* New Riders Publishing.

Ladd, Seth, et al. Building Spring 2 Enterprise Applications. 2007. (ENG.). 335p. per. 42.99 *(978-1-59059-918-1(7))* Apress L. P.

Laddad, Ramnivas. AspectJ in Action: Enterprise AOP with Spring Applications. 2nd ed. 2009. (ENG., Illus.). 568p. pap. 49.99 *(978-1-933988-05-4(3))* Manning Pubns. Co.

Lahman, H. S. Model-Based Development: Applications. rev. ed. 2011. (Illus.). 560p. 64.99 *(978-0-321-77407-1(8))* Addison Wesley Professional.

Lair, Bob & Lair, Robert. Beginning Silverlight 2. Buckingham, Ewan, ed. 2008. (Beginning Ser.). (ENG., Illus.). 296p. pap. 39.99 *(978-1-59059-952-5(7))* Apress L. P.

Lair, Robert. Beginning Silverlight 3. 2009. (ENG., Illus.). 500p. pap. 39.99 *(978-1-4302-2377-1(4))* Apress L. P.

—Beginning Silverlight 4 in C# 3rd ed. 2010. (ENG.). 416p. pap. 39.99 *(978-1-4302-2988-9(8))* Apress L. P.

Lancaster, Mark. Oracle Application Express 4. 0 with Ext JS. 2011. (Illus.). 376p. pap. ***(978-1-84968-106-3(6))*** Packt Publishing, Ltd.

Lano, Kevin. UML 2 Semantics & Applications. 2009. (ENG., Illus.). 400p. 116.00 *(978-0-470-40908-4(8)*, Wiley) Wiley, John & Sons, Inc.

Larsen, Kim G., et al, eds. Quantitative Model-Based Analysis of Real-Time Embedded Systems: The Quasimodo Project. 2012. (Embedded Systems Ser.). (ENG., Illus.). x, 250p. 139.00 *(978-94-007-1368-0(1)*, 9400713681) Springer.

Lau, Sean Q. Modeling E-Commerce Systems- an Application of Generative Software Development Techniques. 2007. 176p. per. *(978-3-8364-2836-1(9))* VDM Verlag Dr. Mueller e.K.

LaVigne, Frank & Cameron, Albert. Microsoft Silverlight 4 Business Application Development: Beginner's Guide. 2010. 446p. pap. 49.99 *(978-1-84719-976-8(3))* Packt Publishing, Ltd. GBR. Dist: Ebsco Publishing.

Lawrence, Ian, et al. Professional Ubuntu Mobile Development. 2009. (ENG., Illus.). 360p. pap. 59.99 *(978-0-470-43676-9(X)*, Wrox) Wiley, John & Sons, Inc.

Layton, Tim & Kowalski, Karl G. Mac Application Development for Dummies. 2011. (ENG., Illus.). 416p. pap. 29.99 *(978-1-118-03222-0(5)*, For Dummies) Wiley, John & Sons, Inc.

Lecky-Thompson, Guy W. Just Enough Web Programming with XHTML, PHP, & MySQL. 2008. (ENG., Illus.). 448p. pap. 29.99 *(978-1-59863-481-5(X))* Course Technology.

Lecrenski, Nick. Silverlight 4: Problem - Design - Solution. 2010. (ENG., Illus.). 528p. pap. 49.99 *(978-0-470-53404-5(4)*, Wrox) Wiley, John & Sons, Inc.

Lecrenski, Nick, et al. Beginning Windows Phone 7 Application Development: Building Windows Phone Applications Using Silverlight & XNA. 2011. (ENG., Illus.). 600p. pap. 34.99 *(978-0-470-91233-1(2)*, Wrox) Wiley, John & Sons, Inc.

Lee, Graham. Test-Driven iOS Development. 2012. (Developer's Library). (ENG.). 256p. pap. 29.99 ***(978-0-321-77418-7(3))*** Addison Wesley Professional.

Lee, Henry & Chuvyrov, Eugene. Beginning Windows Phone 7 Development. 2010. (Illus.). xx, 458p. E-Book ***(978-1-4302-3217-9(X))*** 2010. (ENG., Illus.). 480p. pap. 39.99 *(978-1-4302-3216-2(1))* 2nd ed. 2011. (ENG.). 512p. pap. 39.99 *(978-1-4302-3596-5(9))* Apress L. P.

Lee, Jonathan, et al. Service Life Cycle Tools & Technologies: Methods, Trends, & Advances. 2011. (Illus.). xiii, 341p. ***(978-1-61350-161-0(7))***; 455p. 185.00 ***(978-1-61350-159-7(5))*** IGI Global.

Lee, Wei-Meng. Android Application Development Cookbook: 100 Recipes for Building Winning Apps. 2012. (ENG.). 448p. pap. 39.99 ***(978-1-118-17767-9(3)***, Wrox) Wiley, John & Sons, Inc.

—Beginning Android 4 Application Development. 2012. (ENG., Illus.). 560p. pap. 39.99 ***(978-1-118-19954-1(5)***, Wrox) Wiley, John & Sons, Inc.

—Beginning Android Application Development. 2011. (Illus.). (ENG.). 448p. pap. 39.99 *(978-1-118-01711-1(0)*, Wrox); xx, 428p. E-Book ***(978-1-118-08749-7(6))***; xx, 428p. E-Book ***(978-1-118-08729-9(1))***; xx, 428p. E-Book ***(978-1-118-08780-0(1))*** Wiley, John & Sons, Inc.

—Beginning Android Tablet Application Development. 2011. (ENG., Illus.). 288p. pap. 34.99 *(978-1-118-10673-0(3)*, Wrox) Wiley, John & Sons, Inc.

—Beginning iOS 5 Application Development. 2012. (ENG., Illus.). 656p. pap. 39.99 ***(978-1-118-14425-1(2)***, Wrox) Wiley, John & Sons, Inc.

—Beginning iPad Application Development. 2010. (ENG., Illus.). 600p. pap. 34.99 *(978-0-470-64165-1(7)*, Wrox) Wiley, John & Sons, Inc.

—Beginning iPhone SDK: Programming with Objective-C. 2010. (ENG., Illus.). 552p. pap. 39.99 *(978-0-470-50097-2(2)*, Wrox) Wiley, John & Sons, Inc.

—iOS 4 Application Development. 2010. (ENG., Illus.). 656p. pap. 39.99 *(978-0-470-91802-9(0)*, Wrox) Wiley, John & Sons, Inc.

Leeds, Chris, et al. Microsoft Expression Blend 4. 2011. (ENG., Illus.). 432p. pap. 44.99 *(978-0-7356-3901-0(9))* Microsoft Pr.

Leinecker, Rick & Moore, Andrew. Visual Studio 2010 All-in-One for Dummies. 2010. (ENG., Illus.). 912p. pap. 39.99 *(978-0-470-53943-9(7)*, For Dummies) Wiley, John & Sons, Inc.

Leon, Lordalex & Goralski, Greg. Foundation Flex for Designers. 2008. (ENG., Illus.). 288p. pap. 36.99 *(978-1-59059-877-1(6)*, Friends of Ed) Apress L. P.

Leonard, Anghel. Jsf 2 0 Cookbook. 2010. 396p. pap. *(978-1-84719-952-2(6))* Packt Publishing, Ltd.

—Jsf 2 0 Cookbook: LITE Edition. 2011. 112p. pap. ***(978-1-84969-162-8(2))*** Packt Publishing, Ltd.

—Pro Java 7 NIO. 2. 2011. (ENG.). 296p. pap. 49.99 ***(978-1-4302-4011-2(3))*** Apress L. P.

Leuchner, Marc, et al. Adobe Air: Create - Modify - Reuse. 2008. (ENG., Illus.). 457p. pap. 39.99 *(978-0-470-18207-9(5)*, Wrox) Wiley, John & Sons, Inc.

Leung, Tim & Duran, Yann. Pro Visual Studio LightSwitch 2011 Development. 2012. (ENG.). 736p. pap. 49.99 ***(978-1-4302-4008-2(3))*** Apress L. P.

Levinson, Jeff & Nelson, David. Pro Visual Studio Team System with Team Edition for Database Professionals. 2nd ed. 2007. (Expert's Voice Ser.). (ENG., Illus.). 617p. 64.99 *(978-1-59059-953-2(5))* Apress L. P.

LeVitus, Bob. Incredible iPad Apps for Dummies. 2010. (ENG., Illus.). 240p. pap. 18.99 *(978-0-470-92979-7(0)*, For Dummies) Wiley, John & Sons, Inc.

Li, Qing. Advances in Data & Web Management: Joint International Conferences, APWeb/WAIM 2009, Suzhou, China, April 2-4, 2009, Proceedings. 2009. (Lecture Notes in Computer Science / Information Systems & Applications, incl. Internet/Web, & HCI Ser.). (Illus.). xxi, 685p. pap. 129.00 *(978-3-642-00671-5(X))* Springer.

Liberty, Jesse & Schuman, Corey. Silverlight: Up & Running: A Quick Guide to Silverlight. 2010. 400p. pap. 34.99 *(978-1-4493-8174-5(X))* O'Reilly Media, Inc.

Likness, Jeremy. Designing Silverlight Business Applications: Best Practices for Using Silverlight Effectively in the Enterprise. rev. ed. 2012. (Microsoft . NET Development Ser.). (ENG.). 720p. pap. 49.99 ***(978-0-321-81041-0(4))*** Addison Wesley Professional.

Little, J. Ambrose, et al. Silverlight 3: Programmer's Reference. 2009. (ENG., Illus.). 608p. pap. 49.99 *(978-0-470-38540-1(5)*, Wrox) Wiley, John & Sons, Inc.

Liu, Mike. Wcf 4 0 Multi-Tier Services Development with Linq to Entities. 2010. 348p. pap. *(978-1-84968-114-8(7))* Packt Publishing, Ltd.

Liu, Xiaodong & Li, Yang. Advanced Design Approaches to Emerging Software Systems: Principles, Methodologies, & Tools. 2011. (Illus.). xii, 323p. ***(978-1-60960-737-1(6))*** IGI Global.

Liu, Xiaodong & Li, Yang, eds. Advanced Design Approaches to Emerging Software Systems: Principles, Methodology & Tools. 2011. 348p. 195.00 *(978-1-60960-735-7(X)*, Information Science Reference) IGI Global.

Long, Josh & Mayzak, Steve. Getting Started with Roo. 2011. (ENG., Illus.). 64p. pap. 19.99 ***(978-1-4493-0790-5(6))*** O'Reilly Media, Inc.

Loton, Tony. Mashup Case Studies with Yahoo! Pipes. 2008. (Illus.). 125p. pap. 19.95 *(978-0-9556764-6-8(0))* Lotontech Ltd. GBR. Dist: Lulu Enterprises Inc.

Loudon, Kyle. Developing Large Web Applications: Producing Code That Can Grow & Thrive. 2010. (ENG., Illus.). 304p. pap. 34.99 *(978-0-596-80302-5(8)*, Yahoo Pr.) O'Reilly Media, Inc.

Louvel, Jerome, et al. Restlet in Action: Developing RESTful web APIs in Java. 2012. (ENG.). 450p. pap. 49.99 ***(978-1-935182-34-4(X))*** Manning Pubns. Co.

Lubbers, Peter, et al. Pro HTML5 Programming. 2nd ed. 2011. (ENG.). 352p. pap. 44.99 ***(978-1-4302-3864-5(X))*** Apress L. P.

Lunny, Andrew. PhoneGap Beginner's Guide. 2011. (ENG., Illus.). 242p. pap. ***(978-1-84951-536-8(0))*** Packt Publishing, Ltd.

Lutz, Darren & Moore, Ryan. Pro Expression Blend. 2008. 400p. pap. 39.99 *(978-1-59059-857-3(1))* Apress L. P.

Lyons, Nancy & Wilker, Meghan. Interactive Project Management: Pixels, People, & Process. rev. ed. 2012. (Voices That Matter Ser.). (ENG.). 192p. pap. 24.99 ***(978-0-321-81515-6(7))*** New Riders Publishing.

MacDonald, Matthew. Pro Silverlight 2 in VB 2008. 2008. (ENG.). 632p. pap. 49.99 *(978-1-4302-1602-5(6))* Apress L. P.

—Pro WPF: Windows Presentation Foundation in . Net 3. 0. 2007. (ENG., Illus.). 1000p. pap. 49.99 *(978-1-59059-782-8(6))* Apress L. P.

—Pro WPF in C# 2008: Windows Presentation Foundation with . NET 3. 5. 2nd ed. 2008. (Books for Professionals by Professionals Ser.). (ENG., Illus.). 1040p. pap. 54.99 *(978-1-59059-955-6(1))* Apress L. P.

—Pro WPF with Vb 2008: Windows Presentation Foundation with .NET 3.5. 2008. (Expert's Voice in .NET Ser.). (ENG., Illus.). 1000p. pap. 54.99 *(978-1-59059-962-4(4))* Apress L. P.

—Silverlight 2 Visual Essentials. 2008. (ENG.). 240p. pap. 19.99 *(978-1-4302-1582-0(8))* Apress L. P.

Mack, Moritz. Optimized Distributed Datastore Exchange. 2009. 152p. pap. *(978-3-639-19612-2(0))* VDM Verlag Dr. Mueller e.K.

Mackey, Alex. Introducing . NET 4. 0: With Visual Studio 2010. 2010. (ENG.). 484p. pap. 39.99 *(978-1-4302-2455-6(X))* Apress L. P.

Madden, Lester. Professional Augmented Reality Browsers for Smartphones: Programming for Junaio, Layar & Wikitude. 2011. (ENG., Illus.). 360p. pap. 44.99 *(978-1-119-99281-3(8)*, Wrox) Wiley, John & Sons, Inc.

Maglogiannis, Ilias G. Emerging artificial intelligence applications in computer Engineering. 2007. 163.00 *(978-1-58603-780-2(3))* IOS Pr., Inc.

Mahdavi, Mehregan. Web Data Caching. 2010. 140p. pap. *(978-3-639-12145-2(7))* VDM Verlag Dr. Mueller e.K.

Mak, Gary. Spring Recipes. 2008. (ENG.). 700p. pap. 49.99 *(978-1-59059-979-2(9))* Apress L. P.

Mak, Gary & Long, Josh. Spring Enterprise Recipes: A Problem-Solution Approach. 2009. (Problem-Solution Approach Ser.). (ENG.). 400p. pap. 44.99 *(978-1-4302-2497-6(5))* Apress L. P.

Mak, Gary & Rubio, Daniel. Pro SpringSource Dm Server. 2009. (ENG.). 288p. pap. 39.99 *(978-1-4302-1640-7(9))* Apress L. P.

Mak, Gary, et al. Spring Recipes: A Problem-Solution Approach. 2nd ed. 2010. (ENG.). 1104p. pap. 49.99 *(978-1-4302-2499-0(1))* Apress L. P.

Mamone, Mark. Migrating to iPhone & iPad for . NET Developers. 2011. (ENG.). 316p. pap. 49.99 ***(978-1-4302-3858-4(5))*** Apress L. P.

Margolis, Ben. Enterprise Web 2. 0 with EGL. 2009. (ENG.). 450p. pap. 64.95 *(978-1-58347-091-6(3))* MC Pr., LLC.

—IBM Rational Business Developer with EGL. 2008. (ENG.). 200p. pap. 39.95 *(978-1-58347-066-4(2))* MC Pr., LLC.

Mark, Dave & LaMarche, Jeff. Beginning iPhone Development: Exploring the iPhone SDK. 2008. (ENG.). 536p. pap. 39.99 *(978-1-4302-1626-1(3))* Apress L. P.

—More IPhone 3 Development: Tackling IPhone SDK 3. 2009. (Illus.). xv, 559p. E-Book *(978-1-4302-2743-4(5))* Apress L. P.

Mark, Dave, et al. Beginning IPhone 4 Development: Exploring the IOS SDK. 2011. (Illus.). xvi, 657p. E-Book ***(978-1-4302-3025-0(8))*** Apress L. P.

Mark, David, et al. More iOS 5 Development: Further Explorations of the iOS SDK. 2012. (ENG.). 600p. pap. 39.99 ***(978-1-4302-3807-2(0))*** Apress L. P.

Maskrey, Ken. Building iPhone OS Accessories: Use the iPhone Accessories API to Control & Monitor Devices. 2010. (ENG.). 328p. pap. 59.99 *(978-1-4302-2931-5(4))* Apress L. P.

Mathur, Aditya P. Foundations of Software Testing. 2008. (ENG., Illus.). 689p. 74.99 *(978-81-317-1660-1(0))* Addison Wesley Professional.

Maver, John & Popp, Cappy. Essential Facebook Development: Build Successful Applications for the Facebook Platform. 2009. (Developer's Library). (ENG., Illus.). 480p. pap. 44.99 *(978-0-321-63798-7(4))* Addison Wesley Professional.

Mayo, Joe. Microsoft Visual Studio 2010. 2010. (Illus.). 448p. pap. 39.99 *(978-0-07-166895-8(0)*, 0071668950) McGraw-Hill Osborne.

McChesney, Robert, et al. Advanced Java EE Development for Rational Application Developer 7. 5: Developers' Guidebook. 2nd ed. 2011. 752p. pap. 79.95 *(978-1-931182-31-7(0))* MC Pr., LLC.

McClure, Wallace B., et al. Professional Android Programming with Mono for Android & . NET/C# 2012. (ENG.). 552p. pap. 44.99 *(978-1-118-02643-4(8)*, Wrox) Wiley, John & Sons, Inc.

McCormick, John W., et al. Building Parallel, Embedded, & Real-Time Applications with Ada. 2011. (ENG., Illus.). 386p. 90.00 *(978-0-521-19716-8(3))* Cambridge Univ. Pr.

McCune, Doug & Subramaniam, Deepa. Adobe Flex 3.0. 2008. (ENG., Illus.). 416p. pap. 29.99 *(978-0-470-27792-8(0)*, For Dummies) Wiley, John & Sons, Inc.

McGrath, Mike. Building Android Apps in Easy Steps. 2012. (In Easy Steps Ser.). (ENG., Illus.). 192p. pap. 14.99 ***(978-1-84078-528-9(4))*** Computer Step GBR. Dist: Perseus-PGW.

McMurtry, Craig, et al. Windows Communication Foundation. 2007. (Unleashed Ser.). (ENG., Illus.). 720p. per. 54.99 *(978-0-672-32948-7(4))* Sams.

—Windows Communication Foundation 3.5 Unleashed. 2nd ed. 2008. (Unleashed Ser.). (ENG., Illus.). 768p. pap. 54.99 *(978-0-672-33024-7(5))* Sams.

Mednieks, Zigurd, et al. Programming Android. 2011. (ENG., Illus.). 504p. pap. 44.99 *(978-1-4493-8969-7(4))* O'Reilly Media, Inc.

Mednieks, Zigurd, et al. Programming Android: Java Programming for the New Generation of Mobile Devices. 2nd ed. 2012. (ENG.). 524p. pap. 44.99 ***(978-1-4493-1664-8(6))*** O'Reilly Media, Inc.

Meier, Reto. Professional Android 2 Application Development. 2nd ed. 2010. (ENG., Illus.). 576p. pap. 44.99 *(978-0-470-56552-0(7)*, Wrox) Wiley, John & Sons, Inc.

Meier, Reto. Professional Android 4 Application Development. 3rd ed. 2012. (ENG.). 864p. pap. 44.99 ***(978-1-118-10227-5(4)***, Wrox) Wiley, John & Sons, Inc.

Meloni, Julie C. & Telles, Matt. PHP 6 Fast & Easy Web Development. 2008. (ENG., Illus.). 592p. per. 34.99 *(978-1-59863-471-6(2))* Course Technology.

Mena, Jesus. Machine-to-Machine Marketing (M3) via Anonymous Advertising Apps Anywhere Anytime (A5) 2012. (ENG., Illus.). 436p. pap. 69.95 ***(978-1-4398-8191-0(X))*** Auerbach Pubs., Inc.

Mentzas, Gregoris. Semantic Enterprise Application Integration for Business Processes: Service-Oriented Frameworks. Mentzas, Gregoris & Friesen, Andreas, eds. 2009. 302p. 180.00 *(978-1-60566-804-8(4)*, Business Science Reference) IGI Global.

Mertic, John. Building on SugarCRM. 2011. (ENG.). 80p. pap. 19.99 ***(978-1-4493-0980-0(1))*** O'Reilly Media, Inc.

Meyer, Jeanine. HTML5 & JavaScript Projects. 2011. (ENG.). 448p. pap. 39.99 ***(978-1-4302-4032-7(6))*** Apress L. P.

Meyers, Mike. Working with Animation in Silverlight 1. 0. 2007. (Wrox Briefs Ser.). 27p. 6.99 *(978-0-470-25963-4(9)*, Wrox) Wiley, John & Sons, Inc.

Meyers, Mike & Andrade, Chris. Professional Silverlight 2.0. 2008. 430p. pap. 49.99 *(978-0-470-19393-8(X)*, Wrox) Wiley, John & Sons, Inc.

Michail, Ashraf. Essential Silverlight 3. 2009. (Microsoft . NET Development Ser.). (Illus.). 336p. pap. 44.99 *(978-0-321-55416-1(7))* Addison Wesley Professional.

Microsoft Official Academic Course Staff. Microsoft . Net Framework 2. 0 - Application Development Foundation, Exam 70-536 Textbook, 2 vols. 2010. (ENG., Illus.). 360p. (C). pap. 132.95 ***(978-0-470-18369-4(1)***, Wiley) Wiley, John & Sons, Inc.

Microsoft Official Academic Course Staff. 70-562: Microsoft . Net Framework 3. 5, ASP. NET Application Development, 2 vols. 2010. (ENG., Illus.). 456p. (C). pap. 127.95 *(978-0-470-57810-0(6)*, Wiley) Wiley, John & Sons, Inc.

Microsoft Official Academic Course Staff & Microsoft Corporation Staff. Performance Testing Guidance for Web Applications. 2007. (ENG., Illus.). 288p. per. 34.99 *(978-0-7356-2570-9(0))* Microsoft Pr.

—Team Development with Visual Studio Team Foundation Server. 2007. (ENG., Illus.). 624p. per. 49.99 *(978-0-7356-2571-6(9))* Microsoft Pr.

Microsoft Press Staff & Persse, James. Hollywood Secrets of Project Management Success. 2008. (ENG.). 336p. pap. 39.99 *(978-0-7356-2569-3(7))* Microsoft Pr.

Miller, Michael. Introduction to Google Apps: Productivity Apps. rev. ed. 2011. (ENG., Illus.). 320p. (C). pap. 78.67 ***(978-0-13-272518-7(5)***, Prentice Hall) Prentice Hall PTR.

Mills, Duncan, et al. Oracle Jdeveloper 11g: A Guide to Fusion Web Development. 2009. (Oracle Press Ser.).Tr. of An Introductory Textbook. (ENG., Illus.). 912p. pap., instr.'s hndbk. ed. 64.99 *(978-0-07-160238-9(0)*, 0071602380) McGraw-Hill Osborne.

Millspaugh, Anita & Bradley, Julia Case. Advanced Programming Using Visual Basic 2008. 4th ed. 2009. (ENG., Illus.). 672p. (C). pap. 125.00 *(978-0-07-351722-3(4)*, 0073517224) McGraw-Hill Higher Education.

Minella, Michael T. Pro Spring Batch. 2011. (ENG.). 504p. pap. 49.99 *(978-1-4302-3452-4(0))* Apress L. P.

Misra, Jayadev, et al, eds. FM 2006: Formal Methods: 14th International Symposium on Formal Methods Hamilton, Canada, August 21-27, 2006 Proceedings. 2006. (Lecture Notes in Computer Science Ser.). (Illus.). 620p. pap. 109.00 *(978-3-540-37215-8(6)*, 3540372156) Springer.

MOAC. Microsoft . NET Framework 2. 0 Application Development Foundation, 2 vols. 2010. (ENG., Illus.). 216p. (C). pap. 33.95 ***(978-0-470-18370-0(5)***, Wiley) Wiley, John & Sons, Inc.

Molyneaux, Ian. The Art of Application Performance Testing: Help for Programmers & Quality Assurance. 2009. (ENG., Illus.). 160p. pap. 34.99 *(978-0-596-52066-3(2))* O'Reilly Media, Inc.

Monk, Simon. Arduino + Android Projects for the Evil Genius: Control Arduino with Your Smartphone or Tablet. 2011. (Evil Genius Ser.). (ENG., Illus.). 224p. pap. 25.00 ***(978-0-07-177596-0(X)***, 007177596X, TAB/Electronics) McGraw-Hill Professional Publishing.

Moodie, Matthew. Pro Apache Tomcat 6. Mittal, Kunal, ed. 2007. (Expert's Voice in Java Ser.). (ENG., Illus.). 325p. per. 39.99 *(978-1-59059-785-9(0))* Apress L. P.

Moore, Andrew. Power Programming with Resharper: Optimize . NET Development with the Resharper Add-in to Visual Studio 2008. 2008. (Wrox Briefs Ser.). 6.99 *(978-0-470-39843-2(4)*, Wrox) Wiley, John & Sons, Inc.

Moore, Dana, et al. Professional Rich Internet Applications: AJAX & Beyond. 2007. (ENG., Illus.). 565p. per. 39.99 *(978-0-470-08280-5(1)*, Wrox) Wiley, John & Sons, Inc.

Moroney, Laurence. Beginning Web Development, Silverlight, & ASP. NET AJAX. 2008. (Expert's Voice In . Net Ser.). (ENG., Illus.). 427p. per. 44.99 *(978-1-59059-959-4(4))* Apress L. P.

—Introducing Microsoft Silverlight 3. 3rd ed. 2009. (ENG.). 384p. pap. 39.99 *(978-0-7356-2573-0(5))* Microsoft Pr.

Morris, Simon. Javafx in Action. 2009. (ENG., Illus.). 384p. pap. 44.99 *(978-1-933988-99-3(1))* Manning Pubns. Co.

Moseley, Ralph. Developing Web Applications. 2007. (ENG., Illus.). 410p. per. 60.95 *(978-0-470-01719-7(8)*, Wiley) Wiley, John & Sons, Inc.

Moskowite, Tyler. Getting Started with the Arduino Mega Adk. 2012. (ENG.). 50p. pap. 5.99 ***(978-1-4493-1234-3(9))*** O'Reilly Media, Inc.

Mureta, Chad. App Empire: Make Money, Have a Life, & Let Technology Work for You. 2012. (ENG.). 205p. 24.95 *(978-1-118-10787-4(X)*, Wiley) Wiley, John & Sons, Inc.

Murphy, Jennifer. Developing with Google+ 2012. (ENG.). 50p. pap. 18.99 ***(978-1-4493-1226-8(8))*** O'Reilly Media, Inc.

Myer, Thomas. Beginning PhoneGap. 2011. (ENG., Illus.). 384p. pap. 34.99 ***(978-1-118-15665-0(X)***, Wrox) Wiley, John & Sons, Inc.

Naboulsi, Zain & Ford, Sara. Coding Faster: Getting More Productive with Microsoft Visual Studio - Covers Microsoft Visual Studio 2005, 2008, & 2010. 2011. (ENG.). 480p. pap. 39.99 *(978-0-7356-4992-7(8))* Microsoft Pr.

Nahavandipoor, Vandad. Writing Game Center Apps in iOS: Bringing Your Players into the Game. 2011. (ENG., Illus.). 80p. pap. 19.99 *(978-1-4493-0565-9(2))* O'Reilly Media, Inc.

Nathan, Adam. 101 Windows Phone 7 Apps, Volume I: Developing Apps 1-50. rev. ed. 2011. (ENG., Illus.). 1152p. pap. 59.99 *(978-0-672-33552-5(2))* Sams.

Nayyeri, Keyvan. Professional Visual Studio Extensibility. 2008. (ENG., Illus.). 552p. pap. 49.99 *(978-0-470-23084-8(3)*, Wrox) Wiley, John & Sons, Inc.

Neward, Ted, et al. Professional F# 2. 0. 2010. (ENG., Illus.). 432p. pap. 44.99 *(978-0-470-52801-3(X)*, Wrox) Wiley, John & Sons, Inc.

Nichols, Laura & Leader, Gavin. Sams Teach Yourself Silverlight 4 in 24 Hours. rev. ed. 2011. (Sams Teach Yourself — Hours Ser.). (Illus.). 500p. pap. 34.99 *(978-0-672-33550-1(6))* Sams.

Nolte, Wes & Douglas, Jeff. Salesforce Handbook. 2011. 360p. pap. 35.00 ***(978-1-4461-0853-6(8))*** Lulu Enterprises Inc.

Northrup, Tony. MCTS Exam 70-536: Microsoft. Net Framework Application Development Foundation. 2nd ed. 2008. (ENG.). 832p. pap. 69.99 *(978-0-7356-2619-5(7))* Microsoft Pr.

Northrup, Tony, et al. Designing & Developing Web Applications Using Microsoft .NET Framework, No. 4. 2011. (ENG., Illus.). 304p. pap. 39.99 *(978-0-7356-5726-7(2))* Microsoft Pr.

Noyes, Brian. Developing Applications with Windows Workflow Foundation. 2007. (LiveLessons Ser.). (ENG., Illus.). 80p. 74.99 *(978-0-321-50313-8(9))* Addison Wesley Professional.

Nozzi, Joshua. Mastering Xcode 4: Develop & Design. 2011. (Develop & Design Ser.). (ENG., Illus.). 400p. pap. 49.99 ***(978-0-321-76752-3(7))*** Peachpit Pr.

Nusairat, Joseph Faisal. Beginning JBoss Seam. 2007. (Expert's Voice in JAVA Technology Ser.). (ENG., Illus.). 376p. per. 39.99 *(978-1-59059-792-7(3))* Apress L. P.

Nygard, Michael T. Release It! Design & Deploy Production-Ready Software. 2007. (Pragmatic Programmers Ser.). (ENG., Illus.). 326p. per. 34.95 *(978-0-9787392-1-8(3)*, Pragmatic Bookshelf, The) Pragmatic Programmers, LLC, The.

O'Rourke, Jodie. Flash Mobile Application Development for Dummies. 2011. (ENG., Illus.). 480p. pap. 29.99 *(978-1-118-01254-3(2)*, For Dummies) Wiley, John & Sons, Inc.

Ostrander, Jason. Android UI Fundamentals: Develop & Design. 2012. (Develop & Design Ser.). (ENG.). 320p. pap. 44.99 ***(978-0-321-81458-6(4))*** Peachpit Pr.

Osuna, Alex & Sullivan, Craig. IBM System Storage N Series for SAP. 2007. (Illus.). viii, 64p. *(978-0-7384-9694-8(4))* IBM.

Ouellette, Jason. Development with the Force. Com Platform: Building Business Applications in the Cloud. 2nd rev. ed. 2011. (Developer's Library). (ENG., Illus.). 496p. pap. 49.99 *(978-0-321-76735-6(7))* Addison Wesley Professional.

Pace, Eugenio, et al. Developing Applications for the Cloud on the Microsoft Windows Azure Platform. 2010. (ENG., Illus.). 168p. pap. 29.99 *(978-0-7356-5606-2(1))* Microsoft Pr.

Panetto, Hervé & Boudjlida, Nacer, eds. Interoperability for Enterprise Software & Applications: Proceedings of the Workshops & the Doctorial Symposium of the Second IFAC/IFIP I-ESA International Conference: EI2N, WSI, IS-TSPQ 2006. 2006. (Iste Ser.: 653). (ENG.). 396p. 174.00 *(978-1-905209-61-3(4)*, Wiley-ISTE) Wiley, John & Sons, Inc.

Papakonstantino, Yannis. Patterns for Data-Driven Web Apps. 2012. (ENG.). 300p. pap. 39.99 ***(978-1-4493-0825-4(2))*** O'Reilly Media, Inc.

The check digit for ISBN-10 appears in parentheses after the full ISBN-13

Pardede, Eric, ed. Open & Novel Issues in XML Database Applications: Future Directions & Advanced Technologies. 2009. (Illus.). 394p. 195.00 *(978-1-60566-308-1(5))* IGI Global.

Paries, Jeff. Foundation Silverlight 2 Animation. 2008. (ENG., Illus.). 448p. pap. 39.99 *(978-1-4302-1569-1(0)*, Friends of Ed) Apress L. P.

Parsons, Andrew & Randolph, Nick. Professional Visual Studio 2005. 2006. (ENG., Illus.). 912p. pap. 49.99 *(978-0-7645-9846-3(5)*, Wrox) Wiley, John & Sons, Inc.

Parziale, Geppy & Diaz-Santana, Eva. Location-Based Services for iOS Devices. 2013. (ENG.). 408p. pap. 49.99 ***(978-1-118-10503-0(6)***, Wrox) Wiley, John & Sons, Inc.

Patrick, Tim. Microsoft ADO.NET 4.0. 2010. (ENG.). 440p. pap. 44.99 *(978-0-7356-3888-4(8))* Microsoft Pr.

Paulheim, Heiko. Ontology-based Application Integration. 2011. (ENG., Illus.). xvi, 270p. 99.00 ***(978-1-4614-1429-2(6)***, 1461414296) Springer.

Peachpit Press Staff & Campbell, Duncan. iPhone Application Development with iPhone SDK. 2010. (Visual QuickStart Guide Ser.). (ENG., Illus.). 504p. pap. 34.99 *(978-0-321-71968-3(9))* Peachpit Pr.

Peters, Jeff. Fusebox 5 & FLiP: Master-Class ColdFusion Applications. 2007. per. 39.99 *(978-0-9752647-7-5(X))* Proton Arts.

Petri, Jürgen. NetBeans Platform 6. 8 Developer's Guide: Create professional desktop rich-client Swing applications using the world's only modular Swing Framework. 2010. (Illus.). 250p. pap. *(978-1-84951-176-6(4))* Packt Publishing, Ltd.

Petzold, Charles. Microsoft Silverlight: Programming for Windows Phone 7. 2010. (ENG., Illus.). 792p. pap. 39.99 *(978-0-7356-5667-3(3))* Microsoft Pr.

—Microsoft XNA Framework: Programming for Windows Phone 7. 2010. (ENG., Illus.). 430p. pap. 34.99 *(978-0-7356-5669-7(X))* Microsoft Pr.

Phung, Samuel. Professional Microsoft Windows Embedded CE 6.0. 2008. (ENG., Illus.). 480p. pap. 59.99 *(978-0-470-37733-8(X)*, Wrox) Wiley, John & Sons, Inc.

Piattini, Mario, et al. Handbook of Research on Web Information Systems Quality. 2008. (Illus.). 582p. 245.00 *(978-1-59904-847-5(7))* IGI Global.

Pilone, Dan & Pilone, Tracey. Head First iPhone & iPad Development: A Learner's Guide to Creating Objective-C Applications for the iPhone & iPad. 3rd ed. 2012. (ENG.). 675p. pap. 49.99 ***(978-1-4493-1657-0(3))*** O'Reilly Media, Inc.

Pilone, Tracey & Pilone, Dan. Head First iPhone & iPad Development: A Learner's Guide to Creating Objective-C Applications for the iPhone & iPad. 2nd ed. 2011. (ENG., Illus.). 674p. pap. 49.99 *(978-1-4493-8782-2(9))* O'Reilly Media, Inc.

Plattner, Hasso & Zeier, Alexander. In-Memory Data Management: An Inflection Point for Enterprise Applications. 2011. (Illus.). xvi, 236p. 59.95 *(978-3-642-19362-0(5)*, 3642193625) Springer.

Plenderleith, Jamie & Bunn, Steve. Microsoft Visual Studio 2008 Programming. 2009. (ENG., Illus.). 442p. pap. 49.99 *(978-0-07-160408-6(1)*, 0071604081) McGraw-Hill Osborne.

Podlesak, et al. Restful Web Service in Java. 2010. (Java Ser.). (ENG.). 480p. pap. 49.99 *(978-0-13-701288-6(8))* Prentice Hall PTR.

Polger, Jana & Adamson, Greg, eds. New Generation of Portal Software & Engineering: Emerging Technologies. 2011. (Illus.). 350p. 180.00 *(978-1-60960-571-1(3)*, Information Science Reference) IGI Global.

Porebski, Bartosz, et al. Building PHP Applications with Symfony, CakePHP, & Zend Framework. 2011. (ENG.). 576p. pap. 44.99 *(978-0-470-88734-9(6)*, Wrox) Wiley, John & Sons, Inc.

Potencier, Fabien & Zaninotto, François. The Definitive Guide to Symfony. 2007. (Expert's Voice in Open Source Ser.). (ENG., Illus.). 425p. per. 39.99 *(978-1-59059-786-6(9))* Apress L. P.

Powers, Lars & Snell, Mike. Microsoft Visual Studio 2008 Unleashed. 2008. (Unleashed Ser.). (ENG., Illus.). 1248p. pap. 64.99 *(978-0-672-32972-2(7))* Sams.

PremKumar, Lawrence & Mohan, Praveen. Beginning JavaFX. 2nd ed. 2010. (ENG.). 336p. pap. 39.99 *(978-1-4302-7199-4(X)*, Apress L. P.

Qian, Kai, et al. Embedded Software Development with C. 2009. (ENG., Illus.). xii, 384p. 89.95 *(978-1-4419-0605-2(3)*, 1441906053) Springer.

Raasch, Jon. Smashing WebKit. 2011. (Smashing Magazine Book Ser.: 20). (ENG.). 368p. pap. 44.99 ***(978-1-119-99913-3(8)***, Wiley) Wiley, John & Sons, Inc.

Radaideh, Moh'd A. & Al-Ameed, Hayder. Architecture of Reliable Web Applications Software. 2006. (Illus.). 364p. 99.95 *(978-1-59904-183-4(9))* IGI Global.

Rajshekhar, A. P. Building Dynamic Web 2. 0 Websites with Ruby on Rails. 2008. (Illus.). 250p. per. *(978-1-84719-341-4(2))* Packt Publishing, Ltd.

Ramnath, Rajiv. Android 3 SDK Programming for Dummies. 2011. (ENG.). 408p. pap. 34.99 *(978-1-118-00825-6(1)*, For Dummies) Wiley, John & Sons, Inc.

Randolph, Nick & Fairbairn, Christopher. Professional Windows Phone 7 Application Development: Building Applications & Games Using Visual Studio, Silverlight, & XNA. 2010. (ENG., Illus.). 624p. pap. 44.99 *(978-0-470-89166-7(1)*, Wrox) Wiley, John & Sons, Inc.

Randolph, Nick & Gardner, David. Professional Visual Studio 2008. 2008. (ENG., Illus.). 1032p. pap. 59.99 *(978-0-470-22988-0(8)*, Wrox) Wiley, John & Sons, Inc.

Rauch, Guillermo. Smashing Node. JS: JavaScript Everywhere. 2nd ed. 2012. (Smashing Magazine Book Ser.). (ENG.). 256p. pap. 44.99 ***(978-1-119-96259-5(5)***, Wiley) Wiley, John & Sons, Inc.

Ray, John. iPad Application Development. 2010. (Sams Teach Yourself Ser.). (ENG., Illus.). 696p. pap. 39.99 *(978-0-672-33339-2(2))* Sams.

—iPhone Application Development in 24 Hours. 2nd ed. 2010. (Sams Teach Yourself — Hours Ser.). (ENG., Illus.). 704p. pap. 39.99 *(978-0-672-33220-3(5))* Sams.

Rayns, Chris. Application Development for CICS Web Services. 2nd ed. 2010. (Illus.). xvi, 362p. *(978-0-7384-3385-1(3))* IBM.

—Java Application Development for CICS. 4th ed. 2009. (Illus.). xvi, 308p. *(978-0-7384-3229-8(6))* IBM.

Reagan, Dusty. Twitter Application Development for Dummies. 2010. (ENG., Illus.). 456p. pap. 29.99 *(978-0-470-56862-0(3)*, For Dummies) Wiley, John & Sons, Inc.

Reid, Jon. JQuery Mobile. 2011. (ENG.). 132p. pap. 15.99 ***(978-1-4493-0668-7(3))*** O'Reilly Media, Inc.

Riou, Matthieu. Raven: Scripting Java Builds with Ruby. 2007. (ENG.). 64p. per. 19.99 *(978-1-59059-875-7(X))* Apress L. P.

Ritchie, Stephen D. Pro .NET Best Practices. 2011. (ENG.). 372p. pap. 49.99 ***(978-1-4302-4023-5(7))*** Apress L. P.

Rittgen, Peter. Enterprise Modeling & Computing with UML. 2006. (Illus.). 314p. 94.95 *(978-1-59904-174-2(X))* IGI Global.

Rizk, Anthony. Beginning BlackBerry Development. 2009. (ENG.). 300p. pap. 39.99 *(978-1-4302-7225-0(2))* Apress L. P.

Rocchi, Cesare. Data Visualization with Flash Builder: Designing RIA & AIR Applications with Remote Data Sources. 2011. (Visualizing the Web Ser.). (ENG., Illus.). 316p. pap. 39.95 *(978-0-240-81503-9(3)*, Focal Pr.) Elsevier Science & Technology Bks.

Roche, Kyle. Pro iOS 5 Augmented Reality. 2011. (ENG.). 356p. pap. 39.99 ***(978-1-4302-3912-3(3))*** Apress L. P.

Roche, Ron. Essential iOS Build & Release: A Comprehensive Guide to Building, Packaging, & Distribution. 2012. (ENG.). 118p. pap. 15.99 ***(978-1-4493-1394-4(9))*** O'Reilly Media, Inc.

Rocher, Graeme, et al. The Definitive Guide to Grails: Agile Java Web Development Using This Groovy-Based Framework. 2nd ed. 2009. (ENG.). 648p. pap. 46.99 *(978-1-59059-995-2(0))* Apress L. P.

Rockway, Jonathan & Antano, Solar John. Catalyst 5.8: The Perl MVC Framework. 2010. 250p. pap. *(978-1-84719-924-9(0))* Packt Publishing, Ltd.

Rodger, Richard. Beginning Mobile Application Development in the Cloud. 2011. (ENG., Illus.). 552p. pap. 34.99 *(978-1-118-03469-9(4)*, Wrox) Wiley, John & Sons, Inc.

Rodriguez, Jaime. Building Windows 8 Metro Style Apps with HTML & JavaScript. 2012. (ENG.). 450p. pap. 39.99 ***(978-0-672-33606-5(5))*** Sams.

Rodriguez, Juan R. Building Composite Applications. 2007. (Illus.). xviii, 734p. *(978-0-7384-8941-4(7))* IBM.

Roebuck, Kevin. Cloud Application Development Tools: High-impact Strategies - What You Need to Know. 2011. 136p. pap. ***(978-1-74304-477-3(1)***, Tebbo) Emereo Pty Ltd.

Rogers, Richard A. Learning Android Game Programming: A Hands-on Guide to Building Your First Android Game. 2011. (Learning Ser.). (ENG., Illus.). 480p. pap. 39.99 *(978-0-321-76962-6(7))* Addison Wesley Professional.

Rollins, Mark. The Business of Android Apps Development: Making & Marketing Apps That Succeed. 2011. (ENG., Illus.). 244p. pap. 29.99 ***(978-1-4302-3942-0(5))*** Apress L. P.

Ronald, Grant. Quick Start Guide to Oracle Fusion Development: Oracle JDeveloper & Oracle ADF. 2010. (Oracle Press Ser.). (ENG., Illus.). 224p. pap. 29.99 *(978-0-07-174428-7(2)*, 0071744282) McGraw-Hill Osborne.

Rosenzweig, Gary. My iPad 2 (covers iOS 5) 3rd rev. ed. 2011. (My... Ser.). (ENG., Illus.). 416p. pap. 24.99 ***(978-0-7897-4911-6(4))*** Que.

Rossberg, Joachim. Pro Visual Studio Team System Application Lifecycle Management. 2008. (ENG.). 344p. 59.99 *(978-1-4302-1080-1(X))* Apress L. P.

Rubel, Dan, et al. The Eclipse Graphical Editing Framework (GEF) rev. ed. 2011. (Eclipse Ser.). (ENG., Illus.). 312p. pap. 44.99 *(978-0-321-71838-9(0))* Addison Wesley Professional.

Rubinger, Andrew Lee, et al. Enterprise JavaBeans 3.1. 6th ed. 2010. (ENG., Illus.). 766p. pap. 54.99 *(978-0-596-15802-6(5))* O'Reilly Media, Inc.

Rubio, Daniel. Pro Spring Dynamic Modules for OSGi Service Platforms. 2009. (Pro Ser.). (ENG.). 392p. pap. 46.99 *(978-1-4302-1612-4(3))* Apress L. P.

Rueda, Edwin S. Incorporating Human Experience Quality Attributes in Software Applications. 2008. 160p. pap. *(978-3-639-06581-7(6))* VDM Verlag Dr. Mueller e.K.

Ruest, Nelson & Ruest, Danielle. Virtualization: A Beginner's Guide. 2009. (Beginner's Guide Ser.). (ENG., Illus.). 464p. pap. 39.99 *(978-0-07-161401-6(X)*, 007161401X) McGraw-Hill Osborne.

Ruest, Nelson, et al. MCTS Self-Paced Kit: Configuring Windows Server Virtualization. 2009. (ENG.). 656p. pap. 69.99 *(978-0-7356-2679-9(0))* Microsoft Pr.

Rumbelow, Jamie. Practical CodeIgniter 2 Projects: Building Real-World Apps with CodeIgniter. 2009. (ENG.). 350p. pap. 42.99 *(978-1-4302-1885-2(1))* Apress L. P.

Ryans, Chris. IBM Application Development & Problem Determination. 2008. (Illus.). xii, 214p. *(978-0-7384-3146-8(X))* IBM.

Saad, Ashraf. Soft Computing in Industrial Applications: Recent & Emerging Methods & Techniques. Avineri, Erel et al, eds. 2007. (Advances in Intelligent & Soft Computing Ser.). xiv, 328p. pap. 239.00 *(978-3-540-70704-2(2))* Springer.

Sadtler, Carla. Using IBM WebSphere Message Broker As an ESB with WebSphere Process Server. 2008. (Illus.). xiv, 348p. *(978-0-7384-8554-6(3))* IBM.

—WebSphere Application Server Community Edition 2.0 User Guide. 2008. (Illus.). xiv, 218p. *(978-0-7384-8586-7(1))* IBM.

Sadun, Erica, et al. Taking Your iPad to the Max. 2010. (ENG.). 440p. pap. 29.99 *(978-1-4302-3108-0(4))* Apress L. P.

Saffer, Dan. Designing for Interaction: Creating Smart Applications & Clever Devices. 2006. (Voices That Matter Ser.). (ENG., Illus.). 248p. per. 45.00 *(978-0-321-43206-3(1))* New Riders Publishing.

Sambells, Jeffrey, et al. Beginning Google Maps Applications with Rails & Ajax. 2007. (Expert's Voice in Open Source Ser.). (ENG., Illus.). 365p. per. 34.99 *(978-1-59059-787-3(7))* Apress L. P.

Sanchez, Juan & McIntosh, Andy. Creating Visual Experiences with Flex 3.0. 2008. (Developer's Library). (ENG., Illus.). 432p. pap. 54.99 *(978-0-321-54537-4(0))* Addison Wesley Professional.

Sanderson, Dan. Programming Google App Engine. 2nd ed. 2012. (ENG., Illus.). 500p. pap. 49.99 ***(978-1-4493-9826-2(X)***, Google Pr.) O'Reilly Media, Inc.

Sanderson, Dan. Programming Google App Engine: Build & Run Scalable Web Apps on Google's Infrastructure. 2009. (Animal Guide Ser.). (ENG., Illus.). 394p. pap. 44.99 *(978-0-596-52272-8(X))* O'Reilly Media, Inc.

Sarang, Poornachandra. Practical Liferay: Java-Based Portal Applications Development. 2009. (ENG.). 384p. pap. 59.99 *(978-1-4302-1847-0(9))* Apress L. P.

Sarigumba, Dante & Kao, Robert. BlackBerry Bold for Dummies. 2009. (ENG., Illus.). 360p. pap. 24.99 *(978-0-470-52540-1(1)*, For Dummies) Wiley, John & Sons, Inc.

Sarna, David E. Y. Evernote for Dummies. 2012. (ENG.). 384p. pap. 24.99 ***(978-1-118-10738-6(1)***, For Dummies) Wiley, John & Sons, Inc.

SAS Publishing, creator. SAS 9. 1. 3 Intelligence Platform: Desktop Application Administration Guide. 2006. (Illus.). 96p. 13.95 *(978-1-59994-287-2(9))* SAS Publishing.

—SAS/AF 9. 2 Procedure Guide. 2008. 96p. per. 13.95 *(978-1-59994-005-2(1))* SAS Publishing.

SAS Publishing, Publishing. SAS 9.2 Intelligence Platform: Desktop Application Administration Guide. 2009. vi, 65p. *(978-1-59994-852-2(4)*, SAS Publishing.

Sattler, Alexander. Web GUI Toolkit: Vergleich von Web-GUI-Frameworks in der Java-Anwendungsentwicklung. 2010. 152p. pap. *(978-3-639-27405-9(9))* VDM Verlag Dr. Mueller e.K.

Scanlon, Jeff & Ghoda, Ashish. Accelerated Silverlight 3. 2009. (ENG.). 512p. pap. 39.99 *(978-1-4302-2429-7(0))* Apress L. P.

Schmidt, Heinz, et al. Oracle Application Server Interview Questions: The Unauthorized Oracle Fusion Questions, Answers & Explanations. 2007. 160p. per. 54.95 *(978-1-933804-27-9(0))* Equity Pr.

Schneider, Thomas. SAP Business Bydesign - Application Development. 2011. (ENG., Illus.). 350p. 69.95 *(978-1-59229-367-4(0)*, SAP PR.) Galileo Pr., Inc.

Schoder, Detlef, et al, eds. Peer-to-Peer: Ökonomische, technologische und juristische Perspektiven. 2007. (Xpert. press Ser.). (GER., Illus.). X, 299p. 30.70 *(978-3-540-43708-6(8)*, 3540437088) Springer.

Schuman, Corey. Windows Phone 7 Application Development. rev. ed. 2012. (Developer's Library). (ENG.). 400p. pap. 39.99 *(978-0-672-33222-7(1))* Addison Wesley Professional.

Schwem, Adam. Using OpenGL ES 2. 0 for Android Development: Develop & Design. 2012. (Develop & Design Ser.). (ENG.). 160p. pap. 29.99 ***(978-0-321-79215-0(7))*** Peachpit Pr.

Sellers, Mitchel, et al. Visual Studio 2010 & .NET 4.0, 6 vols. in 1. 2010. (ENG., Illus.). 1272p. pap. 49.99 *(978-0-470-49948-1(6)*, Wrox) Wiley, John & Sons, Inc.

Semko, Vitaly & Marruchi-Foino, Romain. Game & Graphics Programming for iOS & Android with OpenGL ES 2.0. 2012. (ENG., Illus.). 308p. pap. 44.99 ***(978-1-119-97591-5(3)***, Wrox) Wiley, John & Sons, Inc.

Sempf, Bill & Jausovec, Peter. VSTO for Dummies. 2010. (ENG., Illus.). 336p. pap. 29.99 *(978-0-470-04647-0(3)*, For Dummies) Wiley, John & Sons, Inc.

Sen, Robi, et al. Android in Action. 3rd rev. ed. 2011. (ENG.). 664p. pap. 49.99 *(978-1-61729-050-3(5))* Manning Pubns. Co.

Shabdar, Ali. Foundation Zoho: Work & Create Online. 2009. (ENG.). 400p. pap. 29.99 *(978-1-4302-1991-0(2)*, Friends of Ed) Apress L. P.

Sharp, John. Windows Communication Foundation 4 Step by Step. 2010. (ENG., Illus.). 736p. pap. 54.99 *(978-0-7356-4556-1(6))* Microsoft Pr.

Shaw, Zed. Mongrel: Learn to Build the Greatest Ruby Web Server Ever. rev. ed. 2011. (Addison-Wesley Professional Ruby Ser.). (ENG.). 325p. pap. 44.99 *(978-0-321-50309-1(0))* Addison Wesley Professional.

Sheriff, Paul D. Fundamentals of Ado Net. 2007. 100p. pap. 19.95 *(978-0-9793748-6-9(3))* PDSA, Inc.

Sheth, A. Semantic-Enabled Advancements on the Web: Applications Across Industries. 2012. ***(978-1-4666-0187-1(6))***; ***(978-1-4666-0185-7(X))*** IGI Global.

Shklar, Leon & Rosen, Richard. Web Application Architecture: Principles, Protocols & Practices. 2nd ed. 2009. (ENG., Illus.). 440p. pap. 60.95 *(978-0-470-51860-1(X)*, Wiley) Wiley, John & Sons, Inc.

Silva, Vladimir. Pro Android Games. 2009. (ENG.). 300p. pap. 39.99 *(978-1-4302-2647-5(1))* Apress L. P.

Simon, Jonathan. Head First Android Development. 2012. (ENG.). 608p. pap. 44.99 *(978-1-4493-9330-4(6))* O'Reilly Media, Inc.

Singham, Roy, et al. The Thoughtworks Anthology: Essays on Software Technology & Innovation. 2008. (Pragmatic Programmers Ser.). (ENG., Illus.). 248p. pap. 38.95 *(978-1-934356-14-2(X)*, Pragmatic Bookshelf, The) Pragmatic Programmers, LLC, The.

Six, Jeff. Application Security for the Android Platform: Processes, Permissions, & Other Safeguards. 2011. (ENG.). 114p. pap. 17.99 ***(978-1-4493-1507-8(0))*** O'Reilly Media, Inc.

Slovak, Ken. Professional Outlook 2007 Programming. 2007. (ENG., Illus.). 454p. per. 49.99 *(978-0-470-04994-5(4)*, Wrox) Wiley, John & Sons, Inc.

Smart, John Ferguson. Jenkins: the Definitive Guide. 2011. (ENG., Illus.). 406p. pap. 44.99 *(978-1-4493-0535-2(0))* O'Reilly Media, Inc.

Smith, Peter. Software Build Systems: Principles & Experience. rev. ed. 2011. (ENG., Illus.). 624p. 59.99 *(978-0-321-71728-3(7))* Addison Wesley Professional.

Smith, Randy. CertPrimer 801: IBM(r) Lotus Notes(r) Domino(r) Exam 801 Certification Primer. 2008. 199p. pap. 39.99 *(978-0-615-19779-1(5))* CertPrimer.

Smith, Scott. Matlab Advanced Gui Development. 2006. 324p. per. 45.00 *(978-1-59858-181-2(3))* Dog Ear Publishing, LLC.

Smith, Steven A., et al. Silverlight 2.0 Web Development: Problem - Design - Solution. 2009. 550p. pap. 44.99 *(978-0-470-24797-6(5)*, Wrox) Wiley, John & Sons, Inc.

Smithwick, Mike & Verma, Mayank. Pro OpenGL ES for Android. 2012. (ENG.). 308p. pap. 49.99 ***(978-1-4302-4002-0(4))*** Apress L. P.

Snell, Mike & Powers, Lars. Microsoft Visual Studio 2010 Unleashed. 2010. (Unleashed Ser.). (ENG., Illus.). 1224p. pap. 59.99 *(978-0-672-33081-0(4))* Sams.

Sobhany, Rana June. Mobilize: Strategies for Success from the Frontlines of the App Revolution. 2011. (ENG., Illus.). 256p. pap. 17.95 *(978-1-59315-645-9(6))* Vanguard Pr.

Sonatype Company Staff. Maven. rev. ed. 2008. (ENG., Illus.). 470p. pap. 34.99 *(978-0-596-51733-5(5))* O'Reilly Media, Inc.

Sosa, Carlos P. IBM System Blue Gene Solution: Blue Gene/P Application Development. 2007. (Illus.). xiv, 300p. pap. *(978-0-7384-8867-7(4))* IBM.

Spaanjaars, Imar. ASP.NET 4.0: In C# & VB. 2010. (ENG., Illus.). 840p. pap. 44.99 *(978-0-470-50221-1(5)*, Wrox) Wiley, John & Sons, Inc.

Srinivas Sajja, Priti & Akerkar, Rajendra. Intelligent Technologies for Web Applications. 2012. (Chapman & Hall/CRC Data Mining & Knowledge Discovery Ser.). (ENG., Illus.). 367p. 89.95 ***(978-1-4398-7162-1(0)***, Chapman & Hall/CRC) CRC Pr. LLC.

Srivastava, Shashwat & Singh, Apeksha. Facebook Application Development with Graph API Cookbook. 2011. 350p. pap. ***(978-1-84969-092-8(8))*** Packt Publishing, Ltd.

St. Laurent, Simon, et al. Learning Rails 3. 2012. (ENG.). 400p. pap. 34.99 ***(978-1-4493-0933-6(X))*** O'Reilly Media, Inc.

Stark, Jonathan & Jepson, Brian. Building Android Apps with HTML, CSS, & JavaScript: Making Native Apps with Standards-Based Web Tools. 2nd ed. 2012. (ENG.). 178p. pap. 29.99 ***(978-1-4493-1641-9(7))*** O'Reilly Media, Inc.

Stay, Jesse & Reagan. Facebook Application Development for Dummies. 2011. (ENG.). 408p. pap. 29.99 *(978-0-470-76873-0(8)*, For Dummies) Wiley, John & Sons, Inc.

Steele, James & To, Nelson. The Android Developer's Cookbook: Building Applications with the Android SDK. 2010. (Developer's Library). (ENG., Illus.). 400p. pap. 44.99 *(978-0-321-74123-3(4))* Addison Wesley Professional.

Steinberg, Daniel H. & Freeman, Eric T. iPad Programming: iPhone Developers. 2010. (ENG., Illus.). 248p. pap. 34.95 *(978-1-934356-57-9(3)*, Pragmatic Bookshelf, The) Pragmatic Programmers, LLC, The.

Steiner, Matthias. Building Extensible Composite Applications with SAP. 2009. (Illus.). 205p. pap. 84.95 *(978-1-59229-287-5(9)*, SAP PR.) Galileo Pr., Inc.

Stephens, Matt & Rosenberg, Doug. Design Driven Testing: Test Smarter, Not Harder. 2010. (ENG.). 368p. pap. 49.99 *(978-1-4302-2943-8(8))* Apress L. P.

Sterling, Paul, et al. Umbraco User's Guide. 2011. (ENG., Illus.). 360p. pap. 44.99 *(978-0-470-56082-2(7)*, Wrox) Wiley, John & Sons, Inc.

Stevens, Chris. Appillionaires: Secrets from Developers Who Struck It Rich on the App Store. 3rd ed. 2011. (ENG., Illus.). 224p. pap. 24.99 ***(978-1-119-97864-0(5)***, Wiley) Wiley, John & Sons, Inc.

Stevens, Chris. Designing for the iPad: Building Applications That Sell. 2011. (ENG., Illus.). 352p. pap. 39.99 *(978-0-470-97678-4(0)*, Wiley) Wiley, John & Sons, Inc.

Stevens, Timothy J. Facebook Unlocked: The Key to Developing Custom Applications. Burleson, Donald, ed. 2010. (IT in-Focus Ser.). (ENG.). 275p. pap. 27.95 *(978-0-9823061-6-1(4))* Rampant TechPress.

Stevenson, Scott. Cocoa & Objective-C: Up & Running - Foundations of Mac, iPhone, & iPod touch Programming. 2010. (ENG., Illus.). 416p. pap. 34.99 *(978-0-596-80479-4(2))* O'Reilly Media, Inc.

Stoecker, Matthew, et al. MCTS Self-Paced Training Kit (Exam 70-505) Microsoft .NET Framework 3.5 - Windows Forms Application Development. 2nd ed. 2009. (ENG.). 816p. pap. 69.99 *(978-0-7356-2637-9(5))* Microsoft Pr.

Stoecker, Matthew A. MCTS Exam 70-511 Kit: Windows Application Development with Microsoft . Net Framework 4. 2011. (ENG., Illus.). 672p. pap. 69.99 *(978-0-7356-2742-0(8))* Microsoft Pr.

Stoecker, Matthew A. & Northrup, Tony. McPd 70-518 Exam Ref: Designing & Developing Windows(r) Applications Using Microsoft(r) .NET Framework 4. 2011. (ENG., Illus.). 336p. pap. 39.99 *(978-0-7356-5723-6(8))* Microsoft Pr.

Stroud, Adam & Milette, Greg. Professional Android Sensor Programming. 2012. (ENG.). 552p. pap. 49.99 ***(978-1-118-18348-9(7)***, Wrox) Wiley, John & Sons, Inc.

Svetla, Mancheva. Successful Industry Building in Transition Countries - Foreign Direct Investment or Local Effort? Software Industries of Bulgaria, Estonia, & Romani. 2008. 80p. pap. *(978-3-639-03475-2(9))* VDM Verlag Dr. Mueller e.K.

Swenson, Erik. Practical SharePoint 2010 Branding & Customization. 2011. (ENG.). 368p. pap. 49.99 ***(978-1-4302-4026-6(1))*** Apress L. P.

Swift, Jonathan, et al. Professional Silverlight 2 for ASP. NET Developers. 2009. (ENG., Illus.). 672p. pap. 49.99 *(978-0-470-27775-1(0),* Wrox) Wiley, John & Sons, Inc.

Swithinbank, Peter. Web Services Feature Pack for Websphere Application Server V6.1. 2008. (Illus.). xviii, 574p. *(978-0-7384-3134-5(6))* IBM.

Sydor, Michael J. APM Best Practices: Realizing Application Performance Management. 2010. (ENG.). 504p. pap. 69.99 *(978-1-4302-3141-7(6))* Apress L. P.

Tavares, Christopher, et al. ATL Internals: Working with ATL 8. 2nd rev. ed. 2006. (Addison-Wesley Object Technology Ser.). (ENG., Illus.). 888p. per. 69.99 *(978-0-321-15962-5(4))* Addison Wesley Professional.

Taylor, Richard & Zechner, Mario. Beginning Android Games. 2011. (ENG., Illus.). 688p. pap. 39.99 *(978-1-4302-3042-7(8))* Apress L. P.

Thelin, Johan. Foundations of Qt Development. 2007. (Expert's Voice in Open Source Ser.). (ENG., Illus.). 528p. per. 54.99 *(978-1-59059-831-3(8))* Apress L. P.

Thompson, Mick. Getting Started with Geo, Couchdb, & Node. Js. 2011. (ENG.). 64p. pap. 24.99 ***(978-1-4493-0752-3(3))*** O'Reilly Media, Inc.

Tine, Verhanneman & Piessens, Frank. Context-Based Access Control for Software Applications. 2008. 144p. pap. *(978-3-639-01890-5(7))* VDM Verlag Dr. Mueller e.K.

Tiwari, Shashank. Professional BlazeDS: Creating Rich Internet Application with Flex & Java. 2009. (ENG., Illus.). 384p. pap. 54.99 *(978-0-470-46489-2(5),* Wrox) Wiley, John & Sons, Inc.

Tiwari, Shashank & Elrom, Elad. AdvancED Flex 3. 2008. (ENG.). 640p. pap. 54.99 *(978-1-4302-1027-6(3),* Friends of Ed) Apress L. P.

Tiwari, Shashank, et al. AdvancED Flex 4. 2010. (ENG.). 560p. pap. 54.99 *(978-1-4302-2483-9(5),* Friends of Ed) Apress L. P.

Tretola, Rich. BSAVA Manual of Beginning Adobe AIR: Building Applications for the Adobe Integrated Runtime. 2008. (ENG., Illus.). 319p. pap. 44.99 *(978-0-470-22904-0(7),* Wrox) Wiley, John & Sons, Inc.

—Developing BlackBerry Tablet Applications with Flex 4.5. 2011. (ENG., Illus.). 116p. pap. 29.99 ***(978-1-4493-0556-7(3))*** O'Reilly Media, Inc.

—Developing iOS Applications with Flex 4. 5. 2011. (ENG.). 134p. pap. 19.99 ***(978-1-4493-0836-0(8))*** O'Reilly Media, Inc.

Tretola, Rich, et al. Professional Adobe Flex 3. 2009. (ENG., Illus.). 1488p. pap. 49.99 *(978-0-470-22364-2(2),* Wrox) Wiley, John & Sons, Inc.

Troelsen, Andrew. Pro Expression Blend 4. 2011. (ENG.). 400p. pap. 49.99 *(978-1-4302-3377-0(X))* Apress L. P.

Tucker, David, et al. Adobe AIR 1.5: Solutions & Examples for Rich Internet Application Developers. 2008. (ENG., Illus.). 448p. pap. 44.99 *(978-0-596-52250-6(9))* O'Reilly Media, Inc.

Tulach, Jaroslav. Practical API Design: Confessions of a Java Framework Architect. 2008. (ENG.). 416p. 74.99 *(978-1-4302-0973-7(9))* Apress L. P.

Turner, James. Developing Enterprise iOS Applications: IPhone & iPad Apps for Companies & Organizations. 2011. (ENG., Illus.). 116p. pap. 24.99 ***(978-1-4493-1148-3(2))*** O'Reilly Media, Inc.

Turner, Kirby & Harrington, Tom. Learning iPad Programming LiveLessons Bundle. 2012. (LiveLessons Ser.). (ENG.). 816p. pap. 69.99 ***(978-0-321-84395-1(9))*** Addison Wesley Professional.

Tyler, Jason. App Inventor for Android: Build Your Own Apps. 2011. (ENG., Illus.). 416p. pap. 34.99 *(978-1-119-99133-5(1),* Wiley) Wiley, John & Sons, Inc.

Tyler, Jason. XDA's Android Hacker's Toolkit: The Complete Guide to Rooting, ROMs & Theming. 2012. (ENG.). 192p. pap. 34.99 ***(978-1-119-95138-4(0),*** Wiley) Wiley, John & Sons, Inc.

Udell, Sterling. Pro Web Gadgets for Mobile & Desktop. 2009. (ENG.). 350p. pap. 39.99 *(978-1-4302-2551-5(3))* Apress L. P.

Upton, David. Codeigniter for Rapid Php Application Development. 2007. 260p. per. *(978-1-84719-174-8(6))* Packt Publishing, Ltd.

Valim, Jose. Crafting Rails Applications: Expert Practices for Everyday Rails Development. 2011. (ENG., Illus.). 184p. pap. 33.00 *(978-1-934356-73-9(5),* Pragmatic Bookshelf, The) Pragmatic Programmers, LLC, The.

van der Linden, Peter. Android Programming. rev. ed. 2012. (ENG.). 480p. pap. 49.99 ***(978-0-13-277763-6(0),*** Prentice Hall) Prentice Hall PTR.

Vaughan, Daniel. Windows Phone 7.5. rev. ed. 2012. (Unleashed Ser.). (ENG.). 1120p. pap. 59.99 *(978-0-672-33348-4(1))* Sams.

Vaughn, William R. & Blackburn, Peter. Hitchhiker's Guide to Visual Studio & SQL Server: Best Practice Architectures & Examples. 7th ed. 2006. (Microsoft Windows Server System Ser.). (ENG., Illus.). 1128p. pap. 64.99 *(978-0-321-24362-1(5))* Addison Wesley Professional.

Vela Nava, Eduardo Alberto, et al. Web Application Obfuscation: '-/WAFs.. Evasion.. Filters//alert(/Obfuscation/)-' 2010. (ENG., Illus.). 296p. pap. 49.95 *(978-1-59749-604-9(9),* Syngress Press) Elsevier Science & Technology Bks.

Velte, Anthony & Velte, Toby. Microsoft Azure Services Platform. 2012. (Illus.). 400p. pap. 40.00 *(978-0-07-171789-2(7),* 0071717897) McGraw-Hill Osborne.

Velte, Toby, et al. Cloud Computing, A Practical Approach. 2009. (ENG., Illus.). 352p. pap. 39.99 *(978-0-07-162694-1(8),* 0071626948) McGraw-Hill Osborne.

Venkatasamy, Prasanna Venkatesan. Armms - an Architectural Reference Model for Multilingual Software. 2009. 212p. pap. *(978-3-639-20403-2(4))* VDM Verlag Dr. Mueller e.K.

Video2brain Staff & Turrall, Robert. Facebook Application Development: Learn by Video. 2011. (Learn by Video Ser.). (ENG.). 48p. 34.99 ***(978-0-321-80958-2(0))*** Peachpit Pr.

Virtual Training Company, prod. ColdFusion MX 7. 2006. cd-rom 99.95 *(978-1-933736-56-3(9))* VTC, Inc.

Vivien, Vladimir. JavaFX 1. 2 Application Development Cookbook. 2010. 332p. pap. 39.99 *(978-1-84719-894-5(5))* Packt Publishing, Ltd. GBR. Dist: Ebsco Publishing.

Vliet, Jurg van, et al. Elastic Beanstalk. 2011. (ENG.). 88p. pap. 29.99 ***(978-1-4493-0664-9(0))*** O'Reilly Media, Inc.

Vo, Khang. Pro iOS Apps Performance Optimization. 2011. (ENG.). 284p. pap. 44.99 *(978-1-4302-3717-4(1))* Apress L. P.

Vora, Pawan. Web Application Design Patterns. 2009. (Interactive Technologies Ser.). (ENG., Illus.). 448p. pap. 59.95 *(978-0-12-374265-0(X),* Morgan Kaufmann) Elsevier Science & Technology Bks.

Wagner, Richard. Adobe AIR for Dummies. 2009. (ENG., Illus.). 360p. pap. 29.99 *(978-0-470-39044-3(1),* For Dummies) Wiley, John & Sons, Inc.

—Beginning iOS Application Development with HTML & JavaScript. 2012. (ENG.). 432p. pap. 34.99 ***(978-1-118-15900-2(4),*** Wrox) Wiley, John & Sons, Inc.

Wagner, Richard. Professional Flash Mobile Development: Creating Android & iPhone Applications. 2011. (ENG., Illus.). 336p. pap. 39.99 *(978-0-470-62007-6(2),* Wrox) Wiley, John & Sons, Inc.

Wahli, Ueli. Experience Java EE! Using WebSphere Application Server Community Edition 2.1. 2009. (Illus.). xxii, 588p. *(978-0-7384-3230-4(X))* IBM.

Walls, Craig. Modular Java: Creating Flexible Applications with OSGi & Spring. 2009. (ENG., Illus.). 260p. pap. 34.95 *(978-1-934356-40-1(9),* Pragmatic Bookshelf, The) Pragmatic Programmers, LLC, The.

—Spring in Action. 3rd rev. ed. 2011. (ENG., Illus.). 424p. pap. 49.99 *(978-1-935182-35-1(8))* Manning Pubns. Co.

Walther, Stephen. Windows 8 Metro Apps with HTML5 & JavaScript Unleashed. 2012. (Unleashed Ser.). (ENG.). 600p. pap. 59.99 ***(978-0-672-33605-8(7))*** Sams.

Wargo, John M. BlackBerry Development Fundamentals. 2009. (ENG., Illus.). 480p. pap. 39.99 *(978-0-321-64742-9(4))* Addison Wesley Professional.

Wargo, John M. PhoneGap Essentials: Building Cross-Platform Mobile Apps. 2012. (ENG.). 384p. pap. 39.99 ***(978-0-321-81429-6(0))*** Addison Wesley Professional.

Warner, Robert & Privat, Michael. Pro Core Data for iOS. 2nd ed. 2011. (ENG.). 400p. pap. 44.99 ***(978-1-4302-3656-6(6))*** Apress L. P.

Warner, Robert & Privat, Michael. Pro Core Data for IOS: Data Access & Persistence Engine for iPhone, iPad, & iPod Touch. 2011. (ENG.). 400p. pap. 39.99 *(978-1-4302-3355-8(9))* Apress L. P.

Warren, Rich. Creating iOS 5 Apps: Develop & Design. rev. ed. 2011. (Develop & Design Ser.). (ENG., Illus.). 560p. pap. 49.99 *(978-0-321-76960-2(0))* Peachpit Pr.

Watts, David. Tuning IBM System X Servers for Performance. 5th ed. 2007. (Illus.). xxviii, 1068p. *(978-0-7384-8979-7(4))* IBM.

Weathersby, Jason, et al. Integrating & Extending BIRT. (Eclipse Ser.). (ENG., 2nd ed. 2008. Illus.). 724p. pap. 54.99 *(978-0-321-58030-6(3))* 3rd rev. ed. 2011. 880p. pap. 54.99 *(978-0-321-77282-4(2))* Addison Wesley Professional.

Weaver, James L. Pro JavaFX Platform: Script, Desktop & Mobile RIA with Java Technology. 2009. (Illus.). xxiii, 543p. E-Book ***(978-1-4302-1876-0(2))*** Apress L. P.

Weaver, James L., et al. Pro JavaFX 2: A Definitive Guide to Rich Clients with Java Technology. 2012. (Pro Ser.). (ENG.). 640p. pap. 49.99 *(978-1-4302-6872-7(7))* Apress L. P.

Welch, John. iOS5 in the Enterprise: Develop & Design - A Hands-On Guide to Managing iPhones & iPads. 2011. (ENG.). 256p. pap. 49.99 ***(978-0-321-81199-8(2))*** Peachpit Pr.

Welch, Shawn. From Idea to App: Creating iOS UI, Animations, & Gestures. rev. ed. 2011. (Illus.). 264p. pap. 34.99 *(978-0-321-76555-0(9))* New Riders Publishing.

Welch, Shawn. iOS 5 Core Frameworks: Develop & Design - Working with Graphics, Location, iCloud, & More. 2011. (Develop & Design Ser.). (ENG.). 320p. pap. 44.99 ***(978-0-321-80350-4(7))*** Peachpit Pr.

Wentk, Richard. iPhone OS Development: Your Visual Blueprint for Developing Apps for Apple's Mobile Devices. 2010. (Visual Blueprint Ser.: 26). (ENG., Illus.). 320p. pap. 29.99 *(978-0-470-55651-1(X),* Visual) Wiley, John & Sons, Inc.

Westfall, Jon, et al. Android Web Apps Development: Develop for Android Using HTML5, CSS3, JavaScript & More Web Standards. 2012. (ENG.). 284p. pap. 34.99 ***(978-1-4302-3957-4(3))*** Apress L. P.

Wheeler, Willie & Wheeler, John. Spring in Practice. rev. ed. 2012. (ENG.). 600p. pap. 44.99 *(978-1-935182-05-4(6))* Manning Pubns. Co.

Whitechapel, Andrew. Windows Phone 7 Development Internals: Covers versions 7. 0 Through 7. 5. 2012. (ENG.). 750p. pap. 59.99 ***(978-0-7356-6325-1(4))*** Microsoft Pr.

Wildermuth, Shawn. Essential Windows Phone 7.5: Application Development with Silverlight. rev. ed. 2011. (Microsoft . NET Development Ser.). (ENG., Illus.). 512p. pap. 39.99 *(978-0-321-75213-0(9))* Addison Wesley Professional.

Wildermuth, Shawn, et al. Microsoft .NET Framework 3.5 Kit: ADO.NET Application Development (Exam 70-561) 2009. (ENG.). 528p. pap. 69.99 *(978-0-7356-2563-1(8))* Microsoft Pr.

Wiley, et al. BlackBerry Application Development for Dummies. 2010. (ENG., Illus.). 408p. pap. 29.99 *(978-0-470-46711-4(8),* For Dummies) Wiley, John & Sons, Inc.

—Silverlight 2. 2008. (Bible Ser.: 522). (ENG., Illus.). 592p. pap. 39.99 *(978-0-470-37500-6(0),* Wiley) Wiley, John & Sons, Inc.

Wilkinson, Colin. Going Live: Launching Your Digital Business. 2012. (Digital Entrepreneurship in the Age of Apps, the Web, & Mobile Devices Ser.). (ENG., Illus.). 64p. (YA). (gr. 7-12). pap. 12.95 ***(978-1-4488-6972-5(2))***; lib. bdg. 31.95 ***(978-1-4488-6927-5(7))*** Rosen Publishing Group, Inc., The.

Williams, Brennon. Microsoft Expression Blend 4. rev. ed. 2011. (Unleashed Ser.). (ENG., Illus.). 384p. pap. 49.99 *(978-0-672-33107-7(1))* Sams.

Williams, Bruce & Athayde, John. The Rails View: Creating a Beautiful & Maintainable User Experience. 2012. (ENG.). 264p. pap. 35.00 ***(978-1-934356-87-6(5),*** Pragmatic Bookshelf, The) Pragmatic Programmers, LLC, The.

Williams, Mark. Cloud Computing: Moving Your Business into the Cloud. 2010. (ENG., Illus.). 160p. pap. 14.95 *(978-0-7494-6130-0(6))* Kogan Page, Ltd. GBR. Dist: Ingram Pub. Services.

Williams, Vanessa L. Visual Studio 2005 All-in-One Desk Reference for Dummies. 2nd rev. ed. 2006. (ENG., Illus.). 888p. pap. 39.99 *(978-0-7645-9775-6(2),* For Dummies) Wiley, John & Sons, Inc.

Williams, Vanessa L. & Leinecker, Rick. Visual Studio 2008 All-in-One Desk Reference for Dummies. 2008. (ENG., Illus.). 840p. pap. 39.99 *(978-0-470-19108-8(2),* For Dummies) Wiley, John & Sons, Inc.

Wilt, Nicholas. CUDA Handbook: The A Comprehensive Guide to GPU Programming. 2012. (ENG.). 512p. pap. 49.99 ***(978-0-321-80946-9(7))*** Addison Wesley Professional.

Winkler, Matt. Windows Workflow Foundation 4. 0 Unleashed. 2010. (Unleashed Ser.). (ENG.). 700p. pap. 49.99 *(978-0-672-33068-1(7))* Sams.

Wischusen, Derek, et al. Flex on Rails: Building Rich Internet Applications with Adobe Flex 3 & Rails 2. 2008. (Developer's Library). (ENG., Illus.). 360p. pap. 49.99 *(978-0-321-54337-0(8))* Addison Wesley Professional.

Wischusen, Jeremy. Professional Cairngorm. 2009. (ENG., Illus.). 360p. pap. 59.99 *(978-0-470-49726-5(2),* Wrox) Wiley, John & Sons, Inc.

Wolber, David, et al. App Inventor. 2011. (ENG., Illus.). 384p. pap. 39.99 *(978-1-4493-9748-7(4))* O'Reilly Media, Inc.

Wooldridge, Dave & Schneider, Michael. The Business of iPhone & iPad App Development: Making & Marketing Apps That Succeed. 2nd ed. 2011. (ENG.). 480p. pap. 29.99 *(978-1-4302-3300-8(1))* Apress L. P.

—The Business of iPhone App Development: Making & Marketing Apps That Succeed. 2010. (ENG.). 408p. pap. 29.99 *(978-1-4302-2733-5(8))* Apress L. P.

Wooldridge, Dave, et al. Beginning iPad Development for iPhone Developers: Mastering the iPad SDK. 2010. (ENG.). 272p. pap. 39.99 *(978-1-4302-3021-2(5))* Apress L. P.

Yaghmour, Karim. Embedded Android: Porting, Extending, & Customizing. 2012. (ENG.). 200p. pap. 33.99 ***(978-1-4493-0829-2(5))*** O'Reilly Media, Inc.

Yang, Haitao. Practice & Research Notes in Relational Database Applications. 2010. (Computer Science, Technology & Applications Ser.). pap. 43.00 *(978-1-61668-850-9(5),* Nova Novinka) Nova Science Pubs., Inc.

Yang, Yu & Xu Yu, Jeffrey, eds. Advances in Data & Web Management: Joint 9th Asia-Pacific Web Conference, APweb 2007 & 8th International Conference on Web-Age Information Management, WAIM 2007 Huang Shan, China, June 16-18, 2007 Proceedings. 2007. (Lecture Notes in Computer Science Ser.). (Illus.). 896p. pap. 149.00 *(978-3-540-72483-4(4))* Springer.

Yantzi, Don & Haji, Nazmin. The Remote System Explorer: Modern Developer Tools for the System I. 2008. (ENG.). 350p. pap. 79.95 *(978-1-58347-081-7(6))* MC Pr., LLC.

Yarmosh, Ken. App Savvy: Turning Ideas into iPad & iPhone Apps Customers Really Want. 2010. (ENG., Illus.). 352p. pap. 29.99 *(978-1-4493-8976-5(7))* O'Reilly Media, Inc.

Young, Mike. Programming Dynamic Websites Using ASP. 2009. 99p. pap. 25.50 *(978-0-9559877-1-7(7))* Young, Mike GBR. Dist: Lulu Enterprises Inc.

Yurga, Tolga. Testing & Testability of Object-Oriented Software Systems Via Metrics. 2011. 216p. pap. ***(978-3-8433-5950-4(4))*** Lambert Academic Publishing.

Zammetti, Frank. Practical Dojo Projects. 2008. (ENG.). 500p. pap. 46.99 *(978-1-4302-1066-5(4))* Apress L. P.

—Practical Ext JS Projects with Gears. 2009. (ENG.). 600p. pap. 44.99 *(978-1-4302-1924-8(6))* Apress L. P.

—Practical Palm Pre WebOS Projects. 2009. (ENG., Illus.). 400p. pap. 39.99 *(978-1-4302-2674-1(9))* Apress L. P.

Zarra, Marcus & Long, Matt. Core Animation: Simplified Animation Techniques for Mac & iPhone Development. 2009. (Apple Core Technology Ser.). (ENG., Illus.). 264p. pap. 44.99 *(978-0-321-61775-0(4))* Addison Wesley Professional.

Zdziarski, Jonathan. iPhone SDK Application Development: Building Applications for the AppStore. 2009. (ENG., Illus.). 400p. pap. 34.99 *(978-0-596-15405-9(4))* O'Reilly Media, Inc.

Zechner, Mario & Green, Robert. Beginning Android 4 Games Development. 2011. (ENG., Illus.). 696p. pap. 39.99 ***(978-1-4302-3987-1(5))*** Apress L. P.

Zelkowitz, Marvin, ed. The Internet & Mobile Technology. 2011. (ENG., Illus.). 360p. pap. 171.00 *(978-0-12-385514-5(4),* Academic Pr.) Elsevier Science & Technology Bks.

Zend Technologies Staff, contrib. by. Zend Framework, 2 vols. 2010. (ENG.). pap. 49.99 *(978-1-4302-2880-6(6))* 3rd ed. pap. 49.99 *(978-1-4302-2883-7(0))* Apress L. P.

Zhang, Liang-Jie, ed. Web Services Research for Emerging Applications: Discoveries & Trends. 2010. 404p. 180.00 *(978-1-61520-684-1(1),* Information Science Reference) IGI Global.

Zheng, Pei, et al. Windows Phone 7 Programming for Android & iOS Developers. 2011. (ENG., Illus.). 360p. pap. 39.99 *(978-1-118-02197-2(5),* Wrox) Wiley, John & Sons, Inc.

Zucker, Daniel & Rischpater, Ray. Beginning Nokia Apps Development: Qt & HTML5 for Symbian & MeeGo. 2010. (ENG., Illus.). 248p. pap. 44.99 *(978-1-4302-3177-6(7))* Apress L. P.

37signals, et al. Getting Real: the smarter, faster, easier way to build a successful web Application. 2009. 194p. pap., pap. 24.99 *(978-0-578-01281-0(2))* 37signals.

APPLICATIONS FOR COLLEGE

see College Applications

APPLICATIONS FOR POSITIONS

see also Resumes (Employment)

Bodine, Paul. Perfect Phrases for Letters of Recommendation. 2009. (Perfect Phrases Ser.). (ENG.). 208p. (C). pap. 10.95 *(978-0-07-162654-5(9),* 0071626549) McGraw-Hill Cos., The.

Calicchio, Denise Lefrak & David, Eunice. High Rise Low Down: Who's Who & What's What in New York's Most Coveted Apartment Houses. 2006. (Illus.). 278p. 24.95 *(978-1-56980-316-5(1))* Barricade Bks., Inc.

Corfield, Rebecca. Preparing the Perfect Job Application: Application Forms & Letters Made Easy. 5th ed. 2009. (Illus.). 176p. pap. *(978-0-7494-5653-5(1))* Kogan Page, Ltd.

Cram101 Textbook Reviews. Outlines & Highlights for Business Communication by Thomas Means. 2011. 408p. pap. 35.95 ***(978-1-61906-161-3(9))*** Cram101 Inc.

Crosby, Olivia. Resumes, Applications, & Cover Letters (2009) rev. ed. 2009. (ENG., Illus.). 12p. 2.75 *(978-0-16-083479-0(1),* Bureau of Labor Statistics) United States Government Printing Office.

Employment Search 360: A Insider's Guide to Job-Changing & Progressing your Career at any Level. 2008. (ENG.). 314p. mass mkt. *(978-0-9748991-1-4(9))* Proactive Publishing, LLC.

Gillis, Rick. The Real Secret to Finding a Job? Make Me Money or Save Me Money! And Other Really Useful Job Search Tactics, Introducing the PRE-RESUME. Bennett, Ronni, ed. 2009. (ENG.). 188p. pap. 21.95 *(978-1-4251-9138-2(X))* Trafford Publishing.

Job Application File. 4th ed. pap. 20.95 *(978-0-8224-2632-5(3))* Globe Fearon Educational Publishing.

Kastros, Anthony. Mastering the Fire Service Assessment Center. 2006. (Illus.). 300p. 49.00 *(978-1-59370-077-5(6))* Fire Engineering Bks. & Videos.

Kennedy, Joyce Lain. Cover Letters for Dummies. 3rd ed. 2009. (ENG., Illus.). 312p. pap. 16.99 *(978-0-470-40221-4(0),* For Dummies) Wiley, John & Sons, Inc.

Krantman, Stanley. Resume Writer's Workbook. 4th ed. 2012. (ENG.). 224p. (C). pap. 107.95 ***(978-0-538-49791-6(2))*** Cengage South-Western.

Kuhnhanss, Christoph. El Arte de Saber Venderse. 2008. (Masterclass (Robin Book) Ser.). (Illus.). 285p. pap. *(978-84-7927-863-2(3))* Robinbk., Ediciones S.L.

Luntz, Charles E. Vocational Guidance by Astrology. 2007. (ENG.). 208p. 39.95 *(978-0-548-08462-5(9))* Kessinger Publishing, LLC.

McGraw-Hill Staff. Resumes for Science Careers. 2nd rev. ed. 2007. (ENG.). 144p. per. 11.95 *(978-0-07-147619-5(9),* 0071476199) McGraw-Hill Cos., The.

McIvor, Brian. Be Interview-Wise: How to Prepare for & Manage Your Interviews. 2008. (ENG., Illus.). 112p. pap. 14.95 ***(978-0-9519738-4-4(3))*** Management Briefs Ltd.

Means, Thomas. Business Communications. 2nd ed. 2009. (ENG.). 96p. (C). pap., pupil's gde. ed. 38.95 *(978-0-538-44959-5(4))* Cengage South-Western.

Means, Thomas L. Business Communication. 2nd ed. 2009. (Introduction to Business Communication Ser.). (ENG.). 672p. (C). 96.95 *(978-0-538-44947-2(0))* Cengage South-Western.

Pal, Suvankar & Mumford, Colin J. Getting That Medical Job: Secrets for Success. 3rd ed. 2011. (ENG., Illus.). 168p. pap. 29.95 *(978-1-4443-3488-3(3),* Wiley-Blackwell) Wiley, John & Sons, Inc.

Paliwal, Mukta & Jones, Justin. Powerhouse Interviewing Workbook. 2010. pap. 16.99 *(978-1-61566-476-4(9))* Tate Publishing & Enterprises, LLC.

Ricketts, K D. How to Pass Police Recruitment Te. 2009. 160p. 22.00 *(978-1-84528-320-9(1))* How To Books GBR. Dist: Parkwest Pubns., Inc.

Schuman, Nancy & Nadler, Burton Jay. The Resume & Cover Letter Phrase Book: What to Write to Get the Job That's Right. 2010. (ENG.). 256p. pap. 10.95 *(978-1-4405-0981-0(6))* Adams Media Corp.

Scudamore, Pat & Catt, Hilton. Successful Job Applications: Learn in a Week, What the Experts Learn in a Lifetime. 2012. (Teach Yourself: General Reference Ser.). (ENG., Illus.). 128p. pap. 12.00 ***(978-1-4441-5889-2(9),*** 1444158899) McGraw-Hill Cos., The.

Teller, Mark. Screw the Recruiter: Beat Corporate America at its Own Game. 2011. (ENG.). 200p. (YA). pap. 19.95 *(978-0-9819723-0-5(6))* Screw, Inc., The.

Watson, Anne. The Definitive Job Book: Rules from the Recruitment Insiders. 2008. (ENG.). 296p. per. 24.95 *(978-1-84112-781-1(7),* Capstone) Wiley, John & Sons, Inc.

Zedlitz, Robert H. Getting a Job Process, Kit. 6th ed. 2010. (Title 1 Ser.). (ENG.). 160p. (C). pap. 42.95 *(978-0-538-45041-6(X))* Cengage South-Western.

APPLICATIONS SOFTWARE

see Application Software

APPLIED ANTHROPOLOGY

Baldi, James K., ed. From Arrogance to Excellence: Leaders & Human Interactions. 2007. 132p. 30.00 *(978-0-9642023-5-1(2))*; (Illus.). pap. 25.00 *(978-0-9642023-4-4(4))* Society for Applied Anthropology.

Cram101 Textbook Reviews & Cram101 Textbook Reviews. Outlines & Highlights for Applying Anthropology: An Introductory Reader 9th by Aaron Podolefsky; Peter Brown; Scott Lacy, ISBN. 2011. 232p. pap. 31.95 ***(978-1-4288-6500-6(4))*** Cram101 Inc.

Cram101 Textbook Reviews Staff. Outlines & Highlights for Cultural Anthropology: An Applied Perspective by Gary Ferraro, ISBN. 2009. 110p. pap. 28.95 *(978-1-4288-9109-8(9))* Cram101 Inc.

Ferraro & Cram101 Textbook Reviews Staff. Cultural Anthropology: An Applied Perspective. 2007. 244p. per. 14.95 *(978-1-4288-2656-4(4))* Cram101 Inc.

Ferraro, Gary. Cultural Anthropology: An Applied Perspective. 7th ed. 2007. (ENG.). 456p. (C). pap. 163.95 *(978-0-495-80409-3(6))* Wadsworth.

Greaves, Thomas C., et al. Vicos & Beyond: A Half Century of Applying Anthropology in Peru. 2010. (Illus.). xiii, 359p. *(978-0-7591-1976-5(7))* AltaMira Pr.

Greaves/Bolton/Zapat. Vicos & Beyond: A Half Century of Applying Anthropology in Peru. 2010. (ENG., Illus.). 358p. 75.00 *(978-0-7591-1974-1(0))* AltaMira Pr.

Guerron-Montero, Carla. Careers in Applied Anthropology in the 21st Century: Perspectives from Academics & Practitioners, Number 29. 2009. (NAPA Bulletin Ser.). (ENG., Illus.). 160p. pap. 28.95 *(978-1-4051-9015-2(9),* Wiley-Blackwell) Wiley, John & Sons, Inc.

Hardin, Rebecca & Clarke, Kamari Maxine, eds. Transforming Ethnographic Knowledge. 2012. (ENG.). 248p. pap. 29.95 ***(978-0-299-24874-1(7))*** Univ. of Wisconsin Pr.

Hedican, Edward J. Applied Anthropology in Canada: Understanding Aboriginal Issues. 2nd ed. 2008. (ENG.). 320p. *(978-0-8020-9907-5(6))*; pap. *(978-0-8020-9541-1(0))* Univ. of Toronto Pr.

Juris, Jeffrey S. Networking Futures: The Movements Against Corporate Globalization. 2008. (Experimental Futures Ser.). (ENG., Illus.). 400p. pap. 26.95 *(978-0-8223-4269-4(3))*; (C). 94.95 *(978-0-8223-4250-2(2))* Duke Univ. Pr.

Lucas, George R., Jr. Anthropologists in Arms: The Ethics of Military Anthropology. 2009. (Critical Issues in Anthropology Ser.). (ENG.). 246p. 75.00 *(978-0-7591-1212-4(6))*; pap. 27.50 *(978-0-7591-1213-1(4))* AltaMira Pr.

Mba, Chuks & Kwankye, Stephen, eds. Population, Health & Development in Ghana Attaining the Millenium Development Goals. 2007. 208p. (C). pap. *(978-9988-647-61-2(1))* Sub-Saharan Pubs. & Traders GHA. Dist: Michigan State Univ. Pr.

Mitterlehner, Beate. Applied Anthropology: Eine Netzwerkanalyse in einer österreichischen Gemeinde. 2010. 104p. pap. *(978-3-639-26194-3(1))* VDM Verlag Dr. Mueller e.K.

Podolefsky, et al. Applying Cultural Anthropology: An Introductory Reader. 9th ed. 2012. (ENG., Illus.). 320p. (C). pap. 65.33 ***(978-0-07-811703-9(8),*** 0078117038) McGraw-Hill Cos., The.

Podolefsky, Aaron & Brown, Peter. Applying Anthropology: An Introductory Reader. 8th rev. ed. 2006. (Illus.). 384p. (C). pap. 50.63 *(978-0-07-353093-2(X),* 9780073530932, McGraw-Hill Humanities, Social Sciences & World Languages) McGraw-Hill Higher Education.

—Applying Cultural Anthropology: An Introductory Reader. 7th rev. ed. 2006. (Illus.). 320p. (C). pap. 49.06 *(978-0-07-353092-5(1),* 9780073530925, McGraw-Hill Humanities, Social Sciences & World Languages) McGraw-Hill Higher Education.

Podolefsky, Aaron, et al. Applying Anthropology: An Introductory. 9th ed. 2008. (ENG., Illus.). 384p. (C). pap. 67.67 *(978-0-07-340535-3(3),* 0073405353) McGraw-Hill Cos., The.

—Applying Anthropology: An Introductory Reader. 10th ed. 2011. (ENG., Illus.). 432p. (C). pap. 67.67 ***(978-0-07-811704-6(6),*** 0078117046) McGraw-Hill Cos., The.

Podolefsky, Aaron, et al. Applying Cultural Anthropology: An Introductory Reader. 8th ed. 2008. (ENG., Illus.). 320p. (C). pap. 65.33 *(978-0-07-340533-9(7),* 0073405337) McGraw-Hill Cos., The.

Sillitoe, Paul, ed. Local Science vs Global Science: Approaches to Indigenous Knowledge in International Development. 2009. (Illus.). 302p. 34.95 *(978-1-84545-648-1(3))* Berghahn Bks., Inc.

Venkatesan, Soumhya & Yarrow, Thomas, eds. Differentiating Development: Beyond an Anthropology of Critique. 2012. (ENG.). 220p. 95.00 ***(978-0-85745-303-7(3))*** Berghahn Bks., Inc.

Visual Interventions: Applied Visual Anthropology. 2009. (Illus.). 338p. 29.95 *(978-1-84545-678-8(5))* Berghahn Bks., Inc.

Wallace, Tim, et al. Applied Research & Practice from the Next Generation: The NAPA Student Achievement Award Winning Papers, 2001-05, Number 27. 2007. (NAPA Bulletin Ser.). (ENG., Illus.). 244p. pap. 31.95 *(978-1-931303-33-0(9),* Wiley-Blackwell) Wiley, John & Sons, Inc.

Walters, Bradley B., et al, eds. Against the Grain: The Vayda Tradition in Human Ecology & Ecological Anthropology. 2008. (ENG., Illus.). 392p. pap. 34.95 *(978-0-7591-1173-8(1))* AltaMira Pr.

Walters, Bradley B. & McCay, Bonnie J. Against the Grain: The Vayda Tradition in Human Ecology & Ecological Anthropology. 2008. (ENG., Illus.). 392p. 80.00 *(978-0-7591-1172-1(3))* AltaMira Pr.

Wasson, Christina, et al, eds. Applying Anthropology in the Global Village. 2011. (ENG., Illus.). 326p. 89.00 ***(978-1-61132-085-5(2))***; pap. 29.95 ***(978-1-61132-086-2(0))*** Left Coast Pr., Inc.

Wasson, Christina, et al. Making History at the Frontier: Women Creating Careers As Practicing Anthropologists, Number 26. 2006. (NAPA Bulletin Ser.: Vol. 26). (ENG., Illus.). 232p. pap. 31.95 *(978-1-931303-29-3(0),* Wiley-Blackwell) Wiley, John & Sons, Inc.

Westbrook, David A. Navigators of the Contemporary: Why Ethnography Matters. 2008. 160p. 50.00 *(978-0-226-88751-7(0))*; (ENG.). pap. 18.00 *(978-0-226-88752-4(9))* Univ. of Chicago Pr.

Yanow, Dvora, et al, eds. Organizational Ethnography: Studying the Complexity of Everyday Life. 2009. 304p. (C). 135.00 *(978-1-84787-045-2(7),* B70457C); pap. 55.00 *(978-1-84787-046-9(5),* B70457P) SAGE Pubns., Ltd. GBR. Dist: SAGE Pubns., Inc.

APPLIED ART

see Art Industries and Trade

APPLIED ETHICS

see also Casuistry

Altman, Matthew C. Kant & Applied Ethics: The Uses & Limits of Kant's Practical Philosophy. 2011. (ENG.). 336p. 99.95 ***(978-0-470-65766-9(9),*** Wiley-Blackwell) Wiley, John & Sons, Inc.

Bonevac, Daniel A. Today's Moral Issues: Classic & Contemporary Perspectives. (ENG.). (C). 6th ed. 2009. 672p. pap. 114.33 *(978-0-07-338669-0(3),* 0073386693) 7th ed. 2012. (Illus.). 656p. pap. 114.33 ***(978-0-07-803821-1(9),*** 0078038219) McGraw-Hill Cos., The.

Boonin, David & Oddie, Graham. What's Wrong? Applied Ethicists & Their Critics. 2nd ed. 2009. (ENG.). 640p. (C). pap. 92.95 *(978-0-19-533780-8(8))* Oxford Univ. Pr., Inc.

Boss, Judith A. Analyzing Moral Issues. 5th ed. 2009. (ENG., Illus.). 752p. (C). pap. 126.67 *(978-0-07-353574-6(5),* 0073535745) McGraw-Hill Cos., The.

—Analyzing Moral Issues. 4th ed. 2007. 804p. pap. 106.88 *(978-0-07-338663-8(4),* 9780073386638, McGraw-Hill Humanities, Social Sciences & World Languages) McGraw-Hill Higher Education.

Chadwick, Ruth. Encyclopedia of Applied Ethics, 4 vols., Set. 2nd ed. 2011. (ENG.). 3464p. 995.00 ***(978-0-12-373632-1(3),*** Academic Pr.) Elsevier Science & Technology Bks.

Clapton, Jayne. A Transformatory Ethic of Inclusion: Rupturing Disability & Inclusion for Intergrality. 2008. 352p. *(978-90-8790-539-2(4))*; pap. *(978-90-8790-538-5(6))* Sense Pubs.

Cohen, Randy. Be Good: How to Navigate the Ethics of Everything. 2012. (ENG.). 320p. 24.95 ***(978-1-4521-0790-5(4))*** Chronicle Bks. LLC.

Corey, Marianne Schneider & Corey, Gerald. Becoming a Helper. 6th ed. 2010. (Introduction to Human Services Ser.). (ENG.). 432p. (C). pap. 120.95 *(978-0-495-81226-5(9))* Brooks/Cole.

Cortina, Adela, et al, eds. Public Reason & Applied Ethics: The Ways of Practical Reason in a Pluralist Society. 2008. (Law, Ethics & Economics Ser.). 204p. 124.95 *(978-0-7546-7287-6(5))* Ashgate Publishing Co.

Cram101 Textbook Reviews & Cram101 Textbook Reviews. Outlines & Highlights for 21st Century Ethical Toolbox by Anthony Weston, Isbn: 9780195309676 0195309677. 2011. 222p. pap. 30.95 ***(978-1-61490-235-5(6))*** Cram101 Inc.

Cram101 Textbook Reviews Staff. Outlines & Highlights for Contemporary Moral Problems by James E White, Isbn: 9780495553205. 2009. 80p. pap. 27.95 *(978-1-4288-7889-1(0))* Cram101 Inc.

Cremaschi, Sergio. Normativity Within the Bounds of Plural Reasons. 2007. (ENG.). 108p. (C). pap. 18.00 ***(978-87-87564-07-6(6))*** Aarhus Universitetsforlag DNK. Dist: ISD.

Davis, James Calvin. In Defense of Civility: How Religion Can Unite America on Seven Moral Issues that Divide Us. 2010. (ENG.). 240p. pap. 20.00 *(978-0-664-23544-4(1))* Westminster John Knox Pr.

Elliott, Deni. Ethical Challenges: Building an Ethics Toolkit. 2008. 72p. pap. 19.95 *(978-1-4343-8802-5(6))* AuthorHouse.

—Ethics in the First Person: A Guide to Teaching & Learning Practical Ethics. 2006. (ENG.). 160p. 88.00 *(978-0-7425-5206-7(3))*; per. 30.95 *(978-0-7425-5207-4(1))* Rowman & Littlefield Publishers, Inc.

Evans, G. R. The Good, the Bad & the Moral Dilemma. 2008. (ENG.). 224p. pap. 12.95 *(978-0-7459-5268-0(2))* Lion Hudson PLC GBR. Dist: Independent Pubs. Group.

Ezra, Ovadia. Moral Dilemmas in Real Life: Current Issues in Applied Ethics. 2010. (Law & Philosophy Library). xxi, 191p. pap. 179.00 *(978-90-481-7043-2(5),* 9048170435) Springer.

Fischer, Michael & Seelmann, Kurt, eds. Ethik im transdisziplinären Sprachgebrauch. 2008. (Ethik transdisziplinär Ser.). 434p. pap. 99.95 *(978-3-631-56774-6(X))* Lang, Peter GmbH, Europaischer Verlag der Wissenschaften DEU. Dist: Lang, Peter.

Fitzpatrick. Applied Ethics & Social Problems: Moral Questions of Birth, Society & Death. 2008. (Illus.). 280p. 99.00 *(978-1-86134-860-9(6))* Policy Pr. GBR. Dist: Chicago Distribution Ctr.

Fitzpatrick, Tony. Applied Ethics & Social Problems: Moral Questions of Birth, Society & Death. 2008. (Illus.). 280p. (C). pap. 39.95 *(978-1-86134-859-3(2))* Policy Pr. GBR. Dist: Chicago Distribution Ctr.

George, Alexander, ed. What Should I Do? Philosophers on the Good, the Bad, & the Puzzling. 2010. (ENG.). 224p. pap. 15.95 *(978-0-19-958612-7(8))* Oxford Univ. Pr., Inc.

Goree, Keith. Ethics in the Workplace. 3rd ed. 2011. (ENG., Illus.). 250p. (C). pap. 61.95 *(978-0-538-49777-0(7))* Cengage South-Western.

Guha, Debashis. Educational Ethics: Practical & Professional Ethics, Vol. 4. 2007. 256p. pap. 14.00 *(978-81-8069-476-9(3))* Concept Publishing Co. IND. Dist: South Asia Bks.

Hogan, Linda, ed. Applied Ethics in a World Church: The Padua Conference. 2008. 287p. pap. 28.00 *(978-1-57075-759-4(3))* Orbis Bks.

Jacques, D. Joseph. Chivalry-Now: The Code of Male Ethics. 2010. (ENG.). 220p. pap. 24.95 *(978-1-84694-284-6(5))* Hunt, John Publishing Ltd. GBR. Dist: National Bk. Network.

Jewell, Paul. Disability Ethics: A Framework for Practitioners, Professionals & Policy Makers. 2010. 240p. pap. 35.00 *(978-1-86335-754-8(8))* Common Ground Publishing Pty, Ltd.

Kershnar, Stephen. Sex, Discrimination, & Violence: Surprising & Unpopular Results in Applied Ethics. 2009. (ENG.). 180p. pap. 29.50 *(978-0-7618-4799-1(5))* Univ. Pr. of America, Inc.

Lachmann, Rainer, et al. Ethische Schlüsselprobleme: Lebensweltlich -systematisch - didaktisch. 2006. (Theologie für lehrerinnen und Lehrer Ser.). (GER.). 384p. (C). pap. 38.00 *(978-3-525-61423-5(3))* Vandenhoeck & Ruprecht GmbH & Co. KG DEU. Dist: ISD.

LaFollette, Hugh, ed. Ethics in Practice: An Anthology. 3rd rev. ed. 2006. (Blackwell Philosophy Anthologies Ser.: Vol. 3). (ENG., Illus.). 768p. per. 74.95 *(978-1-4051-2945-9(X),* Wiley-Blackwell) Wiley, John & Sons, Inc.

Lott, Samuel E. Ethics Issues & Reflections. 2011. (Ethical Issues in the 21st Century Ser.). 195.00 *(978-1-61761-676-1(1))* Nova Science Pubs., Inc.

Lumer, Christoph & Nannini, Sandro, eds. Intentionality Deliberation & Autonomy: The Action- Theoretic Basis of Practical Philosophy. 2007. 326p. 134.95 *(978-0-7546-6058-3(3))* Ashgate Publishing Co.

May, Larry, et al. Applied Ethics: A Multicultural Approach. 5th ed. 2010. (ENG.). 592p. (C). pap. 96.80 *(978-0-205-70808-6(0),* Prentice Hall) Prentice Hall PTR.

Motilal, Shashi. Applied Ethics & Human Rights: Conceptual Analysis & Contextual Applications. 2011. (Anthem Press India Ser.). 372p. pap. 40.00 *(978-93-80601-15-1(8))* Anthem Pr. GBR. Dist: Books International, Inc.

Motilal, Shashi, ed. Applied Ethics & Human Rights: Conceptual Analysis & Contextual Applications. 2010. (Anthem Press India Ser.). (ENG.). 372p. 99.00 *(978-81-907570-7-2(5))* Anthem Pr. GBR. Dist: Books International, Inc.

Reid, Thomas. Thomas Reid on Practical Ethics: Lectures & Papers of Natural Religion, Self-Government, Natural Jurisprudence & the Law of Nations. Haakonssen, Knud, ed. 2007. (Edinburgh Edition of Thomas Reid Ser.). (ENG.). 432p. 124.00 *(978-0-271-03229-0(4))* Pennsylvania State Univ. Pr.

Ryberg, Jesper. New Waves in Applied Ethics. Ryberg, Jesper et al, eds. 2007. (New Waves in Philosophy Ser.). (ENG., Illus.). 296p. pap. 40.00 *(978-0-230-53784-2(7))* Palgrave Macmillan.

Vaughn, Lewis. Contemporary Moral Arguments: Readings in Ethical Issues, 1 vol. 2009. (ENG.). 736p. (C). pap. 82.95 *(978-0-19-538193-1(9))* Oxford Univ. Pr., Inc.

Waldman, Ellen & Pou, Charles. Mediation Ethics: Cases & Commentaries. 2011. (ENG.). 464p. 60.00 *(978-0-7879-9588-1(6),* Jossey-Bass) Wiley, John & Sons, Inc.

Wee, Bert van. Transport & Ethics: Ethics & the Evaluation of Transport Policies & Projects. 2011. (Transport Economics, Management & Policy Ser.). (Illus.). 272p. 115.00 ***(978-1-84980-964-1(X))*** Elgar, Edward Publishing, Inc.

Weinstein, Bruce. Ethical Intelligence: Five Principles for Untangling Your Toughest Problems at Work & Beyond. 2011. (ENG.). 248p. pap. 14.95 *(978-1-60868-054-2(1))* New World Library.

Weston, Anthony. A 21st Century Ethical Toolbox. 2nd ed. 2007. (ENG.). 496p. (C). pap. 64.95 *(978-0-19-530967-6(7))* Oxford Univ. Pr., Inc.

White, James E. Contemporary Moral Problems. 10th ed. 2011. (ENG.). 544p. (C). pap. 132.95 *(978-0-8400-3378-9(8))* Wadsworth.

—Contemporary Moral Problems: War, Terrorism, & Torture. 4th ed. 2011. (ENG.). 128p. (C). pap. 31.95 *(978-1-111-52351-0(7))* Wadsworth.

APPLIED LINGUISTICS

see also Computational Linguistics; Machine Translating; Mathematical Linguistics

Aarts, Bas & McMahon, April, eds. The Handbook of English Linguistics. 2008. (Blackwell Handbooks in Linguistics Ser.). (ENG., Illus.). 824p. pap., instr.'s hndbk. ed. 57.95 *(978-1-4051-8787-9(5),* Wiley-Blackwell) Wiley, John & Sons, Inc.

Al Shatter, Ghassan. Acquisition & Development of Nominal & Verbal Structures in Arabic. 2010. 316p. pap. *(978-3-639-24473-1(7))* VDM Verlag Dr. Mueller e.K.

Ayoun, Dalila. French Applied Linguistics. (Illus.). xvi, 560p. (C). 156.00 *(978-90-272-1972-5(9))* Benjamins, John Publishing Co.

—Studies in French Applied Linguistics. 2008. (Illus.). xiii, 400p. *(978-90-272-1982-4(6))* Benjamins, John Publishing Co.

Bachman, Lyle & Palmer, Adrian. Language Assessment in Practice. Oxford University Press Staff, ed. 2010. (Oxford Applied Linguistics Ser.). (ENG., Illus.). 416p. 33.95 *(978-0-19-442293-2(3))* Oxford Univ. Pr., Inc.

Berns, Margie, ed. Concise Encyclopedia of Applied Linguistics. 2009. (Concise Encyclopedias of Language & Linguistics Ser.). (ENG., Illus.). 1104p. 165.00 *(978-0-08-096502-4(4))* Elsevier Science & Technology Bks.

Block, David, et al. Neoliberalism & Applied Linguistics. 2012. (ENG., Illus.). 176p. (C). 150.00 ***(978-0-415-59204-8(6))*** Routledge.

Burns, Anne & Varshney, Rachel. Doing Qualitative Research in TESOL: A Guide for New Researchers. 2012. (ESL & Applied Linguistics Professional Ser.). (ENG.). 135.00 *(978-0-415-89178-3(7))*; pap. 39.95 *(978-0-415-89179-0(5))* Routledge.

Byrnes. Advanced Language Learning: The Contribution of Halliday & Vygotsky. 2007. (ENG., Illus.). 288p. 160.00 *(978-0-8264-9071-1(9))* Continuum International Publishing Group, Ltd. GBR. Dist: National Bk. Network.

Byrnes, Heidi. Advanced Language Learning: The Contribution of Halliday & Vygotsky. 2009. (ENG., Illus.). 288p. 49.95 *(978-0-8264-4308-3(7))* Continuum International Publishing Group, Ltd. GBR. Dist: National Bk. Network.

Cheng, Winnie. Corpus Linguistics. 2011. (Routledge Introductions to Applied Linguistics Ser.). (ENG., Illus.). 256p. 140.00 *(978-0-415-58546-0(5))*; pap. 36.95 *(978-0-415-58547-7(3))* Routledge.

Coffin, Caroline. Applied Linguistics Methods: A Reader. 2009. (ENG., Illus.). 278p. 135.00 *(978-0-415-54544-0(7))* Routledge.

Coffin, Caroline, et al. Applied Linguistics Methods: A Reader. 2009. (ENG., Illus.). 288p. pap. 39.95 *(978-0-415-54545-7(5))* Routledge.

Cook, Guy. Applied Linguistics in Action. 2009. (ENG., Illus.). 296p. pap. 41.95 *(978-0-415-54547-1(1))* Routledge.

—Applied Linguistics in Action: A Reader: A Reader. 2009. (ENG., Illus.). 296p. 141.00 *(978-0-415-54546-4(3))* Routledge.

Cook, Vivian & Wei, Li, eds. Contemporary Applied Linguistics Vol. 2: Linguistics for the Real World. 2011. (Contemporary Studies in Linguistics Ser.). (ENG.). 264p. pap. 49.95 *(978-1-4411-6960-0(1))* Continuum International Publishing Group, Ltd. GBR. Dist: National Bk. Network.

Cope, Lida, ed. Applied Linguists Needed: Cross-Disciplinary Networking for Revitalization & Education in Endangered Language Contexts. 2012. (ENG.). 136p. (C). 125.00 ***(978-0-415-69543-5(0))*** Routledge.

Davies, Alan. An Introduction to Applied Linguistics. 2nd ed. 2007. (Edinburgh Textbooks in Applied Linguistics Ser.). (ENG.). 224p. (gr. 17). pap. 36.00 *(978-0-7486-3355-5(3))* Edinburgh Univ. Pr. GBR. Dist: Columbia Univ. Pr.

—An Introduction to Applied Linguistics: From Practice to Theory. Mitchell, Keith, ed. 2nd ed. 2007. (Edinburgh Textbooks in Applied Linguistics Ser.). (ENG.). 224p. 110.00 *(978-0-7486-3354-8(5))* Edinburgh Univ. Pr. GBR. Dist: Columbia Univ. Pr.

Dörnyei, Zoltan. Research Methods in Applied Linguistics. 2007. (Oxford Applied Linguistics Ser.). (ENG., Illus.). 336p. 42.44 *(978-0-19-442258-1(5))* Oxford Univ. Pr., Inc.

Duff, Patricia A. Case Study Research in Applied Linguistics. 2007. (Illus.). 248p. 120.00 *(978-0-8058-2358-5(1))* Erlbaum, Lawrence Assocs., Inc.

—Case Study Research in Applied Linguistics. 2007. (Second Language Acquisition Research Ser.). (ENG., Illus.). 248p. pap. 34.95 *(978-0-8058-2359-2(X))* Routledge.

El-Dali, Hosni Mostafa. Applied Linguistics & Translation: Empirical Research Studies. 2011. 412p. pap. ***(978-3-639-32319-1(X))*** VDM Verlag Dr. Mueller e.K.

Elana Shohamy Staff, et al. Linguistic Landscape: Expanding the Scenery. Gorter, Durk, ed. 2008. (ENG., Illus.). 392p. 135.00 *(978-0-415-98872-8(1))* Routledge.

—Linguistic Landscape: Expanding the Scenery. 2008. (ENG., Illus.). 392p. pap. 49.95 *(978-0-415-98873-5(X))* Routledge.

Ellis, Sue, et al, eds. Applied Linguistics & Primary School Teaching. 2011. (ENG., Illus.). 354p. 99.00 *(978-0-521-19354-2(0))* Cambridge Univ. Pr.

Ewald, Jennifer D. & Edstrom, Anne, eds. El español a través de la Lingüística: Preguntas y Respuestas. 2008. (SPA.). 280p. (C). pap. 38.95 *(978-1-57473-027-2(4))*; lib. bdg. 78.95 *(978-1-57473-127-9(0))* Cascadilla Pr.

Flowerdew, John. Discourse in Language Education. 2012. (ENG.). 176p. 115.00 ***(978-0-415-49964-4(X))*** Routledge.

Fortes, Laura. Meanings of 'Error' in Efl Teachers' Discourse. 2010. 144p. pap. *(978-3-639-27861-3(5))* VDM Verlag Dr. Mueller e.K.

Garcia Padrón, Dolores & Fumero Pérez, Maria del Carmen, eds. Tendencias en lingüística general y Aplicada. 2010. (Studien zur romanischen Sprachwissenschaft und interkulturellen Kommunikation Ser.). (SPA., Illus.). 266p. 67.95 *(978-3-631-60411-3(4))* Lang, Peter GmbH, Europaischer Verlag der Wissenschaften DEU. Dist: Lang, Peter.

Gollin, Sandra M. & Hall, David R. Language for Specific Purposes. 2012. (Research & Practice in Applied Linguistics Ser.). (ENG.). 272p. 90.00 *(978-1-4039-4639-3(6))* Palgrave Macmillan.

Groom, Nicholas & Littlemore, Jeanette. Doing Applied Linguistics: A Guide for Students. 2011. (ENG., Illus.). 224p. (C). 90.00 *(978-0-415-56641-4(X))*; pap. 28.95 *(978-0-415-56642-1(8))* Routledge.

Gulzar, Malik Ajmal. Classroom Discourse in Bilingual Context: Effects of Code-Switching on Language Learning in Pakistani Tefl Classroom. 2011. 380p. pap. ***(978-3-639-33222-3(9))*** VDM Verlag Dr. Mueller e.K.

Hall, Christopher, et al. Mapping Applied Linguistics: A Guide for Students & Practitioners. 2011. (ENG., Illus.). 448p. (C). instr.'s gde. ed. 125.00 *(978-0-415-55912-6(X))*; pap., instr.'s gde. ed. 41.95 *(978-0-415-55913-3(8))* Routledge.

Hardacre, Bahiyyih. Issues in Applied Linguistics - Special Issue 18. 2. 2011. (Issues in Applied Linguistics Ser.). (ENG.). 100p. pap. 19.95 ***(978-0-9828354-5-6(0))*** UCLA Graduate Students Assn. Pubns.

Heigham, Juanita, et al, eds. Qualitative Research in Applied Linguistics: A Practical Introduction. 2009. (ENG., Illus.). 240p. 95.00 *(978-0-230-21952-6(7))* Palgrave Macmillan.

Heigham, Juanita & Croker, Robert A., eds. Qualitative Research in Applied Linguistics: A Practical Introduction. 2009. (ENG., Illus.). 240p. pap. 35.00 *(978-0-230-21953-3(5))* Palgrave Macmillan.

Hunston, Susan. Introducing Applied Linguistics: Concepts & Skills. 2009. (ENG., Illus.). 272p. 35.95 *(978-0-415-44767-6(4))* Routledge.

Hunston, Susan & Oakey, David. Doing applied Linguistics. 2009. (ENG., Illus.). 272p. 110.00 *(978-0-415-44768-3(2))* Routledge.

Hyland, Ken, et al, eds. Corpus Applications in Applied Linguistics. 2012. (ENG.). 272p. 150.00 ***(978-1-4411-0780-0(0))*** Continuum International Publishing Group, Ltd. GBR. Dist: National Bk. Network.

Hyland, Ken, et al. Corpus Applications in Applied Linguistics. 2012. 256p. E-Book ***(978-1-4411-8438-2(4))*** Continuum International Publishing Group, Ltd.

Institute of Education, et al. Neoliberalism & Applied Linguistics. 2012. (ENG., Illus.). 176p. (C). pap. 43.95 *(978-0-415-59205-5(4))* Routledge.

A

Jayraj, S. Joseph Arul. Issues in Applied Linguistics. 2011. 156p. pap. (978-3-8433-9400-0(8)) Lambert Academic Publishing.

Jones, Rodney. Health & Risk Communication: An applied linguistics Perspective. 2012. (ENG.). (C). 224p. 130.00 (978-0-415-67259-7(7)); pap. 39.95 (978-0-415-67260-3(0)) Routledge.

Kaplan, Robert B. The Oxford Handbook of Applied Linguistics, 1 vol. 2nd ed. 2010. (Oxford Handbooks Ser.). (ENG., Illus.). 720p. pap. 60.00 (978-0-19-538425-3(3)) Oxford Univ. Pr., Inc.

Kettemann, Bernhard & Marko, Georg. Planing, Gluing, & Painting Corpora: Inside the Applied Corpus Linguist's Workshop, Vol. 24. 2006. 282p. pap. 57.95 (978-0-8204-9922-2(6)) Lang, Peter Publishing, Inc.

Leung, Constant & Jenkins, Jennifer, eds. Reconfiguring Europe: The Contribution of Applied Linguistics. 2006. (British Studies in Applied Linguistics Ser.). (ENG.). 173p. (C). per. 32.95 (978-1-84553-090-7(X)) Equinox Publishing Ltd. GBR. Dist: ISD.

Li, Wei, ed. The Applied Linguistics Reader. 2011. (ENG., Illus.). 552p. (C). 150.00 (978-0-415-56619-3(3)); pap. 43.95 (978-0-415-56620-9(7)) Routledge.

Mahboob, Ahmar. Appliable Linguistics: Texts, Contexts & Meanings. Knight, Naomi, ed. 2010. (ENG., Illus.). 336p. 150.00 (978-1-4411-6415-5(4)) Continuum International Publishing Group, Ltd. GBR. Dist: National Bk. Network.

Mahboob, Ahmar & Knight, Naomi. Appliable Linguistics: Reclaiming the Place of Language in Linguistics. 2012. (ENG.). 336p. pap. 55.00 (978-1-4411-0832-6(7)) Continuum International Publishing Group, Ltd. GBR. Dist: National Bk. Network.

Martynychev, Andrey. On Research Methodology in Applied Linguistics In 2002-2008. 2010. 92p. pap. (978-3-639-28295-5(7)) VDM Verlag Dr. Mueller e.K.

Mehler, Alexander & Romary, Laurent, eds. Handbook of Technical Communication. 2012. (Handbooks of Applied Linguistics [HAL] Ser.). (ENG., Illus.). 600p. E-Book 419.00 (978-3-11-173987-8(2)) De Gruyter, Mouton DEU. Dist: de Gruyter, Walter GmbH & Co. KG.

Mori, Ohta, et al. Japanese Applied Linguistics: Discourse & Social Perspectives. 2008. (ENG., Illus.). 384p. 150.00 (978-0-8264-8961-6(3)) Continuum International Publishing Group, Ltd. GBR. Dist: National Bk. Network.

Nishina, Yasunori. Evaluative Meanings & Disciplinary Values. 2011. 280p. pap. (978-3-8443-8050-7(7)) Lambert Academic Publishing.

Pallotti, Gabriele & Wagner, Johannes. L2 Learning As Social Practice: Conversation-Analytic Perspectives. 2011. (Illus.). xvii, 368p. pap. (978-0-9800459-7-0(5)) National Foreign Language Resource Ctr.

Paltridge, Brian. Continuum Companion to Research Methods in Applied Linguistics. Paltridge, Brian & Phakiti, Aek, eds. 2010. (Continuum Companions Ser.). (ENG., Illus.). 384p. 44.95 (978-0-8264-9925-7(2)); 386p. 140.00 (978-0-8264-9924-0(4)) Continuum International Publishing Group, Ltd. GBR. Dist: National Bk. Network.

Perren, G. E. & Trim, J. L. M., eds. Applications of Linguistics. 2010. (ENG.). 520p. pap. 67.00 (978-0-521-13141-4(3)) Cambridge Univ. Pr.

Perry, Jr., Fred L., Fred L. Research in Applied Linguistics. 2nd rev. ed. 2011. (ENG., Illus.). 312p. 135.00 (978-0-415-88570-6(1)); pap. 41.95 (978-0-415-88571-3(X)) Routledge.

Pini, Gianreto. Applied Generalizability Theory. 2009. (Quantitative Methodology Ser.). (ENG., Illus.). 240p. pap. 39.95 (978-1-84872-829-5(8), Routledge) Taylor & Francis Group GBR. Dist: Taylor & Francis Group.

Porte, Graeme Keith. Replication Research in Applied Linguistics. 2012. (Cambridge Applied Linguistics Ser.). (ENG.). 304p. 84.98 (978-1-107-02165-5(0)); pap. 40.00 (978-1-107-67152-2(3)) Cambridge Univ. Pr.

Richards, Jack & Schmidt, Richard W. Longman Dictionary of Language Teaching & Applied Linguistics. 4th rev. ed. 2010. (ENG., Illus.). 656p. (C). pap. 33.60 (978-1-4082-0460-3(6)) Prentice Hall, ESL Dept.

Ross, Steven John & Seedhouse, Paul. Research Methods for Applied Language Studies: An Advanced Resource Book for Students. 2011. (Routledge Applied Linguistics Ser.). (ENG., Illus.). 392p. 135.00 (978-0-415-55140-3(4)); pap. 39.95 (978-0-415-55141-0(2)) Routledge.

Rost, Michael. Teaching & Researching: Listening. 2nd ed. 2011. (Applied Linguistics in Action Ser.). (ENG., Illus.). 424p. (C). pap. 42.07 (978-1-4082-0507-5(6)) Prentice Hall, ESL Dept.

Saeidi, Mahnaz. Grammar Instruction: Multiple Intelligence-based Focus on Form. 2011. 148p. pap. (978-3-8433-5438-7(3)) Lambert Academic Publishing.

Sager, Juan C. Language Engineering & Translation: Consequences of Automation. (Translation Library: Vol. 1). xx, 345p. pap. 42.95 (978-1-55619-477-1(3)); lib. bdg. 144.00 (978-1-55619-476-4(5)) Benjamins, John Publishing Co.

Seargeant, Philip. World Englishes Rial. 2012. (Routledge Introductions to Applied Linguistics Ser.). (ENG.). 240p. (C). 150.00 (978-0-415-57209-5(6)) Routledge.

Shields, John. Managing Employee Performance & Reward. 2007. (Illus.). 612p. pap. 72.00 (978-0-521-82046-2(4)) Cambridge Univ. Pr.

Simpson, James. The Routledge Handbook of Applied Linguistics. 2011. (Routledge Handbooks in Applied Linguistics Ser.). (ENG., Illus.). 752p. 210.00 (978-0-415-49067-2(7)) Routledge.

Stilwell Peccei Staff. The Language , Society & Power Reader. 2011. (ENG., Illus.). 400p. (C). 120.00 (978-0-415-43082-1(8)); pap. 35.95 (978-0-415-43083-8(6)) Routledge.

Storch, Neomy. The Nature of Pair Interaction. 2009. 396p. pap. (978-3-639-14341-6(8)) VDM Verlag Dr. Mueller e.K.

Tamm, Anne. Reversible lexical databases: Chapters from the development of the tools & data structures for multilingual lexical databases on the example of OMBI. 2010. 92p. pap. (978-3-639-23429-9(4)) VDM Verlag Dr. Mueller e.K.

Tian, Lili. Teacher Codeswitching in a Communicative Efl Context. 2011. 412p. pap. (978-3-639-33220-9(2)) VDM Verlag Dr. Mueller e.K.

Wa-Mbaleka, Safary. A Meta-Analysis Investigating the Effects of Reading on Second Language Learning. 2008. 204p. pap. (978-3-639-00669-8(0)) VDM Verlag Dr. Mueller e.K.

Walker, James A. Variation in Linguistic Systems. 2010. (ENG., Illus.). 176p. 130.00 (978-0-415-99067-7(X)) Routledge.

Wang, Wei. Genre Across Languages & Cultures- Newspaper Commentaries in China & Australi. 2007. 200p. per. (978-3-8364-2872-9(5)) VDM Verlag Dr. Mueller e.K.

Wei, Li. Applied Linguistics: Language for the Real World, 2 vols. Wei, Li & Cook, Vivian, eds. 2009. (Contemporary Studies in Linguistics Ser.). (ENG., Illus.). 264p. 150.00 (978-0-8264-9681-2(4)) Continuum International Publishing Group, Ltd. GBR. Dist: National Bk. Network.

—Contemporary Applied Linguistics, 2 vols., Set. Cook, Vivian, ed. 2009. (Contemporary Studies in Linguistics Ser.). (ENG., Illus.). 504p. 290.00 (978-0-8264-9745-1(4)) Continuum International Publishing Group, Ltd. GBR. Dist: National Bk. Network.

—Language Teaching & Learning Vol. 1, 2 vols. Cook, Vivian, ed. 2009. (Contemporary Studies in Linguistics Ser.). (ENG., Illus.). 288p. 150.00 (978-0-8264-9680-5(6)) Continuum International Publishing Group, Ltd. GBR. Dist: National Bk. Network.

Wei, Li, ed. Bloomsbury Review of Applied Linguistics & Communication 2010. 2010. (ENG., Illus.). X, 268p. 112.00 (978-3-11-022264-7(7)) De Gruyter, Mouton DEU. Dist: de Gruyter, Walter GmbH & Co. KG.

—Bloomsbury Review of Applied Linguistics & Communication 2010: [Print + Online]. 2010. (ENG.). X, 268p. 133.00 (978-3-11-022266-1(3)) De Gruyter, Mouton DEU. Dist: de Gruyter, Walter GmbH & Co. KG.

Wei, Li & Cook, Vivian, eds. Contemporary Applied Linguistics Vol. 1: Language Teaching & Learning. 2011. (Contemporary Studies in Linguistics Ser.). (ENG.). 288p. pap. 49.95 (978-1-4411-5021-9(8)) Continuum International Publishing Group, Ltd. GBR. Dist: National Bk. Network.

Wei, Li: Applied Linguistics Review. 2011 2: Applied Linguistics Review. 2011 2. 2011. (ENG.). IX, 334p. 112.00 (978-3-11-023932-4(9)) De Gruyter, Mouton DEU. Dist: de Gruyter, Walter GmbH & Co. KG.

Wei, Li: Applied Linguistics Review. 2011 2: [Print + Online]. 2011. (ENG.). 133.00 (978-3-11-023934-8(5)) De Gruyter, Mouton DEU. Dist: de Gruyter, Walter GmbH & Co. KG.

APPLIED MECHANICS
see Mechanics, Applied

APPLIED PSYCHOLOGY
see Psychology, Applied

APPLIED SCIENCE
see Technology

APPLIQUE

Anderson, Alex. Hand & Machine Applique: 6 Techniques, 7 Quilt Projects, Full-Size Patterns. 2009. (ENG., Illus.). 64p. pap. 19.95 (978-1-57120-611-4(6)) C & T Publishing.

Anderson, Alex & Aneloski, Liz. Super Simple Quilts #4 with Alex Anderson & Liz Aneloski: 9 Applique Projects to Sew with or Without a Machine. 2009. (ENG., Illus.). 28p. pap. 9.95 (978-1-57120-662-6(0)) C & T Publishing.

Anderson, Laurel. Appliqué Workshop: Mix & Match 10 Techniques to Unlock Your Creativity. 2010. (ENG., Illus.). 96p. pap. 27.95 (978-1-57120-835-4(6)) C & T Publishing.

AQS Editors, Editors. Sawtooth: New Quilts from an Old Favorite. Lasco, Linda Baxter, ed. 2008. (ENG., Illus.). 96p. pap. 24.95 (978-1-57432-960-5(X), 157432960X, American Quilter's Society) Collector Bks.

Armstrong, Carol. Best in Show: 24 Applique Quilts for Dog Lovers. 2009. (ENG., Illus.). 64p. pap. 26.95 (978-1-57120-610-7(8)) C & T Publishing.

Ballard, Alethea. Maverick Quilts: Using Large-Scale Prints, Novelty Fabrics & Panels with Panache. 2011. (Illus.). 80p. pap. 24.95 (978-1-60705-232-6(6)) C & T Publishing.

Becker, Joyce R. Beautifully Embellished Landscapes: 125 Tips & Techniques to Create Stunning Quilts. 2006. (ENG., Illus.). 96p. per. 26.95 (978-1-57120-360-1(5)) C & T Publishing.

Bellino, Vicki. Bloom Creek Quilts. 2010. (ENG.). 96p. pap. (978-1-60468-002-7(4)) Martingale & Co.

Better Homes and Gardens Books Staff. Applique Class. 2011. (Better Homes & Gardens Crafts Ser.: 20). (ENG., Illus.). 160p. 24.99 (978-0-470-88719-6(2), Wiley) Wiley, John & Sons, Inc.

Better Homes and Gardens Editors, et al. 501 Quilt Blocks: A Treasury of Patterns for Patchwork & Applique. 2009. (Crafts Ser.). (ENG., Illus.). 320p. pap. 22.95 (978-0-696-20480-7(0), Wiley) Wiley, John & Sons, Inc.

Blandeau, Sylvie. Applique for Little Ones. 2009. (ENG., Illus.). 144p. pap. 24.99 (978-0-7153-3209-2(0)) David & Charles Pubs. GBR. Dist: F&W Media, Inc.

Brackman, Barbara. Encyclopedia of Appliqué: 2000 Traditional & Modern Designs, Updated History of Appliqué. 2009. (ENG., Illus.). 200p. pap. 29.95 (978-1-57120-651-0(5)) C & T Publishing.

Brandeburg, Barbara & Christopherson, Teri. Quilting for Joy. 2008. (ENG., Illus.). 80p. pap. 26.95 (978-1-56477-849-9(5), That Patchwork Place) Martingale & Co.

Brown, Rachel W. N. Adoration Quilts: Applique Nativity Projects. 2006. (That Patchwork Place Ser.). (ENG., Illus.). 96p. per. 24.95 (978-1-56477-670-9(0)) Martingale & Co.

Burch, Laurel. Laurel Burch Legends: 9 Quilts Inspired by the Earth, Sea & Sky. 2007. (ENG., Illus.). 64p. per. 29.95 (978-1-57120-367-0(2)) C & T Publishing.

Burniston, Carol. Color-Splashed Quilts: Fuse Fun Applique to Your Piecing. 2007. (ENG., Illus.). 48p. pap. 17.95 (978-1-57120-441-7(5)) C & T Publishing.

C and T Publishing Staff. Quilter's Favorites Vol. 1: Traditional Pieced & Appliqued. 2009. (ENG., Illus.). 112p. pap. 24.95 (978-1-57120-795-1(3)) C & T Publishing.

Campbell, Eileen. Ideas for Applique: The Applique Artist's Workbook. 2009. (Milner Craft Ser.). (Illus.). 128p. pap. 17.95 (978-1-86351-388-3(4)) Milner, Sally Publishing Pty, Ltd. AUS. Dist: Sterling Publishing Co., Inc.

Carlson, Susan E. Serendipity Quilts: Cutting Loose Fabric Collage. 2010. (ENG., Illus.). 96p. pap. 27.95 (978-1-57120-830-9(5)) C & T Publishing.

Cirillo, Suzanne Zaruba. Sunbonnet Sue & Scottie Too. 2007. (ENG., Illus.). 80p. pap. 24.95 (978-1-56477-703-4(0), That Patchwork Place) Martingale & Co.

Coleman, Anne. Collage Applique Patch. (Illus.). 96p. pap. 11.95 (978-1-85219-048-4(5)) Bishopsgate Pr., Ltd. GBR. Dist: International Specialized Bk. Services.

Cooke, Jennifer. Design Your Own Tees: Techniques & Inspiration to Stitch, Stamp, Stencil, & Silk-Screen Your Very Own T-Shirts. 2010. (ENG., Illus.). 144p. pap. 21.99 (978-0-312-64424-6(8), St. Martin's Griffin) St. Martin's Pr.

Cotton, Betty. Courthouse Combo: Cotton Theory Quilting: QY41. 2009. (Illus.). 28p. 13.95 (978-0-9772611-2-3(3)) Cotton Theory, LLC.

Curtis, Helga. Herbs, Spices & Fruits of the Bible. 2011. (ENG., Illus.). 48p. pap. 9.95 (978-1-59217-324-2(1)) Annie's Publishing, LLC.

Daley, Sue. New England Paper Piecing: A Faster Approach to a Traditional Favorite. 2012. (ENG., Illus.). 96p. pap. 27.95 (978-1-60705-404-7(3)) C & T Publishing.

Daniel, Nancy Brenan. 101 Applique Blocks. Schmidt, Dianne, ed. 2010. (ENG., Illus.). 112p. pap. 12.95 (978-1-59217-313-6(6), House of White Birches, Inc.) Annie's Publishing, LLC.

Debono, Linda Lum. Sew Sentimental: Easy Scrapbooking Techniques. 2007. (ENG., Illus.). 80p. per. 19.95 (978-1-56477-775-1(8)) Martingale & Co.

Diehl, Kim. Simple Comforts: 12 Cozy Lap Quilts. 2009. (ENG., Illus.). 112p. pap. (978-1-56477-848-2(7)) Martingale & Co.

—Simple Graces: Charming Quilts & Companion Projects. 2010. (ENG., Illus.). 112p. pap. (978-1-56477-992-2(0)) Martingale & Co.

Dietrich, Mimi. Baltimore Basics: Album Quilts from Start to Finish. 2006. (ENG., Illus.). 112p. per. 27.95 (978-1-56477-678-5(6), That Patchwork Place) Martingale & Co.

—Mimi Dietrich's Favorite Applique Quilts. 2007. (That Patchwork Place Ser.). (ENG., Illus.). 96p. per. 26.95 (978-1-56477-679-2(4)) Martingale & Co.

Docherty, Margaret. Birds 'n Roses. rev. ed. 2006. (Applique Masterpiece Ser.). (ENG., Illus.). 128p. 24.95 (978-1-57432-914-8(6), 1574329146, American Quilter's Society) Collector Bks.

—Hearts & Tulips Applique Masterpiece. 2009. (ENG., Illus.). 112p. 28.95 (978-1-57432-974-2(X), 157432974X, American Quilter's Society) Collector Bks.

Durbin, Pat. Fabric + Paint + Thread = Fabulous. 2009. (ENG.). 64p. pap. (978-1-56477-937-3(8)) Martingale & Co.

—Mosaic Picture Quilts: Turn Favorite Photos into Stunning Quilts. 2007. (That Patchwork Place Ser.). (ENG., Illus.). 64p. per. 24.95 (978-1-56477-735-5(9)) Martingale & Co.

Errea, Grace & Osterfeld, Meridith. Impressionist Applique: Exploring Value & Design to Create Artistic Quilts. 2012. (ENG., Illus.). 144p. pap. 29.95 (978-1-60705-467-2(1)) C & T Publishing.

Field, Debbie. Granola Girl Quilting the Great Outdoors/Lodge Look: Dozens of Applique Wildlife Blocks to Create Impressive Quilts, Wallhangings & Home Decorating Projects Plus 24 Quilt Projects from Quilting the Lodge Look. 2007. (Granola Girl Designs Ser.). (Illus.). 207p. pap. 24.95 (978-0-9793711-1-0(2)) Landauer Publishing, LLC.

—Granola Girl Table Toppers: Celebrating the Great Outdoors. 2008. (Granola Girl Designs Ser.). (Illus.). 128p. pap. 24.95 (978-0-9793711-5-8(5)) Landauer Publishing, LLC.

Fronks, Dilys. Dual Image Appliqué. 2010. (ENG., Illus.). 96p. 26.95 (978-1-57432-673-4(2), 1574326732, American Quilter's Society) Collector Bks.

Gabel, Debra. Quilt Blocks Across America: Applique Patterns for 50 States & Washington, D. C. , Mix & Match to Create Lasting Memories. 2011. (Illus.). 64p. pap. 21.95 (978-1-60705-349-1(7)) C & T Publishing.

Gabel, Debra. Quilt Blocks Around the World: 50 Appliqué Patterns for International Cities & More - Mix & Match to Create Lasting Memories. 2012. (ENG., Illus.). 64p. pap. 21.95 (978-1-60705-435-1(3)) C & T Publishing.

Gibbons, Gretchen. Pennies from Heaven. 2010. (ENG., Illus.). 96p. pap. (978-1-60468-001-0(6)) Martingale & Co.

Goldsmith, Becky & Jenkins, Linda. Appliqué Outside the Lines with Piece O'Cake Designs: No Rules-No Ruler. 2009. (Illus.). 64p. pap. 27.95 (978-1-57120-609-1(4)) C & T Publishing.

—Aunt Millie's Garden: 12 Flowering Blocks from Piece O'Cake Designs. 2007. (ENG., Illus.). 16p. pap. 17.95 (978-1-57120-457-8(1)) C & T Publishing.

—Covered with Love: Kids' Quilts & More from Piece O' Cake Designs. 2006. (ENG., Illus.). 64p. pap. 26.95 (978-1-57120-354-0(0)) C & T Publishing.

Green, Deborah "Ismoyo". 100 Applique Motifs. 2008. (ENG.). 128p. pap. 19.99 (978-0-89689-725-0(7)) Krause Pubns.

Greig, Daphne & Mark, Susan. Give & Take Fabric Applique. 2011. (ENG., Illus.). 80p. 24.95 (978-1-60460-005-6(5), 1604600055, American Quilter's Society) Collector Bks.

Handley, Louise. Fabric Silhouettes: Quilted Treasures from the Family Album. 2006. (ENG., Illus.). 64p. pap. 20.95 (978-1-57120-347-2(8)) C & T Publishing.

Hansen, Suzanne. Happy Helpers Seasonal Pattern Book. pap. 8.95 (978-1-57734-307-3(7), 01113542) Covenant Communications, Inc.

Haren, Penny. Penny Haren's Pieced Applique: Introducing Innovative Techniques for Creating Perfect Blocks for Successful Projects. 2008. (Illus.). 128p. 27.95 (978-0-9793711-9-6(8)) Landauer Publishing, LLC.

—Penny Haren's Pieced Applique Intricate Blocks Made Easy: Innovative Techniques for Creating Perfect Blocks for Successful Projects. 2010. (Illus.). 144p. (978-0-9825586-0-7(0)) Landauer Publishing, LLC.

—Penny Haren's Pieced Applique More Blocks & Projects: Innovative Techniques for Creating Perfect Blocks for Successful Projects. 2009. (ENG., Illus.). 128p. 27.95 (978-0-9800688-4-9(3)) Landauer Publishing, LLC.

—Penny Harens Pieced Applique Weekend Projects: A Dozen Quick Projects. 2009. (ENG., Illus.). 80p. pap. 24.95 (978-0-9818040-4-0(7)) Landauer Publishing, LLC.

Hearder, Valerie. Points of View: Landscape Quilts to Stitch & Embellish. 2007. (That Patchwork Place Ser.). (ENG., Illus.). 96p. per. 26.95 (978-1-56477-700-3(6)) Martingale & Co.

Hickey, Mary. Comfort & Joy: 14 Quilts for Christmas. 2007. (That Patchwork Place Ser.). (ENG., Illus.). 112p. per. 27.95 (978-1-56477-763-8(4), That Patchwork Place) Martingale & Co.

Hughes, Rose. Dream Landscapes: Artful Quilts with Fast-Piece Applique. 2008. (ENG., Illus.). 96p. pap. 26.95 (978-1-56477-859-8(2), That Patchwork Place) Martingale & Co.

—Exploring Embellishments: More Artful Quilts with Fast-Piece Appliqué. 2010. (ENG., Illus.). 96p. pap. (978-1-56477-989-2(0)) Martingale & Co.

Humphries, Pamela. Award-Winning Applique Birds. rev. ed. 2007. (ENG., Illus.). 96p. pap. 21.95 (978-1-57432-943-8(X), 157432943X, American Quilter's Society) Collector Bks.

Jansen, Christine. Hooked Rugs & Wool Applique. 2010. (Illus.). 112p. pap. 19.99 (978-0-7643-3473-3(5)) Schiffer Publishing, Ltd.

Johnson, Tammy & Shirer, Avis. Folk-Art Favorites: Quilts from Joined at the Hip. 2009. (ENG., Illus.). 80p. pap. (978-1-56477-884-0(3)) Martingale & Co.

Jones, Carol & Finley, Bobbi. Tile Quilt Revival: Reinventing a Forgotten Form. 2010. (ENG., Illus.). 48p. pap. 23.95 (978-1-57120-801-9(1)) C & T Publishing.

Jones, Liz. Flowers, Hearts & Garlands Quilt. 2011. (ENG., Illus.). 96p. 26.95 (978-1-57432-648-2(1), 1574326481, American Quilter's Society) Collector Bks.

Kidston, Cath. Make! 2008. (Illus.). 176p. pap. 12.95 (978-1-84400-584-0(4)) Quadrille Publishing, Ltd. GBR. Dist: Ingram Pub. Services.

Kingslake, Clare. Folk Quilt Applique. 2011. (ENG., Illus.). 128p. pap. 24.99 (978-0-7153-3826-1(9)) David & Charles Pubs. GBR. Dist: F&W Media, Inc.

Knapp, Susan Brubaker. Applique Petal Party: A Bouquet of 16 Blocks & Flowering Border. 2009. (ENG.). 8p. pap. 17.95 (978-1-57120-861-3(5)) C & T Publishing.

Kooler, Donna. Encyclopedia of Quilting. rev. ed. 2010. (ENG.). 240p. pap. 24.95 (978-1-60900-086-8(2)) Leisure Arts, Inc.

Kygar, Terrie Linn. Creative Quilts from Your Crayon Box. 2012. (ENG., Illus.). 80p. pap. (978-1-60468-080-5(6)) Martingale & Co.

Labanaris, Faye. America's Quilted Garden Blocks. 2011. (ENG., Illus.). 80p. 24.95 (978-1-60460-007-0(1), 1604600071, American Quilter's Society) Collector Bks.

Lammon, Cindy. Flowers All Around: Garden-Inspired Quilts. 2010. (ENG., Illus.). 64p. pap. (978-1-56477-977-9(7)) Martingale & Co.

—Gathered from the Garden: Quilts with Floral Charm. 2008. (ENG., Illus.). 96p. pap. (978-1-56477-813-0(4)) Martingale & Co.

Large, Jeanne & Wicks, Shelley. Urban Country Quilts. 2011. (Illus.). 80p. pap. (978-1-60468-068-3(7)) Martingale & Co.

Lawrence, Angela. Needleturn Appliqué: The Basics & Beyond. 2012. (ENG., Illus.). 112p. pap. 27.95 (978-1-935726-17-3(X)) Landauer Publishing, LLC.

Leichner, Sandra. Hand Appliqué with Embroidery. 2010. (ENG., Illus.). 96p. 26.95 (978-1-57432-677-2(5), 1574326775, American Quilter's Society) Collector Bks.

Leisure Arts. Debbie Mumm(r): Joy Joy Joy. 2008. (ENG.). 96p. pap. 19.95 (978-1-60140-648-4(7)) Leisure Arts, Inc.

Linn, Don. Sophisticated Stitches: Designs for Quilting, Appliqué, Sashiko & Embroidery. 2009. (ENG., Illus.). 80p. pap. 19.95 (978-1-57120-865-1(8)) C & T Publishing.

Lose, Patrick. Poster Quilts with Patrick Lose. 2009. (ENG., Illus.). 48p. pap. 27.95 (978-1-57120-653-4(1)) C & T Publishing.

—Terrific Table Toppers with Patrick Lose: Decorate Your Home with Fast Fusible Appliqué: 10 Quilt Projects. 2009. (ENG., Illus.). 40p. pap. 22.95 (978-1-57120-845-3(3)) C & T Publishing.

Lynch, Cheryl. Quilt Fiesta! Surprising Designs from Mexican Tiles. 2011. (Illus.). 96p. pap. 26.99 (978-1-60468-003-4(2)) Martingale & Co.

Marshall, Suzanne. Adventure & Applique. 2007. (ENG., Illus.). 144p. per. 26.95 (978-1-57432-947-6(2), 1574329472, American Quilter's Society) Collector Bks.

McKenzie, Kay. Inspired by Tradition: 50 Applique Blocks in 5 Sizes. 2011. (ENG., Illus.). 64p. pap. (978-1-60468-022-5(9)) Martingale & Co.

McTavish, Karen. Quilting for Show: A Practical Guide to Successful Competition Quilting. 2007. (ENG., Illus.). 112p. pap. 24.95 *(978-0-9744706-3-4(5))* On-Word Bound Bks., LLC.
Meredith Corporation, compiled by. Holiday Quilt Projects Through the Year: Better Homes & Gardens. 2006. (ENG.). 48p. pap. 10.95 *(978-1-60140-178-6(7))* Leisure Arts, Inc.
Michael, Ursula. Rainy Day Applique: Quick & Easy Fusible Quilts. 2007. (ENG., Illus.). 128p. pap. 24.99 *(978-0-89689-539-3(4))* Krause Pubns.
Mostek, Pamela & Mostek, Rachel. Sew Easy Sewing: Fast, fresh quilts & more fun Projects. 2008. (Illus.). 80p. pap. 21.95 *(978-0-9789513-3-7(6))* All American Crafts.
Mulari, Mary. Embroidery Machine Essentials: Applique Adventures, Vol. 6. 2nd ed. 2006. (ENG., Illus.). 48p. pap. 22.99 *(978-0-89689-405-1(3)*, Antique Tracer) Krause Pubns.
Murty, Nancy Davis & Murty, Nancy Lee. Sisterhood: A Quilting Tradition - 11 Heartwarming Projects to Piece & Appliqué. 2011. (ENG., Illus.). 88p. pap. 24.95 *(978-1-60705-192-3(3))* C & T Publishing.
Oglesby, Bea. Veggies from the Good Earth Applique Album. 2006. (ENG., Illus.). 80p. 21.95 *(978-1-57432-921-6(9)*, 1574329219, American Quilter's Society) Collector Bks.
Olfers, Sibylle & Smith, Sieglinde Schoen. Mother Earth's Quilt Sampler: Appliqué Patterns Inspired by Mother Earth & Her Children. 2009. (ENG., Illus.). 64p. pap. 29.95 *(978-1-933308-22-7(2))* Breckling Pr.
Pederson, Sharon. Machine Applique for the Terrified Quilter. 2008. (That Patchwork Place Ser.). (ENG., Illus.). 112p. pap. 27.95 *(978-1-56477-820-8(7))* Martingale & Co.
—The Rose of Sharon Block Book: Winning Designs from the EQ6 Challenge. 2010. (ENG., Illus.). 112p. pap. *(978-1-60468-011-9(3))* Martingale & Co.
Perri, Kate. Quilt Blocks & Quilts from Your Favourite Fabrics: Recycling Fabrics as You Learn to Quilt. 2008. (Easy Singer Style Ser.). (ENG., Illus.). 112p. pap. 21.99 *(978-1-58923-390-4(5)*, 1589233905, Creative Publishing International) Queyside.
Peterson, Heather Mulder. Favorite Quilts from Anka's Treasures. 2007. (That Patchwork Place Ser.). (ENG., Illus.). 128p. per. 29.95 *(978-1-56477-714-0(6))* Martingale & Co.
Phillips, Tonye Belinda. Hand-Appliqued Quilts: Whimsical Designs & Simple Techniques. 2006. (ENG., Illus.). 128p. 24.95 *(978-1-60059-254-6(6))* Lark Bks.
Pignatelli, Vikki. Quilting by Improvisation: Exploring Curves, Openwork & Dimension. 2007. (ENG., Illus.). 176p. per. 29.95 *(978-0-9641201-9-8(4))* Dragon Threads.
Pike, Joni. Cute as a Button Quilts: 12 Quick Quilts & Playful Projects to Decorate Your Home. 2006. (ENG., Illus.). 80p. pap. 24.95 *(978-1-57120-345-8(1))* C & T Publishing.
Pippen, Sylvia. Paradise Stitched: Sashiko & Applique Quilts. 2009. (ENG., Illus.). 112p. pap. 29.95 *(978-1-57120-617-6(5))* C & T Publishing.
Popa, Julie. A Fresh Look at Seasonal Quilts. 2006. (That Patchwork Place Ser.). (ENG., Illus.). 96p. per. 24.95 *(978-1-56477-680-8(8)*, That Patchwork Place) Martingale & Co.
—Young at Heart Quilts: 15 Designs with Color & Style. 2007. (That Patchwork Place Ser.). (ENG., Illus.). 96p. per. 24.95 *(978-1-56477-681-5(6)*, That Patchwork Place) Martingale & Co.
Price, Caroline. Love to Machine Applique: A Medley of Techniques. 2008. (ENG., Illus.). 96p. pap. 26.95 *(978-1-57432-956-8(1)*, 1574329561, American Quilter's Society) Collector Bks.
Propst, Susan Taylor. Beautiful Blooms: Quilts & Cushions to Applique. 2008. (That Patchwork Place Ser.). (ENG., Illus.). 112p. pap. 27.95 *(978-1-56477-776-8(6)*, That Patchwork Place) Martingale & Co.
Propst, Taylor. Nature's Beauty in Appliqu: Pretty & Practical Projects. 2012. (ENG., Illus.). 96p. pap. ***(978-1-60468-079-9(2))*** Martingale & Co.
Quartermain, Debra. Sweatshirt Remix: Transform Ordinary Sweatshirts into Extraordinary Fashions. 2009. (ENG., Illus.). 128p. pap. 24.99 *(978-0-89689-645-1(5))* Krause Pubns.
Quilted Treasures: Paper Piecing Applique & More. 2006. 72p. 14.95 *(978-1-60140-399-5(2))* Leisure Arts, Inc.
Radtke, Marsha D. A Baltimore Album: 25 Applique Patterns. 2009. (ENG., Illus.). 96p. 26.95 *(978-1-57432-980-3(4)*, 1574329804, American Quilter's Society) Collector Bks.
Roskelley, Camille. Simplify with Camille Roskelley: Quilts for the Modern Home. 2010. (ENG., Illus.). 112p. pap. 21.95 *(978-1-57120-938-2(7))* C & T Publishing.
Schaefer, Kim. Flower Festival: 50 Appliqué Blocks to Grow Your Garden: 9 Quilt Projects. 2009. (ENG., Illus.). 88p. pap. 25.95 *(978-1-57120-529-2(2))* C & T Publishing.
—Quilts, Bibs, Blankies... Oh My! Create Your Own Cute & Cuddly Nursery. 2008. (ENG., Illus.). 64p. pap. 26.95 *(978-1-57120-491-2(1))* C & T Publishing.
—Quilts from Textured Solids: 20 Rich Projects to Piece & Appliqué. 2011. (ENG., Illus.). 80p. pap. 24.95 *(978-1-60705-198-5(2))* C & T Publishing.
Schamber, Sharon & Fincher, Cristy. Piece by Piece Machine Applique. rev. ed. 2007. (ENG., Illus.). 96p. per. 24.95 *(978-1-57432-923-0(5)*, 1574329235, American Quilter's Society) Collector Bks.
Schmidt, Dianne, ed. Learn to Do Applique in Just One Weekend. 2010. (ENG., Illus.). 64p. pap. 9.95 *(978-1-59217-329-7(2)*, House of White Birches, Inc.) Annie's Publishing, LLC.
Scott, Carla & Smith, Leanne. Ladybug & Friends Quilts. 2011. (ENG., Illus.). 96p. 26.95 *(978-1-57432-684-0(8)*, 1574326848, American Quilter's Society) Collector Bks.
Scott, Elizabeth. The ABCs of Words on Quilts: Applique & Embroidery Lettering Techniques, Beautiful Projects, 6 Complete Alphabets. 2007. (ENG., Illus.). 80p. pap. 24.95 *(978-1-57120-371-7(0))* C & T Publishing.
Scott, Michele. Bobbin Quiltin' & Fusin' Fun. 2011. (ENG., Illus.). 96p. 26.95 *(978-1-60460-006-3(3)*, 1604600063, American Quilter's Society) Collector Bks.
Seely, Ann & Stewart, Joyce. I Can't Believe It's Not Piecing! 2010. (ENG., Illus.). 80p. 24.95 *(978-1-57432-669-7(4)*, 1574326694, American Quilter's Society) Collector Bks.
Seward, Linda. The Complete Book of Patchwork, Quilting & Applique. 2010. (ENG., Illus.). 184p. pap. 24.95 *(978-1-55407-604-2(0))* Firefly Bks., Ltd.
Shaffer, Cynthia. Stash Happy: Applique: 25 Fresh Projects for Fabric Lovers. 2012. (Stash Happy Ser.). (ENG., Illus.). 128p. pap. 16.95 ***(978-1-4547-0280-1(X))*** Lark Bks.
Shifrin, Laurie J. Batik Gems: 29 Dazzling Quilt Projects. 2009. (ENG., Illus.). 96p. pap. 27.95 *(978-1-57120-560-5(8))* C & T Publishing.
Sienkiewicz, Elly. Baltimore Elegance: A New Approach to Classic Album Quilts. 2006. (ENG., Illus.). 176p. pap. 29.95 *(978-1-57120-274-1(9))* C & T Publishing.
—Elly Sienkiewicz's Beloved Baltimore Album Quilts: 25 Blocks, 12 Quilts, Embellishment Techniques. 2010. (ENG., Illus.). 128p. pap. 29.95 *(978-1-57120-848-4(8))* C & T Publishing.
Sitar, Edyta. Hop to It: Appliqued Blocks & Projects. 2009. (Illus.). 128p. pap. 27.95 *(978-0-9818040-1-9(2))* Landauer Publishing, LLC.
Sloan, Pat & Leisure Arts Staff. Learn to Machine Quilt with Pat Sloan. 2008. (ENG.). 80p. pap. 16.95 *(978-1-60140-510-4(3))* Leisure Arts, Inc.
—Pat Sloan's Take the Fear Out of Color. 2008. (ENG.). 96p. pap. 19.95 *(978-1-60140-508-1(1))* Leisure Arts, Inc.
—Tour Ireland with Pat Sloan. 2008. (ENG.). 128p. pap. 24.95 *(978-1-60140-522-7(7))* Leisure Arts, Inc.
Smith, Annie. The Ultimate Applique Guidebook: 150 Patterns, Hand & Machine Techniques, History, Step-by-Step Instructions, Keys to Design & Inspiration. 2010. (ENG., Illus.). 160p. pap. 29.95 *(978-1-60705-005-6(5))* C & T Publishing.
Sonnen, Janice. Penny Rugs: Sewing Wool Appliqué. 3rd ed. 2010. (Illus.). 64p. pap. 12.99 *(978-0-7643-3467-2(0))* Schiffer Publishing, Ltd.
Stauffer, Jeanne & Albury, Elisa Sims, eds. 5-10-15 + Fat Quarters. 2010. (ENG., Illus.). 176p. pap. 19.95 *(978-1-59217-299-3(7)*, House of White Birches, Inc.) Annie's Publishing, LLC.
Stauffer, Jeanne & Hatch, Sandra L. Holly Jolly Christmas Quilting. 2007. (Illus.). 175p. *(978-1-59217-184-2(2)*, House of White Birches, Inc.) Annie's Publishing, LLC.
Stein, Marcia. Picture This! Capture the Essence of a Photograph in Your Pictorial Quilt. 2010. (ENG., Illus.). 96p. pap. 27.95 *(978-1-57120-838-5(0))* C & T Publishing.
Sudo, Kumiko. Kake-Jiku: Images of Japan in Applique, Fabric Origami, & Sashiko. 2006. (ENG., Illus.). 160p. pap. 29.95 *(978-1-933308-11-1(7)*, 1257853) Breckling Pr.
Taylor, Cheryl. Inspirational Applique: Reflections of Faith, Hope & Love. 2011. (ENG., Illus.). 96p. pap. ***(978-1-60468-048-5(2))*** Martingale & Co.
Thorpe, Zena. Beautiful Wildflower Applique. 2011. (ENG., Illus.). 96p. 26.95 *(978-1-60460-003-2(9)*, 1604600039, American Quilter's Society) Collector Bks.
Tomaszewski, Cynthia. Quilting Those Flirty '30s. 2011. (ENG.) 112p. pap. *(978-1-56477-978-6(5))* Martingale & Co.
Walker, Cyndi. Pretty Patchwork Quilts. 2012. (ENG., Illus.). 80p. pap. ***(978-1-60468-077-5(6))*** Martingale & Co.
Wall, Cheryl. Country Comforts: Quilts for Casual Living. 2010. (ENG., Illus.). 96p. pap. *(978-1-56477-996-0(3))* Martingale & Co.
Wells, Valori. Simple Start — Stunning Finish: Easy As 1. Fabric Secrets 2. Easy Piecing 3. Quilting Solutions. 2007. (ENG., Illus.). 96p. pap. 27.95 *(978-1-57120-378-6(8))* C & T Publishing.
Wikman, Kajsa. Scandinavian Stitches: 21 Playful Projects with Seasonal Flair. 2010. (Illus.). 128p. pap. 22.95 *(978-1-60705-007-0(2))* C & T Publishing.
Wilkinson, Rosemary. Classic Quilts: Tradition with a Twist - 13 Sensational Patchwork & Appliqué Patterns, 1 vol. 2008. (ENG.). 112p. 24.95 *(978-1-56148-634-2(5))* Good Bks.
Willms, Heather & Willms, Elissa. Christmas Quilts from Hopscotch: Warm & Cozy, Merry & Bright. 2008. (ENG.). 80p. pap. 24.95 *(978-1-56477-868-0(1)*, That Patchwork Place) Martingale & Co.
Wittmack, DeElda. Applique at Play: 19 Sports Blocks to Mix & Match. 2006. (That Patchwork Place Ser.). (Illus.). 64p. per. 19.95 *(978-1-56477-698-3(0)*, That Patchwork Place) Martingale & Co.
Wylie, Kathy K. Sewflakes: Papercut-Applique Quilts. 2008. (ENG., Illus.). 64p. pap. 21.95 *(978-1-57120-495-0(4))* C & T Publishing.
Yosten, Angela. Stop. Go. Quilt. Sew! Make 12 Fun Projects for Boys to Enjoy. 2012. (ENG., Illus.). 112p. pap. 22.95 ***(978-1-60705-484-9(1))*** C & T Publishing.
102 Fleece Appliques. 2006. 64p. per. 13.95 *(978-1-60140-257-8(0))* Leisure Arts, Inc.

APPOMATTOX CAMPAIGN, 1865

Chamberlain, Joshua Lawrence. The Passing of the Armies: An Account of the Final Campaign of the Army of the Potomac. 392p. reprint ed. 98.00 *(978-0-7222-8178-9(1))* Library Reprints, Inc.
Forsyth, George A. Thrilling Days in Army Life. 2010. 246p. pap. 26.75 *(978-1-148-36462-9(5))* BiblioBazaar.
—Thrilling Days in Army Life. 2009. 78p. pap. 14.14 *(978-0-217-73249-9(6))* General Bks. LLC.
—Thrilling Days in Army Life. 224p. 2010. pap. 19.96 *(978-1-162-96616-8(5))* 2007. (ENG.). 39.95 *(978-0-548-12327-0(6))* Kessinger Publishing, LLC.
—Thrilling Days in Army Life. 196p. reprint ed. 88.00 *(978-0-7222-8254-0(0))* Library Reprints, Inc.
Forsyth, George Alexander. Thrilling Days in Army Life: Experiences of the Beecher's Island Battle 1868, the Apache Campaign of 1882, & the American Civil War. 2011. 124p. ***(978-0-85706-501-8(7))***; pap. ***(978-0-85706-502-5(5))*** Leonaur Ltd.
Gray, Samuel Howard. A Confederate Diary of the Retreat from Petersburg, April 3-20 1865. Harwell, Richard Barksdale, ed. 2011. 24p. 35.95 ***(978-1-258-01061-4(5))*** Literary Licensing, LLC.
Marvel, William. Lee's Last Retreat: The Flight to Appomattox. Lt. ed. 2010. (Civil War America Ser.). (ENG., Illus.). 328p. pap. 31.00 *(978-0-8078-6605-4(9))* Univ. of North Carolina Pr.
Tremain, Henry E. The Last Hours of Sheridan's Cavalry: A Reprint of War Memoranda. (Illus.). 563p. reprint ed. lib. bdg. 98.00 *(978-0-7222-4607-8(2))* Library Reprints, Inc.
Tremain, Henry Edwin. The Last Hours of Sheridan's Cavalry: A Reprint of War Memoranda. 563p. reprint ed. 98.00 *(978-0-7222-9378-2(X))* Library Reprints, Inc.
Winik, Jay. April 1865: The Month That Saved America. 2006. (P. S. Ser.). (ENG., Illus.). 512p. pap. 15.99 *(978-0-06-089968-4(9)*, HarperPerennial) HarperCollins Pubs.

APPORTIONMENT (ELECTION LAW)

see also Election Districts

Ali Khan, Zulfiqar & Adnan, Muhammad. Usability Evaluation of Web-Based Gis Applications. 2010. 72p. pap. *(978-3-8383-6323-3(X))* Lambert Academic Publishing.
Ansolabehere, Stephen & Snyder, James. The End of Inequality: One Person, One Vote, & the Transformation of American Politics. 2008. (Issues in American Democracy Ser.). (ENG., Illus.). 336p. (C). pap. 16.30 net. *(978-0-393-93103-7(X)*, 93103) Norton, W. W. & Co., Inc.
Benham, Liza Abram. From Winning Elections to Influencing Policy: The Electoral-Policy Link for Minority Voters. 2008. (Law & Society Ser.). (Illus.). 304p. 75.00 *(978-1-59332-274-8(7))* LFB Scholarly Publishing LLC.
Blum, Edward. The Unintended Consequences of Section 5 of the Voting Rights Act. 2007. (ENG.). 88p. pap. 15.00 *(978-0-8447-4257-1(0)*, AEI Pr.) American Enterprise Institute for Public Policy Research.
Bullock, Charles. Redistricting: The Most Political Activity in America. 2010. (ENG.). 234p. 79.00 *(978-1-4422-0353-2(6))*; pap. 25.00 *(978-1-4422-0354-9(4))* Rowman & Littlefield Publishers, Inc.
Cram101 Textbook Reviews & Cram101 Textbook Reviews. Outlines & Highlights for Redistricting: The Most Political Activity in America by Charles Bullock III, ISBN. 2011. 104p. pap. 28.95 ***(978-1-61461-921-5(2))*** Cram101 Inc.
Eagles, Charles W. Democracy Delayed: Congressional Reapportionment & Urban-Rural Conflict in The 1920s. 2010. (ENG.). 188p. pap. 22.95 *(978-0-8203-3622-0(X))* Univ. of Georgia Pr.
Grofman, Bernard & Handley, Lisa, eds. Redistricting in Comparative Perspective. 2008. (Comparative Politics Ser.). (ENG., Illus.). 264p. 125.00 *(978-0-19-922740-2(3))* Oxford Univ. Pr., Inc.
Jewell, Malcolm Edwin. The Politics of Reapportionment. 2011. (Illus.). 353p. pap. 49.95 ***(978-1-4128-1865-0(6))*** Aldine Transaction.
MacManus, Susan, ed. Mapping Florida's Political Landscape: The Changing Art & Politics of Reapportionment & Redistricting. (Illus.). (C). pap. 75.00 *(978-0-9649227-5-4(4))* Florida Institute of Government, The.
Moncrief, Gary F. Reapportionment & Redistricting in the West. 2012. ***(978-0-7391-6762-5(6))*** 2011. (ENG.). 294p. (gr. 17). 75.00 ***(978-0-7391-6761-8(8))*** Lexington Bks.
Orsino, Roland D. & Trance, Olivia G. The House of Representatives: Apportionment & Redistricting. 2011. (Series: Congressional Policies, Practices & Procedures Ser.). (Illus.). 206p. 95.00 *(978-1-61324-308-4(1))* Nova Science Pubs., Inc.
Reed, Alfred Z. Territorial Basis of Government under the State Constitutions. (Columbia University, Studies in the Social Sciences: No. 106). reprint ed. 39.50 *(978-0-404-51106-7(6))* AMS Pr., Inc.
Rodriguez, Orlando J. Vote Thieves: Illegal Immigration, Redistricting, & Presidential Elections. 2011. 192p. 26.95 *(978-1-59797-671-8(7))* Potomac Bks., Inc.
Rossiter, D. J., et al. The Boundary Commissions: Redrawing the UK's Map of Parliamentary Constituencies. 2009. (ENG., Illus.). 448p. pap. 43.00 *(978-0-7190-8038-8(X))* Manchester Univ. Pr. GBR. Dist: Macmillan.
United States, Congress Senate Committee on the Judiciary Subcommittee on the Constitution, Civil Rights, and Property Rights Staff, contrib. by. Renewing the Temporary Provisions of the Voting Rights ACT: Legislative Options after Lulac V. Perry: Hearing Before the Subcommittee on the Constitution, Civil Rights, & Property Rights of the Committee on the Judiciary, United States Senate, One Hundred Ninth Congress, Second Session, July 13, 2006. 2007. (Illus.). iv, 511p. *(978-0-16-078313-5(5)*, 552-070-35636-3) United States Government Printing Office.
Vandenberg, Martina E., et al. The Realists' Guide to Redistricting: Avoiding the Legal Pitfalls. 2nd ed. 2011. (ENG.). 89p. pap. 49.95 *(978-1-60442-753-7(3))* American Bar Assn.

APPRAISAL

see Assessment; Valuation

APPRAISAL OF BOOKS

see Books and Reading; Criticism; Literature—History and Criticism

APPRECIATION OF ART

see Art Appreciation

APPRECIATION OF MUSIC

see Music Appreciation

APPREHENSION

see Perception

APPRENTICES

see also Education, Cooperative

Bower, Michael. Apprentices Speak Out- the Experiences of Five Women in a Skilled Trade. 2007. 152p. per. *(978-3-8364-1823-2(1))* VDM Verlag Dr. Mueller e.K.
De Munck, Bert. Technologies of Learning: Apprenticeship in Antwerp from the 15th Century to the End of the Ancien Regime. 2008. (Studies in European Urban History (1100-1800) Ser.). (ENG., Illus.). 306p. (C). pap. 94.00 *(978-2-503-52270-8(X))* Brepols Pubs. BEL. Dist: ISD.
Douglas, Paul H. American Apprenticeship & Industrial Education. 2009. 350p. pap. 32.75 *(978-1-116-29983-0(6))*; 350p. 33.99 *(978-1-116-29982-3(8))*; 350p. 33.99 *(978-1-116-29981-6(X))*; (ENG.). 352p. pap. 26.99 *(978-1-116-29985-4(2)*, BiblioLife); (ENG.). 352p. pap. 25.99 *(978-1-116-29986-1(0)*, BiblioLife); 350p. pap. 31.75 *(978-1-116-29984-7(4))* BiblioBazaar.
Farr, Michael, et al. 200 Best Jobs Through Apprenticeships. 2nd ed. 2009. (ENG.). 544p. 24.95 *(978-1-59357-537-3(8))* JIST Publishing.
Hagedorn, Michael. Post-Dated: The Schooling of an Irreverent Bonsai Monk. 2008. (Illus.). 172p. pap. 14.95 *(978-0-9801094-7-4(7))* Crataegus Bks.
Halloway, Lori. Shear Savvy: Secrets & Strategies for Successful Salon Apprenticeships. 2009. (Illus.). 122p. pap. 74.95 *(978-0-9822666-1-8(8))*; (ENG., cd-rom 14.95 *(978-0-9822666-4-9(2))* Willow Tree Pr.
Herndon, Ruth Wallis & Murray, John E. Children Bound to Labor: The Pauper Apprentice System in Early America. 2009. (Illus.). 288p. pap. 24.95 *(978-0-8014-7559-7(7))* Cornell Univ. Pr.
Hoffman, Andrew J. Builder's Apprentice: A Memoir. 2010. 24.95 *(978-1-932399-24-0(0))* Huron River Pr.
Howe, Susanne. Wilhelm Meister & His English Kinsmen. reprint ed. 20.00 *(978-0-404-03367-5(9))* AMS Pr., Inc.
IEC. IEC 1st Year Apprenticeship Student Manual 2009/2010. 4th ed. 2009. (C). 197.00 *(978-1-4354-9803-7(8))* Delmar Cengage Learning.
—IEC 2nd Year Apprenticeship Student Manual 2009/2010. 4th ed. 2009. (C). 154.00 *(978-1-4354-9800-6(3))* Delmar Cengage Learning.
—IEC 4th Year Apprenticeship Student Manual 2009/2010. 4th ed. 2009. (C). 105.75 *(978-1-4354-9794-8(5))* Delmar Cengage Learning.
Matheson, Rosa Marie. Doing Time Inside: Apprenticeship & Training in GWR's Swindon Works. 2011. (ENG., Illus.). 160p. pap. 27.95 ***(978-0-7524-5301-9(7))*** History Pr. Ltd., The GBR. Dist: Independent Pubs. Group.
Motley, James M. Apprenticeship in American Trade Unions. 2010. 70p. pap. 20.00 *(978-1-154-63113-5(3))* General Bks. LLC.
Mottier Lopez, Lucie. Apprentissage Situé: La microculture de classe en Mathématiques. 2008. (Exploration. Collection de la Société Suisse pour la Recherche en Education Ser.). 332p. pap. *(978-3-03911-580-8(4))* Lang, Peter.
Munck. Learning on the Shop Floor: Historical Perspectives on Apprenticeship. Kaplan, Steven L. et al, eds. 2007. (International Studies in Social History). (Illus.). 242p. (C). 90.00 *(978-1-84545-341-1(7))* Berghahn Bks., Inc.
Oakes, Elizabeth H. Ferguson Career Resource Guide to Apprenticeship Programs, 2 vols., Set. 2nd rev. ed. 2006. (Ferguson Career Resource Guide Ser.). 1056p. (C). (gr. 9-18). 150.00 *(978-0-8160-5573-9(4)*, Ferguson Publishing Co.) Facts On File, Inc.
Park, Linda Sue. L Apprenti. pap. 16.95 *(978-2-08-161602-8(5))* Flammarion et Cie FRA. Dist: Distribooks, Inc.
Quinn, Matthew. How to Survive the Apprentice! 2009. 136p. pap. 12.49 *(978-1-4490-1798-9(3))* AuthorHouse.
Smith, Erica & Rauner, Felix, eds. Rediscovering Apprenticeship: Research Findings of the International Network on Innovative Apprenticeship (INAP) 2009. (Technical & Vocational Education & Training: Issues, Concerns & Prospects Ser.). (ENG., Illus.). 175p. 159.00 *(978-90-481-3115-0(4)*, 9048131154) Springer.

APPROPRIATION AND IMPROPRIATION

see Secularization

APPROVAL, SOCIAL

see Social Acceptance

APPROXIMATE COMPUTATION

see also Differential Equations, Partial—Numerical Solutions; Perturbation (Mathematics); Relaxation Methods (Mathematics)

Stepanets, A. I. Uniform Approximations by Trigonometric Polynomials. (ENG.). XII, 483p. 598.00 ***(978-3-11-179455-6(5))*** De Gruyter, Walter Inc.

APPROXIMATION THEORY

see also Chebyshev Systems; Numerical Analysis; Perturbation (Mathematics); Spline Theory

Abdelmalek, Nabih & Malek, William A. Numerical Linear Approximation in C. 2008. (Chapman & Hall/CRC Numerical Analysis & Scientific Computing Ser.). (ENG., Illus.). 968p. 119.95 *(978-1-58488-978-6(0)*, Chapman & Hall/CRC) CRC Pr. LLC.

Adachi, Hirohiko, et al, eds. Hartree-Fock-Slater Method for Materials Science: The DV-X Alpha Method for Design & Characterization of Materials. 2010. (Springer Series in Materials Science Ser.). (Illus.). xvi, 240p. pap. 169.00 *(978-3-642-06384-8(5)*, 3642063845) Springer.

Akram, Muhammad & Imran Shafi, Muhammad. Functional Approach Towards Approximation Problems. 2010. 112p. pap. *(978-3-8383-6350-9(7))* Lambert Academic Publishing.

Anastassiou, George A. Fuzzy Mathematics: Approximation Theory: Approximation Theory. 2010. (Studies in Fuzziness & Soft Computing Ser.). xii, 444p. 199.00 *(978-3-642-11219-5(6)*, 3642112196) Springer.

Anastassiou, George A. & Duman, Oktay. Towards Intelligent Modeling: Statistical Approximation Theory: Statistical Approximation Theory. 2011. (Intelligent Systems Reference Library). xvi, 236p. 129.00 *(978-3-642-19825-0(2)*, 3642198252) Springer.

Andrievskii, Vladimir V. & Blatt, Hans-Peter. Discrepancy of Signed Measures & Polynomial Approximation. 2010. (Springer Monographs in Mathematics Ser.). (Illus.). xiii, 438p. pap. 129.00 *(978-1-4419-3146-7(5)*, 1441931465) Springer.

Antoulas, Athanasios C. Approximation of Large-Scale Dynamical Systems. 2009. (Advances in Design & Control Ser.). (ENG., Illus.). 510p. pap. 99.00 *(978-0-89871-658-0(6))* Society for Industrial and Applied Mathematics.

Approximation Theory. Tampa: Proceedings of a Seminar held in Tampa, Florida, 1985 - 1986. 2008. (Lecture Notes in Mathematics Ser.). pap. 59.95 *(978-3-540-18500-0(3))* Springer.

Aubin, Jean-Pierre. Approximation of Elliptic Boundary-Value Problems. 2007. (Dover Books on Mathematics Ser.). (ENG.). 384p. per. 19.95 *(978-0-486-45791-8(5))* Dover Pubns., Inc.

Axelsson, O. Preconditioned Conjugate Gradient Methods: Proceedings of a Conference held in Nijmegen, The Netherlands, June 19-21, 1989. 2008. (Lecture Notes in Mathematics Ser.). pap. 26.00 *(978-3-540-53515-7(2))* Springer.

Baker, George A. & Graves-Morris, Peter. Padé Approximants. 2nd rev. ed. 2010. (Encyclopedia of Mathematics & its Applications Ser.). (ENG., Illus.). 764p. pap. 130.00 *(978-0-521-13509-2(5))* Cambridge Univ. Pr.

Borkar, Vivek S. Stochastic Approximation: A Dynamical Systems Viewpoint. 2008. (ENG.). 176p. 70.00 *(978-0-521-51592-4(0))* Cambridge Univ. Pr.

Borovskikh, Yu V. & Korolyuk, V. S. Martingale Approximation. (ENG.). XII, 322p. 464.00 ***(978-3-11-182692-9(9))*** De Gruyter, Walter Inc.

Brink, D. M. Semi-Classical Methods for Nucleus-Nucleus Scattering. 2009. (Cambridge Monographs on Mathematical Physics Ser.). (ENG.). 232p. pap. 53.00 *(978-0-521-11438-7(1))* Cambridge Univ. Pr.

Bugeaud, Yann. Approximation by Algebraic Numbers. 2007. (Cambridge Tracts in Mathematics Ser.). (ENG., Illus.). 292p. pap. 60.00 *(978-0-521-04567-4(3))* Cambridge Univ. Pr.

Buhmann, M. D. & Iserles, A., eds. Approximation Theory & Optimization: Tributes to M. J. D. Powell. 2009. (ENG., Illus.). 236p. pap. 53.00 *(978-0-521-11844-6(1))* Cambridge Univ. Pr.

Buhmann, Martin D. Radial Basis Functions: Theory & Implementations. 2009. (Cambridge Monographs on Applied & Computational Mathematics Ser.). (ENG.). 272p. pap. 53.00 *(978-0-521-10133-2(6))* Cambridge Univ. Pr.

Bustamante, Jorge. Algebraic Approximation: A Guide to Past & Current Solutions: A Guide to Past & Current Solutions. 2011. (Frontiers in Mathematics Ser.). (ENG., Illus.). vii, 205p. pap. 59.95 ***(978-3-0348-0193-5(9)***, 3034801939) Birkhauser Verlag AG CHE. Dist: Springer.

Carl, Bernd & Stephani, Irmtraud. Entropy, Compactness & the Approximation of Operators. 2008. (Cambridge Tracts in Mathematics Ser.). (ENG.). 288p. pap. 38.99 *(978-0-521-09094-0(6))* Cambridge Univ. Pr.

Chaitin-Chatelin, Françoise. Spectral Approximation of Linear Operators. 2011. (ENG.). 480p. pap. *(978-0-89871-999-4(2))* Society for Industrial and Applied Mathematics.

Chan, Hock Peng, ed. Probability Approximations & Beyond. 2011. (Lecture Notes in Statistics / Lecture Notes in Statistics - Proceedings Ser.). (ENG., Illus.). xiv, 159p. pap. 79.95 ***(978-1-4614-1965-5(4)***, 1461419654) Springer.

Chen, Louis H. Y., et al. Normal Approximation by Stein's Method. 2010. (Probability & Its Applications Ser.). xii, 405p. 74.95 *(978-3-642-15006-7(3)*, 3642150063) Springer.

Cheney, Ward & Light, Will. A Course in Approximation Theory. 2009. (Graduate Studies in Mathematics Ser.). (Illus.). 359p. 69.00 *(978-0-8218-4798-5(8))* American Mathematical Society.

Cram101 Textbook Reviews & Cram101 Textbook Reviews. Outlines & Highlights for Learning Theory by Felipe Cucker, Isbn: 9780521865593. 2011. 86p. pap. 27.95 ***(978-1-61461-186-8(6))*** Cram101 Inc.

Cruz-Uribe, David, et al. Weights, Extrapolation & the Theory of Rubio de Francia. 2011. (Operator Theory: Advances & Applications Ser.). xiii, 280p. 99.00 *(978-3-0348-0071-6(1)*, 3034800711) Birkhauser Verlag AG CHE. Dist: Springer.

Cucker, Felipe & Zhou, Ding-Xuan. Learning Theory: An Approximation Theory Viewpoint. 2007. (Cambridge Monographs on Applied & Computational Mathematics). (ENG., Illus.). 236p. 74.99 *(978-0-521-86559-3(X))* Cambridge Univ. Pr.

Cuyt, A. Pade Approximants for Operators: Theory & Applications. 2008. (Lecture Notes in Mathematics Ser.). pap. 39.95 *(978-3-540-13342-1(9))* Springer.

De Concini, Corrado & Procesi, Claudio. Topics in Hyperplane Arrangements, Polytopes & Box-Splines. 2010. (Universitext Ser.). (Illus.). xxii, 381p. pap. 69.95 *(978-0-387-78962-0(6)*, 0387789626) Springer.

De Vore, Ronald A. The Approximation of Continuous Functions by Positive Linear Operators. 2008. (Lecture Notes in Mathematics Ser.). 304p. pap. 59.95 *(978-3-540-06038-3(3)*, 3540060383) Springer.

Debruin, M. G. & Vanrossum, H., eds. Pade Approximation & its Applications, Amsterdam 1980: Proceedings of a Conference Held in Amsterdam, The Netherlands, October 29-31, 1980. 2008. (Lecture Notes in Mathematics Ser.). pap. 46.00 *(978-3-540-11154-2(9))* Springer.

Deterministic & Stochastic Error Bounds in Numerical Analysis. 2008. (Lecture Notes in Mathematics Ser.). pap. 26.00 *(978-3-540-50368-2(4))* Springer.

Deutsch, Frank R. Best Approximation in Inner Product Spaces. 2010. (CMS Books in Mathematics Ser.). (Illus.). xv, 338p. pap. 99.00 *(978-1-4419-2890-0(1)*, 1441928901) Springer.

DeVore, Ronald & Kunoth, Angela, eds. Multiscale, Nonlinear & Adaptive Approximation: Dedicated to Wolfgang Dahmen on the Occasion of his 60th Birthday. 2009. (ENG., Illus.). xxiv, 659p. 209.00 *(978-3-642-03412-1(8)*, 3642034128) Springer.

DeVore, Ronald A. & Lorentz, George G. Constructive Approximation. 2010. (Grundlehren der mathematischen Wissenschaften Ser.). (Illus.). x, 449p. pap. 189.00 *(978-3-642-08075-3(8)*, 3642080758) Springer.

Diophantine Approximation & Transcendence Theory: Seminar, Bonn (FRG) May - June 1985. 2008. (Lecture Notes in Mathematics Ser.). pap. 59.95 *(978-3-540-18597-0(6))* Springer.

Diophantine Approximations & Value Distribution Theory. 2008. (Lecture Notes in Mathematics Ser.). pap. 39.95 *(978-3-540-17551-3(2))* Springer.

Doelman, Arjen, et al. The Dynamics of Modulated Wave Trains. 2009. (Memoirs of the American Mathematical Society Ser.). 105p. pap. 66.00 *(978-0-8218-4293-5(5))* American Mathematical Society.

Du, Ding-Zhu, et al. Design & Analysis of Approximation Algorithms. 2011. (Springer Optimization & Its Applications Ser.). (ENG., Illus.). xi, 440p. 74.95 ***(978-1-4614-1700-2(7)***, 1461417007) Springer.

Dzyadyk, Vladislav K. & Shevchuk, Igor A. Theory of Uniform Approximation of Functions by Polynomials. Malyshev, Dmitry V. et al, trs. 2008. (ENG.). XV, 480p. 105.00 *(978-3-11-020147-5(X))* De Gruyter, Walter Inc.

Emanet, Nahit. The Rectilinear Steiner Tree Problem. 2010. 116p. pap. *(978-3-8383-4906-0(7))* Lambert Academic Publishing.

Erlebach, Thomas & Kaklamanis, Christos. Approximation & Online Algorithms: 4th International Workshop, WAOA 2006, Zurich, Switzerland, September 14-15, 2006: Revised Papers. 2007. (Lecture Notes in Computer Science Ser.: Vol. 4368). (Illus.). X, 345p. pap. 79.95 *(978-3-540-69513-4(3)*, 3540695133) Springer.

Fisher, S. W. & Jerome, J. W. Minimum Norm Extremals in Function Spaces. 2008. (Lecture Notes in Mathematics Ser.). 224p. pap. 59.95 *(978-3-540-07394-9(9))* Springer.

Gal, Sorin G. Approximation by Complex Bernstein & Convolution Type Operators, Vol. 8. 2009. (Series on Concrete & Applicable Mathematics: Vol. 8). 352p. 107.00 *(978-981-4282-42-0(1))* World Scientific Publishing Co., Inc.

—Shape-Preserving Approximation by Real & Complex Polynomials. 2008. xiii, 352p. E-Book *(978-0-8176-4703-2(1))* Birkhauser Verlag AG.

—Shape-Preserving Approximation by Real & Complex Polynomials. 2008. 344p. 89.95 *(978-0-8176-4702-5(3)*, 0817647023) Springer.

Gaomez, A. Approximation & Optimization: Proceedings of the International Seminar, held in Havana, Cuba, January 12-16, 1987. 2008. (Lecture Notes in Mathematics Ser.). pap. 46.00 *(978-3-540-50443-6(5))* Springer.

Garnett, J. Analytic Capacity & Measure. 2008. (Lecture Notes in Mathematics Ser.). (ENG.). 148p. pap. 39.95 *(978-3-540-06073-4(1)*, 3540060731) Springer.

Gautschi, Walter, et al, eds. Approximation & Computation: In Honor of Gradimir V. MilovanoviÄ¿. 2010. (Springer Optimization & Its Applications Ser.). (ENG., Illus.). xxii, 484p. 179.00 *(978-1-4419-6593-6(9)*, 1441965939) Springer.

Georgoulis, Emmanuil H., et al, eds. Approximation Algorithms for Complex Systems: Proceedings of the 6th International Conference on Algorithms for Approximation,Ambleside, UK, 31st August - 4th September 2009. 2011. (Springer Proceedings in Mathematics Ser.). (Illus.). x, 307p. 149.00 *(978-3-642-16875-8(2)*, 3642168752) Springer.

Giesl, Peter. Construction of Global Lyapunov Functions Using Radial Basis Functions. 2007. (Lecture Notes in Mathematics Ser.). (Illus.). 166p. per. 49.95 *(978-3-540-69907-1(4))* Springer.

Gil, Amparo, et al. Numerical Methods for Special Functions. 2007. (ENG., Illus.). 430p. pap. 99.00 *(978-0-89871-634-4(9))* Society for Industrial and Applied Mathematics.

Gockenbach, Mark S. Finite Dimensional Linear Algebra. 2010. (Discrete Mathematics & Its Applications Ser.). (ENG., Illus.). 672p. 99.95 *(978-1-4398-1563-2(1)*, CRC Press) Taylor & Francis Group GBR. Dist: Taylor & Francis Group.

Goebel, Ruediger & Trlifaj, Jan. Approximations & Endomorphism Algebras of Modules. 2006. (De Gruyter Expositions in Mathematics Ser.). (ENG.). XXIV, 640p. 196.00 *(978-3-11-011079-1(2))* De Gruyter, Walter Inc.

Govil, N. K., et al. Frontiers in Interpolation & Approximation. 2006. (Pure & Applied Mathematics Ser.: Vol. 282). (ENG., Illus.). 431p. 199.95 *(978-1-58488-636-5(6)*, Chapman & Hall/CRC) CRC Pr. LLC.

Graves-Morris, P., ed. Rational Approximation & Interpolation: Proceedings of the United Kingdom - United States Conference, held at Tampa, Florida, December 12-16, 1983. 2008. (Lecture Notes in Mathematics Ser.). pap. 59.00 *(978-3-540-13899-0(4))* Springer.

Harmand, P., et al. M-Ideals in Banach Spaces & Banach Algebras. 2008. (Lecture Notes in Mathematics Ser.). (Illus.). 395p. pap. 69.95 *(978-3-540-56814-8(X))* Springer.

Hedberg, Lars Inge & Netrusov, Yuri. An Axiomatic Approach to Function Spaces, Spectral Synthesis, & Luzin Approximation. 2007. (Memoirs of the American Mathematical Society Ser.). 97p. pap. 62.00 *(978-0-8218-3983-6(7))* American Mathematical Society.

Holmes, R. B. A Course on Optimization & Best Approximation. 2008. (Lecture Notes in Mathematics Ser.). pap. 59.95 *(978-3-540-05764-2(1))* Springer.

Hu, Pei-Chu & Yang, Chung-Chun. Distribution Theory of Algebraic Numbers. 2008. (De Gruyter Expositions in Mathematics Ser.). (ENG.). XI, 527p. 175.00 *(978-3-11-020536-7(X))* De Gruyter, Walter Inc.

Iske, Armin & Levesley, Jeremy. Algorithms for Approximation: Proceedings of the 5th International Conference, Chester, July 2005. 2010. (ENG., Illus.). xvi, 389p. pap. 129.00 *(978-3-642-06994-9(0)*, 3642069940) Springer.

Ivanov, A. A. The Theory of Approximate Methods & Their Applications to the Numerical Solution of Singular Integral Equations. Anderssen, R.S. & Elliott, D., eds. 2010. (Mechanics: Analysis Ser.). 352p. pap. 359.00 *(978-90-481-8462-0(2)*, 9048184622) Springer.

Jentzen, Arnulf & Kloeden, Peter E. Taylor Approximations for Stochastic Partial Differential Equations. 2011. (ENG., Illus.). 235p. pap. ***(978-1-61197-200-9(0))*** Society for Industrial and Applied Mathematics.

Kalantari, Bahman. Polynomial Root-Finding & Polynomiography. 2009. (Illus.). 480p. 112.00 *(978-981-270-059-9(5))* World Scientific Publishing Co., Inc.

Katkovnik, V. IA, et al. Local Approximation Techniques in Signal & Image Processing. 2006. (Press Monographs). (Illus.). 576p. 99.00 *(978-0-8194-6092-9(3))* SPIE.

Keimel, Klaus & Roth, Walter E. Ordered Cones & Approximation. 2008. (Lecture Notes in Mathematics Ser.). 140p. pap. 39.95 *(978-3-540-55445-5(9))* Springer.

Kitahara, K. Spaces of Approximating Functions with Haar-like Conditions. 2008. (Lecture Notes in Mathematics Ser.). 120p. pap. 26.00 *(978-3-540-57974-8(5))* Springer.

Kohlenbach, Ulrich. Applied Proof Theory. 2008. (Springer Monographs in Mathematics Ser.). (C). 99.00 *(978-3-540-77532-4(3))* Springer.

—Applied Proof Theory: Proof Interpretations & their Use in Mathematics: Proof Interpretations & their Use in Mathematics. 2010. (Springer Monographs in Mathematics Ser.). xx, 536p. pap. 99.00 *(978-3-642-09627-3(1)*, 3642096271) Springer.

Kokhanovsky, Alexander A. Light Scattering Media Optics. 3rd ed. 2010. (Springer Praxis Books / Environmental Sciences Ser.). xxvi, 299p. pap. 179.00 *(978-3-642-05944-5(9)*, 3642059449) Springer.

Komzsik, Louis. Approximation Techniques for Engineers. 2006. (ENG., Illus.). 296p. 129.95 *(978-0-8493-9277-1(2)*, CRC Press) Taylor & Francis Group GBR. Dist: Taylor & Francis Group.

Korneichuk, N. Exact Constants in Approximation Theory. Ivanov, K., tr. from RUS. 2009. (Encyclopedia of Mathematics & its Applications Ser.). (ENG.). 468p. pap. 84.00 *(978-0-521-11156-0(0))* Cambridge Univ. Pr.

Krantz, William B. Scaling Analysis in Modeling Transport & Reaction Processes: A Systematic Approach to Model Building & the Art of Approximation. 2007. (ENG.). 529p. 144.00 *(978-0-471-77261-3(5))* American Institute of Chemical Engineers.

Kresin, Gershon & Mazia, V. G. Sharp Real-Part Theorems: A Unified Approach. 2007. (Lecture Notes in Mathematics Ser.: Vol. 1903). XVI, 144p. pap. 39.00 *(978-3-540-69573-8(7)*, 3540695737) Springer.

Kushner, Harold J. Approximation & Weak Convergence Methods for Random Processes with Applications to Stochastic Systems Theory. 2008. (Signal Processing, Optimization, & Control Ser.). (ENG.). 287p. (gr. 17). pap. 33.00 *(978-0-262-51218-3(1))* MIT Pr.

Kushner, Harold J. & Yin, G. George. Stochastic Approximation & Recursive Algorithms & Applications. 2nd ed. 2010. (Stochastic Modelling & Applied Probability Ser.). (Illus.). xxii, 474p. pap. 115.00 *(978-1-4419-1847-5(7)*, 1441918477) Springer.

Lax, Peter D. & Zalcman, Lawrence. Complex Proofs of Real Theorems. 2011. (University Lecture Ser.). 90p. pap. 29.00 ***(978-0-8218-7559-9(0))*** American Mathematical Society.

Light, W. & Cheney, E. Approximation Theory in Tensor Product Spaces. 2008. (Lecture Notes in Mathematics Ser.). pap. 39.95 *(978-3-540-16057-1(4))* Springer.

Lipparini, Enrico. Modern Many-Particle Physics: Atomic Gases, Nanostructures & Quantum Liquids. 2nd rev. ed. 2008. (Illus.). 151.00 *(978-981-270-931-8(2))*; 582p. pap. 91.00 *(978-981-270-932-5(0))* World Scientific Publishing Co., Inc.

Lladser, Manuel E. Algorithmic Probability & Combinatorics. Mishna, Marni et al, eds. 2010. (Contemporary Mathematics Ser.). (Illus.). 240p. pap. 79.00 *(978-0-8218-4783-1(X))* American Mathematical Society.

Lopez Lagomasino, Guillermo. Recent Trends in Orthogonal Polynomials & Approximation Theory. Arvesú, Jorge et al, eds. 2010. (Contemporary Mathematics Ser.). (Illus.). 298p. pap. 89.00 *(978-0-8218-4803-6(8))* American Mathematical Society.

MacHado, S., ed. Functional Analysis, Holomorphy, & Approximation Theory: Proceedings of the Seminario de Analise Functional Holomorfia e Teoria da Aproximacao, Universidade Federal do Rio de Janeiro, Brazil, August 7-11, 1978. 2008. (Lecture Notes in Mathematics Ser.). 648p. pap. 69.95 *(978-3-540-10560-2(3))* Springer.

Maksimov, Vyacheslav I. Dynamical Inverse Problems of Distributed Systems. (Inverse & Ill-Posed Problems Ser.). (ENG.). VIII, 269p. 464.00 ***(978-3-11-188675-6(1))*** De Gruyter, Walter Inc.

Markovsky, Ivan. Low Rank Approximation: Algorithms, Implementation, Applications. 2011. (Communications & Control Engineering Ser.). (ENG., Illus.). x, 256p. 109.00 ***(978-1-4471-2226-5(7)***, 1447122267) Springer.

Massopust, Peter Robert. Interpolation & Approximation with Splines & Fractals. 2010. (ENG., Illus.). 336p. 80.00 *(978-0-19-533654-2(2))* Oxford Univ. Pr., Inc.

Maz'ya, Vladimir & Schmidt, Günter. Approximate Approximations. 2007. (Mathematical Surveys & Monographs). (Illus.). 349p. 92.00 *(978-0-8218-4203-4(X))* American Mathematical Society.

Mickens, Ronald E. Truly Nonlinear Oscillations: Harmonic Balance, Parameter Expansions, Iteration, & Averaging Methods. 2010. (Illus.). 260p. 96.00 *(978-981-4291-65-1(X))* World Scientific Publishing Co., Inc.

Mirkov, Radoslava. Tree Approximations of Dynamic Stochastic Programs. 2008. 176p. pap. *(978-3-639-06131-4(4))* VDM Verlag Dr. Mueller e.K.

Morgan, K. & Zienkiewicz, O. C. Finite Elements & Approximation. 2006. (Dover Books on Engineering Ser.). (ENG., Illus.). 352p. per. 19.95 *(978-0-486-45301-9(4))* Dover Pubns., Inc.

Neamtu, Marian & Schumaker, Larry, eds. Approximation Theory XIII: San Antonio 2010: San Antonio 2010. 2011. (Springer Proceedings in Mathematics Ser.). (ENG., Illus.). xvii, 415p. 149.00 ***(978-1-4614-0771-3(0)***, 1461407710) Springer.

Neamtu, Marian & Schumaker, Larry L., eds. Approximation Theory XII: San Antonio 2007. 2008. (Illus.). 453p. 100.00 *(978-0-9728482-9-9(0))* Nashboro Pr., Inc.

Neuberger, John. Sobolev Gradients & Differential Equations. 2nd ed. 2009. (Lecture Notes in Mathematics Ser.). xiii, 289p. pap. 59.95 *(978-3-642-04040-5(3)*, 3642040403) Springer.

Oden, J. T. & Reddy, J. N. An Introduction to the Mathematical Theory of Finite Elements. 2011. (Dover Books on Engineering Ser.). (ENG.). 448p. pap. 24.95 *(978-0-486-46299-8(4))* Dover Pubns., Inc.

Panek, Dariusz. On Sharp Extrapolation Theorems. 2010. 88p. pap. *(978-3-8383-8817-5(8))* Lambert Academic Publishing.

Pardalos, Panos M., ed. Approximation & Complexity in Numerical Optimization: Continuous & Discrete Problems. 2010. (Nonconvex Optimization & its Applications Ser.). 594p. pap. 309.00 *(978-1-4419-4829-8(5)*, 1441948295) Springer.

Peitgen, H. O. & Walther, H. -O., eds. Functional Differential Equations & Approximation of Fixed Points: Proceedings, Bonn, July 1978. 2008. (Lecture Notes in Mathematics Ser.). 516p. pap. 69.95 *(978-3-540-09518-7(7))* Springer.

Petrushev, P. P. & Popov, Vasil Atanasov. Rational Approximation of Real Functions. 2011. (Encyclopedia of Mathematics & its Applications Ser.). (ENG.). 384p. pap. 75.00 *(978-0-521-17740-5(5))* Cambridge Univ. Pr.

Phillips, George M. Interpolation & Approximation by Polynomials. 2011. (CMS Books in Mathematics Ser.). (ENG., Illus.). xiv, 312p. pap. 99.00 *(978-1-4419-1810-9(8)*, 1441918108) Springer.

Pinkus, Allan M. On L1-Approximation. 2008. (Cambridge Tracts in Mathematics Ser.). (ENG.). 252p. pap. 53.00 *(978-0-521-05769-1(8))* Cambridge Univ. Pr.

Plotnikov, Anatoly. Problems of the Class Np. 2011. 152p. pap. ***(978-3-8443-9346-0(3))*** Lambert Academic Publishing.

Rational Approximation & its Applications in Mathematics & Physics: Proceedings, Lancut 1985. 2008. (Lecture Notes in Mathematics Ser.). pap. 46.00 *(978-3-540-17212-3(2))* Springer.

Raza, Nauman & Sial, Sultan. Sobolev Gradient Methods. 2010. 116p. pap. *(978-3-8383-8501-3(2))* Lambert Academic Publishing.

Schaback, R. & Scherer, K., eds. Approximation Theory: Proceedings of an International Conference held at Bonn, Germany, June 8-11, 1976. 2008. (Lecture Notes in Mathematics Ser.). 484p. pap. 69.95 *(978-3-540-08001-5(5))* Springer.

Schempp, W. & Zeller, K., eds. Constructive Theory of Functions of Several Variables: Proceedings of a Conference Held at Oberwolfach, April 25 - May 1, 1976. 2008. (Lecture Notes in Mathematics Ser.). 304p. pap. 46.00 *(978-3-540-08069-5(4))* Springer.

Schmidt, Wolfgang M., ed. Diophantine Approximations & Diophantine Equations. 2008. (Lecture Notes in Mathematics Ser.). (Illus.). viii, 217p. pap. 59.95 *(978-3-540-54058-8(X))* Springer.

Schmidt, Wolfgang M., et al. Diophantine Approximation: Festschrift for Wolfgang Schmidt. 2008. (Developments in Mathematics Ser.). 430p. 179.00 *(978-3-211-74279-2(4))* Springer.

Shahriari, Shahriar. Approximately Calculus. 2006. (Illus.). 292p. (C). 50.00 *(978-0-8218-3750-4(8))* American Mathematical Society.

Shapiro, Harold S. Topics in Approximation Theory. 2008. (Lecture Notes in Mathematics Ser.). 284p. pap. 59.95 *(978-3-540-05376-7(X)*, 354005376X) Springer.

Singh, S. P., ed. Approximation Theory, Wavelets & Applications. 2010. (NATO Science Series C: (closed) Ser.). 600p. pap. 489.00 *(978-90-481-4516-4(3)*, 9048145163) Springer.

Stoltenberg-Hansen, V., et al. Mathematical Theory of Domains. 2008. (Cambridge Tracts in Theoretical Computer Science Ser.). (ENG., Illus.). 364p. (C). pap. 74.00 *(978-0-521-06479-8(1))* Cambridge Univ. Pr.

Synge, J. L. The Hypercircle in Mathematical Physics: A Method for the Approximate Solution of Boundary Value Problems. 2012. (ENG.). 440p. pap. 76.99 ***(978-1-107-66655-9(4))*** Cambridge Univ. Pr.

Tichy, Robert F., et al, eds. Diophantine Approximation: Festschrift for Wolfgang Schmidt. 2010. (Developments in Mathematics Ser.). (ENG & FRE.). vii, 422p. pap. 179.00 *(978-3-211-99909-7(4)*, 3211999094) Springer.

Totik, V. Weighted Approximation with Varying Weight. 2008. (Lecture Notes in Mathematics Ser.). 121p. pap. 39.95 *(978-3-540-57705-8(X))* Springer.

Trebels, W. Multipliers for -Bounded Fourier Expansions in Banach Spaces & Approximation Theory. 2008. (Lecture Notes in Mathematics Ser.). 116p. pap. 26.00 *(978-3-540-06357-5(9))* Springer.

Trigub, Roald M. & Belinsky, Eduard S. Fourier Analysis & Approximation of Functions. 2010. xiii, 585p. pap. 149.00 *(978-90-481-6641-1(1)*, 9048166411) Springer.

Weiss, Yair & Freeman, William T. Belief Propagation. Medioni, Gerard & Dickinson, Sven, eds. 2012. (Synthesis Lectures on Computer Vision Ser.). 100p. pap. 35.00 *(978-1-60845-345-0(6))* Morgan & Claypool Pubs.

Wendland, Holger. Scattered Data Approximation. 2010. (Cambridge Monographs on Applied & Computational Mathematics Ser.). (ENG., Illus.). 348p. pap. 67.00 *(978-0-521-13101-8(4))* Cambridge Univ. Pr.

Werner, H. & Bunger, H., eds. Pade Approximations & its Applications: Proceedings of a Conference held at Bad Honnef, Germany, March 7-10, 1983. 2008. (Lecture Notes in Mathematics Ser.). pap. 46.00 *(978-3-540-13364-3(X))* Springer.

Williamson, David P. & Shmoys, David B. The Design of Approximation Algorithms. 2011. (ENG., Illus.). 516p. 55.00 *(978-0-521-19527-0(6))* Cambridge Univ. Pr.

Wuytack, L., ed. Pade Approximation & its Applications: Proceedings of a Conference held in Antwerp, Belgium, 1979. 2008. (Lecture Notes in Mathematics Ser.). 404p. pap. 46.00 *(978-3-540-09717-4(1))* Springer.

Xiu, Dongbin. Numerical Methods for Stochastic Computations: A Spectral Method Approach. 2010. (ENG., Illus.). 152p. (C). 45.00 *(978-0-691-14212-8(2))* Princeton Univ. Pr.

Yserentant, Harry. Regularity & Approximability of Electronic Wave Functions. 2010. (Lecture Notes in Mathematics Ser.). (ENG., Illus.). viii, 182p. pap. 59.95 *(978-3-642-12247-7(7)*, 3642122477) Springer.

Zalcman, Lawrence. Analytic Capacity & Rational Approximation. 2007. (Lecture Notes in Mathematics Ser.). 164p. per. 39.95 *(978-3-540-04220-4(2))* Springer.

Zvyagin, Victor & Vorotnikov, Dmitry. Topological Approximation Methods for Evolutionary Problems of Nonlinear Hydrodynamics. 2008. (De Gruyter Series in Nonlinear Analysis & Applications Ser.). (ENG.). XII, 230p. 147.00 *(978-3-11-020222-9(0))* De Gruyter, Walter Inc.

APRAXIA

Atter, Elizabeth & Drew, Sharon. Can't Play Won't Play: Simply Sizzling Ideas to Getting the Ball Rolling for Children with Dyspraxia. 2008. (ENG., Illus.). 200p. per. *(978-1-84310-601-2(9))* Kingsley, Jessica Ltd.

Boon, Maureen. Understanding Dyspraxia: A Guide for Parents, Teachers & Professionals. 2nd ed. 2010. (ENG., Illus.). 160p. pap. *(978-1-84905-069-2(4))* Kingsley, Jessica Ltd.

Brookes, Geoff. Dyspraxia. 2nd ed. 2007. (SEN Ser.). (ENG.). 196p. 29.95 *(978-0-8264-9235-7(5))* Continuum International Publishing Group, Ltd. GBR. Dist: National Bk. Network.

—The Teaching Assistant's Guide to Dyspraxia. 2007. (Teaching Assistant's Ser.). (ENG.). 152p. 35.95 *(978-0-8264-9760-4(8))* Continuum International Publishing Group, Ltd. GBR. Dist: National Bk. Network.

Colley, Mary. Living with Dyspraxia: A Guide for Adults with Developmental Dyspraxia. 2006. (ENG., Illus.). 28p. per. *(978-1-84310-452-0(0))* Kingsley, Jessica Ltd.

Fish, Margaret. Here's How to Treat Childhood Apraxia of Speech: An Integrated Approach. 2010. (Illus.). 310p. pap. 79.95 *(978-1-59756-589-9(X))* Plural Publishing, Inc.

Grant, David. That's the Way I Think: Dyslexia, Dyspraxia & ADHD Explained. 2nd rev. ed. 2010. (ENG., Illus.). 176p. pap. 30.95 *(978-0-415-56464-9(6))*; 130.00 *(978-0-415-56465-6(4))* Routledge.

Johns, Sarah. Where's My Pen? a Guide to Supporting People with Dyspraxi. 2009. (Illus.). 124p. pap. *(978-1-84991-036-1(7))* Chipmunkapublishing.

Kirby, Amanda & Peters, Lynne. 100 Ideas for Supporting Pupils with Dyspraxia & DCD. 2007. (Continuums One Hundreds Ser.). (ENG.). 128p. 20.95 *(978-0-8264-9440-5(4))* Continuum International Publishing Group, Ltd. GBR. Dist: National Bk. Network.

MacIntyre, Christine. Dyspraxia 5-14: Identifying & Supporting Young People with Movement Difficulties. 2nd ed. 2009. (David Fulton / Nasen Ser.). (ENG., Illus.). 132p. 37.95 *(978-0-415-54396-5(7))*; 105.00 *(978-0-415-54397-2(5))* Routledge.

MacIntyre, Christine. Dyspraxia in the Early Years: Identifying & Supporting Children with Movement Difficulties. 2nd rev. ed. (David Fulton / Nasen Ser.). (Illus.). 2009. XII, 116p. 37.95 *(978-0-415-47684-3(4))* 2008. 136p. 110.00 *(978-0-415-47889-2(8))* Routledge.

Moody, Sylvia. Dyslexia & Employment: A Guide for Assessors, Trainers & Managers. 2009. (ENG.). 256p. 100.00 *(978-0-470-74090-3(6)*, Wiley) Wiley, John & Sons, Inc.

Moody, Sylvia, ed. Dyslexia & Employment: A Guide for Assessors, Trainers & Managers. 2009. (ENG.). 256p. pap. 65.00 *(978-0-470-69478-7(5)*, Wiley) Wiley, John & Sons, Inc.

Penketh, Claire. A Clumsy Encounter: Dyspraxia & Drawing. 2011. 184p. ***(978-94-6091-456-0(X))***; pap. ***(978-94-6091-455-3(1))*** Sense Pubs.

Talukdar, Afroza. Dyspraxia/DCD Pocketbook. 2012. (ENG., Illus.). 128p. pap. ***(978-1-906610-38-8(X)***, Teachers' Pocketbooks) Management Pocketbooks GBR. Dist: Ware-Pak, Inc.

APRIORI
see A Priori

APTITUDE TESTS
see Ability—Testing

APULEIUS

Apuleius, Lucius. The Apologia & Florida of Apuleius of Madaura. Butler, H. E., tr. 2008. 172p. pap. *(978-1-4099-3014-3(9))* Dodo Pr.

Bradley, Keith. Apuleius & Antonine Rome: Historical Essays. 2012. (Phoenix Supplementary Volumes Ser.). (ENG., Illus.). 408p. ***(978-1-4426-4420-5(6))*** Univ. of Toronto Pr.

Gaisser, Julia Haig. The Fortunes of Apuleius & the Golden Ass: A Study in Transmission & Reception. 2008. (Martin Classical Lectures). (ENG., Illus.). 404p. (C). 57.50 *(978-0-691-13136-8(9))* Princeton Univ. Pr.

Keulen, W. H. & Egelhaaf-Gaiser, Ulrike, eds. Aspects of Apuleius' Golden Ass, Vol. III. 2011. (ENG & LAT.). XVI, 256p. ***(978-90-04-22123-9(9))*** BRILL.

Lee, Benjamin Todd, et al, eds. Apuleius & Africa. 2012. (Routledge Monographs in Classical Studies). (ENG.). 272p. (C). 125.00 ***(978-0-415-53309-6(0))*** Routledge.

May, Regine. Apuleius & Drama: The Ass on Stage. 2007. (Oxford Classical Monographs). (ENG.). 400p. 155.00 *(978-0-19-920292-8(3))* Oxford Univ. Pr., Inc.

Nauta, Ruurd R. Desultoria Scientia. Genre in Apuleius' Metamorphoses & Related Texts. Nauta, R. R., ed. 2006. (Caeculus. Papers on Mediterranean Archaeology & Greek & Roman Studies). (FRE & ENG.). 131p. (C). pap. 44.00 *(978-90-429-1846-7(2))* Peeters Pubs. & Booksellers BEL. Dist: Brown, David Bk. Co., The.

Riess, Werner, ed. Paideia at Play: Learning & Wit in Apuleius. 2008. (Ancient Narrative Supplements Ser.). (LAT & ENG.). 302p. (C). 124.00 ***(978-90-77922-41-5(5))*** Barkhuis Publishing NLD. Dist: Brown, David Bk. Co., The.

Schlam, Carl C. The Metamorphoses of Apuleius: On Making an Ass of Oneself. 2011. (ENG.). 192p. pap. 30.00 *(978-0-8078-6588-0(5))* Univ. of North Carolina Pr.

Zimmerman, M. Lectiones Scrupulosae: Essays on the Text & Interpretation of Apuleius' Metamorphoses in Honour of Maaike Zimmerman. Keulen, W. H. et al, eds. 2006. (Ancient Narrative Supplementum Ser.). (FRE & ENG., Illus.). 338p. (C). 116.00 ***(978-90-77922-16-3(4))*** Barkhuis Publishing NLD. Dist: Brown, David Bk. Co., The.

AQABA, GULF OF

Fritz, Glen A. The Lost Sea of Exodus: A Modern Geographical Analysis. 2007. per. *(978-1-59872-745-6(1))* Instant Pub.

Ghannam, Asma. Seismotectonics & Seismic Hazard in the Gulf of Aqaba Region. 2011. 152p. pap. ***(978-3-8443-9987-5(9))*** Lambert Academic Publishing.

AQUACISES
see Aquatic Exercises

AQUACULTURE
see also Fish Culture

Abbas, Sumaira & Ahmed, Iftikhar. Growth Performance of Common Carps in Different Management Practices. 2011. 228p. pap. ***(978-3-8443-0240-0(9))*** Lambert Academic Publishing.

Adeoye, Ayodeji. Fish Nutrition. 2011. 60p. pap. ***(978-3-8443-2909-4(9))*** Lambert Academic Publishing.

Aquaculture. (Illus.). pap. *(978-971-10-2290-7(7))* New Day Pubs., Philippines.

Aquaculture in Alaska: A Resource Potential. *(978-0-914500-03-2(1))* Univ. of Alaska, Institute of Marine Science.

Bassano, Alessio. Freshwater Ecosystems & Aquaculture Research. Carlo, Felice De, ed. 2010. (Environmental Science, Engineering & Technology Ser.). 387p. 129.00 *(978-1-60741-707-1(3))* Nova Science Pubs., Inc.

Bergfjord, Ole Jakob. Essays on Aquaculture, Risk & Politics. 2011. 128p. pap. ***(978-3-8443-0593-7(9))*** Lambert Academic Publishing.

Bert, Theresa M. Ecological & Genetic Implications of Aquaculture Activities. (Reviews: Methods & Technologies in Fish Biology & Fisheries Ser.). 2010. xii, 548p. pap. 209.00 *(978-90-481-6126-3(6)*, 9048161266) 2007. (Illus.). 560p. 209.00 *(978-1-4020-0884-9(8)*, 1402008848) Springer.

Bhujel, Ram C. & Bhujel. Statistics for Aquaculture. 2009. (ENG., Illus.). 240p. 104.95 *(978-0-8138-1587-9(8)*, Wiley-Blackwell) Wiley, John & Sons, Inc.

Bjorndal, Trond & Asche, Frank. The Economics of Salmon Aquaculture. 2nd ed. 2011. (Fishing News Bks.). (ENG., Illus.). 248p. 149.95 *(978-0-85238-289-9(8)*, Wiley-Blackwell) Wiley, John & Sons, Inc.

Blackford, Mansel G. Making Seafood Sustainable: American Experiences in Global Perspective. 2012. (American Business, Politics, & Society Ser.). (Illus.). 296p. (C). 45.00 ***(978-0-8122-4393-2(5))*** Univ. of Pennsylvania Pr.

Brennessel, Barbara. Good Tidings: The History & Ecology of Shellfish Farming in the Northeast. 2008. (Illus.). 228p. 19.95 *(978-1-58465-727-9(8))* Univ. Pr. of New England.

Brister, Deborah J. Organic Aquaculture: the Emeregence of a New Sustainable Industry: The Emergence of a New Sustainable Industry. 2007. (Illus.). 224p. 79.99 *(978-0-8138-2629-5(2)*, Wiley-Blackwell) Wiley, John & Sons, Inc.

Bunting, Stuart. Principles of Sustainable Aquaculture. 2012. (Earthscan Food & Agriculture Ser.). (ENG.). 288p. (C). pap. 49.95 ***(978-1-84971-077-0(5))***; 140.00 ***(978-1-84971-076-3(7))*** Routledge.

Burnell, G. New Technologies in Aquaculture: Improving production efficiency, quality & environmental Image. Burnell, G. & Allan, G., eds. 2009. (Illus.). 800p. 309.95 *(978-1-4398-0109-3(6))* CRC Pr. LLC.

Burnell, G. & Allan, G., eds. New Technologies in Aquaculture: Improving Production Efficiency, Quality & Environmental Management. 2009. (Illus.). 800p. *(978-1-84569-384-8(1))* Woodhead Publishing Ltd.

Cabrita, Elsa, et al, eds. Methods in Reproductive Aquaculture: Marine & Freshwater Species. 2008. (Marine Biology Ser.). (ENG., Illus.). 568p. 113.95 *(978-0-8493-8053-2(7)*, CRC Press) Taylor & Francis Group GBR. Dist: Taylor & Francis Group.

Characterization Ghan. pap. 19.95 *(978-971-8709-89-4(4))* ICLARM PHL. Dist: International Specialized Bk. Services.

Chopra, Kanchan, et al. Biodiversity Land Use Change & Human Well-Being: A Study of Aquaculture in the Indian Sunderbans. 2009. (ENG., Illus.). 360p. 49.95 *(978-0-19-806021-5(1))* Oxford Univ. Pr., Inc.

Chu, Thai Hoanh. Environment & Livelihoods in Tropical Coastal Zones: Managing Agriculture-Fishery-Aquaculture Conflicts. Gowing, J. W. et al, eds. 2006. (Comprehensive Assessment of Water Management in Agriculture Ser.: Vol. 2). (Illus.). 336p. 145.00 *(978-1-84593-107-0(6)*, CABI GBR. Dist: Stylus Publishing, LLC.

Cifuentes, Juan Luis. El Oceano y Sus Recursos XI: Acuicultura. (Ciencia para Todos Ser.). (SPA.). pap. 6.99 *(978-968-16-3433-9(0))* Fondo de Cultura Economica USA.

Coastal Tourism Se Asia. (Illus.). pap. 5.00 *(978-971-8709-07-8(X))* ICLARM PHL. Dist: International Specialized Bk. Services.

Commercial Biotech Agriculture & Aquaculture. *(978-81-204-0827-2(6))* Science Pubs.

Committee on Best Practices for Shellfish Mariculture and the Effects of Commercial Activities in Drakes Estero, Pt. Reyes National Seashore, California. Ecosystem Concepts for Sustainable Bivalve Mariculture. 2010. (ENG.). 190p. pap. 43.00 *(978-0-309-14695-1(X))* National Academies Pr.

Committee on Best Practices for Shellfish Mariculture and the Effects of Commercial Activities in Drakes Estero, Pt. Reyes National Seashore, California & National Research Council Staff. Shellfish Mariculture in Drakes Estero, Point Reyes National Seashore, California. 2009. (ENG.). 138p. pap. 34.00 *(978-0-309-13898-7(1))* National Academies Pr.

Copp, G. H., et al, eds. When Do Fishes Become Juveniles? 2010. (Developments in Environmental Biology of Fishes Ser.). (Illus.). 280p. pap. 169.00 *(978-90-481-5305-3(0)*, 9048153050) Springer.

Creswell, LeRoy. Aquaculture Desk Reference. Hoff, Frank, ed. 3rd rev. ed. pap. 39.00 *(978-0-9662960-3-7(6))* Florida Aqua Farms, Inc.

Culver, Keith & Castle, David, eds. Aquaculture, Innovation & Social Transformation. 2010. (International Library of Environmental, Agricultural & Food Ethics Ser.). xii, 348p. pap. 229.00 *(978-90-481-8002-8(3)*, 9048180023) Springer.

—Aquaculture, Innovation & Social Transformation. 2008. (International Library of Environmental, Agricultural & Food Ethics Ser.). (ENG., Illus.). xii, 348p. 229.00 *(978-1-4020-8834-6(5)*, 1402088345) Springer.

De Silva, Sena S. & Davy, F. Brian, eds. Success Stories in Asian Aquaculture. 2009. (ENG., Illus.). xiv, 214p. 129.00 *(978-90-481-3085-6(9)*, 9048130859) Springer.

Duc, Nguyen Minh. Effects of Us Antidumping in Perfect & Imperfect Competition. 2009. 76p. pap. *(978-3-639-11692-2(5))* VDM Verlag Dr. Mueller e.K.

Eknath, A. E., ed. International Concerns in the Use of Aquatic Germplasm. Date not set. (ICLARM Technical Reports: No. 47). *(978-971-3709-59-7(2))* ICLARM PHL. Dist: International Specialized Bk. Services.

Emilija, Kalnins. Assessing Disease Potential in U. S. Aquaculture Industry. 2010. (Agriculture Issues & Policies Ser.). 200p. 79.00 *(978-1-60741-543-5(7))* Nova Science Pubs., Inc.

Engle, Carole R. Aquaculture Economics & Financing: Management & Analysis. 2010. (ENG., Illus.). 272p. pap. 110.95 *(978-0-8138-1301-1(8)*, Wiley-Blackwell) Wiley, John & Sons, Inc.

Ericsson, Anna. Water Availability & Distribution in Afric. 2011. 60p. pap. ***(978-3-8433-9362-1(1))*** Lambert Academic Publishing.

Filli, Fave. Homestead Aquaculture in Yola, Adamawa State, Nigeri. 2011. 84p. pap. ***(978-3-8443-9546-4(6))*** Lambert Academic Publishing.

Food and Agriculture Organization (Fao), creator. Report of the Global Conference on Small-Scale Fisheries Securing Sustainable Small-Scale Fisheries: Bringing Together Responsible Fisheries & Social Development: Bangkok, Thailand, 13-17 October 2008. 2010. (FAO Fisheries & Aquaculture Report). (ENG, FRE & SPA.). 189p. pap. *(978-92-5-006442-0(X))* Food & Agriculture Organization of the United Nations.

Fotedar, Ravi & Phillips, Bruce, eds. Recent Advances & New Species in Aquaculture. 2011. (ENG., Illus.). 416p. 199.95 *(978-1-4051-7664-4(4)*, Wiley-Blackwell) Wiley, John & Sons, Inc.

Gharti, Kamala. Sahar & ed Sex Nile Tilapia in Polyculture. 2011. 100p. pap. ***(978-3-8443-9249-4(1))*** Lambert Academic Publishing.

Gjedrem, Trygve. Selection & Breeding Programs in Aquaculture. 2010. (ENG.). xvii, 364p. pap. 139.00 *(978-90-481-6840-8(6)*, 9048168406) Springer.

Gjedrem, Trygve & Baranski, Matthew. Selective Breeding in Aquaculture: an Introduction: An Introduction. 2009. (Reviews: Methods & Technologies in Fish Biology & Fisheries Ser.). (ENG., Illus.). xiv, 221p. 179.00 *(978-90-481-2772-6(6)*, 9048127726) Springer.

Hargrave, Barry. Environmental Effects of Marine Finfish Aquaculture. 2010. (Handbook of Environmental Chemistry / Water Pollution Ser.). (Illus.). xvi, 468p. pap. 329.00 *(978-3-642-06444-9(2)*, 3642064442) Springer.

Hargreaves, John A. & Tucker, C. S. Environmental Best Management Practices for Aquaculture. Tucker, Craig S. & Hargreaves, John A., eds. 2008. (ENG., Illus.). 592p. 199.95 *(978-0-8138-2027-9(8)*, Wiley-Blackwell) Wiley, John & Sons, Inc.

Hasan, Mohammad R., ed. Economics of Aquaculture Feeding Practices in Selected Asian Countries. 2008. (Fao Fisheries Technical Paper Ser.). (Illus.). 205p. pap. *(978-92-5-105874-9(1))* Food & Agriculture Organization of the United Nations.

Hoanh, Chu T., et al, eds. Tropical Deltas & Coastal Zones: Community, Environment & Food Production at the Land-water Interface. 2010. (Comprehensive Assessment of Water Management in Agriculture Ser.). (Illus.). 496p. 230.00 *(978-1-84593-618-1(3))* CABI GBR. Dist: Stylus Publishing, LLC.

Holmer, M. Aquaculture in the Ecosystem. 2008. (ENG., Illus.). x, 326p. 159.00 *(978-1-4020-6809-6(3)*, 1402068093) Springer.

Holmer, Marianne, et al, eds. Aquaculture in the Ecosystem. 2010. (ENG.). x, 326p. pap. 159.00 *(978-90-481-7732-5(4)*, 9048177324) Springer.

Huntingford, Felicity, et al, eds. Aquaculture & Behavior. 2012. (ENG., Illus.). 358p. pap. 79.99 *(978-1-4051-3089-9(X)*, Wiley-Blackwell) Wiley, John & Sons, Inc.

ICLARM Report. pap. *(978-971-8709-31-3(2))* ICLARM PHL. Dist: International Specialized Bk. Services.

ICLARM Report 1992. pap. *(978-971-8709-46-7(0))* ICLARM PHL. Dist: International Specialized Bk. Services.

IUCN. Aquaculture: Responsible Practices & Certification. 2010. (ENG.). 70p. pap. 15.00 *(978-2-8317-1217-8(3))* UICN Union Mondiale pour la Nature, Cecile Thiery CHE. Dist: Chicago Distribution Ctr.

Jacobsen, Rowan. The Living Shore: Rediscovering a Lost World. 2009. (ENG.). 176p. 20.00 *(978-1-59691-684-5(2))* Bloomsbury Publishing.

Jobling, Malcolm, et al. Finfish Aquaculture: Species Selection for Diversification. Le François, Nathalie R., ed. 2010. (Illus.). 640p. 255.00 *(978-1-84593-494-1(6))* CABI GBR. Dist: Stylus Publishing, LLC.

Kipkemboi. Fingerponds: Integrated Seasonal Aquaculture in East African Fres. 2007. (ENG., Illus.). 165p. (C). 79.95 *(978-0-415-41696-2(5)*, Taylor & Francis) Taylor & Francis Group GBR. Dist: Taylor & Francis Group.

Lagutov, V., ed. Rescue of Sturgeon Species in the Ural River Basin. 2008. (NATO Science for Peace & Security Series C: Environmental Security Ser.). (ENG., Illus.). xvii, 333p. 219.00 *(978-1-4020-8922-0(8)*, 1402089228) Springer.

Leclercq, Eric. Diversification of Atlantic Salmon Grow-Out Technology. 2011. 92p. pap. ***(978-3-8443-2442-6(9))*** Lambert Academic Publishing.

Lekang, Odd-Ivar. Aquaculture Engineering. 2007. (ENG., Illus.). 352p. 249.95 *(978-1-4051-2610-6(8)*, Wiley-Blackwell) Wiley, John & Sons, Inc.

Leung, PingSun & Engle, Carole R., eds. Shrimp Culture: Economics, Market, & Trade. 2006. (ENG., Illus.). 335p. 239.95 *(978-0-8138-2655-4(1)*, Wiley-Blackwell) Wiley, John & Sons, Inc.

Li, Yan. Spawning Mediated Responses of Pacific Oyster Crassostrea Gigas. 2010. 172p. pap. *(978-3-8383-1827-1(7))* Lambert Academic Publishing.

Liu, Zhanjiang (John). Aquaculture Genome Technologies. 2007. (ENG., Illus.). 584p. 199.95 *(978-0-8138-0203-9(2)*, Wiley-Blackwell) Wiley, John & Sons, Inc.

Lucas, John S. & Southgate, Paul C. Aquaculture: Farming Aquatic Animals & Plants. 2nd ed. 2012. (ENG., Illus.). 648p. pap. 129.95 *(978-1-4051-8858-6(8)*, Wiley-Blackwell) Wiley, John & Sons, Inc.

Megahed, Mohamed & Mohamed, Megahed. Standard Operating Procedure for Marine Shrimp Hatcheries & Farms: Advance Manual for the Production of Penaeid Shrimp. 2011. 164p. pap. ***(978-3-639-32785-4(3))*** VDM Verlag Dr. Mueller e.K.

Mischke, Charles C., ed. Aquaculture Pond Fertilization: Impacts of Nutrient Input on Production. 2012. (ENG.). 308p. 199.95 ***(978-0-470-95922-0(3)***, Wiley-Blackwell) Wiley, John & Sons, Inc.

Molyneaux, Paul. Swimming in Circles: Aquaculture & the End of Wild Oceans. 2007. (ENG., Illus.). 304p. per. 15.95 *(978-1-56025-756-1(3))* Basic Bks.

Montet, Didier & Ray, Ramesh C. Aquaculture Microbiology & Biotechnology, Vol. 1. 2009. (ENG., Illus.). 286p. 99.95 *(978-1-57808-574-3(8))* BIOS Scientific Publishers Ltd. GBR. Dist: Taylor & Francis Group.

Montet, Didier & Ray, Ramesh C., eds. Aquaculture Microbiology & Biotechnology, Vol. 2. 2011. (ENG., Illus.). 295p. 119.95 *(978-1-57808-711-2(2))* BIOS Scientific Publishers Ltd. GBR. Dist: Taylor & Francis Group.

Murphy, Ryan L., ed. Priorities for U. S. Ocean Science & Research. 2011. (Oceanography & Ocean Engineering Ser.). 115.00 *(978-1-61209-706-0(5))* Nova Science Pubs., Inc.

Mustafa, Saleem. Seafood Security in a Changing Climate. 2010. 180p. pap. *(978-3-8383-3886-6(3))* Lambert Academic Publishing.

Nakamura, Takumi. Aquaculture Research Progress. 2008. (Illus.). xii, 315p. 129.00 *(978-1-60456-247-7(1))* Nova Science Pubs., Inc.

Nash, Colin E. The History of Aquaculture. 2011. (ENG., Illus.). 244p. 99.95 *(978-0-8138-2163-4(0)*, Wiley-Blackwell) Wiley, John & Sons, Inc.

Ndah, Hycenth Tim. Adoption & Diffusion of Fish Pond Aquaculture in Cameroon: An empirical study carried out in the Centre, Southwest & Northwest Provinces of Cameroon. 2008. 100p. pap. *(978-3-639-10933-7(3))* VDM Verlag Dr. Mueller e.K.

Nelson, Rebecca L. Acuaponia: Raising Plants & Fish in a Sustainable System. 2007. (SPA., Illus.). 80p. 24.95 *(978-0-9779696-0-9(6))* Nelson/Pade Multimedia.

Nguyen, Linh & SOPARTH PONGQUAN. Farmers' Participation in Aquaculture Development. 2010. 224p. pap. *(978-3-8383-8128-2(9))* Lambert Academic Publishing.

Nkeze, Morfow Paul. Manual for Intensive Fish Farming in the Tropics. 2011. 88p. pap. ***(978-3-8443-2874-5(2))*** Lambert Academic Publishing.

Ochterski, Jim. The Pond Guidebook. 2007. *(978-1-933395-13-5(3))* Natural Resource, Agricultural, & Engineering Service.

Offshore Aquaculture: Challenges of Fish Farming in Federal Waters: Hearing Before the Subcommittee on National Ocean Policy Study of the Committee on Commerce, Science, & Transportation, United States Senate, One Hundred Ninth Congress, Second Session, June 8, 2006. 2011. iii, 86p. ***(978-0-16-088297-5(4)***, 552-070-42602-7) United States Government Printing Office.

Offshore Aquaculture: Hearing Before the Subcommittee on National Ocean Policy Study of the Committee on Commerce, Science, & Transportation, United States Senate, One Hundred Ninth Congress, Second Session, April 6, 2006. 2011. (Illus.). iv, 129p. ***(978-0-16-088211-1(7)***, 552-070-42573-0) United States Government Printing Office.

Organisation for Economic Co-operation and Development Staff, ed. Review of Fisheries in OECD Countries 2002 Vol. 2: Country Statistics 1999-2001. 2007. (Illus.). 380p. pap. *(978-92-64-10205-7(1)*, 53 2003 04 3 P 1) Organization for Economic Cooperation & Development.

Overturf, Ken. Molecular Research in Aquaculture. 2009. (ENG., Illus.). 408p. 232.00 *(978-0-8138-1851-1(6)*, Wiley-Blackwell) Wiley, John & Sons, Inc.

Pandey, Anuradha. Studies of Monogenoidean Parasites of Siluriform Fishes. 2011. 160p. pap. ***(978-3-8443-3130-1(1))*** Lambert Academic Publishing.

Parker, Rick, , Rick. Aquaculture Science. 3rd ed. 2011. (ENG.). 672p. (C). 154.95 *(978-1-4354-8812-0(1))* Delmar Cengage Learning.

Parsons, Jeffrey R. The Last Pescadores of Chimalhuacán, Mexico: An Archaeological Ethnography. 2006. (Illus.). 377p. 28.00 *(978-0-915703-62-3(9))* Univ. of Michigan, Museum of Anthropology, Pubns. Dept.

Pauly, Daniel, et al, eds. The Third International Symposium on Tilapia in Aquaculture. Date not set. (ICLARM Technical Reports: No. 41). 400p. per. 99.95 *(978-971-8709-42-9(8))* ICLARM PHL. Dist: International Specialized Bk. Services.

Ramadan, Afaf-Haniem. Processing a Convenience Products from Carp Fish in Egypt: Healthy Products from Carp Fish. 2011. 136p. pap. ***(978-3-639-29152-0(2))*** VDM Verlag Dr. Mueller e.K.

Recalde Ruiz, Jose Renato. Economic Analysis of Rural & Artisanal Aquaculture in Ecuador. 2011. 64p. pap. ***(978-3-8454-2282-4(3))*** Lambert Academic Publishing.

Romanowski, Nick. Sustainable Freshwater Aquaculture: The Complete Guide from Backyard to Investor. 2006. (ENG., Illus.). 160p. pap. 40.95 *(978-0-86840-835-4(2)*, UNSW Press) NewSouth Publishing AUS. Dist: Independent Pubs. Group.

Rudloe, Anne & Rudloe, Jack. Shrimp: The Endless Quest for Pink Gold. 2009. (FT Press Science Ser.). (ENG.). 272p. 24.99 *(978-0-13-700972-5(0))* FT Press.

Saheb, Azad Ismail & Al-Ablani, Salam. Aquaculture in the Middle East & North Africa: Status & Research Needs. 2011. *(978-1-61209-834-0(7))* Nova Science Pubs., Inc.

Salander, Lawrence M. & Alwell, Dana N. Food Production: New Research. 2011. (Food Science & Technology Ser.). (Illus.). 191p. 129.00 *(978-1-61209-631-5(X))* Nova Science Pubs., Inc.

Sanz-Lá, et al. Environmental Effects of Aquaculture & Oil Spills. 2010. 180p. pap. *(978-3-8383-7763-6(X))* Lambert Academic Publishing.

Saroglia, Marco. Functional Genomics in Aquaculture. Liu, Zhanjiang (John), ed. 2012. (ENG.). 380p. 199.95 ***(978-0-470-96008-0(6)***, Wiley-Blackwell) Wiley, John & Sons, Inc.

Schwartz, Stephen H., ed. Aquaculture Research Trends. 2008. (Illus.). 338p. (C). 129.00 *(978-1-60456-217-0(X))* Nova Science Pubs., Inc.

Selengut, Becky. Good Fish: Sustainable Seafood Recipes from the Pacific Coast. 2011. (ENG., Illus.). 288p. pap. 29.95 *(978-1-57061-662-4(0))* Sasquatch Bks.

Shirajee, Samina. Women & Small-Scale Freshwater Aquaculture in Bangladesh. 2011. 56p. pap. ***(978-3-8454-2400-2(1))*** Lambert Academic Publishing.

Silvestre, Geronimo. Coastal Resources Brunei. (Illus.). x, 214p. pap. 10.00 *(978-971-8709-11-5(8))* ICLARM PHL. Dist: International Specialized Bk. Services.

Soto, Doris, ed. Integrated Mariculture: A Global Review. 2010. (FAO Fisheries & Aquaculture Report). (Illus.). 183p. pap. *(978-92-5-106387-3(7))* Food & Agriculture Organization of the United Nations.

Stickney, Robert R. Aquaculture: An Introductory Text. 2nd ed. 2009. (Illus.). 320p. 125.00 *(978-1-84593-589-4(6))*; pap. 75.00 *(978-1-84593-543-6(8))* CABI GBR. Dist: Stylus Publishing, LLC.

Tidwell, James H. Aquaculture Production Systems. 2012. (ENG.). 440p. 99.95 ***(978-0-8138-0126-1(5)***, Wiley-Blackwell) Wiley, John & Sons, Inc.

Timmons, Michael B. & Ebeling, James M. Recirculating Aquaculture. 2006. per. 89.00 *(978-0-9712646-2-5(7))* Cayuga Aqua Ventures, LLC.

Turchini, Giovanni M., et al, eds. Fish Oil Replacement & Alternative Lipid Sources in Aquaculture. 2010. (ENG., Illus.). 551p. 149.95 *(978-1-4398-0862-7(7)*, CRC Press) Taylor & Francis Group GBR. Dist: Taylor & Francis Group.

Turner, Megan Whalen. Geographies of Rural Families. 2008. 104p. pap. *(978-3-639-05639-6(6))* VDM Verlag Dr. Mueller e.K.

Vadstein, Olav & Olsen, Yngvar, eds. Sustainable Increase of Marine Harvesting: Fundamental Mechanisms & New Concepts: Fundamental Mechanisms & New Concepts. 2010. (Developments in Hydrobiology Ser.). 280p. pap. 149.00 *(978-90-481-6217-8(3)*, 9048162173) Springer.

Verdegem, Marc. Water Use & Re-Use in Aquaculture. 2010. (Illus.). 352p. *(978-1-4051-6284-5(8)*, Wiley-Blackwell) Wiley, John & Sons, Ltd.

Wood, Adrian, et al. Wetland Management & Sustainable Livelihoods in Africa. 2012. (ENG.). 224p. 140.00 ***(978-1-84971-411-2(8))***; pap. 49.95 ***(978-1-84971-412-9(6))*** Earthscan LLC.

World Bank Staff. Changing the Face of the Waters: The Promise & Challenge of Sustainable Aquaculture. 2007. (Agriculture & Rural Development Ser.). (ENG., Illus.). 210p. per. 25.00 *(978-0-8213-7015-5(4)*, 9780821370155) World Bank Pubns.

World Conservation Union. Aquaculture Site Selection & Site Management. 2009. (ENG., Illus.). 303p. pap. 30.00 *(978-2-8317-1171-3(1))* UICN Union Mondiale pour la Nature, Cecile Thiery CHE. Dist: Chicago Distribution Ctr.

Zhou, Xia & R. Hanson, Terry. A Bioeconomic Model of Recirculating Shrimp Production System. 2010. 76p. pap. *(978-3-8383-4501-7(0))* Lambert Academic Publishing.

AQUACULTURE—LAW AND LEGISLATION

Belanger, Robert C., ed. Offshore Aquaculture in the US: Issues & Economics. 2010. (Fish, Fishing, & Fisheries Ser.). 175.50 *(978-1-60741-539-8(9))* Nova Science Pubs., Inc.

Chao, Gloria & Vanderzwaag, David L., eds. Aquaculture Law & Policy: Towards Principled Access & Operations. 2006. (Routledge Advances in Maritime Research Ser.). (Illus.). 552p. 218.00 *(978-0-415-70201-0(1))* Routledge.

Jakobsson, Daniel. Fisheries, Aquaculture & Marine Mammals: Interrelationship, Background & Issues. 2010. (Fish, Fishing & Fisheries Ser.). 117p. 43.00 *(978-1-60741-542-8(9))* Nova Science Pubs., Inc.

Mittal, Anu K. Offshore Marine Aquaculture: Multiple Administrative & Environmental Issues Need to be Addressed in Establishing a U.S. Regulatory Framework. 2008. 53p. pap. 25.00 *(978-1-4379-0567-0(6))* DIANE Publishing Co.

Nolan, Jean T. Offshore Marine Aquaculture. 2009. pap. 43.00 *(978-1-60692-117-3(7))* Nova Science Pubs., Inc.

AQUAFERS

see Aquifers

AQUARIUM PLANTS

Boruchowitz, David E. Freshwater Aquarium Problem Solver. 2006. (Animal Planet Pet Care Library). (Illus.). 112p. 11.95 *(978-0-7938-3761-8(8))* TFH Pubns., Inc.

Geck, Jakob & Schlienwen, Ulrich. Nanoaquarium. 2010. (Complete Pet Owner's Manuals Ser.). (ENG., Illus.). 64p. pap. 8.99 *(978-0-7641-4428-8(6))* Barron's Educational Series, Inc.

Sweeney, Mary Ellen. The 101 Best Aquarium Plants: How to Choose & Keep Hardy, Vibrant, Eyecatching Species that Will Thrive in Your Home Aquarium, 1 vol. 2008. (ENG., Illus.). 192p. pap. *(978-1-890087-19-7(X))* TFH Pubns., Inc.

AQUARIUMS

see also Fish Culture; Goldfish; Marine Aquariums; Tropical Fish; Water Gardens

Amano, Takashi. Nature Aquarium: Complete Works, 1985-2009, 1 vol. 2011. (ENG., Illus.). 264p. 59.95 *(978-0-7938-0649-2(6))* TFH Pubns., Inc.

Andrews, Chris, et al. Manual of Fish Health: Everything You Need to Know about Aquarium Fish, Their Environment & Disease Prevention. 2nd ed. 2010. (ENG., Illus.). 208p. pap. 19.95 *(978-1-55407-691-8(9))* Firefly Bks., Ltd.

Baensch, Hans & Loiselle, Paul V. Marine Aquarist Manual: Comprehensive Edition. (Illus.). 286p. 26.95 *(978-3-89356-130-8(7)*, 16031) Tetra Pr.

Bailey, Mary & Sandford, Gina. Choosing Fish for Your Aquarium. 2010. (ENG., Illus.). 128p. 17.99 *(978-1-84476-748-9(5))* Anness Publishing GBR. Dist: National Bk. Network.

—A Complete Practical Guide & Fish Identifier: Aquariums & Aquarium Fish. 2010. (ENG., Illus.). 256p. 35.00 *(978-0-7548-2007-9(6))* Anness Publishing GBR. Dist: National Bk. Network.

Birkener, Walter. La Tecnica de Acuario (Aquarium Techniques) (SPA.). 128p. *(978-84-315-0115-0(4))* De Vecchi, Editorial, S.A.

Boruchowitz, David & Boruchowitz, David E. The Simple Guide to Freshwater Aquariums, 1 vol. 2nd ed. 2008. (Simple Guide Ser.). (ENG., Illus.). 256p. pap. 17.95 *(978-0-7938-2122-8(3))* TFH Pubns., Inc.

Boruchowitz, David E. Freshwater Aquarium Problem Solver. 2006. (Animal Planet Pet Care Library). (Illus.). 112p. 11.95 *(978-0-7938-3761-8(8))* TFH Pubns., Inc.

—Freshwater Aquariums. 2006. (Animal Planet Pet Care Library). (Illus.). 112p. 11.95 *(978-0-7938-3760-1(X))* TFH Pubns., Inc.

—Mini Aquariums: A Guide to Successful Nano Aquariums, Proper Setup, Maintenance, & Species Selection. 2008. (Illus.). 256p. 34.95 *(978-0-7938-0573-0(2))* TFH Pubns., Inc.

Brunner, Bernd. The Ocean at Home: An Illustrated History of the Aquarium. 2nd enl. rev. ed. 2011. (ENG., Illus.). 160p. pap. 29.00 *(978-1-86189-816-6(9))* Reaktion Bks., Ltd. GBR. Dist: Chicago Distribution Ctr.

Building Blocks of Science: Understanding Cells & DNA Refurbishment Set (Firsthand Learning) 2007. ring bd. *(978-0-89278-026-6(6))* Carolina Biological Supply Co.

Clifton, Bill. The Complete Aquarium Adventure: A Field Trip in a Book. 2009. spiral bd. 18.99 *(978-0-89051-554-9(9))* Master Bks.

Evans, Sean. Tropical Aquarium: Setting up & Caring for Freshwater Fish. 2007. (ENG., Illus.). 160p. 29.95 *(978-1-84537-161-6(5))* New Holland Pubs., Ltd. GBR. Dist: Sterling Publishing Co., Inc.

Fenner, Robert M. The Conscientious Marine Aquarist: A Commonsense Handbook for Successful Saltwater Hobbyists, 1 vol. 2nd ed. 2008. (ENG., Illus.). 456p. *(978-1-890087-99-9(8))* TFH Pubns., Inc.

Flethcer, Nick. What Fish? A Buyer's Guide to Tropical Fish: Essential Information to Help You Choose the Right Fish for Your Tropical Freshwater Aquarium. 2006. (What Pet? Bks.). (ENG., Illus.). 208p. pap. 16.99 *(978-0-7641-3255-1(5))* Barron's Educational Series, Inc.

Gay, Jeremy. Aquarium Manual: The Complete Step-by-Step Guide to Keeping Fish. 2010. (ENG., Illus.). 160p. 32.95 *(978-1-84425-640-2(5)*, 1844256405) Haynes Publishing PLC GBR. Dist: MBI Distribution Services/Quayside Distribution.

Geck, Jakob & Schlienwen, Ulrich. Nanoaquarium. 2010. (Complete Pet Owner's Manuals Ser.). (ENG., Illus.). 64p. pap. 8.99 *(978-0-7641-4428-8(6))* Barron's Educational Series, Inc.

Görner, Veit. One Hundred Fish Fountain. Moll, Frank-Thorsten, ed. 2008. (GER & ENG., Illus.). 80p. 36.00 *(978-3-939583-64-6(2))* Kehrer Verlag Heidelberg, Klaus Kehrer DEU. Dist: Consortium Bk. Sales & Distribution.

Guadagnini, Walter & Ripa, Giuseppe. Giuseppe Ripa: Aquarium. 2009. (ITA & ENG., Illus.). 120p. 55.00 *(978-88-8158-717-9(3))* Charta ITA. Dist: D.A.P./Distributed Art Pubs.

Gutjahr, Axel. Setting up an Aquarium. 2008. (Complete Pet Owner's Manual Ser.). (ENG., Illus.). 64p. pap. 8.99 *(978-0-7641-3944-4(4))* Barron's Educational Series, Inc.

Hamera, Judith. Parlor Ponds: The Cultural Work of the American Home Aquarium, 1850 - 1970. 2012. (ENG., Illus.). 280p. 90.00 ***(978-0-472-07166-1(1))***; pap. 35.00 ***(978-0-472-05166-3(0))*** Univ. of Michigan Pr.

—Parlor Ponds: The Cultural Work of the American Home Aquarium, 1850-1970. 2011. E-Book ***(978-0-472-02810-8(3))*** Univ. of Michigan Pr.

Hargrove, Maddy & Hargrove, Mic. Freshwater Aquariums for Dummies. 2nd rev. ed. 2006. (ENG., Illus.). 368p. per. 21.99 *(978-0-470-05103-0(5)*, For Dummies) Wiley, John & Sons, Inc.

Harper, Don. Aquarium Fish. 2006. (Collins Discover Ser.). (ENG., Illus.). 192p. pap. 16.95 *(978-0-06-089067-4(3)*, Harper Paperbacks) HarperCollins Pubs.

Hiscock, Peter. Community Fish. 2007. (Aquamaster Ser.). (ENG., Illus.). 96p. pap. 9.95 *(978-1-933958-07-1(3))* BowTie Pr.

Indiviglio, Frank. The Everything Aquarium Book: All You Need to Build the Aquarium of Your Dreams. 2nd ed. 2006. (ENG., Illus.). 304p. per. 14.95 *(978-1-59337-715-1(0))* Adams Media Corp.

Johnson, D. Crosby. Never Change Your Fish Water Again! 2008. 100p. pap. 17.95 *(978-1-59858-580-3(0))* Dog Ear Publishing, LLC.

Lougher, Tristan. What Fish? A Buyer's Guide to Marine Fish: Essential Information to Help You Choose the Right Fish for Your Marine Aquarium. 2006. (What Pet? Bks.). (ENG., Illus.). 208p. pap. 14.99 *(978-0-7641-3256-8(3))* Barron's Educational Series, Inc.

Maitre-Alain, Thierry & Piednoir, Christian. Aquariums: The Complete Guide to Freshwater & Saltwater Aquariums. 2009. (ENG., Illus.). 288p. pap. 29.95 *(978-1-55407-462-4(2))* Firefly Bks., Ltd.

Mills, Dick. Teach Yourself Keeping Aquarium Fish. 2007. (Teach Yourself Ser.). (ENG., Illus.). 176p. per. 12.95 *(978-0-07-148456-5(6)*, 0071484566) McGraw-Hill Cos., The.

Mojeta, Angelo. El Acuario Guia para Idearlo (Guide to Create an Aquarium) (SPA.). pap. *(978-84-315-1745-8(X))* De Vecchi, Editorial, S.A.

Rundle, John. Breeding Egglayers. (Illus.). 64p. 5.95 *(978-1-86054-266-4(2)*, INT141) Ringpress Bks., Ltd. GBR. Dist: TFH Pubns., Inc.

Scott, Peter. A Fishkeeper's Guide to Livebearing Fishes. (Illus.). 118p. 10.95 *(978-3-923880-61-4(8)*, 16056) Tetra Pr.

Sharpe, Shirlie. Knack Aquariums: A Step-by-Step Guide to Raising Healthy, Beautiful Fish. 2010. (Knack: Make It Easy Ser.). (ENG., Illus.). 256p. pap. 19.95 *(978-1-59921-622-5(1)*, Knack) Globe Pequot Pr., The.

Sweeney, Mary Ellen. The 101 Best Aquarium Plants: How to Choose & Keep Hardy, Vibrant, Eyecatching Species that Will Thrive in Your Home Aquarium, 1 vol. 2008. (ENG., Illus.). 192p. pap. *(978-1-890087-19-7(X))* TFH Pubns., Inc.

Thaves, Stuart, et al. Setting up a Tropical Aquarium Week by Week. 2009. (ENG., Illus.). 208p. pap. 19.95 *(978-1-55407-482-2(7))* Firefly Bks., Ltd.

Thraves, Stuart, et al. Freshwater Aquariums. 2007. (Aquamaster Ser.). (ENG., Illus.). 96p. per. 9.95 *(978-1-933958-08-8(1))* BowTie Pr.

Tullock, John. Freshwater Aquarium Models: Recipes for Creating Beautiful Aquariums That Thrive. 2006. (ENG., Illus.). 304p. per. 19.99 *(978-0-470-04425-4(X)*, Howell Bk. Hse.) Wiley, John & Sons, Inc.

Waring, Rob. Aquarium on Wheels (US) 2008. (ENG.). 24p. (C). pap. 10.95 *(978-1-4240-4374-3(3))* Cengage Heinle.

AQUATIC ANIMALS

see also Fishes; Freshwater Animals; Marine Animals

Alekseev, V. R., et al. Diapause in Aquatic Invertebrates: Theory & Human Use. 2007. (Monographiae Biologicae Ser.). (Illus.). xix, 257p. 199.00 *(978-1-4020-5679-6(6))* Springer.

Alekseev, Victor R., et al, eds. Diapause in Aquatic Invertebrates: Theory & Human Use. 2010. (Monographiae Biologicae Ser.). (Illus.). xix, 257p. pap. 199.00 *(978-90-481-7425-6(2)*, 9048174252) Springer.

Braun, Christopher L. & Wilson, Jennifer T. Polychlorinated Biphenyls in Supended-Sediment Samples from Outfalls to Meandering Road Creek at Air Force Plant 4, Fort Worth, Texas, 2003-08. 2010. (Illus.). vi, 20p. ***(978-1-4113-2840-2(X))*** United States Geological Survey.

Damiri, Basma. Risk Characterization for Boron & Aquatic Plants & Animals. 2010. 108p. pap. *(978-3-639-22207-4(5))* VDM Verlag Dr. Mueller e.K.

Danovaro, Roberto. Methods for the Study of Deep-Sea Sediments, Their Functioning & Biodiversity. Danovaro, Roberto, ed. 2009. (ENG., Illus.). 458p. 144.95 *(978-1-4398-1137-5(7)*, CRC Press) Taylor & Francis Group GBR. Dist: Taylor & Francis Group.

Dürr, Simone & Thomason, Jeremy. Biofouling. 2010. (ENG., Illus.). 456p. 219.95 *(978-1-4051-6926-4(5)*, Wiley-Blackwell) Wiley, John & Sons, Inc.

Eder, David L. Aquatic Animals: Biology, Habitats & Threats. 2011. (Marine Biology Ser.). (Illus.). 215p. 95.00 ***(978-1-61470-123-1(7))*** Nova Science Pubs., Inc.

FitzSimmons, David. Animals of Ohio's Ponds & Vernal Pools. 2011. (Illus.). xiii, 144p. 48.00 *(978-1-60635-081-2(1))* Kent State Univ. Pr.

Gjedrem, Trygve. Selection & Breeding Programs in Aquaculture. 2010. (ENG.). xvii, 364p. pap. 139.00 *(978-90-481-6840-8(6)*, 9048168406) Springer.

Immunology. Aquatic Animal Health: Oie Global Conference, Bergen, October 2006: Proceedings: Dodet, B., ed. 2007. (Developments in Biologicals Ser.). (Illus.). 190p. (C). pap. *(978-3-8055-8344-2(3))* Karger, S. AG.

Kocher, Thomas D. & Kole, Chittaranjan. Genome Mapping & Genomics in Fishes & Acquatic Animals. 2008. (Genome Mapping & Genomics in Animals Ser.). 200p. 239.00 *(978-3-540-73836-7(3))* Springer.

—Genome Mapping & Genomics in Fishes & Aquatic Animals. 2010. (Genome Mapping & Genomics in Animals Ser.). (Illus.). xxiv, 180p. pap. 239.00 *(978-3-642-09307-4(8)*, 3642093078) Springer.

Marchal, G. & Spincer, Michael. Living in Water. Date not set. (Longman Biology Topics Ser.). (Illus.). 32p. pap. 35.67 *(978-0-582-32304-9(5))* Addison-Wesley Longman, Ltd. GBR. Dist: Trans-Atlantic Pubns., Inc.

Moring, J. Bruce. Polychlorinated Biphenyls in Aquatic Invertebrates & Fish & Observations about Nitrogen & Carbon Isotope Composition in Relation to Trophic Structure & Bioaccumulation Patterns, Lake Worth & Meandering Road Creek, Fort Worth, Texas, 2007-08. 2010. (Illus.). v, 29p. ***(978-1-4113-3094-8(3))*** United States Geological Survey.

Morris, R., et al, eds. Acid Toxicity & Aquatic Animals. 2008. (Society for Experimental Biology Seminar Ser.). (ENG., Illus.). 296p. pap. 58.00 *(978-0-521-05762-2(0))* Cambridge Univ. Pr.

P., Soundarapandian & Varadharajan, D. Identification of Commercially Important Crabs. 2010. 76p. pap. *(978-3-639-28035-7(0))* VDM Verlag Dr. Mueller e.K.

Thewissen, J. G. M. Sensory Evolution on the Threshold: Adaptations in Secondarily Aquatic Vertebrates. Nummela, Sirpa, ed. 2008. (Illus.). 351p. 75.00 *(978-0-520-25278-3(0))* Univ. of California Pr.

Watters, G. Thomas, et al. The Freshwater Mussels of Ohio. 2009. (ENG.). 400p. 82.95 *(978-0-8142-1105-2(4))* Ohio State Univ. Pr.

Weller, Alan & Dover Pictura. Aquatic Life Vector Designs. 2012. (Dover Pictura Electronic Clip Art Ser.). (ENG., Illus.). 128p. pap. 49.95 ***(978-0-486-99196-2(2))*** Dover Pubns., Inc.

Yamamoto, N., et al, eds. Behavior & Nervous System of Aquatic Animals: 7th Symposium, Kanagawa, August 2005: Special Issue: Brain, Behavior & Evolution 2007, 2, 69. (Illus.). 92p. pap. *(978-3-8055-8190-5(4))* Karger, S. AG.

AQUATIC BIOLOGY

see also Aquatic Animals; Aquatic Ecology; Aquatic Organisms; Aquatic Plants; Brackish Water Biology; Freshwater Biology; Marine Biology; Plankton

Biomedical Research Foundation of S. Arizona and University of Arizona. Molecular Methods for Microsporidia Detection: Use of an Inhibitor Control with Real-Time PCR. 2008. (Illus.). 92p. per. *(978-1-60573-019-6(X))* Water Research Foundation.

Bortone, Stephen A., et al, eds. Artifical Reefs in Fisheries Management. 2011. (Marine Biology Ser.). (ENG., Illus.). 368p. 119.95 *(978-1-4398-2007-0(4)*, CRC Press) Taylor & Francis Group GBR. Dist: Taylor & Francis Group.

Cobbald, Jane. Viktor Schauberger: A Life of Learning from Nature. 2007. (Illus.). 170p. per. *(978-0-86315-569-7(3))* Floris Bks.

Dumont, Henri J., ed. The Nile: Origin, Environments, Limnology & Human Use. 2009. (Monographiae Biologicae Ser.). (Illus.). xiv, 818p. 249.00 *(978-1-4020-9725-6(5))* Springer.

Gray, N. F. Water Technology: An Introduction for Environmental Scientists & Engineers. 3rd rev. ed. 2011. (Elsevier Co-Pub Ser.). (ENG., Illus.). 768p. pap. 66.95 *(978-0-84339-303-0(4)*, Butterworth-Heinemann) Elsevier Science & Technology Bks.

Li, Judith L. & Barbour, Michael T., eds. Wading for Bugs: Exploring Streams with the Experts. 2100. (ENG.). 176p. pap. 19.95 ***(978-0-87071-608-9(5))*** Oregon State Univ. Pr.

Lutsenko, Andriy & Palahniuk, Vasyl, eds. Water Microbiology: Types, Analyses & Disease-causing Microorganisms. 2009. (Microbiology Research Advances Ser.). (Illus.). xiii, 364p. 145.00 *(978-1-60741-273-1(X))* Nova Science Pubs., Inc.

Martin, Joel W., et al, eds. Decapod Crustacean Phylogenetics. 2009. (Crustacean Issues Ser.). (ENG., Illus.). 632p. 139.95 *(978-1-4200-9258-5(8)*, CRC Press) Taylor & Francis Group GBR. Dist: Taylor & Francis Group.

Stevenson, R. Jan & Sabater, Sergi, eds. Global Change & River Ecosystems - Implications for Structure, Function & Ecosystem Services. 2010. (Developments in Hydrobiology Ser.). (Illus.). vi, 278p. 189.00 *(978-94-007-0607-1(3)*, 9400706073) Springer.

Straub, Timothy M. Multiplexed Waterborne Pathogen Detection Using DNA Microarrays. 2007. 64p. pap. 149.00 (978-1-58321-514-2(X)) Water Research Foundation.

Verhoeven, Jos T. A., et al. Wetlands & Natural Resource Management. 2010. (Ecological Studies). (Illus.). xxii, 347p. pap. 219.00 (978-3-642-06972-7(X), 364206972X) Springer.

AQUATIC BIRDS

see Water Birds

AQUATIC CHEMISTRY

see Water Chemistry

AQUATIC ECOLOGY

see also Freshwater Ecology; Marine Ecology

Abele, Doris, et al, eds. Oxidative Stress in Aquatic Ecosystems. 2011. (ENG., Illus.). 548p. 159.95 **(978-1-4443-3548-4(0)**, Wiley-Blackwell) Wiley, John & Sons, Inc.

Ali, Elham Mahmoud. Phytoplankton Blooms in Macro-Tidal Estuaries: Processes & Conditions Influencing Phytoplankton Growth & Bloom Initiation Case Study: Southampton Water. 2011. 264p. pap. **(978-3-639-19864-5(6))** VDM Verlag Dr. Mueller e.K.

Alonso, Leeanne E. & Berrenstein, Haydi J., eds. A Rapid Biological Assessment of the Aquatic Ecosystems of the Coppename River Basin, Suriname: Rap Bulletin of Biological Assessment, 39. 2006. (Conservation International Rapid Assessment Program Ser.). (Illus.). 119p. pap. 19.95 (978-1-881173-96-0(8)) Conservation International.

Arts, Michael T., et al, eds. Lipids in Aquatic Ecosystems. 2012. (ENG., Illus.). xx, 380p. pap. 99.00 **(978-1-4419-2783-5(2)**, 1441927832) Springer.

Arts, Michael Theodore, et al. Lipids in Aquatic Ecosystems. Brett, Michael T. et al, eds. 2009. (ENG., Illus.). xx, 380p. 99.00 (978-0-387-88607-7(9), 0387886079) Springer.

Bianchi, Thomas S. & Canuel, Elizabeth A. Chemical Biomarkers in Aquatic Ecosystems. 2011. (ENG., Illus.). 392p. (C). 95.00 (978-0-691-13414-7(6)) Princeton Univ. Pr.

Brock, Theo C. Linking Aquatic Exposure & Effects: Risk Assessment of Pesticides. 2009. (ENG., Illus.). 440p. 133.95 (978-1-4398-1347-8(7), CRC Press) Taylor & Francis Group GBR. Dist: Taylor & Francis Group.

Brönmark, Christer & Hansson, Lars-Anders, eds. Chemical Ecology in Aquatic Systems. 2012. (ENG., Illus.). 336p. 135.00 **(978-0-19-958309-6(9))**; pap. 69.95 **(978-0-19-958310-2(2))** Oxford Univ. Pr., Inc.

Browne, Sheila A., ed. Aquatic Ecosystems. 2011. (Series: Marine Biology Ser.). (Illus.). xi, 229p. 95.00 (978-1-61324-399-2(5)) Nova Science Pubs., Inc.

Buczkó, Krisztina, et al, eds. Palaeolimnological Proxies as Tools for Environmental Reconstruction in Fresh Water. 2009. (Developments in Hydrobiology Ser.). (ENG., Illus.). 327p. 209.00 (978-90-481-3386-4(6), 9048133866) Springer.

Campbell, Ian Charles, ed. The Mekong: Biophysical Environment of an International River Basin. 2009. (Aquatic Ecology Ser.). (ENG., Illus.). 464p. 92.95 (978-0-12-374026-7(6), Academic Pr.) Elsevier Science & Technology Bks.

Collin, Shaun P. & Marshall, N. Justin, eds. Sensory Processing in Aquatic Environments. 2011. (ENG., Illus.). xxi, 446p. pap. 205.00 (978-1-4419-3039-2(6), 1441930396) Springer.

Committee on Sustainable Water and Environmental Management in the California Bay-Delta & National Research Council. A Scientific Assessment of Alternatives for Reducing Water Management Effects on Threatened & Endangered Fishes in California's Bay Delta. 2010. (ENG.). 104p. pap. 28.25 (978-0-309-12802-5(1)) National Academies Pr.

Dobson, Mike, et al. Ecology of Aquatic Systems. 2nd ed. 2009. (ENG., Illus.). 368p. (C). 59.95 (978-0-19-929754-2(1)) Oxford Univ. Pr., Inc.

Fyfe, Suzanne. Hyperspectral Studies of Seagrasses. 2011. 408p. pap. **(978-3-8443-3352-7(5))** Lambert Academic Publishing.

Gensemer, R. Scientific Review of Cyanide Ecotoxicology & Evaluation of Ambient Water Quality Criteria: Evaluating Ecosystem Health. 2007. 124p. (C). pap. (978-1-84339-753-3(6)) IWA Publishing.

George, Glen, ed. The Impact of Climate Change on European Lakes. 2009. (Aquatic Ecology Ser.). (ENG., Illus.). xxvi, 507p. 249.00 (978-90-481-2944-7(3), 9048129443) Springer.

Gessner, Mark O., ed. Litter Decomposition in Aquatic Ecosystems. 2008. (Illus.). 280p. pap. 69.95 (978-1-4051-0858-4(4), Wiley-Blackwell) Wiley, John & Sons, Inc.

Gleason, Robert A. Literature Review & Database of Relations Between Salinity & Aquatic Biota: Applications to Bowdoin National Wildlife Refuge, Montana. 2009. (Illus.). vi, 76p. (978-1-4113-2426-8(9)) United States Geological Survey.

Hanson, Alan R. & Kerekes, Joseph J. Limnology & Aquatic Birds: Proceedings of the Fourth Conferene Working Group on Aquatic Birds of Societas Internationalis Limnologiae (SIL), Sackville, New Brunswick, Canada, August 3-7 2003. 2006. (Developments in Hydrobiology Ser.: Vol. 189). (Illus.). x, 349p. 239.00 (978-1-4020-5167-8(0), 1402051670) Springer.

Hawksworth, David L. & Bull, Alan T., eds. Marine, Freshwater, & Wetlands Biodiversity Conservation. 2010. (Topics in Biodiversity & Conservation Ser.). vi, 402p. pap. 239.00 (978-90-481-7436-2(8), 9048174368) Springer.

Hildrew, Alan, et al, eds. Body Size: The Structure & Function of Aquatic Ecosystems. 2007. (Ecological Reviews Ser.). (ENG., Illus.). 356p. per. 79.99 (978-0-521-67967-1(2)) Cambridge Univ. Pr.

Ittekkot, Venugopalan, et al, eds. The Silicon Cycle: Human Perturbations & Impacts on Aquatic Systems. 2006. (Scientific Committee on Problems of the Environment (SCOPE) Ser.). (ENG., Illus.). 296p. 100.00 (978-1-59726-114-2(9)) Island Pr.

—The Silicon Cycle: Human Perturbations & Impacts on Aquatic Systems. 2006. (Scientific Committee on Problems of the Environment (SCOPE) Ser.). (ENG., Illus.). 296p. pap. 50.00 (978-1-59726-115-9(7)) Island Pr.

Jordan, Stephen J. Estuaries: Classification, Ecology, & Human Impacts. 2012. **(978-1-61942-083-0(X))** Nova Science Pubs., Inc.

Kitching, R. L. Food Webs & Container Habitats: The Natural History & Ecology of Phytotelmata. 2009. (ENG., Illus.). 448p. pap. 58.00 (978-0-521-12000-5(4)) Cambridge Univ. Pr.

Kronvang, Brian, ed. The Interactions Between Sediments & Water. 2011. (Developments in Hydrobiology Ser.). (ENG.). 340p. pap. 119.00 (978-90-481-6299-4(8), 9048162998) Springer.

Lambrakis, Nicolaos, et al, eds. Advances in the Research of Aquatic Environment: Volume 2. 2011. (Environmental Earth Sciences Ser.). (ENG., Illus.). xxviii, 512p. 229.00 **(978-3-642-24075-1(5)**, 3642240755) Springer.

Li, Hong. Spatial Pattern Dynamics in Aquatic Ecosystem Modelling. 2009. (ENG., Illus.). 202p. pap. 75.95 (978-0-415-55897-6(2), CRC Press) Taylor & Francis Group GBR. Dist: Taylor & Francis Group.

Nairne, George H., ed. Aquatic Ecosystem Research Trends. 2008. 89.00 (978-1-60692-772-4(8)) Nova Science Pubs., Inc.

Namiesnik, Jacek & Szefer, Piotr. Analytical Measurements in Aquatic Environments. 2009. (CRC Press Co-Publication Ser.). (Illus.). 503p. (C). (978-1-84339-306-1(9)) IWA Publishing.

Namiesnik, Jacek & Szefer, Piotr, eds. Analytical Measurements in Aquatic Environments. Namiesnik, Jacek & Szefer, Piotr, trs. 2009. (Analytical Chemistry Ser.). (ENG., Illus.). 503p. 133.95 (978-1-4200-8268-5(X), CRC Press) Taylor & Francis Group GBR. Dist: Taylor & Francis Group.

Naselli-Flores, Luigi & Rossetti, Giampaolo, eds. Fifty Years after the Homage to Santa Rosalia: Old & New Paradigms on Biodiversity in Aquatic Ecosystems: Santa Rosalia 50 Years On. 2010. (Developments in Hydrobiology Ser.). 244p. 219.00 (978-90-481-9907-5(7), 9048199077) Springer.

National Marine Fisheries Service (U.S.), ed. Through a Fish's Eye: the Status of Fish Habitats in the United States: The Status of Fish Habitats in the United States. 2011. (ENG., Illus.). 64p. pap. 13.00 (978-0-16-088072-8(6), National Marine Fisheries Service) United States Government Printing Office.

Nielsen, Søren Laurentius, et al, eds. Estuarine Nutrient Cycling: the Influence of Primary Producers: The Fate of Nutrients & Biomass. 2010. (Aquatic Ecology Ser.). (Illus.). xvii, 303p. pap. 139.00 (978-90-481-6693-0(4), 9048166934) Springer.

Nienhuis, P. H. & Gulati, Ramesh D., eds. Ecological Restoration of Aquatic & Semi-Aquatic Ecosystems in the Netherlands (NW Europe) 2011. (Developments in Hydrobiology Ser.). (ENG.). 256p. pap. 169.00 (978-90-481-6174-4(6), 9048161746) Springer.

Orive, Emma, et al, eds. Nutrients & Eutrophication in Estuaries & Coastal Waters. 2010. (Developments in Hydrobiology Ser.). 536p. pap. 289.00 (978-90-481-6123-2(1), 9048161231) Springer.

Phillips, Scott W. Synthesis of U.S. Geological Survey Science for the Chesapeake Bay Ecosystem & Implications for Environmental Management. 2008. pap. (978-1-4113-2021-5(2)) United States Geological Survey.

Polunin, Nicholas, ed. Aquatic Ecosystems: Trends & Global Prospects. 2008. (ENG., Illus.). 512p. 165.00 (978-0-521-83327-1(2)) Cambridge Univ. Pr.

Prast, Mario. Studies on Nitrification in Aquatic Sediments. 2008. 144p. pap. (978-3-639-00591-2(0)) VDM Verlag Dr. Mueller e.K.

Principles of Environmental Stewardship for the Exploration and Study of Subglacial Environments Committee, et al, contrib. by. Exploration of Antarctic Subglacial Aquatic Environments: Environmental & Scientific Stewardship. 2007. (ENG., Illus.). 162p. pap. 38.25 (978-0-309-10635-1(4)) National Academies Pr.

Relini, G. & Ryland, J. Biodiversity in Enclosed Seas & Artificial Marine Habitats: Proceedings of the 39th European Marine Biology Symposium, held in Genoa, Italy, 21-24 July 2004. 2010. (Developments in Hydrobiology Ser.). viii, 272p. pap. 199.00 (978-90-481-7551-2(8), 9048175518) Springer.

Roesner, L. Protocols for Studying Wet Weather Impacts & Urbanization Patterns: WERF Report 03-WSM-3. 2008. 150p. (C). pap. (978-1-84339-787-8(0)) IWA Publishing.

Sakio, Hitoshi & Tamura, Toshikazu, eds. Ecology of Riparian Forests in Japan: Disturbance, Life History & Regeneration. 2008. 308p. 129.00 (978-4-431-76736-7(3)) Springer.

Salina, Irena, ed. Written in Water: Messages of Hope for Earth's Most Precious Resource. 2010. (ENG., Illus.). 304p. 26.00 (978-1-4262-0572-9(4), National Geographic) National Geographic Society.

Schipper, C. A., ed. Assessment of Effects of Chemical Contaminants in Dredged Material on Marine: Ecosystems & Human Health. 2009. (Deltares Select Ser.). 164p. pap. 85.00 (978-1-60750-085-8(X)) IOS Pr., Inc.

Shelton, Richard. To Sea & Back: The Heroic Life of the Atlantic Salmon. 2011. (ENG., Illus.). 224p. pap. 14.95 (978-1-84354-785-3(6)) Atlantic Bks., Ltd. GBR. Dist: Independent Pubs. Group.

Siegert, Martin J., et al. Antarctic Subglacial Aquatic Enviroments. 2011. (978-0-87590-482-5(3)) American Geophysical Union.

Sime-Ngando, Télesphore & Niquil, Nathalie, eds. Disregarded Microbial Diversity & Ecological Potentials in Aquatic Systems. 2011. (Developments in Hydrobiology Ser.). (Illus.). vi, 118p. 139.00 (978-94-007-1197-6(2), 9400711972) Springer.

Snook, Amy. Primary Production in Freshwater. 2010. 128p. pap. (978-3-8383-4111-8(2)) Lambert Academic Publishing.

Tamminen, T. & Kuosa, H., eds. Eutrophication in Planktonic Ecosystems: Food Web Dynamics & Elemental Cycling: Food Web Dynamics & Elemental Cycling. 2011. (Developments in Hydrobiology Ser.). 356p. pap. 229.00 (978-90-481-5041-0(8), 9048150418) Springer.

Yadav, Dr Kamlesh K & Yadav, Kamlesh K. Genotoxicological Evaluation of Some Heavy Metals in Fish. 2011. 184p. pap. **(978-3-8443-8635-6(1))** Lambert Academic Publishing.

Zarriello, Phillip J. Effects of Water Use & Land Use on Streamflow & Aquatic Habitat in the Sudbury & Assabet River Basins, Massachusetts. 2010. (Illus.). xii, 160p. **(978-1-4113-2944-7(9))** United States Geological Survey.

AQUATIC EXERCISES

Alexander, Christine. Water Fitness Lesson Plans & Choreography. 2010. (Illus.). 200p. pap. 32.00 (978-0-7360-9112-1(2)) Human Kinetics Pubs.

Aquatic Exercise Association Staff. Aquatic Fitness Professional Manual. 6th ed. 2010. (ENG., Illus.). 408p. pap. 62.00 (978-0-7360-6767-6(1)) Human Kinetics Pubs.

Baun, MaryBeth Pappas. Fantastic Water Workouts. 2nd ed. 2007. (ENG., Illus.). 264p. per. 19.95 (978-0-7360-6808-6(2)) Human Kinetics Pubs.

Brody, Lori Thein & Geigle, Paula, eds. Aquatic Exercise for Rehabilitation & Training. 2009. (ENG., Illus.). 368p. (C). 79.00 (978-0-7360-7130-7(X)) Human Kinetics Pubs.

Fraleigh, Sondra. Land to Water Yoga: Shin Somatics Moving Way. 2009. 148p. pap. 14.95 (978-0-595-46637-5(0)) iUniverse, Inc.

Grosse, Susan J. Water Learning: Improving Mental, Physical, & Social Skills Through Water Activities. 2007. (ENG., Illus.). 192p. per. 23.00 (978-0-7360-6766-9(3)) Human Kinetics Pubs.

Lees, Terri. Water Fun: 116 Fitness & Swimming Activities for All Ages. 2007. (ENG., Illus.). 192p. per. 19.95 (978-0-7360-6378-4(1)) Human Kinetics Pubs.

Lepore, Monica, et al. Adapted Aquatics Programming: A Professional Guide. 2nd ed. 2007. (ENG., Illus.). 368p. 59.00 (978-0-7360-5730-1(7)) Human Kinetics Pubs.

Rosenstein, Ann A. Water Exercises for Osteoarthritis: The Effective Way to Reduce Pain & Stiffness, While Increasing Endurance & Strength. 2007. (Illus.). 291p. per. 18.00 (978-1-882883-62-2(4)) Idyll Arbor, Inc.

—Water Exercises for Parkinson's: Maintaining Balance, Strength, Endurance, & Flexibility. 2008. (Illus.). 240p. pap. 18.00 (978-1-882883-76-9(4)) Idyll Arbor, Inc.

—Water Exercises for Rheumatoid Arthritis: The Effective Way to Reduce Pain & Inflammation While Increasing Flexibility & Mobility. 2008. 292p. pap. 18.00 (978-1-882883-63-9(2)) Idyll Arbor, Inc.

Spitzer Gibson, Terry-Ann & Hoeger, Werner W. K. Water Aerobics for Fitness & Wellness. 4th ed. 2011. (ENG.). 170p. (C). pap. 51.95 (978-0-8400-4813-4(0)) Brooks/Cole.

AQUATIC FAUNA

see Aquatic Animals

AQUATIC FLORA

see Aquatic Plants

AQUATIC INSECTS

see Insects, Aquatic

AQUATIC ORGANISMS

see also Aquatic Animals; Aquatic Plants; Benthos; Marine Organisms

Barnum, Douglas A., et al, eds. The Salton Sea. 2010. (Developments in Hydrobiology Ser.). (Illus.). 320p. pap. 169.00 (978-90-481-5989-5(X), 904815989X) Springer.

Chapman, Peter M., et al, eds. Ecological Assessment of Selenium in the Aquatic Environment. 2010. (ENG., Illus.). 368p. 129.95 (978-1-4398-2677-5(3), CRC Press) Taylor & Francis Group GBR. Dist: Taylor & Francis Group.

Crompton, T. R. Toxicants in Aqueous Ecosystems: A Guide for the Analytical & Environmental Chemist. 2010. (ENG., Illus.). xvi, 456p. pap. 259.00 (978-3-642-07141-6(4), 3642071414) Springer.

Fott, J., ed. Limnology of Mountain Lakes. 2011. (Developments in Hydrobiology Ser.). (ENG.). 196p. pap. 229.00 (978-90-481-4351-1(9), 9048143519) Springer.

Francis, Robert A., ed. A Handbook of Global Freshwater Invasive Species. 2012. (ENG., Illus.). 484p. (C). 160.00 (978-1-84971-228-6(X)) Routledge.

Gray, N. F. Water Technology: An Introduction for Environmental Scientists & Engineers. 3rd rev. ed. 2010. (ENG., Illus.). 768p. pap. 66.95 (978-1-85617-705-4(X), CRC Press) Taylor & Francis Group GBR. Dist: Taylor & Francis Group.

Handy. Essentials & Non-Essential Trace Elements. 2008. (Illus.). 350p. pap. 189.95 (978-0-415-42953-5(6)) Taylor & Francis Group.

Hawkins, Anthony & Popper, Arthur N., eds. The Effects of Noise on Aquatic Life. 2011. (Advances in Experimental Medicine & Biology Ser.). (ENG., Illus.). xxviii, 695p. 279.00 (978-1-4419-7310-8(9), 1441973109) Springer.

Langston, William J. & Bebianno, Maria J., eds. Metal Metabolism in Aquatic Environments. 2010. (ENG., Illus.). 472p. pap. 189.00 (978-1-4419-4731-4(0), 1441947310) Springer.

O'Sullivan, Emily G., ed. Ballast Water Management: Combating Aquatic Invaders. 2009. (Water Resource Planning, Development & Management Ser.). (Illus.). ix, 174p. 130.50 (978-1-61728-000-9(3)) Nova Science Pubs., Inc.

Rand, Gary M. Fundamentals of Aquatic Toxicology: Effects, Envionmental Fate & Risk Assessment. 3rd rev. ed. 2013. (ENG., Illus.). 139.95 (978-0-415-24849-5(3), CRC Press) Taylor & Francis Group GBR. Dist: Taylor & Francis Group.

Schipper, C. A., ed. Assessment of Effects of Chemical Contaminants in Dredged Material on Marine: Ecosystems & Human Health. 2009. (Deltares Select Ser.). 164p. pap. 85.00 (978-1-60750-085-8(X)) IOS Pr., Inc.

Tjeerdema, Ronald S., ed. Aquatic Life Water Quality Criteria for Selected Pesticides. 2012. (Reviews of Environmental Contamination & Toxicology Ser.: 216). (ENG., Illus.). 160p. 129.00 **(978-1-4614-2259-4(0)**, 1461422590) Springer.

Vrouwenvelder, Johannes Simon, et al. Biofouling of Spiral Wound Membrane Systems. 2011. (Illus.). 360p. (C). pap. (978-1-84339-363-4(8)) IWA Publishing.

Wang, Zaosheng, et al, eds. Mechanisms of Cadmium Toxicity to Various Trophic Saltwater Organisms. 2010. (Environmental Science, Engineering & Technology Ser.). (Illus.). 83p. pap. 43.00 (978-1-60876-646-8(2)) Nova Science Pubs., Inc.

AQUATIC PESTS

see also Marine Borers

Alexander, Jeff. Pandora's Locks: The Opening of the Great Lakes-St. Lawrence Seaway. (ENG., Illus.). 431p. 2011. pap. 19.95 (978-0-87013-872-0(3)) 2009. 29.95 (978-0-87013-857-7(X)) Michigan State Univ. Pr.

Ballast Water Invasive Species Management & Threats to Coral Reefs: Hearing Before the Subcommittee on National Ocean Policy Study of the Committee on Commerce, Science, & Transportation, United States Senate, One Hundred Ninth Congress, First Session, June 15, 2005. 2010. (Illus.). iii, 92p. **(978-0-16-087401-7(7)**, 552-070-42094-1) United States Government Printing Office.

Caffrey, Joseph, et al, eds. Biology, Ecology & Management of Aquatic Plants. 2010. (Developments in Hydrobiology Ser.). 352p. pap. 239.00 (978-90-481-5404-3(9), 9048154049) Springer.

Carlton, James T. & Eldredge, Lucius G. Marine Bioinvasions of Hawaii: The Introduced & Cryptogenic Marine & Estuarine Animals & Plants of the Hawaiian Archipelago. 2009. (Illus.). 202p. (978-1-58178-096-3(6)) Bishop Museum Pr.

Dutartre, A., et al, eds. Macrophytes in Aquatic Ecosystems: from Biology to Management: Proceedings of the 11th International Symposium on Aquatic Weeds, European Weed Research Society. 2006. (Developments in Hydrobiology Ser.: Vol. 190). (Illus.). 263p. 209.00 (978-1-4020-5389-4(4), 1402053894) Springer.

Leppäkoski, Erkki. The International Law on Ballast Water: Preventing Biopollution. 2008. (Illus.). 352p. (C). (978-90-04-16652-3(1)) BRILL.

Leppäkoski, Erkki, et al, eds. Invasive Aquatic Species of Europe Distribution, Impacts & Management. 2010. 600p. pap. 279.00 (978-90-481-6111-9(8), 9048161118) Springer.

United Nations Environment Programme. In dead Water: Merging of climate change with pollution, over-harvest, & infestation in the world's fishing Grounds. Nellemann, Christian et al, eds. 2008. (ENG., Illus.). 62p. pap. 10.00 (978-82-7701-048-9(6)) United Nations Environment Programme KEN. Dist: National Bk. Network.

Wouters, Clara E., ed. Protecting the Great Lakes from Invasive & Nonindigenous Species. 2010. (Environmental Science, Engineering & Technology Ser.). 130.00 (978-1-61728-103-7(4)) Nova Science Pubs., Inc.

AQUATIC PLANTS

see also Aquarium Plants; Freshwater Plants; Marine Plants

Alderton, David & Dorling Kindersley Publishing Staff. Encyclopedia of Aquarium & Pond Fish. 2008. (ENG., Illus.). 400p. (gr. 12). pap. 24.95 (978-0-7566-3678-4(7)) Dorling Kindersley Publishing, Inc.

Amano, Takashi. Nature Aquarium: Complete Works, 1985-2009, 1 vol. 2011. (ENG., Illus.). 264p. 59.95 (978-0-7938-0649-2(6)) TFH Pubns., Inc.

Arber, Agnes. Water Plants: A Study of Aquatic Angiosperms. 2010. (Cambridge Library Collection - Life Sciences Ser.). (Illus.). 460p. pap. 34.99 (978-1-108-01732-9(0)) Cambridge Univ. Pr.

Billing, Kelly & Biles, Paula. The Lotus: Know It & Grow It. 2008. (Illus.). 51p. pap. 15.00 (978-0-9794732-0-3(9)) International Waterlily & Water Gardening Society.

Block, Timothy A. & Rhoads, Ann Fowler. Aquatic Plants of Pennsylvania: A Complete Reference Guide. 2011. (Illus.). 320p. (C). 59.95 (978-0-8122-4306-2(4)) Univ. of Pennsylvania Pr.

Contreras, Sofia A. Effects of Climate Change on Aquatic Invasive Species. 2010. (Climate Change & its Causes, Effects & Prediction Ser.). pap. 38.70 (978-1-61728-005-4(4)) Nova Science Pubs., Inc.

Damiri, Basma. Risk Characterization for Boron & Aquatic Plants & Animals. 2010. 108p. pap. (978-3-639-22207-4(5)) VDM Verlag Dr. Mueller e.K.

Dennis, La Rea J. & Halse, Richard R. Aquatic & Wetland Plants of Oregon with Vegetative Keys. 2008. (Illus.). (C). pap. 40.00 (978-1-60174-068-7(9), Uncial Pr.) GCT, Inc.

Eisler, Ronald. Compendium of Trace Metals & Marine Biota: Volume 1: Plants & Invertebrates, 2 vols. 2009. (ENG.). 638p. 275.00 (978-0-444-53436-1(9), Elsevier Science) Elsevier Science & Technology Bks.

—Compendium of Trace Metals & Marine Biota Vols. 1 & 2: Plants & Invertebrates - Vertebrates, 2 vols. 2009. (ENG.). 1150p. 420.00 (978-0-444-53439-2(3), Elsevier Science) Elsevier Science & Technology Bks.

Harp, Mark & Beck, Alison. Water Garden Plants for Washington & Oregon. 2008. (ENG., Illus.). 238p. per. (978-976-8200-40-2(5)) Lone Pine Publishing International Inc.

Kelly, Simon. Monet's Water Lilies: The Agapanthus Triptych. 2011. (ENG., Illus.). 64p. 16.95 *(978-0-89178-095-3(5))* St. Louis Art Museum.

Kirk, John T. O. Light & Photosynthesis in Aquatic Ecosystems. 3rd rev. ed. 2010. (ENG., Illus.). 662p. pap. 90.00 *(978-0-521-15175-7(9))* Cambridge Univ. Pr.

Lambert, Derek, et al. Pond Plants. 2006. (Aquamaster Ser.). (ENG., Illus.). 96p. pap. 9.95 *(978-1-931993-81-4(5))* BowTie Pr.

Lawson, George. The Royal Water-Lily of South America. 2009. (Gardening in America Ser.). (ENG.). 116p. pap. 10.95 *(978-1-4290-1369-7(9))* Applewood Bks.

Love, Gilly. Creative Water Effects in the Garden. 2012. (ENG., Illus.). 160p. pap. 17.99 ***(978-1-78019-151-5(0))*** Anness Publishing GBR. Dist: National Bk. Network.

Marchal, G. & Spincer, Michael. Living in Water. Date not set. (Longman Biology Topics Ser.). (Illus.). 32p. pap. 35.67 *(978-0-582-32304-9(5))* Addison-Wesley Longman, Ltd. GBR. Dist: Trans-Atlantic Pubns., Inc.

Parsons, Jeffrey R. The Last Pescadores of Chimalhuacán, Mexico: An Archaeological Ethnography. 2006. (Illus.). 377p. 28.00 *(978-0-915703-62-3(9))* Univ. of Michigan, Museum of Anthropology, Pubns. Dept.

Ramey, Vic & University of Florida, prods. Aquatic Plant Identification Deck. 2006. (Illus.). 72p. ring bd. 15.00 *(978-0-9700046-1-1(3)*, CAIP Information Office) Univ. of Florida, Ctr. for Aquatic & Invasive Plants.

Riffle, Robert Lee, et al. Timber Press Pocket Guide to Water Garden Plants. 2008. (ENG., Illus.). 212p. pap. 19.95 *(978-0-88192-846-4(1)*, 0881928461) Timber Pr., Inc.

Robert Wahiti, Gituru. Reproductive Ecology of the Endangered Aquatic Plant Caldesia Grandis. 2010. 124p. pap. *(978-3-639-27003-7(7))* VDM Verlag Dr. Mueller e.K.

Robinson, Peter. Plants for Ponds, Rock & Water Features: Practical Advice on Planning, Planting & Maintaining Rock & Water Gardens Including More Than 300 Stunning Photographs. 2010. (ENG., Illus.). 128p. pap. 17.99 *(978-1-84476-751-9(5))* Anness Publishing GBR. Dist: National Bk. Network.

Simmons, John. Managing the Wet Garden: Plants That Flourish in Problem Places. 2008. (ENG., Illus.). 312p. 39.95 *(978-0-88192-900-3(X)*, 088192900X) Timber Pr., Inc.

Sridhar, Kandikere R. Aquatic Plants & Plant Diseases: Types, Characteristics & Management. 2012. (Series: Botanical Research & Practices Ser.). (Illus.). 278p. 95.00 *(978-1-61324-380-0(4))* Nova Science Pubs., Inc.

Stutzenbaker, Charles D. Aquatic & Wetland Plants of the Western Gulf Coast. 2010. (Illus.). 468p. pap. 40.00 *(978-1-60344-222-0(7))* Texas A&M Univ. Pr.

Walters, Martin & Lavelle, Michael. The Illustrated Encyclopedia of Wild Flowers & Flora of the World: An Expert Reference & Identification Guide to over 1730 Wild Flowers & Plants from Every Continent. Walters, Martin, ed. 2012. (ENG., Illus.). 512p. 35.00 *(978-0-7548-1972-1(8))* Anness Publishing GBR. Dist: National Bk. Network.

Weller, Alan & Dover Pictura. Aquatic Life Vector Designs. 2012. (Dover Pictura Electronic Clip Art Ser.). (ENG., Illus.). 128p. pap. 49.95 ***(978-0-486-99196-2(2))*** Dover Pubns., Inc.

Wiencke, Christian, ed. Biology of Polar Benthic Algae. 2010. (Marine & Freshwater Botany Ser.). (Illus.). 365p. pap. 168.00 *(978-3-11-022970-7(6))* De Gruyter, Walter Inc.

Wu, Meiyin & Kalma, Dennis. Wetland Plants of the Adirondacks: Herbaceous Plants & Aquatic Plants. 2011. 176p. pap. 25.00 *(978-1-4269-6062-8(X))*; pap. 15.00 *(978-1-4269-5843-4(9))* Trafford Publishing.

AQUATIC RESOURCES

see also Algae; Fisheries; Fishery Products; Marine Resources

Bonar, Scott A. Standard Methods for Sampling North American Freshwater Fishes. 2009. 335p. 60.00 *(978-1-934874-10-3(8))* American Fisheries Society.

Detjen, Philipp Thomas. Hydrothermal Vents. 2010. 148p. pap. *(978-3-639-27338-0(9))* VDM Verlag Dr. Mueller e.K.

Dobson, Mike, et al. Ecology of Aquatic Systems. 2nd ed. 2009. (ENG., Illus.). 368p. (C). 59.95 *(978-0-19-929754-2(1))* Oxford Univ. Pr., Inc.

Food and Agriculture Organization. Workshop on status & trends in aquatic genetic Resources: A basis for international policy; 8-10 May 2006, Victoria, British Columbia, Canada. Bartley, Devin M. et al, eds. 2007. (FAO Fisheries Proceedings Ser.: Vol. 5). (Illus.). 184p. pap. *(978-92-5-105818-3(0))* Food & Agriculture Organization of the United Nations.

Le Gal, Y. & Halvorson, H. O., eds. New Developments in Marine Biotechnology. 2010. pap. 199.00 *(978-1-4419-3300-3(X)*, 144193300X) Springer.

Schechter, Michael G., et al. International Governance of Fisheries Ecosystems: Learning from the Past, Finding Solutions for the Future. 2008. (Illus.). xxii, 458p. *(978-1-888569-99-5(9))* American Fisheries Society.

AQUATIC SCIENCES

see also Aquatic Biology; Hydrography; Hydrology; Limnology; Marine Sciences

Heidorn, Keith C. & Whitelaw, Ian. The Field Guide to Natural Phenomena: The Secret World of Optical, Atmospheric & Celestial Wonders. 2010. (ENG., Illus.). 224p. pap. 24.95 *(978-1-55407-707-6(9))* Firefly Bks., Ltd.

Hunter, William, III, ed. Research Progress in Fisheries Science. 2011. (ENG.). 348p. 99.95 *(978-1-926692-65-4(9))* Apple Academic Pr., Inc. CAN. Dist: Taylor & Francis Group.

Noakes, David L. G. Bill Ricker: an Appreciation: An Appreciation. 2010. (Developments in Environmental Biology of Fishes Ser.). vi, 154p. pap. 119.00 *(978-90-481-7175-0(X)*, 904817175X) Springer.

Seuront, Laurent. Fractals & Multifractals in Ecology & Aquatic Science. 2009. (ENG., Illus.). 360p. 89.95 *(978-0-8493-2782-7(2)*, CRC Press) Taylor & Francis Group GBR. Dist: Taylor & Francis Group.

AQUATIC SPORTS

see also Boats and Boating; Canoes and Canoeing; Diving; Fishing; Rafting (Sports); Rowing; Sailing; Swimming; Water Polo; Water Skiing; Yachts and Yachting

Asian Geographic Magazine, creator. Asian Geographic Journal: 101 Things to Do in Asia. 2007. (Illus.). 168p. pap. *(978-981-05-8165-7(3))* Monsoon Bks. Pte. Ltd.

Aslett, Derek. Solent: Cruising Companion. 2nd ed. 2008. (ENG., Illus.). 200p. 49.95 *(978-0-470-98828-2(2)*, Wiley) Wiley, John & Sons, Inc.

D Custom. MasterCraft: Setting a Higher Standard for 40 Years. 2007. 132p. pap. 39.95 *(978-0-9761697-1-0(1))* D Magazine Ltd. Partners.

Dial, Roman. Packrafting! An Introduction & How-to Guide. 2008. pap. *(978-0-9748188-3-2(6))* Beartooth Mountain Pr.

Ege, Alexander. Impact of Events. 2008. 100p. per. *(978-3-8364-3535-2(7))* VDM Verlag Dr. Mueller e.K.

Favret, Ben. Water Skiing & Wakeboarding. 2010. (ENG., Illus.). 200p. pap. 24.95 *(978-0-7360-8634-9(X))* Human Kinetics Pubs.

Hohn, John. The Millennium Tuber: One Man's Journey to Help Save a River. 2007. (Illus.). 186p. per. 29.95 *(978-0-922993-71-0(8))* Marquette Bks., LLC.

Karasa, Al. Sidney's Pub & other salty Yarns. 2007. 163p. pap. 14.95 *(978-0-7414-3993-2(X))* Infinity Publishing.

Knight, Jared. 101 Swimming Pool Games & Activities. 2010. (Illus.). 141p. pap. 19.95 *(978-1-60679-096-0(X))* Coaches Choice.

Knuth, Barbara A. & Siemer, William F., eds. Aquatic Stewardship Education in Theory & Practice. 2007. (American Fisheries Society Symposium Ser.). 187p. 60.00 *(978-1-888569-90-2(5))* American Fisheries Society.

McLeod, Ian. Swimming Anatomy. 2009. (ENG., Illus.). 200p. pap. 21.95 *(978-0-7360-7571-8(2))* Human Kinetics Pubs.

Mehaffy, Bob & Mehaffy, Carolyn. Cruising Guide to the Hawaiian Islands. 2010. 324p. pap. 29.95 *(978-93-983773-0-7(6))* Paradise Cay Pubns.

—Cruising Guide to the Hawaiian Islands. 2nd rev. ed. 2006. (Illus.). 313p. per. 29.95 *(978-0-939837-73-1(0))* Paradise Cay Pubns.

Nolen, Ben M. & Narramore, Robert E. Rivers & Rapids. rev. ed. (Illus.). lib. bdg. 19.95 *(978-0-9632403-9-2(0))* Overview Pr., Inc.

Outdoor Books & Maps. Colorado Lakes & Reservoirs: Fishing & Boating Guide. 2008. (Illus.). 216p. pap. 19.95 *(978-0-930657-54-3(3)*, Outdoor Books & Maps) Adler Publishing Co.

Roberts, Sandra. First Aid Companion. 2011. (ENG.). 24p. pap. 12.95 *(978-0-470-68206-7(X)*, Wiley) Wiley, John & Sons, Inc.

Stienstra, Tom. California Recreational Lakes & Rivers: The Complete Guide to Boating, Fishing, & Water Sports. 4th ed. 2008. (Moon Handbooks Ser.). (ENG., Illus.). 560p. pap. 21.95 *(978-1-59880-018-0(3))* Westview Pr.

Sumpter, Rod. Today's Top Surfboards. 2007. (Illus.). 160p. pap. 29.95 *(978-0-7643-2764-3(X))* Schiffer Publishing, Ltd.

Sumpter, Rod, photos by. The Perfect Curl. 2008. (ENG., Illus.). 144p. 29.95 *(978-1-55868-954-1(0))* Graphic Arts Ctr. Publishing Co.

Sutherland, Bruce, ed. Europe: The Continent. 3rd ed. 2006. (Stormrider Guides). (ENG., Illus.). 190p. pap. 29.95 *(978-0-9539840-3-9(6))* Low Pressure Ltd. GBR. Dist: Perseus-PGW.

Waring, Rob. Water Sports Adventure. 2008. (ENG.). 24p. (C). pap. 10.95 *(978-1-4240-4413-9(8))* Cengage Heinle.

Watson, Tom. Kids Gone Paddlin' The Young Paddler's Guide to Having More Fun Outdoors. 2008. (ENG., Illus.). 96p. (YA). (gr. 3-7). pap. 12.95 *(978-1-58923-371-3(9)*, 1589233719) Quayside.

Young, David & Young, Cheryl. River Running. 2010. 100p. 19.95 *(978-0-9824419-3-0(2))* Perigee Learning, LLC.

AQUATIC SPORTS—SAFETY MEASURES

American Red Cross Staff, contrib. by. American Red Cross Swimming & Water Safety. 3rd ed. 2009. *(978-1-58480-446-8(7))* StayWell Co., The.

AUSTSWIM Staff. Teaching Swimming & Water Safety: The Australian Way. 2nd rev. ed. 2008. (ENG., Illus.). 236p. pap. 39.95 *(978-1-875897-87-2(9)*, Mosby) Elsevier - Health Sciences Div.

Kavanagh, James. Boat & Water Safety: A Waterproof Reference to Safe Practices & Procedures. 2010. (Duraguide Ser.). (ENG.). 2p. 7.95 *(978-1-58355-519-4(6))* Waterford Pr., Inc.

Lees, Terri. Water Fun: 116 Fitness & Swimming Activities for All Ages. 2007. (ENG., Illus.). 192p. per. 19.95 *(978-0-7360-6378-4(1))* Human Kinetics Pubs.

Moran, Kevin. Re-Thinking Drowning Risk. 2009. 220p. pap. *(978-3-639-13003-4(0))* VDM Verlag Dr. Mueller e.K.

AQUEDUCTS

see also names of particular aqueducts

Ashby, Thomas & Richmond, Ian Archibald. The Aqueducts of Ancient Rome. 2010. *(978-1-57898-854-9(3))* Martino Publishing.

Crow, James, et al. The Water Supply of Byzantine Constantinople. 2008. (Journal of Roman Studies Monograph Ser.). (ENG., Illus.). 286p. (C). 100.00 *(978-0-907764-36-6(3))* Society for the Promotion of Roman Studies GBR. Dist: Brown, David Bk. Co., The.

Frontinus. De aquaeductu urbis Romae. Kunderewicz, Cezary, ed. (Bibliotheca scriptorum Graecorum et Romanorum Teubneriana (BT) Ser.). (LAT.). XVIII, 69p. 90.00 ***(978-3-11-181336-3(3))*** De Gruyter, Walter Inc.

Frontinus. Frontinus: de Aquaeductu Urbis Romae. Rodgers, R. H., ed. 2009. (Cambridge Classical Texts & Commentaries Ser.). (ENG., Illus.). 448p. pap. 55.00 *(978-0-521-10118-9(2))* Cambridge Univ. Pr.

Hodge. Roman Aqueducts & Water Supply. (Illus.). 512p. 45.00 *(978-0-7156-2194-3(7))* Duckworth Publishers GBR. Dist: International Publishers Marketing.

Hodge, A. Trevor. Roman Aqueducts & Water Supply. 2nd ed. 2008. (Duckworth Archaeology Ser.). (Illus.). 512p. pap. 54.95 *(978-0-7156-3171-3(3))* Duckworth Publishers GBR. Dist: International Publishers Marketing.

Rinne, Katherine Wentworth. The Waters of Rome: Aqueducts, Fountains, & the Birth of the Baroque City. 2011. (ENG., Illus.). 240p. 65.00 *(978-0-300-15530-3(1))* Yale Univ. Pr.

Yorke, Trevor. Bridges Explained: Viaducts, Aqueducts. 2008. (Illus.). 160p. (C). pap. 23.95 *(978-1-84674-079-4(7))* Countryside Bks. GBR. Dist: Brown, David Bk. Co., The.

AQUEOUS HUMOR

Benos, Dale J. & Simon, Sidney A., contrib. by. The Eye's Aqueous Humor. 2nd ed. 2008. (Current Topics in Membranes Ser.: 62). (ENG., Illus.). 512p. 193.00 *(978-0-12-373894-3(6)*, Academic Pr.) Elsevier Science & Technology Bks.

AQUICULTURE

see Aquaculture

AQUIFERS

Here are entered works on the geology of water-bearing strata. Works on water contained in aquifers are entered under Groundwater.

Abdolnabi, Abdeh Kolahchi. Optimal Groundwater Monitoring Network Design: Optimal Dynamic Monitoring Network Design for Reliable Tracking of Contaminate Plumes in an Aquifer System. 2011. 248p. pap. ***(978-3-639-33089-2(7))*** VDM Verlag Dr. Mueller e.K.

Ahmed, S., et al, eds. Groundwater Dynamics in Hard Rock Aquifers: Sustainable Management & Optimal Monitoring Network Design. 2008. (ENG., Illus.). xiv, 252p. 149.00 *(978-1-4020-6539-2(6)*, 1402065396) Springer.

Ashworth, William. Ogallala Blue: Water & Life on the High Plains. 2007. (ENG.). 330p. per. 16.95 *(978-0-88150-736-2(9)*, 150736) Countryman Pr.

ASTM International Staff, contrib. by. ASTM Standards for Determining Subsurface Hydraulic Properties & Groundwater Modeling. 3rd ed. 2010. *(978-0-8031-8628-6(2))* American Society for Testing & Materials.

Bear, Jacob, et al, eds. Seawater Intrusion in Coastal Aquifers Concepts, Methods & Practices. 2010. (Theory & Applications of Transport in Porous Media Ser.). (Illus.). 640p. pap. 79.95 *(978-90-481-5172-1(4)*, 9048151724) Springer.

Bonotto, Daniel Marcos & Oliveira, Edson Gomes de, eds. (NON) Conventional Approaches Applied to the Study of Brazilian Aquifers. 2009. (Water Resource Planning, Development & Management Ser.). (Illus.). 65p. pap. 43.00 *(978-1-61668-770-0(3)*, Nova Novinka) Nova Science Pubs., Inc.

Bradbury, K. R., et al. Contaminant Transport Through Aquitards: Technical Guidance for Aquitard Assessment. 2007. 172p. pap. 299.00 *(978-1-58321-499-2(2))* Water Research Foundation.

Brown, Craig J. Aquifer Chemistry & Transport Processes in the Zone of Contribution to a Public-Supply Well in Woodbury, Connecticut, 2002-06. 2009. (Illus.). xiv, 158p. *(978-1-4113-2547-0(8))* United States Geological Survey.

Cherry, J. A., et al. Contaminant Transport Through Aquitards: A State-of-the-Science Review. 2007. 148p. pap. 299.00 *(978-1-58321-498-5(4))* Water Research Foundation.

Clark, Brian R., et al. Groundwater Availability of the Mississippi Embayment. 2011. ***(978-1-4113-3134-1(6))*** United States Geological Survey.

Gentry, Randy, et al. Novel Techniques for Investigating Recharge to the Memphis Aquifer. 2006. 97p. pap. 263.00 *(978-1-58321-483-1(6))* Water Research Foundation.

Gurdak, Jason J. Water Quality in the High Plains Aquifer, Colorado, Kansas, Nebraska, New Mexico, Oklahoma, South Dakota, Texas, & Wyoming, 1999-2004. 2009. (Illus.). viii, 63p. *(978-1-4113-2417-6(X))* United States Geological Survey.

Gurdak, Jason J. & Roe, Cassia D. Recharge Rates & Chemistry Beneath Playas of the High Plains Aquifer: A Literature Review & Synthesis. 2009. (Illus.). iv, 39p. *(978-1-4113-2480-0(3))* United States Geological Survey.

Laughton, Rachel H., ed. Aquifers: Formation, Transport & Pollution. 2010. (Environmental Science, Engineering & Technology Ser.). (Illus.). xv, 504p. 195.00 *(978-1-61668-051-0(2))* Nova Science Pubs., Inc.

Laurence, Chery & de Marsily, Ghislain, eds. Aquifer Systems Management: Darcy's Legacy in a World of Impending Water Shortage. 2007. (IAH - Selected Papers on Hydrogeology Ser.). (ENG., Illus.). 596p. 229.95 *(978-0-415-44355-5(5)*, Taylor & Francis) Taylor & Francis Group GBR. Dist: Taylor & Francis Group.

McFarland, E. Randolph & Bruce, T. Scott. The Virginia Coastal Plain Hydrogeologic Framework. 2006. *(978-1-4113-1065-0(9))* United States Geological Survey.

Mehler, Howard S. & Harter, Thomas. Aquifer pump Testing: Estimation of hydrologic parameters with computer Modeling. 2008. (Illus.). 240p. cd-rom 24.95 net. *(978-0-9741100-9-7(4))* Mehler Publishing Co.

Miller, Todd S. & Karig, Daniel E. Geohydrology of the Stratified-Drift Aquifer System in the Lower Sixmile Creek & Willseyville Creek Trough, Tompkins County, New York. 2010. (Illus.). vi, 55p. ***(978-1-4113-3112-9(5))*** United States Geological Survey.

Mlisa, Andiswa. Spatial Decision Support System for Hydrogeological Studies. 2010. 116p. pap. *(978-3-639-21985-2(6))* VDM Verlag Dr. Mueller e.K.

Nelms, David L. & Moberg, Roger M. Hydrogeology & Groundwater Availability in Clarke County, Virginia. 2010. (Illus.). xi, 119p. ***(978-1-4113-2920-1(1))*** United States Geological Survey.

Ouakili, Zoubeir & Chippo, Habib. Aquifers: Types, Impacts, & Conservation. 2012. (Environmental Science, Engineering & Technology Water Resource Planning, Development & Management Ser.). 286p. 95.00 ***(978-1-61942-091-5(0))*** Nova Science Pubs., Inc.

Painter, Scott L., et al. Enhanced Characterization & Representation of Flow Through Karst Aquifers. 2007. 104p. pap. 209.00 *(978-1-58321-489-3(5))* American Water Works Assn.

Paschke, S. S. Groundwater Availability of the Denver Basin Aquifer System, Colorado. 2011. pap. ***(978-1-4113-3121-1(4))*** United States Geological Survey.

Pinaev, Vladimir. Modelling of Natural Attenuation of Chlorinated Solvents Constituents. 2010. 72p. pap. *(978-3-8383-5233-6(5))* Lambert Academic Publishing.

Reese, Ronald S. & Wacker, Michael A. Hydrogeologic & Hydraulic Characterization of the Surficial Aquifer System, & Origin of High Salinity Groundwater, Palm Beach County, Florida. 2009. (Illus.). vii, 42p. *(978-1-4113-2550-0(8))* United States Geological Survey.

Reyes, Betzaida. Occurrence & Distribution of Organic Chemicals & Nutrients & Comparison of Water-Quality Data from Public Drinking-Water Supplies in the Columbia Aquifer in Delaware, 2000-08. 2010. (Illus.). vii, 64p. ***(978-1-4113-3011-5(0))*** United States Geological Survey.

Simmers, Ian, et al, eds. Selected Papers on Aquifer Overexploitation: From the 23rd International Congress of the IAH. (IAH Contributions to Hydrogeology Ser.: Vol. 3). 392p. pap. *(978-3-922705-62-8(6))* Heise, Heinz, GmbH & Company KG, Verlag.

Stanton, Jennifer S. & Qi, Sharon. Ground-Water Quality of the Northern High Plains Aquifer, 1997, 2002-04. 2007. (Illus.). viii, 60p. pap. *(978-1-4113-1171-8(X))* United States Geological Survey.

Topper, Ralf & Raynolds, Bob. Citizen's Guide to Denver Basin Groundwater. 2007. 33p. pap. 8.00 *(978-0-9754075-7-8(0))* Colorado Foundation for Water Education.

Torres, Luis G. & Bandala, Erick R. Remediation of Soils & Aquifers. 2009. 79.00 *(978-1-60741-372-1(8))* Nova Science Pubs., Inc.

Ukarande, Suresh. Numerical Modeling of Coastal Aquifers. 2009. 212p. pap. *(978-3-639-17552-3(2))* VDM Verlag Dr. Mueller e.K.

Walton, William C. Aquifer Test Modeling. 2007. 222p. (C). *(978-1-84339-140-1(6))* IWA Publishing.

—Aquifer Test Modeling. 2006. (ENG., Illus.). 240p. 144.95 *(978-1-4200-4292-4(0)*, CRC Press) Taylor & Francis Group GBR. Dist: Taylor & Francis Group.

Warner, Kelly L. & Arnold, Terri L. Relations That Affect the Probability & Prediction of Nitrate Concentration in Private Wells in the Glacial Aquifer System in the United States. 2010. (Illus.). xi, 73p. ***(978-1-4113-2951-5(1))*** United States Geological Survey.

Wright, Peter R. Hydrogeology & Water Quality in the Snake River Alluvial Aquifer at Jackson Hole Airport, Jackson, Wyoming, September 2008-June 2009. 2010. (Illus.). vi, 54p. ***(978-1-4113-2995-9(3))*** United States Geological Survey.

Yager, Richard M., et al. Halite Brine in the Onondaga Trough near Syracuse, New York: Characterization & Simulation of Variable-Density Flow. 2007. (Scientific Investigations Report Ser.: Vols. 2007-5058). (Illus.). vii, 40p. *(978-1-4113-2003-1(4))* United States Geological Survey.

AQUITAINE (FRANCE)

Barker, Edward Harrison. Wanderings by Southern Waters, Eastern Aquitaine. 2007. (ENG.). 248p. pap. 20.99 *(978-1-4264-4836-2(8))*; 276p. pap. 23.99 *(978-1-4264-4879-9(1))* BiblioBazaar.

Silvestre, Ruth. A Harvest of Sunflowers. 2011. (ENG., Illus.). 352p. 16.95 *(978-0-7490-0843-7(1))* Allison & Busby, Ltd. GBR. Dist: International Publishers Marketing.

—A House in the Sunflowers. 2011. (ENG., Illus.). 288p. pap. 16.95 *(978-0-7490-0838-3(5))* Allison & Busby, Ltd. GBR. Dist: International Publishers Marketing.

Trumbore Jones, A. Noble Lord, Good Shepherd: Episcopal Power & Piety in Aquitaine, 877-1050. 2009. (Brill's Ser. on the Early Middle Ages Ser.). 288p. *(978-90-04-17786-4(8))* BRILL.

ARAB AMERICANS

Abdel-Malek, Kamal. America in an Arab Mirror: Images of America in Arabic Travel Literature, 1668 to 9/11 & Beyond. Abdel-Malek, Kamal & El Kahla, Mouna, eds. 2nd ed. 2011. (ENG.). 240p. pap. 33.00 *(978-0-230-62035-3(3))* Palgrave Macmillan.

Abdelrazek, Amal Talaat. Contemporary Arab American Women Writers: Hyphenated Identities & Border Crossings. 2007. (C). 104.95 *(978-1-934043-71-4(0))* Cambria Pr.

Abdulhadi, Rabad & Alsultany, Evely, eds. Arab & Arab American Feminisms: Gender, Violence, & Belonging. 2010. 408p. 45.00 *(978-0-8156-3223-8(1))* Syracuse Univ. Pr.

Abraham, Nabeel, et al, intros. Arab Detroit 9/11: Life in the Terror Decade. 2011. (Illus.). vii, 413p. pap. 24.95 *(978-0-8143-3500-0(4))* Wayne State Univ. Pr.

Abrhiem, Talil H. A Successful Arab-American Marketing Strategy. 2008. 188p. pap. *(978-3-639-06716-3(9))* VDM Verlag Dr. Mueller e.K.

Abu-Absi, Samir, ed. & frwd. Arab Americans in Toledo: Cultural Assimilation & Community Involvement. 2010. (ENG., Illus.). 298p. pap. 25.00 *(978-0-932259-11-0(1))* Univ. of Toledo Pr., The.

Al-Qubbaj, Kholoud. Acculturation among Arabic Children & Their Families in the U S. 2010. 136p. pap. (978-3-8383-7498-7(3)) Lambert Academic Publishing.
Ameri, Anan & Arida, Holly. Daily Life of Arab Americans in the 21st Century. 2012. E-Book **(978-0-313-37715-0(4)**, Greenwood Pr.) Greenwood Publishing Group, Inc.
Ameri, Anan & Arida, Holly, eds. Daily Life of Arab Americans in the 21st Century, 1 vol. 2012. (Greenwood Press Daily Life Through History Ser.). (Illus.). 261p. 58.00 (978-0-313-37714-3(6), GR7714) Greenwood Publishing Group, Inc.
Arab American National Museum, creator. Telling Our Story: The Arab American National Museum. 2007. (Illus.). 192p. per. 35.00 (978-0-9767977-1-5(2)) Arab American National Museum.
Ayoub, Omaima M. The Hybrid Identity Construction of a Sufi Muslim, Arab Immigrant to the United States. 2007. 112p. 89.95 (978-0-7734-5284-8(2)) Mellen, Edwin Pr., The.
Bakalian, Anny P. & Bozorgmehr, Medhi. Backlash 9/11: Middle Eastern & Muslim Americans Respond. 2009. (ENG., Illus.). 360p. 60.00 (976-0-520-25734-4(0)) Univ. of California Pr.
Bakalian, Anny P., et al. Backlash 9/11: Middle Eastern & Muslim Americans Respond. 2009. (ENG., Illus.). 368p. pap. 24.95 (978-0-520-25735-1(9)) Univ. of California Pr.
Bard, Mitchell. The Arab Lobby: The Invisible Alliance That Undermines America's Interests in the Middle East. 2011. (ENG.). 432p. pap. 14.99 (978-0-06-172597-5(8)) Broadside Bks. GBR. Dist: HarperCollins Pubs.
—The Arab Lobby: The Invisible Alliance That Undermines America's Interests in the Middle East. 2010. 432p. 27.99 (978-0-06-172601-9(X)) HarperCollins Pubs.
Bayoumi, Moustafa. How Does It Feel to Be a Problem? Being Young & Arab in America. 2009. (ENG.). 320p. (gr. 12-18). 16.00 (978-0-14-311541-0(3), Penguin (Non-Classics)) Penguin Group (USA) Inc.
Cainkar, Louise. Homeland Insecurity: The Arab American & Muslim American Experience after 9/11. 2009. (978-0-87154-048-5(7)) Russell Sage Foundation.
Coryn, Chris L. S. Nationalism & Justice for Social Out-Groups. 2008. 80p. pap. (978-3-639-01243-9(7)) VDM Verlag Dr. Mueller e K.
Curiel, Jonathan. Al' America: Travels Through America's Arab & Islamic Roots. (ENG.). 2009. 272p. pap. 16.95 (978-1-59558-481-6(1)) 2008. 246p. 25.95 (978-1-59558-352-9(1), 955352) New Pr., The.
Detroit Arab American Study Team Staff, contrib. by. Citizenship & Crisis: Arab Detroit after 9/11. 2009. (978-0-87154-052-2(5)) Russell Sage Foundation.
Eggers, Dave. Zeitoun. 2010. (Vintage Ser.). (ENG., Illus.). 368p. pap. 15.95 (978-0-307-38794-3(1), Vintage) Knopf Doubleday Publishing Group.
—Zeitoun. 2009. (ENG.). 342p. 24.00 (978-1-934781-63-0(0)) McSweeney's Publishing.
Haddad, Yvonne Yazbeck. Becoming American? The Forging of Arab & Muslim Identity in Pluralist America. 2011. 130p. 19.95 (978-1-60258-406-8(0)) Baylor Univ. Pr.
Haiek, Joseph R. Arab-American Almanac. 6th ed. 2008. (Illus.). 600p. 39.95 (978-0-915652-29-7(3)) News Circle.
Hassan, Wail S. Immigrant Narratives: Orientalism & Cultural Translation in Arab-American & Arab-British Literature, 1 vol. 2011. (ENG.). 288p. 65.00 (978-0-19-979206-1(2)) Oxford Univ. Pr., Inc.
Holsinger, Jennifer Leila. Residential Patterns of Arab Americans: Race, Ethnicity & Spatial Assimilation. 2009. (New Americans). 210p. 62.00 (978-1-59332-346-2(8)) LFB Scholarly Publishing LLC.
Hussein, Lutfi M. The Internet Discourse of Arab-American Groups: A Study in Web Linguistics. 2009. 178p. 99.95 (978-0-7734-4859-9(4)) Mellen, Edwin Pr., The.
Jamal, Amaney & Naber, Nadine, eds. Race & Arab Americans Before & After 9/11: From Invisible Citizens to Visible Subjects. (Arab American Writing Ser.). (Illus.). 378p. 2008. per. 29.95 (978-0-8156-3177-4(4)) 2007. 55.00 (978-0-8156-3152-1(9)) Syracuse Univ. Pr.
Khalil, Dalel B. From Veils to Thongs: An Arab Chick's Survival Guide to Balancing One's Ethnic Identity
in America. 2008. 260p. pap. 15.95 (978-0-595-48168-2(X)) iUniverse, Inc.
Malek, Alia. A Country Called Amreeka: Arab Roots, American Stories. 2009. (ENG., Illus.). 320p. 25.00 (978-1-4165-8972-3(4), Free Pr.) Free Pr.
—A Country Called Amreeka: U. S. History Retold through Arab-American Lives. 2010. (ENG., Illus.). 320p. pap. 15.00 (978-1-4165-8975-4(9), Free Pr.) Free Pr.
Masry, Ferial & Chenard, Susan. Running for All the Right Reasons: A Saudi-born Woman's Pursuit of Democracy. 2009. (Illus.). 232p. 24.95 (978-0-8156-0911-7(6)) Syracuse Univ. Pr.
McCloud, Aminah Beverly. Transnational Muslims in American Society. 2006. (ENG.). 176p. 39.95 (978-0-8130-2971-9(6)) Univ. Pr. of Florida.
Nabhan, Gary Paul. Arab - American: Landscape, Culture, & Cuisine in Two Great Deserts. 2008. (ENG., Illus.). 160p. 40.00 (978-0-8165-2658-1(3)) Univ. of Arizona Pr.
—Arab/American: Landscape, Culture, & Cuisine in Two Great Deserts. 2008. (ENG., Illus.). 160p. pap. 17.95 (978-0-8165-2659-8(1)) Univ. of Arizona Pr.
Nassar-McMillan, Sylvia, et al. Counseling & Diversity: Counseling Arab Americans. 2010. (ENG.). 112p. (C). pap. 16.95 (978-0-618-47039-6(5)) Wadsworth.
Oweis, Fayeq S. Encyclopedia of Arab American Artists, 1 vol. 2007. (Artists of the American Mosaic Ser.). (Illus.). 336p. 85.00 (978-0-313-33730-7(6), GR3730, Greenwood Pr.) Greenwood Publishing Group, Inc.
Prouty, Nada. Uncompromised: The Rise, Fall, & Redemption of an Arab American Patriot in the CIA. 2011. (ENG., Illus.). 288p. 26.00 (978-0-230-11386-2(9)) Palgrave Macmillan.
Sabry, Somaya Sami. Arab-American Women's Writing & Performance: Orientalism, Race & the Idea of the Arabian Nights. 2011. (International Library of Cultural Studies). (ENG., Illus.). 224p. 88.00 (978-1-84885-568-7(0), Tauris Academic Studies) I. B. Tauris & Co., Ltd. GBR. Dist: Macmillan.
Salaita, Steven. Modern Arab American Fiction: A Reader's Guide. 2011. 176p. (978-0-8156-3277-1(0)); pap. (978-0-8156-3253-5(3)) Syracuse Univ. Pr.
Shora, Nawar. The Arab-American Handbook: A Guide to the Arab, Arab-American, & Muslim Worlds. 2008. (Illus.). 335p. pap. 19.95 (978-1-885942-14-2(1)) Cune Pr., LLC.
—The Arab-American Handbook: A Guide to the Arab, Arab-American & Muslim Worlds. 2008. (Bridge Between the Cultures Ser.). (Illus.). 335p. 34.95 (978-1-885942-47-0(8)) Cune Pr., LLC.
Tehranian, John. Whitewashed: America's Invisible Middle Eastern Minority. 2010. (ENG.). 256p. pap. 21.00 (978-0-8147-8273-6(6)) New York Univ. Pr.
Varouhakis, Miron. U S Newspaper Coverage of Arab Americans Pre- & Post-9/11. 2010. 128p. pap. (978-3-8383-6340-0(X)) Lambert Academic Publishing.
Welch, Michael. Scapegoats of September 11th: Hate Crimes & State Crimes in the War on Terror. 2006. (Critical Issues in Crime & Society Ser.). (ENG.). 238p. per. 23.95 (978-0-8135-3896-9(3)) Rutgers Univ. Pr.
Zabel, Darcy. Arabs in the Americas: Interdisciplinary Essays on the Arab Diaspora. 2006. 248p. (C). pap. 31.95 (978-0-8204-8111-1(4)) Lang, Peter Publishing, Inc.

ARAB ARCHITECTURE
see Islamic Architecture

ARAB ART
see Islamic Art

ARAB BA'TH SOCIALIST PARTY
see Hizb al-Ba'th Al-Arabi Al Ishtiraki

ARAB CIVILIZATION
see Civilization, Arab

ARAB COUNTRIES
Here are entered works treating collectively the Arabic-speaking countries of Asia and Africa, or of Asia only. Works on the region consisting of Asia west of Pakistan, northeastern Africa, and occasionally Greece and Pakistan are entered under Middle East.

Allen, Mark & Allen. Arabs. 2007. (ENG.). 160p. 17.95 (978-0-8264-9402-3(1)) Continuum International Publishing Group, Ltd. GBR. Dist: National Bk. Network.
Cordesman, Anthony H. Arab-Israeli Military Forces in an Era of Asymmetric Wars. 2008. (ENG., Illus.). 432p. pap. 35.00 (978-0-8047-5967-0(7)) Stanford Univ. Pr.
Haseeb, Khair el-Din, ed. The Future of the Arab Nation (RLE: the Arab Nation) Challenges & Options, Volume 2. 2012. (Routledge Library Editions: the Arab Nation Ser.). (ENG.). 544p. 165.00 **(978-0-415-62394-0(4))** Routledge.
Lutfiyya, Abdulla M. & Churchill, Charles W., eds. Readings in Arab Middle Eastern Societies & Cultures. (ENG.). XVII, 733p. 210.00 **(978-3-11-175146-7(5))** De Gruyter, Mouton DEU. Dist: de Gruyter, Walter GmbH & Co. KG.
Mejcher-Atassi, Sonja. Reading Across Modern Arabic Literature & Art. 2011. (ENG.). 250p. (C). 117.00 **(978-3-89500-805-4(2))** Reichert, Ludwig Dr. DEU. Dist: Brown, David Bk. Co., The.
United Nations. Statistical Abstract of the ESCWA Region. 2010 (FRE & MUL.). 236p. pap. 50.00 (978-92-1-128338-9(8)) United Nations Pubns.

ARAB COUNTRIES—BIOGRAPHY
Armes, Roy. Arab Filmmakers of the Middle East: A Dictionary. 2010. (ENG., Illus.). 216p. 39.95 (978-0-253-35518-8(4), 0253355184) Indiana Univ. Pr.
Cikar, Jutta & Cikar, Mustafa, compiled by. Arab-Islamic Biographical Index II / Arabischer-Islamischer Biographischer Index II. 2009. (ENG., Illus.). LXXXIV, 1822p. (978-3-598-35496-0(7)) Saur, K. G. Verlag GmbH & Co.
Cleveland, William L. Islam Against the West: Shakib Arslan & the Campaign for Islamic Nationalism. 2011. (ENG.). 248p. pap. 25.00 **(978-0-292-73733-4(5))** Univ. of Texas Pr.
Eddé, Anne-Marie & Todd, Jane Marie. Saladin. 2011. Orig. Title: Saladin. (ENG., Illus.). 704p. 35.00 (978-0-674-05559-9(4), Belknap Pr.) Harvard Univ. Pr.
Fischbach, Michael R. Biographical Encyclopedia of the Modern Middle East & North Africa, 2 vols. 2007. (Illus.). xxix, 929p. (978-1-4144-1891-9(4)); (978-1-4144-1890-2(6)) Cengage Gale.
Gale Cengage Publishing, creator. Who's Who in the Arab World. 18th rev. ed. 2006. (Who's Who in the Arab World Ser.). (Illus.). 1216p. (978-2-903188-23-8(8)) Publitec Publications.
Gensicke, Klaus. The Mufti of Jerusalem & the Nazis: The Berlin Years. 2011. 256p. 74.95 (978-0-85303-844-3(9)) Vallentine Mitchell Pubs. GBR. Dist: International Specialized Bk. Services.
Gubser, Peter. Saladin. 2011. pap. 38.00 (978-1-61143-670-9(2)) Gorgias Pr., LLC.
Irving, Sarah. Leila Khaled: Icon of Palestinian Liberation, 1 vol. 2012. (ENG., Illus.). 168p. 21.00 **(978-0-7453-2951-2(9))** Pluto Pr. GBR. Dist: Macmillan.
Janneh, Sabarr. Learning from the Life of Prophet Muhammad: Peace & Blessing of God be upon Him. 2010. 660p. pap. 25.99 (978-1-4389-4948-2(0)) AuthorHouse.
Lent, Frederick & Bedjan, Paul. The Life of Saint Simeon Stylites: A Translation of the Syriac Text in Bedjan's Acta Martyrum et Sanctorum, Vol. IV. 2008. (978-1-889758-91-6(4), Evolution Publishing & Manufacturing) Arx Publishing.
Matar, Dina. What It Means to Be Palestinian: Stories of Palestinian Peoplehood. 2010. (ENG., Illus.). 224p. 85.00 (978-1-84885-457-4(9)); pap. 28.00 (978-1-84885-363-8(7)) I. B. Tauris & Co., Ltd. GBR. Dist: Macmillan.
Nusseibeh, Sari. Once upon a Country: A Palestinian Life. 2008. (ENG., Illus.). 584p. pap. 17.00 (978-0-312-42710-8(7)) Picador.
Sadek FACOG, Mona. From Kittens to Babies: The Long Journey Home, 1 vol. 2009. 100p. pap. 16.95 (978-1-60813-005-4(3)) PublishAmerica, Inc.

ARAB COUNTRIES—CIVILIZATION
see Civilization, Arab

ARAB COUNTRIES—COMMERCE
Al Suleimany, Majid Said Nasser. Psychology of Arab Management Thinking: Arabian Management Series. 2009. 486p. pap. 60.00 (978-1-4251-8273-1(9)) Trafford Publishing.
Amin, Magdi, et al. After the Spring: Economic Transition in the Arab World. 2012. (ENG., Illus.). 192p. 35.00 **(978-0-19-992492-9(9))** Oxford Univ. Pr., Inc.
Cram101 Textbook Reviews Staff. Outlines & Highlights for Dubai & Co: Global Strategies for Doing Business in the Gulf States by Rehman, ISBN. 2008. 108p. pap. 11.95 (978-1-4288-6450-4(4)) Cram101 Inc.
El Namaki, M. S. S. Strategy & Entrepreneurship in Arab Countries. 2008. (ENG., Illus.). 240p. 95.00 (978-0-230-51564-2(9)) Palgrave Macmillan.
Gale. Major Companies of the Arab World 2012. 35th ed. 2011. (Major Companies of the Arab World Ser.). (ENG.). 1350p. lib. bdg. 1350.00 **(978-1-86099-688-7(4))** Graham & Whiteside, Ltd. GBR. Dist: Cengage Gale.
Major Companies of the Arab World. 34th ed. 2010. 1250.00 (978-1-86099-634-4(5)) Graham & Whiteside, Ltd. GBR. Dist: Cengage Gale.
Rehman, Aamir A. Dubai & Co: Global Strategies for Doing Business in the Gulf States. 2007. (ENG., Illus.). 288p. 27.95 (978-0-07-149413-7(8), 0071494138) McGraw-Hill Cos., The.
Simpfendorfer, Ben. The New Silk Road: How a Rising Arab World Is Turning Away from the West & Rediscovering China. 2009. (ENG.). 256p. 46.00 (978-0-230-58026-8(2)) Palgrave Macmillan.
—The New Silk Road - Revised & Updated: How a Rising Arab World Is Turning Away from the West & Rediscovering China. rev. ed. 2011. (ENG., Illus.). 224p. pap. 22.00 (978-0-230-28485-2(X)) Palgrave Macmillan.
Suleimany, Majid Said Nasser Al. Psychology of Arab Management Thinking. 2009. 486p. 65.00 (978-1-4269-9806-5(6)) Trafford Publishing.
United Nations Staff. External Trade Bulletin of the ESCWA Region. 18th Issue. 2009. (ENG, FRE & MUL.). 116p. pap. 35.00 (978-92-1-128329-0(0)) United Nations Pubns.
United Nations: Economic and Social Commission for Western Asia. External trade bulletin of the ESCWA Region. 2009. (MUL., Illus.). 128p. pap. 30.00 (978-92-1-128322-8(1)) United Nations Pubns.
Zind, Richard G., et al. The World Financial & Oil Market Crises & the Kingdom of Saudi Arabia. 2009. 104.99 (978-1-60497-629-8(2)) Cambria Pr.

ARAB COUNTRIES—DESCRIPTION AND TRAVEL
Eisner, Mike. Photographic Rendezvous: Musandam Oman. 2008. 114p. pap. 46.95 (978-1-4357-1785-5(6)) Lulu Enterprises Inc.
Frost, Shelley. UAE Off-Road Explorer. (Illus.). 316p. (978-976-8182-04-3(0)) Explorer Publishing UAE. Dist: Vine Hse. Distribution.
Hamilton, Alastair. The Arcadian Library: Western Appreciation of Arab & Islamic Civilization. 2011. (ENG., Illus.). 408p. 250.00 (978-0-19-960963-5(2)) Oxford Univ. Pr., Inc.
Locken, E. Travel Journal Oman. 2010. 192p. pap. 19.99 (978-0-557-43890-7(X)) Lulu Enterprises Inc.
Schmitz, Heiner. From Distance Desert Dreams. 2007. 160p. 39.95 (978-3-86568-086-0(0)) Imhof, Michael Verlag GmbH & Co. KG DEU. Dist: Independent Pubs. Group.
Seabrook, William B. Adventures in Arabia: Among the Bedouins, Druses, Whirling Dervishes, & Yezidee Devil Worshipers. 2006. (Gorgias Historic Travels in the Cradle of Civilization Ser.: 11). 347p. 121.00 (978-1-59333-597-7(0)) Gorgias Pr., LLC.
Stark, Freya. A Winter in Arabia: A Journey Through Yemen. 2011. (ENG.). 326p. (gr. 12). 17.00 (978-1-59020-646-1(0)) Overlook Pr., The.
Tidrick, Kathryn. Heart Beguiling Araby: The English Romance with Arabia. 2nd ed. 2009. (ENG., Illus.). 264p. pap. 19.95 (978-1-84885-146-7(4), Tauris Parke Paperbacks) I. B. Tauris & Co., Ltd. GBR. Dist: Macmillan.

ARAB COUNTRIES—ECONOMIC CONDITIONS
Alasrag, Hussein. The Effects of the Global Economic Crisis on the Arab Economy. 2010. 56p. pap. (978-3-8383-4108-8(2)) Lambert Academic Publishing.
—Enhancing the Competitiveness of the Smes in the Arab Countries. 2010. 64p. pap. (978-3-639-25108-1(3)) VDM Verlag Dr. Mueller e.K.
Cram101 Textbook Reviews Staff. Outlines & Highlights for Dubai & Co: Global Strategies for Doing Business in the Gulf States by Rehman, ISBN. 2008. 108p. pap. 11.95 (978-1-4288-6450-4(4)) Cram101 Inc.
Crane, Keith, et al. Future Challenges for the Arab World: The Implications of Demographic & Economic Trends. 2011. (ENG.). 118p. pap. 25.00 (978-0-8330-5100-4(8)) RAND Corp., The.
Elaff, Mohamed. The Economic Integration. 2009. 200p. pap. (978-3-639-20704-0(1)) VDM Verlag Dr. Mueller e.K.
Euromonitor International, contrib. by. New Arab Consumer. 12th rev. ed. 2010. (Illus.). xxxvi, 570p. lib. bdg. (978-1-84264-525-3(0)) Euromonitor International PLC.
Euromonitor International Staff. New Arab Consumer 2011. 4th ed. 2010. 318p. (C). pap. (978-1-84264-536-9(6)) Euromonitor International PLC.
Evans, William & Harris, Daniel J. Politics & Economics of the Middle East. 2008. (Illus.). xiv, 230p. 82.00 (978-1-60456-719-9(8)) Nova Science Pubs., Inc.
Fromherz, Allen James. Qatar: A Modern History. 2012. (ENG., Illus.). 224p. 29.95 **(978-1-58901-910-2(5))** Georgetown Univ. Pr.
Hafez, Mohamed. Modern Contract & Sales Law in the Middle Eastern & Arab Countries. 2011. 496p. pap. **(978-3-8443-0348-3(0))** Lambert Academic Publishing.
Hamid, Suhayr. Ishkaliyat Al-Tanmiyah Fi Al-Watan Al-Arabi. 2007. (ARA., Illus.). 192p. (978-9957-00-308-1(9)) Dar al-Shuru q lil-Nashr wa-al-Tawzi.
Hathaway, Jane & Barbir, Karl K. The Arab Lands under Ottoman Rule: 1516-1800. 2008. (History of the near East Ser.). (ENG., Illus.). 344p. (C). per. 53.33 (978-0-582-41899-8(2)) Longman Publishing Group.
Icon Group International, Inc. Staff, compiled by. The 2006 Economic & Product Market Databook for Doha, Qatar. 2006. 618p. ring bd. 95.00 (978-0-497-80473-2(5)) Icon Group International, Inc.
—The 2006 Economic & Product Market Databook for Jahra, Kuwait. 2006. 618p. ring bd. 95.00 (978-0-497-81941-5(4)) Icon Group International, Inc.
—The 2006 Economic & Product Market Databook for Matrah, Oman. 2006. 618p. ring bd. 95.00 (978-0-497-80977-5(X)) Icon Group International, Inc.
—The 2006 Economic & Product Market Databook for Mukalla, Yemen. 2006. 618p. ring bd. 95.00 (978-0-497-81070-2(0)) Icon Group International, Inc.
—The 2006 Economic & Product Market Databook for Muscat, Oman. 2006. 618p. ring bd. 95.00 (978-0-497-82025-1(0)) Icon Group International, Inc.
Korb, Lawrence J. & Wheeler, Winslow T. Military Reform: A Reference Handbook. 1 vol. 2007. (Contemporary Military, Strategic, & Security Issues Ser.). (Illus.). 256p. 55.00 (978-0-275-99349-8(3), C9349, Praeger Security International) Greenwood Publishing Group, Inc.
Marinov, Marin. Marketing in the Emerging Markets of Islamic Countries. 2007. (ENG., Illus.). 224p. 105.00 (978-1-4039-9173-7(1)) Palgrave Macmillan.
Mirakhor, Abbas & Hamid, Idris Samawi. Islam & Development: The Institutional Framework. 2009. pap. (978-1-59267-106-9(3)) Global Scholarly Pubns.
Moonesar, Immanuel, et al, eds. Actions & Insights - Middle East North Africa: Managing in Uncertain Times, Vol. 2. 2012. (Actions & Insights - Middle East North Africa Ser.). (Illus.). 264p. 49.95 **(978-1-78052-620-1(2))** Emerald Group Publishing Ltd. GBR. Dist: Turpin Distribution Services Ltd.
Noland, Marcus & Pack, Howard. The Arab Economies in a Changing World. (Illus.). 2007. 350p. per. 24.95 (978-0-88132-393-1(4)) 2nd ed. 2011. 362p. pap. 24.95 **(978-0-88132-628-4(3))** Peterson Institute for International Economics.
Rehman, Aamir A. Dubai & Co: Global Strategies for Doing Business in the Gulf States. 2007. (ENG., Illus.). 288p. 27.95 (978-0-07-149413-7(8), 0071494138) McGraw-Hill Cos., The.
Rivlin, Paul. Arab Economies in the Twenty-First Century. 2009. (ENG., Illus.). 328p. (C). 85.00 (978-0-521-89500-2(6)); pap. 25.99 (978-0-521-71923-0(2)) Cambridge Univ. Pr.
Sabri, Nidal Rashid. Financial Markets & Institutions in the Arab Economy. 2008. (C). 89.00 (978-1-60456-137-1(8)) Nova Science Pubs., Inc.
Schlumberger, Oliver, ed. Debating Arab Authoritarianism: Dynamics & Durability in Nondemocratic Regimes. 2007. (ENG., Illus.). 360p. 55.00 (978-0-8047-5776-8(3)) Stanford Univ. Pr.
Shaban, Hickmet. Energy, Water Resources, & Sustainability in the Arab World: Perspective & Prognosis. 2009. 520p. pap. 23.99 (978-1-4363-7350-0(6)) Xlibris Corp.
U N Development Staff, et al. Arab Human Development Report 2005: Towards the Rise of Women in the Arab World. 2007. (ENG., Illus.). 260p. pap. 25.95 (978-0-8047-5530-6(2)) Stanford Univ. Pr.
United Nations Development Programme: Regional Bureau for Arab States, et al. Arab human development Report 2009: Challenges to human security in the Arab Countries. 2009. (Illus.). 288p. pap. 24.95 (978-92-1-126211-7(9)) United Nations Pubns.
Winckler, Onn. Arab Political Demography: Population Growth, Labor Migration & Natalist Policies. 2nd rev. exp. ed. 2009. (ENG.). 328p. 120.00 (978-1-84519-238-9(9)); (Illus.). pap. 60.00 (978-1-84519-240-2(0)) Sussex Academic Pr. GBR. Dist: International Specialized Bk. Services.
World Bank (Afghanistan) Staff. Better Governance for Development in the Middle East & North Africa Vol. 2: The Political Economy of Reforms. Al-Dahdah, Edouard et al, eds. 2010. (MENA Development Report). (ENG.). 500p. pap. 35.00 (978-0-8213-7948-6(8), 9780821379486) World Bank Pubns.

ARAB COUNTRIES—FOREIGN RELATIONS
Abd Allah, Muhammad Ibrahim Abdi. Mushkilat Al-Sumal Al-Gharbi Wa-Atharuha Ala Al-Alaqat Al-Arabiyah-Al-Ifriqiyah: 1960-1988 M. 2010. (ARA.). 223p. (978-977-10-2566-5(X)) Dar al-Fikr al-Arabi.
Alkim, Hassan Hamdan. Arab Foreign Policy-Making in the Twenty-First Century: Domestic Contraints & External Challenges. 2012. (ENG., Illus.). 400p. 65.00 **(978-0-86356-446-8(1))** Saqi Bks. GBR. Dist: Consortium Bk. Sales & Distribution.
Ata M. Hassan, Ata Hassan. An Arab Awakening Tied to Arab Union's Formation: A Techno-Economic Digital Age Revolution for Arab Region Advancement. 2010. 156p. pap. 14.99 (978-1-4269-2165-0(9)) Trafford Publishing.
Bishara, Marwan. The Invisible Arab: The Promise & Peril of the Arab Revolutions. 2012. (ENG.). 272p. (gr. 9). 26.00 **(978-1-56858-708-0(2))** Basic Bks.

Blackwell & Blackwell, Stephen. British Military Intervention & the Struggle for Jordan: King Hussein, Nasser & the Middle East Crisis, 1955-1958. 2008. (British Politics & Society Ser.). (ENG., Illus.). 268p. (C). 138.00 *(978-0-7146-5699-1(2))* Routledge.

Caplan, Neil. The Israel-Palestine Conflict: Contested Histories. 2009. (Contesting the Past Ser.). (ENG., Illus.). 336p. pap. 39.95 *(978-1-4051-7538-8(9))*; 104.95 *(978-1-4051-7539-5(7))* Wiley, John & Sons, Inc. (Wiley-Blackwell).

Coller, Ian. Arab France: Islam & the Making of Modern Europe, 1798-1831. 2010. (ENG., Illus.). 304p. 60.00 *(978-0-520-26064-1(3))*; pap. 24.95 *(978-0-520-26065-8(1))* Univ. of California Pr.

Cram101 Textbook Reviews Staff. Outlines & Highlights for Dubai & Co: Global Strategies for Doing Business in the Gulf States by Rehman, ISBN. 2008. 108p. pap. 11.95 *(978-1-4288-6450-4(4))* Cram101 Inc.

Deng, Francis & Deng, Francis Mading. Frontiers of Unity: An Experiment in Afro-Arab Cooperation. 2009. (ENG., Illus.). 240p. 120.00 *(978-0-7103-1352-2(7))* Routledge.

Djerejian, Edward P. Changing Minds, Winning Peace: A New Strategic Direction for U. S. Public Diplomacy in the Arab & Muslim World. 2007. 79p. pap. 12.95 *(978-0-615-15742-9(4))* Crossbow Bks.

El-Bendary, Mohamed. The Ugly American in the Arab Mind: Why Do Arabs Resent America? 2011. (Illus.). 220p. 27.50 *(978-1-59797-673-2(3))* Potomac Bks., Inc.

Elaff, Mohamed. The Economic Integration. 2009. 200p. pap. *(978-3-639-20704-0(1))* VDM Verlag Dr. Mueller e.K.

Emirates Center for Strategic Studies and Research Staff & Tauris, I. B. Current Transformations & Their Potential Role in Realizing Change in the Arab World. 2007. (ENG.). 522p. 100.00 *(978-9948-00-873-6(1)*, Emirates Center for Strategic Studies) I. B. Tauris & Co., Ltd. GBR. Dist: Macmillan.

Emirates Centre for Strategic Studies and Research Staff & Tauris, I. B. Current Transformations & Their Potential Role in Realizing Change in the Arab World. 2007. (ENG.). 522p. pap. 36.00 *(978-9948-00-874-3(X)*, Emirates Center for Strategic Studies) I. B. Tauris & Co., Ltd. GBR. Dist: Macmillan.

Friedman, Isaiah. British Pan-Arab Policy, 1915-1922. 2009. (ENG., Illus.). 370p. 69.95 *(978-1-4128-1074-6(4))* Transaction Pubs.

Ginor, Isabella & Remez, Gideon. Foxbats over Dimona: The Soviets' Nuclear Gamble in the Six-Day War. 2008. (ENG., Illus.). 304p. pap. 17.00 *(978-0-300-13627-2(7))* Yale Univ. Pr.

Hajji, Tariq Ahmad & Heggy, Tarek. The Arab Cocoon: Progress & Modernity in Arab Societies. 2010. 160p. 59.95 *(978-0-85303-922-8(4))* Vallentine Mitchell Pubs. GBR. Dist: International Specialized Bk. Services.

Harrigan, Jane & El-Said, Hamed, eds. Globalisation, Democratisation & Radicalisation in the Arab World. 2011. (ENG., Illus.). 272p. 105.00 *(978-0-230-27360-3(2))* Palgrave Macmillan.

Heggy, Tarek. The Arab Cocoon: Progress & Modernity in Arab Societies. 2011. 160p. pap. 29.99 *(978-0-85303-892-4(9))* Vallentine Mitchell Pubs. GBR. Dist: International Specialized Bk. Services.

Jones, Alun. Europe & the Arab States. 2006. 220p. pap. *(978-1-84472-030-9(6)*, Routledge) Taylor & Francis Group.

Jones, Alun & Clarke, Julian. Europe & the Arab States. 2008. 224p. 140.00 *(978-1-84472-164-1(7))* Taylor & Francis Group GBR. Dist: Taylor & Francis Group.

Kursun, Zekeriya. The Ottomans in Qatar. 2010. 108.56 *(978-1-61719-110-7(8))* Gorgias Pr., LLC.

Lawson, Fred H. Constructing International Relations in the Arab World. 2006. (ENG.). 224p. 50.00 *(978-0-8047-5372-2(5))* Stanford Univ. Pr.

Lughod, Ibrahim Abu. Arab Rediscovery of Europe: A Study in Cultural Encounters. 2011. (Saqi Essentials Ser.). (ENG.). 200p. pap. 21.95 ***(978-0-86356-403-1(8))*** Saqi Bks. GBR. Dist: Consortium Bk. Sales & Distribution.

Makdisi, Ussama. Faith Misplaced: The Broken Promise of U. S. - Arab Relations, 1820-2001. 2010. (ENG., Illus.). 432p. 28.95 *(978-1-58648-680-8(2))* PublicAffairs.

—Faith Misplaced: The Broken Promise of U. S. -Arab Relations: 1820-2001. 2011. (ENG., Illus.). 432p. pap. 17.99 *(978-1-58648-961-8(5))* PublicAffairs.

Maloney, Suzanne. Iran's Long Reach: Iran as a Pivotal State in the Muslim World. 2008. (Pivotal State Ser.). (Illus.). 156p. pap. 14.95 *(978-1-60127-033-7(X))* U. S. Institute of Peace Pr. (USIP Pr.).

Mills, Robin M. The Myth of the Oil Crisis: Overcoming the Challenges of Depletion, Geopolitics, & Global Warming, 1 vol. 2008. (Illus.). 336p. 44.95 *(978-0-313-35479-3(0)*, C35479, Praeger Pubs.) Greenwood Publishing Group, Inc.

Mohs, Polly A. Military Intelligence & the Arab Revolt: The First Modern Intelligence War. 2007. (Studies in Intelligence Ser.). (ENG., Illus.). 272p. (C). 150.00 *(978-0-415-37280-0(1))* Routledge.

Noueihed, Lin & Warren, Alex. The Battle for the Arab Spring: Revolution, Counter-Revolution & the Making of a New Era. 2012. (ENG., Illus.). 304p. 28.00 ***(978-0-300-18086-2(1))*** Yale Univ. Pr.

Rehman, Aamir A. Dubai & Co: Global Strategies for Doing Business in the Gulf States. 2007. (ENG., Illus.). 288p. 27.95 *(978-0-07-149413-7(8)*, 0071494138) McGraw-Hill Cos., The.

Rivlin, Paul. Arab Economies in the Twenty-First Century. 2009. (ENG., Illus.). 328p. (C). 85.00 *(978-0-521-89500-2(6))*; pap. 25.99 *(978-0-521-71923-0(2))* Cambridge Univ. Pr.

Ro'i, Yaacov & Morozov, Boris, eds. The Soviet Union & the June 1967 Six Day War. 2008. (Cold War International History Project Ser.). (ENG.). 392p. 60.00 *(978-0-8047-5880-2(8))* Stanford Univ. Pr.

Routledge Staff, creator. A Survey of Arab-Israeli Relations. 3rd rev. ed. 2006. (Illus.). 551p. 260.00 *(978-1-85743-394-4(7))* Routledge.

Rugh & Rugh, William A. Engaging the Arab & Islamic Worlds Through Public Diplomacy: A Report & Action Recommendations. 3904. (Illus.). vii, 174p. pap. *(978-0-9764391-0-3(7)*, Branch Line Video) Rusch & Co.

Ryan, Curtis R. Inter-Arab Alliances: Regime Security & Jordanian Foreign Policy. 2009. (Governance & International Relations in the Middle East Ser.). (ENG., Illus.). 272p. 69.95 *(978-0-8130-3307-5(1))* Univ. Pr. of Florida.

Simpfendorfer, Ben. The New Silk Road: How a Rising Arab World Is Turning Away from the West & Rediscovering China. 2009. (ENG.). 256p. 46.00 *(978-0-230-58026-8(2))* Palgrave Macmillan.

—The New Silk Road - Revised & Updated: How a Rising Arab World Is Turning Away from the West & Rediscovering China. rev. ed. 2011. (ENG., Illus.). 224p. pap. 22.00 *(978-0-230-28485-2(X))* Palgrave Macmillan.

Smith, Grant. Visa Denied: How Anti-Arab Visa Policies Destroy US Exports, Jobs & Higher Education. 2007. per. 19.95 *(978-0-9764437-6-6(7))* Institute for Research.

Smith, Lee. The Strong Horse: Power, Politics, & the Clash of Arab Civilizations. 2011. 256p. pap. 14.95 *(978-0-7679-2180-0(1)*, Anchor) Knopf Doubleday Publishing Group.

ARAB COUNTRIES—GUIDEBOOKS

American University in Cairo Press, ed. New Atlas of the Arab World. 2011. (ENG., Illus.). 144p. 39.50 *(978-977-416-419-4(9))* American Univ. in Cairo Pr. EGY. Dist: Oxford Univ. Pr., Inc.

Explorer Publishing, creator. Kuwait Explorer Residents' Guide. 2007. (Explorer (Explorer Publishing) Ser.). (ENG., Illus.). 300p. pap. 24.95 *(978-976-8182-46-3(6))* Explorer Publishing UAE. Dist: Globe Pequot Pr., The.

Peters, James. The Arab World. 3rd ed. 2009. (ARA & ENG., Illus.). 150p. pap., instr.'s hndbk. ed. 18.95 ***(978-1-906768-03-4(X)***, Stacey International) Stacey Publishing GBR. Dist: Midpoint Trade Bks., Inc.

Popp, Georg & Al-Maskari, Juma. Oman: Jewel of the Arabian Gulf. 2010. (Odyssey Illustrated Guides). (ENG., Illus.). 416p. pap. 27.95 *(978-962-217-813-7(8)*, 217813) Airphoto International/Odyssey HKG. Dist: Norton, W. W. & Co., Inc.

Thomas, Gavin. The Rough Guide to Oman. 2011. (ENG., Illus.). 344p. 22.99 *(978-1-84836-598-8(5))* Rough Guides, Ltd. GBR. Dist: Dorling Kindersley Publishing, Inc.

ARAB COUNTRIES—HISTORY

see also Jewish-Arab Relations

Al Jallad, Nader & Monferrer-Sala, Juan Pedro, eds. The Arabic Language Across the Ages. 2010. (ENG., Illus.). 182p. (C). 168.00 *(978-3-89500-765-1(X))* Reichert, Ludwig Dr. DEU. Dist: Brown, David Bk. Co., The.

Al-Jurhumi, Abid bin Sharya. The History, Poetry, & Genealogy of Yemen. 2006. (Gorgias Historical Texts: 16). 185p. 75.00 *(978-1-59333-516-8(4))* Gorgias Pr., LLC.

Al-Naqeeb, Khaldoun Nassan. Society & State in the Gulf & Arab Peninsula (RLE: the Arab Nation) A Different Perspective, Volume 4. 2012. (Routledge Library Editions: the Arab Nation Ser.). (ENG.). 232p. 115.00 ***(978-0-415-62396-4(0))*** Routledge.

Allen, Mark & Allen. Arabs. 2006. (ENG.). 160p. 32.95 *(978-0-8264-9055-1(7))* Continuum International Publishing Group, Ltd. GBR. Dist: National Bk. Network.

Berton, Joseph. T. E. Lawrence & the Arab Revolt: An Illustrated Guide. 2011. (Illus.). 208p. 77.00 ***(978-84-96658-35-6(X))*** Andrea Pr. ESP. Dist: Casemate Pubs. & Bk. Distributors, LLC.

Fromherz, Allen James. Qatar: A Modern History. 2012. (ENG., Illus.). 224p. 29.95 ***(978-1-58901-910-2(5))*** Georgetown Univ. Pr.

Geographie d'Edrisi. 1088p. reprint ed. lib. bdg. 175.00 *(978-0-89241-184-9(8))* Caratzas, Aristide D. Pub.

Ghubash, Hussein. Oman - the Islamic Democratic Tradition. 2008. (Illus.). XIV, 258p. 39.95 *(978-0-415-48132-8(5))* Routledge.

Halm, Heinz. The Arabes: A Short History with Documents. Brown, Allison, tr. from GER. 2011. (Illus.). 260p. pap. *(978-1-55876-546-7(8))* Wiener, Markus Pubs., Inc.

—The Arabs: A Short History. Brown, Allison & Lampert, Thomas, trs. from GER. (Illus.). 172p. 2007. 89.95 *(978-1-55876-416-3(X))* 2006. per. 24.95 *(978-1-55876-417-0(8))* Wiener, Markus Pubs., Inc.

—The Arabs: A Short History with Documents. Brown, Allison & Lampert, Thomas, trs. from GER. 2011. (Illus.). 260p. 89.95 *(978-1-55876-545-0(X))* Wiener, Markus Pubs., Inc.

Hamilton, Alastair. The Arcadian Library: Western Appreciation of Arab & Islamic Civilization. 2011. (ENG., Illus.). 408p. 250.00 *(978-0-19-960963-5(2))* Oxford Univ. Pr., Inc.

Higgins, Andrew. With the SAS & Other Animals. 2011. (Illus.). 256p. 39.95 ***(978-1-84884-486-5(7))*** Pen & Sword Bks. Ltd. GBR. Dist: Casemate Pubs. & Bk. Distributors, LLC.

Hourani, Albert & Ruthven, Malise. A History of the Arab Peoples: With a New Afterword. 2nd ed. 2010. (Illus.). 624p. pap. 18.95 *(978-0-674-05819-4(4)*, Belknap Pr.) Harvard Univ. Pr.

Ibn Ruzayq, Hlgrave;pound;amilgrave;bdquo;d ibn MAring;laquo;hlgrave;pound;ammad. History of the Imoms & Seyyids of 'Omon: From A.D., 661-1856. Badger, George Percy, tr. 2010. (Cambridge Library Collection- Hakluyt First Ser.). (Illus.). 596p. pap. 43.00 *(978-1-108-01138-9(1))* Cambridge Univ. Pr.

Khurdadbeh. Le Livre des Routes & des Provinces par Ibn-Khordadbeh. De Meynard, C. Barbier, tr. (FRE.). 278p. (C). lib. bdg. 60.00 *(978-0-89241-223-5(2))* Caratzas, Aristide D. Pub.

Klaver, Ivo. European Scientific Expeditions to the Arab World, 1761-1881. 2009. (Studies in the Arcadian Library). (ENG., Illus.). 240p. 195.00 *(978-0-19-956889-5(8))* Oxford Univ. Pr., Inc.

Majcher-Atassi, Sonja & Schwartz, John Pedro. Archives Museums & Collecting Practices in the Modern Arab World. 2012. (Illus.). 224p. 99.95 ***(978-1-4094-4616-3(6))*** Ashgate Publishing Co.

Marshu, Ghrighwar Mansur. Al-Fusam Fi Al-Fikr Al-Arabi Al-Muasir. 2007. (ARA.). 350p. *(978-1-59239-701-3(8))* Dar Al-Fikr Al-Mouaser.

Mohs, Polly A. Military Intelligence & the Arab Revolt: The First Modern Intelligence War. 2007. (Studies in Intelligence Ser.). (ENG., Illus.). 272p. (C). 150.00 *(978-0-415-37280-0(1))* Routledge.

Nizaat Al-Hudud Fi Al-Alam Al-Arabi: Min Nihayat Al-Qarn Al-Ishrin Ilá Bidayat Al-Qarn Al-Wahid Wa-Al-Ishrin. 2009. (ARA.). 424p. *(978-977-313-279-8(X))* Markaz al-Mahrusah lil-Buhuth wa-al-Tadrib wa-al-Malumat.

Noland, Marcus & Pack, Howard. The Arab Economies in a Changing World. 2nd ed. 2011. (Illus.). 362p. pap. 24.95 ***(978-0-88132-628-4(3))*** Peterson Institute for International Economics.

Sabry, Tarik, ed. Arab Cultural Studies: Mapping the Field. 2012. (ENG., Illus.). 320p. pap. 31.00 ***(978-1-84885-559-5(1))***; 85.00 ***(978-1-84885-558-8(3))*** I. B. Tauris & Co., Ltd. GBR. Dist: Macmillan.

Saouli, Adham. The Arab State: Dilemmas of Late Formation. 2011. (Routledge Studies in Middle Eastern Politics Ser.). (ENG., Illus.). 176p. (C). 125.00 *(978-0-415-60295-2(5))* Routledge.

Vaiou, Maria. Diplomacy in the Early Islamic World: A Tenth-Century Treatise on Arab-Byzantine Relations. 2012. (Library of Middle East History Ser.). (ENG.). 288p. 92.50 *(978-1-84511-652-1(6)*, Tauris Academic Studies) I. B. Tauris & Co., Ltd. GBR. Dist: Macmillan.

ARAB COUNTRIES—HISTORY—TO 622

see Africa, North—History; Arabs—History—To 622; Middle East—History—To 622

ARAB COUNTRIES—HISTORY—622-1516

see Islamic Empire

ARAB COUNTRIES—HISTORY—1517-1918

Gruzinski, Serge. What Time Is It There? 2011. (ENG.). 200p. 64.95 *(978-0-7456-4752-4(9))*; pap. 22.95 *(978-0-7456-4753-1(7))* Polity Pr. GBR. Dist: Wiley, John & Sons, Inc.

Hathaway, Jane, ed. & contrib. by. The Arab Lands in the Ottoman Era. 2009. (ENG., Illus.). 304p. 60.00 *(978-0-9797559-1-0(3))* Ctr. for Early Modern History.

Matar, N. I. Europe Through Arab Eyes, 1578-1727. 2008. 352p. pap. *(978-0-231-51208-4(2))* Columbia Univ. Pr.

Rogan, Eugene. The Arabs: A History. 2011. (ENG., Illus.). 592p. (gr. 9). pap. 19.99 *(978-0-465-02504-6(8))* Basic Bks.

Stripling, George William Frederick. The Ottoman Turks & the Arabs, 1511-1574. 2011. 138p. 40.95 ***(978-1-258-05407-6(8))*** Literary Licensing, LLC.

ARAB COUNTRIES—HISTORY—1798-

Duri, A. A. The Historical Formation of the Arab Nation (RLE: the Arab Nation), Volume 1. 2012. (Routledge Library Editions: the Arab Nation Ser.). (ENG.). 384p. 130.00 ***(978-0-415-62286-8(7))*** Routledge.

ARAB COUNTRIES—HISTORY—20TH CENTURY

see also Arab-Israeli Conflict; Jewish-Arab Relations

Destani, Bejtullah D. Muslim Minorities in Arab Countries, 1843-1973, 4 vols. 2006. (Cambridge Archive Editions Ser.). (ENG.). 2400p. 2395.00 *(978-1-84097-180-4(0))* Archive Editions, Ltd. GBR. Dist: Cambridge Univ. Pr.

Hamdan, Abd al-Hamid Salih & Hamdan, Jamal. Jamal Hamdan Wa-Turathuhu Al-Fikri. 2007. (ARA.). 226p. *(978-977-232-576-4(4))* Dar Al-Lataif.

McNamara, Robert. The Hashemites? The Dream of Arabia - The Peace Conferences of, 1919-23 & Their Aftermath. 2010. (Makers of the Modern World Ser.). (ENG., Illus.). 220p. 19.95 *(978-1-905791-66-8(6))* Haus Publishing GBR. Dist: Consortium Bk. Sales & Distribution.

Mohs, Polly A. Military Intelligence & the Arab Revolt: The First Modern Intelligence War. 2009. 260p. pap. 39.95 *(978-0-415-49331-4(5))* Routledge.

Schneider, James J. Guerrilla Leader: T. E. Lawrence & the Arab Revolt. 2011. (ENG., Illus.). 368p. 28.00 *(978-0-553-80764-6(1))* Random House Publishing Group.

ARAB COUNTRIES—POLITICS AND GOVERNMENT

Abu-Rabi', Ibrahim, ed. The Contemporary Arab Reader on Political Islam. 2010. 352p. pap. *(978-0-88864-557-9(0))* Univ. of Alberta Pr. CAN. Dist: Michigan State Univ. Pr.

Abu-Rabi', Ibrahim M., ed. The Contemporary Arab Reader on Political Islam, 1 vol. 2010. (ENG.). 352p. 35.00 *(978-0-7453-2889-8(X))*; lib. bdg. 104.00 *(978-0-7453-2890-4(3))* Pluto Pr. GBR. Dist: Macmillan.

Al-Atrash, Ahmed. Inter-Arab Management of Regional Conflicts. 2010. 296p. pap. *(978-3-8383-7646-2(3))* Lambert Academic Publishing.

Al-Faqih, Abdullah. Political Citizenship in the Republic of Yemen: Constitutional, Legal, & Practical Dimensions. 2008. 100p. pap. *(978-3-639-09252-3(X))* VDM Verlag Dr. Mueller e.K.

Al-Jabri, Mohammad Abed A. Democracy, Human Rights & Law in Islamic Thought. 2009. (ENG.). 256p. 89.00 *(978-1-84511-749-8(2))* I. B. Tauris & Co., Ltd. GBR. Dist: Macmillan.

Amin, Magdi, et al. After the Spring: Economic Transition in the Arab World. 2012. (ENG., Illus.). 192p. 35.00 ***(978-0-19-992492-9(9))*** Oxford Univ. Pr., Inc.

Ata M. Hassan, Ata Hassan. An Arab Awakening Tied to Arab Union's Formation: A Techno-Economic Digital Age Revolution for Arab Region Advancement. 2010. 156p. pap. 14.99 *(978-1-4269-2165-0(9))* Trafford Publishing.

Awad, Samir. Persistence of Authoritarianism in the Middle East. 2010. 224p. pap. *(978-3-8383-4269-6(0))* Lambert Academic Publishing.

Ayubi, Nazih N. Over-Stating the Arab State: Politics & Society in the Middle East. 2009. (ENG., Illus.). 320p. pap. 33.00 *(978-1-85043-828-1(5))* I. B. Tauris & Co., Ltd. GBR. Dist: Macmillan.

Barr, James. Setting the Desert on Fire: T. E. Lawrence & Britain's Secret War in Arabia, 1916-1918. (ENG., Illus.). 400p. 2009. pap. 17.95 *(978-0-393-33527-9(5)*, 33527) 2008. 27.95 *(978-0-393-06040-9(3)*, 6040) Norton, W. W. & Co., Inc.

Biddle, Stephen & Friedman, Jeffrey A. The 2006 Lebanon Campaign & the Future of Warfare: Implications for Army & Defense Policy. 2008. pap. *(978-1-58487-362-4(0))* Strategic Studies Institute, U.S. Army War College Commandant (AWCC-DSI/Pubns.).

Billingsley, Anthony. Political Succession in the Arab World: Constitutions, Family Loyalties & Islam. 2010. (Routledge Studies in Middle Eastern Politics Ser.). (ENG., Illus.). 264p. (C). 120.00 *(978-0-415-49536-3(9))* Routledge.

Bishara, Marwan. The Invisible Arab: The Promise & Peril of the Arab Revolutions. 2012. (ENG.). 272p. (gr. 9). 26.00 ***(978-1-56858-708-0(2))*** Basic Bks.

Brichs, Ferran, ed. Political Regimes in the Arab World: Society & the Exercise of Power. 2012. (Routledge Studies in Middle Eastern Politics Ser.). (ENG., Illus.). 304p. (C). 125.00 ***(978-0-415-62566-1(1))*** Routledge.

Browers, Michaelle L. & Browers, Michaelle. Political Ideology in the Arab World: Accommodation & Transformation. 2009. (Cambridge Middle East Studies). (ENG.). 210p. 85.00 *(978-0-521-76532-9(3))*; pap. 32.99 *(978-0-521-74934-3(4))* Cambridge Univ. Pr.

Brown, Nathan J. The Struggle over Democracy in the Middle East: Regional Politics & External Policies. Shahin, Emad, ed. 2009. (UCLA Center for Middle East Development (CMED) Ser.). (Illus.). 212p. 140.00 *(978-0-415-77379-9(2))* Routledge.

Brown, Nathan J. When Victory Is Not an Option: Islamist Movements in Arab Politics. 2012. (ENG.). 272p. 69.95 ***(978-0-8014-5036-5(5))***; pap. 24.95 ***(978-0-8014-7772-0(7))*** Cornell Univ. Pr.

Brown, Nathan J. & Shahin, Emad, eds. The Struggle over Democracy in the Middle East: Regional Politics & External Policies. 2009. (UCLA Center for Middle East Development (CMED) Ser.). (ENG., Illus.). 224p. (C). 44.95 *(978-0-415-77380-5(6))* Routledge.

Cavatorta, Francesco & Durac, Vincent. Civil Society & Democratization in the Arab World: The Dynamics of Activism. 2010. (Routledge Studies in Middle Eastern Politics Ser.). (ENG., Illus.). 192p. (C). 140.00 *(978-0-415-49129-7(0))* Routledge.

Choucair-Vizoso, Julia, ed. Beyond the Facade: Political Reform in the Arab World. 2008. (ENG.). 295p. per. 22.95 *(978-0-87003-239-4(9))* Carnegie Endowment for International Peace.

Cleveland, William L. Islam Against the West: Shakib Arslan & the Campaign for Islamic Nationalism. 2011. (ENG.). 248p. pap. 25.00 ***(978-0-292-73733-4(5))*** Univ. of Texas Pr.

Corr, Edwin G., et al. The Search for Israel-Arab Peace: Learning from the Past & Building Trust. 2007. (Sussex Studies in Peace Politics in the Middle East Ser.). (ENG.). 286p. (C). 67.50 *(978-1-84519-191-7(9))* Sussex Academic Pr. GBR. Dist: International Specialized Bk. Services.

Dirosilia, Benyamin. Yemen: Foreign Relations & Challenges. 2012. (Middle East in Turmoil/Politics & Economics of the Middle East Ser.). 156p. 125.00 ***(978-1-61470-827-8(4))*** Nova Science Pubs., Inc.

Elbadawi, Ibrahim. Democracy in the Arab World: Explaining the Deficit. 2010. pap. 15.00 *(978-0-415-58740-2(9))* Routledge.

Elbadawi, Ibrahim & Makdisi, Samir, eds. Democracy in the Arab World: Explaining the Deficit. 2010. (Routledge Studies in Middle Eastern Politics Ser.). (ENG., Illus.). 352p. (C). 130.00 *(978-0-415-77999-9(5))* Routledge.

Elkhaffif, Mahmoud A. T., et al, eds. Trade Policies Employment & Poverty in Arab Countries. 2012. (Routledge Political Economy of the Middle East & North Africa Ser.). (ENG., Illus.). 368p. (C). 185.00 ***(978-0-415-51945-8(4))*** Routledge.

Emirates Center for Strategic Studies and Research Staff. Future Arabian Gulf Energy Sources: Hydrocarbon, Nuclear or Renewable? 2009. (ENG., Illus.). 472p. 103.00 *(978-9948-00-990-0(8)*, Emirates Center for Strategic Studies) I. B. Tauris & Co., Ltd. GBR. Dist: Macmillan.

Emirates Center for Strategic Studies and Research Staff & Tauris, I. B. Current Transformations & Their Potential Role in Realizing Change in the Arab World. 2007. (ENG.). 522p. 100.00 *(978-9948-00-873-6(1)*, Emirates Center for Strategic Studies) I. B. Tauris & Co., Ltd. GBR. Dist: Macmillan.

Emirates Centre for Strategic Studies and Research Staff & Tauris, I. B. Current Transformations & Their Potential Role in Realizing Change in the Arab World. 2007. (ENG.). 522p. pap. 36.00 *(978-9948-00-874-3(X)*, Emirates Center for Strategic Studies) I. B. Tauris & Co., Ltd. GBR. Dist: Macmillan.

Esber, Rosemarie M. Under the Cover of War: The Zionist Expulsion of the Palestinians. 2008. (Illus.). 440p. 29.95 *(978-0-9815131-7-1(4))* Arabicus Bks. & Media.

Evans, William & Harris, Daniel J. Politics & Economics of the Middle East. 2008. (Illus.). xiv, 230p. 82.00 *(978-1-60456-719-9(8))* Nova Science Pubs., Inc.

Fandy, Mamoun. (un)Civil War of Words: Media & Politics in the Arab World, 1 vol. 2007. (Praeger Security International Ser.). 176p. 49.95 *(978-0-275-99393-1(0)*, C9393, Praeger Security International) Greenwood Publishing Group, Inc.

Farah, Caesar A. Arabs & Ottomans. 2010. 146.12 *(978-1-61719-089-6(6))* Gorgias Pr., LLC.

Filiu, Jean-Pierre. The Arab Revolution: Ten Lessons from the Democratic Uprising. 2011. (ENG.). 208p. 21.95 ***(978-0-19-939829-9(4))*** Oxford Univ. Pr., Inc.

Friedman, Isaiah. British Pan-Arab Policy, 1915-1922. 2009. (ENG., Illus.). 370p. 69.95 *(978-1-4128-1074-6(4))* Transaction Pubs.

Fromherz, Allen James. Qatar: A Modern History. 2012. (ENG., Illus.). 224p. 29.95 ***(978-1-58901-910-2(5))*** Georgetown Univ. Pr.

Gelvin, James L. The Arab Uprisings: What Everyone Needs to Know, 1 vol. 2012. (What Everyone Needs to Know Ser.). (ENG.). 208p. 74.00 ***(978-0-19-989175-7(3))***; pap. 16.95 ***(978-0-19-989177-1(X))*** Oxford Univ. Pr., Inc.

Ghanem, As'ad. Palestinian Politics after Arafat: A Failed National Movement. 2010. (Indiana Series in Middle East Studies). (ENG.). 222p. 65.00 *(978-0-253-35427-3(7)*, 0253354277); pap. 24.95 *(978-0-253-22160-5(9)*, 0253221609) Indiana Univ. Pr.

Ghosh, Bobby & Time Magazine Editors. Time the New Middle East. 2012. (ENG., Illus.). 112p. 24.95 ***(978-1-61893-023-1(0)***, Time Bks.) Time Home Entertainment, Inc.

Ghubash, Hussein. Oman - the Islamic Democratic Tradition. 2008. (Illus.). XIV, 258p. 39.95 *(978-0-415-48132-8(5))* Routledge.

Hammond, Jeremy R. The Rejection of Palestinian Self-Determination. 2009. 79p. pap. 9.99 *(978-0-557-09569-8(7))* Lulu Enterprises Inc.

Hasan, Dhibian Shamam. Historic & Cultural Determinants of Arab Countries Diplomacy: Fundamental Facts, Evolution, Culture, Institutions, Arab Diplomacy in the L. A. S, Arab Group in the U. N. 2011. 260p. pap. ***(978-3-639-33651-1(8))*** VDM Verlag Dr. Mueller e.K.

Ibrahim, Saad E. & Lawson, Kay, eds. Political Parties & Democracy Vol. 5: The Arab World. 2010. (Political Parties in Context Ser.). (Illus.). 252p. 44.95 *(978-0-275-97082-6(5)*, C7082, Praeger Pubs.) Greenwood Publishing Group, Inc.

Kadhim, Kais A. A Discourse Analytical Approach to Stylistic Variations Employed in Arabic Translation of English News Stories: Transmitting Political News Across Linguistic & Cultural Boundaries. 2011. *(978-0-7734-1427-3(4))* Mellen, Edwin Pr., The.

Kanna, Ahmed, ed. The Superlative City: Dubai & the Urban Condition in the Early Twenty-First Century. 2007. (Aga Khan Program of the Graduate School of Design Ser.). (Illus.). 200p. pap. 24.95 *(978-0-9771224-3-1(3))* Harvard Univ., Graduate Schl. of Design.

Kaye, Dalia Dassa & Wehrey, Frederic. More Freedom, Less Terror? Liberalization & Political Violence in the Arab World. 2008. (Illus.). 228p. pap. 39.00 *(978-0-8330-4508-9(3)*, mg-772) RAND Corp., The.

Khalili, Laleh, ed. Politics of the Modern Arab World, 4 vols. 2008. (Critical Issues in Modern Politics Ser.). (ENG., Illus.). 2128p. 1043.00 *(978-0-415-45159-8(0))* Routledge.

—Politics of the Modern Arab World Vol. 1: Critical Concepts in the Modern Politics of the Middle East, 4 vols. 2008. (Illus.). 560p. *(978-0-415-45560-2(X))* Routledge.

—Politics of the Modern Arab World Vol. 2: Critical Concepts in the Modern Politics of the Middle East, 4 vols. 2008. (Illus.). 472p. *(978-0-415-45561-9(8))* Routledge.

—Politics of the Modern Arab World Vol. 3: Critical Concepts in the Modern Politics of the Middle East, 4 vols. 2008. (Illus.). 584p. *(978-0-415-45562-6(6))* Routledge.

—Politics of the Modern Arab World Vol. 4: Critical Concepts in the Modern Politics of the Middle East, 4 vols. 2008. (Illus.). 512p. *(978-0-415-45563-3(4))* Routledge.

Khosrokhavar, Farhad. The New Arab Revolutions That Shook the World, 1 vol. 2012. (ENG.). 256p. 29.95 ***(978-1-61205-083-6(2))*** Paradigm Pubs.

Khouri, Ellen, tr. from ARA. Voice of Hezbollah: The Statements of Sayyed Hassan Nasrallah. 2007. (ENG., Illus.). 320p. per. 19.95 *(978-1-84467-153-3(4)*, 844153) Verso Bks. GBR. Dist: Norton, W. W. & Co., Inc.

Kraetzschmar, Hendrik Jan, ed. The Dynamics of Reform Coalitions in the Arab World. 2012. (ENG.). 224p. (C). 125.00 ***(978-0-415-50638-0(7))*** Routledge.

Levine, Mark. Impossible Peace: Israel/Palestine Since 1989. 2009. (Global History of the Present Ser.). (ENG., Illus.). 240p. pap. 25.95 *(978-1-84277-769-5(6))* Zed Bks., Ltd. GBR. Dist: Macmillan.

—Impossible Peace: Israel/Palestine since 1989. 2009. (Global History of the Present Ser.). (ENG., Illus.). 240p. 85.95 *(978-1-84277-768-8(8))* Zed Bks., Ltd. GBR. Dist: Macmillan.

Lucas, Russell E. The Politics of Arab Monarchies: Legacy, Survival & Reform. 2013. (Routledge Studies in Middle Eastern Politics Ser.). (ENG.). 224p. (C). 120.00 *(978-0-415-49788-6(4))* Routledge.

Lust-Okar, Ellen. Structuring Conflict in the Arab World: Incumbents, Opponents, & Institutions. 2007. (ENG., Illus.). 296p. pap. 58.00 *(978-0-521-03286-5(5))* Cambridge Univ. Pr.

Lynch, Marc. The Arab Uprising: The Unfinished Revolutions of the New Middle East. 2012. (ENG., Illus.). 288p. 26.99 ***(978-1-61039-084-2(9))*** PublicAffairs.

Makdisi, Ussama. Faith Misplaced: The Broken Promise of U. S. - Arab Relations, 1820-2001. 2010. (ENG., Illus.). 432p. 28.95 *(978-1-58648-680-8(2))* PublicAffairs.

—Faith Misplaced: The Broken Promise of U. S. -Arab Relations: 1820-2001. 2011. (ENG., Illus.). 432p. pap. 17.99 *(978-1-58648-961-8(5))* PublicAffairs.

Manea, Elham. The Arab State & Women's Rights: The Trap of Authoritarian Governance. 2011. (Routledge Studies in Middle Eastern Politics Ser.). (ENG., Illus.). 256p. (C). 125.00 *(978-0-415-61773-4(1))* Routledge.

McCaffrey, Paul. The Arab Spring. 2012. ***(978-0-8242-1116-5(2))*** Wilson, H.W.

Muasher, Marwan. The Arab Center: The Promise of Moderation. 2009. (ENG., Illus.). 336p. pap. 20.00 *(978-0-300-15114-5(4))* Yale Univ. Pr.

Noland, Marcus & Pack, Howard. The Arab Economies in a Changing World. 2nd ed. 2011. (Illus.). 362p. pap. 24.95 ***(978-0-88132-628-4(3))*** Peterson Institute for International Economics.

Nonneman. Democracy, Reform & Authoritarianism in the Arab World V1. 2010. 400p. *(978-0-415-47287-6(3))* Routledge.

—Democracy, Reform & Authoritarianism in the Arab World V2. 2010. 400p. *(978-0-415-47286-9(5))* Routledge.

—Democracy, Reform & Authoritarianism in the Arab World V3. 2010. 400p. *(978-0-415-47285-2(7))* Routledge.

—Democracy, Reform & Authoritarianism in the Arab World V4. 2010. 400p. *(978-0-415-47284-5(9))* Routledge.

Noueihed, Lin & Warren, Alex. The Battle for the Arab Spring: Revolution, Counter-Revolution & the Making of a New Era. 2012. (ENG., Illus.). 304p. 28.00 ***(978-0-300-18086-2(1))*** Yale Univ. Pr.

Nsouli, Mona A. & Meho, Lokman I. Censorship in the Arab World: An Annotated Bibliography. annot. ed. 2006. (ENG & MUL.). 192p. per. 60.00 *(978-0-8108-5869-5(X))* Scarecrow Pr., Inc.

Nusseibeh, Hazem. Jerusalemites: A Living Memory. 2010. 456p. pap. 28.95 *(978-9963-610-38-9(2))* International Publishers Marketing.

Ottaway, Marina & Hamzawy, Amr, eds. Getting to Pluralism: Political Actors in the Arab World. 2009. (ENG.). 160p. 49.95 *(978-0-87003-245-5(3))*; pap. 19.95 *(978-0-87003-244-8(5))* Carnegie Endowment for International Peace.

Parolin, Gianluca P. Citizenship in the Arab World: Kin, Religion & Nation-State. 2009. (IMISCOE Research Ser.). 192p. pap. *(978-90-8964-045-1(2)*, Leiden Univ. Pr.) Amsterdam Univ. Pr.

Pratt, Nicola. Democracy & Authoritarianism in the Arab World. 2007. 235p. (C). pap. 22.00 *(978-1-58826-486-2(6))*; lib. bdg. 55.00 *(978-1-58826-461-9(0))* Rienner, Lynne Pubs.

Pryce-Jones, David. The Closed Circle: An Interpretation of the Arabs. 2009. (ENG.). 480p. pap. 18.95 *(978-1-56663-826-5(7)*, Dee, Ivan R. Pub.

Rev. Jihad Cobey. Surviving the Holy War. 2010. 140p. pap. 14.99 *(978-1-4269-2696-9(0))* Trafford Publishing.

Rosen, Lawrence. Varieties of Muslim Experience: Encounters with Arab Political & Cultural Life. 278p. 2011. pap. 26.00 *(978-0-226-72617-5(7))* 2008. (ENG.). 35.00 *(978-0-226-72616-8(9))* Univ. of Chicago Pr.

Routledge Library Editions:the Arab Nation, 4 vols. 2012. (Routledge Library Editions: the Arab Nation Ser.). (ENG.). 1882p. 545.00 ***(978-0-415-62197-7(6))*** Routledge.

Routledge Staff, creator. A Survey of Arab-Israeli Relations. 3rd rev. ed. 2006. (Illus.). 551p. 260.00 *(978-1-85743-394-4(7))* Routledge.

Sabri, Nidal Rashid. Financial Markets & Institutions in the Arab Economy. 2008. (C). 89.00 *(978-1-60456-137-1(8))* Nova Science Pubs., Inc.

Sabry, Tarik, ed. Arab Cultural Studies: Mapping the Field. 2012. (ENG., Illus.). 320p. pap. 31.00 ***(978-1-84885-559-5(1))***; 85.00 ***(978-1-84885-558-8(3))*** I. B. Tauris & Co., Ltd. GBR. Dist: Macmillan.

Sadat, Jehan. My Hope for Peace. 2011. (ENG.). 224p. pap. 15.99 *(978-1-4165-9221-1(0)*, Free Pr.) Free Pr.

Sadiki, Larbi. Rethinking Arab Democratization: Elections without Democracy. (Oxford Studies in Democratization Ser.). (ENG.). 2012. 352p. pap. 40.00 ***(978-0-19-969924-7(0))*** 2009. (Illus.). 288p. 99.00 *(978-0-19-956298-5(9))* Oxford Univ. Pr., Inc.

Saouli, Adham. The Arab State: Dilemmas of Late Formation. 2011. (Routledge Studies in Middle Eastern Politics Ser.). (ENG., Illus.). 176p. (C). 125.00 *(978-0-415-60295-2(5))* Routledge.

Schlumberger. Debating Arab Authoritarianism: Dynamics & Durability in Nondemocratic Regimes. Schlumberger, Oliver, ed. 2008. (ENG.). 360p. pap. 24.95 *(978-0-8047-6333-2(X))* Stanford Univ. Pr.

Schlumberger, Oliver, ed. Debating Arab Authoritarianism: Dynamics & Durability in Nondemocratic Regimes. 2007. (ENG., Illus.). 360p. 55.00 *(978-0-8047-5776-8(3))* Stanford Univ. Pr.

Schumann, Christoph, ed. Nationalism & Liberal Thought in the Arab East: Ideology & Practice. 2010. (SOAS/Routledge Studies on the Middle East Ser.). (ENG., Illus.). 208p. (C). 120.00 *(978-0-415-55410-7(1)*, Routledge) Taylor & Francis Group GBR. Dist: Taylor & Francis Group.

Schumann, Cristoph, ed. Liberal Thought in the Eastern Mediterranean: Late 19th Century until the 1960s. 2008. (Social, Economic & Political Studies of the Middle East Ser.). xiv, 344p. *(978-90-04-16548-9(7))* BRILL.

Seib, Philip. Real-Time Diplomacy: Politics & Power in the Social Media Era. 2012. (ENG., Illus.). 212p. 90.00 ***(978-0-230-33942-2(5))***; pap. 25.00 ***(978-0-230-33943-9(3))*** Palgrave Macmillan.

Shehata, Dina. Islamists & Secularists in Egypt: Opposition, Conflict & Cooperation. 2010. (ENG., Illus.). 180p. 120.00 *(978-0-415-49547-9(4))* Routledge.

Susser, Asher. Challenges to the Cohesion of the Arab State. 2009. (Illus.). 264p. 39.95 *(978-965-224-079-8(6))* Moshe Dayan Ctr. for Middle Eastern & African Studies ISR. Dist: Syracuse Univ. Pr.

Susser, Asher & Landau, Linda, eds. The Middle East: The Impact of Generational Change. Aronsky, Avi, tr. from HEB. 2007. 174p. per. 12.95 *(978-965-224-071-2(0))* Moshe Dayan Ctr. for Middle Eastern & African Studies ISR. Dist: Syracuse Univ. Pr.

Taha, Ibrahim. Arabic Minimalist Story: Genre, Politics & Poetics in the Self-Colonial Era. 2009. (LITERATUREN IM KONTEXT. ARABISCH - PERSISCH - TURKISCH Ser.). (ENG.). 185p. (C). 84.00 *(978-3-89500-666-1(1))* Reichert, Ludwig Dr. DEU. Dist: Brown, David Bk. Co., The.

Tessler, Mark. Public Opinion in the Middle East: Survey Research & the Political Orientations of Ordinary Citizens. 2011. (Indiana Series in Middle East Studies). (ENG.). 400p. 80.00 *(978-0-253-35631-4(8)*, 0253356318); pap. 27.95 *(978-0-253-22315-9(6)*, 0253223156) Indiana Univ. Pr.

That Which Is Not Obligatory Is Prohibited: Censorship & Incitement in the Arab World: Hearing Before the Subcommittee on the Middle East & South Asia of the Committee on Foreign Affairs, House of Representatives, One Hundred Tenth Congress, Second Session, January 22, 2008. 2008. iii, 43p. *(978-0-16-080858-6(8)*, 552-070-37411-6) United States Government Printing Office.

The Emirates Center for Strategic Studies and Research Staff & Tauris, I. B. Future Arabian Gulf Energy Sources: Hydrocarbon, Nuclear or Renewable? 2009. (ENG., Illus.). 472p. pap. 51.00 *(978-9948-00-989-4(4)*, Emirates Center for Strategic Studies) I. B. Tauris & Co., Ltd. GBR. Dist: Macmillan.

Tibi, Bassam. Das Arabische Staatensytem. *(978-3-411-10631-8(X))* Bibliographisches Institut & F. A. Brockhaus AG DEU. Dist: l. b. d., Ltd.

United Nations. State of the World Population Report 2009 Youth Supplement: At the Frontier: Young People & C. 2011. 52p. pap. 15.00 *(978-0-89714-967-9(X))* United Nations Population Fund FJI. Dist: National Bk. Network.

World Bank (Afghanistan) Staff. Better Governance for Development in the Middle East & North Africa Vol. 2: The Political Economy of Reforms. Al-Dahdah, Edouard et al, eds. 2010. (MENA Development Report). (ENG.). 500p. pap. 35.00 *(978-0-8213-7948-6(8)*, 9780821379486) World Bank Pubns.

Yafi, Wissam S. Inevitable Democracy in the Arab World: New Realities in an Ancient Land. 2012. (ENG., Illus.). 224p. 95.00 ***(978-1-137-00802-2(4))***; pap. 28.00 ***(978-1-137-00849-7(0))*** Palgrave Macmillan.

Zott, Lynn, ed. The Arab Spring. 2012. (Opposing Viewpoints Ser.). (ENG., Illus.). 240p. (gr. 10-12). pap. 28.90 ***(978-0-7377-6043-9(5))***; lib. bdg. 41.70 ***(978-0-7377-6042-2(7))*** Cengage Gale. (Greenhaven Pr., Inc.).

ARAB COUNTRIES—RELATIONS—FOREIGN COUNTRIES

Evans, William & Harris, Daniel J. Politics & Economics of the Middle East. 2008. (Illus.). xiv, 230p. 82.00 *(978-1-60456-719-9(8))* Nova Science Pubs., Inc.

Galal, Injy. Us Public Diplomacy in the Middle East: Prospects & Concerns. 2010. 232p. pap. *(978-3-8383-5141-4(X))* Lambert Academic Publishing.

Hammond, Andrew. What the Arabs Think of America, 1 vol. 2007. (Illus.). 246p. 49.95 *(978-1-84645-000-6(4)*, GWP000) Greenwood Publishing Group, Inc.

Haseeb, Khair el-Din, ed. The Arabs & Africa (RLE: the Arab Nation), Volume 3. 2012. (Routledge Library Editions: the Arab Nation Ser.). (ENG.). 736p. 200.00 ***(978-0-415-62395-7(2))*** Routledge.

Karsh, Ephraim & Kumaraswamy, P. R., eds. Islamic Attitudes to Israel. 2009. (ENG.). 206p. (C). pap. 39.95 *(978-0-415-57463-1(3))* Routledge.

Maalouf, Amin. Disordered World::Setting a New Course for the Twenty-First Century. 2011. (ENG.). 288p. 28.00 *(978-1-60819-584-8(8))* Bloomsbury Publishing.

Matar, N. I. Europe Through Arab Eyes, 1578-1727. 2008. 352p. pap. *(978-0-231-51208-4(2))* Columbia Univ. Pr.

Obama, Barack. Remarks by the President on a New Beginning - Cairo University - June 4 2009. 2009. 60p. pap. *(978-1-60796-150-5(4))* Editorial Benei Noaj.

Vaiou, Maria. Diplomacy in the Early Islamic World: A Tenth-Century Treatise on Arab-Byzantine Relations. 2012. (Library of Middle East History Ser.). (ENG.). 288p. 92.50 *(978-1-84511-652-1(6)*, Tauris Academic Studies) I. B. Tauris & Co., Ltd. GBR. Dist: Macmillan.

ARAB COUNTRIES—RELIGION

El-Ahdab. Arbitration with the Arab Countries, Third Edition. 3rd ed. 2010. li, 1200p. 250.00 *(978-90-411-3170-6(1))* Wolters Kluwer Law & Business.

Griffith, Sidney H. The Church in the Shadow of the Mosque: Christians & Muslims in the World of Islam. (Jews, Christians, & Muslims from the Ancient to the Modern World Ser.). (ENG., Illus.). 248p. (C). 2010. pap. 25.95 *(978-0-691-14628-7(4))* 2007. 45.00 *(978-0-691-13015-6(9))* Princeton Univ. Pr.

Heggy, Tarek. The Arab Mind Bound. 2011. 176p. 69.95 *(978-0-85303-894-8(5))* Vallentine Mitchell Pubs. GBR. Dist: International Specialized Bk. Services.

Ibn 'Arabi, Muhyiddin. The Universal Tree & the Four Birds. Jaffray, Angela, tr. from ARA. 2006. (Mystical Treatises of Muhyiddin Ibn 'Ara Ser.). (ENG., Illus.). 135p. pap. 25.95 *(978-0-9534513-9-5(9))* Anqa Publishing GBR. Dist: Independent Pubs. Group.

May, Melanie A. Jerusalem Testament: Palestinian Christians Speak, 1988-2008. 2009. 176p. pap. 22.00 *(978-0-8028-6485-7(6))* Eerdmans, William B. Publishing Co.

Mumayiz, Ibrahim. Society, Religion & Poetry in pre-Islamic Arabia: [English & Arabic]. 2010. 232p. pap. 67.50 *(978-90-441-2512-2(5))* Garant Uitgevers N.V. BEL. Dist: Coronet Bks.

O'Connor, Paul. The Modern Hajj. 2010. 88p. pap. *(978-3-8383-9032-1(6))* Lambert Academic Publishing.

Rudolph, Rachael M. Mobilizing Movements, Mobilizing Contemporary Islamic Resistance. 2008. 212p. pap. *(978-3-639-08752-9(6))* VDM Verlag Dr. Mueller e.K.

ARAB COUNTRIES—SOCIAL CONDITIONS

Abdulla, Rasha A. The Internet in the Arab World: Egypt & Beyond. 175p. (C). 65.95 *(978-0-8204-8673-4(6))*; 2007. (Illus.). xxi, 175p. pap. *(978-0-8204-8674-1(4))* Lang, Peter Publishing, Inc.

Aksikas, Jaafar. Arab Modernities: Islamism, Nationalism, & Liberalism in the Post-Colonial Arab World. 2009. (Postcolonial Studies). 192p. (C). 37.95 *(978-1-4331-0534-0(9))* Lang, Peter Publishing, Inc.

Al-Krenawi, Alean & Graham, John R. Helping Professional Practice with Indigenous Peoples: The Bedouin-Arab Case. 2008. (ENG., Illus.). 220p. pap. 38.99 *(978-0-7618-4407-5(4))* Univ. Pr. of America, Inc.

Al-Qawasmi, Jamal, ed. Regional Architecture & Identity in the Age of Globalization, 3 vols. 2008. (Illus.). 700p. pap. *(978-9957-8602-2-6(4))* Center for Study of Architecture in the Arab Region (CSAAR), The.

Bashri, Maha. The Opinion & Other Opinion: Al-Jazeera's Agenda Setting Function in the Arab Islamic World. 2008. 136p. pap. *(978-3-639-03541-4(0))* VDM Verlag Dr. Mueller e.K.

Cambanis, Thanassis. A Privilege to Die: Inside Hezbollah's Legions & Their Endless War Against Israel. 2011. (ENG., Illus.). 336p. pap. 15.00 *(978-1-4391-4361-2(7)*, Free Pr.) Free Pr.

Carsten, Wieland. Syria: Democracy, Islamism, & Secularism in the Levant. 2006. 223p. 34.95 *(978-1-885942-16-6(8))* Cune Pr., LLC.

El Saadawi, Nawal. The Hidden Face of Eve: Women in the Arab World. Hetata, Sherif, tr. from ARA. 2008. (ENG.). 395p. 90.00 *(978-1-84277-874-6(9))* Zed Bks., Ltd. GBR. Dist: Macmillan.

El Said, Mohammed. The Development of Intellectual Property Protection in the Arab World. 2008. 320p. 119.95 *(978-0-7734-5045-5(9))* Mellen, Edwin Pr., The.

Emirates Center for Strategic Studies and Research Staff & Tauris, I. B. Current Transformations & Their Potential Role in Realizing Change in the Arab World. 2007. (ENG.). 522p. 100.00 *(978-9948-00-873-6(1)*, Emirates Center for Strategic Studies) I. B. Tauris & Co., Ltd. GBR. Dist: Macmillan.

Emirates Centre for Strategic Studies and Research Staff & Tauris, I. B. Current Transformations & Their Potential Role in Realizing Change in the Arab World. 2007. (ENG.). 522p. pap. 36.00 *(978-9948-00-874-3(X)*, Emirates Center for Strategic Studies) I. B. Tauris & Co., Ltd. GBR. Dist: Macmillan.

Fischbach, Michael R. Jewish Property Claims Against Arab Countries. 2008. (ENG., Illus.). 376p. (gr. 17). 45.00 *(978-0-231-13538-2(6))* Columbia Univ. Pr.

Gray, Matthew. Conspiracy Theories in the Arab World: Sources & Politics. 2010. (ENG.). 224p. (C). 140.00 *(978-0-415-57518-8(4))* Routledge.

—Conspiracy Theories in the Arab World: Sources & Politics. 2010. 224p. (C). pap. 49.95 *(978-0-415-57519-5(2)*, Routledge) Taylor & Francis Group GBR. Dist: Taylor & Francis Group.

Haddad, Joumana. I Killed Scheherazade: Confessions of an Angry Arab Woman. 2011. (ENG.). 160p. pap. 14.95 *(978-1-56976-840-2(4)*, Hill, Lawrence Bks.) Chicago Review Pr., Inc.

Hamid, Suhayr. Ishkaliyat Al-Tanmiyah Fi Al-Watan Al-Arabi. 2007. (ARA., Illus.). 192p. *(978-9957-00-308-1(9))* Dar al-Shuruq lil-Nashr wa-al-Tawzi.

Kraidy, Marwan. Reality Television & Arab Politics: Contention in Public Life. 2009. (Communication, Society & Politics Ser.). (ENG., Illus.). 270p. pap. 24.99 *(978-0-521-74904-6(2))* Cambridge Univ. Pr.

Kraidy, Marwan M. Reality Television & Arab Politics: Contention in Public Life. 2009. (Communication, Society & Politics Ser.). (ENG.). 270p. 85.00 *(978-0-521-76919-8(1))* Cambridge Univ. Pr.

Litvak, Meir & Webman, Ester. From Empathy to Denial: Arab Responses to the Holocaust. 2009. (Columbia/Hurst Ser.). (ENG.). 416p. (gr. 17). 30.00 *(978-0-231-70074-0(1))* Columbia Univ. Pr.

Noland, Marcus & Pack, Howard. The Arab Economies in a Changing World. 2nd ed. 2011. (Illus.). 362p. pap. 24.95 ***(978-0-88132-628-4(3))*** Peterson Institute for International Economics.

Noueihed, Lin & Warren, Alex. The Battle for the Arab Spring: Revolution, Counter-Revolution & the Making of a New Era. 2012. (ENG., Illus.). 304p. 28.00 ***(978-0-300-18086-2(1))*** Yale Univ. Pr.

Pal, Amitabh. Islam Means Peace: Understanding the Muslim Principle of Nonviolence Today, 1 vol. 2011. (Illus.). 276p. 44.95 *(978-0-313-38290-1(5)*, A2689C, Praeger Pubs.) Greenwood Publishing Group, Inc.

Ramadan, Tariq. Islam & the Arab Awakening. 2012. (ENG.). 272p. 27.95 ***(978-0-19-993373-0(1))*** Oxford Univ. Pr., Inc.

Satloff, Robert. Among the Righteous: Lost Stories from the Holocaust's Long Reach into Arab Lands. 2007. (ENG., Illus.). 288p. per. 14.95 *(978-1-58648-510-8(5))* PublicAffairs.

Suleiman, Yasir. Arabic, Self & Identity: A Study in Conflict & Displacement, 1 vol. 2011. (ENG., Illus.). 288p. pap. 39.95 *(978-0-19-974700-9(8))* Oxford Univ. Pr., Inc.

U N Development Staff, et al. Arab Human Development Report 2005: Towards the Rise of Women in the Arab World. 2007. (ENG., Illus.). 260p. pap. 25.95 *(978-0-8047-5530-6(2))* Stanford Univ. Pr.

United Nations Development Programme: Regional Bureau for Arab States, et al. Arab human development Report 2009: Challenges to human security in the Arab Countries. 2009. (Illus.). 238p. pap. 24.95 *(978-92-1-126211-7(9))* United Nations Pubns.

Wolf, Robert & Lefkowitz, Zvi. Forgotten Children of the Bible: Conflict & Consequences. 2009. 87p. 18.95 *(978-1-934440-71-1(X)*, Devora Publishing) Simcha Media Group.

World Bank (Afghanistan) Staff. Better Governance for Development in the Middle East & North Africa Vol. 2: The Political Economy of Reforms. Al-Dahdah, Edouard et al, eds. 2010. (MENA Development Report). (ENG.). 500p. pap. 35.00 (978-0-8213-7948-6(8), 9780821379486) World Bank Pubns.

ARAB COUNTRIES—SOCIAL LIFE AND CUSTOMS

al-Jabri, Mohammad Abed. The Formation of Arab Reason: Text, Tradition & the Construction of Modernity in the Arab World. 2011. (Contemp. Arab Scholarship in the Social Sciences Ser.). (ENG.). 320p. 90.00 (978-1-84885-061-3(1)) I. B. Tauris & Co., Ltd. GBR. Dist: Macmillan.

Ali, Samer M. Arabic Literary Salons in the Islamic Middle Ages: Poetry, Public Performance, & the Presentation of the Past. 2010. (ND Poetics of Orality & Literacy Ser.). (ENG.). 280p. pap. 32.00 (978-0-268-02032-3(9)) Univ. of Notre Dame Pr.

Bouhdiba, Abdelwahab. Sexuality in Islam. 2007. (ENG.). 304p. (C). 175.00 (978-0-415-43915-2(9)) Routledge.

C. Arabic History & Culture. 2009. 1125.00 (978-0-415-44131-5(5)) Routledge.

Caton, Steven C. Yemen Chronicle: An Anthropology of War & Mediation. 2006. (ENG., Illus.). 352p. per. 17.00 (978-0-8090-9882-8(2), Hill & Wang) Farrar, Straus & Giroux.

El-Rouayheb, Khaled. Before Homosexuality in the Arab-Islamic World, 1500-1800. 2009. 224p. pap. 20.00 (978-0-226-72989-3(3)) Univ. of Chicago Pr.

Fiennes, Ranulph. Killer Elite. 2011. 400p. mass mkt. 7.99 (978-0-345-52808-7(5), Ballantine Bks.) Random House Publishing Group.

Frangieh, Bassam K. Arabic for Life: A Textbook for Beginning Arabic. 2011. (ARA & ENG., Illus.). 528p. 85.00 (978-0-300-14131-3(9)) Yale Univ. Pr.

Hammond, Andrew. Popular Culture in the Arab World: Arts, Politics, & the Media. 2007. (ENG., Illus.). 272p. per. 24.95 (978-977-416-054-7(1)) American Univ. in Cairo Pr. EGY. Dist: Oxford Univ. Pr., Inc.

Hamzah, Dyala. The Making of the Arab Intellectual: Empire, Public Sphere & the Colonial Coordinates of Selfhood. Hamzah, Dyala, ed. 2012. (SOAS/Routledge Studies on the Middle East Ser.). (ENG.). 224p. (C). 120.00 (978-0-415-48834-1(6)) Routledge.

Khalaf, Samir & Khalaf, Roseanne Saad, eds. Arab Society & Culture. 2010. (ENG.). 551p. pap. 26.95 (978-0-86356-616-5(2)) Saqi Bks. GBR. Dist: Consortium Bk. Sales & Distribution.

Khuri, Fuad I. An Invitation to Laughter: A Lebanese Anthropologist in the Arab World. Khuri, Sonia, ed. 2007. 224p. per. 22.50 (978-0-226-43478-0(8)) Univ. of Chicago Pr.

Khuri, Fuad Ishaq. Invitation to Laughter: A Lebanese Anthropologist in the Arab World. Khuri, Sonia Jalbout, ed. 2007. 224p. 52.50 (978-0-226-43476-6(1)) Univ. of Chicago Pr.

Labib, Tahar & Djedidi, Tahar Labib. Imagining the Arab Other: How Arabs & Non-Arabs View Each Other. Labib, Tahar, ed. 2008. (ENG.). 316p. 84.00 (978-1-84511-384-1(5)) I. B. Tauris & Co., Ltd. GBR. Dist: Macmillan.

Menocal, Mariá Rosa, et al, eds. The Literature of Al-Andalus. 2006. (Cambridge History of Arabic Literature Ser.). (ENG., Illus.). 520p. pap. 95.00 (978-0-521-03023-6(4)) Cambridge Univ. Pr.

Peters, James. The Arab World. 3rd ed. 2009. (ARA & ENG., Illus.). 150p. pap., instr.'s hndbk. ed. 18.95 **(978-1-906768-03-4(X)**, Stacey International) Stacey Publishing GBR. Dist: Midpoint Trade Bks., Inc.

Peters, James. Very Simple Arabia. 2007. (Illus.). 108p. pap. 11.95 (978-1-905299-51-5(6), Stacey International) Stacey Publishing GBR. Dist: Midpoint Trade Bks., Inc.

Pryce-Jones, David. The Closed Circle: An Interpretation of the Arabs. 2009. (ENG.). 480p. pap. 18.95 (978-1-56663-826-5(7)) Dee, Ivan R. Pub.

Rejwan, Nissim. Arabs in the Mirror: Images & Self-Images from Pre-Islamic to Modern Times. 2008. (ENG.). 224p. (C). pap. 24.95 (978-0-292-71728-2(8)) Univ. of Texas Pr.

Rosen, Lawrence. Varieties of Muslim Experience: Encounters with Arab Political & Cultural Life. 278p. 2011. pap. 26.00 (978-0-226-72617-5(7)) 2008. (ENG.). 35.00 (978-0-226-72616-8(9)) Univ. of Chicago Pr.

Sabry, Tarik, ed. Arab Cultural Studies: Mapping the Field. 2012. (ENG., Illus.). 320p. pap. 31.00 **(978-1-84885-559-5(1))**; 85.00 **(978-1-84885-558-8(3))** I. B. Tauris & Co., Ltd. GBR. Dist: Macmillan.

Schumann, Christoph, ed. Nationalism & Liberal Thought in the Arab East: Ideology & Practice. 2010. (SOAS/Routledge Studies on the Middle East Ser.). (ENG., Illus.). 208p. (C). 120.00 (978-0-415-55410-7(1), Routledge) Taylor & Francis Group GBR. Dist: Taylor & Francis Group.

Suleimany, Majid Said Nasser Al. Between Us Only - the Sequel! From Book One of the Same Title. 2009. 432p. 54.00 (978-1-4269-9807-2(4)) Trafford Publishing.

Tripp, Harvey. CultureShock! Bahrain. 2007. (Illus.). 200p. pap. 15.95 (978-981-232-893-9(9)) Marshall Cavendish International (Asia) Private Ltd. SGP. Dist: Marshall Cavendish Corp.

Wunderle, William D. A Manual for American Servicemen in the Arab Middle East: Using Cultural Understanding to Defeat Adversaries & Win the Peace. 2008. (ENG., Illus.). 144p. pap. 9.95 (978-1-60239-277-9(3), 239277) Skyhorse Publishing Co., Inc.

Zaouali, Lilia. Medieval Cuisine of the Islamic World: A Concise History with 174 Recipes. Debevoise, M B, tr. from ITA. 2007. (California Studies in Food & Culture). (Illus.). 224p. 40.00 (978-0-520-24783-3(3)) Univ. of California Pr.

ARAB COUNTRIES—STUDY AND TEACHING

Al-Batal, Mahmoud, ed. Al Arabiyya No. 2: AATA Monographs in Arabic Studies. (C). pap. 35.00 (978-0-9621530-1-3(X)) American Assn. of Teachers of Arabic, The.

ARAB EMPIRE

see Islamic Empire

ARAB-ISRAEL BORDER CONFLICTS, 1949-

see Israel-Arab Border Conflicts, 1949-

ARAB-ISRAEL WAR, 1967

see Israel-Arab War, 1967

ARAB-ISRAEL WAR, 1973

see Israel-Arab War, 1973

ARAB-ISRAELI CONFLICT

Here are entered works on the political and military conflicts between Arabs and Israel, including the question of national rights in the area of the former mandate for Palestine beginning in 1948, and comprehensive works that include the earlier period. Works on the general relations between Arabs and Jews as well as works on the question of national rights in Palestine up to 1948 are entered under Jewish-Arab Relations. Works on general foreign relations between Israel and specific Arab countries are entered under Israel—Foreign Relations—[Place], with an additional entry under [Place]—Foreign Relations—Israel.

see also Entebbe Airport Raid, 1976; Intifada, 1987-1993; Israel-Arab Border Conflicts, 1949-; Israel-Arab War, 1948-1949; Israel-Arab War, 1967; Israel-Arab War, 1973; Jewish-Arab Relations; Lebanon—History—Israeli Intervention, 1982-1984

Abdulaziz Alaoudah, Saad. Managing the Conflict Between Palestine & Israel: The Role of the European Union. 2009. 228p. pap. 21.49 (978-1-4490-0472-9(5)) AuthorHouse.

Abdullah II of Jordan, King. Our Last Best Chance: The Pursuit of Peace in a Time of Peril. 2012. (ENG., Illus.). 400p. (gr. 12). 18.00 **(978-0-14-312030-8(1)**, Penguin (Non-Classics)) Penguin Group (USA) Inc.

Abi-Ezzi, Karen. Peacemaking Strat Israeli-Pal Conf. 2009. (Routledge Studies in Middle Eastern Politics Ser.). 224p. pap. 105.00 (978-0-415-35672-5(5)) Routledge.

Abraham, A. J. The Eternal War: A Psychological Perspective on the Arab-Israeli Conflict. 2011. (ENG.). 156p. pap. 26.95 **(978-0-7618-5631-3(5))** Univ. Pr. of America, Inc.

Abufarha, Nasser. The Making of a Human Bomb: An Ethnography of Palestinian Resistance. 2009. (Cultures & Practice of Violence Ser.). (ENG., Illus.). 288p. 84.95 (978-0-8223-4428-5(9)); pap. 23.95 (978-0-8223-4439-1(4)) Duke Univ. Pr.

Abunimah, Ali. One Country: A Bold Proposal to End the Israeli-Palestinian Impasse. 2007. (ENG., Illus.). 240p. pap. 16.00 (978-0-8050-8666-9(8)) Picador.

Adas, Jane, et al, eds. Burning Issues: Understanding & Misunderstanding the Middle East - a 40-year Chronicle. 2007. (Illus.). 456p. pap. 16.95 (978-0-9701157-0-6(9)) Selwa Pr.

Ahmad, Muslehuddin. Promised Land? A Perspective on Palestinian- Israeli Conflict. 2010. 676p. pap. 33.49 (978-1-4490-1795-8(9)) AuthorHouse.

Ahmadi, Homayun. Palestine, the Forgotten Area. 2010. 66p. pap. 11.00 (978-1-4349-6382-6(9), Red Lead Pr.) Dorrance Publishing Co., Inc.

Akram, Susan, et al, eds. International Law & the Israeli-Palestinian Conflict. 2011. (ENG., Illus.). 352p. (C). 140.00 (978-0-415-57322-1(X)); pap. 49.95 (978-0-415-57323-8(8)) Routledge.

Al-Habil, Wasim. Occupations & the Local Governments for a Palestinian State. 2009. 204p. pap. (978-3-639-17784-8(3)) VDM Verlag Dr. Mueller e.K.

Al-Hout, Shafiq. My Life in the PLO: The Inside Story of the Palestinian Struggle, 1 vol. Makdisi, Jean Said & Asser, Martin, eds. Othman, Laila, tr. from ARA. 2010. (ENG.). 320p. lib. bdg. 104.00 (978-0-7453-2884-3(9)) Pluto Pr. GBR. Dist: Macmillan.

—My Life in the PLO: The Inside Story of the Palestinian Struggle, 1 vol. Makdisi, Jean Said & Asser, Martin, eds. Al-Hout, Hader & Othman, Laila, trs. from ARA. 2010. (ENG., Illus.). 320p. 29.00 (978-0-7453-2883-6(0)) Pluto Pr. GBR. Dist: Macmillan.

Al-Om, Tamara. Constructing Reality: The Palestinian Israeli Conflict. 2010. 160p. pap. (978-3-639-27212-3(9)) VDM Verlag Dr. Mueller e.K.

Al-Omari, Ghaith & Becker, Tal. The Israeli-Palestinian Conflict & Its Resolution: Sources & Discourses. 2012. 428p. pap., pap. 50.00 **(978-1-901362-41-1(8))** Hart Publishing Ltd. GBR. Dist: International Specialized Bk. Services.

Alkim, Hassan Hamdan. Arab Foreign Policy-Making in the Twenty-First Century: Domestic Contraints & External Challenges. 2012. (ENG., Illus.). 400p. 65.00 **(978-0-86356-446-8(1))** Saqi Bks. GBR. Dist: Consortium Bk. Sales & Distribution.

Alon, Mati. Coexistence with Hagar's Offsprings. 2007. 468p. per. 67.00 (978-1-4251-1244-8(7)) Trafford Publishing.

Alon, Mati. The Return to Zion. 2011. 480p. 34.55 **(978-1-4269-6600-2(8))**; pap. 24.55 **(978-1-4269-6598-2(2))** Trafford Publishing.

Aloni, Udi & Butler, Judith. What Does a Jew Want? On Binationalism & Other Specters. 2011. (Insurrections: Critical Studies in Religion, Politics, & Culture Ser.). (ENG., Illus.). 280p. (gr. 17). 60.00 (978-0-231-15758-2(4)) Columbia Univ. Pr.

Aloni, Udi & Zizek, Slavoj. What Does a Jew Want? On Binationalism & Other Specters. 2011. (Insurrections: Critical Studies in Religion, Politics, & Culture Ser.). (ENG., Illus.). 280p. (gr. 17). pap. 19.95 (978-0-231-15759-9(2)) Columbia Univ. Pr.

Amirav, Mosheh. Jerusalem Syndrome: The Palestinian-Israeli Battle for the Holy City. 2009. (ENG., Illus.). 230p. pap. 32.50 (978-1-84519-348-5(2)) Sussex Academic Pr. GBR. Dist: International Specialized Bk. Services.

Amiry, Suad. Nothing to Lose but Your Life: An 18-Hour Journey with Murad. 2010. (ENG.). 176p. pap. 15.00 **(978-99921-42-05-9(7))** Bloomsbury Publishing.

Amit, Zalman & Levit, Daphna. Israeli Rejectionism: A Hidden Agenda in the Middle East Peace Process, 1 vol. 2011. (ENG.). 216p. 30.00 (978-0-7453-3028-0(2)); lib. bdg. 95.00 (978-0-7453-3029-7(0)) Pluto Pr. GBR. Dist: Macmillan.

Aran, Amnon. Israel's Foreign Policy Toward the PLO, 1967-2005: The Impact of Globalization. 2009. (ENG.). 176p. 74.95 (978-1-84519-281-5(8)) Sussex Academic Pr. GBR. Dist: International Specialized Bk. Services.

—Israel's Foreign Policy Towards the PLO: The Impact of Globalization. 2011. 188p. pap. 29.95 (978-1-84519-483-3(7)) Sussex Academic Pr. GBR. Dist: International Specialized Bk. Services.

Arrigoni, Vittorio. Gaza: Stay Human. Filippin, Daniela, tr. 2010. (ENG., Illus.). 184p. pap. 12.95 (978-1-84774-019-9(7)) Kube Publishing Ltd. GBR. Dist: Consortium Bk. Sales & Distribution.

Ashton, Nigel J. The Cold War in the Middle East: Regional Conflict & the Superpowers 1967-73. 2007. pap. 39.95 (978-0-415-54527-3(7)) Routledge.

Ashton, Nigel J., ed. The Cold War in the Middle East. 2007. (Cold War History Ser.). X, 214p. 160.00 (978-0-415-42578-0(6)) Routledge.

Ashuri, Tamar. The Arab-Israeli Conflict in the Media: Producing Shared Memory & National Identity in the Global Television Era. 2010. (Library of Modern Middle East Studies). (ENG.). 288p. 92.50 (978-1-84511-814-3(6), Tauris Academic Studies) I. B. Tauris & Co., Ltd. GBR. Dist: Macmillan.

Assaf, Bruce. Behind the Veil of Radical Islam. 2007. 112p. per. (978-1-55452-252-1(8)) Essence Publishing.

Ateek, Naim Stifan. A Palestinian Christian Cry for Reconciliation. 2008. (Illus.). 240p. pap. 24.00 (978-1-57075-784-6(4)) Orbis Bks.

Atwan, Abdel Bari. A Country of Words: A Palestinian Journey from the Refugee Camp to the Front Page. 2009. (ENG., Illus.). 285p. 29.95 (978-0-86356-621-9(9)) Saqi Bks. GBR. Dist: Consortium Bk. Sales & Distribution.

Avishai, Bernard. The Hebrew Republic: How Secular Democracy & Global Enterprise Will Bring Israel Peace at Last. 2008. (ENG.). 304p. 26.00 (978-0-15-101452-1(3)) Houghton Mifflin Harcourt Trade & Reference Pubs.

Avnery, Uri. Israel's Vicious Circle: Ten Years of Writings on Israel & Palestine, 1 vol. Powell, Sara R., ed. 2008. (ENG.). 240p. lib. bdg. 29.95 (978-0-7453-2823-2(7)) Pluto Pr. GBR. Dist: Macmillan.

Aziz, Shahzad. In the Land of the Ayatollahs Tupac Shakur Is King: Reflections from Iran & the Arab World. 2007. (ENG.). 299p. pap. 14.95 (978-0-9552359-2-4(8)) Amal Pr. GBR. Dist: Independent Pubs. Group.

Azoulay, Ariella. Civil Imagination: A Political Ontology of Photography. 2012. (ENG., Illus.). 256p. 24.95 **(978-1-84467-753-5(2)**, 844753) Verso Bks. GBR. Dist: Norton, W. W. & Co., Inc.

Badran, Amneh & Badran, Amneh Daoud. Zionist Israel & Apartheid South Africa: Civil society & peace building in ethnic-national States. 2009. (ENG., Illus.). 272p. 130.00 (978-0-415-48981-2(4)) Routledge.

Baker, Abeer & Matar, Anat, eds. Threat: Palestinian Political Prisoners in Israel, 1 vol. 2011. (ENG.). 288p. 34.00 (978-0-7453-3020-4(7)); lib. bdg. 100.00 (978-0-7453-3021-1(5)) Pluto Pr. GBR. Dist: Macmillan.

Baltzer, Anna. Witness in Palestine: A Jewish American Woman in the Occupied Territories. 2007. (Illus.). 240p. pap. 35.95 (978-1-59451-307-7(4)) Paradigm Pubs.

Bar-On, Mordechai, ed. Never-Ending Conflict: Israeli Military History. 2006. (Stackpole Military History Ser.). (ENG., Illus.). 261p. per. 16.95 (978-0-8117-3345-8(9)) Stackpole Bks.

Bar-Siman-Tov, Yaacov & Bar-Siman-Tov, Simon. The Israel-Palestinian Conflict: From Conflict Resolution to Conflict Management. 2007. (ENG., Illus.). 304p. 89.00 (978-1-4039-7732-8(1)) Palgrave Macmillan.

Bar-Tal, Daniel & Shnell, Itzhak. The Impacts of Lasting Occupation: Lessons from Israeli Society. 2012. (Series in Political Psychology Ser.). 576p. 99.99 **(978-0-19-986218-4(4))** Oxford Univ. Pr., Inc.

Baracskay, Daniel. The Palestine Liberation Organization: Terrorism & Prospects for Peace in the Holy Land. 2011. E-Book (978-0-313-38152-2(6)); (Illus.). 225p. 44.95 (978-0-313-38151-5(8), A2585C) Greenwood Publishing Group, Inc. (Praeger Pubs.).

Barak, Eitan. Deadly Metal Rain - The Legality of Flechette Weapons in International Law: A Reappraisal Following Israel's Use of Flechettes in the Gaza Strip, (2001-2009) 2011. (ENG., Illus.). XVIII, 262p. **(978-90-04-16719-3(6))** BRILL.

Baramki, Gabriel. Peaceful Resistance: Building a Palestinian University under Occupation, 1 vol. 2009. (ENG., Illus.). 224p. 80.00 (978-0-7453-2932-1(2)); pap. 29.95 (978-0-7453-2931-4(4)) Pluto Pr. GBR. Dist: Macmillan.

Barari, Hassan. Israelism: Arab Scholarship on Israel - A Critical Assessment. 2012. 172p. pap. 19.95 **(978-0-86372-416-9(7)**, Ithaca Pr.) Garnet Publishing, Ltd. GBR. Dist: International Specialized Bk. Services.

Barari, Hassan A. Israelism: Arab Scholarship on Israel, a Critical Assessment. 2009. 172p. 69.95 (978-0-86372-337-7(3), Ithaca Pr.) Garnet Publishing, Ltd. GBR. Dist: International Specialized Bk. Services.

Bardin, Hillel. A Zionist among Palestinians. 2012. (ENG., Illus.). 280p. 29.00 **(978-0-253-00211-2(7)**, 0253002117) Indiana Univ. Pr.

Baroud, Ramzy. My Father Was a Freedom Fighter: Gaza's Untold Story, 1 vol. 2010. (ENG., Illus.). 320p. 80.00 (978-0-7453-2882-9(2)); pap. 18.00 (978-0-7453-2881-2(4)) Pluto Pr. GBR. Dist: Macmillan.

Bartal, Shaul. The Fedayeen Emerge: The Palestine-Israel Conflict, 1949-1956. 2011. 436p. pap. 24.30 **(978-1-4567-8679-3(2))** AuthorHouse.

Bassiouni, M. Cherif & Ben-Ami, Shlomo, eds. A Guide to Documents on the Arab-Palestinian/Israeli Conflict: 1897-2008. 2009. (International & Comparative Criminal Law Ser.). 324p. pap. (978-90-04-17534-1(2)) BRILL.

Bayoumi, Moustafa, ed. Midnight on the Mavi Marmara: The Attack on the Gaza Freedom Flotilla & How It Changed the Course of the Israel/Palestine Conflict. 2010. (ENG.). 280p. pap. 16.00 (978-1-60846-121-9(1)) Haymarket Bks.

Bazzi, Samia. Arab News & Conflict: A Multidisciplinary Discourse Study. 2009. (Illus.). xiv, 222p. (978-90-272-0625-1(2)) Benjamins, John Publishing Co.

Behrendt, Sven. The Secret Israeli-Palestinian Negotiations in Oslo: Their Success & Why the Process Ultimately Failed. (Durham Modern Middle East & Islamic World Ser.). (Illus.). 2012. (ENG.). 176p. (C). pap. 42.95 **(978-0-415-54213-5(8))** 2007. 160p. 150.00 (978-0-415-41592-7(6)) Routledge.

Bellow, Saul. To Jerusalem & Back. 2010. (ENG.). 234p. pap. 19.95 (978-1-4128-1184-2(8)) Transaction Pubs.

Ben-Ami, Shlomo. Scars of War, Wounds of Peace: The Israeli-Arab Tragedy. 2007. 432p. per. 16.95 (978-0-19-532542-3(7)) Oxford Univ. Pr., Inc.

Ben-Eliezer, Uri. Old Conflict, New War: Israel's Politics Toward the Palestinians. 2012. (ENG., Illus.). 320p. 95.00 **(978-1-137-02756-6(8))** Palgrave Macmillan.

Ben-Meir, Alon. A Framework for Arab-Israeli Peace. 92p. pap. 7.95 (978-0-9638319-0-3(9)) Robert Publishing Group.

Ben-Shaul, Nitzan. Violent World: TV News Images of Middle Eastern Terror & War. 2007. (Critical Media Studies: Institutions, Politics, & Culture Ser.). (ENG.). 180p. pap. 31.95 (978-0-7425-3799-6(4)) Rowman & Littlefield Publishers, Inc.

Ben-Shaul, Nitzan & Ben-Shaul, Nitzan S. A Violent World: TV News Images of Middle Eastern Terror & War. 2006. (Critical Media Studies). (ENG.). 180p. 85.00 (978-0-7425-3798-9(6)) Rowman & Littlefield Publishers, Inc.

Ben-Zvi, Abraham. The Origins of the American-Israeli Alliance: The Jordanian Factor. 2007. (Israeli History, Politics & Society Ser.). 111p. 140.00 (978-0-415-41045-8(2)) Routledge.

Ben-zvi, Abraham. The Origins of the American-Israeli Alliance: The Jordanian Factor. 2009. 112p. pap. 39.95 (978-0-415-57680-2(6)) Routledge.

Bennett, Clinton. In Search of Solutions: The Problem of Religion & Conflict. 2009. (Religion & Violence Ser.). (ENG., Illus.). 284p. (C). 34.95 (978-1-84553-240-6(6)); 99.50 (978-1-84553-239-0(2)) Equinox Publishing Ltd. GBR. Dist: ISD.

Bennis, Phyllis. Understanding the Palestinian-Israeli Conflict: A Primer. 2007. (ENG., Illus.). 208p. per. 10.00 (978-1-56656-685-8(1)) Interlink Publishing Group, Inc.

Benvenisti, Eyal, et al, eds. Israel & the Palestinian Refugees. 2007. (Beiträge zum ausländischen Öffentlichen Recht und Völkerrecht Ser.: Vol. 189). (Illus.). viii, 501p. 129.00 (978-3-540-68160-1(4), 3540681604) Springer.

Benvenisti, Meron. Son of the Cypresses: Memories, Reflections, & Regrets from a Political Life. Kaufman-Lacusta, Maxine & Kaufman-Lacusta, Michael, trs. 2007. 253p. 35.00 (978-0-520-23825-1(7)) Univ. of California Pr.

Berg, Mary. The Diary of Mary Berg: Growing up in the Warsaw Ghetto. 2007. (ENG., Illus.). 350p. 24.95 (978-1-85168-472-4(7)) Oneworld Pubns. GBR. Dist: National Bk. Network.

Berko, Anat. The Path to Paradise: The Inner World of Suicide Bombers & Their Dispatchers, 1 vol. Yuval, Elizabeth, tr. from HEB. 2007. (Praeger Security International Ser.). 216p. 49.95 (978-0-275-99446-4(5), C9446, Praeger Security International) Greenwood Publishing Group, Inc.

—The Path to Paradise: The Inner World of Suicide Bombers & Their Dispatchers. Yuval, Elizabeth, tr. from HEB. 2009. (Illus.). 196p. pap. 19.95 (978-1-59797-364-9(5)) Potomac Bks., Inc.

Berlatsky, Noah, ed. The Arab-Israeli Conflict. 2012. (Global Viewpoints Ser.). (ENG., Illus.). 224p. (gr. 10-12). pap. 39.60 **(978-0-7377-5645-6(4))**; lib. bdg. 27.30 **(978-0-7377-5644-9(6))** Cengage Gale. (Greenhaven Pr., Inc.).

Berry, Mike & Philo, Greg. Israel & Palestine: Competing Histories. annot. ed. 2006. (ENG., Illus.). 176p. 64.00 (978-0-7453-2566-8(1)); per. 22.95 (978-0-7453-2565-1(3)) Pluto Pr. GBR. Dist: Macmillan.

Bickerton, Ian. The Arab-Israeli Conflict: A Guide for the Perplexed. 2012. (Guides for the Perplexed Ser.). (ENG., Illus.). 320p. 75.00 (978-1-4411-7370-6(6)); pap. 19.95 (978-1-4411-2872-0(7)) Continuum International Publishing Group, Ltd. GBR. Dist: National Bk. Network.

Bickerton, Ian J. The Arab-Israeli Conflict: A History. 2009. (Reaktion Books - Contemporary Worlds Ser.). (ENG., Illus.). 256p. pap. 24.95 (978-1-86189-527-1(5)) Reaktion Bks., Ltd. GBR. Dist: Chicago Distribution Ctr.

Bickerton, Ian J. & Klausner, Carla L. A History of the Arab-Israeli Conflict. 6th ed. 2009. (ENG.). 448p. (C). pap. 65.00 (978-0-205-75338-3(8), Prentice Hall) Prentice Hall PTR.

Bird, Kai. Crossing Mandelbaum Gate: Coming of Age Between the Arabs & Israelis, 1956-1978. (ENG., Illus.). 448p. 2011. pap. 18.00 (978-1-4165-4441-8(0)) 2010. 30.00 (978-1-4165-4440-1(2)) Scribner. (Scribner).

Bogdanor, Paul & Alexander, Edward, eds. The Jewish Divide over Israel: Accusers & Defenders. 2008. (ENG.). 310p. pap. 29.95 (978-1-4128-0804-0(9)) Transaction Pubs.

Boyle, Francis A. The Palestinian Right of Return under International Law. 2011. (ENG.). 123p. pap. 14.95 (978-0-932863-93-5(0)) Clarity Pr., Inc.

Boyle, Francis Anthony. Breaking All the Rules: Palestine, Iraq, Iran & the Case for Impeachment. 2008. (Illus.). 127p. per. 12.95 *(978-0-932863-59-1(0))* Clarity Pr., Inc.

Brecher, Daniel Cil. A Stranger in the Land: Jewish Identity Beyond Nationalism. Harshav, Barbara, tr. from GER. 2007. (ENG.). 400p. pap. 15.95 *(978-1-59051-211-1(1))* Other Pr., LLC.

Bregman, Ahron. Israel's Wars: A History Since 1947. 3rd ed. (Illus.). 2008. xvii, 337p. 125.00 *(978-0-415-42436-3(4))* 2010. (ENG., 368p. pap. 24.95 *(978-0-415-42438-7(0))* Routledge.

Brog, David & Fuchs, Sarah. Standing with Israel. 2009. 264p. pap. 25.00 *(978-965-229-428-9(4))* Gefen Publishing Hse., Ltd ISR. Dist: Strauss Consultants.

Broomberg, Adam & Chanarin, Oliver, photos by. Chicago, 1 vol. 2008. (ENG., Illus.). 112p. 50.00 *(978-3-86521-307-5(3))* Steidl, Gerhard Druckerei und Verlag DEU. Dist: Innovative Logistics.

Brown, Wesley Haddon & Penner, Peter F. Christian Perspectives on the Israeli-Palestinian Conflict. 2008. 238p. *(978-0-86585-005-7(4))* Carey, William International Univ. Pr.

—Christian Perspectives on the Israeli-Palestinian Conflict. 2008. 238p. *(978-3-937896-57-1(0))* Neufeld, David.

Bunzl, John & Beit-Hallahmi, Benjamin, eds. Psychoanalysis, Identity, & Ideology: Critical Essays on the Israel/Palestine Case. 2010. (ENG.). 248p. pap. 119.00 *(978-1-4419-5299-8(3)*, 1441952993) Springer.

Byman, Daniel. A High Price: The Triumphs & Failures of Israeli Counterterrorism, 1 vol. 2011. (ENG., Illus.). 496p. 34.95 *(978-0-19-539182-4(9))* Oxford Univ. Pr., Inc.

Cambanis, Thanassis. A Privilege to Die: Inside Hezbollah's Legions & Their Endless War Against Israel. 2011. (ENG., Illus.). 336p. pap. 15.00 *(978-1-4391-4361-2(7)*, Free Pr.) Free Pr.

Caplan, Neil. The Israel-Palestine Conflict: Contested Histories. 2009. (Contesting the Past Ser.). (ENG., Illus.). 336p. pap. 39.95 *(978-1-4051-7538-8(9))*; 104.95 *(978-1-4051-7539-5(7))* Wiley, John & Sons, Inc. (Wiley-Blackwell).

Carey, Roane, ed. The Case for Sanctions Against Israel. 2012. (ENG.). 244p. pap. 14.95 *(978-1-84467-450-3(9)*, 844450) Verso Bks. GBR. Dist: Norton, W. W. & Co., Inc.

Caridi, Paola. Hamas: From Resistance to Government. Teti, Andrea, tr. from ITA. 2012. (ENG., Illus.). 416p. pap. 24.95 ***(978-1-60980-382-7(5))*** Seven Stories Pr.

Carlowitz, Detlev. Egypt at War 1973. 2007. 116p. per. 19.95 *(978-1-60441-105-8(8))* PublishAmerica, Inc.

Carse, Henry Ralph. No-One Land: Israel / Palestine 2000-2002. 2012. (Illus.). 135p. pap. 23.95 *(978-0-9561038-6-4(3))* Ziggurat Bks. GBR. Dist: Trans-Atlantic Pubns., Inc.

Carter, Jimmy. Palestine Peace Not Apartheid. 2007. (ENG.). 288p. pap. 15.00 *(978-0-7432-8503-2(4))* Simon & Schuster.

—Palestine Peace Not Apartheid. rev. l.t. ed. 2007. (Thorndike Nonfiction Ser.). 313p. 31.95 *(978-0-7862-9408-4(6))* Thorndike Pr.

—We Can Have Peace in the Holy Land: A Plan That Will Work. 2010. (ENG., Illus.) 256p. pap. 15.00 *(978-1-4391-4069-7(3))* Simon & Schuster.

Castillo, Angela N., ed. The Middle East in Turmoil. 2011. (Series: the Middle East in Turmoil Ser.). 431p. 295.00 *(978-1-61324-241-4(7))* Nova Science Pubs., Inc.

—The Middle East in Turmoil. Volume 2. 2009. (Middle East in Turmoil Ser.). (Illus.). xv, 367p. 175.50 *(978-1-61728-004-7(6))* Nova Science Pubs., Inc.

Catignani, Sergio. Israeli Counter-Insurgency & the Intifadas: Dilemmas of a Conventional Army. 2009. 246p. pap. 39.95 *(978-0-415-57012-1(3))* Routledge.

Chaitin, Julia. Peace-Building in Israel & Palestine: Social Psychology & Grassroots Initiatives. 2011. (ENG., Illus.). 212p. 85.00 *(978-0-230-11508-8(X))* Palgrave Macmillan.

Champagne, Duane & Abu-Saad, Ismael, eds. Contemporary Issues in Palestinian Arab Education. 2006. (Topical Issues of American Behavioral Scientist Ser.: 385). 124p. pap. 24.00 *(978-1-4129-4210-2(1)*, 201385P) SAGE Pubns., Inc.

Charney, Leon. Backdoor Channels. 2011. (ENG.). 392p. pap. 19.95 ***(978-1-56980-462-9(1))*** Barricade Bks., Inc.

Chasnoff, Joel. The 188th Crybaby Brigade: A Skinny Jewish Kid from Chicago Fights Hezbollah - A Memoir. 2010. (ENG., Illus.). 238p. 25.00 *(978-1-4165-4932-1(3)*, Free Pr.) Free Pr.

Cheah, Elena. An Orchestra Beyond Borders: Voices of the West-Eastern Divan Orchestra. 2009. (ENG.). 320p. pap. 19.95 *(978-1-84467-408-4(8)*, 844408) Verso Bks. GBR. Dist: Norton, W. W. & Co., Inc.

Chehab, Zaki. Inside Hamas: The Untold Story of the Militant Islamic Movement. 2008. (ENG.). 256p. pap. 15.95 *(978-1-56858-395-2(8)*, Nation Bks.) Basic Bks.

Chomsky, Noam. Hopes & Prospects. 2010. (ENG.). 336p. pap. 17.00 *(978-1-931859-96-7(5))* Haymarket Bks.

Chomsky, Noam & Pappé, Ilan. Gaza in Crisis: Reflections on Israel's War Against the Palestinians. 2010. (ENG.). 240p. pap. 16.00 *(978-1-60846-097-7(5))* Haymarket Bks.

Coates, Ken. Unholy Land. 2009. 96p. pap. 18.50 *(978-0-85124-765-6(2))* Spokesman Bks. GBR. Dist: Coronet Bks.

Cohen, Samy. Israel's Asymmetric Wars. Schoch, Cynthia, tr. from FRE. 2010. (Sciences Po Series in International Relations & Political Economy Ser.). (ENG.). 208p. 89.00 *(978-0-230-10444-0(4))* Palgrave Macmillan.

Cohn-Sherbok, Dan. Introduction to Zionism & Israel: From Ideology to History. 2012. (ENG., Illus.). 264p. 80.00 *(978-1-4411-2757-0(7))*; pap. 24.95 *(978-1-4411-6052-1(0))* Continuum International Publishing Group, Ltd. GBR. Dist: National Bk. Network.

Cohn-Sherbok, Dan & El Alami, Dawoud Sudqi. Palestine-Israeli Conflict. 3rd ed. 2008. (Beginners Guide (Oneworld) Ser.). (ENG., Illus.). 295p. pap. 14.95 *(978-1-85168-611-7(8))* Oneworld Pubns. GBR. Dist: National Bk. Network.

Collins, John. Global Palestine. 2012. (Columbia/Hurst Ser.). (ENG.). 208p. (gr. 17). 30.00 ***(978-0-231-70310-9(4))*** Columbia Univ. Pr.

Cook, William. The Plight of the Palestinians: A Long History of Destruction. 2010. (ENG., Illus.). 304p. 89.00 *(978-0-230-10037-4(6))* Palgrave Macmillan.

Copeland, Thomas. Drawing a Line in the Sea: The Gaza Flotilla Incident & the Israeli-Palestinian Conflict. 2011. (ENG.). 210p. 60.00 ***(978-0-7391-6732-8(4))*** Lexington Bks.

Copeland, Thomas E., et al. Drawing a Line in the Sea: The 2010 Gaza Flotilla Incident & the Israeli-Palestinian Conflict. 2011. E-Book ***(978-0-7391-6955-1(6))*** Lexington Bks.

Corr, Edwin G., et al. The Search for Israel-Arab Peace: Learning from the Past & Building Trust. 2007. (Sussex Studies in Peace Politics in the Middle East Ser.). (ENG.). 286p. (C). 67.50 *(978-1-84519-191-7(9))* Sussex Academic Pr. GBR. Dist: International Specialized Bk. Services.

Cox, Eric W. Why Enduring Rivalries Do¿or Don¿t¿End. 2010. 210p. 65.00 *(978-1-935049-24-1(0))* FirstForumPress.

Cram101 Textbook Reviews. Outlines & Highlights for a Concise History of the Arab - Israeli Conflict by Bickerton & Klausner, Isbn: 0130903035 0131900048. 2011. 98p. pap. 27.95 ***(978-1-61830-028-7(8))*** Cram101 Inc.

—Outlines & Highlights for Palestine & the Arab-Israeli Conflict by Charles D Smith. 2011. 298p. pap. 32.95 ***(978-1-61905-757-9(3))*** Cram101 Inc.

—Outlines & Highlights for Palestine & the Arab-Israeli Conflict by Charles D Smith, Isbn: 9780312437367. 2011. 356p. pap. 34.95 ***(978-1-61812-477-7(3))*** Cram101 Inc.

Cram101 Textbook Reviews Staff. Outlines & Highlights for History of the Arab-Israeli Conflict by Bickerton, Ian / Klausner, Carla, Isbn: 9780132223355. 2009. 160p. pap. 29.95 *(978-1-4288-9413-6(6))* Cram101 Inc.

—Outlines & Highlights for the Arab-Israeli Conflict by Cq Press, Isbn: 9780195172300. 2009. 168p. pap. 29.95 *(978-1-4288-9553-9(1))* Cram101 Inc.

Crowley, Richard. No Mans Land. 2008. (ENG.). 253p. pap. 26.95 *(978-1-905483-26-6(0))* Liberties Pr. IRL. Dist: Dufour Editions, Inc.

Cypel, Sylvain. Walled: Israeli Society at an Impasse. 2007. (ENG.). 534p. pap. 17.95 *(978-1-59051-210-4(3))* Other Pr., LLC.

Dalin, David & Rothmann, John. Icon of Evil: Hitler's Mufti & the Rise of Radical Islam. 2009. (ENG., Illus.). 245p. pap. 24.95 *(978-1-4128-1077-7(9))* Transaction Pubs.

Dalin, David G. & Rothmann, John F. Icon of Evil: Hitler's Mufti & the Rise of Radical Islam. 2008. (ENG., Illus.). 240p. 26.00 *(978-1-4000-6653-7(0)*, Random House) Random House Publishing Group.

Danon, Danny. Israel: The Will to Prevail. 2012. (ENG., Illus.). 240p. 26.00 ***(978-0-230-34176-0(4))*** Palgrave Macmillan.

Dave Lane, Collected & Edited by. International Documents on Israel & Palestine 1915 To 2008. 2008. 541p. pap. 39.95 *(978-1-4092-1705-3(1))* Lulu Enterprises Inc.

David, Ron. Arabs & Israel for Beginners. 2007. (For Beginners Ser.). (ENG., Illus.). 224p. per. 14.95 *(978-1-934389-16-4(1)*, For Beginners) Steerforth Pr.

Debrauwere-Mill. Israeli-Palestinian Conflict in the Francophone World. Debrauwere-miller, Nathalie, ed. 2009. (Routledge Studies in Cultural History Ser.). (ENG., Illus.). 272p. (C). 125.00 *(978-0-415-99587-0(6))* Routledge.

Dekker, Ted & Medearis, Carl. Tea with Hezbollah: Sitting at the Enemies Table - Our Journey Through the Middle East. 2010. (ENG.). 256p. 22.99 *(978-0-307-58827-2(0)*, Doubleday Religion) Doubleday Religious Publishing Group, The.

Dershowitz. The Case for Peace: How the Arab-israeli Conflict Can Be Resolved. 2006. (ENG.). 256p. pap. 14.95 *(978-0-470-58132-2(8)*, Wiley) Wiley, John & Sons, Inc.

Dershowitz, Alan, et al. The Case Against Israel's Enemies: Exposing Jimmy Carter & Others Who Stand in the Way of Peace. 2009. (ENG.). 304p. pap. 15.95 *(978-0-470-49005-1(5)*, Wiley) Wiley, John & Sons, Inc.

Dershowitz, Alan M. The Case for Peace: How the Arab-Israeli Conflict Can Be Resolved. annot. ed. 2006. (ENG., Illus.). 256p. per. 14.95 *(978-0-470-04585-5(X)*, Wiley) Wiley, John & Sons, Inc.

Di Mauro, Danilo. The Un & the Arab-Israeli Conflict: American Hegemony & un Intervention since 1947. 2012. (Routledge Studies in Middle Eastern Politics Ser.). (ENG., Illus.). 352p. (C). 145.00 *(978-0-415-68562-7(1))* Routledge.

Dombroski, Kenneth. Peacekeeping in the Middle East As an International Regime. 2010. 176p. pap. 39.95 *(978-0-415-88253-8(2))* Routledge.

Dombrowski, Kenneth R. Peacekeeping in the Middle East as an International Regime. 2006. (Studies in International Relations Ser.). (ENG.). 176p. 138.00 *(978-0-415-98105-7(0))* Routledge.

Dowling, Karl. Burying the Hatchet, Not the Past. 2011. 128p. pap. ***(978-3-8443-0274-5(3))*** Lambert Academic Publishing.

Dowty, Alan. Israel-Palestine. 3rd ed. 2012. (ENG.). 280p. pap. 22.95 ***(978-0-7456-5612-0(9))*** Polity Pr. GBR. Dist: Wiley, John & Sons, Inc.

Dowty, Alan. Israel/Palestine. (ENG., 2nd rev. ed. 2008. (Global Political Hot Spots Ser.: 2). Illus.). 276p. pap. 22.95 *(978-0-7456-4243-7(8))* 2nd rev. ed. 2008. (Global Political Hot Spots Ser.: 4). (Illus.). 276p. 69.95 *(978-0-7456-4242-0(X))* 3rd ed. 2012. 280p. 69.95 ***(978-0-7456-5611-3(0))*** Polity Pr. GBR. Dist: Wiley, John & Sons, Inc.

Dumper, Michael. The Arab-Israeli Conflict, 4 vols. Dumper, Michael, ed. 2009. (ENG., Illus.). 1869p. 1295.00 *(978-0-415-44038-7(6))* Routledge.

—Palestinian Refugees: Return, Resettlement, & Reconciliation. 2007. 270p. lib. bdg. 55.00 *(978-1-58826-474-9(2))* Rienner, Lynne Pubs.

Dumper, Michael, ed. Palestinian Refugee Repatriation: Global Perspectives. 2006. (Routledge Studies in Middle Eastern Politics Ser.). (Illus.). 338p. 160.00 *(978-0-415-38497-1(4)*, RU4974X) Routledge.

Dunsky, Marda. Pens & Swords: How the American Mainstream Media Report the Israeli-Palestinian Conflict. 2008. (ENG.). 456p. (gr. 17). pap. 29.50 *(978-0-231-13349-4(9))*; (Illus.). 90.00 *(978-0-231-13348-7(0))* Columbia Univ. Pr.

Egorova, Yulia & Parfitt, Tudor, eds. Jews, Muslims & Mass Media: Mediating The 'Other' 2007. 272p. 39.95 *(978-0-415-44447-7(0))* Routledge.

Eisenberg, Laura Zittrain & Caplan, Neil. Negotiating Arab-Israeli Peace: Patterns, Problems, Possibilities. 2nd ed. 2010. (Indiana Series in Middle East Studies). (ENG., Illus.). 452p. pap. 27.95 *(978-0-253-22212-1(5)*, 0253222125) Indiana Univ. Pr.

El-Hasan, Hasan Afif. Is the Two-State Solution Already Dead? A Political & Military History of the Palestinian-Israeli Conflictf. 2010. *(978-0-87586-792-2(8))*; 288p. pap. 33.95 *(978-0-87586-793-9(6))* Algora Publishing.

Eldar, Akiva & Zertal, Idith. Lords of the Land: The War over Israel's Settlements in the Occupied Territories, 1967-2007. 2009. (ENG.). 576p. pap. 19.95 *(978-1-56858-414-0(8))* Westview Pr.

Elias Chacour Staff. Hoping Against Hope. 2011. xviii, 118p. pap. ***(978-1-85311-906-4(7)***, SCM Pr.) Hymns Ancient & Modern Ltd.

Ellis, Marc H. Judaism Does Not Equal Israel: The Rebirth of the Jewish Prophetic. 2009. (Does Not Equal Ser.). (ENG.). 256p. 24.95 *(978-1-59558-425-0(0)*, 955425) New Pr., The.

—Reading the Torah Out Loud: A Journey of Lament & Hope. 2007. 198p. pap. 21.00 *(978-0-8006-6210-3(5)*, Fortress Pr.) Augsburg Fortress, Pubs.

Enderlin, Charles. The Lost Years: Radical Islam, Intifada, & Wars in the Middle East 2001-2006. Verderber, Suzanne, tr. from FRE. 2007. (ENG., Illus.). 378p. 25.95 *(978-1-59051-171-8(9))* Other Pr., LLC.

Engler, Yves. Canada & Israel: Building Apartheid. 2010. (ENG.). 240p. pap. 19.95 *(978-1-55266-355-4(8))* Fernwood Publishing Co., Ltd. CAN. Dist: Independent Pubs. Group.

Erlich, Reese. The Iran Agenda: The Real Story of U. S. Policy & the Middle East Crisis. 2007. (Illus.). 192p. pap. 14.95 *(978-0-9778253-5-6(3))* Paradigm Pubs.

Farr, Nicholas. Religious Rhetoric in the Palestinian-Israeli Conflict. 2011. 96p. pap. ***(978-3-8433-8840-5(7))*** Lambert Academic Publishing.

Farsoun, Samih K. & Aruri, Naseer. Palestine & the Palestinians: A Social & Political History. 2nd rev. ed. 2006. (ENG., Illus.). 488p. pap. 44.00 *(978-0-8133-4336-5(4))* Westview Pr.

Faruqi, Daanish. From Camp David to Cast Lead: Essays on Israel, Palestine, & the Future of the Peace Process. 2011. (Logos: Perspectives on Modern Society & Culture Ser.). (ENG.). 186p. 65.00 *(978-0-7391-4456-5(1))* Lexington Bks.

Feige, Michael. Settling in the Hearts: Jewish Fundamentalism in the Occupied Territories. 2009. (Illus.). 352p. 54.95 *(978-0-8143-2750-0(8))* Wayne State Univ. Pr.

Feiler, Bruce. Where God Was Born: A Daring Adventure Through the Bible's Greatest Stories. 2007. (P. S. Ser.). (ENG., Illus.). 416p. pap. 14.95 *(978-0-06-057489-5(5)*, William Morrow Paperbacks) HarperCollins Pubs.

Feng, Shaoxie & Wang, Zhong. Zhong Dong de Ge Zi: Feng Shaoxie You Hua Ji = Middle East Pigeon Series: Feng Shaoxie Oil Paintings. 2010. (CHI & ENG., Illus.). 51p. *(978-0-9844493-4-7(5))* International Publishing Hse. for China's Culture.

Finkelstein, Norman. Image & Reality of the Israel-Palestine Conflict 3rd Edition. 3rd ed. 2008. 364p. pap. 21.95 *(978-1-84467-195-3(X))* Verso Bks. GBR. Dist: Norton, W. W. & Co., Inc.

—This Time We Went Too Far: Truth & Consequences of the Gaza Invasion. 2010. 208p. 20.00 *(978-0-9842950-3-6(8))* OR Bks., LLC.

Finkelstein, Norman G. Beyond Chutzpah: On the Misuse of Anti-Semitism & the Abuse of History. 2nd rev. ed. 2008. 488p. pap. 21.95 *(978-0-520-24989-9(5))* Univ. of California Pr.

Firestone, Reuven. Holy War in Judaism: The Fall & Rise of a Controversial Idea. 2012. (ENG.). 384p. 39.95 ***(978-0-19-986030-2(0))*** Oxford Univ. Pr., Inc.

Fischbach, Michael R. Jewish Property Claims Against Arab Countries. 2008. (ENG., Illus.). 376p. (gr. 17). 45.00 *(978-0-231-13538-2(6))* Columbia Univ. Pr.

Flank, Lenny. The Arab-Israeli Conflict: A Documentary History of the Struggle for Peace in Palestine. 2010. 350p. pap. *(978-1-934941-93-5(X))* Red & Black Pubs.

Fleming, Eileen. Third Intifada/Uprising: Nonviolent but with Words Sharper Than a Two-Edged Sword. 2007. (ENG., Illus.). 132p. per. 10.95 *(978-1-4327-0254-0(8))* Outskirts Pr., Inc.

Forer, Richard. Breakthrough: A New Perspective on the Israel-Palestine Conflict: Transforming Fear into Compassion. 2010. pap. 19.95 *(978-0-615-40458-5(8))* Insight Pr.

Fraser, T. G. The Arab-Israeli Conflict. 3rd rev. ed. 2007. (Studies in Contemporary History Ser.). (ENG., Illus.). 240p. 120.00 *(978-0-230-00468-9(7))*; pap. 39.00 *(978-0-230-00469-6(5))* Palgrave Macmillan.

Freedman, Robert O., ed. Contemporary Israel: Domestic Politics, Foreign Policy, & Security Challenges. rev. ed. 2008. (ENG.). 352p. (C). pap. 43.00 *(978-0-8133-4385-3(2))* Westview Pr.

Friel, Howard & Falk, Richard. Israel-Palestine on Record: How the New York Times Misreports Conflict in the Middle East. 2007. (ENG.). 309p. per. 19.95 *(978-1-84467-109-0(7)*, 844109) Verso Bks. GBR. Dist: Norton, W. W. & Co., Inc.

Garfinkle, Adam. Jewcentricity: Why the Jews Are Praised, Blamed, & Used to Explain Just about Everything. 2009. (ENG.). 320p. 25.95 *(978-0-470-19856-8(7)*, Wiley) Wiley, John & Sons, Inc.

Gat, Moshe. In Search of a Peace Settlement: Egypt & Israel between the Wars, 1967-1973. 2012. (ENG., Illus.). 296p. 85.00 ***(978-0-230-37500-0(6))*** Palgrave Macmillan.

Gavron, Daniel. Holy Land Mosaic: Stories of Cooperation & Coexistence Between Israelis & Palestinians. 2007. (ENG.). 226p. 70.00 *(978-0-7425-4012-5(X))*; per. 26.95 *(978-0-7425-4013-2(8))* Rowman & Littlefield Publishers, Inc.

Gawerc, Michelle I. Prefiguring Peace: Israeli-Palestinian Peacebuilding Partnerships. 2012. (ENG.). 310p. (gr. 17). 80.00 ***(978-0-7391-6610-9(7))*** Lexington Bks.

Gaza after the War: What Can Be Built on the Wreckage?: Hearing Before the Subcommittee on the Middle East & South Asia of the Committee on Foreign Affairs, House of Representatives, One Hundred Eleventh Congress, First Session, February 12, 2009. 2009. iii, 116p. *(978-0-16-082993-2(3)*, 552-070-38895-8) United States Government Printing Office.

Gelvin, James L. The Israel-Palestine Conflict: One Hundred Years of War. 2nd rev. ed. 2007. (ENG., Illus.). 298p. 90.00 *(978-0-521-88835-6(2))*; 312p. pap. 27.99 *(978-0-521-71652-9(7))* Cambridge Univ. Pr.

Ghanem, As'ad. Palestinian Politics after Arafat: A Failed National Movement. 2010. (Indiana Series in Middle East Studies). (ENG.). 222p. 65.00 *(978-0-253-35427-3(7)*, 0253354277); pap. 24.95 *(978-0-253-22160-5(9)*, 0253221609) Indiana Univ. Pr.

Ghosheh, Subhi S. Jerusalem: Arab Social Life, Traditions, & Everyday Pleasures. 2011. (ENG., Illus.). 248p. pap. 20.00 *(978-1-56656-788-6(2)*, Olive Branch Pr.) Interlink Publishing Group, Inc.

Gilbert, Martin. The Routledge Atlas of the Arab-Israeli Conflict. 10th rev. ed. 2012. (Routledge Historical Atlases Ser.). (ENG., Illus.). 240p. (C). 115.00 ***(978-0-415-69975-4(4))***; pap. 29.95 ***(978-0-415-69976-1(2))*** Routledge.

Girard, Louis H. Israeli-Arab Negotiations & Issues. 2011. (Politics & Economics of the Middle East Ser.). (Illus.). viii, 153p. 115.00 *(978-1-61761-185-8(9))* Nova Science Pubs., Inc.

Gish, Arthur G. At-Tuwani Journal: Hope & Nonviolent Action in a Palestinian Village. 2008. pap. 17.99 *(978-0-8361-9406-7(3))* Herald Pr.

Gitlin, Todd & Leibovitz, Liel. The Chosen Peoples: America, Israel, & the Ordeals of Divine Election. 2010. (ENG.). 272p. 26.00 *(978-1-4391-3235-7(6))* Simon & Schuster.

Gleis, Joshua L. & Berti, Benedetta. Hezbollah & Hamas: A Comparative Study. 2012. ***(978-1-4214-0614-5(4))***; pap. ***(978-1-4214-0615-2(2))***; E-Book ***(978-1-4214-0671-8(3))*** Johns Hopkins Univ. Pr.

Glick, Caroline. Shackled Warrior. 2008. 448p. 29.95 *(978-965-229-415-9(2))* Gefen Publishing Hse., Ltd ISR. Dist: Gefen Bks.

Gluck, Andrew L., ed. Religion, Fundamentalism, & Violence: An Interdisciplinary Study & Dialogue. 2010. (ENG.). 312p. pap. 27.00 *(978-1-58966-204-9(0))* Univ. of Scranton Pr.

Gluska, Ami. The Israeli Military & the Origins of the 1967 War: Government, Armed Forces & Defence Policy 1963-67. 2007. pap. 39.95 *(978-0-415-54511-2(0))* Routledge.

Golan, Galia. Israel & Palestine: Peace Plans & Proposals from Oslo to Disengagement. 2007. *(978-1-55876-502-3(6))*; 260p. pap. 24.95 *(978-1-55876-503-0(4))* Wiener, Markus Pubs., Inc.

—Israel & Palestine: Peace Plans & Proposals from Oslo to Disengagement — Updated 2008 Edition. (Illus.). 2008. 260p. 68.95 *(978-1-55876-420-0(8))* 2007. ix, 230p. pap. 24.95 *(978-1-55876-421-7(6))* Wiener, Markus Pubs., Inc.

—Moscow & the Middle East. 112p. *(978-1-85567-008-2(9)*, Burns & Oates) Continuum International Publishing Group, Ltd.

—Moscow & the Middle East: New Thinking on Regional Conflict. 112p. pap. *(978-1-85567-009-9(7)*, Burns & Oates) Continuum International Publishing Group, Ltd.

Gold, Dore. The Fight for Jerusalem: Radical Islam, the West, & the Future of the Holy City. 2009. (ENG., Illus.). 372p. pap. 16.95 *(978-1-59698-102-7(4))* Regnery Publishing, Inc., An Eagle Publishing Co.

Goldberg, Jeffrey. Prisoners: A Story of Friendship & Terror. 2008. (Vintage Ser.). (ENG.). 336p. pap. 16.95 *(978-0-375-72670-5(5)*, Vintage) Knopf Doubleday Publishing Group.

Goodman, Hirsh. The Anatomy of Israel's Survival. 2011. (ENG., Illus.). 288p. 26.99 *(978-1-58648-529-0(6))* PublicAffairs.

Gopin, Marc. Bridges across an Impossible Divide: The Inner Lives of Arab & Jewish Peacemakers. 2012. 240p. 29.95 ***(978-0-19-991698-6(5))*** Oxford Univ. Pr., Inc.

Gordon, Hayim. Israel Today. 256p. (C). pap. 32.95 *(978-0-8204-7825-8(3))* Lang, Peter Publishing, Inc.

Gordon, Neve. Israel's Occupation. 2008. (Illus.). 328p. 55.00 *(978-0-520-25530-2(5))*; pap. 26.95 *(978-0-520-25531-9(3))* Univ. of California Pr.

Gorenberg, Gershom. The Unmaking of Israel. 2012. 336p. pap. 14.99 ***(978-0-06-198509-6(0)***, HarperPerennial) 2011. (ENG.). 288p. 25.99 *(978-0-06-198508-9(2))* HarperCollins Pubs.

Gorny, Yosef. From Binational Society to Jewish State: Federal Concepts in Zionist Political Thought, 1920-1990, & the Jewish People. 2006. (Jewish Identities in a Changing World Ser.: Vol. 7). 189p. *(978-90-04-15529-9(5))* BRILL.

Gröndahl, Mia. Gaza Graffiti: Messages of Love & Politics. 2010. (ENG.). 152p. pap. 29.95 *(978-977-416-321-0(4))* American Univ. in Cairo Pr. EGY. Dist: Oxford Univ. Pr., Inc.

Grief, Howard. The Legal Foundation & Borders of Israel under International Law: A Treatise on Jewish Sovereignty over the Land of Israel. 2008. 731p. 49.00 *(978-965-7344-52-1(2))* Mazo Pubs.

Grinberg, Lev. Politics & Violence in Israel/Palestine: Democracy versus Military Rule. 2009. (Routledge Studies in Middle Eastern Politics Ser.). (ENG.). 258p. 135.00 *(978-0-415-48833-4(8))* Routledge.

Grob, Leonard & Roth, John K., eds. Anguished Hope: Holocaust Scholars Confront the Palestinian-Israeli Conflict. 2008. 264p. pap. 25.00 *(978-0-8028-3329-7(2))* Eerdmans, William B. Publishing Co.

Grobman, Alex. Nations United: How the United Nations Is Undermining Israel & the West. 2009. (Illus.). 208p. 19.99 *(978-0-89221-674-1(3)*, Icon Publishing Group) Midpoint Trade Bks., Inc.

Grossman, David & Cohen, Jessica. Writing in the Dark: Essays on Literature & Politics. 2009. (ENG.). 144p. pap. 15.00 *(978-0-312-42860-0(X))* Picador.

Grossman, Naomi, ed. The Expulsion from Gush Katif. 2008. 260p. pap. 14.95 *(978-1-933882-06-2(9))* Southern Hills Pr.

Halevy, Efraim. Man in the Shadows: Inside the Middle East Crisis with a Man Who Led the Mossad. 2008. (ENG.). 320p. pap. 16.99 *(978-0-312-33772-8(8)*, St. Martin's Griffin) St. Martin's Pr.

Hallward, Maia Carter. Struggling for a Just Peace: Israeli & Palestinian Activism in the Second Intifada. 2011. (ENG., Illus.). 288p. 74.95 *(978-0-8130-3652-6(6))* Univ. Pr. of Florida.

Hallward, Maia Carter & Norma, Julie M., eds. Nonviolent Resistance in the Second Intifada: Activism & Advocacy. 2011. (Middle East Today Ser.). (ENG., Illus.). 196p. 85.00 *(978-0-230-11675-7(2))* Palgrave Macmillan.

Halper, Jeff. An Israeli in Palestine: Resisting Dispossession, Redeeming Israel, 1 vol. 2008. (ENG., Illus.). 336p. lib. bdg. 95.00 *(978-0-7453-2227-8(1))* Pluto Pr. GBR. Dist: Macmillan.

Halwani, Raja & Kapitan, Tomis. The Israeli-Palestinian Conflict: Philosophical Essays on Self-Determination, Terrorism & the One-State Solution. 2008. (ENG., Illus.). 256p. 98.00 *(978-0-230-53537-4(2))* Palgrave Macmillan.

Hammond, Andrew. What the Arabs Think of America, 1 vol. 2007. (Illus.). 246p. 49.95 *(978-1-84645-000-6(4)*, GWP000) Greenwood Publishing Group, Inc.

Hammond, Constance A. Shalom/Salaam/Peace: A Liberation Theology of Hope. 2008. (Religion & Violence Ser.). (ENG., Illus.). 236p. (C). 99.95 *(978-1-84553-379-3(8))*; pap. 34.95 *(978-1-84553-380-9(1))* Equinox Publishing Ltd. GBR. Dist: ISD.

Hammond, Jeremy R. The Rejection of Palestinian Self-Determination. 2009. 79p. pap. 9.99 *(978-0-557-09569-8(7))* Lulu Enterprises Inc.

Handelman, Sapir. Conflict & Peacemaking in Israel-Palestine: Theory & Application. 2011. (Routledge Studies in Middle Eastern Politics Ser.). (ENG., Illus.). 160p. (C). 130.00 *(978-0-415-49215-7(7))* Routledge.

Handley, Robert. Dissident Media Monitoring Strategies & U S News Medi. 2011. 152p. pap. ***(978-3-8443-8194-8(5))*** Lambert Academic Publishing.

Hanf, Theodor. Coexistence in Wartime Lebanon: Decline of a State & Rise of a Nation. 2012. (ENG.). 736p. pap. 35.00 ***(978-1-84885-715-5(2))*** I. B. Tauris & Co., Ltd. GBR. Dist: Macmillan.

Harb, Zahera. Channels of Resistance in Lebanon: Liberation Propaganda, Hezbollah & the Media. 2011. (ENG.). 256p. 88.00 *(978-1-84885-120-7(0))*; pap. 28.00 *(978-1-84885-121-4(9))* I. B. Tauris & Co., Ltd. GBR. Dist: Macmillan.

Harms, Gregory & Ferry, Todd M. The Palestine-Israel Conflict: A Basic Introduction, 1 vol. 3rd ed. 2012. (ENG.). 216p. 22.00 ***(978-0-7453-3213-0(7))*** Pluto Pr. GBR. Dist: Macmillan.

Harrison, Bernard. The Resurgence of Anti-Semitism: Jews, Israel, & Liberal Opinion. 2006. (Philosophy & the Global Context Ser.). (ENG.). 240p. 74.00 *(978-0-7425-5226-5(8))*; per. 28.95 *(978-0-7425-5227-2(6))* Rowman & Littlefield Publishers, Inc.

Heller, Joseph. The Israel Palestine Puzzle: I. the Ben-Gurion Magnes Debates: Jewish State or Binational State; II. Israel's Borders in Historical Perspective: the Security-Demography Dilemma. 2008. 98p. pap. 18.00 *(978-1-58790-155-3(2))* Regent Pr.

Hermann, Tamar S. The Israeli Peace Movement: A Shattered Dream. 2009. (ENG., Illus.). 320p. 85.00 *(978-0-521-88409-9(8))* Cambridge Univ. Pr.

Hever, Shir. The Political Economy of Israel's Occupation: Repression Beyond Exploitation, 1 vol. 2010. (ENG., Illus.). 240p. 30.00 *(978-0-7453-2794-5(X))* Pluto Pr. GBR. Dist: Macmillan.

Hilal, Jamil. Where Now for Palestine? The Demise of the Two-State Solution. 2007. (ENG., Illus.). 224p. per. 32.95 *(978-1-84277-840-1(4))* Zed Bks., Ltd. GBR. Dist: Macmillan.

Hirst, David. Beware of Small States: Lebanon, Battleground of the Middle East. 2011. (ENG.). 496p. (gr. 9). pap. 19.99 *(978-1-56858-657-1(4))* Basic Bks.

Hitchcock, Mark. Middle East Burning. 2012. 256p. pap. 13.99 ***(978-0-7369-3996-6(2))*** Harvest Hse. Pubs.

Honderich. Humanity Terrorism Terrorist War. 2007. vi, 206p. pap. *(978-0-8264-9746-8(2))* Continuum International Publishing Group, Ltd.

Honderich, Ted. Right & Wrong, & Palestine, 9-11, Iraq, 7-7 ... 2006. (ENG.). 272p. pap. 18.95 *(978-1-58322-736-7(9))* Seven Stories Pr.

Honig-Parnass, Tikva. False Prophets of Peace: Liberal Zionism & the Struggle for Palestine. 2011. (ENG., Illus.). 350p. pap. 20.00 ***(978-1-60846-130-1(0))*** Haymarket Bks.

Howland, Nina D., et al, eds. Foreign Relations of the United States, 1969-1976, Volume XXV, Arab-Israeli Crisis & War 1973. 2011. (ENG.). 1278p. 78.00 ***(978-0-16-082003-8(0)***, Bureau of Public Affairs, Office of the Historian) United States Government Printing Office.

Hroub, Khaled. Hamas: A Beginner's Guide. (ENG.). 2006. 192p. 79.00 *(978-0-7453-2591-0(2))* 2nd ed. 2010. 224p. 85.00 *(978-0-7453-2973-4(X))* Pluto Pr. GBR. Dist: Macmillan.

—Hamas: Die islamische Bewegung in Palästina, 1 vol. 2nd ed. 2010. (ENG.). 224p. pap. 24.95 *(978-0-7453-2972-7(1))* Pluto Pr. GBR. Dist: Macmillan.

Hulme Jr, Derick L. & Hulme, Derick L. The Israeli-Palestinian Road Map for Peace: A Critical Analysis. 2008. (ENG.). 252p. pap. 42.99 *(978-0-7618-4370-2(1))* Univ. Pr. of America, Inc.

Hunter, Robert & Howard, Michael. Israel, Palestine & the Arab World. 2006. (Adelphi Paper Ser.). (Illus.). 364p. 290.00 *(978-0-415-39863-3(0))* Routledge.

Hurndall, Jocelyn. Defy the Stars: The Life & Death of Tom Hurndall. 2007. (ENG., Illus.). 1p. 32.95 *(978-0-7475-8944-0(5))* Bloomsbury Publishing Plc GBR. Dist: Independent Pubs. Group.

—Defy the Stars: The Life & Tragic Death of Tom Hurndall. 2007. (ENG., Illus.). 320p. pap. 22.00 *(978-0-7475-9102-3(4))* Bloomsbury Publishing Plc GBR. Dist: Independent Pubs. Group.

Inbar, Efraim. Israel's National Security: Issues & Challenges since the Yom Kippur War. 2008. (Israeli History, Politics & Society Ser.). 304p. 150.00 *(978-0-415-44955-7(3))* Routledge.

Indyk, Martin. Innocent Abroad: An Intimate Account of American Peace Diplomacy in the Middle East. 2009. (ENG., Illus.). 512p. 30.00 *(978-1-4165-9429-1(9))* Simon & Schuster.

IPMN-PC. Steadfast Hope: The Palestinian quest for Just Peach. 2009. pap. *(978-1-61584-213-1(6))* Independent Pub.

Irving, Sarah. Leila Khaled: Icon of Palestinian Liberation, 1 vol. 2012. (ENG., Illus.). 168p. 21.00 ***(978-0-7453-2951-2(9))***; lib. bdg. 75.00 ***(978-0-7453-2952-9(7))*** Pluto Pr. GBR. Dist: Macmillan.

Isaksen, Runo. Literature & War: Conversations with Israeli & Palestinian Writers. Dickson, Kari, tr. from NOR. 2008. (ENG.). 256p. pap. 18.00 *(978-1-56656-730-5(0))* Interlink Publishing Group, Inc.

Ismael, Jacqueline S. & Haddad, William W. Barriers to Reconciliation: Case Studies on Iraq & the Palestine-Israel Conflict. Ismael, Jacqueline S. & Haddad, William W., eds. 2006. (ENG., Illus.). 320p. pap. 49.50 *(978-0-7618-3554-7(7))* Univ. Pr. of America, Inc.

Israeli, Raphael. The Oslo Idea: The Euphoria of Failure. 2012. (ENG.). 244p. 34.95 ***(978-1-4128-4611-0(0))*** Transaction Pubs.

Jacobs, Matthew F. Imagining the Middle East: The Building of an American Foreign Policy, 1918-1967. 2011. (ENG.). 336p. 39.95 *(978-0-8078-3488-6(2))* Univ. of North Carolina Pr.

Jayyusi, Lena. Jerusalem Interrupted: Modernity & Colonial Transformation 1917-Present. Jayyusi, Lena, ed. 2012. (ENG., Illus.). 288p. pap. 60.00 *(978-1-56656-787-9(4))* Interlink Publishing Group, Inc.

Johnson, Jeffrey D. The Arabs-The Conflict. 2007. (Illus.). 28p. pap. 3.00 *(978-1-55635-076-4(7)*, Wipf and Stock) Wipf & Stock Pubs.

Johnston, Alan & Grant, Tony. Kidnapped: And Other Dispatches. 2009. (ENG., Illus.). 160p. pap. 12.95 *(978-1-84668-142-4(1))* Profile Bks. Ltd. GBR. Dist: Consortium Bk. Sales & Distribution.

Jones, Clive & Catignani, Sergio, eds. Israel & Hizbollah: An asymmetric conflict in historical & comparative Perspective. 2012. (ENG.). 206p. (C). pap. 39.95 ***(978-0-415-62221-9(2))*** Routledge.

Jones, Nick. Between Terrorism & Civil War. 2007. 176p. 39.95 *(978-0-415-43453-9(X))* Routledge.

Kadayifci-Orellana, S. Ayse. Standing on an Isthmus: Islamic Narratives on Peace & War in Palestinian Territories. 2007. (ENG.). 340p. 78.99 *(978-0-7391-1111-6(6))* Lexington Bks.

Karmi, Ghada. Married to Another Man: Israel's Dilemma in Palestine. 2007. (ENG., Illus.). 320p. 89.00 *(978-0-7453-2066-3(X))*; per. 26.95 *(978-0-7453-2065-6(1))* Pluto Pr. GBR. Dist: Macmillan.

Karsh, Efraim. Israel at Sixty: Rethinking the birth of the Jewish State. Miller, Rory, ed. 2009. (ENG.). 272p. 150.00 *(978-0-415-48317-9(4))* Routledge.

Karsh, Efraim & Kumaraswamy, P. R., eds. Islamic Attitudes to Israel. 2008. (ENG.). 208p. (C). 150.00 *(978-0-415-44025-7(4))* Routledge.

Karsh, Ephraim & Kumaraswamy, P. R., eds. Islamic Attitudes to Israel. 2009. (ENG.). 206p. (C). pap. 39.95 *(978-0-415-57463-1(3))* Routledge.

Kass, Mark. Intercultural Cooperation Between Israelis & Palestinians. 2010. 312p. pap. *(978-3-639-19697-9(X))* VDM Verlag Dr. Mueller e.K.

Kattan, Victor. From Coexistence to Conquest: International Law & the Origins of the Arab-Israel. 2009. (ENG., Illus.). 544p. pap. 48.00 *(978-0-7453-2578-1(5))* Pluto Pr. GBR. Dist: Macmillan.

—From Coexistance to Conquest: International Law & the Origins of the Arab-Israeli Conflict, 1891-1949. 2009. (ENG.). 416p. 144.00 *(978-0-7453-2579-8(3))* Pluto Pr. GBR. Dist: Macmillan.

Kattan, Victor, ed. The Palestine Question in International Law. 2008. (Illus.). 1045p. (C). 160.00 *(978-1-905221-30-1(4))* British Institute of International & Comparative Law GBR. Dist: International Specialized Bk. Services.

Kaufman-Lacusta, Maxine. Refusing to be Enemies: Palestinian & Israeli Nonviolent Resistance to the Israeli Occupation. 2011. Orig. Title: Peace movements. 552p. pap. 24.95 *(978-0-86372-380-3(2)*, Ithaca Pr.) Garnet Publishing, Ltd. GBR. Dist: International Specialized Bk. Services.

Kaunya, Edward Oku. Diplomacy of War. 2010. 112p. pap. *(978-3-639-26955-0(1))* VDM Verlag Dr. Mueller e.K.

Kaye, Dalia Dassa. Talking to the Enemy: Track Two Diplomacy in the Middle East & South Asia. 2007. (Illus.). 164p. per. 25.00 *(978-0-8330-4191-3(6))* RAND Corp., The.

Kern, Kathleen. As Resident Aliens. 2009. 372p. pap. 41.00 *(978-1-55635-233-1(6)*, Cascade Bks.) Wipf & Stock Pubs.

Khalidi, Rashid. The Iron Cage: The Story of the Palestinian Struggle for Statehood. 2007. (ENG.). 288p. per. 17.00 *(978-0-8070-0309-1(3))* Beacon Pr.

Khalili, Laleh. Heroes & Martyrs of Palestine: The Politics of National Commemoration. 2009. (Cambridge Middle East Studies). (ENG.). 276p. pap. 36.99 *(978-0-521-10638-2(9))* Cambridge Univ. Pr.

Khatchadourian, Haig. The Quest for Peace between Israel & the Palestinians. 2011. 184p. pap. 21.00 ***(978-1-61097-057-0(8)***, Wipf and Stock) Wipf & Stock Pubs.

Khatib, Ghassan. Palestinian Politics & the Middle East Peace Process. 2011. 216p. pap. 42.95 ***(978-0-415-67374-7(7))*** Routledge.

Khider, Ibrahim. Muslimgauze: Chasing the Shadow of Bryn Jones. 2009. 224p. *(978-0-946719-42-6(X))* S.A.F. Publishing Ltd.

King of Jordan Abdullah II. Our Last Best Chance: The Pursuit of Peace in a Time of Peril. l.t. ed. 2011. 32.99 *(978-1-4104-3603-0(9))* Thorndike Pr.

Klein, Aaron. The Late Great State of Israel: How Enemies Within & Without Threaten the Jewish Nation's Survival. 2009. 240p. 25.95 *(978-1-935071-08-2(4))* WND Bks, Inc.

Klein, Menachem. The Jerusalem Problem: The Struggle for Permanent Status. 2009. (ENG.). 256p. (C). pap. 29.50 *(978-1-61610-123-7(7))* Orange Grove Bks.

—A Possible Peace Between Israel & Palestine: An Insider's Account of the Geneva Initiative. Watzman, Haim, tr. from HEB. 2007. (ENG.). 256p. (gr. 17). 35.00 *(978-0-231-13904-5(7))* Columbia Univ. Pr.

—The Shift: Israel-Palestine from Border Struggle to Ethnic Conflict. Weitzman, Chaim, tr. 2010. (Columbia/Hurst Ser.). (ENG.). 144p. (gr. 17). 30.00 *(978-0-231-70196-9(0))* Columbia Univ. Pr.

Knopf-Newman, Marcy Jane. The Politics of Teaching Palestine to Americans: Addressing Pedagogical Strategies. 2011. (ENG., Illus.). 272p. 85.00 ***(978-0-230-11688-7(4))*** Palgrave Macmillan.

Knudsen, Are & Hanafi, Sari, eds. Palestinian Refugees: Identity, Space & Place in the Levant. 2010. (Routledge Studies on the Arab-Israeli Conflict Ser.). (ENG., Illus.). 248p. (C). 130.00 *(978-0-415-58046-5(3))* Routledge.

Kolers, Avery. Land, Conflict, & Justice: A Political Theory of Territory. 2009. (ENG., Illus.). 252p. 98.00 *(978-0-521-51677-8(3))* Cambridge Univ. Pr.

Korinman, Michel & Laughland, John. Israel on Israel. Korinman, Michel, ed. 2008. (Illus.). 337p. 85.00 *(978-0-85303-657-9(8))*; pap. 32.95 *(978-0-85303-658-6(6))* Vallentine Mitchell Pubs. GBR. Dist: International Specialized Bk. Services.

Kozodoy, Neal. The Mideast Peace Process: An Autopsy. 2006. (ENG.). 200p. per. 16.95 *(978-1-59403-191-5(6))* Encounter Bks.

Kreimendahl, Ilka. Powder Keg Middle East- the Role of the United States in the Arab-Israeli Conflict. 2007. 112p. per. *(978-3-8364-1543-9(7))* VDM Verlag Dr. Mueller e.K.

Kremer, Shai, photos by. Shai Kremer: Fallen Empires. 2011. (ENG., Illus.). 136p. 50.00 ***(978-1-934435-35-9(X))*** Radius Bks.

Kuentzel, Matthias. Jihad & Jew-Hatred: Islamism, Nazism & the Roots Of 9/11. Meade, Colin, tr. 2009. (ENG.). 180p. pap. 19.95 *(978-0-914386-39-1(5))* Telos Pr., Ltd.

—Jihad & Jew-Hatred: Islamism, Nazism & the Roots Of 9/11. 2007. 200p. 29.95 *(978-0-914386-36-0(0))* Telos Pr., Ltd.

Kumaraswamy, P. R. Historical Dictionary of the Arab-Israeli Conflict. 2006. (Historical Dictionaries of War, Revolution, & Civil Unrest Ser.: Vol. 32). (ENG.). 424p. 115.00 *(978-0-8108-5343-0(4))* Scarecrow Pr., Inc.

—India's Israel Policy. 2010. (ENG., Illus.). 376p. (gr. 17). 55.00 *(978-0-231-15204-4(3))* Columbia Univ. Pr.

Kumaraswamy, P. R. & Woro. The A to Z of the Arab-Israeli Conflict. 2009. (A to Z Guide Ser.: No. 66). (ENG.). 420p. pap. 34.45 *(978-0-8108-5590-8(9))* Scarecrow Pr., Inc.

Kuperman, Ranan D. Cycles of Violence: The Evolution of the Israeli Decision Regime Governing the Use of Limited Military Force. Kuperman, Ranan D., ed. 2007. (Innovations in the Study of World Politics Ser.). (ENG.). 250p. pap. 31.50 *(978-0-7391-2182-5(0))* Lexington Bks.

Kuriansky, Judy. Terror in the Holy Land: Inside the Anguish of the Israeli-Palestinian Conflict, 1 vol. 2006. (Contemporary Psychology Ser.). (Illus.). 296p. 49.95 *(978-0-275-99041-1(9)*, C9041, Praeger Pubs.) Greenwood Publishing Group, Inc.

Kuriansky, Judy, ed. Beyond Bullets & Bombs: Grassroots Peace Building Between Israelis & Palestinians. 2007. (Contemporary Psychology Ser.). (Illus.). 408p. 49.95 *(978-0-275-99880-6(0)*, C9880, Praeger Pubs.) Greenwood Publishing Group, Inc.

Kurtzer, Daniel C. & Lasensky, Scott B. Negotiating Arab-Israeli Peace: American Leadership in the Middle East. 2008. (Illus.). 210p. per. 17.50 *(978-1-60127-030-6(5))* U.S. Institute of Peace Pr. (USIP Pr.).

Lambeth, Benjamin S. Air Operations in Israel's War Against Hezbollah: Learning from Lebanon & Getting It Right in Gaza, 1 vol. 2011. (ENG., Illus.). 442p. (C). pap. 34.00 *(978-0-8330-5146-2(6))* RAND Corp., The.

Laskier, Michael M. & Lev, Yaacov, eds. The Divergence of Judaism & Islam: Interdependence, Modernity, & Political Turmoil. 2011. (ENG., Illus.). 304p. 74.95 *(978-0-8130-3751-6(4))* Univ. Pr. of Florida.

Lassner, Jacob & Troen, S.Ilan. Jews & Muslims in the Arab World. Lassner, Jacob & Troen, S.Ilan, eds. 2007. (ENG., Illus.). 410p. 89.00 *(978-0-7425-5841-0(X))*; pap. 39.95 *(978-0-7425-5842-7(8))* Rowman & Littlefield Publishers, Inc.

Law, Stephen & Law. Israel, Palestine & Terror. 2008. (ENG.). 240p. 29.95 *(978-0-8264-9793-2(4))* Continuum International Publishing Group, Ltd. GBR. Dist: National Bk. Network.

Lentin, Ronit. Thinking Palestine. 2008. (ENG.). 256p. 108.00 *(978-1-84277-906-4(0))* Zed Bks., Ltd. GBR. Dist: Macmillan.

Lentin, Ronit, ed. Thinking Palestine. 2008. (ENG.). 256p. pap. 34.00 *(978-1-84277-907-1(9))* Zed Bks., Ltd. GBR. Dist: Macmillan.

Lerner, Michael. Embracing Israel/Palestine: A Strategy to Heal & Transform the Middle East. 2011. (ENG., Illus.). 448p. pap. 17.95 *(978-1-58394-307-6(2))* North Atlantic Bks.

Lesch, Ann M. & Lustick, Ian S., eds. Exile & Return: Predicaments of Palestinians & Jews. 2008. 368p. (C). pap. 26.50 *(978-0-8122-2052-0(8))* Univ. of Pennsylvania Pr.

Lesch, David W. The Arab-Israeli Conflict: A History. 2007. (ENG., Illus.). 512p. (C). pap. 54.95 *(978-0-19-517230-0(2))* Oxford Univ. Pr., Inc.

Lesch, David W. & Haas, Mark L., eds. The Middle East & the United States: History, Politics, & Ideologies. 5th ed. 2011. (ENG., Illus.). 560p. (C). pap. 50.00 *(978-0-8133-4529-1(4))* Westview Pr.

Levey, Gregory. How to Make Peace in the Middle East in Six Months or Less: Without Leaving Your Apartment. 2010. (ENG., Illus.). 288p. 25.00 *(978-1-4391-5415-1(5)*, Free Pr.) Free Pr.

Levine, Mark. Impossible Peace: Israel/Palestine Since 1989. 2009. (Global History of the Present Ser.). (ENG., Illus.). 240p. pap. 25.95 *(978-1-84277-769-5(6))* Zed Bks., Ltd. GBR. Dist: Macmillan.

—Impossible Peace: Israel/Palestine since 1989. 2009. (Global History of the Present Ser.). (ENG., Illus.). 240p. 85.95 *(978-1-84277-768-8(8))* Zed Bks., Ltd. GBR. Dist: Macmillan.

LeVine, Mark Andrew & Shafir, Gershon, eds. Struggle & Survival in Palestine/Israel. 2012. (ENG.). 464p. 75.00 ***(978-0-520-26252-2(2))***; pap. 34.95 ***(978-0-520-26253-9(0))*** Univ. of California Pr.

Levy, Gideon. The Punishment of Gaza. 2010. (ENG.). 160p. pap. 15.95 *(978-1-84467-601-9(3)*, 844601) Verso Bks. GBR. Dist: Norton, W. W. & Co., Inc.

Levy, Raanan. Land for Peace. 2010. (ENG.). 96p. pap. 17.99 *(978-0-9824428-8-3(2))* 21st Century Pr.

Levy, Rene H. Baseless Hatred: What It Is & What You Can Do about It. 2011. ***(978-965-229-530-9(2))*** 2nd ed. 2012. ***(978-965-229-588-0(4))*** Gefen Bks.

Little, Douglas. American Orientalism: The United States & the Middle East Since 1945. 3rd rev. ed. 2008. (ENG., Illus.). 464p. pap. 29.95 *(978-0-8078-5898-1(6))* Univ. of North Carolina Pr.

Lochery, Neill & Lochery. View from the Fence: The Arab-Israeli Conflict from the Present to Its Roots. 2006. (ENG.). 272p. 29.95 *(978-0-8264-8270-9(8))* Continuum International Publishing Group, Ltd. GBR. Dist: National Bk. Network.

Louër, Laurence. To Be an Arab in Israel. King, John, tr. from FRE. 2007. (ENG.). 224p. (gr. 17). 40.00 *(978-0-231-14068-3(1))* Columbia Univ. Pr.

Machover, Moshe. Israelis & Palestinians: Conflict & Resolution. 2012. (ENG., Illus.). 360p. pap. 24.00 ***(978-1-60846-148-6(3))*** Haymarket Bks.

Mahler. The Arab-Israeli Conflict. 2009. (ENG., Illus.). 312p. (C). 130.00 *(978-0-415-77460-4(8))*; pap. 45.95 *(978-0-415-77461-1(6))* Routledge.

Majali, Abdul Salam, et al. Peacemaking: An Inside Story of the 1994 Jordanian-Israeli Treaty. 2006. (International & Security Affairs Ser.: 4). (ENG.). 324p. (C). 39.95 *(978-0-8061-3765-0(7))* Univ. of Oklahoma Pr.

Makdisi, Saree. Palestine Inside Out: An Everyday Occupation. (ENG., Illus.). 2008. 384p. 24.95 *(978-0-393-06606-7(1)*, 6606) 2010. 387p. pap. 16.95 *(978-0-393-33844-7(4)*, 33844) Norton, W. W. & Co., Inc.

Mandell, Sherri. The Blessing of a Broken Heart. 2nd ed. 2009. (Illus.). 242p. pap. 14.95 *(978-1-59264-151-2(2))* Toby Pr. LLC, The.

Mansour, Botrus. When Your Neighbor Is the Savior. 2011. *(978-1-932717-23-5(4))* Hope Publishing Hse.

Ma'Oz, Moshe, ed. Muslim Attitudes to Jews & Israel: The Ambivalences of Rejection, Antagonism, Tolerance & Cooperation. 2011. 338p. pap. 34.95 ***(978-1-84519-527-4(2))*** Sussex Academic Pr. GBR. Dist: International Specialized Bk. Services.

Marcus, Amy Dockser. Jerusalem 1913: The Origins of the Arab-Israeli Conflict. 2008. (ENG., Illus.). 240p. (gr. 12-18). 15.00 *(978-0-14-311328-7(3)*, Penguin (Non-Classics)) Penguin Group (USA) Inc.

Marmura, Stephen M. E. Hegemony in the Digital Age: The Arab/Israeli Conflict Online. 2008. (Critical Media Studies). (ENG.). 184p. 62.99 *(978-0-7391-1772-9(6))* Lexington Bks.

Marrar, Khalil. The Arab Lobby & Us Foreign Policy. (Illus.). 2010. (ENG.). 286p. pap. 39.95 *(978-0-415-58662-7(3))* 2008. 272p. 140.00 *(978-0-415-77681-3(3))* Routledge.

Marteu, Elisabeth. Civil Organizations & Protest Movements in Israel: Mobilization Around the Israeli-Palestinian Conflict. Marteu, Elisabeth, ed. 2009. (ENG., Illus.). 272p. 95.00 *(978-0-230-61481-9(7))* Palgrave Macmillan.

Matar, Dina. What It Means to Be Palestinian: Stories of Palestinian Peoplehood. 2010. (ENG., Illus.). 224p. 85.00 (978-1-84885-457-4(9)) I. B. Tauris & Co., Ltd. GBR. Dist: Macmillan.

Mati Alon. Not a Vanishing Breed. 2010. 312p. pap. 22.38 (978-1-4269-2176-6(4)) Trafford Publishing.

McGeough, Paul. Kill Khalid: The Failed Mossad Assassination of Khalid Mishal & the Rise of Hamas. (ENG.). 2010. 512p. pap. 19.95 (978-1-59558-501-1(X)) 2009. (Illus.). 477p. 26.95 (978-1-59558-325-3(4), 955325) New Pr., The.

Meir-Levi, David. History Upside Down: The Roots of Palestinian Fascism & the Myth of Israeli Aggression. 2007. (Brief Encounters Ser.). (ENG.). 125p. 20.00 (978-1-59403-192-2(4)) Encounter Bks.

Meotti, Giulio. A New Shoah: The Untold Story of Israel's Victims of Terrorism. 2010. (ENG.). 365p. 27.95 (978-1-59403-477-0(X)) Encounter Bks.

Merino, Noël, ed. The Middle East. 2011. (Current Controversies Ser.). 240p. (ENG.). pap. 27.50 (978-0-7377-5629-6(2), Greenhaven Pr., Inc.); (J). (gr. 9-12). 39.70 (978-0-7377-5628-9(4)) Cengage Gale.

The Middle East: The Road to Peace: Hearing Before the Committee on Foreign Relations, United States Senate, One Hundred Eleventh Congress, First Session, May 14, 2009. 2010. iii, 37p. (978-0-16-085306-7(0), 552-070-40636-1) United States Government Printing Office.

Middle East Peace: Ground Truths, Challenges Ahead: Hearing Before the Committee on Foreign Relations, United States Senate, One Hundred Eleventh Congress, Second Session, March 4, 2010. 2010. iii, 65p. **(978-0-16-086854-2(8)**, 552-070-41766-4) United States Government Printing Office.

The Middle East Peace Process: Progress & Prospects: Hearing Before the Committee on Foreign Relations, United States Senate, One Hundred Tenth Congress, Second Session, September 25, 2008. 2009. iii, 32p. (978-0-16-082536-1(9), 552-070-38565-7) United States Government Printing Office.

Miller, Aaron David. The Much Too Promised Land: America's Elusive Search for Arab-Israeli Peace. 2008. (ENG.). 416p. pap. 17.00 (978-0-553-38414-7(7)) Random House Publishing Group.

Miller, Jennifer. Inheriting the Holy Land: An American's Search for Hope in the Middle East. 2006. (ENG.). 320p. per. 14.95 (978-0-345-46925-0(9), Ballantine Bks.) Random House Publishing Group.

Miller, Rory. Inglorious Disarray: Europe, Israel & the Palestinians since 1967. 2011. (Columbia/Hurst Ser.). (ENG.). 244p. (gr. 17). 35.00 (978-0-231-70256-0(6)) Columbia Univ. Pr.

Milossa, Melese. The Middle East Conflict. 2010. 120p. pap. (978-3-639-25153-1(9)) VDM Verlag Dr. Mueller e K.

Milton-Edwards, Beverley. The Israeli-Palestinian Conflict: A People's War. 2008 (ENG., Illus.). 240p. 140.00 (978-0-415-41044-1(4)); 39.95 (978-0-415-41043-4(6)) Routledge.

Milton-Edwards, Beverley & Farrell, Stephen. Hamas: The Islamic Resistance Movement. 2010. (ENG., Illus.). 340p. 79.95 (978-0-7456-4295-6(0)); pap. 19.95 (978-0-7456-4296-3(9)) Polity Pr. GBR. Dist: Wiley, John & Sons, Inc.

Mishal, Shaul & Sela, Avraham. The Palestinian Hamas: Vision, Violence, & Coexistence. 2006. (ENG., Illus.). 280p. (gr. 17). 85.00 (978-0-231-14006-5(1)); pap. 27.50 (978-0-231-14007-2(X)) Columbia Univ. Pr.

Mitchell, Thomas G. When Peace Fails: Lessons from Belfast for the Middle East. 2010. (ENG., Illus.). 260p. pap. 45.00 (978-0-7864-4852-4(0)) McFarland & Co., Inc. Pubs.

Molinaro, Enrico. The Holy Places of Jerusalem in Middle East Peace Agreements: The Conflict Between Global & State Identities. 2009. (ENG.). 198p. 99.50 (978-1-84519-335-5(0)) Sussex Academic Pr. GBR. Dist: International Specialized Bk. Services.

—The Holy Places of Jerusalem in Middle East Peace Agreements: The Conflict between Global & State Identities. 2010. (ENG.). 210p. pap. 37.50 (978-1-84519-404-8(7)) Sussex Academic Pr. GBR. Dist: International Specialized Bk. Services.

More, Anne Le. International Assistance to the Palestinians after Oslo: Political Guilt, Wasted Money. 2008. (Routledge Studies on the Arab-Israeli Conflict Ser.). (Illus.). 272p. 130.00 (978-0-415-45385-1(2)) Routledge.

Morris, Benny. One State, Two States: Resolving the Israel/Palestine Conflict. 2010. (ENG., Illus.). 256p. pap. 17.00 (978-0-300-16444-2(0)) Yale Univ. Pr.

Morris, Benny & Morris, B. One State, Two States: Resolving the Israel/Palestine Conflict. 2009. (ENG., Illus.). 256p. 26.00 (978-0-300-12281-7(0)) Yale Univ. Pr.

Muasher, Marwan. The Arab Center: The Promise of Moderation. 2009. (ENG., Illus.). 336p. pap. 20.00 (978-0-300-15114-5(4)) Yale Univ. Pr.

Müller, Patrick. Eu Conflict Resolution & the Middle East. 2012. (CSS Studies in Security & International Relations Ser.). (ENG., Illus.). 184p. (C). 135.00 (978-0-415-67699-1(1)) Routledge.

Myers, David N. Between Jew & Arab: The Lost Voice of Simon Rawidowicz. (Tauber Institute Series for the Study of European Jewry Ser.). (ENG., Illus.). 320p. 2009. pap. 29.95 (978-1-58465-854-2(1)) 2008. lib. bdg. 40.00 (978-1-58465-736-1(7)) Univ. Pr. of New England. (Brandeis University Press).

Myre, Greg & Griffin, Jennifer. This Burning Land: Lessons from the Front Lines of the Transformed Israeli-Palestinian Conflict. 2011. (ENG., Illus.). 336p. 25.95 (978-0-470-55090-8(2), Wiley) Wiley, John & Sons, Inc.

Naggar, David. The Case for a Larger Israel: A new vison for Israel, Palestinians & the Middle East. 2007. (Illus.). 243p. pap. (978-1-57746-580-5(6)) DaJe Publishing.

Najjar, Abeer. Conflict over Jerusalem. 2009. 252p. pap. (978-3-639-20093-5(4)) VDM Verlag Dr. Mueller e.K.

Narrett, Eugene E. World War III: And the Rise of the World Security State: the War on the Jews. 2007. per. 22.95 (978-0-9719388-6-1(5)) Lightcatcher Bks.

Nashif, Taysir. Weakness of Nuclear Deterrence in the near East. 2010. 116p. pap. (978-3-8383-7856-5(3)) Lambert Academic Publishing.

Nennhaus, H. Peter. Quo Vadis, Israel? 2007. (ENG.). 123p. per. 11.95 (978-1-4327-1459-8(7)) Outskirts Pr., Inc.

Newman. Israel/Palestine. 2011. (UCLA Center for Middle East Development (CMED) Ser.). (ENG., Illus.). 288p. (C). 154.00 (978-0-415-43478-2(5)); pap. 46.95 (978-0-415-43479-9(3)) Routledge.

Newman, David & Peters, Joel, eds. Routledge Handbook of the Israeli-Palestinian Conflict. 2012. (ENG.). 424p. (C). 200.00 (978-0-415-77862-6(X)) Routledge.

Norman, Julie. The Second Palestinian Intifada: Civil Resistance. 2010. (Routledge Studies in Middle Eastern Politics Ser.). (ENG., Illus.). 176p. (C). 115.00 (978-0-415-77995-1(2), Routledge) Taylor & Francis Group GBR. Dist: Taylor & Francis Group.

Nusseibeh, Hazem. Jerusalemites: A Living Memory. 2010. 456p. pap. 28.95 (978-9963-610-38-9(2)) International Publishers Marketing.

Nusseibeh, Sari. Once upon a Country: A Palestinian Life. 2008. (ENG., Illus.). 584p. pap. 17.00 (978-0-312-42710-8(7)) Picador.

—What Is a Palestinian State Worth? 256p. 2012. (ENG.). pap. 14.95 **(978-0-674-06435-5(6))** 2011. 19.95 (978-0-674-04873-7(3)) Harvard Univ. Pr.

Ochs, Juliana. Security & Suspicion: An Ethnography of Everyday Life in Israel. 2011. (Ethnography of Political Violence Ser.). (Illus.). 216p. (C). 47.50 (978-0-8122-4291-1(2)) Univ. of Pennsylvania Pr.

Ophir, Adi, et al, eds. The Power of Inclusive Exclusion: Anatomy of Israeli Rule in the Occupied Palestinian Territories. 2009. (ENG., Illus.). 641p. (gr. 17). 38.95 (978-1-890951-92-4(7)) Zone Bks.

Oz, Amos. How to Cure A Fanatic. 2010. (ENG.). 104p. pap. 9.95 (978-0-691-14863-2(5)) Princeton Univ. Pr.

Oz, Amos. The Slopes of Lebanon. Goldberg-Bartura, Maurie, tr. 2012. (ENG.). 224p. pap. 15.95 **(978-0-547-63692-4(X)**, Mariner Bks.) Houghton Mifflin Harcourt Trade & Reference Pubs.

Pace, Marie. The Compassionate Listening Project. 2009. 148p. pap. (978-3-639-14856-5(8)) VDM Verlag Dr. Mueller e.K.

Paharik, James. The Long Journey: In Search of Justice & Peace in Jerusalem. 2009. 152p. pap. 14.95 (978-0-8146-3221-5(1)) Liturgical Pr.

Paone, Arthur J. Israel, Our Frankenstein. 2010. (Illus.). 300p. pap. 14.95 (978-0-9746366-3-4(0)) Belmar Pubns.

Pappé, Ilan. The Ethnic Cleansing of Palestine. (ENG., Illus.). 2007. 320p. per. 17.95 (978-1-85168-555-4(3)) 2006. 256p. 27.50 (978-1-85168-467-0(0)) Oneworld Pubns. GBR. Dist: National Bk. Network.

—The Forgotten Palestinians: A History of the Palestinians in Israel. 2011. (ENG., Illus.). 336p. 30.00 (978-0-300-13441-4(X)) Yale Univ. Pr.

—Forgotten Palestinians: A History of the Palestinians in Israel. 2011. (978-83-00-13441-0(7)) Yale Univ. Pr.

—Out of the Frame: The Struggle for Academic Freedom in Israel, 1 vol. 2010. (ENG.). 224p. pap. 22.00 (978-0-7453-2725-9(7)) Pluto Pr. GBR. Dist: Macmillan.

Pappé, Ilan & Hilal, Jamil. Across the Wall: Narratives of Israeli-Palestinian History. 2010. (Library of Modern Middle East Studies). (ENG.). 440p. 95.00 (978-1-84885-345-4(9)) I. B. Tauris & Co., Ltd. GBR. Dist: Macmillan.

Passow, Judah. Shattered Dreams. 2008. (ENG., Illus.). 192p. 44.95 (978-1-905559-06-0(2)) Halban Pubs. GBR. Dist: Independent Pubs. Group.

Pearlman, Wendy. Violence, Nonviolence, & the Palestinian National Movement. 2011. (ENG., Illus.). 304p. 99.00 **(978-1-107-00702-4(X))** Cambridge Univ. Pr.

Pedahzur, Ami. The Triumph of Israel's Radical Right, 1 vol. 2012. (ENG.). 288p. 29.95 **(978-0-19-974470-1(X))** Oxford Univ. Pr., Inc.

Pedahzur, Ami & Perliger, Arie. Jewish Terrorism in Israel. (Columbia Studies in Terrorism & Irregular Warfare Ser.). (ENG.). 264p. (gr. 17). 2011. pap. 22.50 (978-0-231-15447-5(X)) 2009. (Illus.). 29.50 (978-0-231-15446-8(1)) Columbia Univ. Pr.

Peled-Elhanan, Nurit. Palestine in Israeli School Books: Ideology & Propaganda in Education. 2012. (Library of Modern Middle East Studies: No. 82). (ENG.). 224p. 85.00 (978-1-84511-813-6(8), Tauris Academic Studies) I. B. Tauris & Co., Ltd. GBR. Dist: Macmillan.

Peleg, Ilan & Waxman, Dov. Israel's Palestinians: The Conflict Within. 2011. (ENG., Illus.). 272p. 85.00 **(978-0-521-76683-8(4))**; pap. 27.99 **(978-0-521-15702-5(1))** Cambridge Univ. Pr.

Penslar, Derek J. Israel in History: The Jewish State in Comparative Perspective. 2006. (ENG.). 288p. 160.00 (978-0-415-40036-7(8)); per. 47.50 (978-0-415-40037-4(6)) Routledge.

Peretz, Don. Israel & the Palestine Arabs. reprint ed. 31.00 (978-0-404-18984-6(9)) AMS Pr., Inc.

Perry, Donna. The Israeli-Palestinian Peace Movement: Combatants for Peace. 2011. (ENG., Illus.). 288p. 90.00 (978-0-230-12084-6(9)) Palgrave Macmillan.

Philo, Greg & Berry, Mike. More Bad News from Israel, 1 vol. 2011. (ENG., Illus.). 480p. 27.00 (978-0-7453-2978-9(0)); 486p. lib. bdg. 80.00 (978-0-7453-2979-6(9)) Pluto Pr. GBR. Dist: Macmillan.

Pogacnik, Marko & Pogacnik, Ana. How Wide the Heart: The Roots of Peace in Palestine & Israel. Creeger, Catherine E., tr. from GER. 2006. (Illus.). 202p. per. 20.00 (978-1-58420-039-0(1), Lindisfarne Bks.) SteinerBooks, Inc.

Portugali, Juval. Implicate Relations: Society & Space in the Israeli-Palestinian Conflict. 2010. (GeoJournal Library). 224p. pap. 144.00 (978-90-481-4183-8(4), 9048141834) Springer.

Qumsiyeh, Mazin B. Popular Resistance in Palestine: A History of Hope & Empowerment, 1 vol. 2010. (ENG.). 320p. lib. bdg. 95.00 (978-0-7453-3070-9(3)); (Illus.). 30.00 (978-0-7453-3069-3(X)) Pluto Pr. GBR. Dist: Macmillan.

Qurei, Ahmed. From Oslo to Jerusalem: The Palestinian Story of the Secret Negotiations. King, John, III, ed. 2006. (ENG.). 320p. 58.00 (978-1-84511-132-8(X)) I. B. Tauris & Co., Ltd. GBR. Dist: Macmillan.

Qurie, Ahmed. Beyond Oslo, the Struggle for Palestine: Inside the Middle East Peace Process from Rabin's Death to Camp David. 2008. (ENG.). 320p. 47.00 (978-1-84511-946-1(0)) I. B. Tauris & Co., Ltd. GBR. Dist: Macmillan.

Rabinovich, Itamar. Damascus, Jerusalem, & Washington: The Syrian-Israeli Relationship as a U. S. Policy Issue. 2009. (ENG.). 50p. pap. 12.00 (978-0-8157-0324-2(4)) Brookings Institution Pr.

Rabinovich, Itamar. The Lingering Conflict: Israel, the Arabs & the Middle East, 1948-2011. 2011. (ENG.). 308p. 32.95 **(978-0-8157-2228-1(1))** Brookings Institution Pr.

Rane, Halim. Reconstructing Jihad amid Competing International Norms. 2009. (ENG.). 256p. 95.00 (978-0-230-61483-3(3)) Palgrave Macmillan.

Raz, Avi. The Bride & the Dowry: Israel, Jordan, & the Palestinians in the Aftermath of the June 1967 War. 2012. (ENG., Illus.). 480p. 35.00 **(978-0-300-17194-5(3))** Yale Univ. Pr.

Reich, Bernard. A Brief History of Israel. 2nd rev. ed. 2008. (Brief History Ser.). 400p. pap. 19.95 (978-0-8160-7127-2(6), Checkmark Bks.) Facts On File, Inc.

Reilly, Hilda. Prickly Pears of Palestine. 2006. (ENG., Illus.). 230p. pap. 15.95 (978-1-903070-52-9(X)) Eye Bks. GBR. Dist: Independent Pubs. Group.

Reinhart, Tanya. The Road Map to Nowhere: Israel/Palestine Since 2003. 2006. (ENG., Illus.). 160p. pap. 18.00 (978-1-84467-076-5(7), 844076) Verso Bks. GBR. Dist: Norton, W. W. & Co., Inc.

Reiter, Yitzhak. Jerusalem & Its Role in Islamic Solidarity. 2008. (ENG.). 208p. 89.00 (978-0-230-60782-8(9)) Palgrave Macmillan.

—War, Peace & International Relations in Islam: Muslim Scholars on Peace Accords with Israel. 2011. (ENG.). 246p. 65.00 (978-1-84519-471-0(3)); pap. 29.95 (978-1-84519-480-2(2)) Sussex Academic Pr. GBR. Dist: International Specialized Bk. Services.

Reiter, Yitzhak, et al. Holy Places in the Israeli-Palestinian Conflict: Confrontation & Co-Existence. Breger, Marshall & Reiter, Yitzhak, eds. Hammer, Leonard, ed. 2010. (Routledge Studies in Middle Eastern Politics Ser.). (ENG., Illus.). 308p. (C). 130.00 (978-0-415-54901-1(9)) Routledge.

Rensmann, Lars & Schoeps, Julius H., eds. Politics & Resentment: Antisemitism & Counter-Cosmopolitanism in the European Union. 2010. (Jewish Identities in a Changing World Ser.). (Illus.). x, 504p. (978-90-04-19046-7(5)) BRILL.

Rifa'i, Amal. We Just Want to Live Here. Date not set. (978-0-312-31893-2(6)); mass mkt. (978-0-312-99211-8(4), St. Martin's Paperbacks) St. Martin's Pr.

Ring, Kenneth & Abdullah, Ghassan. Letters from Palestine: Palestinians Speak Out about Their Lives, Their Country, & the Power of Nonviolence. 2010. pap. 26.95 (978-1-60494-416-7(1)) Wheatmark.

Riordon, Michael. Our Way to Fight: Israeli & Palestinian Activists for Peace. 2011. (ENG.). 256p. pap. 16.95 (978-1-56976-778-8(5), Hill, Lawrence Bks.) Chicago Review Pr., Inc.

Rogan, Eugene L. & Shlaim, Avi, eds. The War for Palestine: Rewriting the History Of 1948. 2nd rev. ed. 2007. (Cambridge Middle East Studies). (Illus.). 285p. per. 31.99 (978-0-521-69934-1(7)); (ENG., 310p. (C). 94.00 (978-0-521-87598-1(6)) Cambridge Univ. Pr.

Rohan, Deborah. The Olive Grove: A Palestinian Story. 2008. (ENG., Illus.). 420p. pap. 16.95 (978-0-86356-667-7(7)) Saqi Bks. GBR. Dist: Consortium Bk. Sales & Distribution.

Rose, Jacqueline. Proust among the Nations: From Dreyfus to the Middle East. 2012. (ENG., Illus.). 256p. 35.00 (978-0-226-72578-9(2)) Univ. of Chicago Pr.

—The Question of Zion. annot. ed. 2007. (ENG.). 208p. (Orig.). (C). per. 20.95 (978-0-691-13068-2(X)) Princeton Univ. Pr.

Rosenbaum, Barbara. A Time to Speak Out: Independent Jewish Voices on the Middle East. 2008. (ENG.). 306p. pap. 19.95 (978-1-84467-229-5(8), 844229) Verso Bks. GBR. Dist: Norton, W. W. & Co., Inc.

Ross-Nazzal, James. The U.S. Veto & the Polemics of the Question of Palestine in the United Nations Security Council, 1972-2007. 2008. 208p. 109.95 (978-0-7734-5062-2(9)) Mellen, Edwin Pr., The.

Ross, Stewart. Understand the Israeli-Palestinian Conflict: A Teach Yourself Guide. 2nd ed. 2010. (Teach Yourself: Reference Ser.). (ENG.). 224p. pap. 15.00 (978-0-07-174767-7(2), 0071747672) McGraw-Hill Cos., The.

Rotberg, Robert I., ed. Israeli & Palestinian Narratives of Conflict: History's Double Helix. 2006. (Indiana Series in Middle East Studies). (ENG., Illus.). 296p. pap. 24.95 (978-0-253-21857-5(8), 0253218578); 65.00 (978-0-253-34767-1(X), 025334767X) Indiana Univ. Pr.

Routledge Staff, creator. A Survey of Arab-Israeli Relations. 3rd rev. ed. 2006. (Illus.). 551p. 260.00 (978-1-85743-394-4(7)) Routledge.

Roy, Sara. Failing Peace: Gaza & the Palestinian-Israeli Conflict. 2006. (ENG.). 408p. 100.00 (978-0-7453-2235-3(2)) Pluto Pr. GBR. Dist: Macmillan.

Rubenberg, Cheryl A., ed. Encyclopedia of the Israeli-Palestinian Conflict, 3 vols. 2009. (Illus.). 2000p. 395.00 (978-1-58826-686-6(9)) Rienner, Lynne Pubs.

Rubenstein, Richard. Jihad & Genocide. (Studies in Genocide: Religion, History, & Human Rights Ser.: 1). (ENG.). 262p. 2011. pap. 21.95 (978-0-7425-6203-5(4)) 2010. 65.00 (978-0-7425-6202-8(6)) Rowman & Littlefield Publishers, Inc.

Rydelnik, Michael. Understanding the Arab-Israeli Conflict: What the Headlines Haven't Told You. rev. ed. 2007. (ENG.). 256p. per. 14.99 (978-0-8024-2623-9(9)) Moody Pubs.

Sabbagh, Karl. Palestine: History of a Lost Nation. 2008. (ENG., Illus.). 384p. per. 15.00 (978-0-8021-4350-1(4), Grove Pr.) Grove/Atlantic, Inc.

Sacco, Joe. Footnotes in Gaza. 2009. (ENG., Illus.). 432p. 29.95 (978-0-8050-7347-8(7), Metropolitan Bks.) Holt, Henry & Co.

Sadat, Jehan. My Hope for Peace. 2011. (ENG.). 224p. pap. 15.99 (978-1-4165-9221-1(0), Free Pr.) Free Pr.

Safi, Louay. Palestine: Prophetic Principles over Prophecies. 2009. 107p. pap. 14.95 (978-1-4327-3543-2(8)) Outskirts Pr., Inc.

Safieh, Afif. The Peace Process: From Breaktrough to Breakdown. 2011. (ENG., Illus.). 288p. 24.95 (978-0-86356-422-2(4)) Saqi Bks. GBR. Dist: Consortium Bk. Sales & Distribution.

Safty, Adel. Might over Right: How the Zionists Took over Palestine. 240p. 2012. pap. 14.95 **(978-1-85964-326-6(4))** 2009. 25.00 (978-1-85964-212-2(8)) Garnet Publishing, Ltd. GBR. Dist: International Publishers Marketing.

Said, Edward W. Culture & Resistance: Conversations with Edward W. Said. Barsamian, David, ed. 2008. (ENG., Illus.). 224p. pap. 16.00 (978-0-89608-670-8(4)) South End Pr.

Salinas, Moises F. Planting Hatred, Sowing Pain: The Psychology of the Israeli-Palestinian Conflict, 1 vol. 2007. 200p. 49.95 (978-0-275-99005-3(2), C9005, Praeger Pubs.) Greenwood Publishing Group, Inc.

Salinas, Moises F. & Rabia, Hazza Abu. Resolving the Israeli-Palestinian Conflict: Perspectives on the Peace Process. 2009. (978-1-60497-654-0(3)) Cambria Pr.

Salt, Jeremy. The Unmaking of the Middle East: A History of Western Disorder in Arab Lands. (Illus.). 484p. 2009. (ENG.). pap. 22.95 (978-0-520-26170-9(4)) 2008. 45.00 (978-0-520-25551-7(8)) Univ. of California Pr.

Salzman, Philip Carl. Postcolonial Theory & the Arab-Israel Conflict. 2008. vi, 256p. pap. 40.00 (978-0-415-49576-9(8)) Routledge.

Salzman, Philip Carl & Divine, Donna Robinson, eds. Postcolonial Theory & the Arab-Israel Conflict. 2008. CCLVIII, 6p. 140.00 (978-0-415-44325-8(3)) Routledge.

Samy, Shahira. Reparations to Palestinian Refugees: A Comparative Perspective. 2010. (Routledge Studies on the Arab-Israeli Conflict Ser.). (ENG., Illus.). 192p. (C). 120.00 (978-0-415-48579-1(7)) Routledge.

Sasson, Victor. Essays from Occupied Holy Land. 2010. (ENG.). 216p. pap. 17.95 (978-1-4502-2563-2(2)) iUniverse, Inc.

Sayigh, Rosemary. The Palestinians: From Peasants to Revolutionaries. 2nd ed. 2008. (ENG., Illus.). 256p. 108.00 (978-1-84277-963-7(X)); per. 25.95 (978-1-84277-964-4(8)) Zed Bks., Ltd. GBR. Dist: Macmillan.

Schechet, Nita. Disenthralling Ourselves: Rhetoric of Revenge & Reconciliation in Contemporary Israel. 2009. 168p. 43.50 (978-0-8386-4204-7(7)); (ENG.). 43.50 (978-1-61147-410-7(8)) Fairleigh Dickinson Univ. Pr.

Schenker, Hillel & Abu-Zayyad, Ziad, eds. Islamophobia & Anti-Semitism. 2006. viii, 199p. per. 24.95 (978-1-55876-403-3(8)) Wiener, Markus Pubs., Inc.

Schenker, Hillel & Abu Zayyad, Ziad, eds. Islamophobia & Anti-Semitism. 2006. 208p. 68.95 (978-1-55876-402-6(X)) Wiener, Markus Pubs., Inc.

Schulze, Kirsten E. The Arab-Israeli Conflict. 2nd rev. ed. 2008. (Seminar Studies in History Ser.). (ENG., Illus.). 212p. pap. 28.20 (978-0-582-77189-5(7)) Longman Publishing Group.

Scott-Baumann, Michael. Conflict in the Middle East: Israel & the Arabs. 2nd ed. 2007. (Illus.). 64p. pap. 27.50 (978-0-340-92934-6(0), Hodder Murray) Hodder Education GBR. Dist: Trans-Atlantic Pubns., Inc.

—Crisis in the Middle East: Israel & the Arab States, 1945-2007. 2009. (ENG., Illus.). 192p. pap. 17.95 (978-0-340-96658-7(0)) Hodder Education GBR. Dist: Oxford Univ. Pr., Inc.

Seliktar, Ofira. Doomed to Failure? The Politics & Intelligence of the Oslo Peace Process, 1 vol. 2009. (PSI Reports). 244p. 59.95 (978-0-313-36617-8(9), C36617, Praeger Pubs.) Greenwood Publishing Group, Inc.

Shalem, Avinoam, photos by & text. Facing the Wall: The Palestinian-Israeli Barriers. 2011. (ENG., Illus.). 160p. pap. 49.95 **(978-3-86560-948-9(1))** Verlag der Buchhandlung Walther Konig DEU. Dist: D.A.P./Distributed Art Pubs.

Shamir, Jacob. Public Opinion in the Israeli-Palestinian Conflict: From Geneva to Disengagement to Kadima & Hamas. 2007. (Illus.). 64p. pap. (978-1-60127-027-6(5)) U. S. Institute of Peace Pr. (USIP Pr.).

Shamir, Jacob & Zanotti, Jim. Public Opinion & Solution Prospects for Israeli-Palestinian Peace. 2011. (Middle East in Turmoil Ser.). (Illus.). viii, 137p. 89.00 (978-1-60876-062-6(6)) Nova Science Pubs., Inc.

Shamnad, Dr. N. & Shamnad, N. The Palestine Issue. 2011. 60p. pap. **(978-3-8383-5259-6(9))** Lambert Academic Publishing.

Shay, Shaul. Islamic Terror Abductions in the Middle East. 2007. (ENG.). 197p. (C). 67.50 (978-1-84519-167-2(6)) Sussex Academic Pr. GBR. Dist: International Specialized Bk. Services.

Shehadeh, Raja. Palestinian Walks: Forays into a Vanishing Landscape. 2008 (ENG., Illus.). 224p. pap. 15.00 (978-1-4165-6966-4(9), Scribner) Scribner.

Shemer, Ze'ev. Israel: And the Palestinian Nightmare. 2010. 244p. pap. 19.95 (978-1-4502-6660-4(6)) iUniverse, Inc.

Shemesh, Moshe. Arab Politics, Palestinian Nationalism & the Six Day War: The Crystallization of Arab Strategy & Nasir's Descent to War, 1957-1967. 2008. (ENG., Illus.). 345p. (C). 75.00 (978-1-84519-188-7(9)) Sussex Academic Pr. GBR. Dist: International Specialized Bk. Services.

Shepherd, Robin. A State Beyond the Pale: Europe's Problem with Israel. 2010. (ENG.). 192p. *(978-0-7538-2713-0(1)*, Phoenix) Orion Publishing Group, Ltd. GBR. Dist: Independent Pubs. Group.

Shlaim, Avi. Israel & Palestine: Reappraisals, Revisions, Refutations. 2010. (ENG., Illus.). 416p. pap. 22.95 *(978-1-84467-656-9(0)*, 844656) Verso Bks. GBR. Dist: Norton, W. W. & Co., Inc.

—Israel & Palestine: Reflections, Revisions, Refutations. 2009. (ENG., Illus.). 352p. 34.95 *(978-1-84467-366-7(9)*, 844366) Verso Bks. GBR. Dist: Norton, W. W. & Co., Inc.

—Lion of Jordan: The Life of King Hussein in War & Peace. 2009. (Vintage Ser.). (ENG., Illus.). 768p. pap. 19.00 *(978-1-4000-7828-8(8)*, Vintage) Knopf Doubleday Publishing Group.

Shulman, David. Dark Hope: Working for Peace in Israel & Palestine. 2007. (Illus.). 236p. 22.00 *(978-0-226-75574-8(6))* Univ. of Chicago Pr.

Silverburg, Sanford R., ed. Palestine & International Law: Essays on Politics & Economics. alt. ed. 2009. (ENG.). 440p. pap. 49.95 *(978-0-7864-4248-5(4))* McFarland & Co., Inc. Pubs.

Smith, Charles D. Palestine & the Arab-Israeli Conflict: A History with Documents. 7th ed. 2009. (ENG., Illus.). 608p. (C). pap. 54.95 *(978-0-312-53501-8(5))* Bedford/Saint Martin's.

—Palestine & the Arab-Israeli Conflict: A History with Documents. 7th rev. ed. 2010. (ENG., Illus.). 608p. pap. *(978-0-230-24711-6(3))* Palgrave Macmillan.

Smith, Patti, contrib. by. Double Blind: War in Lebanon 2006. 2007. (Illus.). 128p. pap. 39.95 *(978-1-904563-57-0(0))* Trolley GBR. Dist: Prestel Publishing.

Spyer, Jonathan. The Transforming Fire: The Rise of the Israel-Islamist Conflict. 2010. (ENG., Illus.). 240p. 29.95 *(978-1-4411-6663-0(7))* Continuum International Publishing Group, Ltd. GBR. Dist: National Bk. Network.

Stein, David. Israel, God, & America. 2006. (ENG.). 224p. pap. 13.99 *(978-88-89127-27-8(9))* Destiny Image Europe ITA. Dist: Destiny Image Pubs.

Stein, Rebecca L. Itineraries in Conflict: Israelis, Palestinians, & the Political Lives of Tourism. 2008. (ENG., Illus.). 232p. 84.95 *(978-0-8223-4251-9(0))*; pap. 23.95 *(978-0-8223-4273-1(1))* Duke Univ. Pr.

Stern, Sol. A Century of Palestinian Rejectionism & Jew Hatred. 2011. (Encounter Broadsides Ser.). (ENG.). 48p. pap. 5.99 ***(978-1-59403-620-0(9))*** Encounter Bks.

Stewart, Rory, pref. & text. Afghanistan: Broken Promise, 1 vol. 2007. (ENG., Illus.). 112p. pap. 39.95 *(978-88-8158-646-2(0))* Charta ITA. Dist: D.A.P./Distributed Art Pubs.

Strawson, John. Partitioning Palestine: Legal Fundamentalism in the Palestinian-Israeli Conflict. 2010. (ENG.). 288p. 104.00 *(978-0-7453-2324-4(3))* Pluto Pr. GBR. Dist: Macmillan.

Sturkey, Douglas. The Limits of American Power: Prosecuting a Middle East Peace. 2007. (Illus.). 256p. (C). 119.00 *(978-1-84720-243-7(8))* Elgar, Edward Publishing, Inc.

Sufian, Sandy & Levine, Mark, eds. Reapproaching Borders: New Perspectives on the Study of Israel-Palestine. 2007. (ENG., Illus.). 336p. 85.00 *(978-0-7425-4638-7(1))*; per. 32.95 *(978-0-7425-4639-4(X))* Rowman & Littlefield Publishers, Inc.

Suisman, Doug, et al. The Arc: A Formal Structure for a Palestinian State, 1 vol. 3rd ed. 2011. 106p. (C). pap. 35.00 ***(978-0-8330-5120-2(2))*** RAND Corp., The.

Suleiman, Camelia. Language & Identity in the Israel-Palestine Conflict: The Politics of Self-Perception in the Middle East. 2011. (Library of Modern Middle East Studies). (ENG.). 288p. 96.00 *(978-1-84885-819-0(1)*, Tauris Academic Studies) I. B. Tauris & Co., Ltd. GBR. Dist: Macmillan.

Swisher, Clayton E. The Palestine Papers: The End of the Road? 2011. (ENG.). 320p. pap. 21.95 *(978-1-84391-353-5(4))* Hesperus Pr. GBR. Dist: Independent Pubs. Group.

Tamimi, Azzam. Hamas: A History from Within. 2nd rev. ed. 2011. 392p. pap. 25.00 *(978-1-56656-824-1(2)*, Olive Branch Pr.) Interlink Publishing Group, Inc.

Telhami, Shibley, ed. The Sadat Lectures: Words & Images on Peace, 1997-2008. 2010. (Illus.). 130p. pap. 29.95 *(978-1-60127-054-2(2))* U. S. Institute of Peace Pr. (USIP Pr.).

Teller, Neville. One Year in the History of Israel & Palestine. 2011. (ENG.). 300p. pap. ***(978-1-84876-646-4(7))*** Troubadour Publishing Ltd.

Tenenbaum, Boris. Arabo-israil'skie Voiny v Epizodakh i Biographiyakh. 2008.Tr. of Arab-Israeli Wars in Epozodes & Biographies. (RUS., Illus.). 240p. pap. 11.95 *(978-1-934881-09-5(0)*, M-Graphics) M-Graphics Publishing.

Terrill, W. Andrew. Escalation & Intrawar Deterrence during Limited Wars in the Middle East. 2009. pap. *(978-1-58487-406-5(6))* Strategic Studies Institute, U.S. Army War College Commandant (AWCC-DSI/Pubns.).

Tessler, Mark. A History of the Israeli-Palestinian Conflict. 2nd rev. ed. 2009. (Indiana Ser. in Middle East Studies). (ENG., Illus.). 1040p. pap. 35.00 *(978-0-253-22070-7(X)*, 025322070X) Indiana Univ. Pr.

Thomas, Baylis. The Dark Side of Zionism: The Quest for Security through Dominance. 2009. (ENG.). 284p. 48.50 *(978-0-7391-2690-5(3))* Lexington Bks.

—Dark Side of Zionism: The Quest for Security Through Dominance. 2011. (ENG.). 284p. pap. 24.95 *(978-0-7391-2691-2(1))* Lexington Bks.

Tilley, Virginia. The One-State Solution: A Breakthrough for Peace in the Israeli-Palestinian Deadlock. 2010. (ENG., Illus.). 288p. pap. 24.95 *(978-0-472-03449-9(9))* Univ. of Michigan Pr.

Tischauser, Jeffrey. Anti-Arab & Anti-Muslim Bias in American Newspapers: How They Reported the 2006 Israeli-Hezbollah & Israeli-Hamas Wars. 2009. iv, 192p. *(978-0-7734-3901-6(3))* Mellen, Edwin Pr., The.

Torrance, David W. & Taylor, George. Israel, God's Servant: God's Key to the Redemption of the World. 2008. (ENG.). 224p. per. 19.99 *(978-1-84227-554-2(2)*, Paternoster) Authentic Media.

Totten, Michael J. The Road to Fatima Gate: The Beirut Spring, the Rise of Hezbollah, & the Iranian War Against Israel. (ENG.). 2013. 376p. pap. 17.99 ***(978-1-59403-642-2(X))*** 2011. 360p. 27.95 *(978-1-59403-521-0(0))* Encounter Bks.

Tucker, Spencer C. & Roberts, Priscilla Mary, eds. Encyclopedia of the Arab-Israeli Conflict: A Political, Social, & Military History, 4 vols., Set. 2008. (Illus.). 1553p. 395.00 *(978-1-85109-841-5(0)*, ARISWA1C) ABC-CLIO, LLC.

Two Sides of the Same Coin: Jewish & Palestinian Refugees: Hearing Before the Subcommittee on the Middle East & South Asia of the Committee on Foreign Affairs, House of Representatives, One Hundred Tenth Congress, First Session, May 8, 2007. 2007. iii, 42p. *(978-0-16-078996-0(6)*, 552-070-36111-1) United States Government Printing Office.

United Nations Environment Programme Staff. Environmental Assessment of the Gaza Strip: Following the Escalation of Hostilities in December 2008-January 2009. 2010. (ENG., Illus.). 100p. pap. 35.00 *(978-92-807-3041-8(X))* United Nations Environment Programme KEN. Dist: National Bk. Network.

United States, Congress House Committee on Foreign Affairs Subcommittee on the Middle East and South Asia Staff, contrib. by. Next Steps in Israeli-Palestinian Peace Process: Hearing Before the Subcommittee on the Middle East & South Asia of the Committee on Foreign Affairs, House of Representatives, One Hundred Tenth Congress, First Session, February 14, 2007. 2007. iii, 56p. *(978-0-16-078456-9(5)*, 552-070-35742-4) United States Government Printing Office.

Van Esveld, Bill. Rockets from Gaza: Harm to Civilians from Palestinian Armed Groups' Rocket Attacks. 2009. 28p. ***(978-1-56432-521-1(0))*** Human Rights Watch.

Various Bills & Resolutions: Markup Before the Committee on Foreign Affairs, House of Representatives, One Hundred Tenth Congress, Second Session, on H. Res. 1351, H. Res. 1361, H. Res. 1369, H. con. Res. 374, H.R. 6574 & H. Res. 1370, July 24, 2008. 2008. iii, 85p. *(978-0-16-081828-8(1)*, 552-070-38026-4) United States Government Printing Office.

Waisman, Orit Sônia. Body, Language & Meaning in Conflict Situations: A Semiotic Analysis of Gesture-Word Mismatches in Israeli-Jewish & Arab Discourse. 2010. (Illus.). viii, 188p. *(978-90-272-8755-7(4))*; *(978-90-272-1572-7(3))* Benjamins, John Publishing Co.

Wanis-St. John, A. Back Channel Negotiation: Secrecy in the Middle East Peace Process. 2010. (Illus.). 360p. 39.95 *(978-0-8156-3275-7(4))* Syracuse Univ. Pr.

Wasserstein, Bernard. Divided Jerusalem: The Struggle for the Holy City. 3rd ed. 2008. (ENG., Illus.). 456p. pap. 18.00 *(978-0-300-13763-7(X))* Yale Univ. Pr.

—Israelis & Palestinians: Why Do They Fight? Can They Stop? 3rd ed. 2008. (ENG., Illus.). 240p. pap. 18.00 *(978-0-300-13764-4(8))* Yale Univ. Pr.

Waxman, Dov. Pursuit of Peace & the Crisis of Israeli Identity: Defending Defining the Nation. annot. ed. 2006. (ENG.). 264p. 89.00 *(978-1-4039-7458-7(6))* Palgrave Macmillan.

We Just Want to Live Here. Date not set. pap., tchr. ed. *(978-0-312-32292-2(5)*, St. Martin's Paperbacks) St. Martin's Pr.

Weaver, Alain Epp, ed. Under Vine & Fig Tree: Biblical Theologies of Land & the Palestinian-Israeli Conflict. 2007. 204p. pap. 19.95 *(978-1-931038-45-4(7))* Cascadia Publishing Hse., LLC.

Weinberger, Peter Ezra. Co-opting the PLO: A Critical Reconstruction of the Oslo Accords, 1993-1995. 2007. (ENG.). 188p. per. 29.50 *(978-0-7391-2205-1(3))* Lexington Bks.

Weinzimmer, Julianne Melissa. Homeland Conflict & Identity for Palestinian & Jewish Israeli Americans. 2011. (ENG.). 200p. 65.00 *(978-1-59332-454-4(5))* LFB Scholarly Publishing LLC.

White, Andrew. Faith under Fire: What the Middle East Conflict Has Taught Me about God, 1 vol. 2011. (Illus.). 160p. pap. 13.99 *(978-1-85424-962-3(2)*, Monarch Bks.) Lion Hudson PLC GBR. Dist: Kregel Pubns.

Whitfield, Geoffrey. Dynamics of a Journey to Conflict Prevention & Peace in Israel & Palestine via an Olympic Sport. 2011. (ENG.). 122p. pap. 28.50 ***(978-1-60947-025-8(7))*** Emeth Pr.

Whitfield, Geoffrey Victor. Israeli & Palestinian Terrorism: The 'unintentional' Agents. 2009. *(978-0-9819582-3-1(0))* Emeth Pr.

Wibeck, Sören. Ett Land, Två Folk: Israel-Palestina-Konfliktens Historia. 2009. (SWE., Illus.). 384p. *(978-91-85873-29-6(2))* Svenska Historiska media AB.

Wiles, Stanley L. How to Solve the Israeli-Palestinian Conflict. 2009. 48p. pap. 13.95 *(978-1-4389-3515-7(3))* AuthorHouse.

Wilkes, Samuel J. & Jackson, Cynthia N., eds. Hamas in the Middle East: A Closer Look. 2011. (Politics & Economics of the Middle East Ser.). (Illus.). 176p. 95.00 *(978-1-61324-069-4(4))* Nova Science Pubs., Inc.

Williams, Emma. It's Easier to Reach Heaven Than the End of the Street: A Jerusalem Memoir. 2009. 256p. pap. 16.00 *(978-1-56656-789-3(0)*, Olive Branch Pr.) Interlink Publishing Group, Inc.

Wolf, Robert & Lefkowitz, Zvi. Forgotten Children of the Bible: Conflict & Consequences. 2009. 87p. 18.95 *(978-1-934440-71-1(X)*, Devora Publishing) Simcha Media Group.

Yitzhak, Ronen. Abdullah Al-Tall - Arab Legion Officer: Arab Nationalism & Opposition to the Hashemite Regime. 2012. (ENG.). 196p. 74.95 *(978-1-84519-408-6(X))* Sussex Academic Pr. GBR. Dist: International Specialized Bk. Services.

Zeitoun, Mark. Power & Water in the Middle East: The Hidden Politics of the Palestinian-Israeli Water Conflict. (ENG., Illus.). 2011. 240p. pap. 30.00 ***(978-1-84885-997-5(X))*** 2008. 224p. 89.00 *(978-1-84511-464-0(7))* I. B. Tauris & Co., Ltd. GBR. Dist: Macmillan.

Zelnick, Robert. Israel's Unilaterialism: Beyond Gaza. 2006. (Hoover Inst Press Publication). (Illus.). 170p. per. 15.00 *(978-0-8179-4772-9(8))* Hoover Institution Pr.

Zomlot, Husam Said. Building a State under Occupation: Peacemaking & Reconstruction in the Palestinian-Israeli Conflict. 2012. (Library of Modern Middle East Studies: No. 112). (ENG., Illus.). 256p. 92.00 ***(978-1-84885-772-8(1))*** I. B. Tauris & Co., Ltd. GBR. Dist: Macmillan.

Zuhur, Sherifa. HAMAS & Israel: Conflicting Strategies of Group-Based Politics. 2008. pap. *(978-1-58487-371-6(X))* Strategic Studies Institute, U.S. Army War College Commandant (AWCC-DSI/Pubns.).

853 Days: From Gaza Disengagement to de Facto Power?: Hearing Before the Subcommittee on the Middle East & South Asia of the Committee on Foreign Affairs, House of Representatives, One Hundred Tenth Congress, Second Session, March 12, 2008. 2008. iii, 35p. *(978-0-16-080904-0(5)*, 552-070-37439-6) United States Government Printing Office.

ARAB-JEWISH RELATIONS
see Jewish-Arab Relations

ARAB MATHEMATICS
see Mathematics, Arab

ARAB PHILOSOPHY
see Philosophy, Arab

ARAB WORLD
see Arab Countries

ARABESQUES
see also Decoration and Ornament; Grotesque

Castera, Jean-Marc, et al. Arabesques: Decorative Art in Morocco. 2009. (ENG., Illus.). 480p. 170.00 *(978-2-86770-124-5(4))* ACR Edition FRA. Dist: Antique Collectors' Club.

L'Aventurine, Prisse, ed. Arabic Art. 2008. (Ornamental Design Ser.). 240p. pap. 34.95 *(978-2-914199-60-5(0))* L'Aventurine FRA. Dist: Independent Pubs. Group.

ARABIA
see Arabian Peninsula

ARABIAN HORSE

Borden, Spencer. The Arab Horse. 2009. 56p. pap. *(978-0-217-57001-5(1))* Books LLC.

Conn, George H. The Arabian Horse in Americ. 2011. 322p. 50.95 ***(978-1-258-04424-4(2))*** Literary Licensing, LLC.

Haggard, Doreen. The Arabian Desert Horse. 2012. (ENG.). 218p. pap. 49.99 ***(978-1-4662-1962-5(9))*** CreateSpace.

—The Arabian Horse. 2012. (ENG.). 270p. pap. 49.99 ***(978-1-4679-7513-1(3))*** CreateSpace.

Kowalczyk, Andra. Tennessee's Arabian Horse Racing Heritage. 2007. (Images of America Ser.). (Illus.). 127p. per. 19.99 *(978-0-7385-4390-1(X))* Arcadia Publishing.

Landry, Donna. Noble Brutes: How Eastern Horses Transformed English Culture. 2008. (Animals, History, Culture Ser.). (ENG., Illus.). 248p. (gr. 17). 52.00 *(978-0-8018-9028-4(4))* Johns Hopkins Univ. Pr.

Parkinson, Mary Jane. Gladys Brown Edwards: Artist, Scholar, Author. 2006. ix, 163p. *(978-1-929164-38-7(6))* Primedia Enthusiast Pubns.

Reese, Herbert H. Arabian Horse Breeding. 2011. 160p. 41.95 ***(978-1-258-01145-1(X))*** Literary Licensing, LLC.

—Training Arabian Horses. 2011. 96p. 38.95 ***(978-1-258-05765-7(4))*** Literary Licensing, LLC.

Tweedie, W. Arabian Horse: Country & People. (Arab Background Ser.). 412p. 39.95 *(978-0-86685-170-1(4)*, LDL1704) International Bk. Ctr., Inc.

Upton, Peter. The Arab Horse: A Complete Record of the Arab Horses Imported into Britain from the Desert of Arabia from The 1830s. 2007. (ENG., Illus.). 336p. 75.00 *(978-0-9549701-8-5(7))* Barzan Publishing Company GBR. Dist: Interlink Publishing Group, Inc.

ARABIAN PENINSULA
Here are entered works on the countries of the peninsula of Southwest Asia, comprising Bahrain, Kuwait, Oman, Qatar, Saudi Arabia, United Arab Emirates, and Yemen.

Archaeopress, ed. Proceedings of the Seminar for Arabian Studies, Volumes 1-37 DVD, Vols. 1-37. 2009. (ENG.). (C). 990.00 *(978-1-905739-25-7(7))* Archaeopress GBR. Dist: Brown, David Bk. Co., The.

Burckhardt, John Lewis. Notes on the Bedouins & Wahabys: Collected During His Travels in the East. Ouseley, William, ed. 2010. (Cambridge Library Collection - Travel & Exploration Ser.). (ENG.). 402p. pap. 31.99 *(978-1-108-02290-3(1))*; (Illus.). pap. 31.99 *(978-1-108-02289-7(8))* Cambridge Univ. Pr.

Sayce, A. H., ed. Ancient Empires of the East: Herodotos I-III. 2010. (Cambridge Library Collection - Classics Ser.). 540p. pap. 39.99 *(978-1-108-01096-2(2))* Cambridge Univ. Pr.

Simpson, St John & Weeks, Lloyd, eds. Proceedings of the Seminar for Arabian Studies, Volume 37: Papers from the Fortieth Meeting of the Seminar for Arabian Studies Held in London, 27-29 July 2006. 2007. (Seminar for Arabian Studies Ser.). (Illus.). 337p. per. 100.00 *(978-1-905739-10-3(9))* Archaeopress GBR. Dist: Brown, David Bk. Co., The.

ARABIAN PENINSULA—ANTIQUITIES

Bowen Jr, Richard Lebaron, et al. The Early Arabian Necropolis of Ain Jawan: A Pre-Islamic & Early Site on the Persian Gulf. 2011. 72p. 36.95 ***(978-1-258-07009-0(X))*** Literary Licensing, LLC.

Drechsler, Philipp. The Dispersal of the Neolithic over the Arabian Peninsula. 2009. (Bar S Ser.). (ENG., Illus.). 254p. (C). pap. 112.50 *(978-1-4073-0502-8(6))* British Archaeological Reports Ltd. GBR. Dist: Brown, David Bk. Co., The.

Erskine, Steuart. The Vanished Cities of Arabia. 2008. (ENG.). 256p. 175.00 *(978-0-7103-0984-6(8))* Routledge.

Hilprecht, H. V. Drought, Famine, Plague & Pestilence. 2009. 294p. pap. *(978-1-4590-7310-4(X))* Books LLC.

—Drought, Famine, Plague & Pestilence. 2007. (Gorgias Classic Archaeological Reprints Ser.: 9). 88.00 *(978-1-59333-640-0(3))*;2 of 2. 44.00 *(978-1-59333-650-9(0))* Gorgias Pr., LLC.

Hilprecht, H. V. & Robertson, Warren. Drought, Famine, Plague & Pestilence, 1 of 2. 2010. (Gorgias Classic Archaeological Reprints Ser.: 9). pap. 130.00 *(978-1-59333-649-3(7))* Gorgias Pr., LLC.

Huth, Martin. Coinage of the Caravan Kingdoms: Ancient Arabian Coins from the Collection of Martin Huth. 2010. (Ancient coins in na Collections). (ENG., Illus.). 188p. (C). 150.00 ***(978-0-89722-318-8(7))*** American Numismatic Society.

Huth, Martin & Van Alfen, Peter G., eds. Coinage of the Caravan Kingdoms: Studies in Ancient Arabian Monetization. 2011. (Numismatic Studies). (ENG., Illus.). 602p. (C). 250.00 *(978-0-89722-312-6(8))* American Numismatic Society.

McCorriston, Joy. Pilgrimage & Household in the Ancient near East. 2011. (ENG., Illus.). 304p. 90.00 *(978-0-521-76851-1(9))*; pap. 29.99 *(978-0-521-13760-7(8))* Cambridge Univ. Pr.

Starkey, Janet, ed. Proceedings of the Seminar for Arabian Studies: Papers from the Forty-First Meeting of the Seminar for Arabian Studies Held in London, 24-26 July 2008. 2009. (Illus.). 386p. (C). pap. 100.00 *(978-1-905739-23-3(0))* Archaeopress GBR. Dist: Brown, David Bk. Co., The.

—Proceedings of the Seminar for Arabian Studies: Papers from the forty-fourth meeting, London, 22-24 July 2010. 2011. (Seminar for Arabian Studies). (Illus.). 436p. (C). pap. 110.00 ***(978-1-905739-40-0(0))*** Archaeopress GBR. Dist: Brown, David Bk. Co., The.

Starkey, Janet, ed. Proceedings of the Seminar for Arabian Studies 2010. 2010. (ENG., Illus.). 396p. (C). pap. 110.00 *(978-1-905739-33-2(8))* Archaeopress GBR. Dist: Brown, David Bk. Co., The.

Weeks, Lloyd, ed. Proceedings of the Seminar for Arabian Studies, Volume 38: Papers from the forty-first meeting of the Seminar for Arabian Studies held in London, 19-21 July 2007. 2008. (Seminar for Arabian Studies). (Illus.). 344p. (C). pap. 100.00 *(978-1-905739-20-2(6))* Archaeopress GBR. Dist: Brown, David Bk. Co., The.

ARABIAN PENINSULA—DESCRIPTION AND TRAVEL

Aithie, Charles & Aithie, Patricia. Yemen: Jewel of Arabia. 2009. 224p. pap. 30.00 *(978-1-56656-746-6(7)*, Interlink Bks.) Interlink Publishing Group, Inc.

Aithie, Charles & Aithie, Patricia. Yemen, Jewel of Arabia. 2009. (Illus.). 192p. pap. 26.95 ***(978-1-905299-93-5(1)***, Stacey International) Stacey Publishing GBR. Dist: Midpoint Trade Bks., Inc.

Aithie, Patricia. The Burning Ashes of Time: From Steamer Point to Tiger Bay. 2006. (ENG., Illus.). 196p. pap. 17.95 *(978-1-85411-400-6(X))* Seren Bks. GBR. Dist: Independent Pubs. Group.

Barbosa, Duarte. A Description of the Coasts of East Africa & Malabar in the Beginning of the Sixteenth Century. Stanley, Henry E. J., tr. 2007. 260p. 42.95 *(978-0-548-33543-7(5))*; 264p. per. 27.95 *(978-1-4326-9452-4(9))* Kessinger Publishing, LLC.

Batoutah, Ibn. Voyages d'Ibn Batoutah, 4 vols. Defremery, G. & Sanguimetti, B. R., trs. (FRE.). 2047p. reprint ed. lib. bdg. 325.00 *(978-0-89241-177-1(5))* Caratzas, Aristide D. Pub.

Boggs, Richard. The Lost World of Socotra: Yemen's Island of Bliss. 2009. (ENG., Illus.). 160p. pap. 25.00 ***(978-1-905299-95-9(8)***, Stacey International) Stacey Publishing GBR. Dist: Midpoint Trade Bks., Inc.

Burckhardt, John Lewis. Travels in Arabia: An Account of those Territories in Hedjaz which Th. 2007. (ENG.). 450p. pap. 26.99 *(978-1-4346-2026-2(3))* BiblioBazaar.

—Travels in Arabia: An Account of Those Territories in Hedjaz Which the Mohammedans Regard As Sacred. l.t. ed. 2007. (ENG.). 502p. pap. 31.99 *(978-1-4346-2055-2(7))* BiblioBazaar.

—Travels in Arabia: Comprehending an Account of Those Territories in Hadjaz which the Mohammedans Regard as Sacred. Ouseley, William, ed. 2010. (Cambridge Library Collection - Travel & Exploration Ser.). (ENG.). 454p. pap. 34.99 *(978-1-108-02286-6(3))*; (Illus.). 490p. pap. 35.99 *(978-1-108-02285-9(5))* Cambridge Univ. Pr.

—Travels in Arabia Comprehending an Acco. 2006. pap. *(978-1-4068-0081-4(3))* Echo Library.

Burton, Richard F. The Land of Midian Volume 1. 2007. 232p. pap. 20.99 *(978-1-4264-7721-8(X))*; (ENG.). 258p. pap. 23.99 *(978-1-4264-7779-9(1))* BiblioBazaar.

—Personal Narrative of a Pilgrimage to Al-Madinah & Meccah, Vol. II. l.t. ed. 2006. 396p. pap. 24.99 *(978-1-4264-1708-5(X))* BiblioBazaar.

—Personal Narrative of a Pilgrimage to Al-Madinah & Meccah. 2009. 380p. pap. *(978-1-4588-4046-2(8))*; 292p. pap. *(978-0-217-27045-8(X))* Books LLC.

—Personal Narrative of a Pilgrimage to Al-Madinah & Meccah, Volume 1. 2007. (ENG.). 422p. pap. 28.99 *(978-1-4264-1707-8(1))*; 354p. pap. 25.99 *(978-1-4264-1619-4(9))* BiblioBazaar.

—Personal Narrative of a Pilgrimage to Al-Madinah & Meccah, Volume II. 2007. (ENG.). 338p. pap. 23.99 *(978-1-4264-1620-0(2))* BiblioBazaar.

Cheung, Catherine & Devantier, Lyndon. Socotra: A Natural History of the Islands & Their People. 2007. (Illus.). 393p. 59.95 *(978-962-217-770-3(0))* Odyssey Pubns., Ltd. HKG. Dist: Norton, W. W. & Co., Inc.

Clark, Victoria. Yemen: Dancing on the Heads of Snakes. 2010. (ENG., Illus.). 328p. pap. 20.00 *(978-0-300-11701-1(9))* Yale Univ. Pr.

Doughty, Charles. Wanderings in Arabia: The Authorised Abridged Edition of 'Travels in Arabia Deserta' 2009. (ENG., Illus.). 624p. 89.00 *(978-1-84511-810-5(3))*; pap. 31.00 *(978-1-84511-766-5(2))* I. B. Tauris & Co., Ltd. GBR. Dist: Macmillan.

Doughty, Charles Montagu. Travels in Arabia Deserta. 2010. (Cambridge Library Collection - Travel & Exploration Ser.). (ENG.). 712p. pap. 48.00 *(978-1-108-00947-8(6))*; (Illus.). 668p. pap. 48.00 *(978-1-108-00946-1(8))* Cambridge Univ. Pr.

Hawqal, Ibn. The Oriental Geography of Ibn Hawqal, an Arabian Traveller of the Tenth Century. Ouseley, William G., tr. (ARA.). xxxvi, 327p. reprint ed. lib. bdg. 75.00 *(978-0-89241-182-5(1))* Caratzas, Aristide D. Pub.

Ingrams, Harold. Arabia & the Isles. 2008. (Illus.). 412p. *(978-1-4437-2340-4(1))* 2006. 408p. per. *(978-1-4067-2167-6(0))* Read Bks. (Hesperides Pr.).

Lonely Planet Staff & Walker, Jenny. Oman, UAE & Arabian Peninsula. 3rd ed. 2010. (Multi Country Guide Ser.). (ENG., Illus.). 596p. pap. 31.99 *(978-1-74179-145-7(6))* Lonely Planet Pubns.

Nowell, Simone. Oman: The essential guide to customs & Culture. 2009. (Culture Smart! Ser.). (ENG., Illus.). 168p. pap. 9.95 *(978-1-85733-475-3(2))* Kuperard Pubs. GBR. Dist: Random Hse., Inc.

Palgrave, William Giffor. Narrative of A Years Journey Through Cen. 2006. 488p. per. *(978-1-4067-3334-1(2),* Hesperides Pr.) Read Bks.

Philby, Harris S. Sheba's Daughters. reprint ed. 55.00 *(978-0-404-20201-9(2))* AMS Pr., Inc.

Philby, Harry St. John Bridger. Arabia of the Wahhabis. 2008. 504p. pap. 47.00 *(978-1-59740-452-5(7))* ACLS Humanities E-Book.

Rutter, Eldon. The Holy Cities of Arabia, 2 vols., Set. reprint ed. 97.50 *(978-0-404-16543-7(5))* AMS Pr., Inc.

Schneider, Klaus. Boris Becker Wüstenbilder/Desert Images: Mapping Lawrence of Arabia. Schneider, Klaus, ed. 2011. (ENG., Illus.). 80p. 44.95 ***(978-3-86832-053-4(9))*** Wienand GmbH, Druck- & Verlagshaus DEU. Dist: Independent Pubs. Group.

Thesiger, Wilfred. Arabian Sands. rev. ed. 2008. (ENG., Illus.). 400p. (gr. 12-18). 16.00 *(978-0-14-144207-5(7),* Penguin Classics) Penguin Group (USA) Inc.

Thomas, Bertram. Alarms & Excursions in Arabia. 2007. 316p. per. *(978-1-4067-5068-3(9))* Read Bks.

—Arabia Felix. 2008. (Illus.). 448p. *(978-1-4437-2345-9(2))* 2006. 444p. per. *(978-1-4067-2205-5(7))* Read Bks. (Hesperides Pr.).

Wheatcroft, Andrew. Arabia & the Gulf in Original Photographs, 1880-1950. 2007. (Illus.). 200p. 190.00 *(978-0-7103-0016-4(6))* Taylor & Francis Group.

ARABIAN PENINSULA—ECONOMIC CONDITIONS

Chalk, Peter & Smallman, Laurence. Countering Piracy in the Modern Era: Notes from a RAND Workshop to Discuss the Best Approaches for Dealing with Piracy in the 21st Century. 2009. 22p. pap. 20.00 *(978-0-8330-4793-9(0),* cf-269) RAND Corp., The.

Icon Group International, Inc. Staff, compiled by. The 2006 Economic & Product Market Databook for Nizwa, Oman. 2006. 618p. ring bd. 95.00 *(978-0-497-82039-8(0))* Icon Group International, Inc.

—The 2006 Economic & Product Market Databook for Salala, Oman. 2006. 618p. ring bd. 95.00 *(978-0-497-81401-4(3))* Icon Group International, Inc.

—The 2006 Economic & Product Market Databook for Sanaa, Yemen. 2006. 618p. ring bd. 95.00 *(978-0-497-81435-9(8))* Icon Group International, Inc.

Margariti, Roxani Eleni. Aden & the Indian Ocean Trade: 150 Years in the Life of a Medieval Arabian Port. 2007. (Islamic Civilization & Muslim Networks Ser.). (ENG., Illus.). 360p. 62.95 *(978-0-8078-3076-5(3))* Univ. of North Carolina Pr.

Willoughby, John. Political Economy of the Gulf. 2009. 256p. 130.00 *(978-0-415-70070-2(1),* RU42808) Routledge.

ARABIAN PENINSULA—HISTORY

al-Fassi, Hatoon Ajwad. Women in Pre-Islamic Arabia: Nabataea. 2007. (Bar S Ser.). (Illus.). (C). 75.00 *(978-1-4073-0095-5(4))* British Archaeological Reports Ltd. GBR. Dist: Brown, David Bk. Co., The.

Al-Semmari, Fahd. History of the Arabian Peninsula. 2010. (ENG.). 336p. 59.50 *(978-1-84511-688-0(7))* I. B. Tauris & Co., Ltd. GBR. Dist: Macmillan.

Al-Suwaidi, Jamal S., ed. Yemeni War. (Illus.). 120p. *(978-0-86356-300-3(7))* Saqi Bks.

Bertram Thomas. The Arabs - the Life Story of a People Who Have Left Their Deep Impress on the World. 2007. 400p. per. *(978-1-4067-5243-4(6))* Read Bks.

Burton, Richard F. The Land of Midian. 2009. 248p. 27.99 *(978-0-559-08733-2(0))* 2009. 248p. 23.99 *(978-0-559-08748-6(9))* 2009. 248p. pap. 26.75 *(978-0-559-08736-3(5))* 2009. 248p. pap. 25.75 *(978-0-559-08744-8(6))* 2008. 260p. 25.99 *(978-0-554-34257-3(X))* 2008. 260p. 28.99 *(978-0-554-24954-4(5))* BiblioBazaar.

—The Land of Midian. 2009. 160p. pap. *(978-0-217-39155-9(9))*; 162p. pap. *(978-0-217-08523-6(7))*; 156p. pap. *(978-0-217-08525-0(3))* Books LLC.

—The Land of Midian. 2008. 256p. pap. *(978-1-4099-3659-6(7))*; 240p. pap. *(978-1-4099-3657-2(0))* Dodo Pr.

—The Land of Midian. 2008. 400p. *(978-1-4437-3956-6(1),* Obscure Pr.) Read Bks.

Clark, Victoria. Yemen: Dancing on the Heads of Snakes. 2010. (ENG., Illus.). 328p. pap. 20.00 *(978-0-300-11701-1(9))* Yale Univ. Pr.

Crichton, Andrew. The History of Arabia Ancient & Modern by Andrew Crichton with a Map & Engravings. 2006. 424p. pap. 26.99 *(978-1-4255-4628-1(5))*; 428p. per. 26.99 *(978-1-4255-4644-1(7))* MPublishing.

Hainthaler, Theresia. Christliche Araber Vor Dem Islam: Verbreitung und Konfessionelle Zugehorigkeit. eine Hinfuhrung. 2007. (Eastern Christian Studies Ser.). (ENG., Illus.). 188p. (C). pap. 65.00 *(978-90-429-1917-4(5))* Peeters Pubs. & Booksellers BEL. Dist: Brown, David Bk. Co., The.

Hamilton, Alastair. An Arabian Utopia - The Western Discovery of Oman. 2010. (Studies in the Arcadian Library). (ENG., Illus.). 260p. 180.00 *(978-0-19-958160-3(6))* Oxford Univ. Pr., Inc.

Hawqal, Ibn. The Oriental Geography of Ibn Hawqal, an Arabian Traveller of the Tenth Century. Ouseley, William G., tr. (ARA.). xxxvi, 327p. reprint ed. lib. bdg. 75.00 *(978-0-89241-182-5(1))* Caratzas, Aristide D. Pub.

Hulsman, John. To Begin the World over Again: Lawrence of Arabia from Damascus to Baghdad. 2009. (ENG., Illus.). 256p. 27.00 *(978-0-230-61742-1(5))* Palgrave Macmillan.

Jacob, Harold F. Perfumes of Araby: Silhouettes of Al Yemen. 2007. (Folios Archive Library Ser.). 264p. pap. 49.50 *(978-1-85964-139-6(7))* Garnet Publishing, Ltd. GBR. Dist: International Specialized Bk. Services.

MacDonald, M. C. A. & Macdonald, M. C. A. Literacy & Identity in Pre-Islamic Arabia. 2009. (Variorum Collected Studies). (Illus.). 432p. 190.00 *(978-0-7546-5965-5(8))* Ashgate Publishing Co.

Morgan, Michael Hamilton. Arabia: In Search of the Golden Ages. 2010. (ENG., Illus.). 160p. 39.95 *(978-1-60109-055-3(2),* Earth Aware Editions) Mandala Publishing.

Newby, Gordon Darnell. A History of the Jews of Arabia: From Ancient Times to Their Eclipse under Islam. 2009. (Studies in Comparative Religion Ser.). 192p. pap. 24.95 *(978-1-57003-885-3(6))* Univ. of South Carolina Pr.

Potts, D. T. Mesopotamia, Iran & Arabia from the Seleucids to the Sasanians. 2010. (Variorum Collected Studies). (Illus.). 372p. 170.00 *(978-1-4094-0535-1(4))* Ashgate Publishing Co.

Rubin, Uri. Muhammad the Prophet & Arabia. 2011. (Variorum Collected Studies). (Illus.). 360p. 165.00 *(978-1-4094-0846-8(9))* Ashgate Publishing Co.

Valeem, Ehsan Elahi & Tirmizi, S. M. A. Wave Climate of Northern Arabian Sea During Southwest Monsoon Season: Variation & Analysis of Wave Characteristics. 2011. 284p. pap. ***(978-3-639-31657-5(6))*** VDM Verlag Dr. Mueller e.K.

Wallen, John. Burton & Orientalism. 2011. 256p. pap. ***(978-3-8454-0349-6(7))*** Lambert Academic Publishing.

Weeks, Lloyd, ed. Death & Burial in Arabia & Beyond. 2010. (Bar S Ser.). (ENG., Illus.). 372p. (C). pap. 137.50 *(978-1-4073-0648-3(0))* British Archaeological Reports Ltd. GBR. Dist: Brown, David Bk. Co., The.

Wheatcroft, Andrew. Arabia & the Gulf in Original Photographs, 1880-1950. 2007. (Illus.). 200p. 190.00 *(978-0-7103-0016-4(6))* Taylor & Francis Group.

Willis, John M. Unmaking North & South: Cartographies of the Yemeni Past. 2012. (Columbia/Hurst Ser.). (ENG.). 288p. (gr. 17). 55.00 *(978-0-231-70131-0(4))* Columbia Univ. Pr.

ARABIAN PENINSULA—POLITICS AND GOVERNMENT

Sakr, Naomi, ed. Arab Media & Political Renewal: Community, Legitimacy & Public Life. 2007. (Library of Modern Middle East Studies). (ENG., Illus.). 224p. 89.00 *(978-1-84511-433-6(7))* I. B. Tauris & Co., Ltd. GBR. Dist: Macmillan.

Salmoni, Barak A., et al. Regime & Periphery in Northern Yemen: The Huthi Phenomenon. 2010. (ENG.). 408p. pap. 52.00 *(978-0-8330-4933-9(X),* mg-962) RAND Corp., The.

Weir, Shelagh. A Tribal Order: Politics & Law in the Mountains of Yemen. 2007. (Modern Middle East Ser.). (ENG., Illus.). 410p. 50.00 *(978-0-292-71423-6(8))* Univ. of Texas Pr.

Willis, John M. Unmaking North & South: Cartographies of the Yemeni Past. 2012. (Columbia/Hurst Ser.). (ENG.). 288p. (gr. 17). 55.00 *(978-0-231-70131-0(4))* Columbia Univ. Pr.

Willoughby, John. Political Economy of the Gulf. 2009. 256p. 130.00 *(978-0-415-70070-2(1),* RU42808) Routledge.

ARABIAN PENINSULA—SOCIAL CONDITIONS

Al-Suwaidi, Jamal S., ed. Yemeni War. (Illus.). 120p. *(978-0-86356-300-3(7))* Saqi Bks.

Khondker, Habibul Haque & Pieterse, Jan Nederveen. 21st Century Globalization: Perspectives from the Gulf. Reyes-Ruiz, Rafael, ed. 2011. (Encounters Ser.). (ENG.). 264p. pap. 50.00 *(978-9948-15-751-9(6),* Zayed University) I. B. Tauris & Co., Ltd. GBR. Dist: Macmillan.

Manger, Leif. The Hadrami Diaspora: Community-Building on the Indian Ocean Rim. 2010. (Illus.). 220p. 60.00 *(978-1-84545-742-6(0))* Berghahn Bks., Inc.

Willoughby, John. Political Economy of the Gulf. 2009. 256p. 130.00 *(978-0-415-70070-2(1),* RU42808) Routledge.

ARABIAN PENINSULA—SOCIAL LIFE AND CUSTOMS

Adair, John. The Leadership of Muhammad. 2010. (ENG., Illus.). 148p. 19.95 *(978-0-7494-6076-1(8))* Kogan Page, Ltd. GBR. Dist: Ingram Pub. Services.

Blackgrave, Wanda. Here, There, & Back Again. 2009. 236p. 24.99 *(978-1-4490-3891-5(3))*; pap. 15.99 *(978-1-4490-3890-8(5))* AuthorHouse.

Boxberger, Linda, tr. from ARA. & intro. Visits & Customs: The Visit to the Tomb of Propher Hud. Date not set.Tr. of Shakyh 'Abdalqadir Muhammad Al-Sabban. *(978-1-882557-06-6(9))* American Institute for Yemeni Studies.

Bravmann, M.M. The Spiritual Background of Early Islam: Studies in Ancient Arab Concepts. 2008. (C). *(978-90-04-17200-5(9))* BRILL.

Cole, Donald. Bedouins of the Empty Quarter. 2010. (ENG., Illus.). 202p. pap. 29.95 *(978-0-202-36357-8(0))* Aldine Transaction.

Doughty, Charles. Wanderings in Arabia: The Authorised Abridged Edition of 'Travels in Arabia Deserta' 2009. (ENG., Illus.). 624p. 89.00 *(978-1-84511-810-5(3))*; pap. 31.00 *(978-1-84511-766-5(2))* I. B. Tauris & Co., Ltd. GBR. Dist: Macmillan.

Doughty, Charles Montagu. Travels in Arabia Deserta. 2010. (Cambridge Library Collection - Travel & Exploration Ser.). (ENG.). 712p. pap. 48.00 *(978-1-108-00947-8(6))*; (Illus.). 668p. pap. 48.00 *(978-1-108-00946-1(8))* Cambridge Univ. Pr.

Hilden, Joy Totah. Bedouin Weaving of Saudi Arabia & its Neighbours. 2011. (ENG., Illus.). 288p. (C). pap. 70.00 *(978-0-9558894-8-6(0))* Arabian Publishing, Ltd. GBR. Dist: Brown, David Bk. Co., The.

Jung, Dinah. An Ethnography of Fragrance: The Perfumery Arts of 'Adan/Lahj. 2011. (Islamic History & Civilization Ser.: Vol. 84). (Illus.). 278p. *(978-90-04-18725-2(1))* BRILL.

Keane, John. Six Months in the Hijaz: Journeys to Makkah & Madinah 1877-1878. 2007. (ENG.). 512p. 35.00 *(978-0-9549701-1-6(X))* Barzan Publishing Company GBR. Dist: Interlink Publishing Group, Inc.

Lawrence, T. E. Revolt in the Desert. 2008. 328p. *(978-1-84677-420-1(9))*; pap. *(978-1-84677-419-5(5))* Leonaur Ltd.

Lawrence, T. e. & Lawrence, T. E. Seven Pillars of Wisdom: A Triumph. 2011. 550p. 24.95 ***(978-1-61720-182-0(0))***; pap. 14.99 ***(978-1-61720-181-3(2))*** Wilder Pubns., Ltd.

Lyons, Malcolm C. & Lyons, Ursula, trs. from ARA. Tales from 1,001 Nights: Aladdin, Ali Baba & Other Favourites. 2011. (ENG., Illus.). 432p. (gr. 12). 25.00 *(978-0-14-119165-2(1),* Penguin Classics Hardcover) Penguin Group (USA) Inc.

Mandaville, James P. Bedouin Ethnobotany: Plant Concepts & Uses in a Desert Pastoral World. 2011. (ENG., Illus.). 352p. 55.00 *(978-0-8165-2900-1(0))* Univ. of Arizona Pr.

Minoui, Delphine & Ali, Nujood. I Am Nujood, Age 10 & Divorced. 2010. (ENG.). 192p. pap. 12.00 *(978-0-307-58967-5(6),* Three Rivers Pr.) Crown Publishing Group.

Monferrer-Sala, Juan Pedro. Redefining history on Pre-Islamic Accounts. 2010. 95.60 *(978-1-61719-158-9(2))* Gorgias Pr., LLC.

Morgan, Michael Hamilton. Arabia: In Search of the Golden Ages. 2010. (ENG., Illus.). 160p. 39.95 *(978-1-60109-055-3(2),* Earth Aware Editions) Mandala Publishing.

Nowell, Simone. Oman: The essential guide to customs & Culture. 2009. (Culture Smart! Ser.). (ENG., Illus.). 168p. pap. 9.95 *(978-1-85733-475-3(2))* Kuperard Pubs. GBR. Dist: Random Hse., Inc.

Peters, Emrys L. The Bedouin of Cyrenaica: Studies in Personal & Corporate Power. Goody, Jack & Marx, Emanuel, eds. 2007. (Cambridge Studies in Social & Cultural Anthropology Ser.). (ENG., Illus.). 336p. pap. 69.00 *(978-0-521-04046-4(9))* Cambridge Univ. Pr.

Smith, W. Robertson. Kinship & Marriage in Early Arabia. Cook, Stanley A., ed. 2008. 346p. 46.95 *(978-1-4365-6359-8(3))* 2007. (ENG.). 348p. per. 31.95 *(978-0-548-76619-4(3))* Kessinger Publishing, LLC.

Thomas, Bertram. Arabia Felix. 2008. (Illus.). 448p. *(978-1-4437-2345-9(2))* 2006. 444p. per. *(978-1-4067-2205-5(7))* Read Bks. (Hesperides Pr.).

ARABIC ASTRONOMY

see Astronomy, Arabic

ARABIC BALLADS AND SONGS

see Folk Songs, Arabic; Songs, Arabic

ARABIC CALLIGRAPHY

see Calligraphy, Arabic

ARABIC COUNTRIES

see Arab Countries

ARABIC DRAMA

Amin, Dina. Alfred Farag & Egyptian Theater: The Poetics of Disguise, with Four Short Plays & a Monologue. 2008. (Middle East Literature in Translation Ser.). 384p. (C). 34.95 *(978-0-8156-3163-7(4))* Syracuse Univ. Pr.

Badawi, M. M. Early Arabic Drama. 2010. (ENG.). 160p. pap. 27.99 *(978-0-521-13166-7(9))* Cambridge Univ. Pr.

Parkman, Francis. La Salle & the Discovery of the Great West. 2010. 524p. pap. 40.75 *(978-1-149-00578-1(5))* BiblioBazaar.

Sadgrove, P. C. The Egyptian Theatre in the Nineteenth Century: 1799-1882. 2007. 214p. pap. 34.95 *(978-0-86372-322-3(5),* Ithaca Pr.) Garnet Publishing, Ltd. GBR. Dist: International Specialized Bk. Services.

ARABIC FICTION

see also Short Stories, Arabic

Ali, Nabilah Ahmad. Al-Hulm Al-Aswad: Qiraah Lil-Shakhsiyah Al-Niswiyah Fi Athar Katibat Al-Qissah Al-Qasirah Al-Imaratiyat: Dirasah Tatabbuiyah. 2010. (ARA.). 154p. *(978-9948-15-416-7(9))* Ittihad Kuttab Wa-Udaba Al-Imarat.

Calani, Fabio. Contemporary Arab Fiction. 2007. (Routledge Studies in Middle Eastern Literatures Ser.). XII, 180p. 160.00 *(978-0-415-41456-2(3))* Routledge.

Clark, Peter, ed. Emerging Arab Voices: Nadwa 1: A Bilingual Reader. 2011. (ENG.). 320p. pap. 21.95 ***(978-0-86356-414-7(3))*** Saqi Bks. GBR. Dist: Consortium Bk. Sales & Distribution.

Ghanayim, Mahmud. The Quest for a Lost Identity: Palestinian Fiction in Israel. 2008. (Studies in Arabic Language & Literature). (ENG.). 164p. (C). pap. 57.00 *(978-3-447-05768-4(8))* Harrassowitz, Otto Verlag DEU. Dist: ISD.

Glanville, Jo, ed. Qissat: Short Stories by Palestinian Women. 2007. (ENG.). 200p. per. 18.95 *(978-1-84659-012-2(4),* Telegram Bks.) Saqi Bks. GBR. Dist: Consortium Bk. Sales & Distribution.

Hochberg, G. Z. In Spite of Partition: Jews, Arabs & the Limits of Separatist Imagination. 2007. (Translation/Transnation Ser.). (ENG.). 208p. (C). 42.00 *(978-0-691-12875-7(8))* Princeton Univ. Pr.

Hodges, Sydney. The Battle of Hastings & Other Poems. 2010. 194p. pap. 23.75 *(978-1-149-01170-6(X))* BiblioBazaar.

Jayyusi, Salma Khadra & Jayyusi, Salma, eds. Modern Arabic Fiction: An Anthology. 2008. (ENG.). 1064p. (gr. 17). pap. 40.00 *(978-0-231-13255-8(7))* Columbia Univ. Pr.

Khalaf, Roseanne Saad, ed. Hikayat: Short Stories by Lebanese Women. 2007. (ENG.). 200p. per. 18.95 *(978-1-84659-011-5(6),* Telegram Bks.) Saqi Bks. GBR. Dist: Consortium Bk. Sales & Distribution.

Maher, John. Slouching Towards Jerusalem: Reactive Nationalism in the Irish, Israeli & Palestinian Novel. 2012. 254p. 74.95 ***(978-0-7165-3119-7(4))*** Irish Academic Pr. IRL. Dist: International Specialized Bk. Services.

Mustafa, Shakir. Contemporary Iraqi Fiction: An Anthology. 2009. (Middle East Literature in Translation Ser.). 202p. 22.95 *(978-0-8156-0902-5(7))* Syracuse Univ. Pr.

Ouyang, Wen-Chin. Poetics of Love in the Arabic Novel: Nation-State, Modernity & Tradition. 2012. (ENG., Illus.). 320p. (gr. 17). 115.00 ***(978-0-7486-4273-1(0))*** Edinburgh Univ. Pr. GBR. Dist: Columbia Univ. Pr.

Rasul, Muhammad Rasul. Tamthilat Al-Marah Fi Al-Riwayah Al-Imaratiyah: Qiraat Fi Huwiyat Al-Mutakhayyal Al-Ibdai. 2010. (ARA.). 92p. *(978-9948-15-411-2(8))* Ittihad Kuttab Wa-Udaba Al-Imarat.

Seymour-Jorn, Caroline. Cultural Criticism in Egyptian Women's Writing. 2011. 29.95 ***(978-0-8156-3286-3(X))*** Syracuse Univ. Pr.

Shar, Tariq Uthman. Al-Bahth an Nuqtat Al-Sifr: Dirasat Naqdiyah. 2010. (ARA.). 174p. *(978-9959-38-831-5(X))* Majles Tanmiyat al-Ibda at-Thaqafi.

Tamarah, Abd al-Rahman. Jamaliyat Al-Nass Al-Qisasi Al-Maghribi Al-Rahin. 2010. (ARA.). 206p. *(978-9954-0-4197-0(4))* Institut Marocain du Livre, IML.

Walli, Karim. Masadir Naqd Al-Qissah Al-Qasirah Wa-Al-Riwayah Fi Al-Iraq. 2008. (ARA.). 217p. *(978-9957-11-730-6(0))*; *(978-9957-11-727-6(0))* Dar Wail Lil-Nashr.

ARABIC INSCRIPTIONS

see Inscriptions, Arabic

ARABIC LANGUAGE

Abboud, Samer, et al. Harrap's Arabic Phrasebook. 2007. (Harrap's Phrasebook Ser.). (ENG., Illus.). 192p. pap. 7.95 *(978-0-07-148626-2(7),* 0071486267) McGraw-Hill Cos., The.

Abd Allah, Muhammad Hasan. Al-Islamiyah Wa-Al-Ruhiyah Fi Adab Najib Mahfuz, 2 vols. 2010. (ARA., Illus.). 454p. *(978-977-316-282-5(6))* Dar al-Nashr lil-Jamiat.

Abdel-Massih, Ernest T., et al. A Reference Grammar of Egyptian Arabic. 2009. (Georgetown Classics in Arabic Language & Linguistics Ser.). (ENG.). 352p. (C). pap. 32.50 *(978-1-58901-260-8(7))* Georgetown Univ. Pr.

Abdelhaleem, Mahmoud. Routine Formulas Revisited. 2010. 288p. pap. *(978-3-639-24412-0(5))* VDM Verlag Dr. Mueller e.K.

Abdou, Ashraf. Arabic Idioms: A Corpus Based Study. 2011. (Routledge Arabic Linguistics Ser.). (ENG & ARA., Illus.). 192p. (C). 115.00 *(978-0-415-60340-9(4))* Routledge.

Abdul-Raof, Hussein. Arabic Stylistics: A Coursebook. 2006. (ARA & ENG.). 164p. pap. 44.00 ***(978-3-447-04435-6(7))*** Harrassowitz, Otto Verlag DEU. Dist: ISD.

Abed, Shukri B. An Introduction to Spoken Standard Arabic, Pt. 2. 2012. (ARA & ENG., Illus.). 240p. (C). 40.00 *(978-0-300-15904-2(8))* Yale Univ. Pr.

—An Introduction to Spoken Standard Arabic: A Conversational Course. 2010. (ARA & ENG., Illus.). 384p. (C). 45.00 *(978-0-300-14480-2(6))* Yale Univ. Pr.

Abed, Shukri B. & Lucas, Ceil. Focus on Contemporary Arabic. 2006. (Conversations with Native Speakers Ser.). (ENG & ARA., Illus.). 304p. 47.00 *(978-0-300-10948-1(2))* Yale Univ. Pr.

Abu-Chacra, Faruk. Arabic: An Essential Grammar. 2007. (Routledge Essential Grammars Ser.). (ENG., Illus.). 368p. 140.00 *(978-0-415-41572-9(1))*; per. 40.95 *(978-0-415-41571-2(3))* Routledge.

Abu El-Khair, Ibrahim. Arabic Information Retrieval. 2011. 216p. pap. ***(978-3-8443-1300-0(1))*** Lambert Academic Publishing.

AbuZeina, Dia & Elshafei, Moustafa. Cross-Word Modeling for Arabic Speech Recognition. 2011. (SpringerBriefs in Electrical & Computer Engineering / SpringerBriefs in Speech Technology Ser.). (ENG & ARA., Illus.). x, 74p. 49.95 ***(978-1-4614-1212-0(9),*** 14614*2129) Springer.

Adam. Let's Talk Arabic. 2011. 260p. pap. 21.95 *(978-1-4269-5954-7(0))* Trafford Publishing.

Al-Batal, Mahmoud, ed. & intro. The Teaching of Arabic As a Foreign Language: Issues & Directions. 2008. (ENG., Illus.). 376p. (C). pap. 34.95 *(978-0-9621530-9-9(5))* Georgetown Univ. Pr.

Al Ekhnawy, Kama & Ali, Jamal. 'Arabi Liblib: Colloquial Arabic for the Advanced Learner. 2011. 192p. 22.95 *(978-977-416-458-3(X))* American Univ. in Cairo Pr. EGY. Dist: Oxford Univ. Pr., Inc.

Al-Faizi, Faizan Muhammad. The Key to the Sciences: Being a primer in Arabic Phonetics, Morphology & Syntax. 2010. 156p. pap. 43.49 *(978-1-4520-0450-1(1))* AuthorHouse.

Al Jayousi, Ahmad. Arabic Text-to-Speech Synthesizer. 2011. 192p. pap. ***(978-3-639-33583-5(X))*** VDM Verlag Dr. Mueller e.K.

Al-Lughah Wa-Al-Ilam: Amal Al-Yawm Al-Dirasi. 2009. (ARA.). 139p. *(978-9973-10-265-2(7))* Maison Arabe du Livre.

Al-Marrani, Yahya. Prepositions in English & Arabic. 2011. 120p. pap. ***(978-3-8383-5696-9(9))*** Lambert Academic Publishing.

Al-Osaimi, Saleh. Beliefs about Second Language Learning. 2010. 264p. pap. *(978-3-8383-8921-9(2))* Lambert Academic Publishing.

Al-Sabbagh, Rania. Anaphora Resolution in Arabic/English MacHine Translation Systems. 2010. 104p. pap. *(978-3-8383-8684-3(1))* Lambert Academic Publishing.

Al Shatter, Ghassan. Acquisition & Development of Nominal & Verbal Structures in Arabic. 2010. 316p. pap. *(978-3-639-24473-1(7))* VDM Verlag Dr. Mueller e.K.

Aldokhayel, Reyadh. The Event Structure Metaphor. 2009. 144p. pap. *(978-3-639-13385-1(4))* VDM Verlag Dr. Mueller e.K.

Alhawary, Mohammad T. Arabic Second Language Acquisition of Morphosyntax. 2009. (ENG., Illus.). 240p. pap. 50.00 *(978-0-300-14129-0(7))* Yale Univ. Pr.

—Modern Standard Arabic Grammar: A Learner's Guide. 2011. (Blackwell Reference Grammars Ser.). (ARA & ENG., Illus.). 424p. pap. 41.95 *(978-1-4051-5502-1(7))*; 104.95 *(978-1-4051-5501-4(9))* Wiley, John & Sons, Inc. (Wiley-Blackwell).

Ali, Jamal. Language & Heresy in Ismaili Thought: The Kitab al-Zina of Abu Hatim Al-Razi. 2008. (Gorgias Dissertations in Arabic & Islamic Studies: 2). 105.00 *(978-1-59333-781-0(7))* Gorgias Pr., LLC.

Alosh, M. Ahlan Wa Sahlan - Functional Modern Standard Arabic for Beginners 2e (with Free DVD & CD) 2nd ed. 2009. (ARA & ENG., Illus.). 672p. 69.95 *(978-0-300-12272-5(1))* Yale Univ. Pr.

Alosh, Mahdi. Ahlan Wa Sahlan: Functional Modern Standard Arabic for Beginners - Letters & Sounds of the Arabic Language. 2nd ed. 2009. (Illus.). 192p. wbk. ed. 34.00 *(978-0-300-14048-4(7))* Yale Univ. Pr.

Alsheikh, Negmeldin. The Strategic Reading of Arabic Native Speakers in English. 2009. 124p. pap. *(978-3-639-13535-0(0))* VDM Verlag Dr. Mueller e.K.

Amara, M. & Mar'i, Abd Al-Rahman. Language Education Policy: the Arab Minority in Israel: The Arab Minority in Israel. 2010. (Language Policy Ser.). 221p. pap. 199.00 *(978-90-481-6006-8(5)*, 9048160065) Springer.

An Arabic Reading Book. 2010. 92.24 *(978-1-61719-419-1(0))* Gorgias Pr., LLC.

Assimil Staff, ed. Arabisch Ohne Muhe Heute. (Assimil Language Courses Ser.). (ARA & GER.). pap. 125.00 incl. audio *(978-0-8288-2403-3(7))* French & European Pubns., Inc.

Attar, Samar. Modern Arabic: Grammar in Context. (ARA.). 24.95 *(978-0-86685-736-9(2))* International Bk. Ctr., Inc.

—Modern Arabic 2: An Introductory Course for Foreign Students. (ARA.). pap., stu. ed., wbk. ed. 10.95 *(978-0-86685-702-4(8)*, LKL440B) International Bk. Ctr., Inc.

Ayyubi, Hashim Ismail, et al. Syntax der Arabischen Schriftsprache der Gegenwart. 2010. (ARA & GER.). 569p. (C). 168.00 *(978-3-89500-744-6(7))* Reichert, Ludwig Dr. DEU. Dist: Brown, David Bk. Co., The.

Baalbaki, Ramzi, ed. The Early Islamic Grammatical Tradition. 2007. (Formation of the Classical Islamic World Ser.). 416p. 190.00 *(978-0-86078-718-1(4))* Ashgate Publishing Co.

Bacon, Dan, et al. Moroccan Arabic. 3rd rev. ed. 2008. (Lonely Planet Phrasebook Guides). (ARA & ENG., Illus.). 256p. pap. 8.99 *(978-1-74059-187-4(9))* Lonely Planet Pubns.

Badawi, El-Said. Al-Kitab Al-Asasi Vol. 2: A Basic Course for Teaching Arabic to Non-Native Speakers. 2009. (ENG., Illus.). 390p. pap. 39.50 *(978-977-416-232-9(3))* American Univ. in Cairo Pr. EGY. Dist: Oxford Univ. Pr., Inc.

Bahloul, Maher. Structure & Function of the Arabic Verb. 2007. (Routledge Arabic Linguistics Ser.). (ENG., Illus.). 256p. (C). 168.00 *(978-0-415-77215-0(X))* Routledge.

Bakhtiar, Laleh, tr. Sublime Quran Arabic English. 1120p. 2008. 99.95 *(978-1-56744-768-2(6))* Vol. 2. 2009. pap. 74.95 *(978-1-56744-767-5(8))* Kazi Pubns., Inc. (Library of Islam, Ltd.).

Barsoum, Aphram I. & Saleeba, George. Treatise on the Principals of Translation Techniques from Arabic into Syriac. 2010. (ARA & SYR.). pap. 27.52 *(978-1-61719-458-0(1))* Gorgias Pr., LLC.

Basic Saudi Arabic. (Series of Language Courses). 69.95 *(978-1-57050-005-3(3))* Multilingua, Inc.

Bassiouney, Reem. Arabic Sociolinguistics. 2009. (ARA & ENG., Illus.). 224p. (gr. 17). 50.00 ***(978-0-7486-2373-0(6))***; pap. 16.99 ***(978-0-7486-2374-7(4))*** Edinburgh Univ. Pr. GBR. Dist: Columbia Univ. Pr.

Bassiouney, Reem & Katz, E. Graham, eds. Arabic Language & Linguistics. 2012. (Georgetown University Round Table on Languages & Linguistics Ser.). (ENG.). 208p. pap. 44.95 ***(978-1-58901-885-3(0))*** Georgetown Univ. Pr.

Bassnett. Translation in Global News. 2007. XVI, 240p. 41.95 *(978-0-415-40972-8(1))*; 110.00 *(978-0-415-40973-5(X))* Routledge.

Bataineh, Rula F. Apologies. 2009. 160p. pap. *(978-3-639-14686-8(7))* VDM Verlag Dr. Mueller e.K.

Ben Amor, Taoufik. Developing Writing Skills in Arabic. 2012. (Developing Writing Skills Ser.). (ENG & ITA., Illus.). 216p. 150.00 ***(978-0-415-58812-6(X))***; pap. 44.95 ***(978-0-415-58813-3(8))*** Routledge.

Berlitz. Arabic Vocabulary Study Cards. 2010. (Study Cards Ser.). (ENG & ARA.). 1000p. pap. 14.99 *(978-981-268-867-5(6))* APA Publications Services SGP. Dist: Ingram Pub. Services.

Berlitz Guides, creator. Arabic. 2007. (Phrase Book Ser.). (ARA & ENG., Illus.). 224p. pap. 8.95 *(978-981-268-034-1(9))* APA Publications Services SGP. Dist: Ingram Pub. Services.

Bjorsnos, Amund, et al. Chrestomathy of Classical Arabic Prose Literature. 8th rev. ed. 2008. (Porta Linguarum Orientalium Ser.). (ENG & ARA.). 324p. (C). pap. 48.00 *(978-3-447-05801-8(3))* Harrassowitz, Otto Verlag DEU. Dist: ISD.

Bouchentouf, Amine & Bouchentouf. Arabic Phrases for Dummies. 2009. (ARA & ENG., Illus.). 216p. pap. 9.99 *(978-0-470-22523-3(8)*, For Dummies) Wiley, John & Sons, Inc.

Bray, Julia Ashtiany, et al. Media Arabic. 2nd ed. 2013. (New Edinburgh Islamic Surveys Ser.). (ARA & ENG.). 176p. (gr. 17). 130.00 *(978-0-7486-3813-0(X))*; pap. 37.50 *(978-0-7486-3814-7(8))* Edinburgh Univ. Pr. GBR. Dist: Columbia Univ. Pr.

Brustad, Kristen, et al. Al-Kitaab Fii Tacallum Al-Carabiyya: A Textbook for Arabic, Vol. 3. 2007. (ARA & ENG., Illus.). 424p. (C). pap. 59.95 *(978-1-58901-149-6(X))* Georgetown Univ. Pr.

—Al-Kitaab Fii Tacallum Al-Carabiyya Pt. 1: A Textbook for Beginning Arabic. 3rd rev. ed. 2011. (ARA & ENG., Illus.). 384p. (C). 79.95 *(978-1-58901-737-5(4))*; pap. 69.95 *(978-1-58901-736-8(6))* Georgetown Univ. Pr.

—Alif Baa: Introduction to Arabic Letters & Sounds. 3rd rev. ed. 2010. (ARA & ENG., Illus.). 272p. (C). pap. 49.95 *(978-1-58901-632-3(7))* Georgetown Univ. Pr.

—Answer Key for Al-Kitaab Fii Ta Callum Al-Carabiyya Pt. 1: A Textbook for Beginning Arabick for Beginning Arabic. 3rd rev. ed. 2011. (ARA.). 64p. (C). pap. 5.95 *(978-1-58901-738-2(2))* Georgetown Univ. Pr.

Chouairi, Rajaa. Shou fi ma Fi? Intermediate Levantine Arabic. Alosh, Mahdi, ed. 2010. (ENG., Illus.). 240p. (C). pap. 58.00 *(978-0-300-15391-0(0))* Yale Univ. Pr.

Collins UK. Arabic. 2nd ed. 2010. (Collins Gem Ser.). (ENG & ARA., Illus.). 256p. pap. 6.95 *(978-0-00-735849-6(0))* HarperCollins Pubs. Ltd. GBR. Dist: Independent Pubs. Group.

Collins UK Staff. Arabic Phrase Book Pack: The Right Word in Your Pocket. 2008. (Collins Gem Ser.). (ARA & ENG., Illus.). 256p. pap. 9.95 *(978-0-00-724696-0(X))* HarperCollins Pubs. Ltd. GBR. Dist: Independent Pubs. Group.

Damamini, Muhammad ibn Abi Bakr & Matar, Fakhir Jabr. Al-Manhal Al-Safi Fi Sharh Al-Wafi: Wa-Huwa Sharh Lil-Wafi Wa-Huwa Matn Wajiz Fi Al-Nahw Li-Muallifihi Jamal Al-Din Muhammad Ibn Uthman Ibn Umar Al-Balkhi Al-Mutawaffi Fi Hudud Sanat 800 H, 2 vols. 2008. (ARA., Illus.). *(978-2-7451-5322-7(6))* Dar al-Kutub al-Ilmiyah.

Darwash, Mustafā. Tashakkul Al-Dhat Wa-Al-Lughah Fi Mafahim Al-Naqd Al-Manhaji. 2008. (ARA.). 254p. *(978-9961-883-73-0(X))* Office National de la Recherche Géologique et Minière.

De Beaugrande, Robert, et al, eds. Language, Discourse, & Translation in the West & Middle East: Selected & Revised Papers from the Language & Translation Conference, Irbid, Jordan, 1992. (Translation Library: Vol. 7). xii, 256p. lib. bdg. 126.00 *(978-1-55619-685-0(7))* Benjamins, John Publishing Co.

Department Of The Interior, ed. The Transliteration of Arabic & Persian. 2011. 16p. pap. 35.95 ***(978-1-258-05585-1(6))*** Literary Licensing, LLC.

Diehl, Katharine S. The Press Beyond Calcutta-North & East. (Printers & Printing in the East Indies to 1850 Ser.: Vol. VI). *(978-0-89241-395-9(6))* Caratzas, Aristide D. Pub.

Diouri, Mourad. Internet Arabic. 2012. (Essential Middle Eastern Vocabularies Ser.). (ARA & ENG.). 128p. (gr. 17). 80.00 ***(978-0-7486-4492-6(X))***; pap. 20.00 ***(978-0-7486-4491-9(1))*** Edinburgh Univ. Pr. GBR. Dist: Columbia Univ. Pr.

Dorling Kindersley Publishing Staff. Arabic English. 2009. (DK Visual Dictionaries Ser.). (ARA & ENG., Illus.). 360p. (gr. 12). 14.95 *(978-0-7566-4983-8(8))* Dorling Kindersley Publishing, Inc.

El Mallah, Fuzi. Arabic-English Translational Crossover. 2011. 564p. pap. ***(978-3-8454-2850-5(3))*** Lambert Academic Publishing.

Elgibali, Alaa & Korica, Nevenka. Media Arabic: A Coursebook for Reading Arabic News. 2007. (ENG., Illus.). 232p. per. 29.95 *(978-977-416-108-7(4))* American Univ. in Cairo Pr. EGY. Dist: Oxford Univ. Pr., Inc.

Esseesy, Mohssen. Grammaticalization of Arabic Prepositions & Subordinators: A Corpus-Based Study. (Studies in Semitic Languages & Linguistics Ser.). (Illus.). xxiv, 390p. *(978-90-04-18587-6(9))* BRILL.

Evans, Mark. Intelligence & Security Arabic. 2012. (Essential Middle Eastern Vocabularies Ser.). (ARA & ENG., Illus.). 160p. (gr. 17). 80.00 ***(978-0-7486-4662-3(0))***; pap. 20.00 ***(978-0-7486-4661-6(2))*** Edinburgh Univ. Pr. GBR. Dist: Columbia Univ. Pr.

Farghaly, Ali, ed. Arabic Computational Linguistics. 2010. (Illus.). 300p. 70.00 *(978-1-57586-543-0(2))*; pap. 37.50 *(978-1-57586-544-7(0))* CSLI Pubns.

Fassi Fehri, A. Issues in the Structure of Arabic Clauses & Words. 2010. (Studies in Natural Language & Linguistic Theory Ser.). 336p. pap. 289.00 *(978-90-481-4228-6(8)*, 9048142288) Springer.

Fassi Fehri, Abdelkader. Key Features & Parameters in Arabic Grammar. 2012. (Illus.). xx, 358p. ***(978-90-272-5565-5(2))***; ***(978-90-272-7496-0(7))*** Benjamins, John Publishing Co.

Feghali, Maksoud N. Spoken Lebanese. 2007. per. 34.95 *(978-1-59712-148-4(7))* Catawba Publishing Co.

Ferguson, Charles A. & Ani, Moukhtar. Lessons in Contemporary Arabic: Lessons 1-8. 2011. 176p. 42.95 ***(978-1-258-10370-5(2))*** Literary Licensing, LLC.

Fettah, Saliha & Hansen, Gunna. Read Arabic: An Arabic Reader for Arabic Students at All Levels. 2007. 92p. pap. 22.00 *(978-87-7674-161-7(3))* Univ. Pr. of Southern Denmark DNK. Dist: International Specialized Bk. Services.

Frangieh, Bassam K. Arabic for Life: A Textbook for Beginning Arabic. 2011. (ARA & ENG., Illus.). 528p. 85.00 *(978-0-300-14131-3(9))* Yale Univ. Pr.

Ghali, Naglaa. Write It in Arabic, Second Edition: A Workbook & Step-by-Step Guide to Writing the Arabic Alphabet. 2nd ed. 2009. (ARA & ENG.). 136p. pap. 11.95 *(978-0-9730512-3-0(X))* Fun With Arabic CAN. Dist: National Bk. Network.

Gibson, Margaret. Catalogue of the Arabic MSS. 2010. (GRE.). 97.28 *(978-1-61143-066-0(6))* Gorgias Pr., LLC.

Griess, Ihab Joseph. Syntactical Comparisons Between Classical Hebrew & Classical Arabic: A Study Based on the Translation of Mohammad 'Id's Arabic Grammar. 2008. 330p. 119.95 *(978-0-7734-5013-4(0))* Mellen, Edwin Pr., The.

Groffman, G. N. An Introduction to Modern Standard Arabic. 2014. (ENG.). 520p. 49.95 *(978-0-19-927773-5(7))*; 110.00 *(978-0-19-927772-8(9))* Oxford Univ. Pr., Inc.

Habash, Nizar. Arabic Natural Language Processing. 2010. (Synthesis Lectures on Human Language Technologies Ser.). (ARA & ENG., Illus.). 187p. pap. 40.00 *(978-1-59829-795-9(3))* Morgan & Claypool Pubs.

Habel, Kirk & Habel, K. F. Arabic - Complete Idiot's Guide. 2008. (Complete Idiot's Guide Ser.). (ARA & ENG., Illus.). 416p. (gr. 12-18). pap. 21.95 *(978-1-59257-703-3(2)*, Alpha Bks.) Penguin Group (USA) Inc.

Haffner, August & Cheikho, P. L. Dix Anciens Traités de Philologie Arabe. 2007. (Gorgias Historical Grammars Ser.: 7). 76.00 *(978-1-59333-671-4(3))* Gorgias Pr., LLC.

Haidar, Otared. Practice Makes Perfect Arabic Pronouns & Prepositions. 2012. (Practice Makes Perfect Ser.). (ENG.). 192p. pap. 16.00 ***(978-0-07-175973-1(5)***, 0071759735) McGraw-Hill Cos., The.

Halflants, Bruno. Le Conte du Portefaix et des Trois Jeunes Femmes Dans le Manuscrit de Galland (XIVe-XVe Siècles) édition, Traduction et étude du Moyen Arabe D'un Conte des Mille et une Nuits. 2007. (ARA & FRE.). *(978-2-87723-961-5(6))* Peeters Pubs. & Booksellers.

—Le Conte du Portefaix et des Trois Jeunes Femmes Dans le Manuscrit de Galland (XIVe-XVe Siecles) Edition, Traduction et Etude du Moyen Arabe D'un Conte des Millee et une Nuits. 2007. (Publications de l'Institut Orientaliste de Louvain Ser.). (ENG.). 490p. (C). pap. 109.00 *(978-90-429-1874-0(8))* Peeters Pubs. & Booksellers BEL. Dist: Brown, David Bk. Co., The.

Harrap. Harrap's Pocket Arabic Grammar & Script. 2009. (Harrap's Language Guides). (ENG.). 176p. pap. 10.95 *(978-0-07-163617-9(X)*, 007163617X) McGraw-Hill Cos., The.

—Harrap's Pocket Arabic Vocabulary. 2009. (Harrap's language Guides). (ENG.). 320p. pap. 12.95 *(978-0-07-163615-5(3)*, 0071636153) McGraw-Hill Cos., The.

Hasan, Rashid. Dynamism in Modern Standard Arabic. 2010. 160p. pap. *(978-3-8383-8177-0(7))* Lambert Academic Publishing.

Haupt, Paul & Jandora, John. Arabic Tâjir & Assyrian Tamkaru. Rippin, Andrew, ed. 2012. 126.25 *(978-1-60724-045-7(9))* Gorgias Pr., LLC.

Healey, John & Smith, Rex. A Brief Introduction to the Arabic Alphabet. 2009. (Brief Introduction Ser.). (ENG., Illus.). 116p. pap. 11.95 *(978-0-86356-431-4(3))* Saqi Bks. GBR. Dist: Consortium Bk. Sales & Distribution.

Hiddleston, L. G. A Primer of the Colloquial Arabic of Iraq. 2011. 32p. 35.95 ***(978-1-258-00961-8(7))*** Literary Licensing, LLC.

Hunwick, John O. West Africa, Islam, & the Arab World: Studies in Honor of Basil Davidson. 2006. (Illus.). 147p. 88.95 *(978-1-55876-398-2(8))* Wiener, Markus Pubs., Inc.

Intermediate Saudi Arabic. (Series of Language Courses). 125.00 *(978-1-57050-015-2(0))* Multilingua, Inc.

Isaksson, Bo, et al. Circumstantial Qualifiers in Semitic: The Case of Arabic & Hebrew. Isaksson, Bo, ed. 2009. (Abhandlungen Für Die Kunde des Morgenlandes Ser.). (ENG.). 289p. (C). pap. 102.00 *(978-3-447-06111-7(1))* Harrassowitz, Otto Verlag DEU. Dist: ISD.

Istoci I Utoci: Secanje Na Slavoljuba Inica: Zbornik Radova. 2009. (FRE & ENG.). 454p. *(978-86-86419-69-9(0))* Filoloski fakultet, Izdavacka delatnost.

Jeffery, Arthur. The Foreign Vocabulary of the Qur'an. 2006. (Texts & Studies on the Qur'an: Vol. 3). 311p. *(978-90-04-15352-3(7))* BRILL.

—The Foreign Vocabulary of the Qur'an. 2007. (ENG.). 332p. per. *(978-1-4067-0618-5(3))* Read Bks.

Jiyad, Mohammed. ¿¿¿ ¿¿¿¿¿¿ ¿¿¿¿¿¿¿ the Voice of Arab Women. 2011. 292p. pap. ***(978-3-8433-9365-2(6))*** Lambert Academic Publishing.

Jiyad, Mohammed. 101 Fundamental Arabic Grammar Rules. 2010. 76p. pap. *(978-3-8383-8606-5(X))* Lambert Academic Publishing.

Kadhim, Kais. Linguistics Issues in English-Arabic Translation. 2011. 192p. pap. ***(978-3-8443-2305-4(8))*** Lambert Academic Publishing.

—The Translation of English Compounds of the Bbc News Texts into Arabic. 2011. 120p. pap. ***(978-3-8443-1751-0(1))*** Lambert Academic Publishing.

Kapliwatzky, J. Arabic Language & Grammar, 4 vols., Set. Incl. Pt. 1 incl. Key. 16th ed. 196p. 1993. pap. 15.00 *(978-965-09-0120-2(5)*, 73853); Pt. 2. 151p. 1975. pap. 15.00 *(978-965-09-0121-9(3)*, 73854); Pt. 3. 207p. 1976. pap. 15.00 *(978-965-09-0122-6(1)*, 73855); Pt. 4. 224p. 1976. pap. 15.00 *(978-965-09-0123-3(X)*, 73856); (ARA.). Set. pap. 60.00 *(978-965-09-0124-0(8)*, 67739) Mass, Rubin Ltd. ISR. Dist: Lambda Pubs., Inc.

Kendall, Elisabeth. The Top 1,300 Words for Understanding Media Arabic. 2012. (ARA & ENG.). 160p. pap. 16.95 ***(978-1-58901-912-6(1))*** Georgetown Univ. Pr.

Kershul, Kristine K. Arabic. 2nd ed. 2007. (10 Minutes a Day Ser.). (ENG., Illus.). 132p. 26.95 *(978-1-931873-00-0(3))* Bilingual Bks., Inc.

Khalek, Hisham A. & Sheeran, Joan G. Exploring Arabic. 2009. (ARA & ENG., Illus.). x, 278p. pap. 21.95 *(978-0-8219-3881-2(9))* EMC/Paradigm Publishing.

Khalifa, Mahmoud A. Hamid. The Critical Reception of Edward Said's Orientalism in the Arab World: A Critical Study. 2011. 84p. pap. ***(978-3-639-33024-3(2))*** VDM Verlag Dr. Mueller e.K.

King, Stephen. Carrie. 2011. (ENG.). 304p. mass mkt. 7.99 *(978-0-307-74366-4(7)*, Anchor) Knopf Doubleday Publishing Group.

Kluge, Friedrich. Deutsche Sprachgeschichte: Werden und Wachsen Unserer Muttersprache Von Ihren Anfängen Bis Zu Gegenwart. 2010. 364p. pap. 32.75 *(978-1-149-00771-6(0))* BiblioBazaar.

Lahlali, El Mustapha. Advanced Media Arabic. 2008. (ARA.). 302p. (C). pap. 34.95 *(978-1-58901-220-2(8))* Georgetown Univ. Pr.

Language Contact & Language Conflict in Arabic. 2009. 358p. pap. 39.95 *(978-0-415-56779-4(3))* Routledge.

Learn Arabic for English Speakers. (ARA & ENG.). pap. 25.95 *(978-0-87557-004-4(6))* Saphrograph Corp.

Levi, Joseph Abraham & BarCharts Inc., Staff. Arabic Grammar. 2007. (Quick Study Ser.). (ENG.). 6p. 5.95 *(978-1-4232-0275-2(9))* Barcharts, Inc.

Living Language Staff. Arabic Vocabulary. unabr. l.t. ed. 2009. (Flash Forward Ser.). (ENG.). 19.99 *(978-1-4000-0615-1(5)*, Living Language) Random Hse. Information Group.

London Chamber Of Commerce, creator. The Chamber of Commerce Journal. 2010. 450p. pap. 36.75 *(978-1-149-01898-9(4))* BiblioBazaar.

Louis, Samia. Kallimni 'Arabi: An Intermediate Course in Spoken Egyptian Arabic. 2007. (ENG., Illus.). 432p. 29.95 *(978-977-424-977-8(1))* American Univ. in Cairo Pr. EGY. Dist: Oxford Univ. Pr., Inc.

—Lughatuna Al-fusha: A Course in Modern Standard Arabic, Book One. 2010. (ENG.). 416p. pap. 39.95 *(978-977-416-352-4(4))* American Univ. in Cairo Pr. EGY. Dist: Oxford Univ. Pr., Inc.

—Lughatuna Al-Fusha: A New Course in Modern Standard Arabic. 2012. (ENG.). 476p. pap. 39.95 *(978-977-416-392-0(3))* American Univ. in Cairo Pr. EGY. Dist: Oxford Univ. Pr., Inc.

Macdonald, M. C. A., ed. The Development of Arabic As a Written Language. 2010. (ENG., Illus.). 179p. (C). pap. 60.00 *(978-1-905739-34-9(6))* Archaeopress GBR. Dist: Brown, David Bk. Co., The.

Mace, John. Arabic Today. 2nd ed. 2008. (ARA & ENG., Illus.). 384p. (gr. 17). 125.00 *(978-0-7486-3557-3(2))* Edinburgh Univ. Pr. GBR. Dist: Columbia Univ. Pr.

—Arabic Today: A Student, Business & Professional Course in Spoken & Written Arabic. 2nd ed. 2008. (ARA & ENG., Illus.). 384p. (gr. 17). pap. 40.00 *(978-0-7486-3558-0(0))* Edinburgh Univ. Pr. GBR. Dist: Columbia Univ. Pr.

—Arabic Verbs. 2007. (ENG.). 276p. per. 23.95 *(978-0-7818-1229-0(1))* Hippocrene Bks., Inc.

—Business Arabic: An Essential Vocabulary. 2008. (ARA & ENG.). 104p. (gr. 17). pap. 20.00 *(978-0-7486-3339-5(1))* Edinburgh Univ. Pr. GBR. Dist: Columbia Univ. Pr.

—Intermediate Arabic Workbook. 2007. (ENG., Illus.). 1p. per. 29.95 *(978-0-7818-1177-4(5))* Hippocrene Bks., Inc.

Mahfoudhi, Abdessatar. Studies in the Arabic Mental Lexicon. 2010. 208p. pap. *(978-3-639-25046-6(X))* VDM Verlag Dr. Mueller e.K.

Mansouri, Fethi & Alreemawi, Yousef. Instant Arabic: How to Express 1,000 Different Ideas with Just 100 Key Words & Phrases! 2007. (Instant Phrasebook Ser.). (ENG., Illus.). 192p. pap. 6.95 *(978-0-8048-3860-3(7))* Tuttle Publishing.

Marogy, Amal. Kitab Sibawayhi: Syntax & Pragmatics. 2009. *(978-90-04-17816-8(3))* BRILL.

Massey, Keith. Intermediate Arabic for Dummies. 2008. (ARA & ENG., Illus.). 360p. pap. 19.99 *(978-0-470-37337-8(7)*, For Dummies) Wiley, John & Sons, Inc.

McCarus, Ernest N. English Grammar for Students of Arabic: The Study Guide for Those Learning Arabic. Morton, Jacqueline, ed. 2007. (English Grammar Ser.). (ENG & ARA.). 165p. (C). pap. 19.95 *(978-0-934034-35-7(4))* Olivia & Hill Pr., The.

McLoughlin, Leslie J. A Further Course in Colloquial Arabic. (ARA.). 189p. 16.95 *(978-0-86685-277-7(8)*, LDL2778) International Bk. Ctr., Inc.

Michalak-Pikulska, Barbara & Pikulski, Andrzej. Authority, Privacy & Public Order in Islam: Proceedings of the 22nd Congress of L'Union Europeenne des Arabisants et Islamisants, Cracow, Poland 2004. Michalak-Pikulska, B. & Pikulski, A., eds. 2006. (Orientalia Lovaniensia Analecta Ser.: Vol. 148). (FRE & ENG., Illus.). 496p. (C). 130.00 *(978-90-429-1736-1(9))* Peeters Pubs. & Booksellers BEL. Dist: Brown, David Bk. Co., The.

Mohamud, Abdirashid A. Arabic for Reading & Speaking, 2 vols. 2008. (ARA & ENG., 224p. Illus.). 24.99 *(978-0-7641-9427-6(5))*; *(978-0-7641-3908-6(8))* Barron's Educational Series, Inc.

Morrow, John A., et al. Arabic, Islam, & the Allah Lexicon: How Language Shapes Our Conception of God. 2006. (Illus.). 316p. (C). 119.95 *(978-0-7734-5726-3(7))* Mellen, Edwin Pr., The.

Motzki, Harald & Ditters, Everhard, eds. Approaches to Arabic Linguistics: Presented to Kees Versteegh on the Occasion of his Sixtieth Birthday. 2007. (Studies in Semitic Languages & Linguistics Ser.). 794p. *(978-90-04-16015-6(9))* BRILL.

Moutaouakil, Ahmed. Pragmatic Functions in a Functional Grammar of Arabic. (Functional Grammar Series [FGS] Ser.). (ENG.). XI, 156p. 90.00 ***(978-3-11-177775-7(8))*** De Gruyter, Mouton DEU. Dist: de Gruyter, Walter GmbH & Co. KG.

Nacereddine, Abdallah. Fundamental Arabic Textbook. 2008. 436p. pap. 25.49 (978-1-4343-7173-7(5)) AuthorHouse.

—A New Approach to Teaching Arabic Grammar. 2009. 360p. pap. 22.49 (978-1-4490-3986-8(3)) AuthorHouse.

—Nouvelle Approche de L'Enseignement de la Grammaire Arabe. 2009. 396p. pap. 22.49 (978-1-4389-3645-1(1)) AuthorHouse.

Nasir al-Din, Abd Allah. Kitab Mabadi Al-Arabiyah. 2008. (ARA, FRE & ENG.). 245p. (978-1-4343-7174-4(3)) AuthorHouse.

—A New Approach to Teaching Arabic Grammar. 2009. (ARA & ENG.). 26p. (978-1-4490-3985-1(5)) AuthorHouse.

—Nouvelle Approche de L'enseignement de la Grammaire Arabe. 2009. (ARA & FRE.). xxvi, 312p. (978-1-4389-3646-8(X)) AuthorHouse.

Nasr, Raja T. Learn to Read Arabic. (ARA & ENG.). 45p. pap. 14.95 incl. audio (978-0-86685-194-7(1), LDL62027) International Bk. Ctr., Inc.

—The Structure of Arabic: From Sound to Sentence. (ARA.). 251p. 18.95 (978-0-86685-045-2(7), LDL0457) Librairie du Liban Pubns. FRA. Dist: International Bk. Ctr., Inc.

Nasrallah, Nawal & Hassani, Nadia. Beginner's Iraqi Arabic, 2 CDs. 2006. (Hippocrene Beginner's Ser.). (ENG.). 250p. pap. 29.95 (978-0-7818-1098-2(1)) Hippocrene Bks., Inc.

Nouryeh, Christopher. The Art of Narrative in the Holy Qur'an: A Literary Appreciation of a Sacred Text. 2008. 400p. (978-0-7734-5179-7(X)) Mellen, Edwin Pr., The.

Nunn, Daniel. Arabic, 1 vol. 2012. (Languages of the World Ser.). (ENG & ARA.). 32p. (gr. 1-3). pap. 7.99 (978-1-4329-5842-8(9)); lib. bdg. 26.65 (978-1-4329-5834-3(8)) Heinemann-Raintree. (Heinemann First Library).

Obicini, Tommaso & Lucensis, Marcus Bovelius, compiled by. Thesaurus Arabico-Syro-Latinus. 2010. (LAT.). 149.36 (978-1-60724-899-6(9)) Gorgias Pr., LLC.

Odisho, Edward. Linguistic & Cultural Studies in Aramaic & Arabic. 2009. 116.00 (978-1-60724-586-5(8)) Gorgias Pr., LLC.

O'Leary, De Lacy. Colloquial Arabic. 2008. 212p. pap. (978-1-4097-2733-0(5)) Read Bks.

Owens, Jonathan, ed. Arabic as a Minority Language. (Contributions to the Sociology of Language [CSL] Ser.). (ENG.). X, 458p. 300.00 (978-3-11-188095-2(8)) De Gruyter, Mouton DEU. Dist: de Gruyter, Walter GmbH & Co. KG.

Owens, Jonathan & Elgibali, Alaa. Information Structure in Spoken Arabic. 2009. (ENG., Illus.). 270p. 135.00 (978-0-415-77844-2(1)) Routledge.

Peled, Yishai. Word-Order Patterns in Written Arabic: Medieval & Modern Perspectives. 2008. (Studies in Semitic Languages & Linguistics Ser.). 400p. (978-90-04-17062-9(6)) BRILL.

Penton Overseas, Inc. Staff. Arabic: See, Hear, Say & Learn. 2009. (ENG & ARA., Illus.). 240p. 16.95 (978-1-59125-966-4(5)) Penton Overseas, Inc.

Peters, James. The Arab World. 3rd ed. 2009. (ARA & ENG., Illus.). 150p. pap., instr.'s hndbk. ed. 18.95 (978-1-906768-03-4(X), Stacey International) Stacey Publishing GBR. Dist: Midpoint Trade Bks., Inc.

Peters, James. Very Simple Arabia. 2007. (Illus.). 108p. pap. 11.95 (978-1-905299-51-5(6), Stacey International) Stacey Publishing GBR. Dist: Midpoint Trade Bks., Inc.

Qafisheh, Hamdi A. Yemeni Arabic, Bk. 2. (ARA.). 482p. 24.95 (978-0-86685-557-0(2), LDL5572) Librairie du Liban Pubns. FRA. Dist: International Bk. Ctr., Inc.

Saad, Motaz. Arabic Text Classification. 2011. 172p. pap. (978-3-8443-1957-6(3)) Lambert Academic Publishing.

Sahli, Meriem. Becoming Bilingual in Arabic & Danish. 2011. 72p. pap. (978-3-8443-3340-4(1)) Lambert Academic Publishing.

Salameh, Franck. Language, Memory, & Identity in the Middle East: The Case for Lebanon. 2010. (ENG.). 332p. 83.99 (978-0-7391-3738-3(7)) Lexington Bks.

Sara, Solomon I. Sibawayh on Imalah (Inclination) Text, Translation, Notes & Analysis. 2008. (ARA & ENG., Illus.). 200p. (gr. 17). 160.00 (978-0-7486-2795-0(2)) Edinburgh Univ. Pr. GBR. Dist: Columbia Univ. Pr.

Scheindlin, Raymond. 501 Arabic Verbs. 2007. (501 Verb Ser.). (ENG.). 584p. per. 18.99 (978-0-7641-3622-1(4)) Barron's Educational Series, Inc.

Seraye, Abdullah. The Role of Short Vowels & Context in the Reading of Arabic. 2010. 372p. pap. (978-3-639-22173-2(7)) VDM Verlag Dr. Mueller e.K.

Shah, Mustafa. Religious Dogma & the Synthesis of Early Arabic Linguistic Thought. 2007. 220p. 297.50 (978-0-7103-1347-8(0)) Kegan Paul International, Ltd. GBR. Dist: Columbia Univ. Pr.

Shirwani, Haroon. Build Your Arabic Vocabulary with Audio CD, Second Edition. 2nd ed. 2010. (ENG., Illus.). 144p. pap. 25.00 incl. audio compact disk (978-0-07-174293-1(X), 007174293X) McGraw-Hill Cos., The.

Silvestre de Sacy, Antoine I. Anthologie Grammaticale Arabe. reprint ed. 45.00 (978-0-404-11237-0(4)) AMS Pr., Inc.

—Chrestomathie Arabe, 3 vols., Set. reprint ed. 195.00 (978-0-404-11233-2(1)) AMS Pr., Inc.

Smart, Jack & Altorfer, Frances. Spoken Arabic (Of the Arabian Gulf) 3rd ed. 2010. (Teach Yourself Language Ser.). (ENG., Illus.). 400p. pap. 46.00 incl. audio compact disk (978-0-07-174806-3(7), 0071743067); pap. 32.00 (978-0-07-174807-0(5), 0071748075) McGraw-Hill Cos., The.

Socin, A. Arabic Grammar. 2008. 308p. (978-1-4437-2090-8(9)), Hesperides Pr.) Read Bks.

Soltan, Usama. Arabic DeMYSTiFieD with Audio CD. 2013. (Demystified Ser.). (ENG & ARA.). pap. 25.00 incl. audio compact disk (978-0-07-176561-9(1), 0071765611) McGraw-Hill Cos., The.

Soudi, Abdelhadi. Arabic Computational Morphology. 2007. (Text, Speech & Language Technology Ser.). 316p. 169.00 (978-1-4020-6045-8(9)) Springer.

Soudi, Abdelhadi, et al, eds. Arabic Computational Morphology: Knowledge-based & Empirical Methods. 2010. (Text, Speech & Language Technology Ser.). viii, 308p. pap. 169.00 (978-90-481-7515-4(1), 9048175151) Springer.

Stehle, Dorothy. Sibilants & Emphatics in South Arabic. 2011. 40p. 35.95 (978-1-258-03962-2(1)) Literary Licensing, LLC.

Syrayama De Pinto, Marco. Arabisms in Modern Standard Turkish. 2010. 140p. pap. (978-3-639-25476-1(7)) VDM Verlag Dr. Mueller e.K.

Tayii, Ahmad. Al-Tawasul Al-Balaghi Min Al-Musarrah Bi-Hi Ila Al-Maskut Anh. 2008. (ARA., Illus.). 103p. (978-9954-438-39-8(4)) Cujas, Editions.

Tezel, Sina. Arabic Borrowings in Surayt/Turoyo Within the Framework of Phonological Correspondences: In Comparison with Other Semitic Languages. 2011. (Studia Semetica Upsaliensia Ser.). 226p. pap. 72.50 (978-91-554-8058-5(6)) Uppsala Universitet/Acta Universitatis Upsaliensis SWE. Dist: Coronet Bks.

Thatcher, G. W. Arabic Grammar of the Written Language. 2010. 474p. pap. 30.36 (978-1-163-91833-3(4)) 2008. 472p. 52.95 (978-0-548-94134-8(3)) 2007. (ENG.). 472p. per. 37.95 (978-0-548-58470-5(2)) Kessinger Publishing, LLC.

Thomas Cook Publishing Staff, creator. PhraseGuide Arabic. 2007. (Thomas Cook Phraseguides Ser.). (ENG & ARA., Illus.). 96p. per. 7.95 (978-1-84157-668-8(9)) Cook, Thomas Publishing GBR. Dist: Globe Pequot Pr., The.

The Thousand & One Nights. 2009. 366p. pap. (978-0-217-39978-4(9)); 580p. pap. (978-0-217-37462-0(X)) Books LLC.

The Thousand & One Nights, 4 vols. (ARA.). 59.95 (978-0-86685-708-6(7), LDL829) Librairie du Liban Pubns. FRA. Dist: International Bk. Ctr., Inc.

Tien, Anton. Egyptian, Syrian, & North African Handbook: A Simple Phrase Book in English & Arabic for the Use of the Armed Forces & Civilians. 2011. 178p. 42.95 (978-1-258-09920-6(9)) Literary Licensing, LLC.

Ullmann, Manfred. Die Conclusio a Minori Ad Maius Im Arabischen. 2010. (GER.). 31p. pap. (978-3-7696-1653-8(7)) Bayerische Akademie der Wissenschaften.

Versteegh, Kees, et al, eds. Encyclopedia of Arabic Language & Linguistics, Vol. 2. 2006. (Encyclopedia of Arabic Language & Linguistics Ser.). (Illus.). 716p. (978-90-04-14474-3(9)) BRILL.

Wightwick, Jane & Gaafar, Mahmoud. Arabic Verbs & Essentials of Grammar. 2nd ed. 2007. (Verbs & Essentials of Grammar Ser.). (ARA & ENG., Illus.). 160p. per. 13.95 (978-0-07-149805-0(2), 0071498052) McGraw-Hill Cos., The.

—Easy Arabic Reader. 2011. (Easy Reader Ser.). (ENG & ARA., Illus.). 224p. (C). pap. 17.00 (978-0-07-175402-6(4), 0071754024) McGraw-Hill Cos., The.

—Mastering Arabic. 2nd ed. 2009. (ENG.). 1p. pap. 29.95 (978-0-7818-1238-2(0)) Hippocrene Bks., Inc.

—Practice Makes Perfect Arabic Verb Tenses. 2012. (Practice Makes Perfect Ser.). (ENG & ARA.). 304p. pap. 18.00 (978-0-07-175636-5(1), 0071756361) McGraw-Hill Cos., The.

Wightwick, Jane & Gaafar, Mahmoud. Read & Speak Arabic for Beginners. 2nd ed. 2010. (ENG.). 112p. pap. 18.95 incl. audio compact disk (978-0-07-173966-5(1), 0071739661) McGraw-Hill Cos., The.

Woodard, Roger D., ed. The Ancient Languages of Syria-Palestine & Arabia. 2008. (ENG., Illus.). 282p. pap. 50.00 (978-0-521-68498-9(6)) Cambridge Univ. Pr.

Wright, William. A Grammar of the Arabic Language. 2008. 276p. 28.99 (978-0-554-41250-4(0)); pap. 27.75 (978-0-554-41252-8(7)) BiblioBazaar.

—A Grammar of the Arabic Language, 2 vols. in 1. (ARA., Illus.). 450p. 45.00 (978-0-86685-052-0(X), LDL052X) International Bk. Ctr., Inc.

—A Grammar of the Arabic Language Vol-1 & Vol-2 Combined Together. 2007. 796p. per. (978-1-84356-028-9(3)) Wallenberg, Simon Pr.

Yasmin, Hannouna. Essentials of Arabic Machine Translation Evaluation: The Potentials & Limitations. 2011. 500p. pap. (978-3-639-33534-7(1)) VDM Verlag Dr. Mueller e.K.

Younes, Munther. Introduction to Qur'Anic Arabic. 2012. (ENG & ARA., Illus.). 336p. 140.00 (978-0-415-50893-3(2)); pap. 40.00 (978-0-415-50894-0(0)) Routledge.

Zadeh, Travis. The Vernacular Qur'an: Translation & the Rise of Persian Exegesis. 2012. (Qur'anic Studies Ser.). (ENG.). 600p. 125.00 (978-0-19-726512-3(X)) Oxford Univ. Pr., Inc.

Ziadeh, Farhat Jacob & Winder, Richard Bayly. An Introduction to Modern Arabic. 2011. 310p. 48.95 (978-1-258-01545-9(5)) Literary Licensing, LLC.

ARABIC LANGUAGE—BIBLIOGRAPHY

Atiq, Nahid bint Umar ibn Abd Allah. Al-Masail Al-Nahwiyah Fi Kitab Fath Al-Bari Bi-Sharh Sahih Al-Bukhari: Lil-Hafiz Ibn Hajar Al-Asqalani: Jaman Wa-Dirasatan, 2 vols. 2009. (ARA.). 1115p. (978-9960-01-500-2(9)); (978-9960-01-501-9(7)); (978-9960-01-502-6(5)) Al-Rushid Bkstore for Publishing & Distribution.

Bakalla, M. H. Bibliography of Arabic Linguistics. (ENG.). XXXVII, 308p. 210.00 (978-3-11-213079-7(0)) De Gruyter, Walter Inc.

Damamini, Muhammad ibn Abi Bakr & Matar, Fakhir Jabr. Al-Manhal Al-Safi Fi Sharh Al-Wafi: Wa-Huwa Sharh Lil-Wafi Wa-Huwa Matn Wajiz Fi Al-Nahw Li-Muallifihi Jamal Al-Din Muhammad Ibn Uthman Ibn Umar Al-Balkhi Al-Mutawaffi Fi Hudud Sanat 800 H, 2 vols. 2008. (ARA., Illus.). (978-2-7451-5322-7(6)) Dar al-Kutub al-Ilmiyah.

de Tarrazi, Philip. Catalogue of Eastern & Western Arabic Libraries. 2007. (Gorgias Historical Catalogues Ser.: 3). (ARA.). 380.00 (978-1-59333-611-0(X));1 of 4. 95.00 (978-1-59333-711-7(6));2 of 4. 95.00 (978-1-59333-712-4(4));3 of 4. 95.00 (978-1-59333-713-1(2));4 of 4. 95.00 (978-1-59333-762-9(0)) Gorgias Pr., LLC.

Kishk, Ahmad. Al-Nahw Wa-Al-Siyaq Al-Sawti. 2010. (ARA.). 399p. (978-977-215-941-3(4)) Gharib Bookshop.

Sobelman, Harvey. Arabic Dialect Studies: A Selected Bibliography. Sobelman, Harvey, ed. 2011. 108p. 39.95 (978-1-258-06766-3(8)) Literary Licensing, LLC.

Suyuti, et al. Al-Nukat Ala Al-Alfiyah Wa-Al-Kafiyah Wa-Al-Shafiyah Wa-Al-Shudhur Wa-Al-Nuzhah, 2 vols. 2007. (ARA., Illus.). (978-2-7451-5323-4(4)) Dar al-Kutub al-Ilmiyah.

ARABIC LANGUAGE—DIALECTS

Abdel-Malek, Zaki N. The Closed-List Classes of Colloquial Egyptian Arabic. (Janua Linguarum. Series Practica Ser.). (ENG.). 240p. 210.00 (978-3-11-178172-3(0)) De Gruyter, Mouton DEU. Dist: de Gruyter, Walter GmbH & Co. KG.

Aboul-Fetouh, Hilmi Mohammed. A morphological study of Egyptian colloquial Arabic. (Janua Linguarum. Series Practica Ser.). (ENG.). 149p. 210.00 (978-3-11-213890-8(2)); 135.00 (978-3-11-127467-6(5)) De Gruyter, Mouton DEU. Dist: de Gruyter, Walter GmbH & Co. KG.

Al-Khalesi, Yasin M. Modern Iraqi Arabic. 2nd rev. ed. 2006. (ARA & ENG., Illus.). 368p. (C). pap. 54.95 (978-1-58901-130-4(9)) Georgetown Univ. Pr.

Al-Wer, Enam, et al. Arabic Dialectology: In Honour of Clive Holes on the Occasion of His Sixtieth Birthday. Al-Wer & Jong, R. E. de, eds. 2009. (Studies in Semitic Languages & Linguistics Ser.). (Illus.). 256p. (978-90-04-17212-8(2)) BRILL.

Arabian American Oil Company. Pocket Guide to Arabic. 2011. 90p. 38.95 (978-1-258-03160-2(4)) Literary Licensing, LLC.

Bassiouney, Reem. Arabic Sociolinguistics: Topics in Diglossia, Gender, Identity, & Politics. 2009. (ARA.). 336p. (C). pap. 29.95 (978-1-58901-573-9(8)) Georgetown Univ. Pr.

Behnstedt, P. & Behnstedt, Peter. Die nordjemenitischen Dialekte (Glossar) Buchstaben Fa-Ya, 2 vols. 2006. (Jemen-Studien Ser.). (GER., Illus.). 512p. (C). pap. 252.00 (978-3-89500-559-6(2)) Reichert, Ludwig Dr. DEU. Dist: Brown, David Bk. Co., The.

Berjaoui, Nasser. A Moroccan Arabic Secret Language: The X...XinCa Family. 2007. (Illus.). 125p. pap. (978-3-89586-886-3(8)) Lincom GmbH.

Caubet, Dominique, et al, eds. Arabic in the City: Issues in Dialect Contact & Language Variation. 2008. (Routledge Arabic Linguistics Ser.). (ENG., Illus.). 368p. 150.00 (978-0-415-77311-9(3)) Routledge.

Chekayri, Abdellah. Introduction to Moroccan Arabic & Culture. 2011. (ARA & ENG., Illus.). 544p. (C). pap. 59.95 (978-1-58901-693-4(9)) Georgetown Univ. Pr.

Elashiry, Mohammed R. Sounds of Qur'anic Recitation in Egypt: A Phonetic Analysis. 2009. (Illus.). viii, 352p. (978-0-7734-4836-0(5)) Mellen, Edwin Pr., The.

Embarki, Mohamed & Ennaji, Moha. Modern Trends in Arabic Dialectology. 2011. (978-1-56902-346-4(8)); (Illus.). 284p. pap. (978-1-56902-347-1(6)) Red Sea Pr.

Feghali, Habaka J. Gulf Arabic: The Dialects of Kuwait, Bahrain, Qatar, UAE, & Oman: Grammar, Dialogues, & Lexicon. 2008. (ARA & ENG.). 14p. (978-1-931546-49-2(5)) Dunwoody Pr.

Geva-Kleinberger, Aharon. Autochthonous Texts in the Arabic Dialect of the Jews of Tiberias. 2009. (Semitica Viva Ser.). (ARA & ENG.). 224p. (C). 93.00 (978-3-447-05934-3(6)) Harrassowitz, Otto Verlag DEU. Dist: ISD.

Grigore, George. L' arabe Parlé à Mardin: First American Edition: Monographie d'un Parler arabe Périphérique. 2007. (FRE.). 350p. 116.00 (978-1-59333-734-6(5)) Gorgias Pr., LLC.

Harrell, Richard S. The Phonology of Colloquial Egyptian Arabic. 2011. 98p. 38.95 (978-1-258-05200-3(8)) Literary Licensing, LLC.

Harrell, Richard S. A Short Reference Grammar of Moroccan Arabic. 2010. (Georgetown Classics in Arabic Language & Linguistics Ser.). (ARA.). 288p. (C). pap. 29.95 (978-1-58901-761-0(7)) Georgetown Univ. Pr.

Hary, Benjamin H. Translating Religion: Linguistic Analysis of Judeo-Arabic Sacred Texts from Egypt. 2008. (Études Sur le Judaïsme Médiéval Ser.). 384p. (978-90-04-17382-8(X)) BRILL.

Hillelson, S. Sudan Arabic Texts: With Translation & Glossary. 2011. (ENG & ARA.). 244p. pap. 22.99 (978-0-521-22942-5(1)) Cambridge Univ. Pr.

Holes, Clive. Colloquial Arabic of the Gulf. 2nd rev. ed. (Colloquial Ser.). (Illus.). 2009. (ARA & ENG.). 464p. pap. 39.95 (978-0-415-43039-5(9)) 2008. 416p. pap. 44.95 (978-0-415-43229-0(4)) Routledge.

Jenkins, Siona & Lonely Planet Staff. Egyptian Arabic. 3rd rev. ed. 2008. (Lonely Planet Phrasebook: Egyptian Arabic Ser.). (ARA & ENG., Illus.). 286p. pap. 8.99 (978-1-74059-391-5(X)) Lonely Planet Pubns.

Jewish & Muslim Dialects of Moroccan Arabic. 2009. 598p. pap. 39.95 (978-0-415-56778-7(5)) Routledge.

Louis, Samia. Kallimni 'Arabi Aktar: An Upper Intermediate Course in Spoken Egyptian Arabic 3. 2008. (ENG.). 256p. pap. 29.95 (978-977-416-100-1(9)) American Univ. in Cairo Pr. EGY. Dist: Oxford Univ. Pr., Inc.

McLoughlin, Leslie. Arabic (Levantine) 2nd rev. ed. 2009. (Colloquial Ser.). (ARA & ENG., Illus.). 240p. pap. 39.95 (978-0-415-44857-4(3)) Routledge.

Mejdell, Gunvor. Mixed Styles in Spoken Arabic in Egypt: Somewhere Between Order & Chaos. 2006. (Studies in Semitic Languages & Linguistics Ser.: Vol. 48). 502p. (978-90-04-14986-1(4)) BRILL.

Morgenstern, Matthew. Studies in Jewish Babylonian Aramaic Based upon Early Eastern Manuscripts. 2011. (978-1-57506-938-8(5)) Eisenbrauns, Inc.

Mubaraka, Fadel & Ibrahim, Gregorios. The Aramaic Influence in the Vernacular of Sadad. 2009. (ARA.). 150.00 (978-1-60724-250-5(8)) Gorgias Pr., LLC.

Naim, S. L' arabe yemenite de Sanaa. 2009. (langues du Monde Ser.). (ARA & FRE., Illus.). 232p. (C). pap. 41.00 (978-90-429-2280-8(X)) Peeters Pubs. & Booksellers BEL. Dist: Brown, David Bk. Co., The.

Omar, Margaret K. The Acquisition of Egyptian Arabic as a Native Language. (Janua Linguarum. Series Practica Ser.). (ENG.). 206p. 196.00 (978-3-11-175182-5(1)) De Gruyter, Mouton DEU. Dist: de Gruyter, Walter GmbH & Co. KG.

Omar, Margaret K. & Nydell, Margaret K. The Acquisition of Egyptian Arabic as a Native Language. 2007. (Georgetown Classics in Arabic Language & Linguistics Ser.). (ENG., Illus.). 232p. per. 29.95 (978-1-58901-168-7(6)) Georgetown Univ. Pr.

Qafisheh, Hamdi A. A Basic Course in Gulf Arabic. (ARA.). 482p. 25.00 (978-0-86685-048-3(1), LDL0481) International Bk. Ctr., Inc.

Rice, Frank A. & Sa'id, Majed F. Eastern Arabic. 2011. (Georgetown Classics in Arabic Languages & Linguistics Ser.). (ARA.). 440p. pap. 44.95 (978-1-58901-899-0(0)) Georgetown Univ. Pr.

Sabih, Joshua A. & Japheth ben Ali. Japheth Ben Ali's Book of Jeremiah: A Critical Edition & Linguistic Analysis of the Judaeo-Arabic Translation. 2009. (Copenhagen International Seminar Ser.). (HEB, ARA & ENG., Illus.). 520p. (C). 150.00 (978-1-84553-338-0(0)) Equinox Publishing Ltd. GBR. Dist: ISD.

Sobelman, Harvey. Arabic Dialect Studies: A Selected Bibliography. Sobelman, Harvey, ed. 2011. 108p. 39.95 (978-1-258-06766-3(8)) Literary Licensing, LLC.

Sounkalo, Jiddou. Spoken Hassaniya Arabic. 2008. (ARA.). iv, 150p. (978-1-931546-53-9(3)) Dunwoody Pr.

Vollers, Karl. The Modern Egyptian Dialect of Arabic: A Grammar with Exercises, Reading Lessons & Glossaries. 2011. (ENG & ARA.). 290p. pap. 23.99 (978-0-521-23297-5(X)) Cambridge Univ. Pr.

Wagner, Esther-Miriam. Linguistic Variety of Judaeo-Arabic in Letters from the Cairo Genizah. 2010. (Illus.). viii, 268p. (978-90-04-18776-4(6)) BRILL.

Watson, Janet C. E. The Phonology & Morphology of Arabic. 2007. (Phonology of the World's Languages Ser.). (ENG., Illus.). 336p. per. 55.00 (978-0-19-922669-6(5)) Oxford Univ. Pr., Inc.

Wise, Hilary. Arabic at a Glance. 3rd rev. ed. 2008. (At a Glance Ser.). (ARA & ENG., Illus.). 312p. pap. 8.99 (978-0-7641-3766-2(2)) Barron's Educational Series, Inc.

Woidich. Wortatlas der Arabischen Dialekte: Band I: Mensch, Natur, Fauna und Flora. Behnstedt, ed. 2010. (Handbook of Oriental Studies). (GER, ARA, ENG & MUL., Illus.). 240p. (978-90-04-18664-4(6)) BRILL.

Zack, Liesbeth & Schippers, Arie. Middle Arabic & Mixed Arabic: Diachrony & Synchrony. 2012. (ENG & FRE.). (978-90-04-22229-8(4)) BRILL.

ARABIC LANGUAGE—DIALECTS—MALTA

see Maltese Language

ARABIC LANGUAGE—DICTIONARIES

Abid, Abdellatif, ed. The Al-Kitab Al-Asasi Lexicon. 2009. (ENG.). 384p. pap. 39.50 (978-977-416-234-3(X)) American Univ. in Cairo Pr. EGY. Dist: Oxford Univ. Pr., Inc.

Agius, Dionisius A. In the Wake of the Dhow: The Arabian Gulf & Oman. 2010. 272p. pap. 34.95 (978-0-86372-341-4(1), Ithaca Pr.) Garnet Publishing, Ltd. GBR. Dist: International Specialized Bk. Services.

AISI American Genealogical Census Catalog. (Illus.). lib. bdg. 50.00 (978-0-89593-206-8(7), Accelerated Indexing Systems International (AISI)) Genealogical Services.

Al Mayoof, Sarah. The Golden Book of Arabic. 2009. 260p. pap. 22.95 (978-1-4389-6348-8(3)) AuthorHouse.

Buckwalter, Tim. A Frequency Dictionary of Arabic. 2011. (Routledge Frequency Dictionaries Ser.). (ARA & ENG.). 592p. pap. 48.95 (978-0-415-44434-7(9)) Routledge.

Buckwalter, Tim & Parkinson, Dilworth. A Frequency Dictionary of Arabic. 2011. (Routledge Frequency Dictionaries Ser.). (ENG.). 1p. cd-rom 160.00 (978-0-415-60030-9(8)) Routledge.

—A Frequency Dictionary of Arabic: Core Vocabulary for Learners. 2011. (Routledge Frequency Dictionaries Ser.). (ENG & ARA.). 592p. 140.00 (978-0-415-59543-8(6)) Routledge.

Conseil International de la Langue Francaise Sta. Dictionnaire de la Presse et des Medias.Tr. of French-Arabic, Arabic-French Dictionary of the Press & Media. (ARA & FRE.). pap. (978-0-8288-7675-9(4)) French & European Pubns., Inc.

Corriente, Federico, ed. Dictionary of Arabic & allied Loanwords: Spanish, Portuguese, Catalan, Galician & kindred Dialects. 2008. (Handbook of Oriental Studies). xciv, 602p. (C). (978-90-04-16858-9(3)) BRILL.

Dictionary of Arabic Words in Persian & Persian in Arabic Language. 2009. (PER., Illus.). (978-0-615-27583-3(4)) Piraka, Hadi.

Dozy, Reinhart. Detaille Des Noms Vetements. (ARA & FRE.). 445p. 29.95 (978-0-86685-104-6(6), LDL1045) International Bk. Ctr., Inc.

—Supplement aux Dictionnaire Arabe, 2 vols., set. (ARA & FRE.). 1721p. 95.00 (978-0-86685-106-0(2), LDL1062) International Bk. Ctr., Inc.

Dozy, Reinhart P. A. Supplement aux Dictionnaires Arabes. 2006. (Gorgias Historical Dictionaries Ser.: 3). 1760p. 278.00 (978-1-59333-518-2(0)) Gorgias Pr., LLC.

Eid, Mushira & Eid, M., eds. Encyclopedia of Arabic Language & Linguistics, 5 Vols., Set; Vols. 1-5. 2009. (Illus.). 3250p. (978-90-04-17702-4(7)) BRILL.

Ekhnawy, Kamal Al & Ali, Jamal. 'Arabi Liblib: Egyptian Colloquial Arabic for the Advanced Learner: 1: Adjectives & Descriptions. 2010. (ENG.). 128p. pap.

22.95 (978-977-416-399-9(0)) American Univ. in Cairo Pr. EGY. Dist: Oxford Univ. Pr., Inc.

El Mashreq, Dar. Munjid Fi Al Lugha Wal A'lam: Munjio. (ARA., Illus.). 900p. 69.95 (978-0-86685-750-5(8)); stu. ed. 29.95 (978-0-86685-823-6(7)) International Bk. Ctr., Inc.

Endress, Gerhard & Gutas, Dimitri, eds. A Greek & Arabic Lexicon. 2006. (ARA, GEC & ENG.). 130p. pap. (978-90-04-15725-5(5)) BRILL.

—A Greek & Arabic Lexicon, Fascicle 9, bdn - Brhn. 2010. (Handbook of Oriental Studies). (ARA, GEC & ENG.). 128p. pap. (978-90-04-16527-4(4)) BRILL.

Freytag, Georg Wilhelm. Arabic-Latin Lexicon. 2006. (Gorgias Historical Dictionaries Ser.: 2). 2288p. 447.00 (978-1-59333-507-6(5)) Gorgias Pr., LLC.

Freytag, George Wilhelm. Lexicon Arabico-Latinum, 4 vols., Set. (ARA & LAT.). 2257p. 110.00 (978-0-86685-124-4(0), LDL1240) International Bk. Ctr., Inc.

Gasselin, M. Edouard. Dictionnaire Francais-Arabe, 2 vols., Set. (ARA & FRE.). 1800p. reprint ed. 85.00 (978-0-86685-344-6(8), LDL3448) International Bk. Ctr., Inc.

Gottheil, Richard J. H., intro. The Syriac-Arabic Glosses of Isho Bar Ali. 2010. (SYR.). 222.64 (978-1-60724-869-9(7)); 222.64 (978-1-60724-868-2(9)) Gorgias Pr., LLC.

Hulw, Rihab Kamal. Qamus Al-Aswat Al-Lughawiyah: Tarikh Wa-Tatawwur Wa-Lahajat: Arabi - Arabi. 2009. (Illus.). 628p. (978-9953-86-523-2(X)) Dar An-Nahar.

Ibn Ar Rhazi, Mohammed. Mukhtar us-Sihah. rev. ed. (ARA.). 311p. 24.95 (978-0-86685-375-0(8)) International Bk. Ctr., Inc.

Jeffery, Arthur. The Foreign Vocabulary of the Quran. 2007. (Gorgias Historical Grammars Ser.: 11). 75.00 (978-1-59333-751-3(5)) Gorgias Pr., LLC.

Kazimirski, A. B. Dictionnaire Arabe-Francais, 2 vols., Set. (ARA & FRE.). reprint ed. 95.00 (978-0-86685-110-7(0), LDL1100) International Bk. Ctr., Inc.

Kazimirski, A. de Biberstein. Dictionnaire Arabe-Francais. 2006. (Gorgias Historical Dictionaries Ser.: 4). 3030p. 398.00 (978-1-59333-504-5(0)) Gorgias Pr., LLC.

Lane, Edward William & Qamus, Madd A. Lane's Arabic-English Lexicon: Madd al Qamus, 8 vols. (ARA & ENG.). 3064p. 400.00 (978-0-86685-087-2(2), LDL0872) International Bk. Ctr., Inc.

Living Language Staff. IKnow Arabic. unabr. l.t. ed. 2008. (iKnow Ser.). (ENG.). 20p. 13.95 (978-1-4000-0951-0(0), Living Language) Random Hse. Information Group.

Mason, Antony. Soccer. (Butterfly Bks.). (ARA., Illus.). 31p. 11.95 (978-0-86685-606-5(4), LDL6064) Librairie du Liban Pubns. FRA. Dist: International Bk. Ctr., Inc.

McGrane, Stephen. Sit Crooked & Speak Straight. 2008. 168p. pap. 13.95 (978-1-60594-031-1(3), Llumina Pr.) Aeon Publishing Inc.

Mubaraka, Fadel & Ibrahim, Gregorios. The Aramaic Influence in the Vernacular of Sadad. 2009. (ARA.). 150.00 (978-1-60724-250-5(8)) Gorgias Pr., LLC.

Murad, Mikhael & Ibrahim, Gregorios. Arabic-Syriac Dictionary. 2009. (ARA & SYR.). 167.00 (978-1-60724-262-8(1)) Gorgias Pr., LLC.

Oxford, ed. Oxford Essential Arabic Dictionary. 2010. (ENG & ARA.). 416p. pap. 19.95 (978-0-19-956115-5(X)) Oxford Univ. Pr., Inc.

Qashisho, Thomas & Qashisho, Antonios, eds. A Short Arabic-Syriac Dictionary. 2010. (SYR.). pap. 38.80 (978-1-61719-922-6(2)) Gorgias Pr., LLC.

Ronart, Nandy. Lexikon der Arabischen Welt. (GER.). 295.00 (978-0-8288-7969-9(9), M7277) French & European Pubns., Inc.

Rough Guides Staff & Lexus Firm Staff. Egyptian Arabic. 2nd ed. 2006. (Rough Guide Phrasebooks Ser.). (ENG & ARA., Illus.). 296p. pap. 6.99 (978-1-84353-642-0(0)) Rough Guides, Ltd. GBR. Dist: Dorling Kindersley Publishing, Inc.

Saisse, Louis. Dictionnaire Francais-Arabe. (ARA & FRE.). 425p. pap. 14.95 (978-0-86685-112-1(7), LDL1127) International Bk. Ctr., Inc.

Sopeña Staff. Diccionario Esp. - Arabe Arabe - Esp. (Sp. - Arabic Arabic - Sp. Dict) (SPA & ARA., Illus.). 1280p. 52.95 (978-84-303-0163-8(1)) Sopena, Ramon Editorial S.A. ESP. Dist: AIMS International Bks., Inc.

Tahanawi, Muhammad Ala ibn Ali al & Wajih, Muhammad. A Dictionary of the Technical Terms used in the Sciences of the Musalmans. Sprenger, Aloys, ed. 2010. (ARA.). 294.40 (978-1-61719-815-1(3)); 294.40 (978-1-61719-829-8(3)); 294.40 (978-1-61719-830-4(7)); 294.40 (978-1-61719-814-4(5)) Gorgias Pr., LLC.

Tunji, Muhammad. Al-Mujam Al-Dhahabi Fi Al-Dakhil Alá Al-Arabi: Arabi - Arabi. 2009. (ARA.). 629p. (978-9953-86-521-8(3)) Dar An-Nahar.

Versteegh, C. H. M. & Eid, M., eds. Encyclopedia of Arabic Language & Linguistics, Volume 4. 2008. (Encyclopedia of Arabic Language & Linguistics Ser.). (Illus.). vii, 767p. (978-90-04-14476-7(5)) BRILL.

Versteegh, Kees & Eid, Mushira, eds. Encyclopedia of Arabic Language & Linguistics, Vol. 3. 2007. (Encyclopedia of Arabic Language & Linguistics Ser.). 750p. (978-90-04-14475-0(7)) BRILL.

Wahrmund, Adolf. Handwörterbuch der neu-arabischen und deutschen Sprache. 3rd ed. 135.00 **(978-3-11-128476-7(X))** De Gruyter, Walter Inc.

Wightwick, Jane. Arabic Set: Beginner's Quick & Easy Guide to Demystifying Arabic Script. 2006. (Your First 100 Words In... Ser.). (ENG., Illus.). 80p. pap. 17.00 (978-0-07-146928-9(1), 0071469281) McGraw-Hill Cos., The.

Woidich. Wortatlas der Arabischen Dialekte: Band I: Mensch, Natur, Fauna und Flora. Behnstedt, ed. 2010. (Handbook of Oriental Studies). (GER, ARA, ENG & MUL., Illus.). 240p. (978-90-04-18664-4(6)) BRILL.

Yousif, Mohamed. Scientific Terminology, English / Arabic. 2010. 263p. pap. 21.95 (978-1-4457-0768-6(3)) Lulu Enterprises Inc.

ARABIC LANGUAGE—DICTIONARIES—ENGLISH

Adelson-Goldstein, Jayme & Shapiro, Norma, eds. Oxford Picture Dictionary: English - Arabic. 2nd ed. 2008. (Oxford Picture Dictionary 2E Ser.). (ARA & ENG., Illus.). 320p. pap. 24.94 (978-0-19-474010-4(2)) Oxford Univ. Pr., Inc.

Al-Hilfy, Gatie Niema. The Encyclopaedic Crossreference Dictionary of the Quran, Arabic/English: A First Bilingual Quranic Dictionary Mixing the Traditional Arabic Root System & the Non-Arabic Alphabetical Order. 2010. 416p. pap. 32.00 (978-1-4349-9729-6(4), RoseDog Bks.) Dorrance Publishing Co., Inc.

Arabic Manuscripts, Vol. 3. 2011. (ENG.). 285p. pap., pap., pap. **(978-90-04-22145-1(X))** BRILL.

Badawi, El-Said M. & Haleem, Abdel. Arabic-English Dictionary of Qur'anic Usage. 2007. (Handbook of Oriental Studies: Vol. 85). (ARA & ENG.). (C). (978-90-04-14948-9(1)) BRILL.

Badger, George Percy. An Arabic-English Lexicon. 2007. (Gorgias Historical Dictionaries Ser.: 12). 369.00 (978-1-59333-728-5(0));1 of 4. 92.25 (978-1-59333-729-2(9));2 of 4. 92.25 (978-1-59333-730-8(2));3 of 4. 92.25 (978-1-59333-731-5(0));4 of 4. 92.25 (978-1-59333-732-2(9)) Gorgias Pr., LLC.

Cachia, Pierre. A Dictionary of Grammatical Terms (Al-Arif) English - Arabic & Arabic - English. (ARA & ENG.). 200p. 19.95 (978-0-86685-119-0(4), LDL1194) International Bk. Ctr., Inc.

Collins. Everyday Arabic Dictionary. 2011. (ENG.). 450p. pap. 12.00 (978-0-07-176879-5(3), 0071768793) McGraw-Hill Cos., The.

Dorling Kindersley Publishing Staff. Arabic English. 2009. (DK Visual Dictionaries Ser.). (ARA & ENG., Illus.). 360p. (gr. 12). 14.95 (978-0-7566-4983-8(8)) Dorling Kindersley Publishing, Inc.

Elias, A. E. Arabic-English, English-Arabic School Dictionary. 10th ed. (ARA & ENG., Illus.). 800p. 32.00 (978-977-5028-60-0(4)) i. b. d., Ltd.

Gacek, Adam. The Arabic Manuscript Tradition: A Glossary of Technical Terms & Bibliography - Supplement. 2008. (Handbook of Oriental Studies). 320p. (978-90-04-16540-3(1)) BRILL.

HarperCollins Publishers Ltd. Collins Pocket Arabic Dictionary. 2012. (Collins Language Ser.). 640p. pap. 11.99 **(978-0-06-219181-6(0))** HarperCollins Pubs.

Icon Group International, Inc. Staff, compiled by. Webster's Lebanese - English Thesaurus Dictionary. 2008. 52p. ring bd. 28.95 incl. audio compact disk (978-0-497-83574-3(6)) Icon Group International, Inc.

Lane, Edward William & Lane-Poole, Stanley. An Arabic-English Lexicon. 2010. (ARA.). pap. 508.16 (978-1-61143-542-9(0)); (ARA.). pap. 508.16 (978-1-61143-541-2(2)); (ARA.). pap. 508.16 (978-1-61143-539-9(0)); (ARA.). pap. 508.16 (978-1-61143-538-2(2)); (ARA.). pap. 508.16 (978-1-61143-544-3(7)); (ARA.). pap. 508.16 (978-1-61143-545-0(5)); (ARA.). pap. 508.16 (978-1-61143-540-5(4)); pap. 508.16 (978-1-61143-543-6(9)) Gorgias Pr., LLC.

Merriam-Webster Inc. Merriam-Webster's Arabic-English Dictionary. 2010. (ARA & ENG.). 448p. (gr. 7). mass mkt. 6.50 (978-0-87779-860-6(5)) Merriam-Webster, Inc.

Newman, Daniel. Arabic-English Thematic Lexicon. 2007. (ENG & ARA.). 144p. per. 42.95 (978-0-415-42094-5(6)) Routledge.

—Arabic/English Thematic Lexicon. 2007. (ENG & ARA.). 144p. 153.00 (978-0-415-42093-8(8)) Routledge.

Salmone, Anthony. An Advanced Learner's Dictionary: Arabic - English. (ARA & ENG.). 1462p. 45.00 (978-0-86685-089-6(9), LDL0899) International Bk. Ctr., Inc.

Steingass, F. Steingass Learner's Dictionary: Arabic - English. (ARA & ENG.). 1243p. 45.00 (978-0-86685-091-9(0), LDL0910) International Bk. Ctr., Inc.

Wortabet, John & Porter, H. Wortabet Pocket Dictionaries: Arabic - English. (ARA & ENG.). 448p. pap. 8.95 (978-0-86685-093-3(7), LDL0937) International Bk. Ctr., Inc.

Zuhayri, Nabil. Mujam Al-Adawat Al-Nahwiyah Fi Al-Arabiyah: Arabi-Inklizi. 2008. (ARA & ENG.). 19p. (978-9953-86-374-0(1)) Dar An-Nahar.

ARABIC LANGUAGE—HISTORY

Al Jallad, Nader & Monferrer-Sala, Juan Pedro, eds. The Arabic Language Across the Ages. 2010. (ENG., Illus.). 182p. (C). 168.00 (978-3-89500-765-1(X)) Reichert, Ludwig Dr. DEU. Dist: Brown, David Bk. Co., The.

Al-wer, Emam. Variation & Change in Jordanian Arabic: Women, the Vernacular & Linguistic Innovations. 2008. 288p. 100.00 (978-0-415-30282-1(X)) Routledge.

Baalbaki, Ramzi. The Legacy of the Kitab: Sibawayhi's Analytical Methods Within the Context of the Arabic Grammatical Theory. 2008. (Studies in Semitic Languages & Linguistics Ser.). 334p. (978-90-04-16813-8(3)) BRILL.

Behzadi, Lale. Sprache und Verstehen: Al-Gahiz über Die Vollkommenheit des Ausdrucks. 2009. (GER.). 186p. pap. (978-3-447-05696-4(3)) Harrassowitz, Otto Verlag.

Bhuyan, Shariful Islam. Nonconcatenative Morphology & Arabic Agency. 2010. 60p. pap. (978-3-639-22004-9(8)) VDM Verlag Dr. Mueller e.K.

Chejne, Anwar G. The Arabic Language: Its Role in History. 2009. (ENG.). 260p. pap. 50.00 (978-0-8166-5725-4(4)) Univ. of Minnesota Pr.

Hunwick, John. West Africa,Islam & the Arab World. 2006. per. 24.95 (978-1-55876-399-9(6)) Wiener, Markus Pubs., Inc.

Orfali, Bilal & Balabakki, Ramzi. In the Shadow of Arabic - The Centrality of Language to Arabic Culture: Studies Presented to Ramzi Baalbaki on the Occasion of His Sixtieth Birthday. 2011. (ENG., Illus.). XXIV, 572p. **(978-90-04-21537-5(9))** BRILL.

Owens, Jonathan. A Linguistic History of Arabic. 2006. (ENG., Illus.). 328p. 155.00 (978-0-19-929082-6(2)) Oxford Univ. Pr., Inc.

Stetkevych, Jaroslav. The Modern Arabic Literary Language: Lexical & Stylistic Developments. 2006. (Georgetown Classics in Arabic Language & Linguistics Ser.). (ENG.). 160p. per. 16.95 (978-1-58901-117-5(1)) Georgetown Univ. Pr.

Yunis Ali, Mohamed Mohamed. Medieval Islamic Pragmatics. 2009. 284p. pap. 39.95 (978-0-415-56777-0(7)) Routledge.

ARABIC LANGUAGE—PRONUNCIATION

Abdellah, Antar. Perspectives on Linguistics, Tafl & Tefl. 2010. 136p. pap. (978-3-639-26719-8(2)) VDM Verlag Dr. Mueller e.K.

EPLS. Say It Right in Arabic: The Fastest Way to Correct Pronunciation. 2008. (ENG., Illus.). 176p. pap. 10.95 (978-0-07-154458-0(5), 0071544585) McGraw-Hill Cos., The.

Nacereddine, Abdallah. Handbook of Arabic Writing & Pronunciation. 2011. 148p. pap. 13.72 **(978-1-4634-1482-5(X))** AuthorHouse.

—Manuel d'Ecriture et de Prononciation Arabes. 2011. (FRE.). 148p. pap. 12.99 **(978-1-4567-2064-3(3))** AuthorHouse.

ARABIC LANGUAGE—SELF-INSTRUCTION

al-Tonsi, Abbas, et al. Kalaam Gamiil: An Intensive Course in Egyptian Colloquial Arabic. 2010. (ENG.). 256p. 29.95 (978-977-416-315-9(X)) American Univ. in Cairo Pr. EGY. Dist: Oxford Univ. Pr., Inc.

Assimil Staff. Arabisch Zonder Moeite: Arabic for Dutch Speakers. (ARA & DUT.). 28.95 incl. audio (978-0-8288-4365-2(1), M10749) French & European Pubns., Inc.

—Livret Phonetique (l'Arabe Sans Peine 2) Seul: Phonetic Pamphlet in Arabic for French Speakers. (ARA & FRE.). 14.95 (978-0-8288-4357-7(0)) French & European Pubns., Inc.

Barron's, creator. Arabic in No Time, 3 vols. 3rd rev. ed. 2008. (Now You're Talking! CD Packages Ser.). (ARA & ENG., Illus.). 312p. 18.99 (978-0-7641-9371-2(6)) Barron's Educational Series, Inc.

Berlitz, creator. Berlitz Arabic Phrase Book & CD. 2007. (Phrase Book & CD Ser.). (ARA & ENG.). 224p. 12.95 (978-981-268-186-7(6)) APA Publications Services SGP. Dist: Ingram Pub. Services.

Berlitz Publishing, creator. Berlitz Arabic Guaranteed. 2008. (Playaway Adult Nonfiction Ser.). 59.99 (978-1-60640-733-2(3)) Findaway World, LLC.

DiMeo, David F. Arabic for Dummies. 2008. (For Dummies (Playaway Audio) Ser.). 34.99 (978-1-60252-981-6(7)) Findaway World, LLC.

Diouri, Mourad. Read & Write Arabic Script: A Teach Yourself Guide. 2nd ed. 2011. (Teach Yourself Language Ser.). (ENG.). 176p. pap. 18.00 **(978-0-07-177453-6(X)**, 007177453X) McGraw-Hill Cos., The.

EPLS. Say It Right in Arabic: The Fastest Way to Correct Pronunciation. 2008. (ENG., Illus.). 176p. pap. 10.95 (978-0-07-154458-0(5), 0071544585) McGraw-Hill Cos., The.

Euro Talk. Talk More Arabic Classic. 2008. 29.99 (978-1-60077-215-3(3)) TOPICS Entertainment.

—Talk Now! Arabic Classical. 2008. 29.99 (978-1-84352-318-5(3)) TOPICS Entertainment.

—Talk Now! Arabic Egyptian. 2008. 29.99 (978-1-84352-441-0(4)) TOPICS Entertainment.

—Talk Now! Arabic Modern Standard. 2008. 29.99 (978-1-84352-392-5(2)) TOPICS Entertainment.

—World Talk Arabic Egyptian. 2008. 29.99 (978-1-84352-518-9(6)) TOPICS Entertainment.

Ghali, Naglaa. Arabic Grammar Unravelled. 2008. (ENG., Illus.). 160p. pap. 12.95 (978-0-9730512-2-3(1)) Fun With Arabic CAN. Dist: National Bk. Network.

Gokcora, Deniz & Eveyik-Aydin, Evrim. Arabic Instructors' Attitudes on Communicative Language Teaching. 2011. 64p. pap. **(978-3-8383-8380-4(X))** Lambert Academic Publishing.

Living Language. Living Language Arabic. unabr. ed. 2012. (Essential Ser.). (ENG.). 272p. audio compact disk 22.99 (978-0-307-47862-7(9), Living Language) Random Hse. Information Group.

Living Language Staff. Ultimate Arabic Beginner-Intermediate. unabr. l.t. ed. 2009. (Ultimate Basic-Intermed Ser.). (ENG.). 79.99 (978-1-4000-0976-3(6), Living Language) Random Hse. Information Group.

—Ultimate Arabic Beginner-Intermediate (BK) l.t. ed. 2009. (Ultimate Basic-Intermed Ser.). (ENG.). 544p. pap. 19.99 (978-1-4000-0977-0(4), Living Language) Random Hse. Information Group.

Living Language Staff & Bettaieb, Rym. Arabic Script: Reading & Writing. l.t. ed. 2008. (LL Complete Basic Courses Ser.). (ENG.). 144p. pap. 8.99 (978-1-4000-0924-4(3), Living Language) Random Hse. Information Group.

Mansouri, Fethi & Alreemawi, Yousef. Survival Arabic: How to Communicate Without Fuss or Fear — Instantly! 2008. (Survival Ser.). (ARA & ENG.). 144p. per. 6.95 (978-0-8048-3861-0(5)) Tuttle Publishing.

Rjeily, Rana. Cultural Connectives: Bridging the Latin & Arabic Alphabets. 2011. (ENG., Illus.). 112p. 34.95 (978-1-935613-13-8(8)) Batty, Mark Pub., LLC.

Smart, Jack & Altorfer, Frances. Arabic. 4th ed. 2010. (Teach Yourself Language Ser.). (ENG., Illus.). 496p. pap. 29.95 incl. audio compact disk (978-0-07-162779-5(0), 0071627790) McGraw-Hill Cos., The.

—Complete Arabic. 4th ed. 2010. (Teach Yourself Language Ser.). (ENG., Illus.). 496p. pap. 17.95 (978-0-07-162775-7(8), 0071627758) McGraw-Hill Cos., The.

Soltan, Usama. Arabic DeMYSTiFieD with Audio CD. 2013. (Demystified Ser.). (ENG & ARA.). pap. 25.00 incl. audio compact disk **(978-0-07-176561-9(1)**, 0071765611) McGraw-Hill Cos., The.

Wightwick, Jane & Gaafar, Mahmoud. Speak Arabic with Confidence. 2nd ed. 2011. (ENG.). 48p. 19.95 (978-0-07-175150-6(5), 0071751505) McGraw-Hill Cos., The.

Wightwick, Jane, et al. Arabic for Beginners: The Easiest Way to Learn to Communicate Right Away! 2nd ed. 2010. (ARA & ENG., Illus.). 96p. (978-0-07-173965-8(3)) McGraw-Hill Cos., The.

Wininger, William M. Arabic for the Deploying Service Member: Field Manual, 1. 2006. (ENG & ARA., Illus.). 60p. spiral bd. 8.95 (978-0-9791035-1-3(7)) MilitaryMouth.com.

Younes, Munther & Ibrahim, Ragy H. Learn Arabic. 2008. (Fast & Fun Way CD Packages Ser.). (ARA & ENG., Illus.). 192p. 29.99 (978-0-7641-9507-5(7)) Barron's Educational Series, Inc.

—Learn Arabic the Fast & Fun Way. 2008. (Fast & Fun Way Ser.). (ARA & ENG., Illus.). 192p. pap. 18.99 (978-0-7641-4024-2(8)) Barron's Educational Series, Inc.

ARABIC LANGUAGE—WRITING

see Writing, Arabic

ARABIC LITERATURE

see also Arabic Drama; Arabic Fiction; Arabic Poetry; Arabic Prose Literature; Arabic Wit and Humor

Al-Jurhumi, Abid bin Sharya. The History, Poetry, & Genealogy of Yemen. 2006. (Gorgias Historical Texts: 16). 185p. 75.00 (978-1-59333-516-8(4)) Gorgias Pr., LLC.

Ali, Abdul. Indian Origins of Arab-Islamic Scientific & Literary Heritage. 2010. 378p. 67.50 (978-81-7533-203-4(4)) M. D. Pubns. Pvt. Ltd. IND. Dist: Coronet Bks.

An Arabic Reading Book. 2010. 92.24 (978-1-61719-419-1(0)) Gorgias Pr., LLC.

Bayyumi, Mustafá. Al-Muathhirat Al-Islamiyah Fi Qisas Yusuf Al-Sharuni. 2010. (ARA.). 103p. (978-977-291-613-9(4)) Markaz al-Hadarah al-Arabiyah for Information and Publishing.

Blois, Francois De. Arabic, Persian & Gujarati Manuscripts: The Hamdani Collection in the Library of the Institute of Ismaili Studies. 2011. (ENG & ARA., Illus.). 288p. 70.00 **(978-1-84885-764-3(0)**, I. B. Tauris in Assn. with the Ins) I. B. Tauris & Co., Ltd. GBR. Dist: Macmillan.

Davies, H. T. Yusuf al-Shirbini's Brains Confounded by the Ode of Abu Shaduf Expounded (Kitab Hazz al-Quhuf bi-Sharh Qasid Abi Shaduf) Vol. 2: English Translation, Introduction & Notes. 2008. (Orientalia Lovaniensia Analecta Ser.). (ENG.). 495p. (C). 137.00 (978-90-429-1912-9(4)) Peeters Pubs. & Booksellers BEL. Dist: Brown, David Bk. Co., The.

Diem, Werner. Arabische Briefe aus dem 10.-16. Jahrhundert. 2011. (Corpus Papyrorum Raineri (CPR) Ser.). (ARA, GER & ENG., Illus.). 135p. 140.00 **(978-3-11-026046-5(8))** De Gruyter, Walter Inc.

el Khattabi, Bilal abu Hajar. My Arabic letter Book. 2010. 33p. pap. 33.95 (978-1-4092-7308-0(3)) Lulu Enterprises Inc.

El-Shihibi, Fathi. Evolution of Travel Genre in Arabic Literature. 2010. 284p. pap. 22.90 (978-0-557-55306-8(7)) Lulu Enterprises Inc.

Ellis, Alexander George, et al, compiled by. A Descriptive List of the Arabic Manuscripts. 2010. 94.04 (978-1-61143-058-5(5)) Gorgias Pr., LLC.

Inostranzev, M. Iranian Influence on Moslem Literature - Part I. Nariman, G.K., tr. 2007. 140p. per. (978-1-4065-3441-2(2)) Dodo Pr.

Kilito, Abdelfattah. Thou Shalt Not Speak My Language. Hassan, Wail, tr. from ARA. 2008. 144p. 19.95 (978-0-8156-3191-0(X)) Syracuse Univ. Pr.

Lowry, Joseph E. & Stewart, Devin J., eds. Essays in Arabic Literary Biography II: 1350-1850. 2009. (Essays in Arabic Literary Biography Ser.). (ENG.). 440p. (C). pap. 102.00 (978-3-447-05933-6(8)) Harrassowitz, Otto Verlag DEU. Dist: ISD.

Meisami, Julie Scott & Starkey, Paul, eds. Encyclopedia of Arabic Literature. 2010. (ENG.). 862p. pap. 90.00 (978-0-415-57113-5(8)) Routledge.

Mejcher-Atassi, Sonja. Reading Across Modern Arabic Literature & Art. 2011. (ENG.). 250p. (C). 117.00 **(978-3-89500-805-4(2))** Reichert, Ludwig Dr. DEU. Dist: Brown, David Bk. Co., The.

Mesleh, Abdelwadood. Support Vector MacHine Text Classifier for Arabic Articles. 2010. 132p. pap. (978-3-639-27141-6(6)) VDM Verlag Dr. Mueller e.K.

Mingana, Alphonse. Catalogue of the Mingana Collection of Manuscripts. 2006. (Gorgias Historical Catalogues Ser.: 1). 1016p. 398.00 (978-1-59333-541-0(5)) Gorgias Pr., LLC.

Morley, William H. A Descriptive Catalogue of the Historical Manuscripts in the Arabic & Persian Languages. 2010. pap. 36.16 (978-1-61719-183-1(3)) Gorgias Pr., LLC.

Omar Khayyam. Writings of the Sufi: The Mystical Tradition in Islam. 2009. 128p. pap. (978-1-934941-54-6(9)) Red & Black Pubs.

Oriental Literature. 2007. (ENG.). 472p. 52.95 (978-0-548-20599-0(X)); per. 37.95 (978-1-4325-2366-4(X)) Kessinger Publishing, LLC.

Oriental Literature. 2008. 448p. pap. (978-1-4086-8984-4(7)) Read Bks.

Schwartz, Lowell H. & Helmus, Todd C. Barriers to the Broad Dissemination of Creative Works in the Arab World. 2009. 58p. pap. 23.00 (978-0-8330-4730-4(2), MG-879) RAND Corp., The.

Steinschneider, Moritz. Jewish Arabic Literature: An Introduction. 2007. 382p. pap. 65.00 (978-1-59333-858-9(9)) Gorgias Pr., LLC.

Taha, Ibrahim. Arabic Minimalist Story: Genre, Politics & Poetics in the Self-Colonial Era. 2009. (LITERATUREN IM KONTEXT. ARABISCH - PERSISCH - TuRKISCH Ser.). (ENG.). 185p. (C). 84.00 (978-3-89500-666-1(1)) Reichert, Ludwig Dr. DEU. Dist: Brown, David Bk. Co., The.

Wright, William, intro. The Book of Kalilah & Dimnah. 2010. (SYR.). 139.76 (978-1-60724-843-9(3)) Gorgias Pr., LLC.

Zellman, Gail L., et al. Identifying Arabic-Language Materials for Children That Promote Tolerance & Critical Thinking, 1 vol. 2011. (ENG., Illus.). 84p. (C). pap. 20.00 (978-0-8330-5174-5(1)) RAND Corp., The.

ARABIC LITERATURE—BIBLIOGRAPHY

Ahlwardt, Wilhelm. Verzeichnis der arabischen Handschriften. 2010. (GER.). 1548.80 *(978-1-61719-846-5(3))*; 1548.80 *(978-1-61719-854-0(4))*; 1548.80 *(978-1-61719-852-6(8))*; 1548.80 *(978-1-61719-847-2(1))*; 1548.80 *(978-1-61719-849-6(8))*; 1548.80 *(978-1-61719-850-2(1))*; 1548.80 *(978-1-61719-851-9(X))*; 1548.80 *(978-1-61719-848-9(X))*; 1548.80 *(978-1-61719-853-3(6))*; 1548.80 *(978-1-61719-855-7(2))* Gorgias Pr., LLC.

Alam Al-Adab Al-°Arab i Al-Mu° aòSir: Siyar Wa-Siyar Dh at lyah, 2 Vols. *(978-3-515-06770-6(1))* Bow Historical Bks.

Altoma, Salih J. Iraq's Modern Arabic Literature: A Guide to English Translations since 1950. 2010. E-Book *(978-0-8108-7706-1(6))* Scarecrow Pr., Inc.

Ibn al-Nadim, Muhammad ibn Ishaq & Sayyid, Ayman Fu'ad. Kitab Al-Fihrist, 2 vols. 2009. (ARA., Illus.). *(978-1-905122-21-9(7))* Al-Furquan Islamic Heritage Foundation.

Murabit, Abd al-Wahid. Al-Dirasat Al-Adabiyah Al-Maghribiyah Al-Hadithah: Madakhil Bibliyughrafiyah: Min Bidayat Al-Matbaah Ila Sanat 2008. 2010. (ARA.). 435p. *(978-9954-0-4212-0(1))* Institut Marocain du Livre, IML.

Weisweiler, Max. Verzeichnis der Arabischen Handschriften. 2010. 114p. pap. 19.75 *(978-1-147-85230-1(8))* BiblioBazaar.

ARABIC LITERATURE—HISTORY AND CRITICISM

Abu-Deeb, Kamal. The Imagination Unbound: Al-Adab Al-'Aja'ibi & the Literature of the Fantastic. 2008. (ARA & ENG.). 240p. 60.00 *(978-0-86356-636-3(7))* Saqi Bks. GBR. Dist: Consortium Bk. Sales & Distribution.

Abudi, Dalya. Mothers & Daughters in Arab Women's Literature: The Family Frontier. 2010. (Women & Gender: The Middle East & the Islamic World Ser.). 350p. *(978-90-04-18114-4(6))* BRILL.

Aghacy, Samira. Masculine Identity in Fiction. 2009. 232p. 34.95 *(978-0-8156-3237-5(1))* Syracuse Univ. Pr.

Al-Bagdadi, Nadia. A Brief Introduction to Arabic Erotic Literature. 2011. (Brief Introduction Ser.). (ENG.). 150p. pap. 11.95 *(978-0-86356-608-0(1))* Saqi Bks. GBR. Dist: Consortium Bk. Sales & Distribution.

Al-Mallah, Majd Yaser & Fitzpatrick, Coeli. 20th Century Arabic Writers, Vol. 346. 2008. (Dictionary of Literary Biography Ser.). (ENG.). 312p. 315.00 *(978-0-7876-8164-7(4))* Cengage Gale.

al-Musawi, M. J., ed. Arabic Literary Thresholds: Sites of Rhetorical Turn in Contemporary Scholarship. 2009. 448p. *(978-90-04-17689-8(6))* BRILL.

Al-Musawi, Muhsin Jasim. The Islamic Context of the Thousand & One Nights. 2009. (ENG., Illus.). 352p. (gr. 17). 45.00 *(978-0-231-14634-0(5))* Columbia Univ. Pr.

Al-Wasiti, Salman D. Studies in Literature, Criticism & Translation. 2010. 474p. pap. *(978-0-7552-1248-4(7))* Authors OnLine, Ltd.

Alfonso, Esperanza. Islamic Culture Through Jewish Eyes: Al-Andalus from the Tenth to Twelfth Century. 2007. (Routledge Studies in Middle Eastern Literatures Ser.). 224p. 150.00 *(978-0-415-43732-5(6))* Routledge.

Ali, Samer M. Arabic Literary Salons in the Islamic Middle Ages: Poetry, Public Performance, & the Presentation of the Past. 2010. (ND Poetics of Orality & Literacy Ser.). (ENG.). 280p. pap. 32.00 *(978-0-268-02032-3(9))* Univ. of Notre Dame Pr.

Allen, Roger, ed. Essays in Arabic Literary Biography, 1850-1950, No. III. 2010. (Essays in Arabic Literary Biography Ser.). (ENG.). 395p. (C). 102.00 *(978-3-447-06141-4(3))* Harrassowitz, Otto Verlag DEU. Dist: ISD.

Altoma, Salih. Iraq's Modern Arabic Literature: A Guide to English Translations since 1950. 2010. (ENG.). 184p. (gr. 17). 65.00 *(978-0-8108-7705-4(8))* Scarecrow Pr., Inc.

Altoma, Salih J. Iraq's Modern Arabic Literature: A Guide to English Translations since 1950. 2010. E-Book *(978-0-8108-7706-1(6))* Scarecrow Pr., Inc.

Amer, Sahar. Crossing Borders: Love Between Women in Medieval French & Arabic Literatures. 2008. (Middle Ages Ser.). 264p. (C). 59.95 *(978-0-8122-4087-0(1))* Univ. of Pennsylvania Pr.

Arbuthnot, F. F. Arabic Authors. 2009. 184p. 25.99 *(978-0-559-06396-1(2))*; 22.99 *(978-0-559-06412-8(8))*; pap. 21.75 *(978-0-559-06408-1(X))*; pap. 22.75 *(978-0-559-06400-5(4))* BiblioBazaar.

—Arabic Authors. 2009. 154p. pap. *(978-0-217-68740-9(7))* Books LLC.

Arbuthnot, F. f. & Arbuthnot, F. F. Arabic Authors. 2010. (Illus.). 104p. pap. 20.00 *(978-1-153-58749-5(1))* General Bks. LLC.

Ashtiany, Julia, et al, eds. 'Abbasid Belles Lettres. 2008. (Cambridge History of Arabic Literature Ser.). (ENG., Illus.). 536p. pap. 69.00 *(978-0-521-08865-7(8))* Cambridge Univ. Pr.

Azraq, Michel & Ibrahim, Gregorios, trs. Pro Oriente: The Vienna Dialogue. 2009. (ARA.). 104.00 *(978-1-60724-265-9(6))* Gorgias Pr., LLC.

Babayan, Kathryn & Najmabadi, Afsaneh. Islamicate Sexualities: Translations Across Temporal Geographies of Desire. 2008. (Harvard Middle Eastern Monographs: 39). 384p. pap. 19.95 *(978-0-674-03204-0(7))* Harvard Univ., Ctr. for Middle Eastern Studies.

Badawi, M. M., ed. Modern Arabic Literature. 2006. (Cambridge History of Arabic Literature Ser.). (ENG.). 588p. (C). pap. 105.00 *(978-0-521-02853-0(1))* Cambridge Univ. Pr.

Ball, Anna. Gender Politics & the Postcolonial in Palestinian Literature & Film. 2012. (Routledge Research in Postcolonial Literatures Ser.). (ENG., Illus.). 224p. (C). 125.00 *(978-0-415-88862-2(X))* Routledge.

Bardaji, Anna Gil. Traducir Al-Andalus: El discurso del Otro en el Arabismo Espanol. de Conde a Garcia Gomez. 2009. (SPA.). 392p. 119.95 *(978-0-7734-3885-9(8))* Mellen, Edwin Pr., The.

Bauden, Frédéric, et al, eds. Le Repertoire narratif arabe Medieval: Transmission et ouverture. Actes du Colloque international de l'Universite de Liege (15-17 Septembre 2005) 2008. (Bibliotheque de la Faculte de Philosophie et Lettres Ser.). (FRE., Illus.). 369p. (C). pap. 67.00 *(978-2-87019-295-5(9))* Droz, Librairie CHE. Dist: Brown, David Bk. Co., The.

Beeston, A. F. L., et al, eds. Arabic Literature to the End of the Umayyad Period. 2010. (Cambridge History of Arabic Literature Ser.). (ENG., Illus.). 568p. pap. 55.00 *(978-0-521-12621-2(5))* Cambridge Univ. Pr.

Behnam, Gregorius, ed. The Journals al-Mashriq & Lisan Al-Mashriq (1946-1951) 2009. (ARA.). 850.00 *(978-1-60724-531-5(0))*; 850.00 *(978-1-60724-532-2(9))*; 850.00 *(978-1-60724-534-6(5))*; 850.00 *(978-1-60724-530-8(2))*; 850.00 *(978-1-60724-533-9(7))* Gorgias Pr., LLC.

Behzadi, Lale. Sprache und Verstehen: Al-Gahiz über Die Vollkommenheit des Ausdrucks. 2009. (GER.). 186p. pap. *(978-3-447-05698-4(3))* Harrassowitz, Otto Verlag.

Brann, Ross. Power in the Portrayal: Representations of Jews & Muslims in Eleventh-And Twelfth-Century Islamic Spain. 2009. (Jews, Christians, & Muslims from the Ancient to the Modern World Ser.). (ENG.). 212p. (C). pap. 22.95 *(978-0-691-14673-7(X))* Princeton Univ. Pr.

Brenner, Rachel Feldhay. Inextricably Bonded: Israeli Arab & Jewish Writers Re-Visioning Culture. 2010. (ENG., Illus.). 360p. pap. 19.95 *(978-0-299-18964-8(3))* Univ. of Wisconsin Pr.

Brown, Jonathan A. C. Hadith: Muhammad's Legacy in the Medieval & Modern World. 2009. (ENG.). 320p. 90.00 *(978-1-85168-696-4(7))* Oneworld Pubns. GBR. Dist: National Bk. Network.

Cachia, Pierre. Exploring Arab Folk Literature. 2011. (ENG., Illus.). 256p. (gr. 17). 105.00 *(978-0-7486-4086-7(X))* Edinburgh Univ. Pr. GBR. Dist: Columbia Univ. Pr.

Chaussard, Pierre Jean Baptiste. Fêtes et Courtisanes de la Grèce: Supplément Aux Voyages D'anacharsis et D'anténor, Volume 4. 2010. 506p. pap. 39.75 *(978-1-149-01661-9(2))* BiblioBazaar.

Cheikho, Louis. La Litterature Arabe au XIXe Siecle. 2006. (Christianity in the Islamic World Ser.: 2). 551p. 109.00 *(978-1-59333-539-7(3))* Gorgias Pr., LLC.

Cooke, Miriam. Dissident Syria: Making Oppositional Arts Official. 2007. (ENG., Illus.). 208p. 79.95 *(978-0-8223-4016-4(X))*; per. 22.95 *(978-0-8223-4035-5(6))* Duke Univ. Pr.

Cooperson, Michael. Classical Arabic Biography: The Heirs of the Prophets in the Age of Al-Ma'mun. 2008. (Cambridge Studies in Islamic Civilization Ser.). (ENG.). 244p. pap. 36.00 *(978-0-521-08854-1(2))* Cambridge Univ. Pr.

De Saavedra, Miguel Cervantes. Varias Obras inéditas de Cervantes: Sacadas de Codices de la Biblioteca Colombina, con Nuevas Ilustraciones Sobre la Vida Del Autor Y el Quijote. 2010. 524p. pap. 40.75 *(978-1-149-01468-4(7))* BiblioBazaar.

Deheuvels, Luc, et al, eds. Intertextuality in Modern Arabic Literature since 1967. 2010. (Durham Modern Languages Ser.). (ENG.). 228p. pap. 34.95 *(978-0-7190-8189-7(0))* Manchester Univ. Pr. GBR. Dist: Macmillan.

DeYoung, Terri, ed. Essays in Arabic Literary Biography 925-1350: Edited by Terri Deyoung & Mary St. Germain. 2011. (Mizan Ser.). (ENG.). 371p. (C). 105.00 *(978-3-447-06598-6(2))* Harrassowitz, Otto Verlag DEU. Dist: ISD.

Doufikar-Aerts, Faustina. Alexander Magnus Arabicus: A Survey of the Alexander Tradition through Seven Centuries: from Pseudo-Callisthenes to Suri. 2010. (Mediaevalia Groningana New Ser.). (ENG.). 416p. (C). pap. 95.00 *(978-90-429-2183-2(8))* Peeters Pubs. & Booksellers BEL. Dist: Brown, David Bk. Co., The.

Elinson, Alexander E. Looking Back at Al-Andalus: The Poetics of Loss & Nostalgia in Medieval Arabic & Hebrew Literature. 2009. (Brill Studies in Middle Eastern Literatures Ser.). 180p. *(978-90-04-16680-6(7))* BRILL.

Farid, Mahir Shafiq. Fi Al-Adab Wa-Al-Naqd. 2010. (ARA.). 530p. 37.75 *(978-1-149-00217-9(4))* BiblioBazaar.

Fughali, Jamal. Sual Al-Kaynunah: Qiraat Fi Jamaliyat Al-Ibda Al-Jazairi Al-Muasar. 2009. (ARA.). 198p. *(978-9961-62-827-0(6))* Entreprise Nationale des Arts Graphiques.

Gauch, Suzanne. Liberating Shahrazad: Feminism, Postcolonialism, & Islam. 2006. 224p. 60.00 *(978-0-8166-4882-5(4))*; pap. 24.00 *(978-0-8166-4883-2(2))* Univ. of Minnesota Pr.

Ghanayim, Mahmud. The Quest for a Lost Identity: Palestinian Fiction in Israel. 2008. (Studies in Arabic Language & Literature). (ENG.). 164p. (C). pap. 57.00 *(978-3-447-05768-4(8))* Harrassowitz, Otto Verlag DEU. Dist: ISD.

Ghazoul, Ferial, et al. Arab Women Writers: A Critical Reference Guide, 1873-1999. 2008. 540p. 59.50 *(978-977-416-146-9(7))* American Univ. in Cairo Pr. EGY. Dist: Oxford Univ. Pr., Inc.

Giovannucci, Perri. Literature & Development in North Africa: The Modernizing Mission. 2012. (Literary Criticism & Cultural Theory Ser.). (ENG.). 254p. pap. 42.95 *(978-0-415-54164-0(6))* Routledge.

Grob, Eva Mira. Documentary Arabic Private & Business Letters on Papyrus: Form & Function, Content & Context. 2010. (Archiv fa1/4r Papyrusforschung und verwandte Gebiete - Beihefte Ser.). XXI, 271p. 140.00 *(978-3-11-024704-6(6))* De Gruyter, Walter Inc.

Habib, Samar. Arabo-Islamic Texts on Female Homosexuality, 850 - 1780 a D. 2009. 120p. pap. 26.00 *(978-1-934844-11-3(X))* Teneo Pr.

—Female Homosexuality in the Middle East: Histories & Representations. 2009. 216p. 39.95 *(978-0-415-80603-9(8))* 2007. 195p. 128.00 *(978-0-415-95673-4(0))* Routledge.

Hafez, Sabry, ed. Mediating Literary Theory: An Anthology of Modern Arabic Criticism. 2007. (LITERATUREN IM KONTEXT. ARABISCH - PERSISCH - TuRKISCH Ser.). 376p. (C). 134.00 *(978-3-89500-478-0(2))* Reichert, Ludwig Dr. DEU. Dist: Brown, David Bk. Co., The.

Hafez, Sabry & Hafiz, Sabri. The Quest for Identities: The Development of the Modern Arabic Short Story. 2008. (ENG.). 446p. 50.00 *(978-0-86356-363-8(5))* Saqi Bks. GBR. Dist: Consortium Bk. Sales & Distribution.

Hamilton, David James. A Text-Book of Pathology: Systematic & Practical, Volume 2, part 2. 2010. 648p. pap. 46.75 *(978-1-149-00991-8(8))* BiblioBazaar.

Harrison, Burton. Recollections Grave & Gay. 2010. 404p. pap. 34.75 *(978-1-149-01139-3(4))* BiblioBazaar.

Herman, Ottó. Ungarns Spinnen-Fauna. 2010. 162p. pap. 21.75 *(978-1-149-00843-0(1))* BiblioBazaar.

Hissette, R. Commentum medium super libro praedicamentorum Aristotelis. Translatio Wilhelmo de Luna Ads. 2010. (Averroes Latinus Ser.). (FRE.). 270p. (C). 131.00 *(978-90-429-2282-2(6))* Peeters Pubs. & Booksellers BEL. Dist: Brown, David Bk. Co., The.

Hodges, Sydney. The Battle of Hastings & Other Poems. 2010. 194p. pap. 23.75 *(978-1-149-01170-6(X))* BiblioBazaar.

Huart, Clement. A History of Arabic Literature. 2009. 342p. pap. *(978-0-217-33592-8(6))* Books LLC.

—A History of Arabic Literature. 2009. 342p. pap. 21.42 *(978-1-4432-8417-2(3))* General Bks. LLC.

Imangulieva, Aida. Gibran, Rihani & Naimy: East-West Interactions in Early Twentieth-Century Arab Literature. 2010. (ENG.). 256p. pap. 19.95 *(978-1-905937-27-1(X))* Anqa Publishing GBR. Dist: Independent Pubs. Group.

Inostrantzev, M. Iranian Influence on Moslem Literature, Part I. 2008. 168p. 25.99 *(978-0-554-24432-7(2))* 2008. 168p. 22.99 *(978-0-554-33735-7(5))* 2006. (ENG.). 166p. pap. 21.99 *(978-1-4264-6584-0(X))* BiblioBazaar.

Jiyad, Mohammed. Anti-Women Sentiment in Arabic Literature. 2011. 304p. pap. *(978-3-8443-2955-1(2))* Lambert Academic Publishing.

Kendall, Elisabeth. Literature, Journalism & the Avant-Garde: Intersection in Egypt. 2006. (Routledge Studies in Middle Eastern Literatures Ser.). (Illus.). 279p. 160.00 *(978-0-415-38561-9(X))* Routledge.

Kennedy, Philip. Recognition in Arabic Islamic Literature: A Study of Theme,Structure & Narrative. 2008. (Routledge Studies in Middle Eastern Literatures Ser.). 240p. 85.00 *(978-0-415-29774-5(5)*, RoutledgeCurzon) Taylor & Francis Group.

Khalifa, Nouha. Hardship & Deliverance in the Islamic Tradition: Mu'tazilism, Theology & Spirituality in the Writings of Al-Tanuki. 2010. (ENG.). 304p. 92.50 *(978-1-84885-117-7(0)*, Tauris Academic Studies) I. B. Tauris & Co., Ltd. GBR. Dist: Macmillan.

Kluge, Friedrich. Deutsche Sprachgeschichte: Werden und Wachsen Unserer Muttersprache Von Ihren Anfängen Bis Zu Gegenwart. 2010. 364p. pap. 32.75 *(978-1-149-00771-6(0))* BiblioBazaar.

M. Inostrantzev. Iranian Influence on Moslem Literature, Part I. 2006. (ENG.). 148p. pap. 18.99 *(978-1-4264-6525-3(4))* BiblioBazaar.

Malki, Norah Al. Fiction & Reality T E Lawrence's Portrait of the Arabs in Seven Pillars of Wisdom. 2008. 96p. pap. *(978-3-639-11361-7(6))* VDM Verlag Dr. Mueller e.K.

Mehta, Brinda. Rituals of Memory in Contemporary Arab Women's Writing. 2007. 303p. 45.00 *(978-0-8156-3135-4(9))* Syracuse Univ. Pr.

Michalak-Pikulska, Barbara & Pikulski, Andrzej. Authority, Privacy & Public Order in Islam: Proceedings of the 22nd Congress of L'Union Europeenne des Arabisants et Islamisants, Cracow, Poland 2004. Michalak-Pikulska, B. & Pikulski, A., eds. 2006. (Orientalia Lovaniensia Analecta Ser.: Vol. 148). (FRE & ENG., Illus.). 496p. (C). 130.00 *(978-90-429-1736-1(9))* Peeters Pubs. & Booksellers BEL. Dist: Brown, David Bk. Co., The.

Middle Eastern Literature, 3 vols.; set. 2008. 475.00 *(978-1-4144-3653-1(X))* Cengage Gale.

Mirzaq, Abd al-Qadir Muhammad & Adunis. Mashru Adunis Al-Fikri Wa-Al-Ibdai: Ruyah Marifiyah. 2008. 424p. *(978-1-56564-324-6(0))* International Institute of Islamic Thought, The.

Musawi, Muhsin Jasim & Al-Musawi, Muhsin. Islam on the Street: Religion in Modern Arabic Literature. 2009. (ENG.). 304p. 89.00 *(978-0-7425-6206-6(9))* Rowman & Littlefield Publishers, Inc.

Najjar, Jasmina. Being of the Cedars. 2011. 60p. pap. ***(978-3-8443-2749-6(5))*** Lambert Academic Publishing.

Nasif, Awdit & Ibrahim, Gregorios, trs. Pro Oriente: The Vienna Dialogue. 2009. (ARA.). 107.00 *(978-1-60724-266-6(4))* Gorgias Pr., LLC.

Neuwirth. Postmodern Arabic Literature. 2010. (ENG.). 496p. pap. 28.95 ***(978-0-86356-694-3(4))*** Saqi Bks. GBR. Dist: Consortium Bk. Sales & Distribution.

New Jersey. Sewerage Commission, creator. Report of the State Sewerage Commission to the Legislature. 2010. 230p. pap. 25.75 *(978-1-149-00867-6(9))* BiblioBazaar.

Nicholson, Reynold Alleyn. Literary History of the Arabs. 2006. pap. 40.95 *(978-1-4286-3576-0(9))* Kessinger Publishing, LLC.

Nicholson, Reynold Alleyne. A Literary History of the Arabs. 2009. 416p. pap. *(978-1-4589-9078-5(8))* Books LLC.

—A Literary History of the Arabs. 2007. (ENG.). 532p. 55.95 *(978-0-548-12598-4(8))* Kessinger Publishing, LLC.

Parkman, Francis. La Salle & the Discovery of the Great West. 2010. 524p. pap. 40.75 *(978-1-149-00578-1(5))* BiblioBazaar.

Qitt, Mustafá al-Bashir. Majalis Al-Adab Fi Qusur Al-Khulafa Al-Abbasiyin. 2009. (ARA.). 428p. *(978-9957-12-184-6(7))* Dar al-Yazuri li-Nashr.

Rastegar, Kamran. Literary Modernity Between Middle East & Europe. 2007. (Routledge Studies in Middle Eastern Literatures Ser.). (Illus.). XVI, 176p. 160.00 *(978-0-415-42565-0(4))* Routledge.

Sajdi, Dana & Hammond, Marlé, eds. Transforming Loss into Beauty: Essays on Arabic Literature & Culture in Honor of Magda Al-Nowaihi. 2008. (ENG., Illus.). 368p. 34.95 *(978-977-416-102-5(5))* American Univ. in Cairo Pr. EGY. Dist: Oxford Univ. Pr., Inc.

Sallis, Eva. Sheherazade Through the Looking Glass. 2010. (ENG.). 170p. pap. 39.95 ***(978-0-415-59553-7(3))*** Routledge.

Scheiner. Die Eroberung von Damaskus:Quellenkritische Untersuchung zur Historiographie in klassisch-islamischer Zeit: Quellenkritische Untersuchung zur Historiographie in klassisch-islamischer Zeit. 2009. (Islamic History & Civilization Ser.). (GER.). *(978-90-04-17684-3(5))* BRILL.

Schoeler, Gregor. The Genesis of Literature in Islam: From the Aural to the Read. Toorawa, Shawkat M., tr. from GER. 2009. (New Edinburgh Islamic Surveys Ser.). (ENG.). 160p. (gr. 17). 110.00 *(978-0-7486-2467-6(8))*; pap. 32.50 *(978-0-7486-2468-3(6))* Edinburgh Univ. Pr. GBR. Dist: Columbia Univ. Pr.

Seigneurie, Ken. Standing by the Ruins: Elegiac Humanism in Wartime & Postwar Lebanon. 2011. (Modern Language Initiative Ser.). (ENG., Illus.). 256p. 80.00 ***(978-0-8232-3482-0(7))***; pap. 26.00 ***(978-0-8232-3483-7(5))*** Fordham Univ. Pr.

Selim, Samah. The Novel & the Rural Imaginary in Egypt 1880-1985. 2010. (ENG.). 280p. pap. 39.95 ***(978-0-415-59585-8(1))*** Routledge.

Shaaban, Bouthaina. Voices Revealed: Arab Women Novelists, 1898-2000. 2009. 215p. (C). 58.50 *(978-0-89410-871-6(3))*; pap. 22.50 *(978-0-89410-896-9(4))* Rienner, Lynne Pubs.

Siddiq, Muhammad. Arab Culture & the Novel: Genre, Identity, & Agency in Egyptian Fiction. 2007. (Routledge Studies in Middle Eastern Literatures Ser.). 232p. 150.00 *(978-0-415-77260-0(5))* Routledge.

Starkey, Paul. Modern Arabic Literature. 2006. (ENG.). 232p. 49.95 *(978-1-58901-134-2(1))*; pap. 21.95 *(978-1-58901-135-9(X))* Georgetown Univ. Pr.

Taha, Ibrahim. The Palestinian Novel. 2010. (ENG.). 252p. pap. 39.95 *(978-0-415-59555-1(X))* Routledge.

Tamer, Georges. Humor in der Arabischen Kultur: Humor in Arabic Culture. 2009. (GER & ENG., Illus.). XX, 387p. 109.00 *(978-3-11-019825-6(8))* De Gruyter, Walter Inc.

Tijani, I. & Tijani, Ishaq. Male Domination, Female Revolt: Race, Class, & Gender in Kuwaiti Women's Fiction. 2009. 176p. *(978-90-04-16779-7(X))* BRILL.

Toman, Cheryl. On Evelyne Accad: Essays in Literature, Feminism, & Cultural Studies. 2007. xix, 420p. *(978-1-883479-53-4(3))* Summa Pubns., Inc.

Tresilian, David. A Brief Introduction to Modern Arabic Literature. 2008. (Brief Introduction Ser.). (ENG., Illus.). 140p. pap. 11.95 *(978-0-86356-405-5(4))* Saqi Bks. GBR. Dist: Consortium Bk. Sales & Distribution.

Valassopoulos, Anastasia. Contemporary Arab Women Writers: Cultural Expression in Context. 2007. (Routledge Research in Postcolonial Literatures Ser.). (ENG.). 192p. 120.00 *(978-0-415-35355-7(6))* Routledge.

Wilson, Epiphanius, ed. Oriental Literature: The Literature of Arabia. 2007. 180p. per. *(978-1-4065-4970-6(3))* Dodo Pr.

Zadadiqah, Sufyan. Al-Haqiqah Wa-Al-Sarab: Qiraah Fi Al-Bud Al-Sufi Inda Adunis Marjian Wa-Mumarasah. 2008. (ARA.). 598p. *(978-9953-87-517-0(0))* Arab Scientific Pubs.

Ziadeh, Khaled. Neighborhood & Boulevard: Reading Through the Modern Arab City. Selim, Samah, tr. from ARA. 2011. (Theory around the World Ser.). (ENG., Illus.). 192p. 80.00 *(978-0-230-10351-0(8))* Palgrave Macmillan.

ARABIC LITERATURE—TRANSLATIONS INTO ENGLISH

Al Ardhi, Mohammed. Pearls from Arabia. 2010. 187p. pap. 19.95 *(978-1-907784-02-6(0))* Berkshire Academic Pr., Ltd. GBR. Dist: International Specialized Bk. Services.

Al-Hazimi, Mansour, et al, eds. Beyond the Dunes: An Anthology of Modern Saudi Literature. 2006. (ENG.). 500p. 107.00 *(978-1-85043-972-1(9))* I. B. Tauris & Co., Ltd. GBR. Dist: Macmillan.

Al-Sabbagh, Rania. Anaphora Resolution in Arabic/English MacHine Translation Systems. 2010. 104p. pap. *(978-3-8383-8634-3(1))* Lambert Academic Publishing.

Al-Wasiti, Salman D. Studies in Literature, Criticism & Translation. 2010. 474p. pap. *(978-0-7552-1248-4(7))* Authors OnLine, Ltd.

Altoma, Salih. Iraq's Modern Arabic Literature: A Guide to English Translations since 1950. 2010. (ENG.). 184p. (gr. 17). 65.00 *(978-0-8108-7705-4(8))* Scarecrow Pr., Inc.

Altoma, Salih J. Iraq's Modern Arabic Literature: A Guide to English Translations since 1950. 2010. E-Book *(978-0-8108-7706-1(6))* Scarecrow Pr., Inc.

Anonymous. Chinese Literature: Comprising the Analects of Confucius, the Sayings of Mencius, the Shi-King, the Travels of Fa-Hien, & the Sorrows of Han. 2007. (ENG.). 366p. pap. 26.99 *(978-1-4264-3972-8(5))*; 328p. pap. 23.99 *(978-1-4264-3914-8(8))* BiblioBazaar.

Assadi, Jamal. Mohammad Ali Taha's "A Rose to Hafeeza's Eyes" & Other Stories. 2008. 152p. (C). 60.95 *(978-1-4331-0363-6(X))* Lang, Peter Publishing, Inc.

Baffioni, Carmela. On Logic: An Arabic critical edition & English translation of Epistles 10-14. 2010. (ENG & ARA.). 216p. 65.00 *(978-0-19-958652-3(7))* Oxford Univ. Pr., Inc.

Burckhardt, John Lewis. Arabic Proverbs: Or, the Manners & Customs of the Modern Egyptians. Ouseley, William, ed. 2010. (Cambridge Library Collection - Travel & Exploration Ser.). (ENG., Illus.). 246p. pap. 22.99 *(978-1-108-02288-0(X))* Cambridge Univ. Pr.

El Saadawi, Nawal & Horst, Adele Newson, eds. The Essential Nawal el Saadawi. 2010. (Essential Feminists Ser.). (ENG.). 400p. 125.95 (978-1-84813-334-1(0)) Zed Bks., Ltd. GBR. Dist: Macmillan.

Farid, Mahir Shafiq. Fi Al-Adab Wa-Al-Naqd. 2010. (ARA.). 530p. 37.75 (978-1-149-00217-9(4)) BiblioBazaar.

Habib, Bouagada. Orientalism in Translation: The One Thousand & One Nights in 18th Century France & 19th Century England. 2011. 124p. pap. **(978-3-639-30140-3(4))** VDM Verlag Dr. Mueller e.K.

Husni, Ronak. A Practical Manual in Arabic Translation. 2010. 288p. 170.00 (978-0-415-47884-7(7)) Routledge.

—Savior-Faire Plus. 2012. (ENG.). 288p. pap. 51.95 (978-0-415-47885-4(5)) Routledge.

Jayyusi, Salma Khadra, ed. Classical Arabic Stories: An Anthology. 2010. (ENG., Illus.). 400p. (gr. 17). 60.00 (978-0-231-14922-8(0)) Columbia Univ. Pr.

Mustafa, Shakir. Contemporary Iraqi Fiction: An Anthology. 2009. (Middle East Literature in Translation Ser.). 202p. 22.95 (978-0-8156-0902-5(7)) Syracuse Univ. Pr.

Tanimu Jibril, Ahmed. Arabic Words in English. 2010. 140p. pap. (978-3-639-22753-6(0)) VDM Verlag Dr. Mueller e.K.

Wilson, Epiphanius, ed. Oriental Literature: The Literature of Arabia. 2007. 180p. per. (978-1-4065-4970-6(3)) Dodo Pr.

Woidich, Manfred & Heinen-Nasr, Rabha. Al-Kitab Al-mufid: An Introduction to Modern Written Arabic. 2011. (ENG.). 448p. 39.50 (978-977-416-446-0(6)) American Univ. in Cairo Pr. EGY. Dist: Oxford Univ. Pr., Inc.

Wortabet, John. Arabian Wisdom. 2010. 30p. pap. 14.14 (978-1-153-65532-3(2)) General Bks. LLC.

—Arabian Wisdom. 2009. pap. 37.70 (978-1-60724-295-6(8)) Gorgias Pr., LLC.

ARABIC MEDICINE

see Medicine, Arab

ARABIC PHILOSOPHY

see Islamic Philosophy; Philosophy, Arab

ARABIC POETRY

Abu Awwad, Ibrahim. Madkhal Ilá Ilm Ijtima Al-Qasidah. 2009. (ARA.). 328p. (978-9957-12-208-9(8)) Dar al-Yazuri lil-Nashr.

al-Isfahani, Abu al-Faraj Ali. Kitab Al-Aghani: The Book of Songs. 2010. (ARA.). 3330.00 (978-1-60724-702-9(X)); 3330.00 (978-1-60724-719-7(4)); 3330.00 (978-1-60724-706-7(2)); 3330.00 (978-1-60724-707-4(0)); 3330.00 (978-1-60724-718-0(6)); 3330.00 (978-1-60724-704-3(6)); 3330.00 (978-1-60724-697-8(X)); 3330.00 (978-1-60724-726-5(7)); 3330.00 (978-1-60724-699-2(6)); 3330.00 (978-1-60724-721-0(6)); 3330.00 (978-1-60724-703-6(8)); 3330.00 (978-1-60724-724-1(0)); 3330.00 (978-1-60724-720-3(8)); 3330.00 (978-1-60724-722-7(4)); 3330.00 (978-1-60724-700-5(3)); 3330.00 (978-1-60724-728-9(3)); 3330.00 (978-1-60724-723-4(2)); 3330.00 (978-1-60724-698-5(8)); 3330.00 (978-1-60724-717-3(8)); 3330.00 (978-1-60724-701-2(1)); 3330.00 (978-1-60724-725-8(9)); 3330.00 (978-1-60724-727-2(5)); (Illus.). 3330.00 (978-1-60724-708-1(9)); (Illus.). 3330.00 (978-1-60724-705-0(4)) Gorgias Pr., LLC.

Arberry, A. J., tr. from ARA. Moorish Poetry: A Translation of the Pennants an Anthology Compiled in 1243 by the Andalusian Ibn Sa'id. 2010. (ENG.). 220p. pap. 22.99 (978-0-521-17067-3(2)) Cambridge Univ. Pr.

Brookshaw, Dominic Parviz & Rahimieh, Nasrin, eds. Forugh Farrokhzad, Poet of Modern Iran: Exploring her Life & Works. 2010. (ENG, ARA, PER & GER., Illus.). 296p. pap. 34.00 (978-1-84885-156-6(1)) I. B. Tauris & Co., Ltd. GBR. Dist: Macmillan.

—Forugh Farrokhzad, Poet of Modern Iran: Iconic Woman & Feminine Pioneer of New Persian Poetry. 2010. (ENG, ARA, PER & GER., Illus.). 296p. 96.00 (978-1-84885-155-9(3)) I. B. Tauris & Co., Ltd. GBR. Dist: Macmillan.

Dolabani, Yuhanon, ed. Poems of John Bar Ma'dani. 2010. pap. 24.88 (978-1-61719-597-6(9)) Gorgias Pr., LLC.

Holes, Clive, et al, eds. The Nabati Poetry of the United Arab Emirates: Selected Poems, Annotated & Translated into English. 2011. (ARA & ENG.). 250p. pap. 74.95 incl. audio compact disk (978-0-86372-378-0(0), Ithaca Pr.) Garnet Publishing, Ltd. GBR. Dist: International Specialized Bk. Services.

Kashgari, Badia. The Unattainable Lotus: A Bilingual Anthology of Poetry. 2006. (ENG & ARA.). 140p. pap. 12.95 (978-0-86356-362-1(7)) Saqi Bks. GBR. Dist: Consortium Bk. Sales & Distribution.

ARABIC POETRY—HISTORY AND CRITICISM

Al-Ghadeer, Moneera. Desert Voices: Bedouin Women's Poetry in Saudi Arabia. 2009. (Library of Modern Middle East Studies). (ENG.). 288p. 94.00 (978-1-84511-666-8(6), Tauris Academic Studies) I. B. Tauris & Co., Ltd. GBR. Dist: Macmillan.

Amin, Ahmad. Suwar Mushriqah Min Al-Shir Al-Shabi Al-Jazairi: Muhammad Ibn Vaytun, Al-Shaykh Al-Samati, Al-Qadi Abd Allah Ibn Karyu: Dirasat Wa-Namadhij. 2007. (ARA.). 304p. (978-9961-906-99-6(3)) El Hikma (Souk-Ahras).

Asad, Nasir al-Din. Masadir Al-Shir Al-Jahili Wa-Qimatuha Al-Tarikhiyah. 9th ed. 2010. (ARA., Illus.). 724p. (978-9957-23-174-3(X)) Wakeel Books.

Ashshi, Abd Allah. Asilah Shiriyah: Bahth Fi Aliyat Al-Ibda Al-Shiri. 2009. (ARA.). 296p. (978-9961-9857-4-8(5)) Rabitat Koutab El Ikhtilaf.

Bossong, Georg. Poesía en Convivencia: Estudios Sobre la Lírica árabe, Hebrea y Romance en la España de Las Tres Religiones. 2010. 400p. (978-84-9704-533-9(5)) Trea, Ediciones, S.L.

Darwash, Mustafá. Tashakkul Al-Dhat Wa-Al-Lughah Fi Mafahim Al-Naqd Al-Manhajī. 2008. (ARA.). 254p. (978-9961-883-73-0(X)) Office National de la Recherche Géologique et Minière.

Farrin, Raymond. Abundance from Desert. 2010. 304p. 24.95 (978-0-8156-3222-1(3)) Syracuse Univ. Pr.

Gelder, G.J.H.Van & Hammond, Marlé. Takhyil: The Imaginary in Classical Arabic Poetics. 2007. 112p. (C). 60.00 (978-0-906094-74-7(7)) Gibb Memorial Trust, The GBR. Dist: Brown, David Bk. Co., The.

Gruendler, Beatrice. Medieval Arabic Praise Poetry. 2010. (ENG.). 366p. pap. 39.95 **(978-0-415-59579-7(7))** Routledge.

Haidar, Otared. The Prose Poem & the Journal Shi'r: A Study of Literature, Literary Theory & Journalism. 2008. (ARA & ENG.). 324p. (C). 69.95 (978-0-86372-329-2(2), Ithaca Pr.) Garnet Publishing, Ltd. GBR. Dist: International Specialized Bk. Services.

Hammond, Marlé. Beyond Elegy: Classical Arabic Women's Poetry in Context. 2010. (British Academy Postdoctoral Fellowship Monographs). (ENG.). 224p. 85.00 (978-0-19-726472-0(7)) Oxford Univ. Pr., Inc.

Hermes, Nizar F. The [European] Other in Medieval Arabic Literature & Culture: Ninth-Twelfth Century AD. 2012. (New Middle Ages Ser.). (ENG., Illus.). 260p. 85.00 **(978-0-230-10940-7(3))** Palgrave Macmillan.

Hussein, Ali A. The Lightning-Scene in Ancient Arabic Poetry: Function, Narration & Idiosyncrasy in Pre-Islamic & Early Islamic Poetry. 2010. (Arabische Studien Ser.). (ENG.). 302p. (C). pap. 132.00 (978-3-447-05902-2(8)) Harrassowitz, Otto Verlag DEU. Dist: ISD.

Jones, Alan, ed. Early Arabic Poetry: Select Poems. 2011. 582p. 74.95 **(978-0-86372-387-2(X)**, Ithaca Pr.) Garnet Publishing, Ltd. GBR. Dist: International Specialized Bk. Services.

Kennedy, Philip F. Abu Nuwas: A Genius of Poetry. 2007. (Makers of the Muslim World Ser.). (ENG.). 160p. pap. 19.95 (978-1-85168-510-3(3)) Oneworld Pubns. GBR. Dist: National Bk. Network.

Khairallah, As'ad E. Modern Arabic Poetry: Prophecy, Metapoetry, Snapshots. 2008. (Culture & Civilization in the Middle East Ser.). 256p. 130.00 (978-0-415-29775-2(3), RU25399) Routledge.

Khalil, Yasin Yusuf Ayish. Qiraat Fi Tamarrud Al-Shuara Al-Abbasiyin Alá Al-Sultah. 2011. (ARA.). 215p. (978-9957-06-711-3(7)) Dar al-Masirahlil-Nashr wa-al-Tawzi.

Kilani, Mustafá & Adunis. Adunis Wa-Shairiyat Al-Usul: Muqarabah Tawiliyah. (ARA., Illus.). 291p. (978-2-200-51111-1(6)) Armand, Colin.

Lahiani, Raja. Eastern Luminaries Disclosed to Western Eyes: A Critical Evaluation of the Translations of the Mu'allaqat into English & French (1782-2000) 2008. 361p. pap. 86.95 (978-3-03911-014-8(4)) Lang, Peter AG GBR. Dist: Lang, Peter.

Larkin, Margaret. Al-Mutanabbi: Voice of the 'Abbasid Poetic Ideal. 2007. (Makers of the Muslim World Ser.). (ENG.). 160p. 40.00 (978-1-85168-406-9(9)) Oneworld Pubns. GBR. Dist: National Bk. Network.

Manasirah, Izz al-Din. Jamrat Al-Nass Al-Shiri: Muqarabat Fi Al-Shir Wa-Al-Shuara Wa-Al-Hadathah Wa-Al-Failiyah. 2007. 574p. (978-0-00-702260-1(3)); (ARA.). (978-9957-02-260-0(1)) Dar Mijdalawi lil-Nashr wa-al-Tawzi.

Meisami, Julie. Structure & Meaning in Medieval Arabic & Persian Lyric Poetry. 2011. (ENG.). 528p. pap. 39.95 **(978-0-415-61643-0(3))** Routledge.

Miller, Flagg. The Moral Resonance of Arab Media: Audiocassette Poetry & Culture in Yemen. 2007. (Harvard Middle Eastern Monographs: 38). (Illus.). 512p. per. 29.95 (978-0-932885-32-6(2)) Harvard Univ., Ctr. for Middle Eastern Studies.

Mubarak, Muhammad Rida. Al-Shir Wa-Al-Usturah: Istiarat Al-Sard Fi Nusus Khalil Hawi. 2010. (ARA.). 207p. (978-977-5471-76-5(1)) Misr Al-Arabiyah Lil-Nashr Wa-al-Tawzi.

Musawi, Ahmad. Al-Mawlidiyat Fi Al-Adab Al-Jazairi Al-Qadim: Ahd Tilimsan Al-Zayyaniyah: Dirasah. 2008. (ARA., Illus.). 261p. (978-9961-62-741-9(5)) Entreprise Nationale des Arts Graphiques.

Nykl, Alois Richard. Hispano-Arabic Poetry & Its Relations with the Old Provencal Troubadours. 2011. 448p. 56.95 **(978-1-258-02583-0(3))** Literary Licensing, LLC.

P., Stetkevych S. Mute Immortals Speak Pb. 2011. 352p. pap. 29.95 (978-0-8014-8046-1(9)) Cornell Univ. Pr.

Papoutsakis, Nefeli. Desert Travel as a Form of Boasting: A Study of Dur-Rumma's Poetry. 2009. (Arabische Studien Ser.). (ENG.). 206p. (C). pap. 72.00 (978-3-447-06112-4(X)) Harrassowitz, Otto Verlag DEU. Dist: ISD.

Radwan, Noha M. Egyptian Colloquial Poetry in the Modern Arabic Canon: New Readings of Shi'r Al-'Ammiyya. 2012. (Literatures & Cultures of the Islamic World Ser.). (ENG., Illus.). 252p. 85.00 **(978-0-230-34132-6(2))** Palgrave Macmillan.

Rahman, Najat. Literary Disinheritance: The Writing of Home in the Work of Mahmoud Darwish & Assia Djebar. 2007. (ENG.). 196p. 68.50 (978-0-7391-2007-1(7)) Lexington Bks.

Rahman, Najat & Nassar, Hala Khamis, eds. Mahmoud Darwish: Exile's Poet. 2007. (ENG.). 384p. pap. 25.00 (978-1-56656-664-3(9)) Interlink Publishing Group, Inc.

Rand, Michael & Decter, Jonathan P., eds. Studies in Arabic & Hebrew Letters in Honor of Raymond P. Scheindlin. 2007. (Gorgias Précis Portfolios Ser.: 1). (HEB & ENG.). 86.00 (978-1-59333-701-8(9)) Gorgias Pr., LLC.

Rifai, Ahmad Sharafi. Al-Shir Al-Watani Al-Jazairi: Min Sanat 1925 Ilá Sanat 1954. 2010. (ARA.). 318p. (978-9947-26-127-9(1)) Dar ol-hoda.

Saddik, Gohar. Singers in the Wasteland Voices of Protest in Modern Poetry. 2011. 152p. pap. **(978-3-639-31944-6(3))** VDM Verlag Dr. Mueller e.K.

Shams al-Din, Majdi Muhammad. Ibn Quzman Wa-Al-Zajal Fi Al-Andalus. 2010. (ARA.). 458p. 31.75 (978-1-149-00439-5(8)) BiblioBazaar.

Sindawi, Khalid, ed. A Poet of the Abbasid Period. Abu al-Qasim al-Zahi ('Ali B. Ishaq B. Khalaf al-Zahi) 313-352 AH/925-963 CE: His Life & Poetry. 2010. (Codices Arabici Antiqui Ser.). (ARA & ENG.). 180p. (C). pap. 81.00 (978-3-447-06219-0(3)) Harrassowitz, Otto Verlag DEU. Dist: ISD.

Tabatabai, Sassan, ed. Father of Persian Verse: Rudaki & His Poetry. 2011. (Iranian Studies Ser.). 124p. pap. (978-90-8728-092-5(0)) Amsterdam Univ. Pr.

Tayii, Ahmad. Al-Tawasul Al-Balaghi Min Al-Musarrah Bi-Hi Ilá Al-Maskut Anh. 2008. (ARA., Illus.). 103p. (978-9954-438-39-8(4)) Cujas, Editions.

Tobi, Josef. Between Hebrew & Arabic Poetry: Studies in Spanish Medieval Hebrew Poetry. 2010. (Medieval & Renaissance Authors & Texts Ser.). x, 520p. (978-90-04-18499-2(6)) BRILL.

Ubayd, Muhammad Sabir. Shifrat Adunis Al-Shiriyah: Simiya Al-Dall Wa-Lubat Al-Maná. 2009. 159p. (978-9953-87-693-1(2)) Arab Scientific Pubs.

Wagner, Mark S. Like Joseph in Beauty: Yemeni Vernacular Poetry & Arab-Jewish Symbiosis. 2008. (Brill Studies in Middle Eastern Literatures Ser.). 304p. (978-90-04-16840-4(0)) BRILL.

Yaqub, Nadia G. Pens, Swords, & the Springs of Art: The Oral Poetry Dueling of Palestinian Weddings in the Galilee. 2006. (Brill Studies in Middle Eastern Literatures Ser.: Vol. 32). (ENG & ARA.). 378p. (978-90-04-15259-5(8)) BRILL.

ARABIC POETRY—TRANSLATIONS INTO ENGLISH

Abd al-Rahman, Ibrahim Muhammad. Bina Al-Qasidah Inda Ali Al-Jarim. 2009. (ARA.). 400p. (978-977-336-282-9(5)) Dar al-Yaqin.

Abdulaali, Wafaa Abdullatif & Dhahir, Sanna, trs. from ARA. Contemporary Poetry from Iraq by Bushra Al-Bustani: A Facing Page Translation. 2008. 132p. 99.95 (978-0-7734-4912-1(4)) Mellen, Edwin Pr., The.

Arberry, A. J. Poems of Al-Mutanabbī. 2009. (ARA, ACE & ENG.). 164p. pap. 31.99 (978-0-521-10848-5(9)) Cambridge Univ. Pr.

Assadi, Jamal. The Story of a People: An Anthology of Palestinian Poets Within the Green-lines. 2011. (C). 79.95 **(978-1-4331-1603-2(0))** Lang, Peter Publishing, Inc.

Boulus, Sargon. Knife Sharpener: Selected Poems Translated from the Arabic by the Author. 2010. (ENG., Illus.). 144p. pap. 15.00 (978-0-9549666-7-6(8)) Banipal GBR. Dist: Interlink Publishing Group, Inc.

Darwish, Mahmoud. If I Were Another. Joudah, Fady, tr. from ARA. 2009. (ENG., Illus.). 240p. 28.00 (978-0-374-17429-3(6)) Farrar, Straus & Giroux.

—If I Were Another, 1 vol. Joudah, Fady, tr. 2011. (ENG., Illus.). 240p. pap. 22.00 (978-0-374-53247-5(8)) Farrar, Straus & Giroux.

Gelder, G.J.H.Van & Hammond, Marlé. Takhyil: The Imaginary in Classical Arabic Poetics. 2008. (ENG.). 304p. (C). 85.00 (978-0-906094-69-3(0)) Gibb Memorial Trust, The GBR. Dist: Brown, David Bk. Co., The.

Gorton, T. J., ed. Arabia: A Thousand Years of Arabic Verse. 2010. (Poetry of Place Ser.). (ENG.). 117p. pap. 16.95 (978-1-906011-20-8(6)) Eland Bks. GBR. Dist: Dufour Editions, Inc.

Mohammed, Sadek. Flowers of Flame: The Unheard Voices of Iraq. 2008. (ENG.). 96p. pap. 14.95 (978-0-87013-842-3(1)) Michigan State Univ. Pr.

Mumayiz, Ibrahim, ed. Arabesques: Selections of Biography & Poetry from Classical Arabic Literature. 2006. (World Arab Translators' Association Ser.: Vol. 2). (Illus.). 133p. pap. 28.50 (978-90-441-1888-9(9)) Garant Uitgevers N.V. BEL. Dist: Coronet Bks.

Najm, Soheil. Ishtar's Songs: Iraqi Poetry since The 1970s. Najm, Soheil, ed. Mohammed, Sadek R., tr. 2011. 214p. pap. 18.95 **(978-1-935514-17-6(2))** Plain View Pr.

Nasser, Amjad. Shepherd of Solitude. 2010. (ENG.). 175p. pap. 15.00 (978-0-9549666-8-3(6)) Banipal GBR. Dist: Interlink Publishing Group, Inc.

Obank, Margaret, et al. A Crack in the Wall: New Arab Poetry. 2008. (ENG.). 260p. 39.50 (978-0-86356-984-5(6)) Saqi Bks. GBR. Dist: Consortium Bk. Sales & Distribution.

Palmer, E. H., ed. The Poetical Works of Beha-Ed-Din Zoheir of Egypt 2 Part Set: With a Metrical English Translation, Notes & Introduction, 2 vols. 2012. (ENG.). 750p. pap. 71.99 **(978-1-107-61530-4(5))** Cambridge Univ. Pr.

Qurrat al-Ayn, et al. The Quickening: Unknown Poetry of Táhirih. 2011. (978-1-931847-83-4(5)) Baha'i Publishing Trust, U.S.

Smith, Michael, ed. Poems from Other Tongues. Ingelmo, Luis, tr. from ARA. 2011. 108p. pap. **(978-1-84861-134-4(X))** Shearsman Bks.

Tabatabai, Sassan, ed. Father of Persian Verse: Rudaki & His Poetry. 2011. (Iranian Studies Ser.). 124p. pap. (978-90-8728-092-5(0)) Amsterdam Univ. Pr.

ARABIC PROSE LITERATURE

Avicenna. The Physics of the Healing: A Parallel English-Arabic, 2 vols. Davis, Morgan, ed. McGinnis, Jon, tr. from ARA. 2010. (Brigham Young University - Islamic Translation Ser.). (Illus.). 1168p. 49.95 (978-0-8425-2747-7(8), Maxwell, Neal A. Institute for Religious Scholarship) Brigham Young Univ.

Hermes, Nizar F. The [European] Other in Medieval Arabic Literature & Culture: Ninth-Twelfth Century AD. 2012. (New Middle Ages Ser.). (ENG., Illus.). 260p. 85.00 **(978-0-230-10940-7(3))** Palgrave Macmillan.

Landau, Jacob M. A Word Count of Modern Arabic Prose. 2011. 510p. 60.95 **(978-1-258-02240-2(0))** Literary Licensing, LLC.

ARABIC SPEAKING STATES

see Arab Countries

ARABIC STUDIES

see Arab Countries—Study and Teaching; Civilization, Arab

ARABIC WIT AND HUMOR

Jayyusi, Salma Khadra, ed. Tales of Juha: Classic Arab Folk Humor. Sorenson, Matthew et al, trs. from ARA. 2006. (International Folk Tales Ser.). (ENG., Illus.). 128p. per. 12.95 (978-1-56656-641-4(X)) Interlink Publishing Group, Inc.

Owen, Charles A. & Al-Abi, Abu Sa'id, notes. Arabian Wit & Wisdom. 2011. 84.32 (978-1-61143-910-6(8)) Gorgias Pr., LLC.

ARABISM

see Panislamism

ARABS

Here are entered comprehensive works on the Arabs as an ethnic group. Works on the nomadic Arabs are entered under Bedouins.

see also Bedouins; North Africans; Palestinian Arabs

Achcar, Gilbert. The Arabs & the Holocaust: The Arab-Israeli War of Narratives. 2010. (ENG.). 400p. 30.00 (978-0-8050-8954-7(3), Metropolitan Bks.) Holt, Henry & Co.

—The Arabs & the Holocaust: The Arab-Israeli War of Narratives. 2011. (ENG.). 400p. pap. 20.00 (978-0-312-56920-4(3)) Picador.

Aksikas, Jaafar. Arab Modernities: Islamism, Nationalism, & Liberalism in the Post-Colonial Arab World. 2009. (Postcolonial Studies). 192p. (C). 37.95 (978-1-4331-0534-0(9)) Lang, Peter Publishing, Inc.

Alfaro-Velcamp, Theresa. So Far from Allah, So Close to Mexico: Middle Eastern Immigrants in Modern Mexico. 2007. (ENG., Illus.). 286p. pap. 24.95 (978-0-292-71641-4(9)) Univ. of Texas Pr.

Allen, Mark & Allen. Arabs. 2007. (ENG.). 160p. 17.95 (978-0-8264-9402-3(1)) Continuum International Publishing Group, Ltd. GBR. Dist: National Bk. Network.

Barnes, Maude Fiero. Historic Vistas. 2011. 130p. 40.95 **(978-1-258-02808-4(5))** Literary Licensing, LLC.

Bertram Thomas. The Arabs - the Life Story of a People Who Have Left Their Deep Impress on the World. 2007. 400p. per. (978-1-4067-5243-4(6)) Read Bks.

Butler, Grant & Butler, Grant C. Kings & Camels: An American in Saudi Arabia. 2008. (Illus.). 124p. pap. 34.95 (978-1-85964-200-9(4)) Garnet Publishing, Ltd. GBR. Dist: International Specialized Bk. Services.

Cole, Donald. Bedouins of the Empty Quarter. 2010. (ENG., Illus.). 202p. pap. 29.95 (978-0-202-36357-8(0)) Aldine Transaction.

El-Shihibi, Fathi. Arab, Muslim Travelers through the Centuries. 2010. 164p. pap. 22.90 (978-0-557-47860-6(X)) Lulu Enterprises Inc.

Fitch, Florence Mary. Daughter of Abd Salam the Story of A Pea. 2006. pap. 20.95 (978-1-4286-5485-3(2)) Kessinger Publishing, LLC.

Goodrich-Freer, Adela M. Arabs in Tent & Town: An Intimate Account. reprint ed. 37.50 (978-0-404-16438-6(2)) AMS Pr., Inc.

Hainthaler, Theresia. Christliche Araber Vor Dem Islam: Verbreitung und Konfessionelle Zugehorigkeit. eine Hinfuhrung. 2007. (Eastern Christian Studies Ser.). (ENG., Illus.). 188p. (C). pap. 65.00 (978-90-429-1917-4(5)) Peeters Pubs. & Booksellers BEL. Dist: Brown, David Bk. Co., The.

Hajji, Tariq Ahmad & Heggy, Tarek. The Arab Cocoon: Progress & Modernity in Arab Societies. 2010. 160p. 59.95 (978-0-85303-922-8(4)) Vallentine Mitchell Pubs. GBR. Dist: International Specialized Bk. Services.

Izzeddin, Nejla. The Arab World: Past, Present & Future. 2007. (ENG.). 448p. 51.95 (978-0-548-08274-4(X)) Kessinger Publishing, LLC.

Jacob, Harold F. Kings of Arabia: The Rise & Set of the Turkish Sovranty in the Arabian Peninsula. 2007. (Folios Archive Library Ser.). (Illus.). 294p. pap. 49.50 (978-1-85964-198-9(9)) Garnet Publishing, Ltd. GBR. Dist: International Specialized Bk. Services.

Jacobsen, Frode F. Hadrami Arabs in Present-Day Indonesia: An Indonesia-Oriented Group with an Arab Signature. 2009. (Routledge Contemporary Southeast Asia Ser.). (Illus.). XII, 132p. 160.00 (978-0-415-48092-5(2)) Routledge.

Kligman, Mark L. Maqam & Liturgy: Ritual, Music, & Aesthetics of Syrian Jews in Brooklyn. 2008. 34.95 (978-0-8143-3216-0(1)) Wayne State Univ. Pr.

Lawrence, T. E. Revolt in the Desert. 2008. 328p. (978-1-84677-420-1(9)); pap. (978-1-84677-419-5(5)) Leonaur Ltd.

—Revolt in the Desert: The Abridged Edition of Seven Pillars of Wisdom. 2011. (ENG., Illus.). 352p. 18.00 (978-1-84885-665-3(2), Tauris Parke Paperbacks) I. B. Tauris & Co., Ltd. GBR. Dist: Macmillan.

Lawrence, T. e. & Lawrence, T. E. Seven Pillars of Wisdom: A Triumph. 2011. 550p. 24.95 **(978-1-61720-182-0(0))**; pap. 14.99 **(978-1-61720-181-3(2))** Wilder Pubns., Ltd.

Litvak, Meir & Webman, Ester. From Empathy to Denial: Arab Responses to the Holocaust. 2012. (Columbia/Hurst Ser.). (ENG.). 416p. (gr. 17). pap. 22.00 (978-0-231-70075-7(X)) Columbia Univ. Pr.

Marshu, Ghrighwar Mansur. Al-Fusam Fi Al-Fikr Al-Arabi Al-Muasir. 2007. (ARA.). 350p. (978-1-59239-701-3(8)) Dar Al-Fikr Al-Mouaser.

Massad, Joseph A. Desiring Arabs. 2008. (ENG., Illus.). 472p. pap. 22.50 (978-0-226-50959-4(1)) Univ. of Chicago Pr.

Massad, Joseph Andoni. Desiring Arabs. 2007. (ENG., Illus.). 472p. 37.50 (978-0-226-50958-7(3)) Univ. of Chicago Pr.

Matar, N. I. Europe Through Arab Eyes, 1578-1727. 2008. 352p. pap. (978-0-231-51208-4(2)) Columbia Univ. Pr.

McNamara, Robert. The Hashemites? The Dream of Arabia - The Peace Conferences of, 1919-23 & Their Aftermath. 2010. (Makers of the Modern World Ser.). (ENG., Illus.). 220p. 19.95 (978-1-905791-66-8(6)) Haus Publishing GBR. Dist: Consortium Bk. Sales & Distribution.

Nydell, Margaret K. Understanding Arabs: A Contemporary Guide to Arab Society. 5th ed. 2012. (ENG.). 288p. pap. *(978-0-9839558-0-1(8))* Brealey, Nicholas Publishing Ltd.

Podeh, Elie. The Politics of National Celebrations in the Arab Middle East. 2011. (ENG., Illus.). 352p. 95.00 *(978-1-107-00108-4(0))* Cambridge Univ. Pr.

Rejwan, Nissim. Arabs in the Mirror: Images & Self-Images from Pre-Islamic to Modern Times. 2008. (ENG.). 224p. (C). pap. 24.95 *(978-0-292-71728-2(8))* Univ. of Texas Pr.

Rich, Paul. Iraq & Gertrude Bell's the Arab of Mesopotamia. 2008. (Middle East Classics Ser.). (ENG.). 250p. 73.50 *(978-0-7391-2561-8(3))*; per. 26.50 *(978-0-7391-2562-5(1))* Lexington Bks.

Safouan, Moustapha. Why Are the Arabs Not Free? The Politics of Writing. 2007. (Critical Quarterly Book Ser.: 2). (ENG.). 128p. per. 24.95 *(978-1-4051-6171-8(X)*, Wiley-Blackwell) Wiley, John & Sons, Inc.

Sedaghat, Michel. Arabs - All you need to Know. 2010. 136p. pap. 13.00 *(978-1-4457-6512-9(8))* Lulu Enterprises Inc.

Shields, Sarah D. Fezzes in the River: Identity Politics & European Diplomacy in the Middle East on the Eve of World War II, 1 vol. 2011. (Illus.). 320p. 39.95 *(978-0-19-539331-6(7))* Oxford Univ. Pr., Inc.

Shora, Nawar. The Arab-American Handbook: A Guide to the Arab, Arab-American, & Muslim Worlds. 2008. (Illus.). 335p. pap. 19.95 *(978-1-885942-14-2(1))* Cune Pr., LLC.

—The Arab-American Handbook: A Guide to the Arab, Arab-American & Muslim Worlds. 2008. (Bridge Between the Cultures Ser.). (Illus.). 335p. 34.95 *(978-1-885942-47-0(8))* Cune Pr., LLC.

Villiers, Alan. Sons of Sindbad: Sailing with the Arabs in Their Dhows. 2006. (ENG., Illus.). 480p. (C). 50.00 *(978-0-9544792-3-7(8))* Arabian Publishing, Ltd. GBR. Dist: Brown, David Bk. Co., The.

Villiers, Alan John. Sons of Sinbad: The Photographs. 2006. (ENG., Illus.). 224p. 71.95 *(978-0-948065-75-0(3))* National Maritime Museum GBR. Dist: Independent Pubs. Group.

Weaver, Nigel, et al. Edward Bawden in the Middle East. 2008. (ENG., Illus.). 96p. *(978-1-85149-565-8(7)*, Antique Collectors Club Dist) Antique Collectors' Club.

Zogby, James. Arab Voices: What They Are Saying to Us, & Why it Matters. 2010. (ENG.). 256p. 25.00 *(978-0-230-10299-6(9))* Palgrave Macmillan.

Zogby, James. Arab Voices: What They Are Saying to Us, & Why It Matters. 2012. (ENG., Illus.). 272p. pap. 17.00 ***(978-0-230-12068-6(7))*** Palgrave Macmillan.

ARABS—FOLKLORE

Anonymous. The Book of the Thousand Nights & a Night. (ENG.). 2008. 454p. per. 36.75 *(978-1-4375-2892-3(9))* 2008. 398p. per. 33.75 *(978-1-4375-2742-1(6))* 2007. 422p. pap. 26.99 *(978-1-4346-4923-2(7))* 2007. 484p. pap. 30.99 *(978-1-4346-4924-9(5))* BiblioBazaar.

Arabian Nights. 27.95 *(978-0-8488-0866-2(5))* Amereon LTD.

The Book of the Thousand Nights & a Night. 2008. Vol. 1. pap. *(978-1-4065-6554-6(7))* Vol. 1. pap. *(978-1-4065-6557-7(1))* Vol. 2. pap. *(978-1-4065-6555-3(5))* Vol. 3. pap. *(978-1-4065-6556-0(3))* Vol. 5. pap. *(978-1-4065-6558-4(X))* Vol. 6. pap. *(978-1-4065-6559-1(8))* Vol. 7. pap. *(978-1-4065-6560-7(1))* Vol. 8. pap. *(978-1-4065-6561-4(X))* Vol. 9. pap. *(978-1-4065-6562-1(8))* Vol. 10. pap. *(978-1-4065-6553-8(6))* Vol. 11. pap. *(978-1-4065-6564-5(4))* Dodo Pr.

Burton, Richard. The Arabian Nights. 2011. (ENG.). 750p. lthr. 24.95 *(978-1-60710-309-7(5)*, Thunder Bay Pr.) Advantage Pubs. Group.

Burton, Richard F., tr. The Book of the Thousand Nights & a Night. 2008. Vol. 12. 340p. pap. *(978-1-4065-6565-2(2))* Vol. 13. 488p. pap. *(978-1-4065-6566-9(0))* Vol. 14. 308p. pap. *(978-1-4065-6567-6(9))* Vol. 15. 388p. pap. *(978-1-4065-6568-3(7))* Vol. 16. 384p. pap. *(978-1-4065-6569-0(5))* Dodo Pr.

Campbell, C. G. & McLane, Charles B. Tales from the Arab Tribes: The Oral Traditions among the Great Arab Tribes of Southern Iraq. 2007. (ENG., Illus.). 256p. 255.00 *(978-0-7103-1131-3(1))* Routledge.

Dixon, E. Fairy Tales from the Arabian Nights. 2008. 252p. 24.99 *(978-0-554-32112-7(2))* 2008. 252p. 27.99 *(978-0-554-22809-9(2))* 2007. (ENG.). 224p. pap. 20.99 *(978-1-4264-3073-2(6))* 2006. 250p. pap. 22.99 *(978-1-4264-3138-8(4))* BiblioBazaar.

—Fairy Tales from the Arabian Nights. 2007. 160p. per. *(978-1-4068-6152-5(9))* Echo Library.

El-Shamy, Hasan M. A Motif Index of the Thousand & One Nights. 2006. (ENG., Illus.). 696p. 65.00 *(978-0-253-34834-0(X)*, 025334834X) Indiana Univ. Pr.

Lang, Andrew. The Arabian Nights Entertainments. Lt. ed. 2007. (ENG.). 322p. pap. 24.99 *(978-1-4264-5964-1(5))* BiblioBazaar.

Reynolds, Dwight Fletcher. Arab Folklore: A Handbook, 1 vol. 2007. (Greenwood Folklore Handbooks Ser.) (Illus.). 272p. 55.00 *(978-0-313-33311-8(4)*, GR3311, Greenwood Pr.) Greenwood Publishing Group, Inc.

Wiggin, Kate Douglas & Smith, Nora Archibald. The Arabian Nights: Their Best-known Tales. 2007. 286p. pap. 21.99 *(978-1-4346-5249-2(1))*; (ENG.). 318p. pap. 24.99 *(978-1-4346-5250-8(5))* BiblioBazaar.

ARABS—HISTORY

Abushouk, Ahmed Ibrahim & Ibrahim, Hassan Ahmed, eds. Hadhrami Diaspora in Southeast Asia: Identity Maintenance or Assimilation? 2009. (Social, Economic & Political Studies of the Middle East Ser.). 297p. *(978-90-04-17231-9(9))* BRILL.

Bishtawi, Adel S. Origin of the Arabic Numerals: A Natural History of Numbers. 2011. 396p. pap. 25.00 ***(978-1-4567-8586-4(9))*** AuthorHouse.

C. Arabic History & Culture. 2009. 1125.00 *(978-0-415-44131-5(5))* Routledge.

Halm, Heinz. The Arabes: A Short History with Documents. Brown, Allison, tr. from GER. 2011. (Illus.). 260p. pap. *(978-1-55876-546-7(8))* Wiener, Markus Pubs., Inc.

—The Arabs: A Short History. Brown, Allison & Lampert, Thomas, trs. from GER. (Illus.). 172p. 2007. 89.95 *(978-1-55876-416-3(X))* 2006. per. 24.95 *(978-1-55876-417-0(8))* Wiener, Markus Pubs., Inc.

—The Arabs: A Short History with Documents. Brown, Allison & Lampert, Thomas, trs. from GER. 2011. (Illus.). 260p. 89.95 *(978-1-55876-545-0(X))* Wiener, Markus Pubs., Inc.

Hourani, Albert & Ruthven, Malise. A History of the Arab Peoples: With a New Afterword. 2nd ed. 2010. (Illus.). 624p. pap. 18.95 *(978-0-674-05819-4(4)*, Belknap Pr.) Harvard Univ. Pr.

Mccants, William. Founding Gods, Inventing Nations: Conquest & Culture Myths from Antiquity to Islam. 2011. (ENG.). 192p. (C). 35.00 *(978-0-691-15148-9(2))* Princeton Univ. Pr.

Shahid, Irfan & Shahid, I. Byzantium & the Arabs in the Sixth Century, Volume 2, Part 2. 2010. (Dumbarton Oaks Other Titles in Byzantine Studies). (Illus.). 480p. 50.00 *(978-0-88402-347-0(8))* Dumbarton Oaks.

Zabel, Darcy. Arabs in the Americas: Interdisciplinary Essays on the Arab Diaspora. 2006. 248p. (C). pap. 31.95 *(978-0-8204-8111-1(4))* Lang, Peter Publishing, Inc.

ARABS—HISTORY—TO 622

Crone, Patricia. From Arabian Tribes to Islamic Empire: Army, State & Society in the Near East C. 600-850. 2008. (Variorum Collected Studies). 320p. 154.95 *(978-0-7546-5925-9(9))* Ashgate Publishing Co.

ARABS—HISTORY—622-1517

see Islamic Empire

ARABS—HISTORY—1517-

see Arab Countries—History—1517-1918; Arab Countries—History—1798-; Arab Countries—History—20th Century

ARABS—AFRICA

MacMichael, H. A. A History of the Arabs in the Sudan: And Some Account of the People Who Preceded Them & of the Tribes Inhabiting Dagrave. 2010. (Cambridge Library Collection - Travel & Exploration Ser.). (Illus.). 560p. pap. 39.99 *(978-1-108-01026-9(1))* Cambridge Univ. Pr.

—A History of the Arabs in the Sudan: And Some Account of the People Who Preceded Them & of the Tribes Inhabiting Dagrave;Rfaring;Laquo;R. 2010. (Cambridge Library Collection - Travel & Exploration Ser.). (Illus.). 384p. pap. 31.99 *(978-1-108-01025-2(3))* Cambridge Univ. Pr.

Marouf, Nadir, ed. Les Identits Rgionales et la Dialectique Sud-Sud en Question. 2007. (FRE.). 192p. pap. *(978-2-86978-195-5(4))* Council for the Development of Social Science Research in Africa SEN. Dist: Michigan State Univ. Pr.

Mazrui, Ali A. Euro-Jews & Afro-Arabs: The Great Semitic Divergence in World History. Adem, Seifudein, ed. 2008. (ENG.). 508p. per. 68.50 *(978-0-7618-3857-9(0))* Univ. Pr. of America, Inc.

Ouali, Hamid. Agreement, Pronominal Clitics & Negation in Tamazight Berber: A Unified Analysis. 2011. (Continuum Studies in Theoretical Linguistics Ser.). (BER & ENG., Illus.). 208p. 140.00 *(978-1-4411-0127-3(6))* Continuum International Publishing Group, Ltd. GBR. Dist: National Bk. Network.

Shukrallah, Hani. Egypt, the Arabs, & the World: Reflections at the Turn of the Twenty-first Century. 2011. (ENG.). 304p. 27.95 ***(978-977-416-485-6(5))*** American Univ. in Cairo Pr. EGY. Dist: Oxford Univ. Pr., Inc.

ARABS—CANADA

Dahab, F. Elisabeth. Voices of Exile in Contemporary Canadian Francophone Literature. 2009. (After the Empire: the Francophone World & Postcolonial France Ser.). (ENG.). 246p. 62.99 *(978-0-7391-1878-8(1))* Lexington Bks.

Dahab, F. Elizabeth. Voices of Exile in Contemporary Canadian Francophone Literature. 2010. (After the Empire: the Francophone World & Postcolonial France Ser.). (ENG.). 246p. pap. 29.95 *(978-0-7391-1879-5(X))* Lexington Bks.

Eid, Paul. Being Arab: Ethnic & Religious Identity Building among Second Generation Youth in Montreal. 2007. (McGill-Queen's Studies in Ethnic History Ser.). (ENG.). 272p. (C). *(978-0-7735-3221-2(8))*; (Illus.). per. *(978-0-7735-3222-9(6))* McGill-Queen's Univ. Pr.

ARABS—FOREIGN COUNTRIES

Ball, Warwick. Out of Arabia: Phoenicians, Arabs & the Discovery If Europe. 2009. (ENG., Illus.). 272p. pap. 22.95 *(978-1-56656-801-2(3)*, Olive Branch Pr.) Interlink Publishing Group, Inc.

Chiarelli, Leonard C. A History of Muslim Sicily. 2011. (ENG., Illus.). 441p. (C). pap. 50.00 ***(978-99932-7-353-0(8))*** Midsea Bks. Ltd. MLT. Dist: Brown, David Bk. Co., The.

Hanauer, Larry, et al. Managing Arab-Kurd Tensions in Northern Iraq after the Withdrawal of U. S. Troops. 2011. pap. 14.50 ***(978-0-8330-5321-3(3))*** RAND Corp., The.

Matar, Nabil. Europe Through Arab Eyes, 1578-1727. 2008. (ENG.). 344p. (gr. 17). 50.00 *(978-0-231-14194-9(7))* Columbia Univ. Pr.

Memmi, Albert. Decolonization & the Decolonized. Bononno, Robert, tr. from FRE. 2006. 160p. 54.00 *(978-0-8166-4734-7(8))*; per. 17.95 *(978-0-8166-4735-4(6))* Univ. of Minnesota Pr.

Pryce-Jones, David. Betrayal: France, the Arabs, & the Jews. (ENG.). 2008. 190p. pap. 17.95 *(978-1-59403-220-2(3))* 2006. 185p. 23.95 *(978-1-59403-151-9(7))* Encounter Bks.

Soubra, Hani. Letters to Dalia: Reflections on Lebanon & the Middle East. 2010. (ENG.). 224p. 21.95 *(978-1-935212-14-0(1))* Easton Studio Pr., LLC.

ARABS—ISRAEL

Al-Krenawi, Alean, et al. Helping Professional Practice with Indigenous Peoples: The Bedouin-Arab Case. 2008. 89.00 *(978-1-60021-549-0(1))* Nova Science Pubs., Inc.

Cohen. Arabs in Israel. 2007. 220p. 79.50 *(978-0-85303-796-5(5))* Vallentine Mitchell Pubs. GBR. Dist: International Specialized Bk. Services.

LeBor, Adam. City of Oranges: An Intimate History of Arabs & Jews in Jaffa. 2007. (ENG., Illus.). 464p. per. 14.95 *(978-0-393-32984-1(4)*, 32984) Norton, W. W. & Co., Inc.

Sorek, Tamir. Arab Soccer in a Jewish State: The Integrative Enclave. 2010. (Cambridge Cultural Social Studies). (ENG., Illus.). 244p. pap. 30.00 *(978-0-521-13135-3(9))* Cambridge Univ. Pr.

ARABS—PALESTINE

see Palestinian Arabs

ARABS—SPAIN

Bardaji, Anna Gil. Traducir Al-Andalus: El discurso del Otro en el Arabismo Espanol. de Conde a Garcia Gomez. 2009. (SPA.). 392p. 119.95 *(978-0-7734-3885-9(8))* Mellen, Edwin Pr., The.

Conde, Jose A. The Dominion of the Arabs in Spain: A History, 3 vols. 2009. (ENG.). 511p. 499.00 *(978-1-84511-792-4(1))* I. B. Tauris & Co., Ltd. GBR. Dist: Macmillan.

—History of the Dominion of the Arabs in Spain, 3 vols. Foster, Jonathan, tr. reprint ed. 55.00 *(978-0-404-09270-2(5))* AMS Pr., Inc.

Coppee, Henry. History of the Conquest of Spain Vol I. 2006. 492p. per. *(978-1-4067-2188-1(3)*, Hesperides Pr.) Read Bks.

James, David. A History of Early Al-Andalus. 2011. (Culture & Civilization in the Middle East Ser.). (ENG., Illus.). 208p. (C). 125.00 *(978-0-415-66943-6(X))* Routledge.

Lane-Poole, Stanley. The Moors in Spain. 2009. 126p. pap. *(978-1-150-50020-6(4))* Books LLC.

Lane-Poole, Stanley & Gilman, Arthur. The Moors in Spain. 2009. 116.00 *(978-1-60724-320-5(2))* Gorgias Pr., LLC.

Nykl, Alois Richard. Hispano-Arabic Poetry & Its Relations with the Old Provencal Troubadours. 2011. 448p. 56.95 ***(978-1-258-02583-0(3))*** Literary Licensing, LLC.

Poole, Stanley L. The Moors in Spain. (African Heritage Classical Research Studies). 290p. reprint ed. 16.00 *(978-0-938818-65-6(1))* ECA Assocs.

ARABS—UNITED STATES

see also Arab Americans

Chebel d'Appollonia, Ariane & Reich, Simon, eds. Managing Ethnic Diversity After 9/11: Integration, Security, & Civil Liberties in Transatlantic Perspective. 2011. (ENG., Illus.). 318p. pap. 26.95 ***(978-0-8135-5137-1(4))*** Rutgers Univ. Pr.

Halek, Joseph R. Arab-American Almanac. 6th ed. 2008. (Illus.). 600p. 39.95 *(978-0-915652-29-7(3))* News Circle.

Larson, Jayne A. Driving the Saudis: Seven Weeks Behind the Wheel with Some of the World's Richest Princesses, Their Nannies, Servants, & One Royal Hairdresser. 2012. (ENG.). 224p. 23.00 ***(978-1-4516-4001-4(3)***, Free Pr.) Free Pr.

Tischauser, Jeffrey. Anti-Arab & Anti-Muslim Bias in American Newspapers: How They Reported the 2006 Israeli-Hezbollah & Israeli-Hamas Wars. 2009. iv, 192p. *(978-0-7734-3901-6(3))* Mellen, Edwin Pr., The.

ARACHIDES

see Peanuts

ARACHIDONIC ACID

Roman, Richard. Arachidonic Acid Metabolites & Kidney Function. 2012. (Colloquium Series on Integrated Systems Physiology: from Molecule to Function Ser.). 100p. pap. 35.00 *(978-1-61504-204-3(0))* Morgan & Claypool Life Science Publishers.

ARACHNIDA

see also Mites; Scorpions; Spiders

Beccaloni, Jan. Arachnids. 2009. (ENG.). 320p. 45.00 *(978-0-520-26140-2(2))* Univ. of California Pr.

Cokendolpher, J. C., et al. Arachnids associated with wet playas in the Southern High Plains (Llano Estacado), U. S. A., 54. Baker, R. J., ed. 2008. (Illus.). 77p. (C). pap. 21.95 net. *(978-1-929330-16-4(2))* Museum of Texas Tech Univ.

Eisner, Thomas, et al. Secret Weapons: Defenses of Insects, Spiders, Scorpions, & Other Many-Legged Creatures. 2007. (Illus.). 384p. per. 22.50 *(978-0-674-02403-8(6)*, Belknap Pr.) Harvard Univ. Pr.

Hoffman, Anita. El Maravilloso Mundo de los Aracnidos. (Ciencia para Todos Ser.). (SPA.). pap. 6.99 *(978-968-16-4214-3(7))* Fondo de Cultura Economica USA.

Krantz, G. W. & Walter, D. E., eds. A Manual of Acarology. 3rd ed. 2009. (Illus.). 816p. 175.00 *(978-0-89672-620-8(7))* Texas Tech Univ. Pr.

Machado, Glauco, et al, eds. Harvestmen: The Biology of Opiliones. 2007. (Illus.). 608p. 150.50 *(978-0-674-02343-7(9))* Harvard Univ. Pr.

McMonigle, Orin. Scorpions, Windscorpions, Pseudoscorpions, Culturing Ancient Arachnids. 2009. (Illus.). 41p. 14.00 *(978-0-9802401-3-9(1))* Elytra & Antenna.

Simpson, Stephen & Casas, Jérôme. Advance in Insect Physiology: Spider Physiology & Behaviour Physiology. 2011. (ENG.). 240p. 150.00 ***(978-0-12-387668-3(0)***, Academic Pr.) Elsevier Science & Technology Bks.

Stewart, Amy. Wicked Bugs: The Louse That Conquered Napoleon's Army & Other Diabolical Insects. 2011. (ENG., Illus.). 288p. 18.95 *(978-1-56512-960-3(1)*, 1565129601) Algonquin Bks. of Chapel Hill.

Williams, Tim. A Dictionary for Arachnology. 2009. 292p. pap. 24.95 *(978-1-4092-9853-3(1))* Lulu Enterprises Inc.

ARAFAT, YASIR, 1929-2004

Abu Sharif, Bassam & Abu Sharif, Bassam. Arafat & the Dream of Palestine: An Insider's Account. 2009. (ENG., Illus.). 288p. 27.95 *(978-0-230-60801-6(9))* Palgrave Macmillan.

Ghanem, As'ad. Palestinian Politics after Arafat: A Failed National Movement. 2010. (Indiana Series in Middle East Studies). (ENG.). 222p. 65.00 *(978-0-253-35427-3(7)*, 0253354277); pap. 24.95 *(978-0-253-22160-5(9)*, 0253221609) Indiana Univ. Pr.

Pisano, Isabel. Yasir Arafat: La Pasion de un Lider. 2006. (Cronica Actual Ser.). (SPA & ENG., Illus.). 336p. per. 19.95 *(978-84-666-2510-4(0))* Ediciones B ESP. Dist: Independent Pubs. Group.

Rubin. Yasir Arafat: The Last Revolutionary. *(978-0-312-29525-7(1))* Palgrave Macmillan.

ARAGON, LOUIS, 1897-1982

Bieck, Angelika & Schahinian, David. Sprachwandel in Literarischen Übersetzungen: Aragon, Salinger, Orwell. 2009. (Frankfurter Forschungen zur Kultur- und Sprachwissenschaft Ser.). (GER.). 186p. 57.95 *(978-3-631-58679-2(5))* Lang, Peter GmbH, Europaischer Verlag der Wissenschaften DEU. Dist: Lang, Peter.

Kimyongur, A. M. & Kimyongür, Angela. Memory & Politics: Representations of War in the Work of Louis Aragon. 2008. (University of Wales Press - French & Francophone Studies). 176p. 85.00 *(978-0-7083-2088-4(0))* Univ. of Wales Pr. GBR. Dist: Chicago Distribution Ctr.

Piégay-Gros, Nathalie & Aragon. L'esthétique D'Aragon. (FRE.). 283p. *(978-2-7181-9113-3(9))* Sedes.

ARAGON (SPAIN)

Armijo de Castro, Francisco. Viajes de Agua: Las Aguas en el Pirineo Aragonés a Través de Sus Viajeros. 2007. (SPA., Illus.). 197p. *(978-84-935061-3-1(3))* Pirineum Multimedia, S.Coop.

Earenfight, Theresa. The King's Other Body: Maria of Castile & the Crown of Aragon. 2009. (Middle Ages Ser.). (Illus.). 240p. (C). 49.95 *(978-0-8122-4185-3(1))* Univ. of Pennsylvania Pr.

Goodenough, Lady, ed. The Chronicle of Muntaner. 2010. (Hakluyt Society, Second Ser.). 884p. 120.00 *(978-1-4094-2482-6(0))*; 424p. 69.95 *(978-1-4094-1417-9(5))*; 472p. 69.95 *(978-1-4094-1414-8(0))* Hakluyt Society GBR. Dist: Ashgate Publishing Co.

Kagay, Donald J. War, Government & Society in the Medieval Crown of Aragon. 2007. (Variorum Collected Studies). (Illus.). 344p. 165.00 *(978-0-7546-5904-4(6))* Ashgate Publishing Co.

Pieper, Katharina. Der mudejare Bauschmuck im mittelalterlichen Aragon am Beispiel der Stuckfenster: Eine Untersuchung der spanisch-islamischen und christlichen Elemente in Komposition und Einzelformen. 2009. (Iberia Archaeologica Ser.). (GER & SPA.). 319p. (C). 85.00 *(978-3-8053-3982-7(8))* Zabern, Philipp von Verlag, GmbH DEU. Dist: Brown, David Bk. Co., The.

Rodriguez, Jarbel. Captives & Their Saviors in the Medieval Crown of Aragon. 2007. 225p. 69.95 *(978-0-8132-1475-7(0))* Catholic Univ. of America Pr.

Ryan, Michael A. A Kingdom of Stargazers: Astrology & Authority in the Late Medieval Crown of Aragon. 2011. 232p. 45.00 *(978-0-8014-4984-0(7))* Cornell Univ. Pr.

Smith, Damian J. Crusade, Heresy & Inquisition in the Lands of the Crown of Aragon, C. 1167-1276. 2010. (Illus.). 252p. *(978-90-04-18289-9(6))* BRILL.

Smith, Damian J. & Buffery, Helena. The Book of Deeds of James 1 of Aragon: A Translation of the Medieval Catalan Llibre Dels Fets. 2010. (Crusade Texts in Translation Ser.). (Illus.). 424p. pap. 29.95 *(978-1-4094-0150-6(2))* Ashgate Publishing Co.

Swift, F. Darwin. Life & Times of James the First the Co. 2006. pap. 30.95 *(978-1-4286-4174-7(2))* Kessinger Publishing, LLC.

—The Life & Times of James the First the Conqueror: King of Aragon, Valencia & Majorca, Count of Barcelona & Urgel, Lord of Montpellier. 2007. 336p. 45.95 *(978-0-548-13124-4(4))* Kessinger Publishing, LLC.

Vose, Robin. Dominicans, Muslims & Jews in the Medieval Crown of Aragon. 2011. (Cambridge Studies in Medieval Life & Thought: Fourth Ser.). (ENG.). 310p. pap. 39.99 *(978-0-521-18149-5(6))* Cambridge Univ. Pr.

ARAMAIC INSCRIPTIONS

see Inscriptions, Aramaic

ARAMAIC LANGUAGE

see also Mandaean Language; Samaritan Aramaic Language; Syriac Language

Al-Kfamissy, Paul & Botica, Aurelian. The Concept of Intention in the Old Testament, Philo of Alexandria & the Early Rabbinic Literature. 2011. (Gorgias Historical Grammars Ser.: 3). 140.00 *(978-1-59333-653-0(5))* Gorgias Pr., LLC.

Arayathinal, Thomas. Aramaic - Syriac - Grammar, 3 vols., Vol. 1. 2006. (Gorgias Historical Grammars Ser.: 2). 942p. 198.00 *(978-1-59333-512-0(1))* Gorgias Pr., LLC.

Awde, Nicholas, et al. Modern Aramaic (Assyrian/Syriac) Dictionary & Phrasebook. 2006. (ENG & SYR., Illus.). 240p. per. 12.95 *(978-0-7818-1087-6(6))* Hippocrene Bks., Inc.

Baumel & Vermeersch, Peter. The Romani Movement: Minority Politics & Ethnic Mobilization in Contemporary Central Europe. 2007. (ENG.). 280p. 29.95 *(978-1-84545-102-8(3))* Berghahn Bks., Inc.

A

Bauscher, David. English-Aramaic & Aramaic-English Dictionary. 2008. 613p. pap. 37.97 *(978-1-4357-3014-4(3))* Lulu Enterprises Inc.
Cathcart, Kevin J. Targumic & Cognate Studies: Essays in Honour of Martin Mcnamara. Maher, Michael, ed. 2009. (Library of Hebrew Bible/Old Testament Studies, the Ser.). (ENG.). 250p. 44.95 *(978-0-567-60396-8(2),* T&T Clark) Continuum International Publishing Group, Ltd. GBR. Dist: National Bk. Network.
Catholic Catechism in the Mosul Dialect of Aramaic (Sureth) 2010. (SYR.). pap. 22.00 *(978-1-61719-623-2(1))* Gorgias Pr., LLC.
Catholic Catechism in Urmia Aramaic. 2010. (SYR.). pap. 27.28 *(978-1-61719-622-5(3))* Gorgias Pr., LLC.
Chabot, Jean Baptiste & Lawrence, Anton. Aramaic Languages & their Study. Jaqqi, Murad, tr. 2010. pap. 22.60 *(978-1-61719-459-7(X))* Gorgias Pr., LLC.
Ciancaglini, Claudia. Iranian Loanwords in Syriac. 2008. (Beitrage zur Iranistik Ser.). (ENG.). 364p. (C). 116.00 *(978-3-89500-624-1(6))* Reichert, Ludwig Dr. DEU. Dist: Brown, David Bk. Co., The.
Cook, E. M. A Glossary of Targum Onkelos: According to Alexander Sperber's Edition. 2008. (Studies in the Aramaic Interpretation of Scripture). (ARC & ENG.). 336p. (C). *(978-90-04-14978-6(3))* BRILL.
Cowley, Arthur E. Aramaic Papyri of the Fifth Century B.C. 319p. reprint ed. 68.00 *(978-0-7222-9901-2(X))* Library Reprints, Inc.
Davidson, Benjamin. The Analytical Hebrew & Chaldee Lexicon. 2010. (HEB & ARC.). 174.08 *(978-1-61143-417-0(3))* Gorgias Pr., LLC.
Duval, Rubens. Les Dialectes Néo-Araméens de Salamas: Textes sur l¿état actuel de la Perse et contes Populaires. 2008. (Gorgias Historical Grammars Ser.: 12). (FRE & GER.). 98.00 *(978-1-59333-787-2(6))* Gorgias Pr., LLC.
Fox, Samuel. The Neo-Aramaic Dialect of Bohtan. 2010. 100.00 *(978-1-60724-133-1(1))* Gorgias Pr., LLC.
Frank, Yitzchak. Grammar for Gemara & Targum Onkelos. rev. exp. ed. 120p. 26.99 *(978-1-58330-606-2(4))* Feldheim Pubs.
Gesenius, Wilhelm & Tregelles, Samuel Prideaux. Gesenius' Hebrew & Chaldee Lexicon to the Old Testament Scriptures. 2010. (HEB & ARC.). pap. 127.84 *(978-1-61143-312-8(6))* Gorgias Pr., LLC.
Gottheil, Richard J. H. The Judaeo-Aramaean Dialect of Salamas. 2010. (HEB & ARC.). 81.80 *(978-1-61143-396-8(7))* Gorgias Pr., LLC.
Greenblatt, Jared. The Jewish Neo-Aramaic Dialect of Amß#8482;diya. 2010. (Studies in Semitic Languages & Linguistics Ser.). (ARC & ENG.). 650p. *(978-90-04-18257-8(8))* BRILL.
Haberl, Charles G. The Neo-Mandaic Dialect of Khorramshahr. 2009. (Semitica Viva Ser.). (ENG.). 379p. (C). 117.00 *(978-3-447-05874-2(9))* Harrassowitz, Otto Verlag DEU. Dist: ISD.
Isbell, Charles D. Corpus of the Aramaic Incantation Bowls. 2009. 214p. pap. 24.00 *(978-1-60608-106-8(3))* Wipf & Stock Pubs.
Jastrow, Marcus. A Dictionary of the Targumim, the Talmud Babli & Yerushalmi, & the Midrashic Literature. 2007. 624p. per. *(978-956-291-475-8(5))*; 436p. per. *(978-956-291-474-1(7))*; (ENG.). 704p. per. *(978-956-291-476-5(3))* Editorial Benei Noaj.
Jastrow, Marcus, compiled by. A Dictionary of the Targumim. the Talmud Babli & Yerushalmi & the Midrashic Literature. 2010. (HEB & ARC.). 290.48 *(978-1-61143-498-9(X))* Gorgias Pr., LLC.
Khan, G. The Neo-Aramaic Dialect of Barwar, 3 vols. 2008. (ARC & ENG., Illus.). xxxviii, 2175p. *(978-90-04-16765-0(X))* BRILL.
Khan, Geoffrey. The Jewish Neo-Aramaic Dialect of Urmi. 2008. *(978-1-59333-425-3(7))* Gorgias Pr., LLC.
Kuty, R. J. Studies in the Syntax of Targum Jonathan to Samuel. 2010. (Ancient near Eastern Studies Supplement Ser.). 285p. (C). 124.00 *(978-90-429-2211-2(7))* Peeters Pubs. & Booksellers BEL. Dist: Brown, David Bk. Co., The.
Levias, Caspar. A Grammar of the Aramaic Idiom Contained in the Babylonian Talmud. 2011. pap. 23.08 *(978-1-61143-873-4(X))* Gorgias Pr., LLC.
Li, Tarsee. The Verbal System of the Aramaic of Daniel: An Explanation in the Context of Grammaticalization. 2009. (Studies in the Aramaic Interpretation of Scripture). (ARC & ENG.). 215p. *(978-90-04-17514-3(8))* BRILL.
Lipinski, E. Studies in Aramaic Inscriptions & Onomastics, Volume III: Ma'lana. 2010. (Orientalia Lovaniensia Analecta Ser.). (ENG.). 327p. (C). 109.00 *(978-90-429-2380-5(6))* Peeters Pubs. & Booksellers BEL. Dist: Brown, David Bk. Co., The.
Mahar, Danny. Aramaic Made EZ, No. 1. (Illus.). 114p. spiral bd. 49.95 *(978-0-9675989-1-8(5))* Aramaic Bible Society,The.
Margolis, Max L. A Manual of the Aramaic Language of the Babylonian Talmud: Grammar Chrestomathy & Glossaries. 2008. (Illus.). 298p. pap. 17.00 *(978-1-55635-760-2(5))* Wipf & Stock Pubs.
Mayerhofer, Kerstin & Sander, Ruth. Retrograde Hebrew & Aramaic Dictionary. 2010. (Journal of Ancient Judaism. Supplements (JAJ. S) Ser.). (ARC, HEB & ENG.). 258p. (C). 96.00 *(978-3-525-55007-6(3))* Vandenhoeck & Ruprecht GmbH & Co. KG DEU. Dist: ISD.
Meyers, Eric M. & Flesher, Paul Virgil McCracken. Aramaic in Postbiblical Judaism & Early Christianity: Papers from the 2004 National Endowment for the Humanities Summer Seminar at Duke University. 2010. 49.50 *(978-1-57506-178-8(3))* Eisenbrauns, Inc.
Mutzafi, Hezy. The Jewish Neo-Aramaic Dialect of Betanure (Province of Dihok) 2008. (Semitica Viva Ser.). (ARC & ENG.). 432p. (C). 117.00 *(978-3-447-05710-3(6))* Harrassowitz, Otto Verlag DEU. Dist: ISD.
Muzzarelli, P. & David, Francis. Daily Meditations. 2010. (SYR.). 113.36 *(978-1-61143-340-1(1))* Gorgias Pr., LLC.
Planukoche, J. A. H. On the Prevalence of the Aramaean Language in Palestine in the Age of Christ & the Apostles. 2010. 84.56 *(978-1-61143-457-6(2))* Gorgias Pr., LLC.
Powell, Herbert Harry. The Supposed Hebraism in the Grammar of the Biblical Aramaic. 2008. 60p. pap. 5.00 *(978-1-55635-798-5(2))* Wipf & Stock Pubs.
Ronning, John L. The Jewish Targums & John's Logos Theology, 1 vol. 2010. (ENG., Illus.). 400p. *(978-1-59856-306-1(8))* Hendrickson Pubs. Marketing, LLC.
Sara, Solomon I. A Description of Modern Chaldean. (Janua Linguarum. Series Practica Ser.). (ENG.). 114p. (Orig.). 210.00 ***(978-3-11-174941-9(X))*** De Gruyter, Mouton DEU. Dist: de Gruyter, Walter GmbH & Co. KG.
Schuele, Andreas. An Introduction to Biblical Aramaic. 2012. (ENG.). 136p. pap. 30.00 ***(978-0-664-23424-9(0))*** Westminster John Knox Pr.
Shepherd, Michael B. The Verbal System of Biblical Aramaic: A Distributional Approach. 2007. (Studies in Biblical Literature Ser.). 194p. (C). 64.95 *(978-1-4331-0201-1(3))* Lang, Peter Publishing, Inc.
Stevenson, William Barron. Grammar of Palestinian Jewish Aramaic. 2011. pap. 34.40 *(978-1-61143-928-1(0))* Gorgias Pr., LLC.
Strack, Hermann L. Grammatik des Biblisch-Aramaischen: Mit den Nach Handschriften Berichtigten Texten und Einem Worterbuch. 2009. 100p. pap. 6.00 *(978-1-60608-755-8(X),* Wipf and Stock) Wipf & Stock Pubs.
Strong, James & Thomas Nelson Publishing Staff. The New Strong's Guide to Bible Words: An English Index to Hebrew & Greek Words, 0 vols. 2008. 304p. pap. 18.99 *(978-1-4185-3218-5(5))* Nelson, Thomas Inc.
Syriac Noun & Verb Paradigms in the Eastern Pronunciation (Chaldean) 2010. (SYR.). pap. 27.04 *(978-1-61719-620-1(7))* Gorgias Pr., LLC.
Tezel, Sina. Arabic Borrowings in Surayt/Turoyo Within the Framework of Phonological Correspondences: In Comparison with Other Semitic Languages. 2011. (Studia Semetica Uppsaliensia Ser.). 226p. pap. 72.50 *(978-91-554-8058-5(6))* Uppsala Universitet/Acta Universitatis Uppsaliensis SWE. Dist: Coronet Bks.
Tov, Emanuel. Scribal Practices & Approaches Reflected in the Texts Found in the Judean Desert. 2009. 49.95 *(978-1-58983-429-3(1))* Society of Biblical Literature.
Van Pelt, Miles V. Basics of Biblical Aramaic: Complete Grammar, Lexicon, & Annotated Text, 1 vol. 2011. (ENG.). 304p. pap. 44.99 *(978-0-310-49391-4(9))* Zondervan.

ARAMAIC LITERATURE

Casey, Maurice. Aramaic Sources of Mark's Gospel. 2007. (Society for New Testament Studies Monograph Ser.). (ENG.). 292p. pap. 60.00 *(978-0-521-03613-9(5))* Cambridge Univ. Pr.
Chabot, J. B. & Lawrence, Anton Shukri. Aramaic Dialects & Literature. 2010. pap. 22.96 *(978-1-61719-607-2(X))* Gorgias Pr., LLC.
Manna, Jacques Eugène, ed. Selected Passages from Aramaic Literature. 2010. (SYR.). 134.96 *(978-1-61143-341-8(X))* Gorgias Pr., LLC.
Reading Book for Urmia Aramaic. 2010. (SYR.). pap. 23.68 *(978-1-61719-621-8(5))* Gorgias Pr., LLC.
Yakup, Abdurishid, ed. The Prajna-pa-ramita: Texts in Old Uyghur. 2010. (Berliner Turfantexte Ser.). (ENG.). 319p. (C). pap. 174.00 *(978-2-503-52888-5(0))* Brepols Pubs. BEL. Dist: Brown, David Bk. Co., The.

ARAMEANS

Healey, John. Law & Religion Between Petra & Edessa: Studies in Aramaic Epigraphy on the Roman Frontier. 2011. (Variorum Collected Studies). (Illus.). 320p. 154.95 *(978-1-4094-0367-8(X))* Ashgate Publishing Co.
Kraeling, Emil G. Aram & Israel or, Aramaeans in Syria & Mesopotamia. (Columbia University, Oriental Studies: No. 13). reprint ed. 34.00 *(978-0-404-50503-5(1))* AMS Pr., Inc.
Kraeling, Emil G. H. Aram & Israel: The Aramaeans in Syria & Mesopotamia. 2008. 171p. pap. 15.00 *(978-1-60608-394-9(5),* Wipf and Stock) Wipf & Stock Pubs.
Kraeling, Emil G. H. & Gottheil, Richard. Aram & Israel. 2010. pap. 36.52 *(978-1-61143-471-2(8))* Gorgias Pr., LLC.
Stubbs, Elsina. The Life & Institutions of the Aramaic People: A Social History. 2010. 312p. *(978-0-7734-3794-4(0))* Mellen, Edwin Pr., The.

ARAN ISLAND (IRELAND)

Mayr, Andrea. The Aran Islands in Anglo-Irish & Irish Literature: A Literary History & Selected Studies. 2008. (Europäische Hochschulschriften. Reihe 14: Angelsächsische Sprache und Literatur Ser.). 226p. pap. 61.95 *(978-3-631-56599-5(2))* Lang, Peter GmbH, Europaischer Verlag der Wissenschaften DEU. Dist: Lang, Peter.
Nelson, Charles. The Wild Plants of the Burren & the Aran Islands: A Field Guide. 2nd rev. ed. 2008. (ENG., Illus.). 160p. pap. 29.95 *(978-1-905172-67-2(2))* Collins Pr., The IRL. Dist: Dufour Editions, Inc.
O'Rourke, Con. Nature Guide to the Aran Islands. 2007. (ENG., Illus.). 184p. pap. 36.95 *(978-1-84351-078-9(2))* Lilliput Pr., Ltd., The IRL. Dist: Dufour Editions, Inc.
Robinson, Tim. Stones of Aran: Pilgrimage. 2008. (New York Review Books Classics). (ENG., Illus.). 316p. pap. 18.95 *(978-1-59017-277-3(9),* NYRB Classics) New York Review of Bks., Inc., The.
—Stones of Aran: Labyrinth. 2009. (ENG., Illus.). 528p. pap. 22.95 *(978-1-59017-314-5(7))* New York Review of Bks., Inc., The.
Synge, J. M. The Aran Islands. 2009. (Illus.). 170p. pap. *(978-1-4099-6207-6(5))* Dodo Pr.
Synge, J. m. & Synge, John Millington. The Aran Islands. 2010. 98p. 33.95 *(978-1-161-45669-1(4))* Kessinger Publishing, LLC.
Synge, John Millington. The Aran Islands. 2009. 226p. 28.99 *(978-1-115-18341-3(9))* 2009. 226p. 32.99 *(978-1-115-18343-7(5))* 2009. 226p. pap. 25.75 *(978-1-115-18340-6(0))* 2009. (ENG.). 224p. pap. 20.99 *(978-1-115-18333-8(8),* BiblioLife) 2009. (ENG.). 224p. pap. 22.99 *(978-1-115-18335-2(4),* BiblioLife) 2008. (ENG.). 146p. per. 20.75 *(978-1-4375-3108-4(3))* 2008. (ENG.). 164p. per. 21.75 *(978-1-4375-3219-7(5))* 2007. (ENG.). 132p. pap. 18.99 *(978-1-4264-1589-0(3))* BiblioBazaar.
—The Aran Islands. 2009. 96p. pap. *(978-1-151-48024-8(X))* Books LLC.
—The Aran Islands. 2008. (ENG., Illus.). 136p. per. *(978-1-4065-6666-6(7))* Dodo Pr.
—The Aran Islands. 2010. 124p. pap. *(978-1-4076-2561-4(6))* HardPr.
—The Aran Islands. 2010. 98p. pap. 15.16 *(978-1-162-68804-6(1))* Kessinger Publishing, LLC.
—The Aran Islands. 2008. (ENG.). 124p. per. 12.99 *(978-1-59547-751-4(9))* NuVision Pubns., LLC.
—The Aran Islands. 2008. (ENG.). 128p. pap. 11.45 *(978-1-4385-1090-3(X),* Book Jungle) Standard Pubns., Inc.
—Aran Islands. 2006. pap. *(978-1-4068-2129-1(2))* Echo Library.
—The Aran Islands. l.t. ed. 2007. (ENG.). 128p. pap. 19.99 *(978-1-4264-1603-3(2))* BiblioBazaar.
—The Aran Islands. (Collected Works of John Millington Synge). reprint ed. lib. bdg. 98.00 *(978-0-7426-2907-3(4))* Classic Bks.
—Aran Islands & Connemara. 2008. (ENG.). 224p. pap. 22.95 *(978-1-85635-599-5(3))* Mercier Pr., Ltd., The IRL. Dist: Dufour Editions, Inc.
Yeats, Jack B. & Synge, John Millington. The Aran Islands. 2008. (ENG.). 146p. pap. 20.75 *(978-1-4375-1951-8(2))*; 162p. pap. 21.75 *(978-1-4375-1952-5(0))* BiblioBazaar.

ARANDA (AUSTRALIAN PEOPLE)

Austin-Broos, Diane. Arrernte Present, Arrernte Past: Invasion, Violence, & Imagination in Indigenous Central Australia. 2009. (ENG., Illus.). 336p. 70.00 *(978-0-226-03263-4(9))*; pap. 25.00 *(978-0-226-03264-1(7))* Univ. of Chicago Pr.
Brooks, David. A Town Like Mparntwe: A Guide to the Dreaming Tracks & Sites of Alice Springs. 2007. (ENG., Illus.). 32p. pap. 11.95 *(978-1-86465-045-7(1))* IAD Pr. AUS. Dist: Independent Pubs. Group.

ARANEIDA

see Spiders

ARANTA (AUSTRALIAN PEOPLE)

see Aranda (Australian People)

ARAPAHO INDIANS

see Indians of North America—West (U.S.)

ARAPESH (PAPUA NEW GUINEAN PEOPLE)

Mead, Margaret. The Mountain Arapesh, V3-4: Socio-Economic Life & Diary of Events in Alitoa. 2011. 264p. 47.95 ***(978-1-258-07371-8(4))*** Literary Licensing, LLC.

ARARAT, MOUNT (TURKEY)

Larsen, David. Dinosaurs on the Ark. 2009. (Illus.). 368p. pap. 18.95 *(978-1-57258-569-0(2))* TEACH Services, Inc.
Parrot, Friedrich. Journey to Ararat. 2009. 230p. pap. *(978-1-4590-9316-4(X))* Books LLC.
—Journey to Ararat. Cooley, W. D., tr. 2008. 380p. 48.95 *(978-1-4372-5972-8(3))*; pap. 33.95 *(978-1-4371-3280-9(4))* Kessinger Publishing, LLC.

ARARGE LANGUAGE

see Harari Language

ARAUCANIAN LANGUAGE

see Mapuche Language

ARAWAKAN LANGUAGES

Aikhenvald, Alexandra Y. Language Contact in Amazonia. 2010. (ENG., Illus.). 400p. 55.00 *(978-0-19-958824-4(4))* Oxford Univ. Pr., Inc.
Farabee, William Curtis. The Central Arawaks. 2009. (Cambridge Library Collection - Linguistics Ser.). 344p. pap. 28.99 *(978-1-108-00624-8(8))* Cambridge Univ. Pr.
—The Central Arawaks. 2009. (Illus.). 194p. pap. 19.99 *(978-1-150-60282-5(1))* General Bks. LLC.
Goeje, C. H. de. The Arawak Language of Guiana. 2009. (Cambridge Library Collection - Physical Sciences Ser.). (ENG.). 316p. pap. 26.00 *(978-1-108-00768-9(6))* Cambridge Univ. Pr.
Hill, Jonathan D. & Santos-Granero, Fernando, eds. Comparative Arawakan Histories: Rethinking Language Family & Culture Area in Amazonia. 2006. (Illus.). 352p. per. 26.00 *(978-0-252-07384-7(3))* Univ. of Illinois Pr.

ARBITRAGE

Bialkowski, Jedrzej. Between Futures & Spot Markets- an Approach to Modelling Linkages among Financial Markets. 2007. 88p. per. *(978-3-8364-2948-1(9))* VDM Verlag Dr. Mueller e.K.
Björk, Tomas. Arbitrage Theory in Continuous Time. 3rd ed. 2009. (Oxford Finance Ser.). (ENG., Illus.). 512p. 85.00 *(978-0-19-957474-2(X))* Oxford Univ. Pr., Inc.
Burgstaller, Andre. Property & Prices. 2010. (ENG.). 256p. pap. 38.99 *(978-0-521-13406-4(4))* Cambridge Univ. Pr.
Delbaen, Freddy & Schachermayer, Walter. The Mathematics of Arbitrage. 2010. (Springer Finance Ser.). xvi, 371p. pap. 109.00 *(978-3-642-06030-4(7),* 3642060307) Springer.
Dubil, Robert. Financial Engineering & Arbitrage in the Financial Markets. 2011. (Wiley Finance Ser.: 584). (ENG., Illus.). 380p. 75.00 ***(978-0-470-74601-1(7),*** Wiley) Wiley, John & Sons, Inc.
Kirchner, Thomas. Merger Arbitrage: How to Profit from Event-Driven Arbitrage. 2009. (Wiley Finance Ser.: 472). (ENG., Illus.). 355p. 95.00 *(978-0-470-37197-8(8),* Wiley) Wiley, John & Sons, Inc.
Konstantinos, Sfakianakis. Statistical Arbitrage & Long Run Relations: Evidence from Two Different Stock Markets. 2011. 100p. pap. ***(978-3-639-34019-8(1))*** VDM Verlag Dr. Mueller e.K.
NAU, Robert F. Arbitrage & Rational Choice. 2013. (ENG., Illus.). 500p. 89.95 *(978-1-4398-0224-3(6),* Chapman & Hall/CRC) CRC Pr. LLC.
Newcombe, Andrew. Law & Practice of International Investment Treaties: Standards of Treatment. 2009. xxx, 614p. *(978-90-411-2351-0(2))* Kluwer Law International.
Pascucci, Andrea. PDE & Martingale Methods in Option Pricing. 2nd ed. 2010. (Bocconi & Springer Ser.). Orig. Title: Calcolo Stocastico per la Finanza. (ENG., Illus.). xviii, 720p. 84.95 *(978-88-470-1780-1(7),* 8847017807) Springer.
Shah, Rajeev. Sports Arbitrage - How to Place Riskless Bets & Create Tax-Free Investments. 2008. 133p. 41.95 *(978-1-4092-0478-7(2))* Lulu Enterprises Inc.
Stevens, Matthew A. Taxation of Financial Products & Transactions. 2007. (Tax Law & Practice Course Handbook Ser.: No. 763). (Illus.). 318p. *(978-1-4024-0904-2(4))* Practising Law Institute.
United Nations. Convention on the Recognition & Enforcement of Foreign Arbitral Awards (New York, 1958) 2008. (MUL.). 158p. pap. 25.00 *(978-92-1-033105-0(2))* United Nations Pubns.
Wyser-Pratte, Guy & Wyser-pratte. Risk Arbitrage. 2009. (Wiley Investment Classics Ser.: 41). (ENG., Illus.). 304p. pap. 19.95 *(978-0-470-41571-9(1),* Wiley) Wiley, John & Sons, Inc.

ARBITRATION (INTERNATIONAL LAW)

see also Aggression (International Law); Diplomatic Negotiations in International Disputes; Disarmament; International Courts; Jurisdiction (International Law); Mediation, International

Akinci. International Arbitration in Turkey. 2011. 185.00 *(978-90-411-2777-8(1))* Wolters Kluwer Law & Business.
Alavi, Amin M. Legalization of Development in the WTO: Between Law & Politics. 2008. xiv, 243p. 172.00 *(978-90-411-2795-2(X))* Wolters Kluwer Law & Business.
Amerasinghe, C. F. Jurisdiction of Specific International Tribunals. 2008. 600p. *(978-90-04-16238-9(0))* BRILL.
Amerasinghe, Chittharanjan Felix. International Arbitral Jurisdiction. 2011. 380p. *(978-90-04-18133-5(4))* BRILL.
American Arbitration Association. ADR & the Law - 21st Edition. 2007. (ENG.). 400p. 85.00 *(978-1-929446-97-1(7))* JurisNet LLC.
Amos, Sheldon. Political & Legal Remedies for War. 2009. 372p. 26.99 *(978-1-103-54627-5(9))*; pap. 20.99 *(978-1-103-54623-7(6))* BiblioBazaar.
—Political & Legal Remedies for War. 2009. 160p. pap. 19.99 *(978-1-150-37011-3(4))* General Bks. LLC.
—Political & Legal Remedies for War. 2008. 376p. 48.95 *(978-1-4372-5904-9(9))*; pap. 33.95 *(978-1-4371-3207-6(3))* Kessinger Publishing, LLC.
Balch, Thomas. International Courts of Arbitration. 2009. 52p. pap. 16.75 *(978-1-110-48404-1(6))* BiblioBazaar.
Baldissera Santos, Leonardo. The Formal Requirements for Arbitration Agreements. 2010. 72p. pap. *(978-3-8383-7334-8(0))* Lambert Academic Publishing.
Bergman, Linn & Bond, Stephen. SCC Arbitral Awards, 2004-2009. 2011. xiii, 516p. ***(978-1-933833-69-9(6))*** Juris Publishing, Inc.
Blanke. Global Cartel Litigation. 2011. ring bd. *(978-90-411-2712-9(7))* Wolters Kluwer Law & Business.
Blanke, Gordon. The Use & Utility of International Arbitration in EC Commission Merger Remedies: A Novel Supranational Paradigm in the Making? 2006. 342p. (C). 125.00 *(978-90-76871-56-1(6))* Europa Law Publishing, Netherlands NLD. Dist: International Specialized Bk. Services.
Borba, Igor M. International Arbitration in the 21st Century. 2010. 120p. pap. *(978-3-639-23283-7(6))* VDM Verlag Dr. Mueller e.K.
Born, Gary B. International Commercial Arbitration: Commentary & Materials, 2 vols., Vol. 2. 3rd rev. ed. 2009. lvi, 3303p. 455.00 *(978-90-411-2759-4(3))* Wolters Kluwer Law & Business.
Brekoulakis, Stavros L. Third Parties in International Commercial Arbitration. 2011. (ENG.). 304p. 265.00 *(978-0-19-957208-3(9))* Oxford Univ. Pr., Inc.
Brunner, Christoph. Force Majeure under General Contract Principles. 2008. (International Arbitration Law Library). xxxii, 589p. 218.00 *(978-90-411-2792-1(5))* Wolters Kluwer Law & Business.
Carbonneau, Thomas E. & Grey, Zachary, eds. Yearbook on Arbitration & Mediation. 2011. 630p. pap. 69.95 ***(978-1-60042-145-7(8))*** Vandeplas Publishing.
Chamlongrasdr, Dhisadee. Foreign State Immunity & Arbitration, 1 vol. 2007. 238.00 *(978-1-905017-39-3(1))* Cameron May, Ltd. GBR. Dist: Gaunt, Inc.
Cimmino, Désirée. Das UNCITRAL-Modellgesetz über internationale ADR-Verfahren in Wirtschaftsstreitigkeiten. 2008. (Schriften zum Verfahrensrecht Ser.). 360p. pap. 81.95 *(978-3-631-56979-5(3))* Lang, Peter GmbH, Europaischer Verlag der Wissenschaften DEU. Dist: Lang, Peter.
Favalli, D., et al, eds. Selected Papers on International Arbitration. 2011. 144p. pap. 82.50 *(978-94-90947-14-9(8))* Eleven International Publishing NLD. Dist: International Specialized Bk. Services.

Ferrari, Franco & KröLl, Stefan. Conflict of Laws in International Arbitration. 2011. 480p. pap.. pap. 109.00 (978-3-86653-170-3(2)) Sellier - European Law Publishers GmbH DEU. Dist: International Specialized Bk. Services.

Foster, Jhon W. Arbitration & the Hague Court. 2009. 158p. 26.99 (978-1-110-40576-3(6)); pap. 20.75 (978-1-110-40574-9(X)) BiblioBazaar.

Foster, John W. Arbitration & the Hague Court. 2010. 148p. pap. 16.76 (978-1-163-25956-6(X)) 2007. 146p. 35.95 (978-0-548-23688-8(7)) 2007. 148p. per. 20.95 (978-1-4326-3799-6(1)) Kessinger Publishing, LLC.

Foster, John Watson. Arbitration & the Hague Court. 2009. 62p. pap. (978-1-4590-7949-6(3)); 66p. pap. (978-0-217-43889-6(X)) Books LLC.

Friedland, Paul D. Arbitration Clauses for International Contracts 2nd Edition. 2007. (ENG.). 150.00 (978-1-933833-06-4(8)) JurisNet LLC.

Gibson, Christopher S. & Drahozal, Christopher R. The Iran-U. S, Claims Tribunal at 25: The Cases Everyone Needs to Know for Investor-State & International Arbitration. 2007. (ENG.). 450p. 215.00 (978-0-19-532514-0(1)) Oxford Univ. Pr., Inc.

Grando, Michelle T. Evidence, Proof, & Fact-Finding in WTO Dispute Settlement. 2010. (International Economic Law Ser.). (ENG.). 350p. 154.00 (978-0-19-957264-9(X)) Oxford Univ. Pr., Inc.

Griffin, Clifford E. The Race for Fisheries & Hydrocarbons in the Caribbean Basin: The Barbados-Trinidad & Tobago Dispute, Regional Delimitation Implications. 2007. (Illus.). xx, 181p. pap. (978-976-637-316-0(7)) Randle, Ian Pubs., Inc.

Guglya, Leonila. Confidentiality in Enforcement Phase of International Arbitration. 2008. 76p. pap. (978-3-639-07318-8(5)) VDM Verlag Dr. Mueller e.K.

Gusy, Martin F., et al. A Guide to the ICDR International Arbitration Rules. 2011. (ENG.). 312p. 160.00 (978-0-19-959684-3(0)) Oxford Univ. Pr., Inc.

Hartley, Trevor. International Commercial Litigation: Text, Cases & Materials on Private International Law. 2009. (ENG.). 962p. (C). pap. 93.00 (978-0-521-68748-5(9)) Cambridge Univ. Pr.

Heard, H. Roderic, et al. International Commercial Arbitration Advocacy: A Practitioner's Guide for American Lawyers. 2011. (978-1-60156-081-0(8)) National Institute for Trial Advocacy.

Hirst, Francis Wrigley. The Arbiter in Council. 2009. 576p. 44.99 (978-1-116-77539-6(5)); 37.99 (978-1-116-77540-2(9)); pap. 43.75 (978-1-116-77541-9(7)); pap. 42.75 (978-1-116-77542-6(5)) BiblioBazaar.

Holls, Frederick W. The Peace Conference at the Hague & Its Bearings on International Law & Policy. 600p. 2008. 59.95 (978-1-4365-9847-7(8)) 2007. (ENG.). per. 44.95 (978-0-548-80405-6(2)) Kessinger Publishing, LLC.

—The Peace Conference at the Hague & Its Bearings on International Law & Policy. 2007. 604p. per. (978-1-4067-4388-3(7)) Read Bks.

Hopkins, Roger. Arbitration Law Handbook. Horn, Ben, ed. 2007. 1016p. pap. 441.00 (978-1-84311-708-7(8)) Informa Professional GBR. Dist: International Specialized Bk. Services.

Hull, William Isaac. The Two Hague Conferences: And Their Contributions to International Law (1908) 2008. 536p. 55.95 (978-1-4374-4505-3(5)); pap. 40.95 (978-1-4373-4346-5(5)) Kessinger Publishing, LLC.

—The Two Hague Conferences & Their Contributions to International Law. 2009. 524p. 29.99 (978-1-103-21229-3(X)); pap. 23.99 (978-1-103-21228-6(1)) BiblioBazaar.

Icc. Dossier Vi: Written Evidence & Discovery. 2009. (Illus.). 509p. pap. (978-90-411-3183-6(3)) Kluwer Law International.

Jenkins, Jane & Stebbings, Simon. International Construction Arbitration Law. 2006. (Arbitration in Context Ser.: Vol. 1). (Illus.). 442p. (978-90-411-2341-1(5)) Kluwer Law International.

King, Alice. The Consolidation of Claims in Icsid Arbitration. 2010. 92p. pap. (978-3-8383-6968-6(8)) Lambert Academic Publishing.

Klip, André & Sluiter, Göran. Annotated Leading Cases of International Criminal Tribunals: The International Criminal Tribunal for Rwanda 2001-2002. 2007. 1033p. pap. 259.00 (978-90-5095-544-7(4)) Intersentia Uitgevers N.V. BEL. Dist: International Specialized Bk. Services.

Klip, André & Sluiter, Göran, eds. Annotated Leading Cases of International Criminal Tribunals - Volume 13: Timor Leste - the Special Panels for Serious Crimes 2001-2003, 2 vols. 2008. 846p. pap. 259.00 (978-90-5095-673-4(4)) Intersentia Uitgevers N.V. BEL. Dist: International Specialized Bk. Services.

—Annotated Leading Cases of International Criminal Tribunals - Volume 25: The International Criminal Tribunal for Rwanda 2006-2007. 2010. 969p. pap. 259.00 (978-90-5095-916-2(4)) Intersentia Uitgevers N.V. BEL. Dist: International Specialized Bk. Services.

Ladd, William. An Essay on a Congress of Nations for the Adjustment of International Disputes Without Resort to Arms. 2009. 144p. pap. 15.60 (978-1-150-05980-3(X)) General Bks. LLC.

—An Essay on a Congress of Nations for the Adjustment of International Disputes Without Resort to Arms. 2007. 85.00 (978-1-58477-745-8(1)) Lawbook Exchange, Ltd., The.

Lauterpacht, Hersch. The Function of Law in the International Community. 2011. 512p. pap. 60.00 (978-0-19-960881-2(4)) Oxford Univ. Pr., Inc.

Lee, Karen, ed. Iran-U.S. Claims Tribunal Reports, 2004-2009, Vol. 38. 2010. (Iran-U. S. Claims Tribunal Reports). (ENG.). 622p. 265.00 (978-0-521-19753-8(9)) Cambridge Univ. Pr.

Lovric, Daniel. Deference to the Legislature in WTO Challenges to Legislation. 2009. (Illus.). xxvi, 234p. 172.00 (978-90-411-3145-4(0)) Wolters Kluwer Law & Business.

Macmahon, Belinda & Permanent Court of Arbitration Staff, eds. Multiple Party Actions in International Arbitration: Consent, Procedure & Enforcement. 2009. (ENG.). 440p. 195.00 (978-0-19-955172-9(3)) Oxford Univ. Pr., Inc.

Mahan, Alfred Thayer. Armaments & Arbitration. 2009. 162p. pap. (978-1-4590-7996-4(1)) Books LLC.

—Armaments & Arbitration: Or the Place of Force in the International Relations of States (1912) 2009. 272p. 42.95 (978-1-120-23759-0(9)); pap. 27.95 (978-1-120-15818-5(4)) Kessinger Publishing, LLC.

—Armaments & Arbitration, or, the Place of Force in the International Relations of States. 2010. 272p. 34.99 (978-1-140-55868-2(4)) BiblioBazaar.

—Armaments & Arbitration, or, the Place of Force in the International Relations of States. reprint ed. pap. 125.00 (978-1-4047-3931-4(9)) Classic Textbooks.

Martinez-Fraga, Pedro J. The American Influences on International Commercial Arbitration: Doctrinal Developments & Discovery Methods. 2009. (ENG., Illus.). 432p. 152.00 (978-0-521-76588-6(9)) Cambridge Univ. Pr.

Menkel-Meadow, Carrie, ed. International Dispute Resolution, Vol. III. 2012. (Complex Dispute Resolution Ser.). 666p. 350.00 **(978-0-7546-2804-0(3))** Ashgate Publishing Co.

Merrills, J. G. International Dispute Settlement. 5th rev. ed. 2011. (ENG.). 386p. (C). 125.00 (978-0-521-19909-4(3)); pap. 65.00 (978-0-521-15339-3(5)) Cambridge Univ. Pr.

Minor, Raleigh C. A Republic of Nations: A Study of the Organization of a Federal League of Nations. 2009. 360p. 26.99 (978-1-103-76004-6(1)); pap. 20.99 (978-1-103-75998-9(1)) BiblioBazaar.

Mistelis. Arbitrability in International Arbitration. 2009. xxiv, 375p. 185.00 (978-90-411-2730-3(5)) Wolters Kluwer Law & Business.

—Concise Arbitration. 2010. xvi, 1115p. (978-90-411-2609-2(0)) Kluwer Law International.

Mistelis, Loukas A. Arbitration Insights: Twenty Years of the Annual Lecture of the School of International Arbitration, Sponsored by Freshfields Bruckhaus Deringer. Lew, Julian D. M., ed. 2006. (International Arbitration Law Library Series Set Ser.). 506p. (978-90-411-2606-1(6)) Kluwer Law International.

Moore, John B. History & Digest of the International Arbitrations to Which the United States Has Been a Party, 6 vols., Set. reprint ed. 1800.00 (978-0-404-12270-6(1)) AMS Pr., Inc.

Morris, Robert C. International Arbitration & Procedure. 2009. 252p. 30.99 (978-1-110-48399-0(6)); pap. 25.75 (978-1-110-48398-3(8)) BiblioBazaar.

Morrissey, Joseph. International Sales Law & Arbitration: Problems, Cases, & Commentary. 2008. 118.00 (978-0-7355-7707-7(2)) Wolters Kluwer Law & Business.

Müller, Christoph. Swiss Case Law in International Arbitration. 2010. 568p. pap. 199.00 (978-3-86653-150-5(8)) Sellier - European Law Publishers GmbH DEU. Dist: International Specialized Bk. Services.

O'Leary, Rosemary & Fleishman, Rachel, eds. Recent Developments in Conflict Resolution. 2008. (Illus.). 200p. 119.99 (978-1-84855-290-6(4)) Emerald Group Publishing Ltd. GBR. Dist: Turpin Distribution Services Ltd.

Paulsson, Jan. The Idea of Arbitration. 2013. (Clarendon Law Ser.). (ENG.). 250p. 110.00 (978-0-19-956416-3(7)); pap. 45.00 (978-0-19-956417-0(5)) Oxford Univ. Pr., Inc.

Reinisch, August & Knahr, Christina, eds. International Investment Law in Context. 2007. 207p. (C). 88.00 (978-90-77596-48-7(8)) Eleven International Publishing NLD. Dist: International Specialized Bk. Services.

Rogers, Catherine. Ethics in International Arbitration. 2013. (ENG.). 350p. 95.00 (978-0-19-533769-3(7)) Oxford Univ. Pr., Inc.

Rovine, Arthur W. Contemporary Issues in International Arbitration & Mediation: The Fordham Papers. 2010. 485p. (978-90-04-18291-2(8)) BRILL.

Rovine, Arthur W., ed. Contemporary Issues in International Arbitration & Mediation: The Fordham Papers 2007. 2008. xxx, 336p. (C). (978-90-04-16738-4(2)) BRILL.

—Contemporary Issues in International Arbitration & Mediation: The Fordham Papers:2008, Vol. 2. 2009. (Contemporary Issues in International Arbitration & Mediation: the Fordham Papers Ser.). 350p. (978-90-04-17555-6(5)) BRILL.

Salacuse, Jeswald W. The Law of International Investment Treaties. 2010. (Oxford International Law Library). (ENG.). 600p. 209.00 (978-0-19-920605-6(8)) Oxford Univ. Pr., Inc.

Savage & Mcilwrath, Michael. Practical Handbook on International Commercial Arbitration. 2010. (Illus.). 515p. (978-90-411-2610-8(4)) Kluwer Law International.

Schreuer, Christoph H. The ICSID Convention: A Commentary. 2nd ed. 2009. (ENG.). 1592p. 400.00 (978-0-521-88559-1(0)) Cambridge Univ. Pr.

Schwebel, Stephen M. Justice in International Law: Further Selected Writings. 2011. (ENG., Illus.). 384p. 125.00 (978-1-107-00537-2(X)) Cambridge Univ. Pr.

—Justice in International Law: Selected Writings. 2008. (ENG.). 648p. pap. 79.00 (978-0-521-07299-1(9)) Cambridge Univ. Pr.

Schwenzer, Ingeborg & Spagnalo, Lisa, eds. Towards Uniformity: The 2nd Annual MAA Schlechtriem CISG Conference. 2011. 300p. 106.00 (978-94-90947-10-1(5)) Eleven International Publishing NLD. Dist: International Specialized Bk. Services.

Shadikhodjaev, Sherzod. Retaliation in the WTO Dispute Settlement System. 2009. (Illus.). xviii, 292p. 172.00 (978-90-411-2811-9(5)) Wolters Kluwer Law & Business.

Sluiter, Göran. Annotated Leading Cases of International Criminal Tribunals Vol. 16: The International Criminal Tribunal for Timor-Leste July, 2003-2006, 2 vols. Klip, André & Sluiter, Göran, eds. 2009. 931p. pap. 329.00 (978-90-5095-674-1(2)) Intersentia Uitgevers N.V. BEL. Dist: International Specialized Bk. Services.

—Annotated Leading Cases of International Criminal Tribunals Vol. 22: The International Criminal Tribunal for Rwanda 2005. Sluiter, Göran & Klip, André, eds. 2009. (Annotated Leading Cases of International Criminal Tribunals Ser.: Vol. 22). 855p. pap. 259.00 (978-90-5095-851-6(6)) Intersentia Uitgevers N.V. BEL. Dist: International Specialized Bk. Services.

Sluiter, Göran & Klip, André, eds. Annotated Leading Cases of International Criminal Tribunals Vol. 24: The International Criminal Tribunal for Rwanda 9 November 2005- 12 September 2006. 2009. 1002p. pap. 259.00 (978-90-5095-852-3(4)) Intersentia Uitgevers N.V. BEL. Dist: International Specialized Bk. Services.

—Leading Cases of International Criminal Tribunals - The International Criminal Tribunal for the Former Yugoslavia, Vol. 20. annot. ed. 2010. 850p. pap. 259.00 (978-90-5095-915-5(6)) Intersentia Uitgevers N.V. BEL. Dist: International Specialized Bk. Services.

Strong, S. I. Research & Practice in International Commercial Arbitration: Sources & Strategies. 2009. (ENG.). 112p. pap. 85.00 (978-0-19-923830-9(8), Oxford Univ. Pr., Inc.

Tienhaara, Kyla. The Expropriation of Environmental Governance: Protecting Foreign Investors at the Expense of Public Policy. 2009. (ENG.). 340p. 102.00 (978-0-521-11487-5(X)) Cambridge Univ. Pr.

United Nations. Summaries of Judgments Advisory Opinions & Orders of the International Court of Justice: 2003-2007. 2009. (ENG.). 244p. pap. 30.00 (978-92-1-133776-1(3)) United Nations Pubns.

United Nations Conference on Trade and Development Staff, contrib. by. Investor-State Dispute Settlement & Impact on Investment Rulemaking. 2008. (UNCTAD Series on International Investment Policies for Development). (ENG., Illus.). 120p. pap. 20.00 (978-92-1-112720-1(3)) United Nations Pubns.

United Nations Staff. The Protection of National Security in IIAs. 2009. (UNCTAD Series on International Investment Policies for Development). (ENG.). 180p. pap. 23.00 (978-92-1-112772-0(6)) United Nations Pubns.

Van den, Berg. Yearbook Commercial Arbitration Vol Xxxiv 2009. 2009. pap. 296.00 (978-90-411-2807-2(7)) Wolters Kluwer Law & Business.

Van Den Berg, Albert Jan. Yearbook Commercial Arbitration Vol Xxxiii 2008. 2009. 1328p. pap. 296.00 (978-90-411-2830-0(1)) Wolters Kluwer Law & Business.

Várady, Tibor. Language & Translation in International Commercial Arbitration: From the Constitution of the Arbitral Tribunal through Recognition & Enforcement Proceedings. 2006. (ENG.). 324p. 89.95 (978-90-6704-233-8(1)) T.M.C. Asser Pr. NLD. Dist: Springer.

Varady, Tibor, et al. International Commercial Arbitration: A Transnational Perspective. 4th ed. 2009. xxviii, 985p. pap. (978-0-314-19542-5(4)) West Publishing Co., College & Schl. Div.

von Thulen Rhoades, Rufus, et al. Practitioner's Handbook on International Arbitration & Mediation- 2nd Edition. 2007. 1000p. 225.00 (978-1-933833-03-3(3)) JurisNet LLC.

Waibel, Michael. Sovereign Defaults before International Courts & Tribunals. 2011. (Cambridge Studies in International & Comparative Law Ser.). (ENG., Illus.). 424p. 110.00 (978-0-521-19699-4(X)) Cambridge Univ. Pr.

Warne, John. ed. International Commercial Dispute Resolution. 2009. 808p. 385.00 (978-1-84766-134-0(3), Bloomsbury Professional) Bloomsbury Publishing Plc GBR. Dist: International Specialized Bk. Services.

Wehberg, Hans. The Problem of an International Court of Justice. Fenwick, Charles G., tr. 284p. 2008. 43.95 (978-1-4365-5944-7(8)) 2007. (ENG.). per. 28.95 (978-0-548-76568-5(5)) Kessinger Publishing, LLC.

—The Problem of an International Court of Justice. 2008. 263p. 85.00 (978-1-58477-915-5(2)) Lawbook Exchange, Ltd., The.

Wells, Louis T. & Ahmed, Rafiq. Making Foreign Investment Safe: Property Rights & National Sovereignty. 2006. (ENG., Illus.). 392p. 60.00 (978-0-19-531062-7(4)) Oxford Univ. Pr., Inc.

Wild, Alexander, ed. CAS & Football: Landmark Cases: Landmark Cases. 2011. (ASSER International Sports Law Ser.). (ENG., Illus.). xiii, 272p. 139.00 (978-90-6704-807-1(0), 9067048070) T.M.C. Asser Pr. NLD. Dist: Springer.

Wolff, Reinmar. The New York Convention: A Commentary, 0 vols. 2012. (ENG.). 450p. 320.00 **(978-1-84946-196-2(1))** Hart Publishing Ltd. GBR. Dist: International Specialized Bk. Services.

Zartman. Peacemaking Intermatnl Conflct: Methods & Techniques 2nd rev. ed. 2007. 460p. pap. 29.95 (978-1-929223-66-4(8)) U. S. Institute of Peace Pr. (USIP Pr.).

—Peacemaking Intermatnl Conflct: Methods & Techniques. 2nd rev. ed. 2007. 460p. 60.00 (978-1-929223-65-7(X)) U. S. Institute of Peace Pr. (USIP Pr.).

ARBITRATION, INDUSTRIAL

see also Collective Bargaining; Grievance Procedures; Strikes and Lockouts

Allen, Henry J. Party of the Third Part: The Story of the Kansas Industrial Relations Court. 283p. reprint ed. lib. bdg. 98.00 (978-0-7222-4915-4(2)) Library Reprints, Inc.

American Arbitration Association. ADR & the Law - 21st Edition. 2007. (ENG.). 400p. 85.00 (978-1-929446-97-1(7)) JurisNet LLC.

Askwith, George Ranken Askwith. Industrial Problems & Disputes. 2009. 386p. pap. (978-0-217-48970-6(2)) Books LLC.

Aspatore Books Staff, compiled by. Employment Dispute Resolution: Leading Lawyers on Examining Company Policies & Procedures, Obtaining Key Information, & Considering Alternative Dispute Resolution. 2008. 116p. pap. 90.00 (978-0-314-19474-9(6)) Aspatore Bks.

Baer, Walt. Arbitration Strategy for Labor & Management Advocates. 2006. (ENG., Illus.). 265p. per. 49.95 (978-0-7864-2796-3(5)) McFarland & Co., Inc. Pubs.

Berman, Edward. Labor Disputes & the President of the United States. (Columbia University, Studies in the Social Sciences: No. 249). reprint ed. 27.50 (978-0-404-51249-1(6)) AMS Pr., Inc.

Bing, Alexander M. War-Time Strikes & Their Adjustment. 2009. 246p. pap. 21.24 (978-1-150-63808-4(7)) General Bks. LLC.

Brand, John, et al, eds. Labour Dispute Resolution, 1 vol. 2nd ed. 2009. 293p. pap. 52.00 (978-0-7021-7955-6(8)) Juta & Co., Ltd. ZAF. Dist: Gaunt, Inc.

Broida, Peter B. & Davis, Natania M. A Guide to Principles of Federal Sector Arbitration. 2008. viii, 263p. pap. (978-1-934651-03-2(6)) Dewey Pubns., Inc.

Clemente, Michael Anthony N. Handbook on Pleadings, Practice & Procedure Before the Labor Arbiters. 2010. xvi, 796p. (978-971-011-060-5(8)) Central Bks.

Franckiewicz, Matthew M. & Silverman, Daniel. Winning at the NLRB. 2009. (978-1-57018-707-0(X)) BNA Bks.

Gerhart, Paul F. & Befort, Stephen F., eds. Arbitration 2005: The Evolving World of Work. 2006. 472p. 45.00 (978-1-57018-563-2(8), 1563-PRY6) BNA Bks.

Grogan, John. Labour Litigation & Dispute Resolution. 2010. (Illus.). xxxiv, 416p. pap. (978-0-7021-8500-7(0)) Juta & Co., Ltd.

Hobson, J. A. The Conditions of Industrial Peace (Routledge Revivals) 2012. (Routledge Revivals Ser.). (ENG.) 128p. 80.00 **(978-0-415-52538-1(1))** Routledge.

Isaac, Joe & Macintyre, Stuart, eds. The New Province for Law & Order: 100 Years of Australian Industrial Conciliation & Arbitration. 2009. (ENG.). 456p. pap. 48.00 (978-0-521-12057-9(8)) Cambridge Univ. Pr.

Jagtenberg, R. & Sprengers, L. C. J., eds. Effective Resolution of Collective Labour Diputes. 2006. 165p. (C). pap. 60.00 (978-90-76871-61-5(2)) Europa Law Publishing, Netherlands NLD. Dist: International Specialized Bk. Services.

Ko Ting-Tsz. Government Methods of Adjusting Labor Disputes in North America & Australia. (Columbia University, Studies in the Social Sciences: No. 271). reprint ed. 20.00 (978-0-404-51271-2(2)) AMS Pr., Inc.

Leinenweber, Marcus Christian. Landesschlichtungsgesetze. 2011. (Schriften zum Arbeitsrecht und Wirtschaftsrecht Ser.). (GER.). 202p. 62.95 **(978-3-631-61814-1(X))** Lang, Peter GmbH, Europaischer Verlag der Wissenschaften DEU. Dist: Lang, Peter.

Lloyd, Henry Demarest. A Country without Strikes: A Visit to the Compulsory Arbitration Court of New Zealand. 2011. (Cambridge Library Collection - History Ser.). (ENG.). 202p. pap. 19.99 **(978-1-108-03947-5(2))** Cambridge Univ. Pr.

Loughran, Charles S. How to Prepare & Present a Labor Arbitration Case: Strategy & Tactics for Advocates. 2nd ed. 2006. (Illus.). xxxvii, 739p. (978-1-57018-562-5(X)) Bureau of National Affairs, Inc., (BNA), The.

Mistelis. Concise Arbitration. 2010. xvi, 1115p. (978-90-411-2609-2(0)) Kluwer Law International.

Plowman, David H. Holding the Line: Compulsory Arbitration & National Employer Co-Ordination in Australia. 2010. 288p. pap. 42.00 (978-0-521-12596-3(0)) Cambridge Univ. Pr.

Stone, Katherine Van Wezel & Bales, Richard A. Arbitration Law. 2nd ed. 2010. xxiii, 795p. **(978-1-60930-077-7(7)**, Foundation Pr.) West.

Varady, Tibor, et al. International Commercial Arbitration: A Transnational Perspective. 4th ed. 2009. xxviii, 985p. pap. (978-0-314-19542-5(4)) West Publishing Co., College & Schl. Div.

Warham, John. The 49ers: The True Story. 2011. (Illus.). 576p. 37.50 (978-1-84624-587-9(7)) Book Guild, Ltd. GBR. Dist: Trans-Atlantic Pubns., Inc.

"Workplace Fairness: Has the Supreme Court Been Misinterpreting Laws Designed to Protect American Workers from Discrimination?": Hearing Before the Committee on the Judiciary, United States Senate, One Hundred Eleventh Congress, First Session, October 7, 2009. 2010. (Illus.). iii, 309p. (978-0-16-086106-2(3), 552-070-51216-6) United States Government Printing Office.

Zack, Arnold. Arnold Zack: From A to Z. 2007. 314p. pap. 19.95 (978-1-4303-2770-7(7)) Lulu Enterprises Inc.

ARBITRATION, INTERNATIONAL

see Arbitration (International Law)

ARBITRATION AND AWARD

see also Compromise (Law)

Abraham. Alternative Dispute Resolution in Malaysia & Singapore. 2009. (978-90-411-2716-7(X)) Wolters Kluwer Law & Business.

ADR Client Strategies in the EU: Leading Lawyers on Advising Multinational Clients, Navigating Recent Trends, & Understanding the Key Laws Governing ADR in the EU (Inside the Minds) 2009. 152p. pap. 90.00 (978-0-314-21380-8(5)) Aspatore Bks.

ADR Client Strategies in the Middle East & Africa: Leading Lawyers on Assisting Multinational Companies in ADR Proceedings, Understanding Cultural Differences, & Developing Negotiation Tactics (Inside the Minds) 2009. 264p. pap. 110.00 (978-0-314-90950-3(8)) Aspatore Bks.

Aghahosseini, Mohsen. Claims of Dual Nationals & the Development of Customary International Law: Issues Before the Iran-United States Claims Tribunal. 2007. (Developments in International Law Ser.). 302p. (978-90-04-15698-2(4)) BRILL.

Aguilar, Guillermo & Reisman, W. Michael. The Reasons Requirement in International Investment Arbitration: Critical Case Studies. 2008. 364p. (978-90-04-16632-5(7)) BRILL.

Aicher, Josef, et al, eds. Decisions of the Arbitral Panel for in Rem Restitution, Vol. 1. 2008. (Decisions of the Arbitral Panel for in Rem Restit. Ser.: Vol. 1). 479p. 156.00 (978-1-84113-877-0(0)) Hart Publishing Ltd. GBR. Dist: International Specialized Bk. Services.

Alexander, Nadja. International Comparative Mediation: Legal Perspectives. 2009. (Illus.). xxvi, 508p. *(978-90-411-3224-6(4))* Kluwer Law International.

Alfons, Claudia. Recognition & Enforcement of Annulled Foreign Arbitral Awards: An Analysis of the Legal Framework & its Interpretation in Case Law & Literature. 2010. (Völkerrecht, Europarecht und Internationales Wirtschaftsrecht Ser.). 216p. 64.95 *(978-3-631-60378-9(9))* Lang, Peter GmbH, Europaischer Verlag der Wissenschaften DEU. Dist: Lang, Peter.

Alvik, Ivar. Contracting with Sovereignty: State Contracts & International Arbitration. 2011. (ENG.). 346p. 110.00 *(978-1-84113-657-8(3))* Hart Publishing Ltd. GBR. Dist: International Specialized Bk. Services.

Ambrose, Clare, et al. London Maritime Arbitration. 3rd rev. ed. 2009. (Illus.). 611p. 684.00 *(978-1-84311-832-9(7))* Informa Professional GBR. Dist: International Specialized Bk. Services.

American Arbitration Association. ADR & the Law - 21st Edition. 2007. (ENG.). 400p. 85.00 *(978-1-929446-97-1(7))* JurisNet LLC.

Andrews, Neil. The Three Paths of Justice: Court Proceedings, Arbitration, & Mediation in England. 2011. (Ius Gentium: Comparative Perspectives on Law & Justice Ser.). (ENG.). xiv, 296p. 139.00 ***(978-94-007-2293-4(1)***, 9400722931) Springer.

Arnaldez, Jean-Jacques. Collection of Icc Arbitral Awards 2001-2007. 2009. (FRE & ENG.). lxi, 844p. 330.00 *(978-90-411-2877-5(8))* Wolters Kluwer Law & Business.

Art Directors Club of Europe, creator. Best of European Design & Advertising: The Annual of Annuals. 2007. (Best of European Design & Advertising Ser.). (Illus.). 373p. *(978-84-611-3759-6(0))* Actar Birkhauser Distribution.

Ashenfelter, Orley C. & Iyengar, Radha K., eds. Economics of Commercial Arbitration & Dispute Resolution. 2009. (Economic Approaches to Law Ser.). (Illus.). 592p. 270.00 *(978-1-84720-332-8(9))* Elgar, Edward Publishing, Inc.

Association For International Arbitration, ed. Alternative Dispute Resolution in the Energy Sector. 2009. 156p. pap. 50.00 *(978-90-466-0267-6(2))* Maklu Uitgevers N.V. BEL. Dist: International Specialized Bk. Services.

Association for International Arbitration Staff, ed. Chinese Arbitration: A Selection of Pitfalls. 2009. 160p. pap. 40.00 *(978-90-466-0263-8(X))* Maklu Uitgevers N.V. BEL. Dist: International Specialized Bk. Services.

—Interim Measures in International Commercial Arbitration. 2007. 131p. pap. 40.00 *(978-90-466-0144-0(7))* Maklu Uitgevers N.V. BEL. Dist: International Specialized Bk. Services.

—The UNCITRAL Model Law on International Commercial Arbitration: 25 Years: Association for International Arbitration (AIA) Series. 2010. 168p. pap. 58.00 *(978-90-466-0358-1(X))* Maklu Uitgevers N.V. BEL. Dist: International Specialized Bk. Services.

Automobile Arbitration Fairness ACT of 2008: Hearing Before the Subcommittee on Commercial & Administrative Law of the Committee on the Judiciary, House of Representatives, One Hundred Tenth Congress, Second Session, on H.R. 5312, March 6, 2008. 2009. iv, 109p. *(978-0-16-082583-5(0)*, 552-070-38604-1) United States Government Printing Office.

Awards, Honors & Prizes, 3.0. 32nd ed. 2011. pap. 855.00 *(978-1-4144-5805-2(3))* Cengage Gale.

Awards, Honors & Prizes: United States & Canada, 2.0. 32nd ed. 2011. pap. 454.00 *(978-1-4144-5806-9(1))* Cengage Gale.

Baamir, Abdularahman Y. Shari'a Law in Commercial & Banking Arbitration: Law & Practice in Saudi Arabia. 2010. 230p. 114.95 *(978-1-4094-0377-7(7))* Ashgate Publishing Co.

Bacon, Matthew. The Compleat Arbitrator: Or, the Law of Awards & Arbitraments: Containing Plain & Easy Directions to All Kinds of Arbitrators, What Matters Are Proper to Be Submitted to Arbitration, & in What Manner: the Nature & Different Kinds of Submissions, the Parties to the Submission, the Duty & Office of Arbitrators & Umpires: the Right Manner of Making & Delivering up Awards: How Awards Have Been Construed In... 2009. 320p. 125.00 *(978-1-58477-959-9(4))* Lawbook Exchange, Ltd., The.

Baldissera Santos, Leonardo. The Formal Requirements for Arbitration Agreements. 2010. 72p. pap. *(978-3-8383-7334-8(0))* Lambert Academic Publishing.

Baumann, Thomas. Patentstreitigkeiten vor Schiedsgerichten: Eine rechtsvergleichende Betrachtung ausgewählter Probleme nach deutschem und schweizerischem Recht. 2008. (Schriften zum Verfahrensrecht Ser.). 338p. pap. 81.95 *(978-3-631-56526-1(7))* Lang, Peter GmbH, Europaischer Verlag der Wissenschaften DEU. Dist: Lang, Peter.

Berg, Van Den. International Arbitration 2006, Vol. 13. 2008. xiii, 957p. pap. 272.00 *(978-90-411-2691-7(0))* Wolters Kluwer Law & Business.

—Yearbook Commercial Arbitration Vol Xxxi 2006. 2006. (Yearbook Commercial Arbitration Set Ser.). pap. *(978-90-411-2437-1(3))* Kluwer Law International.

Berger, Klaus Peter. Private Dispute Resolution in International Business, 2 vols. 2nd ed. 2009. 118.00 *(978-90-411-3172-0(8))* Wolters Kluwer Law & Business.

Bergsten, Eric E. International Commercial Arbitration Pacific Rim 2008. 2009. 902p. 205.00 *(978-0-19-538702-5(3))* Oxford Univ. Pr., Inc.

Bergsten, Eric E. & Kröll, Stefan. International Arbitration & International Commercial Law: Synergy, Convergence, & Evolution: Liber Amicorum Eric Bergsten. 2011. (Illus.). xxxvi, 842p. ***(978-90-411-3522-3(7))*** Kluwer Law International.

Bhatia, Vijay K., et al, eds. Legal Discourse Across Cultures & Systems. 2008. (ENG.). 356p. (gr. 17). 70.00 *(978-962-209-851-0(7))*; pap. 35.00 *(978-962-209-852-7(5))* Hong Kong Univ. Pr. HKG. Dist: Columbia Univ. Pr.

Bhatia, Vijay K., et al. Discourse & Practice in International Commercial Arbitration: Issues Challenges & Prospects. 2012. (Law, Language & Communication Ser.). (Illus.). 338p. 134.95 ***(978-1-4094-3231-9(9))*** Ashgate Publishing Co.

Bishop, R. Doak & Marchili, Silvia M. Annulment under the ICSID Convention. 2012. (ENG.). 272p. 250.00 ***(978-0-19-965374-4(7))*** Oxford Univ. Pr., Inc.

Blackaby, Nigel, et al. Redfern & Hunter on International Arbitration. 5th ed. 2009. (ENG.). 776p. (C). pap., stu. ed. 95.00 *(978-0-19-955719-6(5))*; 750p. 275.00 *(978-0-19-955718-9(7))* Oxford Univ. Pr., Inc.

Blackshaw, Ian S. Sport, Mediation & Arbitration. 2009. (Asser International Sports Law Ser.). (ENG.). 578p. 139.00 *(978-90-6704-307-6(9))* T.M.C. Asser Pr. NLD. Dist: Springer.

Bland, F. Paul. Consumer Arbitration Agreements: Enforceability & Other Topics. 5th ed. 2007. xxxiv, 590p. pap. *(978-1-60248-018-6(4))* National Consumer Law Ctr., The.

Blazey, Mark L. Insights to Performance Excellence 2009-2010: An Inside Look at the 2009-2010 Baldrige Award Criteria. 2009. 364p. pap. 84.00 *(978-0-87389-755-6(2))* ASQ Quality Pr.

Blokh, Abram M. Soviet Union in the Context of Nobel Prize. 2010. 900p. 111.00 *(978-981-4277-97-6(5))* World Scientific Publishing Co., Inc.

Bockstiegel, et al. Arbitration in Germany: The Model Law in Practice. 2008. (Illus.). 229.00 *(978-90-411-2718-1(6))* Wolters Kluwer Law & Business.

Born. International Arbitration: Cases & Materials. 2011. l, 1263p. ***(978-0-7355-0797-5(X))*** 2010. *(978-0-7355-0796-8(1))* Wolters Kluwer Law & Business. (Aspen Pubs.).

Born. Intl Arbitration & Forum Selection Agreement Planning Drafting 3E. 3rd ed. 2010. 242p. pap. *(978-90-411-3269-7(4))* Kluwer Law International.

Born & Born, Gary. International Arbitration: Cases & Materials. 2010. (Illus.). l, 1263p. pap. ***(978-90-411-3458-5(1)***, Aspen Pubs.) Wolters Kluwer Law & Business.

Born, Gary B. International Commercial Arbitration: Commentary & Materials, 2 vols., Vol. 2. 3rd rev. ed. 2009. lvi, 3303p. 455.00 *(978-90-411-2759-4(3))* Wolters Kluwer Law & Business.

Brand, Ronald A. & Herrup, Paul M. The 2005 Hague Convention on Choice of Courts Agreements: Commentary & Documents. 2008. (ENG.). 336p. 138.00 *(978-0-521-87866-1(7))* Cambridge Univ. Pr.

Brees, Mina A., et al. Arbitration Road Map: A Guide to Clauses, Procedures, & Hearings. 2007. xvi, 110p. *(978-1-892542-42-7(0))* State Bar of Texas-Bks. & Systems.

Brekoulakis, Stavros L. Third Parties in International Commercial Arbitration. 2011. (ENG.). 304p. 265.00 *(978-0-19-957208-3(9))* Oxford Univ. Pr., Inc.

Brown, Chester & Miles, Kate, eds. Evolution in Investment Treaty Law & Arbitration. 2011. (ENG., Illus.). 766p. 160.00 ***(978-1-107-01468-8(9))*** Cambridge Univ. Pr.

Brown, Mark Graham. Baldrige Award Winning Quality: How to Interpret the Baldrige Criteria for Performance Excellence. 17th rev. ed. 2008. (ENG & CHI., Illus.). 384p. pap. 54.95 *(978-1-4200-8014-8(8))* Productivity Pr.

Brunet, Edward J., et al. Alternative Dispute Resolution: The Advocate's Perspective: Cases & Materials. 4th ed. 2011. ***(978-1-4224-9086-0(6))***; xxvii, 888p. ***(978-1-4224-9084-6(X))*** LexisNexis Matthew Bender.

Carbonneau, Thomas E. Arbitration in a Nutshell. (Nutshell Ser.). 2007. 351p. pap. 31.00 *(978-0-314-17223-5(8))* 3rd rev. ed. 2012. 436p. pap. 38.00 ***(978-0-314-27615-5(7))*** West. (West Legalworks).

—Cases & Materials on Arbitration Law & Practice. (American Casebook Ser.). 4th rev. ed. 2007. 837p. 119.00 *(978-0-314-17072-9(3))* 6th rev. ed. 2012. 971p. 171.00 ***(978-0-314-27957-6(1))*** West. (West Legalworks).

—Cases & Materials on Arbitration Law & Practice. 4th ed. 2007. xxvii, 837p. *(978-0-314-17071-2(5))* West Publishing Co., College & Schl. Div.

Carbonneau, Thomas E. & Grey, Zachary, eds. Yearbook on Arbitration & Mediation. 2011. 630p. pap. 69.95 ***(978-1-60042-145-7(8))*** Vandeplas Publishing.

Carey-Thomas, Lizzie & Stout, Katharine. The Turner Prize & British Art. 2008. (ENG., Illus.). 112p. pap. 27.50 *(978-1-85437-742-5(6))* Tate Publishing, Ltd. GBR. Dist: Hachette Bk. Group.

Caron, David D. & Caplan, Lee M. The UNCITRAL Arbitration Rules: A Commentary. 2nd ed. 2012. (ENG.). 1242p. 350.00 ***(978-0-19-969630-7(6))*** Oxford Univ. Pr., Inc.

Carroll, Eileen & MacKie, Karl. International Mediation - The Art of Business Diplomacy. 2nd ed. 2006. (Illus.). 224p. *(978-90-411-2579-8(5))* Kluwer Law International.

Carter, James H. & Fellas, John. International Commercial Arbitration in New York, 1 vol. 2010. (ENG.). 500p. 215.00 *(978-0-19-537562-6(9))* Oxford Univ. Pr., Inc.

Carugati, D. G. R., ed. Millennium Yacht Design Award. 2004-2008: [in English & Italian]. 2008. 147p. pap. 57.50 *(978-88-370-5564-6(1))* Electa ITA. Dist: Trans-Atlantic Pubns., Inc.

CCH Incorporated. China Master Business Law Guide: Case Law. 2009. (Illus.). vii, 320p. *(978-90-411-3222-2(8))* Kluwer Law International.

Chapman, Tony, ed. Architecture 10: RIBA Buildings of the Year. 2011. (RIBA Guides). (ENG., Illus.). 272p. 34.95 *(978-1-85894-539-2(9))* Merrell Pubs. Ltd. GBR. Dist: Perseus Distribution.

Chern, Cyril. International Commercial Mediation. 2008. (Dispute Resolution Guides Ser.). (Illus.). 265p. 270.00 *(978-1-84311-759-9(2))* Informa Professional GBR. Dist: International Specialized Bk. Services.

Chet. Wolf Prize in Agriculture. 2009. 190.00 *(978-981-283-584-0(9))* World Scientific Publishing Co., Inc.

Chow. International Business Transactions 2009 Supplement. 2010. pap. 35.50 *(978-0-7355-8742-7(6))* Wolters Kluwer Law & Business.

Chow, Daniel C. K. & Schoenbaum, Thomas J. International Business Transactions: Problems, Cases, & Materials. 2nd ed. 2010. (Illus.). xxxi, 819p. *(978-0-7355-7962-0(8)*, Aspen Pubs.) Wolters Kluwer Law & Business.

Cimmino, Désirée. Das UNCITRAL-Modellgesetz über internationale ADR-Verfahren in Wirtschaftsstreitigkeiten. 2008. (Schriften zum Verfahrensrecht Ser.). 360p. pap. 81.95 *(978-3-631-56979-5(3))* Lang, Peter GmbH, Europaischer Verlag der Wissenschaften DEU. Dist: Lang, Peter.

Coe. Nafta Chapter Eleven Reports Vol. 2: Awards Rel. 2011. *(978-90-411-2374-9(1))* Kluwer Law International.

Comite Francais De L'Arbitrage Staff. Revue de Larbitrage. (FRE.). *(978-90-411-1903-2(5))* Kluwer Law International.

Committee on the Design of an NSF Innovation Prize & National Research Council. Innovation Inducement Prizes at the National Science Foundation. 2007. (ENG.). 72p. pap. 21.00 *(978-0-309-10465-4(3))* National Academies Pr.

Connerty, Anthony. A Manual of International Dispute Resolution. 2006. (ENG.). 320p. per. 55.00 *(978-0-85092-837-2(0))* Commonwealth Secretariat GBR. Dist: Stylus Publishing, LLC.

Continuing Education of the Bar. A Litigator's Guide to Effective Use of ADR in California: October 2007 Update. 2007. 420p. ring bd. 72.00 *(978-0-7626-1321-2(1))* Continuing Education of the Bar-California.

Coulson, Peter. Coulson on Construction Adjudication. 2nd ed. 2011. (ENG.). 540p. 450.00 *(978-0-19-959722-2(7))* Oxford Univ. Pr., Inc.

Cram101 Textbook Reviews Staff. Outlines & Highlights for Alternative Dispute Resolution: A Conflict Diagnosis Approach by Laurie S. Coltri, ISBN. 2009. 192p. pap. 30.95 *(978-1-4288-2601-4(7))*; 88p. pap. 27.95 *(978-1-4288-8834-0(9))* Cram101 Inc.

Daradkeh, Lafi. Recognition & Enforcement of Foreign Commercial Arbitral Awards. 2010. 280p. pap. *(978-3-8383-7457-4(6))* Lambert Academic Publishing.

de Paiva Muniz, Joaquim T. & Tereza Palhares Basilio, Ana. Arbitration Law of Brazil: Practice & Procedure. 2006. (ENG.). 160.00 *(978-1-929446-98-8(5))* JurisNet LLC.

Delvolve, Jean-Louis. French Arbitration Law & Practice. 2nd rev. ed. 2009. (FRE & ENG.). xxv, 364p. 185.00 *(978-90-411-2690-0(2))* Wolters Kluwer Law & Business.

Demeter, Dalma. International Commercial Arbitration - Ad Hoc versus Institutional: A Practical Guide to make the Proper Choice between Ad Hoc & Institutional Arbitration. 2008. 68p. pap. *(978-3-639-09331-5(3))* VDM Verlag Dr. Mueller e.K.

Diamond, Harriet & Diamond, Linda Eve. Perfect Phrases for Motivating & Rewarding Employees: Hundreds of Ready-to-Use Phrases for Encouraging & Recognizing Employee Excellence. 2nd ed. 2010. (ENG.). 176p. pap. 10.95 *(978-0-07-174243-6(3)*, 0071742433) McGraw-Hill Cos., The.

Dimsey, Mariel. The Resolution of International Investment Disputes: Challenges & Practical Solutions. 2008. 297p. (C). 136.00 *(978-90-77596-52-4(6))* Eleven International Publishing NLD. Dist: International Specialized Bk. Services.

Dugan, Christopher, et al. Investor-State Arbitration, 1 vol. 2008. (ENG.). xxv, 791p. 225.50 *(978-0-379-21544-1(6))* Oxford Univ. Pr., Inc.

Dupuy, Pierre-Marie, et al. Human Rights in International Investment Law & Arbitration. 2009. (International Economic Law Ser.). (ENG.). 640p. 275.00 *(978-0-19-957818-4(4))*; pap. 90.00 *(978-0-19-957819-1(2))* Oxford Univ. Pr., Inc.

E-Discovery in Arbitration: Leading Lawyers on Recovering Electronic Evidence, Meeting New Disclosure Guidelines, & Implementing Measures to Streamline the Process (Inside the Minds) 2010. 104p. pap. 90.00 *(978-0-314-26347-6(0))* Aspatore Bks.

Edler, Franziska. Die Aufhebung von Schiedssprüchen und der Erlass einstweiliger Maßnahmen in Deutschland und Schweden: Ein Rechtsvergleich vor dem Hintergrund der Investitionsschiedsgerichtsbarkeit. 2008. (Studien zum Europäischen und Internationalen Wirtschaftsrecht. Studies in European & International Economic Law Ser.). (GRE.). 338p. pap. 81.95 *(978-3-631-58322-7(2))* Lang, Peter GmbH, Europaischer Verlag der Wissenschaften DEU. Dist: Lang, Peter.

Eijsvoogel, Peter V. & Van Hooijdonk, Marieke. Litigation in the Netherlands: Civil Procedure, Arbitration & Administrative Litigation. 2009. (Dutch Business Law Ser.: Vol. 1). xix, 187p. 79.00 *(978-90-411-2855-3(7))* Wolters Kluwer Law & Business.

Eksi, Nuray, et al. International Commercial Arbitration: A Comparative Study. 2007. xxxix, 424p. *(978-9944-60-191-7(8))* Turkiye Odalar ve Borsalar Birligi.

El-Ahdab. Arbitration with the Arab Countries, Third Edition. 3rd ed. 2010. li, 1200p. 250.00 *(978-90-411-3170-6(1))* Wolters Kluwer Law & Business.

English, James F. The Economy of Prestige: Prizes, Awards, & the Circulation of Cultural Value. 2008. (Illus.). 432p. pap. 22.50 *(978-0-674-03043-5(5))* Harvard Univ. Pr.

Ferrari, Franco & KröLl, Stefan. Conflict of Laws in International Arbitration. 2011. 480p. pap., pap. 109.00 *(978-3-86653-170-3(2))* Sellier - European Law Publishers GmbH DEU. Dist: International Specialized Bk. Services.

Flannery, Louis & Merkin, Robert. Arbitration Act 1996. 4th rev. ed. 2008. 376p. 378.00 *(978-1-84311-778-0(9))* Informa Professional GBR. Dist: International Specialized Bk. Services.

Folberg. Arbitration. 2010. pap. *(978-0-7355-4014-9(4)*, Aspen Pubs.) Wolters Kluwer Law & Business.

Friedland, Paul D. Arbitration Clauses for International Contracts 2nd Edition. 2007. (ENG.). 150.00 *(978-1-933833-06-4(8))* JurisNet LLC.

Froese, Marc D. Canada at the WTO: Trade Litigation & the Future of Public Policy. 2010. (Illus.). 175p. (C). *(978-1-4426-0152-9(3))*; pap. *(978-1-4426-0138-3(8))* Univ. of Toronto Pr.

Frolund, Tina, ed. & compiled by. The Official YALSA Awards Guidebook. 2008. 225p. pap. 55.00 *(978-1-55570-629-6(0))* Neal-Schuman Pubs., Inc.

Gaillard. Legal Theory of International Arbitration. 2010. 196p. *(978-90-04-18641-5(7))* BRILL.

Gaillard, Emmanuel. Aspects philosophiques du droit de l'arbitrage International. 2008. (Pocket Books of the Hague Academy of International Law//les livres de poche de l'Académie de droit international de la Haye Ser.). 240p. (C). pap. *(978-90-04-17148-0(7))* BRILL.

—Legal Theory of International Arbitration. (ENG.). 202p. pap. *(978-90-04-18714-6(6))* BRILL.

Gaillard, Emmanuel, et al. Enforcement of Arbitration Agreements & International Arbitral Awards: The New York Convention 1958 in Practice. Gaillard, Emmanuel & Di Pietro, Domenico, eds. 2008. 988p. 250.00 *(978-1-905017-47-8(2))* Cameron May, Ltd. GBR. Dist: Gaunt, Inc.

Gemmell, Arthur J. Western & Chinese Arbitration: The Arbitral Chain. 2008. (ENG., Illus.). 228p. pap. 38.99 *(978-0-7618-4006-0(0))* Univ. Pr. of America, Inc.

Gola, Pascale, et al, eds. Institutional Arbitration: Tasks & Powers of Different Arbitration Institutions. 2009. 310p. pap. 99.00 *(978-3-86653-126-0(5))* Sellier - European Law Publishers GmbH DEU. Dist: International Specialized Bk. Services.

Golann, Dwight. Mediating Legal Disputes: Effective Strategies for Neutrals & Advocates. 2009. (ENG., Illus.). xix, 370p. pap. 69.95 incl. DVD *(978-1-60442-303-7(X))* American Bar Assn.

Gorshkova, Elena. Witness Evidence in International Commercial Arbitration. 2008. 92p. pap. *(978-3-639-02780-8(9))* VDM Verlag Dr. Mueller e.K.

Greenberg, Simon, et al. International Commercial Arbitration: Asia-Pacific Perspective. 2010. (ENG.). 588p. pap. 80.00 *(978-0-521-69570-1(8))* Cambridge Univ. Pr.

Grigera Naón, Horacio A. & Mason, Paul E. International Commercial Arbitration Practice: 21st Century Perspectives. 2010. *(978-1-4224-2708-8(0))* LexisNexis Matthew Bender.

Haidar, Ali. Global Claims in Construction. 2011. (ENG., Illus.). xii, 276p. 129.00 *(978-0-85729-729-7(5)*, 0857297295) Springer.

Hanessian, Grant, et al. International Arbitration Checklists. 2nd ed. 2009. l, 439p. *(978-1-933833-21-7(1))* Juris Publishing, Inc.

Happ, Richard & Rubins, Noah. Digest of ICSID Awards & Decisions: 2003-2007. 2009. (ENG.). 330p. 330.00 *(978-0-19-955704-2(7))* Oxford Univ. Pr., Inc.

Harris, Bruce, et al. The Arbitration Act 1996: A Commentary. 4th rev. ed. 2007. (ENG.). 520p. pap. 152.99 *(978-1-4051-3996-0(X)*, Wiley-Blackwell) Wiley, John & Sons, Inc.

Hartley, Trevor. International Commercial Litigation: Text, Cases & Materials on Private International Law. 2009. (ENG.). 962p. (C). 179.00 *(978-0-521-86807-5(6))* Cambridge Univ. Pr.

Heard, H. Roderic, et al. International Commercial Arbitration Advocacy: A Practitioner's Guide for American Lawyers. 2011. *(978-1-60156-081-0(8))* National Institute for Trial Advocacy.

Heilbron, Hilary, ed. A Practical Guide to International Arbitration in London. 2008. (Practical Guides Ser.). 356p. 288.00 *(978-1-84311-729-2(0))* Informa Professional GBR. Dist: International Specialized Bk. Services.

Hinchey, John W. & Harris, Troy L. International Construction Arbitration Handbook. 2008. *(978-0-314-99197-3(2))* West Publishing Co., College & Schl. Div.

Hine, Thomas J. & Brubaker, John K. NASD Arbitration Solution: 5 Black Belt Principles to Protect & Grow Your Financial Services Practice. 2007. (ENG., Illus.). 336p. 49.95 *(978-0-470-12632-5(9)*, Wiley) Wiley, John & Sons, Inc.

Hjalmarsson, Johanna & Merkin, Robert. Singapore Arbitration Legislation. Merkin, Robert, ed. annot. ed. 2009. 226p. 378.00 *(978-1-84311-819-0(X))* Informa Professional GBR. Dist: International Specialized Bk. Services.

Hobér, Kaj. International Commercial Arbitration in Sweden. 2011. (ENG.). 416p. 300.00 *(978-0-19-921852-3(8))* Oxford Univ. Pr., Inc.

—Investment Arbitration in Eastern Europe: In Search of a Definition of Expropriation. 2007. 150.00 *(978-1-933833-00-2(9))* JurisNet LLC.

Hofmann, Dieter, et al, eds. Iba Rules of Evidence: Commentary. 2012. 332p. 174.00 ***(978-3-86653-197-0(4))*** Sellier - European Law Publishers GmbH DEU. Dist: International Specialized Bk. Services.

Holbein, James R. & Ranieri, Nick W. NAFTA — North American Free-Trade Agreements: Chapter 11 Investor-State Arbitration. 2007. *(978-0-19-534043-3(4))*; *(978-0-19-534042-6(6))* Oxford Univ. Pr., Inc.

Hopkins, Roger. Arbitration Law Handbook. Horn, Ben, ed. 2007. 1016p. pap. 441.00 *(978-1-84311-708-7(8))* Informa Professional GBR. Dist: International Specialized Bk. Services.

Horn, Henrik & Mavroidis, Petros C., eds. The WTO Case Law Of 2008. 2010. (American Law Institute Reporters Studies on WTO Law Ser.). (Illus.). 296p. pap. 55.00 *(978-0-521-15401-7(4))* Cambridge Univ. Pr.

Horn, Henrik & Mavroidis, Petros C., eds. The WTO Case Law Of 2009. 2011. (American Law Institute Reporters Studies on WTO Law Ser.). (ENG.). 172p. pap. 49.99 ***(978-1-107-68178-1(2))*** Cambridge Univ. Pr.

Howell, David J. Electronic Disclosure in International Arbitration. 2008. (ENG., Illus.). 400p. 125.00 *(978-1-933833-22-4(X))* JurisNet LLC.

Huber, Stephen K. & Weston, Maureen. Arbitration: Cases & Materials. 3rd ed. 2011. xxii, 697p. ***(978-1-4224-8554-5(4))*** LexisNexis Matthew Bender.

Icc. Interest, Auxiliary, & Alternative Remedies: Dossier V from the ICC. 2009. 259p. pap. *(978-90-411-3182-9(5))* Kluwer Law International.

International Bureau of the Permanent Court of Arbitration Staff, compiled by. The Permanent Court of Arbitration: Summaries of Awards 1999-2009. 2010. (ENG.). 250p. 89.95 *(978-90-6704-319-9(2))* T.M.C. Asser Pr. NLD. Dist: Springer.

International Sales & Arbitration: Problems Cases Materials. (Illus.). *(978-90-411-2654-2(6))* Kluwer Law International.

Jacobs, Richard, et al. Liability Insurance in International Arbitration: The Bermuda Form. 2nd rev. ed. 2011. (ENG.). 414p. 190.00 *(978-1-84113-875-6(4))* Hart Publishing Ltd. GBR. Dist: International Specialized Bk. Services.

Jaeger, Markus. Reimbursement for Attorney's Fees: A Comparative Study of the Laws of Switzerland, Germany, France, England, & the United States of America; International Arbitration Rules & the United Nations Conventions of Contracts for the International Sale of Goods (CISG) 2010. 208p. 85.00 *(978-90-77596-98-2(4))* Eleven International Publishing NLD. Dist: International Specialized Bk. Services.

Japan Display Design Association. Display, Commercial Space & Sign Design 36. 2009. (JPN & ENG., Illus.). 420p. 90.00 *(978-4-89737-624-0(6))* Azur Corp. JPN. Dist: Antique Collectors' Club.

Jarvin, Sigvard & Magnusson, Annette. International Arbitration Court Decisions: 2nd Edition. 2nd ed. 2008. (FRE & ENG.). 1400p. 225.00 *(978-1-933833-08-8(4))* JurisNet LLC.

Kahn, Philippe & Walde, Thomas W., eds. Les Aspects Nouveaux de Droit des Investissements Internationaux/New Aspects of International Investment Law. 2007. (Recueil des Cours - Colloques/Workshops/ Law Books of the Academy Ser.). 1036p. *(978-90-04-15372-1(1))* BRILL.

Kantor, Mark. Valuation for Arbitration: Compensation Standards, Valuation Methods & Expert Evidence. 2008. (Illus.). 172.00 *(978-90-411-2735-8(6))* Wolters Kluwer Law & Business.

Kimmelman, Louis & MacGrath, Dana. Judicial Review of Commercial Arbitration Awards. 2009. (ENG.). 400p. 185.00 *(978-0-379-21524-3(1))* Oxford Univ. Pr., Inc.

Kläger, Roland. 'Fair & Equitable Treatment' in International Investment Law. 2011. (Cambridge Studies in International & Comparative Law Ser.). (ENG.). 410p. 5.00 *(978-0-521-19771-7(6))* Cambridge Univ. Pr.

Knahr, Christina, et al, eds. Investment & Commercial Arbitration - Similarities & Divergences. 2010. 197p. 104.00 *(978-90-77596-81-4(X))* Eleven International Publishing NLD. Dist: International Specialized Bk. Services.

Knetsch, Sebastian. Das un-Kaufrecht in der Praxis der Schiedsgerichtsbarkeit. 2011. (Beiträge zum un-Kaufrecht Ser.). (GER.). 206p. 67.95 ***(978-3-631-61698-7(8))*** Lang, Peter GmbH, Europaischer Verlag der Wissenschaften DEU. Dist: Lang, Peter.

Komninos, Assimakis & Radicati Di Brozolo, Luca. International Commercial Arbitration & Eu Competition Law. 2013. 354p. 190.00 ***(978-1-84113-862-6(2))*** Hart Publishing Ltd. GBR. Dist: International Specialized Bk. Services.

Kryvoi. Iel International Centre Settlement Investment Disputes. 2010. (Illus.). 228p. pap. *(978-90-411-3311-3(9))* Kluwer Law International.

Kulick, Andreas. Global Public Interest in International Investment Law. 2012. (Cambridge Studies in International & Comparative Law Ser.: 90). (ENG.). 400p. 120.00 ***(978-1-107-02176-1(6))*** Cambridge Univ. Pr.

Kurkela, Matti, et al. Due Process in International Commercial Arbitration, 1 vol. 2nd ed. 2010. (ENG., Illus.). 488p. 195.00 *(978-0-19-537713-2(3))* Oxford Univ. Pr., Inc.

Kyd, Stewart. A Treatise on the Law of Awards: Revised & Corrected: with Very Considerable Additions from Printed & Manuscript Cases, & an Appendix, Containing a Variety of Useful Precedents. 2nd ed. 2009. 636p. 150.00 *(978-1-58477-960-5(8))* Lawbook Exchange, Ltd., The.

Lamb. Arbitration of Intellectual Property Disputes. 2010. xxvi, 464p. 185.00 *(978-90-411-2725-9(9))* Wolters Kluwer Law & Business.

Landrove, Juan Carlos. Assignment & Arbitration: A Comparative Study. 2009. 219p. pap. 74.00 *(978-3-86653-109-3(5))* Sellier - European Law Publishers GmbH DEU. Dist: International Specialized Bk. Services.

Latty, Franck. La Lex Sportiva: Recherche Sur le Droit Transnational. 2007. (Etudes de Droit International Ser.). 849p. *(978-90-04-15697-5(6))* BRILL.

Lauterpacht, Elihu, ed. ICSID Reports Volume 11, Volume 11. 2007. (International Convention on the Settlement of Investment Disputes Reports). (ENG., Illus.). 526p. 403.99 *(978-0-521-87170-9(0))* Cambridge Univ. Pr.

Lawrence, Robert Z. The United States & the WTO Dispute Settlement System: March 2007. 2007. (ENG.). 56p. per. 10.00 *(978-0-87609-398-6(5))* Council on Foreign Relations.

Leathley. International Dispute Resolution in Latin America: 2E Revised. 2010. *(978-90-411-3268-0(6))* Kluwer Law International.

Leathley, Christian. International Dispute Resolution in Latin America: An Institutional Overview. 2007. xxv, 414p. *(978-90-411-2461-6(6))* Kluwer Law International.

Lee. Arbitration in Brazil: Law & Practice. 2010. *(978-90-411-3201-7(5))* Kluwer Law International.

Liberti, Lahra, et al, eds. Investment Treaty Law: Current Issues Volume II: Nationality & Investment Treaty Claims & Fair & Equitable Treatment in Investment Treaty Law. 2007. 279p. pap. 120.00 *(978-1-905221-08-0(8))* British Institute of International & Comparative Law GBR. Dist: International Specialized Bk. Services.

Liebscher, Christoph. The Austrian Arbitration Act 2006: Text & Notes. 2006. (RUS, FRE, GER & ENG.). xiv, 208p. *(978-90-411-2439-5(X))* Kluwer Law International.

Liebscher, Christoph & Fremuth-Wolf, Alice, eds. Arbitration Law & Practice in Central & Eastern Europe. 2008. (ENG.). ring bd. 195.00 *(978-1-929446-95-7(0))* JurisNet LLC.

A Litigator's Guide to Effective Use of ADR in California: October 2006 Update. 2006. 462p. ring bd. 72.00 *(978-0-7626-1173-7(1),* CP-31101) Continuing Education of the Bar-California.

Lopa, Baharuddin & Yamin, Moh. Undang-Undang Pemberantasan Tindak Pidana Korupsi (Undang-Undang No. 3 Tahun 1971) 2009. (IND.). viii, 236p. *(978-979-414-090-1(2))* Alumni.

López Blanco, Hemán Fabio & Álvarez Niño, Olga Lucía. La Jurisprudencia Arbitral en Colombia: Análisis de Los Principales Laudos, en Materia de Derecho Privado, 2 vols. 2007. (SPA.). pap. 28.00 *(978-958-616-279-1(6))* Universidad Externado de Colombia COL. Dist: Siglo del Hombre.

—La Jurisprudencia Arbitral en Colombia: Análisis de Los Principales Laudos, en Materia de Derecho Privado, 3 vols. 2007. (SPA.). pap. 33.00 *(978-958-710-308-3(4))* Universidad Externado de Colombia COL. Dist: Siglo del Hombre.

Luttrell, Sam. Bias Challenge in International Arbitration. 2009. xix, 296p. *(978-90-411-3191-1(4))* Kluwer Law International.

Mackie. International Medicine: The Art of Business Diplomacy. 2nd ed. 2006. (Illus.). xiv, 224p. pap. 64.00 *(978-1-84592-346-4(4),* Bloomsbury Professional) Bloomsbury Publishing Plc GBR. Dist: International Specialized Bk. Services.

Macmahon, Belinda, ed. The Bank for International Settlements Arbitration Awards of 2002 & 2003/L'Arbitrage Concernant la Banque des Reglements Internationaux Sentences de 2002 Et 2003. 2007. (Permanent Court of Arbitration Award Ser.). (ENG.). 420p. 99.00 *(978-90-6704-234-5(X))* T.M.C. Asser Pr. NLD. Dist: Springer.

Magnetto, Anna. L'arbitrato Di Rodi Fra Samo e Priene. 2008. (ITA & GEC., Illus.). 263p. *(978-88-7642-320-6(6))* Scuola Normale Superiore.

Mandatory Binding Arbitration: Is It Fair & Voluntary?: Hearing Before the Subcommittee on Commercial & Administrative Law of the Committee on the Judiciary, House of Representatives, One Hundred Eleventh Congress, First Session, September 15, 2009. 2010. iv, 305p. *(978-0-16-085240-4(4),* 552-070-40582-8) United States Government Printing Office.

Mandatory Binding Arbitration Agreements: Are They Fair for Consumers?: Hearing Before the Subcommittee on Commercial & Administrative Law of the Committee on the Judiciary, House of Representatives, One Hundred Tenth Congress, First Session, June 12, 2007. 2008. iii, 255p. *(978-0-16-080973-6(8),* 552-070-37498-1) United States Government Printing Office.

Martinez-Fraga, Pedro J. The American Influences on International Commercial Arbitration: Doctrinal Developments & Discovery Methods. 2009. (ENG., Illus.). 432p. 152.00 *(978-0-521-76588-6(9))* Cambridge Univ. Pr.

McArdle, David. Dispute Resolution in Sport. 2012. (Ethics & Sport Ser.). (ENG.). 224p. (C). 125.00 ***(978-0-415-59567-4(3))*** Routledge.

McCreery, Christopher. The Beginner's Guide to Canadian Honours. 2008. (ENG., Illus.). 96p. pap. 19.99 *(978-1-55002-748-8(4))* Dundurn CAN. Dist: Ingram Pub. Services.

McLachlan. Lis Pencens in International Litigation. 2009. (Pocket Books of the Hague Academy of International Law//es livres de poche de l'Académie de droit international de la Haye Ser.). 320p. pap. *(978-90-04-17909-7(7))* BRILL.

McLachlan, Campbell, et al. International Investment Arbitration: Substantive Principles. 2007. (Oxford International Arbitration Ser.). (ENG.). 528p. 434.50 *(978-0-19-928664-5(7))* Oxford Univ. Pr., Inc.

Mendelson, Littler. Employment Arbitration Agreements: A Practical Guide. 2008. ring bd. 315.00 *(978-0-7355-7820-3(6))* Wolters Kluwer Law & Business.

Mistelis. Arbitrability in International Arbitration. 2009. xxiv, 375p. 185.00 *(978-90-411-2730-3(5))* Wolters Kluwer Law & Business.

—Concise Arbitration. 2010. xvi, 1115p. *(978-90-411-2609-2(0))* Kluwer Law International.

Moffitt. Dispute Resolution: Examples & Explanations 2e. 2nd ed. 2011. pap., stu. ed. *(978-0-7355-9956-7(4),* Aspen Pubs.) Wolters Kluwer Law & Business.

Montt, Santiago. State Liability in Investment Treaty Arbitration: Global Constitutional & Administrative Law in the BIT Generation, 0 vols. (ENG.). 2012. 460p. pap. 50.00 *(978-1-84946-213-6(5))* 2009. (Illus.). 416p. 134.00 *(978-1-84113-856-5(8))* Hart Publishing Ltd. GBR. Dist: International Specialized Bk. Services.

Morrissey, Joseph. International Sales Law & Arbitration: Problems, Cases, & Commentary. 2008. 118.00 *(978-0-7355-7707-7(2))* Wolters Kluwer Law & Business.

Moser. Practical Commentary on the Cietac Rules of Arbitration. 2011. *(978-90-411-2511-8(6))* Kluwer Law International.

Möser, Michael. Arbitration in Hong Kong. 2nd rev. ed. 2009. (CHI & ENG., Illus.). xxiii, 278p. pap. 152.00 *(978-90-411-2808-9(5))* Wolters Kluwer Law & Business.

Moser, Michael & Choong, John, eds. Asia Arbitration Handbook. 2012. (ENG.). 1392p. 450.00 ***(978-0-19-969165-4(7))*** Oxford Univ. Pr., Inc.

Moser, Michael J. Investor-State Arbitration: Lessons for Asia. 2008. 252p. pap. 75.00 *(978-1-933833-23-1(8))* JurisNet LLC.

Moses, Margaret L. The Principles & Practice of International Commercial Arbitration. (ENG.). 2008. 358p. pap. 35.00 *(978-0-521-68562-7(1))* 2nd rev. ed. 2012. 360p. 99.00 ***(978-1-107-00878-6(6))*** 2nd rev. ed. 2012. 392p. pap. 35.00 ***(978-1-107-40133-4(X))*** Cambridge Univ. Pr.

Mosimann, Olivier. Anti-Suit Injunctions in International Commercial Arbitration. 2010. 212p. 85.00 *(978-90-77596-99-9(2))* Eleven International Publishing NLD. Dist: International Specialized Bk. Services.

Nagle, Barbara. Conflict & Resolution, Second Edition. 2nd ed. 2007. pap. 62.95 *(978-0-7355-6732-0(8),* Aspen Pubs.) Wolters Kluwer Law & Business.

Nagle-Lechman, Barbara A. Conflict & Resolution. 2nd ed. 2008. xx, 186p. *(978-0-7355-6733-7(6),* Aspen Pubs.) Wolters Kluwer Law & Business.

Nakagawa, Junji, ed. Transparency in International Trade & Investment Dispute Settlement. 2012. (Routledge Research in International Economic Law Ser.). (ENG.). 256p. (C). 160.00 ***(978-0-415-52873-3(9))*** Routledge.

Nammour, Fady. Droit et Pratique de L'arbitrage Interne et International. 3rd ed. 2009. 481p. *(978-2-8027-2822-1(9),* Spotlight Poets) Bruylant, Editions juridiques.

Noussia, Kyriaki. Confidentiality in International Commercial Arbitration: A Comparative Analysis of the Position under English, US, German & French Law. 2010. (ENG.). xiii, 300p. 139.00 *(978-3-642-10223-3(9),* 3642102239) Springer.

One Club Staff. One Show Boxed Set, 2009 Awards, 3 vols. 2010. (One Show Ser.). (ENG., Illus.). 928p. 150.00 *(978-0-929837-43-7(6),* 0929837436) Quayside.

O'Neill, Philip D. O'Neill's International Arbitration: Case Studies & Material Exploring Where Theory Meets Practice in Resolving Commercial Disputes Privately. 2011. (American Casebook Ser.). 170.00 ***(978-0-314-27585-1(1))*** West Publishing Co., College & Schl. Div.

Onyema, Emilia. International Commercial Arbitration & the Arbitrator's Contract. 2012. (ENG.). 280p. pap. 44.95 ***(978-0-415-63149-5(1))*** Routledge.

Oppermann, Julia-Marie. Internationale Handelsschiedsgerichtsbarkeit und Verjährung. 2009. (Studien zum vergleichenden und internationalen Recht. Comparative & International Law Studies). (GER.). 338p. 86.95 *(978-3-631-59132-1(2))* Lang, Peter GmbH, Europaischer Verlag der Wissenschaften DEU. Dist: Lang, Peter.

Pair, Lara. Consolidation in International Commercial Arbitration: ICC & Swiss Rules. 2012. 235p. 97.50 ***(978-94-90947-27-9(X))*** Eleven International Publishing NLD. Dist: International Specialized Bk. Services.

Palo. Arbitration & Mediation in the Southern Mediterranean Countries. 2007. (Illus.). xlii, 244p. 186.00 *(978-90-411-2684-9(8))* Wolters Kluwer Law & Business.

Paparinskis, Martins. The International Minimum Standard & Fair & Equitable Treatment. 2012. (ENG.). 264p. 120.00 ***(978-0-19-969450-1(8))*** Oxford Univ. Pr., Inc.

Partridge, Mark V. B. Alternative Dispute Resolution: An Essential Competency for Lawyers. 2009. (ENG.). 304p. pap. 180.00 *(978-0-19-537205-2(0))* Oxford Univ. Pr., Inc.

Paulsson. The Revised Uncitral Rules. 2011. *(978-90-411-2733-4(X))* Wolters Kluwer Law & Business.

Paulsson, Jan, et al. The Freshfields Guide to Arbitration & ADR: Clauses in International Contracts. 3rd ed. 2010. (Illus.). xiv, 177p. pap. ***(978-90-411-3400-4(X))*** Kluwer Law International.

Permanent Court of Arbitration. The Barbados/Trinidad & Tobago Arbitration Award Of 2006. 2010. (Permanent Court of Arbitration Award Ser.). (Illus.). 160p. 89.95 *(978-90-6704-321-2(4))* T.M.C. Asser Pr. NLD. Dist: Springer.

Permanent Court of Arbitration, The Hague, compiled by. The Iron Rhine (IJzeren Rijn) Arbitration (Belgium-Netherlands) Award Of 2005. 2007. (Permanent Court of Arbitration Award Ser.). (ENG.). 324p. 99.00 *(978-90-6704-235-2(8))* T.M.C. Asser Pr. NLD. Dist: Springer.

Permanent Court of Arbitration, The Hague, The Hague, compiled by. The OSPAR Arbitration (Ireland - United Kingdom) Award Of 2003. 2009. (Permanent Court of Arbitration Award Ser.). (ENG.). 140p. 69.95 *(978-90-6704-295-6(1))* T.M.C. Asser Pr. NLD. Dist: Springer.

Peter, Henry. Arbitration in the Americas Cup: The 32nd Americas Cup Jury & I. 2008. (Illus.). xiv, 439p. 185.00 *(978-90-411-2755-6(0))* Wolters Kluwer Law & Business.

Peterson's Guides Staff. Scholarships, Grants & Prizes. 11th ed. 2006. (ENG.). 936p. per. 32.00 *(978-0-7689-2314-8(X))* Peterson's.

Pitoniak, Scott. Jewel of the Sports World: The Story of the Hickok Belt Award. 2010. (ENG., Illus.). 152p. pap. 24.95 *(978-1-933360-45-4(3),* RIT Pr.) Rochester Institute of Technology, Cary Graphic Arts Pr.

Poudret, Jean-François & Besson, Sébastien. Comparative Law of International Arbitration. 2nd rev. ed. 2007. *(978-0-421-93210-4(4))* Sweet & Maxwell, Ltd.

Prikhodko, I. A., et al. Kommentarii K Postanovleniiu Plenuma Vysshego Arbitrazhnogo Suda Rossiiskoi Federatsii Ot 12 Marta 2007 G. No. 17 "O Primenenii Arbitrazhnogo Protsessualnogo Kodeksa Rossiiskoi Federatsii Pri Peresmotre Vstupivshikh V Zakonnuiu Silu Sudebnykh Aktov Po Vnov Otkryvshimsia Obstoiatelstvam" 2010. (RUS.). 730p. *(978-5-7133-1385-2(9))* Mezdunarodnye Otnosheniya.

Ramsden, P. The Law of Arbitration: South African & International Arbitration, Vol. 1. 2009. 396p. pap. 64.00 *(978-0-7021-8192-4(7))* Juta & Co., Ltd. ZAF. Dist: Gaunt, Inc.

Rautray. Master Guide to Arbitration in India. 2009. 548p. pap. 131.00 *(978-90-411-3159-1(0))* Wolters Kluwer Law & Business.

Reeb. Sports Arbitration. 2010. *(978-90-411-2354-1(7))* Kluwer Law International.

Reed, Lucy, et al. Guide to ICSID Arbitration. 2nd ed. 2010. (Illus.). xvii, 468p. pap. ***(978-90-411-3401-1(8))*** Kluwer Law International.

Reshetnikova, I. V. & Kurgannikova, I. V. Sudebnye Raskhody V Arbitrazhnom Protsesse: Kommentarii I Postaleinye Materialy K Glave 9 Arbitrazhnogo Protsessualnogo Kodeksa Rossiiskoi Federatsii. 2nd ed. 2010. (RUS.). v, 184p. *(978-5-466-00662-9(9))* Volters Kluver.

Richbell, David. Mediation of Construction Disputes. 2008. (ENG., Illus.). 192p. pap. 104.99 *(978-1-4051-6931-8(1),* Wiley-Blackwell) Wiley, John & Sons, Inc.

Riegler, Stefan, et al. Arbitration Law of Austria: Practice & Procedure. 2007. (ENG.). 160.00 *(978-1-933833-07-1(6))* JurisNet LLC.

Rigo Sureda, Andrés. Investment Treaty Arbitration: Judging under Uncertainty. 2012. (Hersch Lauterpacht Memorial Lectures: 20). (ENG.). 166p. 80.00 ***(978-1-107-02251-5(7))*** Cambridge Univ. Pr.

Robbins, David E. Securities Arbitration in the Market Meltdown ERA: Achieving Fairness in Perception & Reality, 2 vols. 2009. pap. *(978-1-4024-1260-8(6))* Practising Law Institute.

Roe, Thomas & Happold, Matthew. Settlement of Investment Disputes under the Energy Charter Treaty. 2011. (Law Practitioner Ser.). (ENG.). 272p. 125.00 *(978-0-521-89938-3(9))* Cambridge Univ. Pr.

Roebuck, Derek. A Miscellany of Disputes. (Illus.). 128p. 40.00 *(978-0-9537730-0-8(0))* Holo Bks.: The Arbitration Pr. GBR. Dist: Gaunt, Inc.

Rogak, Lawrence N. Rogak's New York No-Fault Law & Practice: 2009 Edition. 2009. 740p. pap. 57.95 *(978-1-4401-1179-2(0))* iUniverse, Inc.

Rogers, Catherine A. & Alford, Roger P., eds. The Future of Investment Arbitration. 2009. (ENG.). 402p. 180.00 *(978-0-19-537180-2(1))* Oxford Univ. Pr., Inc.

Rovine, Arthur W. Contemporary Issues in International Arbitration & Mediation: The Fordham Papers. 2010. 485p. *(978-90-04-18291-2(8))* BRILL.

Rovine, Arthur W., ed. Contemporary Issues in International Arbitration & Mediation: The Fordham Papers 2007. 2008. xxx, 336p. (C). *(978-90-04-16738-4(2))* BRILL.

—Contemporary Issues in International Arbitration & Mediation: The Fordham Papers:2008, Vol. 2. 2009. (Contemporary Issues in International Arbitration & Mediation: the Fordham Papers Ser.). 350p. *(978-90-04-17555-6(5))* BRILL.

Russia (Federation) Staff, contrib. by. Arbitrazhnyi Protsessualnyi Kodeks Rossiiskoi Federatsii: Po Sostoianiiu Na 2 Sentiabria 2010 G.: V Red. Federalnykh Zakonov Ot 28.07.2004 No. 80-FZ, Ot 02.11.2004 No. 127-FZ, Ot 31.03.2005 No. 25-FZ ... 2010. (RUS.). 196p. *(978-5-9916-1018-6(5))* Jurajt.

S. 2838: The Fairness in Nursing Home Arbitration ACT: Joint Hearing Before the Subcommittee on Antitrust, Competition Policy, & Consumer Rights of the Committee on the Judiciary & the Special Committee on Aging, United States Senate, One Hundred Tenth Congress, Second Session, June 18, 2008. 2008. iv, 175p. *(978-0-16-082499-9(0),* 552-070-38537-1) United States Government Printing Office.

Sabahi, Burzu. Compensation & Restitution in Investor-State Arbitration: Principles & Practice. 2011. (ENG.). 302p. 140.00 ***(978-0-19-960118-9(6))*** Oxford Univ. Pr., Inc.

Salacuse, Jeswald W. The Law of International Investment Treaties. 2010. (Oxford International Law Library). (ENG.). 600p. 209.00 *(978-0-19-920605-6(8))* Oxford Univ. Pr., Inc.

Sauvant, Karl P., ed. Appeals Mechanism in International Investment Disputes. 2008. (ENG., Illus.). 472p. 180.00 *(978-0-19-534156-0(2))* Oxford Univ. Pr., Inc.

Savage & Mcilwrath, Michael. Practical Handbook on International Commercial Arbitration. 2010. (Illus.). 515p. *(978-90-411-2610-8(4))* Kluwer Law International.

Schaefer. Post M & A Arbitration. 2011. *(978-90-411-2776-1(3))* Wolters Kluwer Law & Business.

Schafer. Icc Arbitration in Practice Second Edition. 2nd ed. 2010. *(978-90-411-3171-3(X))* Wolters Kluwer Law & Business.

Schäfer, Manuela. Die Verträge zur Durchführung des Schiedsverfahrens: Analyse und Vergleich zweier Lösungsmodelle am Beispiel des deutschen und US-amerikanischen Rechtsraums. 2010. (Saarbrücker Studien zum Privat- und Wirtschaftsrecht Ser.). (GER.). 1154p. 195.95 *(978-3-631-59834-4(3))* Lang, Peter GmbH, Europaischer Verlag der Wissenschaften DEU. Dist: Lang, Peter.

Schill, Stephan W. & Schill, Stephan. The Multilateralization of International Investment Law. 2009. (Cambridge International Trade & Economic Law Ser.). (ENG.). 496p. 102.00 *(978-0-521-76236-6(7))* Cambridge Univ. Pr.

Schmal, Peter & Busenkell, Michaela, eds. Internationaler Hochhaus Preis 2008. 2009. (ENG., Illus.). 88p. pap. 28.00 *(978-3-86859-003-6(X))* Jovis Verlag GmbH DEU. Dist: D.A.P./Distributed Art Pubs.

Schmidt, Carsten. Prozessuale Meistbegünstigung im völkerrechtlichen Investitionsschutz. 2008. (Schriftenreihe der August Maria Berges Stiftung für Arbitrales Recht Ser.). 230p. 61.95 *(978-3-631-58356-2(7))* Lang, Peter GmbH, Europaischer Verlag der Wissenschaften DEU. Dist: Lang, Peter.

Schultz, Thomas. Information Technology & Arbitration: A Practioner's Guide. 2006. (Illus.). xxi, 241p. pap. *(978-90-411-2515-6(9))* Kluwer Law International.

Schwarz, Franz T. The Vienna Rules: A Commentary on International Arbitration in Austria. 2009. (GER & ENG.). lxxxi, 1049p. *(978-90-411-2344-2(X))* Kluwer Law International.

Scorey, David, et al. The Bermuda Form: Interpretation & Dispute Resolution of Excess Liability Insurance. 2011. (ENG., Illus.). 512p. 250.00 *(978-0-19-958361-4(7))* Oxford Univ. Pr., Inc.

Shackleton, Stewart. Arbitration Law Reports & Review 2005, 6 vols. 2009. (ENG.). 800p. 750.00 *(978-0-19-920342-0(3))* Oxford Univ. Pr., Inc.

—Arbitration Law Reports & Review 2006, 6 vols. 2009. (Shackleton Arbitration Law Reports). (ENG.). 800p. 770.00 *(978-0-19-955322-8(X))* Oxford Univ. Pr., Inc.

—Arbitration Law Reports & Review 2007. 2011. 800p. 600.00 *(978-0-19-956398-2(5))* Oxford Univ. Pr., Inc.

Shackleton, Stewart, ed. Arbitration Law Reports & Review 2000. 2009. 1150p. 575.00 *(978-0-19-928663-8(9))* Oxford Univ. Pr., Inc.

—Arbitration Law Reports & Review 2002, 6 vols. 2008. (ENG.). 864p. 709.50 *(978-0-19-928661-4(2))* Oxford Univ. Pr., Inc.

—Arbitration Law Reports & Review 2004, 6 vols. 2007. (ENG.). 872p. 880.00 *(978-0-19-928660-7(4))* Oxford Univ. Pr., Inc.

Shadikhodjaev, Sherzod. Retaliation in the WTO Dispute Settlement System. 2009. (Illus.). xviii, 292p. 172.00 *(978-90-411-2811-9(5))* Wolters Kluwer Law & Business.

Silverman, Peter. A Client's Guide to Mediation & Arbitration. 2009. (ENG.). 50p. pap. 29.95 *(978-1-60442-098-2(7))* American Bar Assn.

Smeureanu. Confidentiality International Commercial Arbitration. xix, 232p. *(978-90-411-3226-0(0))* Kluwer Law International.

Sparka, Felix. Jurisdiction & Arbitration Clauses in Maritime Transport Documents: A Comparative Analysis. 2010. (Hamburg Studies on Maritime Affairs Ser.). (ENG.). xviii, 279p. pap. 159.00 *(978-3-642-10221-9(2)*, 3642102212) Springer.

Steingruber, Andrea M. Consent in International Arbitration. 2012. (ENG.). 344p. 250.00 ***(978-0-19-969815-8(5))*** Oxford Univ. Pr., Inc.

Stern, Brigitte & Ruiz Fabri, Hélène, eds. La jurisprudence de l'OMC/ the Case-Law of the WTO: 1999-I. 2006. 600p. *(978-90-04-15400-1(0))* BRILL.

Strong, S. I. Research & Practice in International Commercial Arbitration: Sources & Strategies. 2009. (ENG.). 112p. pap. 85.00 *(978-0-19-923830-9(8))* Oxford Univ. Pr., Inc.

Swinnerton, Iain. Identifying Your World War One Soldier from Badges & Photographs. 2006. (Illus.). 114p. (C). pap. 17.95 *(978-1-86006-128-8(1))* Countryside Bks. GBR. Dist: Brown, David Bk. Co., The.

Tao, Jingzhou. Arbitration Law & Practice in China. 2nd rev. ed. 2008. xxiv, 436p. 165.00 *(978-90-411-2748-8(8))* Wolters Kluwer Law & Business.

Timea, Baltay. Current Trends in Arbitrability in the United States: Arbitrability in the United States. 2011. 88p. pap. ***(978-3-639-33539-2(2))*** VDM Verlag Dr. Mueller e.K.

Trachte-Huber, E. Wendy & Huber, Stephen K. Mediation & Negotiation: Reaching Agreement in Law & Business. 2nd ed. 2007. 104.00 *(978-1-4224-2137-6(6))* LexisNexis Matthew Bender.

Turner, Peter & Mohtashami, Reza. A Guide to the LCIA Arbitration Rules. 2009. (ENG.). 216p. 225.00 *(978-0-19-923443-1(4))* Oxford Univ. Pr., Inc.

Tweeddale, Andrew & Tweeddale, Keren. Arbitration of Commercial Disputes: International & English Law & Practice. 2007. (ENG.). 1128p. per. 160.00 *(978-0-19-921647-5(9))* Oxford Univ. Pr., Inc.

United Nations. Convention on the Recognition & Enforcement of Foreign Arbitral Awards (New York, 1958) 2008. (MUL.). 158p. pap. 25.00 *(978-92-1-033105-0(2))* United Nations Pubns.

—UNCITRAL Model Law on International Commercial Arbitration: 1985 - with Amendments as Adopted In 2006. 2008. (ENG.). 52p. pap. 18.00 *(978-92-1-133773-0(9))* United Nations Pubns.

United Nations Conference on Trade and Development. Investor-State Disputes: Prevention & Alternatives to Arbitration. 2010. (ENG.). 158p. pap. 20.00 *(978-92-1-112793-5(9))* United Nations Pubns.

Vadi, Valentina. Public Health in International Investment Law & Arbitration. 2012. (Routledge Research in International Economic Law Ser.). (ENG.). 256p. (C). 135.00 ***(978-0-415-50749-3(9))*** Routledge.

Van den Berg. Yearbook Commercial Arbitration Volume Xxxv 2010 (Crc) Rev. 2010. pap. *(978-90-411-3209-3(0))* Kluwer Law International.

—50 Years of the New York Convention. 2009. (Illus.). xi, 767p. pap. *(978-90-411-3212-3(0))* Kluwer Law International.

von Mehren, Robert, et al. American Arbitration: Principles & Practice. 2008. (ENG.). 674p. 250.00 *(978-1-4024-1123-6(5))* Practising Law Institute.

von Thulen Rhoades, Rufus, et al. Practitioner's Handbook on International Arbitration & Mediation- 2nd Edition. 2007. 1000p. 225.00 *(978-1-933833-03-3(3))* JurisNet LLC.

Wach, Karl, ed. Tactics in M & A Arbitration. 2008. 350p. 249.00 *(978-3-86653-068-3(4))* Sellier - European Law Publishers GmbH DEU. Dist: International Specialized Bk. Services.

Waelde, Thomas W., et al. A Liber Amicorum: Thomas Wälde: Law Beyond Conventional Thought. 2011. (Illus.). ix, 317p. 120.00 ***(978-1-907174-01-8(X))*** Gaunt, Inc.

Waibel. Backlash Against Investment Arbitration. 2010. liv, 614p. *(978-90-411-3202-4(3))* Kluwer Law International.

Waincymer. Procedure in International Arbitration. 2010. *(978-90-411-3168-3(X))* Wolters Kluwer Law & Business.

Warne, John, ed. International Commercial Dispute Resolution. 2009. 808p. 385.00 *(978-1-84766-134-0(3)*, Bloomsbury Professional) Bloomsbury Publishing Plc GBR. Dist: International Specialized Bk. Services.

Weeramantry, J. Romesh. Treaty Interpretation in Investment Arbitration. 2012. (ENG.). 312p. 250.00 ***(978-0-19-964147-5(1))*** Oxford Univ. Pr., Inc.

Weigand, Frank-Bernd, ed. Practitioner's Handbook on International Commercial Arbitration. 2nd ed. 2010. (ENG.). 1888p. 503.10 *(978-0-19-953486-9(1))* Oxford Univ. Pr., Inc.

Weiler, Todd. Investment Treaty Arbitration & International Law: Volume 1. 2008. (Illus.). 350p. 125.00 *(978-1-933833-18-7(1))* JurisNet LLC.

Widder, Lynnette, ed. Alumi Travel Award 2009. 2009. pap. 18.00 *(978-1-61584-120-2(2))* Independent Pub.

Wunschheim, Clarisse von. Enforcement of Commercial Arbitral Awards in China: Business Laws of China. 2010. (Illus.). xxx, 325p. pap. *(978-0-314-92609-8(7))* West Publishing Co., College & Schl. Div.

Yannaca-Small, Katia. Arbitration under International Investment Agreements: A Guide to the Key Issues, 1 vol. 2010. (ENG.). 790p. 247.50 *(978-0-19-534069-3(8))* Oxford Univ. Pr., Inc.

Yochembeng, Nkengiefac. Settling International Investment Disputes Through Arbitration. 2011. 96p. pap. ***(978-3-8433-8884-9(9))*** Lambert Academic Publishing.

Yuhniwo, Ngenge. The Scope of Arbitrability. 2009. 156p. pap. *(978-3-639-15218-0(2))* VDM Verlag Dr. Mueller e.K.

Zekos, Georgios I. International Commercial & Marine Arbitration. 2008. (Routledge Research in International Commercial Law Ser.). XII, 548p. 140.00 *(978-0-415-46072-9(7)*, Routledge Cavendish) Taylor & Francis Group GBR. Dist: Taylor & Francis Group.

Zhang, Qi. Consultation Within WTO Dispute Settlement: A Chinese Perspective. 2007. (Illus.). 326p. pap. 65.95 *(978-3-03911-239-5(2))*; pap. 65.95 *(978-0-8204-8918-6(2))* Lang, Peter Publishing, Inc.

ARBLAY, FRANCES BURNEY D', 1752-1840
see Burney, Fanny, 1752-1840

ARBLAY, MADAME, D', 1752-1840
see Burney, Fanny, 1752-1840

ARBOR DAY
see also Tree Planting

Egleston, N. H. Arbor Day Leaves. 2007. (Illus.). 76p. per. *(978-1-4065-1786-6(0))* Dodo Pr.

ARBORETUMS
see also Botanical Gardens
also names of individual arboretums

Arboretum, Arnold. Arnold Arboretum: Inventory of Living Collections. (Illus.). 220p. (Orig.). pap. 20.00 *(978-1-878297-02-0(3))* Arnold Arboretum of Harvard Univ.

Bauer, Gene. Botanical Serigraphs: The Gene Bauer Collection. 2010. (ENG.). 264p. 40.00 *(978-1-58948-253-1(0)*, ESRI Pr.) ESRI, Inc.

Camenson, Blythe. Opportunities in Landscape Architecture, Botanical Gardens & Arboreta Careers. 2007. (Opportunities in... Ser.). (ENG.). 160p. per. 13.95 *(978-0-07-147608-9(3)*, 0071476083) McGraw-Hill Cos., The.

Court, Franklin E. Pioneers of Ecological Restoration: The People & Legacy of the University of Wisconsin Arboretum. 2012. E-Book ***(978-0-299-28663-7(0))***; (ENG., Illus.). 336p. pap. 29.95 ***(978-0-299-28664-4(9))*** Univ. of Wisconsin Pr.

Elliott, Paul A., et al. The British Arboretum: Trees, Science & Culture in the Nineteenth Century, 1 vol. 2011. (Science & Culture in the Nineteenth Century Ser.). (ENG.). 320p. 99.00 *(978-1-84893-097-1(6))* Pickering & Chatto Pubs., Ltd. GBR. Dist: Ashgate Publishing Co.

McPherson, Alan. Botanic Gems Indiana Public Gardens: Including Greater Chicago, Dayton, Cincinnati & Louisville. 2009. 136p. pap. 36.49 *(978-1-4343-7772-2(5))* AuthorHouse.

Toomer, Simon. Planting & Maintaining a Tree Collection. 2010. (ENG., Illus.). 232p. 39.95 *(978-0-88192-930-0(1)*, 0881929301) Timber Pr., Inc.

ARBORICULTURE
see also Forests and Forestry; Fruit-Culture; Trees; Urban Forestry

Barnes, Gerry & Williamson, Tom. Ancient Trees in the Landscape: Norfolk's Arboreal Heritage. 2011. (ENG., Illus.). 179p. pap. 50.00 *(978-1-905119-39-4(9))* Windgather Pr. GBR. Dist: Brown, David Bk. Co., The.

Roddick, Chris. The Tree Care Primer. 2007. (Brooklyn Botanic Garden All-Region Guide Ser.). (ENG., Illus.). 120p. per. 9.95 *(978-1-889538-29-7(9))* Brooklyn Botanic Garden.

Watson, Bob. Trees: Their Use, Management, Cultivation & Biology. 2006. (ENG., Illus.). 384p. instr.'s gde. ed. 65.00 *(978-1-86126-885-3(8))* Crowood Pr., Ltd. GBR. Dist: Independent Pubs. Group.

ARBUS, DIANE, 1923-1971

Arbus, Doon. Diane Arbus: An Aperture Monograph. Israel, Marvin, ed. 40th ed. 2011. (ENG., Illus.). 184p. 65.00 ***(978-1-59711-174-4(0))*** Aperture Foundation, Inc.

Bosworth, Patricia. Diane Arbus: A Biography. 2006. (ENG., Illus.). 416p. pap. 18.95 *(978-0-393-32661-1(6)*, 32661) Norton, W. W. & Co., Inc.

Diane, Arbus. Diane Arbus. 2011. (ENG., Illus.). 112p. 75.00 ***(978-1-59711-190-4(2))*** Aperture Foundation, Inc.

—Diane Arbus: A Chronology. 2011. (ENG., Illus.). 177p. pap. 29.95 ***(978-1-59711-179-9(1))*** Aperture Foundation, Inc.

Gibson, Gregory. Hubert's Freaks: The Rare-Book Dealer, the Times Square Talker, & the Lost Photos of Diane Arbus. (ENG.). 288p. 2009. pap. 14.95 *(978-0-15-603308-4(9)*, Mariner Bks.) 2008. (Illus.). 24.00 *(978-0-15-101233-6(4))* Houghton Mifflin Harcourt Trade & Reference Pubs.

Gross, Frederick. Diane Arbus's 1960s: Auguries of Experience. 2012. 248p. 75.00 ***(978-0-8166-7011-6(0))***; pap. 24.95 ***(978-0-8166-7012-3(9))*** Univ. of Minnesota Pr.

Schultz, William Todd. An Emergency in Slow Motion: The Inner Life of Diane Arbus. 2011. (ENG., Illus.). 256p. 25.00 *(978-1-60819-519-0(8))* Bloomsbury Publishing.

ARC, ELECTRIC
see Electric Arc

ARC MEASURES
see also Geodesy

Nicastro, Nicholas. Circumference: Eratosthenes & the Ancient Quest to Measure the Globe. 2008. (ENG., Illus.). 240p. 23.95 *(978-0-312-37247-7(7))* St. Martin's Pr.

ARC WELDING
see Electric Welding

ARCADIAN LITERATURE
see Pastoral Literature

ARCH
see Arches

ARCHAEAN PERIOD
see Geology, Stratigraphic—Archaean

ARCHAEOLOGICAL DATING
see also Radiocarbon Dating

Barta, Miroslav & Vymazalova, Hana, eds. Chronology & Archaeology in Ancient Egypt: The Third Millennium BC. 2008. (ENG.). 319p. (C). 100.00 *(978-80-7308-245-1(4))* Czech Institute of Egyptology CZE. Dist: Brown, David Bk. Co., The.

Bayliss, Alex, et al. Gathering Time: Dating the Early Neolithic Enclosures of Southern Britain & Ireland, 2 vols. 2011. (ENG., Illus.). 992p. (C). 90.00 *(978-1-84217-425-8(8))* Oxbow Bks., Ltd. GBR. Dist: Brown, David Bk. Co., The.

Chhem, R K & Brothwell, D. R. Paleoradiology: Imaging Mummies & Fossils. 2010. (Illus.). xx, 163p. pap. 209.00 *(978-3-642-08024-1(3)*, 3642080243) Springer.

Graslund, Bo. The Birth of Prehistoric Chronology: Dating Methods & Dating Systems in Nineteenth-Century Scandinavian Archaeology. 2008. (New Studies in Archaeology Ser.). (ENG.). 144p. pap. 33.99 *(978-0-521-10388-6(6))* Cambridge Univ. Pr.

Liritzis, Ioannis & Stevenson, Christopher M. Obsidian & Ancient Manufactured Glasses. 2012. ***(978-0-8263-5161-6(1))*** Univ. of New Mexico Pr.

Liritzis, Ioannis & Stevenson, Christopher M., eds. Obsidian & Ancient Manufactured Glasses. 2012. (ENG., Illus.). 240p. 75.00 ***(978-0-8263-5159-3(X))*** Univ. of New Mexico Pr.

Nash, Stephen E., ed. It's about Time: A History of Archaeological Dating in North America. 2008. (ENG.). 305p. pap. 25.00 *(978-0-87480-947-3(9))* Univ. of Utah Pr.

Sagona, C., ed. Beyond the Homeland: Markers in Phoenician Chronology. 2008. (Ancient near Eastern Studies Supplement Ser.). (ENG.). 655p. (C). 142.00 *(978-90-429-2014-9(9))* Peeters Pubs. & Booksellers BEL. Dist: Brown, David Bk. Co., The.

Shiner, Justin. Place as Occupational Histories: An Investigation of the Deflated Surface Archaeological Record of Pine Point & Langwell Stations, Western New South Wales, Australia. 2008. (Bar S Ser.). (Illus.). 140 p. (C). 77.50 *(978-1-4073-0252-2(3))* British Archaeological Reports Ltd. GBR. Dist: Brown, David Bk. Co., The.

Susino, George J. Analysis of Lithic Artefact Microdebitage for Chronological Determination of Archaeological Sites. 2007. (Bar S Ser.). (ENG., Illus.). 146p. (C). pap. 87.50 *(978-1-4073-0024-5(5))* British Archaeological Reports Ltd. GBR. Dist: Brown, David Bk. Co., The.

Wagner, Ganther A. Age Determination of Young Rocks & Artifacts: Physical & Chemical Clocks in Quaternary Geology & Archaeology. Schiegl, S., tr. from GER. 2010. (Natural Science in Archaeology Ser.). (Illus.). xviii, 466p. pap. 235.00 *(978-3-642-08331-0(5)*, 3642083315) Springer.

ARCHAEOLOGICAL SPECIMENS
see Antiquities

ARCHAEOLOGISTS

Allen, Harry & Phillips, Caroline, eds. Bridging the Divide: Indigenous Communities & Archaeology into the 21st Century. 2010. (One World Archaeology Ser.). (ENG., Illus.). 290p. 79.00 *(978-1-59874-392-0(9))* Left Coast Pr., Inc.

Ashmore, Wendy, et al. Voices in American Archaeology. 2010. *(978-0-932839-39-8(8))* Society for American Archaeology.

Bowden, Mark. Pitt Rivers: The Life & Archaeological Work of Lieutenant-General Augustus Henry Lane Fox Pitt Rivers. 2009. (ENG.). 200p. pap. 26.99 *(978-0-521-10622-1(2))* Cambridge Univ. Pr.

Bruchac, Margaret, et al, eds. Indigenous Archaeologies: A Reader on Decolonization. 2010. (Archaeology & Indigenous Peoples Ser.). (ENG., Illus.). 304p. (C). pap. 34.95 *(978-1-59874-373-9(2))* Left Coast Pr., Inc.

Carver, Martin Oswald Hugh. Making Archaeology Happen. 2011. (ENG., Illus.). 184p. (C). pap. 29.95 *(978-1-61132-025-1(9))* Left Coast Pr., Inc.

—Making Archaeology Happen: Design Versus Dogma. 2011. (ENG., Illus.). 184p. (C). 89.00 *(978-1-61132-024-4(0))* Left Coast Pr., Inc.

Chapman, Kenneth Milton. Kenneth Chapman's Santa Fe: Artists & Archaeologists, 1907-1931. 2008. (School for Advanced Research Resident Scholar Ser.). (ENG., Illus.). 200p. pap. 34.95 *(978-1-930618-92-3(1))* School for Advanced Research Pr./SAR Pr.

Childs, Craig. Finders Keepers: A Tale of Archaeological Plunder & Obsession. 2010. (ENG., Illus.). 288p. 24.99 *(978-0-316-06642-6(7))* Little Brown & Co.

Colwell-Chanthaphonh, Chip & Ferguson, T. J., eds. Collaboration in Archaeological Practice: Engaging Descendant Communities. 2007. (Archaeology in Society Ser.). (ENG., Illus.). 300p. 85.00 *(978-0-7591-1053-3(0))*; per. 39.95 *(978-0-7591-1054-0(9))* AltaMira Pr.

Dobres. Fifty Key Archaeologists. 320p. 2013. (ENG.). (C). pap. 28.95 *(978-0-415-77699-8(6))* 2010. 110.00 *(978-0-415-77698-1(8))* Routledge.

Duke, Philip & Hamilakis, Yannis, eds. Archaeology & Capitalism: From Ethics to Politics. 2007. (One World Archaeology Ser.). (ENG., Illus.). 298p. 89.00 *(978-1-59874-270-1(1))* Left Coast Pr., Inc.

Everill, Paul. Invisible Diggers. 2009. (Hmp research Ser.). (ENG., Illus.). 224p. (C). pap. 49.95 ***(978-1-905933-10-5(X))*** Heritage Marketing & Publications, Ltd. GBR. Dist: Brown, David Bk. Co., The.

Fenwick, Joe. Lost & Found II: Rediscovering Ireland's Past. 2009. (Illus.). x, 332p. pap. *(978-1-905569-26-7(2))* Wordwell, Ltd.

Funari, Pedro Paulo, et al. Arqueologia e Historia del Mundo Antiguo: Contribuciones Brasilenas y Espanolas. 2008. (Bar S Ser.). (SPA., Illus.). 103p. (C). 65.00 *(978-1-4073-0279-9(5))* British Archaeological Reports Ltd. GBR. Dist: Brown, David Bk. Co., The.

Hamilakis, Yannis & Duke, Philip, eds. Archaeology & Capitalism: From Ethics to Politics. 2009. (One World Archaeology, Vol. 54 Ser.). (ENG.). 298p. pap. 36.95 *(978-1-59874-271-8(X))* Left Coast Pr., Inc.

Harris, Charles H., III & Sadler, Louis R. The Archaeologist Was a Spy: Sylvanus G. Morley & the Office of Naval Intelligence. 2009. (ENG., Illus.). 464p. pap. 29.95 *(978-0-8263-2938-7(1))* Univ. of New Mexico Pr.

Hart, Siobhan, et al, eds. Indigenous Archaeologies: A Reader on Decolonization. 2010. (Archaeology & Indigenous Peoples Ser.). (ENG., Illus.). 304p. (C). 89.00 *(978-1-59874-372-2(4))* Left Coast Pr., Inc.

Howard, Phil. Archaeological Surveying & Mapping: Recording & Depicting the Landscape. 2007. (ENG., Illus.). 312p. (C). per. 46.95 *(978-0-415-30663-8(9))* Routledge.

Howard, Philip. Surveying Archaeologists. 2007. (ENG., Illus.). 312p. (C). 150.00 *(978-0-415-30662-1(0))* Routledge.

Howe, Bruce. Dear Ancients: Letters of Bruce Howe. 2011. 176p. 42.95 ***(978-1-258-02200-6(1))*** Literary Licensing, LLC.

Jeter, Marvin D., ed. & pref. Edward Palmer's Arkansaw Mounds. 2nd ed. 2010. (ENG., Illus.). 444p. pap. 42.50 *(978-0-8173-5612-5(6))* Univ. of Alabama Pr.

Krall, Katharina. Der NS-Staat und die Ur- und Frühgeschichte: Ein Vergleich der Schriften von Herbert Jankuhn und Hans Reinerth zwischen 1933 und 1939. 2007. (GER.). 112p. *(978-3-8364-2379-3(0))* VDM Verlag Dr. Mueller e.K.

Levy, Thomas E., et al, eds. Crossing Jordan: North American Contributions to the Archaeology of Jordan. 2007. (ENG., Illus.). 518p. (C). 45.00 *(978-1-84553-269-7(4))*; 120.00 *(978-1-84553-268-0(6))* Equinox Publishing Ltd. GBR. Dist: ISD.

McGuire, Randall H. Archaeology as Political Action. 2008. (California Series in Public Anthropology: Vol. 17). (Illus.). 307p. 70.00 *(978-0-520-25490-9(2))*; pap. 31.95 *(978-0-520-25491-6(0))* Univ. of California Pr.

Meskell, Lynn, ed. Cosmopolitan Archaeologies. 2009. (Material Worlds Ser.). (ENG., Illus.). 304p. 89.95 *(978-0-8223-4432-2(7))*; pap. 24.95 *(978-0-8223-4444-5(0))* Duke Univ. Pr.

Rhodes, Robin F., ed. The Acquisition & Exhibition of Classical Antiquities: Professional, Legal, & Ethical Perspectives. 2008. (ENG., Illus.). 192p. pap. 25.00 *(978-0-268-04027-7(3))* Univ. of Notre Dame Pr.

Shapiro, Jason S. Before Santa Fe: Archaeology of the City Different. 2008. (ENG.). 256p. 39.95 *(978-0-89013-521-1(5))* Museum of New Mexico Pr.

Smith, Claire. Indigenous Archaeologies: Decolonising Theory & Practice. 2010. 432p. pap. 39.95 *(978-0-415-58906-2(1))* Routledge.

Stottman, M. Jay. Archaeologists As Activists: Can Archaeologists Change the World? 2010. (Illus.). viii, 207p. *(978-0-8173-8442-5(1))* Univ. of Alabama Pr.

Stottman, M. Jay, ed. & contrib. by. Archaeologists as Activists: Can Archaeologists Change the World? 2nd ed. (ENG., Illus.). 216p. 2011. pap. 29.95 *(978-0-8173-5622-4(3))* 2010. 46.00 *(978-0-8173-1712-6(0))* Univ. of Alabama Pr.

van Ess, Margarethe & Weber-Noldeke, Elisabeth, eds. Dr. Arnold Noldeke. 2008. (GER., Illus.). 347p. (C). 84.00 *(978-3-89500-485-8(5))* Reichert, Ludwig Dr. DEU. Dist: Brown, David Bk. Co., The.

ARCHAEOLOGISTS—BIOGRAPHY

Adams, Amanda. Ladies of the Field: Early Women Archaeologists & Their Search for Adventure, 1 vol. 2010. (ENG., Illus.). 240p. pap. 17.95 *(978-1-55365-433-9(1)*, Greystone Bks.) D&M Pubs. Inc. CAN. Dist: Perseus-PGW.

Adams, William Y. The Road from Frijoles Canyon: Anthropological Adventures on Four Continents. 2009. (ENG., Illus.). 371p. 45.00 *(978-0-8263-4787-9(8))* Univ. of New Mexico Pr.

Arentzen, Wout. W. J. de Wilde (1860-1936) Een vergeten onderzoeker van de Nederlandse Hunebedden. 2010. (ENG & DUT., Illus.). 223p. (C). pap. 52.00 *(978-90-8890-060-0(4))* Sidestone Pr. NLD. Dist: Brown, David Bk. Co., The.

Bahn, Paul G. The Great Archaeologists: The Lives & Legacies of the People Who Discovered the World's Most Famous Archaeological Sites, with over 180 Stunning Photographs: Fabulous Tales of Extraordinary Explorers Such As Heinrich Schliemann, the Excavator of Troy, & Howard Carter, the Discoverer of Tutankhamen's Tomb. 2009. (ENG., Illus.). 96p. pap. 14.99 *(978-1-84476-562-1(8))* Anness Publishing GBR. Dist: National Bk. Network.

Bryan, Betsy M., pref. The Robber Baron Archaeologist: An Essay about the Life of Theodore M. Davis. 2007. (Illus.). 112p. pap. 35.00 *(978-0-9774373-0-6(2))* Tambopata Partners.

Burger, Richard L., ed. The Life & Writings of Julio C. Tello: America's First Indigenous Archaeologist. 2009. (ENG., Illus.). 382p. pap. 39.95 *(978-1-58729-783-0(3))* Univ. of Iowa Pr.

Burrillo, Ralph. Rattlesnake Poetry: Explorations of Ancient Places & Personal Values. 2008. 190p. pap. 13.95 *(978-0-7414-4831-6(9))* Infinity Publishing.

Carr, Lydia C. Tessa Verney Wheeler: Women & Archaeology Before World War Two. 2012. (ENG., Illus.). 317p. 99.00 (978-0-19-964022-5(X)) Oxford Univ. Pr., Inc.
Carrasco, David, et al. Breaking Through Mexico's Past: Digging the Aztecs with Eduardo Matos Moctezuma. 2007. (ENG., Illus.). 195p. 34.95 (978-0-8263-3831-0(3)) Univ. of New Mexico Pr.
Chapman, Janet & Barrie, Karen. Kenneth Milton Chapman: A Life Dedicated to Indian Arts & Artists. 2008. (ENG., Illus.). 384p. 34.95 (978-0-8263-4424-3(0)) Univ. of New Mexico Pr.
Colwell-Chanthaphonh, Chip. Inheriting the Past: The Making of Arthur C. Parker & Indigenous Archaeology. 2009. (ENG., Illus.). 288p. 49.95 (978-0-8165-2655-0(9)); 296p. pap. 24.95 (978-0-8165-2656-7(7)) Univ. of Arizona Pr.
Currelly, Charles Trick. I Brought the Ages Home. 90th ed. 2008. (ENG.). 314p. 39.95 (978-0-88854-445-2(6)) Royal Ontario Museum CAN. Dist: Univ. of Toronto Pr.
D'Arpe, Rosellina & De Rinaldis, Bartolommeo. I Castromediano Di Lymburg e il Loro Archivio: Primi Interventi e Prospettive: Atti Del Convegno Di Studi, Cavallino, 28 Novembre 2008. 2009. (ITA., Illus.). 223p. (978-88-8086-863-7(2)) Congedo Publishing.
Davis, Miriam C. Dame Kathleen Kenyon: Digging up the Holy Land. 2008. (University College London Institute of Archaeology Publications). (ENG., Illus.). 280p. pap. 26.95 (978-1-59874-326-5(0)); 89.00 (978-1-59874-325-8(2)) Left Coast Pr., Inc.
Emberling, Geoff, ed. Pioneers to the Past: American Archaeologists in the Middle East, 1919-1920. 2010. (Oriental Institute Museum Publications). (ENG., Illus.). 160p. (C). pap. 34.95 (978-1-885923-70-7(8)) Oriental Institute of the Univ. of Chicago, The.
Ergin, N. & Redford, S., eds. Perceptions of the Past in the Turkish Republic: Classical & Byzantine Periods. 2010. (Ancient near Eastern Studies Supplement Ser.). (ENG., Illus.). 236p. (C). 115.00 (978-90-429-2264-8(8)) Peeters Pubs. & Booksellers BEL. Dist: Brown, David Bk. Co., The.
Fagan, Brian M. Return to Babylon: Travelers, Archaeologists, & Monuments in Mesopotamia. rev. ed. 2007. (ENG., Illus.). 386p. per. 21.95 (978-0-87081-867-7(8)) Univ. Pr. of Colorado.
Fowler, Don D. The Glen Canyon Country: A Personal Memoir. 2011. (Illus.). (gr. 12). 432p. pap. 39.95 (978-1-60781-134-3(0)); (ENG., 448p. 75.00 (978-1-60781-127-5(8)) Univ. of Utah Pr.
Graham, Ian. The Road to Ruins. 2010. (ENG., Illus.). 546p. 39.95 (978-0-8263-4754-1(1)) Univ. of New Mexico Pr.
Hauser, Kitty. Bloody Old Britain: O. G. S. Crawford & the Archaeology of Modern Life. (ENG., Illus.). 2010. 286p. pap. 18.95 (978-1-84708-077-6(4)) 2008. 224p. pap. 32.95 (978-1-86207-873-4(4)) Granta Bks. GBR. Dist: Independent Pubs. Group.
Hayden, Julian D. Field Man: Life as a Desert Archaeologist. Broyles, Bill & Boyer, Diane E., eds. 2010. (Swc Ser.). (ENG., Illus.). 352p. 45.00 (978-0-8165-2905-6(1)) Univ. of Arizona Pr.
Hume, Ivor Noël. Belzoni: The Giant Archaeologists Love to Hate. 2011. (ENG., Illus.). 320p. 34.95 (978-0-8139-3140-1(1)) Univ. Pr. of Virginia.
—A Passion for the Past: The Odyssey of a Transatlantic Archaeologist. 2010. (ENG., Illus.). 384p. 29.95 (978-0-8139-2977-4(6)) Univ. Pr. of Virginia.
James, T. G. H. Howard Carter: The Path to Tutankhamun. 2nd ed. 2012. (ENG., Illus.). 544p. pap. 23.00 (978-1-84511-258-5(X), Tauris Parke Paperbacks) I. B. Tauris & Co., Ltd. GBR. Dist: Macmillan.
Judd, Neil M. Men Met along the Trail: Adventures in Archaeology. 2009. (ENG., Illus.). 170p. pap. 19.95 (978-0-87480-991-6(6)) Univ. of Utah Pr.
Kerns, Virginia. Journeys West: Jane & Julian Steward & Their Guides. 2010. (ENG., Illus.). 444p. 55.00 (978-0-8032-2508-4(3)) Univ. of Nebraska Pr.
—Scenes from the High Desert: Julian Steward's Life & Theory. 2009. (ENG., Illus.). 448p. pap. 26.00 (978-0-252-07635-0(4)) Univ. of Illinois Pr.
MacGregor, Arthur. Sir John Evans 1823-1908: Antiquity, Commerce & Natural Science in the Age of Darwin. 2009. (ENG., Illus.). 352p. 90.00 (978-1-85444-237-6(6)) Ashmolean Museum GBR. Dist: National Bk. Network.
Mainfort, Robert C. Sam Dellinger: Raiders of the Lost Arkansas. 2008. (Illus.). 229p. 39.95 (978-1-55728-886-8(0)) Univ. of Arkansas Pr.
Malley, Shawn. From Archaeology to Spectacle in Victorian Britain: The Case of Assyria, 1845-1854. 2012. (Illus.). 220p. 99.95 (978-1-4094-2689-9(0)) Ashgate Publishing Co.
Matson, R. G. & Kohler, Timothy, eds. Tracking Ancient Footsteps: William D. Lipe's Contributions to Southwestern Prehistory & Public Archaeology. 2006. (Illus.). 187p. per. (978-0-87422-290-6(7)) Washington State Univ. Pr.
Mullins, Gerry. Dublin Nazi No. 1: The Life of Adolf Mahr. 2008. (ENG., Illus.). 269p. pap. 45.95 (978-1-905483-19-8(8)) Liberties Pr. IRL. Dist: Dufour Editions, Inc.
—Dublin Nazi No. 1: The Life of Adolph Mahr. 2008. (ENG., Illus.). 269p. pap. 31.95 (978-1-905483-20-4(1)) Liberties Pr. IRL. Dist: Dufour Editions, Inc.
Nicholas, George, ed. Being & Becoming Indigenous Archaeologists. (Archaeology & Indigenous Peoples Ser.). (ENG., Illus.). 352p. 2011. pap. 36.95 (978-1-59874-498-9(4)) 2010. lib. bdg. 69.00 (978-1-59874-497-2(6)) Left Coast Pr., Inc.
Patterson, Don. Journey to Xibalba: A Life in Archaeology. 2007. (ENG., Illus.). 312p. (C). 34.95 (978-0-8263-4292-8(2)) Univ. of New Mexico Pr.
Pedley, John G. The Life & Work of Francis Willey Kelsey: Archaeology, Antiquity, & the Arts. 2011. (ENG., Illus.). 480p. 75.00 (978-0-472-11802-1(1)) Univ. of Michigan Pr.
Pedley, John Griffiths. The Life & Work of Francis Willey Kelsey: Archaeology, Antiquity, & the Arts. 2012. E-Book (978-0-472-02805-4(7)) Univ. of Michigan Pr.
Posnansky, Merrick. Africa & Archaeology: Empowering an Expatriate Life. 2009. (ENG., Illus.). 288p. 58.00 (978-1-84511-994-2(0), Radcliffe Pr., The) I. B. Tauris & Co., Ltd. GBR. Dist: Macmillan.
Preston, Christine. The Rise of Man in the Gardens of Sumeria: A Biography of L. A. Waddell. 2009. (ENG., Illus.). 260p. 85.00 (978-1-84519-315-7(6)) Sussex Academic Pr. GBR. Dist: International Specialized Bk. Services.
Reid, J. Jefferson & Whittlesey, Stephanie Michelle. Prehistory, Personality, & Place: Emil W. Haury & the Mogollon Controversy. 2010. (ENG., Illus.). 208p. pap. 19.95 (978-0-8165-2863-9(2)) Univ. of Arizona Pr.
Reid, Jefferson & Whittlesey, Stephanie Michelle. Prehistory, Personality, & Place: Emil W. Haury & the Mogollon Controversy. 2010. (ENG., Illus.). 208p. (C). pap. 19.95 (978-0-8165-2862-2(4)) Univ. of Arizona Pr.
Richardson, Alexandra. Passionate Patron: The Life of Alexander Hardcastle & the Greek Temples of Agrigento. 2009. (ENG., Illus.). 151p. (C). pap. 30.00 (978-1-905739-26-8(1)) Archaeopress GBR. Dist: Brown, David Bk. Co., The.
Ryan, Donald P. Beneath the Sands of Egypt: Adventures of an Unconventional Archaeologist. (ENG.). 304p. 2011. pap. 15.99 (978-0-06-173283-6(4), Harper Paperbacks) 2010. 26.99 (978-0-06-173282-9(5), Morrow, William & Co.) HarperCollins Pubs.
Sabloff, Jeremy A. & Fash, William L., eds. Gordon R. Willey & American Archeology: Contemporary Perspectives. 2007. (ENG., Illus.). 256p. (C). 34.95 (978-0-8061-3805-3(X)) Univ. of Oklahoma Pr.
Sabol Jr., John G. Digging-Deep: An Archaeologist Unearths a Haunted Life. 2009. 252p. pap. 16.95 (978-1-4490-2481-9(5)) AuthorHouse.
Shanks, Hershel. Freeing the Dead Sea Scrolls: And Other Adventures of an Archaeology Outsider. 2010. (ENG., Illus.). 272p. 29.95 (978-1-4411-5217-6(2)) Continuum International Publishing Group, Ltd. GBR. Dist: National Bk. Network.
—Scholars on the Record: Insightful Interviews on Bible & Archaeology. 2009. (Illus.). 254p. (978-1-935335-23-8(5)) Biblical Archaeology Society.
Silberman, Neil Asher. A Prophet from Amongst You: The Life of Yigael Yadin. 2011. 458p. 70.00 (978-1-59740-815-8(8)) ACLS Humanities E-Book.
Sitchin, Zecharia. The Earth Chronicles Expeditions: Journeys to the Mythical Past. 2007. (ENG., Illus.). 1p. pap. 16.00 (978-1-59143-076-6(3)) Bear & Co.
—Journeys to the Mythical Past. (Earth Chronicles Ser.: Bk. 7). (ENG.). 1p. 2009. pap. 18.00 (978-1-59143-108-4(5)) 2007. (Illus.). 24.00 (978-1-59143-080-3(1)) Bear & Co.
South, Stanley. An Archaeological Evolution. 2007. 432p. per. 69.95 (978-0-387-68174-0(4)) Springer.
Steffy, Loren C. The Man Who Thought like a Ship. 2012. (Ed Rachal Foundation Nautical Archaeology Ser.). (ENG., Illus.). 256p. 35.00 (978-1-60344-664-8(8)) Texas A&M Univ. Pr.
Storck, Peter L. Journey to the Ice Age: Discovering an Ancient World. 2006. (ENG., Illus.). 376p. pap. 29.95 (978-0-7748-1029-6(7)) UBC Pr. CAN. Dist: Univ. of Washington Pr.
Swanton, John Reed & Holmes, William Henry. Biographical Memoir of William Henry Holmes, 1846-1933: National Academy of Sciences Biographical Memoirs, V17, Tenth Memoir. 2011. 38p. 35.95 (978-1-258-06848-6(6)) Literary Licensing, LLC.
Uranium Daughter. 2009. 350p. pap. 18.95 (978-0-9655961-6-9(8)) Yellow Cat Publishing.
Wartke, Ralf-B. Auf dem Weg nach Babylon: Robert Koldewey - Ein Archäologenleben. Wartke, Ralf-B., ed. 2008. (Illus.). 192p. (C). 38.00 (978-3-8053-3918-6(6)) Zabern, Philipp von Verlag, GmbH DEU. Dist: Brown, David Bk. Co., The.
Welbourn, Terry. T.C. Lethbridge: The Man Who Saw the Future. 2011. (ENG., Illus.). 360p. pap. 29.95 (978-1-84694-500-7(3)) Hunt, John Publishing Ltd. GBR. Dist: National Bk. Network.
Wendorf, Fred. Desert Days: My Life as a Field Archaeologist. 2008. (Illus.). 640p. 29.95 (978-0-87074-524-9(7)) Southern Methodist Univ. Pr.
Whitfield, Susan. Aurel Stein on the Silk Road. 2006. (Illus.). 143p. reprint ed. 35.00 (978-1-4223-5504-6(7)) DIANE Publishing Co.
Whitteridge, Gordon. Charles Masson of Afghanistan: Explorer, Archaeologist, Numismatist & Intelligence Agent. 2006. (ENG., Illus.). 22.95 (978-974-524-020-9(6)) Orchid Pr. THA. Dist: National Bk. Network.
Williamson, Ronald F. & Bisson, Michael S. The Archaeology of Bruce Trigger: Theoretical Empiricism. 2006. (ENG., Illus.). 320p. (C). per. (978-0-7735-3161-1(0)) McGill-Queen's Univ. Pr.
Wood, W. Raymond. A White-Bearded Plainsman: The Memoirs of Archaeologist W. Raymond Wood. 2011. (ENG., Illus.). 432p. (C). (gr. 13). 49.95 (978-1-60781-130-5(8)) Univ. of Utah Pr.

ARCHAEOLOGY

see also Aerial Photography in Archaeology; Amulets; Antiquities; Architecture, Ancient; Architecture, Primitive; Burial; Cliff-Dwellings; Copper Age; Earthworks (Archeology); Excavations (Archaeology); Hill Figures; Historic Sites; Human Remains (Archaeology); Indians—Antiquities; Industrial Archaeology; Industries, Primitive; Inscriptions; Iron Age; Kitchen-Middens; Mounds; Numismatics; Photography in Archaeology; Picture-Writing; Pyramids; Rock Paintings; Sculpture, Primitive; Seven Wonders of the World; Social Archaeology; Stele (Archaeology); Stone Age; Underwater Archaeology
also subdivision Antiquities under names of countries, cities, etc. and under individual ethnic groups, e.g. Egypt—Antiquities; Mayas—Antiquities

Abramiuk, Marc A. The Foundations of Cognitive Archaeology. 2012. (978-0-262-01768-8(7)) MIT Pr.
Abt, Jeffrey. American Egyptologist: The Life of James Henry Breasted & the Creation of His Oriental Institute. 2012. (ENG., Illus.). 536p. 45.00 (978-0-226-00110-4(5)) Univ. of Chicago Pr.
Adams, William Yewdale & Adams, Ernest W. Archaeological Typology & Practical Reality: A Dialectical Approach to Artifact Classification & Sorting. 2007. (ENG., Illus.). 452p. pap. 56.00 (978-0-521-04867-5(2)) Cambridge Univ. Pr.
Adkins, Lesley & Adkins, Roy. Archaeological Illustration. 2009. (Cambridge Manuals in Archaeology Ser.). (ENG., Illus.). 276p. pap. 36.99 (978-0-521-10317-6(7)) Cambridge Univ. Pr.
AIA 108th Annual Meeting Abstracts, Volume 30. 2007. (ENG.). (C). pap. 19.95 (978-1-931909-17-4(2)) Archaeological Institute of America.
AIA 109th Annual Meeting Abstracts, Volume 31. 2008. (ENG.). 224p. (C). pap. 19.95 (978-1-931909-19-8(9)) Archaeological Institute of America.
Allen, Grant. Science in Arcady. 2008. 244p. 24.99 (978-0-554-37529-8(X)) 2008. 244p. 27.99 (978-0-554-28226-8(7)) 2007. (ENG.). 218p. per. 20.99 (978-1-4346-4943-0(1)) 2007. (ENG.). 244p. per. 22.99 (978-1-4346-4944-7(X)) BiblioBazaar.
—Science in Arcady. 2009. 168p. pap. (978-0-217-54680-5(3)) Books LLC.
—Science in Arcady. 2008. 318p. 45.95 (978-1-4365-2668-5(X)) 2007. (ENG.). 320p. per. 30.95 (978-0-548-68859-5(1)) Kessinger Publishing, LLC.
Ambrus, Victor G. & Aston, Michael. Recreating the Past. 2009. (ENG., Illus.). 120p. pap. 29.95 (978-0-7524-5033-9(6)) History Pr. Ltd., The GBR. Dist: Independent Pubs. Group.
Antela Bernárdez, Borja & Ñaco del Hoyo, Toni. Transforming Historical Landscapes in the Ancient Empires. 2009. (FRE, SPA & ENG., Illus.). 264p. (C). pap. 125.00 (978-1-4073-0460-1(7)) British Archaeological Reports Ltd. GBR. Dist: Brown, David Bk. Co., The.
Arbel, Yoav. Ultimate Devotion: The Historical Impact & Archaeological Expression of Intense Religious Movements. 2009. (Approaches to Anthropological Archaeology Ser.). (ENG., Illus.). 216p. (C). 99.95 (978-1-84553-226-0(0)) Equinox Publishing Ltd. GBR. Dist: ISD.
Archaeological Institute of America. AIA 110th Annual Meeting Abstracts, Volume 32. 2009. (AIA Annual Meeting Abstracts Ser.). (ENG.). 209p. (C). pap. 19.95 (978-1-931909-20-4(2)) Archaeological Institute of America.
Archaeological Institute of America, ed. AIA 111th Annual Meeting Abstracts, Volume 33. 2010. (AIA Annual Meeting Abstracts Ser.). (ENG.). 145p. (C). pap. 19.95 (978-1-931909-21-1(0)) Archaeological Institute of America.
—AIA 112th Annual Meeting Abstracts, Volume 34. 2011. (ENG.). 163p. (C). pap. 19.95 (978-1-931909-22-8(9), Archaeological Institute of America) Archaeological Institute of America.
Archaeology: Unearthing the Mysteries of the Past. 304p. (978-1-4054-8787-0(9)) Parragon, Inc.
Arnold, Jeanne E. & Walsh, Michael R. California's Ancient Past: From the Pacific to the Range of Light. 2010. (978-0-932839-40-4(1)) Society for American Archaeology.
Ashmore, Wendy, et al. Discovering Our Past: A Brief Introduction to Archaeology. 5th ed. 2009. (ENG., Illus.). 320p. (C). pap. 90.00 (978-0-07-353099-4(9), 0073530999) McGraw-Hill Cos., The.
—Voices in American Archaeology. 2010. (978-0-932839-39-8(8)) Society for American Archaeology.
Aspinall, Arnold, et al. Magnetometry for Archaeologists. 2009. (Geophysical Methods for Archaeology Ser.). (ENG., Illus.). 224p. pap. 29.95 (978-0-7591-1348-0(3)) AltaMira Pr.
Aston, Mick & Gerrard, Chris, eds. The Shapwick Project, Somerset: A Rural Landscape Explored. 2007. (Society for Medieval Archaeology Monograph Ser.). 1048p. (C). pap. 90.00 (978-1-905981-86-1(4)) Northern Universities Pr. GBR. Dist: Brown, David Bk. Co., The.
Attema, P., et al. Between Satricum & Antium: Settlement Dynamics in a Coastal Landscape in Latium Vetus. 2011. (Babesch Supplementa Ser.). (ENG.). 259p. (C). pap. 99.00 (978-90-429-2465-9(9)) Peeters Pubs. & Booksellers BEL. Dist: Brown, David Bk. Co., The.
Aubry, Thierry, et al, eds. Space & Time: Which Diachronies, Which Synchronies, Which Scales?/ Typology vs Technology. 2008. (Bar S Ser.). (FRE., Illus.). 222p. (C). 97.50 (978-1-4073-0315-4(5)) British Archaeological Reports Ltd. GBR. Dist: Brown, David Bk. Co., The.
Avebury, Rt. Hon. Lord. Pre Historic Times. 2006. 688p. per. (978-1-4067-2932-0(9), Hesperides Pr.) Read Bks.
Aygun, Cigdem Ozkan, ed. SOMA 2007. 2009. (Bar S Ser.). (Illus.). 469p. (C). 157.50 (978-1-4073-0382-6(1)) British Archaeological Reports Ltd. GBR. Dist: Brown, David Bk. Co., The.
Bahn, Paul. Archaeology: A Very Short Introduction. 2nd ed. 2012. (ENG., Illus.). 152p. pap. 11.95 (978-0-19-965743-8(2)) Oxford Univ. Pr., Inc.
Bailey, Geoff & Parkington, John, eds. The Archaeology of Prehistoric Coastlines. 2009. (New Directions in Archaeology Ser.). (ENG., Illus.). 164p. pap. 31.99 (978-0-521-10841-6(1)) Cambridge Univ. Pr.
Bakels, Corrie C. The Western European Loess Belt: Agrarian History, 5300 BC - AD 1000. 2009. (ENG., Illus.). viii, 295p. 159.00 (978-1-4020-9839-0(1), 1402098391) Springer.
Bakirtzis, Charalambos & Koester, Helmut, eds. Philippi at the Time of Paul & after His Death. 2009. 128p. pap. 16.00 (978-1-60608-929-3(3), Wipf and Stock) Wipf & Stock Pubs.
Balaam, Nicholas & Rackham, James, eds. Issues in Environmental Archaeology: Perspectives on Its Archaeological & Public Role. 2009. (University College London Institute of Archaeology Publications). (ENG., Illus.). 96p. 89.00 (978-0-905853-29-1(6)) Left Coast Pr., Inc.
Barber, Bruno, et al. The City, the Cross & the Star: The Archaeology of Belief 2012. (MoLAS Monograph Ser.). (ENG., Illus.). 100p. (C). pap. 30.00 (978-1-901992-92-2(6)) Museum of London Archaeology Service GBR. Dist: Brown, David Bk. Co., The.
Barnatt, John. The Archaeology of a Great Estate: Chatsworth & Beyond. 2009. (ENG., Illus.). 232p. pap. 40.00 (978-1-905119-27-1(5)) Windgather Pr. GBR. Dist: Brown, David Bk. Co., The.
Battle-Baptiste, Whitney. Black Feminist Archaeology. 2011. (ENG., Illus.). 200p. 89.00 (978-1-59874-378-4(3)); pap. 29.95 (978-1-59874-379-1(1)) Left Coast Pr., Inc.
Beck, Heinrich, et al, eds. Altertumskunde - Altertumswissenschaft - Kulturwissenschaft: Erträge und Perspektiven Nach 40 Jahren Reallexikon der Germanischen Altertumskunde. 2011. (Reallexikon der Germanischen Altertumskunde - Ergänzungsbände Ser.). (GER., Illus.). 800p. 280.00 (978-3-11-027360-1(8)) De Gruyter, Walter Inc.
Bentley, R. Alexander, et al, eds. Handbook of Archaeological Theories. 2007. (ENG., Illus.). 600p. 184.95 (978-0-7591-0032-9(2)) AltaMira Pr.
Berg, Ina, ed. Breaking the Mould: Challenging the Past through Pottery. 2008. (Bar S Ser.). (Illus.). 123p. (C). 70.00 (978-1-4073-0344-4(9)) British Archaeological Reports Ltd. GBR. Dist: Brown, David Bk. Co., The.
Bernbeck, Reinhard & McGuire, Randall H. Ideologies in Archaeology. 2011. (ENG., Illus.). 424p. 60.00 (978-0-8165-2673-4(7)) Univ. of Arizona Pr.
Bevan, Bill. Walk into Prehistory: Discovering the 40 Greatest Ancient Sites of Britain & Ireland. 2011. (ENG., Illus.). 208p. 40.00 (978-0-7112-3177-1(X)) Lincoln, Frances Ltd. GBR. Dist: Perseus-PGW.
Bhreathnach, Edel, et al, eds. Landscapes of Cult & Kingship: Archaeology & Text. 2011. 340p. 70.00 (978-1-84682-219-3(X)) Four Courts Pr. IRL. Dist: International Specialized Bk. Services.
Bicho, Nuno F., et al, eds. Trekking the Shore: Changing Coastlines & the Antiquity of Coastal Settlement. 2011. (Interdisciplinary Contributions to Archaeology Ser.). (ENG., Illus.). xxx, 496p. 169.00 (978-1-4419-8218-6(3), 1441982183) Springer.
Bilsel, Can. Antiquity on Display: Regimes of the Authentic in Berlin's Pergamon Museum. 2012. (Classical Presences Ser.). (ENG., Illus.). 328p. 150.00 (978-0-19-957055-3(8)) Oxford Univ. Pr., Inc.
Bintliff, John & Pearce, Mark, eds. The Death of Archaeological Theory? 2011. (ENG., Illus.). 89p. (C). pap. 26.00 (978-1-84217-446-3(0)) Oxbow Bks., Ltd. GBR. Dist: Brown, David Bk. Co., The.
Blair, Ian & Sankey, David. A Roman Drainage Culvert, Great Fire Destruction Debris & Other Evidence from Hillside Sites North-East of London Bridge: Excavations at Monument House & 13-21 Eastcheap, City of London. 2007. (MoLAS Archaeology Studies Ser.) (Illus.). 91p. (C). pap. 18.00 (978-1-901992-69-4(1)) Museum of London Archaeology Service GBR. Dist: Brown, David Bk. Co., The.
Blancquaert, Geertrui, et al. Understanding the Past: A Matter of Surface-Area. 2011. (Bar S Ser.). (ENG., Illus.). 162p. (C). pap. 90.00 (978-1-4073-0749-7(5)) British Archaeological Reports Ltd. GBR. Dist: Brown, David Bk. Co., The.
Bland, Roger, et al. The Frome Hoard. 2011. (ENG., Illus.). 48p. (C). pap. 10.00 (978-0-7141-2334-9(X)) British Museum Pr. GBR. Dist: Brown, David Bk. Co., The.
Blatherwick, Simon & Bluer, Richard. Great Houses, Moats & Mills on the South Bank of the Thames: Medieval & Tudor Southwark & Rotherhithe. 2009. (MoLAS Monograph Ser.). (ENG., Illus.). 263p. (C). 46.00 (978-1-901992-83-0(7)) Museum of London Archaeology Service GBR. Dist: Brown, David Bk. Co., The.
Blau, Soren & Ubelaker, Douglas, eds. Handbook of Forensic Anthropology & Archaeology. 2011. (World Archaeological Congress Research Ser.). (ENG., Illus.). 534p. pap. 49.95 (978-1-61132-793-9(8)) Left Coast Pr., Inc.
Bloemers, Tom, et al, eds. The Cultural Landscape & Heritage Paradox: Protection & Development of the Dutch Archaeological-historical Landscape & its European Dimension. 2011. (Landscape & Heritage Proceedings Ser.). (Illus.). 739p. pap. (978-90-8964-155-7(6)) Amsterdam Univ. Pr.
Bowen, Thomas. The Record of Native People on Gulf of California Islands. 2009. (ASM Archaeological Ser.). (ENG., Illus.). 102p. pap. 19.95 (978-1-889747-83-5(1)) Arizona State Museum.
Boyarin, Daniel. Talmudic Archaeology. pap. (978-0-8047-3784-5(3)) Stanford Univ. Pr.
Boykin, Kristina. An Analysis of Feature 33 at Van Winkle's Mill Site. 2011. 92p. pap. (978-3-8443-9615-7(2)) Lambert Academic Publishing.
Boytner, Ran, et al, eds. Controlling the Past, Owning the Future: The Political Uses of Archaeology in the Middle East. 2010. (ENG., Illus.). 320p. 60.00 (978-0-8165-2795-3(4)) Univ. of Arizona Pr.
Bradley, David A. & Creagh, Dudley Cecil, contrib. by. Physical Techniques in the Study of Art, Archaeology & Cultural Heritage, Vol. 1. 2006. (Physical Techniques in the Study of Art, Archaeology & Cultural Heritage Ser.: 1). (ENG., Illus.). 232p. 114.00 (978-0-444-52131-6(3), Elsevier Science) Elsevier Science & Technology Bks.
Braje, Todd J. Modern Oceans, Ancient Sites: Archaeology & Marine Conservation on San Miguel Island, California. 2009. (Anthropology of Pacific North America Ser.). (ENG., Illus.). 176p. 50.00 (978-0-87480-984-8(3)) Univ. of Utah Pr.
Brenner, Joni, et al. Life of Bone: Art Meets Science. 2011. (ENG., Illus.). 160p. 50.00 (978-1-86814-539-3(5)) Witwatersrand Univ. Pr. Pubns. ZAF. Dist: Transaction Pubs.

Brisch, Gerald, ed. The Travel Chronicles of Mrs J. Theodore Bent Vol. 3: Southern Arabia & Persia. 2011. (3rdguides Ser.). (ENG., Illus.). 460p. (C). pap. 59.95 *(978-1-905739-13-4(3))* Archaeopress GBR. Dist: Brown, David Bk. Co., The.

Broughton, Jack M. & Cannon, Michael D., eds. Evolutionary Ecology & Archaeology: Applications to Problems in Human Evolution & Prehistory. 2009. (ENG., Illus.). 456p. pap. 50.00 *(978-0-87480-935-0(5))* Univ. of Utah Pr.

Brown, N., et al. The Archaeology of the Essex Coast Vol 2: Excavations at the prehistoric site of the Stumble. 2012. (East Anglian Archaeology Ser.: 143). (ENG., Illus.). 170p. (C). pap. 30.00 ***(978-1-84194-074-8(7))*** East Anglian Archaeology GBR. Dist: Brown, David Bk. Co., The.

Buck Sutton, Susan & Stroulia, Anna. Archaeology in Situ: Sites, Archaeology, & Communities in Greece. 2010. (Greek Studies: Interdisciplinary Approaches Ser.). (ENG., Illus.). 532p. 115.50 *(978-0-7391-3234-0(2))*; pap. 51.50 *(978-0-7391-3235-7(0))* Lexington Bks.

Burger, Richard L. & Salazar, Lucy C., eds. Machu Picchu: Unveiling the Mystery of the Incas. 2008. (ENG., Illus.). 240p. per. 28.00 *(978-0-300-13645-6(5))* Yale Univ. Pr.

Burke, Heather, et al. The Archaeologist's Field Handbook. 2008. (ENG.). 448p. (Orig.). pap. 49.95 *(978-0-7591-0883-7(8))* AltaMira Pr.

Burl, Aubrey. Prehistoric Astronomy & Ritual. 2nd ed. 2008. (Shire Archaeology Ser.). (ENG., Illus.). 72p. pap. 13.95 *(978-0-7478-0614-1(4))* Shire Pubns., Ltd. GBR. Dist: Random Hse., Inc.

Buteux, Simon & Chapman, Henry. Where the Rivers Meet: The Archaeology of Catholme & the Trent-Tame Confluence. 2009. (CBA Research Report). (Illus.). 192p. (C). pap. 30.00 *(978-1-902771-78-6(8))* Council for British Archaeology GBR. Dist: Brown, David Bk. Co., The.

Buteux, Simon, et al. Digging up the Ice Age: Recognising, Recording & Understanding Fossil & Archaeological Remains Found in British Quarries. 2009. (ENG., Illus.). 194p. (C). pap. 30.00 *(978-1-905739-24-0(9))* Archaeopress GBR. Dist: Brown, David Bk. Co., The.

Butler, Jonathan & Leary, Jim. Roman Archaeology in the Upper Reaches of the Walbrook Valley: Excavations at 6-8 Tokenhouse Yard, London EC2. 2012. (PCA Monographs). (ENG., Illus.). 150p. (C). pap. 30.00 ***(978-0-9563054-5-9(8))*** Pre-Construct Archaeology Limited GBR. Dist: Brown, David Bk. Co., The.

Campana, Stefano & Forte, Maurizio, eds. From Space to Place: 2nd International Conference on Remote Sensing in Archaeology: Proceedings of the 2nd International Workshop, CNR, Rome, Italy, December 2-4, 2006. 2006. (Bar S Ser.). (Illus.). 579p. (C). 175.00 *(978-1-84171-998-6(6))* British Archaeological Reports Ltd. GBR. Dist: Brown, David Bk. Co., The.

Campana, Stefano, et al. Space, Time, Place. 2010. (Bar S Ser.). (ENG., Illus.). 426p. (C). pap. 175.00 *(978-1-4073-0659-9(6))* British Archaeological Reports Ltd. GBR. Dist: Brown, David Bk. Co., The.

Capelotti, P. J. The Human Archaeology of Space: Lunar, Planetary & Interstellar Relics of Exploration. 2010. (ENG., Illus.). 199p. pap. 45.00 *(978-0-7864-5859-2(3))* McFarland & Co., Inc. Pubs.

Caple, Chris. Objects: Reluctant Witnesses to the Past. 2006. (Illus.). 266p. 125.00 *(978-0-415-30588-4(8)*, RU05888); per. 37.95 *(978-0-415-30589-1(6)*, RU05896) Routledge.

Caraher, William, et al. Archaeology & History in Roman, Medieval & Post-Medieval Greece: Studies on Method & Meaning in Honor of Timothy E. Gregory. 2008. (Studies on Method & Meaning in Honor of Timothy E. Gregory Ser.). (Illus.). 372p. 134.95 *(978-0-7546-6442-0(2))* Ashgate Publishing Co.

Carlin, Eithne & Kerke, Simon van de. Linguistics & Archaeology in the Americas: The Historization of Language & Society. (ENG.). 300p. *(978-90-04-17362-0(5))* BRILL.

Carr, Lydia C. Tessa Verney Wheeler: Women & Archaeology Before World War Two. 2012. (ENG., Illus.). 317p. 99.00 ***(978-0-19-964022-5(X))*** Oxford Univ. Pr., Inc.

Carver, Martin. The Birth of a Borough: An Archaeological Study of Anglo-Saxon Stafford. 2010. (Illus.). 194p. 99.00 *(978-0-85115-623-1(1)*, Boydell Press) Boydell & Brewer, Ltd. GBR. Dist: Boydell & Brewer, Inc.

Carver, Martin Professor. Archaeological Investigation. 2010. (ENG., Illus.). 480p. (C). 48.95 *(978-0-415-48919-5(9))* Routledge.

Casiday, Augustine. Evagrius Ponticus. 2006. (Early Church Fathers Ser.). (ENG.). 264p. 115.00 *(978-0-415-32446-5(7))* Routledge.

Catling, Christopher & Bahn, Paul. The Illustrated Practical Encyclopedia of Archaeology: The Key Sites, Those Who Discovered Them, & How to Become & Archaeologist. 2010. (ENG., Illus.). 512p. 35.00 *(978-0-7548-2057-4(2))* Anness Publishing GBR. Dist: National Bk. Network.

Chamberlain, Andrew. Demography in Archaeology. 2006. (Cambridge Manuals in Archaeology Ser.). (ENG., Illus.). 256p. (C). 115.00 *(978-0-521-59367-0(0))*; pap. 42.00 *(978-0-521-59651-0(3))* Cambridge Univ. Pr.

Chang, Kwang-Chih. Kao Gu Xue Zhuan Ti Liu Jiang. 2010. (CHI., Illus.). *(978-7-108-03330-7(5))* SDX Joint Publishing, Co.

Chapman, Robert, et al, eds. The Archaeology of Death. 2009. (New Directions in Archaeology Ser.). (ENG., Illus.). 168p. pap. 28.99 *(978-0-521-11078-5(5))* Cambridge Univ. Pr.

Charles Thomas, Newton. Essays on Art & Archaeology. 2010. (Cambridge Library Collection - Archaeology Ser.). (ENG., Illus.). 500p. pap. 37.99 *(978-1-108-01741-1(X))* Cambridge Univ. Pr.

Chauhan, Parth & Garge, Tejas. Pursuing Archaeological Research in India: Ancient Indica Rediscovered. 2009. (World Archaeological Congress Cultural Heritage Manual Ser.). 260p. 110.00 *(978-0-387-76456-6(9))* Springer.

Chazan, Michael. World Prehistory & Archaeology. 2nd ed. 2010. (ENG.). 480p. (C). 82.67 *(978-0-205-78754-8(1))*; 46.67 *(978-0-205-79731-8(8))* Prentice Hall PTR. (Prentice Hall).

—World Prehistory & Archaeology, Books a la Carte Edition. 2nd ed. 2010. (ENG.). 480p. (C). ring bd. 80.67 *(978-0-205-00353-2(2)*, Prentice Hall) Prentice Hall PTR.

—World Prehistory & Archaeology, Books a la Carte Plus MyAnthroLab. 2nd ed. 2010. (ENG.). (C). ring bd. 87.33 *(978-0-205-00354-9(0)*, Prentice Hall) Prentice Hall PTR.

Childs, Craig. Finders Keepers: A Tale of Archaeological Plunder & Obsession. 2010. (ENG., Illus.). 288p. 24.99 *(978-0-316-06642-6(7))* Little Brown & Co.

Clack, Timothy & Brittain, Marcus, eds. Archaeology & the Media. (University College London Institute of Archaeology Publications). (ENG., Illus.). 323p. 2009. pap. 32.95 *(978-1-59874-234-3(5))* 2007. 94.00 *(978-1-59874-233-6(7))* Left Coast Pr., Inc.

Clack, Timothy A. R., ed. Culture, History & Identity: Landscapes of Inhabitation in the Mount Kilimanjaro Area, Tanzania. 2009. (Bar S Ser.). (ENG., Illus.). 303p. (C). pap. 125.00 *(978-1-4073-0449-6(6))* British Archaeological Reports Ltd. GBR. Dist: Brown, David Bk. Co., The.

Clodd, Edward. Primitive Man. 2007. (ENG.). 204p. 39.95 *(978-0-548-00593-4(1))* Kessinger Publishing, LLC.

Cobb, Hannah, et al, eds. Reconsidering Archaeological Fieldwork: Exploring on-Site Relationships Between Theory & Practice. 2012. (ENG., Illus.). x, 183p. 129.00 ***(978-1-4614-2337-9(6))***, 1461423376) Springer.

Cochrane, Ethan & Gardner, Andrew, eds. Evolutionary & Interpretive Archaeologies: A Dialogue. 2011. (Univ col london inst arch Pub Ser.). (ENG., Illus.). 361p. 89.00 *(978-1-59874-426-2(7))*; pap. 34.95 *(978-1-59874-427-9(5))* Left Coast Pr., Inc.

Coimbra, Fernando & Dimitriadis, George. Cognitive Archaeology As Symbolic Archaeology. 2008. (Bar S Ser.). (Illus.). iv, 69p. (C). 57.50 *(978-1-4073-0179-2(9))* British Archaeological Reports Ltd. GBR. Dist: Brown, David Bk. Co., The.

Coleman, Jason. Uncovering History: An Archaeologist's Perspective. 2006. 96p. per. 9.95 *(978-0-9787490-0-2(6))* Bertillion Bks.

Coles, Bryony, ed. Journal of Wetland Archaeology, Volume 6. 2007. (Journal of Wetland Archaeology Ser.). (Illus.). 168p. per. 50.00 *(978-1-84217-210-0(7))* Oxbow Bks., Ltd. GBR. Dist: Brown, David Bk. Co., The.

Connah, Graham. Writing about Archaeology. 2010. (ENG., Illus.). 224p. (C). instr.'s gde. ed. 89.00 *(978-0-521-86850-1(5))*; pap., instr.'s gde. ed. 24.99 *(978-0-521-68851-2(5))* Cambridge Univ. Pr.

Constable, Nick. Atlas of Archaeology. 2008. (Illus.). 192p. 25.00 *(978-1-904668-05-3(4))* Mercury Bks. Ltd. GBR. Dist: International Publishers Marketing.

Cook, Jill. The Discovery of Human Antiquity. 2nd ed. 2012. (Illus.). 300p. 75.00 *(978-0-9817736-9-8(9))* KWS Pubs.

Coolidge, Frederick L. & Beaune, Sophie A. de. Cognitive Archaeology & Human Evolution. de Beaune, Sophie & Coolidge, Frederick L., eds. Wynn, Thomas, ed. 2009. (ENG., Illus.). 200p. (C). 90.00 *(978-0-521-76977-8(9))*; pap. 30.99 *(978-0-521-74611-3(6))* Cambridge Univ. Pr.

Corbishley, Mike. Pinning down the Past: Archaeology, Heritage, & Education Today. 2011. (Heritage Matters Ser.: Volume 5). (Illus.). 400p. 45.00 *(978-1-84383-678-0(5)*, Boydell Press) Boydell & Brewer, Ltd. GBR. Dist: Boydell & Brewer, Inc.

Costen, Michael, ed. People & Places: Essays in Honour of Michael Aston. 2007. (ENG., Illus.). 240p. (C). 100.00 *(978-1-84217-251-3(4))* Oxbow Bks., Ltd. GBR. Dist: Brown, David Bk. Co., The.

Costopoulos, Andre & Lake, Mark W., eds. Simulating Change: Archaeology into the Twenty-first Century. 2010. (Foundations of Archaeological Inquiry Ser.). (ENG.). 96p. pap. 25.00 *(978-0-60781-036-0(0))* Univ. of Utah Pr.

Cram101 Textbook Reviews. Outlines & Highlights for Discovering Our Past: A Brief Introduction to Archaeology by Wendy Ashmore, ISBN. 2010. 78p. pap. 27.95 *(978-1-61654-579-6(8))*; 72p. pap. 27.95 *(978-1-61654-745-5(6))* Cram101 Inc.

—Outlines & Highlights for Images of the Past by Price & Feinman. 2011. 68p. pap. 27.95 ***(978-1-61812-853-9(1))*** Cram101 Inc.

—Outlines & Highlights for Linking to the Past: A Brief Introduction to Archaeology by Kenneth L. Feder, ISBN. 2010. 70p. pap. 27.95 *(978-1-61698-216-4(0))* Cram101 Inc.

Cram101 Textbook Reviews. Outlines & Highlights for Understanding Physical Anthropology & Archaeology by Barry Lewis, Robert Jurmain, Lynn Kilgore, Isbn: 9780534623968. 2011. 320p. pap. 33.95 ***(978-1-4288-7629-3(4))*** Cram101 Inc.

Cram101 Textbook Reviews & Cram101 Textbook Reviews. Outlines & Highlights for Human Antiquity: Introduction to Physical Anthropology & Archaeology by Kenneth L. Feder, Michael Alan Park, ISBN. 2011. 434p. pap. 35.95 ***(978-1-61744-966-6(0))*** Cram101 Inc.

—Outlines & Highlights for Women in Antiquity: Theoretical Approaches to Gender & Archaeology by Sarah Nelson, ISBN. 2011. 86p. pap. 27.95 ***(978-1-61461-918-5(2))*** Cram101 Inc.

Cram101 Textbook Reviews Staff. Outlines & Highlights for Archaeological Theory by Mathew Johnson, Isbn: 9780631202967. 2009. 58p. pap. 26.95 *(978-1-4288-7437-4(2))* Cram101 Inc.

—Outlines & Highlights for Archaeology by Robert L Kelly, Isbn: 9780495602910. 2009. 120p. pap. 28.95 *(978-1-4288-8560-8(9))* Cram101 Inc.

—Outlines & Highlights for Discovering Our Past: A Brief Introduction to Archaeology by Wendy Ashmore, ISBN. 2009. 72p. pap. 27.95 *(978-1-4288-8803-6(9))* Cram101 Inc.

—Outlines & Highlights for Evolution & Prehistory: Human Challenge by William A. Haviland, Bunny Mcbride, Dana Walrath, Harald E. Prins, ISBN. 2009. 78p. pap. 27.95 *(978-1-4288-9037-4(8))* Cram101 Inc.

—Outlines & Highlights for Linking to the Past: A Brief Introduction to Archaeology by Kenneth L. Feder, ISBN. 2009. 60p. pap. 26.95 *(978-1-4288-8436-6(X))* Cram101 Inc.

Cremin, Aedeen. The Enduring Past. (Illus.). 230p. pap. *(978-0-86840-114-0(5)*, UNSW Press) NewSouth Publishing.

Crubezy, Eric, ed. Humans: Evolution & Environment. 2009. (Bar S Ser.). (ENG., Illus.). 165p. (C). pap. 90.00 *(978-1-4073-0603-2(0))* British Archaeological Reports Ltd. GBR. Dist: Brown, David Bk. Co., The.

Cummings, Vicki & Johnston, Robert, eds. Prehistoric Journeys. 2007. 224p. (C). 70.00 *(978-1-84217-250-6(6))* Oxbow Bks., Ltd. GBR. Dist: Brown, David Bk. Co., The.

Curran, Brian A., et al. Obelisk: A History. 2009. (Publications of the Burndy Library). (ENG., Illus.). 384p. (gr. 17). pap. 28.95 *(978-0-262-51270-1(X))* MIT Pr.

Dar, Shimon. Shallale: Ancient City of Carmel. 2009. (Bar S Ser.). (Illus.). 441p. (C). 150.00 *(978-1-4073-0379-6(1))* British Archaeological Reports Ltd. GBR. Dist: Brown, David Bk. Co., The.

Darrin, Ann Garrison & O'Leary, Beth Laura, eds. Handbook of Space Engineering, Archaeology, & Heritage. 2009. (Advances in Engineering Ser.). (ENG., Illus.). 1035p. 164.95 *(978-1-4200-8431-3(3)*, CRC Press) Taylor & Francis Group GBR. Dist: Taylor & Francis Group.

David, Andrew. Palaeolithic & Mesolithic Settlement in Wales. 2007. (Bar Bs Ser.). (ENG., Illus.). 223p. (C). pap. 90.00 *(978-1-4073-0146-4(2))* British Archaeological Reports Ltd. GBR. Dist: Brown, David Bk. Co., The.

David, Bruno & Thomas, Julian, eds. Handbook of Landscape Archaeology. (World Archaeological Congress Research Ser.). (ENG., Illus.). 719p. 2010. pap. 49.95 *(978-1-59874-616-7(2))* 2008. 129.00 *(978-1-59874-294-7(9))* Left Coast Pr., Inc.

De Fabianis, Valeria Manferto & Bourbon, Fabio, eds. The Great Book of Archaeology. Milan, C T M & Cumming Kleeberg, Irene, trs. 2007. (Illus.). 512p. 29.99 *(978-88-540-0826-7(5))* Book Sales, Inc.

De Graaf, Peter. Late Republican-Early Imperial Regional Italian Landscapes & Demography. 2012. (Bar S Ser.). (ENG., Illus.). 98p. (C). pap. 73.00 ***(978-1-4073-0913-2(7))*** British Archaeological Reports Ltd. GBR. Dist: Brown, David Bk. Co., The.

De Nadaillac, Marquis. Manners & Monuments of Prehistoric Peo. 2006. pap. *(978-1-84702-770-2(9))* Echo Library.

de Vries, Imar. Tantalisingly Close: An Archaeology of Communication Desires in Discourses of Mobile Wireless Media. 2012. (MediaMatters Ser.). (ENG., Illus.). 256p. pap. ***(978-90-8964-354-4(0))*** Amsterdam Univ. Pr.

Delgado, James P. Gold Rush Port: The Maritime Archaeology of San Francisco's Waterfront. 2009. (ENG., Illus.). 256p. 45.00 *(978-0-520-25580-7(1))* Univ. of California Pr.

Deng, Honghai. The Co-Evolution of Human Culture & Spherical Artifacts. 2011. 240p. pap. ***(978-3-8443-2555-3(7))*** Lambert Academic Publishing.

Dept of Anthropology-Florida St Univ. Introduction to Archaeological Science Laboratory. rev. ed. 2010. (ENG.). 130p. spiral bd. 55.00 *(978-0-7575-7498-6(X))* Kendall Hunt Publishing Co.

Dimitriadis, George, ed. Landscape in Mind: Dialogue on Space Between Anthropology & Archaeology. 2009. (ENG., Illus.). 130p. (C). pap. 80.00 *(978-1-4073-0539-4(5))* British Archaeological Reports Ltd. GBR. Dist: Brown, David Bk. Co., The.

Downing, Eric. After Images: Photography, Archaeology, & Psychoanalysis & the Tradition of Bildung. 2006. (Kritik: German Literary Theory & Cultural Studies). (Illus.). 372p. 54.95 *(978-0-8143-3301-3(X))* Wayne State Univ. Pr.

Dowson, Thomas. Sculpture & Archaeology. Bonaventura, Paul & Jones, Andrew, Sr., eds. 2011. (Subject/Object: New Studies in Sculpture Ser.). (Illus.). 238p. 99.95 ***(978-0-7546-5831-3(7))*** Ashgate Publishing Co.

Dowson, Thomas A. Archaeology of Art. 2009. (Themes in Archaeology Ser.). (Illus.). 128p. 100.00 *(978-0-415-18894-4(6)*, RU18202) Routledge.

Drennan, Robert D. Statistics for Archaeologists: A Common Sense Approach. 2nd ed. 2009. (Interdisciplinary Contributions to Archaeology Ser.). (Illus.). xv, 333p. 209.00 *(978-1-4419-0412-6(3)*, 1441904123) Springer.

—Statistics for Archaeologists, 2nd Edition: A Common Sense Approach. 2nd ed. 2010. (Interdisciplinary Contributions to Archaeology Ser.). (ENG., Illus.). 335p. pap. 49.95 *(978-1-4419-6071-9(6)*, 1441960716) Springer.

Duke, Philip & Hamilakis, Yannis, eds. Archaeology & Capitalism: From Ethics to Politics. 2007. (One World Archaeology Ser.). (ENG., Illus.). 298p. 89.00 *(978-1-59874-270-1(1))* Left Coast Pr., Inc.

Dyson, Stephen L. In Pursuit of Ancient Pasts: A History of Classical Archaeology in the Nineteenth & Twentieth Centuries. 2006. (ENG., Illus.). 336p. 47.00 *(978-0-300-11097-5(9))* Yale Univ. Pr.

Edward F. Berger, Ed. D. Crow Canyon: Pioneering Education & Archaeology on the Southwestern Colorado Frontier. 2009. 448p. pap. 20.49 *(978-1-4389-6009-8(3))* AuthorHouse.

Edwards, Douglas R. & McCollough, C. Thomas, eds. The Archaeology of Difference: Gender, Ethnicity, Class & the Other in Antiquity. Studies in Honor of Eric M Meyers, 2 vols. 2007. (Annual of the American Schools of Oriental Research Ser.). (ENG.). 429p. (C). 124.95 *(978-0-89757-070-1(7))* American Schls. of Oriental Research.

Elliott, Melinda. Great Excavations: Tales of Early Southwestern Archaeology. (Illus.). 270p. pap. 19.95 *(978-0-933452-43-5(8))* School for Advanced Research Pr./SAR Pr.

Ellis, Anne V. The Estates of Winchcombe Abbey, Gloucestershire. 2009. (Bar Ser.). (ENG., Illus.). 120p. (C). pap. 70.00 *(978-1-4073-0375-8(9))* British Archaeological Reports Ltd. GBR. Dist: Brown, David Bk. Co., The.

Ember, Carol R., et al. Physical Anthropology & Archaeology, Third Canadian Edition. 3rd ed. 2008. (ENG.). 448p. (C). pap. *(978-0-13-205372-3(1))* Pearson Education Canada.

Emerson, Thomas E. Archaic Societies: Diversity & Complexity Across the Midcontinent. McElrath, Dale L., ed. 2009. (Illus.). 891p. (C). 74.00 *(978-1-4384-2701-0(8))*, Suny Pr.) State Univ. of New York Pr.

Endere, Maria Luz. Management of Archaeological Sites & the Public in Argentina. 2007. (Bar S Ser.). (Illus.). 187p. (C). 85.00 *(978-1-4073-0152-5(7))* British Archaeological Reports Ltd. GBR. Dist: Brown, David Bk. Co., The.

Eogan, George, et al. Excavations at Knowth, 3 vols. 2007. (Illus.). 286p. 50.00 *(978-1-904890-37-9(7))* Royal Irish Academy IRL. Dist: International Specialized Bk. Services.

Ergin, N. & Redford, S., eds. Perceptions of the Past in the Turkish Republic: Classical & Byzantine Periods. 2010. (Ancient near Eastern Studies Supplement Ser.). (ENG., Illus.). 236p. (C). 115.00 *(978-90-429-2264-8(8))* Peeters Pubs. & Booksellers BEL. Dist: Brown, David Bk. Co., The.

Evans, Christopher. Grounding Knowledge/Walking Land: Archaeological Research & Ethno-historical Identity in Central Nepal. 2009. (McDonald Institute Monographs). (ENG., Illus.). 223p. (C). 80.00 *(978-1-902937-50-2(3))* McDonald Institute for Archaeological Research GBR. Dist: Brown, David Bk. Co., The.

Evans, Susan Toby & Webster, David L. Archaeology of Ancient Mexico & Central America. 2009. (ENG., Illus.). 992p. pap. 59.95 *(978-0-415-87399-4(1))* Routledge.

Fagan & Cram101 Textbook Reviews Staff. Archaeology. 2007. 180p. per. 12.95 *(978-1-4288-2650-2(5))* Cram101 Inc.

Fagan, Brian. Writing Archaeology, Second Edition: Telling Stories about the Past. 2nd ed. 2010. (ENG.). 216p. 89.00 *(978-1-59874-608-2(1))*; pap. 26.95 *(978-1-59874-609-9(X))* Left Coast Pr., Inc.

Fagan, Brian M. Ancient Lives: An Introduction to Archaeology & Prehistory. 5th rev. ed. 2011. (ENG., Illus.). 528p. (C). pap. 136.80 ***(978-0-205-17807-0(3)***, Prentice Hall) Prentice Hall PTR.

—Ancient Lives: An Introduction to Archaeology & Prehistory, Books a la Carte Edition. 5th ed. 2011. (ENG.). 528p. (C). ring bd. 89.33 ***(978-0-205-17883-4(9)***, Prentice Hall) Prentice Hall PTR.

—Archaeology: A Brief Introduction. 11th rev. ed. 2011. (ENG.). 384p. (C). pap. 82.00 ***(978-0-205-24082-1(8)***, Prentice Hall) Prentice Hall PTR.

—Archaeology: A Brief Introduction, Books a la Carte Edition. 11th ed. 2011. (ENG.). 384p. (C). ring bd. 53.33 ***(978-0-205-24099-9(2)***, Prentice Hall) Prentice Hall PTR.

Feder & Park & Cram101 Textbook Reviews Staff. Human Antiquity. 2007. 204p. per. 13.95 *(978-1-4288-2620-5(3))* Cram101 Inc.

Feder, Kenneth L. Frauds, Myths, & Mysteries: Science & Pseudoscience in Archaeology. (ENG., Illus.). (C). 6th ed. 2007. 408p. pap. 65.67 *(978-0-07-340529-2(9)*, 0073405299) 7th ed. 2010. 416p. pap. 65.67 *(978-0-07-811697-1(X)*, 007811697X) McGraw-Hill Cos., The.

—Frauds, Myths, & Mysteries: Science & Pseudoscience in Archaeology & Index. 6th ed. 2008. (C). 51.25 *(978-0-07-727403-0(2)*, 9780077274030, McGraw-Hill Humanities, Social Sciences & World Languages) McGraw-Hill Higher Education.

—Linking to the Past: A Brief Introduction to Archaeology. 2nd ed. 2007. (ENG.). 496p. (Orig.). (C). pap. 64.95 *(978-0-19-533117-2(6))* Oxford Univ. Pr., Inc.

Feinman, Gary & Price, T. Douglas. Images of the Past. 6th ed. 2009. (ENG., Illus.). 640p. (C). pap. 129.67 *(978-0-07-353105-2(7)*, 0073531057) McGraw-Hill Cos., The.

Figuier, Louis. Primitive Man. 2007. (ENG.). 426p. 51.95 *(978-0-548-04280-9(2))* Kessinger Publishing, LLC.

—Primitive Man by Louis Figuier Rev Translation. 2006. 432p. per. 26.99 *(978-1-4255-4710-3(9))* MPublishing.

Flatman, Joe. Becoming an Archaeologist: A Guide to Professional Pathways. 2011. (ENG., Illus.). 248p. (C). 85.00 *(978-0-521-76772-9(5))*; pap. 25.99 *(978-0-521-73469-1(X))* Cambridge Univ. Pr.

Fogelin, Lars, ed. Religion, Archaeology, & the Material World. 2008. (Illus.). pap. 40.00 *(978-0-88104-093-7(2))* Ctr. for Archaeological Investigations.

Fontana, Bernard L., et al. The Kiva V25, No 3, February 1960. Fontana, Bernard L., ed. 2011. 48p. 35.95 ***(978-1-258-01499-5(8))*** Literary Licensing, LLC.

Ford, Benjamin L., ed. The Archaeology of Maritime Landscapes. 2011. (When the Land Meets the Sea Ser.). (ENG., Illus.). xv, 352p. 129.00 *(978-1-4419-8209-4(4)*, 1441982094) Springer.

Foss, Pedar. Pompeii & Ancient Settlements. Dobbins, John J., ed. 2007. (Routledge Worlds Ser.). (ENG., Illus.). 704p. (C). 250.00 *(978-0-415-17324-7(8))* Routledge.

Franquemont, Abby. Respect the Spindle: Spin Infinite Yarns with One Amazing Tool. 2009. (ENG., Illus.). 136p. pap. 22.95 *(978-1-59668-155-2(1))* Interweave Pr., LLC.

Frischer, Bernard & Dakouri-Hild, Anastasia, eds. Beyond Illustration: 2D & 3D Digital Technologies as Tools for Discovery in Archaeology. 2008. (Bar S Ser.). (ENG., Illus.). 192p. (C). pap. 120.00 *(978-1-4073-0292-8(2))* British Archaeological Reports Ltd. GBR. Dist: Brown, David Bk. Co., The.

Funari, Pedro Paulo A., et al, eds. New Perspectives on the Ancient World. 2008. (Bar S Ser.). (Illus.). 248p. (C). 100.00 *(978-1-4073-0270-6(1))* British Archaeological Reports Ltd. GBR. Dist: Brown, David Bk. Co., The.

Gamble, Clive. Arechaeology: The Basics. 2nd rev. ed. 2007. (Routledge Student Reference Ser.). (ENG., Illus.). 272p. 110.00 *(978-0-415-35974-0(0))*; per. 19.95 *(978-0-415-35975-7(9))* Routledge.

Gardin, J. C. Archaeological Constructs: An Aspect of Theoretical Archaeology. 2009. (ENG.). 216p. (C). pap. 31.99 *(978-0-521-10938-3(8))* Cambridge Univ. Pr.

Gardner, Andrew, ed. Agency Uncovered: Archaeological Perspectives on Social Agency, Power, & Being Human. 2007. (University College London Institute of Archaeology Publications). (ENG., Illus.). 268p. pap. 34.95 *(978-1-59874-211-4(6))* Left Coast Pr., Inc.

Gates, Charles, et al, eds. Sacred Landscapes in Anatolia & Neighboring Regions. 2009. (Bar S Ser.). (ENG., Illus.). 117p. (C). pap. 77.50 *(978-1-4073-0611-7(1))* British Archaeological Reports Ltd. GBR. Dist: Brown, David Bk. Co., The.

Gates, Timothy, et al. Archaeology & Environment in Northumberland: Till-Tweed Studies Volume 2. 2012. (ENG., Illus.). 368p. (C). 80.00 *(978-1-84217-447-0(9))* Oxbow Bks., Ltd. GBR. Dist: Brown, David Bk. Co., The.

Gere, Cathy. Knossos & the Prophets of Modernism. (Illus.). 288p. 2011. pap. 18.00 *(978-0-226-28954-0(0))* 2009. 27.50 *(978-0-226-28953-3(2))* Univ. of Chicago Pr.

Girdwood, Peter, et al. Trac 2009: Proceedings of the Nineteenth Annual Theoretical Roman Archaeology Conference. Shipley, Lucy, ed. 2010. (Trac Ser.). (ENG., Illus.). 152p. (C). pap. 60.00 *(978-1-84217-972-7(1))* Oxbow Bks., Ltd. GBR. Dist: Brown, David Bk. Co., The.

Glassow, Michael A. Exploring Methods of Faunal Analysis: Insights from California Archaeology. Joslin, Terry L., ed. 2012. (ENG.). 276p. (C). pap. 34.95 ***(978-1-931745-87-1(0))*** Cotsen Institute of Archaeology at UCLA.

Gleba, Margarita, et al. North European Symposium for Archaeological Textiles X. Andersson, Eva et al, eds. Mannering, Ulla et al, eds. 2010. (Ancient textiles Ser.). (ENG & GER., Illus.). 328p. (C). 96.00 *(978-1-84217-370-1(7))* Oxbow Bks., Ltd. GBR. Dist: Brown, David Bk. Co., The.

Gnecco, Cristobal & Ayala, Patricia, eds. Indigenous Peoples & Archaeology in Latin America. 2011. (Archaeology & Indigenous Peoples Ser.). (ENG., Illus.). 365p. 94.00 *(978-1-61132-015-2(1))* Left Coast Pr., Inc.

Gould, Richard A. Disaster Archaeology. 2007. (ENG., Illus.). 272p. (gr. 13). 27.95 *(978-0-87480-894-0(4))* Univ. of Utah Pr.

Grajetzki, Wolfram. Court Officials of the Egyptian Middle Kingdom. 2009. 192p. pap. 34.95 *(978-0-7156-3745-6(2))* Duckworth Publishers GBR. Dist: International Publishers Marketing.

Graslund, Bo. The Birth of Prehistoric Chronology: Dating Methods & Dating Systems in Nineteenth-Century Scandinavian Archaeology. 2008. (New Studies in Archaeology Ser.). (ENG.). 144p. pap. 33.99 *(978-0-521-10388-6(6))* Cambridge Univ. Pr.

Greene, Kevin. Archaeology. 5th rev. ed. 2010. (ENG., Illus.). 416p. 135.00 *(978-0-415-49638-4(1))* Routledge.

Greene, Kevin & Moore, Tom. Archaeology. 5th rev. ed. 2010. (ENG., Illus.). 416p. pap. 49.95 *(978-0-415-49639-1(X))* Routledge.

Greenman, E. F. The Young Site: An Archeological Record from Michigan. (Illus.). reprint ed. lib. bdg. 125.00 *(978-0-7222-0091-9(9))* Library Reprints, Inc.

Groneberg, Brigitte, et al. Die Welt der Gotterbilder. 2007. (Beihefte Zur Zeitschrift Für Die Alttestamentliche Wissenschaft Ser.). (GER & ENG., Illus.). VIII, 380p. 154.00 *(978-3-11-019463-0(5))* De Gruyter, Walter Inc.

Güçer, Evrim & Serim, Erkal. Archaeology & Urban Planning. 2011. 156p. pap. ***(978-3-8433-8475-9(4))*** Lambert Academic Publishing.

Guha, Sudeshna. The Marshall Albums: Photography & Archaeology. 2011. (ENG., Illus.). 288p. 75.00 *(978-1-890206-45-1(8))* Mapin Publishing Pvt. Ltd IND. Dist: National Bk. Network.

Hahn, Robert. Archaeology & the Origins of Philosophy. 335p. 2011. pap. 26.95 ***(978-1-4384-3164-2(3)***, Suny Pr.) 2010. (ENG.). 80.00 *(978-1-4384-3165-9(1))* State Univ. of New York Pr.

Hallagher, Erik & Jensen, Jesper, eds. Proceedings of the Danish Institute at Athens, 5. 2007. (Proceedings of the Danish Institute at Athens Ser.). (ENG., Illus.). 212p. (C). pap. 40.00 *(978-87-7288-725-8(7))* Aarhus Universitetsforlag DNK. Dist: ISD.

Hamilakis, Yannis & Duke, P. G. Archaeology & Capitalism: From Ethics to Politics. 2006. 272p. *(978-1-84472-096-5(9)*, Routledge Cavendish); *(978-1-84472-095-8(0))* Taylor & Francis Group.

Hamilakis, Yannis & Duke, Philip, eds. Archaeology & Capitalism: From Ethics to Politics. 2009. (One World Archaeology, Vol. 54 Ser.). (ENG.). 298p. pap. 36.95 *(978-1-59874-271-8(X))* Left Coast Pr., Inc.

Harding Robert, ed. Landscape Archaeology in South Asia. 2006. 336p. pap. 40.00 *(978-1-84472-078-1(0))* Taylor & Francis Group GBR. Dist: Taylor & Francis Group.

Hardy, Karen, ed. Archaeological Invisibility & Forgotten Knowledge. 2011. (Bar S Ser.). (Illus.). 210p. (C). pap. 100.00 *(978-1-4073-0733-6(9))* British Archaeological Reports Ltd. GBR. Dist: Brown, David Bk. Co., The.

Harrison, Rodney & Schofield, John. After Modernity: Archaeological Approaches to the Contemporary Past. 2010. (ENG., Illus.). 320p. 99.00 *(978-0-19-954807-1(2))*; pap. 36.00 *(978-0-19-954808-8(0))* Oxford Univ. Pr., Inc.

Hartman, Carl V. Archaeological Researches on the Pacific Coast of Costa Rica. (Pittsburgh Carnegie Museum Memoirs Ser.: Vol. 3, No. 1). reprint ed. 34.50 *(978-0-404-15932-0(X))* AMS Pr., Inc.

Harvard University, Peabody Museum of Archaeology Staff. Antiquities of the New World: Early Explorations in Archaeology, 18 titles in 19 vols. reprint ed. *(978-0-404-57300-3(2))* AMS Pr., Inc.

Hather, Jon G. Tropical Archaeobotany: Applications & New Developments. 2010. 296p. pap. 39.95 *(978-0-415-58910-9(X))* Routledge.

Haughton, Brian. Hidden History: Lost Civilizations, Secret Knowledge, & Ancient Mysteries. 2007. (ENG., Illus.). 1p. per. 17.99 *(978-1-56414-897-1(1))* Career Pr., Inc.

Haviland, William A., et al. Evolution & Prehistory: The Human Challenge. (ENG., (C). 8th rev. ed. 2007. Illus.). 384p. per. 145.95 *(978-0-495-38190-7(X))* 9th ed. 2010. 400p. pap. 162.95 *(978-0-495-81219-7(6))* 9th ed. 2010. 400p. ring bd. 113.95 *(978-0-8400-3332-1(X))* Wadsworth.

Hawkes, Sonia Chadwick & Smith, Tyler Jo. Collectanea Antiqua: Essays in Memory of Sonia Chadwick Hawkes. Henig, Martin, ed. 2007. (Bar S Ser.). (ENG., Illus.). 166p. (C). pap. 82.50 *(978-1-4073-0108-2(X))* British Archaeological Reports Ltd. GBR. Dist: Brown, David Bk. Co., The.

Hedgepeth, Jessica Dianne. The Domestic Economy of Early Postclassic Rio Viejo, Oaxac. 2010. 212p. pap. *(978-3-639-23169-4(4))* VDM Verlag Dr. Mueller e.K.

Hedman, Matthew. The Age of Everything: How Science Explores the Past. 2008. (ENG., Illus.). 264p. pap. 16.00 *(978-0-226-32293-3(9))* Univ. of Chicago Pr.

Hendriks, Joep, et al, eds. Trac 2008: Proceedings of the Eighteenth Annual Theoretical Roman Archaeology Conference, Amsterdam 2008. 2009. (Illus.). 208p. (C). pap. 70.00 *(978-1-84217-351-0(0))* Oxbow Bks., Ltd. GBR. Dist: Brown, David Bk. Co., The.

Henson, Donald. Doing Archaeology: A Subject Guide for Students. 2012. (Doing... Ser.). (ENG., Illus.). 288p. 90.00 *(978-0-415-60211-2(4))*; pap. 28.95 *(978-0-415-60212-9(2))* Routledge.

Heron, Carl, et al. Archaeological Chemistry. 2nd rev. ed. 2008. (ENG., Illus.). 456p. (C). 64.00 *(978-0-85404-262-3(8))* Royal Society of Chemistry, The GBR. Dist: Ingram Pub. Services.

Hodder. Contemporary Archaeology in Theory: The New Pragmatism. Mrozowski, Stephen A. & Preucel, Robert W., eds. 2nd ed. 2010. (ENG., Illus.). 664p. 110.95 *(978-1-4051-5832-9(8))*; pap. 59.95 *(978-1-4051-5853-4(0))* Wiley, John & Sons, Inc. (Wiley-Blackwell).

Hodder, Ian, ed. The Archaeology of Contextual Meanings. 2009. (New Directions in Archaeology Ser.). (ENG.). 156p. pap. 28.00 *(978-0-521-10640-5(0))* Cambridge Univ. Pr.

Hodder, Ian, et al, eds. Pattern of the Past: Studies in the Honour of David Clarke. 2009. (ENG., Illus.). 456p. pap. 58.00 *(978-0-521-10843-0(8))* Cambridge Univ. Pr.

Högberg, Anders, et al. Scandinavian Flint: An Archaeological Perspective. 2007. (ENG., Illus.). 153p. (C). pap. 31.00 *(978-87-7934-278-1(7))* Aarhus Universitetsforlag DNK. Dist: ISD.

Holtorf, Cornelius. Archaeology Is a Brand! The Meaning of Archaeology in Contemporary Popular Culture. 2007. (ENG., Illus.). 196p. 94.00 *(978-1-59874-178-0(0))* Left Coast Pr., Inc.

—Archeology Is a Brand! The Meaning of Archaeology in Contemporary Popular Culture. 2009. (ENG., Illus.). 196p. per. 29.95 *(978-1-59874-179-7(9))* Left Coast Pr., Inc.

Holtorf, Cornelius & Piccini, Angela. Contemporary Archaeologies: Excavating Now. 2006. 192p. *(978-1-84472-087-3(X))* Taylor & Francis Group.

Holtorf, Cornelius & Piccini, Angela, eds. Contemporary Archaeologies: Excavating Now. 2009. (Illus.). 222p. pap. 56.95 *(978-3-631-57637-3(4))* 2nd rev. ed. 2011. 224p. pap. 56.95 *(978-3-631-61142-5(0))* Lang, Peter GmbH, Europaischer Verlag der Wissenschaften DEU. Dist: Lang, Peter.

Hoopes, John W. The Archaeology of Central America. 2008. (Cambridge World Archaeology Ser.). (Illus.). (C). 110.00 *(978-0-521-84025-5(2))*; pap. 40.00 *(978-0-521-54953-0(1))* Cambridge Univ. Pr.

Hovell, Gillian. Visiting the Past: A Guide to Understanding Britain's Archaeology. 2009. (ENG., Illus.). 176p. pap. 24.95 *(978-0-7524-4833-6(1))* History Pr. Ltd., The GBR. Dist: Independent Pubs. Group.

Hruby, Zachary X. & Flad, Rowan K., eds. Rethinking Craft Specialization in Complex Societies - Archaeological Analyses of the Social Meaning of Production, Number 17. 2010. (APAZ - Archaeological Papers of the American Anthropological Association Ser.: 1). (ENG.). 200p. pap. 33.95 *(978-1-4443-3402-9(6)*, Wiley-Blackwell) Wiley, John & Sons, Inc.

Hub, Berthold. Die Perspektive der Antike: Archäologie einer symbolischen Form. 2008. (Europäische Hochschulschriften. Reihe 20: Philosophie Ser.). (GER.). 410p. pap. 99.95 *(978-3-631-57559-8(9))* Lang, Peter GmbH, Europaischer Verlag der Wissenschaften DEU. Dist: Lang, Peter.

Hubbard, Samuel & Gilmore, Charles W. Biofortean Reprint: The Doheny Scientific Expedition to the Hava Supai Canyon, Northern Arizona. 2011. 24p. pap. 8.00 ***(978-1-61646-068-6(7))*** Coachwhip Pubns.

Huffman, Thomas N. Handbook to the Iron Age: The Archaeology of Pre-Colonial Farming Societies in Southern Africa. 2007. (Illus.). 518p. (C). 84.95 *(978-1-86914-108-0(3))* University of Kwazulu-Natal Press ZAF. Dist: International Specialized Bk. Services.

Hurcombe, Linda. Archaeological Artefacts as Material Culture. 2007. (Illus.). 368p. 130.00 *(978-0-415-32091-7(7))* Routledge.

Hurcombe, Linda M. Archaeological Artefacts as Material Culture. 2007. (Illus.). 286p. per. 39.95 *(978-0-415-32092-4(5))* Routledge.

Ingold, Tim. Archaeology Anthropology Art & Architecture. 2012. (ENG.). 288p. pap. 39.95 *(978-0-415-56723-7(8))* Routledge.

—Archaeology Anthropology Art & Architecture. 2010. 288p. 120.00 *(978-0-415-56722-0(X)*, Routledge) Taylor & Francis Group GBR. Dist: Taylor & Francis Group.

Insoll, Timothy. The Oxford Handbook of the Archaeology of Ritual & Religion. 2012. (Oxford Handbooks Ser.). (ENG., Illus.). 1102p. 150.00 *(978-0-19-923244-4(X))* Oxford Univ. Pr., Inc.

Insoll, Timothy A. Archaeology: The Conceptual Challenge. 2007. (Duckworth Debates in Archaeology Ser.). (Illus.). 144p. per. 24.95 *(978-0-7156-3457-8(7))* Duckworth Publishers GBR. Dist: International Publishers Marketing.

Irina, Golovacheva. Aldous Huxley: Science & Literature: The Archaeology of Knowledge. 2011. 180p. pap. ***(978-3-639-33418-0(3))*** VDM Verlag Dr. Mueller e.K.

Jacobson-Tepfer, Esther & Meacham, James E. Archaeology & Landscape in the Mongolian Altai: An Atlas. 2009. (ENG., Illus.). 224p. 79.95 *(978-1-58948-232-6(8)*, ESRI Pr.) ESRI, Inc.

Jakobsen, T. B. Acta Archaeologica Supplementa VIII: Birth of a World Museum. 2008. (ENG.). 340p. 84.95 *(978-1-4051-8571-4(6)*, Wiley-Blackwell) Wiley, John & Sons, Inc.

Janetski, Joel. Fish Lake OP #16. 2010. (BYU Occasional Papers). (ENG.). 255p. pap. 30.00 *(978-0-9753945-8-8(4))* Univ. of Utah Pr.

Janetski, Joel C. & Smith, Grant C. Hunter Gatherer Archaeology in Utah Valley: Op #12. 2007. (BYU Occasional Papers). (ENG.). 432p. pap. 50.00 *(978-0-9753945-3-3(3))* Univ. of Utah Pr.

Jennings, Jesse D. Proceedings of the 6th Plains Archeological Conference, 1948. (Utah Anthropological Papers: No. 11). reprint ed. 32.00 *(978-0-404-60611-4(3))* AMS Pr., Inc.

Johnson, Steve & Johnson, Matthew. Archaeological Theory: An Introduction. 2nd ed. 2010. (ENG., Illus.). 328p. 110.95 *(978-1-4051-0014-4(1))*; pap. 43.95 *(978-1-4051-0015-1(X))* Wiley, John & Sons, Inc. (Wiley-Blackwell).

Jones, Andy M. & Kirkham, Graeme. Beyond the Core: Reflections on Regionality in Prehistory. 2011. (ENG., Illus.). 114p. (C). pap. 80.00 *(978-1-84217-989-5(6))* Oxbow Bks., Ltd. GBR. Dist: Brown, David Bk. Co., The.

Jones, Richard, ed. Manure Matters: Historical, Archaeological & Ethnographic Perspectives. 2012. (Illus.). 203p. 124.95 ***(978-0-7546-6988-3(2))*** Ashgate Publishing Co.

Jurmain, Robert, et al. Cengage Advantage Book: Essentials of Physical Anthropology. 8th ed. 2010. (ENG.). 448p. (C). pap. 100.95 *(978-0-8400-3321-5(4))* Wadsworth.

Kansa, Eric C., et al, eds. Archaeology 2.0: New Tools for Communication & Collaboration. 2011. (Cotsen Digital Archaeology Ser.). (ENG.). 295p. (C). pap. 39.95 ***(978-1-931745-85-7(4))*** Cotsen Institute of Archaeology at UCLA.

Kaptijn, Eva. Life on the Watershed. Reconstructing Subsistence in a Steppe Region Using Archaeological Survey: A Diachronic Perspective on Habitation in the Jordan Valley. 2009. (ENG.). 471p. (C). pap. 76.00 *(978-90-8890-029-7(9))* Sidestone Pr. NLD. Dist: Brown, David Bk. Co., The.

Kehoe, Alice Beck. Controversies in Archaeology. 2008. (ENG., Illus.). 256p. (C). 89.00 *(978-1-59874-061-5(X))* Left Coast Pr., Inc.

Kehoe, Alice Beck & Pleger, Thomas C. Archaeology: A Concise Introduction. 2007. (Illus.). 125p. (C). pap. 15.95 *(978-1-57766-450-5(7))* Waveland Pr., Inc.

Kerber, Jordan E., ed. Archaeology of the Iroquois: Selected Readings & Research Sources. 2007. (Iroquois & Their Neighbors Ser.). (Illus.). 557p. per. 45.00 *(978-0-8156-3139-2(1))* Syracuse Univ. Pr.

Kimmel, Richard J. World War II Ghosts: Artifacts Can Talk. 2009. (Illus.). 192p. pap. 14.99 *(978-0-7643-3159-6(0))* Schiffer Publishing, Ltd.

King, C. W. Early Christian Numismatics & Other an. 2006. pap. 31.95 *(978-1-4286-4739-8(2))* Kessinger Publishing, LLC.

King, Thomas F. Doing Archaeology: A Cultural Resource Manager's Perspective. 2007. (ENG., Illus.). 168p. pap. 24.95 *(978-1-59874-003-5(2))* Left Coast Pr., Inc.

King, Thomas F. & White, Gregory G. The Archaeological Survey Manual. 2007. (ENG., Illus.). 196p. (C). pap. 36.95 *(978-1-59874-009-7(1))* Left Coast Pr., Inc.

KM Archaeology Collected Works. 2007. per. *(978-0-9748334-8-4(7))* Institute of Classical Archaeology.

Knapp, A. Bernard, ed. Archaeology, Annales, & Ethnohistory. 2009. (New Directions in Archaeology Ser.). (ENG., Illus.). 172p. pap. 31.99 *(978-0-521-10260-5(X))* Cambridge Univ. Pr.

Knippenberg, Sebastiaan. Stone Artefact Production & Exchange among the Lesser Antilles. 2007. (Archaeological Studies Leiden University Ser.). 144p. pap. *(978-90-8728-008-6(4)*, Leiden Univ. Pr.) Amsterdam Univ. Pr.

Kohl, Philip L., et al, eds. Selective Remembrances: Archaeology in the Construction, Commemoration, & Consecration of National Pasts. 2008. (Illus.). 384p. 70.00 *(978-0-226-45058-2(9))*; per. 27.50 *(978-0-226-45059-9(7))* Univ. of Chicago Pr.

Kohring, Sheila & Wynne-Jones, Stephanie. Socialising Complexity: Structure, Interaction & Power in Archaeological Discourse. Kohring, Sheila & Wynne-Jones, Stephanie, eds. 2007. (ENG., Illus.). 248p. (C). pap. 64.00 *(978-1-84217-294-0(8))* Oxbow Bks., Ltd. GBR. Dist: Brown, David Bk. Co., The.

Koutsoumpos, Nikos. Dictionary of Archaeological Terms: English/Greek - Greek/English. 2011. (ENG.). 92p. (C). pap. 19.95 *(978-1-905739-38-7(9))* Archaeopress GBR. Dist: Brown, David Bk. Co., The.

Krieger, William. Can There Be a Philosophy of Archaeology? Processual Archaeology & the Philosophy of Science. 2006. (ENG., Illus.). 160p. 78.99 *(978-0-7391-1249-6(X))* Lexington Bks.

Krzyszkowska, Olga. Cretan Offerings: Studies in Honour of Peter Warren. 2011. (BSA Studies). (ENG., Illus.). 400p. (C). 158.00 *(978-0-904887-62-4(6))* British Schl. at Athens GBR. Dist: Brown, David Bk. Co., The.

Kuijt, Ian. Seeds of Change: Exploring Neolithic Social Complexity. 2008. (Illus.). 272p. 44.95 *(978-0-415-43604-5(4))*; 145.00 *(978-0-415-43268-9(5))* Routledge.

La Niece, Susan, et al, eds. Metals & Mines: Studies in Archaeometallurgy. 2007. (ENG., Illus.). 256p. pap. 100.00 *(978-1-904982-19-7(0))* Archetype Pubns. GBR. Dist: National Bk. Network.

Lang, Andrew. The Clyde Mystery: A Study in Forgeries & Folklore. 2009. 104p. pap. *(978-0-217-07161-1(9))* Books LLC.

—The Clyde Mystery: A Study in Forgeries & Folklore. 2007. (Illus.). 116p. per. *(978-1-4065-2631-8(2))* Dodo Pr.

Lasaponara, Rosa & Masini, Nicola, eds. Satellite Remote Sensing: A New Tool for Archaeology. 2010. (Remote Sensing & Digital Image Processing Ser.). (Illus.). xvi, 359p. 179.00 *(978-90-481-8800-0(8)*, 9048188008) Springer.

Levy, Joel. Lost Histories: Exploring the World's Most Famous Mysteries. 2007. (ENG.). 288p. pap. 17.95 *(978-1-904132-93-6(6))* Vision Paperbacks GBR. Dist: Independent Pubs. Group.

Lewis, Helen & Semple, Sarah. Perspectives in Landscape Archaeology. 2010. (Bar S Ser.). (ENG., Illus.). 119p. (C). pap. 77.50 *(978-1-4073-0579-0(4))* British Archaeological Reports Ltd. GBR. Dist: Brown, David Bk. Co., The.

Lillios, Katina T., ed. Comparative Archaeologies: The American Southwest (AD 900-1600) & the Iberian Peninsula (3000-1500 BC) 2011. (ENG., Illus.). 312p. (C). 60.00 *(978-1-935488-26-2(0))* Oxbow Bks., Ltd. GBR. Dist: Brown, David Bk. Co., The.

Little, Barbara J. & Shackel, Paul A. Archaeology as a Tool of Civic Engagement. Little, Barbara J. & Shackel, Paul A., eds. 2007. (ENG., Illus.). 294p. 80.00 *(978-0-7591-1059-5(X))*; pap. 32.95 *(978-0-7591-1060-1(3))* AltaMira Pr.

López Wario, Luis Alberto. Arqueólogos a Través Del Espejo. 2010. (SPA., Illus.). 271p. *(978-607-484-099-5(7))* Instituto Nacional de Antropología e Historia.

Lovata, Troy. Inauthentic Archaeologies: Public Uses & Abuses of the Past. 2007. (ENG., Illus.). 168p. (C). 94.00 *(978-1-59874-010-3(5))*; pap. 29.95 *(978-1-59874-011-0(3))* Left Coast Pr., Inc.

Lovis, William A., et al. The Geoarchaeology of Lake Michigan Coastal Dunes. 2012. (Environmental Research Ser.). (ENG.). pap. 35.95 ***(978-1-61186-051-1(2))*** Michigan State Univ. Pr.

Lozny, Ludomir R., ed. Comparative Archaeologies: A Sociological View of the Science of the Past. 2011. (ENG.). xv, 852p. 179.00 *(978-1-4419-8224-7(8)*, 1441982248) Springer.

Lyman, R. Lee, et al. Archaeology as a Process: Processualism & Its Progeny. 2007. (ENG., Illus.). 360p. (C). per. 30.00 *(978-0-87480-907-7(X))* Univ. of Utah Pr.

Maeir, Aren M., et al, eds. ¿Go Out & Study the Land¿ (Judges 18:2) Archaeological, Historical & Textual Studies in Honor of Hanan Eshel. 2011. (Supplements to the Journal for the Study of Judaism Ser.). (Illus.). xxxv, 455p. ***(978-90-04-20268-9(4))*** BRILL.

Manzanilla, Linda. La Arqueologia: Una Vision Cientifica. (Ciencia para Todos Ser.). (SPA.). pap. 6.99 *(978-968-16-4374-4(7))* Fondo de Cultura Economica USA.

Marcus, Brittain & Timothy, Clack, eds. Archaeology & the Media. 2006. 224p. *(978-1-84472-155-9(8))* Taylor & Francis Group.

Marlowe, Elizabeth. Shaky Ground. 2012. (ENG.). 160p. pap. 24.95 ***(978-0-7156-4064-7(X))*** Duckworth Publishers GBR. Dist: International Publishers Marketing.

Marriner, Nick. Geoarchaeology of Lebanon's Ancient Harbours. 2009. (ENG., Illus.). 314p. (C). pap. 125.00 *(978-1-4073-0436-6(4))* British Archaeological Reports Ltd. GBR. Dist: Brown, David Bk. Co., The.

Matsumoto, Naoko, et al, eds. Coexistence & Cultural Transmission in East Asia. 2011. (One World Archaeology Ser.). (ENG., Illus.). 288p. 89.00 *(978-1-59874-335-7(X))* Left Coast Pr., Inc.

McGlade, James. Time, Process & Structured Transformation in Archaeology. 2010. 504p. pap. 39.95 *(978-0-415-58909-3(6))* Routledge.

McGuire, Randall H. Archaeology as Political Action. 2008. (California Series in Public Anthropology: Vol. 17). (Illus.). 307p. 70.00 *(978-0-520-25490-9(2))*; pap. 31.95 *(978-0-520-25491-6(0))* Univ. of California Pr.

McNeill, John, ed. King's Lynn & the Fens: Medieval Art, Architecture & Archaeology. 2008. (British Archaeological Association (BAA) Conference Transaction Ser.). (ENG., Illus.). 256p. (C). 144.00 *(978-1-906540-15-9(2))*; pap. 68.00 *(978-1-906540-16-6(0))* Maney Publishing GBR. Dist: Brown, David Bk. Co., The.

Medlycott, Maria. Research & Archaeology Revisited: A Revised Framework for the East of England. 2011. (East Anglian Archaeology Occasional Paper Ser.). (ENG., Illus.). 116p. (C). pap. 20.00 ***(978-0-9510695-6-1(X))*** East Anglian Archaeology GBR. Dist: Brown, David Bk. Co., The.

Menotti, Francesco. Wetland Archaeology & Beyond: Theory & Practice. 2012. (ENG., Illus.). 520p. 185.00 ***(978-0-19-957101-7(5))*** Oxford Univ. Pr., Inc.

Mercer, H. C. Biofortean Reprint: The Lenape Stone. 2011. 104p. pap. 9.00 ***(978-1-61646-077-8(6))*** Coachwhip Pubns.

Meredith-Lobay, Megan. A Contextual Landscape Study of the Early Christian Churches of Argyll. 2009. (ENG., Illus.). 170p. (C). pap. 90.00 *(978-1-4073-0443-4(7))* British Archaeological Reports Ltd. GBR. Dist: Brown, David Bk. Co., The.

Meskell, Lynn. Nature of Heritage: The New South Africa. 2011. (ENG., Illus.). 272p. 99.95 ***(978-0-470-67072-9(X)***, Wiley-Blackwell) Wiley, John & Sons, Inc.

—The Nature of Heritage: The New South Africa. 2011. (ENG., Illus.). 272p. pap. 39.95 ***(978-0-470-67071-2(1)***, Wiley-Blackwell) Wiley, John & Sons, Inc.

Meskell, Lynn, ed. Cosmopolitan Archaeologies. 2009. (Material Worlds Ser.). (ENG., Illus.). 304p. 89.95 *(978-0-8223-4432-2(7))*; pap. 24.95 *(978-0-8223-4444-5(0))* Duke Univ. Pr.

Miller, Daniel & Tilley, Christopher. Ideology, Power & Prehistory. 2008. (New Directions in Archaeology Ser.). (ENG., Illus.). 168p. pap. 31.99 *(978-0-521-09089-6(X))* Cambridge Univ. Pr.

Milwright, Marcus. An Introduction to Islamic Archaeology. 2010. (New Edinburgh Islamic Surveys Ser.). (ENG., Illus.). 320p. (gr. 17). 105.00 *(978-0-7486-2310-5(8))*; pap. 32.50 *(978-0-7486-2311-2(6))* Edinburgh Univ. Pr. GBR. Dist: Columbia Univ. Pr.

Mladenovic, Dragana & Russell, Ben, eds. Trac 2010: Proceedings of the Twentieth Annual Theoretical Roman Archaeology Conference. 2011. (Trac Ser.). (ENG., Illus.). 160p. (C). pap. 64.00 *(978-1-84217-452-4(5))* Oxbow Bks., Ltd. GBR. Dist: Brown, David Bk. Co., The.

Monroe, J. Cameron & Ogundiran, Akinwumi, eds. Power & Landscape in Atlantic West Africa: Archaeological Perspectives. 2012. (ENG., Illus.). 400p. 99.00 ***(978-1-107-00939-4(1))*** Cambridge Univ. Pr.

Monton-Subias, Sandra & Sanchez-Romero, Margarita, eds. Engendering Social Dynamics: The Archaeology of Maintenance Activities. 2008. (Bar S Ser.). (Illus.). 95p. (C). 65.00 *(978-1-4073-0345-1(7))* British Archaeological Reports Ltd. GBR. Dist: Brown, David Bk. Co., The.

Moorey, P.R.S. Archaeology, Artifacts & the Bible. (Illus.). 71p. pap. 6.95 *(978-0-900090-00-4(6))* Ashmolean Museum GBR. Dist: Weatherhill, Inc.

Mootoosamy, Dharen. Introduction to Paleoanthropology. 2010. 132p. pap. *(978-3-8383-3583-4(X))* Lambert Academic Publishing.

Morrissey, Greg. Tools & Change. 2011. 212p. pap. ***(978-3-8383-9164-9(0))*** Lambert Academic Publishing.

Morton, Christopher & Edwards, Elizabeth. Photography, Anthropology & History: Expanding the Frame. 2009. (Illus.). 310p. 114.95 *(978-0-7546-7909-7(8))* Ashgate Publishing Co.

Mullin, David, ed. Places in Between: The Archaeology of Social, Cultural & Geographical Borders & Borderlands. 2011. (ENG., Illus.). 104p. (C). pap. 60.00 *(978-1-84217-983-3(7))* Oxbow Bks., Ltd. GBR. Dist: Brown, David Bk. Co., The.

Murray, Tim. Milestones in Archaeology: A Chronological Encyclopedia, 1 vol. 2007. (Illus.). 639p. 95.00 *(978-1-57607-186-1(3)*, ARCHC) ABC-CLIO, LLC.

Mytum, Harold, ed. Global Perspectives on Archaeological Field Schools: Constructions of Knowledge & Experience. 2012. (ENG., Illus.). viii, 253p. 129.00 ***(978-1-4614-0432-3(0)***, 1461404320) Springer.

Nadaillac, The Marquis de. Manners & Monuments of Prehistoric Peoples. Bell, Nancy, tr. 2007. (Illus.). 328p. per. *(978-1-4065-3059-9(X))* Dodo Pr.

Nash, George & Children, George, eds. The Archaeology of Semiotics & the Social Order of Things. 2008. (Bar S Ser.). (ENG., Illus.). 204p. (C). pap. 90.00 *(978-1-4073-0317-8(1))* British Archaeological Reports Ltd. GBR. Dist: Brown, David Bk. Co., The.

Neer, Richard T. Greek Art & Archaeology: A New History, C. 2500-C. 150 BCE. 2011. (ENG., Illus.). 400p. (C). pap. 80.00 net. ***(978-0-500-28877-1(1)***, 528877) Thames & Hudson.

Nelson, Margaret C. & Strawhacker, Colleen A., eds. Movement Connectivity & Landsc. 2011. (ENG., Illus.). 448p. 75.00 *(978-1-60732-064-7(9))* Univ. Pr. of Colorado.

Neumann, Thomas W. & Sanford, Robert M. Practicing Archaeology: An Introduction to Cultural Resources Archaeology. 2nd ed. 2010. (ENG.). 364p. 99.00 *(978-0-7591-1806-5(X))* AltaMira Pr.

Newman, Phil. The Field Archaeology of Dartmoor. 2011. (ENG., Illus.). 204p. pap. 60.00 *(978-1-84802-033-7(3))* English Heritage GBR. Dist: Brown, David Bk. Co., The.

Una Nueva Mirada Sobre el Patrimonio Histórico: Líneas de Investigación Arquelógica en la Universidad Autónoma de Madrid. 2007. (SPA., Illus.). 373p. *(978-84-8344-106-0(3))* Universidad Autónoma de Madrid.

Nur, Amos & Burgess, Dawn. Apocalypse: Earthquakes, Archaeology, & the Wrath of God. 2008. (ENG., Illus.). 324p. (C). 26.95 *(978-0-691-01602-3(X))* Princeton Univ. Pr.

Obert Layton, Stephen Shennan. A Future for Archaeology. Layton, Robert et al, eds. 2007. (University College London Institute of Archaeology Publications). (ENG.). 269p. pap. 32.95 *(978-1-59874-337-1(6))* Left Coast Pr., Inc.

of Antiquities, The Supreme Council. Mishkah Vol. 3: Egyptian Journal of Islamic Archaeology. 2010. (ENG.). 448p. pap. 34.95 *(978-977-479-247-2(5))* American Univ. in Cairo Pr. EGY. Dist: Oxford Univ. Pr., Inc.

Okamura, Katsuyuki & Matsuda, Akira, eds. New Perspectives in Global Public Archaeology. 2011. (ENG., Illus.). viii, 280p. 129.00 *(978-1-4614-0340-1(5)*, 1461403405) Springer.

Olsen, Bjrnar. In Defense of Things. 2010. (Archaeology in Society Ser.). (ENG., Illus.). 208p. 75.00 *(978-0-7591-1930-7(9))* AltaMira Pr.

Oswin, John. A Field Guide to Geophysics in Archaeology. (Springer Praxis Books / Geophysical Sciences Ser.). xviii, 230p. 2010. (ENG.). pap. 159.00 ***(978-3-642-09539-9(9)***, 3642095399) 2009. (Illus.). 159.00 *(978-3-540-76691-9(X))* Springer.

Otto, Ton, et al, eds. Warfare & Society: Archaeological & Social Anthropological Perspectives. 2006. (ENG., Illus.). 557p. (C). 84.00 *(978-87-7934-110-4(1))* Aarhus Universitetsforlag DNK. Dist: ISD.

Oxenham, Marc & Tayles, Nancy, eds. Bioarchaeology of Southeast Asia. 2009. (Cambridge Studies in Biological & Evolutionary Anthropology Ser.). (ENG., Illus.). 380p. pap. 53.00 *(978-0-521-12065-4(9))* Cambridge Univ. Pr.

Papaodysseus, Constantin, ed. Pattern Recognition & Signal Processing in Archaeometry: Mathematical & Computational Solutions for Archaeology. 2011. 357p. 195.00 *(978-1-60960-786-9(4)*, Information Science Reference) IGI Global.

Parikka, Jussi. What Is Media Archaeology? 2012. (ENG.). 200p. 64.95 ***(978-0-7456-5025-8(2))***; pap. 24.95 ***(978-0-7456-5026-5(0))*** Polity Pr. GBR. Dist: Wiley, John & Sons, Inc.

Parslow, Carla A. Social Interaction in the Prehistoric Natufian: Generating an Interactive Agency Model Using GIS. 2009. (Bar S Ser.). (ENG., Illus.). 120p. (C). pap. 77.50 *(978-1-4073-0399-4(6))* British Archaeological Reports Ltd. GBR. Dist: Brown, David Bk. Co., The.

Past Worlds: Atlas of Archaeology. (Illus.). 319p. *(978-0-681-50263-5(0))* Borders Group, Inc.

Pásztor, Emília. Archaeoastronomy in Archaeology & Ethnography: Papers from the Annual Meeting of SEAC (European Society for Astronomy in Culture), Held in Kecskemét in Hungary in 2004. 2007. (Bar S Ser.). (ENG., Illus.). 179p. (C). pap. 87.50 *(978-1-4073-0081-8(4))* British Archaeological Reports Ltd. GBR. Dist: Brown, David Bk. Co., The.

Pauketat, Timothy R. The Oxford Handbook of North American Archaeology, 1 vol. 2012. (Oxford Handbooks Ser.). (ENG., Illus.). 688p. 150.00 *(978-0-19-538011-8(8))* Oxford Univ. Pr., Inc.

Pearce, J. E. Tales That Dead Men Tell. 2010. 130p. pap. 16.76 *(978-1-162-98716-3(2))* 2007. (ENG.). 128p. 35.95 *(978-0-548-14809-9(0))* 2006. (ENG.). pap. 20.95 *(978-1-4286-6292-6(8))* Kessinger Publishing, LLC.

Pearsall, Deborah M. Encyclopedia of Archaeology, 3 vols. 2008. (Illus.). *(978-0-12-373643-7(9))*; *(978-0-12-548032-1(6))*; *(978-0-12-548031-4(8))* Elsevier Science & Technology Bks. (Academic Pr.).

Perez, Diane M. Pattern Recognition in Nanoscience, Environmental Engineering & Archeology. 2007. 129.00 *(978-1-60021-715-9(X))* Nova Science Pubs., Inc.

Pescarin, Sofia. Reconstructing Ancient Landscape. 2009. (Series Minor Ser.). (ENG., Illus.). 264p. (C). pap. 50.00 *(978-963-9911-09-3(7))* Archaeolingua Alapitvany HUN. Dist: Brown, David Bk. Co., The.

Phillips, Caroline & Allen, Harry, eds. Bridging the Divide: Indigenous Communities & Archaeology into the 21st Century. 2011. (One World Archaeology Ser.). (ENG., Illus.). 290p. pap. 34.95 ***(978-1-59874-393-7(7))*** Left Coast Pr., Inc.

Phoca-Cosmetatou, Nellie. The First Mediterranean Islanders: Initial Occupation & Survival Strategies. 2011. (OUSA Monograph Ser.). (ENG., Illus.). 176p. (C). pap. 70.00 ***(978-1-905905-20-1(3))*** Oxford Univ. Pr. GBR. Dist: Brown, David Bk. Co., The.

Pillsbury, Joanne. Past Presented: Archaeological Illustration & the Ancient Americas. 2012. (Dumbarton Oaks Pre-Columbian Symposia & Colloquia Ser.). 512p. 65.00 ***(978-0-88402-380-7(X))*** Dumbarton Oaks.

Pollard, Joshua, ed. Prehistoric Britain. 2008. (Wiley-Blackwell Studies in Global Archaeology Ser.). (ENG., Illus.). 384p. 116.95 *(978-1-4051-2545-1(4))*; pap. 51.95 *(978-1-4051-2546-8(2))* Wiley, John & Sons, Inc. (Wiley-Blackwell).

Pollard, Justin. The Story of Archaeology: In 50 Great Discoveries. 2007. (Illus.). 255p. *(978-1-84724-011-8(9))* Quercus.

Pollard, Tony, ed. Culloden. 2012. (Illus.). 288p. pap. 29.95 ***(978-1-84884-687-6(8))*** Pen & Sword Bks. Ltd. GBR. Dist: Casemate Pubs. & Bk. Distributors, LLC.

Posamentir, Richard. Chersonesan Studies 1: The Polychrome Grave Stelai from the Early Hellenistic Necropolis. 2010. (ENG., Illus.). 510p. 75.00 *(978-0-292-72312-2(1))* Univ. of Texas Pr.

Potts, D. T., ed. A Companion to the Archaeology of the Ancient near East, 2 vols. 2012. (Blackwell Companions to the Ancient World Ser.: 94). (ENG.). 1500p. 350.00 ***(978-1-4051-8988-0(6)***, Wiley-Blackwell) Wiley, John & Sons, Inc.

Prentiss, Anna, et al, eds. Macroevolution in Human Prehistory: Evolutionary Theory & Processual Archaeology. 2009. (ENG., Illus.). x, 326p. 159.00 *(978-1-4419-0681-6(9)*, 1441906819) Springer.

Preston, Laura, et al, eds. Inside the City in the Greek World: Studies of Urbanism from the Bronze Age to the Hellenistic Period. 2009. (University of cambridge museum of classical archaeology Monograph Ser.). (ENG., Illus.). 143p. (C). pap. 56.00 *(978-1-84217-349-7(9))* Oxbow Bks., Ltd. GBR. Dist: Brown, David Bk. Co., The.

Price & Feinman & Cram101 Textbook Reviews Staff. Images of the Past. 2007. 108p. per. 11.95 *(978-1-4288-2638-0(6))* Cram101 Inc.

Price, T. Douglas & Feinman, Gary M. Images of the Past. 5th ed. 2006. (Illus.). 656p. (C). pap. 104.55 *(978-0-07-340520-9(5)*, 9780073405209) McGraw-Hill Cos., The.

Price, V. B. Canyon Gardens: The Ancient Pueblo Landscapes of the American Southwest. Morrow, Baker H., ed. 2008. (ENG., Illus.). 239p. pap. 24.95 *(978-0-8263-3860-0(7))* Univ. of New Mexico Pr.

Priest, Josiah. American Antiquities & Discoveries in the West. 2009. 294p. pap. *(978-0-217-16763-5(2))*; 304p. pap. *(978-1-4588-0518-8(2))* Books LLC.

—American Antiquities & Discoveries in the West. 2007. (ENG.). 402p. 49.95 *(978-0-548-17617-7(5))*; 404p. per. 34.95 *(978-1-4304-7551-4(X))* Kessinger Publishing, LLC.

—American Antiquities & Discoveries in the West. 2008. 412p. 39.95 *(978-1-4357-5896-4(X))*; pap. 24.95 *(978-1-4357-5895-7(1))* Lulu Enterprises Inc.

Pritchard Parker, Mari & Angeloni, Elvio. Annual Editions: Archaeology. annuals 9th ed. 2009. (Annual Editions Ser.). (ENG., Illus.). 208p. (C). pap. 44.00 *(978-0-07-812774-8(2)*, 0078127742, McGraw-Hill/Dushkin) McGraw-Hill Higher Education.

Pritchard Parker, Mari & Angeloni, Elvio. Annual Editions: Archaeology, 10/e. 10th ed. 2012. (Annual Editions Ser.). (ENG., Illus.). 208p. (C). pap. 44.00 ***(978-0-07-805115-9(0)***, 0078051150, McGraw-Hill/Dushkin) McGraw-Hill Higher Education.

Raab, L. Mark, et al. California Maritime Archaeology: A San Clemente Island Perspective. 2009. (ENG.). 290p. 75.00 *(978-0-7591-1316-9(5))* AltaMira Pr.

Rainbird, Paul, ed. Monuments in the Landscape. 2008. (ENG., Illus.). 224p. 49.95 *(978-0-7524-4283-9(X))* History Pr. Ltd.,The GBR. Dist: Independent Pubs. Group.

Randall, Margaret. Stones Witness. 2007. (ENG.). 176p. pap. 25.00 *(978-0-8165-2643-7(5))* Univ. of Arizona Pr.

Rapp, George. Archaeomineralogy. 2nd ed. 2009. (Natural Science in Archaeology Ser.). (Illus.). xvi, 348p. 199.00 *(978-3-540-78593-4(0))* Springer.

Ray, Nick, et al, eds. Trac 2006: Proceedings of the Sixteenth Annual Theoretical Roman Archaeology Conference. 2007. (Trac Ser.). (ENG., Illus.). 208p. (C). per. 56.00 *(978-1-84217-264-3(6))* Oxbow Bks., Ltd. GBR. Dist: Brown, David Bk. Co., The.

Reid, J. Jefferson & Whittlesey, Stephanie Michelle. Prehistory, Personality, & Place: Emil W. Haury & the Mogollon Controversy. 2010. (ENG., Illus.). 208p. pap. 19.95 *(978-0-8165-2863-9(2))* Univ. of Arizona Pr.

Relaki, Maria & Catapoti, Despina, eds. An Archaeology of Land Ownership. 2012. (Routledge Studies in Archaeology Ser.). (ENG.). 296p. (C). 125.00 *(978-0-415-88618-5(X))* Routledge.

Renfrew & Bahn & Cram101 Textbook Reviews Staff. Archaeology. 2007. 280p. per. 15.95 *(978-1-4288-2632-8(7))* Cram101 Inc.

Rhodes, Robin F., ed. The Acquisition & Exhibition of Classical Antiquities: Professional, Legal, & Ethical Perspectives. 2008. (ENG., Illus.). 192p. pap. 25.00 *(978-0-268-04027-7(3))* Univ. of Notre Dame Pr.

Rieckhoff, Sabine & Sommer, Ulrike, eds. Auf der Suche Nach Identitaten: Volk - Stamm - Kultur - Ethnos. 2007. (Bar S Ser.). (Illus.). 255p. (C). 92.50 *(978-1-4073-0149-5(7))* British Archaeological Reports Ltd. GBR. Dist: Brown, David Bk. Co., The.

Rigeade, Catherine. Les Sepultures de Catastrophe. 2007. (Bar S Ser.). (FRE., Illus.). 129p. (C). 72.50 *(978-1-4073-0137-2(3))* British Archaeological Reports Ltd. GBR. Dist: Brown, David Bk. Co., The.

Rippon, Stephen. Making Sense of an Historic Landscape. 2012. (ENG., Illus.). 440p. 150.00 ***(978-0-19-953378-7(4))*** Oxford Univ. Pr., Inc.

Roberts, Benjamin & Linden, Marc van der, eds. Investigating Archaeological Cultures: Material Culture, Variability, & Transmission. 2011. (ENG., Illus.). viii, 300p. 169.00 *(978-1-4419-6969-9(1)*, 1441969691) Springer.

Roca, Zoran, et al, eds. Landscape, Identities & Development. 2011. (Illus.). 508p. 134.95 *(978-1-4094-0554-2(0))* Ashgate Publishing Co.

Rockman, Marcy & Flatman, Joe, eds. Archaeology in Society: Its Relevance in the Modern World. 2011. (ENG., Illus.). xxiii, 317p. 129.00 *(978-1-4419-9880-4(2)*, 1441998802) Springer.

Roebroeks, Wil, ed. Guts & Brains: An Integrative Approach to the Hominin Record. 2007. (LUP Academic Ser.). (Illus.). 277p. per. *(978-90-8728-014-7(9)*, Leiden Univ. Pr.) Amsterdam Univ. Pr.

Romancuk, Alla I. & Von Heinz Heinen, Herausgegeben. Studien Zur Geschichte und Archaologie des Byzantinischen Cherson. (GER., Illus.). 408p. *(978-90-04-13227-6(9))* BRILL.

Routledge, Bruce. Archaeology & State Theory. 2013. (Duckworth Debates in Archaeology Ser.). 144p. pap. 27.00 *(978-0-7156-3663-3(4))* Duckworth Publishers GBR. Dist: International Publishers Marketing.

Rubertone, Patricia E., ed. Archaeologies of Placemaking: Monuments, Memories, & Engagement in Native North America. 2008. (One World Archaeology Ser.). (ENG., Illus.). 256p. 89.00 *(978-1-59874-155-1(1))* Left Coast Pr., Inc.

Russell, Ian, ed. Images, Representations & Heritage: Moving beyond Modern Approaches to Archaeology. (ENG., Illus.). xxiv, 390p. 2010. pap. 99.00 *(978-1-4419-4075-9(8)*, 1441940758) 2006. 99.00 *(978-0-387-32215-5(9)*, 0387322159) Springer.

Russell, Ian & Koerner, Stephanie, eds. Unquiet Pasts: Risk Society Lived Cultural Heritage Re-Designing Reflexivity. 2010. (Heritage, Culture & Identity Ser.). (Illus.). 442p. 119.95 *(978-0-7546-7548-8(3))* Ashgate Publishing Co.

Sabloff, Jeremy A. Archaeology Matters: Action Archaeology in the Modern World. 2008. (Key Questions in Anthropology Ser.). (ENG., Illus.). 152p. (C). 79.00 *(978-1-59874-088-2(1))* Left Coast Pr., Inc.

Salama, Pierre. Le Reseau Routier de L'Est de l'Africa Dans L'Antiquite Tardive D'Apres les Documents de Pierre Salama. Desanges, J. et al, eds. 2011. (Bibliothèque de l'Antiquité Tardive Ser.). (FRE., Illus.). 345p. (C). pap. 138.00 *(978-2-503-51320-1(4))* Brepols Pubs. BEL. Dist: Brown, David Bk. Co., The.

Saraydar, Stephen C. Replicating the Past: The Art & Science of the Archaeological Experiment. 2008. (Illus.). 172p. (C). pap. 21.50 *(978-1-57766-557-1(0))* Waveland Pr., Inc.

Saunders, Nicholas J. Killing Time: Archaeology & the First World War. 2007. (ENG., Illus.). 256p. 46.95 *(978-0-7509-4519-6(2))* Sutton Publishing.

Saunders, Nicholas J., ed. Beyond the Dead Horizon: Studies in Modern Conflict Archaeology. 2012. (ENG., Illus.). 240p. (C). 104.00 ***(978-1-84217-471-5(1))*** Oxbow Bks., Ltd. GBR. Dist: Brown, David Bk. Co., The.

Scarre, Geoffrey & Scarre, Chris, eds. The Ethics of Archaeology: Philosophical Perspectives on Archaeological Practice. 2007. (ENG.). 332p. 110.00 *(978-0-521-84011-8(2))* Cambridge Univ. Pr.

Schablitsky, Julie M., , Julie M, ed. Box Office Archaeology: Refining Hollywood's Portrayals of the Past. 2007. (ENG., Illus.). 256p. (C). 89.00 *(978-1-59874-055-4(5))* Left Coast Pr., Inc.

Schablitsky, Julie M., ed. Box Office Archaeology: Refining Hollywood's Portrayals of the Past. 2007. (ENG., Illus.). 256p. pap. 26.95 *(978-1-59874-056-1(3))* Left Coast Pr., Inc.

Schmidt, Peter R. Postcolonial Archaeologies in Africa. 2009. (ENG., Illus.). 304p. pap. 34.95 *(978-1-930618-08-4(5))* School for Advanced Research Pr./SAR Pr.

Schneider, Alan L. & Stenger, Alison T. Proceedings of the International Science Conference: Science in Archaeology. 2007. 233p. pap. 25.95 *(978-1-4357-0068-0(6))* Lulu Enterprises Inc.

Scollar, Irwin, et al. Archaeological Prospecting & Remote Sensing. 2009. (Topics in Remote Sensing Ser.). (ENG.). 696p. pap. 84.00 *(978-0-521-11546-9(9))* Cambridge Univ. Pr.

Sebastian, Lynne & Lipe, William D. Archaeology & Cultural Resource Management: Visions for the Future. 2010. 368p. pap. 34.95 *(978-1-934691-16-8(X))* School for Advanced Research Pr./SAR Pr.

Seibert, Jeffery D. & Fernandez, Deepika C. Space & Spatial Analysis in Archaeology. Robertson, Elizabeth C. & Zender, Marc U., eds. 2006. (ENG., Illus.). 430p. per. 65.00 *(978-0-8263-4022-1(9))* Univ. of New Mexico Pr.

Sengupta, Gautam & Gangopadhyay, Kaushik, eds. Achaeology in India: Individuals, Ideas & Instiutions. 2009. 396p. 99.50 *(978-81-215-1202-2(6))* Munshiram Manoharlal Pubs. Private, Ltd. IND. Dist: Coronet Bks.

Shaffer, Stephen B. Voices of the Ancients. 2012. ***(978-1-4621-1022-3(3)***, Council Pr.) Cedar Fort, Inc./CFI Distribution.

Shanks, Hershel. Freeing the Dead Sea Scrolls: And Other Adventures of an Archaeology Outsider. 2010. (ENG., Illus.). 272p. 29.95 *(978-1-4411-5217-6(2))* Continuum International Publishing Group, Ltd. GBR. Dist: National Bk. Network.

Shanks, Michael. The Archaeological Imagination. 2012. (ENG.). 167p. (C). pap. 27.95 *(978-1-59874-362-3(7))* Left Coast Pr., Inc.

Shennan, Stephen. Pattern & Process in Cultural Evolution. 2009. (Origins of Human Behavior & Culture Ser.). (ENG., Illus.). 336p. 60.00 *(978-0-520-25599-9(2))* Univ. of California Pr.

Siliotti, Alberto. Archaeology Treasures. 2008. 432p. 29.99 *(978-88-540-0857-1(5))* White Star ITA. Dist: Book Sales, Inc.

Simpson, Faye A. The Values of Community Archaeology: A Comparative Assessment between the UK & US. 2010. (Bar S Ser.). (ENG., Illus.). 96p. (C). pap. 72.50 *(978-1-4073-0646-9(4))* British Archaeological Reports Ltd. GBR. Dist: Brown, David Bk. Co., The.

Sinclair, Iain, afterword by. Archaeology in Reverse, 1 vol. 2007. (ENG., Illus.). 104p. 70.00 *(978-0-9549405-5-3(5))* Nobody GBR. Dist: D.A.P./Distributed Art Pubs.

Skeates, Robin. An Archaeology of the Senses: Prehistoric Malta. 2010. (ENG., Illus.). 288p. 150.00 *(978-0-19-921660-4(6))* Oxford Univ. Pr., Inc.

Skeates, Robin, et al, eds. The Oxford Handbook of Public Archaeology. 2012. (Oxford Handbooks Ser.). (ENG., Illus.). 736p. 150.00 ***(978-0-19-923782-1(4))*** Oxford Univ. Pr., Inc.

Smith, John. The Third Watch. 2010. 496p. 36.99 *(978-1-60957-669-1(1))*; pap. 24.99 *(978-1-60957-668-4(3))* Xulon Pr., Inc.

Snead, James E. & Allen, Mark W., eds. Burnt Corn Pueblo: Conflict & Conflagration in the Galisteo Basin, A. D. 1250-1325. 2010. (Anthropological Papers). (ENG., Illus.). 160p. pap. 19.95 *(978-0-8165-2949-0(3))* Univ. of Arizona Pr.

Snow, Dean. The Archaeology of North Americ. 2008. 284p. pap. 27.00 *(978-1-59740-665-9(1))* ACLS Humanities E-Book.

Snyder, Thomas F. Archeology Search Book. *(978-0-07-079001-8(9))* Macmillan/McGraw-Hill Schl. Div.

Southall, James Cocke. The # of the # & the # of Man upon the Earth by James C Southall. 2006. 452p. per. 26.99 *(978-1-4255-4971-8(3))* MPublishing.

Southwest Museum Publisher. The Masterkey V24, No 1, January-February 1950. 2011. 34p. 35.95 ***(978-1-258-05359-8(4))*** Literary Licensing, LLC.

Speth, John D. The Paleoanthropology & Archaeology of Big-Game Hunting: Protein, Fat, or Politics? 2010. (Interdisciplinary Contributions to Archaeology Ser.). (Illus.). xxxiii, 325p. 199.00 *(978-1-4419-6732-9(X)*, 144196732X) Springer.

Stanford, Craig, et al. Biological Anthropology & Archaeology. 2008. 496p. (C). pap. 89.33 *(978-0-13-230076-6(1))* Prentice Hall Higher Education.

Stapp, Darby C. & Longnecker, Julia G. Avoiding Archaeological Disasters: Risk Management for Heritage Professionals. 2009. (Techniques & Issues in Cultural Resource Management Ser.). (ENG., Illus.). 176p. 79.00 *(978-1-59874-160-5(8))*; pap. 24.95 *(978-1-59874-161-2(6))* Left Coast Pr., Inc.

Stark, Rebecca. Archaeology, No. 4. Date not set. tchr. ed. 5.95 *(978-1-56644-966-3(9)*, 036-9APB); tchr. ed. 10.95 *(978-0-910857-34-5(2)*, 970-7APT) Educational Impressions.

Stone, Peter & Thomas, Suzie, eds. Metal Detecting & Archaeology. 2009. (Heritage Matters Ser.: Volume 2). (Illus.). 238p. 90.00 *(978-1-84383-415-1(4)*, Boydell Press) Boydell & Brewer, Ltd. GBR. Dist: Boydell & Brewer, Inc.

Stottman, M. Jay. Archaeologists As Activists: Can Archaeologists Change the World? 2010. (Illus.). viii, 207p. *(978-0-8173-8442-5(1))* Univ. of Alabama Pr.

Stottman, M. Jay, ed. & contrib. by. Archaeologists as Activists: Can Archaeologists Change the World? 2nd ed. (ENG., Illus.). 216p. 2011. pap. 29.95 *(978-0-8173-5622-4(3))* 2010. 46.00 *(978-0-8173-1712-6(0))* Univ. of Alabama Pr.

Stout, Adam. Creating Prehistory: Druids, Ley Hunters & Archaeologists in Pre-War Britain. 2008. (ENG., Illus.). 336p. 116.95 *(978-1-4051-5504-5(3))*; pap. 62.95 *(978-1-4051-5505-2(1))* Wiley, John & Sons, Inc. (Wiley-Blackwell).

Suárez, Alex R. & Vásquez, Marc N., eds. Archeology Research Trends. 2008. (Illus.). xi, 204p. (C). 137.00 *(978-1-60456-678-9(7))* Nova Science Pubs., Inc.

Sullivan, Mary & Connell, Samuel. A Case Study in Archaeology: A Student's Perspective. rev. ed. 2011. (ENG.). 96p. pap. 32.00 *(978-0-7575-6295-2(7))* Kendall Hunt Publishing Co.

Sutton, Mark Q. & Arkush, Brooke S. Archaeological Laboratory Methods: An Introduction. 5th ed. 2009. (Illus.). xix, 384p. pap. ***(978-0-7575-5980-8(8))*** 2010. (ENG.). 404p. pap. 74.29 *(978-0-7575-5974-7(3))* Kendall Hunt Publishing Co.

Swaddling, Judith & Prag, John. Seianti Hanunia Tlesnasa: The Story of an Etruscan Noblewoman. 2nd ed. 2007. (Bmp occasional Paper Ser.). (ENG., Illus.). 76p. (C). pap. 48.00 *(978-0-86159-979-0(9))* British Museum Pr. GBR. Dist: Brown, David Bk. Co., The.

Swift, Dan. Roman Waterfront Development at 12 Arthur Street, City of London. 2007. (MoLAS Archaeology Studies). (Illus.). 78p. (C). pap. 18.00 *(978-1-901992-62-5(4))* Museum of London Archaeology Service GBR. Dist: Brown, David Bk. Co., The.

Tait, John. Why the Egyptians Wrote Books. 2010. (University College London Institute of Archeology Publications). (ENG.). 256p. 89.00 *(978-1-59874-305-0(8))* Left Coast Pr., Inc.

TAKALA & Harris. Value of Life Intro Medic2. 2013. pap. 37.95 ***(978-0-415-36640-3(2))*** Routledge.

Talbot, Richard K. & Richens, Lane D. Shifting Sands: The Archaeology of Sand Hollow. 2009. (BYU Occasional Papers). (ENG.). pap. 45.00 *(978-0-87480-981-7(9))* Univ. of Utah Pr.

Taylor, Walter Willard. A Study of Archeology: American Anthropological Association, V50, No. 3, Part 2, July, 1948, Memoir No. 69. Mason, J. Alden & Hallowell, A. Irving, eds. 2011. 262p. 47.95 ***(978-1-258-06647-5(5))*** Literary Licensing, LLC.

Tellinger, Michael. Temples of the African Gods. 2010. 176p. 29.00 *(978-1-920153-08-3(X))* Zulu Planet Pubs. ZAF. Dist: APG Sales & Distribution Services.

Terry, James. Biofortean Reprint: Sculptured Anthropoid Ape Heads. 2011. 32p. pap. 9.00 ***(978-1-61646-069-3(5))*** Coachwhip Pubns.

Thomas, David Hurst & Kelly, Robert L. Archaeology: Down to Earth. 4th ed. 2010. (ENG.). (C). 304p. pap. 122.95 *(978-0-495-81409-2(1))*; 1p. rng bd. 63.95 *(978-0-495-81412-2(1))* Wadsworth.

Thomas, Kenneth W. Experimental Archaeology. 2008. pap. 35.95 *(978-0-415-41862-1(3))*; 108.00 *(978-0-415-41861-4(5))* Routledge.

Thomas, Kenneth W. & Kelly. Archaeology Module 2. 4th ed. 2006. (C). pap. 6.95 *(978-0-495-00405-9(7))* Wadsworth.

Thorp, Robert L. Visiting Historic Beijing: A Guide to Sites & Resources. 2007. (ENG., Illus.). 240p. pap. 24.95 *(978-1-891640-53-7(4))* Floating World Editions.

Thorpe, I. J. Archaeology of Death. 2009. (Themes in Archaeology Ser.). (Illus.). 160p. 100.00 *(978-0-415-22419-2(5)*, RU20575) Routledge.

Thorpe, Nick. Archaeology of Death. 2009. (Themes in Archaeology Ser.). (Illus.). 160p. 21.95 *(978-0-415-22420-8(9)*, RU20576) Routledge.

Timothy, Clack & Marcus, Brittain. Archaeology & the Media. 2006. 224p. *(978-1-84472-156-6(6))* Taylor & Francis Group.

Tourloukis, Vangelis. Early & Mid Pleistocene Arch Record: Current Status & Future Prospects. 2011. (Archaeological Studies Leiden University Ser.). 262p. pap. *(978-90-8728-106-9(4)*, Leiden Univ. Pr.) Amsterdam Univ. Pr.

Turnbaugh & Jurmain & Kilgore & Nelson & Cram101 Textbook Reviews Staff. Understanding Physical Anthropology & Archaeology. 2007. 260p. per. 14.95 *(978-1-4288-2664-9(5))* Cram101 Inc.

Ucko, Peter J., et al, eds. A Future for the Past: Petrie's Palestinian Collection. 2009. (University College London Institute of Archaeology Publications). (ENG.). 180p. pap. 45.00 *(978-0-905853-42-0(3))* Left Coast Pr., Inc.

Urban, Patricia A. & Schortman, Edward. Archaeological Theory in Practice. 2012. (ENG.). 344p. (C). 94.00 *(978-1-59874-628-0(6))*; pap. 34.95 *(978-1-59874-629-7(4))* Left Coast Pr., Inc.

VanPool, Todd L. & Leonard, Robert D. Quantitative Analysis in Archaeology. 2010. (ENG., Illus.). 376p. 104.95 *(978-1-4051-8951-4(7))*; pap. 51.95 *(978-1-4051-8950-7(9))* Wiley, John & Sons, Inc. (Wiley-Blackwell).

Vecchia, Stefano. The Khmers. 2008. (ENG., Illus.). 208p. 35.00 *(978-88-544-0311-5(3))* White Star ITA. Dist: Random Hse., Inc.

Waksman, S. Y. Archaeometric & Archaeological Approaches to Ceramics: Papers Presented at EMAC '05, 8th European Meeting on Ancient Ceramics, Lyon 2005. 2007. (Bar S Ser.). (Illus.). 204p. (C). pap. 87.50 *(978-1-4073-0129-7(2))* British Archaeological Reports Ltd. GBR. Dist: Brown, David Bk. Co., The.

Wallace, Sandra. Ontology of the Material. 2011. (Critical Realism: Interventions Ser.). (ENG.). 192p. 135.00 *(978-0-415-59127-0(9))* Routledge.

Wass, Stephen. The Amateur Archaeologist. 2012. (ENG.). pap. 44.95 ***(978-0-415-51541-2(6))*** Routledge.

Webb, Simon. Unearthing London: The Ancient World Beneath the Metropolis. 2011. (ENG., Illus.). 176p. pap. 24.95 ***(978-0-7524-6274-5(1))*** History Pr. Ltd.,The GBR. Dist: Independent Pubs. Group.

Weigall, Arthur E. P. B. The Treasury of Ancient Egypt: Miscellaneous Chapters on Ancient Egyptian History. 2007. (ENG.). 230p. pap. 20.99 *(978-1-4264-9213-6(8))*; 254p. pap. 23.99 *(978-1-4264-9270-9(7))* BiblioBazaar.

Weik, Terrance M. The Archaeology of Anti-Slavery Resistance. 2012. (American Experience in Archaeological Pespective Ser.). (ENG., Illus.). 176p. 69.95 *(978-0-8130-3759-2(X))* Univ. Pr. of Florida.

Weiss, Harvey. Collapse. 2006. 256p. 27.95 *(978-0-415-93487-9(7))* Routledge.

Wendorf, Fred. Desert Days: My Life as a Field Archaeologist. 2008. (Illus.). 640p. 29.95 *(978-0-87074-524-9(7))* Southern Methodist Univ. Pr.

Wenke, Robert J. & Olszewski, Deborah I. Patterns in Prehistory: Humankind's First Three Million Years. 5th rev. ed. 2006. (ENG., Illus.). 640p. (C). per. 94.95 *(978-0-19-516928-7(X))* Oxford Univ. Pr., Inc.

White, Gregory G. & King, Thomas F. The Archaeological Survey Manual. 2007. (ENG., Illus.). 196p. (C). 94.00 *(978-1-59874-008-0(3))* Left Coast Pr., Inc.

WhiteStar. Great BK of Archaeology. 2007. 29.99 *(978-88-540-0395-8(6))* White Star ITA. Dist: Book Sales, Inc.

Whitley, David S. & Hays-Gilpin, Kelley. Belief in the Past: Theoretical Approaches to the Archaeology of Religion. Whitley, David S. & Hays-Gilpin, Kelley, eds. 2008. (ENG., Illus.). 290p. 89.00 *(978-1-59874-341-8(4))*; pap. 32.95 *(978-1-59874-342-5(2))* Left Coast Pr., Inc.

Wickham, Louise. Gardens in History: A Political Perspective. 2012. (ENG., Illus.). 272p. pap. 60.00 ***(978-1-905119-43-1(7))*** Windgather Pr. GBR. Dist: Brown, David Bk. Co., The.

Wilkinson, Paul. Archaeology: What it Is, where it Is, & how to do It. 2007. (ENG., Illus.). 106p. (C). pap. 24.95 *(978-1-905739-00-4(1))* Archaeopress GBR. Dist: Brown, David Bk. Co., The.

Willems, W. J. H., et al, contrib. by. Archaeological Heritage Management in the Netherlands: Fifty Years State Service for Archaeological Investigations. (Illus.). 366p. *(978-90-232-3304-6(2))* Van Gorcum & Co. B.V.

Williams, John H., ed. The Archaeology of Kent to AD 800. 2007. (Kent History Project Ser.: Volume 8). (Illus.). 304p. 45.00 *(978-0-85115-580-7(4)*, Boydell Press) Boydell & Brewer, Ltd. GBR. Dist: Boydell & Brewer, Inc.

Williams, Philip Lee. The Archaeological Evidence of Noah's Flood. 2011. (ENG., Illus.). 411p. 34.95 *(978-0-9793102-2-5(9))* Christian Leaders & Scholars Pr.

Williamson, Ronald F. The Archaeology of Bruce Trigger: Theoretical Empiricism. Bisson, Michael, ed. 2006. (ENG., Illus.). 320p. (C). *(978-0-7735-3127-7(0))* McGill-Queen's Univ. Pr.

Williamson, Ronald F. & Bisson, Michael S. The Archaeology of Bruce Trigger: Theoretical Empiricism. 2006. (ENG., Illus.). 320p. (C). per. *(978-0-7735-3161-1(0))* McGill-Queen's Univ. Pr.

Winkelman, Michael. Time & Mind Volume 2 Issue 3: The Journal of Archaeology, Consciousness & Culture. Devereux, Paul et al, eds. 2010. (Illus.). 128p. pap. 59.95 *(978-1-84788-441-1(5))* Berg Pubs. GBR. Dist: Macmillan.

Wiseman, James & El-Baz, Farouk, eds. Remote Sensing in Archaeology. 2007. (Interdisciplinary Contributions to Archaeology Ser.). (Illus.). 553p. 149.00 incl. cd-rom *(978-0-387-44453-6(X))* Springer.

Wiseman, James R. & El-Baz, Farouk, eds. Remote Sensing in Archaeology. 2007. (Interdisciplinary Contributions to Archaeology Ser.). (Illus.). 553p. pap. 59.95 incl. cd-rom *(978-0-387-44615-8(X)*, 038744615X) Springer.

Wood, Christopher. Forgery, Replica, Fiction: Temporalities of German Renaissance Art. 2008. (ENG., Illus.). 416p. 55.00 *(978-0-226-90597-6(7))* Univ. of Chicago Pr.

Yeates, Stephen. A Dreaming for the Witches: The Recreation of the Dobunni Primal Myth. 2009. (ENG., Illus.). 256p. (C). pap. 39.95 *(978-1-84217-359-9(8))* Oxbow Bks., Ltd. GBR. Dist: Brown, David Bk. Co., The.

Zahavy, Yitzhak. Archaeology, Stamps & Coins of the State of Israel. 2009. 226p. pap. 19.54 *(978-0-557-12824-2(2))* Lulu Enterprises Inc.

Zehren, Erich. Crescent & the Bull A Survey of Archae. 2006. pap. 33.95 *(978-1-4286-5525-3(3))* Kessinger Publishing, LLC.

Zimmerman, Virginia. Excavating Victorians. 2007. (SUNY Series, Studies in the Long Nineteenth Century). (Illus.). 231p. 65.00 *(978-0-7914-7279-8(5))* State Univ. of New York Pr.

ARCHAEOLOGY—BIBLIOGRAPHY

Price, T. Douglas & Feinman, Gary M., eds. Archaeology at the Millennium: A Sourcebook. 2006. (ENG., Illus.). xvi, 512p. per. 74.95 *(978-0-387-72610-6(1)*, 0387726101) Springer.

ARCHAEOLOGY—DATA PROCESSING

Barceló, Juan A. Computational Intelligence in Archaeology. 2008. 436p. 180.00 *(978-1-59904-489-7(7))* IGI Global.

Cannata, Rosalia. Information Systems in Archaeology. 2011. 112p. pap. ***(978-3-8443-2920-9(X))*** Lambert Academic Publishing.

Farinetti, Emeri. Boeotian Landscapes: A GIS-Based Study for the Reconstruction & Interpretation of the Archaeological Datasets of Ancient Boeotia. 2011. (Bar S Ser.). (ENG., Illus.). 425p. (C). pap. 162.50 *(978-1-4073-0750-3(9))* British Archaeological Reports Ltd. GBR. Dist: Brown, David Bk. Co., The.

Forte, Maurizio, ed. Cyber-Archaeology. 2010. (Bar S Ser.). (ENG., Illus.). 153p. (C). pap. 107.50 *(978-1-4073-0721-3(5))* British Archaeological Reports Ltd. GBR. Dist: Brown, David Bk. Co., The.

Frischer, Bernard, et al, eds. Making History Interactive. 2010. (Bar S Ser.). (ENG., Illus.). 408p. (C). pap. 150.00 *(978-1-4073-0556-1(5))* British Archaeological Reports Ltd. GBR. Dist: Brown, David Bk. Co., The.

Frischer, Bernard & Dakouri-Hild, Anastasia, eds. Beyond Illustration: 2D & 3D Digital Technologies as Tools for Discovery in Archaeology. 2008. (Bar S Ser.). (ENG., Illus.). 192p. (C). pap. 120.00 *(978-1-4073-0292-8(2))* British Archaeological Reports Ltd. GBR. Dist: Brown, David Bk. Co., The.

Kansa, Eric C., et al, eds. Archaeology 2.0: New Tools for Communication & Collaboration. 2011. (Cotsen Digital Archaeology Ser.). (ENG.). 295p. (C). pap. 39.95 ***(978-1-931745-85-7(4))*** Cotsen Institute of Archaeology at UCLA.

Papadopoulos, Constantin. Pattern Recognition & Signal Processing in Archaeometry: Mathematical & Computational Solutions for Archaeology. 2011. ***(978-1-60960-786-3(0))*** IGI Global.

Parcak, Sarah H. Satellite Remote Sensing for Archaeology. 2009. (ENG., Illus.). 320p. 155.00 *(978-0-415-44877-2(8))*; pap. 44.95 *(978-0-415-44878-9(6))* Routledge.

Politis, Dionysios, ed. E-Learning Methodologies & Computer Applications in Archaeology. 2008. (Illus.). 300+p. 180.00 *(978-1-59904-759-1(4)*, IGI Global.

White, Devin Alan & Surface-Evans, Sarah L., eds. Least Cost Analysis of Social Landscapes: Archaeological Case Studies. 2012. (ENG., Illus.). 304p. 55.00 ***(978-1-60781-171-8(5))*** Univ. of Utah Pr.

Wilson, Andrew T., ed. UK Chapter of Computer Applications & Quantitative Methods in Archaeology. 2011. (Bar S Ser.). (Illus.). 87p. (C). pap. 70.00 *(978-1-4073-0732-9(0))* British Archaeological Reports Ltd. GBR. Dist: Brown, David Bk. Co., The.

ARCHAEOLOGY—DATING

see Archaeological Dating

ARCHAEOLOGY—DICTIONARIES

Clodore-Tissot, Tinaig. Dictionary of Archaeological Terms English-French / French - English. 2009. (ENG., Illus.). 142p. (C). pap. 25.95 *(978-1-905739-27-1(3))* Archaeopress GBR. Dist: Brown, David Bk. Co., The.

Cremin, Aedeen, ed. The World Encyclopedia of Archaeology: The World's Most Significant Sites & Cultural Treasures. 2007. (ENG., Illus.). 400p. 59.95 *(978-1-55407-311-5(1))* Firefly Bks., Ltd.

Darvill, Timothy. Concise Oxford Dictionary of Archaeology. 2nd ed. (Oxford Paperback Reference Ser.). (ENG., Illus.). 544p. 2010. pap. 18.95 *(978-0-19-953404-3(7))* 2008. 50.00 *(978-0-19-953405-0(5))* Oxford Univ. Pr., Inc.

Feder, Kenneth L. Encyclopedia of Dubious Archaeology: From Atlantis to the Walam Olum. 2010. E-Book *(978-0-313-37919-2(X)*, Greenwood Pr.); (Illus.). 292p. 85.00 *(978-0-313-37918-5(1)*, GR7918) Greenwood Publishing Group, Inc.

Gay, Jean. Glossaire Archeologique du Moyen age et de la Renaissance. (FRE.). 295.00 *(978-0-7859-0615-5(0)*, F22140) French & European Pubns., Inc.

Khrapunov, Nikita. Archaeology Field Dictionary: English-Russian-English. 2nd ed. 2007. (ENG.). 236p. (C). pap. 15.00 *(978-0-9748334-3-9(6))* Institute of Classical Archaeology.

Kipfer, Barbara Ann. Dictionary of Artifacts. 2007. (ENG., Illus.). 360p. 159.95 *(978-1-4051-1887-3(3)*, Wiley-Blackwell) Wiley, John & Sons, Inc.

—Encyclopedic Dictionary of Archaeology. 2011. (ENG.). 724p. pap. 159.00 *(978-1-4419-3322-5(0)*, 1441933220) Springer.

Silberman, Neil Asher. The Oxford Companion to Archaeology, second Edition, 3 vols. 2nd ed. 2012. (ENG.). 1952p. 450.00 ***(978-0-19-973578-5(6))*** Oxford Univ. Pr., Inc.

Trent, Christopher. Terms Used in Archaeology. 5.95 *(978-0-8022-1737-0(0))* Philosophical Library, Inc.

ARCHAEOLOGY—HISTORY

Alcock, Susan E. & Talalay, Lauren E. In the Field: The Archaeological Expeditions of the Kelsey Museum. 2006. (Kelsey Museum Publication). (ENG., Illus.). 103p. (C). pap. 19.50 *(978-0-9741873-3-4(X))* Kelsey Museum of Archaeology.

Ameborg, Jette. Dynamics of Northern Societies: Proceedings of the S LA/NABO Conference on Arctic & North Atlantic Archaeology, Copenhagen, May 10th-14th 2004. Gronnow, Bjarne, ed. 2006. (Studies in Archaeology & History, Publications from the Na Ser.). (ENG., Illus.). 415p. (C). 42.00 *(978-87-7602-052-1(5))* Aarhus Universitetsforlag DNK. Dist: ISD.

Babes, Mircea & Kaeser, Marc-Antoine, eds. Archaeologists Without Boundaries: Towards a History of International Archaeological Congresses, 1866-2006. 2009. (Bar S Ser.). (FRE & ENG., Illus.). 51p. (C). pap. 60.00 *(978-1-4073-0622-3(7))* British Archaeological Reports Ltd. GBR. Dist: Brown, David Bk. Co., The.

Blix, Goran & Blix, Göran Magnus. From Paris to Pompeii: French Romanticism & the Cultural Politics of Archaeology. 2008. (Illus.). 320p. (C). 59.95 *(978-0-8122-4136-5(3))* Univ. of Pennsylvania Pr.

Boric, Dusan. Archaeology & Memory. Boric, Dusan, ed. 2010. (ENG., Illus.). 215p. (C). 110.00 *(978-1-84217-363-3(4))* Oxbow Bks., Ltd. GBR. Dist: Brown, David Bk. Co., The.

Bowden, Mark. Pitt Rivers: The Life & Archaeological Work of Lieutenant-General Augustus Henry Lane Fox Pitt Rivers. 2009. (ENG.). 200p. pap. 26.99 *(978-0-521-10622-1(2))* Cambridge Univ. Pr.

Brian Ayers Staff. Medieval Europe Around the North Sea (Series: Studies in the Archaeology of Medieval Europe) 2015. 100.00 ***(978-1-904768-49-4(0))*** Equinox Publishing Ltd. GBR. Dist: Brown, David Bk. Co., The.

Ceserani, Giovanna. Italy's Lost Greece: Magna Graecia & the Making of Modern Archaeology, 1 vol. 2012. (Greeks Overseas Ser.). (ENG., Illus.). 348p. 74.00 *(978-0-19-974427-5(0))* Oxford Univ. Pr., Inc.

Church, Minette C., et al. Colorado History: A Context for Historical Archaeology. Cassells, E. Steve, ed. 2007. (ENG., Illus.). 600p. per. *(978-0-9743137-1-9(8))* Alpine Archaeological Consultants, Inc.

Clark, Grahame. Prehistory at Cambridge & Beyond. 2009. (ENG.). 188p. pap. 31.99 *(978-0-521-10194-3(8))* Cambridge Univ. Pr.

Clark, Peter, ed. Bronze Age Connections: Cultural Contact in Prehistoric Europe. 2009. (ENG., Illus.). 196p. (C). pap. 80.00 *(978-1-84217-348-0(0))* Oxbow Bks., Ltd. GBR. Dist: Brown, David Bk. Co., The.

Cline, Eric H. Sailing the Wine-Dark Sea: International Trade & the Late Bronze Age Aegean Bar S591. 2009. (Bar S Ser.: 591). (ENG., Illus.). 326p. (C). pap. 132.50 *(978-1-4073-0417-5(8))* British Archaeological Reports Ltd. GBR. Dist: Brown, David Bk. Co., The.

Colwell-Chanthaphonh. Living Histories: Native Americans & Southwestern Archaeology. 2010. (Issues in Southwest Archaeology Ser.). (ENG., Illus.). 212p. 75.00 *(978-0-7591-1195-0(2))* AltaMira Pr.

Colwell-Chanthaphonh, Chip. Living Histories: Native American Issues & Southwestern Archaeology. 2010. *(978-0-7591-1997-0(X))* AltaMira Pr.

—Living Histories: Native Americans & Southwestern Archaeology. 2010. (Issues in Southwest Archaeology Ser.). (ENG., Illus.). 212p. pap. 29.95 *(978-0-7591-1196-7(0))* AltaMira Pr.

Cram101 Textbook Reviews. Outlines & Highlights for a History of Archaeology: Classical Times to the Twenty-First Century by Brian M. Fagan, ISBN. 2010. 100p. pap. 27.95 *(978-1-61698-479-3(1))* Cram101 Inc.

—Outlines & Highlights for in the Beginning by Brian M Fagan, Isbn: 9780136026891. 2010. 66p. pap. 27.95 *(978-1-61698-462-5(7))* Cram101 Inc.

Cram101 Textbook Reviews Staff. Outlines & Highlights for a History of Archaeology: Classical Times to the Twenty-First Century by Brian M. Fagan, ISBN. 2009. 92p. pap. 27.95 *(978-1-4288-8596-7(X))* Cram101 Inc.

—Outlines & Highlights for in the Beginning by Brian M Fagan, Isbn: 9780136026891. 2009. 64p. pap. 27.95 *(978-1-4288-9028-2(9))* Cram101 Inc.

Cunliffe, Barry, et al, eds. The Oxford Handbook of Archaeology. 2009. (Handbooks in Archaeology Ser.). (ENG., Illus.). 780p. 150.00 *(978-0-19-927101-6(1))* Oxford Univ. Pr., Inc.

Dennison, E. P., et al. Historic Galashiels: Archaeology & Development. 2011. (Scottish Burgh Survey Ser.). (ENG., Illus.). 112p. (C). pap. 20.00 *(978-1-902771-80-9(X))* Council for British Archaeology GBR. Dist: Brown, David Bk. Co., The.

Diaz-Andreu, Margarita. A World History of Nineteenth-Century Archaeology: Nationalism, Colonialism, & the Past. 2008. (ENG., Illus.). 512p. 175.00 *(978-0-19-921717-5(3))* Oxford Univ. Pr., Inc.

Douglas, Alistair, et al. A Roman settlement & bath house at Shadwell: Excavations at Tobacco Dock & Babe Ruth restaurant, the Highway London. 2011. (Pre-construct archaeology Monograph Ser.). (ENG., Illus.). 225p. (C). pap. 40.00 *(978-0-9563054-2-8(3))* Pre-Construct Archaeology Limited GBR. Dist: Brown, David Bk. Co., The.

Emberling, Geoff, ed. Pioneers to the Past: American Archaeologists in the Middle East, 1919-1920. 2010. (Oriental Institute Museum Publications). (ENG., Illus.). 160p. (C). pap. 34.95 *(978-1-885923-70-7(8))* Oriental Institute of the Univ. of Chicago, The.

Fagan & Cram101 Textbook Reviews Staff. In the Beginning. 2007. 272p. per. 14.95 *(978-1-4288-2626-7(2))* Cram101 Inc.

Fagan, Brian M. & DeCorse, Christopher R. In the Beginning. 12th ed. 2008. (ENG.). 576p. (C). pap. 145.33 *(978-0-13-602689-1(3)*, Prentice Hall) Prentice Hall PTR.

Frison, George C., et al. Prehistory of the Plains & Rockies. 3rd ed. 2010. (ENG., Illus.). 668p. (C). lib. bdg. 89.00 *(978-1-59874-467-5(4))* Left Coast Pr., Inc.

Gkiasta. Historiography of Landscape Research. 2008. (Archaeological Studies Leiden University Ser.). pap. *(978-90-8728-036-9(X)*, Leiden Univ. Pr.) Amsterdam Univ. Pr.

Hamerow, Helena, ed. Anglo-Saxon Studies in Archaeology & History, Vol. 17. 2011. (Anglo-saxon studies in archaeology & History Ser.). (ENG., Illus.). 168p. (C). pap. 70.00 *(978-1-905905-18-8(1))* Oxford Univ. Schl. of Archaeology GBR. Dist: Brown, David Bk. Co., The.

Henig, Martin & McNeill, John, eds. The Medieval Cloister in England & Wales: Journal of the British Archaeological Association Volume 159 For 2006. 2007. (Maney Main Publication). (ENG., Illus.). 344p. (C). pap. 55.00 *(978-1-905981-35-9(X))* Maney Publishing GBR. Dist: Brown, David Bk. Co., The.

Hildebrandt, William R. Life on the River: The Archaeology of an Early Native American Culture. 2008. (Illus.). 120p. pap. 13.95 *(978-1-59714-086-7(4))* Heyday.

Hilprecht, H. V. Drought, Famine, Plague & Pestilence. 2009. 294p. pap. *(978-1-4590-7310-4(X))* Books LLC.

—Drought, Famine, Plague & Pestilence. 2007. (Gorgias Classic Archaeological Reprints Ser.: 9). 88.00 *(978-1-59333-640-0(3))*;2 of 2. 44.00 *(978-1-59333-650-9(0))* Gorgias Pr., LLC.

Hilprecht, H. V. & Robertson, Warren. Drought, Famine, Plague & Pestilence, 1 of 2. 2010. (Gorgias Classic Archaeological Reprints Ser.: 9). pap. 130.00 *(978-1-59333-649-3(7))* Gorgias Pr., LLC.

Hirst, K. Kris. Archaeologist's Book of Quotations. 2009. (ENG., Illus.). 136p. pap. 24.95 *(978-1-59874-434-7(8))* Left Coast Pr., Inc.

Hooke, Della & Hooke. The Anglo-Saxon Landscape: The Kingdom of the Hwicce. 2009. (ENG., Illus.). 208p. pap. 33.00 *(978-0-7190-8068-5(1))* Manchester Univ. Pr. GBR. Dist: Macmillan.

Horning, Audrey & Palmer, Marilyn, eds. Crossing Paths or Sharing Tracks? Future Directions in the Archaeological Study of Post-1550 Britain & Ireland. 2009. (Society for Post Medieval Archaeology Monograph Ser.: Volume 5). (Illus.). 438p. 90.00 *(978-1-84383-434-2(0)*, Boydell Press) Boydell & Brewer, Ltd. GBR. Dist: Boydell & Brewer, Inc.

Hunt, Patrick. Ten Discoveries That Rewrote History. 2007. (ENG.). 240p. (gr. 12-18). 15.00 *(978-0-452-28877-5(0),* Plume) Penguin Group (USA) Inc.

In Palestine, American School for Oriental Study and Research & Barton, George A. Second Annual Report of the Managing Committee. 2010. pap. 18.16 *(978-1-61719-388-0(7))* Gorgias Pr., LLC.

In Palestine, American School for Oriental Study and Research & Brown, Francis. Seventh Annual Report of the Managing Committee, 1907-1908. 2010. pap. 19.84 *(978-1-61719-393-4(3))* Gorgias Pr., LLC.

In Palestine, American School for Oriental Study and Research & Lyon, David G. Sixth Annual Report of the Managing Committee, 1906-1907. 2010. pap. 19.12 *(978-1-61719-392-7(5))* Gorgias Pr., LLC.

Khoo, James C. M. Art & Archaeology of Funan: Pre-Khmer Kingdom of the Lower Mekong Valley. 2006. (ENG., Illus.). 45.00 *(978-974-524-035-3(4))* Orchid Pr. THA. Dist: National Bk. Network.

Loendorf, Lawrence L. Thunder & Herds: Rock Art of the High Plains. 2008. (ENG., Illus.). 254p. 94.00 *(978-1-59874-152-0(7));* pap. 32.95 *(978-1-59874-151-3(9))* Left Coast Pr., Inc.

Malley, Shawn. From Archaeology to Spectacle in Victorian Britain: The Case of Assyria, 1845-1854. 2012. (Illus.). 220p. 99.95 ***(978-1-4094-2689-9(0))*** Ashgate Publishing Co.

Martinón-Torres, Marcos & Rehren, Thilo, eds. Archaeology, History & Science: Integrating Approaches to Ancient Materials. 2008. (Univ Col London Inst Arch Pub Ser.). (ENG., Illus.). 218p. 94.00 *(978-1-59874-340-1(6))* Left Coast Pr., Inc.

Murray, Tim & Evans, Christopher. Histories of Archaeology: A Reader in the History of Archaeology. Murray, Tim & Evans, Christopher, eds. 2008. (ENG., Illus.). 440p. 175.00 *(978-0-19-955007-4(7));* pap. 74.00 *(978-0-19-955008-1(5))* Oxford Univ. Pr., Inc.

O'Connor, Anne. Finding Time for the Old Stone Age: A History of Palaeolithic Archaeology & Quaternary Geology in Britain, 1860-1960. 2007. (ENG., Illus.). 480p. 185.00 *(978-0-19-921547-8(2))* Oxford Univ. Pr., Inc.

Oram, R. D., et al. Historic Fraserburgh: Archaeology & Development. 2010. (Scottish Burgh Survey Ser.). (ENG., Illus.). 172p. (C). pap. 20.00 *(978-1-902771-79-3(6))* Council for British Archaeology GBR. Dist: Brown, David Bk. Co., The.

Panhorst, Annette. Looting of Bones in the Teutoburg Forest. 2010. 108p. pap. 20.90 *(978-3-8391-6546-1(6))* Bks. on Demand.

Pluskowski, Aleksander. The Archaeology of the Prussian Crusade: Holy War & Colonisation. 2013. (ENG.). 288p. (C). 135.00 ***(978-0-415-69170-3(2));*** pap. 44.95 ***(978-0-415-69171-0(0))*** Routledge.

Pluskowski, Aleksander, ed. The Ritual Killing & Burial of Animals: European Perspectives. 2012. (ENG., Illus.). 224p. (C). 96.00 *(978-1-84217-444-9(4))* Oxbow Bks., Ltd. GBR. Dist: Brown, David Bk. Co., The.

Reid, Jefferson & Whittlesey, Stephanie Michelle. Prehistory, Personality, & Place: Emil W. Haury & the Mogollon Controversy. 2010. (ENG., Illus.). 208p. (C). pap. 19.95 *(978-0-8165-2862-2(4))* Univ. of Arizona Pr.

Rick, Torben C. & Erlandson, Jon M., eds. Human Impacts on Ancient Marine Ecosystems: A Global Perspective. 2008. (Illus.). 319p. 65.00 *(978-0-520-25343-8(4))* Univ. of California Pr.

Schissler, Hanna & Soysal, Yasemin Nuhoglu, eds. Archives, Ancestors, Practices: Archaeology in the Lights of Its History. 2008. (Illus.). 268p. 95.00 *(978-1-84545-066-3(3))* Berghahn Bks., Inc.

Schmidt, Peter R. & Patterson, Thomas C., eds. Making Alternative Histories. (Advanced Seminar Ser.). (Illus.). 312p. 29.95 *(978-0-933452-92-3(6))* School for Advanced Research Pr./SAR Pr.

Shanks, Michael. The Archaeological Imagination. 2012. E-Book ***(978-1-61132-784-7(9))*** Left Coast Pr., Inc.

Shortland, Andrew, et al, eds. From Mine to Microscope: Advances in the Study of Ancient Technology. 2009. (ENG., Illus.). 246p. (C). 120.00 *(978-1-84217-259-9(X))* Oxbow Bks., Ltd. GBR. Dist: Brown, David Bk. Co., The.

Silverman, Helaine & Isbell, William. Handbook of South American Archaeology. 2008. (Illus.). 870p. 206.00 *(978-0-387-74906-8(3))* Springer.

Stieglitz, Robert R. Tel Tanninim: Excavations at Krokodeilon Polis, 1996-1999. 2006. (American Schools of Oriental Research Archeological Reports: No. 10). (ENG., Illus.). 270p. (C). 84.95 *(978-0-89757-072-5(3))* American Schls. of Oriental Research.

Trigger, Bruce G. A History of Archaeological Thought. 2nd rev. ed. 2006. (ENG., Illus.). 732p. 105.00 *(978-0-521-84076-7(7));* 730p. per. 36.99 *(978-0-521-60049-1(9))* Cambridge Univ. Pr.

White, Carolyn, ed. The Materiality of Individuality: Archaeological Studies of Individual Lives. 2009. (ENG., Illus.). viii, 228p. 129.00 *(978-1-4419-0497-3(2),* 1441904972) Springer.

Whyte, Nicola. Inhabiting the Landscape: Place, Custom & Memory, 1500-1800. 2008. (ENG., Illus.). 189p. pap. 40.00 *(978-1-905119-24-0(0))* Windgather Pr. GBR. Dist: Brown, David Bk. Co., The.

Yoffee, Norman. Negotiating the Past in the Past: Identity, Memory, & Landscape in Archaeological Research. 2008. (ENG., Illus.). 288p. pap. 39.95 *(978-0-8165-2670-3(2))* Univ. of Arizona Pr.

ARCHAEOLOGY—LAW AND LEGISLATION

Green, Penny & Mackenzie, Simon, eds. Criminology & Archaeology: Studies in Looted Antiquities. 2009. (ENG., Illus.). 182p. 94.00 *(978-1-84113-991-3(2));* pap. 46.00 *(978-1-84113-992-0(0))* Hart Publishing Ltd. GBR. Dist: International Specialized Bk. Services.

Greenfield, Jeanette. The Return of Cultural Treasures. 3rd rev. ed. 2007. (ENG., Illus.). 522p. 138.00 *(978-0-521-80216-1(4))* Cambridge Univ. Pr.

Grim, Roger W. Treasure Laws of the United States. 208p. pap. 16.95 *(978-0-9636458-0-7(3))* Grim, Roger W.

Marquez Grant, Nicholas & Fibiger, Linda, eds. The Routledge Handbook of Archaeological Human Remains & Legislation. 2011. (ENG., Illus.). 800p. 240.00 *(978-0-415-58857-7(X))* Routledge.

Sayer, Duncan. Ethics & Burial Archaeology. 2010. (Illus.). 144p. pap. 24.95 *(978-0-7156-3893-4(9))* Duckworth Publishers GBR. Dist: International Publishers Marketing.

Skowronek, Russell K. & Fischer, George R. HMS Fowey Lost & Found: Being the Discovery, Excavation, & Identification of a British Man-of-War Lost off the Cape of Florida in 1748. 2009. (New Perspectives on Maritime History & Nautical Archaeology Ser.). (ENG., Illus.). 256p. 45.00 *(978-0-8130-3320-4(9))* Univ. Pr. of Florida.

Weiss, Elizabeth. Reburying the Past: The Effects of Repatriation & Reburial on Scientific Inquiry. 2008. (Illus.). 137p. 59.00 *(978-1-60456-701-4(5))* Nova Science Pubs., Inc.

ARCHAEOLOGY—METHODOLOGY

see also Animal Remains (Archaeology); Archaeological Dating; Ethnoarchaeology; Photography in Archaeology

Abicht, Matthew J., et al. Landscapes Through the Lens: Aerial Photographs & the Historic Environment. 2010. (ENG., Illus.). 302p. (C). pap. 90.00 *(978-1-84217-981-9(0))* Oxbow Bks., Ltd. GBR. Dist: Brown, David Bk. Co., The.

Anagnostopoulos, Aris & Hamilakis, Yannis, eds. Archaeological Ethnographies: Public Archaeology, Volume 8, No. 2-3. 2009. (Public Archaeology Ser.). 256p. (C). pap. 62.00 *(978-1-906540-73-9(X))* Maney Publishing GBR. Dist: Brown, David Bk. Co., The.

Anderson, Kirsten, et al, eds. Tools of the Trade: Techniques & Innovative Approaches in Archaeology. 2009. (ENG., Illus.). 344p. pap. 40.95 *(978-1-55238-249-3(4))* Univ. of Calgary Pr. CAN. Dist: Chicago Distribution Ctr.

Archer, Steven & Bartoy, Kevin, eds. Between Dirt & Discussion: Methods, Methodology & Interpretation in Historical Archaeology. 2010. (Illus.). xiv, 235p. pap. 129.00 *(978-1-4419-4166-4(5),* 1441941665) Springer.

Archer, Steven N. & Bartoy, Kevin M., eds. Between Dirt & Discussion: Methods, Methodology & Interpretation in Historical Archaeology. 2006. (Illus.). xiv, 235p. 129.00 *(978-0-387-34218-4(4),* 0387342184) Springer.

Artioli, Gilberto. Scientific Methods & Cultural Heritage: An Introduction to the application of materials science to archaeometry & conservation Science. 2010. (ENG., Illus.). 368p. 117.00 *(978-0-19-954826-2(9))* Oxford Univ. Pr., Inc.

Aufderheide, Arthur C. & Rodriguez-Martin, Conrado. The Cambridge Encyclopedia of Human Paleopathology. 2011. (ENG., Illus.). 498p. pap. 85.00 ***(978-1-107-40377-2(4))*** Cambridge Univ. Pr.

Bain, Allison, ed. La Mesure du Passe. 2007. (Bar S Ser.). (FRE & ENG., Illus.). 236p. (C). 105.00 *(978-1-4073-0142-6(X))* British Archaeological Reports Ltd. GBR. Dist: Brown, David Bk. Co., The.

Barnard, H. & Eerkens, Jelmer W. Theory & Practice of Archaeological Residue Analysis. 2007. (Bar S Ser.). (ENG., Illus.). 274p. (C). pap. 90.00 *(978-1-4073-0084-9(9))* British Archaeological Reports Ltd. GBR. Dist: Brown, David Bk. Co., The.

Belford, Paul, et al. Archaeological Practice & Heritage in Great Britain. 2010. (World Archaeological Congress Cultural Heritage Manual Ser.). (ENG.). ix, 225p. 139.00 *(978-0-387-09452-6(0),* 0387094520) Springer.

Bocquet-Appel, Jean-Pierre, ed. Recent Advances in Palaeodemography: Data, techniques, Patterns. 2008. (ENG., Illus.). viii, 294p. 169.00 *(978-1-4020-6423-4(3),* 1402064233) Springer.

—Recent Advances in Palaeodemography: Data, Techniques, Patterns. 2010. (ENG.). viii, 294p. pap. 169.00 *(978-90-481-7637-3(9),* 9048176379) Springer.

Boric, Dusan & Robb, John. Past Bodies: Body-Centered Research in Archaeology. Boric, Dusan & Robb, John, eds. 2008. (ENG., Illus.). 160p. (C). 60.00 *(978-1-84217-341-1(3))* Oxbow Bks., Ltd. GBR. Dist: Brown, David Bk. Co., The.

Brather, Sebastian, et al, eds. Historia Archaeologica: Festschrift far Heiko Steuer zum 70. Geburtstag. 2009. (Reallexikon der Germanischen Altertumskunde - Ergänzungsbände Ser.).Tr. of Historia archaeologica. Papers Presented to Heiko Steuer on the Occasion of his 70th Birthday. (GER., XLVII, 764p. Illus.). 280.00 *(978-3-11-022337-8(6));* 419.00 ***(978-3-11-173996-0(1))*** De Gruyter, Walter Inc.

Brown, Kate, et al. Biomolecular Archaeology: An Introduction. 2011. (ENG., Illus.). 336p. pap. 82.95 *(978-1-4051-7960-7(0),* Wiley-Blackwell) Wiley, John & Sons, Inc.

Brown, Tony, ed. Journal of Wetland Archaeoloy (2010), No. 10. 2011. (Journal of Wetland Archaeology Ser.). (ENG.). 170p. (C). pap. 40.00 *(978-1-84217-445-6(2))* Oxbow Bks., Ltd. GBR. Dist: Brown, David Bk. Co., The.

Brulet, Raymond, et al, eds. Thinking about Space: The Potential of Surface Survey & Contextual Archaeology in the Definition of Space in Roman Times. 2008. (Studies in Eastern Mediterranean Archaeology Ser.). (ENG.). 255p. (C). pap. 131.00 *(978-2-503-51357-7(3))* Brepols Pubs. BEL. Dist: ISD.

Campbell, Paul Douglas. Earth Pigments & Paint of the California Indians: Meaning & Technology. 2007. 29.95 *(978-0-9793780-0-3(1))* Campbell, Paul Douglas.

Carver, Martin Oswald Hugh. Making Archaeology Happen. 2011. (ENG., Illus.). 184p. (C). pap. 29.95 *(978-1-61132-025-1(9))* Left Coast Pr., Inc.

—Making Archaeology Happen: Design Versus Dogma. 2011. (ENG., Illus.). 184p. (C). 89.00 *(978-1-61132-024-4(0))* Left Coast Pr., Inc.

Carver, Martin Professor. Archaeological Investigation. 2010. (ENG., Illus.). 480p. (C). 48.95 *(978-0-415-48919-5(9));* 140.00 *(978-0-415-48918-8(0))* Routledge.

Castaneda, Quetzil E. & Matthews, Christopher N., eds. Ethnographic Archaeologies: Reflections on Stakeholders & Archaeological Practices. 2008. (ENG., Illus.). 220p. 80.00 *(978-0-7591-1134-9(0));* per. 35.95 *(978-0-7591-1135-6(9))* AltaMira Pr.

Catling, Christopher. Discovering the Past Through Archaeology: The Science & Practice of Studying Excavation Materials & Ancient Sites with 300 Colour Photographs, Maps & Detailed Illustrations. 2012. (ENG., Illus.). 128p. pap. 17.99 ***(978-1-84476-995-7(X))*** Anness Publishing GBR. Dist: National Bk. Network.

—Practical Archaeology: A Step-by-Step Guide to Uncovering the Past. 2009. (ENG., Illus.). 256p. (J). 35.00 *(978-0-7548-1747-5(4))* Anness Publishing GBR. Dist: National Bk. Network.

—A Practical Handbook of Archaeology: A Beginner's Guide to Unearthing the Past - an Invaluable Tool for Amateur Archaeologists with 300 Step-by-Step Photographs, Maps & Illustrations from Excavations Around the World. 2011. (ENG., Illus.). 128p. pap. 17.99 *(978-1-84476-793-9(0))* Anness Publishing GBR. Dist: National Bk. Network.

Cavulli, Fabio, et al. Defining a Methodological Approach to Interpret Structural Evidence. 2009. (Bar S Ser.). (Illus.). 148p. (C). pap. 85.00 *(978-1-4073-0621-6(9))* British Archaeological Reports Ltd. GBR. Dist: Brown, David Bk. Co., The.

Clark, John E. & Collins, Michael B., eds. Folsom Technology & Lifeways. 2011. (Lithic Technology, Special Publications). (ENG.). 456p. pap. 45.00 *(978-1-61132-059-6(3))* Left Coast Pr., Inc.

Conneller, Chantal. An Archaeology of Materials: Technologies of Transformation in Early Prehistoric Europe. 2010. (Routledge Studies in Archaeology Ser.). (ENG., Illus.). 168p. (C). 125.00 *(978-0-415-88130-2(7))* Routledge.

Connor, Melissa A. Forensic Methods: Excavation for the Archaeologist & Investigator. 2007. (ENG., Illus.). 272p. 53.95 *(978-0-7591-0936-0(2))* AltaMira Pr.

Cram101 Textbook Reviews. Outlines & Highlights for in the Beginning by Brian M Fagan, Isbn: 9780136026891. 2010. 66p. pap. 27.95 *(978-1-61698-462-5(7))* Cram101 Inc.

Cram101 Textbook Reviews & Cram101 Textbook Reviews. Outlines & Highlights for Quantitative Analysis in Archaeology by Todd VanPool. 2011. 274p. pap. 32.95 ***(978-1-61830-567-1(0))*** Cram101 Inc.

—Outlines & Highlights for the Oxford Handbook of Material Culture Studies by Dan Hicks, Isbn: 9780199218714. 2011. 650p. pap. 41.95 ***(978-1-61461-629-0(9))*** Cram101 Inc.

Cram101 Textbook Reviews Staff. Outlines & Highlights for in the Beginning by Brian M Fagan, Isbn: 9780136026891. 2009. 64p. pap. 27.95 *(978-1-4288-9028-2(9))* Cram101 Inc.

Creagh, Dudley, ed. Physical Techniques in the Study of Art, Archaeology & Cultural Heritage, Vol. 2. 2007. (Physical Techniques in the Study of Art, Archaeology & Cultural Heritage Ser.: 2). (ENG., Illus.). 282p. 106.00 *(978-0-444-52856-8(3),* Elsevier Science) Elsevier Science & Technology Bks.

Cunliffe, Barry, et al, eds. The Oxford Handbook of Archaeology. 2009. (Handbooks in Archaeology Ser.). (ENG., Illus.). 780p. 150.00 *(978-0-19-927101-6(1))* Oxford Univ. Pr., Inc.

Cunningham, Penny, et al. Experiencing Archaeology by Experiment: Proceedings of the Experimental Archaeology Conference, Exeter, 2007. Cunningham, Penny et al, eds. 2008. (ENG., Illus.). 128p. (C). pap. 50.00 *(978-1-84217-342-8(1))* Oxbow Bks., Ltd. GBR. Dist: Brown, David Bk. Co., The.

Desrosiers, Pierre & Sorensen, Mikkel, eds. Technology in Archaeology: Proceedings of the SILA Workshop: the Study of Technology as a method for gaining insight into social & cultural aspects of Prehistory, the National Museum of Denmark, Copenhagen, November 2-4 2005. 2008. (Studies in Archaeology & History, Publications from the Na Ser.). (ENG., Illus.). 205p. (C). 40.00 *(978-87-7602-093-4(2))* Aarhus Universitetsforlag DNK. Dist: ISD.

Dhanjal, Sarah & Moshenska, Gabriel, eds. Community Archaeology: Themes, Methods & Practices. 2012. (ENG., Illus.). 127p. (C). pap. 50.00 *(978-1-84217-432-6(0))* Oxbow Bks., Ltd. GBR. Dist: Brown, David Bk. Co., The.

Edwards, Howell & Vandenabeele, Peter, eds. Analytical Archaeometry. 2012. (ENG.). 400p. 213.00 *(978-1-84973-162-1(4))* Royal Society of Chemistry, The GBR. Dist: Ingram Pub. Services.

Fagan & Cram101 Textbook Reviews Staff. In the Beginning. 2007. 272p. per. 14.95 *(978-1-4288-2626-7(2))* Cram101 Inc.

Fagan, Brian M. Discovery! Unearthing the New Treasures of Archaeology. Fagan, Brian M., ed. 2007. (ENG., Illus.). 256p. 40.00 *(978-0-500-05149-8(6))* Thames & Hudson.

Fagan, Brian M. & DeCorse, Christopher R. In the Beginning. 12th ed. 2008. (ENG.). 576p. (C). pap. 145.33 *(978-0-13-602689-1(3),* Prentice Hall) Prentice Hall PTR.

Fawcett, Clare, et al, eds. Evaluating Multiple Narratives: Beyond Nationalist, Colonialist, Imperialist Archaeologies. 2008. (ENG., Illus.). xii, 217p. pap. 29.95 *(978-0-387-76459-7(3),* 0387764593) Springer.

Ferguson, Jeffrey, ed. Designing Experimental Research in Archaeology: Examining Technology through Production & Use. 2010. (ENG.). 304p. (C). 65.00 *(978-1-60732-038-8(X))* Univ. Pr. of Colorado.

Ferguson, Jeffrey R., ed. Designing Experimental Research in Archaeology: Examining Technology through Production & Use. 2010. (ENG.). 304p. (C). pap. 32.50 *(978-1-60732-022-7(3))* Univ. Pr. of Colorado.

Fish, Suzanne K. & Kowalewski, Stephen A., eds. The Archaeology of Regions: A Case for Full-Coverage Survey. 2009. (Foundations of Archaeology Ser.). (ENG., Illus.). 302p. (C). pap. 42.50 *(978-0-9797731-0-5(5),* Percheron Pr.) Werner, Eliot Pubns., Inc.

Frederiksen, Rune & Marchand, Eckart, eds. Plaster Casts: Making, Collecting & Displaying from Classical Antiquity to the Present. 2011. (Transformationen der Antike Ser.). (ENG., Illus.). XII, 752p. 280.00 ***(978-3-11-173105-6(7))*** De Gruyter, Walter Inc.

Frischer, Bernard, et al, eds. Making History Interactive. 2010. (Bar S Ser.). (ENG., Illus.). 408p. (C). pap. 150.00 *(978-1-4073-0556-1(5))* British Archaeological Reports Ltd. GBR. Dist: Brown, David Bk. Co., The.

Gaffney, Chris, et al. Magnetometry for Archaeologists. 2008. (Geophysical Methods for Archaeology Ser.). (ENG., Illus.). 224p. 75.00 *(978-0-7591-1106-6(5))* AltaMira Pr.

Gailhard, Nicolas. Transformation du Cuivre Au Moyen-Orient du Neolithique a la Fin du 3eme Millenaire: Etude D'une Chaine Technologique. 2009. (FRE., Illus.). 247p. (C). 117.50 *(978-1-4073-0394-9(5))* British Archaeological Reports Ltd. GBR. Dist: Brown, David Bk. Co., The.

Geier, Clarence R., et al, eds. The Historical Archaeology of Military Sites: Method & Topic. 2010. (Illus.). 280p. 50.00 *(978-1-60344-207-7(3))* Texas A&M Univ. Pr.

Gerike, Christian. Effectively Managing Archaeology Projects. 2012. (Techniques & Issues Cult Resources Mgmt Ser.). (ENG.). 160p. 79.00 *(978-1-61132-018-3(6));* pap. 24.95 *(978-1-61132-019-0(4))* Left Coast Pr., Inc.

Gkiasta. Historiography of Landscape Research. 2008. (Archaeological Studies Leiden University Ser.). pap. *(978-90-8728-036-9(X),* Leiden Univ. Pr.) Amsterdam Univ. Pr.

Goldberg, Paul & Macphail, Richard. Exercises in Geoarchaeology. 2007. (Illus.). 160p. pap., lab manual ed. 39.95 *(978-1-4051-1341-0(3),* Wiley-Blackwell) Wiley, John & Sons, Inc.

Grant, Jim, et al. The Archaeology Coursebook: An Introduction to Themes, Sites, Methods & Skills. 3rd rev. ed. 2008. (ENG., Illus.). 480p. 35.95 *(978-0-415-46286-0(X))* Routledge.

Habu, Junko, et al, eds. Evaluating Multiple Narratives: Beyond Nationalist, Colonialist, Imperialist Archaeologies. 2007. (ENG., Illus.). xii, 217p. 79.95 *(978-0-387-71824-8(9),* 0387718249) Springer.

Hardesty, Donald L. & Little, Barbara J. Assessing Site Significance: A Guide for Archaeologists & Historians. 2nd ed. 2009. (Heritage Resource Management Ser.). (ENG.). 254p. 80.00 *(978-0-7591-1126-4(X));* pap. 29.95 *(978-0-7591-1127-1(8))* AltaMira Pr.

Hester, Thomas R., et al. Field Methods in Archaeology: Seventh Edition. 7th ed. 2009. (ENG.). 448p. (C). pap. 69.00 *(978-1-59874-428-6(3))* Left Coast Pr., Inc.

Hodder, Ian. Archaeological Theory Today. 2nd ed. 2012. (ENG., Illus.). 320p. 89.95 ***(978-0-7456-5306-8(5));*** pap. 29.95 ***(978-0-7456-5307-5(3))*** Polity Pr. GBR. Dist: Wiley, John & Sons, Inc.

Hodder, Ian, ed. Symbolic & Structural Archaeology. 2007. (New Directions in Archaeology Ser.). (ENG., Illus.). 200p. pap. 50.00 *(978-0-521-03550-7(3))* Cambridge Univ. Pr.

Hojte, Jakob Munk, ed. Mithridates VI & the Pontic Kingdom. 2009. (Black Sea Studies). (ENG., Illus.). 375p. (C). 60.00 *(978-87-7934-443-3(7))* Aarhus Universitetsforlag DNK. Dist: ISD.

Holdaway, Simon & Wandsnider, LuAnn, eds. Time in Archaeology: Time Perspectivism Revisited. 2008. (ENG., Illus.). 219p. 50.00 *(978-0-87480-929-9(0))* Univ. of Utah Pr.

(Hrsg), Kommission der Deutschen Archäologischen Instituts Frankfurt aM / Hans-Markus Kaenel und Maria R-Alfoldi & Romisch-Germanische, Kommission fur Geschichte des Altertums der Akademie der Wissenschaften und der Literatur Mainz und, eds. Coins in Context I: New perspectives for the interpretation of coin Finds. 2010. (ENG & GER., Illus.). 187p. (C). pap. 45.00 *(978-3-8053-4091-5(5))* Zabern, Philipp von Verlag, GmbH DEU. Dist: Brown, David Bk. Co., The.

Jameson, John H. & Baugher-Perlin, Sherene. Past Meets Present: Archaeologists Partnering with Museum Curators, Teachers & Community Groups. 2007. (ENG., Illus.). xii, 466p. 149.00 *(978-0-387-47666-7(0),* 0387476660) Springer.

John G. Sabol Jr. Bodies of Substance, Fragments of Memories: An Archaeological Sensitivity to Ghostly Presence. 2009. 228p. pap. 15.95 *(978-1-4389-5157-7(4))* AuthorHouse.

Jones, R. E. & Sharpe, L. Going over Old Ground: Perspectives on Archaeological Geophysical & Geochemical Survey in Scotland: Proceedings of a Conference Held at the Department of Archaeology, University of Glasgow, Scotland, August 2003. 2006. (Bar S Ser.). (Illus.). ix, 256p. (C). pap. 100.00 *(978-1-84171-955-9(2))* British Archaeological Reports Ltd. GBR. Dist: Brown, David Bk. Co., The.

Kamermans, H., et al, eds. Archaeological Prediction & Risk Management: Alternatives to Current Practice. 2010. (Archaeological Studies Leiden University Ser.). (Illus.). 162p. pap. *(978-90-8728-067-3(X),* Leiden Univ. Pr.) Amsterdam Univ. Pr.

Kansa, Eric C., et al, eds. Archaeology 2.0: New Tools for Communication & Collaboration. 2011. (Cotsen Digital Archaeology Ser.). (ENG.). 295p. (C). pap. 39.95 ***(978-1-931745-85-7(4))*** Cotsen Institute of Archaeology at UCLA.

Kehoe, Alice Beck. Controversies in Archaeology. 2008. (ENG., Illus.). 256p. (C). 89.00 *(978-1-59874-061-5(X))*; pap. 36.95 *(978-1-59874-062-2(8))* Left Coast Pr., Inc.

Khakhutaishvili, David A. The Manufacture of Iron in Ancient Colchis. 2009. (Bar S Ser.). (Illus.). 132p. (C). 75.00 *(978-1-4073-0389-5(9))* British Archaeological Reports Ltd. GBR. Dist: Brown, David Bk. Co., The.

Killion, Thomas W. Opening Archaeology: Repatriation's Impact on Contemporary Research & Practice. 2008. (School for Advanced Research Advanced Seminar Ser.). (C). pap. 29.95 *(978-1-930618-93-0(X))* School for Advanced Research Pr./SAR Pr.

Kipfer, Barbara Ann. The Archaeologist's Fieldwork Companion. 2006. (ENG., Illus.). 488p. 108.95 *(978-1-4051-1885-9(7))*; pap. 45.95 *(978-1-4051-1886-6(5))* Wiley, John & Sons, Inc. (Wiley-Blackwell).

Kohler, Timothy A. & Leeuw, Sander Ernst van der. The Model-Based Archaeology of Socionatural Systems. 2007. (Illus.). pap. 34.95 *(978-1-930618-87-9(5))* School for Advanced Research Pr./SAR Pr.

Lawall, Mark L. & Lund, John, eds. Pottery in the Archaeological Record: Greece & Beyond. Acts on the International Colloquium held at the Danish & Canadian Institutes in Athens, June 20-22 2008. 2011. (Gosta Enbom Monographs). (ENG., Illus.). 168p. (C). 40.00 ***(978-87-7934-587-4(5))*** Aarhus Universitetsforlag DNK. Dist: ISD.

Leonard, Robert D. & Jones, George T., eds. Quantifying Diversity in Archaeology. 2009. (New Directions in Archaeology Ser.). (ENG., Illus.). 172p. pap. 31.99 *(978-0-521-10850-8(0))* Cambridge Univ. Pr.

Liebmann, Matthew. Archaeology & the Postcolonial Critique. 2010. (Archaeology in Society Ser.). (ENG.). 274p. pap. 29.95 *(978-0-7591-1005-2(0))* AltaMira Pr.

Little, Barbara J. Historical Archaeology: Why the Past Matters. 2007. (ENG., Illus.). 208p. (C). 84.95 *(978-1-59874-022-6(9))*; pap. 24.95 *(978-1-59874-023-3(7))* Left Coast Pr., Inc.

Lock, Gary R. Confronting Scale in Archaeology. 2007. spiral bd. 39.95 *(978-0-387-75701-8(5)*, 0387757015) Springer.

Longo, Laura M., et al, eds. 'Prehistoric Technology' 40 Years Later: Functional Studies & the Russian Legacy. 2008. (Bar S Ser.). (Illus.). 557p. (C). 182.50 *(978-1-4073-0271-3(X))* British Archaeological Reports Ltd. GBR. Dist: Brown, David Bk. Co., The.

Lucas, Gavin. Understanding the Archaeological Record. 2012. (ENG., Illus.). (C). 320p. 99.00 ***(978-1-107-01026-0(8))***; 314p. pap. 32.99 ***(978-0-521-27969-7(0))*** Cambridge Univ. Pr.

Lycett, Stephen & Chauhan, Parth R., eds. New Perspectives on Old Stones: Analytical Approaches to Paleolithic Technologies. 2010. (ENG., Illus.). viii, 345p. 169.00 *(978-1-4419-6860-9(1)*, 1441968601) Springer.

Lyman, R. Lee. Quantitative Paleozoology. 2008. (Cambridge Manuals in Archaeology Ser.). (ENG., Illus.). 372p. (C). 85.00 *(978-0-521-88749-6(6))*; pap. 30.99 *(978-0-521-71536-2(9))* Cambridge Univ. Pr.

Malainey, Mary E. A Consumer's Guide to Archaeological Science: Analytical Techniques. 2011. (Illus.). xx, 603p. E-Book *(978-1-4419-5704-7(9))* Springer.

Mark Aldenderfer Staff. Handbook of Gis in Archaeology - Hardback (Series: Equinox Handbooks in Anthropological Archaeology) 2013. (Equinox handbooks in anthro Arch Ser.). (ENG., Illus.). 286p. (C). 150.00 *(978-1-904768-62-3(8))* Equinox Publishing Ltd. GBR. Dist: ISD.

Mark Aldenderfer Staff & Aldenderfer, Mark S. Handbook of Gis in Archaeology - Paperback (Series: Equinox Handbooks in Anthropological Archaeology) 2013. (Equinox handbooks in anthro Arch Ser.). (ENG., Illus.). 288p. (C). pap. 39.95 *(978-1-904768-63-0(6))* Equinox Publishing Ltd. GBR. Dist: ISD.

Martinón-Torres, Marcos & Rehren, Thilo, eds. Archaeology, History & Science: Integrating Approaches to Ancient Materials. 2008. (Univ Col London Inst Arch Pub Ser.). (ENG., Illus.). 218p. 94.00 *(978-1-59874-340-1(6))* Left Coast Pr., Inc.

Martinon-Torres, Marcos & Rehren, Thilo, eds. Archaeology, History, & Science: Integrating Approaches to Ancient Materials. 2009. (University College London Institute of Archaeology Publications). (ENG.). 218p. pap. 36.95 *(978-1-59874-350-0(3))* Left Coast Pr., Inc.

Matsumura, Shuichi, et al, eds. Simulations, Genetics & Human Prehistory. 2008. (McDonald Institute Monographs Ser.). 240p. 50.00 *(978-1-902937-45-8(7))* McDonald Institute for Archaeological Research GBR. Dist: Brown, David Bk. Co., The.

Miroff, Laurie E. & Knapp, Timothy D., eds. Iroquoian Archaeology & Analytic Scale. 2007. (ENG.). 328p. 48.00 *(978-1-57233-573-8(4))* Univ. of Tennessee Pr.

Misiano-Genovese, Richard. Excavations. 2007. (ENG.). 48p. pap. *(978-0-615-17661-1(5))* La Belle Inutile Editions.

Morse, Dan F. & Morse, Phyllis A. Archaeology of the Central Mississippi Valley. 2nd ed. 2009. (ENG.). 366p. pap. 36.00 *(978-0-8173-5577-7(4))* Univ. of Alabama Pr.

Mortensen, Lena & Hollowell, Julie, eds. Ethnographies & Archaeologies: Iterations of the Past. 2009. (Cultural Heritage Studies). (ENG., Illus.). 320p. 69.95 *(978-0-8130-3366-2(7))* Univ. Pr. of Florida.

Muckle, Robert, ed. Reading Archaeology: An Introduction. 2007. (ENG., Illus.). 368p. pap. *(979-1-55111-876-5(9))* Univ. of Toronto Pr.

Muscio, Hernan Juan & López, Gabriel Eduardo Jose. Theoretical & Methodological Issues in Evolutionary Archaeology: Toward an Unified Darwinian Paradigm. Muscio, Hernan Juan & López, Gabriel Eduardo Jose, eds. 2009. (Bar S Ser.). (FRE & ENG., Illus.). 110p. (C). pap. 75.00 *(978-1-4073-0398-7(8))* British Archaeological Reports Ltd. GBR. Dist: Brown, David Bk. Co., The.

Neustupny, Evzen & Neustupný, Evzen. Archaeological Method. 2009. (ENG.). 204p. pap. 33.99 *(978-0-521-11588-9(4))* Cambridge Univ. Pr.

Owens, Lawrence Stewart & Tassie, Geoffrey John. Standards of Archaeological Excavation: A Fieldguide to the Methodology, Recording Techniques & Conventions. 2010. (Egyptian Cultural Heritage Organisation monograph Ser.). (ENG., Illus.). 600p. (C). pap. 80.00 *(978-1-906137-17-5(X))* Golden Hse. Pubns. GBR. Dist: Brown, David Bk. Co., The.

Papaodysseus, Constantin, ed. Pattern Recognition & Signal Processing in Archaeometry: Mathematical & Computational Solutions for Archaeology. 2011. 357p. 195.00 *(978-1-60960-786-9(4)*, Information Science Reference) IGI Global.

Peterson, Sarah E. Retrieval of Materials with Water Separation Machines. 2009. (Instap archaeological excavation Manual Ser.). (ENG.). 27p. (C). pap. 9.95 *(978-1-931534-53-6(5))* Institute for Aegean Prehistory Pr.

—Thin-Section Petrography of Ceramic Materials. 2009. (Instap archaeological excavation Manual Ser.). (ENG.). 27p. (C). pap. 9.95 *(978-1-931534-55-0(1))* Institute for Aegean Prehistory Pr.

Pezzati, Luca & Salimbeni, Renzo. O3a: Optics for Arts, Architecture, & Archaeology III. 2011. (Proceedings of SPIE Ser.). 248p. pap. 80.00 ***(978-0-8194-8680-6(9))*** SPIE.

Phakorelles, Giorgos, et al. Proceedings of the 4th Symposium of the Hellenic Society for Archaeometry: National Hellenic Research Foundation, Athens, 28-31 May 2003. 2008. (Bar S Ser.). (ENG., Illus.). 638p. (C). pap. 175.00 *(978-1-4073-0188-4(8))* British Archaeological Reports Ltd. GBR. Dist: Brown, David Bk. Co., The.

Plog, Stephen. Stylistic Variation in Prehistoric Ceramics: Design Analysis in the American Southwest. 2008. (New Studies in Archaeology Ser.). (ENG., Illus.). 172p. pap. 39.99 *(978-0-521-07033-1(3))* Cambridge Univ. Pr.

Pollard, Mark, et al. Analytical Chemistry in Archaeology. 2007. (Cambridge Manuals in Archaeology Ser.). (ENG., Illus.). 418p. (C). 124.00 *(978-0-521-65209-4(X))*; per. 57.00 *(978-0-521-65572-9(2))* Cambridge Univ. Pr.

Porter, Anne. Mobile Pastoralism & the Formation of near Eastern Civilizations: Weaving Together Society. 2012. (ENG., Illus.). 400p. 99.00 ***(978-0-521-76443-8(2))*** Cambridge Univ. Pr.

Praetzellis, Adrian. Death by Theory: A Tale of Mystery & Archaeological Theory. 2011. (ENG.). 198p. 60.00 *(978-0-7591-1957-4(0))* 2011. (ENG.). 198p. pap. 21.95 *(978-0-7591-1958-1(9))* 2010. *(978-0-7591-1959-8(7))* AltaMira Pr.

Prag, John. Making Faces: Using Forensic & Archaeological Evidence. 2007. (Illus.). 256p. reprint ed. pap. 20.00 *(978-1-4223-9020-7(9))* DIANE Publishing Co.

Preucel, Robert W. Archaeological Semiotics. 2010. (Social Archaeology Ser.: 5). (ENG., Illus.). 352p. pap. 43.95 *(978-1-4051-9913-1(X)*, Wiley-Blackwell) Wiley, John & Sons, Inc.

Price, T. Douglas & Burton, James H. An Introduction to Archaeological Chemistry. (ENG., Illus.). xxxii, 311p. 2012. pap. 49.95 ***(978-1-4614-3302-6(9)***, 1461433029) 2010. 169.00 *(978-1-4419-6375-8(8)*, 1441963758) Springer.

Quinn, Patrick Sean & Day, Peter Martin. Archaeological Ceramics in Thin Section: A colour Guide. 2012. (ENG., Illus.). x, 190p. 139.00 *(978-3-642-15466-9(2)*, 3642154662) Springer.

Read, Dwight W. Artifact Classification: A Conceptual & Methodological Approach. (ENG., Illus.). 363p. 2009. pap. 34.95 *(978-1-59874-103-2(9))* 2007. 89.00 *(978-1-59874-102-5(0))* Left Coast Pr., Inc.

Renfrew, Colin & Bahn, Paul. Archaeology Essentials: Theories, Methods, & Practice. 2nd ed. 2011. (ENG., Illus.). 336p. (C). pap. 50.00 net. *(978-0-500-28912-9(3)*, 528912) Thames & Hudson.

Rots, Veerle. Prehension & Hafting Traces on Flint Tools: A Methodology. 2010. 304p. 89.50 *(978-90-5867-801-0(6))* Leuven Univ. Pr. BEL. Dist: Cornell Univ. Pr.

Sabloff, Jeremy A. Archaeology Matters: Action Archaeology in the Modern World. 2008. (Key Questions in Anthropology Ser.). (ENG., Illus.). 152p. (C). 79.00 *(978-1-59874-088-2(1))*; pap. 22.95 *(978-1-59874-089-9(X))* Left Coast Pr., Inc.

Salimbeni, Renzo & Pezzati, Luca. O3A: Optics for Arts, Architecture, & Archaeology II: 17-18 June 2009, Munich, Germany. 2009. (Proceedings of SPIE Ser.). (Illus.). 318p. pap. 80.00 ***(978-0-8194-7674-6(9))*** SPIE.

Salimbeni, Renzo, et al. O3A: Optics for Arts, Architecture, & Archaeology: 20-22 June 2007, Munich, Germany. 2007. (Proceedings of SPIE Ser.). (Illus.). 390p. pap. 105.00 *(978-0-8194-6760-7(X))* SPIE.

Sanford, Robert, et al. Cultural Resources Archaeology: An Introduction. 2nd ed. 2010. (ENG.). 274p. pap. 34.95 *(978-0-7591-1846-1(9))* AltaMira Pr.

Sanford, Robert M., et al. Cultural Resources Archaeology: An Introduction. 2nd ed. 2010. (ENG.). 274p. 90.00 *(978-0-7591-1845-4(0))* AltaMira Pr.

Schiffer, Michael B. Studying Technological Change: A Behavioral Approach. 2011. (Foundations of Archaeological Inquiry Ser.). (ENG., Illus.). 240p. pap. 45.00 *(978-1-60781-136-7(7))* Univ. of Utah Pr.

Schiffer, Michael Brian. Behavioral Archaeology: Principles & Practice. 2010. (Equinox handbooks in anthro Arch Ser.). (ENG., Illus.). 230p. (C). 150.00 *(978-1-84553-287-1(2))* Equinox Publishing Ltd. GBR. Dist: ISD.

—Behavioral Archaeology: Principles & Practice. 2010. (Equinox handbooks in anthro Arch Ser.). (ENG., Illus.). 230p. (C). pap. 45.00 *(978-1-84553-288-8(0))* Equinox Publishing Ltd. GBR. Dist: ISD.

Schroeder, H. Crossing Frontiers: The Opportunities & Challenges of Interdisciplinary Approaches to Archaeology: Proceedings of a Conference Held at the University of Oxford, 25-26 June 2005. Schroeder, H. et al, eds. 2007. (Oxford University School of Archaeology Monograph Ser.). (Illus.). 160p. (C). 60.00 *(978-0-9549627-7-7(X))* Oxford Univ. Schl. of Archaeology GER. Dist: Brown, David Bk. Co., The.

Schurmans, Utsav & De Bie, Mare, eds. 2007 Fitting Rocks: Lithic Refitting Examined. 2007. (BAR International Ser.: Vol. 1596). (Illus.). 118p. 77.50 *(978-1-4073-0012-2(1))* Archaeopress GBR. Dist: Brown, David Bk. Co., The.

Seddon, Matthew T., et al. Archaeology in 3D: Deciphering Buried Sites in the Western U.S. 2011. pap. *(978-0-932839-41-1(X))* Society for American Archaeology.

Shankland, David. Archaeology & Anthropology: Past, Present & Future. 2012. (Association of Social Anthropologists Monographs). (ENG.). 256p. 99.95 ***(978-1-84788-966-9(2))*** Berg Pubs. GBR. Dist: Macmillan.

Shanks, Michael. The Archaeological Imagination. 2012. E-Book ***(973-1-61132-784-7(9))***; (ENG.). 167p. (C). lib. bdg. 84.95 *(973-1-59874-361-6(9))* Left Coast Pr., Inc.

Shortland, Andrew, et al, eds. From Mine to Microscope: Advances in the Study of Ancient Technology. 2009. (ENG., Illus.). 246p. (C). 120.00 *(978-1-84217-259-9(X))* Oxbow Bks., Ltd. GBR. Dist: Brown, David Bk. Co., The.

Skibo, James M. Archaeological Anthropology: Perspectives on Method & Theory. 2007. (ENG., Illus.). 320p. 55.00 *(978-0-8165-2517-1(X))* Univ. of Arizona Pr.

Smith, Claire & Burke, Heather. Digging It up down Under: A Practical Guide to Doing Archaeology in Australia. 2007. (World Archaeological Congress Cultural Heritage Manual Ser.). (Illus.). 352p. per. 39.95 *(978-0-387-75700-1(7)*, 0387757007) Springer.

Smith, Laurajane & Waterton, Emma. Heritage, Communities & Archaeology. 2011. (Duckworth Debates in Archaeology Ser.). (Illus.). 144p. pap. 24.95 *(978-0-7156-3681-7(2))* Duckworth Publishers GBR. Dist: International Publishers Marketing.

Sorensen. Heritage Studies. 2009. (ENG., Illus.). 360p. (C). 115.00 *(978-0-415-43184-2(0))*; pap. 41.95 *(978-0-415-43185-9(9))* Routledge.

Spriggs, Matthew. Marxist Perspectives in Archaeology. 2009. (New Directions in Archaeology Ser.). (ENG.). 168p. pap. 31.99 *(978-0-521-10927-7(2))* Cambridge Univ. Pr.

Stahl, Peter W., ed. Archaeology in the Lowland American Tropics: Current Analytical Methods & Applications. 2006. (ENG.). 332p. pap. 69.00 *(978-0-521-02738-0(1))* Cambridge Univ. Pr.

Sutton, Mark Q., et al. Archaeology: The Science of the Human Past. 3rd ed. 2007. (ENG., Illus.). 464p. (C). per. 116.33 *(978-0-205-57237-3(5))* Allyn & Bacon, Inc.

Thomson, Roy, ed. Leather Tanneries: The Archaeological Evidence. 2011. (ENG., Illus.). 160p. pap. 75.00 *(978-1-904982-61-6(1))* Archetype Pubns. GBR. Dist: National Bk. Network.

Torrence, Robin. Production & Exchange of Stone Tools: Prehistoric Obsidian in the Aegean. 2009. (New Studies in Archaeology Ser.). (ENG.). 272p. (C). pap. 36.99 *(978-0-521-10507-1(2))* Cambridge Univ. Pr.

Trigger, Bruce G. Artifacts & Ideas: Essays in Archaeology. 2007. (ENG.). 253p. (gr. 11). pap. 29.95 *(978-1-4128-0650-3(X))* Transaction Pubs.

Tuniz, Claudio. Science for Cultural Heritage: Technological Innovation & Case Studies in Marine & Land Archaeology in the Adriatic Region & Inland. 2010. 300p. 111.00 *(978-981-4307-06-2(8))* World Scientific Publishing Co., Inc.

Turbanti-Memmi, Isabella, ed. Proceedings of the 37th International Symposium on Archaeometry. 2011. (ENG.). xlv, 662p. 399.00 *(978-3-642-14677-0(5)*, 3642146775) Springer.

Unger, A., et al. Conservation of Wood Artifacts: A Handbook. 2010. (Natural Science in Archaeology Ser.). (Illus.). xvii, 578p. pap. 439.00 *(978-3-642-07480-6(4)*, 3642074804) Springer.

Van Beek, Gus W. & Van Beek, Ora. Glorious Mud! Ancient & Contemporary Earthen Design & Construction in North Africa, Western Europe, the near East, & Southwest Asia. 2007. (ENG.). 560p. 99.95 *(978-0-9788460-0-8(1))* Smithsonian Institution Scholarly Pr.

Velho, Alexandra & Kamermans, Hans, eds. Technology & Methodology for Archaeological Practice: Practical Applications for the Past Reconstruction. 2009. (Bar S Ser.). (FRE & ENG., Illus.). 135p. (C). pap. 82.50 *(978-1-4073-0606-3(5))* British Archaeological Reports Ltd. GBR. Dist: Brown, David Bk. Co., The.

Verhagen, Philip. Case Studies in Archaeological Predictive Modeling. 2007. (Archaeological Studies Leiden University Ser.). 256p. pap. *(978-90-8728-007-9(6)*, Leiden Univ. Pr.) Amsterdam Univ. Pr.

Wagner, P. Archaeometry '90. 847p. 131.79 *(978-3-7643-2522-0(4))* Springer.

Weiner, Stephen. Microarchaeology: Beyond the Visible Archaeological Record. 2010. (ENG., Illus.). 414p. (C). 95.00 *(978-0-521-88003-9(3))*; pap. 36.99 *(978-0-521-70584-4(3))* Cambridge Univ. Pr.

Welsh, Tom. Local History on the Ground. 2009. (ENG., Illus.). 160p. pap. 29.95 *(978-0-7524-4798-8(X))* History Pr. Ltd., The GBR. Dist: Independent Pubs. Group.

Whimster, Rowan. The New Antiquarians: 50 Years of Archaeological Innovation in Wessex. 2011. (CBA Research Report). (Illus.). 234p. (C). pap. 40.00 *(978-1-902771-85-4(0))* Council for British Archaeology GBR. Dist: Brown, David Bk. Co., The.

Whittle, Alasdair. Problems in Neolithic Archaeology. 2008. (New Studies in Archaeology Ser.). (ENG., Illus.). 248p. pap. 36.00 *(978-0-521-10389-3(4))* Cambridge Univ. Pr.

Willems, Willem J. H. & Van Den Dries, Monique H., eds. Quality Management in Archaeology. 2007. (Illus.). 159p. per. 56.00 *(978-1-84217-275-9(1))* Oxbow Bks., Ltd. GBR. Dist: Brown, David Bk. Co., The.

Williams, Emily & Peachey, Claire, eds. The Conservation of Archaeological Materials. 2011. (Bar S Ser.). (ENG., Illus.). 244p. (C). pap. 110.00 *(978-1-4073-0657-5(X))* British Archaeological Reports Ltd. GBR. Dist: Brown, David Bk. Co., The.

ARCHAEOLOGY—STUDY AND TEACHING

The Archaeological Fieldwork Opportunities Bulletin (AFOB) 2008. 2008. (Afob Ser.). (Illus.). 224p. pap. 19.95 *(978-1-931909-18-1(0))* Archaeological Institute of America.

Archeology. tchr. ed. 25.95 *(978-0-382-40688-1(5))* Cobblestone Publishing Co.

Baxter, Jane Eva. Archaeological Field Schools: A Guide for Teaching in the Field. 2009. (ENG., Illus.). 192p. pap. 35.00 *(978-1-59874-007-3(5))* Left Coast Pr., Inc.

Burke, Heather & Smith, Claire, eds. Archaeology to Delight & Instruct: Active Learning in the University Classroom. 2007. (One World Archaeology Ser.). (ENG., Illus.). 288p. 94.00 *(978-1-59874-256-5(6))*; pap. 34.95 *(978-1-59874-257-2(4))* Left Coast Pr., Inc.

College of William and Mary, Center for Gifted Education Staff, contrib. by. What a Find ! Analyzing Natural & Cultural Systems: A Problem-Based Learning Unit Designed for 2nd-4th Grade Learners. 2nd ed. 2007. (Illus.). iv, 240p. 57.99 *(978-0-7575-2386-1(2))* Kendall Hunt Publishing Co.

Corbishley, Mike. Archaeology & Education: Principles & Techniques. 2006. 256p. *(978-1-84472-125-2(6))* Taylor & Francis Group.

Cordell, Linda S., et al, eds. Archaeology in America: An Encyclopedia, 4 vols., Set. 2008. (Illus.). 1488p. 499.95 *(978-0-313-33184-8(7)*, GR3184, Greenwood Pr.) Greenwood Publishing Group, Inc.

Galanidou, Nena & Dommasnes, Liv Helga, eds. Telling Children about the Past: An Interdisciplinary Perspective. 2007. (Illus.). 335p. pap. 25.00 *(978-1-879621-40-4(1))* International Monographs in Prehistory.

Grant, Jim, et al. The Archaeology Coursebook: An Introduction to Themes, Sites, Methods & Skills. 3rd rev. ed. 2008. (ENG., Illus.). 480p. 35.95 *(978-0-415-46286-0(X))* Routledge.

Lewis, Nancy Owen & Hagan, Kay Leigh. A Peculiar Alchemy: A Centennial History of the School of American Research, 1907-2007. 2007. (Illus.). 224p. 75.00 *(978-1-930618-84-8(0))*; pap. 34.95 *(978-1-930618-85-5(9))* School for Advanced Research Pr./SAR Pr.

Marquet, Jean-Claude, et al. L'archéologie et L'éducation: De L'école Primaire á L'université = Archaeology & Education: From Primary School to University. 2006. (Bar S Ser.). (ENG & FRE., Illus.). ix,105p. (C). 72.50 *(978-1-84171-940-5(4))* British Archaeological Reports Ltd. GBR. Dist: Brown, David Bk. Co., The.

Millson, Dana C. E., ed. Experimentation & Interpretation: The Use of Experimental Archaeology in the Study of the Past. 2011. (ENG., Illus.). 149p. (C). pap. 60.00 *(978-1-84217-399-2(5))* Oxbow Bks., Ltd. GBR. Dist: Brown, David Bk. Co., The.

Mizoguchi, Koji. Archaeology, Society & Identity in Modern Japan. 2011. (Cambridge Studies in Archaeology Ser.). (ENG., Illus.). 202p. pap. 39.99 *(978-0-521-18779-4(6))* Cambridge Univ. Pr.

Nassaney, Michael S. & Levine, Mary Ann, eds. Archaeology & Community Service Learning. 2009. (Co-published with the Society for Historical Archaeology Ser.). (ENG., Illus.). 256p. 69.95 *(978-0-8130-3351-8(9))* Univ. Pr. of Florida.

Politis, Dionysios, ed. E-Learning Methodologies & Computer Applications in Archaeology. 2008. (Illus.). 300+p. 180.00 *(978-1-59904-759-1(4))* IGI Global.

Sullivan, Mary & Connell, Samuel. A Case Study in Archaeology: A Student's Perspective. 2nd rev. ed. 2012. (ENG.). pap. 32.95 ***(978-0-7575-9776-3(9))*** Kendall Hunt Publishing Co.

ARCHAEOLOGY, BIBLICAL

see Bible—Antiquities

ARCHAEOLOGY, BOTANICAL

see Plant Remains (Archaeology)

ARCHAEOLOGY, CHRISTIAN

see Christian Antiquities

ARCHAEOLOGY, CLASSICAL

see Classical Antiquities

ARCHAEOLOGY, ENVIRONMENTAL

see Environmental Archaeology

ARCHAEOLOGY, INDUSTRIAL

see Industrial Archaeology

ARCHAEOLOGY, MEDIEVAL

Alduc-Le Bagousse, A. & Alduc-Le Bagousse, Armell, eds. Inhumations de prestige ou prestige de l'inhumation? Expressions du pouvoir dans l'au-dela (IVe-XVe Siecle) 2009. (Tables Rondes du Crahm Ser.). (FRE.). 464p. (C). pap. 48.00 *(978-2-902685-67-7(X))* Brepols Pubs. BEL. Dist: Brown, David Bk. Co., The.

Alttoa, Kaur, et al, eds. Castella Maris Baltici, Vols. 3-4. (Illus.). 260p. pap. *(978-83-86206-42-1(X))* Muzeum Zamkowe w Malborku.

Anderson, Sue. A Medieval Cemetery at Mill Lane, Ormesby St Margaret, Norfolk. 2009. (East anglian archaeology Monograph Ser.). (ENG., Illus.). 50p. (C). pap. 18.00 *(978-0-905594-49-1(5))* East Anglian Archaeology GBR. Dist: Brown, David Bk. Co., The.

A

Bateman, Nick, et al. London's Roman Amphitheatre: Guildhall Yard, City of London. 2008. (MoLAS Monograph Ser.). (ENG., Illus.). 259p. (C). 60.00 *(978-1-901992-71-7(3))* Museum of London Archaeology Service GBR. Dist: Brown, David Bk. Co., The.

Beresford, M. W. & Joseph, J. K. S. Medieval England: An Aerial Survey. 2nd ed. 2009. (Cambridge Air Surveys Ser.). (ENG.). 308p. pap. 42.00 *(978-0-521-10936-9(1))* Cambridge Univ. Pr.

Bintliff, John & Stoger, Hanna. Medieval & Post-Medieval Greece: The Corfu Papers. 2009. (Bar S Ser.). (ENG., Illus.). 258p. (C). pap. 115.00 *(978-1-4073-0598-1(0))* British Archaeological Reports Ltd. GBR. Dist: Brown, David Bk. Co., The.

Bluer, Richard & Brigham, Trevor. Roman & Later Development East of the Forum & Cornhill: Excavations at Lloyd's Register, 71 Fenchurch Street, City of London. 2006. (Molas Monograph Ser.). (Illus.). 185p. pap. 42.00 *(978-1-901992-43-4(8))* Museum of London Archaeology Service GBR. Dist: Brown, David Bk. Co., The.

Botár, István. Kövek, Falak, Templomok: Régészeti Kutatások Csík Középkori Templomaiban 2002-2007 Között. 2009. (HUN., Illus.). 110p. *(978-973-665-284-4(X))* Pallas-Akademia.

Brather, Sebastian. Archäologie der westlichen Slawen: Siedlung, Wirtschaft und Gesellschaft im früh- und hochmittelalterlichen Ostmitteleuropa. 2nd ed. 2008. (Reallexikon der Germanischen Altertumskunde - Ergänzungsbände Ser.). (GER., Illus.). XII, 449p. 189.00 *(978-3-11-020609-8(9))* De Gruyter, Walter Inc.

—Zwischen Spätantike und Frühmittelalter: Archäologie des 4. Bis 7. Jahrhunderts Im Westen. 2008. (Reallexikon der Germanischen Altertumskunde - Ergänzungsbände Ser.). (GER., Illus.). VII, 480p. 189.00 *(978-3-11-020049-2(X))* De Gruyter, Walter Inc.

Brather, Sebastian, et al, eds. Historia Archaeologica: Festschrift far Heiko Steuer zum 70. Geburtstag. 2009. (Reallexikon der Germanischen Altertumskunde - Ergänzungsbände Ser.).Tr. of Historia archaeologica. Papers Presented to Heiko Steuer on the Occasion of his 70th Birthday. (GER., XLVII, 764p. Illus.). 280.00 *(978-3-11-022337-8(6))*; 419.00 ***(978-3-11-173996-0(1))*** De Gruyter, Walter Inc.

Briggs, Lawrence Palmer. The Ancient Khmer Empire: Transactions of the American Philosophical Society, V41, Part 1, February 1951. 2011. 300p. 48.95 ***(978-1-258-10377-4(X))*** Literary Licensing, LLC.

Brisbane, Mark, et al, eds. The Archaeology of Medieval Novgorod in Its Wider Context: A Study of Centre/Periphery Relations. 2012. (ENG., Illus.). 350p. (C). 120.00 *(978-1-84217-278-0(6))* Oxbow Bks., Ltd. GBR. Dist: Brown, David Bk. Co., The.

Brorsson, Torbjorn. The Pottery from the Early Medieval Trading Site & Cemetery at Gross Stromkendorf, Lkr. Nordwestmecklenburg: Forschungen zu Gross Stromkendorf III. 2010. (Fruhmittelalterliche Archaologie zwischen Ostsee und Mittelmeer Ser.). (ENG., Illus.). 157p. (C). 50.00 *(978-3-89500-751-4(X))* Reichert, Ludwig Dr. DEU. Dist: Brown, David Bk. Co., The.

Buko, Andrzej. The Archaeology of Early Medieval Poland: Discoveries - Hypotheses - Interpretations. 2007. (East Central & Eastern Europe in the Middle Ages Ser.). (Illus.). 475p. *(978-90-04-16230-3(5))* BRILL.

Carver, M. O. H., ed. The Age of Sutton Hoo: The Seventh Century in North-Western Europe. 2012. (Illus.). 456p. reprint ed. pap. 45.00 *(978-0-85115-361-2(5)*, Boydell Press) Boydell & Brewer, Ltd. GBR. Dist: Boydell & Brewer, Inc.

Clark, John, ed. The Medieval Horse & its Equipment, C. 1150-1450. 2nd ed. 2011. (Medieval Finds from Excavations in London Ser.: Volume 5). (Illus.). 202p. pap. 34.95 *(978-1-84383-679-7(3)*, Boydell Press) Boydell & Brewer, Ltd. GBR. Dist: Boydell & Brewer, Inc.

Cowgill, J., et al. Knives & Scabbards. 2011. (Medieval Finds from Excavations in London Ser.: Volume 1). (Illus.). 184p. pap. 34.95 *(978-1-84383-353-6(0)*, Boydell Press) Boydell & Brewer, Ltd. GBR. Dist: Boydell & Brewer, Inc.

Cramp, Rosemary, et al. Aedificia Nova: Studies in Honor of Rosemary Cramp. 2008. (Illus.). xv, 427p. 80.00 *(978-1-58044-110-0(6))* Medieval Institute Pubns.

Driscoll, Stephen T. & Geddes, Jane, eds. Pictish Progress: New Studies on Northern Britain in the Middle Ages. 2010. (Northern World Ser.). (Illus.). 416p. *(978-90-04-18759-7(6))* BRILL.

Duffy, Seán. Medieval Dublin XI: Proceedings of the Friends of Medieval Dublin Symposium 2009. 2011. (Illus.). 342p. pap. 35.00 *(978-1-84682-276-6(9))* Four Courts Pr. IRL. Dist: International Specialized Bk. Services.

Duffy, Seán, ed. Medieval Dublin IX. 2009. (Illus.). 250p. 65.00 *(978-1-84682-171-4(1))* Four Courts Pr. IRL. Dist: International Specialized Bk. Services.

—Medieval Dublin IX: Proceedings of the Friends of Medieval Dublin Symposium 2007. 2009. (Illus.). 250p. pap. 35.00 *(978-1-84682-172-1(X))* Four Courts Pr. IRL. Dist: International Specialized Bk. Services.

—Medieval Dublin VIII. 2008. (Illus.). 328p. pap. 35.00 *(978-1-84682-043-4(X))* Four Courts Pr. IRL. Dist: International Specialized Bk. Services.

—Medieval Dublin VIII: Proceedings of the Friends of Medieval Dublin Symposium 2006. 2008. (Illus.). 328p. 65.00 *(978-1-84682-042-7(1))* Four Courts Pr. IRL. Dist: International Specialized Bk. Services.

Duffy, Sean, ed. Medieval Dublin X. 2010. (Illus.). 326p. 65.00 *(978-1-84682-220-9(3))* Four Courts Pr. IRL. Dist: International Specialized Bk. Services.

Duffy, Seán, ed. Medieval Dublin X: Proceedings of the Friends of Medieval Dublin Symposium 2008. 2010. (Illus.). 326p. pap. 35.00 *(978-1-84682-221-6(1))* Four Courts Pr. IRL. Dist: International Specialized Bk. Services.

—Medieval Dublin XI: Proceedings of the Friends of Medieval Dublin Symposium 2009. 2011. (Illus.). 342p. 65.00 *(978-1-84682-275-9(0))* Four Courts Pr. IRL. Dist: International Specialized Bk. Services.

Egan, Geoff & Pritchard, Frances. Dress Accessories, C.1150-C.1450. 2010. (Medieval Finds from Excavations in London Ser.: Volume 3). (Illus.). 438p. pap. 34.95 *(978-1-84383-351-2(4)*, Boydell Press) Boydell & Brewer, Ltd. GBR. Dist: Boydell & Brewer, Inc.

Engberg, Nils. Archaeology of Medieval Towns in the Baltic & North Sea Area. 2009. (Illus.). 218p. 42.00 *(978-87-7602-131-3(9))* Univ. Pr. of Southern Denmark DNK. Dist: International Specialized Bk. Services.

Finch, Jonathan & Giles, Katherine. Estate Landscapes: Design, Improvement & Power in the Post-Medieval Landscape - Papers Given at the Estate Landscapes Conference, April 2003, Hosted by the Society for Post-Medieval Archaeology. Finch, Jonathan & Giles, Kate, eds. 2008. (Society for Post Medieval Archaeology Monograph Ser.: Volume 4). (Illus.). 248p. 90.00 *(978-1-84383-370-3(0)*, Boydell Press) Boydell & Brewer, Ltd. GBR. Dist: Boydell & Brewer, Inc.

Flatman, Joe. The Illuminated Ark: Interrogating Evidence from Manuscript Illuminations & Archaeological Remains for Medieval Vessels. 2007. (ENG., Illus.). 242p. (C). pap. 125.00 *(978-1-4073-0058-0(X))* British Archaeological Reports Ltd. GBR. Dist: Brown, David Bk. Co., The.

Gilchrist, Roberta & Reynolds, Andrew, eds. Reflections: 50 Years of Medieval Archaeology, 1957-2007. 2009. (Society for medieval archaeology Monographs). (ENG., Illus.). 537p. (C). 138.00 *(978-1-906540-71-5(3))* Maney Publishing GBR. Dist: Brown, David Bk. Co., The.

Graham-Campbell, James & Valor, Magdalena, eds. The Archaeology of Medieval Europe, Vol. 1: The Eighth to Twelfth Centuries AD, 2 vols. 2007. (ENG., Illus.). 450p. (C). 79.00 *(978-87-7934-288-0(4))*; pap. 52.95 *(978-87-7934-290-3(6))* Aarhus Universitetsforlag DNK. Dist: ISD.

Green, Adrian & Leech, Roger, eds. Cities in the World, 1500-2000. 2006. (Society for Post-Medieval Archaeology Monograph Ser.: Vol. 3). (ENG., Illus.). 336p. (C). 135.00 *(978-1-904350-02-6(X))* Maney Publishing GBR. Dist: Brown, David Bk. Co., The.

Grew, Francis, et al. Shoes & Pattens. 2nd ed. 2011. (Medieval Finds from Excavations in London Ser.: Volume 2). (Illus.). 152p. per. 34.95 *(978-1-84383-238-6(0))* Boydell & Brewer, Inc.

Hansson, Martin. Aristocratic Landscape: Spatial Ideology of the Medieval Aristocracy. 2006. (Lund Studies in Historical Archaeology: Vol. 2). (Illus.). 223p. pap. 85.00 *(978-91-22-02154-4(X))* Almqvist & Wiksell International SWE. Dist: Coronet Bks.

Haour, Anne. Rulers, Warriors, Traders, Clerics: The Central Sahel & the North Sea, 800-1500. 2008. (British Academy Postdoctoral Fellowship Monographs). (ENG., Illus.). 200p. 74.00 *(978-0-19-726411-9(5))* Oxford Univ. Pr., Inc.

Heffernan, Thomas F. Wood Quay: The Clash over Dublin's Viking Past. 2011. (ENG.). 182p. pap. 19.95 ***(978-0-292-72977-3(4))*** Univ. of Texas Pr.

Higham, Nicholas J. & Ryan, Martin J., eds. The Landscape Archaeology of Anglo-Saxon England. 2010. (Pubns Manchester Centre for Anglo-Saxon Studies: Volume 9). (Illus.). 244p. 99.00 *(978-1-84383-582-0(7)*, Boydell Press) Boydell & Brewer, Ltd. GBR. Dist: Boydell & Brewer, Inc.

Ince, Gillian & Ballantyne, Andrew. Paliochora on Kythera: Survey & Interpretation. 2007. (Bar S Ser.). (Illus.). 119p. (C). 62.50 *(978-1-4073-0148-8(9))* British Archaeological Reports Ltd. GBR. Dist: Brown, David Bk. Co., The.

Jakob, Tina. Prevalence & Patterns of Disease in Early Medieval Populations: A Comparison of Skeletal Samples of the 5th-8th Centuries A.D. from Britain & Southwestern Germany. 2009. (Bar S Ser.). (ENG., Illus.). 220p. (C). pap. 115.00 *(978-1-4073-0456-4(9))* British Archaeological Reports Ltd. GBR. Dist: Brown, David Bk. Co., The.

Jones, Richard & Page, Mark. Medieval Villages in an English Landscape. 2006. (Illus.). 27p. (C). 100.00 *(978-1-905119-08-0(9))* Windgather Pr. GBR. Dist: Brown, David Bk. Co., The.

—Medieval Villages in an English Landscape: Beginnings & Ends. 2006. (Illus.). 270p. per. 39.95 *(978-1-905119-09-7(7))* Windgather Pr. GBR. Dist: Brown, David Bk. Co., The.

King, Chris & Sayer, Duncan, eds. The Archaeology of Post-Medieval Religion. 2011. (Society for Post Medieval Archaeology Monograph Ser.: Volume 6). (Illus.). 304p. 50.00 *(978-1-84383-693-3(9)*, Boydell Press) Boydell & Brewer, Ltd. GBR. Dist: Boydell & Brewer, Inc.

Liddiard, Rober, ed. The Medieval Park: New Perspectives. 2007. (Illus.). 256p. pap. 49.95 *(978-1-905119-16-5(X))* Windgather Pr. GBR. Dist: Brown, David Bk. Co., The.

Lyon, J. & Lyon, Jo. Within These Walls: Roman & Medieval Defences North of Newgate at the Merrill Lynch Financial Centre, City of London. 2007. (MoLAS Monograph Ser.). (Illus.). (C). pap. 50.00 *(978-1-901992-68-7(3))* Museum of London Archaeology Service GBR. Dist: Brown, David Bk. Co., The.

Maltby, Mark, ed. Animals & Archaeology in Northern Mediev. 2012. (ENG., Illus.). 300p. (C). 120.00 *(978-1-84217-277-3(8))* Oxbow Bks., Ltd. GBR. Dist: Brown, David Bk. Co., The.

McKasey, John. Ancient Chapels & Churches in Wales. 2007. (ENG., Illus.). 72p. pap. 11.95 *(978-0-86243-665-0(6)*, Virago Press) Y Lolfa GBR. Dist: Dufour Editions, Inc.

Mehofer, Mathias & Pohl, Walter, eds. Archaoelogy of Identity/ Archaologie der Identitat. 2010. (Forschungen zur Geschichte des Mittelalters Ser.). (ENG & GER.). 325p. (C). pap. 77.00 *(978-3-7001-6502-6(1))* Austrian Academy of Sciences Press AUT. Dist: Brown, David Bk. Co., The.

Meier, Dirk. Seafarers, Merchants & Pirates in the Middle Ages. McGeoch, Angus, tr. from GER. 2006. (Illus.). 192p. 34.95 *(978-1-84383-237-9(2))* Boydell & Brewer, Inc.

Millson, Dana C. E., ed. Experimentation & Interpretation: The Use of Experimental Archaeology in the Study of the Past. 2011. (ENG., Illus.). 149p. (C). pap. 60.00 *(978-1-84217-399-2(5))* Oxbow Bks., Ltd. GBR. Dist: Brown, David Bk. Co., The.

Morigi, Tony, et al. The Archaeology of the Gravel Terraces of the Upper & Middle Thames: Early Human Occupation to 1500 BC, 2 vols. Dodd, Anne, ed. 2011. (Thames Valley Landscapes Monograph Ser.). (ENG., Illus.). 521p. (C). 70.00 *(978-0-9549627-8-4(8))* Oxford Archaeological Unit GBR. Dist: Brown, David Bk. Co., The.

Norton, Andrew. Excavations of Medieval & Early Post-Med. 2007. (ENG.). (C). pap. 15.00 *(978-0-904220-41-4(9))* Oxford Univ. Schl. of Archaeology GBR. Dist: Brown, David Bk. Co., The.

Oosthuizen, Susan. Landscapes Decoded: The Origins & Development of Cambridgeshire's Medieval Fields. Fox, Harold & Goose, Nigel, eds. 2007. (ENG., Illus.). 160p. per. 29.95 *(978-1-902806-58-7(1))* Univ. of Hertfordshire Pr. GBR. Dist: Independent Pubs. Group.

Pelzer, C., et al, eds. Oursi Hu-beero: A Medieval House Complex in Burkina Faso, West Africa. 2011. (ENG., Illus.). 285p. (C). pap. 80.00 ***(978-90-8890-067-9(1))*** Sidestone Pr. NLD. Dist: Brown, David Bk. Co., The.

Phillips, Neil. Earthwork Castles of Gwent & Ergyng AD 1050-1250. 2006. (Bar S Ser.). (Illus.). ix,258p. (C). 100.00 *(978-1-84171-977-1(3))* British Archaeological Reports Ltd. GBR. Dist: Brown, David Bk. Co., The.

Pieper, Katharina. Der mudejare Bauschmuck im mittelalterlichen Aragon am Beispiel der Stuckfenster: Eine Untersuchung der spanisch-islamischen und christlichen Elemente in Komposition und Einzelformen. 2009. (Iberia Archaeologica Ser.). (GER & SPA.). 319p. (C). 85.00 *(978-3-8053-3982-7(8))* Zabern, Philipp von Verlag, GmbH DEU. Dist: Brown, David Bk. Co., The.

Pollington, Stephen. Anglo-Saxon Art, Myth & Material Culture from the 4th to 7th Century: Wayland's Work. 2010. (ENG., Illus.). 542p. (C). 170.00 *(978-1-898281-56-6(4))* Anglo-Saxon Bks. GBR. Dist: Brown, David Bk. Co., The.

Potterton, Michael & Seaver, Matthew, eds. Uncovering Medieval Trim. 2009. (Illus.). 384p. 74.50 *(978-1-84682-169-1(X))* Four Courts Pr. IRL. Dist: International Specialized Bk. Services.

Pryor, Francis. Britain in the Middle Ages: An Archaeological History. 2007. (ENG., Illus.). 320p. per. 17.95 *(978-0-00-720362-8(4))* HarperCollins Pubs. Ltd. GBR. Dist: Independent Pubs. Group.

Quiroga, Jorge & Martínez Tejera, A. M. Morir en el Mediterraneo Medieval: Actas Del III Congreso Internacional de Arqueologia, Arte e Historia de la Antigüedad Tardia y Alta Edad Media Peninsular Celebrado en la Universidad Autonoma de Madrid (UAM) y en e Museo de Los Origenes de Madrid (Casa de San Isidro) - 17 y 18 Diciembre de 2007. 2009. (SPA., Illus.). 370p. (C). pap. 145.00 *(978-1-4073-0462-5(3))* British Archaeological Reports Ltd. GBR. Dist: Brown, David Bk. Co., The.

Reynolds, Andrew. Anglo-Saxon Deviant Burial Customs. 2009. (Medieval History & Archaeology Ser.). (ENG., Illus.). 340p. 145.00 *(978-0-19-954455-4(7))* Oxford Univ. Pr., Inc.

Rtkai, Stephanie. Bull Ring Uncovered. 2008. (ENG., Illus.). 440p. (C). 70.00 *(978-1-84217-285-8(9))* Oxbow Bks., Ltd. GBR. Dist: Brown, David Bk. Co., The.

Schofield, John. London, 1100-1600: The Archaeology of a Capital City. 2011. (Studies in the Archaeology of Medieval Europe Ser.). (ENG., Illus.). 320p. (C). 115.00 *(978-1-84553-551-3(0))* Equinox Publishing Ltd. GBR. Dist: ISD.

Schofield, John. London, 1100-1600: The Archaeology of the Capital City. 2011. (Studies in the Archaeology of Medieval Europe Ser.). (ENG., Illus.). 320p. (C). pap. 45.00 ***(978-1-908049-72-8(3))*** Equinox Publishing Ltd. GBR. Dist: ISD.

Scull, Christopher. Early Medieval (Late 5th - Early 8th Centuries AD) Cemeteries at Boss Hall & Buttermarket, Ipswich, Suffolk. 2009. (Society for Medieval Archaeology Monograph Ser.). (ENG., Illus.). 376p. (C). 86.00 *(978-1-906540-18-0(7))* Maney Publishing GBR. Dist: Brown, David Bk. Co., The.

Sloane, Barney. The Augustinian nunnery of St Mary Clerkenwell, London: Excavations 1974-96. 2012. (MoLAS Monograph Ser.). (ENG., Illus.). 300p. (C). 54.00 ***(978-1-907586-11-8(3))*** Museum of London Archaeology Service GBR. Dist: Brown, David Bk. Co., The.

Stirland, Ann. Criminals & Paupers: The Graveyard of St Margaret Fyebriggate in combusto, Norwich. 2009. (East anglian archaeology Monograph Ser.). (ENG., Illus.). 54p. (C). pap. 18.00 *(978-0-905594-47-7(9))* Norfolk Museums Service, Archaeology & Environment Div. GBR. Dist: Brown, David Bk. Co., The.

von Susanne Biegert, Herausgegeben, et al. Kontinuitatsfragen: Mittlere Kaiserzeit - Spatantike, Spatantike - Fruhmittelalter. 2006. (Bar S Ser.). (GER., Illus.). 98p. (C). 67.50 *(978-1-84171-904-7(8))* British Archaeological Reports Ltd. GBR. Dist: Brown, David Bk. Co., The.

ARCHAEOLOGY, SUBMARINE

see Underwater Archaeology

ARCHAEOLOGY AND HISTORY

Abicht, Matthew J., et al. Landscapes Through the Lens: Aerial Photographs & the Historic Environment. 2010. (ENG., Illus.). 302p. (C). pap. 90.00 *(978-1-84217-981-9(0))* Oxbow Bks., Ltd. GBR. Dist: Brown, David Bk. Co., The.

Anderson, S., et al. Historic Whithorn: Archaeology & Development. 2010. (Scottish Burgh Survey Ser.). (ENG., Illus.). 156p. (C). pap. 20.00 *(978-1-902777-93-1(X))* Council for British Archaeology GBR. Dist: Brown, David Bk. Co., The.

Archer, Steven & Bartoy, Kevin, eds. Between Dirt & Discussion: Methods, Methodology & Interpretation in Historical Archaeology. 2010. (Illus.). xiv, 235p. pap. 129.00 *(978-1-4419-4166-4(5)*, 1441941665) Springer.

Baram, Uzi & Carroll, Lynda, eds. A Historical Archaeology of the Ottoman Empire: Breaking New Ground. 2010. (Contributions to Global Historical Archaeology Ser.). 282p. pap. 129.00 *(978-1-4419-3332-4(8)*, 1441933328) Springer.

Baugher-Perlin, Sherene & Spencer-Wood, Suzanne M. Archaeology & Preservation of Gendered Landscapes. 2010. (Illus.). xiv, 392p. E-Book 129.00 *(978-1-4419-1501-6(X))* Springer.

Baugher, Sherene & Spencer-Wood, Suzanne M., eds. Archaeology & Preservation of Gendered Landscapes. 2010. (ENG., Illus.). xiv, 275p. 129.00 *(978-1-4419-1500-9(1)*, 1441915001) Springer.

Beck, Colleen M., et al, eds. Matériel Culture: The Archaeology of Twentieth-Century Conflict. 2012. (One World Archaeology Ser.). (ENG.). 348p. (C). pap. 44.95 ***(978-0-415-51076-9(7))*** Routledge.

Beisaw, April M. & Gibb, James G. The Archaeology of Institutional Life. Beisaw, April M. & Gibb, James G., eds. 2nd ed. 2009. (ENG., Illus.). 288p. pap. 28.95 *(978-0-8173-5516-6(2))* Univ. of Alabama Pr.

Beisaw, April M. & Gibb, James G., eds. The Archaeology of Institutional Life. 2nd ed. 2009. (ENG., Illus.). 288p. 52.50 *(978-0-8173-1637-2(X))* Univ. of Alabama Pr.

Blix, Goran & Blix, Göran Magnus. From Paris to Pompeii: French Romanticism & the Cultural Politics of Archaeology. 2008. (Illus.). 320p. (C). 59.95 *(978-0-8122-4136-5(3))* Univ. of Pennsylvania Pr.

Bradley, James W. Before Albany: An Archaeology of Native-Dutch Relations in the Capital Region, 1600-1664. 2007. (Illus.). xvii, 230p. *(978-1-55557-238-9(3))* Univ. of the State of New York at Buffalo, Schl. of Architecture & Planning.

Brighton, Stephen A. Historical Archaeology of the Irish Diaspora: A Transnational Approach. 2009. (ENG.). 49.95 *(978-1-57233-667-4(6))* Univ. of Tennessee Pr.

Brown, Tony. Environment & Aggregate-Related Archaeology. 2009. (ENG., Illus.). 232p. (C). pap. 70.00 *(978-1-905223-02-2(1))* Oxbow Bks., Ltd. GBR. Dist: Brown, David Bk. Co., The.

Bruce, Mary Jaye & Manning, Sturt W. Tree-Rings, Kings & Old World Archaeology & Environment: Papers Presented in Honor of Peter Ian Kuniholm. 2009. (ENG., Illus.). 336p. (C). 100.00 *(978-1-84217-386-2(3))* Oxbow Bks., Ltd. GBR. Dist: Brown, David Bk. Co., The.

Carandini, Andrea. Rome: Day One. 2011. (ENG., Illus.). 184p. 24.95 *(978-0-691-13922-7(9))* Princeton Univ. Pr.

Chelkowski, Peter J. History & Archaeology. 2011. (ENG.). 136p. (gr. 13). 35.00 *(978-1-60781-037-7(9))* Univ. of Utah Pr.

Clark, Bonnie J. On the Edge of Purgatory: An Archaeology of Place in Hispanic Colorado. 2012. (Historical Archaeology of the American West Ser.). (ENG., Illus.). 176p. 45.00 *(978-0-8032-1372-2(7))* Univ. of Nebraska Pr.

Croucher, Sarah K. & Weiss, Lindsay, eds. The Archaeology of Capitalism in Colonial Contexts: Postcolonial Historical Archaeologies. 2011. (Contributions to Global Historical Archaeology Ser.). (ENG., Illus.). xvii, 315p. 169.00 *(978-1-4614-0191-9(7)*, 1461401917) Springer.

Delgado, James P. Gold Rush Port: The Maritime Archaeology of San Francisco's Waterfront. 2009. (ENG., Illus.). 256p. 45.00 *(978-0-520-25580-7(1))* Univ. of California Pr.

Delle, James A. Out of Many, One People: The Historical Archaeology of Colonial Jamaica. Hauser, Mark W. & Armstrong, Douglas V., eds. 2nd ed. 2011. (Caribbean Archaeology & Ethnohistory Ser.). (ENG., Illus.). 344p. pap. 27.50 *(978-0-8173-5648-4(7))* Univ. of Alabama Pr.

Delle, James A., et al. Out of Many, One People: The Historical Archaeology of Colonial Jamaica. 2011. (Illus.). 336p. *(978-0-8173-8530-9(4))* Univ. of Alabama Pr.

Dellino-Musgrave, Virginia. Maritime Archaeology & Social Relations: British Action in the Southern Hemisphere. 2010. (Springer Series in Underwater Archaeology Ser.). (Illus.). xviii, 198p. pap. 129.00 *(978-1-4419-4142-8(8)*, 1441941428) Springer.

Dennison, E. Patricia, et al. Historic Barrhead: Archaeology & Development. 2008. (Scottish Burgh Survey Ser.). (Illus.). 84p. (C). pap. 20.00 *(978-1-902771-69-4(9))* Council for British Archaeology GBR. Dist: Brown, David Bk. Co., The.

Dixon, Kelly J. Boomtown Saloons: Archaeology & History in Virginia City. 2006. (Wilbur S. Shepperson Series in Nevada History Ser.). (ENG., Illus.). 256p. per. 21.95 *(978-0-87417-703-9(0))* Univ. of Nevada Pr.

Dixon, Kelly J., et al, eds. Archaeology of Desperation: Exploring the Donner Party's Alder Creek Camp. 2011. (ENG., Illus.). 384p. (C). 34.95 *(978-0-8061-4210-4(3))* Univ. of Oklahoma Pr.

Dolamore, Mike. Underground Battlefields: Uncovering the Mines & Tunnels of Vimy Ridge & Beaumont Hamel. 2007. (Illus.). 224p. 39.95 *(978-1-84415-486-9(6))* Pen & Sword Bks. Ltd. GBR. Dist: Casemate Pubs. & Bk. Distributors, LLC.

Dueppen, Stephen A. Egalitarian Revolution in the Savanna: The Origins of a West African Political System. 2012. (Approaches to Anthropological Archaeology Ser.). (ENG., Illus.). 364p. (C). 120.00 ***(978-1-908049-20-9(0))*** Equinox Publishing Ltd. GBR. Dist: ISD.

Dyson, Stephen L. Rome: A Living Portrait of an Ancient City. 2010. (Ancient Society & History Ser.). (ENG., Illus.). 488p. (C). (gr. 13-17). 75.00 *(978-0-8018-9253-0(8))*; pap. 35.00 *(978-0-8018-9254-7(6))* Johns Hopkins Univ. Pr.

Fagan, Brian M. Discovery! Unearthing the New Treasures of Archaeology. Fagan, Brian M., ed. 2007. (ENG., Illus.). 256p. 40.00 *(978-0-500-05149-8(6))* Thames & Hudson.

Faulkner, Charles H. The Ramseys at Swan Pond: The Archaeology & History of an East Tennessee Farm. 2008. (ENG., Illus.). 168p. 39.95 *(978-1-57233-609-4(9))* Univ. of Tennessee Pr.

Finneran. The Archaeology of Ethiopia. 2007. (Illus.). CCXLp. 35.95 *(978-0-415-38647-0(0))* Routledge.

Finneran, Niall. The Archaeology of Ethiopia. 2007. (Illus.). XX, 316p. 120.00 *(978-0-415-38646-3(2))* Routledge.

Foot, William. The Battlefields That Nearly Were: Defending England 1940. 2006. (ENG., Illus.). 288p. 39.95 *(978-0-7524-3849-8(2))* History Pr. Ltd.,The GBR. Dist: Independent Pubs. Group.

Frendo, Anthony J. Pre-Exilic Israel, the Hebrew Bible, & Archaeology: Integrating Text & Artefact. 2011. (Library Hebrew Bible/Old Testament Studies). 144p. 120.00 *(978-0-567-41563-9(5)*, T&T Clark Int'l) Continuum International Publishing Group, Ltd. GBR. Dist: National Bk. Network.

Funari, Pedro P., et al, eds. Session C32: Contemporary Issues in Historical Archaeology. 2010. (Bar S Ser.). (FRE & ENG., Illus.). 162p. (C). pap. 87.50 *(978-1-4073-0559-2(X))* British Archaeological Reports Ltd. GBR. Dist: Brown, David Bk. Co., The.

Funari, Pedro Paulo A., et al, eds. Historical Archaeology: Back from the Edge. 2012. (ENG.). 376p. pap. 42.95 ***(978-0-415-51888-8(1))*** Routledge.

Galanidou, Nena & Dommasnes, Liv Helga, eds. Telling Children about the Past: An Interdisciplinary Perspective. 2007. (Illus.). 335p. pap. 25.00 *(978-1-879621-40-4(1))* International Monographs in Prehistory.

Geier, Clarence R., et al, eds. The Historical Archaeology of Military Sites: Method & Topic. 2010. (Illus.). 280p. 50.00 *(978-1-60344-207-7(3))* Texas A&M Univ. Pr.

Grabow, Sven, et al. Which Past, Whose Future? Treatments of the Past at the Start of the 21st Century - An International Perspective - Proceedings of a Conference Held at the University of York, 20-21 May 2005. 2007. (Bar S Ser.). (ENG., Illus.). 175p. (C). pap. 87.50 *(978-1-4073-0047-4(4))* British Archaeological Reports Ltd. GBR. Dist: Brown, David Bk. Co., The.

Haecker, Charles M. & Mauck, Jeffrey G. On the Prairie of Palo Alto: Historical Archaeology of the U. S. -Mexican War Battlefield. 2009. (Clayton Wheat Williams Texas Life Ser.). (ENG., Illus.). 248p. pap. 29.95 *(978-1-60344-158-2(1))* Texas A&M Univ. Pr.

Halsall, Guy. Cemeteries & Society in Merovingian Gaul: Selected Studies in History & Archaeology, 1992-2009. 2009. *(978-90-04-17999-8(2))* BRILL.

Hardesty, Donald L. Mining Archaeology in the American West: A View from the Silver State. 2010. (Historical Archaeology of the American West Ser.). (ENG., Illus.). 240p. 45.00 *(978-0-8032-2440-7(0))* Univ. of Nebraska Pr.

Hardesty, Donald L. & Little, Barbara J. Assessing Site Significance: A Guide for Archaeologists & Historians. 2nd ed. 2009. (Heritage Resource Management Ser.). (ENG.). 254p. 80.00 *(978-0-7591-1126-4(X))*; pap. 29.95 *(978-0-7591-1127-1(8))* AltaMira Pr.

Hardy, Karen, ed. Archaeological Invisibility & Forgotten Knowledge. 2011. (Bar S Ser.). (Illus.). 210p. (C). pap. 100.00 *(978-1-4073-0733-6(9))* British Archaeological Reports Ltd. GBR. Dist: Brown, David Bk. Co., The.

Hicks, Dan. The Garden of the World: An Historical Archaeology of Sugar Landscapes in the Eastern Caribbean. 2011. (Bar S Ser.). (ENG., Illus.). 119p. (C). pap. 75.00 *(978-1-4073-0046-7(6))* British Archaeological Reports Ltd. GBR. Dist: Brown, David Bk. Co., The.

Hicks, Dan, et al, eds. Envisioning Landscape: Situations & Standpoints in Archaeology & Heritage. (One World Archaeology Ser.). (ENG., Illus.). 304p. 2009. pap. 34.95 *(978-1-59874-282-4(5))* 2007. 89.00 *(978-1-59874-281-7(7))* Left Coast Pr., Inc.

Hicks, Dan & Beaudry, Mary C., eds. The Cambridge Companion to Historical Archaeology. 2006. (ENG., Illus.). 420p. (C). per. 49.00 *(978-0-521-61962-2(9))* Cambridge Univ. Pr.

Hill, Paul & Wileman, Julie. Landscapes of War: The Archaeology of Aggression & Defence. (ENG., Illus.). 224p. pap. 40.00 *(978-0-7524-1963-3(3))* History Pr. Ltd.,The GBR. Dist: Trafalgar Square Publishing.

Hockensmith, Charles D. & Neary, Donna. The Millstone Quarries of Powell County, Kentucky. 2009. (Contributions to Southern Appalachian Studies). (ENG., Illus.). 216p. pap. 45.00 *(978-0-7864-3859-4(2))* McFarland & Co., Inc. Pubs.

Hodder, Ian. Archaeology as Long-Term History. 2009. (New Directions in Archaeology Ser.). (ENG.). 160p. pap. 31.99 *(978-0-521-10786-0(5))* Cambridge Univ. Pr.

Hodder, Ian, ed. The Archaeology of Contextual Meanings. 2009. (New Directions in Archaeology Ser.). (ENG.). 156p. pap. 28.00 *(978-0-521-10640-5(0))* Cambridge Univ. Pr.

Holdaway, Simon & Wandsnider, LuAnn, eds. Time in Archaeology: Time Perspectivism Revisited. 2008. (ENG., Illus.). 219p. 50.00 *(978-0-87480-929-9(0))* Univ. of Utah Pr.

Holly, Donald H., Jr. Hunter-Gatherer Archaeology as Historical Process. Sassaman, Kenneth E., ed. 2011. (Amerind Studies in Archaeology Ser.). (ENG., Illus.). 352p. 60.00 *(978-0-8165-2925-4(6))* Univ. of Arizona Pr.

Hume, Ivor Noel. Something from the Cellar: More of This & That: Selected Essays from the Colonial Williamsburg Journal. 2008. (Illus.). 163p. per. 29.95 *(978-0-87935-229-5(9))* Colonial Williamsburg Foundation.

Interpreting the Early Modern World. 2010. (Contributions to Global Historical Archaeology Ser.). 129.00 *(978-0-387-70758-7(1)*, 0387707581) Springer.

Jameson, John H. & Baugher-Perlin, Sherene. Past Meets Present: Archaeologists Partnering with Museum Curators, Teachers & Community Groups. 2007. (ENG., Illus.). xii, 466p. 149.00 *(978-0-387-47666-7(0)*, 0387476660) Springer.

Kelly, Kenneth G. & Hardy, Meredith D., eds. French Colonial Archaeology in the Southeast & Caribbean. 2011. (Florida Museum of Natural History: Ripley P. Bullen Ser.). (ENG., Illus.). 256p. 74.95 *(978-0-8130-3680-9(1))* Univ. Pr. of Florida.

Kepecs, Susan, et al, eds. Beyond the Blockade: New Currents in Cuban Archaeology. 2nd ed. 2010. (Caribbean Archaeology & Ethnohistory Ser.). (ENG., Illus.). 224p. 35.00 *(978-0-8173-1720-1(1))*; pap. 22.95 *(978-0-8173-5633-0(9))* Univ. of Alabama Pr.

Kepecs, Susan, et al. Beyond the Blockade: New Currents in Cuban Archaeology. 2010. (Illus.). ix, 206p. *(978-0-8173-8492-0(8))* Univ. of Alabama Pr.

Laurence, Ray. Roman Archaeology for Historians. 2012. (Approaching the Ancient World Ser.). (ENG.). 208p. 120.00 ***(978-0-415-50591-8(7))***; pap. 35.95 ***(978-0-415-50592-5(5))*** Routledge.

Lawrence, Susan. Archaeologies of the British: Explorations of Identity in the United Kingdom & Its Colonies 1600-1945. 2010. (Illus.). 320p. pap. 39.95 *(978-0-415-58905-5(3))* Routledge.

Lawrence, Susan & Davies, Peter. An Archaeology of Australia Since 1788. 2010. (Contributions to Global Historical Archaeology Ser.). (Illus.). xx, 424p. 129.00 *(978-1-4419-7484-6(9)*, 1441974849) Springer.

Leone, Mark P. Critical Historical Archaeology. 2010. (ENG., Illus.). 250p. (C). 89.00 *(978-1-59874-396-8(1))*; pap. 29.95 *(978-1-59874-397-5(X))* Left Coast Pr., Inc.

Lin, James C. S. The Search for Immortality - Tomb Treasures of Han China. 2012. (ENG., Illus.). 384p. 75.00 ***(978-0-300-18434-1(4))*** Yale Univ. Pr.

Little, Barbara J. Historical Archaeology: Why the Past Matters. 2007. (ENG., Illus.). 208p. (C). 84.95 *(978-1-59874-022-6(9))*; pap. 24.95 *(978-1-59874-023-3(7))* Left Coast Pr., Inc.

Maisels, Charles Keith. Archaeology of Politics & Power. 2011. (ENG., Illus.). 486p. (C). pap. 65.00 *(978-1-84217-352-7(9))* Oxbow Bks., Ltd. GBR. Dist: Brown, David Bk. Co., The.

Majewski, Teresita & Gaimster, David, eds. International Handbook of Historical Archaeology. (ENG., Illus.). xv, 673p. 2011. pap. 59.95 *(978-1-4419-9923-8(X)*, 144199923X) 2009. 229.00 *(978-0-387-72068-5(5)*, 0387720685) Springer.

Martinon-Torres, Marcos & Rehren, Thilo, eds. Archaeology, History, & Science: Integrating Approaches to Ancient Materials. 2009. (University College London Institute of Archaeology Publications). (ENG.). 218p. pap. 36.95 *(978-1-59874-350-0(3))* Left Coast Pr., Inc.

Mateus, Jose Eduardo, et al, eds. Session C11: Ancient Cultural Landscapes in South Europe - Their Ecological Setting & Evolution. 2010. (Bar S Ser.). (ENG., Illus.). 188p. (C). pap. 95.00 *(978-1-4073-0665-0(0))* British Archaeological Reports Ltd. GBR. Dist: Brown, David Bk. Co., The.

Matthews, Christopher N. Archaeology of American Capitalism. 2010. (American Experience in Archaeological Pespective Ser.). (ENG., Illus.). 256p. 69.95 *(978-0-8130-3524-6(4))* Univ. Pr. of Florida.

Mazrim, Robert. The Sangamo Frontier: History & Archaeology in the Shadow of Lincoln. 2006. (ENG., Illus.). 362p. 60.00 *(978-0-226-51424-6(2))* Univ. of Chicago Pr.

McAnany, Patricia A. & Yoffee, Norman, eds. Questioning Collapse: Human Resilience, Ecological Vulnerability, & the Aftermath of Empire. 2009. (ENG., Illus.). 390p. (C). 95.00 *(978-0-521-51572-6(6))*; pap. 29.99 *(978-0-521-73366-3(9))* Cambridge Univ. Pr.

McAtackney, Laura, et al. Contemporary & Historical Archaeology in Theory. 2007. (ENG., Illus.). 118p. (C). pap. 75.00 *(978-1-4073-0115-0(2))* British Archaeological Reports Ltd. GBR. Dist: Brown, David Bk. Co., The.

McRay, John. Archaeology & the New Testament. *(978-0-687-01678-5(9))* Abingdon Pr.

—Archaeology & the New Testament. 2008. (Illus.). 432p. (C). (gr. 13). pap. 42.99 *(978-0-8010-3606-8(9))* Baker Academic.

Mills, Barbara J. & Walker, William H. Memory Work: Archaeologies of Material Practices. 2008. (School for Advanced Research Advanced Seminar Ser.). pap. 34.95 *(978-1-930618-88-6(3))* School for Advanced Research Pr./SAR Pr.

Minor, Vernon Hyde, ed. Memoirs of the American Academy in Rome: Volume 51 (2006) & Volume 52 (2007) 2007. (Memoirs of the American Academy in Rome Ser.). (ENG., Illus.). 384p. 44.95 *(978-1-879549-14-2(X))* American Academy in Rome.

Moreland, John. Archaeology, Theory & the Middle Ages. 2010. (Duckworth Archaeology Ser.). (Illus.). 192p. pap. 44.95 *(978-0-7156-3689-3(8))* Duckworth Publishers GBR. Dist: International Publishers Marketing.

Olivier, Laurent. Dark Abyss of Time: Memory & Archaeology. 2011. (Archaeology in Society Ser.). (ENG.). 192p. 65.00 ***(978-0-7591-2045-7(5))*** AltaMira Pr.

Palombo, Paula. Las Cuatro Estaciones: Segmentación Del Tiempo y el Espacio en Floridablanca, Costa Patagónica, Siglo XVIII. 2007. (SPA., Illus.). 153p. 5.50 *(978-987-1354-05-4(3))* Teseo ARG. Dist: Sony Electronics.

Patrich, Joseph. Studies in the Archaeology & History of Caesarea Maritima: Caput Judaeae, Metropolis Palaestinae. 2011. (Ancient Judaism & Early Christianity Ser.). (Illus.). 330p. ***(978-90-04-17511-2(3))*** BRILL.

Pisipaty, S. Rama Krishana. Andhra Culture: An Obscure Phase in the Early Historical Archaeology of Andhra Pradesh. 2010. (Illus.). xii, 284p. *(978-81-7320-097-7(1)*, Library of Congress — New Delhi Overseas Office) Agam Kala Prakashan.

Pykles, Benjamin C. Excavating Nauvoo: The Mormons & the Rise of Historical Archaeology in America. 2010. (Critical Studies in the History of Anthropology Ser.). (ENG., Illus.). 416p. 50.00 *(978-0-8032-1893-2(1))* Univ. of Nebraska Pr.

Randsborg, Klavs. Anatomy of Denmark: Archaeology & History from the Ice Age to the Present. 2011. (Illus.). 160p. pap. 24.95 *(978-0-7156-3842-2(4))* Duckworth Publishers GBR. Dist: International Publishers Marketing.

Reece, Richard. Later Roman Empire: An Archaeology AD 150-600. 2007. (ENG., Illus.). 208p. pap. 34.95 *(978-0-7524-4205-1(8))* History Pr. Ltd.,The GBR. Dist: Independent Pubs. Group.

Ringhoff, Mary & Stoner, Edward J. The River & the Railroad: An Archaeological History of Reno. 2011. (Wilber S. Shepperson Series in Nevada History Ser.). (Illus.). 248p. 34.95 *(978-0-87417-843-2(6))* Univ. of Nevada Pr.

Rodriguez Ramos, Reniel. Rethinking Puerto Rican Precolonial History. 2nd ed. 2010. (Caribbean Archaeology & Ethnohistory Ser.). (ENG., Illus.). 288p. 49.75 *(978-0-8173-1702-7(3))*; pap. 29.95 *(978-0-8173-5609-5(6))* Univ. of Alabama Pr.

Rothschild, Nan A. New York City Neighborhoods: The 18th Century. 2008. (Foundations of Archaeology Ser.). (ENG., Illus.). 295p. (C). pap. 42.50 *(978-0-9752738-6-9(8)*, Percheron Pr.) Werner, Eliot Pubns., Inc.

Rotman, Deborah. Historical Archaeology of Gendered Lives. 2009. (Contributions to Global Historical Archaeology Ser.). (ENG., Illus.). xxiii, 265p. 159.00 *(978-0-387-89667-0(8)*, 0387896678) Springer.

Saitta, Dean J. The Archaeology of Collective Action. 2007. (American Experience in Archaeological Perspective Ser.). (ENG., Illus.). 160p. per. 24.95 *(978-0-8130-3070-8(6))* Univ. Pr. of Florida.

Savelev, IU R. Iskusstvo Istorizma I Gosudarstvennyi Zakaz: Vtoraia Polovina XIX — Nachalo XX Veka. 2008. (RUS., Illus.). 304p. *(978-5-903060-60-3(9))* Sovpadenie, Izdatel'stvo.

Schávelzon, Daniel. The Historical Archaeology of Buenos Aires: A City at the End of the World. 2010. (Contributions to Global Historical Archaeology Ser.). 204p. pap. 139.00 *(978-1-4419-3310-2(7)*, 1441933107) Springer.

Schofield, John & Cocroft, Wayne, eds. A Fearsome Heritage: Diverse Legacies of the Cold War. 2009. (University College London Institute of Archaeology Publications). (ENG., Illus.). 334p. pap. 44.95 *(978-1-59874-259-6(0))* Left Coast Pr., Inc.

Schryver, James G., ed. Advances in Methods in Medieval History & Archaeology. 2010. (Illus.). 312p. *(978-90-04-18175-5(X))* BRILL.

Scott, Douglas, et al, eds. Fields of Conflict: Battlefield Archaeology from the Roman Empire to the Korean War. 2009. (Illus.). 450p. pap. 24.95 *(978-1-59797-276-5(2))* Potomac Bks., Inc.

Shepherd. Greek Archaeology for Historians. 2008. pap. 30.95 *(978-0-415-41481-4(4))*; (ENG., Illus.). 224p. 99.00 *(978-0-415-41480-7(6))* Routledge.

Skibo, James M. Archaeological Anthropology: Perspectives on Method & Theory. 2007. (ENG., Illus.). 320p. 55.00 *(978-0-8165-2517-1(X))* Univ. of Arizona Pr.

Smith, Laurajane & Waterton, Emma. Heritage, Communities & Archaeology. 2011. (Duckworth Debates in Archaeology Ser.). (Illus.). 144p. pap. 24.95 *(978-0-7156-3681-7(2))* Duckworth Publishers GBR. Dist: International Publishers Marketing.

Sobin, Gustaf. Aura: Last Essays. 2008. 72p. pap. 14.95 *(978-1-933996-10-3(2))* Counterpath Pr.

—Ladder of Shadows: Reflecting on Medieval Vestige in Provence & Languedoc. 2009. (ENG., Illus.). 208p. 50.00 *(978-0-520-25334-6(5))*; 264p. pap. 24.95 *(978-0-520-25335-3(3))* Univ. of California Pr.

South, Stanley. Archaeology at Colonial Brunswick. 2010. (Illus.). 308p. pap. 20.00 *(978-0-86526-343-7(4))* North Carolina Office of Archives & History.

Stein, Gil. The Archaeology of Colonial Encounters: Comparative Perspectives. (School of American Research Advanced Seminar Ser.). (Illus.). 464p. pap. 24.95 *(978-1-930618-44-2(1))* School for Advanced Research Pr./SAR Pr.

Swanson, Drew A. Remaking Wormsloe Plantation: The Environmental History of a Lowcountry Landscape. 2012. (Environmental History & the American South Ser.). (ENG.). 320p. 34.95 ***(978-0-8203-4177-4(0))*** Univ. of Georgia Pr.

Tenu, Aline. L'expansion Médio-Assyrienne: Approche Archéologique. 2009. (Illus.). 426p. (C). pap. 132.50 *(978-1-4073-0243-0(4))* British Archaeological Reports Ltd. GBR. Dist: Brown, David Bk. Co., The.

Thorp, Robert L. Visiting China's Past: A Guide to Sites & Resources. 2006. (ENG., Illus.). 240p. per. 24.95 *(978-1-891640-33-9(X))* Floating World Editions.

Vandkilde, Helle, ed. Globalisation, Battlefields, Economics: Three Inaugural Lectures in Archaeology. 2007. (ENG., Illus.). 54p. (C). pap. 20.00 *(978-87-7934-374-0(0))* Aarhus Universitetsforlag DNK. Dist: ISD.

Walker, Cameron Jean. Heritage or Heresy: Archaeology & Culture on the Maya Riviera. 2009. (Caribbean Archaeology & Ethnohistory Ser.). (Illus.). 184p. 49.50 *(978-0-8173-1635-8(3))*; pap. 22.50 *(978-0-8173-5514-2(6))* Univ. of Alabama Pr.

Whimster, Rowan. The New Antiquarians: 50 Years of Archaeological Innovation in Wessex. 2011. (CBA Research Report). (Illus.). 234p. (C). pap. 40.00 *(978-1-902771-85-4(0))* Council for British Archaeology GBR. Dist: Brown, David Bk. Co., The.

Wickham-Jones, Caroline & Wickham-Jones, C. R. Orkney: A Historical Guide. 2007. (Illus.). 223p. per. *(978-1-84158-596-3(3)*, Birlinn) Birlinn, Ltd.

Yoffee, Norman & Crowell, Bradley L. Excavating Asian History: Interdisciplinary Studies in Archaeology & History. 2006. (ENG., Illus.). 368p. 55.00 *(978-0-8165-2418-1(1))* Univ. of Arizona Pr.

ARCHBISHOPRICS

see Dioceses

ARCHBISHOPS

see Bishops

ARCHEGENESIS

see Spontaneous Generation

ARCHER, WILLIAM, 1856-1924

Archer, William. Through Afro-America. 295p. reprint ed. 98.00 *(978-0-7222-9703-2(3))* Library Reprints, Inc.

—Through Afro-America. (Works of William Archer). xvi, 295p. reprint ed. 49.00 *(978-0-932051-75-2(8))* Reprint Services Co.

ARCHERY

see also Bow and Arrow; Hunting with Bow and Arrow

Arora, Ankit. Virtual Archery. 2011. 64p. pap. ***(978-3-8454-1648-9(3))*** Lambert Academic Publishing.

Arya, Ravi Prakash, et al. Dhanurveda: The Vedic Military Science. 2008. (Illus.). xv, 214p. *(978-81-87710-49-3(7)*, Library of Congress — New Delhi Overseas Office) Indian Foundation for Vedic Science.

Axford, Ray. Archery Anatomy: An Introduction to Techniques for Improved Performance. 2010. (ENG., Illus.). 164p. pap. 16.95 *(978-0-285-63265-3(5))* Souvenir Pr. Ltd. GBR. Dist: Independent Pubs. Group.

Bell, Graham. The Click of the Stick: Walking the Welsh Coastline from Chester to Chepstow. 2011. 188p. pap. 17.09 ***(978-1-4567-8819-3(1))*** AuthorHouse.

Bradbury, Jim. The Medieval Archer. 2011. (Illus.). 206p. (Orig.). reprint ed. pap. 29.95 *(978-0-85115-675-0(4)*, Boydell Press) Boydell & Brewer, Ltd. GBR. Dist: Boydell & Brewer, Inc.

Bukach, David, et al. An Examination of Prehistoric Stone Bracers from Britain. 2012. (ENG., Illus.). 192p. (C). 90.00 *(978-1-84217-438-8(X))* Oxbow Bks., Ltd. GBR. Dist: Brown, David Bk. Co., The.

Camera, Anthony. Shooting the Stickbow. 2010. 438p. 27.95 *(978-1-60264-544-8(2))* Virtualbookworm.com Publishing, Inc.

Elmer, Robert P. American Archery. 2008. 332p. pap. 29.95 *(978-1-4437-5507-8(9))* Research Pr.

Fadala, Sam. Traditional Archery. 2nd rev. ed. 2011. (ENG., Illus.). 256p. pap. 24.95 *(978-0-8117-0673-5(7))* Stackpole Bks.

Glover, Daniel S., photos by. Traditional Archery from Six Continents: The Charles E. Grayson Collection. 2007. (ENG., Illus.). 272p. (C). 59.95 *(978-0-8262-1751-6(6))* Univ. of Missouri Pr.

Gray, David & Novotny, Lukas, eds. Mounted Archery in the Americas. 2007. 292p. per. 22.00 *(978-1-59048-262-3(X))* Long Riders' Guild Pr., The.

Gross, W. H. Young Beginner's Guide to Shooting & Archery: Tips for Gun & Bow. 2009. (Complete Hunter Ser.). (ENG., Illus.). 128p. pap. 15.99 *(978-1-58923-409-3(X)*, 158923409X) Quayside.

Hastings, T. British Archer 1831 or Tracts on Archery. 2007. 148p. per. *(978-1-84574-370-3(9))* Naval & Military Pr., The.

Haverington, J. K. How to Make a Slingbow. 2009. 72p. pap. 14.95 *(978-1-4401-0298-1(8))* iUniverse, Inc.

Hübschmann, Volkmar, ed. Bow Accessories. 2008. (Illus.). 208p. bds. 34.99 *(978-0-7643-3035-3(7))* Schiffer Publishing, Ltd.

Idiot Proof Archery: How to Shoot Like a Pro, Step by Step (Even If You Have a Real Job!) 2007. per. 29.95 *(978-0-9712812-1-9(1))* Robinhood Video Productions, Inc.

Klens-Bigman, Deborah & Sosnowski, Raymond A. The Way of the Bow: The Kyudo Path to a Disciplined Mind. 2008. (Illus.). 144p. 12.95 *(978-1-60261-312-6(5))* Cliff Road Bks.

Mallory, Stephanie & Habeishi, Beth L. Basic Illustrated Archery. 2008. (Basic Essentials Ser.). (ENG., Illus.). 80p. pap. 9.95 *(978-0-7627-4756-6(0)*, Falcon Guides) Globe Pequot Pr., The.

Needham, Simon S. Archery: The Art of Repetition. 2006. (ENG., Illus.). 160p. pap. 39.95 *(978-1-86126-869-3(6))* Crowood Pr., Ltd. GBR. Dist: Independent Pubs. Group.

Parker, Denise. Denise Parker: A Teenage Archer's Quest for Olympic Glory. 2008. (Illus.). 168p. per. 24.95 *(978-0-9795131-4-1(1))* Woods N' Water Pr., Inc.

Pope, Saxton. Hunting with the Bow & Arrow. Lt. ed. 2007. (ENG.). 232p. pap. 22.99 *(978-1-4264-2609-4(7))* BiblioBazaar.

—Hunting with the Bow & Arrow. 2011. 286p. pap. 12.95 ***(978-1-61427-117-8(8))*** Martino Publishing.

Roth, Erik. With a Bended Bow: Archery in Medieval & Renaissance Europe. 2012. (ENG., Illus.). 256p. 34.95 ***(978-0-7524-6355-1(1))*** History Pr. Ltd.,The GBR. Dist: Independent Pubs. Group.

Soar, Hugh D. H. The Romance of Archery: A Social History of the Longbow. 2008. (ENG., Illus.). 224p. 24.95 *(978-1-59416-067-7(8))* Westholme Publishing.

Thomas, E. Donnall, Jr. Longbows in the Far North. 2007. (ENG., Illus.). 144p. per. 16.95 *(978-0-8117-3434-9(X))* Stackpole Bks.

THOMAS, MARTY. Buff's Blackwidow. 2007. 95p. pap. 15.50 *(978-1-4357-0061-1(9))* Lulu Enterprises Inc.

Yamada, Shoji. Shots in the Dark: Japan, Zen, & the West. Hartman, Earl, tr. from JPN. 2011. (Buddhism & Modernity Ser.). (Illus.). 304p. pap. 22.50 *(978-0-226-94765-5(3))* Univ. of Chicago Pr.

Yamada, Shoji & Yamada, S. Shots in the Dark: Japan, Zen, & the West. Hartman, Earl, tr. from JPN. 2009. (Buddhism & Modernity Ser.). (Illus.). 304p. 35.00 (978-0-226-94764-8(5)) Univ. of Chicago Pr.

ARCHES

Allan, William. Theory of Arches. 124p. 2008. 35.95 (978-0-548-91087-0(1)) 2007. (ENG.). per. 20.95 (978-0-548-58331-9(5)) Kessinger Publishing, LLC.

—Theory of Arches. 2006. 132p. per. 16.99 (978-1-4255-0914-9(2)) MPublishing.

Cain, Wm. Solid & Braced Elastic Arches - Arch Bridges & Roofs. 2007. 180p. 37.95 (978-1-4276-1454-4(7)) Wexford College Pr.

Cain, Wm. (William). A Practical Theory of Voussoir Arches by Prof William Cain, C E. 2006. 128p. per. 16.99 (978-1-4255-0917-0(7)) MPublishing.

Frothingham, Arthur. A Revised List of Roman Memorial & Triumphal Arches. 2009. pap. 20.08 (978-1-60724-507-0(8)) Gorgias Pr., LLC.

Hirschthal, Meyer. Masonry Design: Elements of Masonry Design, & Design of Masonry Arches, Part 1-2. 2011. 206p. 44.95 **(978-1-258-00150-6(0))** Literary Licensing, LLC.

McGowen, S. L. Sacred & Civic Stone Monuments of the Northwest Roman Provinces. 2010. (Bar S Ser.). (ENG., Illus.). 159p. (C). pap. 87.50 (978-1-4073-0650-6(2)) British Archaeological Reports Ltd. GBR. Dist: Brown, David Bk. Co., The.

ARCHES NATIONAL PARK (UTAH)

Fagan, Damian. Arches & Canyonlands National Parks Pocket Guide. 2009. (Falcon Pocket Guides Ser.). (ENG., Illus.). 96p. 9.95 (978-0-7627-4974-4(1), Falcon Guides) Globe Pequot Pr., The.

McRae, Bill, et al. Moon Zion & Bryce: Including Arches, Canyonlands, Capitol Reef, Grand Staircase-Escalante & Moab. 2011. (ENG., Illus.). 304p. pap. 17.99 (978-1-59880-734-9(X)) Avalon Travel Publishing.

McRae, W. C. & Jewell, Judy. Moon Spotlight Arches & Canyonlands National Parks: Including Moab. 2011. (Moon Spotlight Ser.). (ENG.). 104p. pap. 9.99 (978-1-59880-764-6(1)) Avalon Travel Publishing.

Rowley, Edson M. Pictorial of Arches National Park: With Directions to Easily Missed Arches. 2009. (Illus.). 102p. 49.99 (978-1-4363-9553-3(4)); pap. 43.99 (978-1-4363-9552-6(6)) Xlibris Corp.

ARCHETYPE (PSYCHOLOGY)

Aizenstat, Stephen. Imagination & Medicine. Bosnak, Robert, ed. 2009. 217p. pap. 24.95 (978-1-882670-62-8(0)) Spring Journal.

Bain, Jane Bailey. LifeWorks: Using Myth & Archetype to Develop Your Life Story. 2012. (ENG.). 218p. pap. 22.95 **(978-1-78099-038-5(3))** Hunt, John Publishing Ltd. GBR. Dist: National Bk. Network.

Berry, Patricia. Echo's Subtle Body: Contributions to an Archetypal Psychology. 2nd rev. ed. 2008. (ENG.). 192p. pap. 22.00 (978-0-88214-563-1(0)) Spring Pubns., Inc.

Brown, Coleston. Magical Christianity: The Power of Symbols for Spiritual Renewal. rev. ed. 2007. (ENG., Illus.). 182p. pap. 18.95 (978-0-8356-0855-8(7), Quest Bks.) Theosophical Publishing Hse.

Cavaglion, Gabriel. Hermes, the Child & the Mother: Archetypes in Federico Fellini's Dream-Work. 2011. (Psychology of Emotions, Motivations & Actions Ser.). 141p. 69.00 (978-1-61761-338-8(X)) Nova Science Pubs., Inc.

Cobb, Noel. Archetypal Imagination: Glimpses of the Gods in Life & Art. (Studies in Imagination). 288p. pap. 16.95 (978-0-940262-47-8(9), Lindisfarne Bks.) SteinerBooks, Inc.

Deardorff, Daniel. The Other Within: The Genius of Deformity in Myth, Culture, & Psyche. 2008. (ENG.). 264p. pap. 16.95 (978-1-55643-760-1(9)) North Atlantic Bks.

Demarchelier, Patrick, photos by. Dior Couture. 2011. (ENG., Illus.). 250p. 115.00 (978-0-8478-3802-8(1)) Rizzoli International Pubns., Inc.

Dougherty. Underground Springs. 2007. (ENG., Illus.). 312p. (C). 39.95 (978-0-415-40300-9(6)) Routledge.

Dougherty, Nancy J. & West, Jacqueline J. Underground Springs. 2007. (ENG., Illus.). 312p. (C). 110.00 (978-0-415-40301-6(4)) Routledge.

Gilbert, Toni. Gaining Archetypal Vision: A Guidebook for Using Archetypes in Personal Growth & Healing. 2011. (Illus.). 160p. pap. 16.99 **(978-0-7643-3911-0(7)**, Schiffer Publishing Ltd) Schiffer Publishing, Ltd.

Haule, John. Evolution & Archetype. 2010. (ENG., Illus.). 312p. 99.00 (978-0-415-57797-7(7)); pap. 38.95 (978-0-415-57798-4(5)) Routledge.

Hillman, James. Archetypal Psychologies: Reflections in Honor of James Hillman. 2008. 508p. pap. 32.95 (978-1-882670-54-3(X)) Spring Journal.

Hillman, James & Hillman. Animal Presences: Uniform Edition of the Writings of James Hillman. 2007. (ENG.). 336p. 32.00 (978-0-88214-588-4(6)) Spring Pubns., Inc.

Hippard, Victoria. Who Invited Harry Potter? 2009. 160p. pap. (978-3-639-17212-6(4)) VDM Verlag Dr. Mueller e.K.

Jacoby, Mario. Longing for Paradise: Psychological Perspectives on an Archetype. 2006. (Studies in Jungian Psychology by Jungian Analysts Ser.). (Illus.). 229p. per. 30.00 (978-1-894574-17-4(6), 012-169) Inner City Bks. CAN. Dist: Bookworld Trade, Inc.

Jung, C. G. Notes from the Seminar Given In, 1936-1940. 2010. (Jung Seminars Ser.). (ENG., Illus.). 520p. pap. 24.95 (978-0-691-14807-6(4)) Princeton Univ. Pr.

Knapp, Bettina L. Women in Twentieth-Century Literature: A Jungian View. 2008. (ENG.). 256p. per. 24.95 (978-0-271-03431-7(9)) Pennsylvania State Univ. Pr.

Larson, James S. The Theory of Archetypes Revisited. 2008. 79.00 (978-1-60692-432-7(X)) Nova Science Pubs., Inc.

Lippi, Julian. Doing, Knowing & Being: The Athena Factor in Mentoring - Athenic Mentoring. 2008. 264p. pap. (978-3-639-09346-9(1)) VDM Verlag Dr. Mueller e.K.

Mayes, Clifford. The Archetypal Hero's Journey in Teaching & Learning: A Study in Jungian Pedagogy. 2009. pap. (978-1-891859-80-9(3)) Atwood Publishing.

—Inside Education: Depth Psychology in Teaching & Learning. 2007. pap. (978-1-891859-68-7(4)) Atwood Publishing.

McLuhan, Marshall, et al. From Cliché to Archetype. 2011. (978-1-58423-066-3(5)) Gingko Pr., Inc.

Meyer-Grass, Maria, et al. Children's Dreams: Notes from the Seminar Given in 1936-1940. Meyer-Grass, Maria & Jung, Lorenz, eds. Woolfson, Tony & Falzeder, Ernst, trs. from GER. 2007. (Jung Seminars Ser.). (ENG., Illus.). 520p. (C). 55.00 (978-0-691-13323-2(9)) Princeton Univ. Pr.

Meyer, Ruth. Clio's Circle: Entering the Imaginal World of Historians. 2007. (Illus.). 211p. per. 23.95 (978-1-882670-70-3(1)) Spring Journal.

Moore, Robert L. The King Within: Accessing the King in the Male Psyche. 2007. (Illus.). xix, 299p. pap. (978-0-913552-66-7(6)) Exploration Pr.

Nocturnum, Corvis. I. Lucifer: Exploring the Archetype & Origins of the Devil. 2011. (Illus.). 176p. pap. 19.99 **(978-0-7643-3919-6(2)**, Schiffer Publishing Ltd) Schiffer Publishing, Ltd.

Packer, Sharon. Superheroes & Superegos: Analyzing the Minds Behind the Masks, 1 vol. 2009. 275p. 54.95 (978-0-313-35536-3(3), C35536, Praeger Pubs.) Greenwood Publishing Group, Inc.

Parker, Charlotte. Return to Joy. 2010. 176p. 24.95 (978-0-9822851-0-7(8)) Dancing Horse Publishing.

Pearson, Carol & Marr, Hugh K. What Story Are You Living? A Workbook & Guide to Interpreting Results from the Pearson-Marr Archetype Indicator Instrument. 2006. (978-0-935652-78-9(7)) Center for Applications of Psychological Type, Inc.

Robin Robertson, Robertson & Robin Robertson. Jungian Archetypes: Jung, Gödel, & the History of Archetypes. 2009. 324p. pap. 21.95 (978-1-4401-6450-7(9)) iUniverse, Inc.

Schadel, Erwin. Trinität als Archetyp? Erläuterungen zur C. G. Jung, Hegel und Augustinus. 2008. (Schriften zur Triadik und Ontodynamik Ser.). 174p. pap. 49.95 (978-3-631-57927-5(6)) Lang, Peter GmbH, Europaischer Verlag der Wissenschaften DEU. Dist: Lang, Peter.

Singer. In the Footsteps of 'Thresholds of InitiationApos. 2007. (ENG., Illus.). 248p. (C). 42.50 (978-0-415-39793-3(6)); 110.00 (978-0-415-39792-6(8)) Routledge.

Smethers, John E. Scumbag Sewer Rats. 2008. 168p. pap. (978-0-9551503-5-7(3)) Checkpoint Pr.

Solberg, Rooi. Spirit of Archetypes: Cards of Spiritual Guidance. 2009. (Illus.). 128p. pap. 29.95 (978-0-9816901-0-0(6)) Spirit Elan, LLC.

Spring 79: Irish Culture & Depth Psychology Spring 2008. 2008. 296p. pap. 23.95 (978-1-882670-53-6(1)) Spring Journal.

Taschen, Benedikt & Archive for Research in Archetypal Symbolism. Book of Symbols: Reflections on Archetypal Images. 2010. (ENG., Illus.). 810p. 39.99 (978-3-8365-1448-4(6)) TASCHEN DEU. Dist: Ingram Pub. Services.

Ted, Andrews. Treasures of the Unicorn: Return to the Sacred Quest. 2nd rev. ed. 2009. 256p. pap. 14.95 (978-1-888767-62-9(6)) Dragonhawk Publishing.

Todd, Kay. Bidden or Not Bidden God Is Present C G Jung. 2009. 240p. pap. (978-3-639-17472-4(0)) VDM Verlag Dr. Mueller e.K.

Woodward, Susan R. A Sequential Sojourn: Visualizing the Quest of the Archetypal Hero. 2009. 144p. pap. 19.95 (978-0-578-00610-9(3)) Woodward, Susan R.

ARCHIDAMIAN WAR

see Greece—History—Peloponnesian War, 431-404 B.C.

ARCHILOCHUS, FL. 700-650 B.C.

Kivilo, Maarit. Early Greek Poets' Lives: The Shaping of the Tradition. 2010. xii, 270p. (978-90-04-18615-6(8)) BRILL.

Steinruck, Martin. The Suitors in the Odyssey: The Clash Between Homer & Archilochus. 2008. (Hermeneutic Commentaries Ser.: Vol. 2). 162p. (C). 61.95 (978-1-4331-0475-6(X)) Lang, Peter Publishing, Inc.

ARCHIMEDES

Hirshfeld, Alan. Eureka Man: The Life & Legacy of Archimedes. 2009. (ENG., Illus.). 256p. 26.00 (978-0-8027-1618-7(0)) Walker & Co.

Hirshfeld, Alan W. Eureka Man: The Life & Legacy of Archimedes. 2010. (ENG., Illus.). 256p. pap. 17.00 (978-0-8027-7766-9(X)) Walker & Co.

Jaeger, Mary. Archimedes & the Roman Imagination. 2008. (ENG.). 248p. 80.00 (978-0-472-11630-0(4)) Univ. of Michigan Pr.

Netz, Reviel, et al, eds. The Archimedes Palimpsest, 2 vols. 2011. (Archimedes Palimpsest Publications). (ENG & GEC., Illus.). 350p. 140.00 **(978-1-107-01457-2(3))**; 352p. 140.00 **(978-1-107-01437-4(9))** Cambridge Univ. Pr.

Paipetis, S. A. & Ceccarelli, Marco, eds. The Genius of Archimedes — 23 Centuries of Influence on Mathematics, Science & Engineering: Proceedings of an International Conference held at Syracuse, Italy, June 8-10 2010. 2010. (History of Mechanism & Machine Science Ser.). (ENG., Illus.). x, 696p. 229.00 (978-90-481-9090-4(8), 9048190908) Springer.

Pickover, Clifford. Archimedes to Hawking: Laws of Science & the Great Minds Behind Them. 2008. (ENG., Illus.). 480p. 27.95 (978-0-19-533611-5(9)) Oxford Univ. Pr., Inc.

ARCHITECTS

see also Architectural Firms; Women Architects

also names of architects, e.g. Wright, Frank Lloyd, 1869-1959

Abu-Rabi, Ibrahim M., ed. Theodicy & Justice in Modern Islamic Thought: The Case of Said Nursi. 2010. 282p. 99.95 (978-1-4094-0618-1(0)); pap. 34.95 (978-1-4094-0617-4(2)) Ashgate Publishing Co.

Allinson, Kenneth. Architects & Architecture of London. 2008. (ENG., Illus.). 448p. pap. 32.95 (978-0-7506-8337-1(6)) Routledge.

Álvarez, Ana María, ed. Ramon Esteve: Estudio de Arquitectura. 2010. (ENG & SPA., Illus.). 320p. 49.99 (978-84-9936-197-0(8)) Loft Pubns. ESP. Dist: Prestel Publishing.

Andersson, Arthur, et al. Natural Houses: The Residential Architecture of Andersson-Wise. 2010. (ENG., Illus.). 176p. pap. 40.00 (978-1-56898-879-5(6)) Princeton Architectural Pr.

Andrés de San Miguel & Báez Macías, Eduardo. Obras de Fray Andrés de San Miguel. 2nd ed. 2007. (SPA., Illus.). 524p. (978-970-32-4343-3(6)) Universidad Nacional Autónoma de México.

Architectural League of New York Staff. Proof. 2008. (ENG., Illus.). 176p. pap. 24.95 (978-1-56898-743-9(9)) Princeton Architectural Pr.

—Young Architects 12: Resource. 2011. (ENG., Illus.). 176p. pap. 24.95 (978-1-56898-998-3(9)) Princeton Architectural Pr.

Architectural League of New York Staff. Young Architects 13: It's Different. 2012. (ENG.). 176p. pap. 24.95 **(978-1-61689-057-5(6))** Princeton Architectural Pr.

Arup Associates. Unified Design. Brislin, Paul, ed. 2008. (ENG., Illus.). 208p. 55.00 (978-0-470-72331-9(9), Wiley) Wiley, John & Sons, Inc.

Attali, Erieta, photos by. Erieta Attali: In Extremis - Landscape into Architecture. 2011. (ENG & SPA., Illus.). 255p. pap., pap. 29.95 (978-1-883584-66-5(3)) Columbia Univ., Graduate Schl. of Architecture.

Azur. Architecture Highlights Vol. 3. 2011. 250p. 120.00 (978-4-903233-61-1(8)) Azur Corp. JPN. Dist: Antique Collectors' Club.

Baker, William T. American Architecture New Classicists. 2006. (New Classicists Ser.). (ENG., Illus.). 336p. 90.00 (978-1-920744-57-1(6)) Images Publishing Group AUS. Dist: National Bk. Network.

Ballast, David Kent. Schematic Design: ARE Sample Problems & Practice Exam. 2008. (ENG., Illus.). 76p. pap. 120.00 (978-1-59126-125-4(2)) Professional Pubns., Inc.

Ballast, David Kent & O'Hara, PE, Steven E. ARE Review Manual. 2nd ed. 2011. 744p. pap. 320.00 (978-1-59126-322-7(0)) Professional Pubns., Inc.

Bassenian, Aram. Bassenian/Lagoni Architects Boxed Set. 2007. 94.95 (978-0-9721539-4-2(2)) Bassenian/Lagoni Architects, Inc.

Baxter, Denise & Martin, Meredith S. Architectural Space in Eighteenth-Century Europe: Constructing Indentities an Interiors. 2010. (Illus.). 284p. 119.95 (978-0-7546-6650-9(6)) Ashgate Publishing Co.

Beaver, Robyn. Cox Architects & Planners, 1960 - 2010. 2009. (Master Architect Ser.). (ENG., Illus.). 64p. pap. 80.00 (978-1-920744-07-6(X)) Images Publishing Group AUS. Dist: National Bk. Network.

Beaver, Robyn, ed. Dirk Jan Postel: Transparencies. 2008. (Master Architect (Unnumbered) Ser.). (ENG., Illus.). 256p. 59.95 (978-1-86470-210-1(9), Images Publishing Dist Ac) Antique Collectors' Club GBR. Dist: National Bk. Network.

Belcher, Margaret, ed. The Collected Letters of A. W. N. Pugin: Volume 3: 1846-1848. 2009. (Collected Letters of A. W. N. Pugin Ser.). (ENG., Illus.). 672p. 250.00 (978-0-19-922916-1(3)) Oxford Univ. Pr., Inc.

Beltramini, Guido & Loth, Calder. Palladio & His Legacy: A Transatlantic Journey. Hind, Charles & Murray, Irena, eds. 2010. (ENG., Illus.). 180p. pap. 45.00 (978-88-317-0652-0(7)) Marsilio Editori spa ITA. Dist: Random Hse., Inc.

Berens, Hetty, ed. P. J. H. Cuypers (1827-1921) The Complete Works, 1 vol. 2007. (ENG., Illus.). 397p. 75.00 (978-90-5662-574-0(8)) NAi Uitgevers / Publishers Stichting NLD. Dist: D.A.P./Distributed Art Pubs.

Berkus, Barry A. & Berkus, Barry. Sculpting Space. 2006. (House Design Ser.). (ENG., Illus.). 128p. 49.50 (978-1-86470-086-2(2)) Images Publishing Group AUS. Dist: National Bk. Network.

Berrizbeitia, Anita, ed. Michael Van Valkenburgh Associates: Reconstructing Urban Landscapes. 2009. (ENG., Illus.). 320p. 65.00 (978-0-300-13585-5(8)) Yale Univ. Pr.

Białkiewicz, Zbigniew Jan & Ksiezarski, Feliks. Feliks Ksiezarski, 1820-1884: Krakowski Architekt Epoki Historyzmu. 2008. (Illus.). 374p. (978-83-7188-121-3(5)) Ksiegarnia Akademicka, spolka z o.o.

BIS Publishers. Dutch Architects 8. 7th rev. ed. 2009. (ENG., Illus.). 332p. 69.00 (978-90-6369-160-8(2)) Bis B.V., Uitgeverij(BIS Publishers) NLD. Dist: Consortium Bk. Sales & Distribution.

Bonet Castellana, Antoni & Pizza de Nanno, Antonio. Antonio Bonet Castellana. 2010. (ENG & SPA., Illus.). 280p. (978-84-8301-288-8(X)) UPC, S.L., Edicions.

Bonnemaison, Sarah & Eisenbach, Ronit. Installations by Architects: Experiments in Building & Design. 2009. (ENG., Illus.). 192p. pap. 40.00 (978-1-56898-850-4(8)) Princeton Architectural Pr.

Borden, Gail Peter & Meredith, Michael, eds. Matter: Material Processes in Architectural Production. 2011. (ENG., Illus.). 520p. (C). 155.00 (978-0-415-78028-5(4)) Routledge.

Bosman, Jos, et al, texts. Diederendirrix Architects. 2009. (ENG & MUL., Illus.). 296p. 80.00 (978-90-5662-662-4(0)) NAi Uitgevers / Publishers Stichting NLD. Dist: D.A.P./Distributed Art Pubs.

Brandwood, Geoff. The Architecture of Sharpe, Paley & Austin. 2012. (Twentieth-century Architects Ser.). (ENG., Illus.). 272p. (C). 100.00 (978-1-84802-049-8(X)) English Heritage GBR. Dist: Brown, David Bk. Co., The.

Brock, Harald. Die Landsitzarchitektur Simon-Louis du Rys. 2008. (GER., Illus.). 92p. (978-3-89445-402-9(4)) Jonas Verlag fur Kunst & Literatur GmbH.

Bruegmann, Robert. The Architecture of Harry Weese. 2010. (ENG., Illus.). 240p. 59.95 (978-0-393-73193-4(6), 73193) Norton, W. W. & Co., Inc.

Bullivant, Lucy. New Arcadians: Emerging UK Architects. 2012. (ENG., Illus.). 256p. 49.95 **(978-1-85894-548-4(8))** Merrell Pubs. Ltd. GBR. Dist: Perseus Distribution.

Castro, Ricardo L. & Olsberg, Nicholas. Arthur Erickson Critical Works. 2006. (Illus.). 192p. 75.00 (978-0-295-98620-3(4)) Univ. of Washington Pr.

Chan, Soo. SCDA Architects. 2012. (Master Architects Ser.). (ENG., Illus.). 256p. 80.00 (978-1-86470-414-3(4)) Images Publishing Group AUS. Dist: National Bk. Network.

Charrington, Harry & Nava, Vezio, eds. Alvar Aalto: The Mark of the Hand. 2012. (ENG., Illus.). 400p. pap. 58.95 **(978-951-682-995-4(3))** Rakennustieto oy FIN. Dist: Independent Pubs. Group.

Cloepfil, Brad & text. Allied Works Architecture, 2000-2010. 2011. (ENG., Illus.). 440p. 85.00 (978-0-9800242-5-8(0)) Miller, Gregory & Co.

Cohen, Stuart & Hacker, Julie. Transforming the Traditional: The Work of Cohen & Hacker Architects. 2009. (ENG., Illus.). 128p. 50.00 (978-1-86470-335-1(0)) Images Publishing Group AUS. Dist: National Bk. Network.

Cómez Ramos, Rafael. Los Constructores de la España Medieval. 3rd ed. 2009. (SPA., Illus.). 208p. (978-84-472-1176-0(2)) Universidad de Sevilla.

Conzett, Jürg, et al. Marcel Meili, Markus Peter, 1987-2008: Scheidegger & Spiess. Meili, Marcel & Peter, Markus, eds. 2009. (ENG., Illus.). 400p. 110.00 (978-3-85881-714-3(7)) Scheidegger und Spiess AG, Verlag CHE. Dist: Antique Collectors' Club.

Cornes, David L. & Lupton, Sarah. Cornes & Lupton's Design Liability in the Construction Industry. 5th ed. 2012. (ENG.). 352p. 115.00 **(978-1-4443-3006-9(3)**, Wiley-Blackwell) Wiley, John & Sons, Inc.

Craft, Stephen. Ivan Rijavec: Pure Form. 2006. (House Design Ser.: Vol. 8). (ENG., Illus.). 39.50 (978-1-86470-080-0(7)) Images Publishing Group AUS. Dist: National Bk. Network.

DAAB Media Staff, creator. Jean-Marie Massaud, 1 vol. 2008. (ENG, FRE & GER., Illus.). 175p. 29.95 (978-3-937718-88-0(5)) DAAB Media Gmbh DEU. Dist: Innovative Logistics.

—Matali Crasset: Spaces 2000-2007, 1 vol. 2008. (ENG, FRE & GER., Illus.). 175p. 29.95 (978-3-937718-89-7(3)) DAAB Media GmbH DEU. Dist: Innovative Logistics.

Dal Co, Francesco. Tadao Ando: 1994-2009. 2010. (Illus.). 526p. 85.00 (978-3-7913-4454-6(4)) Prestel Publishing.

DaSilva, John R. & Crosbie, Michael J. Architecture of the Cape Cod Summer: The Work of Polhemus Savery DaSilva. 2008. (ENG., Illus.). 264p. 90.00 (978-1-86470-280-4(X)) Images Publishing Group AUS. Dist: National Bk. Network.

de Jong, Erik & Betram, Christian, eds. Michael Van Gessel: Landscape Architect. 2008. (ENG., Illus.). 348p. 95.00 (978-90-5662-038-7(X)) NAi Uitgevers / Publishers Stichting NLD. Dist: D.A.P./Distributed Art Pubs.

De Kooning, Mil & Gerreway, Christophe Van. Stéphane Beel Architects. 2012. (ENG & DUT., Illus.). 304p. 95.00 **(978-90-209-5638-2(8))** Lannoo Pubs./Racine.

Dercon, Chris, ed. Carlo Mollino: Maniera Moderna. 2012. (ENG., Illus.). 312p. pap. 49.95 **(978-3-86335-020-8(0))** Verlag der Buchhandlung Walther Konig DEU. Dist: D.A.P./Distributed Art Pubs.

Dullemen, C. J. van. Tropical Modernity: Life & Work of C.P. Wolff Schoemaker. 2010. (Illus.). 270p. (978-90-8506-879-2(7)) SUN B.V., Uitgeverij.

Dunster, David, et al. Robert Stern: An Architectural Monograph. (Illus.). 124p. pap. 24.95 (978-0-312-68755-7(9)) St. Martin's Pr.

Eastman, Chuck, et al. BIM Handbook: A Guide to Building Information Modeling for Owners, Managers, Designers, Engineers & Contractors. 2nd ed. 2011. (ENG., Illus.). 648p. 85.00 (978-0-470-54137-1(7), Wiley) Wiley, John & Sons, Inc.

Ebner, Peter & Gerstenberg, Frauke. Housing Moves On: Architects & their Views. Höllbacher, Roman, ed. 2008. (GER & ENG., Illus.). 196p. pap. (978-3-211-79173-8(6), 3211791736) Actar Birkhauser Distribution.

EDAS - Design Kommunalka Staff, contrib. by. ABD: Within the Range of Architecture. 2007. (Illus.). 350p. pap. 59.95 (978-3-211-48858-4(8), 3211488588) Springer Wien AUT. Dist: Springer.

Eisenman, Peter. Ten Canonical Buildings: 1950-2000. Heid, Andrew & Lourie, Ariane, eds. 2008. (ENG., Illus.). 304p. 60.00 (978-0-8478-3048-0(9)) Rizzoli International Pubns., Inc.

Engelhorn, Beate. Young Americans: New Architecture in the USA, 1 vol. 2009. (GER & ENG., Illus.). 416p. 99.95 **(978-3-938666-17-3(X))** DOM Pubs. DEU. Dist: Innovative Logistics.

Esaulov, G. V. & Solovev, N. K. Fedor Shekhtel I Epokha Moderna / Fedor Shekhtel & the Epoch of Art Nouveau. 2009. (Illus.). 247p. (978-5-9647-0184-2(1)) Arhitektura-S, Izdatel'stvo.

Ferrater, Carlos & Ferrater, Borja, eds. Ferrater & Partners: Oab. 2011. (ENG., Illus.). 350p. (978-84-92861-23-1(1)) Actar Birkhauser Distribution.

Fest, J. Albert Speer: Conversations with Hitler's Architect. 2007. (Illus.). 180p. pap. 29.95 (978-0-7456-3919-2(4)) Polity Pr. GBR. Dist: Wiley, John & Sons, Inc.

Fest, Joachim. Albert Speer: Conversations with Hitler's Architect. Camiller, Patrick, tr. from GER. 2007. (ENG., Illus.). 180p. 14.95 (978-0-7456-3918-5(6)) Polity Pr. GBR. Dist: Wiley, John & Sons, Inc.

Fisher, Thomas. Ethics for Architects: 50 Dilemmas of Professional Practice. 2010. (ENG., Illus.). 144p. pap. 24.95 (978-1-56898-946-4(6)) Princeton Architectural Pr.

Fontana-Giusti, Gordana. Foucault for Architects. 2012. (Thinkers for Architects Ser.). (ENG., Illus.). 128p. (C). 130.00 (978-0-415-69330-1(6)); pap. 28.95 (978-0-415-69331-8(4)) Routledge.

Fores, Ferrer. Jorn Utzon. Works & Projects. 2006. 306p. pap. 24.00 (978-84-252-2060-9(2)) Trucatriche.

Forner, Johannes. Wohn- & Bürgerhäuser Im Leipziger Musikviertel. 2007. (GER., Illus.). 95p. pap. (978-3-86729-010-4(5)) Heydick, Erika Sax-Verlag Beucha.

Fowle, Bruce, et al, eds. Fox & Fowle Architects: Designing for the Built Realm. 2006. (Master Architect Series VI). (ENG., Illus.). 256p. 65.00 (978-1-920744-00-7(2)) Images Publishing Group AUS. Dist: National Bk. Network.

Frampton, Kenneth. Alvaro Siza: Complete Works. rev. ed. 2006. (ENG., Illus.). 620p. pap. 49.95 (978-0-7148-4633-0(3)) Phaidon Pr., Inc.

Franzen, Brigitte, et al, eds. WESTARCH 1: A New Generation in Architecture. 2011. (ENG., Illus.). 192p. pap. 49.95 (978-3-86859-079-1(X)) Jovis Verlag GmbH DEU. Dist: D.A.P./Distributed Art Pubs.

Füchslin, Marco & Eggstein, Simone. Architekt Hans Eggstein: Bauten und Projekte: Eine Werkdokumentation. 2007. (GER., Illus.). 199p. (978-3-7212-0627-2(4)) Niggli, Arthur Verlag.

Gang, Jeanne. Reveal: Studio Gang Architects. 2011. (ENG., Illus.). 256p. pap. 45.00 (978-1-56898-993-8(8)) Princeton Architectural Pr.

Gholam, Nabil. Nabil Gholam Architects. 2011. (Illus.). 420p. 42.00 (978-84-9936-860-3(3)) Loft Pubns. ESP. Dist: Prestel Publishing.

Goad, Philip & Willis, Julie, eds. The Encyclopedia of Australian Architecture. 2011. (ENG., Illus.). 830p. 180.00 (978-0-521-88857-8(3)) Cambridge Univ. Pr.

Goldberger, Paul & Libeskind, Daniel. Counterpoint: Daniel Libeskind in Conversation with Paul Goldberger. 2008. (ENG., Illus.). 400p. 60.00 (978-1-58093-206-6(1)) Monacelli Pr., Inc.

Gotkin, Michael. Artists' Handmade Houses. 2011. (ENG., Illus.). 240p. 60.00 (978-0-8109-9584-0(0)) Abrams.

Goulthorpe, Mark. The Possibility of (an) Architecture: Collected Essays by Mark Goulthorpe, DECOi Architects. 2008. (Illus.). 224p. 165.00 (978-0-415-77494-9(2)) Routledge.

—The Possibility of (An) Architecture: Collected Essays by Mark Goulthorpe, Decoi Architects. 2008. (Illus.). XVIII, 206p. 44.95 (978-0-415-77495-6(0)) Routledge.

Gregory, Rob. Hopkins: Volume 3. 2012. (Illus.). 360p. 65.00 (978-3-7913-4432-4(3)) Prestel Publishing.

Grima, Joseph. Instant Asia: Fast Forward Through the Architecture of a Changing Continent. 2008. (ENG., Illus.). 262p. pap. 15.99 (978-88-6130-303-4(X)) Skira Editore ITA. Dist: Random Hse., Inc.

Guccione, Margherita. Zaha Hadid: Minimum Series. 2010. (ENG., Illus.). 120p. 19.95 (978-88-6413-021-7(7), Ore Cultura Srl (Acc)) Antique Collectors' Club GBR. Dist: National Bk. Network.

Hafertepe, Kenneth, ed. American Architects & Their Books, 1840-1915. 2007. (Studies in Print Culture & the History of the Book). (Illus.). 303p. 39.95 (978-1-55849-602-6(5)) Univ. of Massachusetts Pr.

Hardt, John. Construction Documents & Services Question & Answer 2009. 2008. (ENG.). 48p. pap. 49.95 (978-1-4277-7035-6(2)) Kaplan Publishing.

—Programming, Planning & Practice Question & Answer 2009. annuals 2008. (ENG.). 56p. pap. 49.95 (978-1-4277-7033-2(6)) Kaplan Publishing.

Hariri, Hariri & Hariri Architecture: Buildings & Projects. 2010. (ENG., Illus.). 256p. 59.95 (978-1-86470-340-5(7), Images Publishing Dist Ac) Antique Collectors' Club GBR. Dist: National Bk. Network.

Harris, Steven. True Life: Steven Harris Architects. 2010. (ENG., Illus.). 240p. 50.00 (978-1-56898-971-6(7)) Princeton Architectural Pr.

Harwood, Elain. Chamberlin, Powell & Bon: 20th Century Architects. 2011. (Twentieth-century Architects Ser.). (Illus.). 160p. (C). pap. 40.00 (978-1-85694-164-8(7)) English Heritage GBR. Dist: Brown, David Bk. Co., The.

Harwood, Elain & Symondson, Anthony. Stephen Dykes Bower. 2011. (Twentieth-century Architects Ser.). (ENG., Illus.). 186p. (C). pap. 40.00 (978-1-85946-398-7(3)) English Heritage GBR. Dist: Brown, David Bk. Co., The.

Hawkes, Dean, ed. Modern Country Homes in England: The Arts & Crafts Architecture of Barry Parker. 2010. (Cambridge Urban & Architectural Studies). (ENG.). 184p. pap. 27.99 (978-0-521-13682-2(2)) Cambridge Univ. Pr.

Henderson, Holley. Becoming a Green Building Professional: A Guide to Careers in Sustainable Architecture, Design, Engineering, Development, & Operations. 2012. (Wiley Series in Sustainable Design Ser.: 33). (ENG., Illus.). 576p. pap. 44.95 (978-0-470-95143-9(5), Wiley) Wiley, John & Sons, Inc.

Henning, Randolph C. The Architecture of Alfred Browning Parker: Miami's Maverick Modernist. 2011. (ENG., Illus.). 400p. 50.00 (978-0-8130-3677-9(1)) Univ. Pr. of Florida.

Hernandez, Felip & Hernandez, Felipe. Bhabha for Architects. 2010. (Thinkers for Architects Ser.). (ENG., Illus.). 148p. 28.95 (978-0-415-47746-8(8)) Routledge.

Hess, Stephen A., et al. Design Professional & Construction Manager Professional Liability Handbook. 2007. (Illus.). xxxvi, 643p. (978-1-59031-786-0(6)) American Bar Assn.

Ho M Staff & Partners For Health Staff. Hpa: the Story of Ho & Partners Architects: Architecture - Witnessing the Progress of Human Civilisation. 2012. (ENG & CHI., Illus.). 240p. 59.95 (978-1-86470-426-6(8)) Images Publishing Group AUS. Dist: National Bk. Network.

Images Publishing, creator. Haigo Shen & Partners: Selected & Current Works. 2006. (Master Architect Series VI). (ENG., Illus.). 240p. 59.95 (978-1-876907-33-4(9), Images Publishing Dist Ac) Antique Collectors' Club GBR. Dist: National Bk. Network.

Images Publishing Group. 2000 Architects, 2 vols., Vol. 2. 2006. (ENG., Illus.). 680p. 95.00 (978-1-920744-93-9(2)) Images Publishing Group AUS. Dist: National Bk. Network.

Images Publishing Group, contrib. by. Architects of the New Millennium. 2006. (ENG., Illus.). 224p. 65.00 (978-1-86470-079-4(3)) Images Publishing Group AUS. Dist: National Bk. Network.

Images Publishing Staff, PUBLISHING. Assar. Binder, Georges, ed. 2008. (Master Architect Series VI). (ENG., Illus.). 256p. 59.95 (978-1-920744-02-1(9), Images Publishing Dist Ac) Antique Collectors' Club GBR. Dist: National Bk. Network.

—Vizzion Architects. Beaver, Robyn, ed. 2009. (Master Architect Ser.). (ENG., Illus.). 304p. 59.95 (978-1-86470-065-7(3), Images Publishing Dist Ac) Antique Collectors' Club GBR. Dist: National Bk. Network.

Jackson, Neil & Jackson, N. Pierre Koenig, 1925-2004: Living with Steel. 2007. (ENG., Illus.). 96p. pap. 9.99 (978-3-8228-4891-3(3)) TASCHEN DEU. Dist: Ingram Pub. Services.

James, Vincent & Yoos, Jennifer. Vjaa: Vincent James Associates Architects. 2007. (ENG., Illus.). 208p. pap. 40.00 (978-1-56898-588-6(6)) Princeton Architectural Pr.

Jodidio, Philip. Architecture Now! Landscape. 2012. (ENG., Illus.). 416p. pap. 39.99 (978-3-8365-3676-9(5)) TASCHEN DEU. Dist: Ingram Pub. Services.

Jodidio, Philip. Santiago Calatrava: 1951: Architect, Engineer, Artist. 2007. (ENG., Illus.). 96p. pap. 9.99 (978-3-8228-4873-9(5)) TASCHEN DEU. Dist: Ingram Pub. Services.

Jodidio, Philip (Ed). Architecture in France. 2006. (ENG, FRE & GER., Illus.). 192p. 29.99 (978-3-8228-5257-6(0)) TASCHEN DEU. Dist: Ingram Pub. Services.

Johnston, George Barnett. Drafting Culture: A Social History of Architectural Graphic Standards. 2008. (ENG., Illus.). 304p. (gr. 17). 39.95 (978-0-262-10122-6(X)) MIT Pr.

Jones, Grant R. & Amidon, Jane. Grant Jones/Jones & Jones - ILARIS: The Puget Sound Plan. 2007. (ENG., Illus.). 144p. pap. 29.95 (978-1-56898-604-3(1)) Princeton Architectural Pr.

Jovis, compiled by. Berliner BDA Architekten 2. 2009. (ENG., Illus.). 176p. 40.00 (978-3-939633-63-1(1)) Jovis Verlag GmbH DEU. Dist: D.A.P./Distributed Art Pubs.

Jungles, Raymond. The Colors of Nature: Subtropical Gardens by Raymond Jungles. 2008. (ENG., Illus.). 224p. 50.00 (978-1-58093-212-7(6), Monacelli Pr., Inc.

Kanner, Stephan. Kanner Architects: 11 Projects. 2006. (ENG., Illus.). 80p. pap. 30.00 (978-0-9774672-3-5(6)) Oro Editions.

Kapfinger, Otto. Wratzfeld, Kopf: Kindergarten Koblach. (Illus.). 76p. (978-3-7757-0880-7(4)) Hatje Cantz Verlag GmbH & Co KG DEU. Dist: D.A.P./Distributed Art Pubs.

Kauppi, Kenneth. Arkitektens Fritidshus. 2010. (SWE., Illus.). 303p. (978-91-7843-288-2(X), Arena) Ashgate Publishing, Ltd.

Kidder, Paul. Gadamer for Architects. 2012. (Thinkers for Architects Ser.). (ENG., Illus.). 144p. (C). 120.00 (978-0-415-52272-4(2)); pap. 28.95 (978-0-415-52273-1(0)) Routledge.

Klein, Caroline. Futuristic: Visions of Future Living, 1 vol. 2012. (ENG & GER., Illus.). 312p. 75.00 (978-3-942597-09-8(8)) DAAB Media Gmbh DEU. Dist: Innovative Logistics.

Koerner, Stefan. Amerikanische Landschaften: J. B. Jackson in der deutschen Rezeption. 2010. (Sozialgeographische Bibliothek Ser.). (GER., Illus.). 111p. (C). pap. 37.00 (978-3-515-09665-2(5)) Steiner, Franz Verlag Wiesbaden GmbH DEU. Dist: Brown, David Bk. Co., The.

Koivisto, Maritta. Concrete Architecture in Finland. 2009. (Illus.). 132p. 69.00 (978-951-682-888-9(4)) Rakennustieto oy FIN. Dist: Independent Pubs. Group.

Kowalski, Karla. Szyszkowitz-Kowalski: Architekturen von 1994-2010. 2011. (ENG., Illus.). 312p. 65.00 (978-3-86859-033-3(1)) Jovis Verlag GmbH DEU. Dist: D.A.P./Distributed Art Pubs.

Krauel, Jacobo. Creative Events. 2010. (ENG., Illus.). 300p. pap. 39.00 (978-84-96969-62-9(2)) Links International (Leading International Key Services Barcelona, S.A.) ESP. Dist: National Bk. Network.

Kruse, Stefan. Hospital Architecture & Design. 2009. (Masterpieces Ser.). (FRE, GER & ENG., Illus.). 304p. 49.95 (978-3-938780-76-3(2)) BRAUN DEU. Dist: National Bk. Network.

Kuhl, Isabel, et al. 50 Architects You Should Know. 2008. (Illus.). 176p. pap. 19.95 (978-3-7913-4043-2(3)) Prestel Publishing.

Kundoo, Anupama, text. Roger Anger: Research on Beauty. 2009. (ENG., Illus.). 192p. 45.00 (978-3-86859-006-7(4)) Jovis Verlag GmbH DEU. Dist: D.A.P./Distributed Art Pubs.

Kuth, Byron, et al. Kuth/Ranieri Architects. 2010. (ENG., Illus.). 192p. pap. 40.00 (978-1-56898-865-8(6)) Princeton Architectural Pr.

Lampens, Juliaan. Juliaan Lampens, 1 vol. Campens, Angelique, ed. 2011. (ENG., Illus.). 152p. pap. 64.00 (978-94-6117-005-7(X)) Exhibitions International BEL. Dist: Innovative Logistics.

Langdalen, Erik Fenstad, et al, eds. Hamsun, Holl, Hamaroy. 2010. (Illus.). 96p. (978-3-03778-214-9(5)) Lars Muller Pubs.

Lapuerta, Jose Maria, ed. Manual de Vivenda Colectiva. 2007. (Illus.). 223p. per. (978-84-96954-14-4(5)) Actar Birkhauser Distribution.

Lasciac, Antonio. Antonio Lasciac, Architetto: Da Gorizia All'impero Ottomano. 2007. (Illus.). 159p. pap. (978-88-7292-501-0(0)) Alinari (IDEA).

Lavin, Sylvia. Form Follows Libido: Architecture & Richard Neutra in a Psychoanalytic Culture. 2007. (ENG., Illus.). 192p. (gr. 17). pap. 18.95 (978-0-262-62213-4(0)) MIT Pr.

Lees-Milne, James. Holy Dread: Diaries 1982-1984. (Illus.). 352p. 45.00 (978-0-7195-6205-1(8)) Murray, John GBR. Dist: Trafalgar Square Publishing.

Leppo, RA/CID, LEED AP, Holly Williams & Ballast, David Kent. Construction Documents & Services: ARE Sample Problems & Practice Exam. 2nd ed. 2011. (ENG.). 114p. pap. 120.00 (978-1-59126-323-4(9)) Professional Pubns., Inc.

Long, Kieran. Hatch: The New Architectural Generation. 2008. (ENG., Illus.). 352p. pap. 35.00 (978-1-85669-562-6(X)) King, Laurence Publishing GBR. Dist: Hachette Bk. Group.

Mallgrave, Harry Francis. Architect's Brain: Neuroscience, Creativity, & Architecture. 2010. (ENG., Illus.). 288p. 128.95 (978-1-4051-9585-0(1), Wiley-Blackwell) Wiley, John & Sons, Inc.

—The Architect's Brain: Neuroscience, Creativity, & Architecture. 2011. (ENG., Illus.). 288p. pap. 34.95 (978-0-470-65825-3(8), Wiley-Blackwell) Wiley, John & Sons, Inc.

Malone, Michael. The Architect's Guide to Residential Design. 2009. (ENG., Illus.). 272p. 59.95 (978-0-07-160563-2(0), 0071605630) McGraw-Hill Professional Publishing.

McCorquodale, Duncan. Pattern Place Purpose: Proctor & Matthews Architects. 2010. (ENG., Illus.). 192p. pap. 55.00 (978-1-906155-60-5(7)) Black Dog Publishing Ltd. GBR. Dist: Perseus Distribution.

McCoy, Ted. A Southern Architecture: The Work of Ted Mccoy. 2008. (Illus.). 176p. 80.00 (978-1-877372-48-3(X)) Otago University Pr. NZL. Dist: International Specialized Bk. Services.

McCullough, Lissa, ed. Conversations with Paolo Soleri. 2012. (ENG.). 96p. pap. 19.95 (978-1-61689-055-1(X)) Princeton Architectural Pr.

Menzel, Lara. Office Architecture & Design. 2009. (Masterpieces Ser.). (FRE, GER & ENG., Illus.). 304p. 49.95 (978-3-938780-77-0(0)) BRAUN DEU. Dist: National Bk. Network.

Meuser, Natascha & Meuser, Philipp. Meuser Architekten: Bauten und Projekte 1995-2010, 1 vol. 2011. (ENG.). 700p. 64.95 (978-3-86922-150-2(X)) DOM Pubs. DEU. Dist: Innovative Logistics.

Mezger, Claudine & Grossmann, Elisabeth. Ueli Berger - Alles in Allem: Arbeiten auf Papier, 1967 2007. Frehner, Matthias, ed. 2008. (Illus.). 112p. pap. 60.00 (978-3-85881-191-2(2)) Scheidegger und Spiess AG, Verlag CHE. Dist: Antique Collectors' Club.

Millette, Daniel M. Vitruvius, Memory, & the Classical Imagination. 2008. 256p. pap. (978-3-639-03310-6(8)) VDM Verlag Dr. Mueller e.K.

Mola, Francesc Zamora. Landschaftsarchitektur, 1 vol. 2010. (ENG, DUT, GER & FRE., Illus.). 619p. pap. 24.95 (978-94-6065-027-7(9)) booQs Publishers bvba BEL. Dist: Innovative Logistics.

Moon, Karen. George Walton: Designer & Architect. (Illus.). 200p. (978-1-873487-01-3(0)) White Cockade Publishing GBR. Dist: Independent Pubs. Group.

Morris, Alison. John Pawson: Plain Space. 2010. (ENG., Illus.). 240p. 75.00 (978-0-7148-5748-0(3)) Phaidon Pr., Inc.

Mosco, Valerio Paolo. Steven Holl: Minimum Series. 2010. (ENG., Illus.). 120p. 19.95 (978-88-6413-022-4(5), Ore Cultura Srl (Acc)) Antique Collectors' Club GBR. Dist: National Bk. Network.

Mostafavi, Mohsen, et al. Mathematical Form: John Pickering & the Architecture of the Inversion Principle. 2007. (Illus.). 72p. 40.00 (978-1-902902-37-1(8)) Princeton Architectural Pr.

MulvannyG2 Architecture. Design at Work. 2008. (Illus.). 148p. 50.00 (978-1-58471-155-1(8)) Visual Reference Pubns., Inc.

Myerson, Deborah & Haughey, Richard M. The Business of Affordable Housing: Ten Developers' Perspectives. 2007. (ENG., Illus.). 136p. per. 49.95 (978-0-87420-977-8(3)) Urban Land Institute.

Nagel, Isolde, ed. José Salinas: Disembodiment. 2010. (ENG., Illus.). 144p. pap. 28.00 (978-3-939633-97-6(6)) Jovis Verlag GmbH DEU. Dist: D.A.P./Distributed Art Pubs.

Neurath, A. Robert. Bratislava Pressburg Pozsony: Jewish Secular Endeavors (1867-1938) 2011. 322p. 99.99 (978-1-4535-6159-1(5)); pap. 89.99 (978-1-4535-6158-4(7)) Xlibris Corp.

Newman, Morris & Beaver, Robyn. Altoon & Porter Architects: Selected Current Works. 2006. (Master Architect Ser.). (ENG., Illus.). 256p. 59.95 (978-1-876907-44-0(4), Images Publishing Dist Ac) Antique Collectors' Club GBR. Dist: National Bk. Network.

Noever, Peter & Prix, Wolf, eds. In the Absence of Raimund Abraham. 2011. (ENG., Illus.). 128p. pap. 40.00 (978-3-7757-2999-4(2)) Hatje Cantz Verlag GmbH & Co KG DEU. Dist: D.A.P./Distributed Art Pubs.

Nouvel, Jean & Coley, Catherine, texts. Jean Prouv#xE9; & Jean Nouvel: Ferembal House. 2011. (ENG., Illus.). 336p. 125.00 (978-2-909187-01-3(2)) Galerie Patrick Seguin FRA. Dist: D.A.P./Distributed Art Pubs.

O'Brien, Patricia J. The Architects & Buildings of Manhattan, Kansas. 2008. (Illus.). vii, 172p. (978-0-9677686-7-0(5)); pap. (978-0-9677686-6-3(7)) Riley County Historical Society.

Obrist, Hans Ulrich. Yona Friedman, 1 vol. 2007. (ENG., Illus.). 126p. per. 22.00 (978-3-86560-171-1(5)) Verlag der Buchhandlung Walther Konig DEU. Dist: D.A.P./Distributed Art Pubs.

Olsberg, Nicholas, ed. & text. Between Earth & Heaven: The Architecture of John Lautner. 2008. (ENG., Illus.). 234p. 60.00 (978-0-8478-3014-5(4)) Rizzoli International Pubns., Inc.

Otmar, Renée & Lau, Dennis. Dennis Lau & Ng Chun Man. 2006. (Master Architect Series V). (ENG., Illus.). 224p. 59.95 (978-1-876907-11-2(8), Images Publishing Dist Ac) Antique Collectors' Club GBR. Dist: National Bk. Network.

Passikoff, Alexander G. A Façade of Buildings: A Collection of Architectural Styles, Architects, & Their Buildings That Make up the Face of New York. 2011. 164p. pap. 49.99 (978-1-4567-9490-3(6)) AuthorHouse.

Pauwels, Wim. Bruno Erpicum, 1983-2008. 2008. (ENG., Illus.). 200p. (978-90-77213-84-1(8), Beta-Plus (Acc)) Antique Collectors' Club.

—Contemporary Architecture & Interiors: Yearbook 2010. 2010. (FRE, GER & ENG., Illus.). 376p. (978-90-8944-016-7(X), Beta-Plus (Acc)) Antique Collectors' Club.

Pennoyer, Peter, et al. Peter Pennoyer Architects: Apartments - Townhouses - Country Houses. 2010. (ENG., Illus.). 240p. 60.00 (978-0-86565-268-2(6)) Vendome Pr., The.

Perez-Gomez, Alberto, et al. Towards an Ethical Architecture: Issues Within the Work of Gregory Henriquez. 2006. (ENG., Illus.). 184p. pap. 29.95 (978-1-894965-50-7(7)) Simply Read Bks. CAN. Dist: Perseus-PGW.

Petit, Emmanuel. Ceci n¿est pas une Reverie: The Architecture of Stanley Tigerman. Rappaport, Nina, ed. 2011. (Illus.). 26p. (978-0-9826385-9-0(0)) Yale Schl. of Architecture.

Plummer, Henry. Nordic Light: Modern Scandinavian Architecture. 2012. (ENG., Illus.). 256p. 60.00 (978-0-500-34275-6(X), 534275) Thames & Hudson.

Ponti, Gio. Gio Ponti: Fascination for Ceramics. 2012. (ENG & ITA., Illus.). 160p. pap. 40.00 (978-88-366-2064-7(7)) Silvana ITA. Dist: D.A.P./Distributed Art Pubs.

Porter, Tom. Will Alsop. 2010. (ENG., Illus.). 176p. pap. 53.95 (978-0-415-54961-5(2)) Routledge.

Princeton Architectural Press Staff. Tom Leader Studio Site Works: Source Books in Landscape Architecture 6. Kenner, Jason, ed. 2010. (ENG., Illus.). 144p. pap. 29.95 (978-1-56898-891-7(5)) Princeton Architectural Pr.

Princeton Architectural Press Staff & Architectural League of New York Staff. Foresight. 2010. (ENG., Illus.). 176p. pap. 24.95 (978-1-56898-887-0(7)) Princeton Architectural Pr.

Puente, Moisés. Conversations with Mies van der Rohe. 2008. (ENG., Illus.). 96p. pap. 19.95 (978-1-56898-753-8(6)) Princeton Architectural Pr.

Pump-Uhlmann, Holger, ed. From Department Store to Stadtgalerie: Buildings for Retail Trade. 2011. (ENG., Illus.). 144p. 60.00 (978-3-86859-105-7(2)) Jovis Verlag GmbH DEU. Dist: D.A.P./Distributed Art Pubs.

Rattenbury, Kester. Cedric Price: Potteries Thinkbelt. Hardingham, Samantha, ed. 2008. (Supercrit Ser.). (ENG., Illus.). 138p. (C). 49.95 (978-0-415-43412-6(2)) Routledge.

Rattenbury, Kester & Hardingham, Samantha, eds. Cedric Price: Potteries Thinkbelt. 2008. (Supercrit Ser.). (ENG., Illus.). 138p. (C). 165.00 (978-0-415-43411-9(4)) Routledge.

Rattenbury, Kester, et al. Architects Today. 2006. (ENG., Illus.). 240p. pap. 19.95 (978-1-85669-492-6(5)) King, Laurence Publishing GBR. Dist: Hachette Bk. Group.

Rauterberg, Hanno. Talking Architecture: Interviews with Architects. 2012. (Illus.). 160p. pap. 19.95 (978-3-7913-4684-7(9)) Prestel Publishing.

Reilly, C. Representative British Architects. 2007. 176p. per. (978-1-905217-73-1(0)) Mills, Jeremy Publishing.

Reisner, Yael. Architecture & Beauty: Conversations with Architects about a Troubled Relationship. 2010. (ENG., Illus.). 264p. pap. 60.00 (978-0-470-84792-3(1), Academy Pr.) Wiley, John & Sons, Inc.

Richardson, Tim. Avant Gardeners: 50 Visionaries of the Contemporary Landscape. 2008. (ENG., Illus.). 352p. 60.00 (978-0-500-51393-4(7)) Thames & Hudson.

Riew, Jayne, et al, eds. The Thomas Jefferson Foundation Medal in Architecture: The First Forty Years, 1966-2005. 2007. (ENG., Illus.). 96p. (gr. 17). per. 19.00 (978-0-9771024-3-3(2)) Univ. Pr. of Virginia.

Ritter, Arno. Hans Peter Worndl. (Illus.). 104p. (978-3-7757-0575-2(9)) Hatje Cantz Verlag GmbH & Co KG DEU. Dist: D.A.P./Distributed Art Pubs.

Ronan, John & Princeton Architectural Press Staff. Explorations: The Architecture of John Ronan. 2010. (ENG., Illus.). 192p. pap. 40.00 (978-1-56898-876-4(1)) Princeton Architectural Pr.

Rooney, E. Ashley. Shingle Style Architecture for the 21st Century. 2010. (Illus.). 176p. 49.99 (978-0-7643-3551-8(0)) Schiffer Publishing, Ltd.

Rosa, Joseph. Douglas Garofalo. 2006. (A+D Ser.). (ENG., Illus.). 96p. pap. 16.95 (978-0-300-12058-5(3)) Art Institute of Chicago.

Roy, Alan R. From Clay to Classrooms: An Architect's Dream to Advance Education in Africa. 2011. 198p. pap. (978-1-897435-67-0(3)) Agio Publishing Hse.

Ryan, Dan. Lean Office Practices for Architects: DLR Associates Series. 2010. 192p. pap. 14.49 (978-1-4490-8481-3(8)) AuthorHouse.

Sachsse, Rolf. Raumbilder Bildräume: Architekten fotografieren. 2009. (GER., Illus.). 116p. (978-3-422-06902-2(X)) Deutscher Kunstverlag GmbH.

Saint, Andrew. Architect & Engineer: A Study in Sibling Rivalry. 2008. (ENG., Illus.). 530p. 65.00 (978-0-300-12443-9(0)) Yale Univ. Pr.

Salim, Faida Noori. The Impact of Globalisation on Architecture & Architectural Ethics. 2011. pap. (978-1-86335-890-3(0)) Common Ground Publishing Pty, Ltd.

Scaglione, Pino, ed. Torino Contemporanea/Contemporary Turin: Guida alle Architetture/Guide to Architecture. 2011. 245p. pap. 24.95 (978-88-95623-44-3(4)) LIST - Laboratorio Editoriale ITA. Dist: Actar Birkhauser Distribution.

Schaal, Hans Dieter. Stadttagebücher: Rom, Venedig, Warschau, Singapur, Kuala Lumpur, Tel Aviv, jerusalem, Lissabon, San Francisco, Las Vegas, Los Angeles, Wien, Paris, Tallinn, Tartu, New York, Moskau, Sankt Petersburg, Barcelona, Genf, Brüssel, London. 12th ed. 2010. (Illus.). 648p. 98.00 *(978-3-936681-31-4(7))* Edition Axel Menges GmbH DEU. Dist: National Bk. Network.

Schaik, Leon van & London, Geoffrey. Procuring Innovative Architecture. 2010. (ENG., Illus.). 240p. (C). pap. 62.95 *(978-0-415-42942-9(0)*, Routledge) Taylor & Francis Group GBR. Dist: Taylor & Francis Group.

Schank Smith, Kendra. Architects Sketches: Dialogue & Design. 2008. (ENG., Illus.). 152p. 59.95 *(978-0-7506-8226-8(4))* Routledge.

Schirren, Matthias & Claus, Sylvia. Hugo Haring: Architekt des Neuen Bauens. (GER., Illus.). 368p. *(978-3-7757-0940-8(1))* Hatje Cantz Verlag GmbH & Co KG DEU. Dist: D.A.P./Distributed Art Pubs.

Schmal, Peter & Wenjun, Zhi, eds. M8 in China: Contemporary Chinese Architects. Zeitgenössische chinesische Architekten. 2010. (ENG., Illus.). 160p. 39.95 *(978-3-86859-025-8(0))* Jovis Verlag GmbH DEU. Dist: D.A.P./Distributed Art Pubs.

Schneekloth, Lynda, et al. Olmsted in Buffalo Niagara. 2011. 108p. mass mkt. 12.95 ***(978-1-931612-24-1(2))*** Univ. at Buffalo, The Urban Design Project, Schl. of Architecture & Planning.

Scott, George Gilbert. Personal & Professional Recollections. 2009. (Illus.). 242p. pap. *(978-0-217-53084-2(2))* Books LLC.

Shaikh, Javeria. Revitalization of Landscape Design at Os Slowackiego. 2010. 68p. pap. *(978-3-639-27480-6(6))* VDM Verlag Dr. Mueller e.K.

Shariff, Yasmin & Tankard, Jane. Towards a New Architect: The Guide for Architecture Students. 2010. (ENG., Illus.). 128p. pap. 37.95 *(978-1-85617-604-0(5))* Routledge.

Skira & Ando, Tadao. Museums. Molinari, Luca, ed. 2009. (ENG., Illus.). 240p. 75.00 *(978-88-6130-680-6(2))* Skira Editore ITA. Dist: Random Hse., Inc.

Slivon, Fred P., Jr. & Albert, Frants. The Next Will Be Better: A Correspondence. 2008. (Illus.). 248p. pap. 14.00 *(978-0-9815269-0-4(X))* Paper Mill Pr.

Solomon, Nancy B. Architecture: Celebrating the Past, Designing the Future. 2008. (Illus.). 424p. 95.00 *(978-1-58471-162-9(0))* Visual Reference Pubns., Inc.

Somer, Kees. The Functional City: The CIAM & Cornelis Van Eesteren, 1928-1960, 1 vol. 2007. (ENG., Illus.). 304p. 75.00 *(978-90-5662-576-4(4))* NAi Uitgevers / Publishers Stichting NLD. Dist: D.A.P./Distributed Art Pubs.

Spens, Michael. Landscape Architecture: Site-Non-Site. 2007. (Architectural Design Ser.: 34). (ENG., Illus.). 146p. per. 55.00 *(978-0-470-03479-8(3)*, Wiley) Wiley, John & Sons, Inc.

Steffens, Jo, ed. Unpacking My Library: Architects & Their Books. 2009. (ENG., Illus.). 192p. 20.00 *(978-0-300-15893-9(9))* Yale Univ. Pr.

Stern, Jewel & Stuart, John A. Ely Jacques Kahn, Architect: Beaux-Arts to Modernism in New York. 2006. (ENG., Illus.). 336p. 60.00 *(978-0-393-73114-9(6)*, 73114) Norton, W. W. & Co., Inc.

Stern, Robert A. M. Robert A. M. Stern: Buildings & Towns. Dixon, Peter Morris, ed. 2007. (ENG., Illus.). 548p. (gr. 12). 85.00 *(978-1-58093-192-2(8))* Monacelli Pr., Inc.

Toivonen, Tuomas, et al. Newly Drawn: Emerging Finnish Architects. 2010. (ENG.). 208p. pap. 63.00 *(978-951-682-940-4(6)*, Art Stock Bks. Ltd/Csi) Continental Sales, Inc.

Trentin, Annalisa, et al. La Lezione Di Pier Luigi Nervi. 2010. (ITA & ENG., Illus.). xiii, 225p. *(978-88-6159-503-3(0))* Bruno, Scholastica, Mondadori.

Unwin, Simon. Exercises in Architecture. 2012. (ENG., Illus.). 224p. (C). 165.00 *(978-0-415-61908-0(4))* Routledge.

Van Schaik, Leon. Procuring Innovative Architecture. 2010. (ENG., Illus.). 240p. (C). 165.00 *(978-0-415-42941-2(2)*, Taylor & Francis) Taylor & Francis Group GBR. Dist: Taylor & Francis Group.

van 't Hoff, Robert. Robert van 't Hoff: Architect of a New Society. 2010. (ENG., Illus.). 156p. 45.00 *(978-90-5662-750-8(3))* NAi Uitgevers / Publishers Stichting NLD. Dist: D.A.P./Distributed Art Pubs.

Vasari, Giorgio & Feser, Sabine. Das Leben des Bramante und des Peruzzi. 2007. (GER., Illus.). 158p. pap. *(978-3-8031-5036-3(1))* Wagenbach, Klaus, GmbH, Verlag.

Verbist, Muriel. Belgian Architects & Their Homes. 2011. (ENG., Illus.). 270p. 55.00 *(978-94-6058-074-1(2)*, Uitgeverij Luster) Antique Collectors' Club GBR. Dist: National Bk. Network.

Vermaas, P. E., et al, eds. Philosophy & Design: From Engineering to Architecture. 2009. (ENG., Illus.). xiv, 362p. pap. 69.95 *(978-90-481-2733-7(5)*, 9048127335) Springer.

Vermaas, Pieter E., et al, eds. Philosophy & Design: From Engineering to Architecture. 2007. (ENG., Illus.). xiv, 362p. 159.00 *(978-1-4020-6590-3(6)*, 1402065906) Springer.

Visser, Frank. Dutch Architects & Their Houses. 2012. (ENG., Illus.). 240p. 55.00 ***(978-94-6058-094-9(7)***, Uitgeverij Luster) Antique Collectors' Club GBR. Dist: National Bk. Network.

Vodopivec, Ales & Znidarsic, Rok. Edvard Ravnikar: Architect & Teacher. 2009. 348p. 89.95 *(978-3-211-99203-6(0))* Springer Wien AUT. Dist: Springer.

Voigt, Wolfgang & May, Roland, eds. Paul Bonatz 1877-1956. 2011. (ENG., Illus.). 320p. 75.00 *(978-3-8030-0729-2(1))* Wasmuth, Ernst J. Verlag GmbH & Co. DEU. Dist: D.A.P./Distributed Art Pubs.

Volker, L. Deciding about Design Quality: Value Judgement of Architectural Design & Decision Making by Public Clients in the Context of European Tendering Regulation. 2010. (ENG., Illus.). 323p. (C). pap. 80.00 *(978-90-8890-053-2(1))* Sidestone Pr. NLD. Dist: Brown, David Bk. Co., The.

Way, Thaïsa. Unbounded Practice: Women & Landscape Architecture in the Early Twentieth Century. 2009. (ENG., Illus.). 320p. (gr. 17). 50.00 *(978-0-8139-2808-1(7))* Univ. Pr. of Virginia.

Webb, Michael. Steven Ehrlich: A Dynamic Serenity. 2006. (House Design Ser.: Vol. 2). (ENG., Illus.). 128p. 49.50 *(978-1-86470-102-9(1))* Images Publishing Group AUS. Dist: National Bk. Network.

Weiss, Klaus-Dieter. Workmanship: Working Philosophy & Design Practice. 2011. (ENG., Illus.). 320p. 69.95 *(978-3-0346-0481-9(5))* Birkhauser Verlag AG CHE. Dist: Actar Birkhauser Distribution.

What Architects Cook up - Asia. 2012. 128p. pap. 39.95 *(978-3-0346-0773-5(3))* Birkhauser Verlag AG CHE. Dist: Actar Birkhauser Distribution.

Williamson, Roxanne Kuter. American Architects & the Mechanics of Fame. 2011. (ENG., Illus.). 298p. pap. 35.00 *(978-0-292-72922-3(7))* Univ. of Texas Pr.

Witt-Dorring, Christian, text. Josef Hoffmann: Interiors 1902-1913. 2009. (ENG., Illus.). 88p. 45.00 *(978-1-931794-20-6(0))* Neue Galerie New York.

Womack, Wayne Marsh. A Philosophy for Planting Design. 2007. (Illus.). xiv, 145p. *(978-0-9744030-5-2(9))* Darbonne & Bartolett Pubs.

Yo.V.A.3 - Young Viennese Architects 3. 2010. 128p. pap. 39.95 *(978-3-7091-0334-0(7))* Springer Wien AUT. Dist: Actar Birkhauser Distribution.

Zuaznabar, Guillermo. Donald Judd: Open Enclosed. 2012. (ENG., Illus.). 128p. 30.00 *(978-84-343-1267-8(0))* Poligrafa, Ediciones, S. A. ESP. Dist: D.A.P./Distributed Art Pubs.

ARCHITECTS—BIOGRAPHY

Abe, Hitoshi & Pollock, Naomi. Hitoshi Abe. 2009. (ENG., Illus.). 208p. 79.95 *(978-0-7148-4665-1(1))* Phaidon Pr., Inc.

Allan, John. Berthold Lubetkin: Architecture & the Tradition of Progress. 2012. (ENG., Illus.). 632p. 59.95 *(978-1-907317-14-9(7))* Black Dog Publishing Ltd. GBR. Dist: Perseus Distribution.

Allen, Stan. Occasions. 2007. *(978-84-96954-97-7(8))* Actar Birkhauser Distribution.

Alysa & Alan the Architects Build the King's Magic Castle. *(978-0-9622514-7-4(X))* Columbia Pubs.

Ames, Anthony. Residential Work, Volume 2: Anthony Ames Architects. 2006. (ENG., Illus.). 240p. 50.00 *(978-0-9774672-4-2(4))* Oro Editions.

Amin, Kamal. Reflections from the Shining Brow: My Years with Frank Lloyd Wright & Olgivanna Lazovich. 2007. (Illus.). 264p. per. 16.95 *(978-1-56474-470-8(1)*, Fithian Pr) Daniel & Daniel, Pubs., Inc.

Anderson, Christy. Inigo Jones & the Classical Tradition. 2006. (ENG., Illus.). 292p. 115.00 *(978-0-521-82027-1(8))* Cambridge Univ. Pr.

Ando, Tadao & Hunter, Matthew. Tadao Ando: Conversations with Students. 2012. (ENG.). 96p. pap. 19.95 ***(978-1-61689-070-4(3))*** Princeton Architectural Pr.

Arbid, George. Karol Schayer, Architect (1900-1971) A Pole in Beirut. 2012. (ENG.). 320p. 69.95 *(978-3-0346-0772-8(5))* Birkhauser Verlag AG CHE. Dist: Actar Birkhauser Distribution.

Armstrong, Christopher Drew. Julien-David Leroy & the Making of Architectural History. 2011. (Classical Tradition in Architecture Ser.). (ENG., Illus.). 320p. (C). 125.00 *(978-0-415-77889-3(1))* Routledge.

Artigas, Isabel. Gaudi 2 Volume Boxed Set: Complete Works, 2 vols. 2007. (ENG, FRE & GER., Illus.). 600p. per. 34.99 *(978-3-8228-5654-3(1))* TASCHEN DEU. Dist: Ingram Pub. Services.

Avery-Quash, Susanna & Sheldon, Julie. Art for the Nation: The Eastlakes & the Victorian Art World. 2011. (ENG., Illus.). 304p. 45.00 *(978-1-85709-507-4(3))* Yale Univ. Pr.

Bachman, Zoltan. Bachman Zoltán. 2010. (HUN, GER & ENG., Illus.). 322p. 54.95 ***(978-963-303-001-1(3))*** Vince Kiado Kft HUN. Dist: Independent Pubs. Group.

Ballantyne, Andrew. Deleuze & Guattari for Architects. 2007. (Thinkers for Architects Ser.). (Illus.). 124p. per. 28.95 *(978-0-415-42116-4(0))* Taylor & Francis Group.

Ban, Shigeru. Paper in Architecture. Rizzoli et al, eds. 2009. (ENG., Illus.). 232p. 65.00 *(978-0-8478-3211-8(2))* Rizzoli International Pubns., Inc.

Bauman, Irena. How to Be a Happy Architect: Bauman Lyons Architects. 2008. (ENG., Illus.). 192p. pap. 39.95 *(978-1-904772-78-1(1))* Black Dog Publishing Ltd. GBR. Dist: Perseus Distribution.

Behnisch, Stefan, et al. Poetry, Property, & Place 01: Stefan Behnisch, Gerald Hines. Rappaport, Nina, ed. 2006. (Edward P. Bass Distinguished Visiting Architecture Fellowship Ser.). (ENG., Illus.). 192p. pap. 35.00 *(978-0-393-73220-7(7)*, 73220) Norton, W. W. & Co., Inc.

Belfoure, Charles. Edmund G. Lind: Anglo-American Architect of Baltimore & the South. 2009. (Illus.). 203p. pap. 27.95 *(978-0-9729743-2-5(6))* Baltimore Architecture Foundation.

Bell, Richard C. The Bridge Builders. 2010. 312p. pap. 16.95 *(978-0-533-16286-4(6))* Vantage Pr., Inc.

Berkovich, Gary. Watching Communism Fail: A Memoir of Life in the Soviet Union. 2008. (ENG., Illus.). 314p. pap. 35.00 *(978-0-7864-4139-6(9))* McFarland & Co., Inc. Pubs.

Biographiq. Sir John Vanbrugh - English Architect & Dramatist (Biography) 2008. 60p. pap. 9.99 *(978-1-59986-389-4(8)*, Biographiq) Filiquarian Publishing, LLC.

Birnbaum, Charles A. & Foell, Stephanie S., eds. Shaping the American Landscape: New Profiles from the Pioneers of American Landscape Design Project. 2009. (ENG.). 496p. (gr. 17). 65.00 *(978-0-8139-2789-3(7))* Univ. Pr. of Virginia.

Bluestein, Howard B. Clouds: Sculptures in the Sky. 2008. (ENG.). 208p. 39.95 *(978-0-300-11036-4(7))* Yale Univ. Pr.

Borutová, Dana & Jurkovic, Dusan. Architekt Dusan Samuel Jurkovic. 2012. (SLO., Illus.). 384p. 99.95 ***(978-80-8085-665-6(6))*** Slovart, Vydavatel'stvo, spol. s.r.o. SVK. Dist: Independent Pubs. Group.

Bragdon, Claude. More Lives Than One. 2006. pap. 24.95 *(978-1-59605-359-5(3)*, Cosimo Classics) Cosimo, Inc.

Brittain-Catlin, Timothy. Leonard Manasseh & Partners: 20th Century Architects. 2011. (Twentieth-century Architects Ser.). (ENG., Illus.). 160p. pap. 40.00 *(978-1-85946-368-0(1))* English Heritage GBR. Dist: Brown, David Bk. Co., The.

Brostom, Caitlin Lempres, et al. The Houses of William Wurster: Frames for Living. 2011. (ENG., Illus.). 224p. 50.00 *(978-1-61689-028-5(2))* Princeton Architectural Pr.

Brown, Gordon S. Incidental Architect: William Thornton & the Cultural Life of Early Washington, D. C., 1794-1828. 2009. (Perspective on Art & Architect Ser.). (ENG.). 192p. pap. 24.95 *(978-0-8214-1863-5(7))* Ohio Univ. Pr.

Brown, Gordon S. & Thornton, William. Incidental Architect: William Thornton & the Cultural Life of Early Washington, D. C., 1794-1828. 2009. (Perspective on Art & Architect Ser.). (ENG., Illus.). 192p. 49.95 *(978-0-8214-1862-8(9))* Ohio Univ. Pr.

Brown-Manrique, Gerardo, text. Rudolf Frankel & Neues Bauen. 2009. (ENG., Illus.). 148p. pap. 50.00 *(978-3-8030-0695-0(3))* Wasmuth, Ernst J. Verlag GmbH & Co. DEU. Dist: D.A.P./Distributed Art Pubs.

Brownell, Blaine Erickson. Matter in the Floating World: Conversations with Leading Japanese Architects & Designers. 2011. (ENG., Illus.). 256p. pap. 40.00 *(978-1-56898-996-9(2))* Princeton Architectural Pr.

Cairney, John. The Quest for Charles Rennie Mackintosh. 2nd ed. 2007. (ENG., Illus.). 300p. per. 16.95 *(978-1-905222-43-8(2))* Luath Pr. Ltd. GBR. Dist: Ingram Pub. Services.

Chacon, Hipolitao Rafael. Original Man. 2008. pap. 35.00 *(978-0-9815760-0-8(1))* Farcountry Pr.

Chacon, Hipolito Rafael. The Original Man: The Life & Work of Montana Architect A. J. Gibson. 2008. (Illus.). 163p. 75.00 *(978-0-9815760-1-5(X))* Univ. of Montana Pr., The.

Chong, Adele, ed. & text. Daan Roosegaarde: Interactive Landscapes. 2011. (ENG., Illus.). 160p. pap. 45.00 *(978-90-5662-754-6(6))* NAi Uitgevers / Publishers Stichting NLD. Dist: D.A.P./Distributed Art Pubs.

Clawley, Alan. John Madin. 2011. (Twentieth-century Architects Ser.). (ENG., Illus.). 148p. pap. 40.00 *(978-1-85946-367-3(3))* English Heritage GBR. Dist: Brown, David Bk. Co., The.

Cobbers, Arnt. Mendelsohn. 2007. (ENG., Illus.). 96p. pap. 9.99 *(978-3-8228-5595-9(2))* TASCHEN DEU. Dist: Ingram Pub. Services.

Colvin, Howard. A Biographical Dictionary of British Architects 1600-1840. 4th ed. 2008. (Paul Mellon Centre for Studies in British Art). (ENG., Illus.). 1264p. 150.00 *(978-0-300-12508-5(9))* Yale Univ. Pr.

Connah, Roger, compiled by. 40/40 Young Architects from Finland. 2nd ed. 2008. (Illus.). 240p. pap. 49.00 *(978-951-682-646-5(6))* Rakennustieto oy FIN. Dist: Independent Pubs. Group.

Corbusier, Le & Le Corbusier. Journey to the East. Zaknic, Ivan, ed. & tr. by. from FRE. 2nd ed. 2007. (ENG., Illus.). 288p. (gr. 17). pap. 23.95 *(978-0-262-62210-3(6))* MIT Pr.

Cothran, James R. Charleston Gardens & the Landscape Legacy of Loutrel Briggs. 2010. (ENG.). 39.95 *(978-1-57003-891-4(0))* Univ. of South Carolina Pr.

Covey, Frances Alden. The Earl Covey Story: A Master Builder in the Adirondacks Who Made Buildings as Beautiful as Nature Herself. rev. ed. 2010. 178p. pap. 20.00 *(978-0-615-34671-7(5))* Hoffer, Terry.

Cramer, J. & Laible, U. Karl Friedrich Schinkel: Guide to His Buildings. 2007. (Illus.). 400p. pap. *(978-3-422-20671-7(X))* Deutscher Kunstverlag GmbH.

Cramer, Johannes, et al, eds. Karl Friedrich Schinkel Guide to His Buildings: Part I: Berlin & Potsdam; Part II: from Aachen Through Mark Brandenburg to St. Petersburg. Wallis, Wendy & Pepper, Ian, trs. from GER. 2007. (Illus.). 400p. pap. 39.95 *(978-3-422-06671-7(3))* Deutscher Kunstverlag GmbH DEU. Dist: Independent Pubs. Group.

Culter Anderson Architects Staff & Cutler, James E. Cutler Anderson. Ojeda, Oscar Riera, ed. 2009. (ENG., Illus.). 440p. 85.00 *(978-0-8478-3223-1(6))* Rizzoli International Pubns., Inc.

DAAB Media Staff, creator. Ferruccio Laviani, 1 vol. 2008. (ENG.). 175p. 29.95 *(978-3-86654-041-5(8))* DAAB Media Gmbh DEU. Dist: Innovative Logistics.

DAAB Media Staff, ed. Patricia Urquiola, 1 vol. 2009. (ENG.). 175p. 29.95 *(978-3-86654-069-9(8))* DAAB Media Gmbh DEU. Dist: Innovative Logistics.

Daix, Pierre, frwd. Main Entrance. 2011. (ENG., Illus.). 80p. 16.00 *(978-2-916275-78-9(9))* Dilecta, Editions FRA. Dist: D.A.P./Distributed Art Pubs.

Dalton, Caroline. John Vanbrugh & the Vitruvian Landscape. 2012. (ENG., Illus.). 256p. (C). 155.00 *(978-0-415-61163-3(6))*; pap. 55.95 *(978-0-415-61164-0(4))* Routledge.

Darling, Elizabeth. Wells Coates: 20th Century Architects. 2012. (Twentieth-century Architects Ser.). (ENG., Illus.). 160p. (C). pap. 40.00 ***(978-1-85946-437-3(8))*** English Heritage GBR. Dist: Brown, David Bk. Co., The.

Davey, Peter. Architecture in Context: Helin Workshop. 2010. (Illus.). 224p. 84.95 *(978-3-0346-0604-2(4))* Birkhauser Verlag AG CHE. Dist: Actar Birkhauser Distribution.

Davis, Arthur Q., mem. It Happened by Design: The Life & Work of Arthur Q. Davis. 2009. (ENG., Illus.). 160p. 50.00 *(978-1-60473-265-8(2))* Univ. Pr. of Mississippi.

Desilets, Deborah. Morris Lapidus: The Architecture of Joy. 2010. (ENG., Illus.). 240p. 65.00 *(978-0-8478-3088-6(8))* Rizzoli International Pubns., Inc.

Diamond, A. J. Sketches: From Here & There, 1 vol. 2011. (ENG., Illus.). 144p. 45.00 *(978-1-55365-591-6(5))* D&M Pubs. Inc. CAN. Dist: Perseus-PGW.

Diedrich, Lisa, ed. Light Volumes: Art & Landscape of Monika Gora. 2011. 208p. 69.95 *(978-3-0346-0757-5(1))* Birkhauser Verlag AG CHE. Dist: Actar Birkhauser Distribution.

Dittel, Deborah. Hans Reynhart: Ein sächsischer Baumeister der Spätgotik. 2008. (GER., Illus.). 116p. *(978-3-8364-8159-5(6))* VDM Verlag Dr. Mueller e.K.

Donati, Cristina & Donati, Maria Cristina. Michael Hopkins. 1976-2006. 2006. (ENG., Illus.). 240p. pap. 34.95 *(978-88-7624-653-1(3))* Skira Editore ITA. Dist: Random Hse., Inc.

Drennan, William R. Death in a Prairie House: Frank Lloyd Wright & the Taliesin Murders. 2008. (ENG., Illus.). 232p. pap. 16.95 *(978-0-299-22214-7(4))* Univ. of Wisconsin Pr.

Dündar, Murat. A Study on Bruno Taut's Way of Thought. 2011. 128p. pap. ***(978-3-8443-0319-3(7))*** Lambert Academic Publishing.

Dunkerley, Michele & Schubart, Hank. Houses Made of Wood & Light: The Life & Architecture of Hank Schubart. 2012. (ENG., Illus.). 208p. 50.00 ***(978-0-292-72942-1(1))*** Univ. of Texas Pr.

Dunkerley, Michele, et al. Houses Made of Wood & Light: The Life & Architecture of Hank Schubart. 2012. E-Book ***(978-0-292-73714-3(9))*** Univ. of Texas Pr.

Dunning, Robert, ed. Jocelin of Wells: Bishop, Builder, Courtier. 2010. (Studies in the History of Medieval Religion Ser.: Volume 36). (Illus.). 236p. 90.00 *(978-1-84383-556-1(8)*, Boydell Press) Boydell & Brewer, Ltd. GBR. Dist: Boydell & Brewer, Inc.

Durough, Allen R. & Rayfield, Wallace A. The Architectural Legacy of Wallace A. Rayfield: Pioneer Black Architect of Birmingham, Alabama. 2nd ed. 2010. (ENG., Illus.). 176p. 32.95 *(978-0-8173-1683-9(3))* Univ. of Alabama Pr.

Essays, Zürich, et al. Sophie Taeuber-Arp: Gestalterin, Architektin, Tänzerin. 2008. (Illus.). 72p. 49.00 *(978-3-85881-196-7(3))* Scheidegger und Spiess AG, Verlag CHE. Dist: Antique Collectors' Club.

Factor, R. Lance. Chapel in the Sky: Knox College's Old Main & Its Masonic Architect. 2009. (ENG.). 180p. 29.95 *(978-0-87580-415-6(2))* Northern Illinois Univ. Pr.

Fairbank, Wilma. Liang & Lin: Partners in Exploring China's Architectural Past. 2009. 256p. (C). pap. 21.95 *(978-0-8122-2040-7(4))* Univ. of Pennsylvania Pr.

Favretti, Rudy J. Jacob Weidenmann: Pioneer Landscape Architect. 2007. (ENG., Illus.). 196p. 49.95 *(978-0-8195-6847-2(3))* Wesleyan Univ. Pr.

Fiorelli, Francesca. Francisco Mangado: Architecture with the Left Hand. 2012. (ENG., Illus.). 400p. 75.00 ***(978-88-572-1236-4(X))*** Skira Editore ITA. Dist: Random Hse., Inc.

Fischer, Joachim, ed. Young European Designers, 1 vol. 2008. (ENG, FRE & GER., Illus.). 399p. 37.95 *(978-3-937718-42-2(7))* DAAB Media Gmbh DEU. Dist: Innovative Logistics.

Fitch, James Marston. James Marston Fitch. 2007. pap. 27.95 *(978-0-7937-3229-6(8))* Norton, W. W. & Co., Inc.

Flint, Anthony. Wrestling with Moses: How Jane Jacobs Took on New York's Master Builder & Transformed the American City. 2011. (Illus.). 272p. pap. 15.00 *(978-0-8129-8136-0(7)*, Random Hse. Trade Paperbacks) Random House Publishing Group.

Frampton, Kenneth. Five North American Architects: An Anthology. 2012. (ENG., Illus.). 240p. pap. 55.00 ***(978-3-03778-256-9(0))*** Lars Muller Pubs. CHE. Dist: Prestel Publishing.

Frampton, Kenneth, et al. Kristin Jarmund. 2008. (Illus.). 205p. *(978-82-530-3094-4(0))* Pax.

Friedland, Roger & Zellman, Harold. The Fellowship: The Untold Story of Frank Lloyd Wright & the Taliesin Fellowship. 2007. (ENG., Illus.). 704p. per. 18.95 *(978-0-06-098866-1(5)*, HarperPerennial) HarperCollins Pubs.

Friedman, Mildred. The Houses. 2009. (Illus.). 320p. 85.00 *(978-0-8478-3060-2(8))* Rizzoli International Pubns., Inc.

Fumihiko, Maki, et al. Fumihiko Maki. 2009. (ENG., Illus.). 320p. 95.00 *(978-0-7148-4956-0(1))* Phaidon Pr., Inc.

Furuyama, Masao. Tadao Ando: 1941. 2006. (Basic Art Ser.). (ENG., Illus.). 96p. pap. 9.99 *(978-3-8228-4895-1(6))* TASCHEN DEU. Dist: Ingram Pub. Services.

Gabellini, Michael. Gabellini: Architecture of the Interior. 2008. (ENG., Illus.). 240p. 65.00 *(978-0-8478-3016-9(0))* Rizzoli International Pubns., Inc.

Gero, Jan. More Me on Me. 2011. 452p. pap. 38.95 ***(978-1-4620-4361-3(5))*** iUniverse, Inc.

Gordon, Max. Max Gordon: Architect for Art. 2011. (ENG., Illus.). 134p. 40.00 *(978-0-615-39579-1(1))* Marquand Bks., Inc.

Gossel, Peter & Roccella, Graziella. Ponti. 2009. (ENG.). 96p. pap. 9.99 *(978-3-8365-0038-8(8))* TASCHEN DEU. Dist: Ingram Pub. Services.

Gottardo, Francesca, ed. Paolo Portoghesi, Architect. 2011. 386p. pap. 40.00 *(978-88-492-2052-0(9))* Gangemi ITA. Dist: International Publishers Marketing.

Grammel, Ursula. Paul Stohrer, 1909-1975: Architekt in der Zeit des Wirtschaftswunders. 2011. (ENG., Illus.). 360p. 98.00 ***(978-3-936681-52-9(X))*** Edition Axel Menges GmbH DEU. Dist: National Bk. Network.

Greene, Isabelle Clara & Waterman, Pamela. Greene Gardens: The Sustainable Landscape Designs of Isabelle Greene. 2007. *(978-1-4236-0093-0(2))* Gibbs Smith, Publisher.

Guastavino, Rafael, 4th. An Architect & His Son: The Immigrant Journey of Rafael Guastavino II & Rafael Guastavino III. 2008. 122p. pap. 19.50 *(978-0-7884-4143-1(4))* Heritage Bks.

Gubler, Jacques, ed. Jean Tschumi: Architecture at Full Scale. 2009. (ENG., Illus.). 224p. 85.00 *(978-88-572-0071-2(X))* Skira Editore ITA. Dist: Random Hse., Inc.

Guilfoyle, Patrick. Twisted Chimneys the Reasons for Being Me. 2009. 350p. 29.50 *(978-1-60860-357-2(1),* Eloquent Bks.) AEG Literary Publishing Services, Inc.

Gunsser, Christoph, et al. Gebaut: Nebel Pössl Architekten. 2007. (Illus.). 122p. *(978-3-7828-1615-1(3))* Kramer, Karl GmbH.

Hadid: Complete Works, 1979-2009. deluxe ed. 2010. *(978-3-8365-1739-3(6))* TASCHEN.

Hadid, Zaha. Zaha Hadid & Hans Ulrich Obrist. 2008. (ENG., Illus.). 136p. pap. 22.00 *(978-3-86560-078-3(6))* Verlag der Buchhandlung Walther Konig DEU. Dist: D.A.P./Distributed Art Pubs.

Halprin, Lawrence. A Life Spent Changing Places. 2011. (Penn Studies in Landscape Architecture Ser.). (Illus.). 280p. (C). 45.00 *(978-0-8122-4263-8(7))* Univ. of Pennsylvania Pr.

Hamerton, Ian, ed. W. A. S. Benson: Arts & Crafts Luminary & Pioneer of Modern Design. 2007. (ENG., Illus.). 352p. *(978-1-85149-476-7(6),* Antique Collectors Club Dist) Antique Collectors' Club.

Haney, David. When Modern Was Green: Life & Work of Landscape Architect Leberecht Migge. 2010. (ENG., Illus.). 344p. (C). 155.00 *(978-0-415-56138-9(8))*; pap. 62.95 *(978-0-415-56139-6(6))* Routledge.

Hardwick, M. Jeffrey. Mall Maker: Victor Gruen, Architect of an American Dream. 2010. 288p. (C). pap. 24.95 *(978-0-8122-2110-7(9))* Univ. of Pennsylvania Pr.

Harris, Penelope. The Architectural Achievement of Joseph Aloysius Hansom (1803-1882) Designing the Hansom Cab, the Birmingham Town Hall, & Churches of the Catholic Revival. 2010. (Illus.). viii, 200p. *(978-0-7734-3851-4(3))* Mellen, Edwin Pr., The.

Hasegawa, Yuko. Kazuyo Sejima + Ryue Nishizawa: SANAA. 2012. (ENG., Illus.). 320p. 79.95 ***(978-0-7148-6388-7(2))*** Phaidon Pr., Inc.

Hawkes, Dave. A Builder's Life. 2009. 68p. pap. 10.49 *(978-1-4389-5005-1(5))* AuthorHouse.

Hayes, Nick. And One Fine Morning: Memories of My Father. 2010. 24.95 *(978-1-932472-98-1(3))* Nodin Pr.

Herreshoff, L. Francis. Captain Nat Herreshoff: The Wizard of Bristol. 2009. (ENG., Illus.). 248p. pap. 29.95 *(978-1-57409-287-5(1))* Sheridan Hse., Inc.

Herrmann, Wolfgang. Gottfried Semper im Exil: Paris, London 1849 bis 1855. Die Entstehungsgeschichte seines grossten theoretischen Werkes "Der Stil" (FRE, GER & ENG., Illus.). 137p. pap. 21.52 *(978-3-7643-0992-3(X),* 376430992X) Birkhauser Boston.

Herzog, Thomas, et al. Thomas Herzog, Architect: Nikolaus Lang, Sculptor Rainer Wittenborn, Painter Joint Works 1972-1966. (ENG & GER., Illus.). 88p. 39.95 *(978-3-7757-0614-8(3))* Hatje Cantz Verlag GmbH & Co KG DEU. Dist: D.A.P./Distributed Art Pubs.

Hettche, Thomas, et al. Fritz Barth, Cannstatter Straße 84, Fellbach: Cannstatter Strasse 84, Fellbach. 2011. (GER & ENG., Illus.). 72p. 49.00 *(978-3-932565-76-2(2))* Edition Axel Menges GmbH DEU. Dist: National Bk. Network.

Hicks, Ashley. David Hicks: A Life of Design. 2009. (ENG., Illus.). 304p. 65.00 *(978-0-8478-3330-6(5))* Rizzoli International Pubns., Inc.

Hiesinger, Kathryn B. & Hadid, Zaha. Zaha Hadid: Form in Motion. 2011. ***(978-0-87633-232-0(7))*** Philadelphia Museum of Art.

Hill, Rosemary. God's Architect: Pugin & the Building of Romantic Britain. 2009. (ENG., Illus.). 656p. 45.00 *(978-0-300-15161-9(6))* Yale Univ. Pr.

Hines, Thomas S. Burnham of Chicago: Architect & Planner. 2nd ed. 2008. (ENG., Illus.). 474p. pap. 22.50 *(978-0-226-34172-9(0))* Univ. of Chicago Pr.

Hockaday, Joan. Greenscapes: Olmsted's Pacific Northwest. 2009. (Illus.). 224p. pap. 29.95 *(978-0-87422-298-2(2))* Washington State Univ. Pr.

Holl, Steven. Steven Holl: Architecture Spoken. 2007. (ENG., Illus.). 304p. 75.00 *(978-0-8478-2920-0(0))* Rizzoli International Pubns., Inc.

Holliday, Kathryn E. Leopold Eidlitz: Architecture & Idealism in the Gilded Age. 2008. (ENG., Illus.). 176p. 55.00 *(978-0-393-73239-9(8),* 73239) Norton, W. W. & Co., Inc.

Holroyd, June. June: Roots of Steel. 2009. 282p. 30.95 *(978-1-4401-5022-7(2))*; pap. 20.95 *(978-1-4401-5020-3(6))* iUniverse, Inc.

Hudson, Karen E. Paul R. Williams: Classic Hollywood Style. 2012. (ENG., Illus.). 240p. 65.00 ***(978-0-8478-3847-9(1))*** Rizzoli International Pubns., Inc.

Hysler-Rubin, Noah. Patrick Geddes & Town Planning. 2011. (ENG., Illus.). 224p. (C). pap. 44.95 *(978-0-415-57867-7(1))* Routledge.

Images Publishing, creator. Cj Lim, Vol. 8. 2006. (Neo Architecture Ser.). (ENG., Illus.). 124p. 49.50 *(978-1-920744-80-9(0))* Images Publishing Group AUS. Dist: National Bk. Network.

—Daryl Jackson Architecture Folio. 2007. (Millennium Ser.). (ENG., Illus.). 256p. 75.00 *(978-1-86470-049-7(1))* Images Publishing Group AUS. Dist: National Bk. Network.

—Goettsch Partners: Selected & Current Works, Goettsch, Kaufman, Nilles, Prendergast, Weldon, Zheng. 2007. (Master Architect Ser.). (ENG., Illus.). 256p. 65.00 *(978-1-86470-168-5(4))* Images Publishing Group AUS. Dist: National Bk. Network.

—Jakob & MacFarlane. 2006. (Neo Architecture Ser.). (ENG., Illus.). 124p. 49.50 *(978-1-920744-83-0(5))* Images Publishing Group AUS. Dist: National Bk. Network.

Images Publishing Group. Murphy/Jahn. 2006. (ENG., Illus.). 256p. 75.00 *(978-1-876907-14-3(2))* Images Publishing Group AUS. Dist: National Bk. Network.

—Valode & Pistre Architectes. 2006. (Master Architect Ser.). (FRE & ENG., Illus.). 236p. 59.95 *(978-1-920744-53-3(3),* Images Publishing Dist Ac) Antique Collectors' Club GBR. Dist: National Bk. Network.

Images Publishing Group & Beaver, Robyn. Hartman-Cox Architects. Beaver, Robyn, ed. 2009. (Master Architect Ser.). (ENG., Illus.). 256p. 85.00 *(978-1-920744-61-8(4))* Images Publishing Group AUS. Dist: National Bk. Network.

Images Publishing Group & Binder, Georges. Jean-Marie Duthilleul et Etienne Tricaud. 2009. (FRE & ENG., Illus.). 248p. 59.95 *(978-1-86470-164-7(1),* Images Publishing Dist Ac) Antique Collectors' Club GBR. Dist: National Bk. Network.

Images Publishing Group & Houben, Francine. Mecanoo. 2008. (DUT & ENG., Illus.). 276p. 59.95 *(978-1-86470-142-5(0),* Images Publishing Dist Ac) Antique Collectors' Club GBR. Dist: National Bk. Network.

Imbert, Dorothee. Between Garden & City: Jean Canneel-Claes & Landscape Modernism. 2009. (ENG., Illus.). 360p. (C). 55.00 *(978-0-8229-4370-9(0))* Univ. of Pittsburgh Pr.

Iredale, Kathryn & Martineau, Sheila. Finding a Good Fit: The Life & Work of Architect Rand Iredale. 2007. (ENG., Illus.). 400p. pap. 39.95 *(978-1-894965-90-3(6))* Simply Read Bks. CAN. Dist: Perseus-PGW.

Jacobson, Hugh Newell. Hugh Newell Jacobsen, Architect. Vignelli, Massimo, ed. 2006. (ENG., Illus.). 352p. 95.00 *(978-1-920744-13-7(4))* Images Publishing Group AUS. Dist: National Bk. Network.

Jacques, David. Lanscape Modernism Renounced: The Career of Christopher Tunnard (1910-1979) 2009. (ENG., Illus.). 288p. 155.00 *(978-0-415-49720-6(5))* Routledge.

—Lanscape Modernism Renounced: The Career of Christopher Tunnard, 1910-1979. 2009. (ENG., Illus.). 288p. pap. 62.95 *(978-0-415-49722-0(1))* Routledge.

Jahanbegloo, Ramin & Rewal, Raj. Talking Architecture: Raj Rewal in Conversation with Ramin Jahanbegloo. 2012. (ENG., Illus.). 162p. pap. 40.00 ***(978-0-19-808294-1(0))*** Oxford Univ. Pr., Inc.

Jefferson, Thomas. Thomas Jefferson, Architect: Original Designs in the Collection of Thomas Jefferson Coolidge, Jr. 205p. reprint ed. 98.00 *(978-0-7222-8716-3(X))* Library Reprints, Inc.

Jekyll, Gertrude. Home & Garden: Notes & Thoughts, Practical & Critical, of a Worker in Both. 2011. (Cambridge Library Collection - Life Sciences Ser.). (ENG., Illus.). 404p. pap. 31.99 ***(978-1-108-03720-4(8))*** Cambridge Univ. Pr.

Jenkins, David, ed. Norman Foster: Works 5. 2009. (Illus.). 592p. 150.00 *(978-3-7913-3258-1(9))* Prestel Publishing.

Jodidio, Philip. Ando: Complete Works. 2007. (FRE, GER & ENG., Illus.). 500p. 39.99 *(978-3-8229-0930-3(6))* TASCHEN DEU. Dist: Ingram Pub. Services.

—Jean-Michel Wilmotte: Product Design. 2010. (Illus.). 312p. 85.00 *(978-3-7913-4407-2(2))* Prestel Publishing.

—Jean Nouvel by Jean Nouvel. Complete Works 1993-2008, 2 vols. 2009. (FRE, GER & ENG., Illus.). 896p. 200.00 *(978-3-8228-5772-4(6))* TASCHEN DEU. Dist: Ingram Pub. Services.

Jodidio, Philip. Kc Jean Nouvel. 2012. (ENG., Illus.). 96p. pap. 9.99 ***(978-3-8365-3080-4(5))*** TASCHEN DEU. Dist: Ingram Pub. Services.

Jodidio, Philip, ed. Shigeru Ban - Complete Works 1985-2010. 2010. (ENG, FRE & GER., Illus.). 464p. 150.00 *(978-3-8365-0735-6(8))* TASCHEN DEU. Dist: Ingram Pub. Services.

Jodidio, Philip & Strong, Janet Adams. I. M. Pei: Complete Works. 2008. (ENG., Illus.). 368p. 85.00 *(978-0-8478-3145-6(0))* Rizzoli International Pubns., Inc.

Jones, Peter. Ove Arup: Masterbuilder of the Twentieth Century. 2006. (ENG., Illus.). 352p. 50.00 *(978-0-300-11296-2(3))* Yale Univ. Pr.

Jones, Peter Blundell. Peter Hubner: Building as a Social Process. 2007. (Work Monographs). (GER & ENG., Illus.). 300p. 89.00 *(978-3-932565-02-1(9))* Edition Axel Menges GmbH DEU. Dist: National Bk. Network.

Kabdebo-Gedeon, Agnes. Bye Bye Budapest: An Autobiography. 2010. (ENG., Illus.). 256p. pap. ***(978-1-84876-614-3(9))*** Troubadour Publishing Ltd.

Karson, Robin. A Genius for Place: American Landscapes of the Country Place Era. 2007. (Illus.). 428p. 65.00 *(978-1-55849-636-1(X))* Univ. of Massachusetts Pr.

King, Henry T., Jr. & King, Henry T. The Two Worlds of Albert Speer: Reflections of a Nuremberg Prosecutor. 2007. (ENG., Illus.). 278p. per. 31.50 *(978-0-7618-3577-6(6))* Univ. Pr. of America, Inc.

Kipnis, Jeffrey & Mayne, Thom. Buildings & Projects, Vol. 5. 2009. (ENG., Illus.). 488p. 85.00 *(978-0-8478-3072-5(1))* Rizzoli International Pubns., Inc.

Klein, Caroline, ed. Piero Lissoni, 1 vol. 2008. (ENG., Illus.). 175p. 29.95 *(978-3-86654-027-9(2))* DAAB Media Gmbh DEU. Dist: Innovative Logistics.

Klotz, Sabine. Fritz Landauer, 1883-1968: Leben Und Werk Eines Judischen. (GER., Illus.). 333p. *(978-3-496-01247-4(1))* Reimer, Dietrich.

Kolberg, Gerhard. Claus Bury: Architectonic Sculptures 1979-1993. (GER & ENG., Illus.). 184p. 39.95 *(978-3-89322-626-9(5))* Edition Cantz DEU. Dist: D.A.P./Distributed Art Pubs.

Koons, David. Gringo on a Chicken Bus. 2009. 320p. pap. 22.95 *(978-0-595-53292-6(6))* iUniverse, Inc.

Kottas, Dimitris. Industrial Design by Architects. 2012. (ENG.). 360p. pap. 39.00 *(978-84-92796-57-1(X))* Links International (Leading International Key Services Barcelona, S.A.) ESP. Dist: National Bk. Network.

Lange, Christiane, text. Ludwig Mies Van der Rohe & Lilly Reich: Furniture & Interiors, 1 vol. 2007. (ENG., Illus.). 208p. 55.00 *(978-3-7757-1921-6(0))* Hatje Cantz Verlag GmbH & Co KG DEU. Dist: D.A.P./Distributed Art Pubs.

Lathrop, Alan K. Minnesota Architects: A Biographical Dictionary. 2010. (Illus.). xiv, 233p. pap. *(978-0-8166-4464-3(0))*; 288p. 39.95 *(978-0-8166-4463-6(2))* Univ. of Minnesota Pr.

Lewis, Diane. Inside-Out: Architecture New York City, 1 vol. 2006. (ENG., Illus.). 160p. pap. 45.00 *(978-88-8158-585-4(5))* Charta ITA. Dist: D.A.P./Distributed Art Pubs.

Li, Shuxue. Lewis Mumford: Critic of Culture & Civilization. 2009. 241p. pap. 49.95 *(978-3-03911-557-0(X))* Lang, Peter AG GBR. Dist: Lang, Peter.

Libeskind, Daniel. Breaking Ground: Adventures in Life & Architecture. 2008. (ENG.). 288p. 28.00 *(978-1-4379-6339-7(0))* DIANE Publishing Co.

Liscombe, R. W. William Wilkins 1778-1839. 2010. (ENG.). 407p. pap. 31.99 *(978-0-521-14467-4(1))* Cambridge Univ. Pr.

Lissmann, Christina, ed. Stephen Williams Architects, 1 vol. 2008. (ENG., Illus.). 176p. 29.95 *(978-3-86654-028-6(0))* DAAB Media Gmbh DEU. Dist: Innovative Logistics.

Little, George & Lewis, David. A Garden Gallery: Inspiration from an Enchanted World of Plants & Artistry. 2008. (ENG., Illus.). 176p. pap. 19.95 *(978-0-88192-914-0(X),* 088192914X) Timber Pr., Inc.

Loring, John. Joseph Urban. 2010. (ENG., Illus.). 224p. 50.00 *(978-0-8109-9026-5(1))* Abrams.

Louna, Lahti. Alvar Aalto-Ex Intimo. 2008. 192p. pap. 26.00 *(978-951-682-619-9(9))* Rakennustieto oy FIN. Dist: Independent Pubs. Group.

Luna, Ian. On the Edge Ten Architects from China. 2007. (ENG., Illus.). 224p. 25.00 *(978-0-8478-2868-5(9))* Rizzoli International Pubns., Inc.

Luxton, Donald. Building the West: The Early Architects of British Columbia. 2nd ed. 2007. (ENG., Illus.). 560p. per. 39.95 *(978-0-88922-554-1(0))* Talonbooks, Ltd. CAN. Dist: Consortium Bk. Sales & Distribution.

Lynn, Catherine & Penabad, Carie. Marion Manley: Miami's First Woman Architect. 2010. (ENG., Illus.). 248p. pap. 34.95 *(978-0-8203-3406-6(5))* Univ. of Georgia Pr.

Maak, Niklas. Le Corbusier: The Architect on the Beach. 2011. (Illus.). 208p. 29.95 ***(978-3-7774-3991-4(6))*** Hirmer Verlag GmbH DEU. Dist: Chicago Distribution Ctr.

Maddex, Diane. Alden B. Dow: Midwestern Modern. 2007. (ENG., Illus.). 264p. 50.00 *(978-0-393-73248-1(7),* 73248) Norton, W. W. & Co., Inc.

Marchand, Bruno, ed. Renato Salvi Architect. 2011. (Illus.). 144p. pap. 49.95 *(978-3-0346-0689-9(3))* Birkhauser Verlag AG CHE. Dist: Actar Birkhauser Distribution.

Marcus, Mette & Juul Holm, Michael, eds. Jörn Utzon: the Architect's Universe, 1 vol. 2008. (ENG., Illus.). 96p. 35.00 *(978-87-91607-11-0(6))* Louisana DNK. Dist: D.A.P./Distributed Art Pubs.

Margulies, et al., Lynn, Lynn & Corner, James. Ian McHarg: Conversations with Students - Dwelling in Nature. Margulies, Lynne et al, eds. 2007. (ENG., Illus.). 112p. pap. 19.95 *(978-1-56898-620-3(3))* Princeton Architectural Pr.

Maria, Josep, et al. Jujol. 2007. (ENG, FRE & GER., Illus.). 158p. 29.99 *(978-3-8228-4406-9(3))* TASCHEN DEU. Dist: Ingram Pub. Services.

Martin, Justin. Genius of Place: The Life of Frederick Law Olmsted. (Merloyd Lawrence Book Ser.). 2012. (ENG., Illus.). 496p. pap. 20.00 ***(978-0-306-82148-6(6))*** 2011. E-Book *(978-0-306-81984-1(8))* 2011. (ENG., Illus.). 496p. 30.00 *(978-0-306-81881-3(7))* Da Capo Pr., Inc.

Mason, Patty Reinert. The National Archives Building: Temple of American History. 2009. *(978-0-9758601-9-9(4))* Foundation for the National Archives.

Mathews, Stanley. From Agit-Prop to Free Space - The Architecture of Cedric Price: "Technology is the Answer but What is the Question? 2007. (ENG., Illus.). 285p. 45.00 *(978-1-904772-52-1(8))* Black Dog Publishing Ltd. GBR. Dist: Perseus Distribution.

Mattor, Theresa. Designing the Maine Landscape. 2009. (ENG., Illus.). 200p. 50.00 *(978-0-89272-729-2(2))* Down East Bks.

McBride, Peter. As an Architect. 2011. 206p. pap. 24.95 ***(978-1-4560-7951-2(4))*** PublishAmerica, Inc.

McCarter, Robert. William Morgan: Selected & Current Works. 2006. (Master Architect Series VI). (ENG., Illus.). 256p. 59.95 *(978-1-876907-02-0(9),* Images Publishing Dist Ac) Antique Collectors' Club GBR. Dist: National Bk. Network.

McGetrick, Brendan, ed. Who Is Architecture: the 2009 Domus China Interviews. 2011. (ENG., Illus.). 131p. pap. 23.00 *(978-988-18816-6-3(8))* Timezone 8 Ltd. HKG. Dist: D.A.P./Distributed Art Pubs.

Meikle, Jim. Thinking Big: The History of Davis Langdon. Black Dog Publishing Staff, ed. 2009. (ENG., Illus.). 256p. 55.00 *(978-1-906155-71-1(2))* Black Dog Publishing Ltd. GBR. Dist: Perseus Distribution.

Miller, Robert L. David M. Schwarz Architects: 2002-2007. 2008. (ENG., Illus.). 240p. pap. 50.00 *(978-0-9679143-5-0(3))* Grayson Publishing.

Mitchell, William Ford. Buildings As History: A Descriptive Catalogue of His Drawings in the Henderson County Public Library: the Architecture of Erle Stillwell. 2006. per. *(978-0-9790753-1-5(9))* Friends of the Henderson County Public Library.

—Buildings as History: A Descriptive Catalogue of His Drawings in the Henderson County Public Library: the Architecture of Erle Stillwell. 2006. *(978-0-9790753-0-8(0))* Friends of the Henderson County Public Library.

Molinelli, Michael. Build Neat Stuff. 2006. 30.00 net. *(978-1-4276-0312-8(X))* Aardvark Global Publishing.

Moretti Srl & Giaconia, Paola. Eric Owen Moss: The Uncertainty of Doing. 2006. (ENG., Illus.). 240p. pap. 34.95 *(978-88-7624-276-2(7))* Skira Editore ITA. Dist: Random Hse., Inc.

Muga, Patricia de, et al. Jean Prouve: Objects & Furniture Design by Architects, 1 vol. 2007. (ENG., Illus.). 128p. 30.00 *(978-84-343-1144-2(5))* Poligrafa, Ediciones, S. A. ESP. Dist: D.A.P./Distributed Art Pubs.

Nashed, Fred. An Ancient Egyptian in Texas. 2010. (Illus.). 208p. pap. 13.95 *(978-1-60264-540-0(X))* Virtualbookworm.com Publishing, Inc.

Neimeyer, Oscar. The Curves of Time: The Memoirs of Oscar Niemeyer. 2007. (POR & ENG., Illus.). 192p. pap. 14.95 *(978-0-7148-4857-0(3))* Phaidon Pr., Inc.

Neutra, Richard. Life & Shape: The Autobiography of Richard Neutra. 2009. (Illus.). 398p. pap. *(978-0-9822251-3-4(X))* Atara Pr.

Niles, Philip. Beauty of the City: A. E. Doyle, Portland's Architect. 2008. (ENG., Illus.). 352p. (C). pap. 29.95 *(978-0-87071-298-2(5))* Oregon State Univ. Pr.

Noever, Peter & Pokorn, Marek, eds. Josef Hoffmann: Autobiography. 2010. (ENG., Illus.). 144p. pap. 30.00 *(978-3-7757-2473-9(7))* Hatje Cantz Verlag GmbH & Co KG DEU. Dist: D.A.P./Distributed Art Pubs.

Noever, Peter & Pokorny, Marek, eds. Josef Hoffmann: Architecture Guide. 2011. (ENG., Illus.). 200p. pap. 40.00 *(978-3-7757-2733-4(7))* Hatje Cantz Verlag GmbH & Co KG DEU. Dist: D.A.P./Distributed Art Pubs.

Northwestern University Library. Walter A. Netsch, FAIA: A Critical Appreciation & Sourcebook. 2008. (ENG., Illus.). 220p. 30.00 *(978-0-8101-2541-4(2))* Northwestern Univ. Pr.

Ochsner, Jeffrey Karl. Lionel H. Pries: Architect, Artist, Educator: from Arts & Crafts to Modern Architecture. 2007. (Illus.). 384p. 60.00 *(978-0-295-98698-2(0))* Univ. of Washington Pr.

Ojeda, Oscar Riera, ed. Romancing the Tropics: Bedmar & Shi. 2006. (ENG., Illus.). 240p. 60.00 *(978-0-9774672-2-8(8))* Oro Editions.

Olmsted, Frederick Law. The Papers of Frederick Law Olmsted: Parks, Politics, & Patronage, 1874-1882, Volume 7. Beveridge, Charles E. et al, eds. 2007. (Papers of Frederick Law Olmsted Ser.). (ENG., Illus.). 784p. (gr. 17). 85.00 *(978-0-8018-8336-1(9))* Johns Hopkins Univ. Pr.

Olsberg, R. Nicholas, et al. Arthur Erickson: Critical Works, 1 vol. 2006. (ENG., Illus.). 256p. *(978-1-55365-154-3(5))* D&M Pubs. Inc.

Paterson, Carrie, ed. Adolf Loos - A Private Portrait. Pontasch, Constance C. & Saunders, Nicholas, trs. from GER. collector's ltd. ed. 2011. (ENG., Illus.). 200p. 24.95 *(978-0-9832540-0-3(1))* DoppelHouse Pr.

Permanyer, Lluis. Gaud#xED; of Barcelona. Permanyer, Lluis, ed. 2012. (ENG., Illus.). 208p. 45.00 ***(978-84-343-1302-6(2))*** Poligrafa, Ediciones, S. A. ESP. Dist: D.A.P./Distributed Art Pubs.

Pevsner, Nikolaus. Matthew Digby Wyatt: The First Cambridge Slade Professor of Fine Art - An Inaugural Lecture. 2010. (ENG.). 72p. pap. 19.99 *(978-0-521-17076-5(1))* Cambridge Univ. Pr.

Pfeiffer, Bruce Brooks. Frank Lloyd Wright: The Heroic Years, 1920-1932. 2009. (ENG., Illus.). 240p. 60.00 *(978-0-8478-3174-6(4))* Rizzoli International Pubns., Inc.

—Frank Lloyd Wright Designs: The Sketches, Plans, & Drawings. 2011. (ENG., Illus.). 420p. 85.00 *(978-0-8478-3570-6(7))* Rizzoli International Pubns., Inc.

Phaidon Press Editors. 10x10_2. 2008. (ENG., Illus.). 464p. pap. 49.95 *(978-0-7148-4864-8(6))* Phaidon Pr. Ltd. GBR. Dist: Hachette Bk. Group.

Phaidon Press Editors, ed. 10x10 - 3: 100 Architects 10 Critics. 2009. (ENG., Illus.). 468p. 90.00 *(978-0-7148-4953-9(7))* Phaidon Pr., Inc.

Poletti, Therese & Paiva, Tom. Art Deco San Francisco: The Architecture of Timothy Pflueger. 2008. (ENG., Illus.). 256p. 55.00 *(978-1-56898-756-9(0))* Princeton Architectural Pr.

Powell, Kenneth. Richard Rogers - Complete Works, 3 vols., Vol. 3. 2006. (ENG., Illus.). 320p. 95.00 *(978-0-7148-4429-9(2))* Phaidon Pr. Ltd. GBR. Dist: Hachette Bk. Group.

Rashid, Karim. KarimSpace. 2009. (ENG., Illus.). 272p. 75.00 *(978-0-8478-3231-6(7))* Rizzoli International Pubns., Inc.

Reich, David. You Could Lose an Eye: My first 80 years in Montreal. 2010. (ENG., Illus.). 200p. 22.95 *(978-1-926824-03-1(2))* Baraka Bks. CAN. Dist: Independent Pubs. Group.

Reisner, Yael. Architecture & Beauty: Conversations with Architects about a Troubled Relationship. 2010. (ENG., Illus.). 264p. 120.00 *(978-0-470-99784-0(2),* Wiley) Wiley, John & Sons, Inc.

Robson, David. Beyond Bawa: Modern Masterworks of Monsoon Asia. 2008. (ENG., Illus.). 224p. 80.00 *(978-0-500-34238-1(5))* Thames & Hudson.

Rocherolle, Gayatri Carole. The Landscape Diaries: Garden of Obsession. 2007. (ENG., Illus.). 172p. pap. 24.95 *(978-1-932646-38-2(8))* Ruder-Finn Pr.

Rodriguez Viqueira, Manuel & Yañez, Enrique. Arquitecto Enrique Yáñez de la Fuente: Memorias. (SPA., Illus.). 160p. *(978-968-18-5183-5(8))* Noriega Editores.

Rogatnick, Abraham J., et al. B.C. Binning. (Illus.). 192p. 50.00 *(978-1-55365-171-0(5))* D&M Pubs. Inc. CAN. Dist: Perseus-PGW.

Rossi, Aldo. A Scientific Autobiography. Venuti, Lawrence, tr. from ITA. 2010. (Oppositions Bks.). (ENG., Illus.). 128p. (gr. 17). pap. 20.95 *(978-0-262-51438-5(9))* MIT Pr.

Rudder, Steffen De. Architect Hugh Stubbins, 1 vol. 2007. (ENG., Illus.). 192p. pap. 35.00 *(978-3-939633-24-2(0))* Jovis Verlag GmbH DEU. Dist: D.A.P./Distributed Art Pubs.

Rykwert, Joseph, et al, contrib. by. Neues Museum Berlin: By David Chipperfield Architects in Collaboration with Julian Harrap. 2010. (ENG., Illus.). 288p. pap. 65.00 *(978-3-86560-704-1(7))* Verlag der Buchhandlung Walther Konig DEU. Dist: D.A.P./Distributed Art Pubs.

Saeks, Diane Dorrans. Orlando Diaz-Azcuy. 2009. (ENG., Illus.). 224p. 60.00 *(978-0-8478-3076-3(4))* Rizzoli International Pubns., Inc.

Saint-Amour, Suzanne. René Richer, 1887-1963, Architecte Maskoutain: Oublier Ne Puis. 2008. (FRE., Illus.). 276p. *(978-2-89634-029-3(7))* GID, Editions.

Sasonoff, Alexander G. Growing up in Rat City & Beyond. 2008. 240p. pap. 14.49 *(978-1-4343-8903-9(0))* AuthorHouse.

Scarpa, Lawrence. John Howey. 2006. (Master Architect Ser.: Vol. 7). (ENG., Illus.). 256p. 59.95 *(978-1-86470-133-3(1))* Images Publishing Dist A/C.

Schulze, Franz & Windhorst, Edward. Mies Van der Rohe: A Critical Biography. 2012. (Illus.). 568p. 45.00 ***(978-0-226-75600-4(9))*** Univ. of Chicago Pr.

Seidler, Harry & Abel, Chris. Early Houses & Recent Houses, 2 vols. 2006. (ENG., Illus.). 144p. 90.00 *(978-1-920744-16-8(9))* Images Publishing Group AUS. Dist: National Bk. Network.

Serraino, Pierluigi & Marx, John. Wandering the Garden of Technology & Passion. 2012. (ENG., Illus.). 192p. 45.00 *(978-1-890449-56-8(3))* Balcony Pr.

Sharp, Dennis & Rendel, Sally. Connell Ward & Lucas: Modernist Architecture in England. 2008. (ENG., Illus.). 224p. 65.00 *(978-0-7112-2768-2(3))* Lincoln, Frances Ltd. GBR. Dist: Perseus-PGW.

Sherman, Darryl. My '70s Book: The When I Was A Kid... Book for the Generation That Grew up in The '70s. 2008. 108p. pap. 11.95 *(978-1-59858-690-9(4))* Dog Ear Publishing, LLC.

Sigurd Lewerentz, Architect. 82.00 *(978-91-85194-71-1(9))* Byggforlaget SWE. Dist: Coronet Bks.

Simpson, Richard V. Herreshoff Yachts: Seven Generations of Industrialists, Inventors & Ingenuity in Bristol. 2007. (Illus.). 152p. pap., per. 21.99 *(978-1-59629-306-9(3))* History Pr., The.

Snodin, Michael, ed. Horace Walpole's Strawberry Hill. 2009. (Lewis Walpole Series in Eighteenth-C Ser.). (ENG., Illus.). 356p. 85.00 *(978-0-300-12574-0(7))* Yale Univ. Pr.

Sokol, David. Seventy Nordic Architects, 1 vol. 2009. (ENG., Illus.). 448p. 58.00 *(978-3-938666-83-8(8))* DOM Pubs. DEU. Dist: Innovative Logistics.

Soros, Susan Weber & Stuart, James. James "Athenian" Stuart: The Rediscovery of Antiquity. 2007. (ENG., Illus.). 688p. 110.00 *(978-0-300-11713-4(2))* Yale Univ. Pr.

Speaks, Michael & El-Khoury, Rodolphe, contrib. by. Architecture & Sensuality: Andrew Bromberg of Aedas, Recent Works. 2007. (ENG., Illus.). 256p. 40.00 *(978-0-9774672-8-0(7))* Oro Editions.

Speer, Albert. Infiltration: How Heinrich Himmler Schemed to Build an SS Industrial Empire. 2010.Tr. of Sklavenstaat: meine Auseinandersetzungen mit der SS. (ENG., Illus.). 402p. pap. 29.95 *(978-4-87187-877-7(5))* Ishi Pr. International.

—Spandau the Secret Diaries. Winston, Richard & Winston, Clara, trs. 2010. 566p. pap. 34.95 *(978-4-87187-879-1(1))* Ishi Pr. International.

Stephan, Regina, ed. Joseph Maria Olbrich. 2010. (ENG., Illus.). 64p. 30.00 *(978-3-7757-2551-4(2))* Hatje Cantz Verlag GmbH & Co KG DEU. Dist: D.A.P./Distributed Art Pubs.

Stone, Hicks. Edward Durell Stone: A Son's Untold Story of a Legendary Architect. 2011. (ENG., Illus.). 336p. 85.00 *(978-0-8478-3568-3(5))* Rizzoli International Pubns., Inc.

Stonehouse, Roger, et al. Colin St John Wilson: Buildings & Projects. 2008. (ENG., Illus.). 509p. 59.95 *(978-1-904772-70-5(6))* Black Dog Publishing Ltd. GBR. Dist: Perseus Distribution.

Sudjic, Deyan. Norman Foster: A Life in Architecture. 2010. (ENG.). 320p. (gr. 12). 37.95 *(978-1-59020-432-0(8))* Overlook Pr., The.

Suzuki, Hiroyuki. Shuhei Endo: Paramodern Architecture. rev. ed. 2006. (ENG., Illus.). 212p. pap. 29.95 *(978-1-904313-43-4(4))* Phaidon Pr., Inc.

Swaback, Vernon D. Believing in Beauty: Conversations with Vernon D. Swaback. 2009. pap. *(978-0-927015-40-0(4))* Bridgewood Pr.

Swenarton, Mark. Building the New Jerusalem: Architecture, Housing & Politics 1900-1930. 2010. (ENG., Illus.). 246p. 80.00 ***(978-1-84806-024-1(6))*** Building Research Establishment GBR. Dist: Taylor & Francis Group.

Symondson, Anthony, et al. Sir Ninian Comper: An Introduction to His Life & Work, with Complete Gazetteer: With, of the Atmosphere of a Church. 2007. (Illus.). 336p. pap. *(978-1-904965-11-4(3))* Spire Bks. Ltd.

Tames, Richard. Robert Adam: An Illustrated Life of Robert Adam, 1728-92. 2008. (Lifelines Ser.). (ENG., Illus.). 48p. per. 12.95 *(978-0-7478-0603-5(9))* Shire Pubns., Ltd. GBR. Dist: Random Hse., Inc.

Tankard, Judith B. Beatrix Farrand: Private Gardens, Public Landscapes. 2009. (ENG., Illus.). 240p. 60.00 *(978-1-58093-227-1(4))* Monacelli Pr., Inc.

Thomas, Jane. Basil Spence: Architect. Long, Philip, ed. 2008. (ENG., Illus.). 128p. pap. *(978-1-906270-00-1(7))* National Galleries of Scotland.

Thompson, Jessica Cargill. 40 Architects Around 40. 25th anniv. ed. 2006. (ENG, FRE & GER., Illus.). 557p. pap. 14.99 *(978-3-8228-5033-6(0))* TASCHEN DEU. Dist: Ingram Pub. Services.

—40 Architects Around 40. 2006. (ITA, POR & SPA.). 576p. pap. 12.99 *(978-3-8228-5034-3(9))* Taschen America, LLC.

Tigerman, Stanley. Designing Bridges to Burn: Architectural Memoirs by Stanley Tigerman. 2011. (ENG., Illus.). 240p. pap. 24.95 *(978-1-935935-07-0(0))* Oro Editions.

Tostrup, Elizabeth. Norwegian Wood: The Thoughtful Architecture of Wenche Selmer. 2006. (ENG., Illus.). 208p. 45.00 *(978-1-56898-593-0(2))* Princeton Architectural Pr.

Tribert, Renee & O'Gorman, James F. Gervase Wheeler: A British Architect in America, 1847-1860. 2012. (Driftless Connecticut Series & Garnet Bks.). (ENG., Illus.). 136p. 35.00 *(978-0-8195-7145-8(8))* Wesleyan Univ. Pr.

Tyack, Geoffrey. John Nash: Architect of the Picturesque. Tyack, Geoffrey, ed. 2012. (ENG., Illus.). 250p. (C). pap. 100.00 ***(978-1-84802-102-0(X))*** English Heritage GBR. Dist: Brown, David Bk. Co., The.

Udsen, Vibe & Moller, Henrik Sten. Jorn Utzon - Houses. 2006. (ENG., Illus.). 240p. 85.00 *(978-87-987597-3-7(6))* Living Architecture Publishing DNK. Dist: Perseus-PGW.

Ujifusa, Steven. A Man & His Ship: America's Greatest Naval Architect & His Quest to Build the S. S. United States. 2012. (ENG., Illus.). 448p. 29.99 ***(978-1-4516-4507-1(4))*** Simon & Schuster.

Vivoni Farage, Enrique. Klumb: Una Arquitectura de Impronta Social. 2006. (Serie Mnemosina Ser.: Vol. 2). (ENG & SPA., Illus.). xiv, 346p. 84.95 *(978-0-8477-2754-4(8))* Univ. of Puerto Rico Pr.

Walker, Fred. Ships & Shipbuilders. 2010. 256p. 45.95 *(978-1-59114-788-6(3))* Naval Institute Pr.

Ward, W. C. Sir John Vanbrugh V1. 2006. pap. 38.95 *(978-1-4286-6103-5(4))* Kessinger Publishing, LLC.

—Sir John Vanbrugh V2. 2006. pap. 34.95 *(978-1-4286-6104-2(2))* Kessinger Publishing, LLC.

Warhaftig, Myra. They Laid the Foundation: Lives & Works of German-Speaking Jewish Architects in Palestine 1918-1948, 1 vol. Lerner, Andrea, tr. from GER. 2nd ed. 2007. (ENG., Illus.). 416p. 40.00 *(978-3-8030-0676-9(7))* Wasmuth, Ernst J. Verlag GmbH & Co. DEU. Dist: D.A.P./Distributed Art Pubs.

Warren, Miles. Miles Warren: An Autobiography. 2009. (ENG., Illus.). 188p. 49.95 *(978-1-877257-76-6(1))* Canterbury Univ. Pr. NZL. Dist: Independent Pubs. Group.

Warrener, Rodney. Martin Travers, an Appreciation. 2006. (ENG., Illus.). 352p. 60.00 *(978-0-906290-70-5(8))* Unicorn Pr., London GBR. Dist: National Bk. Network.

Watkins, Charles & Cowell, Ben. Uvedale Price (1747-1829) Decoding the Picturesque. 2012. (Garden & Landscape History Ser.: Volume 3). (Illus.). 276p. 45.00 ***(978-1-84383-708-4(0)***, Boydell Press) Boydell & Brewer, Ltd. GBR. Dist: Boydell & Brewer, Inc.

Weber, Nicholas Fox. Le Corbusier. 2008. (ENG., Illus.). 848p. 45.00 *(978-0-375-41043-7(0)*, Knopf) Knopf Doubleday Publishing Group.

Webster, Christopher. R. D. Chantrell (1793-1872) & the Architecture of a Lost Generation. 2010. (ENG., Illus.). 347p. (C). 60.00 *(978-1-904965-22-0(9))* Spire Bks. Ltd. GBR. Dist: Brown, David Bk. Co., The.

Weintraub, Alan, photos by. Frank Lloyd Wright: American Master. 2009. (Illus.). 400p. 30.00 *(978-0-8478-3236-1(8))* Rizzoli International Pubns., Inc.

—Frank Lloyd Wright Mid-Century Modern. 2007. (ENG., Illus.). 336p. 55.00 *(978-0-8478-2976-7(6))* Rizzoli International Pubns., Inc.

—Oscar Niemeyer Buildings. 2009. (ENG., Illus.). 368p. 75.00 *(978-0-8478-3190-6(6))* Rizzoli International Pubns., Inc.

Weiss, Ellen. Robert R. Taylor & Tuskegee: An African American Architect Designs for Booker T. Washington. 2011. (ENG.). 400p. 39.95 *(978-1-58838-248-1(6)*, NewSouth Bks.) NewSouth, Inc.

Welch, Diane Y. Lilian J. Rice: Architect of Rancho Santa Fe, California. 2010. (Illus.). 224p. 49.99 *(978-0-7643-3456-6(5))* Schiffer Publishing, Ltd.

Whyte, William. Oxford Jackson: Architecture, Education, Status, & Style 1835-1924. 2006. (Oxford Historical Monographs). (ENG., Illus.). 288p. 150.00 *(978-0-19-929658-3(8))* Oxford Univ. Pr., Inc.

Wild, David. Jazzpaths: An American Photomemento. 2012. (ENG., Illus.). 112p. 35.00 ***(978-0-907259-45-9(6))*** Hyphen Pr. GBR. Dist: Hachette Bk. Group.

Williams, A. Richard. Archipelago: Islands of Living & Learning Architecture. 2009. (ENG.). 456p. pap. 35.00 *(978-0-252-07685-5(0))* Univ. of Illinois Pr.

Wilson, Mark A. & Maybeck, Bernard R. Bernard Maybeck Architect of Elegance. 2011. (ENG., Illus.). 240p. 60.00 *(978-1-4236-1180-6(2))* Gibbs Smith, Publisher.

Wilson, Mark Anthony. Julia Morgan: Architect of Beauty. 2012. (ENG., Illus.). 256p. pap. 30.00 ***(978-1-4236-3654-0(6))*** Gibbs Smith, Publisher.

Woodbridge, Sally B. Bernard Maybeck: Visionary Architect. 2006. (ENG., Illus.). 248p. pap. 45.00 *(978-0-7892-0132-4(1))* Abbeville Pr., Inc.

Wyllie, Romy. Bertram Goodhue. 2007. 55.00 *(978-0-7937-3219-7(0))* Norton, W. W. & Co., Inc.

—Bertram Goodhue: His Life & Residential Architecture. 2007. (ENG., Illus.). 224p. 60.00 *(978-0-393-73219-1(3)*, 73219) Norton, W. W. & Co., Inc.

Yudell, Buzz & Ruble, John. Moore Ruble Yudell Vol. VI: Making Place. 2006. (Master Architect Series VI). (ENG., Illus.). 256p. 59.95 *(978-1-876907-47-1(9)*, Images Publishing Dist Ac) Antique Collectors' Club GBR. Dist: National Bk. Network.

Zacek, Tomas & Trnovska, Katarina. Wave 68-84: Young Slovak Architects. 2010. 216p. pap. 49.00 *(978-80-8085-921-3(3))* Slovart, Vydavateľstvo, spol. s.r.o. SVK. Dist: Independent Pubs. Group.

Zepter, Tobias, text. MODERSOHN & FREIESLEBEN Architekten: Das Leben der Dinge. The Life of Things. 2010. (ENG., Illus.). 176p. 55.00 *(978-3-7757-2487-6(7))* Hatje Cantz Verlag GmbH & Co KG DEU. Dist: D.A.P./Distributed Art Pubs.

Zimmerman, Jean. Love, Fiercely: A Gilded Age Romance. 2012. (ENG., Illus.). 336p. 26.00 *(978-0-15-101447-7(7))* Houghton Mifflin Harcourt Trade & Reference Pubs.

Zimmermann, H. Russell. The Architecture of Eugene Liebert: Teutonic Style in the American Midwest. 2006. (Illus.). 64p. *(978-0-9741403-5-3(X))*; per. *(978-0-9741403-9-1(2))* Christy Co.

ARCHITECTS—DIRECTORIES

Beaver, Robyn. 1000 Architects, 2 vols. 2006. (ENG., Illus.). 95.00 *(978-1-876907-91-4(6))* Images Publishing Group AUS. Dist: National Bk. Network.

Casper, Paul Alexander. Chicago Luxury Home & Condo: The Ultimate Source for Designing, Building, Remodeling, Landscaping, Decorating & Furnishing Chicagoland's Finest Homes & Condos. 2nd ed. 2008. (ENG.). 800p. 24.95 *(978-0-9789734-1-4(0))* Lake Forest Media Group, The.

Cramer, James P. & Paradise Wolford, Jane. Almanac of Architecture & Design 2011. 12th ed. 2011. (Illus.). 606p. pap. 149.00 ***(978-0-9846136-0-1(9))*** Greenway Communications.

Crosbie, Michael J. Architecture for the Gods, Vol. 2. 2006. (Religious Architecture Ser.). (ENG., Illus.). 192p. 65.00 *(978-1-876907-50-1(9))* Images Publishing Group AUS. Dist: National Bk. Network.

GmbH, Birkhäuser. Architekten Profile 2011 / 2012. 2010. (ENG & GER., Illus.). 392p. 95.00 *(978-3-0346-0612-7(5))* Birkhauser Verlag AG CHE. Dist: Actar Birkhauser Distribution.

Otto, Frei & Songel, Juan María. A Conversation with Frei Otto. 2010. (ENG., Illus.). 96p. pap. 19.95 *(978-1-56898-884-9(2))* Princeton Architectural Pr.

Rosenthal, Lisa, contrib. by. Directory of the New Urbanism: 2008 Edition. 2008. per. 89.00 *(978-0-9745021-4-4(6))* New Urban Pubns.

Steuteville, Robert, ed. The Directory of the New Urbanism: 2007 Edition. 2007th ed. 2007. 300p. per. 89.00 *(978-0-9745021-3-7(8))* New Urban Pubns.

ARCHITECTS—LEGAL STATUS, LAWS, ETC.

see also Building Laws; Engineering Law

Dixon, Sheila A., ed. The XL Insurance Contract Guide for Design Professionals: A Risk Management Handbook for Architects & Engineers. 2008. 528p. pap. incl. cd-rom *(978-0-9797213-0-4(X))* X.L. America, Inc.

Herrmann, Robert F. & Menaker & Herrmann LLP. Law for Architects: What You Need to Know. 2012. (ENG.). 224p. 35.00 ***(978-0-393-73345-7(9)***, 73345) Norton, W. W. & Co., Inc.

Imrie, Rob & Street, Emma. Architectural Design & Regulation. 2011. (ENG., Illus.). 376p. 124.99 *(978-1-4051-7966-9(X)*, Wiley-Blackwell) Wiley, John & Sons, Inc.

Speaight, Anthony, ed. Architect's Legal Handbook: The Law for Architects. 9th rev. ed. 2010. (ENG., Illus.). 432p. pap. 56.95 *(978-1-85617-627-9(4))* Routledge.

van Gulijk, Stéphanie. European Architect Law: Towards a New Design. 2009. (Illus.). 250p. pap. 61.95 *(978-90-466-0145-7(5))* Maklu Uitgevers N.V. BEL. Dist: International Specialized Bk. Services.

Volker, L. Deciding about Design Quality: Value Judgement of Architectural Design & Decision Making by Public Clients in the Context of European Tendering Regulation. 2010. (ENG., Illus.). 323p. (C). pap. 80.00 *(978-90-8890-053-2(1))* Sidestone Pr. NLD. Dist: Brown, David Bk. Co., The.

ARCHITECTS—PUBLIC RELATIONS

Elias, Helen. Getting Your Project Published: A Guide to Press Relations for Architects, Designers & Engineers. 2006. (ENG., Illus.). 208p. 52.95 *(978-0-415-34867-6(8))*; 155.00 *(978-0-415-34866-9(8))* Taylor & Francis Group GBR. (Taylor & Francis). Dist: Taylor & Francis Group.

ARCHITECTS AND COMMUNITY

Aberdeen Gardens Heritage Committee. Aberdeen Gardens. 2007. (Images of America Ser.). (ENG., Illus.). 128p. per. 19.99 *(978-0-7385-5292-7(5))* Arcadia Publishing.

Bell, Bryan & Wakeford, Katie. Expanding Architecture: Design As Activism. 2008. (ENG., Illus.). 288p. pap. 34.95 *(978-1-933045-78-8(7)*, Metropolis Bks.) D.A.P./Distributed Art Pubs.

Bentley, Ian & Butina-Watson, Georgia. Identity by Design. 2007. (ENG., Illus.). 298p. pap. 62.95 *(978-0-7506-4767-0(1))* Routledge.

Berelowitz, Lance. Dream City: Vancouver & the Global Imagination, 1 vol. 2010. (ENG., Illus.). 288p. pap. 29.95 *(978-1-55365-170-3(7))* D&M Pubs. Inc. CAN. Dist: Perseus-PGW.

Bess, Philip. Till We Have Built Jerusalem: Architecture, Urbanism, & the Sacred. 2006. (Illus.). 325p. 28.00 *(978-1-932236-96-5(1))*; per. 18.00 *(978-1-932236-97-2(X))* ISI Bks.

Cary, John, ed. The Power of Pro Bono: 40 Stories about Design for the Public Good by Architects & Their Clients, 1 vol. 2010. (ENG.). 288p. 40.00 *(978-1-935202-18-9(9)*, Metropolis Bks.) D.A.P./Distributed Art Pubs.

Cuff, Dana & Sherman, Roger, eds. Fast-Forward Urbanism: Rethinking Architecture's Engagement with the City. 2011. (ENG., Illus.). 288p. pap. 34.95 *(978-1-56898-977-8(6))* Princeton Architectural Pr.

De Rossi, Antonio, ed. Grande Scala: Architecture, Politic & Form. 2011. 336p. pap. 34.95 *(978-88-95623-29-0(0))* LIST - Laboratorio Editoriale ITA. Dist: Actar Birkhauser Distribution.

Hinson, David & Miller, Justin. Designed for Habitat: Collaborations with Habitat for Humanity. 2012. E-Book ***(978-0-203-12347-8(6))*** Routledge.

Hinson, David & Miller, Justin. Habitat x Design: Habitat for Humanity & the Challenge of Design Excellence. 2012. (ENG., Illus.). 208p. (C). 165.00 *(978-0-415-89108-0(6))*; pap. 34.95 *(978-0-415-89109-7(4))* Routledge.

ARCHITECTURAL ACOUSTICS

see also Absorption of Sound; Sound—Measurement

Allard, Jean & Atalla, Noureddine. Propagation of Sound in Porous Media: Modeling Sound Absorbing Materials. 2nd ed. 2009. (ENG., Illus.). 372p. 140.00 *(978-0-470-74661-5(0)*, Wiley) Wiley, John & Sons, Inc.

Ando, Yoichi. Auditory & Visual Sensations. 2009. (ENG., Illus.). xxv, 340p. 159.00 *(978-1-4419-0171-2(X)*, 144190171X) Springer.

Barron, Michael. Auditorium Acoustics. 2nd rev. ed. 2009. (ENG., Illus.). 504p. (C). 165.00 *(978-0-419-24510-0(3)*, RU29200, Spon Pr.) Routledge.

Beranek, Leo. Concert Halls & Opera Houses: Music, Acoustics, & Architecture. 2nd ed. 2010. (ENG., Illus.). pap. 99.00 *(978-1-4419-3038-5(8)*, 1441930388) Springer.

Blesser, Barry & Salter, Linda-Ruth. Spaces Speak, Are You Listening? Experiencing Aural Architecture. 2006. (ENG., Illus.). 456p. (gr. 17). 42.95 *(978-0-262-02605-5(8))* MIT Pr.

Bradley, David Timothy, et al. Acoustical Design of Theatres for Drama Performance: 1985-2010. 2010. (Illus.). 329p. ***(978-0-9846084-5-4(1))*** American Institute of Physics.

Cavanaugh, William J., et al. Architectural Acoustics: Principles & Practice. 2nd ed. 2009. (ENG., Illus.). 352p. 130.00 *(978-0-470-19052-4(3)*, Wiley) Wiley, John & Sons, Inc.

Cirillo, Ettore & Martellotta, Francesco. Worship, Acoustics, & Architecture. 2007. (Illus.). 210p. per. 69.00 *(978-0-906522-44-8(7))* Multi Science Publishing Co., Ltd. GBR. Dist: Independent Pubs. Group.

Fuchs, Helmut V. Schallabsorber und Schalldämpfer: nnovative akustische Konzepte und Bauteile mit praktischen Anwendungen in konkreten Beispielen. 2nd ed. 2006. (VDI-Buch Ser.). (Illus.). XVI, 546p. 129.00 *(978-3-540-35493-2(X)*, 354035493X) Springer.

Hassan, Osama A. B. Building Acoustics & Vibration: Theory & Practice. 2009. 972p. 118.00 *(978-981-283-833-9(3))* World Scientific Publishing Co., Inc.

Howard, Deborah & Moretti, Laura. Sound & Space in Renaissance Venice: Architecture, Music, Acoustics. 2010. (Illus.). 256p. 55.00 *(978-0-300-14874-9(7))* Yale Univ. Pr.

Ilgü, et al. Noise Barrier Effectiveness in Semi Anechoic Chamber. 2011. 68p. pap. ***(978-3-8454-1723-3(4))*** Lambert Academic Publishing.

Jaffe, Lee & Jaffe, J. Christopher. The Acoustics of Performance Halls Spaces for Music from Carnegie Hall to the Hollywood Bowl. 2010. (ENG., Illus.). 208p. 50.00 *(978-0-393-73255-9(X)*, 73255) Norton, W. W. & Co., Inc.

Kleiner, Mendel. Acoustics & Audio Technology. 3rd ed. 2011. pap. *(978-1-60427-052-5(7))* Ross, J. Publishing, Inc.

Kleiner, Mendel, et al. Worship Space Acoustics. 2010. 256p. pap. *(978-1-60427-037-2(3))* Ross, J. Publishing, Inc.

Kuttruff, Heinri & Kuttruff, Heinrich. Room Acoustics. 5th rev. ed. 2009. (ENG., Illus.). 392p. 175.00 *(978-0-415-48021-5(3)*, CRC Press) Taylor & Francis Group GBR. Dist: Taylor & Francis Group.

Leitner, Bernhard. P. U. L. S. E. Raume der Zeit/Spaces in Time. 2008. (GER & ENG., Illus.). 208p. 60.00 *(978-3-7757-2047-2(2))* Hatje Cantz Verlag GmbH & Co KG DEU. Dist: D.A.P./Distributed Art Pubs.

Maekawa, Zyun-iti, et al. Environmental & Architectural Acoustics. 2nd rev. ed. 2010. (ENG., Illus.). 376p. (C). 160.00 *(978-0-415-44900-7(6)*, CRC Press) Taylor & Francis Group GBR. Dist: Taylor & Francis Group.

Mistur, Mark. The Architecture of EMPAC: the Tangible & the Tantalizing: The Curtis R. Priem Experimental Media & Performing Art Center. 2011. (ENG.). 256p. 40.00 *(978-0-578-07240-1(8))* Oro Editions.

Newhouse, Victoria. Site & Sound: The Architecture & Acoustics of New Opera Houses & Concert Halls. 2012. (ENG., Illus.). 256p. 50.00 ***(978-1-58093-281-3(9))*** Monacelli Pr., Inc.

Shea, Mike. How to Build a Small Budget Recording Studio from Scratch 4/E. 4th ed. 2012. (ENG., Illus.). 464p. pap. 25.00 ***(978-0-07-178271-5(0)***, 0071782710, TAB/Electronics) McGraw-Hill Professional Publishing.

Thorburn. Acoustics & Architecture. 2014. (ENG.). 320p. pap. 49.95 ***(978-0-7506-6543-8(2)***, Architectural Pr.) Elsevier Science & Technology Bks.

Victor, John Samuel. Interaction of Low Frequency Sound. 2010. 96p. pap. *(978-3-639-26237-7(9))* VDM Verlag Dr. Mueller e.K.

Vigran, Tor Erik. Building Acoustics. 2008. (ENG., Illus.). 384p. 170.00 *(978-0-415-42853-8(X)*, CRC Press) Taylor & Francis Group GBR. Dist: Taylor & Francis Group.

Waving, Neil, photos by. RA, the Book: The Recording Architecture Book of Studio Design. 2011. (Illus.). 350p. pap. 255.00 ***(978-1-907759-16-1(6))*** M-Y Bks., Ltd. GBR. Dist: Printondemand-worldwide.com.

ARCHITECTURAL CRITICISM

Aalto, Alvar & Fixler, David. Aalto & America. Anderson, Stanford & Fenske, Gail, eds. 2012. (ENG., Illus.). 320p. 75.00 *(978-0-300-17600-1(7))* Yale Univ. Pr.

Aerni, Georg. Sites & Signs: Fotografien von Georg Aerni. Olonetzky, Nadine, ed. 2011. (ENG & GER., Illus.). 311p. 130.00 *(978-3-85881-320-6(6))* Scheidegger und Spiess AG, Verlag CHE. Dist: Chicago Distribution Ctr.

Alanta History Center Staff. Henri Jova, A Classical Intermezzo: An Architect's Life. 2009. (ENG., Illus.). 212p. 50.00 *(978-1-883828-02-8(3))* Atlanta Historical Society, Inc.

Andersen, Michael Asgaard. Nordic Architects Write: A Documentary Anthology. 2008. (Illus.). (ENG.). 432p. (C). pap. 53.95 *(978-0-415-46352-2(1))*; XIV, 418p. 165.00 *(978-0-415-46351-5(3))* Routledge.

Baker, Geoffrey Howard. The Architecture of James Sterling & His Partners James Gowan & Michael Wilford: A Study of Architectural Creativity in the Twentieth Century. 2011. (Illus.). 512p. 134.95 *(978-1-4094-0926-7(0))* Ashgate Publishing Co.

Balliet, Kristy, et al, eds. Visual Catalog: Greg Lynn's Studio at the University of Applied Arts Vienna. 2010. (Edition Angewandte Ser.). (ENG., Illus.). 176p. pap. 29.95 *(978-3-211-99192-3(1)*, 3211991921) Springer.

Bassegoda i Nonell, Joan, et al. La Cátedra de Antoni Gaudí: Estudio Analítico de Su Obra. 2010. (SPA., Illus.). 146p. *(978-84-8301-283-3(9))* UPC, S.L., Edicions.

Belen, Karl, et al, texts. Oase No. 80: on Territories. 2010. (ENG., Illus.). 144p. pap. 35.00 *(978-90-5662-724-9(4))* NAi Uitgevers / Publishers Stichting NLD. Dist: D.A.P./Distributed Art Pubs.

Benjamin, Andrew & Rice, Charles, eds. Walter Benjamin & the Architecture of Modernity. 2009. (Anamnesis Ser.). 226p. pap. 25.00 *(978-0-9805440-2-2(5))* re.press AUS. Dist: Lightning Source, Inc.

Benton, Caroline Maniaque. Le Corbusier & the Maisons Jaoul. 2009. (ENG., Illus.). 160p. pap. 40.00 *(978-1-56898-800-9(1))* Princeton Architectural Pr.

Bills, Mark. Watts Cemetery Chapel: A Guide to the Symbols of Mary Watt's Arts & Crafts Masterpiece. 2010. (ENG., Illus.). 64p. pap. 30.00 *(978-0-85667-692-5(6))* Wilson, Philip Pubs., Ltd. GBR. Dist: Macmillan.

Birksted, J. K. Le Corbusier & the Occult. 2009. (ENG., Illus.). 424p. (gr. 17). 44.95 *(978-0-262-02648-2(1))* MIT Pr.

Borutová, Dana & Jurkovic, Dusan. Architekt Dusan Samuel Jurkovic. 2012. (SLO., Illus.). 384p. 99.95 ***(978-80-8085-665-6(6))*** Slovart, Vydavatel'stvo, spol. s.r.o. SVK. Dist: Independent Pubs. Group.

Boucher, Bruce. Andrea Palladio: The Architect in His Time. 2nd ed. 2007. (ENG., Illus.). 324p. 49.95 *(978-0-7892-0938-2(1))*; 322p. pap. 39.95 *(978-0-7892-0940-5(3))* Abbeville Pr., Inc.

Boyer, M. Christine. Le Corbusier, Homme de Lettres. 2010. (ENG., Illus.). 782p. 70.00 *(978-1-56898-973-0(3))* Princeton Architectural Pr.

Boyer, M. Christine & Le Corbusier. Le Corbusier: Homme de Lettres. 2010. (ENG., Illus.). 782p. pap. 45.00 *(978-1-56898-980-8(6))* Princeton Architectural Pr.

Brooks Pfeiffer, Bruce. Frank Lloyd Wright - complete works 03 Vol. 3: Complete Works, 3 vols. Gssel, Peter, ed. 2009. (ENG, FRE & GER., Illus.). 596p. 200.00 *(978-3-8228-5770-0(X))* TASCHEN DEU. Dist: Ingram Pub. Services.

Brough, John Capen, et al, eds. Perspecta 43 Taboo: The Yale Architectural Journal. 2010. (ENG., Illus.). 210p. (gr. 17). pap. 25.00 *(978-0-262-51479-8(6))* MIT Pr.

Cannon, Patrick F. & Wright, Frank Lloyd. Frank Lloyd Wright's Unity Temple: A Good Time Place. 2009. 80p. 24.95 *(978-0-7649-5149-7(1))* Pomegranate Communications, Inc.

Castanheira, Carlos & Siza, Álvaro. Álvaro Siza - Recent Works. 2009. (ENG., Illus.). 320p. 125.00 *(978-0-7148-4946-1(4))* Phaidon Pr., Inc.

Celant, Germano. Frank O. Gehry: Since 1997. 2010. (ENG., Illus.). 320p. 95.00 *(978-88-572-0179-5(1))* Skira Editore ITA. Dist: Random Hse., Inc.

Charrington, Harry & Nava, Vezio, eds. Alvar Aalto: The Mark of the Hand. 2012. (ENG., Illus.). 400p. pap. 58.95 ***(978-951-682-995-4(3))*** Rakennustieto oy FIN. Dist: Independent Pubs. Group.

Chatel, Guy, et al, texts. Oase No. 79: the Architecture of James Stirling 1964-1992. 2010. (ENG., Illus.). 160p. pap. 35.00 *(978-90-5662-723-2(6))* NAi Uitgevers / Publishers Stichting NLD. Dist: D.A.P./Distributed Art Pubs.

Chu, Hsiao-Yun & Trujillo, Roberto, eds. New Views on R. Buckminster Fuller. 2009. (ENG., Illus.). 248p. pap. 21.95 *(978-0-8047-6279-3(1))* Stanford Univ. Pr.

Chu, Hsiao-Yun & Trujillo, Roberto G. New Views on R. Buckminster Fuller. Chu, Hsiao-Yun & Trujillo, Roberto, eds. 2009. (ENG., Illus.). 248p. 55.00 *(978-0-8047-5209-1(5))* Stanford Univ. Pr.

Cohen, Jean-Louis. Le Corbusier. Gossel, Peter, ed. 25th ed. 2009. (25 Ser.). (ENG., Illus.). 96p. 14.99 *(978-3-8365-1308-1(0))* TASCHEN DEU. Dist: Ingram Pub. Services.

Colomina, Beatriz. Philip Johnson: The Constancy of Change. Petit, Emmanuel J., ed. 2009. (Illus.). 274p. 60.00 *(978-0-300-12181-0(4))* Yale Univ. Pr.

Colquhoun, Alan & Frampton, Kenneth. Collected Essays in Architectural Criticism. 2009. (ENG., Illus.). 336p. 59.95 *(978-1-906155-20-9(8))* Black Dog Publishing Ltd. GBR. Dist: Perseus Distribution.

Constant, Caroline. Eileen Gray. 2007. (ENG., Illus.). 255p. pap. 29.95 *(978-0-7148-4844-0(1))* Phaidon Pr., Inc.

Crinson, Mark. James Stirling. Crinson, Mark, ed. 2009. (ENG., Illus.). 160p. (C). pap. 44.95 *(978-0-415-55059-8(9))* Routledge.

—James Stirling: Early unpublished writings on Architecture. Crinson, Mark, ed. 2009. (ENG., Illus.). 160p. (C). 165.00 *(978-0-415-55058-1(0))* Routledge.

Crinson, Mark. Stirling & Gowan: Architecture from Austerity to Affluence. 2012. (Paul Mellon Centre for Studies in British Art Ser.). (ENG., Illus.). 288p. 75.00 ***(978-0-300-17728-2(3))*** Yale Univ. Pr.

de Koning, Krijn, et al, texts. OASE 84: Models. 2011. (ENG., Illus.). 144p. pap. 35.00 ***(978-90-5662-807-9(0))*** NAi Uitgevers / Publishers Stichting NLD. Dist: D.A.P./Distributed Art Pubs.

Declerck, Joachim, et al, eds. Oase 75. 2008. (ENG., Illus.). 319p. pap. 40.00 *(978-90-5662-674-7(4))* NAi Uitgevers / Publishers Stichting NLD. Dist: D.A.P./Distributed Art Pubs.

Dettingmeijer, Rob, et al, eds. Rietveld's Universe. 2011. (ENG., Illus.). 277p. pap. 47.50 *(978-90-5662-746-1(5))* NAi Uitgevers / Publishers Stichting NLD. Dist: D.A.P./Distributed Art Pubs.

D'Evelyn, Margaret Muther. Venice & Vitruvius: Reading Venice with Daniele Barbaro & Andrea Palladio. 2012. (ENG., Illus.). 504p. 65.00 ***(978-0-300-17451-9(9))*** Yale Univ. Pr.

Domínguez, Luis Angel & Domínguez, Lluís Àngel. Alvar Aalto, Una Arquitectura Dialogica. 2010. (SPA.). 154p. *(978-84-8301-679-4(6))* UPC, S.L., Edicions.

Dotson, Esther Gordon. J. B. Fischer Von Erlach: Architecture as Theater in the Baroque Era. 2012. (ENG., Illus.). 184p. 75.00 ***(978-0-300-16668-2(0))*** Yale Univ. Pr.

Duran, Sergi Costa & Eguaras, Mariana R. 1000 Ideas by 100 Architects. 2009. (ENG., Illus.). 320p. pap. 40.00 *(978-1-59253-573-6(9)*, 1592535739) Quayside.

Durough, Allen R. & Rayfield, Wallace A. The Architectural Legacy of Wallace A. Rayfield: Pioneer Black Architect of Birmingham, Alabama. 2nd ed. 2010. (ENG., Illus.). 176p. 32.95 *(978-0-8173-1683-9(3))* Univ. of Alabama Pr.

Equipo Staff & Papeti, Dissenys. Gaudí: Dibuixos = Dibujos = Drawings, 1 vol. 2007. (CAT, ENG & SPA., Illus.). 128p. pap. 15.95 ***(978-84-8478-069-4(4))*** Triangle Postals, S.L. ESP. Dist: Innovative Logistics.

Ferrari, Fulvio & Ferrari, Napoleone. The Furniture of Carlo Mollino. 2010. (ENG., Illus.). 240p. pap. 39.95 *(978-0-7148-5778-7(5))* Phaidon Pr., Inc.

Fisher, Thomas & Bastianelli-Kerze, Peter. The Invisible Element of Place: The Architecture of David Salmela. 2011. (Illus.). 272p. pap. 39.95 *(978-0-8166-6994-3(5))* Univ. of Minnesota Pr.

Fontana-Giusti, Gordana. Foucault for Architects. 2012. (Thinkers for Architects Ser.). (ENG., Illus.). 128p. (C). 130.00 ***(978-0-415-69330-1(6))***; pap. 28.95 ***(978-0-415-69331-8(4))*** Routledge.

Foscari, Antonio. Andrea Palladio-Unbuilt Venice. 2010. (Illus.). 208p. *(978-3-03778-222-4(6))* Lars Muller Pubs.

Frampton, Kenneth, et al. Adolf Loos: Architecture 1903-1932. 2009. (ENG., Illus.). 180p. 45.00 *(978-1-58093-236-3(3))* Monacelli Pr., Inc.

Fumihiko, Maki, et al. Fumihiko Maki. 2009. (ENG., Illus.). 320p. 95.00 *(978-0-7148-4956-0(1))* Phaidon Pr., Inc.

Gauzin-Müller, Dominique & Ayers, Andrew. Jean-Yves Barrier: Architect & Urbanist, Architecte et Urbaniste. 2009. (Work Monographs). (ENG & FRE., Illus.). 176p. 109.00 *(978-3-932565-24-3(X))* Edition Axel Menges GmbH DEU. Dist: National Bk. Network.

Genís Terri, Jaume. Gaudí, Entre L'arquitectura Cristiana I L'art Contemporani. 2009. (CAT.). 262p. *(978-84-9883-199-3(7))* Publicacions de l'Abadia de Montserrat.

Gerbino, Anthony. François Blondel: Architecture, Erudition, & the Scientific Revolution. 2010. (Classical Tradition in Architecture Ser.). (ENG., Illus.). 344p. (C). 135.00 *(978-0-415-49199-0(1))* Routledge.

Geva, Anat. Frank Lloyd WrightS Sacred Architecture. 2011. (ENG., Illus.). 304p. (C). 70.00 *(978-0-415-77508-3(6))* Routledge.

Gharagozlou, Daniel. Perspecta 44 - Domain. 2011. (Perspecta Ser.). (ENG., Illus.). 192p. (gr. 17). pap. 29.95 ***(978-0-262-51639-6(X))*** MIT Pr.

Gossel, Peter & Roccella, Graziella. Ponti. 2009. (ENG.). 96p. pap. 9.99 *(978-3-8365-0039-8(8))* TASCHEN DEU. Dist: Ingram Pub. Services.

Guggenheim Foundation et. Frank Lloyd Wright: from Inward Outward. 2009. pap. *(978-0-8478-3263-7(5))* Guggenheim, Solomon R. Museum.

Harris, Penelope. The Architectural Achievement of Joseph Aloysius Hansom (1803-1882) Designing the Hansom Cab, the Birmingham Town Hall, & Churches of the Catholic Revival. 2010. (Illus.). viii, 200p. *(978-0-7734-3851-4(3))* Mellen, Edwin Pr., The.

Havik, Klaske, et al, eds. Criticism Revisited. 2010. (ENG., Illus.). 144p. pap. 35.00 *(978-90-5662-752-2(X))* NAi Uitgevers / Publishers Stichting NLD. Dist: D.A.P./Distributed Art Pubs.

Head, Jeffrey. No Nails, No Lumber: The Bubble Houses of Wallace Neff. 2011. (ENG., Illus.). 176p. 24.95 ***(978-1-61689-024-7(X))*** Princeton Architectural Pr.

Heikkinen, Mikka. Zumthor: Spirit of Nature Wood Architecture Award 2006. 2008. (ENG., Illus.). 80p. pap. 66.00 *(978-951-682-807-0(8))* Rakennustieto oy FIN. Dist: Independent Pubs. Group.

Herbert, Gilbert & Richter, Liliane, texts. Through a Clouded Glass: Mendelsohn, Wijdeveld & the Jewish Connection. 2009. (ENG., Illus.). 200p. pap. 60.00 *(978-3-8030-0696-7(1))* Wasmuth, Ernst J. Verlag GmbH & Co. DEU. Dist: D.A.P./Distributed Art Pubs.

Higgott, Andrew. Mediating Modernism. 2006. (Illus.). VIII, 216p. 64.95 *(978-0-415-40177-7(1))* Routledge.

Hildebrand, Grant. Gene Zema, Architect, Craftsman. 2011. (ENG., Illus.). 176p. 60.00 *(978-0-295-99123-8(2))* Univ. of Washington Pr.

Hoffmann, Claus-Wilhelm. Hans Dieter Schaal. Work in Progress: Work in Progress. Werner, Frank R., ed. 2012. (GER & ENG., Illus.). 608p. 119.00 ***(978-3-936681-49-9(X))*** Edition Axel Menges GmbH DEU. Dist: National Bk. Network.

Hopkins, Andrew. Baldassare Longhena & Venetian Baroque Architecture. 2012. (ENG., Illus.). 372p. 85.00 ***(978-0-300-18109-8(4))*** Yale Univ. Pr.

Hrausky, Andrej, et al. Joze Plecnik: Dunaj, Praga, Ljubljana. 2nd ed. 2007. (SLV., Illus.). 231p. *(978-961-231-575-7(2))* Cankarjeva Zalozba.

Hunter, Gill. William White: Pioneer Victorian Architect. 2010. (Illus.). 338p. (C). *(978-1-904965-26-8(1))* Spire Bks. Ltd.

Jenkins, David & Pawley, Martin. The Strange Death of Architectural Criticism: Martin Pawley Collected Writings. 2007. (ENG., Illus.). 448p. 59.95 *(978-1-906155-19-3(4))* Black Dog Publishing Ltd. GBR. Dist: Perseus Distribution.

Jodidio Philip. Kc Renzo Piano. 2012. (ENG.). 96p. pap. 9.99 ***(978-3-8365-3068-2(6))*** TASCHEN DEU. Dist: Ingram Pub. Services.

Jodidio, Philip. Kc Zaha Hadid. 2012. (ENG., Illus.). 96p. pap. 9.99 ***(978-3-8365-3072-9(4))*** TASCHEN DEU. Dist: Ingram Pub. Services.

—Meier. Gossel, Peter, ed. 2010. (ENG, FRE & GER., Illus.). 96p. pap. 9.99 *(978-3-8365-1545-0(8))* TASCHEN DEU. Dist: Ingram Pub. Services.

—Santiago Calatrava: Complete Works 1979 - 2009. 2009. (ENG., Illus.). 536p. 39.99 *(978-3-8365-1023-3(5))* TASCHEN DEU. Dist: Ingram Pub. Services.

Jodidio, Philip, ed. Anco - complete works updated version: Updated Version. 2010. (FRE, GER & ENG., Illus.). 600p. 150.00 *(978-3-8365-0949-7(0))* TASCHEN DEU. Dist: Ingram Pub. Services.

Jodidio, Philip, ed. Tadao Ando,Complete Works 1975-2011. 2012. (ENG., Illus.). 640p. 49.99 ***(978-3-8365-2813-9(4))*** TASCHEN DEU. Dist: Ingram Pub. Services.

Kathrens, Michael C. American Splendor: The Residential Architecture of Horace Trumbauer. 2nd ed. 2011. (Illus.). 335p. 75.00 *(978-0-926494-61-9(9))* Acanthus Pr. LLC.

La Cecla, Franco. Against Architecture. 2012. (Green Arcade Ser.). (ENG.). 144p. pap. 14.95 ***(978-1-60486-406-9(0))*** PM Pr.

Lampens, Juliaan. Juliaan Lampens, 1 vol. Campens, Angelique, ed. 2011. (ENG., Illus.). 152p. pap. 64.00 ***(978-94-6117-005-7(X))*** Exhibitions International BEL. Dist: Innovative Logistics.

Lamprecht, Barbara. Richard Neutra. Gossel, Peter, ed. 25th ed. 2009. (25 Ser.). (ENG., Illus.). 96p. 14.99 *(978-3-8365-1326-5(9))* TASCHEN DEU. Dist: Ingram Pub. Services.

Lamprecht, Barbara Mac & Gössel, Peter. Neutra, Complete Works: 25 Jahre TASCHEN. 2010. (25 Ser.). (FRE, GER & ENG., Illus.). 464p. 69.99 *(978-3-8365-1244-2(0))* TASCHEN DEU. Dist: Ingram Pub. Services.

Lange, Alexandra. Writing about Architecture: Mastering the Language of Buildings & Cities. 2012. (ENG.). 192p. pap. 24.95 ***(978-1-61689-053-7(3))*** Princeton Architectural Pr.

Lavin, Irving. Visible Spirit: The Art of Gianlorenzo Bernini, 3 vols. 2009. (ENG., Illus.). 680p. (C). 300.00 *(978-1-904597-45-2(9))* Pindar Pr. GBR. Dist: Brown, David Bk. Co., The.

—Visible Spirit Vol. 3: The Art of Gian Lorenzo, 3 vols. 2012. (ENG., Illus.). 118p. (C). 300.00 *(978-1-904597-46-9(7))* Pindar Pr. GBR. Dist: Brown, David Bk. Co., The.

Lawrence, Amanda Reeser & Stirling, James. James Stirling: Revisionary Modernist. 2013. (ENG., Illus.). 240p. 50.00 ***(978-0-300-17005-4(X))*** Yale Univ. Pr.

Leedy, Walter C., Jr. Eric Mendelsohn's Park Synagogue: Architecture & Community. Pearman, Sara Jane, ed. 2011. (Sacred Landmarks Ser.). 192p. 45.00 *(978-1-60635-085-0(4))* Kent State Univ. Pr.

Lejeune, Jean-Francois. Modern Architecture & the Mediterranean: Vernacular Dialogues & Contested Identities. Sabatino, Michelangelo, ed. 2010. (ENG., Illus.). 320p. 53.95 *(978-0-415-77634-9(1))* Routledge.

Lejeune, Jean-Francois & Sabatino, Michelangelo, eds. North-South: The Vernacular, the Modern & the Mediterranean. 2010. (ENG., Illus.). 320p. (C). 165.00 *(978-0-415-77633-2(3))* Routledge.

Lin, Zhongjie. Kenzo Tange & the Metabolist Movement. 2010. (Illus.). 288p. 165.00 *(978-0-415-77659-2(7))* Routledge.

—Kenzo Tange & the Metabolist Movement: Urban Utopias of Modern Japan. 2010. (ENG., Illus.). 288p. (C). pap. 53.95 *(978-0-415-77660-8(0))* Routledge.

Linder, Mark. Nothing Less Than Literal: Architecture after Minimalism. 2007. (ENG., Illus.). 294p. (gr. 17). pap. 19.95 *(978-0-262-62208-0(4))* MIT Pr.

Lizárraga Sánchez, Salvador & Anda, Enrique X. de, eds. Cultura Arquitectónica de la Modernidad Mexicana: Antología de Textos, 1922-1963. 2010. (SPA., Illus.). 391p. *(978-607-02-1468-4(4))* Universidad Nacional Autónoma de México.

Long, Christopher. The Looshaus. 2012. (ENG., Illus.). 256p. 50.00 *(978-0-300-17453-3(5))* Yale Univ. Pr.

Ludevid, Jordi. Catalan Architecture 2004-2009: Portrait of a Time. 2009. 19.95 *(978-84-96842-45-8(2))* Colegio de Arquitectos de Catalunya ESP. Dist: Actar Birkhauser Distribution.

Lynn, Catherine & Penabad, Carie. Marion Manley: Miami's First Woman Architect. 2010. (ENG., Illus.). 248p. pap. 34.95 *(978-0-8203-3406-6(5))* Univ. of Georgia Pr.

Marjanovic, Igor, et al. Marina City: Bertrand Goldberg's Urban Vision. 2010. (ENG., Illus.). 176p. pap. 35.00 *(978-1-56898-863-4(X))* Princeton Architectural Pr.

Massey, Jonathan. Crystal & Arabesque: Claude Bragdon, Ornament, & Modern Architecture. 2009. (ENG., Illus.). 352p. (C). 59.95 *(978-0-8229-4362-4(X))* Univ. of Pittsburgh Pr.

Mead, Christopher Curtis. The Architecture of Bart Prince: A Pragmatics of Place. 2nd rev. ed. 2010. (ENG., Illus.). 208p. pap. 39.95 *(978-0-393-73312-9(2)*, 73312) Norton, W. W. & Co., Inc.

Mead, Christopher Curtis & Predock, Antoine. Roadcut: The Architecture of Antoine Predock. 2011. (ENG., Illus.). 210p. 75.00 *(978-0-8263-5009-1(7))* Univ. of New Mexico Pr.

Media, Mountains & Architecture. 2009. *(978-84-95951-61-8(4))* Actar Birkhauser Distribution.

Meister, Chris & Gordon, James Riely. James Riely Gordon: His Courthouses & Other Public Architecture. 2011. 384p. 49.95 ***(978-0-89672-691-8(6))*** Texas Tech Univ. Pr.

Merrill, Michael. Louis Kahn: On the Thoughtful Making of Spaces. 2010. (Illus.). 320p. pap. *(978-3-03778-220-0(X))* Lars Muller Pubs.

Millett, Larry. Disappearance of Sherlock Holmes. 2012. (Fesler-Lampert Minnesota Heritage Ser.). (Illus.). 352p. pap. 14.95 ***(978-0-8166-6993-6(7))*** Univ. of Minnesota Pr.

Moleskine. Moleskine Inspiration & Process in Architecture: Alberto Kalach. 2012. (ENG., Illus.). 272p. 39.95 *(978-88-6613-001-7(X))* Moleskine ITA. Dist: Hachette Bk. Group.

Moneo, Rafael. Rafael Moneo: Remarks on 21 Works. 2010. (ENG., Illus.). 668p. 75.00 *(978-1-58093-216-5(9))* Monacelli Pr., Inc.

Monestiroli, Antonio, ed. Ignazio Gardella. 2009. (ITA., Illus.). 80p. pap. 46.50 *(978-88-370-6928-5(6))* Electa ITA. Dist: Trans-Atlantic Pubns., Inc.

Morgan, Diane. Kant for Architects. (Thinkers for Architects Ser.). (ENG., Illus.). 128p. (C). 2013. 130.00 ***(978-0-415-69868-9(5))*** 2012. pap. 28.95 ***(978-0-415-69869-6(3))*** Routledge.

Murray, Irena & Osley, Julian, eds. Le Corbusier & Britain: An Anthology. 2010. (ENG., Illus.). 360p. pap. 26.95 *(978-0-415-60865-7(1))* Routledge.

Murray, Irena, et al. Le Corbusier & Britain: An Anthology. Osley, Julian, ed. 2008. (ENG., Illus.). 360p. 62.95 *(978-0-415-47994-3(0))* Routledge.

Myers, Tracy. Deborah Berke. 2008. (ENG., Illus.). 240p. 65.00 *(978-0-300-13439-1(8))* Yale Univ. Pr.

Najafi, Sina & Kastner, Jeffrey, eds. Cabinet 41: Infrastructure. 2011. (ENG., Illus.). 112p. pap. 12.00 *(978-1-932698-40-4(X))* Cabinet.

Nero, Irene. Transformations in Architecture. 2009. (Illus.). 172p. pap. *(978-3-8383-0846-3(8))* Lambert Academic Publishing.

Nicoletti, Manfredi. Manfredi Nicoletti: Architect. Giussani, Elena, ed. 2010. 144p. pap. 22.95 *(978-88-492-1172-6(4))* Gangemi ITA. Dist: International Publishers Marketing.

Nogai, Juergen, photos by. Houses of the Sundown Sea: The Architectural Vision of Harry Gesner. 2012. (ENG., Illus.). 240p. 75.00 *(978-1-4197-0049-1(9))* Abrams.

Normann Sandaker, Bjorn. Reflec Span & Spac Tow Theo Crit. 2007. (ENG., Illus.). 224p. (C). 165.00 *(978-0-415-35787-6(X))* Routledge.

—Reflec Span & Spac Tow Theo Crit. 2007. (Illus.). XII, 212p. 64.95 *(978-0-415-35792-0(6))* Routledge.

Ochsendorf, John Allen. Guastavino Vaulting: The Art of Structural Tile. 2010. (ENG., Illus.). 256p. 60.00 *(978-1-56898-741-5(2))* Princeton Architectural Pr.

O'Donnell, Anne Stewart & Voysey, Charles F. A. C. F. A. Voysey: Architect Designer, Individualist. 2011. (Illus.). 108p. 29.95 *(978-0-7649-5884-7(4))* Pomegranate Communications, Inc.

Olsberg, R. Nicholas, et al. Arthur Erickson: Critical Works, 1 vol. 2006. (ENG., Illus.). 256p. *(978-1-55365-154-3(5))* D&M Pubs. Inc.

Pauly, Danièle. Barragán: L'espace et l'ombre, le mur et la Couleur. 2008. (FRE., Illus.). 231p. pap. 59.95 *(978-3-7643-8706-8(8)*, 3764387068) Springer.

Pauwels, Wim, ed. Nathalie Van Reeth. 2009. (ENG., Illus.). 200p. *(978-90-8944-020-4(8)*, Beta-Plus (Acc)) Antique Collectors' Club.

Pennoyer, Peter, et al. The Architecture of Grosvenor Atterbury. 2009. (ENG., Illus.). 288p. 75.00 *(978-0-393-73222-1(3)*, 73222) Norton, W. W. & Co., Inc.

Phaidon Press Editors, ed. 10x10 - 3: 100 Architects 10 Critics. 2009. (ENG., Illus.). 468p. 90.00 *(978-0-7148-4953-9(7))* Phaidon Pr., Inc.

Philippides, Demetres, et al. Pikiones: Hoi Homilies Tou '65. 2009. (GRE., Illus.). 210p. (C). 65.00 ***(978-960-204-288-5(5))*** Ekdotikos Oikos Melissa GRC. Dist: ISD.

Philippou, Styliane. Oscar Niemeyer: Curves of Irreverence. 2008. (ENG., Illus.). 256p. 65.00 *(978-0-300-12038-7(9))* Yale Univ. Pr.

Pimlott, Mark, et al, eds. OASE 76: Context-Specificity. 2009. (ENG., Illus.). 148p. pap. 35.00 *(978-90-5662-660-0(4))* NAi Uitgevers / Publishers Stichting NLD. Dist: D.A.P./Distributed Art Pubs.

Pisani, Mario, ed. Fuksas Architetto. 2010. 144p. pap. 27.95 *(978-88-7448-200-9(0))* Gangemi ITA. Dist: International Publishers Marketing.

Quiring, Claudia. Ernst May: 1886-1970. 2011. (ENG., Illus.). 272p. pap. 60.00 ***(978-3-7913-5132-2(X))*** Prestel Publishing.

Rattenbury. Bernard Tschumi - Parc de la Villette. 2011. (Supercrit Ser.). (ENG., Illus.). 120p. (C). pap. 49.95 *(978-0-415-45788-0(2))* Routledge.

—Richard Rogers: Centre Pompidou. 2011. (Supercrit Ser.). (ENG., Illus.). 176p. (C). 165.00 *(978-0-415-45785-9(8))*; pap. 49.95 *(978-0-415-45786-6(6))* Routledge.

Rattenbury, Kester. Cedric Price: Potteries Thinkbelt. Hardingham, Samantha, ed. 2008. (Supercrit Ser.). (ENG., Illus.). 138p. (C). 49.95 *(978-0-415-43412-6(2))* Routledge.

Rattenbury, Kester & Hardingham, Samantha, eds. Cedric Price: Potteries Thinkbelt. 2008. (Supercrit Ser.). (ENG., Illus.). 138p. (C). 165.00 *(978-0-415-43411-9(4))* Routledge.

Rault, Jasmine. Eileen Gray & the Design of Sapphic Modernity: Staying In. 2011. (Illus.). 196p. 104.95 *(978-0-7546-6961-6(0))* Ashgate Publishing Co.

Reilly, Donna Grant. An American Proceeding: Building the Grant House with Frank Lloyd Wright. 2010. (Illus.). 196p. pap. 22.95 *(978-1-58465-978-5(5))* Univ. Pr. of New England.

Rendell, Jane, et al, eds. Critical Architecture. 2007. (Illus.). XX, 348p. 165.00 *(978-0-415-41537-8(3))* Routledge.

—Critical Architecture. 2007. (Illus.). XX, 348p. 60.95 *(978-0-415-41538-5(1))* Routledge.

Rikala. New Towns. 2007. (Illus.). 224p. 148.75 *(978-0-415-41050-2(9))* Routledge.

Roca, Miguel Angel & Kahn, Louis I. Louis Kahn, Arquetipos y Modernidad. 2009. (SPA., Illus.). 207p. *(978-987-584-343-1(1))* Nobuko.

Roger, Connah & Connah, Roger. Aaltomania. 2008. 144p. pap. 26.00 *(978-951-682-613-7(X))* Rakennustieto oy FIN. Dist: Independent Pubs. Group.

Rogers, Richard. Richard Rogers + Architects: From the House to the City. 2010. (ENG., Illus.). 272p. 45.00 *(978-1-906863-11-1(3))* FIELL Pubng. Ltd. GBR. Dist: D.A.P./Distributed Art Pubs.

Rosa, Joseph. Douglas Garofalo. 2006. (A+D Ser.). (ENG., Illus.). 96p. pap. 16.95 *(978-0-300-12058-5(3))* Art Institute of Chicago.

Rovira i Gimeno, Josep M., et al. Sert: De la Ciutat Funcional Al Disseny Urbà. 2009. (CAT., Illus.). 47p. *(978-84-8301-887-3(X))* UPC, S.L., Edicions.

Ruegg, Arthur & Spechtenhauser, Klaus. Le Corbusier. Meubles et Interieurs, 1905-1965. 2012. (ENG., Illus.). 352p. 200.00 ***(978-3-85881-729-7(5))*** Scheidegger und Spiess AG, Verlag CHE. Dist: Antique Collectors' Club.

Sadao, Shoji. Best of Friends: Isamu Noguchi & Buckminster Fuller. White, Garrett, ed. 2008. 224p. 50.00 *(978-0-9794727-3-2(3))* Five Ties Publishing.

Salingaros, Nikos A. Anti-Architecture & Deconstruction. 2008. (ENG.). 175p. pap. 23.00 *(978-3-937954-09-7(0))* ISI Bks.

—Anti-Architecture & Deconstruction. 2007. 210p. pap. 23.00 (978-3-937954-08-0(2)) Pueschel, Harald , Umbau-Verlag DEU. Dist: Southern Illinois Univ. Pr.

Saunders, William S. The New Architectural Pragmatism: A Harvard Design Magazine Reader. Saunders, William S., ed. 2007. (Harvard Design Magazine Ser.). (Illus.). 208p. 69.00 (978-0-8166-5263-1(5)); per. 22.95 (978-0-8166-5264-8(3)) Univ. of Minnesota Pr.

Saunders, William S., ed. Judging Architectural Value. 2007. (Harvard Design Magazine Ser.). (Illus.). 192p. 69.00 (978-0-8166-5010-1(1)); per. 22.95 (978-0-8166-5011-8(X)) Univ. of Minnesota Pr.

Sbriglio, Jacques. Le Corbusier & Lucien Herve: A Dialogue Between Architect & Photographer. 2011. (ENG.). 296p. 74.95 (978-1-60606-088-9(0), J. Paul Getty Museum) Getty Pubns.

Seijdel, Jorinde & Melis, Liesbeth, eds. Open 17: A Precarious Existence. 2009. (ENG., Illus.). 144p. pap. 30.00 (978-90-5662-694-5(9)) NAi Uitgevers / Publishers Stichting NLD. Dist: D.A.P./Distributed Art Pubs.

Serraino, Pierluigi. Eero Saarinen. Gossel, Peter, ed. 25th ed. 2009. (25 Ser.). (ENG., Illus.). 96p. 14.99 (978-3-8365-1333-3(1)) TASCHEN DEU. Dist: Ingram Pub. Services.

Shepherd, Stanley A. The Stained Glass of A.W.N. Pugin. 2009. (ENG., Illus.). 443p. (C). (978-1-904965-20-6(2)) Spire Bks. Ltd.

Shorto, Sylvia. A Lebanese Perspective: Houses & Other Work - Simone Kosremelli. 2012. (ENG., Illus.). 252p. 60.00 (978-1-86470-471-6(3)) Images Publishing Group AUS. Dist: National Bk. Network.

Silber, John. Architecture of the Absurd: How Genius Disfigured a Practical Art. 2007. (ENG., Illus.). 128p. 27.50 (978-1-59372-027-8(0)) Quantuck Lane Pr. & The Mill Road Collaborative, The.

Smienk, Gerrit & Niemeijer, Johannes. Palladio, the Villa & the Landscape. 2011. (Illus.). 160p. 79.95 (978-3-0346-0712-4(1)) Birkhauser Verlag AG CHE. Dist: Actar Birkhauser Distribution.

Smith, Christine, et al. Building the Kingdom: Giannozzo Manetti on the Material & Spiritual Edifice. 2006. (Arizona Studies in the Middle Ages & the Renaissance). (LAT & ENG.). (C). (978-0-86698-362-4(7)) Arizona State Univ., Arizona Ctr. for Medieval & Renaissance Studies.

Smith, Kathryn. Schindler House. 2010. (978-0-940512-50-4(5)) Hennessey & Ingalls, Inc.

Smith, Richard G. Building the Kingdom Giannozzo Manetti on the Material & Spiritual Edifice. 2007. (Illus.). 518p. 95.00 (978-2-503-52581-5(4)) Brepols Pubs. BEL. Dist: Brown, David Bk. Co., The.

Stonehouse, Roger. Trevor Dannatt: Works & Words. 2009. (ENG., Illus.). 192p. 49.95 (978-1-906155-21-6(6)) Black Dog Publishing Ltd. GBR. Dist: Perseus Distribution.

Sykes, A. Krista, ed. The Architecture Reader: Essential Writings from Vitruvius to the Present. 2007. (ENG., Illus.). 304p. 35.00 (978-0-8076-1579-9(X), 761579); per. 19.95 (978-0-8076-1580-5(3), 761580) Braziller, George Inc.

Tchoban, Sergei. Buildings: Designing along the Code. 2012. (ENG., Illus.). 256p. 85.00 (978-1-86470-388-7(1)) Images Publishing Group AUS. Dist: National Bk. Network.

TF Editores. Dominique Perrault Architecture. 2011. (ENG., Illus.). 208p. 54.00 incl. cd-rom (978-84-92441-62-4(3)) T.F. Editores ESP. Dist: National Bk. Network.

Tribert, Renee & O'Gorman, James F. Gervase Wheeler: A British Architect in America, 1847-1860. 2012. (Driftless Connecticut Series & Garnet Bks.). (ENG., Illus.). 136p. 35.00 (978-0-8195-7145-8(8)) Wesleyan Univ. Pr.

van der Horst, Jan. Movements in Green: Conceptual Landscape Gardening. 2010. (DUT & ENG., Illus.). 192p. 110.00 (978-90-8989-043-6(2)) Lannoo Pubs./Racine.

van Gameren, Dick, et al, eds. DASH 01: the Re-Opened Building Block. 2009. (ENG., Illus.). 144p. pap. 50.00 (978-90-5662-654-9(X)) NAi Uitgevers / Publishers Stichting NLD. Dist: D.A.P./Distributed Art Pubs.

Vidler, Anthony. Histories of the Immediate Present: Inventing Architectural Modernism. 2008. (Writing Architecture Ser.). (ENG., Illus.). 264p. (gr. 17). pap. 25.95 (978-0-262-72051-9(5)) MIT Pr.

Vivoni Farage, Enrique. Klumb: Una Arquitectura de Impronta Social. 2006. (Serie Mnemosina Ser.: Vol. 2). (ENG & SPA., Illus.). xiv, 346p. 84.95 (978-0-8477-2754-4(8)) Univ. of Puerto Rico Pr.

Vodopivec, Ales & Znidarsic, Rok. Edvard Ravnikar: Architect & Teacher. 2009. 348p. 89.95 (978-3-211-99203-6(0)) Springer Wien AUT. Dist: Springer.

Wang, Wilfried, ed. & text. Argentina: Altamira Building & Florencia Raigal House. 2011. (ENG., Illus.). 144p. pap. 40.00 (978-3-8030-0719-3(4)) Wasmuth, Ernst J. Verlag GmbH & Co. DEU. Dist: D.A.P./Distributed Art Pubs.

—Kyriakos Krokos: Fassianos Building, Athens 1990-1995. 2011. (ENG., Illus.). 144p. pap. 40.00 (978-3-8030-0718-6(6)) Wasmuth, Ernst J. Verlag GmbH & Co. DEU. Dist: D.A.P./Distributed Art Pubs.

—Sigurd Lewerentz: St. Petri. 2009. (ENG., Illus.). 144p. pap. 39.90 (978-3-8030-0698-1(8)) Wasmuth, Ernst J. Verlag GmbH & Co. DEU. Dist: D.A.P./Distributed Art Pubs.

Wang, Wilfried & Alter, Kevin, eds. O'Neil Ford Duograph 1 — Chile: House at Punta Pite, 2003-06, Smiljan Radic: Crypt in the Cathedral of Santiago de Chile, 1999-2006, Rodrigo Perez de Arce. 2008. (ENG., Illus.). 128p. pap. 39.90 (978-3-8030-0685-1(6)) Wasmuth, Ernst J. Verlag GmbH & Co. DEU. Dist: D.A.P./Distributed Art Pubs.

Welter, Volker M. Ernst L. Freud, Architect: The Case of the Modern Bourgois Home. 2011. (Space & Place Ser.). (ENG.). 352p. 39.95 (978-0-85745-233-7(9)) Berghahn Bks., Inc.

Wexler, Donald. Steel & Shade: The Architecture of Donald Wexler. 2011. (ENG., Illus.). 132p. pap. 50.00 (978-3-86828-191-0(6)) Kehrer Verlag Heidelberg, Klaus Kehrer DEU. Dist: Consortium Bk. Sales & Distribution.

Wittman, Richard. Architecture, Print Culture & the Public Sphere in Eighteenth-Century France. 2007. (Classical Tradition in Architecture Ser.). (ENG., Illus.). 304p. (C). 165.00 (978-0-415-77463-5(2)) Routledge.

Wood In Culture Association Staff. Renzo Piano: Spirit of Nature Wood Architecture Award 2000. 2008. (ENG., Illus.). 88p. pap. 34.00 (978-951-682-606-9(7)) Rakennustieto oy FIN. Dist: Independent Pubs. Group.

Wright, Frank Lloyd. Frank Lloyd Wright: Art Glass of the Martin House Complex. Jackson-Forsberg, Eric, ed. 2009. 96p. 27.95 (978-0-7649-5150-3(5)) Pomegranate Communications, Inc.

Wulfram, Hartmut. Literarische Vitruvrezeption in Leon Battista Albertis 'de re Aedificatoria' (Beiträge zur Altertumskunde Ser.). (GER.). 441p. 210.00 (978-3-11-184227-1(4)) De Gruyter, Walter Inc.

Younes, Samir. The Imperfect City: On Architectural Judgment. 2012. (Illus.). 240p. 89.95 (978-1-4094-4668-2(9)); 89.95 (978-1-4094-4667-5(0)) Ashgate Publishing Co.

Zantovská Murray, Irena. Looking at European Architecture: A Critical View, 1 vol. 2011. (ENG & FRE., Illus.). 464p. pap. 20.00 (978-2-930391-26-7(X)) Centre International Pour La Ville, L'Architecture Et Le Paysage BEL. Dist: Innovative Logistics.

Zielinski, Siegfried, et al, eds. Variantology 2: On Deep Time Relations of Arts, Sciences & Technologies, 1 vol. 2007. (ENG., Illus.). 350p. per. 45.00 (978-3-86560-050-9(6)) Verlag der Buchhandlung Walther Konig DEU. Dist: D.A.P./Distributed Art Pubs.

Zimmerman, Claire. Ludwig Mies Van der Rohe. Gossel, Peter, ed. 25th ed. 2009. (25 Ser.). (ENG., Illus.). 96p. 14.99 (978-3-8365-1316-6(1)) TASCHEN DEU. Dist: Ingram Pub. Services.

ARCHITECTURAL DESIGN

see also Crime Prevention and Architectural Design

AAD Hamburg. 2011. 192p. pap. 12.95 (978-3-8327-9502-3(2)) teNeues Publishing Co.

AAD Munich. 2011. 192p. pap. 12.95 (978-3-8327-9501-6(4)) teNeues Publishing Co.

AAD Paris. 2011. 192p. pap. 12.95 (978-3-8327-9464-4(6)) teNeues Publishing Co.

AAD Rome. 2011. 192p. pap. 12.95 (978-3-8327-9499-6(9)) teNeues Publishing Co.

Abdelhameed, Wael. The Impact of Computer on Design Capabilities of Architects. 2010. 172p. pap. (978-3-639-13683-8(7)) VDM Verlag Dr. Mueller e.K.

Abulhasan, Nasser B. Light, Sight & Architecture. 2011. 232p. pap. (978-3-8383-9376-6(7)) Lambert Academic Publishing.

Adler, Gerald, et al, eds. Scale. 2011. (ENG., Illus.). 256p. (C). 155.00 (978-0-415-68711-9(X)) Routledge.

Adshead, Julie, ed. Green Buildings & the Law. 2011. (ENG., Illus.). 288p. (C). 115.00 (978-0-415-55926-3(X)) Routledge.

Aeck, Richard. Turnstijl Houses & Cannoli Framing. 2008. 116p. pap. (978-3-639-07847-3(0)) VDM Verlag Dr. Mueller e.K.

Ahlava, Antti & Edelman, Harry F., eds. Managing Urban Design: A Guide to Good Practice. 2008. (ENG., Illus.). 244p. (C). 67.95 (978-0-415-46922-7(8), Taylor & Francis) Taylor & Francis Group GBR. Dist: Taylor & Francis Group.

Ahmed, Hussein. Interaction Interoperability for Distributed Virtual Environments. 2010. 196p. pap. (978-3-639-27745-6(7)) VDM Verlag Dr. Mueller e.K.

Alalouch, Chaham. Hospital Ward Architecture. 2011. 388p. pap. (978-3-8443-3017-5(8)) Lambert Academic Publishing.

Alexander, Christopher. The Battle for the Life & Beauty of the Earth: A Struggle between Two World-Systems. 2012. (ENG., Illus.). 528p. 45.00 (978-0-19-989807-7(3)) Oxford Univ. Pr., Inc.

Ali, A. & Brebbia, Carlos A., eds. Digital Architecture & Construction. 2006. (Transactions on the Built Environment Ser.: 90). (Illus.). 272p. 155.00 (978-1-84564-047-7(0)) WIT Pr GBR. Dist: WIT Pr.

Alibaba, Halil. A System for Selection of Building Elements in Architectural Design. 2010. 180p. pap. (978-3-8383-1504-1(9)) Lambert Academic Publishing.

Allen, Edward & Iano, Joseph. The Architect's Studio Companion: Rules of Thumb for Preliminary Design. 5th ed. 2011. (ENG., Illus.). 496p. 95.00 (978-0-470-64191-0(6), Wiley) Wiley, John & Sons, Inc.

Allen, Stan & McQuade, Marc, eds. Landform Building: Architecture's New Terrain. 2011. (ENG., Illus.). 416p. (978-3-03778-223-1(4)) Lars Muller Pubs.

Almanac of Architecture & Design. 2007. (Illus.). 591p. pap. 49.50 (978-0-9785552-3-8(6), Ostberg) Greenway Communications.

Alonso del Valle, Ricardo. El Lenguaje Del Proyecto. 2009. (SPA., Illus.). 172p. (978-987-584-228-1(1)) Nobuko.

Alpha Planning Inc. Creative Booth Design 2. 2010. (ENG & JPN., Illus.). 280p. 85.00 (978-4-568-50402-6(3)) Azur Corp. JPN. Dist: Antique Collectors' Club.

Altinisik, Melike, et al, contrib. by. Morphē: Mrgd. 2008. (RIEAuropa Concepts Ser.). (ENG., Illus.). 75p. pap. 39.95 (978-3-211-75789-5(9), 3211757899) Springer.

Amaratunga, Dilanthi & Haigh, Richard. Post-Disaster Reconstruction of the Built Environment: Rebuilding for Resilience. 2011. (ENG., Illus.). 336p. 116.99 (978-1-4443-3356-5(9), Wiley-Blackwell) Wiley, John & Sons, Inc.

Ambrose, Gavin & Harris, Paul. Design Thinking: Fragestellung, Recherche, Ideenfindung, Prototyping, Auswahl, Ausführung, Feedback. 2009. (Basics Design Ser.). (ENG., Illus.). 184p. pap. 34.50 (978-2-940411-17-7(4)) AVA Publishing GBR. Dist: Ingram Pub. Services.

Anderson, Jane. Architectural Design. 2010. (Basics Architecture Ser.). (ENG., Illus.). 184p. (C). pap. 32.95 (978-2-940411-26-9(3)) Ava Publishing SA CHE. Dist: Ingram Pub. Services.

Aouad, Ghassan, et al. Constructing the Future: ND Modelling. 2006. (ENG., Illus.). 432p. 175.00 (978-0-415-39171-9(7)) Routledge.

Arabacioglu, Burcin. Interactive Space Design: The New Architectural Design Thinking by Using Intelligent Building Systems in Interior Spaces. 2011. 76p. pap. (978-3-639-33772-3(7)) VDM Verlag Dr. Mueller e.K.

Architectural Desktop 2007 Tutorial Series. 2007. 299.00 incl. cd-rom (978-1-932931-31-0(7)) 4D Design Solutions, LLC.

Architecture & the Brain: A New Knowledge Base from Neuroscience. 2007. 144p. pap. 39.00 (978-0-9785552-1-4(X), Ostberg) Greenway Communications.

Architecture, STUDIOS. Studios Architecture. 2006. (Master Architect Series VI). (ENG., Illus.). 264p. 59.95 (978-1-876907-01-3(0), Images Publishing Dist Ac) Antique Collectors' Club GBR. Dist: National Bk. Network.

Arellanes II, Michael. M a 2: Mutagenesis. 2010. 200p. pap. 65.99 (978-0-557-42642-3(1)) Lulu Enterprises Inc.

ASME Press, creator. Icod 2010: Proceedings of the International Conference on Optimization Design, Wuhan, China, March 18-20 2010. 2010. (Illus.). 436p. pap. (978-0-7918-5958-2(4)) American Society of Mechanical Engineers, The.

Aubin, Paul. Revit Architecture 2011. 2010. (ENG., Illus.). 864p. pap. 93.95 (978-1-111-12493-9(0), AutoDesk Pr.) Delmar Cengage Learning.

Aubin, Paul F. Mastering Revit Architecture, 2010. 2009. (ENG.). 848p. pap. 112.95 (978-1-4390-5715-5(X), AutoDesk Pr.) Delmar Cengage Learning.

—Revit 2011 CourseNotes for Aubin's the Aubin Mastering Series: Mastering Revit Architecture 2011. 2010. (ENG.). 8p. pap. 5.95 (978-1-111-13714-4(5), AutoDesk Pr.) Delmar Cengage Learning.

—Revit Architecture 2012. 2011. (CAD New Releases Ser.). (ENG.). 416p. pap. 55.95 (978-1-111-64853-4(0), AutoDesk Pr.) Delmar Cengage Learning.

Aubin, Paul F. Revit architecture course Notes. 2009. (ENG.). 6p. (C). 9.95 (978-1-4354-9892-1(5)) Delmar Cengage Learning.

Aubin, Paul F., et al. Revit MEP 2011 Course Notes for Aubin/McClelland/Schmid/Stanley's the Aubin Academy Master Series: Revit MEP 2011. 2011. 8p. pap. 4.95 (978-1-111-13794-6(3), AutoDesk Pr.) Delmar Cengage Learning.

Aubin, Paul F. (Paul F. Aubin). Revit Architecture 2012. 2011. (ENG.). 6p. 4.95 (978-1-133-01446-1(1), AutoDesk Pr.) Delmar Cengage Learning.

Augustin, Sally & Coleman, Cindy. The Designer's Guide to Doing Research: Applying Knowledge to Inform Design. 2012. (ENG., Illus.). 344p. 75.00 (978-0-470-60173-0(6), Wiley) Wiley, John & Sons, Inc.

Avermaete, Tom, et al, eds. Invention/Inventie. 2008. (ENG., Illus.). 144p. pap. 34.95 (978-90-5662-619-8(1)) NAi Uitgevers / Publishers Stichting NLD. Dist: D.A.P./Distributed Art Pubs.

Avgeriou, Paris, et al, eds. Relating Software Requirements & Architectures. 2011. (ENG., Illus.). xxviii, 387p. 129.00 (978-3-642-21000-6(7), 3642210007) Springer.

Ayres, Phil, ed. Persistent Modelling. 2012. (ENG., Illus.). 224p. (C). 165.00 (978-0-415-59406-6(5)); pap. 49.95 (978-0-415-59407-3(3)) Routledge.

Azur. Architecture Highlights Vol. 3. 2011. 250p. 120.00 (978-4-903233-61-1(8)) Azur Corp. JPN. Dist: Antique Collectors' Club.

Bachman, Leonard. Strategic Design in Architecture: Bridging the Real & the Ideal. 2012. (ENG., Illus.). 248p. (C). pap. 49.95 (978-0-415-78247-0(3)); 165.00 (978-0-415-78246-3(5)) Routledge.

Bader, Thomas Karl. Adaptability & Structural Design of Stadia. 2008. 136p. pap. (978-3-8364-7868-7(4)) VDM Verlag Dr. Mueller e.K.

Baker, William T. Architectural Excellence: In a Diverse World Culture. 2008. (ENG., Illus.). 128p. 35.00 (978-1-86470-279-8(6)) Images Publishing Group AUS. Dist: National Bk. Network.

Ballast, David Kent. Schematic Design: ARE Sample Problems & Practice Exam. 2008. (ENG., Illus.). 76p. pap. 120.00 (978-1-59126-125-4(2)) Professional Pubns., Inc.

Ballesteros, Mario, et al, eds. Verb Crisis. 2008. (Verb Ser.). (Illus.). 294p. (978-84-96540-97-2(9)) Kunst-Werke Berlin e.V.

Balliet, Kristy, et al, eds. Visual Catalog: Greg Lynn's Studio at the University of Applied Arts Vienna. 2010. (Edition Angewandte Ser.). (ENG., Illus.). 176p. pap. 29.95 (978-3-211-99192-3(1), 3211991921) Springer.

Balmer, Jeffrey & Swisher, Michael. Diagramming the Big Idea: Methods for Architectural Composition. 2012. (ENG., Illus.). 256p. (C). 165.00 (978-0-415-89408-1(5)); pap. 34.95 (978-0-415-89409-8(3)) Routledge.

Bangash, T. Explosion-Resistant Buildings: Design, Analysis, & Case Studies. 2010. (ENG., Illus.). xxi, 784p. pap. 379.00 (978-3-642-05830-1(2), 3642058302) Springer.

Barison, Alessandro. Design for You. 2010. (ITA.). 67p. pap. 9.50 (978-1-4457-2968-8(7)) Lulu Enterprises Inc.

Barrow, Larry & Al Arayedh, Shaima. The Global Housing Crisis: An Industrial Design & Fabrication Opportunity in Architecture. 2008. 212p. pap. (978-3-639-10468-4(4)) VDM Verlag Dr. Mueller e.K.

Belen, Karl, et al, texts. Oase No. 80: on Territories. 2010. (ENG., Illus.). 144p. pap. 35.00 (978-90-5662-724-9(4)) NAi Uitgevers / Publishers Stichting NLD. Dist: D.A.P./Distributed Art Pubs.

Benedikt, Michael. Centerline, Volume 2: The Argument from Design(Ers) 2006. (978-0-934951-08-1(X)) Ctr. for American Architecture & Design, The.

Bentley, Ian & Butina-Watson, Georgia. Identity by Design. 2007. (ENG., Illus.). 298p. pap. 62.95 (978-0-7506-4767-0(1)) Routledge.

Bess, Bernd. About Making Architecture: An International Debate, 1 vol. 2009. (ENG., Illus.). 144p. pap. 38.00 (978-3-938666-22-7(6)) DOM Pubs. DEU. Dist: Innovative Logistics.

Bhatia, Neeraj, et al, eds. Arium: Weather & Architecture. 2010. (ENG., Illus.). 320p. 55.00 (978-3-7757-2540-8(7)) Hatje Cantz Verlag GmbH & Co KG DEU. Dist: D.A.P./Distributed Art Pubs.

Binnekamp, R., ed. Preference-Based Design in Architecture. 2010. pap. 87.00 (978-1-60750-550-1(9)) IOS Pr., Inc.

BIS Publishers Staff & Agkathidis, Asterios. Digital Manufacturing in Design & Architecture: In Design & Architecture. 2011. (ENG., Illus.). 136p. pap. 17.00 (978-90-6369-232-2(3)) Bis B.V., Uitgeverij(BIS Publishers) NLD. Dist: Consortium Bk. Sales & Distribution.

BIS Publishers Staff & Lim, Joseph. Bio-Structural Analogues in Architecture: Joseph Lim Ee Man. 2009. (ENG., Illus.). 250p. pap. 24.95 (978-90-6369-204-9(8)) Bis B.V., Uitgeverij(BIS Publishers) NLD. Dist: Consortium Bk. Sales & Distribution.

Bishop, Justin. Country Style & Design. 2012. (ENG., Illus.). 224p. 50.00 (978-1-86470-448-8(9)) Images Publishing Group AUS. Dist: National Bk. Network.

Black Dog and Leventhal Publishers Staff, ed. The Big Book of Small House Designs: 75 Award-Winning Plans for Your Dream House, 1,250 Square Feet or Less. 2011. (ENG., Illus.). 368p. pap. 17.95 (978-1-57912-887-6(4), 1579128874) Black Dog & Leventhal Pubs., Inc.

Bloemink, Barbara, et al. Design Life Now: National Design Triennial 2006. 2006. (ENG., Illus.). 224p. (978-0-910503-99-0(0)); pap. (978-0-910503-98-3(2)) Assouline FRA. Dist: Perseus Distribution.

Blyth, Alastair. Managing the Brief for Better Design. 2nd ed. 2009. (Illus.). 220p. pap. 62.95 (978-0-415-46031-6(X)); 160.00 (978-0-415-46030-9(1)) Taylor & Francis Group.

Boeckl, Matthias, ed. Architektur. Aktuell 348: The Art of Building. 2009. (Zeitschrift Architektur. Aktuell Ser.). (ENG & GER., Illus.). 168p. pap., pap. 19.95 (978-3-211-89803-1(4)) Springer.

Boekraad, Hugues. My Work Is Not My Work: Pierre Bernard: Design for the Public Domain. 2008. (Illus.). 319p. pap. 49.95 (978-3-03778-087-9(8), 3037780878) Lars Muller Pubs. CHE. Dist: Springer.

Boğaç, Ceren. Architecture for Meaning. 2010. 216p. pap. (978-3-8383-9554-8(9)) Lambert Academic Publishing.

Bokmiller, Don, et al. Mastering Revit MEP 2010. 2009. 950p. pap. 69.99 (978-0-470-53198-3(3), Sybex) Wiley, John & Sons, Inc.

Bolchover, Joshua. Vitamin Green. Phaidon Press Editors, ed. 2012. (ENG.). 352p. 75.00 (978-0-7148-6229-3(0)) Phaidon Pr., Inc.

Borden, Iain, ed. Bartlett Designs: Speculating with Architecture. 2009. (ENG., Illus.). 256p. pap. 45.00 (978-0-470-77279-9(4), Wiley) Wiley, John & Sons, Inc.

Borja-Villel, Manuel J. Drifts & Derivations: Experiences, Journeys & Morphologies. 2011. (ENG.). 301p. pap. 54.95 (978-84-8026-425-9(X)) Museo Nacional Centro de Arte Reina Sofia ESP. Dist: Actar Birkhauser Distribution.

Bosoni, Giampiero. Franco Albini. 2011. (ENG., Illus.). 120p. 45.00 (978-88-6116-141-2(3)) Antique Collectors' Club.

Boubekri, Mohamed. Daylighting, Architecture & Health: Building Design Strategies. 2008. (ENG., Illus.). 160p. pap. 59.95 (978-0-7506-6724-1(9)) Routledge.

Bougdah, Hocine & Zunde, J. M. Integrated Strategies in Architecture. 2006. (Technologies of Architecture Ser.: Vol. 1). (Illus.). 312p. 170.00 (978-0-415-36083-8(8), RU42665) Taylor & Francis Group.

Bougdah, Hocine & Zunde, Joan. Integrated Strategies in Architecture. 2006. (Technologies of Architecture Ser.: Vol. 1). (ENG., Illus.). 312p. (C). per. 39.95 (978-0-415-36084-5(6), RU42666, Taylor & Francis) Taylor & Francis Group GBR. Dist: Taylor & Francis Group.

Bradstreet, Scott. Landscape Design for Architectural Style: European Influenced. 2008. (Illus.). 256p. 49.99 (978-0-7643-3106-0(X)) Schiffer Publishing, Ltd.

Brandt, Robert M., et al. Design Informed: Driving Innovation with Evidence-Based Design. 2010. (ENG., Illus.). 360p. 80.00 (978-0-470-39562-2(1), Wiley) Wiley, John & Sons, Inc.

Branzi, Andrea. Weak & Diffuse Modernity: The World of Projects at the Beginning of the 21st Century. 2006. (ENG., Illus.). 180p. pap. 34.95 (978-88-7624-651-7(7)) Skira Editore ITA. Dist: Random Hse., Inc.

Bratton, Denise, et al. Another Take: 17 Short Stories on Architecture. Angelil, Marc et al, eds. 2011. (Illus.). 277p. 70.00 (978-3-85881-718-1(X)) Scheidegger und Spiess AG, Verlag CHE. Dist: Antique Collectors' Club.

Braun. Swim! Best of Pool Design. 2010. (ENG., Illus.). 400p. pap. 19.95 (978-3-03768-063-6(6), Braun Publish,Csi) Continental Sales, Inc.

Broto, Carles. Wood Cabins. 2009. (ENG.). 192p. pap. 24.99 (978-2-917031-38-4(7)) Links International (Leading International Key Services Barcelona, S.A.) ESP. Dist: National Bk. Network.

Bucsescu, Dan & Eng, Michael. Looking Beyond the Structure: Critical Thinking for Designers & Architects. 2009. (Illus.). 320p. pap. 68.00 (978-1-56367-719-9(9)) Fairchild Bks.

Bullivant, Lucy. Masterplanning Futures. 2012. (ENG., Illus.). 336p. pap. 53.95 (978-0-415-55447-3(0)) Routledge.

Burry, Jane & Burry, Mark. The New Mathematics of Architecture. 2010. (ENG., Illus.). 272p. 55.00 (978-0-500-34264-0(4), 534264) Thames & Hudson.

Burry, Mark. Scripting Cultures: Architectural Design & Programming. 2011. (Architectural Design Primer Ser.). (ENG., Illus.). 272p. 125.00

(978-0-470-74642-4(4)); pap. 50.00 *(978-0-470-74641-7(6))* Wiley, John & Sons, Inc. (Wiley).

Carmona, Matthew, et al, eds. Public Space: The Management Dimension. 2008. (Illus.). VIII, 232p. 53.95 *(978-0-415-39649-3(2))*; 155.00 *(978-0-415-39108-5(3))* Routledge.

Carpo, Mario. The Alphabet & the Algorithm. 2011. (Writing Architecture Ser.). (ENG., Illus.). 184p. (gr. 17). pap. 21.95 *(978-0-262-51580-1(6))* MIT Pr.

Carpo, Mario & Lemerle, Frederique, eds. Perspective, Projections & Design: Technologies of Architectural Representation. 2007. (ENG., Illus.). 208p. (C). 165.00 *(978-0-415-40204-0(2))* Routledge.

Carscadden, Bruce. Carscadden Thrift: Selected Works. McDonald, Ian Ross, ed. 2012. (ENG., Illus.). 112p. 19.95 ***(978-1-897476-40-6(X))*** Simply Read Bks. CAN. Dist: Perseus-PGW.

Castle, Helen, ed. 4dsocial: Interactive Design Environments. 2007. (Architectural Design Ser.). (ENG., Illus.). 128p. per. 50.00 *(978-0-470-31911-6(9), Wiley)* Wiley, John & Sons, Inc.

Ceccato, Cristiano, et al, eds. Advances in Architectural Geometry 2010. 2010. (Illus.). 242p. 69.95 *(978-3-7091-0308-1(8)*, 3709103088) Springer Wien AUT. Dist: Springer.

Chaix & Morel & JSWD Architects, contrib. by. ThyssenKrupp Quartier. 2011. (ENG., Illus.). 144p. 60.00 *(978-3-86859-090-6(0))* Jovis Verlag GmbH DEU. Dist: D.A.P./Distributed Art Pubs.

Chalfont, Garuth. Connection to Nature at the Building Edge. 2011. 352p. pap. ***(978-3-8443-1154-9(8))*** Lambert Academic Publishing.

Charleson, Andrew. Seismic Design for Architects. 2008. (ENG., Illus.). 296p. pap. 59.95 *(978-0-7506-8550-4(6))* Routledge.

Cheah, Fay, ed. Homes, Issues + Processes: Design Collective Architects. 2011. (ENG.). 144p. pap. 29.95 *(978-1-907317-46-0(5))* Black Dog Publishing Ltd. GBR. Dist: Perseus Distribution.

Chen, Gang. LEED ID&C Exam Guide: A Must-Have for the LEED AP ID+C Exam: Study Materials, Sample Questions, Mock Exam, Green Interior Design & Construction, Green Building LEED Certification, & Sustainability. Wenger, Barry, ed. 2010. (Illus.). 248p. pap. 99.95 *(978-0-9843741-0-6(8))* ArchiteG, Inc.

Ching, Francis D. & Juroszek, Steven P. Design Drawing. 2nd ed. 2010. (Wiley Desktop Editions Ser.). (ENG., Illus.). 416p. pap. 60.00 *(978-0-470-53369-7(2), Wiley)* Wiley, John & Sons, Inc.

Ching, Francis D. K., et al. Building Structures Illustrated: Patterns, Systems, & Design. 2009. (ENG., Illus.). 320p. pap. 49.95 *(978-0-470-18785-2(9), Wiley)* Wiley, John & Sons, Inc.

Chipova, Irina. Moscow Architecture & Design. 2007. (And Guides). (Illus.). 191p. pap. 16.95 *(978-3-8327-9156-8(6))* teNeues Publishing Co.

Chirisa, Innocent. Aspects in Urban Layout Design in Zimbabwe. 2011. 64p. pap. ***(978-3-8443-9914-1(3))*** Lambert Academic Publishing.

Chiuini, Michele, et al. Structural Design: A Practical Guide for Architects. 2nd rev. ed. 2007. (ENG., Illus.). 816p. 120.00 *(978-0-471-78904-8(6), Wiley)* Wiley, John & Sons, Inc.

Chopra, Aidan. Introduction to Google SketchUp. 2007. (ENG., Illus.). 480p. (C). pap. 71.95 *(978-0-470-17565-1(6), Wiley)* Wiley, John & Sons, Inc.

Christiane, Sauer. Made of... New Materials Sourcebook for Architecture & Design. 2010. (Illus.). 280p. 78.00 *(978-3-89955-289-8(X))* Die Gestalten Verlag DEU. Dist: Prestel Publishing.

Chueca, Pilar. Today's City Houses. 2009. (ENG.). 240p. pap. 29.99 *(978-84-96969-93-3(2))* Links International (Leading International Key Services Barcelona, S.A.) ESP. Dist: National Bk. Network.

Clark, Roger H. & Pause, Michael. Precedents in Architecture: Analytic Diagrams, Formative Ideas, & Partis. 4th ed. 2012. (ENG., Illus.). 352p. pap. 65.00 ***(978-0-470-94674-9(1)***, Wiley) Wiley, John & Sons, Inc.

Clarke, James. Designing Schools from the Inside Out. 2013. (Future Schools Ser.). (ENG., Illus.). 160p. 49.95 *(978-1-85539-779-8(X))* Continuum International Publishing Group, Ltd. GBR. Dist: National Bk. Network.

Clear, Nic, ed. Architectures of the near Future. 2009. (Architectural Design Ser.: 37). (ENG., Illus.). 136p. pap. 50.00 *(978-0-470-69955-3(8), Wiley)* Wiley, John & Sons, Inc.

Clementi, Alberto, text. Designing after the Earthquake: The Experiences for Abruzzo. 2011. (ENG & ITA.). 288p. pap. 29.95 *(978-88-95623-47-4(9))* LIST - Laboratorio Editoriale ITA. Dist: Actar Birkhauser Distribution.

Colletti, Marjan, ed. Exuberance: New Virtuosity in Contemporary Architecture. 2010. (Architectural Design Ser.). (ENG.). 144p. pap. 45.00 *(978-0-470-71714-1(9), Wiley)* Wiley, John & Sons, Inc.

Connelly, Garrett. Sculptor's Ferrocement Manual. 2008. (Illus.). 76p. pap. *(978-0-9748016-4-3(X))* ferrocement.com.

Cook, Martin. The Design Quality Manual: Improving Building Performance. 2007. (ENG., Illus.). 216p. 130.00 *(978-1-4051-3088-2(1), Wiley-Blackwell)* Wiley, John & Sons, Inc.

Cooperative Design, Visualization, & Engineering. 2008. (Lecture Notes in Computer Science / Information Systems & Applications, incl. Internet/Web, & HCI Ser.). spiral bd. 79.95 *(978-3-540-88010-3(0)*, 3540880100) Springer.

Corkill, P. A., et al. Structure & Architectural Design. 4th rev. ed. Date not set. (Illus.). 224p. (C). reprint ed. pap. *(978-0-9674690-0-3(7))* Market Publishing.

Corser, Robert & Princeton Architectural Press Staff. Fabricating Architecture: Selected Readings in Digital Design & Manufacturing. 2010. (ENG., Illus.). 216p. pap. 29.95 *(978-1-56898-889-4(3))* Princeton Architectural Pr.

Cory, Steve. Ultimate Guide: Porches. 2011. (Home Improvement Ser.). (ENG., Illus.). 192p. (gr. 5). pap. 16.95 *(978-1-58011-491-2(1))* Creative Homeowner.

Cory, Steve & Sunset Books Staff. Masonry. 2010. (ENG.). 304p. pap. 24.95 *(978-0-376-01599-3(5)*, Sunset Bks./Sunset Publishing Corp.) Oxmoor Hse., Inc.

CPI Editors. The Complete Guide to Decks: Plan & Build Your Dream Deck Includes Complete Deck Plans. 5th ed. 2012. (Black & Decker Complete Guide Ser.). (ENG., Illus.). 352p. pap. 24.99 *(978-1-58923-659-2(9)*, 1589236599) Quayside.

—The Complete Guide to Sheds: Utility, Storage, Playhouse, Mini-Barn, Garden, Backyard Retreat, More. 2nd ed. 2011. (Black & Decker Complete Guide Ser.). (ENG., Illus.). 256p. pap. 24.99 *(978-1-58923-660-8(2)*, 1589236602) Quayside.

Cramer, James P. & Paradise Wolford, Jane. Almanac of Architecture & Design 2011. 12th ed. 2011. (Illus.). 606p. pap. 149.00 ***(978-0-9846136-0-1(9))*** Greenway Communications.

Cramer, James P. & Yankopolus, Jennifer Evans, eds. Almanac of Architecture & Design 2007. 2006. (Illus.). 850p. pap. 49.50 *(978-0-9755654-4-5(3)*, Ostberg) Greenway Communications.

Cram101 Textbook Reviews. Outlines & Highlights for Structural Design by James R Underwood. 2011. 80p. pap. 27.95 ***(978-1-61905-921-4(5))*** Cram101 Inc.

—Outlines & Highlights for the Study of Architectural Design by John F Harbeson. 2011. 88p. pap. 27.95 ***(978-1-61905-625-1(9))*** Cram101 Inc.

Cram101 Textbook Reviews & Cram101 Textbook Reviews. Outlines & Highlights for Analysing Architecture by Simon Unwin. 2011. 90p. pap. 27.95 ***(978-1-61830-876-4(9))*** Cram101 Inc.

—Outlines & Highlights for Commercial Drafting & Detailing by Alan Jefferis. 2011. 230p. pap. 31.95 ***(978-1-61830-866-5(1))*** Cram101 Inc.

—Outlines & Highlights for Introducing & Implementing Revit Architecture 2009 by Lay Christopher Fox. 2011. 66p. pap. 27.95 ***(978-1-61830-970-9(6))*** Cram101 Inc.

—Outlines & Highlights for Mastering Revit Architecture 2008 by Eddy Krygiel. 2011. 124p. pap. 28.95 ***(978-1-61830-949-5(8))*** Cram101 Inc.

Creative Publishing International Editors. Black & Decker Here's How... Decks: Build Your Very Own Deck in 12 Easy Steps. 2010. (Black & Decker Here's How Ser.). (ENG., Illus.). 96p. pap. 9.99 *(978-1-58923-492-5(8)*, 1589234928, Creative Publishing International) Quayside.

Crippa, Maria Antonietta, et al. Living Gaudi: The Architect's Complete Vision. 2006. (ENG., Illus.). 252p. 75.00 *(978-0-8478-2435-9(7))* Rizzoli International Pubns., Inc.

Croci, Valentina, ed. The New Europe. 2006. (Architectural Design Ser.: 29). (ENG., Illus.). 128p. pap. 60.00 *(978-0-470-01839-2(9), Academy Pr.)* Wiley, John & Sons, Inc.

Cruz, Marcos & Pike, Steve, eds. Neoplasmatic Design. 2008. (Architectural Design Ser.). (ENG.). 136p. pap. 45.00 *(978-0-470-51958-5(4), Wiley)* Wiley, John & Sons, Inc.

Cruz, Paulo J. Da Sou, ed. Structures & Architecture: ICSA 2010 - 1st International Conference on STructures & Architecture, July 14-16, 2010 in Guimaraes, Portugal. 2010. (ENG., Illus.). 618p. 199.95 *(978-0-415-49249-2(1)*, CRC Press) Taylor & Francis Group GBR. Dist: Taylor & Francis Group.

DAAB Media Staff. Delugan Meissl: Associated Architects, 1 vol. 2008. (ENG, GER, FRE, SPA & ITA., Illus.). 175p. 29.95 *(978-3-937718-87-3(7))* DAAB Media Gmbh DEU. Dist: Innovative Logistics.

DAAB Media Staff, ed. Creative Germany, 1 vol. 2009. (ITA, FRE, GER, SPA & ENG., Illus.). 499p. 99.95 *(978-3-86654-052-1(3))* DAAB Media Gmbh DEU. Dist: Innovative Logistics.

—New York Architecture & Design, 1 vol. 2009. (ENG.). 240p. 59.95 *(978-3-86654-072-9(8))* DAAB Media Gmbh DEU. Dist: Innovative Logistics.

—Patricia Urquiola, 1 vol. 2009. (ENG.). 175p. 29.95 *(978-3-86654-065-9(8))* DAAB Media Gmbh DEU. Dist: Innovative Logistics.

Dabby, Ramsey & Bedi, Ashwani. Structure for Architects: A Primer. 2012. (ENG., Illus.). 272p. 70.00 *(978-0-470-63376-2(X), Wiley)* Wiley, John & Sons, Inc.

Daglio, Laura & Bellini, Oscar. Building Arabia: Expanding the Limits of Architecture. 2010. (ENG., Illus.). 302p. 40.00 *(978-88-544-0450-2(0))* White Star ITA. Dist: Random Hse., Inc.

Dal Co, Francesco, ed. SOM Journal 6. 2010. (ENG., Illus.). 208p. pap. 30.00 *(978-3-7757-2637-5(3))* Hatje Cantz Verlag GmbH & Co KG DEU. Dist: D.A.P./Distributed Art Pubs.

Dastouri Bias, Taraneh. Critical Look to the Developments in Architectural Structures. 2010. 100p. pap. *(978-3-8383-4781-3(1))* Lambert Academic Publishing.

Davids, Rene & Killory, Christine, eds. Detail in Process. 2007. (ENG., Illus.). 208p. 65.00 *(978-1-56898-718-7(8))* Princeton Architectural Pr.

Davis, Patrick. Introducing Autodesk Revit Architecture 2012. 2011. (ENG., Illus.). 720p. pap. 49.99 *(978-1-118-02996-1(8), Sybex)* Wiley, John & Sons, Inc.

Davis, Patrick, et al. Introducing Autodesk Revit Architecture 2011. 2010. (ENG., Illus.). 544p. pap. 49.99 *(978-0-470-64971-8(2), Sybex)* Wiley, John & Sons, Inc.

de Canales, Francisco Gonzalez. Experiments with Life Itself (Spanish Ed.) 2012. (SPA.). 152p. pap. *(978-84-92861-66-8(5))* Actar Birkhauser Distribution.

de Jongh, Robin. SketchUp 7.1 for Architectural Visualization: Create stunning photo-realistic & artistic visuals for your SketchUp models: Beginner's Guide. 2010. (Illus.). 403p. pap. *(978-1-84719-946-1(1))* Packt Publishing, Ltd.

de Reus, Mark & Nataraj, Nirmala. Tropical Experience: Architecture + Design. Goff, Gordon, ed. 2012. (ENG., Illus.). 300p. 50.00 *(978-1-935935-02-5(X))* Oro Editions.

De Rijk, Timo, ed. The World According to Concrete, 1 vol. 2007. (ENG., Illus.). 480p. 75.00 *(978-90-5662-483-5(0))* NAi Uitgevers / Publishers Stichting NLD. Dist: D.A.P./Distributed Art Pubs.

Debeerst, Philippe, photos by. Living in Great Style in Sotogrande, 1 vol. 2011. (ENG.). 256p. 89.50 ***(978-90-8881-029-9(X))*** Exhibitions International BEL. Dist: Innovative Logistics.

Demchak, Greg, et al. Revit Architecture 2010. 2009. (ENG., Illus.). 816p. pap. 59.99 *(978-0-470-45649-1(3), Sybex)* Wiley, John & Sons, Inc.

Design, Hotels, ed. The Design Hotels Book: Edition 2010. 2010. 424p. 69.00 *(978-3-89955-283-6(0))* Die Gestalten Verlag DEU. Dist: Prestel Publishing.

Design Museum Staff. How to Design a House. 2010. (ENG., Illus.). 112p. 20.00 *(978-1-84091-545-7(5)*, Conran Octopus) Octopus Publishing Group GBR. Dist: Hachette Bk. Group.

Design Workshop. Construction Documentation Standards & Best Practices for Landscape Architectural Design. 2009. (ENG.). 128p. pap. 65.00 *(978-0-470-40217-7(2), Wiley)* Wiley, John & Sons, Inc.

Deutscher Designer Club (DDC), ed. Gute Gestaltung / Good Design 07. 2007. (GER & ENG., Illus.). 348p. 54.95 *(978-3-7643-8383-1(6)*, 3764383836) Springer.

Dikbas, Attila, et al, eds. Managing IT in Construction/Managing Construction for Tomorrow. 2009. (ENG.). 886p. 329.95 *(978-0-415-56744-2(0), CRC Press)* Taylor & Francis Group GBR. Dist: Taylor & Francis Group.

Dittmer, Lori. The Future of Architecture. 2012. (What's Next? Ser.). 48p. (gr. 5-12). 23.95 ***(978-1-60818-220-6(7)***, Creative Education) Creative Co., The.

Dockter, Benjamin. Urban Complexity. 2010. 80p. pap. *(978-3-639-23650-7(5))* VDM Verlag Dr. Mueller e.K.

Doherty, Sharon. Heathrow's Terminal 5: History in the Making. 2008. (ENG., Illus.). 372p. 75.00 *(978-0-470-75435-1(4), Wiley)* Wiley, John & Sons, Inc.

Dong, Andy, et al, eds. Computer-Aided Architectural Design Futures 2007: Proceedings of the 12th International CAAD Futures Conference. 2007. 616p. 219.00 *(978-1-4020-6527-9(2)*, 1402065272) Springer.

Doorley, Scott, et al. Make Space: How to Set the Stage for Creative Collaboration. 2012. (ENG., Illus.). 272p. pap. 49.95 ***(978-1-118-14372-8(8)***, Wiley) Wiley, John & Sons, Inc.

Drexle, Hans. Sustainable by Design: Methods for Holistic Housing: Basics, Strategies, Projects. 2012. (ENG.). 272p. 110.00 *(978-3-0346-0768-1(7))* Birkhauser Verlag AG CHE. Dist: Actar Birkhauser Distribution.

Dumarcay, Jacques. Architecture & Its Models in Southeast Asia. 2006. (ENG., Illus.). pap. 17.00 *(978-974-524-027-8(3))* Orchid Pr. THA. Dist: National Bk. Network.

Dutta, Arindam. The Bureaucracy of Beauty: Design in the Age of Its Global Reproducibility. 2006. (Illus.). 364p. 145.00 *(978-0-415-97919-1(6))*; (ENG., Illus.). 352p. per. 49.95 *(978-0-415-97920-7(X))* Routledge.

Dzambazova, Tatjana, et al. Introducing Revit Architecture 2010: BIM for Beginners. 2009. (ENG., Illus.). 512p. pap. 49.99 *(978-0-470-47355-9(X)*, Sybex) Wiley, John & Sons, Inc.

—Mastering Revit Architecture 2009. 2008. (ENG., Illus.). 800p. pap. 59.99 *(978-0-470-29528-1(7), Sybex)* Wiley, John & Sons, Inc.

Eckler, James F. Language of Space & Form: Generative Terms for Architecture. 2012. (ENG., Illus.). 320p. 50.00 *(978-0-470-61844-8(2), Wiley)* Wiley, John & Sons, Inc.

Edwards, Brian. Understanding Architecture Through Drawing. 2nd rev. ed. 2008. (Illus.). CCLXIV, 8p. pap. 69.95 *(978-0-415-44414-9(4))* Taylor & Francis Group.

—Understanding Architecture Through Drawing. 2nd rev. ed. 2008. (ENG., Illus.). 272p. (C). 165.00 *(978-0-415-44413-2(6)*, Taylor & Francis) Taylor & Francis Group GBR. Dist: Taylor & Francis Group.

Elias, Helen. Getting Your Project Published: A Guide to Press Relations for Architects, Designers & Engineers. 2006. (ENG., Illus.). 208p. 52.95 *(978-0-415-34867-6(6))*; 155.00 *(978-0-415-34866-9(8))* Taylor & Francis Group GBR. (Taylor & Francis). Dist: Taylor & Francis Group.

Emery, Garry & Vincent, Emery. Inside Outside In. 2006. (ENG., Illus.). 256p. 55.00 *(978-1-876907-30-3(4))* Images Publishing Group AUS. Dist: National Bk. Network.

Emmitt, Stephen. Architectural Technology. 2nd ed. 2012. (ENG.). 264p. pap. 52.99 ***(978-1-4051-9479-2(0)***, Wiley-Blackwell) Wiley, John & Sons, Inc.

—Design Management for Architects. 2007. (ENG., Illus.). 344p. per. 69.99 *(978-1-4051-3147-6(0)*, Wiley-Blackwell) Wiley, John & Sons, Inc.

Emmitt, Stephen. Lean Design Management. 2012. (Architectural Engineering & Design Management Ser.). (ENG., Illus.). 120p. 140.00 ***(978-1-84971-431-0(2))*** Routledge.

Emmitt, Stephen, et al. Architectural Management: International Research & Practice. Emmitt, Stephen et al, eds. 2009. (ENG., Illus.). 344p. 144.99 *(978-1-4051-7786-3(1)*, Wiley-Blackwell) Wiley, John & Sons, Inc.

Estévez, Alberto T., ed. Genetic Architectures III / Arquitecturas Genéticas III. 2010. (ENG.). 208p. pap. 22.00 *(978-0-930829-68-1(9))* Lumen, Inc.

Fagone, V. & Favata, G. Joe Colombo: Minimum Design. 2011. (ENG., Illus.). 120p. 45.00 ***(978-88-6648-005-1(3))*** Antique Collectors' Club.

Fanella, David A. Design of Low-Rise Reinforced Concrete Buildings. 2009. pap. 79.00 *(978-1-58001-797-8(5))* International Code Council.

FarEast Design. Spa-De Vol. 3: International Review of Interior Design. 2006. (ENG., Illus.). 184p. 45.00 *(978-4-89737-526-7(6))* Azur Corp. JPN. Dist: Antique Collectors' Club.

Farrelly, Lorraine. The Fundamentals of Architecture. 2007. (Fundamentals Ser.). (ENG., Illus.). 176p. pap. 38.50 *(978-2-940373-48-2(5))* AVA Publishing GBR. Dist: Ingram Pub. Services.

—The Fundamentals of Architecture. 2nd rev. ed. 2012. (ENG.). 192p. (C). pap. 38.50 ***(978-2-940411-75-7(1))*** Ava Publishing SA CHE. Dist: Ingram Pub. Services.

Fentress, Curtis. Touchstones of Design. 2010. (ENG., Illus.). 308p. 19.99 *(978-1-86470-401-3(2)*, Images Publishing Dist Ac) Antique Collectors' Club GBR. Dist: National Bk. Network.

Ferre, Albert, ed. From Control to Design: Parametric/Algorithmic Architecture. 2008. (Illus.). 320p. (C). pap. 42.00 *(978-84-96540-79-8(0))* Kunst-Werke Berlin e.V. DEU. Dist: Actar Birkhauser Distribution.

Fisher, Thomas & Bastianelli-Kerze, Peter. The Invisible Element of Place: The Architecture of David Salmela. 2011. (Illus.). 272p. pap. 39.95 *(978-0-8166-6994-3(5))* Univ. of Minnesota Pr.

Flores, Ricardo, ed. Through the Canvas. 2008. 128p. (C). pap. *(978-84-612-4010-4(3))* Actar Birkhauser Distribution.

Foque, Richard. Building Knowledge in Architecture. 2010. (ENG., Illus.). 240p. pap. 42.00 *(978-90-5487-545-1(3)*, VUB Univ. Pr. BEL. Dist: Independent Pubs. Group.

Form Magazine. Entry 2006: Design, Visions & Perspectives. 2006. (Illus.). 82p. pap. 14.95 *(978-3-936560-47-3(1)*, 3936560471) Birkhauser Verlag GmbH DEU. Dist: Springer.

Fountain, Daniel E. Let's Restore Our Land: Church & Community Leaders Working Together to Restore the Land. 2007. (Illus.). 256p. pap. 5.00 *(978-0-9653360-3-1(4))* ECHO, Inc. (Educational Concerns for Hunger Organization).

Fox, Lay Christopher & Balding, James J. Introducing & Implementing Revit Architecture 2010. 2009. (ENG.). 544p. pap. 107.95 ***(978-1-4354-9310-0(9))*** Delmar Cengage Learning.

Fox, Michael & Kemp, Miles. Interactive Architecture. 2009. (ENG., Illus.). 256p. 50.00 *(978-1-56898-836-8(2))* Princeton Architectural Pr.

Frances, Sarah A. Cool Architecture. 2006. (Designing with/for Ser.). (ENG., Illus.). 192p. 49.50 *(978-1-920744-27-4(4))* Images Publishing Group AUS. Dist: National Bk. Network.

Franck, Karen A. & Howard, Teresa Von Sommaruga. Design Through Dialogue: A Guide for Architects & Clients. 2010. (ENG., Illus.). 208p. 130.00 *(978-0-470-72190-2(1), Wiley)* Wiley, John & Sons, Inc.

Franck, Karen A. & Lepori, R. Bianca. Architecture from the Inside Out: From the Body, the Senses, the Site, & the Community. 2nd ed. 2007. (ENG., Illus.). 200p. 145.00 *(978-0-470-05783-4(*))*; pap. 55.00 *(978-0-470-05785-8(8)*, Wiley, John & Sons, Inc. (Academy Pr.).

Frascari, Marco, et al, eds. From Models to Drawings: Imagination & Representation in Architecture. 2010. (ENG., Illus.). 312p. (C). 53.95 *(978-0-415-48798-6(6))* Routledge.

Frascari, Marco & Starkey, Bradley, eds. From Models to Drawings: Imagination & Representation in Architecture. 2007. (ENG., Illus.). 312p. (C). 100.00 *(978-0-415-43113-2(1))* Routledge.

Frausto, Salomon, ed. Hunch 13: Consensus. 2010. (ENG., Illus.). 176p. pap. 35.00 *(978-90-5662-718-8(X))* NAi Uitgevers / Publishers Stichting NLD. Dist: D.A.P./Distributed Art Pubs.

Frederick, Matthew. 101 Things I Learned in Architecture School. 2007. (ENG., Illus.). 216p. (gr. 17). 14.95 *(978-0-252-06266-4(6))* MIT Pr.

—101 Things I Learned in Architecture School: The Ultimate Cheat Sheet for Surviving an Architectural Education. 2007. pap. *(978-0-262-56228-7(6))* MIT Pr.

Frost, Malcolm. Malcolm Frost: Graphic Design for Architects. 2006. (Hands on Graphics Ser.). (ENG., Illus.). 128p. pap. 19.95 *(978-1-876907-72-3(X))* Images Publishing Group AUS. Dist: National Bk. Network.

Gö, et al. Before Architecture. Vor der Architektur. 2 Bde. Residential Building as Motivation - Wohnbau als Anlass - 11. Internationale Architekturausstellung - La Biennale di Venezia 2008. 11th International Architecture Exhibition - La Biennale di Venezia 2008, 3 vols. 2008. (GER & ENG., Illus.). 211p. pap. 49.95 *(978-3-211-09425-9(3))* Springer Wien AUT. Dist: Actar Birkhauser Distribution.

Gao, Arthur. Hopsca. 2011. (ENG., Illus.). 288p. 50.00 *(978-988-19739-0-0(2))* Design Media Publishing Ltd. HKG. Dist: BookMasters Distribution Services (BDS).

Garcia, Mark. Architextiles. 2007. (Architectural Design Ser.: 32). (ENG., Illus.). 136p. pap. 60.00 *(978-0-470-02634-2(0)*, Academy Pr.) Wiley, John & Sons, Inc.

Garcia, Mark, ed. The Patterns of Architecture. 2010. (Architectural Design Ser.). (ENG., Illus.). 144p. pap. 50.00 *(978-0-470-69959-1(0), Wiley)* Wiley, John & Sons, Inc.

Gardner, Donald. Smartbook 3: Thinking at pencil Speed. 2007. (Illus.). spiral bd. 54.95 *(978-0-9777443-3-6(7))* Amtal S.p.A.

Geist, Kevin. How to Build Wooden Gates & Picket Fences. 2nd rev. ed. 2011. (ENG., Illus.). 160p. pap. 24.95 *(978-0-8117-0766-4(0))* Stackpole Bks.

Gengnagel, Christoph, et al, eds. Computational Design Modeling: Proceedings of the Design Modeling Symposium Berlin 2011. 2011. (ENG., Illus.). xvi, 348p. 259.00 ***(978-3-642-23434-7(8)***, 3642234348) Springer.

Gerhard, Mark & Harper, Jeffrey M. Mastering Autodesk 3ds Max Design 2011. 2010. (ENG., Illus.). 960p. pap. 69.99 *(978-0-470-88262-7(X), Sybex)* Wiley, John & Sons, Inc.

Gero, John S., ed. Design Computing & Cognition '04. 2011. (ENG.). x, 635p. pap. 164.00 *(978-90-481-6650-3(0)*, 9048166500) Springer.

—Design Computing & Cognition '06. 2006. (Illus.). xii, 714p. 249.00 *(978-1-4020-5130-2(1)*, 1402051301) Springer.

—Design Computing & Cognition '10. 2010. (ENG., Illus.). xvi, 744p. 399.00 *(978-94-007-0509-8(3)*, 9400705093) Springer.

Gevorkian, Peter. Alternative Energy Systems in Building Design (GreenSource Books) 2009. (ENG., Illus.). 544p. 99.95 (978-0-07-162147-2(4), 0071621474) McGraw-Hill Professional Publishing.
Gibson, David. The Wayfinding Handbook: Information Design for Public Places. 2009. (ENG., Illus.). 152p. pap. 24.95 (978-1-56898-769-9(2)) Princeton Architectural Pr.
Gill, Bob. Bob Gill Illustration. 2006. (ENG., Illus.). 128p. 17.95 (978-1-920744-73-1(8), Images Publishing Dist Ac) Antique Collectors' Club GBR. Dist: National Bk. Network.
Gissen, David, ed. Territory: Architecture Beyond Environment. 2010. (Architectural Design Ser.: 39). (ENG.). 136p. pap. 40.00 (978-0-470-72165-0(0), Wiley) Wiley, John & Sons, Inc.
Gleiniger, Andrea & Vrachliotis, Georg. Code: Between Operation & Narration. 2010. (ENG., Illus.). 120p. pap. 29.95 (978-3-0346-0117-7(4)) Birkhauser Verlag AG CHE. Dist: Actar Birkhauser Distribution.
Godsey, Lisa. Interior Design Materials & Specifications. 2008. 320p. pap. 80.00 (978-1-56367-487-7(4)) Fairchild Bks.
Goldberg, H. Edward. Revit Architecture 2012: A Comprehensive Guide. 2012. (ENG.). 720p. (C). pap. 102.67 (978-0-13-295510-2(5), Prentice Hall) Prentice Hall PTR.
Goldberg, H. Frank. Revit Architecture 2011: A Comprehensive Guide. 2010. (ENG., Illus.). 648p. (C). pap. 106.20 (978-0-13-813483-9(9), Prentice Hall) Prentice Hall PTR.
Goldemberg, Eric, ed. Pulsation in Architecture. 2011. 480p. pap. (978-1-60427-023-5(3)) Ross, J. Publishing, Inc.
Goldschmidt, Gabriela & Porter, William L., eds. Design Representation. 2010. (ENG., Illus.). xviii, 222p. pap. 169.00 (978-1-84996-904-8(3), 1849969043) Springer.
Good, Ken. Discover Smart Bim: An Interactive Guide to ArchiCAD. 2009. (Illus.). 244p. pap. 70.49 (978-1-4490-3678-2(3)) AuthorHouse.
Grigsby, Darcy Grimaldo. Colossal: Engineering Modernity - Suez Canal Statue of Liberty Eiffel Tower Panama Canal. 2009. (Illus.). 224p. pap. 65.00 (978-1-934772-76-8(3)) Periscope Publishing.
Grobman, Yasha & Neuman, Eran, eds. Performalism: Form & Performance in Digital Architecture. 2011. (ENG., Illus.). 224p. (C). 155.00 (978-0-415-58360-2(8)); pap. 74.95 (978-0-415-58361-9(6)) Routledge.
Grosenick, Uta. Art Now 2: Der neue Wegweiser zu 81 internationalen zeitgenössischen Künstlern, Vol. 2. 25th ed. 2008. (FRE, GER & ENG., Illus.). 349p. 14.99 (978-3-8365-0324-2(7)) TASCHEN DEU. Dist: Ingram Pub. Services.
Gu Zhenhong. Approaches to Energy Efficient Building Development: Studying under Chinese Contexts 2008. 100p. pap. (978-3-639-09361-2(5)) VDM Verlag Dr. Mueller e.K.
Guberman, Marc, et al, eds. Perspecta 40 Monster: The Yale Architectural Journal. 2008. (ENG., Illus.). 209p. (gr. 17). pap. 25.00 (978-0-262-57244-6(3)) MIT Pr.
Gullo, Gina & Rinaldi, Angela. Option Selling for Profit: The Builder's Guide for Generating Design Center Revenues & Profits. 2008. 23.95 (978-0-86718-642-0(9)) BuilderBooks.
Guthrie, John. The Architect's Portable Handbook: First-Step Rules of Thumb for Building Design 4/e. 4th ed. 2010. (ENG., Illus.). 688p. pap. 59.95 (978-0-07-163915-6(2), 0071639152) McGraw-Hill Professional Publishing.
Guthrie, John Patten (Pat). Interior Designers Portable Handbook: First-Step Rules of Thumb for the Design of Interiors. 3rd ed. 2012. (ENG., Illus.). 560p. pap. 60.00 (978-0-07-178206-7(0), 0071782060) McGraw-Hill Professional Publishing.
Haeusler, M. Hank. Chromatophoric Architecture. 2010. (ENG., Illus.). 112p. pap. 28.00 (978-3-939633-96-9(8)) Jovis Verlag GmbH DEU. Dist: D.A.P./Distributed Art Pubs.
Hagan, Susannah. Digitalia: Essays on the Digital, the Environmental & the Avant-Garde. 2008. (Illus.). 168p. 55.95 (978-0-415-39546-5(1)); 165.00 (978-0-415-39545-8(3)) Routledge.
Hagberg, Eva. Nature Framed: At Home in the Landscape. 2011. (ENG., Illus.). 216p. 50.00 (978-1-58093-319-3(X)) Monacelli Pr., Inc.
Hahn, Alexander. Mathematical Excursions to the World's Great Buildings. 2012. (ENG., Illus.). 352p. (C). 49.50 (978-0-691-14520-4(2)) Princeton Univ. Pr.
Hanlon, Don & Hanlon. Compositions in Architecture. 2009. (ENG., Illus.). 336p. pap. 60.00 (978-0-470-05364-5(X), Wiley) Wiley, John & Sons, Inc.
Harbeson, John F. The Study of Architectural Design. 2008. (ENG., Illus.). 352p. pap. 45.00 (978-0-393-73128-6(6), 73128) Norton, W. W. & Co., Inc.
Hardt, John. Programming, Planning & Practice Question & Answer 2009. annuals 2008. (ENG.). 56p. pap. 49.95 (978-1-4277-7033-2(6)) Kaplan Publishing.
Haro Lebrija, Fernando de & Fuentes Elizondo, Omar. Inspiración para Vivir. 2009. (ENG & SPA., Illus.). 174p. (978-607-437-028-7(1)) AM Editores.
Hasan, Noor M. S., et al. Non Sway & Sway Methods for Design of Multi-Storey Rc Building: Analysis & Design of Rc Building Frames by Staad. Pro. 2011. 120p. pap. (978-3-639-33650-4(X)) VDM Verlag Dr. Mueller e.K.
Hasbun Ch., Yamil & Gross, Uffe. The Toolbox. 2011. 68p. pap. (978-3-8443-2756-4(8)) Lambert Academic Publishing.
Hauck, Thomas, et al. Infrastructural Urbanism: Designing the Peripheries, 1 vol. 2011. (ENG.). 366p. pap. 39.95 (978-3-86922-131-1(3)) DOM Pubs. DEU. Dist: Innovative Logistics.
Hauschild, Moritz & Karzel, Rudiger. Detail Practice: Digital Processes: Planning, Designing, Production. 2011. (Illus.). 112p. pap. 54.95 (978-3-0346-0725-4(3)) Birkhauser Verlag AG CHE. Dist: Actar Birkhauser Distribution.
Hazem, Mohamed. Nanomaterials & Architecture. 2010. 100p. pap. (978-3-8383-1141-8(8)) Lambert Academic Publishing.
Hensel, Michael. Performance-Oriented Design: Towards an Inclusive Approach to the Architectural Design & the Environment. 2012. (Architectural Design Primer Ser.). (ENG.). 184p. 100.00 (978-0-470-97332-5(3)); pap. 40.00 (978-0-470-97331-8(5)) Wiley, John & Sons, Inc. (Wiley).
Hensel, Michael & Menges, Achim. Versatility & Vicissitude: Performance in Morpho-Ecological Design. 2008. (Architectural Design Ser.). (ENG., Illus.). 144p. pap. 50.00 (978-0-470-51687-4(9), Wiley) Wiley, John & Sons, Inc.
Hensel, Michael, et al. Emergent Technologies & Design: Towards a Biological Paradigm for Architecture. 2010. (ENG., Illus.). 256p. 155.00 (978-0-415-49343-7(9)); pap. 62.95 (978-0-415-49344-4(7)) Routledge.
Hensen, Jan L. M. Building Performance Simulation for Design & Operation. 2011. (ENG., Illus.). 536p. (C). 110.00 (978-0-415-47414-6(0)) Routledge.
Hepler, Dana J., et al. Student Solutions Manual for Hepler/Wallach/Hepler's Drafting & Design for Architecture, 2nd. 9th ed. 2012. (ENG.). 120p. (C). pap. 59.95 (978-1-111-12816-6(2)) Delmar Cengage Learning.
—Workbook for Hepler/Wallach/Hepler's Drafting & Design for Architecture, 2nd. 9th ed. 2012. (ENG.). 240p. (C). pap. 40.95 (978-1-111-12815-9(4)) Delmar Cengage Learning.
Hepler, Dana J. (Dana J. Hepler), et al. Drafting & Design for Architecture. 9th ed. 2012. (ENG.). 800p. (C). 181.95 (978-1-111-12813-5(8)) Delmar Cengage Learning.
Hewitt, Mischa & Telfer, Kevin. Earthships in Europe. 2nd rev. ed. 2012. (ENG., Illus.). 160p. pap. 49.95 (978-1-84806-236-8(2)) Building Research Establishment GBR. Dist: Taylor & Francis Group.
Higgott, Andrew & Wray, Timothy. Camera-Constructs: Photography, Architecture & the Modern City. 2012. (Illus.). 325p. 114.95 (978-1-4094-2145-0(7)) Ashgate Publishing Co.
Hirschberg, Urs, et al, eds. GAM 04: Emerging Realities. 2007. (GER & ENG., Illus.). 244p. per. 39.95 (978-3-211-48860-7(X), 321148860X) Springer Wien AUT. Dist: Actar Birkhauser Distribution.
Höhl, Wolfgang. Interactive Ambient with Open-Source-Software: 3D-Walk-Throughs & Augmented Reality with Blender 2. 43, DART 3. 0 & ARToolKit 2. 72 for Architects. 2008. (ENG., Illus.). 239p. 79.95 (978-3-211-79169-1(8), 3211791698) Springer.
Holzwarth, Hans Werner. Art Now 03, Vol. 3. Holzwarth, Hans Werner & Jones, Tricia, eds. 2009. (FRE, GER & ENG., Illus.). 591p. pap. 39.99 (978-3-8365-0511-6(8)) TASCHEN DEU. Dist: Ingram Pub. Services.
House, Steven & House, Cathi. Houses in the Sun: Light Movement Embrace. 2008. (ENG., Illus.). 296p. 50.00 (978-1-86470-239-2(7)) Images Publishing Group AUS. Dist: National Bk. Network.
Hubertus, Adam. Space, Twisted with Time / Raum, verschraubt mit der Zeit (eng/ger) Architecture Yearbook Graz Styria 2010 / Architekturjahrbuch Graz Steiermark 2010. 2011. (ENG & GER.). 192p. 64.95 (978-3-0346-0792-6(X)) Birkhauser Verlag AG CHE. Dist: Actar Birkhauser Distribution.
Hussain, Raja Rizwan & Wasim, Mohammad. Seismic Retrofitting of Rc Buildings. 2010. 172p. pap. (978-3-639-25055-8(9)) VDM Verlag Dr. Mueller e.K.
Hutterreimann + Cejka Landscape Architects. Specific Landscape: HutterReimann + Cejka Landschaftsarchitekten. 2012. (ENG & GER., Illus.). 160p. 45.00 (978-3-86859-097-5(8)) Jovis Verlag GmbH DEU. Dist: D.A.P./Distributed Art Pubs.
ICC. International Green Construction Code (IGCC) Public Version 2. 0 Print. 2011. pap. (978-1-60983-097-7(0)) International Code Council.
International Code Council. 2012 International Residential Code for One- & Two-Family Dwellings. 2011. (ENG.). pap. 106.00 (978-1-60983-042-7(3)); ring bd. 125.00 (978-1-60983-041-0(5)) International Code Council.
Irace, Fulvio. Gio Ponti. 2011. (ENG., Illus.). 120p. 45.00 (978-88-6116-142-9(1)) Antique Collectors' Club.
Iwamoto, Lisa. Digital Fabrications: Architectural & Material Techniques. 2009. (ENG., Illus.). 144p. pap. 24.95 (978-1-56898-790-3(0)) Princeton Architectural Pr.
Jacoby, Sam & Lee, Christopher, eds. Typological Urbanism: Projective Cities. 2011. (Architectural Design Ser.). (ENG.). 136p. pap. 45.00 (978-0-470-74720-9(X), Wiley) Wiley, John & Sons, Inc.
Jaeger, Falk, ed. Auer + Weber + Associated. 2011. (ENG., Illus.). 144p. pap. 39.95 (978-3-86859-037-1(4)) Jovis Verlag GmbH DEU. Dist: D.A.P./Distributed Art Pubs.
Jaeggi, Martin & Schweiger, Peter, texts. Breaking the Rules: Plakate der Bewegten 1980er Jahre in der Schweiz/Posters from the Turbulent 1980s in Switzerland. 2007. (Poster Collection). (Illus.). 92p. pap. 29.95 (978-3-03778-094-7(0), 3037780940) Lars Muller Pubs. CHE. Dist: Springer.
Jantsch, Axel. Scalable Multi-core Architectures: Design Methodologies & Tools. Jantsch, Axel & Soudris, Dimitrios, eds. 2011. (Illus.). x, 240p. 119.00 (978-1-4419-6777-0(X), 144196777X) Springer.
Jefferis, Alan, et al. Architectural Drafting & Design (Book Only) 6th ed. 2010. (ENG.). (C). 189.95 (978-1-111-32178-9(7)) Delmar Cengage Learning.
Jernigan, Finith, 2nd. BIG BIM little Bim: The Practical Approach to Building Information Modeling Integrated Practice done the right Way! 2008. (ENG., Illus.). 302p. per. 29.95 (978-0-9795699-0-6(7)) 4Site Pr.
Jodidio, Philip. Architecture Now - Restaurants & Bars: Architektur heute! Restaurants & Bars / L'architecture d'aujourd'hui! Restaurants & Bars. 2009. (ENG, FRE & GER., Illus.). 416p. pap. 39.99 (978-3-8365-0376-1(X)) TASCHEN DEU. Dist: Ingram Pub. Services.
Jodidio, Philip. Temporary Architecture Now! 2011. (ENG, FRE & GER., Illus.). 416p. pap. 39.99 (978-3-8365-2328-8(0)) TASCHEN DEU. Dist: Ingram Pub. Services.
Jones, Will. Unbuilt Masterworks of the 21st Century: Inspirational Architecture for the Digital Age. 2009. (ENG., Illus.). 400p. 65.00 (978-0-500-34254-1(7), 534254) Thames & Hudson.
Kachwalla, Nazia. Social Friction in Interior Architecture: Enhancing Social Dynamism in Interior Architecture Through the Use of Social Friction. 2011. (Illus.). 106p. pap. (978-3-8433-9455-0(5)) Lambert Academic Publishing.
Karadimitriou, Nikos, et al. Delivering homes through urban Regeneration: Experiences from France, the Netherlands & the UK. 2011. (Housing, Planning & Design Ser.). 240p. 155.00 (978-0-415-48110-6(4)); pap. 53.95 (978-0-415-48111-3(2)) Routledge.
Kenzari, Bechir, ed. La Rambla: Jordi Bernadó. 2010.Tr. of Out Barcelona - Massimo Vitali. 96p. (978-84-96954-22-9(6)) Actar Birkhauser Distribution.
Khan, Hasan-Uddin. International Style. Jodidio, Philip, ed. 25th ed. 2009. (World Architecture Ser.). (ENG., Illus.). 224p. 14.99 (978-3-8365-1052-3(9)) TASCHEN DEU. Dist: Ingram Pub. Services.
Kibert, Charles. Sustainable Construction: Green Building Design & Delivery. 3rd ed. 2012. (ENG., Illus.). 464p. 85.00 (978-0-470-90445-9(3), Wiley) Wiley, John & Sons, Inc.
Kicklighter, Clois E. Architecture Standard State License 3.5D 2000. 130.00 (978-1-56637-596-2(7)) Goodheart-Willcox Pub.
Kicklighter, Clois E. & Kicklighter, Joan C. Architecture: Residential Drafting & Design. 10th ed. 2008. (ENG.). 848p. (gr. 9-14). 93.28 (978-1-59070-699-2(4)) Goodheart-Willcox Pub.
Kirkbride, Robert. Architecture & Memory: The Renaissance Studioli of Federico da Montefeltro. 2008. (Gutenberg-E Ser.). (ENG., Illus.). 252p. (gr. 17). 60.00 (978-0-231-14248-9(X)) Columbia Univ. Pr.
Klanten, R., et al. Sublime: New Design & Architecture from Japan. 2011. (ENG., Illus.). 288p. 78.00 (978-3-89955-372-7(1)) Die Gestalten Verlag DEU. Dist: Prestel Publishing.
Kobets-Singkh, Olena. Two Mountain Huts. 2010. 160p. pap. (978-3-8383-7704-9(4)) Lambert Academic Publishing.
Koca, Duygu. Understanding Facade Between Design & Manufacturing. 2009. 144p. pap. (978-3-639-17493-9(3)) VDM Verlag Dr. Mueller e.K.
Kogent, Inc. Revit 2010. 2009. 336p. pap. 56.95 (978-0-7637-7630-5(0)) Jones & Bartlett Learning, LLC.
Korniske, Bruce King, ed. Heroes: The Story of Hasbro Children's Hospital. 2010. (ENG., Illus.). 124p. 30.00 (978-1-86470-346-7(6)) Images Publishing Group AUS. Dist: National Bk. Network.
Konrad, Daniela, ed. Interrogating Pop in Architecture. 2009. (ENG., Illus.). 170p. pap. 32.00 (978-3-8030-0694-3(5)) Wasmuth, Ernst J. Verlag GmbH & Co. DEU. Dist: D.A.P./Distributed Art Pubs.
Kopec, David A., et al. Evidence Based Design: A Process for Research & Writing. rev. ed. 2011. (ENG.). 224p. (C). pap. 72.20 (978-0-13-217406-0(5), Prentice Hall) Prentice Hall PTR.
Kottas, Dimitris. Unusual Hotels. 2012. (ENG.). 300p. 45.00 (978-84-15123-20-0(5)) Links International (Leading International Key Services Barcelona, S.A.) ESP. Dist: National Bk. Network.
Krauel, Jacobo. Clubs & Bars Design. 2011. (ENG., Illus.). 240p. 49.00 (978-84-92796-46-5(4)) Links International (Leading International Key Services Barcelona, S.A.) ESP. Dist: National Bk. Network.
—Great Spaces: Home Interiors. 2009. (ENG.). 192p. pap. 24.99 (978-2-917031-36-0(0)) Links International (Leading International Key Services Barcelona, S.A.) ESP. Dist: National Bk. Network.
—Stands: Innovational Design. 2012. (ENG.). 300p. 68.00 (978-84-15123-60-6(4)) Links International (Leading International Key Services Barcelona, S.A.) ESP. Dist: National Bk. Network.
Krygiel, Eddy & Nies, Brad. Green BIM: Successful Sustainable Design with Building Information Modeling. 2008. (ENG., Illus.). 241p. pap. 49.99 (978-0-470-23960-5(3), Sybex) Wiley, John & Sons, Inc.
Krygiel, Eddy, et al. Autodesk Revit Architecture 2012 Essentials. 2011. (ENG., Illus.). 400p. pap. 49.99 (978-1-118-01683-1(1), Sybex) Wiley, John & Sons, Inc.
—Mastering Autodesk Revit Architecture 2011. 2010. (ENG., Illus.). 1168p. pap. 59.99 (978-0-470-62696-2(8), Sybex) Wiley, John & Sons, Inc.
—Mastering Autodesk Revit Architecture 2011: Autodesk Official Training Guide. 2010. (Illus.). xxx, 1122p. E-Book 27.95 (978-0-470-90819-8(X)) Wiley, John & Sons, Inc.
—Mastering Autodesk Revit Architecture 2012. 2011. (ENG., Illus.). 1152p. pap. 69.99 (978-0-470-93749-5(1), Sybex) Wiley, John & Sons, Inc.
La Roche, Pablo. Carbon-Neutral Architectural Design. 2011. (ENG., Illus.). 344p. 99.95 (978-1-4398-4512-7(3), CRC Press) Taylor & Francis Group GBR. Dist: Taylor & Francis Group.
Lab-Volt Staff. Design & Construction: Tech-Design ESeries. 2nd rev. ed. 2010. 39p. 5.00 (978-1-60533-267-3(4)); 77p. 8.00 (978-1-60533-278-9(X)); 34p. ring bd. 4.00 (978-1-60533-279-6(8)) Lab-Volt Systems, Inc.
Laiprakobsup, Narongpon. Inbetween Place. 2008. 160p. pap. (978-3-639-06378-3(3)) VDM Verlag Dr. Mueller e.K.
Lally. Softspace. 2007. (Illus.). 224p. 55.95 (978-0-415-40202-6(6)) Taylor & Francis Group.
Lally, Sean. Softspace: From a Representation of Form to a Simulation of Space. Young, Jessica, ed. 2007. (Illus.). 224p. 165.00 (978-0-415-40201-9(8)) Taylor & Francis Group.
Lally, Sean, ed. Energies: New Material Boundaries. 2009. (Architectural Design Ser.). (ENG., Illus.). 136p. pap. 55.00 (978-0-470-75363-7(3), Wiley) Wiley, John & Sons, Inc.
Lane, Architect Larry. The Designed Office. 2009. 163p. pap. 19.95 (978-0-557-08358-9(3)) Lulu Enterprises Inc.
Lawrence, Sarah & Wilton, Ely John. Piranesi as Designer. 2007. (ENG.). 360p. (978-0-910503-96-9(6)) Assouline FRA. Dist: Perseus Distribution.
—Piranesi as Designer. 2007. (ENG.). 360p. pap. 45.00 (978-0-910503-95-2(8)) Cooper-Hewitt Museum.
Lee, Katy. Libraries. 2011. (ENG., Illus.). 256p. 45.00 (978-988-19740-6-8(2)) Design Media Publishing Ltd. HKG. Dist: BookMasters Distribution Services (BDS).
Legendre, Georges. Mathematics of Space. 2nd ed. 2011. (Architectural Design Ser.). (ENG.). 136p. pap. 45.00 (978-0-470-68980-6(3), Wiley) Wiley, John & Sons, Inc.
Lemerle, Frederique. Perspective, Projections & Design: Technologies of Architectural Representation. 2007. (ENG., Illus.). 208p. (C). per. 71.95 (978-0-415-40206-4(9)) Routledge.
Leonard, Donald P. Designer's Illustrated Guide to NFPA 101. 2007. (Illus.). xvi, 447p. (978-0-87765-632-6(0)) National Fire Protection Assn.
Leroy, Yann Andre. Yann Andre Leroy of Brennan Beer Gorman: The Space Difference. 2007. (Architectural Ser.). (ENG & ITA., Illus.). 100p. 25.00 (978-88-7838-069-1(5), Art Stock Bks. Ltd/Csi) Continental Sales, Inc.
Li, Rebecca. Clubhouse. 2011. (ENG.). 272p. 50.00 (978-988-19740-5-1(4)) Design Media Publishing Ltd. HKG. Dist: BookMasters Distribution Services (BDS).
Liauw, Laurence, ed. New Urban China. 2008. (Architectural Design Ser.). (ENG.). 136p. pap. 50.00 (978-0-470-75122-0(3), Wiley) Wiley, John & Sons, Inc.
Library Association Library Staff & Fisher, Thomas. Architectural Design & Ethics: Tools for Survival. 2008. (ENG., Illus.). 264p. pap. 33.95 (978-0-7506-6985-6(3)) Routledge.
Liebing, Ralph W. The Other Architecture. 2010. (Illus.). 428p. 89.95 (978-3-7091-0262-6(6), 3709102626) Springer Wien AUT. Dist: Springer.
Lim, Joseph. Eccentric Structures in Architecture. 2011. (ENG., Illus.). 160p. pap. 17.00 (978-90-6369-242-1(0)) Bis B.V., Uitgeverij(BIS Publishers) NLD. Dist: Consortium Bk. Sales & Distribution.
Lind, Diana. Brooklyn Modern: Architecture, Interiors & Design. 2008. (ENG., Illus.). 226p. 45.00 (978-0-8478-3043-5(8)) Rizzoli International Pubns., Inc.
Listri, Massimo. Magnificent Baths: Private Indulgences from Baroque to Minimalist. 2012. (ENG., Illus.). 272p. 50.00 (978-0-8478-3650-5(9)) Rizzoli International Pubns., Inc.
Liu, Yu-Tung, ed. Distinguishing Digital Architecture: 6th Far Eastern International Digital Architectural Design Award. 2007. (Illus.). 227p. pap. 49.95 (978-3-7643-8120-2(5), 3764381205) Birkhauser Verlag AG CHE. Dist: Springer.
Lloyd, Scott & Stoll, Katrina, eds. Infrastructure as Architecture. 2011. (ENG., Illus.). 160p. pap. 29.95 (978-3-86859-091-3(9)) Jovis Verlag GmbH DEU. Dist: D.A.P./Distributed Art Pubs.
Locher, Mira. Super Potato Design: The Complete Works of Takashi Sugimoto: Japan's Leading Interior Designer. 2006. (ENG., Illus.). 256p. 49.95 (978-0-8048-3737-8(6)) Tuttle Publishing.
Loft Publications Staff & Quartino, Daniela Santos. New Lobbies & Waiting Rooms. 2008. (Illus.). 330p. 50.00 (978-0-06-137486-9(5), Collins Design) HarperCollins Pubs.
Lootsma, Bart. Reality Bytes: Selected Essays, 1995 to 2010. 2012. (ENG., Illus.). 272p. pap. 49.95 (978-3-7091-0290-9(1), 3709102901) Springer Wien AUT. Dist: Springer.
Louafi, Kamel. Landschaftsinterventionen / Landscape Interventions: Stadtparadiese / City Paradises. 2011. (ENG, ARA, FRE & GER., Illus.). 496p. 65.00 (978-3-86859-107-1(9)) Jovis Verlag GmbH DEU. Dist: D.A.P./Distributed Art Pubs.
Loukissas, Yanni Alexander. Socio-Technological Studies in Architecture. 2012. (ENG., Illus.). 168p. (C). 165.00 (978-0-415-59227-7(5)); pap. 49.95 (978-0-415-59228-4(3)) Routledge.
Lovell, Jenny & Princeton Architectural Press Staff. Building Envelopes: An Integrated Strategy. 2010. (ENG., Illus.). 152p. pap. 24.95 (978-1-56898-818-4(4)) Princeton Architectural Pr.
Luhan, Gregory A. Digispeak: An illustrated guide to digital architecture design Terms. 240p. 2011. pap. 35.95 (978-0-415-77828-2(X)) 2010. 165.00 (978-0-415-77827-5(1)) Routledge.
Lund, Virginia Llego. George Washington Frank's Stone House on the Nebraska Prairie. 2010. 104p. pap. 29.36 (978-1-4269-1102-6(5)) Trafford Publishing.
Luo, Yuhua. Cooperative Design, Visualization, & Engineering: 4th International Conference, CDVE 2007 Shanghai, China, September 16-20, 2007 Proceedings. 2007. (Lecture Notes in Computer Science Ser.). (Illus.). 431p. pap. 89.95 (978-3-540-74779-6(6)) Springer.
—Cooperative Design, Visualization, & Engineering: 6th International Conference, CDVE 2009, Luxembourg, Luxembourg, September 20-23, 2009, Proceedings. 2009. (Lecture Notes in Computer Science / Information Systems & Applications, incl. Internet/Web, & HCI Ser.). (Illus.). xiii, 390p. pap. 83.00 (978-3-642-04264-5(3), 3642042643) Springer.
—Cooperative Design, Visualization, & Engineering: Third International Conference, CDVE 2006, Mallorca, Spain, September 17-20, 2006, Proceedings. 2006. (Lecture Notes in Computer Science Ser.). (Illus.). 338p. pap. 79.95 (978-3-540-44494-7(7), 3540444947) Springer.
Luo, Yuhua, ed. Cooperative Design, Visualization, & Engineering: 7th International Conference, CDVE 2010, Calvia, Mallorca, Spain, September 19-22, 2010, Proceedings. 2010. (Lecture Notes in Computer Science /

Information Systems & Applications, Incl. Internet/Web, & HCI Ser.). xii, 302p. pap. 83.00 *(978-3-642-16065-3(4)*, 3642160654) Springer.

Luo, Yuhua, ed. Cooperative Design, Visualization, & Engineering: 8th International Conference, CDVE 2011, Hong Kong, China, September 11-14, 2011, Proceedings. 2011. (Lecture Notes in Computer Science / Information Systems & Applications, incl. Internet/Web, & HCI Ser.). (ENG., Illus.). xi, 208p. pap. 72.00 ***(978-3-642-23733-1(9)***, 3642237339) Springer.

Maas, Huub. Architectural Form Part 1 an introduction into understanding Buildings. 2008. 240p. pap. 28.30 *(978-1-84753-264-0(0))* Lulu Enterprises Inc.

Mabb, John. Modification of Atrium Design to Improve Performance. 2008. 300p. pap. *(978-3-639-03900-9(9))* VDM Verlag Dr. Mueller e.K.

Machowiak, Aleksandra & Mizielinski, Daniel. H. O. U. S. E. Homes That Are Outrageous, Unbelievable, Spectacular, & Extraordinary - 35 Designs for Fantastic Living. 2012. (ENG.). 160p. 18.99 ***(978-0-06-211375-7(5)***, Collins Design) HarperCollins Pubs.

Madkour, Yehia. Emergent Programmatic Form-Ation. 2009. 196p. pap. *(978-3-639-19930-7(8))* VDM Verlag Dr. Mueller e.K.

Mallory-Hill, Shauna, et al. Enhancing Building Performance. 2nd ed. 2012. (ENG., Illus.). 360p. pap. 115.00 ***(978-0-470-65759-1(6)***, Wiley-Blackwell) Wiley, John & Sons, Inc.

Mao-Lin Chiu, et al, eds. Digital Design: Research & Practice: Research & Practice. 2010. 480p. pap. 229.00 *(978-90-481-6260-4(2)*, 9048162602) Springer.

Marg, Volkwin. Von Gerkan, Marg, & Partners: Stadiums 2010-2015. 2010. (GER & ENG., Illus.). 240p. 75.00 *(978-3-7913-4439-3(0))* Prestel Publishing.

Markovic, Dejan & Brodersen, Robert W. DSP Architecture Design Essentials. 2012. (Electrical Engineering Essentials Ser.). (ENG.). 400p. 129.00 *(978-1-4419-9659-6(1)*, 1441996591) Springer.

Martens, Bob & Brown, Andre, eds. Computer Aided Architectural Design Futures 2005: Proceedings of the 11th International CAAD Futures Conference held at the Vienna University of Technology, Vienna, Austria, on June 20-22 2005. 2010. (ENG.). xii, 481p. pap. 239.00 *(978-90-481-6872-9(4)*, 9048168724) Springer.

Mateo, Josep Lluis, ed. Natural Metaphor: An Anthology of Essays on Architecture & Nature. 2008. (Illus.). 240p. pap. *(978-84-96954-08-3(0))* Actar Birkhauser Distribution.

McCullough, Lissa, ed. Conversations with Paolo Soleri. 2012. (ENG.). 96p. pap. 19.95 ***(978-1-61689-055-1(X))*** Princeton Architectural Pr.

McGrath, Brian. Urban Design Ecologies Reader. 2012. (AD Reader Ser.). (ENG.). 304p. 130.00 ***(978-0-470-97406-3(0))***; pap. 50.00 ***(978-0-470-97405-6(2))*** Wiley, John & Sons, Inc. (Wiley).

McGuire, Penny, intro. Gary Shoemaker: Configuring the Generic Landscape. 2007. (Architectural Ser.). (ENG., Illus.). 100p. 25.00 *(978-88-7838-114-8(4)*, Art Stock Bks. Ltd/Csi) Continental Sales, Inc.

McPeek, Thomas. Collaboration in the Design Studio. 2010. 176p. pap. *(978-3-639-26766-2(4))* VDM Verlag Dr. Mueller e.K.

Menges, Achim. Material Computation: Higher Integration in Morphogenetic Design Architectural Design. 2012. (Architectural Design Ser.). (ENG., Illus.). 144p. pap. 40.00 ***(978-0-470-97330-1(7)***, Wiley) Wiley, John & Sons, Inc.

Menges, Achim. Morpho-Ecologies: Towards Heterogeneous Space in Architectural Design. Hensel, Michael, ed. 2007. (Illus.). 366p. *(978-1-902902-53-1(X))* Architectural Assn.

Metal Roofing Magazine Staff. The Idea Book: An Architectural Design Resource. 2009. (ENG.). cd-rom 24.99 *(978-1-4402-0511-8(6))* Krause Pubns.

Meyer Boake, Terri. Understanding Steel Design: An Architectural Design Manual. 2011. (ENG.). 240p. 99.95 *(978-3-0346-0269-3(3))* Birkhauser Verlag AG CHE. Dist: Actar Birkhauser Distribution.

Millett, Larry. Disappearance of Sherlock Holmes. 2012. (Fesler-Lampert Minnesota Heritage Ser.). (Illus.). 352p. pap. 14.95 ***(978-0-8166-6993-6(7))*** Univ. of Minnesota Pr.

Mistur, Mark. The Architecture of EMPAC: the Tangible & the Tantalizing: The Curtis R. Priem Experimental Media & Performing Art Center. 2011. (ENG.). 256p. 40.00 *(978-0-578-07240-1(8))* Oro Editions.

Mitchell, Maurice, et al. Learning from Delhi: Dispersed Initiatives in Changing Urban Landscapes. 2010. (Illus.). 322p. pap. 69.95 *(978-1-4094-0102-5(2))* Ashgate Publishing Co.

Moe, Kiel & Smith, Ryan E. Building Systems: Technology, Design & Society. 2012. (ENG., Illus.). 272p. (C). 165.00 *(978-0-415-61793-2(6))*; pap. 39.95 *(978-0-415-61794-9(4))* Routledge.

Moghimi, Mahdi. Architectural Design of Compound & Freeform Space Structures. 2010. 536p. pap. *(978-3-8383-4250-4(X))* Lambert Academic Publishing.

Moloney, Jules. Designing Kinetics for Architectural Facades. 2011. (ENG., Illus.). 192p. (C). 165.00 *(978-0-415-61033-9(8))* Routledge.

—Designing Kinetics for Architectural Facades: State Change. 2011. (ENG., Illus.). 192p. (C). pap. 49.95 *(978-0-415-61034-6(6))* Routledge.

Monson, John. The Architecture of Solomon's Temple. 2008. (Illus.). 304p. 55.00 *(978-0-19-532129-6(4))* Oxford Univ. Pr., Inc.

Montoya, Mike. Green Building Fundamentals. 2nd ed. 2010. (ENG., Illus.). 192p. (C). pap. 52.40 *(978-0-13-511108-6(0)*, Prentice Hall) Prentice Hall PTR.

Mooney, Jim. Cost Effective Building Design. 144p. pap. *(978-0-86840-081-5(5)*, UNSW Press) NewSouth Publishing.

Moore, Gary T. & Marans, Robert W., eds. Advances in Environment, Behavior, & Design: Volume 4: Toward the Integration of Theory, Methods, Research, & Utilization. 2010. (Advances in Environment, Behavior & Design Ser.). 396p. pap. 259.00 *(978-1-4419-3258-7(5)*, 1441932585) Springer.

Moraes Zarzar, K. & Guney, A., eds. Understanding Meaningful Environments: Architectural Precedents & the Question of Identity in Creative Design - Volume 4 Research in Design Series. 2008. (Illus.). 388p. pap. 65.00 *(978-1-58603-913-4(X))* IOS Pr., Inc.

Mores, Claudio Marenco & Marsilio. From Fiorucci to the Guerrilla Stores: Shop Displays in Architecture, Marketing & Communications. 2007. (Mode Ser.). (ENG., Illus.). 114p. pap. 19.95 *(978-88-317-8957-8(0))* Marsilio Editori spa ITA. Dist: Random Hse., Inc.

Moss, Elise. AutoCAD Architecture 2012 Fundamentals. 2011. (Illus.). 228p. pap. 69.95 *(978-1-58503-635-6(8)*, SDC Pubns.) Schroff Development Corp.

—Revit Architecture 2008 Basics. 2007. 423p. per. 59.95 *(978-1-58503-376-8(6)*, SDC Pubns.) Schroff Development Corp.

Mounayar, Michel, et al, eds. DCA 20th Anniversary Conference 2007: Proceedings of Design Communication Association: Flow, Filter, Function, Feeling, & Focus. 2007. (Illus.). per. 74.99 *(978-0-615-16881-4(7))* College of Architecture & Planning.

Moussavi, Farshid. The Function of Form. 2009. 384p. pap. *(978-84-96954-73-1(0))* Actar Birkhauser Distribution.

Moussavi, Farshid & Kubo, Michael, eds. The Function of Ornament. 2006. (Illus.). 186p. pap. 29.95 *(978-84-96540-50-7(2))* Kunst-Werke Berlin e.V. DEU. Dist: Actar Birkhauser Distribution.

Muckenheim, Mark & Demel, Juliane. Inspiration: Contemporary Design Methods in Architecture. 2012. (ENG., Illus.). 256p. 49.00 ***(978-90-6369-267-4(6))*** Bis B.V., Uitgeverij(BIS Publishers) NLD. Dist: Consortium Bk. Sales & Distribution.

Museo Nacional Centro de Arte Reina Sofia Staff, contrib. by. Desvios de la Deriva: Experiencias, Travesias y Morfologias. 2010. (SPA., Illus.). 301p. *(978-84-8026-424-2(1))* Museo Nacional Centro de Arte Reina Sofia.

Nagel, Isolde, ed. José Salinas: Disembodiment. 2010. (ENG., Illus.). 144p. pap. 28.00 *(978-3-939633-97-6(6))* Jovis Verlag GmbH DEU. Dist: D.A.P./Distributed Art Pubs.

National Center for Construction Education and Research Staff. Advanced Rigger. 2nd ed. 2011. (ENG.). 200p. (C). pap. 65.33 *(978-0-13-215461-1(7)*, Prentice Hall) Prentice Hall PTR.

Nelson, George. Building a New Europe: Portraits of Modern Architects, Essays by George Nelson, 1935-1936. 2007. (ENG., Illus.). 192p. 45.00 *(978-0-300-11565-9(2))* Yale Univ. Pr.

Nendo, Oki Sato. Nendo, 1 vol. DAAB Media Staff, ed. 2008. (ENG.). 176p. 29.95 *(978-3-86654-068-2(X))* DAAB Media Gmbh DEU. Dist: Innovative Logistics.

Nib, Vol. 10. lthr. *(978-0-687-09041-9(5))* Abingdon Pr.

Nib. 2008. 280p. pap. *(978-88-95623-05-4(3))* Actar Birkhauser Distribution.

Noble, Jonathan Alfred. African Identity in Post-Apartheid Public Architecture: White Skin Black Masks. 2011. (Ashgate Studies in Architecture Ser.). (Illus.). 314p. 124.95 *(978-0-7546-7765-9(6))* Ashgate Publishing Co.

Normann Sandaker, Bjorn. Reflec Span & Spac Tow Theo Crit. 2007. (ENG., Illus.). 224p. (C). 165.00 *(978-0-415-35787-6(X))* Routledge.

—Reflec Span & Spac Tow Theo Crit. 2007. (Illus.). XII 212p. 64.95 *(978-0-415-35792-0(6))* Routledge.

Nwokeji, Jerome Ezeanonye. Bubbles to Concept: Urban Planning Made Easy-A Design Guide for Urban Planning & Architecture. 2011. 60p. pap. 10.00 ***(978-1-60976-851-5(5)***, Eloquent Bks.) AEG Literary Publishing Services, Inc.

O'Brien, Timothy A. & Walsh, Margo Grant. Collecting by Design: Silver & Metalwork of the Twentieth Century from the Margo Grant Walsh Collection. 2008. (ENG., Illus.). 152p. pap. 25.00 *(978-0-300-13892-4(X))* Yale Univ. Pr.

Ochs, Michael Johannes & Johannes Ochs. Tadelakt. 2009. (ENG., Illus.). 112p. pap. 24.95 *(978-0-393-73295-5(9)*, 73295) Norton, W. W. & Co., Inc.

Ochshorn, Jonathan. Structural Elements for Architects & Builders: Design of Columns, Beams, & Tension Elements in Wood, Steel, & Reinforced Concrete. 2009. (ENG., Illus.). 400p. 103.00 *(978-1-85617-771-9(8)*, Butterworth-Heinemann) Elsevier Science & Technology Bks.

Oosterhuis, Kas. ONLogic: Speed & Vision. 2009. (Master Architect Ser.). (ENG., Illus.). 224p. 59.95 *(978-1-86470-286-6(9)*, Images Publishing Dist Ac) Antique Collectors' Club GBR. Dist: National Bk. Network.

—Towards a New Kind of Building: A Designers Guide for Non-Standard Architecture. 2011. (ENG., Illus.). 240p. pap. 37.50 *(978-90-5662-763-8(5))* NAi Uitgevers / Publishers Stichting NLD. Dist: D.A.P./Distributed Art Pubs.

Ortega, Lluís. GSD 08 Platform. 2008. 24.95 *(978-1-934510-16-2(5))* Harvard Univ. Pr.

Oxman, Rivka & Oxman, Robert. The New Structuralism: Design, Engineering & Architectural Technologies. 2010. (Architectural Design Ser.). (ENG.). 136p. pap. 40.00 *(978-0-470-74227-3(5)*, Wiley) Wiley, John & Sons, Inc.

P Baofu Staff. The Future of Information Architecture: A Preface to the New Theory of Taxonomy, Network & Intelligence. 2008. 304p. per. *(978-1-84334-470-4(X)*, Chandos Publishing) Woodhead Publishing Ltd.

—The Future of Information Architecture: A Preface to the New Theory of Taxonomy, Netwrok & Intelligence. 2008. 304p. *(978-1-84334-471-1(8)*, Chandos Publishing) Woodhead Publishing Ltd.

Panache Partners LLC Staff, ed. Perspectives on Design California: Creative Ideas Shared by Leading Design Professionals. 2010. (Perspectives on Design Ser.). (ENG., Illus.). 272p. lib. bdg. 40.00 *(978-1-933415-90-1(8))* Panache Partners, LLC.

Panache Partners Staff. New England: Creative Ideas Shared by Leading Design Professionals. 2010. (Perspectives on Design Ser.). (ENG., Illus.). 272p. lib. bdg. 40.00 *(978-1-933415-57-4(6))* Panache Partners, LLC.

Patterson, Jim. The Cookbook of Comfort. 2009. 92p. pap. 16.50 *(978-1-4389-5990-0(7))* AuthorHouse.

Pauwels, Wim. ArchiNature, Vol. 1. 2010. (ENG., Illus.). 224p. 145.00 *(978-90-8944-052-5(6))* Beta-Plus Pubs. BEL. Dist: Antique Collectors' Club.

—Architectural Stories: By Bernard de Clerck. 2009. (ENG., Illus.). 304p. *(978-90-8944-015-0(1)*, Beta-Plus (Acc)) Antique Collectors' Club.

—Bataille + Ibens. 2010. (ENG., Illus.). 400p. *(978-90-8944-021-1(6)*, Beta-Plus (Acc)) Antique Collectors' Club.

Pauwels, Wim. The 100 Best Swimming Pools. 2012. (ENG., Illus.). 224p. 55.00 ***(978-90-8944-120-1(4))*** Beta-Plus Pubs. BEL. Dist: National Bk. Network.

Pavia, Rosario, ed. Design & Context/PPC Piano Progetto Città: Monobookmagazine. 2011. 192p. pap. 24.95 *(978-2-03-768200-8(X))* LIST - Laboratorio Editoriale ITA. Dist: Actar Birkhauser Distribution.

Perdue, Justin. Scratches & Indentations - Architecture & the Importance of Home. 2009. 148p. pap. *(978-3-639-10784-5(5))* VDM Verlag Dr. Mueller e.K.

Perry, Chris & Hight, Christopher. Collective Intelligence in Design. 2006. (Architectural Design Ser.: 30). (ENG., Illus.). 136p. per. 60.00 *(978-0-470-02652-6(9)*, Academy Pr.) Wiley, John & Sons, Inc.

Pfeiffer, Bruce Brooks. Frank Lloyd Wright Designs: The Sketches, Plans, & Drawings. 2011. (ENG., Illus.). 420p. 85.00 *(978-0-8478-3570-6(7))* Rizzoli International Pubns., Inc.

Picon, Antoine. Digital Culture in Architecture: An Introduction for the Design Professions. 2010. (Illus.). 224p. pap. 59.95 *(978-3-0346-0259-4(6))* Birkhauser Verlag AG CHE. Dist: Actar Birkhauser Distribution.

Pierchala, Joanna Danuta. Transforming Bytom. 2011. 120p. pap. ***(978-3-8443-0695-8(1))*** Lambert Academic Publishing.

Piotrowski, Christine M. Problem Solving & Critical Thinking for Designers. 2011. (ENG., Illus.). 192p. pap. 55.00 *(978-0-470-53671-1(3)*, Wiley) Wiley, John & Sons, Inc.

Poelman, W. & Keyson, D., eds. What Architects & Industrial Designers Can Teach Each Other about Managing the Design Process. 2008. 344p. pap. 79.00 *(978-1-58603-945-5(8))* IOS Pr., Inc.

Pogade, Daniela. The New Office: Planning & Design. 2008. (ENG., Illus.). 240p. 55.00 *(978-84-96969-03-2(7))* Links International (Leading International Key Services Barcelona, S.A.) ESP. Dist: National Bk. Network.

Pomeroy, Jason. Idea House: Future Tropical Living Today. 2011. (ENG., Illus.). 208p. pap. 35.00 *(978-1-935935-10-0(0))* Oro Editions.

Porter, Tom. Will Alsop. 2010. (ENG., Illus.). 176p. pap. 53.95 *(978-0-415-54961-5(2))* Routledge.

Preiser, Wolfgang & Smith, Korydon H. Universal Design Handbook, 2E. 2nd rev. ed. 2010. (ENG., Illus.). 496p. 150.00 *(978-0-07-162923-2(8)*, 0071629238) McGraw-Hill Professional Publishing.

Pressman, Andy. Designing Architecture. 2012. (ENG., Illus.). 208p. (C). 165.00 ***(978-0-415-59515-5(0))***; pap. 29.99 ***(978-0-415-59516-2(9))*** Routledge.

Princeton Architectural Press. Design Diary 2006. 33.00 *(978-3-89986-024-5(1))* Birkhauser Boston.

Proudfoot, Trevor. Conservation of Plaster & Plaster Finishes. 2012. (ENG.). 79.95 ***(978-0-7506-6943-6(8)***, Butterworth-Heinemann) Elsevier Science & Technology Bks.

Psarra, Sophia. Architecture & Narrative: The Formation of Space & Cultural Meaning in Buildings. 2009. (Illus.). (ENG.). 304p. (C). 53.95 *(978-0-415-34376-3(3))*; 320p. 165.00 *(978-0-415-34375-6(5))* Routledge.

Puglisi, Luigi Prestinenza. New Directions in Contemporary Architecture: Evolutions & Revolutions in Building Design since 1988. 2008. (ENG., Illus.). 240p. 140.00 *(978-0-470-51889-2(8)*, Wiley) Wiley, John & Sons, Inc.

—New Directions in Contemporary Architecture: Evolutions & Revolutions in Building Design Since 1988. 2008. (ENG., Illus.). 240p. pap. 45.00 *(978-0-470-51890-8(1)*, Wiley) Wiley, John & Sons, Inc.

Rayner, Judith, et al. Art on Paper - Mounting & Housing. 2007. (ENG., Illus.). 186p. 90.00 *(978-1-873132-99-9(9))* Archetype Pubns. GBR. Dist: National Bk. Network.

Reisner, Yael. Architecture & Beauty: Conversations with Architects about a Troubled Relationship. 2010. (ENG., Illus.). 264p. pap. 60.00 *(978-0-470-84792-3(1)*, Academy Pr.) Wiley, John & Sons, Inc.

Rendell, Jane, et al, eds. Critical Architecture. 2007. (Illus.). XX, 348p. 165.00 *(978-0-415-41537-8(3))* Routledge.

—Critical Architecture. 2007. (Illus.). XX, 348p. 60.95 *(978-0-415-41538-5(1))* Routledge.

Revit Architecture 2008 Essentials Tutorial Series. 2007. 249.00 incl. cd-rom *(978-1-932931-37-2(6))* 4D Design Solutions, LLC.

Revit Architecture 2008 Tutorial Series. 2007. 400.00 incl. cd-rom *(978-1-932931-36-5(8))* 4D Design Solutions, LLC.

Revit Building 9 Fundamentals Tutorial Series. 2007. 199.00 incl. cd-rom *(978-1-932931-34-1(1))* 4D Design Solutions, LLC.

Reycraft, Kirby. Architectural Design, Drafting, & CAD. 2014. (ENG., Illus.). 704p. 99.00 *(978-0-470-05363-8(1)*, Wiley) Wiley, John & Sons, Inc.

Reynolds, Charles E., et al. Reynolds's Reinforced Concrete Designer's Handbook. 11th rev. ed. 2007. (ENG., Illus.). 416p. 180.00 *(978-0-419-25820-9(5))*; per. 74.35 *(978-0-419-25830-8(2))* Taylor & Francis Group GBR. (CRC Press). Dist: Taylor & Francis Group.

Rice, Charles, et al. Post-Traumatic Urbanism: Architectural Design. 2010. (Architectural Design Ser.). (ENG., Illus.). 136p. pap. 40.00 *(978-0-470-74498-7(7)*, Wiley) Wiley, John & Sons, Inc.

Richardson, Forrest L. Of Course: Writings & Pictures about Golf Course Design. 2007. 165.00 *(978-0-9707563-0-5(5))* On Course Publishing.

Richardson, Jamie D., et al. Revit Structure 2010. 2009. (ENG., Illus.). 912p. pap. 69.99 *(978-0-470-52141-0(4)*, Sybex) Wiley, John & Sons, Inc.

Richardson, Phyllis. XS Future: New Ideas, Small Structures. 2009. (ENG., Illus.). 224p. 29.95 *(978-0-7893-2052-0(5))* Universe Publishing.

RIEA.ch, ed. PARKitectOURPARKitectOUR: From Urban Free Flow to Architecture. 2009. (RIEAeuropa Concepts Ser.). (Illus.). 84p. pap. 39.95 *(978-3-211-99183-1(2)*, 3211991332) Springer.

Riera Ojeda, Oscar, ed. Moore Ruble Yudell: Arc of Interaction. 2008. (ENG., Illus.). 112p. 35.00 *(978-0-9795395-0-3(1))* Oro Editions.

Roaf, Susan, et al. Ecohouse. 4th rev ed. 2012. (ENG., Illus.). 544p. pap. 54.95 ***(978-0-415-52677-7(9))*** Routledge.

Roman, Matthew. The Real Perspecta 42 Yale Architectural Journal. Schori, Tal, ed. 2010. (ENG., Illus.). 223p. (gr 17). pap. 25.00 *(978-0-262-51393-7(5))* MIT Pr.

Rossi, J. & Germishuizen, Anton. 10 Metrics: Toward an Integrated Approach on Design. 2010. (ENG., Illus.). 170p. pap. 40.00 *(978-0-9820607-4-2(2))* Oro Editions.

Roth, Manuela. Masterpieces: Villa Architecture + Design. 2011. (Masterpieces Ser.). (ENG., Illus.). 304p. 49.95 *(978-3-03768-089-6(X)*, Braun Publish,Csi) Continental Sales, Inc.

Ryder, Bethan. New Restaurant Design. 2007. (ENG., Illus.). 192p. 45.00 *(978-1-85669-500-8(X))* King, Laurence Publishing GBR. Dist: Hachette Bk. Group.

Rykwert, Joseph. The Judicious Eye: Architecture Against the Other Arts. 2008. (Illus.). 432p. 45.00 *(978-0-226-73261-9(4))* Univ. of Chicago Pr.

Salazar, Jaime, text. Rhythms, Cycles Performances: Ceramics in Architecture. 2010. (ENG.). 160p. pap. 39.95 *(978-84-613-9405-0(4))* Ico López-Rienda ESP. Dist: Actar Birkhauser Distribution.

Salingaros, Nikos A. The Theory of Architecture. 2007. (ENG., Illus.). 278p. (C). per. 31.00 *(978-3-937954-07-3(4))* ISI Bks.

Samuel, Flora. Le Corbusier an the Architectural Promenade. 2010. (Illus.). 232p. 84.95 *(978-3-0346-0607-3(9))* Birkhauser Verlag AG CHE. Dist: Actar Birkhauser Distribution.

Sandaker, Bjorn. The Structural Basis of Architecture. 2nd rev. ed. 2011. (ENG., Illus.). 424p. (C). pap. 39.95 *(978-0-415-41547-7(0))* Routledge.

Sandow Media Corporation. Leading Residential Architects, Vol. 2. 2nd ed. 2008. (ENG., Illus.). 236p. 39.95 *(978-0-9800398-0-1(0))* Sandow Media.

Sanford, Jon A. Universal Design as Rehabilitation Strategy: Design for the Ages. 2012. 248p. ***(978-0-8261-2552-1(2))*** Springer Publishing Co., Inc.

Sassi, Paola. Strategies for Sustainable Architecture. 2006. (ENG., Illus.). 312p. (C). per. 90.95 *(978-0-415-34142-4(6)*, RU426X, Taylor & Francis) Taylor & Francis Group GBR. Dist: Taylor & Francis Group.

Sater, Dan F., II. The Smaller Home: Smart Designs for Your Home. 2008. (Illus.). 176p. pap. 19.95 *(978-0-06-156532-8(6)*, Collins Design) HarperCollins Pubs.

Saunders, William S., ed. Judging Architectural Value. 2007. (Harvard Design Magazine Ser.). (Illus.). 192p. 69.00 *(978-0-8166-5010-1(1))*; per. 22.95 *(978-0-8166-5011-8(X))* Univ. of Minnesota Pr.

Scaglione, Pino. Cosengeles: Small Spontaneous Metropolis. 2011. 192p. pap. 24.95 *(978-88-95623-32-0(0))* LIST - Laboratorio Editoriale ITA. Dist: Actar Birkhauser Distribution.

Scaglione, Pino, ed. Italian High Design & High Technology. 2011. (ENG & ITA.). 207p. 34.95 ***(978-88-95623-34-4(7))*** LIST - Laboratorio Editoriale ITA. Dist: Actar Birkhauser Distribution.

Scaglione, Pino, ed. Monograph. it 2: Landscape Sensitive Design. 2011. 360p. pap. 29.00 *(978-88-95623-21-4(5))* LIST - Laboratorio Editoriale ITA. Dist: Actar Birkhauser Distribution.

Scaglione, Pino, text. Cities in the Nature. 2011. 300p. pap. 34.95 *(978-88-95623-35-1(5))* LIST - Laboratorio Editoriale ITA. Dist: Actar Birkhauser Distribution.

Schalk, Leon van & London, Geoffrey. Procuring Innovative Architecture. 2010. (ENG., Illus.). 240p. (C). pap. 62.95 *(978-0-415-42942-9(0)*, Routledge) Taylor & Francis Group GBR. Dist: Taylor & Francis Group.

Schirmbeck, Egon, et al. Architecture & Space: Design Concepts in the 20th Century, 1 vol. 2011. (ENG & GER.). 224p. pap. 39.95 ***(978-3-86922-180-9(1))*** DOM Pubs. DEU. Dist: Innovative Logistics.

Schmal, Peter Cachola & Busenkell, Michaela, eds. Best Highrises 2010/2011: Die 27 besten Hochhäuser des internationalen Hochhaus Preises 2010. 2011. (ENG., Illus.). 112p. pap. 34.95 *(978-3-86859-089-0(7))* Jovis Verlag GmbH DEU. Dist: D.A.P./Distributed Art Pubs.

Schmidt, Philip. The Complete Guide to Contemporary Sheds: Complete Plans for 12 Sheds, Including Garden Outbuilding, Storage Lean-To, Playhouse, Woodland Cottage, Hobby Studio, Lawn Tractor Barn. 2008. (Black & Decker Complete Guides). (ENG., Illus.). 240p. per. 24.99 *(978-1-58923-335-5(2)*, 1589233352) Quayside.

Schodek, Daniel L. & As, Imdat. Digital Representations in Architecture: Visions in Motion. 2008. (ENG., Illus.). 272p. (C). 165.00 *(978-0-415-42652-7(9))*; 53.95 *(978-0-415-42653-4(7))* Taylor & Francis Group GBR. (Taylor & Francis). Dist: Taylor & Francis Group.

Schulte, Karin & Glaser, Tobias. Messedesign Jahrbuch 2011 / 2012. 2012. (ENG.). 248p. pap. 99.00 *(978-3-89986-157-0(4)*, Avedition Gmbh,Csi) Continental Sales, Inc.

Schumacher, Michael, et al. Move: Dynamic Components & Elements in Architecture. 2010. (ENG., Illus.). 240p. 105.00 *(978-3-7643-9986-3(4))* Birkhauser Verlag AG CHE. Dist: Actar Birkhauser Distribution.

Schwartz, Donald, ed. AutoCAD 2009 Update Tutorial Series. 2008. 99.00 incl. cd-rom *(978-1-932931-40-2(6))* 4D Design Solutions, LLC.

A

Sheil, Bob, ed. Proto Architecture: Analogue & Digital Hybrids. 2008. (Architectural Design Ser.). (ENG., Illus.). 136p. pap. 50.00 *(978-0-470-51947-9(9)*, Wiley) Wiley, John & Sons, Inc.

Shiratuddin, Mohd Fairuz, et al. Virtual Architecture: Modeling & Creation of Real-Time 3D Interactive Worlds. 2008. 615p. pap. 59.95 *(978-1-4357-5642-7(8))* Lulu Enterprises Inc.

Smith, Brian L. 3ds Max Design Architectural Visualization: For Intermediate Users. 2011. (ENG., Illus.). 560p. 64.95 ***(978-0-240-82107-8(6)***, Focal Pr.) Elsevier Science & Technology Bks.

Smith, Michael. The DataCAD 12 Project Book. 2008. 390p. (C). spiral bd. 45.95 *(978-0-9777525-4-6(2))* Technology Education Concepts Inc.

Smith, Valerie, et al. Radical Post-Modernism. 2011. (Architectural Design Ser.). (ENG., Illus.). 136p. pap. 45.00 ***(978-0-470-66988-4(8)***, Wiley) Wiley, John & Sons, Inc.

Speaks, Michael & El-Khoury, Rodolphe, contrib. by. Architecture & Sensuality: Andrew Bromberg of Aedas, Recent Works. 2007. (ENG., Illus.). 256p. 40.00 *(978-0-9774672-8-0(7))* Oro Editions.

Speiregen, Paul & Wertheimer, Lester. Programming, Planning & Practice 2009. 2008. (ENG.). 376p. pap. 111.95 *(978-1-4277-7039-4(5))* Kaplan Publishing.

Speltz, Alexander. Styles of Ornament. 2010. 178p. pap. 26.34 *(978-1-152-80597-2(5))* General Bks. LLC.

Spiller, Neil & Armstrong, Rachel. Protocell Architecture. 2011. (Architectural Design Ser.). (ENG.). 136p. pap. 40.00 *(978-0-470-74828-2(1)*, Wiley) Wiley, John & Sons, Inc.

Spirito, Gianpaola & Terranova, Antonino. The New Urban Giants: The Ultimate Skyscrapers. 2008. (ENG., Illus.). 216p. 19.95 *(978-88-6312-003-5(X))* White Star ITA. Dist: Random Hse., Inc.

Spuybroek, Lars. The Architecture of Continuity. 2009. (ENG., Illus.). 288p. pap. 30.00 *(978-90-5662-637-2(X))* NAi Uitgevers / Publishers Stichting NLD. Dist: D.A.P./Distributed Art Pubs.

—Research & Design: The Architecture of Variation. Spuybroek, Lars, ed. 2009. (ENG., Illus.). 200p. 24.95 *(978-0-500-34257-2(1)*, 534257) Thames & Hudson.

Spuybroek, Lars. Textile Tectonics. 2011. (ENG., Illus.). 224p. 37.50 ***(978-90-5662-802-4(X))*** NAi Uitgevers / Publishers Stichting NLD. Dist: D.A.P./Distributed Art Pubs.

Stamps, Arthur E. Psychology & the Aesthetics of the Built Environment. 2010. (ENG.). 344p. pap. 295.00 *(978-1-4419-5001-7(X)*, 144195001X) Springer.

Staniscia, Stefania, text. Island Ness. 2012. (ENG & ITA.). 196p. pap. 24.95 *(978-88-95623-38-2(X))* LIST - Laboratorio Editoriale ITA. Dist: Actar Birkhauser Distribution.

Steadman, Philip. The Evolution of Designs: Biological Analogy in Architecture & the Applied Arts. Steadman, Philip, ed. 2008. (ENG., Illus.). 320p. (C). 53.95 *(978-0-415-44753-9(4))*; 165.00 *(978-0-415-44752-2(6))* Routledge.

Steane. The Architecture of Light. 2011. (ENG., Illus.). 256p. (C). 155.00 *(978-0-415-39478-9(3))*; pap. 53.95 *(978-0-415-39479-6(1))* Routledge.

Stern, Robert A. M. & Davidson, Cynthia C. Tradition & Invention in Architecture: Conversations & Essays. 2012. (ENG., Illus.). 208p. 40.00 ***(978-0-300-18115-9(9))*** Yale Univ. Pr.

Stern, Robert A. M. & Goldberger, Paul. Robert A. M. Stern: Buildings & Projects, 2004-2009. Dixon, Peter Morris, ed. 2009. (ENG., Illus.). 624p. 75.00 *(978-1-58093-234-9(7))* Monacelli Pr., Inc.

Sternberg, M.D., Esther M. Healing Spaces: The Science of Place & Well-Being. 2010. (ENG.). 352p. pap. 16.95 *(978-0-674-05748-7(1)*, Belknap Pr.) Harvard Univ. Pr.

Stine, Daniel. Residential Design Using Revit Architecture 2008. 2007. 463p. per. 59.95 *(978-1-58503-374-4(X)*, SDC Pubns.) Schroff Development Corp.

Stukin, Stacie. Richard Manion Architecture: New Classicists. 2011. (ENG., Illus.). 200p. 90.00 *(978-1-86470-372-6(5))* Images Publishing Group AUS. Dist: National Bk. Network.

Sulbaran, Tulio, et al. Introduction to ArchiCAD: A BIM Application. 2010. (ENG., Illus.). 240p. (C). pap. 82.95 *(978-1-4283-5664-1(9))* Delmar Cengage Learning.

Szalapaj, Peter John. The Digital Art of Architectural & Engineering Design. 2009. (ENG., Illus.). 288p. pap. 55.95 *(978-1-4051-5697-4(X)*, Wiley-Blackwell) Wiley, John & Sons, Inc.

Tacke, Heinfried, ed. Berlin Architecture & Design S. 2006. 192p. pap. 14.95 *(978-3-8327-9155-1(8))* teNeues Publishing Co.

Taher, Aamer. Sculpting Tropical Spaces: Aamer Architects. 2012. (ENG., Illus.). 200p. 50.00 *(978-1-935935-11-7(9))* Oro Editions.

Taschen & Evergreen, eds. Book of Houses. 2009. (ENG, FRE & GER., Illus.). 384p. 19.99 *(978-3-8365-1155-1(X)*, Evergreen) TASCHEN DEU. Dist: Ingram Pub. Services.

Taschen Publishing, creator. Architecture Materials Wood. 2008. (ENG., Illus.). 255p. pap. 19.99 *(978-3-8365-0403-4(0))* TASCHEN DEU. Dist: Ingram Pub. Services.

Tayyar, Bahram. E-Neighbor-Topia: A Typological Study on the Impacts of Information andCommunication Technologies on Residential Environments. 2008. 180p. pap. *(978-3-639-09481-7(6))* VDM Verlag Dr. Mueller e.K.

TECTUM, contrib. by. Tomorrow's World, 1 vol. 2011. (ENG, DUT, FRE & GER., Illus.). 620p. pap. 24.95 *(978-94-6065-057-4(0))* booQs Publishers bvba BEL. Dist: Innovative Logistics.

Temple, Nicholas, et al, eds. The Humanities in Architectural Design: A Contemporary & Historical Perspective. 2010. (ENG., Illus.). 288p. (C). 165.00 *(978-0-415-55113-7(7))*; pap. 53.95 *(978-0-415-55114-4(5))* Routledge.

Thonik. Thonik: I Am Your Type. 2012. (ENG., Illus.). 256p. pap. 50.00 *(978-90-5662-744-7(9))* NAi Uitgevers / Publishers Stichting NLD. Dist: D.A.P./Distributed Art Pubs.

Thorp, Francis-Jones Morehen. In the Realm of Learning: The University of Sydney's New Law School. 2009. (ENG., Illus.). 160p. 55.00 *(978-1-86470-357-3(1))* Images Publishing Group AUS. Dist: National Bk. Network.

Thorsen, Kjetil, et al, eds. Nordic Talking: 4 1/2 Years in Studio with Kjetil Thorsen. 2009. (ENG., Illus.). 368p. pap. 49.95 *(978-3-211-99213-5(8)*, 3211992138) Springer.

Timmermans, Harry J. P., ed. Design & Decision Support Systems in Architecture. 2010. 268p. pap. 186.00 *(978-90-481-4313-9(6)*, 9048143136) Springer.

Torroja, Eduardo. The Structures of Eduardo Torroja: An Autobiography of an Engineering Accomplishment. 2011. 210p. 44.95 ***(978-1-258-10099-5(1))*** Literary Licensing, LLC.

Triviño, Santi. Houses in Difficult Places. Minguet, Josep Maria & Monsa Staff, eds. 2010. (ENG., Illus.). 96p. pap. 22.50 *(978-84-96429-43-7(1))* Instituto Monsa de Ediciones, S.A. ESP. Dist: Trans-Atlantic Pubns., Inc.

Unwin, Simon. Analysing Architecture. 3rd rev. ed. 2009. (ENG., Illus.). 296p. (C). 165.00 *(978-0-415-48927-0(X))*; pap. 44.95 *(978-0-415-48928-7(8))* Routledge.

—Twenty Buildings Every Architect Should Understand. 2010. (ENG., Illus.). 240p. (C). 165.00 *(978-0-415-55251-6(6))*; pap. 30.95 *(978-0-415-55252-3(4))* Routledge.

van den Heuvel, Dirk, et al, eds. DASH 05: the Urban Enclave. 2011. (ENG., Illus.). 168p. pap. 45.00 ***(978-90-5662-809-3(7))*** NAi Uitgevers / Publishers Stichting NLD. Dist: D.A.P./Distributed Art Pubs.

Van Der Like, Robert Neal & Meehan, Peggy. The Paid-From-Savings Guide to Green Existing Buildings. 2009. (Illus.). i, 100p. pap. ***(978-1-932444-29-2(7))*** U. S. Green Building Council.

van Gameren, Dick, et al, eds. DASH 01: the Re-Opened Building Block. 2009. (ENG., Illus.). 144p. pap. 50.00 *(978-90-5662-654-9(X))* NAi Uitgevers / Publishers Stichting NLD. Dist: D.A.P./Distributed Art Pubs.

Van Schaik, Leon. Procuring Innovative Architecture. 2010. (ENG., Illus.). 240p. (C). 165.00 *(978-0-415-42941-2(2)*, Taylor & Francis) Taylor & Francis Group GBR. Dist: Taylor & Francis Group.

van Schaik, Leon. Spatial Intelligence: New Futures for Architecture. 2008. (Architectural Design Primer Ser.). (ENG., Illus.). 208p. 135.00 *(978-0-470-72322-7(X)*, Wiley) Wiley, John & Sons, Inc.

Van Schaik, Leon. Spatial Intelligence: New Futures for Architecture. 2008. (Architectural Design Primer Ser.). (ENG., Illus.). 208p. pap. 55.00 *(978-0-470-72323-4(8)*, Wiley) Wiley, John & Sons, Inc.

Van Toorn, Roemer, ed. Tangible Traces. 2010. (ENG., Illus.). 248p. pap. 45.00 *(978-90-5662-328-9(1))* NAi Uitgevers / Publishers Stichting NLD. Dist: D.A.P./Distributed Art Pubs.

Vasquez de Velasco, Guillermo, ed. Changing Trends in Architectural Design Education. 2006. (Illus.). 615p. pap. *(978-9957-8602-0-2(8))* Center for Study of Architecture in the Arab Region (CSAAR), The.

Vastapane, Fabienne. Living in great style in Taroudant, 1 vol. 2012. (ENG.). 256p. 89.50 ***(978-90-8881-032-9(X))*** Exhibitions International BEL. Dist: Innovative Logistics.

Veltkamp, M. Free form structural Design. 2007. pap. 65.00 *(978-1-58603-781-9(1)*, Delft University Pr) IOS Pr., Inc.

Vidiella, Àlex Sánchez & Mola, Francesc Zamora. Sourcebook of Contemporary Urban Design. 2012. (ENG.). 640p. 60.00 ***(978-0-06-211358-0(5)***, Collins Design) HarperCollins Pubs.

Vincenzi, Patrizia & Guadagno, Rosi, eds. Luceplan Worldwide. 2009. (ENG., Illus.). 304p. pap. 35.00 *(978-88-572-0023-1(X))* Skira Editore ITA. Dist: Random Hse., Inc.

Vital, Rebeka. Virtual Reality. 2008. 132p. pap. *(978-3-639-08376-7(8))* VDM Verlag Dr. Mueller e.K.

VV Staff. Urbanism. (Architectural Design Ser.). (SPA.). 726p. *(978-84-89861-00-8(5))* Links International (Leading International Key Services Barcelona, S.A.).

Vyzoviti, Sophia. Folding Architecture. 9th ed. 2008. (ENG., Illus.). 144p. pap. 17.00 *(978-90-6369-059-5(2))* Bis B.V., Uitgeverij(BIS Publishers) NLD. Dist: Consortium Bk. Sales & Distribution.

—Supersurfaces. 4th ed. 2008. (ENG., Illus.). 144p. pap. 17.00 *(978-90-6369-121-9(1))* Bis B.V., Uitgeverij(BIS Publishers) NLD. Dist: Consortium Bk. Sales & Distribution.

Waddell, Theodore. Design Without Fashion. 2010. (ENG., Illus.). 192p. 55.00 *(978-88-572-0328-7(X))* Skira Editore ITA. Dist: Random Hse., Inc.

Waller, Sam. Optimisation of Hierarchical & Branched Compression Structures. 2008. 248p. pap. *(978-3-639-07006-4(2))* VDM Verlag Dr. Mueller e.K.

Wang, Liying, et al, eds. Graphic Design in Architecture. 2011. (ENG., Illus.). 432p. 65.00 *(978-988-19739-3-1(7))* Design Media Publishing Ltd. HKG. Dist: BookMasters Distribution Services (BDS).

Wang, Xiangyu & Schnabel, Marc Aurel. Mixed Reality in Architecture, Design, & Construction. Wang, Xiangyu & Schnabel, Marc Aurel, eds. 2008. (ENG., Illus.). xiv, 274p. 119.00 *(978-1-4020-9087-5(0)*, 1402090870) Springer.

Wang, Xiangyu & Tsai, Jerry Jen-Hung, eds. Collaborative Design in Virtual Environments. 2011. (Intelligent Systems, Control & Automation: Science & Engineering Ser.). (Illus.). x, 210p. 179.00 *(978-94-007-0604-0(9)*, 9400706049) Springer.

Watkins, David H. & Hamilton, D. Kirk. Evidence-Based Design for Multiple Building Types. 2008. (ENG., Illus.). 288p. 80.00 *(978-0-470-12934-0(4)*, Wiley) Wiley, John & Sons, Inc.

Waugh, Emily, ed. GSD Platform 3. 2010. 336p. *(978-84-92861-50-7(9))* Actar Birkhauser Distribution.

Weidinger, Hans. Stairways. 2010. (Illus.). 160p. 34.99 *(978-0-7643-3638-6(X))* Schiffer Publishing, Ltd.

Weiler, Susan K. & Scholz-Barth, Katrin. Green Roof Systems: A Guide to the Planning, Design, & Construction of Landscapes over Structure. 2009. (ENG., Illus.). 320p. 80.00 *(978-0-471-67495-5(8)*, Wiley) Wiley, John & Sons, Inc.

Werner, Megan. Model Making. 2011. (ENG., Illus.). 160p. pap. 24.95 *(978-1-56898-870-2(2))* Princeton Architectural Pr.

Wertheimer, Lester. Schematic Design 2009. 2008. (ENG.). 88p. pap. 111.95 *(978-1-4277-7040-0(9))* Kaplan Publishing.

West, Beverley. Functional Building Design. 2010. (Illus.). 256p. pap. 70.00 *(978-1-4051-1477-6(0)*, Wiley-Blackwell) Wiley, John & Sons, Inc.

Westford, Pia. Neighborhood Design & Travel. 2010. 264p. pap. *(978-3-639-25443-3(0))* VDM Verlag Dr. Mueller e.K.

Wien, Architekturzentrum, ed. Lessons from Bernard Rudofsky: Life as a Voyage. 2007. (Illus.). 296p. 64.95 *(978-3-7643-8360-2(7)*, 3764383607) Springer.

Wienand, Norman. Materials, Specification & Detailing: Foundations of Building Design. 2008. (Technologies of Architecture Ser.). (ENG., Illus.). 328p. (C). 165.00 *(978-0-415-40358-0(8)*, Taylor & Francis) Taylor & Francis Group GBR. Dist: Taylor & Francis Group.

Wienand, Sean, illus. Materials, Specification & Detailing: Foundations of Building Design. 2008. (Technologies of Architecture Ser.). 309p. per. 45.95 *(978-0-415-40359-7(6))* Taylor & Francis Group.

Wilhide, Elizabeth. Materials: A Directory for Home Design. (Illus.). 192p. 34.95 *(978-1-84400-042-5(7))* Quadrille Publishing, Ltd. GBR. Dist: Graphic Arts Ctr. Publishing Co.

Williams, Kim. Nexus Network Journal. 2007. (Nexus Network Journal Ser.). Vol. 8, & 2. (Illus.). 121p. pap. 49.95 *(978-3-7643-7761-8(5)*, 3764377615) Vol. 8,2. 144p. pap. 49.95 *(978-3-7643-7747-2(X)*, 376437747X) Birkhauser Boston.

—Nexus Network Journal 11,1: Architecture & Mathematics. Williams, Kim, ed. 2009. (Nexus Network Journal Ser.). (ENG.). 200p. pap. 109.00 *(978-3-7643-8973-4(7)*, 3764389737) Birkhauser Verlag AG CHE. Dist: Springer.

—Nexus Network Journal 9,2: Architecture & Mathematics. 2007. (Nexus Network Journal Ser.). 150p. pap. 69.95 *(978-3-7643-8444-9(1))* Birkhauser Boston.

Williams, Kim, ed. Nexus Network Journal 11,2: Architecture & Mathematics. 2009. (Nexus Network Journal Ser.). (ENG.). 200p. pap. 109.00 *(978-3-7643-8975-8(3)*, 3764389753) Birkhauser Verlag AG CHE. Dist: Springer.

—Nexus Network Journal 11,3: Architecture & Mathematics. 2010. (Nexus Network Journal Ser.). 200p. pap. 109.00 *(978-3-7643-8977-2(X)*, 376438977X) Birkhauser Verlag AG CHE. Dist: Springer.

—Nexus Network Journal 12,1: Architecture & Mathematics. 2011. (Nexus Network Journal Ser.). (ENG.). iv, 160p. pap. 109.00 *(978-3-0346-0517-5(X)*, 303460517X) Birkhauser Verlag AG CHE. Dist: Springer.

—Nexus Network Journal 12,2: Architecture & Mathematics. 2010. (Nexus Network Journal Ser.). (ENG.). iv, 199p. pap. 109.00 *(978-3-0346-0519-9(6)*, 3034605196) Birkhauser Verlag AG CHE. Dist: Springer.

—Nexus Network Journal 12,3: Architecture & Mathematics. 2011. (Nexus Network Journal Ser.). 164p. pap. 109.00 *(978-3-0346-0521-2(8)*, 3034605218) Birkhauser Verlag AG CHE. Dist: Springer.

—Nexus Network Journal 13,1: Architecture & Mathematics. 2011. (Nexus Network Journal Ser.). (ENG.). v, 150p. pap. 109.00 ***(978-3-0348-0159-1(9)***, 3034801599) Birkhauser Verlag AG CHE. Dist: Springer.

—Nexus Network Journal 13,2: Architecture & Mathematics. 2011. (Nexus Network Journal Ser.). (ENG., Illus.). iv, 150p. pap. 109.00 ***(978-3-0348-0170-6(X)***, 303480170X) Birkhauser Verlag AG CHE. Dist: Springer.

—Nexus Network Journal 13,3: Architecture & Mathematics. 2012. (Nexus Network Journal Ser.). (ENG.). iv, 250p. pap. 109.00 ***(978-3-0348-0245-1(5)***, 3034802455) Birkhauser Verlag AG CHE. Dist: Springer.

Williams, Kim, ed. Nexus Network Journal 9,1: Architecture & Mathematics. 2007. (Nexus Network Journal Ser.). 158p. pap. 64.95 *(978-3-7643-8443-2(3))* Birkhauser Verlag AG CHE. Dist: Springer.

Williams, Kim & Wassell, Stephen R., eds. Architecture & Mathematics: Canons of Form-Making in Honour of Andrea Palladio 1508-2008. 2008. (Nexus Network Journal Ser.). (Illus.). 169p. pap. 89.95 *(978-3-7643-8765-5(3))* Birkhauser Verlag AG CHE. Dist: Springer.

Williamson, Leslie. Handcrafted Modern: At Home with Mid-Century Designers. 2010. (ENG., Illus.). 224p. 45.00 *(978-0-8478-3418-1(2))* Rizzoli International Pubns., Inc.

Wilson, Travis Kelly. Drafting & Design: Basics for Interior Design. 2011. (Illus.). 224p. pap. ***(978-1-56367-837-0(3))*** Fairchild Bks.

Wines, James N. Site: Identity in Density. 2006. (Master Architect Series VI). (ENG., Illus.). 256p. 59.95 *(978-1-920744-21-2(5)*, Images Publishing Dist Ac) Antique Collectors' Club GBR. Dist: National Bk. Network.

Wing, Eric. Autodesk Revit Architecture 2011: No Experience Required. 2010. (ENG., Illus.). 984p. pap. 39.99 *(978-0-470-61011-4(5)*, Sybex) Wiley, John & Sons, Inc.

—Autodesk Revit Architecture 2012: No Experience Required. 2011. (ENG., Illus.). 1032p. pap. 39.99 *(978-0-470-94506-3(0)*, Sybex) Wiley, John & Sons, Inc.

Wing, Eric & Wing. Revit Architecture 2010: No Experience Required. 2009. (ENG., Illus.). 984p. pap. 39.99 *(978-0-470-44722-2(2)*, Sybex) Wiley, John & Sons, Inc.

Wnukiewicz, Karol. The Role of Quality Requirements in Software Architecture Design. 2010. 116p. pap. *(978-3-8383-6549-7(6))* Lambert Academic Publishing.

Wolf, Eric Michael. American Art Museum Architecture: Documents & Design. 2010. (ENG., Illus.). 272p. 75.00 *(978-0-393-73280-1(0)*, 73280) Norton, W. W. & Co., Inc.

Wolff, Howard J. 100 Hotels & Resorts: Destinations That Lift the Spirit. McCulloch, Janelle, ed. 2009. (ENG., Illus.). 65.00 *(978-1-86470-160-9(9))* Images Publishing Group AUS. Dist: National Bk. Network.

Wood, Antony, ed. Best Tall Buildings 2008: CTBUH International Award Winning Projects. 2008. (ENG., Illus.). 128p. 51.95 *(978-1-85617-674-3(6)*, Architectural Pr.) Elsevier Science & Technology Bks.

Wright, Frank Lloyd. Frank Lloyd Wright: Art Glass of the Martin House Complex. Jackson-Forsberg, Eric, ed. 2009. 96p. 27.95 *(978-0-7649-5150-3(5))* Pomegranate Communications, Inc.

Xie, Yeal. Guestroom & Bathroom. 2011. (ENG.). 272p. 50.00 *(978-988-19739-9-3(6))* Design Media Publishing Ltd. HKG. Dist: BookMasters Distribution Services (BDS).

Yaneva, Albena. Mapping Controversies in Architecture. 2012. (Illus.). 144p. 99.95 ***(978-1-4094-2669-1(6))***; 99.95 ***(978-1-4094-2668-4(8))*** Ashgate Publishing Co.

Yeang, Ken & Yeang. EcoMasterplanning. 2009. (ENG., Illus.). 256p. 75.00 *(978-0-470-69729-0(6)*, Wiley) Wiley, John & Sons, Inc.

Yee, Roger. Design Excellence. 2010. 176p. 50.00 *(978-1-58471-141-4(8))* Visual Reference Pubns., Inc.

Yoho & Merritt, ed. Craftsman Bungalows: Designs from the Pacific Northwest. 2008. (Dover Architecture Ser.). (ENG., Illus.). 112p. pap. 10.95 *(978-0-486-46875-4(5))* Dover Pubns., Inc.

Younes, Samir. The Imperfect City: On Architectural Judgment. 2012. (Illus.). 240p. 89.95 ***(978-1-4094-4667-5(0))*** Ashgate Publishing Co.

Yudell, Moore Ruble. The Future of Place. Claudel, Matthew, ed. 2011. (ENG.). 392p. 60.00 *(978-988-19739-2-4(9))* Design Media Publishing Ltd. HKG. Dist: BookMasters Distribution Services (BDS).

Zaera-Polo, Alejandro. The Sniper's Log: Architectural Chronicles of Generation-X. 2012. (ENG., Illus.). 198p. pap. *(978-84-92861-22-4(3))* Actar Birkhauser Distribution.

Zec, Peter. Design Innovations Workbook 2000. (Illus.). 336p. 51.83 *(978-3-929638-47-9(9))* Birkhauser Verlag AG CHE. Dist: Chronicle Bks. LLC.

ARCHITECTURAL DETAILS

see Architecture—Details

ARCHITECTURAL DRAWING

see also Architecture—Designs and Plans; Architecture—Details

Abdelhameed, Wael. The Impact of Computer on Design Capabilities of Architects. 2010. 172p. pap. *(978-3-639-13683-8(7))* VDM Verlag Dr. Mueller e.K.

Amoroso, Nadia. Representing Landscapes. 2012. (ENG., Illus.). 280p. (C). pap. 59.95 ***(978-0-415-58957-4(6))*** Routledge.

Amoroso, Nadia. Representing Landscapes: A Visual Collection of Landscape Architectural Drawings. 2012. (ENG., Illus.). 280p. (C). 165.00 *(978-0-415-58956-7(8))* Routledge.

Andrews, Jonathan. Architectural Visions: Contemporary Sketches, Perspectives, Drawings. 2010. (ENG., Illus.). 372p. 49.95 *(978-3-03768-035-3(0)*, Braun Publish,Csi) Continental Sales, Inc.

Aubin, Paul. Revit Architecture 2011. 2010. (ENG., Illus.). 864p. pap. 93.95 *(978-1-111-12493-9(0)*, AutoDesk Pr.) Delmar Cengage Learning.

Aubin, Paul F. AutoCAD Architecture 2011. 2010. (ENG.). 8p. pap. 5.95 *(978-1-111-31059-2(9)*, AutoDesk Pr.) Delmar Cengage Learning.

—Mastering AutoCAD Architecture 2008. 6th rev. ed. 2007. (ENG., Illus.). 1164p. pap. 108.95 *(978-1-4283-1162-6(9)*, AutoDesk Pr.) Delmar Cengage Learning.

—Mastering AutoCAD Architecture 2010. 7th ed. 2009. (ENG., Illus.). 976p. pap. 108.95 *(978-1-4390-5729-2(X)*, AutoDesk Pr.) Delmar Cengage Learning.

—Mastering Revit Architecture, 2010. 2009. (ENG.). 848p. pap. 112.95 *(978-1-4390-5715-5(X)*, AutoDesk Pr.) Delmar Cengage Learning.

—Revit 2011 CourseNotes for Aubin's the Aubin Mastering Series: Mastering Revit Architecture 2011. 2010. (ENG.). 8p. pap. 5.95 *(978-1-111-13714-4(5)*, AutoDesk Pr.) Delmar Cengage Learning.

—Revit Architecture 2012. 2011. (CAD New Releases Ser.). (ENG.). 416p. pap. 55.95 ***(978-1-111-64853-4(0)***, AutoDesk Pr.) Delmar Cengage Learning.

Aubin, Paul F. Revit architecture course Notes. 2009. (ENG.). 6p. (C). 9.95 *(978-1-4354-9892-1(5))* Delmar Cengage Learning.

Aubin, Paul F., et al. CourseNotes for Aubin/McClelland/Schmid/Stanley's the Aubin Academy Master Series: AutoCAD MEP 2011. 2010. (ENG.). 8p. pap. 5.95 *(978-1-111-31053-0(X)*, AutoDesk Pr.) Delmar Cengage Learning.

—Revit MEP 2011 Course Notes for Aubin/McClelland/Schmid/Stanley's the Aubin Academy Master Series: Revit MEP 2011. 2011. 8p. pap. 4.95 *(978-1-111-13794-6(3)*, AutoDesk Pr.) Delmar Cengage Learning.

Aubin, Paul F. (Paul F. Aubin). Revit Architecture 2012. 2011. (ENG.). 6p. 4.95 *(978-1-133-01446-1(1))*; (Illus.). 752p. pap. 93.95 *(978-1-111-64848-0(4))* Delmar Cengage Learning. (AutoDesk Pr.).

Autodesk Official Training Guide Staff. Learning Revit Architecture 2010. 2009. (ENG., Illus.). 768p. pap. 79.99 *(978-1-897177-56-3(9)*, Sybex) Wiley, John & Sons, Inc.

Ballast, David Kent. Architect's Handbook of Construction Detailing. 2nd ed. 2009. (ENG., Illus.). 480p. 90.00 (978-0-470-38191-5(4), Wiley) Wiley, John & Sons, Inc.

Bennett Wirtz, Diana. Hand Drafting for Interior Design. 2009. 200p. pap. 94.00 (978-1-56367-737-3(7)) Fairchild Bks.

Binggeli, Corky & Binggeli. Graphic Standards Field Guide to Commercial Interiors. 2009. (Graphic Standards Field Guide Ser.: 3). (ENG., Illus.). 560p. pap. 75.00 (978-0-470-41295-4(X), Wiley) Wiley, John & Sons, Inc.

Bokmiller, Don, et al. Mastering Revit MEP 2010. 2009. 950p. pap. 69.99 (978-0-470-53198-3(3), Sybex) Wiley, John & Sons, Inc.

Bork, Robert. The Geometry of Creation: Architectural Drawing & the Dynamics of Gothic Design. 2011. (Illus.). 484p. 119.95 (978-0-7546-6062-0(1)) Ashgate Publishing Co.

Brothers, Cammy. Michelangelo, Drawing, & the Invention of Architecture. 2008. (ENG., Illus.). 272p. 65.00 (978-0-300-12489-7(9)) Yale Univ. Pr.

Burkhalter, Marianne. Finding Buildings. Sumi, Christian, ed. 2010. (ENG & GER., Illus.). 174p. 75.00 (978-3-85881-297-1(8)) Scheidegger und Spiess AG, Verlag CHE. Dist: Antique Collectors' Club.

Carpo, Mario & Lemerle, Frederique, eds. Perspective, Projections & Design: Technologies of Architectural Representation. 2007. (ENG., Illus.). 208p. (C). 165.00 (978-0-415-40204-0(2)) Routledge.

Cavataio, Christine. Manual Drafting for Interiors. 2012. (ENG., Illus.). 160p. pap. 50.00 (978-0-470-87940-5(8), Wiley) Wiley, John & Sons, Inc.

Ching, Francis D. K. Architectural Graphics. 5th ed. 2009. (ENG., Illus.). 256p. pap. 45.00 (978-0-470-39911-8(2), Wiley) Wiley, John & Sons, Inc.

Chueca, Pilar. Urban Houses: Houses Now. 2007. (ENG., Illus.). 240p. 39.95 (978-84-96263-01-7(0)) Links International (Leading International Key Services Barcelona, S.A.) ESP. Dist: National Bk. Network.

Clemirison, Antony. Journeys with Pen & Pencil. 2008. (ENG.). 96p. pap. 38.95 (978-1-84368-037-6(8)) Pallas Athene GBR. Dist: Independent Pubs. Group.

Cline, Lydia. Drafting & Visual Presentation for Interior Designers. rev. ed. 2011. (ENG., Illus.). 416p. (C). spiral bd. 90.20 (978-0-13-506421-4(X), Prentice Hall) Prentice Hall PTR.

Cloarec, Françoise. Storr: Architecte de L'ailleurs. 2010. (FRE., Illus.). 170p. (978-2-7529-0485-0(1)) Phebus, Editions.

Crafti, Stephen. Details for Living. 2007. (ENG., Illus.). 200p. 50.00 (978-1-86470-249-1(4)) Images Publishing Group AUS. Dist: National Bk. Network.

Cram101 Textbook Reviews. Outlines & Highlights for Architectural Drafting for Interior Designers by Lydia Cline. 2011. 70p. pap. 27.95 (978-1-61905-989-4(4)) Cram101 Inc.

—Outlines & Highlights for the Study of Architectural Design by John F Harbeson. 2011. 88p. pap. 27.95 (978-1-61905-625-1(9)) Cram101 Inc.

Cram101 Textbook Reviews & Cram101 Textbook Reviews. Outlines & Highlights for Commercial Drafting & Detailing by Alan Jefferis. 2011. 230p. pap. 31.95 (978-1-61830-866-5(1)) Cram101 Inc.

—Outlines & Highlights for Introducing & Implementing Revit Architecture 2009 by Lay Christopher Fox. 2011. 66p. pap. 27.95 (978-1-61830-970-9(6)) Cram101 Inc.

—Outlines & Highlights for Mastering Revit Architecture 2008 by Eddy Krygiel. 2011. 124p. pap. 28.95 (978-1-61830-949-5(8)) Cram101 Inc.

da Costa Meyer, Esther. Frank Gehry: On Line. 2008. (Illus.). 80p. pap. 24.95 (978-0-943012-00-1(7)) Princeton Univ. Art Museum.

Davis, Patrick. Introducing Autodesk Revit Architecture 2012. 2011. (ENG., Illus.). 720p. pap. 49.99 (978-1-118-02996-1(8), Sybex) Wiley, John & Sons, Inc.

Davis, Patrick, et al. Introducing Autodesk Revit Architecture 2011. 2010. (ENG., Illus.). 544p. pap. 49.99 (978-0-470-64971-8(2), Sybex) Wiley, John & Sons, Inc.

Demchak, Greg, et al. Revit Architecture 2010. 2009. (ENG., Illus.). 816p. pap. 59.99 (978-0-470-45649-1(3), Sybex) Wiley, John & Sons, Inc.

Dernie, David & Dernie, Selena. Architectural Drawing. 2010. (ENG., Illus.). 208p. pap. 35.00 (978-1-85669-679-1(0)) King, Laurence Publishing GBR. Dist: Hachette Bk. Group.

Di Castro, Daniela, et al. Disegni Dall'antico Di Pierre-François-Léonard Fontaine, 1762-1855, Architetto Di Napoleone. 2007. (ITA., Illus.). 155p. (C). 39.50 (978-88-596-0216-3(5)) Edizioni Polistampa ITA. Dist: Brown, David Bk. Co., The.

Docci, Mario & Maestri, Diego. Manuale Di Rilevamento Architettonico e Urbano. 2009. (ITA., Illus.). vi, 374p. (978-88-420-9068-7(9)) Laterza.

Dzambazova, Tatjana, et al. Introducing Revit Architecture 2010: BIM for Beginners. 2009. (ENG., Illus.). 512p. pap. 49.99 (978-0-470-47355-9(X), Sybex) Wiley, John & Sons, Inc.

—Mastering Revit Architecture 2009. 2008. (ENG., Illus.). 800p. pap. 59.99 (978-0-470-29528-1(7), Sybex) Wiley, John & Sons, Inc.

Edwards, Brian. Understanding Architecture Through Drawing. 2nd rev. ed. 2008. (Illus.). CCLXIV, 8p. pap. 69.95 (978-0-415-44414-9(4)) Taylor & Francis Group.

—Understanding Architecture Through Drawing. 2nd rev. ed. 2008. (ENG., Illus.). 272p. (C). 165.00 (978-0-415-44413-2(6), Taylor & Francis) Taylor & Francis Group GBR. Dist: Taylor & Francis Group.

Equipo Staff & Papeti, Dissenys. Gaudí: Dibuixos = Dibujos = Drawings, 1 vol. 2007. (CAT, ENG & SPA., Illus.). 128p. pap. 15.95 (978-84-8478-069-4(4)) Triangle Postals, S.L. ESP. Dist: Innovative Logistics.

Farrelly, Lorraine. Drawing for Urban Design. 2011. (ENG., Illus.). 192p. pap. 35.00 (978-1-85669-718-7(5)) King, Laurence Publishing GBR. Dist: Hachette Bk. Group.

—Representational Techniques. 2008. (Basics Architecture Ser.). (ENG., Illus.). 176p. pap. 29.95 (978-2-940373-62-8(0)) AVA Publishing GBR. Dist: Ingram Pub. Services.

Farthing, Stephen, et al. The Sketchbooks of Nicholas Grimshaw. 2010. (ENG., Illus.). 120p. 30.00 (978-1-905711-62-8(X)) Royal Academy of Arts GBR. Dist: Hachette Bk. Group.

Fischer, Ole W. What Architects Desire. 2010. 400p. pap. 39.95 (978-3-7091-0328-9(2)) Springer Wien AUT. Dist: Springer.

Forget, Thomas. The Construction of Drawings & Movies: Models for Presenting Architectural Design & Analysis. 2012. (ENG., Illus.). 272p. (C). 165.00 (978-0-415-89839-3(0)); pap. 49.95 (978-0-415-89840-9(4)) Routledge.

Foster, Norman & text. Norman Foster Set: Drawings, 1958-2008, 2 vols. 2011. (ENG., Illus.). 232p. 150.00 (978-0-9564339-2-3(8)) Ivory Pr. ESP. Dist: D.A.P./Distributed Art Pubs.

Fox, Lay Christopher & Balding, James J. Introducing & Implementing Revit Architecture 2010. 2009. (ENG.). 544p. pap. 107.95 (978-1-4354-9310-0(9)) Delmar Cengage Learning.

Frascari, Marco. Eleven Exercises in the Art of Architectural Drawing. 2011. (ENG., Illus.). 224p. (C). 165.00 (978-0-415-77925-8(1)); pap. 49.95 (978-0-415-77926-5(X)) Routledge.

Frascari, Marco, et al, eds. From Models to Drawings: Imagination & Representation in Architecture. 2010. (ENG., Illus.). 312p. (C). 53.95 (978-0-415-48798-6(6)) Routledge.

Frascari, Marco & Starkey, Bradley, eds. From Models to Drawings: Imagination & Representation in Architecture. 2007. (ENG., Illus.). 312p. (C). 100.00 (978-0-415-43113-2(1)) Routledge.

Gallo, Luciana. Lord Elgin & Ancient Greek Architecture: The Elgin Drawings at the British Museum. 2009. (ENG., Illus.). 362p. (C). 155.00 (978-0-521-88163-0(3)) Cambridge Univ. Pr.

Geraghty, Anthony. The Architectural Drawings of Sir Christopher Wren: At All Souls College, Oxford: A Complete Catalogue. 2007. (Illus.). 296p. 180.00 (978-0-7546-4071-4(X), Lund Humphries Pubs.) Ashgate Publishing, Ltd. GBR. Dist: Ashgate Publishing Co.

Gibbs, Carolyn. The Design Studio: Developing Technical & Creative Skills Using AutoCAD & ADT. 2008. (Illus.). 608p. pap. 90.00 (978-1-56367-442-6(4)) Fairchild Bks.

Gladstone, Stephen. Graphic Standards Field Guide to Home Inspections. 2011. (Graphic Standards Field Guide Ser.: 4). (ENG., Illus.). 496p. pap. 70.00 (978-0-470-54291-0(8), Wiley) Wiley, John & Sons, Inc.

Goldberg, H. Edward. Revit Architecture 2012: A Comprehensive Guide. 2012. (ENG.). 720p. (C). pap. 102.67 (978-0-13-295510-2(5), Prentice Hall) Prentice Hall PTR.

Grabowski, Ralph. Using AutoCAD 2008 Basics. 2007. (ENG., Illus.). 1224p. pap. 112.95 (978-1-4283-1159-6(9), AutoDesk Pr.) Delmar Cengage Learning.

Gregory, Rob. Key Contemporary Buildings: Plans, Sections & Elevation. 2008. (Key Structures: Plans, Sections, Elevations Ser.). (ENG.). 240p. 45.00 (978-0-393-73242-9(8), 73242) Norton, W. W. & Co., Inc.

Groihofer, Brigitte, ed. Raimund Abraham, [Un]Built. 2nd ed. 2011. (Illus.). 348p. 99.00 (978-3-7091-0468-2(8), 3709104688) Springer Wien AUT. Dist: Springer.

Guggenheim Foundation et. Frank Lloyd Wright: from Inward Outward. 2009. pap. (978-0-8478-3263-7(5)) Guggenheim, Solomon R. Museum.

Gussow, Sue Ferguson. Architects Draw: Freehand Fundamentals. 2008. (ENG., Illus.). 160p. pap. 24.95 (978-1-56898-740-8(4)) Princeton Architectural Pr.

Hamad, Munir. AutoCAD(r) 2012 Beginning & Intermediate. 2011. (Illus.). 400p. pap. 39.95 (978-1-936420-20-9(1)) Mercury Learning & Information.

Harbeson, John F. The Study of Architectural Design. 2008. (ENG., Illus.). 352p. pap. 45.00 (978-0-393-73128-6(6), 73128) Norton, W. W. & Co., Inc.

Hepler, Dana J., et al. Student Solutions Manual for Hepler/Wallach/Hepler's Drafting & Design for Architecture, 2nd. 9th ed. 2012. (ENG.). 120p. (C). pap. 59.95 (978-1-111-12816-6(2)) Delmar Cengage Learning.

—Workbook for Hepler/Wallach/Hepler's Drafting & Design for Architecture, 2nd. 9th ed. 2012. (ENG.). 240p. (C). pap. 40.95 (978-1-111-12815-9(4)) Delmar Cengage Learning.

Hepler, Dana J. (Dana J. Hepler), et al. Drafting & Design for Architecture. 9th ed. 2012. (ENG.). 800p. (C). 181.95 (978-1-111-12813-5(8)) Delmar Cengage Learning.

Herem, Thibaud, contrib. by. Draw Me a House: Architectural Ideas, Inspiration & Colouring In. 2012. (ENG., Illus.). 240p. pap. 20.00 (978-0-9562053-7-7(2)) Cicada Bks. GBR. Dist: D.A.P./Distributed Art Pubs.

Hutchison, Edward. Drawing for Landscape Architecture: Sketch to Screen to Site. 2011. (ENG., Illus.). 240p. 65.00 (978-0-500-34271-8(7), 534271) Thames & Hudson.

Jefferis, Alan & Smith, Kenneth. Commercial Drafting & Detailing. 3rd ed. 2009. (ENG.). 624p. (C). pap. 177.95 (978-1-4354-2597-2(9)) Delmar Cengage Learning.

Jefferis, Alan, et al. Architectural Drafting & Design. 6th ed. 2010. (ENG.). (C). wbk. ed. 103.95 (978-1-4354-8164-0(X)); 1152p. 189.95 (978-1-4354-8162-6(3)) Delmar Cengage Learning.

—Architectural Drafting & Design (Book Only) 6th ed. 2010. (ENG.). (C). 189.95 (978-1-111-32178-9(7)) Delmar Cengage Learning.

—AutoCAD 2008 for Architecture. 2007. (ENG., Illus.). 992p. per. 149.95 (978-1-4283-1161-9(0), AutoDesk Pr.) Delmar Cengage Learning.

Jones, Will. Architects' Sketchbooks. 2011. (ENG., Illus.). 352p. 49.95 (978-1-935202-46-2(4), Metropolis Bks.) D.A.P./Distributed Art Pubs.

—Unbuilt Masterworks of the 21st Century: Inspirational Architecture for the Digital Age. 2009. (ENG., Illus.). 400p. 65.00 (978-0-500-34254-1(7), 534254) Thames & Hudson.

Kalfazade, Nihat. Diagrammatic Potency of the Nine Square Grid in Architecture. 2009. 108p. pap. (978-3-639-13659-3(4)) VDM Verlag Dr. Mueller e.K.

Kicklighter, Clois E. Architecture Standard Ind License 3.5D 2000. 52.00 (978-1-56637-599-3(1)) Goodheart-Willcox Pub.

—Architecture Standard State License 3.5D 2000. 130.00 (978-1-56637-596-2(7)) Goodheart-Willcox Pub.

Kim, In-Sung. Drawing Time with Temporal Drawing. 2010. 192p. pap. (978-3-8383-0790-9(9)) Lambert Academic Publishing.

Klick, Peter. The Interior Designer's Launch Pad. 2008. (Illus.). 472p. pap. 80.00 (978-1-56367-504-1(8)) Fairchild Bks.

Koenig, Peter A. Design Graphics: Drawing Techniques for Design Professionals. 3rd rev. ed. 2011. (ENG.). 192p. (C). pap. 63.80 (978-0-13-713696-4(X), Prentice Hall) Prentice Hall PTR.

Kogent, Inc. Revit 2010. 2009. 336p. pap. 56.95 (978-0-7637-7630-5(0)) Jones & Bartlett Learning, LLC.

Korteis, Amy & Seidler, Douglas R. Hand Drawing for Designers: Communicating Ideas Through Architectural Graphics. 2009. (Illus.). 304p. pap. 98.00 (978-1-56367-780-9(6)) Fairchild Bks.

Krygiel, Eddy, et al. Autodesk Revit Architecture 2012 Essentials. 2011. (ENG., Illus.). 400p. pap. 49.99 (978-1-118-01683-1(1), Sybex) Wiley, John & Sons, Inc.

—Mastering Autodesk Revit Architecture 2011. 2010. (ENG., Illus.). 1168p. pap. 59.99 (978-0-470-62696-2(8), Sybex) Wiley, John & Sons, Inc.

—Mastering Autodesk Revit Architecture 2011: Autodesk Official Training Guide. 2010. (Illus.). xxx, 1122p. E-Book 27.95 (978-0-470-90819-8(X)) Wiley, John & Sons, Inc.

—Mastering Autodesk Revit Architecture 2012. 2011. (ENG., Illus.). 1152p. pap. 69.99 (978-0-470-93749-5(1), Sybex) Wiley, John & Sons, Inc.

Kyles, Shannon R. AutoCAD Workbook for Architects & Engineers. 2008. (ENG., Illus.). 296p. pap. 52.95 (978-1-4051-8096-2(X), Wiley-Blackwell) Wiley, John & Sons, Inc.

Lederer, Arno. Charakterköpfe und Käuze: Der Zeichner Arno Lederer. 2011. (ENG & GER., Illus.). 224p. 35.00 (978-3-86859-135-4(4)) Jovis Verlag GmbH DEU. Dist: D.A.P./Distributed Art Pubs.

Lemerle, Frederique. Perspective, Projections & Design: Technologies of Architectural Representation. 2007. (ENG., Illus.). 208p. (C). per. 71.95 (978-0-415-40206-4(9)) Routledge.

Liebing, Ralph W. Handbook of Detailing: The Graphic Anatomy of Construction. 2009. (Illus.). 424p. 89.95 (978-3-211-99134-3(4), 3211991344) Springer.

Liebl-Osborne, Petra. Gestaltungslehren in der Architektenausbildung: An Technischen Universitaten und Hochschulen in Westdeutschland, 1945-1995. (Europaische Hochschulschriften Ser.). (GER., Illus.). 592p. 73.95 (978-3-631-36307-2(9)) Lang, Peter Publishing, Inc.

Lollia, R. Book with grids to draw in Isometric Prospect. 2009. 68p. pap. 12.95 (978-1-4092-5850-6(5)) Lulu Enterprises Inc.

Lucas, Ray. Getting Lost in Tokyo. 2010. 74p. pap. 42.50 (978-1-4461-2985-5(7)) Lulu Enterprises Inc.

Madsen, David A. & Palma, Ron M. Architectural Desktop & It's Applications 2007. 2007. 70.00 (978-1-59070-796-8(6)) Goodheart-Willcox Pub.

—Architectural Drafting Using AutoCad 2010. 6th ed. 2009. (ENG.). 860p. 82.64 (978-1-60525-187-5(9)) Goodheart-Willcox Pub.

McGrath, Brian & Gardner, Jean. Cinemetrics: Architectural Drawing Today. 2007. (ENG., Illus.). 272p. 145.00 (978-0-470-02669-4(3)); per. 55.00 (978-0-470-02671-7(5)) Wiley, John & Sons, Inc. (Wiley).

Melvin, John. The Stones of Oxford: Conjectures on a Cockleshell. 2011. (ENG.). 96p. 40.00 (978-1-906506-13-1(2)) Papadakis Dist A/C.

Mojon, Luc. Michelangelo: Die Entwürfe zu San Giovanni dei Fiorentini. 2009. (GRE & GER., Illus.). 139p. (978-3-03911-577-8(4)) Lang, Peter.

Moleskine. Hand of the Architect, Set. 2009. (ENG & ITA., Illus.). 392p. 50.00 (978-88-6293-233-2(2)) Moleskine ITA. Dist: Hachette Bk. Group.

Moss, Elise. Autodesk AutoCAD Architecture 2008 Fundamentals. 2007. 289p. per. 59.95 (978-1-58503-358-4(8), SDC Pubns.) Schroff Development Corp.

—Revit Architecture 2008 Basics. 2007. 423p. per. 59.95 (978-1-58503-376-8(6), SDC Pubns.) Schroff Development Corp.

Muller, Edward J., et al. Architectural Drawing & Light Construction. 8th ed. 2008. (ENG., Illus.). 792p. (C). 146.00 (978-0-13-513215-9(0), Prentice Hall) Prentice Hall PTR.

O'Gorman, James F. & Condon, Lorna. Drawing Toward Home: Designs for Domestic Architecture from Historic New England. 2010. 59.95 (978-0-88448-328-1(2)) Tilbury Hse. Pubs.

Onstott, Scott. Enhancing Architectural Drawings & Models with Photoshop. 2nd ed. 2010. (ENG., Illus.). 376p. pap. 49.99 (978-0-470-91656-8(7), Sybex) Wiley, John & Sons, Inc.

Pacey, Arnold. Medieval Architectural Drawing. 2010. (ENG., Illus.). 256p. 49.95 (978-0-7524-4404-8(2)) History Pr. Ltd., The GBR. Dist: Independent Pubs. Group.

Pekol, Banu. Late Medieval Architectural & Micro-Architectural Drawings. 2010. (Illus.). 72p. pap. (978-3-8383-5180-3(0)) Lambert Academic Publishing.

Peterson, et al. Mastering Autodesk Revit MEP 2012. 2011. (ENG., Illus.). 648p. pap. 69.99 (978-1-118-06681-2(2), Sybex) Wiley, John & Sons, Inc.

Pfister, Alessandra & Angelini, Piervaleriano. Gli Architetti Gilardi a Mosca: La Raccolta Dei Disegni Conservati in Ticino. 2007. (ITA., Illus.). 244p. (978-88-87624-30-4(5)) Academy Pr.

Piedmont-Palladino, Susan, ed. Tools of the Imagination: Drawing Tools & Technologies from the Eighteenth Century to the Present. 2006. (ENG., Illus.). 128p. 29.95 (978-1-56898-599-2(1)) Princeton Architectural Pr.

Plunkett, Drew. Drawing for Interior Design. 2009. (ENG., Illus.). 192p. pap. 35.00 (978-1-85669-622-7(7)) King, Laurence Publishing GBR. Dist: Hachette Bk. Group.

Price, Lois Olcott. Line, Shade, & Shadow: The Fabrication & Preservation of Architectural Drawings. 2010. (Illus.). xx, 359p. (978-90-6194-420-1(1)) Oak Knoll Pr.

Price, Louis Olcott. Line, Shade & Shadow: The Fabrication & Preservation of Architectural Drawings. 2010. xx, 359p. 95.00 (978-1-58456-237-5(4)) Oak Knoll Pr.

Revit Architecture 2008 Essentials Tutorial Series. 2007. 249.00 incl. cd-rom (978-1-932931-37-2(6)) 4D Design Solutions, LLC.

Revit Architecture 2008 Tutorial Series. 2007. 400.00 incl. cd-rom (978-1-932931-36-5(8)) 4D Design Solutions, LLC.

Revit Building 9 Fundamentals Tutorial Series. 2007. 199.00 incl. cd-rom (978-1-932931-34-1(1)) 4D Design Solutions, LLC.

Richardson, Jamie D., et al. Revit Structure 2010. 2009. (ENG., Illus.). 912p. pap. 69.99 (978-0-470-52141-0(4), Sybex) Wiley, John & Sons, Inc.

Schank Smith, Kendra. Architects Sketches: Dialogue & Design. 2008. (ENG., Illus.). 152p. 59.95 (978-0-7506-8226-8(4)) Routledge.

Schillaci, Fabio. Architectural Renderings: Construction & Design Manual, 1 vol. 2010. (ENG.). 465p. 68.00 (978-3-938666-63-0(3)) DOM Pubs. DEU. Dist: Innovative Logistics.

Schwartz, Donald, ed. AutoCAD 2009 Update Tutorial Series. 2008. 99.00 incl. cd-rom (978-1-932931-40-2(6)) 4D Design Solutions, LLC.

Seidler, Douglas. Digital Drawing for Designers: A Visual Guide to AutoCAD. 2007. (Illus.). 223p. pap. 89.50 (978-1-56367-512-6(9)) Fairchild Bks.

Senseney, John R. The Art of Building in the Classical World: Vision, Craftsmanship, & Linear Perspective in Greek & Roman Architecture. 2011. (ENG., Illus.). 274p. 90.00 (978-1-107-00235-7(4)) Cambridge Univ. Pr.

Skousen, Joel. How to Implement a High Security Shelter in the Home. 2nd rev. ed. (Illus.). 100p. pap. 25.00 (978-1-56861-054-2(8)) Swift Learning Resources.

Smith, Michael. The DataCAD 12 Project Book. 2008. 390p. (C). spiral bd. 45.95 (978-0-9777525-4-6(2)) Technology Education Concepts Inc.

Snyder, Frank M. Building Details. 2007. (ENG.). 144p. 65.00 (978-0-393-73245-0(2), 73245) Norton, W. W. & Co., Inc.

Spankie, Ro. Drawing Out the Interior. 2009. (Basics Interior Architecture Ser.). (ENG., Illus.). 175p. pap. 29.95 (978-2-940373-88-8(4)) AVA Publishing GBR. Dist: Ingram Pub. Services.

Spiller, Neil. Visionary Architecture: Blueprints of the Modern Imagination. (ENG., Illus.). 272p. 2008. per. 39.95 (978-0-500-28655-5(8)) 2007. 60.00 (978-0-500-34226-8(1)) Thames & Hudson.

Stine, Daniel. Commercial Design Using Revit Architecture 2008. 2007. 320p. per. 59.95 (978-1-58503-375-1(8), SDC Pubns.) Schroff Development Corp.

—Residential Design Using AutoCAD 2008. 2007. 418p. per. 59.95 (978-1-58503-367-6(7), SDC Pubns.) Schroff Development Corp.

—Residential Design Using Revit Architecture 2008. 2007. 463p. per. 59.95 (978-1-58503-374-4(X), SDC Pubns.) Schroff Development Corp.

Tchoban, Sergei. Architekturwelten: Sergei Tchoban - Zeichner und Sammler. 2010. (GER & ENG., Illus.). 128p. 45.00 (978-3-86859-047-0(1)) Jovis Verlag GmbH DEU. Dist: D.A.P./Distributed Art Pubs.

Teale, Oscar Schutte. How to Do Architectural Drawing - a Text Book & Practical Guide for Students in Architectural Draftsmanship. 2009. 240p. 28.45 (978-1-4446-5283-3(4)) Harrison House Pubs.

ter Braak, Lex & Jacobs, Edwin, texts. Robbie Cornelissen: the Capacious Memory. 2011. (ENG., Illus.). 128p. pap. 35.00 (978-90-5662-811-6(9)) NAi Uitgevers / Publishers Stichting NLD. Dist: D.A.P./Distributed Art Pubs.

Toledano, Roulhac. A Pattern Book of New Orleans Architecture, 1 vol. 2010. (ENG., Illus.). 256p. 35.00 (978-1-58980-694-8(8)) Pelican Publishing Co., Inc.

Treib, Marc. Thinking through Drawing in an Electronic Age. 2008. (ENG., Illus.). 192p. (C). 165.00 (978-0-415-77560-1(4)); pap. 53.95 (978-0-415-77561-8(2)) Routledge.

van Leeuwen, Jos P. & Timmermans, Harry J. P., eds. Recent Advances in Design & Decision Support Systems in Architecture & Urban Planning. 2010. (ENG.). xv, 358p. pap. 229.00 (978-90-481-6653-4(5), 9048166535) Springer.

Verlagshaus-Braun Editorial Staff, ed. Unusual Architectural Presentation Drawings. 2007. (Illus.). 336p. 59.65 (978-981-245-214-6(1)) Page One Publishing SGP. Dist: Gingko Pr., Inc.

Wang, Xiangyu & Tsai, Jerry Jen-Hung, eds. Collaborative Design in Virtual Environments. 2011. (Intelligent Systems, Control & Automation: Science & Engineering Ser.). (Illus.). x, 210p. 179.00 (978-94-007-0604-0(9), 9400706049) Springer.

Weber, Raphael & Raphael, Weber. A Bit-Serial Implementation of the Aes Encryption Algorithm: Implementation & Space Optimization of the Advanced Encryption Standard for a Bit-Serial Fully Pipelined Architecture. 2011. 120p. pap. (978-3-639-32713-7(6)) VDM Verlag Dr. Mueller e.K.

Weston, Richard. Key Buildings of the Twentieth Century: Plans, Sections & Elevations. 2nd ed. 2010. (Key Architecture Ser.). (ENG., Illus.). 352p. pap. 45.00 (978-0-393-73311-2(4), 73311) Norton, W. W. & Co., Inc.

Wilson, Richard Guy, et al. Thomas Jefferson's Academical Village: The Creation of an Architectural Masterpiece. 2nd rev. ed. 2009. (ENG., Illus.). 144p. 24.95 (978-0-8139-2830-2(3)) Univ. Pr. of Virginia.

Wilson, Travis Kelly. Drafting & Design: Basics for Interior Design. 2011. (Illus.). 224p. pap. (978-1-56367-837-0(3)) Fairchild Bks.

Wing, Eric. Autodesk Revit Architecture 2011: No Experience Required. 2010. (ENG., Illus.). 984p. pap. 39.99 *(978-0-470-61011-4(5)*, Sybex) Wiley, John & Sons, Inc.

—Autodesk Revit Architecture 2012: No Experience Required. 2011. (ENG., Illus.). 1032p. pap. 39.99 *(978-0-470-94506-3(0)*, Sybex) Wiley, John & Sons, Inc.

Wing, Eric & Wing. Revit Architecture 2010: No Experience Required. 2009. (ENG., Illus.). 984p. pap. 39.99 *(978-0-470-44722-2(2)*, Sybex) Wiley, John & Sons, Inc.

Wyatt, Sr.), William G(William GWyatt, Sr.). AutoCAD Architecture 2012 Course Notes for Wyatt's Accessing AUTOCAD Architecture 2012. 2011. (ENG.). 8p. 4.95 *(978-1-111-64833-6(6)*, AutoDesk Pr.) Delmar Cengage Learning.

Wyatt, William G. Accessing AutoCAD Architecture 2009. 2008. (ENG.). 1032p. pap. 140.95 *(978-1-4354-0262-1(6)*, AutoDesk Pr.) Delmar Cengage Learning.

—Accessing AutoCAD Architecture 2011. 2010. (ENG., Illus.). 928p. pap. 113.95 *(978-1-111-12685-8(2)*, AutoDesk Pr.) Delmar Cengage Learning.

—Accessing Autocad Architecture 2012. 2011. (CAD New Releases Ser.). (ENG., Illus.). 800p. pap. 113.95 *(978-1-111-64831-2(X)*, AutoDesk Pr.) Delmar Cengage Learning.

Yee, Rendow. Architectural Drawing: A Visual Compendium of Types & Methods. (ENG., Illus.). 3rd rev. ed. 2007. 688p. pap. 80.00 *(978-0-471-79366-3(3))* 4th ed. 2012. 592p. pap. 75.00 ***(978-1-118-01287-1(9))*** Wiley, John & Sons, Inc. (Wiley).

Younes, Samir & Mazzola, Ettore Maria, eds. Barletta: Sea, Centre & Periphery. 2010. (University of Notre Dame Graduate Program in Architecture, Rome Studies Program Publications). 96p. pap. 35.95 *(978-88-492-0708-8(5))* Gangemi ITA. Dist: International Publishers Marketing.

Zell, Mo. Architectural Drawing Course: Tools & Techniques for 2D & 3D Representation. 2008. (ENG., Illus.). 144p. pap. 23.99 *(978-0-7641-3814-0(6))* Barron's Educational Series, Inc.

ARCHITECTURAL ENGINEERING

see Building; Building, Iron and Steel; Strains and Stresses; Strength of Materials; Structural Analysis (Engineering); Structures, Theory Of

ARCHITECTURAL FIRMS

A/E Board of Directors Cookbook. 2007. per. 245.00 *(978-1-934150-28-3(2))* ZweigWhite.

Alsop and Stormer Architects Staff, contrib. by. Alsop & Stormer: Selected & Current Works. 2006. (Master Architect Ser.). (ENG., Illus.). 256p. 59.95 *(978-1-86470-001-5(7)*, Images Publishing Dist Ac) Antique Collectors' Club GBR. Dist: National Bk. Network.

Architects & Planners, Moore Ruble Yudell. The Future of Place. 2011. (ENG., Illus.). 392p. 25.00 ***(978-1-935935-39-1(9))*** Oro Editions.

Architects & Planners, Moore Ruble Yudell & Yudell, Buzz. The Future of Place. 2011. (ENG.). 392p. 65.00 ***(978-7-5381-6561-6(4))*** Oro Editions.

Beaver, Robyn, ed. KlingStubbins: Palimpsest. 2009. (Master Architect Ser.). (ENG., Illus.). 536p. 85.00 *(978-1-86470-295-8(8))* Images Publishing Group AUS. Dist: National Bk. Network.

—Tsoi/Kobus & Associates: Architecture, Interior Design, Planning. 2009. (ENG., Illus.). 228p. 59.95 *(978-1-86470-284-2(2)*, Images Publishing Dist Ac) Antique Collectors' Club GBR. Dist: National Bk. Network.

Bernheimer, Andrew & Della Valle, Jared. Think/Make: Della Valle Bernheimer. 2009. (ENG., Illus.). 192p. pap. 40.00 *(978-1-56898-781-1(1))* Princeton Architectural Pr.

Betsky, Aaron. UnStudio: The Floating Space. 2007. (ENG., Illus.). 96p. pap. 9.99 *(978-3-8228-4538-7(8))* TASCHEN DEU. Dist: Ingram Pub. Services.

Bimberg, Howard G. Project Management for Designers & Facilities Managers. 3rd ed. 2008. (Illus.). 272p. *(978-1-60427-011-2(X))* Ross, J. Publishing, Inc.

Bullivant, Lucy. New Arcadians: Emerging UK Architects. 2012. (ENG., Illus.). 256p. 49.95 ***(978-1-85894-548-4(8))*** Merrell Pubs. Ltd. GBR. Dist: Perseus Distribution.

Business Comes to the Expert: A Proactive Marketing Plan for Professional Practice Firms. 2008. 198p. pap. 39.00 *(978-0-9785552-5-2(2)*, Ostberg) Greenway Communications.

Canty, Donald. Fisher Friedman: Community Spaces. 2007. (Architectural Ser.). (ENG., Illus.). 144p. pap. 40.00 *(978-88-7838-070-7(9)*, Art Stock Bks. Ltd/Csi) Continental Sales, Inc.

Carscadden, Bruce. Carscadden Thrift: Selected Works. McDonald, Ian Ross, ed. 2012. (ENG., Illus.). 112p. 19.95 ***(978-1-897476-40-6(X))*** Simply Read Bks. CAN. Dist: Perseus-PGW.

CBT Vision Staff. Boston & Beyond: CBT Architects. 2012. (ENG., Illus.). 224p. 59.95 *(978-1-86470-404-4(7))* Images Publishing Group AUS. Dist: National Bk. Network.

CCDI Design Group. CCDI Design Group: Urban Design, Architecture, Consulting, Engineering. 2012. (ENG., Illus.). 256p. 85.00 ***(978-1-86470-461-7(6))*** Images Publishing Group AUS. Dist: National Bk. Network.

Chan, Soo. SCDA Architects. 2012. (Master Architects Ser.). (ENG., Illus.). 256p. 80.00 *(978-1-86470-414-3(4))* Images Publishing Group AUS. Dist: National Bk. Network.

Conrad-Bercah & Office, W. West Workroom: Towards a New Sobriety in Architecture Theory + Practice. 2008. (ENG., Illus.). 224p. per. 45.00 *(978-88-8158-656-1(8))* Charta ITA. Dist: D.A.P./Distributed Art Pubs.

Corbellini, Giovanni. Bioreboot: The Architecture of R & Sie(N) 2010. (ENG.). 228p. pap. 40.00 *(978-1-56898-869-6(9))* Princeton Architectural Pr.

Davis, Susan E. Design Firm Performance Benchmarks 2007. 2006. 52p. pap. 329.00 *(978-1-58673-205-9(6))* Institute of Management & Administration, IOMA.

De Smedt, Julien, ed. Agenda: JDS Architects: Can We Sustain our Ability to Crisis? 2011. 544p. pap. *(978-84-92861-62-0(2))* Actar Birkhauser Distribution.

Denison, Edward. Mcmorran & Whitby. 2009. (Twentieth-century Architects Ser.). (ENG., Illus.). 154p. (C). pap. 40.00 *(978-1-85946-320-8(7))* English Heritage GBR. Dist: Brown, David Bk. Co., The.

Design Workshop, creator. Toward Legacy. 2007. (ENG., Illus.). 288p. 45.00 *(978-0-9749632-6-6(7))* Spacemaker Pr.

DesignIntelligence: Technology Survey 2008. 2008. (Illus.). 71p. pap. 69.95 *(978-0-9785552-7-6(9)*, Ostberg) Greenway Communications.

Dorenbach Architekten Staff, contrib. by. Arbeiten 1971-2009. 2010. (GER., Illus.). 351p. *(978-3-7245-1664-4(9))* Reinhardt, Friedrich AG.

Dougherty, Brian & Besty. Dougherty + Dougherty Architects LLP: Intersections: Architecture & Social Responsibility. Images Publishing Group Editors, ed. 2008. (ENG., Illus.). 124p. 49.95 *(978-1-86470-303-0(2))* Images Publishing Group AUS. Dist: National Bk. Network.

Dowling, Elizabeth Meredith. Harrison Design Associates: A Decade of Work. 2007. (ENG., Illus.). 256p. 59.95 *(978-1-86470-277-4(X)*, Images Publishing Dist Ac) Antique Collectors' Club GBR. Dist: National Bk. Network.

Dullaghan, Anne. Designed in Minnesota: An Exquisite Collection of Minnesota's Finest Designers. 2007. (Illus.). 156p. 39.95 *(978-0-9774451-6-5(X))* DSA Publishing & Design, Inc.

—Designed in Northern California - an Exquisite Collection of Northern California's Finest Designers. 2008. (Illus.). 102p. 39.95 *(978-0-9774451-7-2(8))* DSA Publishing & Design, Inc.

Fitzgerald, D. Window on the Park: New York's Most Prestigious Properties on Central Park. 2009. (ENG., Illus.). 228p. 45.00 *(978-1-86470-276-7(1))* Images Publishing Group AUS. Dist: National Bk. Network.

Gardner, Mark, et al. Habits, Patterns, Algorithms, 1998-2008. Ojeda, Oscar, ed. 2009. (ENG., Illus.). 424p. 75.00 *(978-0-9795395-2-7(8))* Oro Editions.

Gholam, Nabil. Nabil Gholam Architects. 2011. (Illus.). 420p. 42.00 ***(978-84-9936-860-3(3))*** Loft Pubns. ESP. Dist: Prestel Publishing.

Gigon, Annette & Guyer, Mike. Gigon/Guyer Architects: Works & Projects 2001-2011, 1 vol. 2012. (ENG., Illus.). 576p. 85.00 ***(978-3-03778-276-7(5))*** Lars Muller Pubs. CHE. Dist: Prestel Publishing.

Gisolfi, Peter & McGrath, Norman. Finding the Place of Architecture in the Landscape. 2008. (Master Architect (Unnumbered) Ser.). (ENG., Illus.). 296p. 59.95 *(978-1-86470-165-4(X)*, Images Publishing Dist Ac) Antique Collectors' Club GBR. Dist: National Bk. Network.

Goulet, Patrice, et al. Canal, Patrick Rubin, Architecte: Itinéraires du Passeur: Entretien Avec Patrice Goulet. 2008. (FRE & ENG., Illus.). 159p. *(978-2-87143-212-8(0))* Editions du Layeur.

Gunsser, Christoph, et al. Gebaut: Nebel Pössl Architekten. 2007. (Illus.). 122p. *(978-3-7828-1615-1(3))* Kramer, Karl GmbH.

Gunter, Angelika, ed. Projekte Aus/Projects from Berlin. 2008. (ENG., Illus.). 48p. 29.95 *(978-3-939633-15-0(1))* Jovis Verlag GmbH DEU. Dist: D.A.P./Distributed Art Pubs.

Hariri. Hariri & Hariri Architecture: Buildings & Projects. 2010. (ENG., Illus.). 256p. 59.95 *(978-1-86470-340-5(7)*, Images Publishing Dist Ac) Antique Collectors' Club GBR. Dist: National Bk. Network.

Hei, Lam Wo. Wong & Ouyang: Blueprints for Hong Kong the Master Architect Series. Beaver, Robyn, ed. 2008. (ENG., Illus.). 184p. 59.95 *(978-1-86470-304-7(0)*, Images Publishing Dist Ac) Antique Collectors' Club GBR. Dist: National Bk. Network.

Ho M Staff & Partners For Health Staff. Hpa: the Story of Ho & Partners Architects: Architecture - Witnessing the Progress of Human Civilisation. 2012. (ENG & CHI., Illus.). 240p. 59.95 *(978-1-86470-426-6(8))* Images Publishing Group AUS. Dist: National Bk. Network.

HOK. Hok: A Global Design Portfolio. 2009. (ENG., Illus.). 416p. 85.00 *(978-1-86470-314-6(8))* Images Publishing Group AUS. Dist: National Bk. Network.

—Hok Asia. 2009. (ENG., Illus.). 264p. 80.00 *(978-1-86470-318-4(0))* Images Publishing Group AUS. Dist: National Bk. Network.

Hollenstein, Roman. Modern Alternatives: Höller & Klotzner Concrete Architecture. 2008. (ENG, ITA & GER., Illus.). 136p. pap. 39.95 *(978-3-211-79193-6(0)*, 3211791930) Springer.

Hossbach, Benjamin & Lehmhaus, Christian. Phase Eins: The Architecture of Competition 2006-2008, 1 vol. 2009. (ENG., Illus.). 560p. 99.95 *(978-3-938666-88-3(9))* DOM Pubs. DEU. Dist: Innovative Logistics.

Howells, Trevor. Allen Jack & Cottier: Architecture in the Australian Context. 2006. (ENG., Illus.). 204p. 55.00 *(978-1-875359-96-7(6))* Watermark Pr., The AUS. Dist: National Bk. Network.

Images Australia Pty Ltd Staff. Perkins & Will: Selected & Curent Works. 2006. (Master Architect Ser.). (ENG., Illus.). 256p. 59.95 *(978-1-86470-064-0(5)*, Images Publishing Dist Ac) Antique Collectors' Club GBR. Dist: National Bk. Network.

Images Publishing, creator. Cooper, Robertson & Partners: Cities to Gardens. 2007. (Master Architect (Unnumbered) Ser.). (ENG., Illus.). 276p. 59.95 *(978-1-86470-167-8(6)*, Images Publishing Dist Ac) Antique Collectors' Club GBR. Dist: National Bk. Network.

—LS3P Associates Ltd: Selected & Current Works. 2006. (Master Architect Series V). (ENG., Illus.). 256p. 59.95 *(978-1-876907-77-8(0)*, Images Publishing Dist Ac) Antique Collectors' Club GBR. Dist: National Bk. Network.

Images Publishing Group. A. 2R. C Architects. 2012. (ENG.). 256p. 59.95 *(978-1-86470-157-9(9))* Images Publishing Group AUS. Dist: National Bk. Network.

—HKS Architects. 2010. (ENG., Illus.). 368p. 80.00 *(978-1-86470-336-8(9))* Images Publishing Group AUS. Dist: National Bk. Network.

Images Publishing Staff, PUBLISHING. KPF Selected Works: America Europe Asia, 3 vols. 2006. (Millennium Ser.). (ENG., Illus.). 85.00 *(978-1-86470-050-3(5))* Images Publishing Group AUS. Dist: National Bk. Network.

Images Staff. Montois Partners: Selected & Current Works. 2006. (Master Architect Series VI). (ENG., Illus.). 256p. 59.95 *(978-1-86470-069-5(6)*, Images Publishing Dist Ac) Antique Collectors' Club GBR. Dist: National Bk. Network.

Images Staff & Grover, William H. The Enthusiams of Centerbrook: Selected & Current Works. 2006. (Master Architect Ser.). (ENG., Illus.). 256p. 59.95 *(978-1-86470-047-3(5)*, Images Publishing Dist Ac) Antique Collectors' Club GBR. Dist: National Bk. Network.

Jaeger, Falk. Lederer + Ragnarsdottir + Oei: Portfolio. 2008. (GER & ENG., Illus.). 144p. pap. 39.95 *(978-3-939633-56-3(9))* Jovis Verlag GmbH DEU. Dist: D.A.P./Distributed Art Pubs.

Jaeger, Falk, et al. Auer + Weber + Associated. 2011. (ENG., Illus.). 144p. pap. 39.95 *(978-3-86859-037-1(4))* Jovis Verlag GmbH DEU. Dist: D.A.P./Distributed Art Pubs.

Jenkins, David, ed. Foster + Partners: Catalogue. 2012. (Illus.). 400p. 60.00 ***(978-3-7913-4685-4(7))*** Prestel Publishing.

J.J. Pan & Partners. J. J Pan & Partners: Sustainability, Professionalism, Discourse. 2012. (ENG., Illus.). 256p. 59.95 *(978-1-86470-430-3(6))* Images Publishing Group AUS. Dist: National Bk. Network.

Jovis, creator. KSV: Kruger Schuberth Vandreike: Buildings & Projects 1990-2008. 2009. (ENG & GER., Illus.). 144p. 60.00 *(978-3-939633-46-4(1))* Jovis Verlag GmbH DEU. Dist: D.A.P./Distributed Art Pubs.

Kamvasinou, Krystallia & Canz, Simon. Artifice: Dermot Foley Landscape Architects. 2012. (ENG., Illus.). 160p. 45.00 *(978-1-907317-28-6(7))* Black Dog Publishing Ltd. GBR. Dist: Perseus Distribution.

Kara, Hanif, ed. Design Engineering. 2008. *(978-84-96540-66-8(9))* Actar Birkhauser Distribution.

Kowalski, Karla. Szyszkowitz-Kowalski: Architekturen von 1994-2010. 2011. (ENG., Illus.). 312p. 65.00 *(978-3-86859-033-3(1))* Jovis Verlag GmbH DEU. Dist: D.A.P./Distributed Art Pubs.

Kretschmar-Joehnk, Corinna. Creating Hospitality Design. 2009. (ENG & GER., Illus.). 224p. 49.95 *(978-3-03768-039-1(3)*, Braun Publish,Csi) Continental Sales, Inc.

Lars Muller, ed. Fuhrimann Hachler. 2010. (Illus.). 240p. *(978-3-03778-240-8(4))* Lars Muller Pubs.

Levin, Brenda. Levin & Associates Architects: Selected & Current Works. 2006. (ENG., Illus.). 256p. 59.95 *(978-1-86470-089-3(0))* Images Publishing Group AUS. Dist: National Bk. Network.

Louafi, Kamel. Landschaftsinterventionen / Landscape Interventions: Stadtparadiese / City Paradises. 2011. (ENG, ARA, FRE & GER., Illus.). 496p. 65.00 ***(978-3-86859-107-1(9))*** Jovis Verlag GmbH DEU. Dist: D.A.P./Distributed Art Pubs.

Marmol, Leo & Radziner, Ron. Marmol Radziner + Associates: Between Architecture & Construction. 2008. (ENG., Illus.). 176p. pap. 40.00 *(978-1-56898-744-6(7))* Princeton Architectural Pr.

Marte, Stefan & Marte, Bernhard, eds. Marte. Marte: Architecture, 1996-2008. 2008. (ENG., Illus.). 415p. 79.95 *(978-3-211-79199-8(X)*, 321179199X) Springer.

Martinussen, Kent. 3xn: Mind your Behaviour. 2010. (Illus.). 276p. pap. *(978-87-993680-0-6(5))* Actar Birkhauser Distribution.

Mayer, Jürgen, et al. Think & Grow Rich. 2011. (DUT & ENG., Illus.). 240p. *(978-90-5856-355-2(3)*, Stichting Kunstboak (Acc)) Antique Collectors' Club.

McGillick, Paul. Concrete Metal Glass: Hijas Kasturi Associates: Selected Works 1977-2007. 2007. (ENG., Illus.). 188p. 40.00 *(978-981-4155-28-1(4)*, Didier Millet,Csi) Continental Sales, Inc.

McGlade, Dennis C., et al. Olin: Placemaking. 2008. (ENG., Illus.). 320p. 65.00 *(978-1-58093-210-3(X))* Monacelli Pr., Inc.

Meijer, Haiko, et al, texts. Wood Works Onix. 2010. (ENG., Illus.). 320p. 60.00 *(978-90-5662-679-2(5))* NAi Uitgevers / Publishers Stichting NLD. Dist: D.A.P./Distributed Art Pubs.

Minshaw, John & Fox, Celina. John Minshaw Designs. 2009. (ENG., Illus.). 208p. 75.00 *(978-0-7112-2977-8(5))* Lincoln, Frances Ltd. GBR. Dist: Perseus-PGW.

MS Design (Firm) Staff, contrib. by. Luxury Architecture. 2011. (Illus.). 420p. 39.95 ***(978-84-9936-863-4(8))*** Loft Pubns. ESP. Dist: Prestel Publishing.

Muir, Prescott & Pallasmaa, Juhani. It by Bit: Evoking Simplicity from Complexity. 2012. (ENG., Illus.). 204p. 40.00 *(978-1-935935-05-6(4))* Oro Editions.

Norwich, William. Yabu Pushelberg. Horwitz, Carolyn & Iannacci, Anthony, eds. 2009. (ENG., Illus.). 240p. 70.00 *(978-0-9823190-0-0(2))* Architecture Interiors Pr., Inc.

Oosterhuis, Kas. ONLogic: Speed & Vision. 2009. (Master Architect Ser.). (ENG., Illus.). 224p. 59.95 *(978-1-86470-286-6(9)*, Images Publishing Dist Ac) Antique Collectors' Club GBR. Dist: National Bk. Network.

Pauwels, Wim. Ensemble & Associés. 2010. (ENG., Illus.). 192p. *(978-90-8944-022-8(4)*, Beta-Plus (Acc)) Antique Collectors' Club.

Powers, Alan. Aldington, Craig & Collinge. 2009. (Twentieth-century Architects Ser.). (ENG., Illus.). 144p. (C). pap. 40.00 *(978-1-85946-302-4(9))* English Heritage GBR. Dist: Brown, David Bk. Co., The.

Riera Ojeda, Oscar. Sasaki: Intersection & Convergence. Riera Ojeda, Oscar, ed. 2008. (ENG., Illus.). 336p. 65.00 *(978-0-9793801-5-0(4))* Oro Editions.

Rogers, Rob, et al. Rogers Marvel Architects. 2011. (ENG., Illus.). 192p. pap. 40.00 *(978-1-56898-999-0(7))* Princeton Architectural Pr.

Rothman, Laura. 2007 Financial Performance Survey: Of Architecture, Engineering, Planning & Environmental Consulting Firms. 2007. per. 395.00 *(978-1-934150-23-8(1))* ZweigWhite.

Rothman, Laura, et al, eds. 2006 Incentive Compensation Survey: Of Architecture, Engineering, Planning & Environmental Consulting Firms. 2006. per. 395.00 *(978-1-934150-02-3(9))* ZweigWhite.

Rothman, Laura B., et al, eds. A/E Policy Manual. 2006. 248p. pap. 245.00 *(978-1-932372-96-0(2))* ZweigWhite.

—2006 Financial Performance Survey of Architecture, Engineering, Planning & Environmental Consulting Firms. 2006. 272p. pap. 395.00 *(978-1-932372-95-3(4))* ZweigWhite.

—2006 Marketing Survey: Of Architecture, Engineering, Planning & Environmental Consulting Firms. 13th ed. 2006. 326p. pap. 395.00 *(978-1-932372-97-7(0))* ZweigWhite.

—2006 Multi-Office Firm Survey: Of Architecture, Engineering, Planning & Environmental Consulting Firms. 14th ed. 2006. Orig. Title: Satellite Office Survey. 212p. pap. 395.00 *(978-1-932372-99-1(7))* ZweigWhite.

—2006 Project Management Survey: Of Architecture, Engineering, Planning & Environmental Consulting Firms. 11th ed. 2006. 228p. pap. 395.00 *(978-1-932372-98-4(9))* ZweigWhite.

Russ-Bovelino, Andreas, ed. Caramel. 2011. (ENG & GER., Illus.). 400p. 69.95 *(978-3-7091-0511-5(0)*, 3709105110) Springer Wien AUT. Dist: Actar Birkhauser Distribution.

Ryan, Raymund & Tejchman, Filip, contrib. by. La Dallman: Fabricated Landscapes. 2009. pap. 16.95 *(978-0-615-27456-0(0))* Univ. of Wisconsin-Milwaukee Schl. of Architecture & Urban Planning.

Schatzke, Andreas. Dietrich & Dietrich Max-Plank-Institutfur Wissenschaftsgeschichte, Berlin: Opus 74. 2010. (GER & ENG., Illus.). 60p. 49.00 *(978-3-932565-74-8(6))* Edition Axel Menges GmbH DEU. Dist: National Bk. Network.

Schlorhaufer, Bettina, ed. Heinz-Mathoi-Streli Architekten: Buildings & Projects. 2008. (GER & ENG., Illus.). 304p. 59.95 *(978-3-211-75791-8(0)*, 3211757910) Springer.

Schmal, Peter, ed. HPP Architects. 2009. (ENG., Illus.). 240p. 75.00 *(978-3-7757-2307-7(2))* Hatje Cantz Verlag GmbH & Co KG DEU. Dist: D.A.P./Distributed Art Pubs.

Schmal, Peter Cachola. WOHA: Architektur atmet / Breathing Architecture. Busenkell, Micaela, ed. 2012. (GER & ENG., Illus.). 192p. pap. 60.00 ***(978-3-7913-5186-5(9))*** Prestel Publishing.

Schmertz, Mildred. Mitchell: Giurgola Architects. 2008. (ENG., Illus.). 264p. 70.00 *(978-1-86470-274-3(5))* Images Publishing Group AUS. Dist: National Bk. Network.

Siegel, Gwathmey & Associates. Gwathmey Siegel & Associates Architects: Selected Projects. 2010. (ENG., Illus.). 232p. 59.95 *(978-1-86470-334-4(2))* Images Publishing Group AUS. Dist: National Bk. Network.

Smeesters, Hilde. Luxury Living by B+ Villas. 2011. (ENG, DUT & FRE., Illus.). 192p. 130.00 ***(978-2-87550-004-5(X))*** Beta-Plus Pubs. BEL. Dist: Antique Collectors' Club.

Sokol, David. Seventy Nordic Architects, 1 vol. 2009. (ENG., Illus.). 448p. 58.00 *(978-3-938666-83-8(8))* DOM Pubs. DEU. Dist: Innovative Logistics.

Speaks, Michael & El-Khoury, Rodolphe, contrib. by. Architecture & Sensuality: Andrew Bromberg of Aedas, Recent Works. 2007. (ENG., Illus.). 256p. 40.00 *(978-0-9774672-8-0(7))* Oro Editions.

Sweet, Fay. The Bigger Picture. 2011. (ENG., Illus.). 368p. 60.00 *(978-1-906155-79-7(8))* Black Dog Publishing Ltd. GBR. Dist: Perseus Distribution.

The A49 Group. A49: An Asian Spirit in Contemporary Design. 2009. (ENG., Illus.). 420p. 85.00 *(978-1-86470-322-1(9))* Images Publishing Group AUS. Dist: National Bk. Network.

Urbach, Henry. J. Mayer H. Steingraber, Cristina Ines, ed. 2009. (ENG., Illus.). 240p. 75.00 *(978-3-7757-2223-0(8))* Hatje Cantz Verlag GmbH & Co KG DEU. Dist: D.A.P./Distributed Art Pubs.

van Luxemburg, Renz, et al. Inside Outside Petra Blaisse: Interiors & Landscapes. Ota, Kayoko, ed. 2006. (Illus.). 400p. *(978-3-7643-7630-7(9)*, 3764376309) Birkhauser Boston.

Van Severen, David. Office: Kersten Geers David Van Severen. 2010. (ENG., Illus.). 80p. pap. 45.00 *(978-3-7757-2572-9(5))* Hatje Cantz Verlag GmbH & Co KG DEU. Dist: D.A.P./Distributed Art Pubs.

Van Valkenburgh, Michael, et al. Grounded: The Work of Phillips Farevaag Smallenberg. 2011. (ENG., Illus.). 288p. 69.95 *(978-1-897476-20-8(5))* Simply Read Bks. CAN. Dist: Perseus-PGW.

Vinoly, Rafael & Jodidio, Philip. Rafael Vinoly Architects. 2010. (Illus.). 550p. 99.00 *(978-3-7913-5074-5(9))* Prestel Publishing.

Vranckx, Bridget. PTang Studio: A New Approach to Chinese Architecture. 2012. (ENG., Illus.). 256p. 39.99 ***(978-84-9936-862-7(X))*** Loft Pubns. ESP. Dist: Prestel Publishing.

Walden, Gert, ed. Baumschlager - Eberle - Annäherungen Approaches. 2009. (GER & ENG., Illus.). 148p. *(978-3-211-79158-5(2)*, 3211791582) Actar Birkhauser Distribution.

 The check digit for ISBN-10 appears in parentheses after the full ISBN-13

Williams, Keith. Keith Williams: Projects 1. 2010. (Master Architects Ser.). (ENG., Illus.). 224p. 59.95 *(978-1-86470-235-4(4)*, Images Publishing Dist Ac) Antique Collectors' Club GBR. Dist: National Bk. Network.

Woofer, Heather. Axi:Ome: Spatial Practice. 2009. (ENG., Illus.). 144p. pap. 29.95 *(978-0-9814628-5-1(5))* Oro Editions.

Zepter, Tobias, text. MODERSOHN & FREIESLEBEN Architekten: Das Leben der Dinge. The Life of Things. 2010. (ENG., Illus.). 176p. 55.00 *(978-3-7757-2487-6(7))* Hatje Cantz Verlag GmbH & Co KG DEU. Dist: D.A.P./Distributed Art Pubs.

Zinsmeiste, Annett. Update! 90 Jahre Bauhaus - und nun? 2011. (ENG & GER., Illus.). 176p. pap. 39.95 ***(978-3-86859-102-6(8))*** Jovis Verlag GmbH DEU. Dist: D.A.P./Distributed Art Pubs.

Zschokke, Walter, ed. Dietrich / Untertrifaller: Bauten und Projekte seit 2000 / Buildings & Projects since 2000. 2008. (GER & ENG., Illus.). 308p. pap. *(978-3-211-71529-1(0)*, 3211715290) Actar Birkhauser Distribution.

2006-2007 Management Compensation Survey: Of Architecture, Engineering, Planning & Environmental Consulting Firms. 9th ed. 2006. per. 395.00 *(978-1-934150-10-8(X))* ZweigWhite.

2006-2007 Operating Expenses Survey: Of Architecture, Engineering, Planning & Environmental Consulting Firms. 2006. per. 395.00 *(978-1-934150-11-5(8))* ZweigWhite.

2006-2007 Small Firm Survey: Of Architecture, Engineering, Planning & Environmental Consulting Firms. 3rd ed. 2006. per. 295.00 *(978-1-934150-13-9(4))* ZweigWhite.

2006-2007 Successful Firm Survey: Of Architecture, Engineering, Planning & Environmental Consulting Firms. 8th ed. 2006. per. 395.00 *(978-1-934150-14-6(2))* ZweigWhite.

2007 AEC Industry Outlook: Strategy & Insight for Design & Construction Firms. 5th ed. 2006. per. 295.00 *(978-1-934150-12-2(6))* ZweigWhite.

2007 Fee & Billing Survey: Of Architecture, Engineering, Planning & Environmental Consulting Firms. 2007. per. 395.00 *(978-1-934150-21-4(5))* ZweigWhite.

2007 Information Technology Survey: Of Architecture, Engineering, Planning & Environmental Consulting Firms. 2007. per. 395.00 *(978-1-934150-20-7(7))* ZweigWhite.

ARCHITECTURAL INSCRIPTIONS

Butz. The Art of the Hekatompedon Inscription & the Birth of the Stoikhedon Style. 2010. (Monumenta Graeca et Romana Ser.). (Illus.). 210p. *(978-90-04-18308-7(6))* BRILL.

Cardozo Kindersley, Lida. Cutting through the Colleges. 2010. (Illus.). 124p. 20.00 *(978-1-107-00366-8(0))* Cambridge Univ. Pr.

Cole, John Young & Highsmith, Carol M. On These Walls: Inscriptions & Quotations in the Buildings of the Library of Congress. 2008. *(978-0-8444-1200-9(7))* Library of Congress.

Highway Bridge Inspections: Hearing Before the Subcommittee on Highways & Transit of the Committee on Transportation & Infrastructure, House of Representatives, One Hundred Tenth Congress, First Session, October 23, 2007. 2007. (Illus.). xiv, 131p. *(978-0-16-083395-3(7)*, 552-070-39208-4) United States Government Printing Office.

ARCHITECTURAL INTERIORS

see Interior Architecture

ARCHITECTURAL IRONWORK

see also Building Fittings

Baldwin, William P., ed. Ornamental Ironwork of Charleston. 2007. (Illus.). 191p. pap., per. 14.99 *(978-1-59629-367-0(5))* History Pr., The.

Ferrari, Giulio. Italian Ironwork: Medieval, Renaissance, Baroque, Neo Classical. 2010. (Illus.). 112p. 29.99 *(978-0-7643-3560-0(X))* Schiffer Publishing, Ltd.

Robertson, E. Graeme & Robertson, Joan. Cast Iron Decoration: A World Survey. 2007. (ENG., Illus.). 336p. 65.00 *(978-0-500-23254-5(7))* Thames & Hudson.

Roeper, Adalbert. Treasury of Ornamental Ironwork: 16th to 18th Centuries. 2012. (Dover Jewelry & Metalwork Ser.). (GER & ENG., Illus.). 64p. pap. 8.95 *(978-0-486-46016-1(9))* Dover Pubns., Inc.

Sledge, John S. An Ornament to the City: Old Mobile Ironwork. 2006. (ENG., Illus.). 128p. 36.95 *(978-0-8203-2700-6(X))* Univ. of Georgia Pr.

Subes, Raymond. French Art Deco Ironwork Designs. 2007. (Dover Jewelry & Metalwork Ser.). (ENG., Illus.). 48p. per. 9.95 *(978-0-486-45459-7(2))* Dover Pubns., Inc.

ARCHITECTURAL LAW AND LEGISLATION

see Architects—Legal Status, Laws, etc.; Building Laws; Engineering Law

ARCHITECTURAL LIBRARIES

Hamlin, Talbot. Some European Architectural Libraries: Their Methods, Equipment & Administration. reprint ed. 20.00 *(978-0-404-03092-6(0))* AMS Pr., Inc.

ARCHITECTURAL LIGHTING

see Lighting, Architectural and Decorative

ARCHITECTURAL METAL-WORK

see also Art Metal-Work; Building Fittings

Boston Architectural Club. The Metalworker's Art: A Pictorial Celebration. 2011. (Dover Jewelry & Metalwork Ser.). (ENG.). 112p. pap. 14.95 *(978-0-486-47313-0(9))* Dover Pubns., Inc.

Decker, Jules. Treasury of Nineteenth-Century Ornamental Metalwork. 2006. (Dover Jewelry & Metalwork Ser.). (ENG., Illus.). 144p. per. 15.95 *(978-0-486-45222-7(0))* Dover Pubns., Inc.

Vedrenne, Penny. Antique Door Hardware - A Book of Stencils. 2007. 48p. pap. 19.95 *(978-1-4303-2304-4(3))* Lulu Enterprises Inc.

ARCHITECTURAL MODELS

see also Structural Frames—Models

Abhelakh, Anneke, et al, eds. Architecture Bulletin No. 03: Essays on the Designed Environment, 1 vol. 2008. (ENG., Illus.). 80p. per. 22.50 *(978-90-5662-591-7(8))* NAi Uitgevers / Publishers Stichting NLD. Dist: D.A.P./Distributed Art Pubs.

Abruzzo, Emily, et al, eds. Models. 2008. (ENG., Illus.). 244p. pap. 24.95 *(978-1-56898-734-7(X))* Princeton Architectural Pr.

Art Institute of Chicago Staff. Miniature Rooms: The Thorne Rooms at the Art Institute of Chicago. 2nd ed. 2009. (ENG., Illus.). 184p. 45.00 *(978-0-300-14159-7(9))* Art Institute of Chicago.

Black, Kell, creator. Paper New York: Build Your Own Big Apple. 2010. (ENG., Illus.). 48p. pap. 19.95 *(978-0-7893-2079-7(7))* Universe Publishing.

Bruckner, Dietmar. Probabilistic Models in Building Automation. 2008. 144p. per. *(978-3-8364-5720-0(2))* VDM Verlag Dr. Mueller e.K.

de Jongh, Robin. SketchUp 7. 1 for Architectural Visualization: Create stunning photo-realistic & artistic visuals for your SketchUp models: Beginner's Guide. 2010. (Illus.). 403p. pap. *(978-1-84719-946-1(1))* Packt Publishing, Ltd.

Debschitz, Thilo Von. Frank Kunert: Verkehrte Welt - Topsy-Turvy World. 2008. (GER & ENG., Illus.). 72p. 25.00 *(978-3-7757-2132-5(0))* Hatje Cantz Verlag GmbH & Co KG DEU. Dist: D.A.P./Distributed Art Pubs.

Dunn, Nick. The Ecology of the Architectural Model. 2007. (Illus.). 300p. pap. 109.95 *(978-3-03911-004-9(7))* Lang, Peter Publishing, Inc.

Dunn, Nick & Dunn, Richard. Architectural Modelmaking. 2010. (ENG., Illus.). 192p. pap. 35.00 *(978-1-85669-670-8(7))* King, Laurence Publishing GBR. Dist: Hachette Bk. Group.

Falquet, Gilles, et al. Ontologies in Urban Development Projects. 2011. (Advanced Information & Knowledge Processing Ser.). (ENG., Illus.). viii, 241p. 99.00 *(978-0-85729-723-5(6)*, 0857297236) Springer.

Flores, Ricardo, ed. Through the Canvas. 2008. 128p. (C). pap. *(978-84-612-4010-4(3))* Actar Birkhauser Distribution.

Freitag, Andreas. A Controlling Model for the Enterprise Architecture & Soa. 2008. 112p. pap. *(978-3-8364-8519-7(2))* VDM Verlag Dr. Mueller e.K.

Hatakeyama, Naoya. Scales. 2007. (Illus.). 61p. *(978-1-59005-216-7(1))* Nazraeli Pr.

Hertzberger, Herman. The Berlage Institute: Platform for Architecture Culture, Practice & Education, 1990-2010. 2011. (ENG., Illus.). 240p. pap. 45.00 *(978-90-5662-765-2(1))* NAi Uitgevers / Publishers Stichting NLD. Dist: D.A.P./Distributed Art Pubs.

Jetsonen, Jari, ed. Little Big Houses: Working with Architectural Models. 2008. (Illus.). 176p. pap. 39.00 *(978-951-682-645-8(8))* Rakennustieto oy FIN. Dist: Independent Pubs. Group.

Jodidio, Philip. Renzo Piano: Building Workshop 1966 to today. 25th ed. 2008. (FRE, GER & ENG., Illus.). 528p. 39.99 *(978-3-8365-0322-8(0))* TASCHEN DEU. Dist: Ingram Pub. Services.

Jones, Peter & Jones, Kes. Making Model Buildings for Garden Railways. 2011. (ENG., Illus.). 192p. 39.95 ***(978-1-84797-272-9(1)***, 1847972721) Crowood Pr., Ltd. GBR. Dist: MBI Distribution Services/Quayside Distribution.

Khosla, Niti. Framework to Assist Owners to Use Sustainable Site Design Practices. 2008. 388p. pap. *(978-3-8364-8355-1(6))* VDM Verlag Dr. Mueller e.K.

Klanten, R. & Feireiss, L., eds. Beyond Architecture: Imaginitaive Buildings & Fictional Cities. 2009. (Illus.). 208p. *(978-3-89955-235-5(0))* Die Gestalten Verlag.

Knoll, Wolfgang & Hechinger, Martin. Architectural Models: Construction Techniques. Rogier, Francesca, tr. from GER. 2nd ed. 2007. (Illus.). 142p. *(978-1-932159-96-7(7))* Ross, J. Publishing, Inc.

Miro, Eva Pascual I., et al. Advanced Architectural Modelmaking. 2010. (ENG., Illus.). 160p. pap. 40.00 *(978-0-393-73338-9(6)*, 73338) Norton, W. W. & Co., Inc.

Onstott, Scott. Enhancing Architectural Drawings & Models with Photoshop. 2nd ed. 2010. (ENG., Illus.). 376p. pap. 49.99 *(978-0-470-91656-8(7)*, Sybex) Wiley, John & Sons, Inc.

Oswald, Ansgar. Architectural Models. Keil, Uta, ed. 2008. (Illus.). 247p. *(978-981-245-482-9(9))* Page One Publishing.

Saarinen, Eero. Eero Saarinen: Shaping the Future. Pelkonen, Eeva-Liisa & Albrecht, Donald, eds. 2006. (ENG., Illus.). 408p. 65.00 *(978-0-300-11282-5(3))* Yale Univ. Pr.

Weber, Anton & Dustdar, Schahram. Haptic Systems Architecture Modeling. 2011. (ENG., Illus.). ix, 124p. 99.00 *(978-3-7091-0754-6(7)*, 3709107547) Springer.

Yee, Patrick. Origami Architecture: Papercraft Models of the World's Most Famous Buildings. 2011. (ENG., Illus.). 144p. 24.95 *(978-4-8053-1154-7(1))* Tuttle Publishing.

ARCHITECTURAL ORDERS

see Architecture—Orders

ARCHITECTURAL PERIODICALS

see Architecture—Periodicals

ARCHITECTURAL PERSPECTIVE

see Perspective

ARCHITECTURAL PHOTOGRAPHY

Here are entered works on the photography of buildings. Works on photography as used in architectural drawings are entered under the heading Photographic Reproduction of Plans, Drawings, etc.

see also Photography—Interiors

Aerni, Georg. Sites & Signs: Fotografien von Georg Aerni. Olonetzky, Nadine, ed. 2011. (ENG & GER., Illus.). 311p. 130.00 *(978-3-85881-320-6(6))* Scheidegger und Spiess AG, Verlag CHE. Dist: Chicago Distribution Ctr.

Albrecht, Donald. The Mythic City: Photographs of New York by Samuel H. Gottscho, 1925-1940. 2011. (ENG., Illus.). 224p. pap. 29.95 *(978-1-61689-015-5(0))* Princeton Architectural Pr.

Alexander, Christopher James. Julius Shulman's Los Angeles. 2011. (ENG., Illus.). 72p. pap. 9.95 ***(978-1-60606-079-7(1)***, J. Paul Getty Museum) Getty Pubns.

Architekturbild, ed. Neue Heimat: Eurpäischer Architekturfotographiepreis 2009. 2009. (ENG.). 114p. 35.00 *(978-3-89986-117-4(5)*, Avedition Gmbh,Csi) Continental Sales, Inc.

Barnes, Richard, et al. Animal Logic. 2009. (ENG., Illus.). 160p. 65.00 *(978-1-56898-861-0(3))* Princeton Architectural Pr.

Baumann, Kirsten, et al, eds. Modern Greetings/Moderne Grube: Photographed Architecture on Picture Postcards 1919-1939/Fotografierte Architektur Auf Ansichtskarten 1919-1939. 2007. (ENG & GER., Illus.). 38.00 *(978-3-89790-019-6(X))* Arnoldsche Art Pubs. DEU. Dist: Antique Collectors' Club.

Baumgarten, Lothar. Lothar Baumgarten: Air, 1 vol. 2006. (ENG., Illus.). 152p. lthr. 40.00 *(978-3-933807-46-5(8))* Richter Verlag DEU. Dist: D.A.P./Distributed Art Pubs.

Beil. Andreas Gursky, Architecture. 2008. (ENG., Illus.). 112p. 60.00 *(978-3-7757-2177-6(0))* Hatje Cantz Verlag GmbH & Co KG DEU. Dist: D.A.P./Distributed Art Pubs.

Bialobrzeski, Peter. Peter Bialobrzeski: The Raw & the Cooked. 2012. (ENG., Illus.). 160p. 95.00 ***(978-3-7757-3192-8(X))*** Hatje Cantz Verlag GmbH & Co KG DEU. Dist: D.A.P./Distributed Art Pubs.

Bialobrzeski, Peter, photos by. Peter Bialobrzeski: Case Study Homes. 2010. (ENG., Illus.). 84p. 45.00 *(978-3-7757-2469-2(9))* Hatje Cantz Verlag GmbH & Co KG DEU. Dist: D.A.P./Distributed Art Pubs.

Bialobrzeski, Peter, photos by & pref. Peter Bialobrzeski: Paradise Now. 2009. (ENG & GER., Illus.). 132p. 85.00 *(978-3-7757-2332-9(3))* Hatje Cantz Verlag GmbH & Co KG DEU. Dist: D.A.P./Distributed Art Pubs.

Binet, Hélène. Composing with Architecture: The Photographs of Helene Binet. 2012. (ENG., Illus.). 224p. 150.00 *(978-0-7148-6119-7(7))* Phaidon Pr., Inc.

Binet, Helene. Helene Binet. 2009. 160p. 69.95 *(978-0-7148-4942-3(1))* Phaidon Pr., Inc.

Birchfield, James D. Clay Lancaster's Kentucky: Architectural Photographs of a Preservation Pioneer. 2007. (ENG., Illus.). 144p. 50.00 *(978-0-8131-2421-6(2))* Univ. Pr. of Kentucky.

Boeckl, Matthias. Paul Ott. Photographs about Architecture. 2011. (GER.). 224p. 79.95 ***(978-3-7091-0820-8(9))*** Springer Wien AUT. Dist: Actar Birkhauser Distribution.

Bolloch, Joelle. The Eiffel Tower: Photography at the Musee D'Orsay. 2008. (Photography at the Mus?e D'Orsay Ser.). (ENG., Illus.). 96p. pap. 10.00 *(978-88-7439-260-5(5))* 5 Continents ITA. Dist: Hachette Bk. Group.

Botz, Corinne May. Haunted Houses. 2010. (ENG., Illus.). 208p. 40.00 *(978-1-58093-291-2(6))* Monacelli Pr., Inc.

Bourdeau, Robert, et al. Robert Bourdeau: the Station Point: The Station Point. 2011. (ENG., Illus.). 224p. pap. 60.00 ***(978-0-9739739-8-3(6))*** Magenta Publishing for the Arts CAN. Dist: Consortium Bk. Sales & Distribution.

Bovier, Lionel & Bortolotti, Maurizio, eds. Gabriele Basilico & Dan Graham: Unidentified Modern City. 2011. (ENG., Illus.). 80p. pap. 39.95 ***(978-3-03764-218-4(1))*** JRP Ringier Kunstverlag AG CHE. Dist: D.A.P./Distributed Art Pubs.

Brink, Brian Vanden. Ruin: Photographs of a Vanishing America. 2009. (ENG., Illus.). 144p. 65.00 *(978-0-89272-793-3(4))* Down East Bks.

Bryant, Richard, photos by. London. 2011. (ENG., Illus.). 264p. 17.95 *(978-0-7893-2240-1(4))* Universe Publishing.

Burri, René, et al. René Burri. Brasilia: Fotografien 1960-1993. Rüegg, Arthur, ed. 2011. (GER & ENG., Illus.). 224p. 99.00 *(978-3-85881-307-7(9))* Scheidegger und Spiess AG, Verlag CHE. Dist: Antique Collectors' Club.

Campbell, John Martin. Magnificent Failure: A Portrait of the Western Homestead Era. 2008. (ENG.). 200p. 19.95 *(978-0-8061-9964-1(4))* Univ. of Oklahoma Pr.

Campbell, John Martin & Karsmizki, Kenneth W. Magnificent Failure: A Portrait of the Western Homestead Era. 2008. (ENG.). 200p. pap. 14.95 *(978-0-8061-9965-8(2))* Univ. of Oklahoma Pr.

Caponigro, Paul, photos by. Stone Churches of Ireland. 2007. pap. 24.95 *(978-1-888899-39-9(5))*; 100.00 *(978-1-888899-40-5(9))* Lodima Pr.

Carroll, Mary Ellen. Mary Ellen Carroll: Causes, Place, Mistakes, Boredom, Lies, Resemblance, Pleasure, Nothing, Temporality, Affect, Inscription, Envy/Imitation, Utilitarianism, Disappearance, Literalness, Thingness, 1 vol. 2010. (ENG., Illus.). 360p. pap. 50.00 *(978-3-86521-618-2(8))* Steidl, Gerhard Druckerei und Verlag DEU. Dist: Innovative Logistics.

Colomina, Beatriz, et al, texts. Södrakull Frösakull, 1 vol. 2011. (ENG., Illus.). 144p. 85.00 *(978-3-86930-059-7(0))* Steidl, Gerhard Druckerei und Verlag DEU. Dist: Innovative Logistics.

Comazzi, John & Korab, Balthazar. Balthazar Korab: Architect of Photography. 2012. (ENG.). 192p. 40.00 ***(978-1-61689-041-4(X))*** Princeton Architectural Pr.

Cooper, Nicholas. The Photography of Bedford Lemere & Co. 2011. (ENG., Illus.). 288p. 50.00 *(978-1-84802-061-0(9))* English Heritage GBR. Dist: Brown, David Bk. Co., The.

Cornell, Daniell. Backyard Oasis: The Swimming Pool in Southern California Photography, 1945-1982. 2012. (Illus.). 256p. 60.00 ***(978-3-7913-5176-6(1))*** Prestel Publishing.

Cox, Reuben. The Work of Joe Webb: Appalachian Master of Rustic Architecture. 2009. (ENG., Illus.). 120p. 64.95 *(978-0-912330-85-3(6))* Jargon Society, Inc., The.

Crary, Jonathan. Idubai, 1 vol. 2010. (ENG., Illus.). 160p. 38.00 *(978-3-86521-916-9(0))* Steidl, Gerhard Druckerei und Verlag DEU. Dist: Innovative Logistics.

Culvahouse, Tim, ed. The Tennessee Valley Authority: Design & Persuasion. 2007. (ENG., Illus.). 144p. 40.00 *(978-1-56898-684-5(X))* Princeton Architectural Pr.

Curtis, Eleanor. St George's Chapel, Windsor: A Portrait. 2008. (ENG., Illus.). 160p. 49.95 *(978-1-904832-55-3(5))* Giles, D. Ltd. GBR. Dist: Antique Collectors' Club.

D'Agati, Mauro. Alamar: Habana - Cuba, 1 vol. 2010. (ENG & SPA., Illus.). 156p. 75.00 *(978-3-86521-954-1(3))* Steidl, Gerhard Druckerei und Verlag DEU. Dist: Innovative Logistics.

Del Valle, Eduardo & Gómez, Mirta. Eduardo Del Valle & Mirta Gómez: Artist As Witness. 2008. (Illus.). 90p. *(978-1-59005-220-4(X))* Nazraeli Pr.

Derenthal, Ludger & Kuhn, Christine, eds. Ein neuer Blick: Architekturfotografien aus den Staatlichen Museen zu Berlin. 2011. (ENG., Illus.). 416p. 70.00 *(978-3-8030-0704-9(6))* Wasmuth, Ernst J. Verlag GmbH & Co. DEU. Dist: D.A.P./Distributed Art Pubs.

Doron, Itai, photos by. Chokra Mahal. aut. ed. 2010. (Illus.). 104p. 110.00 *(978-1-904212-55-3(7))* Other Criteria GBR. Dist: Abrams.

Dubowitz, Dan. Wastelands. 2010. (ENG., Illus.). 176p. 55.00 ***(978-1-904587-83-5(6))*** Lewis, Dewi Publishing GBR. Dist: Consortium Bk. Sales & Distribution.

Edkins, Diana & Kouwenhoven, Bill. Chonqing - City of Ambition. 2010. (ENG., Illus.). 112p. 55.00 *(978-90-5330-682-6(X))* Mets en Schilt Uitgevers NLD. Dist: Ingram Pub. Services.

Ehrmann-Schindlbeck, Anna-Maria, et al, texts. Philadelphia: Katalog Tuttlingen. 2010. (ENG & GER., Illus.). 48p. pap. 39.95 *(978-3-8296-0440-6(8))* Schirmer/Mosel Verlag GmbH DEU. Dist: Prestel Publishing.

Elliott, David, et al, texts. A Building Is Not a Building. 2009. (ENG., Illus.). 132p. 85.00 *(978-3-7757-2366-4(8))* Hatje Cantz Verlag GmbH & Co KG DEU. Dist: D.A.P./Distributed Art Pubs.

Elwall, Robert. Evocations of Place: The Photography of Edwin Smith. 2007. (ENG., Illus.). 176p. 59.95 *(978-1-85894-373-2(6))* Merrell Pubs. Ltd. GBR. Dist: Perseus Distribution.

Engel, Gerrit. Gerrit Engel: Berlin Architecture. 2008. (Illus.). 340p. *(978-3-8296-0392-8(4))* Schirmer/Mosel Verlag GmbH.

Erban, David, tr. Architektonische Nachhut/Architectural Rearguard, 1 vol. 2008. (ENG., Illus.). 168p. 48.00 *(978-3-86678-052-1(4))* Kerber Verlag DEU. Dist: D.A.P./Distributed Art Pubs.

Falat, Elke, ed. & text. Alexander Rischer: Caput Corvi. 2010. (ENG., Illus.). 76p. pap. 35.00 *(978-3-86678-220-4(9))* Kerber Verlag DEU. Dist: D.A.P./Distributed Art Pubs.

Feraboli, Maria Teresa. City Squares of the World. 2007. (ENG., Illus.). 216p. 19.95 *(978-88-544-0276-8(1)*, White Star) Rizzoli International Pubns., Inc.

Fischer, Roland, photos by. Roland Fischer: Photoworks 1990-2010. 2011. (ENG., Illus.). 218p. pap. 30.00 *(978-988-18816-0-1(9))* Timezone 8 Ltd. HKG. Dist: D.A.P./Distributed Art Pubs.

Frank, Douglas. Stone Beings. 2009. *(978-1-59028-211-3(6)*, William, James & Co.) Franklin, Beedle & Assocs., Inc.

Franke, Simon, ed. Positions. 2010. (ENG & DUT., Illus.). 220p. 80.00 *(978-90-5662-652-5(3))* NAi Uitgevers / Publishers Stichting NLD. Dist: D.A.P./Distributed Art Pubs.

Fredericq, Suzanne & and Marilia Giannini, Suzanne Fredericq. A Walk through the City: Photographer Marco Leonardi's Architectural Washington D. C. 2009. 145p. pap. 50.00 *(978-0-615-32526-2(2))* Estate of Eugene James Martin.

Gand, Gary. Julius Shulman: Chicago Mid-Century Modernism. 2010. (Illus.). 208p. 60.00 *(978-0-8478-3287-3(2))* Rizzoli International Pubns., Inc.

Gautherot, Marcel, photos by. Building Brasilia. 2010. (ENG., Illus.). 192p. 65.00 *(978-0-500-51542-6(5)*, 551542) Thames & Hudson.

Gierstberg, Frits, et al. Eugène Atget: Paris 1898-1924. 2011. (ENG., Illus.). 320p. 71.00 ***(978-84-15253-03-7(6))*** T.F. Editores ESP. Dist: National Bk. Network.

Glass, Christopher. Historic Maine Homes: 200 Years of Great Houses. 2009. (ENG.). 200p. 40.00 *(978-0-89272-799-5(3))* Down East Bks.

Guerrero, Pedro E. Pedro E. Guerrero: A Photographer's Journey. 2007. (ENG., Illus.). 224p. 55.00 *(978-1-56898-590-9(8))* Princeton Architectural Pr.

Guntli, Reto, photos by. Luxury Living New York. 2009. (ENG.). 59.95 *(978-3-8327-9311-1(9))* teNeues Publishing Co.

Gutschow, Beate, photos by. Beate Gütschow: S. 2010. (ENG., Illus.). 72p. 75.00 *(978-3-7757-2528-6(8))* Hatje Cantz Verlag GmbH & Co KG DEU. Dist: D.A.P./Distributed Art Pubs.

Haga, Dan. Urban Atrophy. 2011. (Illus.). 176p. 39.99 *(978-0-7643-3738-3(6)*, Schiffer Publishing Ltd) Schiffer Publishing, Ltd.

Hatakeyama, Naoya. Scales. 2007. (Illus.). 61p. *(978-1-59005-216-7(1))* Nazraeli Pr.

Healey, John. Photographing Washington D. C. Digital Field Guide. 2010. (ENG., Illus.). 320p. pap. 19.99 *(978-0-470-58687-7(7)*, Wiley) Wiley, John & Sons, Inc.

Heckert, Virginia, et al. Some Aesthetic Decisions: The Photographs of Judy Fiskin. 2011. (ENG., Illus.). 368p. 50.00 ***(978-1-60606-081-0(3)***, J. Paul Getty Museum) Getty Pubns.

Helle, Maarten, photos by. Typography & Architecture: Amsterdam in Letters. 2009. (ENG., Illus.). 192p. 37.50 *(978-90-78088-25-7(7))* Valiz NLD. Dist: D.A.P./Distributed Art Pubs.

A

Helmle, Christian, photos by. Weiße Elefanten / White Elephants. 2008. (ENG., Illus.). 128p. 45.00 *(978-3-939633-19-8(4))* Jovis Verlag GmbH DEU. Dist: D.A.P./Distributed Art Pubs.

Hentschel, Martin. Bert Teunissen. Domestic Landscapes. Ein Porträt von Europäern daheim, 1 vol. 2007. (ENG., Illus.). 136p. 50.00 *(978-1-59711-040-2(X))* Aperture Foundation, Inc.

Higgins, Keith. How to Look at a Vancouver Special. 2010. 48p. pap. 9.00 *(978-1-935662-19-8(8))* Publication Studio.

Higgott, Amdrew & Wray, Timothy. Camera-Constructs: Photography, Architecture & the Modern City. 2012. (Illus.). 325p. 114.95 ***(978-1-4094-2145-0(7))*** Ashgate Publishing Co.

Höfer, Candida. Weimar. 2007. 120p. 49.95 *(978-3-8296-0327-0(4))* Schirmer/Mosel Verlag GmbH DEU. Dist: Prestel Publishing.

Hofer, Candida, photos by. Candida Hofer: Bologna Series, 1 vol. 2008. (ENG., Illus.). 68p. 23.00 *(978-88-7757-212-7(4))* Hopefulmonster Editore ITA. Dist: D.A.P./Distributed Art Pubs.

—Louvre: Photographien. 2006. (Illus.). 18p. 49.95 *(978-3-8296-0250-1(2))* Schirmer/Mosel Verlag GmbH DEU. Dist: Prestel Publishing.

Howell, Steven. The Photographer's Guide to New York City. 2010. (Photographer's Guide Ser.). (ENG., Illus.). 96p. pap. 14.95 *(978-0-88150-876-5(4)*, 150876) Countryman Pr.

International Architectural Photographers Staff. Through the Lens: International Architectural Photographers. 2006. (ENG., Illus.). 224p. 55.00 *(978-1-876907-26-6(6))* Images Publishing Group AUS. Dist: National Bk. Network.

Jäger, Joachim, text. Neue Nationalgalerie Berlin: Mies van der Rohe. 2011. (ENG., Illus.). 108p. 30.00 ***(978-3-7757-3145-4(8))*** Hatje Cantz Verlag GmbH & Co KG DEU. Dist: D.A.P./Distributed Art Pubs.

Jewsiewicki, Bogumil. The Beautiful Time: Photography by Sammy Baloji. 2010. (ENG., Illus.). 48p. pap. 22.00 *(978-0-945802-55-6(2))* Museum for African Art.

Jodice, Mimmo, photos by. Citta Visibili/Visible Cities, 1 vol. 2007. (ITA & ENG., Illus.). 144p. 60.00 *(978-88-8158-628-8(2))* Charta ITA. Dist: D.A.P./Distributed Art Pubs.

Kaak, Joachim. Roland Fischer. 2007. 92p. 49.95 *(978-3-87909-826-2(3))* Wienand GmbH, Druck- & Verlagshaus DEU. Dist: Independent Pubs. Group.

Kanfer, Larry. Barns of Illinois. 2009. (ENG., Illus.). 128p. 39.95 *(978-0-252-03274-5(8))* Univ. of Illinois Pr.

Keller, Christopher & Lagae, Johan, eds. Aglaia Konrad: Desert Cities. 2008. (ENG., Illus.). 236p. pap. 75.00 *(978-3-905829-59-4(2))* JRP Ringier Kunstverlag AG CHE. Dist: D.A.P./Distributed Art Pubs.

Kemp, Hans, ed. Doors. 2008. (Illus.). 200p. 16.95 *(978-962-85637-7-7(7))* Visionary World, Ltd. HKG. Dist: AtlasBooks Distribution.

Kim, Ji Young. Transforum Vol. 1. 2009. 120p. pap. 40.00 *(978-0-557-07836-3(9))* Lulu Enterprises Inc.

Knight, Richard. Saarinen's Quest: A Memoir of a Photographer. 2007. pap. 30.00 *(978-0-9746214-4-9(7))* Stout, William Pubs.

Kolehmainen, Ola, photos by. Ola Kolehmainen: Fraction, Abstraction, Recreation, 1 vol. 2007. (ENG., Illus.). 128p. 80.00 *(978-3-7757-1902-5(4))* Hatje Cantz Verlag GmbH & Co KG DEU. Dist: D.A.P./Distributed Art Pubs.

Kopelow, Gerry. Architectural Photography: The Digital Way. 2007. (ENG., Illus.). 144p. pap. 24.95 *(978-1-56898-697-5(1))* Princeton Architectural Pr.

Krementschouk, Andrej. No Direction Home. 2009. (ENG, RUS & GER., Illus.). 112p. 50.00 *(978-3-86828-056-2(1))* Kehrer Verlag Heidelberg, Klaus Kehrer DEU. Dist: Consortium Bk. Sales & Distribution.

Lambton, Lucinda. Lucinda Lambton's Colonial Caribbean. 2012. (Illus.). 224p. 55.95 ***(978-1-906768-37-9(4)***, Stacey International) Stacey Publishing GBR. Dist: Midpoint Trade Bks., Inc.

Lara Morales, Abel & Montero, Pablo. Fortaleza de San Juan de Ulúa, Veracruz. 3rd ed. 2009. (SPA., Illus.). 102p. *(978-607-484-040-7(7))* Instituto Nacional de Antropologia e Historia.

Lark Books Staff, contrib. by. Focus, Passages: Your World, Your Images. 2010. (Focus Ser.). (ENG., Illus.). 180p. 14.95 *(978-1-60059-680-3(0))* Lark Bks.

Lasciac, Antonio. Antonio Lasciac, Architetto: Da Gorizia All'impero Ottomano. 2007. (Illus.). 159p. pap. *(978-88-7292-501-0(0))* Alinari (IDEA).

Lebovich, Bill & Lebovich, William. How to Photograph Historic Structures & Sites. 2012. (ENG., Illus.). 288p. pap. 35.00 ***(978-0-393-73367-9(X)***, 73367) Norton, W. W. & Co., Inc.

Leong, Sze Tsung. History Images, 1 vol. 2008. (ENG., Illus.). 144p. 90.00 *(978-3-86521-274-0(3))* Steidl, Gerhard Druckerei und Verlag DEU. Dist: Innovative Logistics.

Lewis, Richard Anthony. Robert W. Tebbs, Photographer to Architects: Louisiana Plantations In 1926. 2011. (Illus.). 160p. 39.95 ***(978-0-8071-4218-9(2))*** Louisiana State Univ. Pr.

Liedtke, Walter & Verburg, JoAnn. Interruptions, 1 vol. 2010. (ENG., Illus.). 46p. 30.00 *(978-3-86930-118-1(X))* Steidl, Gerhard Druckerei und Verlag DEU. Dist: Innovative Logistics.

Long, Kieran. Hatch: The New Architectural Generation. 2008. (ENG., Illus.). 352p. pap. 35.00 *(978-1-85669-562-6(X))* King, Laurence Publishing GBR. Dist: Hachette Bk. Group.

Lundberg, W. Bruce & Pinto, John A., eds. Steps off the Beaten Path/Sentieri Smarriti E Ritrovati: Nineteenth-Century Photographs of Rome & Its Environs/Roma E Dintorni Nelle Fotografie del Secondo Ottocento. 2008. (ITA & ENG., Illus.). 216p. pap. 59.95 *(978-88-8158-667-7(3))* Charta ITA. Dist: D.A.P./Distributed Art Pubs.

Lyden, Anne M. & Kingsley, Hope. The Photographs of Frederick H. Evans. 2010. (Illus.). 184p. 50.00 *(978-0-89236-988-1(4))* Oxford Univ. Pr., Inc.

Marchand, Yves & Meffre, Romain, photos by. The Ruins of Detroit, 1 vol. 2011. (ENG., Illus.). 200p. 125.00 *(978-3-86930-042-9(6))* Steidl, Gerhard Druckerei und Verlag DEU. Dist: Innovative Logistics.

Matheson, Elizabeth, photos by. Shell Castle: Portrait of a North Carolina House. 2008. 72p. *(978-0-9798226-0-5(2))* Safe Harbor Bks.

Mayne, Thom & Okun, Jenny. Variations: The Architecture Photographs of Jenny Okun. 2006. (ENG., Illus.). 180p. 65.00 *(978-0-9777193-3-4(2))* Five Ties Publishing.

Merkel, Klaus. Trees As Well As Stones. 2011. (ENG., Illus.). 112p. 70.00 ***(978-3-03778-272-9(2))*** Lars Muller Pubs. CHE. Dist: Prestel Publishing.

Michaels, Barbara L., et al, contrib. by. Philip Trager, 1 vol. 2008. (ENG., Illus.). 312p. 75.00 *(978-3-86521-239-9(5))* Steidl, Gerhard Druckerei und Verlag DEU. Dist: Innovative Logistics.

Milstein, Jeffrey. Cuba. 2010. (ENG., Illus.). 128p. 25.00 *(978-1-58093-275-2(4))* Monacelli Pr., Inc.

Moore, Andrew, photos by & text. Andrew Moore: Detroit Disassembled, 1 vol. 2010. (ENG., Illus.). 136p. 50.00 *(978-88-6208-118-4(9))* Damiani ITA. Dist: D.A.P./Distributed Art Pubs.

Moore, Derry, photos by. In House. 2009. (Illus.). 256p. 60.00 *(978-0-8478-3349-8(6))* Rizzoli International Pubns., Inc.

Morgan, Bret. Rustic: Country Houses, Rural Dwellings, Wooded Retreats. 2009. (ENG., Illus.). 228p. 25.00 *(978-0-8478-3300-9(3))* Rizzoli International Pubns., Inc.

Muller, Frank-Heinrich, ed. & photos by. East/For the Record, 1 vol. 2009. (ENG., Illus.). 192p. 55.00 *(978-3-86521-929-9(2))* Steidl, Gerhard Druckerei und Verlag DEU. Dist: Innovative Logistics.

Nefzger, Jurgen. Nocturnes. 2009. (ENG., Illus.). 128p. 45.00 *(978-3-7757-2334-3(X))* Hatje Cantz Verlag GmbH & Co KG DEU. Dist: D.A.P./Distributed Art Pubs.

Nerdinger, Winfried. Fotografie für Architekten: Die Fotosammlung des Architekturmuseumsder TU München. 2011. (GER & ENG., Illus.). 216p. 65.00 ***(978-3-86560-989-2(9))*** Verlag der Buchhandlung Walther Konig DEU. Dist: D.A.P./Distributed Art Pubs.

Niedermayr, Walter. Walter Niedermayr: Recollection. 2011. (ENG, GER & PER., Illus.). 170p. 75.00 *(978-3-7757-2738-9(8))* Hatje Cantz Verlag GmbH & Co KG DEU. Dist: D.A.P./Distributed Art Pubs.

Nilson, Micheline. Architecture in Nineteenth Century Photographs: Essays on Reading A Collection. 2011. (Visual Culture in Early Modernity Ser.). (Illus.). 216p. 104.95 *(978-1-4094-0904-5(X))* Ashgate Publishing Co.

Passage to Angkor. 3rd ed. 2008. (Illus.). 144p. 59.95 *(978-0-9653574-3-2(0))* Friends Without a Border.

Plank, Jeffrey. Aaron Siskind & Louis Sullivan: The Institute of Design Photo Section Project. 2008. (Illus.). 272p. 65.00 *(978-0-9795508-3-6(1))* Stout, William Pubs.

Polidori, Robert, photos by. Parcours Museologique Revisite, 1 vol. 2009. (ENG., Illus.). 744p. 124.90 *(978-3-86521-702-8(8))* Steidl, Gerhard Druckerei und Verlag DEU. Dist: Innovative Logistics.

Purbrick, Louise, contrib. by. British Watchtowers, 1 vol. 2008. (ENG., Illus.). 76p. 50.00 *(978-3-86521-499-7(1))* Steidl, Gerhard Druckerei und Verlag DEU. Dist: Innovative Logistics.

Rappaport, Nina & Yale School of Architecture Staff. The Human City No. 3: Kings Cross. Knight, George & Taylor, Aaron, eds. 2009. (Edward P. Bass Distinguished Visiting Architecture Fellowship Ser.). (ENG., Illus.). 192p. pap. 30.00 *(978-0-393-73247-4(9)*, 73247) Norton, W. W. & Co., Inc.

Rice, Shelley & Saramago, José, texts. Candida Höfer: Em Portugal/in Portugal. 2007. (POR & ENG., Illus.). 125p. 65.00 *(978-3-8296-0279-2(0))* Schirmer/Mosel Verlag GmbH DEU. Dist: Prestel Publishing.

Ross, Andrew. Fiat Lux: 51 Photographs. 2009. (ENG., Illus.). 64p. 30.00 *(978-0-86473-573-7(1))* Victoria Univ. Pr. NZL. Dist: Independent Pubs. Group.

Ross, Richard, photos by. Architecture of Authority, 1 vol. 2007. (ENG., Illus.). 144p. 40.00 *(978-1-59711-052-5(3))* Aperture Foundation, Inc.

Sachsse, Rolf. Raumbilder Bildräume: Architekten fotografieren. 2009. (GER., Illus.). 116p. *(978-3-422-06902-2(X))* Deutscher Kunstverlag GmbH.

Salignac, Eugene De. New York Rises, 1 vol. 2007. (ENG., Illus.). 144p. 40.00 *(978-1-59711-013-6(2))* Aperture Foundation, Inc.

Sandow Media Corporation, creator. Architectural Photographers Sourcebook: A Showcase of Exceptional Architectural Photographers. 2008. (ENG.). 148p. 39.95 *(978-0-9764713-7-0(X))* Sandow Media.

Saville, Lynn, photos by. Night Shift. 2009. (ENG., Illus.). 144p. 45.00 *(978-1-58093-219-6(3))* Monacelli Pr., Inc.

Schaller, Matthias, photos by. Purple Desks, 1 vol. 2009. (ENG., Illus.). 72p. 49.90 *(978-3-86521-597-0(1))* Steidl, Gerhard Druckerei und Verlag DEU. Dist: Innovative Logistics.

Schieber, Randall Lee, photos by. Columbus Impressions. 2011. (Illus.). 80p. pap. 12.95 *(978-1-56037-513-5(2))* Farcountry Pr.

Schiff, Thomas, photos by. Thomas R. Schiff: Prospect. 2012. (ENG., Illus.). 304p. 80.00 ***(978-88-6208-195-5(2))*** Damiani ITA. Dist: D.A.P./Distributed Art Pubs.

Schiff, Thomas R., photos by. Wright Panorama: Elements of Frank Lloyd Wright's Architecture in 360 Degrees. 2010. *(978-1-933197-75-3(7))* Orange Frazer Pr.

Schmidt, Andreas, photos by. Andreas Schmidt: The City. 2010. (ENG & GER., Illus.). 144p. 55.00 *(978-3-7757-2468-5(0))* Hatje Cantz Verlag GmbH & Co KG DEU. Dist: D.A.P./Distributed Art Pubs.

Schneider, Gregor. Die Familie Schneider, 1 vol. 2008. (ENG., Illus.). 184p. 35.00 *(978-3-86521-236-8(0))* Steidl, Gerhard Druckerei und Verlag DEU. Dist: Innovative Logistics.

Schulz, Adrian. Architectural Photography: Composition, Capture, & Digital Image Processing. 2nd ed. 2012. (ENG., Illus.). 240p. pap. 44.95 ***(978-1-933952-88-8(1))*** Rocky Nook.

Schurmbock, Thomas. The Last Decade. 2011. (ENG., Illus.). 144p. 60.00 ***(978-3-86828-159-0(2))*** Kehrer Verlag Heidelberg, Klaus Kehrer DEU. Dist: Consortium Bk. Sales & Distribution.

Scott, A. O. Sanctuary. 2010. (ENG., Illus.). 96p. 60.00 *(978-0-8109-9199-6(3))* Abrams.

Serraino, Pierluigi. Julius Shulman - Modernism Rediscovered: Die wiederentdeckte Moderne. 25th ed. 2009. (ENG, FRE & GER., Illus.). 415p. 29.99 *(978-3-8365-0326-6(3))* TASCHEN DEU. Dist: Ingram Pub. Services.

Shulman, Julius. Julius Shulman: Modernism Rediscovered, 3 vols., Set. Taschen, Benedikt, ed. 2007. (FRE, GER & ENG., Illus.). 1008p. 300.00 *(978-3-8228-4287-4(7))* TASCHEN DEU. Dist: Ingram Pub. Services.

Shulman, Julius, photos by. Julius Shulman Los Angeles: The Birth of a Modern Metroplis. 2011. (ENG., Illus.). 240p. 60.00 *(978-0-8478-3548-5(0))* Rizzoli International Pubns., Inc.

Smith, Joel, contrib. by. The Life & Death of Buildings: On Photography & Time. 2011. (ENG., Illus.). 104p. pap. 40.00 *(978-0-300-17435-9(7))* Yale Univ. Pr.

Smith, Scott B. The Orange Bowl: A Photographic Journey & Architectural Survey. 2009. 132p. pap. 49.50 *(978-1-4389-9611-0(X))* AuthorHouse.

Spierling, Esperanza, ed. Beyond the Picture. 2009. (GER & ENG., Illus.). 70p. pap. 23.00 *(978-3-86678-149-8(0))* Kerber Verlag DEU. Dist: D.A.P./Distributed Art Pubs.

Stappenbeck, Gisela, et al. Erlebtes Bauen: Ost-Berlin, 1959 Bis 1989, 1 vol. 2009. (RUS, FRE, GER & ENG., Illus.). 288p. 64.95 *(978-3-938666-37-1(4))* DOM Pubs. DEU. Dist: Innovative Logistics.

Stefano, et al. New York: Born Back into the Past. 2012. (ENG., Illus.). 144p. 55.00 ***(978-88-6302-056-4(6))*** Alinari (IDEA) ITA. Dist: Antique Collectors' Club.

Stephenson, David. Heavenly Vaults: From Romanesque to Gothic in European Architecture. 2009. (ENG., Illus.). 192p. 65.00 *(978-1-56898-840-5(0))* Princeton Architectural Pr.

Tillim, Guy. Avenue Patrice Lumumba: Guy Tillim. 2009. (POR, FRE & ENG., Illus.). 128p. 65.00 *(978-3-7913-4066-1(2))* Prestel Publishing.

Toczko, David. Shaker Village of Pleasant Hill: 50th Anniversary of the Restoration. 2010. 39.95 *(978-1-935001-60-7(4))* Acclaim Pr., Inc.

Trevarthen, Mike. Suburban Life in Roman Durnovaria: Excavations at the Former County Hospital Site, Dorchester 2000-2001. 2008. (Illus.). 48p. (C). pap. 12.95 *(978-1-874350-46-0(9))* Trust for Wessex Archaeology Ltd. GBR. Dist: Brown, David Bk. Co., The.

Vila-Matas, Enrique & Burkert, Herbert, texts. Santiago de Compostela: Bibliotheken; Begleitpublikation zur Candida Höfer-Ausstellung zur Einweihung des 'City of Culture of Galicia' 2011. (Illus.). 208p. *(978-3-8296-0514-4(5))* Schirmer/Mosel Verlag GmbH.

Vollmer, Wolfgang, et al. City / Image / Cologne: Photographs from 1880 until Today, 1 vol. 2007. (GER & ENG., Illus.). 176p. 55.00 *(978-3-86521-582-6(3))* Steidl, Gerhard Druckerei und Verlag DEU. Dist: D.A.P./Distributed Art Pubs.

Washington-Melchizedek. Hairlem's Storehouse Private Road. 2009. pap. *(978-1-61584-829-4(0))* Independent Pub.

Wasiuta, Mark & Wigley, Mark. Dan Graham's New Jersey. 2012. (ENG., Illus.). 128p. 65.00 ***(978-3-03778-259-0(5))*** Lars Muller Pubs. CHE. Dist: Prestel Publishing.

Weinberg, David. Towering Mirrors, Mirroring Towers: Photographs of Urban Reflections. 2006. (ENG., Illus.). 96p. 50.00 *(978-0-9777531-2-3(3))* Glitterati, Inc.

Wiedenhvfer, Kai, photos by. Wall, 1 vol. 2007. (ENG., Illus.). 104p. 40.00 *(978-3-86521-117-0(8))* Steidl, Gerhard Druckerei und Verlag DEU. Dist: D.A.P./Distributed Art Pubs.

Wolf, Michael. Hong Kong Corner Houses. 2011. (ENG., Illus.). 136p. (gr. 17). 45.00 *(978-988-8028-72-6(3))* Hong Kong Univ. Pr. HKG. Dist: Columbia Univ. Pr.

Woods, Mary N. Beyond the Architect's Eye: Photographs & the American Built Environment. 2009. (Illus.). 368p. (C). 55.00 *(978-0-8122-4108-2(8))* Univ. of Pennsylvania Pr.

Zanta, Marco. Urbaneurope. 2008. (ENG., Illus.). 150p. 49.00 *(978-88-6965-106-9(1))* Contrasto DUE ITA. Dist: Consortium Bk. Sales & Distribution.

ARCHITECTURAL POLYCHROMY

see Color in Architecture

ARCHITECTURAL PRACTICE

Abruzzo, Emily. The Official Catalog for Workshopping: An American Model for Architectural Practice. 2010. (ENG., Illus.). 128p. pap., wbk. ed. 20.00 *(978-1-61689-017-9(7))* Princeton Architectural Pr.

American Institute of Architects Staff. The Architecture Student's Handbook of Professional Practice. 14th ed. 2008. (ENG., Illus.). 720p. pap., stu. ed., instr.'s hndbk. ed. 115.00 *(978-0-470-08869-2(9)*, Wiley) Wiley, John & Sons, Inc.

Art & Build Architects Staff. Art & Build Architects: A Humanistic Approach to Architecture. 2009. (ENG., Illus.). 480p. 80.00 *(978-1-86470-296-5(6))* Images Publishing Group AUS. Dist: National Bk. Network.

Awan, Nishat, et al. Spatial Agency Schneider & Till. 2011. (ENG., Illus.). 224p. 165.00 *(978-0-415-57192-0(8))*; pap. 44.95 *(978-0-415-57193-7(6))* Routledge.

Bougdah, Hocine & Zunde, J. M. Integrated Strategies in Architecture. 2006. (Technologies of Architecture Ser.: Vol. 1). (Illus.). 312p. 170.00 *(978-0-415-36083-8(5)*, RU42665) Taylor & Francis Group.

Bougdah, Hocine & Zunde, Joan. Integrated Strategies in Architecture. 2006. (Technologies of Architecture Ser.: Vol. 1). (ENG., Illus.). 312p. (C). per. 39.95 *(978-0-415-36084-5(6)*, RU42666, Taylor & Francis) Taylor & Francis Group GBR. Dist: Taylor & Francis Group.

Cesal, Eric J. Down Detour Road: An Architect in Search of Practice. 2010. (ENG., Illus.). 240p. (gr. 17). pap. 22.95 *(978-0-262-01461-8(0))* MIT Pr.

Chappell, David & Willis, Andrew. The Architect in Practice. 10th ed. 2010. (ENG., Illus.). 432p. pap. 65.00 *(978-1-4051-9852-3(4)*, Wiley-Blackwell) Wiley, John & Sons, Inc.

Corser, Robert & Princeton Architectural Press Staff. Fabricating Architecture: Selected Readings in Digital Design & Manufacturing. 2010. (ENG., Illus.). 216p. pap. 29.95 *(978-1-56898-889-4(3))* Princeton Architectural Pr.

Cramer, James P. & Simpson, Scott. The Next Architect: A New Twist on the Future of Design. 2006. 148p. pap. 39.00 *(978-0-9755654-8-3(6)*, Ostberg) Greenway Communications.

Daniell, Thomas. After the Crash: Architecture in Post-Bubble Japan. 2008. (ENG., Illus.). 176p. pap. 24.95 *(978-1-56898-776-7(5))* Princeton Architectural Pr.

Demkin, Joseph A. The Architect's Handbook of Professional Practice. Demkin, Joseph A., ed. 14th ed. 2008. (ENG., Illus.). 1040p. 250.00 *(978-0-470-00957-4(8)*, Wiley) Wiley, John & Sons, Inc.

Deutsch, Randy. BIM & Integrated Design: Strategies for Architectural Practice. 2011. (ENG., Illus.). 272p. 75.00 *(978-0-470-57251-1(5)*, Wiley) Wiley, John & Sons, Inc.

Dutoit, Allison, et al, eds. Quality Out of Control: Standards for Measuring Architecture. 2010. (ENG., Illus.). 240p. 165.00 *(978-0-415-55365-0(2))*; pap. 53.95 *(978-0-415-55366-7(0))* Taylor & Francis Group GBR. (Routledge). Dist: Taylor & Francis Group.

Dutoit, Allison, et al. Quality Out of Control: Standards for Measuring Architecture. 2010. 53.95 *(978-0-203-86184-4(1))* Routledge.

Eastman, Chuck, et al. BIM Handbook: A Guide to Building Information Modeling for Owners, Managers, Designers, Engineers & Contractors. 2nd ed. 2011. (ENG., Illus.). 648p. 85.00 *(978-0-470-54137-1(7)*, Wiley) Wiley, John & Sons, Inc.

Ewing, Suzanne, ed. Field/Work. 2010. (ENG., Illus.). 208p. (C). 155.00 *(978-0-415-59539-1(8))* Routledge.

Ewing, Suzanne & Speed, Chris, eds. Field/Work. 2010. (ENG., Illus.). 208p. (C). pap. 53.95 *(978-0-415-59540-7(1))* Routledge.

Franck, Karen A. & Howard, Teresa Von Sommaruga. Design Through Dialogue: A Guide for Architects & Clients. 2010. (ENG., Illus.). 208p. 130.00 *(978-0-470-72190-2(1)*, Wiley) Wiley, John & Sons, Inc.

Franck, Karen A. & Lepori, R. Bianca. Architecture from the Inside Out: From the Body, the Senses, the Site, & the Community. 2nd ed. 2007. (ENG., Illus.). 200p. 145.00 *(978-0-470-05783-4(1))*; pap. 55.00 *(978-0-470-05785-8(8))* Wiley, John & Sons, Inc. (Academy Pr.).

Gerbino, Anthony. François Blondel: Architecture, Erudition, & the Scientific Revolution. 2010. (Classical Tradition in Architecture Ser.). (ENG., Illus.). 344p. (C). 135.00 *(978-0-415-49199-0(1))* Routledge.

Guillén, Mauro F. The Taylorized Beauty of the Mechanical: Scientific Management & the Rise of Modernist Architecture. 2008. (Princeton Studies in Cultural Sociology Ser.). (ENG., Illus.). 232p. (C). pap. 29.95 *(978-0-691-13847-3(8))* Princeton Univ. Pr.

Hardin, Brad. BIM & Construction Management: Proven Tools, Methods, & Workflows. 2009. (ENG., Illus.). 364p. pap. 49.99 *(978-0-470-40235-1(0)*, Sybex) Wiley, John & Sons, Inc.

Hensel, Michael U., ed. Design Innovation for the Built Environment. 2012. (ENG., Illus.). 280p. (C). 165.00 ***(978-0-415-59664-0(5))***; pap. 49.95 ***(978-0-415-59665-7(3))*** Routledge.

Hernandez, Felip & Hernandez, Felipe. Bhabha for Architects. 2010. (Thinkers for Architects Ser.). (ENG., Illus.). 148p. 28.95 *(978-0-415-47746-8(8))* Routledge.

Herrmann, Robert F. & Menaker & Herrmann LLP. Law for Architects: What You Need to Know. 2012. (ENG.). 224p. 35.00 ***(978-0-393-73345-7(9)***, 73345) Norton, W. W. & Co., Inc.

Hickey, John. Practice, Management & Responsibility. 2009. pap. 44.95 *(978-0-415-46191-7(X))* Taylor & Francis Group.

Hyde, Rory. Future Practice. 2012. (ENG., Illus.). 280p. (C). 165.00 ***(978-0-415-53353-9(8))***; pap. 34.95 ***(978-0-415-53354-6(6))*** Routledge.

Ingels, Bjarke. Yes Is More: An Archicomic on Architectural Evolution. 2009. (ENG., Illus.). 400p. pap. 29.99 *(978-3-8365-2010-2(9)*, Evergreen) TASCHEN DEU. Dist: Ingram Pub. Services.

Jackson, Patrick Thaddeus. The Integrated Design-Build Team. 2012. (ENG.). (C). 59.95 *(978-1-4283-5304-6(6))* Delmar Cengage Learning.

Jernigan, Finith, 2nd. BIG BIM little Bim: The Practical Approach to Building Information Modeling Integrated Practice done the right Way! 2008. (ENG., Illus.). 302p. per. 29.95 *(978-0-9795699-0-6(7))* 4Site Pr.

Johnston, George Barnett. Drafting Culture: A Social History of Architectural Graphic Standards. 2008. (ENG., Illus.). 304p. (gr. 17). 39.95 *(978-0-262-10122-6(X))* MIT Pr.

Kahn, Andrea. Constellations: Constructing Urban Design Practices. 2007. *(978-1-883584-45-0(0))* Columbia Univ., Graduate Schl. of Architecture.
Kedan, Elite. Provisional: Emerging Modes of Architectural Practice USA. Dreyfous, Jon & Mutter, Craig, eds. 2009. (ENG.). 288p. pap. 40.00 *(978-1-56898-878-8(8))* Princeton Architectural Pr.
Kossak, Florian, et al, eds. Agency: Working with Uncertain Architectures. 2009. (Illus.). 192p. 165.00 *(978-0-415-56601-8(0))*; (ENG., pap. 53.95 *(978-0-415-56602-5(9))* Routledge.
Langdon, Davis. Spon's Architects' & Builders' Price Book 2011. 136th ed. 2010. (ENG., Illus.). 1168p. 255.00 *(978-0-415-58845-4(6)*, Spon Pr.) Routledge.
Langdon, Davis. Spon's Architects' & Builders' Price Book 2012. 137th rev. ed. 2011. (ENG.). 99999.00 ***(978-0-415-68067-7(0)***, Spon Pr.) Routledge.
Langdon, Davis, ed. Spon's Architects' & Builders' Price Book 2012. 137th rev. ed. 2011. (ENG., Illus.). 848p. 250.00 ***(978-0-415-68063-9(8)***, Spon Pr.) Routledge.
Loukissas, Yanni Alexander. Socio-Technological Studies in Architecture. 2012. (ENG., Illus.). 168p. (C). 165.00 ***(978-0-415-59227-7(5))***; pap. 49.95 ***(978-0-415-59228-4(3))*** Routledge.
Mateo, Josep Lluis. After Crisis: Post-Fordist Conditions for Architecture. Mateo, Josep Lluis & Ivanisin, Krunoslav, eds. 2010. (Illus.). 160p. pap. 39.95 *(978-3-03778-230-9(7))* Lars Muller Pubs. CHE. Dist: Prestel Publishing.
McNeill, Donald. The Global Architect. 2008. (Cultural Spaces Ser.). (Illus.). (ENG.). 192p. (C). pap. 35.95 *(978-0-415-95641-3(2))*; 200p. 130.00 *(978-0-415-95640-6(4))* Routledge.
Perkins, L. Bradford & Perkins Eastman Architects Staff. International Practice for Architects. 2007. (ENG., Illus.). 384p. 85.00 *(978-0-471-76087-0(0)*, Wiley) Wiley, John & Sons, Inc.
Piven, Peter & Perkins, Bradford. Architect's Essentials of Starting, Assessing, & Transitioning a Design Firm. 2008. (Architect's Essentials of Professional Practice Ser.: 17). (ENG., Illus.). 464p. 65.00 *(978-0-470-26106-4(4)*, Wiley) Wiley, John & Sons, Inc.
Princeton Architectural Press Staff. El Segundo. 2007. (ENG., Illus.). 400p. 60.00 *(978-1-56898-700-2(5))* Princeton Architectural Pr.
Rothman, Laura B., et al, eds. 2006 Project Management Survey: Of Architecture, Engineering, Planning & Environmental Consulting Firms. 11th ed. 2006. 228p. pap. 395.00 *(978-1-932372-98-4(9))* ZweigWhite.
Sauerbruch, Matthias & Hutton, Louisa. Sauerbruch Hutton: Colour in Architecture. 2006. (Illus.). 331p. 79.00 *(978-3-03778-083-1(5)*, 3037780835) Lars Muller Pubs. CHE. Dist: Springer.
Sinha, Sumita. Architecture for Rapid Change & Scarce Resources. 2012. (ENG., Illus.). 320p. 165.00 *(978-1-84971-115-9(1))*; pap. 39.95 *(978-1-84971-116-6(X))* Routledge.
Siva, Jessica Pooi Sun. Habitus Shock. 2009. 504p. pap. *(978-3-639-19314-5(8))* VDM Verlag Dr. Mueller e.K.
Slater, Stephen M. Managing Design & Construction: A Resource for Owners. 2007. (Illus.). 160p. 80.00 *(978-0-615-16019-1(0))* Turnberry Planning Inc.
Thompson. Architectural Design Procedures. 3rd ed. 2012. (ENG.). 288p. pap. 39.99 ***(978-0-7506-6559-9(9)***, Architectural Pr.) Elsevier Science & Technology Bks.
Till, Jeremy. Architecture Depends. 2009. (ENG., Illus.). 272p. (gr. 17). 25.95 *(978-0-262-01253-9(7))* MIT Pr.
Trachtenberg, Marvin. Building-in-Time: From Giotto to Alberti & Modern Oblivion. 2010. (ENG., Illus.). 516p. 65.00 *(978-0-300-16592-0(7))* Yale Univ. Pr.
Wonderland, et al, eds. Wonderland Manual for Emerging Architects: How to Establish & Run an Architecture Practice in Europe. 2011. (ENG., Illus.). 352p. 49.95 *(978-3-7091-0822-2(5)*, 3709108225) Springer Wien AUT. Dist: Springer.
Yale School of Architecture Staff. Negotiated Terrains. Kilmer, Heather & Rappaport, Nina, eds. 2009. (Yale School of Architecture Bks.). (ENG., Illus.). 152p. pap. 35.00 *(978-0-393-73323-5(8)*, 73323) Norton, W. W. & Co., Inc.
Yaneva, Albena. The Making of a Building: A Pragmatist Approach to Architecture. 2009. (Illus.). x, 227p. 49.95 *(978-3-03911-952-3(4))* Lang, Peter AG GBR. Dist: Lang, Peter.

ARCHITECTURAL PRACTICE—MANAGEMENT

Chen, Gang. Architectural Practice Simplified: A Survival Guide & Checklists for Building Construction & Site Improvements as well as Tips on Architecture, B. 2009. 190p. pap. 99.95 *(978-1-4327-1189-4(X))* Outskirts Pr., Inc.
DesignIntelligence: Technology Survey 2008. 2008. (Illus.). 71p. pap. 69.95 *(978-0-9785552-7-6(9)*, Ostberg) Greenway Communications.
Elvin, George. Integrated Practice in Architecture: Mastering Design-Build, Fast-Track, & Building Information Modeling. 2007. (ENG., Illus.). 272p. 85.00 *(978-0-471-99849-5(4)*, Wiley) Wiley, John & Sons, Inc.
Emmitt, Stephen. Design Management for Architects. 2007. (ENG., Illus.). 344p. per. 69.99 *(978-1-4051-3147-6(0)*, Wiley-Blackwell) Wiley, John & Sons, Inc.
Emmitt, Stephen, et al. Architectural Management: International Research & Practice. Emmitt, Stephen et al, eds. 2009. (ENG., Illus.). 344p. 144.99 *(978-1-4051-7786-3(1)*, Wiley-Blackwell) Wiley, John & Sons, Inc.
Klein, Rena M. The Architect's Guide to Small Firm Management: Making Chaos Work for Your Small Firm. 2010. (ENG., Illus.). 240p. 75.00 *(978-0-470-46648-3(0)*, Wiley) Wiley, John & Sons, Inc.
Lowell, Waverly B. & Nelb, Tawny Ryan. Architectural Records: Managing Design & Construction Records. 2006. *(978-1-931666-19-0(9))* Scarecrow Pr., Inc.
Poelman, W. & Keyson, D., eds. What Architects & Industrial Designers Can Teach Each Other about Managing the Design Process. 2008. 344p. pap. 79.00 *(978-1-58603-945-5(8))* IOS Pr., Inc.
Rubeling, Albert W. & Rubeling, Albert W., Jr. How to Start & Operate Your Own Design Firm: A Guide for Interior Designers & Architects. 2nd ed. 2007. (ENG.). 256p. per. 24.95 *(978-1-58115-474-0(7)*, 115474, Allworth Pr.) Skyhorse Publishing Co., Inc.
Thompson. Architectural Design Procedures. 3rd ed. 2012. (ENG.). 288p. pap. 39.99 ***(978-0-7506-6559-9(9)***, Architectural Pr.) Elsevier Science & Technology Bks.
Tunstall, Gavin. Managing the Building Design Process. 2nd rev. ed. 2006. (ENG., Illus.). 400p. per. 48.95 *(978-0-7506-6791-3(5))* Routledge.

ARCHITECTURAL RENDERING

see also Architecture—Sketch-Books; Entourage (Architectural Rendering)
Cusson, Roger & Cardoso, Jamie. Realistic Architectural Visualization with 3ds Max & mental Ray. 2nd ed. 2009. (ENG., Illus.), 295p. pap. 54.95 *(978-0-240-81229-8(8)*, Focal Pr.) Elsevier Science & Technology Bks.
Doyle, Michael E. Color Drawing: Design Drawing Skills & Techniques for Architects, Landscape Architects, & Interior Designers. 3rd rev. ed. 2006. (ENG., Illus.). 432p. 69.95 *(978-0-471-74190-9(6)*, Wiley) Wiley, John & Sons, Inc.
Fischer, Ole W. Sehnsucht - The Book of Architectural Longings: German Contribution to the 12th International Architecture Exhibition / Deutscher Beitrag auf der 12. Internationalen Architekturausstellung - La Biennale die Venezia 2010. 2010. 256p. 69.95 *(978-3-7091-0326-5(6))* Springer Wien AUT. Dist: Actar Birkhauser Distribution.
—What Architects Desire. 2010. 400p. pap. 39.95 *(978-3-7091-0328-9(2))* Springer Wien AUT. Dist: Springer.
Guptill, Arthur L. Drawing & Sketching in Pencil. 2007. (Dover Art Instruction Ser.). (ENG., Illus.). 208p. per. 19.95 *(978-0-486-46048-2(7))* Dover Pubns., Inc.
Jones, Will. Architects' Sketchbooks. 2011. (ENG., Illus.). 352p. 49.95 *(978-1-935202-46-2(4)*, Metropolis Bks.) D.A.P./Distributed Art Pubs.
Kapoor, Anish. Architecture Projects, 1 vol. 2011. (ENG., Illus.). 300p. 35.00 *(978-3-86521-999-2(3))* Steidl, Gerhard Druckerei und Verlag DEU. Dist: Innovative Logistics.
Kuhlo, Markus & Eggert, Enrico. Architectural Rendering with 3ds Max & V-Ray: Photorealistic Visualization. 2010. (ENG., Illus.). 224p. pap. 49.95 *(978-0-240-81477-3(0)*, Focal Pr.) Elsevier Science & Technology Bks.
Magonigle, H. Van Buren. Architectural Rendering in Wash. 2007. 220p. per. 24.95 *(978-1-4326-5026-1(2))* Kessinger Publishing, LLC.
Paredes, Cristina. Sketch - Public Buildings: How Architects Conceive Public Buildings. Paredes, Cristina, ed. 2008. (Illus.). 192p. *(978-84-96936-32-4(5))* Loft Pubns.
Schillaci, Fabio. Architectural Renderings. 2010. (ENG., Illus.). 466p. 75.00 *(978-0-470-66410-0(X)*, Wiley) Wiley, John & Sons, Inc.
—Architectural Renderings: Construction & Design Manual, 1 vol. 2010. (ENG.). 465p. 68.00 *(978-3-938666-63-0(3))* DOM Pubs. DEU. Dist: Innovative Logistics.
Smith, Brian L. 3ds Max Design Architectural Visualization: For Intermediate Users. 2011. (ENG., Illus.). 560p. 64.95 ***(978-0-240-82107-8(6)***, Focal Pr.) Elsevier Science & Technology Bks.
Sondermann, Horst. Light Shadow Space: Architectural Rendering with Cinema 4D. 2007. (Illus.). 238p. 69.95 *(978-3-211-48761-7(1)*, 3211487611) Springer Wien AUT. Dist: Springer.
van der Steen, Joep & Boardman, Ted. Rendering with Mental Ray & 3Ds Max. 2nd ed. 2009. (ENG., Illus.). 272p. pap. 54.95 *(978-0-240-81237-3(9)*, Focal Pr.) Elsevier Science & Technology Bks.
Wells, Malcolm. The Earth-Sheltered House: An Architect's Sketchbook. rev. ed. 2009. (ENG.). 192p. pap. 24.95 *(978-1-60358-107-3(3))* Chelsea Green Publishing.

ARCHITECTURAL SERVICES MARKETING

American Institute of Architects Staff. The Architecture Student's Handbook of Professional Practice. 14th ed. 2008. (ENG., Illus.). 720p. pap., stu. ed., instr.'s hndbk. ed. 115.00 *(978-0-470-08869-2(9)*, Wiley) Wiley, John & Sons, Inc.
Blyth, Alastair. Managing the Brief for Better Design. 2nd ed. 2009. (Illus.). 220p. pap. 62.95 *(978-0-415-46031-6(X))*; 160.00 *(978-0-415-46030-9(1))* Taylor & Francis Group.
Gallagher, Brian & Kayler, Kimberly. Leading with Marketing: The Resource for Creating, Building & Managing Successful Architecture/Engineering/Construction Marketing Programs. 2009. 212p. 24.99 *(978-1-4490-5677-3(6))*; pap. 49.95 *(978-1-4490-3967-7(7))* AuthorHouse.
Grosskurth, Lisa K. Marketing Professional Services. 2010. 240p. pap. *(978-3-8383-5069-1(3))* Lambert Academic Publishing.
Kliment, Stephen A. & Kliment, Stephen. Writing for Design Professionals: A Guide to Writing Successful Proposals, Letters, Brochures, Portfolios, Reports, Presentations, & Job Applications for Architects, Engineers, & Interior Designers. 2nd ed. 2006. (ENG., Illus.). 248p. 45.00 *(978-0-393-73185-9(5)*, 73185) Norton, W. W. & Co., Inc.
Linton, Harold. Portfolio Design. 4th ed. 2012. (ENG., Illus.). 224p. 45.00 ***(978-0-393-73253-5(3)***, 73253) Norton, W. W. & Co., Inc.
Reigle, Jack. Positioning for Architecture & Design Firms. 2011. (ENG., Illus.). 224p. 75.00 *(978-0-470-47225-5(1)*, Wiley) Wiley, John & Sons, Inc.
Rubeling, Albert W. & Rubeling, Albert W., Jr. How to Start & Operate Your Own Design Firm: A Guide for Interior Designers & Architects. 2nd ed. 2007. (ENG.). 256p. per. 24.95 *(978-1-58115-474-0(7)*, 115474, Allworth Pr.) Skyhorse Publishing Co., Inc.
Sawczuk, Basil. Marketing & Selling Professional Services in Architecture & Construction. 2009. (ENG., Illus.). 288p. pap. 72.99 *(978-1-4051-8187-7(7)*, Wiley-Blackwell) Wiley, John & Sons, Inc.
Smith, Dana K., et al. Building Information Modeling: A Strategic Implementation Guide for Architects, Engineers, Constructors, & Real Estate Asset Managers. 2009. (ENG., Illus.). 216p. 75.00 *(978-0-470-25003-7(8)*, Wiley) Wiley, John & Sons, Inc.
Williamson, Roxanne Kuter. American Architects & the Mechanics of Fame. 2011. (ENG., Illus.). 298p. pap. 35.00 *(978-0-292-72922-3(7))* Univ. of Texas Pr.
Yudelson, Jerry & Yudelson. Greening Existing Buildings. 2009. (ENG., Illus.). 336p. 79.95 *(978-0-07-163832-6(6)*, 0071638326) McGraw-Hill Professional Publishing.

ARCHITECTURE

Here are entered works on the design and style of structures. Works on the process of construction are entered under Building. General works on structures or edifices are entered under Buildings.
see also Arches; Architecture, Domestic; Architecture, Tropical; Barrier-Free Design; Building; Buildings; Castles; Church Architecture; Classicism in Architecture; Cloisters (Architecture); Color in Architecture; Decoration and Ornament, Architectural; Exhibition Buildings; Follies (Architecture); Historic Buildings; Indian Architecture; Library Architecture; Lighting, Architectural and Decorative; Military Architecture; Modular Coordination (Architecture); Monuments; Naval Architecture; Organic Architecture; Romanticism in Architcture; Skyscrapers; Space Frame Structures; Strains and Stresses; Structural Engineering; Sustainable Architecture
also headings beginning with the word Architectural
Abellan, Miquel. Building: the City: Mediterranean Architecture Details. Abellan, Miquel, ed. 2011. (SPA.). 352p. pap. 37.50 ***(978-84-15223-22-1(6))*** Instituto Monsa de Ediciones, S.A. ESP. Dist: Trans-Atlantic Pubns., Inc.
Abraham, Raimund, et al. Essays on Architecture. 2008. (Newarchitecture (Papadakis Publisher) Ser.). (ENG., Illus.). 234p. pap. 19.50 *(978-1-901092-54-6(X))* Papadakis Dist A/C.
Abruzzo, Emily. The Official Catalog for Workshopping: An American Model for Architectural Practice. 2010. (ENG., Illus.). 128p. pap., wbk. ed. 20.00 *(978-1-61689-017-9(7))* Princeton Architectural Pr.
Accoella, Alfonso. Stone Architecture: Ancient & Modern Construction Skills. 2006. (ITA & ENG., Illus.). 654p. 150.00 *(978-88-7624-696-8(7))* Skira Editore ITA. Dist: Random Hse., Inc.
Alps: Alpine Landscape Project Sustainable. 2011. (ENG & ITA.). 159p. pap. 14.95 *(978-2-03-840000-7(8))* LIST - Laboratorio Editoriale ITA. Dist: Actar Birkhauser Distribution.
American Institute Staff, et al. Architectural Graphic Standards 4. 0. 2008. (Ramsey/Sleeper Architectural Graphic Standards Ser.: 22). (ENG.). 3180.00 *(978-0-470-34441-5(5)*, Wiley) Wiley, John & Sons, Inc.
Anderson, Janice. Palaces. 2009. (ENG., Illus.). 256p. 24.99 *(978-0-7858-2420-6(0)*, 0785824200, Chartwell) Book Sales, Inc.
Anthony, Ethan. The Architecture of Ralph Adams Cram & His Office. 2007. (ENG., Illus.). 160p. 60.00 *(978-0-393-73104-0(9)*, 73104) Norton, W. W. & Co., Inc.
Antique Collectors Club Staff & Architects 49 Staff. Architects, Vol. 49. 2006. (ENG., Illus.). pap. 39.50 *(978-1-875498-81-9(8))* Images Publishing Group AUS. Dist: National Bk. Network.
Antique Collectors Club Staff & Wooley, Ken. Ken Woolley & Ancher Mortlock & Woolley. 2006. (Master Architect Series IV). (ENG., Illus.). 59.95 *(978-1-86470-024-4(6)*, Images Publishing Dist Ac) Antique Collectors' Club GBR. Dist: National Bk. Network.
Architects Design Partnership Staff. Education & Contextualism: Architects Design Partnership. McCorquodale, Duncan, ed. 2007. (ENG., Illus.). 184p. 45.00 *(978-1-904772-71-2(4))* Black Dog Publishing Ltd. GBR. Dist: Perseus Distribution.
Architecture. (Wall Calendars Ser.). (ENG, FRE & GER.). 12.99 *(978-3-8327-1166-5(X))*; (Illus.). spiral bd. 39.99 *(978-3-8327-0991-4(6))*; (ENG, FRE & GER., Illus.). spiral bd. 14.99 *(978-3-8327-1291-4(7))* teNeues Publishing Co.
Armborst, Tobias. The Arsenal of Exclusion/Inclusion: 101 Things that Open & Close the City. 2011. 288p. pap. *(978-84-92861-80-4(0))* Actar Birkhauser Distribution.
Art & Architecture, Set. 2008. 342p. 200.00 *(978-0-415-46403-1(X))* Routledge.
Asensio, Francisco. New Architecture: An International Atlas. 2007. (ENG., Illus.). 512p. 42.00 *(978-0-8109-9282-5(5))* Abrams.
Asish, Robert. Smart Geometry as Architectural Exploration. 2008. (Illus.). 176p. 70.00 *(978-0-415-70065-8(5))* Taylor & Francis Group.
Assouline. Restoration Hardware. 2010. (ENG.). 220p. 65.00 *(978-2-7594-0480-3(3))* Assouline FRA. Dist: Perseus Distribution.
Atkinson, Harriet & Aynsley, Jeremy, eds. The Banham Lectures: Essays on Designing the Future. 2009. (ENG., Illus.). 1p. 49.95 *(978-1-84788-302-5(8))* Berg Pubs. GBR. Dist: Macmillan.
Aureli, Pier Vittorio. The Possibility of an Absolute Architecture. 2011. (Writing Architecture Ser.). (ENG., Illus.). 272p. (gr. 17). pap. 24.95 *(978-0-262-51579-5(2))* MIT Pr.
Avery, Bryan & Heathcote, Edwin. Fragments of Wilderness City: The Work of Bryan Avery. 2011. (ENG., Illus.). 160p. pap. 45.00 *(978-1-904772-56-3(7))* Black Dog Publishing Ltd. GBR. Dist: Perseus Distribution.
Ayres, Phil, ed. Persistent Modelling. 2012. (ENG., Illus.). 224p. (C). 165.00 ***(978-0-415-59406-6(5))***; pap. 49.95 ***(978-0-415-59407-3(3))*** Routledge.
Baca, Murtha, et al. Cataloging Cultural Objects: A Guide to Describing Cultural Works & Their Images. 2006. (Illus.). 396p. per. 75.00 *(978-0-8389-3564-4(8))* American Library Assn.
Ballantyne, Andrew. Architecture. 2010. (Brief Insight Ser.). (ENG.). 192p. (Orig.). 14.95 *(978-1-4027-7542-0(3))* Sterling Publishing Co., Inc.
Balmori, Diana & Sanders, Joel. Groundwork: Between Landscape & Architecture. 2011. (ENG., Illus.). 208p. 50.00 *(978-1-58093-313-1(0))* Monacelli Pr., Inc.
Banner, Fiona. Banner. (Illus.). 176p. 38.00 *(978-1-902854-10-6(1))* Birkhauser Verlag AG CHE. Dist: Chronicle Bks. LLC.
Bar-Eli, Amos. On the Non-Complete. 2011. 164p. pap. ***(978-3-8454-2291-6(2))*** Lambert Academic Publishing.
Barbara, Anna & Perliss, Anthony. Invisible Architecture: Experiencing Places Through the Sense of Smell. 2006. (ENG., Illus.). 264p. pap. 14.99 *(978-88-7624-267-0(8))* Skira Editore ITA. Dist: Random Hse., Inc.
Barman, Christian, et al. Art & Architecture: Balbus or the Future of Architecture Heraclitus or the future of Films Euterpe or the Future of Art The Future of Futurism, 25 vols. 2008. (Illus.). IV, 332p. 215.00 *(978-0-415-46400-0(5))* Routledge.
Barrie, Thomas. The Sacred In-Between: The Mediating Roles of Architecture. 2010. (ENG., Illus.). 288p. (C). 165.00 *(978-0-415-77963-0(4))*; pap. 36.95 *(978-0-415-77964-7(2))* Taylor & Francis Group GBR. (Routledge). Dist: Taylor & Francis Group.
Beale, S. Sophia. The Amateur's Guide to Architecture. 2007. (ENG.). 190p. 37.95 *(978-0-548-04104-8(0))* Kessinger Publishing, LLC.
Beaver, Robyn, ed. VOA Associates Incorporated: Architecture, Planning, Interior Design. 2008. (Master Architect (Unnumberd) Ser.). (ENG., Illus.). 280p. 59.95 *(978-1-876907-34-1(7)*, Images Publishing Dist Ac) Antique Collectors' Club GBR. Dist: National Bk. Network.
Benjamin, Asher. Country Builders Assistant Containing A. 2006. 64p. per. *(978-1-4067-9587-5(9)*, Hesperides Pr.) Read Bks.
Beorkrem, Christopher. Material Strategies in Digital Fabrication. 2012. (ENG., Illus.). 224p. (C). 165.00 ***(978-0-415-53364-5(3))***; pap. 44.95 ***(978-0-415-53366-9(X))*** Routledge.
Bergmann, Bettina Ann. Roman Frescoes from Boscoreale: The Villa of Publius Fannius Synistor in Reality & Virtual Reality. 2010. (Illus.). 48p. 19.95 *(978-1-58839-394-4(1))* Metropolitan Museum of Art, The.
Berkus, Barry A. Architecture/Art/Parallels/Connections. 2006. (ENG., Illus.). 60.00 *(978-1-86470-084-8(X))* Images Publishing Group AUS. Dist: National Bk. Network.
Berkus, Barry A. & Berkus, Barry. Sculpting Space. 2006. (House Design Ser.). (ENG., Illus.). 128p. 49.50 *(978-1-86470-088-6(2))* Images Publishing Group AUS. Dist: National Bk. Network.
Berlin eV UIA, Berlin eV. Uiakongress 2002. pap. 42.00 *(978-3-7643-6751-0(2))* Birkhauser Verlag AG CHE. Dist: Chronicle Bks. LLC.
Bernstein, Phillip & Deamer, Peggy, eds. Building (in) the Future: Recasting Labor in Architecture. 2010. (ENG., Illus.). 216p. pap. 29.95 *(978-1-56898-806-1(0))* Princeton Architectural Pr.
Bilbeisi, Moh'D. Graphic Journaling. rev. ed. 2011. (ENG.). 228p. pap. 61.95 *(978-0-7575-6262-4(0))* Kendall Hunt Publishing Co.
Birnbaum, Daniel, et al, texts. Carsten Höller - Experience. 2011. (ENG., Illus.). 256p. 60.00 ***(978-0-8478-3760-1(2)***, Skira) Rizzoli International Pubns., Inc.
Bizley, Graham. Architecture in Detail. 2007. (ENG., Illus.). 200p. pap. 59.95 *(978-0-7506-8585-6(9))* Routledge.
Blizard, Mark. Architecture: Land Culture Practice. rev. ed. (ENG.). 226p. 2010. pap. 68.25 *(978-0-7575-5907-5(7))* 2008. pap. 70.25 *(978-0-7575-5157-4(2))* Kendall Hunt Publishing Co.
Bloom, Barbara. My Library. 2012. (ENG.). (J). pap. 15.00 ***(978-0-615-61807-4(3))*** Bloomfield Township Public Library.
Bloszies, Charles. Old Buildings, New Designs: Architectural Transformations. 2011. (ENG., Illus.). 144p. pap. 24.95 ***(978-1-61689-035-3(5))*** Princeton Architectural Pr.
Boehm, Werner W. Gut Gezielt, Schuetze. Date not set. (GER., Illus.). 180p. *(978-3-487-08395-7(7))* Olms, Georg Verlag AG.
Boekel, Andrea, ed. Retail Therapy: Store Design Today. 2007. (International Spaces Ser.). (ENG., Illus.). 224p. 55.00 *(978-1-86470-115-9(3))* Images Publishing Group AUS. Dist: National Bk. Network.
Boglachev, S. V. Arkhitektura Starogo Zheleznovodska. 2010. (RUS & ENG., Illus.). 479p. *(978-5-903129-23-2(4))* Syndicat National Des Entreprises Gaies.
Bollnow, Otto Friedrich. Human Space. Kohlmaier, Joseph, ed. Shuttleworth, Christine, tr. from GER. 2011. (ENG.). 320p. pap. 35.00 *(978-0-907259-35-0(9))* Princeton Architectural Pr.
Borden, G. P. Material Precedent. 2010. (ENG., Illus.). 480p. 85.00 *(978-0-470-47729-8(6)*, Wiley) Wiley, John & Sons, Inc.
Borden, Gail Peter & Meredith, Michael, eds. Matter: Material Processes in Architectural Production. 2011. (ENG., Illus.). 520p. (C). pap. 49.95 *(978-0-415-78029-2(2))* Routledge.
Borngasser, Barbara. Early Modern Architecture. Toman, Rolf, ed. 2007. (Illus.). 304p. 39.95 *(978-3-89985-029-1(7))* Feierabend Verlag OHG DEU. Dist: Perseus-PGW.
Bossiere, Olivier. New Museums. (Illus.). 160p. *(978-2-7450-0036-1(5))* Telleri, Editions.
Boussabaine, Halim. Embracing Complexity in the Built Environment. 2008. (ENG., Illus.). 72p. pap. 97.50 *(978-1-84407-640-6(7))* Routledge.
Bovone, Ines. Class A Buildings: The Next Generation = Edifici Di Classe a: La Prossima Generazione. 2009. (ITA & ENG.). *(978-0-87420-126-0(8))*; *(978-0-9818336-0-6(8))* Fenwick Publishing Group, Inc.

Box, Hal. Think Like an Architect. 2007. (Roger Fullington Series in Architecture). (ENG., Illus.). 224p. 45.00 *(978-0-292-71635-3(4))*; pap. 26.95 *(978-0-292-71636-0(2))* Univ. of Texas Pr.

Braun. Facade Greenery. 2011. (ENG., Illus.). 176p. 24.95 *(978-3-03768-075-9(X)*, Braun Publish,Csi) Continental Sales, Inc.

—Waterscapes. 2011. (ENG., Illus.). 176p. 24.95 *(978-3-03768-074-2(1)*, Braun Publish,Csi) Continental Sales, Inc.

Briseno, Alexander. Decoration. Abruzzo, Emily & Solomon, Jonathan D., eds. 2006. (ENG., Illus.). 160p. pap. 24.95 *(978-1-56898-580-0(0))* Princeton Architectural Pr.

Bruno, Giuliana. Atlas of Emotion: Journeys in Art, Architecture, & Film. 2007. (ENG., Illus.). 496p. pap. 44.95 *(978-1-85984-133-4(3)*, 859133) Verso Bks. GBR. Dist: Norton, W. W. & Co., Inc.

Bryce, James. South America. reprint ed. lib. bdg. 48.00 *(978-0-7426-1229-7(5))* Classic Bks.

Buchli, Victor, et al. Home Cultures Volume 6 Issue 3: The Journal of Architecture, Design & Domestic Space. 2010. (Illus.). 128p. pap. 59.95 *(978-1-84788-517-3(9))* Berg Pubs. GBR. Dist: Macmillan.

Building 8: Edmond & Corrigan at Rmit. (Illus.). pap. *(978-1-86395-313-9(2))* Bookman Pr.

Burchard, John Ely. Symbolism in Architecture: The Decline of the Monumental. 2011. 42p. 35.95 ***(978-1-258-04415-2(3))*** Literary Licensing, LLC.

Butcher, Scott D. Yorks Historic Architecture. 2008. 160p. pap. 19.99 *(978-1-59629-503-2(1))* History Pr., The.

Cache, Bernard & Beauce, Patrick. Objectile: Fast-Wood: A Brouillon Project. 2007. (Illus.). 104p. pap. 29.95 *(978-3-211-25238-3(X)*, 321125238X) Springer Wien AUT. Dist: Actar Birkhauser Distribution.

Campbell, David. Stone in Traditional Architecture. 2011. (Illus.). 216p. 45.00 *(978-0-7643-3614-0(2))* Schiffer Publishing, Ltd.

Carabet, Brian & Shand, John. Spectacular Homes of the Carolinas: An Exclusive Showcase of the Carolinas' Finest Designers. Panache Partners LLC., Staff, ed. 2006. (Spectacular Homes Ser.). (ENG., Illus.). 168p. 39.95 *(978-0-9745747-8-3(3))* Panache Partners, LLC.

Carter, Peter. Mies Van der Rohe at Work. 2006. (SPA.). pap. 39.95 *(978-0-7148-9853-7(8))* Phaidon Pr., Inc.

Caruso, Adam. The Feeling of Things. 2009. (ENG., Illus.). 96p. 25.00 *(978-84-343-1186-2(0))* Poligrafa, Ediciones, S. A. ESP. Dist: D.A.P./Distributed Art Pubs.

Castro, Eva, ed. Critical Territories: From Academia to Praxis. 2011. 160p. pap. 34.95 *(978-88-95623-37-5(1))* LIST - Laboratorio Editoriale ITA. Dist: Actar Birkhauser Distribution.

Cato, Ken. Ken Cato: The Dimensions of Designs. 2006. (Hands on Graphics Ser.). (ENG., Illus.). 128p. pap. 19.95 *(978-1-876907-73-0(8))* Images Publishing Group AUS. Dist: National Bk. Network.

Chaiwiwatworakul, Pipat. Daylighting in the Tropics. 2011. 248p. pap. ***(978-3-8443-1339-0(7))*** Lambert Academic Publishing.

Chaplin, Sarah & Stara, Alexandra. Curating Architecture & the City. 2009. (ENG., Illus.). 258p. 165.00 *(978-0-415-48982-9(2))*; pap. 53.95 *(978-0-415-48983-6(0))* Routledge.

Chapman, Tony, ed. Architecture 06: The Guide to the Riba Awards. 2006. (Architecture: the Guide to the Riba Awards Ser.). (ENG., Illus.). 216p. pap. 22.95 *(978-1-85894-342-8(6))* Merrell Pubs. Ltd. GBR. Dist: Perseus Distribution.

Checa, Jorge. Gracian y la Imaginacion Arquitectonica. 28.00 *(978-0-916379-28-5(0))* Scripta Humanistica.

Chen, Aric & Adams, Michael. Hospitality. 2009. (Illus.). 176p. 60.00 *(978-1-58471-153-7(1))* Visual Reference Pubns., Inc.

Chen, Simon. Institutional Choices & Designs in Neighborhood Management. 2010. 348p. pap. *(978-3-8383-6067-6(2))* Lambert Academic Publishing.

Childs, Mark. Urban Composition: Designing Community through Urban Design. 2012. (ENG., Illus.). 144p. pap. 24.95 ***(978-1-61689-052-0(5))*** Princeton Architectural Pr.

Childs, Mark C. Squares: A Public Place Design Guide for Urbanists. 2006. (ENG., Illus.). 230p. (C). pap. 34.95 *(978-0-8263-3004-8(5))* Univ. of New Mexico Pr.

Ching, Francis D. K. & Ching, Francis D. Architecture: Form, Space, & Order. 3rd rev. ed. 2007. (ENG., Illus.). 448p. pap. 49.95 *(978-0-471-75216-5(9)*, Wiley) Wiley, John & Sons, Inc.

Chong, Seng Kwong, et al. Runtime Support Framework for Agile Manufacturing MacHinery. 2010. 220p. pap. *(978-3-639-12385-2(9))* VDM Verlag Dr. Mueller e.K.

Chramosta, Walter M. Ernst Giselbrecht & Gottfried Bechtold: The School in Kaindorf. (Illus.). 64p. *(978-3-7757-0618-6(6))* Hatje Cantz Verlag GmbH & Co KG DEU. Dist: D.A.P./Distributed Art Pubs.

Coleman, Peter. Shopping Environments: Evolution, Planning & Design. 2006. (ENG., Illus.). 472p. 92.95 *(978-0-7506-6001-3(5))* Routledge.

Collectors Club. International Architecture Yearbook, Vol. 5. 2006. (ENG., Illus.). 75.00 *(978-1-86470-017-6(3))* Images Publishing Group AUS. Dist: National Bk. Network.

Cool, Timothy L. Successful Master Planning: More than Pretty Pictures. 2010. 108p. 23.95 *(978-1-4502-2195-5(5))*; pap. 13.95 *(978-1-4502-2197-9(1))* iUniverse, Inc.

Corkill, P. A., et al. Structure & Architectural Design. 4th rev. ed. Date not set. (Illus.). 224p. (C). reprint ed. pap. *(978-0-9674690-0-3(7))* Market Publishing.

Crafti, Stephen. Office. 2006. (ENG., Illus.). 224p. 65.00 *(978-1-920744-65-6(7))* Images Publishing Group AUS. Dist: National Bk. Network.

Cragoe, Carol Davidson. How to Read Buildings: A Crash Course in Architectural Styles. 2008. (ENG., Illus.). 256p. pap. 17.95 *(978-0-8478-3112-8(4))* Rizzoli International Pubns., Inc.

Craig, James A., et al. Resilience. 2012. (Pamphlet Architecture Ser.). (ENG.). 80p. pap. 17.95 ***(978-1-61689-031-5(2))*** Princeton Architectural Pr.

Creighton, Thomas H. Building for Modern Man. 2007. pap. *(978-1-4067-5635-7(0))* Read Bks.

Crosbie, Michael J. Architecture for Architects. 2006. (ENG., Illus.). 55.00 *(978-1-920744-91-5(6)*, Images Publishing Dist Ac) Antique Collectors' Club GBR. Dist: National Bk. Network.

Crosbie, Michael J., et al. Architecture for Science. 2006. (ENG., Illus.). 208p. 65.00 *(978-1-920744-64-9(9))* Images Publishing Group AUS. Dist: National Bk. Network.

Cruickshank, Dan. Adventures in Architecture. (ENG., Illus.). 2009. 392p. pap. 14.95 *(978-0-7538-2416-0(7)*, Phoenix) 2008. 288p. 29.95 *(978-0-297-84444-0(X)*, Weidenfeld & Nicolson) Orion Publishing Group, Ltd. GBR. Dist: Sterling Publishing Co., Inc.

Cumberlidge, Clare. Unlondon. pap. 19.95 *(978-1-902854-18-2(7))* Princeton Architectural Pr.

DAAB Media Staff. Delugan Meissl: Associated Architects, 1 vol. 2008. (ENG, GER, FRE, SPA & ITA., Illus.). 175p. 29.95 *(978-3-937718-87-3(7))* DAAB Media Gmbh DEU. Dist: Innovative Logistics.

DAAB Media Staff, creator. Glass Design, 1 vol. 2008. (ENG, FRE, GER, SPA & ITA., Illus.). 400p. 37.95 *(978-3-937718-35-4(4))* DAAB Media Gmbh DEU. Dist: Innovative Logistics.

DAAB Media Staff, ed. Exhibition Design, 1 vol. 2009. (ITA, FRE, GER, SPA & ENG., Illus.). 384p. 69.95 *(978-3-86654-062-0(0))* DAAB Media Gmbh DEU. Dist: Innovative Logistics.

—Medical Design, 1 vol. 2008. (ENG, FRE, GER, ITA & SPA., Illus.). 400p. 37.95 *(978-3-937718-58-3(3))* DAAB Media Gmbh DEU. Dist: Innovative Logistics.

Dahl, Julian. Architecture Studio. 2006. (Millennium Ser.). (ENG & FRE., Illus.). 256p. 75.00 *(978-1-86470-021-3(1))* Images Publishing Group AUS. Dist: National Bk. Network.

d'Athegrave;nes, Française. French Connection: 100 Years with Danish Architects at L'Ecute;cole. 2010. (Monographs of the Danish Institute at Athens). (ENG., Illus.). 108p. (C). 29.00 *(978-87-7934-567-6(0))* Aarhus Universitetsforlag DNK. Dist: ISD.

De Baeck, Philippe. Apartment Bible, 1 vol. 2008. (ENG., Illus.). 432p. pap. 124.95 *(978-90-76886-68-8(7))* Tectum B.V.B.A. BEL. Dist: Innovative Logistics.

De Visser, John. Old Ontario Houses: Traditions in Local Architecture. 2nd rev. ed. 2009. (ENG., Illus.). 224p. pap. *(978-1-55407-504-1(1))* Firefly Bks., Ltd.

Dean, Carolyn. A Culture of Stone: Inka Perspectives on Rock. 2010. (ENG., Illus.). 320p. 84.95 *(978-0-8223-4791-0(1))*; pap. 23.95 *(978-0-8223-4807-8(1))* Duke Univ. Pr.

Dean, Kathryn. Dean/Wolf Architects: Constructive Continuum. 2011. (ENG., Illus.). 224p. pap. 40.00 *(978-1-56898-829-0(X))* Princeton Architectural Pr.

Dekker, Harm. Serpentine Gallery Pavilion 2010. 2010. 72p. pap. *(978-3-8383-9413-8(5))* Lambert Academic Publishing.

Delbene, Giacomo, ed. Public, Private, Ephemeral. 2008. 150p. pap. *(978-84-612-1509-6(5))* Actar Birkhauser Distribution.

Demand, Thomas, et al. Art, Fashion & Work for Hire: Thomas Demand, Peter Saville, Hedi Slimane, Hans Ulrich Obrist & Cristina Bechtler in Conversation. 2008. (Kunst und Architektur im Gespräch Art & Architecture in Discussion Ser.). (ENG & GER., Illus.). 112p. pap. 39.95 *(978-3-211-75787-1(2)*, 3211757872) Springer.

Desai, Madhuri & Rajagopalan, Mrinalini. Colonial Frames Nationalist Histories: Architecture Modernism & Identity. 2012. (Ashgate Studies in Architecture Ser.). (Illus.). 332p. 119.95 ***(978-0-7546-7880-9(6))*** Ashgate Publishing Co.

D'Hooghe, Alexander. The Liberal Monument: Urban Design & the Late Modern Project. 2010. (ENG., Illus.). 240p. 29.95 *(978-1-56898-824-5(9))* Princeton Architectural Pr.

Discoe, Paul & Quinn, Alexandra. Zen Architecture: The Building Process As Practice. 2008. (ENG., Illus.). 240p. 40.00 *(978-1-4236-0009-1(6))* Gibbs Smith, Publisher.

Dittmer, Lori. The Future of Architecture. 2012. (What's Next? Ser.). 48p. (gr. 5-12). 23.95 ***(978-1-60818-220-6(7)***, Creative Education) Creative Co., The.

Dizik, A. Allen. The Estimator. 12.95 *(978-0-938614-03-6(7))* Stratford Hse. Publishing Co.

Doig, Alan. Theo Van Doesburg: Painting into Architecture, Theory into Practice. 2010. (ENG.). 280p. pap. 42.00 *(978-0-521-12981-7(8))* Cambridge Univ. Pr.

Dolan, Halil. Urban Threshold. 2010. 64p. pap. *(978-3-639-18659-8(1))* VDM Verlag Dr. Mueller e.K.

Downing, Andrew Jackson. Andrew Jackson Downing: Essential Texts. Twombly, Robert, ed. 2012. (ENG., Illus.). 400p. pap. 35.00 ***(978-0-393-73359-4(9)***, 73359) Norton, W. W. & Co., Inc.

Drake, Scott. A Well-Composed Body - Anthropomorphism in Architecture. 2008. 268p. pap. *(978-3-639-06652-4(9))* VDM Verlag Dr. Mueller e.K.

Dubbeldam, Winka. At-INdex. 2007. (ENG., Illus.). 224p. pap. 40.00 *(978-1-56898-535-0(5))* Princeton Architectural Pr.

Duchamp, Marcel. Marcel Duchamp: Plays & Wins. (Illus.). 224p. pap. 18.95 *(978-2-86234-001-2(4))* Marval Editions FRA. Dist: D.A.P./Distributed Art Pubs.

Dudek, Mark. Nurseries: A Design Guide. 2013. (ENG., Illus.). 240p. pap. 49.95 *(978-0-7506-6951-1(9))* Routledge.

Duliere, Aude-Line & Wong, Clara. Monsterpieces: Once upon a Time ... of the 2000s! 2010. (ENG., Illus.). 100p. pap. 19.95 *(978-0-9819857-3-2(4))* Oro Editions.

Dutoit, Allison, et al, eds. Quality Out of Control: Standards for Measuring Architecture. 2010. (ENG., Illus.). 240p. 165.00 *(978-0-415-55365-0(2))*; pap. 53.95 *(978-0-415-55366-7(0))* Taylor & Francis Group GBR. (Routledge). Dist: Taylor & Francis Group.

Dutoit, Allison, et al. Quality Out of Control: Standards for Measuring Architecture. 2010. 53.95 *(978-0-203-86184-4(1))* Routledge.

Earth Pledge Foundation & Earth Pledge, eds. Earth Pledge White Papers: Series on Sustainable Development. 2009. (ENG.). 784p. ring bd. 55.00 *(978-0-9675099-3-8(9))* Earth Pledge Foundation.

Eeles, Peter & Cripps, Peter. The Process of Software Architecting. 2009. (ENG., Illus.). 432p. pap. 54.99 *(978-0-321-35748-9(5))* Addison Wesley Professional.

Emmer, Michele, ed. Imagine Math: Between Culture & Mathematics. 2012. (Matematica e Cultura Ser.). (ENG., Illus.). x, 290p. 89.95 ***(978-88-470-2426-7(9)***, 8847024269) Springer.

Emmitt, Stephen. Architectural Technology. 2nd ed. 2012. (ENG.). 264p. pap. 52.99 ***(978-1-4051-9479-2(0)***, Wiley-Blackwell) Wiley, John & Sons, Inc.

Emmitt, Stephen. Managing Interdisciplinary Projects: A Primer for Architecture, Engineering & Construction. 2010. (ENG., Illus.). 200p. 130.00 *(978-0-415-48170-0(8))*; pap. 44.95 *(978-0-415-48171-7(6))* Routledge.

Engel, Heino, contrib. by. Tragsysteme / Structure Systems, 1 vol. 3rd ed. 2007. (GER & ENG., Illus.). 352p. 60.00 *(978-3-7757-1876-9(1))* Hatje Cantz Verlag GmbH & Co KG DEU. Dist: D.A.P./Distributed Art Pubs.

Engels, Christoph. 1000 Sacred Places: The World's Most Extraordinary Spiritual Sites, 1 vol. 2010. (ENG., Illus.). 960p. pap. 29.99 *(978-3-8331-5480-5(2))* h.f.ullmann DEU. Dist: Innovative Logistics.

Erlhoff, Michael & (ed.), Michael Erlhoff. St. Moritz Design Summit. Erlhoff, Michael, ed. 2007. (ENG., Illus.). 192p. 15.00 *(978-3-89790-175-9(7))* Arnoldsche Art Pubs. DEU. Dist: Antique Collectors' Club.

Exley, Peter & Exley, Sharon. Design for Kids. 2007. (ENG., Illus.). 224p. 60.00 *(978-1-86470-180-7(3))* Images Publishing Group AUS. Dist: National Bk. Network.

Fahmy, Isis. Around the World with Isis. 2006. (ENG., Illus.). 240p. 30.00 *(978-1-901092-49-3(6))* Papadakis Dist A/C.

Fajardo, Julio. Starchitects: Visionary Architects of the Twenty-First Century. 2010. (ENG., Illus.). 592p. pap. 39.99 *(978-0-06-196877-8(3)*, Collins Design) HarperCollins Pubs.

Farrell, Peter. Writing a Built Environment Dissertation: Practical Guidance & Examples. 2011. (ENG., Illus.). 280p. pap. 37.95 *(978-1-4051-9851-6(6)*, Wiley-Blackwell) Wiley, John & Sons, Inc.

Farrelly, Lorraine. Construction & Materiality. 2009. (Basics Architecture Ser.). (ENG., Illus.). 176p. pap. 29.95 *(978-2-940373-83-3(3))* AVA Publishing GBR. Dist: Ingram Pub. Services.

—The Fundamentals of Architecture. 2007. (Fundamentals Ser.). (ENG., Illus.). 176p. pap. 38.50 *(978-2-940373-48-2(5))* AVA Publishing GBR. Dist: Ingram Pub. Services.

—The Fundamentals of Architecture. 2nd rev. ed. 2012. (ENG.). 192p. (C). pap. 38.50 ***(978-2-940411-75-7(1))*** Ava Publishing SA CHE. Dist: Ingram Pub. Services.

Faulkner, William. Introduction to Environmental Design. 2nd rev. ed. 2011. (ENG.). 68.00 ***(978-0-7575-9209-6(0))*** Kendall Hunt Publishing Co.

Fazio, Michael W. Landscape of Transformations: Architecture & Birmingham, Alabama. 2010. (ENG.). 300p. 44.95 *(978-1-57233-687-2(0))* Univ. of Tennessee Pr.

Feireiss, Lukas, ed. Testify! The Consequences of Architecture. 2011. (ENG., Illus.). 240p. pap. 39.95 ***(978-90-5662-823-9(2))*** NAi Uitgevers / Publishers Stichting NLD. Dist: D.A.P./Distributed Art Pubs.

Fentress, Curtis & Chandler, Mary Volez. Public Architecture: The Art Inside. 2011. (ENG., Illus.). 360p. 85.00 *(978-0-9826226-0-5(0))* Oro Editions.

Feria, José María, ed. Territorial Heritage & Development. 2012. (ENG.). 240p. (C). 129.00 ***(978-0-415-62145-8(3)***, CRC Press) Taylor & Francis Group GBR. Dist: Taylor & Francis Group.

Finsterwalder, Rudolf, ed. Form Follows Nature: Eine Geschichte der Natur als Vorbild für Formgebung in Ingenieurbau, Architektur und Kunst - A History of Nature as Model for Design in Engineering, Architecture & Art. 2011. (GER & ENG., Illus.). 512p. 89.95 *(978-3-7091-0855-0(1)*, 3709108551) Springer Wien AUT. Dist: Springer.

Fisher, T. J. & Guste, Roy F. Orleans Embrace with the Secret Gardens of the Vieux Carre. 2007. (ENG., Illus.). 388p. 50.00 *(978-0-9773514-7-3(5))* Morgana Pr. LLC.

Fisher, Thomas. Ethics for Architects: 50 Dilemmas of Professional Practice. 2010. (ENG., Illus.). 144p. pap. 24.95 *(978-1-56898-946-4(6))* Princeton Architectural Pr.

Fitch, James Marston. James Marston Fitch: Selected Writings 1933-1997. Sawin, Martica, ed. 2007. (ENG., Illus.). 320p. per. 27.95 *(978-0-393-73229-0(0)*, 73229) Norton, W. W. & Co., Inc.

Fountain, Daniel E. Let's Restore Our Land: Church & Community Leaders Working Together to Restore the Land. 2007. (Illus.). 256p. pap. 5.00 *(978-0-9653360-3-1(4))* ECHO, Inc. (Educational Concerns for Hunger Organization).

Fox, Austin M. Symbol & Show: The Pan-American Exposition of 1901. (Illus.). 128p. 15.95 *(978-1-879201-33-0(X))* Western New York Wares, Inc.

Fox, Warwick. A Theory of General Ethics: Human Relationships, Nature, & the Built Environment. 2006. (ENG.). 400p. (gr. 17). 68.00 *(978-0-262-06255-8(0))*; per. 30.00 *(978-0-262-56219-5(7))* MIT Pr.

Franke, Anselm, ed. B-Zone: Becoming Europe & Beyond. 2006. (Illus.). 416p. (gr. 13-18). pap. 40.00 *(978-84-96540-05-7(7))* Kunst-Werke Berlin e.V. DEU. Dist: D.A.P./Distributed Art Pubs.

Friedman, Avi. The Nature of Place: A Search for Authenticity. 2011. (ENG., Illus.). 192p. pap. 19.95 ***(978-1-61689-038-4(X))*** Princeton Architectural Pr.

Ganji, Naveen & Basa, Srinivas. Enhanced Nms Tool Architecture. 2010. 88p. pap. *(978-3-8383-6591-6(7))* Lambert Academic Publishing.

Gantenbein, Köbi & Ursprung, Philip. Zumthor sehen. Bilder von Hans Danuser: Nachdenken über Architektur und Fotografie. Gantenbein, Köbi, ed. 2009. (GER & ENG., Illus.). 88p. 60.00 *(978-3-85881-235-3(8))* Scheidegger und Spiess AG, Verlag CHE. Dist: Antique Collectors' Club.

Gao, Arthur. 50 Awarded Architecture. 2011. (ENG.). 304p. 50.00 *(978-988-19740-0-6(3))* Design Media Publishing Ltd. HKG. Dist: BookMasters Distribution Services (BDS).

Garcia, Mark. Diagrams of Architecture. 2010. (AD Reader Ser.). (ENG., Illus.). 320p. 145.00 *(978-0-470-51944-8(4)*, Wiley) Wiley, John & Sons, Inc.

—The Diagrams of Architecture. 2010. (AD Reader Ser.: 1). (ENG., Illus.). 320p. pap. 85.00 *(978-0-470-51945-5(2)*, Wiley) Wiley, John & Sons, Inc.

Gifford, John. Fife. (Illus.). 468p. 65.00 *(978-0-14-071077-9(9))* Penguin Bks., Ltd. GBR. Dist: Trafalgar Square Publishing.

Giurgola, Mitchell & Architects, Mitchell Giurgola. Boomer Buildings: Six Buildings Back from the Brink. 2006. (ENG., Illus.). 162p. 70.00 *(978-1-920744-96-0(7))* Images Publishing Group AUS. Dist: National Bk. Network.

Gould, Jeremy. Plymouth: Vision of a Modern City. 2011. (Informed Conservation Ser.). (ENG., Illus.). 96p. (C). pap. 20.00 *(978-1-84802-050-4(3))* English Heritage GBR. Dist: Brown, David Bk. Co., The.

Goulthorpe, Mark. The Possibility of (an) Architecture: Collected Essays by Mark Goulthorpe, DECOi Architects. 2008. (Illus.). 224p. 165.00 *(978-0-415-77494-9(2))* Routledge.

—The Possibility of (An) Architecture: Collected Essays by Mark Goulthorpe, Decoi Architects. 2008. (Illus.). XVIII, 206p. 44.95 *(978-0-415-77495-6(0))* Routledge.

Greiff, Constance M. Lost America Vol. 1: From the Atlantic to the Mississippi. 2010. (Dover Architecture Ser.). (ENG.). 256p. pap. 24.95 *(978-0-486-47311-6(2))* Dover Pubns., Inc.

—Lost America Vol. 2: From the Mississippi to the Pacific. 2010. (Dover Architecture Ser.). (ENG.). 256p. pap. 24.95 *(978-0-486-47312-3(0))* Dover Pubns., Inc.

Grillner, Katja & Hughes, Rolf. Architecture & Authorship. Anstey, Tim & Grillner, Katja, eds. Hughes, Rolf, ed. 2007. (ENG., Illus.). 205p. pap. 39.95 *(978-1-904772-74-3(9))* Black Dog Publishing Ltd. GBR. Dist: Perseus Distribution.

Grobman, Yasha & Neuman, Eran, eds. Performalism: Form & Performance in Digital Architecture. 2011. (ENG., Illus.). 224p. (C). 155.00 *(978-0-415-58360-2(8))* Routledge.

Guenther, John J. Developing Writing Strategies for Professionals- Meshing Value with Each Professional. 2007. 140p. per. *(978-3-8364-2198-0(4))* VDM Verlag Dr. Mueller e.K.

Guy, Simon & Farmer, Graham. Sustaining Design. 2006. (Architext Ser.). (ENG., Illus.). 192p. 165.00 *(978-0-415-30682-9(5)*, RU25991); pap. 48.95 *(978-0-415-30683-6(3)*, RU25992) Routledge.

Hardingham, Samantha. Experiments in Architecture. (Illus.). 184p. 25.00 *(978-1-902854-21-2(7))* Princeton Architectural Pr.

Hargreaves, Sean. Places. 2011. (ENG.). 160p. 44.95 ***(978-1-933492-59-9(7))*** Design Studio Pr.

Harrison, Rick. Prefurbia: Redesigning the suburbs: from disdainable to Sustainable. 2008. (Illus.). 220p. pap. 89.95 *(978-0-9800596-0-1(7))* Sustainable Land Development International.

Hartoonian, Gevork. Walter Benjamin & Architecture. Hartoonian, Gevork, ed. 2009. (ENG., Illus.). 192p. 125.00 *(978-0-415-48292-9(5))* Routledge.

Heiss, Oliver. Barrier-Free Design: Principles Planning, Examples. 2010. (Detail Practice Ser.). (Illus.). 112p. pap. 54.95 *(978-3-0346-0577-9(3))* Birkhauser Verlag AG CHE. Dist: Actar Birkhauser Distribution.

Hejduk, John, et al. Columbia Documents of Architecture & Theory, Vol. 2. Perrella, Stephen et al, eds. (Illus.). 175p. (C). 15.00 *(978-0-9623829-9-4(X))* Cleveland Ctr. for Contemporary Art.

Hensel, Michael U., ed. Design Innovation for the Built Environment. 2012. (ENG., Illus.). 280p. (C). 165.00 ***(978-0-415-59664-0(5))***; pap. 49.95 ***(978-0-415-59665-7(3))*** Routledge.

Hibbard, Don, et al. Hart Wood: Architectural Regionalism in Hawaii. 2010. 264p. 24.99 *(978-0-8248-3236-0(1))* Univ. of Hawaii Pr.

Hogue, Christian. The Profitable Architect: How to attract new projects & work with clients that understand the value of good Design. 2010. 270p. pap. 37.99 *(978-1-59932-200-1(5))* Advantage Media Group.

Holl, Steven. Pamphlet Architecture 11-20. 2011. (ENG.). 592p. 45.00 *(978-1-61689-016-2(9))* Princeton Architectural Pr.

Hopkins, D. J., et al. Performance & the City. Hopkins, D. J. et al, eds. 2009. (Performance Interventions Ser.). (ENG., Illus.). 264p. 95.00 *(978-0-230-20497-3(X))* Palgrave Macmillan.

Hudson, Jennifer. Restroom: Zeitgenössisches Toilettendesign. 2008. 192p. 145.00 *(978-3-89986-100-6(0))* Avedition DEU. Dist: National Bk. Network.

Huelat, Barbara. Healing Environments: What's the Proof? 2007. (Illus.). 310p. per. 65.00 *(978-0-9668545-3-4(5)*, Medezyn) PeecaPress.

Hyde, Richard, et al. Environmental Brief. 2007. (Illus.). 336p. 165.00 *(978-0-415-29044-9(9)*, RU25082) Taylor & Francis Group.

ICC. International Building Code 2009 New Jersey. 2010. ring bd. 135.00 *(978-1-58001-788-6(6))* International Code Council.

—North Carolina State Building Code: Plumbing Code & Commentary 2006. 2007. pap. 88.00 (978-1-58001-602-5(2)) International Code Council.

—2009 IBC Structural Q & A. 2010. pap. 45.00 (978-1-58001-962-0(5)) International Code Council.

—2009 IFC Q & A. 2010. pap. 45.00 (978-1-58001-970-5(6)) International Code Council.

—2012 IBC PDF Volume - SINGLE. 2011. (ENG.). 122.00 (978-1-60983-126-4(8)) International Code Council.

Iglesia, Rafael E. J. Imaginar la Ciudad. 2010. (SPA., Illus.). 298p. (978-987-584-266-3(4)) Nobuko.

Iliescu, Sanda, ed. The Hand & the Soul: Aesthetics & Ethics in Architecture & Art. 2009. (ENG., Illus.). 320p. (C). (gr. 13-17). pap. 25.00 (978-0-8139-2772-5(2)) Univ. Pr. of Virginia.

Images Australia Pty Ltd Staff. Cyberspace: The World of Digital Architecture. 2006. (ENG., Illus.). 75.00 (978-1-86470-057-2(2)) Images Publishing Group AUS. Dist: National Bk. Network.

—Perkins & Will: Selected & Curent Works. 2006. (Master Architect Ser.). (ENG., Illus.). 256p. 59.95 (978-1-86470-064-0(5), Images Publishing Dist Ac) Antique Collectors' Club GBR. Dist: National Bk. Network.

Images Publishing, creator. Mainstream Green: Sustainable Design by LPA. 2006. (ENG., Illus.). 128p. 49.50 (978-1-86470-122-7(6)) Images Publishing Group AUS. Dist: National Bk. Network.

Images Publishing Group. The City in Architecture: Recent Works of Rocco Design Limited. 2006. (ENG., Illus.). 144p. 55.00 (978-1-876907-22-8(3)) Images Publishing Group AUS. Dist: National Bk. Network.

—International Architecture Yearbook: Millennium. 2006. (ENG., Illus.). 75.00 (978-1-86470-066-4(1)) Images Publishing Group AUS. Dist: National Bk. Network.

—Kids' Spaces: A Pictorial Review. 2006. (International Spaces Ser.). (ENG., Illus.). 224p. 55.00 (978-1-876907-54-9(1)) Images Publishing Group AUS. Dist: National Bk. Network.

Images Publishing Staff, PUBLISHING. Assar. Binder, Georges, ed. 2008. (Master Architect Series VI). (ENG., Illus.). 256p. 59.95 (978-1-920744-02-1(9), Images Publishing Dist Ac) Antique Collectors' Club GBR. Dist: National Bk. Network.

—Educational Spaces Vol. 2: A Pictorial Review. 2006. (Spaces Ser.). (ENG., Illus.). 212p. 55.00 (978-1-86470-033-6(5)) Images Publishing Group AUS. Dist: National Bk. Network.

Images Publishing Staff, PUBLISHING & Lighting Planners Associates Inc Staff. Designing with Light & Shadow. 2006. (ENG., Illus.). 184p. 65.00 (978-1-86470-041-1(6)) Images Publishing Group AUS. Dist: National Bk. Network.

Imtiaz, Shahed. Industrial Workers Housing: Situation, Problems & Suggestions a Case Study of Khulna City, Bangladesh. 2011. 88p. pap. (978-3-639-33410-4(8)) VDM Verlag Dr. Mueller e.K.

Ingold, Tim. Archaeology Anthropology Art & Architecture. 2012. (ENG.). 288p. pap. 39.95 (978-0-415-56723-7(8)) Routledge.

—Archaeology Anthropology Art & Architecture. 2010. 288p. 120.00 (978-0-415-56722-0(X), Routledge) Taylor & Francis Group GBR. Dist: Taylor & Francis Group.

Integrity Burial Boxes Ltd. The Abc's of Building & Marketing A Columbarium Wall. 2011. 80p. pap. 27.08 (978-1-4567-5087-9(9)) AuthorHouse.

International Code Council. International Building Code 2009. 2009. (ENG.). ring bd. 137.00 (978-1-58001-724-4(X)) International Code Council.

—International Building Code Handbook 2009 - Fire- & Life-Safety Provisions. 2009. (ENG.). pap. 99.95 (978-1-58001-878-4(5)) International Code Council.

—2009 International Building Code: Softcover Version. 2009. (ENG.). 1p. pap. 122.00 (978-1-58001-725-1(8)) International Code Council.

—2009 International Energy Conservation Code Fundamentals Workbook. 2009. (ENG.). pap. 40.00 (978-1-111-12852-4(9)) Delmar Cengage Learning.

International Code Council & Thornburg, Doug. Significant Changes to the International Building Code 2012 Edition. 2011. (ENG.). 368p. pap. 44.95 (978-1-111-54246-7(5)) Delmar Cengage Learning.

Izenour, Steven & Hirshorn, Paul. White Towers. 2007. (ENG., Illus.). 208p. (gr. 17). 24.95 (978-0-262-08368-3(X)) MIT Pr.

Jackson, Jere. Diedrich Rulfs: Designing Modern Nacogdoches. 2012. (ENG., Illus.). 368p. 50.00 (978-1-936205-17-2(3)) Austin, Stephen F. State Univ. Pr.

Jodidio, Philip. Architecture & Automobiles. 2011. (ENG., Illus.). 228p. 60.00 (978-1-86470-330-6(X)) Images Publishing Group AUS. Dist: National Bk. Network.

—Minimum Space Maximum Living M2. 2006. (FRE & ENG., Illus.). 176p. 50.00 (978-1-86470-120-3(X)) Images Publishing Group AUS. Dist: National Bk. Network.

—100 Great Extensions & Renovations: 100 Extensions et Renovations Remarquables. 2007. (ENG., Illus.). 344p. 60.00 (978-1-920744-51-9(7)) Images Publishing Group AUS. Dist: National Bk. Network.

Jodidio, Philip, ed. Public Architecture Now! 2010. (ENG, FRE & GER., Illus.). 416p. pap. 39.99 (978-3-8365-1732-4(9)) TASCHEN DEU. Dist: Ingram Pub. Services.

John, Richard, ed. The Classicist No. 9. 2012. (ENG.). 172p. pap. 45.00 (978-0-9642601-3-9(1)) Institute for the Study of Classical Architecture, The.

Johnson, Ben & Bukantas, Ann. Cityscape: Ben Johnson's Liverpool. 2008. (ENG., Illus.). 72p. pap. 24.95 (978-1-84631-157-4(8)) Liverpool Univ. Pr. GBR. Dist: Chicago Distribution Ctr.

Jones, David M. The Art & Architecture of the Incas. 2012. (ENG., Illus.). 128p. pap. 16.99 (978-1-78019-138-6(3)) Anness Publishing GBR. Dist: National Bk. Network.

Joost-Gaugier, Christiane L. Measuring Heaven: Pythagoras & His Influence on Thought & Art in Antiquity & the Middle Ages. 2007. (Illus.). 359p. per. 25.95 (978-0-8014-7409-5(4)) Cornell Univ. Pr.

Kaminer, Tahl. Architecture Crisis & Resuscitation. 2011. (ENG., Illus.). 216p. (C). 155.00 (978-0-415-57823-3(X)); pap. 49.95 (978-0-415-57824-0(8)) Routledge.

Kastner, Joachim Peter. Erwin Heerich: Museum Insel Hombroich. (Illus.). 160p. 24.95 (978-3-7757-0573-8(2)) Hatje Cantz Verlag GmbH & Co KG DEU. Dist: D.A.P./Distributed Art Pubs.

Kidder. Manual Del Arquitecto y Del Constructor 2 Tomos. (SPA.). 1.116p. (978-968-18-3950-5(1), Limusa) Noriega Editores.

Kiendl, Anthony, ed. Informal Architectures: Space & Contemporary Culture. 2008. (ENG., Illus.). 207p. 65.00 (978-1-906155-33-9(X)) Black Dog Publishing Ltd. GBR. Dist: Perseus Distribution.

Kimman, Eduard, et al. Towards O-Impact Buildings & Built Environments. 2011. 224p. pap. 77.00 (978-90-8594-028-9(1)) Techne Pr. NLD. Dist: Chicago Distribution Ctr.

Klanten, R. & Feireiss, L., eds. Beyond Architecture: Imaginitaive Buildings & Fictional Cities. 2009. (Illus.). 208p. (978-3-89955-235-5(0)) Die Gestalten Verlag.

—Utopia Forever: Visions of Architecture & Urbanism. 2011. (Illus.). 256p. pap. (978-3-89955-335-2(7)) Die Gestalten Verlag.

Klingmann, Anna. Brandscapes: Architecture in the Experience Economy. (ENG., Illus.). 378p. (gr. 17). 2010. pap. 19.95 (978-0-262-51503-0(2)) 2007. 31.95 (978-0-262-11303-8(1)) MIT Pr.

Kocatürk, Tuba. Distributed Intelligence in Design. Medjdoub, Benachir, ed. 2011. (ENG., Illus.). 280p. 152.99 (978-1-4443-3338-1(0), Wiley-Blackwell) Wiley, John & Sons, Inc.

Koenig, Gloria. Iconic L.A: Stories of L.A.'s Most Memorable Buildings. 2nd ed. 2006. (978-1-883318-68-0(8)) Angel City Pr.

Kotnik, Jure. New Kindergarten Architecture. 2011. (ENG.). 300p. 68.00 (978-84-15123-53-8(1)) Links International (Leading International Key Services Barcelona, S.A.) ESP. Dist: National Bk. Network.

Kottas, Dimitris. Wood. 2012. (ENG.). 300p. 57.00 (978-84-15123-26-2(4)) Links International (Leading International Key Services Barcelona, S.A.) ESP. Dist: National Bk. Network.

Krascjevic, Margot K. Spatial Pathology: Floating Realities. Woods, Lebbeus, ed. 2007. (Illus.). 111p. per. (978-3-211-71533-8(9), 3211715339) Actar Birkhauser Distribution.

Krauel, Jacobo. Creative Events. 2010. (ENG., Illus.). 300p. pap. 39.00 (978-84-96969-62-9(2)) Links International (Leading International Key Services Barcelona, S.A.) ESP. Dist: National Bk. Network.

Krier, Rob. Architectural Composition. 2010. (ENG., Illus.). 344p. 98.00 (978-3-936681-39-0(2)) Edition Axel Menges GmbH DEU. Dist: National Bk. Network.

Krols, Birgit. Extreme Bars, 1 vol. 2008. (ENG, DUT & FRE., Illus.). 192p. 39.95 (978-90-76886-66-4(0)) Tectum B.V.B.A. BEL. Dist: Innovative Logistics.

—Extreme Venues: Event Locations Around the World, 1 vol. 2009. (FRE, DUT & ENG., Illus.). 192p. 39.95 (978-90-79761-03-6(6)) Tectum B.V.B.A. BEL. Dist: Innovative Logistics.

Kronenburg, David & Kronenburg, Robert. Flexible: Architecture That Responds to Change. 2007. (ENG., Illus.). 240p. 50.00 (978-1-85669-461-2(5)) King, Laurence Publishing GBR. Dist: Hachette Bk. Group.

Kruse, Stefan. Hospital Architecture & Design. 2009. (Masterpieces Ser.). (FRE, GER & ENG., Illus.). 304p. 49.95 (978-3-938780-76-3(2)) BRAUN DEU. Dist: National Bk. Network.

Kurycowicz, Ewa. Architektura — Bezgosny Przekaz Gosnych Emocji: Integracyjna Rola Miejsc Duchowych Dla Mieszkanców Miast XXI Wieku: III Miedzynarodowa Konferencja PR UIA "Miejsca Duchowe", Warszawa, 6 Pazdziernika 2007 Roku. 2007. (FRE, POL & ENG., Illus.). 344p. (978-83-904369-6-8(5)) Novaja skola.

Lahti, Louna. Aalto: 1898-1976 / Paradies für kleine Leute. (FIN.). 96p. pap. 9.99 (978-3-8228-3451-0(3)) Taschen America, LLC.

Larsen, Olga Popovic. Reciprocal Frame Architecture. 2008. (ENG., Illus.). 208p. per. 51.95 (978-0-7506-8263-3(9)) Routledge.

L'Aventurine. Architecture/Architektur. 2007. (Ornamental Design Ser.). (ENG, FRE & GER., Illus.). 288p. per. 14.95 (978-2-914199-35-3(X)) L'Aventurine FRA. Dist: Independent Pubs. Group.

Le Corbusier. Toward an Architecture. Goodman, John, tr. from FRE. 2007. (ENG.). 358p. 50.00 (978-0-89236-899-0(3)) Oxford Univ. Pr., Inc.

Le Corbusier Staff. Toward an Architecture. Goodman, John, tr. from FRE. 2007. (ENG., Illus.). 358p. pap. 24.95 (978-0-89236-822-8(5)) Oxford Univ. Pr., Inc.

Le Gac, Christophe & Gac, Christophe Le. Manuelle Gautrand Architec. 2006. (Neo Architecture Ser.). (ENG., Illus.). 124p. 49.50 (978-1-920744-87-8(8)) Images Publishing Group AUS. Dist: National Bk. Network.

Lees, Stephen. Visions of Architecture. 2011. (ENG., Illus.). 128p. pap. 25.95 (978-1-4081-2881-7(0)) A & C Black GBR. Dist: Macmillan.

Lethaby, W. R. & Powell, Alfred. Architecture, Nature & Magic. 2011. 170p. 42.95 (978-1-258-00196-4(9)) Literary Licensing, LLC.

Levi, Anna Bofill. Generation of Forms: Space to Inhabit, Time to Think. 2010. (ENG.). 80p. pap. 20.00 (978-3-422-06916-9(X), Art Stock Bks. Ltd/Csi) Continental Sales, Inc.

Levin, Veronika, des. Urban Spaces No. 5: Featuring Green Design Strategies. 2008. (Urban Spaces Ser.). (ENG., Illus.). 303p. 60.00 (978-1-58471-105-6(1)) Visual Reference Pubns., Inc.

Leyton, Michael. Shape As Memory. 2006. (Information Technology Revolution in Architecture Ser.). (Illus.). 96p. pap. 15.95 (978-3-7643-7073-2(4), 3764370734) Birkhauser Verlag AG CHE. Dist: Chronicle Bks. LLC.

Lloyd, Thomas, et al. Carmarthenshire & Ceredigion. 2006. (Pevsner Architectural Guides). (ENG., Illus.). 550p. 85.00 (978-0-300-10179-9(1)) Yale Univ. Pr.

Lupkin, Paula. Manhood Factories: YMCA Architecture & the Making of Modern Urban Culture. 2010. (Architecture, Landscape & Amer Culture Ser.). (Illus.). 312p. (ENG.). 82.50 (978-0-8166-4834-4(4)); pap. 27.50 (978-0-8166-4835-1(2)) Univ. of Minnesota Pr.

Lynn, Abraham C. & Reitherman, Robert, eds. AEI 2011: Building Integration Solutions. 2011. 504p. pap. 99.00 (978-0-7844-1168-1(9)) American Society of Civil Engineers.

MacDonald, Joseph A. McGraw-Hill Construction Locator. 2006. (ENG.). 600p. 89.95 (978-0-07-147530-3(3), 0071475303) McGraw-Hill Professional Publishing.

Macy, Christine & Bonnemaison, Sarah, eds. Festival Architecture. 2007. (Classical Tradition in Architecture Ser.). (Illus.). CCCXXX, 14p. 56.95 (978-0-415-70129-7(5)); 165.00 (978-0-415-70128-0(7)) Routledge.

Madge, James & Peckham, Andrew, eds. Narrating Architecture: A Retrospective Anthology. 2006. (Illus.). 496p. 170.00 (978-0-415-37435-4(9), RU74359) Routledge.

Magyar, Peter. Thinkink: Architecture. rev. ed. 2010. (ENG.). 130p. pap. 56.06 (978-0-7575-7906-6(X)) Kendall Hunt Publishing Co.

Maizels, John. Fantasy Worlds. 25th ed. 2007. (FRE, GER & ENG., Illus.). 236p. 14.99 (978-3-8228-3219-6(7)) TASCHEN DEU. Dist: Ingram Pub. Services.

Mallory-Hill, Shauna, et al. Enhancing Building Performance. 2nd ed. 2012. (ENG., Illus.). 360p. pap. 115.00 (978-0-470-65759-1(6), Wiley-Blackwell) Wiley, John & Sons, Inc.

Manaugh, Geoff. BLDGBLOG Book: Architectural Conjecture, Urban Speculation, Landscape Futures. 2009. (ENG., Illus.). 272p. pap. 29.95 (978-0-8118-6644-6(0)) Chronicle Bks. LLC.

Manaugh, Geoff, ed. Landscape Futures. 2011. (Illus.). 224p. pap. (978-0-9764800-9-9(3)) Nevada Museum of Art.

Mandour, M. Alaa. E-Urban. 2010. 132p. pap. (978-3-639-28094-4(6)) VDM Verlag Dr. Mueller e.K.

March, Lionel, ed. The Architecture of Form. 2010. (Cambridge Urban & Architectural Studies). (ENG., Illus.). 508p. pap. 55.00 (978-0-521-13639-6(3)) Cambridge Univ. Pr.

Marmo Studio Staff. Fine Marble in Architecture. Date not set. (Illus.). 192p. (978-0-393-10411-0(7)) Norton, W. W. & Co., Inc.

Masubuchi, Motoi. Staircase As a Lightweight Structure. 2010. 136p. pap. (978-3-639-22684-3(4)) VDM Verlag Dr. Mueller e.K.

Matteson, Donna, et al. Workbook for Matteson/Kennedy/Baur's Project Lead the Way: Civil Engineering & Architecture. 2012. (ENG.). 320p. (C). pap. 29.95 (978-1-4354-4165-1(6)) Delmar Cengage Learning.

Matteson, Donna (Donna Matteson), et al. Civil Engineering & Architecture. 2011. (ENG.). 784p. (C). 124.95 (978-1-4354-4164-4(8)) Delmar Cengage Learning.

Matthaei, Albrecht & Zimmermann, Martin. Stadtbilder Im Hellenismus. 2009. (Die hellenistische Polis als Lebensform Ser.). (GER., Illus.). 424p. (C). 98.00 (978-3-938032-23-7(5)) Antike, Verlag, e.K. DEU. Dist: ISD.

McCabe, Leed Ap Molly. Practical Greening, the Bottom Line on Sustainable Property Develoopement, Investment & Financing. 2010. 180p. pap. 29.95 (978-1-936343-05-8(3)) Peppertree Pr., The.

McCullough, Cynthia S. Evidence-Based Design for Healthcare Facilities. 2009. (978-1-930538-77-1(4)) Sigma Theta Tau International, Ctr. for Nursing Pr.

McGoodwin, Henry. Architectural Shades & Shadows. 2010. (Orig.). 124p. pap. 19.75 (978-1-171-82946-1(9)); 128p. pap. 20.75 (978-1-177-67632-8(X)); 118p. pap. 19.75 (978-1-146-08063-7(8)) BiblioBazaar.

—Architectural Shades & Shadows. 2010. (Illus.). 44p. (Orig.). pap. 14.14 (978-1-154-61550-0(2)) General Bks. LLC.

McHale, John. The Expendable Reader: Articles on Art, Architecture, Design & Media 1951-1978. Kitnick, Alex, ed. 2011. (ENG., Illus.). 295p. pap. 19.95 (978-1-883584-70-2(1)) Columbia Univ., Graduate Schl. of Architecture.

McIntosh, Gillian. Belfast City Hall. 2006. (ENG., Illus.). 160p. 49.95 (978-0-85640-769-7(0)) Blackstaff Pr., Ltd. GBR. Dist: Dufour Editions, Inc.

McQuire, Scott. Media City: Media, Architecture & Urban Space. 2008. (Published in Association with Theory, Culture & Society Ser.). (Illus.). 240p. 121.00 (978-1-4129-0793-4(4), B07934C) SAGE Pubns., Ltd. GBR. Dist: SAGE Pubns., Inc.

Menis, Fernando. Arquitecto/Architecture: Razon + Emocion/Reason + Emotion. 2008. (Illus.). 230p. (978-84-96954-26-7(9)) Actar Birkhauser Distribution.

Mestre, Octavio. Sunlight Houses. Minguet, Josep M. & Trivino, Santi, eds. 2010. (ENG., Illus.). 98p. pap. 22.50 (978-84-96823-72-3(5)) Instituto Monsa de Ediciones, S.A. ESP. Dist: Trans-Atlantic Pubns., Inc.

Meyer, Ulf & Linster, Alain. LX Architecture in the Heart of Europe: Contemporary Architecture in Luxembourg, 2 vols. 2009. (ENG., Illus.). 252p. pap. 49.95 (978-3-938666-69-2(2)) DOM Pubs. DEU. Dist: Innovative Logistics.

Migliore, Ico & Servetto, Mara. Space Morphing: Temporary Architecture. Anderson, Martyn, tr. from ITA. 2008. (ITA & ENG., Illus.). 144p. pap. 45.00 (978-88-7439-449-4(7)) 5 Continents ITA. Dist: Hachette Bk. Group.

Mikkelsen, M. A. & Kocher, A. Lawrence, eds. The Architectural Record, V63, No 2, February 1928. 2011. 266p. 47.95 (978-1-258-06578-2(9)) Literary Licensing, LLC.

Miller, Charlie. Cover Your Assets. 2011. 28p. pap. 15.99 (978-1-4628-8304-2(4)) Xlibris Corp.

Morris, Mark. Models: Architecture & the Miniature. 2006. (Architecture in Practice Ser.: 6). (ENG., Illus.). 216p. per. 65.00 (978-0-470-01592-6(6), Academy Pr.) Wiley, John & Sons, Inc.

Mörtenböck, Peter & Mooshammer, Helge. Networked Cultures: Parallel Architectures & the Politics of Space. 2008. (ENG., Illus.). 320p. (C). pap. 45.00 (978-90-5662-059-2(2)) NAi Uitgevers / Publishers Stichting NLD. Dist: D.A.P./Distributed Art Pubs.

Mortensen, Jorn. Landscape & Memory. 2011. (ENG., Illus.). 160p. pap. 60.00 (978-82-7547-471-9(X)) Pr., Forlaget NOR. Dist: D.A.P./Distributed Art Pubs.

Moss, Eric Owen & Morais, Julianna. Who Says What Architecture Is? 2007. pap. (978-0-9760079-4-4(0)) Southern California Institute of Architecture, The.

Mostafavi, Mohsen, et al. Mathematical Form: John Pickering & the Architecture of the Inversion Principle. 2007. (Illus.). 72p. 40.00 (978-1-902902-37-1(8)) Princeton Architectural Pr.

Motro, Rene, ed. Flexible Composite Materials in Architecture, Construction & Interiors. 2012. (FRE.). 224p. 69.95 (978-3-0346-0709-4(1)) Birkhauser Verlag AG CHE. Dist: Actar Birkhauser Distribution.

Müller, Andreas, ed. Arctic Perspective Cahier No. 1. 2011. (ENG., Illus.). 148p. 30.00 (978-3-7757-2679-5(9)) Hatje Cantz Verlag GmbH & Co KG DEU. Dist: D.A.P./Distributed Art Pubs.

Müller, Lars. Building Books. 2008. (Illus.). 480p. 69.95 (978-3-907078-96-9(9), 3907078969) Springer.

Nagel, Alexander & Wood, Christopher S. Anachronic Renaissance. 2010. (ENG., Illus.). 456p. (gr. 17). 39.95 (978-1-935408-02-4(X)) Zone Bks.

Nanji, Nawazish Godrej. GIVING ARCHITECTURE TO FIRE: 'ATASH BEHRAM', A PERSIAN FIRE TEMPLE. 2008. 108p. pap. (978-3-639-09720-7(3)) VDM Verlag Dr. Mueller e.K.

Nas. Hypercity: The Symbolic Side of Urbanism. Crome, Keith & Williams, James, eds. 2006. (ENG., Illus.). 256p. 158.00 (978-0-7103-1279-2(2)) Routledge.

National Fire Protection Association Staff & Society of Fire Protection Engineers Staff, contrib. by. SFPE Engineering Guide to Performance-Based Fire Protection. 2007. (Illus.). xiii, 207p. (978-0-87765-789-7(0)) National Fire Protection Assn.

National Research Council (U.S.), Transportation Research Board Subcommittee on Bridge Aesthetics Staff & American Association of State Highway and Transportation Officials, Subcommittee on Bridges and Structures Staff, contrib. by. Bridge Aesthetics Sourcebook: Practical Ideas for Short- & Medium-Span Bridges. 2010. (Illus.). viii, 61p. (978-1-56051-485-5(X)) American Assn. of State Highway & Transportation Officials.

Neujens, Karoline. Fabulous Food Concepts. 2012. (ENG., Illus.). 167p. 55.00 (978-94-6058-078-9(5), Uitgeverij Luster) Antique Collectors' Club GBR. Dist: National Bk. Network.

Newman & Pevsner, Nikolaus. West Kent & the Weald. 2nd rev. ed. (Illus.). 688p. 50.00 (978-0-14-071038-0(8)) Penguin Bks., Ltd. GBR. Dist: Trafalgar Square Publishing.

Newman, John. Glamorgan. (Illus.). 720p. 65.00 (978-0-14-071056-4(6)) Penguin Bks., Ltd. GBR. Dist: Trafalgar Square Publishing.

Noble, Allen. Traditional Buildings: A Global Survey of Structural Forms & Cultural Functions. 2007. (International Library of Human Geography Ser.). (ENG., Illus.). 368p. 79.00 (978-1-84511-305-6(5)) I. B. Tauris & Co., Ltd. GBR. Dist: Macmillan.

Nolan, John M. A Guide to Historic Greenville, South Carolina. 2008. (Illus.). 144p. pap. 19.99 (978-1-59629-340-3(3)) History Pr., The.

Nurcombe, Valerie, ed. Information Sources in Architecture & Construction. 2nd ed. (Guides to Information Sources Ser.). (ENG.). (978-3-11-186658-1(0)) Saur, K. G. Verlag GmbH & Co.

Olbrich, Joseph M. Ideen von Olbrich. fac. ed. (GER., Illus.). 196p. 75.00 (978-3-925369-15-5(5)) Arnoldsche Art Pubs. DEU. Dist: Antique Collectors' Club.

Owen, Graham, ed. Iarchitecture, Ethics & Globalization: Ethics, Efficacy & Architecture in the Globalized Economy. 2009. (ENG., Illus.). 256p. (C). pap. 62.95 (978-0-415-32374-1(6)) Routledge.

—Inverting the Iceberg: Ethics, Efficacy & Architecture in the Globalized Economy. 2009. (ENG., Illus.). 256p. (C). 165.00 (978-0-415-32373-4(8)) Routledge.

Ztop, Hülya & Erkal, Sibel. Housing Design & Safety for the Elderly. 2010. (978-1-61728-844-9(6)) Nova Science Pubs., Inc.

Pallasmaa, Juhani. Archipelago: Essays on Architecture for Juhani Pallasmaa. MacKeith, Peter B., ed. 2008. (Illus.). 232p. pap. 63.00 (978-951-682-806-3(X)) Rakennustieto oy FIN. Dist: Independent Pubs. Group.

—The Embodied Image: Imagination & Imagery in Architecture. 2011. (Architectural Design Primer Ser.). (ENG., Illus.). 152p. 110.00 (978-0-470-71191-0(4)); pap. 45.00 (978-0-470-71190-3(6)) Wiley, John & Sons, Inc. (Wiley).

—The Eyes of the Skin: Architecture & the Senses. 3rd ed. 2012. (ENG.). 128p. 45.00 (978-1-119-94128-6(8), Wiley) Wiley, John & Sons, Inc.

Pallasmaa, Juhani. The Thinking Hand: Existential & Embodied Wisdom in Architecture. 2009. (Architectural Design Primer Ser.). (ENG., Illus.). 160p. 130.00 (978-0-470-77928-6(4)); pap. 55.00 (978-0-470-77929-3(2)) Wiley, John & Sons, Inc. (Wiley).

Pankov, Mark. Grassmannians of Classical Building. 2010. 224p. 75.00 (978-981-4317-56-6(X)) World Scientific Publishing Co., Inc.

Paredes, Cristina, ed. Spiritual Architecture: New Religious Buildings. 2009. (Illus.). 256p. pap. (978-84-96936-35-5(X)) Loft Pubns.

Parkstone Press Staff. City Lights. 2010. (Our Earth Ser.). (ENG., Illus.). 192p. 24.95 *(978-1-84484-776-1(4))* Parkstone International GBR. Dist: Ingram Pub. Services.

Parkyn, Neil. Wonders of World Architecture. 2009. (ENG., Illus.). 304p. pap. 29.95 *(978-0-500-28400-1(8)*, 528400) Thames & Hudson.

Pasquini, Phil. Domes, Arches & Minarets: A History of Islamic-Inspired Buildings in America. 2012. (ENG.). 256p. pap. 40.00 ***(978-0-9670016-1-6(7))*** Flypaper Pr.

Patt, Doug. How to Architect. 2012. (ENG., Illus.). 144p. (gr. 17). pap. 12.95 ***(978-0-262-51699-0(3))*** MIT Pr.

Pauwels, Wim. Urban Retreats. 2008. (ENG., Illus.). 208p. *(978-90-77213-98-8(8)*, Beta-Plus (Acc)) Antique Collectors' Club.

Pearson, Michelle. Historic Denver Landmarks for Children & Families. 2007. pap. 10.95 *(978-0-914248-03-3(0))* Historic Denver, Inc.

Peichl, Gustav. Buildings & Projects. (Illus.). 224p. 60.00 *(978-3-7757-0399-4(3))* Hatje Cantz Verlag GmbH & Co KG DEU. Dist: D.A.P./Distributed Art Pubs.

Pelkonen, Eeva-Liisa. Alvar Aalto: Architecture, Modernity, & Geopolitics. 2009. (ENG., Illus.). 228p. 45.00 *(978-0-300-11428-7(1))* Yale Univ. Pr.

Peltason, Ruth & Ong-Yan, Grace, eds. Architect: The Work of the Pritzker Prize Laureates in Their Own Words. 2010. (ENG., Illus.). 376p. 40.00 *(978-1-57912-847-0(5)*, 1579128475) Black Dog & Leventhal Pubs., Inc.

Perez-Gomez, Alberto, et al. Towards an Ethical Architecture: Issues Within the Work of Gregory Henriquez. 2006. (ENG., Illus.). 184p. pap. 29.95 *(978-1-894965-50-7(7))* Simply Read Bks. CAN. Dist: Perseus-PGW.

Pevsner, N. Pevsner#8242;s Architectural Glossary. 2010. (ENG., Illus.). 196p. ***(978-0-300-16721-4(0))*** Yale Univ. Pr.

Pevsner, Nikolaus. Leicestershire & Rutland. 2nd ed. (Illus.). 576p. 65.00 *(978-0-14-071018-2(3))* Penguin Bks., Ltd. GBR. Dist: Trafalgar Square Publishing.

—North Lancashire. (Illus.). 320p. 45.00 *(978-0-14-071037-3(X))* Penguin Bks., Ltd. GBR. Dist: Trafalgar Square Publishing.

—Shropshire. (Illus.). 1p. 40.00 *(978-0-14-071016-8(7))* Penguin Bks., Ltd. GBR. Dist: Trafalgar Square Publishing.

—Worcestershire England, 1968. 384p. 40.00 *(978-0-14-071035-9(3))* Penguin Bks., Ltd. GBR. Dist: Trafalgar Square Publishing.

Pimlott, Mark, et al, texts. Architecture Bulletin: Essays on the Designed Environment, 1 vol. 2007. (ENG., Illus.). 80p. pap. 20.00 *(978-90-5662-544-3(6))* NAi Uitgevers / Publishers Stichting NLD. Dist: D.A.P./Distributed Art Pubs.

Piñón, Helio & Piñón Pallares, Helio. El Proyecto Como (Re)construcción. 2010. (SPA., Illus.). 116p. *(978-84-8301-807-1(1))* UPC, S.L., Edicions.

Popenoe, Brigitte. Nature's Fractal Geometry. 2011. 64p. pap. ***(978-3-8443-9669-0(1))*** Lambert Academic Publishing.

Portilla, J. M. & Ceccarelli, Marco, eds. History of Machines for Heritage & Engineering Development. 2011. (History of Mechanism & Machine Science Ser.). (Illus.). x, 215p. 129.00 *(978-94-007-1250-8(2)*, 9400712502) Springer.

Portoghesi, Paolo, ed. Dwelling on Earth No. 28: For an Architecture of Responsibility. 2011. 96p. pap. 15.00 ***(978-88-492-2128-2(2))*** Gangemi ITA. Dist: International Publishers Marketing.

—Dwelling on Earth, No. 29: For an Architecture of Responsibility. 2011. 96p. pap. 15.00 ***(978-88-492-2175-6(4))*** Gangemi ITA. Dist: International Publishers Marketing.

Prada, Manuel de. Arte y Naturaleza: El Sentido de la Irregularidad en el Arte y la Arquitectura. 2009. (SPA., Illus.). 131p. *(978-987-584-197-0(8))* Nobuko.

Prina, Francesca. Architecture: Elements, Materials, Form. 2009. (Princeton Field Guides to Art Ser.). (ENG., Illus.). 408p. pap. 29.95 *(978-0-691-14150-3(9))* Princeton Univ. Pr.

Princeton Architectural Press Staff, contrib. by. Princeton Fall 06 Catalog. 2006. pap. 0.01 *(978-1-56898-614-2(9))* Princeton Architectural Pr.

ProFile: The Architects' Sourcebook & CD Set 2002. 225.00 incl. cd-rom *(978-1-929999-06-4(2))* Reed Construction Data.

Prudon, Theodore & Prudon, Theodore H. M. Preservation of Modern Architecture. 2008. (ENG., Illus.). 976p. 115.00 *(978-0-471-66294-5(1)*, Wiley) Wiley, John & Sons, Inc.

Puente, Moisés. Conversations with Mies van der Rohe. 2008. (ENG., Illus.). 96p. pap. 19.95 *(978-1-56898-753-8(6))* Princeton Architectural Pr.

Quek, Raymond. Fiction Image Tone: The Metropolis an the Realisation of Archit. 240p. 2012. (ENG., Illus.). (C). 155.00 ***(978-0-415-49292-8(0))*** 2011. pap. 44.95 *(978-0-415-49293-5(9))* Routledge.

Quek, Raymond, et al. Nationalism & Architecture. 2012. (Ashgate Studies in Architecture Ser.). (Illus.). 300p. 119.95 ***(978-1-4094-3385-9(4))*** Ashgate Publishing Co.

Quinn, Bradley. Design Futures. 2011. (ENG., Illus.). 240p. 59.95 *(978-1-85894-540-8(2))* Merrell Pubs. Ltd. GBR. Dist: Perseus Distribution.

Ramzy, Nelly. From Imhotep to Calatrav. 2011. 92p. pap. ***(978-3-8443-8782-7(X))*** Lambert Academic Publishing.

Raskin, Eugene. Architecturally Speaking. 2009. 150p. 35.95 *(978-1-104-85185-9(7))* 2007. (ENG.). 148p. per. 20.95 *(978-0-548-39268-3(4))* Kessinger Publishing, LLC.

Read, Alan, ed. Spaced Out: Architecture, Art & Performance at the Millennium. Date not set. (Illus.). 272p. pap. *(978-0-485-00603-2(0))*; *(978-0-485-00403-8(8))* Continuum International Publishing Group, Ltd.

Reinhold, Martin & Baxi, Kadambari. Multi-National City: Architectural Itineraries. 2007. (Illus.). 200p. per. *(978-84-96540-62-0(6))* Actar Birkhauser Distribution.

Richon, Oliver & Baker, Simon. Image Perspectives. Yeang, Ken & Luxemburg, Rut Blees, eds. 2011. (ENG.). 128p. pap. 19.95 *(978-1-907317-41-5(4))* Black Dog Publishing Ltd. GBR. Dist: Perseus Distribution.

Rjar 16. 6. 2012. (ENG.). pap. 45.95 *(978-0-415-67522-2(7))* Routledge.

Rook, Russell D. Rhyming Hope & History: Theology & Culture in the Work of Robert Jenson. 2011. 240p. pap. 26.00 ***(978-1-60899-600-1(X)***, Pickwick Pubns.) Wipf & Stock Pubs.

Ross, Leslie D. Art & Architecture of the World's Religions, 2 vols. 2009. (Illus.). 395p. 225.00 *(978-0-313-34286-8(5)*, GR4286) Greenwood Publishing Group, Inc.

Roth, Manuela. Masterpieces: Roof Architecture + Design. 2012. (ENG., Illus.). 304p. 49.95 ***(978-3-03768-113-8(6)***, Braun Publish,Csi) Continental Sales, Inc.

Rudolph, Paul. Writings on Architecture. 2009. (ENG., Illus.). 164p. pap. 18.00 *(978-0-300-15092-6(X))* Yale Univ. Pr.

Rugg, Judith & Martin, Craig, eds. Spatialities: The Geographies of Art & Architecture. 2012. (ENG., Illus.). 220p. pap. 50.00 *(978-1-84150-468-1(8))* Intellect, Ltd. GBR. Dist: Chicago Distribution Ctr.

Rush, Fred. On Architecture. 2008. (Thinking in Action Ser.). (ENG., Illus.). 200p. pap. 21.95 *(978-0-415-39619-6(0))* Routledge.

Rush, Fred & Rush, Fred Leland. On Architecture. 2008. (Thinking in Action Ser.). (ENG., Illus.). 200p. 125.00 *(978-0-415-39618-9(2))* Routledge.

Ruskin, John. Lectures on Architecture & Painting. 2008. 148p. per. *(978-1-4065-9300-6(1))* Dodo Pr.

—Lectures on Architecture & Painting. 2007. (Illus.). 296p. per. *(978-1-4067-2884-2(5))* Read Bks.

—The Poetry of Architecture. 2008. 192p. 22.99 *(978-0-554-35812-3(3))*; 25.99 *(978-0-554-26509-4(5))* BiblioBazaar.

—The Poetry of Architecture: Or the Architecture of the Nations of Europe Cons. 2007. (ENG.). 170p. pap. 19.99 *(978-1-4346-1222-9(8))*; 190p. pap. 21.99 *(978-1-4346-1293-9(7))* BiblioBazaar.

—The Poetry of Architecture: or the Architecture of the Nations of Europe Considered in Its Association with Natural Scenery & National Character. 2010. 208p. pap. 44.95 *(978-1-4092-0935-5(0))* Lulu Enterprises Inc.

—The Seven Lamps of Architecture. 2010. 300p. pap. 29.75 *(978-1-142-73530-2(3))* 2010. 236p. pap. 26.75 *(978-1-141-10908-1(5))* 2009. 280p. 24.99 *(978-1-103-78908-5(2))* 2009. 280p. pap. 18.99 *(978-1-103-78900-9(7))* BiblioBazaar.

—The Seven Lamps of Architecture. 2009. 170p. pap. *(978-0-217-76662-3(5))* Books LLC.

—The Seven Lamps of Architecture. 2009. 104p. pap. 19.99 *(978-1-4589-3527-4(2))* General Bks. LLC.

—The Seven Lamps of Architecture. 2007. (ENG.). 284p. 43.95 *(978-0-548-00380-0(7))* Kessinger Publishing, LLC.

—The Seven Lamps of Architecture. 2008. 268p. pap. *(978-1-4437-0595-0(0))* Read Bks.

Russell, MaryAnn & 1st World Publishing. The Feng Shui Factor: Modern Homes, Ancient Blueprint. 2007. 168p. 22.95 *(978-1-4218-9981-7(7))* 1st World Publishing, Inc.

Sakellariou, E. P. A. Sakellarious, an Architect's Vision. 2008. 324p. pap. *(978-960-6691-00-3(4))* Potamos.

Salingaros, Nikos A. The Theory of Architecture. 2007. (ENG., Illus.). 278p. (C). per. 31.00 *(978-3-937954-07-3(4))* ISI Bks.

Scarciglia, Maurizio. Beyond Luxury: Villa Hadriana. 2011. (Illus.). 144p. pap. 49.00 *(978-90-8594-025-8(7))* Techne Pr. NLD. Dist: Chicago Distribution Ctr.

Schittich, Christian. In Detail: Work Environments: Design in Physical Space, Mobility, Communication. 2012. (ENG., Illus.). 176p. 99.95 *(978-3-0346-0724-7(5))* Birkhauser Verlag AG CHE. Dist: Actar Birkhauser Distribution.

Schulitz, Helmut C. Leistungsform / Form Follows Performance: Schulitz Architekten / Arbeiten / Works / 1995-2010. 2010. (ENG & GER.). 260p. 79.95 *(978-3-0346-0115-3(8))* Birkhauser Verlag AG CHE. Dist: Actar Birkhauser Distribution.

Selldorf, Annabelle. Selldorf Architects. 2009. (ENG., Illus.). 176p. 50.00 *(978-1-58093-226-4(6))* Monacelli Pr., Inc.

Sharr, Adam, ed. Architecture & Culture. 2012. (ENG., Illus.). 272p. (C). 165.00 *(978-0-415-60142-9(8))*; pap. 39.95 *(978-0-415-60143-6(6))* Routledge.

Shen, Hong. Functional Architecture. 2010. 160p. pap. *(978-3-639-20001-0(2))* VDM Verlag Dr. Mueller e.K.

Shonfield. Architecture & Film. (Illus.). 272p. *(978-0-485-00413-7(5))*; 256p. pap. *(978-0-485-00611-7(1))* Continuum International Publishing Group, Ltd.

Skira Staff & Molinari, Luca, eds. Y08 the Skira Yearbook of World Architecture 2007-2008. 2008. (ENG., Illus.). 250p. 89.00 *(978-88-6130-587-8(3))* Skira Editore ITA. Dist: Random Hse., Inc.

Slessor, Catherine. Architecture & Design London. Webb, Michael, ed. (Illus.). 96p. pap. 16.00 *(978-0-9641863-7-8(3)*, TUB Pr.) Understanding Business.

Slessor, Catherine, intro. Contemporary Architecture 2, Vol. 2. 2006. (ENG., Illus.). 256p. 75.00 *(978-1-920744-44-1(4))* Images Publishing Group AUS. Dist: National Bk. Network.

Smith, Laura Massino. Tour of Frank Gehry & Other L. A. Architecture. 2007. (Illus.). 112p. pap. 14.95 *(978-0-7643-2715-5(1))* Schiffer Publishing, Ltd.

Söderström, Ola, ed. Re-Shaping Cities: How Global Mobility Transforms Architecture & Urban Form. 2010. (Architext Ser.). (Illus.). 256p. pap. 53.95 *(978-0-415-49291-1(2))* Routledge.

Söderström, Ola & Guggenheim, Michael, eds. Re-Shaping Cities: How Global Mobility Transforms Architecture & Urban Form. 2010. (Illus.). 256p. 165.00 *(978-0-415-49290-4(4))* Routledge.

Solomon, Nancy B. Architecture: Celebrating the Past, Designing the Future. 2008. (Illus.). 424p. 95.00 *(978-1-58471-162-9(0))* Visual Reference Pubns., Inc.

Sowa, Axel, ed. Candide No. 4: Journal for Architectural Knowledge. 2011. (Journal for Architectural Knowledge Ser.). 144p. pap. *(978-84-92861-83-5(5))* Actar Birkhauser Distribution.

Spector, Jayne. Dockyard to Esplanade. 2011. 144p. pap. ***(978-3-8443-0417-6(7))*** Lambert Academic Publishing.

Steane. The Architecture of Light. 2011. (ENG., Illus.). 256p. (C). 155.00 *(978-0-415-39478-9(3))*; pap. 53.95 *(978-0-415-39479-6(1))* Routledge.

Stebbing, Peter, tr. & compiled by. Conversations about Painting with Rudolf Steiner: Recollections of Five Pioneers of the New Art Impulse. 2008. (Illus.). 208p. 35.00 *(978-0-88010-590-3(9))* SteinerBooks, Inc.

Stoddard, Whitney. Reflections on the Architecture of Williams College. Bleezarde, Thomas, ed. 2006. 296p. pap. 12.95 *(978-0-915081-05-9(9))* Williams College.

Stubley, Gordon. Engineers & Integrity. 2008. 11p. 5.95 *(978-0-9794270-5-3(3))* Ctr. for Ethics & Entrepreneurship.

Sudjic, Deyan. The Language of Things: Understanding the World of Desirable Objects. 2009. (ENG., Illus.). 208p. 24.95 *(978-0-393-07081-1(6)*, 7081) Norton, W. W. & Co., Inc.

Taschen Publishing Staff. Architecture Materials - Concrete: concrete béton beton. Kramp, Klaus, ed. 2008. (FRE, GER & ENG., Illus.). 254p. pap. 19.99 *(978-3-8365-0451-5(0))* TASCHEN DEU. Dist: Ingram Pub. Services.

Taylor, William & Levine, Michael. Prospects for an Ethics of Architecture. 2011. (ENG., Illus.). 232p. (C). 155.00 *(978-0-415-58971-0(1))*; pap. 49.95 *(978-0-415-58972-7(X))* Routledge.

Thomas, Lloyd. Material Matters: Architecture & Material Practice. 2007. (Illus.). 272p. 165.00 *(978-0-415-36325-9(X))*; 55.95 *(978-0-415-36326-6(8))* Routledge.

Toff. Architect & Sculptor Ra's a Guide to the Architect & Sculptor Members of the Royal Academy. 2010. (ENG.). 112p. pap. 25.00 *(978-1-906509-08-8(5))* Unicorn Pr., London GBR. Dist: National Bk. Network.

Tomasso, Diane Wray & Paglia, Michael. The Mid-Century Modern House in Denver. 2007. pap. 10.95 *(978-0-914248-02-6(2))* Historic Denver, Inc.

Torrey, Mike. Stone Offerings: Machu Picchu's Terraces of Enlightenment. 2009. 144p. 40.00 *(978-0-9818812-0-1(3))* Lightpoint Pr.

Triviño, Santi. Small Bars. Trivino, Santi et al, eds. 2010. (Architectural Details Ser.). (ENG., Illus.). 256p. 57.50 *(978-84-96823-32-7(6))* Instituto Monsa de Ediciones, S.A. ESP. Dist: Trans-Atlantic Pubns., Inc.

Tuntbas, Adil. Type in Architecture As a Tool of Communication. 2009. 104p. pap. *(978-3-639-13110-9(X))* VDM Verlag Dr. Mueller e.K.

Tzonis, Alexander & Lefaivre, Liane. Architecture of Regionalism in the Age of Globalization: Peaks & Valleys in the Flat World. 2011. (ENG., Illus.). 232p. 155.00 *(978-0-415-57578-2(8))*; pap. 49.95 *(978-0-415-57579-9(6))* Routledge.

Uffelen, Van Chris. Automobile Architecture. 2011. (Architecture in Focus Ser.). (ENG., Illus.). 424p. 99.95 *(978-3-03768-073-5(3)*, Braun Publish,Csi) Continental Sales, Inc.

Ullmann, Franziska. Basics: Architechture andd Dynamics - Energy Dynamics. 2011. (Illus.). 208p. pap. 59.95 *(978-3-7091-0323-4(1)*, 3709103231) Springer Wien AUT. Dist: Springer.

Vallero, Daniel A. & Brasier, Chris. Sustainable Design: The Science of Sustainability & Green Engineering. 2008. (ENG., Illus.). 352p. 90.00 *(978-0-470-13062-9(8)*, Wiley) Wiley, John & Sons, Inc.

van der Werf, Huib Haye, ed. Waterfront Visions. 2010. (ENG., Illus.). 128p. pap. 40.00 *(978-90-5662-730-0(9))* NAi Uitgevers / Publishers Stichting NLD. Dist: D.A.P./Distributed Art Pubs.

van Eck, Caroline & Bussels, Stijn. Theatricality in Early Modern Art & Architecture. 2011. (Art History Special Issues Ser.: 7). (ENG., Illus.). 200p. pap. 39.95 *(978-1-4443-3902-4(8)*, Wiley-Blackwell) Wiley, John & Sons, Inc.

Van Schaik, Leon. Design City Melbourne. 2008. (Interior Angles Ser.: 23). (ENG., Illus.). 288p. pap. 55.00 *(978-0-470-01641-1(8)*, Wiley) Wiley, John & Sons, Inc.

Varios. Le Corbusier: Una Nueva Arquitectura. 2010. 150p. pap. *(978-1-60796-237-3(3))* Editorial Benei Noaj.

Verderber, Stephen F. Sprawling Cities & Our Endangered Public Health. 2012. (ENG., Illus.). 256p. (C). 165.00 *(978-0-415-66532-2(9))*; pap. 55.95 *(978-0-415-66533-9(7))* Routledge.

Verdickt, Tine. Timeless Wood: Outdoor Living with Style. 2011. (ENG, FRE & DUT., Illus.). 192p. 70.00 *(978-90-209-9710-1(6))* Lannoo Pubs./Racine.

Vidler, Anthony. The Scenes of the Street & Other Essays. 2011. (ENG., Illus.). 368p. 50.00 *(978-1-58093-270-7(3))* Monacelli Pr., Inc.

Vidler, Anthony, ed. Architecture Between Spectacle & Use. 2008. (Clark Studies in the Visual Arts). (ENG., Illus.). 240p. per. 24.95 *(978-0-300-12554-2(2))* Yale Univ. Pr.

Vigne, Antoine. Le Corbusier in His Own Words. 2009. (FRE., Illus.). 48p. 19.95 *(978-1-901092-98-1(4))* Papadakis Dist A/C.

Vijayakumar, M. V. & Davis, D. N. Cognition, Metacognition Agents & Architectures. 2010. 208p. pap. *(978-3-8383-7051-4(1))* Lambert Academic Publishing.

Virone, Carmelo. AIUD/G. Honoré, Architectes + Carmelio Virone, écrivain: AIUD/G. Honoré, Architects + Carmelio Virone, Writer: [expo 18 Janvier-17 Février 2007], 1 vol. 2011. (FRE & ENG., Illus.). 174p. pap. 20.00 *(978-2-9600475-5-4(9))* Centre International Pour La Ville, L'Architecture Et Le Paysage BEL. Dist: Innovative Logistics.

Vitali, Anna. Fantastic Feedback about Architecture. 2010. (ENG., Illus.). 52p. pap. *(978-1-84748-499-4(9))* Athena Pr.

Vukovljak, Damir. A Conversation [Framing a Stage]. 2010. 72p. pap. *(978-3-639-25330-6(2))* VDM Verlag Dr. Mueller e.K.

VV Staff. Guggenheim. (SPA.). 192p. *(978-84-96137-92-9(9))* A. Asppan, S.L. Distribuidora Internacional de Libros y Revistas.

Walker, Ralph. The Fly in the Amber: Comments on the Making of Architecture. 2011. 182p. 42.95 ***(978-1-258-04903-4(1))*** Literary Licensing, LLC.

Walker, Stephen. Gordon Matta-Clark: Art, Architecture & the Attack on Modernism. 2009. (ENG., Illus.). 224p. pap. 31.00 *(978-1-84511-966-9(5))* I. B. Tauris & Co., Ltd. GBR. Dist: Macmillan.

Wallpaper Magazine Editors, ed. Basel 2012 - Wallpaper City Guides. 2nd ed. 2011. (ENG., Illus.). 128p. pap., pap. 9.95 *(978-0-7148-6102-9(2))* Phaidon Pr., Inc.

—Santiago 2011 - Wallpaper City Guides. 2011. (ENG.). 128p. pap. 9.95 *(978-0-7148-5937-8(0))* Phaidon Pr., Inc.

Walz, Steffen P. Toward a Ludic Architecture: the Space of Play & Games. 2010. (ENG.). 382p. pap. 21.95 *(978-0-557-28563-1(1))* Lulu Enterprises Inc.

Warwick, Rhona, ed. Arcade: Artists & Place-Making. 2006. (ENG., Illus.). 157p. pap. 29.95 *(978-1-904772-54-5(4))* Black Dog Publishing Ltd. GBR. Dist: Perseus Distribution.

Watkin, David. The Architect King: George III & the Culture of the Enlightenment. 2006. (Illus.). 50.00 *(978-1-902163-50-5(8))* Royal Collection Enterprises Ltd. GBR. Dist: Antique Collectors' Club.

Watts, Andrew. Modern Construction Envelopes (Modern Construction Series) 2010. (Modern Construction Ser.). (Illus.). 522p. 109.00 *(978-3-7091-0257-2(X)*, 370910257X) Springer Wien AUT. Dist: Springer.

Webb, Michael. Swatt Architects: Livable Modern. 2006. (House Design Ser.). (ENG., Illus.). 108p. 49.50 *(978-1-920744-45-8(2))* Images Publishing Group AUS. Dist: National Bk. Network.

Weigel, Viola & Spanke, Daniel, eds. Gereon Krebber: All That Is Solid Melts into Air. 2008. (ENG., Illus.). 104p. 30.00 *(978-3-86678-061-3(3))* Kerber Verlag DEU. Dist: D.A.P./Distributed Art Pubs.

Weinstock, Michael. The Architecture of Emergence: The Evolution of Form in Nature & Civilisation. 2010. (ENG., Illus.). 280p. 175.00 *(978-0-470-06632-4(6))*; pap. 60.00 *(978-0-470-06633-1(4))* Wiley, John & Sons, Inc. (Wiley).

White, Mason & Przybylski, Maya, eds. On Farming: Bracket 1. 2010. (ENG., Illus.). 252p. pap. *(978-84-92861-21-7(5))* Actar Birkhauser Distribution.

Wiberg, Mikael. Interactive Textures for Architecture & Landscaping: Digital Elements & Technologies. 2010. (Illus.). 350p. 180.00 *(978-1-61520-653-7(1))* IGI Global.

Widmann, Nancy. Washington Park. 2007. (Illus.). xii, 240p. pap. 10.95 *(978-0-914248-00-2(6))* Historic Denver, Inc.

Wilson, Colin St. John. The Other Tradition of Modern Architecture: The Uncompleted Project. rev. ed. 2007. (ENG., Illus.). 189p. 29.95 *(978-1-904772-62-0(5))* Black Dog Publishing Ltd. GBR. Dist: Perseus Distribution.

Wilson, Samuel, Jr. A Guide to Architecture of New Orleans, 1 vol. 2011. (ENG., Illus.). 80p. pap. 10.00 *(978-1-879714-18-2(3))* Wilson Jr., Samuel Pubns. Fund of The Louisiana Landmarks Society.

Winters, Edward & Winters. Aesthetics & Architecture. 2007. (Continuum Aesthetics Ser.). (ENG., Illus.). 192p. 27.95 *(978-0-8264-8632-5(0))*; 130.00 *(978-0-8264-8631-8(2))* Continuum International Publishing Group, Ltd. GBR. Dist: National Bk. Network.

Woodcock, Alex. Gargoyles & Grotesques. 2011. (Shire Library). (ENG., Illus.). 64p. pap. 12.95 *(978-0-7478-0831-2(7))* Shire Pubns., Ltd. GBR. Dist: Random Hse., Inc.

Woolley, Ken. Art Works. 2006. (ENG., Illus.). 80p. pap. 21.95 *(978-1-876907-79-2(7))* Images Publishing Group AUS. Dist: National Bk. Network.

The World's Greatest Architecture: Past & Present. 2007. (Illus.). 447p. pap. 12.99 *(978-0-7858-2239-4(9)*, Chartwell) Book Sales, Inc.

Worpole, Ken. The Modern Hospice Movement: The Architecture of Palliative Care. 2009. (ENG., Illus.). 152p. 165.00 *(978-0-415-45179-6(5))* Routledge.

Wright, Frank Lloyd. The Essential Frank Lloyd Wright: Critical Writings on Architecture. Pfeiffer, Bruce Brooks, ed. 2010. (ENG., Illus.). 464p. pap. 24.95 *(978-0-691-14632-4(2))* Princeton Univ. Pr.

Wright, Frank Lloyd. Two Lectures on Architecture. 2011. 64p. 36.95 ***(978-1-258-00985-4(4))*** Literary Licensing, LLC.

Wright, Frank Lloyd & Pfeiffer, Bruce Brooks. The Essential Frank Lloyd Wright: Critical Writings on Architecture. Pfeiffer, Bruce Brooks, ed. 2008. (ENG., Illus.). 464p. (C). 49.95 *(978-0-691-13318-8(2))* Princeton Univ. Pr.

Wyatt, Ken & Hough, Richard. Principles of Structure. 5th rev. ed. 2013. (ENG., Illus.). 224p. (C). pap. 44.95 *(978-0-415-66727-2(5)*, Spon Pr.) Routledge.

Wyatt, Ken J. Principles of Structure. rev. ed. (Illus.). 140p. pap. *(978-0-86840-086-0(6)*, UNSW Press) NewSouth Publishing.

Yale School of Architecture Staff & Kahn, Louis. Turbulence. Rappaport, Nina & Stevens, Leo, eds. 2011. (Yale School of Architecture Bks.). (ENG., Illus.). 184p. pap. 35.00 *(978-0-393-73350-1(5)*, 73350) Norton, W. W. & Co., Inc.

Young-Sub, Kim. Kim Young-Sub: Selected & Current Works. 2006. (Master Architect Series VI). (ENG., Illus.). 256p. 59.95 *(978-1-920744-01-4(0)*, Images Publishing Dist Ac) Antique Collectors' Club GBR. Dist: National Bk. Network.

Zelov, Christopher & Cousineau, Phil. City21: Multiple Views on Urban Futures. 2009. (ENG.). 25.00 *(978-0-9650306-6-3(0))* Knossus Pubs.

2007-2008 Design/Build Survey: Of Design & Construction Firms. 2007. per. 395.00 *(978-1-934150-19-1(3))* ZweigWhite.

ARCHITECTURE—BIBLIOGRAPHY

Bibliographic Guide to Art & Architecture 1998. Date not set. 273.00 *(978-0-7838-0224-4(2),* Macmillan Reference USA) Cengage Gale.

Faleer, Robert A. Church Woodwork in the British Isles, 1100-1535: An Annotated Bibliography. 2009. (ENG., Illus.). 472p. (gr. 17). 110.00 *(978-0-8108-6739-0(7))* Scarecrow Pr., Inc.

Herrmann. Gottfried Sempers theoretische Schriften an der ETH. (GER., Illus.). 271p. 50.95 *(978-3-7643-1239-8(4),* 3764312394) Birkhauser Boston.

Lyell, Arthur Henry. A Bibliographical List Descriptive of Romano-British Architectural Remains in Great Britain. 2010. (Cambridge Library Collection - Archaeology Ser.). (ENG.). 176p. pap. 19.99 *(978-1-108-00890-7(9))* Cambridge Univ. Pr.

ARCHITECTURE—CLIMATIC FACTORS

see Architecture and Climate

ARCHITECTURE—COMPOSITION, PROPORTION, ETC.

see also Space (Architecture)

Adam, Ken, et al. Style & Scale: Or, Do You Have Anxiety?: A Conversation With. 2009. (GER & ENG., Illus.). 120p. pap. 39.95 *(978-3-211-99215-9(4))* Springer Wien AUT. Dist: Actar Birkhauser Distribution.

Adler, Gerald, et al, eds. Scale. 2011. (ENG., Illus.). 256p. (C). pap. 53.95 ***(978-0-415-68712-6(8))*** Routledge.

Arnheim, Rudolf & Arnheim, R. The Dynamics of Architectural Form. 30th anniv. ed. 2009. (ENG., Illus.). 289p. pap. 24.95 *(978-0-520-26125-9(9))* Univ. of California Pr.

Balmer, Jeffrey & Swisher, Michael. Diagramming the Big Idea: Methods for Architectural Composition. 2012. (ENG., Illus.). 256p. (C). 165.00 *(978-0-415-89408-1(5));* pap. 34.95 *(978-0-415-89409-8(3))* Routledge.

Blanciak, François. Siteless: 1001 Building Forms. 2008. (ENG., Illus.). 128p. (gr. 17). pap. 15.95 *(978-0-262-02630-7(9))* MIT Pr.

Boonzaaijer, Karel, et al. Vision: Space for Imagination. 2011. (DUT & ENG., Illus.). 128p. pap. *(978-90-5856-357-6(X),* Stichting Kunstboak (Acc)) Antique Collectors' Club.

Ching, Francis D. K. Architecture: Form, Space, & Order. 2007. 464p. pap. 48.00 incl. cd-rom *(978-0-470-23153-1(X))* Wiley, John & Sons, Inc.

Curtis, Nathaniel Cortlandt. The Secrets of Architectural Composition. 2011. (Dover Architecture Ser.). (ENG.). 288p. pap. 19.95 *(978-0-486-48042-8(9))* Dover Pubns., Inc.

Grobman, Yasha & Neuman, Eran, eds. Performalism: Form & Performance in Digital Architecture. 2011. (ENG., Illus.). 224p. (C). pap. 74.95 *(978-0-415-58361-9(6))* Routledge.

Hanlon, Don & Hanlon. Compositions in Architecture. 2009. (ENG., Illus.). 336p. pap. 60.00 *(978-0-470-05364-5(X),* Wiley) Wiley, John & Sons, Inc.

Harris, James. Fractal Architecture: Organic Design Philosophy in Theory & Practice. 2012. ***(978-0-8263-5202-6(2));*** (ENG., Illus.). 420p. pap. 75.00 ***(978-0-8263-5201-9(4))*** Univ. of New Mexico Pr.

Hight, Christopher. Architectural Principles in the Age of Cybernetics. 2008. (ENG., Illus.). 248p. (C). 165.00 *(978-0-415-38481-0(8))* Routledge.

—Architectural Principles in the Age of Cybernetics. 2007. (Illus.). 239p. per. 54.95 *(978-0-415-38482-7(6))* Taylor & Francis Group.

Kabir, Fatema. Phenomenon of Visual Perception in Architecture. 2010. (Illus.). 60p. pap. *(978-3-8383-7049-1(X))* Lambert Academic Publishing.

Laming, Denis & Vitta, Maurizio. Denis Laming: Invisible Tensions. 2007. (Architectura Ser.). (ENG., Illus.). 100p. pap. 25.00 *(978-88-7838-054-7(7),* Art Stock Bks. Ltd/Csi) Continental Sales, Inc.

Prada, Manuel de. Arte y Naturaleza: El Sentido de la Irregularidad en el Arte y la Arquitectura. 2009. (SPA., Illus.). 131p. *(978-987-584-197-0(8))* Nobuko.

Read, Gray. The Miniature & the Gigantic in Philadelphia Architecture: Essays on Designing the City to Human Scale. 2007. (Illus.). 160p. (C). 99.95 *(978-0-7734-5429-3(2))* Mellen, Edwin Pr., The.

Remery, Michel. Mystery & Matter: On the Relationship Between Liturgy & Architecture in the Thought of Dom Hans Van der Laan OSB (1904-1991) 2011. 668p. *(978-90-04-18296-7(9))* BRILL.

Schofield, P. H. The Theory of Proportion in Architecture. 2011. (ENG.). 170p. pap. 19.99 ***(978-0-521-24315-5(7))*** Cambridge Univ. Pr.

Susanka, Sarah. More Not So Big Solutions for Your Home. 2010. (ENG., Illus.). 160p. pap. 22.95 *(978-1-60085-148-3(7))* Taunton Pr., Inc.

Triviño, Santi. Architectural Shapes. Minguet, Josep Maria, ed. 2011. (ENG & SPA., Illus.). 96p. pap. 24.95 ***(978-84-15223-06-1(4))*** Instituto Monsa de Ediciones, S.A. ESP. Dist: Trans-Atlantic Pubns., Inc.

ARCHITECTURE—CONSERVATION AND RESTORATION

see also Buildings—Repair and Reconstruction

Albanel, Christine. The Hall of Mirrors: History & Restoration. 2007. (ENG., Illus.). 422p. 275.00 *(978-2-87844-088-1(9))* Hudson Hills Pr. LLC.

Andeweg, Marie Therèse. Cost C16 improving the quality of existing urban building Envelopes. 2007. pap. 69.00 *(978-1-58603-735-2(8),* Delft University Pr) IOS Pr., Inc.

Andeweg, Marie Therèse, et al. Cost C16 improving the quality of existing urban building Envelopes. 2007. pap. 69.00 *(978-1-58603-734-5(X),* Delft University Pr) IOS Pr., Inc.

Architectural Record Staff. The Restoration of Colonial Williamsburg in Virginia. (Illus.). 458p. reprint ed. lib. bdg. 98.00 *(978-0-7222-0566-2(X))* Library Reprints, Inc.

Arnold, Anthea. Charleston Saved, 1979-1989. 2010. (ENG., Illus.). 144p. 39.95 *(978-0-7090-9018-2(8))* Hale, Robert Ltd. GBR. Dist: Independent Pubs. Group.

Arrhenius, Thordis. The Fragile Monument: On Conservation & Modernity. 2012. (ENG.). 176p. pap. 29.95 *(978-1-907317-47-7(3))* Black Dog Publishing Ltd. GBR. Dist: Perseus Distribution.

Asti, William Henry. The Chicken Came First: A premier for renewing & sustaining our Communities. 2011. (Our National Conversation Ser.). (ENG., Illus.). 278p. pap. 19.95 *(978-1-935166-20-7(4))* Parkhurst Brothers, Inc., Pubs.

—The Chicken Came First: A Primer for Renewing & Sustaining Our Communities. 2011. (Our National Conversation Ser.). (ENG.). 400p. 29.95 *(978-1-935166-40-5(9))* Parkhurst Brothers, Inc., Pubs.

Bandarin, Francesco & van Oers, Ron. The Historic Urban Landscape: Managing Heritage in an Urban Century. 2nd ed. 2012. (ENG., Illus.). 262p. 92.99 ***(978-0-470-65574-0(7),*** Wiley) Wiley, John & Sons, Inc.

Bianca, Stefano. Karakoram: Hidden Treasures in the Northern Areas of Pakistan. Bianca, Stefano, ed. 2006. (ENG., Illus.). 328p. pap. 60.00 *(978-88-422-1330-7(6))* Allemandi, Umberto & Co. GBR. Dist: National Bk. Network.

Bianca, Stefano, ed. Syria: Medieval Citadels Between East & West. 2007. (ENG., Illus.). 312p. per. 60.00 *(978-88-422-1449-6(3))* Allemandi, Umberto & Co. GBR. Dist: National Bk. Network.

Birnbaum, Charles A., ed. Preserving Modern Landscape Architecture: Proceedings from the Wave Hill Conference. 2006. (Land Marks Ser.: Vol. 10). (ENG.). 84p. pap. 24.95 *(978-1-888931-21-1(3))* Spacemaker Pr.

Bluestone, Daniel. Buildings, Landscapes, & Memory: Case Studies in Historic Preservation. 2010. (ENG., Illus.). 304p. 47.95 *(978-0-393-73318-1(1),* 73318) Norton, W. W. & Co., Inc.

Borie, Alain. Le Lycée Elisa Lemonnier: Leonard, Weissmann. 2010. (FRE., Illus.). *(978-2-35733-106-8(2))* Archibooks.

Born, George Walter. Preserving Paradise: The Architectural Heritage & History of the Florida Keys. 2006. (Illus.). 156p. pap., per. 19.99 *(978-1-59629-152-2(4))* History Pr., The.

Boussaa, Djamel. Urban Conservation in North Africa & the Gulf. 2010. 324p. pap. *(978-3-639-27313-7(3))* VDM Verlag Dr. Mueller e.K.

Breslauer, Ken. Historic Sites & Architecture of St. Petersburg Florida. 2011. (ENG.). 88p. pap. 22.95 ***(978-1-4327-7885-9(4))*** Outskirts Pr., Inc.

Bridgwood, Barry & Lennie, Lindsay. History, Performance & Conservation. 2009. (Technologies of Architecture Ser.). (ENG., Illus.). 352p. (C). 165.00 *(978-0-415-43419-5(X));* pap. 49.95 *(978-0-415-43420-1(3))* Taylor & Francis Group GBR. (Taylor & Francis). Dist: Taylor & Francis Group.

Broach, Barbara Kimberlin, et al. Frank Lloyd Wright's Rosenbaum House: The Birth & Rebirth of an American Treasure. 2006. (Illus.). 80p. 19.95 *(978-0-7649-3763-7(4),* A123) Pomegranate Communications, Inc.

Brunskill, R. W. Traditional Farm Buildings of Britain & Their Conservation. 3rd ed. 2007. (ENG., Illus.). 208p. pap. 40.00 *(978-0-300-12319-7(1))* Yale Univ. Pr.

Carella, Silvio. Architecture religieuse haut-medievale en Italie Meridionale: Le diocese de Benevent. 2011. (Bibliotheque de l'antiquite Tardive Ser.). (FRE., Illus.). 255p. (C). pap. 94.00 *(978-2-503-53388-9(4))* Brepols Pubs. BEL. Dist: Brown, David Bk. Co., The.

Casey, Christine, ed. The Eighteenth-century Dublin Townhouse. 2010. (Illus.). 312p. 65.00 *(978-1-84682-187-5(8))* Four Courts Pr. IRL. Dist: International Specialized Bk. Services.

Castillejo, Marta, et al, eds. Lasers in the Conservation of Artworks: Proceedings of the International Conference Lacona VII, Madrid, Spain, 17 - 21 September 2007. 2008. (ENG., Illus.). 512p. 205.95 *(978-0-415-47596-9(1),* CRC Press) Taylor & Francis Group GBR. Dist: Taylor & Francis Group.

Cather, Sharon, et al. Wall Paintings: Diagnostic Investigations & Research. 2011. (English Heritage Research Transactions Ser.). (ENG., Illus.). 244p. (C). pap. 67.50 *(978-1-84407-328-3(9))* Earthscan LLC.

Choegyal, Lisa & Potton, Craig. Kathmandu Valley Style. 2008. (Illus.). 256p. 65.00 *(978-1-932476-34-7(2))* Serindia Pubns., Inc.

Chusid, Jeffrey M. Saving Wright: The Freeman House & the Preservation of Meaning, Materials, & Modernity. 2011. (ENG., Illus.). 256p. 55.00 *(978-0-393-73302-0(5),* 73302) Norton, W. W. & Co., Inc.

Claxton, Bevis. Country Cottage Conservation: A Guide to Maintenance & Repair, 1 vol. 2010. (ENG., Illus.). 160p. 32.95 *(978-1-84797-179-1(2))* Crowood Pr., Ltd. GBR. Dist: Independent Pubs. Group.

Collings, Janet. Victorian & Edwardian Houses: A Guide to Care & Maintenance. 2008. (ENG., Illus.). 160p. 43.95 *(978-1-84797-057-2(5))* Crowood Pr., Ltd. GBR. Dist: Independent Pubs. Group.

Coureas, Nicholas, et al. Medieval & Renaissance Famagusta: Studies in Architecture Art & History. 2012. (FRE & ENG., Illus.). 330p. 119.95 ***(978-1-4094-3557-0(1))*** Ashgate Publishing Co.

Couture, Francine & Vanlaethem, France. Conservation de L'art Contemporain et de L'architecture Moderne: L'authenticité en Question. 2010. (FRE., Illus.). viii, 158p. *(978-2-89544-136-6(7))* Editions MultiMondes.

Cullinane, John J. Maintaining & Repairing Old & Historic Buildings. 2012. (ENG., Illus.). 240p. 75.00 ***(978-0-470-76757-3(X),*** Wiley) Wiley, John & Sons, Inc.

Denslagen, Wim. Memories of Architecture: Architectural Heritage & Historiography in the Distant Past. 2011. (ENG., Illus.). 194p. pap. 65.95 *(978-90-5589-303-4(X))* Het Spinhuis NLD. Dist: Transaction Pubs.

—Romantic Modernism: Nostalgia in the World of Conservation. 2011. 261p. pap. *(978-90-8964-103-8(3))* Amsterdam Univ. Pr.

Di Giulio, Roberto. COST C16 improving the quality of existing urban building Envelopes. 2007. pap. 69.00 *(978-1-58603-737-6(4),* Delft University Pr) IOS Pr., Inc.

Di Giulio, Roberto, et al. COST C16 improving the quality of existing urban building Envelopes. 2007. pap. 69.00 *(978-1-58603-736-9(6),* Delft University Pr) IOS Pr., Inc.

Diab, Mark C. & A. Ghafar Ahmad. The Conservation & Restoration of Cultural Heritage in the Asia Pacific Regions. 2009. (ENG.). 307p. 90.00 *(978-0-387-09450-2(4))* Springer.

Dickmann, Klaus, et al, eds. Lasers in the Conservation of Artworks: LACONA V Proceedings, Osnabrack, Germany, Sept. 15-18 2003. 2010. (Springer Proceedings in Physics Ser.). (Illus.). xxi, 528p. pap. 319.00 *(978-3-642-06191-2(5),* 3642061915) Springer.

Dietrich, Eva. Die westfälische Denkmalpflege der Nachkriegszeit. Westfalen-Lippe, Landschaftsverband, ed. 2008. (Illus.). 240p. (C). 36.00 *(978-3-8053-3959-9(3))* Zabern, Philipp von Verlag, GmbH DEU. Dist: Brown, David Bk. Co., The.

Ebersberger, Eva, ed. Jorge Otero-Pailos: the Ethics of Dust. 2010. (ENG., Illus.). 104p. pap. 33.00 *(978-3-86560-655-6(5))* Verlag der Buchhandlung Walther Konig DEU. Dist: D.A.P./Distributed Art Pubs.

Finnish Committee for the Restoration of Viipuri Library Staff & Karjalainen, Markku. Alvar Aalto Library in Vyborg: Saving a Modern Masterpiece. 2010. (ENG., Illus.). 144p. pap. 69.00 *(978-951-682-938-1(4),* Art Stock Bks. Ltd/Csi) Continental Sales, Inc.

Greenspan, Anders. Creating Colonial Williamsburg: The Restoration of Virginia's Eighteenth-Century Capital, Second Edition. 2nd ed. 2009. (ENG., Illus.). 248p. 47.50 *(978-0-8078-3343-8(6));* pap. 20.95 *(978-0-8078-5987-2(7))* Univ. of North Carolina Pr.

Guidelines to Overcome Architectural Barriers in Cultural Heritage Sites. 2012. 206p. pap. 42.00 ***(978-88-492-2192-3(4))*** Gangemi ITA. Dist: International Publishers Marketing.

Guido, Sante & Mantella, Guiseppe, eds. Storie di Restauri Nella Chiesa Conventuale di San Giovanni Battista a la Valletta. 2008. (ITA., Illus.). 492p. (C). 285.00 *(978-99932-7-202-1(7))* Midsea Bks. Ltd. MLT. Dist: Brown, David Bk. Co., The.

Jackson, Emily G. Historic Preservation of U. S. Properties. 2011. (Focus on Civilizations & Cultures Ser.). 115.00 *(978-1-61122-736-9(4))* Nova Science Pubs., Inc.

Jodidio, Philip, ed. The Aga Khan Historic Cities Programme: Strategies for Urban Regeneration. 2011. (Illus.). 240p. 75.00 *(978-3-7913-4406-5(4))* Prestel Publishing.

Kissel, Eleonore & Vigneau, Erin. Architectural Photoreproductions: A Manual for Identification & Care. 2nd ed. 2009. 140p. pap. 49.95 *(978-1-58456-216-0(1))* Oak Knoll Pr.

Landesamt fur Denkmalpflege Rheinland-Pfalz/Abteil, ed. Baudenkmäler in Rheinland-Pfalz 2006-2008. 2010. (GER.). 168p. 45.00 *(978-3-8053-4265-0(9))* Zabern, Philipp von Verlag, GmbH DEU. Dist: Brown, David Bk. Co., The.

Leach, Stephen. Saving the Wall. 2012. (Illus.). 192p. pap. 19.95 ***(978-1-4456-0018-5(8))*** Amberley Publishing GBR. Dist: Casemate Pubs. & Bk. Distributors, LLC.

Lebeau, Marc & Suleiman, Antoine, eds. Beydar Studies 1. 2008. (Subartu Ser.). (FRE & ENG.). 327p. (C). pap. 131.00 *(978-2-503-52660-7(8))* Brepols Pubs. BEL. Dist: ISD.

Letellier, Robin, et al. Recording, Documentation, & Information Management for the Conservation of Heritage Places: Guiding Principles, 2 vols. 2011. (Illus.). 388p. *(978-1-873394-94-6(2))* 2007. pap. *(978-0-89236-925-6(6))* Getty Pubns. (Getty Conservation Institute, The).

Lichfield, Nathaniel. Economics in Urban Conservation. 2009. (ENG.). 380p. pap. 51.00 *(978-0-521-10530-9(7))* Cambridge Univ. Pr.

Littlefield, David & Lewis, Saskia. Architectural Voices: Listening to Old Buildings. 2008. (ENG., Illus.). 240p. pap. 60.00 *(978-0-470-01673-2(6),* Wiley) Wiley, John & Sons, Inc.

Liu, Gretchen & Byfield, Graham. Singapore Sketchbook: An Island Observed. 2011. 96p. 30.00 *(978-981-4063-40-6(3),* Didier Millet,Csi) Continental Sales, Inc.

Macdonald, Susan, et al. Conservation of Modern Architecture. 2007. (Illus.). 144p. pap. *(978-1-873394-84-7(5))* Donhead Publishing Ltd.

Malraux, Andre & Lantelme, Michel. La Grande Pitié des Monuments de France: Débats Parlementaires, 1960-1968. (FRE.). 158p. *(978-2-85939-548-3(2))* Presses Universitaires du Septentrion.

Mason, Randall. The Once & Future New York: Historic Preservation & the Modern City. 2009. (ENG., Illus.). 344p. 84.00 *(978-0-8166-5603-5(7));* pap. 27.95 *(978-0-8166-5604-2(5))* Univ. of Minnesota Pr.

Mateyka, Karen Campe. Henry the Stephenson House Mouse: A Diary. 2007. pap. 12.00 *(978-1-933370-07-1(6))* Reedy Pr.

Meiron, Eyal, ed. Planning & Conserving Jerusalem, 1973-2003: The Challenge of an Ancient City. 2009. (Illus.). 482p. 37.00 *(978-965-217-289-1(8))* Yad Izhak Ben-Zvi ISR. Dist: Eisenbrauns, Inc.

Moro, Laura, ed. Taihe Dian: The Hall of Supreme Harmony of the Forbidden City in Beijing. 2010. 140p. pap. 32.95 *(978-88-492-1557-1(6))* Gangemi ITA. Dist: International Publishers Marketing.

Mort, Mike. A Bridge Worth Saving: A Community Guide to Historic Bridge Preservation. 2008. (ENG., Illus.). 143p. pap. 24.95 *(978-0-87013-828-7(6))* Michigan State Univ. Pr.

Morton, W. Brown, III, et al. The Secretary of the Interior's Standards for Rehabilitation & Illustrated Guidelines on Sustainability for Rehabilitating Historic Buildings. 2011. (Illus.). 35p. pap. 7.00 ***(978-0-16-088440-5(3),*** Interior Dept.) United States Government Printing Office.

Nimmrichter, Johann, et al, eds. Lasers in the Conservation of Artworks: LACONA VI Proceedings, Vienna, Austria, Sept. 21 — 25 2005. (Springer Proceedings in Physics Ser.). (Illus.). xxvi, 650p. 2010. pap. 359.00 *(978-3-642-09129-2(6),* 3642091296) 2007. 359.00 *(978-3-540-72129-1(0))* Springer.

Orbasli, Aylin & Grover, Philip. Architectural Conservation: Principles & Practice. 2007. (ENG., Illus.). 240p. pap. 62.99 *(978-0-632-04025-4(4),* Wiley-Blackwell) Wiley, John & Sons, Inc.

Otero-Pailos. Future Anterior Vol. 8, Issue 1: Journal of Historic Preservation History, Theory & Criticism. 2011. (Future Anterior Ser.). 150p. pap. 46.00 *(978-0-8166-7634-7(8))* Univ. of Minnesota Pr.

Otero-Pailos, Jorge. Future Anterior 4-2. 2008. (Future Anterior Ser.). (ENG.). 112p. pap. 20.00 *(978-0-8166-5470-3(0))* Univ. of Minnesota Pr.

Oyarzún, Fernando Pérez, et al. Chilean Modern Architecture since 1950. Quantrill, Malcolm, ed. 2010. (Studies in Architecture & Culture Ser.). (ENG., Illus.). 192p. 45.00 *(978-1-60344-135-3(2))* Texas A&M Univ. Pr.

Pauwels, Wim. Timeless Renovations/Renovations Intemporelles/Tijdloze Renovaties. 2007. (ENG., Illus.). 200p. *(978-90-77213-80-3(5),* Beta-Plus (Acc)) Antique Collectors' Club.

Pendlebury, John & Townshend, Tim. Conservation & the Age of Consensus. 2008. (Illus.). 240p. 155.00 *(978-0-415-24983-6(X));* pap. 53.95 *(978-0-415-24984-3(8))* Routledge.

Piotrowicz, Lynn M. & Osgood, Scott. Building Science 101: A Primer for Librarians. 2010. 136p. *(978-0-8389-1041-2(6))* American Library Assn.

Plank, Jeffrey. Crombie Taylor: Modern Architecture, Building Restoration & the Re-Discovery of Louis Sullivan. 2010. (Illus.). 315p. 65.00 *(978-0-9795508-1-2(5))* Stout, William Pubs.

Radvan, Roxana, ed. Lasers in the Conservation of Artworks VIII. 2010. (ENG., Illus.). 240p. 159.99 *(978-0-415-58073-1(0),* CRC Press) Taylor & Francis Group GBR. Dist: Taylor & Francis Group.

Rettberg, Britta von. Freising: Stadttopographie und Denkmalpflege. 2009. (GER., Illus.). 336p. *(978-3-86568-354-0(1))* Imhof, Michael Verlag GmbH & Co. KG.

Rodwell, Dennis. Conservation & Sustainability in Historic Cities. 2007. (ENG., Illus.). 272p. per. 104.99 *(978-1-4051-2656-4(6),* Wiley-Blackwell) Wiley, John & Sons, Inc.

Ruch, Hans-Jörg & Seifert-Uherkovich, Ludmila, texts. Historic Houses in Engadin: Architectural Interventions, 1 vol. 2008. (ENG., Illus.). 320p. 98.00 *(978-3-86521-720-2(6))* Steidl, Gerhard Druckerei und Verlag DEU. Dist: Innovative Logistics.

Ruggles, D. Fairchild, ed. On Location: Heritage Cities & Sites. 2011. (ENG., Illus.). viii, 244p. 129.00 ***(978-1-4614-1107-9(6),*** 1461411076) Springer.

Rypkema, Don. Feasibility Assessment Manual. 2007. 108p. 40.00 *(978-0-89133-575-7(7))* National Trust for Historic Preservation.

Santifaller, Enrico, et al. Transform: The Revitalization of Buildings: KSP Engel und Zimmerman Architekten. 2008. (GER & ENG., Illus.). 160p. 49.95 *(978-3-7913-4032-6(8))* Prestel Publishing.

Scarzella, Paolo & Zerbinatti, Marco. Recupero e Conservazione Dell'edilizia Storica: L'insieme, le Parti: Interrati e Fondazioni, Partizioni, Coperture, Chiusure e Aggetti. 2009. (ITA., Illus.). 254p. *(978-88-6055-373-7(3))* Alinea.

Schofield, John, et al. Local Heritage Global Context: Cultural Perspectives on Sense of Place. 2010. (Heritage, Culture & Identity Ser.). (Illus.). 230p. 99.95 *(978-0-7546-7829-8(6))* Ashgate Publishing Co.

Semes, Steven, et al. The Future of the Past: A Conservation Ethic for Architecture, Urbanism, & Historic Preservation. 2009. (ENG., Illus.). 272p. 60.00 *(978-0-393-73244-3(4),* 73244) Norton, W. W. & Co., Inc.

Silvestre, Ruth. A House in the Sunflowers. 2011. (ENG., Illus.). 288p. pap. 16.95 *(978-0-7490-0838-3(5))* Allison & Busby, Ltd. GBR. Dist: International Publishers Marketing.

Stamp, Gavin. Lost Victorian Britain: How the Twentieth Century Destroyed the Nineteenth Century's Architectural Masterpieces. 2010. (ENG., Illus.). 192p. 39.95 *(978-1-84513-532-4(6))* Aurum Pr., Ltd. GBR. Dist: Independent Pubs. Group.

Stein, Carl J. Greening Modernism: Preservation, Sustainability, & the Modern Movement. 2010. (ENG., Illus.). 296p. 60.00 *(978-0-393-73283-2(5),* 73283) Norton, W. W. & Co., Inc.

Stubbs, John H. Time Honored: A Global View of Architectural Conservation. 2009. (ENG., Illus.). 448p. 85.00 *(978-0-470-26049-4(1),* Wiley) Wiley, John & Sons, Inc.

Stubbs, John H. & Makas, Emily G. Architectural Conservation in Europe & the Americas. 2011. (ENG., Illus.). 752p. 110.00 *(978-0-470-60385-7(2),* Wiley) Wiley, John & Sons, Inc.

Stureiko, S. A. Antropologiia Arkhitekturnogo Naslediia: Vzgliad Na Belarus. 2010. (RUS., Illus.). 182p. *(978-985-6802-43-3(1))* Junipak, Zakrytae AT.

Theodossopoulos, Dimitris. Structural Design in Building Conservation. 2012. (ENG., Illus.). 272p. (C). 165.00 *(978-0-415-47945-5(2));* pap. 55.95 *(978-0-415-47946-2(0))* Routledge.

Toledano, Roulhac. A Pattern Book of New Orleans Architecture, 1 vol. 2010. (ENG., Illus.). 256p. 35.00 *(978-1-58980-694-8(8))* Pelican Publishing Co., Inc.

Toxey, Anne Parmly. Materan Contradictions: Architecture, Preservation & Politics. 2011. (Ashgate Studies in Architecture Ser.). (Illus.). 380p. 119.95 ***(978-1-4094-1207-6(5))*** Ashgate Publishing Co.

Van Den Heuvel, D. & Mesman, M., eds. The Challenge of Change: Dealing with the Legacy of the Modern Movement - Proceedings of the 10th International DOCOMOMO Conference. 2008. 180p. pap. 135.00 *(978-1-58603-917-2(2))* IOS Pr., Inc.

Versaci, Russell. Creating a New Old House: Yesterday's Character for Today's Home. 2007. (American Institute Architects Ser.). (ENG., Illus.). 218p. pap. 24.95 *(978-1-56158-792-6(3),* Taunton) Taunton Pr., Inc.

Vogt, Jay D. & Rogers, Stephen C. Picturing the Past: South Dakota's Historic Places. 2006. (Historical Preservation Ser.). (Illus.). 107p. *(978-0-9749195-7-7(8),* South Dakota State Historical Society Pr.) South Dakota State Historical Society.

Wharton, Glenn. The Painted King: Art, Activism, & Authenticity in Hawaii. 2011. 42.00 ***(978-0-8248-3495-1(X))***; pap. 19.00 ***(978-0-8248-3612-2(X))*** Univ. of Hawaii Pr.

Williamson, Kenneth. Development & Design of Heritage Sensitive Sites. 2010. (ENG., Illus.). 216p. 155.00 *(978-0-415-48643-9(2))* Routledge.

—Development & Design of Heritage Sensitive Sites: Strategies for Listed Buildings & Conservation Areas. 2010. (ENG., Illus.). 216p. pap. 62.95 *(978-0-415-48644-6(0))* Routledge.

Wood, Anthony & Wood, Anthony C. Preserving New York: Winning the Right to Protect a City's Landmarks. 2007. 448p. 50.00 *(978-0-415-95284-2(0))* Routledge.

Worthing, Derek & Bond, Stephen. Managing Built Heritage. Harris, John, ed. 2008. (ENG., Illus.). 228p. pap. 99.99 *(978-1-4051-1978-8(0),* Wiley-Blackwell) Wiley, John & Sons, Inc.

ARCHITECTURE—CRITICISM

see Architectural Criticism

ARCHITECTURE—DATA PROCESSING

Ahmed, Zeeshan. Variant Handling Using Zac. 2010. 108p. pap. *(978-3-8383-4103-3(1))* Lambert Academic Publishing.

Akgün, Yenal. Perception of Space Through Representation Medi. 2011. 116p. pap. ***(978-3-8443-3403-6(3))*** Lambert Academic Publishing.

Aley, Eric. Metaphorical Visualization- Using Multidimensional Metaphors to Visualize Dat. 2007. 64p. per. *(978-3-8364-2878-1(4))* VDM Verlag Dr. Mueller e.K.

Ali, A. & Brebbia, Carlos A., eds. Digital Architecture & Construction. 2006. (Transactions on the Built Environment Ser.: 90). (Illus.). 272p. 155.00 *(978-1-84564-047-7(0))* WIT Pr GBR. Dist: WIT Pr.

Altinisik, Melike, et al, contrib. by. Morphé: Mrgd. 2008. (RIEAeuropa Concepts Ser.). (ENG., Illus.). 75p. pap. 39.95 *(978-3-211-75789-5(9),* 3211757899) Springer.

Architectural Desktop 2007 Tutorial Series. 2007. 299.00 incl. cd-rom *(978-1-932931-31-0(7))* 4D Design Solutions, LLC.

Aubin, Paul F. Autocad Architecture 2011. 2010. (ENG., Illus.). 984p. pap. 106.95 *(978-1-111-13795-3(1),* AutoDesk Pr.) Delmar Cengage Learning.

Aubin, Paul F. Revit Architecture 2012. 2011. (CAD New Releases Ser.). (ENG.). 416p. pap. 55.95 ***(978-1-111-64853-4(0),*** AutoDesk Pr.) Delmar Cengage Learning.

Aubin, Paul F., et al. Revit MEP 2011 Course Notes for Aubin/McClelland/Schmid/Stanley's the Aubin Academy Master Series: Revit MEP 2011. 2011. 8p. pap. 4.95 *(978-1-111-13794-6(3),* AutoDesk Pr.) Delmar Cengage Learning.

Aubin, Paul F. (Paul F. Aubin). Revit Architecture 2012. 2011. (ENG.). 6p. 4.95 *(978-1-133-01446-1(1),* AutoDesk Pr.) Delmar Cengage Learning.

Cantrell, Bradley & Michaels, Wes. Digital Drawing for Landscape Architecture: Contemporary Techniques & Tools for Digital Representation in Site Design. 2010. (ENG., Illus.). 320p. pap. 75.00 *(978-0-470-40397-6(7),* Wiley) Wiley, John & Sons, Inc.

Chopra, Aidan & Chopra. Google SketchUp 7 for Dummies. 2009. (ENG., Illus.). 472p. pap. 24.99 *(978-0-470-27739-3(4),* For Dummies) Wiley, John & Sons, Inc.

Coates, Paul. The Architecture of Programming. 2010. (ENG., Illus.). 200p. (C). 165.00 *(978-0-415-45187-1(6))*; pap. 62.95 *(978-0-415-45188-8(4))* Routledge.

Corser, Robert & Princeton Architectural Press Staff. Fabricating Architecture: Selected Readings in Digital Design & Manufacturing. 2010. (ENG., Illus.). 216p. pap. 29.95 *(978-1-56898-889-4(3))* Princeton Architectural Pr.

Curry, Zane. AutoCAD 2009 for Interior Design: A 3D Modelling Approach. 2008. (ENG., Illus.). 448p. (C). pap. 112.60 *(978-0-13-234276-6(6),* Prentice Hall) Prentice Hall PTR.

Dollens, Dennis. The Pangolin's Guide to Biomimetics & Digital Architecture. 2007. (ENG., Illus.). 28p. pap. 7.00 *(978-0-930829-62-9(X))* Lumen, Inc.

Dzambazova, Tatjana, et al. Mastering Revit Architecture 2009. 2008. (ENG., Illus.). 800p. pap. 59.99 *(978-0-470-29528-1(7),* Sybex) Wiley, John & Sons, Inc.

Ferrari, Remo. Interaction Between Requirements Engineering & Systems Architecting. 2011. 256p. pap. ***(978-3-8443-1036-8(3))*** Lambert Academic Publishing.

Fiorello, Joe, et al. CAD for Interiors Basics. 2009. (ENG., Illus.). 208p. pap. 55.00 *(978-0-470-18573-5(2),* Wiley) Wiley, John & Sons, Inc.

Fratzeskou, Eugenia. Operative Intersections. 2010. 64p. pap. *(978-3-8383-5193-3(2))* Lambert Academic Publishing.

Gleiniger, Andrea & Vrachliotis, Georg. Code: Between Operation & Narration. 2010. (ENG., Illus.). 120p. pap. 29.95 *(978-3-0346-0117-7(4))* Birkhauser Verlag AG CHE. Dist: Actar Birkhauser Distribution.

Hahn, Alexander. Mathematical Excursions to the World's Great Buildings. 2012. (ENG., Illus.). 352p. (C). 49.50 ***(978-0-691-14520-4(2))*** Princeton Univ. Pr.

Hepler, Dana J., et al. Student Solutions Manual for Hepler/Wallach/Hepler's Drafting & Design for Architecture, 2nd. 9th ed. 2012. (ENG.). 120p. (C). pap. 59.95 *(978-1-111-12816-6(2))* Delmar Cengage Learning.

HOK Inc. Problem Seeking: An Architectural Programming Primer. 5th ed. 2012. (ENG., Illus.). 288p. pap. 55.00 ***(978-1-118-08414-4(4),*** Wiley) Wiley, John & Sons, Inc.

Huang, Joseph Chuen-Huei. Participatory Design for Prefab House. 2008. (Illus.). 248p. pap. *(978-3-639-07528-1(5))* VDM Verlag Dr. Mueller e.K.

Images Australia Pty Ltd Staff. Cyberspace: The World of Digital Architecture. 2006. (ENG., Illus.). 75.00 *(978-1-86470-057-2(2))* Images Publishing Group AUS. Dist: National Bk. Network.

Iwamoto, Lisa. Digital Fabrications: Architectural & Material Techniques. 2009. (ENG., Illus.). 144p. pap. 24.95 *(978-1-56898-790-3(0))* Princeton Architectural Pr.

Jefferis, Alan, et al. AutoCAD 2008 for Architecture. 2007. (ENG., Illus.). 992p. per. 149.95 *(978-1-4283-1161-9(0),* AutoDesk Pr.) Delmar Cengage Learning.

Khadka, Ravi. Model-Driven Development of Service Compositions. 2011. 184p. pap. ***(978-3-8443-8034-7(5))*** Lambert Academic Publishing.

Krygiel, Eddy & Nies, Brad. Green BIM: Successful Sustainable Design with Building Information Modeling. 2008. (ENG., Illus.). 241p. pap. 49.99 *(978-0-470-23960-5(3),* Sybex) Wiley, John & Sons, Inc.

Krygiel, Eddy, et al. Mastering Autodesk Revit Architecture 2011. 2010. (ENG., Illus.). 1168p. pap. 59.99 *(978-0-470-62696-2(8),* Sybex) Wiley, John & Sons, Inc.

Lattanze, Anthony J. Architecting Software Intensive Systems: A Practitioners Guide. 2008. (ENG., Illus.). 416p. 85.95 *(978-1-4200-4569-7(5))* Auerbach Pubs., Inc.

Leeuwen, van, Jos P., Jos P & Timmermans, Harry J. P., eds. Innovations in Design & Decision Support Systems in Architecture & Urban Planning. 2010. (ENG.). xxi, 502p. pap. 279.00 *(978-90-481-7269-6(1),* 9048172691) Springer.

Li, Zude. Architectural Degeneration of Software Systems. 2011. 264p. pap. ***(978-3-8443-1958-3(1))*** Lambert Academic Publishing.

Mao-Lin Chiu, et al, eds. Digital Design: Research & Practice: Research & Practice. 2010. 480p. pap. 229.00 *(978-90-481-6260-4(2),* 9048162602) Springer.

Martens, Bob & Peter, Herbert. ArchiCAD: Best Practice: the Virtual Building Revealed. 2nd ed. 2006. (Illus.). 296p. 69.95 *(978-3-211-32789-0(4),* 3211327894) Springer Wien AUT. Dist: Springer.

Media, Mountains & Architecture. 2009. *(978-84-95951-61-8(4))* Actar Birkhauser Distribution.

Menges, Achim. Material Computation: Higher Integration in Morphogenetic Design Architectural Design. 2012. (Architectural Design Ser.). (ENG., Illus.). 144p. pap. 40.00 ***(978-0-470-97330-1(7),*** Wiley) Wiley, John & Sons, Inc.

Murdock, Kelly L., et al. Google SketchUp & SketchUp Pro 7. 2009. (Bible Ser.: 606). (ENG., Illus.). 552p. pap. 39.99 *(978-0-470-29229-7(6),* Wiley) Wiley, John & Sons, Inc.

Onstott, Scott. 3ds Max & VIZ for Architects (DVD-ROM) 2007. 463p. cd-rom *(978-0-9719583-9-5(4))* Onstott, Scott.

Oosterhuis, Kas. ONLogic: Speed & Vision. 2009. (Master Architect Ser.). (ENG., Illus.). 224p. 59.95 *(978-1-86470-286-6(9),* Images Publishing Group Ac) Antique Collectors' Club GBR. Dist: National Bk. Network.

Ortega-Arjona, Jorge Luis. Architectural Patterns for Parallel Programming. 2009. 304p. pap. *(978-3-639-17324-6(4))* VDM Verlag Dr. Mueller e.K.

Oxman. The Digital in Architecture. 2011. 484p. 165.00 *(978-0-415-46923-4(6))*; pap. 62.95 *(978-0-415-46924-1(4))* Routledge.

Pereira Mosqueira, Fernando. Mitigation Methods of Wind Acceleration for a 39-Story Building. 2011. 60p. pap. ***(978-3-8443-2024-4(5))*** Lambert Academic Publishing.

Revit Architecture 2008 Essentials Tutorial Series. 2007. 249.00 incl. cd-rom *(978-1-932931-37-2(6))* 4D Design Solutions, LLC.

Revit Architecture 2008 Tutorial Series. 2007. 400.00 incl. cd-rom *(978-1-932931-36-5(8))* 4D Design Solutions, LLC.

Revit Building 9 Fundamentals Tutorial Series. 2007. 199.00 incl. cd-rom *(978-1-932931-34-1(1))* 4D Design Solutions, LLC.

Schodek, Daniel L. & As, Imdat. Digital Representations in Architecture: Visions in Motion. 2008. (ENG., Illus.). 272p. (C). 165.00 *(978-0-415-42652-7(9))*; 53.95 *(978-0-415-42653-4(7))* Taylor & Francis Group GBR. (Taylor & Francis). Dist: Taylor & Francis Group.

Schwartz, Donald, ed. AutoCAD 2009 Update Tutorial Series. 2008. 99.00 incl. cd-rom *(978-1-932931-40-2(6))* 4D Design Solutions, LLC.

Smith, Brian. 3ds Max 10 Architectural Visualization: Beginner to Intermediate. 2007. (Illus.). per. 49.95 *(978-0-9792811-0-5(5))* 3D Architectural Training Solutions.

—3ds Max 10 Architectural Visualization: Intermediate to Advanced. 2007. per. 49.95 *(978-0-9792811-1-2(3))* 3D Architectural Training Solutions.

Smith, Brian L. 3ds Max Design Architectural Visualization: For Intermediate Users. 2011. (ENG., Illus.). 560p. 64.95 ***(978-0-240-82107-8(6),*** Focal Pr.) Elsevier Science & Technology Bks.

Smith, Ian F. C. Intelligent Computing in Engineering & Architecture: 13th EG-ICE Workshop 2006 Ascona, Switzerland, June 25-30, 2006 Revised Selected Papers. 2006. (Lecture Notes in Computer Science Ser.). (Illus.). 689p. pap. 129.00 *(978-3-540-46246-0(5),* 3540462465) Springer.

Sondermann, Horst. Light Shadow Space: Architectural Rendering with Cinema 4D. 2007. (Illus.). 238p. 69.95 *(978-3-211-48761-7(1),* 3211487611) Springer Wien AUT. Dist: Springer.

—Photoshop in Architectural Graphics. 2009. (ENG., Illus.). 328p. 69.95 *(978-3-211-71591-8(6),* 3211715916) Springer.

Spiller, Neil. Digital Architecture Now: A Global Survey of Emerging Talent. 2009. (ENG., Illus.). 400p. 65.00 *(978-0-500-34247-3(4))* Thames & Hudson.

Sulbaran, Tulio, et al. Introduction to ArchiCAD: A BIM Application. 2010. (ENG., Illus.). 240p. (C). pap. 82.95 *(978-1-4283-5664-1(9))* Delmar Cengage Learning.

Tierney, Therese. Abstract Space: Beneath the Media Surface. 2007. (ENG., Illus.). 208p. (C). 165.00 *(978-0-415-41510-1(1))*; per. 63.95 *(978-0-415-41509-5(8))* Taylor & Francis Group GBR. (Taylor & Francis). Dist: Taylor & Francis Group.

Timmermans, Harry J. P., ed. Design & Decision Support Systems in Architecture. 2010. 268p. pap. 186.00 *(978-90-481-4313-9(6),* 9048143136) Springer.

van Leeuwen, Jos P. & Timmermans, Harry J. P., eds. Recent Advances in Design & Decision Support Systems in Architecture & Urban Planning. 2010. (ENG.). xv, 358p. pap. 229.00 *(978-90-481-6653-4(5),* 9048166535) Springer.

Vogel, Oliver, et al. Software Architecture: A Comprehensive Framework & Guide for Practitioners. 2011. (ENG., Illus.). xvii, 478p. 69.95 *(978-3-642-19735-2(3),* 3642197353) Springer.

Weber, Raphael & Raphael, Weber. A Bit-Serial Implementation of the Aes Encryption Algorithm: Implementation & Space Optimization of the Advanced Encryption Standard for a Bit-Serial Fully Pipelined Architecture. 2011. 120p. pap. ***(978-3-639-32713-7(6))*** VDM Verlag Dr. Mueller e.K.

Wyatt, William G. Accessing Autocad Architecture 2012. 2011. (CAD New Releases Ser.). (ENG., Illus.). 800p. pap. 113.95 *(978-1-111-64831-2(X),* AutoDesk Pr.) Delmar Cengage Learning.

2007 Information Technology Survey: Of Architecture, Engineering, Planning & Environmental Consulting Firms. 2007. per. 395.00 *(978-1-934150-20-7(7))* ZweigWhite.

ARCHITECTURE—DECORATION AND ORNAMENT

see Decoration and Ornament, Architectural

ARCHITECTURE—DESIGNS AND PLANS

see also Architecture, Domestic—Designs and Plans; Hospitals—Design and Construction; Theaters—Construction

Abrahams, Tim. Ideas Exchange: The Collaborative Studio of Hawkins Brown. 2010. (ENG., Illus.). 208p. 84.95 *(978-3-0346-0231-0(6))* Birkhauser Verlag AG CHE. Dist: Actar Birkhauser Distribution.

Adam, William. Vitruvius Scoticus: Plans, Elevations, & Sections of Public Buildings, Noblemen's & Gentlemen's Houses in Scotland. 2011. (Dover Architecture Ser.). (ENG., Illus.). 256p. pap. 19.95 *(978-0-486-47307-9(4))* Dover Pubns., Inc.

Alan Mascord Design Associates. Mascord Efficient Living: Build a More Sustainable Lifestyle. Higginbotham, Gary & Daby, Matthew, eds. 2008. (Illus.). 154p. 14.95 *(978-0-9788113-1-0(3))* AMDA Pr.

Allenby, Guy. Elements: The Heart of the City. Law, Erica, tr. 2010. (ENG., Illus.). 160p. 50.00 *(978-0-9814628-9-9(8))* Oro Editions.

Andrews, Jonathan. Architectural Visions: Contemporary Sketches, Perspectives, Drawings. 2010. (ENG., Illus.). 372p. 49.95 *(978-3-03768-035-3(0),* Braun Publish,Csi) Continental Sales, Inc.

Arain, Faisal. Design & Construction Interface Discrepancies. 2010. 96p. pap. *(978-3-8383-4726-4(9))* Lambert Academic Publishing.

Architects Design Partnership Staff. Education & Contextualism: Architects Design Partnership. McCorquodale, Duncan, ed. 2007. (ENG., Illus.). 184p. 45.00 *(978-1-904772-71-2(4))* Black Dog Publishing Ltd. GBR. Dist: Perseus Distribution.

Architecture at the Expo. 2008. 240p. pap. *(978-84-96954-41-0(2))* Actar Birkhauser Distribution.

Asensio, Oscar, et al. Invitation & Promotion Design: Ideas with Impact. 2008. (Illus.). 256p. 45.00 *(978-0-06-124199-4(7),* Collins Design) HarperCollins Pubs.

Avroko & Avroko. Best Ugly: Restaurant Concepts & Architecture. 2008. (ENG., Illus.). 256p. 49.95 *(978-0-06-113693-1(X),* Collins Design) HarperCollins Pubs.

Badeslade, J., et al. Vitruvius Britannicus. 2009. (Dover Architecture Ser.). (ENG., Illus.). 304p. pap. 24.95 *(978-0-486-46890-7(9))* Dover Pubns., Inc.

—1739 & 1767-71 Eds., Vol. 2. 60.95 *(978-0-405-09045-5(5))* Ayer Co. Pubs., Inc.

Bahamón, Alejandro. Glass Houses. 2006. (ENG., Illus.). 192p. 39.95 *(978-0-06-089339-2(7),* Collins Design) HarperCollins Pubs.

Baker, William T. American Architecture New Classicists. 2006. (New Classicists Ser.). (ENG., Illus.). 336p. 90.00 *(978-1-920744-57-1(6))* Images Publishing Group AUS. Dist: National Bk. Network.

Bar-Eli, Shoshi. Design Behavior Profiles. 2010. 176p. pap. *(978-3-8383-5389-0(7))* Lambert Academic Publishing.

Becker, Rachel. Physical Performance of Buildings: Integration in the Building Process & Design. 2012. (ENG.). 320p. 90.00 ***(978-0-470-85498-3(7),*** Wiley) Wiley, John & Sons, Inc.

Bellini, Oscar & Daglio, Laura. New Frontiers of Architecture: Dubai. 2010. (ENG., Illus.). 304p. 40.00 *(978-88-544-0411-3(X))* White Star ITA. Dist: Sterling Publishing Co., Inc.

Benjamin, Asher. The American Builder's Companion. 2007. (ENG.). 200p. per. 12.50 *(978-1-60206-781-3(3))* Cosimo, Inc.

Bergdoll, Barry, intro. Small Scale, Big Change. 2010. (ENG., Illus.). 140p. pap. 37.50 *(978-0-87070-784-1(1))* Museum of Modern Art.

Berger, Ursel & Pavel, Thomas, eds. Barcelona Pavilion/Pavillon: Mies Van der Rohe & Kolbe, 1 vol. 2007. (GER & ENG., Illus.). 192p. 29.95 *(978-3-939633-06-8(2))* Jovis Verlag GmbH DEU. Dist: D.A.P./Distributed Art Pubs.

Bergman, David. Sustainable Design: A Critical Guide for Architects & Interior, Lighting, & Environmental Designers. 2012. (ENG., Illus.). 144p. pap. 24.95 *(978-1-56898-941-9(5))* Princeton Architectural Pr.

Billington, Mike. Using the Building Regulations Pt. C: Site Preparation & Resistance to Contaminants & Moisture. 2007. (ENG., Illus.). 232p. per. 54.95 *(978-0-7506-6258-1(1))* Routledge.

Bin, Xu. Iconic Storefronts USA. 2008. (ENG.). 320p. 49.95 *(978-84-96969-66-7(5))* Links International (Leading International Key Services Barcelona, S.A.) ESP. Dist: National Bk. Network.

Bizley, Graham. Architecture in Detail II. 2010. (ENG., Illus.). 224p. pap. 54.95 *(978-0-08-096535-2(0))* Routledge.

Blechinger, Gerhard & Milev, Yana, eds. Emergency Design: Designstrategien Im Arbeitsfeld der Krise. 2007. (Illus.). 171p. pap. 49.95 *(978-3-211-48760-0(3))* Springer Wien AUT. Dist: Springer.

Bohlin Cywinski Jackson Architects Staff. Bohlin Cywinski Jackson: The Nature of Circumstance. 2010. (ENG., Illus.). 420p. 95.00 *(978-0-8478-3293-4(7))* Rizzoli International Pubns., Inc.

Book Industry Services Publishers Staff & Agkathidis, Asterios. Modular Structures in Design & Architecture. 2nd ed. 2009. (ENG., Illus.). 160p. pap. 17.00 *(978-90-6369-206-3(4))* Bis B.V., Uitgeverij(BIS Publishers) NLD. Dist: Consortium Bk. Sales & Distribution.

Borasi, Giovanna & Zardini, Mirko, eds. Sorry, Out of Gas: Architecture's Response to the 1973 Oil Crisis, 1 vol. 2008. (ENG., Illus.). 236p. pap. 49.95 *(978-88-7570-143-7(1))* Corraini ITA. Dist: D.A.P./Distributed Art Pubs.

Bosser, Jacques. La Tour Signal: Un Nouveau Défi Pour la Défense. 2009. (FRE & ENG., Illus.). 160p. *(978-2-7324-3862-7(6))* Editions de la Martiniere.

Bouman, Ole, et al, texts. Architecture of Consequence. 2010. (ENG., Illus.). 168p. pap. 35.00 *(978-90-5662-726-3(0))* NAi Uitgevers / Publishers Stichting NLD. Dist: D.A.P./Distributed Art Pubs.

Bourke, Kathryn. Achieving Whole Life Value in Infrastructure & Buildings. 2010. (ENG., Illus.). 60p. pap. 80.00 *(978-1-86081-737-3(8))* Building Research Establishment GBR. Dist: Taylor & Francis Group.

Boyken, Immo, intro. Otto Ernst Schweizer: Stadium in Vienna. 2011. (GER & ENG., Illus.). 60p. 49.00 *(978-3-932565-75-5(4))* Edition Axel Menges GmbH DEU. Dist: National Bk. Network.

Bradbury, Dominic. Mediterranean Modern. 2006. (ENG., Illus.). 256p. 35.00 *(978-0-500-34227-5(X))* Thames & Hudson.

Brandolini, Sebastiano. Rome: New Architecture. 2008. (ENG., Illus.). 252p. pap. 14.99 *(978-88-6130-534-2(2))* Skira Editore ITA. Dist: Random Hse., Inc.

Brenda, Peggy & Yee, Roger, eds. Jaya Contemporary Design with a Pedigree: Hotel, Resorts, Spas, Residences, 1 vol. 2012. (ENG., Illus.). 296p. 70.00 *(978-0-9834501-1-5(0))* Visual Profile Bks., Inc.

Brookes, Alan J. Building Envelope & Connections. (C). 102.00 *(978-0-8176-2533-7(X))* Birkhauser Boston.

Broto, Carles. Club Design. 2007. (Illus.). 240p. 45.00 *(978-84-96263-67-3(3))* Links International (Leading International Key Services Barcelona, S.A.) ESP. Dist: National Bk. Network.

—Houses Now 3. 2012. (ENG., Illus.). 240p. 39.00 *(978-84-92796-85-4(5))* Links International (Leading International Key Services Barcelona, S.A.) ESP. Dist: National Bk. Network.

Brown, G. Z. & DeKay, Mark. Sun, Wind, & Light: Architectural Design Strategies. 3rd ed. 2013. (ENG., Illus.). 192p. pap. 85.00 ***(978-0-470-94578-0(8),*** Wiley) Wiley, John & Sons, Inc.

Büker, Dieter. Vier Jahrhunderte und vier Jahre: Der Klosterplan von St. Gallen und seine Bedeutung als Dokument frühmittelalterlicher Schriftlichkeit. 2009. (GER.). 244p. 61.95 *(978-3-631-59542-8(5))* Lang, Peter GmbH, Europaischer Verlag der Wissenschaften DEU. Dist: Lang, Peter.

Bunce, Fredrick W. Monuments of India & the Indianized States: The Plans of Major & Notable Temples, Tombs, Palaces, & Pavilions of Bangladesh, Sri Lanka, Java, the Khmer, Pagan, Thailand, Vietnam, & Malaysia, from 3rd C. BCE to CE 1854. 2007. (Illus.). xx, 518p. *(978-81-246-0385-7(5))* D. K. Print World (P) Ltd.

—The Mosques of the Indian Subcontinent: Their Development & Iconography. 2008. 212p. *(978-81-246-0458-8(4))* D. K. Print World (P) Ltd.

Burelli, Augusto Romano & Gennaro, Paola, texts. Die Moschee von Sinan. Sinan's Mosque. 2009. (ENG., Illus.). 116p. pap. 65.00 *(978-3-8030-0693-6(7))* Wasmuth, Ernst J. Verlag GmbH & Co. DEU. Dist: D.A.P./Distributed Art Pubs.

Burton, Neil & Guillery, Peter. Behind the Façade: London House Plans, 1660-1840. 2006. (Illus.). 142p. (C). *(978-1-904965-10-7(5))* Spire Bks. Ltd.

Campbell, Colen. Vitruvius Britannicus: The Classic of Eighteenth-Century British Architecture. 2006. (Dover Architecture Ser.). (ENG., Illus.). 288p. per. 24.95 *(978-0-486-44799-5(5))* Dover Pubns., Inc.

Campos, Cristian. New Supermarket Design. 2007. (Illus.). 330p. 50.00 *(978-0-06-114996-2(9),* Collins Design) HarperCollins Pubs.

Cantrell, Bradley & Michaels, Wes. Digital Drawing for Landscape Architecture: Contemporary Techniques & Tools for Digital Representation in Site Design. 2010. (ENG., Illus.). 320p. pap. 75.00 *(978-0-470-40397-6(7),* Wiley) Wiley, John & Sons, Inc.

Ceccato, Cristiano, et al, eds. Advances in Architectural Geometry 2010. 2010. (Illus.). 242p. 69.95 *(978-3-7091-0308-1(8),* 3709103088) Springer Wien AUT. Dist: Springer.

Chapman, Wid & Rosenfeld, Jeffrey P. Unassisted Living. 2011. (ENG., Illus.). 240p. 45.00 *(978-1-58093-302-5(5))* Monacelli Pr., Inc.

Chen, Yenna. Small Environments. 2007. (Contemporary Design in Detail Ser.). (ENG., Illus.). 192p. 50.00 *(978-1-59253-231-5(4)*, 1592532314, Rockport Publishers) Quayside.

Chicago Tribune Staff. Elegant Small Homes of the Twenties: 99 Designs from a Competition. 2008. (Dover Architecture Ser.). (ENG.). 112p. pap. 14.95 *(978-0-486-46910-2(7))* Dover Pubns., Inc.

Clark, J. Peter. Practical Design, Construction & Operation of Food Facilities. 2008. (Food Science & Technology Ser.). (ENG., Illus.). 328p. 165.00 *(978-0-12-374204-9(8)*, Academic Pr.) Elsevier Science & Technology Bks.

Colquhoun, Ian. RIBA Book of British Housing: 1900 to the Present Day. 2nd rev. ed. 2008. (ENG., Illus.). 416p. pap. 59.95 *(978-0-7506-8254-1(X))* Routledge.

Comstock, William T. Late Victorian Architectural Plans & Details. 2010. (Dover Architecture Ser.). (ENG., Illus.). 192p. pap. 19.95 *(978-0-486-47361-1(9))* Dover Pubns., Inc.

Cook, Peter. Drawing: The Motive Force of Architecture. 2008. (Architectural Design Primer Ser.: 2). (ENG., Illus.). 208p. pap. 55.00 *(978-0-470-03481-1(5)*, Wiley) Wiley, John & Sons, Inc.

Costanzo, Michele. Mvrdv: Works & Projects 1991-2006. 2006. (ENG., Illus.). 240p. pap. 34.95 *(978-88-7624-649-4(5))* Skira Editore ITA. Dist: Random Hse., Inc.

Cram101 Textbook Reviews & Cram101 Textbook Reviews. Outlines & Highlights for Structural Steel Drafting & Design by David C MacLaughlin. 2011. 58p. pap. 26.95 ***(978-1-61830-742-2(8))*** Cram101 Inc.

Crane, Christina & Brown, Denise Scott. Asia Beyond Growth: Urbanization in the World's Fastest-Changing Continent. AECOM Consult, Inc Staff, ed. 2010. (ENG., Illus.). 400p. pap. 40.00 *(978-0-9795395-1-0(X))* Oro Editions.

Crawford, J. H. & Crawford. Carfree Design Manual. 2009. (Illus.). 600p. 45.00 *(978-90-5727-060-4(9))* International Bks. NLD. Dist: Independent Pubs. Group.

Crosbie, Michael J. Architecture for the Books. 2006. (ENG., Illus.). 65.00 *(978-1-876907-49-5(5))* Images Publishing Group AUS. Dist: National Bk. Network.

Crosbie, Michael J. & Crosbie, Michael. Multi-Family Housing: The Art of Sharing. 2006. (ENG., Illus.). 208p. 65.00 *(978-1-876907-69-3(X))* Images Publishing Group AUS. Dist: National Bk. Network.

Cullman, Ellie, et al. Decorating Master Class. 2008. (ENG., Illus.). 224p. 50.00 *(978-0-8109-9390-7(2))* Abrams.

Curators Staff. Tokyo Restaurant Design Collection 2005: A Summary of the Latest Restaurants by Top Interior Designers. 2006. (ENG., Illus.). 336p. 80.00 *(978-4-88357-220-5(X))* Azur Corp. JPN. Dist: Antique Collectors' Club.

DAAB Media Staff, compiled by. Bar Design, 1 vol. 2008. (ENG, GER, FRE, SPA & ITA., Illus.). 399p. 37.95 *(978-3-937718-55-2(9))* DAAB Media Gmbh DEU. Dist: Innovative Logistics.

DAAB Media Staff, creator. Steel Design, 1 vol. 2008. (ENG, GER, FRE, SPA & ITA., Illus.). 399p. 37.95 *(978-3-937718-65-1(6))* DAAB Media Gmbh DEU. Dist: Innovative Logistics.

—Stone Design, 1 vol. 2008. (ENG, GER, FRE, SPA & ITA., Illus.). 382p. 37.95 *(978-3-937718-66-8(4))* DAAB Media Gmbh DEU. Dist: Innovative Logistics.

—Window Design, 1 vol. 2008. (ENG, GER, FRE, SPA & ITA., Illus.). 383p. 37.95 *(978-3-937718-69-9(9))* DAAB Media Gmbh DEU. Dist: Innovative Logistics.

DAAB Media Staff, ed. Hi-Tech Architecture, 1 vol. 2009. (FRE, ITA, GER, SPA & ENG., Illus.). 382p. 59.95 *(978-3-86654-020-0(5))* DAAB Media Gmbh DEU. Dist: Innovative Logistics.

Damkjaer, Camilla. The Aesthetics of Movement. 2010. 272p. pap. *(978-3-8383-1653-6(3))* Lambert Academic Publishing.

Danube Company Staff & Visual Reference Publications Staff. Supermarket & Pastry Shop Design. 2008. (Illus.). 80p. 45.00 *(978-1-58471-151-3(5))* Visual Reference Pubns., Inc.

Daryanani, Danesh, text. Conserving History: Singapore's Heritage Museums. 2010. (ENG., Illus.). 204p. 60.00 *(978-0-9820607-7-3(7))* Oro Editions.

Davies, Colin. Key Houses of the Twentieth Century: Plans, Sections & Elevations. 2006. (Norton Book for Architects & Designers Ser.). (ENG., Illus.). 240p. pap. 45.00 *(978-0-393-73205-4(3)*, 73205) Norton, W. W. & Co., Inc.

de Lapuerta, Jose Maria, ed. Collective Housing: A Manual. 2007. (Illus.). 223p. per. *(978-84-96954-15-1(3))* Actar Birkhauser Distribution.

Descottes, Hervé. Architectural Lighting: Designing with Light & Space. 2011. (ENG., Illus.). 144p. pap. 24.95 *(978-1-56898-938-9(5))* Princeton Architectural Pr.

Designer Club, Deutscher, ed. Gute Gestaltung 11 / Good Design 11. 2011. (Good Design Ser.). (GER & ENG., Illus.). 532p. pap. 49.95 *(978-3-0346-0771-1(7))* Birkhauser Verlag AG CHE. Dist: Actar Birkhauser Distribution.

Dhakal, Rajesh P., et al. Curvature Ductility of Reinforced Concrete Plastic Hinges. 2008. 164p. pap. *(978-3-639-04184-2(4))* VDM Verlag Dr. Mueller e.K.

Di Pasquale, Franzo. Pulse. 2010. 124p. pap. *(978-3-8383-7010-1(4))* Lambert Academic Publishing.

Dimendberg, Edward, et al, texts. Hunch 15: Privacy. 2012. (ENG., Illus.). 176p. pap. 35.00 *(978-90-5662-767-6(8))* NAi Uitgevers / Publishers Stichting NLD. Dist: D.A.P./Distributed Art Pubs.

Dowdle, David, et al, eds. Architectural Engineering & Design Management: Teaching & Learning Building Design & Construction. 2006. (Architectural Engineering & Design Management Ser.). (ENG., Illus.). 160p. per. 94.95 *(978-1-84407-330-6(0))* Routledge.

Drew, Philip. New Tent Architecture. 2008. (ENG., Illus.). 208p. 60.00 *(978-0-500-34243-5(1))* Thames & Hudson.

Dudler, Max. Max Dudler Continuity. 2011. (Illus.). 664p. pap. ***(978-3-7212-0751-4(3))*** Niggli, Arthur Verlag.

École nationale supérieure d'architecture de Normandie Staff, contrib. by. Projets de Fin D'études 2006-2008. 2010. (FRE., Illus.). 109p. *(978-2-915548-51-8(X))* Point de vues, Editions.

Edwards. Facility Design Construction & Finishes. Date not set. (Pharmaceutical Engineering Ser.: Vol. 11). 256p. 170.00 *(978-0-7506-5124-0(5)*, Butterworth-Heinemann) Elsevier Science & Technology Bks.

Eliasson, Olafur & Thorsen, Kjetil. Serpentine Gallery Pavilion 2007. 2007. (Illus.). 125p. 34.95 *(978-3-03778-116-6(5)*, 3037781165) Springer.

Emmick, David J. Into the Cloud. 2009. 193p. pap. 15.97 *(978-0-557-06437-3(6))* Lulu Enterprises Inc.

Emmitt, Stephen. Architectural Engineering & Design Management: Aspects of Building Design Management. 2007. (ENG., Illus.). 80p. pap. 97.50 *(978-1-84407-510-2(9))* Routledge.

Ernst, Christian. Bastard: Choose My Identity. 2006. (GER & ENG., Illus.). 396p. incl. audio compact disk *(978-84-96540-15-6(4))* Actar Birkhauser Distribution.

Evans, Robin. The Fabrication of Virtue: English Prison Architecture, 1750-1840. 2011. (ENG.). 484p. pap. 39.99 *(978-0-521-18133-4(X))* Cambridge Univ. Pr.

Fabricius, Daniela. 100% Favela. 2012. (ENG.). pap. *(978-84-96540-69-9(3))* Actar Birkhauser Distribution.

Farameh, Patrice. Gowest! Cutting Edge Creatives in the United States. 2011. (ENG.). 312p. 75.00 *(978-3-942597-13-5(6))* DAAB Media Gmbh DEU. Dist: Innovative Logistics.

Feddersen, Eckhard & Ludtke, Insa. Wohnen Im Alter. 2009. (GER., Illus.). 247p. *(978-3-7643-8870-6(6))* Birkhauser Verlag AG.

The Field Guide Templates: CD-ROM. 2008. (Illus.). cd-rom 14.95 *(978-0-9800571-1-9(6))* Walnut Cracker Publishing, LLC.

Fischer, Joachim. Design Destinations Worldwide. 2008. (Art & Architecture Ser.). 800p. 69.95 *(978-0-8416-0286-1(7))* American Map Corp.

Fores, Ferrer. Jorn Utzon. Works & Projects. 2006. 306p. pap. 24.00 *(978-84-252-2060-9(2))* Trucatriche.

Frampton, Kenneth, et al, eds. SOM Journal, No. 5. 2009. (ENG., Illus.). 228p. pap. 30.00 *(978-3-7757-2279-7(3))* Hatje Cantz Verlag GmbH & Co KG DEU. Dist: D.A.P./Distributed Art Pubs.

Franck, Karen A. & Howard, Teresa Von Sommaruga. Design through Dialogue: A Guide for Architects & Clients. 2010. (ENG., Illus.). 208p. pap. 60.00 *(978-0-470-87071-6(0)*, Wiley) Wiley, John & Sons, Inc.

Fuchigami, Masayuki & Fuchigam, Masayuki. World Architects 51: Concepts & Works. Fuchigami, Masayuki, ed. 2008. (ENG., Illus.). 328p. 75.00 *(978-4-903348-07-0(5))* Azur Corp. JPN. Dist: Antique Collectors' Club.

Galindo, Michelle. Collection: European Architecture. 2009. (GER, FRE & ENG.). 512p. 49.95 *(978-3-03768-011-7(3)*, Braun Publish,Csi) Continental Sales, Inc.

—Masterpieces: Chalet Architecture + Design. 2009. (Masterpieces Ser.). (FRE, GER & ENG., Illus.). 304p. 49.95 *(978-3-03768-021-6(0)*, Braun Publish,Csi) Continental Sales, Inc.

Gardner, Mark, et al. Habits, Patterns, Algorithms, 1998-2008. Ojeda, Oscar, ed. 2009. (ENG., Illus.). 424p. 75.00 *(978-0-9795395-2-7(8))* Oro Editions.

Gelfand, Lisa. Sustainable School Architecture: Design for Elementary & Secondary Schools. 2010. (ENG., Illus.). 352p. 85.00 *(978-0-470-44543-3(2)*, Wiley) Wiley, John & Sons, Inc.

Geraghty, Anthony. The Architectural Drawings of Sir Christopher Wren: At All Souls College, Oxford: A Complete Catalogue. 2007. (Illus.). 296p. 180.00 *(978-0-7546-4071-4(X)*, Lund Humphries Pubs.) Ashgate Publishing, Ltd. GBR. Dist: Ashgate Publishing Co.

Gerbino, Anthony & Johnston, Stephen. Compass & Rule: Architecture As Mathematical Practice in England. 2009. (ENG., Illus.). 192p. 65.00 *(978-0-300-15093-3(8))* Yale Univ. Pr.

Gero, John S. & Goel, Ashok K. Design Computing & Cognition '08. 2008. (Illus.). 750p. 189.00 *(978-1-4020-8727-1(6))* Springer.

Ghirardo, Diane, et al. SOM Journal 4, 1 vol. 2006. (ENG., Illus.). 192p. pap. 25.00 *(978-3-7757-1803-5(6))* Hatje Cantz Verlag GmbH & Co KG DEU. Dist: D.A.P./Distributed Art Pubs.

Gibbs, James. Gibbs' Book of Architecture: An Eighteenth-Century Classic. 2008. (Dover Architecture Ser.). (ENG., Illus.). 192p. pap. 18.95 *(978-0-486-46601-9(9))* Dover Pubns., Inc.

Gladu, Christian. Small Bungalows, 1 vol. 2007. (ENG., Illus.). 112p. 21.99 *(978-1-4236-0098-5(3))* Gibbs Smith, Publisher.

Gleiniger, Andrea & Vrachliotis, Georg, eds. Muster: Ornament, Struktur und Verhalten. 2009. (Kontext Architektur Ser.). (GER., Illus.). 108p. pap. *(978-3-7643-8953-6(2))* Birkhauser Verlag AG.

Gondevska, Bisera. The Aestheticisation of Architecture. 2010. 60p. pap. *(978-3-8383-4936-7(9))* Lambert Academic Publishing.

Grawe, Christina & Schmal, Peter Cachola, eds. High Society: Aktuelle Hochhausarchitektur und der Internationale Hochhaus Preis 2006/Contemporary Highrise Architecture & the International Highrise Award 2006, 1 vol. 2007. (GER & ENG., Illus.). 160p. 35.00 *(978-3-936314-77-9(2))* Jovis Verlag GmbH DEU. Dist: D.A.P./Distributed Art Pubs.

Greensource Magazine Staff. Emerald Architecture: Case Studies in Green Building. 2008. (ENG., Illus.). 166p. 59.95 *(978-0-07-154411-5(9)*, 0071544119) McGraw-Hill Professional Publishing.

Gregory, Rob. Key Contemporary Buildings: Plans, Sections & Elevation. 2008. (Key Structures: Plans, Sections, Elevations Ser.). (ENG.). 240p. 45.00 *(978-0-393-73242-9(8)*, 73242) Norton, W. W. & Co., Inc.

Guallart, Vicente, ed. Self-Sufficient City: Envisioning the habitat of the Future. 2010. 416p. pap. *(978-84-92861-33-0(9))* Actar Birkhauser Distribution.

Gupta, Prema Katari. Creating Great Town Centers & Urban Villages. 2008. (ENG.). 200p. 99.95 *(978-0-87420-076-8(8))* Urban Land Institute.

Hackman, William & Greenberg, Mark, eds. Inside the Getty. 2008. (Illus.). 152p. pap. 14.95 *(978-0-89236-911-9(6))* Oxford Univ. Pr., Inc.

Hall, Andrew, ed. Details in Architecture: Creative Detailing by Leading Architects. 2009. (ENG., Illus.). 300p. 65.00 *(978-1-86470-342-9(3))* Images Publishing Group AUS. Dist: National Bk. Network.

Hall, Dennis J. & Giglio, Nina M. Graphic Standards Field Guide to Residential Construction. 2011. (Graphic Standards Field Guide Ser.: 18). (ENG., Illus.). 496p. pap. 75.00 *(978-0-470-63504-9(5)*, Wiley) Wiley, John & Sons, Inc.

Halsted, Byron, ed. Barns & Outbuildings: And How to Build Them. 2nd ed. 2008. (Illus.). 235p. pap. 14.95 *(978-1-59921-371-2(0)*, Lyons Pr.) Globe Pequot Pr., The.

Hargreaves, Sean. Places. 2011. (ENG.). 160p. pap. 29.95 *(978-1-933492-49-0(X))* Design Studio Pr.

Hay, D. Roger. D. Roger Hay, the Essence of Root Meaning. 2008. (Illus.). 104p. *(978-88-7838-146-9(2))* L'Arca Edizioni.

Hensel, Michael & Gharleghi, Mehran. Iran: Past, Present & Future Architectural Design. 2012. (Architectural Design Ser.: 41). (ENG.). 160p. pap. 40.00 ***(978-1-119-97450-5(X)***, Wiley) Wiley, John & Sons, Inc.

Hodge, Brian. Building Your Straw Bale Home: From Foundations to the Roof. 2006. (Landlinks Press Ser.). (Illus.). 280p. pap. 61.95 *(978-0-643-09242-6(0))* CSIRO Publishing AUS. Dist: Stylus Publishing, LLC.

Hooper, Charles. The Country House. 2009. (Gardening in America Ser.). (ENG., Illus.). 356p. pap. 22.95 *(978-1-4290-1454-0(7))* Applewood Bks.

Hwang, Irene & Ferre, Albert, eds. Verb Natures. 2007. (Actar's Boogazine Ser.). (Illus.). 244p. (gr. 13-18). pap. *(978-84-96540-21-7(9))* Actar Birkhauser Distribution.

Images Publishing, creator. Cooper, Robertson & Partners: Cities to Gardens. 2007. (Master Architect (Unnumbered) Ser.). (ENG., Illus.). 276p. 59.95 *(978-1-86470-167-8(6)*, Images Publishing Dist Ac) Antique Collectors' Club GBR. Dist: National Bk. Network.

—Haigo Shen & Partners: Selected & Current Works. 2006. (Master Architect Series VI). (ENG., Illus.). 240p. 59.95 *(978-1-876907-33-4(9)*, Images Publishing Dist Ac) Antique Collectors' Club GBR. Dist: National Bk. Network.

Images Publishing Staff, PUBLISHING. Educational Spaces Vol. 2: A Pictorial Review. 2006. (Spaces Ser.). (ENG., Illus.). 212p. 55.00 *(978-1-86470-033-6(5))* Images Publishing Group AUS. Dist: National Bk. Network.

Incerti, Guido, et al. Diller + Scofidio (+ Renfro) The Ciliary Function - Works & Projects 1979-2007. 2007. (ENG., Illus.). 224p. 39.99 *(978-88-6130-267-5(7))* Skira Editore ITA. Dist: Random Hse., Inc.

Institute of Architects, American & American Institute of Architects Staff. Educational Facilities: The American Institute of Architects Exemplary Learning Environment Program. 2006. (ENG., Illus.). 232p. 65.00 *(978-1-86470-098-5(X))* Images Publishing Group AUS. Dist: National Bk. Network.

Jackson, Barbara. Design-Build Essentials. 2010. (ENG.). 432p. (C). 73.95 *(978-1-4283-5303-9(8))* Delmar Cengage Learning.

Jerke, Dennis. Urban Design & the Bottom Line: Optimizing the Return on Perception. 2008. (ENG.). 300p. 79.95 *(978-0-87420-996-9(X))* Urban Land Institute.

Jodidio, Philip. Architecture Now 6! Architektur heute. L'architecture d'aujourd'hui, Vol. 6. 2009. (Architecture Now Ser.). (FRE, GER & ENG., Illus.). 576p. pap. 39.99 *(978-3-8365-0193-4(7))* TASCHEN DEU. Dist: Ingram Pub. Services.

—Architecture Now! 7. 2010. (GER, FRE & ENG., Illus.). 480p. pap. 39.99 *(978-3-8365-1736-2(1))* TASCHEN DEU. Dist: Ingram Pub. Services.

—Architecture Now! 8. 2012. (ENG, FRE & GER., Illus.). 480p. 39.99 ***(978-3-8365-2681-4(6))*** TASCHEN DEU. Dist: Ingram Pub. Services.

—Renzo Piano: Building Workshop 1966 to today. 25th ed. 2008. (FRE, GER & ENG., Illus.). 528p. 39.99 *(978-3-8365-0322-8(0))* TASCHEN DEU. Dist: Ingram Pub. Services.

—100 Contemporary Architects, 2 vols. Volk, Annick, ed. 25th ed. 2008. (FRE, GER & ENG., Illus.). 848p. 59.99 *(978-3-8365-0091-3(4))* TASCHEN DEU. Dist: Ingram Pub. Services.

John, Geraint, et al. Stadia: A Design & Development Guide. 4th rev. ed. 2007. (ENG., Illus.). 320p. per. 63.95 *(978-0-7506-6844-6(X))* Routledge.

Kara, Hanif, ed. Design Engineering. 2008. *(978-84-96540-66-8(9))* Actar Birkhauser Distribution.

Khan, Musaad Zaheer Nazir & RIZWAN HUSSAIN, Raja. Innovative Design Philosophy for Reinforced Concrete Structures. 2011. 156p. pap. ***(978-3-8443-1825-8(9))*** Lambert Academic Publishing.

King, Rebecca. Frank Lloyd Wright Revealed. 2009. (Illus.). 160p. 15.00 *(978-1-905573-10-3(3))* Compendium GBR. Dist: Casemate Pubs. & Bk. Distributors, LLC.

Kissel, Eleonore & Vigneau, Erin. Architectural Photoreproductions: A Manual for Identification & Care. 2nd ed. 2009. 140p. pap. 49.95 *(978-1-58456-216-0(1))* Oak Knoll Pr.

Klein, Caroline. Below Sea Level: Modern Architecture & Design in the Netherlands, 1 vol. 2012. (GER, DUT & ENG.). 312p. 75.00 *(978-3-942597-10-4(1))* DAAB Media Gmbh DEU. Dist: Innovative Logistics.

—Crossing China: Land of the rising Scene, 1 vol. 2012. (ENG.). 312p. 75.00 *(978-3-942597-12-8(8))* DAAB Media Gmbh DEU. Dist: Innovative Logistics.

—Futuristic: Visions of Future Living, 1 vol. 2012. (ENG & GER., Illus.). 312p. 75.00 *(978-3-942597-09-8(8))* DAAB Media Gmbh DEU. Dist: Innovative Logistics.

Kodis, Michelle. Modern Cabin, 1 vol. 2007. (ENG., Illus.). 192p. 39.95 *(978-1-4236-0099-2(1))* Gibbs Smith, Publisher.

Kolarevic, Branko. Manufacturing Material Effects: Rethinking Design & Making in Architecture. Klinger, Kevin R., ed. 2008. (Illus.). 320p. pap. 62.95 *(978-0-415-77575-5(2))*; 165.00 *(978-0-415-77574-8(4))* Routledge.

Kong, Yilin & Dong, Xiaomin. Urban Colourscape Planning. 2010. 68p. pap. *(978-3-8383-1328-3(3))* Lambert Academic Publishing.

Kong, Yuhang. Jian Zhu '09'08: Dang Dai Zhongguo Jian Zhu Chuang Zuo Lun Tan Zuo Pin Ji. 2009. (CHI., Illus.). 351p. *(978-7-5611-4852-5(6))* Dalian Univ. of Technology Electronic & Audio-Visual Pr.

Konstantinidis, Dimitri & Konstantinides, Ares. Aris Konstantinidis, 1913-1993. Cofano, Paola, ed. 2010. (ITA., Illus.). 360p. 179.50 *(978-88-370-5762-6(8))* Electa ITA. Dist: Trans-Atlantic Pubns., Inc.

Kottas, Dimitris & Broto, Carles. Houses Now: Penthouses, Lofts. 2007. (ENG., Illus.). 240p. 39.95 *(978-84-96263-88-8(6))* Links International (Leading International Key Services Barcelona, S.A.) ESP. Dist: National Bk. Network.

Krauel, Jacobo. New Urban Elements. 2007. (Illus.). 179p. 49.00 *(978-84-96263-75-8(4))* Links International (Leading International Key Services Barcelona, S.A.) ESP. Dist: National Bk. Network.

—Sustainable Homes USA. 2008. (ENG.). 240p. 39.95 *(978-84-96424-30-2(8))* Links International (Leading International Key Services Barcelona, S.A.) ESP. Dist: National Bk. Network.

Kundoo, Anupama, text. Roger Anger: Research on Beauty. 2009. (ENG., Illus.). 192p. 45.00 *(978-3-86859-006-7(4))* Jovis Verlag GmbH DEU. Dist: D.A.P./Distributed Art Pubs.

Lab-Volt Staff. Living Spaces: TD Facs ESeries. 2010. 69p. 8.00 *(978-1-60533-127-0(9))*; 17p. 3.00 *(978-1-60533-126-3(0))*; 34p. ring bd. 5.00 *(978-1-60533-128-7(7))* Lab-Volt Systems, Inc.

Lam, George, compiled by. Landscape Design UK: Featuring Plaza & Square, Institutional, Corporate, Recreational, Residential ... Projects. 2007. (ENG., Illus.). 272p. 60.00 *(978-84-96424-82-1(0))* Links International (Leading International Key Services Barcelona, S.A.) ESP. Dist: National Bk. Network.

Leonard, Donald P. Designer's Illustrated Guide to NFPA 101. 2007. (Illus.). xvi, 447p. *(978-0-87765-632-6(0))* National Fire Protection Assn.

Li, Feng. 'Critical' Practice in State-Owned Design Institutes in Post-Mao China. 2010. 140p. pap. *(978-3-8383-6998-3(X))* Lambert Academic Publishing.

Linton, Harold. Urban Reflections: Illustrated World Cities. 2006. (ENG., Illus.). 224p. 65.00 *(978-1-876907-99-0(1))* Images Publishing Group AUS. Dist: National Bk. Network.

Littenberg, Anne-Marie. Hooked Rug Landscapes. 14th rev. ed. 2008. (Illus.). 100p. 24.95 *(978-1-881982-65-4(3))* Stackpole Magazines.

Lockwood, Owen & Provey, Joseph. Outdoor Kitchens: Ideas for Planning, Designing, & Entertaining. 2008. (Home Improvement Ser.). (ENG., Illus.). 224p. (gr. 5). pap. 21.95 *(978-1-58011-349-6(4))* Creative Homeowner.

Loft Publications Staff & Quartino, Daniela Santos. New Lobbies & Waiting Rooms. 2008. (Illus.). 330p. 50.00 *(978-0-06-137486-9(5)*, Collins Design) HarperCollins Pubs.

Low, Kevin Mark. Small Projects. 2010. (ENG., Illus.). 398p. 60.00 *(978-0-9819857-2-5(6))* Oro Editions.

Luescher, Andreas. The Architect's Portfolio: Planning, Design, Production. 2010. (ENG., Illus.). 200p. (C). pap. 34.95 *(978-0-415-77901-2(4))* Routledge.

Lukas, Scott A. The Themed Space: Locating Culture, Nation, & Self. 2007. (ENG.). 346p. per. 36.99 *(978-0-7391-2142-9(1))* Lexington Bks.

Lukas, Scott A., ed. Critical Perspectives on Them. 2007. (ENG.). 346p. 83.99 *(978-0-7391-2141-2(3))* Lexington Bks.

MacLaughlin, David C. & Estrada, Hector. Structural Steel Drafting. 2nd rev. ed. 2009. (ENG.). 256p. (C). pap. 175.95 *(978-1-4018-9032-2(6))* Delmar Cengage Learning.

Madsen, David A., et al. Print Reading for Architecture & Construction Technology. 3rd ed. 2012. (ENG.). 416p. (C). pap. 157.95 ***(978-1-133-12727-7(4))*** Delmar Cengage Learning.

Marriott, Carol. Fundamentals of ANSI/ASHRAE/IESNA Standard 90. 1: ASHRAE eLearning System. 2006. 620.00 *(978-0-12-373996-4(9)*, Elsevier Science) Elsevier Science & Technology Bks.

—Fundamentals of ANSI/ASHRAE/IESNA Standard 90. 1 Site Licence: ASHRAE eLearning System Site Licence. 2006. 620.00 *(978-0-12-373997-1(7)*, Elsevier Science) Elsevier Science & Technology Bks.

Martin, Muscoe & Franta, Gregory. Sustainable Design II. National Council of Architectural Registration Boards, ed. 2007. 138p. pap. 275.00 *(978-0-941575-53-9(5))* National Council of Architectural Registration Boards.

Marugrauf, Monika, ed. Archäologie der Moderne / Archaeology of Modernism: Sanierung Bauhaus Dessau, 1 vol. 2007. (GER & ENG., Illus.). 256p. pap. 35.00 *(978-3-936314-83-0(7))* Jovis Verlag GmbH DEU. Dist: D.A.P./Distributed Art Pubs.

Masson, Kathryn. Stables: Beautiful Paddocks, Horse Barns, & Tack Rooms. 2010. (ENG., Illus.). 256p. 55.00 *(978-0-8478-3314-6(3))* Rizzoli International Pubns., Inc.

Matthews, Stuart & Reeves, Barry. Structural Assessment of Large Panel Systems (Lps) Dwelling Blocks for Accidental Loading: Handbook. 2012. (ENG., Illus.). 312p. pap. 140.00 ***(978-1-84806-200-9(1))*** Building Research Establishment GBR. Dist: Taylor & Francis Group.

McCarter, Robert. William Morgan: Selected & Current Works. 2006. (Master Architect Series VI). (ENG., Illus.). 256p. 59.95 *(978-1-876907-02-0(9)*, Images Publishing Dist Ac) Antique Collectors' Club GBR. Dist: National Bk. Network.

McGrath, Brian. Designing Patch Dynamics. 2008. *(978-1-883584-47-4(7))* Columbia Univ., Graduate Schl. of Architecture.

Meeda, B., et al. Graphics for Urban Design. 2007. (Illus.). 132p. pap. *(978-0-7277-3399-3(0))* Telford, Thomas Ltd.

Melita, Issa. American Onsen: Adapting the Japanese Hot Spring Bathhouse Spa for the American User. 2011. 72p. pap. ***(978-3-639-30181-6(1))*** VDM Verlag Dr. Mueller e.K.

Meniru, Kene. Sketching & Designing Buildings with Computers. 2010. 244p. pap. *(978-3-8383-7068-2(6))* Lambert Academic Publishing.

Messedat, Jons. best designed flagship stores. 2007. (ENG.). 168p. 35.00 *(978-3-89986-083-2(7)*, Avedition Gmbh,Csi) Continental Sales, Inc.

Meuser, Philipp. Construction & Design Manual: Hospitals & Health Centres, 1 vol. 2011. (ENG.). 600p. pap. 169.95 *(978-3-86922-146-5(1))* DOM Pubs. DEU. Dist: Innovative Logistics.

Mills, Criss B. Designing with Models: A Studio Guide to Architectural Process Models. 3rd ed. 2011. (ENG., Illus.). 288p. pap. 65.00 *(978-0-470-49885-9(4)*, Wiley) Wiley, John & Sons, Inc.

Moghimi, Mahdi. Architectural Design of Compound & Freeform Space Structures. 2010. 536p. pap. *(978-3-8383-4250-4(X))* Lambert Academic Publishing.

Moskow, Keith. Sustainable Facilities: Green Design, Construction, & Operations. 2008. (ENG., Illus.). 208p. 69.95 *(978-0-07-149474-8(X)*, 007149474X) McGraw-Hill Professional Publishing.

Nappo, Donato & Vairelli, Stefania. Homes on Move. 2010. 192p. 19.99 *(978-0-8416-7179-9(6))* Langenscheidt Publishing Group.

—Homes on the move: Mobile Architecture, 1 vol. 2010. (ENG & GER., Illus.). 192p. pap. 19.99 *(978-3-8331-5632-8(5))* h.f.ullmann DEU. Dist: Innovative Logistics.

Newell, Philip. Recording Studio Design. 2nd ed. 2007. (ENG., Illus.). 736p. pap. 93.95 *(978-0-240-52086-5(6)*, Focal Pr.) Elsevier Science & Technology Bks.

Ngwaba, Maurice. Major Constraints in Planning, Design,and Construction of a Facility. 2010. 268p. pap. *(978-3-8383-7276-1(X))* Lambert Academic Publishing.

Northwest Home Designing, Inc. Staff. Designment Review, 1988. Lord, Todd, ed. (Illus.). 40p. pap. 8.00 *(978-0-936909-04-2(8))* Northwest Home Designing, Inc.

Nowacki, H. & Lefèvre, Wolfgang. Creating Shapes in Civil & Naval Architecture: A Cross-Disciplinary Comparison. Nowacki, H., ed. 2009. (History of Science & Medicine Library). (Illus.). 448p. *(978-90-04-17345-3(5))* BRILL.

Núñez Covarrubias, Alberto, et al. New Contributions for Modeling & Simulating Hpc Environments. 2011. 248p. pap. ***(978-3-8383-8168-8(8))*** Lambert Academic Publishing.

Oppenheim Architecture + Design. Modern Elegance: Oppenheim Architecture + Design, 1 vol. 2012. (ENG., Illus.). 496p. pap. 70.00 *(978-0-9825989-9-3(8))* Visual Profile Bks., Inc.

Papadakis, Alexandra & Papadakis, Andreas, eds. Innovations: From Experimentation to Realisation. 2006. (ENG., Illus.). 208p. pap. 30.00 *(978-1-901092-46-2(1))* Papadakis Dist A/C.

Pauwels, Wim. Offices: Bureaux-Kantoren. 2007. (and d Ser.). (ENG., Illus.). 200p. *(978-90-77213-79-7(1)*, Beta-Plus (Acc)) Antique Collectors' Club.

—Swimming Pools. Watkinson, Laura, tr. 2006. (ENG., Illus.). 180p. *(978-90-77213-53-7(8)*, Beta-Plus (Acc)) Antique Collectors' Club.

Pereira Mosqueira, Fernando. Mitigation Methods of Wind Acceleration for a 39-Story Building. 2011. 60p. pap. ***(978-3-8443-2024-4(5))*** Lambert Academic Publishing.

Phaidon Press Editors, ed. Building the New Millennium, Architecture at the Start of the 21st Century. 2009. (ENG., Illus.). 160p. 35.00 *(978-0-7148-5600-1(2))* Phaidon Pr., Inc.

Philon, Helen. Silent Splendour: Palaces of the Deccan, 14th-19th Centuries. 2010. (ENG., Illus.). 148p. 68.00 *(978-81-85026-96-1(3))* Marg Pubns. IND. Dist: National Bk. Network.

Pla, Maurici & Pla i Serra, Maurici. Catalonia: A Guide to Modern Architecture, 1880-2007, 1 vol. 2007. (ENG., Illus.). 488p. pap. 63.00 *(978-84-8478-009-0(0))* Triangle Postals, S.L. ESP. Dist: Innovative Logistics.

Plan Staff. New Forms: Plans & Details for Contemporary Architects. 2009. (ENG., Illus.). 240p. 65.00 *(978-0-500-34253-4(9)*, 534253) Thames & Hudson.

Powell, Joe. The New Competitiveness in Design & Construction: 12 Strategies That Will Drive the 21st-Century's Most Successful Firms. 2008. (ENG., Illus.). 216p. 70.00 *(978-0-470-06560-0(5)*, Wiley) Wiley, John & Sons, Inc.

Power, Ethel B. Smaller Houses of The 1920s: 55 Examples. 2007. (Dover Architecture Ser.). (ENG., Illus.). 112p. pap. 12.95 *(978-0-486-46049-9(5))* Dover Pubns., Inc.

Prigge, Walter, ed. Ikone der Moderne / Icon of Modernism: Das Bauhaugebäude in Dessau / The Bauhaus Building Dessau, 1 vol. 2007. (GER & ENG., Illus.). 144p. per. 29.95 *(978-3-936314-84-7(6))* Jovis Verlag GmbH DEU. Dist: D.A.P./Distributed Art Pubs.

Quartino, Daniela Santos & Quartino, Daniela S. New Spas & Resorts. 2007. (Illus.). 330p. 50.00 *(978-0-06-114998-6(5)*, Collins Design) HarperCollins Pubs.

Rahim, Ali & Jamelle, Hina, eds. Elegance. 2007. (Architectural Design Ser.: 33). (ENG.). 128p. pap. 45.00 *(978-0-470-02968-8(4)*, Academy Pr.) Wiley, John & Sons, Inc.

Ramos, Stephen. After Zero. Turan, Neyran, ed. 2009. (Graduate School of Design New Geographies Ser.). (Illus.). 160p. pap. 20.00 *(978-1-934510-20-9(3))* Harvard Univ., Graduate Schl. of Design.

Rappaport, Nina & Yale School of Architecture. Layered Urbanisms. Stanat, Julia, ed. 2008. (Yale School of Architecture Bks.). (ENG., Illus.). 160p. pap. 30.00 *(978-0-393-73250-4(9)*, 73250) Norton, W. W. & Co., Inc.

Rave, Rolf. Modern Architecture in Berlin. 2009. (ENG., Illus.). 280p. pap. 49.90 *(978-3-936681-29-1(5))* Edition Axel Menges GmbH DEU. Dist: National Bk. Network.

Raynsford, Nick. Celebrating Differences: The Work of BPTW Partnership. McCorquodale, Duncan, ed. 2008. (ENG., Illus.). 191p. 55.00 *(978-1-906155-42-1(9))* Black Dog Publishing Ltd. GBR. Dist: Perseus Distribution.

Remoy, H. T., ed. Out of Office. 2010. (Illus.). 260p. pap. 109.00 *(978-1-60750-520-4(7)*, Delft University Pr) IOS Pr., Inc.

Rengel, Roberto. Shaping Interior Space. 92p. pap., instr.'s gde. ed. *(978-1-56367-222-4(7))* Fairchild Bks.

Rengel, Roberto J. Shaping Interior Space. 2nd rev. ed. 2007. (Illus.). 368p. pap. 95.50 *(978-1-56367-518-8(8))* Fairchild Bks.

Riera Ojeda, Oscar. Sasaki: Intersection & Convergence. Riera Ojeda, Oscar, ed. 2008. (ENG., Illus.). 336p. 65.00 *(978-0-9793801-5-0(4))* Oro Editions.

Riggs, Tamye. Typeface: Classic Typography for Contemporary Design. 2009. (ENG.). 256p. pap. 45.00 *(978-1-56898-810-8(9))* Princeton Architectural Pr.

Riordan, John. Restaurants by Design. 2006. (ENG., Illus.). 192p. 45.00 *(978-0-06-089346-0(X)*, Collins Design) HarperCollins Pubs.

Rochlin, Michael Jacob. Ancient L. A. And Other Essays. Date not set. (Illus.). 54p. 39.95 *(978-0-9648304-2-4(6))* Unreinforced Masonry Studio.

Ronner, Heinz, et al. Zahn der Zeit. 2008. (GER.). 128p. pap. 19.95 *(978-3-7643-2969-3(6)*, 3764329696) Springer.

Ross, Michael. Planning & the Heritage. 3rd ed. 2015. pap. 155.00 *(978-0-415-33838-7(7))*; pap. 39.95 ***(978-0-415-33839-4(5))*** Routledge.

Rostagni, Cecilia & Moretti, Luigi. Luigi Moretti, 1907-1973. Rostagni, Cecilia, ed. 2009. (ITA., Illus.). 368p. 175.00 *(978-88-370-5731-2(8))* Electa ITA. Dist: Trans-Atlantic Pubns., Inc.

Saeger, LEED AP, Brad. LEED BD&C Flashcards: Building Design & Construction. 2009. (ENG.). 473p. pap. 32.00 *(978-0-9801638-7-2(0))* Professional Pubns., Inc.

Sanchez, Alex, ed. Urban Terraces & Balconies. 2009. 216p. 40.00 *(978-84-92463-92-3(9))* Loft Pubns. ESP. Dist: Prestel Publishing.

Schafer, Julia, ed. Dora Garcia: Rooms, Conversations. 2008. (ENG., Illus.). 104p. pap. 35.00 *(978-3-939633-16-7(X))* Jovis Verlag GmbH DEU. Dist: D.A.P./Distributed Art Pubs.

Schalenberg, Marc & Bartetzky, Arnold, eds. Urban Planning & the Pursuit of Happiness: European Variations on a universal Theme. 2009. (ENG., Illus.). 208p. pap. 39.95 *(978-3-86859-020-3(X))* Jovis Verlag GmbH DEU. Dist: D.A.P./Distributed Art Pubs.

Schillaci, Fabio. Architectural Renderings. 2010. (ENG., Illus.). 466p. 75.00 *(978-0-470-66410-0(X)*, Wiley) Wiley, John & Sons, Inc.

Schmiedeknecht, Torsten. Rationalist Traces. Peckham, Andrew & Rattray, Charles, eds. 2007. (Architectural Design Ser.). (ENG.). 152p. pap. 50.00 *(978-0-470-02837-7(8)*, Wiley) Wiley, John & Sons, Inc.

Schulz, Daniel. Global Creative Architecture. 2008. (Illus.). 271p. *(978-981-245-543-7(4))* Page One Publishing.

Seki, Akihiko & Brooke, Elizabeth Heilman. Ryokan: Japan's Finest Spas & Inns. 2007. (ENG., Illus.). 208p. 39.95 *(978-0-8048-3839-9(9))* Tuttle Publishing.

Shahfar, Shawn. Leedpass. 2007. 0.01 net. *(978-1-60402-004-5(0))* Independent Pub.

Sherriff, Clare. Boathouses. 2009. (ENG., Illus.). 168p. 75.00 *(978-0-906290-97-2(X))* Unicorn Pr., London GBR. Dist: National Bk. Network.

Shukla, Sunil. Quku: A Mixed Grain Multi-Layered Reconfigurable Architecture. 2010. 200p. pap. *(978-3-8383-1742-7(4))* Lambert Academic Publishing.

Shulman, Allan T. & Camber, Diane. Miami Modern Metropolis: Paradise & Paradox in Midcentury Architecture & Planning. 2009. (ENG., Illus.). 416p. 85.00 *(978-1-890449-51-3(2))* Balcony Pr.

Siddiqui, Iqtidar. Dams & Reservoirs: Planning, Engineering & Maintenance. 2008. (ENG., Illus.). 302p. pap. 35.00 *(978-0-19-547585-2(2))* Oxford Univ. Pr., Inc.

Skansi, Luka, ed. Gino Valle: Deutsche Bank Milano. 2010. (ENG & ITA., Illus.). 120p. pap. 62.50 *(978-88-370-7300-8(3))* Electa ITA. Dist: Trans-Atlantic Pubns., Inc.

Smith, David Lee. Environmental Issues for Architecture. 2011. (ENG., Illus.). 608p. 85.00 *(978-0-470-49709-8(2)*, Wiley) Wiley, John & Sons, Inc.

Snell, David. The Pocket Guide to Building Your Own Home. 2008. (ENG., Illus.). 224p. pap. 24.95 *(978-0-09-192660-1(2))* Ebury Publishing GBR. Dist: Independent Pubs. Group.

Spiller, Neil. Digital Architecture Now: A Global Survey of Emerging Talent. 2009. (ENG., Illus.). 400p. 65.00 *(978-0-500-34247-3(4))* Thames & Hudson.

—Visionary Architecture: Blueprints of the Modern Imagination. (ENG., Illus.). 272p. 2008. per. 39.95 *(978-0-500-28655-5(8))* 2007. 60.00 *(978-0-500-34226-8(1))* Thames & Hudson.

Starling, Felipe, et al, eds. Broad Horizons / Larges Horizons: ADPI Architecture & Engineering. 2011. (ENG., Illus.). 176p. 49.95 *(978-1-907317-15-6(5))* Black Dog Publishing Ltd. GBR. Dist: Perseus Distribution.

Steenbergen, Clemens. Composing Landscapes: Analysis, Typology & Experiments for Design. 2008. (Illus.). 432p. 69.95 *(978-3-7643-8782-2(3)*, 3764387823) Springer.

Stegmeier, Diane. Innovations in Office Design: The Critical Influence Approach to Effective Work Environments. 2008. (ENG., Illus.). 280p. 75.00 *(978-0-471-73041-5(6)*, Wiley) Wiley, John & Sons, Inc.

Stine, Daniel. Commercial Design Using Revit Architecture 2008. 2007. 320p. per. 59.95 *(978-1-58503-375-1(6)*, SDC Pubns.) Schroff Development Corp.

Stratton, Arthur. Elements of Form & Design in Classic Architecture. 2007. 264p. per. *(978-1-905217-83-0(8))* Mills, Jeremy Publishing.

Street-Porter, Tim, photos by. L. A. Modern. 2008. (ENG., Illus.). 248p. 75.00 *(978-0-8478-3067-1(5))* Rizzoli International Pubns., Inc.

Surratt, Tereasa. A Very Modest Cottage: A 1920s Cabin Gets a New Chance at Life. 2010. (ENG., Illus.). 176p. 24.95 *(978-1-58816-797-2(6))* Hearst Communications, Inc.

Terranova, Antonino & Spirito, Gianpaola. The New Urban Giants: The Ultimate Skyscrapers. 2008. (ENG., Illus.). 216p. 19.95 *(978-88-544-0332-1(6))* White Star ITA. Dist: Random Hse., Inc.

Thielemann, Gerhard, et al. Adalbert Erlebach: Das Leben und die Kunst des Meraner Architekten. 2010. (GER., Illus.). 127p. *(978-88-8266-683-5(2))* Athesia.

Thomas-Emberson, Steve. Airport Interiors: Design for Business. 2008. (ENG., Illus.). 232p. 85.00 *(978-0-470-03475-0(0)*, Academy Pr.) Wiley, John & Sons, Inc.

Triviño, Santi. Low Tech Architecture. Monsa Staff et al, eds. 2010. (ENG., Illus.). 96p. pap. 22.50 *(978-84-96823-70-9(9))* Instituto Monsa de Ediciones, S.A. ESP. Dist: Trans-Atlantic Pubns., Inc.

Trulove, James Grayson. 25 Apartments & Lofts under 2500 Square Feet. 2007. (Illus.). 224p. pap. 39.95 *(978-0-06-114989-4(6)*, Collins Design) HarperCollins Pubs.

Tunstall, Gavin. Managing the Building Design Process. 2nd rev. ed. 2006. (ENG., Illus.). 400p. per. 48.95 *(978-0-7506-6791-3(5))* Routledge.

United States, Congress House Committee on Transportation and Infrastructure Subcommittee on Economic Development, Public Buildings, and Emergency Management Staff, contrib. by. The Future of the Federal Courthouse Construction Program: Results of a Government Accountability Office Study on the Judiciary's Rental Obligations: Hearing Before the Subcommittee on Economic Development, Public Buildings, & Emergency Management of the Committee on Transportation & Infrastructure, House of Representatives, One Hundred Ninth Congress, Second Session, Jun3 22, 2006. 2007. (Illus.). v, 296p. *(978-0-16-078034-9(9)*, 552-070-35464-6) United States Government Printing Office.

Utimpergher, Paolo, et al. Frameworks: Ventidue Progetti Di Aldo Parisotto e Massimo Formenton = Twentytwo Projects by Aldo Parisotto & Massimo Formenton. Maltese, E., ed. 2009. (ITA & ENG., Illus.). 256p. 149.50 *(978-88-370-6559-1(0))* Electa ITA. Dist: Trans-Atlantic Pubns., Inc.

Valle, Pietro. Mecanoo: Experimental Pragmatism. 2007. (ENG., Illus.). 212p. pap. 14.99 *(978-88-7624-655-5(X))* Skira Editore ITA. Dist: Random Hse., Inc.

van der Werf, Huib Haye, ed. Waterfront Visions. 2010. (ENG., Illus.). 128p. pap. 40.00 *(978-90-5662-730-0(9))* NAi Uitgevers / Publishers Stichting NLD. Dist: D.A.P./Distributed Art Pubs.

Verlagshaus-Braun Editorial Staff, ed. Unusual Architectural Presentation Drawings. 2007. (Illus.). 336p. 59.95 *(978-981-245-214-6(1))* Page One Publishing SGP. Dist: Gingko Pr., Inc.

Vos, Emmie, ed. Europan 9. 2008. (ENG & DUT., Illus.). 128p. pap. 45.00 *(978-90-5662-006-6(1))* NAi Uitgevers / Publishers Stichting NLD. Dist: D.A.P./Distributed Art Pubs.

Wakita, Osamu A., et al. The Professional Practice of Architectural Working Drawings. 4th ed. 2011. (ENG., Illus.). 688p. 115.00 *(978-0-470-61815-8(9)*, Wiley) Wiley, John & Sons, Inc.

Warrener, Rodney. Martin Travers, an Appreciation. 2006. (ENG., Illus.). 352p. 60.00 *(978-0-906290-70-5(8))* Unicorn Pr., London GBR. Dist: National Bk. Network.

Wegner, Ramona. Messenger in Built Form & Design. 2007. 64p. per. *(978-3-8364-2359-5(6))* VDM Verlag Dr. Mueller e.K.

Wermiel, Sara E. Lighthouses. 2006. (Norton/Library of Congress Visual Sourcebooks in Architecture, Design, & Engineering). (ENG., Illus.). 360p. 75.00 incl. cd-rom *(978-0-393-73166-8(9)*, 73166) Norton, W. W. & Co., Inc.

Weston, Richard. Key Buildings of the Twentieth Century: Plans, Sections & Elevations. 2nd ed. 2010. (Key Architecture Ser.). (ENG., Illus.). 352p. pap. 45.00 *(978-0-393-73311-2(4)*, 73311) Norton, W. W. & Co., Inc.

Willems, Marlous, compiled by. Behind Bars: Design for Cafes & Bars. 2007. (ENG., Illus.). 344p. *(978-3-89955-300-0(4))* Die Gestalten Verlag DEU. Dist: Prestel Publishing.

Williams, Homer. Building Type Basics for Banks & Financial Institutions. 2010. (Building Type Basics Ser.: 16). (ENG., Illus.). 256p. 85.00 *(978-0-470-27862-8(5)*, Wiley) Wiley, John & Sons, Inc.

Willis, Robert & Willis Clark, John. Selections from the Architectural History of the University of Cambridge: King's College & Eton College. 2009. (ENG.). 376p. pap. 30.00 *(978-0-521-14719-4(0))* Cambridge Univ. Pr.

—Selections from the Architectural History of the University of Cambridge: Peterhouse. 2009. (ENG.). 120p. pap. 15.99 *(978-0-521-14714-9(X))* Cambridge Univ. Pr.

—Selections from the Architectural History of the University of Cambridge: St Johns College. 2009. (ENG.). 164p. pap. 15.99 *(978-0-521-14715-6(8))* Cambridge Univ. Pr.

—Selections from the Architectural History of the University of Cambridge: Trinity College. 2009. (ENG.). 368p. pap. 30.00 *(978-0-521-14718-7(2))* Cambridge Univ. Pr.

Wilson, Henry L. The Bungalow Book: Floor Plans & Photos of 112 Houses 1910. 2006. (Dover Architecture Ser.). (ENG., Illus.). 160p. per. 15.95 *(978-0-486-45104-6(6))* Dover Pubns., Inc.

Womersley, Steve. Urban Design Group: Selected & Current Works. 2006. (Master Architect Series VI). (ENG., Illus.). 59.95 *(978-1-876907-07-5(X)*, Images Publishing Dist Ac) Antique Collectors' Club GBR. Dist: National Bk. Network.

Woofer, Heather. Axi:Ome: Spatial Practice. 2009. (ENG., Illus.). 144p. pap. 29.95 *(978-0-9814628-5-1(5))* Oro Editions.

Yee, Roger. Architecture as a Design Partnership. 2012. (ENG., Illus.). 1780p. 60.00 *(978-0-9825989-7-9(1))* Visual Profile Bks., Inc.

—Corporate Interiors, No. 7. 2006. (Corporate Interiors Ser.). (Illus.). 295p. 60.00 *(978-1-58471-092-9(6))* Visual Reference Pubns., Inc.

—Public Spaces. 2010. (Illus.). 290p. 70.00 *(978-1-58471-117-9(5))* Visual Reference Pubns., Inc.

Younes, Samir & Mazzola, Ettore Maria, eds. Como: The Modernity of Tradition. 2010. (University of Notre Dame Graduate Program in Architecture, Rome Studies Program Publications). 96p. pap. 32.95 *(978-88-492-0467-4(1))* Gangemi ITA. Dist: International Publishers Marketing.

Ypma, Herbert. Atlas. 2007. (ENG., Illus.). 528p. pap. 36.95 *(978-0-500-28569-5(1))* Thames & Hudson.

Yu, Jasmin, ed. Exhibitions & Trade Fair Design. 2011. (ENG.). 272p. 50.00 *(978-988-19740-7-5(0))* Design Media Publishing Ltd. HKG. Dist: BookMasters Distribution Services (BDS).

Zepter, Tobias, text. MODERSOHN & FREIESLEBEN Architekten: Das Leben der Dinge. The Life of Things. 2010. (ENG., Illus.). 176p. 55.00 *(978-3-7757-2487-6(7))* Hatje Cantz Verlag GmbH & Co KG DEU. Dist: D.A.P./Distributed Art Pubs.

ARCHITECTURE—DETAILS

see also Ceilings; Church Architecture—Details; Domes; Doors and Doorways; Facades; Fireplaces; Floors; Foundations; Roofs; Screens; Staircases; Weather Vanes; Windows; Woodwork

Allen, Edward & Rand, Patrick. Architectural Detailing: Function - Constructibility - Aesthetics. 2nd rev. ed. 2006. (ENG., Illus.). 336p. pap. 75.00 *(978-0-471-48817-0(8)*, Wiley) Wiley, John & Sons, Inc.

—Architectural Detailing & Wileycpe. com Designing Leakproof Details Course, Set. 2009. (ENG.). 336p. 99.95 *(978-0-470-49040-2(3)*, Wiley) Wiley, John & Sons, Inc.

Boschetti, Joe, ed. Creative Detailing by Some of the World's Leading Architects, Vol. 4. 2006. (Details in Architecture Ser.). (ENG., Illus.). 216p. 65.00 *(978-1-876907-57-0(6))* Images Publishing Group AUS. Dist: National Bk. Network.

Comstock, William T. Late Victorian Architectural Plans & Details. 2010. (Dover Architecture Ser.). (ENG., Illus.). 192p. pap. 19.95 *(978-0-486-47361-1(9))* Dover Pubns., Inc.

Crafti, Stephen. Details for Living. 2007. (ENG., Illus.). 200p. 50.00 *(978-1-86470-249-1(4))* Images Publishing Group AUS. Dist: National Bk. Network.

Cryder, Jo. Entryways & Doorways. 2008. (Illus.). 160p. pap. 29.95 *(978-0-7643-2858-9(1))* Schiffer Publishing, Ltd.

de Haro, Fernando. 100+ Details. 2011. (ENG., Illus.). 136p. pap. 11.95 *(978-607-437-053-9(2))* AM Editores MEX. Dist: Perseus-PGW.

—100+ Stairs & Corridors. 2011. (ENG., Illus.). 136p. pap. 11.95 *(978-607-437-055-3(9))* AM Editores MEX. Dist: Perseus-PGW.

Delbene, Giacomo, ed. Public, Private, Ephemeral. 2008. 150p. pap. *(978-84-612-1509-6(5))* Actar Birkhauser Distribution.

Ford, Edward R. The Architectural Detail. 2011. (ENG.). 336p. pap. 40.00 *(978-1-56898-978-5(4))* Princeton Architectural Pr.

—Five Houses, Ten Details. 2009. (ENG., Illus.). 256p. 40.00 *(978-1-56898-826-9(5))* Princeton Architectural Pr.

Grenfell, Milton Wilfred, ed. Comparative Architectural Details: A Selection from Pencil Points, 1932-1937. 2010. (ENG., Illus.). 280p. 59.95 *(978-0-393-73300-6(9)*, 73300) Norton, W. W. & Co., Inc.

Guild, Robin. The Victorian House Book: A Practical Guide to Home Repair & Decoration. 4th ed. 2008. (ENG., Illus.). 320p. 49.95 *(978-1-55407-371-9(5))* Firefly Bks., Ltd.

Hafke, Jan-Hendrik, et al. Open I Close. 2009. (Illus.). 160p. pap. 59.95 *(978-3-7643-9961-0(9))* Birkhauser Verlag AG CHE. Dist: Springer.

Hall, Andrew, ed. Details in Architecture: Creative Detailing by Leading Architects. 2009. (ENG., Illus.). 300p. 65.00 *(978-1-86470-342-9(3))* Images Publishing Group AUS. Dist: National Bk. Network.

Hopkins, Owen. Reading Architecture: A Visual Lexicon. 2012. (ENG., Illus.). 176p. pap. 29.95 ***(978-1-85669-736-1(3))*** King, Laurence Publishing GBR. Dist: Hachette Bk. Group.

Images Publishing Group. Details in Architecture. 2006. (Vol. 3 Ser.). (ENG., Illus.). Vol. 3. 216p. 65.00 *(978-1-86470-093-0(9))* Vol. 5. 65.00 *(978-1-876907-80-8(0))* Images Publishing Group AUS. Dist: National Bk. Network.

Jefferis, Alan & Smith, Kenneth. Commercial Drafting & Detailing. 3rd ed. 2009. (ENG.). 624p. (C). pap. 177.95 *(978-1-4354-2597-2(9))* Delmar Cengage Learning.

Kelly, J. Frederick. Early Domestic Architecture of Connecticut. 2007. (Illus.). 230p. pap. 29.95 *(978-0-7643-2664-6(3))* Schiffer Publishing, Ltd.

Maliszewski-Pickart, Margaret. Architecture & Ornament: An Illustrated Dictionary. alt. ed. 2009. (ENG.). 208p. pap. 39.95 *(978-0-7864-4335-2(9))* McFarland & Co., Inc. Pubs.

McLeod, Virginia. Detail in Contemporary Landscape Architecture. 2008. (ENG., Illus.). 192p. 50.00 *(978-1-85669-498-8(4))* King, Laurence Publishing GBR. Dist: Hachette Bk. Group.

—Detail in Contemporary Residential Architecture. 2007. (ENG., Illus.). 240p. 50.00 *(978-1-85669-482-7(8))* King, Laurence Publishing GBR. Dist: Hachette Bk. Group.

—Encyclopedia of Detail in Contemporary Residential Architecture. 2010. (ENG., Illus.). 352p. 65.00 *(978-1-85669-692-0(8))* King, Laurence Publishing GBR. Dist: Hachette Bk. Group.

McLeod, Virginia, et al. Detail in Contemporary Timber Architecture. 2010. (ENG., Illus.). 224p. 50.00 *(978-1-85669-641-8(3))* King, Laurence Publishing GBR. Dist: Hachette Bk. Group.

Mestre, Octavio. Building Skins. 2011. (Architectural Details Ser.). (SPA & ENG., Illus.). 224p. pap. 62.50 ***(978-84-15223-17-7(X))*** Instituto Monsa de Ediciones, S.A. ESP. Dist: Trans-Atlantic Pubns., Inc.

Moro, José L. Baukonstruktion vom Prinzip zum Detail: Band 1: Grundlagen. 2006. (Illus.). XXX, 666p. pap. 89.95 *(978-3-540-40613-6(1)*, 3540406131) Springer.

Pla Boada, Ricard & Cirlot, Juan Eduardo. Gaudi, 1 vol. 2011. (ENG., Illus.). 424p. 68.00 *(978-84-8478-034-2(1))* Triangle Postals, S.L. ESP. Dist: Innovative Logistics.

Reiss, Marcia. Architectural Details. 2008. (ENG.). 256p. 25.00 *(978-1-4223-9309-3(7))* DIANE Publishing Co.

Requa, Richard S. Old World Inspiration for American Architecture. 2007. (Illus.). 344p. 59.95 *(978-0-7643-2668-4(6))* Schiffer Publishing, Ltd.

Ruskin, John. The Stones of Venice - The Fall. 2007. 528p. per. 26.95 *(978-1-60206-703-5(1))* Cosimo, Inc.

—The Stones of Venice - The Foundations. 2007. 464p. 39.45 *(978-1-60206-700-4(7))*; per. 24.95 *(978-1-60206-699-1(X))* Cosimo, Inc.

—The Stones of Venice - The Sea Stories. 2007. 452p. (ENG.). 39.45 *(978-1-60206-702-8(3))*; per. 24.95 *(978-1-60206-701-1(5))* Cosimo, Inc.

—Stones of Venice [Introductions]. 2007. 160p. per. *(978-1-4068-4090-2(4))* Echo Library.

—The Stones of Venice,Volume III the Fall. 2007. 528p. 39.45 *(978-1-60206-704-2(X))* Cosimo, Inc.

Ryan, Thomas R., et al. Detailing for Landscape Architects: Aesthetics, Function, Constructibility. 2011. (ENG., Illus.). 272p. pap. 85.00 *(978-0-470-54878-3(9)*, Wiley) Wiley, John & Sons, Inc.

Schmidt, Phil. Porches & Patio Rooms: Sunrooms, Patio Enclosures, Breezeways & Screened Porches. 2009. (Black & Decker Complete Guide Ser.). (ENG., Illus.). 240p. pap. 24.99 *(978-1-58923-420-8(0)*, 1589234200, Creative Publishing International) Quayside.

Sewall, Jock. Mediterranean Architecture: A Sourcebook of Architectural Elements. 2011. (Illus.). 432p. 100.00 ***(978-0-7643-3891-5(9)***, Schiffer Publishing Ltd) Schiffer Publishing, Ltd.

Shipway, Verna Cook. The Mexican House. 3rd ed. 2007. 39.95 *(978-0-940512-47-4(5))* Hennessey & Ingalls, Inc.

Slessor, Catherine. Architecture & Design London. Webb, Michael, ed. (Illus.). 96p. pap. 16.00 *(978-0-9641863-7-8(3)*, TUB Pr.) Understanding Business.

Smith, Gibbs & Farmer, James T., III. Porch Living, 1 vol. 2012. (ENG., Illus.). 144p. 30.00 ***(978-1-4236-2534-6(X))*** Gibbs Smith, Publisher.

Snyder, Frank M. Building Details. 2007. (ENG.). 144p. 65.00 *(978-0-393-73245-0(2)*, 73245) Norton, W. W. & Co., Inc.

Thallon, Rob. Frame Construction. 3rd ed. 2009. (For Pros by Pros Ser.). (ENG., Illus.). 243p. pap. 24.95 *(978-1-60085-023-3(5))* Taunton Pr., Inc.

The Curators. Details in Design. 2006. (Details in Architecture (Image) Ser.). (ENG., Illus.). 216p. 65.00 *(978-1-920744-28-1(2))* Images Publishing Group AUS. Dist: National Bk. Network.

Tuthill, William B. Late Victorian Interiors & Interior Details. 2010. (Dover Architecture Ser.). (ENG., Illus.). 80p. pap. 9.95 *(978-0-486-47603-2(0))* Dover Pubns., Inc.

Vassallo, Marc & Susanka, Sarah. Inside the Not So Big House: Discovering the Details That Bring a Home to Life. 2007. (Susanka Ser.). (ENG., Illus.). 210p. pap. 21.95 *(978-1-56158-984-5(5)*, Taunton) Taunton Pr., Inc.

West, Geoffrey D. Architectural Salvage: A Guide to Selecting, Buying & Using Reclaimed Building Materials, 1 vol. 2010. (ENG., Illus.). 160p. 35.00 *(978-1-84797-207-1(1))* Crowood Pr., Ltd. GBR. Dist: Independent Pubs. Group.

Yorke, Trevor. British Architectural Styles: An Easy Reference Guide. 2008. (Illus.). 64p. (C). pap. 12.95 *(978-1-84674-082-4(7))* Countryside Bks. GBR. Dist: Brown, David Bk. Co., The.

ARCHITECTURE—DICTIONARIES

Ambrose, Gavin, et al. The Visual Dictionary of Architecture. 2008. (Visual Dictionary Ser.). (ENG., Illus.). 288p. pap. 24.95 *(978-2-940373-54-3(X))* AVA Publishing GBR. Dist: Ingram Pub. Services.

Burden, Ernest. Illustrated Dictionary of Architecture 3/E. 3rd ed. 2012. (ENG., Illus.). 576p. pap. 60.00 ***(978-0-07-177293-8(6)***, 0071772936) McGraw-Hill Professional Publishing.

Ching, Francis D. K. A Visual Dictionary of Architecture. 2nd ed. 2011. (ENG., Illus.). 336p. pap. 55.00 *(978-0-470-64885-8(6)*, Wiley) Wiley, John & Sons, Inc.

Colvin, Howard. A Biographical Dictionary of British Architects 1600-1840. 4th ed. 2008. (Paul Mellon Centre for Studies in British Art). (ENG., Illus.). 1264p. 150.00 *(978-0-300-12508-5(9))* Yale Univ. Pr.

Curl, James Stevens. A Dictionary of Architecture & Landscape Architecture. 2nd rev. ed. 2007. (Oxford Paperback Reference Ser.). (ENG., Illus.). 912p. per. 18.95 *(978-0-19-860678-9(8))* Oxford Univ. Pr., Inc.

Davies, Nikolas & Jokiniemi, Erkki. Architect's Illustrated Pocket Dictionary. 2011. (ENG., Illus.). 560p. pap. 33.95 *(978-0-08-096537-6(7))* Routledge.

Garcia Guinea, Miguel Angel, et al. Enciclopedia Del Románico en Aragón: Zaragoza, 2 vols. 2010. (Illus.). *(978-84-89483-67-5(1))*; (SPA., *(978-84-89483-68-2(X))*; (SPA., *(978-84-89483-69-9(8))* Fundacion Santa Maria La Real, Centro de Estudios del Romanico.

Goode, Patrick, ed. The Oxford Companion to Architecture, 2 vols., Set. 2009. (ENG., Illus.). 1136p. 315.00 *(978-0-19-860568-3(4))* Oxford Univ. Pr., Inc.

Gossel, Peter. Modern Architecture A-Z, 2 vols. 2010. (Go Ser.). (ENG., Illus.). 720p. 59.99 *(978-3-8365-2132-1(6))* TASCHEN DEU. Dist: Ingram Pub. Services.

Jokiniemi, Erkki & Davies, Nikolas. Dictionary of Architecture & Building Construction. 2008. (ENG., Illus.). 736p. 59.95 *(978-0-7506-8502-3(6))* Routledge.

Maliszewski-Pickart, Margaret. Architecture & Ornament: An Illustrated Dictionary. alt. ed. 2009. (ENG.). 208p. pap. 39.95 *(978-0-7864-4335-2(9))* McFarland & Co., Inc. Pubs.

Marter, Joan. The Grove Encyclopedia of American Art, 5 vols., Set. 2011. (ENG., Illus.). 2608p. 1045.00 *(978-0-19-533579-8(1))* Oxford Univ. Pr., Inc.

Palmer, Allison. Historical Dictionary of Architecture. 2008. (Historical Dictionaries of Literature & the Arts Ser.). (ENG.). 400p. 104.00 *(978-0-8108-5821-3(5))* Scarecrow Pr., Inc.

Palmer, Allison Lee. The A to Z of Architecture. 108th ed. 2009. (A to Z Guide Ser.: No. 108). (ENG.). 402p. pap. 34.45 *(978-0-8108-6895-3(4))* Scarecrow Pr., Inc.

Paradis, Thomas W. The Greenwood Encyclopedia of Homes Through American History, 4 vols. 2008. (Illus.). 1840p. 399.95 *(978-0-313-33496-2(X)*, GR3496) Greenwood Publishing Group, Inc.

Peter, Gössel, ed. Modern Architecture A to Z, 2 vols. 2007. (ENG., Illus.). 1072p. 300.00 *(978-3-8228-6313-8(0))* TASCHEN DEU. Dist: Ingram Pub. Services.

Ware. Dictionary of Architecture. *(978-0-8022-1809-4(1))* Philosophical Library, Inc.

Zirpolo, Lilian H. Historical Dictionary of Baroque Art & Architecture. 2010. (Historical Dictionaries of Literature & the Arts Ser.). (ENG., Illus.). 642p. 140.00 *(978-0-8108-6155-8(0))* Scarecrow Pr., Inc.

ARCHITECTURE—EARLY WORKS TO 1800

Barnes, Carl F. The Portfolio of Villard de Honnecourt Paris Bibliotheque Nationale de France Ms Fr 19093: Color Facsimile. 2009. (Illus.). 292p. 149.95 *(978-0-7546-5102-4(9))* Ashgate Publishing Co.

Benjamin, Asher. The Country Builder's Assistant. 2007. 68p. per. 8.50 *(978-1-60206-769-1(4))* Cosimo, Inc.

Haines, Richard. Proposals for Building, in Every County, A Working-Alms-House or Hospital. 2007. 48p. per. *(978-1-4065-1563-3(9))* Dodo Pr.

Palladio, Andrea, et al. Palladio's Rome. 2009. (ENG., Illus.). 320p. pap. 35.00 *(978-0-300-15147-3(0))* Yale Univ. Pr.

Plommer, Hugh. Vitruvius & Later Roman Building Manuals. 2009. (Cambridge Classical Studies). (LAT & ENG.). 132p. pap. 31.99 *(978-0-521-10038-0(0))* Cambridge Univ. Pr.

Scamozzi, Vincenzo. Vincenzo Scamozzi: Venetian Architect. 2008. (Illus.). 368p. 120.00 ***(978-90-76863-15-3(6))*** Architectura & Natura Pr. NLD. Dist: Antique Collectors' Club.

Vitruvius. On Architecture. Schofield, Richard, tr. from LAT. 2009. (ENG., Illus.). 464p. (gr. 12-18). pap. 18.00 *(978-0-14-144168-9(2)*, Penguin Classics) Penguin Group (USA) Inc.

—Ten Books on Architecture. 2009. 412p. 32.99 *(978-0-559-10390-2(5))*; 27.99 *(978-0-559-10405-3(7))*; pap. 34.75 *(978-0-559-10394-0(8))*; pap. 33.75 *(978-0-559-10401-5(4))* BiblioBazaar.

—The Ten Books on Architecture. 2008. (Illus.). 284p. pap. *(978-1-4068-7512-6(0))* Echo Library.

Wotton, Henry. The Elements of Architecture. 2008. 112p. 21.99 *(978-0-559-76121-8(X))*; pap. 19.75 *(978-0-559-76117-1(1))* BiblioBazaar.

ARCHITECTURE—ENVIRONMENTAL ASPECTS

Abbott, Gail. Living with White. 2010. (Illus.). 160p. 29.95 *(978-1-906525-24-8(2))* CICO Bks. GBR. Dist: Ryland Peters & Small.

Aggarwal, R. K. Solar Passive Architecture Techniques. 2011. 96p. pap. ***(978-3-8383-6671-5(9))*** Lambert Academic Publishing.

Ahmed, Hussein. Interaction Interoperability for Distributed Virtual Environments. 2010. 196p. pap. *(978-3-639-27745-6(7))* VDM Verlag Dr. Mueller e.K.

Alan Mascord Design Associates. Mascord Efficient Living: Build a More Sustainable Lifestyle. Higginbotham, Gary & Daby, Matthew, eds. 2008. (Illus.). 154p. 14.95 *(978-0-9788113-1-0(3))* AMDA Pr.

Albarazanchi, Najim. Urbanization Effect. 2010. 188p. pap. *(978-3-639-25230-9(6))* VDM Verlag Dr. Mueller e.K.

Almusaed, Amjad. Biophilic & Bioclimatic Architecture: Analytical Therapy for the Next Generation of Passive Sustainable Architecture. 2010. (ENG., Illus.). xxix, 422p. 279.00 *(978-1-84996-533-0(1)*, 1849965331) Springer.

Anker, Peder. From Bauhaus to Eco-house: A History of Ecological Design. 2010. 216p. 34.95 *(978-0-8071-3551-8(8))* Louisiana State Univ. Pr.

Attmann, Osman. Green Architecture: Advanced Technologies & Materials. 2009. (ENG., Illus.). 368p. 79.95 *(978-0-07-162501-2(1)*, 0071625011) McGraw-Hill Professional Publishing.

Azur Corporation Editors. New Look of Environmental Design. 2007. (ENG.). 208p. 60.00 *(978-4-7661-1629-8(1))* Azur Corp. JPN. Dist: National Bk. Network.

Bahamón, Alejandro & Pérez, Patricia. Animals. 2009. (Building/Biology Connection Ser.). (ENG., Illus.). 192p. pap. 35.00 *(978-0-393-73271-9(1)*, 73271) Norton, W. W. & Co., Inc.

—Inspired by Nature - Minerals: The Building/Geology Connection. 2008. (Inspired by Nature Ser.). (ENG., Illus.). 192p. pap. 35.00 *(978-0-393-73260-3(6)*, 73260) Norton, W. W. & Co., Inc.

Bahamón, Alejandro, et al. Inspired by Nature: Plants: The Building/Botany Connection. 2008. (Building/Botany Connection Ser.). (ENG.). 192p. pap. 35.00 *(978-0-393-73251-1(7)*, 73251) Norton, W. W. & Co., Inc.

Baird, George. Sustainable Buildings in Practice: What Users Think. 2010. (ENG., Illus.). 352p. (C). pap. 62.95 *(978-0-415-39932-6(7))* Routledge.

Ballesteros, Mario, et al, eds. Verb Crisis. 2008. (Verb Ser.). (Illus.). 294p. *(978-84-96540-97-2(9))* Kunst-Werke Berlin e.V.

Behr, R. A. Architectural Galss to Resist Seismic & Extreme Climatic Events. Behr, R. A., ed. 2009. (Illus.). 272p. 199.95 *(978-1-4398-0170-3(3))* CRC Pr. LLC.

Birnbaum, Daniel, et al, texts. Carsten Höller - Experience. 2011. (ENG., Illus.). 256p. 60.00 ***(978-0-8478-3760-1(2)***, Skira) Rizzoli International Pubns., Inc.

Bohlin Cywinkski Jackson Architects Staff. Bohlin Cywinski Jackson: The Nature of Circumstance. 2010. (ENG., Illus.). 420p. 95.00 *(978-0-8478-3293-4(7))* Rizzoli International Pubns., Inc.

Bolchover, Joshua & Solomon, Jonathan D., eds. Sustain & Develop, Vol. 13. 2010. (ENG.). 308p. pap. 30.00 *(978-0-692-00088-5(7))* Princeton Architectural Pr.

Borasi, Giovanna & Amemiya, Kozy. Journeys: How Travelling Fruit, Ideas & Buildings Rearrange Our Environment. 2011. (Illus.). 320p. pap. *(978-84-92861-54-5(1))* Actar Birkhauser Distribution.

Borasi, Giovanna, et al. Trajets: Comment la Mobilité des Fruits, des Idées et des Architectures Recompose Notre Environnement. 2011. (FRE., Illus.). 320p. pap. *(978-84-92861-55-2(X))* Actar Birkhauser Distribution.

Bottger. Updating Germany 100 Projects for a Better Future. 2009. (ENG., Illus.). 292p. 55.00 *(978-3-7757-2263-6(7))* Hatje Cantz Verlag GmbH & Co KG DEU. Dist: D.A.P./Distributed Art Pubs.

Broadbent, G & Brebbia, Carlos A., eds. Eco-Architecture II: Harmonisation Between Architecture & Nature. 2008. (WIT Transactions on Ecology & the Environment Ser.: 113). (Illus.). 368p. 242.00 *(978-1-84564-119-1(1))* WIT Pr GBR. Dist: WIT Pr.

Bromberek, Zbigniew. Eco-Resorts: Planning & Design for the Tropics. 2009. (ENG., Illus.). 256p. pap. 64.95 *(978-0-7506-5793-8(6))* Routledge.

Callard, Sarah. The Home: 250 Tips for an Eco Lifestyle. 2009. (Little Green Bks.). (ENG., Illus.). 128p. pap. 12.95 *(978-1-84732-070-4(8))* Carlton Bks., Ltd. GBR. Dist: Sterling Publishing Co., Inc.

Charleson, Andrew. Seismic Design for Architects. 2008. (ENG., Illus.). 296p. pap. 59.95 *(978-0-7506-8550-4(6))* Routledge.

Chueca, Pilar. Today's City Houses. 2009. (ENG.). 240p. pap. 29.99 *(978-84-96969-93-3(2))* Links International (Leading International Key Services Barcelona, S.A.) ESP. Dist: National Bk. Network.

Co, Us Gr Build. New Construction Reference Guide Version 2.2. 3rd ed. 2007. (Illus.). 422p. *(978-1-932444-06-3(8))* U. S. Green Building Council.

Constant, Caroline. Modern Architectural Landscape. 2012. 344p. pap. 30.00 ***(978-0-8166-7635-4(6))***; (Illus.). 90.00 ***(978-0-8166-7307-0(1))*** Univ. of Minnesota Pr.

Cook, Martin Godfrey. The Zero-Carbon House. 2011. (ENG., Illus.). 160p. 29.95 ***(978-1-84797-262-0(4))*** Crowood Pr., Ltd. GBR. Dist: Independent Pubs. Group.

Coppa, Alessandra & D'Amico, Fortunato. Culture-Nature: Green Ethics, Habit, Environment. 2010. (ITA., Illus.). 318p. *(978-88-572-0773-5(0))* Skira Editore.

Daniels, Klaus & Hamann, Ralph. Energy Design for the Post-Fossil Fuel Era. 2009. (GER & ENG., Illus.). 368p. 109.00 *(978-3-936681-25-3(2))* Edition Axel Menges GmbH DEU. Dist: National Bk. Network.

Dennis, Lori. Green Interior Design. 2010. (ENG., Illus.). 160p. pap. 24.95 *(978-1-58115-745-1(2)*, 115745, Allworth Pr.) Skyhorse Publishing Co., Inc.

Design Center Stuttgart Staff, ed. Focus Green: Internationaler Designpreis Baden-Württemberg 2008 und Mia Seeger Preis. 2008. (GER & ENG.). 220p. 78.00 *(978-3-89986-102-0(7)*, Avedition Gmbh,Csi) Continental Sales, Inc.

Dovey & Dovey, Kim. Becoming Places. 2008. (Illus.). xi, 201p. 165.00 *(978-0-415-41636-8(1))* Routledge.

—Becoming Places. 2008. (Illus.). xi, 201p. pap. 47.95 *(978-0-415-41637-5(X))* Routledge.

Drake, Scott. The Elements of Architecture: Principles of Environmental Performance in Buildings. 2009. (ENG., Illus.). 144p. 166.00 *(978-1-84407-716-8(0))* Routledge.

—The Third Skin: Architecture, Technology, & Environment. 2007. (ENG., Illus.). 224p. pap. 56.95 *(978-0-86840-631-3(6)*, UNSW Press) NewSouth Publishing AUS. Dist: Independent Pubs. Group.

Drake, Scott, et al. The Elements of Architecture: Principles of Environmental Performance in Buildings. 2009. (ENG., Illus.). 144p. pap. 48.95 *(978-1-84407-717-5(9))* Routledge.

Dubrau/Li Xiangning, Christian. Contemporary Green Buildings in China: Art & Architecture 2000 bis 2020, 1 vol. 2011. (ENG, GER & CHI., Illus.). 336p. 99.95 *(978-3-86922-128-1(3))* DOM Pubs. DEU. Dist: Innovative Logistics.

Dunster, Bill, et al. The Zed Book: Solutions for a Shrinking World. 2008. (ENG., Illus.). 276p. pap. 63.95 *(978-0-415-39199-3(7)*, Taylor & Francis) Taylor & Francis Group GBR. Dist: Taylor & Francis Group.

Duran, Sergi Costa. Eco House: Practical Ideas for a Greener, Healthier Dwelling. 2010. (ENG., Illus.). 160p. pap. 19.95 *(978-1-55407-782-3(6))* Firefly Bks., Ltd.

Duran, Sergi Costa & Duran, Sergi C. Green Homes: New Ideas for Sustainable Living. 2007. (ENG., Illus.). 192p. 35.00 *(978-0-06-134826-6(0)*, Collins Design) HarperCollins Pubs.

Emmitt, Stephen, ed. Design Management for Sustainability. 2009. (Architectural Engineering & Design Management Ser.). (ENG., Illus.). 104p. pap. 79.95 *(978-1-84407-895-0(7))* Routledge.

Enlow, Clair. The Architecture & Landscape Architecture of Jones & Jones: Living Places. 2007. (Landmarks Ser.). (ENG., Illus.). 88p. pap. 29.95 *(978-0-9749632-4-2(0))* Spacemaker Pr.

Erell, Evyatar, et al. Urban Microclimate: Designing the Spaces Between Buildings. 2010. (ENG., Illus.). 288p. 115.00 *(978-1-84407-467-9(6))* Routledge.

Fasli, Mukaddes. A Model for Sustaining City Identity. 2010. 352p. pap. *(978-3-639-25877-6(0))* VDM Verlag Dr. Mueller e.K.

First in a Series: Greening Washington & the National Capital Region: Hearing Before the Subcommittee on Economic Development, Public Buildings, & Emergency Management of the Committee on Transportation & Infrastructure, House of Representatives, One Hundred Tenth Congress, Second Session, April 17, 2008. 2008. ix, 101p. *(978-0-16-083277-2(2)*, 552-070-39105-3) United States Government Printing Office.

Fitzgibbon, Keith. Westland Road Culverts As Amphibian Conduits. 2008. 216p. pap. *(978-3-639-04671-7(4))* VDM Verlag Dr. Mueller e.K.

Gang, Jeanne. Reveal: Studio Gang Architects. 2011. (ENG., Illus.). 256p. pap. 45.00 *(978-1-56898-993-8(8))* Princeton Architectural Pr.

Garnham, Trevor & Thomas, Randall. Environmental Architecture Context. 2007. (Illus.). XIV, 242p. 165.00 *(978-0-415-36088-3(9)*, RU42668) Taylor & Francis Group.

—The Environments of Architecture. 2007. (Illus.). 233p. per. 44.95 *(978-0-415-36089-0(7)*, RU42669) Taylor & Francis Group.

Gauzin-Muller, Dominique, ed. Ecological Living. 2010. (ENG., Illus.). 412p. 65.00 *(978-2-7427-8322-9(9))* Actes Sud FRA. Dist: D.A.P./Distributed Art Pubs.

Ghirardo, Diane Yvonne. Italy: Modern Architectures in History. 2012. (Reaktion Books - Modern Architectures in History Ser.). (Illus.). 256p. pap. 29.95 *(978-1-86189-864-7(9))* Reaktion Bks., Ltd. GBR. Dist: Chicago Distribution Ctr.

Gissen, David. Subnature: Architecture's Other Environments. 2009. (ENG., Illus.). 240p. pap. 35.00 *(978-1-56898-777-4(3))* Princeton Architectural Pr.

Gissen, David, ed. Territory: Architecture Beyond Environment. 2010. (Architectural Design Ser.: 39). (ENG.). 136p. pap. 40.00 *(978-0-470-72165-0(0)*, Wiley) Wiley, John & Sons, Inc.

Green Homes. 2007. 192p. 35.00 *(978-0-06-149359-1(7)*, Collins Design) HarperCollins Pubs.

Guallart, Vicente, ed. Self-Sufficient City: Envisioning the habitat of the Future. 2010. 416p. pap. *(978-84-92861-33-0(9))* Actar Birkhauser Distribution.

Gutman, Robert, ed. People & Buildings. 2009. (ENG., Illus.). 492p. pap. 44.95 *(978-1-4128-0993-1(2))* Transaction Pubs.

Guy Nordenson and Associates Staff, et al. New Haiti Villages. 2010. (ENG., Illus.). 48p. pap. 19.95 *(978-1-56898-981-5(4))* Princeton Architectural Pr.

Guzowski, Mary. Towards Zero-Energy Architecture: New Solar Design. 2010. (ENG., Illus.). 208p. 45.00 *(978-1-85669-678-4(2))* King, Laurence Publishing GBR. Dist: Hachette Bk. Group.

Haghi, A. K. Advances in Geosciences & the Built Environment. 2009. (Illus.). vi, 194p. 129.00 *(978-1-60741-171-0(7))* Nova Science Pubs., Inc.

Harrison, Ariane Lourie, ed. Architectural Theories of the Environment: Posthuman Territory. 2012. (ENG., Illus.). (C). 155.00 ***(978-0-415-50618-2(2))***; pap. 44.95 ***(978-0-415-50619-9(0))*** Routledge.

Hawkes, Dean. Environment Imagination. 2007. (Illus.). 272p. 165.00 *(978-0-415-36086-9(2))* Taylor & Francis Group.

—The Environmental Imagination: Technics & Poetics of the Architectural Environment. 2007. (Illus.). 233p. per. 54.95 *(978-0-415-36087-6(0))* Taylor & Francis Group.

Heaney, Christopher. Cradle of Gold: The Story of Hiram Bingham, a Real-Life Indiana Jones, & the Search for Machu Picchu. 2011. (ENG., Illus.). 320p. pap. 17.00 *(978-0-230-11204-9(8))* Palgrave Macmillan.

Hensel, Michael & Menges, Achim. Versatility & Vicissitude: Performance in Morpho-Ecological Design. 2008. (Architectural Design Ser.). (ENG., Illus.). 144p. pap. 50.00 *(978-0-470-51687-4(9)*, Wiley) Wiley, John & Sons, Inc.

Hernandez, S., et al, eds. Eco-Architecture III: Harmonisation between Architecture & Nature. 2010. (WIT Transactions on Ecology & the Environment Ser.: 128). (Illus.). 624p. 474.00 *(978-1-84564-430-7(1))* WIT Pr GBR. Dist: WIT Pr.

Hewitt, Mischa & Telfer, Kevin. Earthships in Europe. 2nd rev. ed. 2012. (ENG., Illus.). 160p. pap. 49.95 ***(978-1-84806-236-8(2))*** Building Research Establishment GBR. Dist: Taylor & Francis Group.

IBA Hamburg, ed. Energy Atlas. 2011. (ENG., Illus.). 224p. pap. 39.95 *(978-3-86859-074-6(9))* Jovis Verlag GmbH DEU. Dist: D.A.P./Distributed Art Pubs.

Jodidio, Philip, ed. 100 Contemporary Houses: 25 Jahre TASCHEN, 2 vols. 2012. (25 Ser.). (ENG, FRE & GER., Illus.). 680p. 59.99 ***(978-3-8365-2330-1(2))*** TASCHEN DEU. Dist: Ingram Pub. Services.

Jovis, creator. Metropole: Bilden. 2010. (ENG., Illus.). 296p. pap. 55.00 *(978-3-86859-070-8(6))* Jovis Verlag GmbH DEU. Dist: D.A.P./Distributed Art Pubs.

Kalz, Doreen E. Heating & Cooling Concepts Employing Environmental Energy & Thermo-Active Building Systems: System Analysis & Optimization. 2011. (ENG., Illus.). 219p. pap. 47.72 *(978-3-8396-0176-1(2))* Fraunhofer IRB Verlag DEU. Dist: Silvermine International Bks., LLC.

Keeler, Marian, et al. Fundamentals of Integrated Design for Sustainable Building. 2009. (ENG., Illus.). 360p. 85.00 (978-0-470-15293-5(1), Wiley) Wiley, John & Sons, Inc.

Kellert, Stephen R., et al. Biophilic Design: The Theory, Science & Practice of Bringing Buildings to Life. 2008. (ENG., Illus.). 432p. 80.00 (978-0-470-16334-4(8), Wiley) Wiley, John & Sons, Inc.

Kenda, Barbara, ed. Aeolian Winds & the Spirit in Renaissance Architecture: Academia Eolia Revisited. 2006. (Illus.). 175p. 170.00 (978-0-415-39803-9(7)); per. 63.95 (978-0-415-39804-6(5)) Routledge.

Kuma, Kengo. Anti-Object: The Dissolution & Disintegration of Architecture, 4 vols. 2007. (Illus.). 200p. pap. (978-1-902902-52-4(1)) Architectural Assn.

Kwok, Alison & Grondzik, Walter. The Green Studio Handbook: Environmental Strategies for Schematic Design. 2nd rev. ed. 2011. (ENG., Illus.). 424p. pap. 75.95 (978-0-08-089052-4(0)) Routledge.

La Cecla, Franco. Against Architecture. 2012. (Green Arcade Ser.). (ENG.). 144p. pap. 14.95 (978-1-60486-406-9(0)) PM Pr.

Laiprakobsup, Narongpon. Inbetween Place. 2008. 160p. pap. (978-3-639-06378-3(3)) VDM Verlag Dr. Mueller e.K.

Langeteig, Kendra. The New Asian Home, 1 vol. 2008. (ENG., Illus.). 176p. 29.95 (978-1-4236-0046-6(0)) Gibbs Smith, Publisher.

Lewis, J. Owen. A Green Vitruvius - Second Edition: Principles & Practice of Sustainable Architectural Design. 2nd rev. ed. 2011. (ENG., Illus.). 152p. pap. 59.95 (978-1-84971-191-3(7)) Routledge.

Lewis, J. Owen & Brophy, Vivienne. A Green Vitruvius - Second Edition: Principles & Practice of Sustainable Architectural Design. 2nd rev. ed. 2011. (ENG., Illus.). 152p. 165.00 (978-1-84971-311-5(1)) Routledge.

Lydia, Kallipoliti, ed. EcoRedux: Design Remedies for an Ailing Planet. 2011. (Architectural Design Ser.: 40). (ENG., Illus.). 136p. pap. 40.00 (978-0-470-74662-2(9), Wiley) Wiley, John & Sons, Inc.

Maas, Winy, et al, texts. The Death of Leisure: Towards the Next Resort. 2012. (ENG., Illus.). 352p. pap. 45.00 (978-90-5662-766-9(X)) NAi Uitgevers / Publishers Stichting NLD. Dist: D.A.P./Distributed Art Pubs.

Marshall, Ulysses. Sustainability in Construction. 2011. (Illus.). 412p. 54.95 (978-0-566-08803-2(7), Gower Publishing Co., Ltd.) Ashgate Publishing, Ltd. GBR. Dist: Ashgate Publishing Co.

Mateo, Josep Lluis, ed. Natural Metaphor: An Anthology of Essays on Architecture & Nature. 2008. (Illus.). 240p. pap. (978-84-96954-08-3(0)) Actar Birkhauser Distribution.

Matzner, Florian, et al, eds. (Re)Designing Nature: Aktuelle Formen der Naturgestaltung in der Bildenden Kunst und Landschaftsarchitektur. 2011. (ENG., Illus.). 205p. pap. 45.00 (978-3-7757-2799-0(X)) Hatje Cantz Verlag GmbH & Co KG DEU. Dist: D.A.P./Distributed Art Pubs.

McClure, Wendy R. & Bartuska, Tom J., eds. The Built Environment: A Collaborative Inquiry into Design & Planning. 2nd ed. 2007. (ENG., Illus.). 424p. 75.00 (978-0-470-00752-5(4), Wiley) Wiley, John & Sons, Inc.

McGrath, Brian. Designing Patch Dynamics. 2008. (978-1-883584-47-4(7)) Columbia Univ., Graduate Schl. of Architecture.

Menges, Achim. Morpho-Ecologies: Towards Heterogeneous Space in Architectural Design. Hensel, Michael, ed. 2007. (Illus.). 366p. (978-1-902902-53-1(X)) Architectural Assn.

Miller, Kathryn. Public Libraries Going Green. 2010. (Illus.). 128p. (978-0-8389-1018-4(1)) American Library Assn.

Mithraratne, Nalanie, et al. Sustainable Living: The Role of Whole Life Costs & Values. 2007. (ENG., Illus.). 224p. (C). per. 54.95 (978-0-7506-8063-9(6)) Routledge.

Moirongo, Bernard Otoki. Urban Space Design & Environmental Management for Sustainable Cities. 2011. 352p. pap. (978-3-8443-1955-2(7)) Lambert Academic Publishing.

Molinari, Luca & d'Onofrio, Alessandro, eds. Sustainab. Italy: An Overview of Contemporary Italian Architecture focusing on Sustainability. 2010. 144p. pap. 35.95 (978-88-492-1480-2(4)) Gangemi ITA. Dist: International Publishers Marketing.

Mosco, Valerio Paolo. Naked Architecture. 2012. (ENG., Illus.). 320p. pap. 45.00 (978-88-572-0472-7(3)) Skira Editore ITA. Dist: Random Hse., Inc.

Neuhaus, Fabian, ed. Studies in Temporal Urbanism: The urbanTick Experiment. 2011. (ENG., Illus.). xxx, 283p. 139.00 (978-94-007-0936-2(6), 9400709366) Springer.

Nordenson, Guy, et al. On the Water: Palisade Bay, 1 vol. 2010. (ENG., Illus.). 320p. 50.00 (978-0-87070-785-8(X)) Museum of Modern Art.

Ong, Boon Lay. Beyond Environmental Comfort. 2009. pap. 62.95 (978-0-415-45369-1(0)) Taylor & Francis Group.

Oyarzún, Fernando Pérez, et al. Chilean Modern Architecture since 1950. Quantrill, Malcolm, ed. 2010. (Studies in Architecture & Culture Ser.). (ENG., Illus.). 192p. 45.00 (978-1-60344-135-3(2)) Texas A&M Univ. Pr.

Petschek, Peter & Gass, Siegfried, eds. Constructing Shadows: Tents, Pergolas, Cables, Plants. 2011. (Illus.). 256p. 84.95 (978-3-0346-0714-8(8)) Birkhauser Verlag AG CHE. Dist: Actar Birkhauser Distribution.

Poletto, Marco & Pasquero, Claudia. Systemic Architecture. 2012. (ENG., Illus.). 280p. (C). pap. 53.95 (978-0-415-59608-4(4)) Routledge.

—Systemic Architecture: Operating Manual for the Self Organizing City. 2012. (ENG., Illus.). 280p. (C). 165.00 (978-0-415-59607-7(6)) Routledge.

Quale, John D. Sustainable, Affordable, Prefab: The Ecomod Project. 2012. (ENG., Illus.). 248p. (C). (gr. 13-17). pap. 35.00 (978-0-8139-3233-0(5)); (gr. 17). 60.00 (978-0-8139-3152-4(5)) Univ. Pr. of Virginia.

Quillien, Jenny. Delight's Muse on Christopher Alexander's the Nature of Order: A Summary & Personal Interpretation. 2008. (Illus.). 186p. pap. 65.95 (978-1-4303-1317-5(X)) Lulu Enterprises Inc.

Radovic, Darko. Eco-Urbanity: Towards the Well-Mannered Built Environment. 2009. (ENG., Illus.). 264p. (C). 165.00 (978-0-415-47277-7(6)) Routledge.

Radovic, Darko, ed. Eco-Urbanity: Towards Well-Mannered Built Environments. 2009. (ENG., Illus.). 264p. (C). pap. 49.95 (978-0-415-47278-4(4)) Routledge.

Rahm, Philippe, et al. Environ(ne)ment: Manieres D'Agir Pour Demain/Approaches for Tomorrow. 2007. (ENG & FRE., Illus.). 160p. pap. 22.95 (978-88-7624-959-4(1)) Skira Editore ITA. Dist: Random Hse., Inc.

Rassia, Stamatina Th. & Pardalos, Panos M., eds. Sustainable Environmental Design in Architecture: Impacts on Health. 2011. (Springer Optimization & Its Applications Ser.). (ENG & FRE., Illus.). xviii, 336p. 149.00 (978-1-4419-0744-8(0), 1441907440) Springer.

Reinberg, Georg W. Ökologische Architektur: Entwurf, Planung, Ausführung. 2008. (ENG & GER., Illus.). 348p. (978-3-211-32770-8(3), 3211327703) Actar Birkhauser Distribution.

Richardson, Phyllis. XS Future: New Ideas, Small Structures. 2009. (ENG., Illus.). 224p. 29.95 (978-0-7893-2052-0(5)) Universe Publishing.

Roaf, Susan, ed. Transforming Markets in the Built Environment: Adapting to Climate Change. 2010. (Architectural Science Review Ser.). (ENG., Illus.). 140p. 120.00 (978-1-84971-088-6(0)) Routledge.

Roth, Manuela & Uphaus, Nicolas, eds. Ecological Design. 2008. (Illus.). 223p. pap. 12.95 (978-3-8327-9229-9(5)) teNeues Publishing Co.

Roy, Rob & Roy, Robert L. Stoneview: How to Build an Eco-Friendly Little Guesthouse. 2008. (ENG., Illus.). 240p. per. 25.95 (978-0-86571-597-4(1), 9780865715974) New Society Pubs., Ltd. CAN. Dist: Consortium Bk. Sales & Distribution.

Russ, Thomas & Russ, Thomas H. Site Planning & Design. 2nd ed. 2009. (ENG., Illus.). 528p. instr.'s hndbk. ed. 99.95 (978-0-07-160558-8(4), 0071605584) McGraw-Hill Professional Publishing.

Ryker, Lori. Off the Grid Homes: Case Studies for Sustainable Living, 1 vol. 2007. (ENG., Illus.). 128p. pap. 24.99 (978-1-58685-689-2(8)) Gibbs Smith, Publisher.

Salama Muhaisen, Ahmed. Solar Performance of Courtyard Buildings. 2010. 308p. pap. (978-3-639-27015-0(0)) VDM Verlag Dr. Mueller e.K.

Santini, Claudio & Zilafro, Dafna. Green Is Beautiful: The Eco-Friendly House. 2009. (ENG., Illus.). 216p. 60.00 (978-1-86470-325-2(3)) Images Publishing Group AUS. Dist: National Bk. Network.

Schools Design Forum Workshop. 2011. (ENG., Illus.). 16p. pap. 25.00 (978-1-86081-943-8(5)) Building Research Establishment GBR. Dist: Taylor & Francis Group.

Shove, Elizabeth, et al, eds. Comfort in a Lower Carbon Society. 2009. (Building Research & Information Ser.). (ENG.). 136p. (C). 125.00 (978-0-415-55089-5(0)) Routledge.

Slavid, Ruth. Extreme Architecture: Building for Challenging Environments. 2009. (ENG., Illus.). 208p. 40.00 (978-1-85669-609-8(X)) King, Laurence Publishing GBR. Dist: Hachette Bk. Group.

Smith, David Lee. Environmental Issues for Architecture. 2011. (ENG., Illus.). 608p. 85.00 (978-0-470-49709-8(2), Wiley) Wiley, John & Sons, Inc.

Smith, Peter. Sustainability at the Cutting Edge: Emerging Technologies for Low Energy Buildings. 2nd rev. ed. 2007. (ENG., Illus.). 196p. pap. 51.95 (978-0-7506-8300-5(7)) Routledge.

Speiregen, Paul & Wertheimer, Lester. Site Planning & Design 2009. 2008. (ENG.). 192p. pap. 111.95 (978-1-4277-7041-7(7)) Kaplan Publishing.

Stang, Alanna & Hawthorne, Christopher. The Green House: New Directions in Sustainable Architecture. 2010. (ENG., Illus.). 192p. pap. 24.95 (978-1-56898-950-1(4)) Princeton Architectural Pr.

Steiner, Frederick. Design for a Vulnerable Planet. 2011. (ENG., Illus.). 304p. 45.00 (978-0-292-72385-6(7)) Univ. of Texas Pr.

Strongman, Cathy. The Sustainable Home: The Essential Guide to Eco Building, Renovation & Decoration. 2008. (Illus.). 208p. 34.95 (978-1-85894-430-2(9)) Merrell Pubs. Ltd. GBR. Dist: Perseus Distribution.

Tompazes, Alexandros N. Oikologike Skepse & Architektonike. 2010. (GRE., Illus.). 200p. (C). 85.00 (978-960-204-308-0(3)) Ekdotikos Oikos Melissa GRC. Dist: ISD.

Topp, Leslie, et al, eds. Madness, Architecture & the Built Environment: Psychiatric Spaces in Historial Context. 2007. (Routledge Studies in the Social History of Medicine: Vol. 27). (Illus.). 346p. 156.00 (978-0-415-37529-0(0)) Routledge.

Triviño, Santi. Eco Refurbishment. Minguet, Josep M. & Trivino, Santi, eds. 2010. (SPA., Illus.). 96p. pap. 22.50 (978-84-96823-85-3(7)) Instituto Monsa de Ediciones, S.A. ESP. Dist: Trans-Atlantic Pubns., Inc.

Turenscape Architects Staff, contrib. by. The Art of Survival. 2011. (Illus.). 256p. 39.99 (978-84-9936-861-0(1)) Loft Pubns. ESP. Dist: Prestel Publishing.

Van Lengen, Johan & van Lengen, Johan. The Barefoot Architect: A Handbook for Green Building. 2007. (ENG., Illus.). 704p. pap. 17.95 (978-0-936070-42-1(0)) Shelter Pubns., Inc.

Wanek, Catherine. The Hybrid House: Designing with Sun, Wind, Water, & Earth, 1 vol. 2010. (ENG., Illus.). 144p. 24.99 (978-1-4236-0316-0(8)) Gibbs Smith, Publisher.

Wasiuta, Mark, ed. Environments & Counter-Environments: Experimental Media in Italy: the New Domestic Landscape, MoMA 1972. 2011. 288p. pap. (978-84-92861-98-9(3)) Actar Birkhauser Distribution.

Weiss, Marion & Manfredi, Michael A. Surface/Subsurface. 2007. (ENG., Illus.). 208p. 60.00 (978-1-56898-733-0(1)) Princeton Architectural Pr.

Wilhide, Elizabeth. Eco: An Essential Sourcebook for Environmentallu Friendly Design & Decoration. (Illus.). 184p. 44.95 (978-1-903845-74-5(2)) Quadrille Publishing, Ltd. GBR. Dist: Graphic Arts Ctr. Publishing Co.

Woolley, Tom. Natural Building: A Guide to Materials & Techniques. 2006. (ENG., Illus.). 192p. 45.00 (978-1-86126-841-9(6)) Crowood Pr., Ltd. GBR. Dist: Independent Pubs. Group.

Yeang, Ken. Ecodesign: A Manual for Ecological Design. 2008. (ENG., Illus.). 500p. pap. 65.00 (978-0-470-99778-9(8), Wiley) Wiley, John & Sons, Inc.

Zardini, Mirko, et al. En Imparfaite Santé: La Médicalisation de L'architecture, 1 vol. 2012. (FRE & ENG.). 300p. 70.00 (978-3-03778-284-2(6)) Lars Muller Pubs. CHE. Dist: Prestel Publishing.

—Imperfect Health: The Medicalization of Architecture, 1 vol. 2012. (ENG., Illus.). 300p. 70.00 (978-3-03778-279-8(X)) Lars Muller Pubs. CHE. Dist: Prestel Publishing.

Zaretsky, Michael. Precedents in Zero-Energy Design: Architecture & Passive Design in the 2007 Solar Decathlon. 2009. (ENG., Illus.). 240p. (C). 165.00 (978-0-415-77874-9(3)); pap. 44.95 (978-0-415-77875-6(1)) Routledge.

ARCHITECTURE—EXAMINATIONS, QUESTIONS, ETC.

Aymer, Valerie. Landscape Grading: A Study Guide for the LARE Grading Examination. 2010. 165p. pap. 50.00 (978-0-557-38507-2(5)) Lulu Enterprises Inc.

Ballast, David Kent. Interior Design in a Flash: Rapid Review of Key Topics for the NCIDQ Exam. 2010. (ENG.). 400p. pap. 56.00 (978-1-59126-316-6(6)) Professional Pubns., Inc.

—Interior Design Reference Manual: Everything You Need to Know to Pass the NCIDQ Exam. 5th ed. 2010. (ENG.). 592p. pap. 176.00 (978-1-59126-304-3(2)) Professional Pubns., Inc.

—NCIDQ Section 1 Sample Questions & Practice Exam. 2010. (ENG.). 122p. pap. 88.00 (978-1-59126-306-7(9)) Professional Pubns., Inc.

—NCIDQ Section 2 Sample Questions & Practice Exam. 2010. (ENG.). 114p. pap. 44.00 (978-1-59126-308-1(5)) Professional Pubns., Inc.

—NCIDQ Section 3 Practice Exam for the Interior Design Practicum. 2010. (ENG.). 109p. 104.00 (978-1-59126-310-4(7)) Professional Pubns., Inc.

—Schematic Design: ARE Sample Problems & Practice Exam. 2008. (ENG., Illus.). 76p. pap. 120.00 (978-1-59126-125-4(2)) Professional Pubns., Inc.

Ballast, David Kent & O'Hara, PE, Steven E. ARE Review Manual. 2nd ed. 2011. 744p. pap. 320.00 (978-1-59126-322-7(0)) 2010. (ENG.). 800p. pap. 336.00 (978-1-59126-321-0(2)) Professional Pubns., Inc.

Ballast, FAIA, NCIDQ-Cert. #9425, David Kent. Site Planning & Design: ARE Sample Problems & Practice Exam. 2nd ed. 2008. (ENG.). 94p. pap. 120.00 (978-1-59126-154-4(6)) Professional Pubns., Inc.

Buckner, C. Dale. Concrete Design for the Civil & Structural PE Exams. 2007. (ENG., Illus.). 184p. per. 120.00 (978-1-59126-114-8(7)) Professional Pubns., Inc.

Chen, Gang. Leed Bd & C Exam Guide: A Must-Have for the Leed Ap Bd+C Exam: Comprehensive Study Materials, Sample Questions, Mock Exam, Green Building Design & Construction, Leed Certification, & Sustainability (Leed V3. 0) 2009. 258p. pap. 99.95 (978-1-4327-4572-1(7)) Outskirts Pr., Inc.

—Leed Ga Exam Guide: A Must-Have for the LEED Green Associate Exam. 2009. 398p. pap. 73.95 (978-1-4327-4168-6(3)) Outskirts Pr., Inc.

Cottrell, Michelle. Guide to the Leed Green Associate Exam. 2010. (ENG., Illus.). 208p. pap., instr.'s gde. ed. 55.00 (978-0-470-60829-6(3), Wiley) Wiley, John & Sons, Inc.

Hardt, John. Building Systems Question & Answer 2009. annuals 2008. (ENG.). 48p. pap. 49.95 (978-1-4277-7032-5(8)) Kaplan Publishing.

—Construction Documents & Services Question & Answer 2009. 2008. (ENG.). 48p. pap. 49.95 (978-1-4277-7035-6(2)) Kaplan Publishing.

—Programming, Planning & Practice Question & Answer 2009. annuals 2008. (ENG.). 56p. pap. 49.95 (978-1-4277-7033-2(6)) Kaplan Publishing.

Hubka, David. LEED GA Practice Exams: Green Associate. 2009. (ENG.). 96p. pap. 48.00 (978-1-59126-179-7(1)) Professional Pubns., Inc.

—LEED O&M Practice Exam: Operations & Maintenance. 2009. (ENG.). 102p. (C). pap. 40.00 (978-1-59126-181-0(3)) Professional Pubns., Inc.

Hubka, David & Valtcheva-McGee, Vessela. LEED Homes Practice Exam. 2009. (ENG.). 94p. pap. 40.00 (978-1-59126-183-4(X)) Professional Pubns., Inc.

Hurdt, John. Structural Systems Question & Answer 2009. 2008. (ENG.). 208p. pap. 49.95 (978-1-4277-7034-9(4)) Kaplan Publishing.

Kornblut, Arthur & Wertheimer, Lester. Construction Documents & Services 2009. 2008. (ENG.). 336p. pap. 111.95 (978-1-4277-7038-7(7)) Kaplan Publishing.

LEED Exam Secrets Test Prep Staff, ed. LEED AP Building Design + Construction Exam Secrets Study Guide: LEED Test Review for the Leadership in Energy & Environmental Design Exam. 2011. (C). 91.99 (978-1-61403-580-0(6)) Mometrix Media LLC.

—LEED Green Associate Exam Practice Questions: LEED Practice Tests & Review for the Leadership in Energy & Environmental Design Exam. 2011. (C). 34.99 (978-1-61403-582-4(2)) Mometrix Media LLC.

Leppo, RA/CID, LEED AP, Holly Williams. LEED Prep Homes: What You Really Need to Know to Pass the LEED AP Homes Exam. 2009. (ENG.). 360p. pap. 48.00 (978-1-59126-182-7(1)) Professional Pubns., Inc.

—LEED Prep ID&C: What You Really Need to Know to Pass the LEED AP Interior Design & Construction Exam. 2009. (ENG.). 356p. pap. 48.00 (978-1-59126-186-5(4)) Professional Pubns., Inc.

Leppo, RA/CID, LEED AP, Holly Williams & Ballast, David Kent. Construction Documents & Services: ARE Sample Problems & Practice Exam. 2nd ed. 2011. (ENG.). 114p. pap. 120.00 (978-1-59126-323-4(9)) Professional Pubns., Inc.

—Programming, Planning & Practice: ARE Sample Problems & Practice Exam. 2nd ed. 2010. (ENG.). 102p. pap. 120.00 (978-1-59126-327-2(1)) Professional Pubns., Inc.

Leppo, RA/CID, LEED AP, Holly Williams, et al. LEED Prep BD&C: What You Really Need to Know to Pass the LEED AP Building Design & Construction Exam. 2009. (ENG.). 392p. pap. 48.00 (978-1-59126-184-1(8)) Professional Pubns., Inc.

LinguaForum Research Center Staff. Biology, Archeology, & Anthropology Vol. 3, Vol. 3. 2007. (TOEFL Practice Test Ser.). (ENG., Illus.). 159p. pap. (978-89-556-3091-6(3)) Linguaforum Co., Ltd.

Passman, Charles C. LEED v3 & BD&C Study Guide: Summary of LEED v3 & BD&C Prerequisites & Credits. 2009. (ENG.). 103p. (C). pap. 64.00 (978-0-615-31202-6(0)) Professional Pubns., Inc.

Peot, M Ed, Meghan & Schumacher, LEED AP, Brennan. LEED BD&C Practice Exam: Building Design & Construction. 2009. (ENG.). 112p. pap. 40.00 (978-1-59126-185-8(6)) Professional Pubns., Inc.

Peot, Meghan & Schumacher, Brennan. LEED NC Practice Problems: New Construction. 2007. (ENG., Illus.). 96p. per. 98.00 (978-1-59126-118-6(X)) Professional Pubns., Inc.

Saeger, LEED AP, Brad. LEED BD&C Flashcards: Building Design & Construction. 2009. (ENG.). 473p. pap. 32.00 (978-0-9801638-7-2(0)) Professional Pubns., Inc.

—LEED Homes Flashcards. 2009. (ENG.). 312p. pap. 32.00 (978-0-9801638-6-5(2)) Professional Pubns., Inc.

—LEED ID&C Flashcards: Interior Design & Construction. 2009. (ENG.). 370p. pap. 40.00 (978-0-9801638-8-9(9)) Professional Pubns., Inc.

Shahfar, Shawn. Leedpass. 2007. 0.01 net. (978-1-60402-004-5(0)) Independent Pub.

Speiregen, Paul & Wertheimer, Lester. Programming, Planning & Practice 2009. 2008. (ENG.). 376p. pap. 111.95 (978-1-4277-7039-4(5)) Kaplan Publishing.

Wertheimer, Lester, et al. Architecture History 2009. 2008. (ENG.). 208p. pap. 59.95 (978-1-4277-7824-6(8)) Kaplan Publishing.

Woodson, R. Dodge. National Contractor's Exam Study Guide. Roy, Jane L., ed. 2007. (ENG., Illus.). 358p. per. 39.95 (978-0-07-148907-2(X), 007148907X) McGraw-Hill Professional Publishing.

ARCHITECTURE—HANDBOOKS, MANUALS, ETC.

American Institute of Architects Staff. The Architecture Student's Handbook of Professional Practice. 14th ed. 2008. (ENG., Illus.). 720p. pap., stu. ed., instr.'s hndbk. ed. 115.00 (978-0-470-08869-2(9), Wiley) Wiley, John & Sons, Inc.

Chappell, David. Standard Letters in Architectural Practice. 4th rev. ed. 2008. (ENG.). 368p. 119.99 (978-1-4051-7965-2(1), Wiley-Blackwell) Wiley, John & Sons, Inc.

Demkin, Joseph A. The Architect's Handbook of Professional Practice. Demkin, Joseph A., ed. 14th ed. 2008. (ENG., Illus.). 1040p. 250.00 (978-0-470-00957-4(8), Wiley) Wiley, John & Sons, Inc.

Deplazes, Andrea, ed. Constructing Architecture: Materials, Processes, Structures. Söffker, G. H., tr. from GER. 2nd ed. 2008. (Illus.). 555p. pap., instr.'s hndbk. ed. 69.95 (978-3-7643-8631-3(2), 3764386312) Springer.

Kormoss, Bernard & Caldeira, Marta. Eisenmanual. 2006. (Illus.). 528p. 58.00 (978-3-03778-081-7(9)) Springer.

Littlefield, David. Metric Handbook. 4th rev. ed. 2012. (ENG., Illus.). 880p. pap. 82.95 (978-1-85617-806-8(4)) Routledge.

Meacham, Brian J., et al. Egress Design Solutions: A Guide to Evacuation & Crowd Management Planning. 2007. (ENG., Illus.). 544p. 125.00 (978-0-471-71956-4(0), Wiley) Wiley, John & Sons, Inc.

Neufert, Ernst, et al. Architects' Data. 4th ed. 2012. (ENG., Illus.). 608p. pap. 99.95 (978-1-4051-9253-8(4), Wiley-Blackwell) Wiley, John & Sons, Inc.

Ross, Ann & Hetreed, Jonathan. Architect's Pocket Book. 4th rev. ed. 2011. (ENG., Illus.). 368p. (C). pap. 34.95 (978-0-08-096959-6(3)) Routledge.

Watts, Andrew. Modern Construction Handbook. 2nd ed. 2009. (Modern Construction Ser.). (ENG., Illus.). 504p. 129.00 (978-3-211-99195-4(6), 3211991956) Springer.

ARCHITECTURE—HISTORY

Abalos, Inaki. Coup de Des 4: What's New? Searching for Clues. 2010. 92p. pap. 26.95 (978-84-936901-2-0(0)) Fundacio Mies Van Der Rohe ESP. Dist: Actar Birkhauser Distribution.

Abel, Chris. Sky High: Vertical Architecture. 2008. (ENG.). 120p. 22.00 (978-1-4223-9345-1(3)) DIANE Publishing Co.

Alfoldy, Sandra. The Allied Arts: Architecture & Craft in Postwar Canada. 2012. (McGill-Queen's/Beaverbrook Canadian Foundation Studies in Art History Ser.). (ENG., Illus.). 264p. (C). (978-0-7735-3960-0(3)); pap. (978-0-7735-4003-3(2)) McGill-Queen's Univ. Pr.

Altabe, Joan. Architecture Behind the Scenes. 2009. 280p. pap. 15.99 (978-1-59092-368-9(5), Full Spectrum Information Library) Orchard House Pr.

Architectural League of New York Staff. Resonance. 2009. (ENG., Illus.). 176p. pap. 24.95 (978-1-56898-809-2(5)) Princeton Architectural Pr.

—Young Architects 12: Resource. 2011. (ENG., Illus.). 176p. pap. 24.95 (978-1-56898-998-3(9)) Princeton Architectural Pr.

Argentero, Francesca, ed. Lost in Nature: Jarmund/Vignaes AS Arkitekter (MNAL) 2010. 64p. pap. 23.95 (978-88-492-1476-5(6)) Gangemi ITA. Dist: International Publishers Marketing.

Aslet, Clive. The Edwardian Country House. rev. ed. 2012. (ENG., Illus.). 288p. 50.00 (978-0-7112-3339-3(X)) Lincoln, Frances Ltd. GBR. Dist: Perseus-PGW.

Avidar, Pnina, et al, eds. Posities/Positions, 1 vol. 2006. (ENG., Illus.). 144p. pap. 25.00 *(978-90-5662-486-6(5))* NAi Uitgevers / Publishers Stichting NLD. Dist: D.A.P./Distributed Art Pubs.

Ball, Philip. Universe of Stone: Chartres Cathedral & the Invention of the Gothic. 2009. (ENG.). 336p. pap. 15.99 *(978-0-06-115430-0(X)*, HarperPerennial) HarperCollins Pubs.

Bayard, Emile. Universe of Style: Architecture & Furniture. 2012. (Temporis Ser.). (ENG., Illus.). 256p. 39.95 *(978-1-84484-880-5(9))* Parkstone Pr. USA, Ltd.

Belfoure, Charles. Edmund G. Lind: Anglo-American Architect of Baltimore & the South. 2009. (Illus.). 203p. pap. 27.95 *(978-0-9729743-2-5(6))* Baltimore Architecture Foundation.

Bo Jensen, Thomas. P. V. Jensen-Klint. 2009. (ENG., Illus.). 504p. (C). 125.00 *(978-0-415-55318-6(0))* Routledge.

Borden, Daniel, et al. Architecture: A World History. 2008. (ENG., Illus.). 512p. pap. 22.50 *(978-0-8109-9512-3(3))* Abrams.

Bork, Robert & Mcgehee, Abby. New Approaches to Medieval Architecture. 2011. (AVISTA Studies in the History of Medieval Technology, Science & Art Ser.). (Illus.). 258p. 119.95 *(978-1-4094-2228-0(3))* Ashgate Publishing Co.

Bragdon, Claude. The Beautiful Necessity. 2008. 64p. pap. *(978-1-4099-0732-9(5))* Dodo Pr.

Brandino, Alessandro. Le Stazioni Ferroviarie Di Messina: Dalla Realizzazione Ottocentesca All'intervento Di Angiolo Mazzoni. 2007. (ITA., Illus.). 207p. *(978-88-7758-807-4(1))* Dario, Flaccovio.

Braun Publishing. 1000x European Architecture. 2nd rev. ed. 2011. (ENG., Illus.). 1024p. 125.00 ***(978-3-03768-087-2(3)***, Braun Publish,Csi) Continental Sales, Inc.

Bridgwood, Barry & Lennie, Lindsay. History, Performance & Conservation. 2009. (Technologies of Architecture Ser.). (ENG., Illus.). 352p. (C). 165.00 *(978-0-415-43419-5(X))*; pap. 49.95 *(978-0-415-43420-1(3))* Taylor & Francis Group GBR. (Taylor & Francis). Dist: Taylor & Francis Group.

Brooklyn Museum Staff. Two Dutch Houses: Tradition & Change in Early New York: The Schenck Houses at the Brooklyn Museum. Date not set. *(978-0-87273-123-3(5))* Brooklyn Museum, The.

Butti, Ken & Perlin, John. A Golden Thread: 2500 Years of Solar Architecture & Technology. 2nd rev. ed. Date not set. (Illus.). *(978-0-937948-12-5(8))*; pap. *(978-0-937948-13-2(6))* aatec Pubns.

Cain, William. A Practical Theory of Voussoir Arches. 2010. 138p. pap. 27.45 *(978-1-4455-5211-8(6))* Audubon Pr. & Christian Bk. Service.

Campitelli, Alberta. The Vatican Gardens: An Architectural & Horticultural History. 2009. (ENG., Illus.). 352p. 125.00 *(978-0-7892-1048-7(7))* Abbeville Pr., Inc.

Carré, Dominique. Euralille: Chroniques D'une Métropole en Mutation (1988-2008) 2008. (FRE., Illus.). 180p. pap. *(978-2-915755-16-9(7))* Carre, Dominique editeur.

Carroll, Rutter. Ryder & Yates. 2009. (Twentieth-century Architects Ser.). (ENG., Illus.). 160p. (C). pap. 40.00 *(978-1-85946-266-9(9))* English Heritage GBR. Dist: Brown, David Bk. Co., The.

Castro, Ricardo L. Rogelio Salmona: Tributo. 2009. (SPA.). 200p. 69.50 *(978-958-8306-15-5(9))* Villegas Editores S.A. COL. Dist: Independent Pubs. Group.

Cattermole, Paul. Architectural Excellence: 500 Iconic Buildings. 2008. (ENG., Illus.). 512p. 49.95 *(978-1-55407-358-0(8))* Firefly Bks., Ltd.

Chyutin, Michael & Chyutin, Bracha. Architecture & Utopia: The Israeli Experiment. 2007. (Design & the Built Environment Ser.). (Illus.). 264p. 124.95 *(978-0-7546-4831-4(1))* Ashgate Publishing Co.

Colomina, Beatri, ed. Clip, Stamp, Fold. 2010. (Illus.). 390p. pap. *(978-84-96954-52-6(8))* Actar Birkhauser Distribution.

Cooper, Graham. Project Japan: Architecture & Art Media Edo to Now. 2009. (ENG., Illus.). 240p. 60.00 *(978-1-86470-309-2(1))* Images Publishing Group AUS. Dist: National Bk. Network.

Costa, Xavier. Coup de Des 1: Housing & Public Space. 2010. 109p. pap. 26.95 *(978-84-920495-9-2(6))* Fundacio Mies Van Der Rohe ESP. Dist: Actar Birkhauser Distribution.

Craig, Robert M. The Architecture of Francis Palmer Smith Atlanta's Scholar Architect. 2012. (ENG.). 296p. 60.00 ***(978-0-8203-2898-0(7))*** Univ. of Georgia Pr.

Cram101 Textbook Reviews. Outlines & Highlights for a History of Architecture: Settings & Rituals by Kostof, ISBN. 2011. 648p. pap. 41.95 ***(978-1-61812-817-1(5))*** Cram101 Inc.

—Outlines & Highlights for Buildings Across Time: An Introduction to World Architecture by Michael W. Fazio, ISBN. 2010. 164p. pap. 29.95 *(978-1-61654-051-7(6))* Cram101 Inc.

—Outlines & Highlights for Global History of Architecture by Francis D K Ching, Vikramaditya Prakash, Mark M Jarzombek. 2011. 408p. pap. 35.95 ***(978-1-61906-125-5(2))*** Cram101 Inc.

—Outlines & Highlights for Understanding Architecture: Its Elements, History, & Meaning by Leland Roth. 2011. 162p. pap. 29.95 ***(978-1-61906-126-2(0))*** Cram101 Inc.

—Outlines & Highlights for World History of Architecture by Michael Fazio. 2011. 360p. pap. 34.95 ***(978-1-61906-091-3(4))*** Cram101 Inc.

Cryder, Jo. Towers, Turrets, Cupolas, & Belvederes. 2008. (Illus.). 160p. pap. 34.99 *(978-0-7643-2963-0(4))* Schiffer Publishing, Ltd.

Damluji, Salma Samar, et al. The Architecture of Yemen: From Yafi to Hadramut. 2008. (ENG., Illus.). 304p. 85.00 *(978-1-85669-514-5(X))* King, Laurence Publishing GBR. Dist: Hachette Bk. Group.

Dietz, Adalbert K. Snippets of St. Louis. 2008. 96p. pap. 9.99 *(978-1-933370-69-9(6))* Reedy Pr.

Donin, Gianpiero, ed. Renzo Piano: Piece by Piece. 2010. 163p. pap. 27.95 *(978-88-7448-010-4(5))* Gangemi ITA. Dist: International Publishers Marketing.

Dorenbach Architekten Staff, contrib. by. Arbeiten 1971-2009. 2010. (GER., Illus.). 351p. *(978-3-7245-1664-4(9))* Reinhardt, Friedrich AG.

Duindam, Jeroen Frans Jozef, et al. Royal Courts in Dynastic States & Empires: A Global Perspective. 2011. (Illus.). xvi, 444p. ***(978-90-04-20622-9(1))*** BRILL.

Ergut, Elvan Altan, et al, eds. Rethinking Architectural Historiography. 2006. (Illus.). 251p. per. 71.95 *(978-0-415-36085-2(4)*, RU42667) Routledge.

Fazio, Michael, et al. Buildings across Time: An Introduction to World Architecture. 3rd ed. 2008. (ENG., Illus.). 608p. (C). pap. 123.00 *(978-0-07-305304-2(X)*, 007305304X) McGraw-Hill Cos., The.

—A World History of Architecture. 2nd ed. 2008. (ENG., Illus.). 608p. 110.00 *(978-0-07-154479-5(8)*, 0071544798) McGraw-Hill Professional Publishing.

Finsterwalder, Rudolf. Alvaro Siza: Von der Linie zum Raum / From Line to Space. 2011. 120p. pap. 39.95 ***(978-3-7091-0853-6(5))*** Springer Wien AUT. Dist: Actar Birkhauser Distribution.

Fougeron, Anne. Fougeron Architecture: Opposition/Composition. 2011. (ENG., Illus.). 192p. pap. 40.00 *(978-1-56898-990-7(3))* Princeton Architectural Pr.

Garrison, J. Ritchie. Two Carpenters: Architecture & Building in Early New England, 1799-1859. 2006. (Illus.). 240p. 48.95 *(978-1-57233-485-4(1))* Univ. of Tennessee Pr.

Gauzin-Müller, Dominique & Ayers, Andrew. Jean-Yves Barrier: Architect & Urbanist, Architecte et Urbaniste. 2009. (Work Monographs). (ENG & FRE., Illus.). 176p. 109.00 *(978-3-932565-24-3(X))* Edition Axel Menges GmbH DEU. Dist: National Bk. Network.

Ghirardo, Diane Yvonne. Italy: Modern Architectures in History. 2012. (Reaktion Books - Modern Architectures in History Ser.). (Illus.). 256p. pap. 29.95 *(978-1-86189-864-7(9))* Reaktion Bks., Ltd. GBR. Dist: Chicago Distribution Ctr.

Giedion, Sigfried & Giedion, S. Space, Time & Architecture: The Growth of a New Tradition. 5th rev. enl. ed. 2009. (Charles Eliot Norton Lectures). (Illus.). 960p. pap. 44.00 *(978-0-674-03047-3(8))* Harvard Univ. Pr.

Goodman, Donna. A History of the Future. 2008. (ENG., Illus.). 280p. 45.00 *(978-1-58093-207-3(X))* Monacelli Pr., Inc.

Gray, Fred. Designing the Seaside: Architecture, Society & Nature. 2006. (Illus.). 400p. 60.00 *(978-1-86189-274-4(8))* Reaktion Bks., Ltd. GBR. Dist: Chicago Distribution Ctr.

Gympel, Jan. Story of Architecture. 2008. (Story of Ser.). 128p. pap. 9.95 *(978-0-8416-0191-8(7))* American Map Corp.

Haeusler, M. Hank. Media Facades: History, Technology & Content. 2009. (ENG., Illus.). 250p. 69.00 *(978-3-89986-107-5(8)*, Avedition Gmbh,Csi) Continental Sales, Inc.

Hajiyeva, Sabina. Architecture of the North-Western District of Azerbaijan. 2011. 112p. pap. ***(978-3-8443-1470-0(9))*** Lambert Academic Publishing.

Hale, Jonathan. Merleau-Ponty for Architects. 2010. (Thinkers for Architects Ser.). (ENG., Illus.). 128p. 28.95 *(978-0-415-48072-7(8))* Routledge.

Hall, Michael. Lasting Elegance: English Country Houses 1830-1900. 2009. (ENG., Illus.). 192p. 65.00 *(978-1-58093-256-1(8))* Monacelli Pr., Inc.

Hamlin, A. D. F. History of Architecture. 30.00 *(978-0-8196-2873-2(5))* Biblo & Tannen Booksellers & Pubs., Inc.

Harbison, Robert. Travels in the History of Architecture. (ENG., Illus.). 2011. 288p. pap. 24.95 *(978-1-86189-818-0(5))* 2009. 224p. 35.00 *(978-1-86189-435-9(X))* Reaktion Bks., Ltd. GBR. Dist: Chicago Distribution Ctr.

Harris, Ann Sutherland. Seventeenth Century Art & Architecture. 2nd ed. 2007. (ENG., Illus.). 456p. (C). per. 135.00 *(978-0-13-603372-1(5)*, Prentice Hall) Prentice Hall PTR.

Harwood, Buie, et al. Architecture & Interior Design from the 19th Century Vol. 2: An Integrated History. 2008. (ENG.). 1040p. 157.47 *(978-0-13-093538-5(4)*, Prentice Hall) Prentice Hall PTR.

Hatherley, Owen. A Guide to the New Ruins of Great Britain. 2011. (ENG., Illus.). 400p. pap. 19.95 *(978-1-84467-700-9(1)*, 844700) Verso Bks. GBR. Dist: Norton, W. W. & Co., Inc.

Healy, Brian. Brian Healy: Commonplaces. 2008. (ENG., Illus.). 110p. pap. 24.95 *(978-0-9793801-7-4(0))* Oro Editions.

Hess, Jeffrey A. & Larson, Paul Clifford. St. Paul's Architecture: A History. 2008. (Illus.). 304p. pap. 24.95 *(978-0-8166-3591-7(9))* Univ. of Minnesota Pr.

Hildebrand, Grant. Suyama: A Complex Serenity. 2011. (ENG., Illus.). 176p. 75.00 *(978-0-295-99081-1(3))* Univ. of Washington Pr.

History of Architecture. 2008. 336p. *(978-1-4075-2403-0(8))* Parragon, Inc.

Home, Clothes, Food. 2008. 428p. 245.00 *(978-0-415-46283-9(5))* Routledge.

Hornstein, Shelley. Losing Site: Architecture Memory & Place. 2011. (Ashgate Studies in Architecture Ser.). (Illus.). 182p. 89.95 ***(978-1-4094-0871-0(X))*** Ashgate Publishing Co.

Irving, Mark, ed. 1001 Buildings You Must See Before You Die: The World's Architectural Masterpieces. 2007. (Quintessence Bks.). (ENG., Illus.). 960p. 36.95 *(978-0-7893-1564-9(5))* Universe Publishing.

Isozaki, Arata, ed. Katsura: Imperial Villa. 2011. (ENG., Illus.). 402p. pap. 49.95 ***(978-0-7148-6254-5(1))*** Phaidon Pr., Inc.

Izenour, Steven & Hirshorn, Paul. White Towers. 2007. (ENG., Illus.). 208p. (gr. 17). 24.95 *(978-0-262-08368-3(X))* MIT Pr.

Jarzombek, Mark M. & Prakash, Vikramaditya. A Global History of Architecture. 2nd ed. 2010. (ENG., Illus.). 864p. 95.00 *(978-0-470-40257-3(1)*, Wiley) Wiley, John & Sons, Inc.

Kennedy, Roger G. Greek Revival America. 2010. (ENG., Illus.). 456p. 75.00 *(978-0-8478-3184-5(1))* Rizzoli International Pubns., Inc.

Klich, Lynda & Mogul, Jonathan, eds. The Journal of Decorative & Propaganda Arts: Mexico Theme Issue, Issue 26. 2010. 304p. pap. 50.00 *(978-1-930776-18-0(7))* Wolfson Foundation of Decorative & Propaganda Arts, Inc., The.

Knauer, Kelly & Time Magazine Editors. Great Buildings: The World's Most Influential, Inspiring & Astonishing Structures. 2010. (ENG., Illus.). 160p. 29.95 *(978-1-60320-161-2(0)*, Time Bks.) Time Home Entertainment, Inc.

Krieger, Alex & Saunders, William S. Urban Design. 2009. (Illus.). 320p. 75.00 *(978-0-8166-5638-7(X))* Univ. of Minnesota Pr.

Krieger, Alex & Saunders, William S., eds. Urban Design. 2009. (Illus.). 320p. pap. 25.00 *(978-0-8166-5639-4(8))* Univ. of Minnesota Pr.

Kuhl, Isabel. First: Groundbreaking Moments in Architecture. 2012. (Illus.). 208p. pap. 19.95 ***(978-3-7913-4654-0(7))*** Prestel Publishing.

Kuhl, Isabel. 50 Buildings You Should Know. 2007. (Illus.). 176p. pap. 19.95 *(978-3-7913-3838-5(2))* Prestel Publishing.

Kuhl, Isabel, et al. 50 Architects You Should Know. 2008. (Illus.). 176p. pap. 19.95 *(978-3-7913-4043-2(3))* Prestel Publishing.

Laurence King Publishing Limited Staff. New Chinese Architecture. 2009. (ENG., Illus.). 480p. pap. 40.00 *(978-1-85669-608-1(1))* King, Laurence Publishing GBR. Dist: Hachette Bk. Group.

Lavin, S. & Lavin, Sylvia. Kissing Architecture. 2011. (POINT: Essays on Architecture Ser.). (ENG., Illus.). 136p. (C). 16.95 *(978-0-691-14923-3(2))* Princeton Univ. Pr.

Leach, Andrew. What Is Architectural History? 2010. (What Is History Ser.). (ENG., Illus.). 196p. 64.95 *(978-0-7456-4456-1(2))*; pap. 19.95 *(978-0-7456-4457-8(0))* Polity Pr. GBR. Dist: Wiley, John & Sons, Inc.

Leach, Andrew, et al, eds. Shifting Views: Selected Essays on the Architectural History Of Australia & New Zealand. 2008. (ENG.). 256p. pap. 52.95 *(978-0-7022-3660-0(8))* Univ. of Queensland Pr. AUS. Dist: Independent Pubs. Group.

Lico, Gerard. Arkitekturang Filipino: A History of Architecture & Urbanism in the Philippines. 2010. (Illus.). 617p. pap. 90.00 *(978-971-542-579-7(8))* Univ. of the Philippines Pr. PHL. Dist: Univ. of Hawaii Pr.

Lounsbury, Carl R. Essays in Early American Architectural History: A View from the Chesapeake. 2011. (ENG., Illus.). 288p. (C). (gr. 13-17). pap. 35.00 *(978-0-8139-3229-3(7))* Univ. Pr. of Virginia.

Lynch, Gerard. The History of Gauged Brickwork: Conservation, Repair & Modern Application. 2007. (ENG., Illus.). 464p. 70.95 *(978-0-7506-8272-5(8))* Routledge.

Mallgrave, Harry Francis. Architectural Theory Vol. 2: An Anthology From, 1871-2005. Contandriopoulos, Christina, ed. 2008. (ENG.). 656p. pap. 64.95 *(978-1-4051-0260-5(8)*, Wiley-Blackwell) Wiley, John & Sons, Inc.

Mallgrave, Harry Francis & Goodman, David. Introduction to Architectural Theory: 1968 to the Present. 2011. (ENG., Illus.). 288p. 89.95 *(978-1-4051-8063-4(3)*, Wiley-Blackwell) Wiley, John & Sons, Inc.

Maran, Joseph. Constructing Power - Architecture, Ideology & Social Practice: Konstruktion der Macht - Architektur, Ideologie und soziales Handeln. Juwig, Carsten et al, eds. 2006. (GER, FRE & ENG., Illus.). 384p. 56.95 *(978-3-8258-9314-9(6))* Lit Verlag DEU. Dist: Transaction Pubs.

Martin, Lewis E., illus. Buildings to Enjoy. 144p. 22.00 *(978-0-86469-253-5(6))* Dunmore Pr. NZL. Dist: United Nations Pubns.

Martin, Therese. Queen as King: Politics & Architectural Propaganda in Twelfth-Century Spain. 2006. (Medieval & Early Modern Iberian World Ser.: Vol. 30). (Illus.). 292p. *(978-90-04-15297-7(0))* BRILL.

Mauer, Benedikt. Der Fürst und seine Stadt: Bauten aus der Jan-Wellem-Zeit in Düsseldorf. 2008. (GER., Illus.). 215p. *(978-3-7700-1302-9(6))* Droste Verlag GmbH.

Mazzola, Ettore Maria. Architecture & Town Planning Operating Instructions: Saving Architecture Might Save the Italian Economy. 2011. 280p. pap. 33.95 *(978-88-7448-840-7(8))* Gangemi ITA. Dist: International Publishers Marketing.

McNeill, Donald. The Global Architect. 2008. (Cultural Spaces Ser.). (Illus.). (ENG.). 192p. (C). pap. 35.95 *(978-0-415-95641-3(2))*; 200p. 130.00 *(978-0-415-95640-6(4))* Routledge.

Mehta, Geeta & MacDonald, Deanna. New Japan Architecture: Recent Works by the World's Leading Architects. 2011. (ENG., Illus.). 224p. 49.95 *(978-4-8053-0948-3(2))* Tuttle Publishing.

Meuser, Natascha & Meuser, Philipp. Meuser Architekten: Bauten und Projekte 1995-2010, 1 vol. 2011. (ENG.). 700p. 64.95 ***(978-3-86922-150-2(X))*** DOM Pubs. DEU. Dist: Innovative Logistics.

Meyer, Ulf. Architectural Guide Tokyo, 1 vol. 2011. (ENG.). 200p. 35.95 *(978-3-86922-106-9(2))* DOM Pubs. DEU. Dist: Innovative Logistics.

Micara, Ludovico, et al, eds. The Mediterranean Medina: An International Seminar. 2011. 176p. pap. 37.95 *(978-88-492-1605-9(X))* Gangemi ITA. Dist: International Publishers Marketing.

Millette, Daniel M. Vitruvius, Memory, & the Classical Imagination. 2008. 256p. pap. *(978-3-639-03310-6(8))* VDM Verlag Dr. Mueller e.K.

Mol, Eva. Hidden Complexities of the Frankish Castle: Social Aspects of Space in the Configurational Architecture of Frankish Castles in the Holy Land, 1099-1291. 2012. (Archaeological Studies Leiden University Ser.: 25) (ENG.). 220p. pap. *(978-90-8728-119-9(6)*, Leiden Univ. Pr.) Amsterdam Univ. Pr.

Morgenthaler & Morgenthaler, Hans. The Architect's History of Architecture. 3rd rev. ed. 2011. (ENG.). 288p. pap. 118.00 ***(978-0-7575-9139-6(6))*** Kendall Hunt Publishing Co.

Naginski, Erika. Sculpture & Enlightenment. 2009. (ENG., Illus.). 336p. 45.00 *(978-0-89236-959-1(0))* Oxford Univ. Pr., Inc.

Nesteruk, Peter. A Rhetoric of Time in the Arts. 2011. 304p. pap. ***(978-3-8443-2121-0(7))*** Lambert Academic Publishing.

Ockman, Joan & Williamson, Rebecca. Architecture School: Three Centuries of Educating Architects in North America. 2012. (ENG., Illus.). 400p. (gr. 17). 50.00 ***(978-0-262-01708-4(3))*** MIT Pr.

Olson Sundberg Kundig Allen. Jim Olson Houses, 1998-2008. 2009. (ENG., Illus.). 256p. 65.00 *(978-1-58093-252-3(5))* Monacelli Pr., Inc.

Otis, Calvin N. Sacred & Constructive Art; Its Origin & Progress a Series of Essays by Calvin N Otis. 2006. 308p. per. 23.99 *(978-1-4255-2895-9(3))* MPublishing.

Palmer, Allison. Historical Dictionary of Architecture. 2008. (Historical Dictionaries of Literature & the Arts Ser.). (ENG.). 400p. 104.00 *(978-0-8108-5821-3(5))* Scarecrow Pr., Inc.

Pearson, Christopher E. M. 1000 Monuments of Genius. 2010. (Book Ser.). (ENG., Illus.). 544p. 24.95 *(978-1-84484-463-0(3))* Parkstone International GBR. Dist: Ingram Pub. Services.

Perez-Arroyo, ed. Engaged with Reality. 2008. 176p. *(978-84-96954-60-1(9))* Actar Birkhauser Distribution.

Plank, Jeffrey. Crombie Taylor: Modern Architecture, Building Restoration & the Re-Discovery of Louis Sullivan. 2010. (Illus.). 315p. 65.00 *(978-0-9795508-1-2(5))* Stout, William Pubs.

Portugali, Nili. The Act of Creation & the Spirit of a Place: A Holistic-Phenomenological Approach to Architecture. 2006. (ENG., Illus.). 248p. 69.00 *(978-3-936681-05-5(8))* Edition Axel Menges GmbH DEU. Dist: National Bk. Network.

Powell, Kenneth. Powell & Moya. 2009. (Twentieth-century Architects Ser.). (ENG., Illus.). 160p. (C). pap. 40.00 *(978-1-85946-303-1(7))* English Heritage GBR. Dist: Brown, David Bk. Co., The.

Powell, Kenneth, ed. The Great Builders. 2011. (ENG., Illus.). 304p. 40.00 *(978-0-500-25179-9(7)*, 525179) Thames & Hudson.

Prown, Jules David. The Architecture of the Yale Center for British Art. 2009. (ENG., Illus.). 72p. 35.00 *(978-0-300-14964-7(6))* Yale Ctr. for British Art.

Pryce, Will. World Architecture: The Masterworks. (ENG., Illus.). 320p. 2008. 80.00 *(978-0-500-34248-0(2)*, 534248) 2nd rev. ed. 2011. 40.00 *(978-0-500-34274-9(1)*, 534274) Thames & Hudson.

Radevsky, Anton. The Modern Architecture. 2008. (ENG., Illus.). 6p. 45.00 *(978-0-7893-1802-2(4))* Universe Publishing.

Rappaport, Nina & Yale School of Architecture Staff. The Human City No. 3: Kings Cross. Knight, George & Taylor, Aaron, eds. 2009. (Edward P. Bass Distinguished Visiting Architecture Fellowship Ser.). (ENG., Illus.). 192p. pap. 30.00 *(978-0-393-73247-4(9)*, 73247) Norton, W. W. & Co., Inc.

Ricketts, Annabel, et al. The English Country House Chapel: Building a Protestant Tradition. 2007. (Illus.). 336p. (C). *(978-1-904965-05-3(9))* Spire Bks. Ltd.

Risselada, Max, ed. A Critical Anthology. 2011. (ENG., Illus.). 368p. 45.00 *(978-84-343-1254-8(9))* Polígrafa, Ediciones, S. A. ESP. Dist: D.A.P./Distributed Art Pubs.

Roberts F.R.I.B.A, Trevor. Parsonages & Priesthouses. 2008. (Illus.). 84p. pap. *(978-0-7552-0405-2(0))* Authors OnLine, Ltd.

Rogers, Chris. Michael Pearson. 2011. (ENG., Illus.). 192p. pap. 55.00 *(978-1-906155-73-5(9))* Black Dog Publishing Ltd. GBR. Dist: Perseus Distribution.

Roth, Leland. Understanding Architecture: Its Elements, History, & Meaning. 2nd rev. ed. 2006. (ENG., Illus.). 696p. pap. 59.00 *(978-0-8133-9045-1(1))* Westview Pr.

Roussell, Aage. Norse Building Customs in the Scottish Isles. reprint ed. 34.50 *(978-0-404-16477-5(3))* AMS Pr., Inc.

Ruskin, John. Lectures on Architecture & Painting: Delivered at Edinburgh in November 1853. 2009. 296p. 24.99 *(978-1-103-26494-0(X))*; pap. 18.99 *(978-1-103-26491-9(5))* BiblioBazaar.

Saboya, Marc. Fragments D'architecture Contemporaine à Bordeaux: Ordre et Désordre. 2008. (Marches de L'architecte Ser.). (FRE., Illus.). 109p. pap. *(978-2-915262-69-8(1))* Le Festin.

Saggio, Antonino. Five Masterworks by Louis Sauer. 2010. 64p. pap. 28.50 *(978-1-4461-4559-3(X))* Lulu Enterprises Inc.

Salvaing, Matthieu. Oscar Niemeyer. ltd. ed. 2008. *(978-2-7594-0293-9(2))* Assouline.

Samalavicius, Almantas. Ideas & Structures: Essays in Architectural History. 2011. 130p. pap. 16.00 *(978-1-60899-735-7(7)*, Resource Pubns.) Wipf & Stock Pubs.

Schaal, Hans Dieter. Stadttagebücher: Rom, Venedig, Warschau, Singapur, Kuala Lumpur, Tel Aviv, jerusalem, Lissabon, San Francisco, Las Vegas, Los Angeles, Wien, Paris, Tallinn, Tartu, New York, Moskau, Sankt Petersburg, Barcelona, Genf, Brüssel, London. 12th ed. 2010. (Illus.). 648p. 98.00 *(978-3-936681-31-4(7))* Edition Axel Menges GmbH DEU. Dist: National Bk. Network.

Schank Smith, Kendra. Architects Sketches: Dialogue & Design. 2008. (ENG., Illus.). 152p. 59.95 *(978-0-7506-8226-8(4))* Routledge.

Schonle, Andreas. Architecture of Oblivion: Ruins & Historical Consciousness in Modern Russia. 2011. (ENG., Illus.). 295p. 45.00 *(978-0-87580-651-8(1))* Northern Illinois Univ. Pr.

Schrenk, Lisa D. Building a Century of Progress: The Architecture of Chicago's 1933-34 World's Fair. 2007. (Illus.). 368p. 39.95 *(978-0-8166-4836-8(0))* Univ. of Minnesota Pr.

Seidler, Harry. The Grand Tour. 25th ed. 2007. (ENG., Illus.). 575p. pap. 14.99 *(978-3-8228-3780-1(6))* TASCHEN DEU. Dist: Ingram Pub. Services.

Shanken, Andrew Michael. 194X: Architecture, Planning, & Consumer Culture on the American Home Front. 2009. (Architecture, Landscape & Amer Culture Ser.). (ENG., Illus.). 288p. 75.00 *(978-0-8166-5365-2(8))*; pap. 24.95 *(978-0-8166-5366-9(6))* Univ. of Minnesota Pr.

Smith, Terry E. The Architecture of Aftermath. 2006. (Illus.). 280p. 80.00 *(978-0-226-76468-9(0))* Univ. of Chicago Pr.

Solomon, Susan G. Louis I. Kahn's Jewish Architecture: Mikveh Israel & the Midcentury American Synagogue. 2009. (Brandeis Series in American Jewish History, Culture & Life Ser.). (ENG., Illus.). 236p. lib. bdg. 45.00 *(978-1-58465-788-0(X))* Univ. Pr. of New England.

Sommer, A.L. Den Danske Arkitektur. 2009. (DAN., Illus.). 592p. *(978-87-02-05401-9(9))* Gyldendal.

Steele, James. The Greenwood Encyclopedia of Homes Through World History, 3 vols., Set. 2008. (Illus.). 1100p. 349.95 *(978-0-313-33788-8(8)*, GR3788) Greenwood Publishing Group, Inc.

Stephenson, Charles. Castles: A Global History of Fortified Structures - Ancient, Medieval, & Modern. 2011. (ENG., Illus.). 288p. pap. 29.99 *(978-0-312-54140-8(6)*, St. Martin's Griffin) St. Martin's Pr.

Stern, Robert, frwd. Ike Kligerman Barkley Houses. 2010. (ENG., Illus.). 256p. 60.00 *(978-1-58093-269-1(X))* Monacelli Pr., Inc.

Stevenson, Neil. Architecture Explained. 2007. 76p. (C). 20.00 *(978-0-13-208126-9(1))* Prentice Hall Higher Education.

Stones, Alison. Studies in Arthurian Illustration. 2012. (ENG., Illus.). 560p. (C). 300.00 *(978-1-904597-37-7(8))* Pindar Pr. GBR. Dist: Brown, David Bk. Co., The.

Stroud, Marion Boulton & Wilkins, Amy. Robert Venturi, Denise Scott Brown, & Steven Izenour at Acadia Summer Arts Program. Stroud, Marion Boulton, ed. 2010. (ENG., Illus.). 124p. 30.00 *(978-0-9797642-2-6(X))* A.S.A.P.

Sutherland, Jonathan. World's Greatest Architecture. 2007. 24.99 *(978-0-7858-2271-4(2)*, Chartwell) Book Sales, Inc.

Symondson, Anthony & Harwood, Elain. Chamberlin, Powell & Bon. 2011. (Twentieth-century Architects Ser.). (ENG., Illus.). 160p. (C). pap. 40.00 ***(978-1-85946-397-0(5))*** English Heritage GBR. Dist: Brown, David Bk. Co., The.

Travers, David. Arts & Architecture 1945-54: The Complete Reprint. Weiner, Nina, ed. 2008. (ENG., Illus.). 6076p. reprint ed. pap. 700.00 *(978-3-8228-2678-2(2))* TASCHEN DEU. Dist: Ingram Pub. Services.

Tretiack. Megalomania: Too Much Is Never Enough. 2008. (ENG.). 144p. 50.00 *(978-2-84323-894-9(3))* Assouline FRA. Dist: Perseus Distribution.

Umbach, Maiken. German Cities & Bourgeois Modernism, 1890-1924. 2009. (ENG., Illus.). 288p. 110.00 *(978-0-19-955739-4(X))* Oxford Univ. Pr., Inc.

Van Tussenbroek, Gabri. The Architectural Network of the Van Neurenberg Family in the Low Countries, 1480-1640. Verheijen, Titus & Byrn, Whitney A., trs. 2006. (Architectura Moderna Ser.). (ENG., Illus.). 250p. (C). pap. 131.00 *(978-2-503-51847-3(8))* Brepols Pubs. BEL. Dist: ISD.

Vidler, Anthony. Histories of the Immediate Present: Inventing Architectural Modernism. 2008. (Writing Architecture Ser.). (ENG., Illus.). 264p. (gr. 17). pap. 25.95 *(978-0-262-72051-9(5))* MIT Pr.

Wallick, Karl, et al. KieranTimberlake: A Manual of Work. 2011. (ENG., Illus.). 256p. 55.00 *(978-0-8478-3678-9(9))* Rizzoli International Pubns., Inc.

Ward, James. Historic Ornament: Treatise on Decorative Art & Architectural Ornament. 2007. (ENG.). 436p. 51.95 *(978-0-548-11794-1(2))* Kessinger Publishing, LLC.

Watkin, David. A History of Western Architecture. 5th rev. ed. 2011. (ENG., Illus.). 720p. pap. 40.00 ***(978-1-85669-790-3(8))*** King, Laurence Publishing GBR. Dist: Hachette Bk. Group.

Watkin, David & Laurence King Publishing Limited Staff. A History of Western Architecture. 4th rev. ed. 2010. (ENG., Illus.). 720p. pap. 40.00 *(978-1-85669-459-9(3))* King, Laurence Publishing GBR. Dist: Hachette Bk. Group.

Wertheimer, Lester, et al. Architecture History 2009. 2008. (ENG.). 208p. pap. 59.95 *(978-1-4277-7824-6(8))* Kaplan Publishing.

Weston, Richard. 100 Ideas that Changed Architecture. 2011. (ENG., Illus.). 216p. pap. 29.95 ***(978-1-85669-732-3(0))*** King, Laurence Publishing GBR. Dist: Hachette Bk. Group.

Wharton, Bernard. House, Home, Heart: Artistry & Craftsmanship in the Architecture of Shope Reno Wharton. 2011. (ENG., Illus.). 320p. 85.00 *(978-0-9833889-0-6(3))* Pointed Leaf Pr.

Wrenick, Frank E. & Wrenick, Elaine V., eds. The Streamline Era Greyhound Terminals: The Architecture of W. S. Arrasmith. alt. ed. 2011. (ENG., Illus.). 204p. pap. 38.00 *(978-0-7864-6445-6(3))* McFarland & Co., Inc. Pubs.

Yarwood, Doreen. A Chronology of Western Architecture. 2010. (Dover Architecture Ser.). (ENG.). 224p. pap. 19.95 *(978-0-486-47648-3(0))* Dover Pubns., Inc.

Yglesias, Caren. The Complete House & Grounds: Learning from A. J. Downing's Domestic Architecture. 2012. (ENG., Illus.). 224p. 40.00 *(978-1-935195-24-5(7))* Ctr. for American Places, Inc.

ARCHITECTURE—INFLUENCE OF CLIMATE

see Architecture and Climate

ARCHITECTURE—JUVENILE LITERATURE

see also Tree Houses

Hewitt, Sally & Rowe, Jane. The Homes We Live In. 2010. (Look Around You Ser.). (ENG., Illus.). 32p. (J). (gr. -1). pap. 10.99 *(978-0-237-53132-4(1)*, Evans Brothers, Limited) Evans Publishing Group GBR. Dist: Independent Pubs. Group.

ARCHITECTURE—LANGUAGE

Odgers, Jo, et al, eds. Primitive: Original Matters in Architecture. 2006. (Illus.). 284p. 170.00 *(978-0-415-38538-1(5))* Routledge.

Samuel, Flora. Primitive: Original Matters in Architecture. Odgers, Jo & Sharr, Adam, eds. 2006. (Illus.). 304p. (C). 74.95 *(978-0-415-38539-8(3))* Routledge.

ARCHITECTURE—LAW AND LEGISLATION

see Architects—Legal Status, Laws, etc.; Building Laws; Engineering Law

ARCHITECTURE—MODULAR DESIGN

see Modular Coordination (Architecture)

ARCHITECTURE—ORDERS

Barletta, Barbara. The Origins of the Greek Architectural Orders. 2009. (ENG., Illus.). 232p. (C). pap. 27.99 *(978-0-521-12422-5(0))* Cambridge Univ. Pr.

Ching, Francis D. K. & Ching, Francis D. Architecture: Form, Space, & Order. 3rd rev. ed. 2007. (ENG., Illus.). 448p. pap. 49.95 *(978-0-471-75216-5(9)*, Wiley) Wiley, John & Sons, Inc.

Holland, Leicester. The Origin of the Doric Entablature. 2009. pap. 21.16 *(978-1-60724-442-4(X))* Gorgias Pr., LLC.

ARCHITECTURE—PERIODICALS

American Institute of Architects Staff. The American Institute of Architects Official Guide to the 2007 AIA Contract Documents. 2009. (ENG., Illus.). 496p. 150.00 *(978-0-470-25166-9(2)*, Wiley) Wiley, John & Sons, Inc.

Anker, Andrew. Harvard Architecture Review. 3rd ed. 25.00 *(978-0-262-76001-0(0))* MIT Pr.

Brainard, Gabrielle, et al, eds. Perspecta 41 Grand Tour: The Yale Architectural Journal. 2008. (ENG., Illus.). 185p. (gr. 17). pap. 25.00 *(978-0-262-51225-1(4))* MIT Pr.

Bruckner & Bruckner. Spirit & Space #2. 2010. (Zeitschrift Architektur. Aktuell Ser.). 168p. pap., pap. 19.95 *(978-3-211-99296-8(0))* Springer.

Chapman, Tony. Architecture 09: RIBA Buildings of the Year. 2010. (Illus.). 272p. pap. *(978-1-85894-490-6(2))* Merrell Pubs. Ltd.

Chapman, Tony, ed. Architecture Vol. 8: The Guide to the Riba Awards. 2008. (Illus.). 216p. pap. 22.95 *(978-1-85894-428-9(7))* Merrell Pubs. Ltd. GBR. Dist: Perseus Distribution.

—Architecture 10: RIBA Buildings of the Year. 2011. (RIBA Guides). (ENG., Illus.). 272p. 34.95 *(978-1-85894-539-2(9))* Merrell Pubs. Ltd. GBR. Dist: Perseus Distribution.

DesignIntelligence: Technology Survey 2008. 2008. (Illus.). 71p. pap. 69.95 *(978-0-9785552-7-6(9)*, Ostberg) Greenway Communications.

Europe Foundation, Landscape Architecture, ed. 'scape 2010/1: The International Magazine of Landscape Architecture & Urbanism. 2010. 80p. pap. 19.95 *(978-3-0346-0325-6(8))* Birkhauser Verlag AG CHE. Dist: Actar Birkhauser Distribution.

Fiell, Charlotte & Peter, ed. Domus, 1970-1974, Vol. 7. 2009. (Domus Ser.). (ITA & ENG., Illus.). 580p. 69.99 *(978-3-8365-0957-2(1))* TASCHEN DEU. Dist: Ingram Pub. Services.

—Domus, 1975-1979, Vol. 8. 2009. (Domus Ser.). (ITA, ENG & FRE., Illus.). 580p. 69.99 *(978-3-8365-0958-9(X))* TASCHEN DEU. Dist: Ingram Pub. Services.

—Domus, 1980-1984, Vol. 9. 2009. (Domus Ser.). (ITA & ENG., Illus.). 580p. 69.99 *(978-3-8365-0959-6(8))* TASCHEN DEU. Dist: Ingram Pub. Services.

Frampton, Kenneth, et al, eds. SOM Journal, No. 5. 2009. (ENG., Illus.). 228p. pap. 30.00 *(978-3-7757-2279-7(3))* Hatje Cantz Verlag GmbH & Co KG DEU. Dist: D.A.P./Distributed Art Pubs.

Gutman, Marta & Nelson, Louis P., eds. Buildings & Landscapes Issue Vol. 18, Issue 1: Journal of the Vernacular Architecture Forum. 2011. (Buildings & Landscapes Ser.). 150p. pap. 37.50 *(978-0-8166-7633-0(X))* Univ. of Minnesota Pr.

Harsema, Harry. Scape 2010/02: The International Magazine of Landscape Architecture & Urbanism. 2010. (Scape Ser.). 80p. pap. 19.95 *(978-3-0346-0617-2(6))* Birkhauser Verlag AG CHE. Dist: Actar Birkhauser Distribution.

Hesse, Anna & Schmal, Peter Cachola, eds. Dam Jahrbuch: Architektur in Deutschland/Architecture in Germany. 2006. (Dam Jahrbuch Ser.). (ENG & GER., Illus.). 192p. pap. 45.00 *(978-3-7913-3690-9(8))* Prestel Publishing.

Otero-Pailos. Future Anterior Vol. 8, Issue 1: Journal of Historic Preservation History, Theory & Criticism. 2011. (Future Anterior Ser.). 150p. pap. 46.00 *(978-0-8166-7634-7(8))* Univ. of Minnesota Pr.

Pace, Brian & Killion, Stephen, eds. GlUe: Ball State Department of Architecture Student Journal. 8th ed. 2007. per. 16.00 *(978-0-9707701-5-8(4))* Ball State Univ.

Rainer, Haupl, et al. PLOT 2: Inszenierungen im Raum: Creative Spaces, 2 vols. 2009. (GER & ENG., Illus.). 100p. pap. 19.95 *(978-3-89986-113-6(2))* Avedition DEU. Dist: National Bk. Network.

Schmal, Peter Cachola, et al. Deutsches Architektur Jahrbuch 2011/12: German Architecture Annual 2011/12. 2011. (GER & ENG., Illus.). 212p. pap. 49.95 ***(978-3-7913-5135-3(4))*** Prestel Publishing.

Steiner, Hadas A. Beyond Archigram: The Structure of Circulation. (Illus.). 168p. 2008. 43.95 *(978-0-415-39477-2(5))* 2007. 165.00 *(978-0-415-39476-5(7))* Routledge.

Taschen Publishing Staff. Domus, 1955-1959, Vol. 4. Volk, Annick et al, eds. 2008. (ITA & ENG., Illus.). 580p. 69.99 *(978-3-8365-0954-1(7))* TASCHEN DEU. Dist: Ingram Pub. Services.

—Domus, 1960-1964, Vol. 5. Volk, Annick et al, eds. 2008. (ITA & ENG., Illus.). 580p. 69.99 *(978-3-8365-0955-8(5))* TASCHEN DEU. Dist: Ingram Pub. Services.

—Domus, 1965-1969, Vol. 6. Volk, Annick et al, eds. 2008. (ITA & ENG., Illus.). 580p. 69.99 *(978-3-8365-0956-5(3))* TASCHEN DEU. Dist: Ingram Pub. Services.

Taschen Publishing Staff, et al. Domus, 1928-1939, Vol. 1. Volk, Annick et al, eds. 2008. (ENG., Illus.). 580p. 69.99 *(978-3-8365-0951-0(2))* TASCHEN DEU. Dist: Ingram Pub. Services.

—Domus, 1940-1949, Vol. 2. Volk, Annick et al, eds. 2008. (ENG., Illus.). 580p. 69.99 *(978-3-8365-0952-7(0))* TASCHEN DEU. Dist: Ingram Pub. Services.

van der Wal, Olof, ed. Architecture Bulletin 02: Essays on the Designed Environment, 1 vol. 2007. (ENG., Illus.). 80p. pap. 20.00 *(978-90-5662-556-6(X))* NAi Uitgevers / Publishers Stichting NLD. Dist: D.A.P./Distributed Art Pubs.

Volk, Annick, et al, eds. Domus, 1950-1954, Vol. 3. 2008. (ENG., Illus.). 580p. 69.99 *(978-3-8365-0953-4(9))* TASCHEN DEU. Dist: Ingram Pub. Services.

Williams, Kim. Nexus Network Journal. 2007. (Nexus Network Journal Ser.). Vol. 8, & 2. (Illus.). 121p. pap. 49.95 *(978-3-7643-7761-8(5)*, 3764377615) Vol. 8,2. 144p. pap. 49.95 *(978-3-7643-7747-2(X)*, 376437747X) Birkhauser Boston.

Williams, Kim, ed. Nexus Network Journal 12,1: Architecture & Mathematics. 2011. (Nexus Network Journal Ser.). (ENG.). iv, 160p. pap. 109.00 *(978-3-0346-0517-5(X)*, 303460517X) Birkhauser Verlag AG CHE. Dist: Springer.

—Nexus Network Journal 12,2: Architecture & Mathematics. 2010. (Nexus Network Journal Ser.). (ENG.). iv, 199p. pap. 109.00 *(978-3-0346-0519-9(6)*, 3034605196) Birkhauser Verlag AG CHE. Dist: Springer.

—Nexus Network Journal 12,3: Architecture & Mathematics. 2011. (Nexus Network Journal Ser.). 164p. pap. 109.00 *(978-3-0346-0521-2(8)*, 3034605218) Birkhauser Verlag AG CHE. Dist: Springer.

—Nexus Network Journal 13,1: Architecture & Mathematics. 2011. (Nexus Network Journal Ser.). (ENG.). v, 150p. pap. 109.00 ***(978-3-0348-0159-1(9)***, 3034801599) Birkhauser Verlag AG CHE. Dist: Springer.

—Nexus Network Journal 13,2: Architecture & Mathematics. 2011. (Nexus Network Journal Ser.). (ENG., Illus.). iv, 150p. pap. 109.00 ***(978-3-0348-0170-6(X)***, 303480170X) Birkhauser Verlag AG CHE. Dist: Springer.

—Nexus Network Journal 13,3: Architecture & Mathematics. 2012. (Nexus Network Journal Ser.). (ENG.). iv, 250p. pap. 109.00 ***(978-3-0348-0245-1(5)***, 3034802455) Birkhauser Verlag AG CHE. Dist: Springer.

Williams, Kim, ed. Nexus Network Journal 9,1: Architecture & Mathematics. 2007. (Nexus Network Journal Ser.). 158p. pap. 64.95 *(978-3-7643-8443-2(3))* Birkhauser Verlag AG CHE. Dist: Springer.

Woodson, R. Dodge & Woodson, R. 2009 International Building Code Need to Know: The 20% of the Code You Need 80% of the Time. 2009. (ENG., Illus.). 304p. pap. 29.95 *(978-0-07-159257-4(1)*, 0071592571) McGraw-Hill Professional Publishing.

ARCHITECTURE—PHILOSOPHY

Aldrete-Haas, José Antonio. Arquitectura y Percepción. 2007. (SPA., Illus.). 157p. *(978-968-859-630-2(2))* Universidad Iberoamericana, A.C.

Alexander, Christopher. The Battle for the Life & Beauty of the Earth: A Struggle between Two World-Systems. 2012. (ENG., Illus.). 528p. 45.00 ***(978-0-19-989807-7(3))*** Oxford Univ. Pr., Inc.

Allen, Stan. Practice: Architecture, Technique & Presentation. 2nd rev. exp. ed. 2009. (ENG., Illus.). 288p. (C). 49.95 *(978-0-415-77625-7(2))* Routledge.

—Practice: Architecture, Technique & Representation. 2nd rev. exp. ed. 2009. (ENG., Illus.). 288p. (C). 160.00 *(978-0-415-77624-0(4))* Routledge.

Andersen, Michael Asgaard. Nordic Architects Write: A Documentary Anthology. 2008. (Illus.). (ENG.). 432p. (C). pap. 53.95 *(978-0-415-46352-2(1))*; XIV, 418p. 165.00 *(978-0-415-46351-5(3))* Routledge.

Arakawa, Shusaku & Gins, Madeline. Making Dying Illegal. 2006. (Illus.). 224p. pap. 22.95 *(978-1-931824-22-4(3)*, Roof Bks.) Segue Foundation.

Archer, Steven & Bartoy, Kevin, eds. Between Dirt & Discussion: Methods, Methodology & Interpretation in Historical Archaeology. 2010. (Illus.). xiv, 235p. pap. 129.00 *(978-1-4419-4166-4(5)*, 1441941665) Springer.

Art & Architecture, Set. 2008. 342p. 200.00 *(978-0-415-46403-1(X))* Routledge.

Baek, Jin. Nothingness: Tadao Ando's Christian Sacred Space: Tadao Ando's Christian Sacred Space. 2009. (ENG., Illus.). 224p. (C). 155.00 *(978-0-415-47853-3(7))*; 212p. pap. 53.95 *(978-0-415-47854-0(5))* Routledge.

Baker, William T. Architectural Excellence: In a Diverse World Culture. 2008. (ENG., Illus.). 128p. 35.00 *(978-1-86470-279-8(6))* Images Publishing Group AUS. Dist: National Bk. Network.

Ballantyne, Andrew. Architecture in the Space of Flows. Smith, Christopher, ed. 2011. (ENG., Illus.). 264p. (C). pap. 49.95 *(978-0-415-58542-2(2))* Routledge.

—Deleuze & Guattari for Architects. 2007. (Thinkers for Architects Ser.). (Illus.). 124p. 130.00 *(978-0-415-42115-7(2))* Routledge.

—Deleuze & Guattari for Architects. 2007. (Thinkers for Architects Ser.). (Illus.). 124p. per. 28.95 *(978-0-415-42116-4(0))* Taylor & Francis Group.

Ballantyne, Andrew & Smith, Christopher, eds. Architecture in the Space of Flows. 2011. (ENG., Illus.). 264p. (C). 155.00 *(978-0-415-58541-5(4))* Routledge.

Baudrillard, Jean. Mass Identity Architecture: Architectural Writings of Jean Baudrillard. Proto, Francesco, ed. 2006. (ENG., Illus.). 206p. per. 55.00 *(978-0-470-02715-8(0)*, Academy Pr.) Wiley, John & Sons, Inc.

Benjamin, Andrew & Rice, Charles, eds. Walter Benjamin & the Architecture of Modernity. 2009. (Anamnesis Ser.). 226p. pap. 25.00 *(978-0-9805440-2-2(5))* re.press AUS. Dist: Lightning Source, Inc.

Braham, William. Rethinking Technology: A Reader in Architectural Theory. Hale, Jonathan A. & Sadar, John Stanislav, eds. 2007. (ENG., Illus.). 488p. (C). 165.00 *(978-0-415-34653-5(3))* Routledge.

Braham, William W., et al, eds. Rethinking Architectural Technology: A Reader in Architectural Theory. 2006. (Illus.). 466p. per. 49.95 *(978-0-415-34654-2(1))* Routledge.

Brott, Simone. Architecture for a Free Subjectivity: Deleuze & Guattari at the Horizon of the Real. 2011. 150p. 99.95 *(978-1-4094-1995-2(9))* Ashgate Publishing Co.

Brown, Lori. Feminist Practices: Interdisciplinary Approaches to Women in Architecture. 2011. (Illus.). 400p. 119.95 ***(978-1-4094-2117-7(1))*** Ashgate Publishing Co.

Caicco, Gregory. Architecture, Ethics, & the Personhood of Place. Caicco, Gregory, ed. 2007. (ENG., Illus.). 260p. 50.00 *(978-1-58465-653-1(0))* Univ. Pr. of New England.

Carabet, Brian & Shand, John. Minnesota: Design Philosophies Expressed by Minnesota's Leading Professionals. 2009. (Perspectives on Design Ser.). (ENG.). 304p. 40.00 *(978-1-933415-77-2(0))* Panache Partners, LLC.

Choi, Esther & Trotter, Marrikka. Architecture at the Edge of Everything Else. 2010. (ENG., Illus.). 218p. (gr. 17). 27.95 *(978-0-262-01479-3(3))* MIT Pr.

Cieraad, Irene, ed. At Home: An Anthropology of Domestic Space. 2006. (Illus.). 200p. pap. 19.95 *(978-0-8156-2903-0(6))* Syracuse Univ. Pr.

Cochrane, Ethan & Gardner, Andrew, eds. Evolutionary & Interpretive Archaeologies: A Dialogue. 2011. (Univ col london inst arch Pub Ser.). (ENG., Illus.). 361p. 89.00 *(978-1-59874-426-2(7))* Left Coast Pr., Inc.

Coleman, Nathaniel. Imagining & Making the World: Reconsidering Architecture & Utopia. 2011. (Illus.). 312p. pap. *(978-3-0343-0120-6(0))* Lang, Peter Publishing, Inc.

Connah, Roger & Quantrill, Malcolm. The Ark of Architecture: Selected Writings of Malcolm Quantrill. 2009. (ENG., Illus.). 240p. pap. 69.00 *(978-951-682-892-6(2)*, Art Stock Bks. Ltd/Csi) Continental Sales, Inc.

Corbusier, Le. Towards a New Architecture. 2008. 312p. pap. *(978-965-00-6036-7(7))* Editorial Benei Noaj.

Coyne, Richard. Derrida for Architects. 2011. (Thinkers for Architects Ser.). (ENG., Illus.). 144p. (C). 120.00 *(978-0-415-59178-2(3))*; pap. 28.95 *(978-0-415-59179-9(1))* Routledge.

Crinson, Mark. James Stirling. Crinson, Mark, ed. 2009. (ENG., Illus.). 160p. (C). pap. 44.95 *(978-0-415-55059-8(9))* Routledge.

—James Stirling: Early unpublished writings on Architecture. Crinson, Mark, ed. 2009. (ENG., Illus.). 160p. (C). 165.00 *(978-0-415-55058-1(0))* Routledge.

Crysler, Greig, et al, eds. The SAGE Handbook of Architectural Theory. 2012. (Illus.). 776p. 150.00 *(978-1-4129-4613-1(1)*, B46131C) SAGE Pubns., Ltd. GBR. Dist: SAGE Pubns., Inc.

Davies, Colin. Thinking about Architecture: An Introduction to Architectural Theory. 2011. (ENG., Illus.). 160p. pap. 29.95 ***(978-1-85669-755-2(X))*** King, Laurence Publishing GBR. Dist: Hachette Bk. Group.

de Botton, Alain. The Architecture of Happiness. 2008. (Vintage Ser.). (ENG., Illus.). 288p. pap. 18.00 *(978-0-307-27724-4(0)*, Vintage) Knopf Doubleday Publishing Group.

—The Architecture of Happiness. 2008. (ENG., Illus.). 288p. pap. *(978-0-7710-2607-2(2)*, McClelland & Stewart) McClelland & Stewart CAN. Dist: Random Hse., Inc.

Edwards, Sarah, et al, eds. Writing the Modern City. 2012. (ENG., Illus.). 256p. (C). 155.00 ***(978-0-415-59150-8(3))*** Routledge.

Edwards, Sarah & Charley, Jonathan, eds. Writing the Modern City. 2012. (ENG., Illus.). 256p. (C). pap. 53.95 ***(978-0-415-59151-5(1))*** Routledge.

Eichinger, Gregor & Troger, Eberhard, eds. Touch Me: The Mystery of the Surface. 2010. (Illus.). 240p. pap. 45.00 *(978-3-03778-229-3(3))* Lars Muller Pubs. CHE. Dist: Prestel Publishing.

Eisenman, Peter. AA Words One: Supercritical: Peter Eisenman Meets Rem Koolhaas, 4 vols. 2007. (Illus.). 200p. pap. *(978-1-902902-51-7(3))* Architectural Assn.

Evers, Bernd. Architectural Theory. Thoenes, Christof, ed. 2006. 576p. (SPA.). pap. 12.99 *(978-3-8228-5083-1(7))*; (ITA.). pap. 12.99 *(978-3-8228-5220-0(1))*; (FRE.). pap. 12.99 *(978-3-8228-5084-8(5))*; (POR.). pap. 12.99 *(978-3-8228-5221-7(X))*; (GER.). pap. 12.99 *(978-3-8228-5082-4(9))* Taschen America, LLC.

Fentress, Curtis. Touchstones of Design. 2010. (ENG., Illus.). 308p. 19.99 *(978-1-86470-401-3(2)*, Images Publishing Dist Ac) Antique Collectors' Club GBR. Dist: National Bk. Network.

Fernandez-Solis, Jost. Is Building Construction Approaching the Threshold of Becoming Unsustainable? - a System Theoretic Exploration Towards a Post-Forrester Model for Taml. 2008. 408p. pap. *(978-3-8364-6086-6(6))* VDM Verlag Dr. Mueller e.K.

Fischer, Ole W. Sehnsucht - The Book of Architectural Longings: German Contribution to the 12th international Architecture Exhibition / Deutscher Beitrag auf der 12. internationalen Architekturausstellung - La Biennale die Venezia 2010. 2010. 256p. 69.95 *(978-3-7091-0326-5(6))* Springer Wien AUT. Dist: Actar Birkhauser Distribution.

—What Architects Desire. 2010. 400p. pap. 39.95 *(978-3-7091-0328-9(2))* Springer Wien AUT. Dist: Springer.

Franck, Karen A. & Lepori, R. Bianca. Architecture from the Inside Out: From the Body, the Senses, the Site, & the Community. 2nd ed. 2007. (ENG., Illus.). 200p. 145.00 *(978-0-470-05783-4(1))*; pap. 55.00 *(978-0-470-05785-8(8))* Wiley, John & Sons, Inc. (Academy Pr.).

Gleiniger, Andrea & Vrachliotis, Georg. Code: Between Operation & Narration. 2010. (ENG., Illus.). 120p. pap. 29.95 (978-3-0346-0117-7(4)) Birkhauser Verlag AG CHE. Dist: Actar Birkhauser Distribution.
Glendinning, Miles. Architecture's Evil Empire? The Triumph & Tragedy of Global Modernism. 2010. (ENG.). 176p. pap. 27.95 (978-1-86189-756-5(1)) Reaktion Bks., Ltd. GBR. Dist: Chicago Distribution Ctr.
Goldblatt, David & Paden, Roger. The Aesthetics of Architecture: Philosophical Investigations into the Art of Building. 2011. (Journal of Aesthetics & Art Criticism Ser.: 2). (ENG., Illus.). 200p. pap. 41.95 (978-1-4443-3972-7(9), Wiley-Blackwell) Wiley, John & Sons, Inc.
Hale, Jonathan. Merleau-Ponty for Architects. 2014. (Thinkers for Architects Ser.). (ENG., Illus.). 128p. (C). 130.00 (978-0-415-48071-0(X)) Routledge.
Hays, K. Michael & Hays, K. M. Architecture's Desire: Reading the Late Avant-Garde. 2009. (Writing Architecture Ser.). (ENG., Illus.). 216p. (gr. 17). pap. 20.95 (978-0-262-51302-9(1)) MIT Pr.
Healy, Brian. Brian Healy: Commonplaces. 2008. (ENG., Illus.). 110p. pap. 24.95 (978-0-9793801-7-4(0)) Oro Editions.
Hernandez, Felip & Hernandez, Felipe. Bhabha for Architects. 2010. (Thinkers for Architects Ser.). (Illus.). 148p. 120.00 (978-0-415-47745-1(X)) Routledge.
Hill, Glen. Design, Heidegger, & the Earth. 2008. 196p. pap. (978-3-639-07160-3(3)) VDM Verlag Dr. Mueller e.K.
Iliescu, Sanda, ed. The Hand & the Soul: Aesthetics & Ethics in Architecture & Art. 2009. (ENG., Illus.). 320p. (gr. 17). 55.00 (978-0-8139-2760-2(9)) Univ. Pr. of Virginia.
Jones, Peter Blundell. Oneplanetarchitecture: The Architecture of RAU. 2012. (ENG., Illus.). 320p. 109.00 (978-3-936681-30-7(9)) Edition Axel Menges GmbH DEU. Dist: National Bk. Network.
Koeck, Richard & Roberts, Les, eds. The City & the Moving Image: Urban Projections. 2010. (ENG., Illus.). 320p. 95.00 (978-0-230-24338-5(X)) Palgrave Macmillan.
Krier, Leon & Thadani, Dhiru A. The Architecture of Community. 2011. (ENG., Illus.). 496p. pap. 35.00 (978-1-59726-579-9(9)) Island Pr.
Krier, Leon, et al. The Architecture of Community. 2009. (ENG., Illus.). 496p. 50.00 (978-1-59726-578-2(0)) Island Pr.
Krischanitz, Adolf. Adolf Krischanitz: Architektur ist der Unterschied zwischen Architektur 2010. (ENG., Illus.). 224p. 55.00 (978-3-7757-2408-1(7)) Hatje Cantz Verlag GmbH & Co KG DEU. Dist: D.A.P./Distributed Art Pubs.
Kuma, Kengo. Anti-Object: The Dissolution & Disintegration of Architecture, 4 vols. 2007. (Illus.). 200p. pap. (978-1-902902-52-4(1)) Architectural Assn.
Kunstbibliothek (Berlin, Germany) Staff, contrib. by. Architectural Theory: From the Renaissance to the Present. 25th anniv. ed. 2006. (ENG., Illus.). 575p. pap. 14.99 (978-3-8228-5085-5(3)) TASCHEN DEU. Dist: Ingram Pub. Services.
Lahiji, Nadir, ed. The Political Unconscious of Architecture: Re-Opening Jameson's Narrative. 2011. (Ashgate Studies in Architecture Ser.). (Illus.). 348p. 119.95 (978-1-4094-2639-4(4)) Ashgate Publishing Co.
Last, Nana. Wittgenstein's House: Language, Space, & Architecture. 2008. (ENG., Illus.). 176p. 55.00 (978-0-8232-2880-5(0)) Fordham Univ. Pr.
Leach. Rethinking Architecture: A Reader in Cultural Theory. 2nd ed. 2009. 544p. 44.95 (978-0-415-45783-5(1)); 165.00 (978-0-415-45782-8(3)) Routledge.
Leatherbarrow, David. Architecture Oriented Otherwise. 2008. (ENG., Illus.). 304p. 39.95 (978-1-56898-811-5(7)) Princeton Architectural Pr.
Lim, Ngiom. Critical Meanings in Architecture. 2009. 336p. pap. (978-3-639-16960-7(3)) VDM Verlag Dr. Mueller e.K.
Maak, Niklas. Le Corbusier: The Architect on the Beach. 2011. (Illus.). 208p. 29.95 (978-3-7774-3991-4(6)) Hirmer Verlag GmbH DEU. Dist: Chicago Distribution Ctr.
Maki, Fumihiko & Mulligan, Mark. Nurturing Dreams: Collected Essays on Architecture & the City. Mulligan, Mark, ed. 2008. (ENG., Illus.). 292p. (gr. 17). 29.95 (978-0-262-13500-9(0)) MIT Pr.
Mallgrave, Harry. Modern Architectural Theory: A Historical Survey, 1673-1968. 2009. (ENG., Illus.). 522p. (C). pap. 54.00 (978-0-521-13048-6(4)) Cambridge Univ. Pr.
Mallgrave, Harry Francis. Architect's Brain: Neuroscience, Creativity, & Architecture. 2010. (ENG., Illus.). 288p. 128.95 (978-1-4051-9585-0(1), Wiley-Blackwell) Wiley, John & Sons, Inc.
Mallgrave, Harry Francis & Contandriopoulos, Christina, eds. Architectural Theory Vol. II: An Anthology From, 1871-2005. 2008. (ENG.). 656p. 136.95 (978-1-4051-0259-9(4), Wiley-Blackwell) Wiley, John & Sons, Inc.
Mallgrave, Harry Francis & Goodman, David. Introduction to Architectural Theory: 1968 to the Present. 2011. (ENG., Illus.). 288p. 89.95 (978-1-4051-8063-4(3), Wiley-Blackwell) Wiley, John & Sons, Inc.
—An Introduction to Architectural Theory: 1968 to the Present. 2011. (ENG., Illus.). 208p. pap. 34.95 (978-1-4051-8062-7(5), Wiley-Blackwell) Wiley, John & Sons, Inc.
McCarter, Robert, ed. On & by Frank Lloyd Wright: A Primer of Architectural Principles. 2012. (ENG., Illus.). 372p. pap. 29.95 (978-0-7148-6316-0(5)) Phaidon Pr., Inc.
Mekking, Aart J. J. The Global Built Environment as a Representation of Realities: Why & How Architecture Should Be the Subject of Worldwide Comparison. Roose, Eric, ed. 2009. (ENG., Illus.). 216p. pap. (978-90-8728-063-5(7), Pallas Publications) Amsterdam Univ. Pr.
Miller, Stephen G. The Berkeley Plato: From Neglected Relic to Ancient Treasure, an Archaeological Detective Story. 2009. (ENG., Illus.). 126p. 55.00 (978-0-520-25833-4(9)) Univ. of California Pr.
Mitnick, Keith. Artificial Light: A Narrative Inquiry into the Nature of Abstraction, Immediacy, & Other Architectural Fictions. 2008. (ENG., Illus.). 152p. pap. 24.95 (978-1-56898-749-1(8)) Princeton Architectural Pr.
Mitrovic, Branko & Branko, Mitrovic. Philosophy for Architects. 2011. (ENG., Illus.). 192p. pap. 24.95 (978-1-56898-994-5(6)) Princeton Architectural Pr.
Molinelli, Michael. Build Neat Stuff. 2006. 30.00 net. (978-1-4276-0312-8(X)) Aardvark Global Publishing.
Moravánszky, Ákos & Kirchengast, Albert, eds. Experiments: Architektur zwischen Wissenschaft und Kunst . Theoriebau 2. 2011. (ENG & GER., Illus.). 304p. pap. 40.00 (978-3-86859-040-1(4)) Jovis Verlag GmbH DEU. Dist: D.A.P./Distributed Art Pubs.
Murcutt, Glenn. Glenn Murcutt: University of Washington Master Studios & Lectures. Nicholls, Jim, ed. 2009. (ENG., Illus.). 80p. pap. 30.00 (978-0-295-98958-7(0)) Univ. of Washington Pr.
Novara, A. Auctor in Bibliotheca: Essai sur les textes préfaciels de Vitruve et une philosophie latine du Livre. 2006. (Bibliotheque d'Etudes Classiques Ser.). (ENG.). 188p. (C). pap. 58.00 (978-90-429-1679-1(6)) Peeters Pubs. & Booksellers BEL. Dist: Brown, David Bk. Co., The.
Otero-Pailos, Jorge. Architecture's Historical Turn: Phenomenology & the Rise of the Postmodern. 2010. (Illus.). 320p. 75.00 (978-0-8166-6603-4(2)); pap. 25.00 (978-0-8166-6604-1(0)) Univ. of Minnesota Pr.
Ots, Enn. Decoding Theoryspeak: An Illustrated Guide to Architectural Theory. 2010. (ENG., Illus.). 240p. (C). instr.'s gde. ed. 165.00 (978-0-415-77829-9(8)); pap. 31.95 (978-0-415-77830-5(1)) Routledge.
Paden, Roger. Mysticism & Architecture: Wittgenstein & the Meanings of the Palais Stonborough. 2007. (Toposophia Ser.). (ENG., Illus.). 232p. 73.50 (978-0-7391-1561-9(8)); per. 28.50 (978-0-7391-1562-6(6)) Lexington Bks.
Parcell, Stephen. Four Historical Definitions of Architecture. 2012. (ENG.). 352p. (C). (978-0-7735-3956-3(5)) McGill-Queen's Univ. Pr.
Parcell, Stephen & Perez-Gomez, Alberto. Chora: Intervals in the Philosophy of Architecture. 2007. (Chora: Intervals in the Philosophy of Architecture Ser.). (ENG., Illus.). 360p. pap. (978-0-7735-3262-5(5)) McGill-Queen's Univ. Pr.
Payot, Daniel. Le Philosophe et L'Architecte. 240p. (978-0-8047-3679-4(0)); pap. (978-0-8047-3680-0(4)) Stanford Univ. Pr.
Pedret, Annie. The Real Team 10 Primer. 2012. (ENG., Illus.). 368p. (C). pap. 53.95 (978-0-415-78076-6(4)); 165.00 (978-0-415-78075-9(6)) Routledge.
Perez-Gomez, Alberto & Parcell, Stephen. Chora: Intervals in the Philosophy of Architecture. 2011. (CHORA: Intervals in the Philosophy of Architecture Ser.). 328p. (C). (978-0-7735-3858-0(5)); Vol. 6. pap. (978-0-7735-3859-7(3)) McGill-Queen's Univ. Pr.
Pérez-Gomez, Alberto & Parcell, Stephen, eds. CHORA - Intervals in the Philosophy of Architecture, Vol. 5. 2007. (CHORA: Intervals in the Philosophy of Architecture Ser.). (ENG., Illus.). 360p. (978-0-7735-3260-1(9)) McGill-Queen's Univ. Pr.
Pessler, Monika. UNDISZIPLINIERT / UNDISCIPLINED: Das Phänomen Raum in Kunst, Architektur und Design / The Phenomenon of Space in Art, Architecture & Design. Bast, Gerald, ed. 2008. (ENG & GER., Illus.). 159p. pap. (978-3-211-09411-2(3), 3211094113) Actar Birkhauser Distribution.
Picon, Antoine. French Architects & Engineers in the Age of Enlightenment. 2009. (Cambridge Studies in the History of Architecture Ser.). (ENG., Illus.). 452p. pap. 60.00 (978-0-521-12369-3(0)) Cambridge Univ. Pr.
Piotrowski, Andrzej. Architecture of Thought. 2011. (Illus.). 408p. 105.00 (978-0-8166-7304-9(7)); pap. 35.00 (978-0-8166-7305-6(5)) Univ. of Minnesota Pr.
Portzamparc, Christian De & Sollers, Philippe. Writing & Seeing Architecture. Tihanyi, Catherine, tr. from FRE. 2008. 168p. 57.00 (978-0-8166-4567-1(1)); pap. 18.95 (978-0-8166-4568-8(X)) Univ. of Minnesota Pr.
Puglisi, Luigi Prestinenza, ed. Theoretical Meltdown. 2009. (Architectural Design Ser.). (ENG.). 136p. pap. 80.00 (978-0-470-99779-6(6), Wiley) Wiley, John & Sons, Inc.
Quillien, Jenny. Delight's Muse on Christopher Alexander's the Nature of Order: A Summary & Personal Interpretation. 2008. (Illus.). 186p. pap. 65.95 (978-1-4303-1317-5(X)) Lulu Enterprises Inc.
Rawes Irigaray for Architects. 2007. (Thinkers for Architects Ser.). (ENG., Illus.). 128p. (C). 130.00 (978-0-415-43132-3(8)) Routledge.
Rawes Peg. Irigaray for Architects. 2007. (Thinkers for Architects Ser.). (Illus.). 128p. 28.95 (978-0-415-43133-0(6)) Routledge.
Roberts, Louis O. Man Between Earth & Sky: A Symbolic Awareness of Architecture Through a Process of Creativity. 2009. (Illus.). 272p. 60.00 (978-0-9822407-1-7(6)) Octavio Publishing.
Rossi, Aldo. A Scientific Autobiography. Venuti, Lawrence, tr. from ITA. 2010. (Oppositions Bks.). (ENG., Illus.). 128p. (gr. 17). pap. 20.95 (978-0-262-51438-5(9)) MIT Pr.
Rüedi Ray, Katerina. Bauhaus Dream-House: Modernity & Globalization. 2010. (Architext Ser.). (ENG., Illus.). 240p. (C). pap. 49.95 (978-0-415-47582-2(1)); 165.00 (978-0-415-47581-5(3)) Routledge.
Ryskamp, John. The Philosophy of Postconstructivism. 2010. 160p. pap. 25.95 (978-0-557-53113-4(6)) Lulu Enterprises Inc.
Sala, Nicoletta, ed. Chaos & Complexity in Arts & Architecture. 2006. 178p. (C). 39.00 (978-1-60021-232-1(8)) Nova Science Pubs., Inc.
Saunders, William S., ed. Judging Architectural Value. 2007. (Harvard Design Magazine Ser.). (Illus.). 192p. 69.00 (978-0-8166-5010-1(1)); per. 22.95 (978-0-8166-5011-8(X)) Univ. of Minnesota Pr.
Schaal, Hans Dieter. Stadttagebücher: Rom, Venedig, Warschau, Singapur, Kuala Lumpur, Tel Aviv, Jerusalem, Lissabon, San Francisco, Las Vegas, Los Angeles, Wien, Paris, Tallinn, Tartu, New York, Moskau, Sankt Petersburg, Barcelona, Genf, Brüssel, London. 12th ed. 2010. (Illus.). 648p. 98.00 (978-3-936681-31-4(7)) Edition Axel Menges GmbH DEU. Dist: National Bk. Network.
Schumacher, Patrik S. The Autopoeisis of Architecture: A New Framework for Architecture. 2011. (ENG., Illus.). 478p. pap. 50.00 (978-0-470-77298-0(0), Wiley) Wiley, John & Sons, Inc.
—The Autopoiesis of Architecture: A New Framework for Architecture. 2011. (ENG., Illus.). 478p. 130.00 (978-0-470-77299-7(9), Wiley) Wiley, John & Sons, Inc.
—The Autopoiesis of Architecture Vol. 2: A New Agenda for Architecture. 2012. (ENG., Illus.). 784p. pap. 50.00 (978-0-470-66616-6(1), Wiley) Wiley, John & Sons, Inc.
—The Autopoiesis of Architecture Vol. II: A New Agenda for Architecture. 2012. (ENG., Illus.). 784p. 145.00 (978-0-470-66615-9(3), Wiley) Wiley, John & Sons, Inc.
Semper Gottfried. The Four Elements of Architecture & Other Writings. Mallgrave, Harry Francis & Herrmann, Wolfgang, trs. from GER. 2011. (Res Monographs in Anthropology & Aesthetics Ser.). (ENG.). 336p. pap. 39.99 (978-0-521-18086-3(4)) Cambridge Univ. Pr.
Sharr, Adam. Heidegger for Architects. 2007. (Thinkers for Architects Ser.). (Illus.). 128p. 130.00 (978-0-415-41515-6(2)) Routledge.
—Heidegger for Architects. 2007. (Thinkers for Architects Ser.). (Illus.). 128p. per. 28.95 (978-0-415-41517-0(9)) Taylor & Francis Group.
Smith, Korydon, ed. Introducing Architectural Theory: Debating a Discipline. 2012. (ENG., Illus.). 448p. (C). 165.00 (978-0-415-88837-0(9)); pap. 39.95 (978-0-415-88838-7(7)) Routledge.
Soleri, Paolo. What If? Quaderno 12: Animism vs. Animation. 2008. (ENG., Illus.). 12.00 (978-1-883340-03-2(9)) Cosanti Pr.
—What If? Quaderno 3: Earthcasting. 2nd ed. 2006. (ENG., Illus.). 32p. 12.00 (978-1-883340-02-5(0)) Cosanti Pr.
Sowa, Axel & Schindler, Susanne, eds. Candide. Journal for Architectural Knowledge: Issue 2. 2011. (ENG.). 148p. pap. 24.95 (978-3-8376-1512-8(X)) Transcript Verlag DEU. Dist: Transaction Pubs.
—Candide. Journal of Architectural Knowledge: Issue 3. 2011. (ENG.). 170p. pap. 24.95 (978-3-8376-1542-5(1)) Transcript Verlag DEU. Dist: Transaction Pubs.
Steadman, Philip. The Evolution of Designs: Biological Analogy in Architecture & the Applied Arts. Steadman, Philip, ed. 2008. (ENG., Illus.). 320p. (C). 53.95 (978-0-415-44753-9(4)); 165.00 (978-0-415-44752-2(6)) Routledge.
Stern, Robert A. M. & Goldberger, Paul. Robert A. M. Stern: Buildings & Projects, 2004-2009. Dixon, Peter Morris, ed. 2009. (ENG., Illus.). 624p. 75.00 (978-1-58093-234-9(7)) Monacelli Pr., Inc.
Stoner, Jill. Toward a Minor Architecture. 2012. (ENG., Illus.). 176p. (gr. 17). pap. 19.95 (978-0-262-51764-5(7)) MIT Pr.
Swaback, Vernon D. Believing in Beauty: Conversations with Vernon D. Swaback. 2009. pap. (978-0-927015-40-0(4)) Bridgewood Pr.
Sykes, A. Krista & Princeton Architectural Press Staff. Constructing a New Agenda: Architectural Theory, 1993-2009. 2010. (ENG., Illus.). 512p. pap. 45.00 (978-1-56898-859-7(1)) Princeton Architectural Pr.
Temple, Nicholas. Disclosing Horizons: Architecture, Perspective & Redemptive Space. 2006. (Illus.). 306p. 165.00 (978-0-415-41653-5(1)) Routledge.
Temple, Nicholas & Bandyopadhyay, Soumyen. Thinking Practice: Reflections on Architectural Research & Building Work. 2007. (ENG., Illus.). 191p. pap. 29.95 (978-1-906155-24-7(0)) Black Dog Publishing Ltd. GBR. Dist: Perseus Distribution.
Thoenes, Christof & Evers, Bernd. Architecture Theory, 2 Vol, 2 vols. 2011. (25 Ser.). (ENG., Illus.). 848p. pap. 29.99 (978-3-8365-3198-6(4)) TASCHEN DEU. Dist: Ingram Pub. Services.
Till, Jeremy. Architecture Depends. 2009. (ENG., Illus.). 272p. (gr. 17). 25.95 (978-0-262-01253-9(7)) MIT Pr.
Trachtenberg, Marvin. Building-in-Time: From Giotto to Alberti & Modern Oblivion. 2010. (ENG., Illus.). 516p. 65.00 (978-0-300-16592-0(7)) Yale Univ. Pr.
Vinegar, Aron. Relearning from Las Vegas. Golec, Michael J., ed. 2008. (Illus.). 208p. pap. 25.00 (978-0-8166-5061-3(6)) Univ. of Minnesota Pr.
Vinegar, Aron, et al. Relearning from Las Vegas. Vinegar, Aron & Golec, Michael J., eds. 2008. (Illus.). 208p. 75.00 (978-0-8166-5060-6(8)) Univ. of Minnesota Pr.
Wallenstein, Sven-Olov. Biopolitics & the Emergence of Modern Architecture. 2009. (ENG., Illus.). 96p. 24.95 (978-1-56898-785-9(4)) Princeton Architectural Pr.
Webster, Helena. Bourdieu for Architects. 2010. (Thinkers for Architects Ser.). (ENG., Illus.). 144p. (C). pap. 28.95 (978-0-415-49615-5(2)) Routledge.
—Bourdieu for Architects. 2010. (Thinkers for Architects Ser.). (ENG., Illus.). 144p. (C). 120.00 (978-0-415-49614-8(4), Routledge) Taylor & Francis Group GBR. Dist: Taylor & Francis Group.
Wolf, Eric M. Making an Entrance: Design Philosophy & the Entry in Western Architecture. 2007. (Illus.). 40p. 0.00 net. (978-0-9798369-0-9(5)) New York Schl. of Interior Design.
Wulfram, Hartmut. Literarische Vitruvrezeption in Leon Battista Albertis 'de re Aedificatoria' (Beiträge zur Altertumskunde Ser.). (GER.). 441p. 210.00 (978-3-11-184227-1(4)) De Gruyter, Walter Inc.
Younes, Samir. The Imperfect City: On Architectural Judgment. 2012. (Illus.). 240p. 89.95 (978-1-4094-4668-2(9)) Ashgate Publishing Co.
Zaera-Polo, Alejandro. The Sniper's Log: Architectural Chronicles of Generation-X. 2012. (ENG., Illus.). 198p. pap. (978-84-92861-22-4(3)) Actar Birkhauser Distribution.
Zumthor, Peter. Thinking Architecture. 3rd ed. 2010. (Illus.). 112p. 44.95 (978-3-0346-0585-4(4)) Birkhauser Verlag AG CHE. Dist: Actar Birkhauser Distribution.

ARCHITECTURE—PICTORIAL WORKS

Acconci, Vito, et al. Less: Alternative Living Strategies/Strategie Alternative Dell'abitare. 2008. (ENG., Illus.). 400p. pap. 45.00 (978-88-7439-331-2(8)) 5 Continents ITA. Dist: Hachette Bk. Group.
Alexander, Christopher James. Julius Shulman's Los Angeles. 2011. (ENG., Illus.). 72p. pap. 9.95 (978-1-60606-079-7(1), J. Paul Getty Museum) Getty Pubns.
Andersen, Paul & Salomon, David. The Architecture of Patterns. 2010. (ENG., Illus.). 144p. pap. 24.95 (978-0-393-73293-1(2), 73293) Norton, W. W. & Co., Inc.
Aran, Berge. Austin Val Verde: A Montecito Masterpiece. 2006. (ENG., Illus.). 144p. 50.00 (978-1-890449-39-1(3)) Balcony Pr.
Arzur, Marie-Haude. Lighthouses of the World. 2008. (ENG., Illus.). 240p. 35.00 (978-1-4081-0635-8(3)) A & C Black GBR. Dist: Macmillan.
Ashley, Peter. More London Peculiars: Being Curious Corners of a Capital City. 2007. (ENG., Illus.). 120p. (C). pap. 31.95 (978-1-85074-999-8(X)) English Heritage GBR. Dist: Brown, David Bk. Co., The.
Austin, Dan. Lost Detroit: Stories Behind Motown's Majestic Ruins. 2010. 176p. pap. 24.99 (978-1-59629-940-5(1)) History Pr., The.
Bague, Alejo, et al, photos by. In Detail: Barcelona Contemporary Architecture, 1 vol. 2006. (ENG., Illus.). 160p. 45.00 (978-84-343-1090-2(2)) Poligrafa, Ediciones, S. A. ESP. Dist: D.A.P./Distributed Art Pubs.
Basilico, Gabriele. Cityscapes. 2008. (ENG.). 400p. 95.00 (978-88-6073-430-3(4)) Baldini Castoldi Dalai Editore ITA. Dist: Independent Pubs. Group.
Baumann, Kirsten, et al, eds. Modern Greetings/Moderne Grube: Photographed Architecture on Picture Postcards 1919-1939/Fotografierte Architektur Auf Ansichtskarten 1919-1939. 2007. (ENG & GER., Illus.). 38.00 (978-3-89790-019-6(X)) Arnoldsche Art Pubs. DEU. Dist: Antique Collectors' Club.
Beltramini, Guido & Burns, Howard. Palladio. 2009. (ENG., Illus.). 320p. 115.00 (978-1-905711-24-6(7)) Royal Academy of Arts GBR. Dist: Hachette Bk. Group.
Bernardi, Silvio, et al. Silvio Bernardi Architetto: Living in Cortina D'Ampezzo. 2010. (ITA & ENG., Illus.). 263p. (978-88-370-7859-1(5)) Electa.
Betsky, Aaron, intro. Tate & Snyders Architects: Architecture in a Sprawling Landscape. 2007. (Architectural Ser.). (ENG., Illus.). 100p. pap. 25.00 (978-88-7838-082-0(2), Art Stock Bks. Ltd/Csi) Continental Sales, Inc.
Blancsube, Michel & Hoffmann, Jens, texts. Fernando Ortega. 2010. (ENG., Illus.). 192p. pap. 29.50 (978-968-9056-41-6(7)) Turner, Ediciones S.A. ESP. Dist: D.A.P./Distributed Art Pubs.
Boekel, Andrea, ed. Outdoor Living: Courtyards, Decks & Patios. 2007. (International Spaces Ser.). (ENG., Illus.). 224p. 39.95 (978-1-876907-55-6(X), Images Publishing Dist Ac) Antique Collectors' Club GBR. Dist: National Bk. Network.
Braun Editorial Staff, ed. Architectural Details - Pillars. 2008. (ENG.). 160p. 37.50 (978-3-938780-47-3(9), Braun Publish,Csi) Continental Sales, Inc.
—Architectural Details - Stairs. 2008. (ENG.). 160p. 37.50 (978-3-938780-46-6(0), Braun Publish,Csi) Continental Sales, Inc.
Braun Editors. Cook! Best of Kitchen Design. 2009. (ENG., Illus.). 400p. 19.95 (978-3-03768-013-1(X), Braun Publish,Csi) Continental Sales, Inc.
Broto, Carles. Houses Today. 2012. (ENG.). 200p. 49.00 (978-84-15123-54-5(X)) Links International (Leading International Key Services Barcelona, S.A.) ESP. Dist: National Bk. Network.
—Superb Cabins. 2009. (ENG.). 192p. pap. 24.99 (978-2-917031-37-7(9)) Links International (Leading International Key Services Barcelona, S.A.) ESP. Dist: National Bk. Network.
—Wood Cabins. 2009. (ENG.). 192p. pap. 24.99 (978-2-917031-38-4(7)) Links International (Leading International Key Services Barcelona, S.A.) ESP. Dist: National Bk. Network.
Buchwald, Ari. I Thought Pigs Could Fly! Architectural Details of Cincinnati. 2007. 100p. per. 19.99 (978-0-9798659-1-6(3)) Edgecliff Pr. LLC.
—Right, Angels! 2007. (ENG., Illus.). 60p. per. 14.99 (978-0-9798659-0-9(5)) Edgecliff Pr. LLC.
Carabet, Brian & Shand, John. Minnesota: Design Philosophies Expressed by Minnesota's Leading Professionals. 2009. (Perspectives on Design Ser.). (ENG.). 304p. 40.00 (978-1-933415-77-2(0)) Panache Partners, LLC.
Cattermole, Paul. Architectural Excellence: 500 Iconic Buildings. 2008. (ENG., Illus.). 512p. 49.95 (978-1-55407-358-0(8)) Firefly Bks., Ltd.
Cerver, Francisco Asensio. The World of Contemporary Architecture. 2008. (Art & Architecture Ser.). (Illus.). 998p. pap. 19.95 (978-0-8416-0097-3(X)) American Map Corp.
Chávez Giraldo, Juan David. Medellín: 333 Años, 333 Arquitecturas. 2009. (ENG & SPA., Illus.). 175p. (978-958-728-034-0(2)) Universidad Nacional, Sede Medellín.
Cleary, Richard & Speck, Lawrence W. The University of Texas at Austin. 2011. (ENG., Illus.). 224p. pap. 29.95 (978-1-56898-854-2(0)) Princeton Architectural Pr.
Clive Wilkinson Architects & Chan, Benny, photos by. Interior Spaces of the USA & Canada Vol 7 No. 7: A Pictorial Review. 2006. (International Spaces Ser.). (ENG., Illus.). 224p. 55.00 (978-1-920744-35-9(5)) Images Publishing Group AUS. Dist: National Bk. Network.
Cohen, Jean-Louis & Lodder, Christina. Building the Revolution: Soviet Art & Architecture, 1915-1935. 2011. (ENG., Illus.). 288p. 60.00

(978-1-905711-91-8(3)) Royal Academy of Arts GBR. Dist: Hachette Bk. Group.

Cohen, Stuart & Hacker, Julie. Transforming the Traditional: The Work of Cohen & Hacker Architects. 2009. (ENG., Illus.). 128p. 50.00 *(978-1-86470-335-1(0))* Images Publishing Group AUS. Dist: National Bk. Network.

Congdon-Martin. South Beach Perspectives. 2007. 80p. pap. 9.95 *(978-0-7643-2796-4(8))* Schiffer Publishing, Ltd.

Congdon-Martin, Douglas. South Beach Perspectives. 2007. (Illus.). 80p. pap. 9.95 *(978-0-7643-2766-7(6))* Schiffer Publishing, Ltd.

Connolly, M. Caren & Wasserman, Louis. Wisconsin's Own: Twenty Remarkable Homes. 2010. (ENG., Illus.). 320p. 45.00 *(978-0-87020-452-4(1))* Wisconsin Historical Society.

Cook, Peter. Liquid Threshold. 2007. (Illus.). 332p. pap. 49.95 *(978-0-9562563-0-0(9))* Atelier One GBR. Dist: Actar Birkhauser Distribution.

Cooke, Brian. Construction Practice. 2011. (ENG., Illus.). 400p. pap. 48.99 *(978-1-4443-3668-9(1)*, Wiley-Blackwell) Wiley, John & Sons, Inc.

Cresti, Carlo & Rendina, Claudio. Palazzi of Rome. 2008. (Art & Architecture Ser.). (Illus.). 398p. pap. 24.95 *(978-0-8416-0288-5(3))* American Map Corp.

Cryder, Jo. Entryways & Doorways. 2008. (Illus.). 160p. pap. 29.95 *(978-0-7643-2858-9(1))* Schiffer Publishing, Ltd.

—1000 Shutters & Awnings. 2007. (Illus.). 160p. pap. 29.95 *(978-0-7643-2711-7(9))* Schiffer Publishing, Ltd.

Cullman, Ellie, et al. Decorating Master Class. 2008. (ENG., Illus.). 224p. 50.00 *(978-0-8109-9390-7(2))* Abrams.

Cuno, James, et al. The Modern Wing: Renzo Piano & the Art Institute of Chicago. 2009. (ENG., Illus.). 168p. 60.00 *(978-0-300-14112-2(2))* Art Institute of Chicago.

Daglio, Laura & Bellini, Oscar. Building Arabia: Expanding the Limits of Architecture. 2010. (ENG., Illus.). 302p. 40.00 *(978-88-544-0450-2(0))* White Star ITA. Dist: Random Hse., Inc.

Daniell, Thomas. Houses & Gardens of Kyoto. 2010. (ENG., Illus.). 224p. 39.95 *(978-4-8053-1091-5(X))* Tuttle Publishing.

De Baeck, Philippe. Hotel Bible, 1 vol. 2009. (ENG., Illus.). 432p. 124.95 *(978-90-79761-13-5(3))* Tectum B.V.B.A. BEL. Dist: Innovative Logistics.

de Haro, Fernando & Fuentes, Omar, compiled by. Homes: Architecture Comes to Life. 2011. (ENG., Illus.). 284p. 45.00 ***(978-607-437-082-9(6))*** AM Editores MEX. Dist: Perseus-PGW.

de Nicolay-Mazery, Christiane & Touillon, Bernard. The French Country House. 2008. (ENG., Illus.). 192p. pap. 29.95 *(978-0-86565-194-4(9))* Vendome Pr., The.

Debschitz, Thilo Von. Frank Kunert: Verkehrte Welt - Topsy-Turvy World. 2008. (GER & ENG., Illus.). 72p. 25.00 *(978-3-7757-2132-5(0))* Hatje Cantz Verlag GmbH & Co KG DEU. Dist: D.A.P./Distributed Art Pubs.

deLashmet, Jack, intro. Hamptons Gardens. 2011. (ENG.). 328p. 150.00 *(978-2-7594-0511-4(7))* Assouline FRA. Dist: Perseus Distribution.

Design 360 Concept and Design Magazine, ed. Conceptual Architecture. 2010. (Illus.). 271p. 59.95 *(978-1-58423-383-1(4))* Gingko Pr., Inc.

Designed for Worship. 2006. per. 44.95 *(978-0-9772092-1-7(0))* Booksmith Group, The.

Designers Villas 24 Weekend Homes. 2007. 49.95 *(978-4-7661-1739-4(5))* Graphic-Sha JPN. Dist: Gingko Pr., Inc.

Desilets, Deborah. Morris Lapidus: The Architecture of Joy. 2010. (ENG., Illus.). 240p. 65.00 *(978-0-8478-3088-6(8))* Rizzoli International Pubns., Inc.

Dowling, Elizabeth Meredith. Harrison Design Associates: A Decade of Work. 2007. (ENG., Illus.). 256p. 59.95 *(978-1-86470-277-4(X)*, Images Publishing Dist Ac) Antique Collectors' Club GBR. Dist: National Bk. Network.

Dubowitz, Dan. Wastelands. 2010. (ENG., Illus.). 176p. 55.00 ***(978-1-904587-83-5(6))*** Lewis, Dewi Publishing GBR. Dist: Consortium Bk. Sales & Distribution.

Dumont-Le Cornec, Elisabeth. Wonders of the World: Natural & Man-Made Majesties. 2007. (Illus.). 150p. (gr. 4-7). 24.95 *(978-0-8109-9417-1(8)*, Abrams Bks. for Young Readers) Abrams.

Eastman, Michael. Vanishing America: The End of Main Street Diners, Drive-Ins, Donut Shops, & Other Everyday Monuments. 2008. (ENG., Illus.). 192p. 39.95 *(978-0-8478-3040-4(3))* Rizzoli International Pubns., Inc.

Edwards, Jane. London Style: Streets, Interiors, Details. Hendricks, J. & Taschen, Angelika, eds. 25th ed. 2008. (Icon (Taschen) Ser.). (FRE, GER & ENG., Illus.). 191p. 7.99 *(978-3-8365-0777-6(3))* TASCHEN DEU. Dist: Ingram Pub. Services.

Eldorado Stone (Firm) Staff, contrib. by. The Allure of Permanence. 2008. (Illus.). 156p. *(978-0-615-18661-0(0))* Eldorado Stone, LLC.

Eng, John & Biondo, Adriene. Modern Tract Homes of Los Angeles. 2011. (Illus.). 144p. 39.99 ***(978-0-7643-3865-6(X)***, Schiffer Publishing Ltd) Schiffer Publishing, Ltd.

Exford, Theodore Henry, compiled by. A Historic Look at Wells, Maine & the Homes of Drakes Island: A Brief History of the Brave Defenders of Colonial Wells & the Eventual Development of Its Jewel, Drakes Island. 2009. (Illus.). ix, 329p. *(978-0-89725-859-3(2)*, Penobscot Pr.) Picton Pr.

Fahr-Becker, Gabriele & Frahm, Klaus. Ryokan: A Japanese Tradition. 2008. (Art & Architecture Ser.). (Illus.). 335p. 19.95 *(978-0-8416-0092-8(9))* American Map Corp.

Fajardo, Julio. MegaMalls. 2010. (Illus.). 215p. *(978-981-245-762-2(3))* Page One Publishing.

Feireiss, Kristin, ed. City & Structure: Photographs by H. G. Esch. 2009. (ENG., Illus.). 256p. 60.00 *(978-3-7757-2281-0(5))* Hatje Cantz Verlag GmbH & Co KG DEU. Dist: D.A.P./Distributed Art Pubs.

Ferro, Lisa & Pasti, Chiara. Venice Interiors: Contemporary Houses. 2009. (ENG., Illus.). 184p. 65.00 *(978-88-7200-286-5(9))* Vianello Libri ITA. Dist: Antique Collectors' Club.

Finton, John. Building up a Storm: Exploits of a Builder Extraordinaire. 2012. (ENG., Illus.). 256p. 59.95 *(978-1-86470-439-6(X))* Images Publishing Group AUS. Dist: National Bk. Network.

Form Magazine. Entry 2006: Design, Visions & Perspectives. 2006. (Illus.). 82p. pap. 14.95 *(978-3-936560-47-3(1)*, 3936560471) Birkhauser Verlag GmbH DEU. Dist: Springer.

Fuentes, Omar & de Haro, Fernando. Ideas: Houses. 2008. (ENG., Illus.). 272p. pap. 24.95 *(978-970-9726-79-4(X))* AM Editores MEX. Dist: Perseus-PGW.

—Styles. 2008. (Ideas (AM Editores) Ser.). (ENG., Illus.). 272p. pap. 24.95 *(978-970-9726-78-7(1))* AM Editores MEX. Dist: Perseus-PGW.

Fuentes, Omar & de Haro, Fernando, compiled by. Interiors: Expression & Functionality. 2008. (Interiors Ser.). (ENG., Illus.). 192p. 39.95 *(978-970-9726-94-7(3))* AM Editores MEX. Dist: Perseus-PGW.

Galindo, Michelle. Collection: European Architecture. 2009. (GER, FRE & ENG.). 512p. 49.95 *(978-3-03768-011-7(3)*, Braun Publish,Csi) Continental Sales, Inc.

—Collection: Houses. 2009. (GER, FRE & ENG.). 512p. 89.95 *(978-3-03768-012-4(1)*, Braun Publish,Csi) Continental Sales, Inc.

Gallagher, Robert C., et al. Building Dry-Stack Stone Walls. 2008. (Illus.). 144p. pap. 25.99 *(978-0-7643-3056-8(X))* Schiffer Publishing, Ltd.

Gand, Gary. Julius Shulman: Chicago Mid-Century Modernism. 2010. (Illus.). 208p. 60.00 *(978-0-8478-3287-3(2))* Rizzoli International Pubns., Inc.

Gingko Press, creator. Play! Indoor & Outdoor. 2011. (ENG., Illus.). 313p. 49.95 ***(978-1-58423-436-4(9))*** Gingko Pr., Inc.

Global Brand Shop Windows Design. 2008. 306p. *(978-7-5611-3577-8(7))* Dalian Univ. of Technology Electronic & Audio-Visual Pr.

Greenaway, Peter. L' Italia Delle Città. 2011.Tr. of Italy of the Cities. (ENG, CHI & ITA., Illus.). 340p. pap. 55.00 *(978-88-572-0885-5(0))* Skira Editore ITA. Dist: Random Hse., Inc.

Greenberg, Stanley. Architecture under Construction. 2010. (ENG., Illus.). 120p. 45.00 *(978-0-226-30642-1(9))* Univ. of Chicago Pr.

Gross, Steve & Daley, Susan. Time Wearing Out Memory: Schoharie County. 2008. (ENG., Illus.). 128p. 49.95 *(978-0-393-06644-9(4)*, 6644) Norton, W. W. & Co., Inc.

Guidi, Guido, photos by. Guido Guidi: Carlo Scarpa's Tomba Brion. 2011. (ENG & ITA., Illus.). 160p. 60.00 *(978-3-7757-2624-5(1))* Hatje Cantz Verlag GmbH & Co KG DEU. Dist: D.A.P./Distributed Art Pubs.

Hansen, Inge Lyse. Hellenistic & Roman Butrint. 2009. (ENG & ALB., Illus.). 96p. (C). pap. 24.00 *(978-0-9535556-8-0(2))* Butrint Foundation GBR. Dist: Brown, David Bk. Co., The.

Hariri. Hariri & Hariri Architecture: Buildings & Projects. 2010. (ENG., Illus.). 256p. 59.95 *(978-1-86470-340-5(7)*, Images Publishing Dist Ac) Antique Collectors' Club GBR. Dist: National Bk. Network.

Harker, Michael, photos by & pref. Harker's Courthouses: Visions of an Iowa Icon. 2009. (Illus.). 96p. pap. 28.95 *(978-0-9793779-9-0(4))* WDG Communications, Inc.

Haro Lebrija, Fernando de & Fuentes Elizondo, Omar. Evolución de Las Formas: Evolution of Forms. 2009. (ENG & SPA., Illus.). 211p. *(978-607-437-041-6(9))* AM Editores.

Hendricks, J. & Taschen, Angelika, eds. Tuscany Style: Landscapes, Terraces & Houses, Interiors, Details. 25th ed. 2008. (Icons Ser.). (FRE, GER & ENG., Illus.). 190p. 7.99 *(978-3-8365-0765-3(X))* TASCHEN DEU. Dist: Ingram Pub. Services.

Hettche, Thomas, et al. Fritz Barth, Cannstatter Straße 84, Fellbach: Cannstatter Strasse 84, Fellbach. 2011. (GER & ENG., Illus.). 72p. 49.00 *(978-3-932565-76-2(2))* Edition Axel Menges GmbH DEU. Dist: National Bk. Network.

Hildebrandt, Rachel & Old York Road Historical Society. The Philadelphia Area Architecture of Horace Trumbauer. 2009. (Images of America Ser.). (Illus.). 128p. pap. 21.99 *(978-0-7385-6297-1(1))* Arcadia Publishing.

Hollauf, Isabella. Isabella Hollauf: Spaces for Recreation. 2011. (ENG, ITA, POL, GER & RUM., Illus.). 176p. pap. 29.80 *(978-3-86859-068-5(4))* Jovis Verlag GmbH DEU. Dist: D.A.P./Distributed Art Pubs.

Holt, Victoria. Old, Ruined, Forgotten. 2007. 116p. per. 29.95 *(978-1-4327-0766-8(3))* Outskirts Pr., Inc.

Holzman, Malcolm. Stone Work: Designing with Stone. 2006. (Designing with/for Ser.). (ENG., Illus.). 210p. 70.00 *(978-1-86470-083-1(1))* Images Publishing Group AUS. Dist: National Bk. Network.

Hopkins, Owen. Reading Architecture: A Visual Lexicon. 2012. (ENG., Illus.). 176p. pap. 29.95 ***(978-1-85669-736-1(3))*** King, Laurence Publishing GBR. Dist: Hachette Bk. Group.

Hopwood, Rosalind. Fountains & Water Features: From Ancient Springs to Modern Marvels. 2009. (ENG., Illus.). 208p. 65.00 *(978-0-7112-2751-4(9))* Lincoln, Frances Ltd. GBR. Dist: Perseus-PGW.

Horwitz, Carolyn & Iannacci, Anthony, eds. Natural Histories: Public Art. 2010. (ENG., Illus.). 194p. 70.00 *(978-0-9823190-2-4(9))* Architecture Interiors Pr., Inc.

Hudson, Karen E. Paul R. Williams: Classic Hollywood Style. 2012. (ENG., Illus.). 240p. 65.00 ***(978-0-8478-3847-9(1))*** Rizzoli International Pubns., Inc.

Hyatt, Peter, ed. Masters of Light: Designing the Luminous House. 2007. (ENG., Illus.). 256p. 65.00 *(978-1-86470-172-2(2))* Images Publishing Group AUS. Dist: National Bk. Network.

Images Publishing Group Editors. International Architecture Yearbook, Vol. 7. 2006. (ENG., Illus.). 75.00 *(978-1-86470-103-6(X))* Images Publishing Group AUS. Dist: National Bk. Network.

Images Staff & Images. Interior Spaces of the USA & Canada: A Pictorial Review, Vol. 6. 2006. (ENG., Illus.). 224p. 55.00 *(978-1-86470-107-4(2))* Images Publishing Group AUS. Dist: National Bk. Network.

Imhof, Michael & Krempel, León. Berlin: New Architecture - A Guide to the New Buildings from 1989 to Today. 6th ed. 2009. (ENG., Illus.). 163p. pap. 19.80 *(978-3-935590-15-0(6)*, Art Stock Bks. Ltd/Csi) Continental Sales, Inc.

Ingels, Bjarke. Yes Is More: An Archicomic on Architectural Evolution. 2009. (ENG., Illus.). 400p. pap. 29.99 *(978-3-8365-2010-2(9)*, Evergreen) TASCHEN DEU. Dist: Ingram Pub. Services.

Jodidio, Philip. Architecture Now 6! Architektur heute. L'architecture d'aujourd'hui. (25 Ser.). (Illus.). 2010. (ENG, FRE & GER.). 352p. 14.99 *(978-3-8365-2345-5(0))* Vol. 6. 2009. (FRE, GER & ENG., 576p. pap. 39.99 *(978-3-8365-0193-4(7))* TASCHEN DEU. Dist: Ingram Pub. Services.

—Architecture Now! 7. 2010. (GER, FRE & ENG., Illus.). 480p. pap. 39.99 *(978-3-8365-1736-2(1))* TASCHEN DEU. Dist: Ingram Pub. Services.

—Architecture Now! 8. 2012. (ENG, FRE & GER., Illus.). 480p. 39.99 ***(978-3-8365-2681-4(6))*** TASCHEN DEU. Dist: Ingram Pub. Services.

Jodidio, Philip. 100 Contemporary Architects, 2 vols. Volk, Annick, ed. 25th ed. 2008. (FRE, GER & ENG., Illus.). 848p. 59.99 *(978-3-8365-0091-3(4))* TASCHEN DEU. Dist: Ingram Pub. Services.

Keetman, Tasja, photos by. Pura Vida. 2010. (ENG., Illus.). 180p. 40.00 *(978-0-9819857-7-0(7))* Oro Editions.

Keister, Douglas. 500 Bungalows. 2006. (ENG., Illus.). 508p. pap. 12.95 *(978-1-56158-842-8(3)*, Taunton) Taunton Pr., Inc.

Keister, Douglas, photos by. 500 Cottages. 2006. (ENG., Illus.). 509p. pap. 12.95 *(978-1-56158-843-5(1)*, Taunton) Taunton Pr., Inc.

King, Helen H. Historic Isle of Wight. 2nd ed. 2007. *(978-1-57864-420-9(8))* Donning Co. Pubs.

Klett, Arne A. & Ballmann, Karen. Asian Design Destinations: From the Middle East to the Far East. 2010. 74p. 69.99 *(978-0-8416-7162-1(1))* Langenscheidt Publishing Group.

Koch, Ebba. The Complete Taj Mahal. 2006. (ENG., Illus.). 288p. 75.00 *(978-0-500-34209-1(1))* Thames & Hudson.

Koivisto, Maritta. Concrete Architecture in Finland. 2009. (Illus.). 132p. 69.00 *(978-951-682-888-9(4))* Rakennustieto oy FIN. Dist: Independent Pubs. Group.

Konrad, Benjamin & Novotny, Maik. Eastmodern: Architecture & Design of the 1960s & 1970s in Slovakia. 2007. (ENG., Illus.). 238p. pap. 59.95 *(978-3-211-71531-4(2)*, 3211715312) Springer.

Kos, Eric J. San Francisco Then & Now. 2nd ed. 2009. (Then & Now Thunder Bay Ser.). (ENG.). 144p. 19.95 *(978-1-60710-003-4(7)*, Thunder Bay Pr.) Advantage Pubs. Group.

Kos, Eric J. & Evanosky, Dennis. San Francisco Then & Now (Compact) 2011. (Then & Now Thunder Bay Ser.). (ENG., Illus.). 144p. pap. 12.95 *(978-1-60710-195-6(5)*, Thunder Bay Pr.) Advantage Pubs. Group.

Kratochvil, Antonin, ed. Inside: The Chelsea Hotel. 2007. (ENG., Illus.). 208p. 49.95 *(978-1-57687-406-6(0))* powerHouse Cultural Entertainment, Inc.

Krauel, Jacobo. Today's Wood Houses. 2010. (ENG., Illus.). 240p. 39.00 *(978-84-92796-53-3(7))* Links International (Leading International Key Services Barcelona, S.A.) ESP. Dist: National Bk. Network.

Krzyzanowski, Michal. Laverne: Furniture, Textiles, & Wallcoverings. 2007. (Illus.). 240p. pap. 49.95 *(978-0-7643-2735-3(6))* Schiffer Publishing, Ltd.

Lahtti, Marku & Rakennustieto Publishing Staff. Alvar Aalto: A Gentler Structure for Life. 2009. (ENG, GER, ITA & FIN., Illus.). 176p. 99.00 *(978-951-682-475-1(7))* Rakennustieto oy FIN. Dist: Independent Pubs. Group.

Lam, Benson & Bin, Xu. Iconic storefronts USA. 2009. (ENG.). 502p. 59.00 *(978-84-96969-63-6(0))* Links International (Leading International Key Services Barcelona, S.A.) ESP. Dist: National Bk. Network.

Leroux, John & Holownia, Thaddeus. St. Andrews Architecture, 1604-1966. 2010. (ENG.). 144p. pap. *(978-1-55447-094-5(3))* Gaspereau Pr.

Li, George. Residence Award. 2011. (ENG., Illus.). 320p. 60.00 *(978-988-19738-9-4(9))* Design Media Publishing Ltd. HKG. Dist: BookMasters Distribution Services (BDS).

Linke, Armin & Jovanovic Weiss, Srdjan. Socialist Architecture: The Vanishing ACT. 2012. (ENG., Illus.). 132p. 75.00 ***(978-3-03764-245-0(9))*** JRP Ringier Kunstverlag AG CHE. Dist: D.A.P./Distributed Art Pubs.

Lowell, Guy. Small Italian Villas & Farmhouses. 2008. (Illus.). 314p. bds. 39.95 *(978-0-7643-2706-3(2))* Schiffer Publishing, Ltd.

MacLean, Alex. Up on the Roof: New York's Hidden Skyline Spaces. 2012. (ENG., Illus.). 240p. 50.00 ***(978-1-61689-050-6(9))*** Princeton Architectural Pr.

Manferto De Fabianis, Valeria, ed. Wonders of Italy. 2010. (CubeBook Ser.). (ENG., Illus.). 504p. 14.95 *(978-88-544-0545-5(0))* White Star ITA. Dist: Sterling Publishing Co., Inc.

Martí, Néstor. Old Havana - La Habana Vieja: Spirit of the Living City - El Espiritu de la Ciudad Viva. 2012. (SPA & ENG.). 228p. 49.95 ***(978-0-8173-1762-1(7))*** Univ. of Alabama Pr.

Martin, Mary L. & Skinner, Tina. Architecture of Old Mexico: Vintage Views of Spanish Colonial Courtyards, Facades, Streetscapes & Interiors. 2007. (Illus.). 144p. pap. 29.95 *(978-0-7643-2571-7(X))* Schiffer Publishing, Ltd.

McLeod, Virginia. Detail in Contemporary Bathroom Design. 2009. (ENG., Illus.). 192p. 45.00 *(978-1-85669-590-9(5))* King, Laurence Publishing GBR. Dist: Hachette Bk. Group.

Meek, A. J., photos by. Sacred Light: Holy Places in Louisiana. 2010. (ENG.). 112p. 35.00 *(978-1-60473-741-7(7))* Univ. Pr. of Mississippi.

Morgan, William. American Country Churches. 2006. (ENG., Illus.). 240p. 19.98 *(978-0-8109-8254-3(4))* Abrams.

MulvannyG2 Architecture. Design at Work. 2008. (Illus.). 148p. 50.00 *(978-1-58471-155-1(8))* Visual Reference Pubns., Inc.

Nakamori, Yasufumi. Katsura: Picturing Modernism in Japanese Architecture. 2010. (Illus.). 168p. 50.00 *(978-0-300-16333-9(9))* Museum of Fine Arts, Houston.

Neith, Jack. Power Rooms: Executive Offices, Corporate Lobbies, & Conference Rooms. 2008. (Illus.). 160p. bds. 49.95 *(978-0-7643-2920-3(0))* Schiffer Publishing, Ltd.

Nepilly, Ellen. Hip Dining Japan. 2008. (Illus.). 192p. *(978-981-245-487-4(X))* Page One Publishing.

Olsen, Russell A. Route 66 Lost & Found: Mother Road Ruins & Relics - The Ultimate Collection. 2011. (ENG., Illus.). 420p. pap. 30.00 *(978-0-7603-3998-5(8)*, 0760339988, Voyageur Pr) MBI Publishing Co. LLC.

Pahlke, Eric. San Diego County Victorians. 2008. 80p. pap. *(978-0-9800950-0-5(X))* Our Heritage Pr.

Palmer, Michele. Gingerbread Gems of Willimantic, Connecticut. 2007. (Illus.). 112p. pap. 19.95 *(978-0-7643-2603-5(1))* Schiffer Publishing, Ltd.

Panache Partners LLC Staff, ed. Dream Homes Coastal California: An Exclusive Showcase of the Finest Architects, Designers & Builders of California's Central Coast Including Santa Barbara, San Luis Obispo & Monterey Counties. 2008. (Dream Homes Ser.). (ENG., Illus.). 224p. 34.95 *(978-1-933415-50-5(9))* Panache Partners, LLC.

Paolucci, Antonio. The Tempio Malatestiano in Rimini, 2 vols. Settis, Salvatore, ed. 2011. (ITA & ENG., Illus.). 608p. 815.00 *(978-88-248-0353-3(9))* Panini Franco Cosimo ITA. Dist: National Bk. Network.

Pategas, Stephen G & Pategas, Kristin. Southern Coastal Home Landscaping. 2011. (Landscaping Ser.). (ENG., Illus.). 176p. (gr. 5). pap. 16.95 *(978-1-58011-510-0(1))* Creative Homeowner.

Pawson, John. A Visual Inventory. 2012. (ENG., Illus.). 320p. 49.95 ***(978-0-7148-6350-4(5))*** Phaidon Pr., Inc.

Payne, Richard. Texas Towns & the Art of Architecture: A Photographer's Journey. 2006. (ENG., Illus.). 200p. 49.95 *(978-0-87611-218-2(1))* Texas State Historical Assn.

Penrose, Sefryn. Images of Change: An Archaeology of England's Contemporary Landscape. Penrose, Sefryn, ed. 2007. (ENG., Illus.). 200p. (C). 36.00 *(978-1-905624-14-0(X))* English Heritage GBR. Dist: Brown, David Bk. Co., The.

Phaidon Press Editors, ed. 10x10 - 3: 100 Architects 10 Critics. 2009. (ENG., Illus.). 468p. 90.00 *(978-0-7148-4953-9(7))* Phaidon Pr., Inc.

Pla Boada, Ricard & Cirlot, Juan Eduardo. Gaudi, 1 vol. 2011. (ENG., Illus.). 424p. 68.00 *(978-84-8478-034-2(1))* Triangle Postals, S.L. ESP. Dist: Innovative Logistics.

Powell, Kenneth. 21st Century London: The New Architecture. 2011. (ENG., Illus.). 352p. 34.95 *(978-1-85894-537-8(2))* Merrell Pubs. Ltd. GBR. Dist: Perseus Distribution.

Pryce, Will. World Architecture: The Masterworks. 2008. (ENG., Illus.). 320p. 80.00 *(978-0-500-34248-0(2)*, 534248) Thames & Hudson.

Quartino, Daniela Santos. 200 Outstanding Apartment Ideas. 2009. (200 Home Ideas Ser.). (ENG., Illus.). 800p. 39.95 *(978-1-55407-394-8(4))* Firefly Bks., Ltd.

Rattee, Kathryn, ed. Red Summer in Kensington Gardens. 2012. (ENG., Illus.). 44p. pap. 44.95 *(978-3-86560-860-4(4))* Verlag der Buchhandlung Walther Konig DEU. Dist: D.A.P./Distributed Art Pubs.

Richmond, Arthur P. Cottages of Oak Bluffs: 20 Postcards. 2007. (Illus.). 40p. pap. 9.95 *(978-0-7643-2683-7(X))* Schiffer Publishing, Ltd.

Rindoks, Leslie, ed. Our Vanishing Americana: A North Carolina Portrait. 2006. 44.95 *(978-0-9704651-9-1(X))* Lorimer Pr.

Rooney, E. Ashley. Shingle Style Architecture for the 21st Century. 2010. (Illus.). 176p. 49.99 *(978-0-7643-3551-8(0))* Schiffer Publishing, Ltd.

Ross, Richard, photos by. Architecture of Authority, 1 vol. 2007. (ENG., Illus.). 144p. 40.00 *(978-1-59711-052-5(3))* Aperture Foundation, Inc.

Royal Palaces of Korea. 2009. 56.00 *(978-981-08-0806-8(2))* World Scientific Publishing Co., Inc.

Ruthven, Ianthe. Animal London. 2011. (ENG., Illus.). 174p. pap. 19.95 ***(978-0-224-08704-9(5))*** Random Hse. GBR. Dist: Independent Pubs. Group.

Salvaing, Matthieu. Oscar Niemeyer. ltd. ed. 2008. *(978-2-7594-0293-9(2))* Assouline.

Schaller, Matthias Petrus. Matthias Schaller: Controfacciata, 1 vol. 2008. (ENG., Illus.). 68p. 50.00 *(978-3-86521-674-8(9))* Steidl, Gerhard Druckerei und Verlag DEU. Dist: Innovative Logistics.

Schulz, Daniel. Global Creative Architecture. 2008. (Illus.). 271p. *(978-981-245-543-7(4))* Page One Publishing.

Seavey, Kent. Carmel: A History in Architecture. 2007. (Images of America Ser.). (ENG., Illus.). 128p. per. 19.99 *(978-0-7385-4705-3(0))* Arcadia Publishing.

Seidler, Harry. The Grand Tour. 25th ed. 2007. (ENG., Illus.). 575p. pap. 14.99 *(978-3-8228-3780-1(6))* TASCHEN DEU. Dist: Ingram Pub. Services.

Serraino, Pierluigi. Julius Shulman - Modernism Rediscovered: Die wiederentdeckte Moderne. 25th ed. 2009. (ENG, FRE & GER., Illus.). 415p. 29.99 *(978-3-8365-0326-6(3))* TASCHEN DEU. Dist: Ingram Pub. Services.

Sewall, Jock. Mediterranean Architecture: A Sourcebook of Architectural Elements. 2011. (Illus.). 432p. 100.00 ***(978-0-7643-3891-5(9)***, Schiffer Publishing Ltd) Schiffer Publishing, Ltd.

Sframeli, Maria. Firenze 1892-1895: Immagini Dell'antico Centro Scomparso. 2007. (ITA., Illus.). 319p. (C). 69.50 *(978-88-596-0246-0(7))* Edizioni Polistampa ITA. Dist: Brown, David Bk. Co., The.
Skinner, Tina. Lowcountry Plantations: Georgia & South Carolina. 2010. (Illus.). 144p. 29.99 *(978-0-7643-3415-3(8))* Schiffer Publishing, Ltd.
—Showhouse Review: An Exposé of Interior Decorating Events. 2008. (Illus.). 224p. bds. 44.95 *(978-0-7643-2864-0(6))* Schiffer Publishing, Ltd.
—Wine Cellar Design. 2008. (Illus.). 256p. bds. 49.95 *(978-0-7643-2862-6(X))* Schiffer Publishing, Ltd.
Smith, Joel. More Than One: Photographs in Sequence. Smith, Joel, ed. 2009. (ENG., Illus.). 96p. pap. 25.00 *(978-0-300-14930-2(1))* Yale Univ. Pr.
Smith, Joel, et al. More Than One: Photographs in Sequence. Smith, Joel, ed. 2008. (Illus.). 120p. pap. *(978-0-943012-01-8(5))* Princeton Univ. Art Museum.
Snow, Dan. Listening to Stone: Hardy Structures, Perilous Follies, & Other Tangles with Nature. 2008. (ENG., Illus.). 145p. 23.95 *(978-1-57965-371-2(5),* 1579653715) Artisan.
Stamp, Gavin. Britain's Lost Cities: A Chronicle of Architectural Destruction. 2010. (ENG.). 186p. pap. 29.95 *(978-1-84513-523-2(7))* Aurum Pr., Ltd. GBR. Dist: Independent Pubs. Group.
Stanley. Complete Flooring. 2008. (ENG., Illus.). 240p. pap. 21.95 *(978-0-696-23838-3(1),* Wiley) Wiley, John & Sons, Inc.
Steffens, Jo, ed. Unpacking My Library: Architects & Their Books. 2009. (ENG., Illus.). 192p. 20.00 *(978-0-300-15893-9(9))* Yale Univ. Pr.
Steinbrunn, Robert N. Large Scale Armor Modeling: Building a 1/6 Scale Stuart Tank. 2011. (Illus.). 160p. 45.00 ***(978-0-7643-3953-0(2),*** Schiffer Publishing Ltd) Schiffer Publishing, Ltd.
Stoeltie, Barbara. Rooms to Remember: Interiors Inspired by the Past. 2006. (Illus.). 168p. 45.00 *(978-0-7112-1298-5(8))* Lincoln, Frances Ltd. GBR. Dist: Perseus-PGW.
Tate, Ken. A Classical Journey: The Houses of Ken Tate. 2011. (ENG., Illus.). 438p. 65.00 *(978-1-86470-290-3(7),* Images Publishing Dist Ac) Antique Collectors' Club GBR. Dist: National Bk. Network.
Tei, Shuwa. Intertionalies: Shaping Japan & Beyond. 2011. (ENG., Illus.). 280p. 59.00 ***(978-90-77174-34-0(6))*** Frame Pubs. NLD. Dist: Consortium Bk. Sales & Distribution.
Temple, Nicholas. Disclosing Horizons: Architecture, Perspective & Redemptive Space. 2006. (Illus.). 306p. per. 64.95 *(978-0-415-28357-1(4))* Routledge.
teNeues. Ecological Hotels. 2010. (Illus.). 220p. 59.95 *(978-3-8327-9370-8(4))* teNeues Publishing Co.
Tittoni, Maria Elisa, ed. La Roma di Achille Pinelli: Water Colour Works, 1832-1835. 2010. 73p. pap. 29.95 *(978-88-492-1303-4(4))* Gangemi ITA. Dist: International Publishers Marketing.
Touchaleaume, Eric, ed. Le Corbusier, Pierre Jeanneret: The Indian Story. 2011. (FRE & ENG., Illus.). 600p. 180.00 *(978-2-35340-099-7(X))* Gourcuff Gradenigo FRA. Dist: National Bk. Network.
V., Architekturbild E. In between I Dazwischen: Europäischer Architekturfotografie-Preis 2011. 2011. (ENG.). 120p. 38.00 *(978-3-89985-159-4(0),* Avedition Gmbh,Csi) Continental Sales, Inc.
Verderber, Stephen. Delirious New Orleans: Manifesto for an Extraordinary American City. 2009. (Roger Fullington Series in Architecture). (ENG., Illus.). 288p. 45.00 *(978-0-292-71753-4(9))* Univ. of Texas Pr.
Vilchis, Ricardo Legorreta, et al. Lopez Guerra: Architecture: A Discipline of Service. 2007. (Architectural Ser.). (ENG., Illus.). 144p. pap. 40.00 *(978-88-7838-086-8(5),* Art Stock Bks. Ltd/Csi) Continental Sales, Inc.
Visit London (Organization) Staff, contrib. by. Iconic London. 2007. (ENG., Illus.). 120p. 9.95 *(978-0-7095-8417-9(2))* VisitBritain GBR. Dist: Globe Pequot Pr., The.
Visscher, Jochen, ed. Havana: The Sleeping Beauty. 2008. (GER, SPA & ENG., Illus.). 96p. 19.95 *(978-3-939633-36-5(4))* Jovis Verlag GmbH DEU. Dist: D.A.P./Distributed Art Pubs.
Vranckx, Bridget & Moreno, Esther. 200 Outstanding House Ideas. 2009. (200 Home Ideas Ser.). (ENG., Illus.). 800p. 39.95 *(978-1-55407-393-1(6))* Firefly Bks., Ltd.
Weinberg, David. Towering Mirrors, Mirroring Towers: Photographs of Urban Reflections. 2006. (ENG., Illus.). 96p. 50.00 *(978-0-9777531-2-3(3))* Glitterati, Inc.
Welch, Diane Y. Lilian J. Rice: Architect of Rancho Santa Fe, California. 2010. (Illus.). 224p. 49.99 *(978-0-7643-3456-6(5))* Schiffer Publishing, Ltd.
Whitsitt, Steven Paul & Marth, Jesse. Built with Stone: Eight Contemporary Artisans. 2011. (Illus.). 144p. 39.99 ***(978-0-7643-3941-7(9),*** Schiffer Publishing Ltd) Schiffer Publishing, Ltd.
Williamson, Leslie. Handcrafted Modern: At Home with Mid-Century Designers. 2010. (ENG., Illus.). 224p. 45.00 *(978-0-8478-3418-1(2))* Rizzoli International Pubns., Inc.
Wimczorek, Uwe. Sean Scully: Die Architektur der Farbe. 2008. (ENG., Illus.). 72p. pap. 19.95 *(978-88-7439-315-2(6))* 5 Continents ITA. Dist: Hachette Bk. Group.
Wright, Ruth M. Machu Picchu Revealed. 2008. 128p. 16.95 *(978-1-55566-424-4(5))* Johnson Bks.
Wu, Yang, ed. Atlas of World Architecture. 2011. (ENG.). 508p. 80.00 *(978-988-19739-7-9(X))* Design Media Publishing Ltd. HKG. Dist: BookMasters Distribution Services (BDS).
Zander, Jean-Paul Deridder City of Children, Berlin: City of Transience. 2009. (ENG.). 104p. 60.00 *(978-3-7757-2286-5(6))* Hatje Cantz Verlag GmbH & Co KG DEU. Dist: D.A.P./Distributed Art Pubs.
Zanta, Marco. Urbaneurope. 2008. (ENG., Illus.). 150p. 49.00 *(978-88-6965-106-9(1))* Contrasto DUE ITA. Dist: Consortium Bk. Sales & Distribution.

ARCHITECTURE—PROPORTION

see Architecture—Composition, Proportion, etc.

ARCHITECTURE—PSYCHOLOGICAL ASPECTS

Aldrete-Haas, José Antonio. Arquitectura y Percepción. 2007. (SPA., Illus.). 157p. *(978-968-859-630-2(2))* Universidad Iberoamericana, A.C.
Architecture & the Brain: A New Knowledge Base from Neuroscience. 2007. 144p. pap. 39.00 *(978-0-9785552-1-4(X),* Ostberg) Greenway Communications.
Arnheim, Rudolf & Arnheim, R. The Dynamics of Architectural Form. 30th anniv. ed. 2009. (ENG., Illus.). 289p. pap. 24.95 *(978-0-520-26125-9(9))* Univ. of California Pr.
Augustin, Sally & Augustin. Place Advantage: Applied Psychology for Interior Architecture. 2009. (ENG., Illus.). 320p. 80.00 *(978-0-470-42212-0(2),* Wiley) Wiley, John & Sons, Inc.
Binder, Thomas, et al. Design Things. 2011. (Design Thinking, Design Theory Ser.). (ENG., Illus.). 256p. (gr. 17). 30.00 ***(978-0-262-01627-8(3))*** MIT Pr.
Boubekri, Mohamed. Daylighting, Architecture & Health: Building Design Strategies. 2008. (ENG., Illus.). 160p. pap. 59.95 *(978-0-7506-6724-1(9))* Routledge.
Brott, Simone. Architecture for a Free Subjectivity: Deleuze & Guattari at the Horizon of the Real. 2011. 150p. 99.95 *(978-1-4094-1995-2(9))* Ashgate Publishing Co.
Bruno, Giuliana & Clark, Robin, texts. Automatic Cities. 2009. (ENG., Illus.). 160p. 32.95 *(978-0-934418-71-3(3))* Museum of Contemporary Art, San Diego.
de Botton, Alain. The Architecture of Happiness. 2008. (Vintage Ser.). (ENG., Illus.). 288p. pap. 18.00 *(978-0-307-27724-4(0),* Vintage) Knopf Doubleday Publishing Group.
—The Architecture of Happiness. 2008. (ENG., Illus.). 288p. pap. *(978-0-7710-2607-2(2),* McClelland & Stewart) McClelland & Stewart CAN. Dist: Random Hse., Inc.
Devlin, Ann Sloan. What Americans Build & Why: Psychological Perspectives. 2010. (ENG., Illus.). 316p. (C). 90.00 *(978-0-521-51657-0(9));* pap. 27.99 *(978-0-521-73435-6(5))* Cambridge Univ. Pr.
Dooley, Scott, et al. Make Space: How to Set the Stage for Creative Collaboration. 2012. (ENG., Illus.). 272p. pap. 49.95 ***(978-1-118-14372-8(8),*** Wiley) Wiley, John & Sons, Inc.
Gallagher, Winifred. House Thinking: A Room-by-Room Look at How We Live. 2007. (P. S. Ser.). (ENG., Illus.). 368p. pap. 14.95 *(978-0-06-053880-4(5),* HarperPerennial) HarperCollins Pubs.
Gerber Architekten. Stadtraume Orte Architektur/Urban Spaces Loci Architecture, 1 vol. 2007. (GER & ENG., Illus.). 252p. 65.00 *(978-3-8030-0666-0(X))* Wasmuth, Ernst J. Verlag GmbH & Co. DEU. Dist: D.A.P./Distributed Art Pubs.
Goldberger, Paul. Why Architecture Matters. (Why X Matters Ser.). (Illus.). 304p. 2011. (ENG.). pap. 16.00 *(978-0-300-16817-4(9))* 2009. 26.00 *(978-0-300-14430-7(X))* Yale Univ. Pr.
Gutman, Robert, ed. People & Buildings. 2009. (ENG., Illus.). 492p. pap. 44.95 *(978-1-4128-0993-1(2))* Transaction Pubs.
Hornstein, Shelley. Losing Site: Architecture Memory & Place. 2011. (Ashgate Studies in Architecture Ser.). (Illus.). 182p. 89.95 ***(978-1-4094-0871-0(X))*** Ashgate Publishing Co.
Kelley, Mike. On the Beyond: A Conversation between Mike Kelley, Jim Shaw & John C. Welchman. 2011. (Kunst und Architektur im Gespräch Art & Architecture in Discussion(closed) Ser.). (Illus.). 128p. pap. 39.95 *(978-3-7091-0260-2(X),* 370910260X) Springer Wien AUT. Dist: Springer.
Kenda, Barbara, ed. Aeolian Winds & the Spirit in Renaissance Architecture: Academia Eolia Revisted. 2006. (Illus.). 175p. 170.00 *(978-0-415-39803-9(7));* per. 63.95 *(978-0-415-39804-6(5))* Routledge.
Koeck, Richard. Cine-scapes: Cinematic Spaces in Architecture & Cities. 2012. (ENG., Illus.). 240p. (C). 165.00 *(978-0-415-60078-1(2));* pap. 49.95 *(978-0-415-60079-8(0))* Routledge.
Mac Gregor, Arcelia. Spacing Out_. 2010. 168p. pap. *(978-3-639-22506-8(6))* VDM Verlag Dr. Mueller e.K.
Mahady, Michaela. Welcoming Home: Creating a House That Says Hello. 2010. (ENG., Illus.). 224p. 40.00 *(978-1-4236-0321-4(4))* Gibbs Smith, Publisher.
Mallgrave, Harry Francis. The Architect's Brain: Neuroscience, Creativity, & Architecture. 2011. (ENG., Illus.). 288p. pap. 34.95 *(978-0-470-65825-3(8),* Wiley-Blackwell) Wiley, John & Sons, Inc.
Martinussen, Kent. Sxn: Mind your Behaviour. 2010. (Illus.). 276p. pap. *(978-87-993680-0-6(5))* Actar Birkhauser Distribution.
Moore, William D. Masonic Temples: Freemasonry, Ritual Architecture, & Masculine Archetypes. 2006. (Illus.). 272p. 34.95 *(978-1-57233-496-0(7))* Univ. of Tennessee Pr.
Moss, Gloria. Gender, Design & Marketing: How Gender Drives Our Perception of Design & Marketing. 2009. (Illus.). 268p. 124.95 *(978-0-566-08786-8(3),* Gower Publishing Co., Ltd.) Ashgate Publishing, Ltd. GBR. Dist: Ashgate Publishing Co.
Nanda, Upali. Sensthetics. 2008. 200p. pap. *(978-3-8364-3790-5(2))* VDM Verlag Dr. Mueller e.K.
Odgers, Jo, et al, eds. Primitive: Original Matters in Architecture. 2006. (Illus.). 284p. 170.00 *(978-0-415-38538-1(5))* Routledge.
Pelletier, Louise. Architecture in Words: Theatre, Language & the Sensuous Space of Architecture. 2006. (Illus.). XII, 244p. 165.00 *(978-0-415-39470-3(8),* RT708X) Routledge.
Perdue, Justin. Scratches & Indentations - Architecture & the Importance of Home. 2009. 148p. pap. *(978-3-639-10784-5(5))* VDM Verlag Dr. Mueller e.K.
Quillien, Jenny. Delight's Muse on Christopher Alexander's the Nature of Order: A Summary & Personal Interpretation. 2008. (Illus.). 186p. pap. 65.95 *(978-1-4303-1317-5(X))* Lulu Enterprises Inc.
Richards, Simon. Architect Knows Best Environmental Determinism in Architecture Culture from 1956 to Present. 2012. (Ashgate Studies in Architecture Ser.). (Illus.). 202p. 99.95 ***(978-1-4094-3922-6(4))*** Ashgate Publishing Co.
Ruan, Xing & Hogben, Paul, eds. Topophilia & Topophobia: Reflections on Twentieth-Century Human Habitat. 2008. (Illus.). (ENG.). 248p. (C). 165.00 *(978-0-415-40323-8(5));* CCXXXIV, 14p. 47.95 *(978-0-415-40324-5(3))* Routledge.
Samuel, Flora. Primitive: Original Matters in Architecture. Odgers, Jo & Sharr, Adam, eds. 2006. (Illus.). 304p. (C). 74.95 *(978-0-415-38539-8(3))* Routledge.
Sarquis, Jorge. Investigación y Conocimiento: Filosofía, Artes y Ciencias, Arquitectura, Diseño y Urbanismo: Coloquio. 2010. (SPA., Illus.). 277p. *(978-987-584-256-4(7))* Nobuko.
Smith, Peter F. The Dynamics of Urbanism. 2007. (Illus.). 256p. 190.00 *(978-0-415-41738-9(4))* Routledge.
—Syntax of Cities. 2007. (Illus.). 271p. 180.00 *(978-0-415-41838-6(0))* Routledge.
Susanka, Sarah. The Not So Big House: A Blueprint for the Way We Really Live. 2008. (Susanka Ser.). (ENG., Illus.). 227p. 32.00 *(978-1-60085-047-9(2),* Taunton) Taunton Pr., Inc.
—The Not So Big House Book. 2006. *(978-1-56158-929-6(2))* Taunton Pr., Inc.
Susanka, Sarah & Obolensky, Kira. The Not So Big House: A Blueprint for the Way We Really Live. 10th ed. 2009. (ENG., Illus.). 240p. pap. 24.95 *(978-1-60085-150-6(9))* Taunton Pr., Inc.
Treib, Marc. Spatial Recall: Memory in Architecture & Landscape. 2009. (ENG., Illus.). 272p. (C). 55.95 *(978-0-415-77736-0(4));* 155.00 *(978-0-415-77735-3(6))* Routledge.
Walden, Rotraut, ed. Schools for the Future: Design Proposals from Architectural Psychology. 2008. (Illus.). 264p. pap. 49.00 *(978-0-88937-351-8(5))* Hogrefe Publishing.
Wernick, Jane. Building Happiness: Architecutre to Make You Smile. McCorquodale, Duncan, ed. 2008. (ENG., Illus.). 173p. pap. 45.00 *(978-1-906155-45-9(1))* Black Dog Publishing Ltd. GBR. Dist: Perseus Distribution.
Wescoat, Bonna D. & Ousterhout, Robert G. Architecture of the Sacred: Space, Ritual, & Experience from Classical Greece to Byzantium. 2012. (ENG., Illus.). 440p. 99.00 ***(978-1-107-00823-6(9))*** Cambridge Univ. Pr.

ARCHITECTURE—RESTORATION

see Architecture—Conservation and Restoration

ARCHITECTURE—SKETCH-BOOKS

see also Architectural Rendering; Architecture—Designs and Plans

Schank Smith, Kendra. Architects Sketches: Dialogue & Design. 2008. (ENG., Illus.). 152p. 59.95 *(978-0-7506-8226-8(4))* Routledge.
Tchoban, Sergei. The Head of the Architect: Drawings & Architecture, 1 vol. 2006. (ENG & GER., Illus.). 192p. 60.00 *(978-3-936314-60-1(8))* Jovis Verlag GmbH DEU. Dist: D.A.P./Distributed Art Pubs.

ARCHITECTURE—STUDY AND TEACHING

Ang, Susan. Valuing Practical Experience. 2011. 240p. pap. ***(978-3-8443-2184-5(5))*** Lambert Academic Publishing.
Bairstow, A. & Roaf, Susan. The Oxford Conference: A Re-Evaluation of Education in Architecture. Roaf, S. & Bairstow, A., eds. 2008. (Illus.). 480p. 316.00 *(978-1-84564-206-8(6))* WIT Pr GBR. Dist: WIT Pr.
BarCharts, Inc. Spanish for Construction 2. 2009. (ENG.). 6p. 5.95 *(978-1-4232-0428-2(X))* Barcharts, Inc.
Behnisch, Stefan, et al. Poetry, Property, & Place 01: Stefan Behnisch, Gerald Hines. Rappaport, Nina, ed. 2006. (Edward P. Bass Distinguished Visiting Architecture Fellowship Ser.). (ENG., Illus.). 192p. pap. 35.00 *(978-0-393-73220-7(7),* 73220) Norton, W. W. & Co., Inc.
Belibani, Rosalba & Panunzi, Stefano, eds. E-learning for Architecture. 2011. 160p. pap. 30.00 *(978-88-492-2026-1(X))* Gangemi ITA. Dist: International Publishers Marketing.
Borden, Iain, ed. Bartlett Designs: Speculating with Architecture. 2009. (ENG., Illus.). 256p. 70.00 *(978-0-470-77280-5(8),* Wiley) Wiley, John & Sons, Inc.
Broekhuizen, Dolf, et al, texts. Contemporary Dutch School Architecture. 2009. (ENG., Illus.). 264p. 70.00 *(978-90-5662-656-3(6))* NAi Uitgevers / Publishers Stichting NLD. Dist: D.A.P./Distributed Art Pubs.
Browning, Gavin, ed. The Studio-X New York Guide to Liberating New Forms of Conversation. 2011. (ENG., Illus.). 194p. pap. 15.00 *(978-1-883584-65-8(5))* Columbia Univ., Graduate Schl. of Architecture.
Cramer, James P., ed. America's Best Architecture & Design Schools 2007. 2006. 90p. pap. 39.95 *(978-0-9785552-0-7(1),* Ostberg) Greenway Communications.
D'Hooghe, Alexander & Dunbar, Sarah, eds. Certain Agendas in Architecture: 2006: One Year of Student Research at MIT's Department of Architecture. 2007. (Illus.). 320p. pap. 20.00 *(978-0-9794774-0-9(9))* SA+P Pr.
Dodds, George. Clemson University 2009 Architectural Research Studio. 2010. 261p. pap. 82.30 *(978-0-557-60459-3(1))* Lulu Enterprises Inc.
Frederick, Matthew. 101 Things I Learned in Architecture School. 2007. (ENG., Illus.). 216p. (gr. 17). 14.95 *(978-0-262-06266-4(6))* MIT Pr.
—101 Things I Learned in Architecture School: The Ultimate Cheat Sheet for Surviving an Architectural Education. 2007. pap. *(978-0-262-56228-7(6))* MIT Pr.
French, Touch, ed. Optimistic Architecture Year Book/ Annuel Optimiste D'Architecture. 2008. 360p. *(978-2-9531421-0-5(X))* Actar Birkhauser Distribution.
Hadighi, Mehrdad, et al, contrib. by. Banham in Buffalo: 5 Years of the P. Reyner Banham Fellowships at the University at Buffalo School of Architecture. 2011. (ENG., Illus.). 120p. pap. 24.95 *(978-0-9826226-7-4(8))* Oro Editions.
Hardin, Mary C., ed. From the Studio to the Streets. 2006. (AAHE's Series on Service-Learning in the Disciplines). (Illus.). 240p. (C). pap. 29.50 *(978-1-56377-100-2(4))* Stylus Publishing, LLC.
Henderson, Holley. Becoming a Green Building Professional: A Guide to Careers in Sustainable Architecture, Design, Engineering, Development, & Operations. 2012. (Wiley Series in Sustainable Design Ser.: 33). (ENG., Illus.). 576p. pap. 44.95 ***(978-0-470-95143-9(5),*** Wiley) Wiley, John & Sons, Inc.
Highway Bridge Inspections: Hearing Before the Subcommittee on Highways & Transit of the Committee on Transportation & Infrastructure, House of Representatives, One Hundred Tenth Congress, First Session, October 23, 2007. 2007. (Illus.). xiv, 131p. *(978-0-16-083395-3(7),* 552-070-39208-4) United States Government Printing Office.
Howeler, Eric, ed. GSD Platform 4. 2011. (ENG.). 368p. ***(978-84-15391-00-5(5))*** Actar Birkhauser Distribution.
Janko, Joan. The Chapel of the Assumption of the Virgin in Spissk² Stvrtok. 2008. 96p. pap. *(978-3-639-04289-4(1))* VDM Verlag Dr. Mueller e.K.
Jetsonen, Jari, ed. Little Big Houses: Working with Architectural Models. 2008. (Illus.). 176p. pap. 39.00 *(978-951-682-645-8(8))* Rakennustieto oy FIN. Dist: Independent Pubs. Group.
Laaksonen, Esa. Research & Practice in Architecture. Simons, Tom & Vartola, Anni, eds. 2008. (ENG., Illus.). 124p. pap. 26.00 *(978-951-682-649-6(0))* Rakennustieto oy FIN. Dist: Independent Pubs. Group.
Lee, Katy. University Architecture. 2011. (ENG., Illus.). 256p. 45.00 *(978-988-19740-2-0(X))* Design Media Publishing Ltd. HKG. Dist: BookMasters Distribution Services (BDS).
Liebl-Osborne, Petra. Gestaltungslehren in der Architektenausbildung: An Technischen Universitaten und Hochschulen in Westdeutschland, 1945-1995. (Europaische Hochschulschriften Ser.). (GER., Illus.). 592p. 73.95 *(978-3-631-36307-2(9))* Lang, Peter Publishing, Inc.
Lowell, Waverly, et al, eds. Design on the Edge: A Century of Teaching at the University of California, Berkeley, 1903-2003. 2010. (Illus.). 320p. 65.00 *(978-0-9819667-3-1(X))* Stout, William Pubs.
MacKay-Lyons, Brian & Buchanan, Peter. Ghost: Building an Architectural Vision. 2008. (ENG., Illus.). 224p. pap. 35.00 *(978-1-56898-736-1(6))* Princeton Architectural Pr.
Marty, Myron A. Communities of Frank Lloyd Wright: Taliesin & Beyond. 2009. (Illus.). 316p. 45.00 *(978-0-87580-396-8(2))* Northern Illinois Univ. Pr.
Murcutt, Glenn. Glenn Murcutt: University of Washington Master Studios & Lectures. Nicholls, Jim, ed. 2009. (ENG., Illus.). 80p. pap. 30.00 *(978-0-295-98958-7(0))* Univ. of Washington Pr.
NC State University College of Design. School of Design: Reflections & Recollections: the Kamphoefner Years 1948-1973. 2007. (ENG.). 148p. 19.95 *(978-0-9776635-3-8(1))* NC State Univ. College of Design Pubn.
Ockman, Joan & Williamson, Rebecca. Architecture School: Three Centuries of Educating Architects in North America. 2012. (ENG., Illus.). 400p. (gr. 17). 50.00 ***(978-0-262-01708-4(3))*** MIT Pr.
Quale, John D. Sustainable, Affordable, Prefab: The Ecomod Project. 2012. (ENG., Illus.). 248p. (C). (gr. 13-17). pap. 35.00 ***(978-0-8139-3233-0(5));*** (gr. 17). 60.00 ***(978-0-8139-3152-4(5))*** Univ. Pr. of Virginia.
Richmond, Peter & Dunne, Jack. The World in One School: The History & Influence of the Liverpool School of Architecture 1894-2008. 2009. (ENG., Illus.). 96p. pap. 29.95 *(978-1-84631-165-9(9))* Liverpool Univ. Pr. GBR. Dist: Chicago Distribution Ctr.
Rüedi Ray, Katerina. Bauhaus Dream-House: Modernity & Globalization. 2010. (Architext Ser.). (ENG., Illus.). 240p. (C). pap. 49.95 *(978-0-415-47582-2(1));* 165.00 *(978-0-415-47581-5(3))* Routledge.
Ryan, Dan. Lean Office Practices for Architects: DLR Associates Series. 2010. 192p. pap. 14.49 *(978-1-4490-8481-3(8))* AuthorHouse.
Shariff, Yasmin & Tankard, Jane. Towards a New Architect: The Guide for Architecture Students. 2010. (ENG., Illus.). 128p. pap. 37.95 *(978-1-85617-604-0(5))* Routledge.
Spuybroek, Lars. The Architecture of Continuity. 2009. (ENG., Illus.). 288p. pap. 30.00 *(978-90-5662-637-2(X))* NAi Uitgevers / Publishers Stichting NLD. Dist: D.A.P./Distributed Art Pubs.
Temple. Making Thinking: Beginning Architectural Design Education. rev. ed. 2011. 122p. pap. 32.99 ***(978-0-7575-9250-8(3))*** Kendall Hunt Publishing Co.
Trentin, Annalisa, et al. La Lezione Di Pier Luigi Nervi. 2010. (ITA & ENG., Illus.). xiii, 225p. *(978-88-6159-503-3(0))* Bruno, Scholastica, Mondadori.
Unwin, Simon. Exercises in Architecture. 2012. (ENG., Illus.). 224p. (C). 165.00 *(978-0-415-61908-0(4));* pap. 29.95 *(978-0-415-61909-7(2))* Routledge.
Waugh, Emily, ed. GSD Platform 3. 2010. 336p. *(978-84-92861-50-7(9))* Actar Birkhauser Distribution.
Wertheimer, Lester. Schematic Design 2009. 2008. (ENG.). 88p. pap. 111.95 *(978-1-4277-7040-0(9))* Kaplan Publishing.
Yale School of Architecture Staff. Negotiated Terrains. Kilmer, Heather & Rappaport, Nina, eds. 2009. (Yale School of Architecture Bks.). (ENG., Illus.). 152p. pap. 35.00 *(978-0-393-73323-5(8),* 73323) Norton, W. W. & Co., Inc.

Yale School of Architecture Staff, et al. Learning in Las Vegas: Yale School of Architecture, Edward P. Bass Distinguished Visiting Architecture Fellowship. 2011. (Yale School of Architecture Bks.). (ENG., Illus.). 192p. pap. 35.00 *(978-0-393-73334-1(3),* 73334) Norton, W. W. & Co., Inc.

ARCHITECTURE—TECHNOLOGICAL ASPECTS

Alread, Jason & Leslie, Thomas. Design-Tech: Building Science for Architects. 2006. (ENG., Illus.). 528p. per. 48.95 *(978-0-7506-6557-5(2))* Routledge.

Architecture Studio Staff & Images Publishing Editorial Staff. Buildings: Innovation + Technology: STUDIOS Architecture. 2009. (ENG., Illus.). 96p. 25.00 *(978-1-86470-329-0(6))* Images Publishing Group AUS. Dist: National Bk. Network.

Asefi, Maziar. Transformable & Kinetic Architectural Structures. 2010. 316p. pap. *(978-3-639-25062-6(1))* VDM Verlag Dr. Mueller e.K.

Beaver, Robyn, ed. Tsoi/Kobus & Associates: Architecture, Interior Design, Planning. 2009. (ENG., Illus.). 228p. 59.95 *(978-1-86470-284-2(2),* Images Publishing Dist Ac) Antique Collectors' Club GBR. Dist: National Bk. Network.

Binder, Thomas, et al. Design Things. 2011. (Design Thinking, Design Theory Ser.). (ENG., Illus.). 256p. (gr. 17). 30.00 ***(978-0-262-01627-8(3))*** MIT Pr.

Brownell, Blaine. Material Strategies: Innovative Applications in Architecture. 2011. (ENG.). 160p. pap. 24.95 ***(978-1-56898-986-0(5))*** Princeton Architectural Pr.

Bullivant, Lucy. Masterplanning Futures. 2012. (ENG., Illus.). 336p. pap. 53.95 ***(978-0-415-55447-3(0))*** Routledge.

Bullivant, Lucy. Responsive Environments: Architecture, Art & Design. 2006. (ENG., Illus.). 128p. pap. 39.95 *(978-1-85177-481-4(5))* V & A Pubns. GBR. Dist: Hachette Bk. Group.

Burke, Anthony & Tierney, Therese, eds. Network Practices: New Strategies in Architecture & Design. 2007. (ENG., Illus.). 224p. pap. 29.95 *(978-1-56898-701-9(3))* Princeton Architectural Pr.

Corser, Robert & Princeton Architectural Press Staff. Fabricating Architecture: Selected Readings in Digital Design & Manufacturing. 2010. (ENG., Illus.). 216p. pap. 29.95 *(978-1-56898-889-4(3))* Princeton Architectural Pr.

Eekhout, M., ed. Methodology for Product Development in Architecture. 2009. 215p. pap. 87.00 *(978-1-58603-965-3(2))* IOS Pr., Inc.

Estévez, Alberto T., ed. Genetic Architectures III / Arquitecturas Genéticas III. 2010. (ENG.). 208p. pap. 22.00 *(978-0-930829-68-1(9))* Lumen, Inc.

Glasner, Barbara & Ott, Stephen. Wonder Wood: A Favorite Material for Designers, Architects, & Artists. 2012. (ENG.). 272p. 84.95 *(978-3-0346-0674-5(5))* Birkhauser Verlag AG CHE. Dist: Actar Birkhauser Distribution.

Gramazio, Fabio & Kohler, Matthias. 1. 2008. (Illus.). 160p. pap. 44.95 *(978-3-03778-122-7(X),* 303778122X) Springer.

Gregotti, Vittorio. Architecture, Means & Ends. Cochrane, Lydia G., tr. from ITA. 2010. 152p. 35.00 *(978-0-226-30758-9(1))* Univ. of Chicago Pr.

Heinich, Nadin & Eidner, Franziska, texts. Sensing Space: Technologien für Architekturen der Zukunft. 2009. (ENG & GER., Illus.). 160p. pap. 28.00 *(978-3-939633-95-2(X))* Jovis Verlag GmbH DEU. Dist: D.A.P./Distributed Art Pubs.

Hensel, Michael, et al. Emergent Technologies & Design: Towards a Biological Paradigm for Architecture. 2010. (ENG., Illus.). 256p. 155.00 *(978-0-415-49343-7(9));* pap. 62.95 *(978-0-415-49344-4(7))* Routledge.

Killory, Christine & Davids, Rene, eds. Details, Technology, & Form. 2012. (ENG., Illus.). 208p. 65.00 *(978-1-56898-953-2(9))* Princeton Architectural Pr.

Kokkini, Angeliki. Can Existing Social Housing in Greece Become Energy Efficient? 2010. 112p. pap. *(978-3-639-26874-4(1))* VDM Verlag Dr. Mueller e.K.

Kottas, Dimitris. Metal. 2012. (ENG.). 300p. 57.00 *(978-84-15123-27-9(2))* Links International (Leading International Key Services Barcelona, S.A.) ESP. Dist: National Bk. Network.

Lally. Softspace. 2007. (Illus.). 224p. 55.95 *(978-0-415-40202-6(6))* Taylor & Francis Group.

Lally, Sean. Softspace: From a Representation of Form to a Simulation of Space. Young, Jessica, ed. 2007. (Illus.). 224p. 165.00 *(978-0-415-40201-9(8))* Taylor & Francis Group.

Mavridis, Nikolaos. Grounded Situation Models for Situated Conversational Assistants. 2010. 272p. pap. *(978-3-8383-1242-2(2))* Lambert Academic Publishing.

McLean, William & Silver, Pete. Introduction to Architectural Technology. 2008. (ENG., Illus.). 192p. pap. 29.95 *(978-1-85669-566-4(2))* King, Laurence Publishing GBR. Dist: Hachette Bk. Group.

Meniru, Kene. Sketching & Designing Buildings with Computers. 2010. 244p. pap. *(978-3-8383-7068-2(6))* Lambert Academic Publishing.

Moravánszky, Ákos & Fischer, Ole. Precisions: Architektur zwischen Wissenschaft und Kunst. TheorieBau Band 1. 2008. (GER & ENG., Illus.). 272p. (C). pap. 40.00 *(978-3-939633-42-6(9))* Jovis Verlag GmbH DEU. Dist: D.A.P./Distributed Art Pubs.

Neder, Federico. Fuller Houses: R. Buckminster Fuller's Dymaxion Dwellings & Other Domestic Adventures. 2008. (ENG & FRE., Illus.). 239p. pap. 39.95 *(978-3-03778-141-8(6),* 3037781416) Springer.

Redi, Andrea & Redi, Ivan, texts. Ortlos: Architecture of the Networks, Volume 2. 2012. (ENG., Illus.). 208p. 55.00 ***(978-3-7757-2971-0(2))*** Hatje Cantz Verlag GmbH & Co KG DEU. Dist: D.A.P./Distributed Art Pubs.

Robinson, Luke. Self-aligned Side Gates for Nanowires & Nanotubes: The development & application of a new gatearchitecture for manipulating & defining 1D quantumdots with possibilities for quantum computation. 2008. 100p. pap. *(978-3-639-04971-8(3))* VDM Verlag Dr. Mueller e.K.

Ruwanpura, Janaka, et al, eds. Construction Research Congress 2010: Innovation for Reshaping Construction Practice, Vol. 1. 2010. (ENG., Illus.). 1566p. pap. 275.00 *(978-0-7844-1109-4(3))* American Society of Civil Engineers.

Santos, Gustavo, et al. Video Streaming Optimization in Adsl Architecture. 2010. 116p. pap. *(978-3-8383-6908-2(4))* Lambert Academic Publishing.

Sharples, Stephen P. & Bougdah, Hocine. Environment, Technology & Sustainability. 2009. (Technologies of Architecture Ser.). (ENG., Illus.). 320p. (C). 165.00 *(978-0-415-40378-8(2),* Taylor & Francis) Taylor & Francis Group GBR. Dist: Taylor & Francis Group.

Sinopoli, James M. Smart Buildings Systems for Architects, Owners & Builders. 2009. (ENG., Illus.). 248p. 103.00 *(978-1-85617-653-8(3),* Butterworth-Heinemann) Elsevier Science & Technology Bks.

Strieter, Nathan. Information Bridging. 2011. 188p. pap. ***(978-3-8443-9881-6(3))*** Lambert Academic Publishing.

Taniguchi, Ittetsu, et al. Design Methodology for Reconfigurable Processors. 2011. 100p. pap. ***(978-3-8383-8928-8(X))*** Lambert Academic Publishing.

Tuniz, Claudio. Science for Cultural Heritage: Technological Innovation & Case Studies in Marine & Land Archaeology in the Adriatic Region & Inland. 2010. 300p. 111.00 *(978-981-4307-06-2(8))* World Scientific Publishing Co., Inc.

Van Schaick, J. & Van Der Spek, S. C., eds. Urbanism on Track: Application of Tracking Technologies in Urbanism - Volume 1 Research in Urbanism Series. 2008. 200p. pap. 99.00 *(978-1-58603-817-5(6))* IOS Pr., Inc.

Wujec, Tom, ed. Imagine design Create: How Designers, Architects, & Engineers Are Changing Our World. 2011. (ENG.). 336p. 29.95 ***(978-1-59591-066-0(2))*** Melcher Media.

Yang, Keunbo. Art, soceity, & technology in Architecture. 2010. 342p. pap. 108.00 *(978-0-557-42624-9(3))* Lulu Enterprises Inc.

ARCHITECTURE—VOCATIONAL GUIDANCE

Borden, Iain. Bartlett Works. 203p. 38.00 *(978-1-902854-23-6(3))* Princeton Architectural Pr.

Camenson, Blythe. Careers in Architecture. 2nd ed. 2008. (ENG.). 192p. pap. 16.95 *(978-0-07-154556-3(5),* 0071545565) McGraw-Hill Cos., The.

Jovis Publishing Staff. Architecture: A Woman's Profession. Kullack, Tanja, ed. 2011. (ENG & GER., Illus.). 256p. pap. 35.00 ***(978-3-86859-086-9(2))*** Jovis Verlag GmbH DEU. Dist: D.A.P./Distributed Art Pubs.

Lee, Ken. Pencil It. 2009. 102p. pap. 22.50 *(978-1-4092-9590-7(7))* Lulu Enterprises Inc.

Leppo, Holly Williams. LEED Prep GA: What You Really Need to Know to Pass the LEED Green Associate Exam. 2009. (ENG.). 184p. pap. 64.00 *(978-1-59126-178-0(3))* Professional Pubns., Inc.

Leppo, RA/CID, LEED AP, Holly Williams. LEED Prep O&M: What You Really Need to Know to Pass the LEED AP Operations & Maintenance Exam. 2009. (ENG.). 320p. pap. 48.00 *(978-1-59126-180-3(5))* Professional Pubns., Inc.

Makstutis, Geoffrey, et al. Architecture. 2010. (ENG., Illus.). 248p. pap. 35.00 *(978-1-85669-623-4(5))* King, Laurence Publishing GBR. Dist: Hachette Bk. Group.

Patterson, David W. Getting a Job in Architecture & Design. 2008. (ENG.). 208p. per. 25.00 *(978-0-393-73217-7(7),* 73217) Norton, W. W. & Co., Inc.

Ponte, Tabitha. To BECOME an ARCHITECT (a guide, mostly for Women) 2010. 121p. pap. 16.00 *(978-0-557-31452-2(6))* Lulu Enterprises Inc.

Shariff, Yasmin & Tankard, Jane. Towards a New Architect: The Guide for Architecture Students. 2010. (ENG., Illus.). 128p. pap. 37.95 *(978-1-85617-604-0(5))* Routledge.

Waldrep, Lee W. Becoming an Architect: A Guide to Careers in Design. 2nd ed. 2009. (ENG., Illus.). 352p. pap. 39.95 *(978-0-470-37210-4(9),* Wiley) Wiley, John & Sons, Inc.

ARCHITECTURE—AFRICA

Adjaye, David. African Metropolitan Architecture. Allison, Peter, ed. 2011. (ENG., Illus.). 568p. pap. 100.00 *(978-0-8478-3716-8(5))* Rizzoli International Pubns., Inc.

Adjaye, David & Bouttiaux, Anne-Marie, eds. Geo-Graphics: A Map of Art Practices, Past & Present, 1 vol. 2010. (ENG.). 384p. pap. 55.00 *(978-88-366-1658-9(5))* Silvana ITA. Dist: D.A.P./Distributed Art Pubs.

Baldwin, John D. The Cushite Religion & Architecture. 2006. pap. 9.95 *(978-1-4286-6978-9(7))* Kessinger Publishing, LLC.

Beddow, Tim, photos by. Safari Living. 2006. (Mini Lifestyle Library Ser.). (ENG., Illus.). 168p. 16.95 *(978-1-902686-56-1(X))* Scriptum Editions GBR. Dist: Independent Pubs. Group.

Binder, Georges. Tall Buildings of Europe, Middle East & Africa. 2007. (Tall Buildings Ser.). (ENG., Illus.). 240p. 75.00 *(978-1-876907-81-5(9))* Images Publishing Group AUS. Dist: National Bk. Network.

Bloom, Jonathan M. Arts of the City Victorious: Islamic Art & Architecture in Fatimid North Africa & Egypt. 2008. (ENG., Illus.). 256p. 75.00 *(978-0-300-13542-8(4))* Yale Univ. Pr.

Boness, Stefan & Visscher, Jochen. Asmara: The Frozen City, 1 vol. 2007. (ITA, GER & ENG., Illus.). 96p. 19.95 *(978-3-936314-61-8(6))* Jovis Verlag GmbH DEU. Dist: D.A.P./Distributed Art Pubs.

Boussaa, Djamel. Urban Conservation in North Africa & the Gulf. 2010. 324p. pap. *(978-3-639-27313-7(3))* VDM Verlag Dr. Mueller e.K.

Burton, Jean-Dominique. Jean-Dominique Burton. Porto-Novo: Cite rouge, esprit du lagon Red City, Spirit of the Lagoon, 1 vol. 2011. (ENG & FRE.). 120p. 68.00 ***(978-90-5779-124-6(2))*** Exhibitions International BEL. Dist: Innovative Logistics.

Çelik, Zeynep. Empire, Architecture, & the City: French-Ottoman Encounters, 1830-1914. 2008. (ENG., Illus.). 368p. 60.00 *(978-0-295-98779-8(0))* Univ. of Washington Pr.

—Walls of Algiers: Narratives of the City Through Text & Image. Clancy-Smith, Julia Ann & Terpak, Frances, eds. 2009. (ENG., Illus.). 288p. pap. *(978-0-295-98868-9(1))* Getty Pubns.

Demissie, Fassil. Colonial Architecture & Urbanism in Africa: Interwined & Contested Histories. 2012. (Design & the Built Environment Ser.). (Illus.). 336p. 119.95 ***(978-0-7546-7512-9(2))*** Ashgate Publishing Co.

Denison, Edward, et al. Asmara: Africa's Secret Modernist City. 2007. (ENG., Illus.). 240p. pap. 39.95 *(978-1-85894-382-4(5))* Merrell Pubs. Ltd. GBR. Dist: Perseus Distribution.

Eledi, Joyce Angnayeli. Eco-Tourism & Its Relative Architecture in Ghan. 2011. 96p. pap. ***(978-3-8443-1475-5(X))*** Lambert Academic Publishing.

Frew, Abiot. Low-Cost Housing. 2010. 92p. pap. *(978-3-639-23480-0(4))* VDM Verlag Dr. Mueller e.K.

Jordan, Bibi, photos by. Swahili Chic: The Feng Shui of Africa. 2007. (ENG., Illus.). 288p. 50.00 *(978-1-933784-16-8(4),* Insight Editions) Palace Publishing Group, LP.

Joy, Charlotte L. The Politics of Heritage Management in Mali: From UNESCO to Djenne. 2012. (Critical Cultural Heritage Ser.). (ENG., Illus.). 235p. 89.00 ***(978-1-61132-094-7(1))*** Left Coast Pr., Inc.

Kamalkhan, Kalandar. The Swahili Architecture of Lamu, Keny: Oral Tradition & Space. 2010. 260p. pap. *(978-3-8383-7995-1(0))* Lambert Academic Publishing.

Kimathi, James. Parliaments & Their Architecture: Design Art Technology. 2011. (ENG., Illus.). 1p. 59.95 *(978-1-86470-349-8(0))* Images Publishing Group AUS. Dist: National Bk. Network.

Koolhaas, Rem. Lagos: How It Works. 2007. (Illus.). 800p. pap. 44.95 *(978-3-03778-085-5(1),* 3037780851) Lars Muller Pubs. CHE. Dist: Springer.

Krumhauer, Julia & Taschen, Angelika, eds. African Interiors. 25th ed. 2008. (ENG., Illus.). 719p. 59.99 *(978-3-8365-0870-4(2))* TASCHEN DEU. Dist: Ingram Pub. Services.

Lewcock, Ronald. Non- Western Architecture. Date not set. *(978-0-393-73044-9(1))* Norton, W. W. & Co., Inc.

Louafi, Kamel. Landschaftsinterventionen / Landscape Interventions: Stadtparadiese / City Paradises. 2011. (ENG, ARA, FRE & GER., Illus.). 496p. 65.00 ***(978-3-86859-107-1(9))*** Jovis Verlag GmbH DEU. Dist: D.A.P./Distributed Art Pubs.

Marchand, Trevor H. J. The Masons of Djenné. 2009. (African Expressive Cultures Ser.). (ENG., Illus.). 376p. 75.00 *(978-0-253-31368-3(6),* 0253313686); pap. 29.95 *(978-0-253-22072-1(6),* 0253220726) Indiana Univ. Pr.

Moirongo, Bernard Otoki. Urban Space Design & Environmental Management for Sustainable Cities. 2011. 352p. pap. ***(978-3-8443-1955-2(7))*** Lambert Academic Publishing.

Nettleton, Anitra. African Dream Machines: Style, Identity & Meaning of African Headrests. 2008. (ENG., Illus.). 488p. pap. 39.95 *(978-1-86814-458-7(5))* Witwatersrand Univ. Pr. Pubns. ZAF. Dist: Transaction Pubs.

Requa, Richard S. Old World Inspiration for American Architecture. 2007. (Illus.). 344p. 59.95 *(978-0-7643-2668-4(6))* Schiffer Publishing, Ltd.

Rind, Mareike. Romische Villen in Nordafrika: Nordafrika Untersuchungen zu Architektur und Wirtschaftsweise. 2009. (GER & ENG., Illus.). 133p. (C). pap. 82.50 *(978-1-4073-0588-2(3))* British Archaeological Reports Ltd. GBR. Dist: Brown, David Bk. Co., The.

van Steekelenburg, Ester, ed. Elmina: Building on the Past to Create a Better Future. 2008. 144p. (C). pap. 49.95 *(978-90-6832-473-0(X))* Royal Tropical Institute Pr. (KIT (Koninklijk Instituut voor de Tropen) NLD. Dist: Stylus Publishing, LLC.

ARCHITECTURE—ARGENTINA

Bonet Castellana, Antoni & Pizza de Nanno, Antonio. Antonio Bonet Castellana. 2010. (ENG & SPA., Illus.). 280p. *(978-84-8301-288-8(X))* UPC, S.L., Edicions.

M.Guillermo Perez. Mexico/Argentina/Architects. 2006. (ENG., Illus.). 200p. 60.00 *(978-968-5152-05-1(5))* COEDI MEX, S.A. de C.V. MEX. Dist: Antique Collectors' Club.

Taschen, Angelika, ed. Living in Argentina. 2008. (Taschen's Lifestyle Ser.). (FRE, GER & ENG., Illus.). 196p. 29.99 *(978-3-8365-0845-2(1))* TASCHEN DEU. Dist: Ingram Pub. Services.

—Style Buenos Aires: The Heart of Argentina. ICON. 2008. (Icon (Taschen) Ser.). (FRE, GER & ENG., Illus.). 192p. pap. 9.99 *(978-3-8365-0194-1(5))* TASCHEN DEU. Dist: Ingram Pub. Services.

Wang, Wilfried, ed. & text. Argentina: Altamira Building & Florencia Raigal House. 2011. (ENG., Illus.). 144p. pap. 40.00 *(978-3-8030-0719-3(4))* Wasmuth, Ernst J. Verlag GmbH & Co. DEU. Dist: D.A.P./Distributed Art Pubs.

ARCHITECTURE—ASIA

Anderson, Collin. The Orchard Road Experience: DP Architects. 2012. (ENG., Illus.). 172p. 50.00 ***(978-1-86470-462-4(4))*** Images Publishing Group AUS. Dist: National Bk. Network.

Ang, Susan. Valuing Practical Experience. 2011. 240p. pap. ***(978-3-8443-2184-5(5))*** Lambert Academic Publishing.

Arabacioglu, Feride Pinar. The City & Its Walls: A Research on Istanbul Land Walls. 2011. 112p. pap. ***(978-3-639-32818-9(3))*** VDM Verlag Dr. Mueller e.K.

Architecture as City. 2010. 152p. 69.95 *(978-3-7091-0367-8(3))* Springer Wien AUT. Dist: Springer.

Assavavirulhakarn, Prapod, et al. Past Lives of the Bhudda: Wat Si Chum & the Art of Sukhothai. 2007. (Illus.). 350p. 60.00 *(978-974-9863-22-0(4))* River Bks. THA. Dist: Antique Collectors' Club.

Baimatowa, Nasiba S. 5000 Jahre Architektur in Mittelasien: Lehmziegelgewolbe vom 4. 3. Jt. V. Chr. bis zum Ende des 8. Jhs. N. Chr. 2008. (Archaologie in Iran und Turan Ser.). (GER., Illus.). 492p. (C). 102.00 *(978-3-8053-3906-3(2))* Zabern, Philipp von Verlag, GmbH DEU. Dist: Brown, David Bk. Co., The.

Ball, Warwick. The Monuments of Afghanistan: History, Archaeology & Architecture. 2008. (ENG., Illus.). 384p. 116.00 *(978-1-85043-436-8(0))* I. B. Tauris & Co., Ltd. GBR. Dist: Macmillan.

Bandyopadhyay, Soumyen. Manah: Omani Oasis, Arabian Legacy Architecture & Social History of an Omani Oasis Settlement. 2011. (ENG., Illus.). 352p. 60.00 *(978-1-84631-121-5(7))* Liverpool Univ. Pr. GBR. Dist: Chicago Distribution Ctr.

Bianca, Stefano, ed. Syria: Medieval Citadels Between East & West. 2007. (ENG., Illus.). 312p. per. 60.00 *(978-88-422-1449-6(3))* Allemandi, Umberto & Co. GBR. Dist: National Bk. Network.

Binder, Georges. Tall Buildings of Asia & Australia. 2006. (Tall Buildings Ser.). (ENG., Illus.). 186p. 75.00 *(978-1-86470-075-6(0))* Images Publishing Group AUS. Dist: National Bk. Network.

Bingham-Hall, Patrick, et al. Recent Malaysian Architecture. Bingham-Hall, Patrick, ed. 2007. (ENG., Illus.). 160p. *(978-1-877015-19-9(9))* Pesaro Publishing.

Bravo-Bhasin, Marion & Johnsson, Tatjana Schantz. In Style Asia. 2007. (ENG., Illus.). 200p. 35.00 *(978-84-96263-21-5(5))* Links International (Leading International Key Services Barcelona, S.A.) ESP. Dist: National Bk. Network.

Brown, Rebecca M. & Hutton, Deborah S., eds. A Companion to Asian Art & Architecture. 2011. (Blackwell Companions to Art History Ser.: 9). (ENG., Illus.). 688p. 199.95 *(978-1-4051-8537-0(6),* Wiley-Blackwell) Wiley, John & Sons, Inc.

Bunce, Fredrick W. Monuments of India & the Indianized States: The Plans of Major & Notable Temples, Tombs, Palaces, & Pavilions of Bangladesh, Sri Lanka, Java, the Khmer, Pagan, Thailand, Vietnam, & Malaysia, from 3rd C. BCE to CE 1854. 2007. (Illus.). xx, 518p. *(978-81-246-0385-7(5))* D. K. Print World (P) Ltd.

Chan, Soo. SCDA Architects. 2012. (Master Architects Ser.). (ENG., Illus.). 256p. 80.00 *(978-1-86470-414-3(4))* Images Publishing Group AUS. Dist: National Bk. Network.

Chandra, Jimmy & Warnitchai, Pennung. Seismic Retrofitting of Rc Buildings Using Buckling Restrained Braces. 2011. 184p. pap. ***(978-3-8383-8720-8(1))*** Lambert Academic Publishing.

Chen, Bixia & Nakama, Yuei. Traditional Rural Landscapes in Island Topography in East Asia. 2011. (Environmental Research Advances Ser.). 95.00 ***(978-1-61470-497-3(X))*** Nova Science Pubs., Inc.

Chitrakar, Rajjan Man. Public Open Spaces in Kathmandu Valley. 2011. 116p. pap. ***(978-3-8433-8098-0(8))*** Lambert Academic Publishing.

Choegyal, Lisa & Potton, Craig. Kathmandu Valley Style. 2008. (Illus.). 256p. 65.00 *(978-1-932476-34-7(2))* Serindia Pubns., Inc.

Cooke, Louise. Conservation Approaches to Earthen Architecture in Archaeological Contexts. 2010. (Bar S Ser.). (ENG., Illus.). 177p. (C). pap. 145.00 *(978-1-4073-0688-9(X))* British Archaeological Reports Ltd. GBR. Dist: Brown, David Bk. Co., The.

Crane, Christina & Brown, Denise Scott. Asia Beyond Growth: Urbanization in the World's Fastest-Changing Continent. AECOM Consult, Inc Staff, ed. 2010. (ENG., Illus.). 400p. pap. 40.00 *(978-0-9795395-1-0(X))* Oro Editions.

Cummings, Joe. Chiang Mai Style, 1 vol. 2006. (ENG., Illus.). 232p. 49.00 *(978-981-232-831-1(9))* Marshall Cavendish International (Asia) Private Ltd. SGP. Dist: Marshall Cavendish Corp.

Daryanani, Danesh, text. Conserving History: Singapore's Heritage Museums. 2010. (ENG., Illus.). 204p. 60.00 *(978-0-9820607-7-3(7))* Oro Editions.

Davison, Julian & Tettoni, Luca Invernizzi. Singapore Shophouse. 2011. (ENG., Illus.). 208p. 50.00 ***(978-981-05-9716-0(9))*** King, Laurence Publishing GBR. Dist: Hachette Bk. Group.

Degroot, V. M. Y. Candi, Space & Landscape: A Study on the Distribution, Orientation & Spatial Organization of Central Javanese Temple Remains. 2009. (Mededelingen van het Rijksmuseum voor Volkenkunde Ser.). (ENG.). 512p. (C). pap. 84.00 *(978-90-8890-039-6(6))* Sidestone Pr. NLD. Dist: Brown, David Bk. Co., The.

Dostogir, Md. Saifulla & Dostogir, Saifulla. An Assessment of Level of Implementation of Khulna City Master Plan. 2010. 96p. pap. *(978-3-639-25907-0(6))* VDM Verlag Dr. Mueller e.K.

Dullemen, C. J. van. Tropical Modernity: Life & Work of C.P. Wolff Schoemaker. 2010. (Illus.). 270p. *(978-90-8506-879-2(7))* SUN B.V., Uitgeverij.

Dumarcay, Jacques. Architecture & Its Models in Southeast Asia. 2006. (ENG., Illus.). pap. 17.00 *(978-974-524-027-8(3))* Orchid Pr. THA. Dist: National Bk. Network.

Ewarte, Darren L. Implications of a Changing Regional Architecture in East Asia. 2010. (Asian Political, Economic & Security Issues Ser.). 190p. 115.00 *(978-1-60741-456-8(2))* Nova Science Pubs., Inc.

Falconer, John, et al. Burmese Design & Architecture. 2007. (ENG., Illus.). 224p. pap. 34.95 *(978-0-7946-0463-9(3),* PeriplusEdition) Tuttle Publishing.

Fergusson, James. History of Indian & Eastern Architecture. 2009. 284p. pap. *(978-1-151-43644-3(5))* Books LLC.

Francione, Gianni, et al. Bali Living: Innovative Tropical Design. 2008. (ENG., Illus.). 224p. 44.95 *(978-0-7946-0567-4(2),* PeriplusEdition) Tuttle Publishing.

Freeman, Michael. Asia Home: Inspirational Design Ideas. 2011. (ENG., Illus.). 144p. 24.95 (978-0-8048-3983-9(2)) Tuttle Publishing.

Galindo, Michelle. Collection: Asian Architecture. 2010. (Collection Ser.). (FRE, GER & ENG., Illus.). 512p. 89.95 (978-3-03768-047-6(4), Braun Publish,Csi) Continental Sales, Inc.

Grima, Joseph. Instant Asia: Fast Forward Through the Architecture of a Changing Continent. 2008. (ENG., Illus.). 262p. pap. 15.99 (978-88-6130-303-4(X)) Skira Editore ITA. Dist: Random Hse., Inc.

Gutschow, Niels. Architecture of the Newars: A History of Building Typologies & Details in Nepal. 2011. (978-1-932476-54-5(7)) Serindia Pubns., Inc.

Hajiyeva, Sabina. Architecture of the North-Western District of Azerbaijan. 2011. 112p. pap. (978-3-8443-1470-0(9)) Lambert Academic Publishing.

Hasan, Muhammad Rashidul & ABDUL MOMIN. Integrating Physical Planning in Street Crime Prevention. 2010. 88p. pap. (978-3-639-27699-2(X)) VDM Verlag Dr. Mueller e.K.

Hasan, Perween. Sultans & Mosques: The Early Muslim Architecture of Bangladesh. 2007. (ENG., Illus.). 288p. 89.00 (978-1-84511-381-0(0)) I. B. Tauris & Co., Ltd. GBR. Dist: Macmillan.

Hope, Eliza. Interior Spaces of Asia & the Pacific Rim Vol. 2: A Pictorial Review. 2006. (International Spaces Ser.). (ENG., Illus.). 55.00 (978-1-876907-67-9(3)) Images Publishing Group AUS. Dist: National Bk. Network.

Images Publishing Group. Architects 49 Ltd. 2006. (Master Architect Series VI). (ENG., Illus.). 256p. 65.00 (978-1-876907-09-9(6)) Images Publishing Group AUS. Dist: National Bk. Network.

Inglis, Kim. Bali Home: Inspirational Design Ideas. 2010. (ENG., Illus.). 144p. 24.95 (978-0-8048-3982-2(4)) Tuttle Publishing.

Jahn, Helmut. Suvarnabhumi Airport, Bangkok, Thailand. 2007. (ENG., Illus.). 20.00 (978-3-89986-088-7(8), Avedition Gmbh,Csi) Continental Sales, Inc.

Jaidah, Ibrahim & Bourennane, Malika, eds. The History of Qatari Architecture. 2010. (ENG., Illus.). 336p. 69.00 (978-88-6130-793-3(0)) Skira Editore ITA. Dist: Random Hse., Inc.

J.J. Pan & Partners. J. J Pan & Partners: Sustainability, Professionalism, Discourse. 2012. (ENG., Illus.). 256p. 59.95 (978-1-86470-430-3(6)) Images Publishing Group AUS. Dist: National Bk. Network.

Kawsar, Riazuddin & Arafat Hasan. Redevelopment of Bhairab River Bank. 2011. 132p. pap. (978-3-8443-2411-2(9)) Lambert Academic Publishing.

Klett, Arne A. & Ballmann, Karen. Asian Design Destinations: From the Middle East to the Far East. 2010. 74p. 69.99 (978-0-8416-7162-1(1)) Langenscheidt Publishing Group.

Kusno, Abidin. The Appearances of Memory: Mnemonic Practices of Architecture & Urban Form in Indonesia. 2010. (ENG., Illus.). 352p. 94.95 (978-0-8223-4655-5(9)); pap. 25.95 (978-0-8223-4647-0(8)) Duke Univ. Pr.

Lee-Kalisch, Jeong-hee, et al, eds. Long Life Festschrift in Honour of Roger Goepper. 2006. (Illus.). 289p. pap. (978-0-8204-9855-3(6)) Lang, Peter AG.

Lewcock, Ronald. Non- Western Architecture. Date not set. (978-0-393-73044-9(1)) Norton, W. W. & Co., Inc.

Lim. Asian Alterity. 2007. (Illus.). 222p. 159.00 (978-981-277-107-0(7)) World Scientific Publishing Co., Inc.

Lim, William S. W. Asian Alterity: With Special Reference to Architecture & Urbanism through the Lens of Cultural Studies. 2007. (Illus.). 320p. (C). pap. 99.00 (978-981-270-771-0(9)) World Scientific Publishing Co., Inc.

Listri, Massimo. New Asian Interiors. 2010. (ENG., Illus.). 360p. 50.00 (978-0-500-51546-4(8), 551546) Thames & Hudson.

McGillick, Paul. Concrete Metal Glass: Hijas Kasturi Associates: Selected Works 1977-2007. 2007. (ENG., Illus.). 188p. 40.00 (978-981-4155-28-1(4), Didier Millet,Csi) Continental Sales, Inc.

Mohamad Tajuddin Haji Mohamad Rasdi. Warisan Seni Bina Islam Tradisional Malaysia. 2010. (MAY., Illus.). xiv, 129p. (978-983-46034-8-9(7)) Dewan Bahasa Dan Pustaka.

Nas, Peter J. M. The Past in the Present: Architecture in Indonesia. 2010. (ENG., Illus.). 286p. 50.00 (978-90-6718-296-6(6)) KITLV Pr. NLD. Dist: Univ. of Hawaii Pr.

Nas, Peter J. M., ed. The Past in the Present: Architecture in Indonesia, 1 vol. 2007. (ENG., Illus.). 288p. 59.95 (978-90-5662-572-6(1)) NAi Uitgevers / Publishers Stichting NLD. Dist: D.A.P./Distributed Art Pubs.

Nasongkhla, Sirima. Aesthetics of Tai Cultural Landscapes. 2010. 420p. pap. (978-3-8383-0157-0(9)) Lambert Academic Publishing.

Ojeda, Oscar Riera, ed. Romancing the Tropics: Bedmar & Shi. 2006. (ENG., Illus.). 240p. 60.00 (978-0-9774672-2-8(8)) Oro Editions.

Passage to Angkor. 3rd ed. 2008. (Illus.). 144p. 59.95 (978-0-9653574-3-2(0)) Friends Without a Border.

Permanasari, Eka. Constructing & Contesting the Nation. 2010. 316p. pap. (978-3-8383-5237-4(8)) Lambert Academic Publishing.

Robson, David. Anjalendran: Architect of Sri Lanka. 2009. (ENG., Illus.). 240p. 49.95 (978-0-8048-4038-5(5)) Tuttle Publishing.

Rowe, Peter. Emergent Architectural Territories in East Asian Cities. 2011. (Illus.). 200p. 59.95 (978-3-7643-8815-7(3)) Birkhauser Verlag AG CHE. Dist: Actar Birkhauser Distribution.

Schmal, Peter Cachola. WOHA: Architektur atmet / Breathing Architecture. Busenkell, Micaela, ed. 2012. (GER & ENG., Illus.). 192p. pap. 60.00 (978-3-7913-5186-5(9)) Prestel Publishing.

Sestini, Valerio & Somigli, Enzo. Architettura Himalayana: Architettura Tradizionale Nella Valle Di Kathmandu = Himalayan Architecture: Traditional Architecture in the Kathmandu Valley. 2007. (ITA., Illus.). 366p. (C). 62.00 (978-88-596-0187-6(8)) Edizioni Polistampa ITA. Dist: Brown, David Bk. Co., The.

Sharp, Ilsa. The Fullerton Heritage: Where the Past Meets the Present. 2011. (ENG., Illus.). 80p. 29.95 (978-0-9820607-8-0(5)) Oro Editions.

Shorto, Sylvia. A Lebanese Perspective: Houses & Other Work - Simone Kosremelli. 2012. (ENG., Illus.). 252p. 60.00 (978-1-86470-471-6(3)) Images Publishing Group AUS. Dist: National Bk. Network.

Skinner, Stephen. Feng Shui Style: The Asian Art of Gracious Living. 2009. (ENG., Illus.). 144p. pap. 24.95 (978-0-8048-4052-1(0)) Tuttle Publishing.

Stratton, Carol. What's What in a Wat: Thai Buddhist Temples. 2010. (ENG., Illus.). 104p. pap. 16.95 (978-974-9511-99-2(9)) Silkworm Bks. THA. Dist: Univ. of Washington Pr.

Stronski, Paul. Tashkent. 2010. (Pitt Russian East European Ser.). (ENG., Illus.). 320p. 65.00 (978-0-8229-4394-5(8)) Univ. of Pittsburgh Pr.

—Tashkent: Forging a Soviet City, 1930-1966. 2010. (Pitt Russian East European Ser.). (ENG., Illus.). 320p. pap. 27.95 (978-0-8229-6113-0(X)) Univ. of Pittsburgh Pr.

Suksri, Naengnoi & Piammattawat, Paisarn. Grand Palace & Rattanakosin Island. 2012. (ENG., Illus.). 230p. pap. 30.00 (978-974-9863-41-1(0)) River Bks. THA. Dist: Antique Collectors' Club.

Tadgell, Christopher. The East: Buddhists, Hindus & the Sons of Heaven. 2007. (ENG., Illus.). 924p. 110.00 (978-0-415-40752-6(4)) Routledge.

Taschen, Angelika, ed. Inside Asia, 2 vols. 2007. (Illus.). Vol. 1. (FRE, GER & ENG.). 425p. 59.99 (978-3-8228-4818-0(2)) Vol. 2. (GER., 447p. 59.99 (978-3-8228-4819-7(0)) TASCHEN DEU. Dist: Ingram Pub. Services.

Tettoni, Luca Invernizzi, photos by. Tropical Asian Style. 2007. (ENG., Illus.). 224p. pap. 29.95 (978-0-7946-0399-1(8), PeriplusEdition) Tuttle Publishing.

Tettoni, Luca Invernizzi, et al. Classic Thai: Design * Interiors * Architecture. 2007. (ENG., Illus.). 240p. pap. 34.95 (978-0-7946-0466-0(8), PeriplusEdition) Tuttle Publishing.

Tonkao, Panin. Tracing the City: The Transformation of Spatial Structure & Human Interaction Within the City from the 19th Century. 2011. 136p. pap. (978-3-639-33973-4(8)) VDM Verlag Dr. Mueller e.K.

United Nations University Staff. Dam Safety in Central Asia: Capacity-Building & Regional Cooperation. 2010. (ENG.). 84p. pap. 25.00 (978-92-1-116962-1(3)) United Nations Pubns.

Walker, Barbara. Gathering Places: Balinese Architecture — A Spiritual & Spatial Orientation, 1 vol. 2006. (ENG., Illus.). 288p. 56.50 (978-981-232-918-9(8)) Marshall Cavendish International (Asia) Private Ltd. SGP. Dist: Marshall Cavendish Corp.

—Indochine Style, 1 vol. 2009. (ENG., Illus.). 250p. 57.95 (978-981-232-971-4(4)) Marshall Cavendish International (Asia) Private Ltd. SGP. Dist: Marshall Cavendish Corp.

Wallpaper Magazine Editors, ed. Bangkok 2010 - Wallpaper City Guide. rev. ed. 2010. (Wallpaper* City Guides). (ENG., Illus.). 128p. pap. 9.95 (978-0-7148-5614-8(2)) Phaidon Pr., Inc.

Warren, William & Limapornvanich, Taveepong. Thailand Sketchbook: Portrait of a Kingdom. 2007. (ENG., Illus.). 96p. 30.00 (978-981-4068-28-4(4), Didier Millet,Csi) Continental Sales, Inc.

Waterson, Roxana. The Living House: An Anthropology of Architecture in South-East Asia. 2010. (ENG., Illus.). 300p. 39.95 (978-0-8048-4120-7(9)) Tuttle Publishing.

Weddikkara, Chitrar. The Impact of Professional Culture on Dispute Resolution in the Building Industries of Australia & Sri Lank. 2008. 540p. pap. (978-3-639-08054-4(8)) VDM Verlag Dr. Mueller e.K.

Zabihi, Karina & Jotisalikorn, Chami. Contemporary Asian Bedrooms. 2007. (Contemporary Asian Home Ser.). (ENG., Illus.). 128p. pap. 19.95 (978-0-7946-0467-7(6), PeriplusEdition) Tuttle Publishing.

ARCHITECTURE—AUSTRALIA

Ang, Susan. Valuing Practical Experience. 2011. 240p. pap. (978-3-8443-2184-5(5)) Lambert Academic Publishing.

Annable, Rosemary. A Setting for Justice: Building for the Supreme Court of New South Wales. 2007. (ENG., Illus.). 192p. pap. 44.95 (978-0-86840-917-7(0), UNSW Press) NewSouth Publishing AUS. Dist: Independent Pubs. Group.

Beck, Haig & Cooper, Jackie. Kurilpa Bridge: Brisbane's New Bridge. 2012. (ENG., Illus.). 100p. 39.95 (978-1-86470-408-2(X)) Images Publishing Group AUS. Dist: National Bk. Network.

Bedini, Gilberto, ed. The Villas of Lucca. 2006. (ENG., Illus.). 304p. 65.00 (978-1-920744-72-4(X)) Images Publishing Group AUS. Dist: National Bk. Network.

Bull, Catherin. New Conversations with an Old Landscape: Landscape Architecture in Contemporary Australia. 2006. (ENG., Illus.). 160p. 65.00 (978-1-876907-65-5(7)) Images Publishing Group AUS. Dist: National Bk. Network.

Collectors Classic Antiques Staff. Michael Graves: Selected & Current Works. 2006. (Master Architect Series III). (ENG., Illus.). 59.95 (978-1-875498-73-4(7), Images Publishing Dist Ac) Antique Collectors' Club GBR. Dist: National Bk. Network.

DAAB Media Staff, ed. Australia Architecture, 1 vol. 2008. (ENG, FRE, GER, ITA & SPA., Illus.). 237p. 59.95 (978-3-937718-77-4(X)) DAAB Media Gmbh DEU. Dist: Innovative Logistics.

Foster, Norman Robert. Der Neue Reichstag. (Illus.). 256p. (978-3-7653-2061-3(7)) Brockhaus, F. A., GmbH DEU. Dist: International Bk. Import Service, Inc.

Goad, Philip & Willis, Julie, eds. The Encyclopedia of Australian Architecture. 2011. (ENG., Illus.). 830p. 180.00 (978-0-521-88857-8(3)) Cambridge Univ. Pr.

Gore, James. Representations of History & Nation in Museums. 2010. 364p. pap. (978-3-8383-6298-4(5)) Lambert Academic Publishing.

Hodge, Brian. Building Your Straw Bale Home: From Foundations to the Roof. 2006. (Landlinks Press Ser.). (Illus.). 280p. pap. 61.95 (978-0-643-09242-6(0)) CSIRO Publishing AUS. Dist: Stylus Publishing, LLC.

Howells, Trevor. Allen Jack & Cottier: Architecture in the Australian Context. 2006. (ENG., Illus.). 204p. 55.00 (978-1-875359-96-7(6)) Watermark Pr., The AUS. Dist: National Bk. Network.

Jackson, Davina. Next Wave: New Australian Architecture. 2008. (ENG., Illus.). 256p. 50.00 (978-1-56898-735-4(8)) Princeton Architectural Pr.

Leach, Andrew, et al, eds. Shifting Views: Selected Essays on the Architectural History Of Australia & New Zealand. 2008. (ENG.). 256p. pap. 52.95 (978-0-7022-3660-0(8)) Univ. of Queensland Pr. AUS. Dist: Independent Pubs. Group.

Loo, Yew-Chaye & Chowdhury, Sanaul H. Reinforced & Prestressed Concrete: Analysis & Design with Emphasis on Application of AS3600-2009. 2010. (ENG., Illus.). 462p. pap. 85.00 (978-0-521-14147-5(8)) Cambridge Univ. Pr.

McAuley, Gay, ed. Unstable Ground: Performance & the Politics of Place. 2nd rev. ed. 2008. (Dramaturgies. Textes, Cultures et Représentations. Texts, Cultures & Performances Ser.). 300p. pap. 62.95 (978-90-5201-438-8(8)) P E - Peter Lang BEL. Dist: Lang, Peter.

Memmott, Paul. Gunyah, Goondie & Wurley: The Aboriginal Architecture of Australia. 2008. (ENG., Illus.). 432p. pap. 70.00 (978-0-7022-3245-9(9)) Univ. of Queensland Pr. AUS. Dist: Independent Pubs. Group.

Metcalf, Andrew. Aurora Place: Renzo Piano in Sydney. 2006. (ENG., Illus.). 125p. 40.00 (978-0-949284-53-2(X)) Watermark Pr., The AUS. Dist: National Bk. Network.

—Canberra Architecture. 2006. (Architecture Guides (Watermark Press) Ser.). (ENG., Illus.). 172p. pap. 29.95 (978-0-949284-63-1(7)) Watermark Pr., The AUS. Dist: National Bk. Network.

Ostwald, Michael J. & Fleming, Steven, eds. Museum, Gallery, & Cultural Architecture in Australia, New Zealand, & the Pacific Region: Essays in Antipodean Identity. 2007. 208p. (978-0-7734-5393-7(8)) Mellen, Edwin Pr., The.

Pallavi, Zambre. Proposing a Cultural Landscape Paradigm: A Case Study: Prospect Reservoir at Western Sydney. 2011. 180p. pap. (978-3-639-33059-5(5)) VDM Verlag Dr. Mueller e.K.

Pauwels, Wim. Wood Marsh Architects: Selected Works. 2012. (ENG., Illus.). 224p. 125.00 (978-90-8944-115-7(8)) Beta-Plus Pubs. BEL. Dist: Antique Collectors' Club.

Reed, Dimity, ed. National Museum of Australia: Building Monographs. 2006. (ENG., Illus.). 180p. 70.00 (978-1-876907-39-6(8)) Images Publishing Group AUS. Dist: National Bk. Network.

Ries, Charles P., et al. Improving the Energy Performance of Buildings: Learning from the European Union & Australia. 2009. 60p. pap. 23.00 (978-0-8330-4787-8(6), tr728) RAND Corp., The.

Romanowski, Nick. Planting Wetlands & Dams: A Practical Guide to Wetland Design, Construction & Propagation. 2nd rev. ed. 2010. (Illus.). 126p. pap. 41.00 (978-0-643-09636-3(1)) CSIRO Publishing AUS. Dist: Stylus Publishing, LLC.

Saniga, Andrew. The History of Landscape Architecture in Australia. 2008. (978-0-521-86621-7(9)) 2007. pap. (978-0-521-68514-6(1)) Cambridge Univ. Pr.

Satherley, Shannon. Reconnecting the Interrupted Landscape. 2010. 160p. pap. (978-3-8383-3652-7(6)) Lambert Academic Publishing.

Wallpaper Magazine Editors, ed. Sydney 2011 - Wallpaper City Guide. rev. ed. 2011. (Wallpaper* City Guides). (ENG., Illus.). 128p. pap. 9.95 (978-0-7148-5654-4(1)) Phaidon Pr., Inc.

Willis, Elizabeth. Royal Exhibition Building: A Guide. 2006. (ENG., Illus.). per. 16.95 (978-0-9577471-4-2(4)) Museum Victoria Publishing AUS. Dist: National Bk. Network.

ARCHITECTURE—AUSTRIA

see also Architecture, Domestic—Austria

Aigner, Silvie, ed. Emanzipation und Konfrontation / Emancipation & Confrontation / Emancipacija in konfrontacija: Kunst aus Kärnten von 1945 bis heute. Architektur aus Kärnten seit 1945 und Kunst im öffentlichen Raum heute., 3 vols. 2008. (GER, SLV & ENG., Illus.). 1010p. (978-3-211-75622-5(1), 3211756221) Actar Birkhauser Distribution.

Balliet, Kristy, et al, eds. Visual Catalog: Greg Lynn's Studio at the University of Applied Arts Vienna. 2010. (Edition Angewandte Ser.). (ENG., Illus.). 176p. pap. 29.95 (978-3-211-99192-3(1), 3211991921) Springer.

Bina, Andrea, et al. Architecture Linz 1900-2010. 2012. (GER & ENG., Illus.). 352p. pap. 49.95 (978-3-7091-0831-4(4), 3709108314) Springer Wien AUT. Dist: Springer.

Boeckl, Matthias. Andreas Treusch Architecture. 2010. (GER & ENG., Illus.). 208p. 49.95 (978-3-211-48961-1(4), 3211489614) Springer Wien AUT. Dist: Actar Birkhauser Distribution.

—Space & Texture. Hertl.Architekten. 2009. (Illus.). 208p. (978-3-211-79161-5(2), 3211791612) Actar Birkhauser Distribution.

Drexel, Thomas. Neue Low-Budget-Häuser: Bauen unter 225.000 Euro. 2010. (Illus.). 159p. (978-3-421-03596-7(2)) Deutsche Verlags-Anstalt GmbH.

Fahr-Becker, Gabriele. Wiener Werkstatte: 1903-1932. 25th ed. 2008. (ENG., Illus.). 240p. 14.99 (978-3-8228-3773-3(3)) TASCHEN DEU. Dist: Ingram Pub. Services.

GmbH, Birkhäuser. Architekten Profile 2011 / 2012. 2010. (ENG & GER., Illus.). 392p. 95.00 (978-3-0346-0612-7(5)) Birkhauser Verlag AG CHE. Dist: Actar Birkhauser Distribution.

Grassegger, Friedrich, et al. Bau[t]en für die KünsteBuilding[s] for the Arts: Zeitgenössische Architektur in NiederösterreichContemporary Architecture in Lower Austria. 2009. (GER & ENG., Illus.). 288p. 49.95 (978-3-211-99147-3(6)) Springer Wien AUT. Dist: Actar Birkhauser Distribution.

Hans Wolfsbauer-Schönau Salzburg: Gemälde und Grafiken Paintings & Drawings. 2009. 208p. 49.95 (978-3-211-98121-4(7)) Springer Wien AUT. Dist: Actar Birkhauser Distribution.

Hauenfels, Theresia. Architekturlandschaft Niederösterreich - Waldviertel / Lower Austria - The Architectural Landscape - Waldviertel Region: Architekturlandschaft Niederosterreich - Waldviertel. 2011. (GER & ENG., Illus.). 264p. pap. 39.95 (978-3-7091-0775-1(X)) Springer Wien AUT. Dist: Actar Birkhauser Distribution.

Institute of Architecture, Studio Zaha Hadid, et al, eds. Total Fluidity: Studio Zaha Hadid, Projects 2000 - 2010 University of Applied Arts, Vienna. 2011. (Edition Angewandte Ser.). (ENG., Illus.). 260p. pap. 49.95 (978-3-7091-0486-6(6), 3709104866) Springer Wien AUT. Dist: Springer.

Kapfinger, Otto. Haus Rauch. 2010. (Illus.). 160p. 69.95 (978-3-0346-0110-8(7)) Birkhauser Verlag AG CHE. Dist: Actar Birkhauser Distribution.

—Hermann Kaufmann: WOOD WORKS. 2008. (Illus.). 254p. (978-3-211-79175-2(2), 3211791752) Actar Birkhauser Distribution.

Kapfinger, Otto & Rakennustieto Publishing Staff. Hermann Kaufmann: Spirit of Nature Wood Architecture Award 2010. 2010. (Illus.). 144p. pap. 64.00 (978-951-682-965-7(1)) Rakennustieto oy FIN. Dist: Independent Pubs. Group.

Karner, Herbert, et al. Austrian Academy of Sciences: The Building & its History. 2007. (ENG.). 64p. (C). pap. 14.95 (978-3-7001-3876-1(8)) Austrian Academy of Sciences Press AUT Dist: Brown, David Bk. Co., The.

Kowalski, Karla. Szyszkowitz-Kowalski: Architekturen von 1994-2010. 2011. (ENG., Illus.). 312p. 65.00 (978-3-86859-033-3(1)) Jovis Verlag GmbH DEU. Dist: D.A.P./Distributed Art Pubs.

Long, Christopher. The Looshaus. 2012. (ENG., Illus.). 256p. 50.00 (978-0-300-17453-3(5)) Yale Univ. Pr.

Luthardt, Ernst-Otto. Austria. 2011. (Horizon Ser.). (ENG.). 160p. 34.95 (978-3-8003-1739-4(7)) Verlagshaus Wurzburg GmbH & Co. KG DEU. Dist: Independent Pubs. Group.

Nickl-Weller, Christine & Nickl, Hans. The New Hospital. 2007. (Illus.). 464p. (978-981-245-325-9(3)) Page One Publishing.

Noever, Peter & Pokorny, Marek, eds. Josef Hoffmann: Architecture Guide. 2011. (ENG., Illus.). 200p. pap. 40.00 (978-3-7757-2733-4(7)) Hatje Cantz Verlag GmbH & Co KG DEU. Dist: D.A.F./Distributed Art Pubs.

Noever, Peter & Prix, Wolf, eds. In the Absence of Raimund Abraham. 2011. (ENG., Illus.). 128p. pap. 40.00 (978-3-7757-2999-4(2)) Hatje Cantz Verlag GmbH & Co KG DEU. Dist: D.A.F./Distributed Art Pubs.

Peters, Paulhans. Franz Riepl. Architekt / Architect. 2006. (ENG & GER., Illus.). 224p. 89.00 (978-3-936681-00-0(7)) Edition Axel Menges GmbH DEU. Dist: National Bk. Network.

Reinberg, Georg W. Ökologische Architektur: Entwurf, Planung, Ausführung. 2008. (ENG & GER., Illus.). 348p. (978-3-211-32770-8(3), 3211327703) Actar Birkhauser Distribution.

Rice, John A. The Temple of Night at Schönau: Architecture, Music, & Theater in a Late Eighteenth-Century Viennese Garden. 2006. (Illus.). xv, 257p. (978-0-87169-258-0(9)) American Philosophical Society.

Russ-Bovelino, Andreas, ed. Caramel. 2011. (ENG & GER., Illus.). 400p. 69.95 (978-3-7091-0511-5(0), 3709105110) Springer Wien AUT. Dist: Actar Birkhauser Distribution.

Samitz, August. Hoffmann. 2007. (ENG., Illus.). 96p. pap. 9.99 (978-3-8228-5591-1(X)) TASCHEN DEU. Dist: Ingram Pub. Services.

Stephan, Regina, ed. Joseph Maria Olbrich. 2010. (ENG., Illus.). 64p. 30.00 (978-3-7757-2551-4(2)) Hatje Cantz Verlag GmbH & Co KG DEU. Dist: D.A.P./Distributed Art Pubs.

Tesar, Heinz. Heinz Tesar: Architecture of Layers: Nine Recent Works. 2008. (ENG., Illus.). 128p. 68.00 (978-3-936681-21-5(X)) Edition Axel Menges GmbH DEU. Dist: National Bk. Network.

Weiss, Walter M. Austria. 2011. (Premium Ser.). (ENG., Illus.). 224p. 69.95 (978-3-8003-1965-7(9)) Verlagshaus Wurzburg GmbH & Co. KG DEU. Dist: Independent Pubs. Group.

Yo.V.A.3 - Young Viennese Architects 3. 2010. 128p. pap. 39.95 (978-3-7091-0334-0(7)) Springer Wien AUT. Dist: Actar Birkhauser Distribution.

Zeytinoglu, Arkan, ed. Geometry of Light: The Architecture of Arkan Zeytinoglu. 2011. (Illus.). 350p. 69.95 (978-3-7091-0538-2(2), 3709105382) Springer Wien AUT. Dist: Springer.

ARCHITECTURE—AUSTRIA—VIENNA

Internationale Amtssitz und Konferenzzentrum. VIC-M. New Conference Building Wien / Uno-City. 2010. 120p. 39.95 (978-3-211-89379-1(2)) Springer Wien AUT. Dist: Actar Birkhauser Distribution.

Kapfinger, Otto. Krischanitz, Federle: Neue Welt Schule. (Illus.). 68p. (978-3-7757-0520-2(1)) Hatje Cantz Verlag GmbH & Co KG DEU. Dist: D.A.P./Distributed Art Pubs.

Karner, Herbert, et al. Austrian Academy of Sciences: The Building & its History. 2007. (GER.). 64p. (C). pap. 14.95 (978-3-7001-3875-4(X)) Austrian Academy of Sciences Press AUT. Dist: Brown, David Bk. Co., The.

Lamprecht, Barbara. Richard Neutra. Gossel, Peter, ed. 25th ed. 2009. (25 Ser.). (ENG., Illus.). 96p. 14.99 (978-3-8365-1326-5(9)) TASCHEN DEU. Dist: Ingram Pub. Services.

Noever, Peter & Pokorn, Marek, eds. Josef Hoffmann: Autobiography. 2010. (ENG., Illus.). 144p. pap. 30.00 (978-3-7757-2473-9(7)) Hatje Cantz Verlag GmbH & Co KG DEU. Dist: D.A.P./Distributed Art Pubs.

Sarnitz, August. Architecture in Vienna: 700 Buildings. 2008. (ENG., Illus.). 592p. pap. 49.95 (978-3-211-71578-9(9), 3211715789) Springer.

Semsroth, Klaus, et al. Camillo Sitte Gesamtausgabe 02: Schriften zu Städtebau und Architektur. 2010. (GER., Illus.). 632p. (978-3-205-78566-8(5)) Bohlau Verlag Gmbh & Cie.

teNeues. AAD Vienna: Art Architecture Design. 2010. (Illus.). 168p. pap. 12.95 (978-3-8327-9434-7(4)) teNeues Publishing Co.

Toman, Rolf, ed. Vienna: Art & Architecture. 2008. (Art & Architecture Ser.) (Illus.). 452p. pap. 24.95 (978-0-8416-0290-8(5)) American Map Corp.

ARCHITECTURE—BELGIUM

Anspach, Isabelle, contrib. by. Museum & Gardens van Buuren. 2012. (ENG., Illus.). 128p. 34.00 (978-90-6153-771-7(1)) Mercatorfonds N. V. BEL. Dist: D.A.P./Distributed Art Pubs.

Barthélemy, Jean & Peeters, Pierre. Les Cours de Justice de Mons. 2008. (FRE., Illus.). 132p. (978-2-507-00155-1(0)) Pire, Luc Editions.

Bekaert, Geert & Vandemoortele, Johanna. Belgium at the Fair: Exile on main Street, 1 vol. De Kooning, Mil, ed. 2011. (ENG.). 252p. 50.00 **(978-90-77833-14-8(5))** Exhibitions International BEL. Dist: Innovative Logistics.

Boyken, Immo. Egon Eiermann / Sep Ruf, German Pavilions, Brussels 1958. 2007. (Opus Ser.). (GER & ENG., Illus.). 60p. 39.90 (978-3-932565-62-5(2)) Edition Axel Menges GmbH DEU. Dist: National Bk. Network.

Bucquoye, Moniek E. & Devos, Rika. Belgium Beyond Expectations: The Belgian EU Pavilion at World Expo Shanghai 2010. 2011. (ENG.). 144p. 48.95 (978-90-5487-768-4(5)) VUB Univ. Pr. BEL. Dist: Independent Pubs. Group.

Ceulemans, Hadewijch. Belgium's Best Buildings. 2012. (ENG., Illus.). 160p. pap. 24.95 **(978-94-6058-081-9(5)**, Uitgeverij Luster) Antique Collectors' Club GBR. Dist: National Bk. Network.

De Decker, Cynrik & Roba, Jean-Louis. Doelwit Leuven: De Luchanvallen van 12 en 13 Mei 1944 en de Berging van een Halifax-Bommenwerper Bij Geraardsbergen. (DUT., Illus.). 224p. pap. 29.95 (978-90-72547-61-3(6)) De Krijger BEL. Dist: Casemate Pubs. & Bk. Distributors, LLC.

DE KOONING. Lucien Engels, 1 vol. 2011. (ENG & DUT.). 388p. 60.00 **(978-90-77833-11-7(0))** Exhibitions International BEL. Dist: Innovative Logistics.

De Kooning, Mil & Gerreway, Christophe Van. Stéphane Beel Architects. 2012. (ENG & DUT., Illus.). 304p. 95.00 **(978-90-209-5638-2(8))** Lannoo Pubs./Racine.

Debeerst, Philippe, photos by. Living in Great Style in Knokke-le Zoute: Beautiful homes in Belgium's most exclusive coastal City. 2011. (ENG., Illus.). 256p. 89.50 (978-90-8881-030-5(3)) Exhibitions International BEL. Dist: Innovative Logistics.

Detiffe, Marc, photos by. Architectural heritage in the Making: City of Brussels CPAS, 1 vol. 2011. (ENG, DUT & FRE.). 239p. 70.00 (978-2-930391-38-0(3)) Centre International Pour La Ville, L'Architecture Et Le Paysage BEL. Dist: Innovative Logistics.

Hoffsummer, Patrick, ed. The Roof Frame from the XIth Through XIXth Century: Typology & Development in Northern France & in Belgium. 2010. (Architectura Medii Aevi Ser.). (ENG.). 376p. (C). pap. 131.00 (978-2-503-52987-5(9)) Brepols Pubs. BEL. Dist: ISD.

Lampens, Juliaan. Juliaan Lampens, 1 vol. Campens, Angelique, ed. 2011. (ENG., Illus.). 152p. pap. 64.00 **(978-94-6117-005-7(X))** Exhibitions International BEL. Dist: Innovative Logistics.

Laporte, Stephanie & Pauwels, Wim. New Essentialism: Stephanie Laporte. 2008. (A&d Ser.). (ENG., Illus.). 200p. (978-90-77213-83-4(X), Beta-Plus (Acc)) Antique Collectors' Club.

Mayer, Jürgen, et al. Think & Grow Rich. 2011. (DUT & ENG., Illus.). 240p. (978-90-5856-355-2(3), Stichting Kunstboek (Acc)) Antique Collectors' Club.

Pauwels, Wim. Architectural Stories: By Bernard de Clerck. 2009. (ENG., Illus.). 304p. (978-90-8944-015-0(1), Beta-Plus (Acc)) Antique Collectors' Club.

—Bruno Erpicum, 1983-2008. 2008. (ENG., Illus.). 200p. (978-90-77213-84-1(8), Beta-Plus (Acc)) Antique Collectors' Club.

—Contemporary Classic: Esther Gutmer. Watkinson, Laura, tr. 2008. (and D Ser.). (ENG., Illus.). 200p. (978-90-8944-006-8(2), Beta-Plus (Acc)) Antique Collectors' Club.

—Ensemble & Associés. 2010. (ENG., Illus.). 192p. (978-90-8944-022-8(4), Beta-Plus (Acc)) Antique Collectors' Club.

Taschen, Angelika. ICONS Brussels Style. 2006. (Icons Ser.). (Illus.). 191p. per. 9.99 (978-3-8228-2384-2(8)) TASCHEN DEU. Dist: Ingram Pub. Services.

Verbist, Muriel. Belgian Architects & Their Homes. 2011. (ENG., Illus.). 270p. 55.00 (978-94-6058-074-1(2), Uitgeverij Luster) Antique Collectors' Club GBR. Dist: National Bk. Network.

ARCHITECTURE—BRAZIL

Alter, Kevin & Hoidn, Barbara, eds. Brazil: House in Santa Teresa, 2008 by Angelo Bucci; House at Rio Bonito, 2003 by Carla Juacaba. 2009. (ENG., Illus.). 144p. pap. 40.00 (978-3-8030-0699-8(6)) Wasmuth, Ernst J. Verlag GmbH & Co. DEU. Dist: D.A.P./Distributed Art Pubs.

Andreoli, Elisabetta & Forty, Adrian, eds. Brazil's Modern Architecture. 2007. (ENG., Illus.). 240p. per. 45.00 (978-0-7148-4845-7(X)) Phaidon Pr., Inc.

Baan, Iwan. Brasilia-Chandigarh: Living with Modernity. 2010. (Illus.). 240p. pap. (978-3-03778-228-6(5)) Lars Muller Pubs.

Borja-Villel, Manuel J. Drifts & Derivations: Experiences, Journeys & Morphologies. 2011. (ENG.). 301p. pap. 54.95 (978-84-8026-425-9(X)) Museo Nacional Centro de Arte Reina Sofia ESP. Dist: Actar Birkhauser Distribution.

Brandao, José. The Role of Urban Design in Strategic Planning. 2009. 360p. pap. (978-3-639-14307-2(8)) VDM Verlag Dr. Mueller e.K.

Burri, René, et al. René Burri. Brasilia: Fotografien 1960-1993. Rüegg, Arthur, ed. 2011. (GER & ENG., Illus.). 224p. 99.00 (978-3-85881-307-7(9)) Scheidegger und Spiess AG, Verlag CHE. Dist: Antique Collectors' Club.

Castro, Ana Claudia Veiga de. A São Paulo de Menotti Del Picchia: Arquitetura, Arte e Cidade Nas Crônicas de Um Modernista. 2008. (POR., Illus.). 296p. (978-85-98325-77-4(5)) Alameda Casa Editorial Ltda.

Equipo Staff. Vilanova Artigas. (SPA., Illus.). 210p. 70.00 (978-85-85751-11-1(8)) Instituto Lina B.O. e P.M. Bardi BRA. Dist: Gingko Pr., Inc.

Fabricius, Daniela. 100% Favela. 2012. (ENG.). pap. (978-84-96540-69-9(3)) Actar Birkhauser Distribution.

Gautherot, Marcel, photos by. Building Brasilia. 2010. (ENG., Illus.). 192p. 65.00 (978-0-500-51542-6(5), 551542) Thames & Hudson.

Lara, Fernando Luiz. The Rise of Popular Modernist Architecture in Brazil. 2008. (ENG., Illus.). 160p. 69.95 (978-0-8130-3289-4(X)) Univ. Pr. of Florida.

Mendes da Rocha, Paulo Archias & Artigas, Rosa. Paulo Mendes Da Rocha: Fifty Years, 1957-2007. 2007. (ENG., Illus.). 392p. 85.00 (978-0-8478-2984-2(7)) Rizzoli International Pubns., Inc.

Neimeyer, Oscar. The Curves of Time: The Memoirs of Oscar Niemeyer. 2007. (POR & ENG., Illus.). 192p. pap. 14.95 (978-0-7148-4857-0(3)) Phaidon Pr., Inc.

Philippou, Styliane. Oscar Niemeyer: Curves of Irreverence. 2008. (ENG., Illus.). 256p. 65.00 (978-0-300-12038-7(9)) Yale Univ. Pr.

Pilis, Alexander. Architecture Parallax: São Paulo. 2008. 56p. pap. 13.99 (978-1-4357-1662-9(0)) Lulu Enterprises Inc.

Salvaing, Matthieu. Oscar Niemeyer. ltd. ed. 2008. (978-2-7594-0293-9(2)) Assouline.

Taschen, Angelika, ed. ICON Bahia Style: Exteriors / Interiors / Details. 2009. (ENG.). 192p. pap. 9.99 (978-3-8365-1509-2(1)) TASCHEN DEU. Dist: Ingram Pub. Services.

Wallpaper Magazine Editors, ed. Rio de Janeiro 2011 - Wallpaper City Guide. rev. ed. 2011. (Wallpaper* City Guides). (ENG., Illus.). 128p. pap. 9.95 (978-0-7148-5644-5(4)) Phaidon Pr., Inc.

Weintraub, Alan, photos by. Oscar Niemeyer Buildings. 2009. (ENG., Illus.). 368p. 75.00 (978-0-8478-3190-6(6)) Rizzoli International Pubns., Inc.

Williams, Richard J. Brazil. 2009. (Reaktion Books - Modern Architectures in History Ser.). (ENG., Illus.). 304p. pap. 29.95 (978-1-86189-400-7(7)) Reaktion Bks., Ltd. GBR. Dist: Chicago Distribution Ctr.

Yale School of Architecture Staff. Urban Intersections: São Paolo. Rappaport, Nina & Bilken, Noah, eds. 2011. (Yale School of Architecture Bks.). (ENG., Illus.). 192p. pap. 35.00 (978-0-393-73352-5(1), 73352) Norton, W. W. & Co., Inc.

ARCHITECTURE—BULGARIA

Stoyanova, Proletina. Energy Efficiency Through Green Investment Schemes. 2010. 80p. pap. (978-3-8383-0363-5(6)) Lambert Academic Publishing.

ARCHITECTURE—BURMA

Moore, Elizabeth H. Early Landscapes of Myanmar. 2007. (ENG., Illus.). 220p. pap. 35.00 (978-974-9863-31-2(3)) River Bks. THA. Dist: Antique Collectors' Club.

Roveda, Vittorio & Clark, Joyce. Bayon Reconsidered. 2007. (Illus.). 256p. 85.00 (978-974-9863-05-3(4)) River Bks. THA. Dist: Antique Collectors' Club.

ARCHITECTURE—CANADA

Acomb, Glenn A. LARE Review: Mastering Section C, Site Design. 2007. (ENG., Illus.). 136p. pap. 72.00 (978-1-59126-042-4(6)) Professional Pubns., Inc.

Alfoldy, Sandra. The Allied Arts: Architecture & Craft in Postwar Canada. 2012. (McGill-Queen's/Beaverbrook Canadian Foundation Studies in Art History Ser.). (ENG., Illus.). 264p. (C). **(978-0-7735-3960-0(3))**; pap. **(978-0-7735-4003-3(2))** McGill-Queen's Univ. Pr.

Architects, Henriquez Partners, compiled by. Deconstructing - Reconstructing Woodwards. 2012. (ENG., Illus.). 240p. pap. 14.95 **(978-1-897476-50-5(7))** Simply Read Bks. CAN. Dist: Perseus-PGW.

Berelowitz, Lance. Dream City: Vancouver & the Global Imagination, 1 vol. 2010. (ENG., Illus.). 288p. pap. 29.95 (978-1-55365-170-3(7)) D&M Pubs. Inc. CAN. Dist: Perseus-PGW.

Browne, Kelvin. Bold Visions: The Architecture of the Royal Ontario Museum. 2007. (ENG.). 192p. 39.99 (978-0-88854-457-5(X)); mass mkt. 29.99 (978-0-88854-458-2(8)) Royal Ontario Museum CAN. Dist: Univ. of Toronto Pr.

Browne, Ken. Bold Visions: The Architecture of the Royal Ontario Museum, Souvenir Edition, 1 vol. 2007. (ENG.). 32p. pap. 2.99 (978-0-88854-450-6(2)) Royal Ontario Museum CAN. Dist: Univ. of Toronto Pr.

Carroll, Michael & Rooyakkers, Danita. Atelier BUILD. Carter, Brian, ed. 2010. (Illus.). 64p. pap. 19.50 (978-0-929112-57-2(1)) Tuns Pr. CAN. Dist: Baker & Taylor Bks.

Castro, Ricardo L. & Olsberg, Nicholas. Arthur Erickson Critical Works. 2006. (Illus.). 192p. 75.00 (978-0-295-98620-3(4)) Univ. of Washington Pr.

Chapple, Nina. A Heritage of Stone: Buildings of Niagara, St. Catharines, the Hamilton Escarpment, Paris, Cambridge, Waterloo County, Guelph, Fergus & Elora & St. Marys. 2006. (ENG., Illus.). 128p. pap. (978-1-55028-935-0(7)) Lorimer, James & Co., Ltd., Pubs. CAN. Dist: Casemate Pubs. & Bk. Distributors, LLC.

Ciecieк, Greg. LARE Review: Analytical Aspects of Practice. 2nd ed. 2006. (ENG., Illus.). 64p. pap. 80.00 (978-1-59126-086-8(8)) Professional Pubns., Inc.

Clive Wilkinson Architects & Chan, Benny, photos by. Interior Spaces of the USA & Canada Vol 7 No. 7: A Pictorial Review. 2006. (International Spaces Ser.). (ENG., Illus.). 224p. 55.00 (978-1-920744-35-9(5)) Images Publishing Group AUS. Dist: National Bk. Network.

Coun, Cdn Wood. Wood Design Manual, 2005: The Complete Reference for Wood Design in Canada. (Illus.). (978-0-921628-75-0(7)) Canadian Wood Council/Conseil Canadien du Bois.

Damianos, Lynne. The Bancroft Building & Its People 100 Years of History. 2010. pap. 55.95 (978-0-578-05686-9(0)) Damianos Photography.

Dennis, Richard, et al, eds. The Contemporary Canadian Metropolis. 2012. (ENG.). 200p. pap. 29.95 (978-1-900039-90-1(7)) Institute of Latin American Studies GBR. Dist: Brookings Institution Pr.

Design Centre for Sustainability. Greater Vancouver Greenguide: Seeding Sustainability. 2007. (ENG., Illus.). 202p. per. 22.95 (978-0-9780966-0-1(6), 0978096606) New Society Pubs., Ltd. CAN. Dist: Consortium Bk. Sales & Distribution.

Ferrara, Luigi, et al. Sustainable Building. rev. ed. 2008. (ENG., Illus.). 240p. pap. 39.95 (978-1-55263-957-3(6)) Key Porter Bks. CAN. Dist: Perseus-PGW.

Freeman, Bill. Casa Loma: Canada's Fairy-Tale Castle & Its Owner, Sir Henry Pellatt. 2nd ed. 2012. (ENG., Illus.). 72p. pap. 14.95 **(978-1-4594-0027-6(5))** Lorimer, James & Co., Ltd., Pubs. CAN. Dist: Casemate Pubs. & Bk. Distributors, LLC.

Goodfellow, Margaret & Goodfellow, Phil. Contemporary Architecture in Toronto, 1 vol. Malkin, Helen & Dunton, Nancy, eds. 2010. (ENG., Illus.). 192p. pap., instr.'s gde. ed. 24.95 (978-1-55365-444-5(7)) D&M Pubs. Inc. CAN. Dist: Perseus-PGW.

Hagberg, Eva. Nature Framed: At Home in the Landscape. 2011. (ENG., Illus.). 216p. 50.00 (978-1-58093-319-3(X)) Monacelli Pr., Inc.

Henriquez, Richard, et al. Richard Henriquez: Selected Works, 1967-2003, 1 vol. 2006. (ENG., Illus.). 288p. (978-1-55365-048-5(4)) D&M Pubs. Inc.

Hustak, Alan. Montreal Then & Now (Compact) Norchet, Johanne, tr. 2009. (Then & Now Thunder Bay Ser.). (ENG.). 144p. pap. 12.95 (978-1-59223-968-9(4), Thunder Bay Pr.) Advantage Pubs. Group.

Images Staff & Images. Interior Spaces of the USA & Canada: A Pictorial Review, Vol. 6. 2006. (ENG., Illus.). 224p. 55.00 (978-1-86470-107-4(2)) Images Publishing Group AUS. Dist: National Bk. Network.

Isitt, Mark. White Green: Ten Projects in the Great Outdoors. 2011. (ENG., Illus.). 208p. 50.00 (978-1-85669-737-8(1)) King, Laurence Publishing GBR. Dist: Hachette Bk. Group.

Kalman, Harold & Ward, Robin. Exploring Vancouver: The Architectural Guide, 1 vol. 4th rev. ed. 2012. (ENG., Illus.). 344p. pap. 24.95 **(978-1-55365-866-5(3))** D&M Pubs. Inc. CAN. Dist: Perseus-PGW.

Killory, Christine & Davids, Rene, eds. Details, Technology, & Form. 2012. (ENG., Illus.). 208p. 65.00 (978-1-56898-953-2(9)) Princeton Architectural Pr.

Kluckner, Michael. Vanishing Vancouver. 2012. 224p. pap. 35.00 **(978-1-77050-067-9(7))** Whitecap Bks., Ltd. CAN. Dist: Midpoint Trade Bks., Inc.

Leppo, RA/CID, LEED AP, Holly Williams & Ballast, David Kent. Construction Documents & Services: ARE Sample Problems & Practice Exam. 2nd ed. 2011. (ENG.). 114p. pap. 120.00 (978-1-59126-323-4(9)) Professional Pubns., Inc.

Leroux, John & Holownia, Thaddeus. St. Andrews Architecture, 1604-1966. 2010. (ENG.). 144p. pap. (978-1-55447-094-5(3)) Gaspereau Pr.

Luxton, Donald. Building the West: The Early Architects of British Columbia. 2nd ed. 2007. (ENG., Illus.). 560p. per. 39.95 (978-0-88922-554-1(0)) Talonbooks, Ltd. CAN. Dist: Consortium Bk. Sales & Distribution.

Macdonald, Christopher & Gillies, Veronica. Contemporary Architecture in Vancouver, 1 vol. Dunton, Nancy & Malkin, Helen, eds. 2010. (ENG., Illus.). 192p. pap., instr.'s gde. ed. 24.95 (978-1-55365-445-2(5)) D&M Pubs. Inc. CAN. Dist: Perseus-PGW.

MacKay-Lyons, Brian & Buchanan, Peter. Ghost: Building an Architectural Vision. 2008. (ENG., Illus.). 224p. pap. 35.00 (978-1-56898-736-1(6)) Princeton Architectural Pr.

MacNutt, James W. Building for Democracy: The History & Architecture of the Legislative Buildings of Nova Scotia, Prince Edward Island & New Brunswick. 2010. (ENG., Illus.). 128p. pap. 24.95 (978-0-88780-930-9(8)) Formac Publishing Co., Ltd. CAN. Dist: Casemate Pubs. & Bk. Distributors, LLC.

Malkin, Helen & Dunton, Nancy. A Guidebook to Contemporary Architecture in Montreal, 1 vol. 2008. (ENG., Illus.). 192p. pap. 24.95 (978-1-55365-346-2(7)) D&M Pubs. Inc. CAN. Dist: Perseus-PGW.

Martins-Manteiga, John. Mean City: From Architecture to Design: How Toronto Went Boom! 2008. (ENG., Illus.). 112p. 22.95 (978-1-55263-912-2(6)) Key Porter Bks. CAN. Dist: Perseus-PGW.

Mellin, Robert. Newfoundland Modern: Architecture in the Smallwood Years, 1949-1972. 2011. (McGill-Queen's/Beaverbrook Canadian Foundation Studies in Art History Ser.). (ENG., Illus.). 304p. (C). **(978-0-7735-3902-0(6))** McGill-Queen's Univ. Pr.

Micallef, Shawn. Stroll: Psychogeographic Walking Tours of Toronto. 2010. (ENG., Illus.). 312p. pap. 22.95 (978-1-55245-226-4(3)) Coach Hse. Bks. CAN. Dist: Consortium Bk. Sales & Distribution.

Min, Christa, et al, eds. Vancouver Matters. 2009. (ENG., Illus.). 176p. pap. 19.95 (978-1-897476-10-9(8)) Simply Read Bks. CAN. Dist: Perseus-PGW.

Mindenhall, Dorothy. Unbuilt Victoria. 2012. (ENG., Illus.). 248p. pap. 28.99 **(978-1-4597-0174-8(7))** Dundurn CAN. Dist: Ingram Pub. Services.

Ockman, Joan & Williamson, Rebecca. Architecture School: Three Centuries of Educating Architects in North America. 2012. (ENG., Illus.). 400p. (gr. 17). 50.00 **(978-0-262-01708-4(3))** MIT Pr.

Olsberg, R. Nicholas, et al. Arthur Erickson: Critical Works, 1 vol. 2006. (ENG., Illus.). 256p. (978-1-55365-154-3(5)) D&M Pubs. Inc.

Osbaldeston, Mark. Unbuilt Toronto: A History of the City That Might Have Been. 2008. (ENG., Illus.). 256p. pap. 26.99 (978-1-55002-835-5(9)) Dundurn CAN. Dist: Ingram Pub. Services.

—Unbuilt Toronto 2: More of the City That Might Have Been. 2011. (ENG., Illus.). 272p. pap. 26.99 (978-1-55488-975-4(8), Dundurn Pr.) Dundurn CAN. Dist: Ingram Pub. Services.

Poole, Stephen. Halifax: Discovering Its Heritage. 2nd ed. 2012. (ENG., Illus.). 72p. pap. 19.95 **(978-1-4595-0052-5(0))** Formac Publishing Co., Ltd. CAN. Dist: Casemate Pubs. & Bk. Distributors, LLC.

RSMeans Engineering Dept., ed. Yardsticks for Costing - Canadian Construction Cost Data. 2009. (ENG.). 160p. pap. 154.95 (978-0-87629-221-1(X)) Means, R.S. Co., Inc.

St-Pierre, Jacques & Beauregard, Yves. Le Québec D'antan: à Travers la Carte Postale Ancienne. 2010. (FRE., Illus.). 157p. (978-2-35720-049-4(9), HC) HarperCollins Pubs.

Visser, Thomas Durant. Porches of North America. 2012. (ENG., Illus.). 304p. 39.95 **(978-1-61168-220-5(7))** Univ. Pr. of New England.

Wallpaper Magazine Editors, ed. Wallpaper City Guide Vancouver 2012. 2012. (ENG., Illus.). 128p. pap. 9.95 **(978-0-7148-6307-8(6))** Phaidon Pr. Ltd. GBR. Dist: Hachette Bk. Group.

Ward, Robin. Robin Ward's Heritage West Coast. unabr. ed. (ENG., Illus.). 128p. (978-1-55017-095-5(3)) Harbour Publishing Co., Ltd.

ARCHITECTURE—CARIBBEAN AREA

Atkinson, Lesley-Gail, ed. The Earliest Inhabitants: The Dynamics of the Jamaican Taino. 2006. (Illus.). 215p. per. (978-976-640-149-8(7)) Univ. of the West Indies Pr.

Connors, Michael. Caribbean Houses: History, Style, & Architecture. 2009. (ENG., Illus.). 272p. 60.00 (978-0-8478-3213-2(9)) Rizzoli International Pubns., Inc.

—The Splendor of Cuba: 450 Years of Architecture & Interiors. 2011. (ENG., Illus.). 320p. 85.00 (978-0-8478-3567-6(7)) Rizzoli International Pubns., Inc.

GARDIN, Giancarlo & ROSATI, Massimo. Caribbean Architecture, 1 vol. 2011. (ENG & ITA.). 216p. 78.00 **(978-88-87653-08-3(9))** Archideos Libri ITA. Dist: Innovative Logistics.

González Arestuche, Luis & Recondo Pérez, Ramón. Puentes de Matanzas. 2009. (Illus.). 118p. (978-959-268-165-1(1)) Matanzas, Ediciones.

Griffith, Cathryn. Havana Revisited: An Architectural Heritage. Cluster, Dick, tr. 2010. (ENG., Illus.). 240p. 49.95 (978-0-393-73284-9(3), 73284) Norton, W. W. & Co., Inc.

Guy Nordenson and Associates Staff, et al. New Haiti Villages. 2010. (ENG., Illus.). 48p. pap. 19.95 (978-1-56898-981-5(4)) Princeton Architectural Pr.

Loomis, John A. Revolution of Forms: Cuba's Forgotten Art Schools. rev. ed. 2011. (ENG., Illus.). 190p. pap. 29.95 (978-1-56898-988-4(1)) Princeton Architectural Pr.

Mallea, Hermes. Great Houses of Havana. 2011. (ENG., Illus.). 272p. 75.00 (978-1-58093-288-2(6)) Monacelli Pr., Inc.

Montalvo, Maria Luisa Lobo. Havana: History & Architecture of a Romantic City. Fox, Lorna S., tr. from SPA. 2009. (ENG., Illus.). 320p. 85.00 (978-1-58093-238-7(X)) Monacelli Pr., Inc.

More, Gustavo Luis, ed. Caribbean Modernist Architecture. 2010. (ENG., Illus.). 200p. pap. 30.00 (978-0-87070-775-9(2)) Museum of Modern Art.

Rodriguez, Eduardo Luis, ed. Architecture & Revolution in Cuba, 1959-1969. 2008. 224p. (978-84-96954-16-8(1)) Actar Birkhauser Distribution.

Visscher, Jochen, ed. Havana: The Sleeping Beauty. 2008. (GER, SPA & ENG., Illus.). 96p. 19.95 (978-3-939633-36-5(4)) Jovis Verlag GmbH DEU. Dist: D.A.P./Distributed Art Pubs.

ARCHITECTURE—CHINA

Ahuja, Shilpa. Designing a Chinese Cultural Center in Indi. 2010. 136p. pap. (978-3-8383-5919-9(4)) Lambert Academic Publishing.

Arkaraprasertkul, Non. Shanghai Contemporary: The Politics of Built Form How divergent planning methods transformed Shanghai's urban identity Foreword by Stanford Anderson. 2009. 204p. pap. (978-3-639-09187-8(6)) VDM Verlag Dr. Mueller e.K.

Barmé, Geremie R. The Forbidden City. 2012. (Wonders of the World Ser.). (Illus.). 288p. pap. 14.95 **(978-0-674-06396-9(1))** Harvard Univ. Pr.

Berliner, Nancy. The Emperor's Private Paradise: Treasures from the Forbidden City. 2010. (Illus.). 256p. 65.00 (978-0-300-16389-6(4)) Yale Univ. Pr.

Borysevicz, Mathieu. Learning from Hangzhou. 2009. (ENG., Illus.). 330p. pap. 45.00 (978-988-18033-6-8(5)) Timezone 8 Ltd. HKG. Dist: D.A.P./Distributed Art Pubs.

Cai, Yanxin. Chinese Architecture. 3rd ed. 2011. (Introductions to Chinese Culture Ser.). (Illus.). 186p. pap. 19.99 (978-0-521-18644-5(7)) Cambridge Univ. Pr.

CCDI Design Group. CCDI Design Group: Urban Design, Architecture, Consulting, Engineering. 2012. (ENG., Illus.). 256p. 85.00 ***(978-1-86470-461-7(6))*** Images Publishing Group AUS. Dist: National Bk. Network.

Ciampi, Mario, photos by. Artists in China. 2007. (ENG., Illus.). 240p. *(978-1-905216-04-8(1))* Verba Volant, Ltd.

Clementi, Alberto, ed. ZHONGSHAN Programme: Italia/Cina per le citta - Italy/China for the Cities. 2011. 240p. pap. 29.95 *(978-88-95623-22-1(3))* LIST - Laboratorio Editoriale ITA. Dist: Actar Birkhauser Distribution.

Cody, Jeffrey W., et al, eds. Chinese Architecture & the Beaux-Arts. 2010. (Illus.). 408p. *(978-988-8028-71-9(5))* Hong Kong Univ. Pr.

Cody, Jeffrey W., et al. Chinese Architecture & the Beaux-Arts. 2010. 408p. *(978-0-8248-3456-2(9))* Hong Kong Univ. Pr.

Creation Magazine Staff. Contemporary Architecture in China. Yajun, Jiang, tr. 2011. (Discovering China Ser.). (ENG., Illus.). 128p. 16.95 *(978-1-60220-116-3(1))* Reader's Digest Assn., Inc., The.

Denison, Edward & Ren, Guang Yu. Modernism in China: Architectural Visions & Revolutions. 2008. (ENG., Illus.). 336p. 90.00 *(978-0-470-31928-4(3)*, Wiley) Wiley, John & Sons, Inc.

Dubrau, Christian. Contemporary Architecture in China: Buildings & Projects, 2000-2020. 2010. (ENG., Illus.). 312p. 99.95 *(978-3-86922-120-5(8))* DOM Pubs. DEU. Dist: Innovative Logistics.

Dubrau/Li Xiangning, Christian. Contemporary Green Buildings in China: Art & Architecture 2000 bis 2020, 1 vol. 2011. (ENG, GER & CHI., Illus.). 336p. 99.95 *(978-3-86922-128-1(5))* DOM Pubs. DEU. Dist: Innovative Logistics.

Edelmann, Freder, ed. In the Chinese City/Positions. 2008. 516p. *(978-84-96954-62-5(5))* Actar Birkhauser Distribution.

Edelmann, Frederic. Positions. Edelmann, Freder, ed. 2008. 216p. *(978-84-96954-50-2(1))* Actar Birkhauser Distribution.

Feng, Jiren. Chinese Architecture & Metaphor: Song Culture in the Yingzao Fashi Building Manual. 2012. 53.00 ***(978-0-8248-3363-3(5))*** Univ. of Hawaii Pr.

Fingerhuth, Carl. Learning from the Chinese. 2006. (Illus.). 215p. pap. 49.95 *(978-3-7643-7602-4(3)*, 3764376023) Birkhauser Verlag AG CHE. Dist: Springer.

Flagge, Ingeborg, ed. & text. LUXEMBOURG EXPO PAVILION SHANGHAI: Hermann & Valentiny & Partners. 2011. (ENG., Illus.). 144p. 50.00 *(978-3-86859-062-3(5))* Jovis Verlag GmbH DEU. Dist: D.A.P./Distributed Art Pubs.

Foit-Albert, Beverly & Shunxun, Nan. China's Sacred Sites. 2007. (ENG.). 286p. 49.95 *(978-0-89389-262-3(9))* Himalayan Institute Pr.

Freeman, Michael A. & Wang, Xiao Dan. China Contemporary. 2009. (ENG., Illus.). 264p. 45.00 *(978-0-500-51418-4(6))* Thames & Hudson.

Gu Zhenhong. Approaches to Energy Efficient Building Development: Studying under Chinese Contexts 2008. 100p. pap. *(978-3-639-09361-2(5))* VDM Verlag Dr. Mueller e.K.

Hei, Lam Wo. Wong & Ouyang: Blueprints for Hong Kong the Master Architect Series. Beaver, Robyn, ed. 2008. (ENG., Illus.). 184p. 59.95 *(978-1-86470-304-7(0)*, Images Publishing Dist Ac) Antique Collectors' Club GBR. Dist: National Bk. Network.

Hill, Terry. Solutions for a Modern City: Arup in Beijing. McCorquodale, Duncan, ed. 2008. (ENG., Illus.). 175p. 55.00 *(978-1-906155-47-6(X))* Black Dog Publishing Ltd. GBR. Dist: Perseus Distribution.

HKU Faculty of Architecture. Building the Dragon City. 2011. (ENG., Illus.). 200p. (gr. 17). 50.00 *(978-988-8083-62-6(7))* Hong Kong Univ. Pr. HKG. Dist: Columbia Univ. Pr.

Ho M Staff & Partners For Health Staff. Hpa: the Story of Ho & Partners Architects: Architecture - Witnessing the Progress of Human Civilisation. 2012. (ENG & CHI., Illus.). 240p. 59.95 *(978-1-86470-426-6(8))* Images Publishing Group AUS. Dist: National Bk. Network.

Holdsworth, May. The Palace of Established Happiness: Restoring a Garden in the Forbidden City. 2008. 223p. *(978-7-80047-331-9(7))* Forbidden City Publishing Hse.

Howard, Edwin L. Chinese Garden Architecture: A Collection of Photographs of Minor Chinese Buildings. 2011. 114p. 39.95 ***(978-1-258-01869-6(1))*** Literary Licensing, LLC.

Images Publishing Staff, PUBLISHING & Pan, Joshua Jih. J. J. Pan & Partners. 2006. (Master Architect Ser.). (ENG., Illus.). 256p. 59.95 *(978-1-86470-058-9(0)*, Images Publishing Dist Ac) Antique Collectors' Club GBR. Dist: National Bk. Network.

Jiang, Shuping. Shan Qu Gong Lu Da Kua Yi Xing Peng Dong Jie Gou. 2010. (CHI., Illus.). vi, 363p. *(978-7-03-026142-7(9))* Science Pr.

Klein, Caroline. Ai Weiwei. 2011. (ENG, FRE, GER, ITA & SPA., Illus.). 176p. 35.00 *(978-3-942597-01-2(2))* DAAB Media Gmbh DEU. Dist: Innovative Logistics.

—Crossing China: Land of the rising Scene, 1 vol. 2012. (ENG.). 312p. 75.00 *(978-3-942597-12-8(8))* DAAB Media Gmbh DEU. Dist: Innovative Logistics.

Knapp, Ronald G. Chinese Bridges: Living Architecture from China's Past. 2008. (ENG.). 272p. 49.95 *(978-0-8048-3884-9(4))* Tuttle Publishing.

Kong, Yuhang. Jian Zhu '09'08: Dang Dai Zhongguo Jian Zhu Chuang Zuo Lun Tan Zuo Pin Ji. 2009. (CHI., Illus.). 351p. *(978-7-5611-4852-5(6))* Dalian Univ. of Technology Electronic & Audio-Visual Pr.

Laurence King Publishing Limited Staff. New Chinese Architecture. 2009. (ENG., Illus.). 480p. pap. 40.00 *(978-1-85669-608-1(1))* King, Laurence Publishing GBR. Dist: Hachette Bk. Group.

Leece, Sharon & Freeman, Michael A. China Style. 2008. (ENG., Illus.). 208p. 39.95 *(978-0-7946-0553-7(2)*, PeriplusEdition) Tuttle Publishing.

Leong, Sze Tsung. History Images, 1 vol. 2008. (ENG., Illus.). 144p. 90.00 *(978-3-86521-274-0(3))* Steidl, Gerhard Druckerei und Verlag DEU. Dist: Innovative Logistics.

Li, Feng. 'Critical' Practice in State-Owned Design Institutes in Post-Mao Chin. 2010. 140p. pap. *(978-3-8383-6998-3(X))* Lambert Academic Publishing.

Liauw, Laurence, ed. New Urban China. 2008. (Architectural Design Ser.). (ENG.). 136p. pap. 50.00 *(978-0-470-75122-0(3)*, Wiley) Wiley, John & Sons, Inc.

Lip, Evelyn. Feng Shui in Chinese Architecture. 2009. pap. 23.99 *(978-981-261-634-0(9))* Marshall Cavendish International (Asia) Private Ltd. SGP. Dist: Marshall Cavendish Corp.

Lü, Chuansheng & Gong, Shengqi. Yu Jian Zhu Dui Hua: Pin du Qingdao Deguo Zong du Lou Jiu Zhi Bo Wu Guan = Dialogue with Architecture: Looking into the Museum of the Former German Governor's House in Qingdao. 2009. (CHI., Illus.). 233p. *(978-7-80737-495-4(0))* Shandong Friendship Publishing Hse.

Lu, Xin. China China. 2008. (ENG., Illus.). 112p. pap. 30.00 *(978-3-7757-2147-9(9))* Hatje Cantz Verlag GmbH & Co KG DEU. Dist: D.A.P./Distributed Art Pubs.

Lui, Elizabeth Gill. Open Hearts Open Doors: Reflections on China's Past & Future. 2008. (Illus.). 250p. 50.00 *(978-0-9796165-0-1(6))*; 50.00 *(978-0-9796165-3-2(0))* Cornell Univ. Pr.

Luna, Ian. On the Edge Ten Architects from China. 2007. (ENG., Illus.). 224p. 25.00 *(978-0-8478-2868-5(9))* Rizzoli International Pubns., Inc.

Maas, Winy, text. Hong Kong Fantasies: A Visual Expedition into the Future of a World-Class City. 2012. (ENG., Illus.). 176p. pap. 35.00 *(978-90-5662-764-5(3))* NAi Uitgevers / Publishers Stichting NLD. Dist: D.A.P./Distributed Art Pubs.

Mangan, J. A. & Jinxia, Dong, eds. Building for the Beijing Olympics: Chinese Challenge in the 'Chinese Century' 2008. (Sport in the Global Society Ser.). 250p. 140.00 *(978-0-415-37165-0(1))* Routledge.

Mars, Neville. The Chinese Dream: A Society under Construction. 2008. (ENG., Illus.). 192p. 60.00 *(978-988-99617-1-8(7))* Timezone 8 Ltd. HKG. Dist: D.A.P./Distributed Art Pubs.

McGetrick, Brendan, ed. Who Is Architecture: the 2009 Domus China Interviews. 2011. (ENG., Illus.). 131p. pap. 28.00 *(978-988-18816-6-3(8))* Timezone 8 Ltd. HKG. Dist: D.A.P./Distributed Art Pubs.

McLane, Daisann. ICON Style Shanghai. Taschen, Angelika, ed. 2008. (Icons Ser.). (ENG., Illus.). 190p. pap. 9.99 *(978-3-8365-0481-2(2))* TASCHEN DEU. Dist: Ingram Pub. Services.

Mei, Zhankui. Shanghai Jian Zhu Xiu. 2009. (CHI., Illus.). 7p. *(978-7-80730-749-5(8))* Xuelin Publishing Hse.

Miller, Tracy. The Divine Nature of Power: Chinese Ritual Architecture at the Sacred Site of Jinci. 2007. (Harvard-Yenching Institute Monograph Ser.: 62). (Illus.). 265p. 45.00 *(978-0-674-02513-4(X))* Harvard Univ., Asia Ctr.

Moro, Laura, ed. Taihe Dian: The Hall of Supreme Harmony of the Forbidden City in Beijing. 2010. 140p. pap. 32.95 *(978-88-492-1557-1(6))* Gangemi ITA. Dist: International Publishers Marketing.

Morse, Edward S. Glimpses of China & Chinese Homes. 2007. (ENG.). 236p. 41.95 *(978-0-548-36796-4(5))*; per. 26.95 *(978-0-548-31100-4(5)*, Kessinger Publishing, LLC.

New Spaces for Old Buildings. 2009. (Illus.). 264p. *(978-981-261-490-2(7))* Marshall Cavendish.

Phillips, Christopher. Shanghai Kaleidoscope. 2008. (ENG., Illus.). 144p. 59.99 *(978-0-88854-460-5(X))*; pap. 34.99 *(978-0-88854-461-2(8))* Royal Ontario Museum CAN. Dist: Univ. of Toronto Pr.

Pohl, Ethel Baraona. Watercube. Baraona, Pohl, ed. 2008. 320p. *(978-84-612-4413-5(2))* Actar Birkhauser Distribution.

Rampello, Davide, ed. Expo 2010 Shaghai Italy Pavilion: The City of Man Living the Italian Way. 2010. 88p. pap. 24.50 ***(978-88-370-7865-2(X))*** Electa ITA. Dist: Trans-Atlantic Pubns., Inc.

Santoro, Carlo & Greco, Claudio. Beijing: The New City. 2008. (ENG., Illus.). 272p. pap. 14.99 *(978-88-6130-302-7(1))* Skira Editore ITA. Dist: Random Hse., Inc.

Schmal, Peter & Wenjun, Zhi, eds. M8 in China: Contemporary Chinese Architects. Zeitgenössische chinesische Architekten. 2010. (ENG., Illus.). 160p. 39.95 *(978-3-86859-025-8(0))* Jovis Verlag GmbH DEU. Dist: D.A.P./Distributed Art Pubs.

Shelton, Barrie, et al. The Making of Hong Kong: From Vertical to Volumetric. 2010. (Planning, History & Environment Ser.). (ENG., Illus.). 192p. (C). 120.00 *(978-0-415-48707-8(3))* Routledge.

Smith, Broc. The Tragic Kingdom or; 'Prisoner in a Chinese Theme Park' 2009. 342p. 18.95 *(978-1-60264-415-1(2))*; pap. 13.95 *(978-1-60264-414-4(4))* Virtualbookworm.com Publishing, Inc.

Teo, Dawn, tr. Alternatives Shops. 2007. (Illus.). 267p. 55.00 *(978-981-245-372-0(3))* Page One Publishing SGP. Dist: Gingko Pr., Inc.

Turenscape Architects Staff, contrib. by. The Art of Survival. 2011. (Illus.). 256p. 39.99 ***(978-84-9936-861-0(1))*** Loft Pubns. ESP. Dist: Prestel Publishing.

Vranckx, Bridget. PTang Studio: A New Approach to Chinese Architecture. 2012. (ENG., Illus.). 256p. 39.99 ***(978-84-9936-862-7(X))*** Loft Pubns. ESP. Dist: Prestel Publishing.

Wallpaper Magazine Editors, ed. Beijing 2012 - Wallpaper City Guide. 2nd ed. 2011. (ENG., Illus.). 128p. pap., pap. 9.95 *(978-0-7148-6092-3(1))* Phaidon Pr., Inc.

—Shanghai 2012 - Wallpaper City Guides. 4th ed. 2011. (ENG., Illus.). 128p. pap., pap. 9.95 *(978-0-7148-6204-0(5))* Phaidon Pr., Inc.

Wang, Fawu, et al. Landslide Disaster Mitigation in Three Gorges Reservoir, China. 2009. (Environmental Science & Engineering Ser.). (ENG., Illus.). xiii, 563p. 229.00 *(978-3-642-00131-4(9)*, 3642001319) Springer.

Wang, Shaoqing. Beyond Design: 2010 Shanghai Expo Architecture & Space Design. 2011. (ENG., Illus.). 320p. 95.00 *(978-4-903233-69-7(3))* Azur Corp. JPN. Dist: Antique Collectors' Club.

Wang, Tongzhen. Si Mao Beijing. 2009. (CHI., Illus.). *(978-7-5010-2871-9(0))* Cultural Relics Publishing Hse.

Warr, Anne. Shanghai Architecture. 2008. (Architecture Guides (Watermark Press) Ser.). (Illus.). 338p. pap. 45.00 *(978-0-949284-76-1(9))* Watermark Pr., The AUS. Dist: National Bk. Network.

Weiwei, Ai, et al. Art & Cultural Policy in China: A Conversation between Ai Weiwei, Uli Sigg & Yung Ho Chang, moderated by Peter Pakesch. 2009. (GER & ENG., Illus.). 132p. pap. 39.95 *(978-3-211-89240-4(0))* Springer Wien AUT. Dist: Actar Birkhauser Distribution.

Wolf, Michael. Hong Kong Corner Houses. 2011. (ENG., Illus.). 136p. (gr. 17). 45.00 *(978-988-8028-72-6(3))* Hong Kong Univ. Pr. HKG. Dist: Columbia Univ. Pr.

Xia, Ai & Fen, Qi. CCDI Architecture: Design for China's Future the Millennium Series. 2008. (ENG., Illus.). 256p. 85.00 *(978-1-86470-306-1(7))* Images Publishing Group AUS. Dist: National Bk. Network.

Xue, Charlie Q. L. World Architecture in China. 2012. (ENG.). 220p. pap. 24.95 *(978-1-59265-083-5(X))* Long River Pr.

Yang, Xiying & Li, Hongiei. Reconstituting History & Culture in New Media Art. 2010. 160p. pap. *(978-3-8383-8067-4(3))* Lambert Academic Publishing.

Yanxin, et al. Chinese Architecture. (Illus.). 154p. 16.95 *(978-7-5085-0996-9(X))* China Intercontinental Communication Ctr. CHN. Dist: China Bks. & Periodicals, Inc.

Yao, Kris. Kris Yao/Artech. 2011. (ENG., Illus.). 588p. 80.00 *(978-1-86470-219-4(2))* Images Publishing Group AUS. Dist: National Bk. Network.

Yuen, Belinda K. P. & Yeh, Anthony G. O. High-Rise Building Living in Asian Cities. 2011. (ENG. Illus.). vii, 195p. 129.00 *(978-90-481-9737-8(6)*, 9048197376) Springer.

Zhenning, Fang, et al. Heart-Made: The Cutting Edge of Chinese Contemporary Architecture - Europalia 2009 China, 1 vol. 2010. (ENG.). 208p. 89.00 *(978-90-6153-894-3(7))* Exhibitions International BEL. Dist: Innovative Logistics.

Zhou, Kexi & Qijun, Wang. Chinese Architecture. 2011. (Discovering China Ser.). (ENG., Illus.). 160p. 16.95 *(978-1-60220-118-7(8))* Reader's Digest Assn., Inc., The.

Zhu, Jianfei. Architecture of Modern China: A Historical Critique. 2008. (ENG., Illus.). 336p. (C). pap. 62.95 *(978-0-415-45781-1(5))* Routledge.

—Modern Chinese Architecture: A Historical Critique. 2008. (Illus.). 336p. 165.00 *(978-0-415-45780-4(7))* Routledge.

Zwerger, Klaus. Vanishing Tradition: Architecture & Carpentry of the Dong Minority in China. 2006. (ENG., Illus.). 224p. 50.00 *(978-974-524-061-2(3))* Orchid Pr. THA. Dist: National Bk. Network.

ARCHITECTURE—CZECH REPUBLIC

Architecture, 1990-2008: Czech Republic, Slovakia, Hungary, Poland, 1 vol. 2011. (ENG., Illus.). 200p. pap. 55.00 *(978-80-7437-000-7(3))* Kant CZE. Dist: D.A.P./Distributed Art Pubs.

Hasek, Vladimir & Unger, Josef. Religious Architecture in the Czech Republic in the Light of Geophysical Prospection & Archaeological Excavation. 2010. (Bar S Ser.). (ENG., Illus.). 90p. (C). pap. 125.00 *(978-1-4073-0669-8(3))* British Archaeological Reports Ltd. GBR. Dist: Brown, David Bk. Co., The.

Janatkova, Alena. Modernisierung und Metropole: Architektur und Repräsentation auf den Landesausstellungen in Prag 1891 und Brunn 1928. 2008. (GER., Illus.). 106p. (C). 49.00 *(978-3-515-08599-1(8))* Steiner, Franz Verlag Wiesbaden GmbH DEU. Dist: Brown, David Bk. Co., The.

Kramm, Rüdiger & Dill, Alex. Vila Tugendhat Brno. 2008. (GER & ENG., Illus.). 132p. pap. 45.00 *(978-3-8030-0679-0(1))* Wasmuth, Ernst J. Verlag GmbH & Co. DEU. Dist: D.A.P./Distributed Art Pubs.

Noever, Peter & Pokorny, Marek, eds. Josef Hoffmann: Architecture Guide. 2011. (ENG., Illus.). 200p. pap. 40.00 *(978-3-7757-2733-4(7))* Hatje Cantz Verlag GmbH & Co KG DEU. Dist: D.A.P./Distributed Art Pubs.

Wallpaper Magazine Editors, ed. Wallpaper City Guide - Prague 2011. rev. ed. 2011. (Wallpaper* City Guides). (ENG., Illus.). 128p. pap. 9.95 *(978-0-7148-5634-6(7))* Phaidon Pr., Inc.

Wittlich, Petr. Art-Nouveau Prague. 2009. (ENG., Illus.). 135p. pap. 30.00 *(978-80-246-1346-8(8))* Karolinum, nakladatelstvi Univerzity Karlovy CZE. Dist: Chicago Distribution Ctr.

ARCHITECTURE—DENMARK

Adriansen, Inge. Erindringssteder i Danmark. 2010. (DAN., Illus.). 540p. *(978-87-635-3173-3(9))* Museum Tusculanum Pr.

Bo Jensen, Thomas. P. V. Jensen-Klint. 2009. (ENG., Illus.). 504p. (C). 125.00 *(978-0-415-55318-6(0))* Routledge.

Bundegaard, Christian, ed. Middelfart Sparekasse. 2011. (ENG & DAN.). 203p. pap. *(978-87-993680-1-3(3))* Actar Birkhauser Distribution.

De Smedt, Julien, ed. Agenda: JDS Architects: Can We Sustain our Ability to Crisis? 2011. 544p. pap. *(978-84-92861-62-0(2))* Actar Birkhauser Distribution.

Design Media Publishing Staff & Big Architecture Staff. Big: Bjarke Ingels Group Projects 2001-2010. 2011. (ENG.). 232p. 40.00 *(978-988-19738-6-3(4))* Design Media Publishing Ltd. HKG. Dist: BookMasters Distribution Services (BDS).

Fores, Ferrer. Jorn Utzon. Works & Projects. 2006. 306p. pap. 24.00 *(978-84-252-2060-9(2))* Trucatriche.

Hejler Andersen, Helle & Lind Klogborg, Mathias. Solar City. 2011. 216p. pap. ***(978-3-8443-2105-0(5))*** Lambert Academic Publishing.

Ibler, Marianne. Sustainability: BÆredygtighed. 2011. (DAN & ENG., Illus.). 206p. pap. *(978-87-91872-03-7(0))* Actar Birkhauser Distribution.

—30 New Projects: Global Danish Architecture 5. 2011. (DAN., Illus.). 136p. pap. *(978-87-91872-05-1(7))* Actar Birkhauser Distribution.

Ibler, Marianne, ed. Tradition & Crisis: Global Danish Architecture 4. 2011. (Global Danish Architecture Ser.). (ENG & DAN.). 156p. pap. *(978-87-91872-04-4(9))* Actar Birkhauser Distribution.

Ingels, Bjarke. Yes Is More: An Archicomic on Architectural Evolution. 2009. (ENG., Illus.). 400p. pap. 29.99 *(978-3-8365-2010-2(9)*, Evergreen) TASCHEN DEU. Dist: Ingram Pub. Services.

Marcus, Mette & Juul Holm, Michael, eds. Jorn Utzon: the Architect's Universe, 1 vol. 2008. (ENG., Illus.). 96p. 35.00 *(978-87-91607-11-0(6))* Louisana DNK. Dist: D.A.P./Distributed Art Pubs.

Mathewson, Casey C. M. & Viderikser, Ann, eds. A5 Copenhagen: Architecture, Interiors, Lifestyle. 2012. (ENG., Illus.). 400p. 60.00 *(978-0-9819857-5-6(0))* Oro Editions.

Nielsen, Anette Vilstrup & Fogedgaard Jonsson, Line. Cancer Health Care Centre, Copenhagen. 2011. 216p. pap. ***(978-3-8454-0707-4(7))*** Lambert Academic Publishing.

Sestoft, Jorgen & Christiansen, Jorgen Hegner. Guide to Danish Architecture, 1000-1960, Vol. 1. 2nd ed. (Illus.). 272p. 82.00 *(978-87-7407-155-6(6))* Arkitektens Forlag DNK. Dist: Coronet Bks.

Sestoft, Jorgen, et al. Guide to Danish Architecture, 1960-1995, 2 vols., Vol. 2. (Illus.). 92.00 *(978-87-7407-113-6(0))* Arkitektens Forlag DNK. Dist: Coronet Bks.

Sommer, A.L. Den Danske Arkitektur. 2009. (DAN., Illus.). 592p. *(978-87-02-05401-9(9))* Gyldendal.

Udsen, Vibe & Moller, Henrik Sten. Jorn Utzon - Houses. 2006. (ENG., Illus.). 240p. 85.00 *(978-87-987597-3-7(5))* Living Architecture Publishing DNK. Dist: Perseus-PGW.

Wallpaper Magazine Editors, ed. Copenhagen 2010 - Wallpaper City Guide. rev. ed. 2010. (Wallpaper* City Guides). (ENG., Illus.). 128p. pap. 9.95 *(978-0-7148-5779-4(3))* Phaidon Pr., Inc.

ARCHITECTURE—EGYPT

see also Architecture, Domestic—Egypt

Alsayyad, Nezar. Cairo: Histories of a City. 2011. (Illus.). 352p. 29.95 *(978-0-674-04786-0(9)*, Belknap Pr.) Harvard Univ. Pr.

Barr, James V. The Floating Stones of Egypt. 2011. 128p. 23.95 *(978-1-4502-8748-7(4))*; pap. 13.95 *(978-1-4502-8749-4(2))* iUniverse, Inc.

Behrens-Abouseif, Doris. Cairo of the Mamluks: A History of Architecture & Its Culture. 2008. (ENG., Illus.). 400p. 79.00 *(978-1-84511-549-4(X))* I. B. Tauris & Co., Ltd. GBR. Dist: Macmillan.

Behrens-Abouseif, Doris & Warner, Nicholas. Minarets of Cairo. 2010. (ENG., Illus.). 448p. 80.00 *(978-1-84885-539-7(7))* I. B. Tauris & Co., Ltd. GBR. Dist: Macmillan.

Bryn, Ole Jorgen. Apex: Retracing the Egyptian Pyramids. 2011. 116p. 118.00 ***(978-82-519-2749-9(8))*** Tapir Forlag NOR. Dist: International Specialized Bk. Services.

Clarke, Somers. Ancient Egyptian Masonry: The Building Craft. 2009. 352p. 29.95 *(978-1-4344-5212-2(3))*; pap. 14.95 *(978-1-4344-5119-4(4))* Wildside Pr., LLC.

Coppens, Filip. The Wabet: Tradition & Innovation in Temples of the Ptolemaic & Roman Period. 2008. (ENG., Illus.). 243p. (C). 110.00 *(978-80-7308-190-4(3))* Czech Institute of Egyptology CZE. Dist: Brown, David Bk. Co., The.

Creighton, Scott. The Giza Prophecy. 2012. 352p. pap. 20.00 ***(978-1-59143-132-9(8))*** Bear & Co.

De Haan, H. J. The Large Egyptian Pyramids. 2010. (Bar S Ser.). (ENG., Illus.). 125p. (C). pap. 90.00 *(978-1-4073-0546-2(8))* British Archaeological Reports Ltd. GBR. Dist: Brown, David Bk. Co., The.

The Great Pyramid Secret: Egypt's Amazing Lost Mystery Science Returns. 2010. (Illus.). 394p. pap. 19.95 *(978-0-9720434-6-5(2)*, Scribal Arts) Scribal Arts.

Gundlach, Rolf & Taylor, John H., eds. 4. Symposium zur agyptischen Konigsideologie /4th Symposium on Egyptian Royal Ideology Egyptian Royal Residences: London, June 1st-5th 2004. 2009. (Konigtum, Staat und Gesellschaft fruher Hochkulturen Ser.). (ENG., Illus.). 197p. (C). 72.00 *(978-3-447-05888-9(9))* Harrassowitz, Otto Verlag DEU. Dist: ISD.

Hagen, Rose-Marie & Hagen, Rainer. Egypt: People, Gods, Pharaohs. 25th ed. 2006. (ENG., Illus.). 240p. 14.99 *(978-3-8228-4767-1(4))* TASCHEN DEU. Dist: Ingram Pub. Services.

Hamid, Ahmad. Hassan Fathy & Continuity in Islamic Art & Architecture. 2010. (ENG., Illus.). 224p. 39.95 *(978-977-416-341-8(9))* American Univ. in Cairo Pr. EGY. Dist: Oxford Univ. Pr., Inc.

Hamzah, Khalid. Late Mamluk Patronage: Qansuh Al-Ghuri's Waqf & His Foundation in Cairo. 2009. 152p. pap. *(978-1-59942-922-9(5))* Universal Pubs.

Hewitt, Jim. Egypt Visual Sourcebook: For Artists, Architects, & Designers. 2011. (Illus.). 392p. 59.50 ***(978-977-416-433-0(4))*** American Univ. in Cairo Pr. EGY. Dist: Oxford Univ. Pr., Inc.

Humbert, Jean-Marcel & Price, Clifford, eds. Imhotep Today: Egyptianizing Architecture. 2007. (Encounters with Ancient Egypt series, University College

London Institute of Archaeology Publications). (ENG., Illus.). 340p. pap. 34.95 *(978-1-59874-201-5(9))* Left Coast Pr., Inc.

Lasciac, Antonio. Antonio Lasciac, Architetto: Da Gorizia All'impero Ottomano. 2007. (Illus.). 159p. pap. *(978-88-7292-501-0(0))* Alinari (IDEA).

McKenzie, Judith. The Architecture of Alexandria & Egypt, 300 B. C. — A. D. 700. 2011. (Yale University Press Pelican Histor Ser.). (Illus.). 480p. pap. 56.00 *(978-0-300-17094-8(7))* Yale Univ. Pr.

Meunier, Pascal, photos by. The Last Hammams of Cairo: A Disappearing Bathhouse Culture. 2009. (ENG., Illus.). 144p. 39.95 *(978-977-416-243-5(9))* American Univ. in Cairo Pr. EGY. Dist: Oxford Univ. Pr., Inc.

Nardo, Don, ed. Ancient Egyptian Art & Architecture. 2011. (Eye on Art Ser.). (Illus.). 128p. (YA). (gr. 7-12). 33.45 *(978-1-4205-0674-7(9))* Cengage Gale.

Ockinga, Boyo G. The Tomb of Amenemope at Thebes (TT 148) Volume 1: Architecture, Texts & Decoration. 2009. (ACE Reports). (ENG., Illus.). 149p. (C). pap. 160.00 *(978-0-85668-824-9(X))* Australian Ctr. for Egyptology AUS. Dist: Brown, David Bk. Co., The.

Petrosyan, Petros. Pyramids of the Great Architect of the Universe. 2009. 232p. 27.95 *(978-1-59526-854-9(5))*; (ENG.). pap. 14.95 *(978-1-59526-853-2(7))* Aeon Publishing Inc. (Llumina Pr.).

Rabbat, Nasser. Mamluk History Through Architecture: Monuments, Culture & Politics in Medieval Egypt & Syria. 2010. (Library of Middle East History Ser.). (ENG., Illus.). 288p. *(978-1-84511-964-5(9))* I. B. Tauris & Co., Ltd.

Ramzy, Nelly. Coptic Architecture. 2011. 188p. pap. ***(978-3-8443-2651-2(0))*** Lambert Academic Publishing.

Raphael, Kate. Muslim Fortresses in the Levant. 2010. (Culture & Civilization in the Middle East Ser.). (ENG., Illus.). 288p. (C). 130.00 *(978-0-415-56925-5(7)*, Routledge) Taylor & Francis Group GBR. Dist: Taylor & Francis Group.

Rashid, Karim. Sketch: Karim. 2012. (ENG., Illus.). 280p. 45.00 ***(978-90-77174-61-6(3))*** Frame Pubs. NLD. Dist: Consortium Bk. Sales & Distribution.

Regine, Schulz. Art & Architecture Egypt. 2010. (Art & Architecture Pocket Ser.). 68p. pap. 16.99 *(978-0-8416-7158-4(3))* Langenscheidt Publishing Group.

Romer, John. The Great Pyramid: Ancient Egypt Revisited. 2007. (ENG., Illus.). 586p. 45.00 *(978-0-521-87166-2(2))* Cambridge Univ. Pr.

Rossi, Corinna. Architecture & Mathematics in Ancient Egypt. 2007. (ENG.). 302p. (C). pap. 54.00 *(978-0-521-69053-9(6))* Cambridge Univ. Pr.

Seidel, Matthias & Schulz, Regine. Egypt. 2008. (Art & Architecture Ser.). (Illus.). 608p. 19.95 *(978-0-8416-0147-5(X))* American Map Corp.

—Egypt, 1 vol. 2010. (ENG., Illus.). 608p. pap. 9.99 *(978-3-8331-5281-8(8))* h.f.ullmann DEU. Dist: Innovative Logistics.

Stierlin, Henri. The Pharaohs Master-Builders. 2008. (Illus.). 255p. pap. 23.50 *(978-2-87939-328-5(0))* Terrail, Pierre Editions FRA. Dist: Perseus-PGW.

Stocks, Denys A. Experiments in Egyptian Archaeology: Stoneworking Technology in Ancient Egypt. 2010. 296p. pap. 39.95 *(978-0-415-58894-2(4))* Routledge.

Taschen, creator. Description de L'Egypte. 25th ed. 2007. (ENG, FRE & GER., Illus.). 752p. pap. 14.99 *(978-3-8228-3775-7(X))* TASCHEN DEU. Dist: Ingram Pub. Services.

Van Siclen Books. Hibis Temple Project Volume 3: The Graffiti from the Temple Precinct. 2008. (Illus.). 244p. pap. 75.00 *(978-0-9774373-1-3(0))* Tambopata Partners.

Vörös, Gyozo. Egyptian Temple Architecture: 100 Years of Hungarian Excavations in Egypt, 1907-2007. 2008. (ENG.). 204p. 39.95 *(978-963-662-084-4(9))* American Univ. in Cairo Pr. EGY. Dist: Oxford Univ. Pr., Inc.

Wagner, Joseph & Wegner, Josef W. The Mortuary Temple of Senwosret III at Abydos. 2007. (ENG., Illus.). 459p. (C). 170.00 *(978-0-9740025-4-5(2))* Yale Univ., The Yale Egyptological Seminar.

Wildung, Dietrich. Egypt. Stierlin, Henri, ed. 25th ed. 2009. (25 Ser.). (ENG., Illus.). 224p. 14.99 *(978-3-8365-1030-1(8))* TASCHEN DEU. Dist: Ingram Pub. Services.

ARCHITECTURE—EUROPE

see also Architecture, Domestic—Europe

Abalos, Inaki. Coup de Des 4: What's New? Searching for Clues. 2010. 92p. pap. 26.95 *(978-84-936901-2-0(0))* Fundacio Mies Van Der Rohe ESP. Dist: Actar Birkhauser Distribution.

Acebillo, Josep Antoni. New Urban Metabolism. Alessandro, Martinelli, ed. 2012. (ENG.). 224p. pap. *(978-84-92861-47-7(9))* Actar Birkhauser Distribution.

Aigner, Silvie, ed. Emanzipation und Konfrontation / Emancipation & Confrontation / Emancipacija in konfrontacija: Kunst aus Kärnten von 1945 bis heute. Architektur aus Kärnten seit 1945 und Kunst im öffentlichen Raum heute., 3 vols. 2008. (GER, SLV & ENG., Illus.). 1010p. *(978-3-211-75622-5(1)*, 3211756221) Actar Birkhauser Distribution.

Alofsin, Anthony. When Buildings Speak: Architecture As Language in the Habsburg Empire & Its Aftermath, 1867-1933. 2008. (Illus.). 300p. pap. 45.00 *(978-0-226-01507-1(6))* Univ. of Chicago Pr.

Angles, Magda. In Favour of Public Space: Ten Years of the European Prize for Urban Public Space. 2010. (Illus.). 208p. pap. *(978-84-92861-38-5(X))* Actar Birkhauser Distribution.

Architectural Guide to Ljubljana. ltd. ed. (Illus.). 252p. 85.00 *(978-961-209-252-8(4))* Rokus Publishing Hse. of Ljubljana SVN. Dist: Bks. of Slovenia.

Architekturbild, ed. Neue Heimat: Eurpäischer Architekturfotographiepreis 2009. 2009. (ENG.). 114p. 35.00 *(978-3-89986-117-4(5)*, Avedition Gmbh,Csi) Continental Sales, Inc.

Art & Build Architects Staff. Art & Build Architects: A Humanistic Approach to Architecture. 2009. (ENG., Illus.). 480p. 80.00 *(978-1-86470-296-5(6))* Images Publishing Group AUS. Dist: National Bk. Network.

Association of Architects Staff. UCB Center by ASSAR. Binder, Georges, ed. 2006. (ENG., Illus.). 49.50 *(978-1-86470-056-5(4))* Images Publishing Group AUS. Dist: National Bk. Network.

Atkinson, Rossignolo. The Re-Creation of the European City: Governance Territory & Polycentricity. Rossignolo, Cristiana & Atkinson, Rob, eds. 2009. (ENG., Illus.). 288p. pap. 76.00 *(978-90-8594-022-7(2))* Techne Pr. NLD. Dist: Chicago Distribution Ctr.

Ayán Vila, Xurxo M., et al, eds. Archaeotecture: Second Floor. 2009. (Illus.). 96p. (C). pap. 77.50 *(978-1-4073-0504-2(2))* British Archaeological Reports Ltd. GBR. Dist: Brown, David Bk. Co., The.

Baring-Gould, Sabine. Cliff Castles & Cave Dwellings of Europe. l.t. ed. 2007. (ENG.). 290p. pap. 23.99 *(978-1-4264-3341-2(7))* BiblioBazaar.

Barlow, Nic, photos by. Follies of Europe: Architectural Extravaganzas. 2008. (ENG., Illus.). 256p. *(978-1-870673-56-3(5)*, Antique Collectors Club Dist) Antique Collectors' Club.

Barth, Fritz & Metzel, Olaf. Zeichen des Wehrhaften / Martial Signifiers: Festungsbauten von Francesco di Giorgio Martini / Fortress Complexes by Francesco di Giorgio Martini. 2011. (GER & ENG., Illus.). 128p. 69.00 *(978-3-936681-42-0(2))* Edition Axel Menges GmbH DEU. Dist: National Bk. Network.

Basilico, Gabriele. Cityscapes. 2008. (ENG.). 400p. 95.00 *(978-88-6073-430-3(4))* Baldini Castoldi Dalai Editore ITA. Dist: Independent Pubs. Group.

Baxter, Denise & Martin, Meredith S. Architectural Space in Eighteenth-Century Europe: Constructing Indentities an Interiors. 2010. (Illus.). 284p. 119.95 *(978-0-7546-6650-9(6))* Ashgate Publishing Co.

Bezjak, Roman, photos by. Roman Bezjak: Socialist Moderism. 2011. (GER & ENG., Illus.). 160p. 60.00 ***(978-3-7757-3188-1(1))*** Hatje Cantz Verlag GmbH & Co KG DEU. Dist: D.A.P./Distributed Art Pubs.

Binder, Georges. Tall Buildings of Europe, Middle East & Africa. 2007. (Tall Buildings Ser.). (ENG., Illus.). 240p. 75.00 *(978-1-876907-81-5(9))* Images Publishing Group AUS. Dist: National Bk. Network.

Bischoff, Michael. Castles of the Weser Renaissance. 2009. (ENG.). 304p. 138.00 *(978-3-936681-23-9(6))* Edition Axel Menges GmbH DEU. Dist: National Bk. Network.

Blau, Eve & Rupnik, Ivan. Project Zagreb: Transition as Condition, Strategy, Practice. 2008. (Illus.). 335p. pap. *(978-84-96540-57-6(X))* Actar Birkhauser Distribution.

Bonello, Giovanni. Nostalgias of Malta: Images by Horatio Agius from the 1860s to The 1900s. 2009. (Illus.). 240p. (C). 99.00 *(978-99932-7-257-1(4))* Midsea Bks. Ltd. MLT. Dist: Brown, David Bk. Co., The.

Borutová, Dana & Jurkovic, Dusan. Architekt Dusan Samuel Jurkovic. 2012. (SLO., Illus.). 384p. 99.95 ***(978-80-8085-665-6(6))*** Slovart, Vydavatel'stvo, spol. s.r.o. SVK. Dist: Independent Pubs. Group.

Bradstreet, Scott. Landscape Design for Architectural Style: European Influenced. 2008. (Illus.). 256p. 49.99 *(978-0-7643-3106-0(X))* Schiffer Publishing, Ltd.

Braun Editorial Staff, ed. Architectural Details - Balconies. 2008. (ENG., Illus.). 160p. 37.50 *(978-3-938780-48-0(7)*, Braun Publish,Csi) Continental Sales, Inc.

—Architectural Details - Pillars. 2008. (ENG.). 160p. 37.50 *(978-3-938780-47-3(9)*, Braun Publish,Csi) Continental Sales, Inc.

—Architectural Details - Stairs. 2008. (ENG.). 160p. 37.50 *(978-3-938780-46-6(0)*, Braun Publish,Csi) Continental Sales, Inc.

Braun, Marcus. European Architecture in Details. 2011. (ENG., Illus.). 544p. 19.95 ***(978-3-03768-086-5(5)***, Braun Publish,Csi) Continental Sales, Inc.

Braun Publishing. 1000x European Architecture. 2nd rev. ed. 2011. (ENG., Illus.). 1024p. 125.00 ***(978-3-03768-087-2(3)***, Braun Publish,Csi) Continental Sales, Inc.

Brown, G. Baldwin. The Care of Ancient Monuments: An Account of Legislative & Other Measures Adopted in European Countries for Protecting Ancient Monuments, Objects & Scenes of Natural Beauty, & for Preserving the Aspect of Historical Cities. 2010. (Cambridge Library Collection - Archaeology Ser.). 278p. pap. 23.99 *(978-1-108-01606-3(5))* Cambridge Univ. Pr.

Brown-Manrique, Gerardo, text. Rudolf Frankel & Neues Bauen. 2009. (ENG., Illus.). 148p. pap. 50.00 *(978-3-8030-0695-0(3))* Wasmuth, Ernst J. Verlag GmbH & Co. DEU. Dist: D.A.P./Distributed Art Pubs.

Celik, Matevz. New Architecture in Slovenia. 2007. (ENG., Illus.). 192p. 69.95 *(978-3-211-71487-4(1)*, 3211714871) Springer.

Chapman, Tony. Architecture 09: RIBA Buildings of the Year. 2010. (Illus.). 272p. pap. *(978-1-85894-490-6(2))* Merrell Pubs. Ltd.

—Architecture 11: RIBA Buildings of the Year. 2012. (ENG., Illus.). 272p. 34.95 *(978-1-85894-561-3(5))* Merrell Pubs. Ltd. GBR. Dist: Perseus Distribution.

Chapman, Tony, ed. Architecture Vol. 8: The Guide to the Riba Awards. 2008. (Illus.). 216p. pap. 22.95 *(978-1-85894-428-9(7))* Merrell Pubs. Ltd. GBR. Dist: Perseus Distribution.

—Architecture 07: The Guide to the Riba Awards. 2007. (Architecture: the Guide to the Riba Awards Ser.). (ENG., Illus.). 215p. pap. 22.95 *(978-1-85894-381-7(7))* Merrell Pubs. Ltd. GBR. Dist: Perseus Distribution.

—Architecture 10: RIBA Buildings of the Year. 2011. (RIBA Guides). (ENG., Illus.). 272p. 34.95 *(978-1-85894-539-2(9))* Merrell Pubs. Ltd. GBR. Dist: Perseus Distribution.

Chatenet, Monique, et al, eds. Public Buildings in Early Modern Europe. 2010. (Architectura Moderna Ser.). (ENG, ITA, FRE & GER., Illus.). 408p. (C). pap. 160.00 *(978-2-503-53354-4(X))* Brepols Pubs. BEL. Dist: ISD.

Christine Sciacca Staff. Building the Medieval World. 2010. (Illus.). vii, 96p. *(978-0-7123-5094-5(2)*, J. Paul Getty Museum) Getty Pubns.

Connah, Roger, compiled by. 40/40 Young Architects from Finland. 2nd ed. 2008. (Illus.). 240p. pap. 49.00 *(978-951-682-646-5(6))* Rakennustieto oy FIN. Dist: Independent Pubs. Group.

Costa, Xavier. Coup de Des 1: Housing & Public Space. 2010. 109p. pap. 26.95 *(978-84-920495-9-2(6))* Fundacio Mies Van Der Rohe ESP. Dist: Actar Birkhauser Distribution.

Cram101 Textbook Reviews Staff. Outlines & Highlights for Seventeenth Century Art & Architecture by Ann Sutherland Harris, Isbn: 9780136033721. 2009. 64p. pap. 27.95 *(978-1-4288-9217-0(6))* Cram101 Inc.

Croci, Valentina, ed. The New Europe. 2006. (Architectural Design Ser.: 29). (ENG., Illus.). 128p. pap. 60.00 *(978-0-470-01839-2(9)*, Academy Pr.) Wiley, John & Sons, Inc.

Curcic, Slobodan. Architecture in the Balkans: From Diocletian to Suleyman the Magnificent, C. 300-1550. 2010. (Illus.). 608p. 85.00 *(978-0-300-11570-3(9))* Yale Univ. Pr.

Dam, Torben & Nielsen, Jens Balsby, eds. European Landscape Architecture: Best Practice in Detailing. 2007. (ENG., Illus.). 272p. (C). pap. 65.00 *(978-0-415-30737-6(6))* Routledge.

Delbeke, M. Edmunde & Schraven, Minou, eds. Foundation, Dedication & Consecration in Early Modern Europe. 2011. (ENG., Illus.). XVI, 396p. ***(978-90-04-21757-7(6))*** BRILL.

Disponzio, Joseph, ed. Territories: Contemporary European Landscape Design. 2007. (Landmarks Ser.). (ENG., Illus.). 112p. pap. 29.95 *(978-0-9749632-5-9(9))* Spacemaker Pr.

Dmitrieva, Marina & Kliems, Alfrun, eds. The Post Socialist City. 2010. (ENG., Illus.). 208p. pap. 45.00 *(978-3-86859-018-0(8))* Jovis Verlag GmbH DEU. Dist: D.A.P./Distributed Art Pubs.

Dullemen, C. J. van. Tropical Modernity: Life & Work of C.P. Wolff Schoemaker. 2010. (Illus.). 270p. *(978-90-8506-879-2(7))* SUN B.V., Uitgeverij.

Eckhardt, Frank & Cremaschi, Marco, eds. Changing Places: Urbanity, Citizenship, & Ideology in the New European Neighbourhoods. 2011. (ENG.). 256p. pap. 67.50 ***(978-90-8594-037-1(0))*** Techne Pr. NLD. Dist: Chicago Distribution Ctr.

ETH Studio Basel - Contemporary City Institute Staff, et al. Belgrade. Formal - Informal: A Research on Urban Transformation. 2012. (ENG & GER., Illus.). 256p. 90.00 *(978-3-85881-254-4(4))* Scheidegger und Spiess AG, Verlag CHE. Dist: Antique Collectors' Club.

Evangelisti, Silvia & Cavallo, Sandra. Domestic & Institutional Interiors in Early Modern Europe. 2009. (Visual Culture in Early Modernity Ser.). (Illus.). 314p. 134.95 *(978-0-7546-5647-0(0))* Ashgate Publishing Co.

Fahr-Becker, Gabriele. Art Nouveau. 2008. (Architecture Sculpture Painting Ser.). (Illus.). 425p. pap. 24.95 *(978-0-8416-0057-7(0))* American Map Corp.

Falconi, Giulia, ed. Solar Buildings: European Students' Competition for the Design of Solar Buildings 1995-1996. 2010. (Illus.). 280p. 38.95 *(978-88-7448-750-9(9))* Gangemi ITA. Dist: International Publishers Marketing.

Finnish Committee for the Restoration of Viipuri Library Staff & Karjalainen, Markku. Alvar Aalto Library in Vyborg: Saving a Modern Masterpiece. 2010. (ENG., Illus.). 144p. pap. 69.00 *(978-951-682-938-1(4)*, Art Stock Bks. Ltd/Csi) Continental Sales, Inc.

Fischer, Joachim, ed. Young European Designers, 1 vol. 2008. (ENG, FRE & GER., Illus.). 399p. 37.95 *(978-3-937718-42-2(7))* DAAB Media Gmbh DEU. Dist: Innovative Logistics.

Flury, Aita, ed. Roger Boltshauser - Elementares zum Raum A Primer of Space: Bauten und Projekte Buildings & Projects. 2008. (ENG & GER., Illus.). 230p. *(978-3-211-79179-0(5)*, 3211791795) Actar Birkhauser Distribution.

Franzen, Brigitte, et al, eds. WESTARCH 1: A New Generation in Architecture. 2011. (ENG., Illus.). 192p. pap. 49.95 *(978-3-86859-079-1(X))* Jovis Verlag GmbH DEU. Dist: D.A.P./Distributed Art Pubs.

Galindo, Michelle. Collection: European Architecture. 2009. (GER, FRE & ENG.). 512p. 49.95 *(978-3-03768-011-7(3)*, Braun Publish,Csi) Continental Sales, Inc.

—European Architecture. 2009. (Collection of Architecture Ser.). (FRE, GER & ENG., Illus.). 512p. 89.95 *(978-3-938780-66-4(5))* BRAUN DEU. Dist: National Bk. Network.

Glendinning, Miles, ed. Rebuilding Scotland: The Postwar Vision, 1945-1975. (Illus.). 208p. pap. *(978-1-898410-33-1(X)*, Donald, John) Birlinn, Ltd.

Goldhoorn, Bart & Meuser, Philipp. Capitalist Realism: New Architecture in Russia = Kapitalistischer Realismus: Neue Architektur in Russland, 1 vol. 2009. (RUS, GER & ENG., Illus.). 303p. 99.95 ***(978-3-938666-10-4(2))*** DOM Pubs. DEU. Dist: Innovative Logistics.

Gray, Diane, ed. Mies Van der Rohe Award: European Union Prize for Contemporary Architecture. 2007. (Illus.). 333p. pap. *(978-84-96540-99-6(5))* Actar Birkhauser Distribution.

Greene, David / B. 0. The Imagining of Community in European Art & Architecture, 1140-1617: Envisioning Transcendence of, Authority in, & Foundations for Community. 2010. (Illus.). viii, 203p. *(978-0-7734-3713-5(4))* Mellen, Edwin Pr., The.

Hajiyeva, Sabina. Architecture of the North-Western District of Azerbaijan. 2011. 112p. pap. ***(978-3-8443-1470-0(9))*** Lambert Academic Publishing.

Hall, Thomas. Planning Europe's Capital Cities: Aspects of Nineteenth-Century Urban Development. 2009. (Planning, History & Environment Ser.). (ENG., Illus.). 408p. (C). 44.95 *(978-0-415-55249-3(4))* Routledge.

Helmle, Christian, photos by. Weiße Elefanten / White Elephants. 2008. (ENG., Illus.). 128p. 45.00 *(978-3-939633-19-8(4))* Jovis Verlag GmbH DEU. Dist: D.A.P./Distributed Art Pubs.

Herscher, Andrew. Violence Taking Place: The Architecture of the Kosovo Conflict. 2010. (Cultural Memory in the Present Ser.). (ENG.). 224p. 55.00 *(978-0-8047-6935-8(4))*; pap. 21.95 *(978-0-8047-6936-5(2))* Stanford Univ. Pr.

Hewitt, Mischa & Telfer, Kevin. Earthships in Europe. 2nd rev. ed. 2012. (ENG., Illus.). 160p. pap. 49.95 ***(978-1-84806-236-8(2))*** Building Research Establishment GBR. Dist: Taylor & Francis Group.

Hossbach, Benjamin & Lehmhaus, Christian. Phase Eins: The Architecture of Competition 2006-2008, 1 vol. 2009. (ENG., Illus.). 560p. 99.95 *(978-3-938666-88-3(9))* DOM Pubs. DEU. Dist: Innovative Logistics.

Hrausky, Andrej, et al. Joze Plecnik: Dunaj, Praga, Ljubljana. 2nd ed. 2007. (SLV., Illus.). 231p. *(978-961-231-575-7(2))* Cankarjeva Zalozba.

—Joze Plecnik in Ljubljana & Slovenia: Guide & Maps of All Architectural & Memorial Works of the Greatest Slovenian Architect. 2007. (Illus.). 120p. *(978-961-231-623-5(6))* Cankarjeva Zalozba.

Huisman, Joyce. Piet Boon, 3 vols. 2012. (ENG., Illus.). 632p. ring bd. 380.00 *(978-90-8989-471-7(3))* Lannoo Pubs./Racine.

Hutterreimann + Cejka Landscape Architects. Specific Landscape: HutterReimann + Cejka Landschaftsarchitekten. 2012. (ENG & GER., Illus.). 160p. 45.00 ***(978-3-86859-097-5(8))*** Jovis Verlag GmbH DEU. Dist: D.A.P./Distributed Art Pubs.

Irace, Fulvio. Gio Ponti. 2011. (ENG., Illus.). 120p. 45.00 *(978-88-6116-142-9(1))* Antique Collectors' Club.

Jager, Frank Peter, ed. Old & New: Design Manual for Revitalizing Existing Buildings. 2010. (Illus.). 192p. 99.95 *(978-3-0346-0525-0(0))* Birkhauser Verlag AG CHE. Dist: Actar Birkhauser Distribution.

Janko, Joan. The Chapel of the Assumption of the Virgin in Spissk² Stvrtok. 2008. 96p. pap. *(978-3-639-04289-4(1))* VDM Verlag Dr. Mueller e.K.

Kovacevic, Igor, ed. Urbanity: Twenty Years Later: Projects for Central European Capitals. 2011. 233p. pap. *(978-80-254-8170-7(0))* Actar Birkhauser Distribution.

Kunz, Martin Nicholas. best designed wellness hotels - europe. 2nd ed. 2007. (Best Designed Ser.). (GER & ENG., Illus.). 35.00 *(978-3-89986-090-0(X)*, Avedition Gmbh,Csi) Continental Sales, Inc.

Lawrence, Henry W. City Trees: A Historical Geography from the Renaissance Through the Nineteenth Century. 2008. (Center Bks.). (ENG., Illus.). 352p. (C). (gr. 13-17). pap. 35.00 *(978-0-8139-2800-5(1))* Univ. Pr. of Virginia.

Lejeune, Jean-Francois. Modern Architecture & the Mediterranean: Vernacular Dialogues & Contested Identities. Sabatino, Michelangelo, ed. 2010. (ENG., Illus.). 320p. 53.95 *(978-0-415-77634-9(1))* Routledge.

Lejeune, Jean-Francois & Sabatino, Michelangelo, eds. North-South: The Vernacular, the Modern & the Mediterranean. 2010. (ENG., Illus.). 320p. (C). 165.00 *(978-0-415-77633-2(3))* Routledge.

Luiten, Erik, ed. A Wider View: Cultural Landscapes in Europe. 2012. (ENG.). 256p. 60.00 *(978-90-5662-413-2(X))* NAi Uitgevers / Publishers Stichting NLD. Dist: D.A.P./Distributed Art Pubs.

Mackinney, Loren Carey & MacKinney, Loren Carey. Pre-Gothic Architecture: A Mirror of the Social-Religious Renaissance of the Eleventh Century. 2011. 26p. 35.95 ***(978-1-258-03572-3(3))*** Literary Licensing, LLC.

Maillard-Luypaert, M. Seminaire de Tournai: Histoire, Batiments, Collections. 2008. (FRE.). 321p. (C). 109.00 *(978-90-429-2169-6(2))* Peeters Pubs. & Booksellers BEL. Dist: Brown, David Bk. Co., The.

Meijer, Remy & Geerts, Paul. Shades of Grey. 2011. (ENG & DUT., Illus.). 192p. 80.00 *(978-90-8989-425-0(X))* Lannoo Pubs./Racine.

Mill, Adair, tr. from TUR. Ottoman Architecture. 2010. (ENG., Illus.). 720p. *(978-1-85149-604-4(1)*, Antique Collectors Club Dist) Antique Collectors' Club.

Miralles, Enric & Tagliabue, Benedetta. E M B T Enric Miralles Benedetta Tagliabue Work in Progress. 2006. (SPA., Illus.). 248p. (gr. 13-18). pap. 55.00 *(978-84-96185-13-5(3))* D.A.P./Distributed Art Pubs.

Molinari, Luca. Italo Rota: Projects, Works, Visions 1997-2007. 2008. (ENG., Illus.). 352p. 85.00 *(978-88-7624-641-8(X))* Skira Editore ITA. Dist: Random Hse., Inc.

Mommaas, Hans & van Boom, Nienke, texts. Comeback Cities. 2010. (ENG., Illus.). 256p. pap., pap. 55.00 *(978-90-5662-707-2(4))* NAi Uitgevers / Publishers Stichting NLD. Dist: D.A.P./Distributed Art Pubs.

Morpurgo, Guido. Gregotti & Associates: The Architecture of Urban Design. 2008. (ENG., Illus.). 312p. 85.00 *(978-0-8478-3100-5(0))* Rizzoli International Pubns., Inc.

Naginski, Erika. Sculpture & Enlightenment. 2009. (ENG., Illus.). 336p. 45.00 *(978-0-89236-959-1(0))* Oxford Univ. Pr., Inc.

Nelson, George. Building a New Europe: Portraits of Modern Architects, Essays by George Nelson, 1935-1936. 2007. (ENG., Illus.). 192p. 45.00 *(978-0-300-11565-9(2))* Yale Univ. Pr.

Nielsen, Jens Balsby & Dam, Torben, eds. European Landscape Architecture: Best Practice in Detailing. 2007. (ENG., Illus.). 272p. (C). 155.00 *(978-0-415-30736-9(8))* Routledge.

Norwich, John Julius, intro. Croatia: Aspects of Art, Architecture & Cultural Heritage. 2009. (ENG., Illus.). 224p. 65.00 *(978-0-7112-2921-1(5))* Lincoln, Frances Ltd. GBR. Dist: Perseus-PGW.

Oosterlynck, Stijn, et al, eds. Strategic Spatial Projects: Catalysts for Change. 2010. (RTPI Library Ser.). (ENG., Illus.). 256p. (C). 165.00 *(978-0-415-56683-4(5))*; pap. 53.95 *(978-0-415-56684-1(3))* Routledge.

Ottenheym, Konrad, ed. Unity & Discontinuity: Architectural Relationships Between the Southern & Northern Low Countries (1530-1700) 2007. (Architectura Moderna Ser.). (ENG., Illus.). 428p. (C). pap. 152.00 *(978-2-503-51366-9(2))* Brepols Pubs. BEL. Dist: ISD.

Parcell, Stephen. Four Historical Definitions of Architecture. 2012. (ENG.). 352p. (C). ***(978-0-7735-3956-3(5))*** McGill-Queen's Univ. Pr.

Pauwels, Wim. European Style, Vol. 2. 2010. (ENG., Illus.). 208p. *(978-90-8944-014-3(3)*, Beta-Plus (Acc)) Antique Collectors' Club.

Pauwels, Wim, ed. European Style, Vol. 1. 2009. (ENG., Illus.). 208p. 125.00 *(978-90-8944-013-6(5))* Beta-Plus Pubs. BEL. Dist: Antique Collectors' Club.

Pevsner, Nikolaus. An Outline of European Architecture, 1 vol. 2009. (ENG., Illus.). 256p. 60.00 *(978-1-4236-0493-8(8))* Gibbs Smith, Publisher.

Pfister, Alessandra & Angelini, Piervaleriano. Gli Architetti Gilardi a Mosca: La Raccolta Dei Disegni Conservati in Ticino. 2007. (ITA., Illus.). 244p. *(978-88-87624-30-4(5))* Academy Pr.

Pinto, John. Speaking Ruins: Piranesi, Architects & Antiquity in Eighteenth-Century Rome. 2012. (Thomas Spencer Jerome Lectures). (ENG., Illus.). 376p. 90.00 ***(978-0-472-11821-2(8))*** Univ. of Michigan Pr.

Pollak, Martha D. Cities at War in Early Modern Europe. 2010. (ENG., Illus.). 360p. 99.00 *(978-0-521-11344-1(X))* Cambridge Univ. Pr.

Qualls, Karl D. From Ruins to Reconstruction: Urban Identity in Soviet Sevastopol after World War II. 2009. (Illus.). 272p. 49.95 *(978-0-8014-4762-4(3))* Cornell Univ. Pr.

Rapanic, Zeljko. Od Carske Palace Do Srednjovjekovne Opcine. 2007. (Illus.). 278p. *(978-953-163-299-7(5))* Knjizevni krug Split.

Rattenbury, Richard Rogers: Centre Pompidou. 2011. (Supercrit Ser.). (ENG., Illus.). 176p. (C). 165.00 *(978-0-415-45785-9(8))*; pap. 49.95 *(978-0-415-45786-6(6))* Routledge.

Requa, Richard S. Old World Inspiration for American Architecture. 2007. (Illus.). 344p. 59.95 *(978-0-7643-2668-4(6))* Schiffer Publishing, Ltd.

Richters, Christian, photos by. Steidle + Partner, Alfred-Wegener-Institut, Bremerhaven. 2006. (Opus Ser.). (GER & ENG., Illus.). 60p. 39.90 *(978-3-932565-60-1(6))* Edition Axel Menges GmbH DEU. Dist: National Bk. Network.

Ries, Charles P., et al. Improving the Energy Performance of Buildings: Learning from the European Union & Australia. 2009. 60p. pap. 23.00 *(978-0-8330-4787-8(6)*, tr728) RAND Corp., The.

Ring, Kristien, ed. Emerging Identities - East! Berlin, Bratislava, Budapest, Ljubljana, Prague, Tallinn, Vilnius, Warsaw, 1 vol. 2006. (ENG & GER., Illus.). 178p. 22.00 *(978-3-936314-69-4(1))* Jovis Verlag GmbH DEU. Dist: D.A.P./Distributed Art Pubs.

Risebero, Bill. The Story of Western Architecture. 4th ed. 2012. (ENG., Illus.). 352p. pap. 39.95 ***(978-1-4081-2813-8(6))*** A & C Black GBR. Dist: Macmillan.

Roger, Connah & Connah, Roger. Aaltomania. 2008. 144p. pap. 26.00 *(978-951-682-613-7(X))* Rakennustieto oy FIN. Dist: Independent Pubs. Group.

Rowe, Nina. The Jew, the Cathedral & the Medieval City: Synagoga & Ecclesia in the Thirteenth Century. 2011. (ENG., Illus.). 300p. 90.00 *(978-0-521-19744-1(9))* Cambridge Univ. Pr.

Ruble, Blair A., et al. Cities after the Fall of Communism: Reshaping Cultural Landscapes & European Identity. Czaplicka, John J. et al, eds. 2009. (ENG., Illus.). 384p. (gr. 17). 65.00 *(978-0-8018-9191-5(4))* Johns Hopkins Univ. Pr.

Ruby, Ilka & Ruby, Andreas, eds. Sadar & Vuga: A Review. 2012. (ENG., Illus.). 256p. 85.00 ***(978-3-7757-3143-0(1))*** Hatje Cantz Verlag GmbH & Co KG DEU. Dist: D.A.P./Distributed Art Pubs.

Rupnik, Ivan, ed. A Peripheral Moment: Experiments in Architectural Agency: Croatia 1990-2010. 2011. (Illus.). 320p. pap. *(978-84-92861-57-6(6))* Actar Birkhauser Distribution.

Sabel, Charles F. & Zeitlin, Jonathan, eds. Experimentalist Governance in the European Union: Towards a New Architecture. 2010. (ENG.). 368p. 95.00 *(978-0-19-957249-6(6))* Oxford Univ. Pr., Inc.

Sasin, Tomasz. Renewable Heat & Electricity Supply to Residential Settlements. 2010. 100p. pap. *(978-3-639-26699-3(4))* VDM Verlag Dr. Mueller e.K.

Sato, Akira. Kenchiku ni Okeru Kindai: 19-Seiki Obei No Kenchikuka Kenchiku Sangyo ni Kansuru Kenkyu. 2010. (JPN., Illus.). 489p. *(978-4-8055-0621-9(0))* Chuo Koron Bijutsu Shuppan.

Schmal, Peter Cachola. Stadtgrün / Urban Green: Europäische Landschaftsarchitektur für das 21. Jahrhundert / European Landscape Design for the 21st century. Becker, Annette, ed. 2010. (ENG., Illus.). 232p. 79.95 *(978-3-0346-0313-3(4))* Birkhauser Verlag AG CHE. Dist: Actar Birkhauser Distribution.

Schmiedeknecht, Torsten. Rationalist Traces. Peckham, Andrew & Rattray, Charles, eds. 2007. (Architectural Design Ser.). (ENG.). 152p. pap. 50.00 *(978-0-470-02837-7(8)*, Wiley) Wiley, John & Sons, Inc.

Sciacca, Christine. Building the Medieval World. 2010. (Illus.). 104p. 19.95 *(978-1-60606-006-3(6)*, J. Paul Getty Museum) Getty Pubns.

Sheridan, Michael. Room 606: The Sas House & the Work of Arne Jacobsen. 2011. (ENG., Illus.). 272p. pap. 45.00 *(978-0-7148-6108-1(1))* Phaidon Pr., Inc.

Solis, Julia. Stages of Decay. 2012. (ENG., Illus.). 144p. 34.95 ***(978-1-935613-46-6(4))*** Batty, Mark Pub., LLC.

Stephenson, David. Heavenly Vaults: From Romanesque to Gothic in European Architecture. 2009. (ENG., Illus.). 192p. 65.00 *(978-1-56898-840-5(0))* Princeton Architectural Pr.

Stiftung Landscape Architecture Europe (Lae), Landscape Architecture Europe (Lae), ed. On Site: Landschaftsarchitektur Europa. 2009. (GER., Illus.). 261p. *(978-3-7643-8949-9(4))* Birkhauser Verlag AG.

Stubbs, John H. & Makas, Emily G. Architectural Conservation in Europe & the Americas. 2011. (ENG., Illus.). 752p. 110.00 *(978-0-470-60385-7(2)*, Wiley) Wiley, John & Sons, Inc.

Stureiko, S. A. Antropoliglia Arkhitekturnogo Nasledia: Vzgliad Na Belarus. 2010. (RUS., Illus.). 182p. *(978-985-6802-43-3(1))* Junipak, Zakrytae AT.

Supicic, Ivan. Croatia in the Late Middle Ages & the Renaissance: A Cultural Survey. 2009. (ENG., Illus.). 800p. 110.00 *(978-0-85667-624-6(1))* Wilson, Philip Pubs., Ltd. GBR. Dist: Macmillan.

Tchoban, Sergei. Buildings: Designing along the Code. 2012. (ENG., Illus.). 256p. 85.00 *(978-1-86470-388-7(1))* Images Publishing Group AUS. Dist: National Bk. Network.

Thiebaut, Pierre. Old Buildings Looking for New Use: 61 Examples of Regional Architecture Between Tradition & Modernity. 2007. (ENG., Illus.). 276p. 86.00 *(978-3-936681-08-6(2))* Edition Axel Menges GmbH DEU. Dist: National Bk. Network.

Timmer, Nicole, text. PrixdeRome. NL 2011. 2011. (ENG., Illus.). 112p. pap. 35.00 ***(978-90-5662-812-3(7))*** NAi Uitgevers / Publishers Stichting NLD. Dist: D.A.P./Distributed Art Pubs.

Toman, Rolf, ed. Gothic: Architecture, Sculpture, Painting. 2008. (Architecture Sculpture Painting Ser.). (Illus.). 520p. per. 24.95 *(978-0-8416-0068-3(6))* American Map Corp.

van den Heuvel, Dirk, ed. DASH 03: the Woonerf Today. 2010. (ENG, DUT & MUL., Illus.). 160p. pap. 50.00 *(978-90-5662-739-3(2))* NAi Uitgevers / Publishers Stichting NLD. Dist: D.A.P./Distributed Art Pubs.

van den Heuvel, Dirk, et al, eds. DASH 02: the Luxury City Apartment. 2010. (ENG., Illus.). 176p. pap. 50.00 *(978-90-5662-717-1(1))* NAi Uitgevers / Publishers Stichting NLD. Dist: D.A.P./Distributed Art Pubs.

van der Horst, Jan. Movements in Green: Conceptual Landscape Gardening. 2010. (DUT & ENG., Illus.). 192p. 110.00 *(978-90-8989-043-6(2))* Lannoo Pubs./Racine.

van der Werf, Huib Haye, ed. Waterfront Visions. 2010. (ENG., Illus.). 128p. pap. 40.00 *(978-90-5662-730-0(9))* NAi Uitgevers / Publishers Stichting NLD. Dist: D.A.P./Distributed Art Pubs.

van Dijk, Walter, et al. Coup de Des: Emerging European Architectures. Issue 2. 2009. (Illus.). 89p. pap. *(978-84-920495-7-8(X))* Fundacio Mies Van Der Rohe.

van Meggelen, Bert, ed. Memory & Transformation. 2008. (ENG.). 176p. pap. 55.00 *(978-90-5662-015-8(0))* NAi Uitgevers / Publishers Stichting NLD. Dist: D.A.P./Distributed Art Pubs.

Van Santvoort, Linda, et al, eds. Sources of Regionalism in the Nineteenth Century: Architecture, Art, & Literature. 2008. (KADOC Artes Ser.). (Illus.). 200p. 65.00 *(978-90-5867-649-8(8))* Leuven Univ. Pr. BEL. Dist: Cornell Univ. Pr.

Van Severen, David. Office: Kersten Geers David Van Severen. 2010. (ENG., Illus.). 80p. pap. 45.00 *(978-3-7757-2572-9(5))* Hatje Cantz Verlag GmbH & Co KG DEU. Dist: D.A.P./Distributed Art Pubs.

Van Tussenbroek, Gabri. The Architectural Network of the Van Neurenberg Family in the Low Countries, 1480-1640. Verheijen, Titus & Bym, Whitney A., trs. 2006. (Architectura Moderna Ser.). (ENG., Illus.). 250p. (C). pap. 131.00 *(978-2-503-51847-3(8))* Brepols Pubs. BEL. Dist: ISD.

Varner, Gary R. Gargoyles, Grotesques & Green Men: Ancient Symbolism in European & American Architecture. 2008. 184p. pap. 16.95 *(978-1-4357-1142-6(4))* Lulu Enterprises Inc.

Verlinde, Jan, photos by. Life in Oak-Framed Buildings: Garden Rooms, Pool Houses, Carports, Guesthouses. 2008. (ENG., Illus.). 192p. *(978-90-209-7479-9(3)*, Lannoo Pubs. (Acc)) Antique Collectors' Club.

Vidler, Anthony. Histories of the Immediate Present: Inventing Architectural Modernism. 2008. (Writing Architecture Ser.). (ENG., Illus.). 264p. (gr. 17). pap. 25.95 *(978-0-262-72051-9(5))* MIT Pr.

Virk, Engr. M. Hamza Saeed & Raja Rizwan Hussain. Seismic Vulnerability Assessment of Rc Buildings. 2011. 120p. pap. ***(978-3-8443-2074-9(1))*** Lambert Academic Publishing.

Vodopivec, Ales & Zndarsic, Rok. Edvard Ravnikar: Architect & Teacher. 2009. 348p. 89.95 *(978-3-211-99203-6(0))* Springer Wien AUT. Dist: Springer.

Voigt, Simone. Contemporary Architecture in Eurasia, 1 vol. 2009. (GER & ENG., Illus.). 415p. 99.95 *(978-3-938666-35-7(8))* DOM Pubs. DEU. Dist: Innovative Logistics.

Vrededman de Vries, Jan. Studies in Perspective. 2010. (Dover Architecture Ser.). (ENG., Illus.). 96p. pap. 12.95 *(978-0-486-47332-1(5))* Dover Pubns., Inc.

Wang, Wilfried & Vesely, Dalibor. Eric Parry Architects, Vol. 1. 2nd rev. ed. 2011. (ENG., Illus.). 208p. pap. 39.95 *(978-1-906155-62-9(3))* Black Dog Publishing Ltd. GBR. Dist: Perseus Distribution.

Wescoat, Bonna D. & Ousterhout, Robert G. Architecture of the Sacred: Space, Ritual, & Experience from Classical Greece to Byzantium. 2012. (ENG., Illus.). 440p. 99.00 ***(978-1-107-00823-6(9))*** Cambridge Univ. Pr.

Wolterinck, Marcel & Gelder, Van Conny. Outside In: Wolterinck's Word. 2010. (ENG., Illus.). 336p. 140.00 *(978-90-5897-995-7(4))* Lannoo Pubs./Racine.

Wonderland, et al, eds. Wonderland Manual for Emerging Architects: How to Establish & Run an Architecture Practice in Europe. 2011. (ENG., Illus.). 352p. 49.95 *(978-3-7091-0822-2(5)*, 3709108225) Springer Wien AUT. Dist: Springer.

Worsley, Giles. Inigo Jones & the European Classicist Tradition. 2007. (ENG., Illus.). 240p. 65.00 *(978-0-300-11729-5(9))* Yale Univ. Pr.

Wotton, Henry. The Elements of Architecture. 2010. 120p. pap. 19.75 *(978-1-141-63514-6(3))* BiblioBazaar.

—The Elements of Architecture. 2009. 125p. pap. 14.97 *(978-0-557-11144-2(7))* Lulu Enterprises Inc.

Yudelson, Jerry. Green Building Trends: Europe. 2nd ed. 2009. (ENG.). 192p. pap. 30.00 *(978-1-59726-477-8(6))*; (Illus.). 60.00 *(978-1-59726-476-1(8))* Island Pr.

Zacek, Tomas & Trnovska, Katarina. Wave 68-84: Young Slovak Architects. 2010. 216p. pap. 49.00 *(978-80-8085-921-3(3))* Slovart, Vydavatel'stvo, spol. s.r.o. SVK. Dist: Independent Pubs. Group.

Zanta, Marco. Urbaneurope. 2008. (ENG., Illus.). 150p. 49.00 *(978-88-6965-105-9(1))* Contrasto DUE ITA. Dist: Consortium Bk. Sales & Distribution.

Zantovská Murray, Irena. Looking at European Architecture: A Critical View, 1 vol. 2011. (ENG & FRE., Illus.). 464p. pap. 20.00 *(978-2-930391-26-7(X))* Centre International Pour La Ville, L'Architecture Et Le Paysage BEL. Dist: Innovative Logistics.

Zira, Christina. Three European Standards for Energy Assessment of Buildings. 2010. 128p. pap. *(978-3-639-26667-2(6))* VDM Verlag Dr. Mueller e.K.

Zwerger, Klaus. Wood & Wood Joints: Building Traditions of Europe, Japan & China (Second, Revised & Expanded Edition) 2nd rev. ed. 2012. (ENG., Illus.). 312p. pap. 69.95 *(978-3-0346-0685-1(0))* Birkhauser Verlag AG CHE. Dist: Actar Birkhauser Distribution.

ARCHITECTURE—FINLAND

Charrington, Harry & Nava, Vezio, eds. Alvar Aalto: The Mark of the Hand. 2012. (ENG., Illus.). 400p. pap. 58.95 ***(978-951-682-995-4(3))*** Rakennustieto oy FIN. Dist: Independent Pubs. Group.

Connah, Roger. Sa(LiVaged Modernism. 2008. (ENG., Illus.). 192p. pap. 26.00 *(978-951-682-595-3(6))* Rakennustieto oy FIN. Dist: Independent Pubs. Group.

De Long, David G. Eero Saarinen: Buildings from the Balthazar Korab Archive. Peatross, C. Ford, ed. 2008. (Norton/Library of Congress Visual Sourcebooks in Architecture, Design & Engineering Ser.). (ENG., Illus.). 400p. 100.00 *(978-0-393-73223-8(1)*, 73223) Norton, W. W. & Co., Inc.

Dominguez, Luis Angel & Dominguez, Lluis Angel. Alvar Aalto, Una Arquitectura Dialogica. 2010. (SPA.). 154p. *(978-84-8301-679-4(6))* UPC, S.L., Edicions.

Hautajarvi, Harri. Houses in Finland. 2011. (ENG., Illus.). 240p. 64.95 *(978-951-682-947-3(3))* Rakennustieto oy FIN. Dist: Independent Pubs. Group.

Heikkinen, Mikka. Zumthor: Spirit of Nature Wood Architecture Award 2006. 2008. (ENG., Illus.). 80p. pap. 66.00 *(978-951-682-807-0(8))* Rakennustieto oy FIN. Dist: Independent Pubs. Group.

Holma, M. Alvar Aalto, A Gentler Structure for Life. 2008. 176p. *(978-951-682-457-7(9))* Art Stock.

Jetsonen, Jari, ed. Little Big Houses: Working with Architectural Models. 2008. (Illus.). 176p. pap. 39.00 *(978-951-682-645-8(8))* Rakennustieto oy FIN. Dist: Independent Pubs. Group.

Koivisto, Maritta. Concrete Architecture in Finland. 2009. (Illus.). 132p. 69.00 *(978-951-682-888-9(4))* Rakennustieto oy FIN. Dist: Independent Pubs. Group.

Koivisto, Maritta & Tiainen, Jussi. Concrete Architecture in Finland. 2009. (ENG.). 132p. 69.00 *(978-951-682-889-6(2)*, Art Stock Bks. Ltd/Csi) Continental Sales, Inc.

Kuosma, Kari. Sport Facilities in Finland 1980-2000. 2008. (ENG.). 184p. 34.00 *(978-951-682-599-4(0))* Rakennustieto oy FIN. Dist: Independent Pubs. Group.

Lahti, Louna. Alvar Aalto. Gossel, Peter, ed. 25th ed. 2009. (25 Ser.). (ENG.). 96p. 14.99 *(978-3-8365-1294-7(7))* TASCHEN DEU. Dist: Ingram Pub. Services.

Lahti, Marku & Rakennustieto Publishing Staff. Alvar Aalto: A Gentler Structure for Life. 2009. (ENG, GER, ITA & FIN., Illus.). 176p. 99.00 *(978-951-682-475-1(7))* Rakennustieto oy FIN. Dist: Independent Pubs. Group.

Lehtovuori, Panu & Jallinoja, Reijo. Office Buildings in Finland. 2008. (ENG.). 168p. 69.00 *(978-951-682-808-7(6))* Rakennustieto oy FIN. Dist: Independent Pubs. Group.

Louna, Lahti. Alvar Aalto-Ex Intimo. 2008. 192p. pap. 26.00 *(978-951-682-619-9(9))* Rakennustieto oy FIN. Dist: Independent Pubs. Group.

Makinen, Matti K. & Quantrill, Malcolm. Unmade Bed of Architecture. 2008. (ENG., Illus.). 192p. 49.00 *(978-951-682-761-5(6))* Rakennustieto oy FIN. Dist: Independent Pubs. Group.

Piironen, Esa. Small Houses in Finland. 2008. (ENG., Illus.). 128p. 66.00 *(978-951-682-751-6(9))* Rakennustieto oy FIN. Dist: Independent Pubs. Group.

Rakennustieto Publishing Staff. Finnish Sauna: Design & Construction. 6th ed. 2007. (Illus.). 120p. 39.00 *(978-951-682-856-8(6))* Rakennustieto oy FIN. Dist: Independent Pubs. Group.

Sato, Tomoko, et al. Alvar Aalto: Through the Eyes of Shigeru Ban. Sato, Tomoko, ed. 2007. (ENG., Illus.). 271p. 45.00 *(978-1-904772-64-4(1))* Black Dog Publishing Ltd. GBR. Dist: Perseus Distribution.

Tiainen, Jussi, photos by. Wood Architecture in Finland. 2008. (ENG., Illus.). 144p. 69.00 *(978-951-682-847-6(7))* Rakennustieto oy FIN. Dist: Independent Pubs. Group.

Toivonen, Tuomas, et al. Newly Drawn: Emerging Finnish Architects. 2010. (ENG.). 208p. pap. 63.00 *(978-951-682-940-4(6)*, Art Stock Bks. Ltd/Csi) Continental Sales, Inc.

ARCHITECTURE—FRANCE

see also Architecture, Domestic—France

Abel, Chris. Carre D'Art. 2011. (Illus.). 96p. 29.95 *(978-3-7913-4545-1(1))* Prestel Publishing.

Adam, Peter. Eileen Gray: Her Life & Work. 2009. *(978-3-8296-0420-8(3))* Schirmer/Mosel Verlag GmbH.

Altana, Leonart, ed. Ultimate Paris Design. 2007. 528p. 24.95 *(978-3-8327-9139-1(6))* teNeues Publishing Co.

Alvarez, Jose. Lebenskunst in Paris. (GER.). *(978-3-8067-2820-0(8))* Gerstenberg DEU. Dist: International Bk. Import Service, Inc.

Anderson, Alex Thomas. The Problem of the House: French Domestic Life & the Rise of Modern Architecture. 2006. (ENG., Illus.). 240p. 60.00 *(978-0-295-98632-6(8))* Univ. of Washington Pr.

Bartz, Gabriele & Konig, Eberhard. Art & Architecture Louvre. 2010. (Art & Architecture Pocket Ser.). 626p. pap. 16.99 *(978-0-8416-7159-1(1))* Langenscheidt Publishing Group.

—Louvre. 2008. (Art & Architecture Ser.). (Illus.). 626p. 19.95 *(978-0-8416-0149-9(6))* American Map Corp.

Benton, Caroline Maniaque. Le Corbusier & the Maisons Jaoul. 2009. (ENG., Illus.). 160p. pap. 40.00 *(978-1-56898-800-9(1))* Princeton Architectural Pr.

Blain, Sophie. Les Terres Cuites Architecturales des Eglises du Haut Moyen Age Dans le Nord-Ouest de la France et le Sud-est de L'Angleterre: Application de la Datation Par Luminescence a Larcheologie du Bati. 2011. (Bar S Ser.). (FRE & ENG., Illus.). 221p. (C). pap. 102.50 *(978-1-4073-0744-2(4))* British Archaeological Reports Ltd. GBR. Dist: Brown, David Bk. Co., The.

Blondes, Casey O'Brien. Parisian Hideaways: Exquisite Rooms in Enchanting Hotels. 2009. (ENG., Illus.). 216p. 45.00 *(978-0-8478-3214-9(7))* Rizzoli International Pubns., Inc.

Boekraad, Hugues. My Work Is Not My Work: Pierre Bernard: Design for the Public Domain. 2008. (Illus.). 319p. pap. 49.95 *(978-3-03778-087-9(8)*, 3037780878) Lars Muller Pubs. CHE. Dist: Springer.

Bonechi, Casa. Chateau of Amboise. 48p. pap. *(978-88-7009-225-7(9))* Casa Editrice Bonechi.

Borie, Alain. Le Lycée Elisa Lemonnier. Leonard, Weissmann. 2010. (FRE., Illus.). *(978-2-35733-106-8(2))* Archibooks.

Borrus, Kathy. Five Hundred Buildings of Paris. 2010. (ENG., Illus.). 608p. pap. 19.95 *(978-1-57912-858-6(0)*, 1579128580) Black Dog & Leventhal Pubs., Inc.

Bosser, Jacques. La Tour Signal: Un Nouveau Défi Pour la Défense. 2009. (FRE & ENG., Illus.). 160p. *(978-2-7324-3862-7(6))* Editions de la Martiniere.

Bouroullec, Erwan & Bouroullec, Ronan. Ronan & Erwan Bouroullec. 2008. (ENG., Illus.). 208p. pap. 39.95 *(978-0-7148-4860-0(3))* Phaidon Pr. Ltd. GBR. Dist: Hachette Bk. Group.

Burckhardt, Titus. Chartres & the Birth of the Cathedral. 2010. (ENG., Illus.). 160p. pap. 24.95 *(978-1-933316-77-2(2))* World Wisdom, Inc.

Buren, Daniel, photos by. Daniel Buren: Prospettive, 5 vols. 2008. (ITA & ENG., Illus.). 72p. 15.00 *(978-3-905701-49-4(9))* JRP Ringier Kunstverlag AG CHE. Dist: D.A.P./Distributed Art Pubs.

Calzi, Renata. Gypsy Architecture. 2007. (ENG., Illus.). 160p. 72.00 *(978-3-936681-12-3(0))* Edition Axel Menges GmbH DEU. Dist: National Bk. Network.

Carré, Dominique. Euralille: Chroniques D'une Métropole en Mutation (1988-2008) 2008. (FRE., Illus.). 180p. pap. *(978-2-915755-16-9(7))* Carre, Dominique editeur.

Chapelot, Jean, ed. Trente ans d'archeologie medievale en France: Un bilan pour un avenir Colloque de la Societe d'Archeologie Medievale. 2009. (Publications du Crahm Ser.). (FRE.). 400p. (C). pap. 66.00 *(978-2-902685-63-9(7))* Brepols Pubs. BEL. Dist: Brown, David Bk. Co., The.

Chateau of Blois. 48p. pap. *(978-88-7009-726-9(9))* Casa Editrice Bonechi.

Chronicle Books Staff & Herman, Michael. City Walks Architecture: Paris. 2009. (ENG.). 25p. 18.95 *(978-0-8118-6862-4(1))* Chronicle Bks. LLC.

Cohen, Jean-Louis. Le Corbusier. Gossel, Peter, ed. 25th ed. 2009. (25 Ser.). (ENG., Illus.). 96p. 14.99 *(978-3-8365-1308-1(0))* TASCHEN DEU. Dist: Ingram Pub. Services.

Constant, Caroline. Eileen Gray. 2007. (ENG., Illus.). 255p. pap. 29.95 *(978-0-7148-4844-0(1))* Phaidon Pr., Inc.

Cook, Theodore Andrea. Old Provence. 2009. 196p. pap. *(978-1-4588-3590-1(1))*; 266p. pap. *(978-0-217-24392-6(4))*; 206p. pap. *(978-0-217-26283-5(X))*; 262p. pap. *(978-0-217-24390-2(8))*; 196p. pap. *(978-0-217-52419-3(2))* Books LLC.

DAAB Media Staff, creator. Jean-Marie Massaud, 1 vol. 2008. (ENG, FRE & GER., Illus.). 175p. 29.95 *(978-3-937718-88-0(5))* DAAB Media Gmbh DEU. Dist: Innovative Logistics.

—Matali Crasset: Spaces 2000-2007, 1 vol. 2008. (ENG, FRE & GER., Illus.). 175p. 29.95 *(978-3-937718-89-7(3))* DAAB Media Gmbh DEU. Dist: Innovative Logistics.

Daix, Pierre, frwd. Main Entrance. 2011. (ENG., Illus.). 80p. 16.00 *(978-2-916275-78-9(9))* Dilecta, Editions FRA. Dist: D.A.P./Distributed Art Pubs.

de Nicolay-Mazery, Christiane & Touillon, Bernard. The French Country House. 2008. (ENG., Illus.). 192p. pap. 29.95 (978-0-86565-194-4(9)) Vendome Pr., The.

Dottelonde, Pierre, et al. CNIT, Ou, Les Temps Modernes. 2009. (FRE., Illus.). 157p. (978-2-7491-1311-1(3)) Le Cherche Midi Editeur.

Dover. French Ornamental Ironwork Designs. 2012. (Dover Pictorial Archive Ser.). (ENG.). 112p. pap. 16.95 (978-0-486-48600-0(1)) Dover Pubns., Inc.

Duarte, Paulette, et al. Les Démolitions Dans les Projets de Renouvellement Urbain: Représentations, Légitimités et Traductions. 2010. (FRE., Illus.). 261p. (978-2-296-13298-6(7)) Harmattan Pr.

Dubois, Adrien. Caen Castle: A Ten Centuries Old Fortress Within the Town. 2010. (Publications du Crahm Ser.). (Illus.). 128p. (C). 22.00 (978-2-902685-75-2(0)) Brepols Pubs. BEL. Dist: Brown, David Bk. Co., The.

Ducouret, Bernard, et al. Épernay, Cité du Champagne: Champagne-Ardenne. 2010. (FRE., Illus.). 160p. pap. (978-2-914528-83-2(3)) Lieux Dits Etude Et Mise En Valeur Du Patrimoine.

Duhamel, Pascale. Polyphonie parisienne et architecture au temps de l'art Gothique (1140-1240) 2010. (Varia Musicologica Ser.). (FRE.). 275p. pap. (978-3-03911-613-3(4)) Lang, Peter.

En Bretagne. pap. 27.95 incl. audio compact disk (978-88-7754-756-9(1)) Cideb ITA. Dist: Distribooks, Inc.

En Provence. pap. 27.95 incl. audio compact disk (978-88-7754-335-6(3)) Cideb ITA. Dist: Distribooks, Inc.

Evans, Joan. Monastic Architecture in France: From the Renaissance to the Revolution. 2011. (ENG.). 645p. pap. 60.00 (978-0-521-18084-9(8)) Cambridge Univ. Pr.

Fixot, Michel & Pelletier, J. P. Saint Victor de Marseille: Etude archeologique et Monumentale. 2009. (Bibliotheque de l'antiquite Tardive Ser.). (FRE.). 300p. (C). pap. 73.00 (978-2-503-53257-8(8)) Brepols Pubs. BEL. Dist: Brown, David Bk. Co., The.

Foster, Norman. Millau Viaduct. 2012. (Illus.). 96p. 29.95 (978-3-7913-4687-8(3)) Prestel Publishing.

French, Touch, ed. Optimistic Architecture Year Book/ Annuel Optimiste D'Architecture. 2008. 360p. (978-2-9531421-0-5(X)) Actar Birkhauser Distribution.

Gafsou, Matthieu. Ce Rêve étrange: Le Corbusier à Firminy. 2009. (FRE., Illus.). 106p. (978-2-7424-2695-9(7)) Gallimard, Editions.

Gallois, Philippe & Lantez, Dominique. Logistique: Sustainable Development & Developpement Durable. 2007. (FRE & ENG., Illus.). 121p. (978-2-912604-64-9(5)) PC, Editions.

Gartner, Peter J. Musee D'Orsay. 2008. (Art & Architecture Ser.). (Illus.). 572p. 19.95 (978-0-8416-0050-8(3)) American Map Corp.

Gauzin-Müller, Dominique & Ayers, Andrew. Jean-Yves Barrier: Architect & Urbanist, Architecte et Urbaniste. 2009. (Work Monographs). (ENG & FRE., Illus.). 176p. 109.00 (978-3-932565-24-3(X)) Edition Axel Menges GmbH DEU. Dist: National Bk. Network.

Gerbino, Anthony. François Blondel: Architecture, Erudition, & the Scientific Revolution. 2010. (Classical Tradition in Architecture Ser.). (ENG., Illus.). 344p. (C). 135.00 (978-0-415-49199-0(1)) Routledge.

Gilman, Roger. The Theory of Gothic Architecture & the Effect of Shellfire at Rheims & Soissons. 2009. pap. 20.32 (978-1-60724-449-3(7)) Gorgias Pr., LLC.

Goulet, Patrice, et al. Canal, Patrick Rubin, Architecte: Itinéraires du Passeur: Entretien Avec Patrice Goulet. 2008. (FRE & ENG., Illus.). 159p. (978-2-87143-212-8(0)) Editions du Layeur.

Hamann-Maclean, Richard. Kathedrale von Reims II: Skulp(Text) 2008. (ENG.). (C). 82.00 (978-3-515-06837-6(6)) Steiner, Franz Verlag Wiesbaden GmbH DEU. Dist: Brown, David Bk. Co., The.

Hendricks, J. & Taschen, Angelika, eds. Paris Style. 25th ed. 2008. (Icon (Taschen) Ser.). (FRE., Illus.). 191p. 7.99 (978-3-8365-0775-2(7)) TASCHEN DEU. Dist: Ingram Pub. Services.

Hofer, Candida, photos by. Louvre: Photographien. 2006. (Illus.). 18p. 49.95 (978-3-8296-0250-1(2)) Schirmer/Mosel Verlag GmbH DEU. Dist: Prestel Publishing.

Hoffsummer, Patrick, ed. The Roof Frame from the Xith Through Xixth Century: Typology & Development in Northern France & in Belgium. 2010. (Architectura Medii Aevi Ser.). (ENG.). 376p. (C). pap. 131.00 (978-2-503-52987-5(9)) Brepols Pubs. BEL. Dist: ISD.

ICI Consultants Company. Interior Design for Wellness Space. 2011. (ENG., Illus.). 356p. 60.00 (978-988-19740-1-3(1)) Design Media Publishing Ltd. HKG. Dist: BookMasters Distribution Services (BDS).

Images Publishing, creator. Jakob & MacFarlane. 2006. (Neo Architecture Ser.). (ENG., Illus.). 124p. 49.50 (978-1-920744-83-0(5)) Images Publishing Group AUS. Dist: National Bk. Network.

James, John. In Search of the Unknown in Medieval Architecture. 2007. (Illus.). 686p. (C). 300.00 (978-1-904597-36-0(X)) Pindar Pr. GBR. Dist: Brown, David Bk. Co., The.

James, Russell, text. Cool Guide Paris. 2009. pap. 12.95 (978-3-8327-9295-4(3)) teNeues Publishing Co.

Jodidio, Philip. Jean Nouvel by Jean Nouvel. Complete Works 1993-2008, 2 vols. 2009. (FRE, GER & ENG., Illus.). 896p. 200.00 (978-3-8228-5772-4(6)) TASCHEN DEU. Dist: Ingram Pub. Services.

Jodidio Philip. Kc Jean Nouvel. 2012. (ENG., Illus.). 96p. pap. 9.99 (978-3-8365-3080-4(5)) TASCHEN DEU. Dist: Ingram Pub. Services.

Jodidio, Philip (Ed). Architecture in France. 2006. (ENG, FRE & GER., Illus.). 192p. 29.99 (978-3-8228-5257-6(0)) TASCHEN DEU. Dist: Ingram Pub. Services.

Johnston, Roy. Parisian Architecture of the Belle Epoque. 2007. (ENG.). 216p. 75.00 (978-0-470-01555-1(1), Academy Pr.) Wiley, John & Sons, Inc.

Kesavaperumal, Thirumaran. Impediments of French Architecture Facades in Contemporary Buildings of Puducherry. 2011. 72p. pap. (978-3-8454-1926-8(1)) Lambert Academic Publishing.

La Rivière, Dominique de. La Chapelle de Passy-Buzenval: 1955-1960. 2010. (FRE., Illus.). 191p. (978-2-35039-093-2(4)) Chaudun, Nicolas Editions.

Larousse Staff. Dictionnaire Sachs, No. 2. (FRE.). (978-0-7859-7634-9(5), 2030281034) French & European Pubns., Inc.

—Dictionnaire Sachs-Villate, Vol. 1. (FRE.). (978-0-7859-7633-2(7), 2030281034) French & European Pubns., Inc.

Loiseau, Laurent & Agnelli, Brice. Paris D'Henri IV. (FRE., Illus.). 254p. (978-2-8123-0156-8(2)) Editions du Chene.

Lovelace, Carey, et al. Iannis Xenakis: Composer, Architect, Visionary. 2010. pap. 25.00 (978-0-942324-57-0(9)) Drawing Ctr.

Malraux, Andre & Lantelme, Michel. La Grande Pitié des Monuments de France: Débats Parlementaires, 1960-1968. (FRE.). 158p. (978-2-85939-548-3(2)) Presses Universitaires du Septentrion.

Maniaque-Benton, Caroline. French Encounters with the American Counterculture, 1960-1980. 2011. (Ashgate Studies in Architecture Ser.). (Illus.). 244p. 99.95 (978-1-4094-2386-7(7)) Ashgate Publishing Co.

Martin, Meredith S. Dairy Queens: The Politics of Pastoral Architecture from Catherine De' Medici to Marie-Antoinette. 2011. (Harvard Historical Studies: 176). (Illus.). 336p. 45.00 (978-0-674-04899-7(7)) Harvard Univ. Pr.

Martina, Padberg. Art & Architecture Paris. 2010. (Art & Architecture Pocket Ser.). 48p. pap. 16.99 (978-0-8416-7160-7(5)) Langenscheidt Publishing Group.

McCulloch, Janelle. Paris Secrets: Architecture, Interiors, Quartiers, Corners. 2009. (ENG., Illus.). 300p. 60.00 (978-1-86470-308-5(3)) Images Publishing Group AUS. Dist: National Bk. Network.

Middleton, Robin & Baudouin-Matuszek, Marie-Noelle. Jean Rondelet: The Architect as Technician. 2007. (ENG., Illus.). 368p. 95.00 (978-0-300-11567-3(9)) Yale Univ. Pr.

Mimram, Marc & Desveaux, Delphine. Un Balcon Sur la Loire: Le Pont Léopold-Sédar-Senghor. 2010. (FRE., Illus.). 128p. (978-2-35733-110-5(0)) Archibooks.

Muga, Patricia de, et al. Jean Prouve: Objects & Furniture Design by Architects, 1 vol. 2007. (ENG., Illus.). 128p. 30.00 (978-84-343-1144-2(5)) Poligrafa, Ediciones, S. A. ESP. Dist: D.A.P./Distributed Art Pubs.

Nouvel, Jean & Coley, Catherine, texts. Jean Prouv#xE9; & Jean Nouvel: Ferembal House. 2011. (ENG., Illus.). 336p. 125.00 (978-2-909187-01-3(2)) Galerie Patrick Seguin FRA. Dist: D.A.P./Distributed Art Pubs.

Pearson, Christopher E. M. Designing UNESCO: Art Architecture & International Politics at Mid-Century. 2010. (Illus.). 412p. 134.95 (978-0-7546-6783-4(9)) Ashgate Publishing Co.

Perouse De Montclos, Jean-Marie. Chateaux of the Loire Valley. 2008. (Art & Architecture Ser.). (Illus.). 359p. pap. 24.95 (978-0-8416-0060-7(0)) American Map Corp.

Peter, Gartner. Art & Architecture Musee Dorsay. 2010. (Art & Architecture Pocket Ser.). 572p. pap. 16.99 (978-0-8416-7152-2(4)) Langenscheidt Publishing Group.

Pezzella, Tiziana. Saint-Etienne-Du-Mont: Storia Di una Chiesa Parigina. 2009. (ITA., Illus.). 206p. (978-88-371-1793-1(0)) Pitagora.

Phaidon Press Editors & Wallpaper Magazine Editors. Le Corbusier le Grand, 2 vols. 2008. (ENG., Illus.). 624p. 200.00 (978-0-7148-4668-2(6)) Phaidon Pr., Inc.

Pieper, Jan. Maulnes-En-Tonnerrois: Ein Konstrukt Aus Dem Geiste des Manierismus: Architektur der Skepsis, des Glaubens, der Zivilitoleranz. 2007. (GER & ENG., Illus.). 560p. 218.00 (978-3-936681-07-9(4)) Edition Axel Menges GmbH DEU. Dist: National Bk. Network.

Provence: Art, Architecture, Landscape. 2008. 49.95 (978-0-8416-0398-1(7)) American Map Corp.

Rattee, Kathryn, ed. Red Summer in Kensington Gardens. 2012. (ENG., Illus.). 44p. pap. 44.95 (978-3-86560-860-4(4)) Verlag der Buchhandlung Walther Konig DEU. Dist: D.A.P./Distributed Art Pubs.

Rattenbury, Bernard Tschumi - Parc de la Villette. 2011. (Supercrit Ser.). (ENG., Illus.). 120p. (C). 165.00 (978-0-415-45787-3(4)); pap. 49.95 (978-0-415-45788-0(2)) Routledge.

Ratti, Annie, et al, texts. Yona Friedman. 2009. (ENG., Illus.). 96p. pap. 27.95 (978-88-8158-705-6(X)) Charta ITA. Dist: D.A.P./Distributed Art Pubs.

Rolf, Toman & Christian, Freigang. Provence. 2010. 4p. pap. 24.99 (978-0-8416-7166-9(4)) Langenscheidt Publishing Group.

Rouyer, Eugene, ed. French Architectural Ornament: From Versailles, Fontainebleau & Other Palaces. 2008. (Dover Architecture Ser.). (ENG., Illus.). 96p. per. 14.95 (978-0-486-46140-3(8)) Dover Pubns., Inc.

Ruegg, Arthur & Spechtenhauser, Klaus. Le Corbusier. Meubles et Interieurs, 1905-1965. 2012. (ENG., Illus.). 352p. 200.00 (978-3-85881-729-7(5)) Scheidegger und Spiess AG, Verlag CHE. Dist: Antique Collectors' Club.

Saboya, Marc. Fragments D'architecture Contemporaine à Bordeaux: Ordre et Désordre. 2008. (Marches de L'architecte Ser.). (FRE., Illus.). 109p. pap. (978-2-915262-69-8(1)) Le Festin.

Sadler, Donna L. Reading the Reverse Facade of Reims Cathedral: Royalty & Ritual in 13th-Century France. 2012. (Illus.). 250p. (978-1-4094-3243-2(2)) Ashgate Publishing, Ltd.

Sargent, Anthony & Buchanan, Peter. The Sage Gateshead. 2010. (Illus.). 96p. 24.95 (978-3-7913-4314-3(9)) Prestel Verlag GmbH & Co KG. DEU. Dist: Prestel Publishing.

Saxon, Elizabeth. The Eucharist in Romanesque France: Iconography & Theology. 2006. (Illus.). 324p. 90.00 (978-1-84383-256-0(9)) Boydell & Brewer, Inc.

Stamp, Gavin. The Memorial to the Missing of the Somme. 2007. (Wonders of the World Ser.). (Illus.). 214p. per. 17.00 (978-1-86197-896-7(0)) Profile Bks. Ltd. GBR. Dist: Independent Pubs. Group.

Taillard, Christian. Victor Louis, 1731-1800: Le Triomphe du Goût Français à L'époque Néo-Classique. 2009. (FRE., Illus.). 495p. (978-2-84050-614-0(9)) Presses de l'Universite de Paris-Sorbonne.

Taschen, Angelika, ed. Icon Paris Style 02, Vol. 2. 2009. (ENG.). 192p. pap. 9.99 (978-3-8365-1505-4(9)) TASCHEN DEU. Dist: Ingram Pub. Services.

TF Editores. Dominique Perrault Architecture. 2011. (ENG., Illus.). 208p. 54.00 incl. cd-rom (978-84-92441-62-4(3)) T.F. Editores ESP. Dist: National Bk. Network.

Toman, Rolf, ed. Burgundy: Art, Architecture, Landscape. 2008. (Art & Architecture Ser.). (Illus.). 380p. 49.95 (978-0-8416-0059-1(7)) American Map Corp.

Vellay, Dominique. La Maison de Verre: Pierre Chareau's Modernist Masterwork. 2007. (ENG., Illus.). 160p. 60.00 (978-0-500-51304-0(X)) Thames & Hudson.

Violeau, Jean-Louis & Buckley, Craig, eds. Utopie: Texts & Projects, 1967-1978. Clarke, Jean-Marie, tr. from FRE. 2011. (Semiotext(e) / Foreign Agents Ser.). (ENG., Illus.). 264p. (gr. 17). 24.95 (978-1-58435-095-8(4)) Semiotexte/Smart Art.

Viollet-le-Duc, Eugene-Emmanuel. The Art of Fortification in France, 1000-1600. 2008.Tr. of Dictionnaire raisonné de l¿architecture française du Xle au XVIe Siècle. (Illus.). 754p. cd-rom 39.95 (978-0-9638332-0-4(0)) Editions Tour Blanche.

Vogt, Gunther & Alice, Foxley. Distance & Engagement: Landscape Thinking — Model Making. 2010. (Illus.). 480p. 80.00 (978-3-03778-196-8(3)) Lars Muller Pubs. CHE. Dist: Prestel Publishing.

Webster, Helena. Bourdieu for Architects. 2010. (Thinkers for Architects Ser.). (ENG., Illus.). 144p. (C). pap. 28.95 (978-0-415-49615-5(2)) Routledge.

Wittman, Richard. Architecture, Print Culture & the Public Sphere in Eighteenth-Century France. 2007. (Classical Tradition in Architecture Ser.). (ENG., Illus.). 304p. (C). 165.00 (978-0-415-77463-5(2)) Routledge.

ARCHITECTURE—GERMANY

Abenstein, Edelgard & Fiedler, Jeannine. Berlin, 1 vol. 2009. (ENG., Illus.). 480p. pap. 9.99 (978-3-8331-4566-7(8)) h.f.ullmann DEU. Dist: Innovative Logistics.

Andrews, Jonathan. Architectural Visions: Contemporary Sketches, Perspectives, Drawings. 2010. (ENG., Illus.). 372p. 49.95 (978-3-03768-035-3(0), Braun Publish,Csi) Continental Sales, Inc.

Architects Berlin Chamber Staff. Building Berlin Vol. 1: The Latest Architecture in & out of the Capital. 2012. (ENG., Illus.). 192p. 39.95 (978-3-03768-118-3(7), Braun Publish,Csi) Continental Sales, Inc.

Aschauer, Bernd, et al, texts. Deutsche Nationalbibliothek in Leipzig: Umschlag,Hülle, Inhalt. 2011. (ENG., Illus.). 112p. 45.00 (978-3-7757-2763-1(9)) Hatje Cantz Verlag GmbH & Co KG DEU. Dist: D.A.P./Distributed Art Pubs.

Aynsley, Jeremy. Designing Modern Germany. 2009. (ENG., Illus.). 256p. pap. 35.00 (978-1-86189-401-4(5)) Reaktion Bks., Ltd. GBR. Dist: Chicago Distribution Ctr.

Barkow, Frank & Leibinger, Regine. Barkow Leibinger: An Atlas of Fabrication. 2009. (Illus.). 98p. pap. (978-1-902902-75-3(0)) Architectural Assn.

Barth, Holger. Projekt Sozialistische Stadt: Beitraege zur Bau & Planungsgeschichte der DDR. (GER., Illus.). 275p. (978-3-496-01190-3(4)) Reimer, Dietrich.

Bauer, Merlin. Liebe Deine Stadt: öffentliche Angelegenheiten Köln. 2009. (GER & ENG., Illus.). 479p. (978-3-7743-0412-3(2)) Greven Verlag Koln GmbH.

Baumann, Kirsten & Meuser, Natascha. Ambassadors' Residences, 1 vol. 2009. (ENG., Illus.). 352p. 74.95 (978-3-938666-80-7(3)) DOM Pubs. DEU. Dist: Innovative Logistics.

Beissel, Jeannette. Luxury Houses. 2007. (Illus.). 220p. 59.95 (978-3-8327-9173-5(6)) teNeues Publishing Co.

Bembé Dellinger Architects: Bilder und Pläne pictures & plans 1999 - 2009. 2010. 736p. pap. 69.95 (978-3-7091-0093-6(3)) Springer Wien AUT. Dist: Actar Birkhauser Distribution.

Berlinger, Alexandra, et al. Tat Ort: Berlinger, Berlinger, Fiel. 2007. (Illus.). 127p. pap. 29.95 (978-3-211-25246-8(0), 3211252460) Springer Wien AUT. Dist: Actar Birkhauser Distribution.

Berning, Maria, et al. Berliner Wohnquartiere: Ein Fuehrer durch 60 Siedlungen in Ost & West. 2nd ed. (GER., Illus.). xii, 397p. (978-3-496-01112-5(2)) Reimer, Dietrich.

Binding, Gunther. Methoden und Probleme bei der Datierung von mittelalterlichen Bauwerken. 2009. (Wissenschaftliche Gesellschaft an der Johann Wolfgang Goethe-Universitat Frankfurt, Main u Sitzungsberichte Ser.). (GER., Illus.). 76p. (C). pap. 39.00 (978-3-515-09607-2(8)) Steiner, Franz Verlag Wiesbaden GmbH DEU. Dist: Brown, David Bk. Co., The.

Bottger. Updating Germany 100 Projects for a Better Future. 2009. (ENG., Illus.). 292p. 55.00 (978-3-7757-2263-6(7)) Hatje Cantz Verlag GmbH & Co KG DEU. Dist: D.A.P./Distributed Art Pubs.

Boyken, Immo, intro. Otto Ernst Schweizer: Stadium in Vienna. 2011. (GER & ENG., Illus.). 60p. 49.00 (978-3-932565-75-5(4)) Edition Axel Menges GmbH DEU. Dist: National Bk. Network.

Brawne, Michael. Museum Fur Kunsthandwerk: Frankfurt Am Main 1984 Richard Meier. (Illus.). 60p. 29.95 (978-0-7148-2765-0(7)) Phaidon Pr. Ltd. GBR. Dist: Hachette Bk. Group.

Bredenbeck, Martin, et al. Beethovenhalle Bonn: Konzerthaus. Festsaal. Denkmal. 2010. (Illus.). 207p. (978-3-938803-28-8(2)) Weidle Verlag GmbH.

Brock, Harald. Die Landsitzarchitektur Simon-Louis du Rys. 2008. (GER., Illus.). 92p. (978-3-89445-402-9(4)) Jonas Verlag fur Kunst & Literatur GmbH.

Brown-Manrique, Gerardo, text. Rudolf Frankel & Neues Bauen. 2009. (ENG., Illus.). 148p. pap. 50.00 (978-3-8030-0695-0(3)) Wasmuth, Ernst J. Verlag GmbH & Co. DEU. Dist: D.A.P./Distributed Art Pubs.

Bruells, Holger & Dietzsch, Thomas. Architekturfuehrer Halle an der Saale. (GER.). xxvi, 226p. (978-3-496-01202-3(1)) Reimer, Dietrich.

Buildings & Regions: Annual 2006. 2007. (Illus.). 160p. pap. 39.95 (978-3-8030-0663-9(5)) Wasmuth, Ernst J. Verlag GmbH & Co. DEU. Dist: D.A.P./Distributed Art Pubs.

Cernichov, Jakov. Jacov Cernichov: Sowjetischer Architekt der Avantgarde. (GER., Illus.). 332p. 108.00 (978-3-925369-46-9(5)) Arnoldsche Art Pubs. DEU. Dist: Antique Collectors' Club.

Chaix & Morel & JSWD Architects, contrib. by. ThyssenKrupp Quartier. 2011. (ENG., Illus.). 144p. 60.00 (978-3-86859-090-6(0)) Jovis Verlag GmbH DEU. Dist: D.A.P./Distributed Art Pubs.

Cramer, J. & Laible, U. Karl Friedrich Schinkel: Guide to His Buildings. 2007. (Illus.). 400p. pap. (978-3-422-20671-7(X)) Deutscher Kunstverlag GmbH.

Cramer, Johannes, et al, eds. Karl Friedrich Schinkel Guide to His Buildings: Part I: Berlin & Potsdam; Part II: from Aachen Through Mark Brandenburg to St. Petersburg. Wallis, Wendy & Pepper, Ian, trs. from GER. 2007. (Illus.). 400p. pap. 39.95 (978-3-422-06671-7(3)) Deutscher Kunstverlag GmbH DEU. Dist: Independent Pubs. Group.

Cünzer, Andrea, et al. Neue Architektur in Frankfurt am Main: Architekturführer Frankfurt. 2008. (Illus.). 260p. pap. (978-3-88506-583-8(5)) Junius Verlag GmbH.

DAAB Media Staff, creator. German Football Stadiums, 1 vol. 2008. (ENG, GER, FRE, SPA & ITA., Illus.). 207p. 19.95 (978-3-937718-94-1(X)) DAAB Media Gmbh DEU. Dist: Innovative Logistics.

DAAB Media Staff, ed. Creative Germany, 1 vol. 2009. (ITA, FRE, GER, SPA & ENG., Illus.). 499p. 99.95 (978-3-86654-052-1(3)) DAAB Media Gmbh DEU. Dist: Innovative Logistics.

Danieri, Anna, ed. Canodrom: 00. 00. 00. 2010. 168p. (978-84-92861-37-8(1)) Actar Birkhauser Distribution.

Debschitz, Thilo Von. Frank Kunert: Verkehrte Welt - Topsy-Turvy World. 2008. (GER & ENG., Illus.). 72p. 25.00 (978-3-7757-2132-5(0)) Hatje Cantz Verlag GmbH & Co KG DEU. Dist: D.A.P./Distributed Art Pubs.

Deja-Vu 19: Bauhaus Photo. pap. 25.00 (978-4-309-90339-2(8)) Fiction, Inc. JPN. Dist: D.A.P./Distributed Art Pubs.

Dietrich, Eva. Die westfalische Denkmalpflege der Nachkriegszeit. Westfalen-Lippe, Landschaftsverband, ed. 2008. (Illus.). 240p. (C). 36.00 (978-3-8053-3959-9(3)) Zabern, Philipp von Verlag, GmbH DEU. Dist: Brown, David Bk. Co., The.

Doll, Monika. Forschungen zu Haus Horst in Gelsenkirchen: Tierknochen aus acht Jahrhunderten. 2010. (Denkmalpflege und Forschung in Westfalen Ser.). (GER., Illus.). 169p. (C). 33.00 (978-3-8053-4281-0(0)) Zabern, Philipp von Verlag, GmbH DEU. Dist: Brown, David Bk. Co., The.

Dreher, Sabine, et al. Porsche Museum: Delugan Meissl Associated ArchitectsHG Merz. Delugan Meissl Associated Architects, ed. 2009. (ENG., Illus.). 364p. pap. 79.95 (978-3-211-99736-9(9), 3211997369) Springer.

Dudler, Max. Max Dudler Continuity. 2011. (Illus.). 664p. pap. (978-3-7212-0751-4(3)) Niggli, Arthur Verlag.

Dündar, Murat. A Study on Bruno Taut's Way of Thought. 2011. 128p. pap. (978-3-8443-0319-3(7)) Lambert Academic Publishing.

Duttmann, Martina & Zwoch, Felix, eds. Bauwelt Berlin Annual: Chronik der baulichen Ereignisse 1996 Bis 2001: 1999/2000. (GER., Illus.). 185p. pap. 52.00 (978-3-7643-6278-2(2), 3764362782) Birkhauser Boston.

Ebel-Zepezauer, Wolfgang, et al, eds. Augusteische Marschlager und Siedlungen des 1. bis 9 Jahrhunderts. 2009. (GER & ENG., Illus.). 468p. (C). 51.00 (978-3-8053-3952-0(6)) Zabern, Philipp von Verlag, GmbH DEU. Dist: Brown, David Bk. Co., The.

Eckhard Schulze-Fielitz: Metasprache des Raums / Metalanguage of Space. 2009. 536p. 59.95 (978-3-211-99197-8(2)) Springer Wien AUT. Dist: Actar Birkhauser Distribution.

Engel, Gerrit. Gerrit Engel: Berlin Architecture. 2008. (Illus.). 340p. (978-3-8296-0392-8(4)) Schirmer/Mosel Verlag GmbH.

Engel, Ute & Gajewski, Alexandrea. Mainz & the Middle Rhine Valley: Medieval Art, Architecture, & Archaeology. 2007. (British Archaeological Association Conference Transactions Ser.). (Illus.). 256p. (C). 94.00 (978-1-904350-82-8(8)); 56.00 (978-1-904350-83-5(6)) Northern Universities Pr. GBR. Dist: Brown, David Bk. Co., The.

Falconer, Jonathan. The Dam Busters: Breaking the Great Dams of Western Germany, 16-17 May 1943. 2011. (ENG., Illus.). 256p. pap. 24.95 (978-1-84425-867-3(X), 184425867X) Haynes Publishing PLC GBR. Dist: MBI Distribution Services/Quayside Distribution.

Falk, Cynthia G. & Falk, Cynthia. Architecture & Artifacts of the Pennsylvania Germans: Constructing Identity in Early America. 2008. (ENG., Illus.). 256p. (C). 45.00 (978-0-271-03338-9(X)) Pennsylvania State Univ. Pr.

Föhl, Axel. Architekturführer Ruhrgebiet: Architectural Guide. 2010. (ENG.). 300p. pap. 38.00 (978-3-496-01293-1(5)) Reimer, Dietrich DEU. Dist: Independent Pubs. Group.

Folkerts, Thilo. Topotek 1 Martin Rein-Cano / Lorenz Dexler Rosemarie Trockel: Eine Landschaftsskulptur für München/A Landscape Sculpture for Munich. 2010. (Illus.). 128p. 54.95 (978-3-0346-0591-5(9)) Birkhauser Verlag AG CHE. Dist: Actar Birkhauser Distribution.

Foster, Norman & Abel, Chris. The Reichstag. 2012. (ENG., Illus.). 96p. 29.95 **(978-3-7913-4589-5(3))** Prestel Publishing.

Frampton, Kenneth. Die Entwicklung der Architektur im 20. Jahrhundert: Eine vergleichende Übersicht. Keßler, Norma, tr. 2007. (Illus.). 159p. pap. 39.95 (978-3-211-31196-7(3), 3211311963) Springer.

Freytag, Daniel & Philipps, Thorsten. Berlin Embassies. 2008. (MUL & ENG.). 320p. 69.00 (978-3-86568-389-2(4), Art Stock Bks. Ltd/Csi) Continental Sales, Inc.

Friedewald, Boris. Bauhaus: Living Art. 2009. (Illus.). 128p. pap. 14.95 (978-3-7913-4200-9(2)) Prestel Publishing.

Gannon, Todd. Zaha Hadid: BMW Central Building, Leipzig, Germany. 2006. (ENG., Illus.). 160p. pap. 29.95 (978-1-56898-536-7(3)) Princeton Architectural Pr.

Geipel, Kaye, ed. Hascher Jehle Architektur: Kunstmuseum Stuttgart. 2006. (ENG., Illus.). 92p. 59.00 (978-3-936681-06-2(6)) Edition Axel Menges GmbH DEU. Dist: National Bk. Network.

GmbH, Birkhäuser. Architekten Profile 2011 / 2012. 2010. (ENG & GER., Illus.). 392p. 95.00 (978-3-0346-0612-7(5)) Birkhauser Verlag AG CHE. Dist: Actar Birkhauser Distribution.

Graumann, Antje & Arndt, Nicole. Das Hansaviertel in Berlin: Bedeutung, Rezeption, Sanierung. 2007. (GER., Illus.). 238p. (978-3-86568-287-1(1)) Imhof, Michael Verlag GmbH & Co. KG.

Grube, Hans Achim, ed. Re-Use, 1 vol. 2007. (ENG., Illus.). 128p. (C). pap. 32.00 (978-3-939633-00-6(3)) Jovis Verlag GmbH DEU. Dist: D.A.P./Distributed Art Pubs.

Grube, Michael & Grube, Christel. Ringtreppenturm Rosshafen: Ein Luftschutzturm in Hamburg. 2008. 62p. pap. 18.50 (978-3-8370-1750-2(8)) Bks. on Demand.

Grundel, Paul, et al, eds. Negotiating Spaces: The new Exhibition Building of the Museum of Contemporary Art in Leipzig by as-if. 2011. (ENG., Illus.). 256p. pap. 42.00 (978-3-86859-007-4(2)) Jovis Verlag GmbH DEU. Dist: D.A.P./Distributed Art Pubs.

Guallart, Vicente, et al, contrib. by. Sociopòlis: Project for a City of the Future. 2006. (Illus.). 294p. (gr. 13-18). pap. 45.00 (978-84-95951-83-0(5)) D.A.P./Distributed Art Pubs.

Gunsser, Christoph, et al. Gebaut: Nebel Pössl Architekten. 2007. (Illus.). 122p. (978-3-7828-1615-1(3)) Kramer, Karl GmbH.

Gunter, Angelika, ed. Projekte Aus/Projects from Berlin. 2008. (ENG., Illus.). 48p. 29.95 (978-3-939633-15-0(1)) Jovis Verlag GmbH DEU. Dist: D.A.P./Distributed Art Pubs.

Hadid, Zaha. Zaha Hadid, 1 vol. 2006. (ENG., Illus.). 316p. per. 50.00 (978-0-89207-346-7(2)) Guggenheim, Solomon R. Museum.

HafenCity Hamburg: Neue urbane Begegnungsorte zwischen Metropole und Nachbarschaft / Places of Urban Encounter between Metropolis & NeighborhoodFotografie: Daniel Barthmann, Martin Kohler, Julian Sippel, Theresa Thiele, Katja Ulbrich, Maria NIFI Xerisoti, alle Hamburg. 2010. 460p. 39.95 (978-3-7091-0106-3(9)) Springer Wien AUT. Dist: Actar Birkhauser Distribution.

Hahn, Karoline Judith. Wahrnehmung und Darstellung von Architektur: Eine k¿nstlerisch-praktische Auseinandersetzung und ihre Reflexion am Beispiel der Rotunde der Pinakothek der Moderne in M¿nchen. 2008. (GER., Illus.). 93p. (978-3-8364-7811-3(0)) VDM Verlag Dr. Mueller e.K.

Hake, Sabine. Topographies of Class: Modern Architecture & Mass Society in Weimar Berlin. 2008. (Social History, Popular Culture, & Politics in Germany Ser.). (ENG., Illus.). 336p. (C). 90.00 (978-0-472-07038-1(X)); pap. 40.00 (978-0-472-05038-3(9)) Univ. of Michigan Pr.

Hamm, Oliver G. Hascher Jehle Architektur: Thoughts & Buildings / Gedanken und Bauten, 2 vols. 2010. (Illus.). 352p. 85.00 (978-3-7913-4159-0(6)) Prestel Publishing.

Haney, David. When Modern Was Green: Life & Work of Landscape Architect Leberecht Migge. 2010. (ENG., Illus.). 344p. (C). 155.00 (978-0-415-56138-9(8)); pap. 62.95 (978-0-415-56139-6(6)) Routledge.

Harro, Schweizer. Berlin. 2009. 432p. 59.99 (978-0-8416-1643-1(4)) American Map Corp.

Hesse, Anna & Schmal, Peter Cachola, eds. Dam Jahrbuch: Architektur in Deutschland/Architecture in Germany. 2006. (Dam Jahrbuch Ser.). (ENG & GER., Illus.). 192p. pap. 45.00 (978-3-7913-3690-9(8)) Prestel Publishing.

Hinz, Berthold & Tacke, Andreas. Architekturführer Kassel / An Architectural Guide. 2009. (Architectural Guides). (GER & ENG., Illus.). 320p. pap. 38.00 (978-3-496-01249-8(8), Art Stock Bks. Ltd/Csi) Continental Sales, Inc.

Hofer, Candida. Candida Hofer: Weimar. 2007. (Illus.). 103p. 49.95 (978-3-8296-0346-1(0)) Schirmer/Mosel Verlag GmbH DEU. Dist: Prestel Publishing.

Hoffmann, Claus-Wilhelm. Hans Dieter Schaal. Work in Progress: Work in Progress. Werner, Frank R., ed. 2012. (GER & ENG., Illus.). 608p. 119.00 **(978-3-936681-49-9(X))** Edition Axel Menges GmbH DEU. Dist: National Bk. Network.

Hogener, Barbel, photos by. 'Typ Berlin' Das Corbusierhaus in Charlottenburg. 2009. (ENG., Illus.). 96p. pap. 29.95 (978-3-86859-004-3(8)) Jovis Verlag GmbH DEU. Dist: D.A.P./Distributed Art Pubs.

Hohl, Claudia, et al. World Heritage: Hildesheim Cathedral & Its Treasures. 2007. (ENG., Illus.). 80p. 19.95 (978-3-7954-2003-1(2)) Schnell und Steiner GmbH, Verlag DEU. Dist: Independent Pubs. Group.

H0gsbro, Caroline & Wischmann, Antje, eds. Nortopia. 2010. (ENG., Illus.). 176p. pap. 39.95 (978-3-86859-027-2(7)) Jovis Verlag GmbH DEU. Dist: D.A.P./Distributed Art Pubs.

IBA Hamburg, ed. Energy Atlas. 2011. (ENG., Illus.). 224p. pap. 39.95 (978-3-86859-074-6(9)) Jovis Verlag GmbH DEU. Dist: D.A.P./Distributed Art Pubs.

Ibbeken, Hillert, ed. & photos by. Friedrich August Stüler: The Architectural Work Today / Das architektonische Werk heute. 2007. (GER & ENG., Illus.). 348p. 118.00 (978-3-936681-10-9(4)) Edition Axel Menges GmbH DEU. Dist: National Bk. Network.

Ibler, Marianne. GD: Global Danish Architecture. 2011. (DAN & ENG., Illus.). 234p. pap. (978-87-91872-02-0(2)) Actar Birkhauser Distribution.

Imhof, Michael. Berlin - Architektur und Kunst - Art & Architecture. 2009. (ENG.). 160p. 24.95 (978-3-86568-100-3(X), Art Stock Bks. Ltd/Csi) Continental Sales, Inc.

Imhof, Michael & Krempel, León. Berlin: New Architecture - A Guide to the New Buildings from 1989 to Today. 6th ed. 2009. (ENG., Illus.). 163p. pap. 19.80 (978-3-935590-15-0(6), Art Stock Bks. Ltd/Csi) Continental Sales, Inc.

Jaeger, Falk. Lederer + Ragnarsdottir + Oei: Portfolio. 2008. (GER & ENG., Illus.). 144p. pap. 39.95 (978-3-939633-56-3(9)) Jovis Verlag GmbH DEU. Dist: D.A.P./Distributed Art Pubs.

—Wulf & Partner. 2008. (ENG & GER., Illus.). 144p. pap. 39.95 (978-3-939633-55-6(0)) Jovis Verlag GmbH DEU. Dist: D.A.P./Distributed Art Pubs.

Jaeger, Falk, ed. Auer + Weber + Associated. 2011. (ENG., Illus.). 144p. pap. 39.95 (978-3-86859-037-1(4)) Jovis Verlag GmbH DEU. Dist: D.A.P./Distributed Art Pubs.

—Behnisch Architekten. 2009. (ENG., Illus.). 144p. pap. 39.95 (978-3-939633-83-9(6)) Jovis Verlag GmbH DEU. Dist: D.A.P./Distributed Art Pubs.

Jäger, Joachim, text. Neue Nationalgalerie Berlin: Mies van der Rohe. 2011. (ENG., Illus.). 108p. 30.00 **(978-3-7757-3145-4(8))** Hatje Cantz Verlag GmbH & Co KG DEU. Dist: D.A.P./Distributed Art Pubs.

James, Kathleen. Bauhaus Culture: From Weimar to the Cold War. 2006. (Illus.). 272p. per. 27.50 (978-0-8166-4688-3(0)) Univ. of Minnesota Pr.

James, Russell, text. Cool Guide Berlin. 2009. pap. 24.95 (978-3-8327-9296-1(1)) teNeues Publishing Co.

Jerram, Leif. Germany's Other Modernity: Munich & the Building of Metropolis, 1895-1930. 2008. (ENG., Illus.). 240p. 89.00 (978-0-7190-7607-7(2)) Manchester Univ. Pr. GBR. Dist: Macmillan.

Jovis, creator. KSV: Kruger Schuberth Vandreike: Buildings & Projects 1990-2008. 2009. (ENG & GER., Illus.). 144p. 60.00 (978-3-939633-46-4(1)) Jovis Verlag GmbH DEU. Dist: D.A.P./Distributed Art Pubs.

—Metropole: Bilden. 2010. (ENG., Illus.). 296p. pap. 55.00 (978-3-86859-070-8(6)) Jovis Verlag GmbH DEU. Dist: D.A.P./Distributed Art Pubs.

Kahler, Gert, ed. GMP - GMP von Gerkan, Marg und Partner Architects: Villas Living in Exceptional Locations, 1 vol., Vol. 4. 2007. (ENG & GER., Illus.). 208p. pap. 35.00 (978-3-936314-47-2(0)) Jovis Verlag GmbH DEU. Dist: D.A.P./Distributed Art Pubs.

Kaltwasser, Martin & Kobberling, Folke. Hold It! The Art & Architecture of Public Space: Bricolage Resistance Resources Aesthetics. 2009. (ENG., Illus.). 240p. pap. 39.95 (978-3-86859-029-6(3)) Jovis Verlag GmbH DEU. Dist: D.A.P./Distributed Art Pubs.

Kanz, Roland & Wiener, Jurgen. Architekturführer Düsseldorf. (GER.). (978-3-496-01232-0(3)) Reimer, Dietrich.

Kapfinger, Otto. Wratzfeld, Kopf: Kindergarten Koblach. (Illus.). 76p. (978-3-7757-0880-7(4)) Hatje Cantz Verlag GmbH & Co KG DEU. Dist: D.A.P./Distributed Art Pubs.

Kappel, Kai. Dachau Concentration Camp Memorial Site: Religious Memorials. 2010. (ENG.). 96p. pap. 10.00 (978-3-422-02238-6(4)) Deutscher Kunstverlag GmbH DEU. Dist: Independent Pubs. Group.

Kessler, Katrin. The Buildings of the Jewish Community in Schwedt/Oder. 2008. (ENG.). 64p. pap. 14.95 (978-3-86568-314-4(2)) Imhof, Michael Verlag GmbH & Co. KG DEU. Dist: Independent Pubs. Group.

Kleihues + Kleihues Staff, contrib. by. Josef Paul Kleihues: Galeria Kaufhof Berlin Alexanderplatz, 1 vol. 2007. (ENG., Illus.). 64p. pap. 22.00 (978-3-939633-26-6(7)) Jovis Verlag GmbH DEU. Dist: D.A.P./Distributed Art Pubs.

Klein, Caroline. Superlative Emirates: The New Dimension of Urban Design, 1 vol. 2012. (SPA, GER & ENG.). 240p. 70.00 (978-3-942597-08-1(X)) DAAB Media Gmbh DEU. Dist: Innovative Logistics.

—Zeitgeist: Modern Architecture & Design in Germany, 1 vol. 2012. (SPA, GER & ENG.). 312p. 75.00 (978-3-942597-11-1(X)) DAAB Media Gmbh DEU. Dist: Innovative Logistics.

Knapp, Gottfried. Ernst von Ihne / Heinz Tesar, Bode-Museum, Berlin 2008. (Opus Ser.). (ENG & GER., Illus.). 72p. 52.00 (978-3-932565-63-2(0)) Edition Axel Menges GmbH DEU. Dist: National Bk. Network.

Knebel, Victoria. Preserve & Rebuild: Dresden During the Transformations of 1989-1990 Architecture, Citizens Initiatives & Local Identities. 2007. (Illus.). 203p. pap. 46.95 (978-0-8204-8742-7(2)) Lang, Peter Publishing, Inc.

Koenig, Karl, photos by. Fragments: Architecture of the Holocaust: an Artist's Journey Through the Camps. 2012. (ENG., Illus.). 154p. 75.00 **(978-1-934491-35-5(7))** Fresco Fine Art Pubns., LLC.

Koerner, Stefan. Amerikanische Landschaften: J. B. Jackson in der deutschen Rezeption. 2010. (Sozialgeographische Bibliothek Ser.). (GER., Illus.). 111p. (C). pap. 37.00 (978-3-515-09665-2(5)) Steiner, Franz Verlag Wiesbaden GmbH DEU. Dist: Brown, David Bk. Co., The.

Kretschmar-Joehnk, Corinna. Creating Hospitality Design. 2009. (ENG & GER., Illus.). 224p. 49.95 (978-3-03768-039-1(3), Braun Publish,Csi) Continental Sales, Inc.

Landesamt fur Denkmalpflege Rheinland-Pfalz/Abteil, ed. Baudenkmäler in Rheinland-Pfalz 2006-2008. 2010. (GER.). 168p. 45.00 (978-3-8053-4265-0(9)) Zabern, Philipp von Verlag, GmbH DEU. Dist: Brown, David Bk. Co., The.

Landschaftsarchitekten, Bund Deutscher, ed. Grüner Wohnen / Green Living: Zeitgenössische Deutsche Landschaftsarchitektur / German Contemporary Landscape Architecture. 2011. (GER & ENG.). 176p. 64.95 (978-3-0346-0755-1(5)) Birkhauser Verlag AG CHE. Dist: Actar Birkhauser Distribution.

Lang, Karlheinz, et al. Kulturdenkmäler in Hessen. Landkreis Gießen III: Die Gemeinden Allendorf (Lumda), Biebertal, Heuchelheim, Lollar, Staufenberg und Wettenberg. 2008. (GER., Illus.). (978-3-8062-2177-0(4)) Theiss, Konrad Verlag, GmbH.

Lehmann-Kopp, Dorothee, ed. Werner Ruhnau: Der Raum, das Spiel und die Künste. 2008. (ENG., Illus.). 260p. pap. 55.00 (978-3-939633-13-6(5)) Jovis Verlag GmbH DEU. Dist: D.A.P./Distributed Art Pubs.

Leitner, Bernhard. P. U. L. S. E. Raume der Zeit/Spaces in Time. 2008. (GER & ENG., Illus.). 208p. 60.00 (978-3-7757-2047-2(2)) Hatje Cantz Verlag GmbH & Co KG DEU. Dist: D.A.P./Distributed Art Pubs.

Lepik, Andres, text. Metropol Parasol. 2011. (ENG & SPA., Illus.). 160p. pap., pap. 45.00 **(978-3-7757-2837-9(6))** Hatje Cantz Verlag GmbH & Co KG DEU. Dist: D.A.P./Distributed Art Pubs.

Liebl-Osborne, Petra. Gestaltungslehren in der Architektenausbildung: An Technischen Universitaten und Hochschulen in Westdeutschland, 1945-1995. (Europaische Hochschulschriften Ser.). (GER., Illus.). 592p. 73.95 (978-3-631-36307-2(9)) Lang, Peter Publishing, Inc.

Lloyd Morgan, Conway. Franken Architekten: spatial narratives. 2008. (GER & ENG.). 164p. 76.00 (978-3-89986-105-1(1), Avedition Gmbh,Csi) Continental Sales, Inc.

Loock, Ulrich, ed. Schütte, Thomas.Public/Political. 2012. (ENG., Illus.). 240p. pap. 59.95 **(978-3-86560-414-9(5))** Verlag der Buchhandlung Walther Konig DEU. Dist: D.A.P./Distributed Art Pubs.

Lupfer, Gilbert, et al, contrib. by. Architekturführer Dresden. (GER & ENG., Illus.). xxxviii, 230p. (978-3-496-01179-8(3)) Reimer, Dietrich.

M#xE4;ckler, Christoph. Opernturm Christoph Maeckle. 2011. (ENG., Illus.). 96p. 30.00 (978-3-86859-048-7(X)) Jovis Verlag GmbH DEU. Dist: D.A.P./Distributed Art Pubs.

Maciuika, John V. Before the Bauhaus: Architecture, Politics, & the German State, 1890-1920. 2008. (Modern Architecture & Cultural Identity Ser.). (ENG., Illus.). 402p. pap. 41.99 (978-0-521-72822-5(3)) Cambridge Univ. Pr.

Manso, Iris. Gott dem Erloser und den Gottesdiensten der Reformierten Gewidmet 1753: Die spatbarocke Evangelisch-Reformierte Kirche in Gottingen. 2009. (GER., Illus.). 248p. (C). pap. 68.00 (978-3-525-28000-3(9)) Vandenhoeck & Ruprecht GmbH & Co. KG DEU. Dist: ISD.

Mauer, Benedikt. Der Fürst und seine Stadt: Bauten aus der Jan-Wellem-Zeit in Düsseldorf. 2008. (GER., Illus.). 215p. (978-3-7700-1302-9(6)) Droste Verlag GmbH.

Mehlhorn, Dieter J. Architekturfuehrer Kiel. (GER., Illus.). 206p. (978-3-496-01165-1(3)) Reimer, Dietrich.

Mersch, Margit. Das ehemalige Zisterzienserinnenkloster Vallis Dei in Brenkhausen im 13. und 14. Jahrhundert. 2008. (GER., Illus.). 343p. (C). 53.00 (978-3-8053-3884-4(8)) Zabern, Philipp von Verlag, GmbH DEU. Dist: Brown, David Bk. Co., The.

Meuser, Natascha & Meuser, Philipp. Meuser Architekten: Bauten und Projekte 1995-2010, 1 vol. 2011. (ENG.). 700p. 64.95 **(978-3-86922-150-2(X))** DOM Pubs. DEU. Dist: Innovative Logistics.

Meuser, Philipp. Schlossplatz Eins. Schlossplatz On: European School of Managment & Technology, 1 vol. 2010. (GER, ENG & MUL., Illus.). 160p. 49.95 **(978-3-938666-03-6(X))** DOM Pubs. DEU. Dist: Innovative Logistics.

Meuser, Philipp & Schirmer, Christoph. Hospital Architecture: Specialist Clinics & Medical Departments. 2007. (Illus.). 304p. (978-981-245-494-2(2)) Page One Publishing.

Moleskine. Moleskine Inspiration & Process in Architecture. 2012. (ENG., Illus.). 272p. 39.95 (978-88-6613-002-4(8)) Moleskine ITA. Dist: Hachette Bk. Group.

Multiple. Architekturführer Münster: Architectural Guide. 2009. (Architectural Guides). (ENG.). 320p. pap. 38.00 (978-3-496-01276-4(5), Art Stock Bks. Ltd/Csi) Continental Sales, Inc.

—München / Munich 1: 11 000 / 1: 22 000: München, Allianz-Arena, Messe München, München City, München Großraum, Voralpenland. 2009. (Architectural Guides). (ENG.). 320p. pap. 38.00 (978-3-496-01359-4(1), Art Stock Bks. Ltd/Csi) Continental Sales, Inc.

Naumann, Stephen. Solving the Stadtschloss Dilemma - What an Old Fatade Will Say about New Berlin. 2007. 84p. per. (978-3-8364-2178-2(X)) VDM Verlag Dr. Mueller e.K.

Nickl-Weller, Christine & Nickl, Hans. The New Hospital. 2007. (Illus.). 464p. (978-981-245-325-9(3)) Page One Publishing.

Niedenthal, Clemens, ed. Stations in Germany. 2009. (ENG & GER., Illus.). 174p. 39.95 (978-3-939633-47-1(X)) Jovis Verlag GmbH DEU. Dist: D.A.P./Distributed Art Pubs.

Nohbauer, Hans F. Munich: City of the Arts. 2007. (Illus.). 346p. 99.00 (978-3-7774-6250-9(0)) Hirmer Verlag GmbH DEU. Dist: Perseus-PGW.

Otto, Frei & Songel, Juan Maria. A Conversation with Frei Otto. 2010. (ENG., Illus.). 96p. pap. 19.95 (978-1-56898-884-9(2)) Princeton Architectural Pr.

Pabsch, Matthias. Zweimal Weltstadt: Architektur & Staedtebau am Potsdamer Platz. (GER., Illus.). 135p. (978-3-496-01191-0(2)) Reimer, Dietrich.

Palutzki, Joachim. Architektur in der DDR. (GER., Illus.). 450p. (978-3-496-01222-1(6)) Reimer, Dietrich.

Pawly, Ronald. Hitler's Chancellery: A Palace to Last a Thousand Years. 2009. (ENG., Illus.). 192p. 49.95 (978-1-84797-091-6(5), 1847970915) Crowood Pr., Ltd. GBR. Dist: MBI Distribution Services/Quayside Distribution.

Prix, Wolf D., ed. Form = Raum Netz / Form = Space Net: 10. Internationale Architektur Biennale Venedig. la Biennale di Venezia 2006. 10th International Exhibition of Architecture. la Biennale di Venezia 2006. 2008. (Illus.). 140p. pap. 39.95 (978-3-211-34363-0(6), 3211343636) Springer.

Puhle, Matthias. Aufbruch in die Gotik, 2 vols. 2009. (GER., Illus.). 1124p. (C). 135.00 (978-3-8053-4062-5(1)) Zabern, Philipp von Verlag, GmbH DEU. Dist: Brown, David Bk. Co., The.

Pump-Uhlmann, Holger, ed. From Department Store to Stadtgalerie: Buildings for Retail Trade. 2011. (ENG., Illus.). 144p. 60.00 (978-3-86859-105-7(2)) Jovis Verlag GmbH DEU. Dist: D.A.P./Distributed Art Pubs.

Quiring, Claudia. Ernst May: 1886-1970. 2011. (ENG., Illus.). 272p. pap. 60.00 **(978-3-7913-5132-2(X))** Prestel Publishing.

Rave, Rolf. Modern Architecture in Berlin. 2009. (ENG., Illus.). 280p. pap. 49.90 (978-3-936681-29-1(5)) Edition Axel Menges GmbH DEU. Dist: National Bk. Network.

Regionalverband Ruhr Staff, contrib. by. Unter freiem Himmel / Under the Open Sky: Emscher Landschaftspark / Emscher Landscape Park. 2010. (ENG., Illus.). 232p. 69.95 (978-3-0346-0266-2(9)) Birkhauser Verlag AG CHE. Dist: Actar Birkhauser Distribution.

Rettberg, Britta von. Freising: Stadttopographie und Denkmalpflege. 2009. (GER., Illus.). 336p. (978-3-86568-354-0(1)) Imhof, Michael Verlag GmbH & Co. KG.

Richter, Jana, ed. The Tourist City Berlin: Tourism & Architecture. 2010. (ENG., Illus.). 368p. pap. 39.95 (978-3-03768-058-2(X), Braun Publish,Csi) Continental Sales, Inc.

Richters, Christian, photos by. Coop Himmelb(l)au, BMW-Welt, Munchen. 2009. (GER & ENG., Illus.). 60p. 49.00 (978-3-932565-66-3(5)) Edition Axel Menges GmbH DEU. Dist: National Bk. Network.

Riemenschneider, Tilman, et al. Tilman Riemenschneider, 2 vols. 2007. (GER., Illus.). 656p. pap. 130.00 (978-3-7954-1563-1(2)) Schnell und Steiner GmbH, Verlag DEU. Dist: Independent Pubs. Group.

Riepl, Peter & Riepl, Gabriele. Riepl / Riepl / Architekten: Peter Riepl, Gabriele Riepl. 2007. (Illus.). 287p. (978-3-211-33986-2(8), 3211339868) Actar Birkhauser Distribution.

Robeck, Ulrike & Robeck. Die älteren Hallen des Bochumer Vereins als Zweckbauten und Denkmale der Eisen- und Stahlindustrie. 2010. (Denkmalpflege und Forschung in Westfalen Ser.). (GER.). (C). 33.00 **(978-3-8053-4279-7(9))** Zabern, Philipp von Verlag, GmbH DEU. Dist: Brown, David Bk. Co., The.

Romba, Katherine. Iron Construction & Cultural Discourse. 2008. 180p. pap. (978-3-8364-6570-0(1)) VDM Verlag Dr. Mueller e.K.

Rykwert, Joseph, et al, contrib. by. Neues Museum Berlin: By David Chipperfield Architects in Collaboration with Julian Harrap. 2010. (ENG., Illus.). 288p. pap. 65.00 (978-3-86560-704-1(7)) Verlag der Buchhandlung Walther Konig DEU. Dist: D.A.P./Distributed Art Pubs.

Sachs, Harry & Hoefner, Franz, eds. Piccolo Mondo. 2009. (978-3-89955-248-5(2)) Die Gestalten Verlag.

Sachsse, Rolf. Raumbilder Bildräume: Architekten fotografieren. 2009. (GER., Illus.). 116p. (978-3-422-06902-2(X)) Deutscher Kunstverlag GmbH.

Sack, Manfred. Robert-Bosch-Krankenhaus, Stuttgart: Opus 68. 2010. (ENG., Illus.). 120p. 69.00 (978-3-932565-68-7(1)) Edition Axel Menges GmbH DEU. Dist: National Bk. Network.

—Sonwik, Flensburg. 2007. (Opus Ser.). (GER & ENG., Illus.). 60p. 39.90 (978-3-932565-61-8(4)) Edition Axel Menges GmbH DEU. Dist: National Bk. Network.

Santifaller, Enrico, et al. Transform: The Revitalization of Buildings: KSP Engel und Zimmerman Architekten. 2008. (GER & ENG., Illus.). 160p. 49.95 (978-3-7913-4032-6(8)) Prestel Publishing.

Sauerbruch, Matthias & Hutton, Louisa. Sauerbruch Hutton: Colour in Architecture. 2006. (Illus.). 331p. 79.00 (978-3-03778-083-1(5), 3037780835) Lars Muller Pubs. CHE. Dist: Springer.

Schache, Wolfgang & Sconci, Maria Selene. An Italian Palazzo in Germany: The Embassy in Berlin. 2007. (ENG., Illus.). 124p. 70.00 (978-88-422-1483-0(3)) Allemandi, Umberto & Co. GBR. Dist: Antique Collectors' Club.

Schatzke, Andreas. Dietrich & Dietrich Max-Plank-Institutfur Wissenschaftsgeschichte, Berlin: Opus 74. 2010. (GER & ENG., Illus.). 60p. 49.00 (978-3-932565-74-8(6)) Edition Axel Menges GmbH DEU. Dist: National Bk. Network.

Scheer, Thorsten, ed. Josef Paul Kleihues Volume 1: Works 1966-1980. 2008. (ENG., Illus.). 288p. 100.00 (978-3-7757-2087-8(1)) Hatje Cantz Verlag GmbH & Co KG DEU. Dist: D.A.P./Distributed Art Pubs.

Schenk, Andreas. Architekturfuehrer Mannheim. (GER.). xi, 279p. *(978-3-496-01201-6(3))* Reimer, Dietrich.

Schlimme, Hermann & Sickel, Lothar, eds. Ordnung und Wandel: in der römischen Architektur der Frühen Neuzeit - Kunsthistorische Studien zu Ehren von Christof Thoenes. 2010. (Roemische studien der bibliotheca Hertziana Ser.). (GER., Illus.). 254p. (C). 140.00 *(978-3-7774-2301-2(7))* Hirmer Verlag GmbH DEU. Dist: Brown, David Bk. Co., The.

Schlorhaufer, Bettina & Sudtiroler Kunstlerbund, eds. Walter Dietl, Arnold Gapp, Werner Tscholl: Drei Vinschgauer Architekten Im Portrait/Ritratto Di Tre Architetti Venostani/Portraits of Three Val Venosta Architects. 2007. (Illus.). 311p. *(978-3-211-32767-8(3)*, 3211327673) Actar Birkhauser Distribution.

Schmal, Peter Cachola. Ready for Take-Off: Aktuelle deutsche Exportarchitektur. 2008. (ENG., Illus.). 208p. 60.00 *(978-3-7757-2146-2(0))* Hatje Cantz Verlag GmbH & Co KG DEU. Dist: D.A.P./Distributed Art Pubs.

Schmal, Peter, ed. HPP Architects. 2009. (ENG., Illus.). 240p. 75.00 *(978-3-7757-2307-7(2))* Hatje Cantz Verlag GmbH & Co KG DEU. Dist: D.A.P./Distributed Art Pubs.

Schmal, Peter & van Berkel, Ben, eds. The Pavilion. 2010. (ENG & GER., Illus.). 192p. pap. 40.00 *(978-3-7757-2494-4(X))* Hatje Cantz Verlag GmbH & Co KG DEU. Dist: D.A.P./Distributed Art Pubs.

Schmal, Peter Cachola. Schneider + Schumacher. Schmal, Peter Cachola et al, eds. 2012. (ENG., Illus.). 240p. 60.00 ***(978-3-7913-5147-6(8))*** Prestel Publishing.

Schmal, Peter Cachola, frwd. Structure in Mind: The Architecture of Burkhard Pahl & Monika Weber-Pahl. 2010. (ENG., Illus.). 240p. 60.00 *(978-3-86859-016-6(1))* Jovis Verlag GmbH DEU. Dist: D.A.P./Distributed Art Pubs.

Schmal, Peter Cachola, et al. Deutsches Architektur Jahrbuch 2011/12: German Architecture Annual 2011/12. 2011. (GER & ENG., Illus.). 212p. pap. 49.95 ***(978-3-7913-5135-3(4))*** Prestel Publishing.

Schneider, Gregor, photos by. White Torture: Gregor Schneider, 1 vol. 2007. (ENG., Illus.). 132p. pap. 37.00 *(978-3-86560-216-9(9))* Verlag der Buchhandlung Walther Konig DEU. Dist: D.A.P./Distributed Art Pubs.

Schneider, Romana. Junge Architekten Aus Deutschland: Auslandsbeziehungen. 2008. (GER., Illus.). 192p. *(978-3-938666-76-0(5))*; *(978-3-938666-77-7(3))* DOM Pubs.

—Junge Architekten Aus Deutschland: Auslandsbeziehungen, 2 vols. 2009. (GER & ENG., Illus.). 192p. pap. 49.95 *(978-3-938666-78-4(1))* DOM Pubs. DEU. Dist: Innovative Logistics.

Scholtz, Andrea. Models: Designculture in Germany. 2008. (GER & ENG.). 84p. 32.00 *(978-3-89986-106-8(X)*, Avedition Gmbh,Csi) Continental Sales, Inc.

Schöntube, Ulrich. Emporenbilderzyklen in der Mark Brandenburg: Ein Beitrag zum lutherischen Bildprogramm des 16. -18. Jahrhunderts. 2008. 610p. pap. 124.95 *(978-3-631-56861-3(4))* Lang, Peter GmbH, Europaischer Verlag der Wissenschaften DEU. Dist: Lang, Peter.

Sigel, Paul & Rennison, Lucinda. Architekturführer Potsdam. Architectural Guide to Potsdam. 2009. (Architectural Guides). (GER & ENG., Illus.). 320p. pap. 38.00 *(978-3-496-01325-9(7)*, Art Stock Bks. Ltd/Csi) Continental Sales, Inc.

Skalecki, Georg & Bremen, Rathaus. Rathaus Bremen: With an introduction by Georg Skalecki & photographs by Christian Richters. 2008. (ENG., Illus.). 72p. 59.00 *(978-3-932565-69-4(X))* Edition Axel Menges GmbH DEU. Dist: National Bk. Network.

Sobek, Werner. Werner Sobek: Light Works. 2008. (ENG & GER.). 156p. 60.00 *(978-3-89986-087-0(X)*, Avedition Gmbh,Csi) Continental Sales, Inc.

Sommer, Martin & Sternagel, Thomas. EinSparHaus: Energieeffiziente Architektur. 2009. (GER., Illus.). 163p. pap. *(978-3-86859-013-5(7))* Jovis Verlag GmbH.

Speer, Albert. Infiltration: How Heinrich Himmler Schemed to Build an SS Industrial Empire. 2010.Tr. of Sklavenstaat: meine Auseinandersetzungen mit der SS. (ENG., Illus.). 402p. pap. 29.95 *(978-4-87187-877-7(5))* Ishi Pr. International.

Steidle, Otto & Gagern, Verena Von. Architectural. (Illus.). 144p. 45.00 *(978-3-923922-19-2(1))* Nazraeli Pr. DEU. Dist: D.A.P./Distributed Art Pubs.

Stephan, Regina, ed. Joseph Maria Olbrich. 2010. (ENG., Illus.). 64p. 30.00 *(978-3-7757-2551-4(2))* Hatje Cantz Verlag GmbH & Co KG DEU. Dist: D.A.P./Distributed Art Pubs.

Stimmann, Hans & Albers, Bernd. Berliner Altstadt: Von der DDR-Staatsmitte zur Stadtmitte. 2009. (GER., Illus.). 160p. *(978-3-938666-27-2(7))* DOM Pubs.

Stratigakos, Despina. A Women's Berlin: Building the Modern City. 2008. (Illus.). 256p. 75.00 *(978-0-8166-5322-5(4))*; pap. 24.95 *(978-0-8166-5323-2(2))* Univ. of Minnesota Pr.

Stuler, Anna. Hilmer & Sattler und Albrecht. Architektur und Städtebau / Architecture & Urban Planning: 2004-2010. 2010. (Illus.). 240p. 75.00 *(978-3-7913-4479-9(X))* Prestel Publishing.

Tacke, Heinfried, ed. Berlin Architecture & Design S. 2006. 192p. pap. 14.95 *(978-3-8327-9155-1(8))* teNeues Publishing Co.

Taylor, Brandon. The Nazification of Art: Art, Design, Architecture, Music & Film in the Third Reich. (Illus.). 280p. pap. 24.95 *(978-0-9506783-9-9(2))* Winchester Schl. of Art Pr. GBR. Dist: Paul & Co. Pubs. Consortium, Inc.

teNeues. AAD Berlin: Art Architecture Design. 2010. (Illus.). 168p. pap. 12.95 *(978-3-8327-9433-0(6))* teNeues Publishing Co.

Tiedeke, Thorsten & Vorbeck, Wolfgang. Architekturführer Frankfurt am Main: An Architectural Guide. 2009. (Architectural Guides). (ENG.). 320p. pap. 38.00 *(978-3-496-01236-8(6)*, Art Stock Bks. Ltd/Csi) Continental Sales, Inc.

Tietz, Jurgen & Schneider, Katja. Nieto Sobejano: Das Neue Kunstmuseum in Halle. 2008. (GER., Illus.). 80p. *(978-3-7774-5075-9(8))* Hirmer Verlag GmbH.

Tonon, Benedict. Benedict Tonon: Persepectivization of Architecture. 2010. 272p. 68.00 *(978-3-8030-0712-4(7))* Wasmuth, Ernst J. Verlag GmbH & Co. DEU. Dist: D.A.P./Distributed Art Pubs.

Ullmann, H. F., ed. Berlin. 2009. 480p. pap. 19.99 *(978-0-8416-1015-6(0))* American Map Corp.

Ungers, O. M. Morphologie: City Metaphors. 2011. (GER & ENG., Illus.). 116p. pap. 29.95 ***(978-3-86560-946-5(5))*** Verlag der Buchhandlung Walther Konig DEU. Dist: D.A.P./Distributed Art Pubs.

Urbach, Henry. J. Mayer H. Steingraber, Cristina Ines, ed. 2009. (ENG., Illus.). 240p. 75.00 *(978-3-7757-2223-0(8))* Hatje Cantz Verlag GmbH & Co KG DEU. Dist: D.A.P./Distributed Art Pubs.

Urban, Florian. Neo-Historical East Berlin: Architecture & Urban Design in the German Democratic Republic, 1970-1990. 2009. (Ashgate Studies in Architecture Ser.). (Illus.). 294p. 124.95 *(978-0-7546-7616-4(1))* Ashgate Publishing Co.

Visscher, Jochen, ed. Berlin Modernism. 2008. (GER, SPA & ENG., Illus.). 96p. 19.95 *(978-3-939633-44-0(5))* Jovis Verlag GmbH DEU. Dist: D.A.P./Distributed Art Pubs.

Voigt, Wolfgang & May, Roland, eds. Paul Bonatz 1877-1956. 2011. (ENG., Illus.). 320p. 75.00 *(978-3-8030-0729-2(1))* Wasmuth, Ernst J. Verlag GmbH & Co. DEU. Dist: D.A.P./Distributed Art Pubs.

Vollmer, Wolfgang, et al. City / Image / Cologne: Photographs from 1880 until Today, 1 vol. 2007. (GER & ENG., Illus.). 176p. 55.00 *(978-3-86521-582-6(3))* Steidl, Gerhard Druckerei und Verlag DEU. Dist: D.A.P./Distributed Art Pubs.

Von Gerkan, Meinhard & Marg, Volkwin, eds. Von Gerkan, Marg und Partner: Bauten Buildings. 2007. (GER & ENG., Illus.). 575p. 99.00 *(978-3-7913-3811-8(0))* Prestel Publishing.

Von Halasz, Joachim, ed. Hitler's Buildings - a Photo Book - Volume 1 - First Published in 1939 As 'das Bauen Im Neuen Reich - Erster Band' 2009. 176p. pap. *(978-1-905742-15-8(0))* Foxley Books.

—Hitler's Buildings - a Photo Book - Volume 2 - First Published in 1943 As 'das Bauen Im Neuen Reich - Zweiter Band' 2009. 176p. pap. *(978-1-905742-16-5(9))* Foxley Books.

Wallpaper Magazine Editors, ed. Berlin 2011 - Wallpaper City Guide. 3rd ed. 2011. (ENG., Illus.). 128p. pap. 9.95 *(978-0-7148-6087-9(5))* Phaidon Pr., Inc.

Wallpaper Magazine Editors, ed. Wallpaper City Guide Munich 2012. 2nd ed. 2012. (ENG., Illus.). 128p. pap. 9.95 ***(978-0-7148-6306-1(8))*** Phaidon Pr. Ltd. GBR. Dist: Hachette Bk. Group.

Wallroth, Martin, ed. Avantgarde in Their Day/Ihrer Zeit: Classic Designs by Schliephacke & Ssymmank/Die Design-Klassiker Schliephacke und Ssymmank, 1 vol. 2006. (ENG & GER., Illus.). 96p. per. 29.95 *(978-3-936314-65-6(9))* Jovis Verlag GmbH DEU. Dist: D.A.P./Distributed Art Pubs.

Warhaftig, Myra. They Laid the Foundation: Lives & Works of German-Speaking Jewish Architects in Palestine 1918-1948, 1 vol. Lerner, Andrea, tr. from GER. 2nd ed. 2007. (ENG., Illus.). 416p. 40.00 *(978-3-8030-0676-9(7))* Wasmuth, Ernst J. Verlag GmbH & Co. DEU. Dist: D.A.P./Distributed Art Pubs.

Welzbacher, Christian & text. The Architecture of Democracy. 2009. (ENG., Illus.). 444p. 75.00 *(978-3-7757-2356-5(0))* Hatje Cantz Verlag GmbH & Co KG DEU. Dist: D.A.P./Distributed Art Pubs.

Werquet, Jan. Historismus und Repräsentation: Die Baupolitik Friedrich Wilhelms IV. in der preußischen Rheinprovinz. 2010. (GER., Illus.). 554p. *(978-3-422-06923-7(2))* Deutscher Kunstverlag GmbH.

Weszkalnys, Gisa. Berlin, Alexanderplatz: Transforming Place in a Unified Germany. 2010. (S&P Ser.). (Illus.). 224p. 60.00 *(978-1-84545-723-5(4))* Berghahn Bks., Inc.

Whyte, Iain Boyd. Bruno Taut & the Architecture of Activism. 2010. (Cambridge Urban & Architectural Studies). (ENG.). 296p. pap. 42.00 *(978-0-521-13183-4(9))* Cambridge Univ. Pr.

Wietzorek, Paul. Historic Berlin: Pictures tell the story. 2008. (ENG.). 192p. 14.95 *(978-3-86568-353-3(3)*, Art Stock Bks. Ltd/Csi) Continental Sales, Inc.

Woerner, Martin & Lupfer, Gilbert. Stuttgart: Ein Architekturfuehrer. (GER.). 261p. *(978-3-496-01157-6(2))* Reimer, Dietrich.

Woerner, Martin, et al. Architekturführer Berlin. 6th ed. (GER., Illus.). 540p. *(978-3-496-01211-5(0))* Reimer, Dietrich.

—Architekturführer Hannover: Architectural Guide. Zweisprachige Ausgabe. Deutsch / Englisch. Mit 350 Objekten. Architekten-, Baugattungs-, Straßen- und hist. Register. Mit allen Expo-Bauten und ÖPNV-Plan. 2009. (Architectural Guides). (GER & ENG.). 320p. pap. 38.00 *(978-3-496-01210-8(2)*, Art Stock Bks. Ltd/Csi) Continental Sales, Inc.

Wolf, Connie, et al. Daniel Libeskind & the Contemporary Jewish Museum: New Jewish Architecture from Berlin to San Francisco. 2008. (ENG., Illus.). 128p. 45.00 *(978-0-8478-3165-4(5))* Rizzoli International Pubns., Inc.

Zachau, Reinhard K., et al. Topography & Literature. Berlin & Modernism. 2009. (Deutschsprachige Gegenwartsliteratur und Medien Ser.). (ENG & GER., Illus.). 187p. (C). 53.00 *(978-3-89971-468-5(7))* Vandenhoeck & Ruprecht GmbH & Co. KG DEU. Dist: ISD.

Zeisser, Boris & Lammers, Maartje. 24H Architecture. McCulloch, Janelle, ed. 2007. (Neo Architecture Ser.). (ENG., Illus.). 124p. 49.50 *(978-1-920744-84-7(3))* Images Publishing Group AUS. Dist: National Bk. Network.

Zeller, Thomas. Driving Germany: The Landscape of the German Autobahn, 1930-1970. 2006. (Illus.). 298p. (C). 85.00 *(978-1-84545-309-1(3))* Berghahn Bks., Inc.

Zepter, Tobias, text. MODERSOHN & FREIESLEBEN Architekten: Das Leben der Dinge. The Life of Things. 2010. (ENG., Illus.). 176p. 55.00 *(978-3-7757-2487-6(7))* Hatje Cantz Verlag GmbH & Co KG DEU. Dist: D.A.P./Distributed Art Pubs.

Zimmerman, Claire. Ludwig Mies Van der Rohe. Gossel, Peter, ed. 25th ed. 2009. (25 Ser.). (ENG., Illus.). 96p. 14.99 *(978-3-8365-1316-6(1))* TASCHEN DEU. Dist: Ingram Pub. Services.

Zinsmeiste, Annett. Update! 90 Jahre Bauhaus - und nun? 2011. (ENG & GER., Illus.). 176p. pap. 39.95 ***(978-3-86859-102-6(8))*** Jovis Verlag GmbH DEU. Dist: D.A.P./Distributed Art Pubs.

ARCHITECTURE—GREAT BRITAIN

see also Architecture, Domestic—Great Britain

AA Publishing. Exploring Britain's Churches & Chapels: Inspirational Journeys of Discovery. 2011. (ENG., Illus.). 256p. 39.95 ***(978-0-7495-7074-3(1))*** Automobile Assn. GBR. Dist: Independent Pubs. Group.

Abrahams, Tim. Ideas Exchange: The Collaborative Studio of Hawkins Brown. 2010. (ENG., Illus.). 208p. 84.95 *(978-3-0346-0231-0(6))* Birkhauser Verlag AG CHE. Dist: Actar Birkhauser Distribution.

Acland, Henry W. The Oxford Museum. 2010. (ENG., Illus.). 126p. pap. 10.00 ***(978-1-906267-19-3(7))*** Euston Grove Pr. GBR. Dist: Lightning Source, Inc.

Airs, Malcolm & Tyack, Geoffrey. The Renaissance Villa in Britain 1500-1700. 2007. (Illus.). 276p. *(978-1-904965-13-8(X))* Spire Bks. Ltd.

Allen, J. R. L. Building a Victorian Country Church: An Historical Archaeology of St. Mary the Virgin, Stratfield Mortimer, Berkshire. 2007. (Bar Ser.). (Illus.). 140p. (C). 77.50 *(978-1-4073-0262-1(0))* British Archaeological Reports Ltd. GBR. Dist: Brown, David Bk. Co., The.

Allinson, Kenneth. Architects & Architecture of London. 2008. (ENG., Illus.). 448p. pap. 32.95 *(978-0-7506-8337-1(6))* Routledge.

—London's Contemporary Architecture: An Explorer's Guide. 5th rev. ed. 2009. (ENG., Illus.). 384p. pap. 32.95 *(978-1-85617-801-3(3))* Routledge.

Anderson, Christy. Inigo Jones & the Classical Tradition. (ENG.). 2010. 294p. pap. 36.99 *(978-0-521-18131-0(3))* 2006. (Illus.). 292p. 115.00 *(978-0-521-82027-1(8))* Cambridge Univ. Pr.

Anderson, Will. Diary of an Eco-Builder. 2006. (ENG., Illus.). 256p. pap. 30.00 *(978-1-903998-79-3(4))* Green Bks. GBR. Dist: Chelsea Green Publishing.

Ansari, Humayun, ed. The Making of the East London Mosque, 1910-1951: Minutes of the London Mosque Fund & East London Mosque Trust Ltd. 2011. (Camden Fifth Ser.). (ENG.). 360p. (C). 80.00 ***(978-1-107-01492-3(1))*** Cambridge Univ. Pr.

Antram, Nicholas, et al. Brighton & Hove. 2008. (Pevsner Architectural Guides). (ENG., Illus.). 256p. pap. 40.00 *(978-0-300-12661-7(1))* Yale Univ. Pr.

Arciszewska. Architecture of Distinction. 2009. (Illus.). 304p. pap. 46.95 *(978-0-415-45183-3(3))* Routledge.

Arciszewska, Barbara. Architecture of Distinction. 2009. (Illus.). 304p. 165.00 *(978-0-415-45182-6(5))* Routledge.

Arnold, Anthea. Charleston Saved, 1979-1989. 2010. (ENG., Illus.). 144p. 39.95 *(978-0-7090-9018-2(8))* Hale, Robert Ltd. GBR. Dist: Independent Pubs. Group.

Arnold, Dana. Shaping London, Shaping Lives: Hospitals As Agents of Change in the Metropolis, 1700-1840. 2008. (Illus.). 208p. pap. 46.95 *(978-0-415-32516-5(1))* Routledge.

Arup Associates. Unified Design. Brislin, Paul, ed. 2008. (ENG., Illus.). 208p. 55.00 *(978-0-470-72331-9(9)*, Wiley) Wiley, John & Sons, Inc.

Ashley, Peter. Built for Britain: Bridges to Beach Huts. 2009. (ENG., Illus.). 168p. pap. 19.99 *(978-0-470-74595-3(9)*, Wiley) Wiley, John & Sons, Inc.

—Cross Country: English Buildings & Landscape from Countryside to Coast. 2011. (ENG.). 240p. 45.00 *(978-0-470-68611-9(1)*, Wiley) Wiley, John & Sons, Inc.

—More London Peculiars: Being Curious Corners of a Capital City. 2007. (ENG., Illus.). 120p. (C). pap. 31.95 *(978-1-85074-999-8(X))* English Heritage GBR. Dist: Brown, David Bk. Co., The.

Badeslade, J., et al. Vitruvius Britannicus. 2009. (Dover Architecture Ser.). (ENG., Illus.). 304p. pap. 24.95 *(978-0-486-46890-7(9))* Dover Pubns., Inc.

—1739 & 1767-71 Eds., Vol. 2. 60.95 *(978-0-405-09045-5(5))* Ayer Co. Pubs., Inc.

Baker, Geoffrey Howard. The Architecture of James Sterling & His Partners James Gowan & Michael Wilford: A Study of Architectural Creativity in the Twentieth Century. 2011. (Illus.). 512p. 134.95 *(978-1-4094-0926-7(0))* Ashgate Publishing Co.

Barker, Paul. Freedoms of Suburbia. 2009. (ENG., Illus.). 240p. 40.00 *(978-0-7112-2978-5(3))* Lincoln, Frances Ltd. GBR. Dist: Perseus-PGW.

Barnwell, P. S. & Airs, Malcolm. Houses & the Hearth Tax: The Later Stuart House & Society. Barnwell, P. S., ed. 2006. (CBA Research Report). (Illus.). 202p. pap. 35.00 *(978-1-902771-65-6(6))* Council for British Archaeology GBR. Dist: Brown, David Bk. Co., The.

Bauman, Irena. How to Be a Happy Architect: Bauman Lyons Architects. 2008. (ENG., Illus.). 192p. pap. 39.95 *(978-1-904772-78-1(1))* Black Dog Publishing Ltd. GBR. Dist: Perseus Distribution.

Belcher, Margaret, ed. The Collected Letters of A. W. N. Pugin: Volume 4: 1849-1850. 2012. (Collected Letters of A. W. N. Pugin Ser.). (ENG., Illus.). 748p. 240.00 *(978-0-19-960784-6(2))* Oxford Univ. Pr., Inc.

Bellenger, Dom Aidan, ed. Downside Abbey: An Architectural History. 2012. (ENG., Illus.). 224p. 75.00 *(978-1-85894-542-2(9))* Merrell Pubs. Ltd. GBR. Dist: Perseus Distribution.

Berg, Mary & Jones, Howard. Norman Churches in the Canterbury Diocese. 2009. (ENG., Illus.). 208p. pap. 39.95 *(978-0-7524-4776-6(9))* History Pr. Ltd.,The GBR. Dist: Independent Pubs. Group.

Berman, Alan, ed. Jim Stirling & the Red Trilogy: Three Radical Buildings. 2010. (ENG., Illus.). 128p. 45.00 *(978-0-7112-3144-3(3))* Lincoln, Frances Ltd. GBR. Dist: Perseus-PGW.

Bertram, Mark. Room for Diplomacy: Britain's Diplomatic Buildings Overseas 1800-2000. 2011. (ENG., Illus.). 480p. (C). 90.00 ***(978-1-904965-32-9(6))*** Spire Bks. Ltd. GBR. Dist: Brown, David Bk. Co., The.

Bettley, James & Pevsner, Nikolaus. Essex: The Buildings of England. Pevsner, Nikolaus, ed. 2007. (Pevsner Architectural Guides). (ENG., Illus.). 960p. 85.00 *(978-0-300-11614-4(4))* Yale Univ. Pr.

Black, Alistair, et al. Books, Buildings & Social Engineering: The Past, Present & Future of Early Public Library Buildings in Britain. rev. ed. 2009. (Illus.). 486p. 134.95 *(978-0-7546-7207-4(7))* Ashgate Publishing Co.

Blain, Sophie. Les Terres Cuites Architecturales des Eglises du Haut Moyen Age Dans le Nord-Ouest de la France et le Sud-est de L'Angleterre: Application de la Datation Par Luminescence a Larcheologie du Bati. 2011. (Bar S Ser.). (FRE & ENG., Illus.). 221p. (C). pap. 102.50 *(978-1-4073-0744-2(4))* British Archaeological Reports Ltd. GBR. Dist: Brown, David Bk. Co., The.

Bold, John & Hinchcliffe, Tanis. Discovering London's Buildings: With Twelve Walks. 2009. (ENG., Illus.). 256p. pap. 40.00 *(978-0-7112-2918-1(X))* Lincoln, Frances Ltd. GBR. Dist: Perseus-PGW.

Brandwood, Geoff. The Architecture of Sharpe, Paley & Austin. 2012. (Twentieth-century Architects Ser.). (ENG., Illus.). 272p. (C). 100.00 *(978-1-84802-049-8(X))* English Heritage GBR. Dist: Brown, David Bk. Co., The.

—Living, Leisure & Law: Eight Building Types in England 1800-1914. 2010. (ENG., Illus.). 172p. (C). pap. 35.00 *(978-1-904965-27-5(X))* Spire Bks. Ltd. GBR. Dist: Brown, David Bk. Co., The.

Brodie, Allan. Weymouth's Seaside Heritage. 2008. (Informed Conservation Ser.). (ENG., Illus.). 80p. pap. 16.00 *(978-1-84802-008-5(2))* English Heritage GBR. Dist: Brown, David Bk. Co., The.

Bronstein, Pablo. A Guide to Postmodern Architecture in London. 2008. (ENG., Illus.). 88p. pap. 29.90 *(978-3-86560-173-5(1))* Verlag der Buchhandlung Walther Konig DEU. Dist: D.A.P./Distributed Art Pubs.

Brooks, Alan & Pevsner, Nikolaus. Herefordshire. 2012. (Pevsner Architectural Guides). (ENG., Illus.). 800p. 85.00 ***(978-0-300-12575-7(5))*** Yale Univ. Pr.

Brooks, Alan & Pevsner, Nikolaus. Worcestershire: The Buildings of England. 2007. (Pevsner Architectural Guides). (Illus.). 848p. 85.00 *(978-0-300-11298-6(X))* Yale Univ. Pr.

Brown-Manrique, Gerardo, text. Rudolf Frankel & Neues Bauen. 2009. (ENG., Illus.). 148p. pap. 50.00 *(978-3-8030-0695-0(3))* Wasmuth, Ernst J. Verlag GmbH & Co. DEU. Dist: D.A.P./Distributed Art Pubs.

Brown, R. J. English Village Architecture. 2007. (ENG., Illus.). 304p. pap. 25.00 *(978-0-7090-8278-1(9))* Hale, Robert Ltd. GBR. Dist: Independent Pubs. Group.

Brown, Richard, et al. Trade & Prosperity, War & Poverty: An Archaeological & Historical Investigation into Southampton's French Quarter. 2011. (Oxford Archaeology Monograph Ser.). (ENG.). 375p. (C). pap. 50.00 ***(978-0-904220-67-4(2))*** Oxford Archaeological Unit GBR. Dist: Brown, David Bk. Co., The.

Brunskill, R. W. Brick & Clay Building in Britain. 2009. (ENG., Illus.). 264p. 85.00 *(978-0-300-11687-8(X))* Yale Univ. Pr.

—Traditional Buildings of Cumbria. 2011. (ENG., Illus.). 224p. pap. 45.00 *(978-0-300-17059-7(9))* Yale Univ. Pr.

Bullen, Michael, et al. Hampshire: Winchester & the North. 2010. (Pevsner Architectural Guides). (Illus.). 800p. 85.00 *(978-0-300-12084-4(2))* Yale Univ. Pr.

Bullivant, Lucy. New Arcadians: Emerging UK Architects. 2012. (ENG., Illus.). 256p. 49.95 ***(978-1-85894-548-4(8))*** Merrell Pubs. Ltd. GBR. Dist: Perseus Distribution.

Burton, Anthony. Canal 250: The Story of Britain's Canals. 2011. (ENG., Illus.). 192p. 32.95 ***(978-0-7524-5952-3(X))*** History Pr. Ltd.,The GBR. Dist: Independent Pubs. Group.

Burton, Neil & Guillery, Peter. Behind the Façade: London House Plans, 1660-1840. 2006. (Illus.). 142p. (C). *(978-1-904965-10-7(5))* Spire Bks. Ltd.

Butler, Marianne. London Architecture. 2nd ed. 2012. (ENG., Illus.). 392p. pap. 19.95 ***(978-1-902910-38-3(9))*** Metro Pubns. GBR. Dist: Independent Pubs. Group.

Campbell, Colen. Vitruvius Britannicus: The Classic of Eighteenth-Century British Architecture. 2006. (Dover Architecture Ser.). (ENG., Illus.). 288p. per. 24.95 *(978-0-486-44799-5(5))* Dover Pubns., Inc.

Carroll, Rutter, Ryder & Yates. 2009. (Twentieth-century Architects Ser.). (ENG., Illus.). 160p. (C). pap. 40.00 *(978-1-85946-266-9(9))* English Heritage GBR. Dist: Brown, David Bk. Co., The.

Carscadden, Bruce. Carscadden Thrift: Selected Works. McDonald, Ian Ross, ed. 2012. (ENG., Illus.). 112p. 19.95 ***(978-1-897476-40-6(X))*** Simply Read Bks. CAN. Dist: Perseus-PGW.

Chancellor, Edwin Beresford. A History of the Squares & Palaces of London. 2012. (ENG., Illus.). 864p. 375.00 *(978-1-84885-495-6(1))* I. B. Tauris & Co., Ltd. GBR. Dist: Macmillan.

—The History of the Squares of London: Topographical & Historical. 2010. (Illus.). 582p. pap. 43.75 *(978-1-141-99182-2(9))* BiblioBazaar.

Chapman, Frederic. Architectural Remains of Richmond Twickenham Kew Mortlake & Petersham. 2008. pap. *(978-1-84830-059-0(X)*, Wildhern Pr.) Echo Library.

Chapman, Tony. Architecture 09: RIBA Buildings of the Year. 2010. (Illus.). 272p. pap. *(978-1-85894-490-6(2))* Merrell Pubs. Ltd.

—Architecture 11: RIBA Buildings of the Year. 2012. (ENG., Illus.). 272p. 34.95 *(978-1-85894-561-3(5))* Merrell Pubs. Ltd. GBR. Dist: Perseus Distribution.

Chapman, Tony, ed. Architecture Vol. 8: The Guide to the Riba Awards. 2008. (Illus.). 216p. pap. 22.95 *(978-1-85894-428-9(7))* Merrell Pubs. Ltd. GBR. Dist: Perseus Distribution.

—Architecture 07: The Guide to the Riba Awards. 2007. (Architecture: the Guide to the Riba Awards Ser.). (ENG., Illus.). 215p. pap. 22.95 *(978-1-85894-381-7(7))* Merrell Pubs. Ltd. GBR. Dist: Perseus Distribution.

Charles, J.A., et al. Engineering Guide to Seismic Risk to Dams in the U. K. 2011. (ENG., Illus.). 72p. pap. 130.00 ***(978-0-85125-510-1(8))*** Building Research Establishment GBR. Dist: Taylor & Francis Group.

Charlton, Susannah, et al, eds. British Modern: Architecture & Design in The 1930s. 2007. (Twentieth Century Architecture Ser.: Vol. 8). (ENG., Illus.). 160p. pap. 40.00 *(978-0-9529755-8-8(0))* Twentieth Century Society GBR. Dist: Univ. of Washington Pr.

Chatel, Guy, et al, texts. Oase No. 79: the Architecture of James Stirling 1964-1992. 2010. (ENG., Illus.). 160p. pap. 35.00 *(978-90-5662-723-2(6))* NAi Uitgevers / Publishers Stichting NLD. Dist: D.A.P./Distributed Art Pubs.

Clarke, Helen. Discover Medieval Sandwich: A Guide to its History & Buildings. 2012. (ENG., Illus.). 120p. (C). pap. 19.95 ***(978-1-84217-476-0(2))*** Oxbow Bks., Ltd. GBR. Dist: Brown, David Bk. Co., The.

Clement, Alexander. Brutalism: Post-War British Architecture, 1 vol. 2011. (ENG., Illus.). 160p. 34.95 ***(978-1-84797-230-9(6))*** Crowood Pr., Ltd. GBR. Dist: Independent Pubs. Group.

Coad, Jonathan. Support for the Fleet: British Naval Bases, 1690-1940. 2012. (ENG., Illus.). 320p. (C). pap. 110.00 *(978-1-84802-055-9(4))* English Heritage GBR. Dist: Brown, David Bk. Co., The.

Cohen, Philip & Rustin, Michael J. London's Turning: The Making of Thames Gateway. 2008. (Design & the Built Environment Ser.). (Illus.). 356p. 134.95 *(978-0-7546-7063-6(5))* Ashgate Publishing Co.

Coles, Alex, et al. Salt Bridges: Changing Perceptions of Art, Architecture, & Science. 2010. (Illus.). 192p. 75.00 *(978-3-7913-5026-4(9))* Prestel Publishing.

Coles, Mark. Guidance Note 2: Isolation & Switching, 5th Edition. 5th ed. 2009. (Illus.). 74p. pap. 50.00 *(978-0-86341-856-3(2))* Institution of Engineering & Technology GBR. Dist: Books International, Inc.

Colquhoun, Ian. RIBA Book of British Housing: 1900 to the Present Day. 2nd rev. ed. 2008. (ENG., Illus.). 416p. pap. 59.95 *(978-0-7506-8254-1(X))* Routledge.

Colvin, Howard. A Biographical Dictionary of British Architects 1600-1840. 4th ed. 2008. (Paul Mellon Centre for Studies in British Art). (ENG., Illus.). 1264p. 150.00 *(978-0-300-12508-5(9))* Yale Univ. Pr.

Conway, Moncure Daniel. Travels in South Kensington. 2009. 60p. pap. *(978-0-217-41109-7(6))* Books LLC.

Cookson, Gillian & History Press Staff. Sunderland: Building a City. 2010. (England's Past for Everyone Ser.). (ENG., Illus.). 192p. pap. 27.95 *(978-1-86077-547-5(0))* History Pr. Ltd.,The GBR. Dist: Independent Pubs. Group.

Cossons, Neil & Jenkins, Martin. Liverpool: Seaport City. 2011. (ENG., Illus.). 160p. 32.95 *(978-0-7110-3421-1(4))* Allan, Ian Publishing GBR. Dist: BookMasters Distribution Services (BDS).

Crinson, Mark. Stirling & Gowan: Architecture from Austerity to Affluence. 2012. (Paul Mellon Centre for Studies in British Art Ser.). (ENG., Illus.). 288p. 75.00 ***(978-0-300-17728-2(3))*** Yale Univ. Pr.

Crook, John. English Medieval Shrines. 2011. (Boydell Studies in Medieval Art & Architecture Ser.: Volume 3). (Illus.). 366p. 70.00 ***(978-1-84383-682-7(3)***, Boydell Press) Boydell & Brewer, Ltd. GBR. Dist: Boydell & Brewer, Inc.

Cruickshank, Dan. The Country House Revealed: A Secret History of the British Ancestral Home. 2011. (ENG., Illus.). 288p. 45.00 ***(978-1-84990-206-9(2))*** BBC Worldwide GBR. Dist: Independent Pubs. Group.

Curl, James Stevens. Georgian Architecture: The British Isles, 1717-1830. 2nd rev. ed. 2011. (ENG., Illus.). 444p. (C). 100.00 *(978-1-84802-086-3(4))* English Heritage GBR. Dist: Brown, David Bk. Co., The.

Curtis, Eleanor. St George's Chapel, Windsor: A Portrait. 2008. (ENG., Illus.). 160p. 49.95 *(978-1-904832-55-3(5))* Giles, D. Ltd. GBR. Dist: Antique Collectors' Club.

Dan, Horace & Morgan Willmott, E. English Shop-Fronts Old & New. 2007. 120p. per. *(978-1-905217-74-8(9))* Mills, Jeremy Publishing.

Däster, Uli, et al. Gillian White: Dance in Steel. 40 Years Work. Altorfer, Sabine, ed. 2009. (ENG & GER., Illus.). 160p. 85.00 *(978-3-85881-251-3(X))* Scheidegger und Spiess AG, Verlag CHE. Dist: Antique Collectors' Club.

Datz, Christian & Kullmann, Christof, eds. Ultimate London Design. 2006. (ITA, FRE, GER, SPA & ENG., Illus.). 527p. 24.95 *(978-3-8327-9138-4(8))* teNeues Publishing Co.

Davis Langdon Engineering Services. Spon's Mechanical & Electrical Services Price Book 2011. 42nd ed. 2010. (ENG., Illus.). 800p. 255.00 *(978-0-415-58851-5(0)*, Spon Pr.) Routledge.

Davis, Paul R. Castles of the Welsh Princes. 2011. (ENG., Illus.). 108p. pap. 14.95 ***(978-0-86243-970-5(1))*** Y Lolfa GBR. Dist: Dufour Editions, Inc.

Day, Stephen, et al. The Sainsbury Laboratory: Science, Architecture, Art. 2012. (ENG.). 192p. 29.95 *(978-1-907317-45-3(7))* Black Dog Publishing Ltd. GBR. Dist: Actar Birkhauser Distribution.

Denison, Edward. Mcmorran & Whitby. 2009. (Twentieth-century Architects Ser.). (ENG., Illus.). 154p. (C). pap. 40.00 *(978-1-85946-320-8(7))* English Heritage GBR. Dist: Brown, David Bk. Co., The.

Dimbleby, David. How We Built Britain. 2008. (ENG., Illus.). 1p. pap. 32.95 *(978-0-7475-9287-7(X))* Bloomsbury Publishing Plc GBR. Dist: Independent Pubs. Group.

Dixon, Tom. Tom Dixon: Interior Worlds. 2009. (ENG., Illus.). 688p. 85.00 *(978-0-8478-3239-2(2))* Rizzoli International Pubns., Inc.

Doherty, Sharon. Heathrow's Terminal 5: History in the Making. 2008. (ENG., Illus.). 372p. 75.00 *(978-0-470-75435-1(4)*, Wiley) Wiley, John & Sons, Inc.

Douglis, Evan. Autogenic Structures. 2008. (Illus.). 256p. 165.00 *(978-0-415-77689-9(9))* Taylor & Francis Group.

—Autogenic Structures. 2008. (ENG., Illus.). 256p. (C). pap. 44.95 *(978-0-415-77690-5(2)*, Taylor & Francis) Taylor & Francis Group GBR. Dist: Taylor & Francis Group.

Downie, Craig. Studio Downie Architects. 2006. (Neoarchitecture Ser.). (ENG., Illus.). 124p. 49.50 *(978-1-86470-155-5(2))* Images Publishing Group AUS. Dist: National Bk. Network.

Draper, Peter. The Formation of English Gothic: Architecture & Identity, 1150-1250. 2007. (Paul Mellon Centre for Studies in British Art). (ENG., Illus.). 288p. 80.00 *(978-0-300-12036-3(2))* Yale Univ. Pr.

Driver, Leigh. The Lost Villages of England. (ENG., Illus.). 176p. 2009. pap. 24.95 *(978-1-84773-218-7(6))* 2007. 39.95 ***(978-1-84537-423-5(1))*** New Holland Pubs., Ltd. GBR. Dist: National Bk. Network.

Duany, Andres & Kern, Margareta. Hertfordshire Guide to Growth-2021: How Should the County Grow? 2009. (ENG., Illus.). 52p. pap. 11.95 *(978-1-905313-61-7(6))* Univ. of Hertfordshire Pr. GBR. Dist: Independent Pubs. Group.

Dunning, R. W., ed. A History of the County of Somerset Vol. IX: Glastonbury & Street. 2006. (Victoria County History Ser.). (Illus.). 257p. 165.00 *(978-1-904356-23-3(0))* Victoria County History GBR. Dist: Boydell & Brewer, Inc.

Durant, David. The Smythson Circle: The Story of Six Great English Houses. 2010. (ENG.). 256p. pap. 22.95 *(978-0-7206-1344-5(2))* Owen, Peter Ltd. GBR. Dist: Independent Pubs. Group.

Eastlake, Charles L. A History of the Gothic Revival. 2007. (ENG.). 456p. 52.95 *(978-0-548-09395-5(4))* Kessinger Publishing, LLC.

Edwards, Brian. Green Buildings Pay. 3rd rev. ed. 2012. (ENG., Illus.). 240p. 155.00 *(978-0-415-68534-4(6))*; pap. 55.00 *(978-0-415-68535-1(4))* Routledge.

Edwards, Jane. London Style: Streets, Interiors, Details. Hendricks, J. & Taschen, Angelika, eds. 25th ed. 2008. (Icon (Taschen) Ser.). (FRE, GER & ENG., Illus.). 191p. 7.99 *(978-3-8365-0777-6(3))* TASCHEN DEU. Dist: Ingram Pub. Services.

Elliott, Chris. Egypt in England. 2012. (ENG., Illus.). 336p. (C). pap. 50.00 ***(978-1-84802-088-7(0))*** English Heritage GBR. Dist: Brown, David Bk. Co., The.

Elliott, John & Finniss, Sue. Salisbury: A Walk in the City. 2010. (ENG., Illus.). 88p. (C). 39.95 *(978-1-904965-28-2(8))* Spire Bks. Ltd. GBR. Dist: Brown, David Bk. Co., The.

Evans, Robin. The Fabrication of Virtue: English Prison Architecture, 1750-1840. 2011. (ENG.). 484p. pap. 39.99 *(978-0-521-18133-4(X))* Cambridge Univ. Pr.

Eyles, Allen. London's West End Cinemas. 3rd ed. 2009. (ENG., Illus.). 256p. (gr. 17). pap. 40.00 *(978-0-9558595-0-2(6))* Wallflower Pr. GBR. Dist: Columbia Univ. Pr.

Falconer, Keith, et al. Ancoats: Cradle of Industrialisation. 2011. (Informed Conservation Ser.). (ENG., Illus.). 98p. (C). pap. 20.00 *(978-1-84802-027-6(9))* English Heritage GBR. Dist: Brown, David Bk. Co., The.

Farquhar, Robin & Dicper, Hannah. Iconic Buildings: London. 2012. (ENG., Illus.). 96p. 14.95 ***(978-1-84994-023-8(1)***, Batsford, B. T. Ltd.) Anova Bks. GBR. Dist: Sterling Publishing Co., Inc.

Farrell, Terry. Shaping London: The Patterns & Forms That Make the Metropolis. 2009. (ENG., Illus.). 288p. 75.00 *(978-0-470-69996-6(5)*, Wiley) Wiley, John & Sons, Inc.

Federation of Piling Specialists Staff, et al, contrib. by. ICE Specification for Piling & Embedded Retaining Walls. 2nd ed. 2007. 264p. *(978-0-7277-3358-0(3))* Telford, Thomas Ltd.

Fergusson, Adam. The Sack of Bath. 2011. (Persephone Bks.). (ENG., Illus.). 77p. pap. ***(978-1-903155-83-7(5))*** Persephone Bks. Ltd.

Fisher, Michael. 'Gothic for Ever' A. W. N. Pugin, Lord Shrewsbury, & the Rebuilding of Catholic England. 2012. (ENG., Illus.). 342p. (C). 100.00 ***(978-1-904965-36-7(9))*** Spire Bks. Ltd. GBR. Dist: Brown, David Bk. Co., The.

Foster, Norman. Willis Faber & Dumas. 2012. (Illus.). 96p. 29.95 ***(978-3-7913-4666-1(5))*** Prestel Publishing.

Foster, Norman & Sudjic, Deyan. The Great Court at the British Museum. 2012. (ENG.). 96p. 29.95 ***(978-3-7913-4590-1(7))*** Prestel Publishing.

Foyle, Andrew & Pevsner, Nikolaus. Somerset - North & Bristol. 2011. (Pevsner Architectural Guides). (ENG., Illus.). 800p. 85.00 *(978-0-300-12658-7(1))* Yale Univ. Pr.

Frampton, Kenneth, et al. Custom & Innovation: John Miller + Partners. 2010. (ENG., Illus.). 192p. 55.00 *(978-1-906155-70-4(4))* Black Dog Publishing Ltd. GBR. Dist: Perseus Distribution.

Fraser, Murray & Kerr, Joe. Architecture & the 'Special Relationship' The American Influence on Post-War British Architecture. 2008. (ENG., Illus.). 608p. 100.00 *(978-0-419-20910-2(7)*, RU09107) Routledge.

Fung, Janice & Janice, Fung. Social Housing in Glasgow Volume 2: Decision-Making in Design, Policy & Occupant Intervention. 2011. 668p. pap. ***(978-3-639-29629-7(X))*** VDM Verlag Dr. Mueller e.K.

Furján, Helene. John Soane's Spectacular Theatre. 2011. (ENG., Illus.). 208p. (C). 155.00 *(978-0-415-78157-2(4))*; pap. 54.95 *(978-0-415-78158-9(2))* Routledge.

Fyfe, David Theodore. Architecture in Cambridge: Examples of Architectural Styles from Saxon to Modern Times. 2009. (Cambridge Library Collection - Cambridge Ser.) (ENG., Illus.). 140p. pap. 19.99 *(978-1-108-00241-7(2))* Cambridge Univ. Pr.

Galinou, Mireille. Cottages & Villas: The Birth of the Garden Suburb. 2011. (ENG., Illus.). 480p. 100.00 *(978-0-300-16726-9(1))* Yale Univ. Pr.

Gardiner, Robert. Warships of Napoleonic Era-Rev. 2011. 176p. 74.95 *(978-1-59114-922-4(3))* Naval Institute Pr.

Gardner, Alfred Herbert. Outline of English Architecture. 2008. 236p. *(978-1-4437-2551-4(X))* 2006. 232p. per. *(978-1-4067-3564-2(7)*, Read Bks. (Hesperides Pr.).

Garner, Lawrence. Dry Stone Walls. 2nd ed. 2008. (Shire Library). (ENG., Illus.). 40p. pap. 11.95 *(978-0-7478-0620-2(9))* Shire Pubns., Ltd. GBR. Dist: Random Hse., Inc.

Geraghty, Anthony. The Architectural Drawings of Sir Christopher Wren: At All Souls College, Oxford: A Complete Catalogue. 2007. (Illus.). 296p. 180.00 *(978-0-7546-4071-4(X)*, Lund Humphries Pubs.) Ashgate Publishing, Ltd. GBR. Dist: Ashgate Publishing Co.

Gerbino, Anthony & Johnston, Stephen. Compass & Rule: Architecture As Mathematical Practice in England. 2009. (ENG., Illus.). 192p. 65.00 *(978-0-300-15093-3(8))* Yale Univ. Pr.

Gibbs, James. Gibbs' Book of Architecture: An Eighteenth-Century Classic. 2008. (Dover Architecture Ser.). (ENG., Illus.). 192p. pap. 18.95 *(978-0-486-46601-9(9))* Dover Pubns., Inc.

Gibson, Kathryn & Taylor, Simon. Manningham: Character & Diversity in a Bradford Suburb. 2010. (Informed Conservation Ser.). (ENG., Illus.). 106p. 20.00 *(978-1-84802-030-6(9))* English Heritage GBR. Dist: Brown, David Bk. Co., The.

Girouard, Mark. Elizabethan Architecture. 2009. (Paul Mellon Centre for Studies in British Art). (Illus.). 400p. 65.00 *(978-0-300-09386-5(1))* Yale Univ. Pr.

Grainger, Hilary J. The Architecture of Sir Ernest George. 2011. (ENG., Illus.). 495p. (C). 130.00 *(978-1-904965-31-2(8))* Spire Bks. Ltd. GBR. Dist: Brown, David Bk. Co., The.

Gravett, Christopher. English Castles 1200-1300. 2009. (Fortress Ser.). (ENG., Illus.). 64p. pap. 18.95 *(978-1-84603-374-2(8))* Osprey Publishing, Ltd. GBR. Dist: Random Hse., Inc.

Gray, Fred. Designing the Seaside: Architecture, Society & Nature. 2009. (ENG., Illus.). 400p. pap. 40.00 *(978-1-86189-440-3(6))* Reaktion Bks., Ltd. GBR. Dist: Chicago Distribution Ctr.

Greider, Katharine. The Archaeology of Home: An Epic Set on a 1000 Square Feet of the Lower East Side. 2011. (ENG., Illus.). 352p. 26.99 *(978-1-58648-712-6(4))* PublicAffairs.

Grimshaw, Nicholas. Grimshaw Architecture: The First 30 Years. 2011. (Illus.). 160p. 60.00 *(978-3-7913-5073-8(0))* Prestel Publishing.

Guillery, Peter, ed. Built from Below: British Architecture & the Vernacular. 2010. (ENG., Illus.). 224p. (C). 165.00 *(978-0-415-56532-5(4))* Routledge.

—Built from Below: British Architecture & the Vernacular. 2010. (ENG., Illus.). 224p. (C). pap. 53.95 *(978-0-415-56533-2(2)*, Routledge) Taylor & Francis Group GBR. Dist: Taylor & Francis Group.

Hall, Michael. Lasting Elegance: English Country Houses 1830-1900. 2009. (ENG., Illus.). 192p. 65.00 *(978-1-58093-256-1(8))* Monacelli Pr., Inc.

Hamilton, Susan, et al. Gloucester Cathedral. 2011. (Illus.). 128p. pap. 29.95 *(978-1-85759-667-0(6))* Scala, Editions FRA. Dist: National Bk. Network.

Hamm, Oliver G. Hascher Jehle Architektur: Thoughts & Buildings / Gedanken und Bauten, 2 vols. 2010. (Illus.). 352p. 85.00 *(978-3-7913-4159-0(6))* Prestel Publishing.

Harding, D. W. The Iron Age Round-House: Later Prehistoric Building in Britain & Beyond. 2009. (ENG., Illus.). 350p. 130.00 *(978-0-19-955857-5(4))* Oxford Univ. Pr., Inc.

Hardy, Dennis. From Garden Cities to New Towns: Campaigning for Town & Country Planning 1899-1946. 2011. (Planning, History & Environment Ser.). (ENG.). 352p. pap. 42.95 ***(978-0-415-51173-5(9))*** Routledge.

—From New Towns to Green Politics: Campaigning for Town & Country Planning 1946-1990. 2011. (Planning, History & Environment Ser.). (ENG.). pap. 42.95 ***(978-0-415-51174-2(7))*** Routledge.

Hargreaves, Sean. Places. 2011. (ENG.). 160p. pap. 29.95 *(978-1-933492-49-0(X))* Design Studio Pr.

Harris, Eileen. British Architectural Books & Writers, 1556-1785. 2011. (ENG.). 572p. pap. 70.00 *(978-0-521-28324-3(8))* Cambridge Univ. Pr.

Hart, Stephen. Medieval Church Window Tracery in England. 2010. (Illus.). 184p. 80.00 *(978-1-84383-533-2(9)*, Boydell Press) Boydell & Brewer, Ltd. GBR. Dist: Boydell & Brewer, Inc.

Hart, Vaughan. Inigo Jones: The Architect of Kings. 2011. (Paul Mellon Centre for Studies in British Art Ser.). (ENG., Illus.). 336p. 70.00 *(978-0-300-14149-8(1))* Yale Univ. Pr.

—Sir John Vanbrugh: Storyteller in Stone. 2008. (ENG., Illus.). 256p. 65.00 *(978-0-300-11929-9(1))* Yale Univ. Pr.

Hartwell, Clare & Pevsner, Nikolaus. Lancashire - North. 2009. (Pevsner Architectural Guides). (ENG., Illus.). 800p. 85.00 *(978-0-300-12667-9(0))* Yale Univ. Pr.

Hartwell, Clare, et al. Cheshire. 2011. (Pevsner Architectural Guides). (ENG., Illus.). 800p. 85.00 *(978-0-300-17043-6(2))* Yale Univ. Pr.

Harwood, Elain. Chamberlin, Powell & Bon: 20th Century Architects. 2011. (Twentieth-century Architects Ser.). (Illus.). 160p. (C). pap. 40.00 *(978-1-85946-164-8(7))* English Heritage GBR. Dist: Brown, David Bk. Co., The.

—Nottingham. 2008. (Pevsner Architectural Guides). (ENG., Illus.). 246p. (C). pap. 40.00 *(978-0-300-12666-2(2))* Yale Univ. Pr.

Harwood, Elain & Keate, Delcia. England's Schools: History, Architecture & Conservation. 2010. (Informed Conservation Ser.). (ENG., Illus.). 112p. pap. 20.00 *(978-1-84802-031-3(7))* English Heritage GBR. Dist: Brown, David Bk. Co., The.

Harwood, Elain & Symondson, Anthony. Stephen Dykes Bower. 2011. (Twentieth-century Architects Ser.). (ENG., Illus.). 186p. (C). pap. 40.00 *(978-1-85946-398-7(3))* English Heritage GBR. Dist: Brown, David Bk. Co., The.

Haslam, Richard, et al. Gwynedd. 2009. (Pevsner Architectural Guides). (ENG., Illus.). 800p. 55.00 *(978-0-300-14169-6(6))* Yale Univ. Pr.

Haslam, Ruby M. Reality & Imagery: The Grottoes of Margate & Twickenham. 2009. (Illus.). 116p. *(978-1-84748-349-2(6))* Athena Pr.

Hastings, Maurice. St Stephen's Chapel: And Its Place in the Development of Perpendicular Style in England. 2011. (ENG.). 276p. pap. 23.99 ***(978-0-521-24278-3(9))*** Cambridge Univ. Pr.

Hatherley, Owen. A Guide to the New Ruins of Great Britain. (ENG., Illus.). 2011. 400p. pap. 19.95 *(978-1-84467-700-9(1)*, 844700) 2010. 256p. 29.95 *(978-1-84467-651-4(X)*, 844651) Verso Bks. GBR. Dist: Norton, W. W. & Co., Inc.

Hawker, Brian & Stevens, Howard. The Motorway Achievement: Building the Network in Wales. 2010. (ENG., Illus.). 224p. 49.95 *(978-1-86077-590-1(X))* History Pr. Ltd.,The GBR. Dist: Independent Pubs. Group.

Hawkes, Dean. Architecture & Climate. 2012. (ENG., Illus.). 272p. (C). 165.00 ***(978-0-415-56186-0(8))***; pap. 49.95 ***(978-0-415-56187-7(6))*** Routledge.

Heathcote, David. A Shell Eye on England: The Shell County Guides 1934-1984. 2010. (Illus.). 152p. pap. 36.95 *(978-1-907471-07-0(3))* Libri Publishing Ltd GBR. Dist: Independent Pubs. Group.

Heatherwick, Thomas. Making Ideas. 2012. (ENG., Illus.). 600p. 75.00 ***(978-1-58093-334-6(3))*** Monacelli Pr., Inc.

Hendrix, John. Architecture As Cosmology: Lincoln Cathedral & English Gothic Architecture. 2010. (Illus.). 372p. (C). pap. 49.95 *(978-1-4331-1316-1(3))* Lang, Peter Publishing, Inc.

Hewlett, Henry. Ensuring Reservoir Safety into the Future: Proceedings of the 15th Conference of the British Dam Society at the University of Warwick from 10-13 September 2008. 2008. (Illus.). 448p. *(978-0-7277-3522-5(5))* Telford, Thomas Ltd.

Higgott, Andrew. Mediating Modernism. 2006. (Illus.). VIII, 216p. 64.95 *(978-0-415-40177-7(1))* Routledge.

Howard, Maurice. The Building of Elizabethan & Jacobean England. 2008. (ENG., Illus.). 256p. 60.00 *(978-0-300-13543-5(2))* Yale Univ. Pr.

Howes, Karen. Lebenskunst in London. (GER.). *(978-3-8067-2861-3(5))* Gerstenberg DEU. Dist: International Bk. Import Service, Inc.

Hubbard, Edward & Shippobottom, Michael. A Guide to Port Sunlight Village. 2nd rev. ed. 2006. (Utp Correspondence James Polk Ser.). (ENG., Illus.). 112p. per. 14.95 *(978-0-85323-455-5(8))* Liverpool Univ. Pr. GBR. Dist: Chicago Distribution Ctr.

Hull, Lise. Great Castles of Britain & Ireland. 2009. (ENG., Illus.). 160p. pap. 19.95 *(978-1-84773-130-2(9))* New Holland Pubs., Ltd. GBR. Dist: National Bk. Network.

Hyde, Matthew & Pevsner, Nikolaus. Cumbria: Cumberland, Westmorland & Furness. 2010. (Pevsner Architectural Guides). (ENG., Illus.). 800p. 85.00 *(978-0-300-12663-1(8))* Yale Univ. Pr.

Images Publishing, creator. Cj Lim, Vol. 8. 2006. (Neo Architecture Ser.). (ENG., Illus.). 124p. 49.50 *(978-1-920744-80-9(0))* Images Publishing Group AUS. Dist: National Bk. Network.

Imrie, Rob, et al. Regenerating London: Governance, Sustainability & Community in a Global City. Imrie, Rob et al, eds. 2009. (Illus.). 336p. pap. 48.95 *(978-0-415-43367-9(3))* Routledge.

Innocent, C. F. The Development of English Building Construction. 2011. (ENG.). 308p. pap. 24.99 *(978-0-521-17960-0(6))* Cambridge Univ. Pr.

Jackson, Neil, et al. Saltaire: The Making of a Model Town. 2010. (Illus.). 258p. (C). *(978-1-904965-21-3(0))* Spire Bks. Ltd.

James, Russell, text. Cool Guide London. 2009. pap. 12.95 *(978-3-8327-9294-7(5))* teNeues Publishing Co.

Jenkins, David. Norman Foster Works 3, Vol. 3. 2008. (Norman Foster Works). (Illus.). 564p. 120.00 *(978-3-7913-3257-4(0))* Prestel Publishing.

—Norman Foster Works 6. 2011. (Illus.). 580p. 150.00 *(978-3-7913-3259-8(7))* Prestel Publishing.

Jenkins, David, ed. Norman Foster: Works 5. 2009. (Illus.). 592p. 150.00 *(978-3-7913-3258-1(9))* Prestel Publishing.

Jenner, Michael & Morris, Stephen. Bristol's 100 Best Buildings. 2010. (Illus.). 160p. *(978-1-906593-61-2(2))*; *(978-1-906593-67-4(1))* Redcliffe Pr., Ltd.

Jodidio, Philip. Kc Zaha Hadid. 2012 (ENG., Illus.). 96p. pap. 9.99 ***(978-3-8365-3072-9(4))*** TASCHEN DEU. Dist: Ingram Pub. Services.

Jodidio, Philip. Ten Years Serpentine Gallery Pavilions. 2011. (FRE, GER & ENG., Illus.). 332p. 59.99 (978-3-8365-2613-5(1)) TASCHEN DEU. Dist: Ingram Pub. Services.

Jones, Edward & Woodward, Christopher. A Guide to the Architecture of London. 2009. (ENG., Illus.). 496p. instr.'s gde. ed. 39.95 (978-0-297-85516-3(6), Weidenfeld & Nicolson) Orion Publishing Group, Ltd. GBR. Dist: Sterling Publishing Co., Inc.

Kadish, Sharman. Jewish Heritage in England: An Architectural Guide. 2006. (ENG., Illus.). 240p. pap. 38.00 (978-1-905624-28-7(X)) English Heritage GBR. Dist: Brown, David Bk. Co., The.

Kara, Hanif, ed. Design Engineering. 2008. (978-84-96540-66-8(9)) Actar Birkhauser Distribution.

Kondo, Ariyuki. Robert & James Adam, Architects of the Age of Enlightenment, 1 vol. 2011. (Enlightenment World Ser.). (ENG., Illus.). 224p. 99.00 (978-1-84893-179-4(4)) Pickering & Chatto Pubs., Ltd. GBR. Dist: Ashgate Publishing Co.

Lambton, Lucinda. Palaces for Pigs: Animal Architecture & other Beastly Dwellings. 2011. (ENG., Illus.). 255p. 50.00 (978-1-85074-989-9(2)) English Heritage GBR. Dist: Brown, David Bk. Co., The.

Langdon, Davis. Spon's Civil Engineering & Highway Works Price Book 2011. 2010. (ENG., Illus.). 752p. 275.00 (978-0-415-58847-8(2), Spon Pr.) Routledge.

Langdon, Davis. Spon's Mechanical & Electrical Services Price Book 2013. 44th rev. ed. 2012. (ENG., Illus.). 800p. 255.00 **(978-0-415-69080-5(3)**, Spon Pr.) Routledge.

Lappin, Sarah A. Full Irish: New Architecture in Ireland. 2009. (ENG., Illus.). 240p. 45.00 (978-1-56898-868-9(0)) Princeton Architectural Pr.

Lawrence, Amanda Reeser & Stirling, James. James Stirling: Revisionary Modernist. 2013. (ENG., Illus.). 240p. 50.00 **(978-0-300-17005-4(X))** Yale Univ. Pr.

Lea, Richard & Miele, Chris. Danson House: The Anatomy of a Georgian Villa. 2011. (ENG., Illus.). 112p. pap. 50.00 (978-1-873592-75-5(2)) English Heritage GBR. Dist: Brown, David Bk. Co., The.

Leach, Peter & Pevsner, Nikolaus. Yorkshire West Riding: Leeds, Bradford & the North. 2009. (Pevsner Architectural Guides). (Illus.). 800p. 85.00 (978-0-300-12665-5(4)) Yale Univ. Pr.

Leary, Patrick. The Punch Brotherhood: Table Talk & Print Culture in Mid-Victorian London. 2010. (ENG., Illus.). 197p. 40.00 (978-0-7123-0923-3(3)) British Library, The GBR. Dist: Chicago Distribution Ctr.

Lees, Loretta, et al. Regenerating London: Governance, Sustainability & Community in a Global City. Imrie, Rob & Lees, Loretta, eds. Raco, Mike, ed. 2009. (Illus.). 336p. 155.00 (978-0-415-43366-2(5)) Routledge.

Lehmann, Ann Holyoke & Guratzsch, Dankwart. Rob Krier, Cité Judiciaire, Luxembourg: 1991-2008. 2010. (Illus.). 1136p. 109.00 (978-3-936681-37-6(8)) Edition Axel Menges GmbH DEU. Dist: National Bk. Network.

Lemmen, Hans. Art Deco Tiles. 2012. (Shire Library). (ENG., Illus.). 64p. pap. 12.95 **(978-0-7478-1199-2(7))** Shire Pubns., Ltd. GBR. Dist: Random Hse., Inc.

Li, Shiqiao. Power & Virtue: Architecture & Intellectual Change in England 1660-1730. 2006. (Classical Tradition in Architecture Ser.). (Illus.). 256p. 52.95 (978-0-415-37427-9(8)) Routledge.

Liscombe, R. W. William Wilkins 1778-1839. 2010. (ENG.). 407p. pap. 31.99 (978-0-521-14467-4(1)) Cambridge Univ. Pr.

Littlefield, Daniel C. Liverpool One: Remaking a City Centre. Littlefield, David & Daramola-Martin, Ayo, eds. 2009. (ENG., Illus.). 256p. 70.00 (978-0-470-71409-6(3), Wiley) Wiley, John & Sons, Inc.

Littlefield, David. London (Re)Generation. 2012. (Architectural Design Ser.). (ENG., Illus.). 136p. pap. 45.00 **(978-1-119-99378-0(4)**, Wiley) Wiley, John & Sons, Inc.

Lloyd, David & Pevsner, Nikolaus. Isle of Wight. 2006. (Buildings of England Ser.). (ENG., Illus.). 348p. 65.00 (978-0-300-10733-3(1)) Yale Univ. Pr.

Long, David. English Eccentrics & Their Bizarre Behaviour. 2009. (Illus.). 176p. 39.99 (978-1-84468-055-9(X)) Pen & Sword Bks. Ltd. GBR. Dist: Casemate Pubs. & Bk. Distributors, LLC.

Lovell, Percy & Marcham, William, eds. Parish of St. Pancras Pt. 2: Old St. Pancras & Kentish Town. (London County Council Survey of London Ser.: No. 19). reprint ed. 84.50 (978-0-404-51669-7(6)) AMS Pr., Inc.

Luxford, Julian & McNeill, John, eds. The Medieval Chantry in England & Wales. 2012. (Journal of the British Archaeological Association Ser.). (ENG.). 368p. (C). 88.00 (978-1-907975-16-5(0)) Maney Publishing GBR. Dist: Brown, David Bk. Co., The.

Luxford, Julian M. The Art & Architecture of English Benedictine Monasteries, 1300-1540: A Patronage History. 2008. (Studies in the History of Medieval Religion Ser.: Volume 25). (Illus.). 346p. 90.00 (978-1-84383-153-2(8), Boydell Press) Boydell & Brewer, Ltd. GBR. Dist: Boydell & Brewer, Inc.

Lyell, Arthur Henry. A Bibliographical List Descriptive of Romano-British Architectural Remains in Great Britain. 2010. (Cambridge Library Collection - Archaeology Ser.). (ENG.). 176p. pap. 19.99 (978-1-108-00890-7(9)) Cambridge Univ. Pr.

Lyle, Marjorie. Canterbury History You Can See. 2008. (ENG., Illus.). 128p. pap. 29.95 (978-0-7524-4538-0(3)) History Pr. Ltd., The GBR. Dist: Independent Pubs. Group.

Lynn Pearson Staff. Tile Gazetteer. 2006. (ENG.). 512p. pap. 50.00 (978-0-903685-97-9(3), Richard Dennis Pubns. Di) Antique Collectors' Club GBR. Dist: National Bk. Network.

McCombie, Grace & Buildings Books Trust (Pevsner). Newcastle & Gateshead. 2009. (Pevsner Architectural Guides). (ENG., Illus.). 320p. pap. 40.00 (978-0-300-12664-8(6)) Yale Univ. Pr.

Meikle, Jim. Thinking Big: The History of Davis Langdon. Black Dog Publishing Staff, ed. 2009. (ENG., Illus.). 256p. 55.00 (978-1-906155-71-1(2)) Black Dog Publishing Ltd. GBR. Dist: Perseus Distribution.

Merrick, Jay, ed. John Mcaslan & Partners. 2009. 288p. 89.95 (978-1-85894-473-9(2)) Merrell Pubs. Ltd. GBR. Dist: Perseus Distribution.

Miele, Chris. The Supreme Court of the United Kingdom: History, Art, Architecture. 2010. (Illus.). 221p. pap. (978-1-85894-508-8(9)) Merrell Pubs. Ltd.

Miele, Chris, ed. The Supreme Court: The Creation, Design & Architecture of the Supreme Court of the United Kingdom. 2012. (ENG., Illus.). 224p. 65.00 (978-1-85894-507-1(0)) Merrell Pubs. Ltd. GBR. Dist: Perseus Distribution.

Monckton, Linda & Morris, Richard. Coventry: Medieval Art, Architecture & Archaeology. 2011. (Baa conference transactions Ser.). (ENG., Illus.). 363p. (C). 130.00 (978-1-906540-63-0(2)) Maney Publishing GBR. Dist: Brown, David Bk. Co., The.

Monckton, Linda & Morris, Richard K. Coventry: Medieval Art, Architecture & Archaeology. 2011. (Baa conference transactions Ser.). (ENG., Illus.). 363p. (C). pap. 62.00 (978-1-906540-62-3(4)) Maney Publishing GBR. Dist: Brown, David Bk. Co., The.

Morley, Ian. British Provincial Civic Design & the Building of Late-Victorian & Edwardian Cities, 1880-1914. (Illus.). 388p. (978-0-7734-5090-5(4)) Mellen, Edwin Pr., The.

Morris, Alison. John Pawson: Plain Space. 2010. (ENG., Illus.). 240p. 75.00 (978-0-7148-5748-0(3)) Phaidon Pr., Inc.

Mortimer, Richard & Rodwell, Warwick, eds. Westminster Abbey Chapter House: The History, Art & Architecture of 'A Chapter House Beyond Compare' 2010. (ENG., Illus.). 317p. (C). 99.95 (978-0-85431-295-5(1)) Society of Antiquaries of London GBR. Dist: Brown, David Bk. Co., The.

Mount, Harry & Muller, Marcia. A Lust for Window Sills: A Lover's Guide to British Buildings from Portcullis to Pebble Dash. 2010. (ENG., Illus.). 384p. pap. 14.95 (978-0-349-12106-2(0)) Little, Brown Bk. Group Ltd. GBR. Dist: Independent Pubs. Group.

Murray, Irena & Osley, Julian, eds. Le Corbusier & Britain: An Anthology. 2008. (Illus.). 256p. 65.00 (978-1-85894-466-1(X)) Merrell Pubs. Ltd. GBR. Dist: Perseus Distribution.

—Le Corbusier & Britain: An Anthology. 2010. (ENG., Illus.). 360p. pap. 26.95 (978-0-415-60865-7(1)) Routledge.

Murray, Irena, et al. Le Corbusier & Britain: An Anthology. Osley, Julian, ed. 2008. (ENG., Illus.). 360p. 62.95 (978-0-415-47994-3(0)) Routledge.

Muthesius, Hermann. The English House, 3 vols., Set. Sharp, Dennis, ed. & intro. by. 2007. (ENG., Illus.). 768p. 225.00 (978-0-7112-2688-3(1)) Lincoln, Frances Ltd. GBR. Dist: Perseus-PGW.

Mylne, Robert Scott. Master Masons to the Crown of Scotland A. 2006. pap. 36.95 (978-1-4286-4744-2(9)) Kessinger Publishing, LLC.

Neary, Ged. Rice Ticket. Mould, Paul, ed. 2007. 235p. pap. (978-1-58690-041-0(2)) Mould, Paul Publishing.

Neave, David & Neave, Susan. Hull. 2010. (Pevsner Architectural Guides). (ENG., Illus.). 254p. pap. 40.00 (978-0-300-14172-6(6)) Yale Univ. Pr.

Newman, John & Pevsner, Nikolaus. Shropshire. 2006. (Pevsner Architectural Guides). (ENG., Illus.). 787p. 85.00 (978-0-300-12083-7(4)) Yale Univ. Pr.

Norton, Christopher & Park, David, eds. Cistercian Art & Architecture in the British Isles. 2011. (ENG., Illus.). 541p. pap. 45.00 (978-0-521-18135-8(6)) Cambridge Univ. Pr.

Obrist, Hans Ulrich, ed. Hans Ulrich Obrist & Cedric Price: the Conversation Series. 2010. (ENG., Illus.). 172p. pap. 35.00 (978-3-86560-093-6(X)) Verlag der Buchhandlung Walther Konig DEU. Dist: D.A.P./Distributed Art Pubs.

O'Donoghue, Rod E. L. Medieval Stained Glass in Suffolk Churches: Let the Stained Glass Speak. 2009. (Illus.). 280p. pap. 67.99 (978-1-4389-8955-6(5)) AuthorHouse.

Orrell, John. The Human Stage: English Theatre Design, 1567-1640. 2009. (ENG.). 316p. pap. 42.00 (978-0-521-10945-1(0)) Cambridge Univ. Pr.

Ozelton, E. C. & Baird, J. A. Timber Designers' Manual. 3rd ed. 2006. (ENG., Illus.). 560p. pap. 104.99 (978-1-4051-4671-5(0), Wiley-Blackwell) Wiley, John & Sons, Inc.

Pacey, Arnold. Medieval Architectural Drawing. 2010. (ENG., Illus.). 256p. 49.95 **(978-0-7524-4404-8(2))** History Pr. Ltd., The GBR. Dist: Independent Pubs. Group.

Palin, Will. The Architects Who Made London. 2009. (ENG., Illus.). 160p. pap. 19.95 (978-1-905711-45-1(X)) Royal Academy of Arts GBR. Dist: Abrams.

Paterson, Nigel McCullagh. The Vernacular Architecture & Buildings of Stroud & Chalford. 2006. (Illus.). 344p. per. 33.91 (978-1-4120-9951-6(X)) Trafford Publishing.

Pawson, John. A Visual Inventory. 2012. (ENG., Illus.). 320p. 49.95 **(978-0-7148-6350-4(5))** Phaidon Pr., Inc.

Pearson, Lynn. Piers & Other Seaside Architecture. 2nd ed. 2009. (Shire Library). (ENG., Illus.). 64p. pap. 12.95 (978-0-7478-0693-6(4)) Shire Pubns., Ltd. GBR. Dist: Random Hse., Inc.

—Played on Tyne & Wear: Charting the Heritage of Two Cities at Play. 2010. (Played in Britain Ser.). (ENG., Illus.). 200p. (C). pap. 29.95 (978-1-905624-74-4(3)) English Heritage GBR. Dist: Brown, David Bk. Co., The.

Peter. Form Follows Fun. 2007. (Illus.). 224p. 165.00 (978-0-415-42818-7(1)) Routledge.

Peter, Bruce. Form Follows Fun. 2007. (Illus.). 224p. 63.95 (978-0-415-42819-4(X)) Routledge.

Pevsner, Nikolaus. Building England Cambridgeshire 1970. 2nd rev. ed. (Illus.). 576p. 50.00 (978-0-14-071010-6(8)) Penguin Bks., Ltd. GBR. Dist: Trafalgar Square Publishing.

—Buildings of England: London Docklands. (Illus.). 320p. pap. 24.95 (978-0-14-071096-0(5)) Penguin Bks., Ltd. GBR. Dist: Trafalgar Square Publishing.

—Buildings of England Berkshire 1966. (Illus.). 360p. 45.00 (978-0-14-071030-4(2)) Penguin Bks., Ltd. GBR. Dist: Trafalgar Square Publishing.

—Cheshire. (Buildings of England Ser.). (Illus.). 448p. 45.00 (978-0-14-071042-7(6)) Penguin Group (USA) Inc.

—Cumberland, Westmorland, 1967. (Illus.). 344p. 45.00 (978-0-14-071033-5(7)) Penguin Bks., Ltd. GBR. Dist: Trafalgar Square Publishing.

—Derbyshire. 2nd ed. (Buildings of England Ser.). (Illus.). 416p. 45.00 (978-0-14-071008-3(6)) Penguin Bks., Ltd. GBR. Dist: Trafalgar Square Publishing.

—Dorset. (Illus.). 556p. pap. 50.00 (978-0-14-071044-1(2)) Penguin Bks., Ltd. GBR. Dist: Trafalgar Square Publishing.

—Hampshire Isle Wight, 1967. (Illus.). 848p. pap. 50.00 (978-0-14-071032-8(9)) Penguin Bks., Ltd. GBR. Dist: Trafalgar Square Publishing.

—Herefordshire 1963. (Buildings of England Ser.). (Illus.). 368p. 45.00 (978-0-14-071025-0(6)) Penguin Bks., Ltd. GBR. Dist: Trafalgar Square Publishing.

—Lancashire South. (Buildings of England Ser.). (Illus.). 1p. 45.00 (978-0-14-071036-6(1)) Penguin Bks., Ltd. GBR. Dist: Trafalgar Square Publishing.

—Matthew Digby Wyatt: The First Cambridge Slade Professor of Fine Art - An Inaugural Lecture. 2010. (ENG.). 72p. pap. 19.99 (978-0-521-17076-5(1)) Cambridge Univ. Pr.

—Northumberland. 2nd ed. (Illus.). 600p. 65.00 (978-0-14-071059-5(0)) Penguin Bks., Ltd. GBR. Dist: Trafalgar Square Publishing.

—Nottinghamshire. 2nd ed. (Buildings of England Ser.). (Illus.). 448p. 50.00 (978-0-14-071002-1(7)) Penguin Bks., Ltd. GBR. Dist: Trafalgar Square Publishing.

—Somerset North & Bristol. (Buildings of England Ser.). (Illus.). 516p. 50.00 (978-0-14-071013-7(2)) Penguin Bks., Ltd. GBR. Dist: Trafalgar Square Publishing.

—South & West Somerset. (Illus.). 400p. 45.00 (978-0-14-071014-4(0)) Penguin Bks., Ltd. GBR. Dist: Trafalgar Square Publishing.

—Staffordshire, 1974. (Buildings of England Ser.). (Illus.). 384p. 45.00 (978-0-14-071046-5(9)) Penguin Bks., Ltd. GBR. Dist: Trafalgar Square Publishing.

—Suffolk. 2nd rev. ed. (Illus.). 568p. 50.00 (978-0-14-071020-5(5)) Penguin Bks., Ltd. GBR. Dist: Trafalgar Square Publishing.

—Sussex 1965. (Buildings of England Ser.). (Illus.). 704p. 50.00 (978-0-14-071028-1(0)) Penguin Bks., Ltd. GBR. Dist: Trafalgar Square Publishing.

—Warwickshire, 1966. (Illus.). 1p. 45.00 (978-0-14-071031-1(0)) Penguin Group (USA) Inc.

—Yorkshire North Riding. (Buildings of England Ser.). (ENG., Illus.). 456p. 45.00 (978-0-14-071029-8(9)) Penguin Bks., Ltd. GBR. Dist: Trafalgar Square Publishing.

Pevsner, Nikolaus & Cherry, Brigid. Buildings England Hertfordshire 1977. 2nd ed. (Illus.). 446p. 45.00 (978-0-14-071007-6(8)) Penguin Bks., Ltd. GBR. Dist: Trafalgar Square Publishing.

—Northamptonshire. 2nd rev. ed. (Buildings of England Ser.). (Illus.). 544p. 50.00 (978-0-14-071022-9(1)) Penguin Bks., Ltd. GBR. Dist: Trafalgar Square Publishing.

Pevsner, Nikolaus & Harris. Lincolnshire 1964. 2nd ed. (Buildings of England Ser.). (Illus.). 880p. 65.00 (978-0-14-071027-4(2)) Penguin Bks., Ltd. GBR. Dist: Trafalgar Square Publishing.

Pevsner, Nikolaus & Nairn, C. Surrey. 2nd rev. ed. (Buildings of England Ser.). (Illus.). 600p. 50.00 (978-0-14-071021-2(3)) Penguin Bks., Ltd. GBR. Dist: Trafalgar Square Publishing.

Pevsner, Nikolaus & Radcliff. Essex 1965. 2nd rev. ed. (Buildings of England Ser.). (Illus.). 496p. 45.00 (978-0-14-071011-3(6)) Penguin Bks., Ltd. GBR. Dist: Trafalgar Square Publishing.

Pevsner, Nikolaus & Sherwood. Oxfordshire 1974. (Buildings of England Ser.). (Illus.). 936p. 45.00 (978-0-14-071045-8(0)) Penguin Bks., Ltd. GBR. Dist: Trafalgar Square Publishing.

Phillips, Charles. The Castles & Palaces of the Tudors & Stuarts: The Golden Age of Britain's Historic & Stately Houses. 2009. (ENG., Illus.). 86p. pap. 16.99 (978-1-84476-706-9(X)) Anness Publishing GBR. Dist: National Bk. Network.

Powell, Kenneth. Ahrends, Burton & Koralek. 2012. (Twentieth-century Architects Ser.). (ENG., Illus.). 152p. (C). pap. 40.00 (978-1-85946-166-2(2)) English Heritage GBR. Dist: Brown, David Bk. Co., The.

—New London Architecture 2. 2007. (ENG., Illus.). 240p. 54.95 (978-1-85894-360-2(4)) Merrell Pubs. Ltd. GBR. Dist: Perseus Distribution.

—Powell & Moya. 2009. (Twentieth-century Architects Ser.). (ENG., Illus.). 160p. (C). pap. 40.00 (978-1-85946-303-1(7)) English Heritage GBR. Dist: Brown, David Bk. Co., The.

—Richard Rogers - Complete Works, 3 vols., Vol. 3. 2006. (ENG., Illus.). 320p. 95.00 (978-0-7148-4429-9(2)) Phaidon Pr. Ltd. GBR. Dist: Hachette Bk. Group.

—21st Century London: The New Architecture. 2011. (ENG., Illus.). 352p. 34.95 (978-1-85894-537-8(2)) Merrell Pubs. Ltd. GBR. Dist: Perseus Distribution.

Powers, Alan. Britain: Modern Architectures in History. 2007. (Reaktion Books - Modern Architectures in History Ser.). (ENG., Illus.). 272p. per. 29.95 (978-1-86189-281-2(0)) Reaktion Bks., Ltd. GBR. Dist: Chicago Distribution Ctr.

—Modern: The Modern Movement in Britain. 2007. (ENG., Illus.). 240p. pap. 39.95 (978-1-85894-405-0(8)) Merrell Pubs. Ltd. GBR. Dist: Perseus Distribution.

Powys & Haslam, Richard. Powys. (Illus.). 432p. pap. 45.00 (978-0-14-071051-9(5)) Penguin Bks., Ltd. GBR. Dist: Trafalgar Square Publishing.

Prasad, Sunand. Transformations: The Architecture of Penoyre & Prasad. 2007. (ENG., Illus.). 239p. per. 39.95 (978-1-904772-67-5(6)) Black Dog Publishing Ltd. GBR. Dist: Perseus Distribution.

Rabbitts, Paul. Bandstands. 2011. (Shire Library). (ENG., Illus.). 64p. pap. 12.95 (978-0-7478-0825-1(2)) Shire Pubns., Ltd. GBR. Dist: Random Hse., Inc.

Rapley, John. Britannia & Other Tubular Bridges. (Illus.). 176p. 37.50 (978-0-7524-2753-9(9)) History Pr. Ltd., The GBR. Dist: Trafalgar Square Publishing.

Rattenbury, Kester. Cedric Price: Potteries Thinkbelt. Hardingham, Samantha, ed. 2008. (Supercrit Ser.). (ENG., Illus.). 138p. (C). 49.95 (978-0-415-43412-6(2)) Routledge.

Rattenbury, Kester & Hardingham, Samantha, eds. Cedric Price: Potteries Thinkbelt. 2008. (Supercrit Ser.). (ENG., Illus.). 138p. (C). 165.00 (978-0-415-43411-9(4)) Routledge.

Rawle, T. Oxford Architecture. pap. 29.95 (978-0-233-98865-8(3)) Andre Deutsch GBR. Dist: Trafalgar Square Publishing.

Reilly, C. Representative British Architects. 2007. 176p. per. (978-1-905217-73-1(0)) Mills, Jeremy Publishing.

Rice, Matthew. Rice's Architectural Primer. 2010. (ENG., Illus.). 240p. 18.00 (978-0-7475-9748-3(0)) Bloomsbury Publishing.

Richmond, Peter & Dunne, Jack. The World in One School: The History & Influence of the Liverpool School of Architecture 1894-2008. 2009. (ENG., Illus.). 96p. pap. 29.95 (978-1-84631-165-9(9)) Liverpool Univ. Pr. GBR. Dist: Chicago Distribution Ctr.

Risselada, Max, ed. A Critical Anthology. 2011. (ENG., Illus.). 368p. 45.00 (978-84-343-1254-8(9)) Polígrafa, Ediciones, S. A. ESP. Dist: D.A.P./Distributed Art Pubs.

Roberts, Hugh. For the King's Pleasure: The Furnishing & Decoration of George IV's Apartments at Windsor Castle. 2010. (ENG., Illus.). 464p. 115.00 (978-1-902163-04-8(4)) Royal Collection Enterprises Ltd. GBR. Dist: Chicago Distribution Ctr.

Robinson, John Martin. James Wyatt, 1746-1813: Architect to George III. 2012. (Paul Mellon Centre for Studies in British Art Ser.). (ENG., Illus.). 400p. 75.00 **(978-0-300-17690-2(2))** Yale Univ. Pr.

—Queen Mary's Dolls' House: Official Souvenir Guide. 2012. (ENG., Illus.). 56p. pap. 10.95 **(978-1-85759-763-9(X))** Scala, Editions FRA. Dist: National Bk. Network.

Robinson, Marcus & Rose, Steve. Eye: The Story Behind the London Eye. 2007. (ENG., Illus.). 191p. 39.95 (978-1-906155-08-7(9)) Black Dog Publishing Ltd. GBR. Dist: Perseus Distribution.

Rogers, Richard. Richard Rogers + Architects: From the House to the City. 2010. (ENG., Illus.). 272p. 45.00 (978-1-906863-11-1(3)) FIELL Pubng. Ltd. GBR. Dist: D.A.P./Distributed Art Pubs.

Rolf, Vivien. Bathing Houses & Plunge Pools. 2011. (Shire Library). (ENG., Illus.). 64p. pap. 12.95 (978-0-7478-0809-1(0)) Shire Pubns., Ltd. GBR. Dist: Random Hse., Inc.

Royal Collection Publications. Buckingham Palace - Espanol. 2010. (Illus.). 96p. pap. 7.95 (978-1-902163-38-3(9)) Royal Collection Enterprises Ltd. GBR. Dist: Chicago Distribution Ctr.

Ruthven, Ianthe. Animal London. 2011. (ENG., Illus.). 174p. pap. 19.95 **(978-0-224-08704-9(5))** Random Hse. GBR. Dist: Independent Pubs. Group.

Rybczneki, Witold. The Biography of a Building: How Robert Sainsbury & Norman Foster Built a Great Museum. 2011. (ENG., Illus.). 208p. 29.95 (978-0-500-34276-3(8), 534276) Thames & Hudson.

Salk, Susanna. Weekend Retreats. 2009. (ENG., Illus.). 216p. 45.00 (978-0-8478-3200-2(7)) Rizzoli International Pubns., Inc.

Shariff, Yasmin & Tankard, Jane. Towards a New Architect: The Guide for Architecture Students. 2010. (ENG., Illus.). 128p. pap. 37.95 (978-1-85617-604-0(5)) Routledge.

Sharp, Dennis & Rendel, Sally. Connell Ward & Lucas: Modernist Architecture in England. 2008. (ENG., Illus.). 224p. 65.00 (978-0-7112-2768-2(3)) Lincoln, Frances Ltd. GBR. Dist: Perseus-PGW.

Sharpe, Geoffrey R. Traditional Buildings of the English Countryside: An Illustrated Guide. 2011. (ENG., Illus.). 240p. 75.00 (978-1-84885-614-1(8)); pap. 25.00 (978-1-84511-841-9(3)) I. B. Tauris & Co., Ltd. GBR. Dist: Macmillan.

Shiqiao, Li. Power & Virtue: Architecture & Intellectual Change in England 1660-1730. 2006. (Classical Tradition in Architecture Ser.). (Illus.). 246p. 165.00 (978-0-415-37424-8(3)) Routledge.

Slocombe, Matthew. Traditional Building Materials. 2012. (Shire Library). (ENG., Illus.). 104p. pap. 15.95 **(978-0-7478-0840-4(6))** Shire Pubns., Ltd. GBR. Dist: Random Hse., Inc.

Snodin, Michael, ed. Horace Walpole's Strawberry Hill. 2009. (Lewis Walpole Series in Eighteenth-C Ser.). (ENG., Illus.). 356p. 85.00 (978-0-300-12574-0(7)) Yale Univ. Pr.

Soo, Lydia M. Wren's 'Tracts' on Architecture & Other Writings. 2007. (ENG.). 340p. pap. 72.00 *(978-0-521-04424-0(3))* Cambridge Univ. Pr.

Soriano, Kathleen, et al. Compton Verney. 2011. (ENG., Illus.). 128p. pap. 24.95 *(978-1-85759-560-4(2))* Scala, Editions FRA. Dist: National Bk. Network.

Soros, Susan Weber & Stuart, James. James "Athenian" Stuart: The Rediscovery of Antiquity. 2007. (ENG., Illus.). 688p. 110.00 *(978-0-300-11713-4(2))* Yale Univ. Pr.

Souden, David, et al. The Royal Palaces of London. 2008. (Illus.). 223p. *(978-1-85894-423-4(6))* Merrell Pubs. Ltd.

Stamp, Gavin. Britain's Lost Cities: A Chronicle of Architectural Destruction. 2010. (ENG.). 186p. pap. 29.95 *(978-1-84513-523-2(7))* Aurum Pr., Ltd. GBR. Dist: Independent Pubs. Group.

—Lost Victorian Britain: How the Twentieth Century Destroyed the Nineteenth Century's Architectural Masterpieces. 2010. (ENG., Illus.). 192p. 39.95 *(978-1-84513-532-4(6))* Aurum Pr., Ltd. GBR. Dist: Independent Pubs. Group.

Stevenson, Greg. The 1930s Home. 2008. (Shire Library). (ENG., Illus.). 40p. pap. 11.95 *(978-0-7478-0464-2(8))* Shire Pubns., Ltd. GBR. Dist: Random Hse., Inc.

Stonehouse, Roger. Trevor Dannatt: Works & Words. 2009. (ENG., Illus.). 192p. 49.95 *(978-1-906155-21-6(6))* Black Dog Publishing Ltd. GBR. Dist: Perseus Distribution.

Stratton, Arthur. Introductory Handbook to the Styles of English Architecture, Part: Tudor & Renaissance. 2011. 34p. 35.95 ***(978-1-258-10016-2(9))*** Literary Licensing, LLC.

Survey of London Staff. Northern Clerkenwell & Pentonville, Vol. 47. 2008. (ENG., Illus.). 400p. 150.00 *(978-0-300-13937-2(3))* Yale Univ. Pr.

—South & East Clerkenwell, Vol. 46. 2008. (ENG., Illus.). 400p. 150.00 *(978-0-300-13727-9(3))* Yale Univ. Pr.

Symondson, Anthony & Harwood, Elain. Chamberlin, Powell & Bon. 2011. (Twentieth-century Architects Ser.). (ENG., Illus.). 160p. (C). pap. 40.00 ***(978-1-85946-397-0(5))*** English Heritage GBR. Dist: Brown, David Bk. Co., The.

Tames, Richard. Parliament & its Buildings. 2012. (Shire Library). (ENG., Illus.). 64p. pap. 12.95 ***(978-0-7478-1166-4(0))*** Shire Pubns., Ltd. GBR. Dist: Random Hse., Inc.

Temple, Philip. Survey of London: The Charterhouse. 2010. (Illus.). 320p. 150.00 *(978-0-300-16722-1(9))* Yale Univ. Pr.

Thomson, Nick. Corrugated Iron Buildings: Churches, Houses, Sheds & Huts. 2011. (Shire Library). (ENG., Illus.). 64p. pap. 12.95 *(978-0-7478-0783-4(3))* Shire Pubns., Ltd. GBR. Dist: Random Hse., Inc.

Thornton, Roy. Lost Buildings of Birmingham. 2009. (ENG., Illus.). 160p. pap. 28.95 *(978-0-7509-5099-2(4))* History Pr. Ltd., The GBR. Dist: Independent Pubs. Group.

Thurley, Simon. The Royal Palaces of Stuart England. 2009. 60.00 *(978-0-300-11927-5(5))* Yale Univ. Pr.

Tilley, Christopher. Interpreting Landscapes: Geologies, Topographies, Identities - Explorations in Landscape Phenomenology 3. 2010. (ENG., Illus.). 536p. lib. bdg. 89.00 *(978-1-59874-374-6(0))* Left Coast Pr., Inc.

Tilley, Christopher. Interpreting Landscapes: Geologies, Topographies, Identities; Explorations in Landscape Phenomenology 3. 2012. (ENG.). 536p. pap. 44.95 ***(978-1-59874-375-3(9))*** Left Coast Pr., Inc.

Trinder, Barrie. One Hundred Buildings of East Grinstead. 2006. (ENG., Illus.). 128p. 26.00 *(978-1-86077-381-5(8),* Phillimore & Co.) History Pr. Ltd., The GBR. Dist: Brown, David Bk. Co., The.

Tuttle, Maria & Binney, Marcus. Winfield House. 2008. (ENG., Illus.). 172p. 60.00 *(978-0-500-97678-4(3))* Thames & Hudson.

Tyack, Geoffrey. John Nash: Architect of the Picturesque. Tyack, Geoffrey, ed. 2012. (ENG., Illus.). 250p. (C). pap. 100.00 ***(978-1-84802-102-0(X))*** English Heritage GBR. Dist: Brown, David Bk. Co., The.

Tyack, Geoffrey, et al. Berkshire. 2010. (Pevsner Architectural Guides). (ENG., Illus.). 800p. 85.00 *(978-0-300-12662-4(X))* Yale Univ. Pr.

van den Heuvel, Dirk, et al, eds. DASH 02: the Luxury City Apartment. 2010. (ENG., Illus.). 176p. pap. 50.00 *(978-90-5662-717-1(1))* NAi Uitgevers / Publishers Stichting NLD. Dist: D.A.P./Distributed Art Pubs.

Vesely, Dalibor & Wang, Wilfried. Eric Parry Architects, Vol. 2. 2011. (ENG., Illus.). 208p. pap. 39.95 *(978-1-906155-25-4(9))* Black Dog Publishing Ltd. GBR. Dist: Perseus Distribution.

Vickers, Hugo. The Royal Mews at Buckingham Palace: Official Souvenir Guide. 2012. (ENG., Illus.). 56p. pap. 10.95 ***(978-1-85759-761-5(3))*** Scala, Editions FRA. Dist: National Bk. Network.

Vidler, Anthony. James Frazer Stirling: Notes from the Archive. 2010. (Illus.). 300p. 70.00 *(978-0-300-16723-8(7))* Yale Univ. Pr.

Vogt, Gunther & Alice, Foxley. Distance & Engagement: Landscape Thinking — Model Making. 2010. (Illus.). 480p. 80.00 *(978-3-03778-196-8(3))* Lars Muller Pubs. CHE. Dist: Prestel Publishing.

Wallpaper Magazine Editors, ed. London 2011 - Wallpaper City Guide. 4th ed. 2011. (ENG., Illus.). 128p. pap. 9.95 *(978-0-7148-5941-5(9))* Phaidon Pr., Inc.

Wang, Wilfried & Vesely, Dalibor. Eric Parry Architects, Vols. 1 & 2. 2011. (ENG., Illus.). 416p. pap. 70.00 *(978-1-906155-63-6(1))* Black Dog Publishing Ltd. GBR. Dist: Actar Birkhauser Distribution.

Ward, W. C. Sir John Vanbrugh V1. 2006. pap. 38.95 *(978-1-4286-6103-5(4))* Kessinger Publishing, LLC.

—Sir John Vanbrugh V2. 2006. pap. 34.95 *(978-1-4286-6104-2(2))* Kessinger Publishing, LLC.

Watkin, David & Taylor, John Russell. Carl Laubin: Paintings. 2007. (ENG., Illus.). 224p. 68.00 *(978-0-85667-633-8(0))* Wilson, Philip Pubs., Ltd. GBR. Dist: Macmillan.

Watts, Andrew, ed. Scratching the Surface: New London Facades by London Architects. 2007. (ENG., Illus.). 303p. pap. 39.95 *(978-3-211-71538-3(X),* 321171538X) Springer.

Waugh, Andrew, et al, eds. A Process Revealed. 2009. (GER & ENG., Illus.). 96p. 34.95 *(978-0-9558620-6-9(X))* FUEL Publishing GBR. Dist: D.A.P./Distributed Art Pubs.

Wedd, Kitt. Victorian Housebuilding. 2012. (Shire Library). (ENG., Illus.). 64p. pap. 12.95 ***(978-0-7478-1095-7(8))*** Shire Pubns., Ltd. GBR. Dist: Random Hse., Inc.

Weinreb, Ben. London Architecture. (Illus.). 240p. 49.95 *(978-0-7148-2890-9(4))* Phaidon Pr. Ltd. GBR. Dist: Hachette Bk. Group.

Whitelaw, Jeffery W. Follies. 4th ed. 2008. (Shire Library). (ENG., Illus.). 56p. pap. 12.95 *(978-0-7478-0624-0(1))* Shire Pubns., Ltd. GBR. Dist: Random Hse., Inc.

Wilkie, Kim. Led by the Land. 2012. (ENG., Illus.). 176p. 50.00 ***(978-0-7112-3325-6(X))*** Lincoln, Frances Ltd. GBR. Dist: Perseus-PGW.

Wilkinson, Philip. Pocket Guide to English Architecture. 2009. (Illus.). 144p. pap. 19.99 *(978-1-84468-045-0(2))* Pen & Sword Bks. Ltd. GBR. Dist: Casemate Pubs. & Bk. Distributors, LLC.

Wilkinson, Philip & Ashley, Peter. The English Buildings Book. 2009. (ENG., Illus.). 390p. (C). pap. 40.00 *(978-1-905624-63-8(8))* English Heritage GBR. Dist: Brown, David Bk. Co., The.

Willis, Robert & Willis Clark, John. Selections from the Architectural History of the University of Cambridge: King's College & Eton College. 2009. (ENG.). 376p. pap. 30.00 *(978-0-521-14719-4(0))* Cambridge Univ. Pr.

—Selections from the Architectural History of the University of Cambridge: Peterhouse. 2009. (ENG.). 120p. pap. 15.99 *(978-0-521-14714-9(X))* Cambridge Univ. Pr.

—Selections from the Architectural History of the University of Cambridge: St Johns College. 2009. (ENG.). 164p. pap. 15.99 *(978-0-521-14715-6(8))* Cambridge Univ. Pr.

—Selections from the Architectural History of the University of Cambridge: Trinity College. 2009. (ENG.). 368p. pap. 30.00 *(978-0-521-14718-7(2),* Cambridge Univ. Pr.

Wilson, Vicky. London's Houses. 2011. (ENG., Illus.). 384p. pap. 15.95 *(978-1-902910-36-9(2))* Metro Pubns. GBR. Dist: Independent Pubs. Group.

Woodman, Ellis & Fretton, Tony. Modernity & Reinvention: The Architecture of James Gowan. 2008. (ENG., Illus.). 235p. pap. 55.00 *(978-1-906155-28-5(3))* Black Dog Publishing Ltd. GBR. Dist: Perseus Distribution.

Yale School of Architecture Staff, et al. Urban Integration - Bishopsgate Good Yards: Johnson, Nick & FAT Architects. Rappaport, Nina, ed. 2010. (Yale School of Architecture Bks.). (ENG., Illus.). 192p. pap. 35.00 *(978-0-393-73322-8(X),* 73322) Norton, W. W. & Co., Inc.

Yorke, Trevor. Bridges Explained: Viaducts, Aqueducts. 2008. (Illus.). 160p. (C). pap. 23.95 *(978-1-84674-079-4(7))* Countryside Bks. GBR. Dist: Brown, David Bk. Co., The.

Zimmerman, Claire & Crinson, Mark, eds. Neo-Avant-Garde & Postmodern: Postwar Architecture in Britain & Beyond. 2010. (Studies in British Art Ser.). (Illus.). 432p. 65.00 *(978-0-300-16618-7(4))* Yale Ctr. for British Art.

ARCHITECTURE—GREECE

see Architecture, Greek

ARCHITECTURE—HUNGARY

Architecture, 1990-2008: Czech Republic, Slovakia, Hungary, Poland, 1 vol. 2011. (ENG., Illus.). 200p. pap. 55.00 *(978-80-7437-000-7(3))* Kant CZE. Dist: D.A.P./Distributed Art Pubs.

Bachman, Zoltan. Bachman Zoltán. 2010. (HUN, GER & ENG., Illus.). 322p. 54.95 ***(978-963-303-001-1(3))*** Vince Kiado Kft HUN. Dist: Independent Pubs. Group.

Gerő, András. Public Space in Budapest: The History of Kossuth Square. 2010. (ENG., Illus.). 230p. (gr. 17). 40.00 *(978-0-88033-648-2(X))* Eastern European Monographs.

Juckes, Tim. St. Elizabeth's in Kosice: Town, Court & Church Building in Late Medieval Hungary. 2012. (Architectura Medii Aevi Ser.). (ENG., Illus.). 320p. (C). pap. 123.00 *(978-2-503-53109-0(1))* Brepols Pubs. BEL. Dist: ISD.

Pratt, Lord Michael. Hungary. 2008. (Great Country Houses Of... Ser.). (ENG., Illus.). 143p. 39.95 *(978-0-7892-0891-0(1))* Abbeville Pr., Inc.

Rodriguez, Maria Ines, ed. Architecture with the People, by the People, for the People: Yona Friedman. 2011. (ENG.). 160p. pap. *(978-84-92861-94-1(0))* Actar Birkhauser Distribution.

ARCHITECTURE—INDIA

Albanese, Marilia. Archaeology: Northern India. 2008. (White Star Guides). (ENG., Illus.). 168p. pap. 18.95 *(978-88-544-0041-2(6))* White Star ITA. Dist: Random Hse., Inc.

Baan, Iwan. Brasilia-Chandigarh: Living with Modernity. 2010. (Illus.). 240p. pap. *(978-3-03778-228-6(5))* Lars Muller Pubs.

Babb, Lawrence, et al. Desert Temples: Sacred Centers of Rajasthan in Historical, Art-Historical, & Social Contexts. 2008. 260p. 35.00 *(978-81-316-0106-8(4))* Rawat Pubns. IND. Dist: International Specialized Bk. Services.

Batra, N. L. Delhi's Red Fort by the Yamuna. 2008. (ENG., Illus.). 181p. 50.00 *(978-0-85667-654-3(3))* Wilson, Philip Pubs., Ltd. GBR. Dist: Macmillan.

Bharadwaj, Monisha. India Style. (Illus.). 160p. pap. 32.95 *(978-1-85626-495-2(5))* Cathie, Kyle Ltd. GBR. Dist: Graphic Arts Ctr. Publishing Co.

Bhatia, Gautam. Silent Spaces & Other Stories of Architecture. (Illus.). xii, 315p. *(978-0-14-024609-4(6))* Penguin Group (USA) Inc.

Bunce, Fredrick W. Monuments of India & the Indianized States: The Plans of Major & Notable Temples, Tombs, Palaces, & Pavilions of Bangladesh, Sri Lanka, Java, the Khmer, Pagan, Thailand, Vietnam, & Malaysia, from 3rd C. BCE to CE 1854. 2007. (Illus.). xx, 518p. *(978-81-246-0385-7(5))* D. K. Print World (P) Ltd.

Burton-Page, John. Indian Islamic Architecture: Forms & Typologies, Sites & Monuments. Michell, George, ed. 2007. (Handbook of Oriental Studies. Section 2 South Asia, 18/2 Ser.). (Illus.). 194p. *(978-90-04-16339-3(5))* BRILL.

Chopra, Preeti. A Joint Enterprise: Indian Elites & the Making of British Bombay. 2011. (Illus.). 344p. 82.50 *(978-0-8166-7036-9(6));* pap. 27.50 *(978-0-8166-7037-6(4))* Univ. of Minnesota Pr.

COLOUR, LOCAL. Taj Mahal. (Our World in Colour Ser.). (Illus.). 80p *(978-962-8711-23-9(7))* Local Colour, Ltd. HKG. Dist: 7 Hills Bk. Distributors.

Curm, Mumtaz & Michell, George. Dargahs: Abodes of the Saints. 2011. (ENG., Illus.). 152p. 66.00 ***(978-81-85026-65-7(3))*** Marg Pubns. IND. Dist: National Bk. Network.

Das, Kausik. Development Trend of Private Land Development Projects in Bangladesh. 2010. 88p. pap. *(978-3-639-27176-8(9))* VDM Verlag Dr. Mueller e.K.

Doctor-Pingel, Mona. Poppo Pingel: Auroville Architects Monograph Series. 2012. (ENG., Illus.). 204p. 50.00 *(978-1-935677-11-6(X))* Mapin Publishing Pvt. Ltd IND. Dist: National Bk. Network.

Fergusson, James. History of Indian & Eastern Architecture. 2009. 284p. pap. *(978-1-151-43644-3(5))* Books LLC.

Gobhai, Noshir, et al. Hampi: A Story in Stone. 2009. (Illus.). 196p. *(978-81-903821-6-8(0),* Library of Congress — New Delhi Overseas Office) Eminence Designs.

Havell, E.B. Hand Book of Indian Art. 2006. 280p. per. *(978-1-4067-0254-5(4),* Hesperides Pr.) Read Bks.

Hendricks, J. & Taschen, Angelika, eds. Indian Style: Landscapes, Houses, Interiors, Details. 25th ed. 2008. (Icon (Taschen) Ser.). (ENG., Illus.). 191p. 7.99 *(978-3-8365-0769-1(2))* TASCHEN DEU. Dist: Ingram Pub. Services.

Hoegner, Barbel, photos by. Chandigarh: Living with le Corbusier. 2011. (ENG., Illus.). 144p. 45.00 *(978-3-86859-137-8(0))* Jovis Verlag GmbH DEU. Dist: D.A.P./Distributed Art Pubs.

Jahanbegloo, Ramin & Rewal, Raj. Talking Architecture: Raj Rewal in Conversation with Ramin Jahanbegloo. 2012. (ENG., Illus.). 162p. pap. 40.00 ***(978-0-19-808294-1(0))*** Oxford Univ. Pr., Inc.

Jamkhedkar, A. P. Ajanta. 2009. (Monumental Legacy Ser.). (ENG., Illus.). 112p. 29.95 *(978-0-19-569785-8(5))* Oxford Univ. Pr., Inc.

Kavuri-Bauer, Santhi. Monumental Matters: The Power, Subjectivity, & Space of India's Mughal Architecture. 2011. (ENG., Illus.). 232p. 84.95 *(978-0-8223-4899-3(3));* pap. 23.95 *(978-0-8223-4922-8(1))* Duke Univ. Pr.

Koch, Ebba. The Complete Taj Mahal. 2006. (ENG., Illus.). 288p. 75.00 *(978-0-500-34209-1(1))* Thames & Hudson.

Kundoo, Anupama, text. Roger Anger: Research on Beauty. 2009. (ENG., Illus.). 192p. 45.00 *(978-3-86859-006-7(4))* Jovis Verlag GmbH DEU. Dist: D.A.P./Distributed Art Pubs.

Lambah, Abha Narain & Patel, Alka, eds. The Architecture of the Indian Sultanates. 2007. (Illus.). 116p. 66.00 *(978-81-85026-75-6(0))* Marg Pubns. IND. Dist: National Bk. Network.

mathur, sharad. Space,life & Planning. 2010. 185p. 36.51 *(978-0-557-31818-6(1))* Lulu Enterprises Inc.

Mehrotra, Rahul, text. Architecture in India: Since 1900. 2011. (ENG., Illus.). 312p. 75.00 ***(978-3-7757-3245-1(4))*** Hatje Cantz Verlag GmbH & Co KG DEU. Dist: D.A.P./Distributed Art Pubs.

Michell, George & Pasricha, Amit. Mughal Architecture & Gardens. 2011. (ENG., Illus.). 402p. 89.50 ***(978-1-85149-670-9(X))*** Antique Collectors' Club.

Mitchell, Maurice, et al. Learning from Delhi: Dispersed Initiatives in Changing Urban Landscapes. 2010. (Illus.). 322p. pap. 69.95 *(978-1-4094-0102-5(2))* Ashgate Publishing Co.

Nath, Aman. Dome over India: Rashtrapati Bhavan. 2006. (Illus.). 136p. 95.00 *(978-81-7508-352-3(2))* India Bk. Hse. Pvt., Ltd. IND. Dist: Antique Collectors' Club.

Nath, Ravinder. History of Mughal Architecture: History of Mughal. 2006. 788p. pap. 149.95 *(978-81-7017-414-1(7))* Abhinav Pubns. IND. Dist: Independent Pubs. Group.

Padhi, Braja Kishor. Religious Art & Architecture of North-East India. 2009. (Illus.). xix, 284p. *(978-81-7320-091-5(2),* Library of Congress — New Delhi Overseas Office) Agam Kala Prakashan.

Philon, Helen. Silent Splendour: Palaces of the Deccan, 14th-19th Centuries. 2010. (ENG., Illus.). 148p. 68.00 *(978-81-85026-96-1(3))* Marg Pubns. IND. Dist: National Bk. Network.

Pitkar, Yashwant. The Romance of Red Stone: An Appreciation of Ornament on Islamic Architecture in India. 2011. (ENG., Illus.). 256p. 79.00 *(978-81-900809-4-1(6))* Edition Axel Menges GmbH DEU. Dist: National Bk. Network.

Porter, Louise. Made in India. 2008. (Architectural Design Ser.). (ENG.). 160p. pap. 45.00 *(978-0-470-03476-7(9),* Wiley) Wiley, John & Sons, Inc.

Ramani, Navin. Bombay Art Deco Architecture: A Visual Journey: 1930-1953. Cerwinske, Laura, ed. 2007. (ENG., Illus.). 295p. 34.95 *(978-81-7436-447-0(1))* Roli Bks. Private, Ltd. IND. Dist: Ingram Pub. Services.

Sane, Prajakta. Experiential Shaping of Public Space During Pilgrimage. 2008. 244p. pap. *(978-3-8364-9154-9(0))* VDM Verlag Dr. Mueller e.K.

Scriver, Peter & Prakash, Vikramaditya. Colonial Modernities: Building, Dwelling & Architecture in British India & Ceylon. 2007. (Architext Ser.). (Illus.). 287p. per. 62.95 *(978-0-415-39909-8(2))* Routledge.

Scriver, Peter & Prakash, Vikramaditya, eds. Colonial Modernities: Building, Dwelling & Architecture in British India & Ceylon. 2007. (Architext Ser.). (ENG., Illus.). 304p. (C). 165.00 *(978-0-415-39908-1(4))* Routledge.

Sethi, Sunil. Indian Interiors. Taschen, Angelika, ed. 25th ed. 2009. (Interiors (Taschen) Ser.). (FRE, GER & ENG., Illus.). 279p. 19.99 *(978-3-8365-0995-4(4))* TASCHEN DEU. Dist: Ingram Pub. Services.

Shah, Jagan. Contemporary Indian Architecture. 2008. (ENG., Illus.). 271p. 34.95 *(978-81-7436-446-3(3))* Roli Bks. Private, Ltd. IND. Dist: Ingram Pub. Services.

Touchaleaume, Eric, ed. Le Corbusier, Pierre Jeanneret: The Indian Story. 2011. (FRE & ENG., Illus.). 600p. 180.00 *(978-2-35340-099-7(X))* Gourcuff Gradenigo FRA. Dist: National Bk. Network.

Wallpaper Magazine Editors, ed. Mumbai 2012 - Wallpaper City Guide. 2nd ed. 2012. (ENG., Illus.). 128p. pap. 9.95 ***(978-0-7148-6305-4(X))*** Phaidon Pr. Ltd. GBR. Dist: Hachette Bk. Group.

ARCHITECTURE—INDOCHINA

Hartingh, Bertrand De & Craven-Smith-Milne, Anna. Vietnam Style. 2007. (ENG., Illus.). 208p. 44.95 *(978-0-7946-0018-1(2),* PeriplusEdition) Tuttle Publishing.

Karnchanaporn, Nuttinee. Fear & Domestic Architecture. 2009. 312p. pap. *(978-3-639-15374-3(X))* VDM Verlag Dr. Mueller e.K.

ARCHITECTURE—IRAN

Babaie, Sussan. Isfahan & Its Palaces: Statecraft, Shi'Ism & the Architecture of Conviviality in Early Modern Iran. 2008. (Edinburgh Studies in Islamic Art Ser.). (ENG., Illus.). 288p. (gr. 17). 150.00 *(978-0-7486-3375-3(8))* Edinburgh Univ. Pr. GBR. Dist: Columbia Univ. Pr.

Bier, Lionel. Sarvistan: A Study in Early Iranian Architecture. 2009. 140p. 21.00 *(978-1-59740-333-7(4));* pap. 14.00 *(978-1-59740-335-1(0))* ACLS Humanities E-Book.

Canby, Sheila R. Shah 'Abbas: The Remaking of Iran. 2009. (ENG., Illus.). 280p. (C). pap. 45.00 *(978-0-7141-2452-0(4))* British Museum Pr. GBR. Dist: Brown, David Bk. Co., The.

Grigor, Talinn. The Civilized Nation: Cultural Heritage & Modernity in 20th-Century Iran. 2009. (Illus.). 384p. 55.00 *(978-1-934772-78-2(X))* Periscope Publishing.

Hensel, Michael & Gharleghi, Mehran. Iran: Past, Present & Future Architectural Design. 2012. (Architectural Design Ser.: 41). (ENG.). 160p. pap. 40.00 ***(978-1-119-97450-5(X),*** Wiley) Wiley, John & Sons, Inc.

Jodidio, Philip. Iran: Architecture for Changing Societies - An International Seminar ... 11-17 October 2002, Yazd & Tehran, Iran. 2006. (ENG., Illus.). 218p. 45.00 *(978-88-422-1236-2(9))* Allemandi, Umberto & Co. GBR. Dist: Antique Collectors' Club.

Kennet, Derek & Luft, Paul, eds. Current Research in Sasanian Archaeology, Art & History. 2008. (Bar S Ser.). (ENG., Illus.). 171p. (C). pap. 83.00 *(978-1-4073-0299-7(X))* British Archaeological Reports Ltd. GBR. Dist: Brown, David Bk. Co., The.

Khaghani, Saeid. Islamic Architecture in Iran: Poststructural Theory & the Architectural History of Iranian Mosques. 2012. (International Library of Iranian Studies: No. 34). (ENG., Illus.). 288p. 95.00 *(978-1-84885-729-2(2),* Tauris Academic Studies) I. B. Tauris & Co., Ltd. GBR. Dist: Macmillan.

Minorsky, Vladimir. Geographical Factors in Persian Art. 2011. 83.96 *(978-1-61143-908-3(6))* Gorgias Pr., LLC.

Rezvan, Azita. Regenerating Semi-Open Spaces in Iranian House Architecture. 2010. 108p. pap. *(978-3-639-25369-6(8))* VDM Verlag Dr. Mueller e.K.

Rizvi, Kishwar. The Safavid Dynastic Shrine: Architecture, Religion & Power in Early Modern Iran. 2011. (British Institute of Persian Studies). (ENG., Illus.). 256p. 92.00 *(978-1-84885-354-6(8),* Tauris Academic Studies) I. B. Tauris & Co., Ltd. GBR. Dist: Macmillan.

Termohlen, David E. Did I Learn This Before I Was Born. 2011. 404p. pap. 29.95 ***(978-1-4560-9744-8(X))*** PublishAmerica, Inc.

Zabihi, Saereh. Effects of Modern Movement on Residential Buildings. 2011. 88p. pap. ***(978-3-8443-9662-1(4))*** Lambert Academic Publishing.

ARCHITECTURE—IRELAND

Casey, Christine, ed. The Eighteenth-century Dublin Townhouse. 2010. (Illus.). 312p. 65.00 *(978-1-84682-187-5(8))* Four Courts Pr. IRL. Dist: International Specialized Bk. Services.

Claffey, John A. & Simms, Anngret. Irish Historic Towns Atlas: Tuam. 2009. (Illus.). 20p. pap. 45.00 incl. cd-rom *(978-1-904890-47-8(4))* Royal Irish Academy IRL. Dist: International Specialized Bk. Services.

Dooley, Terence. The Big Houses & Landed Estates of Ireland: A Research Guide. Lyons, Mary Ann, ed. 2007. (Maynooth Research Guides in Local History Ser.: No. 11). (Illus.). 192p. pap. 24.95 *(978-1-85182-964-4(4))* Four Courts Pr. IRL. Dist: International Specialized Bk. Services.

Dublin City Council. The Georgian Squares of Dublin: An Architectural History. 2007. (Dublin City Council Ser.). (Illus.). 161p. (C). 55.00 *(978-0-946841-78-3(0));* pap. 39.95 *(978-0-946841-79-0(9))* Four Courts Pr. IRL. Dist: International Specialized Bk. Services.

Duffy, Patrick. Exploring the History & Heritage of Irish Landscapes. Lyons, Mary Ann, ed. 2007. (Maynooth Research Guides in Local History Ser.). (Illus.). 264p. pap. 24.95 *(978-1-85182-965-1(2))* Four Courts Pr. IRL. Dist: International Specialized Bk. Services.

A

Fewer, Michael, photos by. Doorways of Ireland. 2008. (ENG., Illus.). 112p. 29.95 *(978-0-7112-2881-8(7))* Lincoln, Frances Ltd. GBR. Dist: Perseus-PGW.

Fitzgerald, Mairéad. Castles of Ireland. 2007. (ENG., Illus.). 48p. pap. 12.95 ***(978-0-86278-988-6(5))*** O'Brien Pr., Ltd., The IRL. Dist: Dufour Editions, Inc.

Gray, Eileen. Eileen Gray: Objects & Furniture Design - By Architects. 2012. (ENG., Illus.). 128p. 30.00 *(978-84-343-1265-4(4))* Poligrafa, Ediciones, S. A. ESP. Dist: D.A.P./Distributed Art Pubs.

Harding, D. W. The Iron Age Round-House: Later Prehistoric Building in Britain & Beyond. 2009. (ENG., Illus.). 350p. 130.00 *(978-0-19-955857-5(4))* Oxford Univ. Pr., Inc.

Hull, Lise. Great Castles of Britain & Ireland. 2009. (ENG., Illus.). 160p. pap. 19.95 *(978-1-84773-130-2(9))* New Holland Pubs., Ltd. GBR. Dist: National Bk. Network.

Ireland, Department of the Environment, Heritage and Local Government Staff & Ireland, National Inventory of Architectural Heritage Staff, contrib. by. An Introduction to the Architectural Heritage of County Wexford. 2010. (Illus.). 140p. pap. *(978-1-4064-2173-6(1))* Stationery Office Dublin.

Kamvasinou, Krystallia & Canz, Simon. Artifice: Dermot Foley Landscape Architects. 2012. (ENG., Illus.). 160p. 45.00 *(978-1-907317-28-6(7))* Black Dog Publishing Ltd. GBR. Dist: Perseus Distribution.

Krawczyk, Elzbieta. Futures Thinking in City Planning Processes. 2010. 376p. pap. *(978-3-8383-4215-3(1))* Lambert Academic Publishing.

Lappin, Sarah A. Full Irish: New Architecture in Ireland. 2009. (ENG., Illus.). 240p. 45.00 *(978-1-56898-868-9(0))* Princeton Architectural Pr.

Lyttleton, James. Blarney Castle: An Irish Tower House. 2011. (Illus.). 174p. 60.00 *(978-1-84682-274-2(2))* Four Courts Pr. IRL. Dist: International Specialized Bk. Services.

Malcomson, Anthony. Nathaniel Clements, 1705-77: Arbiter of Taste & Amateur of Architecture. 2012. (Illus.). 320p. 75.00 *(978-1-85182-914-9(8))* Four Courts Pr. IRL. Dist: International Specialized Bk. Services.

Mc Enery, Dermot. Thatched Vernacular Houses of South-East Co Limerick. 2011. 68p. pap. ***(978-3-8443-2795-3(9))*** Lambert Academic Publishing.

McAfee, Pat. Irish Stone Walls: History, Building, Conservation. 2nd rev. ed. 2012. (ENG., Illus.). 176p. pap. 26.95 ***(978-1-84717-234-1(2))*** O'Brien Pr., Ltd., The IRL. Dist: Dufour Editions, Inc.

McCarthy, Michael & O'Neill, Karina, eds. Studies in the Gothic Revival. 2008. (Illus.). 239p. (C). 75.00 *(978-1-84682-022-9(7))* Four Courts Pr. IRL. Dist: International Specialized Bk. Services.

O'Kane, Finola. Ireland & the Picturesque. 2012. ***(978-0-300-18538-6(3))*** Yale Univ. Pr.

O'Keeffe, Tadhg. A Guide to Medieval Irish Architecture for Local Historians. 2012. (Illus.). 160p. 45.00 *(978-1-84682-247-6(5))*; pap. 24.95 *(978-1-84682-248-3(3))* Four Courts Pr. IRL. Dist: International Specialized Bk. Services.

O'Neill, Cathal, et al. AandD Wejchert & Partners. 2008. (FRE & ENG., Illus.). 283p. *(978-0-948037-55-9(5))* Gandon Editions.

Pearson, Peter. Between the Mountains & the Sea. 2nd rev. ed. 2007. (ENG., Illus.). 416p. 32.95 ***(978-0-86278-977-0(X))*** O'Brien Pr., Ltd., The IRL. Dist: Dufour Editions, Inc.

Pevsner, Nikolaus. Buildings Ireland North West Ulster Country. (Illus.). 572p. 50.00 *(978-0-14-071081-6(7))* Penguin Bks., Ltd. GBR. Dist: Trafalgar Square Publishing.

Rothery, Sean. Shops of Ireland. 2009. (ENG., Illus.). 128p. pap. 19.95 *(978-0-7112-3060-6(9))* Lincoln, Frances Ltd. GBR. Dist: Perseus-PGW.

Ryan, Raymund & McCullough, Niall. Rush Library. 2010. (Illus.). 39p. pap. *(978-1-906429-10-2(3))* Associated Editions.

Stalley, Roger, ed. Limerick & South-West Ireland: Medieval Art & Architecture. 2011. (Baa conference transactions Ser.). (ENG., Illus.). 271p. (C). pap. 62.00 *(978-1-907625-08-4(9))* Maney Publishing GBR. Dist: Brown, David Bk. Co., The.

Tuomey, John & O'Donnell, Sheila. O'Donnell + Tuomey: Selected Works. 2006. (ENG., Illus.). 176p. pap. 40.00 *(978-1-56898-601-2(7))* Princeton Architectural Pr.

Wallpaper Magazine Editors. Wallpaper City Guide Dublin 2012. 2012. (ENG., Illus.). 128p. pap. 9.95 ***(978-0-7148-6300-9(9))*** Phaidon Pr., Inc.

ARCHITECTURE—ISRAEL

Azaryahu, Maoz & Troen, S. Ilan, eds. Tel-Aviv, the First Century: Visions, Designs, Actualities. 2011. (Israel Studies Book Ser.). (ENG., Illus.). 480p. 70.00 *(978-0-253-35694-9(6), 0253356946)*; pap. 24.95 *(978-0-253-22357-9(1), 0253223571)* Indiana Univ. Pr.

Duvshani, Gilead, text. Notes on Local Architecture in Israel. 2009. (ENG., Illus.). 268p. 50.00 *(978-3-8030-0689-9(9))* Wasmuth, Ernst J. Verlag GmbH & Co. DEU. Dist: D.A.P./Distributed Art Pubs.

Hatuka, Tali. Violent Acts & Urban Space in Contemporary Tel Aviv: Revisioning Moments. (ENG., Illus.). 248p. 2011. pap. 25.00 *(978-0-292-72882-0(4))* 2010. 55.00 *(978-0-292-72185-2(4))* Univ. of Texas Pr.

Schultz, Anne. Ada Karmi-Melamede & Ram Karmi, Supreme Court of Israel, Jerusalem: Opus 71. 2010. (ENG., Illus.). 60p. 49.00 *(978-3-932565-71-7(1))* Edition Axel Menges GmbH DEU. Dist: National Bk. Network.

Visscher, Jochen, ed. Tel Aviv: The White City. 2012. (ENG & GER., Illus.). 96p. 19.95 ***(978-3-939633-75-4(5))*** Jovis Verlag GmbH DEU. Dist: D.A.P./Distributed Art Pubs.

Wallpaper Magazine Editors. Tel Aviv 2012 - Wallpaper City Guide. 2nd ed. 2011. (ENG., Illus.). 128p. pap. 9.95 *(978-0-7148-6207-1(X))* Phaidon Pr., Inc.

Weizman, Eyal. Hollow Land: Israel's Architecture of Occupation. 2007. (ENG., Illus.). 318p. 34.95 *(978-1-84467-125-0(9), 844125)* Verso Bks. GBR. Dist: Norton, W. W. & Co., Inc.

ARCHITECTURE—ITALY

see also Architecture, Domestic—Italy; Architecture, Roman

Acocella, Alfonso & Turrini, Davide. Travertino Di Siena: Sienese Travertine. 2010. (ITA., Illus.). 297p. *(978-88-6055-513-7(2))* Alinea.

Angela, Tecce. Candida Höfer - Neapel: Photographien. 2010. (GER & ENG., Illus.). 56p. 39.95 *(978-3-8296-0424-6(6))* Schirmer/Mosel Verlag GmbH DEU. Dist: Prestel Publishing.

Anne, Muller Von Der Haegen. Art & Architecture Tuscany. 2010. (Art & Architecture Pocket Ser.). 626p. pap. 16.99 *(978-0-8416-7153-9(2))* Langenscheidt Publishing Group.

Architetti, Stefano, et al. The Maddalena Effect: An Architectural Affair. 2010. (ENG., Illus.). 224p. 50.00 *(978-0-8478-3516-4(2))* Rizzoli International Pubns., Inc.

Baan, Iwan, photos by. MAXXI: Zaha Hadid Architects. 2010. (ENG., Illus.). 164p. 55.00 *(978-0-8478-5800-2(6)*, Skira) Rizzoli International Pubns., Inc.

Barison, Alessandro. Design for You. 2010. (ITA.). 67p. pap. 9.50 *(978-1-4457-2968-8(7))* Lulu Enterprises Inc.

Baumgarten, Lothar. Lothar Baumgarten: Air, 1 vol. 2006. (ENG., Illus.). 152p. lthr. 40.00 *(978-3-933807-46-5(8))* Richter Verlag DEU. Dist: D.A.P./Distributed Art Pubs.

Bavagnoli, Luigi & Padovan, Gianluca. Bibliografia Archeologica, Speleologica e Tecnica Delle Cavità Artificiali Italiane Ed Estere: Primo Contributo (2000 Titoli con Abstract) 2008. (Bar S Ser.). (ITA., Illus.). viii, 291p. (C). pap. 127.50 *(978-1-4073-0226-3(4))* British Archaeological Reports Ltd. GBR. Dist: Brown, David Bk. Co., The.

Beer, Eugene. Italy: History & Landscape. 2009. (Illus.). 400p. 25.00 *(978-1-905573-35-6(9))* Compendium GBR. Dist: Casemate Pubs. & Bk. Distributors, LLC.

Belluzzi, Amedeo, et al. Palazzo Te in Mantua. 2009. (ENG., Illus.). 1214p. 980.00 *(978-88-7686-808-5(9))* Panini Franco Cosimo ITA. Dist: Antique Collectors' Club.

Beltramini, Guido & Burns, Howard. Palladio. 2009. (ENG., Illus.). 320p. 115.00 *(978-1-905711-24-6(7))* Royal Academy of Arts GBR. Dist: Hachette Bk. Group.

Beltramini, Guido & Loth, Calder. Palladio & His Legacy: A Transatlantic Journey. Hind, Charles & Murray, Irena, eds. 2010. (ENG., Illus.). 180p. pap. 45.00 *(978-88-317-0652-0(7))* Marsilio Editori spa ITA. Dist: Random Hse., Inc.

Beltramini, Guido & Zannier, Italo, eds. Carlo Scarpa: Architecture & Design. 2007. (ENG., Illus.). 320p. 65.00 *(978-0-8478-2911-8(1))* Rizzoli International Pubns., Inc.

Bietoletti, Silvestra, et al. Florence: Art & Architecture. 2008. (Art & Architecture Ser.). (Illus.). 528p. pap. 29.95 *(978-0-8416-0067-6(8))* American Map Corp.

Björklund, Erika. Urban Revitalisation Through Lighting Design. 2009. 112p. pap. *(978-3-639-12702-7(1))* VDM Verlag Dr. Mueller e.K.

Blakeslee, Arthur L. Ornament of the Italian Renaissance. 2007. (Dover Pictorial Archive Ser.). (ENG., Illus.). 64p. per. 7.95 *(978-0-486-45453-5(3))* Dover Pubns., Inc.

Bolognesi, Cecilia. Design City Milan. 2007. (Interior Angles Ser.: 27). (ENG., Illus.). 296p. 80.00 *(978-0-470-02683-0(9)*, Academy Pr.) Wiley, John & Sons, Inc.

Bonino, Michele. The Palazzo Dei Lavori Publici: Clients, Designers, Decision Makers. 2006. (Contemporary Architecture in Turin 2 Ser.). (ENG.). 85p. pap. 14.95 *(978-88-422-1404-5(3))* Allemandi, Umberto & Co. GBR. Dist: Antique Collectors' Club.

Bosoni, Giampiero. Franco Albini. 2011. (ENG., Illus.). 120p. 45.00 *(978-88-6116-141-2(3))* Antique Collectors' Club.

Bosworth, R. J. B. Whispering City: Rome & Its Histories. 2011. (ENG., Illus.). 358p. 35.00 *(978-0-300-11471-3(0))* Yale Univ. Pr.

Boucher, Bruce. Andrea Palladio: The Architect in His Time. 2nd ed. 2007. (ENG., Illus.). 324p. 49.95 *(978-0-7892-0938-2(1))*; 322p. pap. 39.95 *(978-0-7892-0940-5(3))* Abbeville Pr., Inc.

Brancaleoni, Fabio, et al. The Messina Strait Bridge: A Challenge & a Dream. 2009. (ENG., Illus.). 334p. 104.95 *(978-0-415-46814-5(0)*, CRC Press) Taylor & Francis Group GBR. Dist: Taylor & Francis Group.

Brandino, Alessandro. Le Stazioni Ferroviarie Di Messina: Dalla Realizzazione Ottocentesca All'intervento Di Angiolo Mazzoni. 2007. (ITA., Illus.). 207p. *(978-88-7758-807-4(1))* Dario, Flaccovio.

Branzi, Andrea. Andrea Branzi. 2008. (ENG.). 112p. 55.00 *(978-0-500-97680-7(5))* Thames & Hudson.

Brigitte, Hintzen Bohlen. Art & Architecture Rome. 2010. (Art & Architecture Pocket Ser.). 626p. pap. 16.99 *(978-0-8416-7154-6(0))* Langenscheidt Publishing Group.

Bucci, Federico, ed. Franco Albini. 2009. (ITA., Illus.). 80p. pap. 46.50 *(978-88-370-6926-1(X))* Electa ITA. Dist: Trans-Atlantic Pubns., Inc.

Burroughs, Charles. The Italian Renaissance Palace Façade: Structures of Authority, Surfaces of Sense. 2009. (Res Monographs in Anthropology & Aesthetics Ser.). (ENG., Illus.). 312p. pap. 42.00 *(978-0-521-10973-4(6))* Cambridge Univ. Pr.

Caldwell, Dorigen & Caldwell, Lesley. Rome: Continuing Encounters Between Past & Present. 2011. (Illus.). 282p. 119.95 ***(978-1-4094-1762-0(X))*** Ashgate Publishing Co.

Castelnuovo, Enrico & Barberis, Walter. La reggia di Venaria e i Savoia. Arte, magnificenza e storia di una corte europea. Catalogo della mostra (12 ottobre 2007-30 marzo 2008), 2 vols. 2008. (ITA & ENG., Illus.). 680p. pap. 90.00 *(978-88-422-1585-1(6))* Allemandi, Umberto & Co. GBR. Dist: National Bk. Network.

Castex, Jean. Architecture of Italy, 1 vol. 2008. (Reference Guides to National Architecture). (Illus.). 288p. 75.00 *(978-0-313-32086-6(1)*, GR2086, Greenwood Pr.) Greenwood Publishing Group, Inc.

Cecchetto, Alberto. Leaf Flame Crystal. Scaglione, Pino, ed. 2007. (Illus.). 221p. pap. *(978-84-96540-77-4(4))* Actar Birkhauser Distribution.

Chiorino, Cristiana & Olmo, Carlo, eds. Pier Luigi Nervi: Architecture as Challenge. 2011. (ENG., Illus.). 240p. pap. 45.00 *(978-88-366-1756-2(5))* Silvana ITA. Dist: D.A.P./Distributed Art Pubs.

Clementi, Alberto. Ecogeotown. 2011. (ENG & ITA.). 208p. pap. 29.95 *(978-88-95623-33-7(9))* LIST - Laboratorio Editoriale ITA. Dist: Actar Birkhauser Distribution.

Clementi, Alberto, ed. ZHONGSHAN Programme: Italia/Cina per le citta - Italy/China for the Cities. 2011. 240p. pap. 29.95 *(978-88-95623-22-1(3))* LIST - Laboratorio Editoriale ITA. Dist: Actar Birkhauser Distribution.

Coffin, David R. Magnificent Buildings, Splendid Gardens. Sellers, Vanessa Bezemer, ed. 2008. (ENG., Illus.). 320p. (C). pap. 42.00 *(978-0-691-13677-6(7))* Princeton Univ. Pr.

Coffin, David R. & Sellers, Vanessa Bezemer. Magnificent Buildings, Splendid Gardens. 2008. (ENG., Illus.). 320p. (C). 85.00 *(978-0-691-13664-6(5))* Princeton Univ. Pr.

Cole, Michael W., ed. Sixteenth-Century Italian Art. 2006. (Blackwell Anthologies in Art History Ser.: 2). (ENG., Illus.). 568p. 136.95 *(978-1-4051-0840-9(1))*; per. 57.95 *(978-1-4051-0841-6(X))* Wiley, John & Sons, Inc. (Wiley-Blackwell).

Conrad-Bercah & Office, W. West Workroom: Towards a New Sobriety in Architecture Theory + Practice. 2008. (ENG., Illus.). 224p. per. 45.00 *(978-88-8158-656-1(8))* Charta ITA. Dist: D.A.P./Distributed Art Pubs.

Corsini, Paolo & Angeli, Giulio. Il Patrimonio Edilizio Dell'Università Di Pisa: Riqualificazione e Nuovi Edifici. 2008. (ITA., Illus.). 118p. *(978-88-8492-579-4(7))* Plus/Pisa University Pr.

Cresti, Carlo & Rendina, Claudio. Palazzi of Rome. 2008. (Art & Architecture Ser.). (Illus.). 398p. pap. 24.95 *(978-0-8416-0288-5(3))* American Map Corp.

Croset, Pierre-Alain. Gino Valle. Croset, Pierre-Alain & Skansi, Luka, eds. 2010. (ITA.). 416p. pap. 135.00 *(978-88-370-7172-1(8))* Electa ITA. Dist: Trans-Atlantic Pubns., Inc.

Dardanello, Giuseppe, et al. Guarini. 2008. (ITA & ENG., Illus.). 564p. 90.00 *(978-88-422-1471-7(X))* Allemandi, Umberto & Co. GBR. Dist: Antique Collectors' Club.

De Rossi, Antonio & Rossi, Antonio De. Modern Alpine Architecture in Piedmont & Valle D'Aosta: Contemporay Architecture in Turin 3. 2006. (Contemporary Architecture in Turin 3 Ser.). (ENG., Illus.). 80p. pap. 14.95 *(978-88-422-1406-9(X))* Allemandi, Umberto & Co. GBR. Dist: Antique Collectors' Club.

Del Vivo, Caterina. Andrea Vaccà e Ridolfo Castinelli: La Costruzione Del Tempio Di Minerva Medica a Montefoscoli. 2009. (Illus.). xii, 181p. *(978-88-467-2406-9(2))* ETS.

Deliyannis, Deborah Mauskopf. Ravenna in Late Antiquity. 2010. (ENG., Illus.). 464p. (C). 99.00 *(978-0-521-83672-2(7))* Cambridge Univ. Pr.

D'Evelyn, Margaret Muther. Venice & Vitruvius: Reading Venice with Daniele Barbaro & Andrea Palladio. 2012. (ENG., Illus.). 504p. 65.00 ***(978-0-300-17451-9(9))*** Yale Univ. Pr.

Di Lieto, Alba & Morgante, Michela. Piero Gazzola: Una Strategia per I Beni Architettonici Nel Secondo Novecento. 2009. (ITA., Illus.). 380p. *(978-88-8314-533-9(X))* Cierre Edizioni.

Donin, Gianpiero, ed. Renzo Piano: Piece by Piece. 2010. 163p. pap. 27.95 *(978-88-7448-010-4(5))* Gangemi ITA. Dist: International Publishers Marketing.

Dubowitz, Dan, et al. Fascismo: Abbandonato. 2010. (ENG., Illus.). 108p. 55.00 ***(978-1-904587-80-4(1))*** Lewis, Dewi Publishing GBR. Dist: Consortium Bk. Sales & Distribution.

Edel Staff. A Venetian Concert: Grand Italian Architecture & Renaissance Music. 2006. (ENG.). 14.95 incl. lp *(978-3-937406-56-5(5))* Edel Classica Gmbh.

Fagone, V. & Favata, G. Joe Colombo: Minimum Design. 2011. (ENG., Illus.). 120p. 45.00 ***(978-88-6648-005-1(3))*** Antique Collectors' Club.

Fain, William H., Jr. & H. Fain Jr., William. Italian Cities & Landscapes: An Architect's Sketchbook. 2007. (ENG., Illus.). 264p. pap. 27.00 *(978-1-890449-32-2(6))* Balcony Pr.

Falconi, Laura. Gio Ponti: Interiors, Objects, Drawings 1920-1976. 2012. (ENG., Illus.). 256p. pap. 50.00 ***(978-88-370-7834-8(X))*** Electa ITA. Dist: National Bk. Network.

Fassino, Giulietta, et al. Turin Architecture Atlas: 1984-2008. Bonino, Michele, ed. 2009. (ENG., Illus.). 152p. 22.00 *(978-88-422-1642-1(9))* Allemandi, Umberto & Co. GBR. Dist: Antique Collectors' Club.

Fenlon, Iain. Piazza San Marco. 2009. (Wonders of the World Ser.). (Illus.). 256p. 19.95 *(978-0-674-02791-6(4))* Harvard Univ. Pr.

Ferrari, Fulvio & Ferrari, Napoleone. The Furniture of Carlo Mollino. 2010. (ENG., Illus.). 240p. pap. 39.95 *(978-0-7148-5778-7(5))* Phaidon Pr., Inc.

Ferretti, Dante. Marche: People & Land. Ponciroli, Virginia, ed. 2007. (Illus.). 248p. 75.00 *(978-88-370-5463-2(7))* Electa ITA. Dist: Trans-Atlantic Pubns., Inc.

Fiadino, Adele. Le Sculture Farnese. Gasparri, Carlo, ed. 2009. (ITA., Illus.). 512p. 162.50 *(978-88-510-0548-1(6))* Electa ITA. Dist: Trans-Atlantic Pubns., Inc.

Finessi, Beppe. Mangiarotti. Finessi, Beppe, ed. 2010. (ENG & ITA., Illus.). 120p. 49.95 *(978-88-7570-220-5(9))* Corraini ITA. Dist: D.A.P./Distributed Art Pubs.

Fiorentino, Luca. The Ghetto Reveals Rome. 2011. 176p. pap. 25.95 *(978-88-492-0824-5(3))* Gangemi ITA. Dist: International Publishers Marketing.

Foscari, Antonio. Andrea Palladio-Unbuilt Venice. 2010. (Illus.). 208p. *(978-3-03778-222-4(6))* Lars Muller Pubs.

Franco, Stella. Franco Stella: 1. Ausgewählte Schriften und Entwürfe. 2. Das humboldt-Forum als moderner Weiterbau des Berliner Schlosses, 1 vol. 2010. (GER & ITA., Illus.). 192p. 38.00 *(978-3-938666-64-7(1))* DOM Pubs. DEU. Dist: Innovative Logistics.

Franzoni, C., et al. The Mausoleum of Galla Placidia in Ravenna. 2009. (ITA & ENG., Illus.). 258p. 400.00 *(978-88-7686-730-9(9))* Panini Franco Cosimo ITA. Dist: National Bk. Network.

Frommel, Christoph Luitpold. The Architecture of the Italian Renaissance. Spring, Peter, tr. from GER. 2007. (ENG., Illus.). 384p. 65.00 *(978-0-500-34220-6(2))* Thames & Hudson.

—L'antica Basilica Di San Lorenzo in Damaso: Indagini Archeologiche Nel Palazzo Della Cancelleria, 1988-1993. 2009. (ITA & ENG., Illus.). *(978-88-8016-911-6(4))*; *(978-88-8016-846-1(0))* De Luca Editori d'Arte.

Fuhrer, Therese, ed. Rom und Mailand in der Spätantike: Repräsentationen städtischer Räume in Literatur, Architektur und Kunst. 2011. (Topoi Ser.).Tr. of Rome & Milan in Late Antiquity. (GER., Illus.). XX, 448p. 112.00 *(978-3-11-022213-5(2))* De Gruyter, Walter Inc.

Fuller, Mia. Moderns Abroad: Architecture, Cities & Italian Imperialism. 2009. (Architext Ser.). (Illus.). 274p. 53.95 *(978-0-415-77985-2(5))* Routledge.

Gardella, Mariella & Alvear, Gonzalo de. Capri Style. 2007. (ENG., Illus.). 180p. 60.00 *(978-1-86470-153-1(6))* Images Publishing Group AUS. Dist: National Bk. Network.

Geiger, J. The First Hall of Fame: A Study of the Statues in the Forum Augustum. 2008. (History & Archaeology of Classical Antiquity Ser.). (C). *(978-90-04-16869-5(9))* BRILL.

Germak, Claudio. Design & Industry in Piedmont: Contemporary Architecture in Turin. No. 7. 2008. (ENG., Illus.). 80p. pap. 14.95 *(978-88-422-1615-5(1))* Allemandi, Umberto & Co. GBR. Dist: Antique Collectors' Club.

Ghirardo, Diane Yvonne. Italy: Modern Architectures in History. 2012. (Reaktion Books - Modern Architectures in History Ser.). (Illus.). 256p. pap. 29.95 *(978-1-86189-864-7(9))* Reaktion Bks., Ltd. GBR. Dist: Chicago Distribution Ctr.

Giacomelli, Milva, et al, eds. Gli architetti italiani in Marocco dall'inizio del protettorato francese ad oggi / les architectes italiens au Maroc du debut du protectorat francais a Aujourd'hui. 2009. (ITA., Illus.). 144p. (C). pap. 30.00 *(978-88-596-0691-8(8))* Polistampa ITA. Dist: Brown, David Bk. Co., The.

Giannetti, Anna & Molinari, Luca. Continuità e Crisi: Ernesto Nathan Rogers e la Cultura Architettonica Italiana Del Secondo Dopoguerra. 2010. (Illus.). xiii, 233p. *(978-88-6055-559-5(0))* Alinea.

Giuffré, M. Teresa. The Baroque Architecture of Sicily. 2008. (ENG., Illus.). 288p. 95.00 *(978-0-500-34239-8(3))* Thames & Hudson.

Giusti, M. Adriana, et al. Guide to Piedmont Architecture: Of the 20th Century. 2009. (ENG., Illus.). 408p. pap. 46.00 *(978-88-422-1639-1(9))* Allemandi, Umberto & Co. GBR. Dist: Antique Collectors' Club.

Gobbi Sica, Grazia. The Florentine Villa: Architecture History Society. 2012. (Classical Tradition in Architecture Ser.). (ENG., Illus.). 224p. (C). pap. 42.95 ***(978-0-415-54317-0(7))*** Routledge.

Gossel, Peter & Roccella, Graziella. Ponti. 2009. (ENG.). 96p. pap. 9.99 *(978-3-8365-0038-8(8))* TASCHEN DEU. Dist: Ingram Pub. Services.

Gottardo, Francesca, ed. Paolo Portoghesi, Architect. 2011. 386p. pap. 40.00 *(978-88-492-2052-0(9))* Gangemi ITA. Dist: International Publishers Marketing.

Goy, Richard J. Building Renaissance Venice: Patrons, Architects, & Builder. 2006. (ENG., Illus.). 256p. 70.00 *(978-0-300-11292-4(0))* Yale Univ. Pr.

—The House of Gold: Building a Palace in Medieval Venice. 2011. (ENG.). 336p. pap. 39.99 *(978-0-521-18134-1(8))* Cambridge Univ. Pr.

Graham, Dan, et al, texts. Museion: KSV: Kruger Schuberth Vandreike. 2009. (ENG, ITA & GER., Illus.). 142p. pap. 50.00 *(978-3-939633-61-7(5))* Jovis Verlag GmbH DEU. Dist: D.A.P./Distributed Art Pubs.

Grandjean de Montigny, Auguste & Famin, A. Tuscan Architecture: The Renaissance Masterpieces. 2012. (Dover Architecture Ser.). (ENG.). 128p. pap. 19.95 ***(978-0-486-48043-5(7))*** Dover Pubns., Inc.

Green, Keith Evan. Gio Ponti & Carlo Mollino: Post-War Italian Architects & the Relevance of Their Work Today. 2006. (Illus.). 304p. *(978-0-7734-5632-7(5))* Mellen, Edwin Pr., The.

Greenaway, Peter. L' Italia Delle Città. 2011.Tr. of Italy of the Cities. (ENG, CHI & ITA., Illus.). 340p. pap. 55.00 *(978-88-572-0885-5(0))* Skira Editore ITA. Dist: Random Hse., Inc.

Guidi, Guido, photos by. Guido Guidi: Carlo Scarpa's Tomba Brion. 2011. (ENG & ITA., Illus.). 160p. 60.00 *(978-3-7757-2624-5(1))* Hatje Cantz Verlag GmbH & Co KG DEU. Dist: D.A.P./Distributed Art Pubs.

Hollenstein, Roman. Modern Alternatives: Höller & Klotzner Concrete Architecture. 2008. (ENG, ITA & GER., Illus.). 136p. pap. 39.95 *(978-3-211-79193-6(0), 3211791930)* Springer.

Hopkins, Andrew. Baldassare Longhena & Venetian Baroque Architecture. 2012. (ENG., Illus.). 372p. 85.00 ***(978-0-300-18109-8(4))*** Yale Univ. Pr.

Hopkins, Keith & Beard, Mary. The Colosseum. 2011. (Wonders of the World Ser.). (Illus.). 224p. pap. 14.95 *(978-0-674-06031-9(8))* Harvard Univ. Pr.

Howard, Deborah. Venice Disputed: Marc'Antonio Barbaro & Venetian Architecture, 1550-1600. 2011. (ENG., Illus.). 320p. 65.00 *(978-0-300-17685-8(6))* Yale Univ. Pr.

Hunyady, Etienne, ed. & photos by. Luxury Houses - Toscana: At Home with Tuscany's Great Families. 2007. (ENG., Illus.). 220p. 24.95 *(978-3-8327-9133-9(7))* teNeues Publishing Co.

Hutton, Edward. Ravenna, a Study. 2006. (ENG.). 242p. pap. 20.99 *(978-1-4264-6171-2(2))* 2007. 268p. pap. 23.99 *(978-1-4264-6226-9(3))* BiblioBazaar.

Imorde, Joseph & Pieper, Jan. Die Grand Tour in Moderne und Nachmoderne. 2008. (Reihe der Villa Vigoni Ser.).Tr. of Grand Tour in the Modern & Post-Modern Age. (GER., Illus.). VI, 281p. pap. *(978-3-484-67020-4(7))* Verlag Max Niemeyer.

Imorde, Joseph & Pieper, Jan, eds. Die Grand Tour in Moderne und Nachmoderne. 2008. (Reihe der Villa Vigoni Ser.).Tr. of Grand Tour in the Modern & Post-Modern Age. (GER.). VI, 281p. 140.00 ***(978-3-11-916036-0(9))*** De Gruyter, Walter Inc.

Italian Architecture for Chinese City. 2011. (ITA & ENG., Illus.). 125p. pap. 26.95 *(978-88-492-2027-8(8))* Gangemi ITA. Dist: International Publishers Marketing.

Jodidio Philip. Kc Renzo Piano. 2012. (ENG.). 96p. pap. 9.99 ***(978-3-8365-3068-2(6))*** TASCHEN DEU. Dist: Ingram Pub. Services.

Kaminski, Marion. Art & Architecture Venice. 2010. (Art & Architecture Pocket Ser.). 578p. pap. 16.99 *(978-0-8416-7161-4(3))* Langenscheidt Publishing Group.

—Venice. 2008. (Art & Architecture Ser.). (Illus.). 578p. 19.95 *(978-0-8416-0053-9(8))* American Map Corp.

—Venice, 1 vol. 2010. (ENG., Illus.). 578p. pap. 9.99 *(978-3-8331-5287-0(7))* h.f.ullmann DEU. Dist: Innovative Logistics.

Kenda, Barbara, ed. Aeolian Winds & the Spirit in Renaissance Architecture: Academia Eolia Revisted. 2006. (Illus.). 175p. 170.00 *(978-0-415-39803-9(7))*; per. 63.95 *(978-0-415-39804-6(5))* Routledge.

Kite, Stephen. Building Ruskin's Italy: Watching Architecture. 2012. (Illus.). 206p. 119.95 ***(978-1-4094-3796-3(5))*** Ashgate Publishing Co.

Klein, Caroline. Paola Navone, 1 vol. 2011. (ENG, FRE, GER, ITA & SPA.). 176p. 35.00 *(978-3-942597-02-9(0))* DAAB Media Gmbh DEU. Dist: Innovative Logistics.

Kramer, Joachim & Kramer, Joachin. Justinianische Kampferkapitelle mit einem Dekor aus Paaren von Zweigen und die Nachfolgeka. 2007. (Spatantike-Fruhes Christentum-Byzanz Ser.). (GER., Illus.). 212p. (C). 143.00 *(978-3-89500-491-9(X))* Reichert, Ludwig Dr. DEU. Dist: Brown, David Bk. Co., The.

Lancaster, Lynne. Concrete Vaulted Construction in Imperial Rome: Innovations in Context. 2009. (ENG.). 296p. (C). pap. 51.99 *(978-0-521-74436-2(9))* Cambridge Univ. Pr.

L'Archivolto Editorial Staff, ed. New Shops in Italy. Vol. 4. 79.95 *(978-88-7685-096-7(1))* Vol. 5. (Illus.). 240p. 79.95 *(978-88-7685-101-8(1))* L'Archivolto ITA. Dist: Digital Manga Publishing.

Leach, Andrew. Manfredo Tafuri. 2009. (ENG.). 250p. pap. 39.95 *(978-90-76714-30-1(4))* Universiteit Gent, Vakgroep Architectuur En Stedenbouw BEL. Dist: D.A.P./Distributed Art Pubs.

Lenci, Ruggero, ed. Pietro Barucci Architetto. 2009. (ITA., Illus.). 320p. pap. 122.50 *(978-88-370-6749-6(6))* Electa ITA. Dist: Trans-Atlantic Pubns., Inc.

Lenza, Cettina, ed. La Stazione Centrale di Napoli: Storia e Architettura di un Palinsesto Urbano. 2010. (ITA.). 190p. pap. 72.50 *(978-88-370-7473-9(5))* Electa ITA. Dist: Trans-Atlantic Pubns., Inc.

Leonardi, Nicola, ed. Oval: Il Palaghiaccio Olimpico Al Lingotto Di Torino/the Speed Skating Arena at Lingotto in Turin. 2007. (ITA & ENG., Illus.). 81p. 34.95 *(978-88-85980-48-8(1))* Centauro ITA. Dist: Perseus-PGW.

Leone, Stephanie. The Palazzo Pamphilj in Piazza Navona: Constructing Identity in Early Modern Rome. 2007. (Studies in Baroque Art Ser.). (Illus.). 400p. 181.00 *(978-1-905375-07-3(7))* Miller, Harvey Pubs. GBR. Dist: Brown, David Bk. Co., The.

Letarouilly, Paul. The Vatican. 2009. (ENG., Illus.). 320p. 125.00 *(978-1-56898-875-7(3))* Princeton Architectural Pr.

Lorenz, Katharina. Bilder machen Räume: Mythenbilder in pompeianischen Häusern. 2008. (Image & Context Ser.).Tr. of Pictures Create Space. Mythological Imagery in Pompeian Houses. (GER., Illus.). XXII, 666p. 147.00 *(978-3-11-019473-9(2))* De Gruyter, Walter Inc.

Lulof, Patricia S. & Rescigno, Carlo, eds. Deliciae Fictiles IV: Architectural Terracottas in Ancient Italy. Images of Gods, Monsters & Heroes. 2011. (GER, ITA & ENG., Illus.). 672p. (C). 80.00 *(978-1-84217-426-5(6))* Oxbow Bks., Ltd. GBR. Dist: Brown, David Bk. Co., The.

Manetti, Renzo. The Language of the Angels: Symbols & Secrets in the Basilica of San Miniato in Florence. 2011. (storia Raccontata Ser.). (ENG., Illus.). 88p. (C). pap. 20.00 ***(978-88-596-0947-6(X))*** Polistampa ITA. Dist: Brown, David Bk. Co., The.

Mazzola, Ettore M. Manfredi Nicoletti: Architecture Symbol Context. Sharp, Dennis, ed. 2011. 144p. pap. 35.95 *(978-88-492-0983-9(5))* Gangemi ITA. Dist: International Publishers Marketing.

Mazzola, Ettore Maria. Architecture & Town Planning Operating Instructions: Saving Architecture Might Save the Italian Economy. 2011. 280p. pap. 33.95 *(978-88-7448-840-7(8))* Gangemi ITA. Dist: International Publishers Marketing.

Meili, Marcel & Schaub, Christoph. Il Girasole - Ein Haus in der nähe von Verona: Ein Film von Christoph Schaub und Marcel Meili. 2010. (Illus.). 48p. 45.00 *(978-3-85881-906-2(9))* Scheidegger und Spiess AG, Verlag CHE. Dist: Antique Collectors' Club.

Mertens, Dieter. Städte und Bauten der Westgriechen: Von der Kolonisation bis zur Krise am Ende des 5. Jh. v. Chr. 2006. (GER., Illus.). 462p. (C). 165.00 *(978-3-7774-2755-3(1))* Hirmer Verlag GmbH DEU. Dist: Brown, David Bk. Co., The.

Milesi, Silvia, ed. Mauro Galantino: Opere e Progetti. 2010. (ITA., Illus.). 240p. pap. 117.50 *(978-88-370-6686-4(4))* Electa ITA. Dist: Trans-Atlantic Pubns., Inc.

Minor, Heather Hyde. The Culture of Architecture in Enlightenment Rome. 2010. (Buildings, Landscapes, & Societies Ser.). (ENG., Illus.). 328p. 95.00 *(978-0-271-03564-2(1))* Pennsylvania State Univ. Pr.

Moleskine. Inspiration & Process in Architecture - Giancarlo de Carlo. 2012. (ENG., Illus.). 272p. 39.95 *(978-88-6613-003-1(6))* Moleskine ITA. Dist: Hachette Bk. Group.

Molinari, Luca & d'Onofrio, Alessandro, eds. Sustainab. Italy: An Overview of Contemporary Italian Architecture focusing on Sustainability. 2010. 144p. pap. 35.95 *(978-88-492-1480-2(4))* Gangemi ITA. Dist: International Publishers Marketing.

Monestiroli, Antonio, ed. Ignazio Gardella. 2009. (ITA., Illus.). 80p. pap. 46.50 *(978-88-370-6928-5(6))* Electa ITA. Dist: Trans-Atlantic Pubns., Inc.

Montagna, Carmelo. Il Tesoro Di Minos: L'architettura Della Gurfa Di Alia Tra Preistoria e Misteri. 2009. (ITA & ENG., Illus.). 61p. *(978-88-88615-94-3(6))* Officina Studi Medievali.

Moore, Charles Herbert. Development & Character of Gothic Architecture. 2008. 356p. pap. *(978-1-4097-1790-4(9))* Read Bks.

Moskowitz, A. -F. The Facade Reliefs of Orvieto Cathedral. 2009. (Studies in Medieval & Early Renaissance Art History Ser.). (ENG., Illus.). 245p. (C). 145.00 *(978-1-905375-27-1(1))* Miller, Harvey Pubs. GBR. Dist: Brown, David Bk. Co., The.

Mueller von der Haegen, Anne & Strasser, Ruth. Tuscany. 2008. (Art & Architecture Ser.). (Illus.). 626p. 19.95 *(978-0-8416-0052-2(X))* American Map Corp.

Napoleone, Caterina, ed. Villa Madama. 2008. (ENG., Illus.). 176p. 85.00 *(978-88-422-1525-7(2))* Allemandi, Umberto & Co. GBR. Dist: Antique Collectors' Club.

National Terra Cotta Society. Terra Cotta of the Italian Renaissance. 2011. 210p. 44.95 ***(978-1-258-04418-3(8))*** Literary Licensing, LLC.

Nenci, Cinzia, et al. The Cathedral of Pisa, 3 vols. Peroni, Adriano, ed. 2008. (ENG., Illus.). 1634p. 1280.00 *(978-88-7686-614-2(0))* Panini Franco Cosimo ITA. Dist: Antique Collectors' Club.

Nethersole, Scott. Devotion by Design: Italian Altarpieces Before 1500. 2011. (ENG., Illus.). 128p. 40.00 *(978-1-85709-525-8(1))* Yale Univ. Pr.

Nevola, Fabrizio. Siena: Constructing the Renaissance City. 2008. (ENG., Illus.). 320p. 65.00 *(978-0-300-12678-5(6))* Yale Univ. Pr.

Nib, Vol. 10. lthr. *(978-0-687-09041-9(5))* Abingdon Pr.

Nib. 2008. 280p. pap. *(978-88-95623-05-4(3))* Actar Birkhauser Distribution.

Nicoletti, Manfredi. Manfredi Nicoletti: Architect. Giussani, Elena, ed. 2010. 144p. pap. 22.95 *(978-88-492-1172-6(4))* Gangemi ITA. Dist: International Publishers Marketing.

Niefanger, Birgit. Taste Italy. 2008. (ENG.). 192p. *(978-90-76886-61-9(X))* Tectum B.V.B.A.

Novembre, Fabio. Fabio Novembre. 2011. (ENG., Illus.). 136p. 80.00 *(978-88-6116-133-7(2))* Antique Collectors' Club.

Nylon Magazine Editors, ed. Pretty: The Nylon Book of Beauty. 2007. (ENG., Illus.). 224p. pap. 24.95 *(978-0-7893-1539-7(4))* McClelland & Stewart CAN. Dist: Random Hse., Inc.

Olmo, Carlo. Il Lingotto: Storia e Guida. 2006. (ENG., Illus.). 52p. pap. 19.95 *(978-88-422-1163-1(X))* Allemandi, Umberto & Co. GBR. Dist: Antique Collectors' Club.

Pace, Sergio, et al. Italia 61: The Nation on Show. 2006. (Contemporary Architecture in Turin Ser.). (ENG.). 80p. pap. 14.95 *(978-88-422-1405-2(1))* Allemandi, Umberto & Co. GBR. Dist: Antique Collectors' Club.

Palladio, Andrea, et al. Palladio's Rome. 2009. (ENG., Illus.). 320p. pap. 35.00 *(978-0-300-15147-3(0))* Yale Univ. Pr.

Pantheon: History & Future - New Technologies Applied to the Cultural Assets. 2010. (ITA., Illus.). 128p. pap. 17.95 *(978-88-492-1301-0(8))* Gangemi ITA. Dist: International Publishers Marketing.

Paolucci, Antonio. The Tempio Malatestiano in Rimini, 2 vols. Settis, Salvatore, ed. 2011. (ITA & ENG., Illus.). 608p. 815.00 *(978-88-248-0353-3(9))* Panini Franco Cosimo ITA. Dist: National Bk. Network.

Payne, Alina A. The Architectural Treatise in the Italian Renaissance: Architectural Invention, Ornament & Literary Culture. 2010. (ENG.). 364p. pap. 45.00 *(978-0-521-17823-5(1))* Cambridge Univ. Pr.

Pecchioli, Eleonora. The Painted Facades of Florence: From the Fifteenth to the Twentieth Century. 2006. (ENG., Illus.). 200p. 85.00 *(978-88-7038-424-6(1))* Centro Di ITA. Dist: Antique Collectors' Club.

Pietro, Silvio San & Gallo, Paola. New Shops 9: Made in Italy. 2010. (ITA & ENG., Illus.). 228p. *(978-88-7685-173-5(9))*, Edizioni L'archivolto (Acc)) Antique Collectors' Club.

Pino, Scaglione, contrib. by. Exploring Contemporary Age. 2010. 240p. pap. *(978-84-92861-04-0(5))* Actar Birkhauser Distribution.

Pisani, David. Vanishing Valletta. 2007. (ENG.). 105p. (C). 75.00 *(978-99932-7-153-6(5))* Midsea Bks. Ltd. MLT. Dist: Brown, David Bk. Co., The.

Pisani, Mario, ed. Fuksas Architetto. 2010. 144p. pap. 27.95 *(978-88-7448-200-9(0))* Gangemi ITA. Dist: International Publishers Marketing.

Ponciroli, Virginia, ed. 011 + Architetture Made in Torino: [in English & Italian]. 2008. 180p. pap. 92.50 *(978-88-370-6245-3(1))* Electa ITA. Dist: Trans-Atlantic Pubns., Inc.

Portoghesi, Paolo. Carlo Mollino: Arabesques. 2009. (ENG., Illus.). 288p. pap. 60.00 *(978-88-370-4857-0(2))* Electa ITA. Dist: D.A.P./Distributed Art Pubs.

Pozzolo, Luca Dal & Benente, Michela. Baroque: 300 Years Old & as Young as Ever - Contemporary Architecture in Turin, No. 4. 2008. (ENG., Illus.). 80p. pap. 14.95 *(978-88-422-1464-9(7))* Allemandi, Umberto & Co. GBR. Dist: Antique Collectors' Club.

Prat, Ramon, ed. Fuksas: Building. 2012. (ENG.). 450p. *(978-84-92861-78-1(9))* Actar Birkhauser Distribution.

Puglisi, Luigi Prestinenza, ed. Italy: A New Architectural Landscape. 2007. (Architectural Design Ser.). (ENG., Illus.). 144p. pap. 50.00 *(978-0-470-03189-8(1), Wiley)* Wiley, John & Sons, Inc.

Puppi, Lionello. Palladio: Introduzione Alle Architetture E Al Pensiero Teorico. 2007. (ENG., Illus.). 464p. 225.00 *(978-88-7743-303-9(5))* Arsenale Editrice SRL ITA. Dist: National Bk. Network.

Racine, Bruno. Lebenskunst in Rom. (GER.). *(978-3-8067-2867-5(4))*, Gerstenberg DEU. Dist: International Bk. Import Service, Inc.

Rampello, Davide, ed. Expo 2010 Shaghai Italy Pavilion: The City of Man Living the Italian Way. 2010. 88p. pap. 24.50 ***(978-88-370-7865-2(X))*** Electa ITA. Dist: Trans-Atlantic Pubns., Inc.

Rehak, Paul. Imperium & Cosmos: Augustus & the Northern Campus Martius. Younger, John G., ed. 2006. (Wisconsin Studies in Classics). (ENG., Illus.). 288p. 60.00 *(978-0-299-22010-5(9))* Univ. of Wisconsin Pr.

Ricci, Mose, ed. University: The eco_university Genua Project. 2010. 240p. pap. *(978-88-95623-26-9(6))* Actar Birkhauser Distribution.

Rimini, Laura Santori & Peregalli, Roberto. The Invention of the Past: Interior Design & Architecture of Studio Peregalli. 2011. (ENG., Illus.). 304p. 75.00 *(978-0-8478-3665-9(7))* Rizzoli International Pubns., Inc.

Romanelli, Giandomenico, ed. Venice: Art & Architecture. 2008. (Art & Architecture Ser.). (Illus.). 735p. pap. 29.95 *(978-0-8416-0096-6(1))* American Map Corp.

Rostagni, Cecilia & Moretti, Luigi. Luigi Moretti, 1907-1973. Rostagni, Cecilia, ed. 2009. (ITA., Illus.). 368p. 175.00 *(978-88-370-5731-2(8))* Electa ITA. Dist: Trans-Atlantic Pubns., Inc.

Ruskin, John. The Stones of Venice. 2010. 652p. pap. 46.75 *(978-1-143-29495-2(5))*; 398p. pap. 33.75 *(978-1-143-63494-9(2))*; 448p. pap. 36.75 *(978-1-143-84455-3(6))*; 410p. pap. 34.75 *(978-1-141-98268-4(4))*; 408p. pap. 34.75 *(978-1-142-18268-7(1))* BiblioBazaar.

—The Stones of Venice. 2009. (Illus.). 516p. pap. *(978-1-150-61730-0(6))*; 366p. pap. *(978-1-4589-3782-7(8))*; 426p. pap. *(978-0-217-39824-4(3))*; 360p. pap. *(978-1-4589-0639-7(6))*; 300p. pap. *(978-0-217-13404-0(1))*; 314p. pap. *(978-0-217-10745-7(1))*; 242p. pap. *(978-0-217-89754-9(1))*; 268p. pap. *(978-0-217-89751-8(7))*; 300p. pap. *(978-0-217-63837-1(6))*; 134p. pap. *(978-0-217-39825-1(1))*; 156p. pap. *(978-0-217-37284-8(8))*; 204p. pap. *(978-0-217-37253-1(X))* Books LLC.

—The Stones of Venice. 2009. 360p. pap. 22.63 *(978-1-4589-0640-3(X))*; 134p. pap. 19.99 *(978-1-4589-3780-3(1))* General Bks. LLC.

—Stones of Venice. 2008. 232p. 27.99 *(978-0-554-23092-4(5))*; 24.99 *(978-0-554-32355-4(8))* BiblioBazaar.

—The Stones of Venice. 2011. 432p. ***(978-1-84902-301-6(8))*** Benediction Classics.

—Stones of Venice: Introductory Chapters & Local Indices for the Use of Travellers While Staying in Venice & Verona. 2006. 200p. pap. 19.99 *(978-1-4264-3687-1(4))* 2007. (ENG.). 268p. pap. 23.99 *(978-1-4264-3744-1(7))* BiblioBazaar.

—The Stones of Venice - The Fall. 2007. 528p. per. 26.95 *(978-1-60206-703-5(1))* Cosimo, Inc.

—The Stones of Venice - The Foundations. 2007. 464p. 39.45 *(978-1-60206-700-4(7))*; per. 24.95 *(978-1-60206-699-1(X))* Cosimo, Inc.

—The Stones of Venice - The Sea Stories. 2007. 452p. (ENG.). 39.45 *(978-1-60206-702-8(3))*; per. 24.95 *(978-1-60206-701-1(5))* Cosimo, Inc.

—Stones of Venice [Introductions]. 2007. 160p. per. *(978-1-4068-4090-2(4))* Echo Library.

—The Stones of Venice,Volume III the Fall. 2007. 528p. 39.45 *(978-1-60206-704-2(X))* Cosimo, Inc.

Sabatino, Michelangelo. Pride in Modesty: Modernist Architecture & the Vernacular Tradition in Italy. (Illus.). 2011. xxvi, 341p. pap. ***(978-1-4426-1282-2(7))*** 2010. 336p. *(978-0-8020-9705-7(7))* Univ. of Toronto Pr.

San Pietro, Silvio & Gallo, Paola. New Restaurants 2 in Italy. 2008. (Nuovi Ambienti Italiani Ser.). (ITA & ENG., Illus.). 196p. *(978-88-7685-152-0(6))*, Edizioni L'archivolto (Acc)) Antique Collectors' Club.

San Pietro, Silvio, et al. New Bars, Cafes & Pubs in Italy. 2008. (Best Interiors Selection Ser.). (ITA & ENG., Illus.). 216p. *(978-88-7685-158-2(5))*, Edizioni L'archivolto (Acc)) Antique Collectors' Club.

—New Exhibits 3: Made in Italy. 2010. (ITA & ENG., Illus.). 200p. *(978-88-7685-151-3(8))*, Edizioni L'archivolto (Acc)) Antique Collectors' Club.

San, Pietro Silvio, et al. Spas Made in Italy. 2010. (ITA & ENG., Illus.). 196p. *(978-88-7685-165-0(8))*, Edizioni L'archivolto (Acc)) Antique Collectors' Club.

Savoy, Daniel. Venice from the Water: Architecture & Myth in an Early Modern City. 2012. (ENG., Illus.). 224p. 65.00 ***(978-0-300-16797-9(0))*** Yale Univ. Pr.

Scaglione, Giuseppe. Dolomiti GeoScape: Geography+Geology= Landscape. Sailer, Gregor, ed. 2011. (ENG & ITA.). 168p. 34.95 *(978-88-95623-30-6(4))* LIST - Laboratorio Editoriale ITA. Dist: Actar Birkhauser Distribution.

Scaglione, Pino. Cosengeles: Small Spontaneous Metropolis. 2011. 192p. pap. 24.95 *(978-88-95623-32-0(0))* L ST - Laboratorio Editoriale ITA. Dist: Actar Birkhauser Distribution.

Scaglione, Pino, ed. Italian High Design & High Technology. 2011. (ENG & ITA.). 207p. 34.95 ***(978-88-95623-34-4(7))*** LIST - Laboratorio Editoriale ITA. Dist: Actar Birkhauser Distribution.

—Monograph. It 3: Citterio/Viel & Partners. 2011. (ENG & ITA.). 360p. pap. 29.95 ***(978-88-95623-45-0(2))*** LIST - Laboratorio Editoriale ITA. Dist: Actar Birkhauser Distribution.

—Torino Contemporanea/Contemporary Turin: Guida alle Architetture/Guide to Architecture. 2011. 245p. pap. 24.95 ***(978-88-95623-44-3(4))*** LIST - Laboratorio Editoriale ITA. Dist: Actar Birkhauser Distribution.

Scaglione, Pino, text. Cities in the Nature. 2011. 300p. pap. 34.95 *(978-88-95623-35-1(5))* LIST - Laboratorio Editoriale ITA. Dist: Actar Birkhauser Distribution.

Scamozzi, Vincenzo. Vincenzo Scamozzi: Venetian Architect. 2008. (Illus.). 368p. 120.00 ***(978-90-76863-15-3(6))*** Architectura & Natura Pr. NLD. Dist: Antique Collectors' Club.

Scarpa, Carlo. Carlo Scarpa: Villa Palazzetto. (Illus.). 128p. 35.00 *(978-4-900398-21-4(7))* Watari-Um JPN. Dist: D.A.P./Distributed Art Pubs.

Schache, Wolfgang & Sconci, Maria Selene. An Italian Palazzo in Germany: The Embassy in Berlin. 2007. (ENG., Illus.). 124p. 70.00 *(978-88-422-1483-0(3))* Allemandi, Umberto & Co. GBR. Dist: Antique Collectors' Club.

Schaller, Matthias Petrus. Matthias Schaller: Controfacciata, 1 vol. 2008. (ENG., Illus.). 68p. 50.00 *(978-3-86521-674-8(9))* Steidl, Gerhard Druckerei und Verlag DEU. Dist: Innovative Logistics.

Scheppe, Wolfgang, ed. Done. Book. 2011. (ENG., Illus.). 368p. 45.00 *(978-3-7757-2773-0(6))* Hatje Cantz Verlag GmbH & Co KG DEU. Dist: D.A.P./Distributed Art Pubs.

—Migropolis Vol. 1: Venice, Atlas of a Global Situation. 2010. (ENG., Illus.). 1344p. 195.00 *(978-3-7757-2465-2(0))* Hatje Cantz Verlag GmbH & Co KG DEU. Dist: D.A.P./Distributed Art Pubs.

Schultz Anne-Catrin. Carlo Scarpa: Layers. 2007. (ENG., Illus.). 148p. 69.00 *(978-3-930698-14-1(5))* Edition Axel Menges GmbH DEU. Dist: National Bk. Network.

Sessa, Ettore. Ernesto Basile, 1857-1932: Fra Accademismo e Moderno, Un'architettura Della Qualità. 2010. (ITA., Illus.). 118p. *(978-88-7804-478-4(4))* Flaccovio.

Settis, Salvatore & Brenk, Beat. La Capella Palatina a Palermo, 3 vols. 2011. (ITA & ENG., Illus.). 1300p. 1325.00 *(978-88-248-0351-9(2))* Panini Franco Cosimo ITA. Dist: National Bk. Network.

Seymour, Frederick H. A. Siena & Her Artists. 2009. 100p. pap. 14.14 *(978-0-217-87505-9(X))* General Bks. LLC.

Sframeli, Maria. Firenze 1892-1895: Immagini Dell'antico Centro Scomparso. 2007. (ITA., Illus.). 319p. (C). 69.50 *(978-88-596-0246-0(7))* Edizioni Polistampa ITA. Dist: Brown, David Bk. Co., The.

Shawe-Taylor, Desmond. The Roman Baroque: An Introduction to Architecture & Sculpture. 2006. (ENG.). 224p. 60.00 *(978-0-300-11938-1(0))* Yale Univ. Pr.

Shenfield, Larry. How Much of the Florence Baptistery Is a Surviving Roman Building? A Re-Evaluation of the Archaeological, Architectural & Artistic Evidence. 2008. (Bar S Ser.). (Illus.). 433p. (C). pap. 157.50 *(978-1-4073-0225-6(6))* British Archaeological Reports Ltd. GBR. Dist: Brown, David Bk. Co., The.

Shipley, Frederick W. Agrippa's Building Activities in Rome. 2008. 97p. pap. 8.00 *(978-1-60608-244-7(2)*, Wipf and Stock) Wipf & Stock Pubs.

Sica, Grazia Gobbi. The Florentine Villa: Architecture History, Society. 2007. (Illus.). 224p. 115.00 *(978-0-415-44397-5(0))* Routledge.

Skansi, Luka, ed. Gino Valle: Deutsche Bank Milano. 2010. (ENG & ITA., Illus.). 120p. pap. 62.50 *(978-88-370-7300-8(3))* Electa ITA. Dist: Trans-Atlantic Pubns., Inc.

Smith, Lorenza. Venice: Art & History. 2011. (Illus.). 192p. 45.00 *(978-88-7743-349-7(3))* Arsenale Editrice SRL ITA. Dist: Antique Collectors' Club.

Sodi, Stefano & Burresi, Mariagiulia. La Basilica Di San Piero a Grado. 2010. (ITA., Illus.). 69p. *(978-88-467-2747-3(9))* ETS.

Stoppani, Teresa. Paradigm Islands - Manhattan & Venice. 2011. (ENG., Illus.). 312p. (C). 125.00 *(978-0-415-56185-3(X))* Routledge.

Strasser, Ruth & Mueller von der Haegen, Anne. Tuscany, 1 vol. 2010. (ENG., Illus.). 626p. pap. 9.99 *(978-3-8331-5286-3(9))* h.f.ullmann DEU. Dist: Innovative Logistics.

Temple, Nicholas. Renovatio Urbis: Architecture, Urbanism & Ceremony in the Rome of Julius II. 2011. (Classical Tradition in Architecture Ser.). (ENG., Illus.). 368p. (C). 130.00 *(978-0-415-47385-9(3))* Routledge.

Thielemann, Gerhard, et al. Adalbert Erlebach: Das Leben und die Kunst des Meraner Architekten. 2010. (GER., Illus.). 127p. *(978-88-8266-683-5(2))* Athesia.

Thomas, Anabel. Garrisoning the Borderlands of Medieval Siena: Sant'angelo in Colle - Frontier Castle under the Government of the Nine (1287-1355) 2011. (Illus.). 444p. 124.95 *(978-1-4094-2603-5(3))* Ashgate Publishing Co.

Thomas, Michael L. & Meyers, Gretchen E., eds. Monumentality in Etruscan & Early Roman Architecture: Ideology & Innovation. 2012. (ENG.). 236p. 60.00 ***(978-0-292-73888-1(9))*** Univ. of Texas Pr.

Thomas, Michael L., et al. Monumentality in Etruscan & Early Roman Architecture: Ideology & Innovation. 2012. E-Book ***(978-0-292-73889-8(7))*** Univ. of Texas Pr.

Tice, James. Giuseppe Vasi's Rome: Lasting Impressions from the Age of the Grand Tour. 2010. (ENG.). 200p. pap. 40.00 *(978-0-87114-297-9(X))* Univ. of Delaware Pr.

Tittoni, Maria Elisa, ed. La Roma di Achille Pinelli: Water Colour Works, 1832-1835. 2010. 73p. pap. 29.95 *(978-88-492-1303-4(4))* Gangemi ITA. Dist: International Publishers Marketing.

Tobriner, Stephen. The Genesis of Noto: An Eighteenth-Century Sicilian City. (Studies in Architecture: No. XXI). (Illus.). 252p. 125.00 *(978-0-302-00543-9(9))* Zwemmer Bks. GBR. Dist: International Specialized Bk. Services.

Toker, Franklin. On Holy Ground: Liturgy, Architecture & Urbanism in the Cathedrals & the Streets of Medieval Florence. 2009. (Florence duomo Project Ser.). (ENG., Illus.). 324p. (C). 160.00 *(978-1-905375-51-6(4))* Miller, Harvey Pubs. GBR. Dist: Brown, David Bk. Co., The.

Toxey, Anne Parmly. Materan Contradictions: Architecture, Preservation & Politics. 2011. (Ashgate Studies in Architecture Ser.). (Illus.). 380p. 119.95 ***(978-1-4094-1207-6(5))*** Ashgate Publishing Co.

Trachtenberg, Marvin. Brunelleschi, Michelozzo, & the Problem of the Pazzi Chapel. 2008. (Illus.). 272p. 60.00 *(978-0-300-11831-5(7))* Yale Univ. Pr.

—Building-in-Time: From Giotto to Alberti & Modern Oblivion. 2010. (ENG., Illus.). 516p. 65.00 *(978-0-300-16592-0(7))* Yale Univ. Pr.

Trentin, Annalisa, et al. La Lezione Di Pier Luigi Nervi. 2010. (ITA & ENG., Illus.). xiii, 225p. *(978-88-6159-503-3(0))* Bruno, Scholastica, Mondadori.

Ulisse, Alberto, text. EnergyCity. 2011. (ENG & ITA.). 196p. pap. 29.95 *(978-88-95623-40-5(1))* LIST - Laboratorio Editoriale ITA. Dist: Actar Birkhauser Distribution.

Utimpergher, Paolo, et al. Frameworks: Ventidue Progetti Di Aldo Parisotto e Massimo Formenton = Twentytwo Projects by Aldo Parisotto & Massimo Formenton. Maltese, E., ed. 2009. (ITA & ENG., Illus.). 256p. 149.50 *(978-88-370-6559-1(0))* Electa ITA. Dist: Trans-Atlantic Pubns., Inc.

Verbavolant, creator. Massimo Mariani: Progetti, 1980-2005. 2006. (ITA & ENG., Illus.). 232p. *(978-1-905216-02-4(5))* Verba Volant, Ltd.

Viola, Anna M., et al. Il Cantiere Di una Prospettiva: Vicende Costruttive Dei Poderi Di Stupinigi Tra XVIII e XIX Secolo. 2009. (ITA., Illus.). 179p. *(978-88-7661-847-5(3))* Celid.

Vroom, Wolbert. Vincenzo Scamozzi: Venetian Architect the Idea of a Universal Architecture - Villas & Country Estates. 2007. (Illus.). 288p. 90.00 *(978-90-76863-09-2(1))* Architectura & Natura Pr. NLD. Dist: Antique Collectors' Club.

Wallpaper Magazine Editors, ed. Rome 2011 - Wallpaper City Guide. 4th ed. 2011. (ENG., Illus.). 128p. pap. 9.95 *(978-0-7148-6090-9(5))* Phaidon Pr., Inc.

—Turin 2012 - Wallpaper City Guide. 2011. (ENG., Illus.). 128p. pap., pap. 9.95 *(978-0-7148-6091-6(3))* Phaidon Pr., Inc.

—Wallpaper* City Guide Milan 2012. rev. ed. 2011. (ENG.). 128p. pap. 9.95 ***(978-0-7148-6329-0(7))*** Phaidon Pr. Ltd. GBR. Dist: Hachette Bk. Group.

Wallpaper Magazine Editors, ed. Wallpaper* City Guide Palermo. 2010. (Wallpaper* City Guides). (ENG., Illus.). 128p. pap. 9.95 *(978-0-7148-5604-9(5))* Phaidon Pr., Inc.

Wasiuta, Mark, ed. Environments & Counter-Environments: Experimental Media in Italy: the New Domestic Landscape, MoMA 1972. 2011. 288p. pap. *(978-84-92861-98-9(3))* Actar Birkhauser Distribution.

Weissmuller, Alberto. Palladio in Venice. 2006. (ENG., Illus.). 168p. 60.00 *(978-88-7200-174-5(9))* Vianello Libri ITA. Dist: Antique Collectors' Club.

Wharton, Edith. Italian Villas & Their Gardens. 2009. 358p. 33.99 *(978-1-115-41875-1(0))*; pap. 31.75 *(978-1-115-41872-0(6))*; (Illus.). 38.99 *(978-1-115-41878-2(5))*; (Illus.). pap. 32.75 *(978-1-115-41873-7(4))* BiblioBazaar.

—Italian Villas & Their Gardens. 2009. 106p. pap. *(978-0-217-84084-2(1))* Books LLC.

Wirtz, Rolf. Art & Architecture Florence. 2010. (Art & Architecture Pocket Ser.). 56p. pap. 16.99 *(978-0-8416-7151-5(6))* Langenscheidt Publishing Group.

Wirtz, Rolf C. Florence. 2008. (Art & Architecture Ser.). (Illus.). 560p. 19.95 *(978-0-8416-0148-2(8))* American Map Corp.

—Florence, 1 vol. 2010. (ENG., Illus.). 560p. pap. 9.99 *(978-3-8331-5282-5(6))* h.f.ullmann DEU. Dist: Innovative Logistics.

Younés, Samir & Mazzola, Ettore Maria. San Giorgio a Liri: Re-integrating the Dispersed City. 2010. (University of Notre Dame Graduate Program in Architecture, Rome Studies Program Publications). 50p. pap. 35.95 *(978-88-492-0870-2(7))* Gangemi ITA. Dist: International Publishers Marketing.

Younes, Samir & Mazzola, Ettore Maria, eds. Artena: The Recovery of Urban Integrity. 2010. (University of Notre Dame Graduate Program in Architecture, Rome Studies Program Publications). 78p. pap. 35.95 *(978-88-492-0578-7(3))* Gangemi ITA. Dist: International Publishers Marketing.

—Como: The Modernity of Tradition. 2010. (University of Notre Dame Graduate Program in Architecture, Rome Studies Program Publications). 96p. pap. 32.95 *(978-88-492-0467-4(1))* Gangemi ITA. Dist: International Publishers Marketing.

Zöllner, Frank, et al. Michelangelo. 2010. (Go Ser.). (ENG., Illus.). 388p. 39.99 *(978-3-8365-2117-8(2))* TASCHEN DEU. Dist: Ingram Pub. Services.

ARCHITECTURE—JAPAN

see also Architecture, Domestic—Japan

AA Publishing Staff. Before Object, after Image: 1996-2006 Koshirakura Landscape. 2007. (Illus.). 228p. *(978-1-902902-55-5(6))* Architectural Assn.

Abe, Hitoshi. Hitoshi Abe: A-Slash, 1 vol. 2008. (ENG., Illus.). 128p. pap. 17.95 *(978-1-891197-39-0(8))* Univ. of Michigan, College of Architecture & Urban Planning.

Abe, Hitoshi & Pollock, Naomi. Hitoshi Abe. 2009. (ENG., Illus.). 208p. 79.95 *(978-0-7148-4665-1(1))* Phaidon Pr., Inc.

Baek, Jin. Nothingness: Tadao Ando's Christian Sacred Space: Tadao Ando's Christian Sacred Space. 2009. (ENG., Illus.). 224p. (C). 155.00 *(978-0-415-47853-3(7))*; 212p. pap. 53.95 *(978-0-415-47854-0(5))* Routledge.

Ban, Shigeru. Paper in Architecture. Rizzoli et al, eds. 2009. (ENG., Illus.). 232p. 65.00 *(978-0-8478-3211-8(2))* Rizzoli International Pubns., Inc.

Bognar, Botond. Beyond the Bubble: The New Japanese Architecture. 2009. (ENG., Illus.). 240p. 79.95 *(978-0-7148-4575-3(2))* Phaidon Pr., Inc.

—Material Immaterial: The New Work of Kengo Kuma. 2009. (ENG., Illus.). 256p. 65.00 *(978-1-56898-874-0(5))*; pap. 40.00 *(978-1-56898-779-8(X))* Princeton Architectural Pr.

Brownell, Blaine Erickson. Matter in the Floating World: Conversations with Leading Japanese Architects & Designers. 2011. (ENG., Illus.). 256p. pap. 40.00 *(978-1-56898-996-9(2))* Princeton Architectural Pr.

Buntrock, Dana. Material & Meaning in Contemporary Japanese Architecture: Tradition & Today. 2010. (ENG., Illus.). 288p. (C). pap. 62.95 *(978-0-415-77891-6(3))* Routledge.

—Materials & Meaning in Contemporary Japanese Architecture: Tradition & Today. 2010. (ENG., Illus.). 288p. (C). 165.00 *(978-0-415-77890-9(5))* Routledge.

Chaplin, Sarah. Japanese Love Hotels: A Cultural History. 2009. 256p. pap. 39.95 *(978-0-415-48754-2(4))* 2007. (Illus.). 241p. 180.00 *(978-0-415-41585-9(3))* Routledge.

Cooper, Graham. Project Japan: Architecture & Art Media Edo to Now. 2009. (ENG., Illus.). 240p. 60.00 *(978-1-86470-309-2(1))* Images Publishing Group AUS. Dist: National Bk. Network.

Corazza, Iago & Ropa, Greta, texts. Japan: Light & Shadows in the Land of the Rising Sun. 2011. (ENG., Illus.). 272p. 45.00 *(978-88-544-0574-5(4))* White Star ITA. Dist: Sterling Publishing Co., Inc.

Cram, Ralph Adams. Impressions of Japanese Architecture. 2010. (Tuttle Classics Ser.). (ENG., Illus.). 160p. pap. 14.95 *(978-4-8053-1107-3(X))* Tuttle Publishing.

Daniell, Thomas. After the Crash: Architecture in Post-Bubble Japan. 2008. (ENG., Illus.). 176p. pap. 24.95 *(978-1-56898-776-7(5))* Princeton Architectural Pr.

—Houses & Gardens of Kyoto. 2010. (ENG., Illus.). 224p. 39.95 *(978-4-8053-1091-5(X))* Tuttle Publishing.

Designers Apartments in Japan Low-Rise: Architect-Designed Low Rise Condominiums. 2007. 49.95 *(978-4-7661-1712-7(3))* Graphic-Sha JPN. Dist: Gingko Pr., Inc.

Designers Compact Shops in Japan: A Selection of 100 Projects. 2007. 49.95 *(978-4-7661-1740-0(9))* Graphic-Sha JPN. Dist: Gingko Pr., Inc.

Edagawa, Yuichiro. Japanese Identities: Architecture Between Aesthetics & Nature. 2008. (GER & ENG., Illus.). 176p. pap. 40.00 *(978-3-939633-38-9(0))* Jovis Verlag GmbH DEU. Dist: D.A.P./Distributed Art Pubs.

Freeman, Michael, contrib. by. The Modern Japanese Tea Room, 1 vol. 2007. (ENG., Illus.). 240p. 49.95 *(978-88-89431-87-0(3))* Damiani ITA. Dist: D.A.P./Distributed Art Pubs.

Fujino, Yozo, et al. Wind Resistant Design of Bridges in Japan: Developments & Practices. 2012. (ENG., Illus.). xii, 256p. 129.00 ***(978-4-431-54045-8(8)***, 4431540458) Springer.

Fuksas, Massimil, ed. Armani Ginza Tower. 2008. pap. *(978-84-96954-42-7(0))* Actar Birkhauser Distribution.

Fumihiko, Maki, et al. Fumihiko Maki. 2009. (ENG., Illus.). 320p. 95.00 *(978-0-7148-4956-0(1))* Phaidon Pr., Inc.

Hildner, Claudia. Small Houses: Contemporary Japanese Dwellings. 2011. 160p. pap. 54.95 *(978-3-0346-0744-5(X))* Birkhauser Verlag AG CHE. Dist: Actar Birkhauser Distribution.

Images Publishing Staff, PUBLISHING. Tai Soo Kim Partners: Selected Works. 2006. (Master Architect Ser.). (Illus.). 248p. 59.95 *(978-1-86470-023-7(8)*, Images Publishing Dist Ac) Antique Collectors' Club GBR. Dist: National Bk. Network.

Isozaki, Arata. Japan-ness in Architecture. Stewart, David B., ed. Kohso, Sabu, tr. from JPN. 2011. (ENG., Illus.). 376p. (gr. 17). pap. 18.95 *(978-0-262-51605-1(5))* MIT Pr.

Isozaki, Arata, ed. Katsura: Imperial Villa. 2011. (ENG., Illus.). 402p. pap. 49.95 ***(978-0-7148-6254-5(1))*** Phaidon Pr., Inc.

Isozaki, Arata, et al. The Contemporary Tea House: Japan's Top Architects Redefine a Tradition, 1 vol. Rich, Glenn, tr. 2007. (ENG., Illus.). 136p. 39.95 *(978-4-7700-3046-7(0))* Kodansha America, Inc.

Ito, Toyo. Toyo Ito. 2009. (ENG., Illus.). 240p. 90.00 *(978-0-7148-4505-0(1))* Phaidon Pr., Inc.

Japanese Commission on Large Dams Staff, contrib. by. Dams in Japan: Past, Present & Future. 2009. (ENG., Illus.). 240p. (C). 124.95 *(978-0-415-49432-8(X)*, CRC Press) Taylor & Francis Group GBR. Dist: Taylor & Francis Group.

Jodidio, Philip. Ando: Complete Works. 2007. (FRE, GER & ENG., Illus.). 500p. 39.99 *(978-3-8228-0930-3(6))* TASCHEN DEU. Dist: Ingram Pub. Services.

Jodidio, Philip, ed. Ando - complete works updated version: Updated Version. 2010. (FRE, GER & ENG., Illus.). 600p. 150.00 *(978-3-8365-0949-7(0))* TASCHEN DEU. Dist: Ingram Pub. Services.

—Shigeru Ban - Complete Works 1985-2010. 2010. (ENG, FRE & GER., Illus.). 464p. 150.00 *(978-3-8365-0735-6(8))* TASCHEN DEU. Dist: Ingram Pub. Services.

Jodidio, Philip, ed. Tadao Ando,Complete Works 1975-2011. 2012. (ENG., Illus.). 640p. 49.99 ***(978-3-8365-2813-9(4))*** TASCHEN DEU. Dist: Ingram Pub. Services.

Klanten, R., et al. Sublime: New Design & Architecture from Japan. 2011. (ENG., Illus.). 288p. 78.00 ***(978-3-89955-372-7(1))*** Die Gestalten Verlag DEU. Dist: Prestel Publishing.

Lin, Zhongjie. Kenzo Tange & the Metabolist Movement. 2010. (Illus.). 288p. 165.00 *(978-0-415-77659-2(7))* Routledge.

—Kenzo Tange & the Metabolist Movement: Urban Utopias of Modern Japan. 2010. (ENG., Illus.). 288p. (C). pap. 53.95 *(978-0-415-77660-8(0))* Routledge.

Locher, Mira & Simmons, Ben. Traditional Japanese Architecture: An Exploration of Elements & Forms. 2010. (ENG., Illus.). 224p. 39.95 *(978-4-8053-0980-3(6))* Tuttle Publishing.

Martin, John H. & Martin, Phyllis G. Tokyo: 34 Walks in the World's Most Exciting City. 2012. (ENG., Illus.). 288p. pap. 24.95 *(978-4-8053-0917-9(2))* Tuttle Publishing.

Mehta, Geeta & MacDonald, Deanna. New Japan Architecture: Recent Works by the World's Leading Architects. 2011. (ENG., Illus.). 224p. 49.95 *(978-4-8053-0948-3(2))* Tuttle Publishing.

Meyer, Ulf. Architectural Guide Tokyo, 1 vol. 2011. (ENG.). 200p. 35.95 *(978-3-86922-106-9(2))* DOM Pubs. DEU. Dist: Innovative Logistics.

Mikan. Mikan: Save the Danchi. 2011. (ENG., Illus.). 144p. pap. 28.00 ***(978-3-86859-085-2(4))*** Jovis Verlag GmbH DEU. Dist: D.A.P./Distributed Art Pubs.

Muller, Lars & Miki, Akiko, eds. Insular Insight: Where Art & Architecture Conspire with Nature. 2011. (ENG., Illus.). 480p. 70.00 ***(978-3-03778-255-2(2))*** Lars Muller Pubs. CHE. Dist: Prestel Publishing.

Nakamori, Yasufumi. Katsura: Picturing Modernism in Japanese Architecture. 2010. (Illus.). 168p. 50.00 *(978-0-300-16333-9(9))* Museum of Fine Arts, Houston.

Nepilly, Ellen. Hip Dining Japan. 2007. (ENG., Illus.). 192p. 39.95 *(978-84-96263-93-2(2))* Links International (Leading International Key Services Barcelona, S.A.) ESP. Dist: National Bk. Network.

—Hip Lounging Japan. 2007. (ENG., Illus.). 192p. 39.95 *(978-84-96263-92-5(4))* Links International (Leading International Key Services Barcelona, S.A.) ESP. Dist: National Bk. Network.

Nihon Dai Damu Kaigi Staff, contrib. by. Dams in Japan: Past, Present, & Future. 2009. (Illus.). xxiv, 232p. *(978-0-203-87735-7(7))* CRC Pr. LLC.

Obrist, Hans Ulrich. Rem Koolhaas, Project Japan. Koolhaas, Rem, ed. 2011. (ENG., Illus.). 684p. 59.99 *(978-3-8365-2508-4(9))* TASCHEN DEU. Dist: Ingram Pub. Services.

Obrist, Hans Ulrich, ed. Hans Ulrich Obrist & Kazuyo Sejima: Conversation Series: Volume 26. 2012. (ENG., Illus.). 110p. pap. 25.00 ***(978-3-86560-927-4(9))*** Verlag der Buchhandlung Walther Konig DEU. Dist: D.A.P./Distributed Art Pubs.

Pare, Richard, photos by. Stone Hill Center: Tadao Ando at the Clark. 2008. (Illus.). 64p. *(978-0-931102-79-0(0))* Clark, Sterling & Francine Art Institute.

—Stone Hill Center: Tadao Ando at the Clark. 2009. (ENG., Illus.). 64p. pap. 19.95 *(978-0-300-14917-3(4))* Yale Univ. Pr.

Qu, Jinling. Japanese Storefront Design. 2011. (ENG., Illus.). 240p. 40.00 *(978-988-19738-0-1(5))* Design Media Publishing Ltd. HKG. Dist: BookMasters Distribution Services (BDS).

Qu, Jinling, ed. Japanese Spa Resorts. 2011. (ENG.). 416p. 60.00 ***(978-988-15-0716-7(2))*** Design Media Publishing Ltd. HKG. Dist: BookMasters Distribution Services (BDS).

Sadler, A. L. Japanese Architecture: A Short History. 2009. (Tuttle Classics Ser.). (ENG., Illus.). 288p. pap. 19.95 *(978-4-8053-1043-4(X))* Tuttle Publishing.

Schmal, Peter, ed. Takaharu + Yui Tezuka: Erinnerte Zukunft, 1 vol. 2009. (ENG & GER., Illus.). 120p. pap. 40.00 *(978-3-86859-021-0(8))* Jovis Verlag GmbH DEU. Dist: D.A.P./Distributed Art Pubs.

Seki, Akihiko & Brooke, Elizabeth Heilman. Ryokan: Japan's Finest Spas & Inns. 2007. (ENG., Illus.). 208p. 39.95 *(978-0-8048-3839-9(9))* Tuttle Publishing.

Shelton, Barrie. Learning from the Japanese City: Looking East in Urban Design. 2nd rev. ed. (Planning, History & Environment Ser.). (ENG., Illus.). 208p. (C). 2013. pap. 62.95 *(978-0-415-55440-4(3))* 2012. 165.00 *(978-0-415-55439-8(X))* Routledge.

Skira & Ando, Tadao. Museums. Molinari, Luca, ed. 2009. (ENG., Illus.). 240p. 75.00 *(978-88-6130-680-6(2))* Skira Editore ITA. Dist: Random Hse., Inc.

Stewart, David. Making of a Modern Japanese Architecture. (Illus.). 304p. pap. 50.00 *(978-4-7700-2933-1(0))* Kodansha International JPN. Dist: Kodansha America, Inc.

Sumner, Yuki, et al. New Architecture in Japan. 2010. (ENG., Illus.). 288p. 49.95 *(978-1-85894-450-0(3))* Merrell Pubs. Ltd. GBR. Dist: Perseus Distribution.

Suzuki, Hiroyuki. Shuhei Endo: Paramodern Architecture. rev. ed. 2006. (ENG., Illus.). 212p. pap. 29.95 *(978-1-904313-43-4(4))* Phaidon Pr., Inc.

Takahashi, Masaaki. Design City Tokyo. 2006. 224p. pap. 40.00 *(978-0-470-09365-8(X))* Wiley, John & Sons, Inc.

Takahashi, Masaaki & Dytham, Klein. Japan: The New Mix - Architecture, Interiors & More. 2007. (ENG., Illus.). 264p. 59.95 *(978-1-86470-267-5(2))* Images Publishing Group AUS. Dist: National Bk. Network.

Tei, Shuwa. Intentionallies: Shaping Japan & Beyond. 2011. (ENG., Illus.). 280p. 59.00 ***(978-90-77174-34-0(6))*** Frame Pubs. NLD. Dist: Consortium Bk. Sales & Distribution.

Tseng, Alice Y. The Imperial Museums of Meiji Japan: Architecture & the Art of the Nation. 2008. (ENG., Illus.). 304p. (C). 60.00 *(978-0-295-98777-4(4))* Univ. of Washington Pr.

Turnbull, Stephen. Japanese Castles in Korea 1592-98. 2007. (Fortress Ser.). (ENG., Illus.). 64p. pap. 16.95 *(978-1-84603-104-5(4))* Osprey Publishing, Ltd. GBR. Dist: Random Hse., Inc.

Wallpaper Magazine Editors. Kyoto 2012 - Wallpaper City Guide. 2012. (ENG., Illus.). 128p. pap. 9.95 ***(978-0-7148-6302-3(5))*** Phaidon Pr., Inc.

Worrall, Julian & Solomon, Erez Golani. 21st Century Tokyo: A Guide to Contemporary Architecture, 1 vol. 2010. (ENG., Illus.). 240p. pap. 20.00 *(978-4-7700-3054-2(1))* Kodansha America, Inc.

Young, David & Young, Michiko. The Art of Japanese Architecture. 2007. (ENG., Illus.). 176p. 39.95 *(978-0-8048-3838-2(0))* Tuttle Publishing.

Zwerger, Klaus. Wood & Wood Joints: Building Traditions of Europe, Japan & China (Second, Revised & Expanded Edition) 2nd rev. ed. 2012. (ENG., Illus.). 312p. pap. 69.95 *(978-3-0346-0685-1(0))* Birkhauser Verlag AG CHE. Dist: Actar Birkhauser Distribution.

ARCHITECTURE—JERUSALEM

Goldhill, Simon. Jerusalem: City of Longing. (Illus.). 368p. 2010. pap. 19.95 *(978-0-674-03468-6(6))* 2008. 27.95 *(978-0-674-02866-1(X))* Harvard Univ. Pr. (Belknap Pr.).

Grabar, Oleg. The Dome of the Rock. 2006. (Illus.). 256p. 22.95 *(978-0-674-02313-0(7)*, Belknap Pr.) Harvard Univ. Pr.

Hawari, Mahmoud K. Ayyubid Jerusalem (1187-1250) An Architectural & Archaeological Study. 2007. (Bar S Ser.). (Illus.). 214p. (C). pap. 90.00 *(978-1-4073-0042-9(3))* British Archaeological Reports Ltd. GBR. Dist: Brown, David Bk. Co., The.

ARCHITECTURE—KOREA

Busquets, Joan, et al. Deconstruction/Construction: The Chenggyecheon Restoration Project in Seoul. 2011. (Green Prize Ser.). (ENG., Illus.). 86p. pap. 19.95 *(978-1-934510-31-5(9))* Harvard Univ., Graduate Schl. of Design.

Han, Sung Mi. Finding the Hidden Design Philosophy in Korean Traditional Space. 2009. 108p. pap. *(978-3-639-15560-0(2))* VDM Verlag Dr. Mueller e.K.

Kim, Sung Hong & Schmal, Peter Cachola, eds. Megacity Network. 2008. (ENG., Illus.). 272p. 49.95 *(978-3-939633-37-2(2))* Jovis Verlag GmbH DEU. Dist: D.A.P./Distributed Art Pubs.

Neumeyer, Fritz & Jung, In Ha, texts. Auf der Suche nach dem Tektonischen Raum: Die Architektur von Jong Soung Kimm. Exploring Tectonic Space: Architecture of Jong Soung Kimm. 2009. (ENG., Illus.). 120p. 50.00 *(978-3-8030-0687-5(2))* Wasmuth, Ernst J. Verlag GmbH & Co. DEU. Dist: D.A.P./Distributed Art Pubs.

Pak, Kwang-Su. Hanok Ul Mal Handa. 2010. (KOR., Illus.). 262p. *(978-89-429-1162-2(5))* Iljin Publishing Co.

Riera Ojeda, Oscar & Woo, Kyu Sung. Geometries. Riera Ojeda, Oscar, ed. 2008. (ENG., Illus.). 112p. 25.00 *(978-0-9793801-6-7(2))* Oro Editions.

Royal Palaces of Korea. 2009. 56.00 *(978-981-08-0806-8(2))* World Scientific Publishing Co., Inc.

Schafer, Julia, ed. Dora Garcia: Rooms, Conversations. 2008. (ENG., Illus.). 104p. pap. 35.00 *(978-3-939633-16-7(X))* Jovis Verlag GmbH DEU. Dist: D.A.P./Distributed Art Pubs.

Sin, Tae-Hyon. Uri Chol Ul Ch'ajaso: Yoksa Sok Ui Uri Sach'al Iyagi. 2010. (KOR., Illus.). 411p. *(978-89-8494-393-3(2))* Hyean Publishing Co.

ARCHITECTURE—LATIN AMERICA

see also Architecture, Domestic—Latin America

del Real, Patricio & Gyger, Helen, eds. Ambiguous Territories: Articulating New Geographies in Latin American Modern Architecture & Urbanism. 2012. (ENG., Illus.). 400p. (C). 165.00 *(978-0-415-89345-9(3))*; pap. 53.95 *(978-0-415-89346-6(1))* Routledge.

Fraser, Valerie. The Architecture of Conquest: Building in the Viceroyalty of Peru, 1535-1635. 2009. (Cambridge Iberian & Latin American Studies). (ENG., Illus.). 220p. pap. 34.00 *(978-0-521-12281-8(3))* Cambridge Univ. Pr.

Hennings Hinojosa, Vania Verónica & Hernández Álvarez, María Elena. De Otros Asuntos e Historias de la Arquitectura: Interpretaciones Poco Conocidas o No Divulgadas. 2009. (SPA., Illus.). xii, 191p. *(978-607-02-0858-4(7))* Universidad Nacional Autónoma de México.

Leguía, Mariana. Latin America at the Crossroads: Architectural Design. 2011. (Architectural Design Ser.). (ENG.). 152p. pap. 40.00 *(978-0-470-66492-6(4)*, Wiley) Wiley, John & Sons, Inc.

Torrent, Horacio. Contemporary Architecture in Latin America. 2009. 240p. 75.00 *(978-0-7148-5731-2(9))* Phaidon Pr., Inc.

Wang, Wilfried & Alter, Kevin, eds. O'Neil Ford Duograph 1 — Chile: House at Punta Pite, 2003-06, Smiljan Radic: Crypt in the Cathedral of Santiago de Chile, 1999-2006, Rodrigo Perez de Arce. 2008. (ENG., Illus.). 128p. pap. 39.90 *(978-3-8030-0685-1(6))* Wasmuth, Ernst J. Verlag GmbH & Co. DEU. Dist: D.A.P./Distributed Art Pubs.

ARCHITECTURE—MALTA

Buhagiar, Victor. Impressions: Aesthetics & Design. 2006. (Illus.). 128p. (C). pap. 23.00 *(978-99932-7-086-7(5))* Midsea Bks. Ltd. MLT. Dist: Brown, David Bk. Co., The.

ARCHITECTURE—MEXICO

see also Maya Architecture

Adriá, Miquel. Humberto Spindola: Paper Interventions in the Architecture of Luis Barragan. 2009. (ENG., Illus.). 64p. 24.95 *(978-84-92480-48-7(3))* RM Verlag, S.L. ESP. Dist: D.A.P./Distributed Art Pubs.

Aeropuertos y Servicios Auxiliares, creator. Asa: Aeropuertos para la Competitividad y el Desarrollo. 2006. (Coleccion Editorial del Gobierno del

Cambio Ser.). (SPA., Illus.). 299p. pap. 24.95 (978-968-16-8117-3(7)) Fondo de Cultura Economica USA.

Andrés de San Miguel & Báez Macías, Eduardo. Obras de Fray Andrés de San Miguel. 2nd ed. 2007. (SPA., Illus.). 524p. (978-970-32-4343-3(6)) Universidad Nacional Autónoma de México.

Barrag#xE0;n, Luis. Luis Barrag#xE1;n: His House. 2011. (ENG., Illus.). 211p. 65.00 (978-84-15118-13-8(9)) RM Verlag, S.L. ESP. Dist: D.A.P./Distributed Art Pubs.

Baum, Sandy. San Miguel's Mexican Exteriors. 2008. (Illus.). 224p. 39.99 (978-0-7643-3004-9(7)) Schiffer Publishing, Ltd.

Blancsube, Michel & Hoffmann, Jens, texts. Fernando Ortega. 2010. (ENG., Illus.). 192p. pap. 29.50 (978-968-9056-41-6(7)) Turner, Ediciones S.A. ESP. Dist: D.A.P./Distributed Art Pubs.

BNKR Arquitecture, creator. Stop: Keep Moving: An Oxymoronic Approach to Architecture. 2011. (ENG., Illus.). 248p. pap. (978-607-7784-07-4(9)) Editorial RM.

Broid, Isaac. Isaac Broid: Arquitectura Urbana. (ENG & SPA., Illus.). 155p. 35.00 (978-968-5616-00-3(0)) Editorial RM MEX. Dist: Trucatriche.

Carranza, Luis E. Architecture as Revolution: Episodes in the History of Modern Mexico. 2010. (ENG., Illus.). 255p. 60.00 (978-0-292-72195-1(1)) Univ. of Texas Pr.

De Anda Alanis, Enrique X. Candela. 2008. (Basic Architecture Ser.). (ENG., Illus.). 96p. pap. 9.99 (978-3-8228-3725-2(3)) TASCHEN DEU. Dist: Ingram Pub. Services.

George, W. Eugene. Lost Architecture of the Rio Grande Borderlands. 2008. (Fronteras Series, sponsored by Texas A&M International University Ser.). (Illus.). 136p. 35.00 (978-1-60344-011-0(9)) Texas A&M Univ. Pr.

Giffords, Gloria Fraser. Sanctuaries of Earth, Stone, & Light: The Churches of Northern New Spain, 1530-1821. 2007. (Southwest Center Ser.). (ENG., Illus.). 480p. 75.00 (978-0-8165-2589-8(7)) Univ. of Arizona Pr.

Haro Lebrija, Fernando de & Fuentes Elizondo, Omar. Evolución de Las Formas: Evolution of Forms. 2009. (ENG & SPA., Illus.). 211p. (978-607-437-041-6(9)) AM Editores.

—Forma y Volumen. 2008. (ENG & SPA., Illus.). 190p. (978-970-9726-95-4(1)) AM Editores.

Hendricks, J. & Taschen, Angelika, eds. Mexico Style. 25th ed. 2008. (Icon (Taschen) Ser.). (FRE., Illus.). 191p. 7.99 (978-3-8365-0771-4(4)) TASCHEN DEU. Dist: Ingram Pub. Services.

Kalach, Alberto. Biblioteca/Vasconcelos/Library, 1 vol. 2007. (ENG., Illus.). 160p. 29.00 (978-968-5208-77-2(8)) R.M. Editorial, S.A. de C.V. MEX. Dist: D.A.P./Distributed Art Pubs.

Klich, Lynda & Mogul, Jonathan, eds. The Journal of Decorative & Propaganda Arts: Mexico Theme Issue, Issue 26. 2010. 304p. pap. 50.00 (978-1-930776-18-0(7)) Wolfson Foundation of Decorative & Propaganda Arts, Inc., The.

Koontz, Rex. Lightning Gods & Feathered Serpents: The Public Sculpture of el Tajín. 2009. (ENG., Illus.). 152p. 60.00 (978-0-292-71899-9(3)) Univ. of Texas Pr.

Lizárraga Sánchez, Salvador & Anda, Enrique X. de, eds. Cultura Arquitectónica de la Modernidad Mexicana: Antología de Textos, 1922-1963. 2010. (SPA., Illus.). 391p. (978-607-02-1468-4(4)) Universidad Nacional Autónoma de México.

López Luján, Leonardo. La Casa de Las Águilas: Un Ejemplo de la Arquitectura Religiosa de Tenochtitlan, 2 vols. 2006. (Antropología Ser.). (SPA., Illus.). 578p. 49.95 (978-968-16-7537-0(1)) Fondo de Cultura Economica USA.

M.Guillermo Perez. Mexico/Argentina/Architects. 2006. (ENG., Illus.). 200p. 60.00 (978-968-5152-05-1(5)) COEDI MEX, S.A. de C.V. MEX. Dist: Antique Collectors' Club.

Martin, Mary L. & Skinner, Tina. Architecture of Old Mexico: Vintage Views of Spanish Colonial Courtyards, Facades, Streetscapes & Interiors. 2007. (Illus.). 144p. pap. 29.95 (978-0-7643-2571-7(X)) Schiffer Publishing, Ltd.

Messina, John. Alamos, Sonora: Architecture & Urbanism in the Dry Tropics. 2008. (Southwest Center Ser.). (ENG., Illus.). 192p. 35.00 (978-0-8165-2651-2(6)) Univ. of Arizona Pr.

Moleskine. Inspiration & Process in Architecture - Alberto Kalach. 2012. (ENG., Illus.). 272p. 39.95 (978-88-6613-004-8(4)) Moleskine ITA. Dist: Hachette Bk. Group.

Olsen, Patrice Eliza. Artifacts of Revolution: Architecture, Society, & Politics in Mexico City, 1920-1940. 2008. (Latin American Silhouettes Ser.). (ENG.). 300p. 80.00 (978-0-7425-5420-7(1)) Rowman & Littlefield Publishers, Inc.

Pauly, Danièle. Barragán: L'espace et l'ombre, le mur et la Couleur. 2008. (FRE., Illus.). 231p. pap. 59.95 (978-3-7643-8706-8(8), 3764387068) Springer.

Prix, Wolf D., ed. The Mexican Roof Revisited (Techo en Mexico 2) 2010. (Edition Angewandte Ser.). (Illus.). 137p. pap. 39.95 (978-3-7091-0471-2(8), 3709104718) Springer.

Rodríguez Viqueira, Manuel & Yáñez, Enrique. Arquitecto Enrique Yáñez de la Fuente: Memorias. (SPA., Illus.). 160p. (978-968-18-5183-5(8)) Noriega Editores.

Saitão, Yutaka, et al. Luis Barragán. 2nd rev. ed. (SPA., Illus.). 452p. (C). (978-968-18-4742-5(3), Limusa) Noriega Editores.

Shipway, Verna Cook. The Mexican House. 3rd ed. 2007. 39.95 (978-0-940512-47-4(5)) Hennessey & Ingalls, Inc.

Stuart, David E. Pueblo Peoples on the Pajarito Plateau: Archaeology & Efficiency. 2010. (ENG., Illus.). 160p. pap. 19.95 (978-0-8263-4911-8(0)) Univ. of New Mexico Pr.

Tate, Carolyn E. Yaxchilan: The Design of a Maya Ceremonial City. 2011. (ENG., Illus.). 328p. pap. 40.00 (978-0-292-73911-6(7)) Univ. of Texas Pr.

Wallpaper Magazine Editors, ed. Mexico City 2012 - Wallpaper City Guide. 2nd ed. 2011. (ENG., Illus.). 128p. pap. 9.95 (978-0-7148-6098-5(0)) Phaidon Pr., Inc.

Ypma, Herbert. Mexican Contemporary. 2010. (World Design Ser.). (ENG., Illus.). 160p. pap. 19.95 (978-0-500-28887-0(9), 528887) Thames & Hudson.

ARCHITECTURE—MIDDLE EAST

al-Asad, Mohammad. Contemporary Architecture & Urbanism in the Middle East. 2012. (ENG., Illus.). 320p. 50.00 (978-0-8130-4017-2(5)) Univ. Pr. of Florida.

Al-Mudhei, Ali. Implementation of Building Codes. 2010. 188p. pap. (978-3-639-25138-8(5)) VDM Verlag Dr. Mueller e.K.

AlRawahi, Architect Khalsa. Charm of Simplicity: Nakhal Fort. 2011. 104p. pap. 41.47 (978-1-4567-7181-2(7)) AuthorHouse.

Bellini, Oscar & Daglio, Laura. New Frontiers of Architecture: Dubai. 2010. (ENG., Illus.). 304p. 40.00 (978-88-544-0411-3(X)) White Star ITA. Dist: Sterling Publishing Co., Inc.

Beyhan, Bolak Hisari?Gil. Narrative Space: In the Black Book by Orhan Pamuk. 2011. 88p. pap. (978-3-639-32811-0(6)) VDM Verlag Dr. Mueller e.K.

Binder, Georges. Tall Buildings of Europe, Middle East & Africa. 2007. (Tall Buildings Ser.). (ENG., Illus.). 240p. 75.00 (978-1-876907-81-5(9)) Images Publishing Group AUS. Dist: National Bk. Network.

Boussaa, Djamel. Urban Conservation in North Africa & the Gulf. 2010. 324p. pap. (978-3-639-27313-7(3)) VDM Verlag Dr. Mueller e.K.

Bretschneider, J., et al, eds. Power & Architecture. Monumental Public Architecture in the Bronze Age near East & Aegean: Proceedings of the International conference 'Power & Architecture' organized by the Katholieke Universiteit Leuven, the Universite Catholique de Louvain & the Westfalischen Wilhelms-Universitat Munster on the 21st & 22nd of November 2002. 2007. (Orientalia Lovaniensia Analecta Ser.). (ENG., Illus.). 212p. (C). 109.00 (978-90-429-1831-3(4)) Peeters Pubs. & Booksellers BEL. Dist: Brown, David Bk. Co., The.

Chi, Jennifer & Heath, Sebastian. Edge of Empires - Pagans, Jews, & Christians at Roman Dura-Europos. 2011. (ENG., Illus.). 120p. (C). pap. 29.95 (978-0-691-15468-8(6)) Princeton Univ. Pr.

Chyutin, Michael & Chyutin, Bracha. Architecture & Utopia: The Israeli Experiment. 2007. (Design & the Built Environment Ser.). (Illus.). 264p. 124.95 (978-0-7546-4831-4(1)) Ashgate Publishing Co.

Curatola, Giovanni, ed. The Art & Architecture of Mesopotamia. 2007. (ENG., Illus.). 280p. 95.00 (978-0-7892-0921-4(7)) Abbeville Pr., Inc.

Curatola, Giovanni & Scarcia, Gianroberto. Art & Architecture of Persia. Shore, Marguerite, tr. from ITA. 2007. (ENG., Illus.). 263p. 95.00 (978-0-7892-0920-7(9)) Abbeville Pr., Inc.

Daglio, Laura & Bellini, Oscar. Building Arabia: Expanding the Limits of Architecture. 2010. (ENG., Illus.). 302p. 40.00 (978-88-544-0450-2(0)) White Star ITA. Dist: Random Hse., Inc.

Eichner, Ina & Tsamakda, Vasiliki, eds. Syrien und seine Nachbarn von der Spatantike bis in die islamische Zeit. 2009. (Spatantike-Fruhes Christentum-Byzanz Ser.). (GER., Illus.). 308p. (C). 168.00 (978-3-89500-674-6(2)) Reichert, Ludwig Dr. DEU. Dist: Brown, David Bk. Co., The.

Farah, Caesar E. The Ottoman Forts & Castles of Yemen: A Photographic & Architectural Analysis. 2011. (Illus.). 180p. 109.95 (978-0-7734-1291-0(3)) Mellen, Edwin Pr., The.

Gholam, Nabil. Nabil Gholam Architects. 2011. (Illus.). 420p. 42.00 (978-84-9936-860-3(3)) Loft Pubns. ESP. Dist: Prestel Publishing.

Golia, Maria. Photography & Egypt. 2009. (Reaktion Books - Exposures Ser.). (ENG., Illus.). 144p. pap. 29.95 (978-1-86189-543-1(7)) Reaktion Bks., Ltd. GBR. Dist: Chicago Distribution Ctr.

Guccione, Margherita. Zaha Hadid: Minimum Series. 2010. (ENG., Illus.). 120p. 19.95 (978-88-6413-021-7(7), Ore Cultura Srl (Acc)) Antique Collectors' Club GBR. Dist: National Bk. Network.

Hadid: Complete Works, 1979-2009. deluxe ed. 2010. (978-3-8365-1739-3(6)) TASCHEN.

Hadid, Zaha. Zaha Hadid: Complete Works. 2009. (ENG., Illus.). 256p. 50.00 (978-0-8478-3301-6(1)) Rizzoli International Pubns., Inc.

Hassanein, Ahmed Taher, et al. Baghdad Arts Deco: Architectural Brickwork, 19201950. 2011. (ENG.). 608p. 39.95 (978-977-416-356-2(7)) American Univ. in Cairo Pr. EGY. Dist: Oxford Univ. Pr., Inc.

Hawker, Ronald. Traditional Architecture of the Arabian Gulf: Building on Desert Tides. 2008. (Illus.). 252p. 170.00 (978-1-84564-135-1(3)) WIT Pr GBR. Dist: WIT Pr.

Hiesinger, Kathryn Bloom, et al. Zaha Hadid: Form in Motion. 2011. (ENG., Illus.). 60p. pap. 18.00 (978-0-300-17982-8(0)) Yale Univ. Pr.

Isenstadt, Sandy & Rizvi, Kishwar, eds. Modernism & the Middle East: Architecture & Politics in the Twentieth Century. 2008. (Studies in Modernity & National Identity). (ENG., Illus.). 328p. 80.00 (978-0-295-98821-4(5)); (C). pap. 30.00 (978-0-295-98794-1(4)) Univ. of Washington Pr.

Jodidio, Philip. Zaha Hadid: Complete Works 1979 - 2009. 2009. (FRE, GER & ENG., Illus.). 500p. 150.00 (978-3-8365-0294-8(1)) TASCHEN DEU. Dist: Ingram Pub. Services.

Jodidio, Philip, ed. The Aga Khan Historic Cities Programme: Strategies for Urban Regeneration. 2011. (Illus.). 240p. 75.00 (978-3-7913-4406-5(4)) Prestel Publishing.

Katodrytis, George, ed. Dubai: Growing Through Architecture. 2012. (Illus.). 288p. 125.00 (978-0-500-34245-9(8)) Thames & Hudson.

Kazimee, B. A, ed. Heritage & Sustainability in the Islamic Built Environment. 2012. (ENG., Illus.). 240p. 192.00 (978-1-84564-624-0(X)) WIT Pr GBR. Dist: WIT Pr.

Kenney, Ellen V. Power & Patronage in Medieval Syria: The Architecture & Urban Works of Tankiz Al-Nasiri. 2009. (978-0-9708199-4-9(3)) Univ. of Chicago, Middle East Documentation Ctr.

Koolhaas, Rem. The Gulf. 2007. (Illus.). 25p. per. 19.95 (978-3-03778-088-6(6), 3037780886) Lars Muller Pubs. CHE. Dist: Springer.

Lewcock, Ronald. Non- Western Architecture. Date not set. (978-0-393-73044-9(1)) Norton, W. W. & Co., Inc.

Mitchell, Kevin, et al, eds. Instant Cities: Emergent Trends in Architecture & Urbanism in the Arab World. 2008. (Illus.). 500p. pap. (978-9957-8602-1-9(6)) Center for Study of Architecture in the Arab Region (CSAAR), The.

Moleskine. Moleskine Inspiration & Process in Architecture: Alberto Kalach. 2012. (ENG., Illus.). 272p. 39.95 (978-88-6613-001-7(X)) Moleskine ITA. Dist: Hachette Bk. Group.

Murray, Michael J. Black Gold Fever. 2007. 300p. (ENG.). 31.99 (978-1-4257-4170-9(3)); per. 21.99 (978-1-4257-4169-3(X)) Xlibris Corp.

Pringle, Denys. The Churches of the Crusader Kingdom of Jerusalem: A Corpus: Volume 2, L-Z (excluding Tyre) 2009. (Churches of the Crusader Kingdom of Jerusalem Ser.). (ENG., Illus.). 484p. pap. 58.00 (978-0-521-10983-3(3)) Cambridge Univ. Pr.

—The Churches of the Crusader Kingdom of Jerusalem: Volume 3, the City of Jerusalem: A Corpus. 2010. (Churches of the Crusader Kingdom of Jerusalem Ser.). (ENG.). 534p. pap. 65.00 (978-0-521-17283-7(7)) Cambridge Univ. Pr.

Roller, Zoe. Beyond Reality. 2011. 124p. pap. (978-3-8443-2878-3(5)) Lambert Academic Publishing.

Sarkis, Hashim. Han Tumertekin: Recent Work. 2007. (Aga Khan Program of the Graduate School of Design Ser.). (Illus.). 64p. per. 24.95 (978-0-935617-71-7(4)) Harvard Univ., Graduate Schl. of Design.

Sarkis, Hashim, et al. Two Squares: Martyrs Square, Beirut, & Sirkeci Square, Istanbul. Sarkis, Hashim, ed. 2006. (Aga Khan Program of the Graduate School of Design Ser.). (Illus.). 200p. per. 19.95 (978-0-935617-39-4(2)) Harvard Univ., Graduate Schl. of Design.

Seeliger, Hans Reinhard & Krumeich, Kirsten. Archäologie der Antiken Bischofssitze. 2007. (Sprachen und Kulturen des Christlichen Orients Ser.). (GER., Illus.). 176p. (C). 84.00 (978-3-89500-501-5(0)) Reichert, Ludwig Dr. DEU. Dist: Brown, David Bk. Co., The.

Stierlin, Henri. Islam: From Baghdad to Cordoba. Stierlin, Henri, ed. 25th ed. 2009. (World Architecture Ser.). (ENG., Illus.). 224p. 14.99 (978-3-8365-1059-2(6)) TASCHEN DEU. Dist: Ingram Pub. Services.

Stronach, D. & Roaf, M. Nush-i Jan I. the Major Buildings of the Median Settlement. 2007. (ENG.). 242p. (C). pap. 116.00 (978-90-429-1850-4(0)) Peeters Pubs. & Booksellers BEL. Dist: Brown, David Bk. Co., The.

Wallpaper Magazine Editors, ed. Dubai 2012 - Wallpaper City Guide. 2nd ed. 2011. (ENG., Illus.). 128p. pap., pap. 9.95 (978-0-7148-6089-3(1)) Phaidon Pr., Inc.

Weber, Stefan. Damascus: Ottoman Modernity & Urban Transformation (1808-1918). 2 vols. 2009. (Proceedings of the danish institute at Damascus Ser.). (ENG., Illus.). 1125p. (C). 245.00 (978-87-7934-424-2(0)) Aarhus Universitetsforlag DNK. Dist: ISD.

ARCHITECTURE—MOROCCO

Massó, Patricia & Kunz, Martin N. Taste Morocco, 3 vols. 2008. (FRE, GER & ENG., Illus.). (978-90-76886-48-0(2)) Tectum B.V.B.A.

Montague, Maryam. Marrakesh by Design: Decorating with All the Colors, Patterns, & Magic of Morocco. 2012. (ENG., Illus.). 264p. 29.95 (978-1-57965-401-6(0)) Artisan.

O'Meara, Simon. Space & Muslim Urban Life: At the Limits of the Labyrinth of Fez. 2007. (Culture & Civilization in the Middle East Ser.). (ENG., Illus.). 176p. 160.00 (978-0-415-38612-8(8)) Routledge.

Vastapane, Fabienne. Living in great style in Taroudant, 1 vol. 2012. (ENG.). 256p. 89.50 (978-90-8881-032-9(X)) Exhibitions International BEL. Dist: Innovative Logistics.

Wallpaper Magazine Editors, ed. Wallpaper* City Guide - Marrakech 2011. rev. ed. 2011. (Wallpaper* City Guides). (ENG., Illus.). 128p. pap. 9.95 (978-0-7148-5714-5(9)) Phaidon Pr., Inc.

ARCHITECTURE—NEAR EAST

see Architecture—Middle East

ARCHITECTURE—NETHERLANDS

Abrahamse, Jaap Evert & Lebesque, Sabine. Eastern Harbour District Amsterdam: Urbanism & Architecture, 1 vol. 2007. (ENG., Illus.). 240p. pap. 80.00 (978-90-5662-553-5(5)) NAi Uitgevers / Publishers Stichting NLD. Dist: D.A.P./Distributed Art Pubs.

Adriaansz, Elly, et al, texts. Villa Park in the City: the Chabot Museum & the Environs of the Museumpark Villas Rotterdam. 2010. (ENG., Illus.). 124p. 40.00 (978-90-5662-651-8(5)) NAi Uitgevers / Publishers Stichting NLD. Dist: D.A.P./Distributed Art Pubs.

Avermaete, Tom, et al, eds. OASE 77: into the Open. Accomodating the Public. 2009. (ENG., Illus.). 128p. pap. 35.00 (978-90-5662-661-7(2)) NAi Uitgevers / Publishers Stichting NLD. Dist: D.A.P./Distributed Art Pubs.

Avidar, Pnina, et al, eds. OASE 73: Gentrification, 1 vol. 2009. (ENG., Illus.). 144p. pap. 30.00 (978-90-5662-584-9(5)) NAi Uitgevers / Publishers Stichting NLD. Dist: D.A.P./Distributed Art Pubs.

Bakker, Daan, et al, eds. Architectuur in Nederland/Architecture in the Netherlands: Jaarboek/Yearbook, 1 vol. 2007. (ENG., Illus.). 176p. per. 60.00 (978-90-5662-581-8(0)) NAi Uitgevers / Publishers Stichting NLD. Dist: D.A.P./Distributed Art Pubs.

Bal, Ufuk. Utilization of Urban Design Principles in Designing the Urban Space. 2011. 232p. pap. (978-3-8443-0270-7(0)) Lambert Academic Publishing.

Bantal, Samir, ed. Architecture in the Netherlands: Yearbook 2009-10. 2010. (ENG., Illus.). 192p. pap. 60.00 (978-90-5662-751-5(1)) NAi Uitgevers / Publishers Stichting NLD. Dist: D.A.P./Distributed Art Pubs.

Beaver, Robyn, ed. Dirk Jan Postel: Transparencies. 2008. (Master Architect (Unnumberd) Ser.). (ENG., Illus.). 256p. 59.95 (978-1-86470-210-1(9), Images Publishing Dist Ac) Antique Collectors' Club GBR. Dist: National Bk. Network.

Berens, Hetty, ed. P. J. H. Cuypers (1827-1921) The Complete Works, 1 vol. 2007. (ENG., Illus.). 397p. 75.00 (978-90-5662-574-0(8)) NAi Uitgevers / Publishers Stichting NLD. Dist: D.A.P./Distributed Art Pubs.

Betsky, Aaron. False Flat: Why Dutch Design Is So Good. 2008. (ENG., Illus.). 400p. pap. 39.95 (978-0-7148-4861-7(1)) Phaidon Pr. Ltd. GBR. Dist: Hachette Bk. Group.

Biegman, Nicolaas. Whipped Cream: And Other Delights of Amsterdam Architecture. 2011. (DUT & ENG., Illus.). 200p. pap. 35.00 (978-94-6022-140-8(8)) Royal Tropical Institute Pr. (KIT (Koninklijk Instituut voor de Tropen) NLD. Dist: Stylus Publishing, LLC.

BIS Publishers. Dutch Architects 8. 7th rev. ed. 2009. (ENG., Illus.). 332p. 69.00 (978-90-6369-160-8(2)) Bis B.V., Uitgeverij(BIS Publishers) NLD. Dist: Consortium Bk. Sales & Distribution.

Boomgaard, Jeroen, ed. & text. High-Rise & Common Ground, 1 vol. 2008. (ENG., Illus.). 361p. (C). pap. 29.95 (978-90-78088-18-9(4)) Valiz NLD. Dist: D.A.P./Distributed Art Pubs.

Boon, Piet. Piet Boon 2. 2006. (ENG.). 200p. 125.00 (978-90-5897-467-9(7)) Lannoo Pubs./Racine.

Bosman, Jos, et al, texts. Diederendirrix Architects. 2009. (ENG & MUL., Illus.). 296p. 80.00 (978-90-5662-662-4(0)) NAi Uitgevers / Publishers Stichting NLD. Dist: D.A.P./Distributed Art Pubs.

Bouman, Ole, et al, texts. Architecture of Consequence. 2010. (ENG., Illus.). 168p. pap. 35.00 (978-90-5662-726-3(0)) NAi Uitgevers / Publishers Stichting NLD. Dist: D.A.P./Distributed Art Pubs.

Bouvier, Pierre, tr. Building Site Enschede: A City Re-Creates Itself, 1 vol. 2007. (ENG., Illus.). 128p. 32.50 (978-90-5662-589-4(6)) NAi Uitgevers / Publishers Stichting NLD. Dist: D.A.P./Distributed Art Pubs.

Boxel, Elma van, et al. Re-Public: Towards a New Spatial Politics/Naar Een Nieuwe Ruimte-Politiek. 2008. (ENG., Illus.). 160p. 39.95 (978-90-5662-625-9(6)) NAi Uitgevers / Publishers Stichting NLD. Dist: D.A.P./Distributed Art Pubs.

Broekhuizen, Dolf, et al, texts. Contemporary Dutch School Architecture. 2009. (ENG., Illus.). 264p. 70.00 (978-90-5662-656-3(6)) NAi Uitgevers / Publishers Stichting NLD. Dist: D.A.P./Distributed Art Pubs.

Chong, Adele, ed. & text. Daan Roosegaarde: Interactive Landscapes. 2011. (ENG., Illus.). 160p. pap. 45.00 (978-90-5662-754-6(6)) NAi Uitgevers / Publishers Stichting NLD. Dist: D.A.P./Distributed Art Pubs.

de Jong, Erik & Betram, Christian, eds. Michael Van Gessel: Landscape Architect. 2008. (ENG., Illus.). 348p. 95.00 (978-90-5662-038-7(X)) NAi Uitgevers / Publishers Stichting NLD. Dist: D.A.P./Distributed Art Pubs.

Declerck, Joachim, et al, eds. Oase 75. 2008. (ENG., Illus.). 319p. pap. 40.00 (978-90-5662-674-7(4)) NAi Uitgevers / Publishers Stichting NLD. Dist: D.A.P./Distributed Art Pubs.

Denslagen, Wim. Romantic Modernism: Nostalgia in the World of Conservation. 2011. 261p. pap. (978-90-8964-103-8(3)) Amsterdam Univ. Pr.

Dijk, Oene & Abhelakh, Anneke, eds. Architecture Bulletin 04. 2008. (ENG.). 80p. pap. 25.00 (978-90-5662-643-3(4)) NAi Uitgevers / Publishers Stichting NLD. Dist: D.A.P./Distributed Art Pubs.

Edens, Catja, et al, texts. Facts & Forms: the Best Buildings by Young Architects in the Netherlands. 2009. (DUT & ENG., Illus.). 128p. pap. 34.00 (978-90-5662-668-6(X)) NAi Uitgevers / Publishers Stichting NLD. Dist: D.A.P./Distributed Art Pubs.

Fabre, Gladys, et al, eds. Van Doesburg & the International Avant-Garde: Constructing a New World. 2010. (ENG., Illus.). 264p. pap. 40.00 (978-1-85437-872-9(4)) Tate Publishing, Ltd. GBR. Dist: Hachette Bk. Group.

Forgeur, Brigitte. Lebenskunst in Amsterdam. (GER.). (978-3-8067-2856-9(9)) Gerstenberg DEU. Dist: International Bk. Import Service, Inc.

Havermans, Frank. Frank Havermans: Architectural Constructions. 2010. (ENG., Illus.). 192p. 50.00 (978-90-5662-701-0(5)) NAi Uitgevers / Publishers Stichting NLD. Dist: D.A.P./Distributed Art Pubs.

Helle, Maarten, photos by. Typography & Architecture: Amsterdam in Letters. 2009. (ENG., Illus.). 192p. 37.50 (978-90-78088-25-7(7)) Valiz NLD. Dist: D.A.P./Distributed Art Pubs.

Hertzberger, Herman. The Berlage Institute: Platform for Architecture Culture, Practice & Education, 1990-2010. 2011. (ENG., Illus.). 240p. pap. 45.00 (978-90-5662-765-2(1)) NAi Uitgevers / Publishers Stichting NLD. Dist: D.A.P./Distributed Art Pubs.

Heuer, Christopher. The City Rehearsed: Object, Architecture, & Print in the Worlds of Hans Vredeman de Vries. 2012. (Classical Tradition in Architecture Ser.). (ENG., Illus.). 312p. (C). pap. 42.95 (978-0-415-54232-6(4)) Routledge.

Houben, Francine, et al, texts. Architecture Bulletin 05. 2009. (ENG., Illus.). 136p. pap. 25.00 *(978-90-5662-669-3(8))* NAi Uitgevers / Publishers Stichting NLD. Dist: D.A.P./Distributed Art Pubs.

Klein, Caroline. Below Sea Level: Modern Architecture & Design in the Netherlands, 1 vol. 2012. (GER, DUT & ENG.). 312p. 75.00 *(978-3-942597-10-4(1))* DAAB Media Gmbh DEU. Dist: Innovative Logistics.

Lagae, Johan, et al, eds. OASE 72: Back to School, 1 vol. 2007. (ENG., Illus.). 144p. pap. 30.00 *(978-90-5662-583-2(7))* NAi Uitgevers / Publishers Stichting NLD. Dist: D.A.P./Distributed Art Pubs.

Lebesque, Sabine, ed. & text. Along the IJ, 1 vol. 2007. (ENG., Illus.). 352p. pap. 30.00 *(978-90-78088-10-3(9))* Valiz NLD. Dist: D.A.P./Distributed Art Pubs.

Luijten, Anne, et al, eds. Architecture in the Netherlands. (ENG., Illus.). 184p. 2011. pap. 60.00 ***(978-90-5662-806-2(2))*** 2009. pap. 60.00 *(978-90-5662-686-0(8))* NAi Uitgevers / Publishers Stichting NLD. Dist: D.A.P./Distributed Art Pubs.

Maas, Winy & Madrazo, Fleix, texts. NL to Do: Reacting to Future Headlines. 2012. (ENG., Illus.). 328p. pap. 45.00 ***(978-90-5662-804-8(6))*** NAi Uitgevers / Publishers Stichting NLD. Dist: D.A.P./Distributed Art Pubs.

Maaskant, Madeleine, et al, contrib. by. Oase #70: Architecture & Literature, 1 vol. 2009. (ENG., Illus.). 144p. pap. 25.00 *(978-90-5662-487-3(3))* NAi Uitgevers / Publishers Stichting NLD. Dist: D.A.P./Distributed Art Pubs.

Marcelis, Ritsaart. Stadspoort Amsterdam. 2010. 148p. pap. *(978-3-8383-7045-3(7))* Lambert Academic Publishing.

Meijer, Haiko, et al, texts. Wood Works Onix. 2010. (ENG., Illus.). 320p. 60.00 *(978-90-5662-679-2(5))* NAi Uitgevers / Publishers Stichting NLD. Dist: D.A.P./Distributed Art Pubs.

Mens, Noor, text. Healthcare Architecture in the Netherlands. 2010. (ENG., Illus.). 352p. 80.00 *(978-90-5662-734-8(1))* NAi Uitgevers / Publishers Stichting NLD. Dist: D.A.P./Distributed Art Pubs.

Moore, Lesley. Dutch Architects, Vol. 9. 2009. (ENG., Illus.). 264p. 80.00 *(978-90-6369-196-7(3))* Bis B.V., Uitgeverij(BIS Publishers) NLD. Dist: Consortium Bk. Sales & Distribution.

Netherlands Art, Architecture & Landscape. Date not set. (Illus.). 400p. 19.95 *(978-3-8290-6471-2(3)*, 521653) Konemann.

Nillesen, Anne Loes & Singelenberg, Jeroen, texts. Amphibious Housing in the Netherlands: Architecture & Urbanism on the Water. 2011. (ENG., Illus.). 160p. pap. 45.00 *(978-90-5662-780-5(5))* NAi Uitgevers / Publishers Stichting NLD. Dist: D.A.P./Distributed Art Pubs.

Oosterhuis, Kas. ONLogic: Speed & Vision. 2009. (Master Architect Ser.). (ENG., Illus.). 224p. 59.95 *(978-1-86470-286-6(9)*, Images Publishing Dist Ac) Antique Collectors' Club GBR. Dist: National Bk. Network.

Palmboom, Frits. Drawing the Ground - Landscape Urbanism Today: The Work of Palmbout Urban Landscapes. 2010. (ENG., Illus.). 200p. 69.95 *(978-3-0346-0263-1(4))* Birkhauser Verlag AG CHE. Dist: Actar Birkhauser Distribution.

Pimlott, Mark, et al, eds. OASE 76: Context-Specificity. 2009. (ENG., Illus.). 148p. pap. 35.00 *(978-90-5662-660-0(4))* NAi Uitgevers / Publishers Stichting NLD. Dist: D.A.P./Distributed Art Pubs.

Provoost, Michelle, ed. Wimby! Hoogvliet: Future, Past & Present of a New Town: Or: the Big Wimby Book, 1 vol. 2008. (ENG., Illus.). 528p. per. 55.00 *(978-90-5662-595-5(0))* NAi Uitgevers / Publishers Stichting NLD. Dist: D.A.P./Distributed Art Pubs.

Provoost, Michelle, et al, eds. Architecture in the Netherlands. 2008. (ENG., Illus.). 184p. pap. 60.00 *(978-90-5662-050-9(9))* NAi Uitgevers / Publishers Stichting NLD. Dist: D.A.P./Distributed Art Pubs.

Remoy, H. T., ed. Out of Office. 2010. (Illus.). 260p. pap. 109.00 *(978-1-60750-520-4(7)*, Delft University Pr) IOS Pr., Inc.

Roose. Architectural Representation Islam. 2009. (ISIM Dissertations Ser.). pap. *(978-90-8964-133-5(5))* Amsterdam Univ. Pr.

Smeesters, Hilde. Luxury Living by B+ Villas. 2011. (ENG, DUT & FRE., Illus.). 192p. 130.00 ***(978-2-87550-004-5(X))*** Beta-Plus Pubs. BEL. Dist: Antique Collectors' Club.

Smith, Neil, et al, texts. Houses of Transformation: Intervening in European Gentrification. 2009. (DUT & ENG., Illus.). 208p. pap. 50.00 *(978-90-5662-060-8(6))* NAi Uitgevers / Publishers Stichting NLD. Dist: D.A.P./Distributed Art Pubs.

Somer, Kees. The Functional City: The CIAM & Cornelis Van Eesteren, 1928-1960, 1 vol. 2007. (ENG., Illus.). 304p. 75.00 *(978-90-5662-576-4(4))* NAi Uitgevers / Publishers Stichting NLD. Dist: D.A.P./Distributed Art Pubs.

Spuybroek, Lars. The Architecture of Continuity. 2009. (ENG., Illus.). 288p. pap. 30.00 *(978-90-5662-637-2(X))* NAi Uitgevers / Publishers Stichting NLD. Dist: D.A.P./Distributed Art Pubs.

ter Braak, Lex & Jacobs, Edwin, texts. Robbie Cornelissen: the Capacious Memory. 2011. (ENG., Illus.). 128p. pap. 35.00 ***(978-90-5662-811-6(9))*** NAi Uitgevers / Publishers Stichting NLD. Dist: D.A.P./Distributed Art Pubs.

Thonik. Thonik: I Am Your Type. 2012. (ENG., Illus.). 256p. pap. 50.00 *(978-90-5662-744-7(9))* NAi Uitgevers / Publishers Stichting NLD. Dist: D.A.P./Distributed Art Pubs.

van der Vaart, Oscar, et al. A Business Approach for the Development of the Future Dutch Coastline. 2010. 108p. pap. *(978-3-8383-7065-1(1))* Lambert Academic Publishing.

Van Stein, Saskia, ed. Bare Facts: the Best Buildings by Young Architects in the Netherlands, 1 vol. 2007. (ENG., Illus.). 128p. (C). pap. 29.95 *(978-90-5662-521-4(7))* NAi Uitgevers / Publishers Stichting NLD. Dist: D.A.P./Distributed Art Pubs.

van 't Hoff, Robert. Robert van 't Hoff: Architect of a New Society. 2010. (ENG., Illus.). 156p. 45.00 *(978-90-5662-750-8(3))* NAi Uitgevers / Publishers Stichting NLD. Dist: D.A.P./Distributed Art Pubs.

Venhoeven, Ton. The Wonderful World of VenhoevenCS Architects. 2009. (Illus.). 296p. *(978-90-5973-073-1(9))* Episode Pubs.

Visser, Frank. Dutch Architects & Their Houses. 2012. (ENG., Illus.). 240p. 55.00 ***(978-94-6058-094-9(7)***, Uitgeverij Luster) Antique Collectors' Club GBR. Dist: National Bk. Network.

Vos, Emmie. Europan 8 in Nederland: Europan 8 in the Netherlands: European Urbanity & Strategic Projects, 1 vol. 2006. (DUT & ENG., Illus.). 144p. pap. 33.00 *(978-90-5662-499-6(7))* NAi Uitgevers / Publishers Stichting NLD. Dist: D.A.P./Distributed Art Pubs.

Vos, Emmie, ed. Europan 9. 2008. (ENG & DUT., Illus.). 128p. pap. 45.00 *(978-90-5662-006-6(1))* NAi Uitgevers / Publishers Stichting NLD. Dist: D.A.P./Distributed Art Pubs.

Wallpaper Magazine Editors, ed. Wallpaper City Guide - Amsterdam 2011. 2nd ed. 2011. (ENG., Illus.). 128p. pap. 9.95 *(978-0-7148-5938-5(9))* Phaidon Pr., Inc.

Zijlstra, H., ed. Analysing Buildings from Context to Detail in Time. Abcd Research Method. 2009. 228p. pap. 79.00 *(978-1-60750-020-9(5))* IOS Pr., Inc.

ARCHITECTURE—NEW ZEALAND

Crafti, Stephen. Beach Houses 2, Vol. 2. 2006. (ENG., Illus.). 55.00 *(978-1-876907-95-2(9))* Images Publishing Group AUS. Dist: National Bk. Network.

—Beach Houses of Australia & New Zealand. 2006. (ENG., Illus.). 210p. 49.50 *(978-1-86470-071-8(8))* Images Publishing Group AUS. Dist: National Bk. Network.

Dhakal, Rajesh P., et al. Curvature Ductility of Reinforced Concrete Plastic Hinges. 2008. 164p. pap. *(978-3-639-04184-2(4))* VDM Verlag Dr. Mueller e.K.

Gatley, Julia, ed. Long Live the Modern: New Zealand's New Architecture, 1904-1984. 2008. (ENG., Illus.). 240p. 44.95 *(978-1-86940-415-4(7))* Auckland Univ. Pr. NZL. Dist: Independent Pubs. Group.

Gore, James. Representations of History & Nation in Museums. 2010. 364p. pap. *(978-3-8383-6298-4(5))* Lambert Academic Publishing.

Leach, Andrew, et al, eds. Shifting Views: Selected Essays on the Architectural History Of Australia & New Zealand. 2008. (ENG.). 256p. pap. 52.95 *(978-0-7022-3660-0(8))* Univ. of Queensland Pr. AUS. Dist: Independent Pubs. Group.

McCoy, Ted. A Southern Architecture: The Work of Ted Mccoy. 2008. (Illus.). 176p. 80.00 *(978-1-877372-48-3(X))* Otago University Pr. NZL. Dist: International Specialized Bk. Services.

Ostwald, Michael J. & Fleming, Steven, eds. Museum, Gallery, & Cultural Architecture in Australia, New Zealand, & the Pacific Region: Essays in Antipodean Identity. 2007. 208p. *(978-0-7734-5393-7(8))* Mellen, Edwin Pr., The.

Sully, Dean. Decolonising Conservation: Caring for Maori Meeting Houses Outside New Zealand. Sully, Dean, ed. 2008. (University College London Institute of Archeology Publications). (ENG., Illus.). 272p. pap. 34.95 *(978-1-59874-310-4(4))* Left Coast Pr., Inc.

Sundt, Richard. Whare Karakia: Maori Church Building, Decoration & Ritual in Aotearoa New Zealand, 1834-1863. 2010. (ENG., Illus.). 240p. 49.95 *(978-1-86940-456-7(4))* Auckland Univ. Pr. NZL. Dist: Independent Pubs. Group.

ARCHITECTURE—NORWAY

Almaas, Ingerid Helsing, ed. Made in Norway: Norwegian Architecture Today. 2010. (Illus.). 144p. pap. 49.95 *(978-3-0346-0559-5(5))* Birkhauser Verlag AG CHE. Dist: Actar Birkhauser Distribution.

Argentero, Francesca, ed. Lost in Nature: Jarmund/Vigsnæs AS Arkitekter (MNAL) 2010. 64p. pap. 23.95 *(978-88-492-1476-5(6))* Gangemi ITA. Dist: International Publishers Marketing.

Fjeld, Per Olaf. Sverre Fehn: The Pattern of Thoughts. 2009. (ENG., Illus.). 304p. 75.00 *(978-1-58093-217-2(7))* Monacelli Pr., Inc.

Jorgensen, Karsten & Stabel, Vilde. Ny Norsk Landskapsarkitektur. 2010. (NOR., Illus.). 271p. *(978-82-05-40305-5(8))* Gyldendal.

ARCHITECTURE—PACIFIC AREA

Diab, Mark C. & A. Ghafar Ahmad. The Conservation & Restoration of Cultural Heritage in the Asia Pacific Regions. 2009. (ENG.). 307p. 90.00 *(978-0-387-09450-2(4))* Springer.

Hildebrand, Grant. Gene Zema, Architect, Craftsman. 2011. (ENG., Illus.). 176p. 60.00 *(978-0-295-99123-8(2))* Univ. of Washington Pr.

Images Publishing Group. Interior Spaces of Asia & the Pacific Rim, Vol. 1. 2006. (ENG., Illus.). 224p. 55.00 *(978-1-876907-16-7(9))* Images Publishing Group AUS. Dist: National Bk. Network.

Judge, Bernard. Waltzing with Brando: Planning a Paradise in Tahiti. 2011. (ENG., Illus.). 289p. pap. 35.00 *(978-0-9826226-4-3(3))* Oro Editions.

Meek, Christopher & Van Den Wymelenberg, Kevin. Daylighting Design in the Pacific Northwest. 2012. (ENG., Illus.). 192p. (C). pap. 45.00 ***(978-0-295-99206-8(9))*** Univ. of Washington Pr.

Ostwald, Michael J. & Fleming, Steven, eds. Museum, Gallery, & Cultural Architecture in Australia, New Zealand, & the Pacific Region: Essays in Antipodean Identity. 2007. 208p. *(978-0-7734-5393-7(8))* Mellen, Edwin Pr., The.

Treib, Mark, et al. West Coast Residential. Bellerby, Greg, ed. rev. ed. 2012. (ENG., Illus.). 120p. 29.95 *(978-1-894965-99-6(X))* Simply Read Bks. CAN. Dist: Perseus-PGW.

ARCHITECTURE—PAKISTAN

Bianca, Stefano. Karakoram: Hidden Treasures in the Northern Areas of Pakistan. Bianca, Stefano, ed. 2006. (ENG., Illus.). 328p. pap. 60.00 *(978-88-422-1330-7(6))* Allemandi, Umberto & Co. GBR. Dist: National Bk. Network.

Cheema, Yasmin. The Historical Quarters of Karachi. 2009. (Illus.). 204p. pap. 29.95 *(978-0-19-597976-3(1))* Oxford Univ. Pr., Inc.

Clark, Sharri R. The Social Lives of Figurines: Recontextualizing the Third Millennium BC Terracotta Figurines from Harappa (Pakistan) 2012. (American School of Prehistoric Research Monograph Ser.). (ENG., Illus.). 512p. (C). 40.00 *(978-1-84217-455-5(X))* Oxbow Bks., Ltd. GBR. Dist: Brown, David Bk. Co., The.

Dar, Shujaat Zamir. Sights in the Sands of Cholistan: Bahawalpur's History & Architecture. Dar, Shujaat Zamir, ed. 2007. (ENG., Illus.). 250p. 85.00 *(978-0-19-547353-7(1))* Oxford Univ. Pr., Inc.

Glover, William J. Making Lahore Modern: Constructing & Imagining a Colonial City. 2007. (Illus.). 280p. 75.00 *(978-0-8166-5021-7(7))*; per. 25.00 *(978-0-8166-5022-4(5))* Univ. of Minnesota Pr.

Khan. The Gardener: Horticulture in Pakistan. 2009. (Illus.). 365p. 35.00 *(978-0-19-547146-5(6))* Oxford Univ. Pr., Inc.

Manzoor, Farkhanda & Syed, Ruhma. Subterranean Termites in Pakistan: Constructional Damages. 2010. 136p. pap. *(978-3-639-25077-0(X))* VDM Verlag Dr. Mueller e.K.

Meister, Michael W. Temples of the Indus: Studies in the Hindu Architecture of Ancient Pakistan. (Illus.). 200p. *(978-90-04-18617-0(4))* BRILL.

Shaikh, Javeria, et al. Low Energy House in Lahore. 2010. 152p. pap. *(978-3-639-25765-6(0))* VDM Verlag Dr. Mueller e.K.

ARCHITECTURE—POLAND

Architecture, 1990-2008: Czech Republic, Slovakia, Hungary, Poland, 1 vol. 2011. (ENG., Illus.). 200p. pap. 55.00 *(978-80-7437-000-7(3))* Kant CZE. Dist: D.A.P./Distributed Art Pubs.

Biakiewicz, Zbigniew Jan & Ksiezarski, Feliks. Feliks Ksiezarski, 1820-1884: Krakowski Architekt Epoki Historyzmu. 2008. (Illus.). 374p. *(978-83-7188-121-3(5))* Ksiegarnia Akademicka, spolka z o.o.

Borowska, Joanna. Opowiesci Z Paacu Saskiego. 2009. (POL., Illus.). 125p. *(978-83-929033-0-7(7))* Green Gallery, Wojciechowska, Izabela.

Kurant, Agnieszka & Wasilkowska, Aleksandra. Emergency Exit. 2011. (ENG., Illus.). 79p. pap. 24.95 ***(978-1-934105-21-4(X))*** Sternberg Pr.

Muthesius, Stefan. Polska - Art, Architecture, Design, 1966-1970. (ENG, FRE, GER & POL.). lib. bdg. 39.95 *(978-3-7845-7612-1(5))* Langewiesche DEU. Dist: Abaris Bks.

O'Neill, Cathal, et al. AandD Wejchert & Partners. 2008. (FRE & ENG., Illus.). 283p. *(978-0-948037-55-9(5))* Gandon Editions.

Purchla, Jacek. The Metamorphoses of the Ravens House. 2009. (Illus.). 237p. *(978-83-89273-65-9(9))* Miedzynarodowe Centrum Kultury.

Warsza, Joanna. Stadion X — Miejsce, Którego Nie Byo: Reader. 2008. (POL & ENG., Illus.). 103p. *(978-83-61407-84-3(7))*; *(978-83-925107-2-7(0))* Krakowska Alternatywa, Fundacja.

ARCHITECTURE—PORTUGAL

Castanheira, Carlos & Siza, Álvaro. Álvaro Siza - Recent Works. 2009. (ENG., Illus.). 320p. 125.00 *(978-0-7148-4946-1(4))* Phaidon Pr., Inc.

Correia, Luís Miguel Maldonado de Vasconcelos. Castelos Em Portugal: Retrato Do Seu Perfil Arquitectónico (1509-1949) 2010. (POR., Illus.). 469p. *(978-989-26-0022-2(3))* Coimbra Editora.

de Moura, Eduardo Souto. The Pritzker Architecture Prize 2011 Eduardo Souto de Moura. 2011. (ENG.). 300p. 55.00 ***(978-988-15-0719-8(7))*** Design Media Publishing Ltd. HKG. Dist: BookMasters Distribution Services (BDS).

Figueiras, Jorge. Álvaro Siza: Modern Redux. 2009. (ENG., Illus.). 208p. 60.00 *(978-3-7757-2298-8(X))* Hatje Cantz Verlag GmbH & Co KG DEU. Dist: D.A.P./Distributed Art Pubs.

Finsterwalder, Rudolf. Alvaro Siza: Von der Linie zum Raum / From Line to Space. 2011. 120p. pap. 39.95 ***(978-3-7091-0853-6(5))*** Springer Wien AUT. Dist: Actar Birkhauser Distribution.

Hespeler-Boultbee, J. J. A Story in Stones: Portugal's Influence on Culture & Architecture in the Highlands of Ethiopia 1493-1634. 2nd ed. 2011. (Illus.). 204p. pap. *(978-1-926585-98-7(4)*, CCB Publishing) CCB Publishing.

Pereira, Paulo. Convent of Christ, Tomar. 2010. (ENG., Illus.). 128p. pap. 29.95 *(978-1-85759-383-9(9))* Scala, Editions FRA. Dist: National Bk. Network.

Redol, Pedro & Silva, Jose Custfidio Vieira da. The Monastery of Batalha. 2007. (ENG., Illus.). 128p. pap. 29.95 *(978-1-85759-382-2(0))* Scala, Editions FRA. Dist: National Bk. Network.

Ribeirinho, Jose, ed. Creating Environments. 2008. 158p. *(978-84-96954-64-9(1))* Actar Birkhauser Distribution.

Siza, Alvaro, et al. O'NFM 1 Bouça: Bouça Residents' Association Housing, Porto 1972-77, 2005-06, 1 vol. 2008. (O'Neil Ford Monograph Ser.: Vol. 1). (ENG., Illus.). 144p. pap. 39.90 *(978-3-8030-0684-4(8))* Wasmuth, Ernst J. Verlag GmbH & Co. DEU. Dist: D.A.P./Distributed Art Pubs.

Wallpaper Magazine Editors, ed. Porto 2012 - Wallpaper City Guide. 2011. (ENG., Illus.). 128p. pap., pap. 9.95 *(978-0-7148-6097-8(2))* Phaidon Pr., Inc.

ARCHITECTURE—PUERTO RICO

Mignucci, Andres. Arquitectura Contemporanea en Puerto Rico. 2009. pap. *(978-1-61623-555-0(1))* Independent Pub.

Pabon Charneco, Arleen. La arquitectura patrimonial puertorriquena y sus Estilos. 2010. (SPA.). 0.00 *(978-0-9827579-0-1(5))* State Historic Preservation Office.

Vivoni Farage, Enrique. Klumb: Una Arquitectura de Impronta Social. 2006. (Serie Mnemosina Ser.: Vol. 2). (ENG & SPA., Illus.). xiv, 346p. 84.95 *(978-0-8477-2754-4(8))* Univ. of Puerto Rico Pr.

ARCHITECTURE—ROME

see Architecture—Italy; Architecture, Roman

ARCHITECTURE—SCANDINAVIA

Andersen, Michael Asgaard. Nordic Architects Write: A Documentary Anthology. 2008. (Illus.). XIV, 418p. 165.00 *(978-0-415-46351-5(3))* Routledge.

Englund, Magnus & Schmidt, Chrystina. Scandinavian Country. 2007. (ENG., Illus.). 144p. *(978-1-84597-353-7(4))* Ryland Peters & Small.

H0gsbro, Caroline & Wischmann, Antje, eds. Nortopia. 2010. (ENG., Illus.). 176p. pap. 39.95 *(978-3-86859-027-2(7))* Jovis Verlag GmbH DEU. Dist: D.A.P./Distributed Art Pubs.

Plummer, Henry. Nordic Light: Modern Scandinavian Architecture. 2012. (ENG., Illus.). 256p. 60.00 ***(978-0-500-34275-6(X)***, 534275) Thames & Hudson.

Sokol, David. Seventy Nordic Architects, 1 vol. 2009. (ENG., Illus.). 448p. 58.00 *(978-3-938666-83-8(8))* DOM Pubs. DEU. Dist: Innovative Logistics.

ARCHITECTURE—SCOTLAND

Adam, Robert. The Works in Architecture of Robert & James Adam, 3 vols. in 1. (Scottish Enlightenment Ser.). reprint ed. 245.00 *(978-0-404-17233-6(4))* AMS Pr., Inc.

Adam, William. Vitruvius Scoticus: Plans, Elevations, & Sections of Public Buildings, Noblemen's & Gentlemen's Houses in Scotland. 2011. (Dover Architecture Ser.). (ENG., Illus.). 256p. pap. 19.95 *(978-0-486-47307-9(4))* Dover Pubns., Inc.

Billings, Robert William. Baronial & Ecclesiastical Antiquities of Scotland , The - 2008. (Illus.). 792p. pap. *(978-1-84530-058-6(0))*; 208p. pap. *(978-1-84530-055-5(6))*; 204p. pap. *(978-1-84530-057-9(2))*; 204p. pap. *(978-1-84530-056-2(4))* Grimsay Pr.

—The Baronial & Ecclesiastical Antiquities of Scotland (1901) 2008. (Illus.). 224p. pap. *(978-1-84530-054-8(8))* Grimsay Pr.

Fawcett, Richard & Rutherford, Allan. Renewed Life for Scottish Castles. 2011. (CBA Research Report). (Illus.). 178p. (C). pap. 40.00 *(978-1-902771-86-1(9))* Council for British Archaeology GBR. Dist: Brown, David Bk. Co., The.

Garnham, Trevor. Melsetter House: Orkney 1898 William Lethaby. (Illus.). 60p. 29.95 *(978-0-7148-2776-6(2))* Phaidon Pr. Ltd. GBR. Dist: Hachette Bk. Group.

Gifford, John. Dundee & Angus - Buildings of Scotland Series. 2012. (Pevsner Architectural Guides). (ENG., Illus.). 800p. 85.00 ***(978-0-300-14171-9(8))*** Yale Univ. Pr.

Gifford, John. Perth & Kinross: The Buildings of Scotland. 2007. (Pevsner Architectural Guides). (ENG., Illus.). 802p. 85.00 *(978-0-300-10922-1(9))* Yale Univ. Pr.

Gow, Ian. Scotland's Lost Houses. 2009. (ENG., Illus.). 192p. pap. 34.95 *(978-1-84513-393-1(5))* Aurum Pr., Ltd. GBR. Dist: Independent Pubs. Group.

—Scottish Houses & Gardens: From the Archives of Country Life. 2008. (Country Life Ser.). (ENG., Illus.). 192p. pap. 37.95 *(978-1-84513-289-7(0))* Aurum Pr., Ltd. GBR. Dist: Independent Pubs. Group.

McWilliam, Colin. Lothian Excluding Edinburgh: Buildings of Scotland. (Buildings of Scotland Ser.). (Illus.). 528p. pap. 50.00 *(978-0-14-071066-3(3))* Penguin Bks., Ltd. GBR. Dist: Trafalgar Square Publishing.

Nielsen, Anette Vilstrup & Fogedgaard Jonsson, Line. Cancer Health Care Centre, Copenhagen. 2011. 216p. pap. ***(978-3-8454-0707-4(7))*** Lambert Academic Publishing.

Paxton, Roland. Dynasty of Engineers: The Stevensons & the Bell Rock. 2011. (Illus.). 128p. *(978-0-9567209-0-0(0))* Whittles Publishing.

Roussell, Aage. Norse Building Customs in the Scottish Isles. reprint ed. 34.50 *(978-0-404-16477-5(3))* AMS Pr., Inc.

Stevenson, Robert Louis. Records of a Family of Engineers. 2011. (Cambridge Library Collection - Technology Ser.). 240p. pap. 22.99 *(978-1-108-02661-1(3))* Cambridge Univ. Pr.

Walker, Frank Arneil. Argyll & Bute. (ENG., Illus.). 688p. 65.00 *(978-0-14-071079-3(5))* Penguin Group (USA) Inc.

Wallpaper Magazine Editors, ed. Edinburgh 2012 - Wallpaper City Guide. 2012. (ENG., Illus.). 128p. pap. 9.95 ***(978-0-7148-6301-6(7))*** Phaidon Pr., Inc.

ARCHITECTURE—SLOVAKIA

Architecture, 1990-2008: Czech Republic, Slovakia, Hungary, Poland, 1 vol. 2011. (ENG., Illus.). 200p. pap. 55.00 *(978-80-7437-000-7(3))* Kant CZE. Dist: D.A.P./Distributed Art Pubs.

Konrad, Benjamin & Novotny, Maik. Eastmodern: Architecture & Design of the 1960s & 1970s in Slovakia. 2007. (ENG., Illus.). 238p. pap. 59.95 *(978-3-211-71531-4(2)*, 3211715312) Springer.

Moravcíková, Henrieta H. Nová Slovenská Architektúra: Výber Z Prác, 1999-2009 = New Slovak Architecture: Selection of Works, 1999-2009. 2010. (SLO & ENG., Illus.). 256p. pap. 80.00 *(978-80-8085-871-1(3))* Slovart, Vydavatel'stvo, spol. s.r.o. SVK. Dist: Independent Pubs. Group.

ARCHITECTURE—SOUTH AFRICA

Allan, Mandy. Hot Afro, 1 vol. 2011. (ENG.). 199p. 78.00 *(978-0-9814287-0-3(3))* Exhibitions International BEL. Dist: Innovative Logistics.

Chipkin, Clive M. Johannesburg Transition: Architecture & Society, 1950 - 2000. 2008. (ENG., Illus.). 490p. 115.00 *(978-1-919855-88-2(2))* STE Pubs. ZAF. Dist: Independent Pubs. Group.

DAAB Media Staff, creator. Cape Town Architecture & Design, 1 vol. 2008. (ENG., Illus.). 233p. 59.95 *(978-3-86654-030-9(2))* DAAB Media Gmbh DEU. Dist: Innovative Logistics.

Deckler, Thorsten, et al. Contemporary South African Architecture in a Landscape: Transition. 2008. (Illus.). 224p. 65.00 (978-1-77013-056-2(X)) Double Storey Bks. ZAF. Dist: International Publishers Marketing.

—Contemporary South African Architecture in a Landscape of Transition. 2008. 216p. pap. 39.95 (978-0-7021-7969-3(8)) Double Storey Bks. ZAF. Dist: International Publishers Marketing.

Noble, Jonathan Alfred. African Identity in Post-Apartheid Public Architecture: White Skin Black Masks. 2011. (Ashgate Studies in Architecture Ser.). (Illus.). 314p. 124.95 (978-0-7546-7765-9(6)) Ashgate Publishing Co.

O'Toole, Sean, et al. Sound, Space, Design: The Architecture of Don Albert & Partners. 2011. (ENG., Illus.). 312p. pap. 45.00 (978-0-620-46570-0(0)) Papadakis Dist A/C.

SHEPHERD, et al. Des Line Spac Mem & Iden Post-Apar. 2007. (Illus.). 328p. 165.00 (978-0-415-70130-3(9)); (ENG., 55.95 (978-0-415-70131-0(7)) Routledge.

Sorrell, Jennifer & Noero, Jo. Jo Noero: The Everyday & the Extraordinary: Three Decades of Architecture: Jo Noero Architects 1982-1998 & Noero Wolff Architects 1998-2009. 2009. (Illus.). 103p. (978-0-620-45436-0(9)) ADA Publishing Co., Inc.

Wallpaper Magazine Editors, ed. Johannesburg 2010. 2010. (Wallpaper* City Guides). (ENG., Illus.). 128p. pap. 9.95 (978-0-7148-5704-6(1)) Phaidon Pr., Inc.

ARCHITECTURE—SOVIET UNION

Akinsha, Konstantin, et al. The Holy Place: Architecture, Ideology, & History in Russia. 2007. (ENG., Illus.). 224p. 38.00 (978-0-300-11027-2(8)) Yale Univ. Pr.

Barsch, Barbara, et al. Lust auf Raum: Neue Innenarchitektur in Russland. 2010. (RUS, GER & ENG., Illus.). 367p. (978-3-938666-24-1(2)) DOM Pubs.

Batalov, A. L. & Smirnova, E. S. Drevnerusskoe Iskusstvo: Ideia I Obraz, Opyty Izucheniia Vizantiiskogo I Drevnerusskogo Iskusstva. 2009. (Illus.). 478p. (978-5-94431-303-4(X)) Severnyj palomnik.

Chaubin, Frederic. Frédéric Chaubin, Cosmic Communist Constructions photographed. 2011. (FRE, GER & ENG., Illus.). 288p. 59.99 (978-3-8365-2519-0(4)) TASCHEN DEU. Dist: Ingram Pub. Services.

Chernikhov, Dmitry Y., ed. Graphic Masterpieces of Yakov G. Chernikhov, 1 vol. 2009. (ENG.). 287p. 199.95 (978-3-938666-61-6(7)) DOM Pubs. DEU. Dist: Innovative Logistics.

Chipova, Irina. Moscow Architecture & Design. 2007. (And Guides). (Illus.). 191p. pap. 16.95 (978-3-8327-9156-8(6)) teNeues Publishing Co.

CHIPOVA, Irina, ed. Speech, 1 vol. 2011. (MUL & ENG., Illus.). 220p. 20.00 (978-3-86922-014-7(7)) DOM Pubs. DEU. Dist: Innovative Logistics.

Cohen, Jean-Louis & Lodder, Christina. Building the Revolution: Soviet Art & Architecture, 1915-1935. 2011. (ENG., Illus.). 288p. 60.00 (978-1-905711-91-8(3)) Royal Academy of Arts GBR. Dist: Hachette Bk. Group.

EDAS - Design Kommunalka Staff, contrib. by. ABD: Within the Range of Architecture. 2007. (Illus.). 350p. pap. 59.95 (978-3-211-48858-4(8), 3211488588) Springer Wien AUT. Dist: Springer.

Esaulov, G. V. & Solovev, N. K. Fedor Shekhtel I Epokha Moderna / Fedor Shekhtel & the Epoch of Art Nouveau. 2009. (Illus.). 247p. (978-5-9647-0184-2(1)) Arhitektura-S, Izdatel'stvo.

Gaydamak, Arcadi. Russian Empire. 2006. (ENG.). 160p. 125.00 (978-5-89480-025-7(0)) Trilistnik, Trefojl RUS. Dist: National Bk. Network.

Goldhoorn, Bart. Project Russia: The independent architechture Mag, 1 vol. 2011. (MUL & ENG., Illus.). 160p. pap. 20.00 (978-3-86922-053-6(8)) DOM Pubs. DEU. Dist: Innovative Logistics.

Konemann Staff. St. Petersburg: Art & Architecture. Date not set. (Illus.). 250p. 29.95 (978-3-8290-5035-7(6), 521828) Konemann.

Krementschouk, Andrej. No Direction Home. 2009. (ENG, RUS & GER., Illus.). 112p. 50.00 (978-3-86828-056-2(1)) Kehrer Verlag Heidelberg, Klaus Kehrer DEU. Dist: Consortium Bk. Sales & Distribution.

Messana, Paola. Soviet Communal Living: An Oral History of the Kommunalka. 2011. (Palgrave Studies in Oral History Ser.). (ENG., Illus.). 184p. 84.00 (978-0-230-11016-8(9)) Palgrave Macmillan.

Meuser, Philipp & Dörries, Cornelia. Russia Now: Modernes Russland: Architektur und Design der Gegenwart, 2 vols. 2009. (RUS, GER & ENG., Illus.). 336p. pap. 64.95 (978-3-938666-72-2(2)) DOM Pubs. DEU. Dist: Innovative Logistics.

Mikhailov, Konstantin. Moskva, Kotoruiu My Poteriali. 2010. (RUS., Illus.). 493p. (978-5-699-43721-4(5)) EKSMO, Izdatel'stvo.

Paperny, Vladimir. Architecture in the Age of Stalin: Culture Two. Hill, John & Barris, Roann, trs. from RUS. 2011. (Cambridge Studies in New Art History & Criticism Ser.). (ENG.). 400p. pap. 75.00 (978-0-521-29260-3(3)) Cambridge Univ. Pr.

Pare, Richard. The Lost Vanguard: Russian Modernist Architecture, 1922-1932. 2007. (ENG., Illus.). 348p. 85.00 (978-1-58093-185-4(5)) Monacelli Pr., Inc.

Permilovskaia, A. B. Russkii Sever Kak Osobaia Territoriia Naslediia. 2010. (RUS., Illus.). 549p. (978-5-85879-581-0(1)); (978-5-7691-2058-9(4)) Pravda Severa, Izdatel'sko-poligraficeskoe Predprijatie.

Poletkina, Olga. School of Art for Juniors. 2011. 76p. pap. (978-3-8443-9902-8(X)) Lambert Academic Publishing.

Prix, Wolf D., ed. Unbuildable Tatlin? 2012. (ENG & GER., Illus.). 144p. pap. 29.95 (978-3-211-99201-2(4)) Springer Wien AUT. Dist: Actar Birkhauser Distribution.

Savelev, IU R. Iskusstvo Istorizma I Gosudarstvennyi Zakaz: Vtoraia Polovina XIX — Nachalo XX Veka. 2008. (RUS., Illus.). 304p. (978-5-903060-60-3(9)) Sovpadenie, Izdatel'stvo.

Schonle, Andreas. Architecture of Oblivion: Ruins & Historical Consciousness in Modern Russia. 2011. (ENG., Illus.). 295p. 45.00 (978-0-87580-651-8(1)) Northern Illinois Univ. Pr.

Sergievskaia, Irina. Moskva, Kotoruiu Vy Nikogda Ne Uvidite. 2010. (RUS., Illus.). 524p. (978-5-699-45545-4(0)) Dksmo-Press, Izdatel'skaja firma.

Voyce, Arthur. Russian Architecture. (978-0-8022-1785-1(0)) Philosophical Library, Inc.

Wallpaper Editors. Moscow 2012 - Wallpaper City Guide. 2nd ed. 2012. (ENG., Illus.). 128p. pap. 9.95 (978-0-7148-6304-7(1)) Phaidon Pr. Ltd. GBR. Dist: Hachette Bk. Group.

Williams, Sidney & Weiss Bricker, Lauren. Steel & Shade. 2011. pap. 50.00 (978-0-9816743-4-6(8)) Palm Springs Art Museum.

Wood, Antony, tr. from RUS. Russian Architecture & the West. 2007. (ENG., Illus.). 480p. 80.00 (978-0-300-10912-2(1)) Yale Univ. Pr.

ARCHITECTURE—SPAIN

AAD Barcelona. 2011. 192p. pap. 12.95 (978-3-8327-9465-1(4)) teNeues Publishing Co.

Almirall, Josep & Almirall Rill, Josep. Human Towers: Touching the Sky with the Hand, 1 vol. 2011. (ENG.). 240p. pap. 16.95 (978-84-8478-473-9(8)) Triangle Postals, S.L. ESP. Dist: Innovative Logistics.

Álvarez, Ana María, ed. Ramon Esteve: Estudio de Arquitectura. 2010. (ENG & SPA., Illus.). 320p. 49.99 (978-84-9936-197-0(6)) Loft Pubns. ESP. Dist: Prestel Publishing.

Architecture at the Expo. 2008. 240p. pap. (978-84-96954-41-0(2)) Actar Birkhauser Distribution.

Art & Architecture: Andalusia. 2009. 536p. 19.95 (978-0-8416-0895-5(4)) American Map Corp.

Asensio, Francisco. Barcelona Style. (SPA., Illus.). 200p. (978-84-89439-57-3(5)) A. Asppan, S.L. Distribuidora Internacional de Libros y Revistas.

Bague, Alejo, et al, photos by. In Detail: Barcelona Contemporary Architecture, 1 vol. 2006. (ENG., Illus.). 160p. 45.00 (978-84-343-1090-2(2)) Polígrafa, Ediciones, S. A. ESP. Dist: D.A.P./Distributed Art Pubs.

Barros Guerton, Javier. About Urban Spain-B&W. 2009. 144p. pap. 20.50 (978-1-4092-8726-1(2)) Lulu Enterprises Inc.

Barros, Javier. About urban Spain. 2009. 144p. pap. 63.50 (978-1-4092-7386-8(5)) Lulu Enterprises Inc.

Bassegoda i Nonell, Joan, et al. La Cátedra de Antoni Gaudí: Estudio Analítico de Su Obra. 2010. (SPA., Illus.). 146p. (978-84-8301-283-3(9)) UPC, S.L., Edicions.

Ben-Dov, Meir. The Golden Age: Synagogues of Spain in History & Architecture. 2009. (Illus.). 256p. 39.95 (978-965-524-016-0(9)) Urim Pubns. ISR. Dist: Lambda Pubs., Inc.

Berger, Ursel & Pavel, Thomas, eds. Barcelona Pavilion/Pavillon: Mies Van der Rohe & Kolbe, 1 vol. 2007. (GER & ENG., Illus.). 192p. 29.95 (978-3-939633-06-8(2)) Jovis Verlag GmbH DEU. Dist: D.A.P./Distributed Art Pubs.

Bofill, Roser, ed. Barcelona: Arquitectura Floral/Floral Architecture. Santamaria, Elia, tr. 2007. (ENG., Illus.). 144p. 85.00 (978-90-5856-223-4(9), Stichting Kunstboak (Acc)) Antique Collectors' Club GBR. Dist: National Bk. Network.

Bonet Castellana, Antoni & Pizza de Nanno, Antonio. Antonio Bonet Castellana. 2010. (ENG & SPA., Illus.). 280p. (978-84-8301-288-8(X)) UPC, S.L., Edicions.

Bonet i Armengol, Jordi, et al. La Sagrada Familia de Gaudí: El Templo Expiatorio Desde Sus Orígenes Hasta Hoy. 2010. (ENG & SPA., Illus.). 303p. (978-84-9785-684-3(8)) Lunwerg Editores, S.A.

Borngasser & Scheffler. Madrid & Prado. 2009. 432p. 59.99 (978-0-8416-1647-9(7)) American Map Corp.

Callefa, Luis Al, ed. Architecture in Transit. 2008. 388p. (978-84-612-3732-6(3)) Actar Birkhauser Distribution.

Castinei, Manuel. Compostela & Europe: The Story of Diego Gelmirez. 2010. (ENG., Illus.). 432p. 90.00 (978-88-572-0493-2(6)) Skira Editore ITA. Dist: Random Hse., Inc.

Cerro Santamaria, Gerardo Del. Bilbao: Basque Pathways to Globalization. 2006. (Current Research in Urban & Regional Studies). (Illus.). 226p. 152.95 (978-0-08-045324-8(4)) Emerald Group Publishing Ltd. GBR. Dist: Turpin Distribution Services Ltd.

Cirlot, Juan Eduardo & Pla Boada, Ricard. Gaudi 2010: Introduction to His Architecture, 1 vol. 2011. (ENG.). 288p. pap. 16.95 (978-84-8478-451-7(7)) Triangle Postals, S.L. ESP. Dist: Innovative Logistics.

Coll, Ramon Faura, ed. Architectures Without Place: 1968/2008. 2010. (Illus.). 288p. pap. (978-84-96842-44-1(4)) Colegio de Arquitectos de Catalunya.

DAAB Media Staff, ed. Barcelona Architecture & Design, 1 vol. 2008. (ITA, FRE, GER, SPA & ENG., Illus.). 237p. 59.95 (978-3-86654-029-3(9)) DAAB Media Gmbh DEU. Dist: Innovative Logistics.

Debeerst, Philippe, photos by. Living in Great Style in Sotogrande, 1 vol. 2011. (ENG.). 256p. 89.50 (978-90-8881-029-9(X)) Exhibitions International BEL. Dist: Innovative Logistics.

Domáenech Girbau, Luis. Arquitectura de Siempre: Los Anos 40 en Espana. (SPA., Illus.). 160p. (978-84-7223-583-0(1), 6070) Tusquets Editores.

Domènech i Casadevall, Gemma & Gil, Rosa Maria. Un Nou Model D'arquitectura Al Servei D'una Idea de País. 2010. (SPA., Illus.). 151p. (978-84-937740-5-9(7)) Dux Editorial, S.L.

Donati, Cristina & Donati, Maria Cristina. Michael Hopkins, 1976-2006. 2006. (ENG., Illus.). 240p. pap. 34.95 (978-88-7624-653-1(3)) Skira Editore ITA. Dist: Random Hse., Inc.

Elliott, Brian. Benjamin for Architects. 2011. (Thinkers for Architects Ser.). (ENG., Illus.) 160p. (C). 120.00 (978-0-415-55814-3(X)); pap. 28.95 (978-0-415-55815-0(8)) Taylor & Francis Group GBR. (Routledge). Dist: Taylor & Francis Group.

Equipo Staff & Papeti, Dissenys. Gaudí: Dibuixos = Dibujos = Drawings, 1 vol. 2007 (CAT, ENG & SPA., Illus.). 128p. pap. 15.95 (978-84-8478-069-4(4)) Triangle Postals, S.L. ESP. Dist: Innovative Logistics.

Espinosa De Los Monteros Rosillo, Patricia & Fernandez De Santaella Martin-Artajo, Joaquin. Spanish Houses: Rustic Mediterranean Style. 2007. (ENG., Illus.). 216p. 50.00 (978-0-8478-2913-2(8)) Rizzoli International Pubns., Inc.

Feduchi, Luis, ed. Abroad. 2011. (ENG., Illus.). 160p. pap. 38.00 (978-3-86859-108-8(7)) Jovis Verlag GmbH DEU. Dist: D.A.P./Distributed Art Pubs.

Fernández Castiñeiras, Enrique & Monterroso Montero, Juan M. Piedra Sobre Agua: El Monacato en Torno a la Ribeira Sacra: Opus Monasticorum IV. 2010. (SPA.). 306p. (978-84-95892-83-6(9)) Fundación Pedro Barrie de la Maza.

Fernandez, Francisco & Jacobs, Michael. Alhambra. 2009. (ENG., Illus.). 192p. pap. 29.95 (978-0-7112-2518-3(4)) Lincoln, Frances Ltd. GBR. Dist: Perseus-PGW.

Ferrater, Carlos. Benidorm: West Beach Promenade. 2011. 120p. (978-84-92861-77-4(0)) Actar Birkhauser Distribution.

Ferrater, Carlos & Ferrater, Borja, eds. Ferrater & Partners: Oab. 2011. (ENG., Illus.). 350p. (978-84-92861-23-1(1)) Actar Birkhauser Distribution.

Ferre, Albert, ed. Patent Constructions: New Architecture Made in Catalonia. 2007. (Illus.). 240p. pap. (978-84-96954-09-0(9)) Actar Birkhauser Distribution.

Fonds Mercator Staff, ed. Calatrava: Sculptectures, 1 vol. 2011. (ENG, DUT & FRE., Illus.). 64p. pap. 48.00 (978-90-6153-950-6(1)) Exhibitions International BEL. Dist: Innovative Logistics.

Gea, Ma Isabel, et al. La Gran Via: Cien Años de Historia. 2010. (SPA., Illus.). 221p. (978-84-9873-079-1(1)) La Libreria, Ediciones.

Genís Terri, Jaume. Gaudí, Entre L'arquitectura Cristiana I L'art Contemporani. 2009. (CAT.). 262p. (978-84-9883-199-3(7)) Publicacions de l'Abadia de Montserrat.

Gerveno, Marta, et al. Promenade: The City of Culture of Galicia. 2011. (ENG., Illus.). 304p. 70.00 (978-88-572-0643-1(2)) Skira Editore ITA. Dist: Random Hse., Inc.

Giffords, Gloria Fraser. Sanctuaries of Earth, Stone, & Light: The Churches of Northern New Spain, 1530-1821. 2007. (Southwest Center Ser.). (ENG., Illus.). 480p. 75.00 (978-0-8165-2589-8(7)) Univ. of Arizona Pr.

Grupo Folcra Edificaciones S.A. Lightweight Skin: A Building Technique Comes to Age. 2010. (Illus.). 216p. (978-84-92861-40-8(1)) Actar Birkhauser Distribution.

Hintzen-Bohlen, Brigitte. Andalusia. 2008. (Art & Architecture Ser.). (Illus.). 536p. 19.95 (978-0-8416-0146-8(1)) American Map Corp.

—Andalusia, 1 vol. 2010. (ENG., Illus.). 536p. pap. 9.99 (978-3-8331-5280-1(X)) h.f.ullmann DEU. Dist: Innovative Logistics.

Hintzen, Bohlen Brigitte. Art & Architecture Andalusia. 2010. (Art & Architecture Pocket Ser.). 536p. pap. 16.99 (978-0-8416-7150-8(8)) Langenscheidt Publishing Group.

Hughes, Robert. Barcelona the Great Enchantress. 2007. (Directions Ser.). (ENG., Illus.). 192p. per. 12.95 (978-1-4262-0131-8(1), National Geographic) National Geographic Society.

Ingrosso, Chiara. Barcelona: City, Architecture, Society, 1975-2015. 2011. (ENG., Illus.). 192p. pap. 45.00 (978-88-572-0056-9(6)) Skira Editore ITA. Dist: Random Hse., Inc.

Irwin, Robert. The Alhambra. 2011. (Wonders of the World Ser.). (Illus.). 224p. pap. 14.95 (978-0-674-06033-3(4)) Harvard Univ. Pr.

Jodidio, Philip. Santiago Calatrava: 1951: Architect, Engineer, Artist. 2007. (ENG., Illus.). 96p. pap. 9.99 (978-3-8228-4873-9(5)) TASCHEN DEU. Dist: Ingram Pub. Services.

—Santiago Calatrava: Complete Works 1979 - 2009. 2009. (ENG., Illus.). 536p. 39.99 (978-3-8365-1023-3(5)) TASCHEN DEU. Dist: Ingram Pub. Services.

Jones, Owen. Ornament & Design of the Alhambra. 2008. (ENG., Illus.). 80p. pap. 15.95 (978-0-486-46524-1(1)) Dover Pubns., Inc.

Konemann Staff. Great Houses of Andalusia. Date not set. (Illus.). 250p. 19.95 (978-3-8290-4068-6(7), 521508) Konemann.

Kosuth, Joseph, ed. At Last I Thought I Understood (Madrid) 2008. 117p. pap. (978-84-96917-17-0(7)) Actar Birkhauser Distribution.

Llatzer, Moix & Moix Puig, Llàtzer. Barcelona: The City of Gaudi, 1 vol. 2008. (ENG.). 240p. pap. 17.95 (978-84-8478-316-9(2)) Triangle Postals, S.L. ESP. Dist: Innovative Logistics.

Malho Fernández, José Luis & Malho Galán, Diego. El Palacio de Maldorado. 2009. (SPA., Illus.). 59p. (978-84-7800-290-0(1)) Ediciones Universidad Salamanca, Spain.

Mansilla + Tunon, ed. The Mansilla + Tunon Studios 2008-2010: Between Rules & Constraints, 1 vol. 2012. (ENG., Illus.). 160p. pap. 45.00 (978-3-03778-281-1(1)) Lars Muller Pubs. CHE. Dist: Prestel Publishing.

Maria, Josep, et al. Jujol. 2007. (ENG, FRE & GER., Illus.). 158p. 29.99 (978-3-8228-4406-9(3)) TASCHEN DEU. Dist: Ingram Pub. Services.

Maria Torres Nada, Jose. Salvador Perez Arroyo: Works. 2010. 240p. pap. (978-84-92861-41-5(X)) Actar Birkhauser Distribution.

Martin, Therese. Queen as King: Politics & Architectural Propaganda in Twelfth-Century Spain. 2006. (Medieval & Early Modern Iberian World Ser.: Vol. 30). (Illus.). 292p. (978-90-04-15297-7(0)) BRILL.

Moneo, Rafael. Rafael Moneo: Remarks on 21 Works. 2010. (ENG., Illus.). 668p. 75.00 (978-1-58093-216-5(9)) Monacelli Pr., Inc.

MS Design (Firm) Staff, contrib. by. Luxury Architecture. 2011. (Illus.). 420p. 39.95 (978-84-9936-863-4(8)) Loft Pubns. ESP. Dist: Prestel Publishing.

Muñoz-Rojas, Olivia. Ashes & Granite: Destruction & Reconstruction in the Spanish Civil War & Its Aftermath. 2011. (ENG., Illus.). 272p. 90.00 (978-1-84519-436-9(5)) Sussex Academic Pr. GBR. Dist: International Specialized Bk. Services.

Obrist, Hans Ulrich. The Magic Box: Dominique Perrault Architecture. 2011. (ENG & SPA.). 208p. pap. (978-84-615-0641-5(3)) Actar Birkhauser Distribution.

Ochsendorf, John Allen. Guastavino Vaulting: The Art of Structural Tile. 2010. (ENG., Illus.). 256p. 60.00 (978-1-56898-741-5(2)) Princeton Architectural Pr.

Perez-Arroyo, ed. Engaged with Reality. 2008. 176p. (978-84-96954-60-1(9)) Actar Birkhauser Distribution.

Pla Boada, Ricard & Cirlot, Juan Eduardo. Gaudi, 1 vol. 2011. (ENG., Illus.). 424p. 68.00 (978-84-8478-034-2(1)) Triangle Postals, S.L. ESP. Dist: Innovative Logistics.

Pla, Maurici & Pla i Serra, Maurici. Catalonia: A Guide to Modern Architecture, 1880-2007, 1 vol. 2007. (ENG., Illus.). 488p. pap. 63.00 (978-84-8478-009-0(0)) Triangle Postals, S.L. ESP. Dist: Innovative Logistics.

Pla, Ricard & Vivas, Pere. Close up Barcelona, 1 vol. 2012. (ENG.). 152p. pap. 15.00 (978-84-8478-481-4(9)) Triangle Postals, S.L. ESP. Dist: Innovative Logistics.

—Close up Batlló, 1 vol. 2012. (ENG.). 152p. pap. 15.00 (978-84-8478-479-1(7)) Triangle Postals, S.L. ESP. Dist: Innovative Logistics.

—Close up Gaudí, 1 vol. 2012. (ENG.). 152p. pap. 15.00 (978-84-8478-480-7(0)) Triangle Postals, S.L. ESP. Dist: Innovative Logistics.

Rasmussen, Ingrid & Grimshaw, Chloe. Ibiza Style. 2007. (ENG., Illus.). 278p. 39.95 (978-1-85894-362-6(0)) Merrell Pubs. Ltd. GBR. Dist: Perseus Distribution.

Requa, Richard S. Old World Inspiration for American Architecture. 2007. (Illus.). 344p. 59.95 (978-0-7643-2668-4(6)) Schiffer Publishing, Ltd.

Robertson, James Alexander. List of Documents in Spanish Archives Relating to the History of the United States. 2008. 384p. 48.95 (978-1-4372-6059-5(4)); pap. 33.95 (978-1-4371-3369-1(X)) Kessinger Publishing, LLC.

—List of Documents in Spanish Archives Relating to the History of the United States. 368p. reprint ed. 98.00 (978-0-7222-7016-5(X)) Library Reprints, Inc.

Rowe, Peter G. Building Barcelona: A Second Renaixenca. 2006. (Illus.). 208p. 22.95 (978-84-96540-28-6(6)) D.A.P./Distributed Art Pubs.

Ruiz-Geli, Encri. Media-ICT Building. 2011. (ENG., Illus.). 344p. pap. (978-84-92861-02-6(9)) Actar Birkhauser Distribution.

Ruiz Geli, Enric & Rifkin, Jeremy. A Green New Deal: From Geopolitics to Biosphere Politics. 2011. (ENG & SPA., Illus.). 96p. pap. (978-84-92861-58-3(4)) Actar Birkhauser Distribution.

Samuel, Flora. Le Corbusier in Detail. 2007. (ENG., Illus.). 264p. per. 46.95 (978-0-7506-6354-0(5)) Routledge.

Schrijver, Lara, et al, eds. OASE No. 71: Urban Formation & Collective Spaces, 1 vol. 2007. (ENG., Illus.). 144p. pap. 25.00 (978-90-5662-522-1(5)) NAi Uitgevers / Publishers Stichting NLD. Dist: D.A.P./Distributed Art Pubs.

Sweeney, Robert. Casa Del Herrero: The Romance of Spanish Colonial. 2009. (ENG., Illus.). 168p. 50.00 (978-0-8478-3327-6(5)) Rizzoli International Pubns., Inc.

Tabales, Miguel Angel. El Alcázar de Sevilla: Reflexiones Sobre Su Origen y Transformación Durante la Edad Media: Memoria de Investigación Arqueológica 2000-2005. 2010. (SPA., Illus.). 367p. (978-84-8266-966-3(4)) Arraez Editores, S.L.

Taschen, ed. Antoni Gaudí. 2009. (GER & ENG., Illus.). 792p. 14.99 (978-3-8365-1165-0(7), Evergreen) TASCHEN DEU. Dist: Ingram Pub. Services.

TF Editores, C. A. The Alhambra & the Generalife. 2011. (ENG., Illus.). 350p. pap. 28.00 (978-84-92441-12-9(7), T.F. Editores, S.L.C.) Antique Collectors' Club GBR. Dist: National Bk. Network.

Tirado, Jesus Bermejo. La Arquitectura Sagrada Iberica: Origenes, Desarrollos y Contextos. 2008. (Bar S Ser.). (SPA., Illus.). 155p. (C). 83.00 (978-1-4073-0287-4(6)) British Archaeological Reports Ltd. GBR. Dist: Brown, David Bk. Co., The.

Torres, Elias. Elias Torres: Zenithal Light. 2006. (Illus.). 296p. (gr. 13-18). pap. 60.00 (978-84-96185-43-2(5)) D.A.P./Distributed Art Pubs.

Torroja, Eduardo. The Structures of Eduardo Torroj: An Autobiography of an Engineering Accomplishment. 2011. 210p. 44.95 (978-1-258-10099-5(1)) Literary Licensing, LLC.

Valdez del Alamo, E. A Palace of the Mind: The Cloister of Silos & Spanish Sculpture of the Twelfth Century. 2012. (ENG., Illus.). 300p. (C). 174.00 (978-2-503-51711-7(0)) Brepols Pubs. BEL. Dist: Brown, David Bk. Co., The.

Vila-Matas, Enrique & Burkert, Herbert, texts. Santiago de Compostela: Bibliotheken; Begleitpublikation zur Candida Höfer-Ausstellung zur Einweihung des 'City of Culture of Galicia' 2011. (Illus.). 208p. (978-3-8296-0514-4(5)) Schirmer/Mosel Verlag GmbH.

VV Staff. The Architecture of Gaudi. (SPA.). 190p. (978-84-96137-87-5(2)) A. Asppan, S.L. Distribuidora Internacional de Libros y Revistas.

—Barcelona: Gaudi & Modernism. (SPA.). 77p. (978-84-89439-51-1(6)) A. Asppan, S.L. Distribuidora Internacional de Libros y Revistas.

—Gaudi & Modernism in Barcelona. (SPA.). 80p. *(978-84-89439-87-0(7))* A. Asppan, S.L. Distribuidora Internacional de Libros y Revistas.

Wake, Eleanor. Framing the Sacred: The Indian Churches of Early Colonial Mexico. 2010. (ENG.). 368p. (C). 65.00 *(978-0-8061-4033-9(X))* Univ. of Oklahoma Pr.

Wallpaper Magazine Editors, ed. Barcelona 2011 - Wallpaper City Guide. 4th ed. 2011. (ENG., Illus.). 128p. pap. 9.95 *(978-0-7148-6094-7(8))* Phaidon Pr., Inc.

—Bilbao 2012 - Wallpaper City Guides. 2nd ed. 2011. (ENG., Illus.). 128p. pap., pap. 9.95 *(978-0-7148-6096-1(4))* Phaidon Pr., Inc.

White, Conrad. Surprising Architecture Ibiza: Conrad White. Loft Publications, ed. 2010. (ENG & SPA., Illus.). 280p. 42.00 *(978-84-9936-203-8(6))* Loft Pubns. ESP. Dist: Prestel Publishing.

ARCHITECTURE—SWEDEN

Björk, Cecilia, et al. Så Byggdes Villan: Svensk Villaarkitektur Från 1890 till 2010. 2009. (SWE., Illus.). 333p. *(978-91-540-6005-4(2))* Statens rad fuer byggnadsforskning.

Blundell Jones, Peter. Gunnar Asplund. 2012. (ENG., Illus.). 240p. pap. 39.95 ***(978-0-7148-6315-3(7))*** Phaidon Pr., Inc.

Cargill, Katrin. Creating the Look: Swedish Style. (Illus.). 144p. 35.00 *(978-0-7112-1082-0(9))* Lincoln, Frances Ltd. GBR. Dist: Perseus-PGW.

Cederlund, Johan. Classical Swedish Architecture. Summerville-Sternerup, Lani, tr. from SWE. 2007. (ENG., Illus.). 272p. 60.00 *(978-0-393-73172-9(3),* 73172) Norton, W. W. & Co., Inc.

Flora, Nicola. Sigurd Lewerentz, 1885-1975. Giardiello, Paolo & Postiglione, Gennaro, eds. rev. ed. 2006. (ENG., Illus.). 400p. per. 49.95 *(978-1-904313-46-5(9))* Phaidon Pr., Inc.

Hall, Thomas, et al. Stockholm: The Making of a Metropolis. 2008. (Planning, History & Environment Ser.). (Illus.). viii, 232p. 115.00 *(978-0-415-33999-5(5))* Routledge.

Jaeger, Falk, ed. Wingårdhs. 2010. (ENG & GER., Illus.). 144p. pap. 39.95 *(978-3-86859-035-7(8))* Jovis Verlag GmbH DEU. Dist: D.A.P./Distributed Art Pubs.

Kong, Yilin & Dong, Xiaomin. Urban Colourscape Planning. 2010. 68p. pap. *(978-3-8383-1328-3(3))* Lambert Academic Publishing.

Martin, Reinhold, et al. Swedish Modernism: Architecture, Consumption & the Welfare State. Wallenstein, Sven-Olov, ed. 2010. (ENG., Illus.). 192p. pap. 39.95 *(978-1-906155-98-8(4))* Black Dog Publishing Ltd. GBR. Dist: Perseus Distribution.

Meijer, Haiko, et al, texts. Wood Works Onix. 2010. (ENG., Illus.). 320p. 60.00 *(978-90-5662-679-2(5))* NAi Uitgevers / Publishers Stichting NLD. Dist: D.A.P./Distributed Art Pubs.

Neville, Kristoffer. Nicodemus Tessin the Elder: Architecture in Sweden in the Age of Greatness. 2009. (Architectura Moderna Ser.). (ENG., Illus.). 275p. (C). pap. 145.00 *(978-2-503-52826-7(0))* Brepols Pubs. BEL. Dist: ISD.

Nickl-Weller, Christine & Nickl, Hans. The New Hospital. 2007. (Illus.). 464p. *(978-981-245-325-9(3))* Page One Publishing.

Palm, Jenny. Energy Efficiency in Households: Policy, Implementation & Everyday Activities. 2011. (Energy Science, Engineering & Technology Energy Policies, Politics & Prices Ser.). 119p. pap. 47.00 ***(978-1-61324-147-9(X))*** Nova Science Pubs., Inc.

Sigurd Lewerentz, Architect. 82.00 *(978-91-85194-71-1(9))* Byggforlaget SWE. Dist: Coronet Bks.

Wallpaper Magazine Editors, ed. Stockholm 2011 - Wallpaper City Guide. rev. ed. 2011. (Wallpaper* City Guides). (ENG., Illus.). 128p. pap. 9.95 *(978-0-7148-5789-3(0))* Phaidon Pr., Inc.

Wang, Wilfried, ed. & text. Sigurd Lewerentz: St. Petri. 2009. (ENG., Illus.). 144p. pap. 39.90 *(978-3-8030-0698-1(8))* Wasmuth, Ernst J. Verlag GmbH & Co. DEU. Dist: D.A.P./Distributed Art Pubs.

ARCHITECTURE—SWITZERLAND

see also Architecture, Domestic—Switzerland

Aerni, Georg. Sites & Signs: Fotografien von Georg Aerni. Olonetzky, Nadine, ed. 2011. (ENG & GER., Illus.). 311p. 130.00 *(978-3-85881-320-6(6))* Scheidegger und Spiess AG, Verlag CHE. Dist: Chicago Distribution Ctr.

Arnaboldi, Michele. Michele Arnaboldi Architect. 2010. (ITA & ENG., Illus.). 184p. 89.95 *(978-3-0346-0355-3(X))* Birkhauser Verlag AG CHE. Dist: Actar Birkhauser Distribution.

Billington, David P. Robert Maillart: Builder, Designer, & Artist. 2008. (ENG., Illus.). 368p. pap. 42.00 *(978-0-521-05742-4(6))* Cambridge Univ. Pr.

Binet, Hélène. Therme Vals. Zumthor, Peter, ed. 2007. (Illus.). 192p. 110.00 *(978-3-85881-704-4(X))* Scheidegger und Spiess AG, Verlag CHE. Dist: Antique Collectors' Club.

Boyer, M. Christine. Le Corbusier, Homme de Lettres. 2010. (ENG., Illus.). 782p. 70.00 *(978-1-56898-973-0(3))* Princeton Architectural Pr.

Brodbeck & Roulet. Brodbeck & Roulet. 2009. (ENG & FRE., Illus.). 256p. 59.95 *(978-1-86470-244-6(3),* Images Publishing Dist Ac) Antique Collectors' Club GBR. Dist: National Bk. Network.

Büker, Dieter. Vier Jahrhunderte und vier Jahre: Der Klosterplan von St. Gallen und seine Bedeutung als Dokument frühmittelalterlicher Schriftlichkeit. 2009. (GER.). 244p. 61.95 *(978-3-631-59542-8(5))* Lang, Peter GmbH, Europaischer Verlag der Wissenschaften DEU. Dist: Lang, Peter.

Conzett, Jürg, et al. Marcel Meili, Markus Peter, 1987-2008: Scheidegger & Spiess. Meili, Marcel & Peter, Markus, eds. 2009. (ENG., Illus.). 400p. 110.00 *(978-3-85881-714-3(7))* Scheidegger und Spiess AG, Verlag CHE. Dist: Antique Collectors' Club.

Della Casa, Francesco. The Rolex Learning Center. 2010. 224p. *(978-2-940222-44-5(4))* Actar Birkhauser Distribution.

Diener, Roger & Abram, Joseph. Diener & Diener. Steinmann, Martin, ed. 2011. (ENG., Illus.). 240p. 75.00 *(978-0-7148-5919-4(2))* Phaidon Pr., Inc.

Dorenbach Architekten Staff, contrib. by. Arbeiten 1971-2009. 2010. (ENG., Illus.). 351p. *(978-3-7245-1664-4(9))* Reinhardt, Friedrich AG.

Dosch, Leza. Kunst und Landschaft in Graubünden: Bilder und Bauten Seit 1780. 2010. (GER., Illus.). 416p. 91.00 ***(978-3-85881-134-9(3))*** Scheidegger und Spiess AG, Verlag CHE. Dist: Antique Collectors' Club.

Füchslin, Marco & Eggstein, Simone. Architekt Hans Eggstein: Bauten und Projekte: Eine Werkdokumentation. 2007. (GER., Illus.). 199p. *(978-3-7212-0627-2(4))* Niggli, Arthur Verlag.

Giannetto, Raffaella Fabiani, ed. Paolo Bürgi Landscape Architect: Discovering the (Swiss) Horizon - Mountain, Lake, & Forest. 2009. (ENG., Illus.). 144p. 29.95 *(978-1-56898-851-1(6))* Princeton Architectural Pr.

Gigon, Annette & Guyer, Mike. Gigon/Guyer Architects: Works & Projects 2001-2011, 1 vol. 2012. (ENG., Illus.). 576p. 85.00 ***(978-3-03778-276-7(5))*** Lars Muller Pubs. CHE. Dist: Prestel Publishing.

GmbH, Birkhäuser. Architekten Profile 2011 / 2012. 2010. (ENG & GER., Illus.). 392p. 95.00 *(978-3-0346-0612-7(5))* Birkhauser Verlag AG CHE. Dist: Actar Birkhauser Distribution.

Graber, Marco & Pulver, Thomas. Raumsequenzen und Urbane Infrastrukturen: Graber Pulver at ETH Zürich. 2009. (ENG., Illus.). 176p. 60.00 *(978-3-85881-260-5(9))* Scheidegger und Spiess AG, Verlag CHE. Dist: Antique Collectors' Club.

Gubler, Jacques, ed. Jean Tschumi: Architecture at Full Scale. 2009. (ENG., Illus.). 224p. 85.00 *(978-88-572-0071-2(X))* Skira Editore ITA. Dist: Random Hse., Inc.

Herrmann. Gottfried Sempers theoretische Schriften an der ETH. (GER., Illus.). 271p. 50.95 *(978-3-7643-1239-8(4),* 3764312394) Birkhauser Boston.

Herrmann, Wolfgang. Gottfried Semper im Exil: Paris, London 1849 bis 1855. Die Entstehungsgeschichte seines grossten theoretischen Werkes "Der Stil" (FRE, GER & ENG., Illus.). 137p. pap. 21.52 *(978-3-7643-0992-3(X),* 376430992X) Birkhauser Boston.

Huber, Werner. Building Bern: A Guide to Contemporary Architecture, 1990-2010. 2010. (Verlag Scheidegger & Spiess-Edition Hochparterre at Scheidegger & Spiess Ser.). (Illus.). 240p. pap. 45.00 *(978-3-85881-722-8(8))* Scheidegger und Spiess AG, Verlag CHE. Dist: Antique Collectors' Club.

Hubertus, Adam. Space, Twisted with Time / Raum, verschraubt mit der Zeit (eng/ger) Architecture Yearbook Graz Styria 2010 / Architekturjahrbuch Graz Steiermark 2010. 2011. (ENG & GER.). 192p. 64.95 ***(978-3-0346-0792-6(X))*** Birkhauser Verlag AG CHE. Dist: Actar Birkhauser Distribution.

Jahn, Helmut, et al, eds. Merck Serono: Geneva. 2008. (ENG., Illus.). 176p. 65.00 *(978-3-89986-095-5(0),* Avedition Gmbh,Csi) Continental Sales, Inc.

Jones, Peter Blundell. Oneplanetarchitecture: The Architecture of RAU. 2012. (ENG., Illus.). 320p. 109.00 *(978-3-936681-30-7(9))* Edition Axel Menges GmbH DEU. Dist: National Bk. Network.

Kung. Christian Kerez: Construction, Privacy, Politics, Conflicts & Obsessions. Kueng, Moritz, ed. 2009. (ENG., Illus.). 200p. pap. 45.00 *(978-3-7757-2280-3(7))* Hatje Cantz Verlag GmbH & Co KG DEU. Dist: D.A.P./Distributed Art Pubs.

Lars Muller, ed. Fuhrimann Hachler. 2010. (Illus.). 240p. *(978-3-03778-240-8(4))* Lars Muller Pubs.

Lichtenstein, Claude. Playfully Rigid: Swiss Architecture, Graphic Design, Product Design 1950-2006. 2007. (Illus.). 299p. 59.95 *(978-3-03778-090-9(8),* 3037780908) Lars Muller Pubs. CHE. Dist: Springer.

Mezger, Claudine & Grossmann, Elisabeth. Ueli Berger - Alles in Allem: Arbeiten auf Papier, 1967 2007. Frehner, Matthias, ed. 2008. (Illus.). 112p. pap. 60.00 *(978-3-85881-191-2(2))* Scheidegger und Spiess AG, Verlag CHE. Dist: Antique Collectors' Club.

Moos, Stanislaus von. Nicht Disneyland: Und Andere Aufsätze über Modernität und Nostalgie. 2010. (GER., Illus.). 240p. 78.00 ***(978-3-85881-162-2(9))*** Scheidegger und Spiess AG, Verlag CHE. Dist: Antique Collectors' Club.

Olgiati, Valerio. Lecture. 2012. (ENG.). 104p. pap. 29.95 *(978-3-0346-0783-4(0))* Birkhauser Verlag AG CHE. Dist: Actar Birkhauser Distribution.

Spiess, Heiner. Das Hallenstadion: Arena der Emotionen. 2010. (GER., Illus.). 280p. 111.00 ***(978-3-85881-164-6(5))*** Scheidegger und Spiess AG, Verlag CHE. Dist: Antique Collectors' Club.

Steinmann, Martin, ed. Tendenzen - Neuere Architektur im Tessin: Tendencies - Recent Architecture in Ticino Tendenze - Architettura recente nel Ticino. 2010. 166p. pap. 79.95 *(978-3-0346-0531-1(5))* Birkhauser Verlag AG CHE. Dist: Actar Birkhauser Distribution.

Vogt, Gunther & Alice, Foxley. Distance & Engagement: Landscape Thinking — Model Making. 2010. (Illus.). 480p. 80.00 *(978-3-03778-196-8(3))* Lars Muller Pubs. CHE. Dist: Prestel Publishing.

Wallpaper Magazine Editors, ed. Zurich 2012 - Wallpaper City Guide. 2012. (ENG., Illus.). 128p. pap. 9.95 ***(978-0-7148-6308-5(4))*** Phaidon Pr. Ltd. GBR. Dist: Hachette Bk. Group.

Weidmann, Ruedi & Holenstein, Karl. Max Vogt. Bauen für die Bahn 1957 - 1989. 2008. (Illus.). 112p. 97.00 *(978-3-85881-185-1(8))* Scheidegger und Spiess AG, Verlag CHE. Dist: Antique Collectors' Club.

Wiedemann, Pascale, et al. Morbus infinitus & Subkutan, 2 vols. 2008. (GER & ENG., Illus.). 184p. 60.00 *(978-3-85881-206-3(4))* Scheidegger und Spiess AG, Verlag CHE. Dist: Antique Collectors' Club.

Züger, Raffele. Switzerlarch: Bank & Bastion. 2011. (ENG., Illus.). 220p. 29.95 ***(978-3-03764-165-1(7))*** JRP Ringier Kunstverlag AG CHE. Dist: D.A.P./Distributed Art Pubs.

ARCHITECTURE—TUNISIA

Hakim, Besim S., ed. Sidi Bou Sa'id, Tunisia: Structure & Form of a Mediterranean Village. 2nd rev. ed. 2009. (ENG., Illus.). 196p. pap. 19.95 *(978-0-9683184-1-6(X))* EmergentCity Pr.

ARCHITECTURE—TURKEY

Akcan, Esra. Architecture in Translation: Germany, Turkey, & the Modern House. 2012. (ENG., Illus.). 424p. 89.95 ***(978-0-8223-5294-5(X))***; pap. 24.95 ***(978-0-8223-5308-9(3))*** Duke Univ. Pr.

Aktuna, Zeynep. The Social Context of Early Apartment Block Development in Istanbul. 2010. 208p. pap. *(978-3-8383-4255-9(0))* Lambert Academic Publishing.

Alkan Meshur, H. Filiz. The Social Environmental Analysis of Qualitative Values in Suburbs. 2010. 128p. pap. *(978-3-639-22907-3(X))* VDM Verlag Dr. Mueller e.K.

Arginhan, Oktay. Safety Level of Precast Prestressed Concrete Bridge Girders. 2011. 136p. pap. ***(978-3-8443-3178-3(6))*** Lambert Academic Publishing.

Avcioglu, Nebahat. Turkish Architecture in Europe 1737-1876: Politics & Visual Narratives of the Other. 2011. (Illus.). 338p. 124.95 *(978-0-7546-6422-2(8))* Ashgate Publishing Co.

Bertram, Carel. Imagining the Turkish House: Collective Visions of Home. 2008. (ENG., Illus.). 360p. (C). pap. 24.95 *(978-0-292-71826-5(8))* Univ. of Texas Pr.

Bozdogan, Sibel & Akcan, Esra. Turkey: Modern Architectures in History. 2012. (Reaktion Books - Modern Architectures in History Ser.). (Illus.). 272p. pap. 29.95 *(978-1-86189-878-4(9))* Reaktion Bks., Ltd. GBR. Dist: Chicago Distribution Ctr.

Burelli, Augusto Romano & Gennaro, Paola, texts. Die Moschee von Sinan. Sinan's Mosque. 2009. (ENG., Illus.). 116p. pap. 65.00 *(978-3-8030-0693-6(7))* Wasmuth, Ernst J. Verlag GmbH & Co. DEU. Dist: D.A.P./Distributed Art Pubs.

Çelik, Zeynep. Empire, Architecture, & the City: French-Ottoman Encounters, 1830-1914. 2008. (ENG., Illus.). 368p. 60.00 *(978-0-295-98779-8(0))* Univ. of Washington Pr.

Celiker, Afet. The Boundaries of Living Spaces. 2011. 140p. pap. ***(978-3-8443-8502-1(9))*** Lambert Academic Publishing.

Cesarz, Michael & Ferreira-Erlenbach, Manina, eds. Meydan Shopping Square: Ein neuer Prototyp von FOA / METRO Group Project in Istanbul. 2008. (ENG., Illus.). 160p. pap. 55.00 *(978-3-939633-30-3(5))* Jovis Verlag GmbH DEU. Dist: D.A.P./Distributed Art Pubs.

Civan, Isilay. From Design to Development - an Analysis of the Go/No-Go Decision-Making Models Used in Istanbul, Turkey. 2008. 204p. per. *(978-3-8364-3646-5(9))* VDM Verlag Dr. Mueller e.K.

Corbusier, Le & Le Corbusier. Journey to the East. Zaknic, Ivan, ed. & tr. by. from FRE. 2nd ed. 2007. (ENG., Illus.). 288p. (gr. 17). pap. 23.95 *(978-0-262-62210-3(6))* MIT Pr.

Curatola, Giovanni, ed. Turkish Art & Architecture: From the Seljuks to the Ottomans. 2010. (ENG., Illus.). 280p. 95.00 *(978-0-7892-1082-1(7))* Abbeville Pr., Inc.

Darnault, Sezim Sezer. Latin Catholic Buildings in Istanbul. 2010. 111.20 *(978-1-61719-127-5(2))* Gorgias Pr., LLC.

Demesnil, Nicole Lemaigre. Architecture Rupestre et Decor Sculpte en Cappadoce. 2010. (Bar S Ser.). (FRE & ENG., Illus.). 306p. (C). pap. 127.50 *(978-1-4073-0569-1(7))* British Archaeological Reports Ltd. GBR. Dist: Brown, David Bk. Co., The.

Dökmeci, Papatya Nur & Yilmazer, Semiha. Architectural & Acoustical Evaluations of Cepa Shopping Center. 2011. 92p. pap. ***(978-3-8454-0348-9(9))*** Lambert Academic Publishing.

dos Santos, Solvi & Torolsan, Berrin. At Home in Turkey. 2008. (ENG., Illus.). 192p. 45.00 *(978-0-500-51424-5(0))* Thames & Hudson.

Freely, John. History of Ottoman Architecture. 2011. (Illus.). 464p. lib. bdg. 194.00 *(978-1-84564-506-9(5))* WIT Pr GBR. Dist: WIT Pr.

Gonenc, Efe. Public Spaces & Istanbul. 2008. 100p. pap. *(978-3-639-04089-0(9))* VDM Verlag Dr. Mueller e.K.

Harrington, Lydia. City Planning & Atatürk's Memorial Tomb in Early Republican Ankar. 2011. 136p. pap. ***(978-3-8383-9502-9(6))*** Lambert Academic Publishing.

Hensel, Michael, et al, eds. Turkey at the Threshold: Architectural Design. 2011. (Architectural Design Ser.). (ENG.). 144p. pap. 45.00 *(978-0-470-74319-5(0),* Wiley) Wiley, John & Sons, Inc.

Hoffmann, Adolf & Luca, Gioia de. Das Asklepieion 05: Die Platzhallen und die zugehörigen Annexbauten in römischer Zeit. 2010. (GER., Illus.). 352p. 235.00 *(978-3-11-018347-4(1))* De Gruyter, Walter Inc.

Kafescioglu, Çigdem. Constantinopolis/Istanbul: Cultural Encounter, Imperial Vision, & the Construction of the Ottoman Capital. 2009. (Buildings, Landscapes, & Societies Ser.). (ENG., Illus.). 392p. 100.00 *(978-0-271-02776-0(2))* Pennsylvania State Univ. Pr.

Koca, Duygu. Understanding Facade Between Design & Manufacturing. 2009. 144p. pap. *(978-3-639-17493-9(3))* VDM Verlag Dr. Mueller e.K.

Morkoc, Selen. A Study of Ottoman Narratives on Architecture: Text,Context & Hermeneutics. 2010. (Illus.). 230p. *(978-1-933146-54-6(0))* Academica Pr., LLC.

Naza-Dönmez, E. Emine. Wooden Mosques of the Samsun Region, Turkey: From the Past to the Present in the Light of Surveys Carried Out in the Years 2001-2003. 2008. (Bar S Ser.). (Illus.). vi, 159p. (C). pap. 80.00 *(978-1-4073-0306-2(6))* British Archaeological Reports Ltd. GBR. Dist: Brown, David Bk. Co., The.

Necipoglu, Gulru. The Age of Sinan: Architectural Culture in the Ottoman Empire. 2010. (ENG., Illus.). 592p. pap. 49.00 *(978-1-86189-253-9(5))* Reaktion Bks., Ltd. GBR. Dist: Chicago Distribution Ctr.

Okcuoglu, Tarkan & Çobanoglu, Ahmet Vefa. Sultanahmet & Süleymaniye. 2012. (ENG., Illus.). 112p. pap. 24.95 *(978-1-85759-629-8(3))* Scala, Editions FRA. Dist: National Bk. Network.

Ousterhout, Robert G. A Byzantine Settlement in Cappadocia. 2nd rev. ed. 2012. (Dumbarton Oaks Studies). (ENG., Illus.). 504p. pap. 50.00 *(978-0-88402-370-8(2))* Dumbarton Oaks.

Zkan, Suha & Jodidio, Philip. A Vision in Architecture: Projects for the Istanbul Zorlu Center. 2012. (ENG., Illus.). 176p. 65.00 ***(978-0-8478-3854-7(4))*** Rizzoli International Pubns., Inc.

Pucci, Marina. Functional Analysis of Space in Syro-Hittite Architecture. 2008. (Bar S Ser.). (ENG., Illus.). 257p. (C). pap. 95.00 *(978-1-4073-0180-8(2))* British Archaeological Reports Ltd. GBR. Dist: Brown, David Bk. Co., The.

Ramsay, William Mitchell & Bell, Gertrude Lowthian. The Thousand & One Churches. Jackson, Mark P. C. & Ousterhout, Robert G., eds. 2008. (Illus.). 618p. (C). 49.95 *(978-1-934536-05-6(9),* Univ. of Pennsylvania Museum of Archaeology & Anthropology) Univ. Museum Pubns.

Roos, Paavo. Survey of Rock-Cut Chamber-Tombs in Caria. (Illus.). 109.00 *(978-91-86098-25-4(X))* Astroms, Paul Forlag SWE. Dist: Coronet Bks.

—Survey of Rock-Cut Chamber Tombs in Caria Pt. 2: Central Caria. 2006. (Studies in Mediterranean Archaeology: LXXII:2). (Illus.). 144p. pap. 110.00 *(978-91-7081-216-3(0))* Astroms, Paul Forlag SWE. Dist: Coronet Bks.

Russell, Francis. Places in Turkey: A Pocket Grand Tour. 2010. (ENG., Illus.). 352p. pap. 24.95 *(978-0-7112-3061-3(7))* Lincoln, Frances Ltd. GBR. Dist: Perseus-PGW.

Saner, Mehmet. Urban Transformations & Political Actors. 2009. 104p. pap. *(978-3-639-13262-5(9))* VDM Verlag Dr. Mueller e.K.

Scott, Rupert, ed. Turkish Coast. 2009. (Through Writers' Eyes Ser.). (ENG., Illus.). 247p. pap. 32.95 *(978-1-906011-09-3(5))* Eland Bks. GBR. Dist: Dufour Editions, Inc.

Turgut, S. & Ceylan, E. C. In the Wake of a Local Government Initiative: Istanbul Kucukcekmece: Urban Regeneration Project. 2012. (ENG., Illus.). 176p. lib. bdg. 160.00 ***(978-1-84564-630-1(4))*** WIT Pr GBR. Dist: WIT Pr.

Ugurlu, Nur Banu. The Roman Nymphaea in the Cities of Asia Minor. 2009. 148p. pap. *(978-3-639-03673-2(5))* VDM Verlag Dr. Mueller e.K.

Wescoat, Bonna Daix. The Temple of Athena at Assos. 2012. (Oxford Monographs on Classical Archaeology Ser.). (ENG., Illus.). 320p. 180.00 *(978-0-19-814382-6(6))* Oxford Univ. Pr., Inc.

Yurekli, Zeynep. Architecture & Hagiography in the Ottoman Empire: The Politics of Bektashi Shrines in the Classical Age. 2012. (Illus.). 200p. ***(978-1-4094-1107-9(9)); (978-1-4094-1106-2(0))*** Ashgate Publishing, Ltd.

ARCHITECTURE—UNITED STATES

see also Architecture, Colonial; Architecture, Domestic—United States

Aalto, Alvar & Fixler, David. Aalto & America. Anderson, Stanford & Fenske, Gail, eds. 2012. (ENG., Illus.). 320p. 75.00 *(978-0-300-17600-1(7))* Yale Univ. Pr.

Abbott, James Archer. The Presidential Dish: Mrs. Woodrow Wilson & the White House China Room. 2007. (Illus.). 40p. 22.50 *(978-0-9798026-0-7(1))* Woodrow Wilson Hse.

Abrams, Brett L. Capital Sporting Grounds: A History of Stadium & Ballpark Construction in Washington, D. C. 2008. (ENG., Illus.). 296p. pap. 39.95 *(978-0-7864-3956-0(4))* McFarland & Co., Inc. Pubs.

Acomb, Glenn A. LARE Review: Mastering Section C, Site Design. 2007. (ENG., Illus.). 136p. pap. 72.00 *(978-1-59126-042-4(6))* Professional Pubns., Inc.

Agan, John. Remembering Minden: Echoes of Our Past. 2009. (American Chronicles Ser.). 19.99 *(978-1-59629-718-0(2))* History Pr., The.

Alanta History Center Staff. Henri Jova, A Classical Intermezzo: An Architect's Life. 2009. (ENG., Illus.). 212p. 50.00 *(978-1-883828-02-8(3))* Atlanta Historical Society, Inc.

Alexander, Christopher James. Julius Shulman's Los Angeles. 2011. (ENG., Illus.). 72p. pap. 9.95 ***(978-1-60606-079-7(1),*** J. Paul Getty Museum) Getty Pubns.

Allsen, Ken. Old Frontenac, Minnesota: Its History & Architecture. 2011. 128p. pap. 19.99 *(978-1-59629-507-0(4))* History Pr., The.

Almanac of Architecture & Design. 2007. (Illus.). 591p. pap. 49.50 *(978-0-9785552-3-8(6),* Ostberg) Greenway Communications.

American Institute of Architects, Institute Of Architects. Catalogue of the First Exhibition. 2008. (ENG., Illus.). 164p. pap. 14.95 *(978-1-4290-9800-7(7))* Applewood Bks.

American Institute of Architects Staff. The American Institute of Architects Official Guide to the 2007 AIA Contract Documents. 2009. (ENG., Illus.). 496p. 150.00 *(978-0-470-25166-9(2),* Wiley) Wiley, John & Sons, Inc.

Andersen, Dennis, intro. Craftsman Bungalows. 2007. (Illus.). pap. 25.00 *(978-0-9629954-2-2(8))* Bk. Club of Washington.

Anderson, J. Seth, et al. Downtown Phoenix. 2012. (Images of America Ser.). (ENG., Illus.). 128p. pap. 21.99 ***(978-0-7385-8523-9(8))*** Arcadia Publishing.

Andrzejewski, Anna Vemer. Building Power: Architecture & Surveillance in Victorian America. 2008. (ENG., Illus.). 272p. 39.00 *(978-1-57233-631-5(5))* Univ. of Tennessee Pr.

Ángel, Félix. Extended Boundary: Latin America & Caribbean Artists in Miami: Frontera Extendida, Artistas Latinoamericanos y Caribeños en Miami. 2008. (Illus.). 62p. *(978-1-59782-071-4(7))* Inter-American Development Bank.

Aran, Berge. Austin Val Verde: A Montecito Masterpiece. 2006. (ENG., Illus.). 144p. 50.00 *(978-1-890449-39-1(3))* Balcony Pr.

Architects, Ennead. Newseum. 2012. (Ennead Profile Ser.). (ENG.). 86p. pap. 11.95 (978-0-9822024-9-4(0)) Oro Editions.

Architectural League of New York Staff. Instability. 2007. (ENG., Illus.). 176p. pap. 24.95 (978-1-56898-637-1(8)) Princeton Architectural Pr.

—Proof. 2008. (ENG., Illus.). 176p. pap. 24.95 (978-1-56898-743-9(9)) Princeton Architectural Pr.

—Resonance. 2009. (ENG., Illus.). 176p. pap. 24.95 (978-1-56898-809-2(5)) Princeton Architectural Pr.

—Young Architects 12: Resource. 2011. (ENG., Illus.). 176p. pap. 24.95 (978-1-56898-998-3(9)) Princeton Architectural Pr.

Architectural League of New York Staff. Young Architects 13: It's Different. 2012. (ENG.). 176p. pap. 24.95 **(978-1-61689-057-5(6))** Princeton Architectural Pr.

Armstrong, Tom. A Singular Vision: Architecture Art Landscape. 2011. (ENG., Illus.). 256p. 85.00 (978-1-59372-043-8(2), 372043) Quantuck Lane Pr. & The Mill Road Collaborative, The.

Austin, Dan. Lost Detroit: Stories Behind Motown's Majestic Ruins. 2010. 176p. pap. 24.99 (978-1-59629-940-5(1)) History Pr., The.

Ayers, Wayne, et al. Indian Rocks Beach. 2010. (Images of America Ser.). (ENG., Illus.). 128p. pap. 21.99 (978-0-7385-8600-7(5)) Arcadia Publishing.

Bailey, Elizabeth, et al, eds. Lunch 6: Student Journal of the University of Virginia School of Architecture. 2011. (Illus.). 224p. pap. 15.00 (978-0-9843671-1-5(X)) Univ. of Virginia Schl. of Architecture.

Ballast, David Kent & O'Hara, PE, Steven E. ARE Review Manual. 2nd ed. 2011. 744p. pap. 320.00 (978-1-59126-322-7(0)) 2010. (ENG.). 800p. pap. 336.00 (978-1-59126-321-0(2)) Professional Pubns., Inc.

Ballast, FAIA, NCIDQ-Cert. #9425, David Kent. Site Planning & Design: ARE Sample Problems & Practice Exam. 2nd ed. 2008. (ENG.). 94p. pap. 120.00 (978-1-59126-154-4(6)) Professional Pubns., Inc.

Banham, Reyner & Banham, R. Los Angeles: The Architecture of Four Ecologies. 2nd ed. 2009. (ENG., Illus.). 296p. pap. 24.95 (978-0-520-26015-3(5)) Univ. of California Pr.

Bassenian/Lagoni Architects. Tuscan & Andalusian Reflections: 20 Beautiful Homes Inspired by Old World Architecture. 2008. (Illus.). 160p. pap. 19.95 (978-0-9721539-5-9(0)) Bassenian/Lagoni Architects, Inc.

Beaver, Robyn. Dattner Architects. Beaver, Robyn, ed. 2009. (ENG., Illus.). 144p. 45.00 (978-1-86470-285-9(0)) Images Publishing Group AUS. Dist: National Bk. Network.

Beaver, Robyn, ed. KlingStubbins: Palimpsest. 2009. (Master Architect Ser.). (ENG., Illus.). 536p. 85.00 (978-1-86470-295-8(8)) Images Publishing Group AUS. Dist: National Bk. Network.

Belfoure, Charles. Edmund G. Lind: Anglo-American Architect of Baltimore & the South. 2009. (Illus.). 203p. pap. 27.95 (978-0-9729743-2-5(6)) Baltimore Architecture Foundation.

Bennett, George Fletcher. Colonial Architecture: Early Examples from the First State. 2006. (Illus.). 213p. pap. 29.95 (978-0-7643-2510-6(8)) Schiffer Publishing, Ltd.

Benson, Robert. Frank Gehry's Loyola Law School: An architectural Tour. 2010. (ENG., Illus.). 72p. pap. 28.50 (978-0-615-38048-3(4)) Loyola Law Schl.

Berenholtz, Richard, photos by. New York Deco. (ENG., Illus.). 2009. 160p. 19.95 (978-1-59962-078-7(2)) 2008. 184p. 125.00 (978-1-59962-053-4(7)) Welcome Enterprises, Inc. (Welcome Bks.).

Bernheimer, Andrew & Della Valle, Jared. Think/Make: Della Valle Bernheimer. 2009. (ENG., Illus.). 192p. pap. 40.00 (978-1-56898-781-1(1)) Princeton Architectural Pr.

Berrizbeitia, Anita, ed. Michael Van Valkenburgh Associates: Reconstructing Urban Landscapes. 2009. (ENG., Illus.). 320p. 65.00 (978-0-300-13585-5(8)) Yale Univ. Pr.

Bessa, Antonio Sergio, ed. Intersections: The Grand Concourse At 100. 2009. (ENG., Illus.). 160p. 45.00 (978-0-8232-3078-5(3)) Fordham Univ. Pr.

Beyer, William E. The History of the Veterans Memorial Bridge. 90th ed. 2009. (Illus.). 612p. (978-0-692-00126-4(3)) Biddle, Oliver.

Bishir, Catherine W. Southern Built: American Architecture, Regional Practice. 2006. (ENG., Illus.). 400p. (gr. 17). 75.00 (978-0-8139-2538-7(X)); per. 35.00 (978-0-8139-2539-4(8)) Univ. Pr. of Virginia.

Blackwell, Russell. The Architects of America: Freemasons & the Growth of the United States. 2012. **(978-0-87586-907-0(6))**; pap. **(978-0-87586-906-3(8))** Algora Publishing.

Blake, Angela M. How New York Became American, 1890-1924. 2009. (ENG., Illus.). 256p. (gr. 17). pap. 25.00 (978-0-8018-9255-4(4)) Johns Hopkins Univ. Pr.

Bluestone, Daniel. Buildings, Landscapes, & Memory: Case Studies in Historic Preservation. 2010. (ENG., Illus.). 304p. 47.95 (978-0-393-73318-1(1), 73318) Norton, W. W. & Co., Inc.

Bone, Kevin & Pollara, Gina, eds. Water-Works: The Architecture & Engineering of the New York City Water Supply. 2007. (ENG., Illus.). 268p. 50.00 (978-1-58093-176-2(6)) Monacelli Pr., Inc.

Bonnell, Bertie. Domino's Farms. 2008. (ENG., Illus.). 248p. 35.00 (978-0-9817162-6-8(1)) Park Publishing.

Bosch, Jennifer Marjorie & Pridmore, Jay, texts. A View from the River: The Chicago Architecture Foundation River Cruise. 2008. 96p. pap. 15.95 (978-0-7649-4532-8(7)) Pomegranate Communications, Inc.

Bottini, Joseph P. & Davis, James L. Utica. 2007. (Then & Now Ser.). (ENG., Illus.). 96p. pap. 21.99 (978-0-7385-5496-9(0)) Arcadia Publishing.

Bower, John, photos by & text. After the Harvest: Indiana's historic grain elevators & feed Mills. 2007. (Illus.). 144p. pap. 22.00 (978-0-9745186-3-3(8)) Studio Indiana.

Bower, Lynn. Silent Workplace: Shops, stores, businesses, & factories where Hoosiers once earned a Living. 2008. (Illus.). 144p. pap. 22.00 (978-0-9745186-4-0(6), 877-547-5073) Studio Indiana.

Bowsher, Alice Meriwether. Community in Alabama: Architecture for Living Together. 2007. (Illus.). 224p. 39.95 (978-0-615-15352-0(6)) Alabama Architectural Foundation.

Bradbury, Dominic. The Iconic House: Architechural Masterworks since 1900. 2009. (ENG., Illus.). 352p. 65.00 (978-0-500-34255-8(5), 534255) Thames & Hudson.

Bradstreet, Scott. Landscape Designfor: Architectural Style United States Original Styles. 2008. (Illus.). 256p. 49.99 (978-0-7643-3107-7(8)) Schiffer Publishing, Ltd.

Bragdon, Claude Fayette, et al. Claude Bragdon & the Beautiful Necessity: Eleven Essays. 2010. (978-1-933360-43-0(7)) Rochester Institute of Technology, Cary Graphic Arts Pr.

Braun Editorial Staff. 1000x Architecture of the Americas. 2008. (ENG., Illus.). 1024p. 125.00 (978-3-938780-56-5(8), Braun Publish,Csi) Continental Sales, Inc.

Bretz, James. Denver's Early Architecture. 2010. (Images of America Ser.). (ENG., Illus.). 128p. pap. 21.99 (978-0-7385-8046-3(5)) Arcadia Publishing.

Bretz, James. Early Denver. 2012. (Postcard History Ser.). (ENG., Illus.). 128p. pap. 21.99 **(978-0-7385-8885-8(7))** Arcadia Publishing.

Briggs, Benjamin. The Architecture of High Point, North Carolina. 2007. 49.99 (978-1-59629-326-7(8)) History Pr., The.

Broderick, Mosette. Triumvirate: McKim, Mead & White: Art, Architecture, Scandal, & Class in America's Gilded Age. 2010. (ENG., Illus.). 608p. 40.00 (978-0-394-53662-0(2), Knopf) Knopf Doubleday Publishing Group.

Brooks, Paul. The Old Manse. 2011. 120p. pap. 12.95 **(978-1-4290-9137-4(1))** Applewood Bks.

Brooks Pfeiffer, Bruce. Frank Lloyd Wright - complete works 03 Vol. 3: Complete Works, 3 vols. Gssel, Peter, ed. 2009. (ENG, FRE & GER., Illus.). 596p. 200.00 (978-3-8228-5770-0(X), TASCHEN DEU. Dist: Ingram Pub. Services.

Brough, John Capen, et al, eds. Perspecta 43 Taboo: The Yale Architectural Journal. 2010. (ENG., Illus.). 210p. (gr. 17). pap. 25.00 (978-0-262-51479-8(6)) MIT Pr.

Brouws, Jeff, photos by. Approaching Nowhere. 2006. (ENG., Illus.). 160p. 65.00 (978-0-393-06274-8(0), 6274) Norton, W. W. & Co., Inc.

Brown, William J. American Colossus: the Grain Elevator, 1843 To 1943. 2010. 464p. pap. 29.99 (978-0-578-01261-2(8)) Colossal Bks.

Bruno, R. Stephanie. New Orleans Streets: A Walker's Guide to Neighborhood Architecture, 1 vol. 2011. (ENG., Illus.). 160p. pap. 15.95 (978-1-58980-874-4(6)) Pelican Publishing Co., Inc.

Buchwald, Ari. I Thought Pigs Could Fly! Architectural Details of Cincinnati. 2007. 100p. per. 19.99 (978-0-9798639-1-6(3)) Edgecliff Pr. LLC.

Buckner, Cory. A. Quincy Jones. 2007. (ENG., Illus.). 272p. per. 29.95 (978-0-7148-4843-3(3)) Phaidon Pr., Inc.

Bush-Brown, Albert, intro. Som: Architecture of Skidmore, Owings & Merrill, 1973-1983. 2009. (ENG., Illus.). 288p. 60.00 (978-1-58093-222-6(3)) Monacelli Pr., Inc.

Bush, David & Parsons, Jim. Hill Country Deco: Modernistic Architecture of Central Texas. 2010. (ENG., Illus.). 224p. 35.00 (978-0-87565-413-3(4)) Texas Christian Univ. Pr.

Business Comes to the Expert: A Proactive Marketing Plan for Professional Practice Firms. 2008. 198p. pap. 39.00 (978-0-9785552-5-2(2), Ostberg) Greenway Communications.

Buskirk, Matthijs. The Capitol Visitor Center: an Addition to Architectural History. 2010. (American Cities Ser.). pap. 43.00 (978-1-60876-144-9(4)) Nova Science Pubs., Inc.

Caldwell, Pat, photos by. The Majesty of Mobile. 2012. E-Book **(978-1-4556-1492-9(0))** Pelican Publishing Co., Inc.

Cameron, Catherine M. Chaco & after in the Northern San Juan: Excavations at the Bluff Great House. 2008. (ENG., Illus.). 280p. 75.00 (978-0-8165-2681-9(8)) Univ. of Arizona Pr.

Cannon, Patrick F. & Sullivan, Louis H. Louis Sullivan: Creating a New American Architecture. 2011. (Illus.). 192p. 39.95 (978-0-7649-5771-0(6)) Pomegranate Communications, Inc.

Cantley, Bryan & Epstein-Jones, Dora, eds. Mechudzu: New Rhetorics for Architecture. 2011. (RIEAeuropa Book-Ser.). (GER & ENG., Illus.). 120p. pap. 49.95 (978-3-7091-0834-5(9), 3709108349) Springer Wien AUT. Dist: Springer.

Cantor, Fred & Davidson, Debra L. Fresh Meadows. 2011. (Images of America Ser.). (ENG., Illus.). 128p. pap. 21.99 **(978-0-7385-7572-8(0))** Arcadia Publishing.

Carabet, Brian & Shand, John. Minnesota: Design Philosophies Expressed by Minnesota's Leading Professionals. 2009. (Perspectives on Design Ser.). (ENG.). 304p. 40.00 (978-1-933415-77-2(0)) Panache Partners, LLC.

Carlson, Heather. The Visual Shift in Design of the Atomic Age. 2010. 72p. pap. (978-3-8383-4956-5(3)) Lambert Academic Publishing.

Carson, Juli & Last, Nana, eds. Paradox & Practice: Architecture in the Wake of Conceptualism. 2007. per. (978-1-884355-07-3(2)) Univ. of California, Irvine, Univ. Art Gallery.

Carson, Mary Eisenman. Miracle on the Prairie. 2008. 96p. pap. 9.95 (978-0-7414-4820-0(3)) Infinity Publishing.

Cary, John, ed. The Power of Pro Bono: 40 Stories about Design for the Public Good by Architects & Their Clients, 1 vol. 2010. (ENG.). 288p. 40.00 (978-1-935202-18-9(9), Metropolis Bks.) D.A.P./Distributed Art Pubs.

Caswell, Meranda L. Elizabethtown. 2012. (Then & Now Ser.). (ENG., Illus.). 96p. pap. 21.99 **(978-0-7385-9166-7(1))** Arcadia Publishing.

Cawthon, Richard J. Lost Churches of Mississippi. 2010. (ENG., Illus.). 240p. 35.00 (978-1-60473-436-2(1)) Univ. Pr. of Mississippi.

CBT Vision Staff. Boston & Beyond: CBT Architects. 2012. (ENG., Illus.). 224p. 59.95 (978-1-86470-404-4(7)) Images Publishing Group AUS. Dist: National Bk. Network.

Celant, Germano. Frank O. Gehry: Since 1997. 2010. (ENG., Illus.). 320p. 95.00 (978-88-572-0179-5(1)) Skira Editore ITA. Dist: Random Hse., Inc.

Cerny, Susan Dinkelspiel. An Architectural Guidebook to San Francisco & the Bay Area. 2007. (ENG., Illus.). 568p. pap. 29.95 (978-1-58685-432-4(1)) Gibbs Smith, Publisher.

Chacon, Hipolito Rafael. Original Man. 2008. pap. 35.00 (978-0-9815760-0-8(1)) Farcountry Pr.

Chacon, Hipolito Rafael. The Original Man: The Life & Work of Montana Architect A. J. Gibson. 2008. (Illus.). 163p. 75.00 (978-0-9815760-1-5(X)) Univ. of Montana Pr., The.

Chalfant, Randolph W. & Belfoure, Charles. Niernsee & Neilson, Architects of Baltimore: Two Careers on the Edge of the Future. 2006. (Illus.). 184p. per. 24.95 net. (978-0-9729743-1-3(8)) Baltimore Architecture Foundation.

Chandler, Joseph E., ed. The Colonial Architecture of Maryland, Pennsylvania & Virginia. (Illus.). reprint ed. lib. bdg. 88.00 (978-0-7222-0963-9(0)) Library Reprints, Inc.

Chappell, David & Willis, Andrew. The Architect in Practice. 10th ed. 2010. (ENG., Illus.). 432p. pap. 65.00 (978-1-4051-9852-3(4), Wiley-Blackwell) Wiley, John & Sons, Inc.

Chappell, Sally A. Kitt. Chicago's Urban Nature: A Guide to the City's Architecture + Landscape. 2007. (ENG., Illus.). 300p. 47.50 (978-0-226-10139-2(8)); pap. 20.00 (978-0-226-10140-8(1)) Univ. of Chicago Pr.

Charles J. Connick: His Education & His Windows in & near Pittsburgh. 2008. (Illus.). 176p. pap. 19.95 (978-0-9788284-3-1(7)) Pittsburgh History & Landmarks Foundation.

Chase, Iris Garnett & Schuetz, Gabriele. South Beach: Faces & Facades. 2007. (Illus.). 128p. pap. 24.95 (978-0-7643-2593-9(0)) Schiffer Publishing, Ltd.

Chicago Tribune Staff. Elegant Small Homes of the Twenties: 99 Designs from a Competition. 2008. (Dover Architecture Ser.). (ENG.). 112p. pap. 14.95 (978-0-486-46910-2(7)) Dover Pubns., Inc.

Chronicle Books Staff & Walker, Alissa. City Walks Architecture: New York. 2009. (ENG.). 25p. 18.95 (978-0-8118-6876-1(1)) Chronicle Bks. LLC.

Chu, David. Frozen Music: A Literary Exploration of California Architecture. 2010. xiii, 247p. pap. (978-1-59714-137-6(2)) Heyday.

Chu, Hsiao-Yun & Trujillo, Roberto, eds. New Views on R. Buckminster Fuller. 2009. (ENG., Illus.). 248p. pap. 21.95 (978-0-8047-6279-3(1)) Stanford Univ. Pr.

Chu, Hsiao-Yun & Trujillo, Roberto G. New Views on R. Buckminster Fuller. Chu, Hsiao-Yun & Trujillo, Roberto, eds. 2009. (ENG., Illus.). 248p. 55.00 (978-0-8047-5209-1(5)) Stanford Univ. Pr.

Cieciek, Greg. LARE Review: Analytical Aspects of Practice. 2nd ed. 2006. (ENG., Illus.). 64p. pap. 80.00 (978-1-59126-086-8(8)) Professional Pubns., Inc.

Clark, Alexandra Walker. Colorado's Historic Hotels. 2011. (Illus.). 240p. pap. 19.99 **(978-1-60949-301-1(X))** History Pr., The.

Claussen, Pamela/L. Crowns: Treasure Trove of Lavish Designs. 2007. (Illus.). 55.00 (978-0-9793297-0-8(1)) Claussen, Pamela.

Clifford, Mary Louise & Clifford, J. Candace. Lighthouses Short & Tall. 2008. (Illus.). 48p. (YA). pap. 4.95 (978-0-9636412-9-8(8)) Cypress Communications.

Clive Wilkinson Architects & Chan, Benny, photos by. Interior Spaces of the USA & Canada Vol 7 No. 7: A Pictorial Review. 2006. (International Spaces Ser.). (ENG., Illus.). 224p. 55.00 (978-1-920744-35-9(5)) Images Publishing Group AUS. Dist: National Bk. Network.

Cloepfil, Brad & text. Allied Works Architecture, 2000-2010. 2011. (ENG., Illus.). 440p. 85.00 (978-0-9800242-5-8(0)) Miller, Gregory & Co.

Cobbers, Arnt. Frank Lloyd Wright: Life & Work. 2008. (Architecture in Focus Ser.). (Illus.). 95p. per. 5.95 (978-0-8416-0087-4(2)) American Map Corp.

Coffin, L. A. & Holden, A. C. Brick Architecture of the Colonial Period in Maryland & Virginia. (Illus.). 29p. reprint ed. lib. bdg. 88.00 (978-0-7222-4677-1(3)) Library Reprints, Inc.

Cohen, Janie. Architectural Improvisation: A History of Vermont's Design/Build Movement 1964-1977. 2009. (Illus.). 84p. pap. 20.00 (978-0-934658-04-1(8), University of Vermont Press) Univ. Pr. of New England.

Cohen, Stan B. & The Svoboda Collection at the Northern Rockies Heritage Center. Missoula. 2008. (Postcard History Ser.). (ENG., Illus.). 128p. pap. 19.99 (978-0-7385-5888-2(5)) Arcadia Publishing.

Colorado Geological Survey. Guide to Swelling Soil for Colorado Homebuyers & Homeowners, Second Edition. 2007. (Illus.). 51p. pap. (978-1-884216-60-2(9)) Colorado Geological Survey.

Conkling, Edgar C. Frederick Law Olmsted's Point Chautauqua: The Story of an Historic Lakeside Community. Dobies, Ann Marie & Banchich, Sue, eds. (Illus.). 135p. 15.00 (978-0-9671480-6-9(5)) Canisius College Pr.

Cooper, Polly & Eldridge, Ted. Savannah Then & Now. 2010. (Then & Now Thunder Bay Ser.). (ENG., Illus.). 144p. 19.95 (978-1-60710-127-7(0), Thunder Bay Pr.) Advantage Pubs. Group.

Corning, Evelyn. Hillside Letters A to Z: A Guide to Hometown Landmarks. 2007. (Illus.). 204p. pap. 20.00 (978-0-87842-533-4(0)) Mountain Pr. Publishing Co., Inc.

Cothran, James R. Charleston Gardens & the Landscape Legacy of Loutrel Briggs. 2010. (ENG.). 39.95 (978-1-57003-891-4(0)) Univ. of South Carolina Pr.

Cousins, Frank. The Colonial Architecture of Salem. 2010. (ENG.). 442p. pap. 36.75 (978-1-176-31491-7(2)) BiblioBazaar.

—The Colonial Architecture of Salem. 2010. 142p. pap. 23.09 (978-1-151-98534-7(1)) General Bks. LLC.

Cousins, Frank & Riley, Phil M. The Colonial Architecture of Salem. 2010. 430p. 41.99 (978-1-140-19722-5(3)) BiblioBazaar.

—The Colonial Architecture of Salem. 2007. (ENG.). 436p. 51.95 (978-0-548-35488-9(X)); per. 36.95 (978-0-548-29746-9(0)) Kessinger Publishing, LLC.

—The Colonial Architecture of Salem. (Illus.). reprint ed. lib. bdg. 98.00 (978-0-7222-0664-5(X)) Library Reprints, Inc.

Cousins, Frank & Riley, Phil Madison. The Colonial Architecture of Salem. 2010. 442p. pap. 35.75 (978-1-146-61856-4(5)); 444p. pap. 35.75 (978-1-146-97251-2(2)); 440p. pap. 35.75 (978-1-143-98405-1(6)) BiblioBazaar.

Cox, Kenyon. The Classic Point of View. 2009. 74p. pap. (978-1-151-54766-8(2)) Books LLC.

Cramer, James P. & Paradise Wolford, Jane. Almanac of Architecture & Design 2011. 12th ed. 2011. (Illus.). 606p. pap. 149.00 **(978-0-9846136-0-1(9))** Greenway Communications.

Cramer, James P. & Simpson, Scott. The Next Architect: A New Twist on the Future of Design. 2006. 148p. pap. 39.00 (978-0-9755654-8-3(6), Ostberg) Greenway Communications.

Cramer, James P. & Yankopolus, Jennifer Evans, eds. Almanac of Architecture & Design 2007. 2006. (Illus.). 850p. pap. 49.50 (978-0-9755654-4-5(3), Ostberg) Greenway Communications.

Cram101 Textbook Reviews. Outlines & Highlights for American Architecture: A History by Leland Roth. 2011. 232p. pap. 31.95 **(978-1-61906-094-4(3))** Cram101 Inc.

Craven, Wayne. Gilded Mansions: Grand Architecture & High Society. 2008. (ENG., Illus.). 352p. 59.95 (978-0-393-06754-5(8), 6754) Norton, W. W. & Co., Inc.

Crosbie, Michael J. Design for Aging: The American Institute of Architects, Vol. 3. 2006. (ENG., Illus.). 240p. 65.00 (978-1-920744-69-4(X)) Images Publishing Group AUS. Dist: National Bk. Network.

—Houses of God: Religious Architecture for a New Millennium, Vol. 3. 2006. (ENG., Illus.). 192p. 65.00 (978-1-920744-97-7(5)) Images Publishing Group AUS. Dist: National Bk. Network.

—New York Dozen: Gen X Architects. 2011. (ENG., Illus.). 224p. 59.95 (978-1-86470-396-2(2)) Images Publishing Group AUS. Dist: National Bk. Network.

Cryder, Jo. Entryways & Doorways. 2008. (Illus.). 160p. pap. 29.95 (978-0-7643-2858-9(1)) Schiffer Publishing, Ltd.

—1000 Shutters & Awnings. 2007. (Illus.). 160p. pap. 29.95 (978-0-7643-2711-7(9)) Schiffer Publishing, Ltd.

CSD Architecture, compiled by. People Architecture. 2006. 80p. pap. 29.95 (978-0-9755654-9-0(4), Ostberg) Greenway Communications.

Culter Anderson Architects Staff & Cutler, James E. Cutler Anderson. Ojeda, Oscar Riera, ed. 2009. (ENG., Illus.). 440p. 85.00 (978-0-8478-3223-1(6)) Rizzoli International Pubns., Inc.

Cuno, James, et al. The Modern Wing: Renzo Piano & the Art Institute of Chicago. 2009. (ENG., Illus.). 168p. 60.00 (978-0-300-14112-2(2)) Art Institute of Chicago.

Curl, Donald Walter. The Boca Raton Resort & Club: Mizner's Inn. 2008. pap. 19.99 (978-1-59629-527-8(9)) History Pr., The.

Curtis, Lisa. Cedarburg. 2011. (Images of America Ser.). (Illus.). 128p. pap. 21.99 **(978-0-7385-8260-3(3))** Arcadia Publishing.

da Costa Meyer, Esther. Frank Gehry: On Line. 2008. (Illus.). 80p. pap. 24.95 (978-0-943012-00-1(7)) Princeton Univ. Art Museum.

DAAB Media Staff, ed. New York Architecture & Design, 1 vol. 2009. (ENG.). 240p. 59.95 (978-3-86654-072-9(8)) DAAB Media Gmbh DEU. Dist: Innovative Logistics.

Dandekar, Hemalata. Michigan Family Farms & Farm Buildings: Landscapes of the Heart & Mind. 2010. (ENG., Illus.). 288p. 70.00 (978-0-472-07105-0(X)); pap. 27.95 (978-0-472-05105-2(9)) Univ. of Michigan Pr.

Daniels, Megan E. Milwaukee's Early Architecture. 2010. (Images of America Ser.). (ENG., Illus.). 128p. pap. 21.99 (978-0-7385-8411-9(8)) Arcadia Publishing.

Danz, Ernst, comment. Som: Architecture of Skidmore, Owings & Merrill, 1950-1962. 2009. (ENG., Illus.). 224p. 45.00 (978-1-58093-220-2(7)) Monacelli Pr., Inc.

Dave, Ogershok, ed. 2011 National Building Cost Manual. 2010. 264p. pap. 53.00 incl. cd-rom (978-1-57218-240-0(7)) Craftsman Bk. Co.

—2011 National Construction Estimator. 2010. 672p. pap. 62.50 incl. cd-rom (978-1-57218-242-4(3)) Craftsman Bk. Co.

Davidson, Cynthia, ed. Tracing Eisenman: Complete Works. 2006. (ENG., Illus.). 400p. 75.00 (978-0-8478-2889-0(1)) Rizzoli International Pubns., Inc.

Davis, Arthur Q., mem. It Happened by Design: The Life & Work of Arthur Q. Davis. 2009. (ENG., Illus.). 160p. 50.00 (978-1-60473-265-8(2)) Univ. Pr. of Mississippi.

de Leon, Monica Ponce, ed. Fellowships in Architecture: Architecture of America, 1960-2009. 2009. (ENG., Illus.). 260p. pap. 35.00 (978-0-9820607-3-5(4)) Oro Editions.

De Long, David G. Auldbrass: Frank Lloyd Wright's Southern Plantation. 2011. (ENG., Illus.). 304p. 60.00 (978-0-8478-3616-1(9)) Rizzoli International Pubns., Inc.

DeAloia, Michael. Lost Cleveland: Seven Wonders of the Sixth City. 2010. (Lost Ser.). (ENG., Illus.). 112p. pap. 19.99 (978-1-59629-878-1(2)) History Pr., The.

Decker, Julie. Expanded View: The New Wing of the Anchorage Museum at Rasmuson Center. 2010. (978-1-56898-892-4(3)) Princeton Architectural Pr.

—True North: New Alaskan Architecture. 2010. (ENG., Illus.). 96p. 29.90 (978-3-03768-020-9(2), Braun Publish,Csi) Continental Sales, Inc.

Delicato, Armando & Khalil, Elias. Detroit's Cass Corridor. 2012. (Images of America Ser.). (ENG., Illus.). 128p. pap. 21.99 **(978-0-7385-8268-9(9))** Arcadia Publishing.

Deliyannis, Melina. Powers Brown Architecture. 2007. (Neoarchitecture Ser.). (ENG., Illus.). 124p. 49.50 (978-1-86470-250-7(8)) Images Publishing Group AUS. Dist: National Bk. Network.

Designed for Worship. 2006. per. 44.95 (978-0-9772092-1-7(0)) Booksmith Group, The.

DesignIntelligence: Technology Survey 2008. 2008. (Illus.). 71p. pap. 69.95 (978-0-9785552-7-6(9), Ostberg) Greenway Communications.

Desilets, Deborah. Morris Lapidus: The Architecture of Joy. 2010. (ENG., Illus.). 240p. 65.00 (978-0-8478-3088-6(8)) Rizzoli International Pubns., Inc.

Devlin, Ann Sloan. What Americans Build & Why: Psychological Perspectives. 2010. (ENG., Illus.). 316p. (C). 90.00 (978-0-521-51657-0(9)); pap. 27.99 (978-0-521-73435-6(5)) Cambridge Univ. Pr.

Dillon, Joan. American Theaters. 2nd ed. 2006. (Illus.). 254p. 39.95 (978-0-7643-2491-8(8)) Schiffer Publishing, Ltd.

Donnelly, Lu, et al. Buildings of Pennsylvania: Pittsburgh & Western Pennsylvania. 2010. (Buildings of the United States Ser.). (ENG., Illus.). 656p. (gr. 17). 75.00 (978-0-8139-2823-4(0)) Univ. Pr. of Virginia.

Dougherty, Brian & Besty. Dougherty + Dougherty Architects LLP: Intersections: Architecture & Social Responsibility. Images Publishing Group Editors, ed. 2008. (ENG., Illus.). 124p. 49.95 (978-1-86470-303-0(2)) Images Publishing Group AUS. Dist: National Bk. Network.

Draeger, James & Speltz, Mark. Fill'er Up: The Glory Days of Wisconsin Gas Stations. 2008. (Places along the Way Ser.). (ENG., Illus.). 208p. 29.95 (978-0-87020-393-0(2)) Wisconsin Historical Society.

Drickamer, Lee C. & Runge, Peter J. Northern Arizona University: Buildings as History. 2011. (ENG., Illus.). 352p. 30.00 (978-0-8165-2981-0(7)) Univ. of Arizona Pr.

Dubbeldam, Winka & DAAB Editors. Architectonics. 2011. (ENG, FRE, GER, ITA & SPA., Illus.). 176p. 35.00 (978-3-942597-00-5(4)) DAAB Media Gmbh DEU. Dist: Innovative Logistics.

Duff, Charles & Clark, Tracey. Baltimore Architecture. 2006. (Then & Now Ser.). (ENG., Illus.). 96p. per. 21.99 (978-0-7385-4281-2(4)) Arcadia Publishing.

Dunlop, Beth. Arquitectonica. pap. 45.00 (978-0-8478-2607-0(4)) Rizzoli International Pubns., Inc.

Durough, Allen R. & Rayfield, Wallace A. The Architectural Legacy of Wallace A. Rayfield: Pioneer Black Architect of Birmingham, Alabama. 2nd ed. 2010. (ENG., Illus.). 176p. 32.95 (978-0-8173-1683-9(3)) Univ. of Alabama Pr.

Eastham, Scott. American Dreamer: Bucky Fuller & the Sacred Geometry of Nature. 2007. (ENG., Illus.). 200p. pap. 58.00 (978-0-7188-3031-1(8)) Lutherworth Pr., The GBR. Dist: Brown, David Bk. Co., The.

Eastman, Michael. Vanishing America: The End of Main Street Diners, Drive-Ins, Donut Shops, & Other Everyday Monuments. 2008. (ENG., Illus.). 192p. 39.95 (978-0-8478-3040-4(3)) Rizzoli International Pubns., Inc.

Eberlein, Harold D. The Architecture of Colonial America. 2007. (ENG.). 368p. per. 33.95 (978-1-4326-5024-7(6)) Kessinger Publishing, LLC.

Eckert, Kathryn Bishop. Buildings of Michigan. 2nd rev. ed. 2012. (Buildings of the United States Ser.). (ENG., Illus.). 672p. (gr. 17). 85.00 **(978-0-8139-3157-9(6))** Univ. Pr. of Virginia.

Elenga, Maureen R. Seattle Architecture: A Walking Guide to Downtown. 2008. (ENG., Illus.). 336p. pap. 20.00 (978-0-615-14129-9(3)) Seattle Architecture Foundation.

Eliminating Waste & Managing Space in Federal Courthouses: GAO Recommendations on Courthouse Construction, Courtroom Sharing, & Enforcing Congressionally Authorized Limits on Size & Cost: Hearing Before the Subcommittee on Economic Development, Public Buildings, & Emergency Management of the Committee on Transportation & Infrastructure, House of Representatives, One Hundred Eleventh Congress, Second Session, May 25, 2010. 2010. (Illus.). x, 167p. **(978-0-16-087059-0(3)**, 552-070-41916-1) United States Government Printing Office.

Ellis, Clifton & Ginsburg, Rebecca, eds. Cabin, Quarter, Plantation: Architecture & Landscapes of North American Slavery. 2010. (Illus.). 264p. 45.00 (978-0-300-12042-4(7)) Yale Univ. Pr.

Engelhorn, Beate. Young Americans: New Architecture in the USA, 1 vol. 2009. (GER & ENG., Illus.). 416p. 99.95 **(978-3-938666-17-3(X))** DOM Pubs. DEU. Dist: Innovative Logistics.

Ennead Architects Staff. Dickinson School of Law. 2012. (Ennead Profile Ser.). (ENG.). 86p. pap. 11.95 (978-0-9822024-8-7(2)) Oro Editions.

—Ennead Profile Series 4: Frank Sinatra School for the Arts. 2012. (Ennead Profile Ser.). (ENG.). 86p. pap. 11.95 (978-0-9822024-7-0(4)) Oro Editions.

—Standard Hotel. 2012. (Ennead Profile Ser.). (ENG.). 86p. pap. 11.95 (978-0-9822024-6-3(6)) Oro Editions.

Ewing, Heather & Ballard, Amy. A Guide to Smithsonian Architecture: An Architectural History of the Smithsonian. 2009. (ENG.). 160p. pap. 14.95 (978-1-58834-261-4(1)) Smithsonian Institution Pr.

Ewing, Heather & Ossman, Laurie. Carrere & Hastings. 2011. (ENG., Illus.). 320p. 75.00 (978-0-8478-3564-5(2)) Rizzoli International Pubns., Inc.

Factor, R. Lance. Chapel in the Sky: Knox College's Old Main & Its Masonic Architect. 2009. (ENG.). 180p. 29.95 (978-0-87580-415-6(2)) Northern Illinois Univ. Pr.

Falk, C. Barns of New York. 2012. pap. **(978-0-8014-7780-5(8))** Cornell Univ. Pr.

Falk, Cynthia G. & Falk, Cynthia. Architecture & Artifacts of the Pennsylvania Germans: Constructing Identity in Early America. 2008. (ENG., Illus.). 256p. (C). 45.00 (978-0-271-03338-9(X)) Pennsylvania State Univ. Pr.

Farameh, Patrice. Gowest! Cutting Edge Creatives in the United States. 2011. (ENG.). 312p. 75.00 (978-3-942597-13-5(6)) DAAB Media Gmbh DEU. Dist: Innovative Logistics.

Federico, Joseph & McHenry, Matthew. Galloway Township. 2011. (Images of America Ser.). (Illus.). 128p. pap. 21.99 (978-0-7385-7411-0(2)) Arcadia Publishing.

Fedynsky, John. Michigan's County Courthouses. 2011. (ENG., Illus.). 216p. pap. 29.95 **(978-0-472-03493-2(6))** Univ. of Michigan Pr.

Felder, Paula S. George Washington's Fredericksburg. 2011. pap. **(978-1-57864-669-2(3))** Donning Co. Pubs.

Feldman, Roberta M. & Wheaton, Jim, eds. The Chicago Greystone in Historic North Lawndale. 2007. (Illus.). 120p. per. 14.95 (978-0-9789650-0-6(0)) City Design Ctr.

Ferriss, Hugh. Power in Buildings: An Artist's View of Contemporary Architecture. 2011. 114p. 39.95 **(978-1-258-10299-9(4))** Literary Licensing, LLC.

Ferriss, Hugh. The Power of Buildings, 1920-1950: A Master Draftsman's Record. 2008. (Dover Architecture Ser.). (ENG., Illus.). 112p. pap. 15.95 (978-0-486-46920-1(4)) Dover Pubns., Inc.

Field, Cynthia R., et al, eds. Paris on the Potomac: The French Influence on the Architecture & Art of Washington, D. C. 2007. (Perspective on Art & Architect Ser.). (Illus.). 208p. 49.95 (978-0-8214-1759-1(2)) Ohio Univ. Pr.

Field, Cynthia R., et al. Paris on the Potomac: The French Influence on the Architecture & Art of Washington, D.C. Field, Cynthia R. et al, eds. 2007. (Perspective on Art & Architect Ser.). (Illus.). 208p. per. 24.95 (978-0-8214-1760-7(6)) Ohio Univ. Pr.

First in a Series: Greening Washington & the National Capital Region: Hearing Before the Subcommittee on Economic Development, Public Buildings, & Emergency Management of the Committee on Transportation & Infrastructure, House of Representatives, One Hundred Tenth Congress, Second Session, April 17, 2008. 2008. ix, 101p. (978-0-16-083277-2(2), 552-070-39105-3) United States Government Printing Office.

Fisher, Terri L. Giles County. 2011. (Then & Now Ser.). (Illus.). 96p. pap. 21.99 (978-0-7385-8716-5(8)) Arcadia Publishing.

Fisher, Thomas & Bastianelli-Kerze, Peter. The Invisible Element of Place: The Architecture of David Salmela. 2011. (Illus.). 272p. pap. 39.95 (978-0-8166-6994-3(5)) Univ. of Minnesota Pr.

Fitch, James Marston. James Marston Fitch. 2007. pap. 27.95 (978-0-7937-3229-6(8)) Norton, W. W. & Co., Inc.

Fitzgerald, D. Window on the Park: New York's Most Prestigious Properties on Central Park. 2009. (ENG., Illus.). 228p. 45.00 (978-1-86470-276-7(1)) Images Publishing Group AUS. Dist: National Bk. Network.

Fleming, Ronald Lee. The Art of Placemaking: Interpreting Community Through Public Art & Urban Design. 2007. (ENG., Illus.). 384p. 49.95 (978-1-85894-371-8(X)) Merrell Pubs. Ltd. GBR. Dist: Perseus Distribution.

Foster, Laura O. Portland City Walks: Twenty Explorations in & Around Town. 2008. (ENG., Illus.). 320p. pap. 19.95 (978-0-88192-885-3(2), 0881928852) Timber Pr., Inc.

Foster, Norman & Giovannini, Joseph. Hearst Tower. 2010. (Illus.). 96p. 24.95 (978-3-7913-4493-5(5)) Prestel Publishing.

Fougeron, Anne. Fougeron Architecture: Opposition/Composition. 2011. (ENG., Illus.). 192p. pap. 40.00 (978-1-56898-990-7(3)) Princeton Architectural Pr.

Fraiser, Jim. The Majesty of Mobile, 1 vol. 2012. (ENG., Illus.). 144p. 24.95 **(978-1-4556-1491-2(2))** Pelican Publishing Co., Inc.

Fraiser, Jim. Vanished Mississippi Gulf Coast, 1 vol. 2006. (ENG., Illus.). 104p. 24.95 (978-1-58980-346-6(9)) Pelican Publishing Co., Inc.

Frampton, Kenneth. Five North American Architects: An Anthology. 2012. (ENG., Illus.). 240p. pap. 55.00 **(978-3-03778-256-9(0))** Lars Muller Pubs. CHE. Dist: Prestel Publishing.

Frampton, Kenneth, et al, eds. SOM Journal, No. 5. 2009. (ENG., Illus.). 228p. pap. 30.00 (978-3-7757-2279-7(3)) Hatje Cantz Verlag GmbH & Co KG DEU. Dist: D.A.P./Distributed Art Pubs.

Frampton, Kenneth, intro. Som: Architecture of Skidmore, Owings & Merrill, 1997-2008. 2009. (ENG., Illus.). 256p. 60.00 (978-1-58093-224-0(X)) Monacelli Pr., Inc.

Freed, Elaine, ed. Architecture as Teacher: Packard Hall at Colorado College. 2007. per. 12.00 (978-0-935052-46-6(1)) Colorado College.

Friedman, Alice T. American Glamour & the Evolution of Modern Architecture. 2010. (Illus.). 272p. 65.00 (978-0-300-11654-0(3)) Yale Univ. Pr.

Gabellini, Michael. Gabellini: Architecture of the Interior. 2008. (ENG., Illus.). 240p. 65.00 (978-0-8478-3016-9(0)) Rizzoli International Pubns., Inc.

Gabriel. Gloucester City. 2011. (Images of America Ser.). (ENG., Illus.). 128p. pap. 21.99 **(978-0-7385-7627-5(1))** Arcadia Publishing.

Gabrielan, Randall. Hoboken: History & Architecture at a Glance. 2011. (Illus.). 160p. 29.99 (978-0-7643-3652-2(5)) Schiffer Publishing, Ltd.

Galindo, Michelle. Collection: U.S. Architecture. 2009. (Collection). (FRE, GER & ENG., Illus.). 512p. 89.95 (978-3-03768-022-3(9), Braun Publish,Csi) Continental Sales, Inc.

Gallagher, John. Great Architecture of Michigan. 2008. 60.00 (978-0-9816144-0-3(X)) Michigan Architectural Foundation.

Gallery, John Andrew. Philadelphia Architecture: A Guide to the City. 3rd ed. 2009. (ENG.). 188p. pap. 25.00 (978-1-58988-047-4(1)) Dry, Paul Bks., Inc.

Gand, Gary. Julius Shulman: Chicago Mid-Century Modernism. 2010. (Illus.). 208p. 60.00 (978-0-8478-3287-3(2)) Rizzoli International Pubns., Inc.

Gang, Jeanne. Reveal: Studio Gang Architects. 2011. (ENG., Illus.). 256p. pap. 45.00 (978-1-56898-993-8(8)) Princeton Architectural Pr.

Ganon, Jill Alison & Gillis, Sandy. At Home: Pasadena. 2007. (Illus.). 184p. 39.95 (978-0-9753939-3-2(6)) Prospect Park Bks., LLC.

Gardner, Denis. Wood, Concrete, Stone, & Steel: Minnesota's Historic Bridges. 2008. pap. (978-0-8166-4667-8(8)) Univ. of Minnesota Pr.

Gatchell, Lynn & Gatchell, Robert J. Painted Ladies: Corbels & Gingerbread. 2008. (Illus.). 160p. pap. 29.99 (978-0-7643-3046-9(2)) Schiffer Publishing, Ltd.

Gatchell, Robert and Lynn. Painted Ladies: Balusters & Columns. 2008. (Illus.). 160p. pap. 29.99 (978-0-7643-3045-2(4)) Schiffer Publishing, Ltd.

General Services Administration's Fiscal Year 2008 Capital Investment & Leasing Program: Hearing Before the Subcommittee on Economic Development, Public Buildings, & Emergency Management of the Committee on Transportation & Infrastructure, House of Representatives, One Hundred Tenth Congress, First Session, May 10, 2007. 2007. (Illus.). viii, 35p. (978-0-16-080702-2(6), 552-070-37295-4) United States Government Printing Office.

Georgia Museum of Art. Decorative Arts in Georgia: Historic Sites, Historic Contexts - The Third Henry D. Green Symposium of the Decorative Arts. Callahan, Ashley, ed. 2008. (ENG.). 158p. pap. 25.00 (978-0-915977-66-6(4)) Univ. of Georgia, Georgia Museum of Art.

Ghosh, S. K., et al. Significant Changes to the Seismic Load Provisions of ASCE 7-10: An Illustrated Guide. 2010. (ENG.). 192p. pap. 85.00 (978-0-7844-1117-9(4)) American Society of Civil Engineers.

Gilbert, Dale, ed. The Clean Waterfront: Portfolio of Clean Marinas. 2008. (Illus.). 23p. (978-0-9771155-2-5(6)) TIGOR, Inc.

Giller, Norman M. & Nelson, Sarah Giller. Designing the Good Life: Norman M. Giller & the Development of Miami Modernism. 2007. (ENG.). 192p. 39.95 (978-0-8130-3071-5(4)) Univ. Pr. of Florida.

Giovanna, Borasi. Other Space Odysseys. 2010. 160p. pap. 29.95 (978-3-03778-193-7(9)) Lars Muller Pubs. CHE. Dist: Prestel Publishing.

Giovannini, Joseph. Materializing the Immaterial: The Architecture of Wallace Cunningham. 2006. (ENG., Illus.). 160p. 55.00 (978-0-9749565-2-7(X)) Yale Univ. Pr.

Gisolfi, Peter & McGrath, Norman. Finding the Place of Architecture in the Landscape. 2008. (Master Architect (Unnumbered) Ser.). (ENG., Illus.). 296p. 59.95 (978-1-86470-165-4(X), Images Publishing Dist Ac) Antique Collectors' Club GBR. Dist: National Bk. Network.

Gladu, Christian. Small Bungalows, 1 vol. 2007. (ENG., Illus.). 112p. 21.99 (978-1-4236-0098-5(3)) Gibbs Smith, Publisher.

Glass, Christopher. Historic Maine Homes: 200 Years of Great Houses. 2009. (ENG.). 200p. 40.00 (978-0-89272-799-5(3)) Down East Bks.

Godfrey, Mark. Abstraction & the Holocaust. 2007. (ENG., Illus.). 304p. 55.00 (978-0-300-12676-1(X)) Yale Univ. Pr.

González, Robert Alexander. Designing Pan-America: U. S. Architectural Visions for the Western Hemisphere. 2011. (ENG., Illus.). 278p. 65.00 (978-0-292-72325-2(3)) Univ. of Texas Pr.

Gooding, Gamalial H. Poetic Reflections. (Illus.). xi, 108p. pap. 12.00 (978-0-9679367-0-3(5), 04055) Divine Life Pubns.

Goodstein, Phil H. North Side Story: Denver's Most Intriguing Neighborhood. 2011. (Illus.). vi, 570p. pap. **(978-0-9742264-6-0(7))** New Social Pubns.

Grady, John & Pollard, Dot. Plainfield, New Jersey's History & Architecture. 2008. (Illus.). 128p. bds. 29.99 (978-0-7643-2915-9(4)) Schiffer Publishing, Ltd.

Gragg, Randy. Where the Revolution Began: Lawrence & Anna Halprin & the Reinvention of Public Spaces. 2009. (ENG.). 100p. pap. 29.95 (978-0-9824392-1-0(0)) Spacemaker Pr.

Graham, Wade. American Eden: From Monticello to Central Park to Our Backyards. 2011. (ENG., Illus.). 480p. 35.00 (978-0-06-158342-1(1)) HarperCollins Pubs.

Grandfield, Daniel. The Relocation of Century of Progress Exhibit Buildings to Beverly Shores, Indiana. 2012. (ENG.). 32p. pap. 10.95 **(978-1-4663-9419-3(6))** CreateSpace.

Grant, Kerry S. The Rainbow City: Celebrating Light, Color & Architecture at the Pan-American Exposition, Buffalo 1901. Buck, David L., ed. (Illus.). 160p. 15.00 (978-0-9671480-5-2(7)) Canisius College Pr.

Green, Betty. Zook: A Look at R. Harold Zook's Unique Architecture. 2009. (Illus.). 152p. pap. 19.95 (978-0-9818126-8-7(6), Ampersand) Ampersand, Inc.

Green Buildings: Benefits to Health, the Environment, & the Bottom Line: Hearing Before the Committee on Environment & Public Works, United States Senate, One Hundred Tenth Congress, First Session, May 15, 2007. 2011. (Illus.). ii, 228p. **(978-0-16-087998-2(1)**, 552-070-42408-3) United States Government Printing Office.

Greenagel, Frank L. A Guide to the Historic Churches of Somerset County, New Jersey. 2006. pap. 24.99 (978-1-59629-202-4(4)) History Pr., The.

Gringeri-Brown, Michelle. Atomic Ranch: Design Ideas for Stylish Ranch Homes, 1 vol. 2006. (ENG., Illus.). 192p. 40.00 (978-1-4236-0002-2(9)) Gibbs Smith, Publisher.

Grunden, Naida. Lean-Led Hospital Design: Creating the Efficient Hospital of the Future. 2012. (ENG., Illus.). 338p. 69.95 (978-1-4398-6828-7(X)) Productivity Pr.

Guarino, Robert E. Beacon Street: A Highway of History. 2011. 128p. pap. 19.99 (978-1-60949-124-6(6)) History Pr., The.

Guggenheim Foundation et. Frank Lloyd Wright: from Inward Outward. 2009. pap. (978-0-8478-3263-7(5)) Guggenheim, Solomon R. Museum.

Gutman, Marta & Nelson, Louis P., eds. Buildings & Landscapes Issue Vol. 18, Issue 1: Journal of the Vernacular Architecture Forum. 2011. (Buildings & Landscapes Ser.). 150p. pap. 37.50 (978-0-8166-7633-0(X)) Univ. of Minnesota Pr.

Gyllenhaal, Ed & Hansen Gyllenhaal, Kirsten. The Bryn Athyn Historic District. 2011. (Images of America Ser.). (Illus.). 128p. pap. 21.99 (978-0-7385-7432-5(5)) Arcadia Publishing.

Hadley Historical Commission (Hadley, Mass.) Staff & Hadley 350th Committee (Hadley, Mass.) Staff, contrib. by. The Town Cemeteries & Gravestones of Hadley, Massachusetts. 2010. (978-1-935052-24-1(1)) White River Pr.

Haga, Dan. Urban Atrophy. 2011. (Illus.). 176p. 39.99 (978-0-7643-3738-3(6), Schiffer Publishing Ltd) Schiffer Publishing, Ltd.

Hage, Christopher & Hage, Rushika. Nicollet Island: History & Architecture. 2010. (Illus.). xi, 196p. pap. 19.95 (978-1-935666-03-5(7)) Nodin Pr.

Hage, Christopher & Hage, Rushika February. Nicollet Island. 2010. (Images of America Ser.). (ENG., Illus.). 128p. pap. 21.99 (978-0-7385-7791-3(X)) Arcadia Publishing.

Halsted, Byron, ed. Barns & Outbuildings: And How to Build Them. 2nd ed. 2008. (Illus.). 235p. pap. 14.95 (978-1-59921-371-2(0), Lyons Pr.) Globe Pequot Pr., The.

Hansen, David A. David A. Hansen: Corporate Campus Architecture. 2006. (ENG., Illus.). 128p. 49.50 (978-1-86470-126-5(9)) Images Publishing Group AUS. Dist: National Bk. Network.

Hansen, Douglas, et al. Code Check Building for California: An Illustrated Guide to the California Building Code. 2008. (Code Check Building Ser.). (ENG., Illus.). 30p. spiral bd. 18.95 (978-1-60085-083-7(9), Taunton) Taunton Pr., Inc.

Hansley, Richard. Asheville's Historic Architecture. 2011. (Illus.). 176p. pap. 19.99 (978-1-60949-107-9(6)) History Pr., The.

Hardee, Lesta Sue & McDonald, Janice. Myrtle Beach Pavilion. 2010. (Images of America Ser.). (ENG., Illus.). 128p. pap. 21.99 (978-0-7385-8601-4(3)) Arcadia Publishing.

Hardt, John. Building Systems Question & Answer 2009. annuals 2008. (ENG.). 48p. pap. 49.95 (978-1-4277-7032-5(8)) Kaplan Publishing.

Hariri. Hariri & Hariri Architecture: Buildings & Projects. 2010. (ENG., Illus.). 256p. 59.95 (978-1-86470-340-5(7), Images Publishing Dist Ac) Antique Collectors' Club GBR. Dist: National Bk. Network.

Harris, Bill. Five Hundred Buildings of New York. 2010. (ENG., Illus.). 608p. pap. 19.95 (978-1-57912-856-2(4), 1579128564) Black Dog & Leventhal Pubs., Inc.

Harris, Steven. True Life: Steven Harris Architects. 2010. (ENG., Illus.). 240p. 50.00 (978-1-56898-971-6(7)) Princeton Architectural Pr.

Hart, Steven. The Last Three Miles: Politics, Murder, & the Construction of America's First Superhighway. 2007. (ENG., Illus.). 216p. 24.95 (978-1-59558-098-6(0)) New Pr., The.

—Last Three Miles: Politics, Murder, & the Construction of America's First Superhighway. 2010. 216p. 25.00 (978-1-4379-7480-5(5)) DIANE Publishing Co.

Harwood, John. The Interface: IBM & the Transformation of Corporate Design, 1945-1976. 2011. (Quadrant Book Ser.). (ENG., Illus.). 336p. 34.95 **(978-0-8166-7039-0(0))** Univ. of Minnesota Pr.

Hastings, Kirk. Doo Wop Motels: Architectural Treasures of the Wildwoods. 2007. (ENG., Illus.). 122p. pap. 19.95 (978-0-8117-3389-2(0)) Stackpole Bks.

Hayes, Richard W. The Yale Building Project: The First 40 Years. 2007. (ENG., Illus.). 272p. pap. 45.00 (978-0-300-12316-6(7)) Yale Univ. Pr.

Healy, Brian. Brian Healy: Commonplaces. 2008. (ENG., Illus.). 110p. pap. 24.95 (978-0-9793801-7-4(0)) Oro Editions.

Heckert, Virginia, et al. Some Aesthetic Decisions: The Photographs of Judy Fiskin. 2011. (ENG., Illus.). 368p. 50.00 **(978-1-60606-081-0(3)**, J. Paul Getty Museum) Getty Pubns.

Hendricks, J. & Taschen, Angelika, eds. New York Style: Exteriors, Interiors, Details. 25th ed. 2008. (Icons Ser.). (ENG., Illus.). 191p. 7.99 (978-3-8365-0773-8(0)) TASCHEN DEU. Dist: Ingram Pub. Services.

Henning, Randolph C. The Architecture of Alfred Browning Parker: Miami's Maverick Modernist. 2011. (ENG., Illus.). 400p. 50.00 (978-0-8130-3677-9(1)) Univ. Pr. of Florida.

Henry, George B. & Braden Albert, Linda. Friendsville. 2011. (Images of America Ser.). (Illus.). 128p. pap. 21.99 (978-0-7385-8238-2(7)) Arcadia Publishing.

Henry, Jay C. Architecture in Texas: 1895-1945. 2009. (ENG., Illus.). 382p. pap. 45.00 (978-0-292-72280-4(X)) Univ. of Texas Pr.

Hertzberg, Mark & Wright, Frank Lloyd. Frank Lloyd Wright's SC Johnson Research Tower. 2010. 80p. 19.95 (978-0-7649-5609-6(4)) Pomegranate Communications, Inc.

Hess, Alan. The Buildings. 2008. (Illus.). 312p. 75.00 (978-0-8478-3093-0(4)) Rizzoli International Pubns., Inc.

Hess, Stephen A., et al. Design Professional & Construction Manager Professional Liability Handbook. 2007. (Illus.). xxxvi, 643p. (978-1-59031-786-0(6)) American Bar Assn.

Hibbard, Don & Hibbard, Don J. Designing Paradise: The Allure of the Hawaiian Resort. 2006. (ENG., Illus.). 216p. 50.00 (978-1-56898-574-9(6)) Princeton Architectural Pr.

Hibbard, Don J., ed. Buildings of Hawaii. 2011. (Buildings of the United States Ser.). (ENG., Illus.). 352p. (gr. 17). 65.00 *(978-0-8139-3094-7(4))* Univ. Pr. of Virginia.

High Museum of Art Staff. John Portman: Art & Architecture. 2009. (ENG., Illus.). 160p. pap. 30.00 *(978-1-932543-30-8(9))* High Museum of Art.

Hildebrand, Grant. Suyama: A Complex Serenity. 2011. (ENG., Illus.). 176p. 75.00 *(978-0-295-99081-1(3))* Univ. of Washington Pr.

Hildebrandt, Rachel & Old York Road Historical Society. The Philadelphia Area Architecture of Horace Trumbauer. 2009. (Images of America Ser.). (Illus.). 128p. pap. 21.99 *(978-0-7385-6297-1(1))* Arcadia Publishing.

Hill, John. Guide to Contemporary New York City Architecture. 2011. (ENG., Illus.). 304p. pap. 29.95 *(978-0-393-73326-6(2)*, 73326) Norton, W. W. & Co., Inc.

Hilliard, Jerry E. An Antebellum Ozark Community & the Civil War: The Archeology of the Second Mount Comfort Church (3wa880), Washington County, Arkansas (1840-Ca. 1865) 2008. *(978-1-56349-102-3(8))* Arkansas Archeological Survey.

Hiltzik, Michael A. Colossus: The Turbulent, Thrilling Saga of the Building of Hoover Dam. 2011. (ENG.). 512p. pap. 17.00 *(978-1-4165-3217-0(X)*, Free Pr.) Free Pr.

Hines, Thomas S. Architecture of the Sun: Los Angeles Modernism, 1900-1970. 2010. (ENG., Illus.). 756p. 95.00 *(978-0-8478-3320-7(8))* Rizzoli International Pubns., Inc.

HKS Inc. Staff, contrib. by. HKS: Selected & Current Works. 2006. (Master Architect Series V: Vol. 5). (ENG., Illus.). 256p. 59.95 *(978-1-876907-00-6(2)*, Images Publishing Dist Ac) Antique Collectors' Club GBR. Dist: National Bk. Network.

Holl, Steven. Steven Holl: Architecture Spoken. 2007. (ENG., Illus.). 304p. 75.00 *(978-0-8478-2920-0(0))* Rizzoli International Pubns., Inc.

—Urbanisms: Working with Doubt. 2009. (ENG., Illus.). 176p. 55.00 *(978-1-56898-679-1(3))* Princeton Architectural Pr.

Holliday, Kathryn E. Leopold Eidlitz: Architecture & Idealism in the Gilded Age. 2008. (ENG., Illus.). 176p. 55.00 *(978-0-393-73239-9(8)*, 73239) Norton, W. W. & Co., Inc.

Hollis, Tim. Pizitz: Your Store. 2010. (ENG., Illus.). 128p. pap. 19.99 *(978-1-59629-993-1(2))* History Pr., The.

Holm, Bill. Cabins of Minnesota. 2007. (Illus.). 128p. 24.95 *(978-0-87351-549-8(8))* Minnesota Historical Society Pr.

Holmes, John R. The Story of Historic Fort Steuben. 2010. (Landmarks Ser.). 128p. pap. 19.99 *(978-1-59629-908-5(8))* History Pr., The.

Holth, Nathan. Chicago's Bridges. 2012. (Shire Library). (ENG., Illus.). 64p. pap. 9.95 ***(978-0-7478-1103-9(2))*** Shire Pubns., Ltd. GBR. Dist: Random Hse., Inc.

Holzman Moss Architects Staff, et al. Theaters 2: Partnerships in Facility Use, Operations, & Management. 2010. (ENG., Illus.). 228p. 75.00 *(978-1-86470-343-6(1))* Images Publishing Group AUS. Dist: National Bk. Network.

Home Heating Crisis: Field Hearing of the Committee on Health, Education, Labor, & Pensions, United States Senate, One Hundred Tenth Congress, Second Session, on Examining the Home Heating Crisis, Focusing on the Responsibility of Our National Government to Respond to the Needs of Families That Are Facing Enormous Personal Challenges, January 17, 2008 (Boston, MA) 2009. (Illus.). iii, 30p. *(978-0-16-083330-4(2)*, 552-070-39154-1) United States Government Printing Office.

Horn, Bradley, text. City Works 3: Student Work 2008-2009, the City College of New York - Bernard & Anne Spitzer School of Architecture. 2010. (Illus.). 160p. pap. 30.00 *(978-84-9936-191-8(9))* Loft Pubns. ESP. Dist: Prestel Publishing.

Hornbostel, Caleb & Wertheimer, Lester. Building Design & Construction Systems 2009. 2008. (ENG.). 288p. pap. 111.95 *(978-1-4277-7036-3(0))* Kaplan Publishing.

Horowitz, Louis J. & Sparkes, Boyden. The Towers of New York: The Memoirs of A Master Builder. 2011. 310p. 50.95 ***(978-1-258-08240-6(3))*** Literary Licensing, LLC.

Horwitz, Carolyn & Iannacci, Anthony, eds. New Tropical Classics: Hawaiian Homes by Shay Zak. 2011. (ENG.). 192p. 65.00 *(978-0-9823190-5-5(3))* Architecture Interiors Pr., Inc.

Howard, Lucia & Weingarten, David. Ranch Houses: Living the California Dream. 2009. (ENG., Illus.). 240p. 50.00 *(978-0-8478-3182-1(5))* Rizzoli International Pubns., Inc.

HRH Prince of Wales Staff, et al, contrib. by. Views of Seaside: Commentaries & Observations on a City of Ideas. 2008. (Illus.). 208p. 45.00 *(978-0-8478-3120-3(5))* Rizzoli International Pubns., Inc.

Hull, Brent & Franck, Christine. Traditional American Rooms: Celebrating Style, Craftsmanship, & Historic Woodwork. 2009. (Winterthur Style Sourcebook Ser.). (ENG.). 179p. pap. 35.00 *(978-1-56523-322-5(0))* Fox Chapel Publishing Co., Inc.

Images Publishing Editorial Staff & Beaver, Robyn, eds. R. M. Kliment & Frances Halsband Architects. 2008. (Master Architect Ser.: Vol. 7). (ENG., Illus.). 256p. 59.95 *(978-1-86470-130-2(7)*, Images Publishing Dist Ac) Antique Collectors' Club GBR. Dist: National Bk. Network.

Images Publishing Group & Beaver, Robyn. Hartman-Cox Architects. Beaver, Robyn, ed. 2009. (Master Architect Ser.). (ENG., Illus.). 256p. 85.00 *(978-1-920744-61-8(4))* Images Publishing Group AUS. Dist: National Bk. Network.

Images Publishing Staff, PUBLISHING. Ross Barney Architects: Process + Projects. 2007. (ENG., Illus.). 124p. 65.00 *(978-1-86470-229-3(X))* Images Publishing Group AUS. Dist: National Bk. Network.

Images Staff & Images. Interior Spaces of the USA & Canada: A Pictorial Review, Vol. 6. 2006. (ENG., Illus.). 224p. 55.00 *(978-1-86470-107-4(2))* Images Publishing Group AUS. Dist: National Bk. Network.

Incerti, Guido, et al. Diller + Scofidio (+ Renfro) The Ciliary Function - Works & Projects 1979-2007. 2007. (ENG., Illus.). 224p. 39.99 *(978-88-6130-067-5(7))* Skira Editore ITA. Dist: Random Hse., Inc.

International Code Council Staff. National Green Building Standard. 2009. (ENG., Illus.). 116p. pap. 35.95 *(978-0-86718-641-3(0))* BuilderBooks.

Jackson, Neil & Jackson, N. Pierre Koenig, 1925-2004: Living with Steel. 2007. (ENG., Illus.). 96p. pap. 9.99 *(978-3-8228-4891-3(3))* TASCHEN DEU. Dist: Ingram Pub. Services.

Jacobsen, Hugh Newell. Hugh Newell Jacobsen. 2007. (ENG., Illus.). 304p. 60.00 *(978-0-8478-2921-7(9))* Rizzoli International Pubns., Inc.

Jacoby, Kam & Ward, Cynthia Carbone. Layers: Composite Photographs from the Lompoc Valley. 2009. pap. *(978-1-61623-715-8(5))* Independent Pub.

Jakle, John A. & Sculle, Keith A. America's Main Street Hotels: Transiency & Community in the Early Auto Age. 2009. (ENG., Illus.). 232p. pap. 29.95 *(978-1-57233-655-1(2))* Univ. of Tennessee Pr.

Jeanfreau, Robert. The Story Behind the Stone. 2012. E-Book ***(978-1-4556-1520-9(X))***; (ENG., Illus.). 96p. pap. 19.95 ***(978-1-4556-1519-3(6))*** Pelican Publishing Co., Inc.

Jervis, John B. Report of John B Jervis in Relation to the Railroad Bridge over the Mississippi River, at Rock Island. 2011. 18p. pap. 11.99 ***(978-1-4181-9086-6(1))*** MPublishing.

Jhabvala, C. S. H. Old Delhi New York. 2008. (ENG., Illus.). 108p. 39.95 *(978-81-7436-573-6(7))* Roli Bks. Private, Ltd. IND. Dist: Ingram Pub. Services.

Jodidio, Philip. Meier. Gossel, Peter, ed. 2010. (ENG, FRE & GER., Illus.). 96p. pap. 9.99 *(978-3-8365-1545-0(8))* TASCHEN DEU. Dist: Ingram Pub. Services.

—Tadao Ando at Naoshima: Art Architecture Nature. 2009. (ENG., Illus.). 200p. 45.00 *(978-0-8478-3232-3(5))* Universe Publishing.

Jodidio, Philip & Strong, Janet Adams. I. M. Pei: Complete Works. 2008. (ENG., Illus.). 368p. 85.00 *(978-0-8478-3145-6(0))* Rizzoli International Pubns., Inc.

John, Roscoe & Robert. Legacies of Faith. 2009. 320p. pap. 19.95 *(978-0-87839-314-5(5))* North Star Pr. of St. Cloud.

Johnson, Philip. The Glass House. 2008. (ENG., Illus.). 80p. 25.00 *(978-2-7594-0167-3(7))* Assouline FRA. Dist: Perseus Distribution.

Jones, Will. How to Read New York: A Crash Course in Big Apple Architecture. 2012. (ENG., Illus.). 256p. pap. 17.95 ***(978-0-7893-2490-0(3))*** Universe Publishing.

Jones, Will. New Transport Architecture: Travel Hubs in the 21st Century. 2006. (ENG., Illus.). 272p. 50.00 *(978-1-84533-218-1(0)*, Mitchell Beazley) Octopus Publishing Group GBR. Dist: Hachette Bk. Group.

Jovanovic Weiss, Srdjan. Camp David: Spectacle of Retreat. 2009. 89p. pap. 34.95 *(978-0-557-04639-3(4))* Lulu Enterprises Inc.

Jr., William S. Caswell. Connecticut & Rhode Island Covered Bridges. 2011. (Images of America Ser.). (ENG., Illus.). 128p. pap. 21.99 ***(978-0-7385-7540-7(2))*** Arcadia Publishing.

Kaiser, Kaiser & Kaiser, Harvey H. The National Park Architecture Sourcebook. 2008. (ENG., Illus.). 608p. pap. 40.00 *(978-1-56898-742-2(0))* Princeton Architectural Pr.

Kamin, Blair. Terror & Wonder: Architecture in a Tumultuous Age. (Illus.). 320p. 2011. (ENG.). pap. 19.00 *(978-0-226-42312-8(3))* 2010. 30.00 *(978-0-226-42311-1(5))* Univ. of Chicago Pr.

Kaufman, William. The Grand American Home. 2008. (ENG., Illus.). 128p. 49.50 *(978-1-86470-181-4(1))* Images Publishing Group AUS. Dist: National Bk. Network.

Keegan, Edward & Chicago Architecture Foundation Staff. Chicago Architecture: 1885 to Today. 2008. (Universe Architecture Ser.). (ENG., Illus.). 224p. pap. 29.95 *(978-0-7893-1533-5(5))* Universe Publishing.

Keil, Robert. Little Boxes: The Architecture of a Classic Midcentury Suburb. 2006. (Illus.). 144p. 35.00 *(978-0-9779236-4-9(9))* Advection Media.

Keister, Douglas. Stories in Stone New York: A Field Guide to New York City Area Cemeteries & Their Residents, 1 vol. 2011. (ENG., Illus.). 256p. 24.99 *(978-1-4236-2102-7(6))* Gibbs Smith, Publisher.

—500 Bungalows. 2006. (ENG., Illus.). 508p. pap. 12.95 *(978-1-56158-842-8(3)*, Taunton) Taunton Pr., Inc.

Keister, Douglas, photos by. 500 Cottages. 2006. (ENG., Illus.). 509p. pap. 12.95 *(978-1-56158-843-5(1)*, Taunton) Taunton Pr., Inc.

Kelly, Nancy V. Rhinebeck's Historic Architecture. 2009. (America's Landmarks Ser.). (ENG., Illus.). 192p. pap. 19.99 *(978-1-59629-606-0(2))* History Pr., The.

Kennedy-Grant, Philip S., et al, eds. AIA New Jersey Guidebook: 150 Best Buildings & Places. 2011. (ENG., Illus.). 224p. pap. 29.95 *(978-0-8135-5126-5(9)*, Rivergate Bks.) Rutgers Univ. Pr.

Kennedy, Roger G. Hidden Cities: The Discovery & Loss of Ancient North American Cities. 2011. (ENG.). 384p. pap. 23.99 ***(978-1-4516-5875-0(3)***, Free Pr.) Free Pr.

Kerst, Adirenne Merola, et al. Rapid City: Historic Downtown Architecture. 2007. (Images of America Ser.). (Illus.). 128p. per. 19.99 *(978-0-7385-4140-2(0))* Arcadia Publishing.

Kieran, Stephen & Timberlake, James. Loblolly House: Elements of a New Architecture. 2008. (ENG., Illus.). 176p. 40.00 *(978-1-56898-747-7(1))* Princeton Architectural Pr.

Killory, Christine & Davids, Rene, eds. Details, Technology, & Form. 2012. (ENG., Illus.). 208p. 65.00 *(978-1-56898-953-2(9))* Princeton Architectural Pr.

Kimball, Fiske. Thomas Jefferson: Architect. (Illus.). 205p. reprint ed. lib. bdg. 98.00 *(978-0-7222-4666-5(8))* Library Reprints, Inc.

—Thomas Jefferson & the First Monument of the Classical Revival in America. (Illus.). 48p. reprint ed. lib. bdg. 88.00 *(978-0-7222-4659-7(5))* Library Reprints, Inc.

King, Bart. An Architectural Guidebook to Portland. 2nd ed. 2007. (Illus.). 320p. pap. 22.95 *(978-0-87071-191-6(1))* Oregon State Univ. Pr.

King, Robert Arthur. Animals in Stone: Architectural Sculpture in New York City. 2009. (ENG., Illus.). 144p. 24.95 *(978-0-393-73286-3(X)*, 73286) Norton, W. W. & Co., Inc.

Kipnis, Jeffrey & Mayne, Thom. Buildings & Projects, Vol. 5. 2009. (ENG., Illus.). 488p. 85.00 *(978-0-8478-3072-5(1))* Rizzoli International Pubns., Inc.

Klingman, John. New in New Orleans Architecture, 1 vol. 2012. (ENG., Illus.). 192p. 26.00 ***(978-1-4556-1537-7(4))*** Pelican Publishing Co., Inc.

Klingman, John P. New in New Orleans Architecture. 2012. E-Book ***(978-1-4556-1538-4(2))*** Pelican Publishing Co., Inc.

Knight, Richard. Saarinen's Quest: A Memoir of a Photographer. 2007. pap. 30.00 *(978-0-9746214-4-9(7))* Stout, William Pubs.

Knight, Vernon J., Jr., et al. Mound Excavations at Moundville: Architecture, Elites, & Social Order. 2010. (ENG., Illus.). 424p. 75.00 *(978-0-8173-1687-7(6))* Univ. of Alabama Pr.

Knoblock, Glenn A. Historic Iron & Steel Bridges in Maine, New Hampshire & Vermont. 2012. (ENG.). 218p. pap. 55.00 *(978-0-7864-4843-2(1))* McFarland & Co., Inc. Pubs.

Koenig, Gloria. Frey. Gossel, Peter, ed. 2008. (Basic Architecture Ser.). (ENG., Illus.). 96p. pap. 9.99 *(978-3-8228-4883-8(2))* TASCHEN DEU. Dist: Ingram Pub. Services.

Koerner, Stefan. Amerikanische Landschaften: J. B. Jackson in der deutschen Rezeption. 2010. (Sozialgeographische Bibliothek Ser.). (GER., Illus.). 111p. (C). pap. 37.00 *(978-3-515-09665-2(5))* Steiner, Franz Verlag Wiesbaden GmbH DEU. Dist: Brown, David Bk. Co., The.

Kohler, Sue & Scott, Pamela, eds. Designing the Nation's Capital: The 1901 Plan for Washington, DC. 2007. (Illus.). 370p. pap. 39.95 *(978-0-16-075223-0(X))* United States Government Printing Office.

Koltun, G. F. Annual Peak-Flow Frequency Characteristics & (Or) Peak Dam-Pool-Elevation Frequency Characteristics of Dry Dams & Selected Streamflow-Gaging Stations in the Great Miami River Basin, Ohio. 2009. (Illus.). iv, 15p. *(978-1-4113-2525-8(7))* United States Geological Survey.

Komiske, Bruce King, ed. Designing the World's Best Children's Hospital Volume 3: The Quest Continues. 2012. (ENG., Illus.). 224p. 70.00 ***(978-1-86470-339-9(3))*** Images Publishing Group AUS. Dist: National Bk. Network.

Komiske, Bruce King, ed. Heroes: The Story of Hasbro Children's Hospital. 2010. (ENG., Illus.). 124p. 30.00 *(978-1-86470-346-7(6))* Images Publishing Group AUS. Dist: National Bk. Network.

Kornblut, Arthur & Wertheimer, Lester. Construction Documents & Services 2009. 2008. (ENG.). 336p. pap. 111.95 *(978-1-4277-7038-7(7))* Kaplan Publishing.

Kos, Eric J. San Francisco Then & Now. 2nd ed. 2009. (Then & Now Thunder Bay Ser.). (ENG.). 144p. 19.95 *(978-1-60710-003-4(7)*, Thunder Bay Pr.) Advantage Pubs. Group.

Kroloff, Reed. Building Community: The Work of Eskew + Dumez + Ripple. 2011. (ENG., Illus.). 220p. 65.00 *(978-0-9826226-2-9(7))* Oro Editions.

Kumar, Rekha. Walkability of Neighborhoods. 2010. 80p. pap. *(978-3-8383-6601-2(8))* Lambert Academic Publishing.

Kuth, Byron, et al. Kuth/Ranieri Architects. 2010. (ENG., Illus.). 192p. pap. 40.00 *(978-1-56898-865-8(6))* Princeton Architectural Pr.

Kwas, Mary L. A Pictorial History of Arkansas's Old State House: Celebrating 175 Years. 2011. (ENG., Illus.). 334p. 49.95 *(978-1-55728-955-1(7))* Univ. of Arkansas Pr.

Kwinter, Sanford. Requiem: For the city at the end of the Millenium. 2010. (ENG.). 122p. pap. *(978-84-92861-20-0(7))* Actar Birkhauser Distribution.

Kylloe, Ralph. Rustic Elegance, 1 vol. 2010. (ENG., Illus.). 256p. 60.00 *(978-1-4236-0549-2(7)*, 1320865) Gibbs Smith, Publisher.

Langdalen, Erik Fenstad, et al, eds. Hamsun, Holl, Hamaroy. 2010. (Illus.). 96p. *(978-3-03778-214-9(5))* Lars Muller Pubs.

Langmead, Donald. Icons of American Architecture: From the Alamo to the World Trade Center, 2 vols. 2009. (Greenwood Icons Ser.). (Illus.). 632p. 175.00 *(978-0-313-34207-3(5)*, GR4207, Greenwood Pr.) Greenwood Publishing Group, Inc.

Larson, Jean Rehkamp. The Farmhouse: New Inspiration for the Classic American Home. 2006. (ENG., Illus.). 217p. pap. 21.95 *(978-1-56158-874-9(1)*, Taunton) Taunton Pr., Inc.

Latham, LaDonna & Hickman County Historical and Genealogical Society. Hickman County. 2010. (Images of America Ser.). (ENG., Illus.). 128p. pap. 21.99 *(978-0-7385-6675-7(6))* Arcadia Publishing.

Laughlin, Robert W. M. & Jurgensen, Melissa C. Kentucky's Covered Bridges. 2007. (Images of America Ser.). (ENG., Illus.). 128p. per. 21.99 *(978-0-7385-4404-5(3))* Arcadia Publishing.

Lavin, Sylvia, contrib. by. Coop Himmelb(l)au: Central Los Angeles High School No. 9 for the Visual & Performing Arts. 2010. (Illus.). 224p. 49.95 *(978-3-7913-4433-1(1))* Prestel Publishing.

Lawrence, Henry W. City Trees: A Historical Geography from the Renaissance Through the Nineteenth Century. 2008. (Center Bks.). (ENG., Illus.). 352p. (C). (gr. 13-17). pap. 35.00 *(978-0-8139-2800-5(1))* Univ. Pr. of Virginia.

Leeds, Valerie Ann. 101 Masterpieces of New York City: Must-See Works of Art & Architecture in the New York Metropolitan Area. 2009. (ENG., Illus.). 232p. pap. 15.95 *(978-1-59350-098-6(X))* Alyson Pubns.

Leedy, Walter C., Jr. Eric Mendelsohn's Park Synagogue: Architecture & Community. Pearman, Sara Jane, ed. 2011. (Sacred Landmarks Ser.). 192p. 45.00 *(978-1-60635-085-0(4))* Kent State Univ. Pr.

Leers, Andrea, et al. Made to Measure: The Architecture of Leers Weinzapfel Associates. 2011. (ENG., Illus.). 176p. 65.00 *(978-1-56898-957-0(1))* Princeton Architectural Pr.

LeFevre, Camille. Charles R. Stinson Architects: Compositions in Nature. Beaver, Robyn, ed. 2008. (Master Architect Ser.). (ENG., Illus.). 256p. 59.95 *(978-1-86470-299-6(0)*, Images Publishing Dist Ac) Antique Collectors' Club GBR. Dist: National Bk. Network.

Leffingwell, Randy. The American Barn. 2009. (ENG.). 192p. 12.99 *(978-0-7858-2586-9(X)*, 078582586X, Crestline) MBI Publishing Co. LLC.

Lekson, Stephen H. The Architecture of Chaco Canyon, New Mexico. 2007. (Chaco Canyon Ser.). (ENG.). 296p. pap. 29.95 *(978-0-87480-948-0(7))* Univ. of Utah Pr.

Lemon, Mark. The Illustrated Alamo 1836: A Photographic Journey. 2008. (ENG., Illus.). 176p. 49.95 *(978-1-933337-18-0(4))* State Hse. Pr.

Lepik, Andres & Stadler, Andreas, eds. Raimund Abraham & The Austrian Cultural Forum New York. 2011. (ENG., Illus.). 128p. 45.00 *(978-3-7757-2725-9(6))* Hatje Cantz Verlag GmbH & Co KG DEU. Dist: D.A.P./Distributed Art Pubs.

Leppo, RA/CID, LEED AP, Holly Williams & Ballast, David Kent. Construction Documents & Services: ARE Sample Problems & Practice Exam. 2nd ed. 2011. (ENG.). 114p. pap. 120.00 *(978-1-59126-323-4(9))* Professional Pubns., Inc.

—Programming, Planning & Practice: ARE Sample Problems & Practice Exam. 2nd ed. 2010. (ENG.). 102p. pap. 120.00 *(978-1-59126-327-2(1))* Professional Pubns., Inc.

Leroux, John. Building a University: The Architecture of UNB. 2010. (ENG., Illus.). 144p. pap. 29.95 *(978-0-86492-623-4(5))* Goose Lane Editions CAN. Dist: Univ. of Toronto Pr.

Leslie, Thomas. Iowa State Fair: Country Comes to Town. 2007. (ENG., Illus.). 168p. pap. 19.95 *(978-1-56898-568-8(1))* Princeton Architectural Pr.

Leung, Yathim. Rethink Dc Metro Stations. 2010. 72p. pap. *(978-3-8383-6665-4(4))* Lambert Academic Publishing.

Leven, David D. & Betts, Stella. Leven Betts: Pattern Recognition. 2008. (ENG., Illus.). 192p. pap. 40.00 *(978-1-56898-782-8(X))* Princeton Architectural Pr.

Levy, Shanti, et al, eds. Lunch: Dialect, Vol. 2. 2007. (Illus.). 152p. per. 10.95 *(978-0-9771024-4-0(0))* Univ. of Virginia Schl. of Architecture.

Lewis, Diane. Inside-Out: Architecture New York City, 1 vol. 2006. (ENG., Illus.). 160p. pap. 45.00 *(978-88-8158-585-4(5))* Charta ITA. Dist: D.A.P./Distributed Art Pubs.

Lewis, Hilary & Vinoly, Roman. Think New York: A Ground Zero Diary. 2006. (ENG., Illus.). 328p. 65.00 *(978-1-920744-74-8(6))* Images Publishing Group AUS. Dist: National Bk. Network.

Lind, Diana. Brooklyn Modern: Architecture, Interiors & Design. 2008. (ENG., Illus.). 226p. 45.00 *(978-0-8478-3043-5(8))* Rizzoli International Pubns., Inc.

—Brooklyn Modern: Stories of Architecture & Design. 2008. (ENG., Illus.). 240p. 45.00 *(978-0-8478-3045-9(4))* Rizzoli International Pubns., Inc.

Linden, Blanche M. G. Silent City on a Hill: Picturesque Landscapes of Memory & Boston's Mount Auburn Cemetery. 2007. (Illus.). 373p. per. 39.95 *(978-1-55849-571-5(1))* Univ. of Massachusetts Pr.

Linton, Meg, text. Gary Lang: Hybrid Variations. 2008. (Illus.). 72p. per. 20.00 *(978-0-9800962-0-0(0))* Cella, Edward Art+Architecture.

Little, M. Ruth. The Town & Gown Architecture of Chapel Hill, North Carolina, 1795-1975. 2006. (Distributed for the Preservation Society of Chapel Hill Ser.). (ENG., Illus.). 320p. 27.95 *(978-0-8078-3072-7(0))* Univ. of North Carolina Pr.

Little, Margaret Ruth. Carolina Cottage: A Personal History of the Piazza House. 2010. (ENG., Illus.). 152p. 22.95 *(978-0-8139-3009-1(X))* Univ. Pr. of Virginia.

Long, George. Katrina Days: Life in New Orleans after Hurricane Katrina. 2007. (Illus.). 83p. 51.99 *(978-1-4257-8751-6(7))* Xlibris Corp.

Longhurst, John & Bethards, Jack M. Magnum Opus: The Building of the Schoenstein Organ at the Conference Center of the Church of Jesus Christ of Latter-Day Saints, Salt Lake City. 2009. *(978-1-60641-199-5(3)*, Deseret Bk. Co.

Lordi, Joseph A. Las Vegas, New Mexico. 2010. (Illus.). 148p. pap. 26.99 ***(978-0-9755718-1-1(8))*** Cartolina Pr.

Loring, John. Joseph Urban. 2010. (ENG., Illus.). 224p. 50.00 *(978-0-8109-9026-5(1))* Abrams.

Lounsbury, Carl. Essays in Early American Architectural History: A View from the Chesapeake. 2011. (ENG., Illus.). 288p. (gr. 17). 65.00 *(978-0-8139-3110-4(X))* Univ. Pr. of Virginia.

Lounsbury, Carl R. Essays in Early American Architectural History: A View from the Chesapeake. 2011. (ENG., Illus.). 288p. (C). (gr. 13-17). pap. 35.00 *(978-0-8139-3229-3(7))* Univ. Pr. of Virginia.

Lovell, Jennifer Wendler & Loevy, Robert D. Exploring the Old North End Neighborhood of Colorado Springs: A Guide to its History & Architecture. 2011. (Illus.). pap. 19.95 ***(978-0-615-44430-7(X))*** Old North End Neighborhood (ONEN).

Lowe, David Garrard. Lost Chicago. 2010. (ENG., Illus.). 272p. pap. 35.00 *(978-0-226-49432-6(2))* Univ. of Chicago Pr.

Lucas, John Paul. Eidos: Angels & Archetypes in Architecture. 2008. 72p. pap. 29.34 *(978-1-4343-9794-2(7))* AuthorHouse.

Lukez, Paul. Suburban Transformations. Lukez, Paul, ed. 2007. (ENG., Illus.). 192p. pap. 40.00 *(978-1-56898-683-8(1))* Princeton Architectural Pr.

Lund, Virginia Llego. George Washington Frank's Stone House on the Nebraska Prairie. 2010. 104p. pap. 29.36 *(978-1-4269-1102-6(5))* Trafford Publishing.

Lusk, Paul. Building to Endure: Design Lessons of Arid Lands. Simon, Alf, ed. 2009. (ENG., Illus.). 310p. (C). 45.00 *(978-0-8263-4797-8(5))* Univ. of New Mexico Pr.

Lynn, Catherine & Penabad, Carie. Marion Manley: Miami's First Woman Architect. 2010. (ENG., Illus.). 248p. pap. 34.95 *(978-0-8203-3406-6(5))* Univ. of Georgia Pr.

Lynn, Greg & Rappolt, Mark, eds. Form. 2008. (ENG., Illus.). 360p. 55.00 *(978-0-8478-3102-9(7))* Rizzoli International Pubns., Inc.

MacLean, Alex. Up on the Roof: New York's Hidden Skyline Spaces. 2012. (ENG., Illus.). 240p. 50.00 ***(978-1-61689-050-6(9))*** Princeton Architectural Pr.

MacLennan, Cheryl. Historic Homes of Jefferson, Texas. 2011. E-Book ***(978-1-4556-1485-1(8))***; (ENG.). 96p. 25.00 *(978-1-4556-1484-4(X))* Pelican Publishing Co., Inc.

Madge, James & Peckham, Andrew, eds. Narrating Architecture: A Retrospective Anthology. 2006. (ENG., Illus.). 516p. (C). per. 55.95 *(978-0-415-38564-0(4))* Routledge.

Mahoney, Patrick J. Frank Lloyd Wright's Walter V. Davidson House: An Examination of a Buffalo Home & Its Cousins from Coast to Coast. 2011. (Illus.). 144p. 44.99 ***(978-0-9824261-3-5(5))***; pap. 34.99 ***(978-0-9824261-4-2(3))*** Buffalo State College, E.H. Butler Library.

Maki, Fumihiko & Pran, Peter C. Peter Pran: Realizations. 2007. (Master Architect Ser.). (ENG., Illus.). 224p. 59.95 *(978-1-86470-194-4(3)*, Images Publishing Dist Ac) Antique Collectors' Club GBR. Dist: National Bk. Network.

Maloof, John. Portage Park. 2008. (Images of America Ser.). (ENG., Illus.). 128p. pap. 21.99 *(978-0-7385-5229-3(1))* Arcadia Publishing.

Maltzan, Michael. Michael Maltzan: No More Play. Varner, Jessica, ed. 2011. (ENG., Illus.). 240p. pap. 50.00 ***(978-3-7757-2846-1(5))*** Hatje Cantz Verlag GmbH & Co KG DEU. Dist: D.A.P./Distributed Art Pubs.

Manhattan Township Historical Society (Ill.) Staff, contrib. by. Manhattan Memories. 2008. (Illus.). 240p. *(978-0-615-24442-6(4))* Manhattan Township Historical.

Maniaque-Benton, Caroline. French Encounters with the American Counterculture, 1960-1980. 2011. (Ashgate Studies in Architecture Ser.). (Illus.). 244p. 99.95 *(978-1-4094-2386-7(7))* Ashgate Publishing Co.

Mann, Nicholas. The Sacred Geometry of Washington, D. C. The Integrity & Power of the Original Design. 2006. (ENG., Illus.). 200p. per. *(978-0-9547230-7-1(4))* Green Magic Pubs.

Marjanovic, Igor, et al. Marina City: Bertrand Goldberg's Urban Vision. 2010. (ENG., Illus.). 176p. pap. 35.00 *(978-1-56898-863-4(X))* Princeton Architectural Pr.

Marmol, Leo & Radziner, Ron. Marmol Radziner + Associates: Between Architecture & Construction. 2008. (ENG., Illus.). 176p. pap. 40.00 *(978-1-56898-744-6(7))* Princeton Architectural Pr.

Marter, Joan. The Grove Encyclopedia of American Art, 5 vols., Set. 2011. (ENG., Illus.). 2608p. 1045.00 *(978-0-19-533579-8(1))* Oxford Univ. Pr., Inc.

Martin, Ernest O. The Beauty of Holiness: Story of the Wayfarers Chapel. 2007. (Illus.). 96p. *(978-1-57864-404-9(6))* Donning Co. Pubs.

Martin, Mary & Roseberry, Dinah. Greetings from Cincinnati. 2007. (Illus.). 128p. pap. 24.95 *(978-0-7643-2561-8(2))* Schiffer Publishing, Ltd.

Marzlock, Ronald. The New York World's Fairs: Queens County Emerging Gateway to the World. 2007. 80p. per. *(978-0-9791607-1-4(5))* Icon Archives, Inc.

Massey, Jonathan. Crystal & Arabesque: Claude Bragdon, Ornament, & Modern Architecture. 2009. (ENG., Illus.). 352p. (C). 59.95 *(978-0-8229-4362-4(X))* Univ. of Pittsburgh Pr.

Masson, Kathryn. Stables: Beautiful Paddocks, Horse Barns, & Tack Rooms. 2010. (ENG., Illus.). 256p. 55.00 *(978-0-8478-3314-6(3))* Rizzoli International Pubns., Inc.

Mathewson, Casey C. M. & Viderksen, Ann, eds. A5 Architecture Series: Los Angeles. 2010. (A5 Architecture Ser.). (ENG., Illus.). 440p. 60.00 *(978-0-9819857-1-8(8))* Oro Editions.

May, Vonn Marie, et al. Celebrating the Cultural Landscape Heritage of Mills College: Using the Past to Inform Campus Planning & Design. 2008. (Illus.). 159p. per. 18.00 *(978-0-9648938-6-3(X))* Mills College, Ctr. for the Bk.

Maynard, W. Barksdale. Buildings of Delaware. 2008. (Buildings of the United States Ser.). (ENG., Illus.). 376p. (gr. 17). 45.00 *(978-0-8139-2702-2(1))* Univ. Pr. of Virginia.

McBrien, Judith Paine. Pocket Guide to Miami Architecture. 2012. (Norton Pocket Guides). (ENG., Illus.). 144p. pap. 24.95 ***(978-0-393-73306-8(8)***, 73306) Norton, W. W. & Co., Inc.

McClure, Michael. Artifact: A Cultural Geography of Wyoming. 2008. (Illus.). 124p. *(978-1-928786-03-0(0))* Wig Raf Publishing, Inc.

McCulloch, Janelle. Dream Hotels USA & the Bahamas: Architectural Hideaways. 2009. (ENG., Illus.). 248p. 60.00 *(978-1-86470-320-7(2))* Images Publishing Group AUS. Dist: National Bk. Network.

McCulloch, Janelle & Boschetti, Joe. American Spaces: An Overview of What's New. McCulloch, Janelle, ed. 2007. (ENG., Illus.). 224p. 55.00 *(978-1-86470-186-9(2))* Images Publishing Group AUS. Dist: National Bk. Network.

McDowell, Steve & Lake, David. BNIM Architects: Nurture: the School of Nursing & Student Community Center. 2007. (ENG., Illus.). 108p. pap. 25.00 *(978-0-9793801-1-2(1))* Oro Editions.

McDowell, Steve & Payne, Andrew. BNIM Architects: Symbiosis the Fayez S. Sarofim Research Building, Building Monograph Series. 2007. (ENG., Illus.). 108p. pap. 25.00 *(978-0-9793801-0-5(3))* Oro Editions.

McGlade, Dennis C., et al. Olin: Placemaking. 2008. (ENG., Illus.). 320p. 65.00 *(978-1-58093-210-3(X))* Monacelli Pr., Inc.

Mead, Christopher Curtis. The Architecture of Bart Prince: A Pragmatics of Place. 2nd rev. ed. 2010. (ENG., Illus.). 208p. pap. 39.95 *(978-0-393-73312-9(2)*, 73312) Norton, W. W. & Co., Inc.

Meier, Richard. Richard Meier, Architect, Vol. 5. 2009. (ENG., Illus.). 432p. 80.00 *(978-0-8478-3069-5(1))*; pap. 55.00 *(978-0-8478-3273-6(2))* Rizzoli International Pubns., Inc.

Meier, Richard & text. Das Museum Frieder Burda von Richard Meier. 2011. (ENG., Illus.). 144p. 30.00 ***(978-3-7757-2812-6(0))*** Hatje Cantz Verlag GmbH & Co KG DEU. Dist: D.A.P./Distributed Art Pubs.

Meister, Chris & Gordon, James Riely. James Riely Gordon: His Courthouses & Other Public Architecture. 2011. 384p. 49.95 ***(978-0-89672-691-8(6))*** Texas Tech Univ. Pr.

Melikian, Robert A. Vanishing Phoenix. 2010. (Images of America Ser.). (Illus.). 128p. pap. 21.99 *(978-0-7385-7881-1(9))* Arcadia Publishing.

Mellins, Thomas & Albrecht, Donald. The American Style. 2011. (ENG., Illus.). 224p. 50.00 *(978-1-58093-285-1(1))* Monacelli Pr., Inc.

Menago, Marilyn. Princeton: History & Architecture. 2007. (Illus.). 128p. pap. 29.95 *(978-0-7643-2626-4(0))* Schiffer Publishing, Ltd.

Menges, Axel, comment. Som: Architecture of Skidmore, Owings & Merrill, 1963-1973. 2009. (ENG., Illus.). 264p. 50.00 *(978-1-58093-221-9(5))* Monacelli Pr., Inc.

Mertins, Detlef, intro. Som: Architecture of Skidmore, Owings & Merrill, 1984-1996. 2009. (ENG., Illus.). 224p. 60.00 *(978-1-58093-223-3(1))* Monacelli Pr., Inc.

Milano, Kenneth W. Historic Cemeteries of Kensington & Fishtown: Palmer, Hanover & West Street Burial Grounds. 2011. 128p. pap. 19.99 *(978-1-60949-242-7(0))* History Pr., The.

Miller, Alex. California Theme Parks. 2010. (Illus.). 128p. pap. 19.99 *(978-0-7643-3478-8(6))* Schiffer Publishing, Ltd.

Miller, Lynden B. & Miller. Parks, Plants, & People: Beautifying the Urban Landscape. 2009. (ENG., Illus.). 208p. 49.95 *(978-0-393-73203-0(7)*, 73203) Norton, W. W. & Co., Inc.

Miller, Marcia M. & Rideout, Orlando, 5th, eds. Architecture in Annapolis: A Field Guide. 25.00 *(978-1-878399-79-3(9))* Division of Historical & Cultural Programs/Maryland Historical Trust Pr.

Miller, Paul. Lost Newport. 2010. 140p. pap. 19.95 *(978-1-4290-9112-1(6))* Applewood Bks.

Miller, Robert L. David M. Schwarz Architects: 2002-2007. 2008. (ENG., Illus.). 240p. pap. 50.00 *(978-0-9679143-5-0(3))* Grayson Publishing.

Miller, Tamara Gaskell, ed. The President's House in Philadelphia: A Reprint of the Pennsylvania Magazine of History & Biography. 2006. (Illus.). 143p. pap. 20.00 *(978-1-4223-5881-8(X))* DIANE Publishing Co.

Millett, Larry. AIA Guide to Downtown Minneapolis. 2010. (ENG.). 128p. pap. 15.95 *(978-0-87351-720-1(2))* Minnesota Historical Society Pr.

—AIA Guide to Downtown St. Paul. 2010. (ENG.). 128p. pap. 15.95 *(978-0-87351-721-8(0))* Minnesota Historical Society Pr.

—AIA Guide to St. Paul's Summit Avenue & Hill District. 2009. (ENG., Illus.). 128p. pap. 15.95 *(978-0-87351-644-0(3))* Minnesota Historical Society Pr.

—AIA Guide to the Minneapolis Lake District. 2009. (ENG., Illus.). 128p. pap. 15.95 *(978-0-87351-645-7(1))* Minnesota Historical Society Pr.

—Aia Guide to the Twin Cities: The Essential Source on the Architecture of Minneapolis & St. Paul. 2007. (Illus.). 448p. per. 29.95 *(978-0-87351-540-5(4))* Minnesota Historical Society Pr.

—Disappearance of Sherlock Holmes. 2012. (Fesler-Lampert Minnesota Heritage Ser.). (Illus.). 352p. pap. 14.95 ***(978-0-8166-6993-6(7))*** Univ. of Minnesota Pr.

—Once There Were Castles: Lost Mansions & Estates of the Twin Cities. 2011. (ENG., Illus.). 376p. 39.95 ***(978-0-8166-7430-5(2))*** Univ. of Minnesota Pr.

Minardi, Joseph. Historic Architecture in West Philadelphia, 1789-1930s. 2011. (Illus.). 192p. *(978-0-7643-3771-0(8)*, Schiffer Publishing Ltd) Schiffer Publishing, Ltd.

Minor, Woodruff. The Architecture of Ratcliff. 2007. (Illus.). 160p. 39.95 *(978-1-59714-042-3(2))* Heyday.

Mires, Peter. Bayou Built: The Legacy of Louisiana's Historic Architecture. 2010. 176p. pap. 15.95 *(978-1-4502-6367-2(4))* iUniverse, Inc.

Mitchell, Ann, photos by. Austin Val Verde: Impressions of a Montecito Masterpiece. 2007. (ENG., Illus.). 144p. 50.00 *(978-1-890449-31-5(8))* Balcony Pr.

Mitchell, William Ford. Buildings As History: A Descriptive Catalogue of His Drawings in the Henderson County Public Library: the Architecture of Erle Stillwell. 2006. per. *(978-0-9790753-1-5(9))* Friends of the Henderson County Public Library.

—Builtings as History: A Descriptive Catalogue of His Drawings in the Henderson County Public Library: the Architecture of Erle Stillwell. 2006. *(978-0-9790753-0-8(0))* Friends of the Henderson County Public Library.

Mobarak, Christyn. Buffalo As an Architectural Museum. 2009. 154p. pap. *(978-3-639-17788-6(6))* VDM Verlag Dr. Mueller e.K.

Mod, Anna. Building Modern Houston. 2012. (Images of America Ser.). (ENG., Illus.). 128p. pap. 21.99 ***(978-0-7385-8524-6(6))*** Arcadia Publishing.

Moe, Kiel. Integrated Design in Contemporary Architecture. 2008. (ENG., Illus.). 208p. 65.00 *(978-1-56898-745-3(5))* Princeton Architectural Pr.

Moeller, G. Martin, Jr. AIA Guide to the Architecture of Washington, D. C. 4th ed. 2006. (ENG., Illus.). 400p. per. 22.95 *(978-0-8018-8468-9(3))* Johns Hopkins Univ. Pr.

—AIA Guide to the Architecture of Washington, D. C. 4th ed. 2006. (ENG., Illus.). 400p. 41.00 *(978-0-8018-8467-2(5))* Johns Hopkins Univ. Pr.

Moeller, G. Martin, Jr. & Fitch, Mary. AIA Guide to the Architecture of Washington, D. C. 5th ed. 2012. (ENG., Illus.). 328p. 50.00 ***(978-1-4214-0269-7(6))***; pap. 24.95 ***(978-1-4214-0270-3(X))*** Johns Hopkins Univ. Pr.

Mohr, Marsha Williamson. Indiana Barns. 2010. (ENG., Illus.). 152p. 29.95 *(978-0-253-35568-3(0)*, 0253355680, Quarry Bks.) Indiana Univ. Pr.

Moore, Andrew, photos by. Andrew Moore: Detroit Disassembled, Limited Edition. 2010. (ENG., Illus.). 128p. 750.00 *(978-88-6208-140-5(5))* Damiani ITA. Dist: D.A.P./Distributed Art Pubs.

Moore, Margaret. Complete Charleston: A Guide to the Architecture, History, Gardens & Food of Charleston, 1. 4th ed. 2007. (Illus.). 324p. (YA). per. *(978-0-9660144-3-3(X))* TM Photography, Inc.

Moorhead, Gerald, illus. Buildings of Texas: Central, South, & Gulf Coast. 2013. (Buildings of the United States Ser.). (ENG.). 704p. (gr. 17). 85.00 ***(978-0-8139-3255-2(6))*** Univ. Pr. of Virginia.

Morgan, William. Monadnock Summer: The Architectural Legacy of Dublin, New Hampshire. 2011. 176p. pap. 29.95 *(978-1-56792-422-0(0))* Godine, David R. Pub.

Mori, Toshiko. Toshiko Mori Architect. 2008. (ENG., Illus.). 216p. (gr. 12). 50.00 *(978-1-58093-191-5(X))* Monacelli Pr., Inc.

Morrison, Hugh. Early American Architecture: From the First Colonial Settlements to the National Period. 2011. (Dover Architecture Ser.). (ENG., Illus.). 640p. reprint ed. pap. 19.95 *(978-0-486-25492-0(5))* Dover Pubns., Inc.

Morrone, Francis, et al. The Municipal Art Society of New York: 10 Architectural Walks in Manhattan. Lynn, Robyn, ed. 2009. (ENG., Illus.). 304p. pap. 29.95 *(978-0-393-73257-3(6)*, 73257) Norton, W. W. & Co., Inc.

Moss, Roger W. & Crane, Tom. Historic Landmarks of Philadelphia. 2008. (Illus.). 320p. 34.95 *(978-0-8122-4106-8(1))* Univ. of Pennsylvania Pr.

Mulligan. The New Californian Architecture. 2009. (Illus.). 192p. pap. 73.50 *(978-0-415-40059-6(7))* Routledge.

Mumford, Eric Paul. Defining Urban Design: CIAM Architects & the Formation of a Discipline, 1937-69. 2009. (Illus.). 262p. 55.00 *(978-0-300-13888-7(1))* Yale Univ. Pr.

Munro, Sarah Baker. Timberline Lodge: The History, Art, & Craft of an American Icon. 2009. (ENG., Illus.). 232p. 34.95 *(978-0-88192-856-3(9)*, 0881928569) Timber Pr., Inc.

Myers, Catherine. The Pass We Remember. 2011. (ENG.). 122p. pap. 0.00 *(978-0-9834136-0-8(6))* No Waste Publishing.

Myers, Tracy. Deborah Berke. 2008. (ENG., Illus.). 240p. 65.00 *(978-0-300-13439-1(8))* Yale Univ. Pr.

Nasar, Jack L. Design by Competition: Making Design Competition Work. 2006. (Environment & Behavior Ser.). (ENG., Illus.). 260p. pap. 53.00 *(978-0-521-02970-4(8))* Cambridge Univ. Pr.

Nash, Eric Peter. Manhattan Skyscrapers. 3rd ed. 2010. (ENG., Illus.). 240p. 50.00 *(978-1-56898-967-9(9))* Princeton Architectural Pr.

Nauman, Robert Allan. On the Wings of Modernism: The United States Air Force Academy. 2008. (ENG., Illus.). 192p. pap. 25.95 *(978-0-252-07515-5(3))* Univ. of Illinois Pr.

Naylor, David. Railroad Stations: The Buildings That Linked the Nation. 2011. (Library of Congress Visual Sourcebooks Ser.). (ENG., Illus.). 336p. 75.00 *(978-0-393-73164-4(2)*, 73164) Norton, W. W. & Co., Inc.

NC State University College of Design. School of Design: Reflections & Recollections: the Kamphoefner Years 1948-1973. 2007. (ENG.). 148p. 19.95 *(978-0-9776635-3-8(1))* NC State Univ. College of Design Pubn.

NCCER. Sustainable Construction Supervisor. rev. ed. 2011. (ENG.). 160p. (C). pap. 66.67 *(978-0-13-215415-4(3))* Pearson Education Canada CAN. Dist: Pearson Education.

Neil, Erik H. & Wayne, Kenneth, eds. Long Island Moderns: Art & Architecture on the North Shore & Beyond. 2009. (Illus.). 128p. pap. 29.95 *(978-1-879195-15-8(1))* Heckscher Museum of Art.

Nelson, Wendell R. Farmhouse in Town: The Turner House of Amherst, Wisconsin. 2007. (Illus.). 36p. pap. 8.95 *(978-0-9746599-5-4(9))* Hawkweed Hollow Pr.

Nettleton, Sarah & Martin, Frank Edgerton. The Simple Home: The Luxury of Enough. 2007. (American Institute Architects Ser.). (ENG., Illus.). 249p. 40.00 *(978-1-56158-831-2(8)*, Taunton) Taunton Pr., Inc.

Neumann, Dietrich, ed. The Structure of Light: Richard Kelly & the Illumination of Modern Architecture. 2011. (Illus.). 224p. 60.00 *(978-0-300-16370-4(3))* Yale Univ. Pr.

Newcomb, Rexford. Architecture of the Old Northwest Territory: A Study of Early Architecture in Ohio, Indiana, Illinois, Michigan, Wisconsin, & Part of Minnesota. 2011. 294p. 48.95 ***(978-1-258-01427-8(0))*** Literary Licensing, LLC.

Newcomb, Rexford. Spanish-Colonial Architecture in the United States. (Illus.). 39p. reprint ed. lib. bdg. 88.00 *(978-0-7222-0212-8(1))* Library Reprints, Inc.

Newman, Morris. Responsive Architecture: Moody Nolan Recent Work. 2008. (ENG., Illus.). 120p. pap. 29.95 *(978-1-890449-46-9(6))* Balcony Pr.

Ngo, Dung. Tom Kundig: Houses. 2006. (ENG., Illus.). 176p. 40.00 *(978-1-56898-605-0(X))* Princeton Architectural Pr.

Nichols, Frederick D. & O'Neal, William B. Architecture in Virginia, 1776-1958: The Old Dominion's Twelve Best Buildings. 2011. 42p. 35.95 ***(978-1-258-06534-8(7))*** Literary Licensing, LLC.

Nickel, Richard, et al. The Complete Architecture of Adler & Sullivan. 2010. (Illus.). 472p. 95.00 *(978-0-9660273-2-7(9))* Nickel, Richard Committee, The.

Niles, Philip. Beauty of the City: A. E. Doyle, Portland's Architect. 2008. (ENG., Illus.). 352p. (C). pap. 29.95 *(978-0-87071-298-2(5))* Oregon State Univ. Pr.

NMH School & Hamilton, eds. Lift Thine Eyes: The Landscape, the Buildings, the Heritage of Northfield Mount Heron School. 2010. 50.00 *(978-0-615-39071-0(4))* NMH Schl.

Nordahl, Darrin. My Kind of Transit: Rethinking Public Transportation in America. 2009. (ENG., Illus.). 176p. 35.00 *(978-1-930066-88-5(0))* Ctr. for American Places, Inc.

Nuxhall, Phillip J. Beauty in the Grove: Spring Grove Cemetery & Arboretum. 2009. *(978-1-933197-52-4(8))* Orange Frazer Pr.

O'Brien, Patricia J. The Architects & Buildings of Manhattan, Kansas. 2008. (Illus.). vii, 172p. *(978-0-9677686-7-0(5))*; pap. *(978-0-9677686-6-3(7))* Riley County Historical Society.

Ochsner, Jeffrey Karl. Lionel H. Pries: Architect, Artist, Educator: from Arts & Crafts to Modern Architecture. 2007. (Illus.). 384p. 60.00 *(978-0-295-98698-2(0))* Univ. of Washington Pr.

Ockman, Joan & Williamson, Rebecca. Architecture School: Three Centuries of Educating Architects in North America. 2012. (ENG., Illus.). 400p. (gr. 17). 50.00 ***(978-0-262-01708-4(3))*** MIT Pr.

O'Donnell, Anne. Motawi Tileworks: Contemporary Handcrafted Tiles in the Arts & Crafts Tradition. 2008. 112p. 29.95 *(978-0-7649-4598-4(X))* Pomegranate Communications, Inc.

O'Gorman, James F. Henry Austin: In Every Variety of Architectural Style. 2009. (ENG., Illus.). 252p. 35.00 *(978-0-8195-6896-0(1))* Wesleyan Univ. Pr.

O'Gorman, James F. & Condon, Lorna. Drawing Toward Home: Designs for Domestic Architecture from Historic New England. 2010. 59.95 *(978-0-88448-328-1(2))* Tilbury Hse. Pubs.

Olmsted, Frederick Law. The Papers of Frederick Law Olmsted: Parks, Politics, & Patronage, 1874-1882, Volume 7. Beveridge, Charles E. et al, eds. 2007. (Papers of Frederick Law Olmsted Ser.). (ENG., Illus.). 784p. (gr. 17). 85.00 *(978-0-8018-8336-1(9))* Johns Hopkins Univ. Pr.

O'Neill, Patrick L. Virginia's Presidential Homes. 2010. (Images of America Ser.). (Illus.). 128p. pap. 21.99 *(978-0-7385-8608-3(0))* Arcadia Publishing.

Onwukwe, Rosemarie. Bloomingdale. 2010. (Images of America Ser.). (ENG., Illus.). 128p. pap. 21.99 *(978-0-7385-6610-8(1))* Arcadia Publishing.

Oosterlynck, Stijn, et al, eds. Strategic Spatial Projects: Catalysts for Change. 2010. (RTPI Library Ser.). (ENG., Illus.). 256p. (C). 165.00 *(978-0-415-56683-4(5))*; pap. 53.95 *(978-0-415-56684-1(3))* Routledge.

Options & Opportunities for Onsite Renewable Energy Integration: Field Hearing Before the Committee on Science & Technology, House of Representatives, One Hundred Eleventh Congress, Second Session, November 15, 2010. 2010. (Illus.). iv, 65p. ***(978-0-16-088291-3(5)***, 552-070-42596-9) United States Government Printing Office.

Ortega, Lluís. GSD 08 Platform. 2008. 24.95 *(978-1-934510-16-2(5))* Harvard Univ. Pr.

Osborne, Mike, photos by. San Antonio's Spanish Missions: A Portrait. 2009. *(978-1-893271-53-1(6))*; (Illus.). 120p. 39.95 *(978-1-893271-52-4(8))* Maverick Publishing Co.

Ozer, Mark N. Northwest Washington, D. C. Tales from West of the Park. 2011. 160p. pap. 19.99 ***(978-1-60949-363-9(X))*** History Pr., The.

Paganelli, Carlo. Hagy Belzberg: Structures & Metaphores. 2007. (Architectural Ser.). (ENG., Illus.). 100p. pap. 25.00 *(978-88-7838-083-7(0)*, Art Stock Bks. Ltd/Csi) Continental Sales, Inc.

Painter, Sue Ann. Architecture in Cincinnati: An Illustrated History of Designing & Building an American City. 2006. (Illus.). 344p. 70.00 *(978-0-8214-1700-3(2))* Ohio Univ. Pr.

—Architecture in Cincinnati: An Illustrated History of Designing & Building an American City. 2006. (Illus.). 344p. per. 35.00 *(978-0-8214-1701-0(0))* Ohio Univ. Pr.

Palmer, Daniel J. Rochester's Downtown Architecture: 1950-1975. 2010. (Images of America Ser.). (Illus.). 128p. pap. 21.99 *(978-0-7385-7250-5(0))* Arcadia Publishing.

Panache Partners LLC Staff, ed. Atlanta: An Architectural Perspective of Atlanta. 2008. (City by Design Ser.). (ENG., Illus.). 250p. 34.95 *(978-1-933415-47-5(9))* Panache Partners, LLC.

Panache Partners LLC., Staff, ed. City by Dallas: An Architectural Perspective of the Dallas, Texas Area. 2008. (City by Design Ser.). (ENG., Illus.). 250p. 34.95 *(978-1-933415-41-3(X))* Panache Partners, LLC.

Panache Partners LLC Staff, ed. City by Design - Denver: An Architectural Perspective of Denver. 2010. (City by Design Ser.). (ENG., Illus.). 288p. lib. bdg. 40.00 *(978-1-933415-89-5(4))* Panache Partners, LLC.

—City by Design San Francisco. 2009. (City by Design Ser.). (ENG., Illus.). 256p. 40.00 *(978-1-933415-49-9(5))* Panache Partners, LLC.

Panchyk, Richard. New York City Skyscrapers. 2010. (Postcard History Ser.). (ENG., Illus.). 128p. pap. 21.99 *(978-0-7385-7296-3(9))* Arcadia Publishing.

Paoluzzo, Marco. America Blues. 2006. (ENG., Illus.). 98p. *(978-3-7165-1054-4(8)*, Benteli Verlags Ag Dist) Antique Collectors' Club.

Parsons, Jim & Bush, David. Houston Deco: Modernistic Architecture of the Texas Coast. 2008. (ENG., Illus.). 128p. pap. 19.95 *(978-1-933979-07-6(0))* Bright Sky Pr.

Passikoff, Alexander G. A Façade of Buildings: A Collection of Architectural Styles, Architects, & Their Buildings That Make up the Face of New York. 2011. 164p. pap. 49.99 **(978-1-4567-9490-3(6))** AuthorHouse.

Payne, Richard. Texas Towns & the Art of Architecture: A Photographer's Journey. 2006. (ENG., Illus.). 200p. 49.95 (978-0-87611-218-2(1)) Texas State Historical Assn.

Pearlman, Jill. Inventing American Modernism: Joseph Hudnut, Walter Gropius, & the Bauhaus Legacy at Harvard. 2007. (Center Bks.). (ENG., Illus.). 272p. (gr. 17). 40.00 (978-0-8139-2602-5(5)) Univ. Pr. of Virginia.

Pelkonen, Eeva-Liisa. Kevin Roche: Architecture as Environment. 2011. (ENG., Illus.). 280p. 65.00 (978-0-300-15223-4(X)) Yale Univ. Pr.

Penner, Barbara. Newlyweds on Tour: Honeymooning in Nineteenth-Century America. 2009. (Becoming Modern: New Nineteenth-Century Studies). (Illus.). 308p. lib. bdg. 55.00 (978-1-58465-773-6(1), University of New Hampshire Press) Univ. Pr. of New England.

Pennoyer, Peter, et al. The Architecture of Grosvenor Atterbury. 2009. (ENG., Illus.). 288p. 75.00 (978-0-393-73222-1(3), 73222) Norton, W. W. & Co., Inc.

Perkins+Will. Perkins+Will. 2011. (ENG., Illus.). 360p. 80.00 (978-1-86470-373-3(3), Images Publishing Dist Ac) Antique Collectors' Club GBR. Dist: National Bk. Network.

Petit, Emmanuel. Ceci n¿est pas une Reverie: The Architecture of Stanley Tigerman. Rappaport, Nina, ed. 2011. (Illus.). 26p. **(978-0-9826385-9-0(0))** Yale Schl. of Architecture.

Pettern, Silvia. Boulder: A Sense of Time & Place Revisited. 2010. (American Chronicles Ser.). (ENG., Illus.). 144p. pap. 19.99 (978-1-59629-974-0(6)) History Pr., The.

Pezzoni, J. Daniel, ed. The Architectural History of Watauga County, North Carolina. 2009. (Illus.). 392p. 65.00 (978-0-615-30736-7(1)) Watauga County Historical Society.

Pfeffer, W. T. The Hand of the Small Town Builder. 2012. **(978-1-56792-329-2(1))** Godine, David R. Pub.

Pfeiffer, Bruce Brooks. Frank Lloyd Wright: The Heroic Years, 1920-1932. 2009. (ENG., Illus.). 240p. 60.00 (978-0-8478-3174-6(4)) Rizzoli International Pubns., Inc.

—Frank Lloyd Wright - complete works 01: Complete Works, 3 vols., Vol. 1. Gossel, Peter, ed. 2011. (ENG, FRE & GER., Illus.). 580p. 200.00 (978-3-8365-0927-5(X)) TASCHEN DEU. Dist: Ingram Pub. Services.

—Frank Lloyd Wright Designs: The Sketches, Plans, & Drawings. 2011. (ENG., Illus.). 420p. 35.00 (978-0-8478-3570-6(7)) Rizzoli International Pubns., Inc.

Pfeiffer, Bruce Brooks & Gössel, Peter. Frank Lloyd Wright 2: 1917-1942, 3 vols., Vol. 2. 2010. (ENG, FRE & GER., Illus.). 480p. 200.00 (978-3-8365-0926-8(1)) TASCHEN DEU. Dist: Ingram Pub. Services.

Pfeiffer, Bruce Brooks & Sidy, Victor E. Under Arizona Skies: The Apprentice Desert Shelters at Frank Lloyd Wright's Taliesin West. 2011. (ENG., Illus.). 80p. 24.95 (978-0-7649-5959-2(X)) Pomegranate Communications, Inc.

Plank, Jeffrey. Crombie Taylor: Modern Architecture, Building Restoration & the Re-Discovery of Louis Sullivan. 2010. (Illus.). 315p. 65.00 (978-0-9795508-1-2(5)) Stout, William Pubs.

Poletti, Therese & Paiva, Tom. Art Deco San Francisco: The Architecture of Timothy Pflueger. 2008. (ENG., Illus.). 256p. 55.00 (978-1-56898-756-9(0)) Princeton Architectural Pr.

Pontynen, Arthur & Miller, Rod. Western culture at the american Crossroads: The Conflict over the Nature of Science & Reason. 2011. (ENG., Illus.). 448p. 34.95 (978-1-935191-74-2(8)) ISI Bks.

Poole, Robert M. On Hallowed Ground: The Story of Arlington National Cemetery. 2010. (ENG.). 368p. pap. 17.00 (978-0-8027-1549-4(4)) Walker & Co.

Power, Ethel B. The Smaller American House. 2007. (Illus.). 100p. pap. 19.95 (978-0-7643-2769-8(0)) Schiffer Publishing, Ltd.

—Smaller Houses of The 1920s: 55 Examples. 2007. (Dover Architecture Ser.). (ENG., Illus.). 112p. pap. 12.95 (978-0-486-46049-9(5)) Dover Pubns., Inc.

Pridmore, Jay. Northwestern University: The Campus Guide. 2009. (ENG., Illus.). 192p. pap. 24.95 (978-1-56898-755-2(2)) Princeton Architectural Pr.

Princeton Architectural Press Staff & Architectural League of New York Staff. Foresight. 2010. (ENG., Illus.). 176p. pap. 24.95 (978-1-56898-887-0(7)) Princeton Architectural Pr.

Progress, Michael Davis & Stephen Moore. 2006. per. 24.95 (978-0-9771696-2-7(6)) Grand Central Pr.

Prown, Jules David. The Architecture of the Yale Center for British Art. 2009. (ENG., Illus.). 72p. 35.00 (978-0-300-14964-7(6)) Yale Ctr. for British Art.

Radford, William A. The Most Popular Homes of the Twenties. 2009. (Dover Architecture Ser.). (ENG., Illus.). 176p. pap. 19.95 (978-0-486-47028-3(8)) Dover Pubns., Inc.

Rajtar, Steve. A Guide to Historic Lakeland, Florida. 2007. pap. 19.99 (978-1-59629-271-0(7)) History Pr., The.

—A Guide to Historic Tampa. 2007. pap. 19.99 (978-1-59629-253-6(9)) History Pr., The.

—101 Glimpses of Bartow. 2008. pap. 14.99 (978-1-59629-533-9(3)) History Pr., The.

Rajtar, Steve & Goodman, Kelly. A Guide to Historic St. Augustine, Florida. 2008. (Illus.). 190p. pap., per. 19.99 (978-1-59629-336-6(5)) History Pr., The.

Rajtar, Steve & Rajtar, Gayle Prince. A Guide to Historic Winter Park. 2008. (History & Guide Ser.). pap. 19.99 (978-1-59629-436-3(1)) History Pr., The.

Rand, Marvin, photos by. Irving J. Gill: Architect, 1870-1936. 2006. (ENG., Illus.). 240p. 50.00 (978-1-58685-446-1(1)) Gibbs Smith, Publisher.

Rashid, Karim. KarimSpace. 2009. (ENG., Illus.). 272p. 75.00 (978-0-8478-3231-6(7)) Rizzoli International Pubns., Inc.

Rattenbury, Kester & Hardingham, Samantha, eds. Robert Venturi & Denise Scott Brown: Learning from Las Vegas. 2008. (Supercrit Ser.). (ENG., Illus.). 160p. (C). 165.00 (978-0-415-43413-3(0)); pap. 49.95 (978-0-415-43414-0(9)) Routledge.

Read, Gray. The Miniature & the Gigantic in Philadelphia Architecture: Essays on Designing the City to Human Scale. 2007. (Illus.). 160p. (C). 99.95 (978-0-7734-5429-3(2)) Mellen, Edwin Pr., The.

Reed, Roger. Building Victorian Boston: The Architecture of Gridley J. F. Bryant. 2006. (Illus.). 256p. 39.95 (978-1-55849-555-5(X)) Univ. of Massachusetts Pr.

Regan, Brian. Gothic Pride: The Story of Building a Great Cathedral in Newark. 2012. (ENG.). 312p. 39.95 **(978-0-8135-5288-0(5)**, Rivergate Bks.) Rutgers Univ. Pr.

Reiss, Marcia. Architectural Details. 2008. (ENG.). 256p. 25.00 (978-1-4223-9309-3(7)) DIANE Publishing Co.

—Architecture in Detail: New York. 2006. (Illus.). 96p. reprint ed. 13.00 (978-1-4223-5386-8(9)) DIANE Publishing Co.

Reiss, Marcia. Lost New York. 2011. (Lost Ser.). (ENG.). 144p. 18.95 **(978-1-86205-935-1(7))** Chrysalis Children's Bks. GBR. Dist: Independent Pubs. Group.

Restemeyer, Virginia & Weiner, E. I. Hip & Hidden Philadelphia: The Unexpected House in a City of Tradition. 2012. (ENG., Illus.). 176p. pap. 29.95 (978-0-9766626-2-4(0)) Probasco Haus Pr.

Rhoads, William Bertolet. Ulster County, New York: The Architectural History & Guide. 2011. (Illus.). 376p. pap. 24.95 **(978-1-883789-70-1(2))** Black Dome Pr. Corp.

Richards, Rand. Historic San Francisco: A Concise History & Guide. 2nd ed. 2011. (Illus.). 320p. per. 17.95 (978-1-879367-05-0(X)) Heritage Hse. Pubs.

Richmond, Arthur P. Cape Cod Lighthouses & Lightships. 2010. (Illus.). 256p. 45.00 (978-0-7643-3545-7(6)) Schiffer Publishing, Ltd.

Riera Ojeda, Oscar. Sasaki: Intersection & Convergence. Riera Ojeda, Oscar, ed. 2008. (ENG., Illus.). 336p. 65.00 (978-0-9793801-5-0(4)) Oro Editions.

Riera Ojeda, Oscar, ed. Moore Ruble Yudell: Arc of Interaction. 2008. (ENG., Illus.). 112p. 35.00 (978-0-9795395-0-3(1)) Oro Editions.

Riew, Jayne, et al, eds. The Thomas Jefferson Foundation Medal in Architecture: The First Forty Years, 1966-2005. 2007. (ENG., Illus.). 96p. (gr. 17). per. 19.00 (978-0-9771024-3-3(2)) Univ. Pr. of Virginia.

Rindoks, Leslie, ed. Our Vanishing Americana: A North Carolina Portrait. 2006. 44.95 (978-0-9704651-9-1(X)) Lorimer Pr.

Rinne, Kathrine, ed. & intro. Architecture for a Hybrid Landscape: Proposals for the California Delta. 2012. (ENG., Illus.). 112p. 25.00 (978-0-9753507-9-9(X)) California College of the Arts.

Ripley, Hubert G. New England Inns & Taverns: The Monograph Series V18, No. 6. Whitehead, Russell F., ed. 2011. 20p. pap. 35.95 **(978-1-258-03320-0(8))** Literary Licensing, LLC.

Ritchie, Daniel L. Built for Learning: A Unified Architectural Vision for the University of Denver. 2008. (Illus.). 208p. 49.95 (978-0-9648871-3-8(4)) Univ. of Denver.

Rizzoli, et al. Thomas Phifer & Partners. 2010. (ENG., Illus.). 350p. 75.00 (978-0-8478-3525-6(1), Skira) Rizzoli International Pubns., Inc.

Rizzoli Staff. Cowboys Stadium: Architecture, Art, Entertainment in the Twenty-First Century. 2010. (ENG., Illus.). 176p. 50.00 (978-0-8478-3536-2(7)) Rizzoli International Pubns., Inc.

Roca, Miguel Angel & Kahn, Louis I. Louis Kahn, Arquetipos y Modernidad. 2009. (SPA., Illus.). 207p. (978-987-584-343-1(1)) Nobuko.

Rochlin, Michael Jacob. Ancient L. A. And Other Essays. Date not set. (Illus.). 54p. 39.95 (978-0-9648304-2-4(6)) Unreinforced Masonry Studio.

Rockhill, Dan. Designing & Building: Rockhill & Associates. Cater, Brian, ed. 2011. (Illus.). 120p. pap. (978-0-929112-59-6(8)) Tuns Pr.

Rogers, Gregory Parker. Cincinnati's Hyde Park: A Brief History of a Queen City Gem. 2010. (Brief History Ser.). (ENG., Illus.). 192p. pap. 21.99 (978-1-59629-900-9(2)) History Pr., The.

Rogers, Rob, et al. Rogers Marvel Architects. 2011. (ENG., Illus.). 192p. pap. 40.00 (978-1-56898-999-0(7)) Princeton Architectural Pr.

Ronan, John & Princeton Architectural Press Staff. Explorations: The Architecture of John Ronan. 2010. (ENG., Illus.). 192p. pap. 40.00 (978-1-56898-876-4(1)) Princeton Architectural Pr.

Rosa, Joseph. Young Chicago. 2007. (A+D Ser.). (ENG., Illus.). 104p. pap. 16.95 (978-0-300-12067-7(2)) Art Institute of Chicago.

Roseman, Frank M. & Watry, Peter J. Chula Vista. 2010. (Then & Now Ser.). (ENG., Illus.). 96p. pap. 21.99 (978-0-7385-8016-6(3)) Arcadia Publishing.

Rosenfeld, Erika & Bohlin, Peter. Thomas L. Bosworth: Building with Light in the Pacific Northwest. 2007. (ENG., Illus.). 356p. 75.00 (978-0-9774672-6-6(0)) Oro Editions.

Rosenfeld, Lucy D. & Harrison, Marina. Architecture Walks: The Best Outings near New York City. 2010. (ENG., Illus.). 288p. pap. 19.95 (978-0-8135-4734-3(2), Rivergate Bks.) Rutgers Univ. Pr.

Rothman, Laura B., et al, eds. 2006 Marketing Survey: Of Architecture, Engineering, Planning & Environmental Consulting Firms. 13th ed. 2006. 326p. pap. 395.00 (978-1-932372-97-7(0)) ZweigWhite.

—2006 Multi-Office Firm Survey: Of Architecture, Engineering, Planning & Environmental Consulting Firms. 14th ed. 2006. Orig. Title: Satellite Office Survey. 212p. pap. 395.00 (978-1-932372-99-1(7)) ZweigWhite.

Rubin, Mary H. Hagerstown. 2010. (Then & Now Ser.). (ENG., Illus.). 96p. pap. 21.99 (978-0-7385-8584-0(X)) Arcadia Publishing.

Rudder, Steffen De. Architect Hugh Stubbins, 1 vol. 2007. (ENG., Illus.). 192p. pap. 35.00 (978-3-939633-24-2(0)) Jovis Verlag GmbH DEU. Dist: D.A.P./Distributed Art Pubs.

Russell, Susan. South Beach Lifeguard Stations. 2008. (Illus.). 80p. bds. 19.95 (978-0-7643-2900-5(6)) Schiffer Publishing, Ltd.

Rutherford, Sarah. Georgian Garden Buildings. 2012. (Shire Library). (ENG., Illus.). 112p. pap. 15.95 **(978-0-7478-1101-5(6))** Shire Pubns., Ltd. GBR. Dist: Random Hse., Inc.

Ryan, Raymund & Tejchman, Filip, contrib. by. La Dallman: Fabricated Landscapes. 2009. pap. 16.95 (978-0-615-27456-0(0)) Univ. of Wisconsin-Milwaukee Schl. of Architecture & Urban Planning.

Ryan, Zoë. Coney Island: Parachute Pavilion Competition. Cohen-Litant, Jonathan, ed. 2007. (ENG., Illus.). 176p. pap. 29.95 (978-1-56898-623-4(8)) Princeton Architectural Pr.

Ryan, Zoe, et al. Bertrand Goldberg: Architecture of Invention. 2011. (ENG., Illus.). 192p. 60.00 (978-0-300-16704-7(0)) Art Institute of Chicago.

Sadao, Shoji. Best of Friends: Isamu Noguchi & Buckminster Fuller. White, Garrett, ed. 2008. 224p. 50.00 (978-0-9794727-3-2(3)) Five Ties Publishing.

Saeks, Diane Dorrans. Orlando Diaz-Azcuy. 2009. (ENG., Illus.). 224p. 60.00 (978-0-8478-3076-3(4)) Rizzoli International Pubns., Inc.

Sahre, Paul. Leisurama Now: The Beach House for Everyone 1964- 2008. (ENG., Illus.). 256p. 40.00 (978-1-56898-709-5(9)) Princeton Architectural Pr.

Sammarco, Anthony Mitchell & Buchanan, Paul. Milton Architecture. 2006. (Scenes of America Ser.). (Illus.). 127p. per. 9.99 (978-0-7385-4569-1(4)) Arcadia Publishing.

Santa Barbara Conservancy. Stone Architecture in Santa Barbara. 2009. (Images of America Ser.). (ENG., Illus.). 128p. pap. 21.99 (978-0-7385-6968-0(2)) Arcadia Publishing.

Sater, Dan F. Dan Sater's Country: Estates. 2007. (Illus.). per. 16.95 (978-1-932553-22-2(3)) Designs Direct Publishing, LLC.

Sater, Dan F., II. The Smaller Home: Smart Designs for Your Home. 2008. (Illus.). 176p. pap. 19.95 (978-0-06-156532-8(6), Collins Design) HarperCollins Pubs.

Sato, Akira. Kenchiku ni Okeru Kindai: 19-Seiki Obei No Kenchikuka Kenchiku Sangyo ni Kansuru Kenkyu. 2010. (JPN., Illus.). 489p. (978-4-8055-0621-9(0)) Chuo Koron Bijutsu Shuppan.

Sau, Arunabha. Low-Energy Passive Solar Residence in Austin, Texas. 2011. 168p. pap. **(978-3-8443-1460-1(1))** Lambert Academic Publishing.

Scarpa, Lawrence. John Howey. 2006. (Master Architect Ser.: Vol. 7). (ENG., Illus.). 256p. 59.95 (978-1-86470-133-3(1)) Images Publishing Dist A/C.

Schaffner, Ingrid, et al, texts. Anne Tyng: Inhabiting Geometry. 2012. (ENG., Illus.). 112p. pap. 30.00 (978-0-88454-121-9(5)) Institute of Contemporary Art, Univ. of Pennsylvania/Graham Foundation.

Schatz, Bob, photos by. Asheville Impressions. 2008. (Illus.). 80p. pap. 9.95 (978-1-56037-432-9(2)) Farcountry Pr.

Schleier, Merrill. Skyscraper Cinema: Architecture & Gender in American Film. 2009. (Illus.). 368p. 85.50 (978-0-8166-4281-6(8)); (ENG., pap. 28.50 (978-0-8166-4282-3(6)) Univ. of Minnesota Pr.

Schmertz, Mildred. Mitchell: Giurgola Architects. 2008. (ENG., Illus.). 264p. 70.00 (978-1-86470-274-3(5)) Images Publishing Group AUS. Dist: National Bk. Network.

Schmitt, Ronald E. Sullivanesque: Urban Architecture & Ornamentation. 2007. (Illus.). 360p. per. 35.95 (978-0-252-07464-6(5)) Univ. of Illinois Pr.

Schrenk, Lisa D. Building a Century of Progress: The Architecture of Chicago's 1933-34 World's Fair. 2007. (Illus.). 368p. 39.95 (978-0-8166-4836-8(0)) Univ. of Minnesota Pr.

Schultz, Anne-Catrin. Skidmore, Owings & Merrill, International Terminal, San Francisco International Airport. 2008. (ENG., Illus.). 60p. 49.00 (978-3-932565-64-9(9)) Edition Axel Menges GmbH DEU. Dist: National Bk. Network.

Schwarzer, Mitchell. Architecture & Design SF. 2nd ed. Date not set. (Architecture & Design Ser.). (Illus.). 80p. pap. 16.00 (978-0-9641863-8-5(1), TUB Pr.) Understanding Business.

—Architecture of the San Francisco Bay Area: History & Guide. 2006. (Illus.). 187p. pap. 29.95 (978-0-9746214-5-6(5)) Stout, William Pubs.

Scott, Felicity D. Architecture or Techno-Utopia: Politics after Modernism. 2010. (ENG., Illus.). 360p. (gr. 17). pap. 19.95 (978-0-262-51406-4(0), MIT Pr.

Scott, John Beldon & Lehnertz, Rodney P. The University of Iowa Guide to Campus Architecture. 2006. (Bur Oak Guide Ser.). (Illus.). 310p. per. 19.95 (978-0-87745-990-3(8)) Univ. of Iowa Pr.

Scott, Pamela. Fortress of Finance: The United States Treasury Building. 2010. 55.00 (978-0-615-36629-6(5)) Treasury Historical Assn.

Seattle Architectural Club Staff. Seattle Architectural Year Book. (Illus.). reprint ed. lib. bdg. 98.00 (978-0-7222-4709-9(5)) Library Reprints, Inc.

Seavey, Kent. Carmel: A History in Architecture. 2007. (Images of America Ser.). (ENG., Illus.). 128p. per. 19.99 (978-0-7385-4705-3(0)) Arcadia Publishing.

Serraino, Pierluigi. Julius Shulman - Modernism Rediscovered: Die wiederentdeckte Moderne. 25th ed. 2009. (ENG, FRE & GER., Illus.). 415p. 29.99 (978-3-8365-0326-6(3)) TASCHEN DEU. Dist: Ingram Pub. Services.

Sexton, Richard. Rosemary Beach, 1 vol. 2007. (ENG., Illus.). 160p. 35.00 (978-1-58980-403-6(1)) Pelican Publishing Co., Inc.

Shacklett, Bill & Lodl, John. Murfreesboro. 2012. (Then & Now Ser.). (ENG., Illus.). 96p. pap. 21.99 **(978-0-7385-9111-7(4))** Arcadia Publishing.

Shanken, Andrew Michael. 194X: Architecture, Planning, & Consumer Culture on the American Home Front. 2009. (Architecture, Landscape & Amer Culture Ser.). (ENG., Illus.). 288p. 75.00 (978-0-8166-5365-2(8)); pap. 24.95 (978-0-8166-5366-9(6)) Univ. of Minnesota Pr.

Shepherd, Barnett. Tottenville: The Town the Oyster Built - A Staten Island Community, Its People, Industry & Architecture. 2010. 261p. pap. 24.99 (978-0-615-34294-8(9)) Tottenville Historical Society.

Shop Architects Staff. SHoP: Out of Practice. 2012. (ENG., Illus.). 420p. 50.00 (978-1-58093-271-4(1)) Monacelli Pr., Inc.

Shulman, Allan T. & Camber, Diane. Miami Modern Metropolis: Paradise & Paradox in Midcentury Architecture & Planning. 2009. (ENG., Illus.). 416p. 85.00 (978-1-890449-51-3(2)) Balcony Pr.

Shulman, Allan T., et al. Miami Architecture: An A1A Guide Featuring Downtown, the Beaches, & Coconut Grove. 2010. (ENG., Illus.). 352p. pap. 29.95 (978-0-8130-3471-3(X)) Univ. Pr. of Florida.

Shulman, Julius. Julius Shulman: Modernism Rediscovered, 3 vols., Set. Taschen, Benedikt, ed. 2007. (FRE, GER & ENG., Illus.). 1008p. 300.00 (978-3-8228-4287-4(7)) TASCHEN DEU. Dist: Ingram Pub. Services.

Siegel, Gwathmey & Associates. Gwathmey Siegel & Associates Architects: Selected Projects. 2010. (ENG., Illus.). 232p. 59.95 (978-1-86470-334-4(2)) Images Publishing Group AUS. Dist: National Bk. Network.

Silver, Robert H., prod. Schwartz/Silver: Arguments for Building. 2007. (Architectural Ser.). (ENG., Illus.). 144p. 40.00 (978-88-7838-088-2(1), Art Stock Bks. Ltd/Csi) Continental Sales, Inc.

Sinovcic, Damir, ed. 100 Florida Architects & Interior Designers. 2010. (ENG., Illus.). 458p. 45.00 (978-1-936344-00-0(9)) Design Bk.

Siry, Joseph M. Carson Pirie Scott: Louis Sullivan & the Chicago Department Store. 2012. (Chicago Architecture & Urbanism Ser.). (ENG., Illus.). 304p. pap. 50.00 (978-0-226-76137-4(1)) Univ. of Chicago Pr.

Skyline: Chicago: The Series. 6.95 (978-1-880005-10-1(7)) Perspectives International, Inc.

Slavick, Ann. Hour Chicago: Twenty-Five Self-Guided 60-Minute Tours of Chicago's Great Architecture & Art. 2008. (ENG., Illus.). 272p. pap. 16.95 (978-1-56663-743-5(0)) Dee, Ivan R. Pub.

Smith, Daniel M., Jr., text. African-Americans & Charleston: Histories Intertwined. 2010. (Illus.). ix, 113p. **(978-0-615-36805-4(0))** Independent Pub.

Smith, Gary Lloyd. Look! There's Your House! 2009. 90p. pap. 30.95 (978-1-60594-358-9(4), Llumina Pr.) Aeon Publishing Inc.

Smith, Joel. More Than One: Photographs in Sequence. Smith, Joel, ed. 2009. (ENG., Illus.). 96p. pap. 25.00 (978-0-300-14930-2(1)) Yale Univ. Pr.

Smith, Joel, et al. More Than One: Photographs in Sequence. Smith, Joel, ed. 2008. (Illus.). 120p. pap. (978-0-943012-01-8(5)) Princeton Univ. Art Museum.

Smith, Ken. Ken Smith: Landscape Architect. 2009. (ENG., Illus.). 240p. 50.00 (978-1-58093-243-1(6)) Monacelli Pr., Inc.

Smith, Laura Massino. Architecture Tours L. A. Guidebook: Downtown. 2007. (Illus.). 64p. pap. 9.99 (978-0-7643-2084-2(X)) Schiffer Publishing, Ltd.

Snelling, Rebecca & Suermondt, Jan. Frank Lloyd Wright Revealed. 2007. (Illus.). 160p. 19.99 (978-0-7858-2079-6(5), Chartwell) Book Sales, Inc.

Snyder, Frank M. Building Details. 2007. (ENG.). 144p. 65.00 (978-0-393-73245-0(2), 73245) Norton, W. W. & Co., Inc.

Sokol, David M. The Noble Room: The Inspired Conception & Tumultuous Creation of Frank Lloyd Wright's Unity Temple. 100th ed. 2008. (Illus.). 181p. 22.95 (978-0-9789270-3-5(6)) Top Five Bks.

Solis, Julia. Stages of Decay. 2012. (ENG., Illus.). 144p. 34.95 **(978-1-935613-46-6(4))** Batty, Mark Pub., LLC.

Solomon, Susan G. Louis I. Kahn's Jewish Architecture: Mikveh Israel & the Midcentury American Synagogue. 2009. (Brandeis Series in American Jewish History, Culture & Life Ser.). (ENG., Illus.). 236p. lib. bdg. 45.00 (978-1-58465-788-0(X)) Univ. Pr. of New England.

Southwest Seattle Historical Society. West Seattle. 2010. (Images of America Ser.). (ENG., Illus.). 128p. pap. 21.99 (978-0-7385-8133-0(X)) Arcadia Publishing.

Southworth, Michael & Southworth, Susan. Boston: Contemporary Landmarks, Urban Design, Parks, Historic Buildings & Neighborhoods. 3rd ed. 2008. (ENG., Illus.). 384p. pap. 29.95 (978-0-7627-4337-7(9)) Globe Pequot Pr., The.

Sparberg Alexiou, Alice. The Flatiron: The New York Landmark & the Incomparable City That Arose with It. 2010. (ENG., Illus.). 320p. 26.99 (978-0-312-38468-5(8), Dunne, Thomas Bks.) St. Martin's Pr.

Speck, Jeff. Walkable City, 1 vol. 2012. (ENG., Illus.). 320p. 27.00 **(978-0-374-28581-4(0))** Farrar, Straus & Giroux.

Spinzia, Raymond E. & Spinzia, Judith A. Long Island's Prominent South Shore Families: Their Estates & their Country Homes in the Towns of Babylon & Islip. 2007. 404p. per. 24.95 (978-1-58939-964-8(1)) Virtualbookworm.com Publishing, Inc.

St Publications Staff, contrib. by. Stores & Retail Spaces 8. 2007. (Illus.). 168p. 35.00 (978-0-944094-57-0(0)) HarperCollins Pubs.

Stadler, Hilar, et al, eds. Las Vegas Studio: Bilder aus dem Archiv von Robert Venturi und Denise Scott Brown. 2009. (Illus.). 193p. 97.00 (978-3-85881-229-2(3)) Scheidegger und Spiess AG, Verlag CHE. Dist: Antique Collectors' Club.

Stadler, Hilar & Stierli, Martino, eds. Las Vegas Studio: Images from the Archive of Robert Venturi & Deise Scott Brown. 2009. (ENG., Illus.). 193p. 60.00 (978-3-85881-717-4(1)) Scheidegger und Spiess AG, Verlag CHE. Dist: Antique Collectors' Club.

Stalcup, Jonathan. Savannah Architectural Tours. 2008. (Illus.). 144p. pap. 14.95 (978-0-7643-2907-4(3)) Schiffer Publishing, Ltd.

Stalnaker, Joy Gilchrist. Ordered & Resolved or Board of Directors Minutes of the Construction of the Asylum at Weston WV (1858-18810. 2009. pap. 32.50 (978-1-61584-908-6(4)) Independent Pub.

Stanley, Ellen E. Indian River County. 2010. (Images of America Ser.). (Illus.). 128p. pap. 21.99 (978-0-7385-8636-6(6)) Arcadia Publishing.

Stella, Frank. Frank Stella: Painting into Architecture. 2007. (ENG., Illus.). 40p. per. 16.95 *(978-0-300-13148-2(8))* Yale Univ. Pr.

Stern, Robert A. M., et al. New York 1930: Architecture & Urbanism Between the Two World Wars. 2009. (ENG., Illus.). 848p. 95.00 *(978-0-8478-3096-1(9))* Rizzoli International Pubns., Inc.

Stern, Jewel & Stuart, John A. Ely Jacques Kahn, Architect: Beaux-Arts to Modernism in New York. 2006. (ENG., Illus.). 336p. 60.00 *(978-0-393-73114-9(6),* 73114) Norton, W. W. & Co., Inc.

Stern, Robert A. M. Robert A. M. Stern: Buildings & Towns. Dixon, Peter Morris, ed. 2007. (ENG., Illus.). 548p. (gr. 12). 85.00 *(978-1-58093-192-2(8))* Monacelli Pr., Inc.

—Robert A. M. Stern: On Campus. 2010. (ENG., Illus.). 576p. 85.00 *(978-1-58093-283-7(5))* Monacelli Pr., Inc.

Stichweh, Dirk. New York Skyscrapers. 2009. (Illus.). 192p. 39.95 *(978-3-7913-4054-8(9))* Prestel Publishing.

Stones, Alison. Studies in Arthurian Illustration. 2012. (ENG., Illus.). 560p. (C). 300.00 *(978-1-904597-37-7(8))* Pindar Pr. GBR. Dist: Brown, David Bk. Co., The.

Stoney, Samuel G. Plantations of the Carolina Low Country. (Illus.). 243p. reprint ed. lib. bdg. 98.00 *(978-0-7222-0520-4(1))* Library Reprints, Inc.

—This Is Charleston. rev. ed. (Illus.). 139p. (Orig.). reprint ed. pap. 6.95 *(978-0-910326-04-9(5))* Carolina Art Assn.

Stoppani, Teresa. Paradigm Islands - Manhattan & Venice. 2011. (ENG., Illus.). 312p. (C). 125.00 *(978-0-415-56185-3(X))* Routledge.

Straker, Cheryl J. & Matheney, Chris. Ohio Statehouse: A Building for the Ages. 2011. *(978-1-57864-682-1(0))* Donning Co. Pubs.

Street-Porter, Tim, photos by. L. A. Modern. 2008. (ENG., Illus.). 248p. 75.00 *(978-0-8478-3067-1(5))* Rizzoli International Pubns., Inc.

—Los Angeles. 2008. (Illus.). 264p. 9.95 *(978-0-8478-3107-4(8))* Rizzoli International Pubns., Inc.

Strom, Steven R. Houston Lost & Unbuilt. 2010. (ENG., Illus.). 200p. 45.00 *(978-0-292-72113-5(7))* Univ. of Texas Pr.

Stroud, Marion Boulton & Wilkins, Amy. Robert Venturi, Denise Scott Brown, & Steven Izenour at Acadia Summer Arts Program. Stroud, Marion Boulton, ed. 2010. (ENG., Illus.). 124p. 30.00 *(978-0-9797642-2-6(X))* A.S.A.P.

Structurally Deficient Bridges in the United States: Hearing Before the Committee on Transportation & Infrastructure, House of Representatives, One Hundred Tenth Congress, First Session, September 5, 2007. 2007. (Illus.). xv, 326p. *(978-0-16-083400-4(7),* 552-070-39213-1) United States Government Printing Office.

Sullivan-Hartung, Maureen. Hidden History of Everglades City & Points Nearby. 2010. (Hidden History Ser.). (ENG., Illus.). 128p. pap. 19.99 *(978-1-59629-744-9(1))* History Pr., The.

Sully, Susan. Southern Cosmopolitan: Sophisticated Southern Style. 2009. (ENG., Illus.). 208p. 50.00 *(978-0-8478-3078-7(0))* Rizzoli International Pubns., Inc.

Susanka, Sarah. The Not So Big House Book. 2006. *(978-1-56158-929-6(2))* Taunton Pr., Inc.

Sutro, Dirk & Princeton Architectural Press Staff. University of California, San Diego. 2010. (ENG., Illus.). 224p. pap., instr.'s gde. ed. 29.95 *(978-1-56898-860-3(5))* Princeton Architectural Pr.

Sweeney, Robert. Casa Del Herrero: The Romance of Spanish Colonial. 2009. (ENG., Illus.). 168p. 50.00 *(978-0-8478-3327-6(5))* Rizzoli International Pubns., Inc.

Tangires, Helen. Public Markets. 2008. (Norton/Library of Congress Visual Sourcebooks in Architecture, Design & Engineering Ser.). (ENG., Illus.). 336p. 75.00 *(978-0-393-73167-5(7),* 73167) Norton, W. W. & Co., Inc.

Tasch, Woody. Inquiries into the Nature of Slow Money: Investing as if Food, Farms, & Fertility Mattered. 2010. (ENG.). 240p. pap. 15.95 *(978-1-60358-254-4(1))* Chelsea Green Publishing.

Taschen, Angelika, ed. New York Style, Vol. 2. 2009. (ENG.). 192p. pap. 9.99 *(978-3-8365-1503-0(2))* TASCHEN DEU. Dist: Ingram Pub. Services.

Tate, Ken. A Classical Journey: The Houses of Ken Tate. 2011. (ENG., Illus.). 438p. 65.00 *(978-1-86470-290-3(7),* Images Publishing Dist Ac) Antique Collectors' Club GBR. Dist: National Bk. Network.

Telegraph Herald (Dubuque, Iowa) Staff, contrib. by. Having a Fine Time in Galena: A Vintage Picture Postcard Collection. 2007. (Illus.). iv, 154p. ***(978-0-9761125-6-3(6))*** Telegraph Herald.

teNeues. AAD New York: Art Architecture Design. 2010. (Illus.). 168p. pap. 12.95 *(978-3-8327-9435-4(2))* teNeues Publishing Co.

teNeues, creator. Ultimate New York Design. 2007. (ENG, FRE & GER., Illus.). 527p. 24.95 *(978-3-8327-9107-0(8))* teNeues Publishing Co.

Texas Historical Commission Staff, contrib. by. The Fulton Mansion State Historic Site, Rockport-Fulton, Texas. 2012. pap. ***(978-1-57864-732-3(0))*** Donning Co. Pubs.

The Southern Illinoisan, Inc. McAndrew Stadium: A Pictorial History, 1937-2009. 2010. 29.95 *(978-0-578-04613-6(X))* Southern Illinoisan, Incorporated, The.

Thimmesh, Hilary & Breuer, Marcel. Marcel Breuer & the Committee of Twelve Plan a Church: A Monastic Memoir. 2011. 19.95 *(978-0-9740992-7-9(9))* St. John's Univ. Pr.

Thomas, George E., et al. Buildings of Pennsylvania: Philadelphia & Eastern Pennsylvania. 2011. (Buildings of the United States Ser.). (ENG., Illus.). 696p. (gr. 17). 75.00 *(978-0-8139-2967-5(9))* Univ. Pr. of Virginia.

Tigerman, Stanley. Designing Bridges to Burn: Architectural Memoirs by Stanley Tigerman. 2011. (ENG., Illus.). 240p. pap. 24.95 *(978-1-935935-07-0(0))* Oro Editions.

Tigerman, Stanley & Petit, Emmanuel. Schlepping Through Ambivalence: Essays on an American Architectural Condition. 2011. (ENG., Illus.). 192p. 45.00 *(978-0-300-17541-7(8))* Yale Univ. Pr.

Tigor. Personal Dock Building: Waterfront Notes for Residential Docks. 2007. (Illus.). 26p. cd-rom 12.00 net. *(978-0-9771155-1-8(8))* TIGOR, Inc.

Toker, Franklin. Buildings of Pittsburgh. 2007. (Buildings of the United States Ser.). (ENG., Illus.). 272p. (gr. 17). 45.00 *(978-0-8139-2658-2(0))* Univ. Pr. of Virginia.

—Pittsburgh: A New Portrait. 2009. (ENG., Illus.). 528p. 34.95 *(978-0-8229-4371-6(9))* Univ. of Pittsburgh Pr.

Toker, Franklin K. Buildings of Pittsburgh. 2007. (Buildings of the United States Ser.). (ENG., Illus.). 272p. pap. 24.95 *(978-0-8139-2650-6(5))* Univ. Pr. of Virginia.

Tolles, Bryant F. Jr. Architecture & Academe: College Buildings in New England Before 1860. 2011. (Illus.). 260p. 50.00 *(978-1-58465-891-7(6))* Univ. Pr. of New England.

Tolles, Bryant Franklin, Jr. & Tolles, Bryant F. Summer by the Seaside: The Architecture of New England Coastal Resort Hotels, 1820-1950. 2008. (ENG., Illus.). 272p. 27.95 *(978-1-58465-576-3(3))* Univ. Pr. of New England.

Tottis, James W. The Guardian Building: Cathedral of Finance. 2008. (Illus.). 160p. 50.00 *(978-0-8143-3385-3(0))* Wayne State Univ. Pr.

Travers, David. Arts & Architecture 1945-54: The Complete Reprint. Weiner, Nina, ed. 2008. (ENG., Illus.). 6076p. reprint ed. pap. 700.00 *(978-3-8228-2678-2(2))* TASCHEN DEU. Dist: Ingram Pub. Services.

Treu, Martin M. Signs, Streets, & Storefronts: A History of American Commercial Art & Architecture. 2012. ***(978-1-4214-0494-3(X))*** Johns Hopkins Univ. Pr.

Tribert, Renee & O'Gorman, James F. Gervase Wheeler: A British Architect in America, 1847-1860. 2012. (Driftless Connecticut Series & Garnet Bks.). (ENG., Illus.). 136p. 35.00 *(978-0-8195-7145-8(8))* Wesleyan Univ. Pr.

Turberg, Edward F. & Pezzoni, J. Daniel. The Architectural History of Richmond County, North Carolina: Based on the Work of Edward F. Turberg & Others. 2007. *(978-1-57864-451-3(8))* Donning Co. Pubs.

Tyler, Norman, et al. Historic Preservation: An Introduction to Its History, Principles, & Practice. 2nd ed. 2009. (ENG., Illus.). 272p. pap. 35.00 *(978-0-393-73273-3(8),* 73273) Norton, W. W. & Co., Inc.

Ugochukwu, Chukwunyere C. Urban Neighborhood Revitalization & Heritage Conservation: The Architecture of Urban Redesign. 2006. (Illus.). 240p. (C). 109.95 *(978-0-7734-5663-1(5))* Mellen, Edwin Pr., The.

Ungermann-Marshall, Yana. Flintridge. 2008. (Images of America Ser.). (ENG., Illus.). 128p. per. 19.99 *(978-0-7385-5585-0(1))* Arcadia Publishing.

U.S. Green Building Council Staff, contrib. by. Existing Buildings: Operations & Maintenance Reference Guide. 2008. (Illus.). 532p. pap. ***(978-1-932444-13-1(0))*** U. S. Green Building Council.

—USGBC LEED AP Homes Study Guide. 2009. (Illus.). 282p. ***(978-1-932444-25-4(4))*** U. S. Green Building Council.

Valderrama, Victor Lobos. A Self Portrait. 2008. 64p. pap. *(978-3-8364-7123-7(X))* VDM Verlag Dr. Mueller e.K.

Vale, Lawrence J., compiled by. Changing Cities: 75 Years of Planning Better Futures at MIT. 2008. (Illus.). 144p. pap. 30.00 *(978-0-9794774-2-3(5))* SA+P Pr.

Van Ravenswaay, Charles. The Arts & Architecture of German Settlements in Missouri: A Survey of a Vanishing Culture. 2nd ed. 2006. (ENG., Illus.). 576p. (C). 59.95 *(978-0-8262-1700-4(1))* Univ. of Missouri Pr.

Varner, Gary. Strangely Wrought Creatures of Life Dea. 2007. 160p. pap. 15.95 *(978-1-4303-0261-2(5))* Lulu Enterprises Inc.

Varner, Gary R. Gargoyles, Grotesques & Green Men: Ancient Symbolism in European & American Architecture. 2008. 184p. pap. 16.95 *(978-1-4357-1142-6(4))* Lulu Enterprises Inc.

Verderber, Stephen. Delirious New Orleans: Manifesto for an Extraordinary American City. 2009. (Roger Fullington Series in Architecture). (ENG., Illus.). 288p. 45.00 *(978-0-292-71753-4(9))* Univ. of Texas Pr.

Vignelli, Massimo, ed. The Grotta House by Richard Meier. 2007. (ENG., Illus.). 120p. 45.00 *(978-0-8478-3009-1(8))* Rizzoli International Pubns., Inc.

Vintage Grand Rapids VII. 2009. 39.95 *(978-0-9785053-2-5(8))* Grand Rapids Pr., The.

Visser, Thomas Durant. Porches of North America. 2012. (ENG., Illus.). 304p. 39.95 ***(978-1-61168-220-5(7))*** Univ. Pr. of New England.

Voelkel, Richard, ed. Architecture: A Window on the Past. (Orange Countiana Ser.). 159p. 40.00 *(978-1-881860-02-0(7));* pap. 32.00 *(978-1-881860-03-7(5))* Orange County Historical Society.

Waddell, Theodore. Design Without Fashion. 2010. (ENG., Illus.). 192p. 55.00 *(978-88-572-0328-7(X))* Skira Editore ITA. Dist: Random Hse., Inc.

Wagner Murray Architects, PA Staff, contrib. by. Visual Performances: Wagner Murray Architects, PA. 2007. pap. *(978-0-89587-354-5(0))* Blair, John F. Pub.

Waldheim, Charles & Ray, Katerina Ruedi, eds. Chicago Architecture: Histories, Revisions, Alternatives. 2007. (Chicago Architecture & Urbanism Ser.). (Illus.). 442p. per. 25.00 *(978-0-226-87039-7(1))* Univ. of Chicago Pr.

Walker, Nathaniel Robert, et al. Building Expectation: Past & Present Visions of the Architectural Future. Walker, Nathaniel Robert, ed. 2011. (Illus.). 24p. ***(978-0-933519-53-4(2))*** Brown Univ., David Winton Bell Gallery.

Walker, Richard A. The Country in the City: The Greening of the San Francisco Bay Area. 2008. (Weyerhaeuser Environmental Bks.). (ENG., Illus.). 424p. pap. 24.95 *(978-0-295-98815-3(0))* Univ. of Washington Pr.

Wallick, Karl, et al. KieranTimberlake: A Manual of Work. 2011. (ENG., Illus.). 256p. 55.00 *(978-0-8478-3678-9(9))* Rizzoli International Pubns., Inc.

Wallpaper Editors, ed. Wallpaper City Guide Chicago 2012. 2012. (ENG., Illus.). 128p. pap. 9.95 ***(978-0-7148-6299-6(1))*** Phaidon Pr., Inc.

Wallpaper Magazine Editors, ed. Los Angeles 2012 - Wallpaper City Guide. 3rd ed. 2011. (ENG., Illus.). 128p. pap., pap. 9.95 *(978-0-7148-6095-4(6))* Phaidon Pr., Inc.

—Miami 2012 - Wallpaper City Guide. 2nd ed. 2011. (ENG., Illus.). 128p. pap. 9.95 *(978-0-7148-6093-0(X))* Phaidon Pr., Inc.

—New York 2011 - Wallpaper City Guide. 4th ed. 2011. (ENG., Illus.). 128p. pap. 9.95 *(978-0-7148-5944-6(3))* Phaidon Pr., Inc.

—San Francisco 2011 - Wallpaper City Guide. rev. ed. 2011. (Wallpaper* City Guides). (ENG., Illus.). 128p. pap. 9.95 *(978-0-7148-5664-3(9))* Phaidon Pr., Inc.

Wallpaper Magazine Editors, ed. Wallpaper City Guide Las Vegas 2012. 2012. (ENG., Illus.). 128p. pap. 9.95 ***(978-0-7148-6303-0(3))*** Phaidon Pr. Ltd. GBR. Dist: Hachette Bk. Group.

Walton-Buchanan, Holly. Historic Houses & Buildings of Reno, Nevada: An Architectural & Historical Guide. 2007. (Illus.). 146p. pap. 14.95 *(978-1-891033-35-3(2))* Black Rock Pr.

Washington-Melchizedek. Halriem's Storehouse Private Road. 2009. pap. *(978-1-61584-829-4(0))* Independent Pub.

Wasserman, James. The Secrets of Masonic Washington: A Guidebook to Signs, Symbols, & Ceremonies at the Origin of America's Capital. 2008. (ENG., Illus.). 1p. pap. 16.95 *(978-1-59477-266-5(5))* Inner Traditions International, Ltd.

Waugh, Emily, ed. GSD Platform 3. 2010. 336p. *(978-84-92861-50-7(9))* Actar Birkhauser Distribution.

Way, Thaisa. Unbounded Practice: Women & Landscape Architecture in the Early Twentieth Century. 2009. (ENG., Illus.). 320p. (gr. 17). 50.00 *(978-0-8139-2808-1(7))* Univ. Pr. of Virginia.

Webb, Michael. The Architecture & Design Los Angeles Guide. 2nd ed. Date not set. (Illus.). 50p. pap. 9.95 *(978-0-9641863-3-0(0),* TUB Pr.) Understanding Business.

—Steven Ehrlich: A Dynamic Serenity. 2006. (House Design Ser.: Vol. 2). (ENG., Illus.). 128p. 49.50 *(978-1-86470-102-9(1))* Images Publishing Group AUS. Dist: National Bk. Network.

Weinberg, David. Towering Mirrors, Mirroring Towers: Photographs of Urban Reflections. 2006. (ENG., Illus.). 96p. 50.00 *(978-0-9777531-2-3(3))* Glitterati, Inc.

Weintraub, Alan, photos by. Frank Lloyd Wright: American Master. 2009. (Illus.). 400p. 30.00 *(978-0-8478-3236-1(8))* Rizzoli International Pubns., Inc.

Weiser, Dennis. Missouri Courthouses: Building Memories. 2006. *(978-1-57864-399-8(6))* Donning Co. Pubs.

Weiss Bricker, Lauren. The Mediterranean House in America. 2008. (ENG., Illus.). 240p. 55.00 *(978-0-8109-7285-8(9))* Abrams.

Weiss, Ellen. Robert R. Taylor & Tuskegee: An African American Architect Designs for Booker T. Washington. 2011. (ENG.). 400p. 39.95 *(978-1-58838-248-1(6),* NewSouth Bks.) NewSouth, Inc.

Weiss, Marion & Manfredi, Michael A. Surface/Subsurface. 2007. (ENG., Illus.). 208p. 60.00 *(978-1-56898-733-0(1))* Princeton Architectural Pr.

Weissbach, Lee Shai. The Synagogues of Kentucky: Architecture & History. 2011. (Perspectives on Kentucky's Past: Architecture, Archaeology, & Landscape Ser.). (ENG., Illus.). 200p. pap. 25.00 *(978-0-8131-3368-3(8))* Univ. Pr. of Kentucky.

Welch, Diane Y. Lilian J. Rice: Architect of Rancho Santa Fe, California. 2010. (Illus.). 224p. 49.99 *(978-0-7643-3456-6(5))* Schiffer Publishing, Ltd.

Wells, Malcolm. The Earth-Sheltered House: An Architect's Sketchbook. rev. ed. 2009. (ENG.). 192p. pap. 24.95 *(978-1-60358-107-3(3))* Chelsea Green Publishing.

Wertheimer, Lester, et al. Architecture History 2009. 2008. (ENG.). 208p. pap. 59.95 *(978-1-4277-7824-6(8))* Kaplan Publishing.

Westmoreland-Doherty, Lisa. Louisville Architectural Tours: 19th Century Gems. 2008. (Illus.). 128p. pap. 14.99 *(978-0-7643-3038-4(1))* Schiffer Publishing, Ltd.

Wexler, Donald. Steel & Shade: The Architecture of Donald Wexler. 2011. (ENG., Illus.). 132p. pap. 50.00 ***(978-3-86828-191-0(6))*** Kehrer Verlag Heidelberg, Klaus Kehrer DEU. Dist: Consortium Bk. Sales & Distribution.

White, Norval, et al. AIA Guide to New York City. 5th ed. 2010. (ENG., Illus.). 1088p. 99.00 *(978-0-19-538385-0(0));* 1056p. pap. 39.95 *(978-0-19-538386-7(9))* Oxford Univ. Pr., Inc.

White, Samuel G. & White, Elizabeth. Stanford White, Architect. 2008. (ENG., Illus.). 320p. 40.00 *(978-0-8478-3079-4(9))* Rizzoli International Pubns., Inc.

White, Warren H. Covered Bridges in the Southeastern United States: A Comprehensive Illustrated Catalog. alt. ed. 2012. (ENG., Illus.). 252p. pap. 40.00 *(978-0-7864-6633-7(2))* McFarland & Co., Inc. Pubs.

Widder, Lynnette, ed. Alumi Travel Award 2009. 2009. pap. 18.00 *(978-1-61584-120-2(2))* Independent Pub.

Wiegers, Robert P. Missouri Armories. 2012. (ENG., Illus.). 216p. pap. 34.95 ***(978-1-61248-063-3(2))*** Truman State Univ. Pr.

Wilkins, Craig L. The Aesthetics of Equity: Notes on Race, Space, Architecture, & Music. 2007. (Illus.). 256p. 75.00 *(978-0-8166-4660-9(0));* per. 25.00 *(978-0-8166-4661-6(9))* Univ. of Minnesota Pr.

William, Ecenbarger & Susan, Ecenbarger. Glory By The Wayside. 2008. 88p. 29.95 *(978-0-9776139-0-8(9))* Passage Pr., Inc.

Williams, A. Richard. Archipelago: Islands of Living & Learning Architecture. 2009. (ENG.). 456p. pap. 35.00 *(978-0-252-07685-5(0))* Univ. of Illinois Pr.

Williams, Frank, text. Frank Williams Architect. 2010. (ENG., Illus.). 224p. 75.00 *(978-0-8478-3475-4(1))* Rizzoli International Pubns., Inc.

Williams, Homer. Building Type Basics for Banks & Financial Institutions. 2010. (Building Type Basics Ser.: 16). (ENG., Illus.). 256p. 85.00 *(978-0-470-27862-8(5),* Wiley) Wiley, John & Sons, Inc.

Wilson, Andrea S. Gettin' Out of the Projects. 2008. 596p. per. 47.95 *(978-1-58112-385-2(X),* Dissertation.com) Universal Pubs.

Wilson, Chris & Polyzoides, Stefanos, eds. The Plazas of New Mexico. 2011. (ENG., Illus.). 342p. 45.00 *(978-1-59534-083-2(1))* Trinity Univ. Pr.

Wilson, Richard Guy. Harbor Hill: Portrait of a House. 2008. (ENG., Illus.). 264p. 60.00 *(978-0-393-73216-0(9),* 73216) Norton, W. W. & Co., Inc.

Wilsted, Thomas. Planning New & Remodeled Archival Facilities. 2007. *(978-1-931666-25-1(3))* Scarecrow Pr., Inc.

Wittenberg, Marie C. Eden Prairie: A Brief History. 2010. 160p. 19.99 *(978-1-59629-941-2(X))* History Pr., The.

Wittman, Albert D. Architecture of Minneapolis Parks. 2010. 15p. 7.99 *(978-0-7385-6042-7(1));* (ENG., Illus.). 128p. pap. 21.99 *(978-0-7385-6026-7(X))* Arcadia Publishing.

Witynski, Karen & Carr, Joe P. Hacienda Courtyards, 1 vol. 2007. (ENG., Illus.). 144p. 29.95 *(978-1-4236-0001-5(0))* Gibbs Smith, Publisher.

Wolfe, Tom. From Bauhaus to Our House. 2009. (ENG.). 128p. pap. 15.00 *(978-0-312-42914-0(2))* Picador.

Wolner, Edward W. Henry Ives Cobb's Chicago: Architecture, Institutions, & the Making of a Modern Metropolis. 2011. (Chicago Architecture & Urbanism Ser.). (ENG., Illus.). 400p. 45.00 *(978-0-226-90561-7(6))* Univ. of Chicago Pr.

Womack, Wayne Marsh. A Philosophy for Planting Design. 2007. (Illus.). xiv, 145p. *(978-0-9744030-5-2(9))* Darbonne & Bartolett Pubs.

Woodbridge, Sally B. Bernard Maybeck: Visionary Architect. 2006. (ENG., Illus.). 248p. pap. 45.00 *(978-0-7892-0132-4(1))* Abbeville Pr., Inc.

Woods, Mary N. Beyond the Architect's Eye: Photographs & the American Built Environment. 2009. (Illus.). 368p. (C). 55.00 *(978-0-8122-4108-2(8))* Univ. of Pennsylvania Pr.

Woodward, Jeannette A. Countdown to a New Library: Managing the Building Project. 2nd ed. 2010. (Illus.). vii, 272p. *(978-0-8389-1012-2(2))* American Library Assn.

Wrenick, Frank E. & Wrenick, Elaine V., eds. The Streamline Era Greyhound Terminals: The Architecture of W. S. Arrasmith. alt. ed. 2011. (ENG., Illus.). 204p. pap. 38.00 *(978-0-7864-6445-6(3))* McFarland & Co., Inc. Pubs.

Wright, Frank Lloyd. Frank Lloyd Wright: Art Glass of the Martin House Complex. Jackson-Forsberg, Eric, ed. 2009. 96p. 27.95 *(978-0-7649-5150-3(5))* Pomegranate Communications, Inc.

—Modern Architecture: Being the Kahn Lectures for 1930. 2008. (ENG., Illus.). 176p. 29.95 *(978-0-691-12937-2(1))* Princeton Univ. Pr.

Wright, Gwendolyn. USA: Modern Architectures in History. 2008. (Reaktion Books - Modern Architectures in History Ser.). (ENG., Illus.). 272p. pap. 29.95 *(978-1-86189-344-4(2))* Reaktion Bks., Ltd. GBR. Dist: Chicago Distribution Ctr.

Yablon, Nick. Untimely Ruins: An Archaeology of American Urban Modernity, 1819-1919. 2010. (ENG., Illus.). 400p. 70.00 *(978-0-226-94663-4(0))* Univ. of Chicago Pr.

Yale School of Architecture Staff. Negotiated Terrains. Kilmer, Heather & Rappaport, Nina, eds. 2009. (Yale School of Architecture Bks.). (ENG., Illus.). 152p. pap. 35.00 *(978-0-393-73323-5(8),* 73323) Norton, W. W. & Co., Inc.

Yale School of Architecture Staff, et al. Learning in Las Vegas: Yale School of Architecture, Edward P. Bass Distinguished Visiting Architecture Fellowship. 2011. (Yale School of Architecture Bks.). (ENG., Illus.). 192p. pap. 35.00 *(978-0-393-73334-1(3),* 73334) Norton, W. W. & Co., Inc.

Yasuda, Anita. Snapshots of San Diego: Sun, Surf & Sand. 2008. (Illus.). 128p. pap. 24.95 *(978-0-7643-2804-6(2))* Schiffer Publishing, Ltd.

Yee, Roger. Educational Environments No. 4: Featuring Green Design Strategies. 2009. (Illus.). 260p. 70.00 net. *(978-1-58471-167-4(1))* Visual Reference Pubns., Inc.

—Healthcare Spaces No. 4. 2008. (Illus.). 300p. 60.00 *(978-1-58471-112-4(4))* Visual Reference Pubns., Inc.

Yee, Roger, ed. HLW At 125: Better Performance By Design, 1 vol. 2010. (ENG., Illus.). 197p. 60.00 *(978-0-9825989-3-1(9))* Visual Profile Bks., Inc.

Yoon, J. Meejin & Höweler, Eric. Expanded Practice: Höweler + Yoon Architecture/My Studio. 2009. (ENG., Illus.). 208p. pap. 40.00 *(978-1-56898-866-5(4))* Princeton Architectural Pr.

Young, Dwight & Gary, Grace Dietzel. Nemours: A Portrait of Alfred I. duPont's Home. 2011. (ENG., Illus.). 308p. 40.00 *(978-0-8478-3659-8(2))* Rizzoli International Pubns., Inc.

Zanow, Lois & Johnston, Sally. Monuments to Heaven: Baltimore's Historic Houses of Worship. 2010. 128p. pap. 38.49 *(978-1-4520-8537-1(4))* AuthorHouse.

Ziga, Charles J. New York Landmarks: A Collection of Architectural & Historical Details. 2011. (Illus.). 64p. 12.95 *(978-0-7893-2223-4(4))* Universe Publishing.

Zittel, Andrea & Vischer, Theodora, texts. Gouachen und Illustrationen / Gouaches & Illustrations, 1 vol. 2008. (GER & ENG., Illus.). 206p. pap. 35.00 *(978-3-86521-722-6(2))* Steidl, Gerhard Druckerei und Verlag DEU. Dist: Innovative Logistics.

ARCHITECTURE—YEMEN

see Architecture, Domestic—Yemen

ARCHITECTURE, ANCIENT

see also Pyramids; Seven Wonders of the World; Temples
also Architecture—Egypt; Architecture, Greek and similar headings

Bretschneider, J., et al, eds. Power & Architecture. Monumental Public Architecture in the Bronze Age near East & Aegean: Proceedings of the international conference 'Power & Architecture' organized by the Katholieke Universiteit Leuven, the Universite Catholique de Louvain & the Westfalischen Wilhelms-Universitat Munster on the 21st & 22nd of November 2002. 2007. (Orientalia Lovaniensia Analecta Ser.). (ENG., Illus.). 212p. (C). 109.00 *(978-90-429-1831-3(4))* Peeters Pubs. & Booksellers BEL. Dist: Brown, David Bk. Co., The.

Bruehler, Bart B. A Public & Political Christ: The Social-Spatial Characteristics of Luke 18:35Ð19:43 & the Gospel as a Whole in Its Ancient Context. 2011. (Princeton Theological Monographs). 422p. pap. 46.00 ***(978-1-60608-851-7(3)***, Pickwick Pubns.) Wipf & Stock Pubs.

Brusasco, Paolo. The Archaeology of Verbal & Nonverbal Meaning: Mesopotamian Domestic Architecture & Its Textual Dimension. 2007. (Bar S Ser.). (ENG., Illus.). 147p. (C). pap. 80.00 *(978-1-4073-0045-0(8))* British Archaeological Reports Ltd. GBR. Dist: Brown, David Bk. Co., The.

Clarie, Thomas C. Pharos: A Lighthouse for Alexandria. 2009. pap. 29.95 *(978-1-934582-12-1(3))* Back Channel Pr.

Clarke, Somers. Ancient Egyptian Masonry: The Building Craft. 2009. 352p. 29.95 *(978-1-4344-5212-2(3))*; pap. 14.95 *(978-1-4344-5119-4(4))* Wildside Pr., LLC.

Coppens, Filip. The Wabet: Tradition & Innovation in Temples of the Ptolemaic & Roman Period. 2008. (ENG., Illus.). 243p. (C). 110.00 *(978-80-7308-190-4(3))* Czech Institute of Egyptology CZE. Dist: Brown, David Bk. Co., The.

Daehner, Jens, et al. The Herculaneum Women & the Origins of Archaeology. 2008. (Illus.). 160p. 50.00 *(978-0-89236-882-2(9))* Oxford Univ. Pr., Inc.

de Grummond, Nancy T. & Edlund-Berry, Ingrid, eds. The archaeology of sanctuaries & ritual in Etruria. 2011. (Illus.). 167p. 87.00 *(978-1-887829-81-6(4))* Journal of Roman Archaeology, LLC.

Eichmann, Ricardo. Uruk: Architektur. 2007. (GER., Illus.). *(978-3-89646-036-3(6))* VML Verlag Marie Leidorf GmbH.

Feuerstein, Gunther. Urban Fiction: Urban Utopias from Antiquity until Today. 2008. (ENG., Illus.). 560p. 138.00 *(978-3-930698-26-4(9))* Edition Axel Menges GmbH DEU. Dist: National Bk. Network.

Gupta, S.P. Elements of Indian Art: Including Temple Architecture, Iconography & Iconometry. 2nd ed. 2007. (SAN & ENG., Illus.). xiv, 146p. *(978-81-246-0214-0(X))* D. K. Print World (P) Ltd.

Hitchins, Derek. The Secret Diaries of Hemiunu, Architect of the Great Pyramid. 2010. 241p. pap. 41.95 *(978-1-4457-4824-5(X))* Lulu Enterprises Inc.

Lavan, Luke, et al, eds. Housing in Late Antiquity: From Palaces to Shops. 2007. (LAA 2005 3. 1 Social & Political Life / 3. 2 Housing Ser.). (Illus.). 538p. *(978-90-04-16228-0(3))* BRILL.

—Objects in Context, Objects in Use: Material Spatiality in Late Antiquity. 2008. (Late Antique Archaeology Ser.). (Illus.). 741p. *(978-90-04-16550-2(9))* BRILL.

Lightbody, David I. Egyptian Tomb Architecture: The Archaeological Facts of Pharaonic Circular Symbolism. 2008. (Bar S Ser.). (ENG., Illus.). 88p. (C). pap. 62.50 *(978-1-4073-0339-0(2))* British Archaeological Reports Ltd. GBR. Dist: Brown, David Bk. Co., The.

Lulof, Patricia S. & Rescigno, Carlo, eds. Deliciae Fictiles IV: Architectural Terracottas in Ancient Italy. Images of Gods, Monsters & Heroes. 2011. (GER, ITA & ENG., Illus.). 672p. (C). 80.00 *(978-1-84217-426-5(6))* Oxbow Bks., Ltd. GBR. Dist: Brown, David Bk. Co., The.

McCormick, Clifford Mark. Palace & Temple: A Study of Architectural & Verbal Icons. (Beihefte zur Zeitschrift fur die alttestamentliche Wissenschaft Ser.). (ENG.). X, 221p. 180.00 ***(978-3-11-179678-9(7))*** De Gruyter, Walter Inc.

McKenzie, Judith. The Architecture of Alexandria & Egypt, 300 B. C. — A. D. 700. 2011. (Yale University Press Pelican Histor Ser.). (Illus.). 480p. pap. 56.00 *(978-0-300-17094-8(7))* Yale Univ. Pr.

Nardo, Don, ed. Ancient Egyptian Art & Architecture. 2011. (Eye on Art Ser.). (Illus.). 128p. (YA). (gr. 7-12). 33.45 *(978-1-4205-0674-7(9))* Cengage Gale.

Ratté, Christopher. Lydian Architecture: Ashlar Masonry Structures at Sardis. 2011. (Archaeological Exploration of Sardis Reports). (ENG., Illus.). 320p. 85.00 *(978-0-674-06060-9(1))* Harvard Univ. Pr.

Rivera, Angelyn Bass & Rainer, Leslie, eds. The Conservation of Decorated Surfaces on Earthen Architecture. 2006. (Symposium Proceedings Ser.). (Illus.). 220p. pap. 75.00 *(978-0-89236-850-1(0))* Oxford Univ. Pr., Inc.

Rodgers, Nigel. The Art & Architecture of Ancient Greece: An Illustrated Account of Classical Greek Buildings, Sculptures & Paintings, Shown in 200 Glorious Photographs & Drawings. 2012. (ENG., Illus.). 128p. pap. 17.99 ***(978-1-84476-802-8(3))*** Anness Publishing GBR. Dist: National Bk. Network.

Rossi, Corinna. Architecture & Mathematics in Ancient Egypt. 2007. (ENG.). 302p (C). pap. 54.00 *(978-0-521-69053-9(6))* Cambridge Univ. Pr.

Stierlin, Henri. The Pharaohs Master-Builders. 2008. (Illus.). 255p. pap. 23.50 *(978-2-87939-328-5(0))* Terrail, Pierre Editions FRA. Dist: Perseus-PGW.

Stocks, Denys A. Experiments in Egyptian Archaeology: Stoneworking Technology in Ancient Egypt. 2010. 296p. pap. 39.95 *(978-0-415-58894-2(4))* Routledge.

Tadgell, Christ. Antiquity: Origins, Classicism & the New Rome. 2007. (ENG., Illus.). 876p. 110.00 *(978-0-415-40750-2(8))* Routledge.

Tadgell, Christopher. The East: Buddhists, Hindus & the Sons of Heaven. 2007. (ENG., Illus.). 924p. 110.00 *(978-0-415-40752-5(4))* Routledge.

Tiradritti, Francesco. Egyptian Wall Painting. 2008. (ENG., Illus.). 392p. 175.00 *(978-0-7892-1008-1(8))* Abbeville Pr., Inc.

Tiradritti, Francesco & Vannini, Sandro. Egyptian Wall Painting. deluxe ed. 2008. (ENG., Illus.). 391p. 150.00 *(978-0-7892-1005-0(3))* Abbeville Pr., Inc.

Truemper, Monika. Graeco-Roman Slave Markets - Fact or Fiction? 2009. (ENG., Illus.). 160p. (C). 45.00 *(978-0-9774094-8-8(1))* Brown, David Bk. Co., The.

Varner, Gary R. Gargoyles, Grotesques & Green Men: Ancient Symbolism in European & American Architecture. 2008. 184p. pap. 16.95 *(978-1-4357-1142-6(4))* Lulu Enterprises Inc.

Watson, Philip. Egyptian Pyramids & Mastaba Tombs. 2009. (Shire Egyptology Ser.: No. 6). (ENG., Illus.). 64p. pap. 13.95 *(978-0-85263-853-8(1))* Shire Pubns., Ltd. GBR. Dist: Random Hse., Inc.

Westgate, Ruth, et al, eds. Building Communities: House, Settlement & Society in the Aegean & Beyond: Proceedings of a Conference Held at Cardiff University, 17-21 April 2001. 2007. (BSA Studies). (ENG., Illus.). 430p. (C). 178.00 *(978-0-904887-56-3(1))* British Schl. at Athens GBR. Dist: Brown, David Bk. Co., The.

Westwell, Ian & Pereira, Robin. Ancient Monuments Revealed. 2007. (Illus.). 160p. 19.99 *(978-0-7858-2080-2(9)*, Chartwell) Book Sales, Inc.

Wightman, G. J. Sacred Spaces: Religious Architecture in the Ancient World. 2007. (Ancient near Eastern Studies: Vol. 22). (ENG.). 1156p. (C). 174.00 *(978-90-429-1803-0(9))* Peeters Pubs. & Booksellers BEL. Dist: Brown, David Bk. Co., The.

Wildung, Dietrich. Egypt. Stierlin, Henri, ed. 25th ed. 2009. (25 Ser.). (ENG., Illus.). 224p. 14.99 *(978-3-8365-1030-1(8))* TASCHEN DEU. Dist: Ingram Pub. Services.

Wright. Ancient Building Technology, Volume 3: Construction, 2 vols. 2009. (Technology & Change in History Ser.). (Illus.). *(978-90-04-17745-1(0))* BRILL.

ARCHITECTURE, ANGLO-SAXON

Crawford, Sally, et al. Form & Order in the Anglo-Saxon World, AD 600-1100. 2009. (Anglo-Saxon Studies in Archaeology & History Ser.). (Illus.). 128p. (C) pap. 70.00 *(978-1-905905-13-3(0))* Oxford Univ. Pr. GBR. Dist: Brown, David Bk. Co., The.

Taylor, H. M. & Taylor, Joan. Anglo-Saxon Architecture 3 Part Set, 3 vols. 2011. (ENG.). 1254p. pap. 105.00 *(978-1-107-69146-9(X))* Cambridge Univ. Pr.

ARCHITECTURE, ANONYMOUS

see Vernacular Architecture

ARCHITECTURE, ARAB

see Islamic Architecture

ARCHITECTURE, ART DECO

see Art Deco (Architecture)

ARCHITECTURE, BAROQUE

Bailey, Gauvin. Andean Hybrid Baroque: Convergent Cultures in the Churches of Colonial Peru. 2010. (History Lang & Cult Spanish Portuguese Ser.). (ENG., Illus.). 1016p. 75.00 *(978-0-268-02222-8(4))* Univ. of Notre Dame Pr.

Bailey, Gauvin Alexander. Baroque & Rococo. 2012. (ENG., Illus.). 448p. pap. 29.95 ***(978-0-7148-5742-8(4))*** Phaidon Pr., Inc.

Castelnuovo, Enrico & Barberis, Walter. La reggia di Venaria e i Savoia. Arte, magnificenza e storia di una corte europea. Catalogo della mostra (12 ottobre 2007-30 marzo 2008), 2 vols. 2008. (ITA & ENG., Illus.). 680p. pap. 90.00 *(978-88-422-1585-1(6))* Allemandi, Umberto & Co. GBR. Dist: National Bk. Network.

Cohen, Gary B. & Szabo, Franz A. J., eds. Embodiments of Power: Building Baroque Cities in Europe. 2008. (Austrian & Habsburg Studies). (Illus.). 320p. (C). 90.00 *(978-1-84545-433-3(2))* Berghahn Bks., Inc.

DAAB Media Staff, ed. Modern Baroque Interiors, 1 vol. 2008. (ENG.). 384p. 59.95 *(978-3-86654-017-0(5))* DAAB Media Gmbh DEU. Dist: Innovative Logistics.

Dardanello, Giuseppe, et al. Guarini. 2008. (ITA & ENG., Illus.). 564p. 90.00 *(978-88-422-1471-7(X))* Allemandi, Umberto & Co. GBR. Dist: Antique Collectors' Club.

De Lucca, Dennis. Jesuits & Fortifications: The Contribution of the Jesuits to Military Architecture in the Baroque Age. 2012. (History of Warfare Ser.). (ENG., Illus.). 400p. ***(978-90-04-21651-8(0))*** BRILL.

Giuffrè, M. Teresa. The Baroque Architecture of Sicily. 2008. (ENG., Illus.). 288p. 95.00 *(978-0-500-34239-8(3))* Thames & Hudson.

Guillen-Nuñez, Cesar. Macao's Church of Saint Paul: A Glimmer of the Baroque in China. 2008. (ENG., Illus.). 196p. (gr. 17). 45.00 *(978-962-209-922-7(X))* Hong Kong Univ. Pr. HKG. Dist: Columbia Univ. Pr.

Pozzolo, Luca Dal & Benente, Michela. Baroque: 300 Years Old & as Young as Ever - Contemporary Architecture in Turin, No. 4. 2008. (ENG., Illus.). 80p. pap. 14.95 *(978-88-422-1464-9(7))* Allemandi, Umberto & Co. GBR. Dist: Antique Collectors' Club.

Riegl, Alois, et al. The Origins of Baroque Art in Rome. Hopkins, Andrew & Witte, Arnold Alexander, eds. 2010. (Texts & Documents Ser.). (ENG., Illus.). 292p. pap. 50.00 *(978-1-60606-041-4(4)*, Getty Research Institute) Getty Pubns.

Robertson-Justiniano, Maria. The Architecture of the Margins: Gongora's Las Soledades. 2008. 200p. pap. *(978-3-8364-5305-9(3))* VDM Verlag Dr. Mueller e.K.

Schlimme, Hermann & Sickel, Lothar, eds. Ordnung und Wandel: in der römischen Architektur der Frühen Neuzeit - Kunsthistorische Studien zu Ehren von Christof Thoenes. 2010. (Roemische studien der bibliotheca Hertziana Ser.). (GER., Illus.). 254p. (C). 140.00 *(978-3-7774-2301-2(7))* Hirmer Verlag GmbH DEU. Dist: Brown, David Bk. Co., The.

Toman, Rolf, ed. Baroque: Architecture - Sculpture - Painting, 1 vol. 2011. (ENG.). 500p. 19.99 ***(978-3-8331-6001-1(2))*** h.f.ullmann DEU. Dist: Innovative Logistics.

Toman, Rolf, ed. Baroque: Architecture, Sculpting, Painting. 2008. (Architecture Sculpture Painting Ser.). (Illus.). 500p. per. 24.95 *(978-0-8416-0058-4(9))* American Map Corp.

Ward, W. C. Sir John Vanbrugh V1. 2006. pap. 38.95 *(978-1-4286-6103-5(4))* Kessinger Publishing, LLC.

—Sir John Vanbrugh V2. 2006. pap. 34.95 *(978-1-4286-6104-2(2))* Kessinger Publishing, LLC.

Zanlungo, Claudia. The Story of Baroque Architecture. 2012. (ENG., Illus.). 144p. pap. 19.95 ***(978-3-7913-4595-6(8))*** Prestel Publishing.

Zirpolo, Lilian H. Historical Dictionary of Baroque Art & Architecture. 2010. (Historical Dictionaries of Literature & the Arts Ser.). (ENG., Illus.). 642p. 140.00 *(978-0-8108-6155-8(0))* Scarecrow Pr., Inc.

ARCHITECTURE, BUDDHIST

see Buddhist Architecture

ARCHITECTURE, BYZANTINE

Beyer, Hermann Wolfgang. Der syrische Kirchenbau. (Studien zur spätantiken Kunstgeschichte Ser.). (GER.). VIII, 183p. 210.00 ***(978-3-11-216114-2(9))***; 135.00 ***(978-3-11-102620-6(5))*** De Gruyter, Walter Inc.

Beyer, Hermann W. Der syrische Kirchenbau. (Studien zur spätantiken Kunstgeschichte Ser.). (GER.). VIII, 183p. 240.00 ***(978-3-11-176217-3(3))*** De Gruyter, Walter Inc.

Cutler, Anthony. Refiguring the Face of God: The Daphni Pantokrator. 2011. (Studies in the Visual Cultures of the Middle Ages Ser.). (ENG., Illus.). 250p. (C). pap. 102.00 *(978-2-503-52766-6(3))* Brepols Pubs. BEL. Dist: Brown, David Bk. Co., The.

Demesnil, Nicole Lemaigre. Architecture Rupestre et Decor Sculpte en Cappadoce. 2010. (Bar S Ser.). (FRE & ENG., Illus.). 306p. (C). pap. 127.50 *(978-1-4073-0569-1(7))* British Archaeological Reports Ltd. GBR. Dist: Brown, David Bk. Co., The.

Eichner, Ina & Tsamakda, Vasiliki, eds. Syrien und seine Nachbarn von der Spatantike bis in die islamische Zeit. 2009. (Spatantike-Fruhes Christentum-Byzanz Ser.). (GER., Illus.). 308p. (C). 168.00 *(978-3-89500-674-6(2))* Reichert, Ludwig Dr. DEU. Dist: Brown, David Bk. Co., The.

Freely, John & akmak, Ahmet S. Byzantine Monuments of Istanbul. 2009. (ENG., Illus.). 342p. (C). pap. 48.00 *(978-0-521-17905-8(X))* Cambridge Univ. Pr.

Gerstel, Sharon E. J. Beholding the Sacred Mysteries: Programs of the Byzantine Sanctuary. 2009. 226p. 34.00 *(978-1-59740-724-3(0))*; pap. 22.00 *(978-1-59740-746-5(1))* ACLS Humanities E-Book.

Hiscock, Nigel. The symbol at your Door: Number & geometry in the religious architecture of the greek & latin middle Ages. 2007. (Illus.). 442p. 134.95 *(978-0-7546-6300-3(0))* Ashgate Publishing Co.

Johnson, Mark J., et al. Approaches to Byzantine Architecture & Its Decoration: Studies in Honor of Slobodan Curcic. 2012. (Illus.). 330p. 124.95 ***(978-1-4094-2740-7(4))*** Ashgate Publishing Co.

Ousterhout, Robert. Master Builders of Byzantium. 2008. (Illus.). 320p. (C). pap. 39.95 *(978-1-934536-03-2(2)*, Univ. of Pennsylvania Museum of Archaeology & Anthropology) Univ. Museum Pubns.

Ousterhout, Robert G. A Byzantine Settlement in Cappadocia. 2nd rev. ed. 2012. (Dumbarton Oaks Studies). (ENG., Illus.). 504p. pap. 50.00 *(978-0-88402-370-8(2))* Dumbarton Oaks.

Piltz, Elisabeth. From Constantine the Great to Kandinsky: Studies in Byzantine & Post-Byzantine Art & Architecture. 2007. (Bar S Ser.). (Illus.). 75p. (C). pap. 65.00 *(978-1-4073-0104-4(7))* British Archaeological Reports Ltd. GBR. Dist: Brown, David Bk. Co., The.

Savelev, IU R. Iskusstvo Istorizma I Gosudarstvennyi Zakaz: Vtoraia Polovina XIX — Nachalo XX Veka. 2008. (RUS., Illus.). 304p. *(978-5-903060-60-3(9))* Sovpacenie, Izdatel'stvo.

Van Millingen, Alexander. Byzantine Churches in Constantinople. 2008. 484p. *(978-1-4437-2475-3(0))* 2006. (ENG.). 480p. per. *(978-1-4067-3141-5(2))* Read Bks. (Hesperides Pr.).

Yerasimos, Stephane. Constantinople: Istanbul's Historical Heritage. 2008. (Art & Architecture Ser.). (Illus.). 400p. pap. 24.95 *(978-0-8416-0062-1(7))* American Map Corp.

ARCHITECTURE, CARLOVINGIAN

see Architecture, Carolingian

ARCHITECTURE, CAROLINGIAN

Fenske, Lutz, et al. Deutsche Königspfalzen: Beiträge Zu Ihrer Historischen und Archäologischen Erforschung. (Veröffentlichungen des Max-Planck-Instituts Für Geschichte Ser.). (GER., Illus.). (C). 2007. 382p. 179.00 *(978-3-525-35600-5(5))* 2006. 240p. 125.00 *(978-3-525-36521-2(7))* Vandenhoeck & Ruprecht GmbH & Co. KG DEU. Dist: ISD.

ARCHITECTURE, CHURCH

see Church Architecture

ARCHITECTURE, CISTERCIAN

see Cistercian Architecture

ARCHITECTURE, CLUNIAC

see Cluniac Architecture

ARCHITECTURE, COLONIAL

see also Architecture—United States; Architecture, Domestic—United States

Architectural Record Staff. The Restoration of Colonial Williamsburg in Virginia. (Illus.). 458p. reprint ed. lib. bdg. 98.00 *(978-0-7222-0566-2(X))* Library Reprints, Inc.

Chandler, Joseph E., ed. The Colonial Architecture of Maryland, Pennsylvania & Virginia. (Illus.). reprint ed. lib. bdg. 88.00 *(978-0-7222-0963-9(0))* Library Reprints, Inc.

Cousins, Frank. The Colonial Architecture of Salem. 2010. (ENG.). 442p. pap. 36.75 *(978-1-176-31491-7(2))* BiblioBazaar.

—The Colonial Architecture of Salem. 2010. 142p. pap. 23.09 *(978-1-151-98534-7(1))* General Bks. LLC.

Cousins, Frank & Riley, Phil M. The Colonial Architecture of Salem. 2010. 430p. 41.99 *(978-1-140-19722-5(3))* BiblioBazaar.

—The Colonial Architecture of Salem. 2007. (ENG.). 436p. 51.95 *(978-0-548-35488-9(X))*; per. 36.95 *(978-0-548-27946-9(0))* Kessinger Publishing, LLC.

—The Colonial Architecture of Salem. (Illus.). reprint ed. lib. bdg. 98.00 *(978-0-7222-0664-5(X))* Library Reprints, Inc.

Cousins, Frank & Riley, Phil Madison. The Colonial Architecture of Salem. 2010. 444p. pap. 35.75 *(978-1-146-97251-2(2))*; 442p. pap. 35.75 *(978-1-146-61856-4(5))*; 440p. pap. 35.75 *(978-1-143-98405-1(6))* BiblioBazaar.

Cryder, Jo. 1000 Shutters & Awnings. 2007. (Illus.). 160p. pap. 29.95 *(978-0-7643-2711-7(9))* Schiffer Publishing, Ltd.

Demissie, Fassil. Colonial Architecture & Urbanism in Africa: Interwined & Contested Histories. 2012. (Design & the Built Environment Ser.). (Illus.). 336p. 119.95 ***(978-0-7546-7512-9(2))*** Ashgate Publishing Co.

Dubow, Jessica. Settling the Self. 2009. (Illus.). 208p. pap. *(978-3-639-17075-7(X))* VDM Verlag Dr. Mueller e.K.

Dullemen, C. J. van. Tropical Modernity: Life & Work of C.P. Wolff Schoemaker. 2010. (Illus.). 270p. *(978-90-8506-879-2(7))* SUN B.V., Uitgeverij.

Eberlein, Harold D. The Architecture of Colonial America. 2007. (ENG.). 368p. per. 33.95 *(978-1-4326-5024-7(6))* Kessinger Publishing, LLC.

Fuller, Mia. Moderns Abroad: Architecture, Cities & Italian Imperialism. (Architext Ser.). (Illus.). 2009. 274p. 53.95 *(978-0-415-77985-2(5))* 2006. (ENG., 288p. (C). 110.00 *(978-0-415-19463-1(6))* Routledge.

—Moderns Abroad: Architecture, Cities, & Italian Imperialism in the Mediterranean & East Africa. 2007. (Architext Ser.). (Illus.). 256p. 48.95 *(978-0-415-19464-8(4))* Routledge.

Hesperides. Colonial Churches. 2007. 392p. per. *(978-1-4067-5944-0(9)*, Hesperides Pr.) Read Bks.

Isham, Norman Morrison. Early American Houses: With a Glossary of Colonial Architectural Terms. 2007. (Dover Architecture Ser.). (ENG., Illus.). 160p. per. 9.95 *(978-0-486-46035-2(5))* Dover Pubns., Inc.

Jewsiewicki, Bogumil. The Beautiful Time: Photography by Sammy Baloji. 2010. (ENG., Illus.). 48p. pap. 22.00 *(978-0-945802-55-6(2))* Museum for African Art.

Kelly, J. Frederick. Early Domestic Architecture of Connecticut. 2007. (Illus.). 230p. pap. 29.95 *(978-0-7643-2664-6(3))* Schiffer Publishing, Ltd.

Kimball, Fiske. Domestic Architecture of the American Colonies & of the Early Republic. 2009. 48p. pap. *(978-1-4590-6713-4(4))* Books LLC.

Lathrop, Elsie. Historic Houses of Early America. 2006. (ENG.). 552p. per. 42.95 *(978-1-4286-5501-0(8))* Kessinger Publishing, LLC.

Nelson, Louis P. The Beauty of Holiness: Anglicanism & Architecture in Colonial South Carolina. 2009. (Richard Hampton Jenrette Series in Architecture & the Decorative Arts Ser.). (ENG., Illus.). 516p. 52.95 *(978-0-8078-3233-2(2))* Univ. of North Carolina Pr.

Newcomb, Rexford. Spanish-Colonial Architecture in the United States. (Illus.). 39p. reprint ed. lib. bdg. 88.00 *(978-0-7222-0212-8(1))* Library Reprints, Inc.

Paul, Linda Leigh. Haciendas: Spanish Colonial Houses in the U. S. & Mexico. 2008. (ENG., Illus.). 224p. 55.00 *(978-0-8478-3099-2(3))* Rizzoli International Pubns., Inc.

Ripley, Hubert G. New England Inns & Taverns: The Monograph Series V18, No. 6. Whitehead, Russell F., ed. 2011. 20p. pap. 35.95 ***(978-1-258-03320-0(8))*** Literary Licensing, LLC.

Skinner, Tina & Ward, Tammy. New England's Architecture: By Wallace Nutting. 2007. (Illus.). 144p. pap. 29.95 *(978-0-7643-2654-7(6))* Schiffer Publishing, Ltd.

Tsai, Hui-Yu Caroline, et al. Taiwan in Japan's Empire-Building: An Institutional Approach to Colonial Engineering. 2009. (Illus.). XVIII, 334p. 140.00 *(978-0-415-44738-6(0))* Routledge.

Wainwright, Paul, photos by. A Space for Faith: The Colonial Meetinghouses of New England. 2010. (Illus.). 128p. 35.00 *(978-0-9817898-5-3(4)*, Jetty Hse.) Randall, Peter E. Pub.

ARCHITECTURE, COMPUTER

see Computer Architecture

ARCHITECTURE, DOMESTIC

see also Adobe Houses; Apartment Houses; Bathrooms; Bedrooms; Cottages; Country Homes; Decks (Architecture, Domestic); House Construction; Living Rooms; Nurseries; Patios; Recreation Rooms; Solar Houses

Adams, Nicky. Glass House: Buildings for Open Living. 2008. (ENG., Illus.). 192p. 45.00 *(978-0-86565-190-6(6))* Vendome Pr., The.

Agari, Masuhiro, ed. Retiring in Style Around the World. 2007. (Illus.). 207p. 49.95 *(978-4-7661-1738-7(7))* Graphic-Sha JPN. Dist: Gingko Pr., Inc.

Allen, Gordon. The Cheap Cottage & Small House. 2007. 188p. per. *(978-1-905217-90-8(0))* Mills, Jeremy Publishing.

Alter, Kevin & Hoidn, Barbara, eds. Brazil: House in Santa Teresa, 2008 by Angelo Bucci; House at Rio Bonito, 2003 by Carla Juacaba. 2009. (ENG., Illus.).

144p. pap. 40.00 *(978-3-8030-0699-8(6))* Wasmuth, Ernst J. Verlag GmbH & Co. DEU. Dist: D.A.P./Distributed Art Pubs.

Andeweg, Marie Therèse. Cost C16 improving the quality of existing urban building Envelopes. 2007. pap. 69.00 *(978-1-58603-735-2(8),* Delft University Pr) IOS Pr., Inc.

Andeweg, Marie Therèse, et al. Cost C16 improving the quality of existing urban building Envelopes. 2007. pap. 69.00 *(978-1-58603-734-5(X),* Delft University Pr) IOS Pr., Inc.

Australian House and Garden Staff & Australian Women's Weekly Staff. House. (ENG., Illus.). 248p. pap. 34.95 *(978-1-86396-285-8(9))* ACP Publishing Pty, Ltd. AUS. Dist: Graphic Arts Ctr. Publishing Co.

Ballantyne, Andrew & Law, Andrew. Tudoresque: In Pursuit of the Ideal Home. 2011. (ENG., Illus.). 272p. 45.00 *(978-1-86189-811-1(8))* Reaktion Bks., Ltd. GBR. Dist: Chicago Distribution Ctr.

Barreneche, Raul A. Modern House Three. 2006. (SPA.). 59.95 *(978-0-7148-9852-0(X))* Phaidon Pr., Inc.

—The Tropical Modern House. 2011. (ENG., Illus.). 240p. 50.00 *(978-0-8478-3412-9(3))* Rizzoli International Pubns., Inc.

Barton Myers Associates. 3 Steel Houses. 2006. (House Design Ser.: Vol. 2). (ENG., Illus.). 128p. 49.50 *(978-1-876907-89-1(4))* Images Publishing Group AUS. Dist: National Bk. Network.

Beck, Haig & Cooper, Jackie. Architectus: Between Order & Opportunity. 2009. (ENG., Illus.). 240p. 65.00 *(978-0-9814628-6-8(3))* Oro Editions.

Bertram, Carel. Imagining the Turkish House: Collective Visions of Home. 2008. (ENG., Illus.). 360p. (C). pap. 24.95 *(978-0-292-71826-5(8))* Univ. of Texas Pr.

Beta-Plus Publishing. Designer Houses: Home Series 10. 2009. (Home Ser.). (ENG., Illus.). 128p. pap. *(978-90-8944-041-9(0),* Beta-Plus (Acc)) Antique Collectors' Club.

—Home Series Set Vols 21-30. 2010. (ENG.). pap. *(978-1-905377-45-9(2),* Beta-Plus (Acc)) Antique Collectors' Club.

Biddulph, Mike. Introduction to Residential Layout. 2006. (ENG., Illus.). 256p. per. 54.95 *(978-0-7506-6205-5(0))* Routledge.

Bilhuber, Jeffrey. Defining Luxury: The Qualities of Life at Home. 2008. (ENG., Illus.). 256p. 65.00 *(978-0-8478-3054-1(3))* Rizzoli International Pubns., Inc.

Bishop, Justin. Country Style & Design. 2012. (ENG., Illus.). 224p. 50.00 *(978-1-86470-448-8(9))* Images Publishing Group AUS. Dist: National Bk. Network.

Black Dog and Leventhal Publishers Staff, ed. The Big Book of Small House Designs: 75 Award-Winning Plans for Your Dream House, 1,250 Square Feet or Less. 2011. (ENG., Illus.). 368p. pap. 17.95 *(978-1-57912-887-6(4),* 1579128874) Black Dog & Leventhal Pubs., Inc.

Boas, Adrian J. Domestic Settings in Crusader States: Sources on Domestic Architecture & Day-to-Day Activities in the Latin East. 2010. (Illus.). 396p. *(978-90-04-18272-1(1))* BRILL.

Bonfato, Antonio Carlos. Macedo Vieira: Ressonâncias Do Modelo Cidade-Jardim. 2008. (Illus.). 245p. *(978-85-7359-700-4(3))* Servico Nacional de Aprendizagem Comercial, Senac.

Booqs Staff, ed. PREFAB HOUSES, 1 vol. 2011. (FRE, DUT, GER & ENG., Illus.). 620p. (J). pap. 24.95 *(978-94-6065-053-6(8))* booQs Publishers bvba BEL. Dist: Innovative Logistics.

Booth, Norman K. & Hiss, James E. Residential Landscape Architecture: Design Process for the Private Residence. (ENG., 576p. (C). 5th ed. 2007. Illus.). 126.40 *(978-0-13-612697-3(9))* 6th ed. 2011. 126.40 *(978-0-13-237619-8(9))* Prentice Hall PTR. (Prentice Hall).

Bradbury, Dominic. Mediterranean Modern. 2006. (ENG., Illus.). 256p. 35.00 *(978-0-500-34227-5(X))* Thames & Hudson.

—New Country Houses. 2007. (ENG., Illus.). 208p. pap. 35.00 *(978-0-7892-0853-8(9))* Abbeville Pr., Inc.

Broto, Carles. Compact Interiors. 2009. (ENG.). 240p. pap. 29.99 *(978-84-96969-96-4(7))* Links International (Leading International Key Services Barcelona, S.A.) ESP. Dist: National Bk. Network.

—Contemporary Wood Houses. 2008. (ENG.). 240p. 39.95 *(978-84-96969-06-3(1))* Links International (Leading International Key Services Barcelona, S.A.) ESP. Dist: National Bk. Network.

—Houses Now 2. George, William et al, trs. 2007. (ENG., Illus.). 240p. 54.95 *(978-84-96424-75-3(8))* Links International (Leading International Key Services Barcelona, S.A.) ESP. Dist: National Bk. Network.

—Houses Now 3. 2012. (ENG., Illus.). 240p. 39.00 *(978-84-92796-85-4(5))* Links International (Leading International Key Services Barcelona, S.A.) ESP. Dist: National Bk. Network.

—Minimalist Interiors. 2007. (ENG., Illus.). 240p. 39.95 *(978-84-96263-02-4(9))* Links International (Leading International Key Services Barcelona, S.A.) ESP. Dist: National Bk. Network.

—New Domestic Interiors. 2009. (ENG.). 239p. pap. 34.99 *(978-84-96969-95-7(9))* Links International (Leading International Key Services Barcelona, S.A.) ESP. Dist: National Bk. Network.

—New Perspectives: Country Houses. 2007. (ENG., Illus.). 256p. pap. 24.95 *(978-84-96424-47-0(2))* Links International (Leading International Key Services Barcelona, S.A.) ESP. Dist: National Bk. Network.

—Small Wood Cabins. 2012. (ENG.). 240p. 47.00 *(978-84-15123-59-0(0))* Links International (Leading International Key Services Barcelona, S.A.) ESP. Dist: National Bk. Network.

—Smart Interiors. 2009. (ENG.). 168p. pap. 24.99 *(978-84-96969-94-0(0))* Links International (Leading International Key Services Barcelona, S.A.) ESP. Dist: National Bk. Network.

—Superb Cabins. 2009. (ENG.). 192p. pap. 24.99 *(978-2-917031-37-7(9))* Links International (Leading International Key Services Barcelona, S.A.) ESP. Dist: National Bk. Network.

—Superb Wood Houses. 2012. (ENG.). 240p. 45.00 *(978-84-15123-34-7(5))* Links International (Leading International Key Services Barcelona, S.A.) ESP. Dist: National Bk. Network.

—Wood Cabins. 2009. (ENG.). 192p. pap. 24.99 *(978-2-917031-38-4(7))* Links International (Leading International Key Services Barcelona, S.A.) ESP. Dist: National Bk. Network.

Broto, Charles. Cozy Wood Interiors. 2008. (ENG.). 300p. pap. 24.00 *(978-84-96969-08-7(8))* Links International (Leading International Key Services Barcelona, S.A.) ESP. Dist: National Bk. Network.

—Smart Home Extensions. 2008. (ENG.). 300p. 57.00 *(978-84-96969-04-9(5))* Links International (Leading International Key Services Barcelona, S.A.) ESP. Dist: National Bk. Network.

Brun, Christine. Small Space Living. 2009. 128p. bds. 34.99 *(978-0-7643-3192-3(2))* Schiffer Publishing, Ltd.

Brusasco, Paolo. The Archaeology of Verbal & Nonverbal Meaning: Mesopotamian Domestic Architecture & Its Textual Dimension. 2007. (Bar S Ser.). (ENG., Illus.). 147p. (C). pap. 80.00 *(978-1-4073-0045-0(8))* British Archaeological Reports Ltd. GBR. Dist: Brown, David Bk. Co., The.

Campbell, David. Wood in Traditional Architecture. 2011. (Illus.). 224p. 45.00 *(978-0-7643-3581-5(2))* Schiffer Publishing, Ltd.

Cappelli, Lucas, ed. Self-Fab House: 2nd Advanced Architecture Contest. 2010. 384p. pap. *(978-84-96954-74-8(9))* Actar Birkhauser Distribution.

Carpenter, William J. & Carpenter. Modern Sustainable Residential Design: A Guide for Design Professionals. 2009. (ENG., Illus.). 352p. 85.00 *(978-0-470-12673-8(6),* Wiley) Wiley, John & Sons, Inc.

Chan, Yenna. Sustainable Environments. 2008. (Contemporary Design in Detail Ser.). (ENG., Illus.). 192p. pap. 25.00 *(978-1-59253-504-0(6),* 1592535046) Quayside.

Chartrand, Jane W. From the Ground Up. 2007. 183p. pap. 15.95 *(978-1-4303-1127-0(4))* Lulu Enterprises Inc.

Cheah, Fay, ed. Homes, Issues + Processes: Design Collective Architects. 2011. (ENG.). 144p. pap. 29.95 *(978-1-907317-46-0(5))* Black Dog Publishing Ltd. GBR. Dist: Perseus Distribution.

Chueca, Pilar. Today's City Houses. 2009. (ENG.). 240p. pap. 29.99 *(978-84-96969-93-3(2))* Links International (Leading International Key Services Barcelona, S.A.) ESP. Dist: National Bk. Network.

Cleary, Mark. The World's Best Beach Houses. 2012. (ENG., Illus.). 296p. 60.00 ***(978-1-86470-442-6(X))*** Images Publishing Group AUS. Dist: National Bk. Network.

Cleary, Mark, ed. 200 Houses. 2011. (ENG., Illus.). 800p. 59.95 *(978-1-86470-436-5(5))* Images Publishing Group AUS. Dist: National Bk. Network.

Cliff, Stafford. Home: 50 Tastemakers Describe What It Is, Where It Is, What It Means. 2007. (ENG., Illus.). 256p. pap. 25.95 *(978-1-57965-349-1(9),* 1579653499) Artisan.

Cohen, Scott & Lexau, Elizabeth. Scott Cohen's Poolscapes: Refreshing Ideas for the Ultimate Backyard Resort. 2011. (Illus.). 160p. *(978-0-7643-3740-6(8),* Schiffer Publishing Ltd) Schiffer Publishing, Ltd.

Coles, Anne & Jackson, Peter. Windtower: Houses of the Bastakia. 2007. (Illus.). 180p. 55.95 ***(978-1-905299-24-9(9),*** Stacey International) Stacey Publishing GBR. Dist: Midpoint Trade Bks., Inc.

Collings, Janet. Victorian & Edwardian Houses: A Guide to Care & Maintenance. 2008. (ENG., Illus.). 160p. 43.95 *(978-1-84797-057-2(5))* Crowood Pr., Ltd. GBR. Dist: Independent Pubs. Group.

Connelly, Megan. Kids' Rooms. 3rd ed. 2008. (Home Decorating Ser.). (ENG., Illus.). 224p. pap. 21.95 *(978-1-58011-389-2(3))* Creative Homeowner.

Connors, Michael. Caribbean Houses: History, Style, & Architecture. 2009. (ENG., Illus.). 272p. 60.00 *(978-0-8478-3213-2(9))* Rizzoli International Pubns., Inc.

Conran, Terence. Small Spaces: The Back to Basics Guide to Home Design, Decoration, & Furnishing. 2010. (ENG., Illus.). 112p. 20.00 *(978-1-84091-552-5(8),* Conran Octopus) Octopus Publishing Group GBR. Dist: Hachette Bk. Group.

—The Ultimate House Book: For Home Design in the Twenty-First Century. 2006. (ENG., Illus.). 144p. 39.95 *(978-1-84091-352-1(5),* Conran Octopus) Octopus Publishing Group GBR. Dist: Hachette Bk. Group.

Costa Duran, Sergi, ed. High Density Housing. 2009. (Illus.). 256p. *(978-84-92463-35-0(X))* Loft Pubns.

Cousins, Matthew. Design Quality in New Housing: Learning from the Netherlands. 2008. (Illus.). 176p. 165.00 *(978-0-415-44769-0(0));* pap. 71.95 *(978-0-415-44770-6(4))* Taylor & Francis Group.

Crafti, Stephen. Affordable Architecture: Great Houses on a Budget. 2010. (ENG., Illus.). 224p. 50.00 *(978-1-86470-392-4(X))* Images Publishing Group AUS. Dist: National Bk. Network.

—Details for Living. 2007. (ENG., Illus.). 200p. 50.00 *(978-1-86470-249-1(4))* Images Publishing Group AUS. Dist: National Bk. Network.

Crafti, Stephen. 21st Century Architecture: Beach Houses. 2011. (ENG., Illus.). 240p. 50.00 ***(978-1-86470-446-4(2))*** Images Publishing Group AUS. Dist: National Bk. Network.

Cusato, Marianne, et al. Get Your House Right: Architectural Elements to Use & Avoid. 2011. (ENG., Illus.). 272p. pap. 19.95 *(978-1-4027-9103-1(8))* Sterling Publishing Co., Inc.

DAAB Media Staff, creator. Door Design, 1 vol. 2008. (ENG, FRE, GER, ITA & SPA., Illus.). 383p. 37.95 *(978-3-937718-56-9(7))* DAAB Media Gmbh DEU. Dist: Innovative Logistics.

DAAB Media Staff, ed. Restroom Design, 1 vol. 2008. (ITA, FRE, GER, SPA & ENG., Illus.). 383p. 37.95 *(978-3-86654-023-1(X))* DAAB Media Gmbh DEU. Dist: Innovative Logistics.

de Canales, Francisco Gonzalez. Experiments with Life Itself. 2012. (ENG., Illus.). 152p. pap. *(978-84-92861-65-1(7))* Actar Birkhauser Distribution.

—Experiments with Life Itself (Spanish Ed.) 2012. (SPA.). 152p. pap. *(978-84-92861-66-8(5))* Actar Birkhauser Distribution.

de Geyter, Eva. Villas: Frank Missotten. 2011. (DUT, FRE, GER & ENG., Illus.). 320p. 85.00 *(978-90-209-9101-7(9))* Lannoo Pubs./Racine.

de Haro, Fernando & Fuentes, Omar. Houses: Expressions with Personality. 2011. (Houses Ser.). (ENG & SPA., Illus.). 210p. 39.95 *(978-607-437-068-3(0))* AM Editores MEX. Dist: Perseus-PGW.

de Haro, Fernando & Fuentes, Omar, compiled by. Homes: Architecture Comes to Life. 2011. (ENG., Illus.). 284p. 45.00 ***(978-607-437-082-9(6))*** AM Editores MEX. Dist: Perseus-PGW.

de Haro, Fernando & Fuentes, Omar, compiled by. Houses: Evolution of Forms. 2011. (Houses Ser.). (ENG & SPA., Illus.). 176p. 39.95 *(978-607-437-038-6(9))* AM Editores MEX. Dist: Perseus-PGW.

Desjarlais, Mary. Beauty on the Streets of Detroit: A history of the housing market in Detroit. 2011. (Illus.). 176p. pap. 19.95 ***(978-0-9836315-0-7(6))*** Cambourne Publishing.

Di Giulio, Roberto. COST C16 improving the quality of existing urban building Envelopes. 2007. pap. 69.00 *(978-1-58603-737-6(4),* Delft University Pr) IOS Pr., Inc.

Di Giulio, Roberto, et al. COST C16 improving the quality of existing urban building Envelopes. 2007. pap. 69.00 *(978-1-58603-736-9(6),* Delft University Pr) IOS Pr., Inc.

DiGioia, Michael. What You Should Know about Building a New Home or Adding an Addition. 2011. 20p. pap. 24.95 ***(978-1-4634-0581-6(2))*** AuthorHouse.

Dinlawarie, Dawud, ed. Urban Living: Visionen neuen Wohnens. 2009. (GER & ENG., Illus.). 144p. 42.00 *(978-3-939633-64-8(X))* Jovis Verlag GmbH DEU. Dist: D.A.P./Distributed Art Pubs.

Donaghey, John E. Building Your Dream House: Architect's Notes. 3rd rev. ed. 2012. (ENG., Illus.). 82p. spiral bd. 18.85 *(978-0-9604298-1-3(6))* Donaghey, John Pubns.

Downing, A. Rural Essays. 2011. (ENG.). 643p. pap. 36.95 ***(978-1-4585-0137-0(X))*** Univ. of Michigan Library.

Downing, Andrew Jackson. Rural Essays by a J Downing Ed, with a Memoir of the Author, by George William Curtis, & a Letter to His Friends, by Frederika Bremer. 2006. 648p. per. 34.99 *(978-1-4255-6679-1(0));* per. 34.99 *(978-1-4255-6686-9(3))* MPublishing.

Drew, Paul & Richards, Ivor. Dwelling: Accordia. 2009. (ENG., Illus.). 128p. 29.95 *(978-1-906155-90-2(9))* Black Dog Publishing Ltd. GBR. Dist: Perseus Distribution.

Driendl, Georg & Lehrl, Gregor, eds. APOPliving: ... apartments, houses, Cities. 2010. (ENG., Illus.). 336p. pap. 69.95 *(978-3-7091-0116-2(6),* 3709101166) Springer.

Dummies Press Staff & DeGunther, Rik. Energy Efficient Homes for Dummies. 2008. (ENG., Illus.). 384p. pap. 21.99 *(978-0-470-37602-7(3),* For Dummies) Wiley, John & Sons, Inc.

Dunlop, Carson. The Illustrated Home. 2nd ed. 2006. (ENG., Illus.). 382p. pap. 85.00 *(978-1-4195-8919-5(9))* Kaplan Publishing.

Duran, Sergi Costa. Eco House: Practical Ideas for a Greener, Healthier Dwelling. 2010. (ENG., Illus.). 160p. pap. 19.95 *(978-1-55407-782-3(6))* Firefly Bks., Ltd.

Duran, Sergi Costa & Duran, Sergi C. Green Homes: New Ideas for Sustainable Living. 2007. (ENG., Illus.). 192p. 35.00 *(978-0-06-134826-6(0),* Collins Design) HarperCollins Pubs.

Ebner, Peter & Gerstenberg, Frauke. Housing Moves On: Architects & their Views. Hollbacher, Roman, ed. 2008. (GER & ENG., Illus.). 196p. pap. *(978-3-211-79173-8(6),* 3211791736) Actar Birkhauser Distribution.

Ebner, Peter, et al. Typologie+ Innovativer Wohnungsbau. 2009. (Illus.). 431p. *(978-3-0346-0086-6(0))* Birkhauser Verlag AG.

Eck, Jeremiah. House in the Landscape: Siting Your Home Naturally. 2010. (ENG., Illus.). 208p. pap. 40.00 *(978-1-56898-823-8(0))* Princeton Architectural Pr.

Femia, Angela. Ik Ben Zo Blij Dat Ik Hier Ben - I Am So Glad That I Am Here. 2008. 60p. pap. *(978-3-639-00533-2(3))* VDM Verlag Dr. Mueller e.K.

Fisher, T. J. Vieux Carré Chic: The Art of Overindulgent Home Decor. 2011. (ENG., Illus.). 224p. 49.95 *(978-0-9773514-5-9(9))* Morgana Pr. LLC.

Frauel, Jacobo. Prefabulous Architecture. 2010. (ENG., Illus.). 300p. pap. 39.00 *(978-84-96969-78-0(9))* Links International (Leading International Key Services Barcelona, S.A.) ESP. Dist: National Bk. Network.

Friedman, Avi & MacBurnie, Ian. Terraced & Row Housing. 2012. (ENG., Illus.). 272p. pap. 53.95 *(978-0-415-77912-8(X))* Routledge.

Friedman, Rodney & Anton, Frank, contrib. by. In Praise of Pragmatism: Fisher Friedman Associates. 2010. (ENG., Illus.). 214p. pap. 45.00 *(978-0-9793801-3-6(8))* Oro Editions.

Fusion Publishing, ed. Luxury Houses Holiday Escapes. 2008. (Luxury Bks.). (Illus.). 220p. 49.95 *(978-3-8327-9225-1(2))* teNeues Publishing Co.

Galindo, Michelle. Country House Architecture + Design. 2011. (Masterpieces Ser.). (ENG., Illus.). 304p. 49.95 *(978-3-03768-072-8(5),* Braun Publish,Csi) Continental Sales, Inc.

Gao, Arthur. Residential Landscape. 2011. (ENG., Illus.). 272p. 50.00 *(978-988-19739-4-8(5))* Design Media Publishing Ltd. HKG. Dist: BookMasters Distribution Services (BDS).

Gardner, E. C. The House That Jill Built, after Jack's Had Proved a Failure. 2007. (Illus.). 204p. per. *(978-1-4065-2757-5(2))* Dodo Pr.

Gardner, Eugene Clarence. Homes & How to Make Them. 2008. (Illus.). 172p. 22.99 *(978-0-554-34203-0(0))* 2008. (Illus.). 172p. 25.99 *(978-0-554-24900-1(6))* 2007. (ENG.). 160p. pap. 19.99 *(978-1-4264-7617-4(5))* 2007. (ENG.). 170p. pap. 21.99 *(978-1-4264-7668-6(X))* BiblioBazaar.

—Homes & How to Make Them. 2009. 140p. pap. *(978-1-150-26362-0(8))* Books LLC.

—Homes & How to Make Them. 2007. (ENG., Illus.). 160p. per. *(978-1-4065-2756-8(4))* Dodo Pr.

—Homes, & How to Make Them by E C Gardner. 2006. 316p. per. 23.99 *(978-1-4255-3032-7(X))* MPublishing.

—The House that Jill Built: A Book on Home Architecture. 2007. per. 14.95 *(978-0-9734676-8-0(1),* Logos Pr.) ThinkBiotech, LLC.

Gavin, Francesca. Creative Space: The Urban Homes of Artists & Creatives. 2009. (ENG., Illus.). 208p. 35.00 *(978-1-85669-588-6(3))* King, Laurence Publishing GBR. Dist: Hachette Bk. Group.

Glassman, Michael. Outdoor Designs for Living. 2009. 128p. pap. 24.99 *(978-0-7643-3180-0(9))* Schiffer Publishing, Ltd.

Gomez, Mariette Himes & Himes, Gomez M. Houses: Inside & Out. 2007. (ENG., Illus.). 256p. 39.95 *(978-0-06-112422-8(2),* Collins Design) HarperCollins Pubs.

Goodman, Jeremiah, illus. Jeremiah: A Romantic Vision. 2011. (ENG.). 208p. 85.00 *(978-1-57687-353-3(6))* powerHouse Cultural Entertainment, Inc.

Goodman, Jeremiah & Albee, Edward. Jeremiah: A Romantic Vision: Limited Editidion. 2007. 208p. pap. 200.00 *(978-1-57687-354-0(4))* powerHouse Cultural Entertainment, Inc.

Graffin, Emmanuelle. Houses by the Sea. 2011. (ENG., Illus.). 224p. pap. 27.95 *(978-0-500-28962-4(X),* 528962) Thames & Hudson.

Grant, Gary. Green Roofs & Façades. 2010. (ENG., Illus.). 84p. pap. 40.00 *(978-1-86081-940-7(0))* Building Research Establishment GBR. Dist: Taylor & Francis Group.

Green Homes. 2007. 192p. 35.00 *(978-0-06-149359-1(7),* Collins Design) HarperCollins Pubs.

Gringeri-Brown, Michelle. Atomic Ranch Midcentury Interiors, 1 vol. 2012. (ENG., Illus.). 192p. 40.00 ***(978-1-4236-1931-4(5))*** Gibbs Smith, Publisher.

Guild, Robin. The Victorian House Book: A Practical Guide to Home Repair & Decoration. 4th ed. 2008. (ENG., Illus.). 320p. 49.95 *(978-1-55407-371-9(5))* Firefly Bks., Ltd.

Habitat Collectif: Concepts, Projets, Realisations. 2006. (In Detail Ser.). (FRE., Illus.). 174p. 59.95 *(978-3-7643-7528-7(0),* 3764375280) Birkhauser Verlag AG CHE. Dist: Springer.

Hales, Shelley. The Roman House & Social Identity. 2009. (ENG., Illus.). 308p. pap. 35.99 *(978-0-521-73509-4(2))* Cambridge Univ. Pr.

Hallett, Anna. Almshouses. 2008. (Shire Library). (ENG., Illus.). 64p. pap. 12.95 *(978-0-7478-0583-0(0))* Shire Pubns., Ltd. GBR. Dist: Random Hse., Inc.

Hamilton, Elizabeth S. Outdoor Spaces: Backyards, Decks, Patios, Porches & Terraces. 2008. (Easy Transformations Ser.). (ENG., Illus.). 144p. pap. 14.95 *(978-1-58816-576-3(0))* Hearst Communications, Inc.

Heathcote, David. Seventies House: Interior Angles. 2008. (Interior Angles Ser.). 240p. pap. 40.00 *(978-0-470-02420-1(8))* Wiley, John & Sons, Inc.

Hiller, Nancy R. A Home of Her Own. 2011. (ENG., Illus.). 240p. pap. 29.95 *(978-0-253-22353-1(9),* 0253223539) Indiana Univ. Pr.

Hockley, Luke & Gardner, Leslie. House: The Wounded Healer on Television. 2010. (ENG.). 232p. (C). pap. 34.95 *(978-0-415-47913-4(4))* Routledge.

—House the Wounded Healer on Television. 2010. (ENG.). 232p. (C). 100.00 *(978-0-415-47912-7(6))* Routledge.

Homes. (Early Intervention Levels Ser.). 23.10 *(978-0-7362-0017-2(7))* Hampton-Brown Bks.

Homes, Vol. 4. (Early Intervention Levels Ser.). 3.85 *(978-1-56334-489-3(0))* Hampton-Brown Bks.

Hopkins, George D., Jr. Creating Your Architectural Style, 1 vol. 2009. (ENG., Illus.). 336p. 49.95 *(978-1-58980-719-8(7))* Pelican Publishing Co., Inc.

Hough, Jessica & Ramirez-Montagut, Monica, eds. Revisiting the Glass House: Contemporary Art & Modern Architecture. 2008. (ENG., Illus.). 134p. pap. 39.95 *(978-0-300-13587-9(4))* Yale Univ. Pr.

House, Steven & House, Cathi. Mediterranean Villages: An Architectural Journey. 2006. (ENG., Illus.). 320p. 70.00 *(978-1-86470-106-7(4))* Images Publishing Group AUS. Dist: National Bk. Network.

Hudson, Karen E. Paul R. Williams: Classic Hollywood Style. 2012. (ENG., Illus.). 240p. 65.00 ***(978-0-8478-3847-9(1))*** Rizzoli International Pubns., Inc.

Humphreys, Phebe. The Practical Book of Garden Architecture. 2008. (Gardening in America Ser.). (ENG.). 520p. pap. 29.95 *(978-1-4290-1299-7(4))* Applewood Bks.

Hunt, Roger & Suhr, Marianne. Old House: A Practical Guide to Care & Repair. 2008. (ENG., Illus.). 208p. instr.'s hndbk. ed. 39.95 *(978-0-7112-2772-9(1))* Lincoln, Frances Ltd. GBR. Dist: Perseus-PGW.

Iaac, ed. Self-Sufficient Housing: 1st Advanced Architecture Contest. 2006. (Illus.). 380p. pap. 33.00 *(978-84-96540-43-9(X))* Kunst-Werke Berlin e.V. DEU. Dist: Actar Birkhauser Distribution.

Iglesia, Rafael E. J. Habitar, Diseñar. 2010. (SPA., Illus.). 235p. *(978-987-584-262-5(1))* Nobuko.

Images & Images. Residential Spaces of the World Vol. 4: A Pictorial Review. 2006. (Residential Spaces Ser.). (ENG., Illus.). 224p. 55.00 *(978-1-86470-032-9(7))* Images Publishing Group AUS. Dist: National Bk. Network.

Images Publishing Group. Payette Associates Inc. 2006. (Master Architect Series VI). (ENG., Illus.). 59.95 *(978-1-876907-05-1(3)*, Images Publishing Dist Ac) Antique Collectors' Club GBR. Dist: National Bk. Network.

Images Publishing Group Editors. 100 of the World's Best Houses. 2006. (ENG., Illus.). 344p. 60.00 *(978-1-876907-42-6(8))* Images Publishing Group AUS. Dist: National Bk. Network.

Images Publishing Staff, PUBLISHING & Beaver, Robyn. Another 100 of the World's Best Houses. 2006. (ENG., Illus.). 352p. 60.00 *(978-1-920744-24-3(X))* Images Publishing Group AUS. Dist: National Bk. Network.

Images Publishing Staff, PUBLISHING, et al. In Residence: McInturff Architects. 2007. (House Design Ser.). (ENG., Illus.). 128p. 49.50 *(978-1-86470-124-1(2))* Images Publishing Group AUS. Dist: National Bk. Network.

Inions, Cynthia. Open-Plan Living: Creating a Stylish & Practical Open-Plan Home. 2007. (ENG., Illus.). 144p. pap. *(978-1-84597-557-9(X))* Ryland Peters & Small.

Jackson, Katy. The Self-Build Survival Guide. 2008. 224p. 26.00 *(978-1-84528-190-8(X))* How To Books GBR. Dist: Parkwest Pubns., Inc.

Jodidio, Philip. Architecture Now! Houses 2. 2011. (ENG, FRE & GER., Illus.). 416p. pap. 39.99 *(978-3-8365-1973-1(9))* TASCHEN DEU. Dist: Ingram Pub. Services.

Jodidio, Philip, ed. 100 Contemporary Houses: 25 Jahre TASCHEN, 2 vols. 2012. (25 Ser.). (ENG, FRE & GER., Illus.). 680p. 59.99 ***(978-3-8365-2330-1(2))*** TASCHEN DEU. Dist: Ingram Pub. Services.

John, Richard. Robert Adam: The Search for a Modern Classicism. 2010. (New Classicists Ser.). (Illus.). 90.00 *(978-1-920744-54-0(1)*, Images Publishing Dist Ac) Antique Collectors' Club GBR. Dist: National Bk. Network.

Johnson, Scott. Tall Building: Image of the Skyscraper. 2008. (ENG., Illus.). 192p. 34.95 *(978-1-890449-47-6(4))* Balcony Pr.

Keister, Douglas. 500 Bungalows. 2006. (ENG., Illus.). 508p. pap. 12.95 *(978-1-56158-842-8(3)*, Taunton) Taunton Pr., Inc.

Kemp, Barry J. & Stevens, Anna. Busy Lives at Amarna Vol. 2: Excavations in the Main City - (Grid 12 & the House of Ranefer, N49.18), 2 vols. 2011. (Excavation Memoirs Ser.). (ENG., Illus.). (C). pap. 130.00 *(978-0-85698-195-1(8))*; pap. 130.00 *(978-0-85698-197-5(4))* Egypt Exploration Society GBR. Dist: Brown, David Bk. Co., The.

Kemsley, Roderick & Platt, Christopher. Dwelling with Architecture. 2012. (ENG., Illus.). 248p. 165.00 ***(978-0-415-56903-3(6))***; pap. 49.95 ***(978-0-415-56904-0(4))*** Routledge.

Kibert, Charles J. Sustainable Construction: Green Building Design & Delivery. 2nd rev. ed. 2007. (ENG., Illus.). 432p. 85.00 *(978-0-470-11421-6(5)*, Wiley) Wiley, John & Sons, Inc.

King, Peter. In Dwelling: Implacability, Exclusion & Acceptance. 2008. (Design & the Built Environment Ser.). (Illus.). 170p. 124.95 *(978-0-7546-4870-3(2))* Ashgate Publishing Co.

Kliczkowski, Hugo. Exclusive Houses/Casas Exclusivas: Sea & Mountain/Mar y Montana. 2006. (Illus.). 215p. 45.00 *(978-84-96304-26-0(4))* HK Bks. ESP. Dist: Ingram Pub. Services.

Konemann Staff. Great Houses of Andalusia. Date not set. (Illus.). 250p. 19.95 *(978-3-8290-4068-6(7)*, 521508) Konemann.

Koones, Sheri. Prefabulous + Sustainable: Building & Customizing an Affordable, Energy-Efficient Home. 2010. (ENG., Illus.). 240p. 25.00 *(978-0-8109-8483-7(0))* Abrams.

Koones, Sheri, illus. Prefabulous: The House of Your Dreams, Delivered Fresh from the Factory. 2007. (ENG.). 218p. 25.00 *(978-1-56158-844-2(X)*, Taunton) Taunton Pr., Inc.

Kottas, Dimitris. The Architect's Handbook. 2007. (ENG., Illus.). 200p. pap. 24.95 *(978-84-96424-26-5(X))* Links International (Leading International Key Services Barcelona, S.A.) ESP. Dist: National Bk. Network.

—Small Interiors. 2007. (ENG., Illus.). 240p. 39.95 *(978-84-96263-87-1(8))* Links International (Leading International Key Services Barcelona, S.A.) ESP. Dist: National Bk. Network.

Krauel, Jacobo. Today's Wood Houses. 2010. (ENG., Illus.). 240p. 39.00 *(978-84-92796-53-3(7))* Links International (Leading International Key Services Barcelona, S.A.) ESP. Dist: National Bk. Network.

—Wood Houses. 2010. (ENG., Illus.). 240p. 39.95 *(978-84-92796-45-8(6))* Links International (Leading International Key Services Barcelona, S.A.) ESP. Dist: National Bk. Network.

Krebs, Jan. Basics Concevoir L'habitat. 2006. (Basics Ser.). (Illus.). 73p. pap. 16.50 *(978-3-7643-7953-7(7)*, 3764379537) Birkhauser Verlag AG CHE. Dist: Springer.

Kunz, Martin N. Seaside Hotels. 2009. 220p. pap. 19.95 *(978-3-8327-9334-0(8))* teNeues Publishing Co.

Kylloe, Ralph. The Log Home Book, 1 vol. 2010. (ENG., Illus.). 144p. 24.99 *(978-1-4236-1708-2(8))* Gibbs Smith, Publisher.

Lane, Barbara Miller, ed. Housing & Dwelling: Perspectives on Modern Domestic Architecture. 2006. (Illus.). 467p. 165.00 *(978-0-415-34655-9(X))*; (ENG., 480p. per. 54.95 *(978-0-415-34656-6(8))* Routledge.

Lang, Damon. New Ideas for Living Outdoors. 2010. (Illus.). 128p. 24.99 *(978-0-7643-3533-4(2))* Schiffer Publishing, Ltd.

Lapuerta, Jose Maria, ed. Manual de Vivenda Colectiva. 2007. (Illus.). 223p. per. *(978-84-96954-14-4(5))* Actar Birkhauser Distribution.

Lara, Fernando Luiz. The Rise of Popular Modernist Architecture in Brazil. 2008. (ENG., Illus.). 160p. 69.95 *(978-0-8130-3289-4(X))* Univ. Pr. of Florida.

Lawlor, Drue & Thomas, Michael A. Residential Design for Aging in Place. 2008. (ENG., Illus.). 272p. 80.00 *(978-0-470-05614-1(2)*, Wiley) Wiley, John & Sons, Inc.

Levitt, David. Housing Design Handbook: A Guide to Good Practice. 2009. (ENG., Illus.). 288p. 62.95 *(978-0-415-49150-1(9))* Routledge.

Light Screens Illustrated: The Stained Glass Windows of Frank Lloyd Wright. 2008. (Illus.). 112p. pap. 24.50 *(978-0-9724559-7-8(3))* Prairie Designs of California.

Long, M. J. The Artists' Studio. 2009. (ENG., Illus.). 192p. 45.00 *(978-1-906155-72-8(0))* Black Dog Publishing Ltd. GBR. Dist: Perseus Distribution.

Lord, Todd, 3rd, ed. The Designment Review. (Residential Design & Market Trends Ser.). (Illus.). 40p. (Orig.). pap. 8.00 *(978-0-936909-00-4(5))* Northwest Home Designing, Inc.

Machowiak, Aleksandra & Mizielinski, Daniel. H. O. U. S. E. Homes That Are Outrageous, Unbelievable, Spectacular, & Extraordinary - 35 Designs for Fantastic Living. 2012. (ENG.). 160p. 18.99 ***(978-0-06-211375-7(5)***, Collins Design) HarperCollins Pubs.

MacLennan, Cheryl. Historic Homes of Jefferson, Texas. 2011. E-Book ***(978-1-4556-1485-1(8))***; (ENG.). 96p. 25.00 *(978-1-4556-1484-4(X))* Pelican Publishing Co., Inc.

Madge, John. Tomorrows Houses. 2006. 336p. per. *(978-1-4067-3470-6(5)*, Hesperides Pr.) Read Bks.

Mahady, Michaela. Welcoming Home: Creating a House That Says Hello. 2010. (ENG., Illus.). 224p. 40.00 *(978-1-4236-0321-4(4))* Gibbs Smith, Publisher.

Mallea, Hermes. Great Houses of Havana. 2011. (ENG., Illus.). 272p. 75.00 *(978-1-58093-288-2(6))* Monacelli Pr., Inc.

Malone, Michael. The Architect's Guide to Residential Design. 2009. (ENG., Illus.). 272p. 59.95 *(978-0-07-160563-2(0)*, 0071605630) McGraw-Hill Professional Publishing.

Mathewson, Casey C. M., ed. Residential Designs for the 21st Century: An International Collection. 2007. (ENG & GER., Illus.). 576p. 69.95 *(978-1-55407-336-8(7))* Firefly Bks., Ltd.

McLeod, Virginia. Detail in Contemporary Residential Architecture. 2007. (ENG., Illus.). 240p. 50.00 *(978-1-85669-482-7(8))* King, Laurence Publishing GBR. Dist: Hachette Bk. Group.

Mead, Stephen P. House Revision: Sustainable Ideas for the Southwest Home. 2007. 176p. pap. 21.95 *(978-0-87358-920-8(3))* Northland Publishing.

Medford, Sarah. At Home with Town & Country. Town and Country Editors, ed. 2010. (ENG., Illus.). 384p. 60.00 *(978-1-58816-697-5(X))* Hearst Communications, Inc.

Meier, Richard. Richard Meier Houses & Apartments. 2007. (ENG., Illus.). 296p. 85.00 *(978-0-8478-2994-1(4))* Rizzoli International Pubns., Inc.

Melvin, Jeremy, et al, contrib. by. Place & Home: The Search for Better Housing - PRP Architects. 2007. (ENG., Illus.). 288p. 52.50 *(978-1-904772-66-8(8))* Black Dog Publishing Ltd. GBR. Dist: Perseus Distribution.

Menge, Shea. The Secrets of Pip Hannah. 2010. 89p. pap. 8.50 *(978-0-557-54090-7(9))* Lulu Enterprises Inc.

Messervy, Julie Moir & Susanka, Sarah. Outside the Not So Big House: Creating the Landscape of Home. 2008. (Susanka Ser.). (ENG., Illus.). 210p. pap. 21.95 *(978-1-60085-020-2(0))* Taunton Pr., Inc.

Minguet, Josep Maria. Family Housing. Minguet, Josep Maria & Vazquez, Oscar Mira, eds. 2009. (ENG & SPA., Illus.). 240p. 99.50 *(978-84-96823-42-6(3))* Instituto Monsa de Ediciones, S.A. ESP. Dist: Trans-Atlantic Pubns., Inc.

—Houses. 2006. (POR, ENG & SPA., Illus.). 256p. pap. 42.50 *(978-84-96429-64-2(4))* Instituto Monsa de Ediciones, S.A. ESP. Dist: Trans-Atlantic Pubns., Inc.

Montaner, Josep Maria. Tools for Inhabiting the Present: Housing in the 21st Century. 2011. (ENG & SPA.). 210p. pap. ***(978-84-614-7504-9(6))*** Actar Birkhauser Distribution.

Montgomery, Gladys. Storybook Cottages: America's Carpenter Gothic Style. 2011. (ENG., Illus.). 224p. 45.00 *(978-0-8478-3619-2(3))* Rizzoli International Pubns., Inc.

Moraes Zarzar, K. & Guney, A., eds. Understanding Meaningful Environments: Architectural Precedents & the Question of Identity in Creative Design - Volume 4 Research in Design Series. 2008. (Illus.). 388p. pap. 65.00 *(978-1-58603-913-4(X))* IOS Pr., Inc.

Morement, Adam. Extensions. 2007. (ENG., Illus.). 256p. 40.00 *(978-1-85669-494-0(1))* King, Laurence Publishing GBR. Dist: Hachette Bk. Group.

Moro, Marco & Spirandelli, Beatrice. Sustainable Living - Masterpieces of Ecological Architecture. 2011. (ENG., Illus.). 272p. 34.95 *(978-88-544-0594-3(9))* White Star ITA. Dist: Sterling Publishing Co., Inc.

Mostaedi, Arian. Great Spaces: Cabins: Small Houses in Nature. 2008. (ENG., Illus.). 240p. 39.95 *(978-84-96263-51-2(7))* Links International (Leading International Key Services Barcelona, S.A.) ESP. Dist: National Bk. Network.

—New Perspectives: Coastal Houses. 2007. (ENG., Illus.). 256p. pap. 24.95 *(978-84-96424-45-6(6))* Links International (Leading International Key Services Barcelona, S.A.) ESP. Dist: National Bk. Network.

Nettleton, Sarah & Martin, Frank Edgerton. The Simple Home: The Luxury of Enough. 2007. (American Institute Architects Ser.). (ENG., Illus.). 249p. 40.00 *(978-1-56158-831-2(8)*, Taunton) Taunton Pr., Inc.

Nillesen, Anne Loes & Singelenberg, Jeroen, texts. Amphibious Housing in the Netherlands: Architecture & Urbanism on the Water. 2011. (ENG., Illus.). 160p. pap. 45.00 *(978-90-5662-780-5(5))* NAi Uitgevers / Publishers Stichting NLD. Dist: D.A.P./Distributed Art Pubs.

Novogratz, Cortney & Novogratz, Robert. Downtown Chic: Designing Your Dream Home - From Wreck to Ravishing. 2009. (ENG., Illus.). 176p. 45.00 *(978-0-8478-3173-9(6))* Rizzoli International Pubns., Inc.

Oates, Marylouise. The Second Home Book: The Can-Do, How-to, Get-Through Guide. 2008. (ENG.). 272p. pap. 17.99 *(978-0-312-37474-7(7)*, St. Martin's Griffin) St. Martin's Pr.

Ojeda, Oscar Riera, ed. Modern to Classic: Residential Estates by Landry Design Group. 2006. (ENG., Illus.). 420p. 75.00 *(978-0-9774672-1-1(X))* Oro Editions.

Ormsbee, Renee Richmond Huntley & Ormsbee, Thomas H. If You're Going to Live in the Country. 2008. 188p. 22.99 *(978-0-554-35825-3(5))* 2008. 188p. 25.99 *(978-0-554-26522-3(2))* 2007. (ENG.). 164p. pap. 19.99 *(978-1-4346-1304-2(6))* 2007. (ENG.). 184p. pap. 21.99 *(978-1-4346-1356-1(9))* BiblioBazaar.

Ormsbee, Thomas H. & Huntley, Richmond. If You're Going to Live in the Country: Achieving Your Rural American Dream. 2008. 152p. pap. 13.95 *(978-1-4357-4334-2(2))* Lulu Enterprises Inc.

Owen, Julian. Kit & Modern Timber Frame Homes: The Complete Guide. 2007. (ENG., Illus.). 192p. 42.95 *(978-1-86126-950-8(1))* Crowood Pr., Ltd. GBR. Dist: Independent Pubs. Group.

Oyarzún, Fernando Pérez, et al. Chilean Modern Architecture since 1950. Quantrill, Malcolm, ed. 2010. (Studies in Architecture & Culture Ser.). (ENG., Illus.). 192p. 45.00 *(978-1-60344-135-3(2))* Texas A&M Univ. Pr.

Pak, Kwang-Su. Hanok Ul Mal Handa. 2010. (KOR., Illus.). 262p. *(978-89-429-1162-2(5))* Iljin Publishing Co.

Palmke, Oda, text. Typen: Good, Bad & Ugly Houses. 2009. (ENG., Illus.). 176p. pap. 25.00 *(978-3-86859-000-5(5))* Jovis Verlag GmbH DEU. Dist: D.A.P./Distributed Art Pubs.

Paris, Chris. Affluence, Mobility & Second Home Ownership. 2010. (Housing & Society Ser.). (ENG., Illus.). 224p. (C). 165.00 *(978-0-415-54891-5(8))*; pap. 60.00 *(978-0-415-54892-2(6))* Routledge.

Parodi, Aníbal & Parodi Rebella, Aníbal. Puertas Adentro: Interioridad y Espacio Doméstico en el S. XX. 2010. (SPA., Illus.). 396p. *(978-84-8301-774-6(1))* UPC, S.L., Edicions.

Parsons, Bret & Colcord, Gerard Rae. Colcord: Home. 2008. *(978-1-883318-88-8(2))* Angel City Pr.

Patterson, Jim. The Cookbook of Comfort. 2009. 92p. pap. 16.50 *(978-1-4389-5990-0(7))* AuthorHouse.

Paul, Linda Leigh. Cottage & Cabin. 2010. (ENG., Illus.). 336p. 35.00 *(978-0-7893-2014-8(2))* Universe Publishing.

—Lakeside Living: Waterfront Houses, Cottages, & Cabins of the Great Lakes. 2010. (ENG., Illus.). 224p. 14.98 *(978-0-7893-2206-7(4)*, Rizzoli Universe Promotional Bks.) Rizzoli International Pubns., Inc.

Pauwels, Jo, et al, photos by. Contemporary Living. 2007. (ENG., Illus.). 204p. *(978-90-77213-77-3(5)*, Beta-Plus (Acc)) Antique Collectors' Club.

Pauwels, Jo & Laloux, Jean-Luc, photos by. Urban Spaces. 2007. (and d Ser.). (ENG., Illus.). 200p. *(978-90-77213-62-9(7)*, Beta-Plus (Acc)) Antique Collectors' Club.

Pauwels, Wim. Archi-Nature Vol. 2: Private Houses in Extraordinary Landscapes. 2011. (ENG., Illus.). 224p. 125.00 *(978-90-8944-064-8(X))* Beta-Plus Pubs. BEL. Dist: Antique Collectors' Club.

—City Houses. 2006. (ENG.). 228p. *(978-90-77213-59-9(7)*, Beta-Plus (Acc)) Antique Collectors' Club.

—Contemporary Architecture & Interiors: Yearbook 2010. 2010. (FRE, GER & ENG., Illus.). 376p. *(978-90-8944-016-7(X)*, Beta-Plus (Acc)) Antique Collectors' Club.

—Contemporary Architecture & Interiors 2009. 2008. (FRE, GER & ENG., Illus.). 416p. *(978-90-8944-004-4(6)*, Beta-Plus (Acc)) Antique Collectors' Club.

—Contemporary Architecture & Interiors Yearbook 2012. 2011. (ENG, DUT & FRE., Illus.). 200p. 140.00 *(978-90-8944-107-2(7))* Beta-Plus Pubs. BEL. Dist: Antique Collectors' Club.

—Contemporary Living Rooms. 2010. (Home Ser.). (ENG., Illus.). 128p. pap. *(978-90-8944-075-4(5)*, Beta-Plus (Acc)) Antique Collectors' Club.

—Cosmopolitan Living. 2010. (Home Ser.). (ENG., Illus.). 128p. pap. *(978-90-8944-083-9(6)*, Beta-Plus (Acc)) Antique Collectors' Club.

—Cosy Living. 2010. (Home Ser.). (ENG., Illus.). 128p. pap. *(978-90-8944-080-8(1)*, Beta-Plus (Acc)) Antique Collectors' Club.

—Country Living. 2007. (ENG., Illus.). 204p. 95.00 *(978-90-77213-64-3(3))* Beta-Plus Pubs. BEL. Dist: Antique Collectors' Club.

—Details in Architecture. 2010. (Home Ser.). (ENG., Illus.). 128p. pap. *(978-90-8944-078-5(X)*, Beta-Plus (Acc)) Antique Collectors' Club.

—Dining Rooms. 2010. (Home Ser.). (ENG., Illus.). 128p. pap. *(978-90-8944-074-7(7)*, Beta-Plus (Acc)) Antique Collectors' Club.

—Fusion Interiors. 2010. (Home Ser.). (ENG., Illus.). 128p. pap. *(978-90-8944-079-2(8)*, Beta-Plus (Acc)) Antique Collectors' Club.

—Home: 14 Private Residences. 2010. (ENG., Illus.). 320p. *(978-90-8944-056-3(9)*, Beta-Plus (Acc)) Antique Collectors' Club.

—Living with Wood. 2008. (ENG., Illus.). 208p. *(978-90-77213-90-2(2)*, Beta-Plus (Acc)) Antique Collectors' Club.

—Minimal Living. Watkinson, Laura, tr. 2008. (ENG., Illus.). 208p. *(978-90-77213-92-6(9)*, Beta-Plus (Acc)) Antique Collectors' Club.

—Modern Classic Homes. 2010. (Home Ser.). (ENG., Illus.). 128p. pap. *(978-90-8944-077-8(1)*, Beta-Plus (Acc)) Antique Collectors' Club.

—Timeless Architecture & Interiors: Yearbook 2009. 2008. (ENG., Illus.). 416p. *(978-90-8944-005-1(4)*, Beta-Plus (Acc)) Antique Collectors' Club.

—Timeless Architecture & Interiors: Yearbook 2010. 2010. (ENG., Illus.). 416p. *(978-90-8944-017-4(8)*, Beta-Plus (Acc)) Antique Collectors' Club.

—Timeless Interiors. 2010. (Home Ser.). (ENG., Illus.). 128p. pap. *(978-90-8944-081-5(X)*, Beta-Plus (Acc)) Antique Collectors' Club.

—Timeless Living, 1995-2005. 2006. (ENG., Illus.). 224p. *(978-90-77213-36-0(8)*, Beta-Plus (Acc)) Antique Collectors' Club.

Pfeiffer, Bruce Brooks & Sidy, Victor E. Under Arizona Skies: The Apprentice Desert Shelters at Frank Lloyd Wright's Taliesin West. 2011. (ENG., Illus.). 80p. 24.95 *(978-0-7649-5959-2(X))* Pomegranate Communications, Inc.

Phaidon Press Editors. The Modernist House. 2009. (ENG., Illus.). 112p. 29.95 *(978-0-7148-4968-3(5))* Phaidon Pr., Inc.

Phipps, Tad. Building a House Day-by-Day. 2007. 80p. per. 10.95 *(978-0-595-43925-6(X))* iUniverse, Inc.

Planel, Philippe. Locks & Lavatories: The Architecture of Privacy. 2006. (Illus.). 64p. reprint ed. pap. 25.00 *(978-1-4223-5682-1(5))* DIANE Publishing Co.

Powers, Richard & Richardson, Phyllis. Living Modern: The Sourcebook of Contemporary Interiors. 2010. (ENG., Illus.). 368p. 60.00 *(978-0-500-51525-9(5)*, 551525) Thames & Hudson.

Predock, Antoine. Architect, Vol. 4. Collins, Brad, ed. 2006. (ENG., Illus.). 256p. 50.00 *(978-0-8478-2849-4(2))* Rizzoli International Pubns., Inc.

PressGingko. When Space Meets Art/When Art Meets Space. 2007. (Illus.). 240p. 39.95 *(978-988-98228-0-4(6))* Viction Workshop, Ltd. HKG. Dist: Gingko Pr., Inc.

Prinzing, Debra. Stylish Sheds & Elegant Hideaways: Big Ideas for Small Backyard Destinations. 2008. (ENG., Illus.). 224p. 30.00 *(978-0-307-35291-0(9)*, Clarkson Potter) Crown Publishing Group.

Quinn, Edward & Smith, John A. Luxury Trains. 2008. (ENG.). 24.95 *(978-3-8327-9267-1(8))* teNeues Publishing Co.

Reesema, Meg Nolan Van. Caribbean Hideaways: Discovering Enchanting Rooms & Private Villas. 2010. (ENG., Illus.). 202p. 50.00 *(978-0-8478-3292-7(9))* Rizzoli International Pubns., Inc.

Reyes, Elizabeth. The Tropical House: Cutting Edge Design in the Philippines. 2010. (ENG., Illus.). 208p. 39.95 *(978-0-8048-4082-8(2))* Tuttle Publishing.

Rice, Charles. The Emergence of the Interior: Architecture, Modernity, Domesticity. 2006. (Illus.). 161p. 165.00 *(978-0-415-38467-4(2))*; (ENG., 176p. per. 62.95 *(978-0-415-38468-1(0))* Routledge.

Richardson, Leah. Interior Wisdom: Designing Your Heart & Home for the Lord. 2009. (ENG.). 167p. 24.95 *(978-1-933979-30-4(5))* Bright Sky Pr.

Richardson, Phyllis. Nano House: Innovations for Small Dwellings. 2011. (ENG., Illus.). 224p. 29.95 *(978-0-500-34273-2(3)*, 534273) Thames & Hudson.

Richmond, Arthur P. The Evolution of the Cape Cod House: An Architectural History. 2011. (Illus.). 256p. 50.00 ***(978-0-7643-3848-9(X)***, Schiffer Publishing Ltd) Schiffer Publishing, Ltd.

Rieth, Timothy & Ferris, Bob. Natural Building: Creating Communities Through Cooperation. 2008. (Illus.). 128p. pap. 24.99 *(978-0-7643-3039-1(X))* Schiffer Publishing, Ltd.

Rosenfeld, Lucy D. The Architect's Garden: 45 Original Landscapes. 2009. (Illus.). 160p. bds. 39.99 *(978-0-7643-3130-5(2))* Schiffer Publishing, Ltd.

Ruch, Hans-Jörg & Seifert-Uherkovich, Ludmila, texts. Historic Houses in Engadin: Architectural Interventions, 1 vol. 2008. (ENG., Illus.). 320p. 98.00 *(978-3-86521-720-2(6))* Steidl, Gerhard Druckerei und Verlag DEU. Dist: Innovative Logistics.

Russell, MaryAnn & 1st World Publishing. The Feng Shui Factor: Modern Homes, Ancient Blueprint. 2007. 168p. per. 15.95 *(978-1-4218-9965-7(5))* 1st World Publishing, Inc.

Ryker, Lori. Off the Grid Homes: Case Studies for Sustainable Living, 1 vol. 2007. (ENG., Illus.). 128p. pap. 24.99 *(978-1-58685-689-2(8))* Gibbs Smith, Publisher.

Saint-Onge, Stephen. No Place Like Home: Tips & Techniques for Real Family-Friendly Home Design. 2011. (ENG., Illus.). 192p. pap. 19.99 *(978-0-470-58577-1(3)*, Wiley) Wiley, John & Sons, Inc.

Samson, A. V. M. Renewing the House: Trajectories of Social Life in the Yucayeque (Community) of el Cabo, Higuey, Dominican Republic, Ad 800 to 1504. 2010. (ENG.). 370p. (C). pap. 76.00 *(978-90-8890-045-7(0))* Sidestone Pr. NLD. Dist: Brown, David Bk. Co., The.

Santini, Claudio & Zilafro, Dafna. Green Is Beautiful: The Eco-Friendly House. 2009. (ENG., Illus.). 216p. 60.00 *(978-1-86470-325-2(3))* Images Publishing Group AUS. Dist: National Bk. Network.

Scarborough, Sam. Cool Spaces for Kids. 2009. (ENG., Illus.). 144p. 19.99 *(978-0-600-61839-3(0)*, Hamlyn) Octopus Publishing Group GBR. Dist: Hachette Bk. Group.

Schittich, Christian, ed. Vivienda y Densidad: Conceptos, Diseno, Construccion. 2007. (In Detail Ser.). (SPA., Illus.). 174p. 59.95 *(978-3-7643-7530-0(2)*, 3764375302) Birkhauser Verlag AG CHE. Dist: Springer.

Schneider, Friederike & Heckmann, Oliver. Floor Plan Manual: Housing. 4th rev. ed. 2011. (ENG & GER., Illus.). 336p. pap. 84.95 *(978-3-0346-0708-7(3))* Birkhauser Verlag AG CHE. Dist: Actar Birkhauser Distribution.

Schroder, Jorg, ed. Landraum: Entwerfen auf dem Land. 2010. (ENG., Illus.). 352p. 59.95 *(978-3-86859-022-7(6))* Jovis Verlag GmbH DEU. Dist: D.A.P./Distributed Art Pubs.

Search, Gay. The Little Book of Quick Fixes for Designing Your Outdoor Space. 2008. (Illus.). 304p. pap. 12.95 *(978-1-84400-578-9(X))* Quadrille Publishing, Ltd. GBR. Dist: Ingram Pub. Services.

A

Segantini, Maria Alessandra. Contemporary Housing. 2008. (ENG., Illus.). 348p. pap. 14.99 *(978-88-6130-535-9(0))* Skira Editore ITA. Dist: Random Hse., Inc.

Serrats, Marta. Space Savers: Platzsparende Ideen in Haus und Wohnung. Loft Publications Staff, ed. 2012. (FRE, DUT, GER & ENG., Illus.). 352p. pap. 24.95 ***(978-94-6065-065-9(1))*** Tectum B.V.B.A. BEL. Dist: Innovative Logistics.

Shamamian, Oscar & Ferguson, Mark. New Traditional Architecture: Ferguson & Shamamian Architects - City & Country Residences. 2011. (ENG., Illus.). 248p. 75.00 *(978-0-8478-3545-4(6))* Rizzoli International Pubns., Inc.

Shamir, Milette. Inexpressible Privacy: The Interior Life of Antebellum American Literature. 2008. (Illus.). 296p. (C). pap. 22.50 *(978-0-8122-2023-0(4))* Univ. of Pennsylvania Pr.

Sin, Court. The One Third You Are Missing - Designing Third Places to Revitalize Downtowns. 2008. 188p. pap. *(978-3-8364-3923-7(9))* VDM Verlag Dr. Mueller e.K.

Sinopoli, James M. Smart Buildings Systems for Architects, Owners & Builders. 2009. (ENG., Illus.). 248p. 103.00 *(978-1-85617-653-8(3)*, Butterworth-Heinemann) Elsevier Science & Technology Bks.

Slavid, Ruth. Wood Houses. 2006. (ENG., Illus.). 208p. 65.00 *(978-0-7892-0888-0(1))* Abbeville Pr., Inc.

Speed, Caroline. Sustainable Dwelling. 2010. 240p. pap. *(978-3-639-22856-4(1))* VDM Verlag Dr. Mueller e.K.

Springer Vienna Architecture Staff, et al, eds. Housing Density. 2012. (ENG., Illus.). 184p. pap. 49.95 *(978-3-7091-0358-6(4)*, 3709103584) Springer Wien AUT. Dist: Springer.

Stamp, Gavin, et al, eds. The Modern House Revisited. 2006. (Twentieth Century Architecture Ser.). (ENG., Illus.). 128p. pap. 20.00 *(978-0-9529755-9-5(9))* Holberton, Paul Publishing GBR. Dist: Casemate Pubs. & Bk. Distributors, LLC.

Stanley. Complete Flooring. 2008. (ENG., Illus.). 240p. pap. 21.95 *(978-0-696-23838-3(1)*, Wiley) Wiley, John & Sons, Inc.

Stathaki, Ellie & Bell, Jonathan. The New Modern House: Redefining Functionalism. 2010. (ENG., Illus.). 240p. 50.00 *(978-1-85669-684-5(7))* King, Laurence Publishing GBR. Dist: Hachette Bk. Group.

Steele, James. The Greenwood Encyclopedia of Homes Through World History, 3 vols., Set. 2008. (Illus.). 1100p. 349.95 *(978-0-313-33788-8(8)*, GR3788) Greenwood Publishing Group, Inc.

Stickley, Gustav. Craftsman Houses: The 1913 Catalog. 2009. (Dover Architecture Ser.). (ENG.). 144p. pap. 14.95 *(978-0-486-47005-4(9))* Dover Pubns., Inc.

Stierstorfer, Klaus. Constructions of Home: Interdisciplinary Studies in Architecture, Law, & Literature. 2010. (Illus.). xii, 359p. *(978-0-404-64259-4(4))* AMS Pr., Inc.

Strahan, David, et al. Contemporary Villas. 2011. (Illus.). 256p. *(978-0-7643-3774-1(2)*, Schiffer Publishing Ltd) Schiffer Publishing, Ltd.

Strongman, Cathy. The Sustainable Home: The Essential Guide to Eco Building, Renovation & Decoration. 2010. (ENG., Illus.). 208p. pap. 19.95 *(978-1-85894-518-7(6))* Merrell Pubs. Ltd. GBR. Dist: Perseus Distribution.

—100 Houses: Modern Designs for Contemporary Living. 2009. (Illus.). 352p. 45.00 *(978-1-85894-469-2(4))* Merrell Pubs. Ltd. GBR. Dist: Perseus Distribution.

Susanka, Sarah. More Not So Big Solutions for Your Home. 2010. (ENG., Illus.). 160p. pap. 22.95 *(978-1-60085-148-3(7))* Taunton Pr., Inc.

Susanka, Sarah & Obolensky, Kira. The Not So Big House: A Blueprint for the Way We Really Live. 10th ed. 2009. (ENG., Illus.). 240p. pap. 24.95 *(978-1-60085-150-6(9))* Taunton Pr., Inc.

Susanka, Sarah, et al. Inside & Outside the Not So Big House. 2006. *(978-1-56158-930-2(6))* Taunton Pr., Inc.

Taher, Aamer. Sculpting Tropical Spaces: Aamer Architects. 2012. (ENG., Illus.). 200p. 50.00 *(978-1-935935-11-7(9))* Oro Editions.

Tanqueray, Rebecca. Small Spaces: Making the Most of the Space You Have. 2007. (ENG., Illus.). 144p. pap. 19.95 *(978-1-84597-360-5(7))* Ryland Peters & Small.

Taschen, ed. Book of Lofts. 2009. (ENG., Illus.). 384p. 19.99 *(978-3-8365-1151-3(7)*, Evergreen) TASCHEN DEU. Dist: Ingram Pub. Services.

Taschen & Evergreen, eds. Book of Houses. 2009. (ENG, FRE & GER., Illus.). 384p. 19.99 *(978-3-8365-1155-1(X)*, Evergreen) TASCHEN DEU. Dist: Ingram Pub. Services.

Taschen, Angelika, ed. Living in Bahia. 2008. (Taschen's Lifestyle Ser.). (FRE, GER & ENG., Illus.). 200p. 29.99 *(978-3-8365-0478-2(2))* TASCHEN DEU. Dist: Ingram Pub. Services.

Taschen Publishing Staff. New Small Apartments. Kramp, Klaus, ed. 2008. (ENG., Illus.). pap. 14.99 *(978-3-8365-0830-8(3))* TASCHEN DEU. Dist: Ingram Pub. Services.

—New Small Houses. Kramp, Klaus, ed. 2008. (FRE, GER & ENG., Illus.). 186p. pap. 14.99 *(978-3-8365-0832-2(X))* TASCHEN DEU. Dist: Ingram Pub. Services.

Tate, Ken. Windy Hill: Ken Tate, Architect. Nelson, Graves, ed. 2006. (ENG., Illus.). 120p. 45.00 *(978-1-920744-68-7(1))* Images Publishing Group AUS. Dist: National Bk. Network.

Tattersall, George. Sporting Architecture. 2007. (ENG.). 144p. 35.95 *(978-0-548-04943-3(2))* Kessinger Publishing, LLC.

Teneues. Luxury Houses Top of the World. 2008. 95.00 *(978-3-8327-9239-8(2))* teNeues Publishing Co.

Trulove, James Grayson. 25 Apartments & Lofts under 1000 Square Feet. 2008. (Illus.). 224p. pap. 39.95 *(978-0-06-134020-8(0))* HarperCollins Pubs.

Tully, Peggy. From the Ground Up: Innovative Green Homes. 2012. (ENG.). 160p. 29.95 ***(978-1-61689-092-6(4))*** Princeton Architectural Pr.

Uffelen, Chris van. Residential Architecture for Senior Citizens. 2012. (ENG., Illus.). 272p. 62.50 ***(978-3-03768-108-4(X)***, Braun Publish,Csi) Continental Sales, Inc.

van Gameren, Dick, et al, eds. DASH 01: the Re-Opened Building Block. 2009. (ENG., Illus.). 144p. pap. 50.00 *(978-90-5662-654-9(X))* NAi Uitgevers / Publishers Stichting NLD. Dist: D.A.P./Distributed Art Pubs.

van Uffelen, Chris. Low Price Houses: Starter Homes, Minimal Houses, Emergency Accommodation. 2010. (ENG., Illus.). 272p. 62.50 *(978-3-03768-062-9(8)*, Braun Publish,Csi) Continental Sales, Inc.

Vassallo, Marc, intro. The Homestead Builder: Practical Hints for Handy-Men. 2nd ed. 2007. (ENG., Illus.). 152p. per. 12.95 *(978-1-59921-153-4(X)*, Lyons Pr.) Globe Pequot Pr., The.

Visser, Frank. Dutch Architects & Their Houses. 2012. (ENG., Illus.). 240p. 55.00 ***(978-94-6058-094-9(7)***, Uitgeverij Luster) Antique Collectors' Club GBR. Dist: National Bk. Network.

Von Gerkan, Meinhard. Architects of Gerkan, Marg & Parners: Volume 5 Furniture, 1 vol. 2007. (GER & ENG., Illus.). 112p. pap. 29.95 *(978-3-939633-21-1(6))* Jovis Verlag GmbH DEU. Dist: D.A.P./Distributed Art Pubs.

Vranckx, Bridget. Small & Chic: High Style for Small Spaces. 2008. (ENG., Illus.). 424p. pap. 35.00 *(978-0-7893-1599-1(8))* Universe Publishing.

Wanek, Catherine. The Hybrid House: Designing with Sun, Wind, Water, & Earth, 1 vol. 2010. (ENG., Illus.). 144p. 24.99 *(978-1-4236-0316-0(8))* Gibbs Smith, Publisher.

—The New Strawbale Home, 1 vol. 2009. (ENG., Illus.). 192p. pap. 24.99 *(978-1-4236-0657-4(4))* Gibbs Smith, Publisher.

Wattson, Louisa. International Beach Houses. 2007. (ENG., Illus.). 192p. 35.00 *(978-0-8109-9296-2(5))* Abrams.

Weiss Bricker, Lauren. The Mediterranean House in America. 2008. (ENG., Illus.). 240p. 55.00 *(978-0-8109-7285-8(9))* Abrams.

Westgate, Ruth, et al, eds. Building Communities: House, Settlement & Society in the Aegean & Beyond: Proceedings of a Conference Held at Cardiff University, 17-21 April 2001. 2007. (BSA Studies). (ENG., Illus.). 430p. (C). 178.00 *(978-0-904887-56-3(1))* British Schl. at Athens GBR. Dist: Brown, David Bk. Co., The.

White, Melvin Ladon. Property Owner's Sewer & Drain Guide. 2007. 42p. pap. 8.00 *(978-0-8059-7610-6(8))* Dorrance Publishing Co., Inc.

Wilhide, Elizabeth. Eco: An Essential Sourcebook for Environmentallu Friendly Design & Decoration. (Illus.). 184p. 44.95 *(978-1-903845-74-5(2))* Quadrille Publishing, Ltd. GBR. Dist: Graphic Arts Ctr. Publishing Co.

Zabihi, Saereh. Effects of Modern Movement on Residential Buildings. 2011. 88p. pap. ***(978-3-8443-9662-1(4))*** Lambert Academic Publishing.

Zarecor, Kimberly Elman. Manufacturing a Socialist Modernity: Housing in Czechoslovakia, 1945-1960. 2011. (Pitt Russian East European Ser.). (ENG., Illus.). 480p. 45.00 *(978-0-8229-4404-1(9))* Univ. of Pittsburgh Pr.

ARCHITECTURE, DOMESTIC—DESIGNS AND PLANS

Abaza, Hussein. Moisture Behavior in Buildings- an Integrated Design & Control Strategy for Efficient & Healthy Buildings. 2007. 188p. per. *(978-3-8364-2933-7(0))* VDM Verlag Dr. Mueller e.K.

Abdel-Gawad, Ahmed. Veiling Architecture: Decoration of Domestic Buildings in Upper Egypt 1672-1950. 2012. (ENG., Illus.). 144p. pap. 22.95 ***(978-977-416-487-3(3))*** American Univ. in Cairo Pr. EGY. Dist: Oxford Univ. Pr., Inc.

Acerboni, Francesca, et al, told to. 100 Houses for 100 Architects. 25th ed. 2008. (ENG., Illus.). 480p. 29.99 *(978-3-8228-3786-3(5))* TASCHEN DEU. Dist: Ingram Pub. Services.

Alex, Sanchez Vidiella & Francesco, Zamora Mola, eds. Renovated Spaces: New Life for Old Homes. 2010. 420p. pap. 35.00 *(978-84-92463-57-2(0))* Loft Pubns. ESP. Dist: Prestel Publishing.

Ambrose, Gavin & Harris, Paul. Design Thinking: Fragestellung, Recherche, Ideenfindung, Prototyping, Auswahl, Ausführung, Feedback. 2009. (Basics Design Ser.). (ENG., Illus.). 184p. pap. 34.50 *(978-2-940411-17-7(4))* AVA Publishing GBR. Dist: Ingram Pub. Services.

Andersen, Dennis, intro. Craftsman Bungalows. 2007. (Illus.). pap. 25.00 *(978-0-9629954-2-2(8))* Bk. Club of Washington.

Architecture for Humanity. Design Like You Give a Damn Vol. 2: Building Change from the Ground Up. 2012. (ENG., Illus.). 336p. pap. 35.00 *(978-0-8109-9702-8(9))* Abrams.

Arco Editorial. Minimalism: History, Fashion, Design, Architecture, Interiors. Cheviakoff, Sofia, ed. 2008. (Art & Architecture Ser.). (Illus.). 999p. pap. 19.95 *(978-0-8416-0088-1(0))* American Map Corp.

Asquith, Lindsay. Space Use & Claim. 2010. 252p. pap. *(978-3-8383-2603-0(2))* Lambert Academic Publishing.

Bacon, Jennifer & Fuhst, Darlene. Designer Dream Homes Craftsman & other Timeless American Dream Homes. 2007. (Illus.). 176p. pap. 14.95 *(978-1-932553-23-9(1))* Designs Direct Publishing, LLC.

Bahamón, Alejandro. Houses/Casas/Hauser. Brunelle, Michael et al, trs. 2008. (Art & Architecture Ser.). (Illus.). 432p. 49.95 *(978-0-8416-0302-8(2))* American Map Corp.

Bahamón, Alejandro, ed. Sketch: Houses: How Architects Conceive Residential Architecture. 2007. (Illus.). 192p. 34.95 *(978-84-95832-63-4(1))* Loft Pubns. ESP. Dist: Prestel Publishing.

Baker, Jennifer. Designer Dream Homes: 150 Upscale House Plans in all Sizes & Styles. 2007. (Illus.). 224p. pap. 16.95 *(978-1-932553-24-6(X))* Designs Direct Publishing, LLC.

Barber, George F. Barber's Turn-of-the-Century Houses: Elevations & Floor Plans. 3rd ed. 2008. (Dover Architecture Ser.). (ENG., Illus.). 160p. pap. 19.95 *(978-0-486-46527-2(6))* Dover Pubns., Inc.

Barge-Munden, Patrice. The Home Project File: A Decorating & Remodeling Organizer. 2007. (Illus.). ring bd. 24.99 *(978-0-9794320-0-2(6))* Innerspace Publishing Co.

Bensley, Bill. Paradise by Design: Tropical Residences & Resorts by Bensley Design Studios. 2008. (ENG., Illus.). 240p. 49.95 *(978-0-7946-0493-6(5)*, PeriplusEdition) Tuttle Publishing.

Berkus, Barry A. & Berkus, Barry. Sculpting Space. 2006. (House Design Ser.). (ENG., Illus.). 128p. 49.50 *(978-1-86470-088-6(2))* Images Publishing Group AUS. Dist: National Bk. Network.

Beta-Plus, creator. Designer Houses/Maisons de Designer/Designerwoningen. 2007. (ENG., Illus.). 208p. *(978-90-77213-76-6(7)*, Beta-Plus (Acc)) Antique Collectors' Club.

Breland and Farmer Designers, Inc. Staff. Home Designs. (Illus.). reprint ed. 104p. pap. 5.95 *(978-0-938007-00-5(9))*; 56p. pap. 5.95 *(978-0-938007-01-2(7))* Breland & Farmer, Designers, Inc.

—House Plans. (Illus.). 104p. reprint ed. pap. 5.95 *(978-0-938007-02-9(5))* Breland & Farmer, Designers, Inc.

Briggs, Robert. Bungalows & Country Residences. 2007. 108p. per. *(978-1-905217-69-4(2))* Mills, Jeremy Publishing.

—Homes for the Country. 2007. 124p. per. *(978-1-905217-70-0(6))* Mills, Jeremy Publishing.

Broadhurst, Ron. Next Houses: Architecture for the Twenty-First Century. 2009. (ENG., Illus.). 256p. 50.00 *(978-0-8109-5401-4(X))* Abrams.

Broto, Carles. Domestic Interiors Now. 2008. (ENG., Illus.). 240p. 55.00 *(978-84-96424-03-6(0))* Links International (Leading International Key Services Barcelona, S.A.) ESP. Dist: National Bk. Network.

—New Concepts in Housing. 2009. (ENG., Illus.). 360p. pap. 34.99 *(978-84-96969-98-8(3))* Links International (Leading International Key Services Barcelona, S.A.) ESP. Dist: National Bk. Network.

—Town Houses. 2006. (ENG., Illus.). 240p. 45.00 *(978-84-96263-74-1(6))* Links International (Leading International Key Services Barcelona, S.A.) ESP. Dist: National Bk. Network.

—Urban Apartment Blocks. 2008. (ENG., Illus.). 240p. 39.95 *(978-84-96263-90-1(8))* Links International (Leading International Key Services Barcelona, S.A.) ESP. Dist: National Bk. Network.

—Wood Cabins: Small Wood Houses. 2007. (ENG., Illus.). 192p. 39.95 *(978-84-96424-07-4(3))* Links International (Leading International Key Services Barcelona, S.A.) ESP. Dist: National Bk. Network.

Browne, Beth. 100 Country Houses: New Rural Architecture. 2009. (ENG., Illus.). 224p. 60.00 *(978-1-86470-332-0(6))* Images Publishing Group AUS. Dist: National Bk. Network.

Building Knowledge Inc. Building Better Homes (3 CD-ROM Set) Habitat for Humanity Construction Edition V1. 1. 2006. cd-rom *(978-0-9745844-4-7(4)*, Building Better Homes) Building Knowledge Inc.

Camps, Colisa. Country in Style. 2008. (ENG., Illus.). 192p. 39.95 *(978-84-96969-21-6(5))* Links International (Leading International Key Services Barcelona, S.A.) ESP. Dist: National Bk. Network.

Catherine Slessor. Glass Houses: Inspirational Homes And. 2011. (ENG., Illus.). 192p. 45.00 *(978-1-84975-132-2(3))* CICO Bks. GBR. Dist: Ryland Peters & Small.

Cerver, Francisco Asensio. Houses of the World. 2008. (Art & Architecture Ser.). (Illus.). 999p. pap. 19.95 *(978-0-8416-0069-0(4))* American Map Corp.

Chivers, Herbert C. 1000 Turn-of-the-Century Houses: With Illustrations & Floor Plans. 2007. (Dover Architecture Ser.). (ENG., Illus.). 256p. per. 18.95 *(978-0-486-45596-9(3))* Dover Pubns., Inc.

Cohen, Stuart & Hacker, Julie. Transforming the Traditional: The Work of Cohen & Hacker Architects. 2009. (ENG., Illus.). 128p. 50.00 *(978-1-86470-335-1(0))* Images Publishing Group AUS. Dist: National Bk. Network.

Colquhoun, Ian. RIBA Book of British Housing: 1900 to the Present Day. 2nd rev. ed. 2008. (ENG., Illus.). 416p. pap. 59.95 *(978-0-7506-8254-1(X))* Routledge.

Coutts, John. Loft Conversions. 2006. (ENG., Illus.). 280p. per. 84.99 *(978-1-4051-3043-1(1)*, Wiley-Blackwell) Wiley, John & Sons, Inc.

Crafti, Stephen. Ivan Rijavec: Pure Form. 2006. (House Design Ser.: Vol. 8). (ENG., Illus.). 39.50 *(978-1-86470-080-0(7))* Images Publishing Group AUS. Dist: National Bk. Network.

—Making the Most of Small Spaces. 2006. (ENG., Illus.). 176p. 35.00 *(978-1-876907-52-5(5))* Images Publishing Group AUS. Dist: National Bk. Network.

Creative Homeowner Press Editors. Best-Selling 1-Story Home Plans. 2010. (Home Plans Ser.). (ENG., Illus.). 288p. (gr. 5). pap. 9.95 *(978-1-58011-482-0(2))* Creative Homeowner.

—Best-Selling House Plans. 2009. (Home Plans Ser.). (ENG., Illus.). 352p. (gr. 5). pap. 10.95 *(978-1-58011-469-1(5))* Creative Homeowner.

—Easy-to-Build, Expandable Home Plans (Lowe's) 2009. (Home Plans Ser.). (ENG., Illus.). 240p. (gr. 5). pap. 9.95 *(978-1-58011-467-7(9))* Creative Homeowner.

Creative Homeowner Press Editors, creator. Downsized Luxury Home Plans. 2008. (Home Plans Ser.). (ENG., Illus.). 240p. pap. 12.95 *(978-1-58011-387-8(7))* Creative Homeowner.

—The New Ultimate Book of Home Plans. rev. ed. 2007. (Home Plans Ser.). (ENG., Illus.). 608p. (gr. 5). pap. 12.95 *(978-1-58011-336-6(2))* Creative Homeowner.

Creative Homeowner Press Editors, ed. Best-Selling 1-Story. 2010. (Home Plans Ser.). (ENG., Illus.). 288p. (gr. 5). pap. 9.95 *(978-1-58011-481-3(4))* Creative Homeowner.

—Best-Selling Country & Farmhouse. 2010. (Home Plans Ser.). (ENG.). 288p. (gr. 5). pap. 9.95 *(978-1-58011-503-2(9))* Creative Homeowner.

—Best-Selling House Plans. 2009. (Home Plans Ser.). (ENG.). 352p. (gr. 5). pap. 10.95 *(978-1-58011-470-7(9))* Creative Homeowner.

—Curb Appeal House Plans Bible. rev. ed. 2006. (ENG., Illus.). 288p. pap. 12.95 *(978-1-58011-323-6(0))* Creative Homeowner.

—One Story House Plans Bible: Over 450 Home Plans in Full Color. rev. ed. 2006. (House Plan Bible Ser.). (ENG., Illus.). 384p. pap. 12.95 *(978-1-58011-325-0(7))* Creative Homeowner.

Cummins, Martin. Designing & Building Your Own Home. 2007. (ENG., Illus.). 176p. pap. 34.95 *(978-1-86126-904-1(8))* Crowood Pr., Ltd. GBR. Dist: Independent Pubs. Group.

Cusato, Marianne. The Value of Design. 2008. pap. 15.00 *(978-0-9760250-8-5(6)*, Plain Paper Pr.) Plain White Pr., LLC.

DAAB Media Staff. Contemporary House Design, 1 vol. 2009. (ITA, FRE, GER, SPA & ENG., Illus.). 383p. 59.95 *(978-3-86654-057-6(4))* DAAB Media Gmbh DEU. Dist: Innovative Logistics.

Daguerre, Mercedes. New Villas in Switzerland. 2012. (ENG., Illus.). 208p. 84.95 *(978-3-0346-0732-2(6))* Birkhauser Verlag AG CHE. Dist: Actar Birkhauser Distribution.

DaVinci Publishing, creator. 100 Best New Houses. 2011. (Illus.). 405p. 65.00 *(978-988-18923-1-7(7))* Gingko Pr., Inc.

de Haro, Fernando & Fuentes, Omar. City Houses. 2006. (Smallbooks Ser.). (ENG., Illus.). 64p. pap. 3.49 *(978-970-9726-42-8(0))* AM Editores MEX. Dist: Perseus-PGW.

—Country Homes. 2007. (Lifestyles, Nature & Architecture Ser.). (ENG., Illus.). 209p. 45.00 *(978-970-9726-76-3(5))* AM Editores MEX. Dist: Perseus-PGW.

—Country Houses. 2006. (Smallbooks Ser.). (ENG., Illus.). 64p. pap. 3.49 *(978-970-9726-41-1(2))* AM Editores MEX. Dist: Perseus-PGW.

de Haro, Fernando & Fuentes, Omar, compiled by. Houses: Distinction with Style. 2008. (Houses Ser.). (ENG., Illus.). 192p. 39.95 *(978-970-9726-92-3(7))* AM Editores MEX. Dist: Perseus-PGW.

Denzer, Anthony. Gregory Ain: The Modern Home as Social Commentary. 2008. (ENG., Illus.). 256p. 60.00 *(978-0-8478-3062-6(4))* Rizzoli International Pubns., Inc.

Designs Direct Publishing. Small Dream Homes: 120 Plans under 3,000 Square Feet. 2008. (Illus.). 176p. pap. 14.95 *(978-1-932553-29-1(0)*, DDP) Designs Direct Publishing, LLC.

Designs Direct Publishing, creator. The Ultimate Book of Designer Dream Homes: Over 475 Best-Selling Plans. 2006. (Illus.). 519p. pap. 14.95 *(978-1-932553-18-5(5))* Designs Direct Publishing, LLC.

Dickinson, Duo. House on a Budget: Making Smart Choices to Build the Home You Want. 2007. (American Institute Architects Ser.). (ENG., Illus.). 208p. pap. 21.95 *(978-1-56158-923-4(3)*, Taunton) Taunton Pr., Inc.

Downing, Andrew Jackson. The Architecture of Country Houses; Including Designs for Cottages, Farm-Houses, & Villas, with Remarks on Interiors, Furniture, & the Best Modes. 2006. 564p. per. 32.99 *(978-1-4255-6186-4(1))* MPublishing.

Dream Home Luxury Home Plans. 2007. (Illus.). 254p. 8.95 *(978-1-893536-12-8(2)*, 163) Garlinghouse, Inc.

Dregni, Eric, et al. Follies of Science: 20th Century Visions of Our Fantastic Future. 2006. (ENG., Illus.). 128p. pap. 19.00 *(978-1-933108-09-4(6))* Consortium Bk. Sales & Distribution.

Drexel, Thomas. Neue Low-Budget-Häuser: Bauen unter 225.000 Euro. 2010. (Illus.). 159p. *(978-3-421-03596-7(2))* Deutsche Verlags-Anstalt GmbH.

Dunlop, Beth & Lombard, Joanna. Great Houses of Florida. 2008. (ENG., Illus.). 256p. 55.00 *(978-0-8478-3097-8(7))* Rizzoli International Pubns., Inc.

E., Lamie. Space Planning: Comprehensive Guide for Residential Interior Space Planning. 2011. 144p. 29.99 ***(978-1-4628-9611-0(1))***; pap. 19.99 ***(978-1-4628-9610-3(3))*** Xlibris Corp.

Elpel, Thomas. Living Homes: Stone Masonry, Log, & Strawbale Construction. 6th ed. 2010. (ENG., Illus.). 256p. pap. 30.00 *(978-1-892784-32-2(7))* HOPS Pr., LLC.

Fajardo, Julio. Designer Apartments. 2011. (ENG.). 480p. 29.99 *(978-3-8331-6010-3(1))* h.f.ullmann DEU. Dist: Innovative Logistics.

Farris, Jerri. Kitchens & Baths for Today & Tomorrow: Ideas for Fabulous New Kitchens & Baths. 2008. (ENG., Illus.). 288p. pap. 24.95 *(978-1-58923-374-4(3)*, 1589233743, Creative Publishing International) Quayside.

Feireiss, Kristin, ed. Architecture in Times of Need: Make it Right - Rebuilding the New Orleans' Lower Ninth Ward. 2009. (Illus.). 360p. pap. 39.95 *(978-3-7913-4276-4(2))* Prestel Publishing.

Firley, Eric & Stahl, Caroline. The Urban Housing Handbook. (ENG., Illus.). 328p. 2011. pap. 50.00 *(978-1-119-98998-1(1))* 2009. 85.00 *(978-0-470-51275-3(X))* Wiley, John & Sons, Inc. (Wiley).

Fishel, Cathy. In-House Design in Practice. 2008. (ENG.). 208p. pap. 25.00 *(978-1-60061-098-1(6)*, HOW Bks.) F&W Media, Inc.

Flagg, Ernest. Flagg's Small Houses: Their Economic Design & Construction 1922. 2006. (Dover Architecture Ser.). (ENG., Illus.). 160p. per. 14.95 *(978-0-486-45197-8(6))* Dover Pubns., Inc.

Ford, Edward R. Five Houses, Ten Details. 2009. (ENG., Illus.). 256p. 40.00 *(978-1-56898-826-9(5))* Princeton Architectural Pr.

Fox, Maxine. Holistic Home: The Homemaker's Guide to Health & Happiness. 2006. (ENG.). 182p. per. 16.95 *(978-1-84409-070-9(1))* Findhorn Pr. GBR. Dist: Independent Pubs. Group.
French, Hilary. Key Urban Housing of the Twentieth Century: Plans, Sections, & Elevations. 2008. (Key Structures: Plans, Sections, Elevations Ser.). (ENG., Illus.). 240p. pap. 45.00 *(978-0-393-73246-7(0),* 73246) Norton, W. W. & Co., Inc.
Fuentes, Omar & de Haro, Fernando, compiled by. Interiors: Expression & Functionality. 2008. (Interiors Ser.). (ENG., Illus.). 192p. 39.95 *(978-970-9726-94-7(3))* AM Editores MEX. Dist: Perseus-PGW.
Fuentes, Omar, et al. Casas20 Houses. 2008. (Illus.). 208p. 39.95 *(978-970-9726-88-6(9))* AM Editores MEX. Dist: Perseus-PGW.
Galindo, Michelle. Collection: Houses. 2009. (GER, FRE & ENG.). 512p. 89.95 *(978-3-03768-012-4(1),* Braun Publish,Csi) Continental Sales, Inc.
Garling House Plans, creator. Builders' First-Choice Home Plans. 2007. (Illus.). 255p. per. 12.95 *(978-1-893536-26-5(2))* Garlinghouse, Inc.
—1,295 Best-Selling Home Plans. 2007. (Illus.). 812p. per. 12.95 *(978-1-893536-25-8(4))* Garlinghouse, Inc.
Garlinghouse, creator. The Best of Coolhouseplans. com: Premiere Issue. 2007. (Illus.). 287p. per. 12.95 *(978-1-893536-23-4(8),* 375-018) Garlinghouse, Inc.
—Smaller, Smarter Home Plans. 2007. (Illus.). 287p. per. 12.95 *(978-1-893536-20-3(3),* 375-015) Garlinghouse, Inc.
Garlinghouse Company, creator. Country & Farmhouse Home Plans. 2007. (Illus.). 398p. per. 9.99 *(978-1-893536-10-4(6),* 161) Garlinghouse, Inc.
—223 Favorite Hillside Homes. 2007. (Illus.). 238p. per. 8.95 *(978-1-893536-15-9(7),* 166) Garlinghouse, Inc.
—402 Affordable Home Plans. 2007. (Illus.). 411p. per. 8.95 *(978-1-893536-13-5(0),* 164) Garlinghouse, Inc.
—532 Ranch Home Plans. 2007. (Illus.). 415p. per. 9.95 *(978-1-893536-18-0(1),* 169) Garlinghouse, Inc.
Garlinghouse staff. Southern Charm. 2007. 239p. pap. 12.95 *(978-1-893536-22-7(X),* 375-017) Garlinghouse, Inc.
Garnett, Larry W. Home Plan Doctor: The Essential Companion for Anyone Buying a Home Design Plan. 2007. (ENG., Illus.). 224p. pap. 18.95 *(978-1-58017-698-9(4),* 1580176984) Storey Publishing, LLC.
Gomme, Andor, et al. Design & Plan in the Country House: From Castle Donjons to Palladian Boxes. 2008. (ENG., Illus.). 352p. 85.00 *(978-0-300-12645-7(X))* Yale Univ. Pr.
Goody, Joan, et al. Housing. 2nd ed. 2010. (Building Type Basics Ser.: 17). (ENG., Illus.). 240p. 80.00 *(978-0-470-40464-5(7),* Wiley) Wiley, John & Sons, Inc.
Grissim, John D. The Grissim Buyer's Guide to Manufactured Homes & Land: How to Find a Reputable Dealer & Negotiate a Fair Price on the Best Kept Secret in American Housing. 2nd exp. rev. ed. 2008. Orig. Title: The Complete Buyer's Guide to Manufactured Homes & Land. (Illus.). 192p. per. 29.95 *(978-0-9725436-2-0(7))* Rainshadow Pubns.
Group, Harold E. Small Houses of the Forties: With Illustrations & Floor Plans. 2007. (Dover Architecture Ser.). (ENG., Illus.). 144p. per. 12.95 *(978-0-486-45598-3(X))* Dover Pubns., Inc.
H. F. Ullmann Staff, creator. Designer Apartments. 2008. (Art & Architectute Ser.). (Illus.). 800p. 69.95 *(978-0-8416-0064-5(3))* American Map Corp.
Habinteg Housing Association. Lifetime Homes Design Guide. 2012. (ENG., Illus.). 60p. pap. 55.95 ***(978-1-84806-188-0(9))*** Building Research Establishment GBR. Dist: Taylor & Francis Group.
Hettche, Thomas, et al. Fritz Barth, Cannstatter Straße 84, Fellbach: Cannstatter Strasse 84, Fellbach. 2011. (GER & ENG., Illus.). 72p. 49.00 *(978-3-932565-76-2(2))* Edition Axel Menges GmbH DEU. Dist: National Bk. Network.
Hirsch, William J., Jr. Designing Your Perfect House: Lessons from an Architect. 2008. (Illus.). 240p. 39.95 *(978-0-9798820-3-6(6))* Dalsimer Pr., Inc.
Hodge, Brooke, ed. Enrique Norten: A House in the City. 2006. (Eliot Noyes Ser.). (Illus.). 72p. pap. 24.95 *(978-0-935617-43-6(4))* Harvard Univ., Graduate Schl. of Design.
Homeowner Press Staff & Creative Homeowner Press Editors. The New Ultimate Book of Home Plans. 2007. (Home Plans Ser.). (ENG., Illus.). 608p. pap. 12.95 *(978-1-58011-354-0(0))* Creative Homeowner.
Ideal Homes. Ideal Homes of the Thirties. 2010. (Dover Architecture Ser.). (ENG.). 144p. pap. 16.95 *(978-0-486-47255-3(8))* Dover Pubns., Inc.
Images Publishing Group. Architects 49 Ltd. 2006. (Master Architect Series VI). (ENG., Illus.). 256p. 65.00 *(978-1-876907-09-9(6))* Images Publishing Group AUS. Dist: National Bk. Network.
Jacobson, Hugh Newell. Hugh Newell Jacobsen, Architect. Vignelli, Massimo, ed. 2006. (ENG., Illus.). 352p. 95.00 *(978-1-920744-13-7(4))* Images Publishing Group AUS. Dist: National Bk. Network.
Jefferis & Smith, Richard G. Residential Design, Drafting,and Detailing Workbo. 2006. (C). pap. 27.95 *(978-1-4180-1278-6(5))* Delmar Cengage Learning.
Jefferis, Alan & Jefferis, Janice. Residential Design, Drafting, & Detailing. 2007. (ENG., Illus.). 896p. (C). 162.95 *(978-1-4180-1275-5(0))* Delmar Cengage Learning.
Jeswald, Peter. Patios & Walkways Idea Book. 2008. (Taunton Home Idea Bks.). (ENG., Illus.). 185p. pap. 19.95 *(978-1-56158-936-4(5))* Taunton Pr., Inc.
Jimenez, Carlos & Hester, Paul. Crowley. 2009. (ENG., Illus.). 112p. 29.95 *(978-0-9814628-7-5(1))* Oro Editions.
Jodidio, Philip. Architecture Now. Houses. 2009. (ENG, FRE & GER., Illus.). 416p. pap. 39.99 *(978-3-8365-0374-7(3))* TASCHEN DEU. Dist: Ingram Pub. Services.
Jordan, Wendy A. Universal Design for the Home: Great-Looking, Great-Living Design for All Ages, Abilities, & Circumstances. 2008. (ENG., Illus.). 208p. pap. 24.99 *(978-1-59253-381-7(7),* 1592533817, Quarry Books) Quayside.
Kahn, Lloyd, intro. Gardeners & Poultry Keepers Guide & Illustrated Catalogue of W. Cooper, Ltd: 500 Drawings of Greenhouses, Farm & Garden Buildings, & Rustic Furniture. abr. ed. 2010. (ENG., Illus.). 308p. 26.95 *(978-0-936070-47-6(1))* Shelter Pubns., Inc.
Kicklighter, Clois E. Architecture 2000: Residential Drawing & Design. (Illus.). 132.00 *(978-1-56637-604-4(1))* Goodheart-Willcox Pub.
—Architecture Standard Ind License 3.5D 2000. 52.00 *(978-1-56637-599-3(1))* Goodheart-Willcox Pub.
Kicklighter, Clois E. & Kicklighter, Joan C. Architecture: Residential Drafting & Design. 10th ed. 2008. (ENG.). 848p. (gr. 9-14). 93.28 *(978-1-59070-699-2(4))* Goodheart-Willcox Pub.
Killory, Christine & Davids, Rene. Details in Contemporary Architecture. 2007. (ENG., Illus.). 208p. 65.00 *(978-1-56898-576-3(2))* Princeton Architectural Pr.
Kottjé, et al. Individuell wohnen in Reihen- und Doppelhäusern: Großzügig ungewöhnlich attraktiv. 2009. (GER., Illus.). 143p. *(978-3-421-03681-0(0))* Deutsche Verlags-Anstalt GmbH.
Lang, Susan. Designing Your Dream Home: Every Question to Ask, Every Detail to Consider, & Everything to Know Before You Build or Remodel, 0 vols. 2008. (Illus.). 384p. pap. 24.99 *(978-1-4016-0352-6(1))* Nelson, Thomas Inc.
Lehtovuori, Olli. Story of Finnish Housing Architecture. 2008. (ENG & FIN., Illus.). 192p. 34.00 *(978-951-682-556-7(7))* Rakennustieto oy FIN. Dist: Independent Pubs. Group.
Lescroart, Yves, text. Manor Houses in Normandy. 2008. (Art & Architecture Ser.). (Illus.). 359p. per. 24.95 *(978-0-8416-0073-7(2))* American Map Corp.
Lindal, Cedar Homes, ed. Living Dreams. 2007. 272p. 24.95 *(978-0-9625396-7-1(8))* Lindal Cedar Homes.
Llorella, Anja. New Minimalist Houses. 2007. (Illus.). 335p. 50.00 *(978-0-06-089316-3(8),* Collins Design) HarperCollins Pubs.
Loon, Yong Ai & Kin, Chai Wai. Timeless Tropical. Kohli, Eddy, ed. 2010. (ENG., Illus.). 128p. 40.00 *(978-0-9820607-9-7(3))* Oro Editions.
MacBean, Ken Mark. Green Design: The Architecture of Affordability. 2008. 78p. pap. 16.95 *(978-1-60474-741-6(2))* PublishAmerica, Inc.
Mack, Lorrie. Patterns in Your Home. 2007. 24.95 *(978-0-06-114986-3(1),* Collins Design) HarperCollins Pubs.
Madden, Chris & Palomba, Sarah Elizabeth. The Soul of a House: Decorating with Warmth, Style, & Comfort. 2010. (ENG., Illus.). 208p. 45.00 *(978-0-8478-3370-2(4))* Rizzoli International Pubns., Inc.
Marshall, Paula, ed. Patios Designs for Living. 2007. (Designs for Living Ser.). (Illus.). 191p. per. 21.95 *(978-0-696-23246-6(4),* Home Depot Bks.) Meredith Bks.
Mascord, Alan & Alan Mascord Design Associates. Mascord Living Spaces: Inspiring Home Plans from Alan Mascord Design Associates. 2007. (Illus.). 160p. per. 11.95 *(978-0-9788113-0-3(5))* AMDA Pr.
Mateo, Josep Lluíí & S. Global Housing Projects Since 1980. Mateo, Josep Llu, ed. 2008. (Illus.). 280p. pap. *(978-84-96954-47-2(1))* Actar Birkhauser Distribution.
Mattewson, Glenn G. A. Deck Construction Based on the 2009 International Residential Code. 2009. (ENG.). pap. 39.95 *(978-1-58001-880-7(7))* International Code Council.
Mazor, Stanley. Design an Expandable House. 2006. 136p. per. 24.99 *(978-1-58832-143-5(6))* Unlimited Publishing LLC.
McInturff, Mark. Mark McInturff. 2006. (ENG., Illus.). 128p. 39.50 *(978-1-86470-100-5(5))* Images Publishing Group AUS. Dist: National Bk. Network.
McLeod, Virginia. Encyclopedia of Detail in Contemporary Residential Architecture. 2010. (ENG., Illus.). 352p. 65.00 *(978-1-85669-692-0(8))* King, Laurence Publishing GBR. Dist: Hachette Bk. Group.
Meinecke, Conrad. Your Cabin in the Woods: A Compilation of Cabin Plans & Philosophy for Discovering Life in the Great Outdoors. 2011. 206p. 44.95 ***(978-1-258-06101-2(5))*** Literary Licensing, LLC.
Melvin, Jeremy. Country Houses Today. 2006. (Interior Angles Ser.: 14). (ENG., Illus.). 208p. 70.00 *(978-0-470-01647-3(7),* Academy Pr.) Wiley, John & Sons, Inc.
Miers, Mary. American Houses: The Architecture of Fairfax & Sammons. 2006. (ENG., Illus.). 240p. 60.00 *(978-0-8478-2857-9(3))* Rizzoli International Pubns., Inc.
Moss, Richard. Bathroom Installations: A Complete Guide Planning, Managing & Completing Your Installation. 2007. (ENG., Illus.). 160p. 45.00 *(978-1-86126-919-5(6))* Crowood Pr., Ltd. GBR. Dist: Independent Pubs. Group.
O'Gorman, James F. & Condon, Lorna. Drawing Toward Home: Designs for Domestic Architecture from Historic New England. 2010. 59.95 *(978-0-88448-328-1(2))* Tilbury Hse. Pubs.
Paul, Linda Leigh. Haciendas: Spanish Colonial Houses in the U. S. & Mexico. 2008. (ENG., Illus.). 224p. 55.00 *(978-0-8478-3099-2(3))* Rizzoli International Pubns., Inc.
Pauwels, Wim. Bathrooms & Bedrooms. Watkinson, Laura, tr. 2008. (ENG., Illus.). 204p. *(978-90-77213-88-9(0),* Beta-Plus (Acc)) Antique Collectors' Club.
—Family Houses. 2006. (ENG., Illus.). 204p. *(978-90-77213-56-8(2),* Beta-Plus (Acc)) Antique Collectors' Club.
Phaidon Press Editors. Living in the New Millennium, Houses at the Start of the 21st Century. 2009. (ENG., Illus.). 160p. 35.00 *(978-0-7148-5599-8(5))* Phaidon Pr., Inc.
Popular Science Monthly Staff. How to Build Cabins, Lodges & Bungalows. 2006. (Dover Woodworking Ser.). (ENG., Illus.). 256p. per. 10.95 *(978-0-486-45132-9(1))* Dover Pubns., Inc.
Powell, Robert. The New Malaysian House. 2008. (ENG., Illus.). 224p. 49.95 *(978-0-7946-0499-8(4),* PeriplusEdition) Tuttle Publishing.
Quartino, Daniela Santos. 200 Outstanding Apartment Ideas. 2009. (200 Home Ideas Ser.). (ENG., Illus.). 800p. 39.95 *(978-1-55407-394-8(4))* Firefly Bks., Ltd.
Riera Ojeda, Oscar, ed. Peter Forbes: Seal Harbor. 2008. (Illus.). 112p. 25.00 *(978-0-9795395-4-1(4))* Oro Editions.
Riera Ojeda, Oscar & Woo, Kyu Sung. Geometries. Riera Ojeda, Oscar, ed. 2008. (ENG., Illus.). 112p. 25.00 *(978-0-9793801-6-7(2))* Oro Editions.
Rockport Publishers Staff, et al, eds. Open Kitchens: Inspired Designs for Modern & Loft Living. 2007. (ENG., Illus.). 192p. 40.00 *(978-1-59253-378-7(7),* 1592533787, Rockport Publishers) Quayside.
Rooney, E. Ashley, et al. Green Homes: Dwellings for the 21st Century. 2008. (Illus.). 160p. bds. 39.99 *(978-0-7643-3033-9(0))* Schiffer Publishing, Ltd.
Samaroo, Melissa. The Complete Guide to Building Backyard Ponds, Fountains, & Waterfalls for Homeowners: Everything You Need to Know Explained Simply. 2011. (Back to Basics Ser.). (ENG.). 288p. pap. 24.95 *(978-1-60138-598-7(6))* Atlantic Publishing Co.
Sanchez, Laura & Sanchez, Alex. Adobe Houses for Today: Flexible Plans for Your Adobe Home. rev. ed. 2008. (ENG., Illus.). 228p. pap. 29.95 *(978-0-86534-662-8(3))* Sunstone Pr.
Sater, Dan. Smaller Home: Creating the Perfect Fit. 2006. (ENG.). 176p. 35.00 *(978-0-06-089189-3(0),* Collins Design) HarperCollins Pubs.
Sater, Dan F., II. Dan Sater's European Classics: Tuscan, Italian, French, Spanish & English: Eighty Designer Home Plans. Bailey, Rickard & Baker, Jennifer, eds. 2007. (Illus.). 191p. pap. 14.95 *(978-1-932553-27-7(4)* DDP) Designs Direct Publishing, LLC.
Sater Design Collection, des. Dan Sater's Design Collection: 95 Luxury Home Plans. 2008. (Illus.). 192p. pap. 12.95 *(978-1-932553-28-4(2),* DDP) Designs Direct Publishing, LLC.
Schneider, Friederike & Heckmann, Oliver. Floor Plan Manual: Housing. 4th rev. ed. 2011. (ENG.). 336p. 110.00 *(978-3-0346-0707-0(5))* Birkhauser Verlag AG CHE. Dist: Actar Birkhauser Distribution.
Schweitzer. Planning & Designing Innovative & Modern School Kitchens & Dining Rooms. 2010. 172p. 59.00 *(978-1-4389-5279-6(1));* pap. 55.00 *(978-1-4389-5278-9(3))* AuthorHouse.
Scutella, Richard M. & Heberle, Dave. How to Plan, Contract & Build Your Own Home. 5th ed. 2010. (ENG., Illus.). 912p. pap. 34.95 *(978-0-07-160330-0(1),* 0071603301) McGraw-Hill Professional Publishing.
Sears Roebuck and Company & Sears Roebuck Staff. Sears Modern Homes 1913. 2006. (Dover Architecture Ser.). (ENG., Illus.). 128p. per. 12.95 *(978-0-486-45264-7(6))* Dover Pubns., Inc.
Seidler, Harry & Abel, Chris. Early Houses & Recent Houses, 2 vols. 2006. (ENG., Illus.). 144p. 90.00 *(978-1-920744-16-8(9))* Images Publishing Group AUS. Dist: National Bk. Network.
Serrats, Marta. Prefab Houses DesignSource. 2012. (ENG., Illus.). 640p. pap. 19.99 ***(978-0-06-211354-2(2),*** Collins Design) HarperCollins Pubs.
Shafer, Jay. The Tumbleweed DIY Book of Backyard Sheds & Tiny Houses: Your Guest Cottage, Writing Studio, Home Office, Backyard Gym, Craft Workshop. 2011. (ENG., Illus.). 144p. pap. 19.95 ***(978-1-56523-704-9(8))*** Fox Chapel Publishing Co., Inc.
Sillah, Andrea, ed. Universal Design Ideas for Style, Comfort & Safety. 2007. (Illus.). 160p. per. 21.95 *(978-0-87629-091-0(8))* Means, R S. Co., Inc.
Skinner, Tina. Building Outdoor Environments with Retaining Walls. 2006. (Illus.). 128p. pap. 24.95 *(978-0-7643-2542-7(6))* Schiffer Publishing, Ltd.
Sloan, Samuel. The Model Architect, Vol. 2. 2007. 204p. per. *(978-0-923891-86-2(2))* Ishi Pr. International.
—The Model Architect Vol. 1: A Series of Original Designs. 2007. 206p. per. 24.95 *(978-0-923891-85-5(4))* Ishi Pr. International.
Smith, Michael & Pittel, Christine. Houses. 2008. (ENG., Illus.). 208p. 50.00 *(978-0-8478-3070-1(5))* Rizzoli International Pubns., Inc.
Standard Homes Company. Best Homes of The 1920s. 2008. (Dover Architecture Ser.). (ENG., Illus.). 80p. per. 10.95 *(978-0-486-45430-6(4))* Dover Pubns., Inc.
Stickley, Gustav. Gustav Stickley's Craftsmen Homes & Bungalows. 2007. (Illus.). 544p. pap. 19.95 *(978-1-60239-082-9(7))* Skyhorse Publishing Co., Inc.
Stine, Daniel. Residential Design Using AutoCAD 2008. 2007. 418p. per. 59.95 *(978-1-58503-367-6(7),* SDC Pubns.) Schroff Development Corp.
Sunset Books Staff & Bradley, Bridget. Backyards. 2009. (Sunset Design Guide Ser.). (ENG., Illus.). 224p. pap. 22.95 *(978-0-376-01348-4(6),* Sunset Bks./Sunset Publishing Corp.) Oxmoor Hse., Inc.
Susanka, Sarah & Obolensky, Kira. The Not So Big House Collection: The Not So Big House & Creating the Not So Big House, 2 vols. 2nd ed. 2009. (ENG., Illus.). 504p. 40.00 *(978-1-60085-152-0(5))* Taunton Pr., Inc.
Tedesco, Paul H. & Tedesco, James/B. Portable & Prefabricated Houses of the Thirties: E. F. Hodgson Company 1935 & 1939 Catalogs Unabridged Reprint. 2007. 19.95 *(978-0-9792059-1-0(3))* JBT Publishing.
Trulove, James Grayson. Great Houses on a Budget. 2008. (Illus.). 191p. pap. 19.95 *(978-0-06-158116-8(X),* Collins Design) HarperCollins Pubs.
Trulove, James Grayson & Trulove, James G. Cabins: The New Style. 2006. (New Style Ser.). (ENG., Illus.). 192p. 35.00 *(978-0-06-089349-1(4),* Collins Design) HarperCollins Pubs.
—The Modern Townhouse: The Latest in Urban & Suburban Designs. 2006. (ENG., Illus.). 192p. 35.00 *(978-0-06-113892-8(4),* Collins Design) HarperCollins Pubs.
Ullman, creator. Contemporary Houses/Moderne Hauser/Maisons Contemporaines/Modernhuizen. 2008. (Art & Architecture Ser.). (Illus.). 1050p. 69.95 *(978-0-8416-0063-8(5))* American Map Corp.
van Gameren, Dick, ed. The Residential Floor Plan: Standard & Idea. 2011. (ENG & DUT., Illus.). 152p. pap. 45.00 *(978-90-5662-757-7(0))* NAi Uitgevers / Publishers Stichting NLD. Dist: D.A.P./Distributed Art Pubs.
Vaux, Calvert. Villas & Cottages. 2011. 348p. pap. 21.95 ***(978-1-4585-0018-2(7))*** Univ. of Michigan Library.
Vaux, Calvert. Villas & Cottages a Series of Designs Prepared for Execution in the United States by Calvert Vaux, Architect Late Downing & Vaux Illustr. 2006. 352p. per. 26.99 *(978-1-4255-3587-2(9))* MPublishing.
Von Einsiedel, Andreas & Thornycroft, Johanna. Dream Homes: 100 Inspirational Interiors. 2007. (ENG., Illus.). 352p. pap. 32.95 *(978-1-85894-349-7(3))* Merrell Pubs. Ltd. GBR. Dist: Perseus Distribution.
von Holst, H. V., ed. Modern American Homes: Prairie & Craftsman Architecture. 2008. (Illus.). 128p. bds. 29.99 *(978-0-7643-3005-6(5))* Schiffer Publishing, Ltd.
Vranckx, Bridget. 150 Best New House Ideas, Vol. 2. 2008. (ENG., Illus.). 600p. 29.95 *(978-0-06-153792-9(6),* Collins Design) HarperCollins Pubs.
Vranckx, Bridget & Moreno, Esther. 200 Outstanding House Ideas. 2009. (200 Home Ideas Ser.). (ENG., Illus.). 800p. 39.95 *(978-1-55407-393-1(6))* Firefly Bks., Ltd.
William S. B. Dana. The Swiss Chalet Book. 2009. 152p. pap. 9.95 *(978-1-60386-188-5(2),* Watchmaker Publishing) Wexford College Pr.
Williams, Paul R. New Homes for Today, 2 vols. 2006. (California Architecture & Architects Ser.: No. 29). (Illus.). 95p. pap. *(978-0-940512-45-0(9))* Hennessey & Ingalls, Inc.
—Paul R. Williams: A Collection of House Plans, 2 vols. 2006. (California Architecture & Architects Ser.: No. 29). (Illus.). *(978-0-940512-44-3(0))* Hennessey & Ingalls, Inc.
—The Small Home of Tomorrow, 2 vols. 2006. (California Architecture & Architects Ser.: No. 29). (Illus.). 95p. pap. *(978-0-940512-46-7(7))* Hennessey & Ingalls, Inc.
Zhang, Donia. Courtyard Houses of Beijing. 2010. 240p. pap. *(978-3-639-99630-2(5))* VDM Verlag Dr. Mueller e.K.

ARCHITECTURE, DOMESTIC—AFRICA

Bourdier, Jean-Paul & Minh-ha, Trinh T. Vernacular Architecture of West Africa: A World in Dwelling. 2011. (ENG., Illus.). 192p. 74.95 *(978-0-415-58543-9(0))* Routledge.
Carucci, Margherita. The Romano-African Domus: Studies in Space, Decoration, & Function. 2008. (Bar S Ser.). (Illus.). xii, 289p. (C). 100.00 *(978-1-4073-0175-4(6))* British Archaeological Reports Ltd. GBR. Dist: Brown, David Bk. Co., The.
Ehrlich, Steven. Steven Ehrlich Houses. 2011. (ENG., Illus.). 240p. 50.00 *(978-1-58093-306-3(8))* Monacelli Pr., Inc.
Mosha, Livin. Architecture of African Dwellings. 2011. 372p. pap. ***(978-3-8443-1573-8(X))*** Lambert Academic Publishing.
Nelson, Steven. From Cameroon to Paris: Mousgoum Architecture in & Out of Africa. 2007. (Illus.). 304p. 55.00 *(978-0-226-57183-6(1))* Univ. of Chicago Pr.
Rodriguez, Luis, ed. Architecture & Revolution in Cuba, 1959-1969. 2008. 224p. 45.00 *(978-84-96540-72-9(3))* Kunst-Werke Berlin e.V. DEU. Dist: Actar Birkhauser Distribution.
Stoeltie, Barbara & Stoeltie, Rene. Living in Morocco: 25 Jahre TASCHEN. Taschen, Angelika, ed. 2011. (25 Ser.). (ENG., Illus.). 280p. 14.99 ***(978-3-8365-3174-0(7))*** TASCHEN DEU. Dist: Ingram Pub. Services.
Wilbaux, Quentin. Marrakesh: The Secret of Courtyard Houses. 2009. (ENG., Illus.). 384p. 120.00 *(978-2-86770-130-6(9))* ACR Edition FRA. Dist: Antique Collectors' Club.

ARCHITECTURE, DOMESTIC—ASIA

Beal, Gillian & Termansen, Jacob. Tropical Style: Contemporary Dream Houses in Malaysia. 2008. (ENG., Illus.). 224p. 39.95 *(978-0-7946-0555-1(9),* PeriplusEdition) Tuttle Publishing.
Bensley, Bill. Paradise by Design: Tropical Residences & Resorts by Bensley Design Studios. 2008. (ENG., Illus.). 240p. 49.95 *(978-0-7946-0493-6(5),* PeriplusEdition) Tuttle Publishing.
Bertram, Carel. Imagining the Turkish House: Collective Visions of Home. 2008. (ENG., Illus.). 360p. (C). pap. 70.00 *(978-0-292-71825-8(X))* Univ. of Texas Pr.
Bhatia, Gautam. MUD the House. 2007. (ENG.). 260p. *(978-81-8386-023-9(0))* India Research Pr. IND. Dist: Independent Pubs. Group.
Bingham-Hall, Patrick, ed. No Boundaries: The Lien Villa Collective. 2010. (ENG., Illus.). 240p. *(978-1-877015-27-4(X))* Pesaro Publishing.
Cheng, Kelley. Groovy Homes: Sexy & Delicious Living Spaces. 2007. (Illus.). 191p. *(978-981-245-267-2(2))* Page One Publishing.
Gerritsen, Marc & Pauwels, Wim. Contemporary Living in Asia. 2011. (ENG., Illus.). 200p. 145.00 *(978-90-8944-088-4(7))* Beta-Plus Pubs. BEL. Dist: Antique Collectors' Club.
Gray, John. Domestic Mandala: Architecture of Lifeworlds in Nepal. 2006. (Anthropology & Cultural History in Asia & the Indo-Pacific Ser.). (Illus.). 180p. 120.00 *(978-0-7546-4538-2(X))* Ashgate Publishing Co.
Inglis, Kim. Tropical Home: Inspirational Design Ideas. 2011. (ENG., Illus.). 144p. 24.95 *(978-0-8048-3980-8(8))* Tuttle Publishing.
Knapp, Ronald G. Chinese Houses of Southeast Asia: The Eclectic Architecture of Sojourners & Settlers. 2010. (ENG., Illus.). 288p. 49.95 *(978-0-8048-3956-3(5))* Tuttle Publishing.

Kopper, Philip. New Southern Classicism: The Residential Architecture of Barry Fox. 2006. (Illus.). 256p. 60.00 *(978-0-932958-26-6(5))* Golden Coast Publishing Co.

Lico, Gerard. Arkitekturang Filipino: A History of Architecture & Urbanism in the Philippines. 2010. (Illus.). 617p. pap. 90.00 *(978-971-542-579-7(6))* Univ. of the Philippines Pr. PHL. Dist: Univ. of Hawaii Pr.

Lococo, Anita. Living in Bali: 25 Jahre TASCHEN. Taschen, Angelika, ed. 2011. (25 Ser.). (ENG., Illus.). 200p. 14.99 ***(978-3-8365-3168-9(2))*** TASCHEN DEU. Dist: Ingram Pub. Services.

Loon, Yong Ai & Kin, Chai Wai. Timeless Tropical. Kohli, Eddy, ed. 2010. (ENG., Illus.). 128p. 40.00 *(978-0-9820607-9-7(3))* Oro Editions.

Manjikian, Lalai. Collective Memory & Home in the Diaspor. 2008. 108p. pap. *(978-3-639-04894-0(6))* VDM Verlag Dr. Mueller e.K.

Pinijvarasin, Wandee. Experiences of Well-Being. 2008. 260p. pap. *(978-3-639-03655-8(7))* VDM Verlag Dr. Mueller e.K.

Powell, Robert. The New Indonesian House. 2011. (ENG., Illus.). 240p. 49.95 *(978-0-8048-4143-6(8))* Tuttle Publishing.

—The New Malaysian House. 2008. (ENG., Illus.). 224p. 49.95 *(978-0-7946-0499-8(4),* PeriplusEdition) Tuttle Publishing.

—Singapore Houses. 2009. (ENG., Illus.). 240p. 49.95 *(978-0-8048-4051-4(2))* Tuttle Publishing.

Quartino, Daniela Santos. Asian Style: Contemporary Asian Living. 2009. (Illus.). 355p. *(978-981-245-675-5(9))* Page One Publishing.

Riera Ojeda, Oscar & Woo, Kyu Sung. Geometries. Riera Ojeda, Oscar, ed. 2008. (ENG., Illus.). 112p. 25.00 *(978-0-9793801-6-7(2))* Oro Editions.

Rooney, E. Ashley. Asian Influenced Architecture & Design. 2010. (Illus.). 144p. 34.99 *(978-0-7643-3383-5(6))* Schiffer Publishing, Ltd.

Schleifer, Simone, ed. Asian Living. Brooke, Amy et al, trs. 2008. (ENG., Illus.). 188p. pap. 14.99 *(978-3-8365-0393-8(X))* TASCHEN DEU. Dist: Ingram Pub. Services.

Sethi, Sunil. Inside Asia Box: 25 Jahre TASCHEN, 2 vols. 2011. (25 Ser.). (ENG., Illus.). 840p. 59.99 ***(978-3-8365-3176-4(3))*** TASCHEN DEU. Dist: Ingram Pub. Services.

ARCHITECTURE, DOMESTIC—AUSTRALIA

Beaver, Robyn. 100 Top Houses from Down Under. 2006. (ENG., Illus.). 352p. 60.00 *(978-1-86470-141-8(2))* Images Publishing Group AUS. Dist: National Bk. Network.

Bingham-Hall, Patrick, ed. & photos by. The Australian House. 2008. (ENG., Illus.). 500p. pap. *(978-1-877015-25-0(3))* Pesaro Publishing.

Butler-Bowdon, Caroline & Pickett, Charles. Homes in the Sky: Apartment Living in Australia. 2007. (ENG., Illus.). 256p. 53.00 *(978-0-522-85316-2(1))* Melbourne Univ. Publishing AUS. Dist: Independent Pubs. Group.

Crafti, Stephen. Beach Houses 2, Vol. 2. 2006. (ENG., Illus.). 55.00 *(978-1-876907-95-2(9))* Images Publishing Group AUS. Dist: National Bk. Network.

—Beach Houses of Australia & New Zealand. 2006. (ENG., Illus.). 210p. 49.50 *(978-1-86470-071-8(8))* Images Publishing Group AUS. Dist: National Bk. Network.

ARCHITECTURE, DOMESTIC—AUSTRIA

Gö, et al. Before Architecture. Vor der Architektur. 2 Bde. Residential Building as Motivation - Wohnbau als Anlass - 11. Internationale Architekturausstellung - La Biennale di Venezia 2008. 11th International Architecture Exhibition - La Biennale di Venezia 2008, 3 vols. 2008. (GER & ENG., Illus.). 211p. pap. 49.95 *(978-3-211-09425-9(3))* Springer Wien AUT. Dist: Actar Birkhauser Distribution.

Peters, Paulhans. Franz Riepl. Architekt / Architect. 2006. (ENG & GER., Illus.). 224p. 89.00 *(978-3-936681-00-0(7))* Edition Axel Menges GmbH DEU. Dist: National Bk. Network.

ARCHITECTURE, DOMESTIC—CANADA

Aldred, Robert. The Little Stone House. 2007. (Illus.). 72p. *(978-0-9697406-4-3(6))* Meany, P. D. Pubs.

Cruickshank, Tom & De Visser, John. Old Toronto Houses. 2nd rev. ed. 2008. (ENG., Illus.). 320p. pap. 39.95 *(978-1-55407-382-5(0))* Firefly Bks., Ltd.

Dubois, Martin. Architecture et Habitat Collectif Au Québec: 65 Immeubles Résidentiels. 2010. (FRE., Illus.). xv, 240p. *(978-2-551-19863-4(1))* Publications du Quebec, Les.

Dunkerley, Michele & Schubart, Hank. Houses Made of Wood & Light: The Life & Architecture of Hank Schubart. 2012. (ENG., Illus.). 208p. 50.00 ***(978-0-292-72942-1(1))*** Univ. of Texas Pr.

Dunkerley, Michele, et al. Houses Made of Wood & Light: The Life & Architecture of Hank Schubart. 2012. E-Book ***(978-0-292-73714-3(9))*** Univ. of Texas Pr.

Higgins, Keith. How to Look at a Vancouver Special. 2010. 48p. pap. 9.00 *(978-1-935662-19-8(8))* Publication Studio.

MacDonald, Chris. West Coast Residential: The Modern & the Contemporary. Bellerby, Greg, ed. 2007. (ENG., Illus.). 120p. 39.95 *(978-1-894965-60-6(4))* Simply Read Bks. CAN. Dist: Perseus-PGW.

MacNutt, James & Tuck, Robert. Heritage Houses of Prince Edward Island: Two Hundred Years of Domestic Architecture. 2006. (ENG., Illus.). 128p. pap. 34.95 *(978-0-88780-711-4(9))* Formac Publishing Co., Ltd. CAN. Dist: Casemate Pubs. & Bk. Distributors, LLC.

MacNutt, James W. Inside Island Heritage Homes: Two Hundred Years of Domestic Architecture on Prince Edward Island. 2008. (ENG., Illus.). 128p. pap. 34.95 *(978-0-88780-745-9(3))* Formac Publishing Co., Ltd. CAN. Dist: Casemate Pubs. & Bk. Distributors, LLC.

Mellin, Robert. Tilting: House Launching, Slide Hauling, Potato Trenching, & Other Tales from a Newfoundland Fishing Village. 2008. (ENG., Illus.). 256p. pap. 24.95 *(978-1-56898-807-8(9))* Princeton Architectural Pr.

Panache Partners LLC Staff. Spectacular Homes of Western Canada: An Exclusive Showcase of the Finest Designers in British Columbia. 2009. (Spectacular Homes Ser.). (ENG., Illus.). 300p. 34.95 *(978-1-933415-71-0(1))* Panache Partners, LLC.

Panache Partners Staff. Spectacular Homes of Toronto: An Exclusive Showcase of the Finest Designers in Ontario. 2009. (Spectacular Homes Ser.). (ENG., Illus.). 300p. 34.95 *(978-1-933415-72-7(X))* Panache Partners, LLC.

Rose, Peter. Houses. 2010. (ENG., Illus.). 160p. 40.00 *(978-1-56898-821-4(4))* Princeton Architectural Pr.

Soules, Matthew, ed. Future Social. 2011. (ENG.). 168p. pap. 19.95 *(978-1-897476-30-7(2))* Simply Read Bks. CAN. Dist: Perseus-PGW.

Treib, Mark, et al. West Coast Residential. Bellerby, Greg, ed. rev. ed. 2012. (ENG., Illus.). 120p. 29.95 *(978-1-894965-99-6(X))* Simply Read Bks. CAN. Dist: Perseus-PGW.

Ward, Peter. A History of Domestic Space: Privacy & the Canadian Home. 2009. (ENG.). 192p. 39.95 *(978-0-7748-0685-5(0))* UBC Pr. CAN. Dist: Univ. of Washington Pr.

Wilson, Alex. Green Building Products: The GreenSpec Guide to Residential Building Materials. Malin, Nadav, ed. 3rd ed. 2008. (ENG., Illus.). 352p. pap. 37.95 *(978-0-86571-600-1(5),* 9780865716001) New Society Pubs., Ltd. CAN. Dist: Consortium Bk. Sales & Distribution.

ARCHITECTURE, DOMESTIC—CHINA

Congzhou, Pan; Bingjie,, Chen; Hongxaun. Chinese Houses: A Pictorial Tour of China's Traditional Dwellings. 2009. 336p. (gr. 12). 29.95 *(978-1-60220-002-9(5))* Reader's Digest Assn., Inc., The.

Li, George. Residence Award. 2011. (ENG., Illus.). 320p. 60.00 *(978-988-19738-9-4(9))* Design Media Publishing Ltd. HKG. Dist: BookMasters Distribution Services (BDS).

Ray, Mary-Ann, et al, texts. Caochangdi, Beijing Inside Out. 2009. (ENG., Illus.). 450p. pap. 24.95 *(978-988-17522-4-6(8))* Timezone 8 Ltd. HKG. Dist: D.A.P./Distributed Art Pubs.

Shan, Deqi. Chinese Vernacular Dwellings. 3rd ed. 2011. (Introductions to Chinese Culture Ser.). (ENG., Illus.). 166p. pap. 19.99 ***(978-0-521-18667-4(6))*** Cambridge Univ. Pr.

Taschen, Angelika, ed. Living in China. 2007. (Taschen's Lifestyle Ser.). (FRE, GER & ENG., Illus.). 195p. 29.99 *(978-3-8228-4275-1(3))* TASCHEN DEU. Dist: Ingram Pub. Services.

ARCHITECTURE, DOMESTIC—COLOMBIA

Cram101 Textbook Reviews & Cram101 Textbook Reviews. Outlines & Highlights for a Culture of Stone: Inka Perspectives on Rock by Carolyn Dean, ISBN. 2011. 86p. pap. 27.95 ***(978-1-61461-747-1(3))*** Cram101 Inc.

Saldarriaga Roa, Alberto. Country Houses in Colombia. 2006. (ENG., Illus.). 304p. 65.00 *(978-958-8156-67-5(X))* Villegas Editores S.A. COL. Dist: Independent Pubs. Group.

ARCHITECTURE, DOMESTIC—EGYPT

Abdel-Gawad, Ahmed. Veiling Architecture: Decoration of Domestic Buildings in Upper Egypt 1672-1950. 2012. (ENG., Illus.). 144p. pap. 22.95 ***(978-977-416-487-3(3))*** American Univ. in Cairo Pr. EGY. Dist: Oxford Univ. Pr., Inc.

Hitchins, Derek. The Pyramid Builder's Handbook. 2010. 228p. pap. 41.95 *(978-1-4457-5165-8(8))* Lulu Enterprises Inc.

Koltsida, Aikaterini. Social Aspects of Ancient Egyptian Domestic Architecture. 2007. (BAR International Ser.: Vol. 1608). (ENG., Illus.). 246p. (C). pap. 92.50 *(978-1-4073-0025-2(3))* British Archaeological Reports Ltd. GBR. Dist: Brown, David Bk. Co., The.

ARCHITECTURE, DOMESTIC—EUROPE

Andeweg, Marie Therèse. Cost C16 improving the quality of existing urban building Envelopes. 2007. pap. 69.00 *(978-1-58603-735-2(8),* Delft University Pr) IOS Pr., Inc.

Andeweg, Marie Therèse, et al. Cost C16 improving the quality of existing urban building Envelopes. 2007. pap. 69.00 *(978-1-58603-734-5(X),* Delft University Pr) IOS Pr., Inc.

Anthony, David W. & Chi, Jennifer Y., eds. The Lost World of Old Europe: The Danube Valley, 5000-3500 BC. 2009. (ENG., Illus.). 240p. (C). 49.95 *(978-0-691-14388-0(9))* Princeton Univ. Pr.

Baart, Theo. Theo Baart: Eiland 7. 2008. (ENG.). 128p. pap. 50.00 *(978-90-5662-003-5(7))* NAi Uitgevers / Publishers Stichting NLD. Dist: D.A.P./Distributed Art Pubs.

Botta, Marina. Towards Sustainable Renovation: Three Research Projects. 2008. 164p. pap. *(978-3-639-09809-9(9))* VDM Verlag Dr. Mueller e.K.

Di Giulio, Roberto. COST C16 improving the quality of existing urban building Envelopes. 2007. pap. 69.00 *(978-1-58603-737-6(4),* Delft University Pr) IOS Pr., Inc.

Di Giulio, Roberto, et al. COST C16 improving the quality of existing urban building Envelopes. 2007. pap. 69.00 *(978-1-58603-736-9(6),* Delft University Pr) IOS Pr., Inc.

Espinosa De Los Monteros Rosillo, Patricia & Fernandez De Santaella Martin-Artajo, Joaquin. Spanish Houses: Rustic Mediterranean Style. 2007. (ENG., Illus.). 216p. 50.00 *(978-0-8478-2913-2(8))* Rizzoli International Pubns., Inc.

Fokdal, Josefine. Power & Space. 2011. (ENG.). 112p. pap. 29.50 *(978-3-8258-1390-1(8))* Lit Verlag DEU. Dist: Transaction Pubs.

Hastings, Robert & Wall, Maria, eds. Sustainable Solar Housing, 2 vols., Set. 2009. (ENG., Illus.). 288p. pap. 110.00 *(978-1-84407-801-1(9))* Routledge.

Hastings, Robert S., et al, eds. Sustainable Solar Housing Vol. 1: Strategies & Solutions, 2 vols. 2009. (ENG., Illus.). 320p. pap. 64.95 *(978-1-84407-799-1(3))* Routledge.

—Sustainable Solar Housing - Exemplary Buildings & Technologies, 2 vols., Vol. 2. 2006. (ENG., Illus.). 608p. pap. 64.00 *(978-1-84407-800-4(0))* Routledge.

Hautajärvi, Harri. Villas & Saunas in Finland. 2nd exp. ed. 2010. (Illus.). 248p. 59.95 *(978-951-682-957-2(0))* Rakennustieto oy FIN. Dist: Independent Pubs. Group.

Helamaa, E. & Jetsonen, J. Alvar Aalto Summer Homes. 2008. 120p. pap. 67.00 *(978-951-682-857-5(4))* Rakennustieto oy FIN. Dist: Independent Pubs. Group.

Hentschel, Martin. Bert Teunissen. Domestic Landscapes. Ein Porträt von Europäern daheim, 1 vol. 2007. (ENG., Illus.). 136p. 50.00 *(978-1-59711-040-2(X))* Aperture Foundation, Inc.

Jetsonen, Jari & Jetsonen, Sirkkaliisa. Alvar Aalto Houses. 2011. (ENG., Illus.). 224p. 50.00 *(978-1-56898-982-2(2))* Princeton Architectural Pr.

Karjalainen, Markku & Patokoski, Riko. Wooden Urban Villages. 2008. (ENG.). 168p. 49.00 *(978-951-682-844-5(2))* Rakennustieto oy FIN. Dist: Independent Pubs. Group.

Kauppi, Kenneth. Arkitektens Fritidshus. 2010. (SWE., Illus.). 303p. *(978-91-7843-288-2(X),* Arena) Ashgate Publishing, Ltd.

Krauel, Jacobo. New House. 2009. (ENG.). 168p. pap. 24.99 *(978-84-96969-97-1(5))* Links International (Leading International Key Services Barcelona, S.A.) ESP. Dist: National Bk. Network.

Lehtovuori, Olli. Story of Finnish Housing Architecture. 2008. (ENG & FIN., Illus.). 192p. 34.00 *(978-951-682-556-7(7))* Rakennustieto oy FIN. Dist: Independent Pubs. Group.

Megas, George A. The Greek House: Its Evolution & Its Relation to the Houses of Other Balkan Peoples. (Ministry of Reconstruction Publications: 37). (GRE.). reprint ed. 27.50 *(978-0-404-16595-6(8))* AMS Pr., Inc.

Messervy, Julie Moir. Home Outside: Creating the Landscape You Love. 2009. (ENG., Illus.). 249p. 30.00 *(978-1-60085-008-0(1))* Taunton Pr., Inc.

Nagel, Per, photos by. Living Museums in Scandinavia. 2nd ed. 2006. (ENG., Illus.). 192p. 85.00 *(978-87-987597-0-6(1))* Living Architecture Publishing DNK. Dist: Perseus-PGW.

Nau, Ottmar, ed. Contemporary Living in an Old Majorcan Mill. 2010. (ENG., Illus.). 176p. 68.00 *(978-3-939633-87-7(9))* Jovis Verlag GmbH DEU. Dist: D.A.P./Distributed Art Pubs.

Pauwels, Wim. European Style, Vol. 2. 2010. (ENG., Illus.). 208p. *(978-90-8944-014-3(3),* Beta-Plus (Acc)) Antique Collectors' Club.

Pauwels, Wim, ed. European Style, Vol. 1. 2009. (ENG., Illus.). 208p. 125.00 *(978-90-8944-013-6(5))* Beta-Plus Pubs. BEL. Dist: Antique Collectors' Club.

Pratt, Lord Michael. The Great Country Houses of the Czech Republic & Slovakia. 2008. (Great Country Houses Of... Ser.). (ENG., Illus.). 144p. 39.95 *(978-0-7892-0893-4(8))* Abbeville Pr., Inc.

—Poland. 2008. (Great Country Houses Of... Ser.). (ENG., Illus.). 143p. 39.95 *(978-0-7892-0890-3(3))* Abbeville Pr., Inc.

Rowlands, Rob, et al, eds. Mass Housing in Europe: Multiple Faces of Development, Change & Response. 2010. (ENG., Illus.). 264p. 95.00 *(978-0-230-00730-7(9))* Palgrave Macmillan.

Tostrup, Elizabeth. Norwegian Wood: The Thoughtful Architecture of Wenche Selmer. 2006. (ENG., Illus.). 208p. 45.00 *(978-1-56898-593-0(2))* Princeton Architectural Pr.

Treberspurg, Mar, ed. SolarCity Linz-Pichling. Blaschke, Beverly, tr. from GER. 2008. (Illus.). 216p. 69.95 *(978-3-211-30562-1(9),* 3211305629) Springer Wien AUT. Dist: Actar Birkhauser Distribution.

Welter, Volker M. Ernst L. Freud, Architect: The Case of the Modern Bourgeois Home. 2011. (Space & Place Ser.). (ENG.). 352p. 39.95 ***(978-0-85745-233-7(9))*** Berghahn Bks., Inc.

ARCHITECTURE, DOMESTIC—FRANCE

Anderson, Alex Thomas. The Problem of the House: French Domestic Life & the Rise of Modern Architecture. 2006. (ENG., Illus.). 240p. 60.00 *(978-0-295-98632-6(8))* Univ. of Washington Pr.

Bardati, Flaminia. Il Bel Palatio in Forma Di Castello: Gaillon Tra Flamboyant e Rinascimento. 2009. (FRE, ITA & ENG., Illus.). 220p. *(978-88-88168-50-0(8))* Campisano Editore.

Cariou, Joel, et al. Sustainable French Timber Houses: L'affaire de Wood. 2006. (ENG., Illus.). 160p. 19.95 *(978-1-86470-179-1(X))* Images Publishing Group AUS. Dist: National Bk. Network.

Cerfontaine, Sandra. Saint Tropez: Contemporary & Timeless. 2010. (ENG., Illus.). 160p. *(978-90-8944-085-3(2),* Beta-Plus (Acc)) Antique Collectors' Club.

Einsiedel, Andreas von, photos by. Provencal Living. 2007. (Mini Lifestyle Library Ser.). (ENG., Illus.). 168p. 16.95 *(978-1-902686-61-5(6))* Scriptum Editions GBR. Dist: Independent Pubs. Group.

Faucon, Régis & Lescroart, Yves. Manor Houses in Normandy - Flexi, 1 vol. 2007. (ENG., Illus.). 360p. pap. 24.99 *(978-3-8331-3523-1(9))* h.f.ullmann DEU. Dist: Innovative Logistics.

Gelis-Didot, Pierre. Paris Mansions & Apartments 1893: Facades, Floor Plans & Architectural Details. 2011. (Dover Architecture Ser.). (ENG.). 112p. pap. 17.95 *(978-0-486-47700-8(2))* Dover Pubns., Inc.

Goulet, Patrice, et al. Canal, Patrick Rubin, Architecte: Itinéraires du Passeur: Entretien Avec Patrice Goulet. 2008. (FRE & ENG., Illus.). 159p. *(978-2-87143-212-8(0))* Editions du Layeur.

Grunwald, Anja, photos by. Unite D'habitation, Marseille. 2008. (Opus Ser.). (GER, ENG & FRE., Illus.). 60p. 52.00 *(978-3-932565-65-6(7))* Edition Axel Menges GmbH DEU. Dist: National Bk. Network.

Kristen, Clive & Johnson, David. A French Restoration: The Pleasures & Perils of Renovating a Property in France. 2006. (Illus.). 222p. per. 20.00 *(978-1-84528-068-0(7))* How To Books GBR. Dist: Parkwest Pubns., Inc.

Lescroart, Yves, text. Manor Houses in Normandy. 2008. (Art & Architecture Ser.). (Illus.). 359p. per. 24.95 *(978-0-8416-0073-7(2))* American Map Corp.

Pauwels, Wim. Contemporary Living in Paris. 2008. (ENG., Illus.). 208p. *(978-90-8944-001-3(1),* Beta-Plus (Acc)) Antique Collectors' Club.

—Contemporary Living in Provence & Côte D'Azur. 2008. (ENG., Illus.). 208p. *(978-90-77213-96-4(1),* Beta-Plus (Acc)) Antique Collectors' Club.

Saharoff, Philippe. Mountain Houses. 2007. (FRE & ENG., Illus.). 240p. 40.00 *(978-1-58479-648-0(0))* Abrams.

Silvestre, Ruth. A House in the Sunflowers. 2011. (ENG., Illus.). 288p. pap. 16.95 *(978-0-7490-0838-3(5))* Allison & Busby, Ltd. GBR. Dist: International Publishers Marketing.

Vadrot, Olivier, et al. Tectoniques Architectes: Unplugged. 2007. (FRE & ENG., Illus.). 252p. *(978-2-84066-197-9(7))* les presses du reel.

ARCHITECTURE, DOMESTIC—GERMANY

Berning, Maria, et al. Berliner Wohnquartiere: Ein Fuehrer durch 60 Siedlungen in Ost & West. 2nd ed. (GER., Illus.). xii, 397p. *(978-3-496-01112-5(2))* Reimer, Dietrich.

Braum, Michael & Millarg, Hartmut. Staedtebau in Hannover: Ein Fuehrer duch 50 Siedlungen. (GER., Illus.). 172p. *(978-3-496-01223-8(4))* Reimer, Dietrich.

Brenner, Winfried & Werkbund, Deutscher. Bruno Taut: Meister des farbigen Bauens in Berlin. Deutscher Werkbund Berlin, ed. 2008. (Urban Planning & Construction Ser.). (GER & ENG., Illus.). 170p. pap. 29.95 *(978-3-935455-82-4(8),* Braun Publish,Csi) Continental Sales, Inc.

Elam, Kimberley & Princeton Architectural Press Staff. Proportion und Komposition. Heuss, Wolfgang, tr. 2006. (GER & ENG., Illus.). 107p. per. 19.95 *(978-1-56898-584-8(3))* Princeton Architectural Pr.

Forner, Johannes. Wohn- & Bürgerhäuser Im Leipziger Musikviertel. 2007. (GER., Illus.). 95p. pap. *(978-3-86729-010-4(5))* Heydick, Erika Sax-Verlag Beucha.

Hettche, Thomas, et al. Fritz Barth, Cannstatter Straße 84, Fellbach: Cannstatter Strasse 84, Fellbach. 2011. (GER & ENG., Illus.). 72p. 49.00 *(978-3-932565-76-2(2))* Edition Axel Menges GmbH DEU. Dist: National Bk. Network.

Himen, Helga. Ringberg Castle on Tegernsee. 2008. 160p. *(978-3-422-06282-5(3))* Deutscher Kunstverlag GmbH.

—Ringberg Castle on Tegernsee. 2008. (ENG.). 160p. 38.00 *(978-3-422-06828-5(7))* Deutscher Kunstverlag GmbH DEU. Dist: Independent Pubs. Group.

Jager, Markus. Berlin Modern Style. 2007. (ENG.). 96p. pap. 9.95 *(978-3-422-02100-6(0))* Deutscher Kunstverlag GmbH DEU. Dist: Independent Pubs. Group.

Kottjé, et al. Individuell wohnen in Reihen- und Doppelhäusern: Großzügig ungewöhnlich attraktiv. 2009. (GER., Illus.). 143p. *(978-3-421-03681-0(0))* Deutsche Verlags-Anstalt GmbH.

Meuser, Philipp & Nielsen, Fried. Stadt und Haus: Berlinische Architektur Im 21. Jahrhundert = Berlin Architecture in the 21st Century. 2009. (RUS, GER, SPA & ENG., Illus.). 1p. pap. 49.95 ***(978-3-938666-43-2(9))*** DOM Pubs. DEU. Dist: Innovative Logistics.

Sack, Manfred. Sonwik, Flensburg. 2007. (Opus Ser.). (GER & ENG., Illus.). 60p. 39.90 *(978-3-932565-61-8(4))* Edition Axel Menges GmbH DEU. Dist: National Bk. Network.

Schätzke, Andreas & Warmburg, Joaquín Medina. Sep Ruf, Kanzerbungalow, Bonn. 2009. (ENG., Illus.). 48p. 49.00 *(978-3-932565-72-4(X))* Edition Axel Menges GmbH DEU. Dist: National Bk. Network.

Sommer, Martin & Sternagel, Thomas. EinSparHaus: Energieeffiziente Architektur. 2009. (GER., Illus.). 163p. pap. *(978-3-86859-013-5(7))* Jovis Verlag GmbH.

Stimmann, Hans. Townhouses, 1 vol. 2011. (ENG.). 150p. 99.95 ***(978-3-86922-144-1(5))*** DOM Pubs. DEU. Dist: Innovative Logistics.

Zander, Jean-Paul Deridder City of Children, Berlin: City of Transience. 2009. (ENG.). 104p. 60.00 *(978-3-7757-2286-5(6))* Hatje Cantz Verlag GmbH & Co KG DEU. Dist: D.A.P./Distributed Art Pubs.

ARCHITECTURE, DOMESTIC—GREAT BRITAIN

Addy, Sidney Oldall. The Evolution of the English House. 2009. 248p. 41.95 *(978-1-104-43561-5(6));* pap. 26.95 *(978-1-104-38863-8(4))* Kessinger Publishing, LLC.

Adjaye, David. David Adjaye: A House for an Art Collector. 2011. (ENG., Illus.). 128p. 50.00 *(978-0-8478-3508-9(1))* Rizzoli International Pubns., Inc.

Ainley, Rosa. 2 Ennerdale Drive: An Unauthorised Biography. 2011. (ENG., Illus.). 173p. pap. 16.95 *(978-1-84694-560-1(7))* O Bks, John Hunt.

Allison, Peter & Allison, David, eds. David Adjaye Houses: Recycling, Reconfiguring, Rebuilding. 2006. (ENG., Illus.). 256p. pap. 34.95 *(978-0-500-28631-9(0))* Thames & Hudson.

Archer, John. Architecture & Suburbia: From English Villa to American Dream House, 1690-2000. 2008. (Illus.). 496p. per. 27.50 *(978-0-8166-4304-2(0))* Univ. of Minnesota Pr.

Aslet, Clive. The Edwardian Country House. rev. ed. 2012. (ENG., Illus.). 288p. 50.00 (978-0-7112-3339-3(X)) Lincoln, Frances Ltd. GBR. Dist: Perseus-PGW.

Aslet, Clive. The English House: The Story of a Nation at Home. 2009. (ENG., Illus.). 1p. 45.00 (978-0-7475-7797-3(8)) Bloomsbury Publishing Plc GBR. Dist: Independent Pubs. Group.

Bell, Yvonne. The Edwardian Home. 2008. (Shire Library). (ENG., Illus.). 56p. pap. 12.95 (978-0-7478-0631-8(4)) Shire Pubns., Ltd. GBR. Dist: Random Hse., Inc.

Binney, Marcus. In Search of the Perfect House: 500 of the Best Buildings in Britain & Ireland. 2008. (Illus.). 256p. 45.00 (978-0-297-84455-6(5), Weidenfeld & Nicolson) Orion Publishing Group, Ltd. GBR. Dist: Sterling Publishing Co., Inc.

Cliff, Stafford. The Way We Live with the Things We Love. 2009. (ENG., Illus.). 256p. 45.00 (978-0-8478-3225-5(2)) Rizzoli International Pubns., Inc.

Colquhoun, Ian. RIBA Book of British Housing: 1900 to the Present Day. 2nd rev. ed. 2008. (ENG., Illus.). 416p. pap. 59.95 (978-0-7506-8254-1(X)) Routledge.

Davies, Michael. Discovering Welsh Houses - A Fascinating Guide to Welsh Architecture Past & Present. 2009. (ENG.). 192p. pap. 25.00 (978-1-905582-13-6(7)) Graffeg GBR. Dist: National Bk. Network.

Denison, Edward & Ren, Guang Yu. The Life of the British Home: An Architectural History. 2012. (ENG., Illus.). 304p. 50.00 (978-0-470-68333-0(3), Wiley) Wiley, John & Sons, Inc.

Designing Quality Buildings: A BRE Guide. 2010. (ENG., Illus.). 360p. 110.00 (978-1-86081-899-8(4)) Building Research Establishment GBR. Dist: Taylor & Francis Group.

Emery, Anthony. Discovering Medieval Houses. 2008. (Shire Discovering Ser.). (ENG., Illus.). 176p. per. 21.95 (978-0-7478-0655-4(1)) Shire Pubns., Ltd. GBR. Dist: Random Hse., Inc.

Evans, Paul. The 1940s Home. 2009. (Shire Library). (ENG., Illus.). 48p. pap. 12.95 (978-0-7478-0736-0(1)) Shire Pubns., Ltd. GBR. Dist: Random Hse., Inc.

Eveleigh, David. Town House Architecture, 1640-1980. 2011. (Shire Library). (ENG., Illus.). 80p. pap. 12.95 (978-0-7478-0832-9(5)) Shire Pubns., Ltd. GBR. Dist: Random Hse., Inc.

Gordon, Catherine. Cotswolds Arts & Crafts Architecture. 2009. (ENG., Illus.). 192p. 37.95 (978-1-86077-548-2(9)) History Pr. Ltd.,The GBR. Dist: Independent Pubs. Group.

Hall, Michael. Waddesdon Manor. 2010. (ENG., Illus.). 320p. 75.00 (978-1-85759-623-6(4)) Scala, Editions FRA. Dist: National Bk. Network.

Harwood, Elain & Powers, Alan. Housing the Twentieth Century Nation. 2008. (Illus.). 176p. pap. 30.00 (978-0-9556687-0-8(0)) Holberton, Paul Publishing GBR. Dist: Casemate Pubs. & Bk. Distributors, LLC.

Hawkes, Dean, ed. Modern Country Homes in England: The Arts & Crafts Architecture of Barry Parker. 2010. (Cambridge Urban & Architectural Studies). (ENG.). 184p. pap. 27.99 (978-0-521-13682-2(2)) Cambridge Univ. Pr.

Heath, Sidney. The Parts of a Manor House & the Parts of a Castle. 2010. 96p. pap. 26.45 (978-1-4455-0388-2(3)) Barclay Pr., Inc.

Horn, Pamela. Life in the Victorian Country House. 2010. (Shire History Ser.). (ENG., Illus.). 128p. pap. 19.95 (978-0-7478-0750-6(7)) Shire Pubns., Ltd. GBR. Dist: Random Hse., Inc.

Jensen, Finn. Modernist Semis & Terraces in England. 2012. (Ashgate Studies in Architecture Ser.). (Illus.). 220p. 99.95 (978-0-7546-7969-1(1)) Ashgate Publishing Co.

Kirk, Jayne. Parham Park: A Sussex House Transformed. 2008. (ENG.). 208p. pap. 27.95 (978-1-86077-485-0(7)) History Pr. Ltd.,The GBR. Dist: Independent Pubs. Group.

Klattenhoff, Henning. London - the Architecture Guide. 2010. (ENG., Illus.). 368p. pap. 29.95 (978-3-03768-030-8(X), Braun Publish,Csi) Continental Sales, Inc.

Lawrence, Richard Russell. The Book of the Edwardian & Interwar House. 2009. (ENG., Illus.). 272p. 64.95 (978-1-84513-340-5(4)) Aurum Pr., Ltd. GBR. Dist: Independent Pubs. Group.

Leighton, Sophie. The 1950s Home. 2009. (Shire Library). (ENG., Illus.). 56p. pap. 12.95 (978-0-7478-0711-7(6)) Shire Pubns., Ltd. GBR. Dist: Random Hse., Inc.

Lewis, Phillipa. House: British Domestic Architecture. 2011. (Illus.). 192p. 39.95 (978-3-7913-4556-7(7)) Prestel Publishing.

Mander, Nicholas. The Cotswold House: Stone Houses & Interiors from the English Countryside. 2009. (ENG., Illus.). 208p. 19.95 (978-0-8478-3180-7(9)) Rizzoli International Pubns., Inc.

Marshall, Duncan & Worthing, Derek. Construction of Houses. 4th rev. ed. 2006. (ENG., Illus.). 300p. (C). pap. 48.95 (978-0-7282-0486-7(X)) Estates Gazette, Ltd. GBR. Dist: Taylor & Francis Group.

Marshall, Duncan, et al. The Construction of Houses. 5th rev. ed. 2012. (ENG., Illus.). 560p. (C). pap. 52.95 (978-0-08-097100-1(8)) Estates Gazette, Ltd. GBR. Dist: Taylor & Francis Group.

Martin, Barbara & Martin, David. Farm Buildings of the Weald 1450-1750. 2009. (ENG., Illus.). 181p. (C). pap. 50.00 (978-1-905223-24-4(2)) Heritage Marketing & Publications, Ltd. GBR. Dist: Brown, David Bk. Co., The.

McCloud, Kevin. Grand Designs: The Blueprint for Building Your Dream Home. 2009. (ENG., Illus.). 288p. pap., instr.'s hndbk. ed. 23.95 (978-0-00-730742-5(X)) HarperCollins Pubs. Ltd. GBR. Dist: Independent Pubs. Group.

McMurray, Matthew. Samuel Powell's House: The Early 18th Century Town House of a Devizes Clothier. 2009. (ENG., Illus.). 153p. (C). 25.00 (978-0-947723-15-6(3)) Wiltshire Archaeological & Natural History Society GBR. Dist: Brown, David Bk. Co., The.

Melville, Ian & Gordon, Ian. Inspections & Reports on Dwellings: Reporting for Sellers. 2008. (ENG., Illus.). 460p. pap. 67.95 (978-0-7282-0450-8(9)) Estates Gazette, Ltd. GBR. Dist: Taylor & Francis Group.

Melville, Ian A. & Gordon, Ian A. Inspections & Reports on Dwellings: Reporting for Buyers. 2007. (ENG., Illus.). 300p. pap. 62.95 (978-0-7282-0449-2(5)) Estates Gazette, Ltd. GBR. Dist: Taylor & Francis Group.

Miers, Mary. The English Country House: From the Archives of Country Life. 2009. (ENG., Illus.). 484p. 85.00 (978-0-8478-3057-2(8)) Rizzoli International Pubns., Inc.

Miller, Mervyn. Hampstead Garden Suburb: Arts & Crafts Utopia? 2nd ed. 2006. (ENG., Illus.). 288p. 65.00 (978-1-86077-404-1(0), Phillimore & Co.) History Pr. Ltd.,The GBR. Dist: Independent Pubs. Group.

Moore, Derry, photos by. In House. 2009. (Illus.). 256p. 60.00 (978-0-8478-3349-8(6)) Rizzoli International Pubns., Inc.

Morgan, Keith N., et al. Buildings of Massachusetts: Metropolitan Boston. 2009. (Buildings of the United States Ser.). (ENG., Illus.). 688p. (gr. 17). 75.00 (978-0-8139-2709-1(9)) Univ. Pr. of Virginia.

Murdoch, Tessa. Noble Households: Eighteenth-Century Inventories of Great English Houses. 2007. (ENG., Illus.). 336p. 90.00 (978-0-9524322-5-8(0)) John Adamson Publishing Consultants GBR. Dist: National Bk. Network.

Musson, Jeremy. The Country Houses of John Vanbrugh. 2009. (Country Life Ser.). (ENG., Illus.). 192p. 75.00 (978-1-84513-097-8(9)) Aurum Pr., Ltd. GBR. Dist: Independent Pubs. Group.

National Trust Books Staff & Garnett, Oliver. Erddig. 2006. (National Trust Guidebooks Ser.). (ENG., Illus.). 96p. pap. 14.95 (978-1-84359-017-0(4)) History Pr. Ltd.,The GBR. Dist: Independent Pubs. Group.

Oliver, Basil. The Cottages of England: Country homes from the 16th to 18th Century. 2007. 228p. per. (978-1-905217-49-6(8)) Mills, Jeremy Publishing.

Ould, E. Old Cottages, Farm Houses & Other Half-Timber Buildings in Shropshire, Herefordshire & Cheshire. 2007. 152p. per. (978-1-905217-71-7(4)) Mills, Jeremy Publishing.

Panache Partners LLC Staff. Perspectives on Design London: Creative Ideas Shared by Leading Design Professionals. 2012. (Perspectives on Design Ser.). (ENG., Illus.). 192p. 50.00 (978-0-9832398-2-6(7)) Panache Partners, LLC.

Perring, Dominic. The Roman House in Britain. 2009. 272p. 39.95 (978-0-415-48878-5(8)) Routledge.

Phillips, Charles & Wilson, Richard. The Complete Illustrated Guide to the Castles, Palaces & Stately Houses of Britain & Ireland: Britain's Magnificent Architectural, Cultural & Historical Heritage Is Celebrated in over 500 Photographs, Fine-Art Paintings, Maps & Drawings. 2008. (ENG., Illus.). 256p. 35.00 (978-0-7548-1740-6(7)) Anness Publishing GBR. Dist: National Bk. Network.

Ravetz, Alison, et al. The Place of Home: English domestic Environments, 1914-2000. 2011. (Planning, History & Environment Ser.). (ENG., Illus.). 243p. pap. 42.95 (978-0-415-51426-2(6)) Routledge.

Ricketts, Annabel, et al. The English Country House Chapel: Building a Protestant Tradition. 2007. (Illus.). 336p. (C). (978-1-904965-05-3(9)) Spire Bks. Ltd.

Smith, Ian MacDonald. Arts & Crafts Master: The Houses & Gardens. 2010. (ENG., Illus.). 240p. 55.00 (978-0-8478-3181-4(7)) Rizzoli International Pubns., Inc.

Stamp, Gavin. Edwin Lutyens: Country Houses. 2009. (ENG., Illus.). 192p. 65.00 (978-1-58093-237-0(1)) Monacelli Pr., Inc.

Steel, John, et al. The English House: 1000 Years of Domestic Architecture. 2007. (ENG., Illus.). 416p. (978-1-85149-523-8(1), Antique Collectors Club Dist) Antique Collectors' Club.

Stevenson, Greg. The 1930s Home. 2008. (Shire Library). (ENG., Illus.). 40p. pap. 11.95 (978-0-7478-0464-2(8)) Shire Pubns., Ltd. GBR. Dist: Random Hse., Inc.

Stourton, James. Great Houses of London. 2012. (ENG., Illus.). 352p. 65.00 (978-0-7112-3366-9(7)) Lincoln, Frances Ltd. GBR. Dist: Perseus-PGW.

Style, Colin & Style, O-lan. House Histories for Beginners. 2006. (ENG., Illus.). 216p. (C). 30.00 (978-1-86077-405-8(9), Phillimore & Co.) History Pr. Ltd.,The GBR. Dist: Brown, David Bk. Co., The.

Swenarton, Mark. Building the New Jerusalem: Architecture, Housing & Politics 1900-1930. 2010. (ENG., Illus.). 246p. 80.00 (978-1-84806-024-1(6)) Building Research Establishment GBR. Dist: Taylor & Francis Group.

Tange, Andrea Kaston. Architectural Identities: Domesticity, Literature & the Victorian Middle Class. 2010. (Illus.). 336p. (978-1-4426-4113-6(4)) Univ. of Toronto Pr.

Watkin, David. The Classical Country House: From the Archives of Country Life. 2010. (Country Life Ser.). (ENG., Illus.). 192p. 75.00 (978-1-84513-593-5(8)) Aurum Pr., Ltd. GBR. Dist: Independent Pubs. Group.

Weaver, Lawrence, ed. The House & Its Equipment. 2007. (ENG.). 224p. per. 24.95 (978-0-548-67037-8(4)) Kessinger Publishing, LLC.

Wilson, Richard & Mackley, Alan. The Building of the Country House. 2006. (ENG., Illus.). 432p. 39.95 (978-1-85285-556-7(8), Hambledon Continuum) Continuum International Publishing Group, Ltd. GBR. Dist: National Bk. Network.

Worsley, Giles. England's Lost Houses: From the Archives of Country Life. 2011. (ENG., Illus.). 192p. pap. 29.95 (978-1-84513-614-7(4)) Aurum Pr., Ltd. GBR. Dist: Independent Pubs. Group.

Worsley, Lucy. If Walls Could Talk: An intimate history of the Home. 2012. (ENG., Illus.). 368p. 27.00 (978-0-8027-7995-3(6)) Walker & Co.

Yorke, Trevor. Arts & Crafts House Styles. 2011. (ENG., Illus.). 64p. pap. 14.95 (978-1-84674-230-9(7)) Countryside Bks. GBR. Dist: Brown, David Bk. Co., The.

—British Architectural Styles: An Easy Reference Guide. 2008. (Illus.). 64p. (C). pap. 12.95 (978-1-84674-082-4(7)) Countryside Bks. GBR. Dist: Brown, David Bk. Co., The.

—The Edwardian House Explained. 2007. (England's Living History Ser.). (ENG., Illus.). 128p. (C). per. 19.95 (978-1-85306-982-6(5)) Countryside Bks. GBR. Dist: Brown, David Bk. Co., The.

—Georgian & Regency Houses Explained. 2007. (England's Living History Ser.). (ENG., Illus.). 128p. (C). pap. 21.95 (978-1-84674-051-0(7)) Countryside Bks. GBR. Dist: Brown, David Bk. Co., The.

—The Victorian House Explained. 2012. (England's Living History Ser.). (ENG., Illus.). 127p. (C). per. 19.95 (978-1-85306-943-7(4)) Countryside Bks. GBR. Dist: Brown, David Bk. Co., The.

—The 1930s House Explained. 2006. (England's Living History Ser.). (Illus.). 128p. pap. 19.95 (978-1-84674-002-2(9)) Countryside Bks. GBR. Dist: Brown, David Bk. Co., The.

—The 1940s & 1950s House Explained: From Blackout to Sunlight. 2010. (ENG., Illus.). 80p. (C). pap. 16.95 (978-1-84674-221-7(8)) Countryside Bks. GBR. Dist: Brown, David Bk. Co., The.

ARCHITECTURE, DOMESTIC—GREECE

Cohen, Ada & Rutter, Jeremy B. Constructions of Childhood in Ancient Greece & Italy. 2007. (Hesperia Supplement Ser.). (ENG., Illus.). 455p. per. 75.00 (978-0-87661-541-6(8)) American Schl. of Classical Studies at Athens.

Glowacki, Kevin & Vogeikoff-Brogan, Natalia, eds. Archaeology of Houses & Households in Ancient Crete. 2011. (Hesperia Supplements Ser.). (ENG.). 497p. (C). pap. 75.00 (978-0-87661-544-7(2)) American Schl. of Classical Studies at Athens.

Morgan, Janett. The Classical Greek House. 2010. (Bristol Phoenix Press - Greece & Rome Live Ser.). (Illus.). 208p. pap. 25.00 (978-1-904675-75-4(1)); 193p. 78.00 (978-1-904675-74-7(3)) Bristol Phoenix Pr. GBR. Dist: Chicago Distribution Ctr.

Vrettakos, Costas & de Nora, Emmanuela. Greek Doors. Eleftheriou, Michael, tr. 2007. (Illus.). 202p. 69.95 (978-960-8350-67-0(0)) Potamos GRC. Dist: Art Stock.

ARCHITECTURE, DOMESTIC—IRELAND

Binney, Marcus. In Search of the Perfect House: 500 of the Best Buildings in Britain & Ireland. 2008. (Illus.). 256p. 45.00 (978-0-297-84455-6(5), Weidenfeld & Nicolson) Orion Publishing Group, Ltd. GBR. Dist: Sterling Publishing Co., Inc.

Blake, Tarquin. Abandoned Mansions of Ireland. 2011. (ENG., Illus.). 338p. 52.95 (978-1-84889-061-9(3)) Collins Pr., The IRL. Dist: Dufour Editions, Inc.

Fennell, James, photos by. The Irish Country House. 2012. (ENG., Illus.). 192p. 29.95 (978-0-86565-282-8(1)) Vendome Pr., The.

Jones, Barbara. Building with Straw Bales: A Practical Guide for the U. K. & Ireland. 2nd rev. ed. 2010. (ENG., Illus.). 184p. pap. 24.95 (978-1-900322-51-5(X)) Green Bks. GBR. Dist: Chelsea Green Publishing.

Lyttleton, James. Blarney Castle: An Irish Tower House. 2011. 174p. pap. 29.95 (978-1-84682-314-5(5)) Four Courts Pr. IRL. Dist: International Specialized Bk. Services.

O'Byrne, Robert. Romantic Irish Homes. 2009. (Illus.). 176p. 40.00 (978-1-906525-72-9(2)) CICO Bks. GBR. Dist: Ryland Peters & Small.

O'Reilly, Seán D. Irish Houses & Gardens: From the Archives of Country Life. 2008. (Country Life Ser.). (ENG., Illus.). 192p. pap. 34.95 (978-1-84513-351-1(X)) Aurum Pr., Ltd. GBR. Dist: Independent Pubs. Group.

ARCHITECTURE, DOMESTIC—ITALY

Bernardi, Silvio, et al. Silvio Bernardi Architetto: Living in Cortina D'Ampezzo. 2010. (ITA & ENG., Illus.). 263p. (978-88-370-7859-1(5)) Electa.

Casciu, Stefano & Pozzana, Mariachiara, eds. Ville e giardini nei dintorni di Firenze: Da Fiesole ad Artimino. 2010. (ITA & ENG., Illus.). 392p. (C). pap. 28.00 (978-88-596-0800-4(7)) Polistampa ITA. Dist: Brown, David Bk. Co., The.

Faliva, Alberto, ed. Ville del Rinascimento Padano. 2010. (ITA.). 120p. pap. 45.00 (978-88-370-7745-7(9)) Electa ITA. Dist: Trans-Atlantic Pubns., Inc.

Ferro, Lisa & Pasti, Chiara. Venice Interiors: Contemporary Houses. 2009. (ENG., Illus.). 184p. 65.00 (978-88-7200-286-5(9)) Vianello Libri ITA. Dist: Antique Collectors' Club.

Fiell, Charlotte & Peter, ed. Domus, 1955-1999, Vol. 12. 2009. (Domus Ser.). (ENG & ITA., Illus.). 580p. 69.99 (978-3-8365-0962-6(8)) TASCHEN DEU. Dist: Ingram Pub. Services.

—Domus, 1985-1989, Vol. 10. 2009. (Domus Ser.). (ENG., Illus.). 580p. 69.99 (978-3-8365-0960-2(1)) TASCHEN DEU. Dist: Ingram Pub. Services.

—Domus, 1990-1994, Vol. 11. 2009. (Domus Ser.). (ENG., Illus.). 580p. 69.99 (978-3-8365-0961-9(X)) TASCHEN DEU. Dist: Ingram Pub. Services.

Gardin, Giancarlo, et al. Lake Villas, 1 vol. 2011. (ENG & ITA.). 232p. pap. 59.30 (978-88-87653-11-3(9)) Archideos Libri ITA. Dist: Innovative Logistics.

Gossel, Peter & Wundram, Manfred. Palladio Basic Architecture. 2009. (ENG.). 96p. pap. 9.99 (978-3-8365-0289-4(5)) TASCHEN DEU. Dist: Ingram Pub. Services.

Goy, Richard J. Venetian Vernacular Architecture: Traditional Housing in the Venetian Lagoon. 2011. (ENG.). 384p. pap. 31.99 (978-0-521-15490-1(1)) Cambridge Univ. Pr.

Grundmann, Stefan, ed. Architekturführer Rom. (GER., Illus.). 384p. pap. 42.00 (978-3-930698-59-2(5)) Edition Axel Menges GmbH DEU. Dist: National Bk. Network.

Hendricks, J. & Taschen, Angelika, eds. Tuscany Style: Landscapes, Terraces & Houses, Interiors, Details. 25th ed. 2008. (Icons Ser.). (FRE, GER & ENG., Illus.). 190p. 7.99 (978-3-8365-0765-3(X)) TASCHEN DEU. Dist: Ingram Pub. Services.

Lauter, Hans. Die Fassade des Hauses IX 1, 20 in Pompeji: Gestalt und Bedeutung. 2009. (GER., Illus.). 193p. (C). 89.00 (978-3-8053-3807-3(4)) Zabern, Philipp von Verlag, GmbH DEU. Dist: Brown, David Bk. Co., The.

Lillie, Amanda. Florentine Villas in the Fifteenth Century: An Architectural & Social History. 2011. (ENG., Illus.). 369p. pap. 45.00 (978-0-521-18138-9(0)) Cambridge Univ. Pr.

Lowell, Guy. Small Italian Villas & Farmhouses. 2008. (Illus.). 314p. bds. 39.95 (978-0-7643-2706-3(2)) Schiffer Publishing, Ltd.

Marzano, Annalisa. Roman Villas in Central Italy: A Social & Economic History. 2007. (Columbia Studies in the Classical Tradition Ser.). 823p. (978-90-04-16037-8(X)) BRILL.

Mattusch, Carol C. Pompeii & the Roman Villa: Art & Culture Around the Bay of Naples. 2008. (978-0-89468-353-4(5)) National Gallery of Art.

Mattusch, Carol C., ed. Pompeii & the Roman Villa: Art & Culture Around the Bay of Naples. 2008. (ENG., Illus.). 360p. 60.00 (978-0-500-51436-8(4), 551436) Thames & Hudson.

Minchilli, Elizabeth Helman & Minchilli, Domenico. Italian Rustic: How to Bring Tuscan Charm into Your Home. 2009. (ENG., Illus.). 226p. 35.00 (978-1-57965-364-4(2), 1579653642) Artisan.

Monicelli, Francesco & Gerolimetto, Cesare. Venetian Villas. 2006. (ENG., Illus.). 100.00 (978-88-7743-285-8(3)) Arsenale Editrice SRL ITA. Dist: Antique Collectors' Club.

Pavanello, Giuseppe & Mancini, Vincenzo. Gli Affreschi Nelle Ville Venete. 2008. (ITA., Illus.). (978-88-317-9899-0(5)); (978-88-317-9694-1(1)) Marsilio Editori spa.

Pavoni, Rosanna. House Museums in Italy: New cultural itineraries; poetry, history, art, architecture, music, arts & crafts, tastes & Traditions. 2011. 160p. pap. 22.95 (978-88-492-1857-2(5)) Gangemi ITA. Dist: International Publishers Marketing.

Pietro, Silvio San & Gallo, Paola. Multilevel Living: New Italian Environments Series. 2010. (ITA & ENG., Illus.). 198p. (978-88-7685-177-3(1), Edizioni L'archivolto (Acc)) Antique Collectors' Club.

Ponciroli, Virginia, ed. 011 + Architettura Made in Torino: [in English & Italian]. 2008. 180p. pap. 92.50 (978-88-370-6245-3(1)) Electa ITA. Dist: Trans-Atlantic Pubns., Inc.

San Pietro, Silvio, et al. New Villas 2: In Italy & Canton Ticino. 2008. (Best Interiors Selection Ser.). (ITA & ENG., Illus.). 208p. (978-88-7685-159-9(3), Edizioni L'archivolto (Acc)) Antique Collectors' Club.

Smienk, Gerrit & Niemeijer, Johannes. Palladio, the Villa & the Landscape. 2011. (Illus.). 160p. 79.95 (978-3-0346-0712-4(1)) Birkhauser Verlag AG CHE. Dist: Actar Birkhauser Distribution.

Wharton, Edith. Italian Villas & Their Gardens: The Original 1904 Edition. 2008. (ENG., Illus.). 284p. 35.00 (978-0-8478-3115-9(9)) Rizzoli International Pubns., Inc.

Widrig, Walter M. The Via Gabina Villas: Sites 10, 11, & 13. 2009. (978-0-89263-015-8(9)); (978-0-89263-020-2(5)) Rice Univ. Pr.

Winter, Nancy A. Symbols of Wealth & Power: Architectural Terracotta Decoration in Etruria & Central Italy, 640-510 B. C. 2009. (Supplements to the Memoirs of the American Academy in Rome Ser.). (ENG., Illus.). 728p. 95.00 (978-0-472-11665-2(7)) Univ. of Michigan Pr.

ARCHITECTURE, DOMESTIC—JAPAN

Atelier Bow-Wow. Atelier Bow-Wow. 2010. (ENG., Illus.). 304p. 65.00 (978-0-8478-3306-1(2)) Rizzoli International Pubns., Inc.

Berthet-Bondet, Isabelle. 20 Maisons Nippones: Un Art D'habiter les Petits Espaces. 2010. (FRE., Illus.). 145p. (978-2-86364-250-4(2)) Parentheses.

Clancy, Judith. Kyoto Machiya Restaurant Guide: Affordable Dining in Elegant Townhouse Spaces. 2012. (ENG., Illus.). 184p. pap. 14.95 (978-1-61172-001-3(X)) Stone Bridge Pr.

Daniels, Inge Maria. The Japanese House: Material Culture in the Modern Home. 2010. (Materializing Culture Ser.). (ENG., Illus.). 320p. pap. 34.95 (978-1-84520-517-1(0)) Berg Pubs. GBR. Dist: Macmillan.

Designers Villas 24 Weekend Homes. 2007. 49.95 (978-4-7661-1739-4(5)) Graphic-Sha JPN. Dist: Gingko Pr., Inc.

Fahr-Becker, Gabriele & Frahm, Klaus. Ryokan: A Japanese Tradition. 2008. (Art & Architecture Ser.). (Illus.). 335p. 19.95 (978-0-8416-0092-8(9)) American Map Corp.

Iwatate, Marcia. Japan Houses: Ideas for 21st Century Living. 2011. (ENG., Illus.). 176p. 29.95 (978-4-8053-1126-4(6)) Tuttle Publishing.

Iwatate, Marcia, et al. Japan Living: Form & Function at the Cutting Edge. 2008. (ENG., Illus.). 256p. 49.95 (978-4-8053-0949-0(0)) Tuttle Publishing.

Morse, Edward S. Japanese Homes & Their Surroundings. 2007. (Tuttle Classics Ser.). (ENG., Illus.). 416p. per. 18.95 (978-4-8053-0889-9(3)) Tuttle Publishing.

Murata, Noboru, photos by. Japanese Living. 2007. (Mini Lifestyle Library Ser.). (ENG., Illus.). 168p. 16.95 (978-1-902686-60-8(8)) Scriptum Editions GBR. Dist: Independent Pubs. Group.

Parramore, Lisa & Gong, Chadine Flood. Japan Home: Inspirational Design Ideas. 2010. (ENG., Illus.). 144p. 24.95 *(978-4-8053-1000-7(6))* Tuttle Publishing.

Perez, Agustin. Sanaa Houses. 2007. (Illus.). 185p. pap. *(978-84-96540-70-5(7))* Actar Birkhauser Distribution.

Roderick, John. Minka: My Farmhouse in Japan. 2007. (ENG., Illus.). 256p. 24.95 *(978-1-56898-731-6(5))* Princeton Architectural Pr.

Shimizu, Fumio, ed. Designers Apartments in Japan High-Rise: Architect-Designed High Rise Condominiums. 2007. 49.95 *(978-4-7661-1713-4(1))* Graphic-Sha JPN. Dist: Gingko Pr., Inc.

Von, Herausgegeben, ed. Living in Japan. 2006. (FRE, GER & ENG., Illus.). 191p. 29.99 *(978-3-8228-4594-3(9))* TASCHEN DEU. Dist: Ingram Pub. Services.

ARCHITECTURE, DOMESTIC—LATIN AMERICA

Arcila-Duque, Juan Carlos. Latin Style: Decorating Your Home with Color, Texture, & Passion, 0 vols. 2008. (Illus.). 228p. 24.99 *(978-1-4016-0365-6(3))* Nelson, Thomas Inc.

Boas, Adrian J. Domestic Settings in Crusader States: Sources on Domestic Architecture & Day-to-Day Activities in the Latin East. 2010. (Illus.). 396p. *(978-90-04-18272-1(1))* BRILL.

Daguerre, Mercedes. Latin American Houses. 2007. (ENG., Illus.). 240p. 49.95 *(978-1-904313-56-4(6))* Electa Architecture GBR. Dist: Hachette Bk. Group.

Haidar, Sylvia. Beach Houses of South America. 2006. (ENG., Illus.). 160p. 49.50 *(978-1-876907-82-2(7))* Images Publishing Group AUS. Dist: National Bk. Network.

Hess, Alan. Casa Modernista: A History of the Brazil Modern House. 2010. (ENG., Illus.). 324p. 75.00 *(978-0-8478-3175-3(2))* Rizzoli International Pubns., Inc.

Perez Hernandez, Julio Caesar. Inside Havana: 25 Jahre TASCHEN. Hernandez, Julio Cesar Perez, ed. 2011. (ENG., Illus.). 240p. 29.99 ***(978-3-8365-3177-1(1))*** TASCHEN DEU. Dist: Ingram Pub. Services.

Quesada, Maria S. Estancias: The Great Houses & Ranches of Argentina. Di Giovanni, Norman Thomas, tr. from SPA. 2007. (ENG., Illus.). 200p. 75.00 *(978-1-55859-270-4(9))* Abbeville Pr., Inc.

ARCHITECTURE, DOMESTIC—MEXICO

de Haro, Fernando & Fuentes, Omar. Houses. 2007. (Houses Ser.). (ENG., Illus.). 194p. 39.95 *(978-970-9726-70-1(6))* AM Editores MEX. Dist: Perseus-PGW.

—Ideas: Colour/Color/Couleur/Farbe. 2008. (ENG., Illus.). 272p. pap. 24.95 *(978-970-9726-77-0(3))* AM Editores MEX. Dist: Perseus-PGW.

Fekete, Devon. Doors of Oaxaca. 2007. (Illus.). 272p. pap. 29.95 *(978-0-7643-2665-3(1))* Schiffer Publishing, Ltd.

Fuentes, Omar & de Haro, Fernando. Ideas: Houses. 2008. (ENG., Illus.). 272p. pap. 24.95 *(978-970-9726-79-4(X))* AM Editores MEX. Dist: Perseus-PGW.

—Styles. 2008. (Ideas (AM Editores) Ser.). (ENG., Illus.). 272p. pap. 24.95 *(978-970-9726-78-7(1))* AM Editores MEX. Dist: Perseus-PGW.

Fuentes, Omar & Haro, Fernando De. Houses: Space, Volume & Textures (Espacio, Volumen y Texturas) 2006. (Houses Ser.). (ENG., Illus.). 192p. 39.95 *(978-970-9726-33-6(1))* AM Editores MEX. Dist: Perseus-PGW.

House, Steven & House, Cathi. Houses in the Sun: Light Movement Embrace. 2008. (ENG., Illus.). 296p. 50.00 *(978-1-86470-239-2(7))* Images Publishing Group AUS. Dist: National Bk. Network.

Kelly, Annie. Casa Mexicana Style. 2006. (ENG., Illus.). 240p. 45.00 *(978-1-58479-528-5(X))* Stewart, Tabori & Chang.

Lara Morales, Abel & Montero, Pablo. Fortaleza de San Juan de Ulúa, Veracruz. 3rd ed. 2009. (SPA., Illus.). 102p. *(978-607-484-040-7(7))* Instituto Nacional de Antropologia e Historia.

Milnes, Sue. Haciendas, Hammocks & Hurricanes: A House in Mexico. 2007. (Illus.). 204p. per. 16.95 *(978-1-84799-981-8(6))* Lulu Enterprises Inc.

Moragues, Jose Nogal. Mansions Volume 2. 2011. (ENG & SPA., Illus.). 200p. 39.95 ***(978-607-437-062-1(1))*** AM Editores MEX. Dist: Perseus-PGW.

Paul, Linda Leigh. Haciendas: Spanish Colonial Houses in the U. S. & Mexico. 2008. (ENG., Illus.). 224p. 55.00 *(978-0-8478-3099-2(3))* Rizzoli International Pubns., Inc.

Rogers, Victoria & Haines, Cal. Santa Fe's Historic McKenzie Neighborhood: A Contemporary Look at Old Architecture. 2011. pap. ***(978-0-86534-813-4(8))*** Sunstone Pr.

Shipway, Verna Cook. The Mexican House. 3rd ed. 2007. 39.95 *(978-0-940512-47-4(5))* Hennessey & Ingalls, Inc.

Shipway, Verna Cook & Shipway, Warren. Houses of Mexico: Origins & Traditions. 2012. (ENG., Illus.). 272p. pap. 32.00 ***(978-1-58979-643-0(8))*** Taylor Trade Publishing.

Skinner, Tina. Mexican Style, Sustainable. 2007. (Illus.). 112p. pap. 19.95 *(978-0-7643-2743-8(7))* Schiffer Publishing, Ltd.

Stoeltie, Barbara & Stoeltie, Rene. Living in Mexico: 25 Jahre TASCHEN. Taschen, Angelika, ed. 2011. (25 Ser.). (ENG., Illus.). 200p. 14.99 ***(978-3-8365-3172-6(0))*** TASCHEN DEU. Dist: Ingram Pub. Services.

ARCHITECTURE, DOMESTIC—PUERTO RICO

Quiles Rodriguez, Edwin R. La Ciudad de Los Balcones. 2009. 184p. 46.95 *(978-0-8477-1525-1(6))* Univ. of Puerto Rico Pr.

ARCHITECTURE, DOMESTIC—SWITZERLAND

Daguerre, Mercedes. New Villas in Switzerland. 2012. (ENG., Illus.). 208p. 84.95 *(978-3-0346-0732-2(6))* Birkhauser Verlag AG CHE. Dist: Actar Birkhauser Distribution.

Kotté, et al. Individuell wohnen in Reihen- und Doppelhäusern: Großzügig ungewöhnlich attraktiv. 2009. (GER., Illus.). 143p. *(978-3-421-03681-0(0))* Deutsche Verlags-Anstalt GmbH.

Ruch, Hans-Jörg & Seifert-Uherkovich, Ludmila, texts. Historic Houses in Engadin: Architectural Interventions, 1 vol. 2008. (ENG., Illus.). 320p. 98.00 *(978-3-86521-720-2(6))* Steidl, Gerhard Druckerei und Verlag DEU. Dist: Innovative Logistics.

Saharoff, Philippe. Mountain Houses. 2007. (FRE & ENG., Illus.). 240p. 40.00 *(978-1-58479-648-0(0))* Abrams.

Smets, Coen. Zimmer Frei! 2010. 92p. pap. *(978-3-8383-7396-6(0))* Lambert Academic Publishing.

William S. B. Dana. The Swiss Chalet Book. 2009. 152p. pap. 9.95 *(978-1-60386-188-5(2),* Watchmaker Publishing) Wexford College Pr.

ARCHITECTURE, DOMESTIC—UNITED STATES

see also Architecture—United States

Abraham, Russell. California Cool: Residential Modernism Reborn. 2010. (ENG., Illus.). 252p. 50.00 *(978-1-86470-398-6(9),* Images Publishing Dist Ac) Antique Collectors' Club GBR. Dist: National Bk. Network.

Abruzzo, Emily, et al, eds. Making a Case, Vol. 14. 2012. (ENG., Illus.). 180p. pap. 24.95 ***(978-0-615-34909-1(9))*** Princeton Architectural Pr.

Allen, John C., Jr. & Smalling, Walter. Uncommon Vernacular: The Early Houses of Jefferson County, West Virginia, 1735-1835. 2011. (ENG., Illus.). 384p. 49.99 *(978-1-933202-87-7(4))* West Virginia Univ. Pr.

Ames, Anthony. Residential Work, Volume 2: Anthony Ames Architects. 2006. (ENG., Illus.). 240p. 50.00 *(978-0-9774672-4-2(4))* Oro Editions.

Andersson, Arthur, et al. Natural Houses: The Residential Architecture of Andersson-Wise. 2010. (ENG., Illus.). 176p. pap. 40.00 *(978-1-56898-879-5(6))* Princeton Architectural Pr.

Archer, John. Architecture & Suburbia: From English Villa to American Dream House, 1690-2000. 2008. (Illus.). 496p. per. 27.50 *(978-0-8166-4304-2(0))* Univ. of Minnesota Pr.

Architects & Planners, Moore Ruble Yudell. The Future of Place. 2011. (ENG., Illus.). 392p. 25.00 ***(978-1-935935-39-1(9))*** Oro Editions.

Architects & Planners, Moore Ruble Yudell & Yudell, Buzz. The Future of Place. 2011. (ENG.). 392p. 65.00 ***(978-7-5381-6561-6(4))*** Oro Editions.

Arrigo, Jan. Plantations & Historic Homes of New Orleans. 2008. (ENG., Illus.). 128p. 25.95 *(978-0-7603-2974-0(5),* 0760329745, Voyageur Pr) MBI Publishing Co. LLC.

Ashworth, Trisha & Nobile, Amy. I Was a Really Good Mom Before I Had Kids: Reinventing Modern Motherhood. 2007. (ENG.). 240p. per. 18.95 *(978-0-8118-5650-8(X))* Chronicle Bks. LLC.

Bacon, Jennifer & Fuhst, Darlene. Designer Dream Homes Craftsman & other Timeless American Dream Homes. 2007. (Illus.). 176p. pap. 14.95 *(978-1-932553-23-9(1))* Designs Direct Publishing, LLC.

Baker, Jennifer. Designer Dream Homes: 150 Upscale House Plans in all Sizes & Styles. 2007. (Illus.). 224p. pap. 16.95 *(978-1-932553-24-6(X))* Designs Direct Publishing, LLC.

Bassenian, Aram. Bassenian/Lagoni Architects Boxed Set. 2007. 94.95 *(978-0-9721539-4-2(2))* Bassenian/Lagoni Architects, Inc.

Bassenian/Lagoni Architects, creator. Homes & Courtyards: 30 Beautifully Designed Homes for Outdoor Living. 2007. (Illus.). 160p. 34.95 *(978-0-9721539-3-5(4))* Bassenian/Lagoni Architects, Inc.

Baylis, Douglas & Perry, Joan. California Houses of Gordon Drake. 2nd ed. 2011. (Illus.). xxii, 91p. 39.95 *(978-0-9795508-8-1(2))* Stout, William Pubs.

Benjamin, Susan S. & Cohen, Stuart Earl. Great Houses of Chicago, 1871-1921. 2008. (Illus.). 336p. 75.00 *(978-0-926494-39-8(2))* Acanthus Pr. LLC.

Berkhofer, George H. No Place Like Home: A History of Domestic Architecture in Springfield & Clark County, Ohio. 2007. *(978-1-933197-25-8(0))* Orange Frazer Pr.

Bernard, Lance V. Architecture & Regional Identity in the San Francisco Bay Area, 1870-1970. 2007. (Illus.). 232p. 109.95 *(978-0-7734-5340-1(7))* Mellen, Edwin Pr., The.

Bialecki, Matthew, et al. The New Bungalow, 1 vol. 2008. (ENG., Illus.). 160p. pap. 19.99 *(978-1-4236-0435-8(0))* Gibbs Smith, Publisher.

Blackburn, Roderic H. Old Homes of New England: Historic Houses in Clapboard, Shingle, & Stone. 2010. (ENG., Illus.). 256p. 55.00 *(978-0-8478-3075-6(6))* Rizzoli International Pubns., Inc.

Blackburn, Winfrey P., Jr. & Gill, R. Scott. Kentucky Houses of Stratton Hammon. 2007. (Illus.). 208p. 60.00 *(978-1-884532-87-0(X))* Butler Bk. Publishing.

Bloomfield, Anne & Bloomfield, Arthur. Gables & Fables: A Portrait of San Francisco's Pacific Heights. 2007. (Illus.). 386p. *(978-1-59714-055-3(4));* per. 19.95 *(978-1-59714-056-0(2))* Heyday.

Bohlin Cywinski Jackson Architects Staff. Bohlin Cywinski Jackson: The Nature of Circumstance. 2010. (ENG., Illus.). 420p. 95.00 *(978-0-8478-3293-4(7))* Rizzoli International Pubns., Inc.

Bonta, Dave & Snyder, Stephen. The New Solar Home, 1 vol. 2009. (ENG., Illus.). 160p. pap. 24.99 *(978-1-4236-0390-0(7))* Gibbs Smith, Publisher.

Booker, Margaret Moore & Booker, Margaret. The Santa Fe House: Historic Residences, Enchanting Adobes & Romantic Revivals. 2009. (ENG., Illus.). 246p. 50.00 *(978-0-8478-3197-5(3))* Rizzoli International Pubns., Inc.

Broach, Barbara Kimberlin, et al. Frank Lloyd Wright's Rosenbaum House: The Birth & Rebirth of an American Treasure. 2006. (Illus.). 80p. 19.95 *(978-0-7649-3763-7(4,* A123) Pomegranate Communications, Inc.

Brooklyn Museum Staff. Two Dutch Houses: Tradition & Change in Early New York: The Schenck Houses at the Brooklyn Museum. Date not set. *(978-0-87273-123-3(5))* Brooklyn Museum, The.

Brostom, Caitlin Lempres, et al. The Houses of William Wurster: Frames for Living. 2011. (ENG., Illus.). 224p. 50.00 *(978-1-61689-028-5(2))* Princeton Architectural Pr.

Browning, Dominique & Gilmour, Lucy. Living Architecture. 2010. (ENG., Illus.). 240p. 75.00 *(978-2-7594-0470-4(6))* Assouline FRA. Dist: Perseus Distribution.

Caemmerer, Alex. Houses of New Orleans. 2008. 80p. 24.99 *(978-0-7643-3117-6(5))* Schiffer Publishing, Ltd.

Cannon, Patrick F. Hometown Architect: The Complete Buildings of Frank Lloyd Wright in Oak Park & River Forest, Illinois. 2006. (Pomegranate Catalog Ser.: No. 118). (Illus.). 144p. 35.00 *(978-0-7649-3746-0(4))* Pomegranate Communications, Inc.

—Prairie Metropolis: Chicago & the Birth of a New American Home. 2008. (Illus.). 160p. 39.95 *(978-0-7649-4595-3(5))* Pomegranate Communications, Inc.

Cannon, Patrick F. & Wright, Frank Lloyd. Frank Lloyd Wright's Unity Temple: A Good Time Place. 2009. 80p. 24.95 *(978-0-7649-5149-7(1))* Pomegranate Communications, Inc.

Carabet, Brian & Shand, John. Dream Homes Colorado: An Exclusive Showcase of Colorado's Finest Architects, Designers & Builders. Panache Partners LLC Staff, ed. 2006. (Dream Homes Ser.). (ENG., Illus.). 208p. 39.95 *(978-1-933415-31-4(2))* Panache Partners, LLC.

—Spectacular Homes of Chicago: An Exclusive Showcase of Chicago's Finest Designers. Panache Partners LLC Staff, ed. 2007. (Spectacular Homes Ser.). (ENG., Illus.). 214p. 39.95 *(978-1-933415-21-5(5))* Panache Partners, LLC.

—Spectacular Homes of Florida: An Exclusive Showcase of Florida's Finest Designers. Panache Partners LLC., Staff, ed. 2006. (Spectacular Homes Ser.). (ENG., Illus.). 216p. 39.95 *(978-1-933415-18-5(5))* Panache Partners, LLC.

Carabet, Brian & Shand, John, eds. Ohio & Pennsylvania: An Exclusive Showcase of Ohio & Pennsylvania's Finest Architects & Builders. 2009. (Dream Homes Ser.). (ENG.). 250p. 34.95 *(978-1-933415-36-9(3))* Panache Partners, LLC.

Carabet, Brian, et al. Dream Homes Southwest: An Exclusive Showcase of Southwest's Finest Architects, Designers & Builders. 2007. (Dream Homes Ser.). (ENG.). 250p. 39.95 *(978-1-933415-08-6(8))* Panache Partners, LLC.

Carolinf, Castor. Architecture Early Homes St. Joseph. 2009. 36p. pap. 16.95 *(978-0-692-00403-6(3))* Serpent Noir Pr.

Casper, Paul Alexander. Chicago Luxury Home & Condo: The Ultimate Source for Designing, Building, Remodeling, Landscaping, Decorating & Furnishing Chicagoland's Finest Homes & Condos. 2nd ed. 2008. (ENG.). 800p. 24.95 *(978-0-9789734-1-4(0))* Lake Forest Media Group, The.

Castaneda, Eliza Cross. Family Home of the New West. unabr. ed. 2006. (ENG., Illus.). 144p. pap. 21.95 *(978-0-87358-902-4(5))* Cooper Square Publishing Llc.

Chandler, Joseph Everett. Some Charleston Mansions: The White Pine Monograph Series on Early American Architecture V14, No. 4. 2011. 28p. 35.95 ***(978-1-258-04129-8(4))*** Literary Licensing, LLC.

Chicago Tribune Staff. Ideal Small Homes of the Twenties: 99 Designs from a Competition. 2008. (Dover Architecture Ser.). (ENG.). 112p. pap. 14.95 *(978-0-486-46910-2(7))* Dover Pubns., Inc.

Coffin, Lewis A. American Country Houses of the Thirties: With Photographs & Floor Plans. 2007. (Dover Books on Architecture Ser.). (ENG., Illus.). 160p. per. 12.95 *(978-0-486-45592-1(0))* Dover Pubns., Inc.

Cohen, Stuart & Hacker, Julie. Transforming the Traditional: The Work of Cohen & Hacker Architects. 2009. (ENG., Illus.). 128p. 50.00 *(978-1-86470-335-1(0))* Images Publishing Group AUS. Dist: National Bk. Network.

Colomina, Beatriz. Domesticity at War. 2007. (ENG., Illus.). 280p. (gr. 17). 49.95 *(978-0-262-03361-9(5))* MIT Pr.

Connolly, M. Caren & Wasserman, Louis. Wisconsin's Own: Twenty Remarkable Homes. 2010. (ENG., Illus.). 320p. 45.00 *(978-0-87020-452-4(1))* Wisconsin Historical Society.

Conry, Jaci. A History Through Houses: Cape Cod's Varied Residential Architecture. 2010. (ENG., Illus.). 160p. pap. 19.99 *(978-1-59629-999-3(1))* History Pr., The.

Cooper, Dan. New Classic American Houses: The Architecture of Albert, Righter & Tittmann. 2009. (ENG., Illus.). 224p. 50.00 *(978-0-86565-253-8(8))* Vendome Pr., The.

Courtney, Steven. The Loveliest Home That Ever Was: The Story of the Mark Twain House in Hartford. 2011. (ENG., Illus.). 144p. pap. 19.95 ***(978-0-486-48634-5(6))*** Dover Pubns., Inc.

Craft, Stephen. H2O Architecture. 2006. (ENG., Illus.). 224p. 39.95 *(978-1-86470-114-2(5),* Images Publishing Dist Ac) Antique Collectors' Club GBR. Dist: National Bk. Network.

Creative Homeowner Press Editors. Best-Selling House Plans. 2009. (Home Plans Ser.). (ENG., Illus.). 352p. (gr. 5). pap. 10.95 *(978-1-58011-469-1(5))* Creative Homeowner.

—Easy-to-Build, Expandable Home Plans (Lowe's) 2009. (Home Plans Ser.). (ENG., Illus.). 240p. (gr. 5). pap. 9.95 *(978-1-58011-467-7(9))* Creative Homeowner.

Creative Homeowner Press Editors, ed. Best-Selling Country & Farmhouse. 2010. (Home Plans Ser.). (ENG.). 288p. (gr. 5). pap. 9.95 *(978-1-58011-503-2(9))* Creative Homeowner.

Cromley, Elizabeth C. The Food Axis: Cooking, Eating, & the Architecture of American Houses. 2010. (ENG., Illus.). 280p. (gr. 17). 50.00 *(978-0-8139-3007-7(3))* Univ. Pr. of Virginia.

Daley, Sue. Catskills Country Style. 2006. (ENG., Illus.). 208p. 17.98 *(978-0-7893-1517-5(3),* Rizzoli Universe Promotional Bks.) Rizzoli International Pubns., Inc.

DaSilva, John R. & Crosbie, Michael J. Architecture of the Cape Cod Summer: The Work of Polhemus Savery DaSilva. 2008. (ENG., Illus.). 264p. 90.00 *(978-1-86470-280-4(X))* Images Publishing Group AUS. Dist: National Bk. Network.

deLashmet, Jack, intro. Hamptons Gardens. 2011. (ENG.). 328p. 150.00 *(978-2-7594-0511-4(7))* Assouline FRA. Dist: Perseus Distribution.

Dennis, Kristen A. Capitol Hill Converted. 2008. (Illus.). 43p. 31.99 *(978-1-4363-0127-5(0))* Xlibris Corp.

Denzer, Anthony. Gregory Ain: The Modern Home as Social Commentary. 2008. (ENG., Illus.). 256p. 60.00 *(978-0-8478-3062-6(4))* Rizzoli International Pubns., Inc.

Designs Direct Publishing. Small Dream Homes: 120 Plans under 3,000 Square Feet. 2008. (Illus.). 176p. pap. 14.95 *(978-1-932553-29-1(0,* DDP) Designs Direct Publishing, LLC.

Desjarlais, Mary. Beauty on the Streets of Detroit: A history of the housing market in Detroit. 2008. (Illus.). 176p. pap. 19.95 *(978-0-9817517-0-2(9))* Desjarlais, Mary.

Diamond, William & Baratta, Anthony. All-American: The Exuberant Style of William Diamond & Anthony Baratta. 2009. (ENG., Illus.). 204p. 95.00 *(978-0-9823585-0-4(4))* Pointed Leaf Pr.

Dietz, Ulysses & Watters, Sam. Dream House: The White House as an American Home. 2009. (Illus.). 306p. 75.00 *(978-0-926494-65-7(1))* Acanthus Pr. LLC.

Dodd, Richard H. Architectural Styles: Orange County. 2009. (Illus.). 277p. *(978-0-615-31323-8(X))* Dodd, Richard H.

Dolkart, Andrew Scott. The Row House Reborn: Architecture & Neighborhoods in New York City, 1908-1929. 2009. (ENG., Illus.). 248p. (gr. 17). 72.00 *(978-0-8018-9158-8(2))* Johns Hopkins Univ. Pr.

Dowling, Elizabeth Meredith. Harrison Design Associates: A Decade of Work. 2007. (ENG., Illus.). 256p. 59.95 *(978-1-86470-277-4(X),* Images Publishing Dist Ac) Antique Collectors' Club GBR. Dist: National Bk. Network.

Downing, Andrew Jackson. The Architecture of Country Houses; Including Designs for Cottages, Farm-Houses, & Villas, with Remarks on Interiors, Furniture, & the Best Modes. 2006. 564p. per. 32.99 *(978-1-4255-6186-4(1))* MPublishing.

Dream Home Luxury Home Plans. 2007. (Illus.). 254p. 8.95 *(978-1-893536-12-8(2),* 163) Garlinghouse, Inc.

Drew, Bernard A. Dr. du Bois Rebuilds His Dream House. 2006. pap. 17.50 *(978-0-941583-30-5(9))* Attic Revivals Pr.

Dunlop, Beth & Lombard, Joanna. Great Houses of Florida. 2008. (ENG., Illus.). 256p. 55.00 *(978-0-8478-3097-8(7))* Rizzoli International Pubns., Inc.

Earls, William D. The Harvard Five in New Canaan: Mid-Century Modern Houses by Marcel Breuer, Landis Gores, John Johansen, Philip Johnson, Eliot Noyes & Others. 2006. (ENG., Illus.). 176p. 39.95 *(978-0-393-73183-5(9),* 73183) Norton, W. W. & Co., Inc.

Eastberg, John C. The Captain Frederick Pabst Mansion: An Illustrated History. 2009. (ENG., Illus.). 272p. 49.95 *(978-0-9823810-0-7(X))* Univ. of Wisconsin Pr.

Eng, John & Biondo, Adrienne. Modern Tract Homes of Los Angeles. 2011. (Illus.). 144p. 39.99 ***(978-0-7643-3865-6(X,*** Schiffer Publishing Ltd) Schiffer Publishing, Ltd.

Exford, Theodore Henry, compiled by. A Historic Look at Wells, Maine & the Homes of Drakes Island: A Brief History of the Brave Defenders of Colonial Wells & the Eventual Development of Its Jewel, Drakes Island. 2009. (Illus.). ix, 329p. *(978-0-89725-859-3(2),* Penobscot Pr) Picton Pr.

Faherty, Duncan. Remodeling the Nation: The Architecture of American Identity, 1776-1858. 2009. (Becoming Modern: New Nineteenth-Century Studies). (ENG., Illus.). 268p. pap. 35.00 *(978-1-58465-772-9(3),* University of New Hampshire Press) Univ. Pr. of New England.

Feireiss, Kristin, ed. Architecture in Times of Need: Make it Right - Rebuilding the New Orleans' Lower Ninth Ward. 2009. (Illus.). 360p. pap. 39.95 *(978-3-7913-4276-4(2))* Prestel Publishing.

Fell, Derek. The Gardens of Frank Lloyd Wright. 2009. (ENG., Illus.). 160p. 40.00 *(978-0-7112-2967-9(8))* Lincoln, Frances Ltd. GBR. Dist: Perseus-PGW.

Felzer, Lissa. The Charleston Freedman's Cottage: An Architectural Tradition. 2008. pap. 19.99 *(978-1-59629-286-4(5))* History Pr., The.

Fish, Prudence Paine. Antique Houses of Gloucester: The Families Who Built Them, the Mayor Who Moved Them & the Changing Face of the Harbor Village. 2007. (Illus.). 116p. pap., per. 29.99 *(978-1-59629-373-1(X))* History Pr., The.

Fitzgerald, F-Stop. Adirondack Style: Great Camps & Rustic Lodges. 2011. (ENG., Illus.). 224p. 50.00 *(978-0-7893-2266-1(8))* Universe Publishing.

Foley, Robert P., et al. Extraordinary Vision. 2010. (Illus.). 128p. 60.00 *(978-0-9725588-0-8(2));* (ENG., pap. 24.95 *(978-0-9725588-1-5(0))* Newport Restoration Foundation.

Fox, Stephen. The Country Houses of John F. Staub. 2007. (Sara & John Lindsey Series in the Arts & Humanities Ser.). (ENG., Illus.). 408p. 75.00 *(978-1-58544-595-0(9))* Texas A&M Univ. Pr.

Fraiser, Jim. The Garden District of New Orleans. 2012. (ENG.). 288p. 49.95 ***(978-1-934110-68-3(X))*** Univ. Pr. of Mississippi.

Gallagher, Winifred. House Thinking: A Room-by-Room Look at How We Live. 2007. (P. S. Ser.). (ENG., Illus.). 368p. pap. 14.95 *(978-0-06-053880-4(5),* HarperPerennial) HarperCollins Pubs.

Garling House Plans, creator. Builders' First-Choice Home Plans. 2007. (Illus.). 255p. per. 12.95 *(978-1-893536-26-5(2))* Garlinghouse, Inc.

Garlinghouse Company, creator. 223 Favorite Hillside Homes. 2007. (Illus.). 238p. per. 8.95 *(978-1-893536-15-9(7),* 166) Garlinghouse, Inc.

Garrison, James. Houses of Philadelphia: Chestnut Hill & the Wissahickon Valley. Morrison, William, ed. 2008. (Illus.). 320p. 69.00 *(978-0-926494-53-4(8))* Acanthus Pr. LLC.

Germany, Lisa. Great Houses of Texas. 2008. (ENG., Illus.). 256p. 55.00 *(978-0-8109-9393-8(7))* Abrams.

Gibbs Smith Publisher Staff, ed. Dream Homes San Diego & Orange County. 2007. lib. bdg. 34.95 *(978-1-933415-39-0(8))* Panache Partners, LLC.

Goldberger, Paul, intro. Modern Views. 2010. (ENG., Illus.). 200p. 70.00 *(978-2-7594-0467-4(6))* Assouline FRA. Dist: Perseus Distribution.

Goody, Joan, et al. Housing. 2nd ed. 2010. (Building Type Basics Ser.: 17). (ENG., Illus.). 240p. 80.00 *(978-0-470-40464-5(7),* Wiley) Wiley, John & Sons, Inc.

Gordon, Maggie. Historical Casitas of la Quinta Cove. 2007. 98p. pap. 12.95 *(978-0-7414-3937-6(9))* Infinity Publishing.

Gorlin, Alexander. Tomorrow's Houses: New England Modernism. 2011. (ENG., Illus.). 256p. 65.00 *(978-0-8478-3399-3(2))* Rizzoli International Pubns., Inc.

Gotkin, Michael. Artists' Handmade Houses. 2011. (ENG., Illus.). 240p. 60.00 *(978-0-8109-9584-0(0))* Abrams.

Green, Allan Wright, ed. & intro. Building the Pauson House: The Letters of Frank Lloyd Wright & Rose Pauson. 2011. (Illus.). 96p. 24.95 *(978-0-7649-5888-5(7))* Pomegranate Communications, Inc.

Gregory, Daniel P. Cliff May & the Modern Ranch House. 2008. (ENG., Illus.). 256p. 60.00 *(978-0-8478-3047-3(0))* Rizzoli International Pubns., Inc.

Gross, Geoffrey, photos by. Great Houses of New England. 2008. (ENG., Illus.). 272p. 55.00 *(978-0-8478-3101-2(9))* Rizzoli International Pubns., Inc.

Gross, Steve & Daley, Sue. Creole Houses: Traditional Homes of Old Louisiana. 2007. (ENG., Illus.). 192p. 37.50 *(978-0-8109-5495-3(8))* Abrams.

Gross, Steve & Daley, Susan. Time Wearing Out Memory: Schoharie County. 2008. (ENG., Illus.). 128p. 49.95 *(978-0-393-06644-9(4),* 6644) Norton, W. W. & Co., Inc.

Group, Harold E. Small Houses of the Forties: With Illustrations & Floor Plans. 2007. (Dover Architecture Ser.). (ENG., Illus.). 144p. per. 12.95 *(978-0-486-45598-3(X))* Dover Pubns., Inc.

Guntli, Reto, photos by. Luxury Living New York. 2009. (ENG.). 59.95 *(978-3-8327-9311-1(9))* teNeues Publishing Co.

Hackett, Cheryl. Newport Shingle Style. 2010. (ENG., Illus.). 128p. 24.95 *(978-0-7112-2937-2(6))* Lincoln, Frances Ltd. GBR. Dist: Perseus-PGW.

Hammel, Bette Jones. Legendary Homes of Lake Minnetonka. 2009. (ENG., Illus.). 208p. 49.95 *(978-0-87351-722-5(9))* Minnesota Historical Society Pr.

Harris, Steven. True Life: Steven Harris Architects. 2010. (ENG., Illus.). 240p. 50.00 *(978-1-56898-971-6(7))* Princeton Architectural Pr.

Harrison, Peter Joel. Pattern Book of American Doors. 2012. 288p. 95.00 ***(978-0-9838632-0-5(2))*** Bauer & Dean Pubs., Inc.

Hawkins, Jay W. Glasshouses & Glass Manufacturers of the Pittsburgh Region: 1795 - 1910. 2009. 612p. 59.95 ***(978-1-4401-1717-6(9))***; pap. 49.95 *(978-1-4401-1494-6(3))* iUniverse, Inc.

Hayward, Mary Ellen. Baltimore's Alley Houses: Homes for Working People since the 1780s. 2008. (Creating the North American Landscape Ser.). (ENG., Illus.). 328p. (gr. 17). 47.00 *(978-0-8018-8834-2(4))* Johns Hopkins Univ. Pr.

Hellman, Caroline. Domesticity & Design in American Womens Lives & Literature. 2011. (Routledge Studies in Nineteenth Century Literature Ser.). (ENG., Illus.). 146p. (C). 125.00 *(978-0-415-88272-9(9))* Routledge.

Henry, Saxon. Four Florida Moderns: The Architecture of Albert E. Alfonso, René Gonzáles, Chad Oppenheim, & Guy Peterson. 2010. (ENG., Illus.). 320p. 50.00 *(978-0-393-73274-0(6),* 73274) Norton, W. W. & Co., Inc.

Hershman, Susan. House Colors: Exterior Color by Style of Architecture. 2008. (ENG., Illus.). 336p. pap. 40.00 *(978-1-58685-690-8(1))* Gibbs Smith, Publisher.

Hertzberg, Mark. Frank Lloyd Wright's Hardy House. 2006. (Illus.). 80p. 19.95 *(978-0-7649-3761-3(8),* A126) Pomegranate Communications, Inc.

Hess, Alan & Stern, Michael E., texts. Julius Shulman: Palm Springs. 2008. (ENG., Illus.). 208p. 55.00 *(978-0-8478-3113-5(2))* Rizzoli International Pubns., Inc.

Hester, Paul & Hardaway, Lisa, photos by. California Romantica: Spanish Colonial & Mission-Style Houses. 2007. (ENG., Illus.). 322p. 65.00 *(978-0-8478-2975-0(8))* Rizzoli International Pubns., Inc.

Hildebrand, Grant. Frank Lloyd Wright's Palmer House. 2007. (ENG., Illus.). 120p. pap. 30.00 *(978-0-295-98640-1(9))* Univ. of Washington Pr.

Hill, Alton McKiver, Sr. The Historic Home of George Poindexter (Poingdestre), Criss-Cross , A Photo Book & History, Before & After. 2008. (Illus.). 73p. lib. bdg. 40.00 *(978-0-9820823-0-0(4))* Al Hill's Desktop Home Publishing Co.

Hill Jones, Crystal, et al. Nashville's Inglewood. 2009. (Images of America Ser.). (Illus.). 128p. pap. 21.99 *(978-0-7385-6827-0(9))* Arcadia Publishing.

Hoagland, Alison K. Mine Towns: Buildings for Workers in Michigan's Copper Country. 2010. (ENG., Illus.). 328p. 75.00 *(978-0-8166-6566-2(4))*; pap. 25.00 *(978-0-8166-6567-9(2))* Univ. of Minnesota Pr.

Holl, Steven. House: Black Swan Theory. 2007. (ENG., Illus.). 176p. 40.00 *(978-1-56898-587-9(8))* Princeton Architectural Pr.

Horwitz, Carolyn, ed. Modern Order: Houses by Robert Gurney. 2009. (ENG., Illus.). 176p. 55.00 *(978-0-9823190-1-7(0))* Architecture Interiors Pr., Inc.

Horwitz, Carolyn & Iannacci, Anthony, eds. Layers Volumes Light: Abramson Teiger Architects. 2011. (ENG.). 163p. 65.00 *(978-0-9823190-4-8(5))* Architecture Interiors Pr., Inc.

Howard, Hugh & Straus, Roger. Houses of the Presidents: Childhood Homes, Family Dwellings, Private Escapes, & Grand Estates. 2012. (ENG., Illus.). 256p. 40.00 ***(978-0-316-13327-2(2))*** Little Brown & Co.

Hunter, Rebecca. Mail-Order Homes: Sears Homes & Other Kit Houses. 2012. (Shire Library). (ENG., Illus.). 64p. pap. 9.95 ***(978-0-7478-1048-3(6))*** Shire Pubns., Ltd. GBR. Dist: Random Hse., Inc.

Hyland, Matthew G. Montpelier & the Madisons: House, Home, & American Heritage. 2007. pap. 19.99 *(978-1-59629-277-2(6))* History Pr., The.

Ideal Homes. Ideal Homes of the Thirties. 2010. (Dover Architecture Ser.). (ENG.). 144p. pap. 16.95 *(978-0-486-47255-3(8))* Dover Pubns., Inc.

Isaacs, Mollie. The Whalehead Club:: A Legacy Preserved. 2006. (Illus.). 140p. *(978-1-57864-379-0(1))* Donning Co. Pubs.

Isenstadt, Sandy. The Modern American House: Spaciousness & Middle Class Identity. Etlin, Richard A., ed. 2006. (Modern Architecture & Cultural Identity Ser.). (ENG., Illus.). 342p. 113.00 *(978-0-521-77013-2(0))* Cambridge Univ. Pr.

Isham, Norman M. Early Connecticut Houses: A Historical & Architectural Study. (Illus.). reprint ed. lib. bdg. 98.00 *(978-0-7222-4971-0(3))* Library Reprints, Inc.

Isham, Norman M. & Brown, Albert F. Early Rhode Island Houses: An Historical & Architectural Study. 2007. (ENG.). 220p. 39.95 *(978-0-548-32909-2(5))*; per. 24.95 *(978-1-4326-8779-3(4))* Kessinger Publishing, LLC.

Isham, Norman Morrison. Early American Houses: With a Glossary of Colonial Architectural Terms. 2007. (Dover Architecture Ser.). (ENG., Illus.). 160p. per. 9.95 *(978-0-486-46035-2(5))* Dover Pubns., Inc.

[Jacques, Daniel Harrison]. The House: A Pocket Manual of Rural Architecture. 2006. 192p. per. 18.99 *(978-1-4255-1509-6(6))* MPublishing.

Jenkinson, Gordon B. Williamsburgh District: A History of Its People & Places. 2006. pap. 21.99 *(978-1-59629-146-1(X))* History Pr., The.

Jimenez, Carlos & Hester, Paul. Crowley. 2009. (ENG., Illus.). 112p. 29.95 *(978-0-9814628-7-5(1))* Oro Editions.

Kahn, Lloyd. Builders of the Pacific Coast. 2008. (ENG., Illus.). 208p. pap. 26.95 *(978-0-936070-43-8(9))* Shelter Pubns., Inc.

Kathrens, Michael C. American Splendor: The Residential Architecture of Horace Trumbauer. 2012. 79.00 ***(978-0-926494-41-1(4))*** 2nd ed. 2011. (Illus.). 335p. 75.00 *(978-0-926494-61-9(9))* Acanthus Pr. LLC.

Kathrens, Michael C. Newport Villas: The Revival Styles, 1885-1935. 2009. (ENG., Illus.). 384p. 85.00 *(978-0-393-73270-2(3),* 73270) Norton, W. W. & Co., Inc.

Keil, Robert. Little Boxes: The Architecture of a Classic Midcentury Suburb. 2006. (Illus.). 144p. 35.00 *(978-0-9779236-4-9(9))* Advection Media.

Kelly, Annie. Litchfield Style: Classic Country Houses of Connecticut. 2011. (Illus.). 176p. 45.00 *(978-0-8478-3577-5(4))* Rizzoli International Pubns., Inc.

Kelly, J. Frederick. Early Domestic Architecture of Connecticut. 2007. (Illus.). 230p. pap. 29.95 *(978-0-7643-2664-6(3))* Schiffer Publishing, Ltd.

Kimball, Fiske. Domestic Architecture of the American Colonies & of the Early Republic. 2009. 48p. pap. *(978-1-4590-6713-4(4))* Books LLC.

King, Helen H. Historic Isle of Wight. 2nd ed. 2007. *(978-1-57864-420-9(8))* Donning Co. Pubs.

Kodis, Michelle. Modern Cabin, 1 vol. 2007. (ENG., Illus.). 192p. 39.95 *(978-1-4236-0099-2(1))* Gibbs Smith, Publisher.

Krauel, Jacobo. Sustainable Homes USA. 2008. (ENG.). 240p. 39.95 *(978-84-96424-30-2(8))* Links International (Leading International Key Services Barcelona, S.A.) ESP. Dist: National Bk. Network.

Kropp, Phoebe S. California Vieja: Culture & Memory in a Modern American Place. 2008. (Illus.). 384p. pap. 26.95 *(978-0-520-25804-4(5))* Univ. of California Pr.

Krupinski, Loretta. Looking Astern: An Artist's View of Maine's Historic Working Waterfronts. 2010. (ENG.). 128p. 29.95 *(978-0-89272-749-0(7))* Down East Bks.

Laignel, Eric, photos by. ICONS Miami Style. 2006. (Icons Ser.). (ENG., Illus.). 191p. per. 9.99 *(978-3-8228-2570-9(0))* TASCHEN DEU. Dist: Ingram Pub. Services.

Landis, Tom. Home Building Consumer's Guide & Video: How to Save Money by Taking Charge of the Design/Build Process. Incl. (Illus.). 1997. pap. *(978-0-9641268-0-0(X))*; 60.00 *(978-0-9641268-1-7(8))* Owner Builder Services.

Landry, Richard. Private Estates: New Architecture by Landry Design Group. 2012. (ENG., Illus.). 328p. 85.00 *(978-0-9826226-5-0(1))* Oro Editions.

Langeteig, Kendra. The New Asian Home, 1 vol. 2008. (ENG., Illus.). 176p. 29.95 *(978-1-4236-0046-6(0))* Gibbs Smith, Publisher.

Lathrop, Elsie. Historic Houses of Early America. 2006. (ENG.). 552p. per. 42.95 *(978-1-4286-5501-0(8))* Kessinger Publishing, LLC.

Lawrance, Gary & Surchin, Anne. Houses of the Hamptons, 1880-1930. 2007. (Architecture of Leisure Ser.). (Illus.). 324p. 85.00 *(978-0-926494-44-2(9))* Acanthus Pr. LLC.

Levick, Melba & Appleton, Marc. California Mediterranean. 2007. (ENG., Illus.). 208p. 50.00 *(978-0-8478-2915-6(4))* Rizzoli International Pubns., Inc.

Liberman, Ann. Governors' Mansions of the South. 2008. (ENG., Illus.). 248p. (gr. 9). 39.95 *(978-0-8262-1785-1(0))* Univ. of Missouri Pr.

Lidz, Maggie. The du Ponts: Houses & Gardens in the Brandywine, 1900-1951. 2009. (Illus.). 218p. 65.00 *(978-0-926494-69-5(4))* Acanthus Pr. LLC.

Linsley, Leslie. Key West: A Tropical Lifestyle. 2007. (ENG.). 224p. (gr. 12). 45.00 *(978-1-58093-197-7(9))* Monacelli Pr., Inc.

—Nantucket: Island Living. 2008. (ENG., Illus.). 224p. 45.00 *(978-1-58479-723-4(1))* Stewart, Tabori & Chang.

Lowell, Waverly B. & Baer, Morley. Living Modern: A Biography of Greenwood Common. 2009. (Illus.). 173p. *(978-0-9795508-6-7(6))* Stout William Pubs.

Lubell, Sam. Living West: New Residential Architecture in Southern California. 2009. (ENG., Illus.). 240p. 50.00 *(978-1-58093-249-3(5))* Monacelli Pr., Inc.

Luhan, Gregory. Live. Light. 2011. (ENG., Illus.). 92p. pap. 24.95 *(978-0-9826226-6-7(X))* Oro Editions.

MacDonald, Chris. West Coast Residential: The Modern & the Contemporary. Bellerby, Greg, ed. 2007. (ENG., Illus.). 120p. 39.95 *(978-1-894965-60-6(4))* Simply Read Bks. CAN. Dist: Perseus-PGW.

Malrose, Mary Alice, ed. Our First Family's Home: The Ohio Governor's Residence & Heritage Garden. 2008. (Illus.). 131p. 35.00 *(978-0-8214-1790-4(8))* Ohio Univ. Pr.

Maloney, Cathy Jean. The Gardener's Cottage in Riverside, Illinois: Living in a Small Masterpiece by Frank Lloyd Wright, Jens Jensen, & Frederick Law Olmsted. 2010. (Center for American Places - Center Books on American Places Ser.). (ENG., Illus.). 128p. 32.50 *(978-1-930066-89-2(9))* Ctr. for American Places, Inc.

Manucy, Albert. Sixteenth-Century St. Augustine: The People & Their Homes. 2008. (ENG., Illus.). 175p. pap. 24.95 *(978-0-8130-3276-4(6))* Univ. Pr. of Florida.

Masson, Kathryn. The California House: Mission - Craftsman - Victorian - Spanish Colonial. 2011. (ENG., Illus.). 256p. 60.00 *(978-0-8478-3585-0(5))* Rizzoli International Pubns., Inc.

—Historic Houses of Virginia: Great Plantation Houses, Mansions, & Country Places. 2006. (ENG., Illus.). 256p. 55.00 *(978-0-8478-2861-6(1))* Rizzoli International Pubns., Inc.

—Hunt Country Style. 2008. (ENG., Illus.). 256p. 55.00 *(978-0-8478-2949-1(9))* Rizzoli International Pubns., Inc.

Mateyunas, Paul J. Long Island North Shore Country Houses: 1890-1950. 2007. (Suburban Domestic Architecture Ser.). (Illus.). 352p. 80.00 *(978-0-926494-37-4(6))* Acanthus Pr. LLC.

Mathews County Historical Society Staff, contrib. by. Historic Homes & Properties of Mathews County, Virginia: Pre-Civil War. 2009. *(978-1-57864-594-7(8))* Donning Co. Pubs.

Mayne, Thom, frwd. Live & Work: Modern Homes & Offices - The Southern California Architecture of Shubin & Donaldson. 2010. (ENG., Illus.). 252p. 60.00 *(978-0-9795395-5-8(2))* Oro Editions.

McAlester, Virginia, et al. Homes of the Park Cities, Dallas: Great American Suburbs. 2008. (ENG., Illus.). 480p. 75.00 *(978-0-7892-0975-4(4))* Abbeville Pr., Inc.

McAlpine, Bobby & Sully, Susan. The Home Within Us: Romantic Houses, Evocative Rooms. 2010. (ENG., Illus.). 240p. 55.00 *(978-0-8478-3289-7(9))* Rizzoli International Pubns., Inc.

McCurry, Chris & Chase, Nan. Bark House Style: Sustainable Designs from Nature, 1 vol. 2008. (ENG., Illus.). 152p. 30.00 *(978-1-4236-0214-9(5))* Gibbs Smith, Publisher.

McCurry, Margaret. Distillations: The Architecture of Margaret Mccurry. 2011. (ENG., Illus.). 240p. 45.00 ***(978-1-935935-06-3(2))*** Oro Editions.

McMillan, Patricia & McMillan, Katharine. Christmas at Historic Houses. 2010. (Illus.). 224p. 45.00 *(978-0-7643-3559-4(6))* Schiffer Publishing, Ltd.

Meeske, Harrison. From Vernacular to Spectacular: Function Follows Form: How Houses Changed Life Styles of the Hudson Valley Dutch, 1700-1830. 2007. (Illus.). 160p. pap. 25.00 *(978-1-930098-77-0(4))* Purple Mountain Pr., Ltd.

Mellins, Thomas & Albrecht, Donald. The American Style. 2011. (ENG., Illus.). 224p. 50.00 *(978-1-58093-285-1(1))* Monacelli Pr., Inc.

Miers, Mary. American Houses: The Architecture of Fairfax & Sammons. 2006. (ENG., Illus.). 240p. 60.00 *(978-0-8478-2857-9(3))* Rizzoli International Pubns., Inc.

Miller, Mary Carol. Lost Mansions of Mississippi, Vol. 2. 2010. (ENG., Illus.). 144p. 35.00 *(978-1-60473-786-8(7))* Univ. Pr. of Mississippi.

Millstein, Cydney & Grove, Carol. Houses of Missouri. 2008. (Illus.). 272p. 65.00 *(978-0-926494-54-1(6))* Acanthus Pr. LLC.

Mockler, Kim. Maurice Fatio: Palm Beach Architect. 2010. (Illus.). 300p. 65.00 *(978-0-926494-09-1(0))* Acanthus Pr. LLC.

Mooney, Barbara Burlison. Prodigy Houses of Virginia: Architecture & the Native Elite. 2008. (ENG., Illus.). 400p. (gr. 17). 65.00 *(978-0-8139-2673-5(4))* Univ. Pr. of Virginia.

Morgan, Bret. Rustic: Country Houses, Rural Dwellings, Wooded Retreats. 2009. (ENG., Illus.). 228p. 25.00 *(978-0-8478-3300-9(3))* Rizzoli International Pubns., Inc.

Morgan, William. Yankee Modern: The Houses of Estes/Twombly. 2009. (ENG., Illus.). 168p. pap. 40.00 *(978-1-56898-817-7(6))* Princeton Architectural Pr.

Morgan, William, et al. The Abrams Guide to American House Styles. Olsen, Richard, ed. 2008. (ENG., Illus.). 424p. per. 21.95 *(978-0-8109-7230-8(1))* Abrams.

Morris, Linny, photos by. The Hawaiian House Now. 2007. (ENG., Illus.). 192p. 42.00 *(978-0-8109-9394-5(5))* Abrams.

Morrison, William, ed. The Work of Dwight James Baum. 2008. (Illus.). 229p. 69.00 *(978-0-926494-48-0(1))* Acanthus Pr. LLC.

Moskow, Keith & Linn, Robert. Martha's Vineyard: Contemporary Living. 2010. (ENG., Illus.). 224p. 50.00 *(978-1-58093-272-1(X))* Monacelli Pr., Inc.

Murphy, Kevin D. The Houses of Greenwich Village. 2008. (ENG., Illus.). 224p. 45.00 *(978-0-8109-9520-8(4))* Abrams.

Murray-Wooley, Carolyn. Early Stone Houses of Kentucky. 2008. (ENG., Illus.). 272p. 50.00 *(978-0-8131-2479-7(4))* Univ. Pr. of Kentucky.

My Passion for Design. 2010. (ENG., Illus.). 288p. (gr. 12). 60.00 *(978-0-670-02213-7(6),* Viking Adult) Penguin Group (USA) Inc.

Nogai, Juergen, photos by. Houses of the Sundown Sea: The Architectural Vision of Harry Gesner. 2012. (ENG., Illus.). 240p. 75.00 *(978-1-4197-0049-1(9))* Abrams.

Nylander, Justin A. Casas to Castles: Florida's Historic Mediterranean Revival Architecture. 2010. (Illus.). 240p. 39.99 *(978-0-7643-3435-1(2))* Schiffer Publishing, Ltd.

O'Connor, Kevin. The Best Homes from This Old House. 2011. (ENG., Illus.). 228p. 35.00 ***(978-1-58479-935-1(8))*** Stewart, Tabori & Chang.

Ojeda, Oscar, ed. Bohlin Cywinski Jackson: Farrar. 2007. (ENG., Illus.). 112p. 25.00 *(978-0-9774672-7-3(9))* Oro Editions.

Old House & Barn Resource Directory: Second Edition. 2nd ed. 2007. *(978-0-9643014-1-2(5))* New Hampshire Preservation Alliance.

Oldham, Mike. Movie Stars' Homes. 2008. (Illus.). 96p. pap. 12.95 *(978-0-7643-2902-9(2))* Schiffer Publishing, Ltd.

Olsberg, Nicholas, ed. & text. Between Earth & Heaven: The Architecture of John Lautner. 2008. (ENG., Illus.). 234p. 60.00 *(978-0-8478-3014-5(4))* Rizzoli International Pubns., Inc.

Ore, Janet. The Seattle Bungalow: People & Houses, 1900-1940. 2006. (ENG., Illus.). 216p. per. 24.95 *(978-0-295-98627-2(1))* Univ. of Washington Pr.

Ossman, Laurie. Great Houses of the South. 2010. (Illus.). 272p. 55.00 *(978-0-8478-3309-2(7))* Rizzoli International Pubns., Inc.

Ozer, Mark N. Massachusetts Avenue in the Gilded Age: Palaces & Privilege. 2010. 128p. pap. 19.99 *(978-1-59629-922-1(3))* History Pr., The.

Pahlke, Eric. San Diego County Victorians. 2008. 80p. pap. *(978-0-9800950-0-5(X))* Our Heritage Pr.

Palmer, Michele. Gingerbread Gems of Willimantic, Connecticut. 2007. (Illus.). 112p. pap. 19.95 *(978-0-7643-2603-5(1))* Schiffer Publishing, Ltd.

Panache Partners, LLC. New England: Showcasing New England's Finest Architects, Designers & Builders. 2008. (Dream Homes Ser.). (ENG., Illus.). 250p. 34.95 *(978-1-933415-48-2(7))* Panache Partners, LLC.

Panache Partners, LLC, ed. Dream Homes Michigan: An Exclusive Showcase of Michigan's Finest Architects, Designers & Builders. 2008. (Dream Homes Ser.). (ENG.). 250p. lib. bdg. 34.95 *(978-1-933415-09-3(6))* Panache Partners, LLC.

Panache Partners LLC Staff. Dream Homes Greater Washington, D. C. A Showcase of the Finest Architects in Maryland, Northern Virginie & Washington, D. C. Weko, Amanda Gibney, ed. 2008. (Dream Homes Ser.). (ENG., Illus.). 288p. 34.95 *(978-1-933415-45-1(2))* Panache Partners, LLC.

Panache Partners LLC., Staff. Dream Homes Minnesota: Showcasing Minnesota's Finest Architects, Designers & Builders. Castelli, Lauren & Parr, Ryan, eds. 2008. (Dream Homes Ser.). (ENG., Illus.). 224p. 34.95 *(978-1-933415-35-2(5))* Panache Partners, LLC.

Panache Partners LLC Staff. Dream Homes Pacific Northwest: An Exclusive Showcase of the Finest Architects, Designers & Builders in Oregon & Washington. Castelli, Lauren, ed. 2008. (Dream Homes Ser.). (ENG., Illus.). 192p. 34.95 *(978-1-933415-01-7(0))* Panache Partners, LLC.

Panache Partners LLC Staff, contrib. by. Tennessee: An Exclusive Showcase of Tennessee's Finest Architects, Designers & Builders. 2009. (Dream Homes Ser.). (ENG., Illus.). 250p. 34.95 *(978-1-933415-04-8(6))* Panache Partners, LLC.

Panache Partners LLC., Staff, creator. Dream Homes of Los Angeles: An Exclusive Showcase of the Finest Architects in Los Angeles. 2008. (Dream Homes Ser.). (ENG., Illus.). 250p. 34.95 *(978-1-933415-06-2(1),* Panache Partners, LLC.

Panache Partners LLC Staff, creator. Dream Homes South Florida: An Exclusive Showcasing South Florida's Finest Architects, Designers & Builders. 2006. (Dream Homes Ser.). (ENG., Illus.). 204p. 39.95 *(978-1-933415-00-0(2))* Panache Partners, LLC.

Panache Partners LLC., Staff, creator. Spectacular Homes of Greater Washington, D. C. An Exclusive Showcase of Designers in Washington D. C. , Northern Virginia & Maryland. 2007. (Spectacular Homes Ser.) (ENG., Illus.). 250p. 39.95 *(978-1-933415-20-8(7))* Panache Partners, LLC.

Panache Partners LLC., Staff, ed. Chicago: An Exclusive Showcase of Chicago's Finest Architects. 2007. (Dream Homes Ser.). (ENG., Illus.). 250p. 34.95 *(978-1-933415-34-5(7))* Panache Partners, LLC.

Panache Partners LLC Staff, ed. Dream Homes Coastal California: An Exclusive Showcase of the Finest Architects, Designers & Builders of California's Central Coast Including Santa Barbara, San Luis Obispo & Monterey Counties. 2008. (Dream Homes Ser.). (ENG., Illus.). 224p. 34.95 *(978-1-933415-50-5(9))* Panache Partners, LLC.

—Dream Homes Florida: An Exclusive Showcase of Florida's Finest Architects, Designers & Builders. 2007. (Dream Homes Ser.). (ENG., Illus.). 271p. 39.95 *(978-1-933415-32-1(0))* Panache Partners, LLC.

—Dream Homes Greater Philadelphia: An Exclusive Showcase of Greater Philadelphia's Finest Architects. 2007. (Dream Homes Ser.). (ENG., Illus.). 271p. 39.95 *(978-1-933415-33-8(9))* Panache Partners, LLC.

—Dream Homes of Northern California: An Exclusive Showcase of Northern California's Finest Architects. 2007. (Dream Homes Ser.). (ENG., Illus.). 250p. 39.95 *(978-1-933415-10-9(X))* Panache Partners, LLC.

—Georgia: An Exclusive Showcase of Georgia's Finest Architects, Designers, & Builders. 2007. (Dream Homes Ser.). (ENG., Illus.). 250p. 34.95 *(978-1-933415-02-4(9))* Panache Partners, LLC.

—Spectacular Homes of New England: An Exclusive Showcase of the Finest Designers in New England. 2007. (Spectacular Homes Ser.). (ENG., Illus.). 264p. 39.95 *(978-1-933415-19-2(3))* Panache Partners, LLC.

Panache Partners Staff, creator. Dream Homes Carolinas: An Exclusive Showcase of the Carolinas' Finest Architects, Designers & Builders. 2007.

(Dream Homes Ser.). (ENG., Illus.). 240p. 39.95 *(978-1-933415-03-1(7))* Panache Partners, LLC.

Paradis, Thomas W. The Greenwood Encyclopedia of Homes Through American History, 4 vols. 2008. (Illus.). 1840p. 399.95 *(978-0-313-33496-2(X)*, GR3496) Greenwood Publishing Group, Inc.

Paul, Linda Leigh. Haciendas: Spanish Colonial Houses in the U. S. & Mexico. 2008. (ENG., Illus.). 224p. 55.00 *(978-0-8478-3099-2(3))* Rizzoli International Pubns., Inc.

Peck, Steven W. Award-winning Green Roof Designs: Green Roofs for Healthy Cities. 2008. (Illus.). 176p. 39.99 *(978-0-7643-3022-3(5))* Schiffer Publishing, Ltd.

Pedersen, Jens. 90 Houses of the Twenties: Cottages, Bungalows & Colonials. 2011. (Dover Architecture Ser.). (ENG.). 128p. pap. 19.95 *(978-0-486-47886-9(6))* Dover Pubns., Inc.

Pennoyer, Peter, et al. Peter Pennoyer Architects: Apartments - Townhouses - Country Houses. 2010. (ENG., Illus.). 240p. 60.00 *(978-0-86565-268-2(6))* Vendome Pr., The.

Phaidon Press Editors, ed. The American House. 2008. (ENG., Illus.). 112p. 29.95 *(978-0-7148-4885-3(9))* Phaidon Pr., Inc.

Pierce, Mary Knowles. An Acquired Taste: American Houses, Rooms & Gardens Explained in A Rapid Primer. 2011. 162p. 41.95 ***(978-1-258-06044-2(2))*** Literary Licensing, LLC.

Preston, Frederick R. Historic Doorways of San Antonio, Texas. 2009. 128p. pap. 19.99 *(978-0-7643-3167-1(1))* Schiffer Publishing, Ltd.

Pure California-35 Inspiring Homes in the New California Tradition: Pure CA, vols. 2, Vol. 1. 2nd ed. 2011. (Illus.). 160p. 24.95 ***(978-0-9721539-7-3(7))*** Bassenian/Lagoni Architects, Inc.

Quale, John D. Sustainable, Affordable, Prefab: The Ecomod Project. 2012. (ENG., Illus.). 248p. (C). (gr. 13-17). pap. 35.00 ***(978-0-8139-3233-0(5))***; (gr. 17). 60.00 ***(978-0-8139-3152-4(5))*** Univ. Pr. of Virginia.

Ranalli, George. George Ranalli: Saratoga. Ojeda, Oscar Riera, ed. 2009. (ENG., Illus.). 112p. 29.95 *(978-0-9814628-8-2(X))* Oro Editions.

Rashkin, Sam. Retooling the U. S. Housing Industry: How We Got Here - Why It's Broken - And How We Fix It. 2010. (ENG.). 320p. (C). pap. 44.95 *(978-1-111-31382-1(2))* Delmar Cengage Learning.

Raymond, Eleanor. Early Domestic Architecture of Pennsylvania. 2007. (Illus.). 160p. pap. 29.95 *(978-0-7643-2590-8(6))* Schiffer Publishing, Ltd.

Reilly, Donna Grant. An American Proceeding: Building the Grant House with Frank Lloyd Wright. 2010. (Illus.). 196p. pap. 22.95 *(978-1-58465-978-5(5))* Univ. Pr. of New England.

Ricciuti, Italo William. New Orleans & Its Environs: The Domestic Architecture 1727-1870. 2008. (Illus.). 144p. pap. 29.99 *(978-0-7643-3069-8(1))* Schiffer Publishing, Ltd.

Richmond, Arthur P. Cottages of Oak Bluffs: 20 Postcards. 2007. (Illus.). 40p. pap. 9.95 *(978-0-7643-2683-7(X))* Schiffer Publishing, Ltd.

—Gingerbread Gems: Victorian Architecture of Oak Bluffs. 2007. (Illus.). 208p. pap. 29.95 *(978-0-7643-2682-0(1))* Schiffer Publishing, Ltd.

Riera Ojeda, Oscar, ed. Peter Forbes: Seal Harbor. 2008. (Illus.). 112p. 25.00 *(978-0-9795395-4-1(4))* Oro Editions.

Rooney, Ashley. Fences, Gates & Walls. 2007. (Illus.). 128p. pap. 24.95 *(978-0-7643-2643-1(0))* Schiffer Publishing, Ltd.

Rooney, Ashley & Brooks, Turner. Shingle Style Homes: Past & Present. 2007. (Illus.). 256p. 39.95 *(978-0-7643-2554-0(X))* Schiffer Publishing, Ltd.

Rooney, E. Ashley. Old Barns, New Homes: A Showcase of Architectural Conversions. 2007. (Illus.). 175p. 34.95 *(978-0-7643-2132-0(3))* Schiffer Publishing, Ltd.

—Shingle Style Architecture for the 21st Century. 2010. (Illus.). 176p. 49.99 *(978-0-7643-3551-8(0))* Schiffer Publishing, Ltd.

Rooney, E. Ashley & Millet, Caroline Dunlop. Today's Historic Interiors. 2011. (Illus.). 192p. 49.99 ***(978-0-7643-3868-7(4)***, Schiffer Publishing Ltd) Schiffer Publishing, Ltd.

Roy, Rob & Roy, Robert L. Stoneview: How to Build an Eco-Friendly Little Guesthouse. 2008. (ENG., Illus.). 240p. per. 25.95 *(978-0-86571-597-4(1)*, 9780865715974) New Society Pubs., Ltd. CAN. Dist: Consortium Bk. Sales & Distribution.

Sandler, Rob & Mehta, Julie. Architecture in Hawaii. 2008. 184p. 39.95 *(978-1-56647-873-1(1))* Mutual Publishing LLC.

Sandow Media Corporation. Leading Residential Landscape Professionals, Vol. 2. 2nd ed. 2008. (ENG., Illus.). 134p. 39.95 *(978-0-9800398-1-8(9))* Sandow Media.

Santi, Federico & Gacher, John. Newport Mansions: Postcards of the Gilded Age. 2006. (Illus.). 112p. pap. 24.95 *(978-0-7643-2497-0(7))* Schiffer Publishing, Ltd.

Sater, Dan F., II. Dan Sater's European Classics: Tuscan, Italian, French, Spanish & English: Eighty Designer Home Plans. Bailey, Rickard & Baker, Jennifer, eds. 2007. (Illus.). 191p. pap. 14.95 *(978-1-932553-27-7(4)*, DDP) Designs Direct Publishing, LLC.

Sater Design Collection, des. Dan Sater's Design Collection: 95 Luxury Home Plans. 2008. (Illus.). 192p. pap. 12.95 *(978-1-932553-28-4(2)*, DDP) Designs Direct Publishing, LLC.

Schoenherr, Matthew. Remodel: Great Home Makeovers from Connecticut to California. 2007. (American Institute Architects Ser.). (ENG., Illus.). 192p. pap. 21.95 *(978-1-56158-924-1(1)*, Taunton) Taunton Pr., Inc.

Seebohm, Caroline. Cottages & Mansions of the Jersey Shore. 2007. (Rivergate Ser.). (ENG., Illus.). 224p. 39.95 *(978-0-8135-4016-0(X))* Rutgers Univ. Pr.

Serraino, Pierluigi. Eero Saarinen. Gossel, Peter, ed. 25th ed. 2009. (25 Ser.). (ENG., Illus.). 96p. 14.99 *(978-3-8365-1333-3(1))* TASCHEN DEU. Dist: Ingram Pub. Services.

Sewall, Jock. Mediterranean Architecture: A Sourcebook of Architectural Elements. 2011. (Illus.). 432p. 100.00 ***(978-0-7643-3891-5(9)***, Schiffer Publishing Ltd) Schiffer Publishing, Ltd.

Sirefman, Susanna. Modern Shoestring: Contemporary Architecture on a Budget. 2008. (ENG., Illus.). 160p. (gr. 12). 40.00 *(978-1-58093-202-8(9))* Monacelli Pr., Inc.

Skinner, Tina. Lowcountry Plantations: Georgia & South Carolina. 2010. (Illus.). 144p. 29.99 *(978-0-7643-3415-3(8))* Schiffer Publishing, Ltd.

Skurman, Andrew. Contemporary Classicism: The Architecture of Andrew Skurman. 2012. (ENG.). 256p. 60.00 ***(978-1-61689-088-9(6))*** Princeton Architectural Pr.

Sloan, Samuel. The Model Architect, Vol. 2. 2007. 204p. per. *(978-0-923891-86-2(2))* Ishi Pr. International.

—The Model Architect Vol. 1: A Series of Original Designs. 2007. 206p. per. 24.95 *(978-0-923891-85-5(4))* Ishi Pr. International.

Smith, Alice R. Huger. The Dwelling Houses of Charleston, South Carolina. 2007. 256p. pap. 24.99 *(978-1-59629-261-1(X))* History Pr., The.

Smith, Bruce. Greene & Greene: Developing a California Architecture, 1 vol. 2011. (ENG.). 192p. 50.00 *(978-1-58685-817-9(3))* Gibbs Smith, Publisher.

Smith, Elisabeth & Smith, Elizabeth. Case Study Houses. Gossel, Peter, ed. 25th ed. 2009. (25 Ser.). (ENG., Illus.). 96p. 14.99 *(978-3-8365-1301-2(3))* TASCHEN DEU. Dist: Ingram Pub. Services.

Smith, Elizabeth A. T. & Smith Elizabeth. Case Study Houses: 1945-1966 / Der kalifornische Impuls. Gssel, Peter, ed. 25th ed. 2009. (ENG., Illus.). 440p. 69.99 *(978-3-8365-1021-9(9))* TASCHEN DEU. Dist: Ingram Pub. Services.

St. Augustine Historical Restoration & Newton, Earle W. Handbook of Colonial St Augustine Architecture. 2011. 56p. 36.95 ***(978-1-258-09757-8(5))*** Literary Licensing, LLC.

Standiford, Les. Washington Burning: How a Frenchman's Vision for Our Nation's Capital Survived Congress, the Founding Fathers, & the Invading British Army. 2009. (ENG., Illus.). 368p. pap. 16.00 *(978-0-307-34645-2(5))* Crown Publishing Group.

Stern, Robert, frwd. Ike Kligerman Barkley Houses. 2010. (ENG., Illus.). 256p. 60.00 *(978-1-58093-269-1(X))* Monacelli Pr., Inc.

Stickley, Gustav. Gustav Stickley's Craftsman Homes & Bungalows. 2009. (ENG., Illus.). 576p. pap. 19.95 *(978-1-60239-303-5(6)*, 239303) Skyhorse Publishing Co., Inc.

Strickland, James Lowell & Sully, Susan. Coming Home: The Southern Vernacular House. 2012. (ENG., Illus.). 224p. 45.00 ***(978-0-8478-3826-4(9))*** Rizzoli International Pubns., Inc.

Susanka, Sarah. The Not So Big House Book. 2006. *(978-1-56158-929-6(2))* Taunton Pr., Inc.

Tedesco, Paul H. & Tedesco, James/B. Portable & Prefabricated Houses of the Thirties: E. F. Hodgson Company 1935 & 1939 Catalogs Unabridged Reprint. 2007. 19.95 *(978-0-9792059-1-0(3))* JBT Publishing.

Thornton, Rosemary Fuller. Sears Homes of Illinois. 2010. 176p. pap. 26.99 *(978-1-59629-939-9(8))* History Pr., The.

Toledano, Roulhac. A Pattern Book of New Orleans Architecture, 1 vol. 2010. (ENG., Illus.). 256p. 35.00 *(978-1-58980-694-8(8))* Pelican Publishing Co., Inc.

Tomorrow's Historic Tulsa Homes. 2010. (Illus.). 128p. 29.95 *(978-0-9759799-7-6(3))* JBW Pubns.

Treib, Mark, et al. West Coast Residential. Bellerby, Greg, ed. rev. ed. 2012. (ENG., Illus.). 120p. 29.95 *(978-1-894965-99-6(X))* Simply Read Bks. CAN. Dist: Perseus-PGW.

Trulove, James Grayson. Great Houses on a Budget. 2008. (Illus.). 191p. pap. 19.95 *(978-0-06-158116-8(X)*, Collins Design) HarperCollins Pubs.

U.S. Green Building Council Staff, contrib. by. Homes Reference Guide. 2008. (Illus.). x, 342p. *(978-1-932444-10-0(6))* National Council of Teachers of English.

Van Luchene, Katie. Home Design Best of Kansas City. 2007. 130p. pap. 29.95 *(978-0-9725314-5-0(9))* Anthem Media, LLC.

Vassallo, Marc. The Barefoot Home: Dressed-down Design for Casual Living. 2006. (ENG., Illus.). 218p. 30.00 *(978-1-56158-807-7(5)*, Taunton) Taunton Pr., Inc.

Vercelloni, Matteo, et al. Lofts & Apartments in NYC 2. San Pietro, Silvio, ed. 2008. (International Architecture & Interiors Ser.). (ENG., Illus.). 200p. *(978-88-7685-154-4(2)*, Edizioni L'archivolto (Acc)) Antique Collectors' Club.

Versaci, Russell. Creating a New Old House: Yesterday's Character for Today's Home. 2007. (American Institute Architects Ser.). (ENG., Illus.). 218p. pap. 24.95 *(978-1-56158-792-6(3)*, Taunton) Taunton Pr., Inc.

—The Roots of Home: Our Journey to a New Old House. 2008. (ENG., Illus.). 265p. 45.00 *(978-1-56158-867-1(9)*, Taunton) Taunton Pr., Inc.

von Holst, H. V., ed. Modern American Homes: Prairie & Craftsman Architecture. 2008. (Illus.). 128p. bds. 29.99 *(978-0-7643-3005-6(5))* Schiffer Publishing, Ltd.

VV Staff. The Best of American Houses. (SPA.). 218p. *(978-987-97781-7-3(0))* HK Bks.

Watters, Sam. Houses of Los Angeles, 1885-1919, 2 vols. 2007. (Urban Domestic Architecture Ser.). (Illus.). 386p. 85.00 *(978-0-926494-30-5(9))* Acanthus Pr. LLC.

—Houses of Los Angeles, 1920-1935 Vol. 2, 2 vols. 2007. (Urban Domestic Architecture Ser.). (Illus.). 402p. 80.00 *(978-0-926494-31-2(7))* Acanthus Pr. LLC.

Way, Terry. Victorian Homes of San Francisco. 2009. (Illus.). 112p. pap. 19.99 *(978-0-7643-3212-8(0))* Schiffer Publishing, Ltd.

Weintraub, Alan, photos by. Frank Lloyd Wright Prairie Houses. 2006. (ENG., Illus.). 272p. 50.00 *(978-0-8478-2858-6(1))* Rizzoli International Pubns., Inc.

Wendell V. Fountain, D. B. A. How to Build a Southwestern House. 2009. (Illus.). 120p. pap. 49.95 *(978-1-4389-4000-7(9))* AuthorHouse.

Wharton, Bernard. House, Home, Heart: Artistry & Craftsmanship in the Architecture of Shope Reno Wharton. 2011. (ENG., Illus.). 320p. 85.00 *(978-0-9833889-0-6(3))* Pointed Leaf Pr.

Wheeler, Daniel, et al, eds. The Historic Chicago Greystone: A User's Guide for Renovating & Maintaining Your Home. 2008. (Illus.). 108p. per. 21.95 *(978-0-9789650-1-3(9))* City Design Ctr.

Wheeler, Gervase. Rural Homes: Or, Sketches of Houses Suited to American Country Life, with original Plans, Designs, andc., by Gervase Wheeler. 2006. 320p. per. 23.99 *(978-1-4255-3174-4(1))* MPublishing.

Whitsitt, Steven P. & Skinner, Tina. Esherick, Maloof, & Nakashima: Homes of the Master Wood Artisans. 2009. (Illus.). 144p. bds. 49.99 *(978-0-7643-3202-9(3))* Schiffer Publishing, Ltd.

—Handmade Houses. 2009. 112p. bds. 29.99 *(978-0-7643-3203-6(1))* Schiffer Publishing, Ltd.

Wiencek, Henry. The Moodys of Galveston & Their Mansion. 2010. (Sara & John Lindsey Series in the Arts & Humanities Ser.). (ENG., Illus.). 136p. pap. 19.95 *(978-1-60344-182-7(4))* Texas A&M Univ. Pr.

Wight Wise, Marsha. Catonsville. 2010. (Then & Now Ser.). (Illus.). 96p. pap. 21.99 *(978-0-7385-8625-0(0))* Arcadia Publishing.

Wilson, Alex. Green Building Products: The GreenSpec Guide to Residential Building Materials. Malin, Nadav, ed. 3rd ed. 2008. (ENG., Illus.). 352p. pap. 37.95 *(978-0-86571-600-1(5)*, 9780865716001) New Society Pubs., Ltd. CAN. Dist: Consortium Bk. Sales & Distribution.

Wilson, David Stark. Houses + Origins: WA Design. 2012. (ENG., Illus.). 224p. 59.95 ***(978-1-86470-466-2(7))*** Images Publishing Group AUS. Dist: National Bk. Network.

Wolf, Thomas A., ed. Historic Sites in Virginia's Northern Neck & Essex County: A Guide. 2011. (ENG., Illus.). 290p. pap. 24.95 *(978-0-692-01167-6(6))*; (gr. 17). 40.00 *(978-0-692-01166-9(8))* Univ. Pr. of Virginia.

Woods, Douglas. The California Casa. 2012. (ENG., Illus.). 360p. 55.00 ***(978-0-8478-3849-3(8))*** Rizzoli International Pubns., Inc.

Woods, Douglas. Classic Homes of Los Angeles. 2010. (ENG., Illus.). 256p. 55.00 *(978-0-8478-3384-9(4))* Rizzoli International Pubns., Inc.

Worthington, Kathy, ed. Chicago Luxury Home & Condo: The Ultimate Source for Designing, Building, Remodeling, Decorating, Furnishing & Landscaping Chicagoland's Finest Homes & Condos. 2007. (ENG., Illus.). 600p. 24.95 *(978-0-9789734-0-7(2))* Lake Forest Media Group, The.

Wyllie, Romy. Bertram Goodhue. 2007. 55.00 *(978-0-7937-3219-7(0))* Norton, W. W. & Co., Inc.

—Bertram Goodhue: His Life & Residential Architecture. 2007. (ENG., Illus.). 224p. 60.00 *(978-0-393-73219-1(3)*, 73219) Norton, W. W. & Co., Inc.

Yglesias, Caren. The Complete House & Grounds: Learning from A. J. Downing's Domestic Architecture. 2012. (ENG., Illus.). 224p. 40.00 *(978-1-935195-24-5(7))* Ctr. for American Places, Inc.

Yockey Jones, L. Beth. Master Builders Association of King & Snohomish Counties: One Hundred Years of Building Community. 2009. (Illus.). 295p. *(978-0-9764839-5-3(5))* Abecedary Pr.

Zeiger, Mimi. Tiny Houses. 2009. (ENG., Illus.). 208p. 29.95 *(978-0-8478-3203-3(1))* Rizzoli International Pubns., Inc.

ARCHITECTURE, DOMESTIC—YEMEN

Damluji, Salma Samar, et al. The Architecture of Yemen: From Yafi to Hadramut. 2008. (ENG., Illus.). 304p. 85.00 *(978-1-85669-514-5(X))* King, Laurence Publishing GBR. Dist: Hachette Bk. Group.

Marchand, Trevor. Minaret Building & Apprenticeship in Yemen. 2012. (ENG.). 285p. (C). pap. 39.95 ***(978-0-415-69544-2(9))*** Routledge.

ARCHITECTURE, ECCLESIASTICAL

see Church Architecture

ARCHITECTURE, GEORGIAN

Curl, James Stevens. Georgian Architecture: The British Isles, 1717-1830. 2nd rev. ed. 2011. (ENG., Illus.). 444p. (C). 100.00 *(978-1-84802-086-3(4))* English Heritage GBR. Dist: Brown, David Bk. Co., The.

Hume-Frazer, Susan. The Architecture of William Lawrence Bottomley. 2007. (American Architect Ser.). (Illus.). 360p. 85.00 *(978-0-926494-23-7(6))* Acanthus Pr. LLC.

Stalcup, Jonathan. Savannah Architectural Tours. 2008. (Illus.). 144p. pap. 14.95 *(978-0-7643-2907-4(3))* Schiffer Publishing, Ltd.

Telfair Museum of Art & Sammons, Tania June. The Owens-Thomas House. 2008. (ENG., Illus.). 64p. 12.95 *(978-0-933075-10-8(3))* Telfair Museum of Art.

Yorke, Trevor. Georgian & Regency Houses Explained. 2007. (England's Living History Ser.). (ENG., Illus.). 128p. (C). pap. 21.95 *(978-1-84674-051-0(7))* Countryside Bks. GBR. Dist: Brown, David Bk. Co., The.

ARCHITECTURE, GOTHIC

see also Cathedrals; Church Architecture; Cistercian Architecture; Decoration and Ornament, Gothic; Gothic Revival (Architecture)

Ball, Philip. Universe of Stone: A Biography of Chartres Cathedral. 2008. (ENG.). 336p. 27.95 *(978-0-06-115429-4(6))* HarperCollins Pubs.

—Universe of Stone: Chartres Cathedral & the Invention of the Gothic. 2009. (ENG.). 336p. pap. 15.99 *(978-0-06-115430-0(X)*, HarperPerennial) HarperCollins Pubs.

Bednorz, Achim. Gothic: Architecture - Sculpture - Painting, 1 vol. Toman, Rolf, ed. 2011. (ENG.). 520p. 19.99 ***(978-3-8331-6007-3(1))*** h.f.ullmann DEU. Dist: Innovative Logistics.

Bernstein, Susan. Housing Problems: Writing & Architecture in Goethe, Walpole, Freud, & Heidegger. 2008. (Meridian: Crossing Aesthetics Ser.). (ENG., Illus.). 216p. 60.00 *(978-0-8047-5854-3(9))*; pap. 21.95 *(978-0-8047-5855-0(7))* Stanford Univ. Pr.

Bloxam, Holbeche Matthew. The Principles of Gothic Ecclesiastical Architecture, Elucidated by Question & Answer. 2007. 124p. (ENG.). 94.99 *(978-1-4280-7621-1(2))*; per. 88.99 *(978-1-4280-7619-8(0))* IndyPublish.com.

Bonde, Sheila. Fortress-Churches of Languedoc: Architecture, Religion & Conflict in the High Middle Ages. 2008. (ENG.). 292p. pap. 34.99 *(978-0-521-05202-3(5))* Cambridge Univ. Pr.

Bonnet, Philippe & Rioult, Jean-Jacques. Bretagne Gothique: L'architecture Religieuse. 2010. (FRE., Illus.). 485p. *(978-2-7084-0883-8(6))* Picard, A.et J. Editions.

Brandon, Raphael & Brandon, J. Arthur. Gothic Architecture: 158 Plates from the Brandons' Treatise 1847. 2007. (Dover Architecture Ser.). (ENG., Illus.). 176p. per. 18.95 *(978-0-486-46010-9(X))* Dover Pubns., Inc.

Branner, Robert. Gothic Architecture. 125p. pap. 15.95 *(978-0-8076-1471-6(8))* Braziller, George Inc.

—Studies of Gothic Architecture. 2012. (ENG., Illus.). 528p. (C). 300.00 *(978-1-904597-35-3(1))* Pindar Pr. GBR. Dist: Brown, David Bk. Co., The.

Burckhardt, Titus. Chartres & the Birth of the Cathedral. 2010. (ENG., Illus.). 160p. pap. 24.95 *(978-1-933316-77-2(2))* World Wisdom, Inc.

De Jonge, K., et al. Gotiek in het hertogdom Brabant. 2009. (DUT.). 272p. (C). pap. 32.00 *(978-90-429-2275-4(3))* Peeters Pubs. & Booksellers BEL. Dist: Brown, David Bk. Co., The.

Decaëns, Henry & Goupy, Didier. Le Mont-Saint-Michel. (FRE & ENG., Illus.). 237p. *(978-2-8123-0194-0(5))* Editions du Chene.

Dittel, Deborah. Hans Reynhart: Ein sächsischer Baumeister der Spätgotik. 2008. (GER., Illus.). 116p. *(978-3-8364-8159-5(6))* VDM Verlag Dr. Mueller e.K.

Draper, Peter. The Formation of English Gothic: Architecture & Identity, 1150-1250. 2007. (Paul Mellon Centre for Studies in British Art). (ENG., Illus.). 288p. 80.00 *(978-0-300-12036-3(2))* Yale Univ. Pr.

Duhamel, Pascale. Polyphonie parisienne et architecture au temps de l'art Gothique (1140-1240) 2010. (Varia Musicologica Ser.). (FRE.). 275p. pap. *(978-3-03911-613-3(4))* Lang, Peter.

Fenske, Gail. The Skyscraper & the City: The Woolworth Building & the Making of Modern New York. 2008. (Illus.). 352p. 65.00 *(978-0-226-24141-8(6))* Univ. of Chicago Pr.

Frothingham, A. L. Introduction of Gothic Architecture into Italy by the French Cistercian Monks. 2009. pap. 25.12 *(978-1-60724-496-7(9))* Gorgias Pr., LLC.

Goy, Richard J. The House of Gold: Building a Palace in Medieval Venice. 2011. (ENG.). 336p. pap. 39.99 *(978-0-521-18134-1(8))* Cambridge Univ. Pr.

Gravett, Christopher. English Castles 1200-1300. 2009. (Fortress Ser.). (ENG., Illus.). 64p. pap. 18.95 *(978-1-84603-374-2(8))* Osprey Publishing, Ltd. GBR. Dist: Random Hse., Inc.

Hamann-Maclean, Richard. Kathedrale von Reims II: Skulp(Text) 2008. (ENG.). (C). 82.00 *(978-3-515-06837-6(6))* Steiner, Franz Verlag Wiesbaden GmbH DEU. Dist: Brown, David Bk. Co., The.

Hastings, Maurice. St Stephen's Chapel: And Its Place in the Development of Perpendicular Style in England. 2011. (ENG.). 276p. pap. 23.99 ***(978-0-521-24278-3(9))*** Cambridge Univ. Pr.

Hendrix, John. Architecture As Cosmology: Lincoln Cathedral & English Gothic Architecture. 2010. (Illus.). 372p. (C). pap. 49.95 *(978-1-4331-1316-1(3))* Lang, Peter Publishing, Inc.

James, John. In Search of the Unknown in Medieval Architecture. 2007. (Illus.). 686p. (C). 300.00 *(978-1-904597-36-0(X))* Pindar Pr. GBR. Dist: Brown, David Bk. Co., The.

Janko, Joan. The Chapel of the Assumption of the Virgin in Spissk² Stvrtok. 2008. 96p. pap. *(978-3-639-04289-4(1))* VDM Verlag Dr. Mueller e.K.

Kavaler, Ethan Matt. Renaissance Gothic. 2012. (ENG., Illus.). 344p. 75.00 ***(978-0-300-16792-4(X))*** Yale Univ. Pr.

Moore, Charles Herbert. Development & Character of Gothic Architecture. 2008. 356p. pap. *(978-1-4097-1790-4(9))* Read Bks.

Opacic, Z. The Year 1300 & the Creation of the New European Architecture. Gajewski, Alexandrea, ed. 2008. (Architectura Medii Aevi Ser.). (ENG.). 235p. (C). pap. 123.00 *(978-2-503-52286-9(6))* Brepols Pubs. BEL. Dist: ISD.

Opacic, Z. & Timmerman, A., eds. Architecture, Liturgy & Identity. 2011. (Studies in Gothic Art Ser.). (ENG., Illus.). 334p. (C). pap. 116.00 *(978-2-503-53167-0(9))* Brepols Pubs. BEL. Dist: ISD.

Paley, F. A. A Manual of Gothic Architecture. 2008. pap. *(978-1-84830-051-4(4)*, Wildhem Pr.) Echo Library.

Parker, John Henry. An Introduction to the Study of Gothic Architecture. 2008. 272p. 42.95 *(978-1-4369-4745-9(6))*; pap. 27.95 *(978-1-4367-7529-8(9))* Kessinger Publishing, LLC.

Prina, Francesca. The Story of Gothic Architecture. 2011. (ENG., Illus.). 144p. pap. 19.95 ***(978-3-7913-4596-3(6))*** Prestel Publishing.

Pugin, A. W. N. Contrasts & True Principles of Pointed or Christian Architecture. 2012. (ENG., Illus.). 244p. (C). 90.00 ***(978-1-904965-37-4(7))*** Spire Bks. Ltd. GBR. Dist: Brown, David Bk. Co., The.

Puhle, Matthias. Aufbruch in die Gotik, 2 vols. 2009. (GER., Illus.). 1124p. (C). 135.00 *(978-3-8053-4062-5(1))* Zabern, Philipp von Verlag, GmbH DEU. Dist: Brown, David Bk. Co., The.

Reeve, M. M., ed. Reading Gothic Architecture. 2008. (Studies in the Visual Cultures of the Middle Ages Ser.). (ENG.). 160p. (C). pap. 94.00 *(978-2-503-52536-5(9))* Brepols Pubs. BEL. Dist: ISD.

Ruskin, John. Nature of Gothic: A Chapter from the Stones of Venice. 2008. (ENG., Illus.). 90p. pap. 9.50 ***(978-1-906267-07-0(3))*** Euston Grove Pr. GBR. Dist: Lightning Source, Inc.

—The Stones of Venice - The Fall. 2007. 528p. per. 26.95 *(978-1-60206-703-5(1))* Cosimo, Inc.

—The Stones of Venice - The Foundations. 2007. 464p. 39.45 *(978-1-60206-700-4(7))*; per. 24.95 *(978-1-60206-699-1(X))* Cosimo, Inc.

—The Stones of Venice - The Sea Stories. 2007. 452p. (ENG.). 39.45 *(978-1-60206-702-8(3))*; per. 24.95 *(978-1-60206-701-1(5))* Cosimo, Inc.

—Stones of Venice [Introductions]. 2007. 160p. per. *(978-1-4068-4090-2(4))* Echo Library.

—The Stones of Venice,Volume III the Fall. 2007. 528p. 39.45 *(978-1-60206-704-2(X))* Cosimo, Inc.

Sadler, Donna L. Reading the Reverse Facade of Reims Cathedral: Royalty & Ritual in 13th-Century France. 2012. (Illus.). 250p. ***(978-1-4094-3243-2(2))*** Ashgate Publishing, Ltd.

Scott, Robert A. The Gothic Enterprise: A Guide to Understanding the Medieval Cathedral - With a New Preface. 2nd ed. 2011. (ENG., Illus.). 306p. pap. 21.95 *(978-0-520-26999-6(3))* Univ. of California Pr.

Sweeney, Jon M. Beauty Awakening Belief: How the Medieval Worldview Inspires Faith Today. 2009. 160p. pap. 20.00 *(978-0-8192-2370-8(0)*, Morehouse Publishing) Church Publishing, Inc.

Toman, Rolf, ed. Gothic: Architecture, Sculpture, Painting. 2008. (Architecture Sculpture Painting Ser.). (Illus.). 520p. per. 24.95 *(978-0-8416-0068-3(6))* American Map Corp.

Wilson, Christopher. Perpendicular Style: Origins & Development. 2007. (ENG.). 320p. 75.00 *(978-0-300-11125-5(8))* Yale Univ. Pr.

ARCHITECTURE, GREEK

see also Greek Revival (Architecture); Temples

also subdivision antiquities under names of cities, e.g. Athens (Greece)—Antiquities

Bangs, Herbert. The Return of Sacred Architecture: The Golden Ratio & the End of Modernism. 2006. (ENG., Illus.). 1p. per. 24.95 *(978-1-59477-132-3(4))* Inner Traditions International, Ltd.

Barletta, Barbara. The Origins of the Greek Architectural Orders. 2009. (ENG., Illus.). 232p. (C). pap. 27.99 *(978-0-521-12422-5(0))* Cambridge Univ. Pr.

Betancourt, Philip. Dams & Water Management Systems of Minoan Pseira. 2012. (ENG., Illus.). 110p. (C). pap. 20.00 ***(978-1-931534-66-6(7))*** Institute for Aegean Prehistory Pr.

Campbell, Gordon. The Grove Encyclopedia of Classical Art & Architecture, 2 vols. 2007. (ENG., Illus.). 1600p. 345.00 *(978-0-19-530082-6(3))* Oxford Univ. Pr., Inc.

Campbell, Misty. An Architectural Prognosis: Greek Medicine & Architecture. 2008. 108p. pap. *(978-3-639-05865-9(8))* VDM Verlag Dr. Mueller e.K.

Economakis, Richard. Acropolis. 2010. (ENG., Illus.). 144p. pap. 16.95 *(978-1-902889-06-1(1)*, Artmedia (Acc)) Antique Collectors' Club GBR. Dist: National Bk. Network.

Emerson, Mary. Greek Sanctuaries: An Introduction. 2007. (Illus.). 144p. per. 24.95 *(978-1-85399-689-4(0))* Bristol Classical Pr. GBR. Dist: International Publishers Marketing.

Frederiksen, Rune. Greek City Walls of the Archaic Period, 900-480 BC. 2011. (Oxford Monographs on Classical Archaeology Ser.). (ENG., Illus.). 320p. 170.00 *(978-0-19-957812-2(5))* Oxford Univ. Pr., Inc.

Gallo, Luciana. Lord Elgin & Ancient Greek Architecture: The Elgin Drawings at the British Museum. 2009. (ENG., Illus.). 362p. (C). 155.00 *(978-0-521-88163-0(3))* Cambridge Univ. Pr.

Georgopoulou, Maria. Venice's Mediterranean Colonies: Architecture & Urbanism. 2011. (ENG., Illus.). 400p. pap. 45.00 *(978-0-521-18434-2(7))* Cambridge Univ. Pr.

Goodyear, W. H. Egyptian Origin of the Ionic Capital & of the Anthemion. 2009. pap. 21.64 *(978-1-60724-432-5(2))* Gorgias Pr., LLC.

Hans, Taeuber, et al, contrib. by. The Bouleuterion at Ephesos. 2011. (Forschungen in Ephesos Ser.). (ENG.). 210p. (C). pap. 88.00 ***(978-3-7001-6541-5(2)***, Austrian Academy of Sciences of Pr.) Austrian Academy of Sciences Press AUT. Dist: Brown, David Bk. Co., The.

I. Vikelas. 2010. (GRE & ENG., Illus.). 340p. (C). pap. 68.00 ***(978-960-6878-32-9(5))*** Kapon, Ekdoseis GRC. Dist: ISD.

Jenkins, Ian. Greek Architecture & Its Sculpture. 2007. (Illus.). 272p. 35.00 *(978-0-674-02388-8(9))* Harvard Univ. Pr.

Kalogeroudis, Georgios. Befestigungsanlagen Im Griechischen Raum in der Bronzezeit und Ihre Entwicklung Von Neolithischer Bis in Archaische Zeit. 2008. (Bar S Ser.). (GER., Illus.). 486p. (C). 162.50 *(978-1-4073-0358-1(9))* British Archaeological Reports Ltd. GBR. Dist: Brown, David Bk. Co., The.

Kissas, Konstantin. Archaische Architektur der Athener Akropolis: Dachziegel - Metopen - Geisa - Akroterbasen. 2008. (Archaeologische Forschungen Ser.). (GER., Illus.). 146p. (C). 66.00 *(978-3-89500-623-4(8))* Reichert, Ludwig Dr. DEU. Dist: Brown, David Bk. Co., The.

Knell, Heiner. Des Kaisers neue Bauten: Hadrians Architektur in Rom, Athen und Tivoli. 2008. (GER., Illus.). 119p. (C). 38.00 *(978-3-8053-3772-4(8))* Zabern, Philipp von Verlag, GmbH DEU. Dist: Brown, David Bk. Co., The.

Konstantinidis, Dimitri & Konstantinides, Ares. Aris Konstantinidis, 1913-1993. Cofano, Paola, ed. 2010. (ITA., Illus.). 360p. 179.50 *(978-88-370-5762-6(8))* Electa ITA. Dist: Trans-Atlantic Pubns., Inc.

Malacrino, Carmelo G. Constructing the Ancient World: Architectural Techniques of the Greeks & Romans. 2010. (Illus.). 224p. 50.00 *(978-1-60606-016-2(3))* Getty Pubns.

Marquand, Allan. Greek Architecture. 2008. (Illus.). 440p. *(978-1-4437-2400-5(9))* 2006. 436p. per. *(978-1-4067-2653-4(2))* Read Bks. (Hesperides Pr.).

McEnroe, John C. Architecture of Minoan Crete: Constructing Identity in the Aegean Bronze Age. 2010. (ENG., Illus.). 220p. 60.00 *(978-0-292-72193-7(5))* Univ. of Texas Pr.

Mertens, Dieter. Städte und Bauten der Westgriechen: Von der Kolonisation bis zur Krise am Ende des 5. Jh. v. Chr. 2006. (GER., Illus.). 462p. (C). 165.00 *(978-3-7774-2755-3(1))* Hirmer Verlag GmbH DEU. Dist: Brown, David Bk. Co., The.

Philippides, Demetres, et al. Pikiones: Hoi Homilies Tou '65. 2009. (GRE., Illus.). 210p. (C). 65.00 ***(978-960-204-288-5(5))*** Ekdotikos Oikos Melissa GRC. Dist: ISD.

Prokkola, Tapio. The Optical Corrections of the Doric Temple. 2011. 266p. pap. 36.00 ***(978-1-936401-76-5(2))*** Two Harbors Pr., Inc.

Rodgers, Nigel. The Art & Architecture of Ancient Greece: An Illustrated Account of Classical Greek Buildings, Sculptures & Paintings, Shown in 200 Glorious Photographs & Drawings. 2012. (ENG., Illus.). 128p. pap. 17.99 ***(978-1-84476-802-8(3))*** Anness Publishing GBR. Dist: National Bk. Network.

Sakellariou, E. P. A. Sakellarious, an Architect's Vision. 2008. 324p. pap. *(978-960-6691-00-3(4))* Potamos.

Schultz, Peter. Structure, Image, Ornament - Architectural Sculpture in the Greek World: Proceedings of an international conference held at the American School of Classical Studies, 27-28 November 2004. Schultz, Peter & von den Hoff, Ralf, eds. 2009. (ENG., Illus.). 248p. (C). 80.00 *(978-1-84217-344-2(8))* Oxbow Bks., Ltd. GBR. Dist: Brown, David Bk. Co., The.

Scranton, Robert L. Greek Architecture: The Great Ages of World Architecture V4. 2011. 128p. 40.95 ***(978-1-258-04164-9(2))*** Literary Licensing, LLC.

Senseney, John R. The Art of Building in the Classical World: Vision, Craftsmanship, & Linear Perspective in Greek & Roman Architecture. 2011. (ENG., Illus.). 274p. 90.00 *(978-1-107-00235-7(4))* Cambridge Univ. Pr.

Smith, T. Roger & Redford, George. Greek Architecture & Greek Sculpture. 2007. (ENG.). 156p. 36.95 *(978-0-548-00359-6(9))* Kessinger Publishing, LLC.

Stierlin, Henri. Greece. 25th ed. 2009. (World Architecture Ser.). (ENG., Illus.). 224p. 14.99 *(978-3-8365-1038-7(3))* TASCHEN DEU. Dist: Ingram Pub. Services.

Stuart, James & Revett, Nicholas. The Antiquities of Athens. 2007. (ENG., Illus.). 496p. 125.00 *(978-1-56898-723-1(4))* Princeton Architectural Pr.

Truemper, Monika. Graeco-Roman Slave Markets - Fact or Fiction? 2009. (ENG., Illus.). 160p. (C). 45.00 *(978-0-9774094-8-8(1))* Brown, David Bk. Co., The.

Tschumi. New Acropolis Museum - Greek Language. 2009. ***(978-0-8478-3436-5(0))*** Rizzoli International Pubns., Inc.

Tzonis, Alexander & Rodi, Alkistis. Greece. 2012. (Reaktion Books - Modern Architectures in History Ser.). (ENG., Illus.). 272p. pap. 29.95 *(978-1-86189-379-6(5))* Reaktion Bks., Ltd. GBR. Dist: Chicago Distribution Ctr.

Wallpaper Magazine Editors, ed. Athens 2012 - Wallpaper City Guide. 2nd ed. 2011. (ENG., Illus.). 128p. pap., pap. 9.95 *(978-0-7148-6101-2(4))* Phaidon Pr., Inc.

Wang, Wilfried, ed. & text. Kyriakos Krokos: Fassianos Building, Athens 1990-1995. 2011. (ENG., Illus.). 144p. pap. 40.00 *(978-3-8030-0718-6(6))* Wasmuth, Ernst J. Verlag GmbH & Co. DEU. Dist: D.A.P./Distributed Art Pubs.

Wire, Elinor, et al. The Lighthouses of Greece. 2010. (ENG.). 168p. 21.95 *(978-1-56164-452-0(8))*; pap. 16.95 *(978-1-56164-460-5(9))* Pineapple Pr., Inc.

ARCHITECTURE, HINDU

see Hindu Architecture

ARCHITECTURE, INDIAN

see Indian Architecture

ARCHITECTURE, INDIC

Asher, Frederick M. Bodh Gaya. 2008. (ENG., Illus.). 120p. 35.00 *(978-0-19-569314-0(0))* Oxford Univ. Pr., Inc.

Bunce, Fredrick W. The Mosques of the Indian Subcontinent: Their Development & Iconography. 2008. 212p. *(978-81-246-0458-8(4))* D. K. Print World (P) Ltd.

Jhabvala, C. S. H. Old Delhi New York. 2008. (ENG., Illus.). 108p. 39.95 *(978-81-7436-573-6(7))* Roli Bks. Private, Ltd. IND. Dist: Ingram Pub. Services.

ARCHITECTURE, INDIGENOUS

see Vernacular Architecture

ARCHITECTURE, INDUSTRIAL

Altoon, Ronald A. Designing the World's Best Retail Centers. 2006. (Designing the World's Best Ser.). (ENG., Illus.). 224p. 70.00 *(978-1-876907-45-7(2))* Images Publishing Group AUS. Dist: National Bk. Network.

Basar, Shumon, et al, eds. With / Without, 1 vol. 2008. (ENG.). 266p. 25.00 *(978-9948-03-453-7(8))* Ministry of Information & Culture, Copyright Section UAE. Dist: D.A.P./Distributed Art Pubs.

DAAB Media Staff, ed. Contemporary Corporate Architecture, 1 vol. 2009. (ITA, FRE, GER, SPA & ENG., Illus.). 383p. 59.95 *(978-3-86654-018-7(3))* DAAB Media Gmbh DEU. Dist: Innovative Logistics.

Fukasawa, Naoto & Morrison, Jasper. Super Normal: Sensations of the Ordinary. 2007. (Illus.). 112p. pap. 34.95 *(978-3-03778-106-7(8)*, 3037781068) Springer.

Gannon, Todd. Zaha Hadid: BMW Central Building, Leipzig, Germany. 2006. (ENG., Illus.). 160p. pap. 29.95 *(978-1-56898-536-7(3))* Princeton Architectural Pr.

Gresleri, Giuliano & Zacchiroli, E. Architettura Industriale. (ENG & ITA., Illus.). 192p. 60.00 *(978-88-89431-01-6(6))* Damiani ITA. Dist: D.A.P./Distributed Art Pubs.

Grube, Hans Achim. New Power: Elektropolis im Wandel. 2008. (GER & ENG., Illus.). 128p. pap. 45.00 *(978-3-939633-27-3(5))* Jovis Verlag GmbH DEU. Dist: D.A.P./Distributed Art Pubs.

Gutierrez & Portefaix, text. City of Production: A Fabulous Opportunity to Experiment with Positive Capitalism, 1 vol. 2012. (ENG., Illus.). 100p. 25.00 *(978-988-98395-7-4(1))* Map Bk. HKG. Dist: D.A.P./Distributed Art Pubs.

Howe, A. Scott & Sherwood, Brent. Out of This World: The New Field of Space Architecture. 2009. 119.95 *(978-1-56347-982-3(6))* American Institute of Aeronautics & Astronautics.

Images Publishing Group. Industrial Spaces Vol. 1: A Pictorial Review. 2006. (International Spaces Ser.). (ENG., Illus.). 55.00 *(978-1-876907-63-1(0))* Images Publishing Group AUS. Dist: National Bk. Network.

Lissmann, Christina, ed. Stephen Williams Architects, 1 vol. 2008. (ENG., Illus.). 176p. 29.95 *(978-3-86654-028-6(0))* DAAB Media Gmbh DEU. Dist: Innovative Logistics.

Martina/Grabensteiner, et al, contrib. by. Winearchitecture: The Winery Boom. 2006. (ENG & GER., Illus.). 224p. (gr. 13-18). 35.00 *(978-3-7757-1687-1(4))* Hatje Cantz Verlag GmbH & Co KG DEU. Dist: D.A.P./Distributed Art Pubs.

Nganga, Stephen, et al. Industrial Infrastructure Planning for Small Manufacturing Enterprises. 2011. 280p. pap. ***(978-3-8433-9373-7(7))*** Lambert Academic Publishing.

Publishing Teneues Staff, ed. BMW from vision to Reality. 2006. 256p. 125.00 *(978-3-8327-9231-2(7))* teNeues Publishing Co.

Robeck, Ulrike & Robeck. Die älteren Hallen des Bochumer Vereins als Zweckbauten und Denkmale der Eisen- und Stahlindustrie. 2010. (Denkmalpflege und Forschung in Westfalen Ser.). (GER.). (C). 33.00 ***(978-3-8053-4279-7(9))*** Zabern, Philipp von Verlag, GmbH DEU. Dist: Brown, David Bk. Co., The.

Sallustio, Luigi. Fighting for Profit & Control in the Mobile Phone Industry. 2011. 172p. pap. ***(978-3-8443-2422-8(4))*** Lambert Academic Publishing.

Uffelen, Van Chris. Factory Design. 2008. (Illus.). 336p. 62.50 *(978-3-03768-005-6(9)*, Braun Publish,Csi) Continental Sales, Inc.

Utgikar, Shrinivas. Factory Designing for Developing Countries. 2010. 146p. pap. 13.80 *(978-0-557-23190-4(6))* Lulu Enterprises Inc.

Wayne, Lucy B. Sweet Cane: The Architecture of the Sugar Works of East Florida. 2010. (ENG., Illus.). 192p. 45.00 *(978-0-8173-1696-9(5))*; pap. 22.50 *(978-0-8173-5592-0(8))* Univ. of Alabama Pr.

Webb, Michael. Adventurous Wine Architecture. 2006. (Designing the World's Best Ser.). (ENG., Illus.). 216p. 60.00 *(978-1-920744-33-5(9))* Images Publishing Group AUS. Dist: National Bk. Network.

Weißer, Lutz. Corporate Process Architecture: Industriebau in der postindustriellen Gesellschaft. Facility Management Institut (FMI), ed. (GER., Illus.). 155p. 30.70 *(978-3-540-41486-5(X)*, 354041486X) Springer.

Wright, Frank Lloyd. Modern Architecture: Being the Kahn Lectures for 1930. 2008. (ENG., Illus.). 176p. 29.95 *(978-0-691-12937-2(1))* Princeton Univ. Pr.

ARCHITECTURE, INTERIOR

see Interior Architecture

ARCHITECTURE, ISLAMIC

see Islamic Architecture

ARCHITECTURE, JEWISH

see Jewish Architecture

ARCHITECTURE, LIBRARY

see Library Architecture

ARCHITECTURE, MAYA

see Maya Architecture

ARCHITECTURE, MEDIEVAL

see also Architecture, Carolingian; Architecture, Norman; Architecture, Romanesque; Castles; Cathedrals

Barnes, Carl F. The Portfolio of Villard de Honnecourt Paris Bibliotheque Nationale de France Ms Fr 19093: Color Facsimile. 2009. (Illus.). 292p. 149.95 *(978-0-7546-5102-4(9))* Ashgate Publishing Co.

Batalov, A. L. & Smirnova, E. S. Drevnerusskoe Iskusstvo: Ideia I Obraz, Opyty Izucheniia Vizantiiskogo I Drevnerusskogo Iskusstva. 2009. (Illus.). 478p. *(978-5-94431-303-4(X))* Severnyj palomnik.

Bell, Gertrude Lowthian. Churches & Monasteries of the Tûr 'Abdîn & Neighbouring Districts. 2010. 94.88 *(978-1-61719-509-9(X))* Gorgias Pr., LLC.

Binding, Gunther. Antike Saulen ALS Spolien in Fruh- Und Hochmittelalterlichen Kirchen und Pfalzen - Materialspolie Oder Bedeutungs-Trager? 2007. (Sitzungsberichte der Wissenschaftlichen Gesellschaft an der Johann Wolfgang Goethe-Universitat Ser.). (ENG.). 49p. (C). pap. 30.00 *(978-3-515-08999-9(3))* Steiner, Franz Verlag Wiesbaden GmbH DEU. Dist: Brown, David Bk. Co., The.

—Methoden und Probleme bei der Datierung von mittelalterlichen Bauwerken. 2009. (Wissenschaftliche Gesellschaft an der Johann Wolfgang Goethe-Universitat Frankfurt, Main u Sitzungsberichte Ser.). (GER., Illus.). 76p. (C). pap. 39.00 *(978-3-515-09607-2(8))* Steiner, Franz Verlag Wiesbaden GmbH DEU. Dist: Brown, David Bk. Co., The.

Blain, Sophie. Les Terres Cuites Architecturales des Eglises du Haut Moyen Age Dans le Nord-Ouest de la France et le Sud-est de L'Angleterre: Application de la Datation Par Luminescence a Larcheologie du Bati. 2011. (Bar S Ser.). (FRE & ENG., Illus.). 221p. (C). pap. 102.50 *(978-1-4073-0744-2(4))* British Archaeological Reports Ltd. GBR. Dist: Brown, David Bk. Co., The.

Boas, Adrian J. Domestic Settings in Crusader States: Sources on Domestic Architecture & Day-to-Day Activities in the Latin East. 2010. (Illus.). 396p. *(978-90-04-18272-1(1))* BRILL.

Bork, Robert & Mcgehee, Abby. New Approaches to Medieval Architecture. 2011. (AVISTA Studies in the History of Medieval Technology, Science & Art Ser.). (Illus.). 258p. 119.95 *(978-1-4094-2228-0(3))* Ashgate Publishing Co.

Borsi, Stefano. Nicolo V e Roma: Alberti, Angelico, Manetti e un grande piano Urbano. 2009. (Biblioteca della Nuova Antologia Ser.). (ITA.). 648p. (C). pap. 54.00 *(978-88-596-0549-2(0))* Edizioni Polistampa ITA. Dist: Brown, David Bk. Co., The.

Brogiolo, Gian Pietro & Ibsen, M., eds. Corpus Architecturae Religiosae Europeae (saec. IV-X), vol. II. I. 2011. (Corpus Architecturae Religiosae Europeae Ser.). (ENG.). 325p. (C). pap. 114.00 ***(978-953-6002-46-7(9))*** Brepols Pubs. BEL. Dist: Brown, David Bk. Co., The.

Bruzelius, Caroline & Tronzo, William. Medieval Naples: An Architectural & Urban History, 400-1400. 2011. (ENG., Illus.). 160p. 30.00 *(978-1-59910-202-3(1))* Italica Pr.

—Medieval Naples: An Architectural & Urban History, 400¿1400. 2011. (ENG., Illus.). 160p. pap. 20.00 *(978-1-59910-203-0(X))* Italica Pr.

Cannon, Jon & Williamson, Beth, eds. The Medieval Art, Architecture & History of Bristol Cathedral: An Enigma Explored. 2011. (Bristol Studies in Medieval Cultures Ser.: Volume 2). (Illus.). 376p. 95.00 *(978-1-84383-680-3(7)*, Boydell Press) Boydell & Brewer, Ltd. GBR. Dist: Boydell & Brewer, Inc.

Caponigro, Paul, photos by. Stone Churches of Ireland. 2007. pap. 24.95 *(978-1-888899-39-9(5))*; 100.00 *(978-1-888899-40-5(9))* Lodima Pr.

Carella, Silvio. Architecture religieuse haut-medievale en Italie Meridionale: Le diocese de Benevent. 2011. (Bibliotheque de l'antiquite Tardive Ser.). (FRE., Illus.). 255p. (C). pap. 94.00 *(978-2-503-53388-9(4))* Brepols Pubs. BEL. Dist: Brown, David Bk. Co., The.

Cassady, Richard F. The Emperor & the Saint: Frederick II of Hohenstaufen, Francis of Assisi, & Journeys to Medieval Places. 2011. (ENG., Illus.). 472p. 35.00 *(978-0-87580-439-2(X))* Northern Illinois Univ. Pr.

Cather, Sharon, et al. Wall Paintings: Diagnostic Investigations & Research. 2011. (English Heritage Research Transactions Ser.). (ENG., Illus.). 244p. (C). pap. 67.50 *(978-1-84407-328-3(9))* Earthscan LLC.

Christine Sciacca Staff. Building the Medieval World. 2010. (Illus.). vii, 96p. *(978-0-7123-5094-5(2)*, J. Paul Getty Museum) Getty Pubns.

Cómez Ramos, Rafael. Los Constructores de la España Medieval. 3rd ed. 2009. (SPA., Illus.). 208p. *(978-84-472-1176-0(2))* Universidad de Sevilla.

Coureas, Nicholas, et al. Medieval & Renaissance Famagusta: Studies in Architecture Art & History. 2012. (FRE & ENG., Illus.). 330p. 119.95 ***(978-1-4094-3557-0(1))*** Ashgate Publishing Co.

Crook, John. English Medieval Shrines. 2011. (Boydell Studies in Medieval Art & Architecture Ser.: Volume 3). (Illus.). 366p. 70.00 ***(978-1-84383-682-7(3)***, Boydell Press) Boydell & Brewer, Ltd. GBR. Dist: Boydell & Brewer, Inc.

Davis, Paul R. Castles of the Welsh Princes. 2011. (ENG., Illus.). 108p. pap. 14.95 ***(978-0-86243-970-5(1))*** Y Lolfa GBR. Dist: Dufour Editions, Inc.

Eaton, Tim. Plundering the Past: Roman Stonework in Medieval Britain. (Illus.). 160p. pap. 27.50 *(978-0-7524-1903-9(X))* History Pr. Ltd.,The GBR. Dist: Trafalgar Square Publishing.

Emery, Anthony. Discovering Medieval Houses. 2008. (Shire Discovering Ser.). (ENG., Illus.). 176p. per. 21.95 *(978-0-7478-0655-4(1))* Shire Pubns., Ltd. GBR. Dist: Random Hse., Inc.

Erlande-Brandenburg, Alain. The Cathedral: The Social & Architectural Dynamics of Construction. 2009. (Cambridge Studies in the History of Architecture Ser.). (ENG., Illus.). 404p. pap. 42.00 *(978-0-521-11037-2(8))* Cambridge Univ. Pr.

Ettel, P., et al, eds. Chateau et Representations: Actes du colloque international de Stirling (Ecosse). 2008. 2010. (Chateau Gaillard Ser.). (ENG, FRE & GER.). 280p. (C). 65.00 *(978-2-902685-77-6(7))* Brepols Pubs. BEL. Dist: Brown, David Bk. Co., The.

Fawcett, Richard. The Architecture of the Scottish Medieval Church, 1100-1560. 2011. (Paul Mellon Centre for Studies in Britis Ser.). (Illus.). 432p. 100.00 *(978-0-300-17049-8(1))* Yale Univ. Pr.

Fenske, Lutz, et al. Deutsche Königspfalzen: Beiträge Zu Ihrer Historischen und Archäologischen Erforschung. (Veröffentlichungen des Max-Planck-Instituts Für Geschichte Ser.). (GER., Illus.). (C). 2007. 382p. 179.00 *(978-3-525-35600-5(5))* 2006. 240p. 125.00 *(978-3-525-36521-2(7))* Vandenhoeck & Ruprecht GmbH & Co. KG DEU. Dist: ISD.

Frommel, Christoph Luitpold. L'antica Basilica Di San Lorenzo in Damaso: Indagini Archeologiche Nel Palazzo Della Cancelleria, 1988-1993. 2009. (ITA & ENG., Illus.). *(978-88-8016-846-1(0))*; *(978-88-8016-911-6(4))* De Luca Editori d'Arte.

Giles, Kate & Dyer, Christopher, eds. Town & Country in the Middle Ages: Contrasts, Contacts & Interconnections, 1100-1500. 2007. (Society for Medieval Archaeology Monograph Ser.). (ENG., Illus.). 300p. (C). per. 55.00 *(978-1-905981-39-7(2))* Maney Publishing GBR. Dist: Brown, David Bk. Co., The.

Gondoin, Stephane W. Twilight of the Medieval Castles. 2008. (Fortresses Ser.). (Illus.). 128p. 44.95 *(978-2-35250-069-8(9))* Histoire et Collections FRA. Dist: Casemate Pubs. & Bk. Distributors, LLC.

Goy, Richard J. The House of Gold: Building a Palace in Medieval Venice. 2011. (ENG.). 336p. pap. 39.99 *(978-0-521-18134-1(8))* Cambridge Univ. Pr.

Greenhalgh, Michael. Marble Past, Monumental Present: Building with Antiquities in the Mediaeval Mediterranean. 2008. (Medieval Mediterranean Ser.). (Illus.). 656p. *(978-90-04-17083-4(9))* BRILL.

Greppi, Paola. Provincia Maritima Italorum: Fortificazioni Altomedievali in Liguria. 2008. (Bar S Ser.). (ITA., Illus.). 157p. (C). pap. 105.00 ***(978-1-4073-0229-4(9))*** British Archaeological Reports Ltd. GBR. Dist: Brown, David Bk. Co., The.

Haddlesey, Richard. Virtual Meccano. 2010. 100p. pap. *(978-3-8383-6291-5(8))* Lambert Academic Publishing.

Hiscock, Nigel. The symbol at your Door: Number & geometry in the religious architecture of the greek & latin middle Ages. 2007. (Illus.). 442p. 134.95 *(978-0-7546-6300-3(0))* Ashgate Publishing Co.

Howard, F. The Medieval Styles of the English Parish Church. 2007. 208p. per. *(978-1-905217-77-9(3))* Mills, Jeremy Publishing.

Hull, Lise. Great Castles of Britain & Ireland. 2009. (ENG., Illus.). 160p. pap. 19.95 *(978-1-84773-130-2(9))* New Holland Pubs., Ltd. GBR. Dist: National Bk. Network.

Juckes, Tim. St. Elizabeth's in Kosice: Town, Court & Church Building in Late Medieval Hungary. 2012. (Architectura Medii Aevi Ser.). (ENG., Illus.). 320p. (C). pap. 123.00 *(978-2-503-53109-0(1))* Brepols Pubs. BEL. Dist: ISD.

Klinkenberg, Emanuel S. Compressed Meanings: The Donor's Model in Medieval Art to Around 1300 Origin - Spread & Significance of an Architectural Image in the Realm of Tension Between Tradition & Likeness. 2009. (Architectura Medii Aevi Ser.). (ENG., Illus.). 310p. (C). pap. 152.00 *(978-2-503-52835-9(X))* Brepols Pubs. BEL. Dist: ISD.

Lilley, Keith D. City & Cosmos: The Medieval World in Urban Form. 2009. (ENG., Illus.). 256p. 49.00 *(978-1-86189-441-0(4))* Reaktion Bks., Ltd. GBR. Dist: Chicago Distribution Ctr.

Lillie, Amanda. Florentine Villas in the Fifteenth Century: An Architectural & Social History. 2011. (ENG., Illus.). 369p. pap. 45.00 *(978-0-521-18138-9(0))* Cambridge Univ. Pr.

Martin, Therese. Reassessing the Roles of Women As 'makers' of Medieval Art & Architecture. 2012. ***(978-90-04-22827-6(6)); (978-90-04-18555-5(0)); (978-90-04-22828-3(4))*** BRILL.

McNeill, John, ed. King's Lynn & the Fens: Medieval Art, Architecture & Archaeology. 2008. (British Archaeological Association (BAA) Conference Transaction Ser.). (ENG., Illus.). 256p. (C). 144.00 *(978-1-906540-15-9(2))*; pap. 68.00 *(978-1-906540-16-6(0))* Maney Publishing GBR. Dist: Brown, David Bk. Co., The.

McNeill, Tom. Faith, Pride & Works: Medieval Church Building. 2006. (ENG., Illus.). 272p. per. 39.95 *(978-0-7524-3643-2(0))* History Pr. Ltd.,The GBR. Dist: Independent Pubs. Group.

Mortlock, D. P. & Roberts, C. V. The Guide to Norfolk Churches. 2nd ed. 2007. (Popular Guide Ser.). (ENG., Illus.). 392p. pap. 58.00 *(978-0-7188-3064-9(4))* Lutherworth Pr., The GBR. Dist: Brown, David Bk. Co., The.

Ó'Carragáin, Tomás. Churches in Early Medieval Ireland: Architecture, Ritual & Memory. 2011. (Paul Mellon Centre for Studies in Britis Ser.). (Illus.). 400p. 100.00 *(978-0-300-15444-3(5))* Yale Univ. Pr.

O'Donoghue, Rod E. L. Medieval Stained Glass in Suffolk Churches: Let the Stained Glass Speak. 2009. (Illus.). 280p. pap. 67.99 *(978-1-4389-8955-6(5))* AuthorHouse.

O'Keeffe, Tadhg. A Guide to Medieval Irish Architecture for Local Historians. 2012. (Illus.). 160p. 45.00 *(978-1-84682-247-6(5))*; pap. 24.95 *(978-1-84682-248-3(3))* Four Courts Pr. IRL. Dist: International Specialized Bk. Services.

Olson, Vibeke. Written in Stone: Studies on the Use of Limestone in Medieval Sculpture & Architecture in Northern Europe & the British Isles. 2011. (AVISTA Studies in the History of Medieval Technology, Science & Art Ser.). (Illus.). 288p. 119.95 *(978-0-7546-6246-4(2))* Ashgate Publishing Co.

Overesch, Manfred. Himmlisches Jerusalem in Hildesheim: St. Michael und das Geheimnis der sakralen Mathematik vor 1000 Jahren. 2009. (GER., Illus.). 332p. (C). 41.00 *(978-3-525-55004-5(9))* Vandenhoeck & Ruprecht GmbH & Co. KG DEU. Dist: ISD.

Pacey, Arnold. Medieval Architectural Drawing. 2010. (ENG., Illus.). 256p. 49.95 ***(978-0-7524-4404-8(2))*** History Pr. Ltd.,The GBR. Dist: Independent Pubs. Group.

Porter, Arthur Kingsley. Lombard Architecture. 2010. 580p. pap. *(978-1-153-01028-3(3))* 2010. 534p. pap. *(978-1-153-01030-6(5))* 2009. 402p. pap. *(978-1-150-56994-4(8))* Books LLC.

—Lombard Architecture. 2009. 646p. pap. 38.41 *(978-0-217-84354-6(9))* General Bks. LLC.

Potter, John F. The Medieval Town Wall of Great Yarmouth, Norfolk, U.K. A Geological Perlustration. 2008. (Bar Ser.). (Illus.). 105p. (C). 67.50 *(978-1-4073-0286-7(8))* British Archaeological Reports Ltd. GBR. Dist: Brown, David Bk. Co., The.

Pringle, Denys. The Churches of the Crusader Kingdom of Jerusalem: A Corpus: Volume 1, A-K (excluding Acre & Jerusalem) 2008. (Churches of the Crusader Kingdom of Jerusalem Ser.). (ENG., Illus.). 360p. pap. 48.00 *(978-0-521-07295-3(6))* Cambridge Univ. Pr.

—The Churches of the Crusader Kingdom of Jerusalem: A Corpus: Volume 2, L-Z (excluding Tyre) 2009. (Churches of the Crusader Kingdom of Jerusalem Ser.). (ENG., Illus.). 484p. pap. 58.00 *(978-0-521-10983-3(3))* Cambridge Univ. Pr.

—The Churches of the Crusader Kingdom of Jerusalem: Volume 3, the City of Jerusalem: A Corpus. 2010. (Churches of the Crusader Kingdom of Jerusalem Ser.). (ENG.). 534p. pap. 65.00 *(978-0-521-17283-7(7))* Cambridge Univ. Pr.

—The City of Jerusalem, 4 vols. 2007. (Churches of the Crusader Kingdom of Jerusalem Ser.). (ENG., Illus.). 532p. 250.00 *(978-0-521-39038-5(9))* Cambridge Univ. Pr.

—A Corpus Vol. 1-3: The Cities of Acre & Tyre with Addenda & Corrigenda, 4 vols. 2009. (Churches of the Crusader Kingdom of Jerusalem Ser.). (ENG., Illus.). 340p. 205.00 *(978-0-521-85148-0(3))* Cambridge Univ. Pr.

Quintavalle, Arturo Carlo. Medioevo: Le Officine: Atti Del Convegno Internazionale Di Studi, Parma, 22-27 Settembre 2009. 2010. (FRE, ITA & ENG., Illus.). 663p. *(978-88-370-7847-8(1))* Electa.

Rapanic, Zeljko. Od Carske Palace Do Srednjovjekovne Opcine. 2007. (Illus.). 278p. *(978-953-163-299-7(5))* Knjizevni krug Split.

Rodwell, Warwick & Atkins, Caroline. St Peter's, Barton-upon-Humber, Lincolnshire: Volume 1, History, Archaeology & Architecture, 2 vols. 2011. (ENG., Illus.). 944p. (C). 150.00 *(978-1-84217-325-1(1))* Oxbow Bks., Ltd. GBR. Dist: Brown, David Bk. Co., The.

Sciacca, Christine. Building the Medieval World. 2010. (Illus.). 104p. 19.95 *(978-1-60606-006-3(6)*, J. Paul Getty Museum) Getty Pubns.

Stalley, Roger, ed. Limerick & South-West Ireland: Medieval Art & Architecture. 2011. (Baa conference transactions Ser.). (ENG., Illus.). 271p. (C). 130.00 *(978-1-907625-07-7(0))*; pap. 62.00 *(978-1-907625-08-4(9))* Maney Publishing GBR. Dist: Brown, David Bk. Co., The.

Stephenson, David. Heavenly Vaults: From Romanesque to Gothic in European Architecture. 2009. (ENG., Illus.). 192p. 65.00 *(978-1-56898-840-5(0))* Princeton Architectural Pr.

Stjerna, Knut Martin. Essays on Questions Connected with the Old English Poem of Beowulf. 2008. (ENG.). 320p. per. *(978-1-4086-6208-3(6))* Read Bks.

Tadgell, Christopher. Modernity. 2012. (ENG., Illus.). 880p. 115.00 *(978-0-415-40756-4(7))* Routledge.

—The West: From the Advent of Christendom to the Eve of Reformation. 2009. (ENG., Illus.). 928p. 110.00 *(978-0-415-40754-0(0))* Routledge.

Thomas, Anabel. Garrisoning the Borderlands of Medieval Siena: Sant'angelo in Colle - Frontier Castle under the Government of the Nine (1287-1355) 2011. (Illus.). 444p. 124.95 *(978-1-4094-2603-5(3))* Ashgate Publishing Co.

Timmermann, A. Real Presence: Sacrament Houses & the Body of Christ, C. 1270-1600. 2010. (Architectura Medii Aevi Ser.). (ENG., Illus.). 442p. (C). pap. 152.00 *(978-2-503-53012-3(5))* Brepols Pubs. BEL. Dist: ISD.

Trachtenberg, Marvin. Dominion of the Eye: Urbanism, Art, & Power in Early Modern Florence. 2008. (ENG., Illus.). 380p. pap. 52.99 *(978-0-521-72825-6(8))* Cambridge Univ. Pr.

Trapp, Eugen. World Heritage Regensburg. 2009. (ENG.). 256p. pap. 19.95 *(978-3-7954-2080-2(6)*, Art Stock Bks. Ltd/Csi) Continental Sales, Inc.

ARCHITECTURE, MILITARY

see Military Architecture

ARCHITECTURE, MODERN

Alison, Jane, ed. The Surreal House. 2010. (Illus.). 352p. 70.00 *(978-0-300-16576-0(5))* Yale Univ. Pr.

Allenby, Guy. Elements: The Heart of the City. Law, Erica, tr. 2010. (ENG., Illus.). 160p. 50.00 *(978-0-9814628-9-9(8))* Oro Editions.

Avermaete, Tom, et al, texts. OASE 82: L'Afrique, c'est Chic. 2011. (ENG., Illus.). 144p. pap. 35.00 *(978-90-5662-775-1(9))* NAi Uitgevers / Publishers Stichting NLD. Dist: D.A.P./Distributed Art Pubs.

Ballantyne, Andrew & Law, Andrew. Tudoresque: In Pursuit of the Ideal Home. 2011. (ENG., Illus.). 272p. 45.00 *(978-1-86189-811-1(8))* Reaktion Bks., Ltd. GBR. Dist: Chicago Distribution Ctr.

Ban, Shigeru. Paper in Architecture. Rizzoli et al, eds. 2009. (ENG., Illus.). 232p. 65.00 *(978-0-8478-3211-8(2))* Rizzoli International Pubns., Inc.

Barrag#xE0;n, Luis. Luis Barrag#xE1;n: His House. 2011. (ENG., Illus.). 211p. 65.00 ***(978-84-15118-13-8(9))*** RM Verlag, S.L. ESP. Dist: D.A.P./Distributed Art Pubs.

Bell, Michael & Kim, Jeannie, eds. Engineered Transparency: The Technical, Visual, & Spatial Effects of Glass. 2008. (ENG., Illus.). 250p. pap. 65.00 *(978-1-56898-798-9(6))* Princeton Architectural Pr.

Bess, Philip. Till We Have Built Jerusalem: Architecture, Urbanism, & the Sacred. 2006. (Illus.). 325p. 28.00 *(978-1-932236-96-5(1))*; per. 18.00 *(978-1-932236-97-2(X))* ISI Bks.

Betsky, Aaron. Out There. Architecture Beyond Building: 11th International Architecture Exhibition la Biennale di Venezia. 2008. (ENG., Illus.). 608p. pap. 110.00 *(978-88-317-9447-3(7))* Marsilio Editori spa ITA. Dist: Random Hse., Inc.

Bingham, Neil. Masterworks: Architecture at the Royal Academy of Arts. 2010. (ENG., Illus.). 248p. 55.00 *(978-1-905711-83-3(2))* Royal Academy of Arts GBR. Dist: Hachette Bk. Group.

Bradbury, Dominic. The Iconic House: Architechural Masterworks since 1900. 2009. (ENG., Illus.). 352p. 65.00 *(978-0-500-34255-8(5)*, 534255) Thames & Hudson.

Broto, Eduard. Today's Iconic Architecture. 2012. (ENG.). 300p. 49.00 *(978-84-92796-93-9(6))* Links International (Leading International Key Services Barcelona, S.A.) ESP. Dist: National Bk. Network.

Browne, Beth. Starchitect Houses: Residential Architecture from the World's Best & Brightest. 2012. (ENG., Illus.). 224p. 59.95 *(978-1-86470-453-2(5))* Images Publishing Group AUS. Dist: National Bk. Network.

California Academy of Sciences Staff & Wels, Susan. California Academy of Sciences: Architecture in Harmony with Nature. 2008. (ENG.). 120p. pap. 29.95 *(978-0-8118-6558-6(4))* Chronicle Bks. LLC.

Callefa, Luis Al, ed. Architecture in Transit. 2008. 388p. *(978-84-612-3732-6(3))* Actar Birkhauser Distribution.

Carta, Maurizio. Creative City. Carta, Maurizio, ed. 2008. 160p. pap. *(978-88-95623-03-0(7))* Actar Birkhauser Distribution.

Cerver, Francisco Asensio. The World of Contemporary Architecture. 2008. (Art & Architecture Ser.). (Illus.). 998p. pap. 19.95 *(978-0-8416-0097-3(X))* American Map Corp.

Chronicle Books Staff, et al. Born Modern: The Life & Design of Alvin Lustig. 2010. (ENG., Illus.). 208p. 50.00 *(978-0-8118-6127-4(9))* Chronicle Bks. LLC.

Cleary, Richard L. The Place Royale & Urban Design in the Ancien Régime. 2011. (ENG., Illus.). 330p. pap. 65.00 *(978-0-521-36998-5(3))* Cambridge Univ. Pr.

Coates, Nigel. Narrative Architecture: Architectural Design Primers Series. 2012. (Architectural Design Primer Ser.). (ENG., Illus.). 168p. 120.00 ***(978-0-470-05745-2(9))***; pap. 50.00 ***(978-0-470-05744-5(0))*** Wiley, John & Sons, Inc. (Wiley).

Cobbers, Arnt. Marcel Breuer: 1902-1981: Form Giver of the Twentieth Century. 2007. (ENG., Illus.). 96p. pap. 9.99 *(978-3-8228-4887-6(5))* TASCHEN DEU. Dist: Ingram Pub. Services.

Cook, Peter. Drawing: The Motive Force of Architecture. 2008. (Architectural Design Primer Ser.: 2). (ENG., Illus.). 208p. pap. 55.00 *(978-0-470-03481-1(5)*, Wiley) Wiley, John & Sons, Inc.

Crane, Sheila. Mediterranean Crossroads: Marseille & Modern Architecture. 2011. (Illus.). 376p. 82.50 *(978-0-8166-5361-4(5))*; pap. 27.50 *(978-0-8166-5362-1(3))* Univ. of Minnesota Pr.

De Smedt, Julien, ed. Agenda: JDS Architects: Can We Sustain our Ability to Crisis? 2011. 544p. pap. *(978-84-92861-62-0(2))* Actar Birkhauser Distribution.

Design 360 Concept and Design Magazine, ed. Conceptual Architecture. 2010. (Illus.). 271p. 59.95 *(978-1-58423-383-1(4))* Gingko Pr., Inc.

Eckhard Schulze-Fielitz: Metasprache des Raums / Metalanguage of Space. 2009. 536p. 59.95 *(978-3-211-99197-8(2))* Springer Wien AUT. Dist: Actar Birkhauser Distribution.

Edwards. The Modern Transport Interchange. 2011. (ENG., Illus.). 208p. (C). 71.95 *(978-0-415-46449-9(8))* Routledge.

Frampton, Kenneth. Modern Architecture: A Critical History. 4th rev. ed. 2007. (World of Art Ser.). (ENG., Illus.). 424p. pap. 24.95 *(978-0-500-20395-8(4)*, 520395) Thames & Hudson.

Franzen, Brigitte, et al, eds. WESTARCH 1: A New Generation in Architecture. 2011. (ENG., Illus.). 192p. pap. 49.95 *(978-3-86859-079-1(X))* Jovis Verlag GmbH DEU. Dist: D.A.P./Distributed Art Pubs.

French, Hilary. New Urban Housing. 2006. (ENG., Illus.). 192p. 50.00 *(978-0-300-11578-9(4))* Yale Univ. Pr.

Giovannini, Joseph. Steven Ehrlich Architects: Multicultural Modernism. 2006. (Master Architect (Unnumbered) Ser.). (ENG., Illus.). 256p. 59.95 *(978-1-86470-184-5(6)*, Images Publishing Dist Ac) Antique Collectors' Club GBR. Dist: National Bk. Network.

Godoli, Ezio & Giacomelli, Milva. Architetti e Ingegneri Italiani in Egitto Dal Diciannovesimo Al Ventunesimo Secolo: Italian Architects & Engineers in Egypt from the Nineteenth to Twentyfirst Century. 2008. (ITA & ENG., Illus.). 235p. *(978-88-88967-97-4(4)*, Spotlight Poets) Maschietto & Musolino.

Goldberger, Paul. Building up & Tearing Down: Reflections on the Age of Architecture. 2009. (ENG., Illus.). 320p. 35.00 *(978-1-58093-264-6(9))* Monacelli Pr., Inc.

Gossel, Peter. Modern Architecture A-Z, 2 vols. 2010. (Go Ser.). (ENG., Illus.). 720p. 59.99 *(978-3-8365-2132-1(6))* TASCHEN DEU. Dist: Ingram Pub. Services.

Grobman, Yasha & Neuman, Eran, eds. Performalism: Form & Performance in Digital Architecture. 2011. (ENG., Illus.). 224p. (C). pap. 74.95 *(978-0-415-58361-9(6))* Routledge.

Herbert, Gilbert & Richter, Liliane, texts. Through a Clouded Glass: Mendelsohn, Wijdeveld & the Jewish Connection. 2009. (ENG., Illus.). 200p. pap. 60.00 *(978-3-8030-0696-7(1))* Wasmuth, Ernst J. Verlag GmbH & Co. DEU. Dist: D.A.P./Distributed Art Pubs.

Herrle, Peter & Schmitz, Stephanus, eds. Constructed Identities: Contemporary Architecture in the South. 2011. (ENG.). 312p. pap. 44.95 *(978-3-643-10276-8(3))* Lit Verlag DEU. Dist: Transaction Pubs.

Hess, Alan. Casa Modernista: A History of the Brazil Modern House. 2010. (ENG., Illus.). 324p. 75.00 *(978-0-8478-3175-3(2))* Rizzoli International Pubns., Inc.

Images Publishing Group Editors. 100 of the World's Best Houses. 2006. (ENG., Illus.). 344p. 60.00 *(978-1-876907-42-6(8))* Images Publishing Group AUS. Dist: National Bk. Network.

Isenstadt, Sandy. The Modern American House: Spaciousness & Middle Class Identity. Etlin, Richard A., ed. 2006. (Modern Architecture & Cultural Identity Ser.). (ENG., Illus.). 342p. 113.00 *(978-0-521-77013-2(0))* Cambridge Univ. Pr.

Jarzombek, Mark. The Psychologizing of Modernity: Art, Architecture & History. 2011. (ENG., Illus.). 340p. pap. 34.99 *(978-0-521-14763-7(8))* Cambridge Univ. Pr.

Kingston Wm. Heath Staff. Vernacular Architecture & Regional Design: Cultural Process & Environmental Response. 2009. (ENG., Illus.). 216p. pap. 64.95 *(978-0-7506-5933-8(5))* Routledge.

Klein, Caroline. Zeitgeist: Modern Architecture & Design in Germany, 1 vol. 2012. (SPA, GER & ENG.). 312p. 75.00 *(978-3-942597-11-1(X))* DAAB Media Gmbh DEU. Dist: Innovative Logistics.

Kondo, Ariyuki. Robert & James Adam, Architects of the Age of Enlightenment, 1 vol. 2011. (Enlightenment World Ser.). (ENG., Illus.). 224p. 99.00 *(978-1-84893-179-4(4))* Pickering & Chatto Pubs., Ltd. GBR. Dist: Ashgate Publishing Co.

Kottas, Dimitris. Glass. 2012. (ENG.). 260p. 57.00 *(978-84-15123-26-6(0))* Links International (Leading International Key Services Barcelona, S.A.) ESP. Dist: National Bk. Network.

Krieger, Alex & Saunders, William S. Urban Design. 2009. (Illus.). 320p. 75.00 *(978-0-8166-5638-7(X))* Univ. of Minnesota Pr.

Krieger, Alex & Saunders, William S., eds. Urban Design. 2009. (Illus.). 320p. pap. 25.00 *(978-0-8166-5639-4(8))* Univ. of Minnesota Pr.

Lathouri, Marina, et al. Intimate Metropolis: Urban Subjects in the Modern City. Palma, Vittoria Di & Lathouri, Marina, eds. Periton, Diana, ed. 2008. (ENG., Illus.). 288p. (C). 155.00 *(978-0-415-41506-4(3))* Routledge.

—Intimate Metropolis: Urban Subjects in the Modern City. Lathouri, Marina et al, eds. 2008. (Illus.). X, 278p. pap. 56.95 *(978-0-415-41507-1(1))* Routledge.

Lejeune, Jean-Francois. Modern Architecture & the Mediterranean: Vernacular Dialogues & Contested Identities. Sabatino, Michelangelo, ed. 2010. (ENG., Illus.). 320p. 53.95 *(978-0-415-77634-9(1))* Routledge.

Lejeune, Jean-Francois & Sabatino, Michelangelo, eds. North-South: The Vernacular, the Modern & the Mediterranean. 2010. (ENG., Illus.). 320p. (C). 165.00 *(978-0-415-77633-2(3))* Routledge.

Lind, Diana. Brooklyn Modern: Stories of Architecture & Design. 2008. (ENG., Illus.). 240p. 45.00 *(978-0-8478-3045-9(4))* Rizzoli International Pubns., Inc.

Lombaerde, P., ed. Early Modern Urbanism & the Grid: Town Planning in the Low Countries in International Context - Exchanges in Theory & Practice 1550-1800. 2011. (Architectura Moderna Ser.). (ENG., Illus.). 272p. (C). pap. 125.00 ***(978-2-503-54073-3(2))*** Brepols Pubs. BEL. Dist: ISD.

Lonsway, Brian. Making Leisure Work: Architecture & the Experience Economy. 2009. (Illus.). 240p. 49.95 *(978-0-415-39802-2(9))*; (ENG., 272p. (C). 120.00 *(978-0-415-39801-5(0))* Routledge.

MacArthur, John. The Picturesque: Architecture, Disgust & Other Irregularities. 2007. (Classical Tradition in Architecture Ser.). (Illus.). 295p. per. 48.95 *(978-1-84472-011-8(X)*, Routledge) Taylor & Francis Group GBR. Dist: Taylor & Francis Group.

Mallgrave, Harry. Modern Architectural Theory: A Historical Survey, 1673-1968. 2009. (ENG., Illus.). 522p. (C). pap. 54.00 *(978-0-521-13048-6(4))* Cambridge Univ. Pr.

Maria Torres Nada, Jose. Salvador Perez Arroyo: Works. 2010. 240p. pap. *(978-84-92861-41-5(X))* Actar Birkhauser Distribution.

McCulloch, Janelle. Dream Hotels: Architectural Hideaways. 2011. (ENG.). 248p. 60.00 ***(978-1-86470-367-2(9))*** Images Publishing Group AUS. Dist: National Bk. Network.

McDonald, Shannon S. The Parking Garage: Design & Evolution of a Modern Urban Form. 2007. (ENG.). 250p. 87.95 *(978-0-87420-998-3(6))* Urban Land Institute.

Millais, Malcolm. Exploding the Myths of Modern Architecture. 2009. (ENG., Illus.). 296p. pap. 29.95 *(978-0-7112-2974-7(0))* Lincoln, Frances Ltd. GBR. Dist: Perseus-PGW.

Moravánszky, Ákos & Kirchengast, Albert, eds. Experiments: Architektur zwischen Wissenschaft und Kunst . Theoriebau 2. 2011. (ENG & GER., Illus.). 304p. pap. 40.00 *(978-3-86859-040-1(4))* Jovis Verlag GmbH DEU. Dist: D.A.P./Distributed Art Pubs.

Mori, Toshiko. Toshiko Mori Architect. 2008. (ENG., Illus.). 216p. (gr. 12). 50.00 *(978-1-58093-191-5(X))* Monacelli Pr., Inc.

Mornement, Adam. Boathouses. 2010. (ENG., Illus.). 176p. 50.00 *(978-0-7112-2868-9(X))* Lincoln, Frances Ltd. GBR. Dist: Perseus-PGW.

Morris, Sarah. On Architecture, Film & Art: A Conversation Between Sarah Morris & Hans Ulrich Obrist. Bechtler, Cristine & Obrist, Hans Ulrich, eds. 2012. (Art & Architecture in Discussion Ser.). (ENG., Illus.). 110p. pap. 39.95 ***(978-3-7091-1031-7(9)***, 3709110319) Springer Wien AUT. Dist: Springer.

Murphy, Douglas. The Architecture of Failure. 2012. (ENG.). 167p. pap. 19.95 ***(978-1-78099-022-4(7))*** Hunt, John Publishing Ltd. GBR. Dist: National Bk. Network.

Murray, Scott. Contemporary Curtain Wall Architecture. 2009. (ENG., Illus.). 288p. 75.00 *(978-1-56898-797-2(8))* Princeton Architectural Pr.

Neumann, Dietrich, ed. The Structure of Light: Richard Kelly & the Illumination of Modern Architecture. 2011. (Illus.). 224p. 60.00 *(978-0-300-16370-4(3))* Yale Univ. Pr.

Oppenheim Architecture + Design. Modern Elegance: Oppenheim Architecture + Design, 1 vol. 2012. (ENG., Illus.). 496p. pap. 70.00 *(978-0-9825989-9-3(8))* Visual Profile Bks., Inc.

Pauwels, Jo, et al, photos by. Contemporary Living. 2007. (ENG., Illus.). 204p. *(978-90-77213-77-3(5)*, Beta-Plus (Acc)) Antique Collectors' Club.

Pauwels, Wim. Contemporary Architecture & Interiors Yearbook 2012. 2011. (ENG, DUT & FRE., Illus.). 200p. 140.00 *(978-90-8944-107-2(7))* Beta-Plus Pubs. BEL. Dist: Antique Collectors' Club.

—World Architecture & Interiors. Watkinson, Laura, tr. from FRE. 2006. (ENG., Illus.). 228p. *(978-90-77213-31-5(7)*, Beta-Plus (Acc)) Antique Collectors' Club.

Pimlott, Mark, et al, texts. OASE 83: Commissioning Architecture. 2011. (ENG., Illus.). 139p. pap. 35.00 (978-90-5662-776-8(7)) NAi Uitgevers / Publishers Stichting NLD. Dist: D.A.P./Distributed Art Pubs.

Price, Travis. The Mythic Modern: Architectural Expeditions into the Spirit of Place. 2012. (ENG., Illus.). 208p. 65.00 (978-0-9826226-8-1(6)) Oro Editions.

Riggs, Tamye. Typeface: Classic Typography for Contemporary Design. 2009. (ENG.). 256p. pap. 45.00 (978-1-56898-810-8(9)) Princeton Architectural Pr.

Rodriguez, Maria Ines, ed. Architecture with the People, by the People, for the People: Yona Friedman. 2011. (ENG.). 160p. pap. (978-84-92861-94-1(0)) Actar Birkhauser Distribution.

Salimei, Guendalina, text. Contemporary Caravanseray. 2011. 160p. pap. 24.95 (978-88-95623-41-2(X)) LIST - Laboratorio Editoriale ITA. Dist: Actar Birkhauser Distribution.

Silber, John. Architecture of the Absurd: How Genius Disfigured a Practical Art. 2007. (ENG., Illus.). 128p. 27.50 (978-1-59372-027-8(0)) Quantuck Lane Pr. & The Mill Road Collaborative, The.

Soo, Lydia M. Wren's 'Tracts' on Architecture & Other Writings. 2007. (ENG.). 340p. pap. 72.00 (978-0-521-04424-0(3)) Cambridge Univ. Pr.

Stewart, David. Making of a Modern Japanese Architecture. (Illus.). 304p. pap. 50.00 (978-4-7700-2933-1(0)) Kodansha International JPN. Dist: Kodansha America, Inc.

Susanka, Sarah & Obolensky, Kira. The Not So Big House Collection: The Not So Big House & Creating the Not So Big House, 2 vols. 2nd ed. 2009. (ENG., Illus.). 504p. 40.00 (978-1-60085-152-0(5)) Taunton Pr., Inc.

Suzuki Hiroyuki Sensei Kentei Ronbunshu Kankokai Staff, contrib. by. Kenchiku Shiko. 2009. (JPN & ENG., Illus.). 575p. (978-4-8055-0622-6(9)) Chuo Koron Bijutsu Shuppan.

Taschen Publishing Staff, et al. Domus, 1928-1939, Vol. 1. Volk, Annick et al, eds. 2008. (ENG., Illus.). 580p. 69.99 (978-3-8365-0951-0(2)) TASCHEN DEU. Dist: Ingram Pub. Services.

Tzonis, Alexander & Rodi, Alkistis. Greece. 2012. (Reaktion Books - Modern Architectures in History Ser.). (ENG., Illus.). 272p. pap. 29.95 (978-1-86189-379-6(5)) Reaktion Bks., Ltd. GBR. Dist: Chicago Distribution Ctr.

Vesely, Dalibor. Architecture in the Age of Divided Representation: The Question of Creativity in the Shadow of Production. 2006. (ENG., Illus.). 524p. (gr. 17). pap. 29.95 (978-0-262-72048-9(5)) MIT Pr.

Vidiella, Alex Sánchez. The Sourcebook of Contemporary Architecture. 2007. (Illus.). 600p. 60.00 (978-0-06-124197-0(0), Collins Design) HarperCollins Pubs.

—The Sourcebook of Contemporary Houses. 2012. (ENG., Illus.). 600p. 60.00 (978-0-06-206730-2(3), Collins Design) HarperCollins Pubs.

—1000 Details in Architecture: CONSEILS D'ARCHITECTURE / ARCHITEKTUR-ELEMENTE / DETAILS IN ARCHITECTUUR, 1 vol. 2010. (FRE, DUT, GER & ENG., Illus.). 617p. pap. 24.95 (978-94-6065-039-0(2)) booQs Publishers bvba BEL. Dist: Innovative Logistics.

Vidiella, Alex Sánchez, et al. The Sourcebook of Contemporary Green Architecture. 2011. (ENG., Illus.). 600p. 60.00 (978-0-06-200462-8(X), Collins Design) HarperCollins Pubs.

Visscher, Jochen, ed. Tel Aviv: The White City. 2012. (ENG & GER., Illus.). 96p. 19.95 (978-3-939633-75-4(5)) Jovis Verlag GmbH DEU. Dist: D.A.P./Distributed Art Pubs.

Weston, Richard. Key Buildings of the Twentieth Century: Plans, Sections & Elevations. 2nd ed. 2010. (Key Architecture Ser.). (ENG., Illus.). 352p. pap. 45.00 (978-0-393-73311-2(4), 73311) Norton, W. W. & Co., Inc.

Williamson, Leslie. Handcrafted Modern: At Home with Mid-Century Designers. 2010. (ENG., Illus.). 224p. 45.00 (978-0-8478-3418-1(2)) Rizzoli International Pubns., Inc.

Wright, Frank Lloyd. What Styles Mean to the Architect: The Architectural Record V63, No. 2, February 1928. Mikkelsen, M. A. & Kocher, A. Lawrence, eds. 2011. 12p. pap. 35.95 (978-1-258-06560-7(6)) Literary Licensing, LLC.

Wujec, Tom, ed. Imagine design Create: How Designers, Architects, & Engineers Are Changing Our World. 2011. (ENG.). 336p. 29.95 (978-1-59591-066-0(2)) Melcher Media.

Zabihi, Saereh. Effects of Modern Movement on Residential Buildings. 2011. 88p. pap. (978-3-8443-9662-1(4)) Lambert Academic Publishing.

Zhu, Jianfei. Architecture of Modern China: A Historical Critique. 2008. (ENG., Illus.). 336p. (C). pap. 62.95 (978-0-415-45781-1(5)) Routledge.

—Modern Chinese Architecture: A Historical Critique. 2008. (Illus.). 336p. 165.00 (978-0-415-45780-4(7)) Routledge.

ARCHITECTURE, MODERN—19TH CENTURY

Belfoure, Charles. Edmund G. Lind: Anglo-American Architect of Baltimore & the South. 2009. (Illus.). 203p. pap. 27.95 (978-0-9729743-2-5(6)) Baltimore Architecture Foundation.

Berens, Hetty, ed. P. J. H. Cuypers (1827-1921) The Complete Works, 1 vol. 2007. (ENG., Illus.). 397p. 75.00 (978-90-5662-574-0(8)) NAi Uitgevers / Publishers Stichting NLD. Dist: D.A.P./Distributed Art Pubs.

Börsch-Supan, Eva, contrib. by. Gottfried Semper und die Mitte des 19. Jahrhunderts: Symposion, Zürich, 2.-6. Dezember 1974. (ITA, GER & ENG., Illus.). 387p. 79.07 (978-3-7643-0829-2(X), 376430829X) Birkhauser Boston.

Cohen, Jean-Louis. The Future of Architecture Since 1889. 2012. (ENG., Illus.). 638p. 75.00 (978-0-7148-4598-2(1)) Phaidon Pr., Inc.

Craven, Wayne. Gilded Mansions: Grand Architecture & High Society. 2008. (ENG., Illus.). 352p. 59.95 (978-0-393-06754-5(8), 6754) Norton, W. W. & Co., Inc.

Garrison, James. Houses of Philadelphia: Chestnut Hill & the Wissahickon Valley. Morrison, William, ed. 2008. (Illus.). 320p. 69.00 (978-0-926494-53-4(8)) Acanthus Pr. LLC.

Hitchcock, Henry Russell. Architecture, Nineteenth & Twentieth Centuries: The Pelican History of Art. Pevsner, Nikolaus, ed. 2011. 720p. 70.95 (978-1-258-01625-8(7)) Literary Licensing, LLC.

Lane, Barbara Miller, ed. Housing & Dwelling: Perspectives on Modern Domestic Architecture. 2006. (Illus.). 467p. 165.00 (978-0-415-34655-9(X)); (ENG., 480p. per. 54.95 (978-0-415-34656-6(8)) Routledge.

Lawrance, Gary & Surchin, Anne. Houses of the Hamptons, 1880-1930. 2007. (Architecture of Leisure Ser.). (Illus.). 324p. 85.00 (978-0-926494-44-2(9)) Acanthus Pr. LLC.

Levine, Neil. Modern Architecture: Representation & Reality. 2010. (ENG., Illus.). 376p. 65.00 (978-0-300-14567-0(5)) Yale Univ. Pr.

Liu, Gretchen & Byfield, Graham. Singapore Sketchbook: An Island Observed. 2011. 96p. 30.00 (978-981-4068-40-6(3), Didier Millet,Csi) Continental Sales, Inc.

Mateyunas, Paul J. Long Island North Shore Country Houses: 1890-1950. 2007. (Suburban Domestic Architecture Ser.). (Illus.). 352p. 80.00 (978-0-926494-37-4(6)) Acanthus Pr. LLC.

Middleton, Robin & Baudouin-Matuszek, Marie-Noelle. Jean Rondelet: The Architect as Technician. 2007. (ENG., Illus.). 368p. 95.00 (978-0-300-11567-3(9)) Yale Univ. Pr.

Millstein, Cydney & Grove, Carol. Houses of Missouri. 2008. (Illus.). 272p. 65.00 (978-0-926494-54-1(6)) Acanthus Pr. LLC.

Murphy, Kevin D. The Houses of Greenwich Village. 2008. (ENG., Illus.). 224p. 45.00 (978-0-8109-9520-8(4)) Abrams.

O'Gorman, James F. Henry Austin: In Every Variety of Architectural Style. 2009. (ENG., Illus.). 252p. 35.00 (978-0-8195-6896-0(1)) Wesleyan Univ. Pr.

Payne, Alina. From Ornament to Object: Genealogies of Architectural Modernism. 2012. (ENG., Illus.). 360p. 65.00 (978-0-300-17533-2(7)) Yale Univ. Pr.

Pennoyer, Peter, et al. The Architecture of Grosvenor Atterbury. 2009. (ENG., Illus.). 288p. 75.00 (978-0-393-73222-1(3), 73222) Norton, W. W. & Co., Inc.

Platt, Charles A. The Architecture of Charles A. Platt. 2007. (978-0-486-45605-8(6)) Dover Pubns., Inc.

Tietz, Jurgen. The Story of Modern Architecture. 2008. (Story of Ser.). (Illus.). 128p. 9.95 (978-0-8416-0357-8(X)) American Map Corp.

White, Samuel G. & White, Elizabeth. Stanford White, Architect. 2008. (ENG., Illus.). 320p. 40.00 (978-0-8478-3079-4(9)) Rizzoli International Pubns., Inc.

Yee, Roger. HLW at 125. 2009. (Illus.). 164p. 60.00 net. (978-1-58471-169-8(8)) Visual Reference Pubns., Inc.

ARCHITECTURE, MODERN—20TH CENTURY

see also Art Deco (Architecture); Constructivism (Architecture); Deconstructivism (Architecture); International Style (Architecture); Modern Movement (Architecture)

Agnoletto, Matteo, et al. Las Obras Maestras de la Arquitectura Moderna. 2007. (SPA., Illus.). 303p. 39.95 (978-970-718-442-8(6), Numen) Advanced Marketing, S. de R. L. de C. V. MEX. Dist: Perseus-PGW.

Aiello, Carlo, ed. Skyscraper for the XXI Century. 2008. (Illus.). 140p. per. 38.95 (978-0-9816658-0-1(2)) EVOLO.

Albrecht, Donald, et al. Global Citizen: The Architecture of Moshe Safdie. 2010. (ENG., Illus.). 144p. 35.00 (978-1-85759-587-1(4)) Scala, Editions FRA. Dist: National Bk. Network.

Allen, Stan. Practice: Architecture, Technique & Presentation. 2nd rev. exp. ed. 2009. (ENG., Illus.). 288p. (C). 49.95 (978-0-415-77625-7(2)) Routledge.

—Practice: Architecture, Technique & Representation. 2nd rev. exp. ed. 2009. (ENG., Illus.). 288p. (C). 160.00 (978-0-415-77624-0(4)) Routledge.

Allen, Stan, ed. Colossal Urbanism. Date not set. (Illus.). 96p. pap. (978-1-883584-12-2(4)) Columbia Univ., Graduate Schl. of Architecture.

Allinson, Kenneth. London's Contemporary Architecture: An Explorer's Guide. 5th rev. ed. 2009. (ENG., Illus.). 384p. pap. 32.95 (978-1-85617-801-3(3)) Routledge.

Álvarez, Ana María, ed. Ramon Esteve: Estudio de Arquitectura. 2010. (ENG & SPA., Illus.). 320p. 49.99 (978-84-9936-197-0(8)) Loft Pubns. ESP. Dist: Prestel Publishing.

Ambasz, Emilio, et al. The Universitas Project: Solutions for a Post-Technological Society, 1 vol. 2006. (ENG., Illus.). 440p. pap. 34.95 (978-0-87070-070-5(7)) Museum of Modern Art.

Anker, Peder. From Bauhaus to Eco-house: A History of Ecological Design. 2010. 216p. 34.95 (978-0-8071-3551-8(8)) Louisiana State Univ. Pr.

Architecture Studio Staff & Images Publishing Editorial Staff. Buildings: Innovation + Technology: STUDIOS Architecture. 2009. (ENG., Illus.). 96p. 25.00 (978-1-86470-329-0(6)) Images Publishing Group AUS. Dist: National Bk. Network.

Attali, Erieta, photos by. Erieta Attali: In Extremis - Landscape into Architecture. 2011. (ENG & SPA., Illus.). 255p. pap., pap. 29.95 (978-1-883584-66-5(3)) Columbia Univ., Graduate Schl. of Architecture.

Aureli, Pier Vittorio. The Project of Autonomy: Politics & Architecture Within & Against Capitalism. 2008. (ENG., Illus.). 80p. 24.95 (978-1-56898-794-1(3)) Princeton Architectural Pr.

Avermaete, Tom, ed. Colonial Modern: Aesthetics of the Past Rebellions for the Future. 2010. (ENG., Illus.). 320p. pap. 49.95 (978-1-907317-11-8(2)) Black Dog Publishing Ltd. GBR. Dist: Perseus Distribution.

Aynsley, Jeremy. Designing Modern Germany. 2009. (ENG., Illus.). 256p. pap. 35.00 (978-1-86189-401-4(5)) Reaktion Bks., Ltd. GBR. Dist: Chicago Distribution Ctr.

Bahamón, Alejandro. Houses/Casas/Hauser. Brunelle, Michael et al, trs. 2008. (Art & Architecture Ser.). (Illus.). 432p. 49.95 (978-0-8416-0302-8(2)) American Map Corp.

Bahamón, Alejandro & Álvarez, María. Light Color Sound: Sensory Effects in Contemporary Architecture. 2010. (ENG., Illus.). 384p. 75.00 (978-0-393-73337-2(8), 73337) Norton, W. W. & Co., Inc.

Baker, Geoffrey Howard. The Architecture of James Sterling & His Partners James Gowan & Michael Wilford: A Study of Architectural Creativity in the Twentieth Century. 2011. (Illus.). 512p. 134.95 (978-1-4094-0926-7(0)) Ashgate Publishing Co.

Ballon, Hilary. The Guggenheim: Frank Lloyd Wright & the Making of the Modern Museum. 2009. (ENG., Illus.). 228p. 65.00 (978-0-89207-385-6(3)) Guggenheim, Solomon R. Museum.

Barreneche, Raul A. Modern House Three. 2006. (SPA.). 59.95 (978-0-7148-9852-0(X)) Phaidon Pr., Inc.

—New Retail. 2008. (ENG., Illus.). 200p. pap. 35.00 (978-0-7148-4862-4(X)) Phaidon Pr. Ltd. GBR. Dist: Hachette Bk. Group.

Baudrillard, Jean. Mass Identity Architecture: Architectural Writings of Jean Baudrillard. Proto, Francesco, ed. 2006. (ENG., Illus.). 206p. per. 55.00 (978-0-470-02715-8(0), Academy Pr.) Wiley, John & Sons, Inc.

Baumann, Kirsten, et al, eds. Modern Greetings/Moderne Grube: Photographed Architecture on Picture Postcards 1919-1939/Fotografierte Architektur Auf Ansichtskarten 1919-1939. 2007. (ENG & GER., Illus.). 38.00 (978-3-89790-019-6(X)) Arnoldsche Art Pubs. DEU. Dist: Antique Collectors' Club.

Bayley, Stephen, et al. Stanton Williams. 2009. (ENG., Illus.). 256p. 49.95 (978-1-906155-87-2(9)) Black Dog Publishing Ltd. GBR. Dist: Actar Birkhauser Distribution.

Beaver, Robyn. Contemporary Architecture, Vol. 1. 2006. (ENG., Illus.). 75.00 (978-1-876907-87-7(8)) Images Publishing Group AUS. Dist: National Bk. Network.

Bekaert, Geert & Vandemoortele, Johanna. Belgium at the Fair: Exile on main Street, 1 vol. De Kooning, Mil, ed. 2011. (ENG.). 252p. 50.00 (978-90-77833-14-8(5)) Exhibitions International BEL. Dist: Innovative Logistics.

Berens, Hetty, ed. P. J. H. Cuypers (1827-1921) The Complete Works, 1 vol. 2007. (ENG., Illus.). 397p. 75.00 (978-90-5662-574-0(8)) NAi Uitgevers / Publishers Stichting NLD. Dist: D.A.P./Distributed Art Pubs.

Berkus, Barry A. Architecture/Art/Parallels/Connections. 2006. (ENG., Illus.). 60.00 (978-1-86470-084-8(X)) Images Publishing Group AUS. Dist: National Bk. Network.

Betsky, Aaron, intro. Tate & Snyders Architects: Architecture in a Sprawling Landscape. 2007. (Architectural Ser.). (ENG., Illus.). 100p. pap. 25.00 (978-88-7838-082-0(2), Art Stock Bks. Ltd/Csi) Continental Sales, Inc.

Big Thom Architects Staff, contrib. by. Bing Thom Works. 2011. (ENG., Illus.). 200p. 65.00 (978-1-56898-959-4(8)) Princeton Architectural Pr.

Boon, Piet. Piet Boon 2. 2006. (ENG.). 200p. 125.00 (978-90-5897-467-9(7)) Lannoo Pubs./Racine.

Boxel, Elma van, et al. Re-Public: Towards a New Spatial Politics/Naar Een Nieuwe Ruimte-Politiek. 2008. (ENG., Illus.). 160p. 39.95 (978-90-5662-625-9(6)) NAi Uitgevers / Publishers Stichting NLD. Dist: D.A.P./Distributed Art Pubs.

Boym, Svetlana. Architecture of the Off-Modern. 2008. (ENG., Illus.). 80p. 24.95 (978-1-56898-778-1(1)) Princeton Architectural Pr.

Braun Editorial Staff. 1000x Architecture of the Americas. 2008. (ENG., Illus.). 1024p. 125.00 (978-3-938780-56-5(8), Braun Publish,Csi) Continental Sales, Inc.

Braun Editorial Staff, ed. Pure Plastic: New Materials for Today's Architecture. 2008. (ENG., Illus.). 256p. 49.95 (978-3-938780-51-0(7), Braun Publish,Csi) Continental Sales, Inc.

Brayer, Marie-Ange. Future City: Experiment & Utopia in Architecture. Migayrou, Frederic & Spiller, Neil, eds. 2007. (ENG., Illus.). 336p. pap. 34.95 (978-0-500-28651-7(5)) Thames & Hudson.

Broto, Carles. New Concepts in Housing. 2009. (ENG., Illus.). 360p. pap. 34.99 (978-84-96969-98-8(3)) Links International (Leading International Key Services Barcelona, S.A.) ESP. Dist: National Bk. Network.

Brown-Manrique, Gerardo, text. Rudolf Frankel & Neues Bauen. 2009. (ENG., Illus.). 148p. pap. 50.00 (978-3-8030-0695-0(3)) Wasmuth, Ernst J. Verlag GmbH & Co. DEU. Dist: D.A.P./Distributed Art Pubs.

Buckner, Cory. A. Quincy Jones. 2007. (ENG., Illus.). 272p. per. 29.95 (978-0-7148-4843-3(3)) Phaidon Pr., Inc.

Bush-Brown, Albert, intro. Som: Architecture of Skidmore, Owings & Merrill, 1973-1983. 2009. (ENG., Illus.). 288p. 60.00 (978-1-58093-222-6(3)) Monacelli Pr., Inc.

Cadwell, Michael. Strange Details. 2007. (Writing Architecture Ser.). (ENG., Illus.). 208p. (gr. 17). pap. 21.95 (978-0-262-53291-4(3)) MIT Pr.

Canizaro, Vincent B., ed. Architectural Regionalism: Collected Writings on Place, Identity, Modernity, & Tradition. 2007. (ENG., Illus.). 464p. pap. 39.95 (978-1-56898-616-6(5)) Princeton Architectural Pr.

Canniffe, Eamonn & Jones, Peter Blundell. Modern Architecture Through Case Studies, 1945-1990. 2007. (ENG., Illus.). 256p. 54.95 (978-0-7506-6374-8(X)) Routledge.

Canty, Donald. Fisher Friedman: Community Spaces. 2007. (Architectural Ser.). (ENG., Illus.). 144p. pap. 40.00 (978-88-7838-070-7(9), Art Stock Bks. Ltd/Csi) Continental Sales, Inc.

Ceferin, Petra & Pozar, Cvetka. Architectural Epicentres: Inventing Architecture, Intervening in Reality. 2008. (Illus.). 164p. (978-961-6669-03-0(5)) Actar Birkhauser Distribution.

Celant, Germano, ed. Rem Koolhaas: Unveiling the Prada Foundation. 2008. (ENG., Illus.). 272p. pap. 90.00 (978-88-87029-42-0(3)) Fondazione Prada ITA. Dist: D.A.P./Distributed Art Pubs.

Cerver, Francisco Asensio. Houses of the World. 2008. (Art & Architecture Ser.). (Illus.). 999p. pap. 19.95 (978-0-8416-0069-0(4)) American Map Corp.

Charlton, Susannah, et al, eds. British Modern: Architecture & Design in The 1930s. 2007. (Twentieth Century Architecture Ser.: Vol. 8). (ENG., Illus.). 160p. pap. 40.00 (978-0-9529755-8-8(0)) Twentieth Century Society GBR. Dist: Univ. of Washington Pr.

Cheney, Sheldon W. New World Architecture. (BCL Ser.: No. II). (Illus.). reprint ed. 55.00 (978-0-404-01487-2(9)) AMS Pr., Inc.

Christiane, Sauer. Made of... New Materials Sourcebook for Architecture & Design. 2010. (Illus.). 280p. 78.00 (978-3-89955-289-8(X)) Die Gestalten Verlag DEU. Dist: Prestel Publishing.

Chueca, Pilar. Urban Houses: Houses Now. 2007. (ENG., Illus.). 240p. 39.95 (978-84-96263-01-7(0)) Links International (Leading International Key Services Barcelona, S.A.) ESP. Dist: National Bk. Network.

Clements, Peter. Principles of Contemporary Architecture Design. Date not set. 152p. pap. 39.95 (978-0-7506-3416-8(2), Butterworth-Heinemann) Elsevier Science & Technology Bks.

Cobbers, Arnt. Mendelsohn. 2007. (ENG., Illus.). 96p. pap. 9.99 (978-3-8228-5595-9(2)) TASCHEN DEU. Dist: Ingram Pub. Services.

Cody, Jeffrey W., et al. Chinese Architecture & the Beaux-Arts. 2010. 408p. (978-0-8248-3456-2(9)) Hong Kong Univ. Pr.

Cohen, Janie. Architectural Improvisation: A History of Vermont's Design/Build Movement 1964-1977. 2009. (Illus.). 84p. pap. 20.00 (978-0-934658-04-1(8), University of Vermont Press) Univ. Pr. of New England.

Cohen, Jean-Louis. Architecture in Uniform: Designing & Building for the Second World War. 2011. (ENG., Illus.). 448p. 50.00 (978-2-7541-0530-9(1)) Yale Univ. Pr.

Coles, Alex, et al. Salt Bridges: Changing Perceptions of Art, Architecture, & Science. 2010. (Illus.). 192p. 75.00 (978-3-7913-5026-4(9)) Prestel Publishing.

Coll, Ramon Faura, ed. Architectures Without Place: 1968/2008. 2010. (Illus.). 288p. pap. (978-84-96842-44-1(4)) Colegio de Arquitectos de Catalunya.

Colomina, Beatriz. Domesticity at War. 2007. (ENG., Illus.). 280p. (gr. 17). 49.95 (978-0-262-03361-9(5)) MIT Pr.

Connah, Roger. Sa(L)Vaged Modernism. 2008. (ENG., Illus.). 192p. pap. 26.00 (978-951-682-596-3(6)) Rakennustieto oy FIN. Dist: Independent Pubs. Group.

Connah, Roger, compiled by. 40/40 Young Architects from Finland. 2nd ed. 2008. (Illus.). 240p. pap. 49.00 (978-951-682-646-5(6)) Rakennustieto oy FIN. Dist: Independent Pubs. Group.

Constant, Caroline. Modern Architectural Landscape. 2012. 344p. pap. 30.00 (978-0-8166-7635-4(6)); (Illus.). 90.00 (978-0-8166-7307-0(1)) Univ. of Minnesota Pr.

Cook, Peter. Liquid Threshold. 2007. (Illus.). 332p. pap. 49.95 (978-0-9562563-0-0(9)) Atelier One GBR. Dist: Actar Birkhauser Distribution.

Craven, Wayne. Gilded Mansions: Grand Architecture & High Society. 2008. (ENG., Illus.). 352p. 59.95 (978-0-393-06754-5(8), 6754) Norton, W. W. & Co., Inc.

Creation Magazine Staff. Contemporary Architecture in China. Yajun, Jiang, tr. 2011. (Discovering China Ser.). (ENG., Illus.). 128p. 16.95 (978-1-60220-116-3(1)) Reader's Digest Assn., Inc., The.

Crinson, Mark. James Stirling. Crinson, Mark, ed. 2009. (ENG., Illus.). 160p. (C). pap. 44.95 (978-0-415-55059-8(9)) Routledge.

—James Stirling: Early unpublished writings on Architecture. Crinson, Mark, ed. 2009. (ENG., Illus.). 160p. (C). 165.00 (978-0-415-55058-1(0)) Routledge.

Curtis, Penelope. Patio & Pavilion: The Place of Sculpture in Modern Architecture. 2008. (Illus.). 160p. pap. 39.95 (978-0-89236-915-7(9)) Oxford Univ. Pr., Inc.

Danz, Ernst, comment. Som: Architecture of Skidmore, Owings & Merrill, 1950-1962. 2009. (ENG., Illus.). 224p. 45.00 (978-1-58093-220-2(7)) Monacelli Pr., Inc.

Davies, Colin. Key Houses of the Twentieth Century: Plans, Sections & Elevations. 2006. (Norton Book for Architects & Designers Ser.). (ENG., Illus.). 240p. pap. 45.00 (978-0-393-73205-4(3), 73205) Norton, W. W. & Co., Inc.

Daza, Ricardo, ed. Looking for Mies. 2008. 200p. pap. (978-84-96954-37-3(4)) Actar Birkhauser Distribution.

Ddg: One World, One Firm. 2012. (ENG., Illus.). 256p. 59.95 (978-1-86470-468-6(3)) Images Publishing Group AUS. Dist: National Bk. Network.

De Anda Alanis, Enrique X. Candela. 2008. (Basic Architecture Ser.). (ENG., Illus.). 96p. pap. 9.99 (978-3-8228-3725-2(3)) TASCHEN DEU. Dist: Ingram Pub. Services.

De Bure, Gilles. Talk about Contemporary Architecture: Who, What, Where, When, How, Why. 2010. (ENG., Illus.). 256p. pap. 24.95 (978-2-08-030131-4(4)) Flammarion et Cie FRA. Dist: Random Hse., Inc.

de Canales, Francisco Gonzalez. Experiments with Life Itself. 2012. (ENG., Illus.). 152p. pap. (978-84-92861-65-1(7)) Actar Birkhauser Distribution

de Haro, Fernando & Fuentes, Omar. Natural Architecture: The Joy of Living in Harmony. 2010. (ENG & SPA., Illus.). 240p. 45.00 (978-607-437-052-2(4)) AM Editores MEX. Dist: Perseus-PGW.

De La Moureyre, Alice, et al. Stables: Majestic Spaces for Horses. 2006. (ENG., Illus.). 192p. 45.00 (978-0-8478-2915-9(8)) Rizzoli International Pubns., Inc.

Decker, Julie & Princeton Architectural Press Staff. Modern North: Architecture on the Frozen Edge. 2010. (ENG., Illus.). 240p. 45.00 *(978-1-56898-899-3(0))* Princeton Architectural Pr.

Deckler, Thorsten, et al. Contemporary South African Architecture in a Landscape of Transition. 2008. 216p. pap. 39.95 *(978-0-7021-7969-3(8))* Double Storey Bks. ZAF. Dist: International Publishers Marketing.

Denison, Edward. Mcmorran & Whitby. 2009. (Twentieth-century Architects Ser.). (ENG., Illus.). 154p. (C). pap. 40.00 *(978-1-85946-320-8(7))* English Heritage GBR. Dist: Brown, David Bk. Co., The.

Denslagen, Wim. Romantic Modernism: Nostalgia in the World of Conservation. 2011. 261p. pap. *(978-90-8964-103-8(3))* Amsterdam Univ. Pr.

Denzer, Anthony. Gregory Ain: The Modern Home as Social Commentary. 2008. (ENG., Illus.). 256p. 60.00 *(978-0-8478-3062-6(4))* Rizzoli International Pubns., Inc.

Dettingmeijer, Rob, et al, eds. Rietveld's Universe. 2011. (ENG., Illus.). 277p. pap. 47.50 *(978-90-5662-746-1(5))* NAi Uitgevers / Publishers Stichting NLD. Dist: D.A.P./Distributed Art Pubs.

Deutscher Designer Club (DDC), ed. Gute Gestaltung / Good Design 07. 2007. (GER & ENG., Illus.). 348p. 54.95 *(978-3-7643-8383-1(6)*, 3764383836) Springer.

Donin, Gianpiero, ed. Renzo Piano: Piece by Piece. 2010. 163p. pap. 27.95 *(978-88-7448-010-4(5))* Gangemi ITA. Dist: International Publishers Marketing.

Dottelonde, Pierre, et al. CNIT, Ou, Les Temps Modernes. 2009. (FRE., Illus.). 157p. *(978-2-7491-1311-1(3))* Le Cherche Midi Editeur.

Dunlop, Beth. Building a Dream: The Art of Disney Architecture. 2011. (ENG., Illus.). 208p. 60.00 *(978-1-4231-2918-9(0)*, Disney Editions) Disney Pr.

Dunster, David, et al. Robert Stern: An Architectural Monograph. (Illus.). 124p. pap. 24.95 *(978-0-312-68755-7(9))* St. Martin's Pr.

Eisenman, Peter. Ten Canonical Buildings: 1950-2000. Heid, Andrew & Lourie, Ariane, eds. 2008. (ENG., Illus.). 304p. 60.00 *(978-0-8478-3048-0(9))* Rizzoli International Pubns., Inc.

Eisenmann, Peter. The Formal Basis of Modern Architecture Dissertation 1963, Facsimile. 2006. (GER., Illus.). 381p. 69.95 *(978-3-03778-071-8(1)*, 3037780711) Lars Muller Pubs. CHE. Dist: Springer.

Evans, Paul. The 1960s Home. 2010. (Shire Library). (ENG., Illus.). 56p. pap. 12.95 *(978-0-7478-0802-2(3))* Shire Pubns., Ltd. GBR. Dist: Random Hse., Inc.

Favole, Paolo. The Story of Contemporary Architecture. 2011. (ENG., Illus.). 160p. pap. 19.95 ***(978-3-7913-4598-7(2))*** Prestel Publishing.

Ferrater, Carlos & Ferrater, Borja, eds. Ferrater & Partners: Oab. 2011. (ENG., Illus.). 350p. *(978-84-92861-23-1(1))* Actar Birkhauser Distribution.

Ferriss, Hugh. Power in Buildings: An Artist's View of Contemporary Architecture. 2011. 114p. 39.95 ***(978-1-258-10299-9(4))*** Literary Licensing, LLC.

Field, Marcus. Future Systems. Keßler, N. & Wieser, M., trs. 208p. 79.00 *(978-3-211-83314-8(5)*, 3211833145) Springer.

Filler, Martin. Makers of Modern Architecture: From Frank Lloyd Wright to Frank Gehry. 2007. (New York Review Bks.). (ENG., Illus.). 352p. 27.95 *(978-1-59017-227-8(2))* New York Review of Bks., Inc., The.

Foerster, Bernd. Man & Masonry. 2011. 66p. 36.95 ***(978-1-258-03176-3(0))*** Literary Licensing, LLC.

Fores, Ferrer. Jorn Utzon. Works & Projects. 2006. 306p. pap. 24.00 *(978-84-252-2060-9(2))* Trucatriche.

Foster, Norman & Jenkins, David. Catalogue, Foster + Partners: Catalogue. 2008. (Illus.). 352p. pap. 39.95 *(978-3-7913-3973-3(7))* Prestel Publishing.

Frampton, Kenneth. Die Entwicklung der Architektur im 20. Jahrhundert: Eine vergleichende Übersicht. Keßler, Norma, tr. 2007. (Illus.). 159p. pap. 39.95 *(978-3-211-31196-7(3)*, 3211311963) Springer.

—The Evolution of 20th Century Architecture: A Synoptic Account. 2007. (Illus.). 159p. pap. 49.95 *(978-3-211-31195-0(5)*, 3211311955) Springer Wien AUT. Dist: Springer.

Frampton, Kenneth, et al, eds. SOM Journal, No. 5. 2009. (ENG., Illus.). 228p. pap. 30.00 *(978-3-7757-2279-7(3))* Hatje Cantz Verlag GmbH & Co KG DEU. Dist: D.A.P./Distributed Art Pubs.

Frampton, Kenneth, intro. Som: Architecture of Skidmore, Owings & Merrill, 1997-2008. 2009. (ENG., Illus.). 256p. 60.00 *(978-1-58093-224-0(X))* Monacelli Pr., Inc.

French, Hilary. Key Urban Housing of the Twentieth Century: Plans, Sections, & Elevations. 2008. (Key Structures: Plans, Sections, Elevations Ser.). (ENG., Illus.). 240p. pap. 45.00 *(978-0-393-73246-7(0)*, 73246) Norton, W. W. & Co., Inc.

Füchslin, Marco & Eggstein, Simone. Architekt Hans Eggstein: Bauten und Projekte: Eine Werkdokumentation. 2007. (GER., Illus.). 199p. *(978-3-7212-0627-2(4))* Niggli, Arthur Verlag.

Fumihiko, Maki, et al. Fumihiko Maki. 2009. (ENG., Illus.). 320p. 95.00 *(978-0-7148-4956-0(1))* Phaidon Pr., Inc.

Gargiani, Roberto. Rem Koolhaas / OMA. 2008. (ENG., Illus.). 352p. (C). 85.00 *(978-0-415-46145-0(6))* Routledge.

Garrison, James. Houses of Philadelphia: Chestnut Hill & the Wissahickon Valley. Morrison, William, ed. 2008. (Illus.). 320p. 69.00 *(978-0-926494-53-4(8))* Acanthus Pr. LLC.

Gartman, David. From Autos to Architecture: Fordism & Architectural Aesthetics in the Twentieth Century. 2009. (ENG.). 400p. 60.00 *(978-1-56898-813-9(3))* Princeton Architectural Pr.

Gatley, Julia, ed. Long Live the Modern: New Zealand's New Architecture, 1904-1984. 2008. (ENG., Illus.). 240p. 44.95 *(978-1-86940-415-4(7))* Auckland Univ. Pr. NZL. Dist: Independent Pubs. Group.

Gatz, Konrad, et al. Color in Architecture: A Guide to Exterior Design. 2011. 194p. 42.95 ***(978-1-258-01740-8(7))*** Literary Licensing, LLC.

Gieselmann, Reinhard. Reinhard Gieselmann - In Search of Style / Auf der Suche nach Stil. 2007. (ENG & GER., Illus.). 224p. 89.00 *(978-3-932565-55-7(X))* Edition Axel Menges GmbH DEU. Dist: National Bk. Network.

Giovannini, Joseph. Materializing the Immaterial: The Architecture of Wallace Cunningham. 2006. (ENG., Illus.). 160p. 55.00 *(978-0-9749565-2-7(X))* Yale Univ. Pr.

Giusti, M. Adriana, et al. Guide to Piedmont Architecture: Of the 20th Century. 2009. (ENG., Illus.). 408p. pap. 46.00 *(978-88-422-1639-1(9))* Allemandi, Umberto & Co. GBR. Dist: Antique Collectors' Club.

Glancey, Jonathan. Modern Architecture. 2009. (ENG., Illus.). 448p. pap. 16.95 *(978-1-84732-049-0(X))* Carlton Bks., Ltd. GBR. Dist: Sterling Publishing Co., Inc.

—Modern World Architecture: Classic Buildings of Our Time. 2011. (ENG., Illus.). 480p. 39.95 *(978-1-84732-729-1(X))* Carlton Bks., Ltd. GBR. Dist: Sterling Publishing Co., Inc.

Glendinning, Miles, ed. Rebuilding Scotland: The Postwar Vision, 1945-1975. (Illus.). 208p. pap. *(978-1-898410-33-1(X)*, Donald, John) Birlinn, Ltd.

Goldberger, Paul, frwd. The Glass House. 2011. (ENG., Illus.). 80p. 25.00 ***(978-0-8478-3816-5(1)***, Skira) Rizzoli International Pubns., Inc.

Goldberger, Paul, intro. Modern Views. 2010. (ENG., Illus.). 200p. 70.00 *(978-2-7594-0467-4(6))* Assouline FRA. Dist: Perseus Distribution.

Greenberg, Allan. Lutyens & the Modern Movement. 2007. (ENG., Illus.). 156p. pap. 19.50 *(978-1-901092-57-8(7))* Papadakis Dist A/C.

Gregory, Daniel P. Cliff May & the Modern Ranch House. 2008. (ENG., Illus.). 256p. 60.00 *(978-0-8478-3047-3(0))* Rizzoli International Pubns., Inc.

Gregory, Rob. Hopkins: Volume 3. 2012. (Illus.). 360p. 65.00 ***(978-3-7913-4432-4(3))*** Prestel Publishing.

Grosenick, Uta. Art Now 2: Der neue Wegweiser zu 81 internationalen zeitgenössischen Künstlern, Vol. 2. 25th ed. 2008. (FRE, GER & ENG., Illus.). 349p. 14.99 *(978-3-8365-0324-2(7))* TASCHEN DEU. Dist: Ingram Pub. Services.

Grupo Folcra Edificaciones S.A. Lightweight Skin: A Building Technique Comes to Age. 2010. (Illus.). 216p. *(978-84-92861-40-8(1))* Actar Birkhauser Distribution.

Gutheim, Frederick & Aalto, Alvar. Alvar Aalto. 2011. 128p. (Orig.). 40.95 ***(978-1-258-01180-2(8))*** Literary Licensing, LLC.

Halpine, Mig. Pickard Chilton - Architecture. 2012. (ENG., Illus.). 500p. 85.00 *(978-1-86470-371-9(7))* Images Publishing Group AUS. Dist: National Bk. Network.

Hart, Sara. Ecoarchitecture: The Work of Ken Yeang. 2011. (ENG., Illus.). 272p. 75.00 *(978-0-470-72140-7(5)*, Wiley) Wiley, John & Sons, Inc.

Hartoonian, Gevork. Crisis of the Object: The Architecture of Theatricality. 2006. (Illus.). 196p. 165.00 *(978-0-415-38546-6(6))*; per. 74.95 *(978-0-415-38547-3(4))* Routledge.

Hassanein, Ahmed Taher, et al. Baghdad Arts Deco: Architectural Brickwork, 19201950. 2011. (ENG.). 608p. 39.95 *(978-977-416-356-2(7))* American Univ. in Cairo Pr. EGY. Dist: Oxford Univ. Pr., Inc.

Hay, D. Roger. D. Roger Hay, the Essence of Root Meaning. 2008. (Illus.). 104p. *(978-88-7838-146-9(2))* L'Arca Edizioni.

Hays, K. Michael & Hays, K. M. Architecture's Desire: Reading the Late Avant-Garde. 2009. (Writing Architecture Ser.). (ENG., Illus.). 216p. (gr. 17). pap. 20.95 *(978-0-262-51302-9(1))* MIT Pr.

Hei, Lam Wo. Wong & Ouyang: Blueprints for Hong Kong the Master Architect Series. Beaver, Robyn, ed. 2008. (ENG., Illus.). 184p. 59.95 *(978-1-86470-304-7(0)*, Images Publishing Dist Ac) Antique Collectors' Club GBR. Dist: National Bk. Network.

Hejduk, Renata & Williamson, Jim, eds. The Religious Imagination in Modern & Contemporary Architecture: A Reader. 2011. (ENG., Illus.). 424p. (C). 155.00 *(978-0-415-78080-3(2))*; pap. 49.95 *(978-0-415-78081-0(0))* Routledge.

Hess, Alan. The Buildings. 2008. (Illus.). 312p. 75.00 *(978-0-8478-3093-0(4))* Rizzoli International Pubns., Inc.

Higgott, Andrew. Mediating Modernism. 2006. (Illus.). VIII, 216p. 64.95 *(978-0-415-40177-7(1))* Routledge.

Hitchcock, Henry Russell. Architecture, Nineteenth & Twentieth Centuries: The Pelican History of Art. Pevsner, Nikolaus, ed. 2011. 720p. 70.95 ***(978-1-258-01625-8(7))*** Literary Licensing, LLC.

Hoffman, Douglas R. Seeking the Sacred in Contemporary Religious Architecture. 2011. 34.95 *(978-1-60635-047-8(1))* Kent State Univ. Pr.

HOK. Hok: A Global Design Portfolio. 2009. (ENG., Illus.). 416p. 85.00 *(978-1-86470-314-6(8))* Images Publishing Group AUS. Dist: National Bk. Network.

Holl, Steven. House: Black Swan Theory. 2007. (ENG., Illus.). 176p. 40.00 *(978-1-56898-587-9(8))* Princeton Architectural Pr.

Holzwarth, Hans Werner. Art Now 03, Vol. 3. Holzwarth, Hans Werner & Jones, Tricia, eds. 2009. (FRE, GER & ENG., Illus.). 591p. pap. 39.99 *(978-3-8365-0511-6(8))* TASCHEN DEU. Dist: Ingram Pub. Services.

Hough, Jessica & Ramirez-Montagut, Monica, eds. Revisiting the Glass House: Contemporary Art & Modern Architecture. 2008. (ENG., Illus.). 134p. pap. 39.95 *(978-0-300-13587-9(4))* Yale Univ. Pr.

House, Steven & House, Cathi. Houses in the Sun: Light Movement Embrace. 2008. (ENG., Illus.). 296p. 50.00 *(978-1-86470-239-2(7))* Images Publishing Group AUS. Dist: National Bk. Network.

Huber, Werner. Building Bern: A Guide to Contemporary Architecture, 1990-2010. 2010. (Verlag Scheidegger & Spiess-Edition Hochparterre at Scheidegger & Spiess Ser.). (Illus.). 240p. pap. 45.00 *(978-3-85881-722-8(8))* Scheidegger und Spiess AG, Verlag CHE. Dist: Antique Collectors' Club.

Huxtable, Ada Louise. On Architecture: Collected Reflections on a Century of Change. 2010. (ENG., Illus.). 496p. pap. 20.00 *(978-0-8027-1767-2(5))* Walker & Co.

Hyatt, Peter & Hyatt, Jenny. Great Glass Buildings. 2006. (Designing with Glass Ser.). (ENG., Illus.). 224p. 70.00 *(978-1-86470-112-8(9))* Images Publishing Group AUS. Dist: National Bk. Network.

Images Publishing Group, contrib. by. Architects of the New Millennium. 2006. (ENG., Illus.). 224p. 65.00 *(978-1-86470-079-4(3))* Images Publishing Group AUS. Dist: National Bk. Network.

Images Publishing Group Editors. International Architecture Yearbook, Vol. 7. 2006. (ENG., Illus.). 75.00 *(978-1-86470-103-6(X))* Images Publishing Group AUS. Dist: National Bk. Network.

Images Publishing Staff, PUBLISHING & Pan, Joshua Jih. J. J. Pan & Partners. 2006. (Master Architect Ser.). (ENG., Illus.). 256p. 59.95 *(978-1-86470-058-9(0)*, Images Publishing Dist Ac) Antique Collectors' Club GBR. Dist: National Bk. Network.

Images Publishing Staff, PUBLISHING, et al. Moshe Safdie, Vol. 2. 2009. (ENG., Illus.). 288p. 85.00 *(978-1-86470-163-0(3))* Images Publishing Group AUS. Dist: National Bk. Network.

Imhof, Michael & Krempel, León. Berlin: New Architecture - A Guide to the New Buildings from 1989 to Today. 6th ed. 2009. (ENG., Illus.). 163p. pap. 19.80 *(978-3-935590-15-0(6)*, Art Stock Bks. Ltd/Csi) Continental Sales, Inc.

In Palestine, American School for Oriental Study and Research & Brown, Francis. Seventh Annual Report of the Managing Committee, 1907-1908. 2010. pap. 19.84 *(978-1-61719-393-4(3))* Gorgias Pr., LLC.

In Palestine, American School for Oriental Study and Research & Lyon, David G. Sixth Annual Report of the Managing Committee, 1906-1907. 2010. pap. 19.12 *(978-1-61719-392-7(5))* Gorgias Pr., LLC.

Jodidio, Philip. Ando: Complete Works. 2007. (FRE, GER & ENG., Illus.). 500p. 39.99 *(978-3-8228-0930-3(6))* TASCHEN DEU. Dist: Ingram Pub. Services.

—Architecture Now 6! Architektur heute. L'architecture d'aujourd'hui. 2010. (25 Ser.). (ENG, FRE & GER., Illus.). 352p. 14.99 *(978-3-8365-2345-5(0))* TASCHEN DEU. Dist: Ingram Pub. Services.

—Calatrava: Complete Works 1979-2007. 2007. (FRE, GER & ENG., Illus.). 528p. 150.00 *(978-3-8228-4711-4(9))* TASCHEN DEU. Dist: Ingram Pub. Services.

Jodidio Philip. Kc Jean Nouvel. 2012. (ENG., Illus.). 96p. pap. 9.99 ***(978-3-8365-3080-4(5))*** TASCHEN DEU. Dist: Ingram Pub. Services.

Jodidio, Philip. Renzo Piano: Building Workshop 1966 to today. 25th ed. 2008. (FRE, GER & ENG., Illus.). 528p. 39.99 *(978-3-8365-0322-8(0))* TASCHEN DEU. Dist: Ingram Pub. Services.

—Santiago Calatrava: Complete Works 1979 - 2009. 2009. (ENG., Illus.). 536p. 39.99 *(978-3-8365-1023-3(5))* TASCHEN DEU. Dist: Ingram Pub. Services.

—Under the Eaves of Architecture: The Aga Khan: Builder & Patron. 2007. (Illus.). 206p. 75.00 *(978-3-7913-3781-4(5))* Prestel Publishing.

—Zaha Hadid: Complete Works 1979 - 2009. 2009. (FRE, GER & ENG., Illus.). 500p. 150.00 *(978-3-8365-0294-8(1))* TASCHEN DEU. Dist: Ingram Pub. Services.

—100 Contemporary Architects, 2 vols. Volk, Annick, ed. 25th ed. 2008. (FRE, GER & ENG., Illus.). 848p. 59.99 *(978-3-8365-0091-3(4))* TASCHEN DEU. Dist: Ingram Pub. Services.

Kahler, Gert, ed. GMP - GMP von Gerkan, Marg und Partner Architects: Villas Living in Exceptional Locations, 1 vol., Vol. 4. 2007. (ENG & GER., Illus.). 208p. pap. 35.00 *(978-3-936314-47-2(0))* Jovis Verlag GmbH DEU. Dist: D.A.P./Distributed Art Pubs.

Keil, Robert. Little Boxes: The Architecture of a Classic Midcentury Suburb. 2006. (Illus.). 144p. 35.00 *(978-0-9779236-4-9(9))* Advection Media.

Keister, Douglas, photos by. 500 Cottages. 2006. (ENG., Illus.). 509p. pap. 12.95 *(978-1-56158-843-5(1)*, Taunton) Taunton Pr., Inc.

Keshavjee, Serena, ed. Winnipeg Modern: Architecture, 1945-1975. 2011. (ENG., Illus.). 304p. pap. 49.95 *(978-0-88755-691-3(4))* Univ. of Manitoba Pr. CAN. Dist: Chicago Distribution Ctr.

Khan, Hasan-Uddin. International Style. Jodidio, Philip, ed. 25th ed. 2009. (World Architecture Ser.). (ENG., Illus.). 224p. 14.99 *(978-3-8365-1052-3(9))* TASCHEN DEU. Dist: Ingram Pub. Services.

Kipnis, Jeffrey & Mayne, Thom. Buildings & Projects, Vol. 5. 2009. (ENG., Illus.). 488p. 85.00 *(978-0-8478-3072-5(1))* Rizzoli International Pubns., Inc.

Knight, Richard. Saarinen's Quest: A Memoir of a Photographer. 2007. pap. 30.00 *(978-0-9746214-4-9(7))* Stout, William Pubs.

Koenig, Gloria. Frey. Gossel, Peter, ed. 2008. (Basic Architecture Ser.). (ENG., Illus.). 96p. pap. 9.99 *(978-3-8228-4883-8(2))* TASCHEN DEU. Dist: Ingram Pub. Services.

Konrad, Benjamin & Novotny, Maik. Eastmodern: Architecture & Design of the 1960s & 1970s in Slovakia. 2007. (ENG., Illus.). 238p. pap. 59.95 *(978-3-211-71531-4(2)*, 3211715312) Springer.

Koolhaas, Rem & Obriist, Hans Ulrich. Serpentine Gallery: 24-Hour Interview Marthon: London. 2007. (Illus.). 256p. pap. *(978-1-904563-69-3(4))* Trolley.

Kottas, Dimitris & Broto, Carles. Houses Now: Penthouses, Lofts. 2007. (ENG., Illus.). 240p. 39.95 *(978-84-96263-88-8(6))* Links International (Leading International Key Services Barcelona, S.A.) ESP. Dist: National Bk. Network.

Krier, Léon, et al. Drawing for Architecture. 2009. (Writing Architecture Ser.). (ENG., Illus.). 248p. (gr. 17). pap. 26.95 *(978-0-262-51293-0(9))* MIT Pr.

Kung. Christian Kerez: Construction, Privacy, Politics, Conflicts & Obsessions. Kueng, Moritz, ed. 2009. (ENG., Illus.). 200p. pap. 45.00 *(978-3-7757-2280-3(7))* Hatje Cantz Verlag GmbH & Co KG DEU. Dist: D.A.P./Distributed Art Pubs.

Kuosma, Kari. Sport Facilities in Finland 1980-2000. 2008. (ENG.). 184p. 34.00 *(978-951-682-599-4(0))* Rakennustieto oy FIN. Dist: Independent Pubs. Group.

La Marche, Jean. The Familiar & the Unfamiliar in Twentieth-Century Architecture. 2008. (ENG., Illus.). 168p. pap. 26.00 *(978-0-252-07561-2(7))* Univ. of Illinois Pr.

Lahtti, Marku & Rakennustieto Publishing Staff. Alvar Aalto: A Gentler Structure for Life. 2009. (ENG, GER, ITA & FIN., Illus.). 176p. 99.00 *(978-951-682-475-1(7))* Rakennustieto oy FIN. Dist: Independent Pubs. Group.

Lampens, Juliaan. Juliaan Lampens, 1 vol. Campens, Angelique, ed. 2011. (ENG., Illus.). 152p. pap. 64.00 ***(978-94-6117-005-7(X))*** Exhibitions International BEL. Dist: Innovative Logistics.

Lane, Barbara Miller, ed. Housing & Dwelling: Perspectives on Modern Domestic Architecture. 2006. (Illus.). 467p. 165.00 *(978-0-415-34655-9(X))*; (ENG., 480p. per. 54.95 *(978-0-415-34656-6(8))* Routledge.

Lawrance, Gary & Surchin, Anne. Houses of the Hamptons, 1880-1930. 2007. (Architecture of Leisure Ser.). (Illus.). 324p. 85.00 *(978-0-926494-44-2(9))* Acanthus Pr. LLC.

Levine, Neil. Modern Architecture: Representation & Reality. 2010. (ENG., Illus.). 376p. 65.00 *(978-0-300-14567-0(5))* Yale Univ. Pr.

Lewis, Paul, et al. Lewis. Tsurumaki. Lewis: Opportunistic Architecture. 2007. (ENG., Illus.). 192p. pap. 40.00 *(978-1-56898-710-1(2))* Princeton Architectural Pr.

Lewis, Roland. Frank Lloyd Wright in Pop-Up. 2009. (ENG.). 36p. 24.95 *(978-1-60710-008-9(8)*, Thunder Bay Pr.) Advantage Pubs. Group.

Lind, Carla. Lost Wright: Frank Lloyd Wright's Vanished Masterpieces. rev. ed. 2008. 176p. 35.00 *(978-0-7649-4596-0(3))* Pomegranate Communications, Inc.

Linke, Armin & Jovanovic Weiss, Srdjan. Socialist Architecture: The Vanishing ACT. 2012. (ENG., Illus.). 132p. 75.00 ***(978-3-03764-245-0(9))*** JRP Ringier Kunstverlag AG CHE. Dist: D.A.P./Distributed Art Pubs.

Littlefield, David & Jones, Will. Great Modern Structures: 100 Years of Engineering Genius. 2012. (ENG., Illus.). 288p. 45.00 ***(978-1-78097-001-1(3))*** Carlton Bks., Ltd. GBR. Dist: Sterling Publishing Co., Inc.

Liu, Gretchen & Byfield, Graham. Singapore Sketchbook: An Island Observed. 2011. 96p. 30.00 *(978-981-4068-40-6(3)*, Didier Millet,Csi) Continental Sales, Inc.

Lobell, John & Kahn, Louis I. Between Silence & Light: Spirit in the Architecture of Louis I. Kahn. 2nd rev. ed. 2008. (ENG., Illus.). 128p. pap. 18.95 *(978-1-59030-604-8(X))* Shambhala Pubns., Inc.

Loeffler, Jane C. The Architecture of Diplomacy: Building America's Embassies. 2nd ed. 2010. (ENG., Illus.). 336p. pap. 24.95 *(978-1-56898-984-6(9))* Princeton Architectural Pr.

M3 360 Modern Architecture III. 2011. (Illus.). 400p. 115.00 ***(978-988-19018-4-2(7))*** Azur Corp. JPN. Dist: Antique Collectors' Club.

Macadam, Alta. Blue Guide Florence. 10th ed. 2011. (Blue Guides). (ENG., Illus.). 400p. pap. 24.95 *(978-1-905131-52-5(6)*, 913152) Blue Guides Ltd. GBR. Dist: Norton, W. W. & Co., Inc.

Macdonald, Susan, et al. Conservation of Modern Architecture. 2007. (Illus.). 144p. pap. *(978-1-873394-84-7(5))* Donhead Publishing Ltd.

Maki, Fumihiko & Pran, Peter C. Peter Pran: Realizations. 2007. (Master Architect Ser.). (ENG., Illus.). 224p. 59.95 *(978-1-86470-194-4(3)*, Images Publishing Dist Ac) Antique Collectors' Club GBR. Dist: National Bk. Network.

Malkin, Helen & Dunton, Nancy. A Guidebook to Contemporary Architecture in Montreal, 1 vol. 2008. (ENG., Illus.). 192p. pap. 24.95 *(978-1-55365-346-2(7))* D&M Pubs. Inc. CAN. Dist: Perseus-PGW.

Maltzan, Michael. Michael Maltzan: No More Play. Varner, Jessica, ed. 2011. (ENG., Illus.). 240p. pap. 50.00 ***(978-3-7757-2846-1(5))*** Hatje Cantz Verlag GmbH & Co KG DEU. Dist: D.A.P./Distributed Art Pubs.

Marble, Scott & Kalden, Katrin, eds. Abstract, 1996-1997. Date not set. (Illus.). 160p. pap. *(978-1-883584-11-5(6))* Columbia Univ., Graduate Schl. of Architecture.

Marmol, Leo & Radziner, Ron. Marmol Radziner + Associates: Between Architecture & Construction. 2008. (ENG., Illus.). 176p. pap. 40.00 *(978-1-56898-744-6(7))* Princeton Architectural Pr.

Massey, Anne. Interior Design since 1900. 3rd rev. ed. 2008. (World of Art Ser.). (ENG., Illus.). 256p. pap. 19.95 *(978-0-500-20397-2(0)*, 520397) Thames & Hudson.

Mateyunas, Paul J. Long Island North Shore Country Houses: 1890-1950. 2007. (Suburban Domestic Architecture Ser.). (Illus.). 352p. 80.00 *(978-0-926494-37-4(6))* Acanthus Pr. LLC.

Matsui, Midori. Psycho Buildings: Artists Take on Architecture. 2008. (ENG., Illus.). 200p. 59.95 *(978-1-85332-268-6(7))* Hayward Gallery Publishing GBR. Dist: D.A.P./Distributed Art Pubs.

Matthews, Henry. Kirtland Cutter: Architect in the Land of Promise. 2007. (McLellan Bks.). (ENG., Illus.). 432p. per. 25.00 *(978-0-295-98766-8(9))* Univ. of Washington Pr.

Mazzola, Ettore M. Manfredi Nicoletti: Architecture Symbol Context. Sharp, Dennis, ed. 2011. 144p. pap. 35.95 *(978-88-492-0983-9(5))* Gangemi ITA. Dist: International Publishers Marketing.

McAlpine, Bobby & Sully, Susan. The Home Within Us: Romantic Houses, Evocative Rooms. 2010. (ENG., Illus.). 240p. 55.00 *(978-0-8478-3289-7(9))* Rizzoli International Pubns., Inc.

McCarter, Robert, ed. On & by Frank Lloyd Wright: A Primer of Architectural Principles. 2012. (ENG., Illus.). 372p. pap. 29.95 ***(978-0-7148-6316-0(5))*** Phaidon Pr., Inc.

McCoy, Esther. Richard Neutra: Masters of World Architecture. (Illus.). 128p. pap. 16.95 *(978-0-8076-1506-5(4))* Braziller, George Inc.

McGillick, Paul. Concrete Metal Glass: Hijas Kasturi Associates: Selected Works 1977-2007. 2007. (ENG., Illus.). 188p. 40.00 *(978-981-4155-28-1(4)*, Didier Millet,Csi) Continental Sales, Inc.

McLachlan, Fiona. Architectural Colour in the Professional Palette. 2012. (ENG., Illus.). 248p. (C). 165.00 ***(978-0-415-59708-1(0))***; pap. 54.95 ***(978-0-415-59709-8(9))*** Routledge.

Mead, Christopher Curtis & Predock, Antoine. Roadcut: The Architecture of Antoine Predock. 2011. (ENG., Illus.). 210p. 75.00 *(978-0-8263-5009-1(7))* Univ. of New Mexico Pr.

Menges, Axel, comment. Som: Architecture of Skidmore, Owings & Merrill, 1963-1973. 2009. (ENG., Illus.). 264p. 50.00 *(978-1-58093-221-9(5))* Monacelli Pr., Inc.

Mertins, Detlef, intro. Som: Architecture of Skidmore, Owings & Merrill, 1984-1996. 2009. (ENG., Illus.). 224p. 60.00 *(978-1-58093-223-3(1))* Monacelli Pr., Inc.

Meyhofer, Dirk, ed. Water Enjoyment: Sustainable Quality, Technology & Design. 2011. (GER & ENG., Illus.). 224p. 49.95 *(978-3-03768-078-0(4)*, Braun Publish,Csi) Continental Sales, Inc.

Millstein, Cydney & Grove, Carol. Houses of Missouri. 2008. (Illus.). 272p. 65.00 *(978-0-926494-54-1(6))* Acanthus Pr. LLC.

Minta, Anna & Nicolai, Bernd, eds. Modernity & Early Cultures: Reconsidering Non Western References for Modern Architecture in a Cross-Cultural Perspective. 2011. (Neue Berner Schriften zur Kunst Ser.). (Illus.). 236p. pap. *(978-3-0343-0508-2(7))* Lang, Peter.

Molinelli, Michael. Build Neat Stuff. 2006. 30.00 net. *(978-1-4276-0312-8(X))* Aardvark Global Publishing.

Monninger, Michael. Coop Himmelblau. Gossel, Peter, ed. 2010. (GER, FRE & ENG., Illus.). 528p. 150.00 *(978-3-8365-1788-1(4))* TASCHEN DEU. Dist: Ingram Pub. Services.

Morpurgo, Guido. Gregotti & Associates: The Architecture of Urban Design. 2008. (ENG., Illus.). 312p. 85.00 *(978-0-8478-3100-5(0))* Rizzoli International Pubns., Inc.

Morris, Linny, photos by. The Hawaiian House Now. 2007. (ENG., Illus.). 192p. 42.00 *(978-0-8109-9394-5(5))* Abrams.

Moussavi, Farshid & Kubo, Michael, eds. The Function of Ornament. 2006. (Illus.). 186p. pap. 29.95 *(978-84-96540-50-7(2))* Kunst-Werke Berlin e.V. DEU. Dist: Actar Birkhauser Distribution.

Mumford, Eric, et al. Hans Hofmann: the Chimbote Project: The Synergistic Promise of Modern Art & Urban Architecture. 2007. (Illus.). 133p. *(978-84-89771-07-9(3))* Actar Birkhauser Distribution.

Muschamp, Herbert. Hearts of the City: The Selected Writings of Herbert Muschamp. 2009. (ENG.). 912p. 50.00 *(978-0-375-40406-1(6))* Knopf, Alfred A. Inc.

Nash, Eric Peter. Manhattan Skyscrapers. 3rd ed. 2010. (ENG., Illus.). 240p. 50.00 *(978-1-56898-967-9(9))* Princeton Architectural Pr.

Newhouse, Victoria. Towards a New Museum. 2007. (ENG., Illus.). 349p. pap. 50.00 *(978-1-58093-180-9(4))* Monacelli Pr., Inc.

Newman, Morris. Responsive Architecture: Moody Nolan Recent Work. 2008. (ENG., Illus.). 120p. pap. 29.95 *(978-1-890449-46-9(6))* Balcony Pr.

Newman, Morris & Beaver, Robyn. Altoon & Porter Architects: Selected Current Works. 2006. (Master Architect Ser.). (ENG., Illus.). 256p. 59.95 *(978-1-876907-44-0(4)*, Images Publishing Dist Ac) Antique Collectors' Club GBR. Dist: National Bk. Network.

Nicoletti, Manfredi. Manfredi Nicoletti: Architect. Giussani, Elena, ed. 2010. 144p. pap. 22.95 *(978-88-492-1172-6(4))* Gangemi ITA. Dist: International Publishers Marketing.

Noever, Peter & Prix, Wolf, eds. In the Absence of Raimund Abraham. 2011. (ENG., Illus.). 128p. pap. 40.00 ***(978-3-7757-2999-4(2))*** Hatje Cantz Verlag GmbH & Co KG DEU. Dist: D.A.P./Distributed Art Pubs.

Norman, Robert A. Next. 2 vols. (Illus.). 464p. Vol. 1. pap. *(978-0-8478-2523-3(X))* Vol. 2. pap. *(978-0-8478-2537-0(X))* Rizzoli International Pubns., Inc.

Nouvel, Jean. Jean Nouvel: Lousiana Manifest. 1 vol. 2008. (ENG., Illus.). 160p. 45.00 *(978-87-91607-33-2(7))* D.A.P./Distributed Art Pubs.

Novembre, Fabio. Fabio Novembre. 2011. (ENG., Illus.). 136p. 80.00 *(978-88-6116-133-7(2))* Antique Collectors' Club.

Nylon Magazine Editors, ed. Pretty: The Nylon Book of Beauty. 2007. (ENG., Illus.). 224p. pap. 24.95 *(978-0-7893-1539-7(4))* McClelland & Stewart CAN. Dist: Random Hse., Inc.

Obrist, Hans Ulrich. Yona Friedman, 1 vol. 2007. (ENG., Illus.). 126p. per. 22.00 *(978-3-86560-171-1(5))* Verlag der Buchhandlung Walther Konig DEU. Dist: D.A.P./Distributed Art Pubs.

Obrist, Hans Ulrich, ed. Hans Ulrich Obrist & Cedric Price: the Conversation Series. 2010. (ENG., Illus.). 172p. pap. 35.00 *(978-3-86560-093-6(X))* Verlag der Buchhandlung Walther Konig DEU. Dist: D.A.P./Distributed Art Pubs.

Obrist, Hans Ulrich & Koolhaas, Rem. Rem Koolhaas, 1 vol. 2007. (ENG., Illus.). 68p. per. 17.95 *(978-3-86560-077-6(8))* Verlag der Buchhandlung Walther Konig DEU. Dist: D.A.P./Distributed Art Pubs.

O'Neill, Cathal, et al. AandD Wejchert & Partners. 2008. (FRE & ENG., Illus.). 283p. *(978-0-948037-55-9(5))* Gandon Editions.

Oshima, Ken, et al. Home Delivery. 2008. (ENG., Illus.). 248p. 45.00 *(978-0-87070-733-9(7))* Museum of Modern Art.

Overy, Paul. Light, Air & Openness: Modern Architecture Between the Wars. 2008. (ENG., Illus.). 256p. 50.00 *(978-0-500-34242-8(3))* Thames & Hudson.

Pabsch, Matthias. Zweimal Weltstadt: Architektur & Staedtebau am Potsdamer Platz. (GER., Illus.). 135p. *(978-3-496-01191-0(2))* Reimer, Dietrich.

Papadakis, Alexandra & Papadakis, Andreas, eds. Innovations: From Experimentation to Realisation. 2006. (ENG., Illus.). pap. 30.00 *(978-1-901092-46-2(1))* Papadakis Dist A/C.

Parkyn, Neil. Superstructures: The World's Greatest Modern Structures. rev. ed. (Illus.). 192p. *(978-1-85894-238-4(1))* Merrell Pubs. Ltd.

Parodi, Aníbal & Parodi Rebella, Aníbal. Puertas Adentro: Interioridad y Espacio Doméstico en el S. XX. 2010. (SPA., Illus.). 396p. *(978-84-8301-774-6(1))* UPC, S.L., Edicions.

Parsons, Bret & Colcord, Gerard Rae. Colcord: Home. 2008. *(978-1-883318-88-8(2))* Angel City Pr.

Parsons, Jim & Bush, David. Houston Deco: Modernistic Architecture of the Texas Coast. 2008. (ENG., Illus.). 128p. 24.95 *(978-1-933979-06-9(2))* Bright Sky Pr.

Pauwels, Wim. Wood Marsh Architects: Selected Works. 2012. (ENG., Illus.). 224p. 125.00 ***(978-90-8944-115-7(8))*** Beta-Plus Pubs. BEL. Dist: Antique Collectors' Club.

Pawson, John. A Visual Inventory. 2012. (ENG., Illus.). 320p. 49.95 ***(978-0-7148-6350-4(5))*** Phaidon Pr., Inc.

Payne, Alina. From Ornament to Object: Genealogies of Architectural Modernism. 2012. (ENG., Illus.). 360p. 65.00 ***(978-0-300-17533-2(7))*** Yale Univ. Pr.

Pedret, Annie. The Real Team 10 Primer. 2012. (ENG., Illus.). 368p. (C). pap. 53.95 *(978-0-415-78076-6(4))*; 165.00 ***(978-0-415-73075-9(6))*** Routledge.

Pennoyer, Peter, et al. The Architecture of Grosvenor Atterbury. 2009. (ENG., Illus.). 288p. 75.00 *(978-0-393-73222-1(3)*, 73222) Norton, W. W. & Co., Inc.

Phaidon Press Editors. The Modernist House. 2009. (ENG., Illus.). 112p. 29.95 *(978-0-7148-4968-3(5))* Phaidon Pr., Inc.

Phaidon Press Editors, ed. The Phaidon Atlas of 21st Century World Architecture. 2008. (ENG., Illus.). 812p. 195.00 *(978-0-7148-4874-7(3))* Phaidon Pr., Inc.

Phaidon Press Editors, ed. 10x10_3. 2011. (ENG., Illus.). 444p. pap. 49.95 ***(978-0-7148-6252-1(5))*** Phaidon Pr., Inc.

Phaidon Press Editors & Wallpaper Magazine Editors. Le Corbusier le Grand, 2 vols. 2008. (ENG., Illus.). 624p. 200.00 *(978-0-7148-4668-2(6))* Phaidon Pr., Inc.

Piazza, Mario, ed. Abitare: 50 Years of Design - The Best of Architecture, Interiors, Photography, Travel, & Trends, 1961-2011. 2010. (ENG & ITA., Illus.). 432p. 85.00 *(978-0-8478-3513-3(8))* Rizzoli International Pubns., Inc.

Platt, Charles A. The Architecture of Charles A. Platt. 2007. *(978-0-486-45605-8(6))* Dover Pubns., Inc.

Porter, Jenelle, ed. Fertilizers: Olin / Eisenman, 1 vol. 2007. (ENG., Illus.). 96p. per. 25.00 *(978-0-88454-109-7(6))* Univ. of Pennsylvania, Institute of Contemporary Art.

Portzamparc, Christian De & Sollers, Philippe. Writing & Seeing Architecture. Tihanyi, Catherine, tr. from FRE. 2008. 168p. 57.00 *(978-0-8166-4567-1(1))*; pap. 18.95 *(978-0-8166-4568-8(X))* Univ. of Minnesota Pr.

Powell, Kenneth. Richard Rogers - Complete Works, 3 vols., Vol. 3. 2006. (ENG., Illus.). 320p. 95.00 *(978-0-7148-4429-9(2))* Phaidon Pr. Ltd. GBR. Dist: Hachette Bk. Group.

Powers, Alan. Aldington, Craig & Collinge. 2009. (Twentieth-century Architects Ser.). (ENG., Illus.). 144p. (C). pap. 40.00 *(978-1-85946-302-4(9))* English Heritage GBR. Dist: Brown, David Bk. Co., The.

—Britain: Modern Architectures in History. 2007. (Reaktion Books - Modern Architectures in History Ser.). (ENG., Illus.). 272p. per. 29.95 *(978-1-86189-281-2(0))* Reaktion Bks., Ltd. GBR. Dist: Chicago Distribution Ctr.

Princeton Architectural Press Staff. El Segundo. 2007. (ENG., Illus.). 400p. 60.00 *(978-1-56898-700-2(5))* Princeton Architectural Pr.

Prix, Wolf D., ed. Studio Prix: University of Applied Arts, 1990-2011. 2012. (Edition Angewandte Ser.). (GER & ENG., Illus.). 250p. pap. 49.95 *(978-3-7091-0844-4(6)*, 3709108446) Springer Wien AUT. Dist: Springer.

Process Architecture 1996. (Illus.). pap. 50.00 *(978-4-89331-096-5(8))* Process Architecture JPN. Dist: International Specialized Bk. Services.

Prouvé, Jean. Jean Prouvé: La Maison Tropicale = Jean Prouvé: The Tropical House. 2009. (FRE & ENG., Illus.). 157p. *(978-2-84426-335-3(6))* Centre National d'Art et de Culture Georges Pompidou.

Prouve, Jean. Jean Prouve: the Tropical House. 2011. (ENG., Illus.). 160p. pap. 40.00 *(978-1-935202-49-3(9))* Editions du Centre Pompidou FRA. Dist: D.A.P./Distributed Art Pubs.

Puglisi, Luigi Prestinenza. New Directions in Contemporary Architecture: Evolutions & Revolutions in Building Design since 1988. 2008. (ENG., Illus.). 240p. 140.00 *(978-0-470-51889-2(8)*, Wiley) Wiley, John & Sons, Inc.

—New Directions in Contemporary Architecture: Evolutions & Revolutions in Building Design Since 1988. 2008. (ENG., Illus.). 240p. pap. 45.00 *(978-0-470-51890-8(1)*, Wiley) Wiley, John & Sons, Inc.

Radford, William A. The Most Popular Homes of the Twenties. 2009. (Dover Architecture Ser.). (ENG., Illus.). 176p. pap. 19.95 *(978-0-486-47028-3(8))* Dover Pubns., Inc.

Rael, Ronald. Earth Architecture. (ENG., Illus.). 2010. 208p. pap. 24.95 *(978-1-56898-945-7(8))* 2008. 192p. 45.00 *(978-1-56898-767-5(6))* Princeton Architectural Pr.

Rattenbury, Kester, et al. Architects Today. 2006. (ENG., Illus.). 240p. pap. 19.95 *(978-1-85669-492-6(5))* King, Laurence Publishing GBR. Dist: Hachette Bk. Group.

Ratti, Annie, et al, texts. Yona Friedman. 2009. (ENG., Illus.). 96p. pap. 27.95 *(978-88-8158-705-6(X))* Charta ITA. Dist: D.A.P./Distributed Art Pubs.

Rauterberg, Hanno. Talking Architecture: Interviews with Architects. 2012. (Illus.). 160p. pap. 19.95 ***(978-3-7913-4684-7(9))*** Prestel Publishing.

Rave, Rolf. Modern Architecture in Berlin. 2009. (ENG., Illus.). 280p. pap. 49.90 *(978-3-936681-29-1(5))* Edition Axel Menges GmbH DEU. Dist: National Bk. Network.

Reyes, Pedro, et al, texts. LAR Fernando Romero: Simplexity. 2011. (ENG., Illus.). 672p. 85.00 *(978-3-7757-2711-2(6))* Hatje Cantz Verlag GmbH & Co KG DEU. Dist: D.A.P./Distributed Art Pubs.

Richter, Markus, ed. Megastructure Reloaded: Due Inkunabeln der 1960er- Jahre in der visionären Architektur, Popkultur und Kunst. Dieser Katalog erscheint anlässlich der Ausstellung. 2008. (ENG., Illus.). 368p. pap. 55.00 *(978-3-7757-2216-2(5))* Hatje Cantz Verlag GmbH & Co KG DEU. Dist: D.A.P./Distributed Art Pubs.

Richters, Christian, photos by. Erick Van Egeraat: 10 Years. 2006. (Master Architect Ser.: Vol. 8). (ENG., Illus.). 256p. 59.95 *(978-1-86470-131-9(5)*, Images Publishing Dist Ac) Antique Collectors' Club GBR. Dist: National Bk. Network.

—UNStudio: Fotografien von Christian Richters. 2009. (ENG & GER., Illus.). 144p. pap. 39.95 *(978-3-939633-84-6(4))* Jovis Verlag GmbH DEU. Dist: D.A.P./Distributed Art Pubs.

Robinson, Joel. Life in Ruins: Architectural Culture & the Question of Death inthe Twentieth Century. 2008. 200p. pap. *(978-3-639-10916-0(3))* VDM Verlag Dr. Mueller e.K.

Rodriguez, Luis, ed. Architecture & Revolution in Cuba, 1959-1969. 2008. 224p. 45.00 *(978-84-96540-72-9(3))* Kunst-Werke Berlin e.V. DEU. Dist: Actar Birkhauser Distribution.

Rosa, Joseph. Young Chicago. 2007. (A+D Ser.). (ENG., Illus.). 104p. pap. 16.95 *(978-0-300-12067-7(2))* Art Institute of Chicago.

Rose, M. Ugly as Sin. 2009. (Illus.). 256p. pap. 18.95 *(978-1-933184-44-9(2))* Sophia Institute Pr.

Rose, Michael S. Ugly as Sin. 2009. (Forthright Edition Ser.). (Illus.). 256p. pap. 18.95 *(978-1-928832-36-2(9))* Sophia Institute Pr.

Rotondi, Michael & Stevens, Clark P. Roto Architecture: Still Points. 2006. (ENG., Illus.). 240p. 65.00 *(978-0-8478-2813-5(1))* Rizzoli International Pubns., Inc.

Rovira i Gimeno, Josep M., et al. Sert: De la Ciutat Funcional Al Disseny Urbà. 2009. (CAT., Illus.). 47p. *(978-84-8301-887-3(X))* UPC, S.L., Edicions.

Rowlands, Rob, et al, eds. Mass Housing in Europe: Multiple Faces of Development, Change & Response. 2010. (ENG., Illus.). 264p. 95.00 *(978-0-230-00730-7(9))* Palgrave Macmillan.

Ruan, Xing & Hogben, Paul, eds. Topophilia & Topophobia: Reflections on Twentieth-Century Human Habitat. 2008. (Illus.). (ENG.). 248p. (C). 165.00 *(978-0-415-40323-8(5))*; CCXXXIV, 14p. 47.95 *(978-0-415-40324-5(3))* Routledge.

Rüedi Ray, Katerina. Bauhaus Dream-House: Modernity & Globalization. 2010. (Architext Ser.). (ENG., Illus.). 240p. (C). pap. 49.95 *(978-0-415-47582-2(1))*; 165.00 *(978-0-415-47581-5(3))* Routledge.

Safdie, Moshe, et al. Moshe Safdie, Vol. 1. 2009. (ENG., Illus.). 268p. 85.00 *(978-1-86470-162-3(5))* Images Publishing Group AUS. Dist: National Bk. Network.

Saint-Amour, Suzanne. René Richer, 1887-1963, Architecte Maskoutain: Oublier Ne Puis. 2008. (FRE., Illus.). 276p. *(978-2-89634-029-3(7))* GID, Editions.

Salingaros, Nikos A. Anti-Architecture & Deconstruction. 2008. (ENG.). 175p. pap. 23.00 *(978-3-937954-09-7(0))* ISI Bks.

—Anti-Architecture & Deconstruction. 2007. 210p. pap. 23.00 *(978-3-937954-08-0(2))* Pueschel, Harald , Umbau-Verlag DEU. Dist: Southern Illinois Univ. Pr.

Salmon, Frank, ed. The Persistence of the Classical: Essays on Architecture Presented to David Watkin. 2008. (ENG., Illus.). 107p. 63.00 *(978-0-85667-661-1(6))* Wilson, Philip Pubs., Ltd. GBR. Dist: Macmillan.

San Pietro, Silvio, et al. New Bars, Cafes & Pubs in Italy. 2008. (Best Interiors Selection Ser.). (ITA & ENG., Illus.). 216p. *(978-88-7685-158-2(5)*, Edizioni L'archivolto (Acc)) Antique Collectors' Club.

Schaal, Hans Dieter. Learning from Hollywood: Architecture & Film , Architektur und Film. 2nd ed. 2010. (ENG & GER., Illus.). 128p. 49.90 *(978-3-936681-34-5(1))* Edition Axel Menges GmbH DEU. Dist: National Bk. Network.

Scheer, Thorsten, ed. Josef Paul Kleihues Volume 1: Works 1966-1980. 2008. (ENG., Illus.). 288p. 100.00 *(978-3-7757-2087-8(1))* Hatje Cantz Verlag GmbH & Co KG DEU. Dist: D.A.P./Distributed Art Pubs.

Schirmbeck, Egon, et al. Architecture & Space: Design Concepts in the 20th Century, 1 vol. 2011. (ENG & GER.). 224p. pap. 39.95 ***(978-3-86922-180-9(1))*** DOM Pubs. DEU. Dist: Innovative Logistics.

Schmal, Peter Cachola. Ready for Take-Off: Aktuelle deutsche Exportarchitektur. 2008. (ENG., Illus.). 208p. 60.00 *(978-3-7757-2146-2(0))* Hatje Cantz Verlag GmbH & Co KG DEU. Dist: D.A.P./Distributed Art Pubs.

Schmertz, Mildred. Mitchell: Giurgola Architects. 2008. (ENG., Illus.). 264p. 70.00 *(978-1-86470-274-3(5))* Images Publishing Group AUS. Dist: National Bk. Network.

Schröpfer, Thomas. Material Design: Informing Architecture by Materiality. 2010. (ENG., Illus.). 216p. 69.95 *(978-3-0346-0035-4(6))* Birkhauser Verlag AG CHE. Dist: Actar Birkhauser Distribution.

Schulze, Franz & Windhorst, Edward. Mies Van der Rohe: A Critical Biography. 2012. (Illus.). 568p. 45.00 ***(978-0-226-75600-4(9))*** Univ. of Chicago Pr.

Scott, Felicity D. Architecture or Techno-Utopia: Politics after Modernism. 2010. (ENG., Illus.). 360p. (gr. 17). pap. 19.95 *(978-0-262-51406-4(0))* MIT Pr.

Serena Keshavjee, ed. Winnipeg Modernism: Mid-Century Modernist Architecture, 1945 To 1975. 2006. (Illus.). 304p. 74.95 *(978-0-88755-181-9(5))* Univ. of Manitoba Pr. CAN. Dist: Michigan State Univ. Pr.

Shane, David Grahame. Urban Design since 1945: A Global Perspective. 2011. (ENG., Illus.). 360p. 125.00 *(978-0-470-51525-9(2))*; pap. 45.00 *(978-0-470-51526-6(0))* Wiley, John & Sons, Inc. (Wiley).

Sharp, Dennis. 20th Century Architecture: A Visual History. 3rd ed. 2006. (ENG., Illus.). 496p. 90.00 *(978-1-86470-085-5(8))* Images Publishing Group AUS. Dist: National Bk. Network.

Sharp, Dennis & Rendel, Sally. Connell Ward & Lucas: Modernist Architecture in England. 2008. (ENG., Illus.). 224p. 65.00 *(978-0-7112-2768-2(3))* Lincoln, Frances Ltd. GBR. Dist: Perseus-PGW.

Sigurd Lewerentz, Architect. 82.00 *(978-91-85194-71-1(9))* Byggforlaget SWE. Dist: Coronet Bks.

Slessor, Catherine. International Architecture Yearbook, Vol. 8. 2006. (ENG., Illus.). 256p. 75.00 *(978-1-876907-43-3(6))* Images Publishing Group AUS. Dist: National Bk. Network.

Smith, Terry E. The Architecture of Aftermath. 2006. (Illus.). 280p. per. 32.50 *(978-0-226-76469-6(9))* Univ. of Chicago Pr.

Smock, William. Bauhaus Ideal: Then & Now. 2009. (ENG., Illus.). 160p. pap. 19.95 *(978-0-89733-590-4(2))* Academy Chicago Pubs., Ltd.

Snelling, Rebecca & Suermondt, Jan. Frank Lloyd Wright Revealed. 2007. (Illus.). 160p. 19.99 *(978-0-7858-2079-6(5)*, Chartwell) Book Sales, Inc.

Spiller, Neil. Visionary Architecture: Blueprints of the Modern Imagination. (ENG., Illus.). 272p. 2008. per. 39.95 *(978-0-500-28655-5(8))* 2007. 60.00 *(978-0-500-34226-8(1))* Thames & Hudson.

Stamp, Gavin, et al, eds. The Modern House Revisited. 2006. (Twentieth Century Architecture Ser.). (ENG., Illus.). 128p. pap. 20.00 *(978-0-9529755-9-5(9))* Holberton, Paul Publishing GBR. Dist: Casemate Pubs. & Bk. Distributors, LLC.

Steiner, Hadas A. Beyond Archigram: The Structure of Circulation. (Illus.). 168p. 2008. 43.95 *(978-0-415-39477-2(5))* 2007. 165.00 *(978-0-415-39476-5(7))* Routledge.

Stern, Robert A. M., et al. New York 1930: Architecture & Urbanism Between the Two World Wars. 2009. (ENG., Illus.). 848p. 95.00 *(978-0-8478-3096-1(9))* Rizzoli International Pubns., Inc.

Stern, Robert A. M. Robert A. M. Stern: Buildings & Towns. Dixon, Peter Morris, ed. 2007. (ENG., Illus.). 548p. (gr. 12). 85.00 *(978-1-58093-192-2(8))* Monacelli Pr., Inc.

—Robert A. M. Stern: On Campus. 2010. (ENG., Illus.). 576p. 85.00 *(978-1-58093-283-7(5))* Monacelli Pr., Inc.

Swaback, Vernon D. The Custom Home: Dreams, Desire, Design. 2006. (ENG., Illus.). 256p. 65.00 *(978-1-876907-40-2(1))* Images Publishing Group AUS. Dist: National Bk. Network.

Symondson, Anthony & Harwood, Elain. Chamberlin, Powell & Bon. 2011. (Twentieth-century Architects Ser.). (ENG., Illus.). 160p. (C). pap. 40.00 ***(978-1-85946-397-0(5))*** English Heritage GBR. Dist: Brown, David Bk. Co., The.

Taschen Publishing, creator. Architecture Materials Glass. 2008. (ENG & GER., Illus.). 252p. pap. 19.99 *(978-3-8365-0405-8(7))* TASCHEN DEU. Dist: Ingram Pub. Services.

—Architecture Now! 3. 25th ed. 2008. (FRE, GER & ENG., Illus.). 352p. 14.99 *(978-3-8365-0314-3(X))* TASCHEN DEU. Dist: Ingram Pub. Services.

Taschen Publishing Staff, et al. Domus, 1940-1949, Vol. 2. Volk, Annick et al, eds. 2008. (ENG., Illus.). 580p. 69.99 *(978-3-8365-0952-7(0))* TASCHEN DEU. Dist: Ingram Pub. Services.

Tchoban, Sergei. Sergei Tchoban: Art. 2010. (ENG., Illus.). 256p. 59.95 *(978-1-86470-389-4(X)*, Images Publishing Dist Ac) Antique Collectors' Club GBR. Dist: National Bk. Network.

The Plan Staff. Plans & Details for Contemporary Architects: Building with Colour. 2011. (ENG., Illus.). 240p. 65.00 *(978-0-500-34267-1(9)*, 534267) Thames & Hudson.

Tiainen, Jussi, photos by. Wood Architecture in Finland. 2008. (ENG., Illus.). 144p. 69.00 *(978-951-682-847-6(7))* Rakennustieto oy FIN. Dist: Independent Pubs. Group.

Tietz, Jurgen. The Story of Modern Architecture. 2008. (Story of Ser.). (Illus.). 128p. 9.95 *(978-0-8416-0357-8(X))* American Map Corp.

Tzonis, Alexander. Santiago Calatrava: The Complete Works. 2007. (ENG., Illus.). 480p. 85.00 *(978-0-8478-2995-8(2))* Rizzoli International Pubns., Inc.

Udsen, Vibe & Moller, Henrik Sten. Jorn Utzon - Houses. 2006. (ENG., Illus.). 240p. 85.00 *(978-87-987597-3-7(6))* Living Architecture Publishing DNK. Dist: Perseus-PGW.

Uffelen, Van Chris. Factory Design. 2008. (Illus.). 336p. 62.50 *(978-3-03768-005-6(9)*, Braun Publish,Csi) Continental Sales, Inc.

Vesely, Dalibor & Wang, Wilfried. Eric Parry Architects, Vol. 2. 2011. (ENG., Illus.). 208p. pap. 39.95 *(978-1-906155-25-4(9))* Black Dog Publishing Ltd. GBR. Dist: Perseus Distribution.

Vidler, Anthony. Architecture Between Spectacle & Use. 2008. (Clark Studies in the Visual Arts). (Illus.). xiii, 184p. *(978-0-931102-66-0(9))* Clark, Sterling & Francine Art Institute.

Vilchis, Ricardo Legorreta, et al. Lopez Guerra: Architecture: A Discipline of Service. 2007. (Architectural Ser.). (ENG., Illus.). 144p. pap. 40.00 *(978-88-7838-086-8(5)*, Art Stock Bks. Ltd/Csi) Continental Sales, Inc.

Villanueva, Paulina & Pinto, Macia. Carlos Raul Villanueva. Marti, W., tr. 180p. 33.38 *(978-3-7643-6117-4(4)*, 3764361174) Birkhauser Boston.

Vinegar, Aron. Relearning from Las Vegas. Golec, Michael J., ed. 2008. (Illus.). 208p. pap. 25.00 *(978-0-8166-5061-3(6))* Univ. of Minnesota Pr.

Vinegar, Aron, et al. Relearning from Las Vegas. Vinegar, Aron & Golec, Michael J., eds. 2008. (Illus.). 208p. 75.00 *(978-0-8166-5060-6(8))* Univ. of Minnesota Pr.

Vinoly, Rafael & Jodidio, Philip. Rafael Vinoly Architects. 2010. (Illus.). 550p. 99.00 *(978-3-7913-5074-5(9))* Prestel Publishing.

Violeau, Jean-Louis & Buckley, Craig, eds. Utopie: Texts & Projects, 1967-1978. Clarke, Jean-Marie, tr. from FRE. 2011. (Semiotext(e) / Foreign Agents Ser.). (ENG., Illus.). 264p. (gr. 17). 24.95 *(978-1-58435-095-8(4))* Semiotexte/Smart Art.

Volk, Annick, et al, eds. Domus, 1950-1954, Vol. 3. 2008. (ENG., Illus.). 580p. 69.99 *(978-3-8365-0953-4(9))* TASCHEN DEU. Dist: Ingram Pub. Services.

Wachten, Junibert & Neubauer, Henrik. Urban Design & Architecture. 2010. 432p. 69.99 *(978-0-8416-7225-3(3))* Langenscheidt Publishing Group.

Wachten, Kunibert & Hendrik, Neubauer. Urban Design & Architecture in the 20th Century, 1 vol. 2010. (ENG., Illus.). 432p. 59.99 *(978-3-8331-5318-1(0))* h.f.ullmann DEU. Dist: Innovative Logistics.

Walden, Gert, ed. Baumschlager - Eberle - Annäherungen Approaches. 2009. (GER & ENG., Illus.). 148p. *(978-3-211-79158-5(2)*, 3211791582) Actar Birkhauser Distribution.

Wang, Wilfried & Vesely, Dalibor. Eric Parry Architects, Vols. 1 & 2. 2011. (ENG., Illus.). 416p. pap. 70.00 *(978-1-906155-63-6(1))* Black Dog Publishing Ltd. GBR. Dist: Actar Birkhauser Distribution.

Warhaftig, Myra. They Laid the Foundation: Lives & Works of German-Speaking Jewish Architects in Palestine 1918-1948, 1 vol. Lerner, Andrea, tr. from GER. 2nd ed. 2007. (ENG., Illus.). 416p. 40.00 *(978-3-8030-0676-9(7))* Wasmuth, Ernst J. Verlag GmbH & Co. DEU. Dist: D.A.P./Distributed Art Pubs.

Watch, Daniel D., et al. Building Type Basics for Research Laboratories. 2nd ed. 2008. (Building Type Basics Ser.: 14). (ENG., Illus.). 288p. 85.00 *(978-0-470-16333-7(X)*, Wiley) Wiley, John & Sons, Inc.

Watkinson, Gordon. Bauhaus Twenty-21: An Ongoing Legacy. Vrachliotis, Georg, ed. 2009. 232p. 89.85 *(978-3-0346-0054-5(2))* Springer.

—Bauhaus Zwanzig - 21: Ideen für ein neues Jahrhundert. 2009. (GER., Illus.). 231p. *(978-3-0346-0055-2(0))* Birkhauser Verlag AG.

Weaving, Andrew. Sarasota Modern. 2006. (ENG., Illus.). 208p. 17.95 *(978-0-8478-2872-2(7))* Rizzoli International Pubns., Inc.

Weiss, Klaus-Dieter. Workmanship: Working Philosophy & Design Practice. 2011. (ENG., Illus.). 320p. 69.95 *(978-3-0346-0481-9(5))* Birkhauser Verlag AG CHE. Dist: Actar Birkhauser Distribution.

Whitaker, William. Crafting a Modern World: The Architecture & Design of Antonin & Noémi Raymond. Helfrich, Kurt & Whitaker, William, eds. 2006. (ENG., Illus.). 352p. 75.00 *(978-1-56898-583-1(5))* Princeton Architectural Pr.

Williams, Richard J. Brazil. 2009. (Reaktion Books - Modern Architectures in History Ser.). (ENG., Illus.). 304p. pap. 29.95 *(978-1-86189-400-7(7))* Reaktion Bks., Ltd. GBR. Dist: Chicago Distribution Ctr.

Witynski, Karen & Carr, Joe P. Hacienda Courtyards, 1 vol. 2007. (ENG., Illus.). 144p. 29.95 *(978-1-4236-0001-5(0))* Gibbs Smith, Publisher.

Wolf, Connie, et al. Daniel Libeskind & the Contemporary Jewish Museum: New Jewish Architecture from Berlin to San Francisco. 2008. (ENG., Illus.). 128p. 45.00 *(978-0-8478-3165-4(5))* Rizzoli International Pubns., Inc.

Wolfe, Tom. From Bauhaus to Our House. 2009. (ENG.). 128p. pap. 15.00 *(978-0-312-42914-0(2))* Picador.

Wood In Culture Association Staff. Renzo Piano: Spirit of Nature Wood Architecture Award 2000. 2008. (ENG., Illus.). 88p. pap. 34.00 *(978-951-682-606-9(7))* Rakennustieto oy FIN. Dist: Independent Pubs. Group.

Woodman, Ellis & Fretton, Tony. Modernity & Reinvention: The\Architecture of James Gowan. 2008. (ENG., Illus.). 235p. pap. 55.00 *(978-1-906155-28-5(3))* Black Dog Publishing Ltd. GBR. Dist: Perseus Distribution.

Wright, Frank Lloyd. Modern Architecture: Being the Kahn Lectures for 1930. 2008. (ENG., Illus.). 176p. 29.95 *(978-0-691-12937-2(1))* Princeton Univ. Pr.

Wright, Gwendolyn. USA: Modern Architectures in History. 2008. (Reaktion Books - Modern Architectures in History Ser.). (ENG., Illus.). 272p. pap. 29.95 *(978-1-86189-344-4(2))* Reaktion Bks., Ltd. GBR. Dist: Chicago Distribution Ctr.

Xenakis, Iannis & Kanach, Sharon E. Music & Architecture: Architectural Projects, Texts, & Realizations. 2008. (ENG., Illus.). 372p. 48.00 *(978-1-57647-107-4(1))* Pendragon Pr.

Yao, Kris. Kris Yao/Artech. 2011. (ENG., Illus.). 588p. 80.00 *(978-1-86470-219-4(2))* Images Publishing Group AUS. Dist: National Bk. Network.

Yee, Roger, ed. HLW At 125: Better Performance By Design, 1 vol. 2010. (ENG., Illus.). 197p. 60.00 *(978-0-9825989-3-1(9))* Visual Profile Bks., Inc.

Yorke, Trevor. Arts & Crafts House Styles. 2011. (ENG., Illus.). 64p. pap. 14.95 *(978-1-84674-230-9(7))* Countryside Bks. GBR. Dist: Brown, David Bk. Co., The.

Yusuf, Majid Nabil Ali. Mithulujiya Al-Alam Al-Qadim Wa-Atharuha Alá Al-Tasmim Al-Mimari Al-Muasir. 2009. (ARA., Illus.). 398p. *(978-977-10-2509-2(0))* Dar al-Fikr al-Arabi.

Zeytinoglu, Arkan, ed. Geometry of Light: The Architecture of Arkan Zeytinoglu. 2011. (Illus.). 350p. 69.95 *(978-3-7091-0538-2(2)*, 3709105382) Springer Wien AUT. Dist: Springer.

Zimmerman, Claire. Ludwig Mies Van der Rohe. Gossel, Peter, ed. 25th ed. 2009. (25 Ser.). (ENG., Illus.). 96p. 14.99 *(978-3-8365-1316-6(1))* TASCHEN DEU. Dist: Ingram Pub. Services.

Züger, Raffele. Switzerlarch: Bank & Bastion. 2011. (ENG., Illus.). 220p. 29.95 ***(978-3-03764-165-1(7))*** JRP Ringier Kunstverlag AG CHE. Dist: D.A.P./Distributed Art Pubs.

Zumthor, Peter. Penser L'architecture: Thinking Architecture, Third Edition (French Edition) 2010. (FRE.). 112p. 44.95 *(978-3-0346-0582-3(X))* Birkhauser Verlag AG CHE. Dist: Actar Birkhauser Distribution.

ARCHITECTURE, MODERN—21ST CENTURY

Abrahams, Tim. Ideas Exchange: The Collaborative Studio of Hawkins Brown. 2010. (ENG., Illus.). 208p. 84.95 *(978-3-0346-0231-0(6))* Birkhauser Verlag AG CHE. Dist: Actar Birkhauser Distribution.

Adjaye, David & McQuade, Mark. The Adjaye Studios 2008-2010: Co-Authoring, 1 vol. 2012. (ENG., Illus.). 276p. pap. 45.00 ***(978-3-03778-282-8(X))*** Lars Muller Pubs. CHE. Dist: Prestel Publishing.

Aga Khan Foundation Staff & Khan, Aga. Intervention Architecture: Building for Change. Johnston, Pamela, ed. 2007. (ENG., Illus.). 192p. pap. 26.00 *(978-1-84511-673-6(9))* I. B. Tauris & Co., Ltd. GBR. Dist: Macmillan.

Agnoletto, Matteo, et al. Las Obras Maestras de la Arquitectura Moderna. 2007. (SPA., Illus.). 303p. 39.95 *(978-970-718-442-8(6)*, Numen) Advanced Marketing, S. de R. L. de C. V. MEX. Dist: Perseus-PGW.

Albrecht, Donald, et al. Global Citizen: The Architecture of Moshe Safdie. 2010. (ENG., Illus.). 144p. 35.00 *(978-1-85759-587-1(4))* Scala, Editions FRA. Dist: National Bk. Network.

Allen, Stan. Occasions. 2007. *(978-84-96954-97-7(8))* Actar Birkhauser Distribution.

Almaas, Ingerid Helsing, ed. Made in Norway: Norwegian Architecture Today. 2010. (Illus.). 144p. pap. 49.95 *(978-3-0346-0559-5(5))* Birkhauser Verlag AG CHE. Dist: Actar Birkhauser Distribution.

Architectural League of New York Staff. Resonance. 2009. (ENG., Illus.). 176p. pap. 24.95 *(978-1-56898-809-2(5))* Princeton Architectural Pr.

Architectural League of New York Staff. Young Architects 13: It's Different. 2012. (ENG.). 176p. pap. 24.95 ***(978-1-61689-057-5(6))*** Princeton Architectural Pr.

Architecture Studio Staff & Images Publishing Editorial Staff. Buildings: Innovation + Technology: STUDIOS Architecture. 2009. (ENG., Illus.). 96p. 25.00 *(978-1-86470-329-0(6))* Images Publishing Group AUS. Dist: National Bk. Network.

Argentero, Francesca, ed. Lost in Nature: Jarmund/Vigsnæs AS Arkitekter (MNAL) 2010. 64p. pap. 23.95 *(978-88-492-1476-5(6))* Gangemi ITA. Dist: International Publishers Marketing.

Asefi, Maziar. Transformable & Kinetic Architectural Structures. 2010. 316p. pap. *(978-3-639-25062-6(1))* VDM Verlag Dr. Mueller e.K.

Attali, Erieta & Assonitis, Alessio. Architects' Journeys. 2011. (ENG., Illus.). 160p. 40.00 *(978-1-883584-67-2(1))* Columbia Univ., Graduate Schl. of Architecture.

Azur. Architecture Highlights Vol. 3. 2011. 250p. 120.00 *(978-4-903233-61-1(8))* Azur Corp. JPN. Dist: Antique Collectors' Club.

Baan, Christine de, et al. Visionary Power: Producing the Contemporary City, 1 vol. 2007. (ENG., Illus.). 288p. per. 50.00 *(978-90-5662-579-5(9))* NAi Uitgevers / Publishers Stichting NLD. Dist: D.A.P./Distributed Art Pubs.

Bahamón, Alejandro & Álvarez, Maria. Light Color Sound: Sensory Effects in Contemporary Architecture. 2010. (ENG., Illus.). 384p. 75.00 *(978-0-393-73337-2(8)*, 73337) Norton, W. W. & Co., Inc.

Bahamón, Alejandro & Sanjinés, Maria Camila. Rematerial: From Waste to Architecture. 2010. (ENG., Illus.). 340p. pap. 49.95 *(978-0-393-73314-3(9)*, 73314) Norton, W. W. & Co., Inc.

Bantal, Samir, ed. Architecture in the Netherlands: Yearbook 2009-10. 2010. (ENG., Illus.). 192p. pap. 60.00 *(978-90-5662-751-5(1))* NAi Uitgevers / Publishers Stichting NLD. Dist: D.A.P./Distributed Art Pubs.

Barkow, Frank & Leibinger, Regine. Barkow Leibinger: An Atlas of Fabrication. 2009. (Illus.). 98p. pap. *(978-1-902902-75-3(0))* Architectural Assn.

Bayley, Stephen, et al. Stanton Williams. 2009. (ENG., Illus.). 256p. 49.95 *(978-1-906155-87-2(9))* Black Dog Publishing Ltd. GBR. Dist: Actar Birkhauser Distribution.

Bell, Buckley & Princeton Architectural Press Staff. Solid States: Concrete in Transition. Buckley, Craig & Bell, Michael, eds. 2010. (ENG., Illus.). 280p. 65.00 *(978-1-56898-895-5(8))* Princeton Architectural Pr.

Bellini, Oscar & Daglio, Laura. New Frontiers of Architecture: Dubai. 2010. (ENG., Illus.). 304p. 40.00 *(978-88-544-0411-3(X))* White Star ITA. Dist: Sterling Publishing Co., Inc.

Bergdoll, Barry, intro. Small Scale, Big Change. 2010. (ENG., Illus.). 140p. pap. 37.50 *(978-0-87070-784-1(1))* Museum of Modern Art.

Bernheimer, Andrew & Della Valle, Jared. Think/Make: Della Valle Bernheimer. 2009. (ENG., Illus.). 192p. pap. 40.00 *(978-1-56898-781-1(1))* Princeton Architectural Pr.

Betsky, Aaron. UnStudio: The Floating Space. 2007. (ENG., Illus.). 96p. pap. 9.99 *(978-3-8228-4538-7(8))* TASCHEN DEU. Dist: Ingram Pub. Services.

Big Thom Architects Staff, contrib. by. Bing Thom Works. 2011. (ENG., Illus.). 200p. 65.00 *(978-1-56898-959-4(8))* Princeton Architectural Pr.

Boeckl, Matthias. Andreas Treusch Architecture. 2010. (GER & ENG., Illus.). 208p. 49.95 *(978-3-211-48961-1(4)*, 3211489614) Springer Wien AUT. Dist: Actar Birkhauser Distribution.

Braun. Competition Architecture. 2010. (Architecture in Focus Ser.). (ENG., Illus.). 242p. 99.95 *(978-3-03768-041-4(5)*, Braun Publish,Csi) Continental Sales, Inc.

Braun Editorial Staff. Relax! Best of Bath Design. 2008. (ENG., Illus.). 400p. pap. 19.95 *(978-3-938780-68-8(1)*, Braun Publish,Csi) Continental Sales, Inc.

—1000x Architecture of the Americas. 2008. (ENG., Illus.). 1024p. 125.00 *(978-3-938780-56-5(8)*, Braun Publish,Csi) Continental Sales, Inc.

Braun Editorial Staff, ed. Pure Plastic: New Materials for Today's Architecture. 2008. (ENG., Illus.). 256p. 49.95 *(978-3-938780-51-0(7)*, Braun Publish,Csi) Continental Sales, Inc.

Britton, Karla, ed. Constructing the Ineffable: Contemporary Sacred Architecture. 2011. (ENG., Illus.). 248p. 50.00 *(978-0-300-17037-5(8))* Yale Univ. Pr.

Broadhurst, Ron. Houses: Modern Natural - Natural Modern. 2010. (ENG., Illus.). 300p. 60.00 *(978-0-8478-3477-8(8))* Rizzoli International Pubns., Inc.

—Next Houses: Architecture for the Twenty-First Century. 2009. (ENG., Illus.). 256p. 50.00 *(978-0-8109-5401-4(X))* Abrams.

Broto, Carles. Facades Design. 2011. (ENG.). 300p. 49.00 *(978-84-92796-83-0(9))* Links International (Leading International Key Services Barcelona, S.A.) ESP. Dist: National Bk. Network.

Browne, Beth. 100 Country Houses: New Rural Architecture. 2009. (ENG., Illus.). 224p. 60.00 *(978-1-86470-332-0(6))* Images Publishing Group AUS. Dist: National Bk. Network.

Browne, Beth, ed. 21st Century Architecture: Apartment Living. 2011. (ENG., Illus.). 224p. 50.00 *(978-1-86470-445-7(4))* Images Publishing Group AUS. Dist: National Bk. Network.

Burkhalter, Marianne. Finding Buildings. Sumi, Christian, ed. 2010. (ENG & GER., Illus.). 174p. 75.00 *(978-3-85881-297-1(8))* Scheidegger und Spiess AG, Verlag CHE. Dist: Antique Collectors' Club.

Ceferin, Petra & Pozar, Cvetka. Architectural Epicentres: Inventing Architecture, Intervening in Reality. 2008. (Illus.). 164p. *(978-961-6669-03-0(6))* Actar Birkhauser Distribution.

Chan, Yenna. Sustainable Environments. 2008. (Contemporary Design in Detail Ser.). (ENG., Illus.). 192p. pap. 25.00 *(978-1-59253-504-0(6)*, 1592535046) Quayside.

Chapman, Tony, ed. Architecture 07: The Guide to the Riba Awards. 2007. (Architecture: the Guide to the Riba Awards Ser.). (ENG., Illus.). 215p. pap. 22.95 *(978-1-85894-381-7(7))* Merrell Pubs. Ltd. GBR. Dist: Perseus Distribution.

Christiane, Sauer. Made of... New Materials Sourcebook for Architecture & Design. 2010. (Illus.). 280p. 78.00 *(978-3-89955-289-8(X))* Die Gestalten Verlag DEU. Dist: Prestel Publishing.

Cohen, Jean-Louis. Le Corbusier. Gossel, Peter, ed. 25th ed. 2009. (25 Ser.). (ENG., Illus.). 96p. 14.99 *(978-3-8365-1308-1(0))* TASCHEN DEU. Dist: Ingram Pub. Services.

Coll, Ramon Faura, ed. Architectures Without Place: 1968/2008. 2010. (Illus.). 288p. pap. *(978-84-96842-44-1(4))* Colegio de Arquitectos de Catalunya.

Colletti, Marjan, ed. Exuberance: New Virtuosity in Contemporary Architecture. 2010. (Architectural Design Ser.). (ENG.). 144p. pap. 45.00 *(978-0-470-71714-1(9)*, Wiley) Wiley, John & Sons, Inc.

Conrad-Bercah & Office, W. West Workroom: Towards a New Sobriety in Architecture Theory + Practice. 2008. (ENG., Illus.). 224p. per. 45.00 *(978-88-8158-656-1(8))* Charta ITA. Dist: D.A.P./Distributed Art Pubs.

Costa Duran, Sergi, ed. High Density Housing. 2009. (Illus.). 256p. *(978-84-92463-35-0(X))* Loft Pubns.

Creation Magazine Staff. Contemporary Architecture in China. Yajun, Jiang, tr. 2011. (Discovering China Ser.). (ENG., Illus.). 128p. 16.95 *(978-1-60220-116-3(1))* Reader's Digest Assn., Inc., The.

Crosbie, Michael J. New York Dozen: Gen X Architects. 2011. (ENG., Illus.). 224p. 59.95 *(978-1-86470-396-2(2))* Images Publishing Group AUS. Dist: National Bk. Network.

Davidson, Cynthia, ed. Log 10 Summer/Fall 2007: Observations on architecture & the contemporary City. 2007. (Illus.). 152p. pap. 10.00 *(978-0-9746521-9-1(9))* Anyone Corp.

—Log 9 Winter/Spring 2007: Observations on architecture & the contemporary City. 2007. (Illus.). 128p. pap. 10.00 *(978-0-9746521-8-4(0))* Anyone Corp.

Ddg: One World, One Firm. 2012. (ENG., Illus.). 256p. 59.95 ***(978-1-86470-468-6(3))*** Images Publishing Group AUS. Dist: National Bk. Network.

De Bure, Gilles. Talk about Contemporary Architecture: Who, What, Where, When, How, Why. 2010. (ENG., Illus.). 256p. pap. 24.95 *(978-2-08-030131-4(4))* Flammarion et Cie FRA. Dist: Random Hse., Inc.

de Haro, Fernando & Fuentes, Omar. Natural Architecture: The Joy of Living in Harmony. 2010. (ENG & SPA., Illus.). 240p. 45.00 *(978-607-437-052-2(4))* AM Editores MEX. Dist: Perseus-PGW.

de Haro, Fernando & Fuentes, Omar, compiled by. Ideas: Natural. 2010. (ENG., Illus.). 272p. pap. 24.95 ***(978-607-437-034-8(6))*** AM Editores MEX. Dist: Perseus-PGW.

de Haro, Fernando & Fuentes, Omar, compiled by. Spaces: Vanguard Expression. 2011. (ENG & SPA., Illus.). 176p. 39.95 *(978-607-437-040-9(0))* AM Editores MEX. Dist: Perseus-PGW.

de Lapuerta, Jose Maria, ed. Collective Housing: A Manual. 2007. (Illus.). 223p. per. *(978-84-96954-15-1(3))* Actar Birkhauser Distribution.

Decker, Julie. True North: New Alaskan Architecture. 2010. (ENG., Illus.). 96p. 29.90 *(978-3-03768-020-9(2)*, Braun Publish,Csi) Continental Sales, Inc.

Decker, Julie & Princeton Architectural Press Staff. Modern North: Architecture on the Frozen Edge. 2010. (ENG., Illus.). 240p. 45.00 *(978-1-56898-899-3(0))* Princeton Architectural Pr.

Deckler, Thorsten, et al. Contemporary South African Architecture in a Landscape of Transition. 2008. 216p. pap. 39.95 *(978-0-7021-7969-3(8))* Double Storey Bks. ZAF. Dist: International Publishers Marketing.

Deliyannis, Melina. Powers Brown Architecture. 2007. (Neoarchitecture Ser.). (ENG., Illus.). 124p. 49.50 *(978-1-86470-250-7(8))* Images Publishing Group AUS. Dist: National Bk. Network.

Della Casa, Francesco. The Rolex Learning Center. 2010. 224p. *(978-2-940222-44-5(4))* Actar Birkhauser Distribution.

Design Media Publishing Staff & Big Architecture Staff. Big: Bjarke Ingels Group Projects 2001-2010. 2011. (ENG.). 232p. 40.00 *(978-988-19738-6-3(4))* Design Media Publishing Ltd. HKG. Dist: BookMasters Distribution Services (BDS).

Di Ozesanmuseum Bamberg & Feireiss, Lukas, eds. Spacecraft: Fleeting Architecture & Hideouts. 2007. (Illus.). 254p. 79.00 *(978-3-89955-192-1(3))* Die Gestalten Verlag DEU. Dist: Prestel Publishing.

Diamond, A. J., et al. Insight & on Site: The Architecture of Diamond & Schmitt, 1 vol. 2008. (ENG., Illus.). 352p. 60.00 *(978-1-55365-277-9(0))* D&M Pubs. Inc. CAN. Dist: Perseus-PGW.

Didelon, Valery, et al. Rotor Coproduction, 1 vol. 2011. (ENG & FRE.). 80p. pap. 25.00 *(978-2-930391-35-9(9))* Centre International Pour La Ville, L'Architecture Et Le Paysage BEL. Dist: Innovative Logistics.

Drew, Philip. New Tent Architecture. 2008. (ENG., Illus.). 208p. 60.00 *(978-0-500-34243-5(1))* Thames & Hudson.

Ebner, Peter, et al. Typologie+ Innovativer Wohnungsbau. 2009. (Illus.). 431p. *(978-3-0346-0086-6(0))* Birkhauser Verlag AG.

École nationale supérieure d'architecture de Normandie Staff, contrib. by. Projets de Fin D'études 2006-2008. 2010. (FRE., Illus.). 109p. *(978-2-915548-51-8(X))* Point de vues, Editions.

EDAS - Design Kommunalka Staff, contrib. by. ABD: Within the Range of Architecture. 2007. (Illus.). 350p. pap. 59.95 *(978-3-211-48858-4(8)*, 3211488588) Springer Wien AUT. Dist: Springer.

Fajardo, Julio. MegaMalls. 2010. (Illus.). 215p. *(978-981-245-762-2(3))* Page One Publishing.

Farrell, Terry. Continuum: Farrells, 2001-2011 - Work of the Hong Kong & London Offices. 2012. (ENG., Illus.). 320p. 75.00 ***(978-1-85669-844-3(0))*** King, Laurence Publishing GBR. Dist: Hachette Bk. Group.

Favole, Paolo. The Story of Contemporary Architecture. 2011. (ENG., Illus.). 160p. pap. 19.95 ***(978-3-7913-4598-7(2))*** Prestel Publishing.

Ferrater, Carlos & Ferrater, Borja, eds. Ferrater & Partners: Oab. 2011. (ENG., Illus.). 350p. *(978-84-92861-23-1(1))* Actar Birkhauser Distribution.

Fischer, Joachim. Water. 2008. (Architecture Compact Ser.). 288p. 22.95 *(978-0-8416-0360-8(X))* American Map Corp.

Fischer, Ole W. What Architects Desire. 2010. 400p. pap. 39.95 *(978-3-7091-0328-9(2))* Springer Wien AUT. Dist: Springer.

Fitzgerald, D. Window on the Park: New York's Most Prestigious Properties on Central Park. 2009. (ENG., Illus.). 228p. 45.00 *(978-1-86470-276-7(1))* Images Publishing Group AUS. Dist: National Bk. Network.

Fletcher, Mark. Islands - Îles - Inseln: Zeitgenössische Architektur am Wasser, 1 vol. 2009. (ENG., Illus.). 360p. pap. 59.99 *(978-3-8331-5200-9(1))* h.f.ullmann DEU. Dist: Innovative Logistics.

Foster, Norman & Jenkins, David. Catalogue, Foster + Partners: Catalogue. 2008. (Illus.). 352p. pap. 39.95 *(978-3-7913-3973-3(7))* Prestel Publishing.

Frampton, Kenneth, intro. Som: Architecture of Skidmore, Owings & Merrill, 1997-2008. 2009. (ENG., Illus.). 256p. 60.00 *(978-1-58093-224-0(X))* Monacelli Pr., Inc.

Gabriel, Jean-Pierre & Gabriel, Jean Pierre. Cosmopolitan Living: Glenn Sestig. 2008. (ENG., Illus.). 200p. *(978-90-77213-82-7(1)*, Beta-Plus (Acc)) Antique Collectors' Club.

Gand, Gary. Julius Shulman: Chicago Mid-Century Modernism. 2010. (Illus.). 208p. 60.00 *(978-0-8478-3287-3(2))* Rizzoli International Pubns., Inc.

Gao, Arthur. Hopsca. 2011. (ENG., Illus.). 288p. 50.00 *(978-988-19739-0-0(2))* Design Media Publishing Ltd. HKG. Dist: BookMasters Distribution Services (BDS).

Giusti, M. Adriana, et al. Guide to Piedmont Architecture: Of the 20th Century. 2009. (ENG., Illus.). 408p. pap. 46.00 *(978-88-422-1639-1(9))* Allemandi, Umberto & Co. GBR. Dist: Antique Collectors' Club.

Glancey, Jonathan. Modern Architecture. 2009. (ENG., Illus.). 448p. pap. 16.95 *(978-1-84732-049-0(X))* Carlton Bks., Ltd. GBR. Dist: Sterling Publishing Co., Inc.

—Modern World Architecture: Classic Buildings of Our Time. 2011. (ENG., Illus.). 480p. 39.95 *(978-1-84732-729-1(X))* Carlton Bks., Ltd. GBR. Dist: Sterling Publishing Co., Inc.

Glendinning, Miles. Architecture's Evil Empire? The Triumph & Tragedy of Global Modernism. 2010. (ENG.). 176p. pap. 27.95 *(978-1-86189-756-5(1))* Reaktion Bks., Ltd. GBR. Dist: Chicago Distribution Ctr.

Gregory, Rob. Key Contemporary Buildings: Plans, Sections & Elevation. 2008. (Key Structures: Plans, Sections, Elevations Ser.). (ENG.). 240p. 45.00 *(978-0-393-73242-9(8)*, 73242) Norton, W. W. & Co., Inc.

Greub, Suzanne & Greub, Thierry, eds. Museums in the 21st Century: Concepts, Projects, Buildings. 2nd ed. 2008. (Illus.). 223p. 60.00 *(978-3-7913-3840-8(4))* Prestel Publishing.

Grobman, Yasha & Neuman, Eran, eds. Performalism: Form & Performance in Digital Architecture. 2011. (ENG., Illus.). 224p. (C). 155.00 *(978-0-415-58360-2(8))* Routledge.

Grupo Folcra Edificaciones S.A. Lightweight Skin: A Building Technique Comes to Age. 2010. (Illus.). 216p. *(978-84-92861-40-8(1))* Actar Birkhauser Distribution.

Halpine, Mig. Pickard Chilton - Architecture. 2012. (ENG., Illus.). 500p. 85.00 (978-1-86470-371-9(7)) Images Publishing Group AUS. Dist: National Bk. Network.

Hart, Sara. Ecoarchitecture: The Work of Ken Yeang. 2011. (ENG., Illus.). 272p. 75.00 (978-0-470-72140-7(5), Wiley) Wiley, John & Sons, Inc.

Hartoonian, Gevork. Architecture & Spectacle: A Critique. 2012. (Illus.). 360p. 124.95 (978-1-4094-2293-8(3)) Ashgate Publishing Co.

Hartoonian, Gevork. Crisis of the Object: The Architecture of Theatricality. 2006. (Illus.). 196p. 165.00 (978-0-415-38546-6(6)); per. 74.95 (978-0-415-38547-3(4)) Routledge.

Hay, D. Roger. D. Roger Hay, the Essence of Root Meaning. 2008. (Illus.). 104p. (978-88-7838-146-9(2)) L'Arca Edizioni.

Heinich, Nadin & Eidner, Franziska, texts. Sensing Space: Technologien für Architekturen der Zukunft. 2009. (ENG & GER., Illus.). 160p. pap. 28.00 (978-3-939633-95-2(X)) Jovis Verlag GmbH DEU. Dist: D.A.P./Distributed Art Pubs.

Hindrichs, Dirk U. & Heusler, Winfried. Fassaden / Façades: Gebäudehüllen für das 21. Jahrhundert / Building Envelopes for the 21st Century. 3rd ed. 2010. (ENG & GER., Illus.). 630p. 105.00 (978-3-7643-9959-7(7)) Birkhauser Verlag AG CHE. Dist: Actar Birkhauser Distribution.

Hirschberg, Urs, ed. GAM 07. Zero Landscape: Unfolding Active Agencies of Landscape. 2011. (Graz Architecture Magazine Ser.). 260p. pap. 29.95 (978-3-7091-0536-8(6)) Springer Wien AUT. Dist: Actar Birkhauser Distribution.

Hoffman, Douglas R. Seeking the Sacred in Contemporary Religious Architecture. 2011. 34.95 (978-1-60635-047-8(1)) Kent State Univ. Pr.

HOK. Hok: A Global Design Portfolio. 2009. (ENG., Illus.). 416p. 85.00 (978-1-86470-314-6(8)) Images Publishing Group AUS. Dist: National Bk. Network.

Holl, Steven. House: Black Swan Theory. 2007. (ENG., Illus.). 176p. 40.00 (978-1-56898-587-9(8)) Princeton Architectural Pr.

House, Steven & House, Cathi. Houses in the Sun: Light Movement Embrace. 2008. (ENG., Illus.). 296p. 50.00 (978-1-86470-239-2(7)) Images Publishing Group AUS. Dist: National Bk. Network.

Hu, Jiasi. International Competition. 2011. (ENG.). 417p. 80.00 (978-988-19738-4-9(8)) Design Media Publishing Ltd. HKG. Dist: BookMasters Distribution Services (BDS).

Huber, Werner. Building Bern: A Guide to Contemporary Architecture, 1990-2010. 2010. (Verlag Scheidegger & Spiess-Edition Hochparterre at Scheidegger & Spiess Ser.). (Illus.). 240p. pap. 45.00 (978-3-85881-722-8(8)) Scheidegger und Spiess AG, Verlag CHE. Dist: Antique Collectors' Club.

Hyatt, Peter & Hyatt, Jenny. Great Glass Buildings. 2006. (Designing with Glass Ser.). (ENG., Illus.). 224p. 70.00 (978-1-86470-112-8(9)) Images Publishing Group AUS. Dist: National Bk. Network.

Images Publishing Group. HKS Architects. 2010. (ENG., Illus.). 368p. 80.00 (978-1-86470-336-8(9)) Images Publishing Group AUS. Dist: National Bk. Network.

Images Publishing Staff, PUBLISHING. Ross Barney Architects: Process + Projects. 2007. (ENG., Illus.). 124p. 65.00 (978-1-86470-229-3(X)) Images Publishing Group AUS. Dist: National Bk. Network.

Imhof, Michael & Krempel, León. Berlin: New Architecture - A Guide to the New Buildings from 1989 to Today. 6th ed. 2009. (ENG., Illus.). 163p. pap. 19.80 (978-3-935590-15-0(6), Art Stock Bks. Ltd/Csi) Continental Sales, Inc.

Ingels, Bjarke. Yes Is More: An Archicomic on Architectural Evolution. 2009. (ENG., Illus.). 400p. pap. 29.99 (978-3-8365-2010-2(9), Evergreen) TASCHEN DEU. Dist: Ingram Pub. Services.

International Code Council, (International Code Council (ICC)) & Marinelli, Dominic. Code Source Accessibility: Codes, Standards, & Guidelines. 2011. (ENG.). 64p. spiral bd. 25.95 (978-1-111-03724-6(8)) Delmar Cengage Learning.

Jackowski, Nannette & de Ostos, Ricardo. Ambiguous Spaces, No. 29. 2008. (ENG., Illus.). 30p. pap. 16.95 (978-1-56898-795-8(1)) Princeton Architectural Pr.

Jackowski, Nannette & Ostos, Ricardo O. C de. Hanging Cemetery of Baghdad. 2007. (RIEAeuropa Concepts Ser.). (Illus.). 71p. pap. 39.95 (978-3-211-48872-0(3), 3211488723) Springer Wien AUT. Dist: Springer.

Jaeger, Falk, ed. Auer + Weber + Associated. 2011. (ENG., Illus.). 144p. pap. 39.95 (978-3-86859-037-1(4)) Jovis Verlag GmbH DEU. Dist: D.A.P./Distributed Art Pubs.

Jodidio, Philip. Architecture Now 6! Architektur heute. L'architecture d'aujourd'hui, Vol. 6. 2009. (Architecture Now Ser.). (FRE, GER & ENG., Illus.). 576p. pap. 39.99 (978-3-8365-0193-4(7)) TASCHEN DEU. Dist: Ingram Pub. Services.

—Architecture Now! 7. 2010. (GER, FRE & ENG., Illus.). 480p. pap. 39.99 (978-3-8365-1736-2(1)) TASCHEN DEU. Dist: Ingram Pub. Services.

—Architecture Now! 8. 2012. (ENG, FRE & GER., Illus.). 480p. 39.99 (978-3-8365-2681-4(6)) TASCHEN DEU. Dist: Ingram Pub. Services.

—Architecture Now! Houses 2. 2011. (ENG, FRE & GER., Illus.). 416p. pap. 39.99 (978-3-8365-1973-1(9)) TASCHEN DEU. Dist: Ingram Pub. Services.

—Architecture Now! Wood. 2011. (FRE, GER & ENG., Illus.). 416p. pap. 39.99 (978-3-8365-2329-5(9)) TASCHEN DEU. Dist: Ingram Pub. Services.

Jodidio Philip. Kc Jean Nouvel. 2012. (ENG., Illus.). 96p. pap. 9.99 (978-3-8365-3080-4(5)) TASCHEN DEU. Dist: Ingram Pub. Services.

Jodidio, Philip. Temporary Architecture Now! 2011. (ENG, FRE & GER., Illus.). 416p. pap. 39.99 (978-3-8365-2328-8(0)) TASCHEN DEU. Dist: Ingram Pub. Services.

—Under the Eaves of Architecture: The Aga Khan: Builder & Patron. 2007. (Illus.). 206p. 75.00 (978-3-7913-3781-4(5)) Prestel Publishing.

—Zaha Hadid: Complete Works 1979 - 2009. 2009. (FRE, GER & ENG., Illus.). 500p. 150.00 (978-3-8365-0294-8(1)) TASCHEN DEU. Dist: Ingram Pub. Services.

Jodidio, Philip & Strong, Janet Adams. I. M. Pei: Complete Works. 2008. (ENG., Illus.). 368p. 85.00 (978-0-8478-3145-6(0)) Rizzoli International Pubns., Inc.

Johnson, Philip & Nakamura, Toshio. Glass House. 2007. (ENG.). 256p. pap. 95.00 (978-1-58093-186-1(3)) Monacelli Pr., Inc.

Johnson, Scott. Tectonics of Place: The Architecture Johnson Fain. 2010. (ENG., Illus.). 256p. 59.95 (978-1-86470-395-5(4), Images Publishing Dist Ac) Antique Collectors' Club GBR. Dist: National Bk. Network.

Johnston, Shalmir. Hks Architecture. 2012. (ENG., Illus.). 368p. 20.00 (978-1-86470-456-3(X)) Images Publishing Group AUS. Dist: National Bk. Network.

Karcher, Aksel, text. Light Perspectives. 2011. 267p. (978-3-9813216-1-6(8)) Actar Birkhauser Distribution.

Kaufman, William. The Grand American Home. 2008. (ENG., Illus.). 128p. 49.50 (978-1-86470-181-4(1)) Images Publishing Group AUS. Dist: National Bk. Network.

Klanten, R., et al, eds. Spacecraft 2: More Fleeting Architecture & Hideouts. 2009. (Illus.). 280p. (978-3-89955-233-1(4)) Die Gestalten Verlag.

Klanten, R. & Feireiss, L., eds. Build-on: Converted Architectures & Transformed Buildings. 2009. (Illus.). 240p. (978-3-89955-259-1(8)) Die Gestalten Verlag.

—Closer to God: Religious Architecture & Sacred Spaces. 2010. (Illus.). 320p. (978-3-89955-313-0(6)) Die Gestalten Verlag.

Kleihues + Kleihues Staff, contrib. by. Josef Paul Kleihues: Galeria Kaufhof Berlin Alexanderplatz, 1 vol. 2007. (ENG., Illus.). 64p. pap. 22.00 (978-3-939633-26-6(7)) Jovis Verlag GmbH DEU. Dist: D.A.P./Distributed Art Pubs.

Konrad, Daniela, ed. Interrogating Pop in Architecture. 2009. (ENG., Illus.). 170p. pap. 32.00 (978-3-8030-0694-3(5)) Wasmuth, Ernst J. Verlag GmbH & Co. DEU. Dist: D.A.P./Distributed Art Pubs.

Kristal, Marc. Immaterial World: Transparency in Architecture. 2011. (ENG., Illus.). 216p. 45.00 (978-1-58093-314-8(9)) Monacelli Pr., Inc.

—Re:Crafted: Interpretations of Craft in Contemporary Architecture & Interiors. 2010. (ENG., Illus.). 208p. 50.00 (978-1-58093-276-9(2)) Monacelli Pr., Inc.

Kung. Christian Kerez: Construction, Privacy, Politics, Conflicts & Obsessions. Kueng, Moritz, ed. 2009. (ENG., Illus.). 200p. pap. 45.00 (978-3-7757-2280-3(7)) Hatje Cantz Verlag GmbH & Co KG DEU. Dist: D.A.P./Distributed Art Pubs.

Kurant, Agnieszka & Wasilkowska, Aleksandra. Emergency Exit. 2011. (ENG., Illus.). 79p. pap. 24.95 (978-1-934105-21-4(X)) Sternberg Pr.

Kwinter Sanford. Far from Equilibrium: Essays on Technology & Design Culture. Davidson, Cynthia, ed. 2008. (Illus.). 191p. (978-84-96540-64-4(2)) Actar Birkhauser Distribution.

Lampens, Juliaan. Juliaan Lampens, 1 vol. Campens, Angelique, ed. 2011. (ENG., Illus.). 152p. pap. 64.00 (978-94-6117-005-7(X)) Exhibitions International BEL. Dist: Innovative Logistics.

Land, Carsten. Missao Portugal 2007: An Ephemeral Home. 2010. 80p. 44.90 (978-3-00-024561-9(8)) Edition Axel Menges GmbH DEU. Dist: National Bk. Network.

Lavin, Sylvia, contrib. by. Coop Himmelb(l)au: Central Los Angeles High School No. 9 for the Visual & Performing Arts. 2010. (Illus.). 224p. 49.95 (978-3-7913-4433-1(1)) Prestel Publishing.

Littlefield, David. London (Re)Generation. 2012. (Architectural Design Ser.). (ENG., Illus.). 136p. pap. 45.00 (978-1-119-99378-0(4), Wiley) Wiley, John & Sons, Inc.

Littlefield, David & Jones, Will. Great Modern Structures: 100 Years of Engineering Genius. 2012. (ENG., Illus.). 288p. 45.00 (978-1-78097-001-1(3)) Carlton Bks., Ltd. GBR. Dist: Sterling Publishing Co., Inc.

Loeffler, Jane C. The Architecture of Diplomacy: Building America's Embassies. 2nd ed. 2010. (ENG., Illus.). 336p. pap. 24.95 (978-1-56898-984-6(9)) Princeton Architectural Pr.

Long, Kieran. Hatch: The New Architectural Generation. 2008. (ENG., Illus.). 352p. pap. 35.00 (978-1-85669-562-6(X)) King, Laurence Publishing GBR. Dist: Hachette Bk. Group.

Lootsma, Bart. Reality Bytes: Selected Essays, 1995 to 2010. 2012. (ENG., Illus.). 272p. pap. 49.95 (978-3-7091-0290-9(1), 3709102901) Springer Wien AUT. Dist: Springer.

Lowther, Clare & Schultz, Sarah. Beachlife: Architecture & Interior Design on the Seaside. 2008. (Illus.). 280p. (978-3-89955-302-4(0)) Die Gestalten Verlag.

Lubell, Sam. Living West: New Residential Architecture in Southern California. 2009. (ENG., Illus.). 240p. 50.00 (978-1-58093-249-3(5)) Monacelli Pr., Inc.

Luhan, Gregory A. Digispeak: An illustrated guide to digital architecture design Terms. 240p. 2011. pap. 35.95 (978-0-415-77828-2(X)) 2010. 165.00 (978-0-415-77827-5(1)) Routledge.

M3 360 Modern Architecture III. 2011. (Illus.). 400p. 115.00 (978-988-19018-4-2(7)) Azur Corp. JPN. Dist: Antique Collectors' Club.

Maki, Fumihiko & Pran, Peter C. Peter Pran: Realizations. 2007. (Master Architect Ser.). (ENG., Illus.). 224p. 59.95 (978-1-86470-194-4(3), Images Publishing Dist Ac) Antique Collectors' Club GBR. Dist: National Bk. Network.

Malkin, Helen & Dunton, Nancy. A Guidebook to Contemporary Architecture in Montreal, 1 vol. 2008. (ENG., Illus.). 192p. pap. 24.95 (978-1-55365-346-2(7)) D&M Pubs. Inc. CAN. Dist: Perseus-PGW.

Mansilla + Tunon, ed. The Mansilla + Tunon Studios 2008-2010: Between Rules & Constraints, 1 vol. 2012. (ENG., Illus.). 160p. pap. 45.00 (978-3-03778-281-1(1)) Lars Muller Pubs. CHE. Dist: Prestel Publishing.

Marmol, Leo & Radziner, Ron. Marmol Radziner + Associates: Between Architecture & Construction. 2008. (ENG., Illus.). 176p. pap. 40.00 (978-1-56898-744-6(7)) Princeton Architectural Pr.

Matsui, Midori. Psycho Buildings: Artists Take on Architecture. 2008. (ENG., Illus.). 200p. 59.95 (978-1-85332-268-6(7)) Hayward Gallery Publishing GBR. Dist: D.A.P./Distributed Art Pubs.

Mazzola, Ettore Maria. Architecture & Town Planning Operating Instructions: Saving Architecture Might Save the Italian Economy. 2011. 280p. pap. 33.95 (978-88-7448-840-7(8)) Gangemi ITA. Dist: International Publishers Marketing.

McAlpine, Bobby & Sully, Susan. The Home Within Us: Romantic Houses, Evocative Rooms. 2010. (ENG., Illus.). 240p. 55.00 (978-0-8478-3289-7(9)) Rizzoli International Pubns., Inc.

McGetrick, Brendan, ed. Who Is Architecture: the 2009 Domus China Interviews. 2011. (ENG., Illus.). 131p. pap. 28.00 (978-988-18816-6-3(8)) Timezone 8 Ltd. HKG. Dist: D.A.P./Distributed Art Pubs.

McLachlan, Fiona. Architectural Colour in the Professional Palette. 2012. (ENG., Illus.). 248p. (C). 165.00 (978-0-415-59708-1(0)); pap. 54.95 (978-0-415-59709-8(9)) Routledge.

McLeod, Virginia, et al. Detail in Contemporary Timber Architecture. 2010. (ENG., Illus.). 224p. 50.00 (978-1-85669-641-8(3)) King, Laurence Publishing GBR. Dist: Hachette Bk. Group.

Mead, Christopher Curtis & Predock, Antoine. Roadcut: The Architecture of Antoine Predock. 2011. (ENG., Illus.). 210p. 75.00 (978-0-8263-5009-1(7)) Univ. of New Mexico Pr.

Mehta, Geeta & MacDonald, Deanna. New Japan Architecture: Recent Works by the World's Leading Architects. 2011. (ENG., Illus.). 224p. 49.95 (978-4-8053-0948-3(2)) Tuttle Publishing.

Meuser, Philipp & Nielsen, Fried. Stadt und Haus: Berlinische Architektur Im 21. Jahrhundert = Berlin Architecture in the 21st Century. 2009. (RUS, GER, SPA & ENG., Illus.). 1p. pap. 49.95 (978-3-938666-43-2(9)) DOM Pubs. DEU. Dist: Innovative Logistics.

Meyhofer, Dirk, ed. Water Enjoyment: Sustainable Quality, Technology & Design. 2011. (GER & ENG., Illus.). 224p. 49.95 (978-3-03768-078-0(4), Braun Publish,Csi) Continental Sales, Inc.

Miller Hull Partnership Staff. The Miller Hull Partnership: Public Works. 2009. (ENG., Illus.). 272p. 50.00 (978-1-56898-754-5(4)) Princeton Architectural Pr.

Mistur, Mark. The Architecture of EMPAC: the Tangible & the Tantalizing: The Curtis R. Priem Experimental Media & Performing Art Center. 2011. (ENG.). 256p. 40.00 (978-0-578-07240-1(8)) Oro Editions.

Moe, Kiel. Integrated Design in Contemporary Architecture. 2008. (ENG., Illus.). 208p. 65.00 (978-1-56898-745-3(5)) Princeton Architectural Pr.

Moffatt, Laura & Heathcote, Edwin. Contemporary Church Architecture. 2007. (ENG., Illus.). 240p. 90.00 (978-0-470-03156-8(5), Wiley) Wiley, John & Sons, Inc.

Monninger, Michael. Coop Himmelblau. Gossel, Peter, ed. 2010. (GER, FRE & ENG., Illus.). 528p. 150.00 (978-3-8365-1788-1(4)) TASCHEN DEU. Dist: Ingram Pub. Services.

Montaner, Josep Maria. Tools for Inhabiting the Present: Housing in the 21st Century. 2011. (ENG & SPA.). 210p. pap. (978-84-614-7504-9(6)) Actar Birkhauser Distribution.

Moore, Lesley. Dutch Architects, Vol. 9. 2009. (ENG., Illus.). 264p. 80.00 (978-90-6369-196-7(3)) Bis B.V., Uitgeverij(BIS Publishers) NLD. Dist: Consortium Bk. Sales & Distribution.

Mores, Claudio Marenco & Marsilio. From Fiorucci to the Guerrilla Stores: Shop Displays in Architecture, Marketing & Communications. 2007. (Mode Ser.). (ENG., Illus.). 114p. pap. 19.95 (978-88-317-8957-8(0)) Marsilio Editori spa ITA. Dist: Random Hse., Inc.

Moretti Srl & Giaconia, Paola. Eric Owen Moss: The Uncertainty of Doing. 2006. (ENG., Illus.). 240p. pap. 34.95 (978-88-7624-276-2(7)) Skira Editore ITA. Dist: Random Hse., Inc.

Morris, Linny, photos by. The Hawaiian House Now. 2007. (ENG., Illus.). 192p. 42.00 (978-0-8109-9394-5(5)) Abrams.

Mostafavi, Mohsen, ed. Aga Khan Award for Architecture 2010: Implicate & Explicate. 2011. (ENG., Illus.). 352p. (978-3-03778-242-2(0)) Lars Muller Pubs.

Motro, Rene, ed. Flexible Composite Materials in Architecture, Construction & Interiors. 2012. (ENG., Illus.). 224p. 69.95 (978-3-7643-8972-7(5)) Birkhauser Verlag AG CHE. Dist: Actar Birkhauser Distribution.

Muschamp, Herbert. Hearts of the City: The Selected Writings of Herbert Muschamp. 2009. (ENG.). 912p. 50.00 (978-0-375-40406-1(6)) Knopf, Alfred A. Inc.

Myerson, Jeremy & Ross, Philip. Radical Office Design. 2006. (978-0-7892-0887-3(3)); (ENG., Illus.). 192p. 65.00 (978-0-7892-0886-6(5)) Abbeville Pr., Inc.

Nash, Eric Peter. Manhattan Skyscrapers. 3rd ed. 2010. (ENG., Illus.). 240p. 50.00 (978-1-56898-967-9(9)) Princeton Architectural Pr.

Obrist, Hans Ulrich & Koolhaas, Rem. Rem Koolhaas, 1 vol. 2007. (ENG., Illus.). 68p. per. 17.95 (978-3-86560-077-6(8)) Verlag der Buchhandlung Walther Konig DEU. Dist: D.A.P./Distributed Art Pubs.

Ojeda, Oscar, ed. 3 x 3: the Architecture of Suyama Peterson Deguchi. 2008. (ENG., Illus.). 112p. 35.00 (978-0-9795395-7-2(9)) Oro Editions.

Oswald, Ansgar. Architectural Models. Keil, Uta, ed. 2008. (Illus.). 247p. (978-981-245-482-9(9)) Page One Publishing.

O'Toole, Sean, et al. Sound, Space, Design: The Architecture of Don Albert & Partners. 2011. (ENG., Illus.). 312p. pap. 45.00 (978-0-620-46570-0(0)) Papadakis Dist A/C.

Panache Partners LLC Staff. Spectacular Homes of Western Canada: An Exclusive Showcase of the Finest Designers in British Columbia. 2009. (Spectacular Homes Ser.). (ENG., Illus.). 300p. 34.95 (978-1-933415-71-0(1)) Panache Partners, LLC.

Panache Partners Staff. Spectacular Homes of Toronto: An Exclusive Showcase of the Finest Designers in Ontario. 2009. (Spectacular Homes Ser.). (ENG., Illus.). 300p. 34.95 (978-1-933415-72-7(X)) Panache Partners, LLC.

Papadakis, Alexandra & Papadakis, Andreas, eds. Innovations: From Experimentation to Realisation. 2006. (ENG., Illus.). pap. 30.00 (978-1-901092-46-2(1)) Papadakis Dist A/C.

Paredes, Cristina. Sketch - Public Buildings: How Architects Conceive Public Buildings. Paredes, Cristina, ed. 2008. (Illus.). 192p. (978-84-96936-32-4(5)) Loft Pubns.

Pauwels, Wim. Contemporary Classic: Esther Gutmer. Watkinson, Laura, tr. 2008. (and D Ser.). (ENG., Illus.). 200p. (978-90-8944-006-8(2), Beta-Plus (Acc)) Antique Collectors' Club.

—Contemporary Living 2010-2011. 2009. (ENG., Illus.). 320p. instr.'s hndbk. ed. (978-90-8944-019-8(4), Beta-Plus (Acc)) Antique Collectors' Club.

Pauwels, Wim. Wood Marsh Architects: Selected Works. 2012. (ENG., Illus.). 224p. 125.00 (978-90-8944-115-7(8)) Beta-Plus Pubs. BEL. Dist: Antique Collectors' Club.

Phaidon Press Editors. Living in the New Millennium, Houses at the Start of the 21st Century. 2009. (ENG., Illus.). 160p. 35.00 (978-0-7148-5599-8(5)) Phaidon Pr., Inc.

—The Modernist House. 2009. (ENG., Illus.). 112p. 29.95 (978-0-7148-4968-3(5)) Phaidon Pr., Inc.

—10x10_2. 2008. (ENG., Illus.). 464p. pap. 49.95 (978-0-7148-4864-8(6)) Phaidon Pr. Ltd. GBR. Dist: Hachette Bk. Group.

Phaidon Press Editors, ed. Building the New Millennium, Architecture at the Start of the 21st Century. 2009. (ENG., Illus.). 160p. 35.00 (978-0-7148-5600-1(2)) Phaidon Pr., Inc.

—The Phaidon Atlas of 21st Century World Architecture. 2008. (ENG., Illus.). 812p. 195.00 (978-0-7148-4874-7(3)) Phaidon Pr., Inc.

—The Phaidon Atlas of 21st Century World Architecture: Travel Edition. 2011. (ENG.). 438p. pap. 24.95 (978-0-7148-4878-5(6)) Phaidon Pr., Inc.

Phaidon Press Editors, ed. 10x10 - 3: 100 Architects 10 Critics. 2009. (ENG., Illus.). 468p. 90.00 (978-0-7148-4953-9(7)) Phaidon Pr., Inc.

Pietro, Silvio San & Gallo, Paola. New Shops 9: Made in Italy. 2010. (ITA & ENG., Illus.). 228p. (978-88-7685-173-5(9), Edizioni L'archivolto (Acc)) Antique Collectors' Club.

Porter, Jenelle, ed. Fertilizers: Olin / Eisenman, 1 vol. 2007. (ENG., Illus.). 96p. per. 25.00 (978-0-88454-109-7(6)) Univ. of Pennsylvania, Institute of Contemporary Art.

Powers, Alan. Aldington, Craig & Collinge. 2009. (Twentieth-century Architects Ser.). (ENG., Illus.). 144p. (C). pap. 40.00 (978-1-85946-302-4(9)) English Heritage GBR. Dist: Brown, David Bk. Co., The.

Price, Travis. The Archaeology of Tomorrow: Architecture & the Spirit of Place. 2006. (ENG., Illus.). 208p. 45.00 (978-1-932771-93-0(X), Earth Aware Editions) Mandala Publishing.

Princeton Architectural Press Staff. El Segundo. 2007. (ENG., Illus.). 400p. 60.00 (978-1-56898-700-2(5)) Princeton Architectural Pr.

Prix, Wolf D. 99+ Selected Student Work. 2009. (Edition Angewandte Ser.). (Illus.). 208p. pap. 29.95 (978-3-211-89798-0(4)) Springer Wien AUT. Dist: Springer.

Prix, Wolf D., ed. Form = Raum Netz / Form = Space Net: 10. Internationale Architektur Biennale Venedig. la Biennale di Venezia 2006. 10th International Exhibition of Architecture. la Biennale di Venezia 2006. 2008. (Illus.). 140p. pap. 39.95 (978-3-211-34363-0(6), 3211343636) Springer.

—Studio Prix: University of Applied Arts, 1990-2011. 2012. (Edition Angewandte Ser.). (GER & ENG., Illus.). 250p. pap. 49.95 (978-3-7091-0844-4(6), 3709108446) Springer Wien AUT. Dist: Springer.

Puglisi, Luigi Prestinenza. New Directions in Contemporary Architecture: Evolutions & Revolutions in Building Design since 1988. 2008. (ENG., Illus.). 240p. 140.00 (978-0-470-51889-2(8), Wiley) Wiley, John & Sons, Inc.

—New Directions in Contemporary Architecture: Evolutions & Revolutions in Building Design Since 1988. 2008. (ENG., Illus.). 240p. pap. 45.00 (978-0-470-51890-8(1), Wiley) Wiley, John & Sons, Inc.

Puglisi, Luigi Prestinenza, ed. Theoretical Meltdown. 2009. (Architectural Design Ser.). (ENG.). 136p. pap. 80.00 (978-0-470-99779-6(6), Wiley) Wiley, John & Sons, Inc.

Rael, Ronald. Earth Architecture. (ENG., Illus.). 2010. 208p. pap. 24.95 (978-1-56898-945-7(8)) 2008. 192p. 45.00 (978-1-56898-767-5(5)) Princeton Architectural Pr.

Rattenbury, Kester, et al. Architects Today. 2006. (ENG., Illus.). 240p. pap. 19.95 (978-1-85669-492-6(5)) King, Laurence Publishing GBR. Dist: Hachette Bk. Group.

Ratti, Annie, et al, texts. Yona Friedman. 2009. (ENG., Illus.). 96p. pap. 27.95 (978-88-8158-705-6(X)) Charta ITA. Dist: D.A.P./Distributed Art Pubs.

Rauterberg, Hanno. Talking Architecture: Interviews with Architects. 2012. (Illus.). 160p. pap. 19.95 (978-3-7913-4684-7(9)) Prestel Publishing.

Redi, Andrea & Redi, Ivan, texts. Ortlos: Architecture of the Networks, Volume 2. 2012. (ENG., Illus.). 208p. 55.00 (978-3-7757-2971-0(2)) Hatje Cantz Verlag GmbH & Co KG DEU. Dist: D.A.P./Distributed Art Pubs.

Richters, Christian, photos by. UNStudio: Fotografien von Christian Richters. 2009. (ENG & GER., Illus.). 144p. pap. 39.95 (978-3-939633-84-6(4)) Jovis Verlag GmbH DEU. Dist: D.A.P./Distributed Art Pubs.

Robinson, Julia Williams & Robinson, Julia W. Institution & Home: Architecture as a Cultural Medium. 2006. (ENG., Illus.). 268p. pap. 74.00 (978-90-8594-007-4(9)) Purdue Univ. Pr.

Rooney, E. Ashley, et al. Green Homes: Dwellings for the 21st Century. 2008. (Illus.). 160p. bds. 39.99 (978-0-7643-3033-9(0)) Schiffer Publishing, Ltd.

Rosenfeld, Gavriel. Building after Auschwitz: Jewish Architecture & the Memory of the Holocaust. 2011. (ENG., Illus.). 448p. 50.00 (978-0-300-16914-0(0)) Yale Univ. Pr.

Ryan, Raymund & McCullough, Niall. Rush Library. 2010. (Illus.). 39p. pap. (978-1-906429-10-2(3)) Associated Editions.

Ryan, Zoe. Building with Water: Concepts Typology Design. 2010. 160p. 89.95 (978-3-0346-0156-6(5)) Birkhauser Verlag AG CHE. Dist: Actar Birkhauser Distribution.

Schleifer, Simone. Converted Spaces. 2006. (Illus.). 380p. pap. 29.99 (978-3-8228-5147-0(7)) TASCHEN DEU. Dist: Ingram Pub. Services.

Schleifer, Simone, ed. Dream Houses by the Seaside. 2006. (ENG., Illus.). 381p. pap. 29.99 (978-3-8228-2787-1(8)) TASCHEN DEU. Dist: Ingram Pub. Services.

Schmal, Peter & van Berkel, Ben, eds. The Pavilion. 2010. (ENG & GER., Illus.). 192p. pap. 40.00 (978-3-7757-2494-4(X)) Hatje Cantz Verlag GmbH & Co KG DEU. Dist: D.A.P./Distributed Art Pubs.

Schrijver, Lara, text. Radical Games. 2010. (ENG., Illus.). 248p. pap. 40.00 (978-90-5662-678-5(7)) NAi Uitgevers / Publishers Stichting NLD. Dist: D.A.P./Distributed Art Pubs.

Schröpfer, Thomas. Material Design: Informing Architecture by Materiality. 2010. (ENG., Illus.). 216p. 69.95 (978-3-0346-0035-4(6)) Birkhauser Verlag AG CHE. Dist: Actar Birkhauser Distribution.

Schulz, Daniel. Global Creative Architecture. 2008. (Illus.). 271p. (978-981-245-543-7(4)) Page One Publishing.

Sejima, Kazuyo. People Meet in Architecture: Biennale Architettura 2010, 2 vols. 2010. (ENG., Illus.). 573p. pap. 90.00 (978-88-317-0651-3(9)) Marsilio Editori spa ITA. Dist: Random Hse., Inc.

Shaoqiang, Wang. M3 360 Modern Architecture No. 4. Shaoqiang, Wang, ed. 2012. (ENG., Illus.). 400p. 115.00 **(978-4-903233-74-1(X))** Azur Corp. JPN. Dist: National Bk. Network.

Sheil, Bob. Manufacturing the Bespoke. 2012. (AD Reader Ser.). (ENG.). 280p. pap. 55.00 **(978-0-470-66582-4(3)**, Wiley) Wiley, John & Sons, Inc.

—Manufacturing the Bespoke: Making & Prototyping Architecture. 2012. (AD Reader Ser.). (ENG.). 280p. 140.00 **(978-0-470-66583-1(1)**, Wiley) Wiley, John & Sons, Inc.

Smith, Adrian. Adrian Smith + Gordon Gill Architecture: Projects & Sustainable Initiatives. 2011. (ENG., Illus.). 500p. 80.00 (978-1-86470-385-6(7)) Images Publishing Group, The.

Smith, Terry E. The Architecture of Aftermath. 2006. (Illus.). 280p. per. 32.50 (978-0-226-76469-6(9)) Univ. of Chicago Pr.

Snoehetta, ed. Snoehetta Works: Architecture. Interior. Landscape. 2009. (Illus.). 320p. 54.95 (978-3-03778-147-0(5), 3037781475) Springer.

Sorkin, Michael. All over the Map: Writing on Buildings & Cities. 2011. (ENG., Illus.). 320p. 34.95 (978-1-84467-323-0(5), 844323) Verso Bks. GBR. Dist: Norton, W. W. & Co., Inc.

Spiller, Neil. Digital Architecture Now: A Global Survey of Emerging Talent. 2009. (ENG., Illus.). 400p. 65.00 (978-0-500-34247-3(4)) Thames & Hudson.

Stathaki, Ellie & Bell, Jonathan. The New Modern House: Redefining Functionalism. 2010. (ENG., Illus.). 240p. 50.00 (978-1-85669-684-5(7)) King, Laurence Publishing GBR. Dist: Hachette Bk. Group.

Stoner, Jill. Toward a Minor Architecture. 2012. (ENG., Illus.). 176p. (gr. 17). pap. 19.95 **(978-0-262-51764-5(7))** MIT Pr.

Strongman, Cathy. 100 Houses: Modern Designs for Contemporary Living. 2009. (Illus.). 352p. 45.00 (978-1-85894-469-2(4)) Merrell Pubs. Ltd. GBR. Dist: Perseus Distribution.

Tchoban, Sergei. Sergei Tchoban: Art. 2010. (ENG., Illus.). 256p. 59.95 (978-1-86470-389-4(X), Images Publishing Dist Ac) Antique Collectors' Club GBR. Dist: National Bk. Network.

The Plan Staff. Plans & Details for Contemporary Architects: Building with Colour. 2011. (ENG., Illus.). 240p. 65.00 (978-0-500-34267-1(9), 534267) Thames & Hudson.

Thiemann, Robert, ed. Frame: the Great Indoors, Issue 77: Nov/Dec 2010. 2011. (Frame: the Great Indoors Ser.). (ENG., Illus.). 240p. pap. 19.95 (978-90-77174-31-9(1)) Frame Pubs. NLD. Dist: Consortium Bk. Sales & Distribution.

—Frame: the Great Indoors, Issue 78: Jan/Feb 2011. 2011. (Frame: the Great Indoors Ser.). (ENG., Illus.). 240p. pap. 19.95 (978-90-77174-32-6(X)) Frame Pubs. NLD. Dist: Consortium Bk. Sales & Distribution.

Thiemann, Robert, ed. Frame: the Great Indoors, Issue 79. 2011. (Frame: the Great Indoors Ser.). (ENG., Illus.). 240p. pap. 19.95 **(978-90-77174-33-3(8))** Frame Pubs. NLD. Dist: Consortium Bk. Sales & Distribution.

Thompson, Jessica Cargill. 40 Architects Around 40. 25th anniv. ed. 2006. (ENG, FRE & GER., Illus.). 557p. pap. 14.99 (978-3-8228-5033-6(0)) TASCHEN DEU. Dist: Ingram Pub. Services.

Tombazis, Alexandros N. Alexandros N. Tombazis & Associates Architects. 2011. (ENG., Illus.). 240p. 59.95 (978-1-86470-378-8(4)) Images Publishing Group AUS. Dist: National Bk. Network.

Turenscape Architects Staff, contrib. by. The Art of Survival. 2011. (Illus.). 256p. 39.99 **(978-84-9936-861-0(1))** Loft Pubns. ESP. Dist: Prestel Publishing.

Uffelen, Chris van. Ecological Architecture. 2009. (ENG., Illus.). 424p. 99.95 (978-3-03768-010-0(5), Braun Publish,Csi) Continental Sales, Inc.

Uffelen, Van Chris. Factory Design. 2008. (Illus.). 336p. 62.50 (978-3-03768-005-6(9), Braun Publish,Csi) Continental Sales, Inc.

van Uffelen, Chis. Ecological Architecture. 2009. (Architecture in Focus Ser.). (Illus.). 424p. 99.95 (978-3-938780-79-4(7)) BRAUN DEU. Dist: National Bk. Network.

Veer, F., ed. Challenging Glass: Conference on Architectural & Structural Applications of Glass. 2008. 676p. 218.00 (978-1-58603-866-3(4)) IOS Pr., Inc.

Verges, Mireia. Light in Architecture. Meyers, Julie, ed. Bagott, Heather, tr. 2008. (ENG., Illus.). 512p. (978-90-76886-74-9(1)) Tectum B.V.B.A.

Vidiella, Alex Sánchez. The Sourcebook of Contemporary Architecture. 2011. (ENG., Illus.). 464p. pap. 19.99 (978-0-06-208369-2(4), Collins Design) HarperCollins Pubs.

Vidiella, Alex Sánchez, et al. 1000 Architectural Details: A Selection of the World's Most Interesting Building Elements. 2010. (ENG., Illus.). 296p. 29.95 (978-1-55407-783-0(4)) Firefly Bks., Ltd.

Vidler, Anthony. Architecture Between Spectacle & Use. 2008. (Clark Studies in the Visual Arts). (Illus.). xiii, 184p. (978-0-931102-66-0(9)) Clark, Sterling & Francine Art Institute.

Vinoly, Rafael & Jodidio, Philip. Rafael Vinoly Architects. 2010. (Illus.). 550p. 99.00 (978-3-7913-5074-5(9)) Prestel Publishing.

Walden, Gert, ed. Baumschlager - Eberle - Annäherungen Approaches. 2009. (GER & ENG., Illus.). 148p. (978-3-211-79158-5(2), 3211791582) Actar Birkhauser Distribution.

Wang, Shaoqing. Beyond Design: 2010 Shanghai Expo Architecture & Space Design. 2011. (ENG., Illus.). 320p. 95.00 (978-4-903233-69-7(3)) Azur Corp. JPN. Dist: Antique Collectors' Club.

Watkinson, Gordon. Bauhaus Zwanzig - 21: Ideen für ein neues Jahrhundert. 2009. (GER., Illus.). 231p. (978-3-0346-0055-2(0)) Birkhauser Verlag AG.

Weiss, Klaus-Dieter. Workmanship: Working Philosophy & Design Practice. 2011. (ENG., Illus.). 320p. 69.95 (978-3-0346-0481-9(5)) Birkhauser Verlag AG CHE. Dist: Actar Birkhauser Distribution.

Widder, Lynnette, ed. Alumi Travel Award 2009. 2009. pap. 18.00 (978-1-61584-120-2(2)) Independent Pub.

Williams, Keith. Keith Williams: Projects 1. 2010. (Master Architects Ser.). (ENG., Illus.). 224p. 59.95 (978-1-86470-235-4(4), Images Publishing Dist Ac) Antique Collectors' Club GBR. Dist: National Bk. Network.

Wood, Anthony. Best Tall Buildings 2009. 2009. (ENG., Illus.). 168p. 50.00 (978-0-415-77974-6(X)) Routledge.

Wood, Antony, ed. Best Tall Buildings 2010. 2010. (ENG., Illus.). 200p. 49.95 (978-0-415-59404-2(9)) Routledge.

—Best Tall Buildings 2011. 2011. (ENG., Illus.). 216p. 49.95 (978-0-415-68326-5(2)) Routledge.

Worrall, Julian & Solomon, Erez Golani. 21st Century Tokyo: A Guide to Contemporary Architecture, 1 vol. 2010. (ENG., Illus.). 240p. pap. 20.00 (978-4-7700-3054-2(1)) Kodansha America, Inc.

Yale School of & Yale School of Architecture. Future-Proofing: 02: Stuart Lipton / Richard Rogers / Chris Wise / Malcolm Smith. Rappaport, Nina & Steffen, Andrew, eds. 2007. (Edward P. Bass Distinguished Visiting Architecture Fellowship Ser.). (ENG., Illus.). 192p. pap. 30.00 (978-0-393-73237-5(1), 73237) Norton, W. W. & Co., Inc.

Yale School of Architecture. Future Proofing. 2007. pap. 28.00 (978-0-7937-3237-1(9)) Norton, W. W. & Co., Inc.

Yanli, Hu, ed. Best Selection of Shanglin. 2010. (Architecture Highlights Ser.). (ENG., Illus.). 416p. 100.00 (978-4-903233-62-8(6)) Azur Corp. JPN. Dist: Antique Collectors' Club.

Yee, Roger. HLW at 125. 2009. (Illus.). 164p. 60.00 net. (978-1-58471-169-8(8)) Visual Reference Pubns., Inc.

Yee, Roger, ed. HLW At 125: Better Performance By Design, 1 vol. 2010. (ENG., Illus.). 197p. 60.00 (978-0-9825989-3-1(9)) Visual Profile Bks., Inc.

Zeytinoglu, Arkan, ed. Geometry of Light: The Architecture of Arkan Zeytinoglu. 2011. (Illus.). 350p. 69.95 (978-3-7091-0538-2(2), 3709105382) Springer Wien AUT. Dist: Springer.

Zumthor, Peter. Penser L'architecture: Thinking Architecture, Third Edition (French Edition) 2010. (FRE.). 112p. 44.95 (978-3-0346-0582-3(X)) Birkhauser Verlag AG CHE. Dist: Actar Birkhauser Distribution.

ARCHITECTURE, MOORISH

see Islamic Architecture

ARCHITECTURE, MUSLIM

see Islamic Architecture

ARCHITECTURE, NAVAL

see Naval Architecture

ARCHITECTURE, NORMAN

Berg, Mary & Jones, Howard. Norman Churches in the Canterbury Diocese. 2009. (ENG., Illus.). 208p. pap. 39.95 (978-0-7524-4776-6(9)) History Pr. Ltd.,The GBR. Dist: Independent Pubs. Group.

Giles, Kate & Dyer, Christopher, eds. Town & Country in the Middle Ages: Contrasts, Contacts & Interconnections, 1100-1500. 2007. (Society for Medieval Archaeology Monograph Ser.). (ENG., Illus.). 300p. (C). per. 55.00 (978-1-905981-39-7(2)) Maney Publishing GBR. Dist: Brown, David Bk. Co., The.

ARCHITECTURE, OTTOMAN

Bachmann, Martin & Tanman, M. Baha. Ahsap Istanbul: Konut Mimarisinden örnekleri = Istanbuls Holzhäuser: Beispiele Seiner Historischen Wohnarchitektur = Wooden Istanbul: Examples from Housing Architecture. 2008. (GER, TUR & ENG., Illus.). 339p. (978-975-9123-55-0(X)) Suna Ve Inan Kirac Vakfi.

Ergul, Emre. Ottoman House. 2009. 136p. pap. (978-3-639-14074-3(5)) VDM Verlag Dr. Mueller e.K.

Farah, Caesar E. The Ottoman Forts & Castles of Yemen: A Photographic & Architectural Analysis. 2011. (Illus.). 180p. 109.95 (978-0-7734-1291-0(3)) Mellen, Edwin Pr., The.

Freely, John. History of Ottoman Architecture. 2011. (Illus.). 464p. lib. bdg. 194.00 (978-1-84564-506-9(5)) WIT Pr GBR. Dist: WIT Pr.

Kafescioglu, Çigdem. Constantinopolis/Istanbul: Cultural Encounter, Imperial Vision, & the Construction of the Ottoman Capital. 2009. (Buildings, Landscapes, & Societies Ser.). (ENG., Illus.). 392p. 100.00 (978-0-271-02776-0(2)) Pennsylvania State Univ. Pr.

Kreyenbroek, Philip G. & Marzolph, Ulrich, eds. Oral Literature of Iranian Languages Vol. 2: Kurdish, Pashto, Balochi, Ossetic, Persian & Tajik. 2010. (History of Persian Literature Ser.). (ENG.). 400p. 95.00 (978-1-84511-918-8(5)) I. B. Tauris & Co., Ltd. GBR. Dist: Macmillan.

Mill, Adair, tr. from TUR. Ottoman Architecture. 2010. (ENG., Illus.). 720p. (978-1-85149-604-4(1), Antique Collectors Club Dist) Antique Collectors' Club.

Morkoc, Selen. A Study of Ottoman Narratives on Architecture: Text,Context & Hermeneutics. 2010. (Illus.). 230p. (978-1-933146-54-6(0)) Academica Pr., LLC.

ARCHITECTURE, POSTMODERN

Aureli, Pier Vittorio. The Project of Autonomy: Politics & Architecture Within & Against Capitalism. 2008. (ENG., Illus.). 80p. 24.95 (978-1-56898-794-1(3)) Princeton Architectural Pr.

Hodge, Brooke & Mears, Patricia. Skin & Bones: Parallel Practices in Fashion & Architecture. 2006. (978-0-914357-96-4(4)) Museum of Contemporary Art, Los Angeles.

Hodge, Brooke, et al. Skin + Bones: Parallel Practices in Fashion & Architecture. 2006. (Illus.). 272p. 50.00 (978-0-500-51318-7(X)) Thames & Hudson.

Jencks, Charles. Critical Modernism: Where Is Post-Modernism Going What Is Post-Modernism? 5th ed. 2007. (ENG., Illus.). 240p. pap. 55.00 (978-0-470-03011-0(9)); 115.00 (978-0-470-03010-3(0)) Wiley, John & Sons, Inc. (Academy Pr.).

—The New Paradigm in Architecture. 8th ed. 2012. 288p. pap. 45.00 (978-0-300-17823-4(9)) Yale Univ. Pr.

—The Story of Post-Modernism. 2nd ed. 2011. (ENG., Illus.). 272p. 110.00 **(978-0-470-68896-0(3)**, Wiley) Wiley, John & Sons, Inc.

—The Story of Post-Modernism: Five Decades of the Ironic, Iconic & Critical in Architecture. 2nd ed. 2011. (ENG., Illus.). 272p. pap. 40.00 **(978-0-470-68895-3(5)**, Wiley) Wiley, John & Sons, Inc.

Krause, Daniel. Postmoderne — über Die Untauglichkeit Eines Begriffs der Philosophie, Architekturtheorie und Literaturtheorie. (GER & ENG.). 163p. pap. (978-3-631-57383-9(9)) Lang, Peter GmbH, Europaischer Verlag der Wissenschaften.

Martin, Reinhold. Utopia's Ghost: Architecture & Postmodernism, Again. 2010. (Illus.). 248p. 75.00 (978-0-8166-6962-2(7)); pap. 25.00 (978-0-8166-6963-9(5)) Univ. of Minnesota Pr.

Pawson, John. Spatium: Fashion Architecture. 2007. (Architectural Ser.). (ENG., Illus.). 1054p. pap. 40.00 (978-88-7838-062-2(8), Art Stock Bks. Ltd/Csi) Continental Sales, Inc.

Rattenbury. Richard Rogers: Centre Pompidou. 2011. (Supercrit Ser.). (ENG., Illus.). 176p. (C). 165.00 (978-0-415-45785-9(8)); pap. 49.95 (978-0-415-45786-6(6)) Routledge.

Reyes, Pedro, et al, texts. LAR Fernando Romero: Simplexity. 2011. (ENG., Illus.). 672p. 85.00 (978-3-7757-2711-2(6)) Hatje Cantz Verlag GmbH & Co KG DEU. Dist: D.A.P./Distributed Art Pubs.

Sauerbruch, Matthias & Hutton, Louisa. Sauerbruch Hutton: Colour in Architecture. 2006. (Illus.). 331p. 79.00 (978-3-03778-083-1(5), 3037780835) Lars Muller Pubs. CHE. Dist: Springer.

Saunders, William S. The New Architectural Pragmatism: A Harvard Design Magazine Reader. Saunders, William S., ed. 2007. (Harvard Design Magazine Ser.). (Illus.). 208p. 69.00 (978-0-8166-5263-1(5)); per. 22.95 (978-0-8166-5264-8(3)) Univ. of Minnesota Pr.

Scott, Felicity D. Architecture or Techno-Utopia: Politics after Modernism. 2010. (ENG., Illus.). 360p. (gr. 17). pap. 19.95 (978-0-262-51406-4(0)) MIT Pr.

Siegel, Charles. An Architecture for Our Time: The New Classicism. 2008. (Illus.). 56p. pap. (978-0-9788728-1-6(9)) Preservation Institute.

Smith, Valerie, et al. Radical Post-Modernism. 2011. (Architectural Design Ser.). (ENG., Illus.). 136p. pap. 45.00 **(978-0-470-66988-4(8)**, Wiley) Wiley, John & Sons, Inc.

Stern, Robert A. M. Architecture on the Edge of Postmodernism: Collected Essays, 1964-1988. Davidson, Cynthia, ed. 2009. (ENG., Illus.). 216p. 40.00 (978-0-300-15397-2(X)) Yale Univ. Pr.

Urban, Florian. Neo-Historical East Berlin: Architecture & Urban Design in the German Democratic Republic, 1970-1990. 2009. (Ashgate Studies in Architecture Ser.). (Illus.). 294p. 124.95 (978-0-7546-7616-4(1)) Ashgate Publishing Co.

ARCHITECTURE, PREHISTORIC

Harding, D. W. The Iron Age Round-House: Later Prehistoric Building in Britain & Beyond. 2009. (ENG., Illus.). 350p. 130.00 (978-0-19-955857-5(4)) Oxford Univ. Pr., Inc.

Moore, Jerry D. The Prehistory of Home. 2012. (ENG., Illus.). 288p. 29.95 **(978-0-520-27221-7(8))** Univ. of California Pr.

Tilley, Christopher. Body & Image: Explorations in Landscape Phenomenology 2. 2008. (ENG., Illus.). 288p. 89.00 (978-1-59874-313-5(9)); pap. 34.95 (978-1-59874-314-2(7)) Left Coast Pr., Inc.

—Interpreting Landscapes: Geologies, Topographies, Identities - Explorations in Landscape Phenomenology 3. 2010. (ENG., Illus.). 536p. lib. bdg. 89.00 (978-1-59874-374-6(0)) Left Coast Pr., Inc.

Tilley, Christopher. Interpreting Landscapes: Geologies, Topographies, Identities; Explorations in Landscape Phenomenology 3. 2012. (ENG.). 536p. pap. 44.95 **(978-1-59874-375-3(9))** Left Coast Pr., Inc.

ARCHITECTURE, PRIMITIVE

Pollock, Harry E. Round Structures of Aboriginal Middle America. (Carnegie Institution of Washington Publications: No. 471). reprint ed. 37.50 (978-0-404-16274-0(6)) AMS Pr., Inc.

ARCHITECTURE, RENAISSANCE

Airs, Malcolm & Tyack, Geoffrey. The Renaissance Villa in Britain 1500-1700. 2007. (Illus.). 276p. (978-1-904965-13-8(X)) Spire Bks. Ltd.

Allsopp, Bruce. A History of Renaissance Architecture. 2011. 250p. 46.95 **(978-1-258-01172-7(7))** Literary Licensing, LLC.

Bardati, Flaminia. Il Bel Palatio in Forma Di Castello: Gaillon Tra Flamboyant e Rinascimento. 2009. (FRE, ITA & ENG., Illus.). 220p. (978-88-88168-50-0(8)) Campisano Editore.

Bayley, John Barrington. Letarouilly on Renaissance Rome: Tbd. Reed, Henry Hope, ed. 2012. (Dover Architecture Ser.). (ENG.). 224p. pap. 21.95 **(978-0-486-48921-6(3))** Dover Pubns., Inc.

Belluzzi, Amedeo, et al. Palazzo Te in Mantua. 2009. (ENG., Illus.). 1214p. 980.00 (978-88-7686-808-5(9)) Panini Franco Cosimo ITA. Dist: Antique Collectors' Club.

Bischoff, Michael. Castles of the Weser Renaissance. 2009. (ENG.). 304p. 138.00 (978-3-936681-23-9(6)) Edition Axel Menges GmbH DEU. Dist: National Bk. Network.

Blakeslee, Arthur L. Ornament of the Italian Renaissance. 2007. (Dover Pictorial Archive Ser.). (ENG., Illus.). 64p. per. 7.95 (978-0-486-45453-5(3)) Dover Pubns., Inc.

Boucher, Bruce. Andrea Palladio: The Architect in His Time. 2nd ed. 2007. (ENG., Illus.). 324p. 49.95 (978-0-7892-0938-2(1)); 322p. pap. 39.95 (978-0-7892-0940-5(3)) Abbeville Pr., Inc.

Burroughs, Charles. The Italian Renaissance Palace Façade: Structures of Authority, Surfaces of Sense. 2009. (Res Monographs in Anthropology & Aesthetics Ser.). (ENG., Illus.). 312p. pap. 42.00 (978-0-521-10973-4(6)) Cambridge Univ. Pr.

Coffin, David R. Magnificent Buildings, Splendid Gardens. Sellers, Vanessa Bezemer, ed. 2008. (ENG., Illus.). 320p. (C). pap. 42.00 (978-0-691-13677-6(7)) Princeton Univ. Pr.

Coffin, David R. & Sellers, Vanessa Bezemer. Magnificent Buildings, Splendid Gardens. 2008. (ENG., Illus.). 320p. (C). 85.00 (978-0-691-13664-6(5)) Princeton Univ. Pr.

Coureas, Nicholas, et al. Medieval & Renaissance Famagusta: Studies in Architecture Art & History. 2012. (FRE & ENG., Illus.). 330p. 119.95 **(978-1-4094-3557-0(1))** Ashgate Publishing Co.

Faliva, Alberto, ed. Ville del Rinascimento Padano. 2010. (ITA.). 120p. pap. 45.00 (978-88-370-7745-7(9)) Electa ITA. Dist: Trans-Atlantic Pubns., Inc.

Frommel, Christoph Luitpold. The Architecture of the Italian Renaissance. Spring, Peter, tr. from GER. 2007. (ENG., Illus.). 384p. 65.00 (978-0-500-34220-6(2)) Thames & Hudson.

Gossel, Peter & Wundram, Manfred. Palladio Basic Architecture. 2009. (ENG.). 96p. pap. 9.99 (978-3-8365-0289-4(5)) TASCHEN DEU. Dist: Ingram Pub. Services.

Goy, Richard J. Building Renaissance Venice: Patrons, Architects, & Builder. 2006. (ENG., Illus.). 256p. 70.00 (978-0-300-11292-4(0)) Yale Univ. Pr.

Hickson, Sally Anne. Women Art & Architectural Patronage in Renaissance Mantua: Matrons Mystics & Monasteries. 2012. (Women & Gender in the Early Modern World Ser.). (Illus.). 204p. 104.95 **(978-1-4094-2752-0(8))** Ashgate Publishing Co.

Howard, Deborah & Moretti, Laura. Sound & Space in Renaissance Venice: Architecture, Music, Acoustics. 2010. (Illus.). 256p. 55.00 (978-0-300-14874-9(7)) Yale Univ. Pr.

Kavaler, Ethan Matt. Renaissance Gothic. 2012. (ENG., Illus.). 344p. 75.00 **(978-0-300-16792-4(X))** Yale Univ. Pr.

Kenda, Barbara, ed. Aeolian Winds & the Spirit in Renaissance Architecture: Academia Eolia Revisted. 2006. (Illus.). 175p. 170.00 (978-0-415-39803-9(7)); per. 63.95 (978-0-415-39804-6(5)) Routledge.

Lillie, Amanda. Florentine Villas in the Fifteenth Century: An Architectural & Social History. 2011. (ENG., Illus.). 369p. pap. 45.00 (978-0-521-18138-9(0)) Cambridge Univ. Pr.

Lindow, James. The Renaissance Palace in Florence: Magnificence & Splendour in Fifteenth-Century Italy. 2007. (Illus.). 286p. 124.95 (978-0-7546-6092-7(3)) Ashgate Publishing Co.

Lowry, Bates. Renaissance Architecture: The Great Ages of World Architecture. 2011. 126p. 40.95 (978-1-258-03839-7(0)) Literary Licensing, LLC.

Mackinney, Loren Carey & MacKinney, Loren Carey. Pre-Gothic Architecture: A Mirror of the Social-Religious Renaissance of the Eleventh Century. 2011. 26p. 35.95 (978-1-258-03572-3(3)) Literary Licensing, LLC.

Mitrovic, Branko & Wessell, Stephen, eds. Andrea Palladio: Villa Cornaro in Piombino Dese. 2007. (Illus.). 71p. 100.00 (978-0-926494-36-7(8)) Acanthus Pr. LLC.

Moskowitz, A. -F. The Facade Reliefs of Orvieto Cathedral. 2009. (Studies in Medieval & Early Renaissance Art History Ser.). (ENG., Illus.). 245p. (C). 145.00 (978-1-905375-27-1(1)) Miller, Harvey Pubs. GBR. Dist: Brown, David Bk. Co., The.

National Terra Cotta Society. Terra Cotta of the Italian Renaissance. 2011. 210p. 44.95 (978-1-258-04418-3(8)) Literary Licensing, LLC.

Nevola, Fabrizio. Siena: Constructing the Renaissance City. 2008. (ENG., Illus.). 320p. 65.00 (978-0-300-12678-5(6)) Yale Univ. Pr.

Orrell, John. The Human Stage: English Theatre Design, 1567-1640. 2009. (ENG.). 316p. pap. 42.00 (978-0-521-10945-1(0)) Cambridge Univ. Pr.

—The Theatres of Inigo Jones & John Webb. 2010. (ENG.). 234p. pap. 22.99 (978-0-521-15489-5(8)) Cambridge Univ. Pr.

Paolucci, Antonio. The Tempio Malatestiano in Rimini, 2 vols. Settis, Salvatore, ed. 2011. (ITA & ENG., Illus.). 608p. 815.00 (978-88-248-0353-3(9)) Panini Franco Cosimo ITA. Dist: National Bk. Network.

Payne, Alina A. The Architectural Treatise in the Italian Renaissance: Architectural Invention, Ornament & Literary Culture. 2010. (ENG.). 364p. pap. 45.00 (978-0-521-17823-5(1)) Cambridge Univ. Pr.

Pieper, Jan. Maulnes-En-Tonnerrois: Ein Konstrukt Aus Dem Geiste des Manierismus: Architektur der Skepsis, des Glaubens, der Ziviltoleranz. 2007. (GER & ENG., Illus.). 560p. 218.00 (978-3-936681-07-9(4)) Edition Axel Menges GmbH DEU. Dist: National Bk. Network.

Puppi, Lionello. Palladio: Introduzione Alle Architetture E Al Pensiero Teorico. 2007. (ENG., Illus.). 464p. 225.00 (978-88-7743-303-9(5)) Arsenale Editrice SRL ITA. Dist: National Bk. Network.

Rouyer, Eugene, ed. French Architectural Ornament: From Versailles, Fontainebleau & Other Palaces. 2008. (Dover Architecture Ser.). (ENG., Illus.). 96p. per. 14.95 (978-0-486-46140-3(8)) Dover Pubns., Inc.

Sadler, Guy Albert. Outline for a Viable Techno Sphere. 2010. 188p. 29.99 (978-1-4535-1157-2(1)); pap. 19.99 (978-1-4535-1156-5(3)) Xlibris Corp.

Servida, Sonia. The Story of Renaissance Architecture. 2011. (ENG., Illus.). 144p. pap. 19.95 (978-3-7913-4597-0(4)) Prestel Publishing.

Tadgell, Christopher. The West: From the Advent of Christendom to the Eve of Reformation. 2009. (ENG., Illus.). 928p. 110.00 (978-0-415-40754-0(0)) Routledge.

Taglialagamba, Sara, ed. Leonardo & Architecture. 2010. (Leonardo Collection). (ENG., Illus.). 152p. (C). pap. 24.95 (978-88-95686-21-9(7)) Cartei, C.B. & Bianchi Edizioni ITA. Dist: Brown, David Bk. Co., The.

Tanner, M. Jerusalem on the Hill: Rome & the Vision of St. Peter's in the Renaissance. 2010. (Studies in Medieval & Early Renaissance Art History Ser.). (ENG., Illus.). 288p. (C). 174.00 (978-1-905375-49-3(2)) Miller, Harvey Pubs. GBR. Dist: Brown, David Bk. Co., The.

Temple, Nicholas. Renovatio Urbis: Architecture, Urbanism & Ceremony in the Rome of Julius II. 2011. (Classical Tradition in Architecture Ser.). (ENG., Illus.). 368p. (C). 130.00 (978-0-415-47385-9(3)) Routledge.

Trachtenberg, Marvin. Brunelleschi, Michelozzo, & the Problem of the Pazzi Chapel. 2008. (Illus.). 272p. 60.00 (978-0-300-11831-5(7)) Yale Univ. Pr.

Vasari, Giorgio & Feser, Sabine. Das Leben des Bramante und des Peruzzi. 2007. (GER., Illus.). 158p. pap. (978-3-8031-5036-3(1)) Wagenbach, Klaus, GmbH, Verlag.

Vredeman de Vries, Jan. Studies in Perspective. 2010. (Dover Architecture Ser.). (ENG., Illus.). 96p. pap. 12.95 (978-0-486-47332-1(5)) Dover Pubns., Inc.

Weissmuller, Alberto. Palladio in Venice. 2006. (ENG., Illus.). 168p. 60.00 (978-88-7200-174-5(9)) Vianello Libri ITA. Dist: Antique Collectors' Club.

ARCHITECTURE, ROCOCO

Bailey, Gauvin Alexander. Baroque & Rococo. 2012. (ENG., Illus.). 448p. pap. 29.95 (978-0-7148-5742-8(4)) Phaidon Pr., Inc.

ARCHITECTURE, ROMAN

see also Architecture—Italy; Temples

Becker, Jeffrey A. & Terrenato, Nicola. Roman Republican Villas: Architecture, Context, & Ideology. 2011. (Papers & Monographs of the American Academy in Rome Ser.). (ENG., Illus.). 152p. (C). 60.00 (978-0-472-11770-3(X)) Univ. of Michigan Pr.

Betsky, Aaron. Uneternal City: Urbanism Beyond Rome. Betsky, Aaron, ed. 2009. (ENG., Illus.). 272p. 65.00 (978-88-317-9617-0(8)) Marsilio Editori spa ITA. Dist: Random Hse., Inc.

Brandolini, Sebastiano. Rome: New Architecture. 2008. (ENG., Illus.). 252p. pap. 14.99 (978-88-6130-534-2(2)) Skira Editore ITA. Dist: Random Hse., Inc.

Brown, Frank. Roman Architecture. 128p. pap. 15.95 (978-0-8076-1472-3(6)) Braziller, George Inc.

Bussagli, Marco, ed. Rome: Art & Architecture. 2008. (Art & Architecture Ser.). (Illus.). 679p. per. 29.95 (978-0-8416-0091-1(0)) American Map Corp.

Campbell, Duncan B. Roman Auxiliary Forts 27 BC-AD 378. 2009. (Fortress Ser.). (ENG., Illus.). 64p. pap. 18.95 (978-1-84603-380-3(2)) Osprey Publishing, Ltd. GBR. Dist: Random Hse., Inc.

Campbell, Gordon. The Grove Encyclopedia of Classical Art & Architecture, 2 vols. 2007. (ENG., Illus.). 1600p. 345.00 (978-0-19-530082-6(3)) Oxford Univ. Pr., Inc.

Carucci, Margherita. The Romano-African Domus: Studies in Space, Decoration, & Function. 2008. (Bar S Ser.). (Illus.). xii, 289p. (C). 100.00 (978-1-4073-0175-4(6)) British Archaeological Reports Ltd. GBR. Dist: Brown, David Bk. Co., The.

Codeluppi, Manuela, ed. Santa Giulia, Brescia: Dalle Domus romane al Museo Della Citta. 2009. (ITA., Illus.). 144p. 67.50 (978-88-370-6299-6(0)) Electa ITA. Dist: Trans-Atlantic Pubns., Inc.

Daehner, Jens, et al. The Herculaneum Women & the Origins of Archaeology. 2008. (Illus.). 160p. 50.00 (978-0-89236-882-2(9)) Oxford Univ. Pr., Inc.

De Angelis, Francesco, ed. Spaces of Justice in the Roman World. 2010. (Columbia Studies in the Classical Tradition Ser.). (Illus.). xii, 434p. (978-90-04-18925-6(4)) BRILL.

De Luca, Araldo, photos by. The Art of Pompeii. 2011. (ENG., Illus.). 176p. 60.00 (978-88-544-0501-1(9)) White Star ITA. Dist: Sterling Publishing Co., Inc.

Delbeke, Maarten. Expressiveness of Building: Gianlorenzo Bernini Sforaz Pallavicino & the Roman Baroque. 2012. (Histories of Vision Ser.). (Illus.). 216p. 124.95 (978-0-7546-3485-0(X)) Ashgate Publishing Co.

Durando, Furio, ed. Italy: A Journey in Search of Great Art & Archaeology. 2010. (ENG., Illus.). 368p. 45.00 (978-88-544-0427-4(6)) White Star ITA. Dist: Random Hse., Inc.

Eaton, Tim. Plundering the Past: Roman Stonework in Medieval Britain. (Illus.). 160p. pap. 27.50 (978-0-7524-1903-9(X)) History Pr. Ltd., The GBR. Dist: Trafalgar Square Publishing.

Ewald, Bjoern C. & Noreña, Carlos F., eds. The Emperor & Rome: Space, Representation, & Ritual. 2010. (Yale Classical Studies). (ENG., Illus.). 378p. 99.00 (978-0-521-51953-3(5)) Cambridge Univ. Pr.

Fraser, Trudie E. Hadrian as Builder & Benefactor in the Western Provinces. 2006. (BAR International Ser.: Vol. 1484). (ENG., Illus.). 194p. (C). 80.00 (978-1-84171-919-1(6)) British Archaeological Reports Ltd. GBR. Dist: Brown, David Bk. Co., The.

Hales, Shelley. The Roman House & Social Identity. 2009. (ENG., Illus.). 308p. pap. 35.99 (978-0-521-73509-4(2)) Cambridge Univ. Pr.

Hanson, W. S., et al. Elginhaugh: A Flavian Fort & Its Annexe, 2 vols. 2007. (ENG., Illus.). 672p. (C). pap. 116.00 (978-0-907764-34-2(7)) Society for the Promotion of Roman Studies GBR. Dist: Brown, David Bk. Co., The.

Hintzen-Bohlen, Brigitte. Rome: And the Vatican City. 2008. (Art & Architecture Ser.). (Illus.). 626p. 19.95 (978-0-8416-0051-5(1)) American Map Corp.

Knell, Heiner. Des Kaisers neue Bauten: Hadrians Architektur in Rom, Athen und Tivoli. 2008. (GER., Illus.). 119p. (C). 38.00 (978-3-8053-3772-4(8)) Zabern, Philipp von Verlag, GmbH DEU. Dist: Brown, David Bk. Co., The.

Kokkinos, Nikos & Politis, Konstantinos D. International Conference, The World of the Herods & the Nabataeans, Held at the British Museum, 17-19 April 2001: [papers], 2 vols. 2007. (Oriens et Occidens. Studien zu antiken Kulturkontakten und ihrem Nachleben (O&O) Ser.). (ENG., Illus.). 327p. (C). pap. 94.00 (978-3-515-08817-6(2)) Steiner, Franz Verlag Wiesbaden GmbH DEU. Dist: Brown, David Bk. Co., The.

Linders, Tullia & Hellstrom, Pontus, eds. Architecture & Society in Hecatomnid Caria. (Illus.). 104p. (978-91-554-2355-1(8)) Uppsala Universitet/Acta Universitatis Uppsaliensis.

Longfellow, Brenda. Roman Imperialism & Civic Patronage: Form, Meaning & Ideology in Monumental Fountain Complexes. 2010. (ENG., Illus.). 292p. 90.00 (978-0-521-19493-8(8)) Cambridge Univ. Pr.

Lyell, Arthur Henry. A Bibliographical List Descriptive of Romano-British Architectural Remains in Great Britain. 2010. (Cambridge Library Collection - Archaeology Ser.). (ENG.). 176p. pap. 19.99 (978-1-108-00890-7(9)) Cambridge Univ. Pr.

Malacrino, Carmelo G. Constructing the Ancient World: Architectural Techniques of the Greeks & Romans. 2010. (Illus.). 224p. 50.00 (978-1-60606-016-2(3)) Getty Pubns.

McGowen, S. L. Sacred & Civic Stone Monuments of the Northwest Roman Provinces. 2010. (Bar S Ser.). (ENG., Illus.). 159p. (C). pap. 87.50 (978-1-4073-0650-6(2)) British Archaeological Reports Ltd. GBR. Dist: Brown, David Bk. Co., The.

Millette, Daniel M. Vitruvius, Memory, & the Classical Imagination. 2008. 256p. pap. (978-3-639-03310-6(8)) VDM Verlag Dr. Mueller e.K.

Minor, Vernon Hyde & Curran, Brian A., eds. Memoirs of the American Academy in Rome Vol. 55. 2011. (Memoirs of the American Academy in Rome Ser.). (ENG., Illus.). 338p. 70.00 (978-1-879549-19-7(0)) American Academy in Rome.

Mladenovic, Dragana & Russell, Ben, eds. Trac 2010: Proceedings of the Twentieth Annual Theoretical Roman Archaeology Conference. 2011. (Trac Ser.). (ENG., Illus.). 160p. (C). pap. 64.00 (978-1-84217-452-4(5)) Oxbow Bks., Ltd. GBR. Dist: Brown, David Bk. Co., The.

Nasrallah, Laura Salah. Christian Responses to Roman Art & Architecture: The Second-Century Church amid the Spaces of Empire. (ENG., Illus.). (C). 2011. 352p. pap. 39.99 (978-1-107-64499-1(2)) 2010. 350p. 99.00 (978-0-521-76652-4(4)) Cambridge Univ. Pr.

Netzer, Ehud. Architecture of Herod, the Great Builder. 2008. 464p. (C). pap. 70.00 (978-0-8010-3612-5(7)) Baker Academic.

Novara, A. Auctor in Bibliotheca: Essai sur les textes préfaciels de Vitruve et une philosophie latine du Livre. 2006. (Bibliotheque d'Etudes Classiques Ser.). (ENG.). 188p. (C). pap. 58.00 (978-90-429-1679-1(6)) Peeters Pubs. & Booksellers BEL. Dist: Brown, David Bk. Co., The.

Perring, Dominic. The Roman House in Britain. 2009. 272p. 39.95 (978-0-415-48878-5(8)) Routledge.

Rind, Mareike. Romische Villen in Nordafrika: Nordafrika Untersuchungen zu Architektur und Wirtschaftsweise. 2009. (GER & ENG., Illus.). 133p. (C). pap. 82.50 (978-1-4073-0588-2(3)) British Archaeological Reports Ltd. GBR. Dist: Brown, David Bk. Co., The.

Rodgers, Nigel. Roman Architecture: An Expert Visual Guide to the Glorious Classical Heritage of Ancient Rome. 2007. (ENG., Illus.). 128p. pap. 17.99 (978-1-84476-291-0(2)) Anness Publishing GBR. Dist: National Bk. Network.

Roos, Paavo. Survey of Rock-Cut Chamber Tombs in Caria Pt. 2: Central Caria. 2006. (Studies in Mediterranean Archaeology: LXXII:2). (Illus.). 144p. pap. 110.00 (978-91-7081-216-3(0)) Astroms, Paul Forlag SWE. Dist: Coronet Bks.

Senseney, John R. The Art of Building in the Classical World: Vision, Craftsmanship, & Linear Perspective in Greek & Roman Architecture. 2011. (ENG., Illus.). 274p. 90.00 (978-1-107-00235-7(4)) Cambridge Univ. Pr.

Shenfield, Larry. How Much of the Florence Baptistery Is a Surviving Roman Building? A Re-Evaluation of the Archaeological, Architectural & Artistic Evidence. 2008. (Bar S Ser.). (Illus.). 433p. (C). pap. 157.50 (978-1-4073-0225-6(6)) British Archaeological Reports Ltd. GBR. Dist: Brown, David Bk. Co., The.

Smith, J. T. Roman Villas. 2010. 412p. pap. 42.95 (978-0-415-62011-6(2)) Routledge.

Spanu, Marcello. The Theatre of Diokaisareia. 2012. (ENG., Illus.). X, 134p. (gr. 17). E-Book 252.00 (978-3-11-174099-7(4)) 2011. 168.00 (978-3-11-022221-0(3)) De Gruyter, Walter Inc.

Stamper, John. The Architecture of Roman Temples: The Republic to the Middle Empire. 2008. (ENG., Illus.). 304p. pap. 36.00 (978-0-521-72371-8(X)) Cambridge Univ. Pr.

Tadgell, Christopher. Antiquity: Origins, Classicism & the New Rome. 2009. (Illus.). 960p. 44.95 (978-0-415-40751-9(6)) Taylor & Francis Group.

Thomas, Edmund. Monumentality & the Roman Empire: Architecture in the Antonine Age. 2008. (ENG., Illus.). 480p. 315.00 (978-0-19-928863-2(1)) Oxford Univ. Pr., Inc.

Thomas, Michael L. & Meyers, Gretchen E., eds. Monumentality in Etruscan & Early Roman Architecture: Ideology & Innovation. 2012. (ENG.). 236p. 60.00 (978-0-292-73888-1(9)) Univ. of Texas Pr.

Thomas, Michael L., et al. Monumentality in Etruscan & Early Roman Architecture: Ideology & Innovation. 2012. E-Book (978-0-292-73889-8(7)) Univ. of Texas Pr.

Thorpe, M. Roman Architecture. (Illus.). 128p. pap. 20.00 (978-1-85399-421-0(9)) Bristol Classical Pr. GBR. Dist: International Publishers Marketing.

Triff, K. A. The Orsini Palace at Monte Giordano: Patronage & Public Image in Renaissance Rome. 2012. (Art & architecture in early modern Italy Ser.). (ENG., Illus.). 300p. (C). 160.00 (978-1-905375-33-2(6)) Miller, Harvey Pubs. GBR. Dist: Brown, David Bk. Co., The.

Tuck, Steven L. Experiencing Rome: A Visual Exploration of Antiquity's Greatest Empire. 2009. pap. 35.00 (978-1-59803-520-9(7)) Teaching Co., LLC, The.

Van Eck, Caroline. Inigo Jones on Stonehenge: Architectural Representation, Memory & Narrative. 2011. (Illus.). 85p. 25.00 (978-90-76863-83-2(0)) Architectura & Natura Pr. NLD. Dist: Antique Collectors' Club.

Van Krimpen-Winckel, Noor. Building History & Design of Atrium-peristyle Houses in the Social Context of Pompeii. 2010. 480p. pap. (978-90-8728-034-5(3), Leiden Univ. Pr.) Amsterdam Univ. Pr.

Welch, Katherine E. The Roman Amphitheatre: From its Origins to the Colosseum. 2009. (ENG., Illus.). 378p. (C). pap. 49.00 (978-0-521-74435-5(0)) Cambridge Univ. Pr.

Wilmott, Tony. Roman Amphitheatres & Spectacula: A 21st Century Perspective. Wilmott, Tony, ed. 2009. (ENG., Illus.). 238p. (C). pap. 110.00 (978-1-4073-0426-7(7)) British Archaeological Reports Ltd. GBR. Dist: Brown, David Bk. Co., The.

Wilpert, Joseph. Roman Mosaics: Over 60 Full-Color Images from the 4th Through the 13th Centuries. 2007. (ENG., Illus.). 64p. per. 15.95 (978-0-486-45469-6(X)) Dover Pubns., Inc.

Wulfram, Hartmut. Literarische Vitruvrezeption in Leon Battista Albertis 'de re Aedificatoria' (Beiträge zur Altertumskunde Ser.). (GER.). 441p. 210.00 (978-3-11-184227-1(4)) De Gruyter, Walter Inc.

ARCHITECTURE, ROMANESQUE

Bednorz, Achim. Romanesque: Architecture - Sculpture - Painting, 1 vol. Toman, Rolf, ed. 2011. (ENG.). 480p. 19.99 (978-3-8331-6005-9(5)) h.f.ullmann DEU. Dist: Innovative Logistics.

Castinei, Manuel. Compostela & Europe: The Story of Diego Gelmirez. 2010. (ENG., Illus.). 432p. 90.00 (978-88-572-0493-2(6)) Skira Editore ITA. Dist: Random Hse., Inc.

Costen, M. D. & Oakes, Catherine. Romanesque Churches of the Loire & Western France. (Illus.). 194p. 35.00 (978-0-7524-1444-7(5)) History Pr. Ltd., The GBR. Dist: Trafalgar Square Publishing.

García Guinea, Miguel Angel, et al. Enciclopedia Del Románico en Aragón: Zaragoza, 2 vols. 2010. (Illus.). (978-84-89483-67-5(1)); (SPA., (978-84-89483-68-2(X)); (SPA., (978-84-89483-69-9(8)) Fundación Santa Maria La Real, Centro de Estudios del Romanico.

Mann, Janice. Romanesque Architecture & Its Sculptural Decoration in Christian Spain, 1000-1120: Exploring Frontiers & Defining Identities. 2009. (ENG., Illus.). 300p. (978-0-8020-9324-0(8)) Univ. of Toronto Pr.

Martin, Therese. Queen as King: Politics & Architectural Propaganda in Twelfth-Century Spain. 2006. (Medieval & Early Modern Iberian World Ser.: Vol. 30). (Illus.). 292p. (978-90-04-15297-7(0)) BRILL.

Maxwell, Robert A. The Art of Medieval Urbanism: Parthenay in Romanesque Aquitaine. 2008. (ENG., Illus.). 360p. 90.00 (978-0-271-02956-6(0)) Pennsylvania State Univ. Pr.

Moss, Rachel. Romanesque Chevron Ornament: The Language of British, Norman & Irish Sculpture in the Twelfth Century. 2009. (Bar S Ser.). (ENG., Illus.). 137p. (C). pap. 82.50 (978-1-4073-0391-8(0)) British Archaeological Reports Ltd. GBR. Dist: Brown, David Bk. Co., The.

Nenci, Cinzia, et al. The Cathedral of Pisa, 3 vols. Peroni, Adriano, ed. 2008. (ENG., Illus.). 1634p. 1280.00 (978-88-7686-614-2(0)) Panini Franco Cosimo ITA. Dist: Antique Collectors' Club.

Prina, Francesca. The Story of Romanesque Architecture. 2012. (ENG., Illus.). 144p. pap. 19.95 (978-3-7913-4630-4(X)) Prestel Publishing.

Seasonwein, Johanna. Princeton & the Gothic Revival, 1870-1930. 2012. (Publications of the Art Museum, Princeton University Ser.). (ENG., Illus.). 128p. (C). 35.00 (978-0-691-15401-5(5)) Princeton Univ. Pr.

Toman, Rolf. Romanesque, 1 vol. 2010. (ENG., Illus.). 480p. pap. 19.99 (978-3-8331-3600-9(6)) h.f.ullmann DEU. Dist: Innovative Logistics.

Toman, Rolf, ed. Romanesque: Architecture, Sculpture, Painting. 2008. (Architecture Sculpture Painting Ser.). (Illus.). 480p. per. 24.95 (978-0-8416-0090-4(2)) American Map Corp.

ARCHITECTURE, RURAL

see Architecture, Domestic; Cottages; Country Homes; Farm Buildings

ARCHITECTURE, SARACENIC

see Islamic Architecture

ARCHITECTURE, SHAKER

see Shaker Architecture

ARCHITECTURE, TROPICAL

Beal, Gillian & Termansen, Jacob. Tropical Style: Contemporary Dream Houses in Malaysia. 2008. (ENG., Illus.). 224p. 39.95 (978-0-7946-0555-1(9), PeriplusEdition) Tuttle Publishing.

Bensley, Bill. Paradise by Design: Tropical Residences & Resorts by Bensley Design Studios. 2008. (ENG., Illus.). 240p. 49.95 (978-0-7946-0493-6(5), PeriplusEdition) Tuttle Publishing.

Bromberek, Zbigniew. Eco-Resorts: Planning & Design for the Tropics. 2009. (ENG., Illus.). 256p. pap. 64.95 (978-0-7506-5793-8(6)) Routledge.

de Reus, Mark & Nataraj, Nirmala. Tropical Experience: Architecture + Design. Goff, Gordon, ed. 2012. (ENG., Illus.). 300p. 50.00 (978-1-935935-02-5(X)) Oro Editions.

Dullemen, C. J. van. Tropical Modernity: Life & Work of C.P. Wolff Schoemaker. 2010. (Illus.). 270p. (978-90-8506-879-2(7)) SUN B.V., Uitgeverij.

Francione, Gianni, et al. Bali Living: Innovative Tropical Design. 2008. (ENG., Illus.). 224p. 44.95 (978-0-7946-0567-4(2), PeriplusEdition) Tuttle Publishing.

Hindrichs, Dirk U. & Daniels, Klaus. Plusminus 20/40 Latitude: Sustainable Building Design in Tropical & Subtropical Regions. 2007. (ENG., Illus.). 448p. 109.00 (978-3-930698-83-7(8)) Edition Axel Menges GmbH DEU. Dist: National Bk. Network.

Konya, Allan & Vandenberg, Maritz. Design Primer for Hot Climates. 2011. (Illus.). 156p. pap. (978-0-9564323-2-2(6)) Archimedia Pr., Ltd.

Nas, Peter J. M. The Past in the Present: Architecture in Indonesia. 2010. (ENG., Illus.). 286p. 50.00 (978-90-6718-296-6(6)) KITLV Pr. NLD. Dist: Univ. of Hawaii Pr.

Nas, Peter J. M., ed. The Past in the Present: Architecture in Indonesia, 1 vol. 2007. (ENG., Illus.). 288p. 59.95 (978-90-5662-572-6(1)) NAi Uitgevers / Publishers Stichting NLD. Dist: D.A.P./Distributed Art Pubs.

Pomeroy, Jason. Idea House: Future Tropical Living Today. 2011. (ENG., Illus.). 208p. pap. 35.00 (978-1-935935-10-0(0)) Oro Editions.

Prouvé, Jean. Jean Prouvé: La Maison Tropicale = Jean Prouvé: The Tropical House. 2009. (FRE & ENG., Illus.). 157p. (978-2-84426-335-3(6)) Centre National d'Art et de Culture Georges Pompidou.

Prouve, Jean. Jean Prouve: the Tropical House. 2011. (ENG., Illus.). 160p. pap. 40.00 (978-1-935202-49-3(9)) Editions du Centre Pompidou FRA. Dist: D.A.P./Distributed Art Pubs.

Tropical Houses: Living in Paradise. 2012. (ENG., Illus.). 224p. 49.95 (978-3-03768-095-7(4), Braun Publish,Csi) Continental Sales, Inc.

van den Dobbelsteen, Andy, et al, eds. Smart Building in a Changing Climate. 2009. (ENG., Illus.). 254p. pap. 69.00 (978-90-8594-024-1(9)) Techne Pr. NLD. Dist: Chicago Distribution Ctr.

Vivoni Farage, Enrique. Klumb: Una Arquitectura de Impronta Social. 2006. (Serie Mnemosina Ser.: Vol. 2). (ENG & SPA., Illus.). xiv, 346p. 84.95 (978-0-8477-2754-4(8)) Univ. of Puerto Rico Pr.

ARCHITECTURE, VERNACULAR

see Vernacular Architecture

ARCHITECTURE, VICTORIAN

see also Gothic Revival (Architecture)

A J Bicknell & Co & Bicknell, A. J. Victorian Wooden & Brick Houses with Details. 2006. (Dover Architecture Ser.). (ENG., Illus.). 112p. per. 12.95 (978-0-486-45103-9(8)) Dover Pubns., Inc.

Ashworth, Trisha & Nobile, Amy. I Was a Really Good Mom Before I Had Kids: Reinventing Modern Motherhood. 2007. (ENG.). 240p. per. 18.95 (978-0-8118-5650-8(X)) Chronicle Bks. LLC.

Blumer & Kuhn Stair Co. Victorian Woodturnings & Woodwork. 2006. (Dover Architecture Ser.). (ENG., Illus.). 144p. per. 14.95 (978-0-486-45114-5(3)) Dover Pubns., Inc.

Collings, Janet. Victorian & Edwardian Houses: A Guide to Care & Maintenance. 2008. (ENG., Illus.). 160p. 43.95 (978-1-84797-057-2(5)) Crowood Pr., Ltd. GBR. Dist: Independent Pubs. Group.

Comstock, William T. Late Victorian Architectural Plans & Details. 2010. (Dover Architecture Ser.). (ENG., Illus.). 192p. pap. 19.95 (978-0-486-47361-1(9)) Dover Pubns., Inc.

Curl, James Stevens. Victorian Architecture: Diversity & Invention. 2007. (Illus.). 635p. (978-1-904965-06-0(7)) Spire Bks. Ltd.

Ferry, Kathryn. The Victorian Home. 2010. (Shire Library). (ENG., Illus.). 112p. pap. 15.95 (978-0-7478-0748-3(5)) Shire Pubns., Ltd. GBR. Dist: Random Hse., Inc.

Guild, Robin. The Victorian House Book: A Practical Guide to Home Repair & Decoration. 4th ed. 2008. (ENG., Illus.). 320p. 49.95 (978-1-55407-371-9(5)) Firefly Bks., Ltd.

Horn, Pamela. Life in the Victorian Country House. 2010. (Shire History Ser.). (ENG., Illus.). 128p. pap. 19.95 (978-0-7478-0750-6(7)) Shire Pubns., Ltd. GBR. Dist: Random Hse., Inc.

Hunter, Gill. William White: Pioneer Victorian Architect. 2010. (Illus.). 338p. (C). (978-1-904965-26-8(1)) Spire Bks. Ltd.

Jackson, Lee M. Victorian London. 2006. (ENG., Illus.). 160p. 29.95 (978-1-84330-734-1(0)) New Holland Pubs., Ltd. GBR. Dist: National Bk. Network.

Leary, Patrick. The Punch Brotherhood: Table Talk & Print Culture in Mid-Victorian London. 2010. (ENG., Illus.). 197p. 40.00 (978-0-7123-0923-3(3)) British Library, The GBR. Dist: Chicago Distribution Ctr.

Pahlke, Eric. San Diego County Victorians. 2008. 80p. pap. (978-0-9800950-0-5(X)) Our Heritage Pr.

Palmer, Michele. Gingerbread Gems of Willimantic, Connecticut. 2007. (Illus.). 112p. pap. 19.95 (978-0-7643-2603-5(1)) Schiffer Publishing, Ltd.

Reed, Roger. Building Victorian Boston: The Architecture of Gridley J. F. Bryant. 2006. (Illus.). 256p. 39.95 (978-1-55849-555-5(X)) Univ. of Massachusetts Pr.

Richmond, Arthur P. Cottages of Oak Bluffs: 20 Postcards. 2007. (Illus.). 40p. pap. 9.95 (978-0-7643-2683-7(X)) Schiffer Publishing, Ltd.

—Gingerbread Gems: Victorian Architecture of Oak Bluffs. 2007. (Illus.). 208p. pap. 29.95 (978-0-7643-2682-0(1)) Schiffer Publishing, Ltd.

Rutherford, Sarah. The Victorian Cemetery. 2009. (Shire Library). (ENG., Illus.). 64p. pap. 12.95 (978-0-7478-0701-8(9)) Osprey Publishing, Ltd. GBR. Dist: Random Hse., Inc.

Way, Terry. Victorian Homes of San Francisco. 2009. (Illus.). 112p. pap. 19.99 (978-0-7643-3212-8(0)) Schiffer Publishing, Ltd.

Wedd, Kit. The Victorian Society Book of the Victorian House. 2008. (ENG., Illus.). 272p. pap. 39.95 (978-1-84513-294-1(7)) Aurum Pr., Ltd. GBR. Dist: Independent Pubs. Group.

Whyte, William. Oxford Jackson: Architecture, Education, Status, & Style 1835-1924. 2006. (Oxford Historical Monographs). (ENG., Illus.). 288p. 150.00 (978-0-19-929658-3(8)) Oxford Univ. Pr., Inc.

ARCHITECTURE AND CLIMATE

see also Architecture, Tropical

AECOM Consult, Inc Staff. Design: Design & Planning for the Age of Climate Change. 2010. (ENG., Illus.). 280p. 40.00 (978-0-9820607-1-1(8)) Oro Editions.

Bhatia, Neeraj, et al, eds. Arium: Weather & Architecture. 2010. (ENG., Illus.). 320p. 55.00 (978-3-7757-2540-8(7)) Hatje Cantz Verlag GmbH & Co KG DEU. Dist: D.A.P./Distributed Art Pubs.

Brown, Robert. Design with Microclimate: The Secret to Comfortable Outdoor Space. 2010. (ENG., Illus.). 192p. pap. 30.00 (978-1-59726-740-3(6)) Island Pr.

—Design with Microclimate: The Secret to Comfortable Outdoor Spaces. 2010. (ENG., Illus.). 192p. 60.00 (978-1-59726-739-7(2)) Island Pr.

Cook, Martin Godfrey. The Zero-Carbon House. 2011. (ENG., Illus.). 160p. 29.95 **(978-1-84797-262-0(4))** Crowood Pr., Ltd. GBR. Dist: Independent Pubs. Group.

Dahl, Torben, ed. Climate & Architecture. 2009. (ENG., Illus.). 168p. 155.00 (978-0-415-56308-6(9)); pap. 44.95 (978-0-415-56309-3(7)) Routledge.

Decker, Julie & Princeton Architectural Press Staff. Modern North: Architecture on the Frozen Edge. 2010. (ENG., Illus.). 240p. 45.00 (978-1-56898-899-3(0)) Princeton Architectural Pr.

Drake, Scott. The Third Skin: Architecture, Technology, & Environment. 2007. (ENG., Illus.). 224p. per. 56.95 (978-0-86840-931-3(6), UNSW Press) NewSouth Publishing AUS. Dist: Independent Pubs. Group.

Erell, Evyatar, et al. Urban Microclimate: Designing the Spaces Between Buildings. 2010. (ENG., Illus.). 288p. 115.00 (978-1-84407-467-9(6)) Routledge.

Hausladen, Gerhard & Liedl, Petra. Building to Suit the Climate: A Handbook. 2012. (ENG., Illus.). 176p. 69.95 (978-3-0346-0728-5(8)) Birkhauser Verlag AG CHE. Dist: Actar Birkhauser Distribution.

Hawkes, Dean. Architecture & Climate. 2012. (ENG., Illus.). 272p. (C). 165.00 **(978-0-415-56186-0(8))**; pap. 49.95 **(978-0-415-56187-7(6))** Routledge.

Hill, Jonathan. Weather Architecture. 2012. (ENG., Illus.). 384p. (C). 165.00 **(978-0-415-66860-6(3))**; pap. 54.95 **(978-0-415-66861-3(1))** Routledge.

Hyde, Richard. Bioclimatic Housing: Innovative Designs for Warm Climates. 2007. (ENG., Illus.). 400p. (C). pap. 89.95 (978-1-84407-284-2(3)) Routledge.

IBA Hamburg, ed. Energy Atlas. 2011. (ENG., Illus.). 224p. pap. 39.95 (978-3-86859-074-6(9)) Jovis Verlag GmbH DEU. Dist: D.A.P./Distributed Art Pubs.

Knaack, U. & Klein, T., eds. The Future Envelope 2: Architecture - Climate - Skin. 2010. (Research in Architectural Engineering Ser.). (Illus.). 150p. pap. 65.00 (978-1-60750-026-1(4)) IOS Pr., Inc.

La Roche, Pablo. Carbon-Neutral Architectural Design. 2011. (ENG., Illus.). 344p. 99.95 (978-1-4398-4512-7(3), CRC Press) Taylor & Francis Group GBR. Dist: Taylor & Francis Group.

Lstiburek, Joseph. Builder's Guide to Cold Climates: Details for Design & Construction. (Illus.). 352p. pap. (978-1-56158-387-4(1), 070519) Taunton Pr., Inc.

Nicol, Fergus, et al. Adaptive Thermal Comfort: The Physics & Physiology of Field Studies & Comfort. 2012. (ENG., Illus.). 208p. (C). pap. 38.35 **(978-0-415-69159-8(1))** Routledge.

Olthuis, Koen & Keuning, David. Float! Building on Water to Combat Urban Congestion & Climate Change. 2010. (ENG., Illus.). 240p. 59.00 (978-90-77174-29-6(X)) Frame Pubs. NLD. Dist: Consortium Bk. Sales & Distribution.

Rice, E. B. Building in the North. 5th ed. 2008. (ENG., Illus.). 100p. pap. 16.95 (978-1-60223-019-4(6)) Univ. of Alaska Pr.

Roaf, Sue, et al. Adapting Buildings & Cities for Climate Change: A 21st Century Survival Guide. 2nd rev. ed. 2009. (ENG., Illus.). 400p. pap. 59.95 (978-1-85617-720-7(3)) Routledge.

Roaf, Susan, ed. Transforming Markets in the Built Environment: Adapting to Climate Change. 2010. (Architectural Science Review Ser.). (ENG., Illus.). 140p. 120.00 (978-1-84971-088-6(0)) Routledge.

Roettger, Betsy, ed. Building after Katrina: Visions for the Gulf Coast. 2007. (ENG., Illus.). 176p. (C). (gr. 13-17). per. 25.00 (978-0-9771024-5-7(9)) Univ. Pr. of Virginia.

Specification for Hot Weather Concreting. 2007. per. (978-0-87031-242-7(1)) American Concrete Institute.

Stankovic, Sinisa, et al. Urban Wind Energy. 2009. (ENG., Illus.). 200p. 97.50 (978-1-84407-282-8(7)) Routledge.

van den Dobbelsteen, Andy, et al, eds. Smart Building in a Changing Climate. 2009. (ENG., Illus.). 254p. pap. 69.00 (978-90-8594-024-1(9)) Techne Pr. NLD. Dist: Chicago Distribution Ctr.

Watson, Donald & Adams, Michele. Design for Flooding: Architecture, Landscape, & Urban Design for Resilience to Climate Change. 2010. (ENG., Illus.). 336p. 85.00 (978-0-470-47564-5(1), Wiley) Wiley, John & Sons, Inc.

Yannas, Simos & Weber, Willi, eds. Lessons from Traditional Architecture: Achieving Climatic Buildings by Studying the Past. 2012. (ENG., Illus.). 208p. 69.95 (978-1-84407-600-0(8)) Routledge.

ARCHITECTURE AND ENERGY CONSERVATION

Abaza, Hussein. Moisture Behavior in Buildings- an Integrated Design & Control Strategy for Efficient & Healthy Buildings. 2007. 188p. per. (978-3-8364-2933-7(0)) VDM Verlag Dr. Mueller e.K.

Asia Business Council. Building Energy Efficiency: Why Green Buildings Are Key to Asia's Future. 2007. 324p. per. 36.00 (978-988-99565-1-6(9)) Inkstone Bks.

Attmann, Osman. Green Architecture: Advanced Technologies & Materials. 2009. (ENG., Illus.). 368p. 79.95 (978-0-07-162501-2(1), 0071625011) McGraw-Hill Professional Publishing.

Bainbridge, David & Haggard, Ken. Passive Solar Architecture: Heating, Cooling, Ventilation & Daylighting Using Natural Flows. 2011. (ENG., Illus.). 300p. pap. 39.95 (978-1-60358-268-1(1)) Chelsea Green Publishing.

Bainbridge, David A. & Haggard, Ken. Passive Solar Architecture: Heating, Cooling, Ventilation, Daylighting & More Using Natural Flows. 2011. (ENG., Illus.). 304p. 85.00 (978-1-60358-296-4(7)) Chelsea Green Publishing.

Bokalders, Varis & Block, Maria. Whole Building Handbook: How to Build Sustainable Houses. 2009. (ENG., Illus.). 704p. pap. 77.95 (978-1-84407-523-2(0)) Routledge.

Borasi, Giovanna & Zardini, Mirko, eds. Sorry, Out of Gas: Architecture's Response to the 1973 Oil Crisis, 1 vol. 2008. (ENG., Illus.). 236p. pap. 49.95 (978-88-7570-143-7(1)) Corraini ITA. Dist: D.A.P./Distributed Art Pubs.

Building Green, Saving Green: Constructing Sustainable & Energy-Efficient Buildings: Hearing Before the Select Committee on Energy Independence & Global Warming, House of Representatives, One Hundred Tenth Congress, Second Session, May 14, 2008. 2010. (Illus.). iii, 144p. **(978-0-16-087419-2(X)**, 552-070-42112-2) United States Government Printing Office.

Chaisuparasmikul, Pongsak. Simplified Building Energy Modeling Tool. 2008. 260p. pap. (978-3-639-00977-4(0)) VDM Verlag Dr. Mueller e.K.

Chen, Gang. Leed Ap Exam Guide: Study Materials, Sample Questions, Mock Exam, Building LEED Certification (LEED-NC) & Going Green. 2008. 244p. pap. 69.95 (978-1-4327-2842-7(3)) Outskirts Pr., Inc.

—Leed Ga Exam Guide: A Must-Have for the LEED Green Associate Exam. 2009. 398p. pap. 73.95 (978-1-4327-4168-6(3)) Outskirts Pr., Inc.

Climate Benefits of Improved Building Energy Efficiency: Hearing Before the Subcommittee on Energy & Air Quality of the Committee on Energy & Commerce, House of Representatives, One Hundred Tenth Congress, Second Session, July 17, 2008. 2011. v, 184p. **(978-0-16-088086-5(6)**, 552-070-42506-3) United States Government Printing Office.

Committee on Predicting Outcomes of Investments in Maintenance and Repair for Federal Facilities & National Research Council. Predicting Outcomes from Investments in Maintenance & Repair for Federal Facilities. 2012. (ENG.). 152p. pap. 40.00 **(978-0-309-22186-3(2))** National Academies Pr.

Cook, Martin Godfrey. The Zero-Carbon House. 2011. (ENG., Illus.). 160p. 29.95 **(978-1-84797-262-0(4))** Crowood Pr., Ltd. GBR. Dist: Independent Pubs. Group.

Cottrell, Michelle. Guide to the Leed Green Associate Exam. 2010. (ENG., Illus.). 208p. pap., instr.'s gde. ed. 55.00 (978-0-470-60829-6(3), Wiley) Wiley, John & Sons, Inc.

Drake, Scott. The Third Skin: Architecture, Technology, & Environment. 2007. (ENG., Illus.). 224p. per. 56.95 (978-0-86840-931-3(6), UNSW Press) NewSouth Publishing AUS. Dist: Independent Pubs. Group.

Dummies Press Staff & DeGunther, Rik. Energy Efficient Homes for Dummies. 2008. (ENG., Illus.). 384p. pap. 21.99 (978-0-470-37602-7(3), For Dummies) Wiley, John & Sons, Inc.

Edwards, Brian. Green Buildings Pay. 3rd rev. ed. 2012. (ENG., Illus.). 240p. 155.00 (978-0-415-68534-4(6)); pap. 55.00 (978-0-415-68535-1(4)) Routledge.

Energy Efficiency in Buildings: Hearing Before the Committee on Energy & Natural Resources, United States Senate, One Hundred Eleventh Congress, First Session, to Provide Recommendations for Reducing Energy Consumption in Buildings, February 26, 2009. 2009. iii, 99p. (978-0-16-083063-1(X), 552-070-38958-0) United States Government Printing Office.

Energy Efficiency of Buildings: Hearing Before the Subcommittee on Energy of the Committee on Energy & Natural Resources, United States Senate, One Hundred Tenth Congress, First Session, to Receive Recommendations on Policies & Programs to Improve the Energy Efficiency of Buildings & to Expand the Role of Electric & Gas Utilities in Energy Efficiency Programs, February 12, 2007. 2007. iii, 62p. (978-0-16-078935-9(4), 552-070-36062-0) United States Government Printing Office.

Energy Efficient Building Retrofits: Hearing Before the Committee on Energy & Natural Resources, United States Senate, One Hundred Eleventh Congress, Second Session, to Review Legislative Proposals Designed to Create Jobs Related to Energy Efficiency, Including a Majority Staff Draft on Energy Efficient Building Retrofits, March 11, 2010. 2010. iii, 127p. (978-0-16-086228-1(0), 552-070-41319-7) United States Government Printing Office.

Ewing, Rex A. Crafting Log Homes Solar Style: An Inspiring Guide to Self-Sufficiency. 2008. (Illus.). 255p. pap. 25.00 (978-0-9773724-4-7(8)) PixyJack Pr., Inc.

First in a Series: Greening Washington & the National Capital Region: Hearing Before the Subcommittee on Economic Development, Public Buildings, & Emergency Management of the Committee on Transportation & Infrastructure, House of Representatives, One Hundred Tenth Congress, Second Session, April 17, 2008. 2008. ix, 101p. (978-0-16-083277-2(2), 552-070-39105-3) United States Government Printing Office.

Gould, Kira, et al. Women in Green: Voices of Sustainable Design. 2007. (Illus.). 246p. per. 24.95 (978-0-9749033-7-8(X)) Ecotone Publishing.

Gu Zhenhong. Approaches to Energy Efficient Building Development: Studying under Chinese Contexts 2008. 100p. pap. (978-3-639-09361-2(5)) VDM Verlag Dr. Mueller e.K.

Hegger, Manfred, et al. Energy Manual: Sustainable Architecture. 2008. (Construction Manuals (englisch) Ser.). (Illus.). 280p. pap. 89.95 (978-3-7643-8830-0(7), 3764388307) Springer.

Hejler Andersen, Helle & Lind Klogborg, Mathias. Solar City. 2011. 216p. pap. **(978-3-8443-2105-0(5))** Lambert Academic Publishing.

Herzog, Thomas, ed. European Charter for Solar Energy in Architecture & Urban Planning. 2008. 128p. 14.95 (978-3-7913-3928-3(1)) Prestel Publishing.

Hootman, Thomas. Net Zero Energy Design. 2012. (ENG., Illus.). 432p. 85.00 **(978-1-118-01854-5(0)**, Wiley) Wiley, John & Sons, Inc.

Hubka, David & Valtcheva-McGee, Vessela. LEED Homes Practice Exam. 2009. (ENG.). 94p. pap. 40.00 (978-1-59126-183-4(X)) Professional Pubns., Inc.

Hyde, Richard. Bioclimatic Housing: Innovative Designs for Warm Climates. 2007. (ENG., Illus.). 400p. (C). pap. 89.95 (978-1-84407-284-2(3)) Routledge.

ICC. International Green Construction Code (IGCC) Public Version 2. 0 Print. 2011. pap. (978-1-60983-097-7(0)) International Code Council.

International Code Council Staff. International Energy Conservation Code 2009: 90. 1-2007 Energy Standard for Building Except Low-Rise Residential Buildings. 2009. (ENG.). pap. 147.00 (978-1-58001-799-2(1)) International Code Council.

Kalz, Doreen E. Heating & Cooling Concepts Employing Environmental Energy & Thermo-Active Building Systems: System Analysis & Optimization. 2011. (ENG., Illus.). 219p. pap. 47.72 (978-3-8396-0176-1(2)) Fraunhofer IRB Verlag DEU. Dist: Silvermine International Bks., LLC.

Kubba, Sam. LEED Practices, Certification, & Accreditation Handbook. 2009. (ENG., Illus.). 528p. pap. 92.95 (978-1-85617-691-0(6), Butterworth-Heinemann) Elsevier Science & Technology Bks.

Lamia, Sara. Housebirth: Your Guide to Buying an Energy-Efficient, Healthy New Home that Pays You Back. 2007. (Illus.). 256p. spiral bd. 24.94 (978-0-9723390-2-5(7)) Home Building Coach, Inc.

LEED Exam Secrets Test Prep Staff, ed. LEED AP Building Design + Construction Exam Flashcard Study System: LEED Test Practice Questions & Review for the Leadership in Energy & Environmental Design Exam. 2011. (C). 62.99 (978-1-61403-581-7(4)) Mometrix Media LLC.

—LEED AP Building Design + Construction Exam Secrets Study Guide: LEED Test Review for the Leadership in Energy & Environmental Design Exam. 2011. (C). 91.99 (978-1-61403-580-0(6)) Mometrix Media LLC.

LeedVisual. LeedVisual GA. LeedVisual, ed. 2009. (ENG.). pap. (978-0-615-33280-2(3)) LeedVisual.

Leppo, RA/CID, LEED AP, Holly Williams. LEED Prep Homes: What You Really Need to Know to Pass the LEED AP Homes Exam. 2009. (ENG.). 360p. pap. 48.00 (978-1-59126-182-7(1)) Professional Pubns., Inc.

—LEED Prep ID&C: What You Really Need to Know to Pass the LEED AP Interior Design & Construction Exam. 2009. (ENG.). 356p. pap. 48.00 (978-1-59126-186-5(4)) Professional Pubns., Inc.

Leppo, RA/CID, LEED AP, Holly Williams, et al. LEED Prep BD&C: What You Really Need to Know to Pass the LEED AP Building Design & Construction Exam. 2009. (ENG.). 392p. pap. 48.00 (978-1-59126-184-1(8)) Professional Pubns., Inc.

Matriti. Epistolae tae V1, 1537-1548: Ex Variis Europae Locis Ab Anno 1537 Ad 1556 Scriptae (1898) 2009. 648p. pap. 45.95 (978-1-104-12336-9(3)) Kessinger Publishing, LLC.

Meckler, Milton. Innovative Energy Design for the '90s. (Illus.). 403p. 64.00 (978-0-88173-123-1(4), 0263) Fairmont Pr., Inc.

Morton, W. Brown, III, et al. The Secretary of the Interior's Standards for Rehabilitation & Illustrated Guidelines on Sustainability for Rehabilitating Historic Buildings. 2011. (Illus.). 35p. pap. 7.00 **(978-0-16-088440-5(3)**, Interior Dept.) United States Government Printing Office.

Options & Opportunities for Onsite Renewable Energy Integration: Field Hearing Before the Committee on Science & Technology, House of Representatives, One Hundred Eleventh Congress, Second Session, November 15, 2010. 2010. (Illus.). iv, 65p. **(978-0-16-088291-3(5)**, 552-070-42596-9) United States Government Printing Office.

Parissien, Steven & Kenda, Barbara, eds. Green Living: Architecture & Planning. 2010. (ENG., Illus.). 208p. 45.00 (978-0-8478-3310-8(0)) Rizzoli International Pubns., Inc.

Peot, M Ed, Meghan & Schumacher, LEED AP, Brennan. LEED BD&C Practice Exam: Building Design & Construction. 2009. (ENG.). 112p. pap. 40.00 (978-1-59126-185-8(6)) Professional Pubns., Inc.

Pushing the Efficiency Envelope: RandD for High-Performance Buildings, Industries, & Consumers: Hearing Before the Subcommittee on Energy & Environment, Committee on Science & Technology, House of Representatives, One Hundred Eleventh Congress, First Session, April 28, 2009. 2009. (Illus.). iv, 102p. (978-0-16-084653-3(6), 552-070-40148-2) United States Government Printing Office.

Reed, Sue. Energy-Wise Landscape Design: A New Approach for Your Home & Garden. 2010. (ENG., Illus.). 304p. pap. 29.95 (978-0-86571-653-7(6), 9780865716537) New Society Pubs., Ltd. CAN. Dist: Consortium Bk. Sales & Distribution.

Roaf, Sue, et al. Ecohouse. 3rd rev. ed. 2007. (ENG., Illus.). 488p. pap. 51.95 (978-0-7506-6903-0(9)) Routledge.

Ryker, Lori. Off the Grid Homes: Case Studies for Sustainable Living, 1 vol. 2007. (ENG., Illus.). 128p. pap. 24.99 (978-1-58685-689-2(8)) Gibbs Smith, Publisher.

Sabnis, Gajanan M. Green House: The Energy Efficient Home. 2nd ed. 2007. (Illus.). 208p. pap. 24.95 (978-0-9772637-1-4(1)) Drylongso Pubns.

Salomon, Shay. Little House on a Small Planet: Simple Homes, Cozy Retreats, & Energy Efficient Possibilities. 2nd ed. 2009. (ENG., Illus.). 304p. pap. 19.95 (978-1-59921-795-6(3), Lyons Pr.) Globe Pequot Pr., The.

Sasin, Tomasz. Renewable Heat & Electricity Supply to Residential Settlements. 2010. 100p. pap. (978-3-639-26699-3(4)) VDM Verlag Dr. Mueller e.K.

Smith, Peter. Sustainability at the Cutting Edge: Emerging Technologies for Low Energy Buildings. 2nd rev. ed. 2007. (ENG., Illus.). 196p. pap. 51.95 (978-0-7506-8300-5(7)) Routledge.

Sommer, Martin & Sternagel, Thomas. EinSparHaus: Energieeffiziente Architektur. 2009. (GER., Illus.). 163p. pap. (978-3-86859-013-5(7)) Jovis Verlag GmbH.

U.S. Green Building Council Staff, contrib. by. Existing Buildings: Operations & Maintenance Reference Guide. 2008. (Illus.). 532p. pap. **(978-1-932444-13-1(0))** U. S. Green Building Council.

Wanek, Catherine. The Hybrid House: Designing with Sun, Wind, Water, & Earth, 1 vol. 2010. (ENG., Illus.). 144p. 24.99 (978-1-4236-0316-0(8)) Gibbs Smith, Publisher.

Waterfield, Patrick. The Energy Efficient Home: A Complete Guide. 2011. (ENG., Illus.). 176p. pap. 24.95 **(978-1-84797-259-0(4))** Crowood Pr., Ltd. GBR. Dist: Independent Pubs. Group.

Williams, Daniel E. Sustainable Design: Ecology, Architecture, & Planning. 2007. (ENG., Illus.). 320p. 85.00 (978-0-471-70953-4(0), Wiley) Wiley, John & Sons, Inc.

Yannas, Simos. Solar Energy & Housing Design, 2 vols., Bk. 2. 2006. (Illus.). 176p. pap. (978-1-870890-37-3(X)) Architectural Assn.

Yeang, Ken. Ecodesign: A Manual for Ecological Design. 2008. (ENG., Illus.). 500p. pap. 65.00 (978-0-470-99778-9(8), Wiley) Wiley, John & Sons, Inc.

Zira, Christina. Three European Standards for Energy Assessment of Buildings. 2010. 128p. pap. (978-3-639-26667-2(6)) VDM Verlag Dr. Mueller e.K.

ARCHITECTURE AND HISTORY

Ames, David L. & Wagner, Richard D. Design & Historic Preservation: The Challenge of Compatibility: Held at Goucher College, Baltimore, Maryland, March 14-16 2002. 2009. (Illus.). xxvii, 197p. 44.50 (978-0-87413-831-3(0)) Univ. of Delaware Pr.

Bevan, Robert. The Destruction of Memory: Architecture at War. 2007. (ENG., Illus.). 240p. per. 20.00 (978-1-86189-319-2(1)) Reaktion Bks., Ltd. GBR. Dist: Chicago Distribution Ctr.

Hollis, Edward. The Secret Lives of Buildings: From the Ruins of the Parthenon to the Vegas Strip in Thirteen Stories. 2010. (ENG., Illus.). 384p. pap. 17.00 (978-0-312-65536-5(3)) Picador.

Kinney, Dale & Brilliant, Richard. Reuse Value Erasure: Critical Views on Spolia & Appropriation in Art & Architecture. 2011. (Illus.). 284p. 119.95 **(978-1-4094-2422-2(7))** Ashgate Publishing Co.

Mires, Peter. Bayou Built: The Legacy of Louisiana's Historic Architecture. 2010. 176p. pap. 15.95 *(978-1-4502-6367-2(4))* iUniverse, Inc.

Passikoff, Alexander G. A Façade of Buildings: A Collection of Architectural Styles, Architects, & Their Buildings That Make up the Face of New York. 2011. 164p. pap. 49.99 **(978-1-4567-9490-3(6))** AuthorHouse.

Pinto, John. Speaking Ruins: Piranesi, Architects & Antiquity in Eighteenth-Century Rome. 2012. (Thomas Spencer Jerome Lectures). (ENG., Illus.). 376p. 90.00 **(978-0-472-11821-2(8))** Univ. of Michigan Pr.

Rees, Mark A., ed. Archaeology of Louisiana. 2010. 352p. pap. 40.00 *(978-0-8071-3705-5(7))*; (Illus.). 95.00 *(978-0-8071-3703-1(0))* Louisiana State Univ. Pr.

Scheiber, Laura L. & Clark, Bonnie J., eds. Archaeological Landscapes on the High Plains. 2008. (ENG., Illus.). xiii, 296p. 60.00 *(978-0-87081-931-5(3))* Univ. Pr. of Colorado.

Shelton, Barrie. Learning from the Japanese City: Looking East in Urban Design. 2nd rev. ed. (Planning, History & Environment Ser.). (ENG., Illus.). 208p. (C). 2013. pap. 62.95 *(978-0-415-55440-4(3))* 2012. 165.00 *(978-0-415-55439-8(X))* Routledge.

Stahl, Ann Brower. Making History in Banda: Anthropological Visions of Africa's Past. 2007. (New Studies in Archaeology). (ENG., Illus.). 292p. pap. 62.00 *(978-0-521-03797-6(2))* Cambridge Univ. Pr.

ARCHITECTURE AND LITERATURE

Bernstein, Susan. Housing Problems: Writing & Architecture in Goethe, Walpole, Freud, & Heidegger. 2008. (Meridian: Crossing Aesthetics Ser.). (ENG., Illus.). 216p. 60.00 *(978-0-8047-5854-3(9))*; pap. 21.95 *(978-0-8047-5855-0(7))* Stanford Univ. Pr.

Blair, Kirstie. Form & Faith in Victorian Poetry & Religion. 2012. (ENG.). 272p. 110.00 **(978-0-19-964450-6(0))** Oxford Univ. Pr., Inc.

Castro, Ana Claudia Veiga de. A São Paulo de Menotti Del Picchia: Arquitetura, Arte e Cidade Nas Crônicas de Um Modernista. 2008. (POR., Illus.). 296p. *(978-85-98325-77-4(5))* Alameda Casa Editorial Ltda.

Edwards, Sarah, et al, eds. Writing the Modern City. 2012. (ENG., Illus.). 256p. (C). 155.00 **(978-0-415-59150-8(3))** Routledge.

Edwards, Sarah & Charley, Jonathan, eds. Writing the Modern City. 2012. (ENG., Illus.). 256p. (C). pap. 53.95 **(978-0-415-59151-5(1))** Routledge.

Eriksen, Roy. The Building in the Text: From Alberti to Shakespeare & Milton. 2008. 220p. per. 23.95 *(978-0-271-02783-8(5))* Pennsylvania State Univ. Pr.

Gleason, William. Sites Unseen: Architecture, Race, & American Literature. 2011. (ENG., Illus.). 288p. 65.00 *(978-0-8147-3246-5(1))*; pap. 22.00 *(978-0-8147-3247-2(X))* New York Univ. Pr.

Gleason, William A. Sites Unseen: Architecture, Race, & American Literature. 2011. (Illus.). 288p. E-Book **(978-0-8147-3248-9(8))** New York Univ. Pr.

Johnson, Anthony Ben Johnson. 2012. (Writers & Their Work Ser.). (ENG.). (C). pap. 26.00 *(978-0-7463-0881-3(7))* Northcote Hse. Publishers, Ltd. GBR. Dist: Brown, David Bk. Co., The.

—Ben Jonson. 2012. (Writers & Their Work Ser.). (ENG.). (C). 80.00 *(978-0-7463-1063-2(3))* Northcote Hse. Publishers, Ltd. GBR. Dist: Brown, David Bk. Co., The.

Lethaby, W. R. Architecture, Mysticism & Myth. 2009. 252p. 27.99 *(978-0-559-07736-4(X))*; 24.99 *(978-0-559-07748-7(3))*; pap. 26.75 *(978-0-559-07739-5(4))*; pap. 17.99 *(978-0-559-07744-9(0))* BiblioBazaar.

Maaskant, Madeleine, et al, contrib. by. Oase #70: Architecture & Literature, 1 vol. 2009. (ENG., Illus.). 144p. pap. 25.00 *(978-90-5662-487-3(3))* NAi Uitgevers / Publishers Stichting NLD. Dist: D.A.P./Distributed Art Pubs.

Martiat, François-Xavier, et al. Le Bouquin Martiat Durnez, Architectes + Frédéric Saenen, écrivain: The Book Martiat Durnez Architects + Frédéric Saenen Writer, 1 vol. 2011. (ENG & FRE., Illus.). 158p. pap. 20.00 *(978-2-9600475-8-5(3))* Centre International Pour La Ville, L'Architecture Et Le Paysage BEL. Dist: Innovative Logistics.

Modena, Letizia. Italo Calvino's Architecture of Lightness. 2011. (Routledge Studies in Twentieth-Century Literature Ser.). (ENG., Illus.). 284p. (C). 125.00 *(978-0-415-88038-1(6))* Routledge.

Psarra, Sophia. Architecture & Narrative: The Formation of Space & Cultural Meaning in Buildings. 2009. (Illus.). (ENG.). 304p. (C). 53.95 *(978-0-415-34376-3(3))*; 320p. 165.00 *(978-0-415-34375-6(5))* Routledge.

Reynolds, Nicole. Building Romanticism: Literature & Architecture in Nineteenth-Century Britain. 2010. (ENG., Illus.). 240p. (C). 70.00 *(978-0-472-11731-4(9))* Univ. of Michigan Pr.

Spurr, David. Architecture & Modern Literature. 2012. E-Book **(978-0-472-02824-5(3))** Univ. of Michigan Pr.

Spurr, David Anton. Architecture & Modern Literature. 2012. (ENG.). 300p. (C). pap. 30.00 **(978-0-472-05171-7(7))** Univ. of Michigan Pr.

—Architecture & Modern Literature. 2012. (ENG., Illus.). 300p. (C). 85.00 **(978-0-472-07171-5(8))** Univ. of Michigan Pr.

ARCHITECTURE AND LITURGY

see Liturgy and Architecture

ARCHITECTURE AND POLITICS

see Architecture and State

ARCHITECTURE AND SOCIETY

Adam, M. & Hardy, M, eds. Tradition Today: Continuity in Architecture & Society. 2008. (Illus.). 160p. 59.00 *(978-1-84564-066-8(7))* WIT Pr GBR. Dist: WIT Pr.

Aga Khan Foundation Staff & Khan, Aga. Intervention Architecture: Building for Change. Johnston, Pamela, ed. 2007. (ENG., Illus.). 192p. pap. 26.00 *(978-1-84511-673-6(9))* I. B. Tauris & Co., Ltd. GBR. Dist: Macmillan.

Aggregate. Governing by Design: Architecture, Economy, & Politics in the Twentieth Century. 2012. (Culture Politics & the Built Environment Ser.). (ENG., Illus.). 300p. pap. 35.00 **(978-0-8229-6178-9(4))** Univ. of Pittsburgh Pr.

Al-Qawasmi, Jamal, ed. Regional Architecture & Identity in the Age of Globalization, 3 vols. 2008. (Illus.). 700p. pap. *(978-9957-8602-2-6(4))* Center for Study of Architecture in the Arab Region (CSAAR), The.

Allen, Joseph R. Taipei: City of Displacements. 2011. (ENG., Illus.). 288p. (C). 75.00 *(978-0-295-99125-2(9))*; pap. 30.00 *(978-0-295-99126-9(7))* Univ. of Washington Pr.

Allison, Eric W. & Peters, Lauren. Historic Preservation & the Livable City. 2011. (ENG., Illus.). 272p. 80.00 *(978-0-470-38192-2(2),* Wiley) Wiley, John & Sons, Inc.

Alsayyad, Nezar. Cairo: Histories of a City. 2011. (Illus.). 352p. 29.95 *(978-0-674-04786-0(9),* Belknap Pr.) Harvard Univ. Pr.

Amaratunga, Dilanthi & Haigh, Richard. Post-Disaster Reconstruction of the Built Environment: Rebuilding for Resilience. 2011. (ENG., Illus.). 336p. 116.99 *(978-1-4443-3356-5(9),* Wiley-Blackwell) Wiley, John & Sons, Inc.

Angles, Magda. In Favour of Public Space: Ten Years of the European Prize for Urban Public Space. 2010. (Illus.). 208p. pap. *(978-84-92861-38-5(X))* Actar Birkhauser Distribution.

Ankerl, Guy. Experimental Sociology of Architecture: A Guide to Theory, Research & Literature. (New Babylon Ser.). (ENG.). XVI, 550p. 210.00 **(978-3-11-180698-3(7))** De Gruyter, Mouton DEU. Dist: de Gruyter, Walter GmbH & Co. KG.

Aquilino, Marie, ed. Beyond Shelter: Architecture & Human Dignity. 2011. (ENG., Illus.). 304p. pap. 35.00 *(978-1-935202-47-9(2),* Metropolis Bks.) D.A.P./Distributed Art Pubs.

Archer, John. Architecture & Suburbia: From English Villa to American Dream House, 1690-2000. 2008. (Illus.). 496p. per. 27.50 *(978-0-8166-4304-2(0))* Univ. of Minnesota Pr.

Architecture for Humanity. Design Like You Give a Damn Vol. 2: Building Change from the Ground Up. 2012. (ENG., Illus.). 336p. pap. 35.00 *(978-0-8109-9702-8(9))* Abrams.

Avcioglu, Nebahat. Turkish Architecture in Europe 1737-1876: Politics & Visual Narratives of the Other. 2011. (Illus.). 338p. 124.95 *(978-0-7546-6422-2(8))* Ashgate Publishing Co.

Awan, Nishat, et al. Spatial Agency Schneider & Till. 2011. (ENG., Illus.). 224p. 165.00 *(978-0-415-57192-0(8))*; pap. 44.95 *(978-0-415-57193-7(6))* Routledge.

Ballantyne, Andrew. Architecture in the Space of Flows. Smith, Christopher, ed. 2011. (ENG., Illus.). 264p. (C). pap. 49.95 *(978-0-415-58542-2(2))* Routledge.

Ballantyne, Andrew, ed. Rural & Urban: Architecture Between Two Cultures. 2009. (ENG., Illus.). 216p. 53.95 *(978-0-415-55213-4(3))* 165.00 *(978-0-415-55212-7(5))* Routledge.

Ballantyne, Andrew & Smith, Christopher, eds. Architecture in the Space of Flows. 2011. (ENG., Illus.). 264p. (C). 155.00 *(978-0-415-58541-5(4))* Routledge.

Bamberg, Angelique. Chatham Village: Pittsburgh's Garden City. 2011. (ENG., Illus.). 208p. 29.95 *(978-0-8229-4406-5(5))* Univ. of Pittsburgh Pr.

Baudrillard, Jean. Mass Identity Architecture: Architectural Writings of Jean Baudrillard. Proto, Francesco, ed. 2006. (ENG., Illus.). 206p. per. 55.00 *(978-0-470-02715-8(0),* Academy Pr.) Wiley, John & Sons, Inc.

Baxter, Denise & Martin, Meredith S. Architectural Space in Eighteenth-Century Europe: Constructing Indentities an Interiors. 2010. (Illus.). 284p. 119.95 *(978-0-7546-6650-9(6))* Ashgate Publishing Co.

Beasley, Ellen. The Alleys & Back Buildings of Galveston: An Architectural & Social History. 2007. (Sara & John Lindsey Series in the Arts & Humanities: 10). (ENG., Illus.). 186p. 39.95 *(978-1-58544-582-0(7))* Texas A&M Univ. Pr.

Bell, Bryan & Wakeford, Katie. Expanding Architecture: Design As Activism. 2008. (ENG., Illus.). 288p. pap. 34.95 *(978-1-933045-78-8(7),* Metropolis Bks.) D.A.P./Distributed Art Pubs.

Bergdoll, Barry, intro. Small Scale, Big Change. 2010. (ENG., Illus.). 140p. pap. 37.50 *(978-0-87070-784-1(1))* Museum of Modern Art.

Bertram, Carel. Imagining the Turkish House: Collective Visions of Home. 2008. (ENG., Illus.). 360p. (C). pap. 70.00 *(978-0-292-71825-8(X))*; pap. 24.95 *(978-0-292-71826-5(8))* Univ. of Texas Pr.

Bianca, Stefano, ed. Syria: Medieval Citadels Between East & West. 2007. (ENG., Illus.). 312p. per. 60.00 *(978-88-422-1449-6(3))* Allemandi, Umberto & Co. GBR. Dist: National Bk. Network.

Bishir, Catherine W. Southern Built: American Architecture, Regional Practice. 2006. (ENG., Illus.). 400p. (gr. 17). 75.00 *(978-0-8139-2538-7(X))*; per. 35.00 *(978-0-8139-2539-4(8))* Univ. Pr. of Virginia.

Borasi, Giovanna & Amemiya, Kozy. Journeys: How Travelling Fruit, Ideas & Buildings Rearrange Our Environment. 2011. (Illus.). 320p. pap. *(978-84-92861-54-5(1))* Actar Birkhauser Distribution.

Borasi, Giovanna, et al. Trajets: Comment la Mobilité des Fruits, des Idées et des Architectures Recompose Notre Environnement. 2011. (FRE., Illus.). 320p. pap. *(978-84-92861-55-2(X))* Actar Birkhauser Distribution.

Bottger, Matthias, et al, eds. TV Towers / Fernsehtürme: 8,559 Meters Politics & Architecture - 8.559 Meter Politik und Architektur. 2010. (ENG., Illus.). 272p. pap. 39.95 *(978-3-86859-024-1(2))* Jovis Verlag GmbH DEU. Dist: D.A.P./Distributed Art Pubs.

Boym, Svetlana. Architecture of the Off-Modern. 2008. (ENG., Illus.). 80p. 24.95 *(978-1-56898-778-1(1))* Princeton Architectural Pr.

Boys, Jos. Towards Creative Learning Spaces. 2011. (ENG., Illus.). 208p. (C). pap. 49.95 *(978-0-415-57064-0(6))* Routledge.

—Towards Creative Learning Spaces: Re-Thinking the Architecture of Post-Compulsory Education. 2011. (ENG., Illus.). 208p. (C). 155.00 *(978-0-415-57062-6(X))* Routledge.

Bozdogan, Sibel & Akcan, Esra. Turkey: Modern Architectures in History. 2012. (Reaktion Books - Modern Architectures in History Ser.). (Illus.). 272p. pap. 29.95 *(978-1-86189-878-4(9))* Reaktion Bks., Ltd. GBR. Dist: Chicago Distribution Ctr.

Brandwood, Geoff. Living, Leisure & Law: Eight Building Types in England 1800-1914. 2010. (ENG., Illus.). 172p. (C). pap. 35.00 *(978-1-904965-27-5(X))* Spire Bks. Ltd. GBR. Dist: Brown, David Bk. Co., The.

Britton, Karla, ed. Constructing the Ineffable: Contemporary Sacred Architecture. 2011. (ENG., Illus.). 248p. 50.00 *(978-0-300-17037-5(8))* Yale Univ. Pr.

Brown, Lori. Feminist Practices: Interdisciplinary Approaches to Women in Architecture. 2011. (Illus.). 400p. 119.95 **(978-1-4094-2117-7(1))** Ashgate Publishing Co.

Bullivant, Lucy. Responsive Environments: Architecture, Art & Design. 2006. (ENG., Illus.). 128p. pap. 39.95 *(978-1-85177-481-4(5))* V & A Pubns. GBR. Dist: Hachette Bk. Group.

Buntrock, Dana. Material & Meaning in Contemporary Japanese Architecture: Tradition & Today. 2010. (ENG., Illus.). 288p. (C). pap. 62.95 *(978-0-415-77891-6(3))* Routledge.

—Materials & Meaning in Contemporary Japanese Architecture: Tradition & Today. 2010. (ENG., Illus.). 288p. (C). 165.00 *(978-0-415-77890-9(5))* Routledge.

Campanella, Thomas. The Concrete Dragon: China's Urban Revolution & What It Means for the World. 2011. (ENG., Illus.). 336p. pap. 24.95 *(978-1-56898-968-6(7))* Princeton Architectural Pr.

Castle, Helen, ed. 4dsocial: Interactive Design Environments. 2007. (Architectural Design Ser.). (ENG., Illus.). 128p. per. 50.00 *(978-0-470-31911-6(9),* Wiley) Wiley, John & Sons, Inc.

Çelik, Zeynep. Walls of Algiers: Narratives of the City Through Text & Image. Clancy-Smith, Julia Ann & Terpak, Frances, eds. 2009. (ENG., Illus.). 288p. pap. *(978-0-295-98868-9(1))* Getty Pubns.

Chopra, Preeti. A Joint Enterprise: Indian Elites & the Making of British Bombay. 2011. (Illus.). 344p. 82.50 *(978-0-8166-7036-9(6))*; pap. 27.50 *(978-0-8166-7037-6(4))* Univ. of Minnesota Pr.

Christine Sciacca Staff. Building the Medieval World. 2010. (Illus.). vii, 96p. *(978-0-7123-5094-5(2),* J. Paul Getty Museum) Getty Pubns.

Chun, Wendy Hui Kyong. Programmed Visions: Software & Memory. 2011. (Software Studies). (ENG., Illus.). 256p. (gr. 17). 32.00 *(978-0-262-01542-4(0))* MIT Pr.

Cieraad, Irene, ed. At Home: An Anthropology of Domestic Space. 2006. (Illus.). 200p. pap. 19.95 *(978-0-8156-2903-0(6))* Syracuse Univ. Pr.

Colomina, Beatriz. Domesticity at War. 2007. (ENG., Illus.). 280p. (gr. 17). 49.95 *(978-0-262-03361-9(5))* MIT Pr.

Correia, Luís Miguel Maldonado de Vasconcelos. Castelos Em Portugal: Retrato Do Seu Perfil Arquitectónico (1509-1949) 2010. (POR., Illus.). 469p. *(978-989-26-0022-2(3))* Coimbra Editora.

Craig, Maurice James. Dublin, 1660-1860: The Shaping of a City. 2007. (ENG., Illus.). 432p. pap. 27.95 *(978-1-905483-11-2(2))* Liberties Pr. IRL. Dist: Dufour Editions, Inc.

Crane, Sheila. Mediterranean Crossroads: Marseille & Modern Architecture. 2011. (Illus.). 376p. 82.50 *(978-0-8166-5361-4(5))*; pap. 27.50 *(978-0-8166-5362-1(3))* Univ. of Minnesota Pr.

Craven, Wayne. Gilded Mansions: Grand Architecture & High Society. 2008. (ENG., Illus.). 352p. 59.95 *(978-0-393-06754-5(8),* 6754) Norton, W. W. & Co., Inc.

Cromley, Elizabeth C. The Food Axis: Cooking, Eating, & the Architecture of American Houses. 2010. (ENG., Illus.). 280p. (gr. 17). 50.00 *(978-0-8139-3007-7(3))* Univ. Pr. of Virginia.

Cuff, Dana & Sherman, Roger, eds. Fast-Forward Urbanism: Rethinking Architecture's Engagement with the City. 2011. (ENG., Illus.). 288p. pap. 34.95 *(978-1-56898-977-8(6))* Princeton Architectural Pr.

de Botton, Alain. The Architecture of Happiness. 2008. (Vintage Ser.). (ENG., Illus.). 288p. pap. 18.00 *(978-0-307-27724-4(0),* Vintage) Knopf Doubleday Publishing Group.

—The Architecture of Happiness. 2008. (ENG., Illus.). 288p. pap. *(978-0-7710-2607-2(2),* McClelland & Stewart) McClelland & Stewart CAN. Dist: Random Hse., Inc.

Delbeke, M. Edmunde & Schraven, Minou, eds. Foundation, Dedication & Consecration in Early Modern Europe. 2011. (ENG., Illus.). XVI, 396p. **(978-90-04-21757-7(6))** BRILL.

Desai, Madhuri & Rajagopalan, Mrinalini. Colonial Frames Nationalist Histories: Architecture Modernism & Identity. 2012. (Ashgate Studies in Architecture Ser.). (Illus.). 332p. 119.95 **(978-0-7546-7880-9(6))** Ashgate Publishing Co.

Devlin, Ann Sloan. What Americans Build & Why: Psychological Perspectives. 2010. (ENG., Illus.). 316p. (C). 90.00 *(978-0-521-51657-0(9))*; pap. 27.99 *(978-0-521-73435-6(5))* Cambridge Univ. Pr.

Dey, Hendrik W. The Aurelian Wall & the Refashioning of Imperial Rome, AD 271-855. 2011. (ENG., Illus.). 376p. 110.00 *(978-0-521-76365-3(7))* Cambridge Univ. Pr.

Dimbleby, David. How We Built Britain. 2008. (ENG., Illus.). 1p. pap. 32.95 *(978-0-7475-9287-7(X))* Bloomsbury Publishing Plc GBR. Dist: Independent Pubs. Group.

Dottelonde, Pierre, et al. CNIT, Ou, Les Temps Modernes. 2009. (FRE., Illus.). 157p. *(978-2-7491-1311-1(3))* Le Cherche Midi Editeur.

Dovey, Kim. Framing Places: Mediating Power in Built Form. 2nd rev. ed. 2008. (Architext Ser.). (Illus.). XIV, 242p. 160.00 *(978-0-415-41634-4(8))*; 53.95 *(978-0-415-41635-1(3))* Routledge.

Easterling, Keller. Enduring Innocence: Global Architecture & Its Political Masquerades. 2007. (ENG., Illus.). 252p. (gr. 17). pap. 15.95 *(978-0-262-55065-9(2))* MIT Pr.

Eaton, Ruth. Ideal Cities: Utopianism & the (un)Built Environment. 2007. 256p. pap. 44.95 *(978-0-500-28669-2(8))* Thames & Hudson.

Emden, Christian, et al, eds. Imagining the City: The Politics of Urban Space, 2 vols., Vol. 8. 2006. (Cultural History & Literary Imagination Ser.: Vols. 7-8). (Illus.). 383p. pap. 71.95 *(978-0-8204-7537-0(8))* Lang, Peter Publishing, Inc.

Emmons, Paul, et al, eds. The Cultural Role of Architecture. 2012. (ENG., Illus.). 256p. (C). 165.00 *(978-0-415-78340-8(2))*; pap. 49.95 *(978-0-415-78341-5(0))* Routledge.

Ericson, Staffan & Riegert, Kristina. Media Houses: Architecture, Media & the Production of Centrality. 2010. (Illus.). (C). 226p. 109.95 *(978-1-4331-0584-5(5))*; 232p. pap. 32.95 *(978-1-4331-0583-8(7))* Lang, Peter Publishing, Inc.

Erlande-Brandenburg, Alain. The Cathedral: The Social & Architectural Dynamics of Construction. 2009. (Cambridge Studies in the History of Architecture Ser.). (ENG., Illus.). 404p. pap. 42.00 *(978-0-521-11037-2(8))* Cambridge Univ. Pr.

Faherty, Duncan. Remodeling the Nation: The Architecture of American Identity, 1776-1858. 2009. (Becoming Modern: New Nineteenth-Century Studies). (ENG., Illus.). 268p. pap. 35.00 *(978-1-58465-772-9(3),* University of New Hampshire Press) Univ. Pr. of New England.

Feireiss, Kristin, ed. Architecture in Times of Need: Make it Right - Rebuilding the New Orleans' Lower Ninth Ward. 2009. (Illus.). 360p. pap. 39.95 *(978-3-7913-4276-4(2))* Prestel Publishing.

Fenlon, Iain. Piazza San Marco. 2009. (Wonders of the World Ser.). (Illus.). 256p. 19.95 *(978-0-674-02791-6(4))* Harvard Univ. Pr.

Fenske, Gail. The Skyscraper & the City: The Woolworth Building & the Making of Modern New York. 2008. (Illus.). 352p. 65.00 *(978-0-226-24141-3(6))* Univ. of Chicago Pr.

Fergusson, Peter. Canterbury Cathedral Priory in the Age of Becket. 2011. (ENG., Illus.). 288p. 85.00 *(978-0-300-17569-1(8))* Yale Univ. Pr.

Finizio, Gino. Architecture & Mobility: Tradition & Innovation. Rooney, Mary, ed. Ray, Leslie, tr. from ITA. 2007. (ENG., Illus.). 272p. per. 30.00 *(978-88-6130-071-2(5))* Skira Editore ITA. Dist: Random Hse., Inc.

Flowers, Benjamin Sitton. Skyscraper: The Politics & Power of Building New York City in the Twentieth Century. 2009. (Illus.). 240p. (C). 39.95 *(978-0-8122-4184-6(3))* Univ. of Pennsylvania Pr.

Foster, Hal. Design & Crime. 2nd ed. 2011. (Radical Thinkers Ser.). (ENG., Illus.). 192p. pap. 15.95 *(978-1-84467-670-5(6),* 844670) Verso Bks. GBR. Dist: Norton, W. W. & Co., Inc.

Friedman, Alice T. American Glamour & the Evolution of Modern Architecture. 2010. (Illus.). 272p. 65.00 *(978-0-300-11654-0(3))* Yale Univ. Pr.

Friedman, Avi. Terraced & Row Housing. 2012. (ENG., Illus.). 272p. 155.00 *(978-0-415-77911-1(1))* Routledge.

Friedman, Avi & MacBurnie, Ian. Terraced & Row Housing. 2012. (ENG., Illus.). 272p. pap. 53.95 *(978-0-415-77912-8(X))* Routledge.

Gartman, David. From Autos to Architecture: Fordism & Architectural Aesthetics in the Twentieth Century. 2009. (ENG.). 400p. 60.00 *(978-1-56898-813-9(3))* Princeton Architectural Pr.

Gehl, Jan. Life Between Buildings: Using Public Space. 2011. (ENG., Illus.). 216p. pap. 40.00 *(978-1-59726-827-1(5),* Island Pr.

Germany, Lisa. Great Houses of Texas. 2008. (ENG., Illus.). 256p. 55.00 *(978-0-8109-9393-8(7))* Abrams.

Ghirardo, Diane Yvonne. Italy: Modern Architectures in History. 2012. (Reaktion Books - Modern Architectures in History Ser.). (Illus.). 256p. pap. 29.95 *(978-1-86189-864-7(9))* Reaktion Bks., Ltd. GBR. Dist: Chicago Distribution Ctr.

Glazer, Nathan. From a Cause to a Style: Modernist Architecture's Encounter with the American City. 2007. (ENG.). 310p. (C). 24.95 *(978-0-691-12957-0(6))* Princeton Univ. Pr.

Gobbi Sica, Grazia. The Florentine Villa: Architecture History Society. 2012. (Classical Tradition in Architecture Ser.). (ENG., Illus.). 224p. (C). pap. 42.95 **(978-0-415-54317-0(7))** Routledge.

Goldberger, Paul. Why Architecture Matters. (Why X Matters Ser.). (Illus.). 304p. 2011. (ENG.). pap. 16.00 *(978-0-300-16817-4(9))* 2009. 26.00 *(978-0-300-14430-7(X))* Yale Univ. Pr.

Greene, David / B. 0. The Imagining of Community in European Art & Architecture, 1140-1617: Envisioning Transcendence of Authority in, & Foundations for Community. 2010. (Illus.). viii, 203p. *(978-0-7734-3713-5(4))* Mellen, Edwin Pr., The.

Guillén, Mauro F. The Taylorized Beauty of the Mechanical: Scientific Management & the Rise of Modernist Architecture. 2008. (Princeton Studies in Cultural Sociology Ser.). (ENG., Illus.). 232p. (C). pap. 29.95 *(978-0-691-13847-3(8))* Princeton Univ. Pr.

Guillery, Peter, ed. Built from Below: British Architecture & the Vernacular. 2010. (ENG., Illus.). 224p. (C). 165.00 *(978-0-415-56532-5(4))* Routledge.

—Built from Below: British Architecture & the Vernacular. 2010. (ENG., Illus.). 224p. (C). pap. 53.95 *(978-0-415-56533-2(2),* Routledge) Taylor & Francis Group GBR. Dist: Taylor & Francis Group.

Gutman, Robert, et al. Architecture from the Outside In. Cuff, Dana & Wriedt, John, eds. 2010. (ENG.). 342p. pap. 40.00 *(978-1-56898-896-2(6))* Princeton Architectural Pr.

Hanser, David, et al. Firmitas Utilitas Venustas: Architecture & Society. 2nd rev. ed. 2011. (ENG.). 194p. spiral bd. 59.00 *(978-0-7575-8801-3(8))* Kendall Hunt Publishing Co.

Harris, Dianne, ed. Second Suburb: Levittown, Pennsylvania. 2010. (Culture Politics & the Built Environment Ser.). (ENG., Illus.). 400p. (C). 45.95 *(978-0-8229-4389-1(1))* Univ. of Pittsburgh Pr.

Hatuka, Tali. Violent Acts & Urban Space in Contemporary Tel Aviv: Revisioning Moments. (ENG., Illus.). 248p. 2011. pap. 25.00 *(978-0-292-72882-0(4))* 2010. 55.00 *(978-0-292-72185-2(4))* Univ. of Texas Pr.

Hennings Hinojosa, Vania Verónica & Hernández Álvarez, María Elena. De Otros Asuntos e Historias de la Arquitectura: Interpretaciones Poco Conocidas o No Divulgadas. 2009. (SPA., Illus.). xii, 191p. *(978-607-02-0858-4(7))* Universidad Nacional Autónoma de México.

Hensel, Michael, et al, eds. Space Reader: Heterogeneous Space in Architecture. 2009. (AD Reader Ser.: 2). (ENG., Illus.). 224p. pap. 60.00 *(978-0-470-51943-1(6))*; 135.00 *(978-0-470-51942-4(8))* Wiley, John & Sons, Inc. (Wiley).

Herrle, Peter & Schmitz, Stephanus, eds. Constructed Identities: Contemporary Architecture in the South. 2011. (ENG.). 312p. pap. 44.95 *(978-3-643-10276-8(3))* Lit Verlag DEU. Dist: Transaction Pubs.

Herscher, Andrew. Violence Taking Place: The Architecture of the Kosovo Conflict. 2010. (Cultural Memory in the Present Ser.). (ENG.). 224p. 55.00 *(978-0-8047-6935-8(4))*; pap. 21.95 *(978-0-8047-6936-5(2))* Stanford Univ. Pr.

Heuer, Christopher. The City Rehearsed: Object, Architecture, & Print in the Worlds of Hans Vredeman de Vries. 2012. (Classical Tradition in Architecture Ser.). (ENG., Illus.). 312p. (C). pap. 42.95 ***(978-0-415-54232-6(4))*** Routledge.

Hill, Jonathan. Weather Architecture. 2012. (ENG., Illus.). 384p. (C). 165.00 ***(978-0-415-66860-6(3))***; pap. 54.95 ***(978-0-415-66861-3(1))*** Routledge.

Hoagland, Alison K. Mine Towns: Buildings for Workers in Michigan's Copper Country. 2010. (ENG., Illus.). 328p. 75.00 *(978-0-8166-6566-2(4))*; pap. 25.00 *(978-0-8166-6567-9(2))* Univ. of Minnesota Pr.

Hollein, Lilli, ed. Urbanism - for Sale: Austrian Contribution to the 7th International Biennial for Architecture in Sao Paulo. 2007. (GER & ENG., Illus.). 119p. *(978-3-211-75783-3(X)*, 321175783X) Actar Birkhauser Distribution.

Hollis, Edward. The Secret Lives of Buildings: From the Ruins of the Parthenon to the Vegas Strip in Thirteen Stories. 2010. (ENG., Illus.). 384p. pap. 17.00 *(978-0-312-65536-5(3))* Picador.

Hornstein, Shelley. Losing Site: Architecture Memory & Place. 2011. (Ashgate Studies in Architecture Ser.). (Illus.). 182p. 89.95 ***(978-1-4094-0871-0(X))*** Ashgate Publishing Co.

Howard, Maurice. The Building of Elizabethan & Jacobean England. 2008. (ENG., Illus.). 256p. 60.00 *(978-0-300-13543-5(2))* Yale Univ. Pr.

Isenstadt, Sandy & Rizvi, Kishwar, eds. Modernism & the Middle East: Architecture & Politics in the Twentieth Century. 2008. (Studies in Modernity & National Identity). (ENG., Illus.). 328p. 80.00 *(978-0-295-98821-4(5))*; (C). pap. 30.00 *(978-0-295-98794-1(4))* Univ. of Washington Pr.

Jacoby, Sam & Lee, Christopher, eds. Typological Urbanism: Projective Cities. 2011. (Architectural Design Ser.). (ENG.). 136p. pap. 45.00 *(978-0-470-74720-9(X)*, Wiley) Wiley, John & Sons, Inc.

James-Chakraborty, Kathleen. Crossing Borders: Space Beyond Disciplines. Strümper-Krobb, Sabine, ed. 2011. (Illus.). 264p. pap. 58.95 *(978-3-0343-0192-3(8))* Lang, Peter AG GBR. Dist: Lang, Peter.

Jenkins, Paul & Forsyth, Leslie. Architecture, Participation, & Society. 2009. (ENG., Illus.). XX, 220p. 165.00 *(978-0-415-54723-9(7))*; pap. 53.95 *(978-0-415-54724-6(5))* Routledge.

Jones, Paul. The Sociology of Architecture: Constructing Identities. 2011. (ENG., Illus.). 288p. pap. 39.95 *(978-1-84631-077-5(6))*; 195p. 95.00 *(978-1-84631-076-8(8))* Liverpool Univ. Pr. GBR. Dist: Chicago Distribution Ctr.

Kaminer, Tahl. Architecture Crisis & Resuscitation. 2011. (ENG., Illus.). 216p. (C). 155.00 *(978-0-415-57823-3(X))*; pap. 49.95 *(978-0-415-57824-0(8))* Routledge.

Kärrholm, Mattias. Retailising Space: Architecture, Retail & the Territorialisation of Public Space. 2012. (Ashgate Studies in Architecture Ser.). (Illus.). 172p. 99.95 ***(978-1-4094-3099-5(5))***; 99.95 ***(978-1-4094-3098-8(7))*** Ashgate Publishing Co.

Kathrens, Michael C. Newport Villas: The Revival Styles, 1885-1935. 2009. (ENG., Illus.). 384p. 85.00 *(978-0-393-73270-2(3)*, 73270) Norton, W. W. & Co., Inc.

Kellert, Stephen R., et al. Biophilic Design: The Theory, Science & Practice of Bringing Buildings to Life. 2008. (ENG., Illus.). 432p. 80.00 *(978-0-470-16334-4(8)*, Wiley) Wiley, John & Sons, Inc.

Kemsley, Roderick & Platt, Christopher. Dwelling with Architecture. 2012. (ENG., Illus.). 248p. 165.00 ***(978-0-415-56903-3(6))***; pap. 49.95 ***(978-0-415-56904-0(4))*** Routledge.

King, Peter. In Dwelling: Implacability, Exclusion & Acceptance. 2008. (Design & the Built Environment Ser.). (Illus.). 170p. 124.95 *(978-0-7546-4870-3(2))* Ashgate Publishing Co.

Komiske, Bruce King, ed. Designing the World's Best Children's Hospital Volume 3: The Quest Continues. 2012. (ENG., Illus.). 224p. 70.00 ***(978-1-86470-339-9(3))*** Images Publishing Group AUS. Dist: National Bk. Network.

Kossak, Florian, et al, eds. Agency: Working with Uncertain Architectures. 2009. (Illus.). 192p. 165.00 *(978-0-415-56601-8(0))*; (ENG., pap. 53.95 *(978-0-415-56602-5(9))* Routledge.

Krier, Leon & Thadani, Dhiru A. The Architecture of Community. 2011. (ENG., Illus.). 496p. pap. 35.00 *(978-1-59726-579-9(9))* Island Pr.

Krier, Leon, et al. The Architecture of Community. 2009. (ENG., Illus.). 496p. 50.00 *(978-1-59726-578-2(0))* Island Pr.

Kronhagel, Christoph. Kronhagel, Mediatecture. 2010. (Illus.). 448p. 89.95 *(978-3-7091-0299-2(5))* Springer Wien AUT. Dist: Springer.

Kuhl, Isabel. First: Groundbreaking Moments in Architecture. 2012. (Illus.). 208p. pap. 19.95 ***(978-3-7913-4654-0(7))*** Prestel Publishing.

Kusno, Abidin. The Appearances of Memory: Mnemonic Practices of Architecture & Urban Form in Indonesia. 2010. (ENG., Illus.). 352p. 94.95 *(978-0-8223-4655-5(9))*; pap. 25.95 *(978-0-8223-4647-0(8))* Duke Univ. Pr.

Lahiji, Nadir, ed. The Political Unconscious of Architecture: Re-Opening Jameson's Narrative. 2011. (Ashgate Studies in Architecture Ser.). (Illus.). 348p. 119.95 *(978-1-4094-2639-4(4))* Ashgate Publishing Co.

Langmead, Donald. Icons of American Architecture: From the Alamo to the World Trade Center, 2 vols. 2009. (Greenwood Icons Ser.). (Illus.). 632p. 175.00 *(978-0-313-34207-3(5)*, GR4207, Greenwood Pr.) Greenwood Publishing Group, Inc.

Leader, Anne. The Badia of Florence: Art & Observance in a Renaissance Monastery. 2011. (ENG., Illus.). 340p. 65.00 *(978-0-253-35567-6(2)*, 0253355672) Indiana Univ. Pr.

Lepik, Andres. Small Scale, Big Change: New Architectures of Social Engagement. 2010. (Illus.). 140p. pap. ***(978-3-0346-0588-5(9))*** Museum of Modern Art.

Lethaby, W. R. Architecture, Mysticism & Myth. 2009. 252p. 24.99 *(978-0-559-07748-7(3))*; 27.99 *(978-0-559-07736-4(X))*; pap. 17.99 *(978-0-559-07744-9(0))*; pap. 26.75 *(978-0-559-07739-5(4))* BiblioBazaar.

Levitt, David. Housing Design Handbook: A Guide to Good Practice. 2009. (ENG., Illus.). 288p. 62.95 *(978-0-415-49150-1(9))* Routledge.

Li, Shiqiao. Power & Virtue: Architecture & Intellectual Change in England 1660-1730. 2006. (Classical Tradition in Architecture Ser.). (Illus.). 256p. 52.95 *(978-0-415-37427-9(8))* Routledge.

Liang, Samuel Y. Mapping Modernity in Shanghai: Space, Gender, & Material Life in the Sojourners' City, 1853-98. 2010. (Asia's Transformations Ser.). (ENG., Illus.). 240p. (C). 138.00 *(978-0-415-56913-2(3))* Routledge.

Longfellow, Brenda. Roman Imperialism & Civic Patronage: Form, Meaning & Ideology in Monumental Fountain Complexes. 2010. (ENG., Illus.). 292p. 90.00 *(978-0-521-19493-8(8))* Cambridge Univ. Pr.

Lu, Duanfang, ed. Third World Modernism: Architecture, Development & Identity. 2010. (ENG., Illus.). 304p. (C). 53.95 *(978-0-415-56458-8(1))*; 155.00 *(978-0-415-56457-1(3))* Routledge.

Lupkin, Paula. Manhood Factories: YMCA Architecture & the Making of Modern Urban Culture. 2010. (Architecture, Landscape & Amer Culture Ser.). (Illus.). 312p. (ENG.). 82.50 *(978-0-8166-4834-4(4))*; pap. 27.50 *(978-0-8166-4835-1(2))* Univ. of Minnesota Pr.

Lynn, Catherine & Penabad, Carie. Marion Manley: Miami's First Woman Architect. 2010. (ENG., Illus.). 248p. pap. 34.95 *(978-0-8203-3406-6(5))* Univ. of Georgia Pr.

Maniaque-Benton, Caroline. French Encounters with the American Counterculture, 1960-1980. 2011. (Ashgate Studies in Architecture Ser.). (Illus.). 244p. 99.95 *(978-1-4094-2386-7(7))* Ashgate Publishing Co.

Mars, Neville. The Chinese Dream: A Society under Construction. 2008. (ENG., Illus.). 192p. 60.00 *(978-988-99617-1-8(7))* Timezone 8 Ltd. HKG. Dist: D.A.P./Distributed Art Pubs.

Martin, Reinhold, et al. Swedish Modernism: Architecture, Consumption & the Welfare State. Wallenstein, Sven-Olov, ed. 2010. (ENG., Illus.). 192p. pap. 39.95 *(978-1-906155-98-8(4))* Black Dog Publishing Ltd. GBR. Dist: Perseus Distribution.

Martin, Therese. Reassessing the Roles of Women As 'makers' of Medieval Art & Architecture. 2012. ***(978-90-04-22827-6(6))***; ***(978-90-04-22828-3(4))***; ***(978-90-04-18555-5(0))*** BRILL.

Martinussen, Kent. 3xn: Mind your Behaviour. 2010. (Illus.). 276p. pap. *(978-87-993680-0-6(5))* Actar Birkhauser Distribution.

Marzano, Annalisa. Roman Villas in Central Italy: A Social & Economic History. 2007. (Columbia Studies in the Classical Tradition Ser.). 823p. *(978-90-04-16037-8(X))* BRILL.

McEnroe, John C. Architecture of Minoan Crete: Constructing Identity in the Aegean Bronze Age. 2010. (ENG., Illus.). 220p. 60.00 *(978-0-292-72193-7(5))* Univ. of Texas Pr.

McNeill, Donald. The Global Architect. 2008. (Cultural Spaces Ser.). (Illus.). (ENG.). 192p. (C). pap. 35.95 *(978-0-415-95641-3(2))*; 200p. 130.00 *(978-0-415-95640-6(4))* Routledge.

Mead, Christopher Curtis & Baltard, Victor. Making Modern Paris: Victor Baltard's Central Markets & the Urban Practice of Architecture. 2012. (ENG.). 320p. ***(978-0-271-05087-4(X))*** Pennsylvania State Univ. Pr.

Media, Mountains & Architecture. 2009. *(978-84-95951-61-8(4))* Actar Birkhauser Distribution.

Mellins, Thomas & Albrecht, Donald. The American Style. 2011. (ENG., Illus.). 224p. 50.00 *(978-1-58093-285-1(1))* Monacelli Pr., Inc.

Merwood-Salisbury, Joanna. Chicago 1890: The Skyscraper & the Modern City. 2009. (Chicago Architecture & Urbanism Ser.). (ENG., Illus.). 208p. 45.00 *(978-0-226-52078-0(1))* Univ. of Chicago Pr.

Miller, Kristine F. Designs on the Public: The Private Lives of New York's Public Spaces. 2007. (Illus.). 200p. 75.00 *(978-0-8166-4909-9(X))*; pap. 25.00 *(978-0-8166-4910-5(3))* Univ. of Minnesota Pr.

Minor, Heather Hyde. The Culture of Architecture in Enlightenment Rome. 2010. (Buildings, Landscapes, & Societies Ser.). (ENG., Illus.). 328p. 95.00 *(978-0-271-03564-2(1))* Pennsylvania State Univ. Pr.

Mitchell, Kevin, et al, eds. Instant Cities: Emergent Trends in Architecture & Urbanism in the Arab World. 2008. (Illus.). 500p. pap. *(978-9957-8602-1-9(6))* Center for Study of Architecture in the Arab Region (CSAAR), The.

Mitchell, Maurice, et al. Learning from Delhi: Dispersed Initiatives in Changing Urban Landscapes. 2010. (Illus.). 322p. pap. 69.95 *(978-1-4094-0102-5(2))* Ashgate Publishing Co.

Mitchell, William J. World's Greatest Architect: Making, Meaning, & Network Culture. 2008. (ENG.). 168p. (gr. 17). pap. 16.95 *(978-0-262-63364-2(7))* MIT Pr.

Moe, Kiel & Smith, Ryan E. Building Systems: Technology, Design & Society. 2012. (ENG., Illus.). 272p. (C). 165.00 *(978-0-415-61793-2(6))*; pap. 39.95 *(978-0-415-61794-9(4))* Routledge.

Monteyne, David. Fallout Shelter: Designing for Civil Defense in the Cold War. 2011. (Architecture, Landscape & Amer Culture Ser.). (Illus.). 352p. 84.00 *(978-0-8166-6975-2(9))*; pap. 27.95 *(978-0-8166-6976-9(7))* Univ. of Minnesota Pr.

Mooney, Barbara Burlison. Prodigy Houses of Virginia: Architecture & the Native Elite. 2008. (ENG., Illus.). 400p. (gr. 17). 65.00 *(978-0-8139-2673-5(4))* Univ. Pr. of Virginia.

Moskow, Keith & Linn, Robert. Small Scale: Creative Solutions for Better City Living. 2010. (ENG., Illus.). 224p. pap. 34.95 *(978-1-56898-975-4(X))* Princeton Architectural Pr.

Noble, Jonathan Alfred. African Identity in Post-Apartheid Public Architecture: White Skin Black Masks. 2011. (Ashgate Studies in Architecture Ser.). (Illus.). 314p. 124.95 *(978-0-7546-7765-9(6))* Ashgate Publishing Co.

Novak, Anna & Schmidle, Elisabeth. The Artistic Legacy of Le Corbusier's Machine a Habiter. (Illus.). 192p. 99.95 *(978-0-7734-5150-6(1))* Mellen, Edwin Pr., The.

Ó'Carragáin, Tomás. Churches in Early Medieval Ireland: Architecture, Ritual & Memory. 2011. (Paul Mellon Centre for Studies in Britis Ser.). (Illus.). 400p. 100.00 *(978-0-300-15444-3(5))* Yale Univ. Pr.

Olmert, Michael. Kitchens, Smokehouses, & Privies. 2009. (Illus.). 208p. 27.95 *(978-0-8014-4791-4(7))* Cornell Univ. Pr.

Ostwald, Michael J. & Fleming, Steven, eds. Museum, Gallery, & Cultural Architecture in Australia, New Zealand, & the Pacific Region: Essays in Antipodean Identity. 2007. 208p. *(978-0-7734-5393-7(8))* Mellen, Edwin Pr., The.

Panin, Tonkao. Architectural Spatiality. 2009. 196p. pap. *(978-3-639-19575-0(2))* VDM Verlag Dr. Mueller e.K.

Pelkonen, Eeva-Liisa. Alvar Aalto: Architecture, Modernity, & Geopolitics. 2009. (ENG., Illus.). 228p. 45.00 *(978-0-300-11428-7(1))* Yale Univ. Pr.

Pérez-Gómez, Alberto. Built upon Love: Architectural Longing after Ethics & Aesthetics. 2008. (ENG.). 264p. (gr. 17). per. 17.95 *(978-0-262-66205-5(1))* MIT Pr.

Peter. Form Follows Fun. 2007. (Illus.). 224p. 165.00 *(978-0-415-42818-7(1))* Routledge.

Peter, Bruce. Form Follows Fun. 2007. (Illus.). 224p. 63.95 *(978-0-415-42819-4(X))* Routledge.

Pimlott, Mark, et al, texts. OASE 83: Commissioning Architecture. 2011. (ENG., Illus.). 139p. pap. 35.00 *(978-90-5662-776-8(7))* NAi Uitgevers / Publishers Stichting NLD. Dist: D.A.P./Distributed Art Pubs.

Piva, Antonio, et al. Architecture & Politics. 2010. 208p. pap. 32.95 *(978-88-492-1318-8(2))* Gangemi ITA. Dist: International Publishers Marketing.

Portzamparc, Christian De & Sollers, Philippe. Writing & Seeing Architecture. Tihanyi, Catherine, tr. from FRE. 2008. 168p. 57.00 *(978-0-8166-4567-1(1))*; pap. 18.95 *(978-0-8166-4568-8(X))* Univ. of Minnesota Pr.

Prokopovych, Markian. Habsburg Lemberg: Architecture, Public Space, & Politics in the Galician Capital, 1772-1914. 2008. (Illus.). 357p. pap. 49.95 *(978-1-55753-510-8(8))* Purdue Univ. Pr.

Proscio, Tony. Affordable Housing's Green Future: Building a Movement for More Efficient, Longer-Lasting, Healthier Housing. 2007. per. *(978-1-932699-24-1(4))* Enterprise Community Partners, Inc.

Reeh, Henrik. Ornaments of the Metropolis: Siegfried Kracauer & Modern Urban Culture. Irons, John, tr. from DAN. 2006. (ENG., Illus.). 264p. (gr. 17). per. 21.95 *(978-0-262-68163-6(3))* MIT Pr.

Rice, John A. The Temple of Night at Schönau: Architecture, Music, & Theater in a Late Eighteenth-Century Viennese Garden. 2006. (Illus.). xv, 257p. *(978-0-87169-258-0(9))* American Philosophical Society.

Richards, Simon. Architect Knows Best Environmental Determinism in Architecture Culture from 1956 to Present. 2012. (Ashgate Studies in Architecture Ser.). (Illus.). 202p. 99.95 ***(978-1-4094-3922-6(4))*** Ashgate Publishing Co.

Ricketts, Annabel, et al. The English Country House Chapel: Building a Protestant Tradition. 2007. (Illus.). 336p. (C). *(978-1-904965-05-3(9))* Spire Bks. Ltd.

Roaf, Susan, ed. Transforming Markets in the Built Environment: Adapting to Climate Change. 2010. (Architectural Science Review Ser.). (ENG., Illus.). 140p. 120.00 *(978-1-84971-088-6(0))* Routledge.

Rowlands, Rob, et al, eds. Mass Housing in Europe: Multiple Faces of Development, Change & Response. 2010. (ENG., Illus.). 264p. 95.00 *(978-0-230-00730-7(9))* Palgrave Macmillan.

Rybczynski, Witold. Makeshift Metropolis: Ideas about Cities. 2011. (ENG.). 256p. pap. 16.99 *(978-1-4165-6126-2(9)*, Scribner) Scribner.

Sadria, Modjtaba. Homogenization of Representations. 2012. (ENG., Illus.). 208p. pap. 39.00 *(978-1-84885-625-7(3))* I. B. Tauris & Co., Ltd. GBR. Dist: Macmillan.

Salim, Faida Noori. Cultural Sustainability & Changing Worldview: Dilemmas of Architecture & the Built Form. 2011. pap. *(978-1-86335-888-0(9))* Common Ground Publishing Pty, Ltd.

Saunders, William S. The New Architectural Pragmatism: A Harvard Design Magazine Reader. Saunders, William S., ed. 2007. (Harvard Design Magazine Ser.). (Illus.). 208p. 69.00 *(978-0-8166-5263-1(5))*; per. 22.95 *(978-0-8166-5264-8(3))* Univ. of Minnesota Pr.

Sawyer, Ann & Bright, Keith. The Access Manual: Auditing & Managing Inclusive Built Environments. 2nd rev. ed. 2006. (ENG., Illus.). 280p. per. 100.00 *(978-1-4051-4626-5(5)*, Wiley-Blackwell) Wiley, John & Sons, Inc.

Schonle, Andreas. Architecture of Oblivion: Ruins & Historical Consciousness in Modern Russia. 2011. (ENG., Illus.). 295p. 45.00 *(978-0-87580-651-8(1))* Northern Illinois Univ. Pr.

Schuldenfrei, Robin, ed. Atomic Dwelling: Anxiety, Domesticity, & Postwar Architecture. 2012. (ENG., Illus.). 320p. (C). 165.00 *(978-0-415-67608-3(8))*; pap. 49.95 *(978-0-415-67609-0(6))* Routledge.

Sciacca, Christine. Building the Medieval World. 2010. (Illus.). 104p. 19.95 *(978-1-60606-006-3(6)*, J. Paul Getty Museum) Getty Pubns.

Scott, Felicity D. Architecture or Techno-Utopia: Politics after Modernism. 2010. (ENG., Illus.). 360p. (gr. 17). pap. 19.95 *(978-0-262-51406-4(0))* MIT Pr.

Scriver, Peter & Prakash, Vikramaditya. Colonial Modernities: Building, Dwelling & Architecture in British India & Ceylon. 2007. (Architext Ser.). (Illus.). 287p. per. 62.95 *(978-0-415-39909-8(2))* Routledge.

Scriver, Peter & Prakash, Vikramaditya, eds. Colonial Modernities: Building, Dwelling & Architecture in British India & Ceylon. 2007. (Architext Ser.). (ENG., Illus.). 304p. (C). 165.00 *(978-0-415-39908-1(4))* Routledge.

Shanken, Andrew Michael. 194X: Architecture, Planning, & Consumer Culture on the American Home Front. 2009. (Architecture, Landscape & Amer Culture Ser.). (ENG., Illus.). 288p. 75.00 *(978-0-8166-5365-2(8))*; pap. 24.95 *(978-0-8166-5366-9(6))* Univ. of Minnesota Pr.

Shellenbarger, Melanie. High Country Summers: Early Second Homes of Colorado, 1880-1940. 2012. (ENG.). 288p. 55.00 ***(978-0-8165-2958-2(2))*** Univ. of Arizona Pr.

Shelton, Barrie. Learning from the Japanese City: Looking East in Urban Design. 2nd rev. ed. (Planning, History & Environment Ser.). (ENG., Illus.). 208p. (C). 2013. pap. 62.95 *(978-0-415-55440-4(3))* 2012. 165.00 *(978-0-415-55439-8(X))* Routledge.

Shepard, Mark. Sentient City: Ubiquitous Computing, Architecture, & the Future of Urban Space. 2011. (ENG., Illus.). 200p. (gr. 17). pap. 24.95 *(978-0-262-51586-3(5))* MIT Pr.

SHEPHERD, et al. Des Line Spac Mem & Iden Post-Apar. 2007. (Illus.). 328p. 165.00 *(978-0-415-70130-3(9))*; (ENG., 55.95 *(978-0-415-70131-0(7))* Routledge.

Shiqiao, Li. Power & Virtue: Architecture & Intellectual Change in England 1660-1730. 2006. (Classical Tradition in Architecture Ser.). (Illus.). 246p. 165.00 *(978-0-415-37424-8(3))* Routledge.

Sica, Grazia Gobbi. The Florentine Villa: Architecture History, Society. 2007. (Illus.). 224p. 115.00 *(978-0-415-44397-5(0))* Routledge.

Sinha, Sumita. Architecture for Rapid Change & Scarce Resources. 2012. (ENG., Illus.). 320p. 165.00 *(978-1-84971-115-9(1))*; pap. 39.95 *(978-1-84971-116-6(X))* Routledge.

Smith, Terry E. The Architecture of Aftermath. 2006. (Illus.). 280p. per. 32.50 *(978-0-226-76469-6(9))* Univ. of Chicago Pr.

Solomon, Daniel. Cosmopolis. Kelbaugh, Douglas, ed. 2012. (ENG., Illus.). 48p. pap. 17.95 *(978-1-891197-44-4(4))* Univ. of Michigan, College of Architecture & Urban Planning.

Soules, Matthew, ed. Future Social. 2011. (ENG.). 168p. pap. 19.95 *(978-1-897476-30-7(2))* Simply Read Bks. CAN. Dist: Perseus-PGW.

Spicer, Andrew & Thofner, Margit. Lutheran Churches in Early Modern Europe. 2012. (Illus.). 476p. 134.95 ***(978-0-7546-6583-0(6))*** Ashgate Publishing Co.

Stanford, Charlotte A. Commemorating the Dead in Late Medieval Strasbourg: The Cathedral Book of Benefactors, 1320-1520. 2011. (Church, Faith & Culture in the Medieval West Ser.). (Illus.). 348p. 124.95 ***(978-1-4094-0136-0(7))*** Ashgate Publishing Co.

Stewart, Rachel. The Town House in Georgian London. 2009. (Paul Mellon Centre for Studies in Britis Ser.). (ENG., Illus.). 192p. 65.00 *(978-0-300-15277-7(9))* Yale Univ. Pr.

Stoner, Jill. Toward a Minor Architecture. 2012. (ENG., Illus.). 176p. (gr. 17). pap. 19.95 ***(978-0-262-51764-5(7))*** MIT Pr.

Stoppani, Teresa. Paradigm Islands - Manhattan & Venice. 2011. (ENG., Illus.). 312p. (C). 125.00 *(978-0-415-56185-3(X))* Routledge.

Swenarton, Mark. Building the New Jerusalem: Architecture, Housing & Politics 1900-1930. 2010. (ENG., Illus.). 246p. 80.00 ***(978-1-84806-024-1(6))*** Building Research Establishment GBR. Dist: Taylor & Francis Group.

Swenarton, Mark, et al, eds. The Politics of Making. 2007. (Illus.). XIV, 290p. 100.00 *(978-0-415-43101-9(8))* Routledge.

—The Politics of Making. 2008. (Illus.). XIV, 290p. 53.95 *(978-0-415-48800-6(1))* Routledge.

Tadgell, Christopher. The West: From the Advent of Christendom to the Eve of Reformation. 2009. (ENG., Illus.). 928p. 110.00 *(978-0-415-40754-0(0))* Routledge.

Tange, Andrea Kaston. Architectural Identities: Domesticity, Literature & the Victorian Middle Class. 2010. (Illus.). 336p. *(978-1-4426-4113-6(4))* Univ. of Toronto Pr.

Taylor, Brian. Architecture & Identity: Reconciling Traditional Cultural Values & Modern Design. 85.00 *(978-0-393-73071-5(9))* Norton, W. W. & Co., Inc.

Taylor, William & Levine, Michael. Prospects for an Ethics of Architecture. 2011. (ENG., Illus.). 232p. (C). 155.00 *(978-0-415-58971-0(1))*; pap. 49.95 *(978-0-415-58972-7(X))* Routledge.

Temple, Nicholas. Renovatio Urbis: Architecture, Urbanism & Ceremony in the Rome of Julius II. 2011. (Classical Tradition in Architecture Ser.). (ENG., Illus.). 368p. (C). 130.00 *(978-0-415-47385-9(3))* Routledge.

Temple, Nicholas, et al, eds. The Humanities in Architectural Design: A Contemporary & Historical Perspective. 2010. (ENG., Illus.). 288p. (C). 165.00 *(978-0-415-55113-7(7))*; pap. 53.95 *(978-0-415-55114-4(5))* Routledge.

Treib, Marc. Spatial Recall: Memory in Architecture & Landscape. 2009. (ENG., Illus.). 272p. (C). 155.00 *(978-0-415-77735-3(6))* Routledge.

Trüby, Stephan. Exit-Architecture: Design Between War & Peace. Payne, Robert, tr. from GER. 2008. (TRACE Transmission in Rhetorics, Arts & Cultural Evolution Ser.). (ENG., Illus.). vi, 113p. pap. 29.95 *(978-3-211-77969-9(8)*, 3211779698) Springer.

Tseng, Alice Y. The Imperial Museums of Meiji Japan: Architecture & the Art of the Nation. 2008. (ENG., Illus.). 304p. (C). 60.00 *(978-0-295-98777-4(4))* Univ. of Washington Pr.

Tyszczuk, Renata, et al, eds. Atlas: Geography, Architecture & Change in an Interdependent World. 2012. (ENG., Illus.). 160p. pap. 29.95 *(978-1-907317-39-2(2))* Black Dog Publishing Ltd. GBR. Dist: Actar Birkhauser Distribution.

Urban, Florian. Tower & Slab: A Global History of Mass Housing. 2011. (ENG., Illus.). 224p. (C). 155.00 *(978-0-415-67628-1(2))*; pap. 39.95 *(978-0-415-67629-8(0))* Routledge.

Van der Hoorn, Mélanie. Indispensable Eyesores: An Anthropology of Undesired Buildings. 2009. (Illus.). 272p. 90.00 *(978-1-84545-530-9(4))* Berghahn Bks., Inc.

Varnelis, Kazys & Sumrell, Robert. Blue Monday: Stories of Absurd Realities & Natural Philosophies. 2007. (Illus.). 175p. pap. 27.00 *(978-84-96540-53-8(7))* Kunst-Werke Berlin e.V. DEU. Dist: Actar Birkhauser Distribution.

Walden, Russell. Triumphs of Change: Architecture Reconsidered. 2011. (ENG., Illus.). 269p. ***(978-3-0343-0672-0(5))*** Lang, Peter.

Waldheim, Charles & Ray, Katerina Ruedi, eds. Chicago Architecture: Histories, Revisions, Alternatives. 2007. (Chicago Architecture & Urbanism Ser.). (Illus.). 442p. per. 25.00 *(978-0-226-87039-7(1))* Univ. of Chicago Pr.

Wealleans, Anne & Avermaete, Tom, eds. Hotel Lobbies & Lounges: The Architecture of Professional Hospitality. 2012. (Interior Architecture Ser.). (ENG., Illus.). 256p. 165.00 *(978-0-415-49652-0(7))*; pap. 49.95 *(978-0-415-49653-7(5))* Routledge.

Webster, Helena. Bourdieu for Architects. 2010. (Thinkers for Architects Ser.). (ENG., Illus.). 144p. (C). pap. 28.95 *(978-0-415-49615-5(2))* Routledge.

Welch, Katherine. The Roman Amphitheatre: From Its Origins to the Colosseum. 2007. (ENG., Illus.). 376p. 99.00 *(978-0-521-80944-3(4))* Cambridge Univ. Pr.

Welch, Katherine E. The Roman Amphitheatre: From its Origins to the Colosseum. 2009. (ENG., Illus.). 378p. (C). pap. 49.00 *(978-0-521-74435-5(0))* Cambridge Univ. Pr.

Wernick, Jane. Building Happiness: Architecutre to Make You Smile. McCorquodale, Duncan, ed. 2008. (ENG., Illus.). 173p. pap. 45.00 *(978-1-906155-46-9(1))* Black Dog Publishing Ltd. GBR. Dist: Perseus Distribution.

White, James W. Mirrors of Memory: Culture, Politics, & Time in Paris & Tokyo. 2011. (ENG., Illus.). 296p. (gr. 17). 39.50 *(978-0-8139-3070-1(7))* Univ. Pr. of Virginia.

Wittman, Richard. Architecture, Print Culture & the Public Sphere in Eighteenth-Century France. 2007. (Classical Tradition in Architecture Ser.). (ENG., Illus.). 304p. (C). 165.00 *(978-0-415-77463-5(2))* Routledge.

Yaari, Monique. Rethinking the French City: Architecture, Dwelling, & Display After 1968. 2008. 528p. 152.00 *(978-90-420-2500-4(X))* Rodopi.

Yeang, Ken & Spector, Arthur, eds. Green Design: From Theory to Practice. 2011. (ENG., Illus.). 144p. 29.95 *(978-1-907317-12-5(0))* Black Dog Publishing Ltd. GBR. Dist: Perseus Distribution.

ARCHITECTURE AND SOLAR RADIATION

Al-Qeeq, Farid. Sustainable Urban Design & Climate. 2010. (Illus.). 412p. pap. *(978-3-639-26228-5(X))* VDM Verlag Dr. Mueller e.K.

Bonta, Dave & Snyder, Stephen. The New Solar Home, 1 vol. 2009. (ENG., Illus.). 160p. pap. 24.99 *(978-1-4236-0390-0(7))* Gibbs Smith, Publisher.

Butti, Ken & Perlin, John. A Golden Thread: 2500 Years of Solar Architecture & Technology. 2nd rev. ed. Date not set. (Illus.). *(978-0-937948-12-5(8))*; pap. *(978-0-937948-13-2(6))* aatec Pubns.

Frontini, Francesco. Daylight & Solar Control in Buildings: General Evaluation & Optimization of a New Angle Selective Glazing. 2011. (ENG., Illus.). 143p. pap. 63.20 *(978-3-8396-0238-6(6))* Fraunhofer IRB Verlag DEU. Dist: Silvermine International Bks., LLC.

German Solar Energy Society Staff. Planning & Installing Photovoltaic Systems: A Guide for Installers, Architects & Engineers. 2nd rev. ed. 2007. (Planning & Installing Ser.). (ENG., Illus.). 396p. pap. 170.00 *(978-1-84407-442-6(0))* Routledge.

Guzowski, Mary. Towards Zero-Energy Architecture: New Solar Design. 2010. (ENG., Illus.). 208p. 45.00 *(978-1-85669-678-4(2))* King, Laurence Publishing GBR. Dist: Hachette Bk. Group.

Herzog, Thomas, ed. European Charter for Solar Energy in Architecture & Urban Planning. 2008. 128p. 14.95 *(978-3-7913-3928-3(1))* Prestel Publishing.

Hobday, Richard. The Light Revolution: Health, Architecture, & the Sun. 2007. (ENG., Illus.). 182p. per. 17.95 *(978-1-84409-087-7(6))* Findhorn Pr. GBR. Dist: Independent Pubs. Group.

Konya, Allan & Vandenberg, Maritz. Design Primer for Hot Climates. 2011. (Illus.). 156p. pap. ***(978-0-9564323-2-2(8))*** Archimedia Pr., Ltd.

Treberspurg, Mar, ed. SolarCity Linz-Pichling. Blaschke, Beverly, tr. from GER. 2008. (Illus.). 216p. 69.95 *(978-3-211-30562-1(9)*, 3211305629) Springer Wien AUT. Dist: Actar Birkhauser Distribution.

Wright, David. The Passive Solar Primer: Sustainable Architecture. 2008. (Illus.). 280p. pap. 29.99 *(978-0-7643-3070-4(5))* Schiffer Publishing, Ltd.

Zaretsky, Michael. Precedents in Zero-Energy Design: Architecture & Passive Design in the 2007 Solar Decathlon. 2009. (ENG., Illus.). 240p. (C). 165.00 *(978-0-415-77874-9(3))*; pap. 44.95 *(978-0-415-77875-6(1))* Routledge.

ARCHITECTURE AND SPACE

see Space (Architecture)

ARCHITECTURE AND STATE

Akcan, Esra. Architecture in Translation: Germany, Turkey, & the Modern House. 2012. (ENG., Illus.). 424p. 89.95 ***(978-0-8223-5294-5(X))***; pap. 24.95 ***(978-0-8223-5308-9(3))*** Duke Univ. Pr.

Basar, Shumon, et al, eds. With / Without, 1 vol. 2008. (ENG.). 266p. 25.00 *(978-9948-03-453-7(8))* Ministry of Information & Culture, Copyright Section UAE. Dist: D.A.P./Distributed Art Pubs.

Bottger, Matthias, et al, eds. TV Towers / Fernsehtürme: 8,559 Meters Politics & Architecture - 8.559 Meter Politik und Architektur. 2010. (ENG., Illus.). 272p. pap. 39.95 *(978-3-86859-024-1(2))* Jovis Verlag GmbH DEU. Dist: D.A.P./Distributed Art Pubs.

Bretschneider, J., et al, eds. Power & Architecture. Monumental Public Architecture in the Bronze Age near East & Aegean: Proceedings of the international conference 'Power & Architecture' organized by the Katholieke Universiteit Leuven, the Universite Catholique de Louvain & the Westfalischen Wilhelms-Universitat Munster on the 21st & 22nd of November 2002. 2007. (Orientalia Lovaniensia Analecta Ser.). (ENG., Illus.). 212p. (C). 109.00 *(978-90-429-1831-3(4))* Peeters Pubs. & Booksellers BEL. Dist: Brown, David Bk. Co., The.

Bruno, Giuliana & Clark, Robin, texts. Automatic Cities. 2009. (ENG., Illus.). 160p. 32.95 *(978-0-934418-71-3(3))* Museum of Contemporary Art, San Diego.

Cabezas, Pablo, et al. A Usable Semantic Osgi Architecture Within the Smart Home Environment. 2010. 172p. pap. *(978-3-639-27416-5(4))* VDM Verlag Dr. Mueller e.K.

Çelik, Zeynep. Empire, Architecture, & the City: French-Ottoman Encounters, 1830-1914. 2008. (ENG., Illus.). 368p. 60.00 *(978-0-295-98779-8(0))* Univ. of Washington Pr.

Cleary, Richard L. The Place Royale & Urban Design in the Ancien Régime. 2011. (ENG., Illus.). 330p. pap. 65.00 *(978-0-521-36998-5(3))* Cambridge Univ. Pr.

Demissie, Fassil. Colonial Architecture & Urbanism in Africa: Interwined & Contested Histories. 2012. (Design & the Built Environment Ser.). (Illus.). 336p. 119.95 ***(978-0-7546-7512-9(2))*** Ashgate Publishing Co.

Di Lieto, Alba & Morgante, Michela. Piero Gazzola: Una Strategia per I Beni Architettonici Nel Secondo Novecento. 2009. (ITA., Illus.). 380p. *(978-88-8314-533-9(X))* Cierre Edizioni.

Domènech i Casadevall, Gemma & Gil, Rosa Maria. Un Nou Model D'arquitectura Al Servei D'una Idea de País. 2010. (SPA., Illus.). 151p. *(978-84-937740-5-9(7))* Dux Editorial, S.L.

du Cros, Hilary & Lee, Yok-Shiu F., eds. Cultural Heritage Management in China: Preserving the Cities of the Pearl River Delta. 2011. (ENG., Illus.). 192p. pap. 42.95 ***(978-0-415-66642-8(2))*** Routledge.

Easterling, Keller. Enduring Innocence: Global Architecture & Its Political Masquerades. 2007. (ENG., Illus.). 252p. (gr. 17). pap. 15.95 *(978-0-262-55065-9(2))* MIT Pr.

Escobar, Jesús. The Plaza Mayor & the Shaping of Baroque Madrid. 2009. (Illus.). 376p. pap. 38.99 *(978-0-521-11153-9(6))* Cambridge Univ. Pr.

Escobar, Jesús. La plaza Mayor y los orígenes del Madrid Barroco. 2009. (SPA.). 264p. 89.00 *(978-84-96431-07-2(X))* Nerea Editorial ESP. Dist: Independent Pubs. Group.

Fierro, Annette. The Glass State: The Technology of the Spectacle Paris, 1981-1998. 2006. (ENG., Illus.). 338p. (gr. 17). per. 23.95 *(978-0-262-56221-8(9))* MIT Pr.

Georgopoulou, Maria. Venice's Mediterranean Colonies: Architecture & Urbanism. 2011. (ENG., Illus.). 400p. pap. 45.00 *(978-0-521-18434-2(7))* Cambridge Univ. Pr.

Hart, Vaughan. Inigo Jones: The Architect of Kings. 2011. (Paul Mellon Centre for Studies in British Art Ser.). (ENG., Illus.). 336p. 70.00 *(978-0-300-14149-8(1))* Yale Univ. Pr.

Hatuka, Tali. Violent Acts & Urban Space in Contemporary Tel Aviv: Revisioning Moments. (ENG., Illus.). 248p. 2011. pap. 25.00 *(978-0-292-72882-0(4))* 2010. 55.00 *(978-0-292-72185-2(4))* Univ. of Texas Pr.

Howard, Deborah. Venice Disputed: Marc'Antonio Barbaro & Venetian Architecture, 1550-1600. 2011. (ENG., Illus.). 320p. 65.00 *(978-0-300-17685-8(6))* Yale Univ. Pr.

Kafescioglu, Çigdem. Constantinopolis/Istanbul: Cultural Encounter, Imperial Vision, & the Construction of the Ottoman Capital. 2009. (Buildings, Landscapes, & Societies Ser.). (ENG., Illus.). 392p. 100.00 *(978-0-271-02776-0(2))* Pennsylvania State Univ. Pr.

Leach. The Politics of Space: Selected Essays. 2009. (Illus.). 208p. 49.95 *(978-0-415-46927-2(9))*; 150.00 *(978-0-415-46926-5(0))* Routledge.

Loeffler, Jane C. The Architecture of Diplomacy: Building America's Embassies. 2nd ed. 2010. (ENG., Illus.). 336p. pap. 24.95 *(978-1-56898-984-6(5))* Princeton Architectural Pr.

Loomis, John A. Revolution of Forms: Cuba's Forgotten Art Schools. rev. ed. 2011. (ENG., Illus.). 190p. pap. 29.95 *(978-1-56898-988-4(1))* Princeton Architectural Pr.

Maciuika, John V. Before the Bauhaus: Architecture, Politics, & the German State, 1890-1920. 2008. (Modern Architecture & Cultural Identity Ser.). (ENG., Illus.). 402p. pap. 41.99 *(978-0-521-72822-5(3))* Cambridge Univ. Pr.

Malmberg, Catherine, ed. The Politics of Design: Competitions for Public Projects. 2006. (ENG.). 127p. pap. 11.95 *(978-0-9778531-4-4(4))* Policy Research Institute for the Region.

Martin, Reinhold, et al. Swedish Modernism: Architecture, Consumption & the Welfare State. Wallenstein, Sven-Olov, ed. 2010. (ENG., Illus.). 192p. pap. 39.95 *(978-1-906155-98-8(4))* Black Dog Publishing Ltd. GBR. Dist: Perseus Distribution.

Masaka, P., ed. The 1996 Zambia National Housing Policy - Volume 31 Sustainable Urban Areas. 2010. (Illus.). 484p. pap. 116.00 *(978-1-60750-566-2(5))* IOS Pr., Inc.

Monteyne, David. Fallout Shelter: Designing for Civil Defense in the Cold War. 2011. (Architecture, Landscape & Amer Culture Ser.). (Illus.). 352p. 84.00 *(978-0-8166-6975-2(9))*; pap. 27.95 *(978-0-8166-6976-9(7))* Univ. of Minnesota Pr.

Nevola, Fabrizio. Siena: Constructing the Renaissance City. 2008. (ENG., Illus.). 320p. 65.00 *(978-0-300-12678-5(6))* Yale Univ. Pr.

Pare, Richard. The Lost Vanguard: Russian Modernist Architecture, 1922-1932. 2007. (ENG., Illus.). 348p. 85.00 *(978-1-58093-185-4(5))* Monacelli Pr., Inc.

Porter, Bernard. The Battle of the Styles: George Gilbert Scott & the FCO. 2011. (ENG., Illus.). 256p. 49.95 *(978-1-4411-6739-2(0))* Continuum International Publishing Group, Ltd. GBR. Dist: National Bk. Network.

Prokopovych, Markian. Habsburg Lemberg: Architecture, Public Space, & Politics in the Galician Capital, 1772-1914. 2008. (Illus.). 357p. pap. 49.95 *(978-1-55753-510-8(8))* Purdue Univ. Pr.

Rizvi, Kishwar. The Safavid Dynastic Shrine: Architecture, Religion & Power in Early Modern Iran. 2011. (British Institute of Persian Studies). (ENG., Illus.). 256p. 92.00 *(978-1-84885-354-6(8)*, Tauris Academic Studies) I. B. Tauris & Co., Ltd. GBR. Dist: Macmillan.

Savelev, IU R. Iskusstvo Istorizma I Gosudarstvennyi Zakaz: Vtoraia Polovina XIX — Nachalo XX Veka. 2008. (RUS., Illus.). 304p. *(978-5-903060-60-3(9))* Sovpadenie, Izdatel'stvo.

Sternbridge, Jim. Fifty State Capitols: The Architecture of Representative Government. 2011. (ENG., Illus.). 128p. pap. 27.95 *(978-0-9830292-0-5(2)*, Coho Publishing) Cohographics.

Trüby, Stephan. Exit-Architecture: Design Between War & Peace. Payne, Robert, tr. from GER. 2008. (TRACE Transmission in Rhetorics, Arts & Cultural Evolution Ser.). (ENG., Illus.). vi, 113p. pap. 29.95 *(978-3-211-77969-9(8)*, 3211779698) Springer.

Wallenstein, Sven-Olov. Biopolitics & the Emergence of Modern Architecture. 2009. (ENG., Illus.). 96p. 24.95 *(978-1-56898-785-9(4))* Princeton Architectural Pr.

Weiwei, Ai, et al. Art & Cultural Policy in China: A Conversation between Ai Weiwei, Uli Sigg & Yung Ho Chang, moderated by Peter Pakesch. 2009. (GER & ENG., Illus.). 132p. pap. 39.95 *(978-3-211-89240-4(0))* Springer Wien AUT. Dist: Actar Birkhauser Distribution.

Yonan, Michael Elia. Empress Maria Theresa & the Politics of Habsburg Imperial Art. 2011. (ENG., Illus.). 232p. 90.00 *(978-0-271-03722-6(9))* Pennsylvania State Univ. Pr.

Zarecor, Kimberly Elman. Manufacturing a Socialist Modernity: Housing in Czechoslovakia, 1945-1960. 2011. (Pitt Russian East European Ser.). (ENG., Illus.). 480p. 45.00 *(978-0-8229-4404-1(9))* Univ. of Pittsburgh Pr.

ARCHITECTURE AND THE AGED

see Barrier-Free Design for Older People

ARCHITECTURE AND THE PHYSICALLY HANDICAPPED

see Barrier-Free Design

ARCHITECTURE AND WOMEN

Cole, Doris. Candid Reflections: Letters from Women in Architecture, 1972 & 2004. 2007. 184p. pap. 24.00 *(978-1-877675-63-8(6))* Midmarch Arts Pr.

Friedman, Alice T. Women & the Making of the Modern House. 2007. (ENG., Illus.). 242p. pap. 29.95 *(978-0-300-11789-9(2))* Yale Univ. Pr.

Gould, Kira, et al. Women in Green: Voices of Sustainable Design. 2007. (Illus.). 246p. per. 24.95 *(978-0-9749033-7-8(X))* Ecotone Publishing.

Greene, Isabelle Clara & Waterman, Pamela. Greene Gardens: The Sustainable Landscape Designs of Isabelle Greene. 2007. *(978-1-4236-0093-0(2))* Gibbs Smith, Publisher.

Hammond, Cynthia Imogen. Architects Angels Activists & the City of Bath 1765-1965: Engaging with Women's Spatial Interventions in Buildings & Landscapes. 2012. (Illus.). 296p. 119.95 ***(978-1-4094-0043-1(3))*** Ashgate Publishing Co.

Hiller, Nancy R. A Home of Her Own. 2011. (ENG., Illus.). 240p. pap. 29.95 *(978-0-253-22353-1(9)*, 0253223539) Indiana Univ. Pr.

Martin, Meredith S. Dairy Queens: The Politics of Pastoral Architecture from Catherine De' Medici to Marie-Antoinette. 2011. (Harvard Historical Studies: 176). (Illus.). 336p. 45.00 *(978-0-674-04899-7(7))* Harvard Univ. Pr.

Mozingo, Louise A. & Jewell, Linda, eds. Women in Landscape Architecture: Essays on History & Practice. 2011. (ENG., Illus.). 238p. pap. 45.00 *(978-0-7864-6164-6(0))* McFarland & Co., Inc. Pubs.

Sewell, Jessica Ellen. Women & the Everyday City: Public Space in San Francisco, 1890-1915. 2011. (Architecture, Landscape & Amer Culture Ser.). (ENG., Illus.). 280p. 75.00 *(978-0-8166-6973-8(2))*; pap. 25.00 *(978-0-8166-6974-5(0))* Univ. of Minnesota Pr.

Stratigakos, Despina. A Women's Berlin: Building the Modern City. 2008. (Illus.). 256p. 75.00 *(978-0-8166-5322-5(4))*; pap. 24.95 *(978-0-8166-5323-2(2))* Univ. of Minnesota Pr.

Whitworth, Lesley & Darling, Elizabeth, eds. Women & the Making of Built Space in England, 1870-1950. 2007. (Illus.). 232p. 124.95 *(978-0-7546-5185-7(1))* Ashgate Publishing Co.

ARCHITECTURE AS A PROFESSION

see Architecture—Vocational Guidance

ARCHITECTURE IN LITERATURE

Benert, Annette. The Architectural Imagination of Edith Wharton: Gender, Class, & Power in the Progressive Era. 2007. (Illus.). 261p. *(978-0-8386-4106-4(7))* Fairleigh Dickinson Univ. Pr.

Bernier, Ronald R. Monument, Moment, & Memory: Monet's Cathedral in the Fin De Siecle France. 2007. 128p. (C). 45.00 *(978-0-8387-5671-3(9))* Bucknell Univ. Pr.

Bernstein, Susan. Housing Problems: Writing & Architecture in Goethe, Walpole, Freud, & Heidegger. 2008. (Meridian: Crossing Aesthetics Ser.). (ENG., Illus.). 216p. 60.00 *(978-0-8047-5854-3(9))*; pap. 21.95 *(978-0-8047-5855-0(7))* Stanford Univ. Pr.

Bridgham, Elizabeth A. Spaces of the Sacred & Profane: Dickens, Trollope, & the Victorian Cathedral Town. (Literary Criticism & Cultural Theory Ser.). (ENG.). 202p. 2012. pap. 42.95 ***(978-0-415-54222-7(7))*** 2007. 135.00 *(978-0-415-97952-8(8))* Routledge.

Chu, David. Frozen Music: A Literary Exploration of California Architecture. 2010. xiii, 247p. pap. *(978-1-59714-137-6(2))* Heyday.

Dragset, Ingar & Elmgreen, Michael & Dragset, Ingar. Elmgreen & Dragset: Home Is the Place You Left. 2008. (ENG., Illus.). 196p. pap. 52.00 *(978-3-86560-473-6(0))* Verlag der Buchhandlung Walther Konig DEU. Dist: D.A.P./Distributed Art Pubs.

Edwards, Sarah, et al, eds. Writing the Modern City. 2012. (ENG., Illus.). 256p. (C). 155.00 ***(978-0-415-59150-8(3))*** Routledge.

Edwards, Sarah & Charley, Jonathan, eds. Writing the Modern City. 2012. (ENG., Illus.). 256p. (C). pap. 53.95 ***(978-0-415-59151-5(1))*** Routledge.

García Yero, Adela María. La Ciudad: Imágenes en Juego. 2008. (SPA., Illus.). 117p. *(978-959-267-193-5(1))* Acana, Ediciones.

Garner, Lori Ann. Structuring Spaces: Oral Poetics & Architecture in Early Medieval England. 2011. (ND Poetics of Orality & Literacy Ser.). (ENG., Illus.). 456p. pap. 45.00 *(978-0-268-02980-7(6))* Univ. of Notre Dame Pr.

Giles, Paul. Hart Crane: The Contexts of the Bridge. 2009. (Cambridge Studies in American Literature & Culture Ser.). (ENG.). 288p. pap. 38.99 *(978-0-521-10700-6(8))* Cambridge Univ. Pr.

Gleason, William. Sites Unseen: Architecture, Race, & American Literature. 2011. (ENG., Illus.). 288p. 65.00 *(978-0-8147-3246-5(1))*; pap. 22.00 *(978-0-8147-3247-2(X))* New York Univ. Pr.

Gleason, William A. Sites Unseen: Architecture, Race, & American Literature. 2011. (Illus.). 238p. E-Book ***(978-0-8147-3248-9(8))*** New York Univ. Pr.

Handa, Rumiko & Potter, James, eds. Conjuring the Real: The Role of Architecture in Eighteenth- And Nineteenth-Century Fiction. 2011. (ENG., Illus.). 232p. pap. 35.00 *(978-0-8032-1743-0(9))* Univ. of Nebraska Pr.

Lambert, Ladina & Ochsner, Andrea, eds. Moment to Monument: The Making & Unmaking of Cultural Significance. 2009. (ENG.). 224p. pap. 39.95 *(978-3-89942-962-6(1))* Transcript Verlag DEU. Dist: Transaction Pubs.

Reynolds, Nicole. Building Romanticism: Literature & Architecture in Nineteenth-Century Britain. 2010. (ENG., Illus.). 240p. (C). 70.00 *(978-0-472-11731-4(9))* Univ. of Michigan Pr.

Rosner, Victoria. Modernism & the Architecture of Private Life. 2008. (Gender & Culture Ser.). (ENG.). 240p. (gr. 17). pap. 25.00 *(978-0-231-13305-0(7))* Columbia Univ. Pr.

Shamir, Milette. Inexpressible Privacy: The Interior Life of Antebellum American Literature. 2006. (Illus.). 296p. (C). pap. 22.50 *(978-0-8122-2023-0(4))* Univ. of Pennsylvania Pr.

Somers, Reneé. Edith Wharton as Spatial Activist & Analyst. 2009. 176p. 39.95 *(978-0-415-80339-7(X))* Routledge.

Twyning, John. Forms of English History in Literature, Language, & Architecture. 2012. (Language, Discourse, Society Ser.). (ENG.). 280p. 85.00 *(978-0-230-02000-9(3))* Palgrave Macmillan.

Walter, Hugo. Magnificent Houses in Twentieth Century European Literature. 2012. ***(978-1-4331-1847-0(5))*** Lang, Peter Publishing, Inc.

Wye, Margaret. Architectural Influences on Jane Austen's Narratives: Structure as an Active Agent of Fictive Knowledge in the Long Eighteenth Century. 2009. (Illus.). 280p. *(978-0-7734-4769-1(5))* Mellen, Edwin Pr., The.

ARCHITECTURES, COMPUTER NETWORK

see Computer Network Architectures

ARCHIVES

see also Business Records; Cartularies; Charters; Court Records; Diplomatics; Libraries; Manuscripts; Public Records

Alexander, Ben & Bastian, Jeannette Allis. Communities & Their Archives: Creating & Sustaining Memory. 2009. (Illus.). 224p. 135.00 ***(978-1-85604-639-8(7))*** Neal-Schuman Pubs., Inc.

Balloffet, Nelly. Preservation & Conservation for Libraries & Archives. *(978-0-8389-1005-4(X))* American Library Assn.

Bernard, Sheila Curran & Rabin, Kenn. Archival Storytelling: A Filmmaker's Guide to Finding, Using, & Licensing Third-Party Visuals & Music. 2008. (ENG., Illus.). 336p. pap. 38.95 *(978-0-240-80973-1(4)*, Focal Pr.) Elsevier Science & Technology Bks.

Blackstone Research Associates Staff. Defining the Document Industry: Economic Impact & Future Growth Trends. EDSF Staff, ed. Date not set. (Illus.). 46p. pap., spiral bd. 200.00 *(978-0-9658790-0-2(3))* Electronic Document Systems Foundation, The.

Bödeker, Hans Erich & Saada, Anne. Bibliothek Als Archiv. 2007. (Veröffentlichungen des Max-Planck-Instituts Für Geschichte Ser.). (GER., Illus.). 313p. (C). 68.00 *(978-3-525-35869-6(5))* Vandenhoeck & Ruprecht GmbH & Co. KG DEU. Dist: ISD.

Buelow, Anna E. & Ahmon, Jess. Digitizing Original Documents. 2010. (Illus.). 192p. pap. 99.95 ***(978-1-85604-711-1(3))*** Neal-Schuman Pubs., Inc.

Burger, Marlene. Bibliographic Style & Reference Techniques: Revised Edition. 2010. 255p. pap. 31.00 *(978-1-86888-550-3(X))* Unisa Press / Uitgewers GBR. Dist: International Specialized Bk. Services.

Burns, Kathryn. Into the Archive: Writing & Power in Colonial Peru. 2010. (ENG., Illus.). 264p. 79.95 *(978-0-8223-4857-3(8))*; pap. 22.95 *(978-0-8223-4868-9(3))* Duke Univ. Pr.

Carpenter, Julie. Project Management in Libraries, Archives & Museums: Working with Government & other External Partners. 2009. (Illus.). 200p. pap. 80.00 *(978-1-84334-566-4(8)*, Chandos Publishing) Woodhead Publishing Ltd. GBR. Dist: Neal-Schuman Pubs., Inc.

Cook, Joyce H. Researching Native Americans in New York State. 2007. 64p. 15.00 *(978-0-9798900-0-0(4))* New York State Council of Genealogical Organization.

Cook, Terry & Samuels, Helen Willa. Controlling the Past: Documenting Society & Institutions: Essays in Honor of Helen Willa Samuels. 2011. *(978-1-931666-36-7(9))* Scarecrow Pr., Inc.

Cotton, Justine & Sharron, David. Engaging Students with Archival & Digital Resources. 2011. (Illus.). 200p. pap. *(978-1-84334-568-8(4)*, Chandos Publishing) Woodhead Publishing Ltd. GBR. Dist: Neal-Schuman Pubs., Inc.

Cox, Richard J. Archival Anxiety & the Vocational Calling. 2011. pap. 35.00 *(978-1-936117-49-9(5))* Litwin Bks., LLC.

—The Demise of the Library School: Personal Reflections on Professional Education in the Modern Corporate University. 2010. pap. 35.00 *(978-1-936117-18-5(5)*, Library Juice Pr.) Litwin Bks., LLC.

—Personal Archives & a New Archival Calling: Readings, Reflections & Ruminations. 2009. pap. 35.00 *(978-0-9802004-7-8(4))* Litwin Bks., LLC.

Dearing, Charles L., et al. ABC of the NRA. (Brookings Institution Reprint Ser.). reprint ed. lib. bdg. 34.00 *(978-0-697-00154-2(7))* Irvington Pubs.

Derclaye, Estelle, ed. Copyright & Cultural Heritage: Preservation & Access to Works in a Digital World. 2011. 264p. 110.00 *(978-1-84980-004-4(9))* Elgar, Edward Publishing, Inc.

Dow, Elizabeth H. Electronic Records in the Manuscript Repository. 2009. (ENG.). 208p. (gr. 17). pap. 50.00 *(978-0-8108-6708-6(7))* Scarecrow Pr., Inc.

Duchein, Michel. Archive buildings & Equipment. (ENG.). 201p. 210.00 ***(978-3-11-215986-6(1))*** De Gruyter, Walter Inc.

—Archive Buildings & Equipment. Walne, Peter, ed. Thomas, David, tr. 2nd ed. (ICA Handbooks Ser.). (ENG.). 232p. ***(978-3-11-186555-3(X))*** Saur, K. G. Verlag GmbH & Co.

Eastwood, Terry & MacNeil, Heather, eds. Currents of Archival Thinking. 1 vol. 2009. 254p. pap. 45.00 *(978-1-59158-656-2(9)*, LU8656) Libraries Unlimited, Inc.

Eidem, Jasper & Ristvet, Lauren. The Royal Archives from Tell Leilan: Old Babylonian Letters & Treaties from the Eastern Lower Town Palace. 2010. (Yale Tell Leilan Research Ser.). (ENG.). 640p. 125.00 *(978-0-300-16545-6(5))* Yale Univ. Pr.

Esch, Deborah. Archival Survival. *(978-0-8047-4047-0(X))* Stanford Univ. Pr.

Forde, Helen. Preserving Archives. 2007. (Illus.). 224p. pap. 99.95 ***(978-1-85604-577-3(3))*** Neal-Schuman Pubs., Inc.

Fossati, Giovanna. From Grain to Pixel: The Archival Life of Film in Transition. 2010. (Framing Film Ser.). (ENG., Illus.). 336p. pap. *(978-90-8964-139-7(4))* Amsterdam Univ. Pr.

Friesinger, Günther, et al, eds. Mind & Matter: Comparative Approaches towards Complexity. 2012. (ENG., Illus.). 230p. pap. 44.95 ***(978-3-8376-1800-6(5))*** Transcript Verlag DEU. Dist: Transaction Pubs.

Graaf, Maurits van der & Eijndhoven, Kwame van. The European Repository Landscape: Inventory Study into the Present Type & Level of OAI-Compliant Digital Respository Activities in the EU. 2008. (Surf/EU-Driver Ser.). (DUT., Illus.). 149p. *(978-90-5356-410-3(1))* Amsterdam Univ. Pr.

Grim, Ronald E. & Block, Debra. Torn in Two. 2011. (Illus.). 152p. pap. 35.00 *(978-0-615-47402-1(0))* Norman B. Leventhal Map Ctr.

Hackman, Larry J. Many Happy Returns: Advocacy & the Development of Archives. 2011. *(978-1-931666-37-4(7))* Scarecrow Pr., Inc.

Harris, V. S. Archives & Justice: A South African Perspective. 2007. *(978-1-931666-18-3(0))* Scarecrow Pr., Inc.

Hill, Jennie. The Future of Archives & Record Keeping: A Reader. 2011. 256p. pap. *(978-1-85604-666-4(4))* Facet Publishing.

Iacovino, Livia. Recordkeeping, Ethics & Law: Regulatory Models, Participant Relationships & Rights & Responsibilities in the Online World. 2010. (Archivist's Library). xv, 339p. pap. 189.00 *(978-90-481-7172-9(5)*, 9048171725) Springer.

Ioannides, Marinos, et al, eds. Digital Heritage: Third International Euro-Mediterranean Conference, EuroMed 2010, Lemesos, Cyprus, November 8-13, 2010. Proceedings. 2010. (Lecture Notes in Computer Science / Information Systems & Applications, incl. Internet/Web, & HCI Ser.). (Illus.). xiv, 550p. pap. 107.00 *(978-3-642-16872-7(8)*, 3642168728) Springer.

James, Russell D. Public Relations & Marketing for Archivists: A How-To-Do-It Manual. 2011. (Illus.). 250p. pap. 75.00 ***(978-1-55570-733-0(5))*** Neal-Schuman Pubs., Inc.

Jimerson, Randall C. Archives Power: Memory, Accountability, & Social Justice. 2009. *(978-1-931666-30-5(X))*; xxi, 442p. pap. *(978-0-8389-1061-0(0))* Scarecrow Pr., Inc.

Ken, Lawrence. Preparing & Safeguarding Accounting Records in the Church Archives. 2009. 160p. per. 12.95 *(978-0-910653-57-2(7))* Red River Pr.

Kirsch, Gesa E. & Rohan, Liz, eds. Beyond the Archives: Research as a Lived Process. 2008. (ENG.). 192p. pap. 35.00 *(978-0-8093-2840-6(2))* Southern Illinois Univ. Pr.

Kirschenbaum, Matthew G., et al. Digital Forensics & Born-Digital Content in Cultural Heritage Collections. 2010. pap. 25.00 net. *(978-1-932326-37-6(5))* Council on Library & Info. Resources.

Lawrence, Ken. An Extensive Look at Museums in the U. S. rev. ed. 2008. (Illus.). 256p. 19.95 *(978-0-910653-15-2(1)*, 8204372, Red River Pr.) Red River Pr.

Lee, Christopher A. I, Digital: Personal Collections in the Digital ERA. 2011. ***(978-1-931666-38-1(5))*** Society of American Archivists.

MacNeil, H. Trusting Records: Legal, Historical, & Diplomatic Perspectives. 2010. (Archivist's Library). 180p. pap. 179.00 *(978-90-481-5572-9(X)*, 904815572X) Springer.

Masanès, Julien, ed. Web Archiving. 2010. (ENG., Illus.). vii, 234p. pap. 89.95 *(978-3-642-06236-0(9)*, 3642062369) Springer.

Meinhold, Alexandra. World Guide to Library, Archive, & Information Science Associations. 2011. (IFLA Publications). (ENG., Illus.). 486p. ***(978-3-11-174196-3(6))*** Saur, K. G. Verlag GmbH & Co.

Merewether, Charles, ed. The Archive. 2006. (Documents of Contemporary Art Ser.). (ENG.). 208p. (gr. 17). pap. 24.95 *(978-0-262-63338-3(8))* MIT Pr.

Millar, Laura. Archives: Principles & Practice. 2010. 256p. 75.00 *(978-1-55570-726-2(2))* Neal-Schuman Pubs., Inc.

—The Story Behind the Book: Preserving Authors' & Publishers' Archives. 2009. (ENG.). 224p. 36.95 *(978-0-9738727-4-3(8)*, Canadian Centre for Studies in Publishing) CCSP Pr. CAN. Dist: Perseus-PGW.

Note, Margot. Managing Image Collections: A Practical Guide. 2010. (Illus.). 200p. 80.00 *(978-1-84334-599-2(4)*, Chandos Publishing) Woodhead Publishing Ltd. GBR. Dist: Neal-Schuman Pubs., Inc.

Osthoff, Simone. Performing the Archive: The transformation of the archive in Contemporary art from repository of documents to art Medium. Schirmacher, Wolfgang, ed. 2009. (Illus.). 208p. pap. 21.95 *(978-0-9825309-0-0(0))* Atropos Pr.

O'Toole, James M. & Cox, Richard J. Understanding Archives & Manuscripts. 2006. (Archival Fundamentals Ser.). *(978-1-931666-20-6(2))* Scarecrow Pr., Inc.

Posner, Ernst & Munden, Kenneth W. Archives & the Public Interest: Selected Essays by Ernst Posner. 2006. *(978-1-931666-16-9(4))* Scarecrow Pr., Inc.

Ridener, John. From Polders to Postmodernism: A Concise History of Archival Theory. 2009. pap. 22.00 *(978-0-9802004-5-4(8))* Litwin Bks., LLC.

Robertson, Craig, ed. Media History & the Archive. 2011. (ENG., Illus.). 136p. (C). 125.00 *(978-0-415-59327-4(1))* Routledge.

Rosenberg, William G. & Blouin, Francis X., Jr. Processing the Past: Contesting Authority in History & the Archives, 1 vol. 2011. (ENG.). 272p. 74.00 *(978-0-19-974054-3(2))* Oxford Univ. Pr., Inc.

Rosenberg, William G. & Blouin, Francis X., Jr., eds. Archives, Documentation, & Institutions of Social Memory: Essays from the Sawyer Seminar. 2007. (ENG., Illus.). 512p. (C). per. 62.50 *(978-0-472-03270-9(4))* Univ. of Michigan Pr.

Rudman, Jack. Archivist. (Career Examination Ser.: C-3681). pap. 34.95 *(978-0-8373-3681-7(3))* National Learning Corp.

Sandifer, Kevin. A Layman's look at Starting a Religious Archives. rev. ed. 2012. 64p. per. 9.95 *(978-0-910653-94-7(1)*, Red River Pr.) Red River Pr.

Schenk, Dietmar. Kleine Theorie des Archivs. 2008. (GER.). 112p. (C). pap. 29.00 *(978-3-515-09143-5(2))* Steiner, Franz Verlag Wiesbaden GmbH DEU. Dist: Brown, David Bk. Co., The.

Schniederjürgen, Axel. World Guide to Library, Archive, & Information Science Associations. 3rd ed. 2010. (IFLA Publications). (ENG.). 486p. *(978-3-11-022637-9(5))* Saur, K. G. Verlag GmbH & Co.

Stavridis, Stavros & Chibo, David, eds. The Assyrians in Australian Archives. 2010. 140.00 *(978-1-60724-993-1(6))* Gorgias Pr., LLC.

Steedman, Carolyn. Dust. 195p. *(978-0-7190-6014-4(1))*; pap. *(978-0-7190-6015-1(X))* Manchester Univ. Pr. GBR. Dist: Macmillan.

Stockinger, P. Digital Audiovisual Archives. 2012. (Iste Ser.: 604). (ENG., Illus.). xvii, 302p. 145.00 ***(978-1-84821-338-8(7)**, Wiley-ISTE)* Wiley, John & Sons, Inc.

—Introduction to Audiovisual Archives. 2012. (Iste Ser.: 603). (ENG.). 145.00 ***(978-1-84821-337-1(9)**, Wiley-ISTE)* Wiley, John & Sons, Inc.

Theimer, Kate. A Different Kind of Web: New Connections Between Archives & Our Users. 2011. ***(978-1-931666-39-8(3))*** Scarecrow Pr., Inc.

Theimer, Kate. Web 2.0 Tools & Strategies: For Archives & Local History Collections. 2009. 79.95 *(978-1-55570-679-1(7))* Neal-Schuman Pubs., Inc.

VV., AA., et al. Memoria y Naturaleza: El Archivo Del Real Jardín Botánico de Madrid. San Pío Aladrén, Pilar, ed. 2009. (ENG & SPA., Illus.). 269p. *(978-84-9785-618-8(X))* Consejo Superior de Investigaciones Cientificas.

Weenink, Kasja, et al. A DRIVER's Guide to European Repositories. 2008. (Surf/EU-Driver Ser.). (Illus.). 215p. *(978-90-5356-411-0(X))* Amsterdam Univ. Pr.

Zhang, Allison & Gourley, Don. Creating Digital Collections: A Practical Guide. 2008. 252p. *(978-1-84334-397-4(5))*; (Illus.). pap. *(978-1-84334-396-7(7))* Woodhead Publishing Ltd. (Chandos Publishing).

ARCHIVES—DATA PROCESSING

Craven, Louise. What Are Archives? Cultural & Theoretical Perspectives: A Reader. 2008. (Illus.). 214p. 114.95 *(978-0-7546-7310-1(3))* Ashgate Publishing Co.

GAMP Good Practice Guide: Electronic Data Archiving. 2007. 147p. *(978-1-931879-52-1(4))* International Society for Pharmaceutical Engineering.

Rieger, Oya Y. Preservation in the Age of Large-Scale Digitization: A White Paper. 2008. (CLIR Publication Ser.). vii, 52p. per. 20.00 net. *(978-1-932326-29-1(4))* Council on Library & Info. Resources.

ARCHIVES—LAW AND LEGISLATION

Behrnd-Klodt, Menzi L. Navigating Legal Issues in Archives. 2008. *(978-1-931666-28-2(8))* Scarecrow Pr., Inc.

Hirtle, Peter B., et al. Copyright & cultural Institutions: Guidelines for digitization for U. S. libraries, archives, & Museums. 2009. (Illus.). 282p. pap. *(978-0-935995-10-7(2))* Cornell Univ. Library, Div. of Rare & Manuscripts Collections.

ARCHIVES—ASIA

Buchanan, George, et al. Digital Libraries: Universal & Ubiquitous Access to Information: 11th International Conference on Asian Digital Libraries, ICADL 2008, Bali, Indonesia, December 2-5, 2008, Proceedings. 2008. (Lecture Notes in Computer Science / Information Systems & Applications, incl. Internet/Web, & HCI Ser.). xiv, 422p. pap. 89.95 *(978-3-540-89532-9(9))* Springer.

Lu, Dongming & Pan, Yunhe. Digital Preservation for Heritages: Technologies & Applications. 2010. (Advanced Topics in Science & Technology in China Ser.). (ENG., Illus.). 219p. 139.00 *(978-3-642-04861-6(7)*, 3642048617) Springer.

Nanbara, Shigeru & Minear, Richard H. War & Conscience in Japan: Nambara Shigeru & the Asia-Pacific War. 2011. (Illus.). xi, 215p. *(978-0-7425-6815-0(6))* Rowman & Littlefield Publishers, Inc.

Stoler, Ann Laura. Along the Archival Grain: Epistemic Anxieties & Colonial Common Sense. (Illus.). (C). 2010. (ENG.). 314p. pap. 23.95 *(978-0-691-14636-2(5))* 2008. 344p. 59.50 *(978-0-691-01578-1(3))* 2008. 344p. pap. 22.95 *(978-0-691-01577-4(5))* Princeton Univ. Pr.

ARCHIVES—CANADA

Avery, Cheryl & Holmlund, Mona. Better off Forgetting? Essays on Archives, Public Policy & Collective Memory. 2010. (ENG.). *(978-1-4426-4167-9(3))*; pap. *(978-1-4426-1080-4(8))* Univ. of Toronto Pr.

Clarke, Arthur C. Amongst Thistles & Thorns. 2011. (Caribbean Modern Classics Ser.). (ENG.). 208p. pap. 17.95 *(978-1-84523-147-7(3))* Peepal Tree Pr., Ltd. GBR. Dist: Independent Pubs. Group.

Morra, Linda M. & Schagerl, Jessica, eds. Basements & Attics, Closets & Cyberspace: Explorations in Canadian Women's Archives. 2012. (Life Writing Ser.). (ENG., Illus.). 355p. (C). 85.00 ***(978-1-55458-632-5(1))*** Wilfrid Laurier Univ. Pr. CAN. Dist: Univ. of Toronto Pr.

Sleigh, Daphne. The Man Who Saved Vancouver: Major James Skitt Matthews, 1 vol. 2008. (ENG., Illus.). 240p. pap. *(978-1-894974-39-4(5))* Heritage Hse.

ARCHIVES—EUROPE

Grimsted, Patricia K., et al, eds. Returned from Russia: Nazi Archival Plunder in Western Europe & Recent Restitution Issues. 2007. (Illus.). 372p. pap. 85.00 ***(978-1-903987-13-1(X))*** Institute of Art & Law GBR. Dist: International Specialized Bk. Services.

Helferty, Seamus. Directory of Irish Archives. Refaussé, Raymond, ed. 5th rev. ed. 2011. 240p. pap. 35.00 *(978-1-84682-246-9(7))* Four Courts Pr. IRL. Dist: International Specialized Bk. Services.

Helferty, Seamus & Refaussé, Raymond, eds. Directory of Irish Archives. 5th rev. ed. 2011. 240p. 65.00 *(978-1-84682-245-2(9))* Four Courts Pr. IRL. Dist: International Specialized Bk. Services.

Holland, Ailsia C. & Manning, Kate, eds. Archivists & Archives. 2006. 230p. (C). 65.00 *(978-1-84682-016-8(2))* Four Courts Pr. IRL. Dist: International Specialized Bk. Services.

Laurentius, Th & Laurentius, Frans. Watermarks, 1650-1700, Found in the Zeeland Archives. 2008. (Illus.). xviii, 354p. 980.00 *(978-90-6194-190-3(3))* HES & DE GRAAF Pubs. BV NLD. Dist: Oak Knoll Pr.

Lewanski, Richard Casimir. Eastern Europe & Russia/Soviet Union: A handbook of West European archival & library Resources. (GER.). XV, 317p. ***(978-3-11-207212-7(X))*** Saur, K. G. Verlag GmbH & Co.

Madas, Edit. Mittelalterliche Lateinische Handschriftenfragmente in Sopron. (LAT & GER., Illus.). 652p. *(978-963-05-8408-1(5))* Akademiai Kiado.

Martin, Cary J. Demotic Papyri from the Memphite Necropolis: In the Collections of the National Museum of Antiquities in Leiden, the British Museum & the Hermitage Museum. 2009. (Palma Ser.). (Illus.). 270p. (C). pap. 115.00 *(978-2-503-53057-4(5))* Brepols Pubs. BEL. Dist: Brown, David Bk. Co., The.

Martinez Reverte, Javier. Expedición Malaspina: Un Viaje Científico-Político Alrededor Del Mundo 1789-1794. 2010. (SPA., Illus.). 142p. *(978-84-7506-957-9(6))* Turner, Ediciones S.A.

O'Neill, Robert Keating. Irish Libraries: Archives, Museums & Genealogical Centres. 2010. (ENG.). 445p. pap. *(978-1-903688-28-1(0))* Ulster Historical Foundation GBR. Dist: Independent Pubs. Group.

Queyroux, Fabienne & Stockting, Bill, eds. Encoding Across Frontiers: Proceedings of the European Conference on Encoded Archival Description & Context (Ead & Eac), Paris, France, 7-8 October 2004. 2006. (ENG., Illus.). 302p. 65.95 *(978-0-7890-3026-9(8))* Routledge.

Shepherd, William Robert. Guide to the Materials for the History of the United States in Spanish Archives. 2009. 114p. 28.99 *(978-1-115-58249-0(6))*; pap. 19.75 *(978-1-115-58252-0(6))* BiblioBazaar.

—Guide to the Materials for the History of the United States in Spanish Archives. 2008. 112p. pap. 19.95 *(978-1-4368-6378-0(3))* Kessinger Publishing, LLC.

Tsipopoulou, Metaxia, et al. The Hieroglyphic Archive at Petras, Siteias. 2010. (Monographs of the Danish Institute at Athens). (ENG., Illus.). 272p. (C). 45.00 *(978-87-7934-293-4(0))* Aarhus Universitetsforlag DNK. Dist: ISD.

Van der Graaf, Maurits. European Repository Landscape 2008: Inventory of Digital Repositories for Research Output. 2009. (Surf/EU-Driver Ser.). 168p. pap. *(978-90-8964-190-8(4))* Amsterdam Univ. Pr.

Wiesebron, Marianne. Brazilië in de Nederlandse Archieven (1624-1654) Documenten in Het Koninklijk Huisarchief en in Het Archief Van de Staten-Generaal = o Brasil Em Arquivos Neerlandeses (1624-1654): Documentos No Arquivo Da Casa Real e No Arquivo DOS Estados Gerais. 2008. (CNWS Publications). (POR, DUT & MUL., Illus.). 605p. *(978-90-5789-157-1(3)*, Leiden Univ. Pr.) Amsterdam Univ. Pr.

ARCHIVES—FRANCE

Moore, Lara Jennifer. Restoring Order: The Ecole des Chartes & the Organization of Archives & Libraries in France, 1820-1870. 2008. 306p. pap. 32.00 *(978-0-9778617-9-8(1))* Litwin Bks., LLC.

Nappo, Tommaso, ed. Index biographique Francais. 2nd ed. (GER.). ***(978-3-11-197551-1(7))***; ***(978-3-11-114550-1(6))*** Saur, K. G. Verlag GmbH & Co.

Soll, Jacob. The Information Master: Jean-Baptiste Colbert's Secret State Intelligence System. 2011. (Cultures of Knowledge in the Early Modern World Ser.). (ENG., Illus.). 328p. pap. 28.95 ***(978-0-472-03464-2(2))*** Univ. of Michigan Pr.

ARCHIVES—GERMANY

Eckert, Astrid M. The Struggle over the Files: The Western Allies & the Return of German Archives after the Second World War. 2012. (Publications of the German Historical Institute Ser.). (ENG.). 440p. 99.00 ***(978-0-521-88018-3(1))*** Cambridge Univ. Pr.

Kornemann, Matthias & Fischer, Axel, eds. The Archive of the Sing-Akademie Zu Berlin Catalogue das Archiv der Sing-Akademie Zu Berlin Katalog. 2009. (ENG & GER., Illus.). 773p. *(978-3-598-11798-5(1))* Saur, K. G. Verlag GmbH & Co.

Schmidt-Czaia, Bettina & Soénius, Ulrich S. Gedächtnisort: Das Historische Archiv der Stadt Köln. 2010. (GER., Illus.). 197p. *(978-3-412-20490-7(0))* Bohlau Verlag Gmbh & Cie.

Wirth, Ingo. Quellenband Zur Sektionstätigkeit Im Pathologischen Institut der Friedrich-Wilhelms-Universität Zu Berlin Von 1856 Bis 1902: Ein Beitrag Zur Virchow-Forschung. 2006. (GER.). 161p. pap. *(978-3-8325-1087-9(7))* Logos Verlag Berlin.

ARCHIVES—GREAT BRITAIN

Barratt, Nick & Gill, Anton. Who Do You Think You Are? Trace Your Family History Back to the Tudors. 2006. (ENG., Illus.). 224p. 29.95 *(978-0-00-723008-2(7))* HarperCollins Pubs. Ltd. GBR. Dist: Independent Pubs. Group.

Bennett, Nicholas. Wonderful to Behold: A Centenary History of the Lincoln Record Society, 1910-2010. 2010. (Publications of the Lincoln Record Society Ser.: Volume 100). (Illus.). 284p. 50.00 *(978-0-901503-88-6(6))* Lincoln Record Society GBR. Dist: Boydell & Brewer, Inc.

—Wonderful to Behold: A Centenary of the Lincoln Record Society, 1910-2010 (volume 100) With Lincolnshire Church Notes made by Gervase Holles (volume 1) 2010. (Publications of the Lincoln Record Society Ser.). 115.00 *(978-0-901503-91-6(6))* Lincoln Record Society GBR. Dist: Boydell & Brewer, Inc.

Blanchard, Gill. Tracing Your East Anglian Ancestors: A Guide for Family Historians. 2009. (Illus.). 224p. pap. 25.99 *(978-1-84415-989-5(2))* Pen & Sword Bks. Ltd. GBR. Dist: Casemate Pubs. & Bk. Distributors, LLC.

Brown, Jonathan. Tracing Your Rural Ancestors. 2011. (Illus.). 192p. pap. 24.95 ***(978-1-84884-227-4(9))*** Pen & Sword Bks. Ltd. GBR. Dist: Casemate Pubs. & Bk. Distributors, LLC.

Cox, Jane. Tracing Your East End Ancestors. 2011. (Illus.). 256p. pap. 29.95 ***(978-1-84884-160-4(4))*** Pen & Sword Bks. Ltd. GBR. Dist: Casemate Pubs. & Bk. Distributors, LLC.

Cunningham, Sean, et al. Foundations of Medieval York: Records edited in honour of David Crook. Cunningham, Sean & Brand, Paul, eds. 2008. (Illus.). 239p. pap. *(978-1-904497-24-0(1))* Borthwick Institute of Historical Research.

Davis, Graeme. Your Family Tree on-Line: How to Trace Your Ancestry from Your Own Computer. 2009. (Illus.). 163p. pap. 20.00 *(978-1-84528-344-5(9))* How To Books GBR. Dist: Parkwest Pubns., Inc.

Edwards, Edward. Libraries & Founders of Libraries. 2010. (Cambridge Library Collection - Printing & Publishing History Ser.). (ENG.). 540p. pap. 39.99 *(978-1-108-01052-8(0))* Cambridge Univ. Pr.

Hall, Hubert. Studies in English Official Historical Documents. 2010. 428p. pap. 35.75 (978-1-177-86788-7(5)); (ENG.). 432p. pap. 35.75 (978-1-177-64103-6(8)); 428p. pap. 35.75 (978-1-146-40773-1(4)); 434p. pap. 35.75 (978-1-147-73033-3(4)); 438p. pap. 35.75 (978-1-145-31961-5(0)) BiblioBazaar.

—Studies in English Official Historical Documents. 2010. 324p. pap. 39.90 (978-1-152-61915-9(2)) General Bks. LLC.

—Studies in English Official Historical Documents. 2009. 424p. 51.95 (978-1-104-58109-1(4)); pap. 36.95 (978-1-104-47296-2(1)) Kessinger Publishing, LLC.

Higgs, Michelle. Tracing Your Medical Ancestors. 2011. (Illus.). 192p. pap. 24.95 (978-1-84884-277-9(5)) Pen & Sword Bks. Ltd. GBR. Dist: Casemate Pubs. & Bk. Distributors, LLC.

Hubert, Hall. Studies in English Official Historical Documents. 2010. (Cambridge Library Collection - History Ser.). 428p. pap. 32.99 (978-1-108-01064-1(4)) Cambridge Univ. Pr.

Kemp, B., ed. Reading Abbey Cartularies, 2 vols., Vol. 1. (Camden Fourth Ser.). 196p. 27.00 (978-0-86193-108-8(4)) Brown, David Bk. Co., The.

Marshall, Oliver. Brazil in British & Irish Archives. 2008. (ENG.). 288p. per. (978-0-9544070-8-7(3)) Centre for Brazilian Studies.

Oates, Jonathan. Tracing Your London Ancestors. 2011. (Illus.). 192p. pap. 24.95 (978-1-84884-130-7(2)) Pen & Sword Bks. Ltd. GBR. Dist: Casemate Pubs. & Bk. Distributors, LLC.

Peek, H. E. & Hall, C. P. Archives of the University Cambridge: An Historical Introduction. 2009. (Cambridge Library Collection - Cambridge Ser.). (ENG., Illus.). 120p. pap. 19.99 (978-1-108-00237-0(4)) Cambridge Univ. Pr.

Rye, Walter. Records & Record Searching. 264p. 2009. 28.99 (978-1-115-10026-7(2)) 2008. 25.99 (978-0-559-71453-5(X)) 2008. pap. 26.75 (978-0-559-71450-4(5)) BiblioBazaar.

—Records & Record Searching. 2009. 218p. pap. (978-0-217-74869-8(4)) Books LLC.

Shepherd, Elizabeth. Archives & Archivists in 20th Century England. 2009. (Illus.). 260p. 114.95 (978-0-7546-4785-0(4)) Ashgate Publishing Co.

Walne, Peter. A Guide to Manuscript Sources for the History of Latin America & the Caribbean in the British Isles. xx, 580p. (978-0-19-818152-1(3)) Bow Historical Bks.

ARCHIVES—ITALY

Di Renso, Elisa & Harris, Neil. Una Biblioteca, Un'alluvione: Il 4 Novembre 1966 Alla Nazionale Di Firenze: Storia Di Un'emergenza. 2009. (ITA., Illus.). 379p. (978-88-7812-201-7(7)) AIB.

Zombardo, Alessia. Il Diplomatico Del Comune Di Montieri Nell'archivio Di Stato Di Siena: 1236-1578. 2008. (ITA.). lxxiv, 323p. (978-88-89073-31-5(4)) Accademia Degli Intronati.

ARCHIVES—SOVIET UNION

Grimsted, Patricia K., et al, eds. Returned from Russia: Nazi Archival Plunder in Western Europe & Recent Restitution Issues. 2007. (Illus.). 372p. pap. 85.00 (978-1-903987-13-1(X)) Institute of Art & Law GBR. Dist: International Specialized Bk. Services.

Kolesnikova, M. E., et al. Stavropolskaia Gubernskaia Uchenaia Arkhivnaia Komissiia: Stranitsy Istorii Arkhivnogo Dela Severnogo Kavkaza. 2007. (RUS., Illus.). 169p. (978-5-85714-054-3(4)) Vestnik Kavkaza, Redakcija gazety.

ARCHIVES—UNITED STATES

Bartlett, Kenneth F. CD: Record Group 52. 2007. cd-rom 15.95 (978-0-7884-4017-5(9)) Heritage Bks.

Bastian, Jeannette Allis & Webber, Donna. Archival Internships: A Guide for Faculty, Supervisors, & Students. 2008. (978-1-931666-26-8(1)) Scarecrow Pr., Inc.

Behrnd-Klodt, Menzi L. Navigating Legal Issues in Archives. 2008. (978-1-931666-28-2(8)) Scarecrow Pr., Inc.

Bolton, Herbert Eugene. Guide to Materials for the History of the United States in the Principal Archives of Mexico. 2008. 576p. pap. 43.95 (978-1-4368-6358-2(9)) Kessinger Publishing, LLC.

—Guide to Materials for the History of the United States in the Principal Archives of Mexico. (Carnegie Institution of Washington Ser.). 553p. reprint ed. 98.00 (978-0-7222-6991-6(9)) Library Reprints, Inc.

Browne, William Hand. CD: Archives of Maryland: Proceedings & Acts of the General Assembly of Maryland, April, 1684-June 1692. 2008. cd-rom 19.95 (978-0-7884-4508-8(1)) Heritage Bks.

Caldwell, Genoa. Early Travel Photography: The Greatest Traveler of His Time. 2010. (25 Ser.). (ENG., Illus.). 29.99 (978-3-8365-2140-6(7)) TASCHEN DEU. Dist: Ingram Pub. Services.

Carson, Bryan. The Law of Libraries & Archives. 2006. (ENG., Illus.). 416p. 85.00 (978-0-8108-5189-4(X)) Scarecrow Pr., Inc.

Center for the National Archives Experience Staff & Foundation for the National Archives Staff, contrib. by. Discovering the Civil War. 2010. pap. (978-0-9841033-2-4(5)) Foundation for the National Archives.

Danielson, Elena S. The Ethical Archivist. 2010. (978-1-931666-34-3(2)) Scarecrow Pr., Inc.

Dearstyne, Bruce W. Leading & Managing Archives & Records Programs: Strategies for Success. 2008. xvii, 347p. 75.00 (978-1-55570-615-9(0)) Neal-Schuman Pubs., Inc.

Delaware Archives, Set, Vols. 1-5. reprint ed. lib. bdg. 300.00 (978-0-404-19514-4(8)) AMS Pr., Inc.

Gracy, David B., II. The State Library & Archives of Texas: A History, 1835-1962. (ENG., Illus.). 264p. 2011. pap. 25.00 (978-0-292-72896-7(4)) 2010. 45.00 (978-0-292-72201-9(X)) Univ. of Texas Pr.

Gray, Glenn R., et al. An American Political Archives Reader. Gray/Melvin/Paul, ed. 2009. (ENG.). 488p. (gr. 17). 85.00 (978-0-8108-6746-8(X)) Scarecrow Pr., Inc.

Hazard, Samuel. General Index to the Colonial Records, in 16 Volumes, & to the Pennsylvania Archives [1st Series] in 12 Volumes, Prepared & Arranged by Samuel Haz. 2006. 664p. per. 36.99 (978-1-4255-6734-7(7)) MPublishing.

Hirtle, Peter B., et al. Copyright & cultural Institutions: Guidelines for digitization for U. S. libraries, archives, & Museums. 2009. (Illus.). 282p. pap. (978-0-935995-10-7(2)) Cornell Univ. Library, Div. of Rare & Manuscripts Collections.

Landis, William E. & Chandler, Robin L. Archives & the Digital Library. 2007. (ENG., Illus.). 286p. 125.00 (978-0-7890-3437-3(9)); per. 77.00 (978-0-7890-3438-0(7)) Routledge.

McIlwaine, H. r. Official Letters of the Governor of the State of Virginia V3: The Letters of Thomas Nelson & Benjamin Harrison, June 7, 1781-February 27 1783. McIlwaine, H. R., ed. 2011. 524p. 60.95 (978-1-258-04820-4(5)) Literary Licensing, LLC.

McIlwaine, H. r. & McIlwaine, H. R. Official Letters of the Governor of the State of Virginia V1, Letters of Patrick Henry, July 1, 1776 to June 1 1778. 2011. 420p. 54.95 (978-1-258-04900-3(7)) Literary Licensing, LLC.

—Official Letters of the Governor of the State of Virginia V2, Letters of Thomas Jefferson, June 1, 1779 to June 3 1781. 2011. 578p. 63.95 (978-1-258-04901-0(5)) Literary Licensing, LLC.

Miller, Cynthia. Managing Congressional Collections. 2008. (978-1-931666-29-9(6)) Scarecrow Pr., Inc.

National Archives: Advisory Committees & Their Effectiveness: Hearing Before the Subcommittee on Information Policy, Census, & National Archives of the Committee on Oversight & Government Reform, House of Representatives, One Hundred Eleventh Congress, First Session, October 20, 2009. 2009. iii, 77p. (978-0-16-085200-8(5), 552-070-40553-4) United States Government Printing Office.

National Archives Staff. Discovering the Civil War. Barry, Sharon, ed. 2010. (Illus.). 208p. 44.95 (978-1-904832-91-1(1)) Giles, D. Ltd. GBR. Dist: Antique Collectors' Club.

—Our Documents: 100 Milestone Documents from the National Archives. 2006. (ENG., Illus.). 256p. (YA). per. 24.95 (978-0-19-530959-1(6)) Oxford Univ. Pr., Inc.

Pacifico, Michele F. & Wilsted, Thomas. Archival & Special Collections Facilities: Guidelines for Archivists, Librarians, Architects, & Engineers. 2009. (978-1-931666-31-2(8)) Scarecrow Pr., Inc.

Pleasants, J. Hall. CD: Archives of Maryland, LVI: Proceedings & Acts of the General Assembly of Maryland, 1758-1761. 2008. cd-rom 19.95 (978-0-7884-4541-5(3)) Heritage Bks.

Ritzenthaler, Mary Lynn. Preserving Archives & Manuscripts. 2nd ed. 2010. (978-1-931666-32-9(6)) Society of American Archivists.

Rosenow, Ty. Myths Unveiled: the Social History of the Evergreen State College. 2009. 110p. pap. 39.95 (978-0-557-09402-8(X)) Lulu Enterprises Inc.

Slay, David H. Georgia Civil War Manuscript Collections: An Annotated Bibliography. 2011. (ENG.). 296p. (C). 100.00 (978-0-8173-1744-7(9)) Univ. of Alabama Pr.

Slay, David Henson. Georgia Civil War Manuscripts Collections: An Annotated Bibliography. 2011. (978-0-8173-8570-5(3)) Univ. of Alabama Pr.

Stewart, Phillip W., compiled by. America's Film Vault: A Reference Guide to the Motion Pictures Held by the U. S. National Archives. 2009. 325p. (ENG.). 44.95 (978-0-9793243-5-2(1)); pap. 39.95 (978-0-9793243-0-7(0)) PMS Pr.

Taubman, Lowell. Marley Blog III. 2009. 446p. pap. 33.06 (978-0-557-09013-6(X)) Lulu Enterprises Inc.

Taylor, John E. Preliminary Inventory of the Records of the Chiefs of Arms: Record Group 177. 2007. pap. 10.00 (978-0-7884-3649-9(X)) Heritage Bks.

Van Tyne, Claude Halstead. The Archives of the Government of the United States in Washington. 215p. reprint ed. 98.00 (978-0-7222-7020-2(8)) Library Reprints, Inc.

Wilkie, Everett C. Guide to Security Considerations & Practices for Rare Book, Manuscript, & Special Collection Libraries. 2011. (978-0-8389-9338-5(9)); pap. (978-0-8389-8592-2(0)); E-Book (978-0-8389-9337-8(0)) Assn. of College & Research Libraries.

Wilsted, Thomas. Planning New & Remodeled Archival Facilities. 2007. (978-1-931666-25-1(3)) Scarecrow Pr., Inc.

Wosh, Peter J., intro. Waldo Gifford Leland & the Origins of the American Archival Profession. 2011. (978-1-931666-40-4(7)) Scarecrow Pr., Inc.

Zamon, Christina. The Lone Arranger: Succeeding in a Small Repository. 2012. (978-1-931666-41-1(5)) Scarecrow Pr., Inc.

ARCHONS

Bullard, Roger A. The Hypostasis of the Archons: The Coptic Text with Translation & Commentary. (Patristische Texte und Studien Ser.). (ENG.). XII, 132p. 210.00 (978-3-11-187907-9(0)) De Gruyter, Walter Inc.

ARCTIC (STEAMSHIP)

American Society of Mechanical Engineers Staff, ed. Proceedings Offshore Mechanics & Arctic Engineering Offshore Technology Symposium: Part A. 524p. 85.00 (978-0-7918-0130-7(6)) ASME Pr.

ARCTIC EXPEDITIONS

see Arctic Regions—Discovery and Exploration

ARCTIC FAUNA

see Zoology—Arctic Regions

ARCTIC FLORA

see Botany—Arctic Regions

ARCTIC OCEAN

Johnsen, Geir, et al, eds. Ecosystem Barents Sea. 2009. 587p. 99.00 (978-82-519-2461-0(8)) Tapir Forlag NOR. Dist: International Specialized Bk. Services.

Jones, Tristan. Ice! 2008. (ENG.). 288p. pap. 16.95 (978-1-57409-273-8(1)) Sheridan Hse., Inc.

Linder, Chris. Science on Ice: Four Polar Expeditions. 2011. (ENG., Illus.). 288p. 40.00 (978-0-226-48247-7(2)) Univ. of Chicago Pr.

Marchenko, Nataliya. Russian Arctic Seas: Navigational conditions & Accidents. 2012. (RUS & ENG., Illus.). xxii, 274p. 129.00 (978-3-642-22124-8(6), 3642221246) Springer.

Stein, R. Arctic Ocean Sediments: Processes, Proxies, & Paleoenvironment. 2008. (Developments in Marine Geology Ser.: 2). (ENG.). 608p. 150.00 (978-0-444-52018-0(X), Elsevier Science) Elsevier Science & Technology Bks.

Vetrov, Alexander & Romankevich, Evgeny. Carbon Cycle in the Russian Arctic Seas. 2010. (ENG., Illus.). x, 332p. pap. 169.00 (978-3-642-05991-9(0), 3642059910) Springer.

ARCTIC PEOPLES

see also Chukchi; Eskimos; Evenki (Asian People); Kamchadals; Khanty Mansi; Sami (European People)

Bjerregaard, Peter. Health Transitions in Arctic Populations. Young, T. Kue, ed. 2008. (ENG., Illus.). 496p. pap. (978-0-8020-9401-8(5)) Univ. of Toronto Pr.

Bruemmer, Fred. Arctic Visions: Pictures from a Vanished World. 2009. (ENG., Illus.). 280p. 40.00 (978-1-55470-092-9(2)) Key Porter Bks. CAN. Dist: Perseus-PGW.

Brumbach, Hetty Jo, ed. & tr. Circumpolar Lives & Livelihood: A Comparative Ethnoarchaeology of Gender & Subsistence. 2008. (ENG., Illus.). 332p. pap. 24.95 (978-0-8032-2078-2(2)) Univ. of Nebraska Pr.

Carpenter, Edmund, ed. Upside Down: Arctic Realities. 2011. (ENG., Illus.). 232p. 50.00 (978-0-300-16938-6(8)) Yale Univ. Pr.

Creery, Ian, et al. Polar Peoples: Native Inhabitants of the Far North. (Orig.). (C). pap. 24.95 (978-1-873194-51-5(X)) Minority Rights Pubns. GBR. Dist: Paul & Co. Pubs. Consortium, Inc.

Ehrlich, Gretel. In the Empire of Ice: Encounters in a Changing Landscape. 2010. (Illus.). 320p. 28.00 (978-1-4262-0574-3(0), National Geographic) National Geographic Society.

Kantner, Seth. Shopping for Porcupine: A Life in Arctic Alaska. (ENG., Illus.). 256p. 2009. pap. 19.95 (978-1-57131-311-9(7)) 2008. 28.00 (978-1-57131-301-0(X)) Milkweed Editions.

King, Alexander D. Living with Koryak Traditions: Playing with Culture in Siberia. 2011. (ENG., Illus.). 348p. pap. 35.00 (978-0-8032-3509-0(7)) Univ. of Nebraska Pr.

Nuttall, Mark. Pipeline Dreams: People, Environment, & the Arctic Energy Frontier. 2011. 200p. pap. 39.95 (978-87-91563-86-7(0)) IWGIA DNK. Dist: Transaction Pubs.

Parry, Bruce & Lewis-Jones, Huw. Arctic: A Journey Around the Arctic Circle to Explore the Lives of People in a Rapidly Changing World. 2012. (ENG., Illus.). 272p. 29.95 (978-1-84486-130-9(9), Conway Maritime Pr.) Anova Bks. GBR. Dist: Sterling Publishing Co., Inc.

Shephard, Roy J. & Rode, Andris. The Health Consequences Of 'Modernisation' Evidence from Circumpolar Peoples. 2008. (Cambridge Studies in Biological & Evolutionary Anthropology Ser.). (ENG., Illus.). 324p. pap. 61.00 (978-0-521-06556-6(9)) Cambridge Univ. Pr.

Sivertsen, Nina. Circumpolar Nursing. 2010. 132p. pap. (978-3-8383-4079-1(5)) Lambert Academic Publishing.

Stuckenberger, Nicole, ed. Thin Ice: Inut Traditions Within a Changing Environment. 2007. (Illus.). 80p. pap. 24.95 (978-0-944722-33-6(4)) Hood Museum of Art.

Turk, Jon. The Raven's Gift: A Scientist, a Shaman, & Their Remarkable Journey Through the Siberian Wilderness. 2010. (ENG., Illus.). 336p. 27.99 (978-0-312-54021-0(3)) St. Martin's Pr.

Vitebsky, Piers. The Reindeer People: Living with Animals & Spirits in Siberia. 2006. (ENG., Illus.). 496p. pap. 26.95 (978-0-618-77357-2(6), Mariner Bks.) Houghton Mifflin Harcourt Trade & Reference Pubs.

Westerdahl, Christer, ed. A Circumpolar Reappraisal: The Legacy of Gutorm Gjessing (1906-1979) 2010. (Bar S Ser.). (ENG., Illus.). 378p. (C). pap. 165.00 (978-1-4073-0696-4(0)) British Archaeological Reports Ltd. GBR. Dist: Brown, David Bk. Co., The.

Young, T. Kue & Bjerregaard, Peter, eds. Health Transitions in Arctic Populations. 2008. (ENG., Illus.). 496p. (978-0-8020-9109-3(1)) Univ. of Toronto Pr.

ARCTIC REGIONS

see also North Pole; Northeast Passage; Northwest Passage

American Society of Mechanical Engineers, Ocean, Offshore, and Arctic Engineering Division Staff, contrib. by. Proceedings of the ASME 29th International Conference on Ocean, Offshore & Arctic Engineering — 2010: Presented at 29th International Conference on Ocean, Offshore & Arctic Engineering: June 6-11, 2010, Shanghai, China. 2010. (Illus.). (978-0-7918-4912-5(0)); (978-0-7918-4911-8(2)); (978-0-7918-4910-1(4)); (978-0-7918-4909-5(0)); (978-0-7918-4913-2(9)); (978-0-7918-4914-9(7)) American Society of Mechanical Engineers, The.

Anderson, Alun. After the Ice: Life, Death, & Geopolitics in the New Arctic. 2009. (ENG.). 272p. 26.99 (978-0-06-157907-3(6)) Smithsonian Institution Pr.

Barrow, John. Voyages of Discovery & Research within the Arctic Regions, from the Year 1818 to the Present Time. 2011. (Cambridge Library Collection - Travel & Exploration Ser.). (ENG., Illus.). 564p. pap. 39.99 (978-1-108-03113-4(7)) Cambridge Univ. Pr.

Beechey, Frederick William. Narrative of a Voyage to the Pacific & Beering's Strait. 2009. 406p. pap. (978-0-217-26148-7(5)) Books LLC.

Belcher, Edward. The Last of the Arctic Voyages: Being a Narrative of the Expedition in H. M. S. Assistance, under the Command of Captain Sir Edward Belcher, C. B. , in Search of Sir John Franklin, during the Years 1852-54. 2011. (Cambridge Library Collection - Travel & Exploration Ser.). (ENG.). 476p. pap. 35.99 (978-1-108-02889-9(6)); (Illus.). 452p. pap. 34.99 (978-1-108-02888-2(8)) Cambridge Univ. Pr.

Berkman, Paul Arthur. Environmental Security in the Arctic Ocean. 2012. (ENG., Illus.). 160p. (C). pap. 45.95 (978-0-85516-153-8(1)) Routledge.

Bernaerts, Arnd. Arctic Heats Up: Spitsbergen 1919 -1939. 2009. 116p. pap. 16.95 (978-1-4401-4087-7(1)) iUniverse, Inc.

Bjerregaard, Peter. Health Transitions in Arctic Populations. Young, T. Kue, ed. 2008. (ENG., Illus.). 496p. pap. (978-0-8020-9401-8(5)) Univ. of Toronto Pr.

Boas, Franz, et al, eds. The Jesup North Pacific Expedition: Publications, 27 vols., Vols.1-11, & Suppl. Album. (Illus.). reprint ed. 1764.00 (978-0-404-58100-8(5)) AMS Pr., Inc.

Brown, Richard. Voyage of the Iceberg: The Story of the Iceberg that Sank the Titanic. 3rd ed. 2012. (ENG.). 156p. (C). pap. 19.95 (978-1-4594-0087-0(9)) Lorimer, James & Co., Ltd., Pubs. CAN. Dist: Casemate Pubs. & Bk. Distributors, LLC.

Byers, Michael. Who Owns the Arctic? Understanding Sovereignty Disputes in the North, 1 vol. 2010. (ENG., Illus.). 192p. pap. 17.95 (978-1-55365-499-5(4)) D&M Pubs. Inc. CAN. Dist: Perseus-PGW.

Calahan, Thomas R. The Arctic Observing Network. 2009. (Illus.). viii, 130p. 69.00 (978-1-60692-847-9(3)) Nova Science Pubs., Inc.

Campbell, Bruce D. Where the High Winds Blow. 2011. 232p. 46.95 (978-1-258-01190-1(5)) Literary Licensing, LLC.

Carpenter, Edmund, ed. Upside Down: Arctic Realities. 2011. (ENG., Illus.). 232p. 50.00 (978-0-300-16938-6(8)) Yale Univ. Pr.

Climate Change & the Arctic: New Frontiers of National Security: Hearing Before the Committee on Foreign Affairs, House of Representatives, One Hundred Eleventh Congress, First Session, March 25, 2009. 2009. (Illus.). iii, 75p. (978-0-16-083293-2(4), 552-070-39121-5) United States Government Printing Office.

Committee on the Scientific Value of Arctic Sea Ice Imagery Derived Products, et al. Scientific Value of Arctic Sea Ice Imagery Derived Products. 2009. (ENG.). 48p. pap. 15.00 (978-0-309-13763-8(2)) National Academies Pr.

De La Lez, Mireilla, photos by. Vanishing World: The Endangered Arctic. 2007. (ENG., Illus.). 270p. 40.00 (978-0-8109-9464-5(X)) Abrams.

DeWeaver, Eric T., et al. Arctic Sea Ice Decline: Observations, Projections, Mechanisms, & Implications. 2008. (978-0-87590-445-0(9)) American Geophysical Union.

Francis, Gavin. True North: Travels in Arctic Europe. 2nd ed. 2009. (ENG., Illus.). 304p. pap. 18.00 (978-1-84697-130-3(6)) BirlinnPolygon GBR. Dist: Interlink Publishing Group, Inc.

Franklin, John. Narrative of a Journey to the Shores of the Polar Sea in the years 1819-20-21-22, Vol. 2. l.t. ed. 2007. (ENG.). 250p. pap. 22.99 (978-1-4264-9909-8(4)) BiblioBazaar.

—Narrative of a Journey to the Shores of the Polar Sea in the years 1819-20-21-22 Volume 2. 2007. (ENG.). 226p. pap. 20.99 (978-1-4264-9528-1(5)) BiblioBazaar.

Freuchen, Peter. Arctic Adventure: My Life in the Frozen North. 2011. 478p. 57.95 (978-1-258-01393-6(2)) Literary Licensing, LLC.

Frolov, Ivan E., et al. Climate Change in Eurasian Arctic Shelf Seas: Centennial Ice Cover Observations. 2009. (Springer Praxis Books / Geophysical Sciences Ser.). (ENG., Illus.). 166p. 179.00 (978-3-540-85874-4(1)) Springer.

Gilder, William H. Schwatka's Search. 2008. 256p. 25.99 (978-0-554-33023-5(7)) 2008. 256p. 28.99 (978-0-554-23720-6(2)) 2007. (ENG.). 220p. pap. 20.99 (978-1-4264-4953-6(4)) 2007. (ENG.). 254p. pap. 23.99 (978-1-4264-5254-3(3)) BiblioBazaar.

—Schwatka's Search. 2007. (ENG.). 152p. per. (978-1-4068-6201-0(0)) Echo Library.

—Schwatka's Search: Sledging in the Arctic in Quest of the Franklin Records. 2007. 204p. per. (978-1-4065-4452-7(3)) Dodo Pr.

—Schwatka's Search: Sledging in the Arctic in Quest of the Franklin Records. 2010. 176p. 30.36 (978-1-169-27563-8(X)); pap. 18.36 (978-1-162-68323-2(6)); 37.95 (978-1-161-45188-7(9)) Kessinger Publishing, LLC.

Ginsberg, William B. Printed Maps of Scandinavia & the Arctic, 1482-1601. 2006. (Illus.). 232p. 95.00 (978-0-9787900-0-4(6)); 225.00 (978-0-9787900-1-1(4)) Septentrionalium Pr.

Hall, Charles Francis. Life with the Esquimaux: The Narrative of Captain Charles Francis Hall of the Whaling Barque George Henry from the 29th May, 1860, to the 13th September 1862. 2011. (Cambridge Library Collection - Anthropology Ser.). (ENG., Illus.). 346p. pap. 28.99 (978-1-108-04138-6(6)) Cambridge Univ. Pr.

—Life with the Esquimaux: The Narrative of Captain Charles Francis Hall of the Whaling Barquenbsp;George Henry from the 29th May, 1860, to the 13th September 1862. 2011. (Cambridge Library Collection - Anthropology Ser.). (ENG., Illus.). 370p. pap. 29.99 (978-1-108-04139-3(6)) Cambridge Univ. Pr.

The High Arctic Relocation: A Report on the 1953-55 Relocation. 190p. pap. (978-0-660-15544-9(3)) Canadian Government Publishing.

Honneland, Geir. International Cooperation & Arctic Governance: Regime Effectiveness & Northern Region Building. Stokke, Olav Schram, ed. 2007. (Routledge Advances in International Relations & Global Politics Ser.). (Illus.). XVIII, 206p. (C). 150.00 (978-0-415-39934-0(3)) Routledge.

Hoogensen, Gunhild & Bazely, Dawn, eds. Environmental Change & Human Security in the Arctic. 2012. (Earthscan Research Editions Ser.). (ENG.). 192p. 127.00 (978-1-84407-549-2(4)) Earthscan LLC.

Jackson, C. Ian. The Artic Journals of William Scoresby the Younger (1789-157) Vol. 3: The Voyages of 1817, 1818 & 1820, 3 vols. 2009. (Hakluyt Society, Third Ser.). (Illus.). 288p. 99.95 (978-0-904180-95-4(6)) Hakluyt Society GBR. Dist: Ashgate Publishing Co.

Jackson, C. Ian, ed. Arctic Journals of William Scoresby the Younger (1789-1857) Vol. 2: The Voyages of 1814, 1815, 1816, 3 vols. 2008. (Hakluyt Society, Third Ser.). (Illus.). 346p. 99.95 (978-0-904180-92-3(1)) Hakluyt Society GBR. Dist: Ashgate Publishing Co.

Jakobsson, Sverrir, ed. Images of the North: Histories - Identities - Ideas. 2009. (Illus.). 292p. pap. 84.00 (978-90-420-2528-8(X)) Rodopi.

Johansen, Hjalmar. With Nansen in the North: A Record of the Fram Expedition In 1893-96. Braekstad, H. L., tr. 2011. (Cambridge Library Collection - Travel & Exploration Ser.). (ENG., Illus.). 394p. pap. 31.99 **(978-1-108-04150-8(7))** Cambridge Univ. Pr.

Kane, Elisha, abr. Adrift in the Arctic Ice Pack. 2009. (Military History Ser.). (ENG.). 412p. pap. 25.95 (978-1-4290-2178-4(0)) Applewood Bks.

Keskitalo, E. C. H. Climate Change & Globalization in the Arctic: An Integrated Approach to Vulnerability Assessment. 2008. (ENG., Illus.). 272p. (C). 136.00 (978-1-84407-528-7(1)) Routledge.

Koenigk, Torben. Arctic Climate Variability. 2007. 132p. per. (978-3-8364-0802-8(3)) VDM Verlag Dr. Mueller e.K.

Koivurova, Timo, et al. Climate Governance in the Arctic. Koivurova, Timo et al, eds. 2009. (Environment & Policy Ser.). (ENG., Illus.). xx, 452p. 179.00 (978-1-4020-9541-2(4)) Springer.

Kraska, James, ed. Arctic Security in an Age of Climate Change. 2011. (ENG., Illus.). 272p. 90.00 **(978-1-107-00660-7(0))** Cambridge Univ. Pr.

Krupnik, Igor, et al. Smithsonian at the Poles: Contributions to International Polar Year Science. 2009. pap. (978-0-9788460-1-5(X)) Smithsonian Institution Scholarly Pr.

Lamson, Cynthia & Zwaag, David L. van der, eds. Transit Management in the Northwest Passage: Problems & Prospects. 2009. (Studies in Polar Research Ser.). (ENG., Illus.). 332p. pap. 61.00 (978-0-521-09337-8(6)) Cambridge Univ. Pr.

Leacock, Stephen. Adventurers of the Far North. 2009. 58p. pap. (978-1-151-73391-7(1)) Books LLC.

—Adventurers of the Far North. 2009. (Illus.). 92p. pap. (978-1-4099-9283-7(7)) Dodo Pr.

—Adventurers of the Far North. (Chronicles of Canada Ser.). 152p. reprint ed. 88.00 (978-0-7222-6772-1(X)) Library Reprints, Inc.

—Adventures of the Far North. (Chronicles of Canada Ser.). 152p. reprint ed. 88.00 (978-0-7222-6793-6(2)) Library Reprints, Inc.

Lemke, Peter & Jacobi, Hans-Werner, eds. Arctic Climate Change: The ACSYS Decade & Beyond. 2011. (Atmospheric & Oceanographic Sciences Library). (ENG., Illus.). xiv, 464p. 179.00 **(978-94-007-2026-8(2)**, 9400720262) Springer.

Leslie, Alexander. The Arctic Voyages of Adolf Erik Nordenskiöld, 1858-1879. 2011. (Cambridge Library Collection - Travel & Exploration Ser.). (ENG., Illus.). 478p. pap. 35.99 **(978-1-108-04148-5(5))** Cambridge Univ. Pr.

Markham, Albert Hastings. The Great Frozen Sea: A Personal Narrative of the Voyage of the Alert during the Arctic Expedition Of 1875-6. 2011. (Cambridge Library Collection - Travel & Exploration Ser.). (ENG., Illus.). 490p. pap. 35.99 **(978-1-108-04149-2(3))** Cambridge Univ. Pr.

Markham, Clements R. The Threshold of the Unknown Region. 2009. 392p. 38.99 (978-1-117-28374-6(7)) BiblioBazaar.

Martin, James, photos by. Planet Ice: A Climate for Change. 2009. (ENG., Illus.). 176p. 39.95 (978-1-59485-085-1(2), Braided River) Mountaineers Bks., The.

McGhee, Robert. The Last Imaginary Place: A Human History of the Arctic World. 2007. (Illus.). 296p. per. 18.00 (978-0-226-50089-8(6)) Univ. of Chicago Pr.

M'Clintock, Francis Leopold. In the Arctic Seas a Narrative of the Discovery of the Fate of Sir John Franklin & His Companions by Captain M'Clintock. 2006. 452p. per. 29.99 (978-1-4255-5006-6(1)) MPublishing.

Mikkelsen, Aslaug & Langhelle, Oluf, eds. Arctic Oil & Gas: Sustainability at Risk? 2008. (Routledge Explorations in Environmental Economics Ser.). (ENG., Illus.). 408p. (C). 180.00 (978-0-415-44330-2(X)) Routledge.

Müller, Andreas, ed. Arctic Perspective Cahier No. 1. 2011. (ENG., Illus.). 148p. 30.00 (978-3-7757-2679-5(9)) Hatje Cantz Verlag GmbH & Co KG DEU. Dist: D.A.P./Distributed Art Pubs.

Nansen, Fridtjof. Farthest North: Being the Record of a Voyage of Exploration of the Ship Fram, 1893-96, & of a Fifteen Months' Sleigh Journey. 2011. (Cambridge Library Collection - Travel & Exploration Ser.). (ENG.). 840p. pap. 53.00 (978-1-108-03093-9(9)); (Illus.). 652p. pap. 45.00 (978-1-108-03092-2(0)) Cambridge Univ. Pr.

—The First Crossing of Greenland. Gepp, Hubert Majendie, tr. 2011. (Cambridge Library Collection - Travel & Exploration Ser.). (ENG., Illus.). 564p. pap. 39.99 (978-1-108-03109-7(9)); 542p. pap. 39.99 **(978-1-108-03110-3(2))** Cambridge Univ. Pr.

Nihoul, Jacques C. J. & Kostianoi, A. G. Influence of Climate Change on the Changing Arctic & Sub-Arctic Conditions. 2009. (NATO Science for Peace & Security Series C: Environmental Security Ser.). (ENG., Illus.). xii, 232p. 219.00 (978-1-4020-9458-3(2)); pap. 99.00 (978-1-4020-9459-0(0)) Springer.

Nordenskiold, A. E. Voyage of the Vega Vol I. 2006. 536p. per. (978-1-4067-2809-5(8), Hesperides Pr.) Read Bks.

Ørbæk, Jon Borre. Arctic Alpine Ecosystems & People in a Changing Environment. 2006. (ENG., Illus.). xxviii, 434p. 239.00 (978-3-540-48512-4(0), 3540485120) Springer.

Osborn, Sherard. Stray Leaves from an Arctic Journal, or, Eighteen Months in the Polar Regions, in Search of Sir John Franklin's Expedition, in the Years 1850-51 / By. 2006. 332p. per. 23.99 (978-1-4255-3295-6(0)) MPublishing.

Parry, Edward. Memoirs of Rear-Admiral Sir W. Edward Parry. 2011. (Cambridge Library Collection - Travel & Exploration Ser.). (ENG., Illus.). 430p. pap. 32.99 **(978-1-108-04137-9(X))** Cambridge Univ. Pr.

Parry, William E. Journal of Voyage of Discovery to Arctic Regions. (Shorey Historical Ser.). 118p. reprint ed. pap. 10.00 (978-0-8466-0046-6(3), S46) Shorey's Bookstore.

Potter, Russell A. Arctic Spectacles: The Frozen North in Visual Culture, 1818-1875. 2007. (Illus.). 258p. 50.00 (978-0-295-98679-1(4)); pap. 35.00 (978-0-295-98680-7(8)) Univ. of Washington Pr.

Przybylak, Rajmund. Variability of Air Temperature & Atmospheric Precipitation in the Arctic. Kearns, John, tr. 2010. (Atmospheric & Oceanographic Sciences Library). 352p. pap. 149.00 (978-90-481-6153-9(3), 9048161533) Springer.

Rawat, Rajiv. Circumpolar Health Atlas. Young, T. Kue, ed. 2012. (ENG., Illus.). 198p. **(978-1-4426-4456-4(7))** Univ. of Toronto Pr.

Sale, Richard, photos by. The Arctic: The Complete Story. 2008. (ENG., Illus.). 640p. 60.00 (978-0-7112-2707-1(1)) Lincoln, Frances Ltd. GBR. Dist: Perseus-PGW.

Sarytschew, Gawrila. Account of A Voyage of Discovery to the. 2006. pap. 21.95 (978-1-4286-5077-0(6)) Kessinger Publishing, LLC.

Serreze, Mark C., et al. The Arctic Climate System. 2009. (Cambridge Atmospheric & Space Science Ser.). (ENG., Illus.). 404p. pap. 60.00 (978-0-521-11600-8(7)) Cambridge Univ. Pr.

Smolka, H. P. Forty Thousand Against the Arctic. 2006. 364p. per. (978-1-4067-2916-0(7), Hesperides Pr.) Read Bks.

Stefansson, Vilhjalmur. My Life with the Eskimo (New Edition) 2007. 676p. per. 42.45 (978-1-59462-651-7(0), 688, Book Jungle) Standard Pubns., Inc.

—Unsolved Mysteries of the Arctic. pap. 12.95 (978-1-878100-95-5(5)) Todd Communications.

Stefansson, Vilhjalmur & Schwartz, Julia Augusta. Northward Ho! an Account of the Far North & Its People. 2011. 194p. 42.95 **(978-1-258-03685-0(1))** Literary Licensing, LLC.

Stuckenberger, Nicole, ed. Thin Ice: Inut Traditions Within a Changing Environment. 2007. (Illus.). 80p. pap. 24.95 (978-0-944722-33-6(4)) Hood Museum of Art.

Sturm, Matthew. Apun: The Arctic Snow. 2009. (ENG., Illus.). 80p. pap., tchr. ed., instr.'s gde. ed. 19.95 (978-1-60223-070-5(6)) Univ. of Alaska Pr.

Swarson, Brandon D. Changes in the Arctic: Background & Issues. 2010. 130.00 (978-1-61728-882-1(9)) Nova Science Pubs., Inc.

Vaughn, Richard & Vaughan, Richard. The Arctic: A History. 2008. (ENG., Illus.). 384p. 34.95 (978-0-7509-4651-3(2)) History Pr. Ltd.,The GBR. Dist: Independent Pubs. Group.

Young, T. Kue & Bjerregaard, Peter, eds. Health Transitions in Arctic Populations. 2008. (ENG., Illus.). 496p. (978-0-8020-9109-3(1)) Univ. of Toronto Pr.

ARCTIC REGIONS—DESCRIPTION AND TRAVEL

Althoff, William. Arctic Mission. 2011. (Illus.). 256p. 39.95 **(978-1-61251-010-1(8))** Naval Institute Pr.

Axelsson, Ragnar, photos by. Last Days of the Arctic. 2011. (ENG., Illus.). 272p. 75.00 (978-0-9555255-2-0(7)) Crymogea ehf. ISL. Dist: D.A.P./Distributed Art Pubs.

Decker, Julie & Princeton Architectural Press Staff. Modern North: Architecture on the Frozen Edge. 2010. (ENG., Illus.). 240p. 45.00 (978-1-56898-899-3(0)) Princeton Architectural Pr.

Doyle, Arthur Conan. Dangerous Work: The Diary of an Arctic Adventure. Lellenberg, Jon & Stashower, Daniel, eds. 2012. (Illus.). 368p. 35.00 **(978-0-226-00905-6(X))** Univ. of Chicago Pr.

Ermolaev, Aleksei. Arctic Scientist, Gulag Survivor: The Biography of Mikhail Mikhailovich Ermolaev, 1905-1991. 2009. (Northern Lights Ser.). (ENG., Illus.). 606p. pap. 46.95 (978-1-55238-256-1(7)) Univ. of Calgary Pr. CAN. Dist: Chicago Distribution Ctr.

Flowers, Pam. Alone Across the Arctic: One Woman's Epic Journey by Dog Team. rev. ed. 2011. (ENG., Illus.). 120p. pap. 12.95 (978-0-88240-836-1(4), Alaska Northwest Bks.) Graphic Arts Ctr. Publishing Co.

Grinnell, George James. Death on the Barrens: A True Story of Courage & Tragedy in the Canadian Arctic. 2010. (ENG., Illus.). 296p. pap. 17.95 (978-1-55643-882-0(6)) North Atlantic Bks.

Henson, Matthew A. A Negro Explorer at the North Pole. 2010. 230p. pap. 24.95 (978-0-557-36669-9(0)) Lulu Enterprises Inc.

Kobalenko, Jerry. Arctic Eden: Journeys Through the Changing High Arctic, 1 vol. 2010. (ENG., Illus.). 200p. 40.00 (978-1-55365-442-1(0), Greystone Bks.) D&M Pubs. Inc. CAN. Dist: Perseus-PGW.

Lynch, Wayne. Planet Arctic: Life at the Top of the World. 2010. (ENG., Illus.). 240p. 40.00 (978-1-55407-632-1(3)) Firefly Bks., Ltd.

Pitt, Michael D. Beyond the End of the Road: A Winter of Contentment North of the Arctic Circle. 2009. (ENG., Illus.). 338p. pap. 19.95 (978-1-897435-36-6(3)) Agio Publishing Hse. CAN. Dist: Lightning Source, Inc.

Schulz, Florian, photos by. To the Arctic. 2011. (ENG., Illus.). 204p. **(978-1-59485-487-3(4))** Mountaineers Bks., The.

Streever, Bill. Cold: Adventures in the World's Frozen Places. 2010. (ENG., Illus.). 320p. pap. 14.99 (978-0-316-04292-5(7), Back Bay Bks.) Little Brown & Co.

Sturm, Matthew. Finding the Arctic: History & Culture along a 2,500-Mile Snowmobile Journey from Alaska to Hudson's Bay. 2012. E-Book **(978-1-60223-164-1(8))**; (ENG., Illus.). 320p. pap. 24.95 **(978-1-60223-163-4(X))** Univ. of Alaska Pr.

Vermeer, Jan & Essen, Frieda van. Arctic. 2009. (ENG., Illus.). 300p. (978-90-78964-21-6(9), Thieme Art (Acc)) Antique Collectors' Club.

Wheeler, Sara. The Magnetic North: Notes from the Arctic Circle, 1 vol. (ENG.). 336p. 2012. pap. 15.00 **(978-0-374-53309-0(1)**, North Point Pr.) 2011. (Illus.). 26.00 (978-0-374-20013-8(0)) Farrar, Straus & Giroux.

ARCTIC REGIONS—DISCOVERY AND EXPLORATION

see also names of exploring expeditions

Abramson, Howard S. Hero in Disgrace: The True Discoverer of the North Pole, Frederick A. Cook. 2010. 288p. pap. 19.95 (978-1-4502-1123-9(2)) iUniverse, Inc.

Althoff, William F. Drift Station: Arctic Outposts of Superpower Science. 2007. (Illus.). 320p. 39.95 (978-1-57488-771-6(8)) Potomac Bks., Inc.

Anderson, William R. & Keith, Don. The Ice Diaries: The Untold Story of the Cold War's Most Daring Mission, 0 vols. 2008. 384p. 24.99 (978-0-7852-2759-5(8)) Nelson, Thomas Inc.

Armstrong, Alexander. A Personal Narrative of the Discovery of the North-West Passage: While in Search of the Expedition under Sir John Franklin. 2011. (Cambridge Library Collection - Travel & Exploration Ser.). (ENG., Illus.). 654p. pap. 45.00 **(978-1-108-03335-0(0))** Cambridge Univ. Pr.

Ballantyne, Robert Michael. The World of Ice: The Whaling Cruise of the Dolphin & the Advent. 2007. (ENG.). 224p. pap. 20.99 (978-1-4346-2276-1(2)); 248p. pap. 22.99 (978-1-4346-2334-8(3)) BiblioBazaar.

Barr, William. Arctic Hell-Ship: The Voyage of HMS Enterprise 1850-1855. 2007. (ENG., Illus.). 332p. 49.95 (978-0-88864-482-4(5)) Univ. of Alberta Pr. CAN. Dist: Michigan State Univ. Pr.

Barrow, John. A Chronological History of Voyages into the Arctic Regions: Undertaken Chiefly for the Purpose of Discovering a North-East, North-West, or Polar Passage between the Atlantic & Pacific. 2011. (Cambridge Library Collection - Travel & Exploration Ser.). (ENG., Illus.). 450p. pap. 32.99 (978-1-108-03083-0(1)) Cambridge Univ. Pr.

Bartlett, Robert A. The Log of Bob Bartlett: The True Story of Forty Years of Seafaring & Exploration. 420p. 2008. 49.95 (978-1-4366-8253-4(3)) 2007. (ENG.). per. 34.95 (978-1-4325-4612-0(0)) Kessinger Publishing, LLC.

Battersby, William. James Fitzjames: The Mystery Man of the Franklin Expedition. 2010. (ENG., Illus.). 224p. 35.00 (978-1-55488-781-1(X)) Dundurn CAN. Dist: Ingram Pub. Services.

Bockstoce, John R. Arctic Discoveries: Images from Voyages of Four Decades in the North. (Illus.). 144p. pap. (978-0-7735-2153-7(4)) McGill-Queen's Univ. Pr.

Brandt, Anthony. The Man Who Ate His Boots: The Tragic History of the Search for the Northwest Passage. 2011. (Illus.). 464p. pap. 16.95 (978-0-307-27656-8(2), Anchor) Knopf Doubleday Publishing Group.

Cavell, Janice & Noakes, Jeff. Acts of Occupation: Canada & Arctic Sovereignty, 1918-25. 2011. (ENG., Illus.). 348p. pap. 37.95 (978-0-7748-1868-1(9)) UBC Pr. CAN. Dist: Univ. of Washington Pr.

Davis-Fisch, Heather. Loss & Cultural Remains in Performance: The Ghosts of the Franklin Expedition. 2012. (Palgrave Studies in Theatre & Performance History Ser.). (ENG., Illus.). 240p. 85.00 **(978-0-230-34032-9(6))** Palgrave Macmillan.

Ehrlich, Gretel. In the Empire of Ice: Encounters in a Changing Landscape. 2010. (Illus.). 320p. 28.00 (978-1-4262-0574-3(0), National Geographic) National Geographic Society.

Emmerson, Charles. The Future History of the Arctic. 2010. (ENG., Illus.). 448p. 28.95 (978-1-58648-636-5(5)) PublicAffairs.

Faber. Infinite Ice Traversing the Arctic & the Alps from 1860 to the Present. 2009. (ENG.). 112p. 45.00 (978-3-7757-2253-7(X)) Hatje Cantz Verlag GmbH & Co KG DEU. Dist: D.A.P./Distributed Art Pubs.

France, Robert L. High Arctic Extreme Science: Environmental Research from the Trans-Ellesmere Island Ski Expedition. 2010. (ENG., Illus.). 167p. pap. 24.95 (978-0-9812434-0-5(1)) Green Frigate Bks.

Franklin, Jane & Elce, Erika Behrisch. As Affecting the Fate of My Absent Husband: Selected Letters of Lady Franklin Concerning the Search for the Lost Franklin Expedition, 1848-1860. 2009. (McGill-Queen's Native & Northern Ser.). (ENG., Illus.). 240p. (C). (978-0-7735-3479-7(2)) McGill-Queen's Univ. Pr.

Franklin, John. The Journey to the Polar Sea. 2008. 508p. 35.99 (978-0-554-24676-5(7)) 2006. (ENG.). 452p. pap. 28.99 (978-1-4264-7069-1(X)) 2007. 504p. pap. 31.99 (978-1-4264-7145-2(9)) BiblioBazaar.

—Thirty Years in the Arctic Regions; 2010. 488p. pap. 38.75 (978-1-145-85189-4(4)) BiblioBazaar.

—Thirty Years in the Arctic Regions: Or, the Adventures of Sir John Franklin. 2010. 486p. pap. 38.75 (978-1-143-15038-8(4)) BiblioBazaar.

—Thirty Years in the Arctic Regions: Or, the adventures of Sir John Franklin. 2010. (ENG.). 482p. pap. 38.75 (978-1-177-99041-7(5)) BiblioBazaar.

—Thirty Years in the Arctic Regions; a Narrative of the Explorations & Adventures of Sir John Franklin. 2006. 480p. per. 29.99 (978-1-4255-5328-9(1)) MPublishing.

—Thirty Years in the Arctic Regions; or, the Adventures of Sir John Franklin. 2009. 218p. pap. (978-1-150-52550-6(9)) Books LLC.

—Thirty Years in the Arctic Regions; or, the Adventures of Sir John Franklin. 2010. (Illus.). 182p. pap. 26.81 (978-1-154-87067-1(7)) General Bks. LLC.

Frolov, Ivan E. & Kornilov, N. A. Rossiiskie Issledovaniia Na Dreifuiushchikh Ldakh Arktiki. 2010. (RUS., Illus.). 624p. (978-5-98364-024-5(0)) Arkticeskij i Antarkticeskij Naucno-issledovatel'skij Institut.

Frolov, Ivan E., et al. The Arctic Basin: Results from the Russian Drifting Stations. 2010. (Springer Praxis Books / Geophysical Sciences Ser.). xxiv, 273p. pap. 239.00 (978-3-642-06328-2(4), 3642063284) Springer.

Gosch, C. C. A. Danish Arctic Expeditions, 1605 To 1620, 2 vols. 2008. (Illus.). 110.00 (978-1-57898-526-5(9)) Martino Publishing.

Gosch, C. C. A., ed. Danish Arctic Expeditions, 1605 to 1620: Volume 1, the Danish Expeditions to Greenland in 1605, 1606, And 1607: In Two Books. 2010. (Cambridge Library Collection - Travel & Exploration Ser.). (ENG., Illus.). 360p. pap. 28.99 (978-1-108-01292-8(2)) Cambridge Univ. Pr.

Hall, Doug. North Pole Tenderfoot: A Rookie Goes on a North Pole Expedition Following in Admiral Peary's Footsteps. 2009. (ENG.). 224p. pap. 17.95 (978-1-57860-328-2(5)) Clerisy Pr.

Hayes, Isaac Israel. An Arctic Boat Journey: In the Autumn of 1854. 2006. 436p. per. 26.99 (978-1-4255-4767-7(2)) MPublishing.

—The Open Polar Sea: A Narrative of a Voyage of Discovery Towards the North Pole, in the Schooner United States. 2007. 490p. 53.95 (978-0-548-16378-8(2)); 492p. per. 38.95 (978-1-4304-6002-2(4)) Kessinger Publishing, LLC.

—The Open Polar Sea: A Narrative of a Voyage of Discovery Towards the North Pole, in the Schooner United States. 2006. 500p. per. 29.99 (978-1-4255-5529-0(2)); per. 29.99 (978-1-4255-5546-7(2)) MPublishing.

Henighan, Tom. Vilhjalmur Stefansson: Arctic Adventurer. 2009. (Quest Biography Ser.). (ENG., Illus.). 216p. pap. 19.99 (978-1-55002-874-4(X)) Dundurn CAN. Dist: Ingram Pub. Services.

Henson, Matthew A. Matthew A. Henson's Historic Arctic Journey: The Classic Account of One of the World's Greatest Black Explorers. 100th ed. 2009. (ENG., Illus.). 224p. 19.95 (978-1-59921-308-8(7), Lyons Pr.) Globe Pequot Pr., The.

—A Negro Explorer at the North Pole. 2010. 230p. pap. 25.75 (978-1-171-05134-3(4)) 2009. 230p. 32.99 (978-1-117-65337-2(4)) 2009. 230p. pap. 20.99 (978-1-117-65339-6(0), BiblioLife) 2009. 230p. pap. 24.75 (978-1-117-65338-9(2)) 2008. 148p. 21.99 (978-0-554-38151-0(6)) 2008. 148p. 24.99 (978-0-554-28848-2(6)) 2007. 130p. pap. 18.99 (978-1-4346-6400-6(7)) 2007. 146p. pap. 19.99 (978-1-4346-6401-3(5)) BiblioBazaar.

—A Negro Explorer at the North Pole. 2007. (Illus.). 132p. per. (978-1-4065-5374-1(3)) Dodo Pr.

—A Negro Explorer at the North Pole. 2010. (Illus.). 68p. pap. 20.00 (978-1-153-75789-8(3)) General Bks. LLC.

Henson, Matthew A. & Henson, Matthew Alexander. Henson at the North Pole. 2008. (Dover Books on Travel, Adventure Ser.). (ENG., Illus.). 128p. pap. 7.95 (978-0-486-45472-6(X)) Dover Pubns., Inc.

Henson, Matthew Alexander. A Negro Explorer at the North Pole. 2010. 76p. pap. 17.50 (978-1-152-74334-2(1)) General Bks. LLC.

Henson, Matthew Alexander, et al. A Negro Explorer at the North Pole. 2010. (ENG.). 238p. pap. 26.75 (978-1-176-43965-8(0)) BiblioBazaar.

Hern, Frances. Arctic Explorers: In Search of the Northwest Passage, 1 vol. 2010. (Amazing Stories Ser.). (ENG., Illus.). 144p. pap. (978-1-926613-29-1(5)) Heritage Hse.

Kane, Elisha Kent. Arctic Explorations: The Second Grinnell Expedition in Search of Sir John Franklin, 1853, '54, '55. by Elisha Kent Kane ... Illustrated by Upwards Of. 2006. 496p. per. 29.99 (978-1-4255-5507-8(1)) MPublishing.

—Arctic Explorations: The Second Grinnell Expedition in Search of Sir John Franklin, 1853,54,55 / by Elisha Kent Kane ... Illustrated by Upwards of Th. 2006. 492p. pap. 29.99 (978-1-4255-5455-2(5)); per. 29.99 (978-1-4255-5454-5(7)) MPublishing.

Kavenna, Joanna. The Ice Museum: In Search of the Lost Land of Thule. 2007. (ENG.). 304p. (gr. 12-18). 15.00 (978-0-14-303846-7(X), Penguin (Non-Classics)) Penguin Group (USA) Inc.

Kennedy, William. A Short Narrative of the Second Voyage of the Prince Albert , in Search of Sir John Franklin. 2006. (Illus.). 202p. 85.00 (978-1-57898-587-6(0)) Martino Publishing.

Kent Kane. Arctic Explorations in the Years 1853,'54,'55: The second Grinnell expedition in search of Sir John Franklin Vol 1. 2007. 500p. per. (978-1-905748-51-8(5)) Rediscovery Bks.

—Arctic Explorations in the Years 1853,'54,'55: The second Grinnell expedition in search of Sir John Franklin Vol 2. 2007. 488p. per. (978-1-905748-52-5(3)) Rediscovery Bks.

Krear, H. Robert. Four Seasons North: Exploration & Research in the Arctic & Subarctic. 2006. (Illus.). xv, 368p. 15.95 (978-0-533-15336-7(0)) Vantage Pr., Inc.

Lainema, Matti & Nurminen, Juha. A History of Arctic Exploration: Discovery, Adventure & Endurance at the Top of the World. 2010. (ENG., Illus.). 352p. 60.00 (978-1-84486-069-2(8), Conway Maritime Pr.) Anova Bks. GBR. Dist: Sterling Publishing Co., Inc.

A

MacMillan, Donald B. How Peary Reached the Pole: The Personal Story of His Assistant. 2008. (ENG., Illus.). 368p. (C). pap. *(978-0-7735-3450-6(4))* McGill-Queen's Univ. Pr.

McGoogan, Ken. Race to the Polar Sea: The Heroic Adventures of Elisha Kent Kane. 2009. (ENG.). 320p. pap. 15.95 *(978-1-58243-532-9(4)*, Counterpoint Pr.) Basic Bks. GBR. Dist: Perseus-PGW.

McGoogan, Kenneth. Race to the Polar Sea: The Heroic Adventures of Elisha Kent Kane. 2008. (ENG., Illus.). 320p. 28.00 *(978-1-58243-440-7(9)*, Counterpoint Pr.) Basic Bks. GBR. Dist: Perseus-PGW.

Moller, Peter Ulf & Okhotina-Lind, N. A. Until Death Do Us Part: The Travels of Anna & Vitus Bering. 2007. (University of Alaska Press - Rasmuson Library Historic Translation Ser.). (GER & ENG., Illus.). 176p. 29.95 *(978-1-889963-94-5(1))* Univ. of Alaska Pr.

Mudge, Zachariah Atwell. Arctic Heroes: Facts & Incidents of Arctic Explorations from the Earliest Voyages to the Discovery of the Fate of Sir John Franklin / by Z. A. Mudge. 2006. 316p. per. 23.99 *(978-1-4255-3072-3(9))* MPublishing.

—North-Pole Voyages. 2006. 396p. per. 26.99 *(978-1-4255-4201-6(8))* MPublishing.

Muir, John. The Cruise of the Corwin. Bade, William Frederic, ed. 2008. (Illus.). 224p. (Orig.). pap. *(978-1-4099-4180-4(9))* Dodo Pr.

Nansen, Fridtjof. Farthest North. 2009. 278p. pap. *(978-0-217-47346-0(6))*; 456p. pap. *(978-0-217-71881-3(7))* Books LLC.

—Farthest North: The Epic Adventure of a Visionary Explorer. 2008. (ENG., Illus.). 528p. pap. 17.95 *(978-1-60239-237-3(4))* Skyhorse Publishing Co., Inc.

—In Northern Mists: Arctic Exploration in Early Times, 2 vols. Chater, Arthur G., tr. (Illus.). reprint ed. 94.50 *(978-0-404-01955-6(2))* AMS Pr., Inc.

Officer, Charles & Page, Jake. A Fabulous Kingdom: The Exploration of the Arctic. 2nd ed. 2012. (ENG., Illus.). 232p. pap. 19.95 *(978-0-19-983780-9(5))* Oxford Univ. Pr., Inc.

Parry, Bruce & Lewis-Jones, Huw. Arctic: A Journey Around the Arctic Circle to Explore the Lives of People in a Rapidly Changing World. 2012. (ENG., Illus.). 272p. 29.95 *(978-1-84486-130-9(9)*, Conway Maritime Pr.) Anova Bks. GBR. Dist: Sterling Publishing Co., Inc.

Parry, Sir William Edward. Three Voyages for the Discovery of a North-West Passage from the Atlantic to the Pacific, & Narrative of an Attempt to Reach the North Pole. 2009. 164p. pap. 25.04 *(978-1-151-07574-1(4))*; 132p. pap. 19.99 *(978-1-150-13400-5(3))* General Bks. LLC.

—Three Voyages for the Discovery of a Northwest Passage from the Atlantic to the Pacific. 2010. (Illus.). 148p. pap. 19.99 *(978-1-154-13824-5(0))* General Bks. LLC.

Parry, W. E. Three Voyages for the Discovery of a Northwest Passage from the Atlantic to the Pacific, & Narrative of an Attempt to Reach the North Pole. 2007. 428p. per. *(978-1-4065-4107-6(9))* Dodo Pr.

Parry, William Edward. Three Voyages for the Discovery of A nor. 2006. pap. *(978-1-84702-395-7(9))* Echo Library.

—Three Voyages for the Discovery of a North-West Passage from the Atlantic to the Pacific, & Narrative of an Attempt to Reach the North Pole. 2010. 336p. pap. 31.75 *(978-1-146-99779-9(5))*; 274p. pap. 27.75 *(978-1-141-57379-0(2))*; 346p. pap. 32.75 *(978-1-141-94686-0(6))* BiblioBazaar.

—Three Voyages for the Discovery of a North-West Passage from the Atlantic to the Pacific, & Narrative of an Attempt to Reach the North Pole. 2009. 144p. pap. 19.99 *(978-1-150-97570-7(9))*; 142p. pap. 19.99 *(978-1-150-13399-2(5))*; 108p. pap. 19.99 *(978-1-150-96848-8(6))* General Bks. LLC.

—Three Voyages for the Discovery of a Northwest Passage. 2007. 168p. per. *(978-1-84702-396-4(7))* Echo Library.

—Three Voyages for the Discovery of a Northwest Passage from the Atlantic to the Pacific. 2010. 356p. pap. 32.75 *(978-1-142-21651-1(9))* BiblioBazaar.

—Three Voyages for the Discovery of a Northwest Passage from the Atlantic to the Pacific, & Narrati. 2008. 264p. 28.99 *(978-0-554-24672-7(4))*; 268p. 28.99 *(978-0-554-24938-4(3))*; 264p. 25.99 *(978-0-554-33975-7(7))*; 268p. 25.99 *(978-0-554-34241-2(3))* BiblioBazaar.

—Three Voyages for the Discovery of a Northwest Passage from the Atlantic to the Pacific, & Narrative of an Attempt to Reach the North Pole. 2010. 334p. pap. 31.75 *(978-1-177-91679-0(7))*; 338p. pap. 31.75 *(978-1-177-82280-0(6))* BiblioBazaar.

—Three Voyages for the Discovery of a Northwest Passage from the Atlantic to the Pacific, & Narrative of an Attempt to Reach the North Pole. 2010. 150p. pap. 12.88 *(978-1-4432-3415-3(X))*; 150p. pap. 23.74 *(978-1-153-72798-3(6))*; 148p. pap. 20.69 *(978-1-152-06869-8(5))* General Bks. LLC.

—Three Voyages for the Discovery of a Northwest Passage from the Atlantic to the Pacific, & Narrative of an Attempt to Reach the North Pole. 2009. 162p. pap. *(978-1-151-30202-1(3))* Books LLC.

—Three Voyages for the Discovery of a Northwest Passage from the Atlantic to the Pacific, & Narrative of an Attempt to Reach the North Pole, 1. 1st. ed. 2006. 260p. pap. 23.99 *(978-1-4264-7141-4(6))* BiblioBazaar.

—Three Voyages for the Discovery of a Northwest Passage from the Atlantic to the Pacific, & Narrative of an Attempt to Reach the North Pole, Volume 2. 2007. 242p. pap. 20.99 *(978-1-4264-7705-8(8))*2. 2006. 266p. pap. 23.99 *(978-1-4264-7763-8(5))* BiblioBazaar.

—Three Voyages for the Discovery of a Northwest Passage from the Atlantic to the Pacific, & Narrative of an Attempt to Reach the North Pole, Volume I. 2006. 236p. pap. 20.99 *(978-1-4264-7065-3(7))* BiblioBazaar.

Peary, Robert E. The North Pole, Its Discovery in 1909 under the Auspices of the Peary Arctic Club, Fully Illustrated. 2011. 322p. *(978-1-84902-294-1(1))* Benediction Classics.

Pihlaja, Päivi Maria. Tiedettä Pohjantähden Alla: Pohjoisen Tutkimus Ja Ruotsin Tiedeseurojen Suhteet Ranskaan 1700-Luvulla. 2009. (FIN., Illus.). 306p. *(978-951-653-373-8(6))* Finska Vetenskap-Societeter.

Richardson, John. Arctic Searching Expedition: A Journal of A Boat-Voyage Through Rupert's Land & the Arctic Sea, in Search of the Discovery Ships under Command of Si. 2006. 528p. per. 29.99 *(978-1-4255-5891-8(7))* MPublishing.

Robinson, Michael F. The Coldest Crucible: Arctic Exploration & American Culture. 2006. (Illus.). 200p. 42.50 *(978-0-226-72184-2(1))* Univ. of Chicago Pr.

Sale, Richard. Scramble for the Arctic: Ownership, Exploitation & Conflict in the Far North. 2009. (ENG., Illus.). 232p. 24.95 *(978-0-7112-3040-8(4))* Lincoln, Frances Ltd. GBR. Dist: Perseus-PGW.

Sandler, Martin W. Resolute: The Epic Search for the Northwest Passage & John Franklin, & the Discovery of the Queen's Ghost Ship. 2008. (ENG., Illus.). 320p. per. 14.95 *(978-1-4027-5861-4(8))* Sterling Publishing Co., Inc.

Scott, Jeremy. Dancing on Ice: A Stirring Tale of Adventure, Risk & Reckless Folly. 2009. (ENG., Illus.). 272p. (gr. 6). 26.00 *(978-1-905847-50-1(5))* Old Street Publishing GBR. Dist: Consortium Bk. Sales & Distribution.

Smucker, Samuel M. Arctic Explorations & Discoveries During the Nineteenth Century Being Detailed Accounts of the Several Expeditions to the North Seas, Both English. 2006. 524p. per. 29.99 *(978-1-4255-5799-7(6))* MPublishing.

Snow, William Parker. The Voyage of the Prince Albert in Search of Sir John Franklin: A Narrative of Every-Day Life in the Arctic Seas. 2010. (Cambridge Library Collection - Travel & Exploration Ser.). (Illus.). 448p. pap. 32.99 *(978-1-108-01966-8(8))* Cambridge Univ. Pr.

Todd, Alden L. Abandoned: The Story of the Greely Arctic Expedition, 1881-1884. 2011. 358p. 51.95 *(978-1-258-01418-6(1))* Literary Licensing, LLC.

Troubetzkoy, Alexis S. Arctic Obsession: The Lure of the Far North. 2011. (ENG., Illus.). 302p. 35.00 *(978-1-55488-855-9(7)*, Dundurn Pr.) Dundurn CAN. Dist: Ingram Pub. Services.

—Arctic Obsession: The Lure of the Far North. 2011. (ENG., Illus.). 304p. 25.99 *(978-0-312-62503-0(0)*, Dunne, Thomas Bks.) St. Martin's Pr.

Wamsley, Douglas. Polar Hayes: The Life & Contributions of Isaac Israel Hayes, M.D. 2008. *(978-0-87169-262-7(7))* American Philosophical Society.

Webb, Peter H. Icebears & Kotick. 2008. (ENG., Illus.). 252p. pap. 17.95 *(978-1-57409-264-6(2))* Sheridan Hse., Inc.

Wilkinson, Alec. The Ice Balloon: S. A. Andrée & the Heroic Age of Arctic Exploration. 2012. (ENG., Illus.). 256p. 25.95 *(978-0-307-59480-8(7)*, Knopf) Knopf Doubleday Publishing Group.

Woodman, Richard. Arctic Convoys 1941-1945. 2007. (Illus.). 532p. per. 32.99 *(978-1-84415-611-5(7))* Pen & Sword Bks. Ltd. GBR. Dist: Casemate Pubs. & Bk. Distributors, LLC.

ARCTIC REGIONS—HISTORY

Ørbaek, Jon Børre, et al, eds. Arctic Alpine Ecosystems & People in a Changing Environment. 2010. (ENG., Illus.). xxviii, 434p. pap. 239.00 *(978-3-642-08014-2(6)*, 3642080146) Springer.

Banerjee, Subhankar. Arctic Voices: Resistance at the Tipping Point. 2012. (ENG., Illus.). 384p. 35.95 *(978-1-60980-385-8(X))* Seven Stories Pr.

Beechey, Frederick William. Narrative of a Voyage to the Pacific & Beering's Strait: To Co-operate with the Polar Expeditions: Performed in His Majesty's Ship Blossom, under the Command of Captain F. W. Beechey in the Years 1825, 26, 27, 28. 2011. (Cambridge Library Collection - Life Sciences Ser.). (ENG.). 488p. pap. 35.99 *(978-1-108-03104-2(8))*; (Illus.). 558p. pap. 39.99 *(978-1-108-03103-5(X))* Cambridge Univ. Pr.

Bessels, Emil. Die Amerikanische Nordpol-Expedition. 2011. (Cambridge Library Collection - Travel & Exploration Ser.). (GER., Illus.). 694p. pap. 48.00 *(978-1-108-04147-8(7))* Cambridge Univ. Pr.

Bravo, Michael & Triscott, Nicola, eds. Arctic Perspective Cahier No. 2: Geopolitics & Autonomy. 2011. (ENG., Illus.). 116p. 30.00 *(978-3-7757-2681-8(0))* Hatje Cantz Verlag GmbH & Co KG DEU. Dist: D.A.P./Distributed Art Pubs.

Buckland, David. UNFOLD (Edition Angewandte) 2010. (Edition Angewandte Ser.). 120p. 49.95 *(978-3-7091-0220-6(0))* Springer Wien AUT. Dist: Springer.

Dickson, Robert R., et al, eds. Arctic-Subarctic Ocean Fluxes: Defining the Role of the Northern Seas in Climate. 2010. (Illus.). x, 738p. pap. 219.00 *(978-90-481-7721-9(9)*, 9048177219) Springer.

Dumond, Don. The Eskimos & Aleuts. 2011. 184p. 27.00 *(978-1-59740-807-3(7))* ACLS Humanities E-Book.

Fairhall, David. Cold Front: Conflict Ahead in Arctic Waters. 2011. (ENG., Illus.). 256p. 26.00 *(978-1-58243-760-6(2)*, Counterpoint) Counterpoint LLC.

Grant, Shelagh. Polar Imperative: A History of Arctic Sovereignty in North America, 1 vol. 2011. (ENG., Illus.). 560p. pap. 27.95 *(978-1-55365-806-1(X))* D&M Pubs. Inc. CAN. Dist: Perseus-PGW.

Grant, Shelagh D. Polar Imperative: A History of Arctic Sovereignty in North America, 1 vol. 2010. (ENG., Illus.). 560p. 39.95 *(978-1-55365-418-6(8))* D&M Pubs. Inc. CAN. Dist: Perseus-PGW.

Gronnow, Bjarne, ed. On the Track of the Thule Culture from Bering Strait to East Greenland: Proceedings of the SILA Conference the Thule Culture - New Perspectives in Inuit Prehistory. Papers in Honour of Hans Christian Gulløv. 2010. (Studies in archaeology & History Ser.). (ENG., Illus.). 263p. (C). 60.00 *(978-87-7602-106-1(8))* Aarhus Universitetsforlag DNK. Dist: ISD.

Gutman, Garik & Reissell, Anni, eds. Eurasian Arctic Land Cover & Land Use in a Changing Climate. 2010. (ENG., Illus.). xxiii, 306p. 129.00 *(978-90-481-9117-8(3)*, 9048191173) Springer.

Heininen, Lassi. Globalization of the Circumpolar North. Southcott, Chris, ed. 2010. 320p. pap. 24.95 *(978-1-60223-078-1(1))* Univ. of Alaska Pr.

Hovelsrud, Grete K. & Smit, Barry, eds. Community Adaptation & Vulnerability in Arctic Regions. 2010. (ENG.). xvi, 353p. 179.00 *(978-90-481-9173-4(4)*, 9048191734) Springer.

Jenness, Stuart E. Stefansson, Dr. Anderson & the Canadian Arctic Expedition, 1913-1918: A Story of Exploration, Science & Sovereignty. 2011. (ENG., Illus.). 400p. (C). pap. 39.95 *(978-0-660-19971-9(8))* Canadian Museum of Civilization/Musee Canadien des Civilisations CAN. Dist: Univ. of Washington Pr.

Johannessen, Ola M., et al. Remote Sensing of Sea Ice in the Northern Sea Route: Studies & Applications. 2010. (Springer Praxis Books / Geophysical Sciences Ser.). (Illus.). xli, 472p. pap. 289.00 *(978-3-642-06378-7(0)*, 3642063780) Springer.

Johansen, Thomas. Petroleum & Indigenous People in the Arctic. 2009. 64p. pap. *(978-3-639-21684-4(9))* VDM Verlag Dr. Mueller e.K.

Kennedy, William. A Short Narrative of the Second Voyage of the Prince Albert, in Search of Sir John Franklin. 2010. (Cambridge Library Collection - Travel & Exploration Ser.). (Illus.). 232p. pap. 22.99 *(978-1-108-01965-1(X))* Cambridge Univ. Pr.

Korte, Jacobus de, et al. A Passion for the Pole: Ethological Research in Polar Regions. 2008. (Circumpolar Studies). (ENG., Illus.). x, 149p. (C). pap. 21.00 *(978-90-77922-40-8(7))* Barkhuis Publishing NLD. Dist: Brown, David Bk. Co., The.

Krupnik, Igor, et al, eds. SIKU: Knowing Our Ice: Documenting Inuit Sea Ice Knowledge & Use. 2010. (ENG., Illus.). xxxi, 501p. pap. 49.95 *(978-90-481-8648-8(X)*, 904818648X) Springer.

Lackenbauer, P. Whitney & Kikkert, Peter. The Canadian Forces & Arctic Sovereignty: Debating Roles, Interests, & Requirements, 1968-1974. 2010. (ENG., Illus.). 398p. (C). pap. 34.95 *(978-1-926804-00-2(7))* Wilfrid Laurier Univ. Pr. CAN. Dist: Univ. of Toronto Pr.

Marshall, Bonnie & Van Deusen, Kira. Far North Tales: Stories from the Peoples of the Arctic Circle, 1 vol. (World Folklore Ser.). (Illus.). 290p. 40.00 *(978-1-59158-761-3(1)*, LU8761) Libraries Unlimited, Inc.

Mikkelsen, Aslaug & Langhelle, Oluf, eds. Arctic Oil & Gas. 2011. (Illus.). 408p. pap. 41.58 *(978-0-415-61982-0(3))* Routledge.

Munz-Krines, Marion. Expeditionen ins Eis: Historische Polarreisen in der Literatur. 2008. (Helicon - Beiträge zur deutschen Literatur Ser.). 240p. pap. 61.95 *(978-3-631-58202-2(1))* Lang, Peter GmbH, Europaischer Verlag der Wissenschaften DEU. Dist: Lang, Peter.

Ostreng, Willy. Shipping in Arctic Waters: A comparison of the Northeast, Northwest & Trans-Polar Passages. 2012. (ENG., Illus.). x, 300p. 179.00 *(978-3-642-16789-8(6)*, 3642167896) Springer.

Parry, Bruce & Lewis-Jones, Huw. Arctic: A Journey Around the Arctic Circle to Explore the Lives of People in a Rapidly Changing World. 2012. (ENG., Illus.). 272p. 29.95 *(978-1-84486-130-9(9)*, Conway Maritime Pr.) Anova Bks. GBR. Dist: Sterling Publishing Co., Inc.

Pienitz, Reinhard, et al, eds. Long-term Environmental Change in Arctic & Antarctic Lakes. 2010. (Developments in Paleoenvironmental Research Ser.). xxx, 562p. pap. 129.00 *(978-90-481-6595-7(4)*, 9048165954) Springer.

Pigott, Peter. From Far & Wide: A Complete History of Canada's Arctic Sovereignty. 2011. (ENG., Illus.). 312p. 35.00 *(978-1-55488-987-7(1))* Dundurn CAN. Dist: Ingram Pub. Services.

Powell, Theodore. The Long Rescue: One of the Great True Adventures of All Time, the Story of the Tragic Greely Expedition. 2011. 390p. 53.95 *(978-1-258-09997-8(7))* Literary Licensing, LLC.

Scoresby, William. An Account of the Arctic Regions: With a History & Description of the Northern Whale-Fishery. 2011. (Cambridge Library Collection - Travel & Exploration Ser.). (ENG.). 630p. pap. 43.00 *(978-1-108-03779-2(8))*; (Illus.). 670p. pap. 45.00 *(978-1-108-03778-5(X))* Cambridge Univ. Pr.

Shumenko, Roman, ed. Arctic Oil & Gas: Development & Concerns. 2011. (Energy Science, Engineering & Technology Ser.). 75.00 *(978-1-61324-862-1(8))* Nova Science Pubs., Inc.

Sorensen, Mikkel. Technology & Tradition in the Eastern Arctic, 2500 Bc-Ad 1200: A Dynamic Technological Investigation of Lithic Assemblages from the Palae-Eskimo Traditions Greenland. 2012. (ENG., Illus.). 418p. 89.00 *(978-87-635-3167-2(4))* Museum Tusculanum Pr. DNK. Dist: Chicago Distribution Ctr.

Strategic Importance of the Arctic in U.S. Policy: Hearing Before a Subcommittee of the Committee on Appropriations, United States Senate, One Hundred Eleventh Congress, Special Hearing, August 20, 2009, Anchorage, AK. 2010. (Illus.). iii, 69p. *(978-0-16-085087-5(8)*, 552-070-40443-1) United States Government Printing Office.

Struzik, Ed. The Big Thaw: Adventures in the Vanishing Arctic. 2011. (ENG.). 288p. pap. 18.95 *(978-0-470-93216-2(3)*, Wiley) Wiley, John & Sons, Inc.

Sturm, Matthew. Finding the Arctic: History & Culture along a 2,500-Mile Snowmobile Journey from Alaska to Hudson's Bay. 2012. E-Book *(978-1-60223-164-1(8))*; (ENG., Illus.). 320p. pap. 24.95 *(978-1-60223-163-4(X))* Univ. of Alaska Pr.

Tennberg, Monica, ed. Governing the Uncertain: Adaptation & Climate in Russia & Finland. 2012. (ENG., Illus.). xvii, 138p. 129.00 *(978-94-007-3842-3(0)*, 9400738420) Springer.

UNESCO Publishing, creator. Climate Change & Arctic Sustainable Development: Scientific, Social, Cultural & Educational Challenges. 2010. (Illus.). 357p. pap. *(978-92-3-104139-6(8))* UNESCO Publishing.

Westerdahl, Christer, ed. A Circumpolar Reappraisal: The Legacy of Gutorm Gjessing (1906-1979) 2010. (Bar S Ser.). (ENG., Illus.). 378p. (C). pap. 165.00 *(978-1-4073-0696-4(0))* British Archaeological Reports Ltd. GBR. Dist: Brown, David Bk. Co., The.

Wheeler, Sara. The Magnetic North: Notes from the Arctic Circle, 1 vol. (ENG.). 336p. 2012. pap. 15.00 *(978-0-374-53309-0(1)*, North Point Pr.) 2011. (Illus.). 26.00 *(978-0-374-20013-8(0))* Farrar, Straus & Giroux.

Wieder, R. K. & Vitt, D. H. Boreal Peatland Ecosystems. 2010. (Ecological Studies). (Illus.). xx, 444p. pap. 249.00 *(978-3-642-06869-0(3)*, 3642068693) Springer.

Zellen, Barry S. Arctic Doom, Arctic Boom: The Geopolitics of Climate Change in the Arctic, 1 vol. 2009. (Security & the Environment Ser.). (Illus.). 232p. 44.95 *(978-0-313-38012-9(0)*, A2052C, Praeger Pubs.) Greenwood Publishing Group, Inc.

ARCTIC REGIONS—JUVENILE LITERATURE

Krykorka, Vladyana. Arctic Land, 3 vols. 2011. (ENG., Illus.). 16p. (J). bds., bds. 5.95 *(978-1-55451-342-0(1))* Annick Pr., Ltd. CAN. Dist: Firefly Bks., Ltd.

ARCTIC SLED DOGS

see Sled Dogs

ARDEATINE MASSACRE, 1944

Raiber, Richard. Anatomy of Perjury: Field Marshal Albert Kesselring, Via Rasella, & the Ginny Mission. Showalter, Dennis E., ed. & pref. by. 2008. (Illus.). 272p. (C). 55.00 *(978-0-87413-994-5(5))* Univ. of Delaware Pr.

ARDENNES, BATTLE OF THE, 1944-1945

Barron, Leo & Cygan, Don. No Silent Night: The Christmas Battle for Bastogne. 2012. 336p. (gr. 12). 26.95 *(978-0-451-23813-9(3)*, N A L Hardcover) Penguin Group (USA) Inc.

Bruning, John R. The Battle of the Bulge: The Photographic History of an American Triumph. 2011. (ENG., Illus.). 300p. pap. 29.99 *(978-0-7603-4126-1(5)*, 0760341265, Zenith Pr.) MBI Publishing Co. LLC.

Cain, Bill. The Battle of the Bulge: Turning Back Hitler's Final Push. 2008. (Graphic Battles of World War II Ser.). (ENG., Illus.). 48p. (gr. 3-8). pap. 14.05 *(978-1-4042-7422-8(7))* Rosen Publishing Group, Inc., The.

Clark, Lloyd. Crossing the Rhine: Breaking into Nazi Germany 1944 & 1945 — the Greatest Airborne Battles in History. 2009. (ENG., Illus.). 448p. pap. 15.00 *(978-0-8021-4430-0(6)*, Grove Pr.) Grove/Atlantic, Inc.

Cole, Hugh M. The Ardennes: The Official History of the Battle of the Bulge. 2011. *(978-1-61001-015-3(9))* Red & Black Pubs.

Collins, Michael & King, Martin. Voices of the Bulge: Untold Stories from Veterans of the Battle of the Bulge. 2011. (ENG., Illus.). 320p. 29.00 *(978-0-7603-4033-2(1)*, 0760340331, Zenith Pr.) MBI Publishing Co. LLC.

Cooke, David & Evans, Wayne. Kampfgruppe Peiper at the Battle of the Bulge. 2008. (Stackpole Military History Ser.). (ENG., Illus.). 224p. pap. 16.95 *(978-0-8117-3481-3(1))* Stackpole Bks.

Davis, John & Riffenburgh, Anne. Up Close. 2008. 174p. 34.95 *(978-1-4357-1584-4(5))* Lulu Enterprises Inc.

Davis Jr, Franklin M. & Davis Jr., Franklin M. Breakthrough: The Epic Story of the Battle of the Bulge. 2011. 160p. 41.95 *(978-1-258-02611-0(2))* Literary Licensing, LLC.

Green, Michael & Brown, James D. War Stories of the Battle of the Bulge. 2010. (ENG., Illus.). 320p. 28.00 *(978-0-7603-3567-0(9)*, 0760336679, Zenith Pr.) MBI Publishing Co. LLC.

Haasler, Timm, et al. Duel in the Mist2: The Leibstandarte During the Ardennes Offensive. 2011. (Illus.). 225p. *(978-0-9841820-6-0(3))* Panzerwrecks.

Kane, Steve. 1st SS Panzer Division in the Bulge. 2008. 216p. 34.95 *(978-1-4357-5450-8(6))* Lulu Enterprises Inc.

Koskimaki, George. Battered Bastards of Bastogne. 2011. (Illus.). 484p. pap. 16.95 *(978-1-61200-074-9(6)*, Casemate) Casemate Pubs. & Bk. Distributors, LLC.

Koskimaki, George. The Battered Bastards of Bastogne: The 101st Airborne & the Battle of the Bulge, December 19, 1944-January 17,1945. 2007. (ENG., Illus.). 560p. mass mkt. 7.99 *(978-0-89141-894-8(6)*, Presidio Pr.) Random House Publishing Group.

McDonald, Robert K. The Hotton Report, 1. 2006. (Illus.). 168p. per. 13.95 *(978-0-9665753-8-5(5))* Finbar Pr.

McManus, John C. Alamo in the Ardennes: The Untold Story of the American Soldiers Who Made the Defense of Bastogne Possible. 2007. (ENG., Illus.). 336p. 24.95 *(978-0-471-73905-0(7)*, Wiley) Wiley, John & Sons, Inc.

McMurdie, William F. Hey, Mac! This Is serious business! A guy could get Killed! 2006. (Illus.). 240p. (YA). pap. 14.95 *(978-0-9779000-1-5(0))* American Home-School Publishing, LLC.

Merriam, Robert E. Dark December: The Full Account of the Battle of the Bulge. 2011. (ENG., Illus.). 248p. pap. 15.95 *(978-1-59416-150-6(X))* Westholme Publishing.

Mitcham, Samuel W., Jr. Panzers in Winter: Hitler's Army & the Battle of the Bulge. 2008. (Stackpole Military History Ser.). (ENG., Illus.). 240p. per. 16.95 *(978-0-8117-3456-1(0))* Stackpole Bks.

Moranda, Robert E. P. & Moranda, George E. Two Wars & One Love: Front-Line Soldiers Remember World War II through the Battle of the Bulge & the Korean Conflict. 2009. 352p. pap. 23.95 *(978-1-4401-3934-5(2))* iUniverse, Inc.

Neillands, Robin. The Battle for the Rhine: The Battle of the Bulge & the Ardennes Campaign 1944. 2007. (ENG.). 456p. (gr. 12). 27.95 *(978-1-58567-787-0(6))* Overlook Pr., The.

Paszek, Donna M. Knechtel, compiled by. Identification of American Soldiers Buried in Temporary Cemetery of GRAND-FAILLY, FRANCE, 1944-1948: Identité des Soldats des Etats-Unis D'Amérique Inhumés Au Cimetière Temporaire de GRAND-FAILLY, FRANCE, 1944-1948. 2011. (FRE & ENG., Illus.). 50p. ***(978-1-55856-538-8(8))*** Closson Pr.

Rawson, Andrew. Steel Storm: Battle of the Bulge 1944-45. 2011. (Battle Story Ser.). (ENG., Illus.). 160p. 16.95 ***(978-0-7524-6268-4(7))*** History Pr. Ltd.,The GBR. Dist: Independent Pubs. Group.

Reynolds, Michael. Devil's Adjutant: Jochen Peiper, Panzer Leader. 2009. (Illus.). 320p. pap. 24.99 *(978-1-84884-010-2(1))* Pen & Sword Bks. Ltd. GBR. Dist: Casemate Pubs. & Bk. Distributors, LLC.

—Men of Steel: The Ardennes & Eastern Front 1944-45. 2009. (Illus.). 368p. pap. 24.99 *(978-1-84884-009-6(8))* Pen & Sword Bks. Ltd. GBR. Dist: Casemate Pubs. & Bk. Distributors, LLC.

Rickard, John Nelson. Advance & Destroy: Patton as Commander in the Bulge. 2011. (American Warriors Ser.). (ENG., Illus.). 528p. 34.95 *(978-0-8131-3455-0(2))* Univ. Pr. of Kentucky.

Riddle, Lyn. First We'll Kill My Husband. 2008. (ENG., Illus.). 320p. 6.99 *(978-0-7860-1720-1(1),* Pinnacle Bks.) Kensington Publishing Corp.

Rusiecki, Stephen M. & Rusiecki, Stephen. The Key to the Bulge: The Battle for Losheimergraben. 2009. (Military History Ser.). (ENG., Illus.). 240p. pap. 18.95 *(978-0-8117-3591-9(5))* Stackpole Bks.

Sears, Stephen. The Battle of the Bulge. 2007. (ENG.). 160p. pap. 9.95 *(978-1-59687-015-4(X))* IBks., Inc.

Siddall, Brian N. 507th in Normandy & Germany: The Complete Jump Rosters & Aircrew for Operations Neptune & Varsity. 2007. (Illus.). ii, 174p. *(978-0-9774470-4-6(9))* EQS Pr.

Spanos, William V. In the Neighborhood of Zero: A World War II Memoir. 2010. (ENG., Illus.). 218p. 29.95 *(978-0-8032-2681-4(0))* Univ. of Nebraska Pr.

Weintraub, Stanley. 11 Days in December: Christmas at the Bulge 1944. 2007. (ENG., Illus.). 224p. (gr. 12-18). 14.00 *(978-0-451-22317-3(9),* N A L Trade) Penguin Group (USA) Inc.

Whiting, Charles. Ardennes the Secret War. 2007. (Spellmount Siegfried Line Ser.). (ENG., Illus.). 216p. 23.95 *(978-1-86227-397-9(9),* Spellmount, Limited Pubs.) History Pr. Ltd.,The GBR. Dist: Independent Pubs. Group.

—Decision at St Vith. 2008. (Spellmount Siegfried Line Ser.). (ENG., Illus.). 296p. pap. 23.95 *(978-1-86227-398-6(7),* Spellmount, Limited Pubs.) History Pr. Ltd.,The GBR. Dist: Independent Pubs. Group.

Wijers, Hans. Battle of the Bulge: Hell at Butgenback/Sieze the Bridges. 2010. (Stackpole Military History Ser.). (ENG., Illus.). 352p. pap. 21.95 *(978-0-8117-3587-2(7))* Stackpole Bks.

—The Battle of the Bulge Vol. 1: The Losheim Gap - Holding the Line. 2009. (Military History Ser.). (ENG., Illus.). 448p. pap. 21.95 *(978-0-8117-3592-6(3))* Stackpole Bks.

Winton, Harold R. Corps Commanders of the Bulge: Six American Generals & Victory in the Ardennes. 2007. (Modern War Studies). (Illus.). 504p. 39.95 *(978-0-7006-1508-7(3))* Univ. Pr. of Kansas.

Zaloga, Steven. Battle of the Bulge: Hitler's Final Gamble, from St. Vith to Bastogne. 2010. (General Military Ser.). (ENG., Illus.). 288p. 25.95 *(978-1-84908-165-8(4))* Osprey Publishing, Ltd. GBR. Dist: Random Hse., Inc.

—Panther vs Sherman: Battle of the Bulge 1944. 2008. (Duel Ser.). (ENG., Illus.). 80p. pap. 17.95 *(978-1-84603-292-9(X))* Osprey Publishing, Ltd. GBR. Dist: Random Hse., Inc.

AREA MEASUREMENT

Hollingum, Ben. Maps & Measurement. 2010. (Understanding Maps of Our World Ser.). (ENG.). 48p. (gr. 6-8). pap. 14.05 *(978-1-4339-3504-6(X),* Stevens, Gareth Secondary Library) Stevens, Gareth Publishing LLLP.

AREA STUDIES

Here are entered general works on area studies, and with local subdivision, works on area studies carried out in specific places. Works on area studies about a particular region, country, etc. are entered under the name of the region, country, etc. with the subdivision Study and Teaching or Research.

see also Geography—Study and Teaching

Building Area Studies Collections. 2007. (Beiträge Zum Buch- und Bibliothekswesen Ser.: Vol. 52). viii, 163p. *(978-3-447-05512-3(X))* Harrassowitz, Otto Verlag.

Lan, Goh Beng, ed. Decentring & Diversifying Southeast Asian Studies: Perspectives from the Region. 2011. 318p. ***(978-981-4311-57-1(X))*** Institute of Southeast Asian Studies.

O'Connell, Mary Ellen & Norwood, Janet Lippe, eds. International Education & Foreign Languages: Keys to Securing America's Future. 2007. (ENG.). 412p. 50.00 *(978-0-309-10494-4(7))* National Academies Pr.

Wesley-Smith, Terence & Goss, Jon D. Remaking Area Studies: Teaching & Learning Across Asia & the Pacific. 2010. (C). 45.00 *(978-0-8248-3321-3(X))* Univ. of Hawaii Pr.

ARENDT, HANNAH, 1906-1975

Allen, Amy. Hannah Arendt. 2008. (International Library of Essays in the History of Social & Political Thought Ser.). 486p. 275.00 *(978-0-7546-2694-7(6))* Ashgate Publishing Co.

Assy, Bethania. Hannah Arendt: An Ethics of Personal Responsibility. 2007. 191p. pap. 43.95 *(978-0-8204-9867-6(X))* Lang, Peter Publishing, Inc.

Baehr, Peter. Hannah Arendt, Totalitarianism, & the Social Sciences. 2010. (ENG.). 248p. 55.00 *(978-0-8047-5650-1(3))* Stanford Univ. Pr.

Berkowitz, Roger, et al, eds. Thinking in Dark Times: Hannah Arendt on Ethics & Politics. 2009. (ENG., Illus.). 288p. 80.00 *(978-0-8232-3075-4(9))* Fordham Univ. Pr.

Birmingham, Peg. Hannah Arendt & Human Rights: The Predicament of Common Responsibility. 2006. (Studies in Continental Thought). (ENG.). 184p. pap. 24.95 *(978-0-253-21865-0(9),* 0253218659) Indiana Univ. Pr.

Bowring, Finn. Hannah Arendt: A Critical Introduction, 1 vol. 2011. (Modern European Thinkers Ser.). (ENG.). 320p. lib. bdg. 100.00 *(978-0-7453-3142-3(4))* Pluto Pr. GBR. Dist: Macmillan.

Brauer, Gerhard. The Problem with Reading Hannah Arendt in English - How Poor Translation Can Impair the Reading & Understanding of Philosophy. 2008. 108p. pap. *(978-3-639-01354-2(9))* VDM Verlag Dr. Mueller e.K.

Breen, Keith. Under Weber's Shadow: Modernity, Subjectivity & Politics in the Work of Habermas Arendt & Macintyre. 2012. 250p. 99.95 ***(978-0-7546-9799-2(1))***; E-Book 99.95 ***(978-0-7546-7908-0(X))*** Ashgate Publishing Co.

Brudny, Michelle-Irene. Hannah Arendt: An Intellectual Biography. 2008. 250p. 24.95 *(978-1-933633-35-0(2))* Melville Hse. Publishing.

Buckler, Steve. Hannah Arendt & Political Theory: Challenging the Tradition. 2011. (ENG.). 256p. (gr. 17). 105.00 *(978-0-7486-3902-1(0))* Edinburgh Univ. Pr. GBR. Dist: Columbia Univ. Pr.

Deutscher, Max. Judgment after Arendt. 2007. 192p. 99.95 *(978-0-7546-5688-3(8))* Ashgate Publishing Co.

Dossa, Shiraz. The Public Realm & the Public Self: The Political Theory of Hannah Arendt. 2008. (ENG.). 168p. pap. 42.95 *(978-1-55458-152-8(4))* Wilfrid Laurier Univ. Pr. CAN. Dist: Univ. of Toronto Pr.

Fleischacker, Samuel. Heidegger's Jewish Followers: Essays on Hannah Arendt, Leo Strauss, Hans Jonas, & Emmanuel Levinas. Fleischacker, Samuel, ed. 2008. 320p. pap. 22.95 *(978-0-8207-0414-2(8))* Duquesne Univ. Pr.

—Heidegger's Jewish Followers: Essays on Hannah Arendt, Leo Strauss, Hans Jonas, & Emmanuel Levinas. 2008. 320p. 56.00 *(978-0-8207-0412-8(1))* Duquesne Univ. Pr.

Fry, Karin A. Arendt 2009. (Guides for the Perplexed Ser.). (ENG.). 176p. 27.95 *(978-0-8264-9986-8(4))*; 90.00 *(978-0-8264-9985-1(6))* Continuum International Publishing Group, Ltd. GBR. Dist: National Bk. Network.

Goldoni, Marco & Mccorkindale, Christopher, eds. Hannah Arendt & the Law, 0 vols. 2012. (ENG.). 382p. 110.00 ***(978-1-84946-143-6(0))*** Hart Publishing Ltd. GBR. Dist: International Specialized Bk. Services.

Grunenberg, Antonia & Meints, Waltraud, eds. Perspektiven politischen Denkens: Zum 100. Geburtstag von Hannah Arendt. 2008. (Hannah Arendt-Studien. Schriftenreihe des Hannah Arendt-Zentrums der Carl von Ossietzky-Universität Oldenburg. Hannah Arendt Studies. Book Ser. on Contemporary Political Thought by the Hannah Arendt Centre of Carl von Ossietzky Universität Oldenburg Ser.). 220p. pap. 49.95 *(978-3-631-56659-6(X))* Lang, Peter GmbH, Europaischer Verlag der Wissenschaften DEU. Dist: Lang, Peter.

Hartouni, Valerie. Visualizing Atrocity: Arendt, Evil, & the Optics of Thoughtlessness. 2012. (ENG.). 232p. pap. 23.00 ***(978-0-8147-6976-8(4))*** New York Univ. Pr.

Horowitz, Irving Louis. Hannah Arendt: Radical Conservative. 2012. (ENG.). 144p. 29.95 ***(978-1-4128-4602-8(1))*** Transaction Pubs.

Horsman, Yasco. Theaters of Justice: Judging, Staging, & Working Through in Arendt, Brecht, & Delbo. 2010. (Cultural Memory in the Present Ser.). (ENG.). 232p. 55.00 *(978-0-8047-7031-6(X))*; pap. 21.95 *(978-0-8047-7032-3(8))* Stanford Univ. Pr.

Hull, Margaret Betz. The Hidden Philosophy of Hannah Arendt. 2010. (ENG.). 200p. pap. 39.95 ***(978-0-415-59301-4(8))*** Routledge.

Kalyvas, Andreas. Democracy & the Politics of the Extraordinary: Max Weber, Carl Schmitt, & Hannah Arendt. (ENG.). 336p. 2009. pap. 32.99 *(978-0-521-13341-8(6))* 2008. 85.00 *(978-0-521-87768-8(7))* Cambridge Univ. Pr.

Kampowski, Stephan. Arendt, Augustine, & the New Beginning: The Action Theory & Moral Thought of Hannah Arendt in the Light of Her Dissertation on St. Augustine. 2008. 384p. pap. 50.00 *(978-0-8028-2724-1(1))* Eerdmans, William B. Publishing Co.

Katz, Jeffrey & Keenan, Thomas. Thinking in Dark Times: Hannah Arendt on Ethics & Politics. Berkowitz, Roger et al, eds. 2009. (ENG., Illus.). 288p. pap. 30.00 *(978-0-8232-3076-1(7))* Fordham Univ. Pr.

King, Peter. Hannah Arendt & the Uses of History: Imperialism, Nation, Race & Genocide. 2007. 292p. (C). 90.00 *(978-1-84545-361-9(1))* Berghahn Bks., Inc.

King, Richard H. Hannah Arendt & the Uses of History: Imperialism, Nation, Race, & Genocide. 2008. 292p. 34.95 *(978-1-84545-589-7(4))* Berghahn Bks., Inc.

Kolk, Philipp zum. Hannah Arendt und Carl Schmitt: Ausnahme und Normalität - Staat und Politik. 2009. (Europäische Hochschulschriften. Reihe 31: Politikwissenschaft Ser.). (GER.). 128p. pap. 28.95 *(978-3-631-59232-8(9))* Lang, Peter GmbH, Europaischer Verlag der Wissenschaften DEU. Dist: Lang, Peter.

Lamboy, Regine. The Real Banality of Evil. 2010. 180p. pap. *(978-3-8383-3967-2(3))* Lambert Academic Publishing.

Lamoureux, Diane. Pensées Rebelles. 2010. (FRE.). 200p. *(978-2-89091-282-3(5))* Editions du Remue-Menage.

Maier-Katkin, Daniel. Stranger from Abroad: Hannah Arendt, Martin Heidegger, Friendship & Forgiveness. 2010. (ENG.). 384p. 26.95 *(978-0-393-06833-7(1),* 6833) Norton, W. W. & Co., Inc.

Meindl, Matthias. Geschmack und Urteilskraft bei Pierre Bourdieu und Hannah Arendt. 2009. (Berliner Arbeiten zur Erziehungs- und Kulturwissenschaft Ser.). (GER.). 141p. pap. *(978-3-8325-2334-3(0))* Logos Verlag Berlin.

Mewes, Horst. Hannah Arendt's Political Humanism. 2009. (Hannah Arendt-Studien. Schriftenreihe des Hannah Arendt-Zentrums der Carl von Ossietzky-Universität Oldenburg. Hannah Arendt Studies. Book Series on Contemporary Political Thought by the Hannah Arendt Centre of Carl von Ossietzky Universität Oldenburg Ser.). 228p. pap. 54.95 *(978-3-631-55374-9(9))* Lang, Peter GmbH, Europaischer Verlag der Wissenschaften DEU. Dist: Lang, Peter.

Nixon, Jon. Interpretive Pedagogies for Higher Education: Arendt, Berger, Said, Nussbaum & Their Legacies. 2012. 176p. E-Book ***(978-1-4411-1265-1(0))***; E-Book ***(978-1-4411-7099-6(5))*** Continuum International Publishing Group, Ltd.

—Interpretive Pedagogies for Higher Education: Arendt, Berger, Said, Nussbaum & Their Legacies. 2012. (ENG.). 192p. 130.00 *(978-1-4411-1715-1(6))* Continuum International Publishing Group, Ltd. GBR. Dist: National Bk. Network.

Owens, Patricia. Between War & Politics: International Relations & the Thought of Hannah Arendt. (ENG.). 232p. 2009. pap. 45.00 *(978-0-19-956604-4(6))* 2007. 60.00 *(978-0-19-929936-2(6))* Oxford Univ. Pr., Inc.

Parekh, Serena. Hannah Arendt & the Challenge of Modernity: A Phenomenology of Human Rights. 2009. 220p. pap. 39.95 *(978-0-415-87666-7(4))* 2008. (ENG.). 234p. 125.00 *(978-0-415-96108-0(4))* Routledge.

Rensmann, Lars & Gandesha, Samir. Arendt & Adorno: Political & Philosophical Investigations. 2012. (ENG.). 368p. 85.00 ***(978-0-8047-7539-7(7))***; pap. 24.95 ***(978-0-8047-7540-3(0))*** Stanford Univ. Pr.

Rosenstock, Bruce. Philosophy & the Jewish Question: Mendelssohn, Rosenzweig, & Beyond. 2nd ed. 2009. (ENG.). 336p. 70.00 *(978-0-8232-3129-4(1))* Fordham Univ. Pr.

Spanos, William V. The Exiles in the City: Hannah Arendt & Edward W. Said in Counterpoint. 2012. 312p. 62.95 ***(978-0-8142-1193-9(3))***; cd-rom 14.95 ***(978-0-8142-9294-5(1))*** Ohio State Univ. Pr.

Steinmeyer, Georg. Siegfried Kracauer als Denker des Pluralismus: Eine Annäherung im Spiegel Hannah Arendts. 2008. (GER.). 234p. *(978-3-86732-030-6(6))* Bottcher, Dr. Frank Lukas Verlag fur Kunst- und Geistesgeschichte.

Stonebridge, Lyndsey. The Judicial Imagination: Writing after Nuremberg. 2011. (ENG., Illus.). 224p. (gr. 17). 105.00 ***(978-0-7486-4235-9(8))*** Edinburgh Univ. Pr. GBR. Dist: Columbia Univ. Pr.

Swift, Simon. Hannah Arendt. 2008. (Routledge Critical Thinkers Ser.). XVI, 176p. 95.00 *(978-0-415-42585-8(9))*; pap. 22.95 *(978-0-415-42586-5(7))* Routledge.

Villa, Dana R. Politics, Philosophy, & Terror. 280p. *(978-0-8047-3257-4(4))*; pap. *(978-0-8047-3258-1(2))* Stanford Univ. Pr.

Williams, John, et al. Hannah Arendt & International Relations: Readings Across the Lines. 2008. (ENG.). 244p. pap. 30.00 *(978-0-230-60613-5(X))* Palgrave Macmillan.

Yakira, Elhanan. Post-Zionism, Post-Holocaust: Three Essays on Denial, Forgetting, & the Delegitimation of Israel. Swirsky, Michael, tr. from HEB. 2009. (ENG.). 356p. 87.00 *(978-0-521-11110-2(2))*; pap. 29.99 *(978-0-521-12786-8(6))* Cambridge Univ. Pr.

Yeatman, Anna, et al. Action & Appearance: Ethics & the Politics of Writing in Arendt. Yeatman, Anna et al, eds. 2011. (ENG.). 230p. 120.00 *(978-1-4411-8680-5(8))*; 232p. pap. 34.95 *(978-1-4411-0173-0(X))* Continuum International Publishing Group, Ltd. GBR. Dist: National Bk. Network.

Young-Bruehl, Elisabeth. Why Arendt Matters. (Why X Matters Ser.). (ENG., Illus.). 240p. 2009. pap. 14.00 *(978-0-300-13619-7(6))* 2006. 22.00 *(978-0-300-12044-8(3))* Yale Univ. Pr.

AREOLAR TISSUE

see Connective Tissues

ARETINO, PIETRO, 1492-1556

Boillet, Elise. L'Arétin et la Bible. 2007. (Travaux d'Humanisme et Renaissance Ser.). (FRE & ENG., Illus.). 592p. (C). 205.00 *(978-2-600-01058-0(0))* Droz, Librairie CHE. Dist: Brown, David Bk. Co., The.

Clubb, Louise George. Pollastra & the Origins of Twelfth Night: Parthenio Commedia (1516) with an English Translation. 2010. (Anglo-Italian Renaissance Studies). (ITA., Illus.). 258p. 104.95 *(978-0-7546-6890-9(8))* Ashgate Publishing Co.

Roeder, Ralph. Renaissance Lawgivers: Savonarola, Machiavelli, Castiglione, & Aretino. 2011. (ENG., Illus.). 558p. pap. 49.95 *(978-1-4128-1824-7(9))* Transaction Pubs.

Van Dyke, Paul. Renascence Portraits. 2010. (ENG.). 452p. pap. 36.75 *(978-1-171-60476-1(9))*; 452p. pap. 36.75 *(978-1-177-18542-4(3))*; 446p. pap. 36.75 *(978-1-177-19840-0(1))*; 446p. pap. 36.75 *(978-1-146-59670-1(7))*; 444p. pap. 36.75 *(978-1-146-42601-5(1))*; 440p. pap. 35.75 *(978-1-147-05365-4(0))* BiblioBazaar.

—Renascence Portraits. 2007. (ENG.). 440p. per. 36.95 *(978-0-548-79856-0(7))* Kessinger Publishing, LLC.

AREZZO (ITALY)

Cygielman, Mario, ed. The Minerva of Arezzo. 2010. (ENG., Illus.). 56p. (C). pap. 15.00 *(978-88-596-0708-3(6))* Polistampa ITA. Dist: Brown, David Bk. Co., The.

ARGENSON, RENE LOUIS VOYER DE PAULMY, MARQUIS D', 1694-1757

Gallanar, Editeur. Rene Louis D Argenson: Essais Dans le Gout de Ceux de Montagne. 2011. 222p. pap. 20.00 ***(978-1-4357-8989-0(X))*** Lulu Enterprises Inc.

ARGENTINA

Caistor, Nick. Argentina in Focus. Date not set. (In Focus Ser.). (Illus.). 80p. pap. 12.00 *(978-0-85345-978-1(9))* Latin America Bureau GBR. Dist: Monthly Review Pr.

De Bonelli, L. Hugh. Travels in Bolivia: A Tour Across the Pampas to Buenos Ayres, 2 Vols, Set. reprint ed. 250.00 *(978-0-7222-9588-5(X))* Library Reprints, Inc.

Hammerton, John A. The Real Argentine: And Impressions of a Year in the Argentine & Uruguay. 453p. reprint ed. 98.00 *(978-0-7222-9579-3(0))* Library Reprints, Inc.

King, J. Anthony. Twenty-Four Years in the Argentine Republic. reprint ed. 57.50 *(978-0-404-03691-1(0))* AMS Pr., Inc.

Mills, George J. Argentina: Physical Features, Natural Resources, Means Of Communication, Manufactures & Industrial Development. 209p. reprint ed. 98.00 *(978-0-7222-9583-0(9))* Library Reprints, Inc.

Ross, Gordon. Argentina & Uruguay. 2009. 246p. pap. *(978-0-217-72370-1(5))* Books LLC.

—Argentina & Uruguay. 2009. 240p. pap. 19.99 *(978-0-217-33718-2(X))* General Bks. LLC.

—Argentina & Uruguay. 308p. reprint ed. 98.00 *(978-0-7222-9618-9(5))* Library Reprints, Inc.

—Argentine & Uruguay. 308p. reprint ed. 98.00 *(978-0-7222-9584-7(7))* Library Reprints, Inc.

ARGENTINA—ARMY

Lake, Eileen. They Also Serve. 2010. 136p. pap. 10.99 *(978-1-4490-5196-9(0))* AuthorHouse.

ARGENTINA—BIOGRAPHY

Ardiles, Ossie. Ossie's Dream: My Autobiography. (ENG., Illus.). 2010. 416p. pap. 14.95 *(978-0-552-15918-0(2))* 2009. 352p. 34.95 *(978-0-593-06213-5(2))* Transworld Publishers Ltd. GBR. Dist: Independent Pubs. Group.

Bascomb, Neal. Hunting Eichmann: How a Band of Survivors & a Young Spy Agency Chased down the World's Most Notorious Nazi. 2010. (ENG., Illus.). 416p. pap. 15.95 *(978-0-547-24802-8(4),* Mariner Bks.) Houghton Mifflin Harcourt Trade & Reference Pubs.

Caioli, Luca. Messi: The Inside Story of the Boy Who Became a Legend. 2012. (ENG., Illus.). 288p. pap. 14.95 ***(978-1-906850-39-5(9))*** Totem Bks. GBR. Dist: Consortium Bk. Sales & Distribution.

Collier, Simon. The Life, Music, & Times of Carlos Gardel. 2009. (Pitt Latin American Studies). (ENG.). 368p. (C). pap. 27.95 *(978-0-8229-8498-6(9))* Univ. of Pittsburgh Pr.

Donda, Victoria. My Name Is Victoria: The Extraordinary Story of one Woman's Struggle to Reclaim her True Identity. Bolin, Magda, tr. from SPA. 2011. (ENG., Illus.). 272p. pap. 15.95 *(978-1-59051-404-7(1))* Other Pr., LLC.

Dosman, Edgar. The Life & Times of Raúl Prebisch, 1901-1986. 2008. (ENG., Illus.). 624p. (C). *(978-0-7735-3412-4(1))* McGill-Queen's Univ. Pr.

Dosman, Edgar J. The Life & Times of Raul Prebisch, 1901-1986. 2010. (ENG., Illus.). 624p. (C). pap. *(978-0-7735-3775-0(9))* McGill-Queen's Univ. Pr.

García, María Amalia. Tomás Maldonado in Conversation with María Amalia García. 2011. (ENG & SPA., Illus.). 136p. 25.00 *(978-0-9823544-3-8(6))* Fundacion Cisneros.

Geil, Harold Alfredo. The Heart of Man; God's Target. 2009. 420p. pap. 22.99 *(978-1-61579-092-0(6))* Xulon Pr., Inc.

Herrera, Matilde. Jose. 2009. (SPA.). 447p. pap. 30.95 *(978-0-557-04124-4(4))* Lulu Enterprises Inc.

Jones, Pamela. Alcides Lanza: Portrait of a Composer. 2007. (ENG., Illus.). 286p. (C). *(978-0-7735-3264-9(1))* McGill-Queen's Univ. Pr.

Kosice, Gyula. Kosice: Autobiografía. 2010. (SPA., Illus.). 270p. *(978-950-533-021-8(9))* Asunto Impreso, Ediciones.

Lamas, Justo. Be What You Want to Be/Se lo Que Tu Quieres Ser: Don't Give up — Reach Your Dreams!/No Te Rindas, Alcanza Tus Suenos! 2009. (SPA & ENG., Illus.). 184p. pap. 9.99 *(978-1-59979-561-4(2),* Casa Creacion) Charisma Media.

Levine, Alex & Novoa, Adriana. ¡Darwinistas! the Construction of Evolutionary Thought in Nineteenth Century Argentina. 2012. (History of Science & Medicine Library). (ENG., Illus.). xvii, 279p. ***(978-90-04-22136-9(0))*** BRILL.

Maradona, Diego Armando. Maradona: The Autobiography of Soccer's Greatest & Most Controversial Star. 2011. (ENG., Illus.). 328p. pap. 14.95 *(978-1-61608-186-7(4),* 608186) Skyhorse Publishing Co., Inc.

McLeay, Ian. Carlos Tevez: The Biography of Manchester City's Super Striker. 2010. (ENG., Illus.). 296p. 24.95 *(978-1-84454-828-6(7))* Blake, John Publishing, Ltd. GBR. Dist: Independent Pubs. Group.

McManners, Hugh. Forgotten Voices of the Falklands: The Real Story of the Falklands War in the Words of Those Who Were There. 2007. (Forgotten Voices Ser.). (ENG., Illus.). 496p. 37.95 *(978-0-09-190880-5(9))* Random Hse. GBR. Dist: Independent Pubs. Group.

Moragas, Libertad O. condena Florencia. Diario de un viaje. Argentina vs. K. 2008. 72p. pap. 14.95 *(978-1-4092-2164-7(4))* Lulu Enterprises Inc.

Noble, Guadalupe & Peicovich, Esteban, eds. Noble: Un Argentino Visionario. 2010. (SPA., Illus.). 239p. *(978-950-07-3186-7(X))* Editorial Sudamericana S.A.

Parker, William B. Argentines of Today, 2 Vols. (Hispanic Notes & Monographs). reprint ed. 250.00 *(978-0-7222-9577-9(4))* Library Reprints, Inc.

Schwartz-Kates, Deborah & Aydinonat, N. Emrah. Alberto Ginastera: A Guide to Research. 2010. (Routledge Music Bibliographies Ser.). (ENG., Illus.). 256p. 150.00 *(978-0-415-97318-2(X))* Routledge.

Shimano, Chie, illus. Che Guevara: A Manga Biography. 2010. (ENG.). 192p. (gr. 12). 15.00 *(978-0-14-311816-9(1)*, Penguin (Non-Classics)) Penguin Group (USA) Inc.

Taiana, Cecilia. Psychoanalysis & the Military Discourse: The Disappearance, Incarceration, & Exile of Argentinean Psychoanalysts in the 1970s. 2013. (ENG.). 256p. 74.95 *(978-0-230-60790-3(X))* Palgrave Macmillan.

Villa, Ricky & Ardiles, Federico. And Still Ricky Villa: My Autobiography. 2010. (ENG., Illus.). 288p. 28.95 ***(978-1-905326-89-1(0))*** Vision Sports Publishing GBR. Dist: SCB Distributors.

ARGENTINA—CIVILIZATION

Luna, Leandro H. Estructura Demográfica, Estilo de Vida y Relaciones Biologicas de Cazadores Recolectores en un Ambiente de Desierto. 2009. (Bar S Ser.). (ITA., Illus.). 363p. (C). 112.50 *(978-1-4073-0366-6(X))* British Archaeological Reports Ltd. GBR. Dist: Brown, David Bk. Co., The.

Olivera, Guillermo. Laboratorios de la Mediatización: La Experimentación con Materiales Mediáticos, la Teoría y la Crítica Cultural Argentina, 1965-1978. 2010. (SPA.). viii, 354p. *(978-3-0343-0201-2(0))* Lang, Peter Publishing, Inc.

ARGENTINA—DESCRIPTION AND TRAVEL

Abraham, Rudolf. Torres del Paine: Trekking in Chile's Premier National Park. 2010. (Illus.). 224p. pap. 24.95 *(978-1-85284-593-3(7))* Cicerone Pr. GBR. Dist: Midpoint Trade Bks., Inc.

Adams, Fiona. Cultureshock Argentina, 1 vol. 2011. (ENG.). 240p. pap. 15.95 *(978-0-7614-6050-3(0))* Marshall Cavendish Corp.

Aeberhard, Danny, et al. Argentina. 4th ed. 2010. (Rough Guide Travel Guides). (ENG., Illus.). 720p. 26.99 *(978-1-84836-521-6(7))* Rough Guides, Ltd. GBR. Dist: Dorling Kindersley Publishing, Inc.

Andrews, Joseph C. Journey from Buenos Ayres Undertaken on Behalf of the Chilian & Peruvian Mining Assn., 1825-26, 2 vols. reprint ed. 82.50 *(978-0-404-00410-1(5))* AMS Pr., Inc.

Bao, Sandra. Buenos Aires. 6th rev. ed. 2011. (City Guide Ser.). (ENG., Illus.). 256p. pap. 19.99 *(978-1-74179-578-3(8))* Lonely Planet Pubns.

Benson, Andrew & Rough Guides Staff. The Rough Guide to Buenos Aires. 2nd ed. 2011. (ENG., Illus.). 320p. 19.99 *(978-1-84836-891-0(7))* Rough Guides, Ltd. GBR. Dist: Dorling Kindersley Publishing, Inc.

Bernhardson, Wayne. Moon Argentina. 2010. (Moon Handbooks Ser.). (ENG., Illus.). 688p. pap. 21.95 *(978-1-59880-675-5(0))* Avalon Travel Publishing.

—Moon Patagonia: Including the Falkland Islands. 2011. (Moon Handbooks Ser.). (ENG., Illus.). 636p. pap. 21.99 *(978-1-59880-932-9(6))* Avalon Travel Publishing.

—National Geographic Traveler: Argentina. 2010. (National Geographic Traveler Ser.). (ENG., Illus.). 336p. pap. 27.95 *(978-1-4262-0519-4(8)*, National Geographic) National Geographic Society.

Bishop, Nathaniel Holmes. The Pampas & Andes a Thousand Miles' Walk Across South America by Nathaniel H Bishop with an Introduction by Edward a Samuels. 2006. 332p. per. 23.99 *(978-1-4255-3307-6(8))* MPublishing.

Bourne, Benjamin Franklin. The Captive in Patagonia or, Life among the Giants a Personal Narrative. 2006. 252p. per. 20.99 *(978-1-4255-2131-8(2))* MPublishing.

Brega, Isabella. Argentina: Wild South America. 2007. (Exploring Countries of the Wor Ser.). (ENG., Illus.). 128p. 9.95 *(978-88-544-0208-9(7)*, White Star) Rizzoli International Pubns., Inc.

Canaparo, Claudio. El Imaginario Patagonia: Ensayo Acerca de la Evolución Conceptual Del Espacio. 2012. (Hispanic Studies: Culture & Ideas Ser.). (SPA., Illus.). 554p. pap. 85.95 ***(978-3-0343-0287-6(8))*** Lang, Peter AG GBR. Dist: Lang, Peter.

Carrasco, Demetrio, et al, photos by. DK Eyewitness Travel Guide: Argentina: Argentina. 2012. (Eyewitness travel Guide Ser.). (ENG.). 352p. pap. 25.00 ***(978-0-7566-8579-9(6))*** Dorling Kindersley Publishing, Inc.

Chaskielberg, Alejandro. La Creciente. 2011. (SPA & ENG., Illus.). ***(978-1-59005-321-8(4))*** Nazraeli Pr.

Cousins, Lucy E. Argentina Handbook. 6th ed. 2011. (Footprint - Handbooks Ser.). (ENG., Illus.). 716p. 25.95 *(978-1-907263-13-2(6))* Footprint Handbooks GBR. Dist: Globe Pequot Pr., The.

—Buenos Aires & the Pampas Footprint Focus. 2011. (Footprint Focus Ser.). (ENG., Illus.). 128p. pap. 11.95 *(978-1-908206-26-8(8))* Footprint Handbooks GBR. Dist: Globe Pequot Pr., The.

Cousins, Lucy E. Northeast Argentina & Uruguay. 2012. (Footprint Focus Ser.). (ENG.). 144p. pap. 12.95 ***(978-1-908206-66-4(7))*** Footprint Handbooks GBR. Dist: Globe Pequot Pr., The.

Cutler, Miriam. Buenos Aires Street Guide. 2011. 80p. pap. 26.50 ***(978-1-59754-653-9(4))*** Editorial Libros en Red.

Dorling Kindersley Publishing Staff. Argentina. 2010. (Eyewitness Travel Guides). (ENG.). 352p. pap. 25.00 *(978-0-7566-6193-9(5))* Dorling Kindersley Publishing, Inc.

—Eyewitness Travel Guides Top Ten Buenos Aires. 2011. (Eyewitness top 10 travel Guide Ser.). (ENG.). 128p. 14.00 *(978-0-7566-7049-8(7))* Dorling Kindersley Publishing, Inc.

Ellam, Patrick & Ellam, June. The Road to Ushuaia: The World's Southest Town. 2011. 396p. pap. 25.95 *(978-1-4502-9953-4(9))* iUniverse, Inc.

Evans, Polly. On a Hoof & a Prayer: Exploring Argentina at a Gallop. 2008. (ENG., Illus.). 320p. pap. 14.00 *(978-0-385-34110-3(5)*, Delta) Random House Publishing Group.

Everton, Macduff. Patagonia, la Última Esperanza. 2012. (ENG & SPA., Illus.). 235p. 65.00 ***(978-0-938531-02-9(6))*** Txcacalcupul Pr.

Ferranti, Helene Smith. Sailing to Antarctica. 2008. (Illus.). ix, 182p. pap. *(978-1-934582-06-0(9))* Back Channel Pr.

Fodor's Travel Publications, Inc. Staff. Argentina: With Wine Country & Chilean Patagonia. 6th ed. 2010. (Full-Color Gold Guides). (ENG., Illus.). 564p. pap. 24.99 *(978-1-4000-0433-1(0)*, Fodor's) Fodor's Travel Pubns.

—Buenos Aires. 3rd ed. 2012. (Full-Color Gold Guides). (ENG.). 336p. pap. 19.99 ***(978-0-307-92836-8(5)***, Fodor's) Fodor's Travel Pubns.

—Buenos Aires: With Side Trips to Gaucho Country, Iguazu, & Uruguay. 2nd ed. 2010. (Full-Color Gold Guides). (ENG., Illus.). 368p. pap. 19.99 *(978-1-4000-0425-6(X)*, Fodor's) Fodor's Travel Pubns.

—Fodor's Argentina, 7th Edition: With Wine Country & Chilean Patagonia. 2012. (Full-color Travel Guide Ser.). (ENG.). 488p. pap. 25.99 ***(978-0-307-92918-1(3)***, Fodor's) Fodor's Travel Pubns.

Fodor's Travel Publications, Inc. Staff. Patagonia. 2008. (Fodor's Gold Guides). (ENG., Illus.). 416p. pap. 21.95 *(978-1-4000-0684-7(8)*, Fodor's) Fodor's Travel Pubns.

Foster, David William. Urban Photography in Argentina: Nine Artists of the Post-Dictatorship ERA. 2007. (ENG., Illus.). 240p. per. 25.00 *(978-0-7864-3121-2(0))* McFarland & Co., Inc. Pubs.

Froggatt, Charles. Buenos Aires. 2007. (Hedonist's Guide to Buenos Aires Ser.). (ENG., Illus.). 208p. im. lthr. 18.95 *(978-1-905428-09-3(1))* Filmer Ltd. GBR. Dist: Perseus-PGW.

Hamwee, Robert. Argentina: A Quick Guide to Customs & Etiquette. 2006. (Culture Smart! Ser.). (ENG., Illus.). 168p. pap. 9.95 *(978-1-85733-328-2(4))* Kuperard Pubs. GBR. Dist: Random Hse., Inc.

Harvard Student Agencies, Inc. Let's Go Buenos Aires: The Student Travel Guide. 2009. (Let's Go Ser.). (ENG., Illus.). 304p. pap. 18.95 *(978-1-59880-311-2(5)*, Let's Go) Avalon Travel Publishing.

Hayskar, Bonnie J., ed. Natural Iguassu: Brazil/Brasil & Argentina. 2010. (ENG, POR & SPA., Illus.). 180p. pap. 24.95 *(978-0-9630180-9-0(4))* PANGAEA.

Head, Francis Bond. Rough Notes Taken during some Rapid Journeys across the Pampas & among the Andes. 2009. (Cambridge Library Collection - Life Sciences Ser.). (ENG.). 328p. pap. 19.99 *(978-1-108-00161-8(0))* Cambridge Univ. Pr.

Herron, Francis. Letters from the Argentine. 2011. 320p. 50.95 ***(978-1-258-08687-9(5))*** Literary Licensing, LLC.

Hudson, W. H. Far Away & Long Ago: A Childhood in Argentina. reprint ed. 64.50 *(978-0-404-03408-5(X))* AMS Pr., Inc.

—Far Away & Long Ago: A Childhood in Argentina. 2006. (ENG.). 246p. pap. 20.99 *(978-1-4264-1379-7(3))*; 228p. pap. 22.99 *(978-1-4264-1432-9(3))* BiblioBazaar.

—Far Away & Long Ago: A Childhood in Argentina. 332p. reprint ed. 98.00 *(978-0-7222-9581-6(2))* Library Reprints, Inc.

—Far Away & Long Ago: A Childhood in Argentina. 2007. (ENG.). 228p. pap. 12.45 *(978-1-60424-746-6(0)*, Book Jungle) Standard Pubns., Inc.

—Far Away & Long Ago: A Childhood in Argentina. 2007. 356p. 32.95 *(978-1-4344-9351-4(2))*; per. 19.95 *(978-1-4344-9350-7(4))* Wildside Pr., LLC.

—Idle Days in Patagonia. 2008. 152p. pap. *(978-1-4099-0534-9(9))* Dodo Pr.

—Idle Days in Patagonia. 2007. (ENG.). 268p. per. 27.95 *(978-1-4325-2148-6(9))* Kessinger Publishing, LLC.

Indij, Guido, ed. 200 - Four Hundred Images Are Worth More Than Four Hundred Thousand. 2012. (ENG., Illus.). 528p. 95.00 *(978-950-889-196-9(3))* La Marca ARG. Dist: D.A.P./Distributed Art Pubs.

Indij, Guido, et al, photos by. Buenos Aires: Out of Series. 2008. (ENG., Illus.). 240p. pap. 25.00 *(978-950-889-165-5(3))* La Marca ARG. Dist: D.A.P./Distributed Art Pubs.

Insight Guides. Argentina Insight Guide. rev. ed. 2009. (Insight Guides). (ENG., Illus.). 384p. pap. 23.99 *(978-981-282-054-9(X))* APA Publications Services SGP. Dist: Ingram Pub. Services.

Insight Guides Staff. Argentina. 2006. (Insight Guides). 350p. 26.95 *(978-981-258-584-4(2))* Langenscheidt Publishing Group.

Johnson, Delores. ARGENTINA RESIDENCY & RETIREMENT: How I Did It. 2008. 98p. pap. 22.50 *(978-1-4357-1244-7(7))* Lulu Enterprises Inc.

King, J. Anthony. Twenty-Four Years in the Argentine Republic. reprint ed. 57.50 *(978-0-404-03691-1(0))* AMS Pr., Inc.

Knopf Guides. Knopf MapGuides: Buenos Aires. 2010. (ENG.). 48p. pap. 9.95 *(978-0-307-26894-5(2)*, Knopf) Knopf Doubleday Publishing Group.

Koebel, William H. The Great South Land: The River Plate & Southern Brazil of Today. 314p. reprint ed. 98.00 *(978-0-7222-9555-7(3))* Library Reprints, Inc.

Kogan, Gabriela. The Authentic Bars, Cafes & Restaurants of Buenos Aires. 2008. (ENG., Illus.). 144p. pap. 14.95 *(978-1-892145-55-0(3))* Little Bookroom.

Locken, E. Travel Journal Argentina. 2010. 192p. pap. 19.99 *(978-0-557-43259-2(6))* Lulu Enterprises Inc.

—Travel Journal Buenos Aires. 2010. 192p. pap. 19.99 *(978-0-557-44589-9(2))* Lulu Enterprises Inc.

Logan, Joy. Aconcagua: The Invention of Mountaineering on America's Highest Peak. 2011. (ENG., Illus.). 272p. pap. 35.00 *(978-0-8165-2950-6(7))* Univ. of Arizona Pr.

Lonely Planet Staff & Bao, Sandra. Argentina. 7th ed. 2010. (Country Guide Ser.). (ENG., Illus.). 660p. pap. 25.99 *(978-1-74179-464-9(1))* Lonely Planet Pubns.

Luongo, Michael. Frommer's Buenos Aires. 4th ed. 2011. (Frommer's Complete Guides). (ENG., Illus.). 288p. pap. 17.99 *(978-1-118-00964-2(9)*, Frommers) Wiley, John & Sons, Inc.

Luongo, Michael, et al. Frommer's Argentina. 3rd ed. 2011. (Frommer's Complete Guides). (ENG., Illus.). 448p. pap. 22.99 *(978-1-118-00978-9(9)*, Frommers) Wiley, John & Sons, Inc.

Mansilla, Lucio V. Una Excursion a Los Indios Ranqueles. 2008. 290p. 28.99 *(978-0-554-86413-6(4))*; 290p. 25.99 *(978-0-554-86419-8(3))*; 270p. pap. 27.75 *(978-0-554-86417-4(7))*; 290p. pap. 28.75 *(978-0-554-86414-3(2))* BiblioBazaar.

Masotta, Carlos, ed. A Postcard Album, 1 vol. 2010. (ENG., Illus.). 504p. pap. 50.00 *(978-950-889-163-1(7))* La Marca ARG. Dist: D.A.P./Distributed Art Pubs.

McCloskey, Erin. Argentina/2 Bradt. 2nd rev. ed. 2011. (Bradt Travel Guide Ser.). (ENG., Illus.). 448p. pap. 27.99 *(978-1-84162-351-1(2))* Bradt Travel Guides GBR. Dist: Globe Pequot Pr., The.

Miers, John. Travels in Chile & la Plata: Including Accounts Respecting the Geography, Geology, Statistics, Government, Finances, Agriculture, Manners & Customs, & the Mining Operations in Chile. 2011. (Cambridge Library Collection - Travel & Exploration Ser.). (ENG.). 572p. pap. 39.99 *(978-1-108-07296-0(8))*; (Illus.). 554p. pap. 39.99 *(978-1-108-07295-3(X))* Cambridge Univ. Pr.

Moss, Chris. Patagonia: A Cultural History. 2008. (Landscapes of the Imagination Ser.). (ENG., Illus.). 256p. 25.00 *(978-0-19-534249-9(6))* Oxford Univ. Pr., Inc.

Newton, Paula & Newton. Viva Travel Guide Argentina. 2011. (ENG.). 650p. pap. 29.99 *(978-0-9825585-0-8(3))* Viva Travel Guides.

Núñez Cabeza de Vaca, Alvar & Morrow, Baker H. The South American Expeditions, 1540-1545. 2011. ***(978-0-8263-5065-7(8))*** Univ. of New Mexico Pr.

Page, Thomas, abr. La Plata, the Argentine Confederation, & Paraguay. 2009. (Military History Ser.). (ENG.). 630p. pap. 36.95 *(978-1-4290-2195-1(0))* Applewood Bks.

Romero, Migdalia. Tango Lover's Guide to Buenos Aires: Insights & Recommendations. 2010. 240p. pap. 18.95 *(978-1-4401-6675-4(7))* iUniverse, Inc.

Ruiz, Maximiliano. Graffiti Argentina. 2008. (Illus.). 152p. ***(978-0-500-51441-2(0))*** Thames & Hudson.

Ryan, Jim. Aconcagua & the Southern Andes. 2nd ed. 2011. (Illus.). 160p. pap. 24.95 ***(978-1-85284-587-2(2))*** Cicerone Pr. GBR. Dist: Midpoint Trade Bks., Inc.

Sahm, Reiner, photos by. Patagonia. 2007. (Illus.). 186p. 59.95 *(978-1-877339-60-8(1))* NZVP Bks. & Calendars Ltd. NZL. Dist: Perseus-PGW.

Schlecht, Neil Edward. Frommer's Buenos Aires Day by Day. 2009. (Frommer's Day by Day - Pocket Ser.: 254). (ENG., Illus.). 192p. pap. 12.99 *(978-0-470-16011-4(X)*, Frommers) Wiley, John & Sons, Inc.

Stephens, Henry. Illustrated Descriptive Argentina. 763p. reprint ed. 148.00 *(978-0-7222-9585-4(5))* Library Reprints, Inc.

Stewart, Charles Samuel. Brazil & la Plata; the Personal Record of a Cruise, by C S Stewart. 2006. 468p. per. 29.99 *(978-1-4255-5179-7(3))* MPublishing.

Thomas Cook Publishing Staff & Egginton, Jane. Argentina. 2nd ed. 2009. (Travellers - Thomas Cook Ser.). (ENG., Illus.). 176p. pap. 16.95 *(978-1-84848-186-2(1))* Cook, Thomas Publishing GBR. Dist: Globe Pequot Pr., The.

Time Out Guides Staff. Argentina & Uruguay: Perfect Places to Stay, Eat & Explore. 2010. (Perfect Places Ser.). (ENG., Illus.). 400p. pap. 22.95 *(978-1-84670-127-6(9))* Time Out Guides Ltd. GBR. Dist: Perseus-PGW.

—Time Out Buenos Aires. (Time Out Shortlist Ser.). (ENG., Illus.). 2009. 192p. pap. 12.95 *(978-1-84670-159-7(7))* 5th ed. 2011. 256p. pap. 19.95 *(978-1-84670-192-4(9))* Time Out Guides Ltd. GBR. Dist: Perseus-PGW.

Time Out Guides Staff, ed. Time Out Selecciones Buenos Aires: Time Out Shortlist Buenos Aires. 2010. (Selecciones Ser.). (SPA.). 184p. pap. 12.95 *(978-84-9801-456-3(5))* Time Out Guides Ltd. GBR. Dist: Perseus-PGW.

Wallpaper Magazine Editors, ed. Wallpaper City Guide - Beunos Aires 2011. 2011. (ENG.). 128p. pap. 9.95 *(978-0-7148-6088-6(3))* Phaidon Pr., Inc.

Wallpaper Magazine Editors, ed. Wallpaper City Guide - Buenos Aires. 2011. (ENG.). 128p. pap. 9.95 ***(978-0-7148-6281-1(9))*** Phaidon Pr., Inc.

ARGENTINA—ECONOMIC CONDITIONS

Auyero, Javier. Patients of the State: The Politics of Waiting in Argentina. 2012. (ENG., Illus.). 192p. 79.95 ***(978-0-8223-5259-4(1))***; pap. 22.95 ***(978-0-8223-5233-4(8))*** Duke Univ. Pr.

Baer, Werner & Fleischer, David V. The Economies of Argentina & Brazil: A Comparative Perspective. 2011. (Illus.). 512p. 195.00 ***(978-1-84980-996-2(8))*** Elgar, Edward Publishing, Inc.

Berg, Janine, et al. Enfrentando el Desafío Del Empleo: Argentina, Brasil y Mexico en una Economía Globalizada. 2009. (SPA., Illus.). 305p. pap. 29.00 *(978-970-722-523-7(8))* Plaza y Valdes, S.A. de C.V. MEX. Dist: Sony Electronics.

Bianchi Villelli, Marcia. Organizar la Diferencia: Prácticas de Consumo en Floridablanco, Costa Patagónica, Siglo XVIII. 2007. (SPA., Illus.). 225p. 7.00 *(978-987-1354-02-3(9))* Teseo ARG. Dist: Sony Electronics.

Borges, M. J. & Borges, Marcelo J. Chains of Gold: Portuguese Migration to Argentina in Transatlantic Perspective. 2009. (Studies in Global Social History Ser.). (Illus.). 355p. *(978-90-04-17648-5(9))* BRILL.

Brown, Jonathan C. A Socioeconomic History of Argentina, 1776-1860. 2008. (Cambridge Latin American Studies). (ENG.). 320p. pap. 42.00 *(978-0-521-10210-0(3))* Cambridge Univ. Pr.

Burgin, Miron. The Economic Aspects of Argentine Federalism, 1820-1852. 2008. 324p. pap. 32.00 *(978-1-59740-617-8(1))* ACLS Humanities E-Book.

Chudnovsky, Daniel & López, Andrés. The Elusive Quest for Growth in Argentina. 2007. (ENG., Illus.). 236p. 89.00 *(978-1-4039-7789-2(5))* Palgrave Macmillan.

Cohen, Michael. Argentina's Economic Growth & Recovery 2001-2008. 2011. (Routledge Studies in the Modern World Economy Ser.). (ENG., Illus.). 312p. (C). 140.00 ***(978-0-415-59480-6(4))*** Routledge.

Cohen, Michael A. Argentina's Economic Growth & Recovery, 2001-2008. 2011. ***(978-0-203-14452-7(X))*** Routledge.

Conde, Roberto Cortès. The Political Economy of Argentina in the Twentieth Century. 2008. (Cambridge Latin American Studies). (ENG., Illus.). 404p. 85.00 *(978-0-521-88232-3(X))* Cambridge Univ. Pr.

della Paolera, Gerardo & Taylor, Alan M., eds. A New Economic History of Argentina. 2011. (ENG.). 418p. pap. 50.00 *(978-0-521-28325-0(6))* Cambridge Univ. Pr.

Demombynes, Gabriel & Verner, Dorte. The Invisible Poor: A Portrait of Rural Poverty in Argentina. 2010. (Country Studies). (ENG.). 135p. pap. 25.00 *(978-0-8213-8207-3(1)*, 9780821382073) World Bank Pubns.

Doing Business in Argentina. Date not set. (Doing Business in Regions & Countries Around the World Ser.). 80p. *(978-1-882390-50-2(4))* Training Management Corp.

Elena, Eduardo. Dignifying Argentina: Peronism, Citizenship, & Mass Consumption. 2011. (Pitt Latin American Studies). (ENG., Illus.). 344p. pap. 27.95 ***(978-0-8229-6170-3(9))*** Univ. of Pittsburgh Pr.

Epstein, Edward & Pion-Berlin, David. Broken Promises? The Argentine Crisis & Argentine Democracy. 2008. (ENG.). 296p. pap. 34.99 *(978-0-7391-2726-1(8))* Lexington Bks.

Esposto, Alexis. Drifting Apart. 2009. 92p. pap. *(978-3-639-19189-9(7))* VDM Verlag Dr. Mueller e.K.

Haverland, Jeanne B. Argentina: Economic, Political & Social Issues. 2008. (Illus.). xi, 155p. 82.00 *(978-1-60456-469-3(5))* Nova Science Pubs., Inc.

Icon Group International, Inc. Staff, compiled by. The 2006 Economic & Product Market Databook for Bahia Blanca, Argentina. 2006. 618p. ring bd. 95.00 *(978-0-497-80119-9(1))* Icon Group International, Inc.

—The 2006 Economic & Product Market Databook for Buenos Aires, Argentina. 2006. 618p. ring bd. 95.00 *(978-0-497-80258-5(9))* Icon Group International, Inc.

—The 2006 Economic & Product Market Databook for Catamarca, Argentina. 2006. 618p. ring bd. 95.00 *(978-0-497-80320-9(8))* Icon Group International, Inc.

—The 2006 Economic & Product Market Databook for Chaco, Argentina. 2006. 618p. ring bd. 95.00 *(978-0-497-80334-6(8))* Icon Group International, Inc.

—The 2006 Economic & Product Market Databook for Chubut, Argentina. 2006. 618p. ring bd. 95.00 *(978-0-497-80375-9(5))* Icon Group International, Inc.

—The 2006 Economic & Product Market Databook for Cordoba, Argentina. 2006. 618p. ring bd. 95.00 *(978-0-497-80408-4(5))* Icon Group International, Inc.

—The 2006 Economic & Product Market Databook for Corrientes, Argentina. 2006. 618p. ring bd. 95.00 *(978-0-497-80414-5(5))* Icon Group International, Inc.

—The 2006 Economic & Product Market Databook for Entre Rios, Argentina. 2006. 618p. ring bd. 95.00 *(978-0-497-79983-0(9))* Icon Group International, Inc.

—The 2006 Economic & Product Market Databook for Formosa, Argentina. 2006. 618p. ring bd. 95.00 *(978-0-497-80545-6(6))* Icon Group International, Inc.

—The 2006 Economic & Product Market Databook for Jujuy, Argentina. 2006. 618p. ring bd. 95.00 *(978-0-497-81958-3(9))* Icon Group International, Inc.

—The 2006 Economic & Product Market Databook for la Pampa, Argentina. 2006. 618p. ring bd. 95.00 *(978-0-497-80801-3(3))* Icon Group International, Inc.

—The 2006 Economic & Product Market Databook for la Plata, Argentina. 2006. 618p. ring bd. 95.00 *(978-0-497-80803-7(X))* Icon Group International, Inc.

—The 2006 Economic & Product Market Databook for la Rioja, Argentina. 2006. 618p. ring bd. 95.00 *(978-0-497-80804-4(8))* Icon Group International, Inc.

—The 2006 Economic & Product Market Databook for Mar del Plata, Argentina. 2006. 618p. ring bd. 95.00 *(978-0-497-80009-3(8))* Icon Group International, Inc.

—The 2006 Economic & Product Market Databook for Mendoza, Argentina. 2006. 618p. ring bd. 95.00 *(978-0-497-81009-2(3))* Icon Group International, Inc.

—The 2006 Economic & Product Market Databook for Misiones, Argentina. 2006. 618p. ring bd. 95.00 *(978-0-497-81028-3(X))* Icon Group International, Inc.

—The 2006 Economic & Product Market Databook for Neuquén, Argentina. 2006. 618p. ring bd. 95.00 *(978-0-497-81113-6(8))* Icon Group International, Inc.

—The 2006 Economic & Product Market Databook for Rio Negro, Argentina. 2006. 618p. ring bd. 95.00 *(978-0-497-81379-6(3))* Icon Group International, Inc.

—The 2006 Economic & Product Market Databook for Rosario, Argentina. 2006. 618p. ring bd. 95.00 *(978-0-497-81365-9(3))* Icon Group International, Inc.

—The 2006 Economic & Product Market Databook for Salta, Argentina. 2006. 618p. ring bd. 95.00 *(978-0-497-81405-2(6))* Icon Group International, Inc.

—The 2006 Economic & Product Market Databook for San Juan, Argentina. 2006. 618p. ring bd. 95.00 *(978-0-497-81423-6(4))* Icon Group International, Inc.

—The 2006 Economic & Product Market Databook for San Luis, Argentina. 2006. 618p. ring bd. 95.00 *(978-0-497-81427-4(7))* Icon Group International, Inc.

—The 2006 Economic & Product Market Databook for San Miguel de Tucuman, Argentina. 2006. 618p. ring bd. 95.00 *(978-0-497-81429-8(3))* Icon Group International, Inc.

—The 2006 Economic & Product Market Databook for Santa Cruz, Argentina. 2006. 618p. ring bd. 95.00 *(978-0-497-81444-1(7))* Icon Group International, Inc.

—The 2006 Economic & Product Market Databook for Santa Fe, Argentina. 2006. 618p. ring bd. 95.00 *(978-0-497-81446-5(3))* Icon Group International, Inc.

—The 2006 Economic & Product Market Databook for Santiago del Estero, Argentina. 2006. 618p. ring bd. 95.00 *(978-0-497-81456-4(0))* Icon Group International, Inc.

—The 2006 Economic & Product Market Databook for Tierra del Fuego, Argentina. 2006. 618p. ring bd. 95.00 *(978-0-497-81679-7(2))* Icon Group International, Inc.

—The 2006 Economic & Product Market Databook for Tucumán, Argentina. 2006. 618p. ring bd. 95.00 *(978-0-497-81733-6(0))* Icon Group International, Inc.

Juarez-Dappe, Patricia. When Sugar Ruled: Economy & Society in Northwestern Argentina, Tucuman, 1876-1916. 2010. (Ohio RIS Latin America Ser.). (ENG., Illus.). 320p. pap. 32.00 *(978-0-89680-274-2(4))* Ohio Univ. Pr.

Lewis, Paul H. The Agony of Argentine Capitalism: From Menem to the Kirchners, 1 vol. 2009. 221p. 65.00 *(978-0-313-37877-5(0)*, C37877); pap. 29.95 *(978-0-313-37879-9(7)*, B37879) Greenwood Publishing Group, Inc. (Praeger Pubs.).

Maute, Jutta. Hyperinflation, Currency Board, & Bust: The Case of Argentina, Vol. 56. 2006. (Hohenheimer Volkswirtschaftliche Schriften Ser.). 289p. pap. 57.95 *(978-0-8204-8708-3(2))* Lang, Peter Publishing, Inc.

Page, Joanna. Crisis & Capitalism in Contemporary Argentine Cinema. 2009. (ENG., Illus.). 248p. 84.95 *(978-0-8223-4457-5(2))*; pap. 23.95 *(978-0-8223-4472-8(6))* Duke Univ. Pr.

Peralta-Ramos, Monica. La Economía Política Argentina: Poder y Clases Sociales (1930-2006) 2007. (Economía Ser.). (SPA.). 453p. pap. *(978-950-557-717-0(6))* Fondo de Cultura Economica.

Pineda, Yovanna. Industrial Development in a Frontier Economy: The Industrialization of Argentina, 1890-1930. 2009. (Social Science History Ser.). (ENG.). 224p. 55.00 *(978-0-8047-5983-0(9))* Stanford Univ. Pr.

Sanchez, Omar. Mobilizing Resources in Latin America: The Political Economy of Tax Reform in Chile & Argentina. 2011. (ENG.). 258p. 85.00 *(978-0-230-11446-3(6))* Palgrave Macmillan.

Sánchez Román, José Antonio. Taxation & Society in Twentieth-Century Argentina. 2012. (Studies of the Americas Ser.). (ENG., Illus.). 256p. 90.00 ***(978-0-230-34126-5(8))*** Palgrave Macmillan.

Santarcángelo, Juan Eduardo. Growth, Employment & Income Distribution. 2010. 204p. pap. *(978-3-8383-5642-6(X))* Lambert Academic Publishing.

Schelhase, Marc. Globalization, Regionalization & Business: Conflict, Convergence & Influence. 2008. (ENG., Illus.). 224p. 89.00 *(978-0-230-57329-1(0))* Palgrave Macmillan.

Tanzi, Vito. Argentina: How one of the richest countries in the world lost its wealth: an Economic Chronicle. 2007. per. 19.95 *(978-0-9795576-0-6(7))* Pinto, Jorge Bks.

United Nations. Development of Technological Capabilities in an Extremely Volatile Economy: The Industrial Sector in Argentina. 2008. (ENG.). 56p. pap. 10.00 *(978-92-1-121670-7(2))* United Nations Pubns.

Veigel, Klaus Friedrich & Veigel, Klaus. Dictatorship, Democracy, & Globalization: Argentina & the Cost of Paralysis, 1973-2001. 2009. (ENG., Illus.). 240p. 65.00 *(978-0-271-03464-5(5))* Pennsylvania State Univ. Pr.

ARGENTINA—ECONOMIC POLICY

Argentina: Business Financing Handbook. (Illus.). 70p. (Orig.). pap. 295.00 *(978-0-7605-1179-4(9))* Rector Pr., Ltd.

Chudnovsky, Daniel & López, Andrés. The Elusive Quest for Growth in Argentina. 2007. (ENG., Illus.). 236p. 89.00 *(978-1-4039-7789-2(5))* Palgrave Macmillan.

Cibils, Alan. EXCHANGE RATE POLICY, CAPITAL CONTROLS, AND ECONOMICSTABILITY: A CGE MODEL OF ARGENTINA. 2008. 212p. pap. *(978-3-639-10640-4(7))* VDM Verlag Dr. Mueller e.K.

Cohen, Michael. Argentina's Economic Growth & Recovery 2001-2008. 2011. (Routledge Studies in the Modern World Economy Ser.). (ENG., Illus.). 312p. (C). 140.00 ***(978-0-415-59480-6(4))*** Routledge.

Cohen, Michael A. Argentina's Economic Growth & Recovery, 2001-2008. 2011. ***(978-0-203-14452-7(X))*** Routledge.

Eaton, Kent. Politicians & Economic Reform in New Democracies. 2008. pap. 28.95 *(978-0-271-02835-4(1))* Pennsylvania State Univ. Pr.

Epstein, Edward & Pion-Berlin, David. Broken Promises? The Argentine Crisis & Argentine Democracy. 2008. (ENG.). 296p. pap. 34.99 *(978-0-7391-2726-1(8))* Lexington Bks.

Esposto, Alexis. Drifting Apart. 2009. 92p. pap. *(978-3-639-19189-9(7))* VDM Verlag Dr. Mueller e.K.

Lewis, Paul H. The Agony of Argentine Capitalism: From Menem to the Kirchners, 1 vol. 2009. 221p. 65.00 *(978-0-313-37877-5(0)*, C37877); pap. 29.95 *(978-0-313-37879-9(7)*, B37879) Greenwood Publishing Group, Inc. (Praeger Pubs.).

Redrado, Martín. No Reserve: The Limit of Absolute Power, 0 vols. unabr. ed. 2011. (ENG.). 288p. pap. 13.95 *(978-1-935597-23-0(X)*, 9781935597230) Amazon Publishing.

Riggirozzi, Pía. Advancing Governance in the South: What Roles for International Financial Institutions in Developing States? 2008. (International Political Economy Ser.). (ENG., Illus.). 224p. 89.00 *(978-0-230-22011-9(8))* Palgrave Macmillan.

Silva-Garbade, Caroline. Determinants of National IMF Policy: A Case Study of Brazil & Argentina. 2011. (Hispano-Americana. Geschichte, Sprache, Literatur Ser.). 254p. 75.95 *(978-3-631-60560-8(9))* Lang, Peter GmbH, Europaischer Verlag der Wissenschaften DEU. Dist: Lang, Peter.

United Nations. Development of Technological Capabilities in an Extremely Volatile Economy: The Industrial Sector in Argentina. 2008. (ENG.). 56p. pap. 10.00 *(978-92-1-121670-7(2))* United Nations Pubns.

World Bank Staff. Argentina: Income Support Policies Toward the Bicentennial. 2009. (Country Studies). (ENG., Illus.). 182p. pap. 20.00 *(978-0-8213-8051-2(6)*, 9780821380512) World Bank Pubns.

ARGENTINA—FOREIGN RELATIONS

Bletz, May E. Immigration & Acculturation in Brazil & Argentina: 1890-1929. 2010. (ENG.). 190p. 84.00 *(978-0-230-10019-0(8))* Palgrave Macmillan.

Lechini de Alvarez, Gladys, et al. Argentina e Brasil: Vencendo Os Preconceitos: As Várias Arestas de Uma Concepção Estratégica. 2009. (POR & SPA., Illus.). 475p. *(978-85-7106-396-9(6))* Revan, Editora Ltda.

Mani, Kristina. Democratization & Military Transformation in Argentina & Chile: Rethinking Rivalry. 2011. (Illus.). 240p. 65.00 *(978-1-935049-40-1(2))* FirstForumPress.

Margheritis, Ana. Argentina's Foreign Policy: Domestic Politics & Democracy Promotion in the Americas. 2010. 150p. 55.00 *(978-1-935049-19-7(4))* FirstForumPress.

Mullins, Martin. In the Shadow of Generals: Foreign Policy Formation in Argentina Brazil & Chile. 2006. (Illus.). 178p. 120.00 *(978-0-7546-4736-2(6))* Ashgate Publishing Co.

Sheinin, David M. K. Argentina & the United States: An Alliance Contained. 2006. (United States & the Americas Ser.). (ENG.). 304p. lib. bdg. 69.95 *(978-0-8203-2808-9(1))* Univ. of Georgia Pr.

—Argentina & the United States: An Alliance Contained. 2006. (United States & the Americas Ser.). (ENG.). 304p. per. 24.95 *(978-0-8203-2809-6(X))* Univ. of Georgia Pr.

Smith Jr., O. Edmund. Yankee Diplomacy V3: U. S. Intervention in Argentina. 2011. 202p. 44.95 ***(978-1-258-06095-4(7))*** Literary Licensing, LLC.

United Nations. Case Concerning Pulp Mills on the River Uruguay: Request for the Indication of Provisional Measures (Argentina V. Uruguay) Order of 13 July 2006. 2007. (Icj Reports of Judgments, Advisory Opinions & Orders Ser.). (ENG, FRE & MUL.). 96p. pap. 10.00 *(978-92-1-071024-4(X))* United Nations Pubns.

—Case Concerning Pulp Mills on the River Uruguay (Argentina V. Uruguay) Order of 13 July 2006. 2007. (Icj Reports of Judgments, Advisory Opinions & Orders Ser.). (ENG, FRE & MUL.). 8p. pap. 4.50 *(978-92-1-071025-1(8))* United Nations Pubns.

—Case Concerning Pulp Mills on the River Uruguay (Argentina V. Uruguay) Order of 14 September 2007. 2009. (ENG, FRE & MUL.). 6p. pap. 4.50 *(978-92-1-071034-3(7))* United Nations Pubns.

Vacs, Aldo Cesar. Discreet Partners: Argentina & the USSR Since 1917. 2009. (Pitt Latin American Studies). (ENG.). 176p. (C). pap. 24.95 *(978-0-8229-8369-9(9))* Univ. of Pittsburgh Pr.

ARGENTINA—HISTORY

Aguilar, Gonzalo. New Argentine Film: Other Worlds. 2011. (New Concepts in Latino American Cultures Ser.). (ENG.). 320p. pap. 28.00 *(978-0-230-10901-8(2))* Palgrave Macmillan.

Amatriain, Ignacio & Algranti, Joaquín. Una Década de Nuevo Cine Argentino, 1995-2005: Industria, Crítica, Formación, Estéticas. 2009. (SPA., Illus.). 222p. *(978-987-1599-02-8(1))* Fundacion Centro Integral Comunicacion, Cultura y Sociedad, CICCUS.

Aversa, Santiago L. Dispatches from Martín García. 2009. 105p. pap. 13.28 *(978-0-557-16156-0(8))* Lulu Enterprises Inc.

—Patrol & ASW Aircraft of the Argentine Navy Vol. I. 2010. 75p. pap. 11.00 *(978-0-557-22402-9(0))* Lulu Enterprises Inc.

Bergero, Adriana J. Intersecting Tango: Cultural Geographies of Buenos Aires, 1900-1930. Young, Richard, tr. from SPA. 2008. (Pitt Illuminations Ser.). (ENG., Illus.). 376p. (C). pap. 27.95 *(978-0-8229-5985-4(2))* Univ. of Pittsburgh Pr.

Brown, Jonathan C. Argentina. 2nd rev. ed. 2010. (Brief History Ser.). 368p. (C). (gr. 9-18). 49.50 *(978-0-8160-7796-0(7))* Facts On File, Inc.

—A Brief History of Argentina. 2nd rev. ed. 2011. (Brief History Ser.). 368p. (C). (gr. 9). pap. 19.95 *(978-0-8160-8361-9(4)*, Checkmark Bks.) Facts On File, Inc.

Camandrett, Sebas. Gilera Motorcycles in Argentina. 2010. 101p. pap. 40.00 *(978-0-557-45182-1(5))* Lulu Enterprises Inc.

Claxton, Robert H. From Parsifal to Perón: Early Radio in Argentina, 1920-1944. 2007. (ENG., Illus.). 248p. 59.95 *(978-0-8130-3090-6(0))* Univ. Pr. of Florida.

Dominguez, Luis L. The Conquest of the River Plate. 2009. 330p. 29.99 *(978-1-113-66708-3(7))*; pap. 31.75 *(978-1-113-66704-5(4))*; pap. 30.75 *(978-1-113-66703-8(6))* BiblioBazaar.

Dreier, Katherine S. Five Months in the Argentine from a Woman's Point of View, 1918 to 1919. 286p. reprint ed. 98.00 *(978-0-7222-9578-6(2))* Library Reprints, Inc.

Duhalde, Eduardo Alberto. Argentina Aflame: My first 120 days in office, from dissolution to Recovery. 2009. (ENG.). lib. bdg. *(978-1-4135-7508-8(0))* El Cid Editor Incorporated.

Edwards, Todd L. Argentina: A Global Studies Handbook, 1 vol. 2008. (Global Studies). (Illus.). 351p. 55.00 *(978-1-85109-986-3(7)*, ARGENT1C) ABC-CLIO, LLC.

Endere, Maria Luz. Management of Archaeological Sites & the Public in Argentina. 2007. (Bar S Ser.). (Illus.). 187p. (C). 85.00 *(978-1-4073-0152-5(7))* British Archaeological Reports Ltd. GBR. Dist: Brown, David Bk. Co., The.

Faingold, Eduardo D. Exile from Argentina: A Jewish Family & the Military Dictatorship (1976-1983) 2008. pap. *(978-1-59311-994-2(1))* Information Age Publishing, Inc.

Fletcher, Ian. The Waters of Oblivion: The British Invasion of the Rio de la Plata, 1806-1807. 2006. (ENG., Illus.). 172p. 39.95 *(978-1-86227-342-9(1))* History Pr. Ltd.,The GBR. Dist: Independent Pubs. Group.

Garramuño, Florencia & Kazumi Stahl, Anna. Primitive Modernities: Tango, Samba, & Nation. 2011. (ENG.). 216p. 85.00 *(978-0-8047-6249-6(X))*; pap. 27.95 *(978-0-8047-6250-2(3))* Stanford Univ. Pr.

Giunta, Andrea. Avant-Garde, Internationalism, & Politics: Argentine Art in the Sixties. Kahn, Peter, tr. from SPA. 2007. (Latin America Otherwise Ser.). (ENG., Illus.). 432p. per. 27.95 *(978-0-8223-3893-2(9))*; 99.95 *(978-0-8223-3877-2(7))* Duke Univ. Pr.

Goebel, Michael. Argentina's Partisan Past: Nationalism & the Politics of History. 2011. (Liverpool University Press - Liverpool Latin American Studies). (ENG., Illus.). 284p. 95.00 *(978-1-84631-238-0(8))* Liverpool Univ. Pr. GBR. Dist: Chicago Distribution Ctr.

Graham-Yooll, Andrew. Goodbye Buenos Aires. 2012. (ENG.). 222p. pap. 29.95 ***(978-1-906011-70-3(2))*** Eland Bks. GBR. Dist: Dufour Editions, Inc.

Gunning, Jeroen & Kegan Paul, Charles. The Handbook of Argentina. 2008. 50.00 *(978-0-7103-1371-3(3))* Kegan Paul International, Ltd. GBR. Dist: Columbia Univ. Pr.

Halperin Donghi, Tulio. Politics Economics & Society in Argentina in the Revolutionary Period. 2009. (Cambridge Latin American Studies). (ENG.). 440p. pap. 55.00 *(978-0-521-10903-1(5))* Cambridge Univ. Pr.

Halperín Donghi, Tulio & Chiaramonte, José Carlos. Proyecto y Construcción de una Nación: 1846-1880. (SPA.). 622p. *(978-950-9122-29-1(7))* Grupo Editorial Planeta S.A.I.C., Ariel.

Healey, Mark Alan. The Ruins of the New Argentina: Peronism & the Remaking of San Juan after the 1944 Earthquake. 2011. (ENG., Illus.). 416p. 94.95 *(978-0-8223-4883-2(7))*; pap. 25.95 *(978-0-8223-4905-1(1))* Duke Univ. Pr.

Hedges, Jill. Argentina: A Modern History. 2011. (ENG., Illus.). 336p. 42.00 *(978-1-84885-654-7(7))* I. B. Tauris & Co., Ltd. GBR. Dist: Macmillan.

Hermosilla, Alejandro. Los Hijos Sin Nombre: El silencio del Olvido. 2010. 400p. pap. *(978-3-8383-1107-4(8))* Lambert Academic Publishing.

Horowitz, Joel. Argentina's Radical Party & Popular Mobilization, 1916-1930. 2008. (ENG.). 192p. pap. 45.00 *(978-0-271-03404-1(1))*; 254p. pap. 26.95 ***(978-0-271-03405-8(X))*** Pennsylvania State Univ. Pr.

Hortiguera, Hugo & Rocha, Carolina, eds. Argentinean Cultural Production During the Neoliberal Years (1989-2001) 2007. 248p. *(978-0-7734-5348-7(2))* Mellen, Edwin Pr., The.

Indij, Guido, ed. 200 - Four Hundred Images Are Worth More Than Four Hundred Thousand. 2012. (ENG., Illus.). 528p. 95.00 *(978-950-889-196-9(3))* La Marca ARG. Dist: D.A.P./Distributed Art Pubs.

Indij, Guido, ed. & text. Peron Mediante, 1 vol. 2007. (ENG & SPA., Illus.). 240p. pap. 25.00 *(978-950-889-136-5(X))* La Marca ARG. Dist: D.A.P./Distributed Art Pubs.

International Committee of Historical Sciences, Comité Argentino Jornadas Staff, contrib. by. Historiografía Argentina, 1958-1988: Una Evaluación CríTica de la Producción HistóRica Nacional. (SPA.). 625p. *(978-950-43-3183-4(1))* Bow Historical Bks.

Julian, Beatrice, et al. The A to Z of the Dirty Wars. 2009. (A to Z Guide Ser.: No. 29). (ENG.). 250p. pap. 34.45 *(978-0-8108-6812-0(1))* Scarecrow Pr., Inc.

King, J. Anthony. Twenty-Four Years in the Argentine Republic. reprint ed. 57.50 *(978-0-404-03691-1(0))* AMS Pr., Inc.

Kirkpatrick, Frederick. History of the Argentine Republic. reprint ed. 40.00 *(978-0-404-03707-9(0))* AMS Pr., Inc.

Kohut, David R. & Vilella, Olga. Historical Dictionary of the Dirty Wars. 2nd ed. 2010. (Historical Dictionaries of War, Revolution, & Civil Unrest Ser.). (ENG., Illus.). 432p. 111.00 *(978-0-8108-5839-8(8))* Scarecrow Pr., Inc.

Levine, Anette H. Cry for Me, Argentina: The Performance of Trauma in the Short Narratives of Aida Bortnik, Griselda Gambaro, & Tununa Mercado. 2008. (ENG.). 46.00 *(978-1-61147-371-1(3))* Fairleigh Dickinson Univ. Pr.

Levine, Annette H. Cry for Me, Argentina: The Performance of Trauma in the Short Narratives of Aída Bortnik, Griselda Gambaro, & Tununa Mercado. 2008. (Illus.). 184p. 46.00 *(978-0-8386-4156-9(3))* Fairleigh Dickinson Univ. Pr.

Lida, Clara E., et al. Argentina, 1976: Estudios en Torno Al Golpe de Estado. 2007. (Estudios Históricos Ser.). (SPA.). 287p. pap. 26.00 *(978-968-12-1301-5(7))* El Colegio de México, A.C., Biblioteca Miguel Cosio Villegas MEX. Dist: Fondo de Cultura Economica USA.

Longoni, Ana & Bruzzone, Gustavo A. El Siluetazo/ The Silhouette. 2008. (SPA., Illus.). 514p. pap. 46.95 *(978-987-1156-83-2(9))* Hidalgo, Adriana Editora S.A. ARG. Dist: Lectorum Pubns., Inc.

Mallea, Eduardo. Las Aguilas. (SPA.). 12.95 *(978-0-7859-0128-0(0)*, S2130) French & European Pubns., Inc.

Martínez Díaz, Nelson. Juan Domingo Peron: Argentine Dictator, 1946-1955. (SPA., Illus.). 160p. 4.95 *(978-84-7679-031-1(7))* Informacion y Revistas ESP. Dist: AIMS International Bks., Inc.

Moses, Bernard. South America on the Eve of Emancipation. 2009. (ENG.). 365p. 38.99 *(978-1-117-57395-3(8))*; 380p. 31.99 *(978-1-113-90116-3(0))* BiblioBazaar.

—South America on the Eve of Emancipation. 2009. 220p. pap. *(978-0-217-99765-2(1))*; 216p. pap. *(978-0-217-99766-9(X))* Books LLC.

—South America on the Eve of Emancipation. 2009. 206p. pap. 19.99 *(978-0-217-55601-9(9))* General Bks. LLC.

—South America on the Eve of Emancipation. 2008. 368p. 48.95 *(978-1-4365-6507-3(3))* 2007. (ENG.). 372p. per. 33.95 *(978-0-548-76541-8(3))* Kessinger Publishing, LLC.

—South America on the Eve of Emancipation. 2007. (ENG.). 368p. per. *(978-1-4067-7090-2(6))* Read Bks.

Moss, Chris. Patagonia: A Cultural History. 2008. (Landscapes of the Imagination Ser.). (ENG., Illus.). 256p. 25.00 *(978-0-19-534249-9(6))* Oxford Univ. Pr., Inc.

Palombo, Paula. Las Cuatro Estaciones: Segmentación Del Tiempo y el Espacio en Floridablanca, Costa Patagónica, Siglo XVIII. 2007. (SPA., Illus.). 153p. 5.50 *(978-987-1354-05-4(3))* Teseo ARG. Dist: Sony Electronics.

Poliester 23: Argentina. pap. 10.00 *(978-1-56466-059-6(1))* Archer Fields, Inc.

Portela, M. Edurne. Displaced Memories: The Poetics of Trauma in Argentine Women's Writing. 2009. 46.50 *(978-0-8387-5732-1(4))* Bucknell Univ. Pr.

Rabassa, J., ed. The Late Cenozoic of Patagonia & Tierra del Fuego. 2008. (Developments in Quaternary Science Ser.: 11). (ENG., Illus.). 524p. 205.00 *(978-0-444-52954-1(3)*, Elsevier Science) Elsevier Science & Technology Bks.

Robertson, William Spence, ed. A History of Argentina. 2011. (ENG.). 584p. pap. 50.00 ***(978-0-8078-6836-2(1))*** Univ. of North Carolina Pr.

Rocha, Carolina. Masculinities in Contemporary Argentine Popular Cinema. 2012. (ENG., Illus.). 240p. 85.00 ***(978-0-230-33818-0(6))*** Palgrave Macmillan.

Ros, Ana. The Post-Dictatorship Generation in Argentina, Chile, & Uruguay: Collective Memory & Cultural Production. 2012. (ENG., Illus.). 256p. 85.00 ***(978-0-230-12060-0(1))*** Palgrave Macmillan.

Rufer, Mario. La Nación en Escenas: Memoria Pública y Usos Del Pasado en Contextos Poscoloniales. 2010. (Estudios de Asia y África Ser.). (SPA., Illus.). 462p. pap. 41.99 *(978-607-462-062-7(8))* El Colegio de México, A.C., Biblioteca Miguel Cosio Villegas MEX. Dist: Fondo de Cultura Economica USA.

Sánchez Román, José Antonio. Taxation & Society in Twentieth-Century Argentina. 2012. (Studies of the Americas Ser.). (ENG., Illus.). 256p. 90.00 ***(978-0-230-34126-5(8))*** Palgrave Macmillan.

Scobie, James R. Argentin: A City & a Nation. 2008. 312p. pap. 30.00 *(978-1-59740-622-2(8))* ACLS Humanities E-Book.

Senatore, María Ximena. Arqueología e Historia en la Colonia Española de Floridablanca: Patagonia, Siglo XVIII. 2007. (SPA., Illus.). 332p. 7.00 *(978-987-1354-08-5(8))* Teseo ARG. Dist: Sony Electronics.

Taylor, McCartney. The Santa Lucia, Argentina Meteorite Fall Of 2008. 2009. 68p. pap. 35.90 *(978-0-557-04436-8(7))* Lulu Enterprises Inc.

Universidad de Buenos Aires, Programa de Historia Oral Staff, contrib. by. Historia, Voces y Memoria: Boletín Del Programa de Historia Oral. 2007. (SPA.). 127p. *(978-950-793-064-5(7))* Imago Mundi, Ediciones.

Weissel, Marcelo Norman. Arqueología de la Boca del Riachuelo. Puerto Urbano de Buenos Aires, Argentina. 2009. (Illus.). 192p. (C). pap. 97.50 *(978-1-4073-0623-0(5))* British Archaeological Reports Ltd. GBR. Dist: Brown, David Bk. Co., The.

Yankelevich, Pablo. Ráfagas de un Exilio: Argentinos en México, 1974-1983. 2009. (Otras Publicaciones Ser.). (SPA., Illus.). 367p. pap. 43.99 *(978-607-462-071-9(7))* El Colegio de México, A.C., Biblioteca Miguel Cosio Villegas MEX. Dist: Fondo de Cultura Economica USA.

ARGENTINA—JUVENILE LITERATURE

Sarmiento, Domingo Faustino. Facundo. 2009. 382p. 29.99 *(978-1-113-93199-3(X))*; 31.99 *(978-1-113-93201-3(5))*; pap. 32.75 *(978-1-113-93195-5(7))* BiblioBazaar.

—Facundo. 2010. 174p. pap. 10.85 *(978-1-153-66476-9(3))* General Bks. LLC.

ARGENTINA—POLITICS AND GOVERNMENT

see also Peronism

Ablard, Jonathan. Madness in Buenos Aires: Patients, Psychiatrists & the Argentine State, 1890-1983. 2008. (Ohio RIS Latin America Ser.). (ENG., Illus.). 300p. pap. 32.00 *(978-0-89680-259-9(0))* Ohio Univ. Pr.

Alconada Mon, Hugo. Los Secretos de la Valija: Del Caso Antonini Wilson a la Petrodiplomacia de Hugo Chávez. 2009. (SPA., Illus.). 303p. 29.00 *(978-950-49-2125-7(6))* Planeta Argentina, Independencia ARG. Dist: Planeta Publishing Corp.

Anderson, Leslie E. Social Capital in Developing Democracies: Nicaragua & Argentina. 2010. (ENG., Illus.). 344p. 85.00 *(978-0-521-19274-3(9))*; 334p. pap. 27.99 *(978-0-521-14084-3(6))* Cambridge Univ. Pr.

Auyero, Javier. Routine Politics & Violence in Argentina: The Gray Zone of State Power. 2007. (Cambridge Studies in Contentious Politics Ser.). (ENG., Illus.). 208p. 80.00 *(978-0-521-87236-2(7))*; per. 26.99 *(978-0-521-69411-7(6))* Cambridge Univ. Pr.

Azcona Pastor, José Manuel. Violencia Política y Terrorismo de Estado en Argentina: Del Totalitarismo de José Uriburu, 1930, a la Dictadura Militar, 1976-1983: Una Visión Bilateral. 2010. 256p. *(978-84-9940-076-1(0))* Biblioteca Nueva, Editorial, S.L.

Baschetti, Roberto. La Clase Obrera Peronista, 2 vols. 2010. (SPA.). *(978-987-9125-91-5(6))*; *(978-987-9125-96-0(7))* De La Campana.

Blind, Peride K. Democratic Institutions of Undemocratic Individuals: Privatizations, Labor, & Democracy in Turkey & Argentina. 2008. (ENG., Illus.). 276p. 95.00 *(978-0-230-61158-0(3))* Palgrave Macmillan.

Brinks, Daniel M. The Judicial Response to Police Killings in Latin America: Inequality & the Rule of Law. 2007. (ENG., Illus.). 302p. 101.00 *(978-0-521-87234-8(0))* Cambridge Univ. Pr.

Burgin, Miron. The Economic Aspects of Argentine Federalism, 1820-1852. 2008. 324p. pap. 32.00 *(978-1-59740-617-8(1))* ACLS Humanities E-Book.

Cafiero, Antonio. Testimonios Sobre America Latina y Deomcracia. 2006. (Coleccion America Latina y Democracia Ser.). (SPA.). 286p. per. *(978-950-07-2772-3(2))* Editorial Sudamericana S.A.

Cane, James. Fourth Enemy: Journalism & Power in the Making of Peronist Argentina, 1930-1955. 2011. (ENG.). 328p. 74.95 ***(978-0-271-04876-5(X))*** Pennsylvania State Univ. Pr.

Carey, Henry F. Reaping What You Sow: A Comparative Examination of Torture Reform in the United States, France, Argentina, & Israel. 2011. xxi, 339p. E-Book ***(978-0-313-36616-1(0)***, Praeger Pubs.) Greenwood Publishing Group, Inc.

Carey, Henry Frank. Reaping What You Sow: A Comparative Examination of Torture Reform in the United States, France, Argentina, & Israel, 1 vol. 2011. (PSI Reports). 339p. 63.00 *(978-0-313-36615-4(2)*, C36615) Greenwood Publishing Group, Inc.

Casiro, Jessica. Angels in Hell: Argentina's Willing Altruists? 2010. 192p. pap. *(978-3-639-17969-9(2))* VDM Verlag Dr. Mueller e.K.

Cox, David & Nabot, Damián. Unveiling the Enigma: Who Stole the Hands of Juan Peron? 2009.Tr. of segunda Muerte. 306p. pap. 16.50 *(978-1-934841-14-3(5))* Zumaya Pubns. LLC.

Crenzel, Emilio. The Memory of the Argentina Disappearances: The Political History of Nunca Mas. 2011. (ENG.). 212p. (C). 125.00 *(978-0-415-88616-1(3))* Routledge.

Cristóforis, Nadia Andrea de & Nadia Andrea, De Cristóforis. Bajo la Cruz Del Sur: Gallegos y Asturianos en Buenos Aires (1820-1870). 2010. (SPA., Illus.). 251p. *(978-84-95892-84-3(7))* Fundación Pedro Barrie de la Maza.

Denissen, Marieke. Winning Small Battles, Losing the War: Police Violence, the Movimento del Dolor & Democracy in Post-Authoritarian Argentina. 2008. 262p. pap. 38.95 *(978-90-5170-964-3(1))* Purdue Univ. Pr.

DuBois, Lindsay. The Politics of the Past in an Argentine Working-Class Neighbourhood. 2008. 284p. pap. *(978-0-8020-9635-7(2))* Univ. of Toronto Pr.

Duhalde, Eduardo Alberto. Argentina Aflame: My first 120 days in office, from dissolution to Recovery. 2009. (ENG.). lib. bdg. *(978-1-4135-7508-8(0))* El Cid Editor Incorporated.

Epstein, Edward & Pion-Berlin, David. Broken Promises? The Argentine Crisis & Argentine Democracy. 2008. (ENG.). 296p. pap. 34.99 *(978-0-7391-2726-1(8))* Lexington Bks.

Feitlowitz, Marguerite. A Lexicon of Terror: Argentina & the Legacies of Torture. rev. ed. 2011. (ENG., Illus.). 416p. pap. 19.95 *(978-0-19-974469-5(6))* Oxford Univ. Pr., Inc.

Finkel, Jodi S. Judicial Reform as Political Insurance: Argentina, Peru, & Mexico in The 1990s. 2008. (ND Kellogg Inst Int'l Studies). (ENG.). 176p. pap. 22.00 *(978-0-268-02887-9(7))* Univ. of Notre Dame Pr.

Gallo, Klaus. The Struggle for an Enlightened Republic: Buenos Aires & Rivadavia. 2006. (ENG.). 91p. per. 24.95 *(978-1-900039-76-5(1))* Institute of Latin American Studies GBR. Dist: Brookings Institution Pr.

Goebel, Michael. Argentina's Partisan Past: Nationalism & the Politics of History. 2011. (Liverpool University Press - Liverpool Latin American Studies). (ENG., Illus.). 284p. 95.00 *(978-1-84631-238-0(8))* Liverpool Univ. Pr. GBR. Dist: Chicago Distribution Ctr.

Haverland, Jeanne B. Argentina: Economic, Political & Social Issues. 2008. (Illus.). xi, 155p. 82.00 *(978-1-60456-469-3(5))* Nova Science Pubs., Inc.

Hedges, Jill. Argentina: A Modern History. 2011. (ENG., Illus.). 336p. 42.00 *(978-1-84885-654-7(7))* I. B. Tauris & Co., Ltd. GBR. Dist: Macmillan.

Herrera, Matilde. Jose. 2009. (SPA.). 447p. pap. 30.95 *(978-0-557-04124-4(4))* Lulu Enterprises Inc.

Hodges, Donald C. Argentina's Dirty War: An Intellectual Biography. 2011. (ENG.). 408p. pap. 35.00 *(978-0-292-72947-6(2))* Univ. of Texas Pr.

Horowitz, Joel. Argentina's Radical Party & Popular Mobilization, 1916-1930. 2008. (ENG.). 192p. pap. 45.00 *(978-0-271-03404-1(1))*; 254p. pap. 26.95 ***(978-0-271-03405-8(X))*** Pennsylvania State Univ. Pr.

Ippolito-O'Donnell, Gabriela. The Right to the City: Popular Contention in Contemporary Buenos Aires. 2011. (ND Kellogg Inst Int'l Studies). (ENG., Illus.). 320p. pap. 38.00 ***(978-0-268-03179-4(7))*** Univ. of Notre Dame Pr.

Irizarry Osorio, Hiram Jost. Argentina & Brazil's Politics of Taxation: 1980s-1990s. 2008. 300p. pap. *(978-3-639-04754-7(0))* VDM Verlag Dr. Mueller e.K.

Juarez-Dappe, Patricia. When Sugar Ruled: Economy & Society in Northwestern Argentina, Tucuman, 1876-1916. 2010. (Ohio RIS Latin America Ser.). (ENG., Illus.). 320p. pap. 32.00 *(978-0-89680-274-2(4))* Ohio Univ. Pr.

Kaminsky, Amy K. Argentina: Stories for a Nation. 2008. 280p. 67.50 *(978-0-8166-4948-8(0))*; pap. 22.50 *(978-0-8166-4949-5(9))* Univ. of Minnesota Pr.

Karush, Matthew B. & Chamosa, Oscar, eds. The New Cultural History of Peronism: Power & Identity in Mid-Twentieth-Century Argentina. 2010. (ENG., Illus.). 320p. 89.95 *(978-0-8223-4721-7(0))* Duke Univ. Pr.

—The New Cultural History of Peronism: Power & Identity in Mid-Twentieth-Century Argentina. 2010. (ENG., Illus.). 320p. pap. 24.95 *(978-0-8223-4738-5(5))* Duke Univ. Pr.

Lida, Clara E., et al. Argentina, 1976: Estudios en Torno Al Golpe de Estado. 2007. (Estudios Históricos Ser.). (SPA.). 287p. pap. 26.00 *(978-968-12-1301-5(7))* El Colegio de México, A.C., Biblioteca Miguel Cosío Villegas MEX. Dist: Fondo de Cultura Economica USA.

Martinez, Alberto B. Baedeker of the Argentine Republic. 479p. reprint ed. 98.00 *(978-0-7222-9582-3(0))* Library Reprints, Inc.

Miller, Jonathan. The Constitution of Argentina: A Contextual Analysis. 2012. (ENG.). 244p. pap. 25.00 *(978-1-84113-941-8(6))* Hart Publishing Ltd. GBR. Dist: International Specialized Bk. Services.

Ollier, Maria. The Political Learning Process of Argentine Left. 2009. 380p. pap. *(978-3-639-15061-2(9))* VDM Verlag Dr. Mueller e.K.

Peralta-Ramos, Monica. La Economía Política Argentina: Poder y Clases Sociales (1930-2006) 2007. (Economía Ser.). (SPA.). 453p. pap. *(978-950-557-717-0(6))* Fondo de Cultura Economica.

Ray, Leslie. Language of the Land: The Mapuche in Argentina & Chile. 2008. (Illus.). 291p. pap. 29.95 *(978-87-91563-37-9(2))* IWGIA DNK. Dist: Transaction Pubs.

Redrado, Martin. No Reserve: The Limit of Absolute Power, 0 vols. unabr. ed. 2011. (ENG.). 288p. pap. 13.95 *(978-1-935597-23-0(X)*, 9781935597230) Amazon Publishing.

Rein, Raanan. Argentine Jews or Jewish Argentines? Essays on Ethnicity, Identity, & Diaspora. 2010. (Jewish Identities in a Changing World Ser.). *(978-90-04-17913-4(5))* BRILL.

—In the Shadow of Perón: Juan Atilio Bramuglia & the Second Line of Argentina's Populist Movement. Grenzeback, Martha, tr. from SPA. 2008. (ENG.). 312p. 70.00 *(978-0-8047-5792-8(5))* Stanford Univ. Pr.

Robben, Antonius C. G. M. Political Violence & Trauma in Argentina. 2007. (Ethnography of Political Violence Ser.). (Illus.). 480p. (C). per. 29.95 *(978-0-8122-2006-3(4))* Univ. of Pennsylvania Pr.

Roberg, Jeffrey L. & Seymoure, Penny. Tourism in Northeastern Argentina: The Intersection of Human & Indigenous Rights with the Environment. 2011. (ENG.). 230p. (gr. 17). 65.00 ***(978-0-7391-3778-9(6))*** Lexington Bks.

Rock, David. Politics in Argentina, 1890-1930: The Rise & Fall of Radicalism. 2009. (Cambridge Latin American Studies). (ENG.). 328p. pap. 42.00 *(978-0-521-10232-2(4))* Cambridge Univ. Pr.

Romanach, Julio, Jr. Civil Code of Argentina 2008: An English Translation with an Introduction & Index. 2nd rev. ed. 2008. 448p. per. 195.00 *(978-1-4004-0010-2(4))* Lawrence Publishing Co.

Root, Regina A. Couture & Consensus: Fashion & Politics in Postcolonial Argentina. 2010. (Cultural Studies of the Americas Ser.). (Illus.). 240p. 75.00 *(978-0-8166-4793-4(3))*; pap. 25.00 *(978-0-8166-4794-1(1))* Univ. of Minnesota Pr.

Sánchez Román, José Antonio. Taxation & Society in Twentieth-Century Argentina. 2012. (Studies of the Americas Ser.). (ENG., Illus.). 256p. 90.00 ***(978-0-230-34126-5(8))*** Palgrave Macmillan.

Spiller, Pablo T. & Tommasi, Mariano. The Institutional Foundations of Public Policy in Argentina: A Transactions Cost Approach. (Political Economy of Institutions & Decisions Ser.). (ENG.). 254p. 2009. pap. 32.99 *(978-0-521-14578-7(3))* 2007. (Illus.). 103.00 *(978-0-521-85474-0(1))* Cambridge Univ. Pr.

Suriano, Juan. Paradoxes of Utopia: Anarchist Culture & Politics in Buenos Aires, 1890-1910. 2010. (ENG.). 288p. pap. 18.95 *(978-1-84935-005-8(X))* AK Pr. GBR. Dist: Consortium Bk. Sales & Distribution.

Turner, Frederick & Miguens, Jose Enrique, eds. Juan Peron & the Reshaping of Argentina. 2009. (Pitt Latin American Studies). (ENG.). 284p. (C). pap. 25.95 *(978-0-8229-8490-0(3))* Univ. of Pittsburgh Pr.

Wood Lange, Catherine. Shaping the Madre Patria - Spanish & Argentinean Icons of The 1940s. 2008. 256p. pap. *(978-3-639-04411-9(8))* VDM Verlag Dr. Mueller e.K.

ARGENTINA—SOCIAL CONDITIONS

ABBE Scientist Research Division Staff. AIDS & HIV in Argentina: Index & Medical Analysis of New Clinical & Research Information. 2008. (ENG., Illus.). 160p. ring bd. 69.95 *(978-0-7883-4958-4(9))* ABBE Pubs. Assn. of Washington, D.C.

Ansolabehere, Pablo. La Ley de Los Profanos: Delito, Justicia y Cultura en Buenos Aires (1870-1940) Caimari, Lila M., ed. 2007. (Historia Ser.). (SPA., Illus.). 276p. pap. *(978-950-557-720-0(6))* Fondo de Cultura Economica.

Armus, Diego. The Ailing City: Health, Tuberculosis, & Culture in Buenos Aires, 1870–1950. 2011. (ENG., Illus.). 432p. 99.95 *(978-0-8223-4999-0(X))*; pap. 27.95 *(978-0-8223-5012-5(2))* Duke Univ. Pr.

Atzeni, Maurizio. Workplace Conflict: Mobilization & Solidarity in Argentina. 2010. (ENG.). 288p. 100.00 *(978-0-230-58464-8(0))* Palgrave Macmillan.

Bergero, Adriana J. Intersecting Tango: Cultural Geographies of Buenos Aires, 1900-1930. Young, Richard, tr. from SPA. 2008. (Pitt Illuminations Ser.). (ENG., Illus.). 376p. (C). pap. 27.95 *(978-0-8229-5985-4(2))* Univ. of Pittsburgh Pr.

Bianchi Villelli, Marcia. Cambio Social y Prácticas Cotidianas en el Orden Colonial: Arqueología Histórica en Floridablanca (San Julián, Siglo XVIII) 2009. (SPA & ENG., Illus.). x, 206p. (C). pap. 112.50 *(978-1-4073-0466-3(6))* British Archaeological Reports Ltd. GBR. Dist: Brown, David Bk. Co., The.

—Organizar la Diferencia: Prácticas de Consumo en Floridablanco, Costa Patagónica, Siglo XVIII. 2007. (SPA., Illus.). 225p. 7.00 *(978-987-1354-02-3(9))* Teseo ARG. Dist: Sony Electronics.

Borges, M. J. & Borges, Marcelo J. Chains of Gold: Portuguese Migration to Argentina in Transatlantic Perspective. 2009. (Studies in Global Social History Ser.). (Illus.). 355p. ***(978-90-04-17648-5(9))*** BRILL.

Brown, Jonathan C. A Socioeconomic History of Argentina, 1776-1860. 2008. (Cambridge Latin American Studies). (ENG.). 320p. pap. 42.00 *(978-0-521-10210-0(3))* Cambridge Univ. Pr.

Castino, Giovanni. The Environmental Standing to Sue in Argentina & Italy. 2011. 80p. pap. ***(978-3-8443-0581-4(5))*** Lambert Academic Publishing.

Demombynes, Gabriel & Verner, Dorte. The Invisible Poor: A Portrait of Rural Poverty in Argentina. 2010. (Country Studies). (ENG.). 135p. pap. 25.00 *(978-0-8213-8207-3(1)*, 9780821382073) World Bank Pubns.

Denissen, Marieke. Winning Small Battles, Losing the War: Police Violence, the Movimiento del Dolor & Democracy in Post-Authoritarian Argentina. 2008. 262p. pap. 38.95 *(978-90-5170-964-3(1))* Purdue Univ. Pr.

Dillon, Erica. Leaving the Psychiatric Hospital. 2007. 200p. per. *(978-3-8364-3469-0(5))* VDM Verlag Dr. Mueller e.K.

DuBois, Lindsay. The Politics of the Past in an Argentine Working-Class Neighbourhood. 2008. 284p. pap. *(978-0-8020-9635-7(2))* Univ. of Toronto Pr.

Durand, Patricia Beatriz. Desarrollo Rural y Organizacion Campesina en la Argentina la Experiencia Del Movimiento Campesino de Santiago Del Estero. 2010. 316p. pap. 31.50 *(978-1-59754-538-9(4))* Editorial Libros en Red.

Feierstein, Daniel. El Genocidio Como Práctica Social: Entre el Nazismo y la Experiencia Argentina. Hacia un análisis del Aniquilamiento Como Reorganizador de las Relaciones Sociales. 2008. (Sociología Ser.). (SPA.). 405p. pap. *(978-950-557-714-9(1))* Fondo de Cultura Economica.

Frederick, Kenneth D. Water Management & Agricultural Development: A Case Study of the Cuyo Region of Argentina. 2011. (RFF Water Policy Set Ser.). (ENG.). 187p. 99.95 *(978-1-61726-085-8(1)*, RFF Pr.) Earthscan LLC.

Gallo, Klaus. The Struggle for an Enlightened Republic: Buenos Aires & Rivadavia. 2006. (ENG.). 91p. per. 24.95 *(978-1-900039-76-5(1))* Institute of Latin American Studies GBR. Dist: Brookings Institution Pr.

González-Bernaldo, Pilar. Civility & Politics in the Origins of the Argentine Nation: Sociabilities in Buenos Aires, 1829-1862. 2007. pap. *(978-0-87903-089-6(5))* Latin American Ctr. of New Music.

Graham-Yooll, Andrew. Goodbye Buenos Aires. 2012. (ENG.). 222p. pap. 29.95 ***(978-1-906011-70-3(2))*** Eland Bks. GBR. Dist: Dufour Editions, Inc.

Hamilton, William. A Perverted Integrity. 2011. 224p. pap. ***(978-3-8443-2888-2(2))*** Lambert Academic Publishing.

Haverland, Jeanne B. Argentina: Economic, Political & Social Issues. 2008. (Illus.). xi, 155p. 82.00 *(978-1-60456-469-3(5))* Nova Science Pubs., Inc.

Juarez-Dappe, Patricia. When Sugar Ruled: Economy & Society in Northwestern Argentina, Tucuman, 1876-1916. 2010. (Ohio RIS Latin America Ser.). (ENG., Illus.). 320p. pap. 32.00 *(978-0-89680-274-2(4))* Ohio Univ. Pr.

Kelly, Helen. Irish 'Ingleses' The Irish Immigrant Experience in Argentina, 1840-1920. 2009. (Illus.). 272p. pap. *(978-0-7165-3008-4(2))* Irish Academic Pr. IRL. Dist: International Specialized Bk. Services.

Kesselheim, Wolfgang. Die Herstellung von Gruppen im Gespräch - analysiert am Beispiel des argentinischen Einwanderungsdiskurses. 2009. (Europäische Hochschulschriften. Reihe 21: Linguistik Ser.). (GER.). 348p. pap. *(978-3-03911-780-2(7))* Lang, Peter.

Oliveri, Marcelo Héctor. El Chamuyo de Las Tribus Urbanas: Lunfardo, Argots y el Todo Vale. 2009. (SPA., Illus.). 112p. *(978-987-23314-1-2(3))*, Del Cachafaz.

Peralta-Ramos, Monica. La Economía Política Argentina: Poder y Clases Sociales (1930-2006) 2007. (Economía Ser.). (SPA.). 453p. pap. *(978-950-557-717-0(6))* Fondo de Cultura Economica.

Ray, Leslie. Language of the Land: The Mapuche in Argentina & Chile. 2008. (Illus.). 291p. pap. 29.95 *(978-87-91563-37-9(2))* IWGIA DNK. Dist: Transaction Pubs.

Rein, Raanan. Argentine Jews or Jewish Argentines? Essays on Ethnicity, Identity, & Diaspora. 2010. (Jewish Identities in a Changing World Ser.). *(978-90-04-17913-4(5))* BRILL.

Robben, Antonius C. G. M. Political Violence & Trauma in Argentina. 2007. (Ethnography of Political Violence Ser.). (Illus.). 480p. (C). per. 29.95 *(978-0-8122-2006-3(4))* Univ. of Pennsylvania Pr.

Roberg, Jeffrey L. & Seymoure, Penny. Tourism in Northeastern Argentina: The Intersection of Human & Indigenous Rights with the Environment. 2011. (ENG.). 230p. (gr. 17). 65.00 ***(978-0-7391-3778-9(6))*** Lexington Bks.

Rodrí, et al. The Constitution of the Field of Rural Development. 2010. 352p. pap. *(978-3-8383-4474-4(X))* Lambert Academic Publishing.

Seymoure, Penny & Roberg, Jeffrey L. Tourism in Northeastern Argentina: The Intersection of Human & Indigenous Rights with the Environment. 2012. ***(978-0-7391-3780-2(8))*** Lexington Bks.

Taub, Emmanuel. Otredad, Orientalismo e Identidad: Nociones Sobre la Construcción de un Otro Oriental en la Revista Caras y Caretas, 1898-1918. 2008. (SPA., Illus.). 129p. 7.50 *(978-987-1354-15-3(0))* Teseo ARG. Dist: Sony Electronics.

Wald, Gabriela. Community Arts & Health Promotion. 2010. (Illus.). 92p. pap. *(978-3-8383-7146-7(1))* Lambert Academic Publishing.

World Bank Staff. Argentina: Income Support Policies Toward the Bicentennial. 2009. (Country Studies). (ENG., Illus.). 182p. pap. 20.00 *(978-0-8213-8051-2(6)*, 9780821380512) World Bank Pubns.

World Bank Staff, contrib. by. Argentine Youth: An Untapped Potential. 2009. (Country Studies). (ENG.). 146p. pap. 25.00 *(978-0-8213-7924-0(0)*, 9780821379240) World Bank Pubns.

ARGENTINA—SOCIAL LIFE AND CUSTOMS

Adams, Fiona. Cultureshock Argentina, 1 vol. 2011. (ENG.). 240p. pap. 15.95 *(978-0-7614-6050-3(0))* Marshall Cavendish Corp.

—Cultureshock Argentina: A Survival Guide to Customs & Etiquette. 2007. (Cultureshock Argentina: A Survival Guide to Customs & Etiquette Ser.). (Illus.). 252p. per. 15.95 *(978-0-7614-5397-0(0))* Marshall Cavendish Corp.

Bietz, May E. Immigration & Acculturation in Brazil & Argentina: 1890-1929. 2010. (ENG.). 190p. 84.00 *(978-0-230-10019-0(8))* Palgrave Macmillan.

Finn, Maria. Hold Me Tight & Tango Me Home. 2010. (ENG.). 223p. pap. 13.95 *(978-1-56512-517-9(7)*, 1565125177) Algonquin Bks. of Chapel Hill.

Grams, Rocky. Asombrados en Argentina: In Awe in Argentina. 2007. 240p. pap. *(978-1-59979-113-5(7))* Charisma Media.

King, John. Sur: A Study of the Argentine Literary Journal & its Role in the Development of a Culture, 1931-1970. 2009. (Cambridge Iberian & Latin American Studies). 244p. pap. 36.99 *(978-0-521-12121-7(3))* Cambridge Univ. Pr.

Lewis, Hope. A Student's Guide to Being Happy in Argentina. 2009. 86p. pap. 15.95 *(978-0-9786854-8-5(2))* Elevator Group, The.

Marschoff, María. Gato Por Liebre: Prácticas Alimenticias en Floridablanca. 2007. (SPA., Illus.). 231p. 7.00 *(978-987-1354-04-7(5))* Teseo ARG. Dist: Sony Electronics.

Masotta, Carlos. Gauchos en las Primeras Postales Fotograficas Argentinas del S. xx/Gauchos in the Early 1900s. Argentine Photo Postcards, 1 vol. 2007. (ENG., Illus.). 120p. pap. 15.00 *(978-950-889-160-0(2))* La Marca ARG. Dist: D.A.P./Distributed Art Pubs.

Masotta, Carlos, ed. Indians in Argentinian Photographic Postcards of the 20th Century, 1 vol. 2007. (ENG., Illus.). 120p. pap. 15.00 *(978-950-889-162-4(9))* La Marca ARG. Dist: D.A.P./Distributed Art Pubs.

Moragas, Libertad O. condena Florencia. Diario de un viaje. Argentina vs. K 2008. 72p. pap. 14.95 *(978-1-4092-2164-7(4))* Lulu Enterprises Inc.

Schneider, Arnd. Appropriation as Practice: Art & Identity in Argentina. 2006. (Studies of the Americas Ser.). (ENG., Illus.). 256p. 95.00 *(978-1-4039-7314-6(8))* Palgrave Macmillan.

Stephen, Ros, ed. Argentinian Tango & Folk Tunes for Violin: With a CD of Performance & Backing Tracks Book/CD. 2011. (ENG.). 108p. pap. 19.99 incl. audio compact disk ***(978-1-84761-250-2(4)***, 1847612504) Schott Music Corp.

Vila, Pablo & Semán, Pablo, eds. Youth Identities & Argentine Popular Music: Beyond Tango. 2012. (ENG., Illus.). 198p. 85.00 *(978-0-230-10463-1(0))* Palgrave Macmillan.

ARGENTINE DRAMA

Graham-Jones, Jean. BAiT: Buenos Aires in Translation. 2008. (ENG.). 220p. pap. 20.00 *(978-0-9790570-3-8(5))* Segal, Martin E. Theatre Ctr.

Graham-Jones, Jean, ed. BAiT: Buenos Aires in Translation: Recent Argentinean Plays. 2007. 226p. pap. 20.00 *(978-0-595-43657-6(9))* Segal, Martin E. Theatre Ctr.

ARGENTINE DRAMA—HISTORY AND CRITICISM

Ford, Katherine. Politics & Violence in Cuban & Argentine Theater. 2010. (ENG.). 244p. 89.00 *(978-0-230-61314-0(4))* Palgrave Macmillan.

Magnarelli, Sharon. Home Is Where the (He)art Is: The Family Romance in Late Twentieth-Century Mexican & Argentine Theatre. 2008. (Bucknell Studies in Latin American Literature & Theory). (C). *(978-0-8387-5707-9(3))* Bucknell Univ. Pr.

Werth, Brenda. Theatre, Performance, & Memory Politics in Argentina. 2010. (ENG., Illus.). 272p. 84.00 *(978-0-230-10434-1(7))* Palgrave Macmillan.

Woodyard, George. Fabula, Sexo Y Poder: Teatro Argentina Al Final Del Siglo XX. 2009. pap. 16.00 *(978-0-578-02201-7(X))* LATR Bks.

ARGENTINE FICTION—HISTORY AND CRITICISM

Boldy, Steven. The Novels of Julio Cortazar. 2010. (Cambridge Iberian & Latin American Studies). (ENG.). 232p. pap. 27.99 *(978-0-521-13678-5(4))* Cambridge Univ. Pr.

Corral, Rose, ed. Entre Ficción y Reflexión: Juan José Saer y Ricardo Piglia. 2007. (Estudios Lingüísticos y Literarios Ser.). (SPA.). 312p. pap. 32.99 *(978-968-12-1288-9(6))* El Colegio de México, A.C., Biblioteca Miguel Cosío Villegas MEX. Dist: Fondo de Cultura Economica USA.

Haywood Ferreira, Rachel. The Emergence of Latin American Science Fiction. 2011. (Early Classics of Science Fiction Ser.). (ENG., Illus.). 320p. (C). 80.00 *(978-0-8195-7081-9(8))*; pap. 29.95 *(978-0-8195-7082-6(6))* Wesleyan Univ. Pr.

Mattalia, Sonia. La Ley y el Crimen: Usos Del Relato Policial en la Narrativa Argentina (1880-2000) 2008. (SPA.). 237p. pap. 24.80 *(978-84-8489-415-5(0))* Iberoamericana Vervuert Publishing Corp.

Nuño Ávila, Anthony. Subjetividades e Identidades Sexuales de la Posmodernidad: El Deseo Homoerótico en la Narrativa de Manuel Puig. 2011.Tr. of Postmodern Subjectivities & Sexual Identities: Homoerotic Desire in the Narrative of Manuel Puig. (SPA & ENG.). 256p. 109.95 *(978-0-7734-3680-0(4))* Mellen, Edwin Pr., The.

Ran, Amalia. Made of Shores: Judeo-Argentinean Fiction Revisited. 2011. (ENG.). 174p. 65.00 ***(978-1-61146-014-8(X))*** Fairleigh Dickinson Univ. Pr.

Sarlo, Beatriz. La Imaginacion Tecnica. pap. *(978-0-8047-3543-8(3))* Stanford Univ. Pr.

—The Technical Imagination: Argentine Culture's Modern Dreams. Callahan, Xavier, tr. from ENG. 2007. (Writing Science Ser.). (SPA & ENG.). 208p. 60.00 *(978-0-8047-3542-1(5))* Stanford Univ. Pr.

Simon, Diana Garcia. Paraiso, Metamorfosis Y Memoria: La Influencia de Proust Y Kafka en la Obra de Mujica Lainez. (Europaische Hochschulschriften Ser.). (SPA., Illus.). 226p. 39.95 *(978-3-631-32639-8(4))* Lang, Peter Publishing, Inc.

ARGENTINE LITERATURE

see also Argentine Drama

Borges, Jorge Luis. On Mysticism. Levine, Suzanne Jill & Kodama, Maria, eds. 2010. (ENG.). 128p. (gr. 12). 14.00 *(978-0-14-310569-5(8)*, Penguin Classics) Penguin Group (USA) Inc.

ARGENTINE LITERATURE—HISTORY AND CRITICISM

Alonso, Carlos J., ed. Julio Cortázar: New Readings. 2011. (Cambridge Studies in Latin American & Iberian Literature Ser.). (ENG., Illus.). 274p. pap. 35.99 *(978-0-521-17496-1(1))* Cambridge Univ. Pr.

Arsillo, Vincenzo & Fiorani, Flavio. Sertão - Pampa: Topografie Dell'immaginario Sudamericano. 2007. (ITA & SPA.). 181p. *(978-88-7543-179-2(5))* Libreria Editrice Cafoscarina.

Black, Sam, ed. Violence in Argentine Literature & Film, 1989-2005. 2010. (Turning Points Ser.). (ENG.). 286p. pap. 39.95 *(978-1-55238-504-3(3))* Univ. of Calgary Pr. CAN. Dist: Chicago Distribution Ctr.

Butler, Rex. Borges' Short Stories: A Reader's Guide. 2010. (Reader's Guides). (ENG.). 160p. 24.95 *(978-0-8264-5213-9(2))* Continuum International Publishing Group, Ltd. GBR. Dist: National Bk. Network.

Butler, Rex & Butler. Borges' Short Stories: A Reader's Guide. 2010. (Reader's Guides). (ENG.). 160p. 90.00 *(978-0-8264-4298-7(6))* Continuum International Publishing Group, Ltd. GBR. Dist: National Bk. Network.

Canaparo, Claudio. El Imaginario Patagonia: Ensayo Acerca de la Evolución Conceptual Del Espacio. 2012. (Hispanic Studies: Culture & Ideas Ser.). (SPA., Illus.). 554p. pap. 85.95 ***(978-3-0343-0287-6(8))*** Lang, Peter AG GBR. Dist: Lang, Peter.

Copertari, Gabriela. Desintegración y Justicia en el Cine Argentino Contemporáneo. 2009. (Monografías A Ser.: Volume 275). (SPA., Illus.). 194p. 90.00 *(978-1-85566-187-5(X)*, Tamesis Bks.) Boydell & Brewer, Ltd. GBR. Dist: Boydell & Brewer, Inc.

Corral, Rose. Roberto Arlt: Una Poética de la Disonancia. 2009. (Estudios Lingüísticos y Literarios Ser.). (SPA., Illus.). 220p. pap. 20.99 *(978-607-462-078-8(4))* El Colegio de México, A.C., Biblioteca Miguel Cosio Villegas MEX. Dist: Fondo de Cultura Economica USA.

Davies, Lloyd Hughes. Projections of Peronism in Argentine Autobiography, Biography & Fiction. 2007. (University of Wales - Iberian & Latin American Studies). 334p. 85.00 *(978-0-7083-2014-3(7))* Univ. of Wales Pr. GBR. Dist: Chicago Distribution Ctr.

Díaz, Gwendolyn Josie & Díaz, Gwendolyn. Women & Power in Argentine Literature: Stories, Interviews, & Critical Essays. 2007. (Texas Pan American Literature in Translation Ser.). (ENG., Illus.). 392p. pap. 24.95 *(978-0-292-71649-0(4))* Univ. of Texas Pr.

Echeverría, Esteban, et al. El Matadero - La Cautiva.Tr. of Slaughterhouse - The Captive. (SPA., Illus.). 224p. 8.50 *(978-84-376-0617-0(9))* Ediciones Cátedra ESP. Dist: Lectorum Pubns., Inc.

Egginton, William & Johnson, David E., eds. Thinking with Borges. 2009. (ENG.). 234p. pap. 24.00 *(978-1-934542-11-8(3))* Davies Group Pubs., The.

Favoretto, Mara. Alegoría e Ironía Bajo Censura en la Argentina Del Proceso (1976-1983) 2010. (SPA.). 129.95 *(978-0-7734-1292-7(1))* Mellen, Edwin Pr., The.

Fontanet, Hernan. Model y subversion en la poetica de Leonidas Lamborghini. 2008. *(978-0-7734-4884-1(5))* Mellen, Edwin Pr., The.

Garramuño, Florencia. La Experiencia Opaca: Literatura y Desencanto. 2009. (Tierra Firme Ser.). (SPA.). 280p. pap. 19.99 *(978-950-557-783-5(4))* Fondo de Cultura Económica.

Gil Guerrero, Herminia. Poética Narrativa de Jorge Luis Borges. 2008. 191p. pap. 24.80 *(978-84-8489-398-1(7))* Iberoamericana Vervuert Publishing Corp.

González Álvarez, José Manuel. En los bordes fluidos . Formas híbridas y autoficción en la escuritura de Ricardo Piglia. 2009. (Perspectivas Hispánicas Ser.). (SPA.). 309p. pap. *(978-3-03911-819-9(6))* Lang, Peter.

Hortiguero, Hugo. La Literatura Cambalachesca en la Novelistica Be Osvaldo Soriano. (SPA.). 304p. 119.95 *(978-0-7734-5180-3(3))* Mellen, Edwin Pr., The.

Huberman, Ariana. Gauchos & Foreigners: Glossing Culture & Identity in the Argentine Countryside. 2010. (ENG.). 184p. 60.00 *(978-0-7391-4904-1(0))* Lexington Bks.

—Gauchos & Foreigners: Glossing Culture & Identity in the Argentine Countryside By. 2010. vii, 147p. *(978-0-7391-4906-5(7))* Lexington Bks.

Jagoe, Eva-Lynn Alicia. The End of the World As They Knew It: Writing Experiences of the Argentine South. 2008. (Bucknell Studies in Latin American Literature & Theory). (C). *(978-0-8387-5697-3(2))* Bucknell Univ. Pr.

Johnson, David E. Kant's Dog: On Borges, Philosophy, & the Time of Translation. 2012. (SUNY series in Latin American & Iberian Thought & Culture Ser.). (ENG.). 272p. 75.00 ***(978-1-4384-4265-5(3))*** State Univ. of New York Pr.

Kefala, Eleni. Peripheral (Post) Modernity: The Syncretist Aesthetics of Borges, Piglia, Kalokyris & Kyriakidis. 2007. 316p. (C). 77.95 *(978-0-8204-8639-0(6))* Lang, Peter Publishing, Inc.

Komi Kallinikos, Christina. Recorridos Urbanos: La Buenos Aires de Roberto Arlt y Juan Carlos Onetti. 2009. (SPA.). 272p. pap. 29.80 *(978-84-8489-490-2(8))* Iberoamericana Vervuert Publishing Corp.

Levine, Anette H. Cry for Me, Argentina: The Performance of Trauma in the Short Narratives of Aida Bortnik, Griselda Gambaro, & Tununa Mercado. 2008. (ENG.). 46.00 *(978-1-61147-371-1(3))* Fairleigh Dickinson Univ. Pr.

Levine, Annette H. Cry for Me, Argentina: The Performance of Trauma in the Short Narratives of Aida Bortnik, Griselda Gambaro, & Tununa Mercado. 2008. (Illus.). 184p. 46.00 *(978-0-8386-4156-9(3))* Fairleigh Dickinson Univ. Pr.

Mackintosh, Fiona J. & Posso, Karl. Árbol de Alejandra: Pizarnik Reassessed. Mackintosh, Fiona J., ed. 2007. (Monografías A Ser.: Volume 248). 182p. 90.00 *(978-1-85566-153-0(5)*, Tamesis Bks.) Boydell & Brewer, Ltd. GBR. Dist: Boydell & Brewer, Inc.

Martín, Florencia. In der Erzählkolonie: Über die Gewalt des Erzählens bei Thomas Bernhard und Sergio Chejfec. 2009. (Europäische Hochschulschriften. Reihe 18: Vergleichende Literaturwissenschaft Ser.). (GER & SPA.). 276p. pap. 74.95 *(978-3-631-58301-2(X))* Lang, Peter GmbH, Europaischer Verlag der Wissenschaften DEU. Dist: Lang, Peter.

Misemer, Sarah M. Moving Forward, Looking Back: Trains, Literature, & the Arts in the River Plate. 2010. (Illus.). 249p. 57.50 *(978-0-8387-5765-9(0))* Bucknell Univ. Pr.

Murray, Edmundo. Becoming Gauchos Ingleses: Diasporic Models in Irish-Argentine Literature. 2009. (Illus.). 156p. lib. bdg. *(978-1-933146-67-6(2)*, Maunsel & Co.) Academica Pr., LLC.

Nahson, Daniel. La Crítica Del Mito: Borges y la Literatura Como Sueño de Vida. 2009. (SPA.). 362p. pap. 36.00 *(978-84-8489-383-7(9))* Iberoamericana Vervuert Publishing Corp.

Olea Franco, Rafael. In Memoriam: Jorge Luis Borges. 2008. (Estudios Lingüísticos y Literarios Ser.). (SPA.). 420p. pap. 38.99 *(978-968-12-1361-9(0))* El Colegio de México, A.C., Biblioteca Miguel Cosio Villegas MEX. Dist: Fondo de Cultura Economica USA.

Portela, M. Edurne. Displaced Memories: The Poetics of Trauma in Argentine Women's Writing. 2009. 46.50 *(978-0-8387-5732-1(4))* Bucknell Univ. Pr.

Premat, Julio. Héroes Sin Atributos: Figuras de Autor en la Literatura Argentina. 2009. (Tierra Firme Ser.). (SPA.). 276p. pap. 25.99 *(978-950-557-778-1(8))* Fondo de Cultura Económica.

Quiroga, Horacio, et al. Cuentos. 2009. (Playaway Young Adult Ser.). (SPA.). 60.00 *(978-1-60775-579-1(3))* Findaway World, LLC.

Richardson, Bill. Borges & Space. 2012. (Hispanic Studies: Culture & Ideas Ser.: 41). (ENG.). 256p. pap. 54.95 ***(978-3-0343-0246-3(0))*** Lang, Peter AG GBR. Dist: Lang, Peter.

Riobó, Carlos. Sub-Versions of the Archive: Manuel Puig's & Severo Sarduy's Alternative Identities. 2011. 231p. *(978-0-8387-5801-4(0))* Bucknell Univ. Pr.

—Sub Versions of the Archive: Manuel Puig's & Severo Sarduy's Alternative Identities. 2010. (ENG.). 236p. 65.00 *(978-1-61148-036-8(1))* Bucknell Univ. Pr.

Sarlo, Beatriz. Jorge Luis Borges: A Writer on the Edge. King, John, ed. 2007. (Critical Studies in Latin American Culture). (ENG.). 176p. (gr. 13). per. 19.95 *(978-1-84467-588-3(2)*, 844588) Verso Bks. GBR. Dist: Norton, W. W. & Co., Inc.

Sasson-Henry, Perla & Sassón-Henry, Perla. Borges 2.0: From Text to Virtual Worlds. 2007. (Latin America: Interdisciplinary Studies). 136p. (C). 58.95 *(978-0-8204-9714-3(2))* Lang, Peter Publishing, Inc.

Schlickers, Sabine. Que Yo También Soy Pueta: La Literatura Gauchesca Rioplatense y Brasileña (Siglos XIX-XX) 2007. (SPA.). 264p. pap. 44.00 *(978-84-8489-327-1(8))* Iberoamericana Vervuert Publishing Corp.

Sierra, Marta. Gendered Spaces in Argentine Women's Literature. 2012. (ENG., Illus.). 254p. 90.00 ***(978-0-230-12085-3(7))*** Palgrave Macmillan.

Thon, Sonia R. Contexto, Estilo y Forma en la Obra de Jorge Luis Borges y Manuel Puig. 2011. 141p. 99.95 *(978-0-7734-1392-4(8))* Mellen, Edwin Pr., The.

ARGENTINE NATIONAL CHARACTERISTICS

see National Characteristics, Argentine

ARGENTINE POETRY—HISTORY AND CRITICISM

Bollig, Benedikt. Néstor Perlongher: The Poetic Search for an Argentine Marginal Voice. 2008. 256p. 85.00 *(978-0-7083-2123-2(2))* Univ. of Wales Pr. GBR. Dist: Chicago Distribution Ctr.

Choi, Myung. Employing the Grotesque as a Communication Strategy: The History of an Artistic Style. 2009. ii, 120p. *(978-0-7734-3844-6(0))* Mellen, Edwin Pr., The.

ARGENTINE REPUBLIC

see Argentina

ARGININE

Jacobs, Nathan L. Arginine Amino Acid. 2011. (Microbiology Research Advances Ser.). (Illus.). xi, 267p. 129.00 *(978-1-61761-981-6(7)*, Nova Biomedical Bks.) Nova Science Pubs., Inc.

ARGONAUTS (GREEK MYTHOLOGY)

see also Jason (Greek Mythology)

Barich, Michael, tr. from LAT. Argonautica. 2009. (Illus.). 256p. pap. 24.00 *(978-1-880977-29-3(X))* XOXOX Pr.

Murgatroyd, Paul & Murgatroyd, P. A Commentary on Book 4 of Valerius Flaccus' Argonautica. 2009. 374p. *(978-90-04-17561-7(X))* BRILL.

ARGONNE, BATTLE OF THE, FRANCE, 1918

Baker, Horace L. Argonne Days in World War I. Ferrell, Robert H., ed. & intro. by. 2007. (ENG., Illus.). 176p. (gr. 9). 29.95 *(978-0-8262-1708-0(7))* Univ. of Missouri Pr.

Baker, Horace L. & Cunningham, Roger D. The Black Citizen-Soldiers of Kansas, 1864-1901. 2008. (ENG., Illus.). 232p. (C). 34.95 *(978-0-8262-1807-0(5))* Univ. of Missouri Pr.

Clodfelter, Micheal. The Lost Battalion & the Meuse-Argonne 1918: America's Deadliest Battle. (ENG., Illus.). 256p. 2006. 55.00 *(978-0-7864-2679-9(9))* 2012. pap. 25.00 ***(978-0-7864-6908-6(0))*** McFarland & Co., Inc. Pubs.

Ferrell, Robert H. America's Deadliest Battle: Meuse-Argonne 1918. 2007. (Modern War Studies). (Illus.). 195p. 29.95 *(978-0-7006-1499-8(0))* Univ. Pr. of Kansas.

—In the Company of Generals: The World War I Diary of Pierpont L. Stackpole. 2009. (ENG.). 208p. (C). 34.95 *(978-0-8262-1870-4(9))* Univ. of Missouri Pr.

Hogan, Martin J. The Shamrock Battalion in the Great War.... Cooke, James, ed. 2007. (ENG., Illus.). 152p. (gr. 9). 24.95 *(978-0-8262-1710-3(9))* Univ. of Missouri Pr.

Lengel, Edward G. To Conquer Hell: The Meuse-Argonne, 1918 the Epic Battle That Ended the First World War. 2009. (ENG., Illus.). 528p. pap. 20.00 *(978-0-8050-8915-8(2)*, Holt Paperback) Holt, Henry & Co.

ARGOT

see Cant; Slang

ARGUELLO, MARIA DE LA CONCEPCION MARCELA, 1791-1857

Davis, John F. California Romantic & Resourceful. 2009. 48p. pap. *(978-1-4099-0470-0(9))* Dodo Pr.

ARGUMENTATION

see Debates and Debating; Logic; Oratory; Reasoning; Syllogism

ARGUMENTS, LEGAL

see Forensic Orations

ARHYTHMIA

see Arrhythmia

ARIANISM

see also Jesus Christ—Divinity; Socinianism; Unitarianism

Gregg, Robert C., ed. Arianism: Historical & Theological Reassessments: Papers from the Ninth International Conference on Patristic Studies. 2006. (Patristic Monograph Ser.). 394p. pap. 37.00 *(978-1-59752-961-7(3)*, Wipf and Stock) Wipf & Stock Pubs.

Gregory, et al. Contre Eunome. 2008. (FRE & GEC.). *(978-2-204-09211-1(8))*; *(978-2-204-08716-2(5))* Editions du Cerf.

Gwatkin, Henry Melvill. The Arian Controversy. 2008. 160p. 25.99 *(978-0-554-27313-6(6))* 2008. 160p. 22.99 *(978-0-554-36616-6(9))* 2007. (ENG.). 140p. pap. 18.99 *(978-1-4346-2941-8(4))* 2007. (ENG.). 160p. per. 21.99 *(978-1-4346-2965-4(1))* BiblioBazaar.

Gwynn, David M. Athanasius of Alexandria: Bishop, Theologian, Ascetic, Father. 2012. (Christian Theology in Context Ser.). (ENG.). 256p. pap. 35.00 ***(978-0-19-921095-4(0))*** Oxford Univ. Pr., Inc.

Gwynn, David M. The Eusebians: The Polemic of Athanasius of Alexandria & the Construction of the 'Arian Controversy' 2007. (Oxford Theological Monographs). (ENG.). 304p. 99.00 *(978-0-19-920555-4(8))* Oxford Univ. Pr., Inc.

Jones, Marvin D. Athanasius' Concept of Eternal Sonship as Revealed in Contra Arianos. 2006. 240p. *(978-0-7734-5644-0(9))* Mellen, Edwin Pr., The.

Nazianzus, St Gregory. Festal Orations. Harrison, Nonna Verna, tr. from GEC. 2008. 184p. pap. 16.00 *(978-0-88141-325-0(9))* St. Vladimir's Seminary Pr.

Newman, John Henry. The Arians of the Fourth Century. 2010. 494p. pap. 34.45 *(978-1-4455-4019-1(3))* Research Pr.

Russell, Paul S. St. Ephraem the Syrian & St. Gregory the Theologian Confront the Arabs. 2010. 103.04 *(978-1-61143-561-0(7))* Gorgias Pr., LLC.

ZHdanovych, Olesia. Arianstvo V Epokhu Konstantyna Velykoho. 2009. (UKR.). 219p. *(978-966-02-5122-9(X))* National Academy of Sciences of Ukraine.

ARIAS

see Songs

ARID REGIONS

see also Deserts; Dry Farming

Bothma, Jacobus du P. Carnivore Ecology in Arid Lands. 2010. (Adaptations of Desert Organisms Ser.). (Illus.). x, 209p. pap. 201.00 *(978-3-642-08213-9(0)*, 3642082130) Springer.

Choubisa, R. K. & Hooja, Rakesh, eds. Administration of Desert & Drought-Prone Arid Areas. 2009. 353p. 55.00 *(978-81-316-0242-3(7))* Rawat Pubns. IND. Dist: International Specialized Bk. Services.

Cole, Lucy. Arid Environments. 2010. (Advanced TopicMaster Ser.). (Illus.). 126p. pap. 29.50 *(978-1-4441-0834-7(4))* Hodder Education GBR. Dist: Trans-Atlantic Pubns., Inc.

Degenovine, Kara M. Semi-Arid Environments: Agriculture, Water Supply, & Vegetation. 2010. 155.00 *(978-1-61761-215-2(4))* Nova Science Pubs., Inc.

Doelman, Trudy. Time to Quarry: The Archaeology of Stone Procurement in Northwestern New South Wales, Australia. 2008. (Bar S Ser.). (ENG., Illus.). 193p. (C). pap. 90.00 *(978-1-4073-0288-1(4))* British Archaeological Reports Ltd. GBR. Dist: Brown, David Bk. Co., The.

El-Naser, Hazim. Management of Scarce Water Resources: A Middle Eastern Experience. 2009. (Progress in Water Resources Ser.: 14). (Illus.). 224p. 160.00 *(978-1-84564-414-7(X))* WIT Pr GBR. Dist: WIT Pr.

Eshtawi, Tamer & A. Abdulla, Fayez. Using Hydrological Models in the Management of a Semi Arid Watershed. 2011. 124p. pap. ***(978-3-8443-2994-0(3))*** Lambert Academic Publishing.

Fernandez-Bernal, Antonio & De La Rosa, Mauricio Alberto, eds. Arid Environments. 2009. 129.00 *(978-1-60692-411-2(7))* Nova Science Pubs., Inc.

Galvin, Kathleen A., et al, eds. Fragmentation in Semi-Arid & Arid Landscapes: Consequences for Human & Natural Systems. 2007. (ENG., Illus.). xviii, 411p. 249.00 *(978-1-4020-4905-7(6)*, 1402049056) Springer.

Grace, J. Kusuma & Sharma, K. L. Assessment of Soil Quality Using Key Indicators. 2010. 240p. pap. *(978-3-639-21392-8(0))* VDM Verlag Dr. Mueller e.K.

Greiff, Sophia. Desert Birds: Desert Birds. 2nd ed. 2011. (ENG & GER., Illus.). 112p. 45.00 ***(978-3-86828-179-8(7))*** Kehrer Verlag Heidelberg, Klaus Kehrer DEU. Dist: Consortium Bk. Sales & Distribution.

Han, Fengxiang X. Biogeochemistry of Trace Elements in Arid Environments. (Environmental Pollution Ser.). 2010. xxvi, 355p. pap. 249.00 *(978-90-481-7508-6(9)*, 9048175089) 2009. (Illus.). xxvi, 366p. 249.00 *(978-1-4020-6023-6(8))* Springer.

Hutchinson, Charles F. & Herrmann, Stefanie M. The Future of Arid Lands - Revisited: A Review of 50 Years of Drylands Research. 2007. (Advances in Global Change Research Ser.). (Illus.). 225p. 239.00 *(978-1-4020-6688-7(0))* Springer.

Issar, Arie S., ed. Progressive Development: To Mitigate the Negative Impact of Global Warming on the Semi-arid Regions. 2010. (Environmental Science & Engineering Ser.). (Illus.). x, 290p. 159.00 *(978-3-642-10639-2(0)*, 3642106390) Springer.

Issar, Arie S. & Resnick, S. D., eds. Runoff, Infiltration & Subsurface Flow of Water in Arid & Semi-Arid Regions. 2010. (Water Science & Technology Library). 196p. pap. 139.00 *(978-90-481-4701-4(8)*, 9048147018) Springer.

Keller, Christopher & Lagae, Johan, eds. Aglaia Konrad: Desert Cities. 2008. (ENG., Illus.). 236p. pap. 75.00 *(978-3-905829-59-4(2))* JRP Ringier Kunstverlag AG CHE. Dist: D.A.P./Distributed Art Pubs.

Koohafkan, Parviz, et al. Water & Cereals in Drylands. 2008. (ENG., Illus.). 120p. 146.00 *(978-1-84407-709-0(8))*; pap. 54.50 *(978-1-84407-708-3(X))* Routledge.

Mainguet, Monique. Aridity: Droughts & Human Development. Reimer, T. O. E., tr. from GER. 2010. (ENG., Illus.). ix, 302p. pap. 152.00 *(978-3-642-08327-3(7)*, 3642083277) Springer.

Mohamed, A. M. O. Principles & Applications of Time Domain Electrometry in Geoenvironmental Engineering. 2006. (ENG., Illus.). 603p. 279.95 *(978-0-415-41129-5(7)*, Taylor & Francis) Taylor & Francis Group GBR. Dist: Taylor & Francis Group.

Mohamed A M O, ed. Arid Land Hydrogeology: in Search of a Solution to a Threatened Resource: Proceedings of the Third Joint Uae-Japan Symposium on Sustainable Gcc Environment & Water Resources (Ewr2006), Abu Dhabi United Arab Emirates, 28-30 January 2006. 2006. (Developments in Arid Regions Research Ser.). (ENG., Illus.). 213p. 157.95 *(978-0-415-41127-1(0)*, Taylor & Francis) Taylor & Francis Group GBR. Dist: Taylor & Francis Group.

Mortimore, Michael. Dryland Opportunities. 2010. (ENG., Illus.). 98p. pap. 16.00 *(978-2-8317-1183-6(5))* UICN Union Mondiale pour la Nature, Cecile Thiery CHE. Dist: Chicago Distribution Ctr.

Museum Im Bellpark Kriens Staff. Guido Baselgia. 2008. (GER & ENG., Illus.). 104p. lthr. 85.00 *(978-3-7757-2098-4(7))* Hatje Cantz Verlag GmbH & Co KG DEU. Dist: D.A.P./Distributed Art Pubs.

Nicholson, Sharon E. Dryland Climatology. 2011. (ENG., Illus.). 528p. 150.00 *(978-0-521-51649-5(8))* Cambridge Univ. Pr.

Oweis, Theib Y., et al. Rainwater Harvesting for Agriculture in Dry Areas. 2012. (ENG.). 266p. (C). 99.95 ***(978-0-415-62114-4(3)***, CRC Press) Taylor & Francis Group GBR. Dist: Taylor & Francis Group.

Schneier-Madanes, Graciela & Courel, Marie-Francoise, eds. Water & Sustainability in Arid Regions: Bridging the Gap Between Physical & Social Sciences. 2009. (ENG., Illus.). xxii, 349p. 199.00 *(978-90-481-2775-7(0)*, 9048127750) Springer.

Sene, El Hadji M., et al. Managing Wetlands in Arid Regions: Lessons Learned. 2006. (ENG., Illus.). 82p. pap. 26.00 *(978-2-8317-0909-3(1))* UICN Union Mondiale pour la Nature, Cecile Thiery CHE. Dist: Chicago Distribution Ctr.

Temesgen Leye Staff. Conservation Tillage Systems & Water Productivity Implications. 2007. (ENG., Illus.). 130p. 57.95 *(978-0-415-43946-6(9)*, Taylor & Francis) Taylor & Francis Group GBR. Dist: Taylor & Francis Group.

Thomas, David S. G. Arid Zone Geomorphology: Process, Form & Change in Drylands. 3rd ed. 2011. (ENG., Illus.). 648p. pap. 99.95 *(978-0-470-51909-7(6)*, Wiley) Wiley, John & Sons, Inc.

Thomas, David S. G., ed. Arid Zone Geomorphology: Process, Form & Change in Drylands. 3rd ed. 2011. (ENG., Illus.). 648p. 167.95 *(978-0-470-51908-0(8)*, Wiley) Wiley, John & Sons, Inc.

Veth, Peter Marius. The Archaeology of Montebello Islands, North-West Australia: Late Quaternary Foragers on an Arid Coastline. 2007. (Bar S Ser.). (ENG., Illus.). 84p. (C). pap. 62.50 *(978-1-4073-0103-7(9))* British Archaeological Reports Ltd. GBR. Dist: Brown, David Bk. Co., The.

Walton, Kenneth. The Arid Zones. 2007. (ENG., Illus.). 175p. pap. 19.95 *(978-0-202-30928-6(2))* Aldine Transaction.

Wani, Suhas P., et al. Integrated Watershed Management in Rainfed Agriculture. 2011. (ENG., Illus.). 496p. (C). 119.95 *(978-0-415-88277-4(X)*, CRC Press) Taylor & Francis Group GBR. Dist: Taylor & Francis Group.

Wheater, Howard, et al, eds. Groundwater Modelling in Arid & Semi-Arid Areas. 2010. (International Hydrology Ser.). (ENG., Illus.). 150p. 109.00 *(978-0-521-11129-4(3))* Cambridge Univ. Pr.

—Hydrological Modelling in Arid & Semi-Arid Areas. 2007. (International Hydrology Ser.). (ENG., Illus.). 206p. 131.00 *(978-0-521-86918-8(8))* Cambridge Univ. Pr.

Wickens, Gerald E. Ecophysiology of Economic Plants in Arid & Semi-Arid Lands. 2010. (Adaptations of Desert Organisms Ser.). (Illus.). xiii, 343p. pap. 289.00 *(978-3-642-08089-0(8)*, 3642080898) Springer.

ARIOSTO, LODOVICO, 1474-1533

DeCoste, Mary-Michelle. Hopeless Love: Boiardo, Ariosto, & Narratives of Queer Female Desire. 2009. (Toronto Italian Studies). (ENG & ITA.). 192p. *(978-0-8020-9684-5(0))* Univ. of Toronto Pr.

Gardner, Edmund G. King of Court Poets A Study of the Work. 2006. pap. 36.95 *(978-1-4286-4748-0(1))* Kessinger Publishing, LLC.

Hanning, Robert W. Serious Play: Desire & Authority in the Poetry of Ovid, Chaucer, & Ariosto. 2010. (Leonard Hastings Schoff Lectures). (ENG.). 312p. (gr. 17). 45.00 *(978-0-231-15210-5(8))* Columbia Univ. Pr.

ARISTIDES, CA. 530-CA. 468 B.C.

Plutarch. Plutarch's Themistocles & Aristides. 2009. 190p. pap. *(978-1-150-58410-7(6))* Books LLC.

ARISTIDES, AELIUS

Harris, W. V. & Holmes, Brooke, eds. Aelius Aristides between Greece, Rome, & the Gods. 2009. (Columbia Studies in the Classical Tradition Ser.). *(978-90-04-17204-3(1))* BRILL.

Hubbell, Harry Mortimer. The Influence of Isocrates on Cicero, Dionysius & Aristides. 2009. 86p. pap. 17.95 *(978-1-120-76448-5(3))* Kessinger Publishing, LLC.

Petsalis-Diomidis, Alexia. Truly Beyond Wonders: Aelius Aristides & the Cult of Asklepios. 2010. (Oxford Studies in Ancient Culture & Representation Ser.). (ENG., Illus.). 380p. 135.00 *(978-0-19-956190-2(7))* Oxford Univ. Pr., Inc.

ARISTIDES, THE JUST

see Aristides, ca. 530-ca. 468 B.C.

ARISTOCRACY

see Aristocracy (Political Science); Aristocracy (Social Class)

ARISTOCRACY (POLITICAL SCIENCE)

Australian Nati J Jupp Staff. Political Parties. 2009. 124p. 104.00 *(978-0-415-55596-8(5))* Routledge.

Cannadine. Pattern Power Politics of 19th Century Towns. (Illus.). xi, 227p. *(978-0-7185-1193-7(X)*, Thoemmes Continuum) Continuum International Publishing Group, Ltd.

Chekalova, A. A. Senat I Senatorskaia Aristokratiia Konstantinopolia: IV — Pervaa Polovina VII Veka. 2010. (RUS., Illus.). 338p. *(978-5-02-037568-0(3))* Nauka.

Corrigan, Matthew T. American Royalty: The Bush & Clinton Families & the Danger to the American Presidency. 2008. (Evolving American Presidency Ser.). (ENG.). 256p. 89.00 *(978-1-4039-8415-9(8))* Palgrave Macmillan.

Corrigan, Matthew T. & Corrigan, Matthew. American Royalty: The Bush & Clinton Families & the Danger to the American Presidency. 2008. (Evolving American Presidency Ser.). (ENG.). 256p. pap. 31.00 *(978-1-4039-8416-6(6))* Palgrave Macmillan.

Doyle, William. Aristocracy: A Very Short Introduction. 2010. (Very Short Introductions Ser.). (ENG., Illus.). 144p. pap. 11.95 *(978-0-19-920678-0(3))* Oxford Univ. Pr., Inc.

—Aristocracy & its Enemies in the Age of Revolution. 2009. (ENG.). 368p. 60.00 *(978-0-19-955985-5(6))* Oxford Univ. Pr., Inc.

Ebrey, Patricia Buckley. The Aristocratic Families in Early Imperial China: A Case Study of the Po-Ling Ts'ui Family. 2009. (Cambridge Studies in Chinese History, Literature & Institutions Ser.). (ENG.). 252p. pap. 34.99 *(978-0-521-10237-7(5))* Cambridge Univ. Pr.

Kilbride, Daniel. An American Aristocracy: Southern Planters in Antebellum Philadelphia. 2006. (Illus.). 216p. 39.95 *(978-1-57003-656-9(X))* Univ. of South Carolina Pr.

Kyriakidis, Savvas. Warfare in Late Byzantium, 1204-1453. 2011. (Illus.). 272p. *(978-90-04-20666-3(3))* BRILL.

North, Christopher. The Transition from Technocracy to Aristocracy in Japan, 1955-2003. 2007. 160p. per. 19.95 *(978-1-58112-305-0(1)*, Dissertation.com) Universal Pubs.

Sneath, David. The Headless State: Aristocratic Orders, Kinship Society, & Misrepresentations of Nomadic Inner Asia. 2007. (ENG., Illus.). 288p. (gr. 17). 60.00 *(978-0-231-14054-6(1))* Columbia Univ. Pr.

ARISTOCRACY (SOCIAL CLASS)

see also Nobility

Bennett, Susan. 'I awleis admired your talent' The artistic life of Georgiana Jane Henderson (neeKeate) (1771-1850) 2008. 164p. pap. *(978-3-639-10913-9(9))* VDM Verlag Dr. Mueller e.K.

Boyer Lewis, Charlene M. Elizabeth Patterson Bonaparte: An American Aristocrat in the Early Republic. 2012. (Illus.). 312p. 34.95 ***(978-0-8122-4430-4(3))*** Univ. of Pennsylvania Pr.

Campbell, Liza. A Charmed Life: Growing up in Macbeth's Castle. 2008. (ENG., Illus.). 352p. pap. 14.95 *(978-0-312-38496-8(3)*, St. Martin's Griffin) St. Martin's Pr.

Carr, William. Arms, Autarky & Aggression: A Study in German Foreign Policy, 1933-1939. 144p. pap. *(978-0-7131-5669-0(4)*, Hodder Arnold) Hodder Education.

Clemens, Gabriele B. Hochkultur als Herrschaftselement: Italienischer und deutscher Adel im langen 19. Jahrhundert. Clemens, Gabriele B. et al, eds. 2011. (Reihe der Villa Vigoni Ser.).Tr. of High Culture as Element of Power. (GER., Illus.). VI, 340p. 126.00 ***(978-3-11-023568-5(4))*** De Gruyter, Walter Inc.

Coclanis, Peter A. Twilight on the South Carolina Rice Fields: Letters of the Heyward Family, 1862-1871. Hollis, Margaret Belser & Stokes, Allen H., eds. 2010. 480p. 39.95 *(978-1-57003-894-5(5))* Univ. of South Carolina Pr.

Crouch, David. The English Aristocracy: 1070-1272: A Social Transformation. 2011. *(978-83-00-11455-9(6))* Yale Univ. Pr.

—The English Aristocracy, 1070-1272: A Social Transformation. 2011. (ENG., Illus.). 352p. 55.00 *(978-0-300-11455-3(9))* Yale Univ. Pr.

d'Este, Antonino. An American Duke. 2010. 126p. pap. 19.94 *(978-0-557-51745-9(1))* Lulu Enterprises Inc.

Dewar, Michael & Harrison, Thomas. Leisured Resistance: Villas, Literature & Politics. 2010. (ENG.). 144p. pap. 40.00 *(978-0-7156-3489-9(5))* Duckworth Publishers GBR. Dist: International Publishers Marketing.

Doyle, William. Aristocracy: A Very Short Introduction. 2010. (Very Short Introductions Ser.). (ENG., Illus.). 144p. pap. 11.95 *(978-0-19-920678-0(3))* Oxford Univ. Pr., Inc.

Elias, Norbert. The Court Society, 3 vols., Vol. 14. Kilminster, Richard, ed. 2010. (Collected Works Norbert Elias Ser.). (ENG.). 344p. 109.95 *(978-1-906359-01-0(6))* Univ. College Dublin Pr. IRL. Dist: Dufour Editions, Inc.

Evergates, Theodore. The Aristocracy in the County of Champagne, 1100-1300. 2007. (Middle Ages Ser.). (Illus.). 424p. (C). 95.95 *(978-0-8122-4019-1(7))* Univ. of Pennsylvania Pr.

Farney, Gary D. Ethnic Identity & Aristocratic Competition in Republican Roman. 2010. (ENG.). 358p. (C). pap. 33.00 *(978-0-521-15180-1(5))* Cambridge Univ. Pr.

—Ethnic Identity & Aristocratic Competition in Republican Rome. 2007. (ENG., Illus.). 358p. 99.99 *(978-0-521-86331-5(7))* Cambridge Univ. Pr.

Fawcett, Edgar. Social Silhouettes: Being the Impressions of Mr. Mark Manhattan. 2010. 378p. pap. 27.16 *(978-1-163-79224-7(1))* 2007. 380p. 48.95 *(978-0-548-55126-4(X))* 2007. (ENG.). 380p. per. 33.95 *(978-0-548-48839-3(8))* Kessinger Publishing, LLC.

Forster, Margaret Elizabeth. Churchill's Grandmama: A Life of Frances, 7th Duchess of Marlborough. 2010. (ENG., Illus.). 256p. 26.95 *(978-0-7524-5552-5(4))* History Pr. Ltd.,The GBR. Dist: Independent Pubs. Group.

Given-Wilson, Chris, et al. War, Government & Aristocracy in the British Isles, C.1150-1500: Essays in Honour of Michael Prestwich. Given-Wilson, Chris et al, eds. 2008. (Illus.). 332p. 90.00 *(978-1-84383-389-5(1)*, Boydell Press) Boydell & Brewer, Ltd. GBR. Dist: Boydell & Brewer, Inc.

Goldsmith, Annabel. No Invitation Required: The Pelham Cottage Years. (ENG., Illus.). 2011. 288p. 15.95 *(978-0-7538-2338-5(1)*, Phoenix) 2010. 192p. 32.95 *(978-0-297-85451-7(8)*, Weidenfeld & Nicolson) Orion Publishing Group, Ltd. GBR. Dist: Independent Pubs. Group.

Hall-Witt, Jennifer. Fashionable Acts: Opera & Elite Culture in London, 1780-1880. 2007. (Becoming Modern: New Nineteenth-Century Studies). (Illus.). 404p. pap. 50.00 *(978-1-58465-625-8(5)*, University of New Hampshire Press) Univ. Pr. of New England.

Hamilton, Elsa. Mighty Subjects: The Dunbar Earls in Scotland C. 1072-1289. 2010. (ENG., Illus.). 324p. pap. 40.95 *(978-1-904607-94-6(2)*, Donald, John) Birlinn, Ltd. GBR. Dist: Independent Pubs. Group.

Helms, Mary W. Access to Origins: Affines, Ancestors, & Aristocrats. 2010. (ENG., Illus.). 272p. pap. 25.00 *(978-0-292-72374-0(1))* Univ. of Texas Pr.

James, Lawrence. Aristocrats: Power, Grace, & Decadence: Britain's Great Ruling Classes from 1066 to the Present. 2011. (ENG., Illus.). 448p. pap. 19.99 *(978-0-312-58379-8(6)*, St. Martin's Griffin) St. Martin's Pr.

Lehnert, Uta. Der Kaiser & die Siegesallee. (GER., Illus.). 414p. *(978-3-496-01189-7(0))* Reimer, Dietrich.

Leighton, D. J. Ripper Suspect: The Secret Lives of Montague Druitt. 2006. (ENG., Illus.). 224p. pap. 24.95 *(978-0-7509-4329-1(7))* Sutton Publishing.

Leney, Joy. Such a Nuisance to Die: The Autobiography of Her Serene Highness Princess Elisabeth de Croy. 2010. (Illus.). 256p. 38.50 *(978-1-84624-448-3(X))* Book Guild, Ltd. GBR. Dist: Trans-Atlantic Pubns., Inc.

Levy, Oscar. The Revival of Aristocracy. 2010. 150p. pap. 21.75 *(978-1-148-95508-7(9))* BiblioBazaar.

—The Revival of Aristocracy. 2009. 76p. pap. *(978-0-217-13207-7(3))* Books LLC.

Livingstone, Amy. Out of Love for My Kin: Aristocratic Family Life in the Lands of the Loire, 1000-1200. 2010. (Illus.). 296p. 45.00 *(978-0-8014-4841-6(7))* Cornell Univ. Pr.

Macknight. Aristocratic Families In Republican France, 1870-1940. 2012. (Studies in Modern French History Ser.). (ENG., Illus.). 272p. 95.00 ***(978-0-7190-8501-7(2))*** Manchester Univ. Pr. GBR. Dist: Macmillan.

Maeda, Momji. Temptation: (Yaoi) 2007. 200p. pap. 12.99 *(978-1-933809-52-6(3))* DramaQueen, L.L.C.

Magenda, Burhan Djabier. East Kalimantan: The Decline of a Commercial Aristocracy. 2010. 164p. pap. *(978-602-8397-21-6(0))* Equinox Publishing Ltd.

McClain, John Padraig. The Harp, the Cross, & the Sword. 2008. 367p. pap. 18.95 *(978-0-7414-4467-7(4))* Infinity Publishing.

Mosley, Charlotte. Wait for Me! Mitford, Deborah, ed. 2010. (ENG., Illus.). 368p. 28.00 *(978-0-374-20768-7(2))* Farrar, Straus & Giroux.

Murland, Jerry. Aristocrats Go to War: Uncovering the Zillebeke Cemetery. 2010. (Illus.). 192p. 39.95 *(978-1-84884-152-9(3))* Pen & Sword Bks. Ltd. GBR. Dist: Casemate Pubs. & Bk. Distributors, LLC.

Neville, Leonora. Authority in Byzantine Provincial Society, 950-1100. 2009. (ENG., Illus.). 224p. pap. 33.00 *(978-0-521-10117-2(4))* Cambridge Univ. Pr.

Newton, Nicholas D. Seeking the Cool Side of the Pillow: A Wayward Youth's Awakening. 2010. 248p. 24.99 *(978-1-4520-4391-3(4))* AuthorHouse.

Niemoeller, Sibylle Sarah & Sell, Baroness Von. Crowns, Crosses, & Stars: My Youth in Prussia, Surviving Hitler, & a Life Beyond. 2012. (ENG., Illus.). 360p. 29.95 ***(978-1-55753-618-1(X))*** Purdue Univ. Pr.

Niessen, Olwen Claire C. Aristocracy, Temperance & Social Reform: The Life of Lady Henry Somerset. 2007. (Library of Victorian Studies). (ENG., Illus.). 288p. 89.00 *(978-1-84511-484-8(1)*, Tauris Academic Studies) I. B. Tauris & Co., Ltd. GBR. Dist: Macmillan.

Fagnamenta, Peter. Prairie Fever: British Aristocrats in the American West, 1830-1890. 2012. (ENG., Illus.). 368p. 27.95 ***(978-0-393-07239-6(8)***, 7239) Norton, W. W. & Co., Inc.

Ricketts, Philadelphia. High-Ranking Widows in Medieval Iceland & Yorkshire: Property, Power, Marriage & Identity in the Twelfth & Thirteenth Centuries. (Illus.). xxii, 492p. *(978-90-04-18471-8(6))* BRILL.

Rollinger, Christian. Solvendi Sunt Nummi: Die Schuldenkultur der Späten Römischen Republik Im Spiegel der Schriften Ciceros. 2009. (GER., Illus.). 265p. (C). pap. 57.00 ***(978-3-938032-29-9(4))*** Antike, Verlag, e.K. DEU. Dist: ISD.

Rosenthal, Joel T. The Purchase of Pardise. 2006. 192p. 180.00 *(978-0-415-41302-2(8))* Routledge.

Rubenhold, Hallie. The Lady in Red: An Eighteenth-Century Tale of Sex, Scandal, & Divorce. 2010. (ENG., Illus.). 320p. pap. 18.99 *(978-0-312-62416-3(6)*, St. Martin's Griffin) St. Martin's Pr.

Sackville-West, Robert. Inheritance: The Story of Knole & the Sackvilles. 2010. (ENG.). 320p. 26.00 *(978-0-8027-7901-4(8))* Walker & Co.

Schama, Chloë. Wild Romance: A Victorian Story of a Marriage, a Trial, & a Self-Made Woman. 2010. (ENG., Illus.). 272p. 24.00 *(978-0-8027-1736-8(5))* Walker & Co.

Scott, Hamish & Simms, Brendan, eds. Cultures of Power in Europe During the Long Eighteenth Century. 2007. (ENG.). 398p. 125.99 *(978-0-521-84227-3(1))* Cambridge Univ. Pr.

Scriven, Marcus. Splendour & Squalor: The Disgrace & Disintegration of Three Aristocratic Dynasties. 2011. (ENG., Illus.). 414p. pap. 16.95 ***(978-1-84354-125-7(4))*** Atlantic Bks., Ltd. GBR. Dist: Independent Pubs. Group.

Sebba, Anne. American Jennie: The Remarkable Life of Lady Randolph Churchill. 2007. (ENG., Illus.). 416p. 26.95 *(978-0-393-05772-0(0)*, 5772) Norton, W. W. & Co., Inc.

Sebba, Anne. That Woman: The Life of Wallis Simpson, Duchess of Windsor. 2012. (ENG., Illus.). 368p. 27.99 ***(978-1-250-00296-9(6))*** St. Martin's Pr.

Simpkin, David. The English Aristocracy at War: From the Welsh Wars of Edward I to the Battle of Bannockburn. 2008. (Warfare in History Ser.: Volume 26). 246p. 90.00 *(978-1-84383-388-8(3)*, Boydell Press) Boydell & Brewer, Ltd. GBR. Dist: Boydell & Brewer, Inc.

Smith, Douglas. Former People: The Final Days of the Russian Aristocracy, 1 vol. 2012. (ENG., Illus.). 496p. 30.00 ***(978-0-374-15761-6(8))*** Farrar, Straus & Giroux.

Stewart, John. Byron & the Websters: The Letters & Entangled Lives of the Poet, Sir James Webster & Lady Frances Webster. 2008. (ENG., Illus.). 224p. pap. 39.95 *(978-0-7864-3240-0(3))* McFarland & Co., Inc. Pubs.

Stonor Saunders, Frances. The Woman Who Shot Mussolini. 2010. (ENG., Illus.). 400p. 30.00 *(978-0-8050-9121-2(1)*, Metropolitan Bks.) Holt, Henry & Co.

Surovtsov, Vicka Markov. Snow & Sand. 2010. 316p. pap. 22.95 *(978-1-4502-5057-3(2))* iUniverse, Inc.

Tempest, Annie. She Talks Venus - He Talks Mars. 2011. (ENG., Illus.). 112p. 19.95 *(978-0-7112-3261-7(X))* Lincoln, Frances Ltd. GBR. Dist: Perseus-PGW.

Tindley, Annie. The Sutherland Estate, 1850-1920: Aristocratic Decline, Estate Management & Land Reform. 2010. (Scottish Historical Review Monographs). (ENG.). 256p. (gr. 17). 80.00 *(978-0-7486-4032-4(0))* Edinburgh Univ. Pr. GBR. Dist: Columbia Univ. Pr.

Urbach, Karina, ed. European Aristocracies & the Radical Right, 1918-1939. 2007. (Studies of the German Historical Institute, London Ser.). (ENG., Illus.). 240p. 165.00 *(978-0-19-923173-7(7))* Oxford Univ. Pr., Inc.

Wasson, Ellis. The Role of Ruling class Adaptability in the British Transition from Ancien Regime to Modern State: The Open Elite of Britain & Ireland from the Middle Ages to the Second World War. 2010. (Illus.). 328p. 119.95 *(978-0-7734-1464-8(9))* Mellen, Edwin Pr., The.

Webb, Nigel & Webb, Caroline. The Earl & His Butler in Constantinople: The Secret Diary of an English Servant among the Ottomans. 2008. (ENG., Illus.). 248p. pap. 26.00 *(978-1-84511-782-5(4))* I. B. Tauris & Co., Ltd. GBR. Dist: Macmillan.

Williams, Ann. The World Before Domesday: The English Aristocracy 900-1066. 2008. (ENG., Illus.). 256p. 130.00 *(978-1-84725-239-5(7))* Continuum International Publishing Group, Ltd. GBR. Dist: National Bk. Network.

Woods, Lawrence M. Horace Plunkett in America: An Irish Aristocrat on the Wyoming Range. 2010. (Western Frontiersmen Ser.). (ENG., Illus.). 296p. (C). 36.95 *(978-0-87062-394-3(X)*, Clark, Arthur H. Co., The) Univ. of Oklahoma Pr.

Woolsey, Kate T. Republics Versus Woman, Constrasting the Treatment Accorded to Woman in Aristocracies with That Meted Out to Her in Democracies. 179p. reprint ed. 88.00 *(978-0-7222-1578-4(9))* Library Reprints, Inc.

ARISTOCRATS

see Aristocracy (Social Class)

ARISTOPHANES

Aristofane, et al. Donne Al Parlamento. 2010. 297p. *(978-88-430-5148-9(2))* Carocci.

Aristophanes. Acharnians, Knights, & Peace. Ewans, Michael, tr. from GEC. 2012. (Oklahoma Series in Classical Culture Ser.). (ENG., Illus.). 304p. pap. 34.95 ***(978-0-8061-4231-9(6))*** Univ. of Oklahoma Pr.

—The Frogs of Aristophanes, with Notes Critical & Explanatory. Mitchell, Thomas, ed. 2007. (ENG.). 566p. 58.95 *(978-0-548-27326-5(X))*; 568p. per. 43.95 *(978-1-4326-7798-5(5))* Kessinger Publishing, LLC.

—Lysistrata, the Women's Festival, & Frogs. Ewans, Michael, tr. from GEC. 2011. (Oklahoma Series in Classical Culture Ser.). (ENG.). 352p. (C). pap. 34.95 *(978-0-8061-4151-0(4))* Univ. of Oklahoma Pr.

Aristophanes & Chantry, M. Scholies Anciennes Aux Grenouilles et Au Ploutos D'Aristophane. 2009. (Fragments Ser.). (GEC & FRE., Illus.). 428p. (C). pap. 56.00 ***(978-2-251-74205-2(0))*** Societe d'edition Les Belles lettres FRA. Dist: ISD.

Austin, Colin & Olson, S. Douglas, eds. Aristophanes Thesmophoriazusae. 2008. (GEC & ENG., Illus.). 472p. pap. 85.00 *(978-0-19-955383-9(1))* Oxford Univ. Pr., Inc.

Beckett, Mischa. Poetry & Philosophy. 2009. 152p. pap. *(978-3-639-14500-7(3))* VDM Verlag Dr. Mueller e.K.

Biles, Zachary P. Aristophanes & the Poetics of Competition. 2011. (ENG.). 302p. 99.00 *(978-0-521-76407-0(6))* Cambridge Univ. Pr.

Cartledge, Paul, ed. Aristophanes & His Theatre of the Absurd. 2008. (Classical World Ser.). (Illus.). 100p. pap. 19.95 *(978-1-85399-114-1(7))* Bristol Classical Pr. GBR. Dist: International Publishers Marketing.

Dunbar, Henry. A Complete Concordance to the Comedies & Fragments of Aristophanes. 2010. (ENG.). 356p. pap. 32.75 *(978-1-176-56023-9(9))*; 378p. pap. 33.75 *(978-1-145-42909-3(2))*; 428p. pap. 35.75 *(978-1-142-93700-3(3))* BiblioBazaar.

Freydberg, Bernard. Philosophy & Comedy: Aristophanes, Logos, & Eros. 2008. (Studies in Continental Thought). (ENG.). 248p. 65.00 *(978-0-253-35106-7(5)*, 0253351065); pap. 24.95 *(978-0-253-21970-1(1)*, 0253219701) Indiana Univ. Pr.

Hall, Edith & Wrigley, Amanda. Aristophanes in Performance, 421 BC-AD 2007: Peace, Birds & Frogs. Hall, Edith & Wrigley, Amanda, eds. 2007. (Legenda Main Ser.). (Illus.). 390p. 89.50 *(978-1-904350-61-3(5))* European Humanities Research Ctr. GBR. Dist: Brown, David Bk. Co., The.

Henderson, Jeffrey. Aristophanes: Essays in Interpretation. 2009. (Yale Classical Studies). 248p. pap. 36.99 *(978-0-521-12466-9(2))* Cambridge Univ. Pr.

Hugill, William Meredith. Panhellenism in Aristophanes. 2011. 118p. 39.95 ***(978-1-258-03464-1(6))*** Literary Licensing, LLC.

Kanavou, Nicoletta. Aristophanes' Comedy of Names: A Study of Speaking Names in Aristophanes. 2010. (Sozomena Ser.). 196p. 112.00 *(978-3-11-024706-0(2))* De Gruyter, Walter Inc.

Kanavou, Nikoletta. Aristophanes' Comedy of Names: A Study of Speaking Names in Aristophanes. 2011. (Sozomena Ser.). (ENG., Illus.). XIII, 228p. 168.00 ***(978-3-11-215014-6(7))*** De Gruyter, Walter Inc.

Kitzbichler, Josefine. Poetische Vergegenwärtigung, historische Distanz: Johann Gustav Droysens Aristophanes-Übersetzung (1835/38) 2011. (Transformationen der Antike Ser.). (GER.). 258p. 112.00 ***(978-3-11-025815-8(3))*** De Gruyter, Walter Inc.

Kloss, Gerrit. Erscheinungsformen komischen Sprechens bei Aristophanes. (Untersuchungen zur antiken Literatur und Geschichte Ser.). (GER.). VIII, 317p. 225.00 ***(978-3-11-180941-0(2))*** De Gruyter, Walter Inc.

Kozak, Lynn, et al. Playing Around Aristophanes: Essays in Celebration of the Completion of the Edition of the Comedies of Aristophanes by Alan Sommerstein. Kozak, Lynn & Rich, John, eds. 2007. 146p. 70.00 *(978-0-85668-771-6(5))* Aris & Phillips GBR. Dist: Brown, David Bk. Co., The.

Lord, Louis E. Aristophanes: His Plays & His Influence. 2011. 198p. 44.95 ***(978-1-258-06706-9(4))*** Literary Licensing, LLC.

Matulay, L., illus. Aristophanes, Five Comedies: The Knights; Lysistrata; The Clouds; The Birds; The Frogs. 20.00 *(978-0-8196-2863-3(8))* Biblo & Tannen Booksellers & Pubs., Inc.

Platter, Charles. Aristophanes & the Carnival of Genres. 2006. (Arethusa Bks.). (ENG.). 272p. (gr. 17). 59.00 *(978-0-8018-8527-3(2))* Johns Hopkins Univ. Pr.

Putz, Babette & Pütz, Babette. The Symposium & Komos in Aristophanes. 2nd rev. ed. 2007. (Illus.). 243p. per. 48.00 *(978-0-85668-772-3(3))* Aris & Phillips GBR. Dist: Brown, David Bk. Co., The.

Revermann, Martin. Comic Business: Theatricality, Dramatic Technique, & Performance Contexts of Aristophanic Comedy. 2006. (ENG., Illus.). 416p. 170.00 *(978-0-19-815271-2(X))* Oxford Univ. Pr., Inc.

Robson, James. Aristophanes: An Introduction. 2010. (Illus.). 192p. pap. 24.95 *(978-0-7156-3452-3(6))* Duckworth Publishers GBR. Dist: International Publishers Marketing.

Rothwell, Jr, Kenneth S., Kenneth S. Nature, Culture, & the Origins of Greek Comedy: A Study of Animal Choruses. 2010. (ENG.). 340p. (C). pap. 36.99 *(978-0-521-17193-9(8))* Cambridge Univ. Pr.

Sidwell, Keith & Sidwell, Keith C. Aristophanes the Democrat: The Politics of Satirical Comedy During the Peloponnesian War. 2009. (Illus.). 424p. 102.00 *(978-0-521-51998-4(5))* Cambridge Univ. Pr.

Stuttard, David, ed. Looking at Lysistrata: Eight Essays & a New Version of Aristophanes' Provocative Comedy. 2010. 144p. pap. 24.95 *(978-1-85399-736-5(6))* Duckworth Publishers GBR. Dist: International Publishers Marketing.

Thiercy, Pascal. Aristophane: Fiction et Dramaturgie. 2007. (FRE., Illus.). 408p. (C). pap. 56.00 ***(978-2-251-32407-4(0))*** Societe d'edition Les Belles lettres FRA. Dist: ISD.

Willi, Andreas. The Languages of Aristophanes: Aspects of Linguistic Variation in Classical Attic Greek. 2007. (Oxford Classical Monographs). (ENG., Illus.). 376p. pap. 75.00 (978-0-19-921510-2(3)) Oxford Univ. Pr., Inc.

Wilson, N. G. & Wilson, Nigel Guy. Aristophanea: Studies on the Text of Aristophanes. 2008. (ENG.). 222p. 125.00 (978-0-19-928299-9(4)) Oxford Univ. Pr., Inc.

Zumbrunnen, John. Aristophanic Comedy & the Challenge of Democratic Citizenship. 2012. 174p. 65.00 (978-1-58046-417-8(3)) Univ. of Rochester Pr.

ARISTOTLE

Adler, Mortimer J. Desires, Right & Wrong: The Ethics of Enough. 2012. (ENG.). 289p. pap. 12.00 (978-1-60419-046-5(9)) Axios Pr.

Aichele, Alexander. Ontologie des Nicht-Seienden: Aristoteles - Metaphysik der Bewegung. 2009. (Neue Studien zur Philosophie Ser.). (GER.). 493p. (C). 123.00 (978-3-525-30522-5(2)) Vandenhoeck & Ruprecht GmbH & Co. KG DEU. Dist: ISD.

Albertus & Resnick, Irven Michael. On the Causes of the Properties of the Elements: (Liber de Causis Proprietatum Elementorum) 2010. pap. (978-0-87462-249-2(2)) Marquette Univ. Pr.

Albertus, et al. Questions Concerning Aristotle's On Animals. 2008. (Fathers of the Church Ser.). 584p. 69.95 (978-0-8132-1519-8(6)) Catholic Univ. of America Pr.

Allendy, Rene. Treason Complex. 2007. (ENG.). 206p. 39.95 (978-0-548-07281-3(7)) Kessinger Publishing, LLC.

Anagnostopoulos, Georgios, ed. A Companion to Aristotle. 2009. (Blackwell Companions to Philosophy Ser.: 51). (ENG.). 672p. 219.95 (978-1-4051-2223-8(4), Wiley-Blackwell) Wiley, John & Sons, Inc.

Angier, Tom. Techne in Aristotle's Ethics: Crafting the Moral Life. 2011. (Continuum Studies in Ancient Philosophy Ser.). (ENG.). 192p. 120.00 (978-0-8264-6271-8(5)) Continuum International Publishing Group, Ltd. GBR. Dist: National Bk. Network.

Aquinas, Thomas. Commentary on Aristotle's on Interpretation. 2012. (ENG.). 300p. 70.00 (978-1-883357-72-6(1)); pap. 30.00 (978-1-883357-73-3(X)) Dumb Ox Bks.

—Commentary on Aristotle's Politics. Regan, Richard J., tr. from LAT. & pref. by. 2007. 224p. (C). 55.00 (978-0-87220-870-4(2)); pap. 19.95 (978-0-87220-869-8(9)) Hackett Publishing Co., Inc.

Aquinas, Thomas & Aristotle. Exposition of the Physics of Aristotle, Books 1-2: A Summary. Conway, Pierre H., tr. 2011. 78p. 37.95 (978-1-258-01965-5(5)) Literary Licensing, LLC.

Aristotle. Aristote: Traite de l'Ame, 2 vols. Rodier, G., tr. (Classical Studies). (FRE & GRE.). reprint ed. lib. bdg. 85.00 (978-0-89197-662-2(0));2. lib. bdg. 42.50 (978-0-697-00046-0(X)) Irvington Pubs.

—Aristotle II: Posterior Analytics, Topica. Tredennick, Hugh & Forster, E. S., trs. 2011. 762p. 72.95 (978-1-258-03196-1(5)) Literary Licensing, LLC.

—Aristotle on His Predecessors: Being the First Book of His Metaphysics. Taylor, A. E., tr. 2007. (ENG.). 164p. 36.95 (978-0-548-09910-0(3)) Kessinger Publishing, LLC.

—Aristotle's Nicomachean Ethics. Bartlett, Robert C. & Collins, Susan D., trs. from GEC. 368p. 2012. (ENG.). pap. 15.00 (978-0-226-02675-6(2)) 2011. 35.00 (978-0-226-02674-9(4)) Univ. of Chicago Pr.

—Aristotle's Poetics. 2010. 146p. pap. 21.75 (978-1-147-47643-9(8)) BiblioBazaar.

—Aristotle's Poetics. 2009. 10.63 (978-0-7848-1700-1(6), Everbind) Marco Bk. Co.

—Art of Poetry: A Greek View of Poetry & Drama. reprint ed. 37.50 (978-0-404-20007-7(9)) AMS Pr., Inc.

—The Essential Aristotle. 2009. 492p. 24.95 (978-1-60459-779-0(8)); pap. 13.99 (978-1-60459-772-1(0)) Wilder Pubns., Ltd.

—The Metaphysics of Aristotle. M'mahon, John Henry, tr. 2007. (ENG.). 562p. 58.95 (978-0-548-15329-1(9)); 564p. per. 43.95 (978-1-4304-4716-0(8)) Kessinger Publishing, LLC.

—On Generation & Corruption. 2009. 100p. pap. 18.75 (978-0-559-06501-9(9)); pap. 18.75 (978-0-559-06508-8(6)) BiblioBazaar.

—On the Heavens. 2009. 108p. pap. 6.99 (978-1-60459-768-4(2)) Wilder Pubns., Ltd.

—The Poetics of Aristotle. Butcher, S. H., tr. 2007. (ENG.). 66p. pap. 18.99 (978-1-4346-9103-3(9)); 62p. pap. 16.99 (978-1-4346-9102-6(0)) BiblioBazaar.

—The Poetics of Aristotle. 2009. 142p. 24.99 (978-1-110-73594-5(4)); pap. 19.75 (978-1-110-73591-4(X)) BiblioBazaar.

—The Poetics of Aristotle. 2009. 172p. pap. (978-1-151-20169-0(3)) Books LLC.

—The Poetics of Aristotle. Twining, Thomas, tr. 2009. 78p. pap. 17.95 (978-1-120-03830-2(8)) Kessinger Publishing, LLC.

—Treatise on Rhetoric. 2009. 430p. pap. (978-1-4589-4440-5(9)) Books LLC.

Aristotle & Rolfes, Eugen. Aristoteles' Metaphysik, Part 1, Books 1-7: Ubersetzt und Mit Einer Einleitung und Erklarenden Anmerkungen Versehen (1904) 2009. 222p. 39.95 (978-1-120-23017-1(9)); pap. 24.95 (978-1-120-15801-7(X)) Kessinger Publishing, LLC.

Aristotle, et al. Aristoteles Metaphysik (German Edition) 2008. 326p. pap. 30.95 (978-1-4371-1793-6(7)) Kessinger Publishing, LLC.

—Aristoteles Metaphysik, Part. 2009. 314p. 45.95 (978-1-120-08271-8(4)); pap. 30.95 (978-1-120-00558-8(2)) Kessinger Publishing, LLC.

Aristotle, et al. Exhortation à la Philosophie: Le Dossier Grec, Aristote. 2011. (Fragments Ser.). (FRE & GEC.). 288p. (C). pap. 53.00 (978-2-251-74210-6(7)) Societe d'edition Les Belles lettres FRA. Dist: ISD.

Aspasius & Aspasius. Aspasius: On Aristotle's Nicomachean Ethics 1-4, 7-8. 2007. (Ancient Commentators on Aristotle Ser.). 236p. 96.95 (978-0-8014-4531-6(0)) Cornell Univ. Pr.

Atwill, Janet M. Rhetoric Reclaimed: Aristotle & the Liberal Arts Tradition. 2010. 254p. pap. 24.95 (978-0-8014-7605-1(4)) Cornell Univ. Pr.

Averroes. Corpus Commentariorum Averrois in Aristotelem, V4, Parts 1-2: Averroes on Aristotle's De Generatione et Corruptione. 2011. 272p. 47.95 (978-1-258-01817-7(9)) Literary Licensing, LLC.

—Long Commentary on the de Anima of Aristotle. 2011. (Yale Library of Medieval Philosophy Ser.). (ENG.). 610p. pap. 55.00 (978-0-300-17829-6(8)) Yale Univ. Pr.

Averroes. On Aristotle's Metaphysics: An Annotated Translation of the So-called Epitome. Amzen, Rüdiger, ed. 2010. (Scientia Graeco-Arabica Ser.). (ENG.). VII, 378p. 112.00 (978-3-11-022001-8(6)) De Gruyter, Walter Inc.

Bailey & Moseley, Alexander. Aristotle. 2010. (Continuum Library of Educational Thought Ser.). (ENG.). 256p. 140.00 (978-1-84706-103-4(6)) Continuum International Publishing Group, Ltd. GBR. Dist: National Bk. Network.

Baltussen, Han, tr. Simplicius: On Aristotle Physics 1. 5-9. 2012. (Ancient Commentators on Aristotle Ser.). 192p. 130.00 (978-0-7156-3857-6(2)) Duckworth Publishers GBR. Dist: International Publishers Marketing.

Baracchi, Claudia. Aristotle's Ethics As First Philosophy. 2007. (ENG.). 356p. (C). 105.00 (978-0-521-86658-3(8)) Cambridge Univ. Pr.

—Aristotle's Ethics as First Philosophy. 2011. 352p. (C). pap. 36.99 (978-1-107-40051-1(1)) Cambridge Univ. Pr.

Barber, Charles & Jenkins, David, eds. Medieval Greek Commentaries on the Nicomachean Ethics. 2009. 244p. (978-90-04-17393-4(5)) BRILL.

Barker, Ernest. The Political Thought of Plato & Aristotle. 2009. 536p. pap. 30.71 (978-1-4589-3165-8(X)) General Bks. LLC.

—The Political Thought of Plato & Aristotle. 2011. 582p. 63.95 (978-1-258-05444-1(2)) Literary Licensing, LLC.

Barnes, J. R. & Calzolari, V., eds. La diffusion de la pensée et des oeuvres néoplatoniciennes dans la tradition arménienne et Greco-syriaque: L'oeuvre de David L'Invicible. 2009. (Philosophia Antiqua Ser.). (FRE.). 232p. (978-90-04-16047-7(7)) BRILL.

Barthold, Lauren Swayne. Gadamer's Dialectical Hermeneutics. 2009. (ENG.). 166p. 57.99 (978-0-7391-3887-8(1)) Lexington Bks.

Beck, Martha Catherine. Interpreting Aeschylus' Agamemnon Through the Categories of Aristotle: How Greek Tragedy Shaped Ethical Citizens. 2011. 272p. 119.95 (978-0-7734-1521-8(1)) Mellen, Edwin Pr., The.

Beere, Jonathan. Doing & Being: An Interpretation of Aristotle's Metaphysics Theta. (Oxford Aristotle Studies Ser.). (ENG.). 2012. 384p. pap. 40.00 (978-0-19-965204-4(X)) 2010. 372p. 90.00 (978-0-19-920670-4(8)) Oxford Univ. Pr., Inc.

Bennett, Owen. The Nature of Demonstrative Proof According to the Principles of Aristotle & St Thomas Aquinas. 2011. 102p. 39.95 (978-1-258-05570-7(8)) Literary Licensing, LLC.

Berry, Paul. Aristotle versus the Atheists: On the Existence of God & the Immortality of the Soul. 2009. 92p. 89.95 (978-0-7734-4899-5(3)) Mellen, Edwin Pr., The.

Berti, E. Dialectique, physique et Metaphysique: Etudes sur Aristote. 2008. (Aristote. Traductions et Etudes Ser.). (FRE.). 510p. (C). pap. 108.00 (978-90-429-2016-3(5)) Peeters Pubs. & Booksellers BEL. Dist: Brown, David Bk. Co., The.

Beullens, Pieter & Bossier, Fernand, eds. Aristoteles Latinus, 17 2.I.1. de Historia Animalium: Translatio Guillelmi de Morbeka. xciv, 174p. (978-90-04-11863-8(2)) BRILL.

Blazek, Pavel. Die mittelalterliche Rezeption der aristotelischen Philosophie der Ehe: Von Robert Grosseteste bis Bartholomäus von Brügge (1246/1247-1309) 2006. (GER.). xi, 440p. (978-90-04-15413-1(2)) BRILL.

Bloch, David. Aristotle on Memory & Recollection: Text, Translation, Interpretation, & Reception in Western Scholasticism. 2007. (Philosophia Antiqua Ser.). (GEC & ENG., Illus.). 276p. (978-90-04-16046-0(9)) BRILL.

Boas, George. Some Assumptions of Aristotle: Transactions of the American Philosophical Society, V49, Part 6 1959. 2011. 100p. 38.95 (978-1-258-04409-1(9)) Literary Licensing, LLC.

Bolton, R. Science, dialectique et Ethique: Essais d'epistemologie Aristotelicienne. 2010. (Aristote. Traductions et Etudes Ser.). 532p. (C). pap. 95.00 (978-90-429-2213-6(3)) Peeters Pubs. & Booksellers BEL. Dist: Brown, David Bk. Co., The.

Bolton, Robert & Lennox, James G., eds. Being, Nature, & Life in Aristotle: Essays in Honor of Allan Gotthelf. 2010. (ENG.). 306p. 99.00 (978-0-521-76844-3(6)) Cambridge Univ. Pr.

Bonitz, Hermann. Aristotelische Studien. 2009. 372p. 33.99 (978-1-110-17652-6(X)); (ENG.). 370p. pap. 25.99 (978-1-110-17643-4(0), BiblioLife); 372p. pap. 31.75 (978-1-110-17648-9(1)); (ENG.). 370p. pap. 26.99 (978-1-110-17645-8(7), BiblioLife) BiblioBazaar.

Booth, Edward. Aristotelian Aporetic Ontology in Islamic & Christian Thinkers. 2008. (Cambridge Studies in Medieval Life & Thought: Third Ser.). (ENG.). 344p. pap. 46.00 (978-0-521-09044-5(X)) Cambridge Univ. Pr.

Bowler, Michael & Bowler. Heidegger & Aristotle: Philosophy as Praxis. 2008. (Continuum Studies in Continental Philosophy Ser.). (ENG.). 180p. 130.00 (978-0-8264-9846-5(9)) Continuum International Publishing Group, Ltd. GBR. Dist: National Bk. Network.

Bradshaw, David. Aristotle East & West: Metaphysics & the Division of Christendom. 2007. (ENG.). 312p. pap. 46.00 (978-0-521-03556-9(2)) Cambridge Univ. Pr.

Brüllmann, Philipp. Die Theorie des Guten in Aristoteles' 'Nikomachischer Ethik' 2010. (Quellen und Studien zur Philosophie Ser.). (GER.). X, 198p. 112.00 (978-3-11-022786-4(X)) De Gruyter, Walter Inc.

Buchanan, Emerson. Aristotle's Theory of Being. 2011. 72p. 36.95 (978-1-258-01582-4(X)) Literary Licensing, LLC.

Burger, Ronna. Aristotle's Dialogue with Socrates: On the Nicomachean Ethics. (ENG.). 2009. 320p. pap. 22.50 (978-0-226-08052-9(8)) 2008. 306p. 35.00 (978-0-226-08050-5(1)) Univ. of Chicago Pr.

Burian, Peter. Plato & Aristotle on Poetry. 2011. (ENG.). 243p. pap. 40.00 (978-0-8078-9816-1(3)) Univ. of North Carolina Pr.

Buridan, Jean & Rijk, Lambertus Marie de. Lectura Erfordiensis in I-VI Metaphysicam Together with the 15th-Century Abbreviatio Caminensis. 2008. (Studia Artistarum Ser.). (FRE & ENG.). 267p. (C). pap. 73.00 (978-2-503-52873-1(2)) Brepols Pubs. BEL. Dist: ISD.

Buridan, Jean, et al. John Buridan Quaestiones super libros de generatione et corruptione Aristotelis: A Critical Edition with an Introduction. 2010. (History of Science & Medicine Library). (LAT & ENG.). 230p. (978-90-04-18504-3(6)) BRILL.

Burns, Anthony. Aristotle & Natural Law. 2011. (Continuum Studies in Ancient Philosophy Ser.). (ENG.). 224p. 120.00 (978-1-84706-555-1(4)) Continuum International Publishing Group, Ltd. GBR. Dist: National Bk. Network.

Burnyeat, Myles. Aristotle's Divine Intellect. 2008. (Aquinas Lecture Ser.). (C). (978-0-87462-175-4(5)) Marquette Univ. Pr.

Caesar, Irene. Why We Should Not Be Unhappy about Happiness Via Aristotle. 2010. 272p. pap. (978-3-8383-4499-7(5)) Lambert Academic Publishing.

Carr, Jeffrey. Aristotle's Use of Genos in Logic, Philosophy, & Science. 2009. (978-1-4331-0321-6(4)) Lang, Peter Publishing, Inc.

Cartland, Jenifer. Aristotle's Liberalism of Virtue. 2011. 196p. pap. (978-3-8443-0069-7(4)) Lambert Academic Publishing.

Castelli, Laura Maria. Problems & Paradigms of Unity: Aristotle's accounts of the One. 2010. (International Aristotle Studies: 6). (ENG.). 304p. (978-3-89665-520-2(5)) Academia Verlag Richarz GmbH.

Caston, Victor, tr. Alexander of Aphrodisias: on Aristotle on the Soul. 2012. 80.00 (978-0-7156-3923-8(4)) Duckworth Publishers GBR. Dist: International Publishers Marketing.

Cavarnos, Constantine. A Dialogue Between Bergson, Aristotle & Philologos. 2011. 58p. 36.95 (978-1-258-00862-8(9)) Literary Licensing, LLC.

Chan, Michael D. Aristotle & Hamilton on Commerce & Statesmanship. 2006. (ENG.). 248p. (C). 44.95 (978-0-8262-1639-7(0)) Univ. of Missouri Pr.

Chang, Lily. Aristotle on Happiness. 2008. 176p. per. (978-3-8364-5413-1(0)) VDM Verlag Dr. Mueller e.K.

Chappell, T. D. J. Values & Virtues: Aristotelianism in Contemporary Ethics. Chappell, Timothy, ed. 2007. (Mind Association Occasional Ser.). (ENG.). 320p. 110.00 (978-0-19-929145-8(4)) Oxford Univ. Pr., Inc.

Cherry, Kevin M. Plato, Aristotle & the Purpose of Politics. 2012. (ENG.). 254p. 95.00 (978-1-107-02167-9(7)) Cambridge Univ. Pr.

Clausen, Marion. Maxima in sensibus veritas? Die platonischen und stoischen Grundlagen der Erkenntniskritik in Ciceros Lucullus. 2008. (Studien zur klassischen Philologie Ser.). (LAT, GER & ENG.). 210p. pap. 56.95 (978-3-631-57837-7(7)) Lang, Peter GmbH, Europaischer Verlag der Wissenschaften DEU. Dist: Lang, Peter.

Collins, Susan D. Aristotle & the Rediscovery of Citizenship. 2009. (ENG.). 208p. pap. 31.99 (978-0-521-11021-1(1)) Cambridge Univ. Pr.

Coope, Ursula. Time for Aristotle: Physics IV. 10-14. 2009. (ENG.). 208p. pap. 39.95 (978-0-19-955670-0(9)) Oxford Univ. Pr., Inc.

Cooper, Lane. Aristotle, Galileo, & the Tower of Pisa. 2007. (ENG.). 104p. per. (978-1-4067-5263-2(0)) Read Bks.

Cope, E. M. Introduction to Aristotle's Rhetoric with Analysis, Notes, & Appendices. (Classical Studies). reprint ed. lib. bdg. 47.00 (978-0-697-00032-3(X)) Irvington Pubs.

—The Rhetoric of Aristotle with a Commentary, 3 vols. Sandys, John E., ed. (Classical Studies). (ENG & GRE.). reprint ed. 1. lib. bdg. 62.00 (978-0-697-00033-0(8))2. lib. bdg. 62.00 (978-0-697-00034-7(6))3. lib. bdg. 62.00 (978-0-697-00035-4(4)) Irvington Pubs.

—The Rhetoric of Aristotle with a Commentary, 3 vols., Set. Cope, E. M. & Sandys, John E., eds. (Classical Studies). (ENG & GRE.). reprint ed. lib. bdg. 177.00 (978-0-89197-922-7(0)) Irvington Pubs.

Corbin, C. David & Swanson, Judith A. Aristotle's 'Politics' A Reader's Guide. 2009. (Reader's Guides). (ENG.). 180p. 95.00 (978-0-8264-8498-7(0)) Continuum International Publishing Group, Ltd. GBR. Dist: National Bk. Network.

Corcilius, Klaus. Streben und Bewegen: Aristoteles' Theorie der animalischen Ortsbewegung. 2008. (Quellen und Studien zur Philosophie Ser.).Tr. of Striving & Movement. Aristotle's Theory of Animal Movement. (GER.). X, 410p. 147.00 (978-3-11-019454-8(6)); 224.00 (978-3-11-173700-3(4)) De Gruyter, Walter Inc.

Corcilius, Klaus & Rapp, Christof, eds. Beitrage zur Aristotelischen Handlungstheorie: Akten der 8. Tagung der Karl und Gertrud Abel-Stiftung vom 08. 11. 07. 2004 in Blankensee. 2008. (Philosophie der Antike (PhA) Ser.). (GER., Illus.). 217p. (C). 68.00 (978-3-515-09057-5(6)) Steiner, Franz Verlag Wiesbaden GmbH DEU. Dist: Brown, David Bk. Co., The.

Coutant, Victor Carlisle Barr, tr. Alexander of Aphrodisias: Commentary on Book Four of Aristotle's Meteorologica. 2011. 102p. 39.95 (978-1-258-01270-0(7)) Literary Licensing, LLC.

Crubellier, Michel, et al, eds. Dunamis: Autour de la puissance chez Aristote. 2008. (Aristote. Traductions et Etudes Ser.). (ENG.). 522p. (C). pap. 95.00 (978-90-429-1972-3(8)) Peeters Pubs. & Booksellers BEL. Dist: Brown, David Bk. Co., The.

Crubellier, Michel & Laks, André, eds. Aristotle's Metaphysics Beta: Symposium Aristotelicum. 2009. (ENG.). 280p. 85.00 (978-0-19-954677-0(0)) Oxford Univ. Pr., Inc.

Curzer, Howard J. Aristotle & the Virtues. 2012. (ENG.). 480p. 99.00 (978-0-19-969372-6(2)) Oxford Univ. Pr., Inc.

Davidson, Thomas. Aristotle & Ancient Educational Ideals. 2010. (ENG.). 288p. pap. 28.75 (978-1-171-82485-5(8)) 2010. 284p. pap. 28.75 (978-1-177-67256-6(1)) 2010. 276p. pap. 27.75 (978-1-177-12695-3(8)) 2010. 288p. pap. 28.75 (978-1-149-29030-9(7)) 2010. 288p. pap. 28.75 (978-1-149-17345-9(9)) 2010. 280p. pap. 27.75 (978-1-149-08792-3(7)) 2010. 284p. pap. 28.75 (978-1-147-03325-0(0)) 2010. 284p. pap. 28.75 (978-1-145-77999-0(9)) 2009. 272p. 24.99 (978-1-103-97616-4(8)) 2009. 272p. pap. 18.99 (978-1-103-97609-6(5)) BiblioBazaar.

—Aristotle & Ancient Educational Ideals. 2009. 148p. pap. 23.56 (978-1-150-06082-3(4)) General Bks. LLC.

—Aristotle & Ancient Educational Ideals. 2010. 270p. 34.36 (978-1-163-36086-6(4)) 2010. 270p. pap. 22.36 (978-1-162-75747-6(7)) 2007. (ENG.). 268p. 42.95 (978-0-548-05024-8(4)) Kessinger Publishing, LLC.

Davis, G. Scott. Warcraft & the Fragility of Virtue: An Essay in Aristotelian Ethics. 2011. 206p. pap. 23.00 (978-1-61097-085-3(3), Wipf and Stock) Wipf & Stock Pubs.

Day, James & Chambers, Mortimer. Aristotle's History of Athenian Democracy: University of California Publications in History, V73. 2011. 234p. 46.95 (978-1-258-06877-6(X)) Literary Licensing, LLC.

De Leemans, Pieter & Goyens, Michele, eds. Aristotle's Problemata in Different Times & Tongues. 2008. (Mediaevalia Lovaniensia, Series I). (ENG & FRE., Illus.). 325p. pap. 59.95 (978-90-5867-524-8(6)) Leuven Univ. Pr. BEL. Dist: Cornell Univ. Pr.

De Santillana, Giorgio & Reiche, Harald A. T. Aristotle & Science: A Critical Controversy. 2011. 158p. 41.95 (978-1-258-02003-3(3)) Literary Licensing, LLC.

Dehmer, Verena Cäcilia & Aristotle. Aristoteles Hispanus: Eine Altspanische Übersetzung Seiner Zoologie Aus Dem Arabischen und Dem Lateinischen. 2007. (Beihefte Zur Zeitschrift Für Romanische Philologie Ser.). (GER & SPA., Illus.). XI, 263p. (978-3-484-52342-5(5)) Verlag Max Niemeyer.

Deslauriers, Marguerite. Aristotle on Definition. 2007. (Philosophia Antiqua Ser.). 256p. (978-90-04-15669-2(0)) BRILL.

Dewan, Lawrence. St. Thomas & Form As Something Divine in Things. 2007. 98p. (C). (978-0-87462-174-7(7)) Marquette Univ. Pr.

Donini, P. L. Aristotle & Determinism. 2010. (Aristote. Traductions et Etudes Ser.). 205p. (C). pap. 70.00 (978-90-429-2194-8(3)) Peeters Pubs. & Booksellers BEL. Dist: Brown, David Bk. Co., The.

Donini, Pierluigi. Commentary & Tradition: Aristotelianism, Platonism, & Post-Hellenistic Philosophy. Bonazzi, Mauro, ed. 2011. (Commentaria in Aristotelem Graeca et Byzantina Ser.). (ENG, FRE & ITA., Illus.). 466p. 280.00 (978-3-11-173095-0(6)) De Gruyter, Walter Inc.

Dougherty, Jude. Wretched Aristotle: Using the Past to Rescue the Future. 2010. (ENG.). 246p. pap. 29.95 (978-0-7391-4007-9(8)) Lexington Bks.

Dougherty, Jude P. Wretched Aristotle: Using the Past to Rescue the Future. 2009. (ENG.). 260p. 78.99 (978-0-7391-4006-2(X)) Lexington Bks.

Dudley, John. Aristotle's Concept of Chance: Accidents, Cause, Necessity, & Determinism. 2012. (SUNY series in Ancient Greek Philosophy Ser.). (Illus.). 416p. 95.00 (978-1-4384-3227-4(5)) State Univ. of New York Pr.

Echeñique, Javier. Aristotle's Conception of Moral Responsibility. 2012. (ENG.). 232p. 95.00 (978-1-107-02158-7(8)) Cambridge Univ. Pr.

Eikeland, Olav. The Ways of Aristotle: Aristotelian Phrónêsis, Aristotelian Philosophy of Dialogue, & Action Research. 2008. 560p. pap. (978-3-03911-471-9(9)) Lang, Peter.

England, Izhak & England, Izhak. Corrective & Distributive Justice: From Aristotle to Modern Times. 2009. (ENG.). 256p. 99.00 (978-0-19-538007-1(X)) Oxford Univ. Pr., Inc.

Evans, John David Gemmill. Aristotle's Concept of Dialectic. 2010. (ENG.). 164p. pap. 22.00 (978-0-521-13426-2(9)) Cambridge Univ. Pr.

Falcon, Andrea. Aristotelianism in the First Century BCE: Xenarchus of Seleucia. 2011. (ENG.). 240p. 95.00 (978-0-521-87650-6(8)) Cambridge Univ. Pr.

Falcon, Andrea. Aristotle & the Science of Nature: Unity without Uniformity. 2008. (ENG.). 160p. pap. 38.99 (978-0-521-04804-0(4)) Cambridge Univ. Pr.

Fendt, Gene. Love Song for the Life of the Mind: An Essay on the Purpose of Comedy. 2007. (Illus.). 324p. 74.95 (978-0-8132-1485-6(8)) Catholic Univ. of America Pr.

Fiasse, G. L' autre et l'amitié chez Aristote et Paul Ricoeur: Analyses éthiques et Ontologiques. 2006. (Bibliotheque Philosophique de Louvain Ser.). (FRE & ENG.). 318p. (C). pap. 73.00 (978-90-429-1747-7(4)) Peeters Pubs. & Booksellers BEL. Dist: Brown, David Bk. Co., The.

Findlay, John Niemeyer. Plato. 2011. (Routledge Revivals Ser.). (ENG.). 500p. 160.00 (978-0-415-68254-1(1)) Routledge.

Fitterer, Robert J. Love & Objectivity in Virtue Ethics: Aristotle, Lonergan, & Nussbaum on Emotions & Moral Insight. 2008. (ENG.). 192p. (978-0-8020-9788-0(X)) Univ. of Toronto Pr.

Follinger, Sabine, ed. Was Ist Leben? Aristoteles Anschauungen zur Entstehung und Funktionsweise von Leben. Akten der Tagung vom 23. 26. August 2006 in Bamberg. 2009. (Philosophie der Antike (PhA) Ser.). (GER.). 432p. (C).

98.00 *(978-3-515-09244-9(7))* Steiner, Franz Verlag Wiesbaden GmbH DEU. Dist: Brown, David Bk. Co., The.

Ford, Andrew Laughlin. Aristotle as Poet: The Song for Hermias & Its Contexts, 1 vol. 2nd ed. 2011. (ENG., Illus.). 272p. 45.00 *(978-0-19-973329-3(5))* Oxford Univ. Pr., Inc.

Fortenbaugh, William W. Aristotle's Practical Side: On his Psychology, Ethics, Politics & Rhetoric. 2006. (Philosophia Antiqua Ser.: Vol. 101). 464p. *(978-90-04-15164-2(8))* BRILL.

Franks, Christopher A. He Became Poor: The Poverty of Christ & Aquinas's Economic Teachings. 2009. 224p. pap. 27.00 *(978-0-8028-3748-6(4))* Eerdmans, William B. Publishing Co.

Friedmann, Isidor. Aristoteles' Analytica bei den Syrern. 2010. pap. 21.04 *(978-1-61719-531-0(6))* Gorgias Pr., LLC.

Fritz, Kurt von. Aristotle's Contribution to the Practice & Theory of Historiography: Howison Lecture 1957. 2011. 28p. 35.95 ***(978-1-258-01395-0(9))*** Literary Licensing, LLC.

Furth, Montgomery. Substance, Form, & Psyche: An Aristotelean Metaphysics. 2007. (ENG.). 316p. (C). pap. 61.00 *(978-0-521-03561-3(9))* Cambridge Univ. Pr.

Garver, Eugene. Aristotle's Politics: Living Well & Living Together. 2012. (ENG.). 312p. 40.00 *(978-0-226-28402-6(6))* Univ. of Chicago Pr.

Gerson, Lloyd P. Aristotle & Other Platonists. 2006. 335p. per. 24.95 *(978-0-8014-7337-1(3)*, ILR Pr.) Cornell Univ. Pr.

Golitsis, Pantelis. Les Commentaires de Simplicius et de Jean Philopon a la Physique D'Aristote: Tradition et Innovation. 2008. (Commentaria in Aristotelem Graeca et Byzantina Ser.). (FRE.). IX, 306p. 147.00 *(978-3-11-019541-5(0))* De Gruyter, Walter Inc.

Goodman, Lenn E. & Talisse, Robert B., eds. Aristotle's Politics Today. 2008. v, 167p. pap. 24.95 *(978-0-7914-7228-6(0))* 2007. 167p. 60.00 *(978-0-7914-7227-9(2))* State Univ. of New York Pr.

Gotthelf, Allan. Teleology, First Principles, & Scientific Method in Aristotle's Biology. 2012. (Oxford Aristotle Studies Ser.). (ENG.). 464p. 99.00 ***(978-0-19-928795-6(3))*** Oxford Univ. Pr., Inc.

Gottlieb, Paula. The Virtue of Aristotle's Ethics. (ENG.). 2011. 261p. pap. 50.00 *(978-0-521-36999-2(1))* 2009. (Illus.). 262p. (C). 92.00 *(978-0-521-76176-5(X))* Cambridge Univ. Pr.

Grandjean, François. Aristoteles' Theorie der praktischen Rationalität. 2008. (Berner Reihe philosophischer Studien Ser.). (GER.). 346p. pap. *(978-3-03911-674-4(6))* Lang, Peter.

Granger, H. Aristotle's Idea of the Soul. 2010. (Philosophical Studies Ser.). 204p. pap. 219.00 *(978-90-481-4700-7(X)*, 904814700X) Springer.

Grant, Alexander. Aristotle. 2008. 202p. 39.95 *(978-1-4365-5505-0(1))* 2007. (ENG.). 204p. per. 24.95 *(978-0-548-76750-4(5))* Kessinger Publishing, LLC.

Greenspan, Daniel. The Passion of Infinity: Kierkegaard, Aristotle, & the Rebirth of Tragedy. 2008. (Kierkegaard Studies. Monograph Ser.). (ENG.). X, 336p. 133.00 *(978-3-11-020396-7(0))* De Gruyter, Walter Inc.

Greenspan, Daniel. The Passion of Infinity: Kierkegaard, Aristotle & the Rebirth of Tragedy. 2008. (Kierkegaard Studies. Monograph Ser.). (ENG.). X, 336p. 210.00 ***(978-3-11-173546-7(X))*** De Gruyter, Walter Inc.

Gregoric, Pavel. Aristotle on the Common Sense. (Oxford Aristotle Studies Ser.). (ENG.). 2012. 266p. pap. 35.00 ***(978-0-19-964009-6(2))*** 2007. (Illus.). 272p. 85.00 *(978-0-19-927737-7(0))* Oxford Univ. Pr., Inc.

Groarke, Louis. Aristotelian Account of Induction: Creating Something from Nothing. 2009. (McGill-Queen's Studies in the History of Ideas Ser.). (ENG., Illus.). 467p. (C). *(978-0-7735-3595-4(0))*; pap. *(978-0-7735-3596-1(9))* McGill-Queen's Univ. Pr.

Gross, Alan G. & Walzer, Arthur E., eds. Rereading Aristotle's Rhetoric. 2008. (ENG., Illus.). 256p. per. 30.00 *(978-0-8093-2847-5(X))* Southern Illinois Univ. Pr.

Grote, George. Aristotle. 2010. 696p. pap. 48.75 *(978-1-143-26181-7(X))* 2009. 476p. 28.99 *(978-0-559-96437-4(4))* 2009. 476p. pap. 22.99 *(978-0-559-96434-3(X))* BiblioBazaar.

—Aristotle. 2009. 310p. pap. *(978-1-151-47950-1(0))* Books LLC.

—Aristotle. 2010. 308p. pap. 38.41 *(978-1-153-40054-1(5))* 2009. 338p. pap. 41.20 *(978-1-151-47990-7(X))* General Bks. LLC.

Grote, George, ed. Aristotle. 2010. 330p. pap. 40.46 *(978-1-153-40052-7(9))* General Bks. LLC.

Grote, George & Robertson, George Croom. Aristotle. 2010. 510p. pap. 39.75 *(978-1-147-36914-4(3))* BiblioBazaar.

Grote, George, et al. Aristotle. 2010. 500p. pap. 38.75 *(978-1-177-69535-0(9))*; 498p. pap. 38.75 *(978-1-177-69522-0(7))* BiblioBazaar.

Hafemann, Burkhard. Aristoteles' Transzendentaler Realismus: Inhalt und Umfang erster Prinzipien in der Metaphysik. (Quellen und Studien zur Philosophie Ser.). (GER.). XI, 357p. 300.00 ***(978-3-11-180879-5(3))*** De Gruyter, Walter Inc.

Halliwell, Stephen. Aristotle's Poetics. 2009. 384p. pap. 34.95 *(978-0-7156-2858-4(5))* Duckworth Publishers GBR. Dist: International Publishers Marketing.

Halper, Edward. Aristotle's 'Metaphysics' A Reader's Guide. 2012. (Readers Guide Ser.). (ENG.). 176p. 95.00 *(978-1-4411-3191-1(4))*; pap. 24.95 *(978-1-4411-0713-8(4))* Continuum International Publishing Group, Ltd. GBR. Dist: National Bk. Network.

Halper, Edward C. One & Many in Aristotle's Metaphysics: Books Alpha to Delta. 2009. (ENG.). 400p. 48.00 *(978-1-930972-21-6(0)*, Parmenides Publishing.

Hamburger, Max. Morals & Law: The Growth of Aristotle's Legal Theory. 2011. 212p. 44.95 ***(978-1-258-02377-5(6))*** Literary Licensing, LLC.

Hamilton, Ross. Accident: A Philosophical & Literary History. 2008. (Illus.). 320p. 37.50 *(978-0-226-31484-6(7))* Univ. of Chicago Pr.

Hampden, R. D. Fathers of Greek Philosophy. 2006. pap. 37.95 *(978-1-4286-4127-3(0))* Kessinger Publishing, LLC.

Hanke, Lewis. Aristotle & the American Indians: A Study in Race Prejudice in the Modern World. 2011. 176p. 42.95 ***(978-1-258-01394-3(0))*** Literary Licensing, LLC.

Haskins, Ekaterina V. Logos & Power in Isocrates & Aristotle. 2009. (Studies in Rhetoric/Communication Ser.). (ENG.). 192p. pap. 24.95 *(978-1-57003-873-0(2))* Univ. of South Carolina Pr.

Hecquet-Devienne, M. & Stevens, A. Aristote, Metaphysique Gamma: Edition, Traduction, Etudes. 2008. (Aristote. Traductions et Etudes Ser.). 482p. (C). pap. 101.00 *(978-90-429-1836-8(5))* Peeters Pubs. & Booksellers BEL. Dist: Brown, David Bk. Co., The.

Heiberg, I. L., ed. Simplicii in Aristotelis de caelo Commentaria. (LAT.). XVI, 780p. 508.00 ***(978-3-11-186889-9(3))*** De Gruyter, Walter Inc.

Heidegger, Martin. Basic Concepts of Aristotelian Philosophy. Metcalf, Robert D. & Tanzer, Mark B., trs. from GER. 2009. (Studies in Continental Thought Ser.). (ENG.). 296p. 39.95 *(978-0-253-35349-8(1)*, 0253353491) Indiana Univ. Pr.

—Phenomenological Interpretations of Aristotle: Initiation into Phenomenological Research. Rojcewicz, Richard, tr. from GER. 2008. (Studies in Continental Thought Ser.). (ENG.). 184p. pap. 19.95 *(978-0-253-22115-5(3)*, 0253221153) Indiana Univ. Pr.

Helmig, Christoph. Forms & Concepts: Concept Formation in the Platonic Tradition. 2012. (Commentaria in Aristotelem Graeca et Byzantina Ser.). (ENG.). 400p. 154.00 ***(978-3-11-026631-3(8))*** De Gruyter, Walter Inc.

Herman, Arthur. The Cave & the Light: Plato Versus Aristotle, & the Struggle for the Soul of Western Civilization. 2014. (ENG., Illus.). 624p. 30.00 *(978-0-553-80730-1(7))* Random House Publishing Group.

Herrick, Marvin T. The Fusion of Horatian & Aristotelian Literary Criticism, 1531-1555: Illinois Studies in Language & Literature V32, No. 1. 2011. 126p. 40.95 ***(978-1-258-04566-1(4))*** Literary Licensing, LLC.

Herzberg, Stephan. Wahrnehmung und Wissen bei Aristoteles: Zur epistemologischen Funktion der Wahrnehmung. (Quellen und Studien zur Philosophie Ser.).Tr. of Perception & Knowledge in Aristotle. the Epistemological Function of Perception. (GER.). X, 239p. 2011. 196.00 ***(978-3-11-174056-0(0))*** 2010. 126.00 *(978-3-11-021236-5(6))* De Gruyter, Walter Inc.

Hill, Rebecca. The Interval: Relation & Becoming in Irigaray, Aristotle, & Bergson. 2012. (ENG.). 208p. 55.00 ***(978-0-8232-3724-1(9))*** Fordham Univ. Pr.

Hiltunen, Ari. Successful Entertainment & Aristotle's Poetics. 2008. 172p. per. *(978-3-8364-3762-2(7))* VDM Verlag Dr. Mueller e.K.

Hintikka, Jaakko. Analyses of Aristotle. 2010. (Jaakko Hintikka Selected Papers). 256p. pap. 309.00 *(978-90-481-6578-0(4)*, 9048165784) Springer.

hler, Martin. Grenzen der Katharsis in den modernen Künsten: Transformationen des aristotelischen Modells seit Bernays, Nietzsche und Freud. Vöhler, Martin & Linck, Dirck, eds. 2009.Tr. of Boundaries of Catharsis in the Modern Arts. (GER., Illus.). XIV, 391p. 109.00 *(978-3-11-020624-1(2))* De Gruyter, Walter Inc

Hochschild, Joshua P., et al, eds. Virtue's End: God in the Moral Philosophy of Aristotle & Aquinas. 2008. (ENG.). 150p. pap. 19.00 *(978-1-58731-901-3(2))* St. Augustine's Pr., Inc.

Höffe, Otfried, ed. Aristotle's "Nicomachean Ethics" 2010. (ENG.) XVI, 260p. ***(978-90-04-17762-8(0))*** BRILL.

Holland, L. Virginia. Counterpoint: Kenneth Burke & Aristotle's Theories of Rhetoric. 2011. 144p. 40.95 ***(978-1-258-02387-4(3))*** Literary Licensing, LLC.

Huby, Pamela & Taylor, C.C.W., trs. from GEC. Simplicius: On Aristotle Physics 1.3-4. 2011. 224p. 130.00 *(978-0-7156-3921-4(8))* Duckworth Publishers GBR. Dist: International Publishers Marketing.

Hussain, Hammad. Aristotle's 'Genetic Account' & the Problem of Induction. 2011. 184p. pap. ***(978-3-8443-2732-8(0))*** Lambert Academic Publishing.

Hyland, Drew A. & Manoussakis, John Panteleimon, eds. Heidegger & the Greeks: Interpretive Essays. 2006. (Studies in Continental Thought). (ENG.). 208p. pap. 24.95 *(978-0-253-21869-8(1)*, 0253218691) Indiana Univ. Pr.

Jaeger, Werner W. Aristotle: Fundamentals of the History of His Development. Robinson, Richard, tr. 2nd ed. reprint ed. 46.00 *(978-0-404-20131-9(8))* AMS Pr., Inc.

Jaffa, Harry V. Thomism & Aristotelianism: A Study of the Commentary by Thomas Aquinas on the Nicomachean Ethics. 2011. 240p. 46.95 ***(978-1-258-05964-4(9))*** Literary Licensing, LLC.

Jancar, Barbara. Monarch Notes on Aristotle's Philosophy. (C). 4.95 *(978-0-671-00506-1(5)*, Arco) Peterson's.

Johansen, T. K. Aristotle on the Sense-Organs. 2007. (Cambridge Classical Studies). (ENG.). 324p. pap. 47.00 *(978-0-521-71473-0(7))* Cambridge Univ. Pr.

Kalbfleisch, Carolus, ed. Simplicii in Aristotelis categorias Commentarium. (LAT.). XXI, 575p. 508.00 ***(978-3-11-186914-8(8))*** De Gruyter, Walter Inc.

Kavanaugh, Leslie. The Architectonic of Philosophy. 2007. (UvA Proefschriften Ser.). pap. *(978-90-5629-416-8(4)*, Leiden Univ. Pr.) Amsterdam Univ. Pr.

Keys, Mary M. Aquinas, Aristotle, & the Promise of the Common Good. 2008. (ENG.). 270p. pap. 30.00 *(978-0-521-72238-4(1))* Cambridge Univ. Pr.

Kiefer, Thomas & Kiefer. Aristotle's Theory of Knowledge. 2007. (Continuum Studies in Ancient Philosophy Ser.). (ENG.). 256p. 120.00 *(978-0-8264-9485-6(4))* Continuum International Publishing Group, Ltd. GBR. Dist: National Bk. Network.

King, R. A. H. Aristotle & Plotinus on Memory. 2009. (Quellen und Studien zur Philosophie Ser.). (ENG.). XIV, 266p. 210.00 ***(978-3-11-173582-5(6))*** De Gruyter, Walter Inc.

King, Richard A. H. Aristotle & Plotinus on Memory. 2009. (Quellen und Studien zur Philosophie Ser.). (ENG.). XIV, 266p. 140.00 *(978-3-11-021462-8(8))* De Gruyter, Walter Inc.

Kirby, Jeremy. Aristotle's Metaphysics: Form, Matter & Identity. 2011. (ENG.). 172p. pap. 34.95 ***(978-1-4411-5461-3(2))*** Continuum International Publishing Group, Ltd. GBR. Dist: National Bk. Network.

Kirby, Jeremy & Kirby. Aristotle's Metaphysics: Form, Matter, & Identity. 2009. (Continuum Studies in Ancient Philosophy Ser.). (ENG.). 172p. 130.00 *(978-1-84706-246-8(6))* Continuum International Publishing Group, Ltd. GBR. Dist: National Bk. Network.

Klosko, George, ed. Arisotle. 2007. (International Library of Essays in the History of Social & Political Thought Ser.). 472p. 250.00 *(978-0-7546-2635-0(0))* Ashgate Publishing Co.

Kohler, Theodor Wolfram. Homo Animal Nobilissimum: Konturen des Spezifisch Menschlichen in der Naturphilosophischen Aristoteleskommentierung des Dreizehnten Jahrhunderts. 2007. (Studien und Texte Zur Geistesgeschichte des Mittelalters Ser.). 986p. *(978-90-04-16289-1(5)*, BRILL.

Konstan, David. The Emotions of the Ancient Greeks: Studies in Aristotle & Classical Literature. 2007. (Robson Classical Lectures). 428p. pap. *(978-0-8020-9558-9(5))* Univ. of Toronto Pr.

Kontos, Pavlos. Aristotle's Moral Realism Reconsidered. 2011. (Routledge Studies in Ethics & Moral Theory Ser.). (ENG.). 210p. (C). 125.00 *(978-0-415-89674-0(6))* Routledge.

Kouremenos, Theokritos. Heavenly Stuff: The constitution of the celestial objects & the theory of homocentric spheres in Aristotle's Cosmology. 2010. (Palingenesia. Schriftenreihe fur Klassische Altertumswissenschaft Ser.). (ENG.). 150p. (C). 75.00 *(978-3-515-09733-8(3))* Steiner, Franz Verlag Wiesbaden GmbH DEU. Dist: Brown, David Bk. Co., The.

Kristjánsson, Kristján. Aristotle Emotions & Education. 2007. 204p. 99.95 *(978-0-7546-6016-3(8))* Ashgate Publishing Co.

Kupreeva, Inna. Philoponus: On Aristotle Meteorology 1.1-3. Kupreeva, Inna, tr. from GEC. 2011. (Illus.). 224p. 130.00 *(978-0-7156-3676-3(6))* Duckworth Publishers GBR. Dist: International Publishers Marketing.

Kupreeva, Inna & Philoponus. Philiponus: On Aristotle Meteorol. 2012. (ENG.). 224p. 130.00 *(978-0-7156-3675-6(8))* Duckworth Publishers GBR. Dist: International Publishers Marketing.

Laks, Andre. Histoire, Doxographie, Verite: Etudes Sur Aristote, Theophraste et la Philosophie Presocratique. 2007. (Aristote. Traductions et Études Ser.). (ENG.). 294p. (C). pap. 70.00 *(978-90-429-1905-1(1))* Peeters Pubs. & Booksellers BEL. Dist: Brown, David Bk. Co., The.

Lang, Helen S. The Order of Nature in Aristotle's Physics: Place & the Elements. 2007. (ENG.). 340p. pap. 72.00 *(978-0-521-04229-1(1))* Cambridge Univ. Pr.

Larkin, Miriam T. Language in the Philosophy of Aristotle. (Janua Linguarum. Series Minor Ser.). (ENG.). 114p. 210.00 ***(978-3-11-177287-5(X))*** De Gruyter, Mouton DEU. Dist: de Gruyter, Walter GmbH & Co. KG.

Leunissen, Mariska. Explanation & Teleology in Aristotle's Science of Nature. 2010. (ENG., Illus.). 264p. 85.00 *(978-0-521-19774-8(0))* Cambridge Univ. Pr.

Lewis, Hunter & Kellogg, Stuart, eds. The Essence of Aristotle: Nicomachean Ethics. 2011. 100p. pap. 12.00 *(978-1-60419-042-7(6))* Axios Pr.

Lewis, Neil & Wood, Rega, eds. Richard Rufus of Cornwall: in Aristoetelis de Generatione et Corruptione. 2011. (Auctores Britannici Medii Aevi Ser.). 350p. 135.00 ***(978-0-19-726499-7(9))*** Oxford Univ. Pr., Inc.

Ljubovic, Amir. The Works in Logic by Bosniac Authors in Arabic. 2008. 250p. (C). *(978-90-04-16856-5(7))* BRILL.

Lloyd, G. E. R. & Owen, G. E. L., eds. Aristotle on Mind & the Senses. 2007. (Cambridge Classical Studies). (ENG.). 376p. pap. 69.00 *(978-0-521-04443-1(X))* Cambridge Univ. Pr.

Lobel, E. Greek Manuscripts of Aristotles Poetics. 2006. pap. 16.95 *(978-1-4286-5611-6(1))* Kessinger Publishing, LLC.

The Logical Nature of Aristote's Enthymeme. 2008. 100p. (C). ring bd. 50.00 *(978-0-9794289-1-3(2))* Frame Publishing.

Lones, Thomas East. Aristotle's Researches in Natural Science. 2010. 194p. pap. *(978-1-151-89948-4(8))* Books LLC.

Long, Christopher. Aristotle on the Nature of Truth. 2010. (ENG.). 292p. 90.00 *(978-0-521-19121-0(1))* Cambridge Univ. Pr.

Lorenz, Hendrik. The Brute Within: Appetitive Desire in Plato & Aristotle. 2009. (Oxford Philosophical Monographs). (ENG.). 240p. pap. 49.95 *(978-0-19-956169-8(9))* Oxford Univ. Pr., Inc.

Loux, Michael J. Primary Ousia" An Essay on Aristotle's Metaphysics" Z & H. 2008. 288p. pap. 29.95 *(978-0-8014-7488-0(4))* Cornell Univ. Pr.

Machuga, Ric. Life, the Universe & Everything: An Aristotelian Philosophy for a Scientific Age. 2012. (ENG.). 324p. pap. 45.00 ***(978-0-7188-9273-9(9))*** Lutherworth Pr., The GBR. Dist: Brown, David Bk. Co., The.

Malm, Mats. The Soul of Poetry Redefined: Vacillations of Mimesis from Aristotle to Romanticism. 2012. (ENG.). 256p. 43.00 ***(978-87-635-3742-1(7))*** Museum Tusculanum Pr. DNK. Dist: Chicago Distribution Ctr.

Manoussakis, John Panteleimon. Heidegger & the Greeks: Interpretive Essays. Hyland, Drew A. & Manoussakis, John Panteleimon, eds. 2006. (Studies in Continental Thought). (ENG.). 208p. 65.00 *(978-0-253-34802-9(1)*, 0253348021) Indiana Univ. Pr.

Margoliouth, D. S. The Homer of Aristotle. 2006. *(978-1-57898-590-6(0))* Martino Publishing.

Marion, Jean-Luc. Descartes's Grey Ontology. Donahue, Sarah E., tr. from FRE. 2012. (ENG.). 320p. (C). 35.00 *(978-1-58731-176-5(3))* St. Augustine's Pr., Inc.

Marshall, Thomas. Aristotle's Theory of Conduct. 2010. 290p. pap. *(978-1-151-89951-4(8))* Books LLC.

—Aristotle's Theory of Conduct. 2007. (ENG.). 598p. 59.95 *(978-0-548-04607-4(7))* Kessinger Publishing, LLC.

—Aristotle's Theory of Conduct. 2008. 600p. pap. *(978-1-4097-8248-3(4))* Read Bks.

Martini, Stefano. Il Senso Dell'udito Nel Corpus Aristotelicum. 2011. (Europäische Hochschulschriften. Reihe 20: Philosophie Ser.). (ITA.). 629p. pap. *(978-3-0343-0362-0(9))* Lang, Peter.

Massie, Pascal. Contingency, Time, & Possibility: An Essay on Aristotle & Duns Scotus. 2010. (ENG.). 316p. 80.00 *(978-0-7391-4929-4(6))* Lexington Bks.

May, Hope. Aristotle's Ethics: Moral Development & Human Nature. 2011. (ENG.). 204p. pap. 44.95 ***(978-1-4411-1930-8(2))*** Continuum International Publishing Group, Ltd. GBR. Dist: National Bk. Network.

May, Hope & May. Aristotle's Ethics: Moral Development & Human Nature. rev. ed. 2010. (Continuum Studies in Ancient Philosophy Ser.). (ENG., Illus.). 208p. 120.00 *(978-0-8264-9110-7(3))* Continuum International Publishing Group, Ltd. GBR. Dist: National Bk. Network.

McCollum, Adam. A Greek & Syriac Index to Sergius of Reshaina's Version of the de Mundo. 2009. 124.40 *(978-1-60724-583-4(3))* Gorgias Pr., LLC.

McInerny, Ralph. Praeambula Fidei: Thomism & the God of the Philosophers. 2006. 313p. per. 34.95 *(978-0-8132-1458-0(0))* Catholic Univ. of America Pr.

McKeon, Richard. Aristotle's Conception of Language & the Arts of Language. 2011. 48p. 35.95 ***(978-1-258-02238-9(9))*** Literary Licensing, LLC.

—Aristotle's Conception of Moral & Political Philosophy. 2011. 42p. 35.95 ***(978-1-258-02237-2(0))*** Literary Licensing, LLC.

—Aristotle's Conception of the Development & the Nature of Scientific Method. 2011. 46p. 35.95 ***(978-1-258-02239-6(7))*** Literary Licensing, LLC.

—The Philosophy of Aristotle. 2011. 108p. 39.95 ***(978-1-258-05251-5(2))*** Literary Licensing, LLC.

McKirahan, Richard D., Jr. Philoponus: On Aristotle Posterior Analytics 1. 1-8. 2008. (Ancient Commentators on Aristotle Ser.). (Illus.). 192p. 130.00 *(978-0-7156-3667-1(7))* Duckworth Publishers GBR. Dist: International Publishers Marketing.

Meghaizel, Henry. Aristotle on Wisdom. 2009. 172p. pap. *(978-3-639-18091-6(7))* VDM Verlag Dr. Mueller e.K.

Merker, Anne. Une Morale Pour les Mortels: L'éthique de Platon et D'Aristote. 2011. (FRE.). 412p. (C). pap. 59.00 ***(978-2-251-42045-5(2))*** Societe d'edition Les Belles lettres FRA. Dist: ISD.

Meyer, Susan Sauvé. Aristotle on Moral Responsibility: Character & Cause. 2012. (ENG.). 240p. 75.00 *(978-0-19-969742-7(6))*; 216p. pap. 35.00 *(978-0-19-969743-4(4))* Oxford Univ. Pr., Inc.

Miller, Jon, ed. Aristotle's Nicomachean Ethics: A Critical Guide. 2011. (Cambridge Critical Guides). (ENG., Illus.). 300p. 85.00 *(978-0-521-51448-4(7))* Cambridge Univ. Pr.

Millett, Stephan. Aristotle's Powers & Responsibility for Nature. 2011. (Berner Reihe philosophischer Studien Ser.). (ENG.). 304p. pap. ***(978-3-0343-0679-9(2))*** Lang, Peter.

Modrak, Deborah K. W. Aristotle's Theory of Language & Meaning. 2009. (ENG., Illus.). 316p. pap. 42.00 *(978-0-521-10398-5(3))* Cambridge Univ. Pr.

Morison, Ben & Ierodiakonou, Katerina, eds. Episteme, Etc: Essays in Honour of Jonathan Barnes. 2012. (ENG.). 384p. 99.00 ***(978-0-19-969648-2(9))*** Oxford Univ. Pr., Inc.

Murphy, Darryl J. The Deficiencies of the Materialist Reading of Aristotle's Psychology. 2009. 90p. pap. *(978-3-639-17631-5(6))* VDM Verlag Dr. Mueller e.K.

Müürsepp, Peeter. Structural Stability As the Core of René Thom's Philosophy. 2010. 132p. pap. *(978-3-8383-6289-2(6))* Lambert Academic Publishing.

Nagle, D. Brendan. The Household as the Foundation of Aristotle's Polis. 2011. (ENG.). 366p. (C). pap. 45.00 ***(978-1-107-40367-3(7))*** Cambridge Univ. Pr.

Natali, C, ed. Aristotle: Metaphysics & Practical Philosophy: Studies in Honour of Enrico Berti. 2011. (Aristote. Traductions et Etudes Ser.). (ENG, ITA & FRE., Illus.). 202p. (C). pap. 82.00 ***(978-90-429-2477-2(2))*** Peeters Pubs. & Booksellers BEL. Dist: Brown, David Bk. Co., The.

Newton, Lloyd A. Medieval Commentaries on Aristotle's Categories. 2008. (Brill's Companions to the Christian Tradition Ser.). 448p. *(978-90-04-16752-0(8))* BRILL.

Nielsen, Lauge O., et al. Thomas Wylton: On the Intellectual Soul. 2011. (ENG & LAT.). 240p. 75.00 *(978-0-19-726461-4(1))* Oxford Univ. Pr., Inc.

Nyvlt, Mark J. Aristotle & Plotinus on the Intellect: Monism & Dualism Revisited. 2012. ***(978-0-7391-6776-2(6))*** 2011. (ENG.). 278p. 75.00 ***(978-0-7391-6775-5(8))*** Lexington Bks.

Oguamanam, Eugene Ezenwa. The Kind of Society Required for Human Flourishing. 2011. 88p. pap. ***(978-3-8443-8106-1(6))*** Lambert Academic Publishing.

Opsomer, Jan & Steel, Carlos, trs. from GEC. Proclus: Ten Questions on Providence. 2012. 192p. 130.00 ***(978-0-7156-3924-5(2))*** Duckworth Publishers GBR. Dist: International Publishers Marketing.

Osborne, Catherine, tr. Philoponus: Physics 1.4-9. 2009. (Ancient Commentators on Aristotle Ser.). (GEC & ENG.). 224p. 130.00 *(978-0-7156-3787-6(8))* Duckworth Publishers GBR. Dist: International Publishers Marketing.

Owens, Joseph. Aristotle's Gradations of Being in Metaphysics E-Z. Gerson, Lloyd P., ed. 2007. 236p. (C). 40.00 *(978-1-58731-028-7(7))* St. Augustine's Pr., Inc.

A

Pack, Spencer J. Aristotle, Adam Smith & Karl Marx: On Some Fundamental Issues in 21st Century Political Economy. 2010. 288p. 125.00 *(978-1-84844-763-9(9))* Elgar, Edward Publishing, Inc.

Pakaluk, Michael & Pearson, Giles, eds. Moral Psychology & Human Action in Aristotle. 2011. (ENG.). 320p. 85.00 *(978-0-19-954654-1(1))* Oxford Univ. Pr., Inc.

Pangle, Lorraine Smith. Aristotle & the Philosophy of Friendship. 2008. (ENG.). 264p. pap. 37.99 *(978-0-521-05267-2(X))* Cambridge Univ. Pr.

Patar, B. Alberti de Saxonia Quaestiones in Aristotelis de Caelo: Edition Critique. 2008. (Philosophes Medievaux Ser.). (FRE.). 555p. (C). pap. 128.00 *(978-90-429-2104-7(8))* Peeters Pubs. & Booksellers BEL. Dist: Brown, David Bk. Co., The.

Patzig, G. Aristotle's Theory of the Syllogism: A Logico-Philogical Study of Book A of the Prior Analytics. Barnes, Jonathan, tr. 2010. (Synthese Library). 240p. pap. 189.00 *(978-90-481-8322-7(7)*, 9048183227) Springer.

Peramatzis, Michail. Priority in Aristotle's Metaphysics. 2011. (Oxford Aristotle Studies Ser.). (ENG.). 352p. 99.00 *(978-0-19-958835-0(X))* Oxford Univ. Pr., Inc.

Perkams, Matthias. Selbstbewusstein in der Spatantike: Die Neuplatonischen Kommentare Zu Aristoteles' de Anima. 2008. (Quellen und Studien Zur Philosophie Ser.). (GER.). XIV, 468p. 147.00 *(978-3-11-020492-6(4))* De Gruyter, Walter Inc.

Peron, Barbara. Mit Aristoteles zu Platon: Heideggers ontologische Ausdeutung der Dialektik im Sophistes. 2008. (Europäische Hochschulschriften. Reihe 20: Philosophie Ser.). 138p. pap. 39.95 *(978-3-631-58077-6(0))* Lang, Peter GmbH, Europaischer Verlag der Wissenschaften DEU. Dist: Lang, Peter.

Philoponus. Philoponus: on Aristotle Physics 4. 10-14. Broadie, Sarah, tr. from GEC. 2011. 224p. 130.00 *(978-0-7156-4088-3(7))* Duckworth Publishers GBR. Dist: International Publishers Marketing.

Polansky, Ronald. Aristotle's de Anima: A Critical Commentary. 2007. (ENG.). 598p. 113.00 *(978-0-521-86274-5(4))* Cambridge Univ. Pr.

Polansky, Ronald M. Aristotle's de Anima: A Critical Commentary. 2010. (ENG.). 596p. pap. 45.00 *(978-0-521-14885-6(5))* Cambridge Univ. Pr.

Poliziano. Angelo Poliziano's Lamia: Text, Translation, & Introductory Studies. 2010. (BK's Studies in Intellectual History Ser.). (LAT & ENG.). 268p. *(978-90-04-18590-6(9))* BRILL.

Price, A. W. Virtue & Reason in Plato & Aristotle. 2011. (ENG.). 368p. 85.00 *(978-0-19-960961-1(6))* Oxford Univ. Pr., Inc.

Proclus & Proclus. Proclus: on Providence. Steel, Carlos, tr. from GEC. 2007. (Ancient Commentators on Aristotle Ser.). 126p. 92.50 *(978-0-8014-4533-0(7))* Cornell Univ. Pr.

Radke-Uhlmann, Gyburg & Schmitt, Arbogast, eds. Philosophie im Umbruch: Der Bruch Mit dem Aristotelismus im Hellenismus und im spaten Mittelalter - Seine Bedeutung fur die Entstehung Eines Epochalen Gegensatzbewusstseins von Antike und Moderne. 2009. (Philosophie der Antike (PhA) Ser.). (GER.). 244p. (C). 71.00 *(978-3-515-09084-1(3))* Steiner, Franz Verlag Wiesbaden GmbH DEU. Dist: Brown, David Bk. Co., The.

Ransome, William Lee & Ransome, William. Moral Reflection. 2008. (ENG.). 240p. 89.00 *(978-0-230-22038-6(X))* Palgrave Macmillan.

Reeve, C. D. C. Action, Contemplation, & Happiness: An Essay on Aristotle. 2012. (ENG.). 320p. 49.95 ***(978-0-674-06373-0(2))*** Harvard Univ. Pr.

Richter, Goetz. The Congruence of Philosophy & Music Silent Harmony & Hidden Contemplation. 2008. 216p. pap. *(978-3-8364-8020-8(4))* VDM Verlag Dr. Mueller e.K.

Rini, Adriane. Aristotle's Modal Proofs: Prior Analytics A8-22 in Predicate Logic. 2010. (New Synthese Historical Library). (Illus.). vi, 246p. 139.00 *(978-94-007-0049-9(0)*, 9400700490) Springer.

Ritter, William Emerson. Why Aristotle Invented the Word Entelechei: Quarterly Review of Biology V7, No. 4, December 1932. 2011. 30p. 35.95 ***(978-1-258-06127-2(9))*** Literary Licensing, LLC.

Roark, Tony. Aristotle on Time: A Study of the Physics. 2011. (ENG., Illus.). 248p. 82.00 *(978-1-107-00262-3(1))* Cambridge Univ. Pr.

Rosenfeld, Jessica. Ethics & Enjoyment in Late Medieval Poetry: Love after Aristotle. 2010. (Cambridge Studies in Medieval Literature Ser.). (ENG.). 256p. 90.00 *(978-1-107-00011-7(4))* Cambridge Univ. Pr.

Rosenthal, Edna & Goldman-Rozental, Ednah. Aristotle & Modernism: Aesthetic Affinities of T.S. Eliot, Wallace Stevens & Virginia Woolf. 2008. (ENG.). 152p. (C). 75.00 *(978-1-84519-171-9(4))* Sussex Academic Pr. GBR. Dist: International Specialized Bk. Services.

Rubinelli, Sara. Ars Topica: The Classical Technique of Constructing Arguments from Aristotle to Cicero. (Argumentation Library). (ENG & GRE.). 2010. xxii, 162p. pap. 159.00 ***(978-90-481-8153-7(4)***, 9048181534) 2009. (Illus.). 210p. 159.00 *(978-1-4020-9548-1(1))* Springer.

Sadri, Farshad. How Early Muslim Scholars Assimilatedm Aristotle & Made Iran the Intellectual Center of the Islamic World: A Study of Falsafah. 2010. iv, 217p. *(978-0-7734-3716-6(9))* Mellen, Edwin Pr., The.

Salem, Eric. In Pursuit of the Good: Intellect & Action in Aristotle's Ethics. 2010. (ENG.). 256p. pap. 22.95 *(978-1-58988-050-4(1))* Dry, Paul Bks., Inc.

Santozki, Ulrike. Die Bedeutung antiker Theorien für die Genese und Systematik von Kants Philosophie: Eine Analyse der drei Kritiken. 2006. (Kantstudien Ser.). (GER.). XIII, 552p. 154.00 *(978-3-11-019121-9(0))* De Gruyter, Walter Inc.

Scheu, Marina. The Categories of Being in Aristotle & St Thomas. 2011. 122p. 40.95 ***(978-1-258-04508-1(7))*** Literary Licensing, LLC.

Schmidt, Arno. Der Glanz des Logos: Die Philosophie der Klassiker. 2008. 212p. pap. *(978-3-8325-1734-2(0))* Logos Verlag Berlin.

Sgarbi, Marco. La Kritik der reinen Vernunft nel contesto della tradizione logica Aristotelica. 2010. (ITA.). pap. 119.40 *(978-3-487-14385-9(2))* Olms, Georg Verlag AG DEU. Dist: Lubrecht & Cramer, Ltd.

Share, Michael. Philoponus: Against Proclus on the Eternity of the World 9-11. 2010. (Ancient Commentators on Aristotle Ser.). 224p. 130.00 *(978-0-7156-3859-0(9))* Duckworth Publishers GBR. Dist: International Publishers Marketing.

Sharples, Robert W., ed. Particulars in Greek Philosophy: The Seventh S.V. Keeling Colloquium in Ancient Philosophy. 2009. 208p. *(978-90-04-18126-7(1))* BRILL.

Shields, Christopher. Aristotle. 2007. (Routledge Philosophers Ser.). (ENG.). 472p. (C). 100.00 *(978-0-415-28331-1(0))*; (Illus.). per. 27.95 *(978-0-415-28332-8(9))* Routledge.

Shields, Christopher John. The Oxford Handbook of Aristotle, 1 vol. 2012. (Oxford Handbooks Ser.). (ENG.). 704p. 150.00 ***(978-0-19-518748-9(2))*** Oxford Univ. Pr., Inc.

Sim, May. Remastering Morals with Aristotle & Confucius. 2007. (ENG.). 138p. 105.00 *(978-0-521-87093-1(3))* Cambridge Univ. Pr.

Sinclair, Mark. Heidegger, Aristotle & the Work of Art: Poiesis in Being. annot. ed. 2007. (ENG.). 256p. 100.00 *(978-1-4039-8978-9(8))* Palgrave Macmillan.

Slote, Michael A. The Impossibility of Perfection: Aristotle, Feminism, & the Complexities of Ethics, 1 vol. 2011. (ENG.). 184p. 45.00 *(978-0-19-979082-1(5))* Oxford Univ. Pr., Inc.

Smith, Andrew, tr. from GEC. Boethius: On Aristotle on Interpretation 1-3. 2010. (Ancient Commentators on Aristotle Ser.). 224p. 130.00 *(978-0-7156-3918-4(8))* Duckworth Publishers GBR. Dist: International Publishers Marketing.

—Boethius: On Aristotle on Interpretation 4-6. 2011. 224p. 130.00 *(978-0-7156-3919-1(6))* Duckworth Publishers GBR. Dist: International Publishers Marketing.

Sokolon, Marlene K. Political Emotions: Aristotle & the Symphony of Reason & Emotion. 2006. 227p. 38.00 *(978-0-87580-361-6(X))* Northern Illinois Univ. Pr.

Spranzi, Marta. The Art of Dialectic Between Dialogue & Rhetoric: The Aristotelian Tradition. 2011. *(978-90-272-1889-6(7))*; *(978-90-272-8684-0(1))* Benjamins, John Publishing Co.

Stables, Andrew. Childhood & the Philosophy of Education: An Anti-Aristotelian Perspective. 2011. (Continuum Studies in Educational Research Ser.). (ENG.). 210p. pap. 49.95 *(978-1-4411-9833-4(4))* Continuum International Publishing Group, Ltd. GBR. Dist: National Bk. Network.

Stables, Andrew & Stables. Childhood & the Philosophy of Education: An anti-Aristotelian Perspective. 2009. (Continuum Studies in Educational Research Ser.). (ENG., Illus.). 210p. 150.00 *(978-0-8264-9972-1(4))* Continuum International Publishing Group, Ltd. GBR. Dist: National Bk. Network.

Steel, Carlos, ed. Aristotle's Metaphysics Alpha: Symposium Aristotelicum. 2012. (ENG.). 496p. 99.00 ***(978-0-19-963998-4(1))*** Oxford Univ. Pr., Inc.

Stewart, J. A. Notes on the Nicomachean Ethics of Aristotle. 2009. 482p. 42.99 *(978-1-113-84891-8(X))*; pap. 22.99 *(978-1-113-84886-4(3))*; pap. 37.75 *(978-1-113-84888-8(X))* BiblioBazaar.

Stocks, John Leofric. Aristotelianism. 2007. (ENG.). 176p. 37.95 *(978-0-548-02271-9(2))* Kessinger Publishing, LLC.

Striker, Gisela. Aristotle's Prior Analytics book I: Translated with an introduction & Commentary. 2009. (Clarendon Aristotle Ser.). (ENG., Illus.). 256p. 110.00 *(978-0-19-925040-0(5))*; pap. 39.95 *(978-0-19-925041-7(3))* Oxford Univ. Pr., Inc.

Studtmann, Paul. The Foundations of Aristotle's Categorial Scheme. 2008. pap. *(978-0-87462-761-9(3))* Marquette Univ. Pr.

Swanson, Judith A. & Corbin, C. David. Aristotle's 'Politics' A Reader's Guide. 2009. (Reader's Guides). (ENG.). 180p. 29.95 *(978-0-8264-8499-4(9))* Continuum International Publishing Group, Ltd. GBR. Dist: National Bk. Network.

Syrianus & Syrianus. Syrianus: On Aristotle's Metaphysics 13-14. Dillon, John, tr. from GEC. 2007. (Ancient Commentators on Aristotle Ser.). 240p. 96.95 *(978-0-8014-4532-3(9))* Cornell Univ. Pr.

Syros, V. Die Rezeption der aristotelischen politischen Philosophie bei Marsilius von Padua: Eine Untersuchung zur ersten Diktion des Defensor Pacis. 2008. (Studies in Medieval & Reformation Traditions: History, Culture, Religion, Ideas). (GER.). 352p. *(978-90-04-16874-9(5))* BRILL.

Syros, Vasileios. Well Begun Is Only Half Done: Tracing Aristotle's Political Ideas in Medieval Arabic, Syriac, Byzantine, & Jewish Sources. 2011. (FRE & ENG.). ***(978-0-86698-436-2(4))*** ACMRS.

Szaif, Jan. Gut des Menschen: Grundzüge und Perspektiven der Ethik des guten Lebens bei Aristoteles und in der Tradition des Peripatos. 2011. (Quellen und Studien zur Philosophie Ser.).Tr. of Good of Man. (GER.). XI, 322p. 137.00 *(978-3-11-019307-7(8))* De Gruyter, Walter Inc.

Szaif, Jan. Gut des Menschen: Grundzüge und Perspektiven der Ethik des Guten Lebens Bei Aristoteles und in der Tradition des Peripatos. 2012. (Quellen und Studien zur Philosophie Ser.).Tr. of Good of Man. (GER., Illus.). XI, 322p. (gr. 17). E-Book 210.00 ***(978-3-11-173108-7(1))*** De Gruyter, Walter Inc.

Taylor, Thomas. Dissertation on the Philosophy of Aristo. 2006. pap. 44.95 *(978-1-4286-4852-4(6))* Kessinger Publishing, LLC.

Telford, Kenneth A. Aristotle's Poetics: Translation & Analysis. 2011. 190p. 42.95 ***(978-1-258-06110-4(4))*** Literary Licensing, LLC.

Thompson, D'Arcy Wentworth. On Aristotle as a Biologist with a Prooemion on Herbert Spencer: Being the Herbert Spencer Lecture Delivered Before the University of Oxford, on February 14, 1913. reprint ed. lib. bdg. *(978-0-7222-3066-4(4))* Library Reprints, Inc.

Todd, Robert B., tr. from GEC. Themistius: On Aristotle Physics 1-3. 2012. 224p. 130.00 *(978-0-7156-3922-1(6))* Duckworth Publishers GBR. Dist: International Publishers Marketing.

—Themistius: Physics 5-8. 2009. (Ancient Commentators on Aristotle Ser.). 204p. 130.00 *(978-0-7156-3664-0(2))* Duckworth Publishers GBR. Dist: International Publishers Marketing.

Topchyan, Aram. David the Invincible, Commentary on Aristotle's Prior Analytics: Critical Old Armenian Text with an English Translation, Introduction & Notes. 2010. (Philosophia Antiqua Ser.). (ARM & ENG.). 230p. *(978-90-04-18719-1(7))* BRILL.

Torrey, Harry Beal & Felin, Frances. Was Aristotle an Evolutionist? 2011. 22p. 35.95 ***(978-1-258-05597-4(X))*** Literary Licensing, LLC.

Tóth, Imre. Fragmente und Spuren nichteuklidischer Geometrie bei Aristoteles. 2010. (Beiträge zur Altertumskunde Ser.). (GER., Illus.). XXIV, 425p. 154.00 ***(978-3-11-022415-3(1))*** De Gruyter, Walter Inc.

Tracy, Theodore James. Physiological theory & the doctrine of the mean in Plato & Aristotle. (Studies in Philosophy Ser.). (ENG.). 396p. 225.00 ***(978-3-11-202138-5(X))***; 149.00 ***(978-3-11-129026-3(3))*** De Gruyter, Mouton DEU. Dist: de Gruyter, Walter GmbH & Co. KG.

Tuominen, Miira. The Ancient Commentators on Plato & Aristotle. 2009. (Ancient Philosophies Ser.). (ENG.). 336p. 65.00 *(978-0-520-25981-2(5))*; pap. 26.95 *(978-0-520-26027-6(9))* Univ. of California Pr.

Vagelpohl, Uwe. Aristotle's Rhetoric in the East: The Syriac & Arabic Translation & Commentary Tradition. 2008. (Islamic Philosophy, Theology & Science Ser.). (Illus.). 357p. (C). *(978-90-04-16681-3(5))* BRILL.

Van Riel, Gerd & Destrée, Pierre, eds. Ancient Perspectives on Aristotle's de Anima. 2010. (Ancient & Medieval Philosophy Ser.). 240p. 55.00 *(978-90-5867-772-3(9))* Leuven Univ. Pr. BEL. Dist: Cornell Univ. Pr.

Vella, John & Vella. Aristotle. 2008. (Guides for the Perplexed Ser.). (ENG.). 176p. 100.00 *(978-0-8264-9707-9(1))* Continuum International Publishing Group, Ltd. GBR. Dist: National Bk. Network.

Vella, John A. & Vella. Aristotle. 2008. (Guides for the Perplexed Ser.). (ENG.). 176p. 22.95 *(978-0-8264-9708-6(X))* Continuum International Publishing Group, Ltd. GBR. Dist: National Bk. Network.

Von Wilamowitz-Moellendorff, Ulrich. Aristoteles und Athen. 2010. 834p. pap. 56.75 *(978-1-149-87065-5(6))*; 438p. pap. 35.75 *(978-1-146-22608-0(X))*; 442p. pap. 35.75 *(978-1-142-27041-4(6))* BiblioBazaar.

Vuillemin, J. De la logique a la Theologie: Cinq etudes sur Aristote. Nouvelle version remaniee et augmentee par l'auteur, editee et prefacee par T. Benatouil. 2008. (Aristote. Traductions et Etudes Ser.). (FRE.). 240p. (C). pap. 74.00 *(978-90-429-2013-2(0))* Peeters Pubs. & Booksellers BEL. Dist: Brown, David Bk. Co., The.

Wagner, Michael F. The Enigmatic Reality of Time: Aristotle, Plotinus, & Today. 2008. (Studies in Platonism, Neoplatonism, & the Platonic Tradition). 374p. (C). *(978-90-04-17025-4(1))* BRILL.

Waitz, Theodore, ed. Aristotelis Organon Graece, 2 vols. (Classical Studies). (GRE & LAT.). reprint ed. lib. bdg. 89.50 *(978-0-89197-663-9(9))*;1. lib. bdg. 44.75 *(978-0-8290-0691-9(5))*;2. lib. bdg. 44.75 *(978-0-697-00022-4(2))* Irvington Pubs.

Walker, William. Paradise Lost & Republican Tradition from Aristotle to Machiavelli. 2009. (Cursor Mundi Ser.). (ENG & LAT.). 332p. (C). 123.00 *(978-2-503-52877-9(5))* Brepols Pubs. BEL. Dist: ISD.

Wallies, Maximilianus, ed. Alexandri quod fertur in Aristotelis sophisticos elenchos Commentaria. (LAT.). XXXII, 238p. 508.00 ***(978-3-11-175158-0(9))*** De Gruyter, Walter Inc.

Ward, Julie K. Aristotle on Homonymy: Dialectic & Science. (ENG.). 2010. 232p. pap. 36.99 *(978-0-521-12847-6(1))* 2007. (Illus.). 230p. 88.00 *(978-0-521-87486-1(6))* Cambridge Univ. Pr.

Warne, Christopher & Warne. Aristotle's 'Nicomachean Ethics' 2006. (Reader's Guides (Continuum Hardcover) Ser.). (ENG.). 176p. 110.00 *(978-0-8264-8554-0(5))* Continuum International Publishing Group, Ltd. GBR. Dist: National Bk. Network.

—Aristotle's Nicomachean Ethics. annot. ed. 2006. (Reader's Guides). (ENG.). 166p. 27.95 *(978-0-8264-8555-7(3))* Continuum International Publishing Group, Ltd. GBR. Dist: National Bk. Network.

Watt, John & Lossl, Josef. Interpreting the Bible & Aristotle in Late Antiquity: The Alexandrian Commentary Tradition from Rome to Baghdad. 2011. (Illus.). 360p. 134.95 ***(978-1-4094-1007-2(2))*** Ashgate Publishing Co.

Weed, Ronald. Aristotle on Stasis: A Moral Psychology of Political Conflict. 2007. 236p. mass mkt. *(978-3-8325-1380-1(9))* Logos Verlag Berlin.

Weinman, Michael & Weinman. Pleasure in Aristotles Ethics. 2007. (Continuum Studies in Ancient Philosophy). (ENG.). 176p. 135.00 *(978-0-8264-9604-1(0))* Continuum International Publishing Group, Ltd. GBR. Dist: National Bk. Network.

Wilberding, James, et al, trs. Porphyry: to Gaurus on How Embryos are Ensouled: With Proclus: Ten Questions on Providence. 2011. (Ancient Commentators on Aristotle Ser.). 192p. 130.00 *(978-0-7156-3858-3(0))* Duckworth Publishers GBR. Dist: International Publishers Marketing.

Winslow, Russell & Winslow. Aristotle & Rational Discovery: Speaking of Nature. 2007. (Continuum Studies in Ancient Philosophy Ser.). (ENG.). 160p. 120.00 *(978-0-8264-9687-4(3))* Continuum International Publishing Group, Ltd. GBR. Dist: National Bk. Network.

Winter, Michael. Rethinking Virtue Ethics. 2011. (Library of Ethics & Applied Philosophy Ser.). (ENG., Illus.). ix, 183p. 139.00 ***(978-94-007-2192-0(7)***, 9400721927) Springer.

Woodfin, Groves. Introducing Aristotle. 2010. (Introducing Ser.). (ENG., Illus.). 176p. 9.95 ***(978-1-84831-169-5(9))*** Totem Bks. GBR. Dist: Consortium Bk. Sales & Distribution.

Yu, Jiyuan. The Ethics of Confucius & Aristotle: Mirrors of Virtue. 2009. 282p. 39.95 *(978-0-415-80305-2(5))* 2007. 276p. 131.00 *(978-0-415-95647-5(1))* Routledge.

Yuan, Jinmei. Can Aristotelian Logic Be Translated into Chinese. 2010. 196p. pap. *(978-3-639-22296-8(2))* VDM Verlag Dr. Mueller e.K.

ARISTOTLE—BIBLIOGRAPHY

Riley, Lyman W. Aristotle Texts & Commentaries to 1700 in the University of Pennsylvania Library. 2011. 108p. 39.95 ***(978-1-258-06441-9(3))*** Literary Licensing, LLC.

Schwab, M. Bibliographie d'Aristote. (Classical Studies). (FRE.). reprint ed. lib. bdg. 50.50 *(978-0-697-00047-7(8))* Irvington Pubs.

Wingate, S. D. The Mediaeval Latin Versions of the Aristotelian Scientific Corpus: With Special Reference to the Biological Works. (Medieval Studies). reprint ed. lib. bdg. 40.00 *(978-0-697-00023-1(0))* Irvington Pubs.

ARITHMETIC

see also Accounting; Addition; Calculators; Computer Arithmetic; Counting; Decimal System; Division; Fractions; Metric System; Multiplication; Numbers, Real; Numeration; Percentage; Ratio and Proportion; Square Root; Subtraction

Adams, Daniel. Adam's New Arithmetic — 2006. 308p. per. 23.99 *(978-1-4255-2940-6(2))* MPublishing.

Addison-Wesley. MML Student Access Kit for Ad Hoc Valuepacks. 7th ed. (Illus.). xxxii, 1234p. *(978-0-321-26252-3(2))* Addison Wesley.

Andersen, Maria H. Prealgebra & Introductory Algebra: An Applied Approach. 2nd ed. 2010. (ENG.). 368p. (C). pap., wbk. ed. 64.95 *(978-0-8400-5351-0(7))* Brooks/Cole.

Aufmann, Richard N. & Lockwood, Joanne. Prealgebra & Introductory Algebra: An Applied Approach. 2nd ed. 2010. (Available 2011 Titles Enhanced Web Assign Ser.). (ENG.). (C). 1008p. pap. 216.95 *(978-0-8400-4808-0(4))*; 352p. pap. 65.95 *(978-0-8400-4930-8(7))* Brooks/Cole.

Baldor, Aurelio. Aritmetica: Teorico - Practica. (SPA.). 29.95 *(978-968-439-213-7(3)*, PC5772) Publicaciones Cultural, S.A. de C.V. MEX. Dist: Continental Bk. Co., Inc.

Baratto, Stefan, et al. Basic Mathematical Skills with Geometry. 7th ed. 2008. (Illus.). xxvi, 866p. 120.00 *(978-0-07-325777-8(X))* McGraw-Hill Higher Education.

—Hutchison's Basic Mathematical Skills with Geometry. 8th ed. 2009. *(978-0-07-338417-7(8))* McGraw-Hill Cos., The.

Berline, ed. Model Theory & Arithmetic: Comptes rendus d'une action thematique programmee du C.N.R.S. sur la theorie des modeles et l'Arithmetique, Paris, France, 1979/80. 2008. (Lecture Notes in Mathematics Ser.). 59.95 *(978-3-540-11159-7(X))* Springer.

Bittinger & Beecher. Developmental Mathematics: College Mathematics & Introductory Algebra. 7th ed. 2006. pap., pap. 156.00 *(978-0-321-51072-3(0))* Addison-Wesley Longman, Inc.

Bittinger & Cram101 Textbook Reviews Staff. Basic Mathematics. 2007. 104p. per. 10.95 *(978-1-4288-3674-7(8))* Cram101 Inc.

Bittinger, Marvin L. Basic College Mathematics. 11th ed. (Bittinger Worktext Ser.). (ENG.). (C). 2009. 816p. pap. 162.00 *(978-0-321-59919-3(5))* 2010. 360p. pap. 36.67 *(978-0-321-62691-2(5))* Addison Wesley.

—Basic College Mathematics. 11th ed. 2009. tchr. ed. *(978-0-321-62286-0(3))* Pearson Education.

—Worksheets for Classroom or Lab Practice for Basic College Mathematics. 11th ed. 2009. (ENG.). 288p. (C). pap. 26.67 *(978-0-321-62728-5(8))* Addison-Wesley Longman, Inc.

Bittinger, Marvin L. & Beecher, Judith A. Developmental Mathematics. (Bittinger Developmental Mathematics Ser.). (ENG., Illus.). (C). 7th ed. 2007. 1344p. per. 176.00 *(978-0-321-33192-2(3))* 8th rev. ed. 2010. 1280p. pap. 176.00 *(978-0-321-73153-1(0))* Addison Wesley.

—Developmental Mathematics. 7th ed. 2007. (Illus.). xxxii, 1234p. *(978-0-321-34830-2(3))* Addison-Wesley Longman, Inc.

—Developmental Mathematics: College Mathematics & Introductory Algebra. 7th ed. 2007. (MathXL Tutorials on CD Ser.). (ENG., Illus.). 1344p. (C). per. 176.00 *(978-0-321-33191-5(5))* Addison Wesley.

—Developmental Mathematics: College Mathematics & Introductory Algebra. 8th ed. 2011. tchr. ed. ***(978-0-321-73082-4(8))*** Pearson Education.

Bittinger, Marvin L. & Beecher, Judith A. MyWorkBook for Developmental Mathematics. 8th rev. ed. 2011. (ENG.). 416p. (C). pap. 31.00 *(978-0-321-73090-9(9))* Addison Wesley.

Brown, Walter Charles. Basic Mathematics. 8th ed. 2009. (ENG., Illus.). 133p. (gr. 6-12). pap. 36.00 *(978-1-60525-086-1(4))* Goodheart-Willcox Pub.

Burnham, Charles Guilford. Burnham's Arithmetic, Revised a New System of Arithmetic, on an Improved Plan: Embracing the Rules of Three, Single & Double, Direct & Inverse . . 2006. 328p. per. 23.99 *(978-1-4255-3252-9(7))* MPublishing.

Çagman, Naim & S. Wainer, Stan. Tiered Arithmetic & Its Applications. 2010. 108p. pap. *(978-3-8383-6561-9(5))* Lambert Academic Publishing.

Consani, Caterina & Connes, Alain, eds. Noncommutative Geometry, Arithmetic, & Related Topics: Proceedings of the Twenty-First Meeting of the Japan-U. S. Mathematics Institute. 2012. (ENG., Illus.). 328p. (gr. 17). 85.00 ***(978-1-4214-0352-6(8))*** Johns Hopkins Univ. Pr.

Cram101 Textbook Reviews. Outlines & Highlights for Developmental Mathematics by Marvin L Bittinger. 2011. 318p. pap. 33.95 ***(978-1-61830-157-4(8))*** Cram101 Inc.

—Outlines & Highlights for Fundamentals of Mathematics by James Van Dyke. 2011. 128p. pap. 28.95 ***(978-1-61830-162-8(4))*** Cram101 Inc.

Cram101 Textbook Reviews Staff. Outlines & Highlights for Basic Mathematical Skills with Geometry by Donald Hutchison, Isbn: 9780073309590. 2009. 128p. pap. 28.95 *(978-1-4288-3896-3(1))* Cram101 Inc.

—Outlines & Highlights for Basic Mathematical Skills with Geometry by Hutchison Isbn. 2007. pap. 9.95 *(978-1-4288-5726-1(5))* Cram101 Inc.

—Outlines & Highlights for Basic Mathematics by Bittinger, Isbn: 9780321319067. 2009. 80p. pap. 27.95 *(978-1-4288-6787-1(2))* Cram101 Inc.

—Outlines & Highlights for Developmental Mathematics: Basic Mathematics & Algebra by Lial, Hornsby, Mcginnis, andSalzman, ISBN. 2009. 196p. pap. 30.95 *(978-1-4288-2845-2(1))*; 158p. pap. 29.95 *(978-1-4288-7604-0(9))* Cram101 Inc.

—Outlines & Highlights for Developmental Mathematics by Elayn Martin-Gay, Isbn: 9780132290906. 2009. 156p. pap. 29.95 *(978-1-4288-3869-7(4))* Cram101 Inc.

—Outlines & Highlights for Integrated Arith & Basic Algebra by Bill E Jordan, William P Palow, Isbn: 9780321442550. 2009. 118p. pap. 28.95 *(978-1-4288-3756-0(6))* Cram101 Inc.

Daboll, Nathan. Daboll's Schoolmaster's Assistant. 2010. 236p. pap. 16.95 *(978-1-4290-4321-2(0))* Applewood Bks.

Davies, Charles. The University Arithmetic, Embracing the Science of Numbers, & Their Numerous Applications, by Charles Davies. 2006. 412p. per. 26.99 *(978-1-4255-4424-9(X))* MPublishing.

Diez, Juan. The Sumario Compendioso of Brother Juan Diez: The Earliest Mathematical Work of the New World. 2007. 108p. per. 23.95 *(978-1-60206-325-9(7))* Cosimo, Inc.

Eaton, James. An Intellectual Arithmetic upon the Inductive Method - with an Introduction to Written Arithmetic. 2010. 176p. pap. 27.95 *(978-1-4455-9652-5(0)*, Kent Pr.) Kent Communications, Ltd.

Eaton, James Stewart. An Intellectual Arithmetic, upon the Inductive Method, with an Introduction to Written Arithmetic. 2010. 178p. pap. 27.95 *(978-1-4460-2108-8(4)*, Kent Pr.) Kent Communications, Ltd.

Ewald, William Bragg, et al. David Hilbert's Lectures on the Foundations of Arithmetic & Logic 1894-1917. 2008. 700p. 99.00 *(978-3-540-20605-7(1)*, 3540206051) Springer.

Ewald, William Bragg, et al. David Hilbert's Lectures on the Foundations of Arithmetic & Logic, 1917-1933. 2008. 600p. 119.00 *(978-3-540-20578-4(0)*, 3540205780) Springer.

Fish, Daniel W. Fish's Arithmetic Number One - Oral & Written on an Entirely New Plan Containing a Great Variety of Useful Drill Tables, Oral, Slate, & Dictation. 2010. 178p. pap. 27.95 *(978-1-4460-1855-2(5))* Research Pr.

—Robinson's Progressive Primary Arithmetic. 2010. 82p. pap. 26.45 *(978-1-4455-7066-2(1))* Harrison House Pubs.

Fletcher, P. Truth, Proof & Infinity: A Theory of Constructive Reasoning. 2010. (Synthese Library). 480p. pap. 269.00 *(978-90-481-5105-9(8)*, 9048151058) Springer.

Frege, Gottlob, et al. The Foundations of Arithmetic: A Logical-Mathematical Investigation into the Concept of Number 1884. 2007. (Longman Library of Primary Sources Ser.). (ENG.). 144p. (C). per. 12.00 *(978-0-321-24189-4(4))* Longman Publishing.

Goetz, Brian, et al. Basic Mathematics. 2010. *(978-0-13-229612-0(8))* Prentice Hall PTR.

Goldstein, Catherine, et al, eds. The Shaping of Arithmetic after C. F. Gauss's Disquisitiones Arithmeticae. 2007. (ENG., Illus.). xii, 578p. 89.95 *(978-3-540-20441-1(5)*, 3540204415) Springer.

Greenleaf, Benjamin. Introduction to the National Arithmetic, on the Inductive System; Combining the Analytic & Synthetic Methods with the Cancelling System; in Which Th. 2006. (Illus.). 328p. per. 23.99 *(978-1-4255-3199-7(7))* MPublishing.

Heck, Richard G. Frege's Theorem. 2011. (ENG.). 356p. 65.00 *(978-0-19-969564-5(4))* Oxford Univ. Pr., Inc.

Heimerl, Joseph M. Basic Arithmetic & Algebra: A Focused Review. 2011. pap. 28.95 *(978-0-7414-6012-7(2))* Infinity Publishing.

Humphreys, J. E. Arithmetic Groups. 2008. (Lecture Notes in Mathematics Ser.). 168p. pap. 39.95 *(978-3-540-09972-7(7))* Springer.

Hutchison, Donald, et al. Basic Math Skills with Geometry. 8th ed. 2009. (ENG.). 192p. (C). pap. 74.67 *(978-0-07-729206-5(5)*, 0077292065, McGraw-Hill Science, Engineering & Mathematics) McGraw-Hill Higher Education.

Jenkins, C. S. Grounding Concepts: An Empirical Basis for Arithmetic Knowledge. 2008. (ENG.). 256p. 74.00 *(978-0-19-923157-7(5))* Oxford Univ. Pr., Inc.

Jordan, Bill. Integrated Arithmetic & Basic Algebra, Books a la Carte Edition plus MyMathLab Student Access Kit. 2012. (ENG.). (C). ring bd. 107.20 ***(978-0-321-82813-2(5))*** Addison Wesley.

—Integrated Arithmetic & Basic Algebra plus MyMathLab Student Access Kit. 2012. (ENG.). (C). pap., pap. 172.00 ***(978-0-321-82814-9(3))*** Addison Wesley.

Jordan, Bill E. & Palow, William P. Integrated Arithmetic & Basic Algebra. (ENG., Illus.). (C). 4th ed. 2007. 1032p. per. 162.00 *(978-0-321-44255-0(5))* 5th rev. ed. 2011. 960p. pap. 162.00 ***(978-0-321-74738-9(0))*** Addison Wesley.

—Integrated Arithmetic & Basic Algebra. 4th ed. 2008. *(978-0-321-49173-2(4))* Addison-Wesley Longman, Inc.

Jordan, Palow & Cram101 Textbook Reviews Staff. Integrated Arithmetic & Basic Algebr. 2007. 120p. per. 11.95 *(978-1-4288-3642-6(X))* Cram101 Inc.

King, George M. Hermit Arithmetic: . everything you wanted to know, but nobody would tell You! 2007. 96p. per. 17.95 *(978-0-595-44417-5(2))* iUniverse, Inc.

Klein, Felix. Elementary Mathematics from an Advanced Standpoint: Arithmetic, Algebra, Analysis. 2007. (ENG.). 288p. per. 11.95 *(978-1-60206-647-2(7))* Cosimo, Inc.

Kowalski, Emmanuel. The Large Sieve & its Applications: Arithmetic Geometry, Random Walks & Discrete Groups. 2008. (Cambridge Tracts in Mathematics Ser.). (ENG., Illus.). 316p. 91.00 *(978-0-521-88851-6(4))* Cambridge Univ. Pr.

Labesse, J. P. Cohomology of Arithmetic Groups & Automorphic Forms: Proceedings of a Conference held in Luminy/Marseille, France, May 22-27, 1989. 2008. (Lecture Notes in Mathematics Ser.). pap. 59.95 *(978-3-540-53422-8(9))* Springer.

Laing, Laura. Math for Grownups: Re-Learn the Arithmetic You Forgot from School So You Can, Calculate how much that raise will really amount to (after taxes) Figure out if that new fridge will actually fit Help a third grader with his fraction homework Convert calories into cardio Tim. 2011. (ENG.). 256p. pap. 14.95 *(978-1-4405-1263-6(9))* Adams Media Corp.

Leach, Daniel. A Theoretical & Practical Arithmetic; Designed for Common Schools & Academies by Daniel Leach & William D Swan. 2006. 280p. per. 23.99 *(978-1-4255-2525-5(3))* MPublishing.

Lial, Margaret L. Developmental Mathematics: Basic Mathematics & Algebra. 2007. *(978-0-321-50664-1(2))* Addison-Wesley Longman, Inc.

—Developmental Mathematics: Basic Mathematics & Algebra. 2nd ed. 2009. tchr. ed. *(978-0-321-59965-0(9))* Pearson Education.

Lial, Margaret L. & Salzman, Stanley A. Essential Mathematics. 3rd ed. 2008. (Lial Paperback Ser.). (ENG.). 544p. (C). pap. 121.33 *(978-0-321-57270-7(X))* Addison Wesley.

Lial, Margaret L., et al. Developmental Mathematics: Basic Mathematics & Algebra. 2nd ed. 2009. (Lial Paperback Ser.). (ENG.). 1368p. (C). pap. 176.00 *(978-0-321-59920-9(9))* Addison Wesley.

—Developmental Mathematics: Basic Mathematics & Algebra, A la Carte Plus Package. 2nd ed. 2010. (ENG.). (C). ring bd. 115.60 *(978-0-321-59968-1(3))* Addison Wesley.

Manin, IU I., et al. Algebra, Arithmetic, & Geometry: In Honor of Y.I. Manin. 2009. (Illus.). E-Book *(978-0-8176-4745-2(7))* Birkhauser Verlag AG.

Manin, Y. K-Theory, Arithmetic & Geometry: Seminar, Moscow University, 1984-1986. 2008. (Lecture Notes in Mathematics Ser.). pap. 59.95 *(978-3-540-18571-0(2))* Springer.

Mann, Horace. Arithmetic, Practically Applied, for Advanced Pupils, & for Private Reference, Designed As a Sequel to Any of the Ordinary Text-Books on the Subject. 2006. 388p. per. 26.99 *(978-1-4255-4109-5(7))* MPublishing.

Marchisotto, Elena A. & Smith, James T. The Legacy of Mario Pieri in Geometry & Arithmetic. 2007. (Illus.). 494p. 139.00 *(978-0-8176-3210-6(7)*, 0817632107) Birkhauser Boston.

Marino, Anthony I. & Fawcett, Harold P. Arithmetic for Successful Living. 2011. 610p. 64.95 ***(978-1-258-06603-1(3))*** Literary Licensing, LLC.

Martin-Gay & Cram101 Textbook Reviews Staff. Prealgebr. 2007. 120p. per. 11.95 *(978-1-4288-3616-7(0))* Cram101 Inc.

Martin-Gay & Martin-Gay, Elayn. Prealgebra & Introductory Algebra, A la Carte with MML/MSL Student Access Kit (adhoc for Valuepacks) 3rd ed. 2010. (ENG.). (C). ring bd. 116.67 *(978-0-321-62379-9(7))* Addison Wesley.

Martin-Gay, Elayn. Developmental Mathematics. 2nd ed. 2010. (Martin-Gay Paperback Ser.). (ENG., Illus.). 1368p. (C). pap. 176.00 *(978-0-321-65274-4(6)*, Prentice Hall) Prentice Hall PTR.

—Prealgebra. 6th ed. 2010. (Martin-Gay Paperback Ser.). (ENG.). 888p. (C). pap. 162.00 *(978-0-321-62886-2(1)*, Prentice Hall) Prentice Hall PTR.

—Prealgebra & Introductory Algebra, Books a la Carte Edition. 3rd ed. 2010. (ENG.). 1248p. (C). ring bd. 105.60 *(978-0-321-69253-5(5))* Addison Wesley.

—Prealgebra & Introductory Algebra plus MyMathLab/MyStatLab/MyStatLab Student Access Code Card. 3rd ed. 2010. (ENG.). (C). pap., pap. 186.00 *(978-0-321-74453-1(5))* Addison Wesley.

—Prealgebra, Books a la Carte Plus MathXL 12-month Student Access Kit. 6th ed. 2010. (ENG.). (C). pap., ring bd. 104.67 *(978-0-321-73222-4(7))* Addison Wesley.

—Prealgebra (Hardcover) 6th ed. 2009. (ENG.). 888p. (C). 162.00 *(978-0-321-64008-6(X))* Addison Wesley.

—Student Organizer for Prealgebra. 6th ed. 2010. (ENG.). 264p. (C). pap. 36.67 *(978-0-321-63402-3(0)*, Prentice Hall) Prentice Hall PTR.

—Student's Solutions Manual for Prealgebra & Introductory Algebra. 3rd ed. 2010. (ENG.). 696p. (C). pap. 36.67 *(978-0-321-64943-0(5)*, Prentice Hall) Prentice Hall PTR.

—Student's Solutions Manual (standalone) for Developmental Mathematics. 2nd ed. 2010. (ENG.). 720p. (C). pap. 36.67 *(978-0-321-65320-8(3)*, Prentice Hall) Prentice Hall PTR.

Martin-Gay, K. Elayn. Developmental Mathematics. 2nd ed. 2010. tchr. ed. *(978-0-321-65314-7(9))* Pearson Education.

—Prealgebra. 6th ed. 2009. *(978-0-321-62919-7(1))* Prentice Hall PTR.

—Prealgebra & Introductory Algebra. 3rd ed. 2010. tchr. ed. *(978-0-321-64373-5(9))* Pearson Education.

McCurdy, D. (Dennis). The New American Order of Arithmetic by D Mccurdy. 2006. 264p. per. 23.99 *(978-1-4255-2357-2(9))* MPublishing.

McKay, Herbert. Odd Numbers. 2009. (Cambridge Library Collection - Mathematics Ser.). (ENG.). 228p. pap. 16.00 *(978-1-108-00282-0(X))* Cambridge Univ. Pr.

Meskens, Ad. Travelling Mathematics - the Fate of Diophantos' Arithmetic. 2010. (Science Networks. Historical Studies). (Illus.). x, 208p. 124.00 *(978-3-0346-0642-4(7)*, 3034606427) Birkhauser Verlag AG CHE. Dist: Springer.

Miller, Julie, et al. Prealgebra & Introductory Algebra. 2012. (ENG., Illus.). 1280p. (C). pap. 176.00 ***(978-0-07-351295-2(8)***, 0073512958, McGraw-Hill Science, Engineering & Mathematics) McGraw-Hill Higher Education.

—Student Solutions Manual for Prealgebra & Introductory Algebra. 2012. (ENG.). 700p. (C). pap. 68.67 ***(978-0-07-758296-8(9)***, 0077582969, McGraw-Hill Science, Engineering & Mathematics) McGraw-Hill Higher Education.

Morey, Cornell. Explanations of the Principles of Arithmetic, on a New Plan by Cornell Morey. 2006. 112p. per. 16.99 *(978-1-4255-0662-9(3))* MPublishing.

Muller, J. M. Handbook of Floating-Point Arithmetic. 2010. (Illus.). xxiii, 572p. E-Book *(978-0-8176-4705-6(8))* Birkhauser Verlag AG.

Pacemaker Staff. Arithmetic Program Plus II. 174.95 *(978-0-8224-0541-2(5))* Globe Fearon Educational Publishing.

—Arithmetic Program Plus III. 174.95 *(978-0-8224-0542-9(3))* Globe Fearon Educational Publishing.

Pacholski, L., et al, eds. Model Theory of Algebra & Arithmetic: Proceedings of the Conference on Applications of Logic to Algebra & Arithmetic held at Karpacz,Poland, September 1-7, 1979. 2008. (Lecture Notes in Mathematics Ser.). 420p. pap. 59.00 *(978-3-540-10269-4(8))* Springer.

Palmer, Thomas H. Arithmetic, Oral & Written, Practically Applied by Means of Suggestive Questions by Thomas H Palmer. 2006. 356p. per. 26.99 *(978-1-4255-3634-3(4))* MPublishing.

Parke, Uriah. Lectures on the Philosophy of Arithmetic & the Adaptation of That Science to the Business Purposes of Life: With Numerous Problems, Curious & Usef. 2006. 400p. per. 26.99 *(978-1-4255-4294-8(8))* MPublishing.

Pearson Education Staff. MyMathWorkbook for Basic Mathematics & Algebra. 2009. (ENG.). 864p. (C). pap. 31.00 *(978-0-321-62849-7(7)*, Prentice Hall) Prentice Hall PTR.

Penna, Judith A., et al. Developmental Mathematics. 7th ed. 2007. (ENG., Illus.). 350p. (C). pap. 36.67 *(978-0-321-34858-6(3))* Addison Wesley.

Perkins, George R. Higher Arithmetic, Designed for the Use of High Schools, Academies, & Colleges with an Appendix by George R Perkins. 2006. 344p. per. 23.99 *(978-1-4255-3483-7(X))* MPublishing.

Quackenbos, George Payn. An Elementary Arithmetic by G P Quackenbos upon the Basis of the Works of Geo R Perkins, Ll D. 2006. 148p. per. 16.99 *(978-1-4255-1086-2(8))* MPublishing.

Ray, Joseph. Key to Rays New Arithmetics Primary Inte. 2006. pap. 27.95 *(978-1-4286-4080-1(0))* Kessinger Publishing, LLC.

—Ray's Arithmetical Key: Containing Solutions to the Questions in Ray's Third Book, & to Some of the Most Difficult Questions in the Second Book. 2006. 226p. per. 20.99 *(978-1-4255-1890-5(7))*; (ENG.). 276p. per. 23.99 *(978-1-4255-2475-3(3))* MPublishing.

—Ray's Higher Arithmetic the Principles of Arithmetic, Analyzed & Practically Applied by Joseph Ray Ed by Chas E Matthews, M A. 2006. 376p. per. 26.99 *(978-1-4255-3891-0(6))* MPublishing.

—Rays New Practical Arithmetic. 2006. pap. 31.95 *(978-1-4286-3925-6(X))* Kessinger Publishing, LLC.

Ray, Joseph. Ray's New Primary Arithmetic for Young Learners. 2011. (Ray's Arithmetic Ser.). (Illus.). 94p. pap. 7.99 ***(978-0-88062-059-8(5))*** Mott Media.

Scheid, Harald & Schwarz, Wolfgang. Elemente der Arithmetik und Algebra. 5th ed. 2008. (Illus.). 323p. pap. *(978-3-8274-1821-0(6))* Spektrum Akademischer Verlag GmbH.

Silverman, Silverman & Mikhalkin, Grigory. The Arithmetic of Elliptic Curves. 2nd ed. 2009. (Graduate Texts in Mathematics Ser.). (ENG., Illus.). xx, 514p. 59.95 *(978-0-387-09493-9(8)*, 0387094938) Springer.

Smith, David Eugene. Rara Arithmetic: A Catalogue of the Arithmetics Written Before the Year 1601. 2007. 544p. pap. 31.95 *(978-1-60206-690-8(6))* Cosimo, Inc.

—Rara Arithmetic: A Catalogue of the Arithmetics Written Before the Year 1601. 2007. (ENG.). 518p. 55.95 *(978-0-548-18187-4(X))* Kessinger Publishing, LLC.

Smith, G. Consumer Mathematics. 43.25 *(978-0-201-20668-5(4))* Addison-Wesley Longman, Inc.

Smith, Roswell Chamberlain. Arithmetic on the Productive System, Accompanied by a Key & Cubical Blocks by Roswell C Smith. 2006. 316p. per. 23.99 *(978-1-4255-3023-5(0))* MPublishing.

—Arithmetic on the Productive System; Accompanied by a Key & Cubical Blocks by Roswell C Smith. 2006. 316p. per. 23.99 *(978-1-4255-3062-4(1))* MPublishing.

Stehlikova, Nada. Structural Understanding in Advanced Mathematical Thinking. 2011. 260p. pap. ***(978-3-8443-1914-9(X))*** Lambert Academic Publishing.

Stick to Multiplication Table. 2009. (J). per. *(978-0-9776045-1-7(9))* Liu.

Thomson, James B. (James Bates). Higher Arithmetic; or, the Science & Application of Numbers; Combining the Analytic & Synthetic Modes of Instruction by James B Thomson. 2006. 428p. per. 26.99 *(978-1-4255-4720-2(6))* MPublishing.

—Higher Arithmetic; or, the Science & Application of Nymbers; Combining the Analytic & Synthetic Modes of Instruction by James B Thomson. 2006. 436p. per. 26.99 *(978-1-4255-4693-9(5))* MPublishing.

—Practical Arithmetic, Uniting the Inductive with the Synthetic Mode of Instruction Also, Illustrating the Principles of Cancelation for Schools And. 2006. 356p. per. 26.99 *(978-1-4255-3577-3(1))* MPublishing.

Trachtenberg, Jakow. The Trachtenberg Speed System of Basic Mathematics. Cutler, Ann, tr. 2011. 274p. pap. 25.95 ***(978-4-87187-709-1(4))*** Ishi Pr. International.

Tschinkel, Yuri & Zarhin, Yuri G., eds. Algebra, Arithmetic, & Geometry: Volume I: In Honor of Y. I. Manin. 2009. (Progress in Mathematics Ser.). (Illus.). 600p. 139.00 *(978-0-8176-4744-5(9))* Birkhauser Boston.

—Algebra, Arithmetic, & Geometry: Volume II: In Honor of Y. I. Manin. 2010. (Progress in Mathematics Ser.). (Illus.). 600p. 139.00 *(978-0-8176-4746-9(5))* Birkhauser Verlag AG CHE. Dist: Springer.

Tumma, Kranthi. Calculations @ the Speed of Light. 2011. 168p. pap. ***(978-3-8443-8945-6(8))*** Lambert Academic Publishing.

Underhill, D. C. The Arithmetical Primer Underhill's New Tablebook; or, Tables of Arithmetic Made Easier by D C Underhill. 2011. 38p. pap. 11.99 ***(978-1-4181-9510-6(3))*** MPublishing.

Van Dyke, James, et al. Cengage Advantage Books: Fundamentals of Mathematics. 10th ed. 2011. (ENG.). 720p. (C). ring bd. 113.95 *(978-1-111-57839-8(7))* Brooks/Cole.

—Fundamentals of Mathematics, Enhanced Edition (with Enhanced WebAssing 1-Semester Printed Access Card) 9th ed. 2009. (Available 2010 Titles Enhanced Web Assign Ser.). (ENG., Illus.). 864p. (C). pap. 183.95 *(978-1-4390-4729-3(4))* Brooks/Cole.

Van Dyke, James (James Van Dyke), et al. Fundamentals of Mathematics. 10th ed. 2011. (ENG.). 240p. (C). pap. 72.95 *(978-1-111-42948-5(0))* Brooks/Cole.

Walker. New Course in Arithmetic. Date not set. (Illus.). x, 416p. pap. 34.65 *(978-0-582-31869-4(6))* Addison-Wesley Longman, Ltd. GBR. Dist: Trans-Atlantic Pubns., Inc.

Walker, Alan. Multiplication in a Flash. 2008. pap. 34.99 *(978-0-9651769-2-5(5))* Krimsten Publishing.

ARITHMETIC—BEFORE 1846

Napier, John. De Arte Logistica Joannis Naperi Merchistonii, Baronis Libri Qui Supersunt. (Maitland Club, Glasgow Publications: No. 47). reprint ed. 37.50 *(978-0-404-52773-0(6))* AMS Pr., Inc.

Talbott, John L. The Western Practical Arithmetic Containing a Great Variety of Exercises, Particularly Adapted to the Currency of the United States: To Which Is A. 2006. 260p. per. 23.99 *(978-1-4255-2270-4(X))* MPublishing.

ARITHMETIC—EXAMINATIONS, QUESTIONS, ETC.

Rudman, Jack. Postal Arithmetic. (General Aptitude & Abilities Ser.: No. CS-20). pap. 23.95 *(978-0-8373-6720-0(4)*, CS-20) National Learning Corp.

ARITHMETIC—FOUNDATIONS

see also Algorithms; Goedel's Theorem; Recursive Functions

Aharoni, Ron. Arithmetic for Parents: A Book for Grownups about Children's Mathematics. Reisner, Danna, tr. from HEB. 2007. (Illus.). 208p. per. 29.95 *(978-0-9779852-5-8(3))* Sumizdat.

Croft, Anthony & Davison, Robert. Foundation Maths. 5th ed. 2010. (Illus.). 584p. pap. *(978-0-273-72940-2(3))* Prentice Hall PTR.

Gillies, Donald. Frege, Dedekind, & Peano on the Foundations of Arithmetic (Routledge Revivals) 2011. (Routledge Revivals Ser.). (ENG.). 118p. 90.00 *(978-0-415-66709-8(7))* Routledge.

Halmos, Paul R. Naive Set Theory. 2011. 114p. pap. 11.95 ***(978-1-61427-131-4(3))*** Martino Publishing.

Sentilles, Dennis. A Bridge to Advanced Mathematics. 2011. (Dover Books on Mathematics Ser.). (ENG.). 416p. pap. 24.95 *(978-0-486-48219-4(7))* Dover Pubns., Inc.

Thurston, H. A. The Number System. 2007. (Dover Books on Mathematics Ser.). (ENG., Illus.). 144p. per. 9.95 *(978-0-486-45806-9(7))* Dover Pubns., Inc.

ARITHMETIC—HISTORY

Dantzig, Tobias & Mazur, Joseph. Number: The Language of Science. 2007. (ENG., Illus.). 416p. (gr. 12-18). pap. 17.00 *(978-0-452-28811-9(8)*, Plume) Penguin Group (USA) Inc.

El Bahry, Mohamed. Hey! Do You Know the History & Evolution of the Numbers? 2010. 80p. pap. 20.90 *(978-3-8391-4594-4(5))* Bks. on Demand.

Goldstein, Catherine, et al, eds. The Shaping of Arithmetic after C. F. Gauss's Disquisitiones Arithmeticae. 2010. (ENG., Illus.). xii, 578p. pap. 89.95 *(978-3-642-05802-8(7)*, 3642058027) Springer.

ARITHMETIC—JUVENILE LITERATURE

Cummings M.A., Alyece B. Painless Fractions. 3rd rev. ed. 2012. (Painless Ser.). (ENG., Illus.). 264p. pap. 9.99 ***(978-1-4380-0000-8(6))*** Barron's Educational Series, Inc.

Greathouse, Lisa. At the Playground: Level K. 2011. (Mathematics Readers Ser.). 32p. (gr. k-k). pap. 8.99 ***(978-1-4333-3432-0(1))*** Teacher Created Materials, Inc.

Piddock, Claire. Regrouping. 2010. (ENG.). 24p. (J). pap. *(978-0-7787-6794-7(9))* Crabtree Publishing Co.

Tango Books Staff. Addition. 2012. (Number Pops Ser.). (ENG., Illus.). 12p. (J). (gr. -1-k). 10.99 ***(978-1-85707-846-6(2))*** Tango Bks. GBR. Dist: Independent Pubs. Group.

ARITHMETIC—PROBLEMS, EXERCISES, ETC.

see also Arithmetic—Examinations, Questions, etc.

Beveridge, Colin. Numeracy Tests for Dummies. 2012. (ENG., Illus.). 344p. pap. 14.99 ***(978-1-119-95318-0(9)***, For Dummies) Wiley, John & Sons, Inc.

Blair, Jamie, et al. Student Solutions Manual for Prealgebra. 4th ed. 2009. (ENG.). 312p. (C). pap. 36.67 *(978-0-321-58834-0(7)*, Prentice Hall) Prentice Hall PTR.

Davis, Stephen. Math Games Galore: Numbers & Operations. 2009. pap. 12.99 *(978-1-59198-981-3(7))* Creative Teaching Pr., Inc.

Dukes, Owner Dorothy. Basic Addition Practive Vol. 2. 2009. 49p. pap. 11.46 *(978-0-557-03532-8(5))* Lulu Enterprises Inc.

Farmer, August & Huntington, Janet. Food Problems. 2008. (Cooking in America Ser.). (ENG.). 116p. pap. 9.95 *(978-1-4290-1191-4(2))* Applewood Bks.

Houghton Mifflin Company Staff, contrib. by. Houghton Mifflin Matemáticas, 2 vols. 2007. (SPA & ENG., Illus.). *(978-0-618-80729-1(2))*; *(978-0-618-80730-7(6))* Houghton Mifflin Harcourt Publishing Co.

Jitendra, Asha K. Solving Math Word Problems: Teaching Students with Learning Disabilities Using Schema-Based Instruction. 2007. 60.00 *(978-1-4164-0245-9(4))* PRO-ED, Inc.

Krafel, Alysia, et al. Patterns in Arithmetic: Student Workbook: Book 3. 2007. (Illus.). 396p. ring bd. 26.00 *(978-0-9729248-7-0(6))* Pattern Pr.

—Patterns in Aritmetic; Book 3: Student Workbook. 2007. (Illus.). 396p. spiral bd. *(978-0-9729248-8-7(4))* Pattern Pr.

Lial, Margaret L., et al. Developmental Mathematics: Basic Mathematics & Algebra. 2nd ed. 2009. (ENG.). 616p. (C). pap. 36.67 *(978-0-321-59970-4(5))* Addison-Wesley Longman, Inc.

Onish, Liane B. Fun-Flap Math: Fractions & Decimals: 30+ Super-Motivating, Self-Checking Manipulatives That Help Students Practice Fraction & Decimal Skills. 2010. (ENG.). 48p. (gr. 3-5). pap. 10.99 *(978-0-545-20927-4(7)*, Teaching Resources) Scholastic, Inc.

Scholastic, Inc. Staff, contrib. by. The Great Big Idea Book: Language Arts - Dozens & Dozens of Just-Right Activities for Teaching the Topics & Skills Kids Really Need to Master. 2009. (Great BIG Idea Book Ser.). (ENG.). 224p. (gr. 2-3). pap. 23.99 *(978-0-545-14700-2(X)*, Teaching Resources) Scholastic, Inc.

—The Great Big Idea Book: Math - Dozens & Dozens of Just-Right Activities for Teaching the Topics & Skills Kids Really Need to Master. 2009. (Great BIG Idea Book Ser.). (ENG.). 224p. (gr. 2-3). pap. 23.99 *(978-0-545-14701-9(8)*, Teaching Resources) Scholastic, Inc.

Shiotsu, Vicky. Build-A-Skill Instant Books: Fractions. 2009. pap. 5.99 *(978-1-59198-980-6(9))* Creative Teaching Pr., Inc.

—Build-A-Skill Instant Books: Multiplication & Division. 2009. pap. 5.99 *(978-1-59198-977-6(9))* Creative Teaching Pr., Inc.

Smith, Heidi, et al. Great at My Job but Crap at Numbers. 2010. (Illus.). 224p. pap. *(978-1-4441-0225-3(7))* Hodder Education.

Staszkow, Ronald. Math Skills: Arithmetic with Introductory Algebra & Geometry. 7th rev. ed. 2007. (ENG.). 634p. pap. 80.80 *(978-0-7575-4612-9(9))* Kendall Hunt Publishing Co.

Vilmos, William. Instruction for Tests in the Armed Forces. 2011. 128p. 40.95 ***(978-1-258-10365-1(6))*** Literary Licensing, LLC.

Williams, Edward & Prindle, Katie. E-Z Arithmetic. 5th ed. 2011. (Barron's E-Z Ser.). (ENG.). 496p. pap. 16.99 *(978-0-7641-4466-0(9))* Barron's Educational Series, Inc.

ARITHMETIC—STUDY AND TEACHING

Barnett-Clarke, Carne & Ramirez, Alma B. Math Pathways & Pitfalls Early & Whole Number Concepts with Algebra Readiness: Lessons & Teaching Manual Grade K & Grade 1. 2010. (ENG.). 320p. (gr. k-1). pap. 165.00 *(978-0-914409-58-8(1)*, 9780914409588) WestEd.

The Best Stuff for Multiplying & Dividing, Teacher's Edition (CD-ROM) Count, Notice & Remember Math Intervention MD-1. 2nd ed. 2006. (Count, Notice, & Remember Ser.: 13). tchr. ed. 95.00 incl. cd-rom *(978-1-888976-39-7(X)*, 530CD) Mastery Learning Systems.

Cain, Michael. Amusement Park Math: A Ten-Minute Daily Math Adventure. 2007. (ENG., Illus.). 160p. (gr. 4-6). per. 19.95 *(978-1-59363-291-5(6))* Prufrock Pr.

Cawley, John F., et al. Teaching Math to Students with Learning Disabilities: Implications & Solutions. 2008. (ENG.). 174p. 95.00 *(978-1-57886-824-7(6))*; pap. 43.95 *(978-1-57886-825-4(4))* Rowman & Littlefield Education.

Charner, Kathy. Learn Every Day about Numbers. Charner, Kathy, ed. 2009. (Learn Every Day Ser.). (ENG., Illus.). 128p. pap. 12.95 *(978-0-87659-090-4(3))* Gryphon Hse., Inc.

Classical Learning Universe. Math Success: Student Book: Effective Problem Solving Strategies for Addition & Subtraction. 2007. *(978-0-9763376-5-2(7))* Classical Learning Universe, LLC.

—Math Success: Student Book: Effective Problem Solving Strategies for Multiplication & Division. 2007. *(978-0-9763376-3-8(0))* Classical Learning Universe, LLC.

—Math Success: Teacher Book: Effective Problem Solving Strategies for Addition & Subtraction. 2007. *(978-0-9763376-4-5(9))* Classical Learning Universe, LLC.

—Math Success: Teacher Book: Effective Problem Solving Strategies for Multiplication & Division. 2007. *(978-0-9763376-2-1(2))* Classical Learning Universe, LLC.

Davies, Charles. Grammar of Arithmetic; or, an Analysis of the Language of Figures & Science of Numbers by Charles Davies. 2006. 148p. per. 16.99 *(978-1-4255-1092-3(2))* MPublishing.

Dillon, Diann. A Comparison of Multiple-Choice & Open-Ended Assessments. 2010. 88p. pap. *(978-3-8383-3641-1(0))* Lambert Academic Publishing.

Dukes, Dorothy. Math Essentials. 2009. 120p. pap. 12.50 *(978-0-557-20268-3(X))* Lulu Enterprises Inc.

Encyclopaedia Britannica, Inc., compiled by. Mathematics in Context: Fraction Times 2006 Teacher Guide. 2009. (gr. 5-8). 31.75 *(978-1-60835-019-3(3))* Encyclopaedia Britannica, Inc.

—Mathematics in Context: More or Less. 2009. (gr. 5-8). 31.75 *(978-1-60835-002-5(9))* Encyclopaedia Britannica, Inc.

—Mathematics in Context: Rates & Ratios. 2009. (gr. 5-8). 8.75 *(978-1-59339-994-8(4))*; 8.75 *(978-1-59339-982-5(0))* Encyclopaedia Britannica, Inc.

—Mathematics in Context: Rates & Ratios 2006 Teacher Guide. 2009. (gr. 5-8). 31.75 *(978-1-60835-016-2(9))* Encyclopaedia Britannica, Inc.

Krafel, Alysia, et al. Patterns in Arithmetic: Parent/Teacher Guide: Book 3. 2007. (Illus.). 326p. spiral bd. 50.00 *(978-0-9729248-6-3(8))* Pattern Pr.

LaRose, Denise. Early Childhood Mathematics Activities, Grades PreK-1: Literacy, Language, & Learning. 2010. (Early Childhood Activities Ser.). (Illus.). 176p. pap. 29.99 incl. cd-rom *(978-1-4258-0699-6(6))* Shell Educational Publishing.

Maxwell Group. Arithmetic in English: An Arithmetic Vocabulary Workbook. 2nd ed. 2008. (ENG.). 78p. ring bd. 15.00 *(978-1-885401-11-3(6))* Maxwell Group, The.

Parent Child Press, prod. Math Works: Montessori Math & the Developing Brain. 2008. (Illus.). 78p. pap. 16.00 *(978-0-939195-38-1(0))* Parent Child Pr., Inc.

Piccirilli, Richard & Piccirilli, Richard S. Mastering Math Facts - Addition & Subtraction: A Practical Approach for Helping Students Learn & Retain Math Facts with Efficiency & Confidence. 2009. (Mastering Math Facts Ser.). (ENG.). 144p. (gr. 1-3). pap. 18.99 *(978-0-545-06405-7(8)*, Teaching Resources) Scholastic, Inc.

Piccirilli, Richard, et al. Multiplication & Division: A Practical Approach for Helping Students Learn & Retain Math Facts with Efficiency & Confidence. 2009. (Mastering Math Facts Ser.). (ENG.). 144p. (gr. 3-6). pap. 18.99 *(978-0-545-06404-0(X)*, Teaching Resources) Scholastic, Inc.

Sandusky, Lois & Norman, Erika. Hands-on Math. 2009. pap. 9.99 *(978-1-59198-462-7(9))* Creative Teaching Pr., Inc.

Sevaly, Karen. Simple Addition & Subtraction Mats. 2007. (ENG.). (J). (gr. k-2). 14.99 *(978-0-439-92035-3(3))* Scholastic, Inc.

Sharp, Brian. Numeracy: Supporting Children Who Struggle with Basic Skills. 2008. (Thirty Three Ways to Help With.... Ser.). (Illus.). XII, 124p. pap. 39.95 *(978-0-415-46896-1(5))* Routledge.

Simpson, Jeff. Addition, Subtraction & Place Value Teacher Edition. Simpson, Marilyn, ed. 2007. (Count, Notice & Remember Ser.: Volume I, AS). tchr. ed. 95.00 incl. cd-rom *(978-1-888976-42-7(X))* Mastery Learning Systems.

—Addition, Subtraction & Place Value Teacher Edition: Count, Notice & Remember Math Intervention Volume I, AS. Simpson, Marilyn, ed. 2007. (Count, Notice & Remember Ser.: Volume I, AS). tchr. ed., ring bd. 95.00 *(978-1-888976-40-3(3))* Mastery Learning Systems.

Simpson, Jeffrey L. Core Processes of Mathematics, Teacher Edition: Count, Notice & Remember Math Intervention, Volume 4. Simpson, Marilyn Bohlen, ed. 2007. ring bd. 99.95 *(978-1-888976-52-6(7))* Mastery Learning Systems.

—Core Processes of Mathematics, Teacher Edition CD-ROM: Count, Notice & Remember Math Intervention, Volume 4. Simpson, Marilyn Bohlen, ed. 2007. ring bd. 99.95 *(978-1-888976-54-0(3))* Mastery Learning Systems.

—Fractions & Decimals, Teacher Edition: Count, Notice & Remember Math Intervention, Volume 2. Simpson, Marilyn Bohlen, ed. 2007. tchr. ed., ring bd. 149.95 *(978-1-888976-46-5(2))* Mastery Learning Systems.

—Fractions & Decimals, Teacher Edition CD-ROM: Count, Notice & Remember Math Intervention, Volume 2. Simpson, Marilyn Bohlen, ed. 2007. cd-rom *(978-1-888976-48-9(9))* Mastery Learning Systems.

—Functions & Equations, Teacher Edition: Count, Notice & Remember Math Intervention, Volume 5. Simpson, Marilyn Bohlen, ed. 2007. ring bd. 99.95 *(978-1-888976-55-7(1))* Mastery Learning Systems.

—Functions & Equations, Teacher Edition CD-ROM: Count, Notice & Remember Math Intervention, Volume 5. Simpson, Marilyn Bohlen, ed. 2007. cd-rom 99.95 *(978-1-888976-57-1(8))* Mastery Learning Systems.

Steele, Robert. The Earliest Arithmetics in English. 2009. (ENG.). 103p. pap. 18.99 *(978-1-117-15771-9(7)*, BiblioLife) BiblioBazaar.

—The Earliest Arithmetics in English. 2010. 84p. pap. 12.72 *(978-1-152-24617-1(8))* General Bks. LLC.

Stern, Margaret & Gould, Toni S. Structural Arithmetic I. 2007. (ENG., Illus.). 96p. (J). pap. 12.00 *(978-0-9779132-1-3(X)*, 7080) Stern Math, LLC.

Stern, Margaret & Toni S., Gould. Structural Arithmetic II: Teacher's Guide & Answer Key. 2007. (Illus.). 91p. (J). pap. 12.00 *(978-0-9779132-2-0(8))* Stern Math, LLC.

Wilson, Nancy. The Wilson Multiplication Memorization Method. 2006. (Illus.). 271p. per. 20.95 *(978-1-59886-135-8(2))* Tate Publishing & Enterprises, LLC.

Woody, Clifford. Measurements of Some Achievements in Arithmetic. 2009. 76p. pap. 16.75 *(978-1-116-69304-1(6))*; pap. 17.75 *(978-1-116-69303-4(8))* BiblioBazaar.

Wright, Robert J., et al. Teaching Number: Advancing Children's Skills & Strategies. 2nd rev. ed. 2006. (Math Recovery Ser.). (Illus.). 264p. (C). 99.00 *(978-1-4129-2184-8(8)*, B21848C); pap. 42.95 *(978-1-4129-2185-5(6)*, B21848P) SAGE Pubns., Ltd. GBR. Dist: SAGE Pubns., Inc.

ARITHMETIC—STUDY AND TEACHING (ELEMENTARY)

Ashlock, Robert B. Error Patterns in Computation: Using Error Patterns to Help Each Student Learn. 10th ed. 2009. (ENG.). 288p. (C). pap. 36.80 *(978-0-13-500910-9(3))* Allyn & Bacon, Inc.

Barnett-Clarke, Carne & Ramirez, Alma B. Math Pathways & Pitfalls Percents, Ratios, & Proportions with Algebra Readiness: Lessons & Teaching Manual Grade 6, Grade 7, & Grade 8. 2010. (ENG.). 368p. (gr. 6-8). pap. 165.00 *(978-0-914409-61-8(1)*, 9780914409618) WestEd.

Barnett-Clarke, Carne, et al. Math Pathways & Pitfalls: Fractions & Decimals with Algebra Readiness. 2010. (Illus.). iv, 358p. ***(978-0-914409-66-3(2))***; ***(978-0-914409-62-5(X))***; ***(978-0-914409-63-2(8))*** WestEd.

Battista, Michael. Cognition-Based Assessment & Teaching of Place Value: Building on Students' Reasoning. 2012. 112p. pap. 24.38 ***(978-0-325-04343-2(4)***, E04343) Heinemann.

Cassandra, Moore. Letter/Number Master. 2007. (Illus.). (J). spiral bd. 15.95 *(978-1-886297-29-6(0))* Omega Publishing Hse.

Charlesworth, Eric. Addition & Subtraction Facts: 40+ Reproducible Puzzles That Motivate Students to Practice & Master Math Facts. 2010. (Super Sudoku Math Ser.). (ENG.). 48p. (gr. 2-3). pap. 10.99 *(978-0-545-17457-2(0)*, Teaching Resources) Scholastic, Inc.

—Fractions & Decimals: 40+ Reproducible Puzzles That Motivate Students to Practice & Master Key Math Skills. 2010. (Super Sudoku Math Ser.). (ENG.). 48p. (gr. 3-6). pap. 10.99 *(978-0-545-15044-6(2)*, Teaching Resources) Scholastic, Inc.

—Multiplication & Division Facts: 40+ Reproducible Puzzles That Motivate Students to Practice & Master Math Facts. 2010. (Super Sudoku Math Ser.). (ENG.). 48p. (gr. 3-5). pap. 10.99 *(978-0-545-15045-3(0)*, Teaching Resources) Scholastic, Inc.

English, Richard. Teaching Arithmetic in Primary Schools. 2012. (ENG., Illus.). 144p. pap. ***(978-0-85725-725-3(0))*** Learning Matters Ltd.

LearningExpress Staff. Eighth Grade Math Review. 2009. (ENG.). 200p. pap. 14.95 *(978-1-57685-712-0(3))* LearningExpress, LLC.

Onish, Liane. Multiplication & Division Facts: 50+ Reproducible Activity Sheets That Help Students Master Multiplication & Division Facts. 2010. (Solve-the-Riddle Math Practice Ser.). (ENG.). 64p. (gr. 2-4). pap. 11.99 *(978-0-545-16326-2(9)*, Teaching Resources) Scholastic, Inc.

—Solve-the-Riddle Math Practice: Addition & Subtraction: 50+ Reproducible Activity Sheets That Help Students Master Addition & Subtraction Skills. 2010. (ENG.). 64p. (gr. 2-3). pap. 11.99 *(978-0-545-16325-5(0)*, Teaching Resources) Scholastic, Inc.

Parrish, Sherry. Number Talks: Helping Children Build Mental Math & Computation Strategies, Grades K-5. 2010. *(978-1-935099-16-1(7))*; (Illus.). xli, 390p. *(978-1-935099-15-4(9))* Math Solutions.

Schliemann, Analucia Dias, et al. Bringing Out the Algebraic Character of Arithmetic: From Children's Ideas to Classroom Practice. 2006. (Studies in Mathematical Thinking & Learning). (Illus.). 144p. 150.00 incl. cd-rom *(978-0-8058-4338-5(8))* Erlbaum, Lawrence Assocs., Inc.

—Bringing Out the Algebraic Character of Arithmetic: From Children's Ideas to Classroom Practice. 2006. (Studies in Mathematical Thinking & Learning). (ENG., Illus.). 160p. pap. 27.95 *(978-0-8058-5873-0(3))* Routledge.

Sophian, Catherine. The Origins of Mathematical Knowledge in Childhood. 216p. 2009. pap. 62.95 *(978-0-415-87770-1(9))* 2007. (ENG., Illus.). (C). 77.00 *(978-0-8058-5758-0(3))* Routledge.

Spangler, David B. Strategies for Teaching Whole Number Computation: Using Error Analysis for Intervention & Assessment. 2010. (Illus.). 224p. pap. 38.95 *(978-1-4129-8106-4(9)*, B81064P) Corwin Pr.

Thompson, Ian. Teaching & Learning Early Number. 2nd ed. 2008. (ENG., Illus.). 256p. (C). pap. 48.00 *(978-0-335-23411-0(9)*, 0335234119) McGraw-Hill Education GBR. Dist: McGraw-Hill Cos., The.

Turley, Sandy. The Fact Family: A Teaching Rhyme about Inverse Number Relationships. 2006. (ENG., Illus.). (J). lib. bdg. 26.95 *(978-0-9778548-1-3(7))* Helps4Teachers.

Wickett, Maryann & Hendrix-Martin, Eunice. Beyond the Bubble: How to Use Multiple-Choice Tests to Improve Math Instruction, Grades 4-5. 2011. (ENG.). 320p. (C). (gr. 4-5). pap. 24.00 *(978-1-57110-818-0(1))*; *(978-1-57110-899-9(8))* Stenhouse Pubs.

ARITHMETIC—1961-

Hirschfeld, J. & Wheeler, W. H. Forcing, Arithmetic, Division Rings. 2008. (Lecture Notes in Mathematics Ser.). 280p. pap. 59.95 *(978-3-540-07157-0(1))* Springer.

ARITHMETIC, COMMERCIAL

see Business Mathematics

ARITHMETIC, MENTAL

see Mental Arithmetic

ARITHMETIC, PHARMACEUTICAL

see Pharmaceutical Arithmetic

ARITHMETICAL ABILITY

see Mathematical Ability

ARIZONA

Wojna, Lisa & Soderberg, Paul. Arizona Trivia: Weird, Wacky & Wild. 2008. (ENG., Illus.). 240p. pap. *(978-1-897278-49-9(7))* Blue Bike Bks. CAN. Dist: Lone Pine Publishing.

ARIZONA—ANTIQUITIES

Alofsin, Anthony & Wright, Frank Lloyd. Frank Lloyd Wright, Art Collector: Secessionist Prints from the Turn of the Century. 2012. E-Book ***(978-0-292-73722-8(X))***; (ENG., Illus.). 132p. 40.00 ***(978-0-292-73721-1(1))*** Univ. of Texas Pr.

Altschul, Jeffrey & Rankin, Adrianne G. Fragile Patterns: The Archaeology of the Western Papagueria. 2008. (ENG.). 760p. 49.95 *(978-1-879442-98-6(1))* Statistical Res.

Bernardini, Wesley. Hopi Social Memory in Stone. 2007. (Archeological Ser.). (ENG.). 215p. 24.95 *(978-1-889747-82-8(3))* Arizona State Museum.

Bicknell, Robin Scott. Arizona's Rock Art: Guide to Rock Art Sites. 2008. 192p. pap. 15.95 *(978-1-4327-3329-2(X))* Outskirts Pr., Inc.

Bostwick, Todd W. Beneath the Runways: Archaeology of Sky Harbor International Airport. 2008. 123p. pap. *(978-1-882572-42-7(4))* Pueblo Grande Museum.

Breternitz, Cory Dale, et al, eds. Data Recovery at Six Sites in the 66 Acre Desert Rose Development in South Phoenix, Arizona. 2008. (Pueblo Grande Museum Occasional Papers: 9). 226p. pap. 0.00 *(978-1-882572-41-0(6))* Pueblo Grande Museum.

Colton, Harold S. A Survey of Prehistoric Sites in the Region of Flagstaff, Arizona. reprint ed. 59.00 *(978-0-403-03702-5(6))* Scholarly Pr., Inc.

Dallett, Nancy C. At the Confluence of Change. 2008. (Illus.). 256p. pap. 29.95 *(978-1-58369-113-7(8))* Western National Parks Assn.

Downum, Christian E. & contrib. by. Hisatsinom: Ancient Peoples in a Land Without Water. 2011. 59.95 *(978-1-934691-11-3(9))*; pap. 24.95 *(978-1-934691-12-0(7))* School for Advanced Research Pr./SAR Pr.

Gage, Gina / S. & Craig, Douglas B. Excavations at Pueblo Del Rio (AZ T:12, Pueblo Grande Museum Occasional Papers No. 4. 2009. 378p. pap. *(978-1-882572-44-1(0))* Pueblo Grande Museum.

Gregonis, Linda M. The Hardy Site at Fort Lowell Park, Tucson, Arizona: Revised Edition. 2011. (ASM Archaeological Ser.). (ENG.). 296p. pap. 14.95 *(978-1-889747-86-6(6))* Univ. of Arizona Pr.

Gregonis, Linda M. & Hartmann, Gayle Harrison. Whiptail Ruin (AZ BB:10:3 [ASM]) A Classic Period Community in the Northeastern Tucson Basin. 2011. (ASM Archaeological Ser.). (ENG.). 310p. pap. 24.95 *(978-1-889747-88-0(2))* Univ. of Arizona Pr.

Gregory, David A. Excavations in the Santa Cruz River Floodplain: Further Investigations at Los Pozos. 2007. (Illus.). viii, 142p. *(978-1-886398-58-0(5))* Ctr. for Desert Archaeology.

Haynes, C. Vance, Jr. & Huckell, Bruce B. Murray Springs: A Clovis Site with Multiple Activity Areas in the San Pedro Valley, Arizona. 2007. (Anthropological Papers of the University of Arizona). (ENG., Illus.). 288p. pap. 24.95 *(978-0-8165-2579-9(X))* Univ. of Arizona Pr.

Hinton, Richard Josiah. 1,000 Old Arizona Mines: With A Gallery of Old Photographs. 2011. 126p. 40.95 ***(978-1-258-06142-5(2))*** Literary Licensing, LLC.

Judd, Neil M. Archaeological Observations North of the Rio Colorado. 2010. (ENG., Illus.). 190p. pap. 19.95 *(978-1-60781-022-3(0))* Univ. of Utah Pr.

Lange, Richard C. Echoes in the Canyons: The Archaeology of the Southeastern Sierra Ancha, Central Arizona. 2006. (Arizona State Museum Archaeological Ser.). (Illus.). 358p. pap. 39.95 incl. cd-rom *(978-1-889747-80-4(7))* Univ. of Arizona Pr.

Mabry, Jonathan B. Las Capas: Early Irrigation & Sedentism in a Southwestern Floodplain. 2008. (Illus.). xxii, 457p. pap. ***(978-1-886398-62-7(3))*** Ctr. for Desert Archaeology.

Malotki, Ekkehart. The Rock Art of Arizona: Art for Life's Sake. 2008. (Illus.). 194p. pap. 35.00 *(978-1-885772-38-1(6))* Kiva Publishing, Inc.

Mindeleff, Cosmos. The Cliff Ruins of Canyon de Chelly, Arizona. 2007. 128p. 94.99 *(978-1-4280-7582-5(8))*; per. 88.99 *(978-1-4280-7583-2(6))* IndyPublish.com.

Mindeleff, Cosmos. The Cliff Ruins of Canyon de Chelly, Arizona - with Original Illustrations & Index - Sixteenth Annual Report of the Bureau of Ethnology to the Secre. 2011. 180p. ***(978-1-84902-387-0(5))*** Benediction Classics.

Neuzil, Anna A. In the Aftermath of Migration: Renegotiating Ancient Identity in Southeastern Arizona. 2008. (ENG., Illus.). 136p. pap. 17.95 *(978-0-8165-2736-6(9))* Univ. of Arizona Pr.

Ravesloot, John C., et al, eds. The Prehistory of the Marsh Station Road Site (AZ EE:2:44 [ASM]), Cienega Creek, Southeastern Arizona. 2011. (ASM Archaeological Ser.). (ENG.). 456p. pap. 29.95 *(978-1-889747-87-3(4))* Univ. of Arizona Pr.

Rice, Glen E. & Czarzasty, John L., eds. Las Cremaciones: A Hohokam Ball Court Center in the Phoenix Basin. 2008. (Pueblo Grande Museum Occasional Papers: 6). 239p. pap. *(978-1-882572-43-4(2))* Pueblo Grande Museum.

Schroeder, Albert H. Archeological Excavations at Willow Beach, Arizona, 1950. (Utah Anthropological Papers: No. 50). reprint ed. 35.00 *(978-0-404-60650-3(4))* AMS Pr., Inc.

Wellman, Kevin D., ed. The Valley Farms Sites: Prehistoric Floodplain Agriculture on the Santa Cruz River in Southern Arizona. 2008. (SWCA Anthropological Research Papers). (ENG., Illus.). 242p. pap. 30.00 *(978-1-931901-22-2(8))* SWCA, Inc.

Wells, Christian & Wells, E. Christian. From Hohokam to O'Odham. 2006. (GRIC Anthropological Research Papers). (ENG.). 74p. pap. 12.95 *(978-0-9723347-2-3(6))* Gila River Indian Community Cultural Resource Management Program.

Wilcox, David R. Archaeology of Perry Mesa & Its World. 2007. (ENG.). 300p. 20.00 *(978-0-9718786-9-3(2))* Bilby Research Ctr., Northern Arizona Univ.

Wileman, Julie. War & Rumors of War: The Evidential Base for the Recognition of Warfare in Prehistory. 2009. (Bar S Ser.). (ENG., Illus.). 171p. (C). pap. 90.00 *(978-1-4073-0516-5(6))* British Archaeological Reports Ltd. GBR. Dist: Brown, David Bk. Co., The.

Zoll, Kenneth / J. Sinagua Sunwatchers: An Archaeoastronomy Survey of the Sacred Mountain Basin. 2008. (Illus.). 88p. pap. 10.95 *(978-0-9820378-0-5(5))* WAC Pr.

—Understanding the Rock Art of Sedona. 2009. (ENG., Illus.). 52p. pap. 10.95 *(978-0-9820378-1-2(3))* WAC Pr.

ARIZONA—BIOGRAPHY

Acuña, Dorothy Chapman. Short Stories from el Barrio Libre, 1 vol. 2009. 78p. pap. 14.95 *(978-1-61546-297-1(X))* PublishAmerica, Inc.

Adkins, Bee & Keeling, Duane. Between Now & Then. 2009. 122p. 29.88 *(978-0-557-06242-3(X))* Lulu Enterprises Inc.

Alcock, John. When the Rains Come: A Naturalist's Year in the Sonoran Desert. 2009. (ENG., Illus.). 336p. (C). 45.00 *(978-0-8165-2835-6(7))*; 288p. pap. 21.95 *(978-0-8165-2762-5(8))* Univ. of Arizona Pr.

Anderson, Ray C. My First 88 Years: Minnesota to Arizona. 2007. 20.00 *(978-0-9706710-2-8(4))* Elan Pr.

Atchinson, Glenn A. A Sliver of Light Out of Darkness: Gathering Truth Through Life Stories. 2008. 80p. pap. 8.95 *(978-0-595-53253-7(5))* iUniverse, Inc.

Audretsch, Robert W. Shaping the Park & Saving the Boys: The Civilian Conservation Corps at Grand Canyon, 1933-1942. 2011. 140p. pap. 19.95 ***(978-1-4575-0529-4(0))*** Dog Ear Publishing, LLC.

Barnes, Mary Ellen. The Road to Mount Lemmon: A Father, A Family, & the Making of Summerhaven. 2009. (ENG., Illus.). 224p. pap. 17.95 *(978-0-8165-2781-6(4))* Univ. of Arizona Pr.

Barney, Ollie O. The Life & Times of Ollie Barney: An Arizona Native Son. 2006. 357p. pap. 18.95 *(978-0-7414-3609-2(4))* Infinity Publishing.

Bates, Albert R. Jack Swilling: Arizona's Most Lied about Pioneer. 2007. 128p. per. 12.95 *(978-1-58736-965-0(6))* Wheatmark.

Beagley, David. One Lost Boy: His Escape from Polygamy. 2008. 112p. pap. 9.99 *(978-1-59955-204-0(3))* Cedar Fort, Inc./CFI Distribution.

Bellile, Donald L. The Hybrid Man. 2010. 80p. pap. 10.97 *(978-1-4269-3209-0(X))* Trafford Publishing.

Benford, Tom & Theis, Andrea Benford. Standing Tall: A Father's Lessons Through His Daughter's Cancer. 2011. 176p. pap. 19.95 *(978-1-4520-4395-1(7))* AuthorHouse.

Berkowitz, Paul. The Case of the Indian Trader: Billy Malone & the National Park Service Investigation at Hubbell Trading Post. 2011. (ENG., Illus.). 376p. pap. 24.95 ***(978-0-8263-4860-9(2))*** Univ. of New Mexico Pr.

Bhatti, Sardar Ahmed. Snippets from My Life: Hong kong & Beyond. 2011. 136p. pap. 19.99 ***(978-1-4628-5273-4(4))*** Xlibris Corp.

Billy Stiles: Chasing the Wind. 2009. (Illus.). 256p. pap. 16.95 *(978-0-9769940-3-9(8))* Santa Cruz Valley Pr.

Butler, Elias & Myers, Tom. Grand Obsession: Harvey Butchart & the Exploration of the Grand Canyon. 2007. (Illus.). 457p. *(978-0-9700973-5-4(2))* Puma Pr.

Cady, John H. Arizona's Yesterday: Being the Narrative of John H. Cady, Pioneer. Woon, Basil, ed. 2007. (ENG.). 140p. 35.95 *(978-0-548-43310-2(0))*; per. 20.95 *(978-0-548-41079-0(8))* Kessinger Publishing, LLC.

Castro, Raul H. & August, Jack L., Jr. Adversity Is My Angel: The Life & Career of Raúl H. Castro. 2009. (ENG., Illus.). 192p. pap. 21.95 *(978-0-87565-378-5(2))* Texas Christian Univ. Pr.

Chen, Stanley S. As I Remembered: A Memoir. 2010. 188p. pap. 16.95 *(978-1-4502-3985-1(4))* iUniverse, Inc.

Christensen, Randy. Ask Me Why I Hurt: The Kids Nobody Wants & the Doctor Who Heals Them. 2011. (ENG.). 288p. pap. 19.00 ***(978-0-307-71901-0(4))*** Broadway Bks.

Clardy, Susan & Hammon, Frank Malcolm. Sometimes the Blues: The Letters & Diaries of Frank Hammon, a Lonely Frontiersman in Globe & Phoenix, 1882-1889. 2007. (Illus.). vii, 313p. *(978-0-910037-47-1(7))* Arizona Historical Society.

Cleere, Jan. Outlaw Tales of Arizona, 2nd: True Stories of the Grand Canyon State's Most Infamous Crooks, Culprits, & Cutthroats. 2nd ed. 2012. (Outlaw Tales Ser.). (ENG., Illus.). 176p. pap. 14.95 ***(978-0-7627-7233-9(6)***, TwoDot) Globe Pequot Pr., The.

Clemans, Charles. Harpo, War Survivor, Basketball Wizard: How one courageous young Mexican American faced impossible Odds... twice. 2009. 108p. pap. 11.95 *(978-1-60494-227-9(4))* Wheatmark.

Coe, Steven R. Touching the Universe: My Favorite Twenty Nights Viewing the Sky. 2011. 248p. 32.95 *(978-1-4620-0249-8(8))*; pap. 22.95 *(978-1-4620-0247-4(1))* iUniverse, Inc.

Dabovich, Chris. Chihuahua Hill: Bisbee, Arizona. 2010. 92p. pap. 11.95 *(978-1-4502-3701-7(0))* iUniverse, Inc.

Dalen. University Hospitals: Doctors & Patients. 2009. 236p. pap. 14.95 *(978-1-59330-603-8(2))* Aventine Pr.

Davis, James Ivey. My Life & Thoughts. 2011. 370p. 30.95 ***(978-1-4502-9880-3(X))***; pap. 20.95 ***(978-1-4502-9879-7(6))*** iUniverse, Inc.

Davis, Paul D. Family, Friends & Follies. 2009. 316p. pap. 15.95 *(978-1-4389-9767-4(1))* AuthorHouse.

Dean, Kevan N. & Brown, Terry L. Ezekiel, Yuma's Native Son: A Journey through the eyes of a Centenarian: Bishop Herman E. Dean. 2011. 208p. 29.99 *(978-1-4567-1245-7(4))*; pap. 19.99 *(978-1-4567-1246-4(2))* AuthorHouse.

DeArment, Robert K. & DeMattos, Jack. A Rough Ride to Redemption: The Ben Daniels Story. 2010. (ENG.). 264p. (C). 29.95 *(978-0-8061-4112-1(3))* Univ. of Oklahoma Pr.

Escapule, Betty Foster. The Five Fosters. 2009. 288p. 29.99 *(978-1-4415-5473-4(4))*; pap. 19.99 *(978-1-4415-5472-7(6))* Xlibris Corp.

Esquer, Cecilia D. The Lie about My Inferiority-Revolution of a Chicana Activist. 2010. pap. 24.95 *(978-1-4507-1883-7(3))* Independent Pub.

Fahlman, Betsy. The Cowboy's Dream: The Mythic Life & Art of Lon Megargee. (Illus.). 144p. pap. 35.00 *(978-0-87842-497-9(0)*, 1525) Mountain Pr. Publishing Co., Inc.

Foster Escapule, Betty. The Five Fosters. 2007. (ENG., Illus.). 239p. 34.00 *(978-0-9797168-0-5(2))* B & C Enterprises.

Gilbert, Two Rivers Church, compiled by. Not by Chance. 2007. pap. 14.95 *(978-0-9792475-7-6(8))* Good Catch Publishing.

Gordon A. Hunsaker. Gunfights & Gunfighters: Reflections from a Phoenix Police Officer. 2010. 344p. 33.95 *(978-1-4502-0721-8(9))*; pap. 23.95 *(978-1-4502-0720-1(0))* iUniverse, Inc.

Goss, Bob. Confessions of a Gringo Spanish Teacher. 2008. 100p. pap. 16.95 *(978-1-60474-735-5(8))* PublishAmerica, Inc.

Harrison McMichael, Susan. Box 7: Black Canyon Stage Route. 2010. pap. 13.95 *(978-0-7414-6117-9(X))* Infinity Publishing.

Hatch, Jo Ann. Lore & Legend: Adventure & History in the White Mountains of Arizona. 2007. (Illus.). 172p. per. 14.95 *(978-0-9773648-6-2(0))* Legend eXpress Publishing.

Henderson, John R. Attachments: To Those Who Can. 2010. 180p. 25.95 *(978-1-4502-3761-1(4))*; (ENG.). pap. 15.95 *(978-1-4502-3760-4(6))* iUniverse, Inc.

Henderson, Odell. Stuff from My Head & Heart. 2011. pap. 12.95 ***(978-0-7414-6622-8(8))*** Infinity Publishing.

Henry, Bonnie. Tucson Memories. 2006. *(978-1-59152-034-4(7))* Arizona Daily Star.

Jacobson, James R. Hope for Tomorrow's Families/A Model That Values Variety. 2009. 160p. 23.25 *(978-1-60860-490-6(X)*, Eloquent Bks.) AEG Literary Publishing Services, Inc.

Joling, Robert J. J. D. On the Way to the Courthouse! 2011. 270p. 29.99 ***(978-1-4568-9688-1(1))***; pap. 19.99 ***(978-1-4568-9687-4(3))*** Xlibris Corp.

Kemp, Aaron W. It Takes Practice. 2010. 108p. (ENG.). 22.92 *(978-1-4269-3149-9(2))*; pap. 11.92 *(978-1-4269-3148-2(4))* Trafford Publishing.

Kroloff, Reed. Arizona Modern. 55.00 *(978-0-8478-2601-8(5))* Rizzoli International Pubns., Inc.

Lassey, Bill & Lassey, Marie. Fabulous Journey. 2008. 400p. pap. 25.95 *(978-1-4401-0306-3(2))* iUniverse, Inc.

Lawrence F. Lihosit, F. Lihosit & Lawrence F. Lihosit. South of the Frontera: A Peace Corps Memoir. 2010. 316p. pap. 22.95 *(978-1-4502-1858-0(X))* iUniverse, Inc.

Ledoux, Gary. Nantan: The Life & Times of John P. Clum Vol. 2. 2008. 416p. 49.00 *(978-1-4251-7425-5(6))* Trafford Publishing.

Leo, Mabel. Mob Mole: Mr. Smooth aka Jack Durant. 2008. 225p. mass mkt. 15.00 *(978-0-9650787-5-7(2))* MIBS Publishing.

Lowe, Sam. Speaking Ill of the Dead: Jerks in Arizona History. 2012. (Speaking Ill of the Dead: Jerks in Histo Ser.). (ENG., Illus.). 240p. pap. 16.95 ***(978-0-7627-2815-2(9))*** Globe Pequot Pr., The.

Luttrell, Jean. The Last Old-Time Ranger: John H. Riffey. 2007. (Illus.). 152p. pap. 14.95 *(978-0-9795055-1-5(8))* Vishnu Temple Pr.

Lyon, Cherstin M. Prisons & Patriots: Japanese American Wartime Citizenship, Civil Disobedience, & Historical Memory. 2011. (Illus.). 256p. E-Book ***(978-1-4399-0188-5(0))*** Temple Univ. Pr.

Lyons, Bettina. Zeckendorfs & Steinfelds: Merchant Princes of the American Southwest. 2008. *(978-0-910037-49-5(3))* Arizona Historical Society.

Maricle, Francoise. Hold on to Your Dreams: Regardless of Your Past. 2008. 244p. pap. 14.95 *(978-1-59858-655-8(6))* Dog Ear Publishing, LLC.

Martins, Olu. A Journey Interrupted. 2007. 68p. per. 9.99 *(978-1-60266-718-1(7))* Xulon Pr., Inc.

McCarville, Mary Michele. American Doctor. 2009. 243p. 70.22 *(978-0-615-23854-8(8))* McCarville, Mary Michele.

McKanna, Clare V., Jr. Court-Martial of Apache Kid, the Renegade of Renegades. 2009. (Illus.). 256p. 29.95 *(978-0-89672-652-9(5))* Texas Tech Univ. Pr.

Means, Andrew. Some Memories Growing up with Marty Robb. 2007. 136p. per. 13.95 *(978-1-60145-105-7(9))* Booklocker.com, Inc.

Messersmith, Dan W. Kingman. 2010. (Images of America Ser.). (Illus.). 128p. pap. 21.99 *(978-0-7385-7930-6(0))* Arcadia Publishing.

Miller, Neil. Kartchner Caverns: How Two Cavers Discovered & Saved One of the Wonders of the Natural World. 2008. (ENG., Illus.). 224p. pap. 15.95 *(978-0-8165-2516-4(1))* Univ. of Arizona Pr.

Moehringer, J. R. The Tender Bar: A Memoir. 2006. (ENG.). 432p. pap. 14.99 *(978-0-7868-8876-4(8))* Hyperion Pr.

Moore, Robert J. The Civilian Conservation Corps in Arizona's Rim Country: Working in the Woods. 2006. (ENG., Illus.). 176p. 34.95 *(978-0-87417-677-3(8))* Univ. of Nevada Pr.

Nassar, Dave & Barrett-Lee, Lynne. Giant George: Life with the World's Biggest Dog. l.t. ed. 2012. (ENG.). 293p. 32.99 ***(978-1-4104-4836-1(3))*** Thorndike Pr.

Nasser, Dave. Giant George: Life with the World's Biggest Dog. 2012. (ENG., Illus.). 272p. pap. 12.95 ***(978-1-84983-282-3(X))*** Simon & Schuster, Ltd. GBR. Dist: Independent Pubs. Group.

Nasser, Dave & Barrett-Lee, Lynne. Giant George: Life with the World's Biggest Dog. 2012. ***(978-1-4555-1144-0(7))*** Grand Central Publishing.

Nichols, Ericka & Bracamontes, Maria, trs. Documented Dreams: A Testimony of the Plight of a Generation of Young Latinos Caught in a Social Dilemma. 2008. (ENG & SPA., Illus.). 86p. per. 25.00 *(978-0-9797814-3-8(4))* Hispanic Institute of Social Issues.

Nichols, Paul. Just Seven Blocks from the Mexican Border: Growing up in the 1950s... A Southern Arizona Memoir. 2009. 270p. pap. 14.95 *(978-0-9823859-1-3(9))* Inheritance Pr.

No One Succeeds Alone. 2007. per. *(978-1-59916-193-8(1))* Printing Systems.

Norman, Mildred. Henry's Daughter: My Journeys Through the 20th Century. 2007. (ENG.). 327p. per. 14.95 *(978-1-58985-056-9(4))* Five Star Pubns., Inc.

Owers, Geoffrey. Their Effort Was Like Toothpaste: a Story of Trophies Won & Life Changed. 2010. 353p. pap. 19.25 *(978-0-557-36436-7(1))* Lulu Enterprises Inc.

Oxford, Isabel M. Children of the Sun. 2011. pap. 9.99 ***(978-1-61777-183-5(X))*** Tate Publishing & Enterprises, LLC.

Payne, Tom. My Life with Barbara: A Love Story. 2007. 144p. 19.95 *(978-1-4327-0928-0(3))*; (ENG.). per. 10.95 *(978-1-4327-1463-5(5))* Outskirts Pr., Inc.

Peterman, Melinda Gay & notes. Our Arizona Heritage: Memories of Gay Killian & Max Killian. 2009. 902p. *(978-0-9633640-1-2(4))* Killian, C. Max.

Phillips, Beverly Jane. From Heaven to My Heart: God's Journey with Me. 2011. 396p. 35.95 *(978-1-4502-5995-8(2))*; pap. 25.95 *(978-1-4502-5993-4(6))* iUniverse, Inc.

Preston, Donald. I Love You One Thousand Houses: A Memoir. 2009. 204p. pap. 17.95 *(978-1-4401-4384-7(6))* iUniverse, Inc.

Reale, Rick. Tires Optional. 2011. 108p. pap. 13.95 *(978-1-4327-7127-0(2))* Outskirts Pr., Inc.

Reeves, Buster. Dark Night, Bright Morning: One Family, under God, Indivisible. 2010. pap. 11.99 *(978-1-61663-686-9(6))* Tate Publishing & Enterprises, LLC.

Ring, Bob, et al. Frontier Lady of Letters: The Heroic Love Story of Ines Fraser. 2007. (ENG.). 192p. per. 19.95 *(978-1-58736-775-5(0))* Wheatmark.

Rivera, Al. The Barefoot Shoeshine Boy. 2008. 156p. 22.49 *(978-1-4389-2121-1(7))*; pap. 15.49 *(978-1-4389-2120-4(9))* AuthorHouse.

Rodebush, Emmitt. The Accidental Millionaire: The Unusual Life of E. L. Rodebush. 2007. 60p. per. 9.95 *(978-0-595-34176-4(4))* iUniverse, Inc.

Rogers, Patricia A. From Sedona to Vegas. 2007. 272p. pap. 16.95 *(978-0-9762026-2-2(X))* Rogers, Patricia.

Rosok, Ingwald Andreas. Retrospect: An Autobiography. Norlie, O. M., ed. 2011. 346p. 51.95 ***(978-1-258-10085-8(1))*** Literary Licensing, LLC.

Sandy, Eveline. What Did I Do Wrong? 2011. 164p. 25.95 *(978-1-4502-9991-6(1))*; pap. 15.95 *(978-1-4502-9989-3(X))* iUniverse, Inc.

Sherman, Jason. Diary of a Widowed Dad. 2009. 168p. pap. 14.95 *(978-1-60844-062-7(1))* Dog Ear Publishing, LLC.

Shortridge, L. W. Flatlined in Phoenix: A True Story of My after-Death Experience, 1 vol. 2010. 76p. pap. 19.95 *(978-1-4512-8669-4(4))* PublishAmerica, Inc.

Sotelo, Joe. Burro Alley. 2006. per. 19.95 *(978-0-9771167-7-5(8))* Hispanic Institute of Social Issues.

Spicer, Edward H. People of Pascua. Sands, Kathleen Mullen & Spicer, Rosamond B., eds. 2011. (ENG., Illus.). 331p. pap. 30.00 *(978-0-8165-2967-4(1))* Univ. of Arizona Pr.

Spragg-Braude, Stacia. To Walk in Beauty: A Navajo Family's Journey Home. 2009. (ENG., Illus.). 200p. 45.00 *(978-0-89013-554-9(1))* Museum of New Mexico Pr.

Summerhayes, Martha. Vanished Arizona: Recollections of the Army Life by a New England Woman. 2007. (ENG.). 212p. pap. 20.99 *(978-1-4346-1429-2(8))*; 232p. pap. 22.99 *(978-1-4346-1523-7(5))* BiblioBazaar.

—Vanished Arizona Recollections of the A. 2006. pap. *(978-1-4068-3140-5(9))* Echo Library.

Trombino, Mark & Dickerson, John. Life Is Short: Living & Losing the American Dream at 3-Feet Tall. 2008. 104p. pap. 14.95 *(978-0-7414-4664-0(2))* Infinity Publishing.

Tucker, Donald W. The Two-Edged Sword. 2010. 272p. pap. 15.99 *(978-1-60844-566-0(6))* Dog Ear Publishing, LLC.

Turner, Eleanor. Adventures at Castle Dome. 2009. 50p. pap. 15.00 *(978-0-557-15709-9(9))* Lulu Enterprises Inc.

Valdez, Linda, told to. A Doctor's Legacy: A Memoir of Merlin K. Duval, Founding Dean of Arizona's First Medical School. 2009. (ENG., Illus.). 302p. 29.95 *(978-0-615-28393-7(4))* Legacy Publishing.

Verbout, Scott. An Asperger Journey: My Lifelong Battle with Autism. 2011. 76p. pap. 10.95 *(978-1-4502-9535-2(5))* iUniverse, Inc.

Walsh, Mike. Kaeleb's Dad. 2007. 48p. per. 16.95 *(978-1-4241-9056-0(8))* PublishAmerica, Inc.

ARIZONA—CENSUS

Arizona Census Index 1900. (Illus.). lib. bdg. *(978-0-89593-217-4(2)*, Accelerated Indexing Systems International (AISI)) Genealogical Services.

Arizona Census Index 1910. (Illus.). lib. bdg. *(978-0-89593-218-1(0)*, Accelerated Indexing Systems International (AISI)) Genealogical Services.

ARIZONA—DESCRIPTION AND TRAVEL

Acree, Laurie Dee. Rambling along the Rim: The 50 Best Day Hikes in the White Mountains of Arizona. 2010. pap. 15.95 *(978-0-7414-5835-3(7))* Infinity Publishing.

Aleshire, Peter. Desert Rivers: From Lush Headwaters to Sonoran Sands. 2006. (Arizona Highways Special Scenic Collections). (Illus.). 80p. pap. 12.95 *(978-1-893860-17-9(5))* Arizona Highways.

Anderson, Lisa A., et al. Mesa. 2008. (Images of America Ser.). (ENG., Illus.). 128p. per. 21.99 *(978-0-7385-4842-5(1))* Arcadia Publishing.

Anderson, Parker & Ruffner, Elisabeth. The Elks Opera House. 2012. (Images of America Ser.). (ENG., Illus.). 128p. pap. 21.99 ***(978-0-7385-8542-0(4))*** Arcadia Publishing.

Annerino, John. Dead in Their Tracks: Crossing America's Desert Borderlands in the New Era. 2009. (ENG., Illus.). 320p. pap. 17.95 *(978-0-8165-2765-6(2))* Univ. of Arizona Pr.

Arizona. (Proseries Wall Map Ser.). 229.00 *(978-0-528-85856-7(4))* Rand McNally.

Arizona Development Board. An Adventure with the Arizona Mountain Men Who Tamed the Frontier Wilderness for Amazing Arizon. 2011. 58p. 36.95 ***(978-1-258-01516-9(1))*** Literary Licensing, LLC.

Arizona Highways Magazine, ed. Arizona Highways Photography Guide: How & Where to Make Great Photographs. 2008. (Arizona Highways: Travel Arizona Collection). (Illus.). 335p. pap. 24.95 *(978-1-932082-84-5(0))* Arizona Highways.

Ascarza, William. Southeastern Arizona Mining Towns. 2011. (Images of America Ser.). (Illus.). 128p. pap. 21.99 ***(978-0-7385-8516-1(5))*** Arcadia Publishing.

Ascarza, William. Tucson Mountains. 2010. (Images of America Ser.). (ENG., Illus.). 128p. pap. 21.99 *(978-0-7385-7923-8(8))* Arcadia Publishing.

Audretsch, Robert W. Grand Canyon's Phantom Ranch. 2012. (Images of America Ser.). (ENG., Illus.). 128p. pap. 21.99 ***(978-0-7385-8525-3(4))*** Arcadia Publishing.

Ayers, Steve & Camp Verde Historical Society. Camp Verde. 2010. (Images of America Ser.). (Illus.). 128p. pap. 21.99 *(978-0-7385-7912-2(2))* Arcadia Publishing.

Babbitt, James E. & DeGraff III, John G. Flagstaff. 2009. (Images of America Ser.). (ENG., Illus.). 128p. pap. 21.99 *(978-0-7385-7115-7(6))* Arcadia Publishing.

Barr, Betty. Around Sonoita. 2009. (Images of America Ser.). (ENG., Illus.). 128p. pap. 21.99 *(978-0-7385-7143-0(1))* Arcadia Publishing.

Bates, Denise E., et al. Goodyear. 2010. (Images of America Ser.). (ENG., Illus.). 128p. pap. 21.99 *(978-0-7385-7117-1(2))* Arcadia Publishing.

Beaver, Deanna & The Parker Area Historical Society. Parker. 2008. 128p. pap. 19.99 *(978-0-7385-5638-3(6))* Arcadia Publishing.

Berger, Todd & Deuschle, Carolyn, eds. Grand Canyon Reflections. 2011. (ENG.). 48p. 7.95 *(978-1-934656-12-9(7))* Grand Canyon Assn.

Bohrer, Vorsila. Pre-Ceramic Subsistence in Two Rock Shelters. 2007. (Arizona State Museum Archaeological Ser.). (ENG.). 235p. pap. 24.95 *(978-1-889747-81-1(5))* Arizona State Museum.

Bolesta, Murray. Moods of the Santa Ritas of Southern Arizona: A Celebration of Southern Arizona Image Gallery. 2007. 60p. per. 19.95 *(978-0-9797842-1-7(2))* CactusHuggers Publishing Co.

Bonechi, Casa. Lake Powell Monument Valley. 64p. *(978-88-7009-215-8(1))* Casa Editrice Bonechi.

Bowden, Charles & Ranney, Chuck. Jack Dykinga's Grand Canyon. 2008. 112p. 39.95 *(978-1-932082-87-6(5))* Arizona Highways.

Boyer, Diane E. & Webb, Robert H. Damming Grand Canyon: The 1923 USGS Colorado River Expedition. 2007. (ENG., Illus.). 280p. (gr. 13). 34.95 *(978-0-87421-660-8(5)*, Utah State Univ. Pr.) Univ. Pr. of Colorado.

Brock, Patricia & Maricopa Historical Society. Maricopa. 2011. (Images of America Ser.). (Illus.). 128p. pap. 21.99 *(978-0-7385-7995-5(5))* Arcadia Publishing.

Brown, Christopher. Path of Beauty: Photographic Adventures in the Grand Canyon. 2010. (ENG., Illus.). 128p. 39.99 *(978-0-312-59835-8(1))* St. Martin's Pr.

Brownold, Tom. The Grandest Ride. 2010. (ENG., Illus.). 48p. pap. 8.95 *(978-1-933855-43-1(6))* Rio Nuevo Pubs.

Bryant, Kathleen. Sedona & Red Rock Country. 2011. (Illus.). 64p. pap. 9.95 *(978-1-933855-65-3(7))* Rio Nuevo Pubs.

Burdick, Clifford. Snowbird Express Yuma Bound: Get Out of the Snow & Enjoy the Sun! 2009. 168p. pap. 15.95 *(978-1-4327-1753-7(7))* Outskirts Pr., Inc.

Burgess, Nancy & Ariz, Karen Despain on behalf of the Yavapai County. Around Yavapai County: Celebrating Arizona's Centennial. 2011. (Images of America Ser.). (ENG., Illus.). 128p. pap. 21.99 ***(978-0-7385-7962-7(9))*** Arcadia Publishing.

Buscher, Dick. Historic Photos of Arizona. 2009. (Historic Photos Ser.). (ENG.). 206p. 39.95 *(978-1-59652-518-4(5))* Turner Publishing Co.

Butcher, Scott D. Tombstone: Relive the Gunfight at the OK Corral. 2010. (Illus.). 96p. pap. 9.99 *(978-0-7643-3425-2(5))* Schiffer Publishing, Ltd.

—Tucson Perspectives. 2011. (Illus.). 80p. *(978-0-7643-3712-3(2)*, Schiffer Publishing Ltd) Schiffer Publishing, Ltd.

Campbell, Marty. Arizona Family Field Trips. 2006. per. 16.95 *(978-0-9722286-1-9(6))* AZ Adventures.

Carson, Thomas. Ranching, Sport & Travel. 2009. (Illus.). 200p. pap. *(978-1-4099-5114-8(6))* Dodo Pr.

—Ranching, Sport & Travel. 2007. 136p. per. *(978-1-4068-4405-4(5))* Echo Library.

—Ranching, Sport & Travel. 2007. (ENG.). 196p. pap. 11.45 *(978-1-60424-789-3(4)*, Book Jungle) Standard Pubns., Inc.

—Ranching Sport & Travel. 2008. 224p. 27.99 *(978-0-554-28077-6(9))* 2008. 224p. 24.99 *(978-0-554-37380-5(7))* 2007. (ENG.). 198p. pap. 19.99 *(978-1-4346-4643-9(2))* 2007. (ENG.). 220p. pap. 22.99 *(978-1-4346-4644-6(0))* BiblioBazaar.

Chandler, R. J. The World of God. 2010. 44p. pap. 29.95 *(978-0-557-59067-4(1))* Lulu Enterprises Inc.

Clark, Victoria. A Journey Through Northern Arizona. 2008. (Illus.). 128p. pap. 24.99 *(978-0-7643-3010-0(1))* Schiffer Publishing, Ltd.

Cleere, Jan. Amazing Girls of Arizona: True Stories of Young Pioneers. 2007. (ENG., Illus.). 200p. pap. 12.95 *(978-0-7627-4135-9(X)*, TwoDot) Globe Pequot Pr., The.

Conklin, Les & Greater Pinnacle Peak Association. Pinnacle Peak. 2011. (Images of America Ser.). (ENG., Illus.). 128p. pap. 21.99 *(978-0-7385-7984-9(X))* Arcadia Publishing.

Cool Springs Press Publications Staff. Desert Gardens: A Photographic Tour of the Arizona-Sonora Desert Museum. Brusca, Richard C., ed. 2010. (ENG.). 176p. 34.95 *(978-1-59186-458-5(5)*, 1591864585) Cool Springs Pr.

Costa Mesa Historical Society. Early Costa Mesa. 2009. (Images of America Ser.). (ENG., Illus.). 128p. pap. 21.99 *(978-0-7385-6976-5(3))* Arcadia Publishing.

Cowan, Bill. Verde Valley. 2011. (Images of America Ser.). (ENG., Illus.). 128p. per. 21.99 (978-0-7385-8514-7(9)) Arcadia Publishing.

Cozzens, Samuel Woodworth. The Marvellous Country, or, Three Years in Arizona & New Mexico Containing an Authentic History of This Wonderful Country & Its Ancient Civilizat. 2006. 608p. per. 34.99 (978-1-4255-6474-2(7)) MPublishing.

Crago, Jody A., et al. Chandler. 2012. (Images of America Ser.). (ENG., Illus.). 128p. pap. 21.99 (978-0-7385-8521-5(1)) Arcadia Publishing.

Creighton, Kimberly J. Mt. Baldy. 2009. (Images of America Ser.). (ENG., Illus.). 128p. pap. 21.99 (978-0-7385-5999-5(7)) Arcadia Publishing.

Cross, Jean. Prescott Valley. 2009. (Images of America Ser.). (ENG., Illus.). 128p. pap. 21.99 (978-0-7385-7070-9(2)) Arcadia Publishing.

Davis, Hester A. Remembering Awatovi: The Story of an Archaeological Expedition in Northern Arizona, 1935-1939. 2008. (Illus.). 240p. (Peabody Museum Ser.). 35.00 (978-0-87365-912-3(0)); (Peabody Museum Monographs: 10). pap. 18.95 (978-0-87365-911-6(2)) Peabody Museum of Archaeology & Ethnology, Harvard Univ., Pubns. Dept.

DeGraff III, John G. Flagstaff. 2011. (Postcard History Ser.). (Illus.). 128p. pap. 21.99 (978-0-7385-8510-9(6)) Arcadia Publishing.

DeLuse,, Stephanie R., Stephanie R & Bates,, Denise E., Denise E. Arizona State University. 2012. (Campus History Ser.). (ENG., Illus.). 128p. pap. 21.99 (978-0-7385-9545-0(4)) Arcadia Publishing.

DeSoucy, M. David. Arizona Rangers. 2008. (Images of America Ser.). (ENG., Illus.). 128p. per. 21.99 (978-0-7385-4831-9(6)) Arcadia Publishing.

Downey, Lynn & Desert Caballeros Western Museum. Wickenburg. 2012. (Images of America Ser.). (ENG., Illus.). 128p. pap. 21.99 (978-0-7385-8504-8(1)) Arcadia Publishing.

Eickemeyer, Carl. Over the Great Navajo Trail. 2007. 268p. 42.95 (978-0-548-43586-1(3)); pap. 27.95 (978-0-548-41369-2(X)) Kessinger Publishing, LLC.

Ellis, Catherine H. Holbrook & the Petrified Forest. 2007. (Images of America Ser.). (ENG., Illus.). 128p. per. 21.99 (978-0-7385-4885-2(5)) Arcadia Publishing.

—Snowflake. 2008. (Images of America Ser.). (ENG., Illus.). 128p. pap. 19.99 (978-0-7385-4838-8(3)) Arcadia Publishing.

Ellis, Catherine H. & Turner, D. L. The White Mountains of Apache County. 2010. (Images of America Ser.). (Illus.). 128p. pap. 21.99 (978-0-7385-6690-0(X)) Arcadia Publishing.

Elsner, Jodey & Peoria Arizona Historical Society. Peoria. 2010. (Images of America Ser.). (Illus.). 128p. pap. 21.99 (978-0-7385-7110-2(5)) Arcadia Publishing.

Eppinga, Jane. Tombstone. 2010. (Postcard History Ser.). (Illus.). 128p. pap. 21.99 (978-0-7385-7933-7(5)) Arcadia Publishing.

Fowler, Don D. The Glen Canyon Country: A Personal Memoir. 2011. (Illus.). 432p. (gr. 12). pap. 39.95 (978-1-60781-134-3(0)) Univ. of Utah Pr.

Gartell, Barry, ed. Times Past: Reflections from Arizona History. 2008. (ENG., Illus.). 263p. 49.95 (978-0-615-25117-2(X)) Arizona Capitol Times.

George Wharton, James. The Grand Canyon of Arizona; How to See It. 2007. 236p. pap. 20.99 (978-1-4346-1776-7(9)); (ENG.). 262p. pap. 23.99 (978-1-4346-1945-7(1)) BiblioBazaar.

Giordano, Gerard. The Verde River: Bartlett & Horseshoe Dams. 2010. (Images of America Ser.). 128p. pap. 21.99 (978-0-7385-7889-7(4)) Arcadia Publishing.

Graziano, Margaret. Lady Lost: The Story of the Honeymoon Cottage in Jerome, AZ. 2009. 184p. 15.95 (978-1-58985-152-8(8)) Five Star Pubns., Inc.

Haak, Wilbur A., et al. Globe. 2008. (Images of America Ser.). (ENG., Illus.). 128p. per. 21.99 (978-0-7385-4833-3(2)) Arcadia Publishing.

Hamblin, W. Kenneth. Anatomy of the Grand Canyon: Panoramas of the Canyon's Geology. 2008. (ENG.). 144p. 49.95 (978-1-934656-01-3(1)); pap. (978-1-934656-02-0(X)) Grand Canyon Assn.

Hayostek, Cindy. Douglas. 2009. (Images of America Ser.). (ENG., Illus.). 128p. pap. 21.99 (978-0-7385-7065-5(6)) Arcadia Publishing.

James, George Wharton. The Grand Canyon of Arizona: How to See It. 2007. (ENG.). 336p. per. 30.95 (978-1-4326-4540-3(4)) Kessinger Publishing, LLC.

—The Grand Canyon of Arizona; How to See It. 2011. 354p. pap. 32.75 (978-1-178-82377-6(6)) 2010. (ENG.). 348p. pap. 32.75 (978-1-171-69874-6(7)) 2008. 264p. 25.99 (978-0-554-36122-2(1)) 2008. 264p. 28.99 (978-0-554-26819-4(1)) BiblioBazaar.

—The Grand Canyon of Arizona; How to See It. 2009. 192p. pap. (978-1-150-72276-9(2)) Books LLC.

—The Grand Canyon of Arizona; How to See It. 2007. 224p. per. (978-1-4065-1833-7(6)) Dodo Pr.

—The Grand Canyon of Arizona; How to See It. 2010. (Illus.). 142p. pap. 23.09 (978-1-153-74500-0(3)) General Bks. LLC.

—The Grand Canyon of Arizona How to See It. 2009. (ENG.). 340p. 36.99 (978-1-117-25365-7(1)); pap. 30.75 (978-1-117-25366-4(X)); pap. 23.99 (978-1-117-25367-1(8), BiblioLife) BiblioBazaar.

Jasper, Joy Waldron. USS Arizona. (Illus.). pap. (978-0-312-31012-7(9)) St. Martin's Pr.

Kelly, William J. Arizona in The '50s: Captain James H. Tevis. 2007. 135p. per. 25.00 (978-0-9790261-1-9(3)) Barr, Betty.

Killebrew, Helen & Verde Historical Society. Cottonwood. 2011. (Images of America Ser.). (Illus.). 128p. pap. 21.99 (978-0-7385-7999-3(8)) Arcadia Publishing.

Kinsley, Shaw. Tubac. 2009. 128p. pap. 21.99 (978-0-7385-7864-4(9)); (ENG., Illus.). 15p. pap. 7.99 (978-0-7385-7869-9(X)) Arcadia Publishing.

Klump, Kathy & Tenney, Peta-Anne. Willcox. 2009. (Images of America Ser.). (ENG., Illus.). 128p. pap. 21.99 (978-0-7385-7177-5(6)) Arcadia Publishing.

Kolb, Ellsworth Leonardson. Through the Grand Canyon from Wyoming to Mexico. 2008. 248p. 24.99 (978-0-554-34376-1(2)) 2008. 248p. 27.99 (978-0-554-25073-1(X)) 2007. (ENG.). 218p. pap. 20.99 (978-1-4264-8124-6(1)) 2007. (ENG.). 244p. pap. 22.99 (978-1-4264-8196-3(9)) BiblioBazaar.

Kutner, E. W., et al. McMullen Valley. 2008. (Images of America Ser.). (ENG., Illus.). 128p. pap. 21.99 (978-0-7385-5851-6(6)) Arcadia Publishing.

Kyi, Tanya Lloyd & Kyi, Tanya Lloyd. Arizona. 2010. (ENG., Illus.). 96p. pap. 12.95 (978-1-55285-770-0(0)) Whitecap Bks., Ltd. CAN. Dist: Midpoint Trade Bks., Inc.

Ladd, Gary. Grand Canyon: Views Beyond the Beauty. 2008. (ENG.). 82p. pap. 14.95 (978-0-938216-89-6(9)) Grand Canyon Assn.

Lamb, Susan. Arizona Scenic Seasons: The Unique Landscapes of Spring, Summer, Autumn, & Winter. 2009. 112p. mass mkt. 39.99 (978-0-9822788-0-2(2)) Arizona Highways.

Larson, Peggy Pickering & Ascarza, William. Arizona-Sonora Desert Museum. 2010. (Images of America Ser.). (Illus.). 128p. pap. 21.99 (978-0-7385-8671-7(4)) Arcadia Publishing.

Lawton, Paul J. Old Tucson Studios. 2008. (Images of America Ser.). (ENG., Illus.). 128p. pap. 21.99 (978-0-7385-5629-1(7)) Arcadia Publishing.

Lee, Katie. Glen Canyon Betrayed: A Sensuous Elegy. 2006. Orig. Title: All My Rivers Are Gone: A Journey of Discovery Through Glen Canyon. (Illus.). 276p. per. 16.95 net. (978-1-892327-06-2(6)) Fretwater Pr.

Lindahl, Larry, photos by. Arizona Kicks on Route 66. 2012. pap. (978-1-933855-76-9(2), Rio Nuevo Pubs.) Rio Nuevo Pubs.

Locken, E. Travel Journal Arizona. 2009. 198p. pap. 20.97 (978-0-557-07869-1(5)) Lulu Enterprises Inc.

Lopez, Kathy & Morgan Ranch Park Association Inc. Williamson Valley Road. 2011. (Images of America Ser.). (ENG., Illus.). 128p. pap. 21.99 (978-0-7385-7987-0(4)) Arcadia Publishing.

Marriott, Barbara & Oro Valley Historical Society. Oro Valley. 2008. (Images of America Ser.). (Illus.). 127p. per. 19.99 (978-0-7385-4834-0(0)) Arcadia Publishing.

Maxa, Christine. Arizona's Salsa Trail - Adventures in Culinary Tourism in Southeast Arizona. 2008. (Illus.). 175p. pap. 20.00 (978-0-9785824-3-2(8)) Jamax Publishers Pr.

Maxa, Christine Maxa. Wickenburg Adventures: The Official Backcountry Guide. 2007. per. 16.95 net. (978-0-9790814-0-8(8)) Wickenburg Chamber of Commerce.

McIntyre, Allan J., et al. The Tohono O'Odham & Pimeria Alta. 2008. (Images of America Ser.). (ENG., Illus.). 128p. pap. 21.99 (978-0-7385-5633-8(5)) Arcadia Publishing.

McKeand, Bret & Sun Cities Area Historical Society. Sun City. 2011. (Images of America Ser.). (Illus.). 128p. pap. 21.99 (978-0-7385-7951-1(3)) Arcadia Publishing.

McNamee, Gregory. Mark Klett: Saguaros, 1 vol. 2007. (ENG., Illus.). 106p. 75.00 (978-1-934435-00-7(7)) Radius Bks.

—Monumental Places: National Parks & Monuments in the Grand Canyon State. 2007. (Arizona Highways Special Scenic Collection). (Illus.). 80p. per. 14.95 (978-1-932082-78-4(6)) Arizona Highways.

Meck, Verlyne. Buckeye. 2010. (Then & Now Ser.). (ENG., Illus.). 96p. pap. 21.99 (978-0-7385-7924-5(6)) Arcadia Publishing.

Messersmith, Dan W. Kingman. 2010. (Images of America Ser.). (Illus.). 128p. pap. 21.99 (978-0-7385-7930-6(0)) Arcadia Publishing.

Miller, Raymond E. Prescott. 2010. (Postcard History Ser.). (Illus.). 128p. pap. 21.99 (978-0-7385-7906-1(8)) Arcadia Publishing.

Muench, David, photos by. Arizona. 2007. (ENG., Illus.). 191p. 50.00 (978-1-55868-986-2(9)) Graphic Arts Ctr. Publishing Co.

Mullaly, Katie & Ohlde, Patrick, H. Finding Ghosts in Phoenix. 2010. (Illus.). 160p. pap. 14.99 (978-0-7643-3583-9(9)) Schiffer Publishing, Ltd.

Mullaly, Katie & Ohlde, J. Patrick. Tucson's Most Haunted. 2009. 160p. pap. 14.99 (978-0-7643-3153-4(1)) Schiffer Publishing, Ltd.

Munk, Joseph A. Arizona Sketches. 2008. 104p. pap. (978-1-4099-0378-9(8)) Dodo Pr.

Munk, Joseph Amasa. Southwest Sketches. 311p. reprint ed. 98.00 (978-0-7222-6472-0(0)) Library Reprints, Inc.

Murray, Vincent. Gila Bend. 2012. (Images of America Ser.). (ENG., Illus.). 128p. pap. 21.99 (978-0-7385-8475-1(4)) Arcadia Publishing.

Nickell, Anna, et al. Pearce & Sunsites. 2011. (Images of America Ser.). (ENG., Illus.). 128p. pap. 21.99 (978-0-7385-8473-7(8)) Arcadia Publishing.

Nickens, Paul & Nickens, Kathleen. Old San Carlos. 2008. (Images of America Ser.). (Illus.). 128p. pap. 21.99 (978-0-7385-5891-2(5)) Arcadia Publishing.

Parr, Barry. Explore! Big Sur Country: A Guide to Exploring the Coastline, Byways, Mountains, Trails, & Lore. 2007. (Exploring Ser.). (ENG., Illus.). 272p. pap. 17.95 (978-0-7627-3568-6(6), Falcon Guides) Globe Pequot Pr., The.

Powers, Richard L. & the Superstition Mountain Historical Society, and the Gila County Historical Society Museum. Apache Trail. 2008. (Images of America Ser.). (ENG., Illus.). 128p. pap. 21.99 (978-0-7385-5862-2(1)) Arcadia Publishing.

Preston, Ralph N. & Preston, Monte L. Arizona Ghost Town Sites. (Illus.). pap. 11.00 (978-0-9657558-8-7(6)) Pioneer Pr.

Pyle, Jayne Peace & Pyle, Jinx. Payson. 2010. (Images of America Ser.). (Illus.). 128p. pap. 21.99 (978-0-7385-8457-7(6)) Arcadia Publishing.

Ratz, Thomas Alan. Grand Canyon National Park. 2009. (Postcard History Ser.). (ENG., Illus.). 128p. pap. 21.99 (978-0-7385-7856-9(8)) Arcadia Publishing.

Reiser, Ronald J. Arizona Passport. 2007. 36p. pap. (978-0-9625515-2-9(X)) Reiser, R. J. & Co.

Rio Nuevo Publishers, ed. Arizona: Scenic Wonders of the Grand Canyon State. 2011. (Illus.). 80p. pap. 11.95 (978-1-933855-44-8(4)) Rio Nuevo Pubs.

—The Grand Canyon: From Rim to River. 2010. (ENG., Illus.). 64p. pap. 9.95 (978-1-933855-42-4(8)) Rio Nuevo Pubs.

Rowe, Jeremy. Early Maricopa County: 1871-1920. 2011. (Images of America Ser.). (Illus.). 128p. pap. 21.99 (978-0-7385-7416-5(3)) Arcadia Publishing.

Ryan Bryson, Janice & Shappee Wood, Kathleen. Irish Arizona. 2009. (Images of America Ser.). (ENG., Illus.). 128p. pap. 21.99 (978-0-7385-5647-5(5)) Arcadia Publishing.

Schumacher, Carol A. & Tomerlin, Danielle M. Superior & Queen Valley. 2011. (Images of America Ser.). (Illus.). 128p. pap. 21.99 (978-0-7385-7965-8(3)) Arcadia Publishing.

Snell, Dawn & Casa Grande Valley Historical Society. Casa Grande. 2011. (Images of America Ser.). (Illus.). 128p. pap. 21.99 (978-0-7385-7953-5(X)) Arcadia Publishing.

Sonderman, Joe. Route 66 in Arizona. 2010. (Images of America Ser.). (ENG., Illus.). 128p. pap. 21.99 (978-0-7385-7942-9(4)) Arcadia Publishing.

Speelman, Mike. Historic Photos of Tucson. 2007. (Historic Photos Ser.). (ENG., Illus.). 204p. 39.95 (978-1-59652-370-8(0)) Turner Publishing Co.

Squire, Jerry & City of Avondale. Avondale. 2008. (Images of America Ser.). (ENG., Illus.). 128p. pap. 19.99 (978-0-7385-4843-2(X)) Arcadia Publishing.

Stansfield, Charles A. Haunted Arizona: Ghosts & Strange Phenomena of the Grand Canyon State. 2010. (Haunted Ser.). (ENG., Illus.). 128p. pap. 10.95 (978-0-8117-3620-6(2)) Stackpole Bks.

Steckner, Susie & The Mesa Historical Museum. Cactus League: Spring Training. 2012. (Images of America Ser.). (ENG., Illus.). 128p. pap. 21.99 (978-0-7385-8534-5(3)) Arcadia Publishing.

Steuber, Midge & Jerome Historical Society Archives Staff. Jerome. 2008. (Images of America Ser.). (ENG., Illus.). 128p. pap. 21.99 (978-0-7385-5882-0(6)) Arcadia Publishing.

Stocking, George, photos by. Arizona Wonder & Light. 2007. (Wonder & Light Ser.). (ENG.). 84p. pap. 14.95 (978-0-9777933-8-9(9)) Mountain Trail Pr. LLC.

Suagee, E. K. & San Pedro Valley Arts and Historical Society. Around Benson. 2009. (Images of America Ser.). (ENG., Illus.). 128p. pap. 21.99 (978-0-7385-5892-9(3)) Arcadia Publishing.

Summerhayes, Martha. Vanished Arizona: Recollections of the Army Life by a New England Woman. 2007. (ENG.). 212p. pap. 20.99 (978-1-4346-1429-2(8)); 232p. pap. 22.99 (978-1-4346-1523-7(5)) BiblioBazaar.

—Vanished Arizona Recollections of the A. 2006. pap. (978-1-4068-3140-5(9)) Echo Library.

—Vanished Arizona, Recollections of the Army Life by a New England Woman. 2007. 188p. per. 13.99 (978-1-59547-759-0(4)) NuVision Pubns., LLC.

Sydnor, Douglas B. Scottsdale Architecture. 2010. (Images of America Ser.). (ENG., Illus.). 128p. pap. 21.99 (978-0-7385-7877-4(0)) Arcadia Publishing.

Taylor, Jean. Our Trip to Arizona from Missouri, 1 vol. 2010. 80p. pap. 19.95 (978-1-4489-3824-7(4)) PublishAmerica, Inc.

Tegeler, Dorothy. Moving to Arizona. 5th ed. 2008. (Illus.). 204p. pap. 12.95 (978-1-889786-39-1(X)) Gem Guides Bk. Co.

Thybony, Scott. Walnut Canyon National Monument. 2006. (Illus.). 16p. pap. 4.95 (978-1-877856-72-3(X)) Western National Parks Assn.

Tingley, Joseph, et al. A Geologic & Natural History Tour through Nevada & Arizona along U. S. Highway 93 with GPS Coordinates. 2009. (Illus.). 174p. spiral bd. (978-1-888035-13-1(7)) Nevada Bureau of Mines & Geology.

Trailing Louis L'Amour in Arizona. 2008. (Trailing Louis L'Amour Ser.). (ENG.). pap. (978-0-9650298-5-8(9)) MBAR Publishing.

Trimble, Marshall. Ash Fork. 2008. (Images of America Ser.). (ENG., Illus.). 128p. per. 19.99 (978-0-7385-4832-6(4)) Arcadia Publishing.

Turner, D. L. & Ellis, Catherine H. Latter-day Saints in Mesa. 2009. (Images of America Ser.). (ENG., Illus.). 128p. pap. 21.99 (978-0-7385-5857-8(5)) Arcadia Publishing.

Turner, Jack. Landscapes on Glass: Lantern Slides for the Rainbow Bridge-Monument Valley Expedition. 2010. (Illus.). 127p. pap. (978-1-887805-31-5(1)) Durango Herald Small Pr. Co.

Vail, Tom, et al. Your Guide to the Grand Canyon. 2008. (True North Ser.). 124p. spiral bd. (978-0-89051-501-3(8)) Master Bks.

Vega, Santos C. Mexicans in Tempe. 2009. (Images of America Ser.). (ENG., Illus.). 128p. pap. 21.99 (978-0-7385-7056-3(7)) Arcadia Publishing.

Whitehurst, Patrick. Grand Canyon's Tusayan Village. 2010. (Images of America Ser.). (Illus.). 128p. pap. 21.99 (978-0-7385-7890-3(8)) Arcadia Publishing.

—Williams. 2008. (Images of America Ser.). (Illus.). 128p. pap. 21.99 (978-0-7385-5885-1(0)) Arcadia Publishing.

Wildfang, Frederic B., et al. Tempe. 2010. (Then & Now Ser.). (Illus.). 96p. pap. 21.99 (978-0-7385-7926-9(2)) Arcadia Publishing.

Woodward, Heather. Ghosts of Central Arizona. 2010. (Illus.). 192p. pap. 14.99 (978-0-7643-3387-3(9)) Schiffer Publishing, Ltd.

Woosley, Anne I. & Arizona Historical Society. Early Tucson. 2008. (Images of America Ser.). (ENG., Illus.). 128p. pap. 21.99 (978-0-7385-5646-8(7)) Arcadia Publishing.

Zindell, Deborah. Arizona of Yesteryear. 2009. (ENG.). 192p. 45.00 (978-1-60710-016-4(9), Thunder Bay Pr.) Advantage Pubs. Group.

ARIZONA—DIRECTORIES

Market Data Retrieval, creator. MDR School Directory: Arizona, 51 vols. 29th ed. 2006. (MDR's School Directory Arizona Ser.). 144p. 52.00 (978-1-57953-487-5(2)) Market Data Retrieval.

ARIZONA—ECONOMIC CONDITIONS

Hallock, Dale C. From Cowboys & Sodbusters to a Mega-Residential Community: A Pictorial History of Gilbert, Arizona. 2007. (978-1-57864-440-7(2)) Donning Co. Pubs.

Haskins, Victoria K. Matrons & Maids: Regulating Indian Domestic Service in Tucson, 1914 — 1934. 2012. (ENG.). 240p. 50.00 (978-0-8165-2960-5(4)) Univ. of Arizona Pr.

Pry, Mark E. & Andersen, Fred. Building the Grand Canyon State: Public Works in Arizona History. 2006. per. 24.95 (978-0-9786730-1-7(8)) American Public Works Assn., Arizona Chapter.

Zoellner, Tom. A Safeway in Arizona: What the Gabrielle Giffords Shooting Tells Us about the Grand Canyon State & Life in America. 2011. (ENG.). 288p. (gr. 12). 26.95 (978-0-670-02320-2(5), Viking Adult) Penguin Group (USA) Inc.

ARIZONA—GENEALOGY

Peterman, Melinda Gay & notes. Our Arizona Heritage: Memories of Gay Killian & Max Killian. 2009. 902p. (978-0-9633640-1-2(4)) Killian, C. Max.

ARIZONA—GUIDEBOOKS

Abbott, Lon & Cook, Terri. Geology Underfoot in Northern Arizona. 2007. (Geology Underfoot Ser.). (Illus.). 321p. per. 18.00 (978-0-87842-528-0(4)) Mountain Pr. Publishing Co., Inc.

Abbott, Lon & Freedman, Lew. Weekend Rock: Arizona: Trad & Sport Routes from 5. 0 To 5. 10a. 2006. (Weekend Rock Ser.). (ENG., Illus.). 285p. per. 19.95 (978-0-89886-965-1(X)) Mountaineers Bks., The.

Adams, Sharen & Mallman, Sharon, eds. Arizona Wildlife Viewing Guide. 2007. (Watchable Wildlife (Adventure Publications) Ser.). (Illus.). 240p. pap. 14.95 (978-1-59193-141-6(X)) Adventure Pubns., Inc.

Adkison, Ron. Grand Canyon National Park. 2010. (Best Easy Day Hikes Ser.). (ENG.). 112p. pap. 19.95 (978-0-7627-5971-2(2), Falcon Guides) Globe Pequot Pr., The.

—Grand Canyon National Park: A Guide to the Best Hiking Adventures on the North & South Rims. Adkison, Ben, ed. 3rd ed. 2011. (Regional Hiking Ser.). (ENG., Illus.). 256p. pap. 18.95 (978-0-7627-6060-2(5), Falcon Guides) Globe Pequot Pr., The.

—Grand Staircase — Escalante & the Glen Canyon Region. 2nd ed. 2010. (Best Easy Day Hikes Ser.). (ENG., Illus.). 128p. pap. 9.95 (978-0-7627-6096-1(6), Falcon Guides) Globe Pequot Pr., The.

—Hikes Grand Canyon National Park. 3rd ed. 2010. (Best Easy Day Hikes Ser.). (ENG., Illus.). 96p. pap. 9.95 (978-0-7627-5527-1(X), Falcon Guides) Globe Pequot Pr., The.

Aitchison, Stewart W. Grand Canyon's North Rim & Beyond: A Guide to the North Rim & the Arizona Strip. 2008. (ENG.). 96p. pap. 12.95 (978-0-938216-92-6(9)) Grand Canyon Assn.

Anderson, Richard J. The Heart of the Vortex: An insiders guide to the magic & mystery of Sedona's Vortexes. 2nd exp. ed. 2007. per. 15.95 (978-0-9765897-7-8(X)) Sedona Wind Publishing.

Andres, Dennis. Sedona: The Essential Guide. 2006. (Illus.). viii, 233p. per. 16.95 (978-0-9721202-3-4(8)) Meta Adventures Publishing & DIA Publishing.

Arizona & the Grand Canyon. 3rd ed. 2012. (Insight Guides). (Illus.). 368p. pap. 23.99 (978-1-78005-051-5(8)) APA Publications Services SGP. Dist: Ingram Pub. Services.

Bailey, Christine K. Explorer′s Guide Phoenix, Scottsdale, Sedona & Central Arizona: A Great Destination. 2nd ed. 2011. (Great Destinations Ser.). (ENG., Illus.). 224p. pap. 19.95 (978-1-58157-118-9(6), 157118) Countryman Pr.

Bailowitz, Richard A. & Brodkin, Hank. Finding Butterflies in Arizona: A Guide to the Best Sites. 2007. (Illus.). 233p. per. 22.50 (978-1-55566-352-0(4)) Johnson Bks.

Bicknell, Robin Scott. Arizona's Rock Art: Guide to Rock Art Sites. 2008. 192p. pap. 15.95 (978-1-4327-3329-2(X)) Outskirts Pr., Inc.

Bischoff, Matt C. Arizona Hot Springs. 2nd ed. 2007. (Touring Guides). (ENG., Illus.). 128p. per. 14.95 (978-0-7627-3640-9(2), Falcon Guides) Globe Pequot Pr., The.

Bitler, Teresa. Arizona. 2008. (Great Escapes Ser.). (ENG., Illus.). 192p. pap. 16.95 (978-0-88150-741-6(5), 150741) Countryman Pr.

Blair, Gerry. Arizona: A Guide to 75 of the State's Best Rockhounding Sites. 2nd ed. 2008. (Rockhounding Ser.). (ENG., Illus.). 232p. pap. 15.95 (978-0-7627-4449-7(9), Falcon Guides) Globe Pequot Pr., The.

Blond, Becca, et al. Arizona, New Mexico & the Grand Canyon Trips. 2009. (Regional Guide Ser.). (ENG., Illus.). 352p. pap. 19.99 (978-1-74179-729-9(2)) Lonely Planet Pubns.

Bryant, Kathleen. Moon Grand Canyon. 2011. (Moon Handbooks Ser.). (ENG., Illus.). 284p. pap. 17.99 (978-1-59880-899-5(0)) Avalon Travel Publishing.

Carlson, Jack & Stewart, Elizabeth. Superstition Wilderness Trails East: Hikes, Horse Rides, & History. 2009. 352p. pap. 16.95 (978-1-884224-08-9(3)) Clear Creek Publishing.

Carpenter, Tom. Great Places Arizona. 2011. 512p. pap. 29.95 (978-1-932098-84-6(4)) Wilderness Adventures Pr., Inc.

Christensen, Shane. Frommer's Grand Canyon National Park. (Park Guides). (ENG., 216p. 7th ed. 2010. Illus.). pap. 12.99 (978-0-470-54130-2(X)) 8th ed. 2012. pap. 12.99 (978-1-118-11804-7(9)) Wiley, John & Sons, Inc. (Frommers).

Church, Mike & Church, Terri. Southwest Camping Destinations: RV & Car Camping Destinations in Arizona, New Mexico, & Utah. 2nd ed. 2008.

(Camping Destinations Ser.). (ENG., Illus.). 544p. pap. 19.95 (978-0-9749471-9-8(9)) Rolling Homes Pr.
Dallett, Nancy C. At the Confluence of Change. 2008. (Illus.). 256p. pap. 29.95 (978-1-58369-113-7(8)) Western National Parks Assn.
Discovery Channel (Firm) Staff, contrib. by. Arizona & the Grand Canyon. 2nd ed. 2009. (Insight Guides). (ENG., Illus.). 368p. pap. 23.99 (978-981-282-055-6(8)) APA Publications Services SGP. Dist: Ingram Pub. Services.
Dishner, Jackie, et al. Arizona: Drives, Day Trips & Weekend Excursions. 2009. (Backroads & Byways Ser.). (ENG., Illus.). 216p. pap. 17.95 (978-0-88150-815-4(2), 150815) Countryman Pr.
DK Publishing. DK Eyewitness Travel Guide: Arizona & the Grand Canyon: Arizona & the Grand Canyon. 2012. (Eyewitness travel Guide Ser.). (ENG.). 176p. pap. 20.00 **(978-0-7566-8574-4(5))** Dorling Kindersley Publishing, Inc.
Dorling Kindersley Publishing Staff. Arizona & the Grand Canyon. 2010. (Eyewitness Travel Guides). (ENG.). 176p. pap. 20.00 (978-0-7566-6179-3(X)) Dorling Kindersley Publishing, Inc.
Drickamer, Lee C. & Runge, Peter J. Northern Arizona University: Buildings as History. 2011. (ENG., Illus.). 352p. 30.00 (978-0-8165-2981-0(7)) Univ. of Arizona Pr.
Entertainment Publications, Inc. Staff, compiled by. Tucson 2009 Entertainment Book. 2008. pap. 40.00 (978-1-59878-659-0(8)) Entertainment Pubns., Inc.
Ficker, Jeff. Moon Phoenix, Scottsdale & Sedona. 2010. (Moon Handbooks). (ENG., Illus.). 244p. pap. 17.95 (978-1-59880-247-4(X)) Avalon Travel Publishing.
Fodor's Travel Publications, Inc. Staff. Fodor's Arizona & the Grand Canyon 2012. 2011. (Full-Color Gold Guides). (ENG., Illus.). 544p. pap. 20.99 (978-0-679-00950-4(7), Fodor's) Fodor's Travel Pubns.
—Grand Canyon National Park. 2008. (Pocket Guides). (ENG., Illus.). 192p. pap. 10.95 (978-1-4000-0747-9(X), Fodor's) Fodor's Travel Pubns.
Frank, Susan & Frank, Phil. Grand Canyon: Insider Advice from Ranger Jack. 2008. (ENG., Illus.). 220p. pap. 16.95 (978-1-59880-128-6(7)) Westview Pr.
Gateway To Sedona. Gateway to Sedona Visitor & Web Guide. 2007. per. 8.50 (978-0-9797059-0-8(8)) Trade Winds Advertising Inc.
Ginnodo, Bill & Ginnodo, Celia. Seven Perfect Days in Arizona: A Guided Driving Tour. 2009. (978-0-9656587-4-4(0)) Pride Publications, Inc.
Green, Stewart M. Scenic Driving Arizona. 3rd ed. 2009. (Scenic Driving Ser.). (ENG., Illus.). 224p. pap. 15.95 (978-0-7627-5054-2(5), Falcon Guides) Globe Pequot Pr., The.
Grubbs, Bruce. Arizona: A Guide to Arizona's Greatest Hiking Adventures. 3rd ed. 2007. (State Hiking Ser.). (ENG., Illus.). 368p. per. 16.95 (978-0-7627-4085-7(X), Falcon Guides) Globe Pequot Pr., The.
—Best Easy Day Hikes Flagstaff. 2nd ed. 2009. (Best Easy Day Hikes Ser.). (ENG., Illus.). 96p. pap. 9.95 (978-0-7627-5106-8(4), Falcon Guides) Globe Pequot Pr., The.
—Best Easy Day Hikes Tucson. 2009. (Best Easy Day Hikes Ser.). (ENG., Illus.). 96p. pap. 9.95 (978-0-7627-5250-8(5), Falcon Guides) Globe Pequot Pr., The.
—Grand Canyon National Park Pocket Guide. 2008. (Falcon Pocket Guides Ser.). (ENG., Illus.). 96p. 9.95 (978-0-7627-4805-1(2), Falcon Guides) Globe Pequot Pr., The.
—Hiking Northern Arizona: A Guide to Northern Arizona's Greatest Hiking Adventures. 3rd ed. 2008. (Regional Hiking Ser.). (ENG., Illus.). 320p. pap. 16.95 (978-0-7627-4142-7(2), Falcon Guides) Globe Pequot Pr., The.
—Sedona. 2nd ed. 2009. (Best Easy Day Hikes Ser.). (ENG., Illus.). 112p. pap. 9.95 (978-0-7627-5119-8(3), Falcon Guides) Globe Pequot Pr., The.
Hait, Pam. Day Trips from Phoenix, Tucson, & Flagstaff: Getaway Ideas for the Local Traveler. 11th ed. 2011. (Day Trips Ser.). (ENG.). 304p. pap. 14.95 (978-0-7627-6461-7(9)) Globe Pequot Pr., The.
Harris, Richard. Hidden Arizona: Including Phoenix, Tucson, Sedona, & the Grand Canyon. 6th ed. 2008. (Hidden Travel Ser.). (ENG.). 392p. pap. 18.95 (978-1-56975-657-7(0)) Ulysses Pr.
Hinckley, Jim & James, Kerrick. Ghost Towns of the Southwest: Your Guide to the Historic Mining Camps & Ghost Towns of Arizona & New Mexico. 2010. (ENG., Illus.). 256p. pap. 21.99 (978-0-7603-3221-4(5), 0760332215, Voyageur Pr) MBI Publishing Co. LLC.
Hull, Tim. Moon Arizona. 2011. (Moon Handbooks Ser.). (ENG., Illus.). 448p. pap. 19.99 (978-1-59880-731-8(5)) Avalon Travel Publishing.
—Moon Tucson. 2009. (Moon Handbooks Ser.). (ENG., Illus.). 264p. pap. 17.95 (978-1-59880-208-5(5)) Avalon Travel Publishing.
James, David A., photos by. Cycling Arizona: The Statewide Road Biking Guide. 2007. (Illus.). 280p. pap. 19.95 (978-1-56579-537-2(7)) Westcliffe Pubs.
James, Kerrick, photos by. Backroads of Arizona: Your Guide to Arizona's Most Scenic Backroad Adventures. 2006. (ENG., Illus.). 160p. pap. 21.99 (978-0-7603-2589-3(4), 0760326894, Voyageur Pr) MBI Publishing Co. LLC.
Jordan, Will. Flyfisher's Guide to Arizona. 2008. (Flyfisher's Guides). (Illus.). 294p. per. 28.95 (978-1-932098-54-9(2)) Wilderness Adventures Pr., Inc.
Kaiser, James. Grand Canyon: The Complete Guide - Grand Canyon National Park. 4th ed. 2011. (ENG., Illus.). 304p. pap. 22.95 (978-0-9825172-1-5(1)) Destination Pr.
Kavanagh, James. Arizona Butterflies & Moths: An Introduction to Familiar Species. 2008. (Pocket Naturalist - Waterford Press Ser.). (ENG., Illus.). 1p. 5.95 (978-1-58355-424-1(6)) Waterford Pr., Inc.
Kelsey, Michael R. Hiking & Exploring the Paria River. 5th ed. 2010. (Illus.). 384p. pap. 19.95 (978-0-944510-26-1(4)) Kelsey Publishing.
Kovacevic, Katarina. Phoenix & Scottsdale: The Best Restaurants, Markets & Local Culinary Offerings. 2011. (Food Lovers' Ser.). (ENG.). 288p. pap. 14.95 (978-0-7627-7314-5(6)) Globe Pequot Pr., The.
Kramer, Jon & Martinez, Julie. Arizona Journey Guide: A Driving & Hiking Guide to Ruins, Rock Art, Fossils & Formations. 2006. (Illus.). 272p. pap. 16.95 (978-1-59193-140-9(1)) Adventure Pubns., Inc.
Kreitel, David. Mohave County, AZ Road Guide & Section Maps. 2007. 34.99 (978-0-9796478-0-2(0), MO-6500-3) Mohave VU.
Lane, Brian J. Hikernut's Grand Canyon Companion: A Guide to Hiking & Backpacking the Most Popular Trails into the Canyon: Bright Angel, South Kaibab, & North Kaibab Trails. Bryant, Kathleen, ed. 2008. (ENG.). 96p. per. 9.95 (978-0-9790230-0-2(9)) Sense of Nature, A.
Lonely Planet Staff & Balfour, Amy C. Lonely Planet Arizona, 50 vols. 2nd rev. ed. 2011. (Regional Guide Ser.). (ENG., Illus.). 360p. pap. 22.99 (978-1-74059-675-6(7)) Lonely Planet Pubns.
Mangum, Richard. Sedona Hikes: 130 Day Hikes & 5 Vortex Sites around Sedona, Arizona. 9th rev. ed. 2007. Orig. Title: Sedona Hikes. 256p. pap. 16.95 (978-1-891517-08-2(2)) Hexagon Pr., Inc.
Mangum, Richard K. Flagstaff Hikes: 97 Day Hikes around Flagstaff, Arizona. 6th rev. ed. 2007. (Illus.). 192p. per. 16.95 (978-1-891517-04-4(X)) Hexagon Pr., Inc.
Manning. What Is Arizona Really Like? pap. 6.95 (978-0-918080-96-7(7)) Rio Nuevo Pubs.
Martin, Todd. Arizona Technical Canyoneering: Rappelling, Swimming & Exploring the Remote & Beautiful Canyons of Arizona. 2007. (Illus.). 256p. per. 19.95 (978-0-9789614-1-1(2), Todd's Desert Hiking Guide) Canyoneering USA.
Martin, Tom. Day Hikes from the River: A Guide to 100 Hikes from Camps along the Colorado River in the Grand Canyon. 4th ed. 2010. (Illus.). 244p. pap. 21.95 (978-0-9795055-4-6(2)) Vishnu Temple Pr.
Martin, Tom & Whitis, Duwain. Guide to the Colorado River in the Grand Canyon. 4th ed. 2008. (Illus.). 110p. spiral bd. (978-0-9776749-9-2(1)) RiverMaps, LLC.
Massey, Peter, et al. Arizona Trails Northeast Region. 2007. (Illus.). 255p. per. 19.95 (978-1-930193-02-4(5)) Adler Publishing Co.
—Arizona Trails South Region. 2007. (Trails Ser.). (Illus.). 225p. per. 24.95 (978-1-930193-03-1(3)) Adler Publishing Co.
—Arizona Trails West Region. 2006. (Illus.). 201p. per. 19.95 (978-1-930193-00-0(9)) Adler Publishing Co.
Maxa, Christine. Arizona - Explorer's Guide. 2nd ed. 2010. (Explorer's Guides). (ENG., Illus.). 360p. pap. 21.95 (978-0-88150-894-9(2), 150894) Countryman Pr.
—An Explorer's Guide: Arizona. 2007. (Explorer's Guide Arizona Ser.). (ENG., Illus.). 432p. per. 18.95 (978-0-88150-715-7(6)) Countryman Pr.
Miner, Carrie & Frasure, Carrie. Arizona: A Guide to Unique Places. 7th ed. 2009. (Off the Beaten Path Ser.). (ENG., Illus.). 192p. pap. 14.95 (978-0-7627-5021-4(9)) Globe Pequot Pr., The.
Mitchell, David N. The Insider's Arizona Guidebook. 2006. (Arizona Highways: Travel Arizona Collection). (Illus.). 416p. pap. 22.95 (978-1-932082-24-1(7)) Arizona Highways.
Mitchell, James R. Gem Trails of Arizona. 2010. (Illus.). 272p. pap. 14.95 (978-1-889786-47-6(0)) Gem Guides Bk. Co.
Mullaly, Katie & Ohlde, J. Patrick. Scare-izona: A Guide to Arizona's Legendary Haunts. 2008. (Illus.). 224p. pap. 14.95 (978-0-7643-2844-2(1)) Schiffer Publishing, Ltd.
Muller, Seth. Canyon Crossing: Experiencing Grand Canyon from Rim to Rim. 2011. (978-1-934656-13-6(5)); (ENG.). 272p. pap. 16.95 (978-1-934656-11-2(9)) Grand Canyon Assn.
Negri, Sam. Arizona Highways: the Back Roads. 5th ed. 2007. (Arizona Highways: Travel Arizona Collection). (Illus.). 248p. pap. 19.95 (978-1-932082-77-7(8)) Arizona Highways.
Olmon, Kirstin & Phillips, Kelly. Arizona. 2008. (Best in Tent Camping Ser.). (ENG., Illus.). 176p. pap. 14.95 (978-0-89732-648-3(2)) Menasha Ridge Pr., Inc.
Padegimas, Tony. Day & Overnight Hikes: Tonto National Forest. 2008. (Day & Overnight Hikes Ser.). (ENG., Illus.). 176p. pap. 14.95 (978-0-89732-639-1(3)) Menasha Ridge Pr., Inc.
—Five-Star Trails: Flagstaff & Sedona: Your Guide to the Area's Most Beautiful Hikes. 2011. (Five-Star Trails Ser.). (ENG., Illus.). 240p. pap. 15.95 (978-0-89732-927-9(9)) Menasha Ridge Pr., Inc.
Preston, Thomas & Preston, Elizabeth. The Double Eagle Guide to Western State Parks: Volume 4 Desert Southwest, 4 of 6. 4th ed. 2007. (Double Eagle Guides Ser.: 4). 21.95 (978-1-932417-18-0(4), Double Eagle Guides) Discovery Publishing.
Rails-to-Trails Conservancy Staff. Rail-Trails West: California, Arizona, & Nevada - The Official Rails-to-Trails Conservancy Guidebook. 2009. (Rail-Trails Ser.). (ENG.). 264p. pap. 16.95 (978-0-89997-489-7(9)) Wilderness Pr.
Samson, Karl. Frommer's Arizona & the Grand Canyon 2012. 7th ed. 2011. (Frommer's Colour Complete Guides). (ENG., Illus.). 576p. pap. 21.99 (978-1-118-01727-2(7), Frommers) Wiley, John & Sons, Inc.
Smith, Julian. Navajo & Hopi Country. 2009. (Moon Spotlight Ser.). (ENG.). 60p. pap. 7.95 (978-1-59880-270-2(4)) Avalon Travel Publishing.
Steele-Carlin, Sherril. LifeTips 101 Grand Canyon Tips. 2007. 9.99 (978-1-60275-030-2(0)) LifeTips.
Tenny, Ted. Goldfield Mountain Hikes. 2006. (Illus.). 192p. pap. 16.95 (978-1-889786-33-9(0)) Gem Guides Bk. Co.
Thybony, Scott. The Painted Desert: Land of Wind & Stone. 2006. (Desert Places Ser.). (ENG., Illus.). 96p. pap. 14.95 (978-0-8165-2480-8(7)) Univ. of Arizona Pr.
Treat, Wesley. Weird Arizona: Your Travel Guide to Arizona's Local Legends & Best Kept Secrets. 2007. (Weird Ser.). (ENG., Illus.). 256p. 19.95 (978-1-4027-3938-5(9)) Sterling Publishing Co., Inc.
Votto, Mary Paganelli. Insiders' Guide to Tucson, 7th. 7th ed. 2012. (Insiders' Guide Ser.). (ENG., Illus.). 400p. pap. 16.95 (978-0-7627-7324-4(3), Insiders' Guide) Globe Pequot Pr., The.
Wallner, Jeff & Urreiztieta, Melissa. Cactus Forest Drive: Saguaro National Park. 2006. (Illus.). 12p. 2.00 (978-1-58369-096-3(4)) Western National Parks Assn.
Ward, Greg & Rough Guides Staff. The Grand Canyon - Rough Guide. 3rd ed. 2011. (ENG., Illus.). 244p. pap. 19.99 (978-1-84836-744-9(9)) Rough Guides, Ltd. GBR. Dist: Dorling Kindersley Publishing, Inc.
Warren, Scott S. 100 Classic Hikes in Arizona. 3rd rev. ed. 2007. (100 Hikes Ser.). (ENG., Illus.). 253p. pap. 21.95 (978-1-59485-025-7(9)) Mountaineers Bks., The.
Weir, Bill. National Geographic Traveler: Arizona, 4th Edition. 4th ed. 2011. (National Geographic Traveler Ser.). (ENG., Illus.). 272p. pap. 22.95 (978-1-4262-0713-6(1), National Geographic) National Geographic Society.
Wenk, Elizabeth. One Best Hike: Grand Canyon: Everything You Need to Know to Successfully Hike from the Rim to the River - & Back. 2010. (One Best Hike Ser). (ENG., Illus.). 120p. pap. 14.95 (978-0-89997-491-0(0)) Wilderness Pr.
Westerman, Kim, et al. Tucson. 2009. (Great Destinations Ser.). (ENG., Illus.). 232p. pap. 19.95 (978-1-58157-046-5(5), 157046) Countryman Pr.
Williams, Tyler. Arizona Summits South. 2009. pap. 19.95 (978-0-9664919-5-1(5)) Funhog Pr.
—Paddling Arizona. 2007. 256p. pap. 19.95 (978-0-9664919-4-4(7)) Funhog Pr.
Wilson, Jeanne, et al. Arizona Trails Central Region. 2006. (Illus.). 251p. per. 19.95 (978-1-930193-01-7(7)) Adler Publishing Co.
Witt, Greg. Exploring Havasupai: A Guide to the Heart of the Grand Canyon. 2010. (ENG., Illus.). 208p. pap. 19.95 (978-0-89732-654-4(7)) Menasha Ridge Pr., Inc.
Woodward, Heather. Arizona's Haunted Hotspots. 2011. (Illus.). 160p. (978-0-7643-3748-2(3), Schiffer Publishing Ltd) Schiffer Publishing, Ltd.
Yanagihara, Wendy. Grand Canyon National Park, 36 vols. 3rd rev. ed. 2012. (National Parks Ser.). (ENG., Illus.). 256p. pap. 19.99 (978-1-74179-404-5(8)) Lonely Planet Pubns.
Youman, Becky. Open Road's Best of Arizona. 3rd ed. 2011. (ENG., Illus.). 240p. pap. 12.95 (978-1-59360-136-2(0)) Open Road Publishing.
Young, Mary E. Arizona Waterways: A pocket guide to boating & fishing in Arizona. 2007. (978-0-9776524-1-9(6)) Argan Publishers LLC.

ARIZONA—HISTORY

Aitchison, Stewart W. Grand Canyon's North Rim & Beyond: A Guide to the North Rim & the Arizona Strip. 2008. (ENG.). 96p. pap. 12.95 (978-0-938216-92-6(9)) Grand Canyon Assn.
Anderson, Lisa A., et al. Mesa. 2008. (Images of America Ser.). (ENG., Illus.). 128p. per. 21.99 (978-0-7385-4842-5(1)) Arcadia Publishing.
Anderson, Parker & Ruffner, Elisabeth. The Elks Opera House. 2012. (Images of America Ser.). (ENG., Illus.). 128p. pap. 21.99 **(978-0-7385-8542-0(4))** Arcadia Publishing.
Annerino, John. Arizona: A Photographic Tribute. 2012. (ENG., Illus.). 128p. 17.95 (978-0-7627-7425-8(8)) Globe Pequot Pr., The.
Ascarza, William. Southeastern Arizona Mining Towns. 2011. (Images of America Ser.). (Illus.). 128p. pap. 21.99 **(978-0-7385-8516-1(5))** Arcadia Publishing.
Ascarza, William. Tucson Mountains. 2010. (Images of America Ser.). (ENG., Illus.). 128p. pap. 21.99 (978-0-7385-7923-8(8)) Arcadia Publishing.
Audretsch, Robert W. Grand Canyon's Phantom Ranch. 2012. (Images of America Ser.). (ENG., Illus.). 128p. pap. 21.99 **(978-0-7385-8525-3(4))** Arcadia Publishing.
Babbitt, James E. & DeGraff III, John G. Flagstaff. 2009. (Images of America Ser.). (ENG., Illus.). 128p. pap. 21.99 (978-0-7385-7115-7(6)) Arcadia Publishing.
Bakarich, Sarah Grace. Gunsmoke: The True Story of Old Tombstone. 2011. 202p. 44.95 **(978-1-258-00322-7(8))** Literary Licensing, LLC.
Barnes, Mary Ellen. The Road to Mount Lemmon: A Father, A Family, & the Making of Summerhaven. 2009. (ENG., Illus.). 224p. pap. 17.95 (978-0-8165-2781-6(4)) Univ. of Arizona Pr.
Barr, Betty. Around Sonoita. 2009. (Images of America Ser.). (ENG., Illus.). 128p. pap. 21.99 (978-0-7385-7143-0(1)) Arcadia Publishing.
Bates, Albert R. Jack Swilling: Arizona's Most Lied about Pioneer. 2007. 128p. per. 12.95 (978-1-58736-965-0(6)) Wheatmark.
Bates, Denise E., et al. Goodyear. 2010. (Images of America Ser.). (ENG., Illus.). 128p. pap. 21.99 (978-0-7385-7117-1(2)) Arcadia Publishing.
Beaver, Deanna & The Parker Area Historical Society. Parker. 2008. 128p. pap. 19.99 (978-0-7385-5638-3(6)) Arcadia Publishing.
Berger, Todd R., ed. Reflections of Grand Canyon Historians: Ideas, Arguments, & First-Person Accounts. 2008. (ENG.). 224p. pap. 15.00 (978-1-934656-00-6(3)) Grand Canyon Assn.
Blanton, Shirley R. Tempe. 2007. (Images of America Ser.). (Illus.). 127p. per. 19.99 (978-0-7385-4888-3(X)) Arcadia Publishing.
Brock, Patricia & Maricopa Historical Society. Maricopa. 2011. (Images of America Ser.). (Illus.). 128p. pap. 21.99 (978-0-7385-7995-5(5)) Arcadia Publishing.
Brown, Stanley C. The Tale of Two Rivers: Pioneer Settlement in Arizona. 2007. 206p. pap. 24.95 (978-1-60441-300-7(X)) PublishAmerica, Inc.
Brownold, Tom. The Grandest Ride. 2010. (ENG., Illus.). 48p. pap. 8.95 (978-1-933855-43-1(6)) Rio Nuevo Pubs.
Burgess, Nancy & Ariz, Karen Despain on behalf of the Yavapai County. Around Yavapai County: Celebrating Arizona's Centennial. 2011. (Images of America Ser.). (ENG., Illus.). 128p. pap. 21.99 **(978-0-7385-7962-7(9))** Arcadia Publishing.
Burruel, Jose Maria. Mexicans in Scottsdale. 2007. (Images of America Ser.). (ENG., Illus.). 128p. per. 19.99 (978-0-7385-4826-5(X)) Arcadia Publishing.
Burton, Lance W. The Wigwam Resort. 2007. (Images of America Ser.). (ENG., Illus.). 128p. per. 21.99 (978-0-7385-4825-8(1)) Arcadia Publishing.
Chadwick, W. Guy. God in the Foundations of Arizona Government. 2007. (Illus.). 180p. pap. 12.00 (978-0-9795707-0-4(0)) Arizona Call to Prayer.
Clark, Victoria. A Journey Through Northern Arizona. 2008. (Illus.). 128p. pap. 24.99 (978-0-7643-3010-0(1)) Schiffer Publishing, Ltd.
Cleere, Jan. Outlaw Tales of Arizona, 2nd: True Stories of the Grand Canyon State's Most Infamous Crooks, Culprits, & Cutthroats. 2nd ed. 2012. (Outlaw Tales Ser.). (ENG., Illus.). 176p. pap. 14.95 **(978-0-7627-7233-9(6)**, TwoDot) Globe Pequot Pr., The.
Collins, Thomas P. Stage-Struck Settlers in the Sun-Kissed Land: The Amateur Theatre in Territorial Prescott, 1868-1903. 2007. 132p. per. 12.95 (978-1-58736-783-0(1)) Wheatmark.
Colwell-Chanthaphonh, Chip. Massacre at Camp Grant: Forgetting & Remembering Apache History. 2007. (ENG., Illus.). 176p. 40.00 (978-0-8165-2584-3(6)); pap. 17.95 (978-0-8165-2585-0(4)) Univ. of Arizona Pr.
Conklin, Les & Greater Pinnacle Peak Association. Pinnacle Peak. 2011. (Images of America Ser.). (ENG., Illus.). 128p. pap. 21.99 (978-0-7385-7984-9(X)) Arcadia Publishing.
Costa Mesa Historical Society. Early Costa Mesa. 2009. (Images of America Ser.). (ENG., Illus.). 128p. pap. 21.99 (978-0-7385-6976-5(3)) Arcadia Publishing.
Cowan, Bill. Verde Valley. 2011. (Images of America Ser.). (ENG., Illus.). 128p. pap. 21.99 **(978-0-7385-8514-7(9))** Arcadia Publishing.
Crago, Jody A., et al. Chandler. 2012. (Images of America Ser.). (ENG., Illus.). 128p. pap. 21.99 **(978-0-7385-8521-5(1))** Arcadia Publishing.
Creighton, Kimberly J. Mt. Baldy. 2009. (Images of America Ser.). (ENG., Illus.). 128p. pap. 21.99 (978-0-7385-5999-5(7)) Arcadia Publishing.
Cross, Jean. Prescott Valley. 2009. (Images of America Ser.). (ENG., Illus.). 128p. pap. 21.99 (978-0-7385-7070-9(2)) Arcadia Publishing.
Crutchfield, James A. Arizona: Thirty-Six Remarkable Events That Shaped History. 2nd ed. 2009. (It Happened in Ser.). (ENG., Illus.). 160p. pap. 14.95 (978-0-7627-5420-5(6)) Globe Pequot Pr., The.
Cummings, Laura L. Pachucas & Pachucos in Tucson: Situated Border Lives. 2009. (ENG., Illus.). 264p. pap. 34.95 (978-0-8165-2737-3(7)) Univ. of Arizona Pr.
Cutting, Robert. Trouble in Tombstone. 2007. (Timeline Ser.). (Illus.). 48p. pap. 8.99 (978-1-4190-4406-9(0)) Houghton Mifflin Harcourt Supplemental Pubs.
DeGraff III, John G. Flagstaff. 2011. (Postcard History Ser.). (Illus.). 128p. pap. 21.99 **(978-0-7385-8510-9(6))** Arcadia Publishing.
DeSoucy, M. David. Arizona Rangers. 2008. (Images of America Ser.). (ENG., Illus.). 128p. per. 21.99 (978-0-7385-4831-9(6)) Arcadia Publishing.
Downey, Lynn & Desert Caballeros Western Museum. Wickenburg. 2012. (Images of America Ser.). (ENG., Illus.). 128p. pap. 21.99 **(978-0-7385-8504-8(1))** Arcadia Publishing.
Ellis, Catherine. Oracle & the San Pedro River Valley. 2008. (Images of America Ser.). (ENG., Illus.). 128p. pap. 21.99 (978-0-7385-5639-0(4)) Arcadia Publishing.
Ellis, Catherine H. Snowflake. 2008. (Images of America Ser.). (ENG., Illus.). 128p. pap. 19.99 (978-0-7385-4838-8(3)) Arcadia Publishing.
Ellis, Catherine H. & Turner, D. L. The White Mountains of Apache County. 2010. (Images of America Ser.). (Illus.). 128p. pap. 21.99 (978-0-7385-6690-0(X)) Arcadia Publishing.
Elsner, Jodey & Peoria Arizona Historical Society. Peoria. 2010. (Images of America Ser.). (Illus.). 128p. pap. 21.99 (978-0-7385-7110-2(5)) Arcadia Publishing.
Eppinga, Jane. Around Tombstone: Ghost Towns & Gunfights. 2009. (Images of America Ser.). (ENG., Illus.). 128p. pap. 21.99 (978-0-7385-7127-0(X)) Arcadia Publishing.
Fudala, Joan. Desert Highlands: A Vision in the Desert: 25th Anniversary Commemorative Tribute, 1983-2008. 2008. (978-1-57864-504-6(2)) Donning Co. Pubs.
—Golf in Scottsdale. 2008. (Images of Sports Ser.). (ENG., Illus.). 128p. pap. 19.99 (978-0-7385-5632-1(7)) Arcadia Publishing.
—Scottsdale. 2007. (Images of America Ser.). (ENG., Illus.). 128p. per. 21.99 (978-0-7385-4875-3(8)) Arcadia Publishing.
Gartell, Barry, ed. Times Past: Reflections from Arizona History. 2008. (ENG., Illus.). 263p. 49.95 (978-0-615-25117-2(X)) Arizona Capitol Times.
Giordano, Gerard. The Verde River: Bartlett & Horseshoe Dams. 2010. (Images of America Ser.). 128p. pap. 21.99 (978-0-7385-7889-7(4)) Arcadia Publishing.
Goodwin, Kathy, creator. Zopilote Press: Exploring the History of East Santa Cruz County, Volume II. 2007. (Illus.). 80p. per. 18.00 (978-0-9779694-3-2(6)) Zopilote.
Grady, Patrick. Homesteading along the Creek: Pioneer Life in Cave Creek, Arizona, 1890-1940. 2009. pap. 20.00 (978-0-615-33059-4(2)) Arizona Pioneer Pr.
Griffith, Jim. A Border Runs Through It: Journeys in Regional History & Folklore. 2011. (Illus.). 128p. 17.95 **(978-1-933855-62-2(2))** Rio Nuevo Pubs.

Guinn, Jeff. The Last Gunfight: The Real Story of the Shootout at the O. K. Corral-And How It Changed the American West. 2011. (ENG., Illus.). 416p. 27.00 (978-1-4391-5424-3(4)) Simon & Schuster.

Haak, Wilbur A., et al. Globe. 2008. (Images of America Ser.). (ENG., Illus.). 128p. per. 21.99 (978-0-7385-4833-3(2)) Arcadia Publishing.

Hallock, Dale C. From Cowboys & Sodbusters to a Mega-Residential Community: A Pictorial History of Gilbert, Arizona. 2007. (978-1-57864-440-7(2)) Donning Co. Pubs.

Hatch, Jo Ann. Lore & Legend: Adventure & History in the White Mountains of Arizona. 2007. (Illus.). 172p. per. 14.95 (978-0-9773648-6-2(0)) Legend eXpress Publishing.

Hayostek, Cindy. Douglas. 2009. (Images of America Ser.). (ENG., Illus.). 128p. pap. 21.99 (978-0-7385-7065-5(6)) Arcadia Publishing.

Hefley, Flood. Grand Canyon Trivia Trek. 2010. 200p. pap. 16.95 (978-1-55566-430-5(X)) Johnson Bks.

Heidinger, Lisa Schnebly & Trevillyan, Janeen. Sedona. 2007. (Images of America Ser.). (ENG., Illus.). 128p. per. 21.99 (978-0-7385-4800-5(6)) Arcadia Publishing.

Henry, Bonnie. Tucson Memories. 2006. (978-1-59152-034-4(7)) Arizona Daily Star.

Herman, Daniel Justin. Hell on the Range: A Story of Honor, Conscience, & the American West. 2010. (Lamar Series in Western History Ser.). (ENG., Illus.). 400p. 45.00 (978-0-300-13736-1(2)) Yale Univ. Pr.

Hubbard, Samuel & Gilmore, Charles W. Biofortean Reprint: The Doheny Scientific Expedition to the Hava Supai Canyon, Northern Arizona. 2011. 24p. pap. 8.00 **(978-1-61646-068-6(7))** Coachwhip Pubns.

Hudnall, Ken & Hudnall, Sharon. Spirits of the Border: The History & Mystery of Arizona. 2007. 260p. per. 16.95 (978-1-933951-10-2(9)) Omega Pr.

Hunt, Sharon E. Vail & Colossal Cave Mountain Park. 2007. (Images of America Ser.). (Illus.). 128p. per. 19.99 (978-0-7385-4882-1(0)) Arcadia Publishing.

Huso, Jani, et al. Show Low. 2009. (Images of America Ser.). (ENG., Illus.). 128p. pap. 21.99 (978-0-7385-7138-6(5)) Arcadia Publishing.

Keleher, William. Turmoil in New Mexico, 1846-1868. 2007. 592p. per. 40.00 (978-0-86534-621-5(6)) Sunstone Pr.

Kelly, William J. Arizona in The '50s: Captain James H. Tevis. 2007. 135p. per. 25.00 (978-0-9790261-1-9(3)) Barr, Betty.

Kelsey, Michael R. Hiking & Exploring the Paria River. 5th ed. 2010. (Illus.). 384p. pap. 19.95 (978-0-944510-26-1(4)) Kelsey Publishing.

Killebrew, Helen & Verde Historical Society. Cottonwood. 2011. (Images of America Ser.). (Illus.). 128p. pap. 21.99 **(978-0-7385-7999-3(8))** Arcadia Publishing.

Kinsley, Shaw. Tubac. 2009. 128p. pap. 21.99 (978-0-7385-7864-4(9)); (ENG., Illus.). 15p. pap. 7.99 (978-0-7385-7869-9(X)) Arcadia Publishing.

Kiser, William S. Turmoil on the Rio Grande: History of the Mesilla Valley, 1846-1865. 2011. (Elma Dill Russell Spencer Series in the West & Southwest Ser.). (ENG., Illus.). 304p. 35.00 (978-1-60344-296-1(0)) Texas A&M Univ. Pr.

Klump, Kathy & Tenney, Peta-Anne. Willcox. 2009. (Images of America Ser.). (ENG., Illus.). 128p. pap. 21.99 (978-0-7385-7177-5(6)) Arcadia Publishing.

Knuckey, Gene. Chrysotile Arizona 1914 To 1945. 2007. (ENG.). 60p. per. 11.95 (978-1-58736-769-4(6)) Wheatmark.

Kutner, E. W., et al. McMullen Valley. 2008. (Images of America Ser.). (ENG., Illus.). 128p. pap. 21.99 (978-0-7385-5851-6(6)) Arcadia Publishing.

Lamberton, Ken. Dry River: Stories of Life, Death, & Redemption on the Santa Cruz. 2011. (ENG., Illus.). 288p. pap. 24.95 (978-0-8165-2921-6(3)) Univ. of Arizona Pr.

Lauer, Charles D. Tales of Arizona Territory. 2008. (Illus.). 160p. (Orig.). pap. 14.95 (978-0-914846-47-5(7), Golden West Publishers) American Traveler Pr.

Lawton, Paul J. Old Tucson Studios. 2008. (Images of America Ser.). (ENG., Illus.). 128p. pap. 21.99 (978-0-7385-5629-1(7)) Arcadia Publishing.

Ledoux, Gary. Nantan: The Life & Times of John P. Clum Vol. 2. 2008. 416p. 49.00 (978-1-4251-7425-5(6)) Trafford Publishing.

Lindahl, Larry, photos by. Arizona Kicks on Route 66. 2012. pap. **(978-1-933855-76-9(2)**, Rio Nuevo Pubs.) Rio Nuevo Pubs.

Lopez, Kathy & Morgan Ranch Park Association Inc. Williamson Valley Road. 2011. (Images of America Ser.). (ENG., Illus.). 128p. pap. 21.99 **(978-0-7385-7987-0(4))** Arcadia Publishing.

Lowe, Sam. Mysteries & Legends of Arizona: True Stories of the Unsolved & Unexplained. 2010. (Mysteries & Legends Ser.). (ENG., Illus.). 208p. pap. 14.95 (978-0-7627-5546-2(6)) Globe Pequot Pr., The.

Lowe, Sam. Speaking Ill of the Dead: Jerks in Arizona History. 2012. (Speaking Ill of the Dead: Jerks in Histo Ser.). (ENG., Illus.). 240p. pap. 16.95 **(978-0-7627-2815-2(9))** Globe Pequot Pr., The.

Luttrell, Jean. The Last Old-Time Ranger: John H. Riffey. 2007. (Illus.). 152p. pap. 14.95 (978-0-9795055-1-5(8)) Vishnu Temple Pr.

Lynch, Mona Pauline. Sunbelt Justice: Arizona & the Transformation of American Punishment. 2009. (Critical Perspectives on Crime & Law Ser.). (ENG., Illus.). 280p. 70.00 (978-0-8047-6284-7(8)); pap. 24.95 (978-0-8047-6285-4(6)) Stanford Univ. Pr.

Mallett, Daryl F. Falcon Field. 2009. 128p. pap. 21.99 (978-0-7385-7137-9(7)) Arcadia Publishing.

Marriott, Barbara & Oro Valley Historical Society. Oro Valley. 2008. (Images of America Ser.). (Illus.). 127p. per. 19.99 (978-0-7385-4834-0(0)) Arcadia Publishing.

Masich, Andrew E. The Civil War in Arizona: The Story of the California Volunteers, 1861-1865. 2008. (ENG., Illus.). 384p. (C). pap. 26.95 (978-0-8061-3900-5(5)) Univ. of Oklahoma Pr.

McBlane, Dick. The Chandler, Arizona Fire Department: A History of Service & Tradition. 2012. **(978-1-57864-737-8(1))** Donning Co. Pubs.

McClintock, James H. Mormon Settlement in Arizona. 2008. 356p. 31.99 (978-0-554-23063-4(1)) BiblioBazaar.

—Mormon Settlement in Arizona: A Record of Peaceful Conquest of the Desert. 2007. (ENG.). 318p. pap. 23.99 (978-1-4264-3657-4(2)); 354p. pap. 26.99 (978-1-4264-3714-4(5)) BiblioBazaar.

McIntyre, Allan J., et al. The Tohono O'Odham & Pimeria Alta. 2008. (Images of America Ser.). (ENG., Illus.). 128p. pap. 21.99 (978-0-7385-5633-8(5)) Arcadia Publishing.

McKeand, Bret & Sun Cities Area Historical Society. Sun City. 2011. (Images of America Ser.). (Illus.). 128p. pap. 21.99 (978-0-7385-7951-1(3)) Arcadia Publishing.

M'Closkey, Kathy. Swept under the Rug: A Hidden History of Navajo Weaving. 2008. (University of Arizona Southwest Centre Ser.). (ENG., Illus.). 336p. (C). pap. 27.95 (978-0-8263-2832-8(6)) Univ. of New Mexico Pr.

McNeill, Joe. Arizona's Little Hollywood: Sedona & Northern Arizona's Forgotten Film History 1923-1973. 2010. 60.00 (978-0-615-32321-3(9)) Bar225 Media LLC.

Meck, Verlyne. Buckeye. (Then & Now Ser.). (ENG., Illus.). 2010. 96p. pap. 21.99 (978-0-7385-7924-5(6)) 2007. 128p. per. 19.99 (978-0-7385-4889-0(8)) Arcadia Publishing.

Messersmith, Dan W. Kingman. 2010. (Images of America Ser.). (Illus.). 128p. pap. 21.99 (978-0-7385-7930-6(0)) Arcadia Publishing.

Michael, R. Massacre at Wickenburg: Arizona's Greatest Mystery. 2007. (ENG., Illus.). 168p. pap. 14.95 (978-0-7627-4453-4(7), Falcon Guides) Globe Pequot Pr., The.

Moore, Robert J. The Civilian Conservation Corps in Arizona's Rim Country: Working in the Woods. 2006. (ENG., Illus.). 176p. 34.95 (978-0-87417-677-3(8)) Univ. of Nevada Pr.

Mowry, Sylvester. Arizona & Sonora: The Geography, History, & Resources of the Silver Region of North America. 2006. (ENG.). 256p. per. 23.99 (978-1-4255-2174-5(6)) MPublishing.

Murray, Vincent. Gila Bend. 2012. (Images of America Ser.). (ENG., Illus.). 128p. pap. 21.99 **(978-0-7385-8475-1(4))** Arcadia Publishing.

Nelson, Robert. Early Yuma. 2006. (Images of America Ser.). (ENG., Illus.). 128p. pap. 21.99 (978-0-7385-4857-9(X)) Arcadia Publishing.

Nickell, Anna, et al. Pearce & Sunsites. 2011. (Images of America Ser.). (ENG., Illus.). 128p. pap. 21.99 **(978-0-7385-8473-7(8))** Arcadia Publishing.

Nickens, Paul & Nickens, Kathleen. Native Americans of Arizona. 2007. (Postcard History Ser.). (ENG., Illus.). 128p. per. 21.99 (978-0-7385-4884-5(7)) Arcadia Publishing.

—Old San Carlos. 2008. (Images of America Ser.). (Illus.). 128p. pap. 21.99 (978-0-7385-5891-2(5)) Arcadia Publishing.

Poston, Charles D. Building a State in Apache Land. 2009. 60p. pap. (978-1-4099-5719-5(5)) Dodo Pr.

—Building a State in Apache Land. 2006. pap. (978-1-4068-1218-3(8)) Echo Library.

Powers, Richard L. & the Superstition Mountain Historical Society, and the Gila County Historical Society Museum. Apache Trail. 2008. (Images of America Ser.). (ENG., Illus.). 128p. pap. 21.99 (978-0-7385-5862-2(1)) Arcadia Publishing.

Pyle, Jayne Peace & Pyle, Jinx. Payson. 2010. (Images of America Ser.). (Illus.). 128p. pap. 21.99 (978-0-7385-8457-7(6)) Arcadia Publishing.

Ratz, Thomas Alan. Grand Canyon National Park. 2009. (Postcard History Ser.). (ENG., Illus.). 128p. pap. 21.99 (978-0-7385-7856-9(8)) Arcadia Publishing.

Reiser, Ronald J. Arizona Passport. 2007. 36p. pap. (978-0-9625515-2-9(X)) Reiser, R. J. & Co.

Rio Nuevo Publishers, ed. Arizona: Scenic Wonders of the Grand Canyon State. 2011. (Illus.). 80p. pap. 11.95 (978-1-933855-44-8(4)) Rio Nuevo Pubs.

Rowe, Jeremy. Arizona Real Photo Postcards: A History & Portfolio. 2007. (ENG., Illus.). 182p. 45.00 (978-1-887694-26-1(9)); pap. 35.00 (978-1-887694-29-2(3)) Mautz, Carl Publishing.

Ruland-Thorne, Kate. Gold, Greed & Glory: The Territorial History of Prescott & the Verde Valley 1864-1912. 2007. 284p. per. 27.95 (978-1-4137-9322-2(3)) PublishAmerica, Inc.

Ryan Bryson, Janice & Shappee Wood, Kathleen. Irish Arizona. 2009. (Images of America Ser.). (ENG., Illus.). 128p. pap. 21.99 (978-0-7385-5647-5(5)) Arcadia Publishing.

Salge, David. Around San Tan Mountain. 2007. (Images of America Ser.). (ENG., Illus.). 128p. per. 19.99 (978-0-7385-4895-1(2)) Arcadia Publishing.

Salmon, M. H. Gila Libre! New Mexico's Last Wild River. 2008. (ENG., Illus.). 141p. pap. 19.95 (978-0-8263-4082-5(2)) Univ. of New Mexico Pr.

Sanchez, Joseph P., et al. Between Two Countries: A History of Coronado National Mmemorial 1939-1990. 2007. (Illus.). 356p. 32.95 (978-1-890689-18-6(1), Rio Grande Bks.) LPD Pr.

Sauder, Robert A. The Yuma Reclamation Project: Irrigation, Indian Allotment, & Settlement along the Lower Colorado River. 2009. (ENG., Illus.). 296p. 44.95 (978-0-87417-783-1(9)) Univ. of Nevada Pr.

Schneider, Silke. Arizona's Spanish Barbs: The Story of the Wilbur-Cruce Horses. 2007. 108p. per. 25.95 (978-1-59800-849-4(8)) Outskirts Pr., Inc.

Schumacher, Carol A. & Tomerlin, Danielle M. Superior & Queen Valley. 2011. (Images of America Ser.). (Illus.). 128p. pap. 21.99 (978-0-7385-7965-8(3)) Arcadia Publishing.

Sheridan, Thomas E. Arizona: A History. 2012. (Southwest Center Ser.). (ENG., Illus.). 488p. pap. 26.95 **(978-0-8165-0693-4(0))** Univ. of Arizona Pr.

Sletten, Carol & Kramer, Eric. Story of the American West: Told Through the Lives of Apaches, Mountain Men, Hispanics, Soldiers, Mormons, Cowboys, Blacks, Outlaws & Others, Who Struggled in Arizona's White Mountains, One of the Last Untamed Regions of the West. 2011. (ENG., Illus.). 448p. pap. 26.95 (978-0-615-41476-8(1)) Wolf Water Pr.

Snell, Dawn & Casa Grande Valley Historical Society. Casa Grande. 2011. (Images of America Ser.). (Illus.). 128p. pap. 21.99 **(978-0-7385-7953-5(X))** Arcadia Publishing.

Sperlin, O. B. & Miles, Charles. Building a State. 620p. reprint ed. lib. bdg. 128.00 (978-0-7222-0514-3(7)) Library Reprints, Inc.

Squire, Jerry & City of Avondale. Avondale. 2008. (Images of America Ser.). (ENG., Illus.). 128p. pap. 19.99 (978-0-7385-4843-2(X)) Arcadia Publishing.

St Clair, Carol J. Coffelt & St Clair, Charles S. Glendale. 2006. (Images of America Ser.). (ENG., Illus.). 128p. per. 21.99 (978-0-7385-4866-1(9)) Arcadia Publishing.

Steckner, Susie & The Mesa Historical Museum. Cactus League: Spring Training. 2012. (Images of America Ser.). (ENG., Illus.). 128p. pap. 21.99 **(978-0-7385-8534-5(3))** Arcadia Publishing.

Steuber, Midge & Jerome Historical Society Archives Staff. Jerome. 2008. (Images of America Ser.). (ENG., Illus.). 128p. pap. 21.99 (978-0-7385-5882-0(6)) Arcadia Publishing.

Suagee, E. K. & San Pedro Valley Arts and Historical Society. Around Benson. 2009. (Images of America Ser.). (ENG., Illus.). 128p. pap. 21.99 (978-0-7385-5892-9(3)) Arcadia Publishing.

Sydnor, Douglas B. Scottsdale Architecture. 2010. (Images of America Ser.). (ENG., Illus.). 128p. pap. 21.99 (978-0-7385-7877-4(0)) Arcadia Publishing.

Thybony, Scott. The Incredible Grand Canyon: Cliffhangers & Curiosities from America's Greatest Canyon. 2007. (ENG., Illus.). 120p. pap. 14.95 (978-0-938216-94-0(5)) Grand Canyon Assn.

Tietjen, Gary. Encounter with the Frontier. 2007. per. (978-0-9800813-0-5(0)) DMT Publishing.

Trimble, Marshall. Ash Fork. 2008. (Images of America Ser.). (ENG., Illus.). 128p. per. 19.99 (978-0-7385-4832-6(4)) Arcadia Publishing.

Turner, D. L. & Ellis, Catherine H. Latter-day Saints in Mesa. 2009. (Images of America Ser.). (ENG., Illus.). 128p. pap. 21.99 (978-0-7385-5857-8(5)) Arcadia Publishing.

Turner, Jim. Arizona: A Celebration of the Grand Canyon State, 1 vol. 2011. (ENG., Illus.). 336p. 40.00 (978-1-4236-0742-7(2)) Gibbs Smith, Publisher.

Unraveling the Treasure Enigma at Tumacacori Arizona. 2007. cd-rom (978-0-9633813-2-3(6)) Oliver, Gary Don.

Vega, Santos C. Mexicans in Tempe. 2009. (Images of America Ser.). (ENG., Illus.). 128p. pap. 21.99 (978-0-7385-7056-3(7)) Arcadia Publishing.

Waters, Frank. The Earp Brothers of Tombstone: The Story of Mrs. Virgil Earp. 2011. 254p. 47.95 **(978-1-258-04526-5(5))** Literary Licensing, LLC.

Whitehurst, Patrick. Williams. 2008. (Images of America Ser.). (Illus.). 128p. pap. 21.99 (978-0-7385-5885-1(0)) Arcadia Publishing.

Wildfang, Frederic B. & Sharlot Hall Museum Archives. Prescott. 2006. (Images of America Ser.). (Illus.). 127p. per. 21.99 (978-0-7385-4858-6(8)) Arcadia Publishing.

Wildfang, Frederic B., et al. Tempe. 2010. (Then & Now Ser.). (Illus.). 96p. pap. 21.99 (978-0-7385-7926-9(2)) Arcadia Publishing.

Wilson, James L. Cracking the Golden Egg: In Hot Pursuit of the Lost Dutchman Mine. 2007. (ENG., Illus.). 152p. pap. 20.95 (978-1-59299-257-7(9)) Inkwater Pr.

Wolfe, Barbara Brooks. Power, Passion, & Prejudice: Shootout in the Galiuro Mountains. 2008. (Illus.). 172p. pap. 12.95 (978-0-9799341-7-9(6)) Imago Pr.

Woosley, Anne I. & Arizona Historical Society. Early Tucson. 2008. (Images of America Ser.). (ENG., Illus.). 128p. pap. 21.99 (978-0-7385-5646-8(7)) Arcadia Publishing.

Yadon, Laurence J. & Anderson, Dan. Arizona Gunfighters, 1 vol. 2010. (ENG., Illus.). 360p. pap. 16.95 (978-1-58980-651-1(4)) Pelican Publishing Co., Inc.

ARIZONA—MAPS

Benchmark Maps Staff, creator. Arizona Road & Recreation Atlas. 6th ed. 2007. (Benchmark Map: Arizona Road & Recreation Atlas Ser.). 111p. pap. 22.95 (978-0-929591-97-1(6)) Map Link.

Great Pacific Map Co. Staff. Recreation Map Arizona. 2006. 3.95 (978-0-88126-214-8(5)) Great Pacific Recreation Maps & Guides.

Green, Stewart M. Phoenix. 2nd ed. 2009. (Best Easy Day Hikes Ser.). (ENG., Illus.). 120p. pap. 9.95 (978-0-7627-5108-2(8), Falcon Guides) Globe Pequot Pr., The.

Grubbs, Bruce. Best Easy Day Hikes Flagstaff. 2nd ed. 2009. (Best Easy Day Hikes Ser.). (ENG., Illus.). 96p. pap. 9.95 (978-0-7627-5106-8(1), Falcon Guides) Globe Pequot Pr., The.

Mangum, Richard. Sedona Hikes: 130 Day Hikes & 5 Vortex Sites around Sedona, Arizona. 9th rev. ed. 2007. Orig. Title: Sedona Hikes. 256p. pap. 16.95 (978-1-891517-08-2(2)) Hexagon Pr., Inc.

Preston, Ralph N. & Preston, Monte L. Arizona Gold & Gem Maps. (Illus.). pap. 11.00 (978-0-9657558-7-0(8)) Pioneer Pr.

Rand McNally, creator. Rand Mcnally City Map Book: Arizona Cities. 2010. (Rand Mcnally City Map Bks.). (Illus.). 64p. pap. 7.99 (978-0-528-88228-9(7)) Rand McNally.

—The Thomas Guide Phoenix Street Guide. 2007. (Thomas Guide Phoenix Metropolitan Area Street Guide & Directory Ser.). 1388p. pap. 24.95 (978-0-528-86052-6(0)) Rand McNally.

—The Thomas Guide Tucson Street Guide. 2007. (Thomas Guide Tucson Metropolitan Area Street Guide & Directory Ser.). 2158p. pap. 19.95 (978-0-528-86053-9(4)) Rand McNally.

Trails Illustrated Staff & Other Publisher Map Staff. Map Grand Canyon Bright Az. 2011. 11.95 (978-1-56695-495-2(9)) National Geographic Maps.

ARIZONA—POLITICS AND GOVERNMENT

Chadwick, W. Guy. God in the Foundations of Arizona Government. 2007. (Illus.). 180p. pap. 12.00 (978-0-9795707-0-4(0)) Arizona Call to Prayer.

Moussalli, Stephanie D. The Fiscal Case against Statehood: Accounting for Statehood in New Mexico & Arizona. 2012. (ENG.). 224p. (gr. 17). 65.00 **(978-0-7391-6699-4(9))** Lexington Bks.

Osselaer, Heidi J. Winning Their Place: Arizona Women in Politics, 1883-1950. (ENG.). 248p. 2011. pap. 24.95 (978-0-8165-0239-4(0)) 2009. (Illus.). 45.00 (978-0-8165-2733-5(4)) Univ. of Arizona Pr.

Santa Ana, Otto & Gonzalez de Bustamante, Celeste. Arizona Firestorm: Global Immigration Realities, National Media, & Provincial Politics. 2012. (ENG.). 328p. (gr. 17). 80.00 **(978-1-4422-1415-6(5))** Rowman & Littlefield Publishers, Inc.

Stevens, Sharon McKenzie. A Place for Dialogue: Language, Land Use, & Politics in Southern Arizona. 2007. (American Land & Life Ser.). (ENG., Illus.). 232p. 37.95 (978-1-58729-534-8(2)) Univ. of Iowa Pr.

Vierra, Jerry. Traffic Citation Scheme. 2008. 128p. pap. 19.95 (978-1-60610-925-0(1)) PublishAmerica, Inc.

Zoellner, Tom. A Safeway in Arizona: What the Gabrielle Giffords Shooting Tells Us about the Grand Canyon State & Life in America. 2011. (ENG.). 288p. (gr. 12). 26.95 **(978-0-670-02320-2(5)**, Viking Adult) Penguin Group (USA) Inc.

ARIZONA—SOCIAL CONDITIONS

Benally, Malcolm D. Bitter Water: Diné Oral Histories of the Navajo-Hopi Land Dispute. 2011. (First Peoples: New Directions in Indigenous Studies). (ENG & NAV., Illus.). 136p. pap. 19.95 (978-0-8165-2898-1(5)) Univ. of Arizona Pr.

Burns, Tammy & Burns, Russell. Your Guide to Assisted Living in Arizon. 2010. 74p. pap. 12.95 (978-0-557-43305-6(3)) Lulu Enterprises Inc.

Christensen, Randy. Ask Me Why I Hurt: The Kids Nobody Wants & the Doctor Who Heals Them. 2011. 288p. 24.99 (978-0-307-71899-0(9)) Broadway Bks.

CQ Press, ed. Arizona Crime in Perspective 2010 Edition, 00 vols. rev. ed. 2010. 24p. pap. 32.00 (978-1-60871-436-0(5)) CQ Pr.

—Arizona Education in Perspective 2010-2011 Editon, 00 vols. rev. ed. 2010. 24p. pap. 32.00 (978-1-60871-437-7(3)) CQ Pr.

—Arizona Health Care in Perspective 2010 Edition, 00 vols. rev. ed. 2010. 24p. pap. 32.00 (978-1-60871-438-4(1)) CQ Pr.

—Arizona in Perspective 2010 Edition, 00 vols. rev. ed. 2010. 24p. pap. 32.00 (978-1-60871-439-1(X)) CQ Pr.

Cummings, Laura L. Pachucas & Pachucos in Tucson: Situated Border Lives. 2009. (ENG., Illus.). 264p. pap. 34.95 (978-0-8165-2737-3(7)) Univ. of Arizona Pr.

Duffy, Sean. All Desert Roads. 2010. 280p. pap. (978-3-8383-7243-3(3)) Lambert Academic Publishing.

Esparza, Adrian X. & Donelson, Angela J. Colonias in Arizona & New Mexico: Border Poverty & Community Development Solutions. 2008. (ENG.). 208p. pap. 19.95 (978-0-8165-2652-9(4)) Univ. of Arizona Pr.

Hallock, Dale C. From Cowboys & Sodbusters to a Mega-Residential Community: A Pictorial History of Gilbert, Arizona. 2007. (978-1-57864-440-7(2)) Donning Co. Pubs.

Haskins, Victoria K. Matrons & Maids: Regulating Indian Domestic Service in Tucson, 1914 — 1934. 2012. (ENG.). 240p. 50.00 **(978-0-8165-2960-5(4))** Univ. of Arizona Pr.

Hickey, Maeve, photos by. Ambos Nogales: Intimate Portraits of the U. S. -Mexico Border. (Southwest Ser.). (Illus.). 138p. pap. 17.95 (978-1-930618-07-7(7)) School for Advanced Research Pr./SAR Pr.

Martinelli, Phylis Cancilla. Undermining Race: Ethnic Identities in Arizona Copper Camps, 1880-1920. 2009. (ENG., Illus.). 240p. 50.00 (978-0-8165-2745-8(8)) Univ. of Arizona Pr.

McBlane, Dick. The Chandler, Arizona Fire Department: A History of Service & Tradition. 2012. **(978-1-57864-737-8(1))** Donning Co. Pubs.

Morgan, Scott, ed. Arizona in Perspective 2011, 00 vols. rev. ed. 2011. 24p. pap. 32.00 (978-1-4522-0011-8(4)) CQ Pr.

Otero, Lydia R. La Calle: Spatial Conflicts & Urban Renewal in a Southwest City. 2010. (ENG., Illus.). 288p. pap. 24.95 (978-0-8165-2888-2(8)) Univ. of Arizona Pr.

Stucki, Larry R. Copper Mines, Company Towns, Indians, Mexicans, Mormons, Masons, Jews, Muslims, Gays, Wombs, Mcdonalds, & the March of Dimes: Survival of the Fitte. 2009. 532p. 44.95 (978-1-4269-1335-8(4)) Trafford Publishing.

—Copper Mines, Company Towns, Indians, Mexicans, Mormons, Masons, Jews, Muslims, Gays, Wombs, Mcdonalds, & the March of Dimes: Survival of the Fittest in & Far Beyond the Deserts of Arizona, New Mexico, & Utah: What is the secret of human-created systems that continue to thrive long after their creators; what has led to the failure of others to Survive? 2009. 532p. pap. 34.95 (978-1-4269-1334-1(6)) Trafford Publishing.

Zoellner, Tom. A Safeway in Arizona: What the Gabrielle Giffords Shooting Tells Us about the Grand Canyon State & Life in America. 2011. (ENG.). 288p. (gr. 12). 26.95 **(978-0-670-02320-2(5)**, Viking Adult) Penguin Group (USA) Inc.

ARIZONA—SOCIAL LIFE AND CUSTOMS

Ayers, Steve & Camp Verde Historical Society. Camp Verde. 2010. (Images of America Ser.). (Illus.). 128p. pap. 21.99 (978-0-7385-7912-2(2)) Arcadia Publishing.

Bahr, Donald. How Mockingbirds Are: O'odham Ritual Orations. 2011. (North American Native Peoples, Past & Present Ser.). (Illus.). 128p. 45.00 (978-1-4384-3525-1(8), Suny Pr.) State Univ. of New York Pr.

Barnes, Mary Ellen. The Road to Mount Lemmon: A Father, A Family, & the Making of Summerhaven. 2009. (ENG., Illus.). 224p. pap. 17.95 (978-0-8165-2781-6(4)) Univ. of Arizona Pr.

Bates, Denise E., et al. Goodyear. 2010. (Images of America Ser.). (ENG., Illus.). 128p. pap. 21.99 (978-0-7385-7117-1(2)) Arcadia Publishing.

Berkowitz, Paul. The Case of the Indian Trader: Billy Malone & the National Park Service Investigation at Hubbell Trading Post. 2011. (ENG., Illus.). 376p. 34.95 (978-0-8263-4859-3(9)) Univ. of New Mexico Pr.

Brock, Patricia & Maricopa Historical Society. Maricopa. 2011. (Images of America Ser.). (Illus.). 128p. pap. 21.99 (978-0-7385-7995-5(5)) Arcadia Publishing.

Buscher, Dick. Historic Photos of Arizona. 2009. (Historic Photos Ser.). (ENG.). 206p. 39.95 (978-1-59652-518-4(5)) Turner Publishing Co.

DeGraff III, John G. Flagstaff. 2011. (Postcard History Ser.). (Illus.). 128p. pap. 21.99 **(978-0-7385-8510-9(6))** Arcadia Publishing.

Duncklee, John. Coyotes I Have Known. 2008. 164p. pap. 14.95 (978-0-595-53243-8(8)) iUniverse, Inc.

Elsner, Jodey & Peoria Arizona Historical Society. Peoria. 2010. (Images of America Ser.). (Illus.). 128p. pap. 21.99 (978-0-7385-7110-2(5)) Arcadia Publishing.

Fewkes, Jesse W. The Snake Ceremonials at Walpi. 126p. reprint ed. 88.00 (978-0-7222-9671-4(1)) Library Reprints, Inc.

Fudala, Joan. Desert Highlands: A Vision in the Desert: 25th Anniversary Commemorative Tribute, 1983-2008. 2008. (978-1-57864-504-6(2)) Donning Co. Pubs.

Griffith, Jim. A Border Runs Through It: Journeys in Regional History & Folklore. 2011. (Illus.). 128p. 17.95 **(978-1-933855-62-2(2))** Rio Nuevo Pubs.

Hatch, Jo Ann. Lore & Legend: Adventure & History in the White Mountains of Arizona. 2007. (Illus.). 172p. per. 14.95 (978-0-9773648-6-2(0)) Legend eXpress Publishing.

Henry, Bonnie. Tucson Memories. 2006. (978-1-59152-034-4(7)) Arizona Daily Star.

Herring, Patricia Roche. Life & Society at the Royal Spanish Presidio of San Agustin del Tucson, 1775-1856. 2009. 180p. pap. 15.95 (978-1-60494-196-8(0)) Wheatmark.

Hickey, Maeve, photos by. Ambos Nogales: Intimate Portraits of the U. S. -Mexico Border. (Southwest Ser.). (Illus.). 138p. pap. 17.95 (978-1-930618-07-7(7)) School for Advanced Research Pr./SAR Pr.

Konstan, Victor. What's the Point? 2011. 216p. pap. 12.95 **(978-1-4269-7929-3(0))** Trafford Publishing.

Lowe, Sam. Mysteries & Legends of Arizona: True Stories of the Unsolved & Unexplained. 2010. (Mysteries & Legends Ser.). (ENG., Illus.). 208p. pap. 14.95 (978-0-7627-5546-2(6)) Globe Pequot Pr., The.

McKeand, Bret & Sun Cities Area Historical Society. Sun City. 2011. (Images of America Ser.). (Illus.). 128p. pap. 21.99 (978-0-7385-7951-1(3)) Arcadia Publishing.

Meck, Verlyne. Buckeye. 2010. (Then & Now Ser.). (ENG., Illus.). 96p. pap. 21.99 (978-0-7385-7924-5(6)) Arcadia Publishing.

Messersmith, Dan W. Kingman. 2010. (Images of America Ser.). (Illus.). 128p. pap. 21.99 (978-0-7385-7930-6(0)) Arcadia Publishing.

Rowe, Jeremy. Early Maricopa County: 1871-1920. 2011. (Images of America Ser.). (Illus.). 128p. pap. 21.99 (978-0-7385-7416-5(3)) Arcadia Publishing.

Sass, Sherry, text. The Life of the Santa Cruz River: A Rambler's Guide. 2006. (Illus.). 32p. 2.95 (978-1-58369-084-0(0)) Western National Parks Assn.

Snell, Dawn & Casa Grande Valley Historical Society. Casa Grande. 2011. (Images of America Ser.). (Illus.). 128p. pap. 21.99 **(978-0-7385-7953-5(X))** Arcadia Publishing.

Spicer, Edward H. People of Pascua. Sands, Kathleen Mullen & Spicer, Rosamond B., eds. 2011. (ENG., Illus.). 331p. pap. 30.00 (978-0-8165-2967-4(1)) Univ. of Arizona Pr.

Spragg-Braude, Stacia. To Walk in Beauty: A Navajo Family's Journey Home. 2009. (ENG., Illus.). 200p. 45.00 (978-0-89013-554-9(1)) Museum of New Mexico Pr.

ARIZONA (SHIP)

see USS Arizona (Ship)

ARIZONA, UNIVERSITY OF

see University of Arizona

ARIZONA CARDINALS (FOOTBALL TEAM)

Triumph Books Staff. Arizona Cardinals Super Bowl Champions. 2009. 128p. pap. 14.95 (978-1-60078-296-1(5)) Triumph Bks.

Triumph Books Staff, ed. Desert Storm: Kurt Warner & the Arizona Cardinals' Unforgettable Run to the Super Bowl. 2009. (ENG.). 128p. pap. 14.95 (978-1-60078-305-0(8)) Triumph Bks.

ARIZONA DIAMONDBACKS (BASEBALL TEAM)

Euchner, Charles C. The Last Nine Innings: Inside the Real Game Fans Never See. 2007. (ENG., Illus.). 320p. per. 14.95 (978-1-4022-0754-9(9)) Sourcebooks, Inc.

Travers, Steven. Diamondbacks Essential: Everything You Need to Know to Be a Real Fan! 2007. (Essential (Triumph) Ser.). (ENG., Illus.). 176p. 19.95 (978-1-57243-944-3(0)) Triumph Bks.

ARIZONA STATE PRISON

Rapp, Keith & Davis, Robert. Hostage: An account of the longest prison hostage siege in United States history. 2007. per. (978-0-9790999-8-4(6)) Printmedia Bks.

ARK, NOAH'S

see Noah's Ark

ARK OF THE COVENANT

Arnold, William R. Ephod & Ark: A Study in the Records & Religion of the Ancient Hebrews. 2008. 176p. pap. 15.00 (978-1-55635-766-4(4)) Wipf & Stock Pubs.

Berkley, Grant. The Discovery of the Ark of the Covenant. 2007. 372p. 50.38 (978-1-4251-4190-5(0)) Trafford Publishing.

Bernstein, Henrietta. Ark of the Covenant & Holy Grail: The Symbolism Behind the Mystery. rev. ed. 2007. 272p. pap. 21.95 (978-0-87516-833-3(7), Devorss Pubns.) DeVorss & Co.

Budge, E. A. Wallis. The Kebra Nagast. 2007. 284p. per. 19.95 (978-1-59654-410-9(4)) Disruptive Publishing.

Emerys, Chevalier. Revelation of the Holy Grail. 2007. 365p. pap. 29.95 (978-0-615-15978-5(1)) Hogan, Timothy W.

Foster, Charles. Tracking the Ark of the Covenant: By Camel, Foot & Ancient Ford in Search of Antiquity's Greatest Treasure, 1 vol. 2008. (Illus.). 256p. pap. 13.99 (978-0-8254-6152-1(9), Monarch Bks.) Lion Hudson PLC GBR. Dist: Kregel Pubns.

Joseph, Frank & Beaudoin, Laura. Opening the Ark of the Covenant: The Secret Power of the Ancients, the Knights Templar Connection, & the Search for the Holy Grail. 2007. (ENG., Illus.). 1p. per. 17.99 (978-1-56414-903-9(X), 1259651) Career Pr., Inc.

Miller, Patrick D. & Roberts, J. J. M. The Hand of the Lord: A Reassessment of the "Ark Narrative" of 1 Samuel. 2007. 15.95 (978-1-58983-294-7(9)) Society of Biblical Literature.

Munro-Hay, Stuart. The Quest for the Ark of the Covenant: The True History of the Tablets of Moses. 2006. (ENG., Illus.). 288p. pap. 26.00 (978-1-84511-248-6(2)) I. B. Tauris & Co., Ltd. GBR. Dist: Macmillan.

Newton, Richard. The Jewish Tabernacle: And Its Furniture in their Typical Teachings. 2009. 398p. pap. 25.00 (978-1-59925-212-4(0)) Solid Ground Christian Bks.

Page, Nick. What Happened to the Ark of the Covenant? And Other Bible Mysteries. 2007. (ENG., Illus.). 216p. pap. 13.99 (978-1-85078-751-8(4)) Authentic Media.

Parfitt, Tudor. The Lost Ark of the Covenant: Solving the 2,500-Year-Old Mystery of the Fabled Biblical Ark. 2009. 384p. pap. 14.99 (978-0-06-137104-2(1), HarperOne) HarperCollins Pubs.

Rezetko, Robert. Source & Revision in the Narratives of David's Transfer of the Ark: Text, Language & Story in 2 Samuel 6 & 1 Chronicles 13, 15-16. 6th ed. 2007. (Library of Hebrew Bible/Old Testament Studies: Vol. 470). (ENG.). 432p. 180.00 (978-0-567-02612-5(4), T&T Clark Int'l) Continuum International Publishing Group, Ltd. GBR. Dist: National Bk. Network.

ARKANSAS

Carter, Clarence E., ed. The Territory of Arkansas, 1819-1825. (Territorial Papers of the United States: Vol. 19). reprint ed. 138.60 (978-0-404-01469-8(0)) AMS Pr., Inc.

—The Territory of Arkansas, 1825-1829. (Territorial Papers of the United States: Vol. 20). reprint ed. 138.60 (978-0-404-01470-4(4)) AMS Pr., Inc.

—The Territory of Arkansas, 1829-1836. (Territorial Papers of the United States: Vol. 21). reprint ed. 138.60 (978-0-404-01471-1(2)) AMS Pr., Inc.

Eddlemon, Sherida K. Index to the Arkansas General Land Office, 1820-1907: Covering the Counties of: Monroe, Lee, Woodruff, White, Crittenden, Independence, Lonoke, St. Francois, Prairie & Cross, Vol. 3. 2008. 344p. pap. 30.00 (978-0-7884-1044-4(X), No. E109) Heritage Bks.

Smith, Myron J. The Css Arkansas: A Confederate Ironclad in Western Waters. 2011. (ENG., Illus.). 360p. 45.00 (978-0-7864-4726-8(5)) McFarland & Co., Inc. Pubs.

York, Courtney & York, Gerlene. Poinsett County Arkansas Census, 1850. 54p. (Orig.). pap. 12.00 (978-0-916660-05-5(2)) House of York.

ARKANSAS—ANTIQUITIES

Boykin, Kristina. An Analysis of Feature 33 at Van Winkle's Mill Site. 2011. 92p. pap. **(978-3-8443-9615-7(2))** Lambert Academic Publishing.

Cherry, James F. The Headpots of Northeast Arkansas & Southern Pemiscot County, Missouri. 2009. (Illus.). 384p. 59.95 (978-1-55728-897-4(6)) Univ. of Arkansas Pr.

Hilliard, Jerry E. An Antebellum Ozark Community & the Civil War: The Archeology of the Second Mount Comfort Church (3wa880), Washington County, Arkansas (1840-Ca. 1865) 2008. (978-1-56349-102-3(8)) Arkansas Archeological Survey.

Kwas, Mary L. Digging for History at Old Washington. 2009. (Illus.). 170p. 34.95 (978-1-55728-898-1(4)) Univ. of Arkansas Pr.

Rolingson, Martha Ann. Toltec Mounds: Archeology of the Mound-and-Plaza Complex. 2011. (ENG., Illus.). pap. (978-1-56349-104-7(4)) Arkansas Archeological Survey.

ARKANSAS—BIOGRAPHY

Allen, Bill. Livin'... Lovin'... & Laughin' 2010. 436p. 37.35 (978-0-557-29763-4(X)) Lulu Enterprises Inc.

Allen, Desmond Walls, compiled by. Index to Arkansas Goodspeed Biographical Sketches. 2007. pap. 22.00 (978-1-56546-390-5(0)) Arkansas Research, Inc.

Beals, Melba Patillo. Warriors Don't Cry: A Searing Memoir of the Battle to Integrate Little Rock's Central High. 2007. (ENG., Illus.). 240p. (YA). (gr. 7-12). mass mkt. 6.99 (978-1-4169-4882-7(1), Simon Pulse) Simon Pulse.

—Warriors Don't Cry: A Searing Memoir of the Battle to Integrate Little Rock's Central High. abr. ed. 2007. (ENG., Illus.). 226p. 17.20 (978-1-4178-1397-1(0)) Turtleback Bks.

Big Hat Law: Arkansas & Its State Police, 1935-2000. 2008. 208p. pap. 19.95 (978-0-9800897-4-5(3)) Butler Ctr. for Arkansas Studies.

Bish, Jan Douglas. Light & Shadow. 2006. 106p. pap. 10.95 (978-0-7414-3521-7(7)) Infinity Publishing.

Bishop, A. W. Loyalty on the Frontier: Or Sketches of Union Men of the South-West with Incidents & Adventures in Rebellion on the Border. Scott, Kim Allen, ed. 2007. 228p. per. 19.95 (978-1-55728-840-0(2)) Univ. of Arkansas Pr.

Bolsterli, Margaret Jones. Things You Need to Hear: Collected Memories of Growing up in Arkansas, 1890-1980. 2012. (ENG., Illus.). 160p. 24.95 **(978-1-55728-978-0(6))** Univ. of Arkansas Pr.

Brown, Frank W. Guardian of the Memories: Searcy. 2008. 172p. 27.50 (978-1-4251-6757-8(8)) Trafford Publishing.

Brown, Judge Gerald Parker. The Clod-Hoppin' Judge: Memoirs of Judge Gerald Parker Brown. 2011. 112p. 22.95 (978-1-4620-0311-2(7)); pap. 12.95 (978-1-4620-0309-9(5)) iUniverse, Inc.

Caldwell, Jackie L. Dreams Remembered: A Memoir. 2009. 164p. 25.95 (978-1-4401-2745-8(X)); pap. 15.95 (978-1-4401-0141-0(8)) iUniverse, Inc.

Cavitt, William F. & Gwise, Thomas E. I Once Could See, but Now I'm Blind. 2010. 144p. pap. 11.99 (978-1-4490-7434-0(0)) AuthorHouse.

Chappel, Roland. Chapel Chimes: The Story of a Little Known Baptist Preacher. 2011. 156p. pap. 13.95 **(978-1-61507-885-1(1))** Cross Bks. Publishing.

Chauncey, James Wilburn. Eyewitness to Heaven: A Glimpse into the Obscure. 2011. (ENG.). 215p. pap. 13.99 **(978-1-61346-013-9(9))** Tate Publishing & Enterprises, LLC.

Coleman, Ewell R. A Life on the Black River in Arkansas: A Pioneering Banker's Memoir. 2008. 124p. pap. 16.95 (978-1-935106-06-7(6)) Butler Ctr. for Arkansas Studies.

Courtney, Gary D. Carl Janaway - Smartest Bandit of the Cookson Hills. 2008. 364p. pap. 26.15 (978-1-4259-9588-1(8)) AuthorHouse.

Cox, Ben J. To Mam: The Long Road Home. 2008. 520p. 28.95 (978-1-4327-2711-6(7)); pap. 24.95 (978-1-4327-2262-1(4)) Outskirts Pr., Inc.

Curtis, Ann. A Farmer's Daughter... Amazed by Grace. 2007. 336p. 19.95 (978-0-9788080-1-3(0)) Open Ear Pubs.

Davis, William. Rambling Boy & Friends: A Story of a Boy Growing Up. 2008. 148p. 22.49 (978-1-4389-1736-8(8)); pap. 11.99 (978-1-4389-1737-5(6)) AuthorHouse.

Dillard, Tom W. Statesmen, Scoundrels, & Eccentrics: A Gallery of Amazing Arkansans. 2010. (ENG., Illus.). 264p. pap. 22.95 (978-1-55728-927-8(1)) Univ. of Arkansas Pr.

Echols, Damien. Damien Echols: Life after Death. 2012. (ENG., Illus.). 384p. (gr. 12). 26.95 **(978-0-399-16020-2(5)**, Blue Rider Pr.) Penguin Group (USA) Inc.

Finch, Henrietta Roberts. God's Amazing Grace. 2008. 152p. pap. 13.99 (978-1-60647-285-9(2)) Xulon Pr., Inc.

Fiser, Sandra & Fiser, Tom. A Change of Heart. 2010. 148p. 30.95 (978-1-61507-193-7(8)); pap. 13.95 (978-1-61507-192-0(X)) Cross Bks. Publishing.

Fulton County History Book Committee (Ark.) Staff, contrib. by. Fulton County, Arkansas: History & Families. 2008. (Illus.). 536p. (978-0-9798802-8-5(9)) Acclaim Pr., Inc.

Goodspeed's Biographical & Historical Memoirs of Central Arkansas. 2007. cd-rom 9.95 (978-1-56546-383-7(8)) Arkansas Research, Inc.

Goodspeed's Biographical & Historical Memoirs of Eastern Arkansas. 2007. cd-rom 9.95 (978-1-56546-382-0(X)) Arkansas Research, Inc.

Goodspeed's Biographical & Historical Memoirs of Northeast Arkansas. 2007. cd-rom 9.95 (978-1-56546-381-3(1)) Arkansas Research, Inc.

Goodspeed's Biographical & Historical Memoirs of Southern Arkansas. 2007. cd-rom 9.95 (978-1-56546-384-4(6)) Arkansas Research, Inc.

Goodspeed's Biographical & Historical Memoirs of Western Arkansas. 2007. cd-rom 9.95 (978-1-56546-385-1(4)) Arkansas Research, Inc.

Goodspeed's Historical Reminiscenses & Biographical Memoirs of Conway County, Arkansas. 2007. cd-rom 9.95 (978-1-56546-388-2(9)) Arkansas Research, Inc.

Goodspeed's Histories of Arkansas, eight volumes on one CD. 2007. cd-rom 39.95 (978-1-56546-389-9(7)) Arkansas Research, Inc.

Goodspeed's History of Benton, Washington, Carroll, Madison, Crawford, Franklin, & Sebastian Counties, Arkansas. 2007. cd-rom 9.95 (978-1-56546-386-8(2)) Arkansas Research, Inc.

Graddy, Thomas R. Patches & Beyond: My Memoirs. 2009. 180p. pap. 16.95 (978-1-4401-4335-9(8)) iUniverse, Inc.

Halbrook, William Erwin. A School Man of the Ozarks: Being an Autobiography of William Erwin Halbrook. 2006. per. 9.25 (978-0-9779859-1-3(1)) Rock Island Pr.

Hanley, Steven & Hanley, Ray. Malvern. 2010. (Images of America Ser.). (Illus.). 128p. pap. 21.99 (978-0-7385-8626-7(9)) Arcadia Publishing.

Harrison, A. Cleveland. A Little Rock Boyhood: Growing up in the Great Depression. 2010. (ENG., Illus.). 375p. 29.95 (978-1-935106-18-0(X)) Butler Ctr. for Arkansas Studies.

Hedges, William D. From Life in the Hamptons to a Life of Poverty in Arkansas. 2011. 144p. 29.99 **(978-1-4568-8699-8(1))**; pap. 19.99 **(978-1-4568-8698-1(3))** Xlibris Corp.

Hempstead, Fay. Hempstead's Historical Review of Arkansas, three-volume set on CD. 2007. cd-rom 19.95 (978-1-56546-391-2(9)) Arkansas Research, Inc.

Herndon, Dallas T. Centennial History of Arkansas, three-volume set on CD. 2006. cd-rom 19.95 (978-1-56546-377-6(3)) Arkansas Research, Inc.

Higgins, Billy D. The Barling Darling: Hal Smith in American Baseball. 2009. (Illus.). 246p. pap. 19.95 (978-1-935106-09-8(0)) Butler Ctr. for Arkansas Studies.

History & Families: Boone County, Arkansas. 2008. (Illus.). 320p. **(978-1-935001-07-2(8))** Acclaim Pr., Inc.

Irland, Basia. Water Library. 2007. (ENG., Illus.). 248p. 45.00 (978-0-8263-3675-0(2)) Univ. of New Mexico Pr.

Jones Bolsterli, Margaret. During Wind & Rain: The Jones Family Farm in the Arkansas Delta, 1848-2006. 2008. (Illus.). 144p. pap. 16.95 (978-1-55728-871-4(2)) Univ. of Arkansas Pr.

Kesee, Rip. My Life, My Story, My Pain. 2010. 108p. 21.49 (978-1-4520-3659-5(4)); pap. 10.99 (978-1-4520-3658-8(6)) AuthorHouse.

Kirk, John A. Beyond Little Rock: The Origins & Legacies of the Central High Crisis. 2007. 213p. 64.95 (978-1-55728-850-9(X)); per. 22.50 (978-1-55728-851-6(8)) Univ. of Arkansas Pr.

Knotts, Burton Ray, compiled by. Historical & Genealogical Abstracts from Randolph County, Arkansas, Newspapers Of 1919. 2006. pap. 33.00 (978-1-56546-378-3(1)) Arkansas Research, Inc.

Kwas, Mary L. Digging for History at Old Washington. 2009. (Illus.). 170p. 34.95 (978-1-55728-898-1(4)) Univ. of Arkansas Pr.

Lanier, Carlotta Walls & Page, Lisa Frazier. A Mighty Long Way: My Journey to Justice at Little Rock Central High School. 2010. (ENG., Illus.). 336p. pap. 16.00 (978-0-345-51101-0(8), One World/Ballantine) Random House Publishing Group.

Laymon, Sherry. Fearless: John L. Mcclellan, United States Senator. 2011. pap. 29.99 **(978-1-61346-486-1(X))** Tate Publishing & Enterprises, LLC.

Leavell, Roland Quinche. An Unashamed Workman: The Biography of Landrum Pinson Leavell. 2011. 154p. 41.95 **(978-1-258-06481-5(2))** Literary Licensing, LLC.

A Life on the Black River in Arkansas: A Pioneering Banker's Memoir. 2008. 124p. pap. 33.95 (978-0-9800897-8-3(6)); 34.95 (978-1-935106-04-3(X)) Butler Ctr. for Arkansas Studies.

Magee, Mary. Red: The Legacy of Coach Jimmy Red Parker: Beyond Football. 2007. pap. 22.95 (978-1-930709-64-5(1)) HAWK Publishing Group.

Mainfort, Robert C. Sam Dellinger: Raiders of the Lost Arkansas. 2008. (Illus.). 229p. 39.95 (978-1-55728-886-8(0)) Univ. of Arkansas Pr.

Margolick, David. Elizabeth & Hazel: Two Women of Little Rock. l.t. ed. 2011. lib. bdg. 33.95 **(978-1-61173-256-6(5))** Ctr. Point Large Print.

—Elizabeth & Hazel: Two Women of Little Rock. 2011. (Playaway Adult Nonfiction Ser.). (ENG.). 54.99 **(978-1-61637-118-0(8))** Findaway World, LLC.

—Elizabeth & Hazel: Two Women of Little Rock. 2011. (Illus.). 320p. 26.00 (978-0-300-14193-1(9)) Yale Univ. Pr.

Mears, Nancy. Messges from the Throne Room. 2008. 144p. pap. 14.95 (978-1-59858-599-5(1)) Dog Ear Publishing, LLC.

Moran, Michael J. Proudly We Speak Your Name: Forty-Four Years at Little Rock Catholic High School. 2009. (Illus.). 144p. 24.95 (978-1-935106-07-4(4)) Butler Ctr. for Arkansas Studies.

Morell, Paula M. & Branton, Suzanne, eds. Tales from the South: Volume II. 2007. 200p. pap. 15.95 (978-0-9785648-6-5(3)) Temenos Publishing.

Morell, Paula Martin & Corum, Elaine Tomlinson, eds. Tales from the South: Volume I, Vol. 1. 2006. 272p. per. 14.95 (978-0-9785648-3-4(9)) Temenos Publishing.

Neal, Richard McKenzie. The Long Road Home: A philosophical Journey. 2009. 216p. 24.99 (978-1-4490-3185-5(4)); pap. 14.49 (978-1-4490-3184-8(6)) AuthorHouse.

Norrell, Tom. Turning Hope into a Second Chance, 1 vol. 2009. (ENG.). 84p. pap. 16.95 (978-1-60749-201-6(6)) PublishAmerica, Inc.

Oveson, Letty P. Heartaches & Blessings While Parenting My Mom. 2009. 128p. 22.50 (978-1-60693-802-7(9), Eloquent Bks.) AEG Literary Publishing Services, Inc.

Parnell, Todd. The Buffalo, Ben, & Me. 2007. (ENG., Illus.). 136p. (gr. 9). 24.95 (978-0-8262-1752-3(4)) Univ. of Missouri Pr.

Pershall, Stacy. Loud in the House of Myself: Memoir of a Strange Girl. (ENG.). 2012. 240p. pap. 14.95 **(978-0-393-34079-2(1)**, 34079) 2011. 232p. 24.95 (978-0-393-06692-0(4), 6692) Norton, W. W. & Co., Inc.

Presson, Jerry Wayne. The Life & Times of Jerry Wayne Presson. 2007. 60p. per. 15.99 (978-1-4257-8353-2(8)) Xlibris Corp.

A Pryor Commitment: The AUTOB of David Pryor. 2008. 388p. 29.95 (978-0-9800897-3-8(5)) Butler Ctr. for Arkansas Studies.

Pryor, David. A Pryor Commitment: The Autobiography of David Pryor. 2009. (Illus.). 416p. pap. 19.95 (978-1-935106-10-4(4)) Butler Ctr. for Arkansas Studies.

Rattlehead, David. The Life & Adventures of an Arkansas Doctor. 2009. 104p. pap. (978-0-217-35460-8(2)) Books LLC.

Rhodes, Bill. Pick of the Litter, 1 vol. 2010. 86p. pap. 19.95 (978-1-4489-3880-3(5)) PublishAmerica, Inc.

—Scholar from the Holler. 2007. (ENG.). 104p. per. 16.95 (978-1-4241-5254-4(2)) PublishAmerica, Inc.

Rice, Mary E. The Rainbow Crane. 2006. (ENG.). 260p. per. 14.95 (978-0-7414-3578-1(0)) Infinity Publishing.

Roberts, Terrence. Lessons from Little Rock. 2009. (ENG.). 200p. 24.95 (978-1-935106-11-1(2)) Butler Ctr. for Arkansas Studies.

Robinson, E. R. The Heart of the Toiler's Martyr. 2011. 76p. 36.95 **(978-1-258-04676-7(8))** Literary Licensing, LLC.

Sherley, Charles. Life in Arkansas: (When I Was a Boy), 1 vol. 2010. 48p. pap. 16.95 *(978-1-4489-5469-8(X))* PublishAmerica, Inc.

Skelton, Bettie Bears. A Shelter after the Storm. 2010. 110p. pap. 13.00 *(978-0-557-56841-3(2))* Lulu Enterprises Inc.

Smith, Elizabeth. Finding My Way Home. 2011. 248p. pap. 19.99 ***(978-1-4257-8998-5(6))*** Xlibris Corp.

Smith, Margret. Diary of a Resort Owner. 2007. 200p. per. 24.95 *(978-1-4241-4588-1(0))* PublishAmerica, Inc.

Stobaugh, Robert B. Starting from Arkansas: Four Continents, Four Countries, Four Kids. 2012. (ENG.). 427p. 30.00 ***(978-0-578-09693-3(5))*** Stobaugh, Robert B.

Swinger, Patricia. Hard Work, Good People, & 100,000 Boats: 50 Years of Boat-Building with Zach McClendon. 2009. 152p. *(978-1-57864-576-3(X))* Donning Co. Pubs.

Takiff, Michael. A Complicated Man: The Life of Bill Clinton as Told by Those Who Know Him. 2011. (ENG., Illus.). 528p. pap. 23.00 *(978-0-300-17768-8(2))* Yale Univ. Pr.

Teske, Steven. Unvarnished Arkansas: The Naked Truth about Nine Famous Arkansans. 2012. (ENG.). 160p. pap. 19.95 ***(978-1-935106-35-7(X))*** Butler Ctr. for Arkansas Studies.

Watson, Rob. My Journey: A Poet's Life, 1 vol. 2009. 75p. pap. 16.95 *(978-1-61546-664-1(9))* PublishAmerica, Inc.

Will Clift. Out of Arkansas: A True Story Based on an Outright Lie. 2009. 68p. pap. 9.95 *(978-1-4269-1937-4(9))* Trafford Publishing.

Willis, James. What Almost Did Not Happen: A Self-Portrait. 2011. 404p. 35.95 ***(978-1-4620-4046-9(2))***; pap. 25.95 ***(978-1-4620-4045-2(4))*** iUniverse, Inc.

Wood, Larry. Ozarks Gunfights & Other Notorious Incidents, 1 vol. 2010. (ENG., Illus.). 240p. pap. 15.95 *(978-1-58980-703-7(0))* Pelican Publishing Co., Inc.

Work Projects Administration. Slave Narratives: a Folk History of Slavery in the United States from Interviews with Former Slaves: Arkansas Narratives, Part 1. 2007. (ENG.). 242p. pap. 20.99 *(978-1-4264-4829-4(5))* BiblioBazaar.

—Slave Narratives: a Folk History of Slavery in the United States from Interviews with Former Slaves: Arkansas Narratives, Part 2. l.t. ed. 2007. (ENG.). 274p. pap. 23.99 *(978-1-4264-4872-0(4))* BiblioBazaar.

—Slave Narratives: A Folk History of Slavery in the United States from Interviews with Former Slaves: Arkansas Narratives, Part 5. 2007. (ENG.). 260p. pap. 21.99 *(978-1-4264-4743-3(4))* BiblioBazaar.

—Slave Narratives: A Folk History of Slavery in the United States from Interviews with Former Slaves: Arkansas Narratives, Part 6. l.t. ed. 2007. (ENG.). 294p. pap. 23.99 *(978-1-4264-4781-5(7))* BiblioBazaar.

—Slave Narratives: A Folk History of Slavery in the United States from Interviews with Former Slaves: Arkansas Narratives, Part 7. 2006. 180p. pap. 19.99 *(978-1-4264-4692-4(6))* BiblioBazaar.

—Slave Narratives: A Folk History of Slavery in the United States from Interviews with Former Slaves: Arkansas Narratives, Part 8. l.t. ed. 2007. (ENG.). 204p. pap. 22.99 *(978-1-4264-4723-5(X))* BiblioBazaar.

Zeller, Joyce. Hidden History of Eureka Springs. 2011. 128p. pap. 19.99 ***(978-1-60949-376-9(1))*** History Pr., The.

Zoller, Bob. Boy, Am I Ever Lucky! the Life & Times of Robert J Zoller. 2008. 312p. pap. 23.95 *(978-1-59858-570-4(3))* Dog Ear Publishing, LLC.

ARKANSAS—CENSUS

Arkansas Census Index, 1880. (Illus.). lib. bdg. *(978-0-89593-225-9(3)*, Accelerated Indexing Systems International (AISI)) Genealogical Services.

Arkansas Census Index, 1880 Mortality Schedules. (Illus.). lib. bdg. *(978-0-89593-226-6(1)*, Accelerated Indexing Systems International (AISI)) Genealogical Services.

Jackson, Ronald V. Arkansas Federal Census Index, 1820. (Illus.). lib. bdg. 48.00 *(978-0-89593-710-0(7)*, Accelerated Indexing Systems International (AISI)) Genealogical Services.

ARKANSAS—DESCRIPTION AND TRAVEL

Boyles, Carolyn & Pipkin, Patsy. Searcy. 2012. (Images of America Ser.). (ENG., Illus.). 128p. pap. 21.99 ***(978-0-7385-9101-8(7))*** Arcadia Publishing.

Carroll, Margo & Welch, Peggy. The Ozark Trail Guidebook. 2nd ed. 2009. 194p. pap. 18.95 *(978-0-9761231-1-8(8))* Enjoy the Journey, LLC.

Ernst, Tim. Arkansas Autumn: Spectacular Fall Photos of the Natural State. 2010. (Illus.). 144p. 34.95 *(978-1-882906-70-3(5))* Cloudland.net Publishing.

—Arkansas Portfolio III. 2011. (Illus.). 144p. 34.95 ***(978-1-882906-74-1(8))*** Cloudland.net Publishing.

Ernst, Tim. Buffalo River Dreams. 2010. (ENG., Illus.). 132p. 29.95 *(978-1-882906-59-8(4))* Cloudland.net Publishing.

Ferguson, Heather D. Arkansas City. 2008. (Images of America Ser.). (ENG., Illus.). 128p. pap. 19.99 *(978-0-7385-5240-8(2))* Arcadia Publishing.

Gill, John Purifoy. Open House: The Arkansas Governor's Mansion & Its Place in History. 2011. (ENG., Illus.). 240p. 50.00 *(978-1-935106-26-5(0))* Butler Ctr. for Arkansas Studies.

Hales, James. Rogers Arkansas 1881-2006. 2007. (Illus.). 168p. pap. 19.95 *(978-0-9790190-0-5(1))* St. Josephs Ozark Pr.

Hanley, Steven, Ray. Main Street Arkansas: The Hearts of Arkansas Cities & Towns - as Portrayed in Postcards & Photographs. 2009. (Illus.). 224p. 33.95 *(978-1-935106-12-8(0))*; (ENG., pap. 19.95 *(978-1-935106-13-5(9))* Butler Ctr. for Arkansas Studies.

Hanley, Ray. Little Rock. 2007. (Then & Now Ser.). (ENG., Illus.). 96p. per. 21.99 *(978-0-7385-4422-9(1))* Arcadia Publishing.

—A Place Apart: A Pictorial History of Hot Springs, Arkansas. 2011. (Illus.). 190p. pap. 22.50 *(978-1-55728-954-4(9))* Univ. of Arkansas Pr.

Hanley, Ray & Hanley, Steven. Arkansas County. 2008. (Images of America Ser.). (ENG., Illus.). 128p. pap. 19.99 *(978-0-7385-5340-5(9))* Arcadia Publishing.

Hanley, Steven & Hanley, Ray. Malvern. 2010. (Images of America Ser.). (Illus.). 128p. pap. 21.99 *(978-0-7385-8626-7(9))* Arcadia Publishing.

Harris, Monte. Bentonville. 2011. (Images of America Ser.). (ENG., Illus.). 128p. pap. 21.99 *(978-0-7385-8724-0(9))* Arcadia Publishing.

Heady, Mary & Spencer, Mark. Monticello. 2011. (Images of America Ser.). (ENG., Illus.). 128p. pap. 21.99 ***(978-0-7385-8789-9(3))*** Arcadia Publishing.

Henry, James P. Resources of the State of Arkansas, with Description of Counties, Railroads, Mines, & the City of Little Rock. 2006. 136p. per. 16.99 *(978-1-4255-0950-7(9))* MPublishing.

Joseph, Timothy. Historic Photos of Little Rock. 2009. (Historic Photos Ser.). (ENG.). 206p. 39.95 *(978-1-59652-379-1(4))* Turner Publishing Co.

Kovalcik, Timothy M. The Great Passion Play. 2008. (Images of America Ser.). (ENG., Illus.). 128p. pap. 19.99 *(978-0-7385-5324-5(7))* Arcadia Publishing.

Kwas, Mary L. A Pictorial History of Arkansas's Old State House: Celebrating 175 Years. 2011. (ENG., Illus.). 334p. 49.95 *(978-1-55728-955-1(7))* Univ. of Arkansas Pr.

Lowe, Alan & Hall, Jason. The Ghosts of Little Rock: Tales of the City's Most Haunted Places. Koone, D. W., ed. 2008. pap. 9.95 *(978-1-4276-3560-0(9))* Aardvark Global Publishing.

Lyon, Marguerite. Hurrah for Arkansas: From Razorbacks to Diamonds. 2011. 312p. 50.95 ***(978-1-258-08151-5(2))*** Literary Licensing, LLC.

Nuttall, Thomas. A Journal of Travel into Arkansa Territory, during the Year 1819: With Occasional Observations on the Manners of the Aborigines. 2011. (Cambridge Library Collection - Travel & Exploration Ser.). (ENG., Illus.). 320p. pap. 28.99 ***(978-1-108-03249-0(4))*** Cambridge Univ. Pr.

Nuttall, Thomas. Nuttall's Journal: Of Travels into the Arkansa Territory October 2, 1818-February 18 1820. 2007. (Travel in America Ser.). (ENG.). 372p. 49.95 *(978-1-4290-0068-0(6))*; per. 24.95 *(978-1-4290-0069-7(4))* Applewood Bks.

Parker, H. Wayne, et al. Forrest City & St. Francis County. 2008. (Images of America Ser.). (ENG., Illus.). 128p. pap. 19.99 *(978-0-7385-5422-8(7))* Arcadia Publishing.

Parnell, Todd. The Buffalo, Ben, & Me. 2007. (ENG., Illus.). 136p. (gr. 9). 24.95 *(978-0-8262-1752-3(4))* Univ. of Missouri Pr.

Polston, Mike & Polston, Debra Carrington. Cabot. 2012. (Images of America Ser.). (ENG., Illus.). 128p. pap. 21.99 ***(978-0-7385-9102-5(5))*** Arcadia Publishing.

Spencer, Mark. A Haunted Love Story: The Ghosts of the Allen House. 2012. (ENG., Illus.). 240p. pap. 15.95 ***(978-0-7387-3073-8(4))*** Llewellyn Pubns.

Stepanoff, Bonnie. Big Spring Autumn. 2008. (Illus.). 148p. pap. 16.95 *(978-1-931112-86-4(X))* Truman State Univ. Pr.

Thwaites, Reuben Gold. Early Western Travels, 1748-1846: Nuttall's Travels into the Arkansa Territory 1819, Vol. XIII. 2007. cd-rom 15.95 *(978-0-7884-4418-0(2))* Heritage Bks.

UFOs, The. Bizarrkansas Volume One. 2010. 87p. pap. 16.00 *(978-0-557-34802-2(1))* Lulu Enterprises Inc.

Underwood, Ed. Haunted Jonesboro. 2011. 128p. pap. 19.99 ***(978-1-60949-366-0(4))*** History Pr., The.

Williams, Joshua. Hope. 2010. (Images of America Ser.). (ENG., Illus.). 128p. pap. 21.99 *(978-0-7385-8596-3(3))* Arcadia Publishing.

2006-2007 Class Trip Directory South West Central. 2006. per. 9.95 *(978-0-9743329-9-4(2))* Family Pubns.

ARKANSAS—DIRECTORIES

MDR School Directories, 2006-07: Arkansas, 51 vols. 29th ed. 2006. 141p. 70.00 *(978-1-57953-488-2(0))* Market Data Retrieval.

2007 Arkansas Manufacturers Register. 2006. per. 93.00 *(978-1-58202-439-4(1))* Manufacturers' News, Inc.

ARKANSAS—ECONOMIC CONDITIONS

Downs, William, Jr. Stories of Survival: Arkansas Farmers During the Great Depression. 2011. (ENG., Illus.). 304p. pap. 19.95 *(978-0-9824295-5-6(X))* Phoenix International, Inc.

Henry, James P. Resources of the State of Arkansas, with Description of Counties, Railroads, Mines, & the City of Little Rock. 2006. 136p. per. 16.99 *(978-1-4255-0950-7(9))* MPublishing.

Rosen, Marjorie. Boom Town: How Wal-Mart Transformed an All-American Town into an International Community. 2009. (ENG., Illus.). 288p. 24.95 *(978-1-55652-948-1(1))* Chicago Review Pr., Inc.

Williams, C. Fred. Historic Little Rock: An Illustrated History. 2008. (Illus.). 148p. *(978-1-893619-82-1(6))* Historical Publishing Network.

ARKANSAS—GENEALOGY

Allen, Desmond Walls, compiled by. Abstracts from Masonic Records: Grand Lodge of Arkansas, 1880-1883. 2007. pap. 29.00 *(978-1-56546-379-0(X))* Arkansas Research, Inc.

—Abstracts from the Sharp County Record Newspaper Published in Evening Shade, Arkansas 1917. 2006. pap. 25.00 *(978-1-56546-342-4(0))* Arkansas Research, Inc.

—Arkansas Death Record Index, 1934-1940. 2nd ed. 2006. pap. 55.50 *(978-1-56546-343-1(9))* Arkansas Research, Inc.

—Index to Arkansas Goodspeed Biographical Sketches. 2007. pap. 22.00 *(978-1-56546-390-5(0))* Arkansas Research, Inc.

Barnes, Cathy, compiled by. Index to the Arkansas Gazette, July through December 1900. 2007. pap. 24.00 *(978-1-56546-380-6(3))* Arkansas Research, Inc.

Boyd, Gregory A. Family Maps of Cleburne County, Arkansas, Deluxe Edition: With Homesteads, Roads, Waterways, Towns, Cemeteries, & More. 2006. (Illus.). 270p. lib. bdg. 51.99 *(978-1-4203-0378-0(3))*; spiral bd. 38.00 *(978-1-4203-0377-3(5))* Arphax Publishing Co.

—Family Maps of Lawrence County, Arkansas, Deluxe Edition: With Homesteads, Roads, Waterways, Towns, Cemeteries, Railroads, & More. 2007. (Illus.). 220p. (ENG.). lib. bdg. 49.99 *(978-1-4203-0689-7(8))*; spiral bd. 36.00 *(978-1-4203-0688-0(X))* Arphax Publishing Co.

—Family Maps of Madison County, Arkansas, Deluxe Edition: With Homesteads, Roads, Waterways, Towns, Cemeteries, Railroads, & More. 2008. (ENG., Illus.). 418p. lib. bdg. 57.99 *(978-1-4203-0908-9(0))*; spiral bd. 46.00 *(978-1-4203-0907-2(2))* Arphax Publishing Co.

—Family Maps of Nevada County, Arkansas, Deluxe Edition: With Homesteads, Roads, Waterways, Towns, Cemeteries, Railroads, & More. 2007. (Illus.). 254p. lib. bdg. 51.99 *(978-1-4203-0651-4(0))*; spiral bd. 38.00 *(978-1-4203-0650-7(2))* Arphax Publishing Co.

Boyes, Karen. Wilderness Pioneers of America Genealogy. 2008. (Illus.). pap. *(978-0-615-17592-8(9)*, Gateway Pr.) White-Bowden Assocs.

Brown, Algie D. & Brown, Bryan T. Brown's Bulletin: Memoirs of a Louisiana Family on the Move, 1876-1973. 2008. (Illus.). 651p. *(978-0-578-00315-3(5))* Bodcau Publishing.

Chapman, Marcia, compiled by. Columbia County, Arkansas Cemeteries. 2008. 60.00 *(978-0-9816451-0-0(0))* Arkansas Genealogical Society, Inc.

—Columbia County, Arkansas Obituary Index, 1948-2004. 2008. 50.00 *(978-0-9816451-1-7(9))* Arkansas Genealogical Society, Inc.

Eddlemon, Sherida K. Index to the Arkansas General Land Office, 1820-1907: Covering the Counties of AK, Desha, Chicot, Jefferson, Phillips. 2008. 306p. pap. 28.00 *(978-0-7884-0902-8(6)*, E112) Heritage Bks.

—Index to the Arkansas General Land Office, 1820-1907: Covering the Counties of Miller, Lafayette, Columbia, Ouchita, Calhoun & Clark, Vol. 10. 2008. pap. 29.00 *(978-0-7884-2049-8(6))* Heritage Bks.

—Index to the Arkansas General Land Office, 1820-1907: Covering the Counties of Washington, Crawford & Sebastian. 2008. 326p. pap. 29.00 *(978-0-7884-1121-2(7)*, E107) Heritage Bks.

—Index to the Arkansas General Land Office, 1820-1907 Vol. 2: Covering the Counties of; Union, Bradley & Ashley. 2008. 348p. pap. 30.00 *(978-0-7884-0930-1(1)*, E111) Heritage Bks.

Fulton County History Book Committee (Ark.) Staff, contrib. by. Fulton County, Arkansas: History & Families. 2008. (Illus.). 536p. *(978-0-9798802-8-5(9))* Acclaim Pr., Inc.

Goodspeed's A Reminiscent History of the Ozark Region. 2007. cd-rom 9.95 *(978-1-56546-387-5(0))* Arkansas Research, Inc.

History & Families: Boone County, Arkansas. 2008. (Illus.). 320p. ***(978-1-935001-07-2(8))*** Acclaim Pr., Inc.

Russell, Oscar G., compiled by. Index of Death Notices Appearing in the Arkansas Democrat-Gazette 1992. 2006. pap. 42.00 *(978-1-56546-363-9(3))* Arkansas Research, Inc.

—Index of Death Notices Appearing in the Arkansas Democrat-Gazette 1994. 2006. pap. 41.00 *(978-1-56546-365-3(X))* Arkansas Research, Inc.

—Index of Death Notices Appearing in the Arkansas Democrat-Gazette 1995. 2006. pap. 41.00 *(978-1-56546-366-0(8))* Arkansas Research, Inc.

—Index of Death Notices Appearing in the Arkansas Democrat-Gazette 1996. 2006. pap. 40.00 *(978-1-56546-367-7(6))* Arkansas Research, Inc.

—Index of Death Notices Appearing in the Arkansas Democrat-Gazette 1997. 2006. pap. 46.00 *(978-1-56546-368-4(4))* Arkansas Research, Inc.

—Index of Death Notices Appearing in the Arkansas Democrat-Gazette 1998. 2006. pap. 41.00 *(978-1-56546-369-1(2))* Arkansas Research, Inc.

—Index of Death Notices Appearing in the Arkansas Democrat-Gazette 1999. 2006. pap. 46.00 *(978-1-56546-370-7(6))* Arkansas Research, Inc.

—Index of Death Notices Appearing in the Arkansas Democrat-Gazette 2000. 2006. pap. 41.00 *(978-1-56546-371-4(4))* Arkansas Research, Inc.

—Index of Death Notices Appearing in the Arkansas Democrat-Gazette 2001. 2006. pap. 42.00 *(978-1-56546-372-1(2))* Arkansas Research, Inc.

—Index of Death Notices Appearing in the Arkansas Democrat-Gazette 2002. 2006. pap. 40.00 *(978-1-56546-373-8(0))* Arkansas Research, Inc.

—Index of Death Notices Appearing in the Arkansas Democrat-Gazette 2003. 2006. pap. 36.00 *(978-1-56546-374-5(9))* Arkansas Research, Inc.

—Index of Death Notices Appearing in the Arkansas Democrat-Gazette 2004. 2006. pap. 35.00 *(978-1-56546-375-2(7))* Arkansas Research, Inc.

—Index of Death Notices Appearing in the Arkansas Democrat-Gazette 2005. 2006. pap. 55.00 *(978-1-56546-376-9(5))* Arkansas Research, Inc.

—Index of Death Notices Appearing in the Arkansas Gazette 1914. 2006. pap. *(978-1-56546-344-8(7))* Arkansas Research, Inc.

—Index of Death Notices Appearing in the Arkansas Gazette 1915. 2006. pap. 25.00 *(978-1-56546-345-5(5))* Arkansas Research, Inc.

—Index of Death Notices Appearing in the Arkansas Gazette 1916. 2006. pap. 26.00 *(978-1-56546-346-2(3))* Arkansas Research, Inc.

—Index of Death Notices Appearing in the Arkansas Gazette 1917. 2006. pap. 22.00 *(978-1-56546-347-9(1))* Arkansas Research, Inc.

—Index of Death Notices Appearing in the Arkansas Gazette 1918. 2006. pap. 66.00 *(978-1-56546-348-6(X))* Arkansas Research, Inc.

—Index of Death Notices Appearing in the Arkansas Gazette 1919. 2006. pap. 26.00 *(978-1-56546-349-3(8))* Arkansas Research, Inc.

—Index of Death Notices Appearing in the Arkansas Gazette 1920. 2006. pap. 27.00 *(978-1-56546-350-9(1))* Arkansas Research, Inc.

—Index of Death Notices Appearing in the Arkansas Gazette 1921. 2006. pap. 35.00 *(978-1-56546-351-6(X))* Arkansas Research, Inc.

—Index of Death Notices Appearing in the Arkansas Gazette 1922. 2006. pap. 34.00 *(978-1-56546-352-3(8))* Arkansas Research, Inc.

—Index of Death Notices Appearing in the Arkansas Gazette 1923. 2006. pap. 33.00 *(978-1-56546-353-0(6))* Arkansas Research, Inc.

—Index of Death Notices Appearing in the Arkansas Gazette 1924. 2006. pap. 34.00 *(978-1-56546-354-7(4))* Arkansas Research, Inc.

—Index of Death Notices Appearing in the Arkansas Gazette 1925. 2006. pap. 38.00 *(978-1-56546-355-4(2))* Arkansas Research, Inc.

—Index of Death Notices Appearing in the Arkansas Gazette 1926. 2006. pap. 41.00 *(978-1-56546-356-1(0))* Arkansas Research, Inc.

—Index of Death Notices Appearing in the Arkansas Gazette 1927. 2006. pap. 44.00 *(978-1-56546-357-8(9))* Arkansas Research, Inc.

—Index of Death Notices Appearing in the Arkansas Gazette 1928. 2006. pap. 41.00 *(978-1-56546-358-5(7))* Arkansas Research, Inc.

—Index of Death Notices Appearing in the Arkansas Gazette 1929. 2006. pap. 55.00 *(978-1-56546-359-2(5))* Arkansas Research, Inc.

—Index of Death Notices Appearing in the Arkansas Gazette 1960. 2006. pap. 37.00 *(978-1-56546-360-8(9))* Arkansas Research, Inc.

—Index of Death Notices Appearing in the Arkansas Gazette 1990. 2006. pap. 38.00 *(978-1-56546-361-5(7))* Arkansas Research, Inc.

—Index of Death Notices Appearing in the Arkansas Gazette 1991. 2006. pap. 42.00 *(978-1-56546-362-2(5))* Arkansas Research, Inc.

Toms, Marie & Brown, Earma. Peppers Family Legacy. 2008. 172p. pap. 11.95 *(978-0-9797701-2-8(2))* Butterfly Pr.

Tumbo, Silas C. Tumbo's Tales of the Ozarks, Nine Volumes on CD. Allen, Desmond Walls, ed. 2007. cd-rom 39.95 *(978-1-56546-392-9(7))* Arkansas Research, Inc.

ARKANSAS—GUIDEBOOKS

Chamberlin, Johnnie. Trails of Little Rock: Hiking, Biking, & Kayaking Trails in Little Rock. 2009. (ENG., Illus.). 80p. (gr. 12). pap. 12.00 *(978-1-935166-10-8(7))* Parkhurst Brothers, Inc., Pubs.

DeLano, Patti. Arkansas: A Guide to Unique Places. 9th ed. 2008. (Off the Beaten Path Ser.). (ENG., Illus.). 240p. pap. 14.95 *(978-0-7627-4856-3(7))* Globe Pequot Pr., The.

Ernst, Tim. Arkansas Nature Lover's Guidebook: How to Find 101 Scenic Areas in the Natural State. 2010. (ENG., Illus.). 224p. pap. 19.95 *(978-1-882906-58-1(6))* Cloudland.net Publishing.

Ernst, Tim Ernst. Arkansas Waterfalls: Scenic Icons of the Natural State. Ernst, Tim Ernst & Ernst, Pam, eds. 2010. (ENG., Illus.). 132p. 29.95 *(978-1-882906-61-1(6))* Cloudland.net Publishing.

Kavanagh, James. Arkansas Trees & Wildflowers: An Introduction to Familiar Species. 2008. (Pocket Naturalist - Waterford Press Ser.). (ENG., Illus.). 1p. 5.95 *(978-1-58355-404-3(1))* Waterford Pr., Inc.

Molloy, Johnny. Explorer's Guide 50 Hikes in the Ozarks: Walks, Hikes, & Backpacks in the Mountains, Wildernesses & Geological Wonders of Arkansas & Missouri. 2008. (Explorer's 50 Hikes Ser.). (ENG., Illus.). 256p. pap. 16.95 *(978-0-88150-735-5(0)*, 150735) Countryman Pr.

Wilkerson, Lyn. Slow Travels-Arkansas. 2009. 108p. pap. 13.00 *(978-0-557-09474-5(7))* Lulu Enterprises Inc.

Wood, Jana. Arkansas. 2010. (Explorer's Guides). (ENG., Illus.). 320p. pap. 21.95 *(978-0-88150-892-5(6)*, 150892) Countryman Pr.

ARKANSAS—HISTORY

Akins, Jerry. Hangin' Times in Fort Smith: A History of Executions in Judge Parker's Court. 2012. (ENG.). 268p. pap. 22.50 ***(978-1-935106-34-0(1))*** Butler Ctr. for Arkansas Studies.

Arkansas. (Rand Mcnally Wall Maps Ser.). 229.00 *(978-0-528-86148-2(4))* Rand McNally.

Arkansas. Adjutant-'s Office. Report of the Adjutant General of Arkansas, for the Period of the Late Rebellion, & to November 1 1866. 2006. 292p. per. 23.99 *(978-1-4255-2658-0(6))* MPublishing.

The Arkansas Journey Program Kit: All components for the Arkansas Journey, 1 vol. 2009. 149.95 *(978-1-4236-0714-4(7))* Gibbs Smith, Publisher.

Arnold, Morris S. The Rumble of a Distant Drum: The Quapaws & Old World Newcomers, 1673-1804. 2007. (Illus.). 230p. per. 18.95 *(978-1-55728-839-4(9))* Univ. of Arkansas Pr.

Baer, Frances Lisa. Resistance to Public School Desegregation: Little Rock, Arkansas, & Beyond. 2008. (Law & Society Ser.). 336p. 80.00 *(978-1-59332-260-1(7))* LFB Scholarly Publishing LLC.

Baker, T. Lindsay, ed. Confederate Guerrilla: The Civil War Memoir of Joseph M. Bailey. 2007. 34.95 *(978-1-55728-838-7(0))* Univ. of Arkansas Pr.

Bender, Robert Patrick. Worthy of the Cause for Which They Fight: The Civil War Diary of Brigadier General Harris Reynolds, 1861-1865. 2011. (ENG., Illus.). 343p. pap. 34.95 ***(978-1-55728-971-1(9))*** Univ. of Arkansas Pr.

Bishop, A. W. Loyalty on the Frontier: Or Sketches of Union Men of the South-West with Incidents & Adventures in Rebellion on the Border. Scott, Kim Allen, ed. 2007. 228p. per. 19.95 *(978-1-55728-840-0(2))* Univ. of Arkansas Pr.

Bolsterli, Margaret Jones. Things You Need to Hear: Collected Memories of Growing up in Arkansas, 1890-1980. 2012. (ENG., Illus.). 160p. 24.95 ***(978-1-55728-978-0(6))*** Univ. of Arkansas Pr.

Boyles, Carolyn & Pipkin, Patsy. Searcy. 2012. (Images of America Ser.). (ENG., Illus.). 128p. pap. 21.99 ***(978-0-7385-9101-8(7))*** Arcadia Publishing.

Cantrell, Doyne "Two Wolves". Western Cherokee Nation of Arkansas & Missouri - A History - A Heritage. 2009. (ENG.). 131p. pap. 16.99 *(978-0-557-07892-9(X))* Lulu Enterprises Inc.

Christ, Mark K. Civil War Arkansas 1863: The Battle for a State. 2010. (Campaigns & Commanders Ser.). (ENG.). 336p. (C). 34.95 *(978-0-8061-4087-2(9))* Univ. of Oklahoma Pr.

CHRIST, Mark K. Getting used to being shot At. 2010. (Illus.). 248p. pap. 24.95 *(978-1-55728-939-1(5))* Univ. of Arkansas Pr.

Cottrell, Steve. Haunted Ozark Battlefields: Civil War Ghost Stories & Brief Battle Histories, 1 vol. 2010. (ENG., Illus.). 116p. pap. 12.95 *(978-1-58980-877-5(0))* Pelican Publishing Co., Inc.

Dedmondt, Glenn. Flags of Civil War Arkansas. 2009. (Flag Ser.). (ENG., Illus.). 160p. pap. 22.00 *(978-1-58980-190-5(3))* Pelican Publishing Co., Inc.

Dierks, Don. Full Circle, 1957-2002: A Historical Narrative on the Timberlands of Dierks Forests, Inc. Which Became Hot Springs Village. 2010. (Illus.). 84p. ***(978-0-9844722-1-5(5)***, Orbit Books) Cedar Mountain Bks., LLC.

Dillard, Tom W. Statesmen, Scoundrels, & Eccentrics: A Gallery of Amazing Arkansans. 2010. (ENG., Illus.). 264p. pap. 22.95 *(978-1-55728-927-8(1))* Univ. of Arkansas Pr.

Dougan, Michael B. The Die Is Cast: Arkansas Goes to War 1861. Christ, Mark K., ed. 2010. (ENG., Illus.). 160p. pap. 19.95 *(978-1-935106-15-9(5))* Butler Ctr. for Arkansas Studies.

Eddlemon, Sherida K. Index to the Arkansas General Land Office, 1820-1907: Covering the Counties of: Jackson, Clay, Greene, Sharp, Lawrence, Mississippi, Craighead, Poinsett & Randolph. 2008. 212p. pap. 23.50 *(978-0-7884-1384-1(8)*, E1384) Heritage Bks.

—Index to the Arkansas General Land Office, 1820-1907: Covering the Counties of Scott, Logan, Montgomery, Pike, Sevier & Polk. 2008. pap. 26.00 *(978-0-7884-1884-6(X))* Heritage Bks.

—Index to the Arkansas General Land Office, 1820-1907: Covering the Counties of Washington, Crawford & Sebastion. 2008. 326p. pap. 29.00 *(978-0-7884-1121-2(7)*, E107) Heritage Bks.

—Index to the Arkansas General Land Office, 1820-1907 Vol. 2: Covering the Counties of; Union, Bradley & Ashley. 2008. 348p. pap. 30.00 *(978-0-7884-0930-1(1)*, E111) Heritage Bks.

Edwards, John N. Shelby & His Men: The War in the West. (Illus.). 551p. reprint ed. lib. bdg. 98.00 *(978-0-7222-0676-8(3))* Library Reprints, Inc.

Edwards, John Newman. Shelby & His Men: The War in the West. 551p. reprint ed. 98.00 *(978-0-7222-8367-7(9))* Library Reprints, Inc.

Ferguson, Heather D. Arkansas City. 2008. (Images of America Ser.). (ENG., Illus.). 128p. pap. 19.99 *(978-0-7385-5240-8(2))* Arcadia Publishing.

Forsyth, Michael J. The Red River Campaign of 1864 & the Loss by the Confederacy of the Civil War. alt. ed. 2010. (ENG., Illus.). 192p. pap. 35.00 *(978-0-7864-4499-1(1))* McFarland & Co., Inc. Pubs.

Fulton County History Book Committee (Ark.) Staff, contrib. by. Fulton County, Arkansas: History & Families. 2008. (Illus.). 536p. *(978-0-9798802-8-5(9))* Acclaim Pr., Inc.

Gill, John Purifoy. Open House: The Arkansas Governor's Mansion & Its Place in History. 2011. (ENG., Illus.). 240p. 50.00 *(978-1-935106-26-5(0))* Butler Ctr. for Arkansas Studies.

Goodspeed's A Reminiscent History of the Ozark Region. 2007. cd-rom 9.95 *(978-1-56546-387-5(0))* Arkansas Research, Inc.

Goodspeed's Biographical & Historical Memoirs of Central Arkansas. 2007. cd-rom 9.95 *(978-1-56546-383-7(8))* Arkansas Research, Inc.

Goodspeed's Biographical & Historical Memoirs of Eastern Arkansas. 2007. cd-rom 9.95 *(978-1-56546-382-0(X))* Arkansas Research, Inc.

Goodspeed's Biographical & Historical Memoirs of Northeast Arkansas. 2007. cd-rom 9.95 *(978-1-56546-381-3(1))* Arkansas Research, Inc.

Goodspeed's Biographical & Historical Memoirs of Southern Arkansas. 2007. cd-rom 9.95 *(978-1-56546-384-4(6))* Arkansas Research, Inc.

Goodspeed's Biographical & Historical Memoirs of Western Arkansas. 2007. cd-rom 9.95 *(978-1-56546-385-1(4))* Arkansas Research, Inc.

Goodspeed's Historical Reminiscenses & Biographical Memoirs of Conway County, Arkansas. 2007. cd-rom 9.95 *(978-1-56546-388-2(9))* Arkansas Research, Inc.

Goodspeed's Histories of Arkansas, eight volumes on one CD. 2007. cd-rom 39.95 *(978-1-56546-389-9(7))* Arkansas Research, Inc.

Goodspeed's History of Benton, Washington, Carroll, Madison, Crawford, Franklin, & Sebastian Counties, Arkansas. 2007. cd-rom 9.95 *(978-1-56546-386-8(2))* Arkansas Research, Inc.

Hales, James. Rogers Arkansas 1881-2006. 2007. (Illus.). 168p. pap. 19.95 *(978-0-9790190-0-5(1))* St. Josephs Ozark Pr.

Hanley, Steven, Ray. Main Street Arkansas: The Hearts of Arkansas Cities & Towns - as Portrayed in Postcards & Photographs. 2009. (Illus.). 224p. 33.95 *(978-1-935106-12-8(0))*; (ENG.). pap. 19.95 *(978-1-935106-13-5(9))* Butler Ctr. for Arkansas Studies.

Hanley, Ray & Hanley, Steven. Arkansas County. 2008. (Images of America Ser.). (ENG., Illus.). 128p. pap. 19.99 *(978-0-7385-5340-5(9))* Arcadia Publishing.

Hanley, Ray & Hanley, Steven G. Remembering Arkansas Confederates & the 1911 Little Rock Veterans Reunion. 2006. (Images of America Ser.). (ENG., Illus.). 128p. per. 21.99 *(978-0-7385-4298-0(9))* Arcadia Publishing.

Harris, Monte. Bentonville. 2011. (Images of America Ser.). (ENG., Illus.). 128p. pap. 21.99 *(978-0-7385-8724-0(9))* Arcadia Publishing.

Heady, Mary & Spencer, Mark. Monticello. 2011. (Images of America Ser.). (ENG., Illus.). 128p. pap. 21.99 ***(978-0-7385-8789-9(3))*** Arcadia Publishing.

Hempstead, Fay. Hempstead's Historical Review of Arkansas, three-volume set on CD. 2007. cd-rom 19.95 *(978-1-56546-391-2(9))* Arkansas Research, Inc.

Herndon, Dallas T. Centennial History of Arkansas, three-volume set on CD. 2006. cd-rom 19.95 *(978-1-56546-377-6(3))* Arkansas Research, Inc.

Hicks, Timothy, illus. University of Arkansas All Americans 1928-1997. Date not set. 39.95 *(978-1-891087-01-1(0))* WEHCO Publishing.

History & Families: Boone County, Arkansas. 2008. (Illus.). 320p. ***(978-1-935001-07-2(8))*** Acclaim Pr., Inc.

Jacoway, Elizabeth. Turn Away Thy Son: Little Rock, the Crisis That Shocked the Nation. 2008. 477p. pap. 19.95 *(978-1-55728-878-3(X))* Univ. of Arkansas Pr.

Kennedy, Thomas C. A History of Southland College: The Society of Friends & Black Education in Arkansas. 2009. (ENG., Illus.). 424p. 45.00 *(978-1-55728-916-2(6))* Univ. of Arkansas Pr.

Kilpatrick, Judith. There When We Needed Him: Wiley Austin Branton, Civil Rights Warrior. 2007. (Illus.). 221p. 32.50 *(978-1-55728-848-6(8))* Univ. of Arkansas Pr.

Knotts, Burton Ray, compiled by. Historical & Genealogical Abstracts from Randolph County, Arkansas, Newspapers Of 1919. 2006. pap. 33.00 *(978-1-56546-378-3(1))* Arkansas Research, Inc.

Kovalcik, Timothy M. The Great Passion Play. 2008. (Images of America Ser.). (ENG., Illus.). 128p. pap. 19.99 *(978-0-7385-5324-5(7))* Arcadia Publishing.

Kuczynski, Terri L. & Central Delta Historical Society. Monroe County. 2009. (Images of America Ser.). (ENG., Illus.). 128p. pap. 21.99 *(978-0-7385-6821-8(X))* Arcadia Publishing.

Kujawa, Stan. Historic Places Fayetteville Arkansas. 2007. (Illus.). 150p. spiral bd. 32.00 *(978-0-9705280-9-4(4))* Camelot Consulting.

Kwas, Mary L. A Pictorial History of Arkansas's Old State House: Celebrating 175 Years. 2011. (ENG., Illus.). 334p. 49.95 *(978-1-55728-955-1(7))* Univ. of Arkansas Pr.

Lewis, Catherine & Richard. Race, Politics & Memory. 2007. (Illus.). 270p. (C). pap. 22.95 *(978-1-55728-857-8(7))* Univ. of Arkansas Pr.

Lewis, Catherine M. & Lewis, J. Richard, eds. Race, Politics, & Memory: A Documentary History of the Little Rock School Crisis. 2007. (Illus.). 242p. 65.00 *(978-1-55728-856-1(9))* Univ. of Arkansas Pr.

Lord, Allyn & Rogers Historical Museum Staff. Historic Monte Ne. 2006. (Images of America Ser.). (ENG., Illus.). 128p. per. 21.99 *(978-0-7385-4336-9(5))* Arcadia Publishing.

Margolick, David. Elizabeth & Hazel: Two Women of Little Rock. Lt. ed. 2011. lib. bdg. 33.95 ***(978-1-61173-256-6(5))*** Ctr. Point Large Print.

—Elizabeth & Hazel: Two Women of Little Rock. 2011. (Playaway Adult Nonfiction Ser.). (ENG.). 54.99 ***(978-1-61637-118-0(8))*** Findaway World, LLC.

—Elizabeth & Hazel: Two Women of Little Rock. 2011. (Illus.). 320p. 26.00 *(978-0-300-14193-1(9))* Yale Univ. Pr.

Mary Frances Hodges. John Newton Sarber & Sarber County, Arkansas. 2009. 144p. 25.00 *(978-1-4389-5826-2(9))*; pap. 18.95 *(978-1-4389-5825-5(0))* AuthorHouse.

Mills, Margie I. Turn South for Arkansas: The Story of the Daltons of Faulkner County. 2011. 100p. 38.95 ***(978-1-258-05433-5(7))*** Literary Licensing, LLC.

Monks, William. A History of Southern Missouri & Northern Arkansas: Being an Account of the Early Settlements, the Civil War, the Ku-Klux, & Times of Peace. (Illus.). 247p. reprint ed. lib. bdg. 98.00 *(978-0-7222-0735-2(2))* Library Reprints, Inc.

—A History of Southern Missouri & Northern Arkansas: Being an Account of the Early Settlements, the Civil War, the Ku-Klux, & Times of Peace. Bradbury, John F. et al, eds. 2006. (Illus.). 194p. per. 19.95 *(978-1-55728-832-5(1))* Univ. of Arkansas Pr.

Paradise, Tom. Arkansas: An Illustrated Atlas. 2011. 52p. 19.95 *(978-1-935106-25-8(2))* Butler Ctr. for Arkansas Studies.

Parker, H. Wayne, et al. Forrest City & St. Francis County. 2008. (Images of America Ser.). (ENG., Illus.). 128p. pap. 19.99 *(978-0-7385-5422-8(7))* Arcadia Publishing.

Polston, Mike & Polston, Debra Carrington. Cabot. 2012. (Images of America Ser.). (ENG., Illus.). 128p. pap. 21.99 ***(978-0-7385-9102-5(5))*** Arcadia Publishing.

Ready, Booted, & Spurred: Arkansas in the U.S. - Mexican War. 2008. 216p. 39.95 *(978-1-935106-05-0(8))*; pap. 19.95 *(978-0-9800897-5-2(1))* Butler Ctr. for Arkansas Studies.

Reed, Roy. Looking Back at the Arkansas Gazette: An Oral History. 2009. (Illus.). 378p. 34.95 *(978-1-55728-899-8(2))* Univ. of Arkansas Pr.

Robinson II, Charles Frank. Engaging Missouri: An Epic Drama of Love, Honor, & Redemption across the Color Line. 2007. 208p. per. 14.95 *(978-0-595-43432-9(0))* iUniverse, Inc.

Stone, Patricia. The Adandonment of Happy Hollow. 2011. 92p. pap. ***(978-3-8383-3666-4(6))*** Lambert Academic Publishing.

Teske, Steven. Unvarnished Arkansas: The Naked Truth about Nine Famous Arkansans. 2012. (ENG.). 160p. pap. 19.95 ***(978-1-935106-35-7(X))*** Butler Ctr. for Arkansas Studies.

Tumbo, Silas C. Tumbo's Tales of the Ozarks, Nine Volumes on CD. Allen, Desmond Walls, ed. 2007. cd-rom 39.95 *(978-1-56546-392-9(7))* Arkansas Research, Inc.

Vaught, Elsa, ed. The Diary of an Unknown Soldier: September 5, 1862 to December 7 1862. 2011. 56p. 36.95 ***(978-1-258-09580-2(7))*** Literary Licensing, LLC.

Wappel, Anthony J. & Simpson, Ethel C. Once upon Dickson: An Illustrated History, 1868-2000. 2008. (Illus.). xii, 403p. 22.50 *(978-0-9768007-7-4(2))* Phoenix International, Inc.

Whitaker, Robert. On the Laps of Gods: The Red Summer of 1919 & the Struggle for Justice That Remade a Nation. 2009. (ENG., Illus.). 400p. pap. 16.00 *(978-0-307-33983-6(1)*, Three Rivers Pr.) Crown Publishing Group.

Williams, C. Fred. Historic Little Rock: An Illustrated History. 2008. (Illus.). 148p. *(978-1-893619-82-1(6))* Historical Publishing Network.

Williams, Joshua. Hope. 2010. (Images of America Ser.). (ENG., Illus.). 128p. pap. 21.99 *(978-0-7385-8596-3(3))* Arcadia Publishing.

Woody, Velma B. Branscum & Teske, Steven. Homefront Arkansas: Arkansans Face Wartime Past & Present. 2009. (ENG.). 200p. pap. 15.00 *(978-0-9800897-9-0(4))* Butler Ctr. for Arkansas Studies.

Zeller, Joyce. Hidden History of Eureka Springs. 2011. 128p. pap. 19.99 ***(978-1-60949-376-9(1))*** History Pr., The.

ARKANSAS—MAPS

American Map, creator. Little Rock/Hot Springs Arkansas Street Atlas. 2009. (American Map Ser.). (Illus.). 152p. pap. 17.99 *(978-0-8416-1631-5(0))* American Map Corp.

Boyd, Gregory A. Family Maps of Cleburne County, Arkansas, Deluxe Edition: With Homesteads, Roads, Waterways, Towns, Cemeteries, & More. 2006. (Illus.). 270p. lib. bdg. 51.99 *(978-1-4203-0378-0(3))*; spiral bd. 38.00 *(978-1-4203-0377-3(5))* Arphax Publishing Co.

—Family Maps of Lawrence County, Arkansas, Deluxe Edition: With Homesteads, Roads, Waterways, Towns, Cemeteries, Railroads, & More. 2007. (Illus.). 220p. (ENG.). lib. bdg. 49.99 *(978-1-4203-0689-7(8))*; spiral bd. 36.00 *(978-1-4203-0688-0(X))* Arphax Publishing Co.

—Family Maps of Madison County, Arkansas, Deluxe Edition: With Homesteads, Roads, Waterways, Towns, Cemeteries, Railroads, & More. 2008. (ENG., Illus.). 418p. lib. bdg. 57.99 *(978-1-4203-0908-9(0))*; spiral bd. 46.00 *(978-1-4203-0907-2(2))* Arphax Publishing Co.

—Family Maps of Nevada County, Arkansas, Deluxe Edition: With Homesteads, Roads, Waterways, Towns, Cemeteries, Railroads, & More. 2007. (Illus.). 254p. lib. bdg. 51.99 *(978-1-4203-0651-4(0))*; spiral bd. 38.00 *(978-1-4203-0650-7(2))* Arphax Publishing Co.

Paradise, Tom. Arkansas: An Illustrated Atlas. 2011. 52p. 19.95 *(978-1-935106-25-8(2))* Butler Ctr. for Arkansas Studies.

Rand McNally, creator. Rand Mcnally City Map Book: West Arkansas Cities. 2010. (Rand Mcnally City Map Bks.). (Illus.). 56p. pap. 7.99 *(978-0-528-83227-2(9))* Rand McNally.

—Rand Mcnally Fayetteville, Springdale & Rogers Street Guide: Including Bentonville. 2007. (Illus.). pap. 14.95 *(978-0-528-86575-3(3))* Rand McNally.

ARKANSAS—POLITICS AND GOVERNMENT

Big Hat Law: Arkansas & Its State Police, 1935-2000. 2008. 208p. 39.95 *(978-1-935106-01-2(5))* Butler Ctr. for Arkansas Studies.

Brown, Robert L. Defining Moments: Historic Decisions by Arkansas Governors from McMath Through Huckabee. 2010. (ENG., Illus.). 105p. (C). pap. 19.95 *(978-1-55728-944-5(1))* Univ. of Arkansas Pr.

Dougan, Michael B. The Die Is Cast: Arkansas Goes to War 1861. Christ, Mark K., ed. 2010. (ENG., Illus.). 160p. pap. 19.95 *(978-1-935106-15-9(5))* Butler Ctr. for Arkansas Studies.

Eccleston, Stacey M., et al. Workers' Compensation in Arkansas: Administrative Inventory. 5th ed. 2007. per. 135.00 *(978-1-931906-45-6(9))* Workers Compensation Research Institute.

Huckabee, Mike. Character Makes a Difference: Where I'm from, Where I've Been, & What I Believe. 2007. (ENG.). 227p. per. 11.99 *(978-0-8054-4677-7(X)*, B&H Bks.) B&H Publishing Group.

Parry, Janine A. & Wang, Richard P. Readings in Arkansas Government & Politics. 2009. 75.00 *(978-1-55728-902-5(6))*; pap. 39.95 *(978-1-55728-903-2(4))* Univ. of Arkansas Pr.

ARKANSAS—SOCIAL CONDITIONS

Bayless, Stephanie & Browndervile, Greg Alan. Deep down in the Delta: Folktales & Poems. 2012. (ENG.). 96p. pap. 19.95 ***(978-1-935106-33-3(3))*** Butler Ctr. for Arkansas Studies.

CQ Press, ed. Arkansas Crime in Perspective 2010 Edition, 00 vols. rev. ed. 2010. 24p. pap. 32.00 *(978-1-60871-440-7(3))* CQ Pr.

—Arkansas Health Care in Perspective 2010 Edition, 00 vols. rev. ed. 2010. 24p. pap. 32.00 *(978-1-60871-442-1(X))* CQ Pr.

—Arkansas in Perspective 2010 Edition, 00 vols. rev. ed. 2010. 24p. pap. 32.00 *(978-1-60871-443-8(8))* CQ Pr.

Davis, Lynn A. They Said It Couldn't. 2009. 260p. pap. 29.95 *(978-1-4276-3963-9(9))* Aardvark Global Publishing.

Disaster Declarations: Where Is FEMA in a Time of Need?: Full Hearing of the Committee on Homeland Security, House of Representatives, One Hundred Tenth Congress, First Session, March 15, 2007. 2009. iii, 39p. *(978-0-16-084851-3(2)*, 552-070-40252-7) United States Government Printing Office.

Esralew, Rachel A. & Tortorelli, Robert L. Nutrient Concentrations, Loads, & Yields in the Eucha-Spavinaw Basin, Arkansas & Oklahoma, 2002-09. 2010. (Illus.). vi, 61p. ***(978-1-4113-2922-5(8))*** United States Geological Survey.

Gordon, Fon. Caste & Class: The Black Experience in Arkansas, 1880-1920. 2007. (ENG.). 200p. per. 22.95 *(978-0-8203-3130-0(9))* Univ. of Georgia Pr.

Jennings, Jay. Carry the Rock: Race, Football, & the Soul of an American City. 2010. (ENG., Illus.). 280p. 25.99 *(978-1-60529-637-1(6))* Rodale Pr., Inc.

Morgan, Scott, ed. Arkansas in Perspective 2011, 00 vols. rev. ed. 2011. 24p. pap. 32.00 *(978-1-4522-0015-6(7))* CQ Pr.

Turner, F. W. The People of Princeton. 2007. 124p. per. 19.95 *(978-1-4241-9319-6(2))* PublishAmerica, Inc.

Williams, Johnny E. African American Religion & the Civil Rights Movement in Arkansas. 2008. (ENG.). 177p. pap. 25.00 *(978-1-60473-186-6(9))* Univ. Pr. of Mississippi.

ARKANSAS—SOCIAL LIFE AND CUSTOMS

Bates, Daisy. The Long Shadow of Little Rock. 2007. (ENG., Illus.). 260p. per. 18.95 *(978-1-55728-863-9(1))* Univ. of Arkansas Pr.

Bates, Daisy. The Long Shadow of Little Rock: A Memoir. 2011. 268p. 47.95 ***(978-1-258-09783-7(4))*** Literary Licensing, LLC.

Bolsterli, Margaret Jones. Things You Need to Hear: Collected Memories of Growing up in Arkansas, 1890-1980. 2012. (ENG., Illus.). 160p. 24.95 ***(978-1-55728-978-0(6))*** Univ. of Arkansas Pr.

Hanley, Steven & Hanley, Ray. Malvern. 2010. (Images of America Ser.). (Illus.). 128p. pap. 21.99 *(978-0-7385-8626-7(9))* Arcadia Publishing.

Harrison, A. Cleveland. A Little Rock Boyhood: Growing up in the Great Depression. 2010. (ENG., Illus.). 375p. 29.95 *(978-1-935106-18-0(X))* Butler Ctr. for Arkansas Studies.

Heady, Mary & Spencer, Mark. Monticello. 2011. (Images of America Ser.). (ENG., Illus.). 128p. pap. 21.99 ***(978-0-7385-8789-9(3))*** Arcadia Publishing.

House, Don. Not a Good Sign. 2010. (ENG., Illus.). 128p. pap. 29.95 *(978-0-9824295-0-1(9))* Phoenix International, Inc.

Jones Bolsterli, Margaret. During Wind & Rain: The Jones Family Farm in the Arkansas Delta, 1848-2006. 2008. (Illus.). 144p. pap. 16.95 *(978-1-55728-871-4(2))* Univ. of Arkansas Pr.

Joseph, Timothy. Historic Photos of Little Rock. 2009. (Historic Photos Ser.). (ENG.). 206p. 39.95 *(978-1-59652-379-1(4))* Turner Publishing Co.

Mills, Margie I. Turn South for Arkansas: The Story of the Daltons of Faulkner County. 2011. 100p. 38.95 ***(978-1-258-05433-5(7))*** Literary Licensing, LLC.

Stepenoff, Bonnie. Big Spring Autumn. 2008. (Illus.). 148p. pap. 16.95 *(978-1-931112-86-4(X))* Truman State Univ. Pr.

Stone, Patricia. The Adandonment of Happy Hollow. 2011. 92p. pap. ***(978-3-8383-3666-4(6))*** Lambert Academic Publishing.

Thompson, Brock. The Un-Natural State: Arkansas & the Queer South. 2010. (ENG., Illus.). 275p. 29.95 *(978-1-55728-943-8(3))* Univ. of Arkansas Pr.

Williams, Joshua. Hope. 2010. (Images of America Ser.). (ENG., Illus.). 128p. pap. 21.99 *(978-0-7385-8596-3(3))* Arcadia Publishing.

Zeller, Joyce. Hidden History of Eureka Springs. 2011. 128p. pap. 19.99 ***(978-1-60949-376-9(1))*** History Pr., The.

ARKANSAS RIVER VALLEY

DuVal, Kathleen. The Native Ground: Indians & Colonists in the Heart of the Continent. 2007. (Early American Studies). (Illus.). 336p. (C). per. 24.95 *(978-0-8122-1939-5(2))* Univ. of Pennsylvania Pr.

Hada, Ken. The River White: A Confluence of Brush & Quill. 2011. (Illus.). 116p. pap. 30.00 ***(978-0-9833052-6-2(9))*** Mongrel Empire Pr.

Moorehead, Warren K. Archaeology of the Arkansas River Valley. reprint ed. *(978-0-404-15634-3(7))* AMS Pr., Inc.

ARKHAM HOUSE

Courtemanche, Brian & Sanborn, Matt. Arkham Now: Revisiting the Legend-Haunted City. 2010. (Call of Cthulhu Roleplaying Ser.). (ENG., Illus.). 176p. pap. 27.95 *(978-1-56882-321-8(5))* Chaosium, Inc.

ARLINGTON COUNTY (VA.)

Gilmore, Matthew, text. Historic Photos of Arlington County. 2007. (Historic Photos Ser.). (ENG., Illus.). 205p. 39.95 *(978-1-59652-396-8(4))* Turner Publishing Co.

ARLINGTON NATIONAL CEMETERY (ARLINGTON, VA.)

Arlington National Cemetery: A Photographic Tour. 2007. *(978-1-57864-450-6(X))* Donning Co. Pubs.

Arlington National Cemetery: An Update from the New Administration: Hearing Before the Subcommittee on Disability Assistance & Memorial Affairs of the Committee on Veterans' Affairs, U.S. House of Representatives, One Hundred Twelfth Congress, First Session, June 23, 2011. 2011. iii, 55p. ***(978-0-16-090141-6(3)***, 552-070-43844-1) United States Government Printing Office.

Atkinson, Rick. Where Valor Rests: Arlington National Cemetery. 2009. (ENG., Illus.). 192p. 18.95 *(978-1-4262-0456-2(6)*, National Geographic) National Geographic Society.

—Where Valor Rests: Arlington National Cemetery. 2007. (ENG., Illus.). 192p. 30.00 *(978-1-4262-0089-2(7)*, National Geographic) National Geographic Society.

Brundick, Tara & Brundick, Patricia. On Behalf of a Grateful Nation. 2007. 68p. pap. 25.98 *(978-0-615-15244-8(9))* Brundick, Tara.

Callihan, David L. With Full Military Honors: Civil War Generals Buried at Arlington National Cemetery. 2009. 222p. pap. 30.00 *(978-0-7884-4934-5(6))*; (Illus.). xi, 208p. *(978-0-7884-8186-4(X))* Heritage Bks.

Dodge, George W. Arlington National Cemetery. 2006. (Images of America Ser.). (ENG., Illus.). 128p. per. 21.99 *(978-0-7385-4326-0(8))* Arcadia Publishing.

Globe Pequot Press Staff & Parzych, Cynthia. Arlington National Cemetery: A Walking Tour Through History. 2009. (Timeline Ser.). (ENG., Illus.). 96p. pap. 15.95 *(978-0-7627-5329-1(3))* Globe Pequot Pr., The.

Knudsen, Robert C. A Living Treasure: Seasonal Photographs of Arlington National Cemetery. 2008. (Illus.). 200p. 29.95 *(978-1-59797-272-7(X))* Potomac Bks., Inc.

Peters, James Edward. Arlington National Cemetery: Shrine to America's Heroes. 2008. 350p. pap. 15.95 *(978-1-890627-92-8(5))* Woodbine Hse.

A

Poole, Robert M. On Hallowed Ground: The Story of Arlington National Cemetery. (ENG.). 368p. 2010. pap. 17.00 *(978-0-8027-1549-4(4))* 2009. 28.00 *(978-0-8027-1548-7(6))* Walker & Co.

Review of Army Investigation of Arlington National Cemetery: Committee on Armed Services, House of Representatives, One Hundred Eleventh Congress, Second Session, Hearing Held June 30, 2010. 2010. iii, 74p. ***(978-0-16-087394-2(0)**,* 552-070-42087-8) United States Government Printing Office.

United States, Congress House Committee on Veterans' Affairs Subcommittee on Disability Assistance and Memorial Affairs Staff, contrib. by. Policy & Operational Issues Facing Arlington National Cemetery & the American Battle Monuments Commission: Hearing Before the Committee on Veterans' Affairs, House of Representatives, Subcommittee on Disability Assistance & Memorial Affairs, One Hundred Ninth Congress, Second Session, March 30, 2006. 2007. iii, 27p. *(978-0-16-078009-7(8),* 552-070-35430-1) United States Government Printing Office.

ARM

Dines, David M., et al. Complex Upper Extremity Trauma: Acute & Reconstructive Solutions. 2008. 203p. 159.95 *(978-3-13-142241-5(6))* Thieme Medical Pubs., Inc.

Goldfarb, Charles A., et al. A Pocketbook Manual of Hand & Upper Extremity Anatomy: Primus Manus. 2010. (ENG., Illus.). 256p. pap. 74.99 *(978-1-60831-466-9(9))* Lippincott Williams & Wilkins.

Knoll, Daniela. Arm Movement Analysis Before & after Birth. 2008. 108p. pap. *(978-3-8364-8925-6(2))* VDM Verlag Dr. Mueller e.K.

Lorich, Dean G., et al, eds. Solutions for Complex Upper Extremity Trauma. 2008. (ENG., Illus.). 272p. 169.99 *(978-1-58890-504-8(7))* Thieme Medical Pubs., Inc.

Pereira da Silva, Jose Antonio & Woolf, Anthony D. Rheumatology of the Upper Limbs in Clinical Practice. 2011. (ENG., Illus.). vii, 142p. pap. 59.95 ***(978-1-4471-2241-8(0)**,* 1447122410) Springer.

Peterson, Caryl E. Upper Extremity: Guide to the Prosected Cadaver. rev. ed. 2011. (ENG.). 110p. pap. 40.57 *(978-0-7575-6044-6(X))* Kendall Hunt Publishing Co.

Rocon, Eduardo & Pons, José L. Exoskeletons in Rehabilitation Robotics: Tremor Suppression. 2011. (Springer Tracts in Advanced Robotics Ser.). (Illus.). xviii, 138p. 109.00 *(978-3-642-17658-6(5),* 3642176585) Springer.

Rohde, Rachel S. & Millett, Peter J. Evaluation & Management of Common Upper Extremity Disorders: A Practical Handbook. 2011. (ENG., Illus.). 304p. pap. 48.95 *(978-1-55642-949-1(5))* SLACK, Inc.

Yao, Jeffrey. Year Book of Hand & Upper Limb Surgery 2010. 2010. (Year Bks.: 2010). (ENG.). 325p. 176.00 *(978-0-323-06832-1(4),* Mosby) Elsevier - Health Sciences Div.

Yao, Jeffrey. Year Book of Hand & Upper Limb Surgery 2011 - E-Book1. 2011. E-Book ***(978-0-323-08736-0(1))*** Elsevier - Health Sciences Div.

Yao, Jeffrey & Steinmann, Scott P. Year Book of Hand & Upper Limb Surgery 2012. 2012. (Year Bks.: 2012). (ENG.). 272p. 173.00 ***(978-0-323-08881-7(3)**,* Mosby) Elsevier - Health Sciences Div.

ARMADA, 1588

Fremont-Barnes, Gregory. Victory vs Redoutable: Ships of the Line at Trafalgar 1805. 2008. (Duel Ser.). (ENG., Illus.). 80p. pap. 17.95 *(978-1-84603-134-2(6))* Osprey Publishing, Ltd. GBR. Dist: Random Hse., Inc.

Konstam, Angus. The Great Expedition: Sir Francis Drake on the Spanish Main 1585-86. 2011. (Raid Ser.). (ENG., Illus.). 80p. pap. 18.95 *(978-1-84908-245-7(6))* Osprey Publishing, Ltd. GBR. Dist: Random Hse., Inc.

Walker, Bryce. Armada. (Illus.). 176p. 24.00 *(978-1-84447-111-9(X))* Time Life Value GBR. Dist: Mercury Bks. Ltd.

Williams, Patrick. Armada. 2008. (ENG., Illus.). 240p. pap. 22.95 *(978-0-7524-2976-2(0))* History Pr. Ltd.,The GBR. Dist: Independent Pubs. Group.

ARMADILLOS

Wyrick, Priscilla B. & Bavoil, Patrik M., eds. Chlamydia: Genomics & Pathogenesis. 2007. (ENG., Illus.). 550p. (C). 272.00 *(978-1-904933-21-2(1),* Taylor & Francis) Taylor & Francis Group GBR. Dist: Taylor & Francis Group.

ARMAMENTS

see Military Readiness; Military Weapons

ARMAMENTS INDUSTRIES

see Defense Industries

ARMED FORCES

see also Air Forces; Armies; Military Service, Voluntary; Militia; National Service; Navies; Sailors; Sociology, Military; Soldiers; Strategic Forces

also specific branches of the Armed Forces under names of countries, e.g. France—Army; or subdivision Armed Forces under countries, e.g. United States—Armed Forces

Abrahamson, James & O'Meara, Andrew. LEADERSHIP: Combat Leaders & Lessons. 2008. 215p. pap. 18.00 *(978-0-615-25574-3(4))* Stand Up America.

—Leadership:Combat Leaders & Lessons. 2008. 215p. 32.00 *(978-0-615-25578-1(7))* Stand Up America.

Amara, Jomana & Hendricks, Ann, eds. Military Health Care. 2012. (Cass Military Studies). (ENG.). 256p. (C). 135.00 ***(978-0-415-52402-5(4))*** Routledge.

Armstrong, Nicholas J. & Chura-Beaver, Jacqueline. Harnessing Post-Conflict Transitions: A Conceptual Primer. 2010. (PKSOI Papers). *(978-1-58487-464-5(3))* Strategic Studies Institute, U.S. Army War College Commandant (AWCC-DSI/Pubns.).

Avakov, Aleksandr V. Quality of Life, Balance of Power & Nuclear Weapons: A Statistical Yearbook for Statesmen & Citizens. 2008. xiv, 312p. 45.00 *(978-0-87586-595-9(X));* pap. 26.95 *(978-0-87586-594-2(1))* Algora Publishing.

Avakov, Alexander V. Quality of Life, Balance of Power, & Nuclear Weapons: A Statesman's & Citizen's Statistical Yearbook. 2011. 202p. pap. 29.95 *(978-0-87586-820-2(7))* Algora Publishing.

—Quality of Life, Balance of Power, & Nuclear Weapons: A Statesman's & Citizen's Statistical Yearbook. 2011. 202p. pap. 19.95 *(978-0-87586-819-6(3))* Algora Publishing.

—Quality of Life, Balance of Power, & Nuclear Weapons: A Statistical Yearbook for Statesmen & Citizens. 2010. (Quality of Life, Balance of Power, & Nuclear Weapons Ser.). 181p. 45.00 *(978-0-87586-775-5(8));* pap. 26.95 *(978-0-87586-774-8(X))* Algora Publishing.

—Quality of Life, Balance of Power & Nuclear Weapons (2009) A Statistical Yearbook for Statesmen & Citizens. 2009. 326p. pap. 26.95 *(978-0-87586-675-8(1))* Algora Publishing.

Aybet, Gülnur & Moore, Rebecca R., eds. NATO in Search of a Vision. 2010. (ENG., Illus.). 288p. pap. 29.95 *(978-1-58901-630-9(0))* Georgetown Univ. Pr.

Barany, Zoltan D. The Soldier & the Changing State: Building Democratic Armies in Africa, Asia, Europe, & the Americas. 2012. (ENG.). 392p. (C). 75.00 ***(978-0-691-13768-1(4))**;* pap. 29.95 ***(978-0-691-13769-8(2))*** Princeton Univ. Pr.

Bertell, Rosalie. Planet Earth: The Latest Weapon of War. 262p. 30.00 *(978-0-7043-4428-0(9))* Women's Pr., Ltd., The GBR. Dist: Trafalgar Square Publishing.

Brooks, Risa & Stanley, Elizabeth, eds. Creating Military Power: The Sources of Military Effectiveness. 2007. (ENG., Illus.). 264p. 55.00 *(978-0-8047-5399-9(7))* Stanford Univ. Pr.

Bruneau, Thomas & Trinkunas, Harold. Global Politics of Defense Reform. 2008. (Initiatives in Strategic Studies: Issues & Policies Ser.). (ENG.). 312p. 100.00 *(978-0-230-60444-5(7))* Palgrave Macmillan.

Clayton, Bert/Allen. Cocky's Boy. 2009. pap. 19.95 *(978-1-934956-20-5(1))* Elderberry Press, Inc.

Closmann, Charles E., ed. War & the Environment: Military Destruction in the Modern Age. 2009. (Williams-Ford Texas A&M University Military History Ser.). (ENG.). 256p. 40.00 *(978-1-60344-115-5(8));* (Illus.). 222p. pap. 22.00 *(978-1-60344-169-8(7))* Texas A&M Univ. Pr.

Cole, Bernard. Taiwan's Security: History & Prospects. 2008. 272p. 39.95 *(978-0-415-46082-8(4))* Routledge.

Conboy, Ken. Fank: A History of the Cambodian Armed Forces 1970-1975. 2011. 286p. pap. ***(978-979-3780-86-3(X))*** Equinox Publishing Ltd.

CQ Press Staff. Worldwide Directory of Defense Authorities 2007, 00 vols. rev. ed. 2007. pap. 616.00 *(978-0-87289-268-2(9))* CQ Pr.

Crowcy, Terry. Military Mayhem: 2,500 Years of Soldierly Sleaze & Scandal. 2010. (General Military Ser.). (ENG., Illus.). 320p. pap. 12.00 *(978-1-84908-147-4(6))* Osprey Publishing, Ltd. GBR. Dist: Random Hse., Inc.

Cucolo, Ginger. Dog Tags: The History, Personal Stories, Cultural Impact, & Future of Military Identification. 2011. 344p. pap. 14.95 ***(978-0-9833057-0-5(6))*** Allen House Publishing.

Davis, Robert T., II. The U. S. Army & the Media in the 20th Century. Combat Studies Institute (U.S.), ed. 2009. (Long War Series Occasional Paper Ser.). (ENG.). 135p. pap. 13.00 *(978-0-9823283-4-7(6),* Dept. of the Army) United States Government Printing Office.

Department of the Army Staff. U. S. Army Leadership Handbook: Skills, Tactics, & Techniques for Leading in Any Situation. 2012. (ENG.). 216p. pap. 14.95 ***(978-1-61608-562-9(2)**,* 608562) Skyhorse Publishing Co., Inc.

Environmental Change & Security Program Report Issue 12. 2007. per. *(978-0-9745919-3-3(9))* Environmental Change & Security Program.

Fenema, Paul van. Managing Military Organisations: Theory & Practice. Soeters, Joseph & Beeres, Robert, eds. 2010. (Cass Military Studies). (ENG., Illus.). 304p. (C). 138.00 *(978-0-415-48406-0(5))* Routledge.

Friedman, Lauri S. National Security. 2009. (OPPOSING VIEWPOINTS VISUALS Ser.). (ENG.). 144p. (YA). (gr. 7-12). 35.75 *(978-0-7377-4481-1(2))* Cengage Gale.

G. Caforio G. Kummel Staff. Armed Forces & Conflict Resolution. 2008. (Illus.). xiz, 411p. 200.00 *(978-1-84855-122-0(3))* Emerald Group Publishing Ltd. GBR. Dist: Turpin Distribution Services Ltd.

Gilroy, Curtis & Williams, Cindy, eds. Service to Country: Personnel Policy & the Transformation of Western Militaries. 2007. (BCSIA Studies in International Security Ser.). (ENG., Illus.). 400p. (gr. 17). 55.00 *(978-0-262-07276-2(9));* pap. 28.00 *(978-0-262-57235-4(4))* MIT Pr.

Glenn, Russell W. Counterinsurgency in a Test Tube: Analyzing the Success of the Regional Assistance Mission to Solomon Islands (RAMSI) 2007. (Illus.). 190p. per. 30.00 *(978-0-8330-4027-5(8),* mg551) RAND Corp., The.

Hall & Markowski, Stefan. Defence Procurement & Industry Policy. 2006. (Routledge Studies in Defence & Peace Economics Ser.). (Illus.). 256p. 150.00 *(978-0-415-36288-7(1))* Routledge.

Hartley, Keith & Sandler, Todd, eds. The Economics of Defence Spending: An International Survey. 2011. (Routledge Revivals Ser.). (ENG.). 306p. 130.00 *(978-0-415-61544-0(5))* Routledge.

Hinton, Clete. CD: Arc of Crisis 1979. 2007. cd-rom 15.95 *(978-0-7884-4189-9(2))* Heritage Bks.

Horn, Bernd & Walker, Robert W., eds. Guide du Leadership Militaire. 2008. (FRE & ENG., Illus.). 632p. pap. 59.95 *(978-1-55002-767-9(0),* Dundurn Pr.) Dundurn CAN. Dist: Ingram Pub. Services.

Human Rights Watch (Organization) Staff, contrib. by. Paramilitaries' Heirs: The New Face of Violence in Colombia. 2010. (Illus.). 124p. ***(978-1-56432-594-5(6))*** Human Rights Watch.

Jane's Military Communications. 28th rev. ed. 2007. (Jane's Military Communications Ser.). (Illus.). 810p. *(978-0-7106-2806-0(4))* Jane's Information Group.

Jowett, Philip. Armies of the Balkan Wars 1912-13: The Priming Charge for the Great War. 2011. (Men-at-Arms Ser.). (ENG., Illus.). 48p. pap. 17.95 *(978-1-84908-418-5(1))* Osprey Publishing, Ltd. GBR. Dist: Random Hse., Inc.

Kimball, Raymond A. Transformation under Fire: A Historical Case Study with Modern Parallels. 2007. (Letort Papers). *(978-1-58487-319-8(1))* Strategic Studies Institute, U.S. Army War College Commandant (AWCC-DSI/Pubns.).

King, Anthony. The Transformation of Europe's Armed Forces: From the Rhine to Afghanistan. 2011. (ENG., Illus.). 326p. 90.00 *(978-0-521-76094-2(1))* Cambridge Univ. Pr.

Konstam, Angus. Ancient World Commanders. 2009. (Illus.). 192p. 19.95 *(978-1-906347-29-1(8))* Compendium GBR. Dist: Casemate Pubs. & Bk. Distributors, LLC.

Leuprecht, Christian, ed. Defending Democracy & Securing Diversity. 2010. (ENG., Illus.). 260p. (C). 125.00 *(978-0-415-57649-9(0),* Routledge) Taylor & Francis Group GBR. Dist: Taylor & Francis Group.

Leuprecht, Christian, et al. Mission Critical: Smaller Democracies' Role in Global Stability Operations. 2010. (Queen's Policy Studies Ser.). (ENG., Illus.). 312p. (C). pap. *(978-1-55339-244-6(2))* McGill-Queen's Univ. Pr.

Libicki, Martin C., et al. Global Demographic Change & Its Implications for Military Power. 2011. (ENG.). 170p. pap. 32.00 ***(978-0-8330-5177-6(6))*** RAND Corp., The.

Lioe, Kim Eduard. Armed Forces in Law Enforcement Operations? - the German & European Perspective. 2010. (ENG.). xviii, 236p. 139.00 *(978-3-642-15433-1(6),* 3642154336) Springer.

MacFarlane, John. Triquet's Cross: A Study of Military Heroism. 2009. (ENG., Illus.). 232p. (C). *(978-0-7735-3577-0(2))* McGill-Queen's Univ. Pr.

Manning, David F. Global Arms of Collegiality: A Close-Up of the Command & General Staff College, International Military Student Program at Fort Leavenworth, Kansas. 2nd ed. 2010. (Illus.). 297p. pap. ***(978-1-4507-4617-5(9))*** Independent Pub.

Martinez, Marco. Hard Corps: From Gangster to Marine Hero. 2008. (ENG.). 256p. 16.00 *(978-0-307-38305-1(9),* Three Rivers Pr.) Crown Publishing Group.

McConville, Teri & Cleary, Laura Richards, eds. Managing Defence in a Democracy. 2006. (Cass Military Studies). (ENG., Illus.). 288p. (C). 178.00 *(978-0-415-39563-2(1))* Routledge.

McDonald, Daniel P. & Parks, Kizzy M., eds. Managing Diversity & Inclusion in the Military. 2012. (Cass Military Studies). (ENG., Illus.). 296p. (C). 135.00 *(978-0-415-58636-8(4))* Routledge.

Micheletti, Eric. World Elite Forces. (Military History Ser.). (Illus.). 158p. 29.95 *(978-2-908182-25-5(4))* Histoire et Collections FRA. Dist: Casemate Pubs. & Bk. Distributors, LLC.

Mitchell, Jon. Careers after the Armed Forces: How to Decide on the Right Career & Make a Successful Transition. 2009. (ENG., Illus.). 160p. pap. 17.95 *(978-0-7494-5530-9(6))* Kogan Page, Ltd. GBR. Dist: Ingram Pub. Services.

Moroney, Jennifer D. P. & Blacker, Nancy E. Building Partner Capabilities for Coalition Operations. 2007. 122p. pap. 22.00 *(978-0-8330-4211-8(4),* mg635) RAND Corp., The.

Operations in Iraq: Hearing Before the Committee on Armed Services, House of Representatives, One Hundred Ninth Congress, First Session, Hearing Held, September 29, 2005. 2007. iii, 52p. *(978-0-16-079295-3(9),* 552-070-36373-4) United States Government Printing Office.

Orr, Aileen. Wojtek the Bear: Polish War Hero. 2010. (ENG., Illus.). 224p. 19.95 *(978-1-84158-845-2(8))* Birlinn, Ltd. GBR. Dist: Casemate Pubs. & Bk. Distributors, LLC.

Paquette, Laure. Counterinsurgency & the Armed Forces. 2009. (Defense, Security & Strategy Ser.). 69.00 *(978-1-60741-763-7(4))* Nova Science Pubs., Inc.

Privott, Daryl R. Military Recruiting on College Campuses: Legal, Theoretical & Practical Implications of Rumsfeld V. FAIR. 2010. (Law & Society Ser.). 184p. 65.00 *(978-1-59332-444-5(8))* LFB Scholarly Publishing LLC.

Raffin, Anne. Youth Mobilization in Vichy Indochina & Its Legacies, 1940 to 1970. 2008. (After the Empire: The Francophone World & Postcolonial France Ser.). (ENG., Illus.). 282p. pap. 31.50 *(978-0-7391-2811-4(6))* Lexington Bks.

Ramírez, María Clemencia. Between the Guerrillas & the State: The Cocalero Movement, Citizenship, & Identity in the Colombian Amazon. Klatt, Andy, tr. 2011. (ENG., Illus.). 328p. 89.95 *(978-0-8223-5000-2(9))* Duke Univ. Pr.

Ray, Susan L. & Ray, K., eds. Healing from the Trauma of Peacekeeping. 2010. (Health Psychology Research Focus Ser.). 199p. 89.00 *(978-1-60876-404-4(4))* Nova Science Pubs., Inc.

Reid, Stuart. Frederick the Great's Allies. 2010. (Men-at-Arms Ser.). (ENG., Illus.). 48p. pap. 17.95 *(978-1-84908-177-1(8))* Osprey Publishing, Ltd. GBR. Dist: Random Hse., Inc.

Repeal of Law & Policies Governing Service by Openly Gay & Lesbian Service Members: Committee on Armed Services, House of Representatives, One Hundred Twelfth Congress, First Session, Hearing Held April 7, 2011. 2011. iii, 80p. ***(978-0-16-089983-6(4)**,* 552-070-43767-3) United States Government Printing Office.

Schanes, Daniela. Serbien Im Ersten Weltkrieg. 2011. (Neue Forschungen zur ostmittel- und südosteuropäischen Geschichte. New Researches on East Central & South East European History. Recherches nouvelles sur l'histoire de l'Europe centrale et orientale Ser.). (GER., Illus.). 392p. 90.95 ***(978-3-631-61844-8(1))*** Lang, Peter GmbH, Europaischer Verlag der Wissenschaften DEU. Dist: Lang, Peter.

Simon/Abdel-Moneim. A Handbook of Military Conscription & Composition the World Over. 2011. (ENG.). 218p. 65.00 ***(978-0-7391-6751-9(0))*** Lexington Bks.

Sloan, Elinor. Military Transformation & Modern Warfare: A Reference Handbook, 1 vol. 2008. (Contemporary Military, Strategic, & Security Issues Ser.). 200p. 55.00 *(978-0-275-99405-1(8),* C9405, Praeger Security International) Greenwood Publishing Group, Inc.

Soeters, Joseph L. Cultural Diversity in the Armed Forces: An International Comparison. 2007. pap. 39.95 *(978-0-415-54510-5(2))* Routledge.

Soeters, Joseph L. & Van der Meulen, Jan, eds. Cultural Diversity in the Armed Forces: An International Comparision. 2007. (Cass Military Studies). (Illus.). 217p. 160.00 *(978-0-415-39202-0(0))* Routledge.

Standards of Military Commissions & Tribunals: Hearing Before the Committee on Armed Services, House of Representatives, One Hundred Ninth Congress, Second Session, Hearing Held, July 26, 2006. 2007. iii, 133p. *(978-0-16-079947-1(3),* 552-070-36774-8) United States Government Printing Office.

Sterling, Christopher H., ed. Military Communications: From Ancient Times to the 21st Century, 1 vol. 2007. (Illus.). 565p. 95.00 *(978-1-85109-732-6(5),* MILCOM1C) ABC-CLIO, LLC.

Tucker, David. Confronting the Unconventional: Innovation & Transformation in Military Affairs. 2006. (Letort Papers: No. 14). vi, 81p. pap. *(978-1-58487-254-2(3))* Strategic Studies Institute, U.S. Army War College Commandant (AWCC-DSI/Pubns.).

Vilens, Alexander. Suicide & the Military. Sher, Leo, ed. 2009. 89.00 *(978-1-60876-201-9(7),* Nova Biomedical Bks.) Nova Science Pubs., Inc.

Weitz, Richard. The Reserve Policies of Nations: A Comparative Analysis. 2007. *(978-1-58487-304-4(3))* Strategic Studies Institute, U.S. Army War College Commandant (AWCC-DSI/Pubns.).

Westwell, Ian. World War II Commanders. 2009. (Illus.). 192p. 19.95 *(978-1-906347-31-4(X))* Compendium GBR. Dist: Casemate Pubs. & Bk. Distributors, LLC.

Wirls, Daniel. Irrational Security: The Politics of Defense from Reagan to Obama. 2010. (ENG., Illus.). 256p. (C). (gr. 13-17). 60.00 *(978-0-8018-9438-1(7));* pap. 30.00 *(978-0-8018-9439-8(5))* Johns Hopkins Univ. Pr.

Yarger, Harry R., ed. Short of General War: Perspectives on the use of Military Power in the 21st Century. 2010. (Carlisle Papers Ser.). (Illus.). vi, 281p. pap. *(978-1-58487-431-7(7))* Strategic Studies Institute, U.S. Army War College Commandant (AWCC-DSI/Pubns.).

Zabecki, David T. Chief of Staff: The Principal Officers Behind History's Great Commanders, 2 vols. 2008. (Illus.). 243p. 37.95 *(978-1-59114-991-0(6))* Naval Institute Pr.

—Chief of Staff, Volume 1: The Principal Officers Behind History's Great Commanders: Napoleonic Wars to World War I, 2 vols. 2008. (Illus.). 241p. 39.95 *(978-1-59114-990-3(8))* Naval Institute Pr.

ARMED FORCES—CIVIC ACTION

Binnendijk, Hans, et al, eds. Civilian Surge: Key to Complex Operations. 2009. (ENG., Illus.). 326p. pap. 29.00 *(978-0-16-083166-9(0),* National Defense University) United States Government Printing Office.

Davis, Lynn E., et al. Hurricane Katrina: Lessons for Army Planning & Operations. 2007. (Illus.). 106p. per. 23.00 *(978-0-8330-4167-8(3),* mg603) RAND Corp., The.

Head, Michael & Mann, Scott. Domestic Deployment of the Armed Forces: Military Powers Law & Human Rights. 2009. (International & Comparative Criminal Justice Ser.). 214p. 114.95 *(978-0-7546-7346-0(4))* Ashgate Publishing Co.

Wright, Donald P., et al. A Different Kind of War: the United States Army in Operation ENDURING FREEDOM, October 2001 - September 2005: The United States Army in Operation ENDURING FREEDOM, October 2001 - September 2005. Combat Studies Institute (U.S.) & Contemporary Operations Study Team (U.S.), eds. 2010. (ENG., Illus.). 414p. pap. 44.00 *(978-0-9823283-1-6(1),* Dept. of the Army) United States Government Printing Office.

ARMED FORCES—JOURNALISM

see Journalism, Military

ARMED FORCES—MEDALS, BADGES, DECORATIONS, ETC.

see Military Decorations

ARMED FORCES—POLITICAL ACTIVITY

Bienen, Henry, ed. & pref. The Military & Modernization. 2009. (ENG.). 270p. pap. 29.95 *(978-0-202-36305-9(8))* Aldine Transaction.

Cook, Steven A. Ruling, but Not Governing: The Military & Political Development in Egypt, Algeria, & Turkey. 2007. 208p. 55.00 *(978-0-8018-8590-7(6))* Johns Hopkins Univ. Pr.

—Ruling but Not Governing: The Military & Political Development in Egypt, Algeria, & Turkey. 2007. (ENG.). 208p. (gr. 17). per. 27.95 *(978-0-8018-8591-4(4))* Johns Hopkins Univ. Pr.

DeRosa, Christopher S. & DeRosa, Christopher. Politica Indoctrination in the U. S. Army from World War II to the Vietnam War. 2006. (Studies in War, Society, & the Military). (ENG.). 336p. 24.95 *(978-0-8032-1734-8(X))* Univ. of Nebraska Pr.

Hong, Ch'ol. Kunbu Ui Chongch'i Ch'amyo Wa Minjuhwa Kwajong. 2009. (KOR., Illus.). 552p. pap. *(978-89-26-80303-5(1))*; E-Book *(978-89-26-80304-2(X))* Korean Studies Information Co., Ltd.

Schlichte, Klaus. Der Staat in der Weltgesellschaft: Politische Herrschaft in Asien, Afrika und Lateinamerika. 2009. 220p. pap. 42.00 *(978-3-593-37881-7(7))* Campus Verlag GmbH DEU. Dist: Chicago Distribution Ctr.

Schlichte, Klaus & Schlichte, K. Der Staat in der Weltgesellschaft: Politische Herrschaft in Asien, Afrika und Lateinamerika. 2009. (ENG.). 256p. pap. 42.00 *(978-3-593-38817-5(0))* Campus Verlag GmbH DEU. Dist: Chicago Distribution Ctr.

ARMED FORCES—PRAYERS AND DEVOTIONS

Cairney, Paul D. On Target: Bible-Based Leadership for Military Professionals. 2010. 196p. pap. 21.49 *(978-1-4520-7230-2(2))* AuthorHouse.

Church Publishing Staff & Domestic And Foreign Missionary Society Staff. A Prayer Book for the Armed Services. 3rd rev. ed. 2007. 192p. pap. 5.00 *(978-0-89869-565-6(1))* Church Publishing, Inc.

Estes, Arthur J. & Estes, Jeane E. Paratrooper Chaplain. Lynd, Cindy, ed. 2008. 220p. 32.86 *(978-1-4251-7853-6(7))* Trafford Publishing.

Fenelon, Marge, compiled by. Reveille for the Soul: Prayers for Military Life: Prayers. 2010. 96p. pap. 9.99 *(978-0-7648-1878-3(3))* Liguori Pubns.

Ortiz, Michael. God & Country: Reflections for Catholics in the Military. 2007. 60p. per. 2.95 *(978-0-86716-577-7(4))* Franciscan Media.

Parr, S. Battlefield Prayers: Desert. 2006. (ENG.). 162p. pap. 6.95 *(978-0-9765010-2-2(3))* Word Prodns.

Quintard, Charles Todd. The Confederate Soldier's Pocket Manual of Devotions: Including Balm for the Weary & the Wounded. 2009. 176p. pap. 18.00 *(978-0-88146-175-6(X))* Mercer Univ. Pr.

Tittle, Matthew & Tittle, Gail, eds. Bless All Who Serve: Sources of Hope, Comfort & Faith for Military Personnel & Their Families. 2010. (ENG.). 1p. pap. 8.00 *(978-1-55896-566-9(1),* Skinner Hse. Bks.) Unitarian Universalist Assn.

Wright, Venita Hampton. Simple Acts of Moving Forward: 60 Suggestions for Getting Unstuck. 2009. (ENG.). 152p. pap. 12.95 *(978-0-8294-2812-4(7))* Loyola Pr.

ARMED FORCES—RECRUITING, ENLISTMENT, ETC.

see Recruiting and Enlistment

ARMED FORCES—VOCATIONAL GUIDANCE

Committee on Examination of the U.S. Air Force's Science, Technology, Engineering, and Mathematics (STEM) Workforce Needs in the Future and Its Strategy to Meet Those Needs & National Research Council. Examination of the U. S. Air Force's Science, Technology, Engineering, & Mathematics (STEM) Workforce Needs in the Future & Its Strategy to Meet Those Needs. 2010. (ENG.). 176p. pap. 40.50 *(978-0-309-14197-0(4))* National Academies Pr.

Committee on Science, Technology, Engineering, and Mathematics Workforce Needs for the U.S. Department of Defense and the U.S. Defense Industrial Base, et al. Report of a Workshop on Science, Technology, Engineering, & Mathematics (STEM) Workforce Needs for the U. S. Department of Defense & the U. S. Defense Industrial Base. 2012. (ENG.). 78p. pap. 35.00 ***(978-0-309-25180-8(X))*** National Academies Pr.

Herbert, Don. 63 Days & a Wake-up: Your Survival Guide to United States Army Basic Combat Training. 2007. 192p. per. 16.95 *(978-0-595-42511-2(9))* iUniverse, Inc.

Lewis, Audie G. Career Progression Guide. 3rd rev. ed. 2008. (ENG., Illus.). 157p. pap. 14.95 *(978-0-8117-3491-2(9))* Stackpole Bks.

McNair, Phil & Stielow, Fred. Identity Series: Finding Success as a Millitary Student. rev. ed. 2012. (IDentity Ser.). (ENG.). 48p. (C). pap. 13.33 ***(978-0-13-288695-6(2))*** Addison Wesley.

ARMED FORCES—FOREIGN COUNTRIES

see also Military Occupation

Ronn, Harald. Complexity & Leadership. 2010. 196p. pap. *(978-3-639-26299-3(X))* VDM Verlag Dr. Mueller e.K.

Sloan, James. Militarisation of Peacekeeping in the Twenty-First Century. 2011. (Studies in International Law Ser.: No. 35). (ENG.). 336p. 120.00 *(978-1-84946-114-6(7))* Hart Publishing Ltd. GBR. Dist: International Specialized Bk. Services.

ARMED FORCES ATTACHES

see Military Attaches

ARMED FORCES NEWSPAPERS

see Journalism, Military

ARMED FORCES IN FOREIGN COUNTRIES

see Armed Forces—Foreign Countries

ARMED MERCHANT SHIPS

see also World War, 1914-1918—Naval Operations; World War, 1939-1945—Naval Operations

Browning, Robert M. United States Merchant Marine Casualties of World War II. rev. ed. 2011. (ENG., Illus.). 419p. pap. 75.00 *(978-0-7864-4600-1(5))* McFarland & Co., Inc. Pubs.

Cullen, Patrick & Berube, Claude, eds. Private Maritime Security in the 21st Century: Market Responses to Piracy, Terrorism & Waterborne Security Risks. 2012. (Cass Series: Naval Policy & History Ser.). (ENG., Illus.). 272p. (C). 135.00 ***(978-0-415-68862-8(0))*** Routledge.

ARMED SERVICES VOCATIONAL APTITUDE BATTERY

Ace Academics, ed. Asvab: Exam Prep Software on CD-ROM! Exambusters CD-ROM Study Cards. 2007. (Exambusters Ser.). cd-rom 12.95 *(978-1-57633-212-2(8),* Exambusters) Ace Academics, Inc.

AFQT Exam Secrets Test Prep Staff, ed. AFQT Practice Questions: AFQT Practice Tests & Exam Review for the Armed Forces Qualification Test. 2011. 34.99 *(978-1-61403-486-5(9))* Mometrix Media LLC.

American BookWorks Corporation. CliffsNotes ASVAB Cram Plan. 2010. (ENG., Illus.). 408p. pap. 14.99 *(978-0-470-62024-3(2),* Cliff Notes) Wiley, John & Sons, Inc.

ASVAB Exam Secrets Test Prep Staff, ed. ASVAB Practice Questions: ASVAB Practice Tests & Exam Review for the Armed Services Vocational Aptitude Battery. 2011. 34.99 *(978-1-61403-490-2(7))* Mometrix Media LLC.

Consumer Dummies Staff & Powers, Rod. ASVAB AFQT for Dummies. 2010. (ENG., Illus.). 336p. pap. 14.99 *(978-0-470-56652-7(3),* For Dummies) Wiley, John & Sons, Inc.

Duran, Terry L. Barron's ASVAB Flash Cards: Armed Services Vocational Aptitude Battery. 2010. (ENG.). 404p. 18.99 *(978-0-7641-9783-3(5))* Barron's Educational Series, Inc.

Grayson, Fred N. CliffsNotes ASVAB. 2nd ed. 2010. (ENG., Illus.). 504p. pap. 24.99 *(978-0-470-56683-1(3),* Cliff Notes) Wiley, John & Sons, Inc.

Kaplan. Kaplan ASVAB. 9th ed. 2011. (ENG.). 444p. pap. 19.99 *(978-1-60714-878-4(1))* Kaplan Publishing.

Learning Express Editors. ASVAB Success. 3rd ed. 2011. (ENG.). 208p. pap. 16.95 *(978-1-57685-785-4(9))* LearningExpress, LLC.

LearningExpress Editors. Asvab - Power Practice. 2010. (ENG.). 288p. pap. 17.95 *(978-1-57685-749-6(2))* LearningExpress, LLC.

—ASVAB Core Review (Complete Preparation Guides). (ENG.). 3rd rev. ed. 2009. 192p. pap. 14.95 *(978-1-57685-666-6(6))* 4th ed. 2012. 208p. pap. 14.95 ***(978-1-57685-890-5(1))*** LearningExpress, LLC.

LearningExpress Staff. ASVAB. 4th rev. ed. 2010. (Complete Preparation Guides). (ENG.). 312p. pap. 19.95 *(978-1-57685-741-0(7))* LearningExpress, LLC.

—ASVAB Success. 2nd rev. ed. 2007. (ASVAB Success Ser.). (ENG., Illus.). 192p. per. 16.00 *(978-1-57685-543-0(0))* LearningExpress, LLC.

Ostrow, Scott A. & DeAngelis, Therese. Master the ASVAB: Score High & Launch Your Military Career. 21st ed. 2008. (ENG., Illus.). 672p. (YA). pap. 18.95 *(978-0-7689-2603-3(3),* Arco) Peterson's.

—Master the Asvab: Score Higher - Guaranteed. 4th ed. 2008. (ENG., Illus.). 672p. (YA). pap. 26.95 *(978-0-7689-2602-6(5),* Arco) Peterson's.

Peterson's. Master the ASVAB Basics. DeAngelis, Therese, ed. 8th ed. 2010. (ENG.). 374p. (YA). pap. 15.95 *(978-0-7689-2829-7(X),* Arco) Peterson's.

Powers, Rod. ASVAB for Dummies. 3rd ed. 2010. (ENG.). 408p. pap. 18.00 *(978-0-470-63760-9(9))*; (Illus.). pap. 26.99 *(978-0-470-63761-6(7))* Wiley, John & Sons, Inc. (For Dummies).

Princeton Review Staff. Cracking the ASVAB, 3rd Edition. 2010. (College Test Preparation Ser.). (ENG.). 352p. pap. 18.00 *(978-0-375-42967-5(0),* Princeton Review) Random Hse. Information Group.

Proctor, Pat, et al. ASVAB AFQT Cram Plan. 2010. (ENG.). 312p. pap. 12.99 *(978-0-470-59889-4(1),* Cliff Notes) Wiley, John & Sons, Inc.

Research and Education Association Staff. ASVAB Flashcards: Score High on the ASVAB for Better Military Placement! 2011. (Military (ASVAB) Test Preparation Ser.). (ENG.). 352p. pap. 15.95 *(978-0-7386-0908-9(0))* Research & Education Assn.

Riebs, Karl W. & Reeves, Kalinda. ASVAB Exam Cram: Armed Services Vocational Aptitude Battery. 2nd ed. 2009. (Exam Cram Ser.). (ENG., Illus.). 456p. pap. 29.99 *(978-0-7897-4225-4(X))* Que.

Rudman, Jack. Armed Forces Tests (AFT-ASVAB) (Admission Test Ser.: Vol. 34). 54.95 *(978-0-8373-5134-6(0))* National Learning Corp.

Sourcebooks, Inc Staff. My Max Score ASVAB: Armed Services Vocational Aptitude Battery: Maximize Your Score in Less Time. 2012. (My Max Score Ser.). (ENG.). 496p. pap. 14.99 *(978-1-4022-4492-6(4))* Sourcebooks, Inc.

Stradley, Laura & Kavanagh, Robin. The Complete Idiot's Guide to the ASVAB. 2010. (Complete Idiot's Guide Ser.). (ENG., Illus.). 400p. (gr. 12). 18.95 *(978-1-59257-983-9(3),* Alpha Bks.) Penguin Group (USA) Inc.

—The Pocket Idiot's Guide to the ASVAB. 2009. (Pocket Idiot's Guide Ser.). (ENG.). 208p. (gr. 12-18). 9.95 *(978-1-59257-982-2(5),* Alpha Bks.) Penguin Group (USA) Inc.

Walker-Hammond, Wallie. ASVAB: Your Total Solution. 7th ed. 2010. (Military (ASVAB) Test Preparation Ser.). (ENG.). 576p. (gr. 12). pap. 26.95 *(978-0-7386-0643-9(X))*; pap. 20.95 *(978-0-7386-0642-2(1))* Research & Education Assn.

Walker-Hammond, Wallie. ASVAB AFQT Crash Course. 2011. (Military (ASVAB) Test Preparation Ser.). (ENG.). 304p. pap. 12.95 ***(978-0-7386-0904-1(8))*** Research & Education Assn.

Wall, Janet. McGraw-Hill's ASVAB, Second Edition. 2nd ed. 2009. (ENG., Illus.). 608p. (C). pap. 18.95 *(978-0-07-162661-3(1),* 0071626611) McGraw-Hill Cos., The.

Wall, Janet & Wall, Janet E. McGraw-Hill's ASVAB Basic Training for the AFQT, Second Edition. 2nd ed. 2009. (ACE & ENG., Illus.). 336p. (C). pap. 13.95 *(978-0-07-163282-9(4),* 0071632824) McGraw-Hill Cos., The.

Wall, Janet E. ASVAB. 2nd ed. 2009. (ENG.). 608p. pap. 29.95 incl. cd-rom *(978-0-07-162665-1(4),* 0071626654) McGraw-Hill Cos., The.

—A Top Score: ASVAB Reading & Math. 2010. (McGraw-Hill's Top 50 Skills Ser.). (ENG.). 192p. pap. 20.00 incl. cd-rom *(978-0-07-171801-1(X),* 007171801X) McGraw-Hill Cos., The.

Wynne, Sharon A. ASVAB Armed Services Vocational Aptitude Battery Study Guide. 2011. (ENG.), 350p. pap. 24.99 *(978-1-60787-107-1(6))* XAMonline, Inc.

ARMENIA (REPUBLIC)

Alekseev, V. P., et al. Contributions to the Archaeology of Armenia. Field, Henry, ed. Krimgold, Arlene, tr. (Harvard University, Peabody Museum of Archaeology & Ethnology, Russian Translation Ser.: Vol. 3, No. 3). reprint ed. lib. bdg. 76.50 *(978-0-404-52646-7(2))* AMS Pr., Inc.

Tozer, Henry F. Turkish Armenia & Eastern Asia Minor. reprint ed. 35.00 *(978-0-404-16462-1(5))* AMS Pr., Inc.

ARMENIA (REPUBLIC)—BIOGRAPHY

Apkarian, Sooren. My Armenian Heritage. 2007. 144p. pap. 8.76 *(978-0-615-15265-3(1))* Apkarian, Sooren Simon.

Arakelyan, Mikayel. Mesrop of Xizan: An Armenian Master of the Seventeenth Century. 2011. (ENG.). 128p. (C). pap. 40.00 *(978-0-9553393-3-2(2))* Holberton, Paul Publishing GBR. Dist: Univ. of Washington Pr.

Balakian, Grigoris. Armenian Golgotha. Balakian, Peter, tr. 2010. (Vintage Ser.). (ENG., Illus.). 576p. pap. 20.00 *(978-1-4000-9677-0(4),* Vintage) Knopf Doubleday Publishing Group.

Earle, Scott. Yerevan Journal. 2007. 160p. (YA). pap. 19.50 *(978-0-615-14420-7(9))* Larkspur Bks.

Mahari, Antonina, et al. My Odyssey: From the Green Fields of Lithuania, Through Exile in Siberia, to a New Life in Armenia. 2011. (Illus.). *(978-0-9648787-6-1(3))* Armenian International Women's Assoc. (AIWA).

Marcus, Ralph, intro. The Armenian Life of Marutha of Maipherkat. 2011. 83.12 *(978-1-61143-831-4(4))* Gorgias Pr., LLC.

Movsisian Foess, Mary L. My Armenian Genesis: The last Survivor. 2010. 268p. pap. 23.98 *(978-0-557-26888-7(5))* Lulu Enterprises Inc.

Paulson, J. Barrie. Hripsime. 2007. (ENG.). 124p. per. 19.95 *(978-1-4241-6602-2(0))* PublishAmerica, Inc.

Vosbikian, Irene. Bedros. pap. 16.00 *(978-0-7388-4760-3(7))* Xlibris Corp.

ARMENIA (REPUBLIC)—DESCRIPTION AND TRAVEL

Aghababyan, Anahit. Protected Areas & Tourism Development. 2010. 84p. pap. *(978-3-639-22268-5(7))* VDM Verlag Dr. Mueller e.K.

Barkley, Henry C. A Ride through Asia Minor & Armenia: Giving a Sketch of the Characters, Manners, & Customs of Both the Mussulman & Christian Inhabitants. 2011. (Cambridge Library Collection - Travel & Exploration Ser.). (ENG.). 366p. pap. 29.99 ***(978-1-108-03757-0(7))*** Cambridge Univ. Pr.

Boyajian, Dickran H. A Light Through the Iron Curtain. 2011. 92p. 38.95 ***(978-1-258-06437-2(5))*** Literary Licensing, LLC.

Holding, Nicholas. Armenia. 3rd ed. 2011. (Bradt Travel Guide Ser.). (ENG., Illus.). 256p. pap. 25.99 *(978-1-84162-345-0(6))* Bradt Travel Guides GBR. Dist: Globe Pequot Pr., The.

Karanian, Matthew & Kurkjian, Robert. Armenia & Karabagh: The Stone Garden Guide. 2nd ed. 2006. per. 24.95 *(978-0-9672120-9-8(X))* Stone Garden Productions.

Locken, E. Travel Journal Armenia. 2009. 192p. pap. 20.95 *(978-0-557-07999-5(3))* Lulu Enterprises Inc.

Noble, John. Georgia, Armenia & Azerbaijan. 4th rev. ed. 2012. (Multi Country Guide Ser.). (ENG., Illus.). 328p. pap. 25.99 ***(978-1-74179-403-8(X))*** Lonely Planet Pubns.

Noble, John, et al. Georgia, Armenia & Azerbaijan. 3rd rev. ed. 2008. (Lonely Planet Georgia, Armenia & Azerbaijan Ser.). (ENG., Illus.). 364p. pap. 24.99 *(978-1-74104-477-5(4))* Lonely Planet Pubns.

Oshagan, Ara, photos by. Father Land. 2010. (ENG., Illus.). 156p. 45.00 *(978-1-57687-548-3(2),* powerHouse Bks.) powerHouse Cultural Entertainment, Inc.

Vigo, Graziella, photos by. Armenia: The Holy Land - The Cradle of Christianity. 2010. (ARM, RUS, ITA, FRE & ENG., Illus.). 240p. 85.00 *(978-88-572-0410-9(3))* Skira Editore ITA. Dist: Random Hse., Inc.

ARMENIA (REPUBLIC)—ECONOMIC CONDITIONS

Beman Press Staff & World Trade Organization Staff. Trade Policy Review: Armenia 2010. 2010. (ENG.). 144p. pap. 75.00 *(978-1-59888-435-7(2))* Beman Assocs.

Gabrielyan, Nune. Investigation on Factors Affecting Fdi Flow to Armeni. 2011. 72p. pap. ***(978-3-8433-9059-0(2))*** Lambert Academic Publishing.

Hovakimyan, Aleksey. Rural Clusters & Structural Transformation. 2010. 64p. pap. *(978-3-639-27702-9(3))* VDM Verlag Dr. Mueller e.K.

Icon Group International, Inc. Staff, compiled by. The 2006 Economic & Product Market Databook for Abovian, Armenia. 2006. 618p. ring bd. 95.00 *(978-0-497-79946-5(4))* Icon Group International, Inc.

—The 2006 Economic & Product Market Databook for Alaverdi, Armenia. 2006. 618p. ring bd. 95.00 *(978-0-497-80025-3(X))* Icon Group International, Inc.

—The 2006 Economic & Product Market Databook for Artashat, Armenia. 2006. 618p. ring bd. 95.00 *(978-0-497-80086-4(1))* Icon Group International, Inc.

—The 2006 Economic & Product Market Databook for Artik, Armenia. 2006. 618p. ring bd. 95.00 *(978-0-497-80087-1(X))* Icon Group International, Inc.

—The 2006 Economic & Product Market Databook for Ashtarak, Armenia. 2006. 618p. ring bd. 95.00 *(978-0-497-80093-2(4))* Icon Group International, Inc.

—The 2006 Economic & Product Market Databook for Charentsavan, Armenia. 2006. 618p. ring bd. 95.00 *(978-0-497-80340-7(2))* Icon Group International, Inc.

—The 2006 Economic & Product Market Databook for Dilijan, Armenia. 2006. 618p. ring bd. 95.00 *(978-0-497-80461-9(1))* Icon Group International, Inc.

—The 2006 Economic & Product Market Databook for Echmiadzin, Armenia. 2006. 618p. ring bd. 95.00 *(978-0-497-80501-2(4))* Icon Group International, Inc.

—The 2006 Economic & Product Market Databook for Goris, Armenia. 2006. 618p. ring bd. 95.00 *(978-0-497-80610-1(X))* Icon Group International, Inc.

—The 2006 Economic & Product Market Databook for Gyumri, Armenia. 2006. 618p. ring bd. 95.00 *(978-0-497-80633-0(9))* Icon Group International, Inc.

—The 2006 Economic & Product Market Databook for Hoktemberian, Armenia. 2006. 618p. ring bd. 95.00 *(978-0-497-80652-1(5))* Icon Group International, Inc.

—The 2006 Economic & Product Market Databook for Hrazdan, Armenia. 2006. 618p. ring bd. 95.00 *(978-0-497-80659-0(2))* Icon Group International, Inc.

—The 2006 Economic & Product Market Databook for Kamo, Armenia. 2006. 618p. ring bd. 95.00 *(978-0-497-80713-9(0))* Icon Group International, Inc.

—The 2006 Economic & Product Market Databook for Kaphan, Armenia. 2006. 618p. ring bd. 95.00 *(978-0-497-80721-4(1))* Icon Group International, Inc.

—The 2006 Economic & Product Market Databook for Kirovakan, Armenia. 2006. 618p. ring bd. 95.00 *(978-0-497-80751-1(3))* Icon Group International, Inc.

—The 2006 Economic & Product Market Databook for Massis, Armenia. 2006. 618p. ring bd. 95.00 *(978-0-497-80969-0(9))* Icon Group International, Inc.

—The 2006 Economic & Product Market Databook for Sevan, Armenia. 2006. 618p. ring bd. 95.00 *(978-0-497-81511-0(7))* Icon Group International, Inc.

—The 2006 Economic & Product Market Databook for Stepanavan, Armenia. 2006. 618p. ring bd. 95.00 *(978-0-497-81568-4(0))* Icon Group International, Inc.

—The 2006 Economic & Product Market Databook for Yerevan, Armenia. 2006. 618p. ring bd. 95.00 *(978-0-497-81250-8(9))* Icon Group International, Inc.

Mitra, Saumya, et al. The Caucasian Tiger: Sustaining Economic Growth in Armenia. 2007. (Stand Alones Ser.). (ENG., Illus.). 400p. per. 45.00 *(978-0-8213-6811-4(7),* 9780821368114) World Bank Pubns.

Shayegh Soheil & Shayegh, Soheil. Environmental Impact Assessment of Copper Production: A Case Study on Alaverdi Copper Factory in Armenia. 2008. 96p. pap. *(978-3-639-09444-2(1))* VDM Verlag Dr. Mueller e.K.

ARMENIA (REPUBLIC)—FOREIGN RELATIONS

Congressional Budget Office (U.S.), compiled by. Budget & Economic Outlook: an Update (2008) 2008. (ENG.). 75p. pap. 13.00 *(978-0-16-081513-3(4),* 552-070-37869-3, Congressional Budget Office) United States Government Printing Office.

Cox, Caroline, et al. Heroes & Zeros: Bible Discovery for Families. 2010. (Illus.). 48p. (J). pap. *(978-1-873166-79-6(6))* Good Bk. Co.

Dodds, Brandon. Victory Dance. 2008. 97p. pap. 16.95 *(978-0-578-00047-3(4))* Southern Cross Publishing.

Gabrielyan, Nune. Investigation on Factors Affecting Fdi Flow to Armeni. 2011. 72p. pap. ***(978-3-8433-9059-0(2))*** Lambert Academic Publishing.

Hakobyan, Levon. Haykakan Petakan utyan Verakangnman (Hayots Hartsi Hangutsalutsman) Hayetsakarg. (ARM.). 143p. *(978-99941-57-61-7(2))* Antares, Ltd.

Insel, Ahmet, et al. Erkkhosutyun Haykakan Tabui Shurj. 2010. (ARM., Illus.). 131p. *(978-9939-816-14-2(6))* Van Aryan Publishing Hse. Co., Ltd.

Manandyan, Hakob & Bournoutian, George A. Tigranes II & Rome: A New Interpretation Based on Primary Sources. 2007. *(978-1-56859-166-7(7))* Mazda Pubs., Inc.

Mirzoyan, Alla. Armenia, the Regional Powers, & the West: Between History & Geopolitics. 2010. (ENG.). 256p. 89.00 *(978-0-230-61866-4(9))* Palgrave Macmillan.

Ordubadi, Mammad. Years of Blood: A History of the Armenian-Muslim Clashes in the Caucasus, 1905-1906. 2011. 205p. pap. 34.95 *(978-0-86372-390-2(X),* Ithaca Pr.) Garnet Publishing, Ltd. GBR. Dist: International Specialized Bk. Services.

Parsumean-Tatoyean, Seda. The Armenians in the Medieval Islamic World: Paradigms of InteractionSeventh to Fourteenth Centuries. 2011. (ENG., Illus.). 235p. 39.95 ***(978-1-4128-4577-9(7))*** Transaction Pubs.

ARMENIA (REPUBLIC)—HISTORY

see also Armenian Massacres, 1915-1923; Armenian Question

Adalian, Rouben. Historical Dictionary of Armenia. 2nd ed. 2010. (Historical Dictionaries of Europe Ser.). (ENG., Illus.). 750p. 158.00 *(978-0-8108-6096-4(1))* Scarecrow Pr., Inc.

Agatangeghos. The Lives of Saint Gregory: The Armenian, Greek, Arabic, & Syriac Versions of the History Attributed to Agathangelos. 2010. *(978-0-88206-118-4(6))* Caravan Bks.

Arakel & Bournoutian, George A., texts. Book of History. 2010. *(978-1-56859-172-8(1))* Mazda Pubs., Inc.

Avetisyan, Pavel, et al. The Archaeology & Geography of Ancient Transcaucasian Societies Vol. 1: The Foundations of Research & Regional Survey in the Tsaghkahovit Plain, Armenia. 2009. (Oriental Institute Publications). (ENG., Illus.). 540p. (C). 90.00 *(978-1-885923-62-2(7))* Oriental Institute of the Univ. of Chicago, The.

Badalyan, R. S., et al. Bronze & Early Iron Age Archaeological Sites in Armenia. I. Mt. Aragats & Its Surrounding. 2007. (Bar S Ser.). (ENG., Illus.). 319p. (C). pap. 112.50 *(978-1-4073-0139-6(X))* British Archaeological Reports Ltd. GBR. Dist: Brown, David Bk. Co., The.

Cetin, Fethiye. My Grandmother: A Memoir. Freely, Maureen, tr. from TUR. 2008. (ENG., Illus.). 116p. 21.95 *(978-1-84467-169-4(0),* 844169) Verso Bks. GBR. Dist: Norton, W. W. & Co., Inc.

Dashdondog, Bayarsaikhan. The Mongols & the Armenians (1220-1335) 2010. (Brill's Inner Asian Library). (Illus.). 224p. *(978-90-04-18635-4(2))* BRILL.

Erickson, John. The Road to Berlin, Vol. 2. 2007. (Cassell Military Paperbacks Ser.). (ENG., Illus.). 896p. pap. 12.95 *(978-0-304-36540-1(8))* Cassell Guides GBR. Dist: Sterling Publishing Co., Inc.

Esayi Hasan Jalaleants & Bournoutian, George A. A Brief History of the Aghuank Region: Patmutiwn Hamarot Aghuanits Erkri: A History of Karabagh & Ganje from 1702-1723. 2009. (ARM & ENG., Illus.). xi, 124p. *(978-1-56859-171-1(3))* Mazda Pubs., Inc.

Garsoïan, Nina G. De Vita Sua. 2011. *(978-1-56859-288-6(4))* Mazda Pubs., Inc.

Ghazareans, Ara. Collections of the Armenian Cultural Foundation Series. 2007. *(978-0-9674621-6-5(9))* Armenian Cultural Foundation.

Hakobyan, Levon. Haykakan Petakanutyan Verakangnman (Hayots Hartsi Hangutsalutsman) Hayetsakarg. (ARM.). 143p. *(978-99941-57-61-7(2))* Antares, Ltd.

Haroyan, Lusine. Nagorno Karabagh Conflict. 2009. 64p. pap. *(978-3-639-08615-7(5))* VDM Verlag Dr. Mueller e.K.

Hovannisian, Richard, ed. The Armenian Genocide: Cultural & Ethical Legacies. 2007. (ENG., Illus.). 461p. pap. 29.95 *(978-1-4128-0619-0(4))*; (gr. 11). 49.95 *(978-0-7658-0367-2(4))* Transaction Pubs.

Hovannisian, Richard G. Armenian Pontus: The Trebizond-Black Sea Communities. 2008. *(978-1-56859-155-1(1))* Mazda Pubs., Inc.

Jones, Lynn. Between Byzantium & Islam: Aght'Amar & the Visual Construction of Medieval Aremenian Rulership. 2007. (Illus.). 160p. 114.95 *(978-0-7546-3852-0(9))* Ashgate Publishing Co.

Koolakian, Robert George. Armenian Struggle for Justice: A Story of the American Committee for the Independence of Armenia 1915-1920. 2007. per. *(978-1-934548-00-4(6))* Armenian Research Ct.

Kouymjian, Dickran. Between Paris & Fresno: Armenian Studies in Honor of Dickran Kouymjian. 2008. (Armenian Studies). (C). *(978-1-56859-168-1(3))* Mazda Pubs., Inc.

Künzler, Jakob, et al. In the Land of Blood & Tears: Experiences in Mesopotamia During the World War. 2007. *(978-0-9674621-8-9(5))* Armenian Cultural Foundation.

Kurkjian, Vahan M. A History of Armenia. 2008. 412p. pap. 45.95 *(978-1-60444-012-6(0))* IndoEuropeanPublishing.com.

Lewy, Guenter. The Armenian Massacres in Ottoman Turkey: A Disputed Genocide. 2007. (Utah Series in Turkish & Islamic Stud Ser.). (ENG., Illus.). 384p. per. 23.00 *(978-0-87480-890-2(1))* Univ. of Utah Pr.

Libaridian, Gerard J. Modern Armenia: People, Nation, State. 2007. (ENG.). 338p. (gr. 11). pap. 29.95 *(978-1-4128-0648-0(8))* Transaction Pubs.

Manandyan, Hakob & Bournoutian, George A. Tigranes II & Rome: A New Interpretation Based on Primary Sources. 2007. *(978-1-56859-166-7(7))* Mazda Pubs., Inc.

Melkonian, Markar & Melkonian, Marker. My Brother's Road: An American's Fateful Journey to Armenia. 2008. (ENG., Illus.). 344p. pap. 21.00 *(978-1-84511-530-2(9))* I. B. Tauris & Co., Ltd. GBR. Dist: Macmillan.

Mirzoyan, Alla. Armenia, the Regional Powers, & the West: Between History & Geopolitics. 2010. (ENG.). 256p. 89.00 *(978-0-230-61866-4(9))* Palgrave Macmillan.

Moses. History of the Armenians. 2006. *(978-0-88206-111-5(9))* Caravan Bks.

Muskhelishvili, David. Some Issues of Georgian History in Armenian Historiography. 2011. (Focus on Civilizations & Cultures Ser.). 129.00 *(978-1-61761-336-4(3))* Nova Science Pubs., Inc.

Payaslian, Simon. The History of Armenia. 2008. (Palgrave Essential Histories Ser.). (ENG.). 304p. 89.00 *(978-0-230-60064-5(6))* Palgrave Macmillan.

—The Political Economy of Human Rights in Armenia: Authoritarianism & Democracy in a Former Soviet Republic. 2011. (International Library of Historical Studies: No. 75). (ENG., Illus.). 384p. 95.00 *(978-1-84885-811-4(6)*, Tauris Academic Studies) I. B. Tauris & Co., Ltd. GBR. Dist: Macmillan.

Stone, Michael E. Apocrypha, Pseudepigrapha & Armenian Studies. Collected Papers: Volume II, 2 vols. 2006. (Orientalia Lovaniensia Analecta Ser.: Vols. 144-145). (ARM & ENG., Illus.). 489p. (C). 108.00 *(978-90-429-1644-9(3))* Peeters Pubs. & Booksellers BEL. Dist: Brown, David Bk. Co., The.

Stone, Michael E. & Stone, Michael Edward. Apocrypha, Pseudepigrapha & Armenian Studies. Collected Papers: Volume I, 2 vols. 2006. (Orientalia Lovaniensia Analecta Ser.: Vols. 144-145). (ARM & ENG., Illus.). 466p. (C). 119.00 *(978-90-429-1643-2(5))* Peeters Pubs. & Booksellers BEL. Dist: Brown, David Bk. Co., The.

Topchyan, Aram & Topchyan, A. The Problem of the Greek Sources of Movses Xorenac'i's History of Armenia. 2006. (Hebrew University Armenian Studies: Vol. 7). (ENG.). 145p. (C). pap. 61.00 *(978-90-429-1662-3(1))* Peeters Pubs. & Booksellers BEL. Dist: Brown, David Bk. Co., The.

Von Voss Staff. Portraits of Hope: Armenians in the Contemporary World. 2007. (Illus.). 400p. 39.95 *(978-1-84545-257-5(7))* Berghahn Bks., Inc.

ARMENIA (REPUBLIC)—POLITICS AND GOVERNMENT

Boyajian, Artashes. Failed Transition? 2009. 60p. pap. *(978-3-639-13037-9(5))* VDM Verlag Dr. Mueller e.K.

Ghazarian, Vatche, compiled by. Minutes of the Armenian National Delegation. 2007. (ARM.). *(978-1-931834-24-7(5)*, Mayreni) Mayreni Publishing.

Ishkanian, Armine. Democracy Building & Civil Society in Post-Soviet Armenia. 2012. (Routledge Contemporary Russia & Eastern Europe Ser.). (ENG.). 216p. (C). pap. 42.95 ***(978-0-415-54117-6(4))*** Routledge.

Krüger, Heiko. The Nagorno-Karabakh Conflict: A Legal Analysis. 2010. (ENG.). xii, 164p. 119.00 *(978-3-642-11787-9(2)*, 3642117872) Springer.

Manjikian, Lalai. Collective Memory & Home in the Diaspor. 2008. 108p. pap. *(978-3-639-04894-0(6))* VDM Verlag Dr. Mueller e.K.

Margaryan, Satenik. Penal Reform in a Society in Transition: An Institutional Analysis of Penal Reform in the Republic of Armenia. 2008. 184p. pap. *(978-3-8364-9064-1(1))* VDM Verlag Dr. Mueller e.K.

Melkonian, Markar & Melkonian, Marker. My Brother's Road: An American's Fateful Journey to Armenia. 2008. (ENG., Illus.). 344p. pap. 21.00 *(978-1-84511-530-2(9))* I. B. Tauris & Co., Ltd. GBR. Dist: Macmillan.

Mirzoyan, Alla. Armenia, the Regional Powers, & the West: Between History & Geopolitics. 2010. (ENG.). 256p. 89.00 *(978-0-230-61866-4(9))* Palgrave Macmillan.

Mitra, Saumya, et al. The Caucasian Tiger: Sustaining Economic Growth in Armenia. 2007. (Stand Alones Ser.). (ENG., Illus.). 400p. per. 45.00 *(978-0-8213-6811-4(7)*, 9780821368114) World Bank Pubns.

Mooradian, Tom. The Repatriate: Love, Basketball, & the KGB. 2008. (Illus.). pap. 24.95 *(978-0-9802296-3-9(4))* Moreradiant Publishing.

Mukherjee, Amitava. Frontiers in PRA & PLA: PRA & PLA in Applied Research. 2010. (ENG., Illus.). 466p. 79.95 *(978-81-7188-724-8(4))* Academic Foundation IND. Dist: Independent Pubs. Group.

Payaslian, Simon. The Political Economy of Human Rights in Armenia: Authoritarianism & Democracy in a Former Soviet Republic. 2011. (International Library of Historical Studies: No. 75). (ENG., Illus.). 384p. 95.00 *(978-1-84885-811-4(6)*, Tauris Academic Studies) I. B. Tauris & Co., Ltd. GBR. Dist: Macmillan.

Stefes, Christoph H. Understanding Post-Soviet Transitions: Corruption, Collusion & Clientelism. 2006. (Euro-Asian Studies). (ENG., Illus.). 224p. 110.00 *(978-1-4039-3658-5(7))* Palgrave Macmillan.

United Nations. Road Map for Mainstreaming Ageing in Armenia. 2011. (ENG.). 104p. pap. 20.00 ***(978-92-1-117038-2(9))*** United Nations Pubns.

ARMENIA (REPUBLIC)—SOCIAL CONDITIONS

Anjargolian, Sara. How We Live: Life on the Margins in Armenia. 2010. (Illus.). 96p. 40.00 *(978-0-615-38584-6(2))* Anjargolian, Sara Photography.

(Hagop Melik-Hagopian), Raffi. Khatchagoghi Hishatakarana by Raffi [Language: Armenian]. 2009. 300p. pap. 24.00 *(978-1-60444-051-5(1))* IndoEuropeanPublishing.com.

Mooradian, Tom. The Repatriate: Love, Basketball, & the KGB. 2008. (Illus.). pap. 24.95 *(978-0-9802296-3-9(4))* Moreradiant Publishing.

Simonyan, Lena. Constuction & Validation of a Task-Based Test in Armenian Context. 2011. 92p. pap. ***(978-3-8443-8383-6(2))*** Lambert Academic Publishing.

Terzian, Shelley. Curriculum Reform in Post-Soviet Armeni. 2010. 292p. pap. *(978-3-639-24969-9(0))* VDM Verlag Dr. Mueller e.K.

ARMENIA (REPUBLIC)—SOCIAL LIFE AND CUSTOMS

Khachaturian, Lisa. Cultivating Nationhood in Imperial Russia: The Periodical Press & the Formation of a Modern Armenian Identity. 2009. (ENG.). 250p. 49.95 *(978-1-4128-0848-4(0))* Transaction Pubs.

Marshall, Bonnie. The Flower of Paradise & Other Armenian Tales, 1 vol. 2007. (World Folklore Ser.). (Illus.). 252p. 40.00 *(978-1-59158-367-7(5)*, LU3675) Libraries Unlimited, Inc.

Oshagan, Ara, photos by. Father Land. 2010. (ENG., Illus.). 156p. 45.00 *(978-1-57687-548-3(2)*, powerHouse Bks.) powerHouse Cultural Entertainment, Inc.

ARMENIAN AMERICANS

Aghanian, Denise. The Armenian Diaspora: Cohesion & Fracture. 2007. (ENG.). 224p. per. 37.99 *(978-0-7618-3683-4(7))* Univ. Pr. of America, Inc.

Ahnert, Margaret. The Knock at the Door: A Mother's Survival of the Armenian Genocide. 2007. (Illus.). 240p. 24.95 *(978-0-8253-0512-2(8))* Beaufort Bks., Inc.

Aslanian, Sebouh David. From the Indian Ocean to the Mediterranean: The Global Trade Networks of Armenian Merchants from New Julfa. 2011. (California World History Library). (ENG., Illus.). 336p. 49.95 *(978-0-520-26687-2(0))* Univ. of California Pr.

Bakalian, Anny P. Armenian-Americans: From Being to Feeling Armenian. 2011. (ENG.). 523p. pap. 39.95 ***(978-1-4128-4227-3(1))*** Transaction Pubs.

Forgotten Bread: First-Generation Armenian American Writers. 2007. (Illus.). 481p. *(978-1-59714-069-0(4))* Heyday.

Garsoïan, Nina G. De Vita Sua. 2011. *(978-1-56859-288-6(4))* Mazda Pubs., Inc.

Goulian, Jon-Jon. The Man in the Gray Flannel Skirt. 2011. (Illus.). 336p. 25.00 *(978-1-4000-6811-1(8)*, Random House) Random House Publishing Group.

Hovannisian, Garin K. Family of Shadows: A Century of Murder, Memory, & the Armenian American Dream. 2011. (ENG.). 276p. pap. 16.99 *(978-0-06-179214-4(4)*, Harper Paperbacks) 2010. 304p. 27.99 *(978-0-06-179208-3(X))* HarperCollins Pubs.

Jendian, Matthew A. Becoming American, Remaining Ethnic: The Case of Armenian-Americans in Central California. 2008. (Law & Society Ser.). 226p. 80.00 *(978-1-59332-261-8(5))* LFB Scholarly Publishing LLC.

Kherdian, David, ed. Forgotten Bread: First-Generation Armenian American Writers. 2008. (Illus.). 481p. pap. 21.95 *(978-1-59714-068-3(6))* Heyday.

Mooradian, Tom. The Repatriate: Love, Basketball, & the KGB. 2008. (Illus.). pap. 24.95 *(978-0-9802296-3-9(4))* Moreradiant Publishing.

Partamian, Stepan, compiled by. Yes, We Have: Contributions of American-Armenians to the United States of America. 2009. (Illus.). 143p. 19.95 *(978-0-615-30247-8(5))* Armenian Arts Fund.

Pilibosian, Helene. My Literary Profile: A Memoir. 2010. (Illus.). 324p. pap. 20.00 *(978-1-929966-08-0(3))* Ohan Pr.

ARMENIAN ART

see Art, Armenian

ARMENIAN CHURCH

Agatangeghos. The Lives of Saint Gregory: The Armenian, Greek, Arabic, & Syriac Versions of the History Attributed to Agathangelos. 2010. *(978-0-88206-118-4(6))* Caravan Bks.

Arpee, Leon. The Armenian Awakening. 2010. 250p. 32.99 *(978-1-117-93915-5(4))*; pap. 26.75 *(978-1-117-93916-2(2))* BiblioBazaar.

—The Armenian Awakening. 2009. 144p. pap. *(978-1-4588-6455-0(3))* Books LLC.

Auge, I. Eglises en Dialogue: Armeniens et Byzantins dans la seconde moitie du XIIe Siecle. 2011. (Corpus Scriptorum Christianorum Orientalium Ser.). (FRE.). 317p. (C). pap. 109.00 *(978-90-429-2357-7(1))* Peeters Pubs. & Booksellers BEL. Dist: Brown, David Bk. Co., The.

Boyajian, Dickran H. A Light Through the Iron Curtain. 2011. 92p. 38.95 ***(978-1-258-06437-2(5))*** Literary Licensing, LLC.

Ervine, Roberta R., ed. Worship Traditions in Armenia & the Neighboring Christian East: An International Symposium in Honor of the 40th Anniversary of St. Nersess Armenian Seminary. 2006. (ENG., Illus.). 346p. (C). 35.00 *(978-0-88141-304-5(6))* St. Vladimir's Seminary Pr.

Ghazarian, Vatche. Memoirs. 2008. per. *(978-1-931834-26-1(1)*, Mayreni) Mayreni Publishing.

Heyer, Friedrich, ed. Die Kirche Armeniens: Eine Volkskirche zwischen Ost und West. (Die Kirchen der Welt Ser.). (GER.). 232p. 210.00 ***(978-3-11-178441-0(X))*** De Gruyter, Walter Inc.

Krikorian, Mesrob K. Christology of the Oriental Orthodox Churches: Christology in the Tradition of the Armenian Apostolic Church. 2010. 310p. pap. 74.95 *(978-3-631-58121-6(1))* Lang, Peter GmbH, Europaischer Verlag der Wissenschaften DEU. Dist: Lang, Peter.

Marchese, Ronald & Breu, Marlene. Splendor & Pageantry: Textile Treasures from the Armenian Orthodox Churches of Istanbul. 2011. 397p. pap. 155.00 *(978-9944-424-78-3(1))* Citlembik/Nettleberry Pubns. TUR. Dist: National Bk. Network.

Minassian, Oshagan. A History of the Armenian Holy Apostolic Orthodox Church in the United States (1888-1944) 2010. 432p. 30.00 net. *(978-1-931834-35-3(0)*, Mayreni) Mayreni Publishing.

Panoyan, Kevork. Classification of Hymns of the Armenian Apostolic Church Vol. 1. 2009. (ARM., Illus.). 120p. pap. 25.00 *(978-0-9842573-1-7(4))* Drazark Pr.

Sarkissian, Karekin. The Council of Chalcedon & the Armenian Church: With Maps. (Orthodoxies & Heresies in the Early Church Ser.). (Illus.). reprint ed. 41.50 *(978-0-404-62393-7(X))* AMS Pr., Inc.

Stone, Nira, et al. The Armenians: Art, Culture & Religion. 2007. (ENG., Illus.). 96p. pap. 24.95 *(978-1-904832-37-9(7))* Giles, D. Ltd. GBR. Dist: Antique Collectors' Club.

Terian, Abraham. Macarius of Jerusalem: Letter to the Armenians, AD 335) 2008. (ENG & ARM.). 184p. 30.00 *(978-0-88141-323-6(2))* St. Vladimir's Seminary Pr.

Tourian, Leon. The Handbook of Divine Liturgy of the Armenian Apostolic Holy Church. 2011. 90p. 38.95 ***(978-1-258-04850-1(7))*** Literary Licensing, LLC.

Yagjian, Ralph A. The Divine Liturgy of the Armenian Church. Kasparian, Amak & Papazian, Dennis, eds. 2011. 66p. 36.95 ***(978-1-258-04515-9(X))*** Literary Licensing, LLC.

ARMENIAN GENOCIDE, 1915-1923

see Armenian Massacres, 1915-1923

ARMENIAN LANGUAGE

Archer, Paschal & Brand, John. A Dictionary English-Armenian. 2010. (ARM.). 181.76 *(978-1-61143-373-9(8))* Gorgias Pr., LLC.

Bedrossian, Matthias. New Armenian-English Dictionary. (ARM & ENG.). 816p. 49.95 *(978-0-86685-122-0(4)*, LDL1224) International Bk. Ctr., Inc.

—New Dictionary Armenian-English. 2009. 818p. pap. 85.00 *(978-1-60608-399-4(6)*, Wipf and Stock) Wipf & Stock Pubs.

Bedrossian, Matthias & Mathews, Edward G. Bedrossian's Armenian-English Dictionary. 2010. (ARM.). 176.00 *(978-1-61719-886-1(2))* Gorgias Pr., LLC.

Chyukyurian, Grigo. English Armenian; Armenian English Dictionary: A Dictionary of the Armenian Language. 2007. 664p. per. *(978-1-84356-014-2(3))* Wallenberg, Simon Pr.

Ciakciak, Emmanuele. Dizionario Armeno-Italiano. 2010. (ARM.). 346.96 *(978-1-60724-841-5(7))*; 346.96 *(978-1-60724-840-8(9))* Gorgias Pr., LLC.

Coneybeare, Frederick. On the Western Text of the Acts as Evidenced by Chrysostom. 2009. pap. 20.44 *(978-1-60724-608-4(2))* Gorgias Pr., LLC.

Dwight, Harrison Gray Otis. Catalogue of All Works Known to Exist in the Armenian Language: Of a Date Earlier than the Seventeenth Century. 2007. per. 29.00 *(978-1-59333-869-5(4))* Gorgias Pr., LLC.

Eastern Armenian. unabr. ed. (ARM.). 115.00 incl. audio Norton, Jeffrey Pubs., Inc.

Euro Talk. Talk Now! Armenian. 2008. 29.99 *(978-1-84352-409-0(0))* TOPICS Entertainment.

Ghazarian, Vatche. English-Armenian Dictionary. 2007. (ARM.). *(978-1-931834-20-9(2)*, Mayreni) Mayreni Publishing.

Ginosyan, Hranush & Sargsyan, Shoghik. Learning Style & Strategy Choices of Armenian University Learners. 2010. 132p. pap. *(978-3-8383-4072-2(8))* Lambert Academic Publishing.

Gyulazyan, Irena. The European Language Portfolio in Armenian Primary Education. 2009. 60p. pap. *(978-3-639-13107-9(X))* VDM Verlag Dr. Mueller e.K.

Icon Group International, Inc. Staff, compiled by. Webster's Armenian - English Thesaurus Dictionary. 2008. 564p. ring bd. 28.95 incl. audio compact disk *(978-0-497-83427-2(8))* Icon Group International, Inc.

Jordan, Hermann & Lüdtke, Willy, intros. Armenische Irenaeusfragmente. 2010. 107.72 *(978-1-61719-516-7(2))* Gorgias Pr., LLC.

Martirosyan, Hrach K. Etymological Dictionary of the Armenian Inherited Lexicon. 2008. (Leiden Indo-European Etymological Dictionary Ser.). 1000p. *(978-90-04-17337-8(4))* BRILL.

Sakayan, Dora. Eastern Armenian: For the English-Speaking World: A Contrastive Approach. (ARM & ENG., Illus.). xxviii, 535p. *(978-5-8084-0890-6(3))* Yerevan Univ. Pr.

Tragut, Jasmine. Modern Eastern Armenian. 2009. *(978-90-272-3814-6(6))* Benjamins, John Publishing Co.

ARMENIAN LITERATURE

Adalian, Rouben. Historical Dictionary of Armenia. 2nd ed. 2010. (Historical Dictionaries of Europe Ser.). (ENG., Illus.). 750p. 158.00 *(978-0-8108-6096-4(1))* Scarecrow Pr., Inc.

Aghajanian, Alfred, ed. Armenian Literature: Comprising poetry, drama, folklore, & classic Traditions. 2007. 276p. per. 19.95 *(978-1-60444-000-3(7))* IndoEuropeanPublishing.com.

Anonymous. Armenian Literature. 2007. (ENG.). 168p. pap. 19.99 *(978-1-4264-4696-2(9))*; 190p. pap. 21.99 *(978-1-4264-4727-3(2))* BiblioBazaar.

Boyajian, Zabelle C. & Raffi, Aram. An Anthology of Legedns & Poems of Armeni. 2008. 216p. pap. 24.95 *(978-1-60444-015-7(5))* IndoEuropeanPublishing.com.

Conybeare, F. C., ed. The Apology & Acts of Apollonius: And Other Monuments of Early Christianity. 2007. 368p. pap. 35.00 *(978-1-55635-275-1(1)*, Wipf and Stock) Wipf & Stock Pubs.

ARMENIAN LITERATURE—HISTORY AND CRITICISM

Parlakian, Nishan. Notable Women in Armenian Drama,1850-1970: An Anthology. 2008. *(978-0-935411-23-2(2)*, Armenian Heritage Press) National Assn. for Armenian Studies & Research.

Russell, James R. Bosphorus Nights: The Complete Lyric Poems of Bedros Tourian. 2006. (Harvard Armenian Texts & Studies: 10). (ARM & ENG., Illus.). 250p. 39.95 *(978-0-935411-22-5(4))* Harvard Univ. Pr.

Stone, Michael E. Apocrypha, Pseudepigrapha & Armenian Studies. Collected Papers: Volume II, 2 vols. 2006. (Orientalia Lovaniensia Analecta Ser.: Vols. 144-145). (ARM & ENG., Illus.). 489p. (C). 108.00 *(978-90-429-1644-9(3))* Peeters Pubs. & Booksellers BEL. Dist: Brown, David Bk. Co., The.

Stone, Michael E. & Stone, Michael Edward. Apocrypha, Pseudepigrapha & Armenian Studies. Collected Papers: Volume I, 2 vols. 2006. (Orientalia Lovaniensia Analecta Ser.: Vols. 144-145). (ARM & ENG., Illus.). 466p. (C). 119.00 *(978-90-429-1643-2(5))* Peeters Pubs. & Booksellers BEL. Dist: Brown, David Bk. Co., The.

ARMENIAN MASSACRES, 1915-1923

Affirmation of the United States Record on the Armenian Genocide Resolution: Markup Before the Committee on Foreign Affairs, House of Representatives, One Hundred Tenth Congress, First Session, on H. Res. 106, October 10, 2007. 2008. iii, 147p. *(978-0-16-080124-2(9)*, 552-070-36863) United States Government Printing Office.

Ahnert, Margaret. The Knock at the Door: A Mother's Survival of the Armenian Genocide. 2007. (Illus.). 240p. 24.95 *(978-0-8253-0512-2(8))* Beaufort Bks., Inc.

Akcam, Taner. Armenian Problem Has Been Solved. 2012. (Human Rights & Crimes against Humanity Ser.). (ENG., Illus.). 528p. (C). 39.50 ***(978-0-691-15333-9(7))*** Princeton Univ. Pr.

Akçam, Taner. A Shameful Act: The Armenian Genocide & the Question of Turkish Responsibility. 2007. (ENG., Illus.). 496p. pap. 18.00 *(978-0-8050-8665-2(X))* Picador.

Alayarian, Aida, ed. Consequences of Denial. 2008. (Illus.). 229p. (C). pap. 38.95 *(978-1-85575-565-9(3))* Karnac Bks. GBR. Dist: Stylus Publishing, LLC.

Armenian Atrocities & Terrorism - Testimonies & Witnesses. Date not set. 75p. pap. 10.00 *(978-0-9661157-0-3(8))* Assembly of Turkish American Assns.

Balakian, Grigoris. Armenian Golgotha. Balakian, Peter, tr. 2010. (Vintage Ser.). (ENG., Illus.). 576p. pap. 20.00 *(978-1-4000-9677-0(4)*, Vintage) Knopf Doubleday Publishing Group.

Balakian, Peter. Black Dog of Fate: A Memoir. 10th rev. ed. 2009. (ENG.). 304p. pap. 16.95 *(978-0-465-01019-6(9))* Perseus Bks. Group.

Balakian, Peter, et al. Armenian Golgotha. Balakian, Peter & Sevag, Aris, trs. from ARM. 2009. (ENG., Illus.). 560p. 35.00 *(978-0-307-26288-2(X)*, Knopf) Knopf Doubleday Publishing Group.

Dadrian, Vahakn N. & Akçam, Taner. Judgment at Istanbul: The Armenian Genocide Trials. 2011. (ENG.). 376p. 10.00 ***(978-0-85745-251-1(7))*** Berghahn Bks., Inc.

Dündar, Fuat. Crime of Numbers: The Role of Statistics in the Armenian Question (1878-1918) 2010. (ENG., Illus.). 254p. 49.95 *(978-1-4128-1100-2(7))* Transaction Pubs.

Freedman, Jeri. The Armenian Genocide. 2008. (Illus.). 64p. lib. bdg. 29.25 *(978-1-4042-1825-3(4))* Rosen Publishing Group, Inc., The.

Ghazarian, Vatche, compiled by. Boghos Nubar's Papers & the Armenian Question. 2007. (ARM.). *(978-1-931834-23-0(7)*, Mayreni) Mayreni Publishing.

Göçek, Fatma Müge. A Question of Genocide: Armenians & Turks at the End of the Ottoman Empire, 1 vol. Suny, Ronald Grigor & Naimark, Norman M., eds. 2011. (ENG., Illus.). 464p. 34.95 *(978-0-19-539374-3(0))* Oxford Univ. Pr., Inc.

Gunter, Michael M. Armenian History & the Question of Genocide. 2011. (ENG., Illus.). 208p. 85.00 *(978-0-230-11059-5(2))* Palgrave Macmillan.
Hovannisian, Garin K. Family of Shadows: A Century of Murder, Memory, & the Armenian American Dream. 2011. (ENG.). 276p. pap. 16.99 *(978-0-06-179214-4(4)*, Harper Paperbacks) 2010. 304p. 27.99 *(978-0-06-179208-3(X))* HarperCollins Pubs.
Hovannisian, Richard, ed. The Armenian Genocide: Cultural & Ethical Legacies. 2007. (ENG., Illus.). 461p. pap. 29.95 *(978-1-4128-0619-0(4))*; (gr. 11). 49.95 *(978-0-7658-0367-2(4))* Transaction Pubs.
Insel, Ahmet, et al. Erkkhosutyun Haykakan Tabui Shurj. 2010. (ARM., Illus.). 131p. *(978-9939-816-14-2(6))* Van Aryan Publishing Hse. Co., Ltd.
Kaligian, Dikran. Armenian Organization & Ideology under Ottoman Rule: 1908-1914. 2009. (ENG., Illus.). 270p. 59.95 *(978-1-4128-0775-3(1))* Transaction Pubs.
Kaligian, Dikran Mesrob. Armenian Organization & Ideology under Ottoman Rule, 1908-1914. 2011. (ENG.). 272p. pap. 29.95 *(978-1-4128-4245-7(X))* Transaction Pubs.
Karagueuzian, Hrayr & Auron, Yair. A Perfect Injustice: Genocide & Theft of Armenian Wealth. 2009. (ENG., Illus.). 183p. 39.95 *(978-1-4128-1001-2(9))* Transaction Pubs.
Kévorkian, Raymond. The Armenian Genocide: A Complete History. 2011. (ENG., Illus.). 1008p. 80.00 *(978-1-84885-561-8(3))* I. B. Tauris & Co., Ltd. GBR. Dist: Macmillan.
Kieser, Hans-Lukas. A Quest for Belonging. 2010. 139.64 *(978-1-61719-103-9(5))* Gorgias Pr., LLC.
Knapp, Grace H., et al. The Tragedy of Bitlis. 2009. 172p. 37.95 *(978-1-104-42602-6(1))*; pap. 22.95 *(978-1-104-40390-4(0))* Kessinger Publishing, LLC.
Künzler, Jakob, et al. In the Land of Blood & Tears: Experiences in Mesopotamia During the World War. 2007. *(978-0-9674621-8-9(5))* Armenian Cultural Foundation.
Lewy, Guenter. The Armenian Massacres in Ottoman Turkey: A Disputed Genocide. 2007. (Utah Series in Turkish & Islamic Stud Ser.). (ENG., Illus.). 384p. per. 23.00 *(978-0-87480-890-2(1))* Univ. of Utah Pr.
Libaridian, Gerard J. Modern Armenia: People, Nation, State. 2007. (ENG.). 338p. (gr. 11). pap. 29.95 *(978-1-4128-0648-0(8))* Transaction Pubs.
McCarthy, Justin. The Turk in America: The Creation of an Enduring Prejudice. 2010. (Utah Series in Turkish & Islamic Stud Ser.). (ENG., Illus.). 611p. pap. 39.95 *(978-1-60781-013-1(1))* Univ. of Utah Pr.
Semerdjian, Éric. Mémoire de la Douceur Qui Vient: Turcs, Arméniens: Sortir de L'empêchement. 2010. (FRE.). 62p. *(978-2-296-13317-4(7))* Harmattan Pr.
Ungor, Ugur & Polatel, Mehmet. Confiscation & Colonization: The Young Turk Seizure of Armenian Property. 2011. (ENG., Illus.). 224p. 120.00 *(978-1-4411-3578-0(2))* Continuum International Publishing Group, Ltd. GBR. Dist: National Bk. Network.
Winter, Jay, ed. America & the Armenian Genocide Of 1915. 2008. (Studies in the Social & Cultural History of Modern Warfare Ser.). (ENG., Illus.). 332p. pap. 46.00 *(978-0-521-07123-9(2))* Cambridge Univ. Pr.

ARMENIAN QUESTION

see also Armenian Massacres, 1915-1923

Akcam, Taner. Armenian Problem Has Been Solved. 2012. (Human Rights & Crimes against Humanity Ser.). (ENG., Illus.). 528p. (C). 39.50 ***(978-0-691-15333-9(7))*** Princeton Univ. Pr.
Benson, E. F. Crescent & Iron Cross. 2008. 152p. 24.99 *(978-0-554-23453-3(X))* 2008. 152p. 21.99 *(978-0-554-32756-3(2))* 2007. (ENG.). 134p. pap. 18.99 *(978-1-4264-4444-9(3))* BiblioBazaar.
—Crescent & Iron Cross. 2007. (ENG.). 124p. per. *(978-1-4065-4831-0(6))* Dodo Pr.
—Crescent & Iron Cross. 2010. (Illus.). 86p. pap. 12.85 *(978-1-4432-0643-3(1))* General Bks. LLC.
—Crescent & Iron Cross. 2010. 100p. pap. *(978-1-4076-1033-7(3))* HardPr.
—Crescent & Iron Cross. 2009. (ENG.). 132p. pap. 10.96 *(978-1-4385-1939-5(7)*, Book Jungle) Standard Pubns., Inc.
—The Crescent & Iron Cross. 2010. 106p. 27.96 *(978-1-169-24288-3(X))*; pap. 15.96 *(978-1-162-65880-3(0))* Kessinger Publishing, LLC.
—Crescent & Iron Cross. l.t. ed. 2007. (ENG.). 148p. pap. 19.99 *(978-1-4264-4512-5(1))* BiblioBazaar.
Benson, E. f. & Benson, E. F. Crescent & Iron Cross. 2010. 246p. 32.99 *(978-1-140-51283-7(8))*; pap. 26.75 *(978-1-140-51284-4(6))* BiblioBazaar.
—The Crescent & Iron Cross. 2010. 106p. 34.95 *(978-1-161-42745-5(7))* Kessinger Publishing, LLC.
Benson, E. f. 1867-1940. Crescent & Iron Cross. 2010. (ENG.). 290p. pap. 28.75 *(978-1-177-96625-2(5))* BiblioBazaar.
Benson, Edward Frederic. Crescent & Iron Cross. 2010. 250p. pap. 26.75 *(978-1-144-08864-2(X))* BiblioBazaar.
—Crescent & Iron Cross. 2009. 100p. pap. *(978-1-151-39144-5(1))* Books LLC.
—Crescent & Iron Cross: The theories of the old & the new Turks-the end of the Armenian question -the question of Syria & Palestine... 2010. 148p. pap. 15.00 *(978-1-60444-080-5(5))* IndoEuropeanPublishing.com.
Dündar, Fuat. Crime of Numbers: The Role of Statistics in the Armenian Question (1878-1918) 2010. (ENG., Illus.). 254p. 49.95 *(978-1-4128-1100-2(7))* Transaction Pubs.
El-Ghusein, Fa'iz. Martyred Armenia. 2007. 48p. per. *(978-1-4065-1792-7(5))* Dodo Pr.
Ghazarian, Vatche, compiled by. Boghos Nubar's Papers & the Armenian Question. 2007. (ARM.). *(978-1-931834-23-0(7)*, Mayreni) Mayreni Publishing.
Hakobyan, Levon. Haykakan Petakanutyan Verakangnman (Hayots Hartsi Hangutsalutsman) Hayetsakarg. (ARM.). 143p. *(978-99941-57-61-7(2))* Antares, Ltd.
Laycock, Joanne. Imagining Armenia: Orientalism, Ambiguity & Intervention, 1879-1925. 2009. (Cultural History of Modern War Ser.). (ENG., Illus.). 272p. 94.00 *(978-0-7190-7817-0(2))* Manchester Univ. Pr. GBR. Dist: Macmillan.
Naayem, Joseph & Bryce, Lord. Shall this Nation Die? 2010. 126.80 *(978-1-61719-041-4(1))* Gorgias Pr., LLC.

ARMENIANS

Alayarian, Aida, ed. Consequences of Denial. 2008. (Illus.). 229p. (C). pap. 38.95 *(978-1-85575-565-9(3))* Karnac Bks. GBR. Dist: Stylus Publishing, LLC.
Balakian, Grigoris. Armenian Golgotha. Balakian, Peter, tr. 2010. (Vintage Ser.). (ENG., Illus.). 576p. pap. 20.00 *(978-1-4000-9677-0(4)*, Vintage) Knopf Doubleday Publishing Group.
Balakian, Peter, et al. Armenian Golgotha. Balakian, Peter & Sevag, Aris, trs. from ARM. 2009. (ENG., Illus.). 560p. 35.00 *(978-0-307-26288-2(X)*, Knopf) Knopf Doubleday Publishing Group.
Cetin, Fethiye. My Grandmother: A Memoir. Freely, Maureen, tr. from TUR. 2008. (ENG., Illus.). 116p. 21.95 *(978-1-84467-169-4(0)*, 844169) Verso Bks. GBR. Dist: Norton, W. W. & Co., Inc.
Dadayan, Khachatur. Aproyan Gerdastani Patmutyun: XVId.-XXd. Arajin Karord. 2010. (ARM., Illus.). 207p. *(978-99941-2-443-5(9))* Gasprint Ltd., Publishing Hse.
Freedman, Jeri. The Armenian Genocide. 2008. (Illus.). 64p. lib. bdg. 29.25 *(978-1-4042-1825-3(4))* Rosen Publishing Group, Inc., The.
Ghazareans, Ara. The Armenian Review: A Bibliography & Index (1948-2008) 2010. *(978-0-9674621-9-6(3))* Armenian Cultural Foundation.
Guclu, Yucel. Armenians & the Allies in Cilicia, 1914-1923. 2009. (Utah Series in Turkish & Islamic Stud Ser.). (ENG.). 296p. pap. 25.00 *(978-0-87480-955-5(8))* Univ. of Utah Pr.
Heydarov, Tale, ed. The Armenian Question - 3 Volume Set: Russian Archive Documents & Publications, 3 vols. 2011. (RUS & ENG., Illus.). 1712p. 270.00 ***(978-0-86372-409-1(4)***, Ithaca Pr.) Garnet Publishing, Ltd. GBR. Dist: International Specialized Bk. Services.
—The Armenian Question - Volume 2: Russian Archive Documents & Publications, 3 vols. 2011. (RUS & ENG., Illus.). 624p. 98.50 ***(978-0-86372-405-3(1)***, Ithaca Pr.) Garnet Publishing, Ltd. GBR. Dist: International Specialized Bk. Services.
—The Armenian Question - Volume 3: Russian Archive Documents & Publications, 3 vols. 2011. (RUS & ENG., Illus.). 352p. 74.95 ***(978-0-86372-406-0(X)***, Ithaca Pr.) Garnet Publishing, Ltd. GBR. Dist: International Specialized Bk. Services.
Hovannisian, Richard G. Armenian Kars & Ani. 2011. *(978-1-56859-157-5(8))* Mazda Pubs., Inc.
—Armenian Pontus: The Trebizond-Black Sea Communities. 2008. *(978-1-56859-155-1(1))* Mazda Pubs., Inc.
Hovannisian, Richard G. & Payaslian, Simon. Armenian Cilicia. 2008. (Illus.). (C). *(978-1-56859-154-4(3))* Mazda Pubs., Inc.
Hülagü, M. Metin, et al. Armenians in the Ottoman Society: Erciyes University, 1st International Social Studies Symposium (EUSAS-I), 2 vols. 2008. (Illus.). *(975-9944-0664-0-2(0))* Erciyes Universitesi.
Kalemkiarian, Hagop Boghos, et al. The Enduring Family History of Boghos Hagop Kalemkiarian, (1865-1947) Memoirs. 2007. (Illus.). xiv, 66p. *(978-0-9800801-0-0(X))* Sahag Mesrob Pr. West Publishing.
Kaligian, Dikran Mesrob. Armenian Organization & Ideology under Ottoman Rule, 1908-1914. 2011. (ENG.). 272p. pap. 29.95 *(978-1-4128-4245-7(X))* Transaction Pubs.
Kouymjian, Dickran. Between Paris & Fresno: Armenian Studies in Honor of Dickran Kouymjian. 2008. (Armenian Studies). (C). *(978-1-56859-168-1(3))* Mazda Pubs., Inc.
McCarthy, Justin, et al. The Armenian Rebellion at Van. 2006. (Utah Series in Turkish & Islamic Stud Ser.). (ENG., Illus.). 304p. per. 25.00 *(978-0-87480-870-4(7))* Univ. of Utah Pr.
Parsumean-Tatoyean, Seda. The Armenians in the Medieval Islamic World: Paradigms of InteractionSeventh to Fourteenth Centuries. 2011. (ENG., Illus.). 235p. 39.95 ***(978-1-4128-4577-9(7))*** Transaction Pubs.
Payaslian, Simon. The History of Armenia. 2008. (Palgrave Essential Histories Ser.). (ENG.). 304p. 89.00 *(978-0-230-60064-5(6))* Palgrave Macmillan.
—The History of Armenia: From the Origins to the Present. 2007. (Palgrave Essential Histories Ser.). (ENG.). 304p. pap. 18.95 *(978-1-4039-7467-9(5))* Palgrave Macmillan.
Stone, Nira, et al. The Armenians: Art, Culture & Religion. 2007. (ENG., Illus.). 96p. pap. 24.95 *(978-1-904832-37-9(7))* Giles, D. Ltd. GBR. Dist: Artique Collectors' Club.
Super, Mary. A Massacre Averted: An Armenian Town, an American Nurse, & the Turkish Army They Resisted. 2010. *(978-1-55876-532-0(8))*; pap. *(978-1-55876-533-7(6))* Wiener, Markus Pubs., Inc.
Windle, Holly. Baghdad Barcarolle: How an Iraqi-Armenian Woman Became Iraq's Foremost Classical Pianist. 2008. *(978-1-932472-78-3(9))* Nodin Pr.

ARMENIANS—FOREIGN COUNTRIES

Adalian, Rouben. Historical Dictionary of Armenia. 2nd ed. 2010. (Historical Dictionaries of Europe Ser.). (ENG., Illus.). 750p. 158.00 *(978-0-8108-6096-4(1))* Scarecrow Pr., Inc.
Chaliand, Gerard. Memory of My Memory. 2007. 68p. (C). per. 15.00 *(978-1-903656-67-9(2)*, Gomidas Institute Bks.) Taderon Pr. GBR. Dist: Whitehurst & Clark.
Dadrian, Vahakn N. & Akçam, Taner. Judgment at Istanbul: The Armenian Genocide Trials. 2011. (ENG.). 376p. 10.00 ***(978-0-85745-251-1(7))*** Berghahn Bks., Inc.
Federal Writers' Project, Massachusetts. The Armenians in Massachusetts. (American Guide Ser.). reprint ed. 42.50 *(978-0-404-57926-5(4))* AMS Pr., Inc.
Ghazareans, Ara. Collections of the Armenian Cultural Foundation Series 2007. *(978-0-9674621-6-5(9))* Armenian Cultural Foundation.
Göçek, Fatma Müge. A Question of Genocide: Armenians & Turks at the End of the Ottoman Empire, 1 vol. Suny, Ronald Grigor & Naimark, Norman M., eds. 2011. (ENG., Illus.). 464p. 34.95 *(978-0-19-539374-3(0))* Oxford Univ. Pr., Inc.
Heydarov, Tale, ed. The Armenian Question - Volume 1: Russian Archive Documents & Publications, 3 vols. 2011. (RUS & ENG., Illus.). 736p. 98.50 ***(978-0-86372-404-6(3)***, Ithaca Pr.) Garnet Publishing, Ltd. GBR. Dist: International Specialized Bk. Services.
Hovannisian, Richard G. & Payaslian, Simon. Armenian Constantinople. 2010. *(978-1-56859-156-8(X))* Mazda Pubs., Inc.
Kaligian, Dikran. Armenian Organization & Ideology under Ottoman Rule: 1908-1914. 2009. (ENG., Illus.). 270p. 59.95 *(978-1-4128-0775-3(1))* Transaction Pubs.
Karagueuzian, Hrayr & Auron, Yair. A Perfect Injustice: Genocide & Theft of Armenian Wealth. 2009. (ENG., Illus.). 183p. 39.95 *(978-1-4128-1001-2(9))* Transaction Pubs.
Keusseyan, Krikor. Colors of the Prism. 2009. (ARM., Illus.). 336p. pap. *(978-1-931834-32-2(6)*, Mayreni) Mayreni Publishing.
Kotchikian, Asbed. The Dialectics of Small States - Foreign Policy Making in Armenia & Georgi. 2008. 188p. pap. *(978-3-639-05539-9(X))* VDM Verlag Dr. Mueller e.K.
Lewy, Guenter. The Armenian Massacres in Ottoman Turkey: A Disputed Genocide. 2007. (Utah Series in Turkish & Islamic Stud Ser.). (ENG., Illus.). 384p. per. 23.00 *(978-0-87480-890-2(1))* Univ. of Utah Pr.
Richoux, Sylvie. Karine Arabian: The Armenians in Fashion 17-21st Centuries. 2009. (FRE & ENG., Illus.). 152p. pap. 34.80 *(978-2-7572-0083-4(6)*, Art Stock Bks. Ltd/Csi) Continental Sales, Inc.
Simeon & Boumoutian, George A. The Travel Accounts of Simeon of Poland. 2007. (Armenian Studies: No. 10). (Illus.). 349p. (C). pap. 45.00 *(978-1-56859-161-2(6))* Mazda Pubs., Inc.
Simonian, Hovann H., ed. The Hemshin: History, Society & Identity in the Highlands of Northeast Turkey. 2007. (Caucasus World Ser.). (ENG., Illus.). 472p. (C). 160.00 *(978-0-7007-0656-3(9)*, RU29929) Routledge.
Temelkuran, Ece. Deep Mountain. 2010. (ENG., Illus.). 288p. 26.95 *(978-1-84467-423-7(1)* 844423) Verso Bks. GBR. Dist: Norton, W. W. & Co., Inc.
Vartivarian, Hagop. Meetings - 2. 2007. Orig. Title: Hantibumner - 2. (ARM.). 440p. per. *(978-1-931834-27-8(X)*, Mayreni) Mayreni Publishing.
Von Voss Staff. Portraits of Hope: Armenians in the Contemporary World. 2007. (Illus.). 400p. 39.95 *(978-1-84545-257-5(7))* Berghahn Bks., Inc.
Winter, Jay, ed. America & the Armenian Genocide Of 1915. 2008. (Studies in the Social & Cultural History of Modern Warfare Ser.). (ENG., Illus.). 332p. pap. 46.00 *(978-0-521-07123-9(2))* Cambridge Univ. Pr.

ARMENIANS—UNITED STATES

see also Armenian Americans

Apelian, Virginia Matosian. Musa Dagh Girl. 2011. 548p. 38.99 ***(978-1-61215-552-4(9))*** pap. 26.99 ***(978-1-61215-551-7(0))*** Xulon Pr., Inc.
Mardikian, George M. Song of America: Fascinating Narrative of an Armenian Immigrant. 2011. 320p. 50.95 ***(978-1-258-09300-6(6))*** Literary Licensing, LLC.
Minassian, Oshagan. A History of the Armenian Holy Apostolic Orthodox Church in the United States (1888-1944) 2010. 432p. 30.00 net. *(978-1-931834-35-3(0)*, Mayreni) Mayreni Publishing.

ARMIES

see also Artillery; Cavalry; Disarmament; Infantry; Mercenary Troops; Militarism; Recruiting and Enlistment; Sociology, Military

also Armies of individual countries, e.g. Great Britain—Army

Ahram, Ariel I. Proxy Warriors: The Rise & Fall of State-Sponsored Militias. 2011. (ENG., Illus.). 208p. 65.00 *(978-0-8047-7358-4(0))*; pap. 21.95 *(978-0-8047-7359-1(9))* Stanford Univ. Pr.
Clarke, John L., ed. Armies in Homeland Security: American & European Perspectives. 2006. (ENG., Illus.). 259p. pap. 22.00 *(978-0-16-076812-5(8)*, National Defense University) United States Government Printing Office.
Coggins, Jack. Soldiers & Warriors: An Illustrated History. 2006. (ENG., Illus.). 384p. per. 19.95 *(978-0-486-45257-9(3))* Dover Pubns., Inc.
Flanagan, Tim. The Army & Defense Resource Allocation: The Bronze Medal Ain't good Enough in a Three-Man Race. 2007. (Carlisle Papers in Security Strategy). *(978-1-58487-315-0(9))* Strategic Studies Institute, U.S. Army War College Commandant (AWCC-DSI/Pubns.).
Gabriel, Richard A. Soldiers' Lives Through History: The Ancient World. 2006. (Soldiers' Lives through History Ser.). (Illus.). 328p. 65.00 *(978-0-313-33348-4(3)*, GR3348, Greenwood Pr.) Greenwood Publishing Group, Inc.
Heyman, Charles, ed. The British Army: A Pocket Guide, 2002-2003. rev. ed. (Military Reference Ser.). (Illus.). 207p. pap. 8.95 *(978-0-85052-867-1(4))* Pen & Sword Bks. Ltd. GBR. Dist: Casemate Pubs. & Bk. Distributors, LLC.
Jowett, Philip. Chinese Warlord Armies, 1911-30. 2010. (Men-at-Arms Ser.). (ENG., Illus.). 48p. pap. 17.95 *(978-1-84908-402-4(5))* Osprey Publishing, Ltd. GBR. Dist: Random Hse., Inc.
Knight, Ian. Voices from the Zulu War. 2011. (Illus.). 280p. pap. 32.95 *(978-1-84832-590-6(8)*, Frontline) Pen & Sword Bks. Ltd. GBR. Dist: Casemate Pubs. & Bk. Distributors, LLC.
Koodziejczyk, Tomasz, et al. Oficerowie Grup Dyspozycyjnych: Socjologiczna Analiza Procesu Bezpieczenstwa Narodowego. 2008. (SLO & POL., Illus.). 486p. *(978-83-229-2969-8(2))* Uniwersytet Wroclawski, Wydawnictwo, spolka z o.o.
Parkinson, George Ellis. I Just Had to Get on with It. 2011. 172p. pap. 16.77 ***(978-1-4567-7273-4(2))*** AuthorHouse.
Peers, Chris. Central Africa: Tribal & Colonial Armies in the Congo, Gabon, Rwanda, Burundi, Northern Rhodesia & Nyasaland, 1800 To 1900. 2011. (Armies of the 19th Century: Africa Ser.). (Illus.). 200p. 63.00 *(978-1-901543-23-0(4))* Foundry Bks. GBR. Dist: Casemate Pubs. & Bk. Distributors, LLC.
Ray, Fred Eugene. Land Battles in 5th Century B. C. Greece: A History & Analysis of 173 Engagements. 2008. (ENG., Illus.). 323p. 55.00 *(978-0-7864-3534-0(8))* McFarland & Co., Inc. Pubs.
Ray, Fred Eugene. Land Battles in 5th Century BC Greece: A History & Analysis of 173 Engagements. alt. ed. 2011. (ENG., Illus.). 323p. pap. 35.00 ***(978-0-7864-6773-0(8))*** McFarland & Co., Inc. Pubs.
Smith, Digby. Armies of the Seven Years War: Commanders, Equipment, Uniforms & Strategies of the 'First World War' 2012. (ENG., Illus.). 320p. 45.00 ***(978-0-7524-5923-3(6))*** History Pr. Ltd., The GBR. Dist: Independent Pubs. Group.
Smith, Digby George. Armies of 1812: The Grand Armée & the Armies of Austria, Prussia, Russia & Turkey. 2009. (ENG., Illus.). 224p. pap. 34.95 *(978-1-86227-414-3(2))* History Pr. Ltd., The GBR. Dist: Independent Pubs. Group.
Stone, David J. Fighting for the Fatherland: The Story of the German Soldier from 1648 to the Present Day. 2009. 466p. pap. 19.95 *(978-1-59797-186-7(3))* Potomac Bks., Inc.
—Fighting for the Fatherland: The Story of the German Soldier from 1648 to the Present Day. 2006. (Illus.). 466p. 29.95 *(978-1-59797-069-3(7))* Potomac Bks., Inc.
Urban, William. Matchlocks to Flintlocks. 2012. (Illus.). 304p. 50.00 ***(978-1-84832-628-6(9)***, Frontline) Pen & Sword Bks. Ltd. GBR. Dist: Casemate Pubs. & Bk. Distributors, LLC.

ARMIES—DISCIPLINE

see Military Discipline

ARMIES—MUSIC

see Military Music

ARMIES—STAFFS

see also Marshals

Ladenheim, J. C. Grant's Keeper: The Life of John A. Rawlins. 2011. (Illus.). 286p. pap. 25.50 ***(978-0-7884-5333-5(5))*** Heritage Bks.
Ladenheim, Jules C. Grant's Keeper: The Life of John A. Rawlins. 2011. (Illus.). x, 274p. ***(978-0-7884-8791-0(4))*** Heritage Bks.
Reynolds, Michael. Devil's Adjutant: Jochen Peiper, Panzer Leader. 2009. (Illus.). 320p. pap. 24.99 *(978-1-84884-010-2(1))* Pen & Sword Bks. Ltd. GBR. Dist: Casemate Pubs. & Bk. Distributors, LLC.
Von Ludendorff, Eric. The General Staff & Its Problems, 2 vols., Set. Holt, F. A., tr. reprint ed. 44.00 *(978-0-8290-0495-3(5))* Irvington Pubs.
Wilkerson, Joseph. The Disarmament School. 2010. 84p. pap. *(978-3-8383-4924-4(5))* Lambert Academic Publishing.

ARMIES—SUPPLIES

see Military Supplies

ARMINIANISM

see also Calvinism; Methodism

Arminius, James. Arminius Speaks: Essential Writings on Predestination, Free Will, & the Nature of God. Wagner, John D., ed. 2010. 406p. pap. 45.00 *(978-1-61097-030-3(6)*, Wipf and Stock) Wipf & Stock Pubs.
Beckley, Daniel F. The Balancing Act Arminianism V. Calvinism. 2007. per. 16.95 *(978-0-9771809-5-0(6))* Painted WORD Studios.
Clarke, F. Stuart. The Ground of Election: Jacobus Arminius' Doctrine of the Work & Person of Christ. 2006. (Studies in Christian History & Thought Ser.). 214p. pap. 24.00 *(978-1-59752-919-8(2)*, Wipf and Stock) Wipf & Stock Pubs.
Colie. Light & Enlightenment. 2009. (ENG.). 180p. pap. 31.99 *(978-0-521-10823-2(3))* Cambridge Univ. Pr.
Foster, Randolph Sinks. Objections to Calvinism As It Is, in a Series of Letters Addressed to Rev N L Rice by R S Foster, with an Appendix, Containing Replies & Rejoin. 2006. 312p. per. 23.99 *(978-1-4255-2962-8(3))* MPublishing.
Gill, John. The Cause of God & Truth. 2009. 168p. pap. *(978-1-150-75681-8(0))* Books LLC.
Hunt, David. A Calvinist's Honest Doubts Resolved: By Reason & God's Amazing Grace. 2007. (ENG.). 104p. per. 7.99 *(978-1-928660-34-7(7))* Berean Call, The.
McCulloh, Gerald O., ed. Man's Faith & Freedom: The Theological Influence of Jacobus Arminius. 2011. 128p. 40.95 ***(978-1-258-08210-9(1))*** Literary Licensing, LLC.

—Man's Faith & Freedom: The Theological Influence of Jacobus Arminius. 2007. 128p. pap. 17.00 *(978-1-55635-160-0(7)*, Wipf and Stock) Wipf & Stock Pubs.

Meij-Tolsma, M. van der, ed. Arminius, Arminianism, & Europe: Jacobus Arminius (1559/60-1609) 2009. (Brill's Ser. in Church History Ser.). (Illus.). 320p. *(978-90-04-17887-8(2))* BRILL.

Olson, Roger E. Arminian Theology: Myths & Realities. 2006. (ENG.). 250p. 25.00 *(978-0-8308-2841-8(9)*, IVP Acad.) InterVarsity Pr.

Piper, John. TULIP: The Pursuit of God's Glory in Salvation. 2009. (John Piper Small Group Ser.). 216p. pap. 12.99 *(978-1-4335-0763-2(3))* Crossway.

Punt, Neal. A Theology of Inclusivism. 2008. pap. *(978-0-945315-46-9(5))* Northland Bks.

Stanglin, Keith D. & McCall, Thomas H. Jacob Arminius: Theologian of Grace. 2012. (ENG.). 224p. 99.00 ***(978-0-19-975566-0(3))***; pap. 27.95 ***(978-0-19-975567-7(1))*** Oxford Univ. Pr., Inc.

ARMINIUS, PRINCE OF THE CHERUSCI

Kuehnemund, Richard. Arminius or the Rise of a National Symbol. (North Carolina University, Studies in the Germanic Languages & Literatures: No. 8). reprint ed. 27.00 *(978-0-404-50908-8(8))* AMS Pr., Inc.

Wagner-Egelhaaf, Martina. Hermanns Schlachten: Zur Literaturgeschichte eines nationalen Mythos. 2008. (GER., Illus.). 347p. pap. *(978-3-89528-714-5(8))* Kopp, Dr. Detlev, u. Dr. Michael Vogt, Aisthesis Verlag.

ARMINIUS, JACOBUS, 1560-1609

Arminius, Jacobus & Gunter, W. Stephen. Arminius & His Declaration of Sentiments: An Annotated Translation with Introduction & Theological Commentary. 2012. pap. ***(978-1-60258-568-3(7))*** Baylor Univ. Pr.

Arminius, James. The Works of James Arminius. 2011. 554p. pap. ***(978-1-84902-375-7(1))*** Benediction Classics.

Clarke, F. Stuart. The Ground of Election: Jacobus Arminius' Doctrine of the Work & Person of Christ. 2006. (Studies in Christian History & Thought: Ser.). 214p. pap. 24.00 *(978-1-59752-919-8(2)*, Wipf and Stock) Wipf & Stock Pubs.

den Boer, William. God's Twofold Love: The Theology of Jacob Arminius (1559-1609) Gootjes, Albert, tr. 2010. (Reformed Historical Theology Ser.). (ENG.). 342p. (C). 117.00 *(978-3-525-56908-5(4))* Vandenhoeck & Ruprecht GmbH & Co. KG DEU. Dist: ISD.

McCulloh, Gerald O., ed. Man's Faith & Freedom: The Theological Influence of Jacobus Arminius. 2011. 128p. 40.95 ***(978-1-258-08210-9(1))*** Literary Licensing, LLC.

—Man's Faith & Freedom: The Theological Influence of Jacobus Arminius. 2007. 128p. pap. 17.00 *(978-1-55635-160-0(7)*, Wipf and Stock) Wipf & Stock Pubs.

Meij-Tolsma, M. van der, ed. Arminius, Arminianism, & Europe: Jacobus Arminius (1559/60-1609) 2009. (Brill's Ser. in Church History Ser.). (Illus.). 320p. *(978-90-04-17887-8(2))* BRILL.

Randall House Publications. The Works of James Arminius. 2007. 174.99 *(978-0-89265-567-0(4))* Randall Hse. Pubns.

Stanglin, Keith D. Arminius on the Assurance of Salvation: The Context, Roots, & Shape of the Leiden Debate, 1603-1609. 2007. (Brill's Series in Church History Ser.). (Illus.). 285p. *(978-90-04-15608-1(9))* BRILL.

Stanglin, Keith D. & McCall, Thomas H. Jacob Arminius: Theologian of Grace. 2012. (ENG.). 224p. 99.00 ***(978-0-19-975566-0(3))***; pap. 27.95 ***(978-0-19-975567-7(1))*** Oxford Univ. Pr., Inc.

ARMOR

see also Shields; Weapons

Adam, Guy & Maréchal, Jacques. Jousts & Tournaments from the Xi to the Xv Centuries. 2010. (Illus.). 112p. pap. 24.95 *(978-2-35250-103-9(2))* Histoire et Collections FRA. Dist: Casemate Pubs. & Bk. Distributors, LLC.

Barbier-Mueller, J. Gabriel, ed. Art of Armor: Samurai Armor from the Ann & Gabriel Barbier-Mueller Museum. 2011. (ENG., Illus.). 360p. 65.00 *(978-0-300-17636-0(8))* Yale Univ. Pr.

Barton, Kathy. The Shrink Wrapped Armor of God. 2010. 108p. pap. 10.99 *(978-1-4490-8735-7(3))* AuthorHouse.

Brayley, Martin J. Modern Body Armour. 2011. (ENG., Illus.). 160p. 34.95 *(978-1-84797-248-4(9)*, 1847972489) Crowood Pr., Ltd. GBR. Dist: MBI Distribution Services/Quayside Distribution.

Cannan, Fergus. Scottish Arms & Armour. 2009. (Shire Collections). (ENG., Illus.). 120p. pap. 19.95 *(978-0-7478-0698-1(5))* Shire Pubns., Ltd. GBR. Dist: Random Hse., Inc.

Capwell, Tobias & Edge, David. Masterpieces of European Arms & Armour from the Wallace Collection. 2011. (Illus.). 192p. pap. 50.00 ***(978-0-900785-86-3(1))*** Holberton, Paul Publishing GBR. Dist: Casemate Pubs. & Bk. Distributors, LLC.

Clip Art. Dover Digital Design Source #15: Arms & Armor. Grafton, Carol Belanger, ed. 2012. (Dover Electronic Clip Art Ser.). (ENG.). 128p. pap. 19.95 ***(978-0-486-99182-5(2))*** Dover Pubns., Inc.

Demmin, Auguste. An Illustrated History of Arms & Armour. 2008. pap. *(978-1-84830-049-1(2)*, Wildhern Pr.) Echo Library.

Department of Defense Body Armor Programs. 2008. (Illus.). iv, 225p. *(978-0-16-082679-5(9)*, 552-070-38696-3) United States Government Printing Office.

East, Richard. The Power of Armor. 2009. 52p. pap. 15.51 *(978-0-557-03187-0(7))* Lulu Enterprises Inc.

Fliegel, Stephen N. Arms & Armor: The Cleveland Museum of Art. 2007. (Illus.). 200p. *(978-0-940717-93-0(X))* Cleveland Museum of Art.

—Arms & Armor: The Cleveland Museum of Art. rev. ed. 2008. (ENG., Illus.). 200p. 55.00 *(978-0-940717-92-3(1))* Distribution General.

Force Protection Equipment Programs for Operations in Iraq & Afghanistan: Joint Hearing Before the Seapower & Expeditionary Forces Subcommittee Meeting Jointly with Air & Land Forces Subcommittee of the Committee on Armed Services, House of Representatives, One Hundred Eleventh Congress, Second Session, Hearing Held March 17, 2010. 2010. (Illus.). iv, 97p. ***(978-0-16-087052-1(6)***, 552-070-41909-8) United States Government Printing Office.

Franks, L. Advances in Ceramic Armor III: Ceramic Engineering & Science Proceedings. Salem, Jonathan & Zhu, Dongming, eds. 2007. (Ceramic Engineering & Science Proceedings Ser.). (ENG., Illus.). 224p. 111.00 *(978-0-470-19636-6(X)*, Wiley-American Ceramic Society) Wiley, John & Sons, Inc.

Franks, Lisa Prokurat, ed. Advances in Ceramic Armor IV: Ceramic Engineering & Science Proceedings. 2008. (Ceramic Engineering & Science Proceedings Ser.: 50). (ENG., Illus.). 242p. 89.95 *(978-0-470-34497-2(0)*, Wiley-American Ceramic Society) Wiley, John & Sons, Inc.

Frieder, Braden. Chivalry & the Perfect Prince: Tournaments, Art, & Armor at the Spanish Habsburg Court. 2008. (Sixteenth Century Essays & Studies). (Illus.). 256p. 65.00 *(978-1-931112-69-7(X))* Truman State Univ. Pr.

Frielinghaus, Heide. Die Helme von Olympia: Ein Beitrag zu Waffenweihungen in griechischen Heiligtümern. 2011. (Olympische Forschungen Ser.). (GER.). 179.00 ***(978-3-11-024596-7(5))*** De Gruyter, Walter Inc.

Glad, Damien. Origine et Diffusion de L'équipement Défensif Corporel en Méditerranée Orientale (IVe-VIIIe S.) Contribution à L'étude Historique et Archéologique des Armées Antiques et Médiévales. 2009. (Bar S Ser.). (FRE & ENG., Illus.). 164p. (C). pap. 97.50 *(978-1-4073-0246-1(9))* British Archaeological Reports Ltd. GBR. Dist: Brown, David Bk. Co., The.

Horn, Kenneth, et al. Lightening Body Armor: Arroyo Support to the Army Response to Section 125 of the National Defense Authorization Act for Fiscal Year 2011, 1 vol. 2012. (ENG.). 64p. (C). pap. 24.50 ***(978-0-8330-5844-7(4))*** RAND Corp., The.

Howlett, Simon. Modern British Webbing Equipment. 2010. (Europa Militaria Ser.). (ENG., Illus.). 64p. 19.95 *(978-1-84797-140-1(7)*, 1847971407) Crowood Pr., Ltd. GBR. Dist: MBI Distribution Services/Quayside Distribution.

James, Simon. The Excavations at Dura-Europos conducted by Yale University & the French Academy of Inscriptions & Letters 1928 to 1937. Final Report VII: The Arms & Armour & other Military Equipment. 2nd ed. 2010. (Illus.). 336p. (C). pap. 80.00 *(978-1-84217-371-8(5))* Oxbow Bks., Ltd. GBR. Dist: Brown, David Bk. Co., The.

Jones, George W., creator. Arms & Armor In-Miniature. 2008. (Illus.). 40p. 39.95 *(973-0-9797779-8-1(4))* George Publishing.

Jones, Robert W. Bloodied Banners: Martial Display on the Medieval Battlefield. 2010. (Warfare in History Ser.: Volume 29). (Illus.). 228p. 90.00 *(978-1-84383-561-5(4)*, Boydell Press) Boydell & Brewer, Ltd. GBR. Dist: Boydell & Brewer, Inc.

Kaminski, J. & Sim, David. Roman Imperial Armour: The Production of Early Imperial Military Armour. 2012. (ENG., Illus.). 336p. (C). pap. 50.00 *(978-1-84217-435-7(5))* Oxbow Bks., Ltd. GBR. Dist: Brown, David Bk. Co., The.

Khorasani, Manouchehr Moshtagh. Arms & Armour from Iran: The Bronze Age to the End of the Qajar Period. 2006. (Illus.). 700p. 199.00 *(978-3-932942-22-8(1))* Legat-Verlag GmbH & Company KG DEU. Dist: Independent Pubs. Group.

Kottenkamp, F. The History of Chivalry & Armour: With 60 Full-Color Plates. 2007. (Dover Books on History, Political & Social Science Ser.). (Illus.). 128p. per. 22.95 *(978-0-486-45742-0(7))* Dover Pubns., Inc.

LaCroix, Paul. Knights, Weapons & Armor. Grafton, Carol Belanger, ed. 2007. (Dover Electronic Clip Art Ser.). (ENG., Illus.). 48p. pap. 14.95 *(978-0-486-99872-5(X))* Dover Pubns., Inc.

Laking, Guy F. A Record of European Armour & Arms Through Seven Centuries, 5 vols., Set. (Illus.). reprint ed. 295.00 *(978-0-404-18344-8(1))* AMS Pr., Inc.

Lannoy, Francois de & Gilliot, Christophe. Weapons & Armour Medieval. 2008. (Illus.). 192p. 29.95 *(978-2-84048-251-2(7))* Editions Heimdal FRA. Dist: Casemate Pubs. & Bk. Distributors, LLC.

Mann, Sir James & Capwell, Tobias. Masterpieces of European Arms & Armour in the Wallace Collection. 2011. (Illus.). 192p. 250.00 ***(978-0-900785-93-1(4))*** Holberton, Paul Publishing GBR. Dist: Casemate Pubs. & Bk. Distributors, LLC.

Meyrick, Samuel Rush. Full-Color Knights & Armour CD-ROM & Book. 2007. (Dover Electronic Clip Art Ser.). (ENG., Illus.). 48p. pap. 19.95 *(978-0-486-99843-5(6))* Dover Pubns., Inc.

Michaux, Marie-Anne. Swords & Saucepans. 2011. 176p. pap. ***(978-3-8443-9348-4(X))*** Lambert Academic Publishing.

Mortimer, Paul. Woden's Warriors: Warfare, Beliefs, Arms & Armour in Northern Europe during the 6-7th Cent. 2012. (ENG., Illus.). 304p. (C). 90.00 ***(978-1-898281-60-3(2))*** Anglo-Saxon Bks. GBR. Dist: Brown, David Bk. Co., The.

Oakeshott, Ewart. European Weapons & Armour: From the Renaissance to the Industrial Revolution. 2012. (Illus.). 312p. pap. 29.95 ***(978-1-84383-720-6(X)***, Boydell Press) Boydell & Brewer, Ltd. GBR. Dist: Boydell & Brewer, Inc.

Ogawa, Morihiro, ed. Art of the Samurai: Japanese Arms & Armor, 1156-1868. 2009. (Illus.). 356p. 65.00 *(978-0-300-14205-1(6))* Yale Univ. Pr.

Ogawa, Morihiro & Harada, Kazutoshi. Art of the Samurai: Japanese Arms & Armor, 1156-1868. 2009. 65.00 *(978-1-58839-345-6(3))* Metropolitan Museum of Art, The.

Patterson, Angus. Fashion & Armour in Renaissance Europe: Proud Lookes & Brave Attire. 2009. (ENG., Illus.). 112p. 30.00 *(978-1-85177-581-1(1))* V & A Pubns. GBR. Dist: Hachette Bk. Group.

Ruble, Ron. ARMS & ARMOUR of Archduke Eugen, 1927 Auction Catalog. 2008. 264p. pap. 27.50 *(978-1-4357-1804-3(6))* Lulu Enterprises Inc.

Schwartz, Adam. Reinstating the Hoplite: Arms, Armour & Phalanx Fighting in Archaic & Classical Greece. 2009. (Historia - Einzelschriften Ser.). (ENG., Illus.). 337p. (C). 97.00 *(978-3-515-09330-9(3))* Steiner, Franz Verlag Wiesbaden GmbH DEU. Dist: Brown, David Bk. Co., The.

Solis, William M. Defense Logistics: Several Factors Limited the Production & Installation of Army Truck Armor During Current Wartime Operations. 2006. (Illus.). 63p. (C). pap. 20.00 *(978-1-4223-0708-3(5))* DIANE Publishing Co.

Soyars, by Andrew. Hail, Ye Knights of the King. 2009. 111p. pap. 12.99 *(978-0-557-03464-2(7))* Lulu Enterprises Inc.

Suenaga, M. Pictorial History of Ancient Japanese Weapons, Armour & Artifacts. 100p. pap. 20.00 *(978-0-87556-702-0(9))* Saifer, Albert Pub.

Sumner, G. Arms & Armour of Imperial Roman Soldier. 2009. (Illus.). 320p. 60.00 *(978-1-84832-512-8(6)*, Frontline) Pen & Sword Bks. Ltd. GBR. Dist: Casemate Pubs. & Bk. Distributors, LLC.

Swab, Jeffrey J. & Franks, Lisa, eds. Advances in Ceramic Armor V. 2009. (Ceramic Engineering & Science Proceedings Ser.: 509). (ENG., Illus.). 246p. 94.95 *(978-0-470-45755-9(4)*, Wiley-American Ceramic Society) Wiley, John & Sons, Inc.

Terjanian, Pierre. Princely Armor in the Age of Durer: A Renaissance Masterpiece in the Philadelphia Museum of Art. 2012. (ENG., Illus.). 56p. pap. 18.00 *(978-0-300-17631-5(7))* Yale Univ. Pr.

Travis, Hilary & John. Roman Body Armour. 2011. (Illus.). 176p. 40.00 ***(978-1-4456-0359-9(4))*** Amberley Publishing GBR. Dist: Casemate Pubs. & Bk. Distributors, LLC.

University of Toronto Press. Armor & Masculinity in the Italian Renaissance. 2010. (Toronto Italian Studies). (ITA & ENG., Illus.). 272p. *(978-1-4426-4055-9(3))* Univ. of Toronto Pr.

Van De Ven, Tim. The Limits of Transparency. 2011. 88p. pap. ***(978-3-8443-1087-0(8))*** Lambert Academic Publishing.

ARMORED CARS (TANKS)

see Tanks (Military Science)

ARMORED MILITARY VEHICLES

see Armored Vehicles, Military

ARMORED VEHICLES, MILITARY

see also Half-Track Vehicles, Military; Tanks (Military Science)

Across the Reef: The Amphibious Tracked Vehicle at War. 256p. pap. 35.00 *(978-0-7881-2665-9(2))* DIANE Publishing Co.

Amphibious Operations: Hearing Before the Subcommittee on Seapower & Projection Forces of the Committee on Armed Services, House of Representatives, One Hundred Twelfth Congress, First Session, Hearing Held March 16, 2011. 2011. (Illus.). iii, 47p. ***(978-0-16-089509-8(X)***, 552-070-43468-2) United States Government Printing Office.

Army & Marine Corps Force Protection Programs: Joint Hearing Before the Air & Land Forces Subcommittee Meeting Jointly with Seapower & Expeditionary Forces Subcommittee of the Committee on Armed Services, House of Representatives, One Hundred Eleventh Congress, First Session, Hearing Held, February 4, 2009. 2010. iv, 96p. *(978-0-16-085072-1(X)*, 552-070-4-429-5) United States Government Printing Office.

The Army's M1114 Up-Armor High Mobility Multipurpose Wheeled Vehicle (UAH) Distribution Strategy: Hearing Before the Committee on Armed Services, House of Representatives, One Hundred Ninth Congress, First Session, Hearing Held, October 20, 2005. 2008. (Illus.). iii, 67p. *(978-0-16-080716-9(6)*, 552-070-37324-1) United States Government Printing Office.

Bishop, Chris. German Panzers in World War II. rev. ed. 2007. (Order of Battle Ser.). (ENG., Illus.). 192p. pap. 19.95 *(978-0-7603-3116-3(2)*, 0760331162, Zenith Pr.) MBI Publishing Co. LLC.

—Panzergrenadier Divisions, 1939-45. 2007. (Essential Vehicle Identification Guide Ser.). (Illus.). 192p. 34.95 *(978-1-905704-29-3(1))* Amber Bks. GBR. Dist: Casemate Pubs. & Bk. Distributors, LLC.

Blakeman, Seth T. Arming America at War: A Model for Rapid Defense Aquisition in Time of War. 2010. *(978-1-61735-062-7(1))*; pap. *(978-1-61735-061-0(3))*; E-Book *(978-1-61735-063-4(X))* Information Age Publishing, Inc.

Bradford, George. Allied Armored Fighting Vehicles 1: 72 Scale. 2009. (World War II AFV Plans Ser.). (ENG., Illus.). 96p. pap. 14.95 *(978-0-8117-3570-4(2))* Stackpole Bks.

—Axis Armored Fighting Vehicles 1: 72 Scale. 2009. (World War II AFV Plans Ser.). (ENG., Illus.). 96p. pap. 14.95 *(978-0-8117-3572-8(9))* Stackpole Bks.

—British Armored Fighting Vehicles. 2008. (World War II Afv Plans Ser.). (ENG., Illus.). 96p. per. 14.95 *(978-0-8117-3453-0(6))* Stackpole Bks.

—Cold War Armored Fighting Vehicles. 2010. (World War II AFV Plans Ser.). (ENG., Illus.). 96p. pap. 14.95 *(978-0-8117-0678-0(8))* Stackpole Bks.

—German Early War Armored Fighting Vehicles. 2007. (World War II Armored Fighting Vehicle Plans Ser.). (ENG., Illus.). 95p. per. 14.95 *(978-0-8117-3341-0(6))* Stackpole Bks.

—German Late War Armored Fighting Vehicles. 2007. (World War II Afv Plans Ser.). (ENG., Illus.). 93p. per. 14.95 *(978-0-8117-3355-7(6))* Stackpole Bks.

—Other Axis & Allied Armored Fighting Vehicles. 2008. (World War II Afv Plans Ser.). (ENG., Illus.). 112p. per. 14.95 *(978-0-8117-3455-4(2))* Stackpole Bks.

—Russian Armored Fighting Vehicles. 2007. (World War II Afv Plans Ser.). (ENG., Illus.). 86p. per. 14.95 *(978-0-8117-3356-4(4))* Stackpole Bks.

—1914-1938 Armored Fighting Vehicles. 2010. (World War II AFV Plans Ser.). (ENG., Illus.). 96p. pap. 14.95 *(978-0-8117-0568-4(4))* Stackpole Bks.

Clark, Alex. Small-Scale Armour Modelling. 2011. (Modelling Masterclass Ser.). (ENG., Illus.). 192p. 39.95 *(978-1-84908-414-7(9))* Osprey Publishing, Ltd. GBR. Dist: Random Hse., Inc.

Combat Vehicle Active Protection Systems: Hearing Before the Tactical Air & Land Forces Subcommittee of the Committee on Armed Services, House of Representatives, One Hundred Ninth Congress, Second Session: Hearing Held, September 21, 2006. 2007. (Illus.). iii, 75p. *(978-0-16-079752-1(7)*, 552-070-36670-9) United States Government Printing Office.

Dancey, Peter. USAF Air Combat Command & Air Mobility Command. 2010. 102p. pap. 28.50 *(978-1-4461-5515-8(3))* Lulu Enterprises Inc.

Demaret, Henry. L' AIFV au Service de l'Armee Belge. (Belgique Sous les Armes Ser.: Tome 2). (FRE., Illus.). 68p. pap. 18.95 *(978-90-72547-32-3(2))* De Krijger BEL. Dist: Casemate Pubs. & Bk. Distributors, LLC.

The Department of Defense's Rapid Acquisition Process: Is It a Model for Improving Acquisition?: Hearing Before the Panel on Defense Acquisition Reform of the Committee on Armed Services, House of Representatives, One Hundred Eleventh Congress, First Session, Hearing Held October 8, 2009. 2010. (Illus.). iii, 92p. *(978-0-16-086572-5(7)*, 552-070-41570-0) United States Government Printing Office.

Doherty, Richard. Humber Light Reconnaissance Car 1941-45. 2011. (New Vanguard Ser.). (ENG., Illus.). 48p. pap. 17.95 *(978-1-84908-310-2(X))* Osprey Publishing, Ltd. GBR. Dist: Random Hse., Inc.

Doyle, David. M50A1 Ontos. 2010. (Illus.). 72p. pap. ***(978-0-89747-618-8(2))*** Squadron Signal Pubns.

—M88 Armored Recovery Vehicle. 2010. (Illus.). 80p. pap. ***(978-0-89747-599-0(2))*** Squadron Signal Pubns.

Edmundson, Gary. Modelling the Sturmgeschütz III. 2006. (Osprey Modelling Ser.: No. 22). (ENG., Illus.). 80p. pap. 19.95 *(978-1-84176-949-3(5))* Osprey Publishing, Ltd. GBR. Dist: Random Hse., Inc.

Edmundson, Gary, et al. Modelling Armoured Vehicles. 2008. (Osprey Modelling Ser.). (ENG., Illus.). 80p. pap. 19.95 *(978-1-84603-287-5(3))* Osprey Publishing, Ltd. GBR. Dist: Random Hse., Inc.

Expeditionary Fighting Vehicle Program Update: Hearing Before the Seapower & Expeditionary Forces Subcommittee of the Committee on Armed Services, House of Representatives, One Hundred Tenth Congress, First Session, Hearing Held, June 26, 2007. 2008. (Illus.). iii, 66p. *(978-0-16-082458-6(3)*, 552-070-38501-1) United States Government Printing Office.

Feist, Uwe. Panzerspahwagen. 2008. (ENG., Illus.). 150p. 49.95 *(978-1-930571-30-3(5))* Ryton Pubns.

Feliciano, Christian N. The Army's Future Combat System Program. 2009. (Defense, Security & Strategies Ser.). (Illus.). 148p. 69.00 *(978-1-60741-262-5(4))* Nova Science Pubs., Inc.

Fletcher, David. The Rolls-Royce Armoured Car. 2012. (New Vanguard Ser.). (ENG., Illus.). 48p. pap. 17.95 ***(978-1-84908-580-9(3))*** Osprey Publishing, Ltd. GBR. Dist: Random Hse., Inc.

Force Protection Equipment Programs for Operations in Iraq & Afghanistan: Joint Hearing Before the Seapower & Expeditionary Forces Subcommittee Meeting Jointly with Air & Land Forces Subcommittee of the Committee on Armed Services, House of Representatives, One Hundred Eleventh Congress, Second Session, Hearing Held March 17, 2010. 2010. (Illus.). iv, 97p. ***(978-0-16-087052-1(6)***, 552-070-41909-8) United States Government Printing Office.

Foss, Christopher F. & Strickland, Richard, eds. Janes Armour Artillery Upgrades 2006/07. 19th rev. ed. 2006. (Jane's Armour & Artillery Ser.). (Illus.). 693p. *(978-0-7106-2748-3(3))* Jane's Information Group.

Fuller, John F. Armored Warfare. reprint ed. 32.50 *(978-0-404-20102-9(4)*, UG446) AMS Pr., Inc.

Gott, Kendall D. Breaking the Mold: Tanks in the Cities. 2006. (ENG., Illus.). 148p. pap. 12.00 *(978-0-16-076223-9(5)*, Dept. of the Army) United States Government Printing Office.

Green, Michael & Brown, James D. M2/M3 Bradley at War. rev. ed. 2007. (At War Ser.). (ENG., Illus.). 128p. pap. 19.95 *(978-0-7603-2523-0(5)*, 0760325235, Zenith Pr.) MBI Publishing Co. LLC.

Haskew, Michael. Postwar Armored Fighting Vehicles: 1945-Present. 2010. (Essential Vehicle Identification Guide Ser.). (Illus.). 192p. 34.95 *(978-1-907446-28-3(1))* Amber Bks. GBR. Dist: Casemate Pubs. & Bk. Distributors, LLC.

Jane's Armour & Artillery: The World's Authority on Battlefield Armour & Artillery. 560.00 *(978-0-7106-2309-6(7))* Jane's Information Group, Inc.

Jane's Armour & Artillery Upgrades: Upgrade Your Subsystems Information. 510.00 *(978-0-7106-2310-2(0))* Jane's Information Group, Inc.

Johnson, David E. & Gordon, John, IV. Observations on Recent Trends in Armored Forces. 2010. 14p. pap. 20.00 *(978-0-8330-4927-8(5))* RAND Corp., The.

Laugier, Didier. Sturmartillerie. 2011. (FRE., Illus.). 400p. 79.95 ***(978-2-84048-285-7(1))*** Editions Heimdal FRA. Dist: Casemate Pubs. & Bk. Distributors, LLC.

—Sturmartillerie Ii. 2011. (FRE., Illus.). 144p. 59.95 ***(978-2-84048-306-9(8))*** Editions Heimdal FRA. Dist: Casemate Pubs. & Bk. Distributors, LLC.

Livesey, Jack. Armoured Fighting Vehicles of World Wars I & II: Features 90 Landmark Vehicles from 1900-1945 with over 370 Archive Photographs. 2007. (ENG., Illus.). 128p. pap. 16.99 *(978-1-84476-370-2(6))* Anness Publishing GBR. Dist: National Bk. Network.

—Modern Armored Fighting Vehicles: From 1946 to the Present Day: an Illustrated A-Z Guide to AFVs of the World, Featuring 76 Vehicles & 330

Stunning Photographs. 2008. (ENG., Illus.). 128p. pap. 16.99 *(978-1-84476-462-4(1))* Anness Publishing GBR. Dist: National Bk. Network.

Mine Resistant Ambush Protected (MRAP) Vehicle Program: Joint Hearing Before the Seapower & Expeditionary Forces Subcommittee Meeting Jointly with Air & Land Forces Subcommittee of the Committee on Armed Services, House of Representatives, One Hundred Tenth Congress, First Session, Hearing Held, July 19, 2007. 2008. (Illus.). iv, 93p. *(978-0-16-082613-9(6),* 552-070-38631-9) United States Government Printing Office.

Prigent, John. Armour Modelling. 2006. (Modelling Masterclass Ser.). (ENG., Illus.). 192p. 39.95 *(978-1-84176-974-5(6))* Osprey Publishing, Ltd. GBR. Dist: Random Hse., Inc.

Riccio, Ralph. Afvs in Irish Service Since 1922: From the National Army to the Irish Defence Forces. 2010. (Green Ser.). (Illus.). 184p. pap. 58.00 *(978-83-61421-19-1(X))* Stratus, Wydawnictwo, Juszczak, Artur POL. Dist: Casemate Pubs. & Bk. Distributors, LLC.

Rottman, Gordon. Vietnam Gun Trucks. 2011. (New Vanguard Ser.). (ENG., Illus.). 48p. pap. 17.95 *(978-1-84908-355-3(X))* Osprey Publishing, Ltd. GBR. Dist: Random Hse., Inc.

Rottman, Gordon L. Stryker Combat Vehicles. 2006. (New Vanguard Ser.: Vol. 121). (ENG., Illus.). 48p. pap. 17.95 *(978-1-84176-930-1(4))* Osprey Publishing, Ltd. GBR. Dist: Random Hse., Inc.

Sawodny, Wolfgang. German Armored Trains 1904-1945. 2010. (Illus.). 428p. 99.99 *(978-0-7643-3523-5(5))* Schiffer Publishing, Ltd.

Skaarup, Harold A. Ironsides: Canadian Armoured Fighting Vehicle Museums & Monuments. 2011. 368p. pap. 33.95 ***(978-1-4620-3464-2(0))*** iUniverse, Inc.

Spielberger, Walter J. Armored Vehicles of the German Army 1905-1945. 2008. (Illus.). 176p. 49.95 *(978-0-7643-2941-8(3))* Schiffer Publishing, Ltd.

Spielberger, Walter J. & Doyle, Hilary L. Special Panzer Variants: Development - Production - Operations. 2007. (Illus.). 160p. 49.95 *(978-0-7643-2622-6(8))* Schiffer Publishing, Ltd.

The Status of Tactical Wheeled Vehicle Armoring Initiatives & Improvised Explosive Device (IED) Jammer Initiatives on Operation Iraqi Freedom: Hearing Before the Committee on Armed Services, House of Representatives, One Hundred Ninth Congress, First Session, Hearing Held, May 5, 2005. 2008. (Illus.). iv, 159p. *(978-0-16-080758-9(1),* 552-070-37362-4) United States Government Printing Office.

Stickland, Richard & Foss, Christopher F., eds. Jane's Armour & Artillery Upgrades: 2007-2008. 20th rev. ed. 2007. (Jane's Armour & Artillery Upgrades Ser.). (Illus.). 702p. *(978-0-7106-2795-7(5))* Jane's Information Group.

Time-Life Editors. New Faces of War: Armoured Fist. (Illus.). 196p. 24.00 *(978-1-84447-223-9(X))* Time Life Value GBR. Dist: Mercury Bks. Ltd.

Uddin, N., ed. Blast Protection of Civil Infrastructures & Vehicles Using Composites. 2010. (ENG., Illus.). 448p. 219.95 *(978-1-4398-2771-0(0),* CRC Press) Taylor & Francis Group GBR. Dist: Taylor & Francis Group.

—Blast Protection of Civil Infrastructures & Vehicles Using Composites. 2010. (Illus.). 448p. 240.00 *(978-1-84569-399-2(X))* Woodhead Publishing Ltd. GBR. Dist: Taylor & Francis Group.

Ware, Pat. World War Two Armoured Cars. 2009. 192p. 39.95 *(978-0-7110-3394-8(3))* Allan, Ian Publishing GBR. Dist: Casemate Pubs. & Bk. Distributors, LLC.

World Market for Armoured & Military Logistic Vehicles. 695.00 *(978-0-7106-1218-2(4))* Jane's Information Group, Inc.

Yeide, Harry. The Infantry's Armor: The U.S. Army's Separate Tank Battalions in World War II. 2010. (ENG., Illus.). 400p. 29.95 *(978-0-8117-0595-0(1))* Stackpole Bks.

Zaloga, Steven J. Modeling US Armor of World War 2. 2009. (Modelling Masterclass Ser.). (ENG., Illus.). 192p. 39.95 *(978-1-84603-398-8(5))* Osprey Publishing, Ltd. GBR. Dist: Random Hse., Inc.

—U. S. Armour Camouflage & Markings, 1917-45. (Vanguard Ser.: No. 39). (Illus.). 48p. pap. 10.95 *(978-0-85045-515-1(4),* 9328) Osprey Publishing, Ltd. GBR. Dist: Stackpole Bks.

Zimmerman, W. X-47 Unmanned Combat Air Vehicle. 2007. 36p. per. 17.81 *(978-1-934840-03-0(3))* Nimble Bks. LLC.

ARMORED VESSELS

see Warships

ARMORIC LANGUAGE

see Breton Language

ARMORIES

see also Arsenals

Lane, Frederic Chapin. Venetian Ships & Shipbuilders of the Renaissance. 296p. 2008. 43.95 *(978-1-4366-9085-0(4))* 2007. (ENG.). per. 28.95 *(978-1-4325-5601-3(0))* Kessinger Publishing, LLC.

Todd, Nancy L. New York's Historic Armories: An Illustrated History. 2006. (Illus.). 322p. 50.00 *(978-0-7914-6911-8(5))* State Univ. of New York Pr.

Wiegers, Robert P. Missouri Armories. 2012. (ENG., Illus.). 216p. pap. 34.95 ***(978-1-61248-063-3(2))*** Truman State Univ. Pr.

ARMS, COATS OF

see Devices (Heraldry); Heraldry

ARMS AND ARMOR

see Armor; Weapons

ARMS AND ARMOR, ANCIENT

see Weapons, Ancient

ARMS CONTROL

see also Arms Race; Military Readiness

Abhinandan, Netajee. China's Adaptation to Global Regimes: Dilemmas & Debates. 2011. 264p. pap. ***(978-3-8454-1598-7(3))*** Lambert Academic Publishing.

Albright, David. Peddling Peril: How the Secret Nuclear Trade Arms America's Enemies. 2010. (ENG., Illus.). 304p. 27.00 *(978-1-4165-4931-4(5),* Free Pr.) Free Pr.

Anderton, Charles H. & Carter, John R. Principles of Conflict Economics: A Primer for Social Scientists. 2009. (ENG., Illus.). 344p. (C). 2.00 *(978-0-521-87557-8(9));* pap. 39.00 *(978-0-521-69865-8(0))* Cambridge Univ. Pr.

Art & Waltz & Cram101 Textbook Reviews Staff. The Use of Force: Military Power & International Politics. 2007. 140p. per. 11.95 *(978-1-4288-2204-7(6))* Cram101 Inc.

Barak, Eitan. Deadly Metal Rain - The Legality of Flechette Weapons in International Law: A Reappraisal Following Israel's Use of Flechettes in the Gaza Strip, (2001-2009) 2011. (ENG., Illus.). XVIII, 262p. ***(978-90-04-16719-3(6))*** BRILL.

Bellany, Ian, ed. Terrorism & Weapons of Mass Destruction: Responding to the Challenge. 2009. (Illus.). 246p. pap. 39.95 *(978-0-415-57065-7(4))* Routledge.

Björk, Kjell. Ridding the World of Landmines: The Governance of Mine Action. 2012. 348p. pap. 35.95 ***(978-1-61233-555-1(1),*** Brown Walker Pr.) Universal Pubs.

Blank, Stephen J. Russia & Arms Control: Are There Opportunities for the Obama Administration? 2009. pap. *(978-1-58487-381-5(7))* Strategic Studies Institute, U.S. Army War College Commandant (AWCC-DSI/Pubns.).

Blix, Hans. Why Nuclear Disarmament Matters. 2008. (Boston Review Bks.). (ENG.). 112p. (gr. 17). 14.95 *(978-0-262-02644-4(9))* MIT Pr.

Bonomo, James, et al. Stealing the Sword: Limiting Terrorist Use of Advanced Conventional Weapons. 2007. (Illus.). 146p. per. 20.00 *(978-0-8330-3965-1(2))* RAND Corp., The.

Borrie, John & Randin, Vanessa Martin. Thinking Outside the Box in Multilateral Disarmament & Arms Control Negotiations. 2007. (ENG., Illus.). 292p. pap. 35.00 *(978-92-9045-187-7(4))* United Nations Pubns.

Borrie, John, et al. The value of diversity in multilateral disarmament Work. 2009. (ENG.). 100p. pap. 19.00 *(978-92-9045-193-8(9))* United Nations Pubns.

Burns, Richard Dean. The Evolution of Arms Control: From Antiquity to the Nuclear Age, 1 vol. 2009. (Praeger Security International Ser.). 251p. 49.95 *(978-0-313-37574-3(7),* C37574) Greenwood Publishing Group, Inc.

Caldicott, Helen & Eisendrath, Craig. War in Heaven: The Arms Race in Outer Space. 2007. 280p. pap. 26.95 *(978-1-59558-224-9(X));* (ENG.). 166p. 23.95 *(978-1-59558-114-3(6))* New Pr., The.

Caldwell IV, William B., et al, frwds. The U. S. Army Stability Operations Field Manual: U. S. Army Field Manual No. 3-07. 2009. (ENG., Illus.). 352p. pap. 15.00 *(978-0-472-03390-4(5))* Univ. of Michigan Pr.

Cambridge University Press, creator. Small Arms Survey: Guns & the City. 2007. (Small Arms Survey Ser.). (ENG., Illus.). 368p. 99.99 *(978-0-521-88039-8(4));* per. 41.00 *(978-0-521-70654-4(8))* Cambridge Univ. Pr.

Cattaneo, Silvia, et al. Implementing the United Nations Programme of Action on Small Arms & Light Weapons: Analysis of the national reports submitted by states from 2002 To 2008. 2009. (ENG.). 192p. pap. 32.00 *(978-92-9045-191-4(2))* United Nations Pubns.

Chinese Academy of Sciences Staff, et al. Trends in Science & Technology Relevant to the Biological & Toxin Weapons Convention. 2011. (ENG.). 164p. pap. 42.00 *(978-0-309-21071-3(2))* National Academies Pr.

—Trends in Science & Technology Relevant to the Biological & Toxin Weapons Convention: Summary of an International Workshop: October 31 to November 3, 2010, Beijing, China. 2011. (ENG.). 56p. pap. 21.00 *(978-0-309-20929-8(3))* National Academies Pr.

Committee on Improving Metrics for the Department of Defense, et al. Improving Metrics for the Department of Defense Cooperative Threat Reduction Program. 2012. (ENG.). 118p. pap. 38.00 ***(978-0-309-22255-6(9))*** National Academies Pr.

Cooper, Neil & Mutimer, David, eds. Arms Control for the 21st Century. 2011. (ENG., Illus.). 280p. (C). 145.00 ***(978-0-415-68883-3(3))*** Routledge.

Cram101 Textbook Reviews Staff. Outlines & Highlights for Peace & Conflict Studies by Charles P Webel, David P Barash, Isbn: 9781412961202. 2009. 196p. pap. 29.95 *(978-1-4288-8444-1(0))* Cram101 Inc.

Daase, Christopher & Meier, Oliver, eds. Arms Control in the 21st Century: Between Coercion & Cooperation. 2012. (Routledge Global Security Studies). (ENG., Illus.). 248p. (C). 135.00 ***(978-0-415-69817-7(0))*** Routledge.

Dando, Malcolm R., et al, eds. Verification of the Biological & Toxin Weapons Convention. 2010. (NATO Science Partnership Sub-Series: 1: Ser.). 260p. pap. 189.00 *(978-90-481-5537-8(1),* 9048155371) Springer.

Dokos, Thanos P. Countering the Proliferation of Weapons of Mass Destruction: NATO & EU Options in the Mediterranean & the Middle East. 2007. (Contemporary Security Studies). (Illus.). 230p. 150.00 *(978-0-7146-5606-9(2),* RU33538) Routledge.

—Weapons of Mass Destruction in the Mediterranean: Options for NATO & the EU. 2007. 256p. pap. 39.95 *(978-0-7146-8499-4(5),* RU34017) Routledge.

Elliot, Jeffrey M. The Arms Control, Disarmament, & Military Security Dictionary. 2007. (ENG.). 364p. 39.95 *(978-1-4344-9051-3(3));* per. 24.95 *(978-1-4344-9052-0(1))* Wildside Pr., LLC. (Borgo Pr.).

FAULKNER, Frank. Moral Entrepreneurs & the Campaign to Ban Landmines. 2007. (At the Interface/Probing the Boundaries Ser.: 35). 272p. per. 73.00 *(978-90-420-2230-0(2))* Rodopi.

Fidler, David P. & Gostin, Lawrence O. Biosecurity in the Global Age: Biological Weapons, Public Health, & the Rule of Law. 2007. (ENG., Illus.). 320p. 29.95 *(978-0-8047-5029-5(7),* Stanford Law & Politics) Stanford Univ. Pr.

Forsberg, Randall, ed. Arms Control in the New Era: Linked Restraints on Arms Deployment, Production, & Trade. Date not set. (CSIA Studies in International Security: No. N). 256p. pap. 17.95 *(978-0-262-56094-8(1));* (Illus.). (C). 39.95 *(978-0-262-06182-7(1))* MIT Pr.

Foster, John Watson. Limitation of Armament on the Great Lakes. 2009. 68p. pap. 16.95 *(978-1-104-23910-7(8))* Kessinger Publishing, LLC.

Garcia, Denise. Disarmament Diplomacy & Human Security: Regimes, Norms & Moral Progress in International Relations. 2012. (ENG., Illus.). 231p. (C). pap. 39.95 ***(978-0-415-53245-7(0))*** Routledge.

Garcia, Denise. International Arms Trade. 2011. (Routledge Global Security Studies). (ENG., Illus.). 256p. (C). 138.00 *(978-0-415-58003-8(X))* Routledge.

Gaspari, Adelfo. Proliferation Control Regimes. 2009. (Weapons of Mass Destruction Ser.). 171p. 79.00 *(978-1-60741-115-4(6))* Nova Science Pubs., Inc.

Gillespie, Alexander. A History of the Laws of War Vol. 1: The Customs & Laws of War with Regards to Combatants & Captives. 2011. (ENG.). 278p. 90.00 *(978-1-84946-204-4(6))* Hart Publishing Ltd. GBR. Dist: International Specialized Bk. Services.

—A History of the Laws of War Vol. 3: The Customs & Laws of War with Regards to Arms Control. 2011. (ENG.). 180p. 90.00 *(978-1-84946-206-8(2))* Hart Publishing Ltd. GBR. Dist: International Specialized Bk. Services.

Glynn, Patrick. Closing Pandora's Box: Arms Races, Arms Control, & the History of the Cold War. 2006. 445p. reprint ed. 30.00 *(978-1-4223-5371-4(0))* DIANE Publishing Co.

Hamilton, Keith, et al. Arms & Disarmament in Diplomacy. Hamilton, Keith & Johnson, Edward, eds. 2008. 202p. (C). 85.00 *(978-0-85303-756-9(6));* pap. 34.95 *(978-0-85303-757-6(4))* Vallentine Mitchell Pubs. GBR. Dist: International Specialized Bk. Services.

Hansen & Grinevsky. Making Peace: Confidence & Security in a New Europe. 2009. 700p. 41.50 *(978-1-60693-586-6(0),* Eloquent Bks.) AEG Literary Publishing Services, Inc.

Harmon, Christopher et al. Toward a Grand Strategy Against Terrorism. 2010. (Textbook Ser.). (ENG., Illus.). 448p. (C). pap. 98.00 *(978-0-07-352779-6(3),* 0073527793, McGraw-Hill/Dushkin) McGraw-Hill Higher Education.

Hearing on National Defense Authorization ACT for Fiscal Year 2011 & Oversight of Previously Authorized Programs Before the Committee on Armed Services, House of Representatives, One Hundred Eleventh Congress, Second Session: Terrorism, Unconventional Threats & Capabilities Subcommittee Hearing on Budget Request for the Defense Threat Reduction Agency & Chemical Biological Defense Program & Counterproliferation Initiatives, Hearing Held April 14, 2010. 2010. iii, 71p. ***(978-0-16-086635-7(9),*** 552-070-41613-7) United States Government Printing Office.

Heyes, Alan. The Global Partnership Against WMD: Success & Shortcomings of G8 Threat Reduction Since 9/11. 2012. (Whitehall Papers). (ENG.). 160p. (C). pap. 42.95 ***(978-0-415-51862-8(8))*** Routledge.

Hristov, Jasmin. Blood & Capital: The Paramilitarization of Colombia. 2009. (Ohio RIS Latin America Ser.). (ENG., Illus.). 320p. pap. 28.00 *(978-0-89680-267-4(1))* Ohio Univ. Pr.

Iiss. Arms Control & Arms Reduction, 3 vols., Vol. 3. 2006. (Adelphi Papers Reissue Hardback Ser.). (Illus.). 328p. 290.00 *(978-0-415-39827-5(4))* Routledge.

Implementing the 2006 Quadrennial Defense Review (QDR) Recommendations to Combat Weapons of Mass Destruction (WMD) Hearing Before the Terrorism, Unconventional Threats & Capabilities Subcommittee of the Committee on Armed Services, House of Representatives, One Hundred Ninth Congress, Second Session, Hearing Held April 5, 2006. 2007. iii, 62p. *(978-0-16-079186-4(3),* 552-070-36274-6) United States Government Printing Office.

Joyner, Daniel H. Arms Control Law. 2012. (International Law of Peace & Security Ser.). 632p. 300.00 ***(978-0-7546-2953-5(8))*** Ashgate Publishing Co.

Joyner, Daniel H. International Law & the Proliferation of Weapons of Mass Destruction. 2009. (ENG.). 304p. 143.00 *(978-0-19-920490-8(X))* Oxford Univ. Pr., Inc.

Karp, Aaron. The Politics of Destroying Surplus Small Arms: Inconspicuous Disarmament. 2009. 268p. pap. 40.00 *(978-0-415-55783-2(6))* Routledge.

Kayes, D. Christopher. Leadership, Loyalty & Deception: Lessons learned from the race to find Weapons of Mass Destruction. 2009. (ENG.). 256p. 45.00 *(978-0-230-52482-8(6))* Palgrave Macmillan.

Kopel, David B. Aiming for Liberty: The Past, Present, & Future of Freedom & Self-Defense. 2009. 192p. pap. 20.00 *(978-0-936783-58-1(3))* Merril Pr.

Krohn, Axel. Overcoming Armed Violence in a Complex World: Essays in Honour of Herbert Wulf. Brzoska, Michael, ed. 2009. 288p. pap. 45.95 *(978-3-940755-33-9(8))* Budrich-Esser, Barbara DEU. Dist: International Specialized Bk. Services.

Kubbig, Bernd W., ed. Arms Control & Proliferation in the Middle East: Overcoming the Security Dilemma. 2012. (Routledge Global Security Studies). (ENG., Illus.). 360p. (C). 130.00 *(978-0-415-60111-5(8))* Routledge.

Landau, Emily B. Arms Control in the Middle East: Constructing Cooperative Process, Defining Security Threats, & the Conduct of Regional Politics. 2006. (ENG.). 253p. 85.00 *(978-1-84519-028-6(9))* Sussex Academic Pr. GBR. Dist: International Specialized Bk. Services.

Larsen, Jeffrey A. & Wirtz, James J. eds. Arms Control & Cooperative Security. 2009. 285p. (C). 63.00 *(978-1-58826-684-2(2));* pap. 24.50 *(978-1-58826-660-6(5))* Rienner, Lynne Pubs.

Lefevre, Peggy. Can International Law Achieve the Effective Disarmament of Chemical Weapons. 2008. 244p. pap. *(978-3-639-01898-1(2))* VDM Verlag Dr. Mueller e.K.

Leitenberg, Milton & Zilinskas, Raymond A. The Soviet Biological Weapons Program. 2012. (ENG., Illus.). 800p. 55.00 ***(978-0-674-04770-9(2))*** Harvard Univ. Pr.

Maresca, Louis & Maslen, Stuart, eds. The Banning of Anti-Personnel Landmines: The Legal Contribution of the International Committee of the Red Cross 1955-1999. 2008. (ENG.). 700p. pap. 84.00 *(978-0-521-06451-4(1))* Cambridge Univ. Pr.

Meier, Oliver, ed. Technology Transfers & Non-Proliferation of Weapons of Mass Destruction: Between Control & Cooperation. 2012. (Routledge Global Security Studies). (ENG.). 240p. (C). 135.00 ***(978-0-415-53580-9(8))*** Routledge.

Nystuen, Gro & Casey-Maslen, Stuart. The Convention on Cluster Munitions: A Commentary. 2010. (ENG.). 708p. 198.50 *(978-0-19-959900-4(9))* Oxford Univ. Pr., Inc.

Oxford University Press, creator. Armaments, Disarmament, & International Security. 2007. (SIPRI Yearbook Ser.). (ENG.). 792p. 199.00 *(978-0-19-923021-1(8))* Oxford Univ. Pr., Inc.

Pirseyedi, Bobi. Arms Control & Iranian Foreign Policy: Diplomacy of Discontent. 2012. (Routledge Studies in Middle Eastern Politics Ser.). (ENG.). 320p. (C). 125.00 *(978-0-415-61165-7(2))* Routledge.

Prevention of Proliferation of Biological Weapons in States Beyond the Former Soviet Union Committee, et al. Countering Biological Threats: Challenges for the Department of Defense's Nonproliferation Program Beyond the Former Soviet Union. 2009. (ENG.). 196p. pap. 44.00 *(978-0-309-13176-6(6))* National Academies Pr.

Researcher, C. Q., ed. Issues in Peace & Conflict Studies: Selections from CQ Researcher. 2010. (Illus.). 544p. (C). pap. 36.00 *(978-1-4129-9291-6(5),* B92916P) SAGE Pubns., Inc.

Ritter, Scott. Dangerous Ground: America's Failed Arms Control Policy, from FDR to Obama. 2010. (ENG.). 464p. (gr. 9). 29.95 *(978-1-56858-399-0(0))* Perseus Bks. Group.

Rogers, Damien. Subaltern Killers: Controlling Small Arms & Light Weapons. 2009. 300p. 124.95 *(978-0-7546-7538-9(6))* Ashgate Publishing Co.

Routledge, creator. Arms Control & Arms Reduction, 3 vols. 2006. (Adelphi Papers). (ENG., Illus.). 438p. (C). 290.00 *(978-0-415-39824-4(X))* Routledge.

—Arms Control & Arms Reduction: 40 Years of the Adelphi Papers, 3 vols. 2006. (Adelphi Papers). (Illus.). 410p. 290.00 *(978-0-415-39825-1(8))* Routledge.

Russell, James. Globalization & WMD Proliferation: Terrorism, Transnational Networks, & International Security. Wirtz, James J., ed. 2008. (Routledge Global Security Studies). (Illus.). 192p. 140.00 *(978-0-415-43394-5(0))* Routledge.

Rutherford, Ken. Disarming States: The International Movement to Ban Landmines. 2010. (Illus.). xxiv, 226p. E-Book *(978-0-313-39397-6(4),* Praeger Pubs.) Greenwood Publishing Group, Inc.

Rutherford, Kenneth R. Disarming States: The International Movement to Ban Landmines, 1 vol. 2010. (Praeger Security International Ser.). (Illus.). 226p. 49.95 *(978-0-313-39396-9(6),* A3410C, Praeger Pubs.) Greenwood Publishing Group, Inc.

Schram, Martin. Avoiding Armageddon: Our Future, Our Choice. 2006. (Illus.). 356p. reprint ed. 26.00 *(978-1-4223-5459-9(8))* DIANE Publishing Co.

Sims, Nicholas. The Future of Biological Disarmament: Strengthening the Treaty Ban on Weapons. 2009. (LSE International Studies Ser.). (ENG.). 240p. 140.00 *(978-0-415-47580-8(5))* Routledge.

Small Arms Survey, Geneva, Geneva. Small Arms Survey 2008: Risk & Resilience. 2008. (Small Arms Survey Ser.). (ENG.). 320p. (C). pap. 35.00 *(978-0-521-70655-1(6));* (Illus.). 83.00 *(978-0-521-88040-4(8))* Cambridge Univ. Pr.

Small Arms Survey, Geneva, Geneva. Small Arms Survey 2011: States of Security. 2011. (Small Arms Survey Ser.). (ENG., Illus.). 328p. 99.00 ***(978-0-521-19712-0(0));*** pap. 34.99 ***(978-0-521-14686-9(0))*** Cambridge Univ. Pr.

Small Arms Survey Staff. Small Arms Survey 2010: Gangs, Groups, & Guns. 2010. (Small Arms Survey Ser.) (ENG., Illus.). 352p. 80.00 *(978-0-521-19711-3(2))* Cambridge Univ. Pr.

Smithson, Amy. Germ Gambits: The Bioweapons Dilemma, Iraq & Beyond. 2011. (ENG.). 384p. 95.00 ***(978-0-8047-7552-6(4));*** pap. 29.95 ***(978-0-8047-7553-3(2))*** Stanford Univ. Pr.

Stavrianakis, Anna. Taking Aim at the Arms Trade: NGOS, Global Civil Society & the World Military Order. 2010. (ENG.). 224p. 125.95 *(978-1-84813-268-9(9));* pap. 39.95 *(978-1-84813-269-6(7))* Zed Bks., Ltd. GBR. Dist: Macmillan.

Stockholm International Peace Research Institute. Armaments, Disarmament & International Security. 2006. (SIPRI Yearbook Ser.). (ENG.). 928p. 199.00 *(978-0-19-929873-0(4))* Oxford Univ. Pr., Inc.

—SIPRI Yearbook 2010: Armaments, Disarmament & International Security. 2010. (SIPRI Yearbook Ser.). (ENG., Illus.). 624p. 185.00 *(978-0-19-958112-2(6))* Oxford Univ. Pr., Inc.

—SIPRI Yearbook 2011: Armaments, Disarmament & International Security. 2011. (SIPRI Yearbook Ser.). (ENG.). 592p. 185.00 *(978-0-19-969552-2(0))* Oxford Univ. Pr., Inc.

Stockholm International Peace Research Institute Staff, Stockholm International Peace Research Institute. Armaments, Disarmament, & International Security

A

2008. 2008. (SIPRI Publication). (ENG.). 792p. 165.00 *(978-0-19-954895-8(1))* Oxford Univ. Pr., Inc.

Stopa, Peter J. & Bartoszcze, Michael A., eds. Rapid Methods for Analysis of Biological Materials in the Environment. 2012. (NATO Science Partnership Sub-Series: 1: Ser.). (ENG.). 324p. pap. 171.00 *(978-90-481-5455-5(3),* 9048154553) Springer.

Tabassi, Lisa Woolomes, compiled by. OPCW: the Legal Texts. 2nd rev. ed. 2010. (Illus.). 774p. 189.00 *(978-90-6704-318-2(4))* T.M.C. Asser Pr. NLD. Dist: Springer.

The Strategic Posture Review Commission. America's Strategic Posture: The Final Report of the Congressional Commission on the Strategic Posture of the United States. 2009. 184p. pap. 14.95 *(978-1-60127-045-0(3))* U. S. Institute of Peace Pr. (USIP Pr.).

Trbovich, Ana & Trbovich, Ana S. A Legal Geography of Yugoslavia's Disintegration. 2008. (ENG., Illus.). 536p. 90.00 *(978-0-19-533343-5(8))* Oxford Univ. Pr., Inc.

United Nations. ODA Occasional Papers: Assessing the United Nations Register of Conventional Arms. 2009. (ENG.). 44p. pap. 10.00 *(978-92-1-142269-6(8))* United Nations Pubns.

United Nations, Office for Disarmament Affairs Staff. The United Nations Disarmament Yearbook 2010, Pt. 2 Vol. 35. 2011. (ENG., Illus.). 380p. pap. 27.50 ***(978-92-1-142279-5(5))*** United Nations Pubns.

United Nations, Office for Disarmament Affairs Staff, contrib. by. Small Arms & Light Weapons: Selected United Nations Documents. 2008th ed. 2008. (ENG.). 108p. pap. 17.95 *(978-92-1-142264-1(7))* United Nations Pubns.

—United Nations Seminar on Implementing UN Security Council Resolution 1540 in Latin America & the Caribbean, 27-28 November 2006 Lima, Peru. 2008. (ODA Occasional Papers: No. 13). (ENG., Illus.). 208p. pap. 17.50 *(978-92-1-142259-7(0))* United Nations Pubns.

United Nations Staff. Unacceptable Harm: A History of How the Treaty to Ban Cluster Munitions was Won. 2009. (ENG.). 516p. pap. 65.00 *(978-92-9045-196-9(3))* United Nations Pubns.

—Verification in all its Aspects including the Role of the United Nations in the Field of Verification (Russian Edition) 2009. (Disarmament Study Ser.). (RUS.). 58p. pap. 12.00 *(978-92-1-442008-8(4))* United Nations Pubns.

United Nations: Office for Disarmament Affairs. The United Nations Disarmament Yearbook. 2011. (ENG., Illus.). 236p. pap. 70.00 ***(978-92-1-142278-8(7))*** United Nations Pubns.

Vicziany. Controlling Arms & Terror in the Asia Pacific after Bali & Iraq. 2007. (Illus.). 320p. (C). 137.00 *(978-1-84542-405-3(0))* Elgar, Edward Publishing, Inc.

Viotti, Paul R. Arms Control & Global Security: A Document Guide, 2 vols. 2010. (Praeger Security International Ser.). 569p. 104.95 *(978-0-313-35430-4(8),* C35430) Greenwood Publishing Group, Inc.

Walker, John R. Britain & Disarmament: The UK & Nuclear Biological & Chemical Weapons Arms Control & Programmes, 1956-75. 2012. 322p. 124.95 ***(978-1-4094-3580-8(6))*** Ashgate Publishing Co.

Webel, Charles P. & Barash, David P. Peace & Conflict Studies. 2nd ed. 2008. (Illus.). 544p. (C). pap. 102.00 *(978-1-4129-6120-2(3),* B61202P) SAGE Pubns., Inc.

Wetter, Anna. Enforcing European Union Law on Exports of Dual-Use Goods: National Enforcement of EU Regulation 1334/2000 on Exports of Dual-Use Goods. Oxford Editors, ed. 2009. (SIPRI Research Reports). (ENG.). 160p. pap. 75.00 *(978-0-19-954896-5(X))* Oxford Univ. Pr., Inc.

Williams, Jody, et al, eds. Banning Landmines: Disarmament, Citizen Diplomacy, & Human Security. 2008. (National State Papers (rl Ser.). (ENG., Illus.). 348p. 90.00 *(978-0-7425-6240-0(9));* pap. 37.95 *(978-0-7425-6241-7(7))* Rowman & Littlefield Publishers, Inc.

Williams, Robert E. & Viotti, Paul R. Arms Control: History, Theory, & Policy, 2 vols. 2012. (Praeger Security International Ser.). 784p. 189.00 *(978-0-275-99820-2(7),* C9820); E-Book ***(978-0-275-99821-9(5),*** Praeger Pubs.) Greenwood Publishing Group, Inc.

Wolf, Charles, Jr., et al. Enhancement by Enlargement: The Proliferation Security Initiative. 2008. 80p. pap. 23.50 *(978-0-8330-4579-9(2),* mg806) RAND Corp., The.

Woolf, Amy F. Nonproliferation & Threat Reduction Assistance. 2008. (Illus.). 91p. pap. 39.00 *(978-1-60456-849-3(6))* Nova Science Pubs., Inc.

Worth, Richard. In the Shadow of the Battleship: Considering the Cruisers of World War II. 2008. 48p. pap. 24.11 *(978-1-934840-52-8(1))* Nimble Bks. LLC.

Yihdego, Zeray. The Arms Trade & International Law. 2007. (ENG.). 380p. 110.00 *(978-1-84113-746-9(4))* Hart Publishing Ltd. GBR. Dist: International Specialized Bk. Services.

Zellen, Barry Scott. State of Doom: Bernard Brodie, the Bomb, & the Birth of the Bipolar World. 2011. (ENG., Illus.). 352p. 150.00 ***(978-1-4411-5984-7(3));*** pap. 49.95 ***(978-1-4411-2462-3(4))*** Continuum International Publishing Group, Ltd. GBR. Dist: National Bk. Network.

ARMS INDUSTRY

see Weapons Industry

ARMS RACE

see also Arms Control; Arms Transfers; Disarmament; Military Readiness

Art & Waltz & Cram101 Textbook Reviews Staff. The Use of Force: Military Power & International Politics. 2007. 140p. per. 11.95 *(978-1-4288-2204-7(6))* Cram101 Inc.

Basrur, Rajesh M. South Asia's Cold War: Nuclear Weapons & Conflict in Comparative Perspective. 2009. 172p. pap. 39.95 *(978-0-415-57035-0(2))* Routledge.

Behnen, Michael. Rüstung - Bündnis - Sicherheit: Dreibund und Informeller Imperialismus, 1900-1908. (GER.). XI, 516p. 210.00 ***(978-3-11-181778-1(4))*** De Gruyter, Walter Inc.

Caldicott, Helen. The New Nuclear Danger: George W. Bush's Military-Industrial Complex. 320p. pap. 30.00 *(978-0-908011-65-0(2))* Scribe Pubns. AUS. Dist: Independent Pubs. Group.

Caldicott, Helen & Eisendrath, Craig. War in Heaven: The Arms Race in Outer Space. 2007. 280p. pap. 26.95 *(978-1-59558-224-9(X));* (ENG.). 166p. 23.95 *(978-1-59558-114-3(6))* New Pr., The.

Cambridge University Press, creator. Small Arms Survey: Guns & the City. 2007. (Small Arms Survey Ser.). (ENG., Illus.). 368p. 99.99 *(978-0-521-88039-8(4));* per. 41.00 *(978-0-521-70654-4(8))* Cambridge Univ. Pr.

Carroll, James. House of War: The Pentagon & the Disastrous Rise of American Power. 2007. (ENG., Illus.). 688p. pap. 15.95 *(978-0-618-87201-5(9))* Houghton Mifflin Harcourt Trade & Reference Pubs.

Central Intelligence Agency (U.S.), et al, eds. Penetrating the Iron Curtain: Resolving the Missile Gap with Technology: Resolving the Missile Gap with Technology. 2012. (ENG., Illus.). 56p. 14.00 ***(978-0-16-089972-0(9),*** Central Intelligence Agency) United States Government Printing Office.

Chakma, Bhumitra. Politics of Nuclear Weapons in South Asia. 2011. 278p. 114.95 *(978-1-4094-2625-7(4))* Ashgate Publishing Co.

Dokos, Thanos P. Countering the Proliferation of Weapons of Mass Destruction: NATO & EU Options in the Mediterranean & the Middle East. 2007. (Contemporary Security Studies). (Illus.). 230p. 150.00 *(978-0-7146-5606-9(2),* RU33538) Routledge.

—Weapons of Mass Destruction in the Mediterranean: Options for NATO & the EU. 2007. 256p. pap. 39.95 *(978-0-7146-8499-4(6),* RU34017) Routledge.

Ganguly, Sumit & Kapur, S. Paul, eds. Nuclear Proliferation in South Asia: Crisis Behaviour & the Bomb. 2010. 240p. pap. 39.95 *(978-0-415-58211-7(3))* Routledge.

Gordin, Michael D. Red Cloud at Dawn: Truman, Stalin, & the End of the Atomic Monopoly. 2010. (ENG., Illus.). 416p. pap. 18.00 *(978-0-312-65542-6(8))* Picador.

Gormley, Dennis. Missile Contagion. 2010. 0288p. pap. 21.95 *(978-1-59114-332-1(2))* Naval Institute Pr.

Gormley, Dennis M. Missile Contagion: Cruise Missile Proliferation & the Threat to International Security, 1 vol. 2008. (Praeger Security International Ser.). (Illus.). 272p. 54.95 *(978-0-275-99836-3(3),* C9836, Praeger Security International) Greenwood Publishing Group, Inc.

Hoffman, David. The Dead Hand: The Untold Story of the Cold War Arms Race & Its Dangerous Legacy. 2010. (ENG., Illus.). 608p. pap. 16.95 *(978-0-307-38784-4(4),* Anchor) Knopf Doubleday Publishing Group.

Iiss. Proliferation & Non-Proliferation. 2006. (Illus.). 328p. 290.00 *(978-0-415-39828-2(2))* Routledge.

Kapur, S. Paul. Dangerous Deterrent: Nuclear Weapons Proliferation & Conflict in South Asia. 2007. (Studies in Asian Security Ser.). (ENG.). 280p. 65.00 *(978-0-8047-5549-8(3));* per. 24.95 *(978-0-8047-5550-4(7))* Stanford Univ. Pr.

Lavoy, Peter. Nuclear Weapons Proliferation in the Next Decade. 2007. pap. 40.00 *(978-0-415-49522-6(9))* Routledge.

Lavoy, Peter, ed. Nuclear Weapons Proliferation in the Next Decade. 2008. (ENG.). 249p. (C). 158.00 *(978-0-415-44322-7(9))* Routledge.

Lee, Rachel. Asia's Nuclear Futures. 2011. (Routledge Security in Asia Pacific Ser.). (ENG.). 240p. (C). 150.00 *(978-0-415-42825-5(4))* Routledge.

Maiolo, Joseph. Cry Havoc: How the Arms Race Drove the World to War, 1931-1941. (ENG., Illus.). 504p. (gr. 9). 2012. pap. 19.99 ***(978-0-465-03229-7(X))*** 2010. 35.00 *(978-0-465-01114-8(4))* Basic Bks.

Nikitin, A, ed. Lessons to be Learned from Non-Proliferation Failures & Successes - Volume 48 NATO Science for Peace & Security Series - E: Human & Societal Dynamics. 2009. 160p. pap. 167.00 *(978-1-58603-932-5(6))* IOS Pr., Inc.

Quester, George H. Preemption, Prevention & Proliferation: The Threat & Use of Weapons in History. 2009. (ENG., Illus.). 221p. 39.95 *(978-1-4128-1041-8(8))* Transaction Pubs.

Reiss, Edward. The Strategic Defense Initiative. 2008. (Cambridge Studies in International Relations). (ENG.). 264p. pap. 53.00 *(978-0-521-05400-3(1))* Cambridge Univ. Pr.

Rhodes, Richard. The Twilight of the Bombs: Recent Challenges, New Dangers, & the Prospects for a World Without Nuclear Weapons. 2010. (ENG., Illus.). 384p. 27.95 *(978-0-307-26754-2(7),* Knopf) Knopf Doubleday Publishing Group.

—Twilight of the Bombs: Recent Challenges, New Dangers, & the Prospects for a World Without Nuclear Weapons. 2011. (Vintage Ser.). (ENG., Illus.). 480p. pap. 17.00 *(978-0-307-38741-7(0),* Vintage) Knopf Doubleday Publishing Group.

Rhodes, Richard Lee. Arsenals of Folly: The Making of the Nuclear Arms Race. 2008. (Vintage Ser.). (Illus.). 432p. pap. 16.95 *(978-0-375-71394-1(8),* Vintage) Knopf Doubleday Publishing Group.

Sathasivam, Kanishkan. Keeping up with the Joneses. 2009. 204p. pap. *(978-3-639-20217-5(1))* VDM Verlag Dr. Mueller e.K.

Schreier, Fred. WMD Proliferation: Reforming the Security Sector to Meet the Threat. 2009. 348p. 60.00 *(978-1-59797-421-9(8));* pap. 29.95 *(978-1-59797-422-6(6))* Potomac Bks., Inc.

Seitz, Adam C. & Cordesman, Anthony H. Iranian Weapons of Mass Destruction: The Birth of a Regional Nuclear Arms Race?, 1 vol. 2009. (Praeger Security International Ser.). (Illus.). 400p. 54.95 *(978-0-313-38088-4(0),* A2233C, Praeger Pubs.) Greenwood Publishing Group, Inc.

Small Arms Survey, Geneva, Geneva. Small Arms Survey 2011: States of Security. 2011. (Small Arms Survey Ser.). (ENG., Illus.). 328p. 99.00 ***(978-0-521-19712-0(0));*** pap. 34.99 ***(978-0-521-14686-9(0))*** Cambridge Univ. Pr.

Sokolski, Henry, ed. Pakistan's Nuclear Future: Reining in the Risk. 2009. pap. *(978-1-58487-422-5(8))* Strategic Studies Institute, U.S. Army War College Commandant (AWCC-DSI/Pubns.).

Sokolski, Henry D., ed. Pakistan's Nuclear Future: Worries Beyond War. 2008. lib. bdg. *(978-1-58487-333-4(7))* Strategic Studies Institute, U.S. Army War College Commandant (AWCC-DSI/Pubns.).

Trenear-Harvey, Glenmore S. Historical Dictionary of Atomic Espionage. 2011. (Historical Dictionaries of Intelligence & Counterintelligence Ser.). (ENG.). 264p. 75.00 *(978-0-8108-7180-9(7))* Scarecrow Pr., Inc.

Van Ham, Peter. Managing Problems of Anti-Proliferation Regimes in the 1990's. 128p. *(978-1-85567-136-2(0));* pap. *(978-1-85567-137-9(9))* Continuum International Publishing Group, Ltd. (Burns & Oates).

ARMS SALES

see Arms Transfers

ARMS TRAFFIC

see Arms Transfers

ARMS TRANSFERS

see also Arms Race; Defense Industries; Military Assistance

A.Q. Khan's Nuclear Wal-Mart: Out of Business or under New Management?: Joint Hearing Before the Subcommittee on the Middle East & South Asia & the Subcommittee on Terrorism, Nonproliferation, & Trade of the Committee on Foreign Affairs, House of Representatives, One Hundred Tenth Congress, First Session, June 27, 2007. 2007. v, 50p. *(978-0-16-079512-1(5),* 552-070-36490-1) United States Government Printing Office.

Bertges, Florian. Der fragmentierte europäische Verteidigungsmarkt: Sektorenanalyse und Handlungsoptionen. 2009. (Europäische Hochschulschriften. Reihe 31: Politikwissenschaft Ser.). (GER.). 288p. pap. 74.95 *(978-3-631-58297-8(8))* Lang, Peter GmbH, Europaischer Verlag der Wissenschaften DEU. Dist: Lang, Peter.

Bialos, Jeffrey P., et al. Fortresses & Icebergs: The Evolution of the Transatlantic Defense Market & the Implications for U.S. National Security Policy, 2 vols. 2009. (Illus.). xiii, 698p. pap. ***(978-0-9841341-2-0(3));*** pap. ***(978-0-9841341-1-3(5))*** Ctr. for Transatlantic Relations.

Blank, Stephen. Rosoboronexport: Arms Sales & the Structure of Russian Defense Industry. 2007. vi, 102p. pap. *(978-1-58487-271-9(3))* Strategic Studies Institute, U.S. Army War College Commandant (AWCC-DSI/Pubns.).

—Shrinking Ground: Russia's Decline in Global Arms Sale. 2011. (ENG.). 53p. pap. 20.00 *(978-0-9816905-7-5(2))* Jamestown Foundation, The.

Bourne, Mike. Arming Conflict: The Proliferation of Small Arms. 2007. (Global Issues Ser.). (ENG., Illus.). 256p. 112.00 *(978-0-230-01933-1(1))* Palgrave Macmillan.

Boyne, Sean. Gunrunners: The Covert Arms Trail to Ireland. 2006. (ENG., Illus.). 476p. 30.95 ***(978-0-86278-908-4(7))*** O'Brien Pr., Ltd., The IRL. Dist: Dufour Editions, Inc.

Brzoska, Michael & Frederic, S. Pearson. Arms & Warfare: Escalation, de-Escalation, & Negotiation. 2006. 316p. reprint ed. 27.00 *(978-1-4223-5296-0(X))* DIANE Publishing Co.

Cattaneo, Silvia, et al. Implementing the United Nations Programme of Action on Small Arms & Light Weapons: Analysis of the national reports submitted by states from 2002 To 2008. 2009. (ENG.). 192p. pap. 32.00 *(978-92-9045-191-4(2))* United Nations Pubns.

Chu, Vivian S. Gun Trafficking & the Southwest Border. 2010. 27p. (C). pap. 20.00 *(978-1-4379-2914-0(1))* DIANE Publishing Co.

Corera, Gordon. Shopping for Bombs: Nuclear Proliferation, Global Insecurity, & the Rise & Fall of the A. Q. Khan Network. 2006. (ENG., Illus.). 304p. 28.00 *(978-0-19-530495-4(0))* Oxford Univ. Pr., Inc.

Defeating Al-Qaeda's Air Force: Pakistan's F-16 Program in the Fight Against Terrorism: Hearing Before the Subcommittee on the Middle East & South Asia of the Committee on Foreign Affairs, House of Representatives, One Hundred Tenth Congress, Second Session, September 16, 2008. 2008. iii, 40p. *(978-0-16-081971-1(7),* 552-070-38143-1) United States Government Printing Office.

Examination of AEY Contracts with the U.S. Government: Hearing Before the Committee on Oversight & Government Reform, House of Representatives, One Hundred Tenth Congress, Second Session, June 24, 2008. 2009. iii, 96p. *(978-0-16-083036-5(2),* 552-070-38931-8) United States Government Printing Office.

Export Controls on Satellite Technology: Hearing Before the Subcommittee on Terrorism, Nonproliferation, & Trade of the Committee on Foreign Affairs, House of Representatives, One Hundred Eleventh Congress, First Session, April 2, 2009. 2009. iii, 78p. *(978-0-16-083647-3(6),* 552-070-39358-7) United States Government Printing Office.

Farah. Merchant of Death: Money, Guns, Planes, & the Man Who Makes War Possible. 2008. (ENG.). 320p. pap. 15.95 *(978-0-470-58042-4(9),* Wiley) Wiley, John & Sons, Inc.

Farah, Douglas & Braun, Stephen. Merchant of Death: Money, Guns, Planes, & the Man Who Makes War Possible. (ENG., Illus.). 320p. 2008. pap. 15.95 *(978-0-470-26196-5(X))* 2007. 25.95 *(978-0-470-04866-5(2))* Wiley, John & Sons, Inc. (Wiley).

Feinstein, Andrew. The Shadow World: Inside the Global Arms Trade. rev. ed. 2012. (ENG.). 704p. pap. 18.00 ***(978-1-250-01395-8(X))*** Picador.

Frantz, Douglas & Collins, Catherine. Fallout: The True Story of the CIA's Secret War on Nuclear Trafficking. 2011. (ENG.). 304p. 26.00 *(978-1-4391-8306-9(6),* Free Pr.) Free Pr.

Gilby, Nicolas. No-Nonsense Guide to the Arms Trade. 2009. (ENG., Illus.). 144p. pap. 13.95 *(978-1-906523-17-6(7))* New Internationalist Pubns., Ltd. GBR. Dist: Consortium Bk. Sales & Distribution.

Grant, Jonathan A. Rulers, Guns, & Money: The Global Arms Trade in the Age of Imperialism. 2007. (Illus.). 304p. 57.50 *(978-0-674-02442-7(7))* Harvard Univ. Pr.

Greene, Owen & Marsh, Nicholas, eds. Small Arms, Crime & Conflict: Global Governance & the Threat of Armed Violence. 2011. (Routledge Studies in Peace & Conflict Resolution Ser.). (ENG., Illus.). 320p. (C). 130.00 *(978-0-415-56700-8(9))* Routledge.

Grimmett, Richard F. Conventional Arms Transfers to Developing Nations, 1999-2006. 2008. (Illus.). viii, 123p. pap. 39.00 *(978-1-60456-419-8(9))* Nova Science Pubs., Inc.

Guns, Drugs & Violence: The Merida Initiative & the Challenge in Mexico: Hearing Before the Subcommittee on the Western Hemisphere of the Committee on Foreign Affairs, House of Representatives, One Hundred Eleventh Congress, First Session, March 18, 2009. 2009. (Illus.). iii, 108p. *(978-0-16-083915-3(7),* 552-070-39604-7) United States Government Printing Office.

Hoyt, Timothy D. Military Industry & Regional Defense Policy: India, Iraq, & Israel. 2006. (Cass Military Studies). (ENG., Illus.). 304p. (C). 160.00 *(978-0-7146-5714-1(X))* Routledge.

Impacts of U.S. Export Control Policies on Science & Technology Activities & Competitiveness: Hearing Before the Committee on Science & Technology, House of Representatives, One Hundred Eleventh Congress, First Session, February 25, 2009. 2009. (Illus.). iv, 138p. *(978-0-16-083524-7(0),* 552-070-39247-5) United States Government Printing Office.

Investigation into the Sale of Sensitive, In-Demand Military Equipment & Supplies on the Internet: Hearing Before the Subcommittee on National Security & Foreign Affairs of the Committee on Oversight & Government Reform, House of Representatives, One Hundred Tenth Congress, Second Session, April 10, 2008. 2009. (Illus.). iii, 103p. *(978-0-16-083745-6(6),* 552-070-39447-8) United States Government Printing Office.

Investing in Tragedy: China's Money, Arms, & Politics in Sudan. 2008. pap. 10.00 *(978-0-9799975-1-8(8))* Human Rights First.

Irwin, Andrew & Krauland, Edward. International Traffic in Arms Regulations Handbook. 2008. 815p. pap. 95.00 *(978-0-314-99016-7(X))* West.

Irwin, Andrew D., et al. International Traffic in Arms Regulations Desk Reference. 2008. 478p. pap. 149.00 *(978-0-314-99013-6(5))* West Publishing Co., College & Schl. Div.

Kroenig, Matthew. Exporting the Bomb: Technology Transfer & the Spread of Nuclear Weapons. 2010. (Cornell Studies in Security Affairs Ser.). (Illus.). 248p. 68.50 *(978-0-8014-4857-7(3));* pap. 22.95 *(978-0-8014-7640-2(2))* Cornell Univ. Pr.

Merino, Noël. The Arms Trade. 2009. (Current Controversies Ser.). (ENG., Illus.). 240p. (gr. 10-12). 27.50 *(978-0-7377-4317-3(4));* pap. 39.70 *(978-0-7377-4318-0(2))* Cengage Gale. (Greenhaven Pr., Inc.).

Michell, Simon. Fighter Aircraft Retrofits: Markets & Programs. (Illus.). 312p. 695.00 *(978-0-7106-1432-2(2))* Jane's Information Group, Inc.

Mitchell, Robert & Campbell, Jeff. Conventional Arms Transfers among Developing Nations: Trends & Data. 2012. ***(978-1-61942-203-2(4))*** Nova Science Pubs., Inc.

Money, Guns, & Drugs: Are U.S. Inputs Fueling Violence on the U.S.-Mexico Border?: Hearing Before the Subcommittee on National Security & Foreign Affairs of the Committee on Oversight & Government Reform, House of Representatives, One Hundred Eleventh Congress, First Session, March 12, 2009. 2010. (Illus.). iii, 77p. *(978-0-16-086538-1(7),* 552-070-41536-0) United States Government Printing Office.

Moran, Sebastian G. Pakistan: Issues & Developments. 2011. (Asian Political, Economic & Security Issues Ser.). 115.00 *(978-1-61761-768-3(7))* Nova Science Pubs., Inc.

National Research Council. Space Science & the International Traffic in Arms Regulations: Summary of a Workshop. 2008. (ENG.). 44p. pap. 15.00 *(978-0-309-11609-1(0))* National Academies Pr.

Nepram, Binalakshmi, ed. India & the Arms Trade Treaty. 2008. (ENG.). 325p. 34.95 *(978-81-8386-075-8(3))* India Research Pr. IND. Dist: Independent Pubs. Group.

Paul, Joel Richard. Unlikely Allies: How a Merchant, a Playwright, & a Spy Saved the American Revolution. 2010. (ENG.). 416p. (gr. 12). 16.00 *(978-1-59448-487-2(2),* Riverhead Trade (Paperbacks)) Penguin Group (USA) Inc.

Pavlich, Katie. Fast & Furious: Barack Obama's Bloodiest Scandal & Its Shameless Cover-up. 2012. (ENG.). 224p. 27.95 ***(978-1-59698-321-2(3))*** Regnery Publishing, Inc., An Eagle Publishing Co.

Phythian, Mark. The Business of Arms: Blurring the Boundaries of Legality. 2006. (Transnational Crime Ser.). 256p. 130.00 *(978-0-415-33604-8(X))* Routledge.

Phythian, Mark, ed. Under the Counter & over the Border: Aspects of the Contemporary Trade in Illicit Arms. 2010. 200p. pap. 89.95 *(978-90-481-5569-9(X),* 904815569X) Springer.

Rodman, David. Arms Transfers to Israel: The Strategic Logic Behind American Military Assistance. 2007. (ENG., Illus.). 144p. (C). 55.00 *(978-1-84519-178-8(1))* Sussex Academic Pr. GBR. Dist: International Specialized Bk. Services.

Rogers, Damien. Subaltern Killers: Controlling Small Arms & Light Weapons. 2009. 300p. 124.95 *(978-0-7546-7538-9(6))* Ashgate Publishing Co.

Small Arms Survey Staff. Small Arms Survey 2010: Gangs, Groups, & Guns. 2010. (Small Arms Survey Ser.). (ENG., Illus.). 352p. 80.00 *(978-0-521-19711-3(2))* Cambridge Univ. Pr.

Stavrianakis, Anna. Taking Aim at the Arms Trade: NGOS, Global Civil Society & the World Military Order. 2010. (ENG.). 224p. 125.95 *(978-1-84813-268-9(9))*; pap. 39.95 *(978-1-84813-269-6(7))* Zed Bks., Ltd. GBR. Dist: Macmillan.

Stohl, Rachel & Grillot, Suzette. The International Arms Trade. 2009. (WCMW - War & Conflict in the Modern World Ser.: 7). (ENG.). 176p. 64.95 *(978-0-7456-4153-9(9))*; pap. 22.95 *(978-0-7456-4154-6(7))* Polity Pr. GBR. Dist: Wiley, John & Sons, Inc.

Stohl, Rachel, et al. The Small Arms Trade: A Beginner's Guide. 2007. (Beginner's Guides (Oneworld) Ser.). (ENG.). 192p. pap. 14.95 *(978-1-85168-476-2(X))* Oneworld Pubns. GBR. Dist: National Bk. Network.

Storey, William Kelleher. Guns, Race, & Power in Colonial South Africa. 2012. (African Studies). (ENG., Illus.). 398p. pap. 29.99 ***(978-1-107-40396-3(0))*** Cambridge Univ. Pr.

Sutton, John L., et al. The Arms Trade & Defence Economics. 2006. (Adelphi Papers). (Illus.). 216p. 200.00 *(978-0-415-39829-9(0))* Routledge.

Tan, Andrew T. H. The Global Arms Trade. 2010. (Routledge International Handbooks Ser.). (ENG., Illus.). 416p. instr.'s hndbk. ed. 300.00 *(978-1-85743-497-2(8))* Routledge.

Thomas, Mark. As Used on the Famous Nelson Mandela: Underground Adventures in the Arms & Torture Trade. 2007. (ENG., Illus.). 352p. pap. 15.00 *(978-0-09-190922-2(8))* Random Hse. GBR. Dist: Independent Pubs. Group.

Tirman, John. Spoils of War. 2011. (ENG.). 320p. pap. 19.99 *(978-1-4516-3161-6(8)*, Free Pr.) Free Pr.

Treaties: Hearing Before the Committee on Foreign Relations, United States Senate, One Hundred Tenth Congress, Second Session, May 21, 2008. 2008. iii, 107p. *(978-0-16-082547-7(4)*, 552-070-38576-2) United States Government Printing Office.

United Nations. ODA Occasional Papers: Assessing the United Nations Register of Conventional Arms. 2009. (ENG.). 44p. pap. 10.00 *(978-92-1-142269-6(8))* United Nations Pubns.

U.S. Efforts to Combat Arms Trafficking to Mexico: Report from the Government Accountability Office (GAO): Hearing Before the Subcommittee on the Western Hemisphere of the Committee on Foreign Affairs, House of Representatives, One Hundred Eleventh Congress, First Session, June 19, 2009. 2009. (Illus.). iii, 52p. *(978-0-16-083758-6(8)*, 552-070-39460-5) United States Government Printing Office.

Various Bills & Resolutions: Markup Before the Committee on Foreign Affairs, House of Representatives, One Hundred Tenth Congress, First Session, on H.R. 982, H.R. 1469, H.R. 1405, H.R. 1441, H.R. 1678, H. con. Res. 100, H. Res. 100, H. Res. 125, H. Res. 158, H. Res. 196, H. Res. 240, H. Res. 267, & H.R. 1681, March 27, 2007. 2007. iv, 183p. *(978-0-16-078905-2(2)*, 552-070-36046-8) United States Government Printing Office.

Viëtor, Marcel. Russian Foreign Policy Between Security & Economics: Exporting Gas & Arms to Belarus & China, 1990-2009. 2011. (ENG.). 112p. 29.95 *(978-3-643-10414-4(6))* Lit Verlag DEU. Dist: Transaction Pubs.

Why Taiwan Matters: Hearing Before the Committee on Foreign Affairs, House of Representatives, One Hundred Twelfth Congress, First Session. 2011. (Illus.). ***(978-0-16-089327-8(5)***, 552-070-43319-8 (pt. 1)); ***(978-0-16-089997-3(4)***, 552-070-43319-8 (pt. 1)) United States Government Printing Office.

Yihdego, Zeray. The Arms Trade & International Law. 2007. (ENG.). 380p. 110.00 *(978-1-84113-746-9(4))* Hart Publishing Ltd. GBR. Dist: International Specialized Bk. Services.

ARMSTRONG, HERBERT W.

Doudna, Greg. Showdown at Big Sandy: Youthful Creativity Confronts Bureaucratic Inertia at an Unconventional Bible College in East Texas, 1. 2006. 540p. per. 56.00 *(978-0-9789838-0-2(7))* Scrollery, The.

Flurry, Stephen. Raising the Ruins: The Fight to Revive the Legacy of Herbert W. Armstrong. 2006. (Illus.). 415p. 19.95 *(978-0-9745507-1-8(X))* Philadelphia Church of God.

ARMSTRONG, LANCE, 1971-

Armstrong, Lance. Comeback 2.0: Up Close & Personal. 2009. (ENG., Illus.). 208p. 27.99 *(978-1-4391-7314-5(1)*, Touchstone) Touchstone.

—Lance Armstrong: Images of a Champion. rev. ed. 2006. (ENG., Illus.). 248p. pap. 24.95 *(978-1-59486-506-0(X))* Rodale Pr., Inc.

Coyle, Daniel. Lance Armstrong's War: One Man's Battle Against Fate, Fame, Love, Death, Scandal, & a Few Other Rivals on the Road to the Tour de France. 2010. (ENG.). 384p. pap. 14.99 *(978-0-06-178371-5(4)*, Harper Paperbacks) HarperCollins Pubs.

Johanson, Paula. Lance Armstrong: A Biography. 2011. E-Book *(978-0-313-38691-6(9)*, Greenwood Pr.) Greenwood Publishing Group, Inc.

Johanson, Paula Marie. Lance Armstrong: A Biography, 1 vol. 2011. (Greenwood Biographies Ser.). (Illus.). 153p. 35.00 *(978-0-313-38690-9(0)*, A3127C) Greenwood Publishing Group, Inc.

Strickland, Bill. Tour de Lance: The Extraordinary Story of Cycling's Most Controversial Champion. 2011. (ENG., Illus.). 336p. pap. 16.00 *(978-0-307-58995-8(1)*, Three Rivers Pr.) Crown Publishing Group.

Walsh, David. From Lance to Landis: Inside the American Doping Controversy at the Tour de France. 2007. (ENG., Illus.). 352p. 24.95 *(978-0-345-49962-2(X)*, Ballantine Bks.) Random House Publishing Group.

Wilcockson, John. Lance: The Making of the World's Greatest Champion. (ENG.). 2010. 432p. pap. 15.95 *(978-0-306-81874-5(4))* 2009. (Illus.). 416p. 26.00 *(978-0-306-81587-4(7))* Da Capo Pr., Inc.

ARMSTRONG, LOUIS, 1900-1971

Anderson, Gene Henry & Budds, Michael J. The Original Hot Five Recordings of Louis Armstrong. 2006. *(978-1-57647-120-3(9))* Pendragon Pr.

Brothers, Thomas. Louis Armstrong's New Orleans. 2007. (ENG., Illus.). 400p. per. 17.95 *(978-0-393-33001-4(X)*, 33001) Norton, W. W. & Co., Inc.

Brower, Steven. Satchmo: The Wonderful World & Art of Louis Armstrong. 2009. (ENG., Illus.). 256p. 37.50 *(978-0-8109-9528-4(X))* Abrams.

Goffin, Robert. Horn of Plenty: The Story of Louis Armstrong. Bezou, James F., tr. 316p. 2008. 45.95 *(978-1-4367-1087-9(1))* 2007. (ENG.). per. 30.95 *(978-1-4325-1848-6(8))* Kessinger Publishing, LLC.

Harker, Brian. Louis Armstrong's Hot Five & Hot Seven Recordings, 1 vol. 2011. (Oxford Studies in Recorded Jazz Ser.). (ENG., Illus.). 192p. pap. 16.95 *(978-0-19-538840-4(2))* Oxford Univ. Pr., Inc.

Nollen, Scott Allen. Louis Armstrong: The Life, Music & Screen Career. alt. ed. 2010. (ENG., Illus.). 239p. pap. 38.00 *(978-0-7864-4918-7(7))* McFarland & Co., Inc. Pubs.

Riccardi, Ricky. What a Wonderful World: The Magic of Louis Armstrong's Later Years. 2012. (ENG., Illus.). 416p. pap. 16.95 ***(978-0-307-47329-5(5)***, Vintage) Knopf Doubleday Publishing Group.

Stein, Daniel. Music Is My Life: Louis Armstrong, Autobiography, & American Jazz. 2012. (Jazz Perspectives Ser.). (ENG.). 360p. (C). 80.00 ***(978-0-472-07180-7(7))***; (Illus.). pap. 45.00 ***(978-0-472-05180-9(6))*** Univ. of Michigan Pr.

Stricklin, David. Louis Armstrong. 2010. (ENG.). 200p. 26.00 *(978-1-56663-836-4(4))* Dee, Ivan R. Pub.

Teachout, Terry. Pops: A Life of Louis Armstrong. (ENG., Illus.). 496p. 2010. pap. 16.95 *(978-0-547-38637-9(0)*, Mariner Bks.) 2009. 30.00 *(978-0-15-101089-9(7))* Houghton Mifflin Harcourt Trade & Reference Pubs.

ARMSTRONG, NEIL, 1930-

Hansen, James R. First Man: The Life of Neil A. Armstrong. 2008. (ENG.). 769p. 30.00 *(978-1-4223-9334-5(8))* DIANE Publishing Co.

—First Man: The Life of Neil A. Armstrong. 2006. (ENG., Illus.). 784p. pap. 18.00 *(978-0-7432-5751-0(0))* Simon & Schuster.

ARMY

see Armies

also France—Armee; United States—Army, and similar headings

ARMY NEWSPAPERS

see Journalism, Military

ARMY SCHOOLS

see Military Education

ARMY SPOUSES

Attaud, Ivette. My Life, My Soul - Surviving, Healing & Thriving after an Abusive Relationship: Part 1: Surviving. 2011. 232p. mass mkt. 15.95 *(978-0-615-44061-3(4))* MLMS Publishing.

Biank, Tanya. Army Wives: The Unwritten Code of Military Marriage. 2007. (ENG.). 288p. pap. 14.99 *(978-0-312-33351-5(X)*, St. Martin's Griffin) St. Martin's Pr.

Brandl, Ulrich, ed. Frauen und Romisches Militar. 2008. (Bar S Ser.). (GER.). 155p. (C). pap. 80.00 *(978-1-4073-0198-3(5))* British Archaeological Reports Ltd. GBR. Dist: Brown, David Bk. Co., The.

Cardoza, Thomas. Intrepid Women: Cantinières & Vivandières of the French Army. 2010. (ENG., Illus.). 312p. 39.95 *(978-0-253-35451-8(X)*, 025335451X) Indiana Univ. Pr.

Carrington, Frances E. My Army Life & the Fort Phil Kearney M. 2006. pap. 33.95 *(978-1-4286-5113-5(6))* Kessinger Publishing, LLC.

Dimbleby, Kitty. Daffodil Girls: Meet the Women Behind Our Heroes. 2011. (ENG., Illus.). 288p. 24.95 ***(978-0-7535-3964-4(0))*** Virgin Bks. Ltd. GBR. Dist: Independent Pubs. Group.

Eaton, Charlotte A., et al. Ladies of Waterloo: The Experiences of Three Women During the Campaign Of 1815. 2009. 268p. pap. *(978-1-84677-643-4(0))* Leonaur Ltd.

Hanna, Martha. Your Death Would Be Mine: Paul & Marie Pireaud in the Great War. 2008. (Illus.). 352p. pap. 21.00 *(978-0-674-03051-0(6))* Harvard Univ. Pr.

Horn, Sara. Weekend Warrior No More: Help & Hope for Reserve & Guard Families During Deployment. 2009. 224p. pap. 24.95 *(978-1-59797-366-3(1))* Potomac Bks., Inc.

Krajeski, Mama. Household Baggage: The Moving Life of a Military Wife (2nd Edition) 2008. 188p. pap. 15.00 *(978-1-932279-56-6(3))* Wyatt-MacKenzie Publishing.

Mello, Stephanie Anne. Once in a Wifetime. 2008. 152p. pap. 24.95 *(978-1-60441-998-6(9))* PublishAmerica, Inc.

Mock, Janelle H. Portraits of the Toughest Job in the Army: Voices & Faces of Modern Army Wives. 2007. 260p. (ENG.). 29.95 *(978-0-595-86978-7(5))*; per. 19.95 *(978-0-595-42615-7(8))* iUniverse, Inc.

Roe, Frances M.A. Army Letters from an Officer's Wife, 1871-1888. 2007. 188p. per. *(978-1-4068-3989-0(2))* Echo Library.

Roe, Frances Marie Antoinette Mack. Army Letters from an Officer's Wife: 1871-1888. 2007. (ENG.). 294p. pap. 21.99 *(978-1-4264-5013-6(3))*; 322p. pap. 24.99 *(978-1-4264-5314-4(0))* BiblioBazaar.

Smith, Shannon D. Give Me Eighty Men: Women & the Myth of the Fetterman Fight. (Women in the West Ser.). (ENG., Illus.). 2010. 264p. pap. 18.95 *(978-0-8032-3425-3(2)*, Bison Bks.) 2008. 262p. 39.95 *(978-0-8032-1541-2(X))* Univ. of Nebraska Pr.

Steinkamp, Mary. Mara- A True Story of Faith & Forgiveness. 2008. (Illus.). 64p. per. *(978-1-55452-243-9(9)*, Guardian Bks.) Essence Publishing.

Summerhayes, Martha. Vanished Arizona Recollections of the A. 2006. pap. *(978-1-4068-3140-5(9))* Echo Library.

—Vanished Arizona, Recollections of the Army Life by a New England Woman. 2007. 188p. per. 13.99 *(978-1-59547-759-0(4))* NuVision Pubns., LLC.

ARMY SUPPLIES

see Military Supplies

ARMY WAGONS

see Vehicles, Military

ARMY WIVES

see Army Spouses

ARNAZ, DESI, 1917-1986

Sanders, Coyne S. & Gilbert, Tom. Desilu: The Story of Lucille Ball & Desi Arnaz. 2011. (ENG.). 400p. pap. 16.99 *(978-0-06-202001-7(3))* HarperCollins Pubs.

ARNDT, ERNST MORITZ, 1769-1860

Erhart, Walter & Koch, Arne. Ernst Moritz Arndt (1769-1860) Deutscher Nationalismus - Europa - Transatlantische Perspektiven / German Nationalism - European Visions - American Interpretations. 2007. (Studien und Texte Zur Sozialgeschichte der Literatur Ser.). (GER & ENG., Illus.). VIII, 302p. pap. *(978-3-484-35112-7(8))* Verlag Max Niemeyer.

ARNHEM, BATTLE OF, ARNHEM, NETHERLANDS, 1944

Bennett, David. Magnificent Disaster: The Failure of Market Garden, the Arnhem Operation, September 1944. 2011. (Illus.). 352p. pap. 18.95 *(978-1-935149-89-7(X))* Casemate Pubs. & Bk. Distributors, LLC.

—Magnificent Disaster: The Failure of the Market Garden, the Arnhem Operation, September 1944. 2008. (Illus.). 352p. 32.95 *(978-1-932033-85-4(8))* Casemate Pubs. & Bk. Distributors, LLC.

Brown, Chris. Arnhem 1944. 2012. (Battle Story Ser.). (ENG., Illus.). 160p. 17.95 ***(978-0-7524-6311-7(X))*** History Pr. Ltd.,The GBR. Dist: Independent Pubs. Group.

Clark, Lloyd. Crossing the Rhine: Breaking into Nazi Germany 1944 & 1945 — the Greatest Airborne Battles in History. 2009. (ENG., Illus.). 448p. pap. 15.00 *(978-0-8021-4430-0(6)*, Grove Pr.) Grove/Atlantic, Inc.

Gardner, Ian, et al. Deliver Us from Darkness: The Untold Story of Third Battalion 506 Parachute Infantry Company During Market Garden. 2012. (ENG., Illus.). 344p. 27.95 ***(978-1-84908-717-9(2))*** Osprey Publishing, Ltd. GBR. Dist: Random Hse., Inc.

Irwin, Will. Abundance of Valor: Resistance, Survival, & Liberation: 1944-45. 2012. (ENG., Illus.). 432p. pap. 22.95 ***(978-0-8032-4068-1(6))*** Univ. of Nebraska Pr.

Kershaw, Robert J. It Never Snows in September: The German View of Market-Garden & the Battle of Arnhem, September 1944. (ENG., Illus.). 2009. 448p. pap. 16.95 *(978-0-7110-3322-1(6))* 2007. 364p. 24.95 *(978-0-7110-3062-6(6))* Allan, Ian Publishing GBR. Dist: BookMasters Distribution Services (BDS).

Lynch, Tim. Operation Market Garden: The Legend of the Waal Crossing. 2011. (ENG., Illus.). 192p. pap. 24.95 ***(978-0-7524-5825-0(6))*** History Pr. Ltd.,The GBR. Dist: Independent Pubs. Group.

McManus, John C. September Hope: The American Side of a Bridge Too Far. 2012. (ENG.). 512p. (gr. 12). 27.95 ***(978-0-451-23706-4(4)***, N A L Hardcover) Penguin Group (USA) Inc.

Middlebrook, Martin. Arnhem 1944: The Airborne Battle. 2009. (Illus.). 512p. 50.00 *(978-1-84884-075-1(6))* Pen & Sword Bks. Ltd. GBR. Dist: Casemate Pubs. & Bk. Distributors, LLC.

—Arnhem 1944: The Airborne Battle. 2011. (Stackpole Military History Ser.). (ENG., Illus.). 528p. pap. 21.95 *(978-0-8117-0826-5(8))* Stackpole Bks.

Neillands, Robin. The Battle for the Rhine: The Battle of the Bulge & the Ardennes Campaign 1944. 2007. (ENG.). 456p. (gr. 12). 27.95 *(978-1-58567-797-0(6))* Overlook Pr., The.

Neillands, Robin & Neillands, Robin. The Battle for the Rhine: The Battle for the Bulge & the Ardennes Campaign 1944. 2008. (ENG., Illus.). 352p. (gr. 12). pap. 18.95 *(978-1-59020-028-5(4))* Overlook Pr., The.

Peters, M. L. Glider Pilots at Arnhem. 2009. (Illus.). 256p. 39.99 *(978-1-84415-763-1(6))* Pen & Sword Bks. Ltd. GBR. Dist: Casemate Pubs. & Bk. Distributors, LLC.

Ritchie, Sebastian. Arnhem: Myth & Reality. 2011. (ENG., Illus.). 272p. 34.95 ***(978-0-7090-8991-9(0))*** Hale, Robert Ltd. GBR. Dist: Independent Pubs. Group.

Sliz, John. Storm Boat Kings: The 23Rd R. C. E. at Arnhem 1944. 2009. (Illus.). 128p. 24.95 *(978-1-55125-103-5(5))* Vanwell Publishing, Ltd. CAN. Dist: Casemate Pubs. & Bk. Distributors, LLC.

Spezzano, Remy. Kampfraum Arnheim: A Photo Study of the German Soldier Fighting in & Around Arnhem September 1944. 2010. (World War 2 Ser.). (Illus.). 288p. 55.00 *(978-0-9657584-9-9(4))* RZM Imports, Inc.

Sutherland, Jonathan & Canwell, Diane. Battlefield General: Arnhem 1944. 2011. (Illus.). 176p. pap. 19.95 ***(978-1-84884-484-1(0))*** Pen & Sword Bks. Ltd. GBR. Dist: Casemate Pubs. & Bk. Distributors, LLC.

Tout, Ken. In the Shadow of Arnhem: The Battle for the Lower MAAS, Steptember - November 1944. 2009. (ENG., Illus.). 256p. pap. 27.95 *(978-0-7524-5194-7(4))* History Pr. Ltd.,The GBR. Dist: Independent Pubs. Group.

Urquhart, R. E. Arnhem. 2008. (Illus.). 256p. pap. 28.95 *(978-1-84415-537-8(4))* Pen & Sword Bks. Ltd. GBR. Dist: Casemate Pubs. & Bk. Distributors, LLC.

ARNIM, BETTINA VON, 1785-1859

Bunzel, Wolfgang. "Die Welt Umwälzen" Bettine Von Arnim Geb. Brentano (1785-1859) 2009. (Illus.). 126p. *(978-3-9811109-7-5(8))* Freies Deutsches Hochstift, Frankfurter Goethe-Museum.

Oehlke, Waldemar. Bettina Von Arnims Briefromane. 2010. 380p. pap. 33.75 *(978-1-147-35783-7(8))* BiblioBazaar.

Rolland, Romain. Goethe & Beethoven. Pfister, G. A. & Kemp, E. S., trs. 332p. 2008. 45.95 *(978-1-4366-8784-3(5))* 2007. (ENG.). per. 30.95 *(978-1-4326-3009-6(1))* Kessinger Publishing, LLC.

Walden, Edward. Beethoven's Immortal Beloved: Solving the Mystery. 2011. (Illus.). xxxviii, 145p. E-Book *(978-0-8108-7774-0(0))*; (ENG., 194p. (gr. 17). 49.95 *(978-0-8108-7773-3(2))* Scarecrow Pr., Inc.

Wallenborn, Markus. Frauen, Dichten, Goethe: Die Produktive Goethe-Rezeption Bei Charlotte Von Stein, Marianne Von Willemer und Bettina Von Arnim. 2006. (Untersuchungen Zur Deutschen Literaturgeschichte Ser.). (GER., Illus.). 349p. 98.00 *(978-3-484-32129-8(6))* De Gruyter, Walter Inc.

ARNIM, LUDWIG ACHIM, FREIHERR VON, 1781-1831

Arnim, Ludwig Achim & Burwick, Roswitha. Werke und Briefwechsel: Historisch-Kritische Ausgabe. 2007. (GER., Illus.). XIV, 1161p. *(978-3-484-15602-9(3))* Verlag Max Niemeyer.

Arnim, Ludwig Achim von. Schaubahne I. Pietsch, Yvonne, ed. 2010. (GER., Illus.). VIII, 905p. *(978-3-484-15613-5(9))* Verlag Max Niemeyer.

Dietzsch, Steffen. Achim von Arnim und sein Kreis. Dietzsch, Steffen & Ludwig, Ariane, eds. 2010. (Schriften der Internationalen Arnim-Gesellschaft Ser.).Tr. of Achim von Arnim & His Circle. (GER.). VIII, 383p. 182.00 *(978-3-11-023308-7(8))* De Gruyter, Walter Inc.

Dietzsch, Steffen & Ludwig, Ariane, eds. Achim von Arnim und sein Kreis. 2010. (Schriften der Internationalen Arnim-Gesellschaft Ser.).Tr. of Achim von Arnim & His Circle. (GER.). VIII, 383p. 280.00 ***(978-3-11-175325-6(5))*** De Gruyter, Walter Inc.

Härtl, Heinz, ed. Briefwechsel III (1805-1806) 2011. (GER.). 1104p. 308.00 *(978-3-11-025069-5(1))* De Gruyter, Walter Inc.

Hori, Misako. Das Wunderhorn: Zur Konzeptionellen Bedeutung der Titelkupfer Zu Achim Von Arnims und Clemens Brentanos Liedersammlung des Knaben Wunderhorn. (GER., Illus.). 233p. pap. 51.95 *(978-3-631-57390-7(1))* Lang, Peter GmbH, Europaischer Verlag der Wissenschaften DEU. Dist: Lang, Peter Publishing, Inc.

Metz, Christian. Die Narratologie der Liebe: Achim Von Arnims Gräfin Dolores. 2012. (Studien zur deutschen Literatur Ser.). (GER.). VII, 453p. (gr. 17). 140.00 ***(978-3-11-026520-0(6))*** De Gruyter, Walter Inc.

Pape, Walter. Romantische Metaphorik des Fliessens: Körper, Seele, Poesie: Schönburger Kolloquium der Internationalen Arnim-Gesellschaft. 2007. (Schriften der Internationalen Arnim-Gesellschaft Ser.). (GER., Illus.). X, 285p. pap. *(978-3-484-10877-6(0))* Verlag Max Niemeyer.

ARNOLD, BENEDICT, 1741-1801

Abbatt, William. The Crisis of the Revolution: The Story of Arnold & Andre. 119p. reprint ed. 88.00 *(978-0-7222-9252-4(7))* Library Reprints, Inc.

—The CRISIS of the REVOLUTION; Being the Story of Arnold & Andre, Now for the First Time Collected from All Sources, & illustrated with Views of All Places Identified with It. 2007. (Illus.). 280p. pap. 39.95 *(978-1-60105-130-1(1)*, 6D7E) Scholar's Bookshelf.

Arnold, Isaac Newton. The Life of Benedict Arnold. 444p. reprint ed. 98.00 *(978-0-7222-9263-1(5))* Library Reprints, Inc.

Codman, John. Arnold's Expedition to Quebec. 2009. 376p. 33.99 *(978-1-110-17687-8(2))*; pap. 32.75 *(978-1-110-17683-0(X))* BiblioBazaar.

—Arnold's Expedition to Quebec. 2009. 198p. pap. *(978-0-217-17554-8(5))* Books LLC.

—Arnold's Expedition to Quebec. 2008. 368p. 46.95 *(978-1-4369-8358-7(4))*; pap. 31.95 *(978-1-4367-8126-8(4))* Kessinger Publishing, LLC.

—Arnold's Expedition to Quebec. Abbatt, William, ed. 2007. (ENG.). 464p. per. 37.95 *(978-0-548-65120-9(5))* Kessinger Publishing, LLC.

—Arnold's Expedition to Quebec. 340p. reprint ed. 98.00 *(978-0-7222-9264-8(3))* Library Reprints, Inc.

—Arnold's Expedition to Quebec. 2007. (ENG.). 368p. per. *(978-1-4067-5273-1(8))* Read Bks.

Darley, Stephen. Voices from A Wilderness Expedition: The Journals & Men of Benedict Arnold's Expedition to Quebec In 1775. 2011. 324p. 36.95 ***(978-1-4567-6108-0(0))***; pap. 24.95 ***(978-1-4567-6106-6(4))*** AuthorHouse.

Desjardin, Thomas A. Through a Howling Wilderness: Benedict Arnold's March to Quebec 1775. 2007. (ENG., Illus.). 256p. pap. 16.99 *(978-0-312-33905-0(4)*, St. Martin's Griffin) St. Martin's Pr.

Drewery, Ellis Warren. Benedict Arnold - Master of the American Rebellion. 2011. 376p. 99.99 ***(978-1-61170-024-4(8))*** Robertson Publishing.

Gould, Dudley C. Benedict Arnold. 2006. (Illus.). 72p. pap. 9.95 *(978-0-913337-61-5(7))* Southfarm Pr.

Hill, George Caning. Benedict Arnold: A Biography. 295p. reprint ed. 98.00 *(978-0-7222-9266-2(X))* Library Reprints, Inc.

Palmer, Dave R. George Washington & Benedict Arnold: A Tale of Two Patriots. 2006. (ENG., Illus.). 424p. 29.95 *(978-1-59698-020-4(6))* Regnery Publishing, Inc., An Eagle Publishing Co.

Palmer, Dave Richard. George Washington & Benedict Arnold: A Tale of Two Patriots. 2010. (ENG.). 424p. pap. 18.95 *(978-1-59698-640-4(9))* Regnery Publishing, Inc., An Eagle Publishing Co.

Smith, Justin Harvey. Arnold's March from Cambridge to Quebec: A Critical Study Together with a Reprint of Arnold's Journal. 2009. (Illus.). 518p. reprint ed. pap. 39.00 *(978-1-55613-194-3(1))* Heritage Bks.

Smith, Richard B. Ethan Allen & the Capture of Fort Ticonderoga: America's First Victory. 2010. (ENG., Illus.). 128p. pap. 19.99 *(978-1-59629-920-7(7))* History Pr., The.

Sparks, Jared. The Life & Treason of Benedict Arnold. 2009. 360p. 26.99 *(978-1-103-41390-4(2))* 2009. 360p. pap. 20.99 *(978-1-103-41387-4(2))* 2008. 361p. 29.99 *(978-0-559-02552-5(1))* 2008. 361p. 31.99 *(978-0-559-02537-2(8))* 2008. 361p. pap. 32.75 *(978-0-559-02539-6(4))* 2008. 361p. pap. 31.75 *(978-0-559-02546-4(7))* BiblioBazaar.

—The Life & Treason of Benedict Arnold. 2008. 348p. 46.95 *(978-1-4374-0565-1(7))*; pap. 31.95 *(978-1-4373-1834-0(7))* Kessinger Publishing, LLC.

—The Life & Treason of Benedict Arnold. 335p. reprint ed. 98.00 *(978-0-7222-8554-1(X))*; 98.00 *(978-0-7222-9269-3(4))* Library Reprints, Inc.

Todd, Charles Burr. The Real Benedict Arnold. 2009. 92p. pap. *(978-0-217-13045-5(3))* Books LLC.

—The Real Benedict Arnold. 2010. 260p. 42.95 *(978-1-120-99658-9(9))*; pap. 27.95 *(978-1-120-92115-4(5))* Kessinger Publishing, LLC.

—The Real Benedict Arnold. 235p. reprint ed. 98.00 *(978-0-7222-9271-6(6))* Library Reprints, Inc.

Wegars, Priscilla. Imprisoned in Paradise: Japanese Internee Road Workers at the World War II Kooskia Internment Camp. 2010. (ENG., Illus.). 323p. pap. 19.95 *(978-0-89301-550-3(4))* Caxton Pr.

York, Mark A. Patriot on the Kennebec: Major Reuben Colburn, Benedict Arnold & the March to Quebec 1775. 2012. 128p. pap. 19.99 ***(978-1-60949-500-8(4))*** History Pr., The.

ARNOLD, EBERHARD, 1883-1935

Arnold, Eberhard & Hollander, Emmy von. Love Letters. 2007. (Illus.). x, 306p. *(978-0-87486-939-2(0))* Plough Publishing Hse.

ARNOLD, EDDY, 1918-2008

Streissguth, Michael. Eddy Arnold: Pioneer of the Nashville Sound. 2009. (American Made Music Ser.). (ENG., Illus.). 302p. pap. 25.00 *(978-1-60473-269-6(5))* Univ. Pr. of Mississippi.

ARNOLD, EDWIN, SIR, 1832-1904

Wright, Brooks. Interpreter of Buddhism to the West: Edwin Arnold. 2011. 186p. 42.95 ***(978-1-258-08961-0(0))*** Literary Licensing, LLC.

ARNOLD, HENRY HARLEY, 1886-1950

Wolk, Herman S. Cataclysm: General Hap Arnold & the Defeat of Japan. 2010. (ENG., Illus.). 344p. 24.95 *(978-1-57441-281-9(7))* Univ. of North Texas Pr.

ARNOLD, MATTHEW, 1822-1888

Alexander, Edward. Matthew Arnold & John Stuart Mill. 2009. (ENG.). 332p. 140.00 *(978-0-415-55550-0(7))* Routledge.

Arnold, Matthew. Culture & Anarchy. 2009. 164p. pap. 11.25 *(978-1-60459-701-1(1))* Wilder Pubns., Ltd.

—God & the Bible: A Review of Objections to Literature & Dogma. 2007. (ENG.). 386p. 48.95 *(978-0-548-02716-5(1))* Kessinger Publishing, LLC.

—God & the Bible: A Review of Objections to "Literature & Dogma" reprint ed. lib. bdg. 98.00 *(978-0-7426-2171-8(5))* Classic Bks.

—Heinrich Heine. reprint ed. lib. bdg. 98.00 *(978-0-7426-2161-9(8))* Classic Bks.

—Heinrich Heine. 2008. 88p. pap. 17.95 *(978-1-4368-6808-2(4))* Kessinger Publishing, LLC.

—The Note-Books of Matthew Arnold. reprint ed. lib. bdg. 98.00 *(978-0-7426-2173-2(1))* Classic Bks.

—The Works of Matthew Arnold, 15 vols. (BCL Ser.: No. 1). reprint ed. 810.00 *(978-0-404-00450-7(4))* AMS Pr., Inc.

—The Works of Matthew Arnold. 2009. 194p. pap. *(978-0-217-61575-4(9))*; 192p. pap. *(978-0-217-89885-0(8))*; 190p. pap. *(978-1-4589-4387-3(9))*; 236p. pap. *(978-0-217-61571-6(6))*; 178p. pap. *(978-0-217-28762-3(X))*; 252p. pap. *(978-0-217-80611-4(2))*; 170p. pap. *(978-0-217-61572-3(4))*; 200p. pap. *(978-0-217-91788-9(7))*; 164p. pap. *(978-0-217-91787-2(9))* Books LLC.

—Works of Matthew Arnold, 15 vols. reprint ed. lib. bdg. 900.00 *(978-0-7812-0170-4(5))* Reprint Services Co.

Bickley, Francis L. Matthew Arnold & His Poetry. (Poetry & Life Ser.). reprint ed. 16.00 *(978-0-404-52501-9(6))* AMS Pr., Inc.

Bolus-Reichert, Christine. The Age of Eclecticism: Literature & Culture in Britain, 1815-1885. 2009. (ENG.). 352p. 54.95 *(978-0-8142-1103-8(8))*; cd-rom 14.95 *(978-0-8142-9201-3(1))* Ohio State Univ. Pr.

Caufield, James Walter. Overcoming Matthew Arnold: Ethics in Culture & Criticism. 2012. 242p. 99.95 ***(978-1-4094-2651-6(3))*** Ashgate Publishing Co.

Dietz, Mark David. An Awkward Echo: Matthew Arnold & John Dewey. 2010. 282p. *(978-1-60752-399-4(X))*; pap. *(978-1-60752-398-7(1))* Information Age Publishing, Inc.

Dixon, James Main. Matthew Arnold. 2009. 104p. pap. *(978-0-217-78203-6(5))* Books LLC.

Faverty, Frederic E. Matthew Arnold the Ethnologist. (Northwestern University, Humanities Ser.: No. 27). reprint ed. 36.50 *(978-0-404-50727-5(1))* AMS Pr., Inc.

Gates, Lewis E. Three Studies in Literature. 2008. 222p. 39.95 *(978-1-4365-1378-4(2))* 2007. (ENG.). 224p. per. 24.95 *(978-0-548-71448-5(7))* Kessinger Publishing, LLC.

Hicks, John, et al. Critical Studies in Arnold, Emerson, & Newman. 180p. 2008. 37.95 *(978-1-4367-0360-4(3))* 2007. (ENG.). per. 22.95 *(978-1-4325-5688-4(6))* Kessinger Publishing, LLC.

Lippincott, Benjamin Evans. Victorian Critics of Democracy: Carlyle, Ruskin, Arnold, Stephen, Maine, Lecky. 2009. (ENG.). 292p. pap. 50.00 *(978-0-8166-5928-9(1))* Univ. of Minnesota Pr.

Logan, Peter Melville. Victorian Fetishism: Intellectuals & Primitives. (SUNY series, Studies in the Long Nineteenth Century Ser.). 2010. 218p. pap. 23.95 *(978-0-7914-7662-8(6)*, Suny Pr.) 2009. (Illus.). 208p. 55.00 *(978-0-7914-7661-1(8))* State Univ. of New York Pr.

Paul, Herbert W. Matthew Arnold. 2007. (ENG.). 194p. 37.95 *(978-0-548-03009-7(X))*; 200p. 39.95 *(978-0-548-11248-9(7))* Kessinger Publishing, LLC.

Russell, G. W. E. Matthew Arnold. 2007. 116p. per. *(978-1-4068-4101-5(3))* Echo Library.

Russell, G. W. E., ed. Matthew Arnold. 2007. (ENG.). 318p. 45.95 *(978-0-548-07576-0(X))* Kessinger Publishing, LLC.

Russell, George William Erskine. Matthew Arnold. 2008. 204p. 22.99 *(978-0-554-35453-8(5))* 2008. 204p. 25.99 *(978-0-554-26150-8(2))* 2007. (ENG.). 180p. pap. 19.99 *(978-1-4346-0544-3(2))* 2007. (ENG.). 200p. pap. 21.99 *(978-1-4346-0619-8(8))* BiblioBazaar.

—Matthew Arnold. 2009. 150p. pap. *(978-0-217-78200-5(0))* Books LLC.

Sagovsky, Nicholas. Between Two Worlds: George Tyrrell's Relationship to the Thought of Matthew Arnold. 2008. (ENG.). 212p. pap. 31.99 *(978-0-521-09770-3(3))* Cambridge Univ. Pr.

Saintsbury, George. Matthew Arnold. 2008. 176p. 22.99 *(978-0-554-39656-9(4))*; 25.99 *(978-0-554-30353-6(1))* BiblioBazaar.

—Matthew Arnold. 2009. 116p. pap. *(978-0-217-01735-0(5))* Books LLC.

—Matthew Arnold. 2007. 144p. per. *(978-1-4065-4284-4(9))* Dodo Pr.

—Matthew Arnold. 2008. 240p. 41.95 *(978-1-4365-1599-3(8))* 2007. (ENG.). 244p. per. 26.95 *(978-0-548-71074-6(0))* Kessinger Publishing, LLC.

White, Greenough. Matthew Arnold & the Spirit of the Age. 2009. 110p. pap. *(978-0-217-01738-1(X))* Books LLC.

ARNOLD, THOMAS, 1795-1842

Strachey, Lytton. Eminent Victorians. 2009. 124p. (Orig.). pap. *(978-0-217-94522-6(8))* Books LLC.

—Eminent Victorians. 2008. 236p. (Orig.). pap. *(978-1-4065-7560-6(7))* Dodo Pr.

—Eminent Victorians. 2006. (Dover Value Editions Ser.). (ENG., Illus.). 272p. (Orig.). per. 9.95 *(978-0-486-45136-7(4))* Dover Pubns., Inc.

—Eminent Victorians. 2006. (ENG.). (Orig.). pap. *(978-1-4068-3120-7(4))* Echo Library.

—Eminent Victorians. Sutherland, John, ed. 2009. (Oxford World's Classics Ser.). (ENG., Illus.). 336p. (Orig.). pap. 12.95 *(978-0-19-955501-7(X))* Oxford Univ. Pr., Inc.

—Eminent Victorians. 2009. 216p. (Orig.). pap. 9.15 *(978-1-60459-747-9(X))* Wilder Pubns., Ltd.

AROMATHERAPY

Here are entered works on therapy using massage with essential oils, sometimes combined with inhalation of essences and use of herbal infusions.

Aromatherapy. Date not set. (Mind, Body & Spirit Ser.). 96p. pap. 4.98 *(978-0-7525-8879-7(6))* Parragon, Inc.

Berton, Hélène. The Essential Guide to Natural Skin Care: Choosing Botanicals, Oils & Extracts for Simple & Healthy Beauty. 2012. (ENG., Illus.). 240p. pap. 16.95 ***(978-0-7387-2927-5(2))*** Llewellyn Pubns.

Brown, Denise Whichello. Change Your Mood with Aromatherapy. 2011. (Teach Yourself Ser.). (ENG., Illus.). 362p. pap. 15.95 *(978-1-4441-0105-8(6)*, Hodder & Stoughton) Hodder General Publishing Div. GBR. Dist: Independent Pubs. Group.

Bruder, Leslie. Hot Stone Massage: A Three Dimensional Approach. 2009. (LWW in Touch Ser.). (ENG., Illus.). 256p. pap. 50.99 *(978-0-7817-6327-1(4))* Lippincott Williams & Wilkins.

Bull, Ruah & Keim, Joni. Daily Aromatherapy: Transforming the Seasons of Your Life with Essential Oils. 2008. (ENG., Illus.). 400p. pap. 18.95 *(978-1-55643-693-2(9))* North Atlantic Bks.

Clark, Marge. Essential Oils & Aromatics: A Step-by-Step Guide for Use in Massage & Aromatherapy. 2008. (ENG., Illus.). 96p. 16.95 *(978-1-933317-73-1(6))* Silverleaf Pr.

Clarke, Sue, ed. Essential Chemistry for Aromatherapy. 2nd ed. 2009. (ENG., Illus.). 320p. pap. 54.95 *(978-0-443-10403-9(4)*, Churchill Livingstone) Elsevier - Health Sciences Div.

Corkhill, Melissa. Natural Remedies: Self-Sufficiency. 2011. (Self-Sufficiency Ser.). (ENG., Illus.). 128p. 12.95 *(978-1-61608-348-9(4)*, 608348) Skyhorse Publishing Co., Inc.

Dave, Vivek, et al. Aromatherapy. 2011. 136p. pap. ***(978-3-8443-8659-2(9))*** Lambert Academic Publishing.

Davis, Patricia. Subtle Aromatherapy. (Illus.). 256p. (Orig.). pap. 23.95 *(978-0-8464-4295-0(7))* Beekman Bks., Inc.

Devereux, Charla. Bookinabox; Aromatherapy. 2009. (Book-in-A-Box Ser.). (ENG.). 384p. 14.95 *(978-1-85906-240-1(7))* Connections Bk. Publishing, Ltd. GBR. Dist: Red Wheel/Weiser.

Ellis, William R. Vibrational Energy Healing. Living, John M., ed. 2008. 272p. pap. *(978-0-9686323-7-6(8))* Living, John M.

Evans, Mark, et al. Book of Step-by-Step Massage & Aromatherapy: The Power of Massage, Aromatherapy, Shiatsu & Reflexology for Health & Wellbeing, Shown in More Than 200 Colour Photographs. 2010. (ENG., Illus.). 96p. pap. 16.99 *(978-1-84476-765-6(5))* Anness Publishing GBR. Dist: National Bk. Network.

Fialdini, Marcia. Earthly Essentials: A Face & Body Recipe Guide Book. 2011. 92p. pap. 11.95 *(978-1-4620-0490-4(3))* iUniverse, Inc.

Fitzsimmons, J. & Bousquet, P. M. Aromaterapia para los Cuatro Estaciones. (SPA.). 208p. 16.00 *(978-84-89920-81-1(8)*, 87405) Ediciones Oniro S.A. ESP. Dist: Lectorum Pubns., Inc.

Glover, Dennis W. The History of Respiratory Therapy: Discovery & Evolution. 2010. 156p. 24.49 *(978-1-4490-1491-9(7))*; pap. 17.95 *(978-1-4490-1490-2(9))* AuthorHouse.

Graddy, Karen Renee. The Spa Recipe Book. 2006. 77p. pap. 14.95 *(978-0-7414-3566-8(7))* Infinity Publishing.

Harrison, Jimm. Aromatherapy: Therapeutic Use of Essential Oils for Esthetics. 2007. (ENG., Illus.). 416p. per. 54.50 *(978-1-4018-9895-3(5)*, Milady Publishing Co.) Delmar Cengage Learning.

Hoare, Joanna. The Complete Aromatherapy Tutor: A Structured Course to Achieve Professional Expertise. 2010. (ENG., Illus.). 256p. pap. 19.99 *(978-1-85675-284-8(4)*, Gaia Books) Octopus Publishing Group GBR. Dist: Hachette Bk. Group.

Jehn, Judy & Caywood, Kathryn. Aromatherapy for the Soul: Spiritual & Emotional Empowerment with Essential Oils. 2008. (Illus.). iv, 150p. *(978-0-9818290-0-5(7))* Vision Publishing.

Jenkins, Nicola. Aromatherapy in Essence. 2007. (ENG., Illus.). 160p. pap. 24.50 *(978-0-340-92606-2(6))* Hodder Arnold Pubs.

Jones, Elizabeth Anne. Awaken to Healing Fragrance: The Power of Essential Oil Therapy. 2010. (ENG., Illus.). 360p. pap. 18.95 *(978-1-55643-875-2(3))* North Atlantic Bks.

Jones, Larissa. Aromaterapia. (SPA.). 19.95 *(978-0-9720682-1-5(X))* Evergreen Aromatherapy.

—Aromatherapy for Body, Mind & Spirit. pap. 19.95 *(978-0-9720682-0-8(1))* Evergreen Aromatherapy.

Keville, Kathi. The Little Book of Aromatherapy. 2009. (ENG., Illus.). 176p. pap. 11.99 *(978-1-58091-195-5(1)*, Crossing Pr.) Ten Speed Pr.

Keville, Kathi & Green, Mindy. Aromatherapy: A Complete Guide to the Healing Art. 2nd rev. ed. 2008. (ENG., Illus.). 256p. pap. 19.99 *(978-1-58091-189-4(7)*, Crossing Pr.) Ten Speed Pr.

Lamun, Laura. The Garden of Earth: Living Remedies & Earth-Honoring Practices, 3 vols., Vol. 1. 2008. (ENG., Illus.). 219p. pap. 15.95 *(978-0-9801513-0-5(9))* Little Moon Rises Publishing Co.

Lawless. Home Aromatherapy Kit. 29.95 *(978-1-85626-205-7(7))* Cathie, Kyle Ltd. GBR. Dist: Trafalgar Square Publishing.

McGilvery, Carole, et al. Stressbusting Book of Yoga, Massage & Aromatherapy: A step-by-step guide to spiritual & physical Well-being. 2011. (ENG., Illus.). 256p. pap. 24.99 *(978-1-84476-924-7(0))* Anness Publishing GBR. Dist: National Bk. Network.

Milford, Francine. Aroma~Care#8482; Make your Own Magical Blends. 2008. 92p. pap. 12.99 *(978-1-4357-2316-0(3))* Lulu Enterprises Inc.

—Aroma~Care#8482; Pet Aromatherapy. 2007. 88p. pap. 12.99 *(978-0-615-15172-4(8))* Milford, Francine.

PallasDowney, Rhonda. Aromatherapy & Essential Oils. 2010. 44p. pap. 4.95 *(978-1-58054-166-4(6))* Woodland Publishing, Inc.

Pepper, Kathleen. Essential Oils & Meditation. 2007. (ENG., Illus.). 64p. pap. 11.95 *(978-1-905398-12-6(3))* Polair Publishing GBR. Dist: SCB Distributors.

Perez, Nicole. The Aromatherapy Workshop. (Illus.). 192p. pap. 29.95 *(978-1-86126-256-1(6))* Crowood Pr., Ltd. GBR. Dist: Trafalgar Square Publishing.

Price, Shirley & Price, Len. Aromatherapy for Health Professionals. 4th ed. 2011. (ENG., Illus.). 400p. pap. 60.95 ***(978-0-7020-3564-7(5)*** , Churchill Livingstone) Elsevier - Health Sciences Div.

Quezada, Maria. Finding infinity, vol. 1: an easy aromatherapy guide to blending essential oils (the anti-aging Secrets) 2010. 178p. pap. 15.95 *(978-0-557-55001-2(7))* Lulu Enterprises Inc.

Reader's Digest Editors. Massage & Aromatherapy: Simple Techniques to Use at Home to Relieve Stress, Promote Health, & FeelGreat. 2011. (ENG.). (gr. 12). 24.95 *(978-1-60652-339-1(2))* Reader's Digest Assn., Inc., The.

Schiller, Carol & Schiller, David. The Aromatherapy Encyclopedia: A Concise Guide to over 385 Plant Oils, 1 vol. 2008. (ENG., Illus.). 128p. pap. *(978-1-59120-228-8(0))* Basic Health Pubns., Inc.

Schiller, David & Schiller, Carol. Aromatherapy for Life Empowerment: Using Essential Oils to enhance body, Mind, Sprit Well-Being, 1 vol. 2011. (ENG.). 224p. pap. *(978-1-59120-285-1(X))* Basic Health Pubns., Inc.

Schnaubelt, Kurt. The Healing Intelligence of Essential Oils. 2011. (ENG.). 1p. pap. 19.95 ***(978-1-59477-425-6(0))*** Inner Traditions International, Ltd.

—The Healing Intelligence of Essential Oils: The Science of Advanced Aromatherapy. 2011. E-Book ***(978-1-59477-815-5(9))***, Healing Arts Pr.) Inner Traditions International, Ltd.

Selby, A. R. & Selby, Anna. Aromaterapia. (SPA.). 202p. 12.50 *(978-84-922523-0-5(8)*, 86306) Ediciones Oniro S.A. ESP. Dist: Lectorum Pubns., Inc.

Shutes, Jade & Weaver, Christina. Aromatherapy for Bodyworkers. 2007. (ENG., Illus.). 400p. (C). per. 53.00 *(978-0-13-173737-2(6)*, Prentice Hall) Prentice Hall PTR.

Sibley, Veronica. Soluciones de Aromaterapia: Aceites Esenciales para Elevar la Mente, el Cuerpo y el Espiritu. Larousse Staff & Larousse/Marabout Editors, eds. 2007. (Marabout Ser.). (SPA & ENG., Illus.). 128p. pap. 7.95 *(978-970-22-1406-9(8))* Larousse, Ediciones, S. A. de C. V. MEX. Dist: Houghton Mifflin Harcourt Trade & Reference Pubs.

Stuart, Catherine. The Complete Book of Massage & Aromatherapy: A Practical Illustrated Step-by-Step Guide to Achieving Relaxation & Well-Being with Top-to-Toe Body Treatments & Essential Oils. 2007. (ENG., Illus.). 512p. 29.99 *(978-0-7548-1641-6(9))* Anness Publishing GBR. Dist: National Bk. Network.

Taylor, Michelle Caple. Aromatherapy for the Marriage: A Self-Help Inspirational Book for Marriage Ministry & Couples. 2009. 122p. pap. 17.95 *(978-1-61546-630-6(4))* PublishAmerica, Inc.

Totilo, Rebecca Park. Heal with Essential Oil: Nature's Medicine Cabinet. 2010. 262p. pap. 24.99 *(978-0-9827264-0-2(6))* Rebecca at the Well Foundation.

—Heal with Oil: How to Use the Essential Oils of Ancient Scripture. 2008. 112p. pap. 14.99 *(978-0-9749115-4-0(2))* Rebecca at the Well Foundation.

Tulloch, Caro. Aromatherapy Chart. (Illus.). pap. 9.95 *(978-0-86315-595-6(2)*, 1742) Floris Bks. GBR. Dist: SteinerBooks, Inc.

Valentin, Alfonso & Valentín, Alfonso. Aromaterapia. 2010. (SPA.). 208p. pap. *(978-84-87190-98-8(7))* Videocinco, S.A.

White, Judith. Home Spa: Creating Your Own Spa Experience with Aromatherapy. 2006. (ENG., Illus.). 144p. per. 9.95 *(978-1-4019-1148-5(X))* Hay Hse., Inc.

Wildwood, Christine. Guia Facil de Aromaterapia. (SPA., Illus.). 160p. *(978-84-7927-505-1(7))* Robinbk., Ediciones S.L. ESP. Dist: Lectorum Pubns., Inc.

Worwood, Valerie Ann. Aromatherapy for the Soul: Healing the Spirit with Fragrance & Essential Oils. 2nd ed. 2006. (ENG., Illus.). 364p. per. 19.95 *(978-1-57731-562-9(6))* New World Library.

AROMATIC COMPOUNDS

Badger, G. M. The Structures & Reactions of the Aromatic Compounds. 2009. 470p. pap. 55.00 *(978-0-521-10884-3(5))* Cambridge Univ. Pr.

Busslinger, Nicole. Armonia de Fragancias. (SPA.). 226p. *(978-84-7223-819-0(9)*, 6100) Tusquets Editores.

Cserháti, Tibor. Chromatography of Aroma Compounds & Fragrances. 2010. (ENG., Illus.). xii, 392p. 199.00 *(978-3-642-01655-4(3)*, 3642016553) Springer.

Elshahed, Mostafa. Anaerobic Biodegradation of Monoaromatic Compounds. 2008. 180p. pap. *(978-3-639-08264-7(8))* VDM Verlag Dr. Mueller e.K.

Haines, Pierre A. & Hendrickson, Milton D. Polycyclic Aromatic Hydrocarbons: Pollution, Health Effects & Chemistry. 2009. (Polymer Science & Technology Ser.). 145.00 *(978-1-60741-462-9(7)*, Nova Biomedical Bks.) Nova Science Pubs., Inc.

Heipieper, Hermann. Bioremediation of Soils Contaminated with Aromatic Compounds: Proceedings of the NATO Advanced Research Workshop on Bioremediation of Soils Contaminated with Aromatic Compounds, Tartu, Estonia, 1-3 July 2004. (Nato Science Series: IV: Earth & Environmental Sciences Ser.). (ENG.). xxvi, 130p. (C). 2007. pap. 79.95 *(978-1-4020-5692-5(3)*, 1402056923) 2006. 219.00 *(978-1-4020-5691-8(5)*, 1402056915) Springer London, Ltd. GBR. Dist: Springer.

Herrera, Lisandra Cubero. Mass Spectrometry of Polycyclic Aromatic Compounds from Petroleum. 2008. 260p. pap. *(978-3-639-06765-1(7))* VDM Verlag Dr. Mueller e.K.

Hoggett, J. G., et al. Nitration & Aromatic Reactivity. 2009. (ENG., Illus.). 256p. pap. 36.99 *(978-0-521-10494-4(7))* Cambridge Univ. Pr.

Mujiburohman, Muhammad. Studies on Pervaporation for Recovery of Natural Aroma Compound. 2008. 164p. pap. *(978-3-639-08322-4(9))* VDM Verlag Dr. Mueller e.K.

Rauf, Abdul & Farshori, Nida Nayyar. Microwave-Induced Synthesis of Aromatic Heterocycles. 2011. (SpringerBriefs in Molecular Science / Green Chemistry for Sustainability Ser.). (ENG., Illus.). viii, 93p. pap. 49.95 *(978-94-007-1484-7(X)*, 940071484X) Springer.

Rusanov, Alexander L. & Belomoina, Nataliya M. Aromatic Polyethers Based on Heterocyclic Monomers. 2011. (Chemistry Research & Applications Ser.). 175p. pap. 43.00 *(978-1-61761-792-8(X))* Nova Science Pubs., Inc.

Whitmore, Frank C. Organic Chemistry, Volume Two: Part III: Aromatic Compounds Part IV: Heterocyclic Compounds Part V: Organophosphorus & Organometallic Compounds. 2011. (Dover Books on Chemistry Ser.). (ENG.). 416p. pap. 24.95 ***(978-0-486-60701-6(1))*** Dover Pubns., Inc.

Zylstra, Gerben J. Microbial Degradation of Aromatic Compounds. Kukor, Jerome J., ed. 2008. 600p. 139.95 *(978-0-8247-2528-0(X))* CRC Pr. LLC.

AROMATIC PLANTS

see also Essences and Essential Oils; Potpourris (Scented Floral Mixtures)

Acharya, Ram Prasad, et al. Value Chain Analysis of Maps of Mid & Far Western Region of Nepal. 2011. 116p. pap. ***(978-3-8454-0734-0(4))*** Lambert Academic Publishing.

Ahmad, Iftikhar, et al. Medicinal Plants: As Poverty Alleviator in Northern KPK, Pakistan. 2010. 104p. pap. *(978-3-639-28357-0(0))* VDM Verlag Dr. Mueller e.K.

Akhila, Anand, ed. Essential Oil Bearing Grasses: The Genus Cymbopogon. 2009. (Medicinal & Aromatic Plants - Industrial Profiles Ser.). (ENG., Illus.). 262p. 144.95 *(978-0-8493-7857-7(5)*, CRC Press) Taylor & Francis Group GBR. Dist: Taylor & Francis Group.

Aryal, Bimal. Plant Extracts & Their Antifungal Activity Against Fusarium Oxysporum. 2011. 64p. pap. ***(978-3-8443-9884-7(8))*** Lambert Academic Publishing.

Bajaj, Y. P. S., ed. Medicinal & Aromatic Plants XI. 2010. (Biotechnology in Agriculture & Forestry Ser.). (Illus.). xix, 420p. pap. 549.00 *(978-3-642-08363-1(3)*, 3642083633) Springer.

Bogers, Robert J., et al, eds. Medicinal & Aromatic Plants: Agricultural, Commercial, Ecological, Legal, Pharmacological & Social Aspects.

(Wageningen UR Frontis Ser.). 2008. xviii, 309p. 179.00 *(978-1-4020-5447-1(5))* 2007. XVIII, 309p. pap. 109.00 *(978-1-4020-5448-8(3)*, 1402054483) Springer.

Chadha, K. L. & Gupta, Rajendra, eds. Medicinal & Aromatic Plants. (Advances in Horticulture Ser.: Vol. 11). (Illus.). xxxx, 953p. *(978-81-85048-29-1(0))* Malhotra Publishing Hse, (M P H).

Clark, Marge. Essential Oils & Aromatics: A Step-by-Step Guide for Use in Massage & Aromatherapy. 2008. (ENG., Illus.). 96p. 16.95 *(978-1-933317-73-1(6))* Silverleaf Pr.

David, Elizabeth. Spices, Salt & Aromatics in the English Kitchen. 2008. 279p. 29.95 *(978-1-902304-66-3(7))* Grub Street GBR. Dist: Casemate Pubs. & Bk. Distributors, LLC.

Dwivedi, Sumeet & Pankaj K. Sahu. Database on Medicinal & Aromatic Plants of Madhya Pradesh, Indi. 2011. 92p. pap. ***(978-3-8433-8413-1(4))*** Lambert Academic Publishing.

Gaire, Damodar. Medicinal & Aromatic Plants. 2011. 76p. pap. ***(978-3-8443-0298-1(0))*** Lambert Academic Publishing.

Hawkins, Jessie. Lavender: Growing & Using Lavender for Fragrance, Mood & Body Care. 2008. (ENG., Illus.). 72p. 15.95 *(978-1-933317-78-6(7))* Silverleaf Pr.

Hossain, M. Farid, et al. Aromatic Rice. 2011. 236p. pap. ***(978-3-8443-9822-9(8))*** Lambert Academic Publishing.

Jain, S. Mohan & Saxena, Praveen K. Protocols for in Vitro Cultures & Secondary Metabolite Analysis of Aromatic & Medicinal Plants. 2009. (Illus.). xv, 411p. *(978-1-60327-287-2(9))* Humana Pr.

Jain, S. Mohan & Saxena, Praveen K., eds. Protocols for in Vitro Cultures & Secondary Metabolite Analysis of Aromatic & Medicinal Plants. 2009. (Methods in Molecular Biology Ser.). (ENG., Illus.). xviii, 350p. 129.00 *(978-1-60327-286-5(0))* Humana Pr.

Lansky, Ephraim Philip & Paavilainen, Helena Maaria. Figs. 2010. (Medicinal & Aromatic Plants - Industrial Profiles Ser.). (ENG., Illus.). 415p. 119.95 *(978-1-4200-8966-0(8)*, CRC Press) Taylor & Francis Group GBR. Dist: Taylor & Francis Group.

Medicinal & Aromatic Plants IX. 2011. (Biotechnology in Agriculture & Forestry Ser.). (ENG., Illus.). xix, 414p. pap. 589.00 *(978-3-642-08229-0(7)*, 3642082297) Springer.

Medicinal & Aromatic Plants VIII. 2010. (Biotechnology in Agriculture & Forestry Ser.). (Illus.). xxii, 476p. pap. 689.00 *(978-3-642-08201-6(7)*, 3642082017) Springer.

Nagata, Toshiyuki & Ebizuka, Yutaka. Medicinal & Aromatic Plants XII. 2010. (Biotechnology in Agriculture & Forestry Ser.). (Illus.). xvii, 348p. pap. 359.00 *(978-3-642-07503-2(7)*, 3642075037) Springer.

Odoux, Eric & Grisoni, Michel, eds. Vanilla. 2010. (Medicinal & Aromatic Plants - Industrial Profiles Ser.). (ENG., Illus.). 420p. 119.95 *(978-1-4200-8337-8(6)*, CRC Press) Taylor & Francis Group GBR. Dist: Taylor & Francis Group.

Oztekin, Serdar & Martinov, Milan. Medicinal & Aromatic Crops: Harvesting, Drying, & Processing. 2007. (ENG., Illus.). 312p. pap. 59.95 *(978-1-56022-975-9(6)*, CRC Press) Taylor & Francis Group GBR. Dist: Taylor & Francis Group.

Ztekin, Serdar & Martinov, Milan. Medicinal & Aromatic Crops: Harvesting, Drying, & Processing. 2007. (ENG., Illus.). 320p. 104.95 *(978-1-56022-974-2(8)*, CRC Press) Taylor & Francis Group GBR. Dist: Taylor & Francis Group.

Piesse, G. W. Septimus. The Art of Perfumery & Methods of Obtaining the Aromas of Plants: How to make perfumes, scented powders, aromatic vinegars, dentifrices, pomatums, cosmetics, perfumed soap & More! 2008. 212p. pap. 14.95 *(978-1-4357-4120-1(X))* Lulu Enterprises Inc.

Simon, James, et al, eds. African Natural Plant Products. 2012. (ENG., Illus.). 448p. 139.95 *(978-1-4398-2176-3(3)*, CRC Press) Taylor & Francis Group GBR. Dist: Taylor & Francis Group.

Sun, Li. Characterisation of Strawberry Aroma at Super Oxygen Condition. 2011. 68p. pap. ***(978-3-8443-9453-5(2))*** Lambert Academic Publishing.

Tomecko, Denise. Buddhist Healing in Laos: The Fragrant Forest. 2009. (ENG., Illus.). 152p. pap. 29.95 *(978-974-524-078-0(8))* Orchid Pr. THA. Dist: National Bk. Network.

Valerio, Lucia, ed. Il Giardino dei Profumi: Italian Villas' Gardens & their Flowers. 2011. (ENG & ITA., Illus.). 160p. 145.00 ***(978-88-370-8575-9(3))*** Electa ITA. Dist: National Bk. Network.

AROMATIC PLANT PRODUCTS
see Essences and Essential Oils

ARON, RAYMOND, 1905-1983

Aron, Raymond. Political Reason in the Age of Ideology: Essays in Honor of Raymond Aron. Frost, Bryan-Paul & Mahoney, Daniel, eds. 2007. (Festschriften Ser.). (ENG.). 330p. (gr. 11). 49.95 *(978-0-7658-0353-5(4))* Transaction Pubs.

Davis, Reed. A Politics of Understanding: The International Thought of Raymond Aron. 2009. (Political Traditions in Foreign Policy Ser.). 232p. 42.50 *(978-0-8071-3517-4(8))* Louisiana State Univ. Pr.

Judt, Tony. The Burden of Responsibility: Blum, Camus, Aron, & the French Twentieth Century. 2007. (ENG., Illus.). 204p. per. 17.50 *(978-0-226-41419-5(1))* Univ. of Chicago Pr.

Lapparent, Olivier de. Raymond Aron et L'Europe: Itinéraire d'un Européen dans le Siècle. 2010. (Convergences Ser.). (FRE.). 183p. pap. *(978-3-0343-0416-0(1))* Lang, Peter.

ARP, BILL
see Smith, Charles Henry, 1826-1903

ARP, HANS, 1888-1966

Robertson, Eric. Arp: Painter, Poet, Sculptor. 2006. (ENG., Illus.). 256p. 60.00 *(978-0-300-10690-9(4))* Yale Univ. Pr.

ARRANGEMENT (MUSIC)
see also Instrumentation and Orchestration

Alexander, Peter. Professional Orchestration 16-Stave Ruled Orchestral Sketchbook. 2007. 104p. pap. 9.95 *(978-0-939067-68-8(4))* Alexander Publishing.

—Professional Orchestration 16-Stave Unruled Orchestral Sketchbook. 2007. 104p. pap. 9.95 *(978-0-939067-69-5(2))* Alexander Publishing.

Alexander, Peter Lawrence. Professional Orchestration: Orchestrating the Melody Within the String Section. 2008. 596p. pap. 59.95 *(978-0-939067-06-0(4))* Alexander Publishing.

—Professional Orchestration: Orchestrating the Melody Within the Woodwinds & Brass. 2009. 714p. pap. 64.95 *(978-0-939067-93-0(5))* Alexander Publishing.

—Professional Orchestration: Solo Instruments & Instrumentation Notes. 2008. 804p. pap. 69.95 *(978-0-939067-70-1(6))* Alexander Publishing.

American Academy of Orthopaedic Surgeons (AAOS). Intermediate. 2007. 698p. pap. 67.95 *(978-0-7637-5675-8(X))* Jones & Bartlett Learning, LLC.

Carter, Peggy. Hammered Dulcimer Arrangements for Special Occasions, 1 vol. 2007. (ENG., Illus.). 96p. spiral bd. 19.95 *(978-0-7866-7421-3(0))* Mel Bay Pubns., Inc.

Eddington, R. Jelani. The Art of Theatre Organ Arranging, Volume 1. 2009. (Illus.). 130p. spiral bd. 34.95 *(978-0-9823385-0-6(3))* RJE Productions LLC.

Erickson, Frank. Arranging for the Concert Band Workbook. 2009. 118p. pap. 24.95 *(978-0-910927-06-2(5))* Alfred Publishing Co., Inc.

Guest, Bill. String Band Classics: Fiddle, 1 vol. 2006. (ENG., Illus.). 56p. pap. 17.95 *(978-0-7866-4932-7(1)*, 96689bcd) Mel Bay Pubns., Inc.

Hal Leonard Corp., creator. Pop/Rock Piano Favorites. 2010. (ENG.). 140p. pap. 19.99 *(978-1-60378-156-5(0)*, 1603781560) Cherry Lane Music Co.

Klapuri, Anssi & Davy, Manuel, eds. Signal Processing Methods for Music Transcription. 2010. (ENG., Illus.). xii, 440p. pap. 169.00 *(978-1-4419-4035-3(9)*, 1441940359) Springer.

Kregor, Jonathan. Liszt as Transcriber. 2010. (ENG., Illus.). 314p. 90.00 *(978-0-521-11777-7(1))* Cambridge Univ. Pr.

Leanza, Frank. Arranging & Orchestration Ideas. 2011. (ENG.). 209p. pap. 15.95 ***(978-1-934849-54-5(5))*** Zip Publishing.

—The Golden Encyclopedia of Music Theory & Arranging. 2011. (Illus.). 263p. ***(978-0-934687-67-6(6))*** Crystal Pubs.

Letsch, Glenn. 25 Great Bass Lines: Transcriptions * Lessons * Bios * Photos. 2010. (ENG.). 84p. pap. 19.99 incl. audio compact disk *(978-1-4234-6056-5(1)*, 1423460561) Leonard, Hal Corp.

Libertino, Dan, ed. Pro Charts for Jazz Guitar. 2010. (ENG.). 32p. pap. 14.99 incl. audio compact disk *(978-1-4234-9771-4(6)*, 1423497716) Leonard, Hal Corp.

Pacheco, Beau A. Guitar Building Basics: Acoustic Assembly at Home. 2010. (ENG., Illus.). 144p. pap. 27.95 *(978-1-929133-82-6(0)*, 1929133820) Wolfgang Pubns., Inc.

Rooksby, Rikky. Arranging Songs: How to Put the Parts Together. 2008. (Music Ser.). (ENG., Illus.). 190p. pap. 22.95 incl. audio compact disk *(978-0-87930-896-4(6)*, 0879308966, Backbeat Books) Leonard, Hal Corp.

Sussman, Richard & Abene, Michael. Jazz Composition & Arranging in the Digital Age, 1 vol. 2012. (ENG., Illus.). 544p. 99.00 *(978-0-19-538099-6(1))*; 416p. pap. 39.95 *(978-0-19-538100-9(9))* Oxford Univ. Pr., Inc.

Tomaro, Mike & Wilson, John. Instrumental Jazz Arranging: A Comprehensive & Practical Guide. 2009. (ENG., Illus.). 536p. pap. 49.99 incl. audio compact disk *(978-1-4234-5274-4(7)*, 1423452747) Leonard, Hal Corp.

Wallberg, Gunther. Die Schutzfahigkeit von Bearbeitungen Gemeinfreier Werke der Ernsten Musik im Europaischen Vergleich. (GER.). 296p. 43.95 *(978-3-631-39234-8(6))* Lang, Peter Publishing, Inc.

ARRAS (FRANCE)

Bilton, David. The German Army at Arras: Rare Photographs from Wartime Archives. 2008. (Illus.). 160p. pap. 24.95 *(978-1-84415-768-6(7))* Pen & Sword Bks. Ltd. GBR. Dist: Casemate Pubs. & Bk. Distributors, LLC.

Reed, Paul. Walking Arras. 2007. (Illus.). 240p. pap. 24.95 *(978-1-84415-619-1(2))* Pen & Sword Bks. Ltd. GBR. Dist: Casemate Pubs. & Bk. Distributors LLC.

ARRAY LOGIC, PROGRAMMABLE
see Programmable Array Logic

ARREST
see also Bail; Juvenile Detention Homes

Anderson, James F. & Thompson, Bankole. American Criminal Procedures. 2007. 330p. pap. 35.00 *(978-1-59460-237-5(9))* Carolina Academic Pr.

Biddulph, Sarah. Legal Reform & Administrative Detention Powers in China. 2008. (Cambridge Studies in Law & Society). (ENG.). 502p. 120.00 *(978-0-521-86940-9(4))* Cambridge Univ. Pr.

Coven, Mark S., ed. Arrest, Search & Seizure Citator 2007. annuals 2007. pap. 125.00 *(978-1-57589-443-0(2))* Massachusetts Continuing Legal Education, Inc.

Devi, Bellary Uma. Arrest, Detention, & Criminal Justice System: A Study in the Context of the Constitution of India. 2012. (ENG.). 428p. 75.00 ***(978-0-19-807599-8(5))*** Oxford Univ. Pr., Inc.

Eig, Jonathan. Get Capone: The Secret Plot That Captured America's Most Wanted Gangster. 2011. (ENG., Illus.). 480p. pap. 16.00 *(978-1-4165-8060-7(3))* Simon & Schuster.

—Get Capone: The Secret Plot That Captured America's Most Wanted Gangster. Lt. ed. 2010. 710p. 31.99 *(978-1-4104-2743-4(9))* Thorndike Pr.

Eisenhardt, Thilo. Der Jugendarrest: Eine Chance der Kriminalprävention. 2010. (Studien zur Psychologie und Kriminalität Ser.). (GER.). 122p. pap. 28.95 *(978-3-631-60073-8(X))* Lang, Peter GmbH, Europaischer Verlag der Wissenschaften DEU. Dist: Lang, Peter.

Guild, Elspeth, ed. Constitutional Challenges to the European Arrest Warrant, Vol. 1. 2006. 272p. pap. 45.00 *(978-90-5850-184-4(1))* Gaunt, Inc.

Richards, Laura, et al. Policing Domestic Violence. 2008. (Blackstone's Practical Policing Ser.). (ENG., Illus.). 250p. pap. 85.00 *(978-0-19-923674-9(7)*, Blackstone Pr.) Oxford Univ. Pr. GBR. Dist: Oxford Univ. Pr., Inc.

Voorhees, Harvey Cortlandt. The Law of Arrest: In Civil & Criminal Actions. 2nd ed. 2011. 287p. 58.00 ***(978-1-60449-110-4(8))*** Gaunt, Inc.

Whitson, Sarah Leah & Gorvin, Ian. Group Denial: Repression of Kurdish Political & Cultural Rights in Syria. 2009. (Illus.). 63p. pap. ***(978-1-56432-560-0(1))*** Human Rights Watch.

2010 CA Legal & Search & Seizure Sourceguide. 2010. 77p. pap. 19.99 *(978-1-56325-153-5(1))* Lawtech Publishing Co., Ltd.

ARREST—CANADA

Coughlan, Stephen & Luther, Glen. Detention & Arrest. 2010. (Essentials of Canadian Law Ser.). 370p. pap. *(978-1-55221-193-9(2))* Irwin Law, Inc.

ARREST (POLICE METHODS)
see also Police Pursuit Driving

Carson, Dale C. & Denham, Wes. Arrest-Proof Yourself: An Ex-Cop Reveals How Easy It Is for Anyone to Get Arrested, How Even a Single Arrest Could Ruin Your Life, & What to Do If the Police Get in Your Face. 2007. (ENG., Illus.). 288p. pap. 14.95 *(978-1-55652-637-4(7))* Chicago Review Pr., Inc.

Comerford, James F. Massachusetts Motor Vehicle Stops Benchbook 2010 Edition. 2010. 0.00 *(978-1-889916-08-8(0))* Flaschner, Franklin N Judicial Institute, Inc.

Davis, Lisa & Krinke, Karri. Defensive Tactics: Training for Life. 2007. *(978-0-9786018-4-3(X))* Sparrow Media Group, Inc.

Fichera, Massimo. The Implementation of the European Arrest Warrant in the European Union: Law, Policy & Practice. 2011. (Supranational Criminal Law Ser.: Vol. 10). 267p. pap. 91.00 *(978-94-000-0172-5(X))* Intersentia Uitgevers N.V. BEL. Dist: International Specialized Bk. Services.

Phillips, Deborah. Implementing Mandatory Arrest Laws - the Arrest & Criminal Charge Decisions. 2008. 156p. per. *(978-3-8364-3801-8(1))* VDM Verlag Dr. Mueller e.K.

Ross, Darrell L. & Chan, Ted, eds. Sudden Deaths in Custody. 2010. (Forensic Science & Medicine Ser.). (Illus.). 248p. pap. 149.00 *(978-1-61737-591-0(8)*, 1617375918) Humana Pr.

Suggs, Eldridge. Real Law Talk: Your First Arrest What Will Happen Next? 2011. 24p. pap. 16.98 *(978-1-4520-9964-4(2))* AuthorHouse.

ARREST, CARDIAC
see Cardiac Arrest

ARREST RECORDS
see Criminal Records

ARRHYTHMIA

AAOS, creator. First Aid, CPR, & AED. 5th ed. 2007. per. 45.50 *(978-0-7637-4664-3(9))* Jones & Bartlett Learning, LLC.

Abedin, Zainul, et al. ECG Interpretation: The Self-Assessment Approach. 2nd rev. ed. 2007. (ENG., Illus.). 240p. per. 76.95 *(978-1-4051-6749-9(1)*, Wiley-Blackwell) Wiley, John & Sons, Inc.

Acker, Lesha. Powdered Donuts on Monday: Appreciating Life's Simple Pleasures in Times of Adversity. 2010. 102p. pap. 13.95 *(978-1-4327-5959-9(0))* Outskirts Pr., Inc.

Aehlert, Barbara J. ECGs Made Easy - Book & Pocket Reference Package. 4th ed. 2009. (ENG., Illus.). 368p. (C). pap. 59.95 *(978-0-323-06924-3(X)*, Mosby/JEMS) Elsevier - Health Sciences Div.

Al-Ahmad, Amin, et al, eds. Electroanatomical Mapping: An Atlas for Clinicians. 2008. (ENG., Illus.). 280p. 152.95 *(978-1-4051-5702-5(X)*, Wiley-Blackwell) Wiley, John & Sons, Inc.

—Ventricular Arrhythmias & Sudden Cardiac Death: Mechanism, Ablation, & Defibrillation. 2008. (ENG., Illus.). 360p. 185.95 *(978-1-4051-6114-5(0)*, Wiley-Blackwell) Wiley, John & Sons, Inc.

Aliot, Etienne, et al, eds. Catheter Ablation of Atrial Fibrillation. 2008. (ENG., Illus.). 280p. 185.95 *(978-1-4051-6349-1(6)*, Wiley-Blackwell) Wiley, John & Sons, Inc.

Almas, Tabish. Mathematical Models of Failing Heart. 2008. 220p. pap. *(978-3-639-04295-5(6))* VDM Verlag Dr. Mueller e.K.

American College of Emergency Physicians (ACEP). EACLS Study Guide - Express PDF. 2nd rev. ed. 2009. pap. 15.95 *(978-0-7637-8613-7(6))* Jones & Bartlett Learning, LLC.

American Heart Association, creator. Heartsaver Child & Infant Poster Pack. 2011. (ENG.). 39.75 ***(978-1-61669-062-5(3))*** American Heart Assn., Inc.

Antzelevitch, Charles. Basic Science for the Clinical Electrophysiologist, an Issue of Cardiac Electrophysiology Clinics. 2011. (Clinics: Internal Medicine Ser.: 3-1). (ENG.). 200p. 75.00 *(978-1-4557-0423-1(7)*, Saunders) Elsevier - Health Sciences Div.

Atwood, Sandra, et al. Introduction to Basic Cardiac Dysrhythmias. 4th rev. ed. 2011. (ENG., Illus.). 416p. (C). pap. 51.95 *(978-0-323-08532-8(6)*, Mosby/JEMS) Elsevier - Health Sciences Div.

Back Sternick, Eduardo & Wellens, Hein J. J. Variants of Ventricular Preexcitation: Recognition & Treatment. 2006. (ENG., Illus.). 168p. 115.95 *(978-1-4051-4843-6(8)*, Wiley-Blackwell) Wiley, John & Sons, Inc.

Bartolozzi, Fabio, et al, eds. Manual of Surgical Treatment of Atrial Fibrillation. 2008. (ENG., Illus.). 272p. 125.95 *(978-1-4051-4032-4(1)*, Wiley-Blackwell) Wiley, John & Sons, Inc.

Bashir, Yaver, et al. Cardiac Electrophysiology & Catheter Ablation. 2010. (ENG., Illus.). 576p. pap. 75.00 *(978-0-19-955018-0(2))* Oxford Univ. Pr., Inc.

Basson, Craig T. & Lerman, Bruce B. Ischemic Heart Disease & Arrhythmias. 2009. 379.00 *(978-1-933864-58-7(3))* Demos Medical Publishing, LLC.

Baum, Kristin & Thompson, Gale, eds. ECG Interpretation. 2008. (Incredibly Easy! Ser.). (ENG., Illus.). 256p. pap. 25.99 *(978-0-7817-8308-8(9))* Lippincott Williams & Wilkins.

Bayés de Luna, Antonio, et al, eds. Arrhythmias & Sudden Death in Athletes. 2010. (Developments in Cardiovascular Medicine Ser.). 176p. pap. 105.00 *(978-90-481-5470-8(7)*, 9048154707) Springer.

Billman, George Edward. Novel Therapeutic Targets for Antiarrhythmic Drugs. 2010. (ENG., Illus.). 586p. 166.00 *(978-0-470-26100-2(5)*, Wiley) Wiley, John & Sons, Inc.

Bredikis, Audrius & Wilber, David. Cryoablation of Cardiac Arrhythmias: Expert Consult - Online & Print. 2011. (ENG., Illus.). 256p. 149.00 *(978-1-4377-1615-3(6)*, Saunders) Elsevier - Health Sciences Div.

Capucci. Sudden Cardiac Death. 2006. (ENG., Illus.). 212p. 160.00 *(978-1-84184-578-4(7))* Taylor & Francis Group.

Cerutti, Sergio, et al. Understanding Atrial Fibrillation: The Signal Processing Contribution. 2009. (Synthesis Lectures on Biomedical Engineering Ser.). 240p. pap. 50.00 *(978-1-59829-296-1(X))* Morgan & Claypool Pubs.

Cohen, Todd J. A Patient's Guide to Heart Rhythm Problems. 2010. (Johns Hopkins Press Health Book Ser.). (ENG., Illus.). 232p. pap. 16.95 *(978-0-8018-9775-7(0))*; (gr. 17). 45.00 *(978-0-8018-9774-0(2))* Johns Hopkins Univ. Pr.

Corrado, Domenico, et al. Arrhythmogenic Cardiomyopathy: Cardiac Electrophysiology Clinics. 2011. (Clinics: Internal Medicine Ser.: 3-2). (ENG.). 176p. 75.00 *(978-1-4377-2428-8(0)*, Saunders) Elsevier - Health Sciences Div.

Cram101 Textbook Reviews & Cram101 Textbook Reviews. Outlines & Highlights for Basic Arrhythmias by Gail Walraven, Isbn: 9780135002384. 2011. 294p. pap. 32.95 ***(978-1-61461-514-9(4))*** Cram101 Inc.

de Luna, Antonio Bayés. Clinical Arrhythmology. 2011. (ENG., Illus.). 440p. 157.95 *(978-0-470-65636-5(0)*, Wiley-Blackwell) Wiley, John & Sons, Inc.

De Ponti, Roberto. From Signals to Colours: A Case-Based Atlas of Electroanatomic Mapping in Complex Atrial Arrhythmias. 2007. (Illus.). 201p. 179.00 *(978-88-470-0648-5(1))* Springer.

—From Signals to Colours: A Case-based Atlas of Electroanatomic Mapping in Complex Atrial Arrhythmias. 2010. (Illus.). xiv, 202p. pap. 179.00 *(978-88-470-1558-6(8)*, 8847015588) Springer.

Dhein, S. Cardiovascular Gap Junctions. 2nd rev. ed. (Advances in Cardiology Ser.: Vol. 42). (Illus.). 298p. *(978-3-8055-8077-9(0))* Karger, S. AG.

Furniss, Steve, et al. Fast Facts: Fast Facts. 2010. (Illus.). 148p. pap. 25.00 ***(978-1-903734-88-9(6))*** Health Pr., Ltd. GBR. Dist: BookMasters Distribution Services (BDS).

Grauer, Ken. Arrhythmia Management & Cardiac Arrest: Arrhythmia Management & Cardiac Arrest: A Pocket Brain Approach. 2007. (ENG., Illus.). 106p. pap. 16.00 *(978-0-9663389-1-1(X))* KG/EKG Pr.

Gussak, Ihor, et al, eds. Cardiac Repolarization. 2010. (Contemporary Cardiology Ser.). (Illus.). 568p. pap. 219.00 *(978-1-61737-336-7(2)*, 1617373362) Humana Pr.

Gussak, Ihor, et al. Electrical Diseases of the Heart: Genetics, Mechanisms, Treatment, Prevention. 2007. (Illus.). 968p. 279.00 *(978-1-84628-853-1(3))* Springer.

Hayes, David L. & Asirvatham, Samuel J. Dictionary of Cardiac Pacing, Defibrillation, Resynchronization & Arrhythmias. 2nd ed. 2007. (ENG., Illus.). 320p. 49.00 *(978-0-9790164-0-0(1))* Cardiotext Publishing.

Ho, Reginald T. Electrophysiology of Arrhythmias: Practical Images for Diagnosis & Ablation. 2009. (ENG., Illus.). 384p. 104.95 *(978-1-60547-590-5(4))* Lippincott Williams & Wilkins.

Huang, Shoei K. Stephen & Wood, Mark A. Catheter Ablation of Cardiac Arrhythmias. 2nd ed. 2010. (ENG., Illus.). 672p. 195.00 *(978-1-4377-1368-8(8)*, Saunders) Elsevier - Health Sciences Div.

Huff, Jane. ECG Workout: Exercises in Arrhythmia Interpretation. 6th rev. ed. 2011. (Illus.). 384p. pap. 51.99 *(978-1-4511-1553-6(9))* Lippincott Williams & Wilkins.

Issa, Ziad, et al. Clinical Arrhythmology & Electrophysiology: A Companion to Braunwald's Heart Disease. 2008. (ENG., Illus.). 520p. 218.00 *(978-1-4160-5998-1(9)*, Saunders) Elsevier - Health Sciences Div.

Jalife, Jose, et al. Basic Cardiac Electrophysiology for the Clinician. 2nd ed. 2009. (ENG., Illus.). 360p. 115.95 *(978-1-4051-8333-8(0)*, Wiley-Blackwell) Wiley, John & Sons, Inc.

Jenkins, Peggy. Nurse to Nurse ECG Interpretation. 2009. (Nurse to Nurse Ser.). (ENG., Illus.). 336p. 32.00 *(978-0-07-159283-3(0)*, 0071592830) McGraw-Hill Professional Publishing.

Jevon, Philip. ECGs for Nurses. 2nd ed. 2009. (Essential Clinical Skills for Nurses Ser.: 13). (ENG., Illus.). 296p. pap. 44.99 *(978-1-4051-8162-4(1)*, Wiley-Blackwell) Wiley, John & Sons, Inc.

Josephson, Mark E. Clinical Cardiac Electrophysiology: Techniques & Interpretations. 4th rev. ed. 2008. (ENG., Illus.). 912p. 245.99 *(978-0-7817-7739-1(9))* Lippincott Williams & Wilkins.

A

Kass, Robert E. & Clancy, Colleen E. Basis & Treatment of Cardiac Arrhythmias. 2010. (Handbook of Experimental Pharmacology Ser.). (Illus.). ix, 361p. pap. 469.00 *(978-3-642-06396-1(9)*, 3642063969) Springer.

Kohl, Peter, et al. Cardiac Mechano-Electric Coupling & Arrhythmias. 2nd ed. 2011. (ENG., Illus.). 512p. 245.00 *(978-0-19-957016-4(7))* Oxford Univ. Pr., Inc.

Kowey, Peter R. & Naccarelli, Gerald V. Advances in Antiarrhythmic Drug Therapy, an Issue of Cardiac Electrophysiology Clinics. 2010. (Clinics: Internal Medicine Ser.: 2-3). (ENG., Illus.). ix, 326p. 75.00 *(978-1-4377-2429-5(9)*, Saunders) Elsevier - Health Sciences Div.

Kunz, Michele G. Zombie Notes Bradycardia - Heart Blocks. Kunz, Joseph C., Jr., ed. & des. by. 2011. 2p. mass mkt. 4.99 *(978-1-933230-49-8(5))* Dickson Keanaghan, LLC.

Lewis, Kathryn M. Multiple Lead ECGs: A Practical Analysis of Arrhythmias. 2009. (ENG.). 528p. (C). pap. 58.95 *(978-1-4354-4124-8(9))* Delmar Cengage Learning.

Liong Bing Liem & Downar, Eugene, eds. Progress in Catheter Ablation: Clinical Application of New Mapping & Ablation Technology. 2012. (Developments in Cardiovascular Medicine Ser.). (ENG., Illus.). 608p. pap. 389.00 *(978-90-481-5882-9(6)*, 9048158826) Springer.

Lippincott. ACLS Review Made Incredibly Easy. 2nd rev. ed. 2012. (Incredibly Easy! Ser.). (ENG.). 352p. pap. 43.99 *(978-1-60831-288-7(7))* Lippincott Williams & Wilkins.

Macfarlane, Peter W., et al, eds. Cardiac Arrhythmias & Mapping Techniques. 2011. (ENG., Illus.). xii, 346p. pap. 79.95 ***(978-0-85729-876-8(3)***, 0857298763) Springer.

Mugera, Charles. Ventricular Fibrillation: Novel insights into pharmacology & Mechanisms. 2011. 100p. pap. ***(978-3-8443-2934-6(X))*** Lambert Academic Publishing.

Natale, Andrea & Jalife, Jose, eds. Atrial Fibrillation: From Bench to Bedside. 2008. (Contemporary Cardiology Ser.). (Illus.). 453p. 119.00 *(978-1-58829-856-0(6))* Springer.

Natale, Andrea & Raviele, Antonio. Atrial Fibrillation Ablation: The State of the Art Based on the Venicechart International Consensus Document. 2007. (ENG., Illus.). 104p. pap. 62.95 *(978-1-4051-8038-2(2)*, Wiley-Blackwell) Wiley, John & Sons, Inc.

—Ventricular Tachycardia - Fibrillation Ablation: The State of the Art Based on the Venicechart International Consensus Document. 2009. (ENG., Illus.). 152p. pap. 66.99 *(978-1-4443-3073-1(X)*, Wiley-Blackwell) Wiley, John & Sons, Inc.

Natale, Andrea & Raviele, Antonio, eds. Atrial Fibrillation Ablation 2011: The State of the Art Based on the Venicechart International Consensus Document. 2nd rev. ed. 2011. (ENG.). 232p. pap. 65.95 ***(978-0-470-67415-4(6)***, Wiley-Blackwell) Wiley, John & Sons, Inc.

Olshansky. Arrhythmias Essentials. rev. ed. 2011. 352p. pap. 34.95 *(978-0-7637-7476-9(6))* Jones & Bartlett Learning, LLC.

Prion, Silvia. Genetics of Cardiac Arrhythmias, an Issue of Cardiac Electrophysiology Clinics. 2010. (Clinics: Internal Medicine Ser.: 2-4). (ENG.). 75.00 *(978-1-4557-0304-3(4)*, Saunders) Elsevier - Health Sciences Div.

Rzavi, Mehdi & Razavi, Mehdi. Cardiac Rhythm Devices: A Case-Based Approach to Management. 2011. (Illus.). xiv, 175p. pap. 199.00 *(978-1-933864-67-9(2))* Demos Medical Publishing, LLC.

Saksena, Sanjeev & Camm, A. John. Electrophysiological Disorders of the Heart: Expert Consult - Online & Print. 2nd ed. 2011. (ENG., Illus.). 1488p. 279.00 *(978-1-4377-0285-9(6)*, Saunders) Elsevier - Health Sciences Div.

Sankaranarayanan, Rajiv, et al, eds. Treatment of Ventricular Fibrillation. 2010. (Cardiology Research & Clinical Developments Ser.). pap. 43.00 *(978-1-60876-850-9(3)*, Nova Biomedical Bks.) Nova Science Pubs., Inc.

Scheinman, Melvin M. & Akhtar, Masood. Advances in Arrhythmia Analyses: A Case-Based Approach, an Issue of Cardiac Electrophysiology Clinics. 2010. (Clinics: Internal Medicine Ser.: 2-2). (ENG.). 75.00 *(978-1-4377-1799-0(3)*, Saunders) Elsevier - Health Sciences Div.

Singh, B. J., et al, eds. Electropharmacological Control of Cardiac Arrhythmias. 2007. (Illus.). 350p. 80.00 *(978-0-87993-514-6(6)*, Wiley-Blackwell) Wiley, John & Sons, Inc.

Springhouse Publishing Company Staff. ECG Interpretation. 2009. (Incredibly Easy! Ser.). (ENG., Illus.). 288p. pap. 36.99 *(978-1-60547-235-5(2))* Lippincott Williams & Wilkins.

Springhouse Publishing Company Staff, ed. Nursing Know-How: Interpreting ECGs. 2008. (ENG., Illus.). 320p. 47.99 *(978-0-7817-9206-6(1))* Lippincott Williams & Wilkins.

Steinberg, Jonathan S., ed. Atrial Fibrillation after Cardiac Surgery. 2010. (Developments in Cardiovascular Medicine Ser.). 184p. pap. 279.00 *(978-1-4419-5112-0(1)*, 1441951121) Springer.

Tarkowicz, Ira R. Progress in Cardiac Arrythmia Research. 2007. 185.00 *(978-1-60021-796-8(6))* Nova Science Pubs., Inc.

Thakur, Ranjan K. & Natale, Andrea. Atrial Fibrillation: Medical Clinics. 2007. (Clinics: Internal Medicine Ser.: 92-1). (ENG., Illus.). 240p. 65.00 *(978-1-4160-5860-1(5)*, Saunders) Elsevier - Health Sciences Div.

—Atrial Fibrillation, an Issue of Cardiology Clinics. 2009. (Clinics: Internal Medicine Ser.: 27-1). (ENG., Illus.). 240p. 99.00 *(978-1-4377-0456-3(5)*, Saunders) Elsevier - Health Sciences Div.

Thiene, Gaetano, et al, eds. Arrhythmogenic RV Cardiomyopathy/Dysplasia: Recent Advances. 2007. (Illus.). 217p. 189.00 *(978-88-470-0489-4(6)*, 8847004896) Springer.

Tsiperfal, Angela, et al, eds. Cardiac Arrhythmia Management: A Practical Guide for Nurses & Allied Professionals. 2011. (ENG., Illus.). 516p. pap. 89.99 *(978-0-8138-1667-8(X)*, Wiley-Blackwell) Wiley, John & Sons, Inc.

Valentinuzzi, Max E. Cardiac Fibrillation-Defibrillation: Clinical & Engineering Aspects. 2010. (Illus.). 304p. 119.00 *(978-981-4293-63-1(6))* World Scientific Publishing Co., Inc.

Vespry, Lynn A. Cardiac Arrythmia Research Advances. 2007. 79.00 *(978-1-60021-795-1(8))* Nova Science Pubs., Inc.

Vespry, Lynn A., ed. Cardiac Arrythmia Research Advances. 2008. 185.00 *(978-1-60021-794-4(X))* Nova Science Pubs., Inc.

Walraven, Gail. Basic Arrhythmias. 7th ed. 2010. (ENG., Illus.). 640p. (C). pap. 98.67 *(978-0-13-500238-4(9)*, Prentice Hall) Prentice Hall PTR.

Wang, Paul & Al-Ahmad, Amin. Advances in ICD Therapy: Cardiac Electrophysiology Clinics. 2011. (Clinics: Internal Medicine Ser.: 3-3). (ENG.). 75.00 *(978-1-4557-0424-8(5)*, Saunders) Elsevier - Health Sciences Div.

Wesley, Keith. Basic Dysrhythmias & Acute Coronary Syndromes: Interpretation & Management. 4th ed. 2011. (ENG.). 232p. (C). pap. 19.95 *(978-0-323-03973-4(1)*, Mosby/JEMS) Elsevier - Health Sciences Div.

—Huszar's Basic Dysrhythmias & Acute Coronary Syndromes: Interpretation & Management Text & Pocket Guide Package, 2 vols. 4th ed. 2011. (ENG.). 524p. (C). pap. 56.95 *(978-0-323-03974-1(X)*, Mosby/JEMS) Elsevier - Health Sciences Div.

Wilber, David J., et al, eds. Catheter Ablation of Cardiac Arrhythmias: Basic Concepts & Clinical Applications. 3rd rev. ed. 2008. (ENG., Illus.). 392p. 165.95 *(978-1-4051-3117-9(9)*, Wiley-Blackwell) Wiley, John & Sons, Inc.

Wren, Christopher. Concise Guide to Pediatric Arrhythmias. 2011. (ENG., Illus.). 198p. pap. 64.95 ***(978-0-470-65855-0(X)***, Wiley-Blackwell) Wiley, John & Sons, Inc.

Yan, Gan-Xin & Kowey, Peter R., eds. Management of Cardiac Arrhythmias. 2nd ed. 2010. (Contemporary Cardiology Ser.). (Illus.). xii, 560p. 279.00 *(978-1-60761-160-8(0)*, 1607611600) Humana Pr.

Zimetbaum, Peter J. & Josephson, Mark E., eds. Practical Clinical Electrophysiology. 2008. (ENG., Illus.). 320p. 136.99 *(978-0-7817-6603-6(6))* Lippincott Williams & Wilkins.

ARROW (FIGHTER PLANES)

see Pfeil (Fighter Planes)

ARROWS

see Bow and Arrow

ARSENAL FOOTBALL CLUB

Callow, Nick & Martin, Neil. The Little Book of Arsenal: More Than 185 Hotshot Quotes! 2nd ed. 2011. (ENG.). 192p. pap. 4.95 *(978-1-84732-680-5(3))* Carlton Bks., Ltd. GBR. Dist: Independent Pubs. Group.

Donnelley, Paul. Arsenal - On This Day. 2011. (On This Day Ser.). (ENG., Illus.). 160p. 14.95 ***(978-1-905411-36-8(7))*** Pitch Publishing (Brighton) Ltd. GBR. Dist: Independent Pubs. Group.

Fynn, Alex & Whitcher, Kevin. Arsènal: The Making of a Modern Superclub. 3rd rev. ed. 2011. (ENG., Illus.). 318p. pap. 14.95 ***(978-1-907637-31-5(1))*** Vision Sports Publishing GBR. Dist: SCB Distributors.

Gold, Adam. The Arsenal Miscellany. 2nd rev. ed. 2008. (ENG., Illus.). 160p. 14.95 ***(978-1-905326-45-7(9))*** Vision Sports Publishing GBR. Dist: SCB Distributors.

Hayes, Dean. Arsenal: The Football Facts. 2008. (ENG., Illus.). 394p. per. 14.95 *(978-1-84454-433-2(8))* Blake, John Publishing, Ltd. GBR. Dist: Independent Pubs. Group.

Joseph, Paul. When Football Was Football: Arsenal: A Nostalgic Look at a Century of the Club. 2010. (ENG., Illus.). 208p. 29.95 *(978-1-84425-947-2(1)*, 1844259471) Haynes Publishing PLC GBR. Dist: MBI Distribution Services/Quayside Distribution.

Matthews, Tony. Who's Who of Arsenal. 2007. (ENG., Illus.). 334p. pap. 22.95 *(978-1-84596-232-6(X))* Mainstream Publishing Co., Ltd. GBR. Dist: Independent Pubs. Group.

Oldfield, Tom. Cesc Fabregas. 2010. (World Cup Heroes Ser.). (ENG., Illus.). 122p. pap. 10.95 *(978-1-84358-176-5(0))* Blake, John Publishing, Ltd. GBR. Dist: Independent Pubs. Group.

—Young Gun: The Biography of Cesc Fabregas. 2009. (ENG., Illus.). 260p. 29.95 *(978-1-84454-642-8(X))* Blake, John Publishing, Ltd. GBR. Dist: Independent Pubs. Group.

Spurling, Jon. Highbury: The Story of Arsenal in N5. 2007. (ENG., Illus.). 368p. pap. 32.95 *(978-0-7528-7639-9(2))* Orion Publishing Group, Ltd. GBR. Dist: Independent Pubs. Group.

Whitcher, Kevin. The Pocket Book of Arsenal. 2nd rev. ed. 2010. (ENG., Illus.). 160p. 14.95 ***(978-1-905326-92-1(0))*** Vision Sports Publishing GBR. Dist: SCB Distributors.

Williams, Andy. Robin Van Persie. 2011. (ENG., Illus.). 262p. 24.95 ***(978-1-84358-376-9(3))*** Blake, John Publishing, Ltd. GBR. Dist: Independent Pubs. Group.

ARSENALS

see also Military Museums

Committee on Risk-Based Approaches for Securing the DOE Nuclear Weapons Complex & National Research Council. Understanding & Managing Risk in Security Systems for the DOE Nuclear Weapons Complex. 2011. (ENG.). 300p. pap. 15.00 *(978-0-309-20884-0(X))* National Academies Pr.

Iversen, Kristen. Full Body Burden: Growing up in the Nuclear Shadow of Rocky Flats. 2012. (ENG., Illus.). 416p. 25.00 ***(978-0-307-95563-0(X)***, Crown) Crown Publishing Group.

Kraemer, Robin A. U. S. Nuclear Stockpile: Maintenance & Replacement of Warheads. 2009. (Defense, Security & Strategies Ser.). 79.00 *(978-1-60741-483-4(X))* Nova Science Pubs., Inc.

Krause, H., ed. Conversion Concepts for Commercial Application & Disposal Technologies of Energetic Systems. 2011. (NATO Science Partnership Sub-Series: 1: Ser.). (ENG.). 292p. pap. 289.00 *(978-90-481-4880-6(4)*, 9048148804) Springer.

Schulte, N., ed. Dismantlement & Destruction of Chemical, Nuclear & Conventional Weapons. 2010. (NATO Science Partnership Sub-Series: 1: Ser.). 260p. pap. 219.00 *(978-90-481-4817-2(0)*, 9048148170) Springer.

ARSENIC

Ashfaque, Khandaker. Arsenic Mobilization in Groundwater. 2009. 248p. pap. *(978-3-639-10102-7(2))* VDM Verlag Dr. Mueller e.K.

Borsanyi, Matyas. Best Practice Guide on the Control of Arsenic in Drinking Water. 2013. (Best Practice Guides on Metals & Related Substances in Drinking Water Ser.). 120p. (C). pap. *(978-1-84339-385-6(9))* IWA Publishing.

Bundschuh, Jochen, et al, eds. Natural Arsenic in Groundwaters of Latin America. 2008. (Arsenic in the Environment Ser.). (ENG., Illus.). 782p. 219.95 *(978-0-415-40771-7(0)*, Taylor & Francis) Taylor & Francis Group GBR. Dist: Taylor & Francis Group.

Bundschuh, Jochen & Hollander, Hartmunt, eds. In-Situ Remediation of Arsenic-Contaminated Sites. 2012. (Arsenic in the Environment Ser.). (ENG.). 350p. (C). 129.95 ***(978-0-415-62085-7(6)***, CRC Press) Taylor & Francis Group GBR. Dist: Taylor & Francis Group.

Bunnett, J. F. & Mikolajczyk, Marian, eds. Arsenic & Old Mustard: Chemical Problems in the Destruction of Old Arsenical & 'Mustard' Munitions: Chemical Problems in the Destruction of Old Arsenical & 'Mustard' Munitions. 2010. (NATO Science Partnership Sub-Series: 1: Ser.). 224p. pap. 160.00 *(978-90-481-5069-4(8)*, 9048150698) Springer.

Gosselin, Jack D. & Fancher, Ike M. Environmental Health Risks: Lead Poisoning & Arsenic Exposure. 2009. (Environmental Health - Physical, Chemical & Biological Factors Ser.). 129.00 *(978-1-60741-781-1(2))* Nova Science Pubs., Inc.

Henke, Kevin, et al. Arsenic: Environmental Chemistry, Health Threats & Waste Treatment. 2009. (ENG., Illus.). 588p. 210.00 *(978-0-470-02758-5(4)*, Wiley) Wiley, John & Sons, Inc.

Hung-Yi & Chen, Chien-Jen. Health Hazards of Environmental Arsenic Poisoning: From Epidemic to Pandemic. 2010. (Illus.). 350p. 124.00 *(978-981-4291-81-1(1))* World Scientific Publishing Co., Inc.

Jahn, Thomas P. & Bienert, Gerd P., eds. MIPs & Their Roles in the Exchange of Metalloids. 2010. (Advances in Experimental Medicine & Biology Ser.). (ENG., Illus.). xvi, 146p. 159.00 *(978-1-4419-6314-7(6)*, 1441963146) Springer.

Jean, Jiin-Shuh, et al, eds. Arsenic 2010: Proceedings of the Third International Congress on Arsenic in the Environment. 2010. (ENG.). 652p. 179.95 *(978-0-415-57898-1(1)*, CRC Press) Taylor & Francis Group GBR. Dist: Taylor & Francis Group.

Jean, Jiin-Shuh, et al. The Taiwan Crisis: A Showcase of the Global Arsenic Problem. 2010. (Arsenic in the Environment Ser.). (ENG., Illus.). 234p. 89.95 *(978-0-415-58510-1(4)*, CRC Press) Taylor & Francis Group GBR. Dist: Taylor & Francis Group.

Latif, Muhammad & Mahmood, Sajid. Arsenic: Dangerous & harmful for Health. 2010. 104p. pap. *(978-3-639-25133-3(4))* VDM Verlag Dr. Mueller e.K.

M Khan, Bayezid, et al. Environmental Biology. 2011. 128p. pap. ***(978-3-8443-1364-2(8))*** Lambert Academic Publishing.

Matschullat, Jörg, ed. Arsenic - Natural & Anthropogenic. 2011. (Arsenic in the Environment Ser.). (ENG.). 238p. 129.95 *(978-0-415-54928-8(0)*, CRC Press) Taylor & Francis Group GBR. Dist: Taylor & Francis Group.

Pal, Priyabrata. Detection & Removal of Heavy Metal Ions & Removal Using Packed Bed. 2011. 200p. pap. ***(978-3-8443-2533-1(6))*** Lambert Academic Publishing.

Phan, Kongkea & Kim, Kyoung-Woong. Arsenic & Trace Element Calamities in Cambodi. 2011. 56p. pap. ***(978-3-8383-2371-8(8))*** Lambert Academic Publishing.

Ranjan, Deeksha & S. H. Hasan. Biosorptive Remediation of Arsenic & Selenium. 2011. 272p. pap. ***(978-3-8443-3199-8(9))*** Lambert Academic Publishing.

Ravenscroft, Peter, et al. Arsenic Pollution: A Global Synthesis. 2009. (RGS-IBG Book Ser.: 26). (ENG., Illus.). 616p. pap. 69.95 *(978-1-4051-8601-8(1))*; 129.95 *(978-1-4051-8602-5(X))* Wiley, John & Sons, Inc. (Wiley-Blackwell).

Ray, Sajal & SAHA, Sanjib. Arsenic Toxicity in Estuarine Mudcrab. 2011. 188p. pap. ***(978-3-8443-3035-9(6))*** Lambert Academic Publishing.

Santini, Joanna M. & Ward, Seamus A., eds. The Metabolism of Arsenite. 2012. (Arsenic in the Environment Ser.). (ENG., Illus.). 218p. 119.95 ***(978-0-415-69719-4(0)***, CRC Press) Taylor & Francis Group GBR. Dist: Taylor & Francis Group.

Shams, Shahriar. Arsenic Evaluation & Mitigation Using Gis & Expert System. 2011. 76p. pap. ***(978-3-8443-0636-1(6))*** Lambert Academic Publishing.

Singh, Sushant. Arsenic Contamination in Water, Soil, & Food Materials in Bihar. 2011. 260p. pap. ***(978-3-8443-2099-2(7))*** Lambert Academic Publishing.

Sorlini, Sabrina & COLLIVIGNARELLI, Carlo. Arsenic in Water for Human Consumption. 2011. 144p. pap. ***(978-3-8443-9597-6(0))*** Lambert Academic Publishing.

Sun, Hongzhe, ed. Biological Chemistry of Arsenic, Antimony & Bismuth. 2011. (ENG., Illus.). 400p. 175.00 *(978-0-470-71390-7(9)*, Wiley) Wiley, John & Sons, Inc.

Technical Learning College, compiled by. TLC's Arsenic CEU Training Course. 2007. 175p. *(978-0-9799928-4-1(2))* Technical Learning College.

Thomas, Mary Ann. Relation Between Solid-Phase & Dissolved Arsenic in the Ground-Water System Underlying Northern Preble County, Ohio. 2008. (Illus.). iv, 56p. pap. *(978-1-4113-2322-3(X))* United States Geological Survey.

Tran, Trung Kien & Ross, William. Arsenic Contamination Awareness of Residents in the Hanoi Area,Vietnam. 2010. 128p. pap. *(978-3-639-28462-1(3))* VDM Verlag Dr. Mueller e.K.

Whorton, James C. The Arsenic Century: How Victorian Britain was Poisoned at Home, Work, & Play. 2010. (ENG., Illus.). 424p. 29.95 *(978-0-19-957470-4(7))* Oxford Univ. Pr., Inc.

Whorton, James C. The Arsenic Century: How Victorian Britain Was Poisoned at Home, Work, & Play. 2011. (ENG., Illus.). 440p. pap. 18.95 ***(978-0-19-960599-6(8))*** Oxford Univ. Pr., Inc.

ARSENIC POISONING

Ahuja, Satinder. Arsenic Contamination of Groundwater: Mechanism, Analysis, & Remediation. 2008. (ENG., Illus.). 404p. 178.00 *(978-0-470-14447-3(5)*, Wiley-Interscience) Wiley, John & Sons, Inc.

Bharti, Virendra Kumar & Mills, Shirley. Cancer, Arsenic, Mortality & Their Relationship. 2010. 76p. pap. *(978-3-8383-1974-2(5))* Lambert Academic Publishing.

Cullen, William R. Is Arsenic an Aphrodisiac? The Sociochemistry of an Element. 2008. (ENG., Illus.). 428p. 107.00 *(978-0-85404-363-7(2))* Royal Society of Chemistry, The GBR. Dist: Ingram Pub. Services.

Gosselin, Jack D. & Fancher, Ike M. Environmental Health Risks: Lead Poisoning & Arsenic Exposure. 2009. (Environmental Health - Physical, Chemical & Biological Factors Ser.). 129.00 *(978-1-60741-781-1(2))* Nova Science Pubs., Inc.

Lamb, Amanda. Deadly Dose: The Untold Story of a Homicide Investigator's Crusade for Truth & Justice. 2008. (ENG., Illus.). 304p. (gr. 12-18). 7.99 *(978-0-425-22196-9(2)*, Berkley) Penguin Group (USA) Inc.

Meliker, Jaymie R. Lifetime Exposure to Arsenic in Drinking Water- Application to a Bladder Cancer Case-Control Study. 2007. 332p. per. *(978-3-8364-2942-9(X))* VDM Verlag Dr. Mueller e.K.

Moldovan, Brett J. & Henry, M. Jim. Fate & Transport of Arsenic in Uranium Mine Tailings. 2008. 200p. pap. *(978-3-639-00524-0(4))* VDM Verlag Dr. Mueller e.K.

Yu, Guangqian. Arsenic in China: Occurrence & Health Effects: A Reprint from the Journal, ¿Environmental Health Perspectives¿. 2007. (Illus.). 26p. (C). pap. 15.00 *(978-1-4223-1454-8(5))* DIANE Publishing Co.

ARSON

Decker, John F. & Ottley, Bruce L. Arson Law & Prosecution. 2009. 596p. 73.00 *(978-1-59460-590-1(4))* Carolina Academic Pr.

Dickens, Geoffrey L., et al, eds. Firesetting & Mental Health: Theory, Research & Practice. 2012. 288p. pap. 70.00 ***(978-1-908020-37-6(7))*** Royal College of Psychiatrists GBR. Dist: Turpin Distribution Services Ltd.

Doley, Rebekah M. A Snapshot of Serial Arson in Australi. 2010. 164p. pap. *(978-3-8383-1128-9(0))* Lambert Academic Publishing.

Dooley, Terence. The Murders at Wildgoose Lodge. 2007. (Illus.). 285p. 55.00 *(978-1-84682-085-4(5))* Four Courts Pr. IRL. Dist: International Specialized Bk. Services.

Fisher, Robin Gaby. After the Fire: A True Story of Friendship & Survival. 2010. (ENG.). 288p. pap. 14.99 *(978-0-316-06622-8(2)*, Back Bay Bks.) Little Brown & Co.

Harmon, Daniel E. Careers in Explosives & Arson Investigation. 2008. (Careers in Forensics Ser.). (Illus.). 64p. (J). (gr. 4-7). lib. bdg. 29.25 *(978-1-4042-1346-3(5)*, Rosen Central) Rosen Publishing Group, Inc., The.

Kapusinski, George T. The Hulett Hotel Fire on Lake George. 2012. 128p. pap. 19.99 ***(978-1-60949-261-8(7))*** History Pr., The.

Langdon, Grant Dinehart. Scandal in the Courtroom Vol. 1: Found Guilty Without Trial. 2007. (Illus.). 116p. per. 16.95 *(978-0-9790860-0-7(0))* Langdon, Grant Dinehart.

Massey, Don, ed. & compiled by. Circus Fire Memories: Survivor Recollections of July 6 1944. 2006. (Illus.). 178p. per. 10.00 *(978-1-930601-22-2(0))* Willow Brook Pr.

Mellon & Chandler, Russell. Fire & Arson Investigation. 2009. (ENG.). 560p. (C). pap. 91.95 *(978-1-4180-0960-1(1))* Delmar Cengage Learning.

Redsicker, David R. Practical Fire & Arson Investigation. 3rd ed. 2009. (Illus.). 576p. 99.95 *(978-0-8493-2133-7(6))* CRC Pr. LLC.

Strain, Christopher B. Burning Faith: Church Arson in the American South. 2008. (Southern Dissent Ser.). (ENG., Illus.). 224p. 34.95 *(978-0-8130-3239-9(3))* Univ. Pr. of Florida.

Wells, Jon. Heat: A Firefighter's Story. 2006. (ENG., Illus.). 256p. pap. *(978-1-55028-928-2(4))* Lorimer, James & Co., Ltd., Pubs. CAN. Dist: Casemate Pubs. & Bk. Distributors, LLC.

ART

Here are entered general works on the visual arts. Works on the arts in general, including the visual arts, literature, and the performing arts are entered under Arts.

see also Aesthetics; Anatomy, Artistic; Animal Painting and Illustration; Antiques; Architecture; Art Nouveau; Art Objects; Artists; Arts and Crafts Movement; Bronzes; Caricature; Christian Art and Symbolism; Classicism in Art; Collage; Collectors and Collecting; Color in Art; Commercial Art; Communism and Art; Composition (Art); Costume; Creation (Literary, Artistic, etc.); Cubism; Decoration and Ornament; Design, Decorative; Drawing; Erotic Art; Etching; Ethnic Art; Expressionism (Art); Feminism and Art; Folk Art; Futurism (Art); Glass Art; Graphic Arts; Homosexuality and Art; Human Figure in Art; Idealism in Art; Illumination of Books and Manuscripts; Illustration of Books; Indian Art; Influence (Literary, Artistic, etc.); Interior Decoration; Law and Art; Line (Art); Mannerism (Art); Marine Art; Mass Media and Art; Medicine and Art; Mosaics; Mural Painting and Decoration; Music in Art; Naturalism in Art; Painting; Photography, Artistic; Photography of Art; Pictures; Portraits; Posters; Primitivism in Art

also subdivision Art under special headings, e.g. Jesus Christ—Art; also Animals in Art; Birds in Art; Nude in Art; Sea in Art, and similar headings

Adams, Henry. Viktor Schreckengost: American Davinci. Morton, Sunny McClellan, ed. 2006. (Illus.). 213p. pap. 34.95 *(978-1-59490-220-8(8))* Tide-Mark Pr., Ltd.

Adamson, Glenn. Thinking Through Craft. 2007. (ENG., Illus.). 224p. pap. 29.95 *(978-1-84520-647-5(9))* Berg Pubs. GBR. Dist: Macmillan.

Aguilera, Steven. A New Perspective #8213; Universal Edition. 2008. 188p. pap. 29.95 *(978-0-578-00038-1(5))* Artistech Bks.

Allen, Felicity. Your Sketchbook, Your Self. 2011. (ENG., Illus.). 48p. pap. 12.95 *(978-1-85437-969-6(0))* Tate Publishing, Ltd. GBR. Dist: Hachette Bk. Group.

Allston, Washington. Lectures on Art. 2008. 172p. 25.99 *(978-0-554-23560-8(9))* 2008. 172p. 22.99 *(978-0-554-32863-8(1))* 2006. 154p. pap. 19.99 *(978-1-4264-4677-1(2))* 2007. (ENG.). 170p. pap. 21.99 *(978-1-4264-4708-2(6))* BiblioBazaar.

—Lectures on Art, & Poems, by Washington Allston Ed by Richard Henry Dana, Jr. 2006. 396p. per. 26.99 *(978-1-4255-4175-0(5))* MPublishing.

Anderson, Isaac, et al. Mixed Media Workshop: A multifaceted approach to creating unique works of art-step by Step. 2012. (ENG., Illus.). 144p. 19.95 *(978-1-60058-238-7(9),* 1600582389) Foster, Walter Publishing, Inc.

Annerino, John. The Virgin of Guadalupe: Art & Legend. 2012. (ENG., Illus.). 112p. 21.99 ***(978-1-4236-2471-4(8))*** Gibbs Smith, Publisher.

Appel, Rosaire. Morpheme Pages. 2009. 68p. pap. 11.97 *(978-0-557-03591-5(0))* Lulu Enterprises Inc.

Art & Architecture, Set. 2008. 342p. 200.00 *(978-0-415-46403-1(X))* Routledge.

Ashbee, Charles Robert. Where the Great City Stands. 2008. 256p. pap. *(978-1-905217-96-0(X))* Mills, Jeremy Publishing.

Asher, Frederick M. & Beaven, Lisa. The Art Museum. Phaidon Press Editors, ed. 2011. (ENG., Illus.). 992p. 200.00 ***(978-0-7148-5652-0(5))*** Phaidon Pr., Inc.

Baillio, Joseph. "A Hermit in the Garden" - Hubert Robert (1733-1808) A New Acquisition for the Speed Art Museum. (Illus.). 32p. pap. 7.95 *(978-0-9612276-3-0(X))* Speed, J. B. Art Museum.

Bal, Mieke & Hernández-Navarro, Miguel Á, eds. Art & Visibility in Migratory Culture: Conflict, Resistance, & Agency. 2012. (Illus.). 345p. pap. 93.00 ***(978-90-420-3263-7(4))*** Rodopi.

Balmond, Cecil. Element. 2007. (Illus.). 288p. 45.00 *(978-3-7913-3778-4(5))* Prestel Publishing.

Bean, Joseph W., compiled by. Fetish & Fetters: A Selection of Art Work by the Hun. 2006. (Illus.). 80p. per. 19.95 *(978-1-887895-35-4(3))* Nazca Plains Corp., The.

Beever, Julian. Pavement Chalk Artist: The Three-Dimensional Drawings of Julian Beever. 2nd enl. ed. 2012. (ENG., Illus.). 128p. 29.95 ***(978-1-77085-159-7(3))*** Firefly Bks., Ltd.

Behind the Curtains. 2007. *(978-0-9771990-1-3(0))* Big Kid Bks.

Bell, Clive. Since Cezanne. 2009. 256p. 24.99 *(978-1-103-49592-4(5))* 2009. 256p. pap. 18.99 *(978-1-103-49590-0(9))* 2008. 164p. 22.99 *(978-0-554-33935-1(8))* 2008. 164p. 25.99 *(978-0-554-24632-1(5))* BiblioBazaar.

—Since Cezanne. 2008. 254p. 42.95 *(978-1-4372-2162-6(9))*; pap. 27.95 *(978-1-4370-9277-6(2))* Kessinger Publishing, LLC.

—Since Cézanne. 2006. (ENG.). 146p. pap. 18.99 *(978-1-4264-7025-7(8))*; 160p. pap. 21.99 *(978-1-4264-7101-8(7))* BiblioBazaar.

Bennett, Audrey Grace. Engendering Interaction with Images. 2012. (ENG., Illus.). 96p. pap. 40.00 *(978-1-84150-481-0(5))* Intellect, Ltd. GBR. Dist: Chicago Distribution Ctr.

Beta Tank. Taxing Art: When Objects Travel. 2011. (Illus.). 160p. pap. *(978-3-89955-346-8(2))* Die Gestalten Verlag.

Brusen, Claus. Imaginaire II: Magic Realism. 2012. (FRE & ENG., Illus.). 176p. 49.95 *(978-87-992147-4-7(1))* Fantasmus-Art DNK. Dist: Independent Pubs. Group.

Brykina, Nadja, ed. Yuri Zltonikov: Monograph. 2011. (Illus.). 256p. ***(978-3-9523522-0-5(9))*** Brykina, Nadja Gallery AG.

Buikema, Rosemarie & Tuin, Iris van der. Doing Gender in Media, Art & Culture. 2009. (ENG., Illus.). 304p. (C). 160.00 *(978-0-415-49382-6(X))* Routledge.

—Doing Gender in Media, Art & Culture. Buikema, Rosemarie & Van Der Tuin, Iris, eds. 2009. (ENG., Illus.). 304p. (C). pap. 46.95 *(978-0-415-49383-3(8))* Routledge.

Carman, Bliss. The Friendship of Art. 2008. 324p. 28.99 *(978-0-559-76147-8(3))*; pap. 29.75 *(978-0-559-76145-4(7))* BiblioBazaar.

—The Friendship of Art. 2009. 56p. pap. *(978-0-217-62622-4(X))* Books LLC.

—The Friendship of Art. 2009. 128p. pap. 14.14 *(978-1-4589-1620-4(0))*; 138p. pap. 14.14 *(978-0-217-38597-8(4))* General Bks. LLC.

—The Friendship of Art. 2007. (ENG.). 320p. 45.95 *(978-0-548-03712-6(4))* Kessinger Publishing, LLC.

Carter, David E. Creativity 38. 2009. (ENG., Illus.). 400p. 55.00 *(978-0-06-180833-3(4),* Collins Design) HarperCollins Pubs.

Chen, Hongshou & Lu, Minghua. Shu, Hua, Yin, Hu: Chen Hongshou de Yi Shu. (CHI & ENG., Illus.). 313p. 46.00 *(978-962-7101-74-1(5))* Art Media Resources, Inc.

Cheney, Sheldon. Expressionism in Art. 2007. (ENG.). 440p. per. *(978-1-4067-0455-6(5))* Read Bks.

Cherry, Deborah, ed. About Mieke Bal. 2008. (Art History Special Issues Ser.). (ENG., Illus.). 200p. pap. 39.95 *(978-1-4051-8656-6(9),* Wiley-Blackwell) Wiley, John & Sons, Inc.

Chorpenning, Joseph F., ed. Human Encounter in the Salesian Tradition: Collected Essays Commemorating the 4th Centenary of the Initial Encounter of St. Francis de Sales & St. Jane Frances de Chantal. 2007. (FRE., Illus.). 426p. 35.00 *(978-0-9800371-0-4(7))* Oblates of St. Francis de Sales, Inc.

Clark Keefe, Kelly. Invoking Mnemosyne: Art, Memory, & the Uncertain Emergence of a Feminist Embodied Methodology. 2010. 112p. *(978-94-6091-230-6(3))*; pap. *(978-94-6091-229-0(X))* Sense Pubs.

Clave, Antoni, photos by. Antoni Clave: A World of Art. 2010. (ENG & SPA., Illus.). 320p. pap. 35.00 *(978-84-7506-906-7(1))* Turner, Ediciones S.A. ESP. Dist: D.A.P./Distributed Art Pubs.

Clement, Page. Principles & Practice in Art. Date not set. (Illus.). 128p. pap. *(978-0-05-005082-8(6))* Addison-Wesley Longman, Inc.

Clutton-Brock, A. Essays on Art. 2007. (ENG.). 84p. per. *(978-1-4068-4641-6(4))* Echo Library.

Clutton-Brock, Arthur. Essays on Art. 2007. (ENG.). 88p. per. 16.99 *(978-1-4346-9541-3(7))*; 100p. per. 18.99 *(978-1-4346-9542-0(5))* BiblioBazaar.

Cohn, Marjorie B., et al. Dear Print Fan: A Festschrift for Marjorie B. Cohn. Bowen, Craigen W. & Dackerman, Susan, eds. 2006. (ENG., Illus.). 334p. 65.00 *(978-1-891771-21-7(3),* Harvard Art Museum (Acc)) Antique Collectors' Club GBR. Dist: National Bk. Network.

Connery, M. Cathrene, et al. Dancing with the Muses: A Cultural-Historical Activity Theory (CHAT) Approch to Play, Meaning-Making, & Creativity. 2010. (Educational Psychology: Critical Pedagogical Perspectives Ser.). 256p. (C). 119.95 *(978-1-4331-0706-1(6))*; pap. 34.95 *(978-1-4331-0705-4(8))*, Lang, Peter Publishing, Inc.

Coomaraswamy, Ananda Kentish. Figures of Speech or Figures of Thought? The Traditional View of Art. Wroth, William, ed. 2007. (Perennial Philosophy Ser.). (ENG., Illus.). 288p. per. 24.95 *(978-1-933316-34-5(9))* World Wisdom, Inc.

Coomaraswamy, Ananda Kentish. Why Exhibit Works of Art. 2011. 146p. 40.95 ***(978-1-258-04328-5(9))*** Literary Licensing, LLC.

Cortissoz, Royal. Personalities in Art. 2007. 492p. per. *(978-1-4067-4439-5(7))* Read Bks.

Costache, Irina D. The Art of Understanding Art. 2012. (ENG.). 280p. pap. 39.95 ***(978-0-470-65834-5(7),*** Wiley-Blackwell) Wiley, John & Sons, Inc.

Coverey, P. & Highfield, R. The Secret Art: Beyond Chaos. Date not set. pap. *(978-0-449-90833-4(X),* Fawcett) Random House Publishing Group.

Cox, Kenyon. Artist & Public & Other Essays on Art Subjects. 2008. (Illus.). 116p. pap. *(978-1-4099-4225-2(2))* Dodo Pr.

—Artist & Public & Other Essays on Art Subjects. 2008. (Illus.). 84p. pap. *(978-1-4068-2557-2(3))* Echo Library.

—Painters & Sculptors. 2009. 122p. pap. *(978-0-217-88286-6(2))* Books LLC.

Cram101 Textbook Reviews. Outlines & Highlights for Shaping Space by Zelanski & Fisher. 2011. 202p. pap. 30.95 ***(978-1-61812-884-3(1))*** Cram101 Inc.

Crane, Lucy. Art & the Formation of Taste. 2009. 324p. 25.99 *(978-1-103-29026-0(6))*; pap. 19.99 *(978-1-103-29023-9(1))* BiblioBazaar.

—Art & the Formation of Taste. 2009. 94p. pap. 14.14 *(978-1-151-59185-2(8))* General Bks. LLC.

Cropper, Elizabeth, ed. Dialogues in Art History, from Mesopotamian to Modern: Readings for a New Century. 2009. (Studies in the History of Art Ser.). (ENG., Illus.). 424p. 70.00 *(978-0-300-12162-9(8))* National Gallery of Art.

Crow, David. Left to Right: The Cultural Shift from Words to Pictures. 2006. (Required Reading Range Ser.). (ENG., Illus.). 192p. pap. 39.95 *(978-2-940373-36-9(1))* AVA Publishing GBR. Dist: Ingram Pub. Services.

Damiani, Luca. Kirimatuli: Art, Design & Subconscious. 2010. (Illus.). 80p. pap. *(978-1-85756-705-2(6))* Janus Publishing Co.

De Lucia, Joseph. More artwork done in Paint. 2010. 47p. pap. 49.98 *(978-0-557-49812-3(0))* Lulu Enterprises Inc.

De Montherlant, Henry. Chant de Mimos, Pasiphae. (Col. Las Peintres du Livre). (FRE., Illus.). 39.95 *(978-0-8288-9635-1(6),* F115610) French & European Pubns., Inc.

Delaunay, Sonia. Color Moves: Art & Fashion by Sonia Delaunay. 2011. (ENG., Illus.). 200p. pap. 35.00 *(978-0-910503-84-6(2))* Cooper-Hewitt Museum.

Dessanay, Margherita & Valli, Marc. Microworlds. 2011. (ENG., Illus.). 144p. pap. 19.95 ***(978-1-85669-787-3(8))*** King, Laurence Publishing GBR. Dist: Hachette Bk. Group.

DeWitte, Debra J., et al. Gateways to Art: An Introduction to the Visual Arts. 2011. (ENG., Illus.). 630p. (C). spiral bd. pap. 95.00 net. ***(978-0-500-28956-3(5),*** 523956) Thames & Hudson.

Doering, Deborah Adams. 360: Deborah Adams Doering. 2009. (Illus.). 48p. pap. 30.00 *(978-0-615-31977-3(7))* Aestus Bivium Co.

Donahue, M. Patricia. Nursing, the Finest Art: An Illustrated History. 3rd ed. 2010. (ENG.). 416p. 59.95 *(978-0-323-05305-1(X),* Mosby) Elsevier - Health Sciences Div.

Drayton, Cynthia A. JFK & Art. 2006. (Illus.). 128p. 35.00 *(978-0-7112-2342-4(4))* Lincoln, Frances Ltd. GBR. Dist: Perseus-PGW.

Du Bois, Henri Pene. French Folly in Maxims of Art. 2006. pap. 22.95 *(978-1-4286-4627-8(2))* Kessinger Publishing, LLC.

Du Bois, Henri Pene, tr. French Folly in Maxims of Art. 2007. (ENG.). 184p. 37.95 *(978-0-548-13516-7(9))* Kessinger Publishing, LLC.

Ecker, Berthold, ed. Die sechziger Jahre: Eine phantastische Moderne The 1960s: A Fantastic Modernism. 2011. (ENG & GER.). 550p. 49.95 ***(978-3-7091-0743-0(1))*** Springer Wien AUT. Dist: Actar Birkhauser Distribution.

Eisenstein, Sergei. Towards a Theory of Montage Vol. 2, 3 vols., Vol. 2. Taylor, Richard, ed. Glenny, Michael, tr. from RUS. 2010. (ENG., Illus.). 448p. pap. 35.00 *(978-1-84885-356-0(4))* I. B. Tauris & Co., Ltd. GBR. Dist: Macmillan.

—Writings, 1922-1934 Vol. 1: Sergei Eisenstein Selected Works, 3 vols. Taylor, Richard, ed. 2010. (ENG., Illus.). 344p. pap. 35.00 *(978-1-84885-355-3(6))* I. B. Tauris & Co., Ltd. GBR. Dist: Macmillan.

Eisenstein, Sergei M. Sergei Eisenstein Selected Works, 3 vols. Taylor, Richard, ed. 2011. (ENG., Illus.). 344p. pap. 85.00 *(978-1-84885-358-4(0))* I. B. Tauris & Co., Ltd. GBR. Dist: Macmillan.

—Writings, 1934-1947 Vol. 3: Sergei Eisenstein Selected Works, 3 vols. Taylor, Richard, ed. Powell, William, tr. from RUS. 2010. (ENG., Illus.). 384p. pap. 35.00 *(978-1-84885-357-7(2))* I. B. Tauris & Co., Ltd. GBR. Dist: Macmillan.

Elbaz, Lorenzo. Mediterranean Graphicity. Minguet, Josep Maria, ed. 2011. (ENG & SPA., Illus.). 192p. pap. 62.50 ***(978-84-15223-15-3(3))*** Instituto Monsa de Ediciones, S.A. ESP. Dist: Trans-Atlantic Pubns., Inc.

Eld, Wendy. A Mouse's Guide to Childhood. 2008. (ENG.). (J). 24.95 ***(978-0-9821821-0-9(4))*** Crazy Over Animals.

Emmer, M. The Visual Mind II. 2006. (Leonardo Bks.). (ENG., Illus.). 712p. (gr. 17). per. 28.00 *(978-0-262-55063-5(6))* MIT Pr.

European Comm. Art & Scientific Research Are Free: Towards a Culture of Life. (Illus.). 96p. pap. 42.00 *(978-88-7778-102-4(5))* SEMAR ITA. Dist: SPD-Small Pr. Distribution.

Falconer, Morgan. The Art Lovers' Guide - New York: The Finest Art in New York by Museum, Artist, or Period. 2011. (Illus.). 240p. pap. 19.95 *(978-0-8478-3627-7(4),* Skira) Rizzoli International Pubns., Inc.

Fallah, Amir H. Beautiful/Decay: Class Clowns. 2012. (ENG.). 164p. pap. 20.00 *(978-0-9824745-6-3(3))* Beautiful/Decay.

—Beautiful/Decay: Future Perfect. 2011. (ENG.). 164p. pap. 20.00 *(978-0-9824745-5-5(5))* Beautiful/Decay.

Fallah, Amir H., compiled by. Beautiful/Decay: Psychonauts. 2011. (ENG.). 164p. pap. 20.00 ***(978-0-9824745-4-9(7))*** Beautiful/Decay.

Farameh, Patrice. Gowest! Cutting Edge Creatives in the United States. 2011. (ENG.). 312p. 75.00 *(978-3-942597-13-5(6))* DAAB Media Gmbh DEU. Dist: Innovative Logistics.

—New on the Catwalk: Emerging Fashion Labels. 2011. (ENG., Illus.). 400p. 95.00 *(978-3-942597-15-9(2))* DAAB Media Gmbh DEU. Dist: Innovative Logistics.

—Skull Style: Skulls in Contemporary Art & Design - Metallic Black. 2011. (ENG., Illus.). 496p. 125.00 *(978-0-9830831-3-9(4))* Curated Collection, The.

Featured Artists, Vol. 1. 2010. (Illus.). 96p. *(978-960-98774-1-9(9))* Katik Niki-Mediaplan Publishing.

Fichner-Rathus, Lois. Foundations of Art & Design: An Enhanced Media Edition. 2011. (ENG.). 360p. (C). spiral bd. 103.95 *(978-1-111-83026-7(6))* Wadsworth.

Fick, Bill. Black Book. 2010. 104p. pap. 12.95 *(978-0-557-51607-0(2))* Lulu Enterprises Inc.

Finsterwalder, Rudolf, ed. Form Follows Nature: Eine Geschichte der Natur als Vorbild für Formgebung in Ingenieurbau, Architektur und Kunst - A History of Nature as Model for Design in Engineering, Architecture & Art. 2011. (GER & ENG., Illus.). 512p. 89.95 *(978-3-7091-0855-0(1),* 3709108551) Springer Wien AUT. Dist: Springer.

Fliedl, Konstanze, et al, eds. Handbuch der Kunstzitate. 2 Bände: Malerei, Skulptur, Fotografie in der Deutschsprachigen Literatur der Moderne, 2 vols. 2011. (GER., Illus.). XXII, 966p. 419.00 ***(978-3-11-020500-8(9))*** De Gruyter, Walter Inc.

Foster, Hal. The Art-Architecture Complex. 2011. (ENG., Illus.). 316p. 26.95 *(978-1-84467-689-7(7),* 844689) Verso Bks. GBR. Dist: Norton, W. W. & Co., Inc.

Foster, Walter T. The Influence of Bones & Muscles on Form. 2012. (Dover Anatomy for Artists Ser.). (ENG., Illus.). 64p. pap. 9.95 ***(978-0-486-48285-9(5))*** Dover Pubns., Inc.

Frantz, Marc & Crannell, Annalisa. Viewpoints: Mathematical Perspective & Fractal Geometry in Art. 2011. (Illus.). xi, 232p. *(978-0-691-15091-8(5))*; (ENG., 258p. (C). 45.00 *(978-0-691-12592-3(9))* Princeton Univ. Pr.

Freeman-Zachery, Rice. Living the Creative Life: Ideas & Inspirations from Working Artists. 2007. (ENG., Illus.). 144p. per. 22.99 *(978-1-58180-994-7(8))* F&W Media, Inc.

Friedrichs, Arnd & Finger, Kerstin, eds. 220°C Virus Monobloc. 2010. (Illus.). 224p. pap. *(978-3-89955-317-8(9))* Die Gestalten Verlag.

Gallagher, David, ed. World Cinema & the Visual Arts. 2012. (New Perspectives on World Cinema Ser.). (ENG., Illus.). 202p. 99.00 ***(978-0-85728-438-9(X))*** Anthem Pr. GBR. Dist: Books International Inc.

Gallatin, A. E., ed. Of Art: Plato to Picasso, Aphorisms & Observations. 2011. 70p. 36.95 ***(978-1-258-03153-4(1))*** Literary Licensing, LLC.

Gansterer, Nikolaus. Drawing a Hypothesis: Figures of Thought. 2011. (Edition Angewandte Ser.). (ENG., Illus.). 352p. pap. 59.95 *(978-3-7091-0802-4(0),* 3709108020) Springer Wien AUT. Dist: Springer.

Gardner, Sarah. Art Beyond the Lens: Working with Digital Textures. 2012. (ENG.). 192p. pap. 34.95 ***(978-0-240-82409-3(1),*** Focal Pr.) Elsevier Science & Technology Bks.

Gaultier, Paul. The Meaning of Art: Its Nature, Role & Value. 2007. (ENG.). 304p. 43.95 *(978-0-548-04337-0(X))* Kessinger Publishing, LLC.

Gaut, Berys. Art, Emotion & Ethics. 2009. (ENG.). 288p. pap. 37.95 *(978-0-19-957152-9(X))* Oxford Univ. Pr., Inc.

George, Waldemar. Formes, 6 vols., Vol. 1. (Contemporary Art Ser.). (Illus.). reprint ed. 253.95 *(978-0-405-00727-9(2))* Ayer Co. Pubs., Inc.

Glowacka, Dorota. Disappearing Traces: Holocaust Testimonials, Ethics, & Aesthetics, 1 vol. 2012. (ENG., Illus.). 304p. (C). pap. 30.00 ***(978-0-295-99169-6(0))***; 70.00 ***(978-0-295-99168-9(2))*** Univ. of Washington Pr.

Golten, Lionel. Art & the Unconscious. 2007. (ENG.). 188p. 37.95 *(978-0-548-05798-8(2))* Kessinger Publishing, LLC.

Goldin, Amy. Amy Goldin: Art in a Hairshirt Art Criticism, 1964-1978. Kushner, Robert, ed. 2012. (ENG., Illus.). 220p. pap. 19.95 ***(978-1-55595-342-3(5))*** Hudson Hills Pr. LLC.

Goldman, Paul. Looking at Prints, Drawings & Watercolours: A Guide to Technical Terms. 2nd rev. ed. 2006. (Illus.). 72p. pap. 18.95 *(978-0-89236-871-6(3))* Oxford Univ. Pr., Inc.

Goldstein, Harriet. Art in Every Day Life. 2007. (ENG.). 508p. per. *(978-1-4067-5290-8(8))* Read Bks.

Gutierrez & Portefaix, text. City of Production: A Fabulous Opportunity to Experiment with Positive Capitalism, 1 vol. 2012. (ENG., Illus.). 100p. 25.00 *(978-988-98395-7-4(1))* Map Bk. HKG. Dist: D.A.P./Distributed Art Pubs.

Hamerton, Philip Gilbert. Portfolio Papers. 2009. (ENG.). 399p. 38.99 *(978-1-117-69665-2(0))*; 400p. pap. 33.75 *(978-1-117-69666-9(9))* BiblioBazaar.

—Portfolio Papers. 2009. 172p. pap. *(978-1-150-58469-5(6))* Books LLC.

Hanson, John Charlie. When Words Get in the Way: Three Stories of Beauty, Integrity & Freedom. 2010. (ENG., Illus.). 52p. 18.95 *(978-0-931674-81-5(6))* Tristan Publishing, Inc.

Harrison, Frederic. Realities & Ideals: Social, Political, Literary & Artistic. 462p. reprint ed. 98.00 *(978-0-7222-1667-5(X))* Library Reprints, Inc.

Hartley, Marsden. Adventures in the Arts. 2008. 204p. 22.99 *(978-0-554-38082-7(X))*; 25.99 *(978-0-554-28779-9(X))* BiblioBazaar.

—Adventures in the Arts. 2009. 156p. pap. *(978-0-217-67628-1(6))* Books LLC.

—Adventures in the Arts: Informal Chapters on Painters, Vaudeville & Poets. 2009. 276p. 24.99 *(978-1-103-87605-5(0))*; pap. 18.99 *(978-1-103-87797-3(6))* BiblioBazaar.

—Adventures in the Arts: Informal Chapters on Painters, Vaudeville & Poets. 2007. 160p. per. *(978-1-4065-3343-9(2))* Dodo Pr.

—Adventures in the Arts: Informal Chapters on Painters, Vaudeville & Poets. 2007. 276p. 42.95 *(978-0-548-43756-8(4))*; per. 27.95 *(978-0-548-41560-3(9))* Kessinger Publishing, LLC.

Harvey, Jake, et al. Stone: A Legacy & Inspiration for Art. 2011. (ENG.). 192p. pap. 45.00 *(978-1-907317-37-8(6))* Black Dog Publishing Ltd. GBR. Dist: Perseus Distribution.

Hawksley, Lucinda. 50 British Artists You Should Know. 2011. (Illus.). 160p. pap. 19.95 *(978-3-7913-4538-3(9))* Prestel Publishing.

Hayes, Clay. Gig Posters, Vol. 2. 2011. (ENG., Illus.). 208p. pap. 40.00 *(978-1-59474-543-0(9))* Quirk Bks.

Hayward. Artwork. Date not set. (Illus.). 96p. pap. 89.95 *(978-0-582-05295-6(5))* Addison-Wesley Longman, Ltd. GBR. Dist: Trans-Atlantic Pubns., Inc.

Hazlitt, William. On the Elgin Marbles. 2008. (On Ser.). (ENG.). 112p. pap. 13.95 *(978-1-84391-602-4(9))* Hesperus Pr. GBR. Dist: Independent Pubs. Group.

Hendee, Karel. Dig This! 2013 Calendar. 2012. (ENG., Illus.). 28p. pap. 14.99 ***(978-0-9853025-1-1(8))*** Hendee, Karel Artworks.

—For the Love of Trees: 2013 Calendar. 2012. (ENG., Illus.). 24p. pap. 14.99 ***(978-0-9853025-0-4(X))*** Hendee, Karel Artworks.

Henri, Robert. The Art Spirit. 2007. (ENG., Illus.). 288p. per. 19.95 *(978-0-465-00263-4(3))* Basic Bks.

Hight, Christopher & Robinson, Michael. Re:mediations 1. 2010. 78p. pap. 26.40 *(978-0-557-29414-5(2))* Lulu Enterprises Inc.

Hind, C. Lewis. The Consolations of a Critic. 2009. 168p. 26.99 *(978-1-113-66737-3(0))*; pap. 20.75 *(978-1-113-66733-5(8))*; pap. 21.75 *(978-1-113-66735-9(4))* BiblioBazaar.

—The Consolations of a Critic. 2007. (ENG.). 166p. 36.95 *(978-0-548-04422-3(8))* Kessinger Publishing, LLC.

Hockney, David & Hockney, David. Hockney on Art: Conversations with Paul Joyce. 2009. (ENG., Illus.). 264p. pap. 24.95 *(978-1-4087-0157-7(X))* Little, Brown Bk. Group Ltd. GBR. Dist: Independent Pubs. Group.

Hoffmann, Konrad, et al. Zeitenspiegelung: Zur Bedeutung von Traditionen in Kunst & Kunstwissenschaft. (GER., Illus.). 497p. *(978-3-496-01192-7(0))* Reimer, Dietrich.

Holly, Michael Ann & Smith, Marquard. What Is Research in the Visual Arts? Obsession, Archive, Encounter. 2008. (Illus.). xxvi, 215p. *(978-0-931102-80-6(4))* Clark, Sterling & Francine Art Institute.

Holohan, Patrick. Color My Vacation. 2007. 5.99 net. *(978-1-60402-335-0(X))* Independent Pub.

Hosseini, Debra. Artism: The Art of Autism. Martinex,, Rosa C., Rosa C, ed. 2011. 144p. 34.95 ***(978-0-9831308-0-2(9),*** Sicoli Group) Exceptional Resources, Inc.

Huebner, Berna G., ed. I Remember Better When I Paint: Art & Alzheimer's: Opening Doors, Making Connections. 2011. (Illus.). 132p. pap. 19.95 net. ***(978-0-9761364-4-6(9))*** Bethesda Communications Group.

Hume, Helen D. The Art Teacher's Book of Lists. 2nd ed. 2010. (J-B Ed: Book of Lists Ser.: 66). (ENG., Illus.). 416p. pap. 32.95 *(978-0-470-48208-7(7),* Jossey-Bass) Wiley, John & Sons, Inc.

Huneker, James. Promenades of an Impressionist. 2009. 402p. pap. 34.75 *(978-1-116-00917-0(X))* 2008. 288p. 25.99 *(978-0-554-33897-2(1))* 2008. 288p. 28.99 *(978-0-554-24594-2(9))* 2006. (ENG.). 254p. pap. 21.99 *(978-1-4264-6905-3(5))* 2007. 284p. pap. 23.99 *(978-1-4264-6987-9(X))* BiblioBazaar.

—Promenades of an Impressionist. 2008. (ENG.). 264p. per. *(978-1-4065-6902-5(X))* Dodo Pr.

—Promenades of an Impressionist. 2007. (ENG.). 184p. per. *(978-1-4068-1371-5(0))* Echo Library.

—Promenades of an Impressionist. 2008. 408p. 49.95 *(978-1-4372-6448-7(4))*; 404p. pap. 34.95 *(978-1-4371-3787-3(3))* Kessinger Publishing, LLC.

Ingold, Tim. Archaeology Anthropology Art & Architecture. 2012. (ENG.). 288p. pap. 39.95 *(978-0-415-56723-7(8))* Routledge.

—Archaeology Anthropology Art & Architecture. 2010. 288p. 120.00 *(978-0-415-56722-0(X)*, Routledge) Taylor & Francis Group GBR. Dist: Taylor & Francis Group.

Jackson, Christine E. Fish in Art. 2012. (Illus.). 256p. 39.00 ***(978-1-86189-899-9(1))*** Reaktion Bks., Ltd. GBR. Dist: Chicago Distribution Ctr.

Jaeger, Falk, ed. Beneath Sweeping Canopies/Unter Schwingenden Dachern: The New Stuttgart Trade Fair Centre/Die Neue Messe Stuttgart. 2007. (ENG., Illus.). 20.00 *(978-3-89986-091-7(8)*, Avedition Gmbh,Csi) Continental Sales, Inc.

James, Henry. Picture & Text. 2007. (ENG.). 200p. 39.95 *(978-0-548-12211-2(3))* Kessinger Publishing, LLC.

Joost-Gaugier, Christiane L. Measuring Heaven: Pythagoras & His Influence on Thought & Art in Antiquity & the Middle Ages. 2007. (Illus.). 359p. per. 25.95 *(978-0-8014-7409-5(4))* Cornell Univ. Pr.

Kacunko, Slavko & Leach, Dawn. Image-Problem? Medienkunst und Performance Im Kontext der Bilddiskussion. 2007. (GER & ENG., Illus.). 235p. pap. *(978-3-8325-1473-0(2))* Logos Verlag Berlin.

Kaye, Donna. Musing Art. 2011. 72p. pap. 25.48 *(978-1-4567-3655-2(8))* AuthorHouse.

Kersey, Geoff. Mediterranean Landscapes in Watercolour. 2011. (Ready to Paint Ser.). (ENG., Illus.). 72p. pap. 17.95 *(978-1-84448-647-2(8))* Search Pr., Ltd. GBR. Dist: Independent Pubs. Group.

Kim, Alice. Art & Globalization. Elkins, James & Valiavicharska, Zhivka, eds. 2010. (Stone Art Theory Institutes Ser.). (Illus.). 272p. 85.00 *(978-0-271-03716-5(4))* Pennsylvania State Univ. Pr.

King, Scott. Scott King. 2010. (ENG., Illus.). 232p. pap. 55.00 *(978-3-03764-118-7(5))* JRP Ringier Kunstverlag AG CHE. Dist: D.A.P./Distributed Art Pubs.

Kingwell, Mark. Opening Gambits: Essays on Art & Philosophy. 2009. (ENG., Illus.). 296p. 27.95 *(978-1-55470-073-8(6))* Key Porter Bks. CAN. Dist: Perseus-PGW.

Kleiner, Fred S. Drawing upon Art for Gardner's Art Through the Ages: A Concise Global History, 2nd. 2nd ed. 2009. (ENG.). 192p. (C). pap. 50.95 *(978-0-495-57236-7(5))* Wadsworth.

Klipper, Stuart. A City As Once Seen: Photographs by Stuart Klipper. 2008. (Illus.). 45p. 675.00 *(978-0-935052-48-0(8))* Colorado College.

Kornhauser, Elizabeth Mankin. American Moderns on Paper: Masterworks from the Wadsworth Atheneum Museum of Art. 2010. (Illus.). 216p. 60.00 *(978-0-300-15166-4(7))* Yale Univ. Pr.

Krall, Linda & Runyen, Amy. Artist's Block Cured! 201 Ways to Unleash Your Creativity. 2012. (ENG., Illus.). 128p. pap. 19.95 *(978-1-60058-255-4(9)*, 1600582559) Foster, Walter Publishing, Inc.

Labat, Tony & Novakov, Anna. Liquid Architecture. 2009. 43p. pap. 26.90 *(978-0-557-20483-0(6))* Lulu Enterprises Inc.

LaBelle, Brandon, ed. Surface Tension Supplement No. 4: Manual for the Construction of a Sound as a Device to Elaborate Social Connection. 2011. (ENG., Illus.). 104p. pap. 19.00 *(978-0-9772594-8-9(X))* Errant Bodies Pr.

LaBelle, Brandon & Martinho, Claudia, eds. Site of Sound: of Architecture & the Ear Vol 2. 2011. (ENG., Illus.). 304p. pap. 27.00 ***(978-0-9827439-0-4(4))*** Errant Bodies Pr.

Labno, Jeannie. Commemorating the Polish Renaissance Child: Funeral Monuments & Their European Context. 2011. (Illus.). 472p. 134.95 *(978-0-7546-6825-1(8))* Ashgate Publishing Co.

Lanier, Lee. Maya Studio Projects: Texturing & Lighting. 2011. (ENG., Illus.). 272p. pap. 49.99 *(978-0-470-90327-8(9)*, Sybex) Wiley, John & Sons, Inc.

Le Bourgeois, John Y. Art & Forbidden Fruit: Hidden Passion in the Life of William Morris. 2006. (ENG.). 152p. per. 40.00 *(978-0-7188-3059-5(8))* Lutherworth Pr., The GBR. Dist: Brown, David Bk. Co., The.

Legge, Elizabeth M. & Soussloff, Catherine M. Editing the Image: Strategies in the Production & Reception of the Visual - Including Papers Given at the Thirty-Ninth Annual Conference on Editorial Problems, University of Toronto, 7-8 November 2003. Cheetham, Mark & Legge, Elizabeth M., eds. Soussloff, Catherine M., ed. 2008. (Illus.). 240p. *(978-0-8020-9248-9(9))* Univ. of Toronto Pr.

Lehrer, Jonah. Proust Was a Neuroscientist. 2008. (ENG., Illus.). 256p. pap. 14.95 *(978-0-547-08590-6(7)*, Mariner Bks.) Houghton Mifflin Harcourt Trade & Reference Pubs.

Lopes, Dominic McIver & Kieran, Matthew, eds. Knowing Art: Essays in Aesthetics & Epistemology. 2007. (Philosophical Studies Ser.). XXIV, 168p. pap. 49.95 *(978-1-4020-6785-3(2)*, 1402067852) Springer.

Losi, Stefano. Under the Burnt Walls. 2010. 112p. pap. 37.60 *(978-0-578-04109-4(X))* Violent Dances Fade.

Lowry, Bates. The Visual Experience: An Introduction to Art. 2007. (ENG.). 272p. per. 27.95 *(978-0-548-45214-1(8))* Kessinger Publishing, LLC.

Lucas, Raymond. You Are Cordially Invited... 2010. 59p. pap. 36.95 *(978-1-4461-7548-4(0))* Lulu Enterprises Inc.

Mack, John. The Art of Small Things. 2008. (Illus.). 224p. 24.95 *(978-0-674-02693-3(4))* Harvard Univ. Pr.

Maillet, Arnaud. The Claude Glass: Use & Meaning of the Black Mirror in Western Art. Fort, Jeff, tr. from FRE. 2009. (ENG., Illus.). 306p. (gr. 17). pap. 21.95 *(978-1-890951-48-1(X))* Zone Bks.

Marshall, Robert W. Finding Rock Art in the Southwest. (Illus.). 32p. reprint ed. pap. 5.95 *(978-0-9659167-0-7(7))* Canyon Moon Pubns.

Möseneder, Karl. Paracelsus und die Bilder: Über Glauben, Magie und Astrologie im Reformationszeitalter. 2009. (Frühe Neuzeit Ser.).Tr. of Paracelsus & the Images. (GER., Illus.). VIII, 384p. *(978-3-484-36640-4(0))* Verlag Max Niemeyer.

McAuley's. The World Would Be A Better Place If... 2011. 28p. pap. 12.03 *(978-1-4567-3581-4(0))* AuthorHouse.

McDonald, Quinn. Raw Art Journaling. 2011. (ENG., Illus.). 128p. pap. 24.99 *(978-1-4403-0855-0(1)*, North Light Bks.) F&W Media, Inc.

McGee, Mike & Frankel, David. Manuel Pardo: Universo Soñado in Technicolor. 2011.Tr. of Universal Dream in Technicolor. (Illus.). 277p. 45.00 ***(978-0-9817987-6-9(4))*** Grand Central Pr.

McHale, John. The Expendable Reader: Articles on Art, Architecture, Design & Media 1951-1978. Kitnick, Alex, ed. 2011. (ENG., Illus.). 295p. pap. 19.95 ***(978-1-883584-70-2(1))*** Columbia Univ., Graduate Schl. of Architecture.

McNaughton, Frances. Modelling Fairies in Sugar. rev. ed. 2011. (ENG., Illus.). 96p. pap. 19.95 *(978-0-9549761-2-5(6))* Search Pr., Ltd. GBR. Dist: Independent Pubs. Group.

McNaughton, Frances. Sensational Sugar Animals. 2012. (ENG., Illus.). 128p. pap. 24.95 ***(978-1-84448-744-8(X))*** Search Pr., Ltd. GBR. Dist: Independent Pubs. Group.

McRae Books. Demons. 2010. (Magnet Art Bks.). (ENG.). 24p. 5.95 *(978-88-6098-169-1(7))* McRae Bks. Srl ITA. Dist: Independent Pubs. Group.

Mehigan, Timothy J. Frameworks, Artworks, Place: The Space of Perception in the Modern World. Mehigan, Tim, ed. 2008. (Illus.). 264p. per. 78.00 *(978-90-420-2362-8(7))* Rodopi.

Merrett, Andy. PicWords. 2010. 47p. pap. 16.95 *(978-1-4457-6869-4(0))* Lulu Enterprises Inc.

Merrill, Yvonne Y. Hands-On Alaska. (Illus.). 20.00 *(978-0-9643177-0-3(2))* KITS Publishing.

Meyer, Anna. Internetionale: 2001-2006, 1 vol. 2007. (GER & ENG., Illus.). 248p. pap. 35.00 *(978-3-939633-22-8(4))* Jovis Verlag GmbH DEU. Dist: D.A.P./Distributed Art Pubs.

Michel, Karen. Green Guide for Artists: Nontoxic Recipes, Green Art Ideas, & Resources for the Eco-Conscious Artist. 2009. (ENG., Illus.). 128p. pap. 22.99 *(978-1-59253-518-7(6)*, 1592535186) Quayside.

Migone, Christof, text. Sonic Somatic: Performances of the Unsound Body. 2012. (ENG., Illus.). 298p. pap. 21.00 ***(978-0-9827439-4-2(7))*** Errant Bodies Pr.

Mitchell, W. J. T. What Do Pictures Want? The Lives & Loves of Images. 2006. (ENG., Illus.). 408p. per. 27.50 *(978-0-226-53248-6(8))* Univ. of Chicago Pr.

Molesworth, Helen, et al, texts. Dance, Draw. 2011. (ENG., Illus.). 176p. pap. 55.00 ***(978-3-7757-3163-8(6))*** Hatje Cantz Verlag GmbH & Co KG DEU. Dist: D.A.P./Distributed Art Pubs.

Morgan, Les. The Significance of Diaspora Politics in the Visual Arts: Art, Protest & Belonging. 2008. 144p. pap. *(978-3-639-08964-6(2))* VDM Verlag Dr. Mueller e.K.

Morris, William. Hopes & Fears for Art. 2008. 224p. 24.99 *(978-0-559-41285-1(1))* 2008. 224p. pap. 24.75 *(978-0-559-41283-7(5))* 2008. 160p. 22.99 *(978-0-554-38790-1(5))* 2008. 160p. 25.99 *(978-0-554-29487-2(7))* 2007. (ENG.). 140p. per. 18.99 *(978-1-4346-7746-4(X))* BiblioBazaar.

—Hopes & Fears for Art. 2007. 136p. per. *(978-1-4065-4601-9(1))* Dodo Pr.

—Hopes & Fears for Art. 2010. (ENG.). 228p. pap. 25.75 *(978-1-171-79903-0(9))* 2010. 232p. pap. 25.75 *(978-1-177-16951-6(7))* 2010. 230p. pap. 25.75 *(978-1-177-16955-4(X))* 2010. 232p. pap. 25.75 *(978-1-177-16945-5(2))* 2010. 228p. pap. 25.75 *(978-1-176-70644-6(6))* 2010. 232p. pap. 25.75 *(978-1-145-73986-4(5))* 2009. 226p. 28.99 *(978-1-110-85688-6(1))* 2009. 226p. pap. 24.75 *(978-1-110-85686-2(5))* 2009. (ENG.). 224p. pap. 22.99 *(978-1-110-85683-1(0)*, BiblioLife) 2009. (ENG.). 224p. pap. 20.99 *(978-1-110-85682-4(2)*, BiblioLife) BiblioBazaar.

—Hopes & Fears for Art. 2009. 98p. pap. *(978-1-151-72064-1(X))*; pap. *(978-1-151-35236-1(5))* Books LLC.

—Hopes & Fears for Art. 2010. (Illus.). 92p. pap. 20.00 *(978-1-153-62923-2(2))* General Bks. LLC.

—Hopes & Fears for Art. 2010. 122p. 28.76 *(978-1-169-25130-4(7))*; pap. 16.76 *(978-1-162-66668-6(4))*; 35.95 *(978-1-161-43533-7(6))* Kessinger Publishing, LLC.

—Hopes & Fears for Art. 2009. (ENG.). 132p. pap. 10.95 *(978-1-4385-2586-0(9)*, Book Jungle) Standard Pubns., Inc.

—Hopes & Fears for Art. l.t. ed. 2007. (ENG.). 156p. per. 21.99 *(978-1-4346-7747-1(8))* BiblioBazaar.

Mortensen, Jorn. Landscape & Memory. 2011. (ENG., Illus.). 160p. pap. 60.00 ***(978-82-7547-471-9(X))*** Pr., Forlaget NOR. Dist: D.A.P./Distributed Art Pubs.

Mosley, Jonathan & Warren, Sophie. Beyond Utopia. 2012. (ENG., Illus.). 112p. pap. 19.00 ***(978-0-9827439-3-5(9))*** Errant Bodies Pr.

Muskett, G. M. Mycenaean Art: A Psychological Approach. 2007. (Bar S Ser.). (ENG., Illus.). 75p. (C). pap. 72.50 *(978-1-4073-0075-7(X))* British Archaeological Reports Ltd. GBR. Dist: Brown, David Bk. Co., The.

Natural World Museum Staff, contrib. by. Art in Action: Nature, Creativity, & Our Collective Future. 2007. (ENG., Illus.). 176p. 45.00 *(978-1-932771-77-0(8))* Mandala Publishing.

Nelson, Maggie. The Art of Cruelty: A Reckoning. 2012. (ENG.). 304p. pap. 16.95 ***(978-0-393-34314-4(6)***, 34314) Norton, W. W. & Co., Inc.

Nimmrichter, Johann, et al, eds. Lasers in the Conservation of Artworks: LACONA VI Proceedings, Vienna, Austria, Sept. 21 — 25 2005. 2010. (Springer Proceedings in Physics Ser.). (Illus.). xxvi, 650p. pap. 359.00 *(978-3-642-09129-2(6)*, 3642091296) Springer.

Obert, Christopher & Fischer, Charles, compiled by. Pen & Brush: A Collection of Poetry & Art. 2006. (ENG., Illus.). 88p. 14.95 *(978-0-9749291-3-2(1)*, Pear Tree Publishing) Obert, Christopher Publishing.

Ocvirk, Otto, et al. Art Fundamentals: Theory & Practice. 11th ed. 2008. (ENG., Illus.). 336p. (C). pap. 116.67 *(978-0-07-352652-2(5)*, 0073526525) McGraw-Hill Cos., The.

Ocvirk, Otto G. Art Fundamentals: Theory & Practice. 12th ed. 2012. pap. ***(978-0-07-337927-2(1))*** McGraw-Hill Cos., The.

O'Neil, Polly. Surfaces & Textures: A visual Sourcebook. 2011. (ENG., Illus.). 160p. pap. 29.95 *(978-0-7136-8859-7(9))* A & C Black GBR. Dist: Macmillan.

Oxis, Yannis. MOONs2. 2010. 70p. pap. 30.95 *(978-1-4457-2966-4(0))* Lulu Enterprises Inc.

Packer, Boyd K. The Earth Shall Teach Thee. 2011. (Illus.). 200p. ***(978-0-8425-2806-1(7)***, Brigham Young Univ. Religious Studies Ctr.) Brigham Young Univ.

"Papis", Wagner Anarca. Drawings Sketchbook. 2010. 712p. 34.99 *(978-1-4500-4760-9(2))*; pap. 23.99 *(978-1-4500-4759-3(9))* Xlibris Corp.

Parker Farris, Teresa, ed. Patricia Cronin: All Is Not Lost. 2012. (ENG.). pap. 50.00 ***(978-0-9668595-1-5(0))*** Newcomb Art Gallery.

Pearce, Harry. Conundrums: Typographic Conundrums. 2009. (ENG., Illus.). 176p. 14.99 *(978-0-06-182659-7(6))* HarperCollins Pubs.

Pedersen, B. Martin. 100 Best Advertising Annual 2011, 1 vol. 2010. (ENG., Illus.). 237p. 70.00 *(978-1-932026-62-7(2))* Graphis, U.S., Inc.

Pegazzano, Donatella. Committenza e Collezionismo Nel Cinquecento: La Famiglia Corsi a Firenze Tra Musica e Scultura. 2010. (ITA., Illus.). 76p. *(978-88-7970-451-9(6))* Edifir.

Pereira, Irene Rice. The Nature of Space: A Metaphysical & Aesthetic Inquiry. 2011. 72p. 36.95 ***(978-1-258-05196-9(6))*** Literary Licensing, LLC.

The Perfect World Tour. 2006. (Illus.). 68p. per. 29.99 *(978-0-9787922-1-3(1))* Perfectus Arts.

Pergola, Tom, compiled by. Great Art: www.tompergolastudios.com. 2007. (Illus.). 196p. 69.95 *(978-0-9758870-1-1(7))* Beverly Hills Publishing.

Pezzati, Luca & Salimbeni, Renzo. O3a: Optics for Arts, Architecture, & Archaeology III. 2011. (Proceedings of SPIE Ser.). 248p. pap. 80.00 ***(978-0-8194-8680-6(9))*** SPIE.

Pírez, Norberto Marrero. Privacidad. Linares, Yudania Monés & García Santana, Juan Félix, trs. 2011.Tr. of Privacy. (Illus.). 60p. 2000.00 net. ***(978-0-9816044-5-9(5)***, Aqui en la lucha) Red Trillium Pr.

Pitman, Bonnie & Hirzy, Ellen. Ignite the Power of Art: Advancing Visitor Engagement in Museums. 2011. (ENG., Illus.). 238p. pap. 25.00 *(978-0-300-16754-2(7))* Dallas Museum of Art.

Pitman, Joanna. The Dragon's Trail: The Biography of Raphael's Masterpiece. 2008. (ENG., Illus.). 304p. pap. 19.99 *(978-0-7432-6514-0(9)*, Touchstone) Touchstone.

Pooke. Art History: The Basics. 2007. (Basics Ser.). (ENG., Illus.). 288p. 110.00 *(978-0-415-37309-8(3))* Routledge.

Pooke, Grant & Newall, Diana. Art History. 2007. (Basics Ser.). (ENG., Illus.). 288p. pap. 19.95 *(978-0-415-37308-1(5))* Routledge.

Porter, Fairfield. Art in Its Own Terms (BAD ISBN DNU) 2008. (ENG., Illus.). 288p. pap. 22.50 *(978-0-87846-743-3(2))* Museum of Fine Arts, Boston.

Poynter, Edward J. Ten Lectures on Art. 2009. 298p. 30.99 *(978-1-116-21184-9(X))*; 298p. 34.99 *(978-1-116-21183-2(1))*; 298p. pap. 27.75 *(978-1-116-21186-3(6))*; 298p. pap. 28.75 *(978-1-116-21185-6(8))*; (ENG.). 296p. pap. 23.99 *(978-1-116-21187-0(4)*, BiblioLife); (ENG.). 296p. pap. 21.99 *(978-1-116-21188-7(2)*, BiblioLife) BiblioBazaar.

—Ten Lectures on Art. 2007. 294p. 43.95 *(978-0-548-16390-0(1))*; 296p. per. 28.95 *(978-1-4304-6014-5(8))* Kessinger Publishing, LLC.

Raske, Hilde. The Language of Color in the First Goetheanum: A Study of Rudolf Steiner's Art. 388p. 50.00 *(978-3-906633-19-0(5))* Keller, Walter Verlag CHE. Dist: SteinerBooks, Inc.

Rauch, Neo. Neo Rauch. 2007. 248p. 50.00 *(978-3-8321-7732-4(9))* DuMont DEU. Dist: D.A.P./Distributed Art Pubs.

Reynolds, Joshua. Discourses. 2010. 146p. pap. *(978-1-152-23397-3(1))* Books LLC.

—Seven Discourses on Art. Morley, Henry, tr. 2006. (ENG.). 102p. pap. 19.99 *(978-1-4264-0240-1(6))* BiblioBazaar.

—Seven Discourses on Art. 2009. 112p. pap. *(978-1-4099-6429-2(9))* Dodo Pr.

Rishel, Joseph. Revelaciones: Las Artes en América Latina, 1492-1820. Stratton-Pruitt, Suzanne, ed. 2007. (Arte Universal Ser.). (SPA.). 576p. 119.99 *(978-968-16-8429-7(X))*; pap. 89.99 *(978-968-16-8428-0(1))* Fondo de Cultura Economica USA.

Rittermann, Janet, ed. Kunst und Forschung. Art & research: Können Künstler Forscher Sein? Can artists be researchers? 2011. (GER.). 192p. pap. 39.95 ***(978-3-7091-0752-2(0))*** Springer Wien AUT. Dist: Actar Birkhauser Distribution.

Robin, Tabitha. The Color of Life. 2008. 70p. pap. 25.00 *(978-1-4357-2735-9(5))* Lulu Enterprises Inc.

Rossi, Daniel. Everyone We Know. 2010. 48p. pap. 22.00 *(978-0-557-35248-7(7))* Lulu Enterprises Inc.

Roubichou. Meeting the French Impressionists at Grounds for Sculpture. 2012. (ENG.). pap. ***(978-0-9853721-0-1(9))*** Sculpture Foundation, Inc., The.

Rowell, Margit. Cotton Puffs, Q-Tips, Smoke & Mirrors: The Drawings of Ed Ruscha, 1 vol. 2008. (ENG., Illus.). 261p. 45.00 *(978-3-88243-965-6(3))* Steidl, Gerhard Druckerei und Verlag DEU. Dist: Innovative Logistics.

Ruby, Ilka, et al, texts. Relax: (chiarenza & hauser & co), 2 vols. 2007. (ENG., Illus.). 408p. 65.00 *(978-3-938821-56-5(6))* Verlag fur Moderne Kunst DEU. Dist: D.A.P./Distributed Art Pubs.

Ruffner, Ginny & Foster, Bruce. The Imagination Cycle. 2008. (Illus.). 18p. *(978-1-60530-804-3(8))* Museum of Northwest Art.

Ruskin, John. A Joy for Ever. 2008. 156p. 25.99 *(978-0-554-27546-8(5))*; 22.99 *(978-0-554-36849-8(8))* BiblioBazaar.

—A Joy for Ever. 2007. (ENG.). 132p. per. *(978-1-4065-6367-2(6))* Dodo Pr.

—A Joy for Ever. 2007. 100p. per. *(978-1-4068-4085-8(8))* Echo Library.

—Lectures on Art: Delivered before the University of Oxford in Hilar. 2007. (ENG.). 126p. pap. 18.99 *(978-1-4264-9600-4(1))*; 140p. pap. 19.99 *(978-1-4264-9981-4(7))* BiblioBazaar.

—Political Economy of Art. 2007. (ENG.). 260p. 42.95 *(978-0-548-11147-5(2))* Kessinger Publishing, LLC.

—The Two Paths. 2007. (ENG.). 132p. per. *(978-1-4065-6376-4(5))* Dodo Pr.

—The Two Paths. 2007. 108p. per. *(978-1-4068-4096-4(3))* Echo Library.

Russo, Scott, ed. Matchbook Art. 2012. (Pictorial Archive Ser.). (ENG.). 128p. pap. 19.95 ***(978-0-486-48443-3(2))*** Dover Pubns., Inc.

Ryan, Paul. Paul Valery et le Dessin: Preface De Martine Rouart. (FRE., Illus.). 352p. pap. 65.95 *(978-3-631-56414-1(7))* Lang, Peter GmbH, Europaischer Verlag der Wissenschaften DEU. Dist: Lang, Peter Publishing, Inc.

Salleh, Hood. Crafts & the Visual Arts. Jamal, Datuk Syed Ahmad, ed. 2007. (ENCYCLOPEDIA of MALAYSIA Ser.). (ENG., Illus.). 144p. 29.95 *(978-981-3018-57-0(7)*, Didier Millet,Csi) Continental Sales, Inc.

Santora, Patricia B., et al, eds. Addiction & Art. 2010. (ENG., Illus.). 184p. 29.95 *(978-0-8018-9481-7(6))* Johns Hopkins Univ. Pr.

Sayre, Henry M. A World of Art. 6th ed. (ENG.). (C). 2010. 46.67 *(978-0-205-80007-0(6))* 2009. 576p. pap. 152.67 *(978-0-205-67720-7(7))* Prentice Hall PTR. (Prentice Hall).

Scholastic, Inc. Staff & Hale, Christy. All about Me Art Activities: 20 Easy, Step-by-Step Projects That Celebrate Kids' Individuality — And Build Classroom Community. 2009. (ENG.). 64p. (gr. -1-1). pap. 14.99 *(978-0-439-53150-4(0)*, Teaching Resources) Scholastic, Inc.

schultz, dan. 10 Years (softcover) 2008. 110p. pap. 47.50 *(978-0-615-18722-8(6))* Schultz, Dan LaV.

Scott, David. The Art & Aesthetics of Boxing. 2009. (ENG., Illus.). 224p. 40.00 *(978-0-8032-1386-9(7))* Univ. of Nebraska Pr.

Seder, Anton, ed. Dragons, Birds & Incredible Sea Creatures. 2012. (Dover Pictorial Archive Ser.). (ENG., Illus.). 96p. pap. 19.95 ***(978-0-486-48447-1(5))*** Dover Pubns., Inc.

Shallcross, Bozena. Through the Poet's Eye: The Travels of Zagajewski, Herbert, & Brodsky. 2009. (ENG., Illus.). 212p. pap. 19.95 *(978-0-8101-2592-6(7))* Northwestern Univ. Pr.

Sherrow, Joanne. Vector + Raster Fun with Fashion Design: Part II. 2009. (ENG.). 56p. (C). pap. 27.00 ***(978-0-9826341-0-3(2))*** Sherrow, Joanne.

Shipps, Steve. (Re)Thinking Art: A Guide for Beginners. 2008. (ENG., Illus.). 184p. per., instr.'s gde. ed. 33.95 *(978-1-4051-5563-2(9)*, Wiley-Blackwell) Wiley, John & Sons, Inc.

—(Re)Thinking "Art" A Guide for Beginners. 2008. (ENG., Illus.). 184p. 99.95 *(978-1-4051-5562-5(0)*, Wiley-Blackwell) Wiley, John & Sons, Inc.

Shneiderman, Ben. CC 2007: Creativity & Cognition 2007: Seeding Creativity — Tools, Media, & Environments: June 13-15, 2007: Washington, D.C., USA. 2007. (Illus.). xiii, 313p. pap. *(978-1-59593-712-4(9))* Assn. for Computing Machinery.

Showcard & Ticket Writing. rev. ed. (Illus.). 96p. pap. *(978-0-908237-96-8(0)*, UNSW Press) NewSouth Publishing.

Simonson, Lee. Minor Prophecies. 2009. 58p. pap. *(978-0-217-25833-3(6))* Books LLC.

Steinhoff, Judith. Sienese Painting after the Black Death: Artistic Pluralism, Politics, & the New Art Market. 2007. (ENG., Illus.). 288p. 107.99 *(978-0-521-84664-6(1))* Cambridge Univ. Pr.

Storck, Timo. Spiel am Werk: Eine psychoanalytisch-begriffskritische Untersuchung kunstlerischer Arbeitsprozesse. 2010. (ENG.). 369p. (C). 68.00 *(978-3-89971-580-4(2))* Vandenhoeck & Ruprecht GmbH & Co. KG DEU. Dist: ISD.

Stork, David G. & Coddington, Jim. Computer Image Analysis in the Study of Art: 28-29 January 2008, San Jose, California, USA. 2008. (Proceedings of SPIE Ser.). (Illus.). 200p. pap. 70.00 *(978-0-8194-6982-3(3))* SPIE.

Styhre, Alexander. Perception & Organization: Art, Music, Media. 2008. (ENG., Illus.). 272p. (C). 105.00 *(978-0-230-51615-1(7))* Palgrave Macmillan.

Thaler, Lisa. Look up, the Sun Is Shining: The Life & Art of Sasha Kolin / Lisa Thaler. 2008. (Illus.). xi, 460p. pap. *(978-1-877675-68-3(7))* Midmarch Arts Pr.

Thomashoff, Hans-Otto & Sukhanova, Ekaterina. The Person in Art: Conceptual & Pictorial Frames on Art & Mental Health. 2008. 98.00 *(978-1-60456-922-3(0))* Nova Science Pubs., Inc.

Thompson, Jon. The Collected Writings of Jon Thompson. Akerman, Jeremy & Daly, Eileen, eds. 2011. (ENG., Illus.). 536p. pap. ***(978-1-905464-37-1(1))*** Ridinghouse.

Titan Books & Robinson, Martin. Halo: The Art of Building Worlds. 2011. (ENG., Illus.). 192p. reprint ed. 29.95 *(978-0-85768-562-9(7)*, Titan Bks.) Titan Bks. Ltd. GBR. Dist: Random Hse., Inc.

Townsend, Joyce. Preparation for Painting: The Artist's Choice & Its Consequences. 2008. (ENG., Illus.). 208p. pap. 80.00 *(978-1-904982-32-6(8))* Archetype Pubns. GBR. Dist: National Bk. Network.

Trimble, Michael R. The Soul in the Brain: The Cerebral Basis of Language, Art, & Belief. 2007. (ENG., Illus.). 304p. (gr. 17). 38.00 *(978-0-8018-8481-8(0))* Johns Hopkins Univ. Pr.

Tupitsyn, Victor. The Museological Unconscious: Communal (Post)Modernism in Russia. 2012. (ENG., Illus.). 352p. (gr. 17). pap. 17.95 ***(978-0-262-51751-5(5))*** MIT Pr.

Tymieniecka, A-T., ed. Enjoyment: From Laughter to Delight in Philosophy, Literature, the Fine Arts, & Aesthetics. 2012. (Analecta Husserliana Ser.: 56). (ENG., Illus.). 332p. pap. 239.00 *(978-90-481-4889-9(8)*, 9048148898) Springer.

University of Georgia Staff. Place to Belong. 45.00 *(978-0-8203-1395-5(5))* Univ. of Georgia Pr.

Valdeon, Julio. La Baja Edad Media. (Biblioteca Iberoamericana Ser.). (SPA.). 96p. pap. 16.50 *(978-84-7525-444-9(6)*, ANY446) Grupo Anaya, S.A. ESP. Dist: Continental Bk. Co., Inc.

van den Berk, Tjeu. The Eccentric Artist: Jung's Perspectives on Art & Its Creation. 2012. (ENG., Illus.). 176p. 99.00 *(978-0-415-61027-8(3))*; pap. 36.95 *(978-0-415-61028-5(1))* Routledge.

Vandi, Loretta. La Trasformazione del Motivo Dell'Acanto Dell'Antichita al XV Secolo: Ricerche di Teoria e Storia Dell'Ornamento. (Publications Universitaires Europeennes). (ITA.). 53.95 *(978-3-906767-76-5(0))* Lang, Peter CHE. Dist: Lang, Peter Publishing, Inc.

Victionary, ed. Dark Inspiration: Grotesque Illustrations, Art & Design. 2010. (Illus.). 271p. pap. *(978-988-19438-1-1(7))* Victionary.

Vivanti, Luca. Tisettanta: Forty Years of Design, Forty Years of Home. Vivanti, Luca, ed. 2011. (ENG & ITA.). 160p. 89.50 ***(978-88-370-8616-9(4))*** Trans-Atlantic Pubns., Inc.

Wainwright, A. A Fifth Lakeland Sketchbook. 2006. (Lakeland Sketchbooks Ser.). (Illus.). 24.95 *(978-0-7112-2337-0(8))* Lincoln, Frances Ltd. GBR. Dist: Perseus-PGW.

—A Fourth Lakeland Sketchbook. 2006. (Lakeland Sketchbooks Ser.). (Illus.). 24.95 *(978-0-7112-2336-3(X))* Lincoln, Frances Ltd. GBR. Dist: Perseus-PGW.

—A Lakeland Sketchbook. 2008. (Lakeland Sketchbooks Ser.). (Illus.). 80p. 24.95 *(978-0-7112-2333-2(5))* Lincoln, Frances Ltd. GBR. Dist: Perseus-PGW.

—A Second Lakeland Sketchbook. 2006. (Lakeland Sketchbooks Ser.). (Illus.). 24.95 *(978-0-7112-2334-9(3))* Lincoln, Frances Ltd. GBR. Dist: Perseus-PGW.

—A Third Lakeland Sketchbook. 2006. (Lakeland Sketchbooks Ser.). (Illus.). 24.95 *(978-0-7112-2335-6(1))* Lincoln, Frances Ltd. GBR. Dist: Perseus-PGW.

Waterhouse, Jo. Indie Craft. 2010. (ENG., Illus.). 128p. pap. 19.95 *(978-1-85669-696-8(0))* King, Laurence Publishing GBR. Dist: Hachette Bk. Group.

Weinzapfel, Adam. Zapfels. 2011. (Illus.). 58p. pap. 24.99 ***(978-1-4634-1406-1(4))*** AuthorHouse.

Weller, Alan & Dover Staff. Fairy Tale Art. 2012. (Pictura Ser.). (ENG., Illus.). 128p. pap. 39.95 ***(978-0-486-99191-7(1))*** Dover Pubns., Inc.

Wilde, Oscar. Decay of Lying. 2009. (Oneworld Classics Ser.). (ENG.). 150p. 15.95 *(978-1-84749-067-4(0))* Alma Classics GBR. Dist: Independent Pubs. Group.

Winter, Gundolf, et al. Das Raumbild: Bilder jenseits ihrer Flächen. 2009. (GER., Illus.). 363p. *(978-3-7705-4741-8(1))* Wilhelm/Fink#GmbH & Co. Verlags-KG.

Wolfson, Rutger, ed. This Is the Flow: the Museum as a Space for Ideas. 2009. (ENG., Illus.). 260p. pap. 32.50 *(978-90-78088-24-0(9))* Valiz NLD. Dist: D.A.P./Distributed Art Pubs.

Wood, Ashley. Sparrow: Ashley Wood. 2008. (Illus.). 48p. 11.99 *(978-1-60010-223-3(9))* Idea & Design Works, LLC.

Wright, Erica. Why Things Look the Way They Do. 2009. 336p. pap. *(978-3-639-13217-5(3))* VDM Verlag Dr. Mueller e.K.

Wyman, Melissa. Fight Therapy. 2010. 60p. pap. *(978-3-8383-5679-2(9))* Lambert Academic Publishing.

Yot, Richard J., et al. Light for Visual Artists: Understanding & Using Light in Art & Design. 2011. (ENG., Illus.). 176p. pap. 29.95 *(978-1-85669-660-9(X))* King, Laurence Publishing GBR. Dist: Hachette Bk. Group.

Zdebik, Jakub. Deleuze & the Diagram: Aesthetic Threads in Visual Organisation. 2012. (Continuum Studies in Continental Philosophy Ser.). (ENG.). 240p. 120.00 ***(978-1-4411-1560-7(9))*** Continuum International Publishing Group, Ltd. GBR. Dist: National Bk. Network.

—Deleuze & the Diagram: Aesthetic Threads in Visual Organization. 2012. E-Book ***(978-1-4411-7872-5(4))*** Continuum International Publishing Group, Ltd.

Zeegen, Lawrence. What Is Illustration? 2009. (Essential Design Handbooks Ser.). (ENG., Illus.). 256p. 35.00 *(978-2-88893-033-4(1)*, 2888930331) RotoVision SA CHE. Dist: Quayside.

Zeki, Semir. Splendors & Miseries of the Brain: Love, Creativity, & the Quest for Human Happiness. 5th ed. 2008. (ENG., Illus.). 256p. pap. 31.95 *(978-1-4051-8557-8(0)*, Wiley-Blackwell) Wiley, John & Sons, Inc.

Zekowski, Arlene. Cardinals & Saints. 2006. pap. 22.95 *(978-1-4286-5434-1(8))* Kessinger Publishing, LLC.

Zekowski, Arlene & Berne, Stanley. Cardinals & Saints. 2007. (ENG.). 188p. 37.95 *(978-0-548-14216-5(5))* Kessinger Publishing, LLC.

Zimmermann, Philip. Long Story Short: An Artist's Book. (Illus.). 154p. 50.00 *(978-0-932526-84-7(5))* Nexus Pr.

Zorach, Marguerite. Clever Fresno Girl: The Travel Writings of Marguerite Thompson Zorach (1908-1915) 2008. (Illus.). 264p. 55.00 *(978-0-87413-035-5(2))* Univ. of Delaware Pr.

Zybok, Oliver & Richard, Birgit, eds. Dead Lines. 2012. (ENG., Illus.). 256p. 60.00 ***(978-3-7757-3005-1(2))*** Hatje Cantz Verlag GmbH & Co KG DEU. Dist: D.A.P./Distributed Art Pubs.

ART—ANALYSIS, INTERPRETATION, APPRECIATION

see Aesthetics; Art—Philosophy; Art—Study and Teaching; Art Appreciation; Art Criticism; Painting; Pictures

ART—ANECDOTES

Mileti, Nick James. The Unscrupulous: Scams, Cons, Fakes, & Frauds that Poison the Fine Arts. 2009. 314p. pap. 20.00 *(978-1-59954-003-0(7))* Bordighera Incorporated.

Mould, Philip. The Art Detective: Adventures of an Antiques Roadshow Appraiser. 2011. (ENG.). 272p. (gr. 12). 16.00 *(978-0-14-311916-6(3)*, Penguin (Non-Classics)) Penguin Group (USA) Inc.

Spooner, Shearjashub. Anecdotes of Painters, Engravers, Sculptors & Architects, & Curiosities of Art, Volume III. 2007. (ENG.). 214p. pap. 20.99 *(978-1-4264-5185-0(7))*; 238p. pap. 22.99 *(978-1-4264-5486-8(4))* BiblioBazaar.

ART—BIBLIOGRAPHY

Bibliographic Guide to Art & Architecture 1998. Date not set. 273.00 *(978-0-7838-0224-4(2)*, Macmillan Reference USA) Cengage Gale.

Crandall, Richard C. & Crandall, Susan M. An Annotated Bibliography of Inuit Art. alt. annot. ed. 2007. (ENG.). 464p. per. 95.00 *(978-0-7864-3091-8(5))* McFarland & Co., Inc. Pubs.

Ford, Simon, ed. Information Sources in Art, Art History & Design. (Guides to Information Sources Ser.). (ENG.). XX, 220p. ***(978-3-11-184923-2(6))*** Saur, K. G. Verlag GmbH & Co.

Geck, Francis Joseph. Bibliography of Italian Early Renaissance Art. 2011. 44p. 35.95 ***(978-1-258-02103-0(X))*** Literary Licensing, LLC.

Lombardi, Elena, ed. L'Archivio Di Giovanni Poggi (1880-1961) Soprintendente Alle Gallerie Fiorentine. 2011. (Dagli Archivi delle Arti Ser.). (ITA., Illus.). 466p. (C). pap. 40.00 ***(978-88-596-0831-8(7))*** Polistampa ITA. Dist: Brown, David Bk. Co., The.

O'Neal, William Bainter. Jefferson's Buildings at the University of Virgini: The Rotunda. 2011. 98p. 38.95 ***(978-1-258-08757-9(X))*** Literary Licensing, LLC.

Pooke, Grant & Newall, Diana. Fifty Key Texts in Art History. 2011. xxxiii, 243p. E-Book ***(978-0-203-13878-6(3))*** Routledge.

Pooke, Grant & Newall, Diana, eds. Fifty Key Texts in Art History. 2012. (Routledge Key Guides). (ENG.). 288p. 110.00 ***(978-0-415-48705-4(6))***; pap. 29.95 ***(978-0-415-49770-1(1))*** Routledge.

Rooses, Max. Art in Flanders. 2010. 378p. pap. 33.75 *(978-1-177-79168-7(4))*; 366p. pap. 32.75 *(978-1-142-12865-4(2))* BiblioBazaar.

—Art in Flanders. 2009. 188p. pap. *(978-1-151-73666-6(X))* Books LLC.

—Art in Flanders. 356p. 2010. 37.56 *(978-1-165-36184-7(1))* 2009. 46.95 *(978-1-104-07211-7(4))* 2009. pap. 31.95 *(978-1-104-03622-5(3))* Kessinger Publishing, LLC.

Schimmelman, Janice Gayle. Books on Art in Early America: Books on Art, Aesthetics & Instruction Available in American Libraries & Bookstores Through 1815. 2007. (ENG.). 292p. 65.00 *(978-1-58456-214-6(5))* Oak Knoll Pr.

ART—CATALOGS

see also Art—Exhibitions

Acconci, Vito & Buchloh, B. H. D. A Bit of Matter & a Little Bit More: The Collection & the Archives of Herman & Nicole Daled. Wilmes, Ulrich, ed. 2011. (ENG., Illus.). 456p. pap. 95.00 *(978-3-86560-763-8(2))* Verlag der Buchhandlung Walther Konig DEU. Dist: D.A.P./Distributed Art Pubs.

Ades, Dawn, et al, contrib. by. Surrealist Art: The Lindy & Edwin Bergman Collection at the Art Institute of Chicago. (Illus.). 256p. pap. *(978-0-500-27995-3(0))* Thames & Hudson.

Agustin, Perez Rubio, ed. Discursive Variants. 2010. (ENG., Illus.). 320p. pap. *(978-84-92861-27-9(4))* Actar Birkhauser Distribution.

Ai, Weiwei & Meile, Urs. Ai Weiwei Works, 2004-2007. 2008. (ENG., Illus.). 219p. pap. 39.00 *(978-3-905829-27-3(4))* JRP Ringier Kunstverlag AG CHE. Dist: D.A.P./Distributed Art Pubs.

Akay & Baranowski, Peter. Urban Recreation: City Art by Akay & Peter. 2006. (ENG., Illus.). 192p. 29.95 *(978-91-973981-7-6(9))* Dokument forlag, Fotograf Malcolm Jacobsson SWE. Dist: SCB Distributors.

Alber, Dave. Myth & Medium. 2007. 72p. pap. 25.60 *(978-1-4116-6126-4(5))* Lulu Enterprises Inc.

Albersmeier, Sabine. The Art of Ancient Greece. 2008. (ENG., Illus.). 176p. 47.00 *(978-0-85667-643-7(8))* Wilson, Philip Pubs., Ltd. GBR. Dist: Macmillan.

—The Art of Ancient Greece: The Walters Art Museum. 2008. (ENG., Illus.). 176p. pap. 27.95 *(978-0-85667-646-8(2))* Wilson, Philip Pubs., Ltd. GBR. Dist: Macmillan.

Allegaert, Sophie & Mestdagh, Chris. Colorful Retreats: By Chris Mestdagh. 2010. (ENG., Illus.). 192p. pap. *(978-90-5856-336-1(7)*, Stichting Kunstboak (Acc)) Antique Collectors' Club.

Antonaccio, Carla M. & Dillon, Sheila, eds. The Past Is Present: The Kempner Collection of Classical Antiquities at the Nasher Museum. 2011. (ENG., Illus.). 236p. pap. 40.00 *(978-0-938989-35-6(9))* Duke Univ. Pr.

Arendar, Hanna. Silver Tableware of the 17th-20th Centuries: Collection in the V.V. Tarnovsky Chernihiv Historical Museum, Ukraine. 2010. (ENG & UKR.). 176p. 49.00 *(978-966-7845-25-4(7)*, Art Stock Bks. Ltd/Csl) Continental Sales, Inc.

Arntzen, Etta. Krannert Art Museum: Selected Works. 2009. (ENG., Illus.). 360p. 39.95 *(978-1-883015-41-1(3))* Krannert Art Museum.

Art Basel, ed. Art 41 Basel. 2010. (ENG., Illus.). 750p. pap. 70.00 *(978-3-7757-2607-8(1))* Hatje Cantz Verlag GmbH & Co KG DEU. Dist: D.A.P./Distributed Art Pubs.

Art Institute of Chicago Staff, contrib. by. The Essential Guide. 3rd ed. 2009. (Illus.). 336p. pap. *(978-0-86559-229-2(2))* Art Institute of Chicago.

Asano, Shugo & Smith, Lawrence, intros. British Museum, Vol. 1. (Illus.). 268p. 300.00 *(978-0-87011-855-5(2))* Kodansha America, Inc.

Assemani, Stephen Evodius & Assemani, Joseph Simon. Catalog of Syriac & Garshuni Manuscripts in the Vatican Library. 2010. (LAT.). 303.76 *(978-1-60724-905-4(7))*; 303.76 *(978-1-60724-904-7(9))* Gorgias Pr., LLC.

Avery, Charles. Bertos: The Triumph of Motion. 2008. (ENG., Illus.). 400p. 100.00 *(978-88-422-1556-1(2))* Allemandi, Umberto & Co. GBR. Dist: Antique Collectors' Club.

Axsom, Richard H. 100 Years, 100 Works of Art: Introduction to the Collection of the Grand Rapids Art Museum. 2010. *(978-0-615-39126-7(5))* Yale Univ. Pr.

Bü, et al. Maler der Brücke: Die Sammlung Hermann Gerlinger in der Auswahl - Katalog. 2009. (GER., Illus.). 119p. *(978-3-89812-618-2(8))* Mitteldeutscher Verlag GmbH, MDV.

Backe-Dahmen, Annika. Die Rückkehr der Götter: Berlins verborgener Olymp. 2009. (ENG.). 424p. 69.00 *(978-3-7954-2113-7(6)*, Art Stock Bks. Ltd/Csi) Continental Sales, Inc.

Bailey, Colin B. Building the Frick Collection: An Introduction to the House & Its Collections. 2006. (ENG., Illus.). 128p. 24.95 *(978-1-85759-381-5(2))* Scala, Editions FRA. Dist: National Bk. Network.

Bal, Julien. Tapisserie. 2008. (DUT & FRE.). 212p. (C). 102.00 *(978-90-429-2164-1(1))* Peeters Pubs. & Booksellers BEL. Dist: Brown, David Bk. Co., The.

Barbara Cooper Re: Growth. 2007. pap. 20.00 *(978-0-942342-14-7(3))* Bellevue Arts Museum.

Barbier, Gilles. Gilles Barbier, 1 vol. 2006. (ENG., Illus.). 64p. 35.00 *(978-3-905701-19-7(7))* JRP Ringier Kunstverlag AG CHE. Dist: D.A.P./Distributed Art Pubs.

Barnes, Lucinda & Baas, Jacquelynn. Measure of Time, 1 vol. 2007. (ENG., Illus.). 176p. pap. 25.00 *(978-0-9719397-6-9(4))* Univ. of California, Berkeley Art Museum & Pacific Film Archive.

Barovier, Marino, ed. Venetian Glass: From Modern to Contemporary. 2009. (ITA & ENG., Illus.). 400p. pap. 19.95 *(978-88-7179-208-8(4)*, Ore Cultura Srl (Acc)) Antique Collectors' Club GBR. Dist: National Bk. Network.

Barratt, Carrie Rebora & Zabar, Lori. American Portrait Miniatures in the Metropolitan Museum of Art. 2010. (Illus.). 328p. 65.00 *(978-0-300-14895-4(X))* Yale Univ. Pr.

—American Portrait Miniatures in the Metropolitan Museum of Art. 2010. (Illus.). xii, 316p. 65.00 *(978-1-58839-357-9(7))* Metropolitan Museum of Art, The.

Barriault, Anne B. Selections from the Virginia Museum of Fine Arts. 2nd rev. ed. 2007. (ENG., Illus.). 376p. 45.00 *(978-0-917046-82-7(X))* Virginia Museum of Fine Arts.

Barriault, Anne B. & Davidson, Kay M. Selections from the Virginia Museum of Fine Arts. 2007. (Illus.). xix, 355p. pap. *(978-0-917046-81-0(1))* United States Holocaust Memorial Museum.

Barron, Stephanie. Envisioning Modernism: The Janice & Henri Lazarof Collection. 2012. (Illus.). 224p. 49.95 ***(978-3-7913-5201-5(6))*** Prestel Publishing.

Barter, Judith A. & Obniski, Monica. For Kith & Kin: The Folk Art Collection at the Art Institute of Chicago. 2012. (ENG., Illus.). 112p. 30.00 ***(978-0-300-17972-9(3))*** Art Institute of Chicago.

Bartholomew, Terese, et al. Later Chinese Jades: Ming Dynasty to Early Twentieth Century. 2007. (ENG.). 368p. 95.00 *(978-0-939117-41-3(X))* Asian Art Museum of San Francisco.

Bast, Gerald, ed. Mit Eigenen Augen/with Their Own Eyes: KunstlerInnen Aus der Ehemaligen Meisterklasse Maria Lassnig/Former Students of Maria Lassnig. 2008. (GER & ENG., Illus.). 176p. pap. *(978-3-211-77840-1(3)*, 3211778403) Actar Birkhauser Distribution.

Baumhauer, Till Ansgar, ed. Till Ansgar Baumhauer: Stranger Sampling. 2010. (ENG., Illus.). 120p. 45.00 *(978-3-86678-271-6(3))* Kerber Verlag DEU. Dist: D.A.P./Distributed Art Pubs.

Bayer, Andrea & Rodeschini, Maria Cristina. Bellini, Titian, & Lotto: North Italian Paintings from the Accademia Carrara, Bergamo. 2012. (ENG., Illus.). 80p. pap. 19.95 ***(978-0-300-17956-9(1))*** Yale Univ. Pr.

Bead Review 3. 2008. 126p. pap. 21.00 *(978-0-9770831-5-2(2))* Pearson, Brad.

Beal, Graham William John & Mancoff, Debra N. Treasures of the DIA: The Detroit Institute of Arts. 2007. *(978-0-89558-160-0(4))* Detroit Institute of Arts.

Beek, Wim Van Der. Jos Dirix: Sculptures Cyclical Life. 2009. (DUT & ENG., Illus.). 120p. *(978-90-78964-29-2(4)*, Thieme Art (Acc)) Antique Collectors' Club.

Behrendt, Kurt A. The Art of Gandhara in the Metropolitan Museum of Art. 2007. 24.95 *(978-1-58839-224-4(4))* Metropolitan Museum of Art, The.

Beresford, Laura. Folk Art from the American Museum in Britain. 2011. (ENG., Illus.). 128p. pap. 35.00 *(978-1-85759-676-2(5))* Scala, Editions FRA. Dist: National Bk. Network.

Bernice Pauahi Bishop Museum Staff, ed. Images From The Bernice Pauahi Bishop Museum Art Collection. 2008. 16.95 *(978-1-58178-076-5(1))* Bishop Museum Pr.

Berry, Ian, ed. Tim Rollins & K. O. S. 2009. (ENG., Illus.). 220p. (gr. 17). 39.95 *(978-0-262-01355-0(X))* MIT Pr.

Berwick, John, tr. Masterpieces of the Kunsthaus Zurich. 2010. (ENG., Illus.). 44p. 30.00 *(978-3-7757-2545-3(8))* Hatje Cantz Verlag GmbH & Co KG DEU. Dist: D.A.P./Distributed Art Pubs.

Beuys, Joseph, et al. Mythos Volume 2, 1 vol. 2007. (GER & ENG., Illus.). 160p. 62.00 *(978-3-86560-182-7(0))* Kunsthaus Bregenz AUT. Dist: D.A.P./Distributed Art Pubs.

Bierens, Cornel, et al. Private Passion: Artists' Jewelry of the 20th Century. Joris, Yvònne, ed. 2010. (ENG., Illus.). 176p. 70.00 *(978-3-89790-320-3(2))* Arnoldsche Art Pubs. DEU. Dist: National Bk. Network.

Biesenbach, Klaus, et al, texts. Greater New York 2010, 1 vol. 2010. (ENG.). 250p. pap. 19.00 *(978-0-9841776-2-2(0))* P.S.1 Contemporary Art Ctr.

Birge, Debra L. The World of My Little Pony (r): An Unauthorized Guide for Collectors. 2nd rev. exp. ed. 2008. (Schiffer Book for Collectors Ser.). (Illus.). 128p. pap. 24.95 *(978-0-7643-2878-7(6))* Schiffer Publishing, Ltd.

Birnie, Annabelle. Art in the Office. 2007. (ENG., Illus.). 240p. 45.00 *(978-90-400-8255-9(3))* Waanders B.V., Uitgeverij NLD. Dist: National Bk. Network.

Bissell, R. Ward, et al. Masters of Italian Baroque Painting: The Detroit Institute of Arts. 2006. (Master Paintings from Dia Ser.). (ENG., Illus.). 176p. 65.00 *(978-1-904832-05-8(9))* Giles, D. Ltd. GBR. Dist: Antique Collectors' Club.

Blaas-Pratscher, Katharina. Öffentliche Kunst, Kunst im öffentlichen Raum Niederösterreich, Band 9: / Public Art Lower Austria, Volume 9. 2009. (GER & ENG., Illus.). 256p. 59.95 *(978-3-211-99013-1(5))* Springer Wien AUT. Dist: Actar Birkhauser Distribution.

Blaas-Pratscher, Katharina, ed. Öffentliche Kunst, Kunst im öffentlichen Raum Niederösterreich, Band 10: / Public Art Lower Austria, Volume 10. 2012 (Public Art Lower Austria Ser.). (ENG & GER., Illus.). 224p. 49.95 ***(978-3-7091-0780-5(6))*** Springer Wien AUT. Dist: Actar Birkhauser Distribution.

Bleiberg, Edward & Cooney, Kathlyn M. To Live Forever: Egyptian Treasures from the Brooklyn Museum. 2008. (ENG., Illus.). 152p. 39.95 *(978-1-904832-52-2(0))* Giles, D. Ltd. GBR. Dist: Antique Collectors' Club.

Blondeau, Marc & Meaudre, Thierry, eds. A. C. I., Art Catalogue Index. 2009. (ENG., Illus.). 512p. 95.00 *(978-3-905829-53-2(3))* JRP Ringier Kunstverlag AG CHE. Dist: D.A.P./Distributed Art Pubs.

Bober, Phyllis & Rubinstein, Ruth. Renaissance Artists & Antique Sculpture: A Handbook of Sources. New, revised, & updated Edition. 2nd ed. 2010. (Studies in Medieval & Early Renaissance Art History Ser.). (ENG., Illus.). 581p. (C). 217.00 *(978-1-905375-60-8(3))* Miller, Harvey Pubs. GBR. Dist: Brown, David Bk. Co., The.

Bocuse, Paul & Pinard, Yves. Food in the Louvre. 2010. (ENG., Illus.). 80p. 19.95 *(978-2-08-122821-4(1))* Flammarion et Cie FRA. Dist: Random Hse., Inc.

Böhm, Florian, ed. Commedia Dell'Arte - Couture Edition. 2010. 320p. 170.00 *(978-3-0346-0544-1(7))* Birkhauser Verlag AG CHE. Dist: Actar Birkhauser Distribution.

Bois, Yve-Alain & Ruscha, Edward. Edward Ruscha Vol. I: Catalogue Raisonné of the Paintings, 1 vol. 2008. (ENG., Illus.). 469p. (gr. 13-18). 200.00 *(978-3-88243-972-4(6))* Steidl, Gerhard Druckerei und Verlag DEU. Dist: Innovative Logistics.

Bomford, David. Seeing the Collections at the Getty Center. 2009. (Illus.). 64p. pap. 10.95 *(978-0-89236-962-1(0))* Oxford Univ. Pr., Inc.

Bonevardi, Gustavo & Bennett, John, eds. Bonevardi: Chasing Shadows, Constructing Art. 2007. (ENG., Illus.). 448p. 60.00 *(978-0-292-71436-6(X))* Univ. of Texas Pr.

Borovsky, Alexander, et al, texts. Alexander Kosolapov: Sots Art. 2010. (ENG., Illus.). 184p. 55.00 *(978-3-86678-227-3(6))* Kerber Verlag DEU. Dist: D.A.P./Distributed Art Pubs.

Boyajian, Ani. Stuart Davis: A Catalogue Raisonne, 3 vols., Set. Rutkoski, Mark, ed. 2007. (Illus.). 1604p. 300.00 *(978-0-300-10981-8(4))* Yale Univ. Art Gallery.

Brand, Heather, ed. Red Hot: Asian Art Today from the Chaney Family Collection. 2008. (ENG., Illus.). 208p. pap. 39.95 *(978-0-300-13889-4(X))* Museum of Fine Arts, Houston.

Brattig, Patricia, ed. Meissen: Barockes Porzellan. 2010. (ENG., Illus.). 432p. 85.00 *(978-3-89790-329-6(6))* Arnoldsche Art Pubs. DEU. Dist: Antique Collectors' Club.

Brettell, Richard R., et al. The Metropolitan Museum of Art Vol. 3: Nineteenth - And Twentieth - Century Paintings. 2010. (ENG., Illus.). 496p. (C). 125.00 *(978-0-691-14536-5(9))* Princeton Univ. Pr.

Brilliant, Virginia. The John & Mable Ringling Museum of Art. 2011. (ENG., Illus.). 64p. pap. 7.95 ***(978-1-85759-694-6(3))*** Scala, Editions FRA. Dist: National Bk. Network.

Brilliant, Virginia. The John & Mable Ringling Museum of Art: Curator's Choice. 2010. (ENG., Illus.). 80p. pap. 9.95 *(978-1-85759-643-4(9))* Scala, Editions FRA. Dist: National Bk. Network.

Brown, Elizabeth. Kiki Smith: Photographs. 2010. (Illus.). 208p. 49.95 *(978-3-7913-4465-2(X))* Prestel Publishing.

Brüggebors, Nadine, text. Andy Denzler Paintings: The Human Nature Project. 2011. (ENG., Illus.). 128p. 55.00 *(978-3-7757-2803-4(1))* Hatje Cantz Verlag GmbH & Co KG DEU. Dist: D.A.P./Distributed Art Pubs.

Bryan, Brett, des. What's Not Ta Like (Second Edition) The Art of Joe Capobianco. 2007. (Illus.). 218p. per. 50.00 net. *(978-0-9727160-5-5(X))* PrestoArt, Inc.

Bua, Justin. The Beat of Urban Art: The Art of Justin Bua. 2006. 160p. 100.00 *(978-0-06-114479-0(7)*, ReganBooks) HarperCollins Pubs.

Büche, Wolfgang & Gerlinger, Hermann. Painters of the Brücke: Selected from the Collection of Hermann Gerlinger. 2009. (Illus.). 119p. *(978-3-89812-622-9(6))* Mitteldeutscher Verlag GmbH, MDV.

Bühl, Gudrun, ed. Dumbarton Oaks: The Collections. 2008. (Dumbarton Oaks Collection Ser.). (Illus.). 384p. pap. 24.95 *(978-0-88402-354-8(0))* Dumbarton Oaks.

Bühler, Kathleen, et al. Switzerlart: A Collection of Swiss Art in Five Chapters. 2011. (ENG., Illus.). 380p. 29.95 ***(978-3-03764-164-4(9))*** JRP Ringier Kunstverlag AG CHE. Dist: D.A.P./Distributed Art Pubs.

Bujok, Elke & Mueller, Claudius, eds. Weiter als der Horizont: Kunst der Welt. 2008. (GER., Illus.). 288p. (C). pap. 49.00 *(978-3-7774-3895-5(2))* Hirmer Verlag GmbH DEU. Dist: Brown, David Bk. Co., The.

Busch, Jason, ed. & text. Carnegie Museum of Art: Decorative Arts & Design. 2010. (ENG., Illus.). 224p. pap. 19.95 *(978-0-88039-052-1(2))* Carnegie Museum of Art, The.

Caccioli, D. A. The Villanovan, Etruscan, & Hellenistic Collections in the Detroit Institute of Arts. 2009. 270p. *(978-90-04-17230-2(0))* BRILL.

Calza, Gian Carlo, ed. Hiroshige: Master of Nature. 2009. (ENG., Illus.). 304p. pap. 75.00 *(978-88-572-0106-1(6))* Skira Editore ITA. Dist: Random Hse., Inc.

Cameron, Dan & Power, Kevin. Juliao Sarmento Vol. 1: 1990-1992. Cameron, Dan, ed. 2009. (ENG & SPA., Illus.). 64p. pap. 35.00 *(978-84-343-1195-4(X))* Polígrafa, Ediciones, S. A. ESP. Dist: D.A.P./Distributed Art Pubs.

Caneva, Caterina. Museo D'arte Sacra Dell'Abbazia Di Vallombrosa: Guida Alla Visita Del Museo e Alla Scoperta Del Territorio. 2007. (Piccoli, grandi Musei Ser.). (Illus.). 257p. (C). 24.00 *(978-88-596-0212-5(2))* Polistampa ITA. Dist: Brown, David Bk. Co., The.

Capponi, Howard B. & Sessions, James Milton. James Milton Sessions: American World War II Artist & Premier Brush Reporter. 2007. (Illus.). 66p. 31.99 *(978-1-4257-3121-2(X))* Xlibris Corp.

Caramelle, Ernst. Ernst Caramelle. 2009. pap. 20.00 *(978-1-883597-08-5(0))* Markey, Lawrence Inc.

Carder, James N. American Art at Dumbarton Oaks. 2011. (Dumbarton Oaks Collection Ser.). (ENG., Illus.). 136p. pap. 20.95 *(978-0-88402-366-1(4))* Dumbarton Oaks.

Cardiff, Janet & Miller, George Bures. Janet Cardiff & George Bures Miller: Pandemonium, 1 vol. 2006. (ENG., Illus.). 47p. 25.00 *(978-0-9649221-2-9(6)*, Eastern State Penitentiary Historic Site) Prison Sentences/Moore College of Art & Design.

Cass, Claire. The Masters Box Set: Masterpieces of French Art Pottery, 1885-1910 & Clement Massier: Master of Iridescence, 2. 2007. (Illus.). 204p. 75.00 *(978-0-9788371-4-3(2))* Jason Jacques Gallery Pr. The.

Catalogue Entries by the Curators of Birmingham Museum of Art Staff. Birmingham Museum of Art: Guide to the Collection. 2011. (ENG., Illus.). 272p. pap. 35.00 *(978-1-904832-77-5(6))* Giles, D. Ltd. GBR. Dist: Antique Collectors' Club.

Catalogue Raisonne Staff. Liudmila Kondakova. Date not set. (Illus.). 32p. pap. *(978-0-9648085-1-5(X))* Jenkintown Pr.

Cavalchini, Pieranna, et al, texts. Stefano Arienti: The Asian Shore. 2008. (ENG., Illus.). 76p. 34.95 *(978-88-8158-654-7(1))* Charta ITA. Dist: D.A.P./Distributed Art Pubs.

Cerizza, Luca, ed. Town Hidden under Concrete - Passageway, 1 vol. 2007. (SPA & ENG., Illus.). 80p. 15.00 *(978-3-905701-92-0(8))* JRP Ringier Kunstverlag AG CHE. Dist: D.A.P./Distributed Art Pubs.

Charles R. Mack. European Art in the Columbia Museum of Art, Including the Samuel H. Kress Collection, Volume One: The Thirteenth through the Sixteenth Century. 2009. (ENG.). 304p. pap. 29.95 *(978-1-57003-806-8(6))* Univ. of South Carolina Pr.

Christo & Jeanne Claude. Christo & Jeanne-Claude: Early Works 1958-64. 2010. (ENG & GER., Illus.). 192p. pap. 35.00 *(978-3-941100-79-4(3))* DruckVerlag Kettler GmbH DEU. Dist: D.A.P./Distributed Art Pubs.

City Museum Freiburg. Augustiner Museum: Masterpieces from the Middle Ages to the Baroque. 2010. (ENG.). 200p. pap. 28.00 *(978-3-422-06949-7(6)*, Art Stock Bks. Ltd/Csi) Continental Sales, Inc.

Cloudman, Ruth H. The Speed Art Museum: Highlights from the Collection. 2007. (ENG., Illus.). 240p. pap. 16.95 *(978-1-85894-409-8(0))* Merrell Pubs. Ltd. GBR. Dist: Perseus Distribution.

Coatsworth, Elizabeth. Western Yorkshire. 2008. (Corpus of Anglo-Saxon Stone Sculpture Ser.). (ENG., Illus.). 350p. 74.00 *(978-0-19-726425-6(5))* Oxford Univ. Pr., Inc.

Cock, Jan de. Denkmal III, 5 vols. 2008. (Illus.). 650p. *(978-90-808424-3-4(5))* Atelier Jan de Cock.

Coe, Debbie & Randy. Fenton Art Glass: A Centennial of Glass Making 1907 To 2007. 2007. (Schiffer Book for Collectors Ser.). (Illus.). 192p. pap. 35.00 *(978-0-7643-2794-0(1))* Schiffer Publishing, Ltd.

Cosh, Stephen R. & Neal, David S. Roman Mosaics of Britain Vol. 4: West Britain, Incorporating Wales, 4 vols. 2010. (ENG., Illus.). 470p. (C). 320.00 *(978-0-85431-294-8(3))* Society of Antiquaries of London GBR. Dist: Brown, David Bk. Co., The.

—Roman Mosaics of Britain Volume III: South-east Britain, 2 vols. 2008. (ENG., Illus.). 625p. (C). 400.00 *(978-0-85431-289-4(7))* Society of Antiquaries of London GBR. Dist: Brown, David Bk. Co., The.

Crosman, Christopher B. & Shapiro, Emily D. Celebrating the American Spirit: Masterworks from Crystal Bridges Museum of American Art. 2011. (ENG., Illus.). 356p. 60.00 ***(978-1-55595-371-3(9))*** Hudson Hills Pr. LLC.

Cullen, Deborah, ed. Nexus New York: Latin/American Artists in the Modern Metropolis. 2009. (ENG., Illus.). 288p. pap. 45.00 *(978-0-300-15896-0(3))* Yale Univ. Pr.

Cuno, James, selected by. Master Paintings in the Art Institute of Chicago. 3rd ed. 2009. (ENG., Illus.). 168p. 39.95 *(978-0-300-15103-9(9))* Art Institute of Chicago.

Curators Gallery Staff. Whitworth Art Gallery: Art Spaces. 2011. (ENG., Illus.). 64p. pap. 7.95 *(978-1-85759-585-7(8))* Scala, Editions FRA. Dist: National Bk. Network.

Curators of the Museum Staff. Fitzwilliam Museum. 2006. (ENG., Illus.). 256p. pap. 45.00 *(978-1-85759-344-0(8))* Scala, Editions FRA. Dist: National Bk. Network.

Curators of the Newark Museum Staff. Newark Museum: Selected Works. Venn, Beth F., ed. 2009. (ENG., Illus.). 168p. pap. 24.95 *(978-1-85759-588-8(2))* Scala, Editions FRA. Dist: National Bk. Network.

Curators of the The Royal Collection Staff. Treasures: The Royal Collection. Roberts, Jane, ed. 2010. (Illus.). 256p. 30.00 *(978-1-905686-05-6(6))* Royal Collection Enterprises Ltd. GBR. Dist: Chicago Distribution Ctr.

—Treasures: The Royal Collection. 2008. (ENG.). 256p. 50.00 *(978-1-85759-568-0(8))* Scala, Editions FRA. Dist: National Bk. Network.

Cushner, Jeremy, et al, eds. Copro/Nason Fine Art: Catalogue Raissone. 2007. (Illus.). 267p. 39.95 *(978-0-86719-676-4(9))* Last Gasp of San Francisco.

Czestochowski, Joseph S. & Swann, James. James Swann Prints: A Catalogue Raisonne. 2009. *(978-0-9716408-4-9(X))* International Arts.

Czestochowski, Joseph S., et al. Associated American Artists: Catalogue Raisonne, 1934-2000. 2010. *(978-0-9716408-6-3(6))* International Arts.

Daneo, Angelica. The Kress Collection at the Denver Art Museum. 2011. (ENG., Illus.). 168p. pap. 25.00 *(978-0-914738-69-5(0))* Denver Art Museum.

Danilowitz, Brenda & Weber, Nicolas Fox. The Prints of Josef Albers: A Catalogue Raisonné, 1915-1976. 2010. (ENG., Illus.). 240p. 95.00 *(978-1-55595-324-9(7))* Hudson Hills Pr. LLC.

Danto, Arthur C. June Wayne, a Catalogue Raisonne, 1936-2006: The Art of Everything. Conway, Robert, ed. 2007. (ENG.). 544p. (C). 125.00 *(978-0-8135-3824-2(6))* Rutgers Univ. Pr.

David Joseph Herrle. 158p. 4.99 *(978-0-9706843-0-1(4))* Herrle, David Joseph.

Dawson, Aileen. English & Irish Delftware 1570-1840. 2010. (ENG., Illus.). 320p. (C). 70.00 *(978-0-7141-2810-8(4))* British Museum Pr. GBR. Dist: Brown, David Bk. Co., The.

De, Aditi, et al. Lines from an Artistic Life: The Drawings of Adimoolam. 2008. (Illus.). 164p. 70.00 *(978-0-85331-982-5(0)*, Lund Humphries Pubs.) Ashgate Publishing, Ltd. GBR. Dist: Ashgate Publishing Co.

de Guitaut, Caroline. Royal Fabergé. 2011. (Illus.). 156p. 24.95 *(978-1-905686-37-7(4))* Royal Collection Enterprises Ltd. GBR. Dist: Chicago Distribution Ctr.

De Pillis, Mario S. & Goodwillie, Christian. Gather up the Fragments: The Andrews Shaker Collection. 2008. (ENG., Illus.). 400p. 75.00 *(978-0-300-13760-6(5))* Yale Univ. Pr.

Debroise, Olivier, ed. Informe. 2010. (ENG & SPA., Illus.). 246p. 40.00 *(978-968-9056-35-5(2))* Turner, Ediciones S.A. ESP. Dist: D.A.P./Distributed Art Pubs.

DeFurio, Steve, photos by. The World of Andy Anderson. 2007. (Illus.). 68p. 34.99 *(978-0-9799984-0-9(9))* High Noon Western Americana.

Deputy Director of Curatorial Affairs Staff & Departmental Curators of the Museum Staff. Cincinnati Art Museum: Collection Highlights. 2009. (ENG., Illus.). 392p. 49.95 *(978-1-904832-53-9(9))* Giles, D. Ltd. GBR. Dist: Antique Collectors' Club.

Des Rochers, Jacques, ed. Quebec & Canadian Art: The Montreal Museum of Fine Arts' Collection: Volume I. 2012. (ENG., Illus.). 400p. 55.00 ***(978-2-89192-355-2(3))*** Abrams.

Di Ozesanmuseum Bamberg, et al, eds. Fragiles: Porcelain, Glass & Ceramics. 2008. (Illus.). 279p. *(978-3-89955-208-9(3))* Die Gestalten Verlag.

Dolkart, Judith F., et al. Masterworks - The Barnes Foundation. 2012. (ENG., Illus.). 374p. 40.00 ***(978-0-8478-3806-6(4)***, Skira) Rizzoli International Pubns., Inc.

Dorfles, Gillo & Hockemeyer, Lisa. The Hockemeyer Collection: 20th Century Italian Ceramic Art. 2009. (GER, ITA & ENG., Illus.). 240p. (C). 138.00 *(978-3-7774-2271-8(1))* Hirmer Verlag GmbH DEU. Dist: Brown, David Bk. Co., The.

Draper, James David. Cameo Appearances. 2008. (ENG., Illus.). 56p. pap. 19.95 *(978-0-300-14145-0(9))* Yale Univ. Pr.

Dreishpoon, Douglas, ed. The Long Curve: 150 Years of Visionary Collecting at the Albright-Knox Art Gallery. 2011. (ENG., Illus.). 268p. 65.00 ***(978-88-572-1040-7(5))*** Skira Editore ITA. Dist: Random Hse., Inc.

Dubois, Hughes, photos by. Solomon Islands Art: The Conru Collection. 2008. (ENG., Illus.). 256p. 125.00 *(978-88-7439-493-7(4))* 5 Continents ITA. Dist: Hachette Bk. Group.

Duggan, Ginger Gregg & Fox, Judith Hoos. Under Control. 2010. (Illus.). 60p. pap. 25.00 *(978-1-883015-43-5(X))* Univ. of Washington Pr.

Dulce, Román, et al. American Selections from the Samuel P. Harn Museum of Art. 2009. (ENG., Illus.). 160p. pap. 29.95 *(978-0-9762552-8-4(6))* Univ. Pr. of Florida.

Duncan, Alastair. High Style: Masterworks from the Bernard & Sylvia Ostry Collection in the Royal Ontario Museum. 2006. (ENG., Illus.). 148p. *(978-0-88854-446-9(4))* Royal Ontario Museum.

Dunkley, Tina Maria & Cullum, Jerry. In the Eye of the Muses: Selections from the Clark Atlanta University Art Collection. 2012. ***(978-0-615-59005-9(5))*** Massachusetts College of Art.

Dunlap, William. Dunlap. 2006. (ENG., Illus.). 144p. 45.00 *(978-1-57806-904-0(1))* Univ. Pr. of Mississippi.

Dupui-Labbé, Dominique, et al. Picasso Horses. 2010. (ENG., Illus.). 176p. 65.00 *(978-1-55595-360-7(3))* Hudson Hills Pr. LLC.

Duvivier, C., et al. Gregory Masurovsky: Drawings. Somogy Edition D'Art Staff, ed. 2008. (FRE & ENG., Illus.). 112p. pap. *(978-2-7572-0147-3(6))* Somogy Editions d'Art.

Eaton, Erica & Smelt, Tara. The Minutiae of Visionaries: Experiments Toward Social Evolution. 2010. 168p. pap. 54.40 *(978-0-578-03235-1(X))* Evolutionary Girls.

Eder, Martin. Martin Eder: Der Blasse Tanz. 2010. (GER & ENG., Illus.). 320p. 65.00 *(978-3-7913-4442-3(0))* Prestel Verlag GmbH & Co KG. DEU. Dist: Prestel Publishing.

Egli, Michael, et al. Meisterwerke und Kleinode: Sammlung der Peyerschen Tobias Stimmer-Stiftung, Museum zu Allerheiligen, Schaffhausen. Gesamtkatalog. The Swiss Institute for Art Research SIK-ISEA. Essays by Walter R. C. Abegglen, ed. 2010. (Illus.). 156p. ***(978-3-85881-135-6(1))*** Antique Collectors' Club.

Ekhtiar, Maryam. Masterpieces from the Department of Islamic Art in the Metropolitan Museum of Art. 2011. (Illus.). xiii, 431p. ***(978-1-58839-434-7(4))***; pap. ***(978-1-58839-435-4(2))*** Metropolitan Museum of Art, The.

Ekserdjian, David, ed. Treasures from Budapest: European Masterpieces from Leonardo to Schiele. 2011. (ENG., Illus.). 288p. 60.00 *(978-1-905711-80-2(8))* Royal Academy of Arts GBR. Dist: Hachette Bk. Group.

El Glaoui, Hassan & Churchill, Winston. Meetings in Marrakech: The Paintings of Hassan el Glaoui & Winston Churchill. Glaoui, Touria El, ed. 2012. (ENG., Illus.). 96p. pap. 40.00 ***(978-88-572-1241-8(6))*** Skira Editore ITA. Dist: Random Hse., Inc.

Elaine, James, et al, texts. Hammer Projects. 2009. (ENG., Illus.). 432p. 60.00 *(978-0-943739-35-9(7))* Hammer Museum.

Elliott, Patrick. Another World: Dalí, Magritte, Miró & the Surrealists. 2011. (ENG., Illus.). 224p. pap. *(978-1-906270-30-8(9))* National Galleries of Scotland.

Ellis, Marianne. Embroideries & Samplers from Islamic Egypt. 2006. (ENG., Illus.). 96p. 39.95 *(978-1-85444-154-6(X)*, 154X) Ashmolean Museum GBR. Dist: Antique Collectors' Club.

Ellis, Ray G. By the Light of the Moon: Paintings of Ray Ellis. 2007. (Illus.). 108p. 40.00 *(978-0-9641967-5-9(1))* Compass Publishing.

Emison, Patricia. The Simple Art: Printed Images in an Age of Magnificence. 2006. (Illus.). 100p. per. 25.00 *(978-0-9648953-5-5(8))* Univ. of New Hampshire, Museum of Art.

English, Darby. How to See a Work of Art in Total Darkness. 2007. (ENG., Illus.). 376p. (gr. 17). 32.00 *(978-0-262-05083-8(8))* MIT Pr.

Erdman, Matthijs. Nieuw Realisme: 159 Kunstwerken Uit de Collectie Van Het Voormalige Scheringa Museum Voor Realisme. 2010. (DUT., Illus.). 232p. *(978-90-8910-182-2(9))* D'jonge Hond.

Esher Collection. (Illus.). 18p. Pt. 2. pap. 85.00 *(978-1-56762-036-8(1))*Pt. 3. pap. 85.00 *(978-1-56762-037-5(X))* Modern Learning Pr.

Faber, Paul & Floor, Rob. African Signs. 2010. (Illus.). 210p. 45.00 *(978-94-6022-080-7(0))* Royal Tropical Institute Pr. (KIT (Koninklijk Instituut voor de Tropen) NLD. Dist: Stylus Publishing, LLC.

Fabre, Jan. Jan Fabre: Hortus Corpus. 2011. (ENG., Illus.). 224p. 50.00 ***(978-90-5662-816-1(X))*** NAi Uitgevers / Publishers Stichting NLD. Dist: D.A.P./Distributed Art Pubs.

Fabre, Jan & Di Pietrantonio, Giacinto. Jan Fabre: Homo Faber: Drawings, Performances, Photoworks, Films, Sculptures & Installations. 2009. (ENG., Illus.). 400p. 100.00 *(978-90-6153-649-9(9))* Mercatorfonds N. V. BEL. Dist: D.A.P./Distributed Art Pubs.

Fahlman, Betsy. Wonders of Work & Labor: The Steidle Collection of American Industrial Art. 2008. (Illus.). 176p. 50.00 *(978-0-615-23428-1(3))* Earth & Mineral Sciences Museum & Art Gallery.

Fairey, Shepard. May Day. 2011. (Illus.). 133p. *(978-1-58423-428-9(8))* Gingko Pr., Inc.

Falberg, Bill, ed. United States Multiple Advertising & Discount Postal Cards: A Handbook Originally in 1982 by David G. Nussmann, Charles A. Fricke & George S. Norton. 2007. (Illus.). 180p. *(978-0-9800112-0-3(5))* United Postal Stationery Society.

Farnsworth, Donald, photos by. The Magnolia Tapestry Project. 2007. (Illus.). 129p. 58.00 *(978-0-9799164-2-7(9))* Magnolia Editions.

Farrell, Jennifer. Get There First, Decide Promptly: The Richard Brown Baker Collection of Postwar Art. 2012. (ENG., Illus.). 372p. 50.00 *(978-0-300-15302-6(3))* Yale Univ. Art Gallery.

Fennimore, Donald L. Delaware Silver: The Col. Kenneth P. & Regina I. Brown Collection. 2008. *(978-1-893287-10-5(6))*; pap. *(978-1-893287-11-2(4))* Biggs, Sewell C. Museum of American Art.

—Iron at Winterthur. 2010. (ENG.). 428p. 45.00 *(978-1-4379-7079-1(6))* DIANE Publishing Co.

Fenz, Werner, et al, eds. Kunst im öffentlichen Raum Steiermark. Art in Public Space Styria: Projekte / Projects 2007-2008. 2010. 344p. pap. *(978-3-7091-0118-6(2))* Actar Birkhauser Distribution.

Fillmore, Sarah. Jacques Hurtubise: Catalogue Raisonné. 2011. (FRE & ENG., Illus.). 256p. 60.00 ***(978-0-86492-662-3(6))*** Goose Lane Editions CAN. Dist: Univ. of Toronto Pr.

Fishel, Catharine & Gardner, Bill. LogoLounge 3: 2000 International Identities by Leading Designers. 2009. (ENG., Illus.). 376p. pap. 19.99 *(978-1-59253-510-1(0)*, 1592535100, Rockport Publishers) Quayside.

Fisher Sterling, Susan. Women Artists: The National Museum of Women in the Arts. 2nd ed. 2010. (Tiny Folio Ser.). (ENG., Illus.). 320p. 11.95 *(978-0-7892-1053-1(3))* Abbeville Pr., Inc.

Fliegel, Stephen N. Arms & Armor: The Cleveland Museum of Art. 2007. (Illus.). 200p. *(978-0-940717-93-0(X))* Cleveland Museum of Art.

—Arms & Armor: The Cleveland Museum of Art. rev. ed. 2008. (ENG., Illus.). 200p. 55.00 *(978-0-940717-92-3(1))* Distribution General.

Flood, Kathy. Warman's Jewelry: Identification & Price Guide. 4th ed. 2010. (ENG., Illus.). 288p. pap. 29.99 *(978-1-4402-0801-0(8))* Krause Pubns.

Flynn, Ron. The Audubon Price Guide Book. 2008. 252p. pap. 59.95 *(978-1-4357-0809-9(1))* Lulu Enterprises Inc.

Folga-Januszewska, Dorota & Majewski, Lech. The Mystic Middle Ages. 2008. 160p. 50.00 *(978-83-87730-59-8(9))* Bosz, Szymanik i wspolnicky POL. Dist: Independent Pubs. Group.

Fomsgaard, Jes & D.C.A. Gallery, contrib. by. Jes Fomsgaard: DCA Gallery. (Illus.). *(978-87-88223-60-6(4))* Galerie Asbaek.

Fomsgaard, Jes & Thau, Carsten. Jes Fomsgaard: Incorporating Architecture. 2009. (DAN, MUL & ENG., Illus.). 116p. *(978-87-92420-05-3(2))* Bogværket.

Foucart-Walter, Elisbeth, et al. Jewels in the Louvre. 2009. (ENG., Illus.). 80p. 19.95 *(978-2-08-030078-2(4))* Flammarion et Cie FRA. Dist: Random Hse., Inc.

—Love: In the Louvre. 2009. (ENG., Illus.). 80p. 19.95 *(978-2-08-030077-5(6))* Flammarion et Cie FRA. Dist: Random Hse., Inc.

Fox Weber, Nicholas & Danilowitz, Brenda, eds. The Prints of Anni Albers: Catalogue Raisonne. 2009. (ENG., Illus.). 200p. 70.00 *(978-84-92480-52-4(1))* RM Verlag, S.L. ESP. Dist: D.A.P./Distributed Art Pubs.

Frank, Michael & Reilly Sacco, Louise. The Museum of Bad Art: Masterworks. 2008. (ENG., Illus.). 128p. 14.95 *(978-1-58008-911-1(9))* Ten Speed Pr.

Franses, Michael. Textiles Carpets: Part One. 2012. (Nkd collection of islamic Art Ser.). (ENG.). (C). 180.00 *(978-1-874780-78-6(1))* Kibo Foundation (UK), Ltd. GBR. Dist: Brown, David Bk. Co., The.

Franz Gertsch: Large-Scale Woodcuts. pap. *(978-3-7165-0537-3(4))* Benteli Verlag.

Freda, Anthony. Freda. 2008. (Illus.). 22.99 *(978-1-4257-9063-9(1))* Xlibris Corp.

Fredericq, Suzanne. Catalogue of the Inaugural Art Exhibit Eugene J. Martin: Spice of Life. 2009. 38p. 19.70 *(978-0-9825704-0-1(6))* Estate of Eugene James Martin.

Frei, Mathias, et al. Hugo Atzwanger: 1883 - 1960 Maler, Zeichner, Lichtbildner, Heimatkundler. 2010. (GER., Illus.). 151p. *(978-88-8266-703-0(0))* Athesia.

Freiman, Lisa, ed. Adam Ames & Andrew Bordwin: Type A. 2010. (ENG., Illus.). 128p. 55.00 *(978-3-7757-2529-3(6))* Hatje Cantz Verlag GmbH & Co KG DEU. Dist: D.A.P./Distributed Art Pubs.

Friede, John, et al, eds. New Guinea Highlands: Art from the Jolika Collection. 2011. (Illus.). 672p. 120.00 *(978-3-7913-5055-4(2))* Prestel Publishing.

Friedel, Helmut & Hoberg, Annegret, eds. The Blue Rider: A Dance in Colour: Watercolours, Drawings & Prints from the Lenbachhaus Munich. 2011. (Illus.). 264p. 65.00 *(978-3-7774-3271-7(7))* Hirmer Verlag GmbH DEU. Dist: Chicago Distribution Ctr.

Gan, Stephen. Visionaire No. 27: Homme. 150.00 *(978-1-888645-08-8(3))* Visionaire Publishing.

Gardner, Bill & Fishel, Catharine. LogoLounge 5: 2,000 International Identities by Leading Designers. 2009. (ENG., Illus.). 192p. 50.00 *(978-1-59253-527-9(5)*, 1592535275) Quayside.

Genius Loci. 2011. 110p. 29.95 *(978-84-937610-9-7(5))* Fundacio Joan Miro ESP. Dist: Actar Birkhauser Distribution.

Gilje, Karianne Bjellås, ed. Grete Prytz Kittelsen: The Art of Enamel Design. 2012. (ENG., Illus.). 296p. 55.00 ***(978-0-393-73331-0(9)***, 73331) Norton, W. W. & Co., Inc.

Gill, Gagan & Lal, Sham. Ram Kumar: A Journey Within. 2010. (ENG., Illus.). 239p. 55.00 *(978-81-87737-08-7(5)*, Vadehra Art Gallery (Acc)) Antique Collectors' Club GBR. Dist: National Bk. Network.

Giusti, Annamaria & Koeppe, Wolfram, eds. Art of the Royal Court: Treasures in Pietre Dure from the Palaces of Europe. 2008. (ENG., Illus.). 428p. 65.00 *(978-0-300-13672-2(2))* Yale Univ. Pr.

Giusti Galardi, Giovanna. Vivere in Coppia Al Museo: Percorsi in Libertà Alla Galleria Degli Uffizi. 2010. (Illus.). 71p. *(978-88-8347-560-3(7))* Sillabe.

Gleissner, Stephen. Sue Jean Covacovich: Pioneer Kansas Abstract Artist. 2006. (Illus.). 36p. 15.00 *(978-0-939324-52-1(0))* Wichita Art Museum.

Gold & Silver Plate Catalog: Exhibition of Historic Plate at Goldsmith Hall, 2 vols. pap. 25.00 *(978-0-87556-424-1(0))* Saifer, Albert Pub.

Goldberg, Joseph, et al. Joseph Goldberg: Jeweled Earth. 2008. (Thomas T. Wilson Ser.). (ENG., Illus.). 80p. 29.95 *(978-0-295-98767-5(7))* Univ. of Washington Pr.

Goldstein, Ann, et al. This Is Not to Be Looked At: Highlights from the Permanent Collection of the Museum of Contemporary Art, Los Angeles. 2008. (ENG., Illus.). 384p. 59.95 *(978-1-933751-07-8(X))* Museum of Contemporary Art, Los Angeles.

Gonzalez, Mark. Solid-Colored Dinnerware: Depression to Mid-Century. 2008. (Schiffer Book for Collectors Ser.). (Illus.). 160p. pap. 29.95 (978-0-7643-2846-6(8)) Schiffer Publishing, Ltd.

Gordon, Robert & Butterfield, Deborah. Deborah Butterfield. 2010. (ENG., Illus.). 196p. pap. 40.00 (978-0-8109-8947-4(6)) Abrams

Gorecki, Joachim. Die Fundmünzen der Römischen Zeit in Deutschland: Abteilung IV: Rheinland-Pfalz. Band 1, Nachtrag 1: Stadt Mainz. 2006. (GER., Illus.). 591p. 99.00 (978-3-8053-3643-7(8)) Zabern, Philipp von Verlag, GmbH DEU. Dist: Brown, David Bk. Co., The.

Goring, E., et al. Kevin Coates: A Hidden Alchemy - Goldsmithing - Jewels & Tablepieces. 2008. (ENG., Illus.). 312p. 75.00 (978-3-89790-284-8(2)) Arnoldsche Art Pubs. DEU. Dist: Antique Collectors' Club.

Grabner, et al. Can I Come over to Your House? The First Ten Years of the Suburban 1999-2009. 2009. (978-1-61623-082-1(7)) Independent Pub.

Grasslin, Karola & Cadere, André. André Cadere: Catalogue Raisonné. 2009. (FRE, GER & ENG., Illus.). 208p. pap. 45.00 (978-3-86560-358-6(0)) Verlag der Buchhandlung Walther Konig DEU. Dist: D.A.P./Distributed Art Pubs.

Gunn, Ann V. The Prints of Wilhelmina Barns-Graham: A Complete Catalogue. 2007. (Illus.). 160p. 80.00 (978-0-85331-969-6(3), Lund Humphries Pubs.) Ashgate Publishing, Ltd. GBR. Dist: Ashgate Publishing Co.

Gurganus, Allan, text. James Castle. 2007. (Illus.). 72p. per. 30.00 (978-1-883597-07-8(2)) Markey, Lawrence Inc.

Gust, Frauke, et al, texts. Concepts of Love. 2009. (ENG., Illus.). 144p. pap. 25.00 (978-3-86560-427-9(7)) Verlag der Buchhandlung Walther Konig DEU. Dist: D.A.P./Distributed Art Pubs.

Halfpenny, Patricia A., et al. Success to America: Creamware for the American Market. 2010. (ENG., Illus.). 304p. (978-1-85149-631-0(9), Antique Collectors Club Dist) Antique Collectors' Club.

Hall, Sarah J. & McPherson, Craig. Steel: Pittsburgh Drawings by Craig Mcpherson. 2008. (Illus.). 48p. pap. 14.95 (978-0-9703425-9-1(4)) Frick Art & Historical Ctr.,The.

Halsey, William & Blackman, Lynne. William Halsey: Mastery of the Modern. 2006. (978-0-9785365-1-0(7)) Charleston Renaissance Gallery, The.

Hamilton, Ann. Ann Hamilton: An Inventory of Objects, 1 vol. 2006. (ENG., Illus.). 264p. 60.00 (978-0-9743648-5-8(1)) Miller, Gregory & Co.

Haniel, Franz, ed. The Haniel Collection. 2011. (ENG., Illus.). 320p. 89.00 (978-3-8030-3351-2(9)) Wasmuth, Ernst J. Verlag GmbH & Co. DEU. Dist: D.A.P./Distributed Art Pubs.

Hans Hofmann: Exuberant Eye. 2007. per. (978-0-9795323-0-6(2)) KN Gallery.

Hanson, Marin F. & Crews, Patricia Cox, eds. American Quilts in the Modern Age, 1870-1940: The International Quilt Study Center Collections. 2009. (ENG., Illus.). 496p. 90.00 (978-0-8032-2054-6(5)) Univ. of Nebraska Pr.

Harding, A. & N. Victorian Staffordshire Figures 1835-1875: Book Four. 2007. (Illus.). 320p. pap. 95.00 (978-0-7643-2762-9(3)) Schiffer Publishing, Ltd.

Harris, Adam Duncan. Wildlife in American Art: Masterworks from the National Museum of Wildlife Art. 2009. (ENG.). 320p. (C). 55.00 (978-0-8061-4015-5(1)) Univ. of Oklahoma Pr.

Harrison, Jeff, et al. Collecting with Vision: Treasures from the Chrysler Museum of Art. 2007. (ENG., Illus.). 160p. 35.00 (978-1-904832-33-1(4)) Giles, D. Ltd. GBR. Dist: Antique Collectors' Club.

Hartop, Christopher. British & Irish Silver in the Fogg Art Museum, Harvard University Art Museums. 2007. (Illus.). 263p. (978-1-891771-46-0(9)) Harvard Univ. Art Museums.

Haustein-Bartsch, Eva & Wolf, Norbert, eds. Icons. 2008. (ENG., Illus.). 96p. pap. 9.99 (978-3-8228-5478-5(6)) TASCHEN DEU. Dist: Ingram Pub. Services.

Hayon, Jaime. Jaime Hayon Works. 2008. (Illus.). 317p. (978-3-89955-207-2(5)) Die Gestalten Verlag.

Hazen, Peggy. A Museum Visitor's Guide. 2006. per. 10.00 (978-1-59971-857-6(X)) Aardvark Global Publishing.

Hebgin-Barnes, Penny. The Medieval Stained Glass of Cheshire. 2010. (ENG., Illus.). 642p. 210.00 (978-0-19-726469-0(7)) Oxford Univ. Pr., Inc.

Heckscher, Morrison H. The American Wing at the Metropolitan Museum of Art: A Walking Guide. 2012. (ENG., Illus.). 96p. pap. 9.95 (978-1-85759-742-4(7)) Scala, Editions FRA. Dist: National Bk. Network.

Heilingsetzer, Semiran, ed. Thage: Malerei zwischen Konvention und Avantgarde. 2009. (GER.). 159p. 47.95 (978-3-631-58203-9(X)) Lang, Peter GmbH, Europaischer Verlag der Wissenschaften DEU. Dist: Lang, Peter.

Helke, Gun-Dagmar. Deckelterrinen des 18. Jahrhunderts aus Fayence und Zinn: Eine Sammlung auf Gut Hohen Luckow. 2007. (GER., Illus.). 144p. (C). pap. 42.00 (978-3-7774-3865-8(0)) Hirmer Verlag GmbH DEU. Dist: Brown, David Bk. Co., The.

Heller, Ena Giurescu. Reluctant Partners: Art & Religion in Dialogue. 2006. (Illus.). 200p. 29.50 (978-1-58516-772-2(X)) American Bible Society.

Hemachandra, Ray & Galloway, Julia. 500 Vases: Contemporary Explorations of a Timeless Form. 2010. (500 Ser.). (ENG., Illus.). 420p. pap. 24.95 (978-1-60059-246-1(5)) Lark Bks.

Henderson, James D., Jr. Royal Austria Porcelain. 2008. (Illus.). 272p. bds. 59.95 (978-0-7643-2820-6(4)) Schiffer Publishing, Ltd.

Herford, Marta. 'Ad Absurdum' Energien des Absurden von der klassischen Moderne zur Gegenwart.Energies of the Absurd from modernism til today. 2009. (GER & ENG., Illus.). 1152p. 29.50 (978-3-86678-130-6(X)) Kerber Verlag DEU. Dist: D.A.P./Distributed Art Pubs.

Hertz, Betti-Sue. Eleanor Antin: Historical Takes. 2008. (Illus.). 128p. pap. 45.00 (978-3-7913-4055-5(7)) Prestel Publishing.

Hess, Donald & Steiner, Myrtha, texts. Hess Art Collection. 2010. (ENG., Illus.). 372p. 60.00 (978-3-7757-2139-4(8)) Hatje Cantz Verlag GmbH & Co KG DEU. Dist: D.A.P./Distributed Art Pubs.

Hicks, Alistar. Contemporary Art at Deutsche Bank. (Illus.). 167p. 39.95 (978-3-89322-825-6(X)) Edition Cantz DEU. Dist: D.A.P./Distributed Art Pubs.

Hicks, Bob, et al. Beth Van Hoesen: Catalogue Raisonne of Limited-Edition Prints, Books, & Portfolios. 2011. (ENG., Illus.). 592p. 95.00 (978-1-55595-344-7(1)) Hudson Hills Pr. LLC.

Higgott, Suzanne. Wallace Collection Catalogue of Glass & Limoges Painted Enamels. 2011. (Illus.). 400p. 175.00 (978-0-900785-85-6(3)) Holberton, Paul Publishing GBR. Dist: Casemate Pubs. & Bk. Distributors, LLC.

Hill, J. D., ed. Masterpieces of the British Museum. 2009. (ENG., Illus.). 288p. (C). pap. 35.00 (978-0-7141-5068-0(1)) British Museum Pr. GBR. Dist: Brown, David Bk. Co., The.

Hinton, Jack. The Art of German Stoneware Ceramics, 1300-1900: From the Charles W. Nichols Collection & the Philadelphia Museum of Art. 2012. (ENG., Illus.). 60p. pap. 20.00 (978-0-300-17978-1(2)) Yale Univ. Pr.

Hirst, Damien. The Death of God. Beard, Jason, ed. 2008. (ENG., Illus.). 170p. pap. 65.00 (978-1-904212-13-3(1)); 168p. pap. 200.00 (978-1-904212-27-0(1)) Other Criteria GBR. Dist: Hachette Bk. Group.

Holladay, Wilhelmina Cole. A Museum of Their Own: The National Museum of Women in the Arts, 1987-2007. 2008. (ENG., Illus.). 240p. 50.00 (978-0-7892-1003-6(7)) Abbeville Pr., Inc.

Holler, Carsten. Carsten Holler. 2011. (ENG., Illus.). 288p. 75.00 (978-3-7757-2395-4(1)) Hatje Cantz Verlag GmbH & Co KG DEU. Dist: D.A.P./Distributed Art Pubs.

Houdouin, Guy. Odon: Sourcier, Sorcier, Magicien. 2010. (FRE & ENG., Illus.). 304p. 110.00 (978-2-35340-041-6(8)) Gourcuff Gradenigo FRA. Dist: National Bk. Network.

Hovens, Pieter. The American Indian Material Culture: Ten Kate Collection, 1882-1888. 2010. (ENG., Illus.). 282p. pap. 39.00 (978-3-9811620-1-1(3)) ZKF Pubs. DEU. Dist: Univ. of Nebraska Pr.

Hu, Philip K. Later Chinese Bronzes: The Saint Louis Art Museum & Robert E. Kresko Collections. Steiner, Mary Ann, ed. 2008. (ENG & CHI., Illus.). 208p. pap. 39.95 (978-0-89178-092-2(0)) St. Louis Art Museum.

Huldisch, Henriette & Momin, Shamim M. Whitney Biennial 2008. 2008. (ENG., Illus.). 288p. pap. 45.00 (978-0-300-13689-0(7)) Yale Univ. Pr.

Huping, Xu. Treasures of the Nanjing Museum. 2006. (ENG., Illus.). 128p. pap. (978-962-86215-1-4(3)) London Editions (HK), Ltd.

Husfloen, Kyle. Antique Trader Pottery & Porcelain Ceramics. 6th ed. 2009. (ENG., Illus.). 768p. pap. 25.99 (978-0-89689-933-9(0)) Krause Pubns.

Husslein-Arco, Agnes. Barock: Meisterwerke Im Belvedere. 2008. (GER., Illus.). 367p. (978-3-901508-43-1(0)) Bibliothek der Provinz, Verlag fur Litteratur Kunst & Musikalien.

Iles, Chrissie, et al. A Decade in Conversation: A Ten-Year Celebration of the Bucksbaum Award, 2000-2010 - With Interviews with Paul Pfeiffer, Irit Batsry, Raymond Pettibon, Mark Bradford, & Omer Fast. 2010. (Illus.). 88p. 19.95 (978-0-300-16755-9(5)) Yale Univ. Pr.

Ilsoe, Harald. Biblioteker til Salg: Om danske bogauktioner og Kataloger 1661-1811. 280p. 54.00 (978-87-635-0447-8(2)) Museum Tusculanum Pr. DNK. Dist: Chicago Distribution Ctr.

Impey, Oliver R., et al. Dragons, Tigers & Bamboo: Japanese Porcelain & Its Impact on Europe, 1 vol. 2009. (ENG., Illus.). 192p. 49.95 (978-1-55365-434-6(X)) D&M Pubs. Inc. CAN. Dist: Perseus-PGW

Israel, Nico. Meg Cranston. 2008. (ENG., Illus.). 202p. pap. 49.00 (978-3-905829-34-1(7)) JRP Ringier Kunstverlag AG CHE. Dist: D.A.P./Distributed Art Pubs.

J Paul Getty Museum. The J. Paul Getty Museum Handbook of the Collections. 7th ed. 2007. (Illus.). 336p. 26.95 (978-0-89236-886-0(1)); pap. 16.95 (978-0-89236-887-7(X)) Oxford Univ. Pr., Inc.

J. Paul Getty Museum Staff, contrib. by. The Antiquities Collection. 2nd ed. 2010. (978-0-89236-997-3(3), J. Paul Getty Museum) Getty Pubns.

Jaeger, Falk, ed. Wingårdhs. 2010. (ENG & GER., Illus.). 144p. pap. 39.95 (978-3-86859-035-7(8)) Jovis Verlag GmbH DEU. Dist: D.A.P./Distributed Art Pubs.

Jaffe, David. Rubens's Massacre of the Innocents in the Thomson Collection. 2009. (Illus.). 128p. pap. 50.00 (978-1-903470-81-7(1)) Holberton, Paul Publishing GBR. Dist: Casemate Pubs. & Bk. Distributors, LLC.

The James T. Bialac Collection: Selected Works. 2012. (978-0-8061-4299-9(5)); pap. (978-0-8061-4304-0(5)) Univ. of Oklahoma Pr.

Jensen, Sergej, et al. Sergej Jensen, 1 vol. 2011. (ENG & GER., Illus.). 300p. pap. 60.00 (978-3-942405-06-5(7)) Die Gestalten Verlag DEU. Dist: Prestel Publishing.

Jirka-Schmitz, Patrizia. The World of Netsuke: The Werdelmann Collection at the Museum Kunst. 2007. (ENG., Illus.). 320p. 135.00 (978-3-89790-209-1(5)) Arnoldsche Art Pubs. DEU. Dist: Antique Collectors' Club.

John Young: Silhouettes & Polychromes. pap. (978-1-86395-399-3(X)) Bookman Pr.

Johns, Catherine. The Hoxne Late Roman Treasure: Gold Jewellery & Silver Plate. 2010. (ENG., Illus.). 288p. (C). 120.00 (978-0-7141-1817-8(6)) British Museum Pr. GBR. Dist: Brown, David Bk. Co., The.

Johns, Elizabeth, et al. One Hundred Stories: Highlights from the Washington County Museum of Fine Arts. 2008. (ENG., Illus.). 232p. 49.95 (978-1-904832-54-6(7)) Giles, D. Ltd. GBR. Dist: Antique Collectors' Club.

Johnson, Donald-Brian & Pina, Leslie. Deco Decor: Porcelain, Glass, & Metal Accessories for the Home. 2009. (Illus.). 240p. bds. 69.99 (978-0-7643-3178-7(7)) Schiffer Publishing, Ltd.

Johnson, Jacqueline. Classic Perfume Advertising: 1920-1970. 2007. (Illus.). 192p. pap. 39.95 (978-0-7643-2741-4(0)) Schiffer Publishing, Ltd.

Joo, Michael, et al. Joo, 87-07. 2008. (ENG., Illus.). 260p. 150.00 (978-1-904212-10-2(7)) Other Criteria GBR. Dist: Hachette Bk. Group.

Kadour, Ric Kasini, afterword by. 2007 Art's Alive Festival of Fine Art Festival Catalog. 2007. per. 25.00 (978-0-9771397-2-9(7)) Kasini Hse.

Kaeppler, Adrienne L. & Kaeppler, Adrienne Lois. Polynesia: The Mark & Carolyn Blackburn Collection of Polynesian Art. 2010. (Illus.). xxxv, 410p. (978-1-883528-38-6(0)) Al Pohaku Pr.

Kaeppler, Adrienne Lois. Polynesia: The Mark & Carolyn Blackburn Collection of Polynesian Art. 2010. (Illus.). xxxv, 410p. (978-1-883528-40-9(2)) Al Pohaku Pr.

Kaltwasser, Martin & Kobberling, Folke. Ressource Stadt - City as a Resource: One man's trash is another man's treasure, 1 vol. 2007. (ENG & GER., Illus.). 128p. pap. 29.95 (978-3-939633-07-5(0)) Jovis Verlag GmbH DEU. Dist: D.A.P./Distributed Art Pubs.

Kames, Andrea & Thistlethwaite, Mark. Modern Art Museum of Fort Worth: 110 Masterworks. Auping, Michael, tr. & intro. by. 2006. (ENG., Illus.). 45.00 (978-1-903942-14-7(4), Third Millenium Pub Ltd) Antique Collectors' Club GBR. Dist: National Bk. Network.

Kaneda, Shirley & text. Shirley Kaneda: New Paintings. 2007. (Illus.). 30p. per. (978-0-9795501-0-2(6)) Danese.

Karapetian, Vartan, et al. Armenia: Imprints of a Civilization. 2012. (ENG., Illus.). 408p. 75.00 (978-88-572-1244-9(0)) Skira Editore ITA. Dist: Random Hse., Inc.

Kargl, Georg, ed. Carter - an Arm with Hair: (the Vienna Catalogue, 1973) 2008. (Illus.). 176p. 29.95 (978-3-7082-3254-6(2)) Skarabaeus AUT. Dist: SCB Distributors.

Kasner, Stephen. Stephen Kasner: Works: 1993-2006. 2007. (Illus.). 160p. pap. 29.95 (978-0-9764035-6-2(0)) Scapegoat Publishing.

Kasner, Stephen & Hellion, Dwid. Stephen Kasner: Works 1993-2006. 160p. 39.95 (978-0-9764035-5-5(2)) Scapegoat Publishing.

Keefe, John Webster. Fabergé: The Hodges Family Collection. O'Shello, Wanda, ed. 2009. (ENG., Illus.). 310p. 65.00 (978-0-89494-108-5(9)) New Orleans Museum of Art.

Kelvingrove Art Gallery Staff. The Curators & Employees of Kelvingrove Art Gallery & Museum. 2009. (ENG., Illus.). 128p. pap. 20.00 (978-0-85667-665-9(9)) Wilson, Philip Pubs., Ltd. GBR. Dist: Macmillan.

Kemp, Dominic, et al. Terry Frost Prints: A Catalogue Raisonne. 2010. (Illus.). 304p. 90.00 (978-1-84822-035-5(9), Lund Humphries Pubs.) Ashgate Publishing, Ltd. GBR. Dist: Ashgate Publishing Co.

Kennedy, S. B. & Henry, Paul. Paul Henry: Paintings, Drawings, Illustrations. 2007. (ENG., Illus.). 416p. 125.00 (978-0-300-11712-7(4)) Yale Univ. Pr.

Kerr, Kavar, selected by. The Heart of a Collection: National Museum of Wildlife Art: Highlights of the NMWA Collection. 2012. (978-1-57864-707-1(X)) Donning Co. Pubs.

Keusch, Beat & Voss, Jan, eds. Dieter Roth: Souvenirs. 2011. (GER & ENG., Illus.). 152p. 85.00 (978-3-7757-2818-8(X)) Hatje Cantz Verlag GmbH & Co KG DEU. Dist: D.A.P./Distributed Art Pubs.

Kilimnik, Karen & Schaffner, Ingrid. Karen Kilimnik, 1 vol. 2007. (ENG., Illus.). 207p. 45.00 (978-0-88454-110-3(X)) Univ. of Pennsylvania, Institute of Contemporary Art.

King, Emily & Schouwenberg, Louise, texts. The ABC of De Designpolitie. 2008. (ENG., Illus.). 480p. 45.00 (978-90-78088-21-9(4)) Valiz NLD. Dist: D.A.P./Distributed Art Pubs.

Kinsey, Bernard W. & Kinsey, Shirley Pooler. The Kinsey Collection, Collector's Edition: Shared Treasures of Bernard & Shirley Kinsey: Where Art & History Intersect. 2010. (Illus.). 160p. 99.95 (978-0-9826225-1-3(1)) Allen, Charles Imaging Experts.

Kisluk-Grosheide, Danielle O. & Munger, Jeffrey. The Wrightsman Galleries for French Decorative Arts, the Metropolitan Museum of Art. 2010. (Illus.). 272p. 40.00 (978-0-300-15520-4(4)) Yale Univ. Pr.

Kisluk-Grosheide, Danielle O. & Munger, Jeffrey H. The Wrightsman Galleries for French Decorative Arts, the Metropolitan Museum of Art. 2010. (Illus.). xii, 259p. 40.00 (978-1-58839-366-1(6)) Metropolitan Museum of Art, The.

Kjellgren, Eric. Oceania: Art of the Pacific Islands in the Metropolitan Museum of Art. 2007. 24.95 (978-1-58839-238-1(4)); 45.00 (978-1-58839-237-4(6)) Metropolitan Museum of Art, The.

Klein, Holger A. Sacred Gifts & Worldly Treasures: Medieval Masterworks from the Cleveland Museum of Art. 2007. (Illus.). 319p. (978-94-071-7916-8(6)) Cleveland Museum of Art.

Koeppe, Wolfram, et al. The Robert Lehman Collection at the Metropolitan Museum of Art V15 - European & Asian Decorative Arts. 2012. (ENG., Illus.). 400p. (C). 95.00 (978-0-691-15490-9(2)) Princeton Univ. Pr.

Kondoleon, Christine, et al. Classical Art. 2008. (ENG., Illus.). 240p. pap. 22.50 (978-0-87846-728-0(9)) Museum of Fine Arts, Boston.

Kosel, Janine. Norwegian Handknits: Heirloom Designs from Vesterheim Museum. 2012. (ENG., Illus.). 144p. pap. 24.99 (978-0-7603-4255-8(5), 0760342555, Voyageur Pr) MBI Publishing Co. LLC.

Kounellis, Jannis. Kounellis. 2011. (ENG & ITA., Illus.). 132p. 40.00 (978-88-366-1801-9(4)) Silvana ITA. Dist: D.A.P./Distributed Art Pubs

Kriska, Fedor. Kamila Stanclova. 2010. (ENG.). 208p. 120.00 (978-80-8085-788-2(1)) Slovart, Vydavatel'stvo, spol. s.r.o. SVK. Dist: Independent Pubs. Group.

Kronberg Frederiksen, Nanna, text. French Art at Ordrupgaard: Complete Catalogue of Paintings, Sculptures, Pastels, Drawings, & Prints. 2011. (ENG., Illus.). 544p. 120.00 (978-3-7757-2671-9(3)) Hatje Cantz Verlag GmbH & Co KG DEU. Dist: D.A.P./Distributed Art Pubs.

Kuniholm, Peter I., et al. A Guide to the Classical Collections of Cornell University. Terrell, Jane S., ed. 2nd ed. 2011. (Published by the Herbert F. Johnson Museum of Art, Cornell University Press, & Archaeology & Art Publications Ser.). (Illus.). 80p. reprint ed. pap. 19.95 (978-1-934260-08-1(8)) Cornell Univ., Herbert F. Johnson Museum of Art.

Kunstler, Mort. The Civil War Paintings of Mort Kunstler: Vol. 3: the Gettysburg Campaign. 2007. (Civil War Paintings Ser.). (ENG., Illus.). 240p. 18.95 (978-1-58182-558-9(7)) Turner Publishing Co.

Lange, Amanda Elizabeth. Delftware at Historic Deerfield, 1600-1800. 2006. (ENG., Illus.). 50.00 (978-0-9666769-1-4(2)) Historic Deerfield Inc.

Langer, Lawrence L. Return to Vilna in the Art of Samuel Bak, 1. 2007. (Illus.). 118p. 50.00 (978-1-879985-17-9(9), Pucker Art Pubns.) Pucker Gallery.

Langmuir, Erika. Angels. 2010. (ENG., Illus.). 96p. pap. 15.00 (978-1-85709-484-8(0)) Yale Univ. Pr.

Lansdell, Avril. Canal Arts & Crafts. 2nd ed. 2008. (Shire Library). (ENG., Illus.). 56p. pap. 12.95 (978-0-7478-0586-1(5)) Shire Pubns., Ltd. GBR. Dist: Random Hse., Inc.

Lapatin, Kenneth & Wight, Karol, eds. The Antiquities Collection. 2nd rev. ed. 2010. (Illus.). 264p. pap., instr.'s hndbk. ed. 19.95 (978-0-89236-998-0(1), J. Paul Getty Museum) Getty Pubns.

Lascault, Gilbert. In Folio: Gouaches et Aquarelles de Candida Romero. 2012. (FRE & ENG., Illus.). 112p. pap. 30.00 (978-2-35340-025-6(6)) Gourcuff Gradenigo FRA. Dist: National Bk. Network.

Le Fur, Yves, ed. Musée du Quai Branly: The Collection - Art from Africa, Asia, Oceania, & the Americas. 2009. (ENG., Illus.). 480p. 95.00 (978-2-08-122579-4(4)) Flammarion et Cie FRA. Dist: Random Hse., Inc.

Leeman, Fred, et al. Odilon Redon & Emile Bernard: Masterpieces from the Andries Bonger Collection. 2009. (ENG., Illus.). 156p. 55.00 (978-90-400-8589-5(7)) Waanders B.V., Uitgeverij NLD. Dist: National Bk Network.

Leighton, John, ed. Masterpieces from the National Galleries of Scotland. 2012. (ENG., Illus.). 272p. pap. (978-1-906270-01-8(5)) National Galleries of Scotland.

Leveque, Jean-Jacques, et al. Nadia Saikali. 2012. (ENG & FRE., Illus.). 120p. 38.95 (978-2-7572-0351-4(7)) Somogy Editions d'Art FRA. Dist: Independent Pubs. Group.

Levinson, Orde & Jenkins, David Fraser. The Prints of John Piper: Quality & Experiment - A Catalogue Raisonné 1923-91. Levinson, Orde, ed. 3rd rev. exp. ed. 2010. (Illus.). 232p. 250.00 (978-1-84822-063-8(4), Lund Humphries Pubs.) Ashgate Publishing, Ltd. GBR. Dist: Ashgate Publishing Co.

Liefkes, Reino & Young, Hilary, eds. Masterpieces of World Ceramics. 2008. (ENG., Illus.). 144p. 60.00 (978-1-85177-527-9(7)) V & A Pubns. GBR. Dist: Hachette Bk. Group.

Light Work Staff & Gonchar, Nancy, eds. John Wood. (Illus.). 24p. 7.50 (978-0-935445-01-5(3)) Light Work Visual Studies, Inc.

Lilly, Sonja. A Published Gallery. 2009. 396p. 77.80 (978-1-882918-28-7(2), I C Art) InnerCircle Publishing.

Lippard, Lucy. Joyce Kozloff: Voyages. 2007. pap. 15.00 (978-0-9774965-7-0(0)) DC Moore Gallery.

Lombardi, Elena, ed. L' Archivio Di Giovanni Poggi (1880-1961) Soprintendente Alle Gallerie Fiorentine. 2011. (Dagli Archivi delle Arti Ser.). (ITA., Illus.). 436p. (C). pap. 40.00 (978-88-596-0831-8(7)) Polistampa ITA. Dist: Brown, David Bk. Co., The.

Lowry, Glenn D., text. Masterworks of Modern Art: From the Museum of Modern Art, New York, 1 vol. 2011. (ENG., Illus.). 302p. 60.00 (978-88-8117-298-6(4)) Scala Grp. ITA. Dist: D.A.P./Distributed Art Pubs.

Lynes, Barbara Buhler & O'Keeffe, Georgia. The Georgia O'Keeffe Museum Collections. 2007. (ENG., Illus.). 352p. 70.00 (978-0-8109-0957-1(X)) Abrams.

MacAdam, Barbara J. American Art at Dartmouth: Highlights from the Hood Museum of Art. 2007. (Illus.). ix, 244p. (978-1-58465-667-8(0)) Hood Museum of Art.

—American Art at Dartmouth: Highlights from the Hood Museum of Art. 2007. (ENG., Illus.). 256p. pap. 40.00 (978-1-58465-668-5(9)) Hood Museum of Art.

Mack, Heinz. Ars Urbana. Kunst für die Stadt. Heinz Mack. 2008. (GER & ENG., Illus.). 388p. 110.00 (978-3-7774-4065-1(5), Art Stock Bks. Ltd/Csi) Continental Sales, Inc.

Mackenzie, Colin. Masterworks of Chinese Art: The Nelson-Atkins Museum of Art, 1 vol. 2011. (ENG., Illus.). 104p. 24.95 (978-0-615-48882-0(X)) Nelson-Atkins Museum of Art, The.

Madden, David, et al. Richard Anuskiewicz: Paintings & Sculptures 1945-2001. 2011. (ENG., Illus.). 272p. 85.00 (978-88-7038-483-3(7)) Centro Di ITA. Dist: Antique Collectors' Club.

Manley, Bill. Egyptian Treasures. 2010. (ENG., Illus.). 176p. 29.95 (978-1-905267-17-0(7)) NMS Enterprises Ltd. - Publishing GBR. Dist: National Bk. Network.

Marchant, Deborah DeWit & Piercy, Marge. Painting Cats. 2008. (978-1-59028-208-3(6), William, James & Co.) Franklin, Beedle & Assocs. Inc.

Mark Dagley - Shaped Canvas. 2008. (Illus.). 16p. pap. 15.00 (978-0-9677326-9-5(7)) Abaton Bk. Co.

Martin Llopis Paloma, ed. Alejandra Icaza: Marshmallows. 2011. (ENG., Illus.). 144p. 40.00 (978-84-7506-912-8(6)) Turner, Ediciones S.A. ESP. Dist: D.A.P./Distributed Art Pubs.

Martin, Mary L. & Skinner, Tina. The Ultimate Collector's Guide to Surfing Postcards. 2008. (Illus.). 160p. pap. 29.95 *(978-0-7643-2909-8(X))* Schiffer Publishing, Ltd.

Masiero, Roberto, ed. Tobia Scarpa. 2009. (ITA., Illus.). 400p. 175.00 *(978-88-370-6930-8(8))* Electa ITA. Dist: Trans-Atlantic Pubns., Inc.

Matheson. Corpus Vasorum Antiquorum. United States of America / Corpus Vasorum Antiquorum. 2011. (Corpus Vasorum Antiquorum. United States of America Ser.). (ENG.). 98p. (C). 143.00 ***(978-3-8053-4348-0(5))*** Zabern, Philipp von Verlag, GmbH DEU. Dist: Brown, David Bk. Co., The.

Matt, Gerald, et al, texts. Don Juan: Or Two Plus Two Equals Four or Lust Is the Only Swindle I Wish Permanence, 1 vol. 2006. (ENG., Illus.). 144p. 35.00 *(978-3-938821-36-7(1))* Verlag fur Moderne Kunst DEU. Dist: D.A.P./Distributed Art Pubs.

Mauritshuis, creator. Flowers in the Mauritshuis. 2008. (ENG., Illus.). 72p. pap. 29.95 *(978-90-400-8345-7(2))* Waanders B.V., Uitgeverij NLD. Dist: National Bk. Network.

Mayr, Juan & Botero, Clara Isabel. Museo Del Oro: Patrimonio Milenario de Colombia. 2007. (Tezontle Ser.). (SPA., Illus.). 271p. pap. 50.99 *(978-958-38-0134-1(8))* Fondo de Cultura Economica USA.

McGill, Forrest & Chirapravati, M. L. Pattaratorn. Emerald Cities: Arts of Siam & Burma 1775-1950. 2009. (ENG., Illus.). 224p. 49.00 *(978-0-939117-50-5(9))* Asian Art Museum of San Francisco.

McLean, Kathleen. Minneapolis Institute of Arts: Handbook of the Collection. 2007. (Illus.). 328p. *(978-0-912964-99-7(5))* Minneapolis Institute of Arts.

McMenamin, Donna. Popular Arts of Mexico, 1850-1950. 2nd rev. ed. 2009. (ENG & SPA., Illus.). 240p. 59.99 *(978-0-7643-3284-5(8))* Schiffer Publishing, Ltd.

McNair, Anne. Catalogue of the Lady Ludlow Collection of English Porcelain at the Bowes Museum. 2007. (ENG., Illus.). 400p. 75.00 *(978-0-906290-88-0(0))* Unicorn Pr., London GBR. Dist: National Bk. Network.

McNutt, Jennifer Complo & Holland, Ashley, eds. We Are Here: The Eiteljorg Contemporary Art Fellowship 2011, 1 vol. 2011. (ENG., Illus.). 120p. pap. 26.95 ***(978-0-295-99179-5(8))*** Univ. of Washington Pr.

McQuarrie, Ralph. The Art of Ralph Mcquarrie. 2007. 125.00 *(978-0-9791580-0-1(1))* dreams and visions pr.

McSweeney's Books Staff. 826NYC Art Show. 2007. (ENG., Illus.). 24p. 39.00 *(978-1-932416-80-0(3))* McSweeney's Publishing.

Meedendorp, Teio, ed. Drawings & Prints by Vincent van Gogh: In the Collection of the Kroller-Muller Museum. 2009. (Illus.). 192p. 99.95 *(978-90-78964-05-6(7)*, Leiden Univ. Pr.) Amsterdam Univ. Pr. NLD. Dist: Chicago Distribution Ctr.

Menzies, Jackie, et al. Asian Collections: The Art Gallery of New South Wales. (Illus.). 352p. pap. 39.95 *(978-0-7347-6351-8(4))* Art Media Resources, Inc.

Mercurio, Gianni. Roy Lichtenstein: Meditations on Art. 2010. (Illus.). 372p. 100.00 *(978-88-572-0460-4(X))* Skira Editore ITA. Dist: Random Hse., Inc.

Merriam, Daniel. The Eye of a Dreamer: The Art of Daniel Merriam. 2007. (Illus.). 128p. 45.00 *(978-0-9797157-0-9(9))* Monarch Editions, Inc.

Merritt, Ray, ed. Shared Space. 2010. (ENG., Illus.). 334p. 60.00 *(978-88-6208-108-5(1))* Damiani ITA. Dist: D.A.P./Distributed Art Pubs.

Metropolitan Museum of Art (New York, N.Y.) Staff, contrib. by. The Metropolitan Museum of Art Guide. 2012. ***(978-1-58839-455-2(7))*** Metropolitan Museum of Art, The.

Mezian, Nadia, et al. Tamy Tazi - Caftans. 2011. (ENG & FRE., Illus.). 192p. 75.00 *(978-88-572-0323-2(9))* Skira Editore ITA. Dist: Random Hse., Inc.

Michael, Thomas & Cuhaj, George. Collecting World Coins: Circulating Issues 1901 - Present. 12th ed. 2008. (ENG., Illus.). 1008p. pap. 40.00 *(978-0-89689-713-7(3))* Krause Pubns.

Michie, Thomas S. Selected Works. 2008. (Illus.). 319p. *(978-0-911517-82-8(0))* United States Holocaust Memorial Museum.

Miller, Preston & Corey, Carolyn. The New Four Winds Guide to Indian Weaponry, Trade Goods, & Replicas. 2007. (Schiffer Book for Collectors Ser.). (Illus.). 176p. pap. 29.95 *(978-0-7643-2634-9(1))* Schiffer Publishing, Ltd.

Miracco, Renato. Italian Artists in New York. 2010. (ITA & ENG., Illus.). 152p. pap. 49.95 *(978-88-8158-747-6(5))* Charta ITA. Dist: D.A.P./Distributed Art Pubs.

Mitchinson, David. Celebrating Moore: Works from the Collection of the Henry Moore Foundation. rev. ed. 2006. (Illus.). 360p. pap. 40.00 *(978-0-85331-944-3(8)*, Lund Humphries Pubs.) Ashgate Publishing, Ltd. GBR. Dist: Ashgate Publishing Co.

Miyasaki, George. George Miyasaki. 2007. (Illus.). 95p. pap. 36.00 *(978-0-9799164-3-4(7))* Magnolia Editions.

Mohamed, Bashir. The Arts of the Muslim Knight: The Furusiyya Art Foundation Collection. 2008. (ENG., Illus.). 416p. 100.00 *(978-88-7624-877-1(3))* Skira Editore ITA. Dist: Random Hse., Inc.

Moles, Kathleen & Arnaud, Jean-Pierre. John Franklin Koenig: Northwest Master, Home & Away. 2008. (Illus.). 74p. pap. 20.00 *(978-0-938506-13-3(7))* Whatcom Museum of History & Art.

Moleskine Cahiers. (FRE., Illus.). 136p. pap. 29.95 *(978-3-928762-65-6(6))* Richter Verlag DEU. Dist: D.A.P./Distributed Art Pubs.

Mondadori Electa, ed. Museo del Novecento: The Collection. 2010. 373p. 75.00 *(978-88-370-7992-5(3))* Electa ITA. Dist: Trans-Atlantic Pubns., Inc.

Morris, Edward & Curators, Senior. The Walker Art Gallery. 2007. (ENG., Illus.). 96p. pap. 24.95 *(978-1-85759-037-1(6))* Scala, Editions FRA. Dist: National Bk. Network.

Morris, Francis, ed. The Tate Modern Handbook. 2nd ed. 2006. (ENG., Illus.). 240p. pap. 35.00 *(978-1-85437-577-3(6))* Tate Publishing, Ltd. GBR. Dist: Hachette Bk. Group.

Morstad, Julie. Milk Teeth. 2011. (ENG., Illus.). 104p. pap. 16.95 *(978-1-897299-45-6(1))* Drawn & Quarterly Pubns. CAN. Dist: Macmillan.

Moschel, Ulrike, ed. Ulrike Möschel: Als ich ein Junge war. 2011. (ENG., Illus.). 70p. 45.00 *(978-3-86678-435-2(X))* Kerber Verlag DEU. Dist: D.A.P./Distributed Art Pubs.

Mossinger, Ingrid & Drechsel, Kerstin, eds. Wolfgang Mattheuer: The Prints-the Hartmut Koch Donation. 2010. (ENG., Illus.). 256p. 78.00 ***(978-3-86832-034-3(2))*** Wienand GmbH, Druck- & Verlagshaus DEU. Dist: Independent Pubs. Group.

Motti, Gianni. Gianni Motti, 1 vol. 2006. (GER & ENG., Illus.). 252p. pap. 35.00 *(978-3-905701-10-4(3))* JRP Ringier Kunstverlag AG CHE. Dist: D.A.P./Distributed Art Pubs.

Mueller, Hans-Joachim. Walter Moroder: Skulpturen. 2007. 160p. 69.95 *(978-3-87909-896-5(4))* Wienand GmbH, Druck- & Verlagshaus DEU. Dist: Independent Pubs. Group.

Multi-Cultural Masterpieces. (Illus.). 18p. pap. 79.00 *(978-1-56762-045-0(0))* Modern Learning Pr.

Multiple. Irdische Paradiese. Earthly Paradises: Meisterwerke aus der Kasser Art Foundation. 2009. (ENG.). 450p. 48.00 *(978-3-422-06906-0(2)*, Art Stock Bks. Ltd/Csi) Continental Sales, Inc.

Munayyer, Hanan Karaman. Traditional Palestinian Costume: Origins & Evolution. 2011. (ENG., Illus.). 448p. 200.00 *(978-1-56656-825-8(0)*, Olive Branch Pr.) Interlink Publishing Group, Inc.

Musacchio, Humberto. El Taller de Gráfica Popular. 2007. (Tezontle Ser.). (SPA.). 214p. 49.95 *(978-968-16-7703-9(X))* Fondo de Cultura Economica USA.

Musée de design et d'arts appliqués contemporains Staff, contrib. by. L'art du Verre Contemporain: Contemporary Glass Art = Zeitgenössische Glaskunst, 1 vol. 2007. (ENG., Illus.). 405p. 80.00 *(978-2-88453-127-6(0))* La Bibliotheque des Arts FRA. Dist: D.A.P./Distributed Art Pubs.

Museo del Prado Staff & Bettagno, Alessandro, contrib. by. The Prado Museum: (collection of Paintings) (Illus.). 669p. *(978-90-6153-371-9(6))* Mercatorfonds N. V.

Museum of Fine Arts, Houston Staff, contrib. by. Masterpieces from the Museum of Fine Arts, Houston: Director's Choice. 2010. (Illus.). 208p. 50.00 *(978-0-300-16372-8(X))* Museum of Fine Arts, Houston.

Nachtigäller, Roland, et al. Dennis Oppenheim: Public Projects. 2009. (ENG., Illus.). 148p. pap. 45.00 *(978-88-8158-695-0(9))* Charta ITA. Dist: D.A.P./Distributed Art Pubs.

NADA Art Fair, compiled by. NADA Catalogue. 2009. (ENG., Illus.). 216p. pap. 20.00 *(978-0-9820947-2-3(8))* PictureBox, Inc.

Nelson-Atkins Museum of Art Staff, contrib. by. The Nelson-Atkins Museum of Art: A Handbook of the Collection. 7th ed. 2008. *(978-0-942614-38-1(0))*; pap. *(978-0-942614-39-8(9))* Nelson-Atkins Museum of Art, The.

Nemmers, Laura K., et al, eds. Samuel P. Harn Museum of Art: Twenty Years - The Collection Catalogue. 2010. (ENG., Illus.). 288p. 50.00 *(978-0-8130-3513-0(9))* Univ. Pr. of Florida.

Neubauer, Susanne, ed. Anne-Mie van Kerckhoven: Nothing More Natural. 2009. (DUT, FRE, GER & ENG., Illus.). 272p. pap. 69.95 *(978-3-86560-528-3(1))* Verlag der Buchhandlung Walther Konig DEU. Dist: D.A.P./Distributed Art Pubs.

Neutres, Jerome. New Delhi, New Wave. Neutres, Jerome, ed. 2008. (ITA & ENG., Illus.). 288p. 70.00 *(978-88-6208-023-1(9))* Damiani ITA. Dist: D.A.P./Distributed Art Pubs.

New-York Historical Society. Museum and. Catalogue of the Museum & Gallery of Art of the New York Historical Society 1873. 2006. 156p. per. 18.99 *(978-1-4255-1162-3(7))* MPublishing.

Newbery, Timothy. The Robert Lehman Collection XIII: Frames. 2007. (ENG., Illus.). 520p. (C). 125.00 *(978-0-691-13483-3(9))* Princeton Univ. Pr.

Newbery, Timothy J. The Robert Lehman Collection. 2007. (Illus.). xiii, 465p. 100.00 *(978-1-58839-269-5(4))* Metropolitan Museum of Art, The.

Nickl, Peter & Jeffries, Susan. Gilbert Portanier: Oeuvre 2000-2009. 2009. (ENG., Illus.). 200p. 85.00 *(978-3-89790-289-3(3))* Arnoldsche Art Pubs. DEU. Dist: Antique Collectors' Club.

Nicosia, Nic. Nic Nicosia. 2012. (ENG., Illus.). 264p. 75.00 ***(978-0-292-74369-4(6))*** Univ. of Texas Pr.

Noel, William & Weiss, Daniel. Book of Kings: Art, War & the Morgan Library's Medieval Picture Bible. 2006. (ENG., Illus.). 55.00 *(978-1-903942-16-1(0))* Third Millenium Publishing GBR. Dist: National Bk. Network.

Noelle, Alexander J., ed. American Reflections: The Collection of Dr. Timothy Mclaughlin. 2011. (Illus.). 80p. pap. 19.95 *(978-0-9724497-0-0(1))* New Britain Museum of American Art.

Noever, Peter, ed. & text. 20/21: MAK Collection of Contemporary Art. 2010. (ENG., Illus.). 244p. pap. 40.00 *(978-3-941185-29-6(2))* Verlag fur Moderne Kunst DEU. Dist: D.A.P./Distributed Art Pubs.

Noon, Patrick J. & Bonington, Richard Parkes. Richard Parkes Bonington: The Complete Paintings. 2009. (ENG., Illus.). 472p. 125.00 *(978-0-300-13421-6(5))* Yale Univ. Pr.

Norman Rockwell Museum, et al. American Chronicles: The Art of Norman Rockwell. 2007. (Illus.). 275p. 45.00 *(978-0-9615273-2-7(3))* Rockwell, Norman Museum.

Normand-Romain, Antoinette Le. The Bronzes of Rodin: Catalogue of Works in the Musee Rodin, 2 vols. 2007. (Illus.). 800p. 320.00 *(978-2-7118-4939-0(2)*, Lund Humphries Pubs.) Ashgate Publishing, Ltd. GBR. Dist: Ashgate Publishing Co.

North Carolina Museum of Art Staff, contrib. by. North Carolina Museum of Art: Handbook of the Collections. 2010. pap. *(978-0-88259-992-2(5))* North Carolina Museum of Art.

Nottage, James H., et al. Generations: The Helen Cox Kersting Collection of Southwestern Cultural Arts. 2011. (ENG., Illus.). 460p. 75.00 *(978-0-9798495-1-0(9))* Eiteljorg Museum.

Obrist, Hans Ulrich, ed. Pars Pro Toto II. 2009. (ENG., Illus.). 256p. pap. 90.00 *(978-3-86828-055-5(3))* Kehrer Verlag Heidelberg, Klaus Kehrer DEU. Dist: Consortium Bk. Sales & Distribution.

Ofili, Chris. Chris Ofili: Afro Margin. 2010. (ENG., Illus.). 24p. pap. 50.00 *(978-1-934435-22-9(8))* Radius Bks.

Oldham, Todd. Charley Harper: An Illustrated Life. 2011. (ENG., Illus.). 420p. 29.95 *(978-1-934429-82-2(1))* AMMO Bks., LLC.

Oldknow, Tina & Russell, Cristine. Voices of Contemporary Glass: The Heineman Collection. 2009. (ENG., Illus.). 382p. 85.00 *(978-1-55595-314-0(X))* Hudson Hills Pr. LLC.

O'Leary, Elizabeth, et al. American Art at the Virginia Museum of Fine Arts. 2010. (ENG., Illus.). 432p. (gr. 17). 50.00 *(978-0-917046-94-0(3))* Univ. Pr. of Virginia.

O'Leary, Elizabeth L. American Art at the Virginia Museum of Fine Arts. 2010. (Illus.). ix, 422p. pap. *(978-0-917046-93-3(5))* Virginia Museum of Fine Arts.

O'Neal, William Bainter. Jefferson's Buildings at the University of Virgini: The Rotunda. 2011. 98p. 38.95 ***(978-1-258-08757-9(X))*** Literary Licensing, LLC.

Ornstein-Van Slooten, Eva. The Rembrandt House: A Catalogue of Rembrandt Etchings. Van Der Veen, Jaap, ed. 2006. (ENG., Illus.). 176p. pap. 19.95 *(978-90-400-8851-3(9))* Waanders B.V., Uitgeverij NLD. Dist: National Bk. Network.

Osian, creator. Osian's Forty Masterpieces: The Masterpieces & Museum-Quality Series. 2006. (ENG., Illus.). 240p. pap. 65.00 *(978-1-890206-83-3(0))* Mapin Publishing Pvt. Ltd IND. Dist: National Bk. Network.

P., Paul. Nonchaloir. 2007. 156p. 3500.00 *(978-1-57687-387-8(0))* powerHouse Cultural Entertainment, Inc.

Page One, creator. T-Shirt Design. 2008. (Cube Collection Ser.). (Illus.). 672p. *(978-981-245-551-2(5))* Page One Publishing.

Pakesch, Peter, et al, texts. Public Spaces, Two Audiences: Works & Documents from the Herbert Collection. 2006. (Illus.). 430p. 50.00 *(978-84-89771-20-8(0))* Verlag der Buchhandlung Walther Konig DEU. Dist: D.A.P./Distributed Art Pubs.

Pal, Pratapatditya. East Meets West. 2010. (Illus.). 196p. 45.00 *(978-93-80581-00-2(9))* Marg Pubns. IND. Dist: National Bk. Network.

Paloscia, Pax. Let the Kids Play. 2007. (ENG., Illus.). 96p. pap. 29.00 *(978-88-88493-20-6(4))* Drago Arts & Communication ITA. Dist: SCB Distributors.

Pardo, Patrick, et al. John Baldessari Catalogue Raisonne: Volume One: 1956-1974. 2012. (ENG., Illus.). 472p. 200.00 ***(978-0-300-17448-9(9))*** Yale Univ. Pr.

Parsons, Tom & Royal Collection Staff. 100 Treasures of Buckingham Palace. 2010. (Illus.). 224p. pap. 9.95 *(978-1-902163-92-5(3))* Royal Collection Enterprises Ltd. GBR. Dist: Chicago Distribution Ctr.

Peck, Amelia. American Quilts & Coverlets in the Metropolitan Museum of Art. 2009. (ENG., Illus.). 320p. 29.95 *(978-0-300-15903-5(X))* Yale Univ. Pr.

Pero, Linda Szekeley, et al. American Chronicles: The Art of Norman Rockwell. 2009. (ENG., Illus.). 276p. pap. 30.00 *(978-0-9615273-3-4(1))* Rockwell, Norman Museum.

Petrova, E. A. & Petrova, Yevgenia, eds. Abstraction in Russia, 2 vols. 2006. (ENG., Illus.). pap. 160.00 *(978-3-935298-50-6(1)*, Palace Editions) Mandala Publishing.

Petrova, Yevgenia. Drawing & Watercolours in Russian Culture: The First Half of the Nineteenth Century. 2006. (ENG., Illus.). 288p. 110.00 *(978-3-938051-32-0(9)*, Palace Editions) Mandala Publishing.

Petrova, Yevgenia, ed. Art from Cuba: The Ludwig Collection. 2006. (MUL & ENG., Illus.). 242p. 80.00 *(978-3-935298-27-8(7)*, Palace Editions) Mandala Publishing.

—Twosome. 2006. (MUL & ENG., Illus.). 85.00 *(978-3-935298-40-7(4)*, Palace Editions) Mandala Publishing.

Petullo, Anthony. Art Without Category: British & Irish Art from the Anthony Petullo Collection. 2009. (Illus.). 84p. *(978-1-60743-122-0(X))* Independent Pub.

Phillips, Jim. Skateboard Art of Jim Phillips. 2007. (Illus.). 208p. pap. 29.95 *(978-0-7643-2807-7(7))* Schiffer Publishing, Ltd.

Picasso, Pablo, illus. Picasso's Paintings, Watercolors, Drawings & Sculpture - A Comprehensive Illustrated Catalogue. Turn of the Century - 1900-1901. 2010. (Picasso's Paintings, Watercolors, Drawings & Sculpture Ser.). 304p. 150.00 *(978-1-55660-323-5(1))* Wofsy, Alan Fine Arts.

Piccus, Robert Peter. Sacred & Secular: The Piccus Collection of Tibetan Rugs. 2011. ***(978-1-932476-55-2(5))*** Serindia Pubns., Inc.

Pietsch, Ulrich. Early Meissen Porcelain: The Wark Collection from the Cummer Museum of Art & Gardens. 2011. (ENG., Illus.). 576p. 99.95 *(978-1-904832-79-9(2))* Giles, D. Ltd. GBR. Dist: Antique Collectors' Club.

Piggott, Stuart & Daniel, Glyn E. A Picture Book of Ancient British Art. 2011. (ENG., Illus.). 90p. pap. 21.99 *(978-0-521-17640-8(9))* Cambridge Univ. Pr.

Pimentel, Ursula M. Brinkmann & Francey, Mary F. A History of Giving: The Marriner S. Eccles Foundation. 2007. (Illus.). 80p. *(978-0-9657215-3-0(1))* Utah Museum of Fine Arts.

Pitman, Bonnie. Dallas Museum of Art: A Guide to the Collection. 2012. (ENG., Illus.). 368p. pap. 24.95 ***(978-0-300-17963-7(4))*** Dallas Museum of Art.

Ponciroli, Virginia, ed. Nunziante Opere 1995-2010: [in English & Italian]. 2010. 208p. 99.50 ***(978-88-370-7790-7(4))*** Electa ITA. Dist: Trans-Atlantic Pubns., Inc.

Powell, Melissa, ed. Huichol Art & Culture: Balancing the World. 2010. (ENG.). 176p. pap. *(978-0-89013-563-1(0))* Museum of New Mexico Pr.

Prentice, Helaine Kaplan. Suzhou: Shaping an Ancient City for the New China. 2006. (Land Marks Ser.: Vol. 8). (ENG., Illus.). 64p. pap. 24.95 *(978-1-888931-15-0(9))* Spacemaker Pr.

Preziosi, Donald. Classic American Diners: Collectible Postcards & Matchcovers. 2007. (Schiffer Book Ser.). (Illus.). 176p. 39.95 *(978-0-7643-2610-3(4))* Schiffer Publishing, Ltd.

Putman, Andree & Bonifassi, Catherine. Andrée Putman: Ambassadrice du Style. 2010. (Illus.). 119p. *(978-2-08-124634-8(1))* Editions Flammarion.

Quinze, Arne. Arne Quinze: Modern Contemporary. 2011. (ENG., Illus.). 300p. 70.00 *(978-3-7757-2693-1(4))* Hatje Cantz Verlag GmbH & Co KG DEU. Dist: D.A.P./Distributed Art Pubs.

Raby, Julian, intro. Ideals of Beauty: Asian & American Art in the Freer & Sackler Galleries. 2010. (World of Art Ser.). (ENG., Illus.). 192p. pap. 19.95 *(978-0-500-20403-0(9)*, 520403) Thames & Hudson.

Radical Structures. 2007. (Illus.). pap. 10.00 *(978-0-9677326-8-8(9))* Abaton Bk. Co.

Ravenal, John B. Modern & Contemporary Art at the Virginia Museum of Fine Arts. 2007. (ENG., Illus.). 252p. 19.50 *(978-0-917046-80-3(3))* Virginia Museum of Fine Arts.

Ray, Rex. Rex Ray: Art + Design. 2007. (ENG., Illus.). 160p. 35.00 *(978-0-8118-5975-2(4))* Chronicle Bks. LLC.

Refice, Paola. Museo D'arte Sacra Della Collegiata Di San Lorenzo a Montevarchi: Guida Alla Visita Del Museo e Alla Scoperta Del Territorio. 2007. (Piccoli, grandi Musei Ser.). (ITA & ENG., Illus.). 203p. (C). 24.00 *(978-88-596-0208-8(4))* Polistampa ITA. Dist: Brown, David Bk. Co., The.

Reinhard-Felice, Mariantonia, ed. Oskar Reinhart Collection 'Am Römerholz' Winterthur: Complete Catalogue. 2006. (Illus.). 712p. (C). 120.00 *(978-1-903470-38-1(2))* Holberton, Paul Publishing GBR. Dist: Casemate Pubs. & Bk. Distributors, LLC.

Rennert, Jack. Posters of the Belle Epoque: The Wine Spectator Collection. 2007. (ENG., Illus.). 222p. 75.00 *(978-0-7570-0064-5(9))* Square One Pubs.

Reno, Jesse. Truth Will Measure: The Art of Jesse Reno. 2007. 132p. per. 29.99 *(978-0-9776051-3-2(2))* Another Sky Pr.

Rewald, Sabine & Dabrowski, Magdalena. The American Matisse: The Dealer, His Artists, His Collection. 2010. (ENG., Illus.). 208p. 60.00 *(978-0-300-15510-5(7))* Yale Univ. Pr.

—The American Matisse: The Dealer, His Artists, His Collection: The Pierre & Maria-Gaetana Matisse Collection. 2010. (Illus.). ix, 195p. 60.00 *(978-1-58839-352-4(6))* Metropolitan Museum of Art, The.

Reynolds, Andi Milam. Collection of the National Quilt Museum. 2009. *(978-1-57432-987-2(1)*, American Quilter's Society) Collector Bks.

Ribalta, Jorge, text. Relational Objects: Macba Collection 2002-2007. 2010. (ENG.). 272p. pap. 39.95 *(978-84-92505-12-8(5))* Museu d'Art Contemporani de Barcelona ESP. Dist: Actar Birkhauser Distribution.

Ricchi, Daria, et al, texts. Giny Vos: Singing in the Dark. 2011. (ENG., Illus.). 192p. pap. 45.00 *(978-90-78088-33-2(8))* Valiz NLD. Dist: D.A.P./Distributed Art Pubs.

Rice, William S. William S. Rice: California Block Prints. 2009. 80p. 24.95 *(978-0-7649-4803-9(2))* Pomegranate Communications, Inc.

Riley, C. M. Art at Lincoln Center: The Public Art & List Print & Poster Collections. 2008. (Illus.). 240p. 75.00 *(978-0-470-16913-1(3)*, Wiley) Wiley, John & Sons, Inc.

Riley, Charles A., II, et al. Art at Lincoln Center: The Public Art & List Print & Poster Collections. 2009. (ENG., Illus.). 228p. 75.00 *(978-0-470-28494-0(3)*, Wiley) Wiley, John & Sons, Inc.

Riviere, Henri. Thirty-Six Views of the Eiffel Tower: A Turn-of-the-Century Tribute to the City of Light. 2010. (ENG & FRE., Illus.). 108p. 22.95 *(978-0-8118-7698-8(5))* Chronicle Bks. LLC.

Robinson, James. Masterpieces Medieval Art. 2008. (ENG., Illus.). 320p. 39.95 *(978-0-7141-2815-3(5))* British Museum Pr. GBR. Dist: Brown, David Bk. Co., The.

Rocheleau, Caroline M. Ancient Egyptian Art: Systematic Catalogue of the Collection, North Carolina Museum of Art, Raleigh. 2012. ***(978-0-88259-996-0(8))*** North Carolina Museum of Art.

Rodrigue, George. George Rodrigue Prints: A Catalogue Raisonné 1970-2007. 2008. (ENG., Illus.). 256p. 55.00 *(978-0-8109-9517-8(4))* Abrams.

Rodriguez, Alfredo, et al. Alfredo Rodriguez - A Life in Color: A Life in Color. Rodriguez, Alfredo & Walters, Jeannine, eds. 2007. (Illus.). 192p. 125.00 *(978-0-9792747-0-1(2))* Heritage Gallery.

Roe, Sonia & Ellis, Andrew. Oil Paintings in Public Ownership in Cambridgeshire: The Fitzwilliam Museum. Roe, Sonia, ed. 2007. (Oil Paintings in Public Ownership Ser.). (SPA & ENG., Illus.). 240p. 85.00 *(978-1-904931-12-6(X))* Public Catalogue Foundation, The GBR. Dist: National Bk. Network.

Roehmer, Marion. Siegburger Steinzeug: Die Sammlung Schulte in Meschede. 2008. (Denkmalpflege und Forschung in Westfalen Ser.). (GER., Illus.). 546p. (C). 68.00 *(978-3-8053-3453-2(2))* Zabern, Philipp von Verlag, GmbH DEU. Dist: Brown, David Bk. Co., The.

Rogers, James G., Jr., et al. The Art of Downing Barnitz: A Retrospective Exhibition. 2007. 18.00 *(978-0-9714065-1-3(0))* Florida Southern College, Melvin Art Gallery.

Romney, Émile & Bandou, Mireille. Art Public: Une Collection D'art Contemporain en Guadeloupe. 2010. (FRE, SPA & ENG., Illus.). 175p. *(978-2-08-124504-4(3))* Editions Flammarion.

Rondeau, James. Judith Neisser Collection: Minimal & Postminimal Innovation. 2011. (Contemporary Collecting Ser.). (ENG., Illus.). 160p. 35.00 *(978-0-300-17024-5(6))* Art Institute of Chicago.

Rooney, Dawn F. Khmer Ceramics: Beauty & Meaning. 2010. (ENG., Illus.). 216p. *(978-974-9863-88-6(7),* River Bks. Pr. Dist A C) Antique Collectors' Club.

Rosado, Jesus & Schweigert, Scott A. Carlos Luna: Personal Histories. 2006. (ENG & SPA., Illus.). 154p. 50.00 *(978-0-9791753-0-5(5))* Arnold, Suzanne H. Art Gallery.

Roselione-Valadez, Juan, ed. How Soon Now. 2011. (ENG., Illus.). 175p. pap. 39.95 ***(978-0-9821195-3-2(4))*** Rubell Family Collection.

Rouart, Denis & Rey, Jean-Dominique. Monet: Water Lilies. 2008. (ENG., Illus.). 178p. 49.95 *(978-2-08-030076-8(8))* Flammarion et Cie FRA. Dist: Random Hse., Inc.

Ruscha, Ed. Edward Ruscha: Catalogue Raisonne of Works on Paper. 2009. (Illus.). 600p. 210.00 *(978-3-86521-832-2(6))* Steidl, Gerhard Druckerei und Verlag DEU. Dist: D.A.P./Distributed Art Pubs.

Rush, Michael. The Rose Art Museum Collection. 2009. (ENG., Illus.). 288p. 60.00 *(978-0-8109-5574-5(1))* Abrams.

Sagmeister, S. & Koehler, D. W. OUBEY MINDKISS. 2010. (ENG.). 240p. pap. 178.00 *(978-3-422-06797-4(3))* Deutscher Kunstverlag GmbH DEU. Dist: Independent Pubs. Group.

Sahin, Seracettin. The Museum of Turkish & Islamic Arts: Fourteen Centuries of Glory. 2009. (ENG., Illus.). 340p. 59.95 *(978-1-935295-02-0(0))* Blue Dome Pr.

Sanders, Scott. Picture Perfect: Designing the New American Family Home. 2010. (ENG., Illus.). 176p. 65.00 *(978-0-9823585-1-1(2),* Pointed Leaf Pr.

Sandon, John. The Ewers-Tyne Collection of Worcester Porcelain at Cheekwood. 2007. (ENG., Illus.). 224p. *(978-1-85149-558-0(4),* Antique Collectors Club Dist) Antique Collectors' Club.

Sandusky, Phil. Painting Katrina, 1 vol. 2007. (ENG., Illus.). 96p. 19.95 *(978-1-58980-477-7(5))* Pelican Publishing Co., Inc.

Sartain, Dorthea & Derrick, Peter. Guide to the Collections of the Bronx County Archives. 2007. 72p. *(978-0-941980-54-8(5))* Bronx County Historical Society, The.

Scaglioia, Manuele, ed. The Islamic Ceramics of the Laura Collection. 2011. (ITA & ENG., Illus.). 160p. 47.00 *(978-88-422-1843-2(X))* Allemandi, Umberto & Co. GBR. Dist: Antique Collectors' Club.

Schellmann, Jorg, ed. Forty Are Better Than One: Contemporary Art Production Munchen New York 1969-2009. 2010. (ENG., Illus.). 456p. 70.00 *(978-3-7757-2236-0(X))* Hatje Cantz Verlag GmbH & Co KG DEU. Dist: D.A.P./Distributed Art Pubs.

Scheps, Marc & Kounellis, Jannis. Jannis Kounellis: XXII Stations on an Odyssey 1969-2010. 2010. (Illus.). 360p. 120.00 *(978-3-7913-5012-7(9))* Prestel Verlag GmbH & Co KG. DEU. Dist: Prestel Publishing.

Scholten, Frits. The Robert Lehman Collection. 2011. (Illus.). xiii, 274p. ***(978-1-58839-441-5(7))*** Metropolitan Museum of Art, The.

Schoonmaker, Trevor. Street Level: Mark Bradford, William Cordova, & Robin Rhode. 2007. (ENG., Illus.). 96p. pap. 19.95 *(978-0-938989-28-8(6))* Duke Univ. Pr.

Schoonmaker, Trevor, ed. Barkley L. Hendricks: Birth of the Cool. 2008. (ENG., Illus.). 140p. 39.95 *(978-0-938989-31-8(6))* Duke Univ. Pr.

Schorr, Collier, ed. Freeway Balconies. 2008. (ENG., Illus.). 128p. 65.00 *(978-0-89207-374-0(8))* Guggenheim, Solomon R. Museum.

Schretlen, Helen. Loving Art: The William & Anna Singer Collection. 2007. (ENG., Illus.). 224p. 60.00 *(978-90-400-8234-4(0))* Allemandi, Umberto & Co. GBR. Dist: National Bk. Network.

Schroder, Tim. British & Continental Gold & Silver in the Ashmolean Museum, 3 Vols., Set. 2010. (ENG., Illus.). 500p. 650.00 *(978-1-85444-220-8(1))* Ashmolean Museum GBR. Dist: National Bk. Network.

Schulz, Regine & Seidel, Matthias. Egyptian Art. 2009. pap. *(978-0-911886-70-2(2))* Walters Art Museum, US.

Scott, John F. & Johnson-Kelly, Laura W. A New World: Pre-Columbian Art from the Carroll Collection. Johnson-Kelly, Laura W., ed. 2008. (Illus.). 152p. pap. *(978-1-934260-02-9(9))* Cornell Univ., Herbert F. Johnson Museum of Art.

Seidel, Matthias, et al. Egyptian Art: The Walters Art Museum. 2009. (ENG., Illus.). 192p. 45.00 *(978-1-904832-57-7(1))* Giles, D. Ltd. GBR. Dist: Antique Collectors' Club.

Seiwert, Wolf-Dieter. Jewellery from the Orient: Treasures from the Dr. Bir Collection. 2010. (ENG., Illus.). 320p. 85.00 *(978-3-89790-319-7(9))* Arnoldsche Art Pubs. DEU. Dist: Antique Collectors' Club.

Sen, He. He Sen: Paintings. 2010. (ENG., Illus.). 160p. 50.00 *(978-88-6208-137-5(5))* Damiani ITA. Dist: D.A.P./Distributed Art Pubs.

Shapton, Leanne. Important Artifacts & Personal Property from the Collection of Lenore Doolan & Harold Morris, Including Books, Street Fashion, & Jewelry. 2009. (ENG., Illus.). 144p. pap. 18.00 *(978-0-374-17530-6(6))* Farrar, Straus & Giroux.

Shchurik, Natalia Leonidovna. Kuban I Velikie Pobedy Rossii: V Tvorchestve Khudozhnikov Krasnodarskogo Kraia. 2010. (RUS., Illus.). 157p. *(978-5-91050-082-6(1))* Diapazon-V.

Shields, Conal. Kenneth Thomson the Collector. 2009. (Illus.). 128p. pap. 50.00 ***(978-1-903470-79-4(X))*** Holberton, Paul Publishing GBR. Dist: Casemate Pubs. & Bk. Distributors, LLC.

Shields, Scott A., et al. The Crocker Art Museum Collection: Unveiled. Shields, Scott A., ed. 2010. (Illus.). 544p. *(978-1-884038-19-8(0))* Crocker Art Museum.

Siegmann, William. African Art: A Century at the Brooklyn Museum. 2009. (Illus.). 296p. pap. *(978-0-87273-163-9(4))* Brooklyn Museum, The.

—African Art: A Century at the Brooklyn Museum. 2009. (Illus.). 304p. *(978-3-7913-4321-1(1))* Prestel Verlag GmbH & Co KG.

Simari, Maria Matilde & Bisceglia, Anna. Museo D'arte Sacra e Religiosità Popolare "Beato Angelico" a Vicchio: Guida Alla Visita Del Museo e Alla Scoperta Del Territorio. 2008. (Piccoli, grandi Musei Ser.). (Illus.). 404p. (C). 24.00 *(978-88-596-0381-8(1))* Polistampa ITA. Dist: Brown, David Bk. Co., The.

Singleton, Douglas, ed. Wangechi Mutu: A Shady Promise. Scardoni, Chiara, tr. 2008. (ENG., Illus.). 144p. 50.00 *(978-88-6208-021-7(2))* Damiani ITA. Dist: D.A.P./Distributed Art Pubs.

Sirmans, Franklin, ed. & contrib. by. NeoHooDoo: Art for a Forgotten Faith. 2008. (ENG., Illus.). 144p. 45.00 *(978-0-300-13418-6(5))* Yale Univ. Pr.

Smith, Joel. Saul Steinberg: Illuminations. 2006. (Illus.). 288p. 65.00 *(978-0-300-11586-4(5))* Yale Univ. Pr.

Society of Publication Designers Staff. 45th Publication Design Annual. 2011. (ENG., Illus.). 336p. 60.00 *(978-1-59253-669-6(7),* 1592536697) Quayside.

Solomon R Guggenheim Foundation, creator. The Hugo Boss Prize, 1 vol. 2007. (ENG., Illus.). 108p. pap. 29.95 *(978-0-89207-361-0(6))* Guggenheim, Solomon R. Museum.

Spalding, Julian & Rough Guides Staff. The Best Art You've Never Seen: 100 Hidden Treasures from Around the World. 2010. (ENG., Illus.). 288p. 22.99 *(978-1-84836-271-0(4))* Rough Guides, Ltd. GBR. Dist: Dorling Kindersley Publishing, Inc.

Speed, Julie. Speed Art, 2003-2009. 2009. (ENG., Illus.). 188p. 55.00 *(978-0-292-71994-1(9))* Univ. of Texas Pr.

Spencer, Tracy. The Arts for Every Day: A Practical Introduction. 2nd rev. ed. 2010. (ENG., Illus.). 92p. pap. 50.71 *(978-0-7575-7913-3(8))* Kendall Hunt Publishing Co.

Stafford, Kim, text. In the Presence of Books. 2007. (Illus.). 112p. per. *(978-1-59028-196-3(9))* Franklin, Beedle & Assocs., Inc.

Stampolidis, Nicholas & Sotirakopoulou, Peggy. Aegean Waves: Artworks of the Early Cycladic Culture in the Museum of Cycladic Art. Hardy, David, tr. 2008. (ENG., Illus.). 224p. 65.00 *(978-88-6130-346-1(3))* Rizzoli International Pubns., Inc.

Starr, Figura. German Expressionism: The Graphic Impulse - Masterworks from the Museum of Modern Art. 2011. (ENG., Illus.). 288p. 60.00 *(978-0-87070-795-7(7))* Museum of Modern Art.

Steffensen. Tal R Etchings Masters & Method. 2008. (ENG., Illus.). 276p. 195.00 *(978-3-7757-2163-9(0))* Hatje Cantz Verlag GmbH & Co KG DEU. Dist: D.A.P./Distributed Art Pubs.

Stephens, Simon. Ship Models in the Thomson Collection. 2009. (Illus.). 128p. pap. 50.00 ***(978-1-903470-82-4(X))*** Holberton, Paul Publishing GBR. Dist: Casemate Pubs. & Bk. Distributors, LLC.

Sterling, Linder. Linder: Works 1976-2006, 1 vol. 2006. (ENG., Illus.). 144p. 70.00 *(978-3-905701-60-9(X))* JRP Ringier Kunstverlag AG CHE. Dist: D.A.P./Distributed Art Pubs.

Stevenson, John A. & Wood, Donald A. Dragons & Lotus Blossoms: Vietnamese Ceramics from the Birmingham Museum of Art, 1 vol. 2011. (ENG., Illus.). 320p. pap. 45.00 ***(978-0-295-99162-7(3))*** Univ. of Washington Pr.

Stichting Kunstboek. Bonsai: Noelanders Trophy 10 Years. 2010. (ENG., Illus.). 224p. *(978-90-5856-341-5(3),* Stichting Kunstboek (Acc)) Antique Collectors' Club.

Stingel, Rudolf. Rudolf Stingel. 2011. (ENG., Illus.). 84p. 80.00 ***(978-3-7913-4581-9(8))*** Prestel Publishing.

Stiver, David J. The Art & Image of the Cross. 2007. (Illus.). 125p. pap. *(978-0-9794266-2-9(6))* 23rd Street Pr.

Stringer, John, et al. Closet Circus: The Lloyd & Elizabeth Horn Collection of Contemporary Western Australian Art. 2008. 224p. pap. 49.95 *(978-1-921361-27-2(1))* Fremantle Pr. AUS. Dist: Independent Pubs. Group.

Suera, Vincenzo. Junior Pop Textures, Vol. 1. 2010. (ENG., Illus.). 144p. 135.00 incl. DVD *(978-88-88766-04-1(9))* Arkivia Bks. ITA. Dist: National Bk. Network.

—Techno Pop Textures, Vol. 1. 2010. (ENG., Illus.). 144p. 135.00 incl. DVD *(978-88-88766-01-0(4))* Arkivia Bks. ITA. Dist: National Bk. Network.

Sultana, Sharon. The National Museum of Archaeology: The Neolithic Period. 2006. (ENG., Illus.). 40p. (C). pap. 9.95 *(978-99932-7-076-8(8))* Midsea Bks. Ltd. MLT. Dist: Brown, David Bk. Co., The.

Sumberg, Bobbie. Textiles: Collection of the Museum of International Folk Art. 2010. (ENG., Illus.). 250p. 60.00 *(978-1-4236-0650-5(7))* Gibbs Smith, Publisher.

Sumner, Ann. The Barber Institute of Fine Arts: Director's Choice. 2011. (ENG., Illus.). 80p. pap. 12.95 *(978-1-85759-652-6(8))* Scala, Editions FRA. Dist: National Bk. Network.

Syndram, Dirk. Juwelenkunst des Barock: Johann Melchior Dinglinger im Grünen Gewölbe. 2008. (Illus.). 240p. (C). 47.00 *(978-3-7774-4445-1(6))* Hirmer Verlag GmbH DEU. Dist: Brown, David Bk. Co., The.

Szperling, Severin. A Catalog of Holocaust Medals: A History Etched in Metal. 2010. pap. 98.95 *(978-1-60494-421-1(8))* Wheatmark.

Szymczyk, Adam & Filipovic, Elena. When Things Cast No Shadow. 2008. (GER & ENG., Illus.). 592p. pap. 45.00 *(978-3-905829-58-7(4))* JRP Ringier Kunstverlag AG CHE. Dist: D.A.P./Distributed Art Pubs.

Tamas, Klara & Hobbick, Cade. Klara Tamas: Tapestries, Paintings, Drawings, Posters. 2008. (Illus.). 31.99 *(978-1-4257-9634-1(6))* Xlibris Corp.

Tamura, Rieko, photos by. Taizo Kuroda, White Porcelain. 2008. (Illus.). 28p. pap. *(978-0-9626731-0-8(2))* Yoshii Gallery.

Tan, Fiona, et al. Mirror Maker. 2006. (GER, DAN, ENG, FIN & SWE., Illus.). 384p. 40.00 *(978-3-936636-89-5(3))* Kehrer Verlag Heidelberg, Klaus Kehrer DEU. Dist: Consortium Bk. Sales & Distribution.

Taschen Staff. Giger. Date not set. (SPA.). pap. 4.99 *(978-3-8228-8780-6(3))* TASCHEN DEU. Dist: Digital Manga Publishing.

Tedesch, Martha & Dahm, Kristi. John Marin's Watercolors: A Medium for Modernism. 2011. (ENG., Illus.). 192p. 50.00 *(978-0-300-16637-8(0))* Art Institute of Chicago.

The Curators and Employees of Kelvingrove Art Gallery and Museum. Kelvingrove Art Gallery & Museum: The Curators & employees of Kelvingrove Art Gallery & Museum. 2009. (ENG., Illus.). 128p. pap. 20.00 *(978-0-85667-667-3(5))* Wilson, Philip Pubs., Ltd. GBR. Dist: Macmillan.

Thormann, Olaf. Vessel Sculpture. 2009. (GER & ENG., Illus.). 480p. 85.00 *(978-3-89790-288-6(5))* Arnoldsche Art Pubs. DEU. Dist: Antique Collectors' Club.

Tianbing Li: Me & My Brother. 2008. (Illus.). 55p. pap. 40.00 *(978-0-9790942-2-4(4))* L & M Arts.

Tibol, Raquel & Rivera, Diego. Diego Rivera: Great Illustrator. 2008. (ENG., Illus.). 308p. 65.00 *(978-968-9345-00-8(1))* R.M. Editorial, S.A. de C.V. MEX. Dist: D.A.P./Distributed Art Pubs.

Toikka, Oiva, et al. Birds by Toikka. 2008. (FIN & ENG., Illus.). 159p. pap. *(978-951-0-34905-2(4))* Osakeyhtio, Werner Soderstrom.

Top Design Studio & Top, Peleg. Design for Special Events: 500 of the Best Logos, Invitations, & Graphics. 2008. (ENG., Illus.). 320p. 50.00 *(978-1-59253-416-6(3),* 1592534163) Quayside.

Tortoriello, Lyn & Lyons, Deborah. Bakelite Jewelry: The Art of the Carver. 2008. (Illus.). 192p. 39.99 *(978-0-7643-2914-2(6))* Schiffer Publishing, Ltd.

Tretiak, Daniel. The life & works of haku Maki. 2007. 132p. per. 39.95 *(978-1-4327-0575-6(X))* Outskirts Pr., Inc.

Trockel, Rosemarie. Jedes Tier Ist Eine Kunstlerin: Every Animal Is a Female Artist. ltd. ed. (Illus.). 64p. 100.00 *(978-91-87952-10-4(6))* Propexus AB SWE. Dist: D.A.P./Distributed Art Pubs.

Tuli, Neville. A Historic Epic: India in the Making 1757-1950: From Surrender to Revolt: Swaraj to Responsibility. (Masterpieces & Museum Quality Ser.). (Illus.). 288p. 75.00 *(978-81-88204-11-3(0))* Mapin Publishing Pvt. Ltd IND. Dist: Antique Collectors' Club.

—A Historical Mela: the ABC of India: The Art, Book & Cinema. (Masterpieces & Museum Quality Ser.). (Illus.). 320p. 60.00 *(978-81-88204-07-6(2))* Mapin Publishing Pvt. Ltd IND. Dist: Antique Collectors' Club.

—Osian's A Historical Mela: The Art, Books & Cinema. 2006. (ENG., Illus.). pap. 60.00 *(978-1-890206-49-9(0))* Mapin Publishing Pvt. Ltd IND. Dist: National Bk. Network.

—Osians Historical Series III. 2007. 65.00 *(978-0-944142-52-3(4))* Antique Collectors' Club.

Tuli, Neville, text. India: A Historical Lila: Auctions of Indian Modern & Contemporary Paintings, Drawings & Graphic Art. 2006. (Paintings, Drawings & Graphic Art Ser.). (ENG., Illus.). 224p. pap. 50.00 *(978-1-890206-39-0(3))* Mapin Publishing Pvt. Ltd IND. Dist: National Bk. Network.

Updike, Robin & Dailey, Michael. Michael Dailey: Color, Light, Time, & Place - Selected Works, 1965-2007. 2008. (ENG., Illus.). 48p. *(978-0-295-98830-6(4))* Univ. of Washington Pr.

Vallejo, Boris & Bell, Julie. Boris Vallejo & Julie Bell: The Ultimate Illustrations. 2009. (ENG.). 192p. pap. 24.99 *(978-0-06-115173-6(4),* Collins Design) HarperCollins Pubs.

—Imaginistix: The Art of Boris Vallejo & Julie Bell. 2007. (ENG., Illus.). 192p. 29.95 *(978-0-06-113846-1(0),* Collins Design) HarperCollins Pubs.

Van Dyke, Kristina. African Art: From the Menil Collection. 2008. (Illus.). 239p. pap. *(978-0-939594-64-1(1))* Menil Foundation.

Van Hoesen, Beth, et al. 5,000 Years of Chinese Jade: Featuring Selections from the National Museum of History, Taiwan, & the Arthur M. Sackler Gallery, Smithsonian Institution, 1 vol. 2011. (ENG., Illus.). 130p. pap. 29.95 ***(978-0-615-47180-8(3))*** San Antonio Museum of Art.

Vanstiphout, Wouter & van den Boogerd, Dominic, texts. Jeroen Doorenweerd. 2009. (ENG & DUT., Illus.). 208p. pap. 45.00 *(978-90-5662-676-1(C))* NAi Uitgevers / Publishers Stichting NLD. Dist: D.A.P./Distributed Art Pubs.

Vedova, Emilio. Emilio Vedova, 1 vol. 2006. (ENG & ITA., Illus.). 144p. pap. 45.00 *(978-88-8158-583-0(9))* Charta ITA. Dist: D.A.P./Distributed Art Pubs.

Veleanu, Mircea. Netsuke. 2008. (Illus.). 256p. bds. 79.95 *(978-0-7643-2647-3(6))* Schiffer Publishing, Ltd.

Victoria and Albert Museum Staff. The Victoria & Albert Museum: Pocket Address Book 2008. 2007. (Illus.). 112p. 9.95 *(978-0-7112-2794-1(2))* Lincoln, Frances Ltd. GBR. Dist: Perseus-PGW.

Villet, Jeffrey M. The Complete Prints Maxime Lalanne, Catalogue, Raisonne, Lithographs, & Etchings: Third Edition Expanded. 2010. pap. *(978-1-4507-3423-3(5))* Independent Pub.

Vingtrinier, Beatrice & Lis, Michel. Flowers in the Louvre. 2010. (ENG., Illus.). 80p. 19.95 *(978-2-08-122820-7(3))* Flammarion et Cie FRA. Dist: Random Hse., Inc.

Vogtherr, Christoph. The Wallace Collection: Director's Choice. 2012. (ENG., Illus.). 80p. pap. 14.95 ***(978-1-85759-770-7(2))*** Scala, Editions FRA. Dist: National Bk. Network.

Von Halasz, Joachim, ed. Hitler's Degenerate Art - the Exhibition Catalogue - First Published in 1937 As Entartete Kunst Austellungsnhrer' 2008. 48p. pap. *(978-1-905742-08-0(8))* Foxley Books.

Voorhies, James. Exact Imagination: Exhibition Catalogue, Columbus College of Art & Design. 2008. per. *(978-0-9797476-1-8(9))* Columbus College of Art & Design.

—Taking Shelter: Exhibition Catalogue, Columbus College of Art & Design. 2008. per. *(978-0-9797476-2-5(7))* Columbus College of Art & Design.

Voss, Roy, text. Daniel Sturgis: Don't Argue, 2007- exhibition catalog with an essay by Roy Voss. 2007. (Illus.). per. *(978-0-9774221-1-1(9))* Broan, Cynthia Gallery.

VV Staff. Rafael. (Colección Art Book). (SPA., Illus.). 144p. *(978-84-8156-251-4(3))* Sociedad Editorial Electa Espana ESP. Dist: Lectorum Pubns., Inc.

Wachmann, Wiebke Maria. Spaces 98-03. 64p. *(978-3-89955-063-4(3))* Die Gestalten Verlag.

Warner, Ian & Posgay, Mike. The World of Wade Ireland. 2007. (Illus.). 160p. pap. 29.95 *(978-0-7643-2618-9(X))* Schiffer Publishing, Ltd.

Warren, Isensee. Warren Isensee. 2008. (Illus.). 34p. per. *(978-0-9795501-2-6(2))* Danese.

Warren, Jeremy. Beauty & Power: Renaissance & Baroque Bronzes from the Collection of Peter Marino. 2010. (ENG., Illus.). 288p. 90.00 *(978-0-900785-77-1(2))* Holberton, Paul Publishing GBR. Dist: Univ. of Washington Pr.

Waschek, Matthias, ed. Portrait/Homage/Embodiment. 2006. 0.00 net. *(978-0-9714648-5-8(5))* Pulitzer Foundation For The Arts.

Wasserman, Krystyna. The Book As Art: Artists' Books from the National Museum of Women in the Arts. 2nd ed. 2011. (ENG., Illus.). 208p. pap. 34.95 *(978-1-56898-992-1(X))* Princeton Architectural Pr.

Weidensaul, Scott. Ned Smith's Game News Covers. 2006. (ENG., Illus.). 144p. pap. 24.95 *(978-0-8117-3301-4(7))* Stackpole Bks.

Weiss, Jeffrey, text. The Helga & Walther Lauffs Collection Vol. 1, 1 vol. 2010. (ENG., Illus.). 416p. 175.00 *(978-3-86521-850-6(4))* Steidl, Gerhard Druckerei und Verlag DEU. Dist: Innovative Logistics.

Welch, Stuart Cary. Rajasthani Miniatures. 2006. (ENG.). 48p. pap. 15.00 *(978-0-942324-10-5(2),* Harvard Art Museum (Acc)) Antique Collectors' Club GBR. Dist: National Bk. Network.

Weller, Alan. Mehndi Tattoo Flash CD-ROM & Book. 2011. (Dover Electronic Clip Art Ser.). (ENG., Illus.). 48p. pap. 19.95 *(978-0-486-99093-4(1))* Dover Pubns., Inc.

Wengel, Doug & Wengel, Pat. Comic Character Metal Sand Toys. 2008. (Illus.). 176p. bds. 39.95 *(978-0-7643-2851-0(4))* Schiffer Publishing, Ltd.

Wenjun, Zhang. The Henan Museum. 2010. (ENG., Illus.). 192p. pap. 35.00 *(978-1-85759-633-5(1))* Scala, Editions FRA. Dist: National Bk. Network.

Wenley, Robert. French Bronzes in the Wallace Collection. 2006. (ENG., Illus.). 112p. pap. 24.95 *(978-0-900785-79-8(0))* Wallace Collection GBR. Dist: National Bk. Network.

Whitaker, Jim, et al. Josef Originals: Charming Figurines. 3rd rev. exp. ed. 2008. (Schiffer Book for Collectors Ser.). (Illus.). 128p. pap. 29.95 *(978-0-7643-2837-4(9))* Schiffer Publishing, Ltd.

White, Colin. A Guide to the Printed Work of Jessie M. King. 2007. (Illus.). 238p. 90.00 *(978-1-58456-204-7(8))* Oak Knoll Pr.

Whitehouse, David. Islamic Glass in the Corning Museum of Glass. 2010. (Illus.). *(978-0-87290-175-9(0))* Corning Museum of Glass.

Whiteley, Jon. Poussin to Cezanne: French Drawings & Watercolours. 2006. (Ashmolean Handbooks: Vol. 19). (ENG., Illus.). 112p. pap. 15.95 *(978-1-85444-168-3(X),* 168X) Ashmolean Museum GBR. Dist: Antique Collectors' Club.

Whitney Gallery of Western Art Staff, contrib. by. Timeless Treasures: 50 Favorites from the Whitney Gallery of Western Art. 2008. pap. *(978-0-931618-68-0(1))* Buffalo Bill Historical Ctr.

Wiedemann, Julius, ed. Illustration Now 2. 2007. (FRE, GER & ENG., Illus.). 480p. per. 39.99 *(978-3-8228-3016-1(X))* TASCHEN DEU. Dist: Ingram Pub. Services.

William Hayes Ackland Art Memorial Art Center. William Hayes Ackland Memorial Art Center Catalogue of the Collection: Volume 1, Painting & Selected Sculpture. 2011. (ENG.). 224p. pap. 40.00 ***(978-0-8078-6895-9(7))*** Univ. of North Carolina Pr.

Williams, Dyfri. Masterpieces of Classical Art. 2009. (ENG., Illus.). 360p. 45.00 *(978-0-292-72147-0(1))* Univ. of Texas Pr.

Williams, Jay, ed. Pleasant Journeys & Good Eats along the Way: The Paintings of John Baeder. 2007. (ENG., Illus.). 112p. pap. 30.00 *(978-1-934110-22-5(1))* Univ. Pr. of Mississippi.

Williamson, Laila & Young, Serinity, eds. Body & Spirit: Tibetan Medical Paintings. 2009. (ENG., Illus.). 264p. pap. 45.00 *(978-0-295-98869-6(X))* Univ. of Washington Pr.

Willingham, et al. Silver Stained Roundels & Unipartite Panels Before the French Revolution Flanders Vol. 1: The Province of Antwerp. 2007. (Corpus vitrearum, belgium, Checklists Ser.). (Illus.). 464p. 138.00 *(978-1-905375-25-7(5))* Brepols Pubs. BEL. Dist: Brown, David Bk. Co. The.

Wodzinska, Anna. A Manual of Egyptian Pottery, Volume 2: Naqada III - Middle Kingdom. 2009. (Aera field manual Ser.). (ENG., Illus.). 245p. (C). spiral bd. 40.00 *(978-0-9779370-5-9(4))* Ancient Egypt Research Assocs.

Wolf, Norbert & Lorenz, Ralph, eds. Brucke. 2008. (Basic Genre Ser.). (ENG., Illus.). 96p. pap. 9.99 *(978-3-8228-5474-7(3))* TASCHEN DEU. Dist: Ingram Pub. Services.

Wolff, Martha. Kings, Queens, & Courtiers: Art in Early Renaissance France. 2011. (ENG., Illus.). 208p. 60.00 *(978-0-300-17025-2(4))* Art Institute of Chicago.

Woloholian, Stephan. Harvard Art Museum Handbook. Woloholian, Stephan, ed. 2008. (Harvard Art Museum Ser.). (Illus.). 288p. pap. 24.95 *(978-1-891771-50-7(7))* Harvard Univ. Art Museums.

Wood, J. Copies & Adaptations from Renaissance & Later Artists: Italian Masters. Raphael & his School, 2 vols. 2010. (Corpus Rubenianum Ludwig Burchard Ser.). (ENG., Illus.). 717p. (C). 261.00 (978-1-905375-39-4(5)) Miller, Harvey Pubs. GBR. Dist: Brown, David Bk. Co., The.

Wood, John. Copies & Adaptations from Renaissance & Later Artists: Italian Masters. Titian & North Italian Art, 2 vols. 2010. (Corpus Rubenianum Ludwig Burchard Ser.). (ENG., Illus.). 680p. (C). 261.00 (978-1-905375-40-0(9)) Miller, Harvey Pubs. GBR. Dist: Brown, David Bk. Co., The.

Woodward, Hiram W. The Sacred Sculpture of Thailand: The Alexander B. Griswold Collection, the Walters Art Gallery. (Illus.). 328p. (978-0-500-97457-5(8)) Thames & Hudson.

Wooton, David. Peter Coker RA. 2006. (ENG., Illus.). 180p. (978-1-871136-76-0(8)) Beetles, Chris Ltd.

Yeager, Ira H., Jr. Ira Yeager Indian Paintings: Forty Years of Indians. 2007. 123p. per. 29.95 (978-0-9791423-0-7(X)) Yeager's, Ira Studio.

Yoo, Hee-Gwone & Regina, Kristen A., compiled by. Visual Resources from Russia & Eastern Europe in the New York Public Library: A Checklist. 2008. (Illus.). 140.00 (978-0-88354-046-6(0)) Ross Publishing Incorporated.

York, Karen S. Sons of Adam, Daughters of Eve: Biblical Images in Art from Tulsa Collections. 2007. (Illus.). 110p. pap. (978-0-9799851-0-2(2)) Sherwin Miller Museum of Jewish Art, The.

Zelevansky, Lynn. Carnegie Museum of Art: Director's Choice. 2010. (ENG., Illus.). 80p. pap. 14.95 (978-1-85759-653-3(6)) Scala, Editions FRA. Dist: National Bk. Network.

Zobel, Joseph. Antique Vienna Bronzes. 2008. (Illus.). 256p. bds. 79.95 (978-0-7643-2849-7(2)) Schiffer Publishing, Ltd.

ART—COLLECTORS AND COLLECTING

see also Art As an Investment

Altshuler, Bruce. Collecting the New: Museums & Contemporary Art. 2007. (ENG., Illus.). 208p. (C). per. 21.95 (978-0-691-13373-7(5)) Princeton Univ. Pr.

Andersen, Margaret & Thomas, Neil F. Living Art: The Life of Paul R. Jones, African American Art Collector. 2009. (Illus.). 144p. 32.50 (978-0-87413-073-7(5)) Univ. of Delaware Pr.

Ardizzone, Heidi. An Illuminated Life: Belle Da Costa Greene's Journey from Prejudice to Privilege. 2007. (ENG., Illus.). 592p. 35.00 (978-0-393-05104-9(8), 5104) Norton, W. W. & Co., Inc.

Arenski, Jay, et al. Swiss Carvings: Art of the Black Forest. 2007. (ENG., Illus.). 184p. (978-1-85149-493-4(6), Antique Collectors Club Dist) Antique Collectors' Club.

Asensio, P. Minimal - the Big Book of Minimalism. 2008. 599p. (978-981-245-588-8(4)) Page One Publishing.

Attaboy! Hi-Fructose Collected Edition: Under the Counter Culture. 2008. (ENG., Illus.). 250p. 39.95 (978-0-86719-702-0(1)) Last Gasp of San Francisco.

Aymerich, Marta. Symbols, Pictograms & Silhouettes. 2008. (Illus.). incl. cd-rom (978-84-96774-35-3(X)) Index Bks., Spain.

Bader, Alfred. Chemistry & Art: Further Adventures of a Chemist Collector. 2009. (ENG., Illus.). 312p. 29.95 (978-0-297-85512-5(3)) Orion Publishing Group, Ltd. GBR. Dist: Independent Pubs. Group.

Bamberger, Alan. The Art of Buying Art - 2nd Edition. Benson, Jodie, ed. 2007. 284p. per. 24.95 (978-1-933295-20-6(1)) LTB Gordonsart, Inc.

Barbero, Luca Massimo. Carlo Cardazzo: Una Nuova Visione Dell'arte. Barbero, Luca Massimo, ed. 2009. (ITA., Illus.). 400p. 117.50 (978-88-370-6534-8(5)) Electa ITA. Dist: Trans-Atlantic Pubns., Inc.

Bargna, Ivan & Parodi da Passano, M. Giovanna. L'Africa Delle Meraviglie: Arti Africane Nelle Collezioni Italiane = the Wonders of Africa: African Arts in Italian Collections. 2011. (ITA & ENG., Illus.). 204p. pap. 60.00 (978-88-366-1949-8(5)) Silvana ITA. Dist: D.A.P./Distributed Art Pubs.

Bassegoda i Hugas, Bonaventura. Col·leccionistes, Col·leccions I Museus: Episodis de la Història Del Patrimoni Artístic de Catalunya. 2007. (CAT., Illus.). 291p. (978-84-475-3166-0(X)) Univ. de Barcelona Pubns.

Beard, Rick, et al. Packaging Presidents: A Book Illustrating the Merrill C. Berman Collection. 2008. (Illus.). 200p. pap. (978-0-9799182-1-6(9)) Abraham Lincoln Presidential Library Foundation.

Bell, Esther & Gere, Charlotte. Studying Nature: Oil Sketches from the Thaw Collection. 2011. (978-0-87598-160-4(7)) Pierpont Morgan Library.

Bellini, Andrea, et al, eds. Collecting Contemporary Art. 2009. (ENG., Illus.). 128p. pap. 15.00 (978-3-03764-015-9(4)) JRP Ringier Kunstverlag AG CHE. Dist: D.A.P./Distributed Art Pubs.

Bennett, Jim. Authenticating Ancient Indian Artifacts: How to Recognize Reproduction & Altered Artifacts. rev. ed. 2008. (ENG., Illus.). 240p. 29.95 (978-1-57432-555-3(8), 1574325558) Collector Bks.

Berzock, Kathleen Bickford & Clarke, Christa, eds. Representing Africa in American Art Museums: A Century of Collecting & Display. 2010. (Mclellan Book Ser.). (ENG., Illus.). 320p. pap. 40.00 (978-0-295-98961-7(0)) Univ. of Washington Pr.

Black, Peter, ed. "My Highest Pleasures" William Hunter's Art Collection. 2011. (ENG., Illus.). 192p. 50.00 (978-1-903470-31-2(5)) Holberton, Paul Publishing GBR. Dist: Casemate Pubs. & Bk. Distributors, LLC.

Bonami, Francesco & Gingeras, Alison, eds. La Collezione Di Punta Della Dogana: The Catalogue of the Contemporary Art Center in Venice. 2009. (ITA & FRE., Illus.). 300p. 115.00 (978-88-370-6994-0(4)) Electa ITA. Dist: Trans-Atlantic Pubns., Inc.

Borys, Stephen D., ed. The John & Mable Ringling Museum of Art: A guide to the Collections. 2008. (Illus.). per. (978-0-916758-52-3(4)) Ringling, John & Mable Museum of Art Foundation, The.

Breitz, Candice. Candice Breitz: Inner & Outer Space. 2009. (GER & ENG., Illus.). 120p. pap. 45.00 (978-3-86560-546-7(X)) Verlag der Buchhandlung Walther Konig DEU. Dist: D.A.P./Distributed Art Pubs.

Brotherton, Barbara. A Community of Collectors: 75 Anniversary Gifts to the Seattle Art Museum. Ishikawa, Chiyo, ed. 2008. (ENG., Illus.). 304p. (978-0-932216-60-1(9)) Seattle Art Museum.

Brown, Shana Julia. Pastimes: From Art & Antiquarianism to Modern Chinese Historiography. 2011. 232p. 48.00 (978-0-8248-3498-2(4)) Univ. of Hawaii Pr.

Bryce, Alan D. Art Smart: The Intelligent Guide to Investing in the Canadian Art Market. 2007. (ENG., Illus.). 176p. pap. 24.99 (978-1-55002-676-4(3), Dundurn Pr.) Dundurn CAN. Dist: Ingram Pub. Services.

Buck, Louisa & Greer, Judith C. Owning Art: Contemporary Art Collectors Handbook, 1 vol. 2007. (ENG.). 276p. 30.00 (978-0-9546999-1-8(2)) Cultureshock Media Ltd. GBR. Dist: D.A.P./Distributed Art Pubs.

Burns, Cherie. Searching for Beauty: The Life of Millicent Rogers. 2011. (ENG., Illus.). 384p. 27.99 (978-0-312-54724-0(2)) St. Martin's Pr.

Campbell, Sara. Collector without Walls: Norton Simon & His Hunt for the Best. 2010. (Illus.). 260p. 65.00 (978-0-9726681-8-7(7)) Norton Simon Museum.

—Collector without Walls: Norton Simon & His Hunt for the Best. 2010. (Illus.). 480p. 65.00 (978-0-300-16672-9(9)) Yale Univ. Pr.

Cantero, David, illus. Club Life. 2008. pap. (978-3-86787-013-9(6)) Bruno Gmunder Verlag GmbH.

Carder, James N., ed. A Home of the Humanities: The Collecting & Patronage of Mildred & Robert Woods Bliss. 2011. (Dumbarton Oaks Collection Ser.). (ENG., Illus.). 200p. 65.00 (978-0-88402-365-4(6)) Dumbarton Oaks.

Carminati, Marco. Il David in Carrozza. 2009. (ITA., Illus.). 296p. (978-88-304-2622-1(9)) Longanesi.

Cartwright, Derrick R. & Brown, Bill. Personal Views: Regarding Private Collections in San Diego. 2006. (978-0-937108-39-0(1)) San Diego Museum of Art.

Cattelan, Maurizio, et al, eds. Charley Independents. 2011. (ENG., Illus.). 356p. pap. 30.00 (978-1-935202-31-8(6)) D.A.P./Distributed Art Pubs.

Chinese Arts Auction Records 2000: 2000 Fine Arts 1/1/99 - 12/31/99. (Illus.). 500p. pap. 59.95 (978-957-99189-9-2(6)) Chinese Art Bks. Cultural Enterprise Co., Ltd. TWN. Dist: Art Media Resources, Inc.

Christian, Kathleen Wren. Empire Without End: Antiquities Collections in Renaissance Rome, C. 1350-1527. 2010. (Illus.). 288p. 70.00 (978-0-300-15421-4(6)) Yale Univ. Pr.

Clarke, Mathew S. From Fire to Form Metalsmith: Sculpture from the Modern Blacksmith & Metalsmith. 2009. (Illus.). 256p. bds. 50.00 (978-0-7643-3247-0(3)) Schiffer Publishing, Ltd.

Clemence, Paul & Davidow, Julie. Miami: Contemporary Artists. 2007. (Illus.). 288p. pap. 49.95 (978-0-7643-2647-9(3)) Schiffer Publishing, Ltd.

Clements, Monica Lynn & Clements, Patricia Rosser. Cameos: Classical to Costume. 2nd exp. rev. ed. 2008. (Illus.). 224p. bds. 59.99 (978-0-7643-2994-4(4)) Schiffer Publishing, Ltd.

Colangelo, Carmon, et al. On the Margins. 2008. (Illus.). 64p. 30.00 (978-0-936316-25-3(X)) Washington Univ., Mildred Lane Kemper Art Museum.

Colley, Robert, ed. Stone Canoe: A Journal of Arts & Ideas from Upstate New York, #2. 2009. 404p. pap. 20.00 (978-0-9791944-1-2(5)) Syracuse Univ. Pr.

Connor, Michael, et al, contrib. by. The New Normal. 2008. (ENG., Illus.). 144p. pap. 29.95 (978-0-916365-79-0(4)) Independent Curators International.

Cushing, Stanley Ellis & Dearinger, David B. Acquired Tastes: 200 Years of Collecting for the Boston Athenaeum. 2007. (Illus.). 388p. 65.00 (978-0-934552-73-8(8)) Boston Athenaeum Library.

Daros-Latinamerica Collec Staff. Face to Face. 2008. (ENG., Illus.). 288p. 55.00 (978-3-7757-2112-7(6)) Hatje Cantz Verlag GmbH & Co KG DEU. Dist: D.A.P./Distributed Art Pubs.

Davila-Villa, Ursula, ed. & intro. Recovering Beauty: The 1990s in Buenos Aires. 2011. (ENG., Illus.). 144p. pap. 25.00 (978-0-9815738-5-4(1)) Blanton Museum of Art, Univ. of Texas at Austin.

de Waal, Edmund. A Hare with Amber Eyes: A Family's Century of Art & Loss. 2010. (ENG., Illus.). 368p. 26.00 (978-0-374-10597-6(9)) Farrar, Straus & Giroux.

—The Hare with Amber Eyes: A Hidden Inheritance. 2011. (ENG., Illus.). 368p. pap. 16.00 (978-0-312-56937-2(8)) Picador.

Dobson, Austin. Horace Walpole A Memoir with an Appendix. 2006. pap. 31.95 (978-1-4286-5212-5(4)) Kessinger Publishing, LLC.

Doctor Roncero, Rafael, ed. The Musac Collection, Volume II. 2007. (Illus.). 623p. (978-84-96954-20-5(X)) Charta.

Dreyfus, Renee. Legion of Honor: Selected Works. 2008. (ENG., Illus.). 160p. pap. 14.95 (978-1-85759-407-2(X)) Scala, Editions FRA. Dist: National Bk. Network.

Dunn-Morton, Julie. 160 Years of Art at the St. Louis Mercantile Library: A Handbook to the Collections: an Anniversary Publication, 1846-2006. 2008. (ENG., Illus.). 196p. (gr. 9). 39.95 (978-0-9639804-9-6(1)) Univ. of Missouri Pr.

Duveen, James Henry. Secrets of an Art Dealer. 2007. 312p. per. (978-1-4067-6914-2(2)) Read Bks.

Earle, Peggy. Legacy: Walter Chrysler Jr. & the Untold Story of Norfolk's Chrysler Museum of Art. 2008. (ENG.). 216p. 22.95 (978-0-8139-2718-3(8)) Univ. Pr. of Virginia.

Ebrey, Patricia Buckley. Accumulating Culture: The Collections of Emperor Huizong. 2008. (ENG., Illus.). 576p. 65.00 (978-0-295-98778-1(2)) Univ. of Washington Pr.

Eccles, Tom, frwd. At Home/Not at Home. 2010. (ENG., Illus.). 168p. 40.00 (978-1-936192-07-6(1)) Ctr. for Curatorial Studies, The.

Eeg-Tverbakk. Lars O Ramberg. 2009. (ENG.). 248p. 60.00 (978-3-7757-2038-0(3)) Hatje Cantz Verlag GmbH & Co KG DEU. Dist: D.A.P./Distributed Art Pubs.

Faber, Paul. Africa at the Tropenmuseum: Collections at the Tropenmuseum. 2012. (Illus.). 168p. 50.00 (978-94-6022-119-4(X)) Royal Tropical Institute Pr. (KIT (Koninklijk Instituut voor de Tropen) NLD. Dist: Stylus Publishing, LLC.

Fairclough, Oliver, et al. Turner to Cézanne: Masterpieces from the Davies Collection, National Museum Wales. 2009. (ENG., Illus.). 176p. 60.00 (978-1-55595-299-0(2)) Hudson Hills Pr. LLC.

Fern, Alan, et al. One Hundred Stories: Highlights from the Washington County Museum of Fine Arts. 2008. (Illus.). 232p. pap. 29.95 (978-0-914495-02-4(X)) Washington County Museum of Fine Arts.

Fietzek, Gerti, ed. Maria Eichhorn: the Artist's Contract. 2009. (ENG., Illus.). 336p. pap. 49.95 (978-3-86560-421-7(8)) Verlag der Buchhandlung Walther Konig DEU. Dist: D.A.P./Distributed Art Pubs.

George, Sasha. The Art World of Sasha's Innovations. 2010. 76p. pap. 30.00 (978-1-4520-7920-2(X)) AuthorHouse.

Getty, J. Paul. The Joys of Collecting. 2011. (ENG., Illus.). 80p. pap. 9.95 (978-1-60606-087-2(2), J. Paul Getty Museum) Getty Pubns.

Gonzalez, Mark. Solid-Colored Dinnerware: Depression to Mid-Century. 2008. (Schiffer Book for Collectors Ser.). (Illus.). 160p. pap. 29.95 (978-0-7643-2846-6(8)) Schiffer Publishing, Ltd.

Goodwin, James. International Art Markets: The Essential Guide for Collectors & Investors. 2010. (ENG., Illus.). 448p. pap. 45.95 (978-0-7494-5592-7(6)) Kogan Page, Ltd. GBR. Dist: Ingram Pub. Services.

Grave, Johannes. Der "ideale Kunstkörper" Johann Wolfgang Goethe Als Sammler Von Druckgraphiken und Zeichnungen. 2007. (Asthetik Um 1800 Ser.). (GER., Illus.). 648p. (C). 100.00 (978-3-525-47503-4(9)) Vandenhoeck & Ruprecht GmbH & Co. KG DEU. Dist: ISD.

Greenberger Rafferty, Sara, et al, contrib. by. North Drive Press: Ndp#3. 2006. (Illus.). 35.00 (978-1-933045-41-2(8)) North Drive Pr.

Gwily, Ruth, ed. Cycle. 2008. 142p. (978-84-612-1482-2(X)) Actar Birkhauser Distribution.

Hanson, Craig Ashley. The English Virtuoso: Art, Medicine, & Antiquarianism in the Age of Empiricism. 2009. (ENG., Illus.). 344p. 50.00 (978-0-226-31587-4(8)) Univ. of Chicago Pr.

Hein, Jorgen. The Treasure Collection at Rosenborg Castle: The Inventories of 1696 & 1718 - Royal Heritage & Collecting in Denmark-Norway, 1500-1900, 3 vols. Jones, Glyn et al, trs. 2009. (Illus.). 846p. 285.00 (978-87-635-0131-6(7)) Museum Tusculanum Pr. DNK. Dist: Chicago Distribution Ctr.

Herzog, Hans-Michael & Steffen, Katrin, eds. Painted: Beate Gunther, Richard Allen Morris, Guillermo Kuitca. 2009. (ENG., Illus.). 172p. pap. 60.00 (978-3-7757-2328-2(5)) Hatje Cantz Verlag GmbH & Co KG DEU. Dist: D.A.P./Distributed Art Pubs.

Hofer, Andreas. The Long Tomorrow. 2009. (GER, SPA & ENG., Illus.). 72p. pap. 45.00 (978-3-86560-511-5(7)) Verlag der Buchhandlung Walther Konig DEU. Dist: D.A.P./Distributed Art Pubs.

Hunt, William. William Hunt: Tempting Fate by Swimming Alone, 1 vol. 2009. (ENG., Illus.). 1p. 30.00 (978-90-73362-83-3(0)) Witte De With Centre for Contemporary Art NLD. Dist: D.A.P./Distributed Art Pubs.

Hunter, Lisa. The Intrepid Art Collector: The Beginner's Guide to Finding, Buying, & Appreciating Art on a Budget. 2006. (ENG., Illus.). 368p. per. 13.95 (978-0-307-23713-2(3), Three Rivers Pr.) Crown Publishing Group.

Hutchinson, Elizabeth. The Indian Craze: Primitivism, Modernism, & Transculturation in American Art, 1890-1915. 2009. (Objects/Histories Ser.). (ENG., Illus.). 304p. 89.95 (978-0-8223-4390-5(8)); pap. 24.95 (978-0-8223-4408-7(4)) Duke Univ. Pr.

Ice, Joyce, ed. On Collecting: From Private to Public, Featuring Folk & Tribal Art from the Diane & Sandy Besser Collection. 2009. (ENG., Illus.). 176p. pap. (978-0-295-98888-7(6)) Univ. of Washington Pr.

International Directory of Arts 2011. 35th ed. 2011. (ENG., Illus.). 2986p. (978-3-11-916803-8(3)) Saur, K. G. Verlag GmbH & Co.

International Directory of Arts 2012. 36th ed. 2012. (ENG., Illus.). XXIV, 2954p. E-Book 769.00 (978-3-11-916308-8(2)) De Gruyter, Walter Inc.

Jersey City Museum Staff. First Look: The Essential Guide to Jersey City Museum. 2007. (ENG., Illus.). 224p. per. 29.95 (978-0-8135-3963-8(3)) Rutgers Univ. Pr.

Jones, Laura K., ed. A Hedonist's Guide to Art. 2010. (Hedonist's Guide To... Ser.). (ENG., Illus.). 240p. 20.00 (978-1-905428-50-2(2), HG2) Filmer Ltd. GBR. Dist: Perseus-PGW.

Joshi, Angela, ed. A Sister's Love Is Forever: A Very Special Collection to Share with a Sister Who Is More than Family... She's a Friend for Life, 1 vol. 2011. (Illus.). 96p. pap. 13.95 (978-1-59842-622-9(2)) Blue Mountain Arts Inc.

K. G. Saur Editorial Staff, ed. International Directory of Arts, 3 vols. 31st rev. ed. 2006. 2,800p. (978-3-598-23113-1(X)) Saur, K. G. Verlag GmbH & Co.

Kcosa, Leonard D. DeMaio Ksma. The Artful Dodger: Collecting & Investing in Fine Art Without a Spare Million in Pocket Change. 2010. (Illus.). 129p. pap. 15.95 (978-1-4327-5249-1(9)) Outskirts Pr., Inc.

Keevill, Elizabeth & Eyres, Kevin. Dali. 2009. (Todo Arte Ser.). (ENG.). 384p. pap. 19.00 (978-84-9794-050-4(4)) Edimat Libros, S. A. ESP. Dist: Independent Pubs. Group.

Knorr, Daniel. Daniel Knorr: Carte de Artist. 2008. (Illus.). 200p. pap. 248.00 (978-3-86560-239-8(8)) Verlag der Buchhandlung Walther Konig DEU. Dist: D.A.P./Distributed Art Pubs.

Knowles, Valerie. From Telegrapher to Titan: The Life of William C. Van Horne. 2010. (Railroads Past & Present Ser.). (ENG., Illus.). 504p. pap. 29.95 (978-0-253-22250-3(8), 0253222508) Indiana Univ. Pr.

Korero Books Staff, et al. Burlesque Poster Design: The Art of Tease. 2009. (ENG., Illus.). 178p. 39.95 (978-0-9553398-2-0(0)) Korero Books LLP GBR. Dist: Independent Pubs. Group.

Kraus Connelly, Bonnie. Everything's Coming up Sock Monkeys! Art, History & Business of the American Sock Monkey. 2007. (Illus.). 161p. 34.95 (978-0-9790323-0-1(X)) In My Own Dream Pub.

Lamp, Frederick John, et al, contrib. by. Accumulating Histories: African Art from the Charles B. Benenson Collection at the Yale University Art Gallery. 2012. (ENG., Illus.). 328p. 75.00 (978-0-300-16992-8(2)) Yale Univ. Art Gallery.

Learning Group. Collecting Systems: Learning Book #001. 2006. (Illus.). 64p. pap. 10.00 (978-0-945323-09-9(3)) WhiteWalls, Inc.

LePere, Gene Hirshhorn. Little Man in a Big Hurry. 2009. (ENG.). 271p. 26.95 (978-0-533-16079-2(0)) Vantage Pr., Inc.

Lerner, Ralph E. & Bresler, Judith. All about Tax Tips for Collectors. 2008. (ENG., Illus.). 263p. pap. 29.95 (978-1-4024-1071-0(9)) Practising Law Institute.

Li, Yishan. 500 Manga Creatures. 2008. 528p. pap. 19.95 (978-0-06-165050-5(1), Collins Design) HarperCollins Pubs.

Lillehoj, Elizabeth, ed. Acquisition: Art & Ownership in EDO-Period Japan. 2007. (ENG., Illus.). 208p. per. 50.00 (978-1-891640-50-6(X)) Floating World Editions.

Maberly, Joseph. The Print Collector. 2009. 254p. pap. (978-0-217-28238-3(5)); 124p. pap. (978-0-217-60541-0(9)) Books LLC.

Mabuchi, Aiko, ed. Mabuchi: William Anderson: the Pictorial Arts of Japan: Western sources on japanese art & japonism, Series 4. 2008. 2700p. 825.00 (978-4-86166-028-3(9)) Synapse, Edition JPN. Dist: Taylor & Francis Group.

Maclean, Malcolm & Dorgan, Theo. Leabhar Mor. 2008. (ENG., Illus.). 336p. 49.95 (978-1-84717-113-9(3)) O'Brien Pr., Ltd., The IRL. Dist: Dufour Editions, Inc.

Macleod, Dianne Sachko. Enchanted Lives, Enchanted Objects: American Women Collectors & the Making of Culture, 1800-1940. 2008. (Illus.). 328p. 50.00 (978-0-520-23729-2(3)) Univ. of California Pr.

Mannini, Lucia. Le stanze dei Tesori: Collezionisti e antiquari a Firenze tra Ottocento e Novecento. 2011. (Piccoli, grandi Musei Ser.). (ENG & ITA., Illus.). 312p. (C). 75.00 (978-88-596-0965-0(8)) Polistampa ITA. Dist: Brown, David Bk. Co., The.

Martin, Mary L. & Skinner, Tina. The Ultimate Collector's Guide to Surfing Postcards. 2008. (Illus.). 160p. pap. 29.95 (978-0-7643-2909-8(X)) Schiffer Publishing, Ltd.

Marzio, Peter C. American Art & Philanthropy: Twenty Years of Collecting at the Museum of Fine Arts, Houston. 2010. (ENG., Illus.). 388p. 75.00 (978-0-300-16756-6(3)) Museum of Fine Arts, Houston.

Mazaroff, Stanley. Henry Walters & Bernard Berenson: Collector & Connoisseur. 2010. (ENG., Illus.). 248p. (gr. 17). 40.00 (978-0-8018-9512-8(X)) Johns Hopkins Univ. Pr.

Mcharg, Robert G. Him Book. 2007. (Illus.). 208p. 29.99 (978-1-904563-62-4(7)) Trolley GBR. Dist: Prestel Publishing.

McLean, Fred. New Zealand Art for Investment. 160p. pap. 19.95 (978-0-908876-88-4(2)) Transpress NZL. Dist: Pacific Island Bks.

McPhee, Sarah. Bernini's Beloved: A Portrait of Costanza Piccolomini. 2012. (ENG., Illus.). 280p. 45.00 (978-0-300-17527-1(2)) Yale Univ. Pr.

Mellor, Douglas. Still. 2007. pap. 24.95 (978-1-888899-43-6(3)); 100.00 (978-1-888899-44-3(1)) Lodima Pr.

Metrick-Chen, Lenore. Collecting Objects/Excluding People: Chinese Subjects & American Visual Culture, 1830-1900. 2012. (ENG.). 320p. 85.00 (978-1-4384-4325-6(0)) State Univ. of New York Pr.

Migdal, Marcin. Sketchozine. Com Vol. 1: The Ultimate Collection of Artwork & Interviews from World's Most Talented Artists. 2011. (ENG.). 150p. pap. 34.95 (978-1-4663-8390-6(9)) CreateSpace.

—Sketchozine. com Vol. 2 SEXY THINGS: The ultimate Collection of Artwork & Interviews from World's Most Talented Artists. 2011. (ENG.). 134p. pap. 34.95 (978-1-4679-7544-5(3)) CreateSpace.

—Sketchozine. com: Vol. 4 CUTESIES: The ultimate Collection of Artwork & Interviews from World's Most Talented Artists. 2011. (ENG.). 146p. pap. 34.95 (978-1-4664-0266-9(0)) CreateSpace.

Mileti, Nick James. The Unscrupulous: Scams, Cons, Fakes, & Frauds that Poison the Fine Arts. 2009. 314p. pap. 20.00 (978-1-59954-003-0(7)) Bordighera Incorporated.

Miniaturensammlung Tansey, ed. Miniaturen des Rokoko aus der Sammlung Tansey. 2008. (GER., Illus.). 428p. (C). 119.00 (978-3-7774-4335-5(2)) Hirmer Verlag GmbH DEU. Dist: Brown, David Bk. Co., The.

Moure, Nancy Dustin Wall. Historical Collections Council Newsletters, January 1999-May 2006 & Miscellaneous Articles. 2006. (Publications in Southern California Art: 9). 741p. 80.00 (978-0-9614622-9-1(9)) Dustin Pubns.

Muller, Melissa & Tatzkow, Monika. Lost Lives, Lost Art: Jewish Collectors, Nazi Art Theft, & the Quest for Justice. 2010. (ENG., Illus.). 248p. 40.00 (978-0-86565-263-7(5)) Vendome Pr., The.

Munder, Heike, ed. Migros Museum fur Gegenwartskunst. 2008. (ENG., Illus.). 416p. 115.00 (978-3-905829-42-6(8)) JRP Ringier Kunstverlag AG CHE. Dist: D.A.P./Distributed Art Pubs.

MURPHY, David Richard. The art of st. john Davies. 2008. 36p. 21.50 (978-1-4357-6020-2(4)) Lulu Enterprises Inc.

Museum of Illustration, ed. What Are You Like? Self Revealing Artworks by People in the Public Eye. 2008. (ENG.). 96p. pap. 55.00 *(978-0-9559496-0-9(2))* Pallas Athene GBR. Dist: Independent Pubs. Group.

National Museum of the American Indian (U.S.), George Gustav Heye Center Staff, contrib. by. Indigenous Motivations: Recent Acquisitions from the National Museum of the American Indian. 2006. (NMAI Editions Ser.). 80p. pap. *(978-1-933565-03-3(9))* Smithsonian National Museum of the American Indian.

Niemeyer Chini, Valerie & Chini, Valerie Niemeyer. Stefano Bardini e Wilhelm Bode: Mercanti e connaisseur fra Ottocento e Novecento. 2009. (ITA., Illus.). 288p. (C). pap. 54.00 *(978-88-596-0668-0(3))* Polistampa ITA. Dist: Brown, David Bk. Co., The.

North, Michael, ed. Artistic & Cultural Exchanges Between Europe & Asia, 1400-1900: Rethinking Markets, Workshops & Collections. 2010. (Illus.). 216p. 124.95 *(978-0-7546-6937-1(8))* Ashgate Publishing Co.

Okwunodu Ogbechie, Sylvester. Making History: African Collectors & the Canon of African Art. 2012. (ENG., Illus.). 256p. 70.00 *(978-88-7439-571-2(X))* 5 Continents ITA. Dist: Abrams.

Ortiz, Diego, ed. Yours Faithfully. 2008. 114p. pap. *(978-84-611-7815-5(7))* Actar Birkhauser Distribution.

Ottmann, Klaus. Still Points: Site Santa Fe's Sixth International Biennial Exhibition: Volumes I & II, 1 vol. 2006. (ENG., Illus.). 272p. lthr. 50.00 *(978-0-9764492-3-2(4))* Site Santa Fe.

Panza, Giuseppe. Giuseppe Panza: Memories of a Collector. 2008. (ENG., Illus.). 416p. pap. 37.50 *(978-0-7892-0944-3(6))* Abbeville Pr., Inc.

Parkett, compiled by. Art Works - 25 Years: The 200 Editions Made for Parkett since 1984. 2009. (ENG., Illus.). 517p. pap. 45.00 *(978-3-907582-25-1(X))* Parkett Verlag AG CHE. Dist: D.A.P./Distributed Art Pubs.

Patterson, Jan. Smart Book: The Smart Mart to the Arts. 3rd ed. Date not set. pap. 24.95 *(978-0-9643197-2-1(1))* Patterson Marketing.

Perrella, Lynne. Art Making, Collections, & Obsessions: An Intimate Exploration of the Mixed-Media Work & Collections of 35 Artists. 2008. (ENG., Illus.). 160p. 26.99 *(978-1-59253-363-3(9),* 1592533639) Quayside.

Pezzano, Chiara & Morolli, Gabriele. La galleria d'Arte Moderna di Firenze: Il luogo, le Collezioni (1784-1914) 2009. (ITA., Illus.). 240p. (C). pap. 30.00 *(978-88-596-0572-0(5))* Polistampa ITA. Dist: Brown, David Bk. Co., The.

Ploeg, Peter van der, et al, contrib. by. Princely Patrons: The Collection of Frederick Henry of Orange & Amalia of Solms in the Hague. (Illus.). 276p. *(978-90-400-9193-3(5))* Waanders B.V., Uitgeverij.

Polo, Roberto I., et al. Roberto Polo: The Eye. 2011. (ENG., Illus.). 688p. 150.00 *(978-0-7112-3252-5(0))* Lincoln, Frances Ltd. GBR. Dist: Perseus-PGW.

Polsky, Richard. The Art Prophets: The Artists, Dealers, & Tastemakers Who Shook the Art World. 2011. (ENG., Illus.). 272p. 24.95 *(978-1-59051-406-1(8))* Other Pr., LLC.

—I Sold Andy Warhol (Too Soon) 2009. (ENG.). 288p. 23.95 *(978-1-59051-337-8(1))* Other Pr., LLC.

Potvin, John & Myzelev, Alla, eds. Material Cultures, 1740-1920: The Meanings & Pleasures of Collecting. 2009. (Illus.). 250p. 124.95 *(978-0-7546-6144-3(X))* Ashgate Publishing Co.

Preziosi, Don & Skinner, Tina. Peep-Machine Pin-Ups: 1940s-1950s Mutoscope Art. 2006. (Illus.). 128p. pap. 29.95 *(978-0-7643-2511-3(6))* Schiffer Publishing, Ltd.

Preziosi, Donald. Classic American Diners: Collectible Postcards & Matchcovers. 2007. (Schiffer Book Ser.). (Illus.). 176p. 39.95 *(978-0-7643-2610-3(4))* Schiffer Publishing, Ltd.

Pucci, Ralph & Pucci. Show. 2009. (ENG.). 192p. 75.00 *(978-0-9801557-8-5(9))* Glitterati, Inc.

Qing, Zhang, et al, texts. The Shanghai Papers. 2009. (ENG., Illus.). 136p. pap. 45.00 *(978-3-7757-2322-0(6))* Hatje Cantz Verlag GmbH & Co KG DEU. Dist: D.A.P./Distributed Art Pubs.

Randall, Christopher. The Brush & the Stone: The Dr. Dean Edell Collection of Chinese Art. (Illus.). 142p. 85.00 *(978-1-878529-54-1(4))* Art Media Resources, Inc.

Ray, Judah. Inspiration Manifesto. 2008. 39p. 404.70 *(978-1-4357-4222-2(2))* Lulu Enterprises Inc.

Reece, Thad. The Lunchbox Kid! 2010 Collector's Pictorial Price Guide for Metal Lunchboxes. 2010. 172p. pap. 99.00 *(978-1-4520-0746-5(2))* AuthorHouse.

Reid, Michael. How to Buy & Sell Art. 2nd rev. ed. 2008. (ENG., Illus.). xv, 351p. 24.95 *(978-1-74175-369-1(4))* Allen & Unwin AUS. Dist: Independent Pubs. Group.

Reuter, Laurel, ed. The Disappeared/Los Desaparecidos 1 vol. 2006. (ENG & SPA., Illus.). 112p. pap. 34.95 *(978-88-8158-604-2(5))* D.A.P./Distributed Art Pubs.

Riley, C. M. Art at Lincoln Center: The Public Art & List Print & Poster Collections. 2008. (Illus.). 240p. 75.00 *(978-0-470-16913-1(3),* Wiley) Wiley, John & Sons, Inc.

Rittersma, Rentgenier C., ed. Luxury in the Low Countries: Miscellaneous Reflections on Netherlandish Material Culture, 1500 to the Present. 2011. 272p. pap. 34.95 *(978-90-5487-797-4(9))* VUB Univ. Pr. BEL. Dist: Independent Pubs. Group.

Salisbury, Martin. Artists at the Fry: A Guide to the Works in the Fry Art Gallery. 2008. (ENG., Illus.). 96p. pap. *(978-0-9537810-2-7(X),* Frye Art Gallery The) Antique Collectors' Club.

Sanchez-Jauregui Alpanes, Maria Dolores & Wilcox, Scott, eds. The English Prize: The Capture of the Westmorland, an Episode of the Grand Tour. 2012. (ENG., Illus.). 400p. 75.00 *(978-0-300-17605-6(8))* Yale Univ. Pr.

Sanger, Martha Frick Symington. Helen Clay Frick: Bittersweet Heiress. 2007. (ENG., Illus.). 386p. 40.00 *(978-0-8229-4341-9(7))* Univ. of Pittsburgh Pr.

Satiat, Nadine. Gertrude Stein. 2010. (FRE., Illus.). 1288p. *(978-2-08-121992-2(1))* Flammarion et Cie.

Schaffner, Ingrid, text. Douglas Blau. 2009. (ENG., Illus.). 80p. pap. 30.00 *(978-0-88454-115-8(0))* Univ. of Pennsylvania, Institute of Contemporary Art.

Seely, Jana & Collins, Keri. Faces of Hearst Castle. 2007. (Illus.). 96p. 19.95 *(978-0-9792156-3-6(3))* Hearst Castle Pr.

Sharf, Frederic. Art of Collecting: The Spaulding Brothers & Their Legacy, 1 vol. 2008. (ENG., Illus.). 144p. pap. 24.95 *(978-0-87846-723-5(8))* Museum of Fine Arts, Boston.

Skinner, Tina. Found Object Art II. 2009. (Illus.). 176p. bds. 49.99 *(978-0-7643-3162-6(0))* Schiffer Publishing, Ltd.

Skinner, Tina & Sam Hilu Collection Staff. Nomadic Embroideries: India's Tribal Textile Art. 2008. (Illus.). 208p. 49.99 *(978-0-7643-3032-2(2))* Schiffer Publishing, Ltd.

Smith, Travis. Kitschmasland! Christmas Decor from the 1950s to The 1970s. 2nd rev. ed. 2008. (Illus.). 160p. pap. 29.99 *(978-0-7643-2978-4(2))* Schiffer Publishing, Ltd.

Spoons, Bwana. Welcome to Forest Island. 2009. (Illus.). 144p. 30.00 *(978-1-60309-040-7(1))* Top Shelf Productions.

Staatliche Museum Kassel Staff. Old Masters Gallery, Kassel. 2006. (ENG., Illus.). 136p. pap. 29.95 *(978-1-85759-329-7(4))* Scala, Editions FRA. Dist: National Bk. Network.

Stepan, Peter. Picasso's Collection of African & Oceanic Art: Masters of Metamorphosis. 2006. (Illus.). 136p. 85.00 *(978-3-7913-3691-6(6))* Prestel Publishing.

Stolwijk, Chris, et al, contrib. by. Theo Van Gogh, 1857-1891: Art Dealer, Collector, & Brother of Vincent. 2006. (Illus.). 232p. 45.00 *(978-90-400-9359-3(8))* Waanders B.V., Uitgeverij NLD. Dist: Antique Collectors' Club.

Stourton, James. Great Collectors of Our Time: Art Collecting Since 1945. 2007. (ENG., Illus.). 480p. 85.00 *(978-1-85759-514-7(9))* Scala, Editions FRA. Dist: National Bk. Network.

Stourton, James & Sebag-Montefiore, Charles. The British As Art Collectors: From the Tudors to the Present. 2012. (ENG., Illus.). 400p. 100.00 ***(978-1-85759-749-3(4))*** Scala, Editions FRA. Dist: National Bk. Network.

Strauss, Cindi. Pioneers of Contemporary Glass: Highlights from the Barbara & Dennis Dubois Collection. 2009. (ENG., Illus.). 96p. pap. 19.95 *(978-0-300-14695-0(7))* Museum of Fine Arts, Houston.

Strongman, Jay. Tiki Mugs: Cult Artifacts of Polynesian Pop. 2008. (ENG., Illus.). 176p. 39.95 *(978-0-9553398-1-3(2))* Korero Books LLP GBR. Dist: Independent Pubs. Group.

Suriano, Gregory. Tea Art: A Modern Look at Vintage Tea Graphics. 2008. (Illus.). 112p. pap. 24.99 *(978-0-7643-2811-4(5))* Schiffer Publishing, Ltd.

Theatre, Sketch. The Art of Sketch Theatre Volume 1. 2011. (ENG.). 240p. 40.00 ***(978-1-61404-003-3(6))*** Baby Tattoo Bks.

Thompson, Don. The $12 Million Stuffed Shark: The Curious Economics of Contemporary Art. 2010. (ENG., Illus.). 272p. pap. 17.00 *(978-0-230-62059-9(0))* Palgrave Macmillan.

Thompson, Donald N. The $12 Million Stuffed Shark: The Curious Economics of Contemporary Art. 2008. (ENG., Illus.). 272p. 26.00 *(978-0-230-61022-4(6))* Palgrave Macmillan.

Todd, Pamela. The Arts & Crafts Companion. 2008. (ENG.). 320p. pap. 24.95 *(978-0-9553046-7-5(9))* Palazzo Editions, Ltd. GBR. Dist: Independent Pubs. Group.

Topsfield, Andrew & Hodgkin, Howard. Visions of Mughal India: The Collection of Howard Hodgkin. 2012. (ENG., Illus.). 200p. pap. 50.00 ***(978-1-85444-263-5(5))*** Ashmolean Museum GBR. Dist: National Bk. Network.

Twist, Anthony. A Life of John Julius Angerstein, 1735-1823: Widening Circles in Finance, Philanthropy & the Arts in Eighteenth Century London. 2006. (Illus.). 620p. 149.95 *(978-0-7734-5583-2(3))* Mellen, Edwin Pr., The.

Upper Playground, creator. Upper Playground, Volume 1. 2007. (Illus.). 19.95 *(978-0-9790862-2-9(1))* Upper Playground Pubng.

van Brakel, Koos & Legêne, Susan, eds. Collecting on Cultural Crossroads: Collection Policies & Approaches (2008-2011) at the Tropenmuseum. 2008. (Bulletins of the Royal Tropical Institute Ser.). 106p. (C). pap. 35.00 *(978-90-6832-647-5(3))* Royal Tropical Institute Pr. (KIT (Koninklijk Instituut voor de Tropen)) NLD. Dist: Stylus Publishing, LLC.

Veleanu, Mircea. Netsuke. 2008. (Illus.). 256p. bds. 79.95 *(978-0-7643-2847-3(6))* Schiffer Publishing, Ltd.

Vivian, Frances. A Life of Frederick, Prince of Wales, 1707-1751: A Connoisseur of the Arts. White, Roger, ed. 2007. (Illus.). 512p. lib. bdg. *(978-0-7734-5547-4(7))* Mellen, Edwin Pr., The.

Waanders Editors. Room for Art: In Seventeenth-Century Antwerp. 2010. (ENG., Illus.). 144p. 49.50 *(978-90-400-7655-8(3))* Waanders B.V., Uitgeverij NLD. Dist: National Bk. Network.

Waterfield, Hermione & King, J. C. H. Provenance: Twelve Collectors of Ethnographic Art in England, 1760-1990. 2009. (Illus.). 175p. *(978-1-903470-97-3(5))* Holberton, Paul Publishing.

Weber, Nicholas Fox. The Clarks of Cooperstown. 2007. (ENG., Illus.). 448p. 35.00 *(978-0-307-26347-6(9),* Knopf) Knopf Doubleday Publishing Group.

Wendorf, Richard. The Literature of Collecting & Other Essays. 2008. 49.95 *(978-1-58456-230-6(7))* Oak Knoll Pr.

West, Paige. The Art of Buying Art: An Insider's Guide to Collecting Contemporary Art. 2007. (Illus.). 208p. 39.95 *(978-0-06-079459-0(3),* Collins Design) HarperCollins Pubs.

Whalen, Nomi. She Collects Collections. 2009. 96p. pap. 28.99 *(978-1-4389-4354-1(7))* AuthorHouse.

Wineapple, Brenda. Sister Brother: Gertrude & Leo Stein. 2008. (ENG., Illus.). 536p. pap. 25.00 *(978-0-8032-1753-9(6),* Bison Bks.) Univ. of Nebraska Pr.

Wolfe, Tom. Carving Santas for Today: With Tom Wolfe. 2008. (Illus.). 64p. pap. 14.99 *(978-0-7643-3082-7(9))* Schiffer Publishing, Ltd.

Wright, Barnaby, et al. Cézanne's Card Players. 2010. (ENG., Illus.). 160p. pap. 40.00 *(978-1-907372-08-7(3))* Holberton, Paul Publishing GBR. Dist: Univ. of Washington Pr.

Zenko, Adachi. My Life in Japanese Art & Gardens: From Entrepreneur to Connoisseur. 2010. (ENG.). 256p. 29.95 *(978-1-933330-86-0(4))* Stone Bridge Pr.

Ziskin, Rochelle. Sheltering Art: Collecting & Social Identity in Early Eighteenth-Century Paris. 2012. (ENG.). 360p. ***(978-0-271-03785-1(7))*** Pennsylvania State Univ. Pr.

Zobel, Joseph. Antique Vienna Bronzes. 2008. (Illus.). 256p. bds. 79.95 *(978-0-7643-2849-7(2))* Schiffer Publishing, Ltd.

ART—COMPETITIONS

Berry, Ian, et al, texts. Oliver Herring: TASK. 2012. (ENG., Illus.). 176p. pap. 33.00 ***(978-0-945558-34-7(1))*** Univ. Galleries of Illinois State Univ.

Koekebakker, Olof, text. PrixdeRome. NL 2010. 2010. (ENG., Illus.). 120p. pap. 35.00 *(978-90-5662-753-9(8))* NAi Uitgevers / Publishers Stichting NLD. Dist: D.A.P./Distributed Art Pubs.

Pedersen, B. Martin. Graphis Photography Annual 2009. 2009. (Illus.). 256p. 70.00 *(978-1-932026-50-4(9))* Graphis, U.S., Inc.

—100 Best Photography Annual 2011, 1 vol. 2011. (ENG., Illus.). 256p. 70.00 *(978-1-932026-63-4(0))* Graphis, U.S., Inc.

Thornton, Sarah. Seven Days in the Art World. (ENG., Illus.). 2009. 256p. pap. 15.95 *(978-0-393-33712-9(X),* 33712) 2008. 304p. 24.95 *(978-0-393-06722-4(X),* 6722) Norton, W. W. & Co., Inc.

ART—COMPOSITION

see Composition (Art)

ART—COMPUTER NETWORK RESOURCES

Amerika, Mark. Meta/Data: A Digital Poetics. 2007. (Leonardo Bks.). (ENG., Illus.). 460p. (gr. 17). 35.95 *(978-0-262-01233-1(2))* MIT Pr.

Amerika, Mark & Amerika, M. Meta/data: A Digital Poetics. 2009. (Leonardo Bks.). (ENG., Illus.). 460p. (gr. 17). pap. 19.95 *(978-0-262-51314-2(5))* MIT Pr.

David, Gerard B. The Art Signature File. 6th ed. 2012. (Illus.). 685p. pap. 29.95 *(978-1-884939-10-5(4))* Antoine Versailles Publishing.

Joubert, Lindy, ed. Educating in the Arts: The Asian Experience, Twenty-Four Essays. 2008. (Education in the Asia-Pacific Region: Issues, Concerns & Prospects Ser.). (Illus.). 300p. 179.00 *(978-1-4020-6366-2(5))* Springer.

Reas, Casey & Fry, Ben. Processing: A Programming Handbook for Visual Designers & Artists. 2007. (ENG., Illus.). 736p. 52.00 *(978-0-262-18262-1(9))* MIT Pr.

ART—CONSERVATION AND RESTORATION

Arthur M. Sackler Gallery (Smithsonian Institution) Staff, contrib. by. Gods of Angkor: Bronzes from the National Museum of Cambodia. 2010. pap. *(978-0-934686-17-4(3))* Freer Gallery of Art, Smithsonian Institution.

Bewer, Francesca G. A Laboratory for Art: Harvard's Fogg Museum & the Emergence of Conservation in America, 1900-1950. 2010. (Illus.). 365p. *(978-1-891771-53-8(1))* Harvard Univ. Art Museums.

Brignolo, Armando & Giannella, Salvatore. The Nicolas: Restoration Tales in a Family History. 2011. (Illus.). 144p. 55.00 *(978-88-422-1660-5(7))* Allemandi, Umberto & Co. GBR. Dist: Antique Collectors' Club.

Britt, Salvesen & Stratis, Harriet K., eds. The Broad Spectrum: Studies in the Materials, Techniques, & Conservation of Color on Paper. 2006. (Conservation of Color on Paper Ser.). (ENG., Illus.). 264p. 160.00 *(978-1-873132-57-9(3))* Archetype Pubns. GBR. Dist: National Bk. Network.

Brown, A. Jean E. The Postprints of the Image Re-Integration Conference: 15th-17th September 2003. 2007. (ENG., Illus.). 164p. pap. 30.00 *(978-1-904794-23-3(8))* Northumbria University Press GBR. Dist: Independent Pubs. Group.

Buckley, Barbara, compiled by. Stretchers & Strainers, Vol. 2. 2008. (Illus.). ring bd., pupil's gde. ed. 65.00 *(978-0-9760501-1-7(0))* American Institute for Conservation of Historic & Artistic Works.

Caneva, Caterina. Tre Piccoli, Grandi Musei e Altre Testimonianze, Scritti 2002-2008. Paolini, Claudio, ed. 2009. (Interventi e Testimonianze Ser.). (ITA., Illus.). 144p. (C). pap. 28.00 *(978-88-596-0692-5(6))* Polistampa ITA. Dist: Brown, David Bk. Co., The.

Couture, Francine & Vanlaethem, France. Conservation de L'art Contemporain et de L'architecture Moderne: L'authenticité en Question. 2010. (FRE., Illus.). viii, 158p. *(978-2-89544-136-6(7))* Editions MultiMondes.

Hermens, Erma & Fiske, Tina. Art, Conservation & Authenticities: Material, Concept, Context. 2010. (ENG., Illus.). 280p. pap. 90.00 *(978-1-904982-51-7(4))* Archetype Pubns. GBR. Dist: National Bk. Network.

Horie, C. V. Materials for Conservation: Organic consolidants, adhesives & Coatings. 2nd rev. ed. 2010. (ENG., Illus.). 504p. pap. 74.95 *(978-0-7506-6905-4(5))* Routledge.

Hummelen, IJsbrand M. C. & Sillé, Dionne. Modern Art - Who Cares? An Interdisciplinary Research Project & an International Symposium on the Conservation of Modern & Contemporary Art. 2006. (ENG., Illus.). 450p. pap. 90.00 *(978-1-904982-02-9(6))* Archetype Pubns. GBR. Dist: National Bk. Network.

James & James, Carlo. Visual Identification & Analysis of Old Master Drawing Techniques. 2010. (Illus.). 85p. *(978-88-222-6014-7(7))* Olschki.

Keneghan, Brenda & Betts, Louise. Plastics: Looking at the Future & Learning from the Past. 2009. (ENG., Illus.). 208p. pap. 90.00 *(978-1-904982-43-2(3))* Archetype Pubns. GBR. Dist: National Bk. Network.

MacFarland, Paul. Framing Art on Canvas: Standard Preservation Practice. 2008. (Illus.). 64p. pap. *(978-0-9663189-5-1(1))* PFM PubCo.

Mack, John. Preserving the Cultural Heritage of Africa: Crisis or Renaissance? Yoshida, Kenji, ed. 2010. (Illus.). 224p. pap. 29.95 *(978-0-85255-982-5(8),* Currey, James) Boydell & Brewer, Ltd. GBR. Dist: Boydell & Brewer, Inc.

Miller, James. Mounting Objects with Clear Film. 2008. 32p. 15.00 *(978-0-938655-23-7(X))* Columba Publishing Co., Inc.

Newman, Richard, text. Conservation: MFA Highlights. 2011. (ENG., Illus.) 200p. pap. 22.50 *(978-0-87846-729-7(7))* Museum of Fine Arts, Boston.

Podany, Jerry. Advances in the Protection of Museum Collections from Earthquake Damage: Papers from a Conference Held at the J. Paul Getty Museum, May 2006. 2008. (Illus.). 240p. pap. 75.00 *(978-0-89236-908-9(6))* Oxford Univ. Pr., Inc.

Save Venice Inc., intro. Save Venice Inc: Four Decades of Restoration. 2010. (ENG.). pap. 65.00 *(978-0-9623364-1-6(6))* Save Venice, Inc.

Schädler-Saub, Ursula & Weyer, Angela. Theory & Practice in the Conservation of Modern & Contemporary Art: Reflections on the Roots & the Perspectives. 2010. (ENG., Illus.). 210p. 90.00 *(978-1-904982-54-8(9))* Archetype Pubns. GBR. Dist: National Bk. Network.

Schinzel, Hiltrud. Touching Vision: Essays on Restoration Theory & the Perception of Art. 2008. (ENG., Illus.). 262p. pap. 28.95 *(978-90-5487-352-5(3))* VUB Univ. Pr. BEL. Dist: Independent Pubs. Group.

Townsend, Joyce H., ed. Art of the Past: Sources & Reconstructions. 2007. (ENG., Illus.). 144p. pap. 75.00 *(978-1-904982-01-2(8))* Archetype Pubns. GBR. Dist: National Bk. Network.

Wilholt, Jennifer J. Common Ground Between Crafts Collectives & Conservation: Protecting Natural Resources Through Artisan Production. 2008. 128p. pap. *(978-3-639-09858-7(7))* VDM Verlag Dr. Mueller e.K.

Xi'an. Unter der gelben Erde. 2007. (GER., Illus.). 224p. (C). 34.00 ***(978-3-8053-3604-8(7))*** Zabern, Philipp von Verlag, GmbH DEU. Dist: Brown, David Bk. Co., The.

ART—CRITICISM

see Art Criticism

ART—DICTIONARIES

Callan, Georgina O'Hara & Glover, Cat. The Thames & Hudson Dictionary of Fashion & Fashion Designers. 2nd rev. ed. 2008. (World of Art Ser.). (ENG., Illus.). 296p. pap. 19.95 *(978-0-500-20399-6(7),* 520399) Thames & Hudson.

Campbell, Gordon. The Grove Encyclopedia of Northern Renaissance Art, 3 vols. 2009. (Grove Art Ser.). (ENG., Illus.). 1300p. (C). 357.00 *(978-0-19-533467-8(1))* Oxford Univ. Pr., Inc.

Chilvers, Ian. The Oxford Dictionary of Art & Artists. 4th ed. 2009. (Oxford Paperback Reference Ser.). (ENG., Illus.). 736p. pap. 18.99 *(978-0-19-953294-0(X))* Oxford Univ. Pr., Inc.

Chilvers, Ian & Glaves-Smith, John. A Dictionary of Modern & Contemporary Art. 2nd ed. (ENG., Illus.). 784p. 2010. pap. 19.95 *(978-0-19-923966-5(5))* 2009. 65.00 *(978-0-19-923965-8(7))* Oxford Univ. Pr., Inc.

Clarke, Michael. The Concise Dictionary of Art Terms. 2nd ed. 2010. (ENG., Illus.). 288p. (Orig.). 17.95 *(978-0-19-956992-2(4))* Oxford Univ. Pr., Inc.

Couperie, Pierre, et al. Encyclopédie de la Bande Dessinee, 3 vols., Set. pap. 85.00 *(978-0-7859-0741-1(6),* M-6093) French & European Pubns., Inc.

Dempsey, Amy. Styles, Schools & Movements: The Essential Encyclopaedic Guide to Modern Art. 2nd rev. ed. 2011. (ENG., Illus.). 312p. pap. 31.95 *(978-0-500-28844-3(5),* 528844) Thames & Hudson.

Edited by the Dipartimento Educazione del Castello di Rivoli Museo d'Arte Contemporanea & the Istituto dei Sordi di Torino. Dictionary of Contemporary Art in Italian Sign Language: Silence Speaks about Art. 2011. (ITA & ENG., Illus.). 208p. pap. 37.00 *(978-88-422-1841-8(3))* Allemandi, Umberto & Co. GBR. Dist: Antique Collectors' Club.

Encyclopaedia Britannica, Inc., compiled by. Britannica Encyclopaedia of Art & Britannica Biographical Encyclopaedia of Artists, 9 vols. 2007. *(978-1-59339-537-7(X))* Encyclopaedia Britannica, Inc.

—My First Britannica: The Arts. 2008. (gr. 7-12). *(978-1-59339-403-5(9))* Encyclopaedia Britannica, Inc.

Evans, David. Critical Dictionary. 2011. (ENG.). 192p. pap. 29.95 *(978-1-907317-49-1(X))* Black Dog Publishing Ltd. GBR. Dist: Perseus Distribution.

Frank, Jane. Science Fiction & Fantasy Artists of the Twentieth Century: A Biographical Dictionary. 2009. (ENG.). 534p. 135.00 *(978-0-7864-3423-7(6))* McFarland & Co., Inc. Pubs.

García Guinea, Miguel Angel, et al. Enciclopedia Del Románico en Aragón: Zaragoza, 2 vols. 2010. (Illus.). (SPA.). *(978-84-89483-68-2(X));* (SPA., *(978-84-89483-69-9(8));* *(978-84-89483-67-5(1))* Fundacion Santa Maria La Real, Centro de Estudios del Romanico.

Giorgi, Rosa. Saints & Their Symbols. 2012. (ENG., Illus.). 420p. 19.95 ***(978-1-4197-0224-2(6))*** Abrams.

Hall, James. Dictionary of Subjects & Symbols in Art. 2nd rev. ed. 2007. (ENG., Illus.). 400p. pap. 44.00 *(978-0-8133-4393-8(3))* Westview Pr.

Hernert, Read. Diccionario del Arte y los Artistas. (SPA., Illus.). 412p. 39.95 *(978-84-233-2377-7(3)*, DE773) Ediciones Destino ESP. Dist: Continental Bk. Co., Inc.

Hourihane, Colum. The Grove Encyclopedia of Medieval Art & Architecture. 2012. (ENG.). 4070p. 895.00 ***(978-0-19-539536-5(0))*** Oxford Univ. Pr., Inc.

Karraker, D. Gene. Looking at European Frames: A Guide to Terms, Styles, & Techniques. 2010. (Looking at Ser.). (Illus.). 88p. pap. 18.95 *(978-0-89236-981-2(7))* Oxford Univ. Pr., Inc.

Kienholz, Lyn. L. A. Rising: SoCal Artists Before 1980. Betinski, Elizabeta & Nelson, Corinne, eds. 2011. (Illus.). 516p. 75.00 net. *(978-0-917571-13-8(4))* California/International Arts Foundation.

Laffont, Robert. Dictionnaire des Oeuvres de Tous les Temps et de Tous les Pays: Litterature.Tr. of Dictionary of the Works of All Times & Places. (FRE.). 882p. pap. 45.00 *(978-0-7859-4622-9(5))* French & European Pubns., Inc.

Lidwell, William, et al. Universal Principles of Design: 125 Ways to Enhance Usability, Influence Perception, Increase Appeal, Make Better Design Decisions, & Teach Through Design. 2nd rev. ed. 2010. (ENG., Illus.). 272p. pap. 30.00 *(978-1-59253-587-3(9)*, 1592535879) Quayside.

Marter, Joan. The Grove Encyclopedia of American Art, 5 vols., Set. 2011. (ENG., Illus.). 2608p. 1045.00 *(978-0-19-533579-8(1))* Oxford Univ. Pr., Inc.

Marter, Joan M. The Grove Encyclopedia of American Art. 2011. (Illus.). E-Book ***(978-0-19-973926-4(9))*** Oxford Univ. Pr., Inc.

Milam, Jennifer D. Historical Dictionary of Rococo Art. 2011. (Historical Dictionaries of Literature & the Arts Ser.). (ENG.). 334p. 80.00 *(978-0-8108-6183-1(6))* Scarecrow Pr., Inc.

Milam, Jennifer Dawn. Historical Dictionary of Rococo Art. 2011. E-Book *(978-0-8108-7952-2(2))* Scarecrow Pr., Inc.

Murphy, Bruce F. Benet's Reader's Encyclopedia. 5th ed. 2008. (ENG.). 1232p. 60.00 *(978-0-06-089016-2(9))* HarperCollins Pubs.

Oweis, Fayeq S. Encyclopedia of Arab American Artists, 1 vol. 2007. (Artists of the American Mosaic Ser.). (Illus.). 336p. 85.00 *(978-0-313-33730-7(6)*, GR3730, Greenwood Pr.) Greenwood Publishing Group, Inc.

Ripley, George. Cyclopedia of Literature & the Fine Arts Comp & Arranged by George Ripley & Bayard Taylor. 2006. 668p. per. 36.99 *(978-1-4255-6782-8(7))* MPublishing.

Room, Adrian. A Dictionary of Art Titles: The Origins of the Names & Titles of 3,000 Works of Art. alt. ed. 2008. (ENG.). 294p. pap. 39.95 *(978-0-7864-3889-1(4))* McFarland & Co., Inc. Pubs.

Thieme, Ulrich. Allgemeines Lexikon der Bildenden Kunstler, 25 vols. (GER.). 2395.00 *(978-0-7859-8354-5(6)*, 3423059079) French & European Pubns., Inc.

Ward, Gerald W. R. The Grove Encyclopedia of Materials & Techniques in Art. 2008. (ENG., Illus.). 864p. 160.00 *(978-0-19-531391-8(7))* Oxford Univ. Pr., Inc.

Waters, Clara Erskine Clement. A Handbook of Legendary & Mythological Art. 2009. 212p. pap. *(978-0-217-15873-2(0))*; 310p. pap. *(978-0-217-67037-1(7))*; 216p. pap. *(978-1-4432-8367-0(3))*; 338p. pap. *(978-1-4432-8365-6(7))* Books LLC.

Zirpolo, Lilian H. The A to Z of Renaissance Art. 93rd ed. 2009. (A to Z Guide Ser.: No. 93). (ENG.). 632p. pap. 34.45 *(978-0-8108-6880-9(6))* Scarecrow Pr., Inc.

—Historical Dictionary of Baroque Art & Architecture. 2010. (Historical Dictionaries of Literature & the Arts Ser.). (ENG., Illus.). 642p. 140.00 *(978-0-8108-6155-8(0))* Scarecrow Pr., Inc.

—Historical Dictionary of Renaissance Art. 2007. (Historical Dictionaries of Literature & the Arts Ser.: No. 21). (ENG., Illus.). 632p. 133.00 *(978-0-8108-5800-8(2))* Scarecrow Pr., Inc.

ART—DIRECTORIES

Art Guide 2009 Staff. Contemporary Europe Art Guide 2009. 2009. (ENG., Illus.). 368p. pap. 45.00 *(978-3-7757-2336-7(6))* Hatje Cantz Verlag GmbH & Co KG DEU. Dist: D.A.P./Distributed Art Pubs.

Giancarlo Politi Editore, ed. Art Diary International 2007-2008: The World Art Directory, 1 vol. 2007. (ENG., Illus.). 570p. pap. 30.00 *(978-88-7816-143-6(8))* Politi, Giancarlo Editore ITA. Dist: D.A.P./Distributed Art Pubs.

Gilbert, Jennifer. Free Art Spaces: Artist's Directory of Alternative Exhibit Spaces. Long, Christpher, ed. (Illus.). 72p. (Orig.). pap. *(978-1-887724-00-5(1))* Fremantle Pr./DeHavilland.

International Directory of Arts 2011. 35th ed. 2011. (ENG., Illus.). 2986p. ***(978-3-11-916803-8(3))*** Saur, K. G. Verlag GmbH & Co.

International Directory of Arts 2012. 36th ed. 2012. (ENG., Illus.). XXIV, 2954p. E-Book 769.00 ***(978-3-11-916308-8(2))*** De Gruyter, Walter Inc.

K. G. Saur Editorial Staff, ed. International Directory of Arts, 3 vols. 31st rev. ed. 2006. 2,800p. *(978-3-598-23113-1(X))* Saur, K. G. Verlag GmbH & Co.

Marquis. American Art Directory 2007-2008. 61st ed. 2006. 1046p. 299.00 *(978-0-87217-843-4(9))* National Register Publishing.

National Register Publishing, creator. American Art Directory. 63rd ed. 2008. (American Art Directory Ser.). 1035p. 371.25 *(978-0-87217-755-0(6))* National Register Publishing.

National Register Publishing Co. Staff. American Art Directory. 65th ed. 2011. 1086p. 297.00 *(978-0-87217-764-2(5))* National Register Publishing.

Peterson's Guides Staff, creator. College Guide for Visual Arts Majors 2007. 12th ed. 2006. (ENG., Illus.). 416p. per. 24.00 *(978-0-7689-2172-4(4))* Peterson's.

Theatre Communications Group, creator. Theatre Directory 2007-2008: 35th Annual Edition. 35th ed. 2007. (Theatre Directory Ser.). (ENG.). 280p. pap. 14.95 *(978-1-55936-320-4(7))* Theatre Communications Group, Inc.

Writer's Digest Books Editors. 2010 Artist's & Graphic Designer's Market. 34th ed. 2009. (ENG.). 560p. pap. 29.99 *(978-1-58297-583-2(3)*, Writer's Digest Bks.) F&W Media, Inc.

Writer's Digest Books Editors, et al, eds. 2011 Artist's & Graphic Designer's Market. 35th ed. 2010. (ENG., Illus.). 576p. pap. 34.99 *(978-1-58297-955-7(3)*, Writer's Digest Bks.) F&W Media, Inc.

ART—EARLY WORKS TO 1800

Borghini, Raffaello & Ellis, Lloyd H., Jr. Il Riposo. 2008. (Lorenzo Da Ponte Italian Library). 384p. *(978-0-8020-9743-9(X))* Univ. of Toronto Pr.

Isager, Jacob. Pliny on Art & Society: The Elder Pliny's Chapters on the History of Art. 2010. 256p. pap. 39.95 *(978-0-415-58901-7(0))* Routledge.

Lavin, Marilyn Aronberg. Artists' Art in the Renaissance. 2009. (ENG., Illus.). 230p. (C). 220.00 *(978-1-904597-43-8(2))* Pindar Pr. GBR. Dist: Brown, David Bk. Co., The.

Reynolds, Joshua. Seven Discourses on Art. 2007. 80p. per. *(978-1-4068-3846-6(2))* Echo Library.

—Seven Discourses on Art. 2010. 70p. pap. 8.75 *(978-1-4432-4844-0(4))* General Bks. LLC.

Reynolds, Joshua. Seven Discourses on Art. 2010. 96p. pap. 15.16 *(978-1-162-68353-9(8))*; 27.16 ***(978-1-169-23628-8(6))***; 33.95 *(978-1-161-45218-1(4))* Kessinger Publishing, LLC.

ART—ECONOMIC ASPECTS

Bamberger, Alan. The Art of Buying Art - 2nd Edition. Benson, Jodie, ed. 2007. 284p. per. 24.95 *(978-1-933295-20-6(1))* LTB Gordonsart, Inc.

Basa, Lynn. The Artist's Guide to Public Art: How to Find & Win Commissions. 2008. (ENG., Illus.). 240p. pap. 19.95 *(978-1-58115-501-3(8)*, 115501, Allworth Pr.) Skyhorse Publishing Co., Inc.

Battenfield, Jackie. The Artist's Guide: How to Make a Living Doing What You Love. 2009. (ENG., Illus.). 400p. pap. 17.95 *(978-0-306-81652-9(0))* Perseus Bks. Group.

Bifo, Franco Berardi, et al, contrib. by. E-Flux Journal: Are You Working Too Much? Post-Fordism, Precarity, & the Labor of Art. 2011. (ENG., Illus.). 212p. pap. 15.00 ***(978-1-934105-31-3(7))*** Sternberg Pr.

Boll, Dirk, text. Art for Sale, 1 vol. 2011. (ENG.). 192p. pap. 25.00 *(978-3-7757-2815-7(5))* Hatje Cantz Verlag GmbH & Co KG DEU. Dist: D.A.P./Distributed Art Pubs.

Cameron, Angus & Gregory, Burke, texts. Goldin & Senneby: Headless. 2010. (ENG., Illus.). 80p. pap. 19.00 *(978-1-894212-26-7(6))* Power Plant, The CAN. Dist: D.A.P./Distributed Art Pubs.

Catterall, Lee. Great Dali Art Fraud. 2009. 400p. 29.95 *(978-965-229-460-9(8))* Gefen Publishing Hse., Ltd ISR. Dist: Strauss Consultants.

Center for Cultural Innovation, prod. Business of Art: An Artist's Guide to Profitable Self-Employment. 2008. 265p. pap. 34.95 *(978-0-9793555-0-9(8))* Ctr. for Cultural Innovation.

Constance, Smith. Art Office, Second Edition. 2007. (ENG.). 112p. pap. 14.95 *(978-0-940899-28-5(0))* ArtNetwork.

Elwins, Dannie. Secrets to Selling Your Crafts at Craft Shows. 2009. 48p. pap. 16.99 *(978-0-557-15587-3(8))* Lulu Enterprises Inc.

Ferrell, Robyn. Sacred Exchanges: Images in Global Context. 2012. (Columbia Themes in Philosophy, Social Criticism, & the Arts Ser.). (ENG., Illus.). 192p. (gr. 17). 50.00 ***(978-0-231-14880-1(1))*** Columbia Univ. Pr.

Findlay, Michael. The Value of Art: Money, Power, Beauty. 2012. (Illus.). 208p. 29.95 ***(978-3-7913-4638-0(5))*** Prestel Publishing.

Frattarolo, Eleonora & Cremonini, Leonardo. La Necessità Dell'arte Oggi: Rappresentare o Presentare?: Atti Del Convegno. 2010. (ITA.). 95p. *(978-88-8016-988-8(2))* De Luca Editori d'Arte.

Freybourg, Anne Maria & Freybourg, Anne Marie. Die Inszenierung des Künstlers. 2008. (GER., Illus.). 111p. pap. *(978-3-86859-031-9(5))* Jovis Verlag GmbH.

Gale, Peggy, et al. Art at Work/L'Art Au Travail: rt Bank of the Canada Council of the Arts/ le Banque d'Oeuvres d'Art du Conseil des Arts du Canada. Henry, Victoria, ed. 2007. (ENG & FRE., Illus.). 144p. pap. 45.00 *(978-0-86492-429-2(1))* Goose Lane Editions CAN. Dist: Univ. of Toronto Pr.

Gielen, Pascal, text. The Murmuring of the Artistic Multitude. 2010. (ENG., Illus.). 368p. pap. 28.95 *(978-90-78088-34-9(6))* Valiz NLD. Dist: D.A.P./Distributed Art Pubs.

Goodwin, James. International Art Markets: The Essential Guide for Collectors & Investors. 2010. (ENG., Illus.). 448p. pap. 45.95 *(978-0-7494-5592-7(6))* Kogan Page, Ltd. GBR. Dist: Ingram Pub. Services.

Grant, Daniel. Selling Art Without Galleries: Toward Making a Living from Your Art. 2006. (ENG.). 256p. per. 19.95 *(978-1-58115-460-3(7)*, 115460, Allworth Pr.) Skyhorse Publishing Co., Inc.

Grazian, David. On the Make: The Hustle of Urban Nightlife. 2008. (ENG., Illus.). 296p. 25.00 *(978-0-226-30567-7(8))* Univ. of Chicago Pr.

Guerzoni, Guido. Apollo & Vulcan: The Art Markets in Italy, 1400-1700. 2011. (ENG., Illus.). 384p. 54.95 *(978-1-61186-006-1(7))* Michigan State Univ. Pr.

Hagoort, Giep & Kooyman, Rene, eds. Creative Industries: Colourful Fabric in Multiple Dimensions. 2010. 224p. pap. 25.00 *(978-90-5972-353-5(8))* Eburon Academic Pubs. NLD. Dist: Chicago Distribution Ctr.

Harowitz, N. Art of the Deal: Contemporary Art in a Global Financial Market. 2011. (ENG., Illus.). 384p. (C). 39.50 *(978-0-691-14832-8(5))* Princeton Univ. Pr.

Hunter, Lisa. The Intrepid Art Collector: The Beginner's Guide to Finding, Buying, & Appreciating Art on a Budget. 2006. (ENG., Illus.). 368p. per. 13.95 *(978-0-307-23713-2(3)*, Three Rivers Pr.) Crown Publishing Group.

Ivey, Bill J. Arts, Inc: How Greed & Neglect Have Destroyed Our Cultural Rights. 2008. (Illus.). 342p. 40.00 *(978-0-520-24112-1(6))* Univ. of California Pr.

Kcosa, Leonard D. DeMaio Ksma. The Artful Dodger: Collecting & Investing in Fine Art Without a Spare Million in Pocket Change. 2010. (Illus.). 129p. pap. 15.95 *(978-1-4327-5249-1(9))* Outskirts Pr., Inc.

Kieft, Royston. Paint & Grow Rich. 2010. 164p. pap. *(978-1-921578-86-1(6))* BookPal.

Lü, Peng. Zhongguo Dang Dai Yi Shu de Li Shi Jin Cheng Yu Shi Chang Hua Qu Shi. 2010. (CHI.). *(978-7-301-16243-9(X))* Beijing University Pr.

Mayer International Auction 1990. 179.00 *(978-3-906985-15-2(6))* M, Edition CHE. Dist: D.A.P./Distributed Art Pubs.

Moeran, Brian & Alacovska, Ana. Creative Industries: Critical Readings, 4 vols. 2012. (ENG.). 1600p. 895.00 ***(978-1-84788-778-8(3))*** Berg Pubs. GBR. Dist: Macmillan.

Molesworth, Helen. This Will Have Been: Art, Love, & Politics in the 1980s. 2012. (ENG., Illus.). 448p. pap. 50.00 ***(978-0-300-18110-4(8))*** Yale Univ. Pr.

Nieves, Marysol. Taking Aim! The Business of Being an Artist Today. 2011. (ENG., Illus.). 200p. 100.00 ***(978-0-8232-3413-4(4))*** Fordham Univ. Pr.

Nieves, Marysol, ed. Taking Aim! The Business of Being an Artist Today. 2011. (ENG., Illus.). 200p. pap. 25.00 ***(978-0-8232-3414-1(2))*** Fordham Univ. Pr.

NY Foundation for the Arts and Artspire Staff. The Profitable Artist: A Handbook for All Artists in the Performing, Literary, & Visual Arts. 2011. (ENG.). 256p. pap. 24.95 *(978-1-58115-872-4(6)*, 115872, Allworth Pr.) Skyhorse Publishing Co., Inc.

Page, John R. & Bayer, Thomas M. The Development of the Art Market in England: Money as Muse, 1730-1900, 1 vol. 2011. (Financial History Ser.). (ENG., Illus.). 288p. 99.00 *(978-1-84893-043-8(7))* Pickering & Chatto Pubs., Ltd. GBR. Dist: Ashgate Publishing Co.

Polsky, Richard. I Sold Andy Warhol (Too Soon) 2009. (ENG.). 288p. 23.95 *(978-1-59051-337-8(1))* Other Pr., LLC.

—I Sold Andy, Warhol (Too Soon) 2011. 288p. pap. 15.95 *(978-1-59051-456-6(4))* Other Pr., LLC.

Puu, Tõnu. Arts, Sciences, & Economics: A Historical Safari. 2006. (ENG., Illus.). xii, 193p. 129.00 *(978-3-540-34423-0(3)*, 3540344233) Springer.

Robertson, Iain & Chong, Derrick. The Art Business. Robertson, Iain & Chong, Derrick, eds. 2008. (ENG., Illus.). 246p. (C). 150.00 *(978-0-415-39157-3(1))*; pap. 54.95 *(978-0-415-39158-0(X))* Routledge.

Ruskin, John. A Joy for Ever: (and Its Price in the Market) 2007. (ENG.). 138p. pap. 18.99 *(978-1-4346-3450-4(7))*; 152p. pap. 21.99 *(978-1-4346-3451-1(5))* BiblioBazaar.

Santagata, Walter. The Culture Factory: Creativity & the Production of Culture. Finnel, Susan, tr. from ITA. 2010. Orig. Title: La fabbrica della Cultura. (ENG., Illus.). xiii, 110p. 119.00 *(978-3-642-13357-2(6)*, 3642133576) Springer.

Smith, Constance, et al. Advanced Strategies for Art Marketing. 2011. (ENG.). 192p. pap. 19.95 ***(978-0-940899-55-1(8))*** ArtNetwork.

Sparkman, Donald. Selling Graphic & Web Design. 3rd rev. ed. 2006. (ENG., Illus.). 240p. per. 24.95 *(978-1-58115-459-7(3)*, 115459, Allworth Pr.) Skyhorse Publishing Co., Inc.

Sullivan, Edward J. The Language of Objects in the Art of the Americas. 2007. (ENG., Illus.). 336p. 65.00 *(978-0-300-11106-4(1))* Yale Univ. Pr.

Taylor, Mark C. Confidence Games: Money & Markets in a World Without Redemption. 2008. (Religion & Postmodernism Ser.). (Illus.). 416p. pap. 24.00 *(978-0-226-79168-5(8))* Univ. of Chicago Pr.

Thompson, Don. The $12 Million Stuffed Shark: The Curious Economics of Contemporary Art. 2010. (ENG., Illus.). 272p. pap. 17.00 *(978-0-230-62059-9(0))* Palgrave Macmillan.

Thompson, Donald N. The $12 Million Stuffed Shark: The Curious Economics of Contemporary Art. 2008. (ENG., Illus.). 272p. 26.00 *(978-0-230-61022-4(6))* Palgrave Macmillan.

Towse, Ruth, ed. Recent Developments in Cultural Economics. 2007. (International Library of Critical Writings in Economics Ser.). (Illus.). 752p. (C). 360.00 *(978-1-84542-385-8(2))* Elgar, Edward Publishing, Inc.

Williams, Theo Stephan. The Graphic Designer's Guide to Pricing, Estimating, & Budgeting. 3rd ed. 2010. (ENG.). 256p. pap. 24.95 *(978-1-58115-713-0(4)*, 115713, Allworth Pr.) Skyhorse Publishing Co., Inc.

—The Interior Designer's Guide to Pricing, Estimating, & Budgeting. 2nd ed. 2010. (ENG., Illus.). 256p. pap. 24.95 *(978-1-58115-718-5(5)*, 115718, Allworth Pr.) Skyhorse Publishing Co., Inc.

ART—EDUCATION

see Art—Study and Teaching

ART—EXAMINATIONS, QUESTIONS, ETC.

Asch, Gayle A. AP Art History Crash Course. 2012. (Advanced Placement (AP) Crash Course Ser.). (ENG.). 224p. (C). (gr. 10-12). pap. 12.95 ***(978-0-7386-1004-7(6))*** Research & Education Assn.

Ballast, David Kent. IDEX Essentials: the Power to Pass the IDEX California Exam. 2009. (ENG.). 480p. pap. 192.00 *(978-1-59126-189-6(9))* Professional Pubns., Inc.

Byrouty M.Ed., Mary Beth. Barron's New Jersey ASK6 Language Arts Literacy Test. 2008. (ENG.). 168p. pap. 12.99 *(978-0-7641-3942-0(8))* Barron's Educational Series, Inc.

Chmiel, Frank, et al. AP Art History. 2012. (Advanced Placement (AP) Test Preparation Ser.). (ENG.). 512p. (gr. 11-12). pap. 29.95 ***(978-0-7386-1075-7(5))*** Research & Education Assn.

DSST Exam Secrets Test Prep Staff, ed. DSST Art of the Western World Exam Secrets Study Guide: DSST Test Review for the Dantes Subject Standardized Tests. 2011. 62.99 *(978-1-61403-517-6(2))* Mometrix Media LLC.

Hubka, David. LEED ID&C Practice Exam: Interior Design & Construction. 2009. (ENG.). 104p. pap. 40.00 *(978-1-59126-187-2(2))* Professional Pubns., Inc.

NMTA Exam Secrets Test Prep Staff, ed. NMTA Visual Arts (22) Secrets Study Guide: NMTA Test Review for the New Mexico Teacher Assessments. 2011. (C). 62.99 *(978-1-61403-611-1(X))* Mometrix Media LLC.

ORELA Exam Secrets Test Prep Staff, ed. ORELA Art Flashcard Study System: ORELA Test Practice Questions & Exam Review for the Oregon Educator Licensure Assessments. 2011. (C). 62.99 *(978-1-61403-630-2(6))* Mometrix Media LLC.

—ORELA Art Secrets Study Guide: ORELA Test Review for the Oregon Educator Licensure Assessments. 2011. (C). 62.99 *(978-1-61403-629-6(2))* Mometrix Media LLC.

Weinthal, Edie & Hade, Patricia. Barron's New Jersey Language Arts Literacy HPSA. 2nd rev. ed. 2008. (ENG.). 240p. pap. 14.99 *(978-0-7641-4017-4(5))* Barron's Educational Series, Inc.

WEST-E Exam Secrets Test Prep Staff, ed. WEST-E Visual Arts (033) Secrets Study Guide: WEST-E Test Review for the Washington Educator Skills Tests-Endorsements. 2011. (C). 62.99 *(978-1-61403-778-1(7))* Mometrix Media LLC.

Wood, Dorothy & Wood, Ashley. Beading - 200 Q&A: Questions Answered on Everything from Basic Stitches to Finishing Touches. 2010. (ENG.). 224p. 18.99 *(978-0-7641-6359-3(0))* Barron's Educational Series, Inc.

Wynne, Sharon. CSET Art Sample Subtest 140. 2008. (Xam Cset Ser.). (ENG.). 76p. pap. 16.50 *(978-1-58197-397-6(7))* XAMonline, Inc.

—MTEL Visual Art Sample Test 17. XAMonline, ed. 2007. (Xam Mtel Ser.). (ENG.). 72p. per. 16.50 *(978-1-58197-893-3(6))* XAMonline, Inc.

ART—EXHIBITIONS

Abate, Nicolò dell', et al. Nicolò Dell'Abate Alla Corte Dei Boiardo: Il Paradiso Ritrovato. 2009. (ITA., Illus.). 334p. *(978-88-366-1383-0(7))* Silvana.

Abdul, Lisa & Caragliano, Renata. Lisa Abdul. 2009. (ITA & ENG., Illus.). 172p. 45.00 *(978-88-7757-223-3(X))* Hopefulmonster Editore ITA. Dist: D.A.P./Distributed Art Pubs.

Ackermann, Marion, et al. Big Picture: Orte/Projektionen. 2012. (ENG., Illus.). 130p. 49.95 ***(978-3-86678-528-1(3))*** Kerber Verlag DEU. Dist: D.A.P./Distributed Art Pubs.

Ackley, Clifford, et al, texts. Splendor & Elegance. 2009. (ENG., Illus.). 160p. 55.00 *(978-0-87846-738-9(6))* Museum of Fine Arts, Boston.

Actar, creator. From I to J: Isabel Coixet/John Berger. 2009. (Illus.). 89p. *(978-84-96954-85-4(4))* Actar Birkhauser Distribution.

Adams, Henry. Vincent Campanella: Classical Abstractionist. 2007. (Illus.). 60p. per. 10.00 *(978-0-9615372-8-9(0))* Albrecht-Kemper Museum of Art.

Ades, Dawn, et al, contrib. by. Surrealist Art: The Lindy & Edwin Bergman Collection at the Art Institute of Chicago. (Illus.). 256p. pap. *(978-0-500-27995-3(0))* Thames & Hudson.

Adjaye, David & Bouttiaux, Anne-Marie, eds. Geo-Graphics: A Map of Art Practices, Past & Present, 1 vol. 2010. (ENG.). 384p. pap. 55.00 *(978-88-366-1658-9(5))* Silvana ITA. Dist: D.A.P./Distributed Art Pubs.

Agustí, Anna. Tapies Obra Completa: Volume 8: 1998-2004, 1 vol. 2006. (ENG., Illus.). 528p. 295.00 *(978-84-88786-83-8(2))* Polígrafa, Ediciones, S. A. ESP. Dist: D.A.P./Distributed Art Pubs.

Albany Institute of History and Art Staff. Paul Cushman: The Work & World of an Early 19th Century Albany Potter. 2007. (Albany Institute of History & Art Ser.). (Illus.). 142p. pap. 34.95 *(978-0-939072-15-6(7)*, Suny Pr.) State Univ. of New York Pr.

Alberro, Alexander. Dan Graham Models to Projects 1978 to 1995. Date not set. (Illus.). 52p. (Orig.). pap. *(978-0-944219-13-3(6))* Goodman, Marian Gallery.

Albers, Josef & Judd, Donald. Donald Judd & Josef Albers: Color, Material, Space. 2012. (ENG., Illus.). 128p. 65.00 *(978-3-937572-98-7(8))* Richter Verlag DEU. Dist: D.A.P./Distributed Art Pubs.

Ali, Laylah, illus. Laylah Ali: Typology, 1 vol. 2007. (ENG.). 48p. per. 20.00 *(978-0-943836-30-0(1))* Pennsylvania Academy of the Fine Arts.

Allen, Jennifer, et al, texts. Monumentalism. 2011. (ENG., Illus.). 264p. pap. 30.00 *(978-90-5662-773-7(2))* NAi Uitgevers / Publishers Stichting NLD. Dist: D.A.P./Distributed Art Pubs.

Allen, Karen, ed. Al & Al. 2008. (ENG., Illus.). 63p. pap. 25.00 *(978-1-84631-148-2(9))* Liverpool Univ. Pr. GBR. Dist: Chicago Distribution Ctr.

Allen, Siemon, et al. Julie Mehretu: City Sitings, 1 vol. 2009. (ENG.). 88p. 40.00 *(978-0-89558-161-7(2))* Detroit Institute of Arts.

Allen, Terry. Jim Roche: Glory Roads, 1 vol. 2011. (ENG., Illus.). 88p. pap. 22.50 ***(978-1-889282-23-7(5))*** Florida State Univ., Museum of Fine Arts.

Amadiume, Ifi. Black Womanhood: Images, Icons, & Ideologies of the African Body. Thompson, Barbara, ed. 2008. (ENG., Illus.). 376p. (C). *(978-0-295-98770-5(7))* Hood Museum of Art.

Ambrosini, Lynne, et al. Monet in Giverny: Landscapes of Reflection. Leca, Benedict, ed. 2012. 88p. pap. ***(978-0-931537-41-7(X))*** Cincinnati Art Museum.

Amorales, Carlos. Carlos Amorales: Caca Grande. 2010. (ENG., Illus.). 66p. pap. 25.00 *(978-84-92480-64-7(5))* RM Verlag, S.L. ESP. Dist: D.A.P./Distributed Art Pubs.

Anderson, Nancy K. George de Forest Brush: The Indian Paintings. 2008. (Illus.). vii, 239p. *(978-0-89468-347-3(0))* National Gallery of Art.

Anderson, Nancy K., et al. George de Forest Brush: The Indian Paintings. 2008. (Illus.). 224p. 65.00 *(978-1-84822-006-5(5)*, Lund Humphries Pubs.) Ashgate Publishing, Ltd. GBR. Dist: Ashgate Publishing Co.

Anderson, Susan M. Collecting California: Selections from Laguna Art Museum. 2009. *(978-0-940872-36-3(6))* Laguna Art Museum Store.

Andrade, Edna & Paschall, Douglas. Sensational: Edna Andrade's Drawings: Woodmere Art Museum, March 25-June 24, 2007. 2007. (Illus.). 32p. *(978-1-888008-19-7(9))* Woodmere Art Museum, Inc.

Andre, Carl. Carl Andre. 2011. (ENG., Illus.). 152p. pap. 55.00 ***(978-3-86560-999-1(6))*** Verlag der Buchhandlung Walther Konig DEU. Dist: D.A.P./Distributed Art Pubs.

Andreae, Bernard. Kleopatra und die Caesaren: Katalogband zur Ausstellung im Bucerius Kunst Forum, Hamburg. 2006. (GER., Illus.). 264p. (C). pap. 42.00 *(978-3-7774-3245-8(8))* Hirmer Verlag GmbH DEU. Dist: Brown, David Bk. Co., The.

Anisimova, Elena, et al. Art Nouveau During the Reign of the Last Tsars. 2008. (Illus.). 128p. 40.00 *(978-0-85331-987-0(1)*, Lund Humphries Pubs.) Ashgate Publishing, Ltd. GBR. Dist: Ashgate Publishing Co.

Annichiarico, Silvana, ed. Dritto Rovescio / Right Wrong Side: Woven Threads among Art, Design & Mass Creativity. 2010. (ENG & ITA., Illus.). 230p. pap. 55.00 *(978-88-370-6919-3(7)*, Mondadori Electa (Acc)) Antique Collectors' Club GBR. Dist: National Bk. Network.

Antcliffe, Mark & Greene, Vivien, eds. The Vorticists. 2010. (ENG., Illus.). 192p. pap. 39.95 *(978-1-85437-885-9(6))* Tate Publishing, Ltd. GBR. Dist: Hachette Bk. Group.

Antonelli, Paola. Talk to Me: Design & the Communication Between People & Objects. 2011. (ENG., Illus.). 208p. pap. 35.00 ***(978-0-87070-796-4(5))*** Museum of Modern Art.

Aranda-Alvarado, Rocío, et al, contrib. by. El Museo's Bienal: The (S) Files 2011. 2011. (Illus.). 194p. pap. 25.00 *(978-1-882454-02-0(2))* El Museo del Barrio.

Armleder, John, et al, eds. Voids. 2009. (ENG., Illus.). 528p. 80.00 *(978-3-03764-036-4(7))* JRP Ringier Kunstverlag AG CHE. Dist: D.A.P./Distributed Art Pubs.

Arnett, Matt, et al. Mary Lee Bendolph, Gee's Bend Quilts, & Beyond. Metcalf, Eugene W., ed. 2006. (ENG., Illus.). 72p. 26.95 *(978-0-9719104-8-5(0))* Tinwood Bks.

Aronson, Julie. Bessie Potter Vonnoh: Sculptor of Women. 2008. (ENG., Illus.). 308p. 60.00 *(978-0-8214-1800-0(9))*; pap. 39.95 *(978-0-8214-1801-7(7))* Ohio Univ. Pr.

Arrhenius, Sara, et al. Tomás Saraceno: 14 Billions. 2012. (SWE & ENG., Illus.). 192p. 75.00 *(978-88-572-0857-2(5))* Skira Editore ITA. Dist: Random Hse., Inc.

Art to Hear Staff. Art to Hear: Metamorphoses of the Face from Rodin to Picasso. 2009. (ENG., Illus.). 52p. 30.00 *(978-3-7757-2416-6(8))* Hatje Cantz Verlag GmbH & Co KG DEU. Dist: D.A.P./Distributed Art Pubs.

Arthur M. Sackler Gallery (Smithsonian Institution) Staff, contrib. by. Gods of Angkor: Bronzes from the National Museum of Cambodia. 2010. pap. *(978-0-934686-17-4(3))* Freer Gallery of Art, Smithsonian Institution.

Aruz, Joan, et al, eds. Beyond Babylon: Art, Trade, & Diplomacy in the Second Millennium B. C. 2008. (ENG., Illus.). 548p. 75.00 *(978-0-300-14143-8(2))* Yale Univ. Pr.

Aruz, Joan, et al. Beyond Babylon: Art, Trade, & Diplomacy in the Second Millennium B.C. 2008. (Illus.). xxiii, 524p. 75.00 *(978-1-58839-295-4(3))* Metropolitan Museum of Art, The.

Ashbery, John, prologue by. Jess: To & from the Printed Page, 1 vol. 2007. (ENG., Illus.). 112p. pap. 29.95 *(978-0-916365-75-2(1))* Independent Curators International.

Askevold, David & Diviney, David. David Askevold: Il était une Fois Dans L'est. 2011. (FRE.). 160p. 50.00 ***(978-0-86492-666-1(9))*** Goose Lane Editions CAN. Dist: Univ. of Toronto Pr.

Assouline, ed. Provoking Magic: Lighting of Ingo Maurer. 2007. (ENG., Illus.). 160p. pap. *(978-0-910503-94-5(X))* Assouline FRA. Dist: Perseus Distribution.

Attenborough, David, et al. Amazing Rare Things: The Art of Natural History in the Age of Discovery. 2007. (ENG., Illus.). 224p. 37.50 *(978-0-300-12547-4(X))* Yale Univ. Pr.

Aubenas, Sylvie, et al. The Lens of Impressionism: Photography & Painting along the Normandy Coast, 1850-1874. 2009. (ENG., Illus.). 208p. 50.00 *(978-1-55595-325-6(5))* Hudson Hills Pr. LLC.

Auer, Barbara & Hubl, Michael, texts. Angela Glajcar: Works in Paper & Plastic 2007-2009. 2010. (ENG., Illus.). 96p. pap. 40.00 *(978-3-86678-284-6(5))* Kerber Verlag DEU. Dist: D.A.P./Distributed Art Pubs.

Augaitis, Daina, et al. Brian Jungen, 1 vol. 2010. (ENG.). 176p. pap. 35.00 *(978-1-55365-562-6(1))* D&M Pubs. Inc. CAN. Dist: Perseus-PGW.

Augaitus, Daina. Raven Travelling: Two Centuries of Haida Art. 2008. (Illus.). 182p. pap. 39.95 *(978-0-295-98818-4(5))* Univ. of Washington Pr.

Augaitus, Daina, et al. Raven Travelling: Two Centuries of Haida Art. 2006. (Illus.). 182p. 60.00 *(978-0-295-98619-7(0))* Univ. of Washington Pr.

Auping, Michael. Declaring Space: Mark Rothko, Barnett Newman, Lucio Fontana, Yves Klein. 2007. (Illus.). 176p. pap. *(978-0-929865-28-7(6))* Modern Art Museum of Fort Worth.

Aurisch, Helga Kessler & Czymmek, Götz. German Impressionist Landscape Painting: Liebermann - Corinth - Slevogt. 2010. (Illus.). 256p. 70.00 ***(978-3-89790-321-0(0))*** Arnoldsche Art Pubs. DEU. Dist: Antique Collectors' Club.

Avril, Ellen. Ancient Artistry: Pre-Chinese Ceramics & Jades from the Shatzman Collection. 2006. (Illus.). 55p. pap. 15.00 *(978-0-9646042-2-3(1))* Cornell Univ., Herbert F. Johnson Museum of Art.

Azari, Shoja, et al, texts. Women Without Men. 2011. (ENG & PER., Illus.). 120p. pap. 39.95 ***(978-88-8158-806-0(4))*** Charta ITA. Dist: D.A.P./Distributed Art Pubs.

Bacon, Francis. Francis Bacon - A Terrible Beauty, 1 vol. 2009. (ENG., Illus.). 208p. pap. 34.95 *(978-3-86930-027-6(2))* Steidl, Gerhard Druckerei und Verlag DEU. Dist: Innovative Logistics.

Bader, Graham, text. Arturo Herrera: Boy & Dwarf, 1 vol. 2007. (ENG., Illus.). 88p. 50.00 *(978-3-935567-38-1(3))* Holzwarth Pubns. DEU. Dist: D.A.P./Distributed Art Pubs.

Badiola, Txomin. Proforma. 2011. 304p. pap. *(978-84-92861-92-7(4))* Actar Birkhauser Distribution.

Baechler, Donald. Donald Baechler: XL + XS. 2010. (ENG., Illus.). 144p. 45.00 *(978-88-366-1536-0(8))* Silvana ITA. Dist: D.A.P./Distributed Art Pubs.

Baert, B., et al. Noli me Tangere: Mary Magdelene: One Person, Many Images. 2006. (Documenta Libraria Ser.). (ENG., Illus.). 125p. (C). pap. 35.00 *(978-90-429-1807-8(1))* Peeters Pubs. & Booksellers BEL. Dist: Brown, David Bk. Co., The.

Bagnoli, Martina. Treasures of Heaven: Saints, Relics, & Devotion in Medieval Europe. 2010. (Illus.). xviii, 259p. pap. *(978-0-911886-74-0(5))* Cleveland Museum of Art.

B.A.I. Staff, ed. Delvaux and the Antiquity, 1 vol. 2010. (ENG.). 189p. pap. 40.00 *(978-90-8586-541-4(7))* Exhibitions International BEL. Dist: Innovative Logistics.

BAI Staff, ed. A Passage to Asia: 35 Centuries of Exchange Between Asia & Europe, 1 vol. 2010. (ENG.). 271p. 60.00 *(978-90-8586-565-0(4))* Exhibitions International BEL. Dist: Innovative Logistics.

Bailey, Douglass, et al. Unearthed: A Comparative Study of Jomon Dogu & Neolithic Figurines. 2010. (Illus.). 176p. (C). pap. 39.95 *(978-0-9545921-2-7(3))* Sainsbury Centre for the Visual Arts GBR. Dist: Brown, David Bk. Co., The.

Baillio, Joseph. The Odyssey Continues: Masterworks from the New Orleans Museum of Art & from private New Orleans Collections. 2006. per. 45.00 *(978-0-9657856-3-1(7))* Wildenstein & Co., Inc.

Baker, Christopher. J. M. W. Turner: The Vaughan Bequest. 2007. (ENG., Illus.). 112p. pap. *(978-1-903278-89-5(9))* National Galleries of Scotland.

Baldessari, John. John Baldessari: Noses & Ears, etc. (Part Three) 2007. (Illus.). 51p. 40.00 *(978-1-880641-06-4(2))* Margo Leavin Gallery.

Balken, Debra Bricker. John Storrs: Machine-Age Modernist. 2010. (ENG., Illus.). 112p. pap. 29.95 *(978-0-934552-79-0(7))* Boston Athenaeum Library.

Ballester Moreno, Antonio. Antonio Ballester Moreno. 2008. (Illus.). pap. 20.00 *(978-0-9778819-7-0(0))* Peres Projects, Los Angeles Berlin.

Bann, Stephen & Whiteley, Linda. Painting History: Delaroche & Lady Jane Grey. 2010. (ENG., Illus.). 180p. 45.00 *(978-1-85709-479-4(4))* Yale Univ. Pr.

Barbolani di Montauto, Novella & Chappell, Miles L. Colorire Naturale e Vero: Figline, il Cigoli e I Suoi Amici. 2008. (citta degli Uffizi Ser.). (ITA., Illus.). 176p. (C). 50.00 *(978-88-596-0481-5(8))* Polistampa ITA. Dist: Brown, David Bk. Co., The.

Barcham, William, et al. Passion in Venice: Crivelli to Tintoretto & Veronese - The Man of Sorrows in Venetian Art. 2011. (ENG., Illus.). 176p. 45.00 *(978-1-904832-82-9(2))* Giles, D. Ltd. GBR. Dist: Antique Collectors' Club.

Bargna, Ivan & Parodi da Passano, M. Giovanna. L'Africa Delle Meraviglie: Arti Africane Nelle Collezioni Italiane = the Wonders of Africa: African Arts in Italian Collections. 2011. (ITA & ENG., Illus.). 204p. pap. 60.00 ***(978-88-366-1949-8(5))*** Silvana ITA. Dist: D.A.P./Distributed Art Pubs.

Barker, Elizabeth E. & Wright, Joseph. Joseph Wright of Derby in Liverpool. Kidson, Alex & Barker, Elizabeth, eds. 2008. (ENG., Illus.). 224p. (C). 75.00 *(978-0-300-11745-5(0))* Yale Ctr. for British Art.

Barlow, Stephen. Guillermo Kuitca: Stage Fright. 2007. (Illus.). 80p. 45.00 *(978-0-9799458-0-9(1))* Sperone Westwater.

Barnet, Will, illus. Will Barnet: A Sketchbook, 1932-1934. 2009. (ENG.). 90p. 49.95 *(978-0-8076-1597-3(8)*, 761597) Braziller, George Inc.

Barney, Matthew, et al. Matthew Barney. 2008. (GER & ENG., Illus.). 239p. 50.00 *(978-3-939894-09-4(5))* Goetz, Ingvild, Kunstverlag, GmbH DEU. Dist: D.A.P./Distributed Art Pubs.

Barry X Ball. pap. 25.00 *(978-2-903004-12-5(9))* Galerie Isy Brachot FRA. Dist: D.A.P./Distributed Art Pubs.

Bartholomew, Terese Tse & Johnston, John. The Dragon's Gift: The Sacred Arts of Bhutan. 2008. (Illus.). 400p. *(978-1-932476-35-4(0))*; 390p. pap. *(978-1-932476-36-1(9))* Serindia Pubns., Inc.

Bartholomew, Terese Tse & Tsuruta, Kaz. Hidden Meanings in Chinese Art. 2012. (ENG., Illus.). 352p. pap. 45.00 ***(978-0-939117-37-6(1))*** Asian Art Museum of San Francisco.

Barzel, Amnon. Hans Hartung. 2007. (FRE & ENG., Illus.). 296p. *(978-88-7439-395-4(4))* 5 Continents.

Baskins, Cristelle. The Triumph of Marriage: Painted Cassoni of the Renaissance. 2008. (Illus.). 264p. 45.00 *(978-1-934772-86-7(0))* Periscope Publishing.

Basualdo, Carlos, et al. Bruce Nauman: Topological Gardens. 2009. (ITA & ENG., Illus.). 240p. *(978-0-87633-217-7(3))* Philadelphia Museum of Art.

Batchen, Geoffrey. What of Shoes? Van Gogh & Art History. 2009. (ENG.). 48p. pap. 14.95 *(978-3-86502-218-9(9)*, Art Stock Bks. Ltd/Csi) Continental Sales, Inc.

Battesti, Jacques. L'objet Dans Tous Ses états! Musée Basque et de L'histoire de Bayonne = Objektua Bere Izate Guztietan!: Baionako Euskal Museoa. 2009. (BAQ & FRE., Illus.). 95p. *(978-2-915262-94-0(2))* Le Festin.

Baumann, Leonie, et al, eds. Crosskick: European Art Academies as Guests in German Kunstvereine. 2009. (ENG., Illus.). 210p. pap. 39.95 *(978-3-86560-518-4(4))* Verlag der Buchhandlung Walther Konig DEU. Dist: D.A.P./Distributed Art Pubs.

Baume, Nicholas, ed. Anish Kapoor: Past, Present, Future. 2008. (ENG., Illus.). 143p. (gr. 17). 29.95 *(978-0-262-02659-8(7))* MIT Pr.

Bayer, Andrea. Art & Love in Renaissance Italy. 2008. (Illus.). xv, 376p. 45.00 *(978-1-58839-301-2(1))*; 65.00 *(978-1-58839-300-5(3))* Metropolitan Museum of Art, The.

Bayer, Andrea, ed. & contrib. by. Art & Love in Renaissance Italy. 2008. (ENG., Illus.). 392p. 65.00 *(978-0-300-12411-8(2))* Yale Univ. Pr.

Beattie, May H. Carpets of Central Persia: With Special Reference to Rugs of Kirman: Exhibition Catalogue. 2007. (Illus.). 104p. reprint ed. pap. 27.00 *(978-1-4223-6822-0(X))* DIANE Publishing Co.

Becker, Cynthia & Loughran, Kristyne, contrib. by. Desert Jewels: North African Jewelry & Photography from the Xavier Guerrand-Hermes Collection. 2009. (Illus.). 95p. pap. 19.95 *(978-0-945802-52-5(8))* Museum for African Art.

Bell, Ralf & Ehmann, Antje, eds. Serious Games: Krieg Medien Kunst. 2011. (ENG & GER., Illus.). 208p. 45.00 ***(978-3-7757-2991-8(7))*** Hatje Cantz Verlag GmbH & Co KG DEU. Dist: D.A.P./Distributed Art Pubs.

Bell, Marc, ed. Nog a Dod: Prehistoric Canadian Psychedooolia, 1 vol. 2006. (ENG., Illus.). 224p. per. 24.95 *(978-1-894994-16-3(7))* PictureBox, Inc.

Bell, Nicholas. A Revolution in Wood: The Bresler Collection. 2010. (ENG., Illus.). 152p. 45.00 *(978-1-58834-304-8(9))* Smithsonian Institution Pr.

Bellour, Raymond. David Claerbout. 2008. (ENG., Illus.). 160p. pap. 45.00 *(978-3-905829-38-9(X))* JRP Ringier Kunstverlag AG CHE. Dist: D.A.P./Distributed Art Pubs.

Bendolph, Mary Lee, et al. Gee's Bend: The Architecture of the Quilt. 2006. (ENG., Illus.). 224p. 50.00 *(978-0-9719104-5-4(6))* Tinwood Bks.

Bennett, Ralph Kinney. Ligonier 250 the Fort, the Town, the Valley: How We Came to Be & Who We Are. 2008. 100p. pap. *(978-0-9717475-7-9(1))* Laurel Valley Graphics, Inc.

Bercht, Fatima. Viva David Tineo: A Retrospective of Tucson's Muralist & Art Educator. 2010. (Illus.). 64p. pap. 20.00 *(978-0-911511-38-0(X))* Tucson Museum of Art.

Berg, et al. Julian Rosefeldt: Film Works. 2008. (ENG., Illus.). 176p. 60.00 *(978-3-7757-2171-4(1))* Hatje Cantz Verlag GmbH & Co KG DEU. Dist: D.A.P./Distributed Art Pubs.

Bergh, Susan. Wari: Lords of the Ancient Andes. 2012. (ENG., Illus.). 304p. 60.00 ***(978-0-500-51656-0(1)***, 551656) Thames & Hudson.

Berman, Avis, text. Bill Scott: Looking Through. 2007. pap. *(978-0-9759954-8-0(0))* Taggart, Hollis Galleries.

Bernasek, Lisa. Artistry of the Everyday: Beauty & Craftsmanship in Berber Art. 2008. (Peabody Museum Collections Ser.). (Illus.). 128p. pap. 21.95 *(978-0-87365-405-0(6))* Peabody Museum of Archaeology & Ethnology, Harvard Univ., Pubns. Dept.

Berns, Marla C., et al, eds. Central Nigeria Unmasked: Arts of the Benue River Valley. 2011. (ENG., Illus.). 608p. 100.00 ***(978-0-9778344-6-4(8))*** Univ. of California, Los Angeles, Fowler Museum of Cultural History.

—Central Nigeria Unmasked: Arts of the Benue River Valley, 1 vol. 2011. (ENG., Illus.). 608p. pap. 75.00 ***(978-0-9778344-5-7(X))*** Univ. of California, Los Angeles, Fowler Museum of Cultural History.

Berrin, Kathleen & Fields, Virginia M. Olmec: Colossal Masterworks of Ancient Mexico. 2010. pap. *(978-0-88401-131-6(3))* Fine Arts Museums of San Francisco.

Berrin, Kathleen & Fields, Virginia M., eds. Olmec: Colossal Masterworks of Ancient Mexico. 2010. (Illus.). 272p. 65.00 *(978-0-300-16676-7(1)*, Yale Univ. Pr.

Berry, Ian & Lewis, Tom, eds. Lives of the Hudson. 2010. (Illus.). 224p. 49.95 *(978-3-7913-5047-9(1))* Prestel Publishing.

Berti, Fausto. La Farmacia Storica Fiorentina: I "Fornimenti" in Maiolica Di Montelupo, Secc. XV- XVIII. 2010. (ITA., Illus.). 224p. (C). pap. 58.00 *(978-88-596-0797-7(3))* Polistampa ITA. Dist: Brown, David Bk. Co., The.

Bertsch, von M., et al. Kosmos Runge. Der Morgen der Romantik: Katalog zur Ausstellung in Hamburg; Hamburger Kunsthalle; 3.12.2010-13.03.2011 und in München; Kusthalle der Hypo-Kulturstiftung; 13.05.2011-04.09.2011. Howoldt, J. et al, eds. 2011. (GER., Illus.). 360p. (C). 59.00 *(978-3-7774-3061-4(7))* Hirmer Verlag GmbH DEU. Dist: Brown, David Bk. Co., The.

Berzock, Kathleen Bickford & Clarke, Christa, eds. Representing Africa in American Art Museums: A Century of Collecting & Display. 2010. (Mclellan Book Ser.). (ENG., Illus.). 320p. pap. 40.00 *(978-0-295-98961-7(0))* Univ. of Washington Pr.

Besten, Liesbeth Den. On Jewellery: A Compendium of International Contemporary Art Jewellery. 2012. (ENG., Illus.). 240p. 50.00 *(978-3-89790-349-4(0))* Arnoldsche Art Pubs. DEU. Dist: Antique Collectors' Club.

Betsky, Aaron. Out There. Architecture Beyond Building: 11th International Architecture Exhibition la Biennale di Venezia. 2008. (ENG., Illus.). 608p. pap. 110.00 *(978-88-317-9447-3(7))* Marsilio Editori spa ITA. Dist: Random Hse., Inc.

Beuys, Joseph, illus. Joseph Beuys: Sculpture & Drawing, 1 vol. 2008. (ENG.). 64p. 45.00 *(978-0-9773568-6-7(8))* Zwirner & Wirth.

Beuys, Joseph, et al. Beuys, Pourquoi Faites-Vous des Multiples? 2010. (FRE & ENG., Illus.). 96p. pap. 40.00 *(978-2-35340-030-0(2))* Gourcuff Gradenigo FRA. Dist: National Bk. Network.

—Mythos Volume 2, 1 vol. 2007. (GER & ENG., Illus.). 160p. 62.00 *(978-3-86560-182-7(0))* Kunsthaus Bregenz AUT. Dist: D.A.P./Distributed Art Pubs.

Bezzenberger, Tilman & Esche, Charles, texts. Maria Eichhorn: Aktiengesellschaft. 2008. (ENG., Illus.). 304p. pap. 49.95 *(978-3-86560-244-2(4))* Verlag der Buchhandlung Walther Konig DEU. Dist: D.A.P./Distributed Art Pubs.

Bianco, Juliette M., et al, contrib. by. Wenda Gu at Dartmouth: The Art of Installation. 2008. (Illus.). 160p. pap. 35.00 *(978-1-58465-707-1(3))* Hood Museum of Art & Univ. Pr. of New England.

Biancolini Fea, Daniela, et al. Il Tesoro Della Sindone: Mirabilia Del Sacro e Incisioni Sindoniche Di Umberto II Di Savoia. 2010. (ITA., Illus.). 124p. *(978-88-7889-242-2(4))* Piazza C.

Biennials - art on a global scale (Edition Angewandte) 2010. (Edition Angewandte Ser.). 144p. pap. 49.95 *(978-3-7091-0250-3(2))* Springer Wien AUT. Dist: Springer.

Biesenbach, Klaus, et al, contrib. by. Take Your Time: Olafur Eliasson. 2007. (ENG., Illus.). 272p. 50.00 *(978-0-500-09340-5(7))* Thames & Hudson.

Biesenbach, Klaus, ed. Political, Minimal. 2009. (ENG & GER., Illus.). 148p. pap. 45.00 *(978-3-941185-07-4(1))* Verlag fur Moderne Kunst DEU. Dist: D.A.P./Distributed Art Pubs.

Biesenbach, Klaus, ed. & text. Into Me / Out of Me, 1 vol. 2007. (GER & ENG., Illus.). 580p. pap., pap. 60.00 *(978-3-7757-2041-0(3))* Hatje Cantz Verlag GmbH & Co KG DEU. Dist: D.A.P./Distributed Art Pubs.

Binder, Lisa M., ed. El Anatsui: When I Last Wrote to You about Africa, 1 vol. 2011. (ENG., Illus.). 170p. 50.00 *(978-0-945802-56-3(0))* Museum for African Art.

Binstock, Jonathan P. & Blake, Jeremy. Wild Choir: Cinematic Portraits by Jeremy Blake. 2007. *(978-0-88675-080-0(6))* Corcoran Gallery of Art.

Birk, Sandow. The Depravities of War - Sandow Birk. 2007. per. 22.95 *(978-0-9771696-9-6(3))* Grand Central Pr.

Birky Greene, Stacie. Junk Mail Takes Flight. 2009. 34p. pap. 16.95 *(978-0-557-04469-6(3))* Lulu Enterprises Inc.

Birnbaum, Daniel, text. What Good Is the Moon? 2010. (ENG., Illus.). 368p. 60.00 *(978-3-7757-2666-5(7))* Hatje Cantz Verlag GmbH & Co KG DEU. Dist: D.A.P./Distributed Art Pubs.

Black, Patti Carr. American Masters of the Mississippi Gulf Coast: George Ohr, Dusti Bonge, Walter Anderson, Richmond Barthe. 2008. (ENG., Illus.). 99p. 35.00 *(978-1-60473-205-4(9))* Univ. Pr. of Mississippi.

—The Mississippi Story. Dietrick, Robin C., ed. 2007. (ENG., Illus.). 132p. 29.95 *(978-1-887422-14-7(5))* Univ. Pr. of Mississippi.

Blake, Peter, illus. An Alphabet, 1 vol. 2008. (ENG.). 64p. 35.00 *(978-0-9552154-5-2(5))* Stolper, Paul GBR. Dist: D.A.P./Distributed Art Pubs.

Blanchard, Rebecca & Davenport, Nancy. Contemporary Coast Salish Art. (Illus.). pap. 35.00 *(978-1-55365-104-8(9))* D&M Pubs. Inc. CAN. Dist: Perseus-PGW.

Blistene, Bernard, et al. The Museum That Did Not Exist: Daniel Buren. 2010. (Illus.). 352p. 85.00 *(978-3-7913-4499-7(4))* Prestel Publishing.

Bloemink, Barbara, et al. Design Life Now: National Design Triennial 2006. 2006. (ENG., Illus.). 224p. *(978-0-910503-99-0(0))*; pap. *(978-0-910503-98-3(2))* Assouline FRA. Dist: Perseus Distribution.

Blom, Ina, text. Saadane Afif: Technical Specifications. 2009. (ENG., Illus.). 148p. 25.00 *(978-90-73362-84-0(9))* Witte De With Centre for Contemporary Art NLD. Dist: D.A.P./Distributed Art Pubs.

Blühm, Andreas. The Moon: "Houston, Tranquility Base Here. the Eagle Has Landed" 2009. pap. *(978-0-89090-170-0(8))* Museum of Fine Arts, Houston.

Bohl, Henning. Henning Bohl: Kunstverein Braunschweig E.V. Kunstverein Für Die Rheinlande und Westfalen Düsseldorf, 1 vol. 2006. (GER & ENG., Illus.). 56p. pap. 20.00 *(978-3-86560-012-7(3))* Verlag der Buchhandlung Walther Konig DEU. Dist: D.A.P./Distributed Art Pubs.

Bolland, Denise, ed. Expo Revisited-Issues of Affordable Housing, South Brisbane & West End 1983-2008. 2008. (Illus.). 420p. *(978-0-9806490-0-0(5))* Bolland, Denise.

Bollmann, Karl. Castle in the Air: õhuLoss: Jewellery from Estonia. 2011. (ENG & EST., Illus.). 296p. 85.00 ***(978-3-89790-359-3(8))*** Arnoldsche Art Pubs. DEU. Dist: Antique Collectors' Club.

Bollmann, Karl & Schrage, Dieter. Elisabeth Defner: Man - Nature - Cosmos Jewellery & Objects. 2012. (ENG & GER., Illus.). 248p. 85.00 ***(978-3-89790-353-1(9))*** Arnoldsche Art Pubs. DEU. Dist: National Bk. Network.

Bonafoux, Pascal & Bidaine, Philippe. Boris Zaborov. 2008. (ENG., Illus.). 160p. 80.00 *(978-88-6130-122-1(3))* Skira Editore ITA. Dist: Random Hse., Inc.

Bondil, Nathalie, ed. Cuba: Art & History from 1868 to Today. 2009. (Illus.). 368p. pap. 49.95 *(978-3-7913-4394-5(7))* Prestel Publishing.

Bondil, Nathalie & Bouthours, Jean-Michel, eds. Van Dongen. 2009. (Illus.). 351p. *(978-2-7541-0326-8(0))* Hazan, Fernand, Editeur.

Bongioanni, Alessandro. Treasures of Tutankhamun & the Egyptian Museum of Cairo. 2008. 632p. 19.99 *(978-88-540-0850-2(8))* White Star ITA. Dist: Book Sales, Inc.

Bonn, Landschaftsverband Rheinland / LVR-LandesMuseum, ed. Alter in der Antike: Die Blüte des Alters aber ist die Weisheit. 2009. (GER., Illus.). 192p. (C). 38.00 *(978-3-8053-3979-7(8))* Zabern, Philipp von Verlag, GmbH DEU. Dist: Brown, David Bk. Co., The.

Bonnet, Anne-Marie, et al, eds. Auguste Rodin: Der Kuss - Die Paare. 2006. (GER., Illus.). 184p. (C). pap. 42.00 *(978-3-7774-3225-0(3))* Hirmer Verlag GmbH DEU. Dist: Brown, David Bk. Co., The.

Bonnet, Frédéric, ed. General Idea: A Retrospective 1969-1994. 2011. (ENG., Illus.). 224p. 39.95 *(978-3-03764-162-0(2))* JRP Ringier Kunstverlag AG CHE. Dist: D.A.P./Distributed Art Pubs.

Borchardt-Hume, Achim, ed. Per Kirkeby. 2009. (ENG., Illus.). 176p. pap. 26.95 *(978-1-85437-821-7(X))* Tate Publishing, Ltd. GBR. Dist: Hachette Bk. Group.

Bouguereau, William Adolphe & Zafran, Eric. In the Studios of Paris: William Bouguereau & His American Students: Exhibition. 2006. (Illus.). 211p. pap. *(978-0-86659-028-0(5))* Yale Univ. Pr.

Bourgeois, Louise, et al. Art & Fashion: Between Skin & Clothing. 2012. (ENG., Illus.). 136p. 55.00 ***(978-3-86678-538-0(0))*** Kerber Verlag DEU. Dist: D.A.P./Distributed Art Pubs.

Bourgeois, Louise, et al. Moi, Eugénie Grandet. 2010. (FRE., Illus.). 135p. *(978-2-07-013101-3(7))* Gallimard, Editions.

Bourguignon, Katherine M., ed. Impressionist Giverny: A Colony of Artists, 1885-1915. 2007. (Illus.). 224p. pap. 49.00 *(978-0-932171-52-8(4))* Terra Foundation for American Art.

Bovier, Lionel, ed. Justin Lieberman. 2009. (ENG., Illus.). 64p. 35.00 *(978-3-03764-008-1(1))* JRP Ringier Kunstverlag AG CHE. Dist: D.A.P./Distributed Art Pubs.

Bowron, Edgar Peters, et al. Pompeo Batoni: Prince of Painters in Eighteenth-Century Rome. 2007. 240p. pap. *(978-0-89090-158-8(9))* Yale Univ. Pr.

Boyden, Frank. Coexistence with Fire: Wood-Fired Ceramics by Frank Boyden, 1985-2006. 2008. (Illus.). 245p. *(978-0-9816728-2-3(5))* American Museum of Ceramic Art.

Boym, Svetlana, text. Territories of Terror: Mythologies & Memories of the Gulag in Contemporary Russian-American Art. 2007. (ENG., Illus.). 64p. pap. 20.00 *(978-1-881450-25-2(2))* Boston Univ., Art Gallery.

Bracewell, Michael, text. Gilbert & George: Jack Freak Pictures. 2010. (ENG., Illus.). 176p. 45.00 *(978-3-7757-2505-7(9))* Hatje Cantz Verlag GmbH & Co KG DEU. Dist: D.A.P./Distributed Art Pubs.

Bragdon, Claude Fayette, et al. Claude Bragdon & the Beautiful Necessity: Eleven Essays. 2010. *(978-1-933360-43-0(7))* Rochester Institute of Technology, Cary Graphic Arts Pr.

Brandon, Laura & Ogden, Glenn. A Brush with War: Military Art from Korea to Afghanistan. 2009. (ENG., Illus.). 72p. pap. 19.95 *(978-0-660-19854-5(1))* Canadian Museum of Civilization/Musee Canadien des Civilisations CAN. Dist: Univ. of Washington Pr.

Branzi, Andrea. What Is Italian Design? The Seven Obsessions [in English & Italian]. Annicchiarico, Silvana, ed. 2008. 470p. pap. 92.50 *(978-88-370-5981-1(7))* Electa ITA. Dist: Trans-Atlantic Pubns., Inc.

Brasile, Jeanne & Bianchino, Gianluca, eds. Dialogue with an Ancient Forest. 2008. (Illus.). 12p. *(978-0-9793954-1-3(0))* Walsh Gallery.

Brattig, Patricia, ed. Meissen: Barockes Porzellan. 2010. (ENG., Illus.). 432p. 85.00 *(978-3-89790-329-6(6))* Arnoldsche Art Pubs. DEU. Dist: Antique Collectors' Club.

Breazeale, William, et al. The Language of the Nude: Four Centuries of Drawing the Human Body. 2008. (Illus.). 168p. 80.00 *(978-0-85331-988-7(X)*, Lund Humphries Pubs.) Ashgate Publishing, Ltd. GBR. Dist: Ashgate Publishing Co.

Breitwieser, Sabine & Steirischer Herbst, eds. Utopia & Monument: Exhibition for the Public Space - Steirischer Herbst 2009-2010. 2011. (Illus.). 224p. 49.95 *(978-3-7091-0772-0(5)*, 3709107725) Springer Wien AUT. Dist: Springer.

Breitz, Candice. Candice Breitz. The Scripted Life. OEuvreverzeichnis der Videoinstallationen 1999 - 2010: The Scripted Life. 2010. (ENG & GER., Illus.). 232p. 68.00 *(978-3-86560-782-9(9))* Kunsthaus Bregenz AUT. Dist: D.A.P./Distributed Art Pubs.

Bremen, Kunsthalle & Bremen, the Kunsthalle, eds. Paula Modersohn-Becker und die Kunst in Paris Um 1900: Von Cezanne bis Picasso. 2007. (GER., Illus.). 359p. (C). pap. 60.00 *(978-3-7774-3535-0(X))* Hirmer Verlag GmbH DEU. Dist: Brown, David Bk. Co., The.

Bremer-David, Charissa. Paris: Life & Luxury in the Eighteenth Century. 2011. (ENG., Illus.). 164p. 45.00 *(978-1-60606-052-0(X)*, J. Paul Getty Museum) Getty Pubns.

Brennan, Marcia. Curating Consciousness: Mysticism & the Modern Museum. 2010. (ENG., Illus.). 304p. (gr. 17). 29.95 *(978-0-262-01378-9(9))* MIT Pr.

Brenneman, David. Toulouse-Lautrec & Friends: The Irene & Howard Stein Collection. 2010. 30.00 *(978-1-932543-41-4(4))* High Museum of Art.

Brettell, Richard R. Pissarro's People. 2011. (Illus.). 304p. 65.00 *(978-3-7913-5118-6(4))* Prestel Publishing.

Brettell, Richard R. & Dickerson, C. D. From the Private Collections of Texas: European Art, Ancient to Modern. 2009. (Illus.). xv, 455p. pap. *(978-0-912804-51-4(3))* Kimbell Art Museum.

Breuer, Gerda, et al, texts. Interieur, Exterieur: Living in Art. 2009. (ENG., Illus.). 280p. 60.00 *(978-3-7757-2297-1(1))* Hatje Cantz Verlag GmbH & Co KG DEU. Dist: D.A.P./Distributed Art Pubs.

Breuer, Karin. Japanesque: The Japanese Print in the Era of Impressionism. 2010. (Illus.). 160p. 34.95 *(978-3-7913-5082-0(X))* Prestel Publishing.

Brewster, Anna Richards. Anna Richards Brewster, American Impressionist. Maxwell, Judith Kafka, ed. 2008. (Illus.). 216p. 45.00 *(978-0-520-25749-8(9))* Univ. of California Pr.

Brinkgreve, Francine. Sumatra: Crossroads Of. 2010. 204p. 38.00 *(978-90-6718-356-7(3))* KITLV Pr. NLD. Dist: Univ. of Hawaii Pr.

Britton-Newell, Laurie & Newell, Laurie Britton. Out of the Ordinary: Spectacular Craft. 2007. (ENG., Illus.). 144p. 45.00 *(978-1-85177-524-8(2))* V & A Pubns. GBR. Dist: Hachette Bk. Group.

Brock, Charles, et al. American Modernism: The Shein Collection. 2010. *(978-0-89468-365-7(9))* National Gallery of Art.

Brodner, Steve, ed. Artists Against the War. 2011. (ENG., Illus.). 120p. 19.95 *(978-1-59929-030-0(8))* Underwood Books.

Bronx Museum of the Arts Staff. Quisqueya Henriquez: The WORLD OUTSIDE A Survey Exhibition 1991-2007. 2007. (Illus.). 65p. per. 32.00 *(978-0-917535-00-0(6))* Bronx Museum of the Arts, The.

Brown, Harrison Bird & Routhier, Jessica Skwire. Vividly True to Nature: Harrison Bird Brown, 1831-1915. 2007. (Illus.). 32p. pap. *(978-0-916857-45-5(X))*; pap. *(978-0-916857-47-9(6))* Portland Museum of Art.

Brown-May, Andrew, et al. Australian Impressionism. McQueen, Humphrey, ed. 2007. (ENG., Illus.). 352p. pap. 39.95 *(978-0-7241-0281-5(7))* National Gallery of Victoria AUS. Dist: National Bk. Network.

Brown, Peter O. Walter Goodman's the Printseller's Window. 2009. pap. 15.00 net. *(978-0-918098-12-2(2))* Memorial Art Gallery of the Univ. of Rochester.

Brownlee, Andrea Barnwell & Oliver, Valerie Cassel. Cinema Remixed & Reloaded: Black Women & the Moving Image Since 1970. 2008. (ENG., Illus.). 82p. (C). *(978-0-295-98864-1(9))* Contemporary Arts Museum, Houston.

Bruce, Katie & Hollows, Victoria. Towards an Engaged Gallery: Contemporary art & human Rights. 2007. (Illus.). 96p. per. *(978-0-902752-88-7(X))* Glasgow Museums.

Brusen, Claus. Dante: The Divine Comedy. 2012. (ENG., Illus.). 96p. pap. 29.95 *(978-87-992147-2-3(5))* Fantasmus-Art DNK. Dist: Independent Pubs. Group.

—Quadrant Fantasy. 2012. (ENG.). 96p. pap. 29.95 *(978-87-992147-7-8(6))* Fantasmus-Art DNK. Dist: Independent Pubs. Group.

Buchanan, Roderick. Histrionics. 2007. (Illus.). 30p. *(978-0-902752-85-6(5))* Glasgow Museums.

Buche, Wolfgang. Lyonel Feininger. 2010. (GER., Illus.). 176p. (C). 53.00 *(978-3-7774-2681-5(4))* Hirmer Verlag GmbH DEU. Dist: Brown, David Bk. Co., The.

Buchmann, Sabeth, et al, texts. unExhibit. 2011. (ENG., Illus.). 150p. pap. 60.00 ***(978-3-86984-202-8(4))*** Verlag fur Moderne Kunst DEU. Dist: D.A.P./Distributed Art Pubs.

Buckingham, Matthew & Hickson, Patricia. Improbable Horse. 2009. (ENG., Illus.). 114p. pap. 15.00 *(978-1-879003-52-1(X))* Des Moines Art Ctr.

Buetti, Daniele, illus. Maybe You Can Be One of Us. 2008. (ENG.). 240p. 60.00 *(978-3-7757-2095-3(2))* Hatje Cantz Verlag GmbH & Co KG DEU. Dist: D.A.P./Distributed Art Pubs.

Buhrs, Michael & Brandlhuber, Margot Th., eds. Frederic Lord Leighton: A Princley Painter of the Victorian Age. 2009. (Illus.). 208p. 35.00 *(978-3-7913-4383-9(1))* Prestel Publishing.

Bul, Lee. Lee Bul: On Every New Shadow. 2008. (ENG.). 128p. 40.00 *(978-0-500-97498-8(5))* Thames & Hudson.

Buranelli, Francesco. Between God & Man: Angels in Italian Art. Dietrick, Robin C., ed. 2007. (ENG., Illus.). 192p. 34.95 *(978-1-887422-15-4(3))* Univ. Pr. of Mississippi.

Buren, Anne Van. Illuminating Fashion: Dress in the Art of Medieval France & the Netherlands, 1325-1515. Wieck, Roger S., ed. 2011. (ENG., Illus.). 448p. 95.00 *(978-1-904832-90-4(3))* Giles, D. Ltd. GBR. Dist: National Bk. Network.

Burke, Gregory, ed. Lawrence Weiner: the Other Side of A Cul-de-Sac. 2009. (ENG., Illus.). 48p. 35.00 *(978-1-894212-25-0(8))* Power Plant, The CAN. Dist: D.A.P./Distributed Art Pubs.

Burke, Gregory, text. Universal Code: Art & Cosmology in the Information Age. 2010. (ENG., Illus.). 136p. 58.00 *(978-1-894212-28-1(2))* Power Plant, The CAN. Dist: D.A.P./Distributed Art Pubs.

Burton, Bruce, des. Katie Holten: Paths of Desire, 1 vol. 2007. (ENG., Illus.). 120p. per. 25.00 *(978-0-9777528-3-6(6))* Contemporary Art Museum St. Louis.

Butler, Jon & Cooper, Helen A. Life, Liberty, & the Pursuit of Happiness: Art & the American Experience, 1660-1900. 2008. pap. *(978-0-89467-966-7(X))* Yale Univ. Pr.

Buvelot, Quentin. Made in Holland: Highlights from the Collection of Eijk & Rose-Marie de Mol Van Otterloo. 2011. 152p. pap. 50.00 *(978-90-400-7744-9(4))* Waanders B.V., Uitgeverij NLD. Dist: National Bk. Network.

Cachin, Francoise. Treasures of the Musee D'Orsay. (ITA & JPN., Illus.). 320p. *(978-88-86482-29-5(9))* Leonardo International ITA. Dist: Abbeville Pr., Inc.

Cage, John. The Anarchy of Silence: John Cage & Experimental Art. 2010. (Illus.). 295p. pap. 59.95 *(978-84-92505-14-2(1))* Museu d'Art Contemporani de Barcelona ESP. Dist: Actar Birkhauser Distribution.

Calit2, Gallery. A Light Green Light: Toward Sustainability in Practice. 2010. 44p. pap. 27.49 *(978-0-578-06223-5(2))* gallery@calit2.

—Overheard. 2010. 48p. pap. 28.51 *(978-0-578-05311-0(X))* gallery@calit2.

—Tijuana/San Diego: Cooperation & Confrontation at the Interface. 2010. 100p. pap. 44.00 *(978-0-578-04780-5(2))* gallery@calit2.

Calit2, Gallery & @calit2, gallery. Scalable City. 2010. 68p. pap. 34.75 *(978-0-578-00316-0(3))* gallery@calit2.

Cameron, Angus & Gregory, Burke, texts. Goldin & Senneby: Headless. 2010. (ENG., Illus.). 80p. pap. 19.00 *(978-1-894212-26-7(6))* Power Plant, The CAN. Dist: D.A.P./Distributed Art Pubs.

Campbell, Caroline. Love & Marriage in Renaissance Florence. 2009. (Illus.). 128p. pap. 50.00 ***(978-1-903470-91-6(9))*** Holberton, Paul Publishing GBR. Dist: Casemate Pubs. & Bk. Distributors, LLC.

Campbell, Caroline, ed. Temptation in Eden: Lucas Cranach's Adam & Eve. 2007. (ENG., Illus.). 128p. 50.00 *(978-1-903470-54-1(4))* Holberton, Paul Publishing GBR. Dist: Univ. of Washington Pr.

Campbell, Thomas P., et al. Tapestry in the Baroque: Threads of Splendor. 2007. 35.00 *(978-1-58839-230-5(9))*; 75.00 *(978-1-58839-229-9(5))* Metropolitan Museum of Art, The.

Campeggi, Silvano & Righi, Giuliana. Verso Campaldino: Dal Pian Di Ripoli Alla Battaglia. 2010. (ITA & ENG., Illus.). 119p. *(978-88-7970-471-7(0))* Edifir.

Campens, Angelique, et al. For Reasons of State. 2009. (Independent Study Program Ser.). (ENG., Illus.). 48p. pap. 16.95 *(978-0-300-14694-3(9))* Yale Univ. Pr.

Capwell, Tobias. Noble Art of the Sword. 2012. (Illus.). 264p. pap. 65.00 ***(978-0-900785-43-6(8))*** Holberton, Paul Publishing GBR. Dist: Casemate Pubs. & Bk. Distributors, LLC.

Carpenter, John T. The Artist's Touch, the Craftsman's Hand: Three Centuries of Japanese Prints in the Portland Art Museum, 1 vol. Graybill, Maribeth, ed. 2011. (ENG., Illus.). 348p. 45.00 ***(978-1-883124-32-8(8))*** Portland Art Museum.

Carr, Carolyn Kinder & Miles, Ellen Gross. Capital Portraits: Treasures from the Washington Private Collections. 2011. (ENG.). 200p. 49.95 *(978-1-935623-00-7(1))* Smithsonian Institution Scholarly Pr.

Carter, J. C., ed. The Gravestones of Chersonesos: Research & Conservation. 2006. (ENG., Illus.). 91p. (C). pap. 25.00 *(978-975-8071-47-0(5))* Institute of Classical Archaeology.

Cash, Sarah & Ormond, Richard. Sargent & the Sea. 2009. (ENG., Illus.). 192p. 50.00 *(978-0-300-14360-7(5))* Yale Univ. Pr.

Cassidy-Geiger, Maureen & Arnhold, Henry. The Arnhold Collection of Meissen Porcelain, 1710-50. 2008. (ENG., Illus.). 800p. 275.00 *(978-1-904832-44-7(X))* Giles, D. Ltd. GBR. Dist: Antique Collectors' Club.

Castelnuovo, Enrico & Barberis, Walter. La reggia di Venaria e i Savoia. Arte, magnificenza e storia di una corte europea. Catalogo della mostra (12 ottobre 2007-30 marzo 2008), 2 vols. 2008. (ITA & ENG., Illus.). 680p. pap. 90.00 *(978-88-422-1585-1(6))* Allemandi, Umberto & Co. GBR. Dist: National Bk. Network.

Castro, Iné, et al. Paradiese der Südsee: Mythos und Wirklichkeit. 2008. (GER., Illus.). 248p. (C). 53.00 *(978-3-8053-3915-5(1))* Zabern, Philipp von Verlag, GmbH DEU. Dist: Brown, David Bk. Co., The.

Casula Powerhouse, compiled by. Liverpool Art Society 10th Annual Exhibition. 2007. *(978-1-876418-81-6(8))* Casula Powerhouse.

—A show about Joe. 2007. per. *(978-1-876418-79-3(6))* Casula Powerhouse.

Caterina Proto Pisani, Rosanna. La Valle Dei Tesori: Capolavori Allo Specchio. 2006. (Piccoli, grandi Musei Ser.). (ITA & ENG., Illus.). 185p. (C). 29.50 *(978-88-596-0068-8(5))* Edizioni Polistampa ITA. Dist: Brown, David Bk. Co., The.

Celant, Germano. Anselm Kiefer. 2007. (ENG., Illus.). 524p. 100.00 *(978-88-6130-101-6(0))* Skira Editore ITA. Dist: Random Hse., Inc.

—Frank O. Gehry: Since 1997. 2010. (ENG., Illus.). 320p. 95.00 *(978-88-572-0179-5(1))* Skira Editore ITA. Dist: Random Hse., Inc.

—Paolo Canevari. Celant, Germano, ed. 2011. (ITA & ENG., Illus.). 312p. pap. 87.50 *(978-88-370-7603-0(7)*, Mondadori Electa (Acc)) Antique Collectors' Club GBR. Dist: National Bk. Network.

—Tobias Rehberger: on Otto. Celant, Germano et al, eds. 2008. (ENG., Illus.). 120p. 160.00 *(978-88-87029-39-0(3))* Fondazione Prada ITA. Dist: D.A.P./Distributed Art Pubs.

Celant, Germano, ed. Roter Sand und ein gefundenes Glück. 2008. (ENG., Illus.). 180p. pap. 94.00 *(978-3-86560-178-0(2))* Fondazione Prada ITA. Dist: D.A.P./Distributed Art Pubs.

Centre d'art contemporain (Geneva, Switzerland) Staff, contrib. by. Wouldn't It Be Nice: Wishful Thinking in Art & Design. 2008. (FRE & ENG., Illus.). 300p. pap. 42.00 *(978-3-905829-24-2(X))* JRP Ringier Kunstverlag AG CHE. Dist: D.A.P./Distributed Art Pubs.

Chagall, Marc, et al. Marc Chagall: Der Maler Am Fenster. 2009. (GER., Illus.). 167p. (C). 45.00 *(978-3-7774-6025-3(7))* Hirmer Verlag GmbH DEU. Dist: Brown, David Bk. Co., The.

Chapelle Des Deaux-Arts, ed. Academia: Qui es-tu?, 1 vol. 2010. (FRE.). 348p. 115.00 *(978-90-76979-65-6(0))* Exhibitions International BEL. Dist: Innovative Logistics.

Chapin, Mary Weaver. Posters of Paris: Toulouse-Lautrec & His Contemporaries. 2012. pap. ***(978-3-7913-6407-0(3))*** Prestel Verlag GmbH & Co KG.

Chaplin, Sarah & Stara, Alexandra. Curating Architecture & the City. 2009. (ENG., Illus.). 258p. 165.00 *(978-0-415-48982-9(2))*; pap. 53.95 *(978-0-415-48983-6(0))* Routledge.

Chapman, Martin. Cartier & America. Levine, Karen, ed. 2010. (Illus.). 176p. 29.95 *(978-3-7913-5015-8(3))* Prestel Publishing.

Chariau, Joelle, ed. Drawing Fashion: A Century of Fashion Illustration. 2011. (Illus.). 240p. 49.95 *(978-3-7913-5102-5(8))* Prestel Publishing.

Chemiakin, Michel. Chemiakin: Art & Life, 2 vols., Set. (Illus.). 1200p. 400.00 *(978-0-88962-327-9(9))* Chemiakin Bks.

Chen, April, et al. V 0. 0. 2010. 184p. pap. 59.20 *(978-0-557-13754-1(3))* Lulu Enterprises Inc.

Chhangur, Emelie & Zaccagnini, Carla. Carla Zaccagnini: No. It Is Opposition. Maranda, Michael, ed. 2010. (POR, SPA & ENG., Illus.). 112p. pap. 25.00 *(978-0-921972-57-0(1))* Art Gallery of York Univ. CAN. Dist: D.A.P./Distributed Art Pubs.

Chiarenza, Carl. Pictures Come from Pictures: Selected Photographs, 1955-2007. 2008. (ENG., Illus.). 128p. pap. 19.95 *(978-1-56792-358-2(5))* Godine, David R. Pub.

Chihuly, Dale, illus. Dale Chihuly: A Celebration. 2011. (ENG.). 128p. 19.95 *(978-1-4197-0000-2(6))* Abrams.

Childs, Adrienne L., et al. Evolution: Five Decades of Printmaking. 2007. (Illus.). 128p. 30.00 *(978-0-7649-4204-4(2)*, A141) Pomegranate Communications, Inc.

Chow, Brian G. & Sun, Seunghye. The Lure of Painted Poetry: Japanese & Korean Art. 2011. (Illus.). 120p. 50.00 *(978-1-55595-364-5(6))* Hudson Hills Pr. LLC.

Chowdhry, Pritika. Visceral Mappings: Transdiasporic Art Practices. 2007. (Illus.). 50p. pap. 24.95 *(978-0-9797340-0-7(2))* Chowdhry, Pritika.

Christiansen, Keith, et al. The Renaissance Portrait: From Donatello to Bellini. 2011. 65.00 ***(978-1-58839-425-5(5))***; (Illus.). xii, 420p. pap. 45.00 ***(978-1-58839-426-2(3))*** Metropolitan Museum of Art, The.

Cindy Ho & Christine Mathieu, eds. Quentin Roosevelt's China: Ancestral Realms of the Naxi: 2011. (Illus.). 200p. 75.00 *(978-0-9845190-1-9(7))* Rubin Museum of Art.

Cirincione, Janine, intro. Feng Zhengjie. 2007. (Illus.). 32p. 10.00 *(978-0-9798486-0-5(1))* Tilton Gallery.

Claire Gittings, et al. The National Portrait Gallery Book of Elizabeth I. 2006. (4-Fold Ser.). (ENG., Illus.). 9.95 *(978-1-85759-429-4(0))* Scala, Editions FRA. Dist: National Bk. Network.

Clark, Carol & Deas, Charles. Charles Deas & 1840s America. 2009. (Charles M. Russell Center on Art & Photography of the American West Ser.). (ENG.). 248p. (C). 39.95 *(978-0-8061-4030-8(5))*; pap. *(978-0-8061-4048-3(8))* Univ. of Oklahoma Pr.

Clark, Garth. Ian Ingram: Divining. 2010. (Illus.). 40p. 30.00 *(978-0-9826397-0-2(8))* Friedman, Barry Ltd.

Clark, Kirk. Celebration of Spirit. 2007.Tr. of Celebracion de Espiritu. (Illus.). 144p. 40.00 *(978-0-9774935-0-0(4))* Clark, Kirk.

Clark, Martin. Michael Stevenson. 2008. (ENG., Illus.). 64p. 19.00 *(978-3-905829-48-8(7))* JRP Ringier Kunstverlag AG CHE. Dist: D.A.P./Distributed Art Pubs.

Clarke, Lorraine & Richardson, Ruth. Lorraine Clarke: Nosce Te Ipsum. 2007. (ENG., Illus.). 24p. pap. 11.95 *(978-1-905313-42-6(X))* Univ. of Hertfordshire Pr. GBR. Dist: Independent Pubs. Group.

Clayton, Martin & da Vinci, Leonardo. Leonardo da Vinci: The Divine & the Grotesque. 2010. (ENG., Illus.). 181p. 45.00 *(978-1-902163-97-0(4))* Royal Collection Enterprises Ltd. GBR. Dist: Chicago Distribution Ctr.

Cleijne, Edgar. Heart of Darkness, 1 vol. 2006. (ENG., Illus.). 96p. per. 27.00 *(978-0-935640-85-4(1))* Walker Art Ctr.

Clemente, Francesco. Francesco Clemente: The Sopranos. 2008. (ENG., Illus.). 40p. 29.95 *(978-88-8158-698-1(3))* Charta ITA. Dist: D.A.P./Distributed Art Pubs.

Clifford, Timothy, et al. The Three Graces. 2006. (ENG., Illus.). 112p. pap. *(978-0-903598-59-0(0))* National Galleries of Scotland.

Clifton, James, et al, contrib. by. Scripture for the Eyes: Bible Illustration in Netherlandish Prints of the Sixteenth Century. 2009. (Illus.). 224p. pap. 49.95 *(978-0-9777839-3-9(6))* Museum of Biblical Art.

Clifton, James & Scatone, Leslie M. The Plains of Mars: European War Prints, 1500-1825, from the Collection of the Sarah Campbell Blaffer Foundation. 2009. pap. *(978-0-89090-167-0(8))* Yale Univ. Pr.

Clifton, James, et al. The Plains of Mars: European War Prints, 1500-1825, from the Collection of the Sarah Campbell Blaffer Foundation. 2009. (ENG., Illus.). 254p. 65.00 *(978-0-300-13722-4(2))* Yale Univ. Pr.

Coates, Marcus. Marcus Coates: The Trip. 2011. (ENG., Illus.). 88p. pap. 22.95 ***(978-3-86560-985-4(6))*** Verlag der Buchhandlung Walther Konig DEU. Dist: D.A.P./Distributed Art Pubs.

Cobb, Benjamin & Linn, Susan. Kids Design Glass. 2009. (ENG., Illus.). 132p. 40.00 *(978-0-295-98937-2(8))* Univ. of Washington Pr.

Coetzee, Mark, ed. Keith Haring: Against All Odds. 2009. (ENG., Illus.). 288p. 60.00 *(978-0-9821195-0-1(X))* Rubell Family Collection.

Coffin, Sarah D. Set in Style: The Jewelry of Van Cleef & Arpels. 2011. pap. ***(978-0-910503-86-0(9))*** Princeton Architectural Pr.

Cohen, Beth. The Colors of Clay: Special Techniques in Athenian Vases. (Illus.). 2008. 384p. pap. 44.95 *(978-0-89236-942-3(6))* 2006. (ENG., 288p. 85.00 *(978-0-89236-571-5(4))* Oxford Univ. Pr., Inc.

Collection Videos & Films Isabelle & Jean-Conrad Lemaitre. 2008. (ENG.). 255p. pap. 55.00 *(978-3-86560-392-0(0))* Verlag der Buchhandlung Walther Konig DEU. Dist: D.A.P./Distributed Art Pubs.

Collins, Curtis J., et al. A New Brunswick Trilogy: Philip Iverson, Francis Coutellier, Sarah Maloney, 3 vols. (FRE & ENG., Illus.). pap. 12.95 *(978-0-920674-45-1(3))* Beaverbrook Art Gallery CAN. Dist: Goose Lane Editions.

Columbia Musuem of Art. Carolina Collects. 2011. (Distributed for the South Carolina State Museum Ser.). 44p. pap. 14.95 ***(978-0-9818064-0-2(6))*** Univ. of South Carolina Pr.

Connor, Michael, et al, contrib. by. The New Normal. 2008. (ENG., Illus.). 144p. pap. 29.95 *(978-0-916365-79-0(4))* Independent Curators International.

Conrads, Margaret C., ed. Romancing the West: Alfred Jacob Miller in the Bank of America Collection. 2010. (ENG., Illus.). 136p. pap. 34.95 *(978-0-615-35171-1(9))* Nelson-Atkins Museum of Art, The.

Constable, John & Chivian-Cobb, Hermine. Constable's Oil Sketches, 1809-29: The Maria Bicknell Years. 2007. (Illus.). 152p. *(978-1-58821-149-1(5))* Salander - O'Reilly Publishing.

Cook, Colin & Shambaugh, Bill. Colin Cook und Bill Shambaugh: Drawings with Bill. 2009. (ENG.). 64p. 30.00 *(978-3-86828-069-2(3))* Kehrer Verlag Heidelberg, Klaus Kehrer DEU. Dist: Consortium Bk. Sales & Distribution.

Cooke, Lynne, ed. Thomas Schutte. 2010. (ENG., Illus.). 208p. 49.95 *(978-3-7913-5050-9(1))* Prestel Publishing.

Cooke, Lynne & Oursler, Tony. Tony Oursler 1997-2007. 2008. (ENG., Illus.). 144p. 79.00 (978-3-905829-25-9(8)) JRP Ringier Kunstverlag AG CHE. Dist: D.A.P./Distributed Art Pubs.

Cooks, Bridget R. Exhibiting Blackness: African Americans & the American Art Museum. 2011. (Illus.). 240p. pap. 29.95 (978-1-55849-875-4(3)) Univ. of Massachusetts Pr.

Cooksey, Susan, et al. Resonance & Inspiration: New Works by Magdalene Odundo. 2006. 14.95 (978-0-9762552-2-2(7)) Harn Museum of Art.

Cooney, John D. & Riefstahl, Elizabeth. Pagan & Christian Egypt: Egyptian Art from the First to the Tenth Century. 2011. 198p. 42.95 (978-1-258-03750-5(5)) Literary Licensing, LLC.

Cormack, Robin & Vassiliki, Maria. Byzantium, 330-1453. 2008. (ENG., Illus.). 496p. 115.00 (978-1-905711-26-0(3)) Royal Academy of Arts GBR. Dist: Hachette Bk. Group.

Corrêa Do Lago, Pedro & Corrêa Do Lago, Bia. Frans Post, 1612-1680: Catalogue Raisonné. 2008. (ENG., Illus.). 448p. 200.00 (978-88-7439-394-7(6)) 5 Continents ITA. Dist: Hachette Bk. Group.

Cort, Louise Allison & Jett, Paul, eds. Gods of Angkor: Bronzes from the National Museum of Cambodia. 2010. (ENG., Illus.). 160p. pap. 40.00 (978-0-295-99042-2(2)) Sackler, Arthur M. Foundation, The.

Costa, Xavier, ed. Ai Wei Wei: With Milk, find something everybody can Use. 2010. 40p. pap. 19.95 (978-84-92861-46-0(0)) Fundacio Mies Van Der Rohe ESP. Dist: Actar Birkhauser Distribution.

Coyle, Heather Campbell, et al. John Sloan's New York. 2007. pap. 40.00 (978-0-9771644-1-7(1)) Delaware Art Museum, The.

—John Sloan's New York. 2007. (ENG., Illus.). 208p. 50.00 (978-0-300-12619-8(0)) Yale Univ. Pr.

Coyne, Petah & Lloyd, Ann Wilson. Petah Coyne: Vermilion Fog. 2008. (ENG., Illus.). 88p. 39.95 (978-88-8158-684-4(3)) Charta ITA. Dist: D.A.P./Distributed Art Pubs.

Crisante, Cristina D. & Gransingh, Vania, eds. Giambattista Tiepolo: Tra Scherzo e Capriccio. 2010. (ITA.). 112p. pap. 45.00 (978-88-370-7725-9(4)) Electa ITA. Dist: Trans-Atlantic Pubns., Inc.

Croft, Brenda L. Culture Warriors: National Indigenous Art Triennial '07. Clark, Deborah & Jenkins, Susan, eds. 2008. (Illus.). 218p. pap. (978-0-642-54133-8(7)) National Gallery of Australia.

Cross, Elizabeth. Allan Mitelman: Works on Paper 1966-2004. 2006. (Illus.). 143p. 24.95 (978-0-7241-0250-1(7)) National Gallery of Victoria AUS. Dist: Antique Collectors' Club.

Crow, Thomas. John Chamberlain: New Sculpture. 2012. (ENG., Illus.). 144p. 100.00 (978-0-8478-3766-3(1)) Rizzoli International Pubns., Inc.

Crowell, Aron & Worl, Rosita, eds. Living Our Cultures, Sharing Our Heritage: The First Peoples of Alaska. 2010. (ENG., Illus.). 312p. 50.00 (978-1-58834-270-6(0)) Smithsonian Institution Pr.

Crown Foundation, The. Jaume Plensa. 2008. (ENG., Illus.). 240p. 60.00 (978-3-7757-2080-9(4)) Hatje Cantz Verlag GmbH & Co KG DEU. Dist: D.A.P./Distributed Art Pubs.

Crutchfield, Margo A. Beyond the Line: The Art of Diana Cooper. 1 vol. 2008. (ENG., Illus.). 120p. per. 29.99 (978-1-880353-37-0(7)) Cleveland Ctr. for Contemporary Art.

Cubbs, Joanne & Metcalf, Eugene W., eds. Hard Truths: The Art of Thornton Dial. 2011. (Illus.). 240p. 45.00 (978-3-7913-5058-5(7)) Prestel Publishing.

Cueff, Alain & Maurer, Simon. Marie Jose Burki: These Days. 1 vol. 2007. (ENG., Illus.). 176p. 50.00 (978-3-86521-479-9(7)) Steidl, Gerhard Druckerei und Verlag DEU. Dist: Innovative Logistics.

Cueto, Lola. Lola Cueto: Trascendencia Mágica, 1897-1978. 2009. (SPA., Illus.). 218p. (978-607-7622-30-7(3)) Direccion General de Publicaciones del Consejo Nacional para la Cultura y las Artes.

Cullen, Fintan. Ireland on Show: Art Union & Nationhood. 2012. (Illus.). 124.95 (978-1-4094-3109-1(6)) Ashgate Publishing Co.

Cummings, Hildegard. Charles Ethan Porter: African-American Master of Still Life. Barr, Pamela, ed. 2008. (Illus.). 112p. per. 35.00 (978-0-9724497-6-2(0)) New Britain Museum of American Art.

Cummings, Hildegard, et al. J. Alden Weir: A Place of His Own. (Illus.). 99p. 14.50 (978-0-918386-43-4(8)) William Benton Museum of Art.

Cunningham, C. C., ed. Art in New England: The Arts & Crafts of New England & A Survey of the Taste of Its People. 2011. 616p. 64.95 (978-1-258-08854-5(1)) Literary Licensing, LLC.

Curiger, Bice. Hypermental: Rampant Reality, 1950-2000. 39.95 (978-3-906574-11-0(3)) Kunsthaus Zurich, Zurcher Kunstgesellschaft CHE. Dist: D.A.P./Distributed Art Pubs.

Curtis, Robin. John Bock. 2008. (ENG., Illus.). 176p. pap. 54.00 (978-3-86560-261-9(4)) Verlag der Buchhandlung Walther Konig DEU. Dist: D.A.P./Distributed Art Pubs.

Curtis, Shelley, ed. This Bountiful Place: Art about Agriculture: the Permanent Collection. 2007. (Illus.). 256p. per. 26.00 (978-0-87595-303-8(4)) Oregon Historical Society Pr.

Cushing, Stanley Ellis & Dearinger, David B. Acquired Tastes: 200 Years of Collecting for the Boston Athenaeum. 2007. (Illus.). 388p. 65.00 (978-0-934552-73-8(8)) Boston Athenaeum Library.

D'Agati, Mauro. Alamar: Habana - Cuba. 1 vol. 2010. (ENG & SPA., Illus.). 156p. 75.00 (978-3-86521-954-1(3)) Steidl, Gerhard Druckerei und Verlag DEU. Dist: Innovative Logistics.

D'Alessandro, Jill & De Borchgrave, Isabelle. Pulp Fashion: The Art of Isabelle de Borchgrave. 2011. (Illus.). 104p. (978-3-7913-5105-6(2)) Fine Arts Museums of San Francisco.

Dalgleish, George & Fothringham, Henry Steuart. Silver: Made in Scotland. 2008. (ENG., Illus.). 256p. pap. 55.00 (978-1-905267-13-2(4)) NMS Enterprises Ltd. - Publishing GBR. Dist: National Bk. Network.

Dallett, Joseph B., et al. Romeyn de Hooghe: Virtuoso Etcher. 2009. (Illus.). 96p. pap. (978-1-934260-11-1(8)) Cornell Univ., Herbert F. Johnson Museum of Art.

David & Chie Hammons. 2008. (Illus.). 22p. 35.00 (978-0-9790942-4-8(0)) L & M Arts.

David, Caroline, ed. Frontières Invisibles - Invisible Borders. 2009. (FRE & ENG., Illus.). 224p. pap. (978-90-5856-315-6(4), Stichting Kunstboek (Acc)) Antique Collectors' Club.

David Joseph Herrle. 158p. 4.99 (978-0-9706843-0-1(4)) Herrle, David Joseph.

Davis, Margaret Leslie. Mona Lisa in Camelot: How Jacqueline Kennedy & Da Vinci's Masterpiece Charmed & Captivated a Nation. 2009. (ENG.). 304p. pap. 15.95 (978-0-306-81843-1(4)) Da Capo Pr., Inc.

Davy, Jennifer, et al. Material Culture: 16 February/6 April 2008, Fort Worth Contemporary Arts. 2010. (ENG., Illus.). 48p. pap. 19.95 (978-0-9801617-0-0(3)) Texas Christian Univ. Pr.

A Day in Pompeii. 2007. per. (978-1-933245-08-9(5)) Documentary Media LLC.

de Brugerolle, Marie, et al, texts. Not to Play with Dead Things. 2010. (ENG., Illus.). 176p. pap. 35.00 (978-3-03764-071-5(5)) JRP Ringier Kunstverlag AG CHE. Dist: D.A.P./Distributed Art Pubs.

De Bunes Ibarra, Miguel Angel, et al. The Invention of Glory: Afonso V & the Pastrana Tapestries. 2012. (ENG., Illus.). 104p. 65.00 (978-1-55595-375-1(1)) Hudson Hills Pr. LLC.

De Concilis, Ettore. Ettore De Concilis: Opere 1982-2009. 2009. (ITA., Illus.). 155p. (978-88-7831-236-4(3), Spotlight Poets) Cigno Galileo Galilei.

De Montclos, Brigitte. Moscow: Splendours of the Romanovs. 2009. (ENG., Illus.). 304p. 50.00 (978-88-572-0256-3(9)) Skira Editore ITA. Dist: Random Hse., Inc.

De Oliveira, Nicolas & Pirotte, Philippe, eds. Stefan Bruggemann. 2008. (ENG., Illus.). 64p. 35.00 (978-3-905829-64-8(9)) JRP Ringier Kunstverlag AG CHE. Dist: D.A.P./Distributed Art Pubs.

De Rocchi, Francesco & Pontiggia, Elena. Il Chiarismo: Omaggio a de Rocchi: Luce e Colore a Milano Negli Anni Trenta. 2010. (ITA., Illus.). 175p. (978-88-572-0724-7(2)) Skira Editore.

De Rooij, Willem & De Rijke, Jeroen, illus. Jeroen de Rijke & Willem de Rooij. 1 vol. 2007. (ENG.). 112p. per. 35.00 (978-2-940271-33-7(X)) JRP Ringier Kunstverlag AG CHE. Dist: D.A.P./Distributed Art Pubs.

Debailleux, Francois. Benoit Luyckx. 2006. (ENG., Illus.). 104p. 35.00 (978-90-400-9093-6(9)) Waanders B.V., Uitgeverij NLD. Dist: National Bk. Network.

Debono, Sandro. Uncorsanding Caravaggio & His Art in Malta. 2007. 56p. (C). pap. 9.95 (978-99932-7-164-2(0)) Midsea Bks. Ltd. MLT. Dist: Brown, David Bk. Co., The.

Debreczeny, Karl. The Black Hat Eccentric: Artistic Visions of the Tenth Karmapa. 2012. (ENG., Illus.). 320p. 75.00 (978-0-9772131-0-8(2)) Rubin Museum of Art.

Debreczeny, Karl, ed. The Tenth Karmapa: Tibet's Eccentric Master Revealed. 2012. (ENG.). pap. 60.00 (978-0-9772131-6-0(1)) Rubin Museum of Art.

Decan, Liesbeth. Axelleration: Evelyne Axel,1964-1972. 2012. (ENG & GER., Illus.). 112p. pap. 40.00 (978-90-209-9947-1(8)) Lannoo Pubs./Racine.

Deena, Chalabi, et al, eds. Told, Untold, Retold: 23 Stories of Journeys Through Time & Place. 2011. (ARA & ENG., Illus.). 280p. pap. 65.00 (978-88-572-0819-0(2)) Skira Editore ITA. Dist: Random Hse., Inc.

Dejanoff, Plamen, photos by. Dejanoff. 2008. (ENG., Illus.). 160p. pap. 49.00 (978-3-905701-58-6(8)) JRP Ringier Kunstverlag AG CHE. Dist: D.A.P./Distributed Art Pubs.

Dellenbaugh, Virginia. Markus Schinwald. 2008. (GER & ENG., Illus.). 208p. 39.00 (978-3-905829-22-8(3)) JRP Ringier Kunstverlag AG CHE. Dist: D.A.P./Distributed Art Pubs.

Delsaux, Cedric, photos by. Murakami Versailles. 2011. (ENG., Illus.). 256p. 85.00 (978-2-915173-72-7(9)) Barral, Xavier Editions FRA. Dist: D.A.P./Distributed Art Pubs.

Demange, F. Glass, Gilding, & Grand Design: Art of Sasanian Iran (224-642) 2007. (Illus.). 47p. (978-0-87848-106-4(0)) Asia Society, Inc.

Denver Art Museum Staff. The Masterworks of Charles M. Russell: A Retrospective of Paintings & Sculpture. Troccoli, Joan Carpenter, ed. 2009. (Charles M. Russell Center Series on Art & Photography of the American West Ser.). (ENG.). 304p. pap. 39.95 (978-0-8061-4097-1(6)) Univ. of Oklahoma Pr.

Denver Art Museum Staff, contrib. by. Denver Art Museum: Highlights from the Collection. 2006. (ENG., Illus.). 64p. pap. 8.95 (978-1-85759-432-4(0)) Scala, Editions FRA. Dist: National Bk. Network.

Denver Museum of Art Staff, ed. West Point Points West. 2008. (ENG.). 80p. pap. 10.95 (978-0-8061-9968-9(7)) Denver Art Museum.

Dercon, Chris, ed. Carlo Mollino: Maniera Moderna. 2012. (ENG., Illus.). 312p. pap. 49.95 (978-3-86335-020-8(0)) Verlag der Buchhandlung Walther Konig DEU. Dist: D.A.P./Distributed Art Pubs.

Derksen, Tessa & Shen, Chen. Iconic 15: The ROM's Must-See Treasures. 2010. (ENG & FRE.). 80p. pap. 5.00 (978-0-88854-467-4(7)) Royal Ontario Museum CAN. Dist: Univ. of Toronto Pr.

DeRose, Elizabeth C. & Johns, Jasper. Jasper Johns: From Plate to Print. 2006. (ENG., Illus.). 112p. 24.00 (978-0-89467-963-6(5)) Yale Univ. Art Gallery.

Descatoire, Christine. Treasures of the Black Death. 2009. (ENG., Illus.). 112p. pap. 40.00 (978-0-900785-95-5(0)) Holberton, Paul Publishing GBR. Dist: Casemate Pubs. & Bk. Distributors, LLC.

Desroches, Jean-Paul, et al. Fils du Ciel. 2009. (FRE., Illus.). 231p. (978-90-6153-887-5(4)); (978-90-6153-886-8(6)) Mercatorfonds N. V.

Detweiler, Susan Gray. American Presidential China: The Robert L. McNeil, Jr., Collection at the Philadelphia Museum of Art. 2008. (ENG., Illus.). 91p. 24.95 (978-0-300-13593-0(9)) Yale Univ. Pr.

Diaz de León, Francisco. Francisco Díaz de León. 2011. (ENG., Illus.). 160p. 45.00 (978-84-936123-6-8(7)) RM Verlag, S.L. ESP. Dist: D.A.P./Distributed Art Pubs.

Dichter, Claudia, ed. Horst Ademeit: Secret Universe. 2011. (ENG., Illus.). 112p. pap. 44.95 (978-3-86560-997-7(X)) Verlag der Buchhandlung Walther Konig DEU. Dist: D.A.P./Distributed Art Pubs.

Diederichsen, Diedrich & Danbolt, Mathias, texts. Pauline Boudry & Renate Lorenz: Temporal Drag. 2011. (ENG., Illus.). 172p. pap. 40.00 (978-3-7757-2988-8(7)) Hatje Cantz Verlag GmbH & Co KG DEU. Dist: D.A.P./Distributed Art Pubs.

Dillon, Brian, et al, texts. Walking in My Mind. 2009. (ENG., Illus.). 160p. pap. 40.00 (978-1-85332-277-8(6)) Hayward Gallery Publishing GBR. Dist: D.A.P./Distributed Art Pubs.

Dillow, Katie. Spanish Modernism in Nineteenth-France. 2011. 76p. pap. (978-3-8433-8466-7(5)) Lambert Academic Publishing.

Dine, Jim, photos by. This Is How I Remember Now: Portraits; Photographs. 1 vol. 2008. (ENG., Illus.). 328p. 70.00 (978-3-86521-603-8(X)) Steidl, Gerhard Druckerei und Verlag DEU. Dist: Innovative Logistics.

DiQuinzio, Apsara, ed. The Air We Breathe: Artists & Poets Reflect on Marriage Equality. 2011. (ENG., Illus.). 172p. 19.95 (978-0-918471-86-4(9)) San Francisco Museum of Modern Art.

Diviney, David. David Askevold: Once upon a Time in the East. 2011. (ENG.). 160p. 50.00 (978-0-86492-659-3(6)) Goose Lane Editions CAN. Dist: Univ. of Toronto Pr.

Dixon, Annette & Chapin, Mary Weaver. The Dancer: Degas, Forain, Toulouse-Lautrec. 2008. (ENG., Illus.). 256p. 39.95 (978-1-883124-27-4(1)) Portland Art Museum.

Djurberg, Nathalie. The Parade: Nathalie Djurberg with Music by Hans Berg. 2011. (ENG., Illus.). 192p. pap. 24.99 (978-1-935963-04-2(X)) Walker Art Ctr.

Dobney, Jayson Kerr. Guitar Heroes: Legendary Craftsmen from Italy to New York. 2011. (Illus.). 48p. 14.95 (978-1-58839-422-4(0)) Metropolitan Museum of Art, The.

Doherty, Willie. Fuera de Posición: Out of Position. 1 vol. 2007. (SPA & ENG., Illus.). 102p. pap. 20.00 (978-968-9056-03-4(4)) Turner, Ediciones S.A. ESP. Dist: D.A.P./Distributed Art Pubs.

Dohm, Katharina & Hoffmann, Justin, texts. Kunstmaschinen Maschinenkunst. 2008. (GER & ENG.). 184p. pap. 40.00 (978-3-939583-40-0(5)) Kehrer Verlag Heidelberg, Klaus Kehrer DEU. Dist: Consortium Bk. Sales & Distribution.

Dole-Recio, Lecia. Lecia Dole-Recio. 1 vol. 2006. (ENG., Illus.). 48p. per. 24.95 (978-0-914357-98-3(0)) Museum of Contemporary Art, Los Angeles.

Dolkart, Judith F., et al. James Tissot: The Life of Christ. 2009. (ENG., Illus.). 304p. 59.95 (978-1-85894-496-8(1)) Merrell Pubs. Ltd. GBR. Dist: Perseus Distribution.

Donato, Gerald. Gerald Donato: Reinventing the Game. 2007. (Illus.). 62p. (978-0-935519-30-3(0)) Anderson Gallery.

Doring, Jurgen. Power to the Imagination: Artists, Posters & Politics. 2011. (ENG & GER., Illus.). 168p. 29.95 (978-3-7774-3881-8(2)) Hirmer Verlag GmbH DEU. Dist: Chicago Distribution Ctr.

Doshi, Balkrishna, et al. Scapes: Laura de Santillana & Alessandro Diaz de Santillana. 1 vol. 2012. (ENG., Illus.). 128p. 55.00 (978-0-295-99188-7(7)) Univ. of Washington Pr.

Doucet, Jacques. Jacques Doucet: Le CoBrA Français. 2010. (FRE, DUT & ENG., Illus.). 191p. (978-2-35733-111-2(9)) Archibooks.

Dragset, Ingar & Elmgreen, Michael & Dragset, Ingar. Elmgreen & Dragset: Home Is the Place You Left. 2008. (ENG., Illus.). 196p. pap. 52.00 (978-3-86560-473-6(0)) Verlag der Buchhandlung Walther Konig DEU. Dist: D.A.P./Distributed Art Pubs.

Drain, Jim & Peterson, Ara. Hypnogocogia. 2007. (Illus.). 30p. per. (978-0-9778686-2-9(1)) Deitch, Jeffrey Inc.

Drescher, Jürgen, et al. Jürgen Drescher: Arbeiten Bis Heute: Galerie Isabella Czarnowska, Berlin, Mai 36 Galerie Zürich. 2008. (GER & ENG., Illus.). 144p. 64.00 (978-3-86560-330-2(0)) Verlag der Buchhandlung Walther Konig DEU. Dist: D.A.P./Distributed Art Pubs.

Drutt, Matthew. Anna Gaskell: Half Life. 2007. (ENG.). 96p. 40.00 (978-0-300-12475-0(9)) Yale Univ. Pr.

Dubois, Hughes, et al. Masters of the Americas: In Praise of the Pre-Columbian Artists - The Dora & Paul Janssen Collection. Le Fort, Genevieve, ed. 2008. (FRE & ENG., Illus.). 400p. 120.00 (978-88-7439-258-2(3)) 5 Continents ITA. Dist: Hachette Bk. Group.

Dudek, Peter. Photasm. Adler, Tracy, ed. (Illus.). 12p. pap. 5.00 (978-1-885998-24-8(4)) Hunter College Art Galleries.

Duke, Marc. The Art Festival Handbook. 2008. 276p. 24.95 (978-0-615-19813-2(9)); (ENG.). pap. 16.95 (978-0-615-19814-9(7)) Virtualbookworm.com Publishing, Inc.

Dumas, Marlene. Marlene Dumas: Selected Works. 1 vol. 2006. (ENG., Illus.). 94p. 35.00 (978-0-9708884-8-8(1)) Zwirner & Wirth.

Dunbar, Elizabeth & Berry, Ian. Dario Robleto: Alloy of Love. 2008. (Illus.). 296p. (978-0-9765723-6-7(2)) Tang, Frances Young Teaching Museum & Art Gallery at Skidmore College, The.

Durant, Sam, ed. Black Panther: The Revolutionary Art of Emory Douglas. 2007. (ENG., Illus.). 208p. pap. 35.00 (978-0-8478-2944-6(8)) Rizzoli International Pubns., Inc.

Dursum, Brian Angus. Clay & Brush: The Ceramic Art of China. 2007. (Illus.). 141p. per. 29.95 (978-0-9788213-1-9(9)) Lowe Art Museum.

Dzama, Marcel. Marcel Dzama: Behind Every Curtain. 2011. (ENG., Illus.). 80p. pap. 22.00 (978-1-935202-62-2(6)) Zwirner, David Inc.

Earle, Joe, et al. Japanese Art & Design. Earle, Joe, ed. 2009. (ENG., Illus.) 236p. pap. 39.95 (978-1-85177-562-0(5)) V & A Pubns. GBR. Dist: Hachette Bk. Group.

Earle, Susan, ed. Aaron Douglas: African American Modernist. 2007. (ENG., Illus.). 272p. 60.00 (978-0-300-12180-3(6)) Yale Univ. Pr.

Ebner, Martin & Zeyfang, Florian, eds. Poor Man's Expression: Technology, Experimental Film, Conceptual Art. 2011. (ENG., Illus.). 231p. pap. 34.95 (978-1-934105-01-6(5)) Sternberg Pr.

Ecker, Berthold, et al. stark bewölkt / Clouds up High: flüchtige Erscheinungen des Himmels / Fleeting Figures in the Sky. 2009. (GER & ENG., Illus.). 224p. 39.95 (978-3-211-89113-1(7)) Springer Wien AUT. Dist: Actar Birkhauser Distribution.

Edwards, Paul. Wyndham Lewis Portraits. 2009. (Illus.). 112p. pap. 34.95 (978-1-58423-320-6(6)) Gingko Pr., Inc.

Eikelmann, Renate, ed. Die Wittelsbacher und das Reich der Mitte: 400 Jahre China und Bayern. Katalogbuch zur Ausstellung in München, 27.03.2009-26.07.2009, Bayerisches Nationalmuseum. 2009. (GER., Illus.). 592p. (C). 65.00 (978-3-7774-9045-8(8)) Hirmer Verlag GmbH DEU. Dist: Brown, David Bk. Co., The.

Eikelmann, Renate & Renate Eikelmann. The Cleveland Museum of Art: Meisterwerke von 300 Bis 1550. 2007. (GER., Illus.). 304p. (C). pap. 56.00 (978-3-7774-3565-7(1)) Hirmer Verlag GmbH DEU. Dist: Brown, David Bk. Co., The.

Eisenman, Stephen. Design in the Age of Darwin: From William Morris to Frank Lloyd Wright. 2008. (ENG., Illus.). 140p. pap. 36.95 (978-0-8101-5204-5(5)) Northwestern Univ. Pr.

Eleey, Peter & Bither, Philip. Trisha Brown: So That the Audience Does Not Know Whether I Have Stopped Dancing. 2008. (ENG., Illus.). 96p. 29.95 (978-0-935640-91-5(6)) Walker Art Ctr.

Eliasson, Olafur, ed. Olafur Eliasson. 2008. (CAT, SPA & ENG., Illus.). 232p. (978-84-934730-7-5(3)) Actar Birkhauser Distribution.

Elkemir, Sabiah. From Cordoba to Samarquand. 2006. 224p. 50.00 (978-88-7439-334-3(2)) 5 Continents ITA. Dist: Antique Collectors' Club.

Ellegood, Anne, et al, texts. Ivan Navarro: Threshold. 2009. (ENG., Illus.). 80p. pap. 37.95 (978-88-8158-728-5(9)) Charta ITA. Dist: D.A.P./Distributed Art Pubs.

Ellen Zweig. 2006. (978-0-9776417-6-5(7)) CUE Art Foundation.

Ellis, Anita J. & Meyn, Susan Labry. Rookwood & the American Indian: Masterpieces of American Art Pottery from the James J. Gardner Collection. 2007. (Illus.). 280p. 50.00 (978-0-8214-1739-3(8)); pap. 30.00 (978-0-8214-1740-9(1)) Ohio Univ. Pr.

Ellis, George R. Oceanic Art: A Celebration of Form. 2009. pap. (978-0-937108-46-8(4)) San Diego Museum of Art.

Emberling, Geoff & Hanson, Katharyn, eds. Catastrophe! The Looting & Destruction of Iraq's Past. 2008. (Oriental Institute Museum Publications). (ENG., Illus.). 88p. (C). pap. 29.95 (978-1-885923-56-1(2)) Oriental Institute of the Univ. of Chicago, The.

Encounters: Richard Painter. 2006. (Illus.). 12p. pap. 8.00 (978-1-885820-22-8(4)) Huntsville Museum of Art.

Endedijk, Leo & Dumas, Charles E. Masters of Mills: From Rembrandt to Mondriaan. 2007. (ENG., Illus.). 232p. pap. 35.00 (978-90-400-8291-7(X)) Waanders B.V., Uitgeverij NLD. Dist: National Bk. Network.

Energies. pap. 39.95 (978-90-5006-034-9(X)) Stedelijk Museum NLD. Dist: D.A.P./Distributed Art Pubs.

Enlightenment, des. After the Reality. 1 vol. 2007. (ENG., Illus.). 52p. pap. 20.00 (978-0-9753243-8-7(1)) Deitch, Jeffrey Inc.

Enwezor, Okuwi, et al. Overlapping. 2010. (ENG., Illus.). 288p. 75.00 (978-88-8158-784-1(X)) Charta ITA. Dist: D.A.P./Distributed Art Pubs.

Epprecht, Katharina, ed. Kannon: Divine Compassion: Early Buddhist Art from Japan. 2007. (Reitberg Museum, Zurich Ser.). (ENG., Illus.). 196p. 50.00 (978-3-907077-30-6(X)) Holberton, Paul Publishing GBR. Dist: Univ. of Washington Pr.

Ernesto Tatafiore. 80.00 (978-91-7936-034-4(3)) Kalejdoskop SWE. Dist: D.A.P./Distributed Art Pubs.

Esche, Charles, et al, eds. Citizens & Subjects: The Netherlands, for Example. 1 vol. 2007. (ENG., Illus.). 336p. pap. 29.00 (978-3-905770-73-5(3)) JRP Ringier Kunstverlag AG CHE. Dist: D.A.P./Distributed Art Pubs.

Essl, Karlheinz, et al. Neo Rauch & Rosa Loy: Hinter den Gärten: Behind the Gardens. 2011. (ENG., Illus.). 160p. 49.95 (978-3-7913-5142-1(7)) Prestel Publishing.

Evans & Frankel, Susannah. The House of Viktor & Rolf. 2008. (Illus.). 256p. 59.95 (978-1-85894-460-9(0)) Merrell Pubs. Ltd. GBR. Dist: Perseus Distribution.

Evans, Mark & Browne, Clare. Raphael: Cartoons & Tapestries for the Sistine Chapel. 2011. (ENG., Illus.). 132p. 24.95 (978-1-85177-634-4(6)) V & A Pubns. GBR. Dist: Hachette Bk. Group.

EXORB - Laurie Hassold. 2006. per. 0.00 *(978-0-9771696-3-4(4))* Grand Central Pr.
Expanded Original Staff. Cornelia Sollfrank: Expanded Original. 2009. (GER & ENG., Illus.). 144p. pap. 40.00 *(978-3-7757-2390-9(0))* Hatje Cantz Verlag GmbH & Co KG DEU. Dist: D.A.P./Distributed Art Pubs.
Faietti, Marzia, ed. Fausto Melotti Graphiko's. 2010. (ITA., Illus.). 248p. pap. 72.50 *(978-88-370-7700-6(9))* Electa ITA. Dist: Trans-Atlantic Pubns., Inc.
Fairey, Shepard. E Pluribus Venom: Shepard Fairey Recent Work. 2008. (Illus.). 128p. 29.95 *(978-1-58423-295-7(1))* Gingko Pr., Inc.
Fang, Jing Pei, et al. Elegance of the Qing Court: Reflections of a Dynasty Through Its Art. 2008. *(978-0-936364-35-3(1))* Joslyn Art Museum.
Fansa, Mamoun & Ritzau, Carsten. Von der Kunst mit Vögeln zu Jagen: das Falkenbuch Friedrichs II.: Kulturgeschichte und Ornithologie: Begleitband zur Sonderausstellung "Kaiser Friedrich II. (1194-1250). Welt und Kultur des Mittelmeerraums" im Landesmuseum für Natur und Mensch Oldenburg. 2008. (GER., Illus.). 160p. (C). 38.00 *(978-3-8053-3868-4(6))* Zabern, Philipp von Verlag, GmbH DEU. Dist: Brown, David Bk. Co., The.
Farnsworth, Donald, photos by. The Magnolia Tapestry Project. 2007. (Illus.). 129p. 58.00 *(978-0-9799164-2-7(9))* Magnolia Editions.
Farocki, Harun. Harun Farocki: Nebeneinander. 2008. (ENG., Illus.). 130p. pap. 48.00 *(978-3-86560-286-2(X))* Verlag der Buchhandlung Walther Konig DEU. Dist: D.A.P./Distributed Art Pubs.
Fattori, Giovanni. I Luoghi Di Giovanni Fattori Nell'Accademia Di Belle Arti Di Firenze: Passato e Presente. 2008. (ITA., Illus.). 383p. (C). 56.00 *(978-88-564-0035-9(9))* Edizioni Polistampa ITA. Dist: Brown, David Bk. Co., The.
Feher, Tony. Tony Feher. 2012. (ENG., Illus.). 264p. 60.00 ***(978-0-9826813-3-6(X))*** Miller, Gregory & Co.
Feininger, Lyonel & Büche, Wolfgang. Lyonel Feininger: Zurück in Amerika, 1937-1956. 2009. (Illus.). 229p. pap. *(978-3-7774-9085-4(7))* Hirmer Verlag GmbH.
Feng, Shaoxie & Zhu, Xiaodan. Bai Nian Guangzhou: Feng Shaoxie You Hua Ji = Guangzhou Impression: Canton's Splendor over 200 Years: Feng Shaoxie Oil Paintings. 2010. (CHI & ENG., Illus.). 90p. *(978-0-9844493-3-0(7))* International Publishing Hse. for China's Culture.
Fer, Briony, et al. Transmission: The Art of Matta & Gordon Matta-Clark, 1 vol. 2007. (ENG., Illus.). 144p. pap. 34.95 *(978-0-937108-37-6(5))* San Diego Museum of Art.
Ferguson, Russell, et al. Larry Johnson. 2009. *(978-0-943739-38-0(1))* Yale Univ. Pr.
Ferretti Bocquillon, Marina, ed. Maximilien Luce: Neo-Impressionist. 2011. (ENG., Illus.). 144p. 39.50 *(978-88-366-1777-7(8))* Silvana ITA. Dist: D.A.P./Distributed Art Pubs.
Fields, Virginia, et al. Children of the Plumed Serpent: The Legacy of Quetzalcoatl in Ancient Mexico. 2012. (ENG., Illus.). 256p. 65.00 ***(978-1-85759-741-7(9))*** Scala, Editions FRA. Dist: National Bk. Network.
Figura, Starr, text. Editions 07. 2007. (Illus.). *(978-0-9667505-7-7(8))* Lower East Side Printshop, Inc.
Fink, Lois Marie & Staiti, Paul, contrib. by. American Artists & the Louvre. 2007. (Illus.). 147p. pap. 49.95 *(978-2-7541-0097-7(0))* Hazan, Fernand, Editeur FRA. Dist: Gingko Pr., Inc.
Finkel, Rose Brein. The Craft & Art Show Calendar. 2007. 64p. pap. 6.00 *(978-0-9788978-1-9(1))* Finkel, Rose Brein.
Finn, David. Leonda Finke. 2006. (ENG., Illus.). 200p. 65.00 *(978-1-932646-21-4(3))* Ruder-Finn Pr.
Finzi, Silvia, et al, eds. Architectures et architectes italiens au Maghreb: Actes du colloque international tenu aux Archives Nationales de Tunisie (Tunis, 10-12 Decembre 2009) 2011. (ITA & FRE., Illus.). 256p. (C). pap. 35.00 ***(978-88-596-0726-7(4))*** Polistampa ITA. Dist: Brown, David Bk. Co., The.
Fischer, Felice. The Art of Japanese Craft: 1875 to the Present. 2008. (ENG., Illus.). 60p. (C). pap. 19.95 *(978-0-300-14212-9(9))* Yale Univ. Pr.
Fischer, Ole W. Sehnsucht - The Book of Architectural Longings: German Contribution to the 12th international Architecture Exhibition / Deutscher Beitrag auf der 12. internationalen Architekturausstellung - La Biennale die Venezia 2010. 2010. 256p. 69.95 *(978-3-7091-0326-5(6))* Springer Wien AUT. Dist: Actar Birkhauser Distribution.
—What Architects Desire. 2010. 400p. pap. 39.95 *(978-3-7091-0328-9(2))* Springer Wien AUT. Dist: Springer.
Fisher, Susan Greenberg. Picasso & the Allure of Language. 2009. (Yale University Art Gallery Ser.). (Illus.). 272p. pap. 40.00 *(978-0-300-13546-6(7))* Yale Univ. Pr.
FitzGerald, Michael A., et al. Picasso: Im Atelier des Künstlers. 2010. (GER., Illus.). 247p. (C). pap. 49.00 *(978-3-7774-3281-6(4))* Hirmer Verlag GmbH DEU. Dist: Brown, David Bk. Co., The.
Flavin, Dan. Series & Progressions, 1 vol. 2010. (ENG., Illus.). 165p. 68.00 *(978-3-86930-146-4(5))* Steidl, Gerhard Druckerei und Verlag DEU. Dist: Innovative Logistics.
Fleck, Robert, text. Oda Jaune: First Water. 2011. (ENG., Illus.). 240p. 85.00 *(978-3-7757-2677-1(2))* Hatje Cantz Verlag GmbH & Co KG DEU. Dist: D.A.P./Distributed Art Pubs.
Fleischeslust -oder die Lust an der Darstellung des Fleischlichen. 2010. (Illus.). 84p. pap. 49.00 ***(978-3-85881-208-7(0))*** Scheidegger und Spiess AG, Verlag CHE. Dist: Antique Collectors' Club.
Fleming, Peggy & Fleming, Jennifer. Crown Me! Capital Pool Checkers Club. 2010. (Illus.). 111p. *(978-0-9676322-2-3(6))* Three Sisters Pr.
Folie, Sabine, ed. & text. Modernism As a Ruin: An Archaeology of the Present. 2010. (GER & ENG., Illus.). 236p. 60.00 *(978-3-941185-82-1(9))* Verlag fur Moderne Kunst DEU. Dist: D.A.P./Distributed Art Pubs.
Fomsgaard, Jes & D.C.A. Gallery, contrib. by. Jes Fomsgaard: DCA Gallery. (Illus.). *(978-87-88223-60-6(4))* Galerie Asbaek.
Forrester, Gillian, ed. Rebecca Salter: Into the Light of Things. 2011. (ENG., Illus.). 282p. 60.00 *(978-0-300-17042-9(4))* Yale Univ. Pr.
Foster, Kathleen A. Thomas Chambers: American Marine & Landscape Painter, 1808-1869. 2008. (Illus.). xi, 171p. *(978-0-87633-205-4(X))*; *(978-0-87633-204-7(1))* Philadelphia Museum of Art.
—Thomas Chambers: American Marine & Landscape Painter, 1808-1869. 2008. (ENG., Illus.). 184p. 50.00 *(978-0-300-14105-4(X))* Yale Univ. Pr.
Fox Weber, Nicholas & Danilowitz, Brenda, eds. Josef Albers: Homage to the Square. 2009. (ENG., Illus.). 52p. 50.00 *(978-84-92480-38-8(6))* RM Verlag, S.L. ESP. Dist: D.A.P./Distributed Art Pubs.
Franciolli, Marco, et al, eds. Gutai. 2011. (ENG & ITA., Illus.). 264p. pap. 49.95 *(978-88-366-1815-6(4))* Silvana ITA. Dist: D.A.P./Distributed Art Pubs.
Francis, Doris, ed. Faith & Transformation: Votive Offerings & Amulets from the Alexander Girard Collection. 2007. (ENG., Illus.). 160p. pap. 29.95 *(978-0-89013-504-4(5))* Museum of New Mexico Pr.
Frank, Peter, et al. Transcendental Realism: The Art of Adi Da Samraj. 2007. (Illus.). 49p. *(978-1-57097-228-7(1))* Dawn Horse Pr.
Franke, Anselm & Demeester, Ann, eds. Valerie Mannaerts: an Exhibition, Another Exhibition. 2011. (ENG., Illus.). 144p. 34.00 ***(978-1-934105-36-8(8))*** Sternberg Pr.
Franke, Anselm & Folie, Sabine, eds. Animism: Modernity through the Looking Glass. 2012. (ENG & GER., Illus.). 228p. pap. 59.95 ***(978-3-86335-070-3(7))*** Verlag der Buchhandlung Walther Konig DEU. Dist: D.A.P./Distributed Art Pubs.
Franklin, David & Schütze, Sebastian. Caravaggio & His Followers in Rome. 2011. (Illus.). x, 333p. ***(978-0-88884-891-8(9))*** Yale Univ. Pr.
—Caravaggio & les Peintres Caravagesques à Rome. 2011. (FRE., Illus.). x, 333p. ***(978-0-88884-892-5(7))*** Yale Univ. Pr.
Franklin, John Hope & Wardlaw, Alivia J. Collecting African American Art: The Museum of Fine Arts, Houston. 2009. (ENG., Illus.). 152p. pap. 35.00 *(978-0-300-15291-3(4))* Museum of Fine Arts, Houston.
Franks, Pamela & Steele, Robert E. Embodied: Black Identities in American Art from the Yale University Art Gallery. 2010. *(978-0-89467-977-3(5))* Yale Univ. Art Gallery.
Franzke, Andreas. Stephan Balkenhol. public: Die Skulpturen im öffentlichen Raum 1984-2008. 2009. (GER & ENG., Illus.). 144p. 60.00 *(978-3-7757-2293-3(9))* Hatje Cantz Verlag GmbH & Co KG DEU. Dist: D.A.P./Distributed Art Pubs.
Frazetta, Frank. Frazetta: Illustrations Arcanum. Jones, Valarie, ed. (Illus.). 72p. (Orig.). 75.00 *(978-1-885730-01-5(2))*; pap. 29.95 *(978-1-885730-00-8(4))* Verotik.
Fred Jones Jr. Museum of Art Staff, et al, contrib. by. The Eugene B. Adkins Collection: Selected Works. 2011. (ENG., Illus.). 304p. 60.00 *(978-0-8061-4100-8(X))*; pap. 29.95 *(978-0-8061-4101-5(8))* Univ. of Oklahoma Pr.
Frehner, Matthias, et al, texts. Edward Burne-Jones: the Earthly Paradise. 2010. (ENG., Illus.). 232p. 60.00 *(978-3-7757-2517-0(2))* Hatje Cantz Verlag GmbH & Co KG DEU. Dist: D.A.P./Distributed Art Pubs.
Frehner, Matthias, et al. Form, Color, Illumination: Suzan Frecon Painting. 2008. (ENG., Illus.). 112p. 35.00 *(978-0-300-12552-8(6))* Yale Univ. Pr.
French, Anne & Waterfield, Giles. Below Stairs: 400 Years of Servants' Portraits. 2006. (Illus.). 45.00 *(978-1-85514-509-2(X))* National Portrait Gallery Pubns. GBR. Dist: Antique Collectors' Club.
Freshman, Phil. Time & Tide: The Changing Art of the Asmat of New Guinea. 14th ed. 2009. (Illus.). 128p. *(978-0-9800484-2-1(7))* Minneapolis Institute of Arts.
Fuchs, Rudi, contrib. by. With a Probability of Being Seen. Dorothee & Konrad Fischer: Archives of an Attitude. 2011. 384p. 65.00 *(978-84-92505-44-9(3))* Museu d'Art Contemporani de Barcelona ESP. Dist: Actar Birkhauser Distribution.
Fusco, Coco, et al, texts. Making Art Global, Part 1: The Third Havana Biennial 1989, Exhibition Histories Vol. 2. 2012. (ENG., Illus.). 250p. pap. 27.50 ***(978-3-86560-993-9(7))*** Afterall Publishing GBR. Dist: D.A.P./Distributed Art Pubs.
Fusening, T. & Taatgen, Alice. Hans von Aachen, 1552-1615. 2010. (ENG.). 300p. 48.00 *(978-3-422-06972-5(0))* Deutscher Kunstverlag GmbH DEU. Dist: Independent Pubs. Group.
Galassi, Susan Grace & McCully, Marilyn. Picasso's Drawings, 1890-1921: Reinventing Tradition. 2011. (ENG., Illus.). 224p. 60.00 *(978-0-300-17073-3(4))* Yale Univ. Pr.
Gale, Matthew & Daniel, Marko. Miró: The Ladder of Escape. 2011. (Illus.). 240p. ***(978-1-85437-944-3(5))*** D.A.P./Distributed Art Pubs.
Gallegos, Randy R. The Art of Gallegos: Dreaming in Black & White. 2007. (Illus.). 64p. per. 19.95 *(978-0-9797025-1-8(8))* Daydream Graphics.
Galleria degli Uffizi Staff, contrib. by. Medusa: Il Mito, L'antico e I Medici. 2008. (I mai Visti Ser.). (ITA., Illus.). 139p. (C). 29.50 *(978-88-596-0513-3(X))* Edizioni Polistampa ITA. Dist: Brown, David Bk. Co., The.
Gallery at Barnsdall Art Park Directors Staff, et al. Lax '92. (Illus.). 126p. (Orig.). pap. 25.00 *(978-1-882299-01-0(9))* Municipal Art Gallery.
Gandini, Manuela. Gigi Rigamonti: Cross Stories. Gandini, Manuela, ed. 2009. (ENG., Illus.). 96p. pap. 29.95 *(978-88-8158-736-0(X))* Charta ITA. Dist: D.A.P./Distributed Art Pubs.
Garcia, Carmela. Carmela Garcia: Constelacion. 2008. (ENG., Illus.). 110p. 45.00 *(978-84-7506-820-6(0))* Turner, Ediciones S.A. ESP. Dist: D.A.P./Distributed Art Pubs.
Garvey, Susan G. & Beaverbrook Art Gallery Staff. Theatrum Mundi: The Marion McCain Atlantic Art Exhibition 1997. 93p. pap. 7.95 *(978-0-920674-42-0(9))* Beaverbrook Art Gallery CAN. Dist: Goose Lane Editions.
Gastaldon, Vidya. Vidya Gastaldon: Call It What You Like. 2009. (ENG., Illus.). 160p. pap. 45.00 *(978-3-905829-84-6(3))* JRP Ringier Kunstverlag AG CHE. Dist: D.A.P./Distributed Art Pubs.
Gaudaire-Thor, Jean. Trafiquer dans L'inconnu... Arthur Rimbaud. 2008. (ENG.). 224p. pap. 60.00 *(978-2-35340-023-2(X))* Gourcuff Gradenigo FRA. Dist: National Bk. Network.
Gauss, Ulrike, ed. Marc Chagall: The Lithographs. (Illus.). 416p. *(978-3-7757-0799-2(9))* Hatje Cantz Verlag GmbH & Co KG DEU. Dist: D.A.P./Distributed Art Pubs.
Gayford, Martin & Lyles, Anne. Constable Portraits: The Painter & His Circle. 2010. (Illus.). 160p. 35.00 *(978-1-85514-398-2(4))* National Portrait Gallery Pubns. GBR. Dist: National Bk. Network.
Geeraerts, Ann & Vanackere, Luc. Sleeping Beauties. 2012. (ENG., Illus.). 128p. 35.50 ***(978-90-5856-385-9(5))*** Stichting Kunstboek Bvba BEL. Dist: National Bk. Network.
Geest, Joost de & Vekemans, Bruno. Bruno Vekemans: Kinshasa Congo. 2009. (FRE, DUT, GER & ENG., Illus.). 112p. 45.00 *(978-90-77207-19-2(8)*, Art Stock Bks. Ltd/Csi) Continental Sales, Inc.
Gelitin. Gelitin: Chinese Synthese Leberkase, 1 vol. 2006. (ENG., Illus.). 64p. 35.00 *(978-3-86560-081-3(6))* Kunsthaus Bregenz AUT. Dist: D.A.P./Distributed Art Pubs.
Georganteli, Eurydice, et al. Sacred & Profane. 2010. (ENG., Illus.). 128p. 40.00 *(978-1-904832-80-5(6))* Giles, D. Ltd. GBR. Dist: Antique Collectors' Club.
George, Hardy S., et al. Paris 1900. George, Hardy S. & Pavelka, Jeffrey J., eds. 2008. (Illus.). 174p. per. 35.00 *(978-0-911919-08-0(2))* Oklahoma City Museum of Art.
Gerald, Matt, pref. Chen Zhen: The Body as Landscape, 1 vol. 2007. (MUL & ENG., Illus.). 96p. per. 40.00 *(978-3-939738-30-5(1))* Verlag fur Moderne Kunst DEU. Dist: D.A.P./Distributed Art Pubs.
Gerrard, John, photos by. John Gerrard. 2011. (ENG., Illus.). 176p. 55.00 ***(978-84-938340-3-6(3))*** Ivory Pr. ESP. Dist: D.A.P./Distributed Art Pubs.
Ghiberti, Lorenzo, et al. The Gates of Paradise: Lorenzo Ghiberti's Renaissance Masterpiece. 2007. (Illus.). 182p. pap. *(978-1-932543-16-2(3))* High Museum of Art.
Gierstberg, Frits, et al. Eugène Atget: Paris 1898-1924. 2011. (ENG., Illus.). 320p. 71.00 ***(978-84-15253-03-7(6))*** T.F. Editores ESP. Dist: National Bk. Network.
Giger, H. R. & Stutzer, Beat. HR Giger- das Schaffen vor Alien, 1961-1976. 2010. (GER., Illus.). 168p. 95.00 ***(978-3-85881-195-0(5))*** Scheidegger und Spiess AG, Verlag CHE. Dist: Antique Collectors' Club.
Gilbert, et al, contrib. by. Gilbert & George: 4 Octobre 1997-4 Janvier 1998, Musee d'Art Moderne de la Ville de Paris. (Illus.). 432p. *(978-2-87900-360-3(1))* Paris-Musées, Association.
Gillick, Liam, et al. Meaning Liam Gillick. Szewczyk, Monika, ed. & intro. by. 2009. (ENG., Illus.). 218p. (gr. 17). pap. 24.95 *(978-0-262-51351-7(X))* MIT Pr.
Gioni, Massilmiliano, text. After Nature. 2008. (ENG., Illus.). 122p. pap. 24.95 *(978-0-915557-92-9(4))* New Museum of Contemporary Art, The.
Girait-Miracle, Daniel & Altaio, Vicenc. Visualkultur. Cat: Art/Design/Books. 2007. (Illus.). 339p. per. *(978-84-96540-93-4(6))* Actar Birkhauser Distribution.
Giroire, Cécile & Roger, Daniel. Roman Art from the Louvre. 2009. (ENG., Illus.). 280p. pap. 45.00 *(978-1-885444-35-6(4))* Hudson Hills Pr. LLC.
Gittings, Claire & Gittings, Clare. The Tudors. 2006. (ENG., Illus.). 9.95 *(978-1-85759-430-0(4))* Scala, Editions FRA. Dist: National Bk. Network.
Glancy, Michael. Michael Glancy: Infinite Obsessions. 2011. (Illus.). 228p. ***(978-0-9826397-2-6(4))*** Arnoldsche Art Pubs.
Gleissner, Stephen. Sue Jean Covacovich: Pioneer Kansas Abstract Artist. 2006. (Illus.). 36p. 15.00 *(978-0-939324-52-1(0))* Wichita Art Museum.
Goetz, Ingvild, ed. Fast Forward 2: The Power of MotionMedia Art Sammlung Goetz. 2010. (ENG & GER., Illus.). 320p. 75.00 *(978-3-7757-2604-7(7))* Hatje Cantz Verlag GmbH & Co KG DEU. Dist: D.A.P./Distributed Art Pubs.
Goetz, Ingvild & Löckemann, Karsten, eds. Mens Agitat Molem. 2010. (ENG., Illus.). 152p. 45.00 *(978-3-939894-12-4(5))* Goetz, Ingvild, Kunstverlag, GmbH DEU. Dist: D.A.P./Distributed Art Pubs.
Goetz, Ingvild & Urbaschek, Stephan, eds. Schichtwechsel: Von der Kohlekrise zum Strukturwandel. 2012. (ENG., Illus.). 160p. pap. 30.00 ***(978-3-7757-2973-4(9))*** Hatje Cantz Verlag GmbH & Co KG DEU. Dist: D.A.P./Distributed Art Pubs.
Gogh, Vincent van, et al. Van Gogh & the Colors of the Night. 2008. (Illus.). 160p. pap. *(978-0-87070-737-7(X))* Museum of Modern Art.
Goldman, Stephen & Swindler, Rebecca, eds. Barsamian: 20 Years-Searching for the Answer. 2011. 20p. *(978-0-9845213-1-9(3))* Holocaust Memorial Ctr.
Gorbaty, Norman. Norman Gorbaty: Works of a Modern Master. 2009. *(978-0-9764756-7-5(7))* QCC Art Gallery.
Gordon, Kim. Kim Gordon: Chronicles, 1 vol., Vol. 2. 2006. (ENG., Illus.). 32p. per. 20.00 *(978-3-905714-13-5(2))* Nieves CHE. Dist: D.A.P./Distributed Art Pubs.
Gorschlüter, Peter. Afro Modern: Journeys Through the Black Atlantic. Barson, Tanya, ed. 2010. (ENG., Illus.). 208p. 32.50 *(978-1-85437-923-8(2))* Tate Publishing, Ltd. GBR. Dist: Hachette Bk. Group.
Goswamy, B. N. & Smith, Caron. I see no Stranger: Early Sikh Art & Devotion. 2006. (ENG., Illus.). 216p. 65.00 *(978-1-890206-04-8(0))* Mapin Publishing Pvt. Ltd IND. Dist: National Bk. Network.
Grabowska-Konwent, Anna. Zoografika: Gnieznienskie Spotkania Z Plakatem: Spotkanie 8: Plakat, Grafika, Druki Ze Zbiorów Muzeum Narodowego W Poznaniu. 2009. (POL., Illus.). 189p. *(978-83-61391-16-6(9))* Muzeum Poczatkow Panstwa Polskiego w Gnieznie.
Grafton, Carol Belanger, ed. Victorian Design from the Crystal Palace Exhibition. 2010. (Dover Pictorial Archive Ser.). (ENG., Illus.). 128p. pap. 19.95 *(978-0-486-47219-5(1))* Dover Pubns., Inc.
Grammel, Soren & Kunstverein, Grazer, eds. Der Symolische Auftraggeber/the Symbolic Commissioner. 2011. (ENG & GER., Illus.). 224p. 34.00 ***(978-1-934105-35-1(X))*** Sternberg Pr.
Granet, François-Marius, et al. Granet: Roma e Parigi, la Natura Romantica. Cavina, Anna Ottani, ed. 2009. (ITA., Illus.). 128p. 57.50 *(978-88-370-6900-1(6))* Electa ITA. Dist: Trans-Atlantic Pubns., Inc.
Granoff, Phyllis. Victorious Ones: Jain Images of Perfection. 2010. (Illus.). 308p. pap. 75.00 *(978-0-944142-83-7(4))* Grantha Corp.
—Victorious Ones: Jain Images of Perfection. 2010. (ENG.). 304p. 75.00 *(978-0-944142-82-0(6))* Mapin Publishing Pvt. Ltd IND. Dist: National Bk. Network.
Granoff, Phyllis, ed. Victorious Ones: Jain Images of Perfection. 2009. (Illus.). 308p. *(978-81-89995-29-4(4))* Serindia Pubns., Inc.
Granser, Peter. Sun City. 2006. (ENG & GER., Illus.). 128p. *(978-3-7165-1303-3(2)*, Benteli Verlags Ag Dist) Antique Collectors' Club.
Grayson, Kathy, ed. Panic Room: Selections from the Dakis Joannou Works on Paper Collection, 1 vol. 2007. (ENG., Illus.). 160p. pap. 30.00 *(978-0-9778686-3-6(X))* Deitch, Jeffrey Inc.
Green, Christopher & Picasso, Pablo. Life & Death in Picasso: Still Life/Figure, C. 1907-1933. 2009. (ENG., Illus.). 192p. 50.00 *(978-0-500-09348-1(2)*, 509348) Thames & Hudson.
Green, Christopher, et al. Modern Antiquity: Picasso, de Chirico, Léger, Picabia. 2011. (ENG., Illus.). 176p. 39.95 *(978-0-89236-977-5(9)*, J. Paul Getty Museum) Getty Pubns.
Green, Nancy E. Joie de Vivre: Art Nouveau & Art Deco Ceramics from the Shatzman Collection. 2009. (Illus.). 71p. *(978-1-934260-10-4(X))* Cornell Univ., Herbert F. Johnson Museum of Art.
Greenaway, Peter. L'ultima cena di Leonardo-Leonardo's Last Supper. 2008. (ITA & ENG., Illus.). 160p. 75.00 *(978-88-8158-691-2(6))* Charta ITA. Dist: D.A.P./Distributed Art Pubs.
Gregory, Jarrett & Valdez, Sarah, eds. Ostalgia. 2011. (ENG., Illus.). 120p. pap. 35.00 ***(978-0-915557-96-7(7))*** New Museum of Contemporary Art, The.
Greub, Suzanne, ed. Gauguin Polynesia. 2012. (Illus.). 400p. 59.95 ***(978-3-7774-4261-7(5))*** Hirmer Verlag GmbH DEU. Dist: Chicago Distribution Ctr.
Gribling, Frank. Frank Gribling: At a Sligh. pap. 25.00 *(978-90-5006-057-8(9))* Stedelijk Museum NLD. Dist: D.A.P./Distributed Art Pubs.
Groihofer, Brigitte, ed. Raimund Abraham, [Un]Built. 2nd ed. 2011. (Illus.). 348p. 99.00 *(978-3-7091-0468-2(8)*, 3709104688) Springer Wien AUT. Dist: Springer.
Gronlund, Melissa, ed. Frieze Projects: Artists' Commissions & Talks 2003-2005, 1 vol. 2007. (ENG., Illus.). 320p. pap. 26.00 *(978-0-9553201-0-1(0))* Frieze GBR. Dist: D.A.P./Distributed Art Pubs.
Groos, Ulrike. Palermo. 2007. (Illus.). 280p. pap. 60.00 *(978-3-8321-9015-6(5))* Merrell Pubs. Ltd. GBR. Dist: Perseus Distribution.
Grotowski, Piotr, ed. Arms & Armour of the Warrior Saints: Tradition & Innovation in Byzantine Iconography (843-1261) Brzezinski, Richard, tr. 2010. (Medieval Mediterranean Ser.). (Illus.). 704p. *(978-90-04-18548-7(8))* BRILL.
Guardiola, Juan, ed. India: Auteur Films, Independent Documentaries & Video Art (1890-2008) 2009. (Illus.). 213p. pap. *(978-84-96917-46-0(0))* Caja de Madrid.
Guegan, Stephane & Thomine-Berrada, Alice, eds. Birth of Impressionism: Masterpieces from the Musee D'Orsay. 2010. (Illus.). 256p. 50.00 *(978-3-7913-5045-5(5))* Prestel Publishing.
Guerrero, Raul. Raul Guerrero: The Whaling Bar: la Jolla. 2007. (Illus.). 10.00 *(978-0-9744804-7-3(9)*, Athenaeum Music & Arts Library) Library Assn. of La Jolla.
Guggisberg, Monica & Baldwin, Philip. Circus of Spheres. 2008. (ENG & FRE., Illus.). 88p. 30.00 *(978-88-7439-177-6(3))* 5 Continents ITA. Dist: Hachette Bk. Group.
Gunn, Michael & Peltier, Philippe, eds. New Ireland: Art of the South Pacific. 2008. (ENG., Illus.). 304p. pap. 60.00 *(978-88-7439-369-5(5))* 5 Continents ITA. Dist: Hachette Bk. Group.
Gurney, George. Variations on America: Masterworks of the American Art Forum, Smithsonian American Art Museum. 2008. *(978-0-9790678-0-8(4))* Smithsonian American Art Museum.
Gurney, George, et al. Variations on America: Masterworks from American Art Forum Collections. 2006. (ENG., Illus.). 192p. 30.00 *(978-1-904832-42-3(3))* Giles, D. Ltd. GBR. Dist: Antique Collectors' Club.
Gust, Frauke, et al, texts. Concepts of Love. 2009. (ENG., Illus.). 144p. pap. 25.00 *(978-3-86560-427-9(7))* Verlag der Buchhandlung Walther Konig DEU. Dist: D.A.P./Distributed Art Pubs.
Gute, Charles & Prandoni, Alessandro, eds. Magic Line, 1 vol. De Martin, Maria Pia et al, trs. 2007. (ITA, GER & ENG., Illus.). 112p. pap. 39.95 *(978-88-8158-632-5(0))* Charta ITA. Dist: D.A.P./Distributed Art Pubs.
Gwilt, Joanna. French Porcelain for English Palaces: Sèvres from the Royal Collection. 2010. (Illus.). 200p. pap. 25.00 *(978-1-905686-14-8(5))* Royal Collection Enterprises Ltd. GBR. Dist: Chicago Distribution Ctr.

Gygax, Raphael & Munder, Heike, eds. Dawn Mellor. 2009. (ENG & GER., Illus.). 64p. 35.00 *(978-3-905829-98-3(3))* JRP Ringier Kunstverlag AG CHE. Dist: D.A.P./Distributed Art Pubs.

Haas, Philip & Warner, Malcolm. Butchers, Dragons, Gods & Skeletons: Film Installations by Philip Haas. 2009. (Illus.). ix, 94p. *(978-0-912804-50-7(5))* Kimbell Art Museum.

Haggerty, Michael, tr. Bertozzi & Casoni: Le Bugie Dell'arte. 2008. (ENG., Illus.). 112p. 40.00 *(978-88-6208-005-7(0))* Damiani ITA. Dist: D.A.P./Distributed Art Pubs.

Haifeng, Ni. Ni Haifeng: the Return of the Shreds. 2008. (ENG., Illus.). 80p. pap. 29.95 *(978-90-71655-22-7(9))* Valiz NLD. Dist: D.A.P./Distributed Art Pubs.

Haldemann, Anita. Les yeux enchantés: Zeichnungen und Druckgraphik des Surrealismus. 2008. (GER., Illus.). 150p. *(978-3-86678-144-3(X))* Kerber Verlag.

Hall, Grace Cynthia. The Wadsworth Trail. 2007. (YA) pap. 10.95 *(978-0-9792509-0-3(0))* Stevens County Historical Society & Museum.

Hanover, Princess Caroline of, frwd. Yinka Shonibare, MBE. 2011. (ENG & FRE., Illus.). 176p. pap. 34.95 *(978-88-7439-564-4(7))* 5 Continents ITA. Dist: Hachette Bk. Group.

Hanru, Hou. Global Multitude. Hanru, Hou, ed. 2008. 160p. pap. *(978-84-935844-4-3(4))* Actar Birkhauser Distribution.

Hanzal, Carla, et al. Romare Bearden: Southern Recollections. 2011. (ENG., Illus.). 144p. 44.95 *(978-1-904832-98-0(9))* Giles, D. Ltd. GBR. Dist: National Bk. Network.

Haraha, Sebastian & Welsch, Robert L. Coaxing the Spirits to Dance: Art & Society in the Papuan Gulf of New Guinea. 2006. (ENG., Illus.). 128p. pap. 40.00 *(978-0-944722-30-5(X))* Hood Museum of Art.

Harbuz, Ann, et al. Ann Harbuz: Sao Paulo & Seattle. 19.95 *(978-0-920085-55-4(5))* Dunlop Art Gallery CAN. Dist: Coteau Bks.

Harper, James G. Verso: The Flip Side of Master Drawings. 2006. (ENG., Illus.). 72p. pap. 15.00 *(978-1-891771-19-4(1))* Harvard Univ. Art Museums.

Harper, Paula, contrib. by. Elena Presser: Works on the Music of Johann Sebastian Bach. 16p. (Orig.). (C). *(978-0-9630869-2-1(8))* Univ. of Wyoming Art Museum.

Harris, Adam Duncan & Kuhn, Bob. Bob Kuhn: Drawing on Instinct. 2012. ***(978-0-8061-4300-2(2))***; pap. ***(978-0-8061-4301-9(0))*** Univ. of Oklahoma Pr.

Harris, Susan & Howard, Jan. Pat Steir: Drawing Out of Line. 2010. pap. 35.00 *(978-0-615-34382-2(1))* RISD Museum.

Hart, Mary Louise. The Art of Ancient Greek Theater. 2010. (Illus.). 176p. 50.00 *(978-1-60606-037-7(6)*, J. Paul Getty Museum) Getty Pubns.

Harthorn, Sandy. Devorah Sperber: Threads of Perception. 2010. (ENG., Illus.). 56p. pap. 22.50 *(978-0-295-98960-0(2))* Univ. of Washington Pr.

Hatje Cantz, compiled by. Art to Hear: Bauhaus. 2009. (ENG., Illus.). 48p. 30.00 *(978-3-7757-2451-7(6))* Hatje Cantz Verlag GmbH & Co KG DEU. Dist: D.A.P./Distributed Art Pubs.

Hayes, Paul Tucker. Claude Monet: Late Work. 2010. (ENG., Illus.). 216p. 100.00 *(978-0-8478-3603-1(7))* Rizzoli International Pubns , Inc.

Hazoume, Romuald. Romuald Hazoumé: My Paradise - Made in Porto-Novo. 2010. (ENG., Illus.). 144p. 40.00 *(978-3-7757-2645-0(4))* Hatje Cantz Verlag GmbH & Co KG DEU. Dist: D.A.P./Distributed Art Pubs.

Heartney, Eleanor. Kenneth Snelson: Forces Made Visible. 2009. (ENG., Illus.). 200p. 75.00 incl. cd-rom *(978-1-55595-243-3(7))* Hudson Hills Pr. LLC.

Heartney, Eleanor, et al. John Buck: Iconography. 2008. (Illus.). 144p. *(978-0-910524-37-7(8))* Eastern Washington State Historical Society.

Heffley, Scott. Bold Improvisation: Searching for African-American Quilts - the Heffley Collection. 2007. 124p. mass mkt. 29.95 *(978-1-933466-25-5(1))* Kansas City Star Bks.

Hegyi, Lorand. Passage to Europe: Realities, References, Reflections. 2008. (ENG., Illus.). 160p. pap. 29.95 ***(978-88-7439-168-4(4))*** 5 Continents ITA. Dist: Hachette Bk. Group.

Heiser, Jorg, et al. Romantischer Konzeptualismus/Romantic Conceptualism. 2008. (GER & ENG., Illus.). 216p. 39.50 *(978-3-86678-073-6(7))* Kerber Verlag DEU. Dist: D.A.P./Distributed Art Pubs.

Heiss, Alanna, et al, texts. Federico Diaz & E Area: Resonance, 1 vol. 2009. (ENG., Illus.). 500p. 95.00 *(978-88-8158-721-6(1))* Charta ITA. Dist: D.A.P./Distributed Art Pubs.

Helsinger, Elizabeth K. The Writing of Modern Life: The Etching Revival in France, Britain, & the U. S. , 1850-1940. 2009. (Illus.). 104p. pap. 20.00 *(978-0-935573-45-9(3))* Univ. of Chicago, David & Alfred Smart Museum.

Hempel, Lothar, illus. Alphabet City, 1 vol. 2007. (ENG.). 160p. pap. 45.00 *(978-3-905770-47-6(4))* JRP Ringier Kunstverlag AG CHE. Dist: D.A.P./Distributed Art Pubs.

Henderson, Sue, et al, texts. Space Antics Sue Henderson, David Marsden, Penny Mason. 2011. (Illus.). 4p. mass mkt. ***(978-0-9808003-5-7(8))*** Burnie Regional Art Gallery.

Henkel, David, et al. Land of the Morning: The Philippines & its People. 2011. 176p. pap. 30.00 ***(978-971-0579-07-5(X))*** Artpostasia Inc. PHL. Dist: National Bk. Network.

Heon, Laura, text. Barry X Ball, 1 vol. 2007. (ENG., Illus.). 80p. 20.00 *(978-0-9764492-4-9(2))* Site Santa Fe.

Herndon-Consagra, Francesca & Crenshaw, Paul. Rembrandt: Master Etchings from St. Louis Collections. Steiner, Mary A., ed. 2006. (Illus.). 172p. pap. 29.95 *(978-0-89178-089-2(0))* St. Louis Art Museum.

Herold, Georg. Georg Herold. Sunny Side Up. 2011. (ENG., Illus.). 68p. 35.00 ***(978-3-931355-69-2(1))*** Verlag der Buchhandlung Walther Konig DEU. Dist: D.A.P./Distributed Art Pubs.

Herrero, Marta. Irish Intellectuals & Aesthetics: The Making of a Modern Art Collection. 2007. (Illus.). 214p. pap. 30.00 *(978-0-7165-3328-3(6))* Irish Academic Pr. IRL. Dist: International Specialized Bk. Services.

Hertz, Betty-Sue. Transmission: The Art of Matta & Gordon Matta-Clark. 2006. (Illus.). 112p. pap. 27.50 *(978-0-937108-38-3(3))* San Diego Museum of Art.

Hess, Clarke. Lancaster county Privy Bags. 2009. pap. 12.95 *(978-1-61658-284-5(7))* Independent Pub.

Heuser, Mechthild. Tell im Visier: Plakate aus der Schweizerischen Nationalbibliothek. 2010. (GER., Illus.). 392p. pap. 81.00 ***(978-3-85881-202-5(1))*** Scheidegger und Spiess AG, Verlag CHE. Dist: Antique Collectors' Club.

Heyes-Moore, Balshaw. Mary Kelly: Projects, 1973-2010. Heyse-Moore, Dominique, ed. 2011. (ENG., Illus.). 140p. pap. 39.95 *(978-0-7190-8628-1(0))* Manchester Univ. Pr. GBR. Dist: Macmillan.

Heynen, Julian. Joe Scanlan. 2008. (ENG., Illus.). 112p. 38.00 *(978-3-86678-062-0(1))* Kerber Verlag DEU. Dist: D.A.P./Distributed Art Pubs.

Hickey, Dave, intro. Julian Stanczak. 2008. (Illus.). 48p. pap. *(978-0-9795501-3-3(0))* Danese.

Hiebert, Fredrik. Afghanistan: Hidden Treasures from the National Museum, Kabul. Cambon, Pierre, ed. 2008. (ENG., Illus.). 304p. pap. 30.00 *(978-1-4262-0295-7(4))* National Geographic Society.

Hiesinger, Kathryn B. & Hadid, Zaha. Zaha Hadid: Form in Motion. 2011. ***(978-0-87633-232-0(7))*** Philadelphia Museum of Art.

Higgs, Matthew, et al. McDermott & McGough: An Experience of Amusing Chemistry: Photographs, 1990-1890. 2008. (ENG., Illus.). 224p. 95.00 *(978-88-8158-672-1(X))* Charta ITA. Dist: D.A.P./Distributed Art Pubs.

High Museum of Art Staff. The Art of Golf. 2012. (ENG., Illus.). 96p. 29.95 ***(978-1-932543-44-5(9))*** High Museum of Art.

Hill, Gary, et al. Gary Hill: I Believe It Is an Image. (Illus.). 30.00 *(978-4-900398-18-4(7))* Watari-Um JPN. Dist: D.A.P./Distributed Art Pubs.

Hindman, Sandra. Toward an Art History of Medieval Rings: A Private Collection. 2007. (Illus.). 260p. pap. 40.00 *(978-1-903470-64-0(1))* Holberton, Paul Publishing GBR. Dist: Casemate Pubs. & Bk. Distributors, LLC.

Hinton, Jack. The Art of German Stoneware, 1300-1900, from the Charles W. Nichols Collection & the Philadelphia Museum of Art. 2012. ***(978-0-87633-236-8(X))*** Philadelphia Museum of Art.

Hirsch, Robert & Nickard, Gary, texts. World in a Jar: War & Trauma. 2008. (Illus.). 40p. *(978-0-939784-27-1(0))* CEPA Gallery.

Hirst, Damien. Poisons + Remedies. 2011. (ENG., Illus.). 88p. pap. 100.00 ***(978-1-935263-19-7(6))*** Abrams.

Hirst, Damien. Romance in the Age of Uncertainty. Beard, Jason, ed. 2008. (ENG., Illus.). 144p. pap. 90.00 *(978-0-9542363-7-3(8))* Other Criteria GBR. Dist: Hachette Bk. Group.

Hively, Charles, ed. 3x3 Illustration Annual No. 3. 2007. 8p. per. 24.95 *(978-0-9755158-3-9(7))* 3x3 Magazine.

Hobbs, Philippa. Through the Looking Glass: Representations of Self by South African Women Artists. (C). pap., tchr. ed., suppl. ed. *(978-0-9584688-6-2(9))* Krut, David Publishing.

Hofer, Andreas. The Long Tomorrow. 2009. (GER, SPA & ENG., Illus.). 72p. pap. 45.00 *(978-3-86560-511-5(7))* Verlag der Buchhandlung Walther Konig DEU. Dist: D.A.P./Distributed Art Pubs.

—Phantom Gallery, 1 vol. 2009. (ENG & GER., Illus.). 144p. 48.00 *(978-3-86521-733-7(9))* Steidl, Gerhard Druckerei und Verlag DEU. Dist: Innovative Logistics.

Hoffman, Sheila K. Crafted to Perfection: The Nancy & Alan Cameros Collection of Southwestern Pottery. Hoffman, Bryce T., ed. 2007. (Illus.). 188p. *(978-0-9769919-1-5(8))* Rockwell Museum of Western Art.

Hoffmann, Leni. leni hoffmann: RGB: Künstlerbuch. 2010. (GER & ENG., Illus.). 144p. pap. 59.95 *(978-3-8321-9290-7(5))* DuMont DEU. Dist: D.A.P./Distributed Art Pubs.

Hogan, Linda, text. Jaune Quick-to-See Smith: She Paints the Horse. 2008. (Illus.). 48p. pap. 15.00 *(978-0-9614971-5-6(7))* Nicolaysen Art Museum.

Holder, Will, ed. For the Blind Man in the Dark Room Looking for the Black Cat That Isn't There. 2009. (ENG., Illus.). 176p. pap. 40.00 *(978-0-9777528-6-7(0))* Contemporary Art Museum St. Louis.

Holding, Julie. Hau Pei Jen: Bold Horizons in Ink & Color. 2010. 96p. pap. 32.50 *(978-1-4490-9679-3(4))* AuthorHouse.

Holert, Tom. Marc Camille Chaimowicz - Celebration? Realife. 2007. (One Work Ser.). (ENG., Illus.). 112p. (gr. 17). 35.00 *(978-1-84638-030-3(8))*; pap. 16.00 *(978-1-84638-029-7(4))* Afterall Publishing GBR. Dist: MIT Pr.

Hollein, Max. Julian Schnabel. Moos, David & Schnabel, Julian, eds. 2009. (ENG., Illus.). 432p. 90.00 *(978-88-6130-317-1(X))* Skira Editore ITA. Dist: Random Hse., Inc.

Holler, Carsten. Carsten Holler. 2011. (ENG., Illus.). 288p. 75.00 *(978-3-7757-2395-4(1))* Hatje Cantz Verlag GmbH & Co KG DEU. Dist: D.A.P./Distributed Art Pubs.

Holmes, David J. Wayfarers All: Selections from the Kenneth Grahame Collection of David J. Holmes. 2008. (ENG., Illus.). 46p. pap. 15.00 *(978-1-60583-011-7(9))* Grolier Club of New York, The.

Holtzberg, Maggie. Keepers of Tradition: Art & Folk Heritage in Massachusetts. 2008. (Illus.). 199p. pap. 24.95 *(978-1-55849-640-8(8))* Univ. of Massachusetts Pr.

Homburg, Cornelia, ed. Vincent Van Gogh: Timeless Country - Modern City. 2011. (ENG., Illus.). 280p. 75.00 *(978-88-572-0825-1(7))* Skira Editore ITA. Dist: Random Hse., Inc.

Hooper, Steven. Pacific Encounters: Art & Divinity in Polynesia, 1760-1860. 2006. (Illus.). 288p. pap. 46.00 *(978-0-8248-3084-7(9))* Univ. of Hawaii Pr.

Hoptman, Laura, ed. Brion Gysin. 2010. (ENG., Illus.). 192p. 39.95 *(978-1-85894-521-7(6))* Merrell Pubs. Ltd. GBR. Dist: Perseus Distribution.

Horn, Gabriele. Sigalit Landau. 2008. (GER & ENG., Illus.). 290p. 45.00 *(978-3-7757-2104-2(5))* Hatje Cantz Verlag GmbH & Co KG DEU. Dist: D.A.P./Distributed Art Pubs.

Horn, Roni. Roni Horn aka Roni Horn, 1 vol. 2009. (ENG., Illus.). 432p. 70.00 *(978-3-86521-831-5(8))* Steidl, Gerhard Druckerei und Verlag DEU. Dist: Innovative Logistics.

Horowitz, Deborah E., et al. Ethiopian Art. 2006. (ENG., Illus.). 30.00 *(978-1-903942-02-4(0))* Third Millenium Publishing GBR. Dist: National Bk. Network.

Horvath, Andreas. Yakutia: Siberia of Siberiea. 2006. (ENG & GER.). 160p. 65.00 *(978-3-7165-1295-1(8)*, Benteli Verlags Ag Dist) Antique Collectors' Club GBR. Dist: National Bk. Network.

House, John & Hopkins, David. Impressionists by the Sea. 2007. (ENG., Illus.). 156p. 55.00 *(978-1-903973-88-2(0))* Royal Academy of Arts GBR. Dist: Hachette Bk. Group.

Houston, David. The making of an Exhibition. 2008. pap. *(978-0-9772544-4-6(5))* Ogden Museum of Southern Art, The.

Howard, Judy. Centennial Stitches: Oklahoma History in Quilts. 2007. (Illus.). 120p. 39.95 *(978-0-9762375-1-8(2))* Dorcas Publishing.

Huber, Patrick. Sarah Morris: 1972. 2008. (ENG., Illus.). 64p. 35.00 *(978-3-905829-47-1(9))* JRP Ringier Kunstverlag AG CHE. Dist: D.A.P./Distributed Art Pubs.

Hudson, Suzanne, text. Katja Strunz, 1 vol. 2007. (ENG., Illus.). 140p. 44.00 *(978-3-86560-161-2(3))* Verlag der Buchhandlung Walther Konig DEU. Dist: D.A.P./Distributed Art Pubs.

Hug, Alfons, et al. The Tropics: Views from the Middle of the Globe. 2009. (ENG., Illus.). 344p. 69.00 *(978-3-86678-166-5(0))* Kerber Verlag DEU. Dist: D.A.P./Distributed Art Pubs.

Hung, Wu. Displacement: The Three Gorges Dam & Contemporary Chinese Art. 2008. (Illus.). 160p. pap. 30.00 *(978-0-935573-46-6(1))* Univ. of Chicago, David & Alfred Smart Museum.

Hunt, David, et al, texts. Terminal stage. 2008. (ENG., Illus.). 72p. 49.95 *(978-88-8158-683-7(5))* Charta ITA. Dist: D.A.P./Distributed Art Pubs.

Hunt, Ian, et al. The Self as a Stranger: Simon Lewty. 2010. (ENG., Illus.). 192p. 49.95 *(978-1-907317-07-1(4))* Black Dog Publishing Ltd. GBR. Dist: Perseus Distribution.

Husslein-Arco, Agnes. Prince Eugene: Commander Philosopher. 2010. (ENG.). 360p. 75.00 *(978-3-7774-2551-1(6)*, Art Stock Bks. Ltd/Csi) Continental Sales, Inc.

Imperato, Gavin H. & Imperato, Pascal James. Bundu, Sowei Headpieces of the Sande Society of West Africa: The Imperato Family Collection. 2012. ***(978-1-936658-10-7(0))*** Kilima Hse. Pubs.

In the USSR & Beyond. pap. 45.00 *(978-90-5006-049-3(8))* Stedelijk Museum NLD. Dist: D.A.P./Distributed Art Pubs.

Infinite Distance - Architectural Compositions by Helen Lundeberg. 2007. 40.00 *(978-0-9749421-6-2(2))* Stern, Louis Fine Arts, Inc.

Inselmann, Andrea. Stop. look. listen: An exhibition of video Works. 2008. (Illus.). 184p. *(978-1-934260-03-6(7))* Cornell Univ., Herbert F. Johnson Museum of Art.

Inspired Design: The Mentoring Stamp. 2008. (Illus.). 48p. pap. 35.00 *(978-0-87391-059-0(1))* Smith College Pubns.

International Fine Art Expositions Staff. Art Miami 95. (Illus.). 348p. *(978-1-886639-01-0(9))* International Fine Art Expositions.

Iosifescu, Grigore. The Black Cat & Those Eleven Days in the Mahoning County Jail. 2011. 126p. pap. 19.99 ***(978-1-4535-5816-4(0))*** Xlibris Corp.

Iozzo, Mario, ed. The Chimaera of Arezzo. 2009. (Illus.). 52p. (C). (ITA.). pap. 15.00 *(978-88-596-0627-7(6))*; (ENG., pap. 15.00 *(978-88-596-0628-4(4))* Polistampa ITA. Dist: Brown, David Bk. Co., The.

Isser, Johanna von, et al. Die Burgenzeichnerin Johanna Von Isser-Grossrubatscher (1802-1880) 2010. (GER., Illus.). 391p. *(978-88-8266-713-9(8))* Athesia.

Jacir, Emily & Wäspe, Roland. Emily Jacir. 2008. (GER & ENG., Illus.). 96p. 65.00 *(978-3-939738-57-2(3))* Verlag fur Moderne Kunst DEU. Dist: D.A.P./Distributed Art Pubs.

Jackson, David Paul. The Nepalese Legacy in Tibetan Painting. 2010. (Masterworks of Tibetan Painting Ser.). (ENG., Illus.). 288p. 75.00 *(978-0-9772131-8-4(8))* Rubin Museum of Art.

—The Nepalese Stylistic Legacy in Tibetan Painting: From Early Beri to Ngor. 2010. pap. *(978-0-9772131-7-7(X))* Serindia Pubns., Inc.

Jacobson, Heidi Zuckerman & Deller, Jeremy. "Marlon Brando, Pocahontas, & Me" 2009. (ENG., Illus.). 72p. 35.00 *(978-0-934324-43-4(3))* Aspen Art Museum.

Jannin Kounellis: Via Del. 39.50 *(978-90-5006-050-9(1))* Stedelijk Museum NLD. Dist: D.A.P./Distributed Art Pubs.

Jespersen, T. Christine, et al. The Anatomy of Body Worlds: Critical Essays on the Plastinated Cadavers of Gunther Von Hagens. Jespersen, T. Christine et al, eds. 2008. (ENG., Illus.). 276p. pap. 45.00 *(978-0-7864-3656-9(5))* McFarland & Co., Inc. Pubs.

Jeu De Paume, Paris. Eija-Liisa Ahtila. 2008. (GER & ENG., Illus.). 192p. pap. 55.00 *(978-3-7757-2133-2(9))* Hatje Cantz Verlag GmbH & Co KG DEU. Dist: D.A.P./Distributed Art Pubs.

Jimenez, Ariel. A Constructive Vision. 2010. (ENG., Illus.). 344p. 65.00 *(978-0-9823544-0-7(1))* Fundacion Cisneros.

Johanson, George. Equivalents: Portraits of Oregon Artists. pap. *(978-1-883124-13-7(1))* Portland Art Museum.

John, Simpson. The Begram Hoard: Indian Ivories from Afghanistan. 2011. (ENG., Illus.). 96p. (C). pap. 15.95 *(978-0-7141-1178-0(3))* British Museum Pr. GBR. Dist: Brown, David Bk. Co., The.

Johnson, Tim & Wright, Will. Krazy! The Delirious World of Anime - Comics - Video Games - Art. Grenville, Bruce & Wilson, Charles Reagan, eds. 2008. (Illus.). 276p. pap. 36.95 *(978-0-520-25784-9(7))* Univ. of California Pr.

Johnson, Vivien. Clifford Possum Tjapaltjarri. 2007. (Illus.). 256p. 55.00 *(978-0-7308-3053-5(5))* Art Gallery of South Australia AUS. Dist: Antique Collectors' Club.

Jonas, Joan. Joan Jonas: Timelines: Transparencies in a Dark Room. 2007. (Illus.). 169p. pap. *(978-84-89771-44-4(8))* Museu d'Art Contemporari de Barcelona.

Jones, Kellie. Now Dig This! Art & Black Los Angeles, 1960-1980. 2011. (ENG., Illus.). 352p. 60.00 ***(978-3-7913-5136-0(2))*** Prestel Publishing.

Jones, Kimberly, et al. In the Forest of Fontainebleau: Painters & Photographers from Corot to Monet. 2008. (ENG., Illus.). 220p. 60.00 *(978-0-300-13897-9(0))* Yale Univ. Pr.

Jones, Laura K., ed. A Hedonist's Guide to Art. 2010. (Hedonist's Guide To... Ser.). (ENG., Illus.). 240p. 20.00 *(978-1-905428-50-2(2)*, HG2) Filmer Ltd. GBR. Dist: Perseus-PGW.

Jones, Lois Mailou & Hanzal, Carla M. Lois Mailou Jones: A Life in Vibrant Color. 2009. *(978-0-9762300-8-3(9))* Mint Museum, The.

Jones, William E. Tearoom. 2008. (Illus.). 43p. 14.00 *(978-0-9786830-8-5(0)*, 2nd Cannons Pubns.

Jonone & Rock, John One. Jonone Rock. 2009. (Illus.). 40p. 33.00 *(978-88-88493-51-0(4))* Drago Arts & Communication ITA. Dist: SCB Distributors.

Julien, Issac. Isaac Julien: True North-Fantome Afrique, 1 vol. 2006. (GER & ENG., Illus.). 100p. 50.00 *(978-3-7757-1867-7(2))* Hatje Cantz Verlag GmbH & Co KG DEU. Dist: D.A.P./Distributed Art Pubs.

Julin, Richard & Praun, Tessa, eds. Pipilotti Rist Congratulations! 2007. (Illus.). 159p. 34.95 *(978-3-03778-108-1(4)*, 3037781084) Springer.

Juncosa, Enrique & Pellizzi, Francesco, texts. Ray Smith: Works, 1 vol. 2006 (ENG., Illus.). 320p. 75.00 *(978-84-343-1092-6(9))* Polígrafa, Ediciones, S. A. ESP. Dist: D.A.P./Distributed Art Pubs.

Jung, Christine & Heuser, August. Thierry Boissel. 2012. (ENG, FRE & GER., Illus.). 160p. 70.00 ***(978-3-89790-369-2(5))*** Arnoldsche Art Pubs. DEU. Dist: National Bk. Network.

Kacharava, Darejan & Kvirkvelia, Guram. Wine, Worship, & Sacrifice. Chi, Jennifer Y., ed. 2008. (Illus.). 216p. (C). 40.00 *(978-0-691-13856-5(7))* Princeton Univ. Pr.

Kaellgren, Peter, text. Wedgwood: Artistry & Innovation. 2009. (ENG., Illus.). 128p. pap. 25.00 *(978-0-88854-466-7(9))* Royal Ontario Museum CAN. Dist: Univ. of Toronto Pr.

Kahn, Tobi, et al. Tobi Kahn: Sacred Spaces for the 21st Century. Heller, Ena Giurescu, ed. 2009. (ENG., Illus.). 112p. 39.95 *(978-1-904832-64-5(4))* Giles, D. Ltd. GBR. Dist: Antique Collectors' Club.

Kaiser, Philipp & Kwon, Miwon. Ends of the Earth: Art of the Land To 1974. 2012. (Illus.). 264p. 60.00 ***(978-3-7913-5194-0(X))*** Prestel Publishing.

Kamps, Toby, text. No Zoning: Artists Engage Houston. 2009. (ENG., Illus.). 136p. pap. 24.95 *(978-1-933619-19-4(8))* Contemporary Arts Museum, Houston.

Kandeler-Fritsch, Martina, et al, texts. Industrial Furniture: Prototypes of the Modern Era. 2012. (ENG & GER., Illus.). 128p. pap. 45.00 ***(978-3-86984-219-6(9))*** Verlag fur Moderne Kunst DEU. Dist: D.A.P./Distributed Art Pubs.

Karapetian, Vartan, et al. Armenia: Imprints of a Civilization. 2012. (ENG., Illus.). 408p. 75.00 ***(978-88-572-1244-9(0))*** Skira Editore ITA. Dist: Random Hse., Inc.

Karpova, E. V. & Petrova, Yevgenia. Portraiture in Russia XX Century: From the Collection of the State Russian Museum in St. Petersburg. Petrova, Yevgenia, ed. 2006. (ENG., Illus.). 408p. 85.00 *(978-3-935298-11-7(0)*, Palace Editions) Mandala Publishing.

Karmay, Samten G. & Watt, Jeff. Bon, the Magic Word: The Indiginous Religion of Tibet. 2007. (Illus.). 231p. pap. *(978-0-9772131-2-2(9))* Serindia Pubns., Inc.

Katlan, Alexander. The Black & White Exhibitions of the Salmagundi Sketch Club 1878 to 1887: A Guide to Etchings, Engravings, Drawings, Sculpture, Ceramics, Oils, & Monotypes. 2007. (Illus.). 273p. *(978-0-9791290-0-1(1))* Katlan, Alexander Conservator, Inc.

Katz, Alex. Alex Katz. 2008. (ENG., Illus.). 88p. 15.00 *(978-3-905770-79-7(2))* JRP Ringier Kunstverlag AG CHE. Dist: D.A.P./Distributed Art Pubs.

Katz, Janice. Beyond Golden Clouds: Japanese Screens from the Art Institute of Chicago & the Saint Louis Art Museum. 2009. (Illus.). 216p. pap. *(978-0-86559-232-2(2))* Art Institute of Chicago.

Katz, Janice, ed. Beyond Golden Clouds: Japanese Screens from the Art Institute of Chicago & the Saint Louis Art Museum. 2009. (ENG., Illus.). 216p. 55.00 *(978-0-300-11948-0(8))* Art Institute of Chicago.

Katz, Jonathan D. & Ward, David C. Hide/Seek: Difference & Desire in American Portraiture. 2010. (ENG., Illus.). 296p. 45.00 *(978-1-58834-299-7(9))* Smithsonian Institution Pr.

Katzew, Ilona, ed. Contested Visions in the Spanish Colonial World. 2011. (ENG., Illus.). 320p. 70.00 *(978-0-300-17664-3(3))* Yale Univ. Pr.

Kawauchi, Rinko, photos by. Rinko Kawauchi: Illuminance. 2011. (ENG., Illus.) 352p. 60.00 *(978-1-59711-144-7(9))* Aperture Foundation, Inc.

Kearns, James & Vaisse, Pierre. "Ce Salon à Quoi Tout Se Ramène" Le Salon de Peinture et de Sculpture, 1791-1890. 2009. (French Studies of the Eighteenth & Nineteenth Centuries Ser.). (FRE., Illus.). 164p. 48.95 *(978-3-03910-931-9(6))* Lang, Peter AG GBR. Dist: Lang, Peter.

Keller, Christoph, ed. Andree Korpys / Markus Löffler. 2009. (ENG., Illus.). 256p. pap. 28.00 *(978-3-905829-74-7(6))* JRP Ringier Kunstverlag AG CHE. Dist: D.A.P./Distributed Art Pubs.

Keller, Christoph & Perret, Mai-Thu, eds. Mai-Thu Perret: Land of Crystal. 2008. (ENG., Illus.). 240p. pap. 49.00 *(978-3-905701-55-5(3))* JRP Ringier Kunstverlag AG CHE. Dist: D.A.P./Distributed Art Pubs.

Kelley, Jeff & Tsuruta, Kaz. Rocks into Gold: Zhan Wang - Sculptures from the Sierra. 2008. (ENG.). 88p. pap. 24.95 *(978-0-939117-45-1(2))* Asian Art Museum of San Francisco.

Kelley, Mike. Mike Kelley: Arenas. 2011. (ENG., Illus.). 44p. 30.00 *(978-1-61623-718-9(X))* Skarstedt Gallery.

Kelly, Ellsworth. Ellsworth Kelly: Reliefs 2009-2010. 2011. (ENG., Illus.). 48p. 45.00 ***(978-1-880146-56-9(8))*** Marks, Matthew Gallery.

Kelly, Jerry, et al. The Work of the Stamperia Valdonega: 1948-2008. 2009. (Illus.). 96p. 35.00 *(978-1-60583-021-6(6))* Grolier Club of New York, The.

Kelly, Sarah E., et al. The Age of American Impressionism: Masterpieces from the Art Institute of Chicago. Barter, Judith A., ed. 2011. (Contemporary Collecting Ser.). (ENG., Illus.). 160p. 50.00 *(978-0-300-17574-5(4))* Art Institute of Chicago.

Kelly, Simon. Monet's Water Lilies: The Agapanthus Triptych. 2011. (ENG., Illus.). 64p. 16.95 *(978-0-89178-095-3(5))* St. Louis Art Museum.

Kenna, Michael. Monique's Kindergarten. (Illus.). 112p. 45.00 *(978-3-923922-55-0(8))* Nazraeli Pr. DEU. Dist: D.A.P./Distributed Art Pubs.

Kent, Rachel & Hobbs, Rober. Yinka Shonibare MBE. 2008. (Illus.). 208p. 55.00 *(978-3-7913-4123-1(5))* Prestel Publishing.

Kent, Rachel, et al. Yinka Shonibare MBE. 2008. (ENG., Illus.). 208p. *(978-1-921034-25-1(4))*; 224p. pap. *(978-1-921034-29-9(7))* Museum of Contemporary Art - Sydney AUS. Dist: Bookwise International.

Kerin, Melissa R. Artful Beneficence: Materials & Meanings of Himalayan Art: Selections from the David Nalin Himalayan Art Collection. 2009. *(978-0-9772131-5-3(3))* Serindia Pubns., Inc.

Kerkhoven, Ronald A. R. & Museum van der Togt, contrib. by. Beauties, Beasts, & Birds: Corneille & His Collection of African Art. (Illus.). 103p. *(978-90-6825-222-4(4))* Uniepers B.V./Denis.

Keys, Melissa & text. The Weight of History. 2007. (Illus.). 4p. *(978-0-9775782-4-5(0))* Monash Univ. Museum of Art.

Khalili, Nassir. The Arts of Islam: Treasures from the Nasser D. Khalili Collection. 2010. (ENG.). 400p. (gr. 12). 65.00 *(978-1-59020-393-4(3))* Overlook Pr., The.

Khan, Jeff & Hale, Meg, eds. Remote: Next Wave's focus on screen culture & Art. 2008. (Illus.). 22p. pap. *(978-0-9775158-2-0(6))* Next Wave Festival.

Khemir, Sabiha. Beauty & Belief: Crossing Bridges with the Arts of Islamic Culture. 2012. ***(978-0-8425-2811-5(3))*** Rutgers Univ. Pr.

Khemir, Sabiha, et al. From Cordoba to Samarqand: Masterpieces from the New Islamic Art Museum in Doha. 2008. (ENG., Illus.). 224p. 50.00 *(978-88-7439-316-9(4))* 5 Continents ITA. Dist: Hachette Bk. Group.

Kim, Clara, et al. Snake River: Charles Gaines & Edgar Arceneaux: Roy & Edna Disney/CalArts Theater. Kim, Clara, ed. 2006. (ENG.). pap. 40.00 *(978-0-9749831-5-8(2))* California Institute of the Arts.

Kippenberger & Pakesch, Peter. Modell: Kippenberger. 2008. (GER & ENG., Illus.). 200p. pap. 49.95 *(978-3-86560-311-1(4))* Verlag der Buchhandlung Walther Konig DEU. Dist: D.A.P./Distributed Art Pubs.

Kippenberger, Martin. Martin Kippenberger, 1 vol. Friedrich Christian Flick Collection, ed. 2006. (ENG., Illus.). 184p. 50.00 *(978-3-8321-7579-5(2))* DuMont DEU. Dist: D.A.P./Distributed Art Pubs.

Kippenberger, Martin, illus. Martin Kippenberger: No Drawing No Cry. 496p. pap. 52.00 *(978-3-88375-449-9(8)*, B10014) Verlag der Buchhandlung Walther Konig DEU. Dist: D.A.P./Distributed Art Pubs.

Kirkpatrick, Diane & Sheridan, Sonia Landy. The Art of Sonia Landy Sheridan. 2009. (Illus.). 72p. pap. 24.95 *(978-0-944722-38-1(5))* Hood Museum of Art.

Kittelmann, Udo. Michel Majerus. 2008. (GER & ENG., Illus.). 120p. pap. 49.00 *(978-3-905770-85-8(7))* JRP Ringier Kunstverlag AG CHE. Dist: D.A.P./Distributed Art Pubs.

Kittelmann, Udo, ed. Elaine Sturtevant: Author of the Quixote. 2009. (ENG., Illus.). 48p. 45.00 *(978-3-86560-472-9(2))* Verlag der Buchhandlung Walther Konig DEU. Dist: D.A.P./Distributed Art Pubs.

Kittelmann, Udo & Brill, Dorothée, eds. Carsten Höller: Soma / Dokomente / Documents. 2011. (ENG., Illus.). 128p. pap. 25.00 *(978-3-7757-2764-8(7))* Hatje Cantz Verlag GmbH & Co KG DEU. Dist: D.A.P./Distributed Art Pubs.

Klant, Michael. Art Brands: Wenn Hunde Beuys Fressen/When Dogs Eat Beuys. 2008. (GER & ENG., Illus.). 120p. pap. 30.00 *(978-3-7757-2116-5(9))* Hatje Cantz Verlag GmbH & Co KG DEU. Dist: D.A.P./Distributed Art Pubs.

Klaus, Kemp & Keiko, Ueki-Polet, eds. Less & More: The Design Ethos of Dieter Rams. 2010. (GER & ENG., Illus.). 808p. pap. 78.00 *(978-3-89955-277-5(6))* Die Gestalten Verlag DEU. Dist: Prestel Publishing.

Klein, Holger A., et al. Sacred Gifts & Worldly Treasures: Medieval Masterworks from the Cleveland Museum of Art. 2008. (ENG., Illus.). 320p. 45.00 *(978-0-940717-91-6(3))* Distribution General.

Klein, Richard & Wilson, Fred. Fred Wilson: Black Like Me, 1 vol. 2006. (ENG., Illus.). 64p. 29.95 *(978-1-888332-25-4(5))* Aldrich Museum of Contemporary Art, Inc., The.

Klenell, Ingalena, et al. Glimmering Gone: Ingalena Klenell & Beth Lipman. 2011. (ENG., Illus.). 96p. pap. 60.00 *(978-0-295-99080-4(5))* Museum of Glass.

Kloss, William, et al. Art in the White House: A Nation's Pride. 2nd ed. 2007. (ENG.). 408p. 29.95 *(978-1-931917-01-8(9))* White Hse. Historical Assn.

Knape, Gunilla, ed. Graciela Iturbide: The Hasselblad Award 2008, 1 vol. 2009. (ENG., Illus.). 144p. 45.00 *(978-3-86521-733-2(8))* Steidl, Gerhard Druckerei und Verlag DEU. Dist: Innovative Logistics.

Knorr, Daniel. Daniel Knorr: Carte de Artist. 2008. (Illus.). 200p. pap. 248.00 *(978-3-86560-239-8(8))* Verlag der Buchhandlung Walther Konig DEU. Dist: D.A.P./Distributed Art Pubs.

Koda, Harold & Bolton, Andrew. Poiret. 2007. (Illus.). 224p. 65.00 *(978-1-58839-223-7(6))* Metropolitan Museum of Art, The.

Koeppe, Wolfram. Vienna Circa 1780: An Imperial Silver Service Rediscovered. 2010. 35.00 *(978-1-58839-368-5(2))* Metropolitan Museum of Art, The.

Koeppe, Wolfram, et al. Art of the Royal Court: Treasures in Pietre Dure from the Palaces of Europe. 2008. (Illus.). xvi, 412p. 65.00 *(978-1-58839-288-6(0))* Metropolitan Museum of Art, The.

Koestenbaum, Wayne, et al. Jack Pierson: Angel Youth. 2008. (ENG., Illus.). 436p. pap. 59.95 *(978-88-8158-677-6(0))* Charta ITA. Dist: D.A.P./Distributed Art Pubs.

Komaroff, Linda, ed. Gifts of the Sultan: The Arts of Giving at the Islamic Courts. 2011. (ENG., Illus.). 336p. 65.00 *(978-0-300-17110-5(2))* Yale Univ. Pr.

Kondoleon, Christine, text. Aphrodite & the Gods of Love. 2011. (ENG., Illus.). 256p. 55.00 *(978-0-87846-756-3(4))* Museum of Fine Arts, Boston.

König, Kasper, et al. Remembering Forward: Australian Aboriginal Painting since 1960. 2011. (ENG., Illus.). 188p. (C). 50.00 *(978-1-907372-14-8(8))* Holberton, Paul Publishing GBR. Dist: Univ. of Washington Pr.

Koutsomallis, Kyriakos. Ancient Greece & Masson: The Goulandris Foundation. 2007. (ENG., Illus.). 180p. 60.00 *(978-88-422-1497-7(3))* Allemandi, Umberto & Co. GBR. Dist: Antique Collectors' Club.

Koutsomallis, Kyriakos, et al. Henri de Toulouse-Lautrec: Woman as Myth. 2006. (ENG., Illus.). 240p. 75.00 *(978-88-422-1046-7(3))* Allemandi, Umberto & Co. GBR. Dist: Antique Collectors' Club.

Kratsman, Miki. Miki Kratsman: All about Us. 2011. (ENG., Illus.). 102p. pap. 29.95 ***(978-1-934105-45-0(7))*** Sternberg Pr.

Kreilkamp, Vera. Rural Ireland: The Inside Story. 2012. (ENG., Illus.). 300p. pap. 45.00 ***(978-1-892850-18-8(4))*** McMullen Museum of Art, Boston College.

Kress, W. John & Sherwood, Shirley. The Art of Plant Evolution. 2010. (Illus.). 320p. (ENG.). 53.00 *(978-1-84246-421-2(3))*; pap. 41.00 *(978-1-84246-417-5(5))* Kew Publishing GBR. Dist: Chicago Distribution Ctr.

Krimko, Stuart, ed. Tobias Putrih: 99-07. 2008. (ENG., Illus.). 180p. 37.00 *(978-3-905770-71-1(7))* JRP Ringier Kunstverlag AG CHE. Dist: D.A.P./Distributed Art Pubs.

Krishna, Kalyan, et al. In Adoration of Krishna: Pichhwais of Shrinathji, Tapi Collection. 2008. (ENG., Illus.). 225p. 100.00 *(978-81-905935-0-2(1))* Roli Bks. Private, Ltd. IND. Dist: Ingram Pub. Services.

Krody, Sumru Belger & Çakmut, Feza. Colors of the Oasis: Central Asian Ikats. 2010. *(978-0-87405-033-2(2))*; pap. *(978-0-87405-034-9(0))* Textile Museum.

Kungnip Chungang Pangmulgwan (Korea) Staff & Museum of Fine Arts, Houston Staff, contrib. by. Treasures from the National Museum of Korea. 2007. *(978-0-89090-159-5(7))*; pap. *(978-0-89090-161-8(9))* Museum of Fine Arts, Houston.

Kunstmuseum Bern & Fibicher, Bernhard, eds. Six Feet Under: Autopsie unseres Umgangs mit Toten, 1 vol. Bohan, Ann Marie & Drews, David, trs. 2007. (GER & ENG., Illus.). 224p. 66.00 *(978-3-86678-019-4(2))* Kerber Verlag DEU. Dist: D.A.P./Distributed Art Pubs.

Kurjakovic, Daniel, ed. Album: On & Around Urs Fischer, Yves Netzhammer, Ugo Rondinone, & Christine Streuli, Participating at the 52nd Venice Biennale 2007, 1 vol. 2007. (ENG., Illus.). 320p. per. 25.00 *(978-3-905770-70-4(9))* JRP Ringier Kunstverlag AG CHE. Dist: D.A.P./Distributed Art Pubs.

Kurtz Lansing, Amy & Burdan, Amanda C. Lyme in Mind: The Clement C. Moore Collection. 2009. (Illus.). 64p. pap. *(978-0-615-28438-5(8))* Griswold, Florence Museum.

Kurzmeyer, Roman. Viereck und Kosmos: Kunstler, Lebensreformer, Okkultisten, Spiritisten in Amden 1901-1912. Max Nopper, Josua Klein, Fidus, Otto Meyer-Amden. (Edition Voldemeer Ser.). (GER., Illus.). 258p. 44.95 *(978-3-211-83371-1(4)*, 3211833714) Springer.

Kwon, Miwon. James Turrell. 2012. (ENG., Illus.). 80p. 100.00 ***(978-0-8478-3712-0(2))*** Rizzoli International Pubns., Inc.

L&M Arts, prod. Willem de Kooning 1981 - 1986. 2007. (Illus.). 80p. 60.00 *(978-0-9790942-1-7(6))* L & M Arts.

Laclotte, Michel. Treasures of the Louvre. (ITA., Illus.). 384p. 11.95 *(978-88-86482-30-1(2))* Leonardo International ITA. Dist: Abbeville Pr., Inc.

LaGamma, Alisa & Giuntini, Christine. The Essential Art of African Textiles: Design Without End. 2008. (ENG., Illus.). 72p. pap. 19.95 *(978-0-300-14962-3(X))* Yale Univ. Pr.

Lake, Prince Dav, ed. Winslow Homers Empire State. 2010. (Illus.). 84p. pap. 19.99 *(978-0-8156-8155-7(0))* Syracuse Univ. Pr.

Lakra, Dr. & López, Jerónimo. Dr. Lakra. 2010. (ENG., Illus.). 116p. 35.00 *(978-84-92480-86-9(6))* RM Verlag, S.L. ESP. Dist: D.A.P./Distributed Art Pubs.

Lally, Janice. The Australian Aboriginal Collection in the Museum Fnr Völkerkunde, Berlin. 2008. 488p. pap. *(978-3-639-03491-2(0))* VDM Verlag Dr. Mueller e.K.

Lam, Peter Y. K. Ethereal Elegance: Porcelain Vases of the Imperial Qing - The Huaihaitang Collection. 2008. 400p. 135.00 *(978-962-7101-84-0(2))* Art Museum Chinese Univ. of Hong Kong DEU. Dist: Art Media Resources, Inc.

Lamberton, Daniel, comment. On the River Through the Valley of Fire: The Collaborative Ceramics of Frank Boyden & Tom Coleman. 2008. (Illus.). 141p. *(978-0-9816728-1-6(7))* American Museum of Ceramic Art.

Lanchner, Carolyn & Miró, Joan. Joan Miró. 2008. (ENG., Illus.). 48p. pap. 9.95 *(978-0-87070-725-4(6))* Museum of Modern Art.

Landy, Michael. Michael Landy: H2ny. 2007. (Illus.). 93p. *(978-1-905464-07-4(X))* Ridinghouse.

Langdon, Helen. The Art of Salvator Rosa. 2010. (ENG., Illus.). 200p. 60.00 *(978-1-907372-01-8(6))* Holberton, Paul Publishing GBR. Dist: Univ. of Washington Pr.

Lange, Amanda E. Chinese Export Art at Historic Deerfield. 2006. (ENG., Illus.). 272p. 65.00 *(978-0-9666769-4-5(7))* Historic Deerfield Inc.

Lange, C. Alfons Mucha. Gaillemin, J. -L. et al, eds. (GER., Illus.). 356p. (C). 65.00 *(978-3-7774-7035-1(X))* Hirmer Verlag GmbH DEU. Dist: Brown, David Bk. Co., The.

Lange, Christiane & Diederen, Roger, eds. Das Ewige Auge: Von Rembrandt bis Picasso. Meisterwerke der Sammlung Jan Krugier und Marie-Anne Krugier-Poniatowski. 2007. (GER., Illus.). 511p. (C). 56.00 *(978-3-7774-3695-1(X))* Hirmer Verlag GmbH DEU. Dist: Brown, David Bk. Co., The.

Lange, Christiane & Frehner, Matthias. Giacometti, Hodler, Klee. Das Kunstmuseum Bern zu Gast: Katalog zur Ausstellung in München, Kunsthallle der Hypo-Kulturstiftung; 17.09.2010-09.01.2111. Frehner, Matthias & Lange, C., eds. 2010. (GER., Illus.). 236p. (C). 59.00 *(978-3-7774-2931-1(7))* Hirmer Verlag GmbH DEU. Dist: Brown, David Bk. Co., The.

Langer, Lawrence. Adam & Eve in the Art of Samuel Bak. Choi, Justine, ed. 2012. (Illus.). 120p. 50.00 ***(978-1-879985-25-4(X))*** Pucker Gallery.

Langmuir, Erika. Angels. 2010. (ENG., Illus.). 96p. pap. 15.00 *(978-1-85709-484-8(0))* Yale Univ. Pr.

Lars Muller Publishers, creator. Super Normal: Published by Lars Muller Publishers on the Occasion of the First Super Normal Exhibition, in Tokyo, June 2006, Curated by Jasper Morrison & Naoto Fukasawa. 2006. (Illus.). 16p. per. 11.95 *(978-3-03778-084-8(3)*, 3037780843) Lars Muller Pubs. CHE. Dist: Springer.

Lawing, Douglas, et al. The Spirit of Modernism: The John R. Eckel, Jr. Foundation Gift to the Museum of Fine Arts, Houston. 2011. pap. ***(978-0-89090-175-5(9))*** Museum of Fine Arts, Houston.

Lawrence, Priscilla O. & Lemmon, Alfred E. Common Routes: St. Domingue-Louisiana. 2006. 126p. *(978-2-85056-966-1(6))* Somogy Editions d'Art.

Lawrence, Sarah & Wilton, Ely John. Piranesi as Designer. 2007. (ENG.). 360p. *(978-0-910503-96-9(6))* Assouline FRA. Dist: Perseus Distribution.

—Piranesi as Designer. 2007. (ENG.). 360p. pap. 45.00 *(978-0-910503-95-2(8))* Cooper-Hewitt Museum.

Le Feuvre, Lisa & Morton, Tom. British Art Show 7: In the Days of the Comet. 2011. (ENG., Illus.). 192p. pap. 35.00 *(978-1-85332-286-0(5))* Hayward Gallery Publishing GBR. Dist: D.A.P./Distributed Art Pubs.

Lebenstein, Jan. Jan Lebenstein: Warszawa — Paryz: Prace Z Lat 1956-1972: Zacheta Narodowa Galeria Sztuki, 25 Czerwca-28 Sierpnia 2010. Koczowski, Piotr & Szewczyk, Agnieszka, trs. 2010. (POL., Illus.). 199p. *(978-83-89945-48-8(7))* Zacheta, Panstwowa Galeria Sztuki.

Ledezma, Juan. The Sites of Latin American Abstraction/Los Sitios de la Abstraccion Lationoamericana. 2008. (ENG., Illus.). 248p. 75.00 *(978-88-8158-664-6(9))* Charta ITA. Dist: D.A.P./Distributed Art Pubs.

Lee, Paul. Paul Lee. 2008. (Illus.). pap. 40.00 *(978-0-9778819-8-7(9))* Peres Projects, Los Angeles Berlin.

Legat-Verlag Staff, ed. Icons. 2006. 368p. 59.95 *(978-3-932942-20-4(5))* Legat-Verlag GmbH & Company KG DEU. Dist: Independent Pubs. Group.

Lehmann, Ulrike, ed. Michael Laube: In Between. 2010. (ENG., Illus.). 180p. 60.00 *(978-3-7757-2514-9(8))* Hatje Cantz Verlag GmbH & Co KG DEU. Dist: D.A.P./Distributed Art Pubs.

Leinz, Gottlieb & Wiesinger, Véronique, eds. Alberto Giacometti: Die Frau auf dem Wagen - Triumph und Tod. Katalogbuch zur Ausstellung in Duisburg, Stiftung Wilhelm Lehmbruck-Museum, 31.01.2010-18.04.2010. 2010. (ENG & GER., Illus.). 224p. (C). 53.00 *(978-3-7774-2411-8(0))* Hirmer Verlag GmbH DEU. Dist: Brown, David Bk. Co., The.

Leismann, B. & Padberg, M. W. intimacy! Baden in der Kunst. 2010. (ENG.). 320p. 78.00 *(978-3-86832-020-6(2)*, Art Stock Bks. Ltd/Csi) Continental Sales, Inc.

Lemonedes, Heather, et al. Paul Gauguin: Durchbruch zur Moderne. 2009. (Illus.). 247p. *(978-2-7427-8695-4(3))*; *(978-90-79310-13-5(1))*; *(978-1-935294-00-9(8))*; *(978-0-940717-60-2(3))*; *(978-3-7757-2426-5(5))*; *(978-3-7757-2533-0(4))* Cleveland Museum of Art.

Leonard, Anne. The Tragic Muse: Art & Emotion, 1700-1900. 2011. (ENG., Illus.). 128p. pap. 30.00 *(978-0-935573-49-7(6))* Univ. of Chicago, David & Alfred Smart Museum.

Leonardo & Melani, Margherita. Leonardo Da Vinci: The European Genius: Paintings & Drawings: Exhibition in the Basilica of Koekelberg, Brussels, in Celebration of the 50th Anniversary of the Treaty of Rome for the Constitution of the European Community (1957-2007) Pedretti, Carlo, ed. 2008. (FRE & ENG., Illus.). 176p. (C). pap. 76.00 ***(978-88-95686-00-4(4))*** Cartei, C.B. & Bianchi Edizioni ITA. Dist: Brown, David Bk. Co., The.

Lermer, Andrea & Shalem, Avinoam, eds. After One Hundred Years: The 1910 Exhibition Meisterwerke muhammedanischer Kunst Reconsidered. 2010. (Islamic History & Civilization Ser.). (GER & ENG., Illus.). 440p. *(978-90-04-19001-6(5))* BRILL.

Lerner, Leslie, et al. Under the Radar: Leslie Lerner. 2008. (Illus.). 31p. *(978-0-915171-75-0(9))* Katonah Gallery.

Lettera27 Staff. Young Guns & the Undiscovered Letter, 2 vols. Art Directors Club Staff, ed. 2009. (ENG., Illus.). 356p. 40.00 *(978-0-8118-6945-4(8))* Chronicle Bks. LLC.

Levitov, Karen & Shiff, Richard. Camille Pissarro: Impressions of City & Country. 2007. (ENG., Illus.). 96p. pap. 19.95 *(978-0-300-12479-8(1))* Yale Univ. Pr.

Lewallen, Constance. A Rose Has No Teeth: Bruce Nauman in The 1960s. 2007. (Illus.). 235p. 45.00 *(978-0-520-25085-7(0))* Univ. of California Pr.

Lewis, Andrea R., ed. Bead International 2008 & Beyond Basketry: The Dairy Barn Arts Center. 2008. (ENG., Illus.). 152p. pap. 24.95 *(978-0-8214-1812-3(2))* Ohio Univ. Pr.

Lewitt, Sol. Sol Lewitt, 1 vol. 2006. (ITA & ENG., Illus.). 102p. pap. 28.00 *(978-88-89431-59-7(8))* Damiani ITA. Dist: D.A.P./Distributed Art Pubs.

Libby, Alexandra & Stanton, Thomas. Venice in the Age of Canaletto. 2009. (Illus.). 224p. 60.00 *(978-3-7913-8000-1(1))* Prestel Publishing.

Lichtenstein, Roy. Roy Lichtenstein Reflected. 2011. (ENG., Illus.). 64p. 40.00 *(978-0-9814578-6-4(X))* Mitchell-Innes & Nash.

Lichtenstein, Roy & Cowart, Jack. Lichtenstein in Process. 2009. (Illus.). 44p. *(978-0-915171-77-4(5))* Katonah Gallery.

Lidtke, Thomas, frwd. A Corner of the World: The Art of Lois Ireland Zwettler. 2007. (Illus.). 24p. per. *(978-0-9710228-0-5(1))* Museum of Wisconsin Art.

Lightseed. pap. 35.00 *(978-4-900398-12-2(8))* Watari-Um JPN. Dist: D.A.P./Distributed Art Pubs.

Lin, James C. S. The Immortal Stone: Chinese Jades from the Neolithic Period to the Twentieth Century. 2009. (Illus.). 160p. 60.00 *(978-1-85759-581-9(5))* Scala Pubs., Ltd. GBR. Dist: Antique Collectors' Club.

Linden, Liz, ed. The Best Surprise Is No Surprise, 1 vol. 2007. (ENG., Illus.). 296p. pap. 39.95 *(978-3-905770-05-6(9))* JRP Ringier Kunstverlag AG CHE. Dist: D.A.P./Distributed Art Pubs.

Linton, Meg, text. Gary Lang: Hybrid Variations. 2008. (Illus.). 72p. per. 20.00 *(978-0-9800962-0-0(0))* Cella, Edward Art+Architecture.

Lippit, Yukio. Colorful Realm: Japanese Bird-and-Flower Paintings by Ito Jakuchu. 2012. (ENG., Illus.). 224p. 50.00 ***(978-0-226-48460-0(2))*** Univ. of Chicago Pr.

Lister, Ken, ed. Canada Collects: The Passionate Eye, 1 vol. 2007. (ENG., Illus.). 192p. 24.99 *(978-0-88854-453-7(7))* Royal Ontario Museum CAN. Dist: Univ. of Toronto Pr.

Liuming, Ma, photos by. Ma Liuming: Performances, Paintings, Sculptures. 2008. (ENG., Illus.). 232p. 50.00 *(978-88-6208-001-9(8))* Damiani ITA. Dist: D.A.P./Distributed Art Pubs.

Liversidge, Peter. Proposals for Liverpool. 2009. (ENG.). 142p. pap. 29.95 *(978-1-84631-205-2(1))* Liverpool Univ. Pr. GBR. Dist: Chicago Distribution Ctr.

Lloyd, Christopher. Impressionism: Pastels, Watercolors, Drawings. 2011. ***(978-0-944110-96-6(7))*** Milwaukee Art Museum.

Lo Sardo, Eugenio. The She-Wolf & the Sphinx: Rome & Egypt from History to Myth. Lo Sardo, Eugenio, ed. 2008. (Illus.). 216p. 65.00 *(978-88-370-6223-1(0))* Electa ITA. Dist: Trans-Atlantic Pubns., Inc.

Lochnan, Katharine. Black Ice: David Blackwood's Prints of Newfoundland, 1 vol. 2011. (ENG., Illus.). 224p. pap. 40.00 *(978-1-55365-779-8(9))* D&M Pubs. Inc. CAN. Dist: Perseus-PGW.

Loftus, Barbara. Sigismund's Watch: A Tiny Catastrophe. 2011. (ENG., Illus.). 112p. pap. 45.00 ***(978-0-85667-709-0(4))*** Wilson, Philip Pubs., Ltd. GBR. Dist: Macmillan.

Lombardi, Enrico. Edoardo Albinati: Voci Nel Buio/Voices in the Dark: Enrico Lombardi: Immagini/Images, 1 vol. 2006. (ENG., Illus.). 104p. per. 29.95 *(978-88-8158-582-3(0))* D.A.P./Distributed Art Pubs.

Longwell, Alicia G. Sand: Memory, Meaning & Metaphor. 2008. (Illus.). 150p. pap. *(978-0-943526-52-2(3))* Parrish Art Museum, The.

Longwell, Alicia G., intro. First Impressions: Nineteenth-Century American Master Prints. 2010. (Illus.). 96p. *(978-0-943526-55-3(8))* Parrish Art Museum, The.

Longwell, Alicia Grant. First Impressions: Nineteenth-Century American Master Prints. 2010. (ENG., Illus.). 96p. 39.95 *(978-1-904832-75-1(X))* Giles, D. Ltd. GBR. Dist: Antique Collectors' Club.

Losty, Jeremiah P. Indian Miniatures from the James Ivory Collection. 2011. (Illus.). 220p. pap. 65.00 *(978-0-9553306-7-4(X)*, Frahcesco Galloway (Acc)) Antique Collectors' Club GBR. Dist: National Bk. Network.

Lowrey, Carol & Lever, Hayley. Hayley Lever & the Modern Spirit. 2010. (Illus.). 48p. pap. ***(978-1-935617-05-1(2))*** Spanierman Gallery.

Lowry, Carol. A Legacy of Art: Paintings & Sculptures by Artist Life Members of the National Arts Club. 2008. (ENG., Illus.). 216p. 60.00 *(978-0-615-15499-2(9))* Hudson Hills Pr. LLC.

Lozano-Hemmer, Rafael. Rafael Lozano-Hemmer: Algunas Cosas Pasan Mas Veces Que Todo el Tiempo/Some Things Happen More Often Than All of the Time, 1 vol. 2007. (ENG & SPA., Illus.). 176p. 34.00 *(978-84-7506-792-6(1))* Turner, Ediciones S.A. ESP. Dist: D.A.P./Distributed Art Pubs.

Lozano, Lee. Seek the Extremes, Volume II, 1 vol. 2006. (ENG., Illus.). 80p. 35.00 *(978-3-938821-49-7(3))* Verlag fur Moderne Kunst DEU. Dist: D.A.P./Distributed Art Pubs.

Lu, Wensheng & Murray, Julia K. Confucius. Lee Barrett, J. May, ed. 2010. (Illus.). 200p. pap. *(978-0-9774054-5-9(1))* China Institute Gallery, China Institute in America.

Luca, Francesca de, ed. Santi poeti Navigatoria. 2009. (I mai Visti Ser.). (ITA., Illus.). 144p. (C). 30.00 *(978-88-596-0713-7(2))* Polistampa ITA. Dist: Brown, David Bk. Co., The.

Luciano, Eleonora, et al. Antico. 2011. (Illus.). 224p. 55.00 (978-1-907372-27-8(X)) Holberton, Paul Publishing GBR. Dist: Casemate Pubs. & Bk. Distributors, LLC.

Luckert, Steven & Bachrach, Susan. State of Deception: The Power of Nazi Propaganda. 2009. (ENG., Illus.). 288p. 45.00 (978-0-89604-714-3(8), 47143) Norton, W. W. & Co., Inc.

Luders, Marc. Marc Lüders. 2010. (ENG., Illus.). 176p. 55.00 (978-3-7757-2515-6(6)) Hatje Cantz Verlag GmbH & Co KG DEU. Dist: D.A.P./Distributed Art Pubs.

Lui, Elizabeth G. Closed Mondays. (Illus.). 136p. 50.00 (978-3-923922-73-4(6)) Nazraeli Pr. DEU. Dist: D.A.P./Distributed Art Pubs.

Lüth, Nanna & Wilcke, Jole. Pöpp68: Privat, öffentlich, Persönlich, Politisch: Partizipation Einwände Trotzdem: Texte, Gespräche und Beteiligung = Participation Objections Anyhow: Texts, Dialogues & Participation. 2009. (FRE, GER & ENG., Illus.). 294p. pap. (978-3-938515-24-2(4)) Neue Gesellschaft.

Lüthi, Urs & Barbero, Luca Massimo. Urs Lüthi: Just Another Story about Leaving. Forin, Elena, ed. 2010. (ITA & ENG., Illus.). 208p. 90.00 (978-88-370-7464-7(6)) Electa ITA. Dist: Trans-Atlantic Pubns., Inc.

Luzzatto, Sylvia, ed. Buccellati: Timeless Art. 2009. (ENG., Illus.). 208p. 85.00 (978-88-7439-508-8(6)) 5 Continents ITA. Dist: Hachette Bk. Group.

Lycett, Joseph & McPhee, John. Joseph Lycett: Convict Artist. 2008. (ENG., Illus.). 285p. 69.95 (978-1-876991-21-0(6)) Historic Houses Trust of New South Wales AUS. Dist: National Bk. Network.

Lynes, Barbara Buhler & Weinberg, Jonathan. Shared Intelligence: American Painting & the Photograph. 2011. (ENG., Illus.). 274p. 39.95 (978-0-520-26906-4(3)) Univ. of California Pr.

M/M (Paris). M/M (Paris) No. 2: Inventory. 2009. (ENG., Illus.). 320p. pap. 35.00 (978-1-905620-30-2(6)) Haunch of Venison GBR. Dist: D.A.P./Distributed Art Pubs.

MacAulay, David, contrib. by. What a Circus! the Art of Etienne Delessert. 2011. (Illus.). 40p. pap. 17.95 (978-1-59288-026-3(6)) Carle, Eric Museum of Picture Bk. Art, The.

Maccari, Mino & Vallora, Marco. I Maccari Di Maccari. 2009. (ITA., Illus.). 238p. (978-88-202-1930-7(1)) Mazzotta.

Mack, Angela D. & Hoffius, Stephen G., eds. Landscape of Slavery: The Plantation in American Art. 2008. (Illus.). 166p. 49.95 (978-1-57003-719-1(1)); pap. 24.95 (978-1-57003-720-7(5)) Univ. of South Carolina Pr.

Macomber, Ben. The Jewel City. 2008. 204p. 27.99 (978-0-554-22428-2(3)) 2008. 204p. 24.99 (978-0-554-31731-1(1)) 2007. (ENG.). 190p. pap. 19.99 (978-1-4264-2329-1(2)) 2007. (ENG.). 202p. pap. 22.99 (978-1-4264-2377-2(2)) BiblioBazaar.

*Made in Pennsylvania: A Folk Art Tradition. 2007. 29.95 (978-0-931241-35-2(9)) Antique Collectors' Club.

Made of Stone. pap. 25.00 (978-2-903004-06-4(4)) Galerie Isy Brachot FRA. Dist: D.A.P./Distributed Art Pubs.

Maggi Hambling & Andrew Lambirth. Maggi Hambling: The Works & Conversations with Andrew Lambirth. 2006. (ENG., Illus.). 240p. 85.00 (978-0-906290-84-2(8)) Unicorn Pr., London GBR. Dist: National Bk. Network.

Mahony, Claire O. Brunel & the Art of Invention. 2007. (ENG., Illus.). 64p. per. 15.95 (978-1-904537-50-2(2), Sansom (Acc)) Antique Collectors' Club GBR. Dist: National Bk. Network.

Maier-Aichen, Hansjerg, ed. New Talents: State of the Arts. Stand der Dinge. 2009. (ENG & GER., Illus.). 176p. pap. 35.00 (978-3-89986-110-5(8), Avedition Gmbh,Csi) Continental Sales, Inc.

Malani, Nalini, illus. Nalini Malani, 1 vol. 2007. (ENG.). 144p. 55.00 (978-88-8158-644-8(4)) Charta ITA. Dist: D.A.P./Distributed Art Pubs.

Malaskauskas, Raimundas. Loris Greaud. 2008. (ENG., Illus.). 80p. pap. 15.00 (978-3-905829-50-1(9)) JRP Ringier Kunstverlag AG CHE. Dist: D.A.P./Distributed Art Pubs.

Malik, Anne E. A New & Native Beauty: The Art & Craft of Greene & Greene. Bosley, Edward R., ed. 2008. (Illus.). 272p. 75.00 (978-1-85894-452-4(X)) Merrell Pubs. Ltd. GBR. Dist: Perseus Distribution.

Malk, Kadri, et al. Just Must: Black International Jewellery. 2009. (EST & ENG., Illus.). 216p. 70.00 (978-3-89790-296-1(6)) Arnoldsche Art Pubs. DEU. Dist: Antique Collectors' Club.

Mallet, J. V. G. Xanto: Pottery-Painter, Poet, Man of the Italian Renaissance. 2011. (Illus.). 216p. pap. 45.00 (978-0-900785-98-6(5)) Holberton, Paul Publishing GBR. Dist: Casemate Pubs. & Bk. Distributors, LLC.

Manasseh, Cyrus. The Problematic of Video Art in Museum, 1968-1990. 2009. 114.99 (978-1-60497-650-2(0)) Cambria Pr.

Mangion, Eric, ed. Half Square Half Crazy. 2008. (ENG., Illus.). 176p. per. 32.00 (978-3-905829-06-8(1)) JRP Ringier Kunstverlag AG CHE. Dist: D.A.P./Distributed Art Pubs.

Mangold, Robert & Dreishpoon, Douglas. Beyond the Line: Paintings & Project, 2000-2008. 2009. (ENG., Illus.). 128p. 150.00 (978-0-8109-5487-8(7)) Abrams.

Mann, Vivian B., ed. & contrib. by. Uneasy Communion: Jews, Christians, & the Altarpieces of Medieval Spain. 2010. 49.95 (978-0-9777839-6-0(0)) Museum of Biblical Art.

Mannini, Lucia. Le stanze dei Tesori: Collezionisti e antiquari a Firenze tra Ottocento e Novecento. 2011. (Piccoli, grandi Musei Ser.). (ENG & ITA., Illus.). 312p. (C). 75.00 (978-88-596-0965-0(8)) Polistampa ITA. Dist: Brown, David Bk. Co., The.

Maranda, Michael, ed. The Saskia Olde Wolbers Files: And While I Have Been Lying Here Perfectly Still. 2009. (ENG., Illus.). 136p. pap. 20.00 (978-0-921972-53-2(9)) Art Gallery of York Univ. CAN. Dist: D.A.P./Distributed Art Pubs.

Marcadé, Jean-Claude. Futurism. Ottinger, Didier, ed. 2009. (ENG., Illus.). 360p. pap. 60.00 (978-88-7439-496-8(9)) 5 Continents ITA. Dist: Hachette Bk. Group.

Marchetti, Luca & Quinz, Emanuele, eds. Dysfashional. 2007. (Illus.). 148p. pap. (978-84-934879-9-7(6)) Actar Birkhauser Distribution.

Marden, Brice. Brice Marden: Letters. 2011. (ENG., Illus.). 48p. 45.00 (978-1-880146-55-2(X)) Marks, Matthew Gallery.

Mari, Bartomeu. Asier Mendizabal. Mari, Bartomeu, ed. 2008. 180p. (978-84-89771-51-2(0)) Actar Birkhauser Distribution.

Mari, Enzo, ed. Paolo Ulian: Tra Gioco e Discarica. 2010. (ENG & ITA., Illus.). 96p. pap. 42.50 (978-88-370-7512-5(X)) Electa ITA. Dist: Trans-Atlantic Pubns., Inc.

Marignoli, Duccio K. & Mascelloni, Enrico. A Thousand & One Days: Pakistani Women Artists. 2006. (ENG.). 126p. pap. 12.95 (978-0-937426-73-9(3)) Honolulu Academy of the Arts.

Marincola, Paula, ed. What Makes a Great Exhibition? Questions of Practice. 2007. (ENG., Illus.). 176p. pap. 19.95 (978-0-9708346-1-4(6)) Reaktion Bks., Ltd. GBR. Dist: Chicago Distribution Ctr.

Mariné, Óscar. Design Is Everything. 2011. (SPA & ENG., Illus.). 280p. 52.00 (978-84-92441-09-9(7), T.F. Editores, S.L.C.) Antique Collectors' Club GBR. Dist: National Bk. Network.

Mark, Lisa, ed. Sterling Ruby: MOCA Focus. 2008. (ENG., Illus.). 152p. pap. 24.95 (978-1-933751-10-8(X)) Museum of Contemporary Art, Los Angeles.

Markel, Stephen. India's Fabled City: The Art of Courtly Lucknow. 2010. (978-0-87587-206-3(9)) Los Angeles County Museum of Art.

Markonish, Denise. Petah Coyne: Everything That Rises Must Converge. 2010. (ENG., Illus.). 128p. pap. 25.00 (978-0-300-16770-2(9)) Yale Univ. Pr.

Marling, Karal Ann & Wegener, Corine A. Wind & Whimsy: Weathervanes & Whirligigs from Twin Cities Collections. 2007. (Illus.). 63p. (978-0-912964-97-3(9)) Minneapolis Institute of Arts.

Marman, Jennifer & Borins, Daniel. Jennifer Marman & Daniel Borins: Project for a New American Century. 2009. (ENG., Illus.). 64p. (978-0-921972-55-6(5)) Art Gallery of York Univ.

Marshall, Christopher R., ed. Sculpture & the Museum. 2011. (Subject/Object: New Studies in Sculpture Ser.). (Illus.). 286p. 99.95 (978-1-4094-0910-6(4)) Ashgate Publishing Co.

Marshall, Jennifer Jane. Machine Art 1934. 2012. (ENG., Illus.). 240p. 45.00 (978-0-226-50715-6(7)) Univ. of Chicago Pr.

Martin, Andy. Ideas Have Legs: Ian Mcmillan vs. Andy Martin, 1 vol. 2006. (ENG., Illus.). 120p. pap. 25.00 (978-0-9550061-5-9(5)) FUEL Publishing GBR. Dist: D.A.P./Distributed Art Pubs.

Martin, Uli. U3 - Corporate Culture: Art, Plastics & Recycling. 2007. (ENG., Illus.). 192p. 75.00 (978-3-89790-196-4(X)) Arnoldsche Art Pubs. DEU. Dist: Antique Collectors' Club.

Martinelli, Roberta & Musée de l'armée France. Mito e Bellezza. Bartolli, Moreno D., ed. 2010. (ITA., Illus.). 336p. pap. 93.50 (978-88-370-7448-7(4)) Electa ITA. Dist: Trans-Atlantic Pubns., Inc.

Martiniz-Ruiz, Barbaro. Art & Emancipation in Jamaica: Isaac Mendes Belisario & His Worlds. Barringer, Tim & Forrester, Gillian, eds. 2007. (Illus.). 612p. 75.00 (978-0-300-11661-8(6)) Yale Ctr. for British Art.

Martorelli, Barbara. George Barbier: The Birth of Art Deco. 2009. (ENG.). 176p. 50.00 (978-88-317-9646-0(1)) Marsilio Editori spa ITA. Dist: Random Hse., Inc.

Marx, Annegret, et al. Arise & Go Toward the South: 2000 Years of Christianity in Ethiopia. 2009. (GER & ENG., Illus.). 368p. 59.00 (978-3-932942-28-0(0)) Legat-Verlag GmbH & Company KG DEU. Dist: Independent Pubs. Group.

Mas. Five centuries of Images: Masterworks of the MAS, 1 vol. 2011. (ENG.). 240p. 86.00 (978-90-8586-577-3(8)) Exhibitions International BEL. Dist: Innovative Logistics.

Mason, Charles. Spinach Green & Mutton-fat White: Chinese Jades of the Qing Dynasty (1644-1911) 2006. per. 24.95 (978-0-9762552-1-5(9)) Ham Museum of Art.

Mason, Darielle. Kantha: The Embroidered Quilts of Bengal from the Jill & Sheldon Bonovitz Collection & the Stella Kramrisch Collection of the Philadelphia Museum of Art. 2010. (Illus.). xiii, 290p. (978-0-87633-219-1(X)); (978-0-87633-218-4(1)) Philadelphia Museum of Art.

Massimiliano, Gioni, et al. The Younger Than Jesus Artist Directory. 2009. (ENG., Illus.). 480p. pap. 49.95 (978-0-7148-4981-2(2)) Phaidon Pr., Inc.

Matheson, Susan B. Art for Yale: A History of the Yale University Art Gallery. 2006. (ENG., Illus.). 30.00 (978-0-89467-953-7(8)) Yale Univ. Art Gallery.

Matisse, Henri. Les Esquimaux Vus Par Matisse: Georges Duthuit: Une Fête en Cimmérie. 2010. (FRE., Illus.). 128p. (978-2-7541-0527-9(1)) Hazan, Fernand, Editeur.

Matta-Clark, Gordon & Sussman, Elisabeth. Gordon Matta-Clark "You Are the Measure" 2007. (Illus.). 239p. (978-0-87427-156-0(8)) Whitney Museum of American Art.

Matter, Mercedes. Mercedes Matter. 2010. (ENG., Illus.). 276p. 55.00 (978-0-615-30990-3(9)) Borghi, Mark Fine Art.

Matthews, Nancy Mowll & Kennedy, Elizabeth, eds. Prendergast in Italy. 2009. (Illus.). 192p. 55.00 (978-1-85894-483-8(X)) Merrell Pubs. Ltd. GBR. Dist: Perseus Distribution.

Mattusch, Carol C. Pompeii & the Roman Villa: Art & Culture Around the Bay of Naples. 2008. (978-0-89468-353-4(5)) National Gallery of Art.

Mattusch, Carol C., ed. Pompeii & the Roman Villa: Art & Culture Around the Bay of Naples. 2008. (ENG., Illus.). 360p. 60.00 (978-0-500-51436-8(4), 551436) Thames & Hudson.

Maudsley, Catherine. Art & Imitation in China. 2006. (ENG.). 350p. (gr. 17). 75.00 (978-962-7287-51-3(2)) Hong Kong Univ. Pr. HKG. Dist: Columbia Univ. Pr.

Mayer, Carol E. Transitions of a Still Life. 2007. (ENG., Illus.). 128p. 40.00 (978-1-895636-83-3(3)); pap. 26.95 (978-1-895636-82-6(5)) Anvil Pr. CAN. Dist: Univ. of Toronto Pr.

Mayer, Katharina, et al. Katharina Mayer, Paula Modersohn-Becker: Eine Begegnung. 2008. (GER., Illus.). 55p. (978-3-9810296-2-8(3), Spotlight Poets) Bottcherstrae GmbH.

Mayer-Thurman, Christa C. & Wayne, June. June Wayne's Narrative Tapestries: Tidal Waves, DNA, & the Cosmos. 2010. (Illus.). 36p. pap. (978-0-86559-243-8(8)) Art Institute of Chicago.

Mazow, Leo G. & Benton, Thomas Hart. Shallow Creek: Thomas Hart Benton & American Waterways. 2007. (Penn State Press Ser.). (ENG., Illus.). 60p. per. 24.95 (978-0-911209-66-2(2)) Pennsylvania State Univ. Pr.

Mazow, Leo G. & Murphy, Kevin M. Taxing Visions: Financial Episodes in Late Nineteenth-Century American Art. 2010. (ENG.). 80p. pap. 24.95 (978-0-911209-68-6(9)) Pennsylvania State Univ. Pr.

McCamon, Dave. Life Drawings: Beginnings, Plans & Dreams. 2006. (ENG., Illus.). 91p. 29.95 (978-1-933341-02-6(5)) CRM.

McClure, Michael. Artifact: A Cultural Geography of Wyoming. 2008. (Illus.). 124p. (978-1-928786-03-0(0)) Wig Raf Publishing, Inc.

McClusky, Pamela. Ancestral Modern: Australian Aboriginal Art. 2012. (ENG., Illus.). 176p. 50.00 (978-0-300-18003-9(9)) Yale Univ. Pr.

McCombs, W. Douglas, ed. Horsing Around: 19th Century Cast Iron Hitching Posts. 2008. (Albany Institute of History & Art Ser.). (Illus.). 76p. pap. 26.95 (978-0-939072-17-0(3), Suny Pr.) State Univ. of New York Pr.

McCormick, Melissa & Tokyo National Museum Staff. Elegant Perfection: Masterpieces of Courtly & Religious Art from the Tokyo National Museum. 2012. (ENG., Illus.). 128p. 45.00 (978-0-300-17593-6(0)) Museum of Fine Arts, Houston.

McCracken, John. John Mccracken: Sketchbook. 2008. (ENG., Illus.). 168p. 65.00 (978-1-934435-12-0(0)) Radius Bks.

McEvilley, Thomas, et al, texts. Kara Walker: My Complement, My Enemy, My Oppressor, My Love, 1 vol. 2007. (ENG., Illus.). 432p. 49.95 (978-0-935640-86-1(X)) Walker Art Ctr.

McGee, Barry. Barry McGee. 2010. (ENG., Illus.). 176p. 49.95 (978-88-6208-096-5(4)) Damiani ITA. Dist: D.A.P./Distributed Art Pubs.

McGee, Mike & Roche, Joanna. The Curiosities of Janice Lowry. 2011. (Illus.). 268p. 45.00 (978-0-9817987-4-5(8)) Grand Central Pr.

McGill, Donald Fraser Gould. The Michael Winner Collection of Donald McGill. 2007. (ENG., Illus.). 82p. pap. (978-1-871136-96-8(2)) Beetles, Chris Ltd.

McGinnis, Mark & Vinti, Carlo. Front Forty Profiles, No. 1. 2010. (Front Forty Press - Front Forty Profiles Ser.). (ITA & ENG., Illus.). 144p. pap. 20.00 (978-0-9825458-0-5(0)) Front Forty Pr.

McGowin, Ed. Name Change: One Artist - Twelve Personas - Thirty-Five Years. 2006. (ENG., Illus.). 100p. 30.00 (978-1-57806-970-5(X)) Univ. Pr. of Mississippi.

McIver, Beverly, et al. Reflections: Portraits by Beverly McIver. 2011. pap. (978-0-88259-997-7(6)) North Carolina Museum of Art.

McKinney, Rose Mary. Hans Friedrich Grohs A Memento Mori for Elisabeth Grohs Treskow. McKinney, Rose Mary, tr. 2011. (Illus.). 52p. 75.00 (978-0-9830254-0-5(1)) Frauken Grohs Collinson-Grohs Collection Trust.

McMaster, Gerald. Inuit Modern: Masterworks from the Samuel & Esther Sarick Collection, 1 vol. 2011. (ENG., Illus.). 288p. pap. 50.00 (978-1-55365-778-1(0), Douglas & McIntyre) D&M Pubs. Inc. CAN. Dist: Perseus-PGW.

McMillen, Michael C., et al. Michael C. McMillen: Train of Thought. 2011. (Illus.). 192p. (978-3-7913-5125-4(7)) Oakland Museum.

McNutt, Jennifer Complo & Holland, Ashley. Art Quantum: The Eiteljorg Fellowship for Native American Fine Art 2009. Nottage, James, ed. 2010. (ENG., Illus.). 96p. pap. 26.95 (978-0-295-98996-9(3)) Univ. of Washington Pr.

McPhee, Constance C. & Orenstein, Nadine. Infinite Jest: Caricature & Satire from Leonardo to Levine. 2011. 45.00 (978-1-58839-429-3(8)) Metropolitan Museum of Art, The.

McPhee, Constance C. & Orenstein, Nadine M. Infinite Jest: Caricature & Satire from Leonardo to Levine. 2011. (Illus.). 224p. 45.00 (978-0-300-17561-3(7)) Yale Univ. Pr.

McPherson, Tara. Lonely Heart: The Art of Tara McPherson. 2006. (Illus.). 112p. 22.95 (978-1-59582-102-7(3)) Dark Horse Comics.

McWilliam, Neil, ed. A Bibliography of Salon Criticism in Paris from the Ancien Règime to the Restoration, 1699-1827, Vol. 1. 2008. (Cambridge Studies in the History of Art Ser.). (ENG.). 284p. pap. 38.99 (978-0-521-06914-4(9)) Cambridge Univ. Pr.

Mead Art Museum, et al. Orra White Hitchcock (1796-1863) An Amherst Woman of Art & Science. 2011. (ENG., Illus.). 114p. pap. 39.95 (978-0-914337-23-2(8)) Amherst College, Mead Art Museum.

Meijer, W. Arnold & Dijk, Jacobus van. Objects for Eternity: Egyptian Antiquities from the W. Arnold Meijer Collection. 2006. (Illus.). 280p. 45.00 (978-3-8053-3651-2(9)) Zabern, Philipp von Verlag, GmbH DEU. Dist: Brown, David Bk. Co., The.

Melissa Richardson Banks Staff, ed. Papel Chicano: Works on Paper from the Collection of Cheech Marin. 2007. 96p. 24.99 (978-0-9724735-5-2(6)) La Mano Pr.

Mendini, Alessandro. Alessandro Mendini: Wunderkammer Design. 2012. (ENG & GER., Illus.). 204p. 40.00 (978-3-86984-255-4(5)) Verlag fur Moderne Kunst DEU. Dist: D.A.P./Distributed Art Pubs.

Mennekes, Friedhelm. Gerhard Trieb: Apocalypsis Variations. 2007. 176p. (978-3-87909-903-0(0)) Wienand GmbH, Druck- & Verlagshaus.

Mentasti, Rosa Barovier, ed. Exquisite Glass Ornaments: The Nineteenth-Century Glass Revival. 2011. (ENG., Illus.). 124p. 39.50 (978-88-317-0650-6(0)) Marsilio Editori spa ITA. Dist: Random Hse., Inc.

Menz, Casar & Roethlisberger. Jean Etienne Liotard: The Catalogue of the Exhibition at the Frick Collection. 2006. 120p. (978-2-85056-947-0(X)) Somogy Editions d'Art.

Merali, Shaheen, ed. Re-Imagining Asia: A Thousand Years of Separation. 2008. (ENG., Illus.). 364p. pap. 29.95 (978-0-86356-653-0(7)) Saqi Bks. GBR. Dist: Consortium Bk. Sales & Distribution.

Metcalf, Bruce & Mayfield, Signe. The Miniature Worlds of Bruce Metcalf: September 28-December 21, 2008: Palo Alto Art Center. 2008. (Illus.). 120p. (978-0-9636922-8-3(3)) Palo Alto Art Ctr.

Meyer, Anna. Internetionale: 2001-2006, 1 vol. 2007. (GER & ENG., Illus.). 248p. pap. 35.00 (978-3-939633-22-8(4)) Jovis Verlag GmbH DEU. Dist: D.A.P./Distributed Art Pubs.

Meyer, Horst Peter, et al. Horst Peter Meyer, Feind Fabrik. 2008. (GER., Illus.). 88p. (978-3-930128-91-4(8)) Stadtische Museen Jena, Bibliothek.

Meyer, Jonathan. Great Exhibitions: London - New York - Paris - Philadelphia, 1851-1900. 2006. (ENG., Illus.). 400p. (978-1-85149-527-6(4), Antique Collectors Club Dist) Antique Collectors' Club.

Meyn, Susan L. & Farny, Henry François. Henry Farny Paints the Far West. 2007. (978-0-931537-32-5(0)) Cincinnati Art Museum.

Michaud, Philippe-Alain & Lebovici, Elisabeth. A L'Attaque: Adel Abdessemed, 1 vol. 2007. (FRE & ENG., Illus.). 224p. pap. 29.00 (978-3-905770-45-2(8)) JRP Ringier Kunstverlag AG CHE. Dist: D.A.P./Distributed Art Pubs.

Middlebrook, Jason & Lombino, Mary-Kay. Jason Middlebrook: Live with Less. 2009. (Illus.). 56p. pap. (978-0-910763-37-0(2)) Univ. at Albany, Univ. Art Museum.

Miessgang, Thomas, text. Punk: No One Is Innocent: Art, Style, Revolt. 2008. (ENG., Illus.). 250p. pap. 60.00 (978-3-940748-18-8(8)) Verlag fur Moderne Kunst DEU. Dist: D.A.P./Distributed Art Pubs.

Mihai, Aurelia, illus. Unter Freiem Himmel/in the Open Air. 2008. (ENG.). 96p. pap. 29.50 (978-3-86678-056-9(7)) Kerber Verlag DEU. Dist: D.A.P./Distributed Art Pubs.

Mik, Aernout. Aernout Mik. 2009. (ENG., Illus.). 96p. pap. 24.95 (978-0-87070-742-1(6)) Museum of Modern Art.

Mik, Aernout. Communitas, 1 vol. 2011. (ENG., Illus.). 295p. pap. 48.00 (978-3-86930-297-3(6)) Steidl, Gerhard Druckerei und Verlag DEU. Dist: Innovative Logistics.

Miksic, John N., et al. Southeast Asian Ceramics: New Light on Old Pottery. 2010. (ENG., Illus.). 176p. 50.00 (978-981-4260-13-8(4), Didier Millet,Csi) Continental Sales, Inc.

Milazzo, Richard & McCarron, Andrew, texts. First Mark: El Primer Trazo, 1 vol. 2007. (ENG., Illus.). 264p. 80.00 (978-88-8158-649-3(5)) Charta ITA. Dist: D.A.P./Distributed Art Pubs.

Miller, Lillian B. Rembrandt Peale 1778-1860: A Life in the Arts: an Exhibition at the Historical Society of Pennsylvania. Hevner, Carol Eaton, ed. Parker, Peter J., tr. 2006. (Illus.). 121p. reprint ed. pap. 25.00 (978-1-4223-5827-6(5)) DIANE Publishing Co.

Miller, R. A. Lord Love You: Works by R. A. Miller from the Mullis Collection. 2009. (ENG., Illus.). 32p. 25.00 (978-0-915977-70-3(2)) Univ. of Georgia, Georgia Museum of Art.

Mingei International Museum Staff, contrib. by. ¡VIVA MÉXICO! HEROES & ARTISANS: A Commemorative Exhibition Celebrating the Independence Bicentennial & Revolution Centennial = HÉROES y ARTESANOS: Una Exhibición Conmemorativa Que Celebra el Bicentenario de la Independencia y el Centenario de la Revolución. 2010. (SPA & ENG., Illus.). 20p. (978-0-914155-24-9(5)) Mingei International Museum.

Mintz, Robert. Japanese Cloisonné Enamels: The Stephen W. Fisher Collection. 2009. pap. (978-0-911886-71-9(0)) Walters Art Museum, US.

Mirko: Archetype & Mythology, 1937-1968. 2010. 48p. pap. 26.95 (978-88-492-1240-2(2)) Gangemi ITA. Dist: International Publishers Marketing.

Mishori, Efrat. Mika Rottenberg. 2011. (ENG., Illus.). 204p. 45.00 (978-0-9826813-0-5(5)) Miller, Gregory & Co.

Mitchell, Mark D. & Inness, George. George Inness in Italy. 2011. (978-0-87633-226-9(2)) Philadelphia Museum of Art.

Mobley, Amanda. The Canopy Overhead: The Later Years of Dwight Kirsch. 2008. (ENG., Illus.). 28p. 10.00 (978-0-938932-18-5(7)) Univ. of Nebraska, Ctr. for Great Plains Studies.

Mocquet, Marlène. Marlène Mocquet. 2009. (Illus.). 111p. (978-2-906461-79-6(2)) 5 Continents.

Modigliani, Amedeo, et al. Il Mistico Profano: Omaggio a Modigliani. Claudio, Strinati, ed. 2010. (ITA., Illus.). 176p. pap. 63.50 (978-88-370-7517-0(0)) Electa ITA. Dist: Trans-Atlantic Pubns., Inc.

Moeller, Magdalena M. Ernst Ludwig Kirchner in Berlin. 2008. (Illus.). 200p. (C). pap. 55.00 (978-3-7774-4485-7(5)) Hirmer Verlag GmbH DEU. Dist: Brown, David Bk. Co., The.

Moll, Frank-Thorsten & Görner, Veit, eds. Araki Meets Hokusai. 2008. (GER & ENG., Illus.). 288p. 70.00 (978-3-939583-78-3(2)) Kehrer Verlag Heidelberg, Klaus Kehrer DEU. Dist: Consortium Bk. Sales & Distribution.

Mondloch, Kate. Screens: Viewing Media Installation Art. 2010. (Electronic Mediations Ser.). (ENG., Illus.). 208p. 75.00 *(978-0-8166-6521-1(4))*; pap. 25.00 *(978-0-8166-6522-8(2))* Univ. of Minnesota Pr.

Mondriaan Stichting Staff. Disorient. 2009. (ENG.). 128p. pap. 42.00 *(978-3-86828-068-5(5))* Kehrer Verlag Heidelberg, Klaus Kehrer DEU. Dist: Consortium Bk. Sales & Distribution.

Morgan, Susan. Joan Jonas: I Want to Live in the Country (and Other Romances) 2006. (One Work Ser.). (ENG., Illus.). 112p. (gr. 17). pap. 16.00 *(978-1-84638-025-9(1))* Afterall Publishing GBR. Dist: MIT Pr.

—Joan Jonas - I Want to Live in the Country: And Other Romances. 2007. (One Work Ser.). (ENG., Illus.). 112p. (gr. 17). 35.00 *(978-1-84638-026-6(X))* Afterall Publishing GBR. Dist: MIT Pr.

Morris, Frances, ed. Yayoi Kusama. 2012. (ENG., Illus.). 208p. 49.95 ***(978-1-935202-81-3(2))*** D.A.P./Distributed Art Pubs.

Morrison, Elizabeth & Hedeman, Anne Dawson. Imagining the Past in France: History in Manuscript Painting, 1250-1500. 2010. (ENG., Illus.). 384p. 80.00 *(978-1-60606-028-5(7))*; pap. 49.95 *(978-1-60606-029-2(5))* Getty Pubns. (J. Paul Getty Museum).

Morton, Mary, ed. Oudry's Painted Menagerie: Portraits of Exotic Animals in Eighteenth-Century France. 2007. 192p. (ENG.). 60.00 *(978-0-89236-879-2(9))*; (Illus.). pap. 40.00 *(978-0-89236-889-1(6))* Oxford Univ. Pr., Inc.

Moss, Matthew, illus. Les Aventures de Rembrandt. 2007.Tr. of Adventures of Rembrandt. (FRE.). 120p. pap. *(978-0-943884-04-2(7))* Conservation Pr.

Mossaed, Mahvash. Dear Dr. B. Encounters of a Volunteer at a County Hospital. 2007. *(978-0-9796912-1-8(4))* Zodeak G42nd Publishing.

Mossinger, Ingrid, ed. Cesare Lucchini: What Remains. 2009. (ENG., Illus.). 120p. 45.00 *(978-3-86678-213-6(6))* Kerber Verlag DEU. Dist: D.A.P./Distributed Art Pubs.

Motherwell, Robert. Open. 2010. (ENG., Illus.). 183p. 65.00 *(978-1-901785-12-8(2))* 21 Publishing GBR. Dist: D.A.P./Distributed Art Pubs.

Mowry, Robert D., ed. A Tradition Redefined: Modern & Contemporary Chinese Ink Paintings from the Chu-Tsing Li Collection, 1950-2000. 2008. (ENG., Illus.). 244p. per. 50.00 *(978-0-300-12672-3(7))* Yale Univ. Pr.

Mulas, Ugo, photos by. Fausto Melotti with Photos by Ugo Mulas. 2009. (ENG., Illus.). 80p. pap. 27.95 *(978-88-8158-716-2(5))* Charta ITA. Dist: D.A.P./Distributed Art Pubs.

Muller, Christopher & Richards, Derek, texts. Ding Dong Art Festival 2006. 2007. (Illus.). 158p. pap. 20.00 *(978-1-58423-269-8(2))* Gingko Pr., Inc.

Mullin, Glenn H. Buddha in Paradise: A Celebration in Himalayan Art. 2007. *(978-0-9772131-1-5(0))* Serindia Pubns., Inc.

Mulot, Jean-Pierre. Profile: A Collection of Drawings & Paintings. 2006. (Illus.). 180p. per. 24.95 *(978-0-9759312-0-2(2))* Mulot, Jean Pierre.

Munari, Bruno & Bianchino, Gloria. Bruno Munari: Il Disegno, il Design. 2009. (ITA & ENG., Illus.). 248p. pap. 65.00 *(978-88-7570-160-4(1))* Corraini ITA. Dist: D.A.P./Distributed Art Pubs.

Munder, Heike. The Garden of Forking Paths: An Anthology about Contemporary Follies. 2012. (GER & ENG., Illus.). 248p. 69.95 ***(978-3-03764-232-0(7))*** JRP Ringier Kunstverlag AG CHE. Dist: D.A.P./Distributed Art Pubs.

Munder, Heike, ed. Migros Museum fur Gegenwartskunst. 2008. (ENG., Illus.). 416p. 115.00 *(978-3-905829-42-6(8))* JRP Ringier Kunstverlag AG CHE. Dist: D.A.P./Distributed Art Pubs.

—Robert Kusmirowski. 2009. (ENG., Illus.). 68p. pap. 75.00 *(978-3-905770-52-0(0))* JRP Ringier Kunstverlag AG CHE. Dist: D.A.P./Distributed Art Pubs.

Munder, Heike, et al. Peter Saville Estate 1-127: Migros Museum Fur Gegenwartskunst Zurich, 1 vol. 2007. (ENG., Illus.). 272p. pap. 50.00 *(978-3-905701-66-1(9))* JRP Ringier Kunstverlag AG CHE. Dist: D.A.P./Distributed Art Pubs.

Murase, Miyeko. Through the Seasons: Japanese Art in Nature. 2008. *(978-0-931102-77-6(4))* Clark, Sterling & Francine Art Institute.

—Through the Seasons: Japanese Art in Nature. 2009. (ENG., Illus.). 84p. pap. 19.95 *(978-0-300-14188-7(2))* Yale Univ. Pr.

Musac, Leon. Cerith Wyn Evans. 2008. (SPA & ENG., Illus.). 176p. 70.00 *(978-3-7757-2131-8(2))* Hatje Cantz Verlag GmbH & Co KG DEU. Dist: D.A.P./Distributed Art Pubs.

Musée du Louvre, contrib. by. The Louvre & the Ancient World: Greek, Etruscan, Roman, Egyptian, & near Eastern Antiquities from the Musée du Louvre. 2007. 35.00 *(978-1-932543-19-3(8))* High Museum of Art.

Museum für Gestaltung Zürich. Global Design. 2010. (Illus.). 320p. pap. 60.00 *(978-3-03778-210-1(2))* Lars Muller Pubs. CHE. Dist: Prestel Publishing.

Nachtigaller, Roland, ed. Sonja Alhauser: Immerzu. 2008. (Illus.). 104p. pap. 34.00 *(978-3-86560-256-5(8))* Verlag der Buchhandlung Walther Konig DEU. Dist: D.A.P./Distributed Art Pubs.

Nachtigaller, Roland, et al, texts. Martin Walde: A Second Home for Schrödinger's Cat. 2010. (ENG., Illus.). 232p. pap. 50.00 *(978-3-7757-2623-8(3))* Hatje Cantz Verlag GmbH & Co KG DEU. Dist: D.A.P./Distributed Art Pubs.

Nagy, Clinton, ed. Splendid Heritage-Deluxe Cloth Edition. 2009. (Illus.). 207p. 135.00 *(978-0-87480-961-9(4))* Univ. of Utah Pr.

Nash, Susie. No Equal in Any Land: Andre Beauneveu, Artist to the Courts of France & Flanders. 2008. (Illus.). 216p. pap. 60.00 *(978-1-903470-66-4(8))* Holberton, Paul Publishing GBR. Dist: Casemate Pubs. & Bk. Distributors, LLC.

Nassau County Museum of Art Staff, contrib. by. Long Island Collects: Cézanne, Degas, Renoir & Chagall Come to Long Island. 2009. (Illus.). 28p. *(978-0-9815644-3-2(7))* Nassau County Museum of Art.

—Tiffany. 2008. (Illus.). 48p. pap. *(978-0-9815644-2-5(9))* Nassau County Museum of Art.

National Galleries of Scotland Staff, contrib. by. Henry Raeburn & His Printmakers. 2007. (Illus.). 32p. pap. *(978-1-903278-90-1(2))* National Galleries of Scotland.

National Museum of the American Indian (U.S.), George Gustav Heye Center Staff, contrib. by. Off the Map: Landscape in the Native Imagination. 2007. (Illus.). 88p. *(978-1-933565-08-8(X))* Smithsonian National Museum of the American Indian.

Nauman, Bruce. Bruce Nauman: Live or Die. 2010. (ENG., Illus.). 240p. 59.95 *(978-3-8321-9284-6(0))* DuMont DEU. Dist: D.A.P./Distributed Art Pubs.

Nefkens, Han. Pipilotti Rist: Friendly game: Electronic Feelings. 2010. (CAT, SPA & ENG., Illus.). 152p. 34.95 *(978-84-92861-56-9(8))* Fundacio Joan Miro ESP. Dist: Actar Birkhauser Distribution.

Nes, Adi, et al. Access to Israel. 2008. (GER & ENG., Illus.). 116p. pap. 40.00 *(978-3-86560-463-7(3))* Verlag der Buchhandlung Walther Konig DEU. Dist: D.A.P./Distributed Art Pubs.

Neuburger, Susanne & Franzen, Brigitte, eds. Hyper Real: The Passion of the Real in Painting & Photography. 2011. (ENG & GER., Illus.). 400p. 49.95 *(978-3-86560-929-8(5))* Verlag der Buchhandlung Walther Konig DEU. Dist: D.A.P./Distributed Art Pubs.

Neuenschwander, Rivane. Rivane Neuenschwander: A Day Like Any Other, 1 vol. 2011. (ENG & POR., Illus.). 244p. pap. 49.95 *(978-0-915557-93-6(2))* New Museum of Contemporary Art, The.

Neuhaus, Eugen. The Art of the Exposition. 2007. (ENG.). 80p. pap. 16.99 *(978-1-4346-4169-4(4))*; 88p. pap. 18.99 *(978-1-4346-4232-5(1))* BiblioBazaar.

—The Art of the Exposition. 2007. (ENG.). 76p. per. *(978-1-4065-3088-9(3))* Dodo Pr.

—The Art of the Exposition. 2007. (ENG.). pap. *(978-1-4068-3509-0(9))* Echo Library.

—The Art of the Exposition. 2007. (ENG.). 166p. 36.95 *(978-0-548-02534-5(7))* Kessinger Publishing, LLC.

—The Galleries of the Exposition. 2007. (ENG.). 76p. per. *(978-1-4065-3089-6(1))* Dodo Pr.

—The Galleries of the Exposition. 2007. (ENG.). 80p. per. *(978-1-4068-3673-8(7))* Echo Library.

Nicolai, Olaf & text. Olaf Nicolai Arbeiten/Works 2003-2006, 1 vol. 2007. (ENG., Illus.). 56p. pap. 30.00 *(978-3-938821-23-7(X))* Verlag fur Moderne Kunst DEU. Dist: D.A.P./Distributed Art Pubs.

Niederer, Caro. Waiting for Returns. 2010. (ENG., Illus.). 128p. 45.00 *(978-3-86521-628-1(5))* Steidl, Gerhard Druckerei und Verlag DEU. Dist: D.A.P./Distributed Art Pubs.

Nittve, Lars, text. Time & Place Vol. 3: Los Angeles 1957-1968, Vol. 3. 2008. (ENG., Illus.). 142p. pap. 50.00 *(978-3-86521-640-3(4))* Steidl, Gerhard Druckerei und Verlag DEU. Dist: D.A.P./Distributed Art Pubs.

Noble, Nancy & Buckberrough, Sherry. Women Artists @ New Britain Museum. 2011. (Illus.). 96p. pap. 25.00 *(978-0-9724497-2-4(8))* New Britain Museum of American Art.

Noever, Peter, ed. Bruno Gironcoli: The Unbegotten. (ENG & GER., Illus.). 160p. pap. 45.00 *(978-3-7757-0678-0(X))* Hatje Cantz Verlag GmbH & Co KG DEU. Dist: D.A.P./Distributed Art Pubs.

—How Many Billboards? 2010. (ENG., Illus.). 160p. pap. 40.00 *(978-3-86984-039-0(0))* Verlag der Buchhandlung Walther Konig DEU. Dist: D.A.P./Distributed Art Pubs.

Nogueira, Carlos. Desenhos Construções e Outros Acidentes: Drawings Constructions & Other Accidents. 2008. (Illus.). 111p. *(978-972-37-1392-3(6))* Assirio e Alvim.

Obey: Supply & Demand: The Art of Shepard Fairey. 2008. (ESP., Illus.). 360p. 59.95 *(978-1-58423-244-5(7))* Gingko Pr., Inc.

O'Brien, Timothy A. & Walsh, Margo Grant. Collecting by Design: Silver & Metalwork of the Twentieth Century from the Margo Grant Walsh Collection. 2008. (ENG., Illus.). 152p. pap. 25.00 *(978-0-300-13892-4(X))* Yale Univ. Pr.

Obrist, Hans Ulrich, ed. Jeff Koons: Popeye Series, 1 vol. 2009. (ENG., Illus.). 88p. pap. 39.95 *(978-3-86560-666-2(0))* Verlag der Buchhandlung Walther Konig DEU. Dist: D.A.P./Distributed Art Pubs.

Obrist, Hans Ulrich, et al, eds. Luke Fowler. 2009. (GER & ENG., Illus.). 96p. 35.00 *(978-3-03764-046-3(4))* JRP Ringier Kunstverlag AG CHE. Dist: D.A.P./Distributed Art Pubs.

—Victor Man. 2008. (ENG., Illus.). 64p. 35.00 *(978-3-905829-31-0(2))* JRP Ringier Kunstverlag AG CHE. Dist: D.A.P./Distributed Art Pubs.

Ochoa, Elena, ed. Frequency: Michal Rovner. 2009. (SPA & ENG., Illus.). 175p. pap. 65.00 *(978-0-9559613-8-0(6))* Ivory Pr. ESP. Dist: Actar Birkhauser Distribution.

Ogawa, Morihiro & Harada, Kazutoshi. Art of the Samurai: Japanese Arms & Armor, 1156-1868. 2009. 65.00 *(978-1-58839-345-6(3))* Metropolitan Museum of Art, The.

O'Hare, Mary Kate. Constructive Spirit: Abstract Art in South & North America, 1920s-50s. 2010. 196p. 39.95 *(978-0-7649-5274-6(9))* Pomegranate Communications, Inc.

Okada, Koichiro, et al. Masters of Bamboo: Artistic Lineages in the Lloyd Cotsen Japanese Basket Collection. 2008. (ENG., Illus.). 144p. pap. 25.00 *(978-0-939117-40-6(1))* Asian Art Museum of San Francisco.

Oliver, Valerie Cassel, et al. Donald Moffett: The Extravagant Vein. 2011. (ENG., Illus.). 224p. 65.00 *(978-0-8478-3727-4(0)*, Skira) Rizzoli International Pubns., Inc.

O'Neil, Robyn. Robyn O'Neil: the World has Won. A Final Bow Was Taken. 2010. (ENG., Illus.). 68p. pap. 25.00 *(978-1-879003-57-6(0))* Des Moines Art Ctr.

O'Neill, Liam & Ní Shúilleabháin, Brenda. Corca Dhuibhne. 2010. (ENG., Illus.). 224p. 159.95 *(978-0-86322-408-9(3))* Brandon/Mount Eagle Pubns., Ltd. IRL. Dist: Dufour Editions, Inc.

O'Neill, Paul. Curating Subjects: Occasional Table, 1 vol. 2007. (ENG.). 232p. pap. 30.00 *(978-0-949004-16-1(2))* Open Editions GBR. Dist: D.A.P./Distributed Art Pubs.

Ono, Yoko. Yoko Ono: Touch Me. 2009. (ENG., Illus.). 72p. 37.95 *(978-88-8158-696-7(7))* Charta ITA. Dist: D.A.P./Distributed Art Pubs.

Onori, Lorenza Mochi, ed. Raffaello e Urbino: La sua formazione e I rapporti con la citta Natale. 2009. (ITA., Illus.). 320p. pap. 67.50 *(978-88-370-6812-7(3))* Electa ITA. Dist: Trans-Atlantic Pubns., Inc.

Ophuis, Ronald. Ronald Ophuis. 2008. (ENG., Illus.). 152p. pap. 55.00 *(978-3-905829-32-7(0))* JRP Ringier Kunstverlag AG CHE. Dist: D.A.P./Distributed Art Pubs.

Opper, Thorsten. Hadrian: Empire & Conflict. 2010. (Illus.). 224p. pap. 21.95 *(978-0-674-05742-5(2))* Harvard Univ. Pr.

O'Reilly, Sally & Allen, Jonathan, texts. Magic Show. 2010. (ENG., Illus.). 116p. pap. 30.00 *(978-1-85332-281-5(4))* Hayward Gallery Publishing GBR. Dist: D.A.P./Distributed Art Pubs.

Ortega, Damian, et al. Do It Yourself: Damian Ortega. 2009. (SPA & ENG., Illus.). 208p. 40.00 *(978-0-8478-3438-9(7)*, Skira) Rizzoli International Pubns., Inc.

Ortega, Luis Felipe. Ocupación: Luis Felipe Ortega, 1 vol. 2007. (ENG & SPA., Illus.). 48p. 19.00 *(978-968-9056-05-8(0))* Turner, Ediciones S.A. ESP. Dist: D.A.P./Distributed Art Pubs.

Os, H. W. Van, et al. Dreaming of Italy. 2007. (ENG., Illus.). 128p. 39.50 *(978-90-400-8222-1(7))* Waanders B.V., Uitgeverij NLD. Dist: National Bk. Network.

O'Toole, Judith. Different Views in Hudson River School Painting. 2008. (ENG.). 160p. (gr. 17). pap. 27.95 *(978-0-231-13821-5(0))* Columbia Univ. Pr.

Otto Keunzli: 3rd Eye. 30.00 *(978-90-5006-051-6(X))* Stedelijk Museum NLD. Dist: D.A.P./Distributed Art Pubs.

Oudsten, Frank den. Space, Time, Narrative: On the Art of Exhibiting Today. 2011. (Illus.). 512p. 99.95 *(978-0-7546-7655-3(2))* Ashgate Publishing Co.

Owens, Susan, et al. Amazing Rare Things: The Art of Natural History in the Age of Discovery. 2009. (ENG., Illus.). 224p. pap. 24.95 *(978-0-9798456-2-8(9)*, 979842) Kales Pr.

Paik, Nam June. Nam June Paik. Lee, Sook-Kyung & Rennert, Susanne, eds. 2011. (ENG., Illus.). 208p. 45.00 *(978-1-85437-924-5(0))* Tate Publishing, Ltd. GBR. Dist: Hachette Bk. Group.

Palazzo Fortuny Staff, ed. In-finitum: L'Infinito del non-finito, 1 vol. 2010. (ITA., Illus.). 339p. 115.00 *(978-90-76979-81-6(2))* Exhibitions International BEL. Dist: Innovative Logistics.

Paper Dreams. 2007. (Illus.). 12p. pap. *(978-0-9717365-4-2(5))* Palos Verdes Art Ctr.

Parker, Samuel K., et al. What Is a Trade? Donald Fels & Signboard Painters of South India. 2008. (Illus.). 80p. pap. *(978-0-924335-26-6(2))* Tacoma Art Museum.

Parmiggiani, Claudio & Clair, Jean. Claudio Parmiggiani: Apocalypsis Cum Figuris. 2008. (FRE, ITA & ENG., Illus.). 404p. 50.00 *(978-88-422-1575-2(9))* Allemandi, Umberto & Co. GBR. Dist: Antique Collectors' Club.

Parr, Martin & Weski, Thomas. Parrworld, 2 vols. 2008. (Illus.). *(978-1-57110-693-3(6))* Aperture Foundation, Inc.

Parshall, Peter, et al. The Darker Side of Light: Arts of Privacy, 1850-1900. 2009. *(978-0-89468-354-1(3))* National Gallery of Art.

Passos Leite, Maria Fernanda. René Lalique at the Calouste Gulbenkian Museum. 2009. (ENG., Illus.). 136p. 40.00 *(978-88-572-0042-2(6))* Skira Editore ITA. Dist: Random Hse., Inc.

Patel, Divia, et al. Cinema India: The Art of Bollywood. 2007. (Illus.). 63p. pap. 19.95 *(978-0-7241-0280-8(9))* National Gallery of Victoria AUS. Dist: Antique Collectors' Club.

Paul, Carole. The Borghese Collections & the Display of Art in the Age of the Grand Tour. 2008. (Illus.). 358p. 134.95 *(978-0-7546-6134-4(2))* Ashgate Publishing Co.

Peabody Museum Publisher. Twenty-Five Centuries of Peruvian Art: 700 B. C. to 1800 A. D. 2011. 68p. 36.95 ***(978-1-258-09128-6(3))*** Literary Licensing, LLC.

Pearson, Joshua T. Alphabhetto. 2011. 56p. pap. 25.95 ***(978-1-4634-0772-8(6))*** AuthorHouse.

Peckl, Manfred. Another Girl, Another World, 1 vol. 2006. (ENG & GER., Illus.). 19p. 35.00 *(978-3-938821-34-3(5))* Verlag fur Moderne Kunst DEU. Dist: D.A.P./Distributed Art Pubs.

Peirce, Donald. Art & Enterprise: American Decorative Art 1825-1917 - The Virginia Carroll Crawford Collection. 2006. (ENG., Illus.). 464p. 60.00 *(978-0-939802-87-6(2))* High Museum of Art.

Pellegrini, Sonia. L'officina Del Volo: Futurismo, Pubblicità e Design, 1908-1938. 2009. (ITA., Illus.). 235p. *(978-88-366-1468-4(X))* Silvana.

Pemberton, John, 3rd. African Beaded Art: Power & Adornment. 2008. (Illus.). 224p. pap. *(978-0-87391-058-3(3))* Smith College Pubns.

Penwarden, Charles, et al, trs. Pierre & Gilles: Double Jeopardy 1976 To 2007. 2007. (ENG & GER., Illus.). 459p. 59.99 *(978-3-8228-4650-6(3))* TASCHEN DEU. Dist: Ingram Pub. Services.

Perell, Josep, ed. Sommerer & Mignonneau: Living Systems. 2011. 96p. pap. *(978-84-92861-79-8(7))* Actar Birkhauser Distribution.

Pergam, Elizabeth A. The Manchester Art Treasures Exhibition of 1857: Entrepreneurs, Connoisseurs & the Public. 2011. (Illus.). 396p. 124.95 *(978-1-4094-1830-6(8))* Ashgate Publishing Co.

Perjovschi, Dan. Mad Cow, Bird Flu, Global Village. 2007. (ENG., Illus.). 120p. 17.95 *(978-1-84467-166-3(6)*, 844166) Verso Bks. GBR. Dist: Norton, W. W. & Co., Inc.

Pernice, Manfred. Manfred Pernice: Que-Sah. 2011. (ENG & GER., Illus.). 208p. pap. 70.00 *(978-3-940748-53-9(6))* Verlag fur Moderne Kunst DEU. Dist: D.A.P./Distributed Art Pubs.

Perry, Claire. The Great American Hall of Wonders: Art, Science, & Invention in the Nineteenth Century. 2011. (ENG., Illus.). 256p. 65.00 *(978-1-904832-97-3(0))* Giles, D. Ltd. GBR. Dist: Antique Collectors' Club.

—The Great American Hall of Wonders: Art, Science, & Invention in the Nineteenth Century. 2011. *(978-0-9790678-9-1(8))* Smithsonian American Art Museum.

Pesenti, Allegra, et al. Zarina: Paper Like Skin. 2012. (ENG., Illus.). 128p. 39.95 ***(978-3-7913-5166-7(4))*** Prestel Publishing.

Peters, Ruudt & Mallol, Mònica Gaspar. Lingam: Fertility Now. den Hout, Guus van, ed. 2010. (ENG., Illus.). 128p. 50.00 *(978-3-89790-325-8(3))* Arnoldsche Art Pubs. DEU. Dist: Antique Collectors' Club.

Petrova, Yevgenia, ed. Play & Passion in Russian Fine Art. 2006. (ENG., Illus.). 360p. 75.00 *(978-3-930775-62-0(X)*, Palace Editions) Mandala Publishing.

Petschnig, Mária, contrib. by. Maria Petschnig: Master Bedroom. 2011. (ENG., Illus.). 65p. pap. ***(978-3-9502046-2-9(8))*** Fotohof Editions.

Pietromarchi, Bartolomeo, ed. Antarctica: [in English & Italian]. 2008. 176p. 57.50 *(978-88-370-6337-5(7))* Electa ITA. Dist: Trans-Atlantic Pubns., Inc.

Piggott, Stuart. Early Celtic Art: From Its Origins to Its Aftermath. 2008. (ENG., Illus.). 77p. pap. 39.95 *(978-0-202-36186-4(1))* Aldine Transaction.

Pincus-Witten, Robert, text. Circa 70: Lynda Benglis Louise Bourgeois. 2007. (Illus.). 26p. per. 25.00 *(978-0-9797397-4-3(8))* Cheim & Read.

Pinkert, Marvin, et al. The Public Vaults Unlocked: Discovering American History in the National Archives. 2006. (Archives Ser.). (ENG., Illus.). 176p. 40.00 *(978-1-904832-17-1(2))* Giles, D. Ltd. GBR. Dist: Antique Collectors' Club.

Pinkney, Jerry. Jerry Pinkney: Aesop's Fables & Other Tails. 2007. (Illus.). 17p. pap. *(978-0-9795872-1-4(2))* Brandywine River Museum.

Plankensteiner, Barbara. Benin. 2010. (ENG., Illus.). 136p. pap. 34.95 *(978-88-7439-410-4(1))* 5 Continents ITA. Dist: Hachette Bk. Group.

Platt, Susan & LeBaron, Michelle. Loud Bones: The Jewelry of Nancy Worden. 2009. (ENG., Illus.). 128p. 40.00 *(978-0-924335-28-0(9))*; pap. 24.95 *(978-0-924335-29-7(7))* Tacoma Art Museum.

Ploof, John, ed. The Object of Labor: Art, cloth, & Cultural Production. 2006. (Illus.). 408p. per. *(978-0-9637817-5-8(8))* Schl. of the Art Institute of Chicago, The.

Pluvinge, Gonzague. Expo 58: Between Utopia & Reality. 2008. (ENG., Illus.). 208p. pap. *(978-2-87386-541-2(5)*, Lannoo Pubs. (Acc)) Antique Collectors' Club.

Poirier, Anne & Poirier, Patrick, illus. Anne e Patrick Poirier, 1 vol. 2007. (ITA & ENG.). 102p. pap. 30.00 *(978-88-89431-99-3(7))* Damiani ITA. Dist: D.A.P./Distributed Art Pubs.

Poledna, Mathias. Mathias Poledna: Western Recording, 1 vol. 2006. (ENG., Illus.). 156p. pap. 30.00 *(978-90-73362-67-3(9))* D.A.P./Distributed Art Pubs.

Poltamees, Welleran. Weird & Wonderful: Discoveries from the Mysterious World of Forgotten Children's Books. Darling, Harold, ed. 2010. (ENG.). 112p. (J). (gr. -1-3). pap. 18.95 *(978-1-59583-385-3(4)*, Green Tiger Pr.) Laughing Elephant.

Pongracz, Patricia C., et al. The Christian Story: Five Asian Artists Today. 2007. (ENG., Illus.). 168p. pap. 39.95 *(978-1-904832-20-1(2))* Giles, D. Ltd. GBR. Dist: Antique Collectors' Club.

Ponti, Gio. Gio Ponti: Fascination for Ceramics. 2012. (ENG & ITA., Illus.). 160p. pap. 40.00 ***(978-88-366-2064-7(7))*** Silvana ITA. Dist: D.A.P./Distributed Art Pubs.

Portal, Jane. Terra Cotta Warriors: Guardians of China's First Emperor. 2008. (ENG., Illus.). 96p. 14.95 *(978-1-4262-0380-0(2)*, National Geographic) National Geographic Society.

Porter, Jenelle, ed. Fertilizers: Olin / Eisenman, 1 vol. 2007. (ENG., Illus.). 96p. per. 25.00 *(978-0-88454-109-7(6))* Univ. of Pennsylvania, Institute of Contemporary Art.

Post, Melissa G. Preston Singletary: Echoes, Fire, & Shadows. 2009. (ENG., Illus.). 152p. 45.00 *(978-0-295-98918-1(1))* Univ. of Washington Pr.

Powell, Amy Knight. Depositions: Scenes from the Late Medieval Church & the Modern Museum. 2012. (ENG., Illus.). 384p. (gr. 17). 34.95 ***(978-1-935408-20-8(8))*** Zone Bks.

Prentice, Helaine Kaplan. Suzhou: Shaping an Ancient City for the New China. 2006. (Land Marks Ser.: Vol. 8). (ENG., Illus.). 64p. pap. 24.95 *(978-1-888931-15-0(9))* Spacemaker Pr.

PressGingko. When Space Meets Art/When Art Meets Space. 2007. (Illus.). 240p. 39.95 *(978-988-98228-0-4(6))* Viction Workshop, Ltd. HKG. Dist: Gingko Pr., Inc.

Priem, Ruud. Rembrandt & the Golden Age of Dutch Art: Treasures from the Rijksmuseum, Amsterdam. Hunter-Stiebel, Penelope, ed. 2007. (ENG., Illus.). 144p. 29.95 *(978-1-883124-23-6(9))* Portland Art Museum.

—Vermeer, Rembrandt & the Golden Age of Dutch Art: Masterpieces of the Rijksmuseum, 1 vol. 2009. (ENG., Illus.). 240p. pap. 39.95 *(978-1-55365-471-1(4))* D&M Pubs. Inc. CAN. Dist: Perseus-PGW.

Primordial Images of a Modern Mystic - Myron Conan Dyal. 2007. per. 24.95 *(978-0-9771696-5-8(0))* Grand Central Pr.

Princenthal, Nancy, ed. Joyce Kozloff: Co-Ordinates. 2009. (ENG., Illus.). 132p. 45.00 *(978-0-9768488-8-2(0))* Dickinson College, The Trout Gallery.

Pritchard, Jane & Marsh, Geoffrey, eds. Diaghilev & the Golden Age of the Ballet Russes 1909-1929. 2010. (ENG., Illus.). 240p. 55.00 *(978-1-85177-613-9(3))* V & A Pubns. GBR. Dist: Hachette Bk. Group.

Proser, Adriana, ed. Pilgrimage & Buddhist Art. 2010. (Illus.). 224p. 65.00 *(978-0-300-15566-2(2))* Yale Univ. Pr.

Pucci, Idanna, ed. Brazza in Congo: A Life & Legacy. 2009. (ENG., Illus.). 240p. 40.00 *(978-1-884167-94-2(2))* Umbrage Editions.

Pucci, Ralph. Show. deluxe ed. 2009. 192p. 150.00 *(978-0-9801557-9-2(7))* Glitterati, Inc.

Puhle, Matthias. Aufbruch in die Gotik, 2 vols. 2009. (GER., Illus.). 1124p. (C). 135.00 *(978-3-8053-4062-5(1))* Zabern, Philipp von Verlag, GmbH DEU. Dist: Brown, David Bk. Co., The.

Putnam, James. Art & Artifact: The Museum as Medium. 2nd rev. ed. 2009. (ENG., Illus.). 216p. pap. 34.95 *(978-0-500-28835-1(6)*, 528835) Thames & Hudson.

Quarcoopome, Nii O. & Arlt, Veit. Through African Eyes: The European in African Art, 1500 to Present. 2010. pap. 55.00 *(978-0-89558-163-1(9))* Detroit Institute of Arts.

Rabbia, Luisa. Luisa Rabbia: Traveling under the Same Sky. 2010. (ENG., Illus.). 160p. 45.00 *(978-88-7757-244-8(2))* Hopefulmonster Editore ITA. Dist: D.A.P./Distributed Art Pubs.

Rabottini, Alessandro. Aaron Curry: Bad Dimension. 2010. (ENG., Illus.). 180p. pap. 49.95 *(978-3-86560-745-4(4))* Verlag der Buchhandlung Walther Konig DEU. Dist: D.A.P./Distributed Art Pubs.

Racette, Sherry Farrell. Clearing a Path: New Ways of Seeing Traditional Indigenous Art. Robertson, Carmen, ed. 2009. (ENG.). 80p. 29.95 *(978-0-88977-226-7(6))* Canadian Plains Research Ctr. CAN. Dist: Univ. of Toronto Pr.

Radke, Gary & contrib. by. The Gates of Paradise: Lorenzo Ghiberti's Renaissance Masterpiece. 2007. (Illus.). 182p. 45.00 *(978-1-932543-15-5(5))* High Museum of Art.

Radke, Gary M., ed. The Gates of Paradise: Lorenzo Ghiberti's Renaissance Masterpiece. 2007. (ENG., Illus.). 184p. 45.00 *(978-0-300-12615-0(8))* Yale Univ. Pr.

Rainer, Arnulf. Arnulf Rainer. Visages. 2011. (GER & ENG., Illus.). 132p. 59.95 ***(978-3-8321-9370-6(7))*** DuMont DEU. Dist: D.A.P./Distributed Art Pubs.

Raspail, Thierry, et al. Marlène Mocquet. 2010. (ENG & FRE., Illus.). 112p. 34.95 *(978-88-7439-522-4(1))* 5 Continents ITA. Dist: Hachette Bk. Group.

Ratcliff, Carter & Paley, Albert. Albert Paley in the 21st Century. Gribaudo, Paola, ed. 2010. *(978-0-615-35392-0(4))* Paley Studios Ltd.

Rathbone, Eliza E. & Halford-MacLeod, Johanna. Art Beyond Isms: Masterworks from el Greco to Picasso in the Phillips Collection. 2006. (ENG., Illus.). pap. 22.00 *(978-1-903942-08-6(X))* Third Millenium Publishing GBR. Dist: National Bk. Network.

Ratti, Annie. Annie Ratti, 1 vol. 2007. (ENG., Illus.). 112p. pap. 34.95 *(978-88-8158-630-1(4))* Charta ITA. Dist: D.A.P./Distributed Art Pubs.

Raymond, Yasmil, et al, texts. Abstract Resistance. 2010. (ENG., Illus.). 96p. pap. 9.99 *(978-0-935640-95-3(9))* Walker Art Ctr.

Reading, Nigel & Wyatt, Gary. Manawa: Pacific Heartbeat - A Celebration of Contemporary Maori & Pacific Northwest Coast Art, 1 vol. (ENG., Illus.). 144p. pap. 35.00 *(978-1-55365-139-0(1))* D&M Pubs. Inc. CAN. Dist: Perseus-PGW.

Rehberger, Tobias. Flach. 2010. (GER., Illus.). 160p. *(978-3-942405-00-3(8))* Die Gestalten Verlag.

Reilly, Maura, et al. Richard Bell: Uz vs. Them. 2011. (Illus.). 80p. pap. *(978-1-885444-40-0(0))* American Federation of Arts, The.

—Richard Bell: Uz vs. Them. 2011. (ENG., Illus.). 80p. 35.00 *(978-1-904832-95-9(4))* Giles, D. Ltd. GBR. Dist: Antique Collectors' Club.

Remba, Natania. Surrounded by Water: Expressions of Freedom & Isolation in Contemporary Cuban Art. 2008. (Illus.). 64p. pap. 15.00 *(978-1-881450-28-3(7))* Boston Univ., Art Gallery.

Rembrandt Harmenszoon van Rijn. Rembrandt & the Face of Jesus. 2011. (Illus.). xv, 255p. *(978-0-87633-228-3(9))*; *(978-0-87633-227-6(0))* Philadelphia Museum of Art.

Rembrandt Harmenszoon van Rijn & Tucker, Mark S. Rembrandt & the Face of Jesus. DeWitt, Lloyd, ed. 2011. (ENG., Illus.). 256p. 65.00 *(978-0-300-16957-7(4))* Yale Univ. Pr.

Rembrandt Harmenszoon van Rijn, et al. Rembrandt: Three Faces of the Master. 2008. *(978-0-931537-33-2(9))* Cincinnati Art Museum.

Rene Magritte. 75.00 *(978-2-903004-07-1(2))* Galerie Isy Brachot FRA. Dist: D.A.P./Distributed Art Pubs.

Restany, Pierre & De Vreee, Freddy. Cremer: Grafiek, 1956-1998 = Prints, 1956-1998. (DUT & ENG., Illus.). 252p. pap. *(978-90-6868-210-6(5))* Thoth, Uitgeverij.

Reuther, Manfred, ed. Emil Nolde: Die Südseereise 1913 - 1914. 2008. (GER & ENG., Illus.). 144p. *(978-3-8321-9083-5(X))* DuMont.

Reuther, Manfred & Klar, Alexander, eds. Emil Nolde und Emil Schumacher. Verwandte Seelen / Kindred Spirits. 2011. (ENG., Illus.). 144p. 45.00 *(978-3-8321-9351-5(0))* DuMont DEU. Dist: D.A.P./Distributed Art Pubs.

Rewald, Sabine. Rooms with a View: The Open Window in the 19th Century. 2011. (Illus.). xiii, 190p. pap. 30.00 ***(978-1-58839-413-2(1))*** Metropolitan Museum of Art, The.

Rheims, Bettina & Bramly, Serge. Bettina Rheims & Serge Bramly. 25.00 *(978-3-929078-29-9(5))* Kehayoff Verlag DEU. Dist: Prestel Publishing.

Rhode, Robin. Robin Rhode: Who Saw Who. 2009. (ENG., Illus.). 120p. 40.00 *(978-1-85332-271-6(7))* Hayward Gallery Publishing GBR. Dist: D.A.P./Distributed Art Pubs.

Ribas, Joao, ed. Frances Stark: This Could Become a Gimick [sic] or an Honest Articulation of the Workings of the Mind. 2011. (ENG., Illus.). 200p. pap. 20.00 *(978-0-938437-75-8(5))* Massachusetts Institute of Technology, List Visual Arts Ctr.

Richard Tuttle. 75.00 *(978-90-12-06665-5(4))* S. D. U. Uitgeverij NLD. Dist: D.A.P./Distributed Art Pubs.

Richards, Judith, frwd. Phantasmagoria: Specters of Absence, 1 vol. 2007. (ENG., Illus.). 72p. 24.95 *(978-0-916365-76-9(X))* Independent Curators International.

Richardt, Ferdinand, et al. Ferdinand Richardt: Drawings of America, 1855-1859. 2007. *(978-0-915895-31-1(5))* Munson-Williams-Proctor Institute.

Richoux, Sylvie. Karine Arabian: The Armenians in Fashion 17-21st Centuries. 2009. (FRE & ENG., Illus.). 152p. pap. 34.80 *(978-2-7572-0083-4(6)*, Art Stock Bks. Ltd/Csi) Continental Sales, Inc.

Richter, Markus, ed. Megastructure Reloaded: Due Inkunabeln der 1960er- Jahre in der visionären Architektur, Popkultur und Kunst. Dieser Katalog erscheint anlässlich der Ausstellung. 2008. (ENG., Illus.). 368p. pap. 55.00 *(978-3-7757-2216-2(5))* Hatje Cantz Verlag GmbH & Co KG DEU. Dist: D.A.P./Distributed Art Pubs.

Richter Verlag Publishing, creator. Hans Arp: Die Natur der Dinge, 1 vol. 2008. (ENG., Illus.). 236p. 95.00 *(978-3-937572-74-1(0))* Richter Verlag DEU. Dist: D.A.P./Distributed Art Pubs.

Riggs, Timothy. At the Heart of Progress: Coal, Iron, & Steam Since 1750. 2009. (Distributed for the Ackland Art Museum Ser.). (ENG., Illus.). 50p. pap. 15.95 *(978-0-8078-5980-3(X))* Univ. of North Carolina Pr.

Rinder, Lawrence, et al. Create. 2011. (ENG., Illus.). 179p. pap. 27.50 *(978-0-9719397-9-0(9))* Univ. of California, Berkeley Art Museum & Pacific Film Archive.

Riopelle, Christopher. Manet to Picasso: The National Gallery. 2007. (ENG., Illus.). 72p. pap. 14.95 *(978-1-85709-333-9(X))* Yale Univ. Pr.

Rishel, Joseph J. The Arts in Latin America, 1492-1820. 2006. (Philadelphia Museum of Art Ser.). (ENG., Illus.). 592p. 75.00 *(978-0-300-12003-5(6))* Yale Univ. Pr.

Rishel, Joseph J. & Stratton, Suzanne L. The Arts in Latin America, 1492-1820. 2006. (Philadelphia Museum of Art Ser.). (Illus.). xxiii, 568p. *(978-0-87633-251-1(3))*; *(978-0-87633-250-4(5))* Philadelphia Museum of Art.

Robert Hull Fleming Museum. Material Pursuits. 2007. *(978-0-934658-00-3(5))* Fleming, Robert Hull Museum.

Robinson, J. Dennis. Maritime Portsmouth: The Sawtelle Collection. Candee, Richard M., ed. 2011. (Illus.). 212p. 35.00 ***(978-0-915819-38-6(4))*** Portsmouth Marine Society, The.

Roche, Catherine. Fleeting Beauty: Japanese Woodblock Prints. 2010. *(978-0-932216-66-3(8))* Seattle Art Museum.

Rodeschini, Maria. Future of Futurism. di Pietrantonio, Giancinto, ed. 2007. 240p. pap. 65.00 *(978-88-370-5663-6(X))* Electa ITA. Dist: Trans-Atlantic Pubns., Inc.

Rodgers, Susan, et al. Gold Cloths of Sumatra: Indonesia's Songkets from Ceremony to Commodity. 2010. (Illus.). 148p. pap. 44.00 *(978-90-6718-312-3(1))* KITLV Pr. NLD. Dist: Univ. of Hawaii Pr.

Roger, Daniel & Giroire, Cecile. Roman Art from the Louvre. 2007. (ENG., Illus.). 280p. 65.00 *(978-1-55595-283-9(6))* Hudson Hills Pr. LLC.

Rogers, James G., Jr. et al. The Art of Downing Barnitz: A Retrospective Exhibition. 2007. 18.00 *(978-0-9714065-1-3(0))* Florida Southern College, Melvin Art Gallery.

Rogge, Claudia, photos by. Claudia Rogge: A Retrospective. 2010. (RUS, GER & ENG., Illus.). 128p. 60.00 *(978-3-7757-2574-3(1))* Hatje Cantz Verlag GmbH & Co KG DEU. Dist: D.A.P./Distributed Art Pubs.

Román, Dulce María & Oliver-Smith, Kerry. Paradigms & the Unexpected: Modern & Contemporary Art from the Shey Collection. 2007. *(978-0-9762552-6-0(X))*; pap. *(978-0-9762552-7-7(8))* Harn Museum of Art.

Rondinone, Ugo & Tarsia, Andrea. Ugo Rondinone: Zero Built a Nest in My Navel, 1 vol. 2006. (ENG., Illus.). 320p. 55.00 *(978-3-905701-52-4(9))* JRP Ringier Kunstverlag AG CHE. Dist: D.A.P./Distributed Art Pubs.

Roosen, Maria. Maria Roosen: My Friends, 1 vol. 2006. (ENG., Illus.). 32p. pap. 15.00 *(978-90-78088-07-3(9))* Valiz NLD. Dist: D.A.P./Distributed Art Pubs.

Rose, Peter, selected by. Doulton Studio Notes: A Miscellany of Amateur Contributions, 1883-1887. 2007. (ENG., Illus.). 169p. 40.00 *(978-0-903685-02-3(7)*, Richard Dennis Pubns. Di) Antique Collectors' Club GBR. Dist: National Bk. Network.

Rosefeldt, Julian. Julian Rosefeldt: Living in Oblivion, 2 vols. 2011. (GER & ENG., Illus.). 104p. pap. 43.50 *(978-3-86678-414-7(7))* Kerber Verlag DEU. Dist: D.A.P./Distributed Art Pubs.

Rosenberg, Angela. Valeria Heisenberg: Bilder 2000-2005, 1 vol. 2007. (ENG & GER., Illus.). 82p. 45.00 *(978-3-938025-68-0(9))* Kerber Verlag DEU. Dist: D.A.P./Distributed Art Pubs.

Rosenberg, Pierre & Christiansen, Keith. Poussin & Nature: Arcadian Visions. 2008. (Illus.). xvii, 414p. 65.00 *(978-1-58839-242-8(2))* Metropolitan Museum of Art, The.

Rosenberg, Pierre & Christiansen, Keith, eds. Poussin & Nature: Arcadian Visions. 2008. (ENG., Illus.). 432p. 65.00 *(978-0-300-13668-5(4))* Yale Univ. Pr.

Rosenquist, James. James Rosenquist. 2009. (ENG., Illus.). 78p. 75.00 *(978-1-905620-15-5(6))* Haunch of Venison GBR. Dist: D.A.P./Distributed Art Pubs.

Rosenthal, Mark. Jasper Johns - Drawings. 2007. (ENG., Illus.). 80p. pap. 30.00 *(978-0-300-12501-6(1))* Yale Univ. Pr.

Rossler, Patrick, text. The Bauhaus at the Newsstand / Das Bauhaus am Kiosk: die neue linie 1929-1943. 2010. (ENG & GER., Illus.). 160p. pap. 46.50 *(978-3-86678-282-2(9))* Kerber Verlag DEU. Dist: D.A.P./Distributed Art Pubs.

Rousseau, Valerie, tr. Sound & Fury: the Art of Henry Darger. 2009. (ENG., Illus.). 80p. 40.00 *(978-0-9778783-4-5(1))* Edlin, Andrew Gallery.

Rowe, M. Jessica. Albert Paley: Portals & Gates. 2007. (Illus.). 143p. 35.00 *(978-0-9798111-0-4(4))* Ilca State Univ., Univ. Museum.

Royal BC Museum Staff, et al. Exhibit Companion, 1 vol. 2007. (Royal Bc Museum Ser.). (ENG., Illus.). 60p. pap. 9.45 *(978-0-7726-5602-5(9))* Royal British Columbia Museum CAN. Dist: Heritage Group Distribution.

Rozensztroch, Daniel & Slavin, Shiri. Brush. 2006. (FRE & ENG., Illus.). 256p. 29.95 *(978-0-9727661-6-6(2))* Pointed Leaf Pr.

Rubin, David S. John Hernandez: Zoe's Room. 2009. (Illus.). 26p. pap. 8.00 *(978-1-883502-19-5(5))* San Antonio Museum of Art.

—Ry Cooder / Vincent Valdez: El Chavez Ravine. Rubin, David S., ed. 2009. (Illus.). 24p. pap. *(978-1-883502-18-8(7))* San Antonio Museum of Art.

—Waterflow. Rubin, David S., ed. 2009. (Illus.). 24p. (YA). pap. 8.00 *(978-1-883502-20-1(9))* San Antonio Museum of Art.

Rubinstein, Donald. Paul Jacoulet's Vision of Micronesia. 2007. 40p. pap. 30.00 *(978-0-9800331-0-6(1))* Univ. of Guam, Micronesian Area Research Ctr.

Ruedin, Pascal. Beaux-arts et représentation Nationale: La participation des artites suisses aux expositions universelles de Paris (1855-1900) 2010. (atelier. Travaux d'Histoire de l'art et de Muséologie/das Atelier. Arbeiten zur Kunstgeschichte und Museumskunde/the Workshop. Art History & Museum Studies). (FRE.). 693p. pap. *(978-3-0343-0041-4(7))* Lang, Peter.

Ruf, Beatrix, ed. Sean Landers. 2008. (ENG., Illus.). 160p. pap. 55.00 *(978-3-905829-87-7(8))* JRP Ringier Kunstverlag AG CHE. Dist: D.A.P./Distributed Art Pubs.

Rugg, Judith & Sedgwick, Michele, eds. Issues in Curating Contemporary Art & Performance. 2008. (Illus.). 272p. 60.00 *(978-1-84150-162-8(X))* Intellect, Ltd. GBR. Dist: Chicago Distribution Ctr.

Rugg, Kim. Don't Mention the War. 2008. 56p. pap. 24.50 *(978-1-4357-1247-8(1))* Lulu Enterprises Inc.

Ruppersberg, Allen. Allen Ruppersberg: One of Many - Origins & Variants, 1 vol. 2006. (ENG., Illus.). 215p. pap. 50.00 *(978-3-86560-029-5(8))* Verlag der Buchhandlung Walther Konig DEU. Dist: D.A.P./Distributed Art Pubs.

Ruscha, Edward. Ed Ruscha: Industrial Strength. 2008. (ENG., Illus.). 60p. 40.00 *(978-0-9724556-4-0(7))* Fabric Workshop, Inc.

Rushmore, Michael. The Thousands: Painting Outside, Breaking In. 2010. (Illus.). 40p. 33.00 *(978-88-88493-53-4(0))* Drago Arts & Communication ITA. Dist: SCB Distributors.

Russell, Charles M. & Denver Art Museum Staff. The Masterworks of Charles M. Russell: A Retrospective of Paintings & Sculpture. Troccoli, Joan Carpenter, ed. 2009. (Charles M. Russell Center Series on Art & Photography of the American West Ser.). (ENG.). 304p. (C). 65.00 *(978-0-8061-4081-0(X))* Univ. of Oklahoma Pr.

Russmann, Edna R. Unearthing the Truth: Egypt's Pagan & Coptic Sculpture. 2009. *(978-0-87273-162-2(6))* Brooklyn Museum, The.

Ruston, Annabelle & Sims, Mike. Starting up a Gallery. 2011. (ENG.). 240p. pap. 22.95 *(978-0-7136-8475-9(5))* A & C Black GBR. Dist: Macmillan.

Ryan, Judith. Across the Desert: Aboriginal Batik from Central Australia. 2009. (ENG., Illus.). 168p. pap. 37.50 *(978-0-7241-0299-0(X))* National Gallery of Victoria AUS. Dist: National Bk. Network.

Saad, Rhonda & Schlegel, Amy Ingrid. Empire & Its Discontents. Koles, Jeanne Vee, ed. 2009. (ENG., Illus.). 72p. pap. 20.00 *(978-1-880593-07-3(6))* Tufts Univ. Gallery.

Saarinen, Eero. Eero Saarinen: Shaping the Future. Pelkonen, Eeva-Liisa & Albrecht, Donald, eds. 2011. (Illus.). 464p. pap. 50.00 *(978-0-300-12237-4(3))* Yale Univ. Pr.

Saarinen, Eero, et al. Eero Saarinen: Shaping the Future. 2006. (Illus.). xv, 382p. pap. *(978-0-9724881-2-9(X))* Yale Univ. Pr.

Sacco, David C. David C. Sacco: An American Master. Goldman, Rita, ed. (Illus.). 48p. 25.00 *(978-0-9638842-0-6(4))* Master Touch Gallery.

Sachs, Sid & Minioudaki, Kalliopi, eds. Seductive Subversion: Women Pop Artists 1958-1968. 2010. (ENG., Illus.). 248p. 50.00 *(978-0-7892-1065-4(7))* Abbeville Pr., Inc.

Sachs, Tom. Tom Sachs, 1 vol. 2006. (ENG., Illus.). 196p. 145.00 *(978-88-87029-37-6(7))* Fondazione Prada ITA. Dist: D.A.P./Distributed Art Pubs.

Sala Rekalde (Bilbao, prod. Haegue Yang Asymmetric Equality. 2008. (Illus.). 215p. pap. 40.00 *(978-0-9749831-9-6(5))* California Institute of the Arts.

salter, michael. Visual. 2008. 150p. pap. 49.50 *(978-0-615-18878-2(8))* Salter, Michael A.

Samman, Nadim, ed. One of a Thousand Ways to Defeat Entropy: Hans Op de Beeck, Adrian Ghenie, Ryoichi Kurokawa, Alexander Ponomarev. 2011. (ENG., Illus.). 160p. 60.00 ***(978-3-7757-3189-8(X))*** Hatje Cantz Verlag GmbH & Co KG DEU. Dist: D.A.P./Distributed Art Pubs.

Samuel P. Harn Museum of Art Staff, contrib. by. Continuity & Change: Three Generations of Ethiopian Artists. 2007. (Illus.). 124p. *(978-0-9762552-3-9(5))* Harn Museum of Art.

Sanders, Jay, et al, eds. Performa 2007. 2010. (ENG., Illus.). 340p. pap. 45.00 *(978-3-03764-034-0(0))* JRP Ringier Kunstverlag AG CHE. Dist: D.A.P./Distributed Art Pubs.

Sangster, Gary. Lead Pencil Studio: Annie Han + Daniel Mihalyo: After. 2009. (ENG., Illus.). 56p. pap. 22.50 *(978-0-295-98934-1(3))* Univ. of Washington Pr.

Sans, Jerome, ed. It's Not Only Rock & Roll Baby! 2008. 244p. pap. *(978-84-935844-6-7(0))* Actar Birkhauser Distribution.

Sant, Toni. Franklin Furnace & the Spirit of the Avant-Garde: A History of the Future. 2011. (ENG., Illus.). 184p. pap. 25.00 *(978-1-84150-371-4(1))* Intellect, Ltd. GBR. Dist: Chicago Distribution Ctr.

Sasabuchi, Fumie, illus. Fumie Sasabuchi, 1 vol. 2007. (ENG.). 104p. 35.00 *(978-3-938821-65-7(5))* Verlag fur Moderne Kunst DEU. Dist: D.A.P./Distributed Art Pubs.

Saumade, Pascal. L'Art Modeste Sous les Bombes. 2007. (FRE & ENG., Illus.). 136p. 29.00 *(978-2-85980-009-3(3))* Kitchen 93 FRA. Dist: SCB Distributors.

Savides, Nick. Nick Savides: New York/Paris. 2009. (Illus.). 28p. pap. 10.00 *(978-0-9747030-6-0(0))* Nabi Pr.

Schaffner, Ingrid & Kuoni, Carin, eds. The Puppet Show. 2008. (ENG., Illus.). 128p. pap. 35.00 *(978-0-88454-113-4(4))* Univ. of Pennsylvania, Institute of Contemporary Art.

Schafhausen, Nicolaus & Gray, Zoe, eds. Cosima von Bonin: Source Book 9. 2011. (ENG., Illus.). 208p. pap. 15.00 *(978-90-73362-91-8(1))* Witte De With Centre for Contemporary Art NLD. Dist: D.A.P./Distributed Art Pubs.

Schatz, Silke, illus. Silke Schatz: Radical Self/Wurzelkind, 1 vol. 2007. (GER & ENG.). 96p. 45.00 *(978-3-938025-78-9(6))* Kerber Verlag DEU. Dist: D.A.P./Distributed Art Pubs.

Scher, Paula. Rock Paper Show: Flatstock Volume One. 2011. (ENG., Illus.). 312p. 59.99 *(978-0-9843028-0-2(8))* Soundscreen Design.

Schlegel, Amy Ingrid & Parrika, Jussi. I Am the Animal. 2011. (Illus.). 18p. pap. 10.00 ***(978-1-880593-10-3(6))*** Tufts Univ. Gallery.

Schleif, Nina & Zweite, Armin, eds. Pablo Picasso. Künstlerbücher: Werke aus der Sammlung Udo und Anette Brandhorst. 2010. (GER., Illus.). 300p. (C). 59.00 *(978-3-7774-3101-7(X))* Hirmer Verlag GmbH DEU. Dist: Brown, David Bk. Co., The.

Schmal, Peter, ed. HPP Architects. 2009. (ENG., Illus.). 240p. 75.00 *(978-3-7757-2307-7(2))* Hatje Cantz Verlag GmbH & Co KG DEU. Dist: D.A.P./Distributed Art Pubs.

Schmidt, A. M. & Westerdijk, P. The Cutting Edge: West Central African 19th Century Throwing Knives in the National Museum of Ethnology Leiden. 2010. (Illus.). 112p. 44.00 *(978-90-5450-007-0(7))* KITLV Pr. NLD. Dist: Univ. of Hawaii Pr.

Schmitz, Britta, ed. Ays Erkmen: Weggefährten. 2009. (GER & ENG., Illus.). 224p. pap. 45.00 *(978-3-86560-516-0(6))* Verlag der Buchhandlung Walther Konig DEU. Dist: D.A.P./Distributed Art Pubs.

Schmitz-Von Ledebur, Katja. Habsburg Treasures: Renaissance Tapestries from the Kunsthistorisches Museum, Vienna. 2010. *(978-0-9767102-8-8(5))* International Arts & Artists.

Schmuckli, Claudia & Weiss, Allen S. Leonardo Drew: Existed. Schmuckli, Claudia, ed. 2009. (ENG., Illus.). 208p. 59.95 *(978-1-904832-58-4(X))* Giles, D. Ltd. GBR. Dist: Antique Collectors' Club.

Schnapp, Jeffrey T., ed. Speed Limits. 2009. (ENG., Illus.). 320p. pap. 39.30 *(978-88-572-0175-7(9))* Skira Editore ITA. Dist: Random Hse., Inc.

Schneider, Angela & Daemgen, Anke, eds. Jannis Kounellis: In der Neuen Nationalgalerie/in the Neue Nationalgalerie. 2008. (GER & ENG., Illus.). 240p. 60.00 *(978-3-7757-2108-0(8))* Hatje Cantz Verlag GmbH & Co KG DEU. Dist: D.A.P./Distributed Art Pubs.

Schneider, Gregor, photos by. White Torture: Gregor Schneider, 1 vol. 2007. (ENG., Illus.). 132p. pap. 37.00 *(978-3-86560-216-9(9))* Verlag der Buchhandlung Walther Konig DEU. Dist: D.A.P./Distributed Art Pubs.

Schneider, Tim, ed. Peter Wegner. 2007. (Illus.). *(978-0-9704427-6-5(9))* Griffin, W. L. Editions.

Scholder, Fritz. Flirting with Possessions. (Illus.). 92p. 24.95 *(978-3-923922-57-4(4))* Nazraeli Pr. DEU. Dist: D.A.P./Distributed Art Pubs.

—Rot/Red. (Illus.). 56p. 35.00 *(978-3-923922-29-1(9))* Nazraeli Pr. DEU. Dist: D.A.P./Distributed Art Pubs.

Schorr, Collier, ed. Freeway Balconies. 2008. (ENG., Illus.). 128p. 65.00 *(978-0-89207-374-0(8))* Guggenheim, Solomon R. Museum.

Schreier, Christian & Haldemann, Anita, eds. Rosemarie Trockel: Drawings, Collages, & Book Drafts. 2010. (ENG., Illus.). 164p. pap. 60.00 *(978-3-7757-2613-9(6))* Hatje Cantz Verlag GmbH & Co KG DEU. Dist: D.A.P./Distributed Art Pubs.

Schretlen, Helen. Loving Art: The William & Anna Singer Collection. 2007. (ENG., Illus.). 224p. 60.00 *(978-90-400-8234-4(0))* Allemandi, Umberto & Co. GBR. Dist: National Bk. Network.

Schroder, Tim. Hiroshi Suzuki. 2010. (ENG., Illus.). 80p. pap. 24.95 *(978-1-85759-625-0(0))* Scala, Editions FRA. Dist: National Bk. Network.

Schroth, Sarah, ed. Irwin Kremen: Beyond Black Mountain, 1966-2006. 2007. (ENG., Illus.). 72p. pap. 24.95 *(978-0-938989-29-5(4))* Duke Univ. Pr.

Schroth, Sarah & Baer, Ronni. El Greco to Velazquez: Art During the Reign of Philip III. 2008. 351p. pap. 40.00 *(978-0-87846-727-3(0))*; (ENG., Illus.). 352p. 65.00 *(978-0-87846-726-6(2))* Museum of Fine Arts, Boston.

Schubiger, Irene, ed. & text. Reconstructing Swiss Video Art: From the 1970s & 1980s. 2010. (ENG., Illus.). 184p. pap. 50.00 *(978-3-03764-054-8(5))* JRP Ringier Kunstverlag AG CHE. Dist: D.A.P./Distributed Art Pubs.

Schuppli, Madeleine & De Vries, Janneke, eds. Mark Wallinger. 2008. (ENG., Illus.). 160p. pap. 55.00 *(978-3-905829-78-5(9))* JRP Ringier Kunstverlag AG CHE. Dist: D.A.P./Distributed Art Pubs.

Schutz, Dana. Dana Schutz: If It Appears in the Desert. 2009. (ENG., Illus.). 40p. pap. 60.00 *(978-3-931355-48-7(9))* Verlag der Buchhandlung Walther Konig DEU. Dist: D.A.P./Distributed Art Pubs.

Schwartz, Constance. ¡Latinas! Latin American Women in Art. 2010. (Illus.). pap. *(978-0-9815644-6-3(1))* Nassau County Museum of Art.

—The Sea Around Us. 2010. (Illus.). 28p. pap. *(978-0-9815644-8-7(8))* Nassau County Museum of Art.

Schwarz, Michael, et al. LienhardvonMonkiewitsch: Colourand Space, 1 vol. Schwarz, Michael, ed. 2007. (ENG & GER., Illus.). 208p. 55.00 *(978-3-938025-54-3(9))* Kerber Verlag DEU. Dist: D.A.P./Distributed Art Pubs.

Sconci, Maria Selene & Robinson, Christopher. Maiolica Medievale: Una Moderna Interpretazione. 2006. (ITA & ENG., Illus.). 63p. (C). 13.00 *(978-88-596-0094-7(4))* Edizioni Polistampa ITA. Dist: Brown, David Bk. Co., The.

Scott, Margaret. Fashion in the Middle Ages. 2011. (ENG., Illus.). 112p. 19.95 *(978-1-60606-061-2(9)*, J. Paul Getty Museum) Getty Pubns.

Seattle Art Museum Staff, contrib. by. Ancestral Modern: Australian Aboriginal Art: Kaplan & Levi Collection. 2012. ***(978-0-932216-67-0(6))*** Yale Univ. Pr.

Seeing the Light - Postmodern Luminous Landscapes by Frederick S. Wight. 2008. lib. bdg. 40.00 *(978-0-9749421-8-6(9))* Stern, Louis Fine Arts, Inc.

Segal, George. Street Scenes. 2008. (ENG., Illus.). 80p. 34.95 *(978-0-913883-34-1(4))* Madison Art Ctr., Inc.

Seifermann, Ellen, et al, texts. André Butzer: Viele Tote im Heimatland: Fanta, Sprite, H-Milch, Micky und Donald! Gemälde/Paintings 1999-2008. 2010. (ENG., Illus.). 120p. 45.00 *(978-3-86678-297-6(7))* Kerber Verlag DEU. Dist: D.A.P./Distributed Art Pubs.

Seimons, Mark & Weiwei, Ai. Ai Weiwei. 2009. (ENG & GER., Illus.). 120p. pap. 29.95 *(978-3-7913-5014-1(5))* Prestel Publishing.

Seligman, Rachel, ed. Union College Senior Invitational. 2008. (Illus.). per. *(978-0-9763207-7-7(0))* Union College, Mandeville Gallery.

Seligman, Rachel, ed. & compiled by. ReView: Five Union Alumni. 2007. (Illus.). 12p. per. 3.00 net. *(978-0-9763207-5-3(4))* Union College, Mandeville Gallery.

Serrats, Marta & Mola, Francesc Zamora. Affordable Exhibition Design. 2011. (ENG., Illus.). 256p. 45.00 *(978-0-06-196882-2(X)*, Collins Design) HarperCollins Pubs.

Sever, Nancy & Haynes, Peter, comments. Phillip Hughes: Mountains of the Mind. 2008. (Illus.). 36p. pap. *(978-0-9804606-0-5(3))* Australian National University - Drill Hall Gallery.

Seyfarth, Ludwig, et al, texts. Timm Ulrichs: Betreten der Ausstellung verboten. Werke von 1960-2010. 2011. (ENG., Illus.). 160p. 60.00 *(978-3-7757-2794-5(9))* Hatje Cantz Verlag GmbH & Co KG DEU. Dist: D.A.P./Distributed Art Pubs.

Sframeli, Maria & Nitti, Patrizia. Trésor des Médicis. 2010. (FRE., Illus.). 271p. *(978-2-08-124505-1(1))* Editions Flammarion.

Shabout, Nada M. Dafatir: Contemporary Iraqi Book Art. 2007. pap. *(978-1-889886-08-4(4))* Univ. of North Texas Art Gallery.

Shark, Bud. The Legend of Bud Shark & His Indelible Ink. 2010. (ENG., Illus.). 228p. 60.00 *(978-0-945367-37-6(6))* Hardy Marks Pubns.

Shatanawi, Mirjam. Tehran Studio Works: The Art of Khosrow Hassanzadeh. 2007. (ARA, ENG & PER., Illus.). 160p. pap. 22.95 *(978-0-86356-670-7(7))* Saqi Bks. GBR. Dist: Consortium Bk. Sales & Distribution.

Sheehy, Sheehy. Cabinet of Curiosities. 2006. (Illus.). 128p. pap. 29.95 *(978-0-8166-4470-4(5))* Univ. of Minnesota Pr.

Shein. Theatrical Exhibitions. 197p. *(978-0-88978-006-4(4))* Arsenal Pulp Pr.

Sheldon, George F. Hugh Williamson: Physician, Patriot & Founding Father. 2009. (ENG., Illus.). 340p. pap. 39.00 *(978-1-59102-770-6(5)*, Humanity Bks.) Prometheus Bks., Pubs.

Sherer, Scott A. The Lam Collection of Aboriginal Art. 2008. 79p. *(978-1-933979-19-9(4))* Bright Sky Pr.

Sherwood, Shirley & Rix, Martyn. Treasures of Botanical Art: Icons from the Shirley Sherwood & Kew Collections. 2008. (ENG., Illus.). 272p. *(978-1-84246-368-0(3)*, Royal Botanic Gardens Edinburg) Antique Collectors' Club.

Shi, Jinsong. Ne Zha 2008: A Child Boutique. 2008. (CHI., Illus.). 102p. pap. 30.00 *(978-0-9787666-9-6(5))* Chambers Fine Art LLC.

Shields, Scott A. & Harrison, Alfred C., Jr. Edwin Deakin: California Painter of the Picturesque. 2008. (Pomegranate Catalog Ser.). (Illus.). 120p. 30.00 *(978-0-7649-4351-5(0))* Pomegranate Communications, Inc.

Shirahara, Yukiko. Japan Envisions the West: 16th-19th Century Japanese Art from Kobe City Museum. 2007. (ENG., Illus.). 216p. *(978-0-295-98740-8(5))* Seattle Art Museum.

Shoemaker, Innis Howe. Adventures in Modern Art: The Charles K. Williams II Collection. 2009. (ENG., Illus.). 336p. 60.00 *(978-0-300-14978-4(6))* Yale Univ. Pr.

Sibeth, Achim, ed. Being Object, Being Art, 1 vol. 2010. (ENG.). 324p. 75.00 *(978-3-8030-3338-3(1))* Wasmuth, Ernst J. Verlag GmbH & Co. DEU. Dist: D.A.P./Distributed Art Pubs.

Signer, Roman. Roman Signer: Vernissage: Invitations for Exhibitions 1973-2008. =Waspe, Roland & Mettler, Max, eds. 2008. (Illus.). 240p. 85.00 *(978-3-85881-224-7(2))* Scheidegger und Spiess AG, Verlag CHE. Dist: Antique Collectors' Club.

Signs of Life 2007. 2007. 12.00 *(978-0-9618302-3-6(9))*; 3rd ed. 12.95 *(978-0-9785501-0-3(2))* Lorene Pubns.

Signs of Life 2008. 2008. 12.00 *(978-0-9618302-4-3(7))* Lorene Pubns.

Silber, Mark & Nels, Nelson, photos by. Portraits & Voices: Workers of Seven Mills. 2007. (Illus.). 56p. pap. 14.00 *(978-0-9799307-0-6(7))* Museum L-A.

Silber, Mark & Nelson, Nels, photos by. Portraits & Voices: Workers of Seven Mills. 2007. (Illus.). 56p. pap. 24.00 incl. DVD *(978-0-9799307-1-3(5))* Museum L-A.

Silver, Larry & Wyckoff, Elizabeth, eds. Grand Scale: Monumental Prints in the Age of Dürer & Titian. 2008. (Illus.). 176p. 50.00 *(978-0-300-13879-5(2))* Yale Univ. Pr.

Simon, Joan & Faxon, Susan C. Sheila Hicks: 50 Years. 2010. (ENG., Illus.). 256p. 65.00 *(978-0-300-12164-3(4))* Yale Univ. Pr.

Simpson, Bennett & Iles, Chrissie, eds. Dan Graham: Beyond. 2009. (ENG., Illus.). 348p. (gr. 17). pap. 44.95 *(978-1-933751-12-2(6))* MIT Pr.

Sims, Lowery Stokes, text. The Persistence of Geometry: Form, Content, & Culture in the Collection of the Cleveland Museum of Art. 2007. (ENG., Illus.). 128p. pap. 22.50 *(978-0-940717-86-2(7))* Cleveland Museum of Art.

Skira. Bjarne Melgaard: Jealous. Arbu, Grete et al, eds. 2010. (ENG., Illus.). 96p. pap. 29.95 *(978-88-572-0465-9(0))* Skira Editore ITA. Dist: Random Hse., Inc.

Skira-Rizzoli Staff. Skira Fall 2004 Catalog. *(978-88-8491-994-6(0))* Skira Editore ITA. Dist: Macmillan.

Skotnes, Pippa, ed. Rock Art Made in Translation: Framing Images of & from the Landscape. 2011. (ENG., Illus.). 104p. pap. 24.95 *(978-1-4314-0080-5(7))* Jacana Media ZAF. Dist: Independent Pubs. Group.

Sloan, Mark, ed. Aldwyth: Collage & Assemblage 1991-2009. 2010. (ENG., Illus.). 112p. pap. 29.95 *(978-0-615-26885-9(4))* Halsey Institute of Contemporary Art.

Slobodkina, Esphyr, et al. Rediscovering Slobodkina: A Pioneer of American Abstraction. 2009. (ENG., Illus.). 184p. 60.00 *(978-1-55595-312-6(3))* Hudson Hills Pr. LLC.

Sloterdijk, Peter. Sigmar Polke. Fudge, Anthony & Koenig, Ruth, trs. from DUT. (Illus.). 88p. pap. 35.00 *(978-90-5006-077-6(3))* Stedelijk Museum NLD. Dist: D.A.P./Distributed Art Pubs.

Smith, Alison. Watercolour. 2011. (ENG., Illus.). 208p. pap. 39.95 *(978-1-85437-913-9(5))* Tate Publishing, Ltd. GBR. Dist: Hachette Bk. Group.

Smith, Cynthia, et al, texts. Design for the Other 90% 2007. (ENG., Illus.). 144p. pap. 24.95 *(978-0-910503-97-6(4))* Cooper-Hewitt Museum.

Smith, Jason. Gwynn Hansen Piggott: A Survey 1955 - 2005. 2006. (ENG., Illus.). 112p. pap. 26.50 *(978-0-7241-0265-5(5))* National Gallery of Victoria AUS. Dist: National Bk. Network.

Smith, Michael & White, Joshua, illus. Mike's World, 1 vol. 2008. (ENG.). 140p. per. 30.00 *(978-0-9771453-9-3(5))* Blanton Museum of Art, Univ. of Texas at Austin.

Smith, Valerie, et al, texts. Juan Downey: the Invisible Architect. 2011. (ENG., Illus.). 200p. pap. 35.00 *(978-0-938437-76-5(3))* Massachusetts Institute of Technology, List Visual Arts Ctr.

Smithson, Pete. Installing Exhibitions. 2010. (ENG., Illus.). 208p. pap., instr.'s gde. ed. 29.95 *(978-1-4081-1016-4(4))* A & C Black GBR. Dist: Macmillan.

Soares, Valeska, et al. Seducoes, 1 vol. 2007. (ENG & SPA., Illus.). 200p. 55.00 *(978-3-7757-1884-4(2))* Hatje Cantz Verlag GmbH & Co KG DEU. Dist: D.A.P./Distributed Art Pubs.

Soberón, Edgar. Movements in Stillness: The Still-Life Paintings of Edgar Soberón. 2009. *(978-0-89280-052-0(6))* Montgomery Museum of Fine Arts.

Solakov, Nedko & Perjovschi, Dan. Dan Perjovschi, Nedko Solakov: Walls & Floor (Without the Ceiling) Kluturkontakt Austria, ed. 2008. (GER & ENG., Illus.). 96p. pap. 40.00 *(978-3-940748-19-5(6))* Verlag fur Moderne Kunst DEU. Dist: D.A.P./Distributed Art Pubs.

Sonoma County Museum. Marguerite Wildenhain: Selected Works from the Forrest L. Merrill Collection. 2007. (Illus.). 48p. pap. 17.00 *(978-0-9798537-6-0(1))* Sonoma County Museum.

Sorrell, Jennifer & Noero, Jo. Jo Noero: The Everyday & the Extraordinary: Three Decades of Architecture: Jo Noero Architects 1982-1998 & Noero Wolff Architects 1998-2009. 2009. (Illus.). 103p. *(978-0-620-45436-0(9))* ADA Publishing Co., Inc.

Spanierman Gallery Staff, contrib. by. American Works on Paper: 1800 to the Present. 2010. (Illus.). 56p. *(978-1-935617-02-0(8))* Spanierman Gallery.

Spector, Nancy. Pierre Huyghe. 2009. 160p. 49.95 *(978-0-7148-4582-1(5))* Phaidon Pr., Inc.

—Theanyspacewhatever. 2008. (ENG., Illus.). 256p. 49.95 *(978-0-89207-377-1(2))* Guggenheim, Solomon R. Museum.

Spector, Nancy, ed. Richard Prince, 1 vol. 2007. (ENG., Illus.). 368p. 60.00 *(978-0-89207-363-4(2))* Guggenheim, Solomon R. Museum.

Spector, Nancy & Prince, Richard. Richard Prince. 2007. (Illus.). 371p. *(978-0-89207-364-1(0))* Guggenheim, Solomon R. Museum.

Spencer, Tracy. The Arts for Every Day: A Practical Introduction. 2nd rev. ed. 2010. (ENG., Illus.). 92p. pap. 50.71 *(978-0-7575-7910-3(8))* Kendall Hunt Publishing Co.

Spiegel, Dianne Hendricks & Speigel, Lee. How to Put on a Great Craft Show: First Time & Every Time. 2008. (Illus.). 68p. pap. 24.95 *(978-0-9655193-8-0(4))* Craftmasters Bks. & Videos.

Splendid Grief: Darren Waterstpm & the Afterlife of Leland Stanford Jr. 2009. (Illus.). 38p. pap. 22.00 *(978-0-937031-29-2(1))* Cantor, Iris & B. Gerald Ctr. for Visual Arts at Stanford Univ.

Springfield Library and Museums Association. The Legacy of Currier. 2010. pap. 19.95 *(978-0-916746-00-1(3))* Springfield Library & Museum Assn.

Staatliches Museum für angewandte Kunst und Design Staff, contrib. by. Dorothea Prühl: Colliers. 2009. (GER & ENG., Illus.). 96p. 85.00 *(978-3-89790-301-2(6))* Arnoldsche Art Pubs. DEU. Dist: Antique Collectors' Club.

Staatsgemäldesammlungen, Bayersche & Rott, Herbert W., eds. George Stubbs. 2011. (Illus.). 224p. 49.95 ***(978-3-7913-5170-4(2))*** Prestel Publishing.

Stallings, Tyler, et al. Gabriela León: Sunday Walk to the Zócalo of Oaxaca. Stallings, Tyler, ed. 2008.Tr. of Gabriela león: Paseo Dominical por el zócalo de Oaxaca. (ENG & SPA.). 40p. pap. *(978-0-932173-21-8(7))* Sweeney Art Gallery.

Stamm, Rainer, ed. Paula Modersohn-Becker und die Mumienportraits: Eine Hommage zum 100. Todestag der Künstlerin. Katalogbuch zur Ausstellung: Bremen, 14.10.2007-24.02.2008, Kunstsammlung Böttcherstraße. 2007. (GER., Illus.). 220p. (C). pap. 53.00 *(978-3-7774-3735-4(2))* Hirmer Verlag GmbH DEU. Dist: Brown, David Bk. Co., The.

Stauffer, Karl, et al. "Verfluchter Kerl!" Karl Stauffer-Bern, Maler, Radierer, Plastiker. 2007. (Illus.). 240p. *(978-3-03823-362-6(5))* Neue Zurcher Zeitung, NZZ, Buchverlag.

Steiner, Barbara, ed. The Captured Museum. 2011. (ENG., Illus.). 256p. pap. 40.00 *(978-3-86859-059-3(5))* Jovis Verlag GmbH DEU. Dist: D.A.P./Distributed Art Pubs.

Steinmann, Martin, ed. Tendenzen - Neuere Architektur im Tessin: Tendencies - Recent Architecture in Ticino Tendenze - Architettura recente nel Ticino. 2010. 166p. pap. 79.95 *(978-3-0346-0531-1(5))* Birkhauser Verlag AG CHE. Dist: Actar Birkhauser Distribution.

Stella, Frank. Frank Stella: Painting into Architecture. 2007. (Illus.). 40p. 16.95 *(978-1-58839-268-8(6))* Metropolitan Museum of Art, The.

Stibbon, Emma. Emma Stibbon. 2010. (ENG., Illus.). 80p. 45.00 *(978-3-86678-275-4(6))* Kerber Verlag DEU. Dist: D.A.P./Distributed Art Pubs.

Stiles, Kristine, ed. States of Mind: Dan & Lia Perjovschi. 2007. (ENG., Illus.). 236p. pap. 35.00 *(978-0-938989-30-1(8))* Duke Univ. Pr.

Stolwijk, Chris, et al, contrib. by. Theo Van Gogh, 1857-1891: Art Dealer, Collector, & Brother of Vincent. 2006. (Illus.). 232p. 45.00 *(978-90-400-9359-3(8))* Waanders B.V., Uitgeverij NLD. Dist: Antique Collectors' Club.

Stoppini, Luca, ed. Fausto Melotti. 2009. (ITA., Illus.). 80p. pap. 57.50 *(978-88-370-6662-8(7))* Electa ITA. Dist: Trans-Atlantic Pubns., Inc.

Stoschek. Julia Stoschek Collection No. 1: Destroy She Said. 2008. (ENG., Illus.). 304p. 70.00 *(978-3-7757-2231-5(9))* Hatje Cantz Verlag GmbH & Co KG DEU. Dist: D.A.P./Distributed Art Pubs.

Stratton-Pruitt, Suzanne L., et al, eds. The Virgin, Saints, & Angels: South American Paintings 1600-1825 from the Thoma Collection. 2006. (ENG., Illus.). 288p. 55.00 *(978-88-7624-613-5(4))* Skira Editore ITA. Dist: Random Hse., Inc.

Strauber, Susan, et al. Women in Impressionism: From Mythical Feminine to Modern Woman. Sondergaard, Sidsel Maria, ed. 2007. (ENG., Illus.). 288p. 55.00 *(978-88-7624-787-3(4))* Skira Editore ITA. Dist: Random Hse., Inc.

Strauss, Cindi. Pioneers of Contemporary Glass: Highlights from the Barbara & Dennis Dubois Collection. 2009. (ENG., Illus.). 96p. pap. 19.95 *(978-0-300-14695-0(7))* Museum of Fine Arts, Houston.

Strauss, Dorothea, ed. Carsten Nicolai: Static Fades. 2008. (ENG., Illus.). 160p. pap. 49.00 *(978-3-905770-63-6(6))* JRP Ringier Kunstverlag AG CHE. Dist: D.A.P./Distributed Art Pubs.

Stromberg, Gobi & Mallet Cárdenas, Ana Elena. Silver Seduction: The Art of Mexican Modernist Antonio Pineda. 2008. (Illus.). 188p. pap. *(978-0-9778344-0-2(9))* Univ. of California, Los Angeles, Fowler Museum of Cultural History.

Stula, Nancy & Robinson, David Miller. At Home & Abroad: The Transcendental Landscapes of Christopher Pearce Cranch (1813-1892) 2007. (ENG., Illus.). 196p. per. 35.00 *(978-1-878541-10-9(2))* Univ. Pr. of New England.

Sultan, Terrie, ed. Chantal Akerman: Moving Through Time & Space, 1 vol. 2008. (ENG., Illus.). 72p. 24.95 *(978-0-9778028-5-2(X))*; 40.00 *(978-0-941193-40-5(3))* Blaffer Art Museum.

Sumner, Ann, ed. Court on Canvas: Tennis in Art. 2011. (ENG., Illus.). 176p. pap. 35.00 *(978-0-85667-706-9(X))* Wilson, Philip Pubs., Ltd. GBR. Dist: Macmillan.

Sun, Seunghye. The Lure of Painted Poetry: Japanese & Korean Art. 2011. (Illus.). 109p. ***(978-1-935294-04-7(0))*** Cleveland Museum of Art.

Sung, Hou-Mei. Decoded Messages: The Symbolic Language of Chinese Animal Painting. 2009. (Illus.). xv, 271p. *(978-0-931537-35-6(5))* Yale Univ. Pr.

Sureda, Joan, photos by. Goya & Italy. 2008. (ENG., Illus.). 310p. pap. 69.00 *(978-84-7506-808-4(1))* Turner, Ediciones S.A. ESP. Dist: D.A.P./Distributed Art Pubs.

Swergold, Leopold, et al. Treasures Rediscovered: Chinese Stone Sculpture from the Sackler Collections at Columbia University. 2008. (Illus.). x, 115p. *(978-1-884919-21-3(9))* Columbia Univ., The Miriam & Ira D. Wallach Art Gallery.

Syson, Luke, et al. Renaissance Siena: Art for a City. 2008. (ENG., Illus.). 372p. 65.00 *(978-1-85709-392-6(5))* Yale Univ. Pr.

Szabo, Joyce M. Art from Fort Marion: The Silberman Collection. (Western Legacies Ser.). (ENG.). 208p. 2009. pap. 29.95 *(978-0-8061-3889-3(0))* 2008. (Illus.). (C). 49.95 *(978-0-8061-3883-1(1))* Univ. of Oklahoma Pr.

Szymusiak, Dominique. La donation Alice Teriade: La collection d'un editeur D'art. 2008. (ENG.). 120p. pap. 45.00 *(978-2-35340-038-6(8))* Gourcuff Gradenigo FRA. Dist: National Bk. Network.

Takeover. 2007. pap. *(978-0-9778084-1-0(6))* Hyde Park Art Center, The.

Talerman, Margaretha & Savage, Robert E. Nobel: Celebrating a Century of the Nobel Prizes: Exhibition Catalogue. 2007. (Illus.). 17p. reprint ed. pap. 15.00 *(978-1-4223-6558-8(1))* DIANE Publishing Co.

Tam, Karen. Karen Tam. 2007. pap. 8.00 *(978-0-9797964-1-8(5))* CUE Art Foundation.

Tamayo, Museo. Brian Nissen: Cuatro Cuartetos. 2006. 119p. pap. 54.00 *(978-968-5979-12-2(X))* Trucatriche.

Tartuferi, Angelo, ed. Arte a Figline Valdarno: Dal Maestro della Maddalena a Masaccio. 2010. (citta degli Uffizi Ser.). (ITA., Illus.). 200p. (C). 60.00 *(978-88-596-0832-5(5))* Polistampa ITA. Dist: Brown, David Bk. Co., The.

Taschen Staff. Giger. Date not set. (SPA.). pap. 4.99 *(978-3-8228-8780-6(3))* TASCHEN DEU. Dist: Digital Manga Publishing.

Tatham, David & Prince, David Lake. Winslow Homer's Empire State: Houghton Farm & Beyond. 2010. (Illus.). 84p. *(978-0-8156-8179-3(8))* Syracuse Univ. Pr.

Taylor, Michael R. Marcel Duchamp: Étant Donnés. 2009. *(978-0-87633-211-5(4))*; *(978-0-87633-210-8(6))* Philadelphia Museum of Art.

Telfair Museum of Art & Sammons, Tania June. The Story of Silver in Savannah: Creating & Collecting since the 18th Century. 2010. (ENG., Illus.). 128p. 24.95 *(978-0-933075-13-9(8))* Telfair Museum of Art.

Telfair Museum of Art Staff. Picturing Savannah: The Art of Christopher A. D. Murphy. 2008. (ENG., Illus.). 120p. pap. 29.95 *(978-0-933075-07-8(3))* Telfair Museum of Art.

Tellgren, Anna, ed. & text. The History Book, 1 vol. 2009. (ENG., Illus.). 500p. 75.00 *(978-3-86521-642-7(0))* Steidl, Gerhard Druckerei und Verlag DEU. Dist: Innovative Logistics.

Temkin, Ann. Color Chart: Reinventing Color, 1950 to Today, 1 vol. 2008. (ENG., Illus.). 248p. 55.00 *(978-0-87070-731-5(0))* Museum of Modern Art.

Templeton, Ed, photos by. Ed Templeton: the Cemetery of Reason. 2010. (ENG., Illus.). 160p. pap. 39.95 *(978-90-75679-34-2(3))* Vereniging voor het Museum van Hedendaagse Kunst BEL. Dist: D.A.P./Distributed Art Pubs.

The Tender among Us: Project Series 32: Liat Yossifor. 2007. (Illus.). 24p. pap. 10.00 *(978-0-9786996-3-5(7))* Pomona College Museum of Art.

ter Braak, Lex & Jacobs, Edwin, texts. Robbie Cornelissen: the Capacious Memory. 2011. (ENG., Illus.). 128p. pap. 35.00 ***(978-90-5662-811-6(9))*** NAi Uitgevers / Publishers Stichting NLD. Dist: D.A.P./Distributed Art Pubs.

The Pace Gallery, prod. Kiki Smith: Lodestar. 2010. (Illus.). 44p. 40.00 *(978-1-935410-10-2(5))* Pace Gallery, The.

—Robert Mangold: Ring Paintings. 2011. (Illus.). 30p. pap. 30.00 *(978-1-935410-18-8(0))* Pace Gallery, The.

Thomas, Nene. Parting the Veil: The Art of Nene Thomas. 2010. (ENG.). 128p. pap. 25.00 *(978-0-9744612-9-8(6))* Chimera Publishing.

Thompson, Barbara, ed. Black Womanhood: Images, Icons, & Ideologies of the African Body. 2008. (ENG., Illus.). 376p. pap. 50.00 *(978-0-295-98771-2(5))* Hood Museum of Art.

Thompson, Ralph, et al. Writers Who Paint Painters Who Write: 3 Jamaican Artists. 2008. (ENG.). 64p. pap. 19.95 *(978-1-84523-064-7(7))* Peepal Tree Pr., Ltd. GBR. Dist: Independent Pubs. Group.

Thomsen, Hans Bjarne. The Floating World: Ukiyo-e Prints from the Wallace B. Rogers Collection of the Lauren Rogers Museum of Art. Chancey, Jill R., ed. 2008. (ENG., Illus.). 29.95 *(978-0-935903-10-2(0))* Lauren Rogers Museum of Art.

Thomson, Belinda, ed. Gauguin: Maker of Myth. 2010. (ENG., Illus.). 256p. 55.00 *(978-0-691-14886-1(4))* Princeton Univ. Pr.

Thomson, Richard, et al. Toulouse-Lautrec & Montmartre. 2006. (Illus.). 293p. pap. 39.50 *(978-0-691-12904-4(5))* Princeton Univ. Pr.

Thoret, Jean-Baptiste, et al. Dennis Hopper & the New Hollywood. 2010. (ENG., Illus.). 192p. 50.00 *(978-2-08-030099-7(7))* Flammarion et Cie FRA. Dist: Random Hse., Inc.

Thornton, Sarah. Seven Days in the Art World. (ENG., Illus.). 2009. 256p. pap. 15.95 *(978-0-393-33712-9(X)*, 33712) 2008. 304p. 24.95 *(978-0-393-06722-4(X)*, 6722) Norton, W. W. & Co., Inc.

Thorpe, Mackenzie. A Crossroads. 2007. *(978-0-9753664-1-7(6))* Chase Group, The.

Thunfors, Jacquelyn. Journalist Without Words: 19 Years Painting International Conversations. 2007. (Illus.). 116p. per. *(978-1-4243-2937-3(X))* Riverside Publishing Co.

Thurber, T. Barton. European Art at Dartmouth: Highlights from the Hood Museum of Art. 2008. (Illus.). ix, 222p. *(978-1-58465-738-5(3))*; (ENG., 232p. pap. 40.00 *(978-1-58465-724-8(3))* Hood Museum of Art.

Thurmer, Robert, frwd. Each in Their Own Voice: African American Artists in Cleveland, 1970 - 2005. 2009. (Illus.). 56p. pap. 10.00 *(978-0-615-26752-4(1))* Cleveland State University Art Gallery.

Thyssen-Bornemisza Art Contemporary. Kuba: Journey Against the Current. 2006. (Illus.). 182p. pap. *(978-3-211-36513-7(3)*, 3211365133) Actar Birkhauser Distribution.

Tianbing Li: Me & My Brother. 2008. (Illus.). 55p. pap. 40.00 *(978-0-9790942-2-4(4))* L & M Arts.

Tiberini, Elvira Stefania. Women in Charge: Contemporary Inuit Artists. 2012. (ITA, FRE & ENG., Illus.). 64p. pap. 24.95 *(978-88-89854-65-5(0))* Officina Libraria srl ITA. Dist: Antique Collectors' Club.

Tice, James. Giuseppe Vasi's Rome: Lasting Impressions from the Age of the Grand Tour. 2010. (ENG.). 200p. pap. 40.00 *(978-0-87114-297-9(X))* Univ. of Delaware Pr.

Tingley, Nancy. Arts of Ancient Vietnam: From River Plain to Open Sea. 2009. (ENG., Illus.). 368p. 60.00 *(978-0-300-14696-7(5))* Museum of Fine Arts, Houston.

—Buddhas. 2009. 120p. 29.95 *(978-0-7649-4800-8(8))* Pomegranate Communications, Inc.

Todts, Herwig. Goya Redon Ensor: Grotesque Paintings & Drawings. 2009. (ENG., Illus.). 240p. *(978-90-209-8342-5(3)*, Lannoo Pubs. (Acc)) Antique Collectors' Club.

Tokar Miller, Nancy. Nancy Tokar Miller... in Retrospect. 2009. (ENG., Illus.). 140p. pap. *(978-0-9814840-4-4(2))* Univ. of Arizona Museum of Art.

Tomasso Brothers Fine Art Staff. Scultura III. 2010. (ENG., Illus.). 80p. (C). 50.00 *(978-1-907372-15-5(6))* Holberton, Paul Publishing GBR. Dist: Univ. of Washington Pr.

Torelli, Mario & Sgubini Moretti, Anna Maria. Etruschi: Le Antiche Metropoli Del Lazio. Torelli, Mario & Moretti, Anna Maria, eds. 2009. (ITA., Illus.). 304p. 77.50 *(978-88-370-6620-8(1))* Electa ITA. Dist: Trans-Atlantic Pubns., Inc.

Torfs, Ana. Ana Torfs. Album/Tacks A+B. 2010. (ENG & GER., Illus.). 204p. 60.00 *(978-3-86984-015-4(3))* Verlag der Buchhandlung Walther Konig DEU. Dist: D.A.P./Distributed Art Pubs.

TORST, creator. Studio Najbrt: Life Happiness Surprise, 1 vol. 2007. (CZE & ENG., Illus.). 272p. 48.00 *(978-80-7215-298-8(X))* TORST CZE. Dist: D.A.P./Distributed Art Pubs.

Townsend, Richard F. & Pope, Elizabeth Irene. Ballplayers, Gods, & Rainmaker Kings: Masterpieces from Ancient Mexico. 2010. (SPA., Illus.). 47p. pap. ***(978-0-86559-242-1(X))*** Art Institute of Chicago.

Traugott, Joseph. Sole Mates: Cowboy Boots & Art. 2010. (ENG.). 124p. *(978-0-89013-565-5(7))* Museum of New Mexico Pr.

Treptow, Tanya. Daily Life Ornamented: The Medieval Persian City of Rayy. 2007. (Oriental Institute Museum Publications Ser.). (ENG., Illus.). 64p. (C). pap. 24.95 *(978-1-885923-51-6(1))* Oriental Institute of the Univ. of Chicago, The.

Trnek, Renate & Dervis, Martina. The Picture Gallery, Academy of Fine Arts, Vienna. 2006. (ENG., Illus.). 128p. pap. 29.95 *(978-1-85759-415-7(0))* Scala, Editions FRA. Dist: National Bk. Network.

Troelenberg, Eva-Maria. Eine Ausstellung Wird Besichtigt: Die Münchner "Ausstellung Von Meisterwerken Muhammedanischer Kunst" 1910 in Kultur- und Wissenschaftsgeschichtlicher Perspektive. 2011. (GER., Illus.). 532p. pap. *(978-3-631-60515-8(3))* Lang, Peter Publishing, Inc.

Trouve, Tatiana, text. Tatiana Trouve: il Grande Ritratto. 2010. (ENG & GER., Illus.). 150p. pap. 49.95 *(978-3-86560-753-9(5))* Verlag der Buchhandlung Walther Konig DEU. Dist: D.A.P./Distributed Art Pubs.

Trümpler, Stefan & Clarke, Brian. Brian Clarke. Life & Death. 2011. (ENG., Illus.). 80p. 45.00 *(978-3-7165-1671-3(6))* Benteli Verlag CHE. Dist: Antique Collectors' Club.

Tsai, Eugenie & Biggers, Sanford. Sanford Biggers: Sweet Funk — an Introspective. 2011. ***(978-0-87273-169-1(3))*** Brooklyn Museum, The.

Tsai, Eugenie & Lee, Mingwei. Lee Mingwei: The Moving Garden. 2011. ***(978-0-87273-168-4(5))*** Brooklyn Museum, The.

Tuli, Neville. Osian's A Historical Epic: From Surrender to Revolt, Swaraj to Responsibility. 2006. (ENG., Illus.). 45.00 *(978-1-890206-51-2(2))* Mapin Publishing Pvt. Ltd IND. Dist: National Bk. Network.

Tunga. Tunga: Laminated Souls. 2008. (ENG., Illus.). 136p. 69.00 *(978-3-935567-41-1(3))* Holzwarth Pubns. DEU. Dist: D.A.P./Distributed Art Pubs.

Turner, compiled by. Banquete: Nodes & Networks. 2009. (ENG., Illus.). 366p. 50.00 *(978-84-7506-845-9(6))* Turner, Ediciones S.A. ESP. Dist: D.A.P./Distributed Art Pubs.

Turrell, James. James Turrell: Air Mass. (Illus.). 118p. 40.00 *(978-1-85332-101-6(X))* South Bank Ctr. GBR. Dist: D.A.P./Distributed Art Pubs.

Tuttle, Susan. Exhibition 36: Mixed Media Demonstrations + Explorations. 2008. (ENG., Illus.). 160p. pap. 24.99 *(978-1-60061-104-9(4)*, North Light Bks.) F&W Media, Inc.

Twombly, Cy. Cy Twombly: Photographs, Prints & Works on Paper from the Grosshaus Collection. 2011. (ENG., Illus.). 216p. pap. 55.00 ***(978-3-86335-035-2(9))*** Verlag der Buchhandlung Walther Konig DEU. Dist: D.A.P./Distributed Art Pubs.

Uelsberg, Gabriele & Holthuis, Gabriele. Christoph Loos: Nann-Paradox. 2007. 148p. 49.95 *(978-3-87909-891-0(3))* Wienand GmbH, Druck- & Verlagshaus DEU. Dist: Independent Pubs. Group.

Uhlig, Helmut. On the Path to Enlightenment: The Berti Aschmann Foundation of Tibetan Art at the Museum Rietberg Zürich. 2011. (ENG., Illus.). 226p. (C). 50.00 *(978-3-907070-60-4(7))* Holberton, Paul Publishing GBR. Dist: Univ. of Washington Pr.

Umberger, Leslie. Messages & Magic: 100 Years of Collage & Assemblage in American Art. 2008. (Illus.). 78p. *(978-0-9710703-7-0(7))* Kohler, John Michael Arts Ctr.

Umberger, Leslie & Chaloupka, Amy. American Story. 2009. *(978-0-9710703-8-7(5))* Kohler, John Michael Arts Ctr.

Unbroken Ties: Dialogues in Cuban Art. 2008. (ENG & SPA., Illus.). 81p. pap. 24.95 *(978-0-9678056-6-5(X))* Nova Southeastern Univ., Museum of Art Fort Lauderdale.

Universitat de Barcelona, Centre de Recerca de Dones Staff, contrib. by. Col·lecció D'Art I Punt D'Investigació "La Relació", Duoda, Universitat de Barcelona: Documents 2000-2008. 2009. (CAT & SPA., Illus.). 114p. *(978-84-475-3414-2(6))* Univ. de Barcelona Pubns.

Upstone, Robert. Sickert in Venice. 2009. (ENG., Illus.). 160p. pap. 45.00 *(978-1-85759-583-3(1))* Scala, Editions FRA. Dist: National Bk. Network.

Urban, Otto. Decadence - In Morbid Colours Bohemia: Art & the Idea of Decadence in the Bohemian Lands, 1880-1914. 2011. (ENG., Illus.). 410p. 85.00 *(978-80-86300-84-9(6))* Nakladatelstvi Arbor vitae CZE. Dist: D.A.P./Distributed Art Pubs.

Urbaschek, Stephan, ed. Andreas Hofer: Andy Hope 1930. 2010. (ENG., Illus.). 192p. pap. 45.00 *(978-3-939894-13-1(3))* Goetz, Ingvild, Kunstverlag, GmbH DEU. Dist: D.A.P./Distributed Art Pubs.

—Fast Forward: Media Art - the Goetz Collection, 1 vol. 2006. (GER & ENG., Illus.). 532p. 60.00 *(978-3-7757-1865-3(6))* Hatje Cantz Verlag GmbH & Co KG DEU. Dist: D.A.P./Distributed Art Pubs.

Ursprung, Philip, et al, texts. L/B: Beautiful Book. 2009. (ENG., Illus.). 164p. 35.00 *(978-3-905829-90-7(8))* JRP Ringier Kunstverlag AG CHE. Dist: D.A.P./Distributed Art Pubs.

Vaccari, Franco. Esposizioni in Tempo Reale, 1 vol. 2007. (ITA & ENG., Illus.). 250p. 60.00 *(978-88-89431-82-5(2))* Damiani ITA. Dist: D.A.P./Distributed Art Pubs.

Vallières, Nicole & Cooper, Cynthia. 90 Treasures, 90 Stories, 90 Years. 2012. (Illus.). 268p. (C). pap. ***(978-1-895615-16-6(X))*** McGill-Queen's Univ. Pr.

Van Beirendonck, Walter. Walter Van Beirendonck: Dream the World Awake. 2012. (ENG., Illus.). 240p. 90.00 ***(978-90-209-6112-6(8))*** Lannoo Pubs./Racine.

Van Claerbergen, Ernst Vegelin & Wright, Barnaby, eds. Renoir at the Theatre: Looking at la Loge. 2008. (Courtauld Institute of Art Gallery Ser.). (Illus.). 128p. pap. 40.00 *(978-1-903470-73-2(0))* Holberton, Paul Publishing GBR. Dist: Casemate Pubs. & Bk. Distributors, LLC.

van den Heuvel, Maartje, ed. Nature as Artifice. 2008. (ENG.). 288p. 80.00 *(978-90-5662-028-8(2))* NAi Uitgevers / Publishers Stichting NLD. Dist: D.A.P./Distributed Art Pubs.

Van der Sman, Gert Jan. Lorenzo & Giovanna: Life & Art in Renaissance Florence. 2011. (ENG., Illus.). 160p. pap. 25.00 *(978-88-7461-128-7(5))* Mandragora ITA. Dist: Antique Collectors' Club.

van Dijk, Janneke & Legêne, Susan. The Netherlands East Indies at the Tropenmuseum. 2011. (Collections at the Tropenmuseum Ser.). 200p. 45.00 *(978-90-6832-751-9(8))* Royal Tropical Institute Pr. (KIT (Koninklijk Instituut voor de Tropen)) NLD. Dist: Stylus Publishing, LLC.

van Duyn, Edna, ed. Michael Borremans: Weight. 2006. (ENG., Illus.). 88p. 45.00 *(978-3-7757-2130-1(4))* Hatje Cantz Verlag GmbH & Co KG DEU. Dist: D.A.P./Distributed Art Pubs.

Van Himbeeck, Clem, et al, eds. Xtra Strong/Light Composites. 2006. (ENG & DUT.). 95p. (Orig.). pap. 16.30 *(978-90-5867-562-0(9))* Leuven Univ. Pr. BEL. Dist: Cornell Univ. Pr.

Van Lieshout, Erik. This Can't Go On: Stay with Me, 1 vol. 2007. (GER & ENG., Illus.). 305p. pap. 39.95 *(978-3-905770-29-2(6))* JRP Ringier Kunstverlag AG CHE. Dist: D.A.P./Distributed Art Pubs.

Van Mol, Jan. Labfiles #01. 2010. 56p. pap. 24.50 *(978-0-557-67524-1(3))* Lulu Enterprises Inc.

Van Suchtelen, Ariane, et al. Rubens & Brueghel: A Working Friendship. Woollett, Anne, ed. 2006. (Illus.). 270p. 65.00 *(978-0-89236-847-1(0))* Oxford Univ. Pr., Inc.

Varadinis, Miriam, ed. Mircea Cantor. 2011. (ENG & GER., Illus.). 224p. pap. 45.00 ***(978-3-86828-107-1(X))*** Kehrer Verlag Heidelberg, Klaus Kehrer DEU. Dist: Consortium Bk. Sales & Distribution.

Vedova, Emilio. Emilio Vedova, 1 vol. 2006. (ENG & ITA., Illus.). 144p. pap. 45.00 *(978-88-8158-583-0(9))* Charta ITA. Dist: D.A.P./Distributed Art Pubs.

Verlag, Hirmer. Geisterbahn und Glanzrevue: Otto Dix, Aquarelle und Gouachen. Katalogbuch zur Ausstellung: Hamburg, 16.06.2007-09.09.2007, Bucerius Kunstforum. 2007. (GER., Illus.). 216p. (C). 52.50 *(978-3-7774-3635-7(6))* Hirmer Verlag GmbH DEU. Dist: Brown, David Bk. Co., The.

Verlag, Hirmer & Hirmer Verlag. Goldrausch: Die Pracht der Goldledertapeten. 2006. (GER., Illus.). 152p. (C). pap. 28.00 *(978-3-7774-3285-4(7))* Hirmer Verlag GmbH DEU. Dist: Brown, David Bk. Co., The.

—Meisterwerke mittelalterlicher Kunst au dem Nationalmuseum Warschau. 2006. (GER., Illus.). 192p. (C). pap. 42.00 *(978-3-7774-3275-5(X))* Hirmer Verlag GmbH DEU. Dist: Brown, David Bk. Co., The.

—Tibet: Kloester oeffnen ihre Schatzkammern. 2006. (GER., Illus.). 664p. (C). pap. 63.00 *(978-3-7774-3115-4(X))* Hirmer Verlag GmbH DEU. Dist: Brown, David Bk. Co., The.

Verwoert, Jan, contrib. by. Michaela Melian: Speicher. 2009. (ENG., Illus.). 160p. 55.00 *(978-3-86560-454-5(4))* Verlag der Buchhandlung Walther Konig DEU. Dist: D.A.P./Distributed Art Pubs.

Verzotti, Giorgio & Bernardelli, Francesco, texts. Claudio Guarino. 2009. (ENG.). 168p. pap. 45.00 *(978-88-8158-671-4(1))* Charta ITA. Dist: D.A.P./Distributed Art Pubs.

Verzotti, Giorgio & Michaud, Francois. Gabriele Di Matteo - Jackson Pollock. 2009. (ITA, FRE & ENG., Illus.). 128p. pap. 49.95 *(978-88-8158-719-3(X))* Charta ITA. Dist: D.A.P./Distributed Art Pubs.

Vetter-Liebnow, Gisela. Friedrich Karl Waechter: Zeichenkunst. 2009. (GER., Illus.). 384p. (C). 72.00 *(978-3-7774-9095-3(4))* Hirmer Verlag GmbH DEU. Dist: Brown, David Bk. Co., The.

Vezzoli, Francesco. Francesco Vezzoli: A True Hollywood Story. 2009. (ENG., Illus.). 118p. 45.00 *(978-1-894212-12-0(6))* Power Plant, The CAN. Dist: D.A.P./Distributed Art Pubs.

Victoria and Albert Museum Staff, et al. A Grand Design: The Art of the Victoria & Albert Museum. (Illus.). 431p. *(978-1-85177-217-9(0))* V & A Pubns.

Vigna, Lena. Laced with History. 2009. *(978-0-9710703-6-3(9))* Kohler, John Michael Arts Ctr.

—Provocative Clay. 2007. *(978-0-9710703-4-9(2))* Kohler, John Michael Arts Ctr.

Vingtrinier, Beatrice & Lis, Michel. Flowers in the Louvre. 2010. (ENG., Illus.). 80p. 19.95 *(978-2-08-122820-7(3))* Flammarion et Cie FRA. Dist: Random Hse., Inc.

Vinzent, Jutta, text. Overcoming Dictatorships. 2009. (ENG., Illus.). 96p. pap. 32.00 *(978-3-86678-178-8(4))* Kerber Verlag DEU. Dist: D.A.P./Distributed Art Pubs.

Virginia Museum of Fine Arts Staff, contrib. by. Making History: 20th-Century African American Art. 2012. ***(978-1-934351-00-0(8))*** Virginia Museum of Fine Arts.

Vogel, Annette. Gustav Klimt: Beethovenfries. Zeichnungen. Vogel, Annette, ed. 2010. (GER., Illus.). 160p. (C). pap. 39.00 *(978-3-7774-2881-9(7))* Hirmer Verlag GmbH DEU. Dist: Brown, David Bk. Co., The.

Vogelzang, Marije & Schouwenberg, Louise. Eat Love: Food Concepts by Eating-Designer Marije Vogelzang. 2009. (ENG., Illus.). 160p. 49.00 *(978-90-6369-200-1(5))* Bis B.V., Uitgeverij(BIS Publishers) NLD. Dist: Consortium Bk. Sales & Distribution.

von der Schulenberg, Stephan Graf & Simon, Rainald. Birth of Form: Early Chinese Ceramics at the Museum of Applied Arts, Frankfurt. 2006. (Arts, Frankfurt Ser.). (ENG, GER & CHI., Illus.). 518p. 50.00 *(978-1-891640-21-6(6))* Floating World Editions.

Von Halasz, Joachim, ed. Hitler's Art 1937 - the Great German Art Exhibition 1937 in the House of German Art in Munich - Official Exhibition Catalogue / First Published As Gro. 2008. 200p. pap. *(978-1-905742-09-7(6))* Foxley Books.

—Hitler's Art 1938 - the Great German Art Exhibition 1938 - in the House of German Art in Munich - Official Exhibition Catalogue / First Published As ' 2009. 192p. pap. *(978-1-905742-22-6(3))* Foxley Books.

—Hitler's Art 1939 - the Great German Art Exhibition 1939 - in the House of German Art in Munich - Official Exhibition Catalogue / First Published As ' 2009. 212p. pap. *(978-1-905742-23-3(1))* Foxley Books.

—Hitler's Day of German Art 1937 - First Published As 'Tag der Deutschen Kunst Mnnchen 1937' 2009. 52p. pap. *(978-1-905742-20-2(7))* Foxley Books.

—Hitler's Day of German Art 1938 - the Programme of the Procession - First Published As 'Zwe tausend Jahre Deutsche Kunst - Festzug Am Tag der Deutsche. 2009. 48p. pap. *(978-1-905742-21-9(5))* Foxley Books.

—Hitler's Day of German Art 1939 / First Published As 'Tag der Deutschen Kunst 1939' 2008. 48p. pap. *(978-1-905742-10-3(X))* Foxley Books.

—Hitler's Degenerate Art - the Exhibition Catalogue - First Published in 1937 As Entartete Kunst Ausstellungsnhrer' 2008. 48p. pap. *(978-1-905742-08-0(8))* Foxley Books.

von Huene, Stephan. Stephan von Huene: The Song of the Line/Die Zeichnungen 1950-1999. 2010. (ENG., Illus.). 144p. 45.00 *(978-3-7757-2642-9(X))* Hatje Cantz Verlag GmbH & Co KG DEU. Dist: D.A.P./Distributed Art Pubs.

Voorhies, James. Exact Imagination: Exhibition Catalogue, Columbus College of Art & Design. 2008. per. *(978-0-9797476-1-8(9))* Columbus College of Art & Design.

Waanders Editors. Black Is Beautiful: Rubens to Dumas. 2008. (ENG., Illus.). 336p. 45.00 *(978-90-400-8497-3(1))* Waanders B.V., Uitgeverij NLD. Dist: National Bk. Network.

Waggoner, Diane, et al. The Pre-Raphaelite Lens: British Photography & Painting, 1848-1875. 2010. (Illus.). 240p. 65.00 *(978-1-84822-067-6(7)*, Lund Humphries Pubs.) Ashgate Publishing, Ltd. GBR. Dist: Ashgate Publishing Co.

Walker, Barry, ed. Singular Multiples: The Peter Blum Edition Archive, 1980-1994. 2006. (Houston Museum of Fine Arts Ser.). (ENG., Illus.). 408p. 75.00 *(978-0-300-11447-3(8))* Yale Univ. Pr.

Walker, Hamza, et al, texts. Restless Empathy. 2010. (ENG., Illus.). 192p. pap. 40.00 *(978-0-934324-49-6(2))* Aspen Art Museum.

Walker, Hamzah. Anne-Mie Van Kerckhoven. 2012. (ENG., Illus.). 216p. 95.00 ***(978-90-209-9937-2(0))*** Lannoo Pubs./Racine.

Walker, Kara, text. Bureau of Refugees. 2008. (ENG., Illus.). 120p. pap. 39.95 *(978-88-8158-686-3(X))* Charta ITA. Dist: D.A.P./Distributed Art Pubs.

Wallace, Kevin. River of Destiny: The Life & Work of Binh Pho. 2006. pap. 35.00 *(978-0-9712772-6-7(5))* Long Beach Museum of Art.

Wallis, Brian, et al, eds. Strangers: The First ICP Triennial of Photography & Video, 1 vol. 2008. (ENG., Illus.). 288p. pap. 45.00 *(978-3-88243-929-8(7))* Steidl, Gerhard Druckerei und Verlag DEU. Dist: Innovative Logistics.

Walsh, Dan. Dan Walsh: Paintings. 2008. (ENG., Illus.). 112p. 49.95 *(978-0-9753921-0-2(7))* Cooper, Paula Gallery.

Ware, Chris. Uninked: Paintings, Sculpture & Graphic Works by Five Cartoonists. 2007. *(978-0-910407-59-5(2))* Phoenix Art Museum.

Warhol, Andy. Cars: Andy Warhol, Sylvie Fleury, Robert Longo, Vincent Szarek. 2010. (ENG & GER., Illus.). 248p. 60.00 *(978-3-7757-2582-8(2))* Hatje Cantz Verlag GmbH & Co KG DEU. Dist: D.A.P./Distributed Art Pubs.

Warnock, John, et al. Splendid Heritage: Perspectives on American Indian Arts. Nagy, Clinton, ed. 2009. (ENG., Illus.). 207p. pap. 49.95 *(978-0-87480-960-2(6))* Univ. of Utah Pr.

Waschek, Matthias, ed. Portrait/Homage/Embodiment. 2006. 0.00 net. *(978-0-9714648-5-8(5))* Pulitzer Foundation For The Arts.

—Water. 2007. 0.00 *(978-0-9714648-6-5(3))* Pulitzer Foundation For The Arts.

Waschek, Matthias & Mani, Camran, eds. Dan Flavin: Constructed Light. 2008. 0.00 *(978-0-9714648-7-2(1))* Pulitzer Foundation For The Arts.

Waschek, Matthias, et al. The Louvre & the Masterpiece. 2008. 35.00 *(978-1-932543-28-5(7))* High Museum of Art.

Watban, Rose. Picasso: Fired with Passion. 2007. (ENG., Illus.). 128p. pap. 27.95 *(978-1-905267-11-8(8))* NMS Enterprises Ltd. - Publishing GBR. Dist: National Bk. Network.

Waters, John. Unwatchable, 1 vol. 2006. (ENG., Illus.). 96p. per. 30.00 *(978-0-9779503-0-0(1))* Boesky, Marianne Gallery.

Watson, Wendy. Italian Renaissance Ceramics: The Howard S. & Janet H. Stein Collection. 2006. (Illus.). 224p. 45.00 *(978-0-87633-154-5(1))* Philadelphia Museum of Art.

Watteau, Antoine & Baetjer, Katharine. Watteau, Music, & Theater. 2009. 35.00 *(978-1-58839-335-7(6))* Metropolitan Museum of Art, The.

Weber, Heidi. Heidi Weber 50 Years Ambassador for Le Corbusier 1958-2008: Heidi Weber 50 Jahre Botschafterin für Le Corbusier 1958-2008. 2009. (Illus.). 205p. pap. *(978-3-0346-0249-5(9))* Birkhauser Verlag AG.

Weibel, Peter & Beitin, Andreas, eds. Elmgreen & Dragset - Celebrity: The One & the Many. 2011. (ENG., Illus.). 384p. 59.95 *(978-3-86560-908-3(2))* Verlag der Buchhandlung Walther Konig DEU. Dist: D.A.P./Distributed Art Pubs.

Weisbeck, Markus, ed. William Forsythe: Suspense. 2008. (ENG & GER., Illus.). 148p. pap. 55.00 *(978-3-905829-75-4(4))* JRP Ringier Kunstverlag AG CHE. Dist: D.A.P./Distributed Art Pubs.

Weisberg, Gabriel, ed. & text. Illusions of Reality. 2011. (ENG., Illus.). 224p. 50.00 *(978-90-6153-941-4(2))* Mercatorfonds N. V. BEL. Dist: D.A.P./Distributed Art Pubs.

Weislogel, Andrew C., text. Studied Elegance: Italian Master Drawings from the Askin Collection. 2007. (Illus.). 56p. per. *(978-1-934260-01-2(0))* Cornell Univ., Herbert F. Johnson Museum of Art.

Weislogel, Andrew C. & Iacono, Domenic J. A Changing Landscape: Prints & Drawings 1570-1670 from the Arthur & Arlene Elkind Collection. 2006. (Illus.). 52p. pap. 5.00 *(978-0-9646042-1-6(3))* Cornell Univ., Herbert F. Johnson Museum of Art.

Welchman, John, et al. Joseph Kosuth: Ni Apparence ni Illusion, 1 vol. 2011. (ENG & FRE.). 164p. 98.00 ***(978-94-90693-03-9(0))*** Exhibitions International BEL. Dist: Innovative Logistics.

Wesley, Eric. Eric Wesley, 1 vol. 2006. (ENG., Illus.). 60p. pap. 24.95 *(978-0-914357-97-1(2))* Museum of Contemporary Art, Los Angeles.

West, Franz. Franz West: White Elephant. 2010. (ENG., Illus.). 64p. 30.00 *(978-84-92480-80-7(7))* RM Verlag, S.L. ESP. Dist: D.A.P./Distributed Art Pubs.

Westheider, Ortrud. Sturz in die Welt: Die Kunst des Manierismus in Europa. Mit Beiträgen von Szilvia Bodnár, Eszter Ágnes Czoma, Anna Ecsedy, Ildikó Ember, Miklós Gálos, Zsuzsa Gonda, Annamária Gosztola, Zoltán Kárpáti, Szilárd Papp, Manga Pattantyús, Michael Philipp, Judit Sebő, Miriam Szőcs, Júlia Tátrai, Vilmos Tátrai, Michael Thimann und Axel Vécsey. Philipp, Michael- & Westheider, Ortrus, eds. 2008. (GER., Illus.). 216p. (C). 55.00 *(978-3-7774-4455-0(3))* Hirmer Verlag GmbH DEU. Dist: Brown, David Bk. Co., The.

—Zwischen Himmel und Hölle: Kunst des Mittelalters von der Gotik bis Baldung Grien. Katalogbuch zur Ausstellung Hamburg 19.09.2009-10.01.2010 Bucerius Kunst Forum. Westheider, Ortrud & Philipp, Michael, eds. 2009. (GER., Illus.). 256p. (C). 64.00 *(978-3-7774-2201-5(0))* Hirmer Verlag GmbH DEU. Dist: Brown, David Bk. Co., The.

Westheider, Ortrud & Philipp, Michael. Marc Chagall: Lebenslinien. Westheider, Ortrud & Philipp, Michael, eds. 2010. (ENG., Illus.). 232p. (C). 49.00 *(978-3-7774-2961-8(9))* Hirmer Verlag GmbH DEU. Dist: Brown, David Bk. Co., The.

Westheider, Ortrud & Philipp, Michael, eds. Schrecken und Lust: Die Versuchung des heiligen Augustinus von Hieronymus Bosch bis Max Ernst. 2008. (GER., Illus.). 215p. (C). pap. 60.00 *(978-3-7774-3945-7(2))* Hirmer Verlag GmbH DEU. Dist: Brown, David Bk. Co., The.

Wheelock, Arthur K., Jr., et al. Jan Lievens: A Dutch Master Rediscovered. 2008. (ENG., Illus.). 320p. (C). 65.00 *(978-0-300-14213-6(7))* Yale Univ. Pr.

Whitaker, Lucy & Clayton, Martin. Italian Paintings & Drawings: The Royal Collection. 2007. (ENG., Illus.). 192p. pap. 19.95 *(978-1-85759-486-7(X))* Scala, Editions FRA. Dist: National Bk. Network.

Whitehouse, David. Medieval Glass for Popes, Princes, & Peasants. 2010. (Illus.). 274p. ***(978-0-87290-177-3(7))*** Corning Museum of Glass.

Whitman, Robert. Robert Whitman Local Report. Martin, Julie, ed. 2007. (Illus.). per. 27.50 *(978-0-931286-09-4(3)*, Experiments in Art & Technology.

Wieder, John, ed. Nick Mauss & Ken Okiishi: A Fair to Meddling Story. 2008. (ENG., Illus.). 84p. pap. 28.00 *(978-3-905829-33-4(9))* JRP Ringier Kunstverlag AG CHE. Dist: D.A.P./Distributed Art Pubs.

Wiehager, Renate, ed. Art & Stars & Cars. 2011. (ENG., Illus.). 216p. pap. 50.00 ***(978-3-7757-3185-0(7))*** Hatje Cantz Verlag GmbH & Co KG DEU. Dist: D.A.P./Distributed Art Pubs.

Wiggins, Colin & Paterson, Don. Alison Watt: Phantom. 2008. (ENG., Illus.). 72p. 30.00 *(978-1-85709-412-1(3))* Yale Univ. Pr.

Wilcox, Scott, et al. Sun, Wind, & Rain: The Art of David Cox. 2008. (ENG., Illus.). 272p. 75.00 *(978-0-300-11744-8(2))* Yale Univ. Pr.

Wilke, Hannah. Hannah Wilke: Gestures. 2010. (ENG., Illus.). 108p. pap. 29.95 *(978-0-9795629-2-1(9))* Neuberger Museum of Art.

Willers, Karl. Milton Avery & the End of Modernism. 2011. 80p. pap. 20.00 ***(978-0-615-40181-2(3)**, Suny Pr.)* State Univ. of New York Pr.

Williams, Christopher. Secession, 1 vol. 2007. (ENG., Illus.). 96p. pap. 25.00 *(978-3-86560-041-7(7))* Verlag der Buchhandlung Walther Konig DEU. Dist: D.A.P./Distributed Art Pubs.

Williams, Dyfri. The Warren Cup. 2006. (British Museum Objects in Focus Ser.). (Illus.). 64p. pap. 12.95 *(978-0-7141-2260-1(2))* British Museum Pr. GBR. Dist: Brown, David Bk. Co., The.

Williams, Susan L., ed. Children's Vision of the Future: 2007/2008 Crayola Juried Art Exhibition. 2008. (Illus.). 92p. per. 24.99 incl. audio *(978-0-86696-330-5(8))* Binney & Smith, Inc.

Williamson, Paul. Medieval & Renaissance Treasures from the V&A. Motture, Peta, ed. 2007. (ENG., Illus.). 96p. 27.50 *(978-1-85177-526-2(9))* V & A Pubns. GBR. Dist: Hachette Bk. Group.

Willsdon, Clare A. P. Impressionist Gardens. 2011. (Illus.). 184p. pap. 25.00 *(978-1-906270-28-5(7))* National Galleries of Scotland GBR. Dist: National Bk. Network.

Winters, Laurie, et al. Biedermeier: The Invention of Simplicity. 2006. *(978-0-944110-85-0(1))*; pap. *(978-0-944110-89-8(4))* Milwaukee Art Museum.

Wiseman, Ari, ed. Matthew Monahan, 1 vol. 2007. (ENG., Illus.). 96p. pap. 29.95 *(978-1-933751-02-3(9))* Museum of Contemporary Art, Los Angeles.

Wolk-Simon, Linda. Raphael at the Metropolitan: The Colonna Altarpiece. 2006. (ENG., Illus.). 76p. per. 19.95 *(978-0-300-11790-5(6))* Yale Univ. Pr.

Wood, John, photos by. On the Edge of Clear Meaning, 1 vol. 2008. (ENG., Illus.). 176p. 65.00 *(978-3-86521-689-2(7))* Steidl, Gerhard Druckerei und Verlag DEU. Dist: Innovative Logistics.

Wood, Wilma. The Vanishing Landscape. 2007. pap. 27.95 *(978-1-55059-340-2(4))* Detselig Enterprises, Ltd. CAN. Dist: Temeron Bks., Inc.

Woodford, Annie. Ice: Tracing the Line of Existence. 2010. (Illus.). 55p. *(978-0-9565536-0-7(5))* Timeforce Pr.

Wool, Christopher, photos by. Christopher Wool: Pattern Paintings 1987-2000. 2008. (ENG., Illus.). 48p. pap. 25.00 *(978-0-9709090-7-7(1))* Skarstedt Fine Art.

Woollacott, Richard. Contemporary Ceramics A Dairy Barn Invitational: A Dairy Barn Invitational. 2007. (Illus.). 72p. per. 21.95 *(978-0-9717158-2-0(3))* Dairy Barn Southeastern Ohio Cultural Arts Ctr., The.

Woollett, Anne T., et al. Rubens & Brueghel: A Working Friendship. 2006. (Illus.). 270p. pap. 45.00 *(978-0-89236-848-8(9))* Oxford Univ. Pr., Inc.

Wright, Barnaby, ed. Walter Sickert: The Camden Town Nudes. 2008. (Illus.). 111p. 50.00 *(978-1-903470-59-6(5))* Holberton, Paul Publishing GBR. Dist: Univ. of Washington Pr.

Wright, Barnaby, et al. Cezanne's Card Players. 2010. (ENG., Illus.). 160p. pap. 40.00 *(978-1-907372-11-7(3))* Holberton, Paul Publishing GBR. Dist: Univ. of Washington Pr.

Wright, Frank Lloyd, et al, contrib. by. Frank Lloyd Wright & the Living City. (Illus.). 334p. *(978-3-931936-11-2(2))* Vitra Design Museum GmbH.

Wright, Micah Ian. Surveillance Means Security! Remixed War Propaganda. 2006. (ENG., Illus.). 128p. per. 21.95 *(978-1-58322-741-1(5))* Seven Stories Pr.

Wroth, William & Gavin, Robin Farwell, eds. Converging Streams: Art of the Hispanic & Native American Southwest from Preconquest Times to the Twentieth Century. 2010. (ENG.). 256p. *(978-0-89013-568-6(1))*; pap. *(978-0-89013-570-9(3))* Museum of New Mexico Pr.

Wyatt, Gary. Susan Point. (Illus.). pap. 39.95 *(978-1-55054-810-5(7))* D&M Pubs. Inc. CAN. Dist: Perseus-PGW.

Wyeth, Jamie. Farm Work by Jamie Wyeth. 2011. (Illus.). 108p. pap. 24.95 *(978-0-9795872-4-5(7))* Brandywine River Museum.

Wylie, Charles, et al, texts. On Kawara: 10 Tableaux & 16,952 Pages. 2008. (ENG., Illus.). 192p. 50.00 *(978-0-300-13734-7(6))* Dallas Museum of Art.

Xandra Eden & Gary Indiana. Dike Blair: Now & Again. 2010. (ENG., Illus.). 96p. pap. 35.00 *(978-1-890949-12-9(4))* Univ. of North Carolina at Greensboro, Weatherspoon Art Museum.

Yale University, Art Gallery Staff, contrib. by. Art for Yale: Collecting for a New Century: Celebrating the Yale University Art Gallery's 175th Anniversary & the Centennial of Paul Mellon's Birth. 2007. *(978-0-89467-969-8(4))* Yale Univ. Art Gallery.

Yamane, Kazuyo. Grassroots Museums for Peace in Japan. 2009. 364p. pap. *(978-3-639-16691-0(4))* VDM Verlag Dr. Mueller e.K.

Yee, Lydia. Urban Mythologies: The Bronx Represented since the 1960s. pap. 30.00 *(978-0-917535-26-0(X))* Bronx Museum of the Arts, The.

Yount, Sylvia. Private Passion, Public Promise: The James W. & Frances G. Mcglothlin Collection of American Art. 2010. (ENG., Illus.). 96p. (gr. 17). 30.00 *(978-0-917046-95-7(1))* Univ. Pr. of Virginia.

Yuran, Noam & Khader, Hassan, texts. Wanderland: Israel-Palestine, 1 vol. 2007. (GER & ENG., Illus.). 128p. per. 35.00 *(978-3-86678-035-4(4))* Kerber Verlag DEU. Dist: D.A.P./Distributed Art Pubs.

Zdenek. Thomas Helbig Homo Homini Lupus. 2008. (ENG., Illus.). 208p. 60.00 *(978-3-7757-2164-6(9))* Hatje Cantz Verlag GmbH & Co KG DEU. Dist: D.A.P./Distributed Art Pubs.

Zeisler, Wilfred & Bouchenot-Déchin, Patricia. The Magnificence & Grandeur of the Royal Houses in Europe. Catherine, Armin & Arminjon, Catherine, eds. 2012. (ENG., Illus.). 368p. 70.00 ***(978-88-572-1117-6(7))*** Skira Editore ITA. Dist: Random Hse., Inc.

Zelevansky, Lynn & Sussman, Elisabeth, eds. Paul Thek: Diver, A Retrospective. 2010. (ENG., Illus.). 304p. 65.00 *(978-0-300-16595-1(1))* Yale Univ. Pr.

Zhen, Chen. Chen Zhen: 1991-2000 Unrealized, 1 vol. 2007. (ENG., Illus.). 224p. per. 40.00 *(978-3-939738-31-2(X))* Verlag fur Moderne Kunst DEU. Dist: D.A.P./Distributed Art Pubs.

Zhenqing, Gu, et al, eds. To Each His Own, 1 vol. Yu, Xu, tr. 2008. (ENG., Illus.). 151p. pap. 40.00 *(978-988-99264-3-4(1))* Timezone 8 Ltd. HKG. Dist: D.A.P./Distributed Art Pubs.

Zybok, Oliver, ed. & text. Rowena Dring: Falls the Shadow. 2009. (ENG & GER., Illus.). 80p. 45.00 *(978-3-86678-222-8(5))* Kerber Verlag DEU. Dist: D.A.P./Distributed Art Pubs.

ART—EXPERTISING

see also Painting—Expertising

Crumpacker, Darrel & Master of the Die. Identifying Master of the Die: Re-examining Sixteenth Century Italian Printmaking. 2010. 48p. 20.00 *(978-0-9667532-9-5(1))* Blue Moon - Lee Pr.

Fine, Gary Alan. Everyday Genius: Self-Taught Art & the Culture of Authenticity. 2006. (Illus.). 344p. per. 35.00 *(978-0-226-24951-3(4))* Univ. of Chicago Pr.

Lenain, Thierry. Art Forgery: The History of a Modern Obsession. 2012. (Illus.). 384p. 55.00 *(978-1-86189-850-0(9))* Reaktion Bks., Ltd. GBR. Dist: Chicago Distribution Ctr.

Mould, Philip. The Art Detective: Adventures of an Antiques Roadshow Appraiser. 2011. (ENG.). 272p. (gr. 12). 16.00 *(978-0-14-311916-6(8)*, Penguin (Non-Classics)) Penguin Group (USA) Inc.

Niemeyer Chini, Valerie & Chini, Valerie Niemeyer. Stefano Bardini e Wilhelm Bode: Mercanti e connaisseur fra Ottocento e Novecento. 2009. (ITA., Illus.). 288p. (C). pap. 54.00 *(978-88-596-0668-0(3))* Polistampa ITA. Dist: Brown, David Bk. Co., The.

ART—FEDERAL AID

see Federal Aid to the Arts

ART—FINANCE

see also Federal Aid to the Arts

Robertson, Clive. Policy Matters: Administrations of Art & Culture. 2006. (ENG., Illus.). 288p. per. 19.95 *(978-0-920397-36-7(0))* Y Y Z Artists Outlet CAN. Dist: LitDistCo.

ART—FORGERIES

see Forgery of Works of Art

ART—GALLERIES AND MUSEUMS

see Art Museums

ART—GOVERNMENT POLICY

see Art and State

ART—HISTORIOGRAPHY

Adams, Laurie Schneider. The Methodologies of Art: An Introduction. 2nd ed. 2009. (ENG.). 312p. (C). pap. 36.00 *(978-0-8133-4450-8(6))* Westview Pr.

Allen, Gwen. Artists' Magazines: An Alternative Space for Art. 2011. (ENG., Illus.). 376p. (gr. 17). 37.95 *(978-0-262-01519-6(6))* MIT Pr.

Arnold, Dana, ed. Art History: Contemporary Perspectives on Method. 2010. (Art History Special Issues Ser.: 5). (ENG., Illus.). 184p. pap. 34.95 *(978-1-4443-3359-6(3)*, Wiley-Blackwell) Wiley, John & Sons, Inc.

Bagley, Robert W., et al. Max Loehr & the Study of Chinese Bronzes: Style & Classification in the History of Art. 2008. (Illus.). 199p. 55.00 *(978-1-933947-41-9(1))* Cornell Univ. East Asia Program.

Bailey, Chris & Gardiner, Hazel. Revisualizing Visual Culture. 2010. (Digital Research in the Arts & Humanities Ser.). (Illus.). 206p. 99.95 *(978-0-7546-7568-6(8))* Ashgate Publishing Co.

Barolsky, Paul. A Brief History of the Artist from God to Picasso. 2010. (ENG.). 152p. 49.95 *(978-0-271-03675-5(3))* Pennsylvania State Univ. Pr.

Batchen, Geoffrey. What of Shoes? Van Gogh & Art History. 2009. (ENG.). 48p. pap. 14.95 *(978-3-86502-218-9(9)*, Art Stock Bks. Ltd/Csi) Continental Sales, Inc.

Birkle, G., et al. Denkraume Zwischen Kunst Und Wissenschaft. (GER., Illus.). 530p. *(978-3-496-01097-5(5))* Reimer, Dietrich.

Brush, Kathryn. The Shaping of Art History: Wilhelm Vöge, Adolph Goldschmidt, & the Study of Medieval Art. 2010. (ENG.). 280p. pap. 39.99 *(978-0-521-14762-0(X))* Cambridge Univ. Pr.

Brzyski, Anna, ed. Partisan Canons. 2007. (ENG., Illus.). 376p. (C). 94.95 *(978-0-8223-4085-0(2))*; per. 26.95 *(978-0-8223-4106-2(9))* Duke Univ. Pr.

Carrier, David. A World Art History & Its Objects. 2008. (ENG., Illus.). 176p. 55.00 *(978-0-271-03414-0(9))* Pennsylvania State Univ. Pr.

—World Art History & Its Objects. 2009. (ENG., Illus.). 176p. pap. 27.95 *(978-0-271-03415-7(7))* Pennsylvania State Univ. Pr.

Caskey, Jill, et al. Confronting the Borders of Medieval Art. 2011. XVI, 230p. pap. ***(978-90-04-20749-3(X))*** BRILL.

Cheney, Liana De. Giorgio Vasari's Prefaces: Art & Theory; with a foreword by Wolfram Prinz. 2012. (LAT, ITA & ENG., Illus.). lxxiii, 333p. (C). 47.95 ***(978-1-4331-0799-3(6))*** Lang, Peter Publishing, Inc.

Cram101 Textbook Reviews. Outlines & Highlights for Look! Fundamentals of Art History by Anne DAlleva, ISBN. 2011. 94p. pap. 27.95 ***(978-1-61812-450-0(1))*** Cram101 Inc.

Crow, Thomas. La Inteligencia del Arte. 2008. (Arte Universal Ser.). 155p. pap. *(978-968-16-7236-2(4))* Fondo de Cultura Economica.

D'Alleva, Anne. Look! Art History Fundamentals. 3rd ed. 2010. (ENG.). 184p. (C). pap. 38.20 *(978-0-205-76871-4(7)*, Prentice Hall) Prentice Hall PTR.

—Methods & Theories of Art History. 2009. (ENG., Illus.). 192p. pap. 18.95 *(978-1-85669-417-9(8))* King, Laurence Publishing GBR. Dist: Hachette Bk. Group.

Davis, W. A General Theory of Visual Culture. 2011. (ENG., Illus.). 432p. (C). 55.00 *(978-0-691-14765-9(5))* Princeton Univ. Pr.

Dilly, Heinrich. Altmeister moderner Kunstgeschichte: Kunstgeschichte zur Einführung. (GER.). *(978-3-496-01203-0(X))* Reimer, Dietrich.

Emison, Patricia. The Shaping of Art History: Meditations on a Discipline. 2008. (ENG., Illus.). 104p. pap. 25.00 *(978-0-271-03306-8(1))* Pennsylvania State Univ. Pr.

Emison, Patricia A. & Emison, Patricia. The Shaping of Art History: Meditations on a Discipline. 2008. (ENG., Illus.). 104p. 40.00 *(978-0-271-03305-1(3))* Pennsylvania State Univ. Pr.

Frank, Mitchell & Adler, Daniel. German Art History & Scientific Thought: Beyond Formalism. 2012. (Illus.). 194p. 114.95 ***(978-1-4094-4023-9(0))*** Ashgate Publishing Co.

Grant, Catherine, et al, eds. Creative Writing & Art History. 2012. (Art History Special Issues Ser.: 8). (ENG., Illus.). 208p. pap. 39.95 ***(978-1-4443-5039-5(0)***, Wiley-Blackwell) Wiley, John & Sons, Inc.

Grau, Oliver. MediaArtHistories. 2010. (Leonardo Bks.). (ENG., Illus.). 488p. (gr. 17). pap. 23.00 *(978-0-262-51498-9(2))* MIT Pr.

Groseclose & Wierich. Internationalizing Hist American Art. pap. 35.00 *(978-0-271-03088-3(7))* Pennsylvania State Univ. Pr.

Guillon, Roland. Harmonie, Rythme et Sociétés: Genèse de L'art Contemporain. 2010. (FRE.). 199p. pap. *(978-2-296-13086-9(0))* Harmattan Pr.

Hatfield, Rab, ed. Sandro Botticelli Herbert Horn. 2009. 160p. pap. 24.95 *(978-88-95250-04-5(4))* Syracuse Univ. Pr.

Hills, Helen, ed. Rethinking the Baroque. 2011. (Illus.). 286p. 124.95 *(978-0-7546-6685-1(9))* Ashgate Publishing Co.

Imesch, Kornelia. Inscriptions/Transgressions: Kunstgeschichte und Gender Studies = Histoire de L'art et études Genre. 2008. (FRE, GER & ENG., Illus.). 317p. 71.95 *(978-3-03911-308-8(9))* Lang, Peter Publishing, Inc.

Iversen, Margaret & Melville, Stephen W. Writing Art History: Disciplinary Departures. 2010. (ENG., Illus.). 256p. 85.00 *(978-0-226-38825-0(5))*; pap. 30.00 *(978-0-226-38826-7(3))* Univ. of Chicago Pr.

Lesure, Richard G. Interpreting Ancient Figurines: Context, Comparison, & Prehistoric Art. 2011. (ENG., Illus.). 276p. 95.00 *(978-0-521-19745-8(7))* Cambridge Univ. Pr.

Mathur, Saloni. The Migrant's Time: Rethinking Art History & Diaspora. 2011. (Illus.). xix, 251p. ***(978-1-935998-03-7(X))*** Clark, Sterling & Francine Art Institute.

Michaud, Philippe-Alain. Aby Warburg & the Image in Motion. Hawkes, Sophie, tr. from FRE. 2007. (ENG., Illus.). 382p. (gr. 17). per. 25.00 *(978-1-890951-40-5(4))* Zone Bks.

Noever, Peter, et al, eds. Alois Riegl Revisited: Beiträge zu Werk und Rezeption - Contributions to the Opus & its Reception. 2010. (VERoFFENTLICHUNGEN der KOMMISSION FuR KUNSTGESCHICHTE Ser.). 148p. (C). pap. 73.00 *(978-3-7001-6498-2(X))* Austrian Academy of Sciences Press AUT. Dist: Brown, David Bk. Co., The.

Olin, Margaret. The Nation Without Art: Examining Modern Discourses on Jewish Art. 2007. (Texts & Contexts Ser.). (ENG., Illus.). 308p. pap. 24.95 *(978-0-8032-2233-5(5))* Univ. of Nebraska Pr.

Pellizzi, Francesco, ed. West by Nonwest, Vol. 42. 2006. (Illus.). 272p. pap. 30.00 *(978-0-87365-842-3(6))* Peabody Museum of Archaeology & Ethnology, Harvard Univ., Pubns. Dept.

Preziosi, Donald, ed. The Art of Art History: A Critical Anthology. 2nd ed. 2009. (Oxford History of Art Ser.). (ENG., Illus.). 624p. 29.95 *(978-0-19-922984-0(8))* Oxford Univ. Pr., Inc.

Soussloff, Catherine M. The Subject in Art: Portraiture & the Birth of the Modern. 2006. (ENG., Illus.). 192p. 79.95 *(978-0-8223-3658-7(8))*; per. 22.95 *(978-0-8223-3670-9(7))* Duke Univ. Pr.

ART—HISTORY

Ackroyd, Norman & Dunn, Douglas. Silent Tides. 2009. (ENG., Illus.). 160p. 120.00 *(978-1-903973-68-4(6))* Royal Academy of Arts GBR. Dist: Hachette Bk. Group.

Adams, Laurie. A History of Western Art Revised, Student Edition & World Views Package. 4th ed. 2009. (Art Ser.). (ENG.). pap., pap. 129.00 *(978-0-07-895096-4(1)*, 0078950961) McGraw-Hill Higher Education.

Adams, Laurie Schneider. Art: A Beginner's Guide. 2012. (ENG., Illus.). 240p. pap. 14.95 ***(978-1-85168-853-1(6))*** Oneworld Pubns. GBR. Dist: National Bk. Network.

—Art Across Time, Vol. 2. 4th ed. 2010. (ENG.). 640p. (C). pap. 142.67 *(978-0-07-735371-1(4)*, 0077353714) McGraw-Hill Cos., The.

—Art across Time Combined. 4th ed. 2010. (ENG., Illus.). 1088p. (C). pap. 157.33 *(978-0-07-337923-4(9)*, 0073379239) McGraw-Hill Cos., The.

—A History of Western Art. (ENG., Illus.). 640p. (C). 4th rev. ed. 2006. per. 143.33 *(978-0-07-352646-1(0)*, 0073526460) 5th ed. 2010. pap. 143.33 *(978-0-07-337922-7(0)*, 0073379220) McGraw-Hill Cos., The.

Aigner, Silvie, ed. Emanzipation und Konfrontation / Emancipation & Confrontation / Emancipacija in konfrontacija: Kunst aus Kärnten von 1945 bis heute. Architektur aus Kärnten seit 1945 und Kunst im öffentlichen Raum heute., 3 vols. 2008. (GER, SLV & ENG., Illus.). 1010p. *(978-3-211-75622-5(1)*, 3211756221) Actar Birkhauser Distribution.

Allard, Sebastien, et al. Citizens & Kings: Portraits in the Age of Enlightenment. 2007. (ENG., Illus.). 368p. 85.00 *(978-1-903973-23-3(6))* Royal Academy of Arts GBR. Dist: Hachette Bk. Group.

Allen, Felicity. Education. 2011. (Whitechapel: Documents of Contemporary Art Ser.). (ENG.). 240p. (gr. 17). pap. 24.95 *(978-0-262-51636-5(5))* MIT Pr.

Allen, J. Romilly. Celtic Art in Pagan & Christian Times. 2010. 414p. 39.96 *(978-1-169-33887-6(9))*; 49.95 *(978-1-161-60727-7(7))* Kessinger Publishing, LLC.

—Celtic Art in Pagan & Christian Times. 2008. (ENG.). 424p. per. *(978-1-4086-5308-1(7))* Read Bks.

Alpatov, Mikhail. Russian Impact on Art. Wolf, Martin L., ed. Litvinov, Ivy, tr. 2011. 406p. 54.95 ***(978-1-258-07522-4(9))*** Literary Licensing, LLC.

Alternative Pick. 10th anniv. ed. 60.00 *(978-0-7893-6251-3(1))* Universe Publishing.

Álvarez-Mon, Javier & Garrison, Mark B. Elam & Persia. 2010. 79.50 *(978-1-57506-166-5(X))* Eisenbrauns, Inc.

Art Directors Club, ed. ADC Bush 2000: German Art Directors Club Annual. (Illus.). 626p. 99.00 *(978-3-87439-530-4(8))* Universitatsdruckerei & Verlag H. Schmidt GmbH & Co. DEU. Dist: Gingko Pr., Inc.

Asch, Gayle A. AP Art History Crash Course. 2012. (Advanced Placement (AP) Crash Course Ser.). (ENG.). 224p. (C). (gr. 10-12). pap. 12.95 ***(978-0-7386-1004-7(6))*** Research & Education Assn.

Babelon, Jean. Histoire de l'Art Vol. 2: L'Europe Medievale. (FRE.). 1748p. *(978-0-8288-7601-8(0))* French & European Pubns., Inc.

—Histoire de l'Art Vol. 3: Renaissance, Baroque, Romantisme. (FRE.). 1704p. *(978-0-8288-7602-5(9))* French & European Pubns., Inc.

BarCharts, Inc. Art History 1. 2010. (ENG.). 6p. 5.95 *(978-1-4232-1494-6(3))* Barcharts, Inc.

Barrow, John. The Artful Universe Expanded. 2nd ed. 2011. (ENG., Illus.). 336p. pap. 19.95 *(978-0-19-960133-2(X))* Oxford Univ. Pr., Inc.

Barter, Judith A. & Downs, Jennifer M. American Modernism at the Art Institute of Chicago: From World War I to 1955. 2009. (ENG., Illus.). 368p. 75.00 *(978-0-300-11738-7(8))* Art Institute of Chicago.

Barzun, Jacques. History As a Liberal Art: Journal of the History of Ideas, V6, No. 1, January 1945. Randall Jr., John Herman, ed. 2011. 16p. pap. 35.95 ***(978-1-258-03658-4(4))*** Literary Licensing, LLC.

Baxandall, Michael. Episodes: A Memory Book. 2010. (ENG., Illus.). 144p. 24.95 *(978-0-7112-3115-3(X))* Lincoln, Frances Ltd. GBR. Dist: Perseus-PGW.

Beaulieu, Jill, et al, eds. Refracting Vision: Essays on the Writings of Michael Fried. 2012. (ENG., Illus.). 407p. (C). per. 35.00 *(978-1-86487-024-4(9))* Power Pubns. AUS. Dist: Univ. of Washington Pr.

Bell, Clive. Art. 2008. 188p. 25.99 *(978-0-554-26107-2(3))* 2008. 188p. 22.99 *(978-0-554-35410-1(1))* 2007. (ENG.). 168p. pap. 19.99 *(978-1-4346-0389-0(X))* 2007. (ENG.). 186p. pap. 21.99 *(978-1-4346-0462-0(4))* BiblioBazaar.

—Art. 2008. 320p. 45.95 *(978-1-4366-4789-2(4))*; pap. 30.95 *(978-0-548-90130-4(9))* Kessinger Publishing, LLC.

—Art. 2008. (ENG.). 156p. pap. 11.95 *(978-1-4385-0174-1(9))*; pap. 12.45 *(978-1-4385-0894-8(8))* Standard Pubns., Inc. (Book Jungle).

Bell, Julian. Mirror of the World. 2007. (ENG., Illus.). 496p. 45.00 *(978-0-500-23837-0(5))* Thames & Hudson.

—Mirror of the World: A New History of Art. 2010. (ENG., Illus.). 496p. pap. 34.95 *(978-0-500-28754-5(6)*, 528754) Thames & Hudson.

Bhattacharyya, A. K. & Padaliptacarya. Historical Development of Jaina Iconography: A Comprehensive Study. 2010. (SAN & ENG., Illus.). xviii, 339p. *(978-81-8090-231-4(5)*, Library of Congress — New Delhi Overseas Office) Bhartiya Kala Prakashan.

Bishop, Claire. Installation Art. 2010. (ENG., Illus.). 144p. pap. 32.50 *(978-1-85437-518-6(0))* Tate Publishing, Ltd. GBR. Dist: Hachette Bk. Group.

Black, Michael. Leonardo, Romancia & R: Art History. 2009. (Illus.). 128p. pap. *(978-1-84991-004-0(9))* Chipmunkapublishing.

Bogh, Mikkel, et al, eds. Images of Culture: Art History as Cultural History. 2012. (Illus.). 250p. pap. 43.00 *(978-87-635-0478-2(2))* Museum Tusculanum Pr. DNK. Dist: Chicago Distribution Ctr.

Bradley, David A. & Creagh, Dudley Cecil, contrib. by. Physical Techniques in the Study of Art, Archaeology & Cultural Heritage, Vol. 1. 2006. (Physical Techniques in the Study of Art, Archaeology & Cultural Heritage Ser.: 1). (ENG., Illus.). 232p. 114.00 *(978-0-444-52131-6(3)*, Elsevier Science) Elsevier Science & Technology Bks.

Brommer, Frank, ed. Discover Art History. 3rd ed. (Illus.). tchr. ed. *(978-0-87192-313-4(0))*; 68p. tchr. ed. 234.95 *(978-0-87192-312-7(2))* Davis Pubns., Inc.

Brommer, Gerald F. Discover Art History: Overhead Transparencies. 74.95 *(978-0-87192-310-3(6))* Davis Pubns., Inc.

Brown, Shana Julia. Pastimes: From Art & Antiquarianism to Modern Chinese Historiography. 2011. 232p. 48.00 ***(978-0-8248-3498-2(4))*** Univ. of Hawaii Pr.

Bryan-Wilson, Julia. Art Workers: Radical Practice in the Vietnam War Era. 2009. (ENG., Illus.). 256p. 60.00 *(978-0-520-25728-3(6))* Univ. of California Pr.

Buchholz, Elke Linda, et al. Art: A World History. 2007. (ENG., Illus.). 512p. per. 21.95 *(978-0-8109-9442-3(9))* Abrams.

Buck, Stephanie & Hohenstatt, Peter. Raffaello Santi, Known as Raphael: 1483-1520. 2008. (Masters of Italian Art Ser.). (Illus.). 120p. per. 9.95 *(978-0-8416-0083-6(X))* American Map Corp.

BURGESS. Art & Design: Teaching School Subjects 11-19. 2008. (Illus.). 204p. 130.00 *(978-0-415-36739-4(5))*; pap. 42.95 *(978-0-415-36740-0(9))* Routledge.

Butovski, Viktor & Orlova, Maria. The Russian Ornament Sourcebook, 1 vol. 2011. (ENG., Illus.). 336p. 39.95 *(978-1-908126-02-3(7))* Vivays Pubng. Ltd. GBR. Dist: Innovative Logistics.

Calvo Serraller, Francisco. The Moustache of la Gioconda: Eduardo Arroyo. 2009. 184p. 50.00 *(978-84-96763-19-7(6))* Museo Nacional Centro de Arte Reina Sofia ESP. Dist: Actar Birkhauser Distribution.

Candlin, Fiona. Art, Museums & Touch. 2010. (Rethinking Art's Histories Ser.). (ENG., Illus.). 240p. 90.00 *(978-0-7190-7933-7(0))* Manchester Univ. Pr. GBR. Dist: Macmillan.

Carey, Sorcha. Pliny's Catalogue of Culture: Art & Empire in the Natural History. 2007. (Oxford Studies in Ancient Culture & Representation Ser.). (ENG., Illus.). 224p. per. 75.00 *(978-0-19-920765-7(8))* Oxford Univ. Pr., Inc.

Carl, Klaus H. & Charles, Victoria. Baroque Art. 2009. (Art of Century Ser.). (ENG., Illus.). 200p. 19.95 *(978-1-84484-621-4(0))* Parkstone International GBR. Dist: Ingram Pub. Services.

Carr-Gomm, Sarah. The Secret Language of Art: The Illustrated Decoder of Symbols & Figures in Western Painting. 2008. (ENG.). 256p. pap.

(978-1-84483-710-6(6)) Duncan Baird Pubs. GBR. Dist: Sterling Publishing Co., Inc.

Charles, Victoria & Carl, Klaus H. Medieval Art in Europe from 987 To 1489. 2012. (Must Ser.). (ENG.). 400p. 49.95 (978-1-906981-03-7(5)) Parkstone Pr. USA, Ltd.

Charles, Victoria & Weber, Frederick Parkes. Art of the Eternal. 2012. (Temporis Ser.). (ENG., Illus.). 256p. 39.95 (978-1-84484-827-0(2)) Parkstone International GBR. Dist: Ingram Pub. Services.

Charles, Victoria, et al. World History of Art, 5 vols. 2012. (Prestige Ser.). (ENG, FRE & GER., Illus.). 256p. 99.00 (978-1-84484-669-6(5)) Parkstone International GBR. Dist: Ingram Pub. Services.

Ching, Dora C. & Smith, Judith. Bridges to Heaven: Essays on East Asian Art in Honor of Professor Wen C. Fong, 2 vols. 2011. (Publications of the Department of Art & Archaeology, Princeton University Ser.). (ENG., Illus.). 992p. (C). 175.00 (978-0-691-15298-1(5)) Princeton Univ. Pr.

Chmiel, Frank, et al. AP Art History. 2012. (Advanced Placement (AP) Test Preparation Ser.). (ENG.). 512p. (gr. 11-12). pap. 29.95 (978-0-7386-1075-7(5)) Research & Education Assn.

Clarke, Mark. The Art of All Colours: Mediaeval Recipe Books for Painters & Illuminators. 2007. (ENG., Illus.). 152p. pap. 50.00 (978-1-873132-72-2(7)) Archetype Pubns. GBR. Dist: National Bk. Network.

Cook, Clarence. Art & Artists of Our Time. 2010. 106p. pap. 19.75 (978-1-155-05084-3(3)); 104p. pap. 20.00 (978-1-155-05088-1(6)); (Illus.). 104p. pap. 20.00 (978-1-155-05092-8(4)); (Illus.). 210p. pap. 29.31 (978-1-155-00584-3(8)) General Bks. LLC.

Cram101 Textbook Reviews. Outlines & Highlights for a History of Western Art by Adams. 2011. 96p. pap. 27.95 (978-1-61906-257-3(7)) Cram101 Inc.

—Outlines & Highlights for a History of Western Art by Adams, Isbn: 007282719x 0072997680. 2011. 424p. pap. 36.95 (978-1-61812-787-7(X)) Cram101 Inc.

—Outlines & Highlights for Art History: 18th - 21st Century by Marilyn Stokstad, ISBN. 2010. 68p. pap. 27.95 (978-1-61698-268-3(3)) Cram101 Inc.

—Outlines & Highlights for Art History: A View of the West, Combined by Marilyn Stokstad, Patrick Frank, D. Fairchild Ruggles, ISBN. 2010. 166p. pap. 29.95 (978-1-61698-257-7(8)) Cram101 Inc.

—Outlines & Highlights for Art History, Combined by Marilyn Stokstad, Isbn: 9780132368544. 2010. 236p. pap. 31.95 (978-1-61698-250-8(0)) Cram101 Inc.

—Outlines & Highlights for Art Historys History by Vernon Hyde Minor, Isbn: 9780130851338. 2010. 106p. pap. 28.95 (978-1-61698-265-2(9)) Cram101 Inc.

—Outlines & Highlights for Art Past Art Present by David G Wilkins, Bernard Schultz, Katheryn M Linduff, Isbn: 9780136011002. 2010. 128p. pap. 28.95 (978-1-61698-260-7(8)) Cram101 Inc.

—Outlines & Highlights for Gardners Art Through the Ages: A Concise Global History (with ArtStudy Online Printed Access Card & Timeline) by Fred S. Kle. 2010. 166p. pap. 29.95 (978-1-61698-262-1(4)) Cram101 Inc.

—Outlines & Highlights for Gardners Art Through the Ages: Backpack Edition, Book C by Fred S. Kleiner. 2011. 282p. pap. 32.95 (978-1-61490-892-0(3)) Cram101 Inc.

—Outlines & Highlights for Gardners Art Through the Ages: Backpack Edition Set by Fred S. Kleiner, ISBN. 2011. 338p. pap. 37.95 (978-1-61490-168-6(6)) Cram101 Inc.

—Outlines & Highlights for Gardners Art Through the Ages: The Western Perspective by Fred S. Kleiner, Christin J. Mamiya, ISBN. 2010. 210p. pap. 30.95 (978-1-61698-254-6(3)) Cram101 Inc.

—Outlines & Highlights for Gardners Art Through the Ages: The Western Perspective, Volume I by Fred S. Kleiner. 2011. 348p. pap. 33.95 (978-1-61490-891-3(5)) Cram101 Inc.

—Outlines & Highlights for Gardners Art Through the Ages: The Western Perspective (with Art Study & Timeline Printed Access Card) by Fred S. Kleiner, 2010. 218p. pap. 30.95 (978-1-61698-251-5(9)) Cram101 Inc.

—Outlines & Highlights for Gardners Art Through the Ages by Fred S Kleiner, Isbn: 9780495793434 0495793434 9780495573678 0495573671. 2011. 212p. pap. 30.95 (978-1-61490-169-3(4)) Cram101 Inc.

—Outlines & Highlights for Gardners Art Through the Ages by Fred S Kleiner, Isbn: 9780495794486 0495794481. 2011. 338p. pap. 30.95 (978-1-61490-183-9(X)) Cram101 Inc.

—Outlines & Highlights for Gardners Art Through the Ages the Western Perspective, Volume II by Fred S Kleiner, Isbn: 9780495573654 0495573655 97804955. 2011. 84p. pap. 27.95 (978-1-61490-153-2(8)) Cram101 Inc.

—Outlines & Highlights for Gardners Art Through the Ages, Volume I, Chapters 1-18 (with Artstudy Stud by Fred S Kleiner, Christin J Mamiya, Isbn: 978. 2010. 100p. pap. 27.95 (978-1-61698-261-4(6)) Cram101 Inc.

—Outlines & Highlights for Jansons Basic History of Western Art by Penelope Davies. 2011. 146p. pap. 29.95 (978-1-61906-006-7(X)) Cram101 Inc.

—Outlines & Highlights for Jansons History of Art: Western Tradition, Volume 2 by Penelope J. E. Davies, Joseph Jacobs, Walter B. Denny, David L. Simon, 2010. 66p. pap. 27.95 (978-1-61698-255-3(1)) Cram101 Inc.

—Outlines & Highlights for the Creative Impulse: An Introduction to the Arts by Dennis J. Sporre, ISBN. 2010. 166p. pap. 29.95 (978-1-61698-252-2(7)) Cram101 Inc.

Cram101 Textbook Reviews. Outlines & Highlights for the Visual Arts: A History by Honour & Fleming, ISBN. 2011. 698p. pap. 42.95 (978-1-61812-702-0(0)) Cram101 Inc.

Cram101 Textbook Reviews & Cram101 Textbook Reviews. Outlines & Highlights for Art Across Time Volume Two by Laurie Adams, Isbn: 9780077353711. 2011. 140p. pap. 28.95 (978-1-61461-824-9(0)) Cram101 Inc.

—Outlines & Highlights for Gardners Art Through the Ages: Backpack Edition, Book A, Antiquity by Fred S. Kleiner. 2011. 214p. pap. 30.95 (978-1-61830-657-9(X)) Cram101 Inc.

—Outlines & Highlights for Visual Arts: History by Hugh Honour, ISBN. 2011. 666p. pap. 41.95 (978-1-61490-524-0(X)) Cram101 Inc.

Cram101 Textbook Reviews Staff. Outlines & Highlights for Art Across Time, Volume II by Laurie Schneider Adams, Isbn: 9780072969740. 2009. 184p. pap. 29.95 (978-1-4288-9505-8(1)) Cram101 Inc.

—Outlines & Highlights for Art History: 18th - 21st Century by Marilyn Stokstad, ISBN. 2009. 58p. pap. 26.95 (978-1-4288-9102-9(1)) Cram101 Inc.

—Outlines & Highlights for Art History: A View of the West, Combined by Marilyn Stokstad, Patrick Frank, D. Fairchild Ruggles, ISBN. 2009. 140p. pap. 28.95 (978-1-4288-9214-9(1)) Cram101 Inc.

—Outlines & Highlights for Art History, Combined by Marilyn Stokstad, Isbn: 9780132368544. 2009. 212p. pap. 30.95 (978-1-4288-9223-1(0)) Cram101 Inc.

—Outlines & Highlights for Art History, Volume One by Marilyn Stokstad, Isbn: 9780131743205. 2009. 94p. pap. 27.95 (978-1-4288-9558-4(2)) Cram101 Inc.

—Outlines & Highlights for Art History, Volume Two by Marilyn Stokstad, Isbn: 9780131991408. 2009. 118p. pap. 28.95 (978-1-4288-9500-3(0)) Cram101 Inc.

—Outlines & Highlights for Art Past Art Present by David G Wilkins, Bernard Schultz, Katheryn M Linduff, Isbn: 9780136011002. 2009. 108p. pap. 28.95 (978-1-4288-9168-5(4)) Cram101 Inc.

—Outlines & Highlights for Art Past, Art Present by David G Wilkins, Isbn: 9780132357166. 2009. 126p. pap. 28.95 (978-1-4288-9472-3(1)) Cram101 Inc.

—Outlines & Highlights for Artforms: An Introduction to the Visual Arts by Patrick Frank, ISBN. 2009. 144p. pap. 28.95 (978-1-4288-9605-5(8)) Cram101 Inc.

—Outlines & Highlights for Gardners Art Through the Ages: A Concise Global History (with ArtStudy Online Printed Access Card & Timeline) by Fred S. Kle. 2009. 148p. pap. 29.95 (978-1-4288-9126-5(9)) Cram101 Inc.

—Outlines & Highlights for Gardners Art Through the Ages: A Global History by Fred S. Kleiner, ISBN. 2009. 214p. pap. 30.95 (978-1-4288-9401-3(2)) Cram101 Inc.

—Outlines & Highlights for Gardners Art Through the Ages: A Global History, Vol. 1 by Fred S. Kleiner, ISBN. 2009. 106p. pap. 28.95 (978-1-4288-9402-0(0)) Cram101 Inc.

—Outlines & Highlights for Gardners Art Through the Ages: A Global History, Vol. 2 by Fred S. Kleiner, ISBN. 2009. 144p. pap. 28.95 (978-1-4288-9403-7(9)) Cram101 Inc.

—Outlines & Highlights for Gardners Art Through the Ages: The Western Perspective (with Art Study & Timeline Printed Access Card) by Fred S. Kleiner, 2009. 186p. pap. 30.95 (978-1-4288-9219-4(2)) Cram101 Inc.

—Outlines & Highlights for Gardners Art Through the Ages, Volume I, Chapters 1-18 (with Artstudy Stud by Fred S Kleiner, Christin J Mamiya, Isbn: 978. 2009. 82p. pap. 27.95 (978-1-4288-9136-4(6)) Cram101 Inc.

—Outlines & Highlights for History of Art: Western Tradition, Volume I by Penelope J. E. Davies, ISBN. 2009. 64p. pap. 27.95 (978-1-4288-9495-2(0)) Cram101 Inc.

Cross, Elizabeth & Gott, Ted. Edvard Munch: The Frieze of Life. 2006. (ENG., Illus.). 184p. pap. 39.95 (978-0-7241-0254-9(X)) National Gallery of Victoria AUS. Dist: National Bk. Network.

Cuss, Terence Camerer. The English Watch: 1585-1970 A Unique Alliance of Art, Design & Inventive Genius. 2008. (ENG., Illus.). 504p. (978-1-85149-583-7(6), Antique Collectors Club Dist) Antique Collectors' Club.

Dalli Regoli, Gigetta. Verrocchio, Lorenzo di Credi, Francesco di Simone Ferrucci. 2008. (Drawing Gallery Ser.). (ENG., Illus.). 92p. pap. 14.95 (978-88-7439-063-7(8)) 5 Continents ITA. Dist: Hachette Bk. Group.

Dalmia, Yashodhara & Hashmi, Salima. Memory, Metaphor, Mutations: The Contemporary Art of India & Pakistan. 2007. (ENG., Illus.). 239p. 199.00 (978-0-19-567347-0(6)) Oxford Univ. Pr., Inc.

Darring, Walt. The Ur-Board Book. 2011. 126p. pap. 14.95 (978-0-557-49490-3(7)) Lulu Enterprises Inc.

Davidts, Wouter, et al, texts. The Fall of the Studio. 2009. (ENG., Illus.). 249p. pap. 27.50 (978-90-78088-29-5(X)) Valiz NLD. Dist: D.A.P./Distributed Art Pubs.

Davies, Penelope, et al. History of Art: The Western Tradition. 8th ed. 2010. (ENG.). (C). 1184p. 109.33 (978-0-205-80075-9(0)); 46.67 (978-0-205-80072-8(6)) Prentice Hall PTR. (Prentice Hall).

—Janson's Basic History of Western Art. 8th ed. 2008. (ENG.). 688p. (C). pap. 140.67 (978-0-13-603912-9(X), Prentice Hall) Prentice Hall PTR.

Davies, Penelope J. E. Janson's History of Art: The Western Tradition. 7th ed. 2007. (Illus.). (978-0-13-500632-0(5)) Pearson Education Canada.

Davies, Penelope J. E., et al. Janson's History of Art, Vol. 2. 8th ed. 2010. (ENG.). 736p. (C). ring bd. 94.67 (978-0-205-79563-5(3), Prentice Hall) Prentice Hall PTR.

—Janson's History of Art: The Western Tradition. 7th ed. 2006. (ENG., Illus.). pap. (978-0-13-239783-9(9)) Pearson Education Canada.

—Janson's History of Art: The Western Tradition, Volume I, 2 vols. 8th ed. 2010. (ENG., Illus.). 528p. (C). pap. 145.00 (978-0-205-68518-9(8), Prentice Hall) Prentice Hall PTR.

—Janson's History of Art: The Western Tradition, Volume I, Books a la Carte Plus MyArtsLab. 8th ed. 2010. (ENG.). (C). ring bd. 101.33 (978-0-205-80049-0(1), Prentice Hall) Prentice Hall PTR.

—Janson's History of Art: The Western Tradition, Volume II, Books a la Carte Plus MyArtsLab. 8th ed. 2010. (ENG.). (C). ring bd. 101.33 (978-0-205-80050-6(5), Prentice Hall) Prentice Hall PTR.

—Janson's History of Art Vol. 1: The Western Tradition. 8th ed. 2010. (ENG.). 520p. (C). ring bd. 94.67 (978-0-205-79562-8(5), Prentice Hall) Prentice Hall PTR.

—Janson's History of Art Vol. 2: The Western Tradition, 2 vols. 8th ed. 2010. (ENG., Illus.). 408p. (C). pap. 145.00 (978-0-205-68519-6(6), Prentice Hall) Prentice Hall PTR.

—Janson's History of Art Portable Edition Book 2, 4 vols. 8th rev. ed. 2010. (ENG., Illus.). 272p. (C). 75.33 (978-0-205-16113-3(8), Prentice Hall) Prentice Hall PTR.

Davis, Anita Price. New Deal Art in Virginia: The Oils, Murals, Reliefs & Frescoes & Their Creators. 2009. (ENG., Illus.). 223p. pap. 45.00 (978-0-7864-4185-3(2)) McFarland & Co., Inc. Pubs.

Dehan, Amy Miller. Outside the Ordinary: Contemporary Art in Glass, Wood, & Ceramics from the Wolf Collection. 2009. (ENG.). 176p. pap. 30.00 (978-0-8214-1861-1(0)) Ohio Univ. Pr.

Devambez, Pierre. Histoire de l'Ar Vol. 1: Le Monde Non Chretien. (FRE.). 2240p. 140.00 (978-0-8288-7697-1(5)) French & European Pubns., Inc.

Didi-Huberman, Georges. Confronting Images: Questioning the Ends of a Certain History of Art. (Illus.). 288p. pap. 35.00 (978-0-271-02472-1(0)) Pennsylvania State Univ. Pr.

Dorra, Henri. Art in Perspective: A Brief History. (Orig.). 2010. 350p. 27.96 (978-1-169-69838-3(7)) 2010. 350p. 34.95 (978-1-161-68435-3(2)) 2007. (ENG.). 348p. per. 31.95 (978-0-548-38686-6(2)) Kessinger Publishing, LLC.

Dressendörfer, Werner. Thornton: Temple of Flora. Lamers-Schuetze, Petra, ed. l.t. ed. 2008. (Illus.). 110p. 150.00 (978-3-8228-5273-6(2)) TASCHEN DEU. Dist: Ingram Pub. Services.

El-Shahawy, Abeer. Recherche sur la decoration des tombes thebaines du Nouvel Empire: Originalites iconographiques et Innovations. 2010. (Internet-Beitrage Zur Agyptologie und Sudanarchaologie Ser.: XIII). (FRE.). 400p. (C). pap. 80.00 (978-1-906137-19-9(6)) Golden Hse. Pubns. GBR. Dist: Brown, David Bk. Co., The.

Elkins, James. Chinese Landscape Painting as Western Art History. 2010. (ENG., Illus.). 208p. (gr. 17). 45.00 (978-962-209-000-2(1)) Hong Kong Univ. Pr. HKG. Dist: Columbia Univ. Pr.

—Chinese Landscape Painting As Western Art History. 2010. 208p. (978-9971-69-523-1(5)) Hong Kong Univ. Pr.

—Is Art History Global? 2006. (Art Seminar Ser.: Vol. 3). (ENG., Illus.). 472p. 35.95 (978-0-415-97785-2(1)) Routledge.

Elkins, James, ed. Is Art History Global? 2006. (Art Seminar Ser.: Vol. 3). (ENG., Illus.). 128p. 125.00 (978-0-415-97784-5(3)) Routledge.

Fairbanks, Arthur. Athenian Lekythoi with Outline Drawing in Glaze Varnish on a White Ground. 2010. 720p. pap. 49.75 (978-1-143-00263-2(6)) BiblioBazaar.

Faure, Elie. Ancient Art: History of Art. Pach, Walter, tr. 2011. 380p. 53.95 (978-1-258-01388-2(6)) Literary Licensing, LLC.

—The Italian Renaissance. 2011. 176p. 42.95 (978-1-258-04969-0(4)) Literary Licensing, LLC.

—Mediaeval Art: History of Art V2. Pach, Walter, tr. 2011. 462p. 57.95 (978-1-258-02980-7(4)) Literary Licensing, LLC.

Ferino, S., ed. Tizian versus Seisenegger: Das Portait Karls V mit Hund. ein Holbeinstreit. 2006. (Museums at the Crossroads Ser.). (ITA, FRE, GER, SPA & ENG., Illus.). 184p. (C). pap. 109.00 (978-2-503-51506-9(1)) Brepols Pubs. BEL. Dist: ISD.

Fichner-Rathus, Lois. Understanding Art: A Concise History. 8th ed. 2007. (ENG., Illus.). 336p. (C). pap. 85.95 (978-0-495-10168-0(0)) Wadsworth.

Fiero, Gloria & Adams, Laurie. Art Across Time Vol. 1: Prehistory to the Fourteenth Century. 4th ed. 2010. (ENG., Illus.). 544p. (C). pap. 142.67 (978-0-07-735373-5(0), 0077353730) McGraw-Hill Cos., The.

Ford, Simon, ed. Information Sources in Art, Art History & Design. (Guides to Information Sources Ser.). (ENG.). XX, 220p. (978-3-11-184923-2(6)) Saur, K. G. Verlag GmbH & Co.

Frank, Patrick L. & Preble, Sarah. Prebles' Artforms. 10th ed. 2011. (ENG.). (C). 46.67 (978-0-205-22774-7(0), Prentice Hall) Prentice Hall PTR.

Gaehtgens, Thomas W. & Zelljadt, Katja, eds. Getty Research Journal. (Getty Research Journal Ser.). (ENG., No. 2. 2010. Illus.). 228p. pap. 50.00 (978-1-60606-017-9(1))No. 3. 2011. 234p. pap. 50.00 (978-1-60606-063-6(5)) Getty Pubns. (Getty Research Institute).

Gallup, Alison, et al, eds. Great Paintings of the Western World. (Illus.). 320p. (978-0-88363-259-8(4)) Levin, Hugh Lauter Assocs.

Gaut, Berys, ed. Thinking about Art: Classic & Contemporary Philosophical Readings. 2009. 560p. 34.00 (978-0-415-40576-8(9)); 122.00 (978-0-415-40575-1(0)) Routledge.

Geczy, Adam. Art: Histories, Theories & Exceptions. 2008. (ENG., Illus.). 1p. 109.95 (978-1-84520-700-7(9)); 224p. pap. 29.95 (978-1-84520-701-4(7)) Berg Pubs. GBR. Dist: Macmillan.

Geczy, Adam & Karaminas, Vicki. Fashion & Art. 2012. (ENG., Illus.). 224p. (C). pap. 29.95 (978-1-84788-783-2(X)) Berg Pubs. GBR. Dist: Macmillan

Geczy, Adam & Karaminas, Vicki, eds. Fashion & Art. 2012. (ENG., Illus.). 224p. (C). 99.95 (978-1-84788-784-9(8)) Berg Pubs. GBR. Dist: Macmillan.

Gere, Charlie. Art, Time & Technology. 2006. (Culture Machine Ser.). (ENG., Illus.). 240p. 109.95 (978-1-84520-134-0(5)) Berg Pubs. GBR. Dist: Macmillan.

Giedraityte, Goda. Swords in Images: Representation, Development, & Message. 2008. 120p. pap. (978-3-639-07422-2(X)) VDM Verlag Dr. Mueller e.K.

Glorieux-Desouche, Isabelle. How to Talk to Children about World Art. 2010. (ENG., Illus.). 176p. pap. 19.95 (978-0-7112-3091-0(9)) Lincoln, Frances Ltd. GBR. Dist: Perseus-PGW.

Gompertz, Will. What Are You Looking At? The Surprising, Shocking, & Sometimes Strange Story of One Hundred Years of Modern Art. 2012. (ENG., Illus.). 320p. (gr. 12). 27.95 (978-0-525-95267-1(5), Dutton Adult) Penguin Group (USA) Inc.

Grosse, Ernst. The Beginnings of Art. 2009. 216p. pap. (978-0-217-62205-9(4)); 208p. pap. (978-0-217-29077-7(9)) Books LLC.

Grousset, Rene. Chinese Art & Culture. 2009. 514p. 55.95 (978-1-104-85208-5(X)) 2007. (ENG.). 512p. per. 40.95 (978-0-548-39185-3(8)) Kessinger Publishing, LLC.

Grundtvig, Birgitte, et al, eds. Image, Eye & Art in Calvino: Writing Visibility. 2006. (Legenda Main Ser.). (ENG., Illus.). 2p. (C). 69.00 (978-1-904350-59-0(3)) European Humanities Research Ctr. GBR. Dist: Brown, David Bk. Co., The.

Hagen, Rose-Marie, et al. 100 Masterpieces in Detail, 3 vols. 2010. (Go Ser.). (ENG., Illus.). 720p. 59.99 (978-3-8365-1549-8(0)) TASCHEN DEU. Dist: Ingram Pub. Services.

Haidar, Navina Najat & Sardar, Marika, eds. Sultans of the South: Arts of India's Deccan Courts, 1323-1687. 2011. (ENG., Illus.). 336p. pap. 50.00 (978-0-300-17587-5(6)) Yale Univ. Pr.

Harris, Jonatha. Art History: The Key Concepts. 2006. (Routledge Key Guides). (ENG.). 360p. 110.00 (978-0-415-31976-8(5)) Routledge.

Harris, Jonathan. Art History: The Key Concepts. 2006. (Routledge Key Guides). (ENG.). 360p. per. 26.95 (978-0-415-31977-5(3)) Routledge.

—Dead History, Live Art? Spectacle, Subjectivity & Subversion in Visual Culture since the 1960s. Harris, Jonathan, ed. 2008. (Liverpool University Press - Tate Liverpool Critical Forum Ser.). (ENG., Illus.). 256p. pap. 40.00 (978-0-85323-438-8(8)) Liverpool Univ. Pr. GBR. Dist: Chicago Distribution Ctr.

Harrison, Charles. An Introduction to Art. 2010. (ENG., Illus.). 320p. pap. 30.00 (978-0-300-10915-3(6)) Yale Univ. Pr.

Heck, Michele-Caroline. Histoire de l'histoire de l'art Septentrional. 2009. (Art Theory (1400-1800) Ser.). (FRE., Illus.). 216p. (C). pap. 80.00 (978-2-503-53093-2(1)) Brepols Pubs. BEL. Dist: Brown, David Bk. Co., The.

Hein, Jorgen. The Treasure Collection at Rosenborg Castle: The Inventories of 1696 & 1718 - Royal Heritage & Collecting in Denmark-Norway, 1500-1900, 3 vols. Jones, Glyn et al, trs. 2009. (Illus.). 846p. 285.00 (978-87-635-0131-6(7)) Museum Tusculanum Pr. DNK. Dist: Chicago Distribution Ctr.

Heine, Florian. First: Groundbreaking Moments in Art. 2012. (Illus.). 208p. pap. 19.95 (978-3-7913-4569-7(9)) Prestel Publishing.

Herbert, James. Creating the AHRC: An Arts & Humanities Research Council for the United Kingdom in the Twenty-first Century. 2008. (ENG., Illus.). 100p. pap. 24.95 (978-0-19-726429-4(3)) Oxford Univ. Pr., Inc.

Hermens, Erma & Townsend, Joyce. Sources & Serendipity: Testimonies of Artists' Practice. 2010. (ENG., Illus.). 208p. pap. 75.00 (978-1-904982-52-4(2)) Archetype Pubns. GBR. Dist: National Bk. Network.

History of Art: Slides. 7th rev. ed. 2007. 1032p. 250.97 (978-0-13-193459-7(7)) Prentice Hall (Schl. Div.).

Hodel, Page. Monday Hearts for Madalene. 2010. (ENG., Illus.). 112p. 16.95 (978-1-58479-778-4(9)) Stewart, Tabori & Chang.

Holly, Michael Ann & Smith, Marquard, eds. What Is Research in the Visual Arts? Obsession, Archive, Encounter. 2009. (Clark Studies in the Visual Arts Ser.). (ENG., Illus.). 246p. pap. 24.95 (978-0-300-13413-1(4)) Yale Univ. Pr.

Honour, Hugh & Fleming, John F. The Visual Arts: A History, Revised Edition. 7th ed. 2009. (ENG., Illus.). 1004p. (C). pap. 167.67 (978-0-205-66535-8(7), Prentice Hall) Prentice Hall PTR.

Hoppin, James M. Great Epochs in Art History. 2009. (ENG.). 282p. 34.99 (978-1-117-08627-9(5)); pap. 27.75 (978-1-117-08628-6(3)) BiblioBazaar.

—Great Epochs in Art History. 2007. (ENG.). 274p. 42.95 (978-0-548-01347-7(2)) Kessinger Publishing, LLC.

Hoving, Kirsten. Joseph Cornell & Astronomy: A Case for the Stars. 2008. (ENG., Illus.). 336p. (C). 52.50 (978-0-691-13498-7(7)) Princeton Univ. Pr.

Hub, Berthold. Die Perspektive der Antike: Archäologie einer symbolischen Form. 2008. (Europäische Hochschulschriften. Reihe 20: Philosophie Ser.). (GER.). 410p. pap. 99.95 (978-3-631-57559-8(9)) Lang, Peter GmbH, Europaischer Verlag der Wissenschaften DEU. Dist: Lang, Peter.

Huntington, Daniel. Manual of the Fine Arts, Critical & Historical with an Introduction by D Huntington. 2006. 488p. per. 29.99 (978-1-4255-5402-6(4)) MPublishing.

I Love Art II. pap. 35.00 (978-4-900398-16-0(0)) Watari-Um JPN. Dist: D.A.P./Distributed Art Pubs.

Janson, H. W., et al. Janson's History of Art: The Western Tradition. 8th ed. 2010. (ENG., Illus.). 1184p. (C). 179.00 (978-0-205-68517-2(X), Prentice Hall) Prentice Hall PTR.

Jirat-Wasiutynski, Vojtech, ed. Modern Art & the Idea of the Mediterranean. 2007. (ENG., Illus.). 480p. (978-0-8020-9170-3(9)) Univ. of Toronto Pr.

Johnston, Ella Bond. A History of the Art Association of Richmond, Indiana. (Illus.). 48p. reprint ed. lib. bdg. 88.00 (978-0-7222-0601-0(1)) Library Reprints, Inc.

Kac, E. Signs of Life: Bio Art & Beyond. Kac, Eduardo, ed. 2009. (Leonardo Bks.). (ENG., Illus.). 432p. (gr. 17). pap. 19.95 (978-0-262-51321-0(8)) MIT Pr.

Kaminski, Marion. Titian: Tiziano Vecellio: 1488/1490-1576. 2008. (Masters of Italian Art Ser.). (Illus.). 140p. pap. 9.95 (978-0-8416-0084-3(8)) American Map Corp.

Keith Haring Foundation Staff. Haring: Heart to Heart. 10.95 (978-3-8238-4668-0(X)) teNeues Publishing Co.

Kelleher, Diane Elizabeth. How to Research, Write & Publish an Art History Book in American Art. 2011. 48p. pap. 10.95 **(978-1-4634-6799-9(0))** AuthorHouse.
Kenaan-Kedar, Nurith. Ha-Madonah Shel Siah Ha-Tsabar: Masoret Ve-Hidush Ba-Tsiyur Ha-Notsri Ba-Arets Ba-Meot Ha-19 Veha-20: Kenesiyat Ha-Bikur Be-En-Kerem U-Khenesiyat Ba-Besorah Be-Natsrat. 2009. (HEB., Illus.). 158p. (978-965-217-300-3(2)) Yad Izhak Ben-Zvi.
Klein, Sheri. Art & Laughter. 2007. (Art and... Ser.). (ENG., Illus.). 168p. 94.00 (978-1-84511-233-2(4)) I. B. Tauris & Co., Ltd. GBR. Dist: Macmillan.
Kleiner, Fred S. Art Through the Ages Vol. 1: A Global History, 4 vols. 13th ed. 2009. (ENG.). 272p. (C). pap. 176.95 (978-0-495-79442-4(2)) Wadsworth.
—Gardner's Art Through the Ages: A Concise Global History. 2nd ed. 2008. (ENG., Illus.). 608p. (C). pap. 168.95 (978-0-495-50379-8(7)) Wadsworth.
—Gardner's Art Through the Ages: A Concise History of Western Art. 2nd ed. 2010. (ENG.). 512p. (C). pap. 149.95 (978-1-4240-6998-9(X)) Wadsworth.
—Gardner's Art through the Ages: A Global History. 14th ed. 2012. (ENG.). 1120p. (C). 207.95 **(978-0-495-91543-0(2))** Wadsworth.
—Gardner's Art through the Ages: A Global History (with Arts CourseMate with eBook Online Digital Image Printed Access Card) 14th ed. 2012. (ENG.). 1216p. (C). 207.56 **(978-0-495-91542-3(4))** Wadsworth.
—Gardner's Art Through the Ages: Backpack Edition, Book A. 2009. (ENG.). 272p. (C). pap. 79.95 (978-0-495-79448-6(1)) Wadsworth.
—Gardner's Art Through the Ages: Backpack Edition, Book B. 2010. (ENG.). 224p. (C). pap. 79.95 (978-0-495-79452-3(X)) Wadsworth.
—Gardner's Art through the Ages: Backpack Edition, Book C. 2009. (ENG.). 272p. (C). pap. 79.95 (978-0-495-79456-1(2)) Wadsworth.
—Gardner's Art Through the Ages: Backpack Edition, Book D. 2009. (ENG.). 272p. (C). pap. 79.95 (978-0-495-79462-2(7)) Wadsworth.
—Gardner's Art Through the Ages: Modern Europe & America. 13th ed. 2009. (ENG.). 272p. (C). pap. 79.95 (978-0-495-79459-2(7)) Wadsworth.
—Gardner's Art Through the Ages: Renaissance & Baroque. 13th ed. 2009. (ENG.). 272p. (C). pap. 79.95 (978-0-495-79455-4(4)) Wadsworth.
—Gardner's Art Through the Ages: The Western Perspective. 13th ed. 2008. (ENG.). 880p. (C). 197.95 (978-0-495-57356-2(6)) Wadsworth.
—Gardner's Art Through the Ages: The Western Perspective, Volume I. 13th ed. 2009. (ENG.). 464p. (C). pap. 161.95 (978-0-495-57361-6(2)) Wadsworth.
—Gardner's Art Through the Ages: The Western Perspective, Volume II. 13th ed. 2009. (ENG.). 496p. (C). pap. 161.95 (978-0-495-57365-4(5)) Wadsworth.
—Gardner's Art through the Ages: The Western Perspective (with Art Study & Timeline Printed Access Card) 13th ed. 2008. (ENG.). 880p. (C). 197.95 (978-0-495-57355-5(8)) Wadsworth.
—Gardner's Art Through the Ages Bk. B: A Global History. 13th ed. 2009. (ENG.). 224p. (C). pap. 79.95 (978-0-495-79451-6(1)) Wadsworth.
—Gardner's Art Through the Ages Vol. 1: The Western Perspective. 13th ed. 2009. (ENG.). 464p. (C). pap. 161.95 (978-0-495-57360-9(4)) Wadsworth.
—Gardner's Art Through the Ages Vol. 1, Bk. A: A Global History. 13th ed. 2009. (ENG.). 272p. (C). pap. 79.95 (978-0-495-79447-9(3)) Wadsworth.
—Gardner's Art Through the Ages Vol. 2: The Western Perspective. 13th ed. 2009. (ENG.). 496p. (C). pap. 161.95 (978-0-495-57364-7(7)) Wadsworth.
Kleiner, Fred S. & Baxter, Clark. Art Through the Ages Vol. 1: A Global History. 13th ed. 2008. (ENG., Illus.). 1104p. (C). 215.95 (978-0-495-09307-7(6)) Wadsworth.
Kleiner, Fred S. & Mamiya. Gardner's Art Through the Ages: A Global History. 13th ed. 2008. (ENG.). 24p. (C). 18.95 (978-0-495-50175-6(1)) Wadsworth.
Kleiner, Fred S. & Mamiya, Christin J. Gardner's Art Through the Ages: A Concise Global History. 2nd ed. 2008. (ENG.). 608p. (C). pap. 168.95 (978-0-495-50346-0(0)) Wadsworth.
—Gardner's Art Through the Ages: A Concise History of Western Art. (ENG., Illus.). (C). 2007. 496p. pap. 151.95 (978-0-534-60511-7(7)) 2007. 256p. stu. ed., per. 28.95 (978-0-534-60517-9(6)) 2nd ed. 2010. 512p. pap. 149.95 (978-1-4240-6922-4(X)) Wadsworth.
—Gardner's Art Through the Ages: Non-Western Perspectives. 13th ed. 2008. (ENG.). 288p. (C). pap. 120.95 (978-0-495-79343-4(4)) Wadsworth.
—Gardner's Art through the Ages: Non-Western Perspectives (with ArtyStudy, Timeline Printed Access Card) 13th ed. 2009. (ENG.). 288p. (C). pap. 132.95 (978-0-495-57367-8(1)) Wadsworth.
—Infotrac Workbook-Gard Art Through/Ages: Conc His/Westrn Art. 2007. (C). pap. 13.95 (978-0-534-60518-6(4)) Wadsworth.
Knell, Simon, et al, eds. National Museums. 2010. (ENG., Illus.). 504p. (C). pap. 46.95 (978-0-415-54774-1(1), Routledge) Taylor & Francis Group GBR. Dist: Taylor & Francis Group.
—National Museums: New Studies from Around the World. 2010. (ENG., Illus.). 504p. (C). 130.00 (978-0-415-54773-4(3)) Routledge.
Korey, Michael. Power of Geometry. 2007. 64p. pap. 14.95 (978-3-422-06726-4(4)) Deutscher Kunstverlag GmbH DEU. Dist: Independent Pubs. Group.
Lavin, Irving. The Form of Meaning / the Meaning of Form Vol. 1: Studies in the History of Art from Late Antiquity to Jackson Pollack. 2013. (ENG., Illus.). 680p. (C). 300.00 (978-1-899828-40-1(0)) Pindar Pr. GBR. Dist: Brown, David Bk. Co., The.
Leddy, Annette & Conwell, Donna. Farewell to Surrealism: The Dyn Circle in Mexico. 2012. **(978-1-60606-118-3(6))** Getty Pubns.
Lee, Pamela M. Art History since the Sixties. 2012. (Theories of Modernism & Postmodernism in the Visual Arts Ser.). (ENG., Illus.). 192p. (C). pap. 31.95 (978-0-415-98880-3(2)) Routledge.
Lewis. Slideguide/Test Packet for Lewis/Lewis' the Grand Tour: A Brief History of Art. 2009. (C). pap. 6.95 (978-0-495-00986-3(5)) Wadsworth.
Lewis, Mark. Art & the Moving Image: A Critical Reader. Leighton, Tanya, ed. 2008. (ENG., Illus.). 480p. pap. 39.95 (978-1-85437-625-1(X)) Tate Publishing, Ltd. GBR. Dist: Hachette Bk. Group.
Lorenz, Detlef. Reklamekunst um 1900 - Kuenstlerlexikon fuer Sammelbilder. (GER., Illus.). 237p. (978-3-496-01220-7(X)) Reimer, Dietrich.
Lossing, Benson John. Outline History of the Fine Arts. 2009. 160p. pap. (978-0-217-24550-0(1)) Books LLC.
—Outline History of the Fine Arts. 2008. 332p. 45.95 (978-1-4372-4773-2(3)); pap. 30.95 (978-1-4371-2009-7(1)) Kessinger Publishing, LLC.
Magritte, Rene. Irony by Vision. 45.00 (978-4-900398-14-6(4)) Watari-Um JPN. Dist: D.A.P./Distributed Art Pubs.
Maldonado Ortiz, Carlos. Rarámuri: Freedom at Twilight - Memories from the Tarahumara. 2010. 168p. pap. 52.49 (978-1-4490-3376-7(8)) AuthorHouse.
Maleuvre, Didier. The Horizon: A History of Our Infinite Longing. 2011. (ENG., Illus.). 392p. 29.95 (978-0-520-26743-5(5)) Univ. of California Pr.
Manca, Joseph, et al. 1000 Sculptures of Genius. 2007. (ENG., Illus.). 543p. 24.95 (978-1-84484-215-5(0)) Parkstone International GBR. Dist: Ingram Pub. Services.
Mann, Vivian B., ed. Jewish Texts on the Visual Arts. 2011. (ENG.). 258p. pap. 50.00 **(978-1-107-40366-6(9))** Cambridge Univ. Pr.
Mansfield, Elizabeth. Making Art History: A Changing Discipline & Its Institutions. 2007. (Illus.). 274p. 140.00 (978-0-415-37234-3(8)); per. 45.95 (978-0-415-37235-0(6)) Routledge.
Mansfield, Elizabeth C. The Perfect Foil: FranCois-Andre Vincent & the Revolution in French Painting. 2011. (ENG., Illus.). 320p. 105.00 **(978-0-8166-7580-7(5))**; pap. 35.00 **(978-0-8166-7581-4(3))** Univ. of Minnesota Pr.
Maritain, Jacques. Art & Scholasticism with Other Essays. 2007. pap. 16.99 (978-1-59986-847-9(4), FQ Classics) Filiquarian Publishing, LLC.
Marzona, Daniel. Minimal Art: Taschen. 2009. (25 Ser.). (ENG., Illus.). 96p. 14.99 (978-3-8365-1406-4(0)) TASCHEN DEU. Dist: Ingram Pub. Services.
Massing, Jean-Michel. Studies in Imagery. 2007. (FRE & ENG., Illus.). 446p. (C). 300.00 (978-1-899828-98-2(2)) Pindar Pr. GBR. Dist: Brown, David Bk. Co., The.
Mayer, Claudia. Art: From Prehistoric Art until Modernism. (Illus.). 19p. 9.95 (978-3-7701-7048-7(2)) DuMont DEU. Dist: Advanced Global Distribution Services.
Merewether, Potts. After the Event: New Perspectives on Art History. Potts, John & Merewether, Charles, eds. 2011. (Rethinking Art's Histories Ser.). (ENG., Illus.). 272p. 89.95 (978-0-7190-8173-6(4)) Manchester Univ. Pr. GBR. Dist: Macmillan.
Messensee, Caroline & Kraftner, Johann. Splendours of the Princely Collections of Liechenstein: Brueghel, Rembrandt, Rubens. 2011. (ENG.). 256p. 60.00 (978-2-35340-106-2(6)) Gourcuff Gradenigo FRA. Dist: National Bk. Network.
Mey, Kerstin. Art & Obscenity. 2007. (Art and... Ser.). (ENG., Illus.). 168p. 94.00 (978-1-84511-234-9(2)); pap. 27.00 (978-1-84511-235-6(0)) I. B. Tauris & Co., Ltd. GBR. Dist: Macmillan.
Michel, ed. Histoire de l'Art, 8 tomes en 15. (978-0-8288-7900-2(1)) French & European Pubns., Inc.
Mirzoeff, Nicholas. The Right to Look: A Counterhistory of Visuality. 2011. (ENG., Illus.). 408p. 89.95 (978-0-8223-4895-5(0)) Duke Univ. Pr.
Moller, Simon Dybbroe. Like Origami Gone Wrong, 1 vol. 2007. (ENG., Illus.). 100p. 29.00 (978-3-905770-33-9(4)) JRP Ringier Kunstverlag AG CHE. Dist: D.A.P./Distributed Art Pubs.
Moore, Colin. Propaganda Prints: A History of Art in the Service of Social & Political Change. 2011. (ENG., Illus.). 200p. 55.00 (978-1-4081-0591-7(8)) A & C Black GBR. Dist: Macmillan.
Munsterberg, Hugo. A Short History of Chinese Art. (978-0-8022-1170-5(4)) Philosophical Library, Inc.
Museum of Fine Arts, Houston Staff, contrib. by. Looking at Art: An Art History Survey at the Museum of Fine Arts, Houston. 2009. pap. (978-0-89090-169-4(4)) Museum of Fine Arts, Houston.
Naredi-Rainer, Paul. Imitatio. (GER.). (978-3-496-01242-9(0)) Reimer, Dietrich.
Nesteruk, Peter. A Rhetoric of Time in the Arts. 2011. 304p. pap. **(978-3-8443-2121-0(7))** Lambert Academic Publishing.
Onians, John. The Art Atlas. 2008. (ENG., Illus.). 352p. 55.00 (978-0-7892-0961-0(6)) Abbeville Pr., Inc.
Onyile, Onyile Bassey. Ancestral Spirits Embodied in Ekpu Figurines of the Oron People: A Study in Nigerian Traditional Art. 2007. (Illus.). 264p. 109.95 (978-0-7734-5334-0(2)) Mellen, Edwin Pr., The.
Osborne, Richard & Sturgis, Dan. Art Theory for Beginners. 2009. (For Beginners Ser.). (ENG., Illus.). 192p. pap. 14.99 (978-1-934389-47-8(1), For Beginners) Steerforth Pr.
Osborne, Robin, et al, eds. Art's Agency & Art History. 2007. (New Interventions in Art History Ser.: 21). (ENG., Illus.). 240p. 110.95 (978-1-4051-3537-5(9), Wiley-Blackwell) Wiley, John & Sons, Inc.
Osborne, Robin & Tanner, Jeremy, eds. Art's Agency & Art History. 2007. (New Interventions in Art History Ser.). (ENG., Illus.). 226p. pap. 44.95 (978-1-4051-3538-2(7), Wiley-Blackwell) Wiley, John & Sons, Inc.
Oxford University Press Staff, ed. Art History VSI Set: Consisting of Art History VSI, Modern Art VSI, Dada & Surrealism VSI, Renaissance Art VSI, & Contemporary Art VSI. 2006. pap. 35.00 (978-0-19-532597-3(4)) Oxford Univ. Pr., Inc.
Paglia, Camille. Glittering Images: A Journey Through Art from Egypt to Star Wars. 2012. (ENG., Illus.). 224p. 30.00 **(978-0-375-42460-1(1)**, Pantheon) Knopf Doubleday Publishing Group.
Pearson, Mark Edward. Art History. 2011. (ENG.). (C). 40.00 **(978-0-205-20389-5(2)**, Prentice Hall) Prentice Hall PTR.
Phaidon Press Editors. La Anunciation. 2008. (SPA.). pap. 12.95 (978-0-7148-9820-9(1)) Phaidon Pr., Inc.
—10,000 Years of Art. 2009. (ENG., Illus.). 544p. pap. 12.95 (978-0-7148-4969-0(3)) Phaidon Pr., Inc.
Phaidon Press Editors, ed. 30,000 Years of Art: The Story of Human Creativity Across Time & Space. 2007. (ENG., Illus.). 1072p. 59.95 (978-0-7148-4789-4(5)) Phaidon Pr., Inc.
Phakorelles, Giorgos, et al. Proceedings of the 4th Symposium of the Hellenic Society for Archaeometry: National Hellenic Research Foundation, Athens, 28-31 May 2003. 2008. (Bar S Ser.). (ENG., Illus.). 688p. (C). pap. 175.00 (978-1-4073-0188-4(8)) British Archaeological Reports Ltd. GBR. Dist: Brown, David Bk. Co., The.
Pollock, Griselda & Turvey-Sauron, Victoria, eds. The Sacred & the Feminine: Imagination & Sexual Difference. 2008. (New Encounters: Arts, Cultures, Concepts Ser.). (ENG., Illus.). 320p. pap. 31.00 (978-1-84511-521-0(X)); 89.00 (978-1-84511-520-3(1)) I. B. Tauris & Co., Ltd. GBR. Dist: Macmillan.
Pooke, Grant & Newall, Diana. Fifty Key Texts in Art History. 2011. xxxiii, 243p. E-Book **(978-0-203-13878-6(3))** Routledge.
Pooke, Grant & Newall, Diana, eds. Fifty Key Texts in Art History. 2012. (Routledge Key Guides). (ENG.). 288p. 110.00 **(978-0-415-48705-4(6))**; pap. 29.95 **(978-0-415-49770-1(1))** Routledge.
Pooke, Grant & Whitham, Graham. Art History. 2nd ed. 2009. (Teach Yourself: Reference Ser.). (ENG.). 224p. pap. 14.95 (978-0-07-162586-9(0), 0071625860) McGraw-Hill Cos., The.
—Understand Art History. 2011. (Teach Yourself Ser.). (ENG., Illus.). 224p. pap. 19.95 (978-1-4441-0497-4(7), Hodder & Stoughton) Hodder General Publishing Div. GBR. Dist: Independent Pubs. Group.
Pope, Karen. Homage to the Creative Spirit: The Paintings of Jenness Cortez. 2011. (Illus.). 125p. 40.00 (978-0-9753752-4-2(5)) AMI Pubs.
Prettejohn, Elizabeth. The Art of the Pre-Raphaelites. 2007. (ENG., Illus.). 304p. per. 39.95 (978-1-85437-726-5(4)) Tate Publishing, Ltd. GBR. Dist: Hachette Bk. Group.
Quinlan, Marjorie L. Frank Lloyd Wright's Darwin D. Martin House: Rescue a Landmark. 13.95 (978-1-879201-32-3(1)) Western New York Wares, Inc.
Ramirez, Mari C., ed. ICAA Versions & Inversions: Perspectives on Avant-Garde Art in Latin America. 2006. (Perspectives on Avant Ser.). (SPA & ENG., Illus.). 272p. pap. 40.00 (978-0-300-11652-6(7)) Yale Univ. Pr.
Ran, Faye. A History of Installation Art & the Development of New Art Forms: Technology & the Hermeneutics of Time & Space in Modern & Postmodern Art from Cubism to Installation. 2009. (Illus.). 266p. (C). 75.95 (978-1-4331-0519-7(5)) Lang, Peter Publishing, Inc.
Reuss, Solange ich liebe: Gedichte und Fotografie. (Illus.). 84p. 36.95 (978-3-9805017-2-9(8)) Edition Reuss, Germany DEU. Dist: Last Gasp of San Francisco.
Roslak, Robyn. Neo-Impressionism & Anarchism Politics in Fin-de-Siecle France: Painting Politics & Landscape. 2007. (Illus.). 232p. 124.95 (978-0-7546-5711-8(6)) Ashgate Publishing Co.
Rubiés, Joan Pau & Calaresu, Melissa. Exploring Cultural History: Essays in Honour of Peter Burke. Vivo, Filippo de, ed. 2010. (Illus.). 394p. 134.95 (978-0-7546-6750-6(2)) Ashgate Publishing Co.
Rudman, Jack. Art History. (Undergraduate Program Field Tests Ser.: Vol. 1). 49.95 (978-0-8373-6051-5(X), Passbooks) National Learning Corp.
Saccardi, Marianne C. Art in Story: Teaching Art History to Elementary School Children, 1 vol. 2nd ed. 2006. (Illus.). 484p. pap. 35.00 (978-1-59158-359-2(4), LU3594, Teacher Ideas Pr.) Libraries Unlimited, Inc.
Sadao, Tsuneko S. & Wada, Stephanie. Discovering the Arts of Japan: A Historical Overview. 2010. (ENG., Illus.). 284p. pap. 29.95 (978-0-7892-1035-7(5)) Abbeville Pr., Inc.
Schama, Simon. The Power of Art. 2006. (Illus.). 448p. 55.00 (978-0-06-117610-4(9), Ecco) HarperCollins Pubs.
Scott, Diana G. Approaches to Art History. rev. ed. 2010. (ENG.). 250p. pap. 83.79 (978-0-7575-3887-2(8)) Kendall Hunt Publishing Co.
Sedlmayr, Hans. Art in Crisis: The Lost Center. Battershaw, Brian, tr. from GER. 2006. (ENG., Illus.). 289p. (gr. 11). pap. 29.95 (978-1-4128-0607-7(0)) Transaction Pubs.
Sherman, Van. Our Playhouse. 2007. per. (978-0-9794860-6-7(8)) Town & Country Reprographics.
Sinclair, Christine, et al, eds. Education in the Arts: Principles & Practices for Teaching. 2008. (ENG., Illus.). 215p. pap. 75.00 (978-0-19-556056-5(6)) Oxford Univ. Pr., Inc.
Sitte, Camillo, et al. Camillo Sitte Gesamtausgabe 05: Schriften zu Kunsttheorie und Kunstgeschichte. (GER., Illus.). 696p. (978-3-205-78458-6(8)) Bohlau Verlag GmbH u. Co. KG.
Smith, Matthew. The Total Work of Art. 2007. (ENG., Illus.). 240p. 120.00 (978-0-415-97795-1(9)) Routledge.
Smith, Matthew Wilson. The Total Work of Art: From Bayreuth to Cyberspace. 2007. (ENG., Illus.). 240p. per. 33.95 (978-0-415-97796-8(7)) Routledge.
Smith, Paul & Wilde, Carolyn, eds. A Companion to Art Theory. 2007. (Blackwell Companions in Cultural Studies: 21). (ENG., Illus.). 552p. 209.95 (978-0-631-20762-7(7), Wiley-Blackwell) Wiley, John & Sons, Inc.
Soucek, Priscilla P. Content & Context of the Visual Arts in the Islamic World. 2009. 300p. 45.00 (978-1-59740-738-0(0)); pap. 30.00 (978-1-59740-760-1(7)) ACLS Humanities E-Book.
Steinhoff, Judith & Smith, Timothy B. Art as Politics in Late Medieval & Renaissance Siena. 2012. (Illus.). 250p. **(978-1-4094-0066-0(2))** Ashgate Publishing Co.
Sterling, Charles. Peinture Medievale a Paris 1300-1500, 2 vols. (FRE., Illus.). 280p. 200.00 (978-2-85047-002-8(3)) La Bibliotheque des Arts FRA. Dist: D.A.P./Distributed Art Pubs.
Stokstad & Stokstad, Marilyn. Art: A Brief History. 2010. (Illus.). xxi, 634p. pap. (978-0-558-65233-3(6)) Pearson Learning Solutions.
Stokstad, et al. Art History, Volume 1, Books a la Carte Edition. 4th ed. 2010. (ENG.). 648p. (C). ring bd. 98.67 (978-0-205-79557-4(9), Prentice Hall) Prentice Hall PTR.
—Art History, Volume 2, Books a la Carte Edition. 4th ed. 2010. (ENG.). 696p. (C). ring bd. 98.67 (978-0-205-79558-1(7), Prentice Hall) Prentice Hall PTR.
Stokstad, Marilyn. Art History. 3rd ed. 2007. (ENG., Illus.). pap. 185.40 (978-0-13-512940-1(0)) Addison-Wesley Longman, Inc.
—Art History, Portable Editions Books 1,2,3. 4th ed. 2010. 648p. (C). pap., pap., pap. 120.00 (978-0-205-00462-1(8)) Pearson Education Canada CAN. Dist: Pearson Education.
—Art History, Portable Editions Books 1,2,4,6 with MyArtsLab. 4th ed. 2010. 1096p. (C). 146.67 (978-0-205-00468-3(7)) Pearson Education Canada CAN. Dist: Pearson Education.
Stokstad, Marilyn & Cothren, Michael. Art: A Brief History. 4th ed. 2010. (ENG.). (C). 46.67 (978-0-205-80080-3(7), Prentice Hall) Prentice Hall PTR.
—Art: A Brief History. 5th rev. ed. 2011. (ENG., Illus.). 640p. (C). pap. 148.67 **(978-0-205-01702-7(9)**, Prentice Hall) Prentice Hall PTR.
—Art History. 4th ed. (ENG.). (C). 2011. 46.67 **(978-0-205-19498-8(2))** 2011. 1240p. 109.33 **(978-0-205-17759-2(X))** 2010. 46.67 **(978-0-205-80009-4(2))** 2010. 1240p. 109.33 **(978-0-205-80036-0(X))** Vol. 1. 2011. 46.67 **(978-0-205-17756-1(5))** Vol. 1. 2011. 648p. 109.33 **(978-0-205-17757-8(3))** Vol. 2. 2011. 696p. 109.33 **(978-0-205-20192-1(X))** Vol. 2. 2011. 46.67 **(978-0-205-19488-9(5))** Prentice Hall PTR. (Prentice Hall).
—Art History Portable, Book 3: A View of the World, Part One. 4th ed. 2010. (ENG.). 192p. (C). pap. 53.33 (978-0-205-79093-7(3), Prentice Hall) Prentice Hall PTR.
—Art History Portable, Book 4: 14th-17th Century Art. 4th ed. 2010. (ENG.). 296p. (C). pap. 80.00 (978-0-205-79094-4(1), Prentice Hall) Prentice Hall PTR.
—Art History Portable, Book 5: A View of the World, Part Two. 4th ed. 2010. (ENG.). 160p. (C). pap. 53.33 (978-0-205-79095-1(X), Prentice Hall) Prentice Hall PTR.
—Art History, Portable Editions Books 1,2. 4th ed. 2010. (ENG.). 1096p. (C). pap., pap. 118.00 (978-0-205-00469-0(5), Prentice Hall) Prentice Hall PTR.
—Art History, Portable Editions Books 1,2 with MyArtsLab. 4th ed. 2010. (ENG.). 528p. (C). pap., pap. 124.00 (978-0-205-00470-6(9), Prentice Hall) Prentice Hall PTR.
—Art History, Portable Editions Books 1,2,3 with MyArtsLab. 4th ed. 2010. (ENG.). 648p. (C). pap., pap., pap. 130.33 (978-0-205-00463-8(6), Prentice Hall) Prentice Hall PTR.
—Art History, Portable Editions Books 1,2,3,4,5,6 with MyArtsLab. 4th ed. 2010. (ENG.). 1240p. (C). pap., pap., pap. 157.73 (978-0-205-00461-4(X), Prentice Hall) Prentice Hall PTR.
—Art History, Portable Editions Books 1,2,4,6. 4th ed. 2010. (ENG.). 1096p. (C). pap., pap., pap. 150.67 (978-0-205-00467-6(9), Prentice Hall) Prentice Hall PTR.
—Art History, Portable Editions Books 3,5. 4th ed. 2010. (ENG.). 352p. (C). pap., pap. 85.33 (978-0-205-00543-7(8), Prentice Hall) Prentice Hall PTR.
—Art History, Portable Editions Books 3,5 with MyArtsLab. 4th ed. 2010. (ENG.). 352p. (C). pap., pap. 86.27 (978-0-205-00544-4(6), Prentice Hall) Prentice Hall PTR.
—Art History, Portable Editions Books 4,5,6. 4th ed. 2010. (ENG.). 696p. (C). pap., pap., pap. 124.00 (978-0-205-00464-5(4), Prentice Hall) Prentice Hall PTR.
—Art History, Portable Editions Books 4,5,6 with MyArtsLab. 4th ed. 2010. (ENG.). 696p. (C). pap., pap., pap. 130.33 (978-0-205-00465-2(2), Prentice Hall) Prentice Hall PTR.
—Art History, Portable Editions Books 4,6. 4th ed. 2010. (ENG.). 568p. (C). pap., pap. 118.00 (978-0-205-00474-4(1), Prentice Hall) Prentice Hall PTR.
—Art History, Portable Editions Books 4,6 with MyArtsLab. 4th ed. 2010. (ENG.). 568p. (C). pap., pap. 118.00 (978-0-205-00475-1(X), Prentice Hall) Prentice Hall PTR.
—Art History Portables Book 6: 18th -21st Century. 4th ed. 2010. (ENG.). 272p. (C). pap. 80.00 (978-0-205-79096-8(8), Prentice Hall) Prentice Hall PTR.
—Art History, Volume 1. 4th ed. 2010. (ENG.). 648p. (C). pap. 151.00 (978-0-205-74420-6(6), Prentice Hall) Prentice Hall PTR.
—Art History, Volume 1, Books a la Carte Plus NEW MyArtsLab. 4th ed. 2011. (ENG.). (C). ring bd. 105.33 (978-0-205-21600-0(5), Prentice Hall) Prentice Hall PTR.
—Art History, Volume 2. 4th ed. 2010. (ENG.). 696p. (C). pap. 151.00 (978-0-205-74421-3(4), Prentice Hall) Prentice Hall PTR.
—Art History, Volume 2, Books a la Carte Plus MyArtsLab. 4th ed. 2010. (ENG.). (C). ring bd. 105.33 (978-0-205-79561-1(7), Prentice Hall) Prentice Hall PTR.
Stokstad, Marilyn & Cothren, Michael. Art History, Volume 2, Books a la Carte Plus NEW MyArtsLab. 4th ed. 2011. (ENG.). (C). ring bd. 105.33 **(978-0-205-21601-7(3)**, Prentice Hall) Prentice Hall PTR.
Stokstad, Marilyn & Cothren, Michael W. Art. 4th ed. 2009. (ENG.). 656p. (C). pap. 148.67 (978-0-13-605909-7(0), Prentice Hall) Prentice Hall PTR.

Stokstad, Marilyn, et al. Art History. 4th ed. (Illus.). 2011. xli, 1198p. *(978-0-205-74423-7(0))* 2010. (ENG., 1240p. (C). 189.00 *(978-0-205-74422-0(2)*, Prentice Hall) Prentice Hall PTR.
Stone, Harry. Stage Effect Sensations: An Astounding History Revealing Amazing Mechanical Devices. 2011. 104p. pap. 17.23 ***(978-1-4520-5520-6(3))*** AuthorHouse.
Strickland, Carol & Boswell, John. The Annotated Mona Lisa: A Crash Course in Art History from Prehistoric to Post-Modern. Brown, Patty, ed. 2nd ed. 2007. (ENG., Illus.). 216p. (Orig.). pap. 22.99 *(978-0-7407-6872-9(7))* Andrews McMeel Publishing.
Symons, Arthur. From Toulouse Lautrec to Rodin with Some Personal Impressions. 2007. (ENG., Illus.). 272p. 42.95 *(978-0-548-02201-6(1))* Kessinger Publishing, LLC.
TASCHEN, Angelika, ed. Masterpieces in Detail - 2012. 2011. (ENG.). 13.99 *(978-3-8365-2943-3(2))* TASCHEN DEU. Dist: Ingram Pub. Services.
Tehrani, Rachid. Shahrzad: History, 1 vol. 2006. (ENG., Illus.). 320p. pap. 22.00 *(978-3-905701-50-0(2))* JRP Ringier Kunstverlag AG CHE. Dist: D.A.P./Distributed Art Pubs.
Tkacz, Michael W. The Second Liberal Art: A Guide to Traditional Logic. rev. ed. 2011. (ENG.). 308p. spiral bd. 43.99 *(978-0-7575-8574-6(4))* Kendall Hunt Publishing Co.
Townsend, Chris. Art & Death. 2008. (Art and... Ser.). (ENG., Illus.). 168p. 79.00 *(978-1-84511-662-0(3))*; pap. 28.00 *(978-1-84511-663-7(1))* I. B. Tauris & Co., Ltd. GBR. Dist: Macmillan.
Trumble, Angus. Love & Death: Art in the Age of Queen Victoria. 2007. (Illus.). 240p. 45.00 *(978-0-7308-3076-4(4)*, 30764) Art Gallery of South Australia AUS. Dist: Antique Collectors' Club.
Turner, Adriana & Warren, Jeremy, eds. Auctions, Agents & Dealers: The Mechanisms of the Art Market 1660-1830. 2008. (Studies in the history of Collections). (ENG., Illus.). 173p. (C). pap. 50.00 *(978-1-903767-10-8(5))* Archaeopress GBR. Dist: Brown, David Bk. Co., The.
van den Brink, Peter. ArtMatters: Netherlands Technical Studies in Art. 2006. (Illus.). 128p. (C). 75.00 *(978-90-400-8728-8(8))* Waanders B.V., Uitgeverij NLD. Dist: Antique Collectors' Club.
Van der Stighelen, Katlijne & Watteeuw, Bert, eds. Pokerfaced: Flemish & Dutch Baroque Faces Unveiled. 2011. (Museum at the Crossroads Ser.). (DUT, ENG & GER., Illus.). 277p. (C). pap. 109.00 *(978-2-503-52564-8(4))* Brepols Pubs. BEL. Dist: ISD.
Vermeulen, Ingrid. Picturing Art History: The Rise of the Illustrated History of Art in the Eighteenth Century. 2010. (ENG., Illus.). 359p. pap. *(978-90-8964-031-4(2))* Amsterdam Univ. Pr.
Die Visuelle Geschichte der Kunst. (GER.). *(978-3-8067-4503-0(X))* Gerstenberg DEU. Dist: International Bk. Import Service, Inc.
Walker, Roslyn Adele. The Arts of Africa at the Dallas Museum of Art. 2010. (ENG., Illus.). 304p. 75.00 *(978-0-300-13895-5(4)*, Dallas Museum of Art.
Weller, Dennis P., et al, contrib. by. Rembrandt in America: Collecting & Connoisseurship. 2011. (ENG., Illus.). 224p. pap. 60.00 *(978-0-8478-3685-7(1)*, Skira) Rizzoli International Pubns., Inc.
Weller, Dennis P., intro. & text. Rembrandt: Paintings in America. 2011. (Illus.). 224p. pap. 50.00 *(978-0-8478-3687-1(8)*, Skira) Rizzoli International Pubns., Inc.
Wilder, Frank Van. Fine Art Annual 2001. 1538p. 89.00 *(978-2-85299-038-8(5))* Editions Van Wilder FRA. Dist: Antique Collectors' Club.
Wilder, Jesse Bryant. Art History for Dummies. 2007. (ENG., Illus.). 464p. per. 24.99 *(978-0-470-09910-0(0)*, For Dummies) Wiley, John & Sons, Inc.
Wilkins, David, et al. Art Past, Art Present (with MyArtKit Student Access Code Card) 6th ed. 2009. (ENG.). 672p. (C). pap. 141.40 *(978-0-205-77297-1(8)*, Prentice Hall) Prentice Hall PTR.
Wilkins, David G., et al. Art Past Art Present. 6th ed. 2008. (ENG., Illus.). 672p. (C). pap. 141.40 *(978-0-13-235716-6(X)*, Prentice Hall) Prentice Hall PTR.
Willard, Ashton Rollins. History of Modern Italian Art. 2009. 294p. pap. *(978-0-217-22357-7(5))*; 268p. pap. *(978-0-217-22220-4(X))* Books LLC.
William Hauptman, et al. Ingres. 2008. (Gallery of the Arts Ser.). (ENG., Illus.). 112p. 18.95 *(978-88-7439-263-6(X))* 5 Continents ITA. Dist: Hachette Bk. Group.
Williams, Robert. Art Theory: An Historical Introduction. 2nd ed. 2009. (ENG., Illus.). 344p. 104.95 *(978-1-4051-8414-4(0)*, Wiley-Blackwell) Wiley, John & Sons, Inc.
Williams, Robert & Williams. Art Theory: An Historical Introduction. 2nd rev. ed. 2009. (ENG., Illus.). 344p. pap. 38.95 *(978-1-4051-7553-1(2)*, Wiley-Blackwell) Wiley, John & Sons, Inc.
Winckelmann, Johann Joachim, et al. Schriften und Nachlass: Anmerkungen Uber Die Geschichte Der Kunst Des Altertums. 2008. (Schriften und Nachlass Ser.). (GER., Illus.). 280p. (C). 69.00 *(978-3-8053-3844-8(9))* Zabern, Philipp von Verlag, GmbH DEU. Dist: Brown, David Bk. Co., The.
Wyss, Beat. Hegel's Art History & the Critique of Modernity: The 'Sorrow of Perfect' in the Aesthetics of German Idealism & Modern Art Criticism. 2008. (Res Monographs in Anthropology & Aesthetics). (ENG., Illus.). 308p. pap. 63.00 *(978-0-521-06680-8(8))* Cambridge Univ. Pr.
Zijlmans, Kitty & van Damme, Wilfried, eds. World Art Studies. 2008. (ENG., Illus.). 464p. (C). pap. 39.95 *(978-90-78088-22-6(2))* Valiz NLD. Dist: D.A.P./Distributed Art Pubs.

ART—HISTORY—20TH CENTURY
see Art, Modern—20th Century—History

ART—HISTORY—21ST CENTURY
see Art, Modern—21st Century—History

ART—JUVENILE LITERATURE
Aher, W. Jude. Tiny Sky Dancer. 2010. 33p. pap. 15.00 *(978-0-557-58297-6(0))* Lulu Enterprises Inc.
Brezina, Thomas. Who Can Crack the Da Vinci Code? (Illus.). 112p. pap. 16.95 *(978-3-7913-3426-4(3))* Prestel Publishing.
Scholastic, Inc. Staff. How to Draw Heroes & Villains. 2010. (Freerealms Ser.). (ENG.). 32p. (J). pap. 4.99 *(978-0-545-24273-8(8))* Scholastic, Inc.
Spence, David. Monet. 2010. (Great Artists & Their World Ser.). 48p. 32.80 *(978-1-84898-313-7(1))* Black Rabbit Bks.

ART—LAW AND LEGISLATION
see Law and Art

ART—MARKETING
Art Sales Index: Companies-Products-Services, 2 vols. (Illus.). 1200p. 295.00 *(978-0-7605-0632-5(9))* Rector Pr., Ltd.
Benhamou-Huet, Judith. The Worth of Art. 2007. (ENG.). 127p. per. 30.00 *(978-2-7594-0147-5(2))* Assouline FRA. Dist: Perseus Distribution.
Bernstein, Joanne Scheff. Arts Marketing Insights: The Dynamics of Building & Retaining Performing Arts Audiences. 2006. (ENG., Illus.). 320p. 27.95 *(978-0-7879-7844-0(2)*, Jossey-Bass) Wiley, John & Sons, Inc.
Bloch, Janet. Strategic Marketing Tools for Visual Artists. 2011. (ENG.). 121p. (gr. 10). pap. 18.95 *(978-0-615-41857-5(0))* Bloch Publishing.
Bowstead, Jay McCauley. A Guide to Preparing your Portfolio. 2011. (ENG., Illus.). 128p. pap. 25.95 *(978-1-4081-1436-0(4))* A & C Black GBR. Dist: Macmillan.
Brown, Kate. Imagining Marketing. 2007. (Illus.). 320p. 42.50 *(978-0-415-43968-8(X))* Routledge.
Carr, Eugene. Sign-up for Culture: The Arts Marketer's Guide to Building an Effective E-mail List (Second Edition) 2007. 87p. per. 19.95 *(978-0-9729141-5-4(3))* Patron Technology, Inc.
—Wired for Culture: How E-mail Is Revolutionizing Arts Marketing (Third Edition) 2007. per. 19.95 *(978-0-9729141-4-7(5))* Patron Technology, Inc.
Center for Cultural Innovation, prod. Business of Art: An Artist's Guide to Profitable Self-Employment. 2008. 265p. pap. 34.95 *(978-0-9793555-0-9(8))* Ctr. for Cultural Innovation.
Clazie, Ian. Creating Your Digital Portfolio: The Essential Guide to Showcasing Your Design Work Online. 2010. (ENG.). 192p. pap. 35.00 *(978-1-4403-1023-2(8)*, HOW Bks.) F&W Media, Inc.
Constance, Smith. Art Marketing 101: A Handbook for the Fine Artist. 3rd ed. 2007. (ENG., Illus.). 288p. pap. 19.95 *(978-0-940899-49-0(3))* ArtNetwork.
Crawford, Tad & Mellon, Susan. The Artist-Gallery Partnership: A Practical Guide to Consigning Art. 3rd ed. 2008. (ENG., Illus.). 216p. pap. 19.95 *(978-1-58115-645-4(6)*, 115645, Allworth Pr.) Skyhorse Publishing Co., Inc.
DeWolf, Holly. Breaking into Freelance Illustration: A Guide for Artists, Designers & Illustrators. 2009. (ENG.). 272p. pap. 19.99 *(978-1-60061-197-1(4)*, HOW Bks.) F&W Media, Inc.
Domini, Mathias. Return Forecasting in the Art Market. 2011. 76p. pap. ***(978-3-8443-9805-2(8))*** Lambert Academic Publishing.
Dvorák, Robert Regis. Selling Art 101, 2nd Edition: The Art of Creative Selling. 2009. (ENG.). 192p. pap. 19.95 *(978-0-940899-96-4(5))* ArtNetwork.
Fine, Gary Alan. Everyday Genius: Self-Taught Art & the Culture of Authenticity. 2006. (Illus.). 344p. per. 35.00 *(978-0-226-24951-3(4))* Univ. of Chicago Pr.
Foote, Cameron S. The Business Side of Creativity: The Complete Guide to Running a Small Graphics Design or Communications Business. 3rd rev. ed. 2006. (ENG., Illus.). 440p. per. 35.00 *(978-0-393-73207-8(X)*, 73207) Norton, W. W. & Co., Inc.
—The Creative Business Guide to Running a Graphic Design Business. rev. ed. 2009. (ENG., Illus.). 416p. pap. 35.00 *(978-0-393-73299-3(1)*, 73299) Norton, W. W. & Co., Inc.
French, Ylva & Runyard, Sue. Marketing & Public Relations for Museums & Cultural Heritage Organisations. 2011. (ENG., Illus.). 384p. (C). 140.00 *(978-0-415-61045-2(1))* Routledge.
French, Ylva & Runyard, Susan. Marketing & Public Relations for Museums, Galleries, Cultural & Heritage Attractions. 2011. (ENG., Illus.). 384p. (C). pap. 47.95 *(978-0-415-61046-9(X))* Routledge.
Gibson, William. Art & Money in the Writings of Tobias Smollett. 2006. (Bucknell Studies in Eighteenth-Century Literature & Culture). (Illus.). (C). *(978-0-8387-5637-9(9))* Bucknell Univ. Pr.
Gleeson, Helen. Bear Basics & Beyond: An Inspirational Guide. the Teddy Bear Making Basics, Through to Creating & Promoting your Own Unique Collection. 2011. 127p. (ENG.). pap. 54.95 *(978-1-4327-6835-5(2))*; pap. 49.95 *(978-1-4327-6822-5(0))* Outskirts Pr., Inc.
Gordon Jr., Steve, et al. 100 Habits of Successful Freelance Designers: Insider Secrets for Working Smart & Staying Creative. 2009. (100 Habits Ser.). (ENG., Illus.). 192p. 40.00 *(978-1-59253-512-5(7)*, 1592535127, Rockport Publishers) Quayside.
Grant, Daniel. Selling Art Without Galleries: Toward Making a Living from Your Art. 2006. (ENG.). 256p. per. 19.95 *(978-1-58115-460-3(7)*, 115460, Allworth Pr.) Skyhorse Publishing Co., Inc.
Graphic Artists Guild Staff, ed. Graphic Artist's Guild Handbook of Pricing & Ethical Guidelines. 13th ed. 2010. (ENG., Illus.). 352p. pap. 39.99 *(978-0-932102-15-7(8))* Graphic Artists Guild.
Guerzoni, Guido. Apollo & Vulcan: The Art Markets in Italy, 1400-1700. 2011. (ENG., Illus.). 384p. 54.95 *(978-1-61186-006-1(7))* Michigan State Univ. Pr.
Harowitz, N. Art of the Deal: Contemporary Art in a Global Financial Market. 2011. (ENG., Illus.). 384p. (C). 39.50 *(978-0-691-14832-8(5))* Princeton Univ. Pr.
Heller, Steven & Talarico, Lita. Design Entrepreneur: Turning Graphic Design into Goods That Sell. 2008. (Design Field Guide Ser.). (ENG., Illus.). 240p. pap. 40.00 *(978-1-59253-421-0(X)*, 159253421X) Quayside.
—The Design Entrepreneur: Turning Graphic Design into Goods That Sell. 2011. (Design Field Guide Ser.). (ENG., Illus.). 240p. pap. 25.00 *(978-1-59253-706-8(5)*, 1592537065, Fair Winds Press) Quayside.
Jonckheere, Koenraad. The Auction of King William's Paintings (1713) 2008. (C). *(978-90-272-4962-3(8))*; pap. *(978-90-272-4963-0(6))* Benjamins, John Publishing Co.
Keller, Maura. Design Matters: Portfolios 01: An Essential Primer for Today's Competitive Market. 2010. (ENG., Illus.). 192p. pap. 24.99 *(978-1-59253-602-3(6)*, 1592536026) Quayside.
Kieft, Royston. Paint & Grow Rich. 2010. 164p. pap. *(978-1-921578-86-1(6))* BookPal.
McAndrew, Clare. The Art Economy: An Investor's Guide to the Art Market. 2012. (ENG.). 280p. pap. 39.95 *(978-1-905785-60-5(7))* Liffey Pr., The IRL. Dist: Dufour Editions, Inc.
Michels, Caroll. How to Survive & Prosper As an Artist: Selling Yourself Without Selling Your Soul. 6th ed. 2009. (ENG.). 400p. pap. 21.99 *(978-0-8050-8848-9(2)*, Owl Bks.) Holt, Henry & Co.
Milford, Francine. 100+ Ideas for Artists. 2009. 152p. pap. 19.99 *(978-0-557-06983-5(1))* Lulu Enterprises Inc.
Niemeyer Chini, Valerie & Chini, Valerie Niemeyer. Stefano Bardini e Wilhelm Bode: Mercanti e connaisseur fra Ottocento e Novecento. 2009. (ITA., Illus.). 288p. (C). pap. 54.00 *(978-88-596-0668-0(3))* Polistampa ITA. Dist: Brown, David Bk. Co., The.
North, Michael, ed. Artistic & Cultural Exchanges Between Europe & Asia, 1400-1900: Rethinking Markets, Workshops & Collections. 2010. (Illus.). 216p. 124.95 *(978-0-7546-6937-1(8))* Ashgate Publishing Co.
NY Foundation for the Arts and Artspire Staff. The Profitable Artist: A Handbook for All Artists in the Performing, Literary, & Visual Arts. 2011. (ENG.). 256p. pap. 24.95 *(978-1-58115-872-4(6)*, 115872, Allworth Pr.) Skyhorse Publishing Co., Inc.
Olwin, Anne. Business of Art. 2007. 5.95 *(978-1-934396-05-6(2))* Creativity Pr.
Perkins, Shel. Talent Is Not Enough: Business Secrets for Designers. 2nd ed. 2010. (Voices That Matter Ser.). (ENG., Illus.). 448p. pap. 39.99 *(978-0-321-70202-9(6))* New Riders Publishing.
Pollack, Barbara, text. The Wild, Wild East: an American Art Critic's Adventures in China. 2010. (ENG., Illus.). 208p. pap. 24.95 *(978-988-18034-9-8(7))* Timezone 8 Ltd. HKG. Dist: D.A.P./Distributed Art Pubs.
Polsky, Richard. The Art Prophets: The Artists, Dealers, & Tastemakers Who Shook the Art World. 2011. (ENG., Illus.). 272p. 24.95 *(978-1-59051-406-1(8))* Other Pr., LLC.
—I Sold Andy Warhol (Too Soon) 2009. (ENG.). 288p. 23.95 *(978-1-59051-337-8(1))* Other Pr., LLC.
Robertson, Iain. A New Art from Emerging Markets. 2011. (Illus.). 208p. pap. 50.00 *(978-1-84822-019-5(7)*, Lund Humphries Pubs.) Ashgate Publishing, Ltd. GBR. Dist: Ashgate Publishing Co.
Robertson, Iain & Chong, Derrick. The Art Business. Robertson, Iain & Chong, Derrick, eds. 2008. (ENG., Illus.). 246p. (C). 150.00 *(978-0-415-39157-3(1))*; pap. 54.95 *(978-0-415-39158-0(X))* Routledge.
Rowley, Lee. How to Market & Sell Your Art, Music, Photographs, & Handmade Crafts Online: Turn Your Hobby into a Cash Machine. 2008. (ENG.). 288p. per. 24.95 *(978-1-60138-146-0(8))* Atlantic Publishing Co.
Russell, Alex. The Fundamentals of Printed Textile Design. 2011. (ENG., Illus.). 208p. (C). pap. 38.50 *(978-2-940411-47-4(6))* Ava Publishing SA CHE. Dist: Ingram Pub. Services.
Simanskaite, Marija. Generation of Artist's Brand Image in Fine Art Licensing Business. 2011. 72p. pap. ***(978-3-8443-0265-3(4))*** Lambert Academic Publishing.
Smith, Constance, et al. Advanced Strategies for Art Marketing. 2011. (ENG.). 192p. pap. 19.95 ***(978-0-940899-55-1(8))*** ArtNetwork.
Stanfield, Alyson Blair. I'd Rather Be in the Studio! The Artist's No-Excuse Guide to Self-Promotion. 2008. (Illus.). 249p. 24.95 *(978-0-9742725-6-0(2))* Pentas Pr.
Tangled Baubles, Bangles & Beads. 2011. (ENG.). 50p. ring bd. 19.95 *(978-0-9799207-2-1(8))* Palette Publishing.
Taylor, Fig. How to Create a Portfolio & Get Hired: A Guide for Graphic Designers & Illustrators. 2010. (ENG., Illus.). 144p. pap. 30.00 *(978-1-85669-672-2(3))* King, Laurence Publishing GBR. Dist: Hachette Bk. Group.
Thompson, Don. The $12 Million Stuffed Shark: The Curious Economics of Contemporary Art. 2010. (ENG., Illus.). 272p. pap. 17.00 *(978-0-230-62059-9(0))* Palgrave Macmillan.
Thompson, Donald N. The $12 Million Stuffed Shark: The Curious Economics of Contemporary Art. 2008. (ENG., Illus.). 272p. 26.00 *(978-0-230-61022-4(6))* Palgrave Macmillan.
Thornton, Sarah. Seven Days in the Art World. (ENG., Illus.). 2009. 256p. pap. 15.95 *(978-0-393-33712-9(X)*, 33712) 2008. 304p. 24.95 *(978-0-393-06722-4(X)*, 6722) Norton, W. W. & Co., Inc.
Tummers, Anna & Jonckheere, Koenraad, eds. Art Market & Connoisseurship: A Closer Look at Paintings by Rembrandt, Rubens & Their Contemporaries. 2009. (Amsterdam Studies in the Dutch Golden Age Ser.). (ENG., Illus.). 192p. pap. *(978-90-8964-032-1(0)*, Leiden Univ. Pr.) Amsterdam Univ. Pr.
Upton, Jennifer N., ed. American Indian Arts & Crafts: The Misrepresentation Problem. 2012. (Fine Arts, Music & Literature Ser.). 82p. pap. 47.00 ***(978-1-62100-417-2(1))*** Nova Science Pubs., Inc.
Visocky O'Grady, Jennifer & O'Grady Ken. A Designer's Research Manual: Succeed in Design by Knowing Your Clients & What They Really Need. 2009. (Design Field Guide Ser.). (ENG., Illus.). 192p. pap. 25.00 *(978-1-59253-557-6(7)*, 1592535577) Quayside.
White, Jack. Malady of Art: FEAR. 2010. 283p. pap. 29.95 *(978-0-557-33545-9(0))* Lulu Enterprises Inc.
—Mastery of Self Promotion. 2010. 199p. pap. 29.95 *(978-0-557-33951-8(0))* Lulu Enterprises Inc.
—Methods of Success. 2010. 158p. pap. 29.95 *(978-0-557-34752-0(1))* Lulu Enterprises Inc.
—Mystery of Making IT. 2010. 307p. pap. 29.95 *(978-0-557-33016-4(5))* Lulu Enterprises Inc.
Williams, Theo Stephan. The Interior Designer's Guide to Pricing, Estimating, & Budgeting. 2nd ed. 2010. (ENG., Illus.). 256p. pap. 24.95 *(978-1-58115-718-5(5)*, 115718, Allworth Pr.) Skyhorse Publishing Co., Inc.
Woodward, Michael. Licensing Art 101. 3rd ed. 2007. (Licensing Art 101 Ser.). (ENG., Illus.). 192p. per. 19.95 *(978-0-940899-84-1(1))* ArtNetwork.
Writer's Digest Books Editors, et al, eds. 2011 Artist's & Graphic Designer's Market. 35th ed. 2010. (ENG., Illus.). 576p. pap. 34.99 *(978-1-58297-955-7(3)*, Writer's Digest Bks.) F&W Media, Inc.

ART—MUSEUMS
see Art Museums

ART—OUTLINES, SYLLABI, ETC.
Cram101 Textbook Reviews. Outlines & Highlights for a World of Art by Sayre, Isbn: 0130474800 0131759531. 2011. 472p. pap. 36.95 ***(978-1-61812-851-5(5))*** Cram101 Inc.
—Outlines & Highlights for a World of Art by Sayre, Isbn: 0132221861 9780132221863. 2011. 460p. pap. 36.95 ***(978-1-61812-705-1(5))*** Cram101 Inc.
—Outlines & Highlights for Art Across Time by Laurie Schneider Adams, Isbn: 9780072965254 9780072969795 9780072969726 0072965258. 2011. 648p. pap. 41.95 ***(978-1-61812-333-6(5))*** Cram101 Inc.
—Outlines & Highlights for Art Across Time, Volume I by Laurie Schneider Adams, Isbn: 9780072969726 0072969725. 2011. 518p. pap. 37.95 ***(978-1-61812-353-4(X))*** Cram101 Inc.
—Outlines & Highlights for Art & Creative Development for Young Children by J Englebright Fox. 2011. 144p. pap. 28.95 ***(978-1-61905-222-2(9))*** Cram101 Inc.
—Outlines & Highlights for Art History: 18th - 21st Century by Marilyn Stokstad, ISBN. 2010. 68p. pap. 27.95 *(978-1-61698-268-3(3))* Cram101 Inc.
—Outlines & Highlights for Art History: A View of the West, Combined by Marilyn Stokstad, Patrick Frank, D. Fairchild Ruggles, ISBN. 2010. 166p. pap. 29.95 *(978-1-61698-257-7(8))* Cram101 Inc.
—Outlines & Highlights for Art History: Ancient Art by Marilyn Stokstad, ISBN. 2011. 178p. pap. 29.95 ***(978-1-61812-556-9(7))*** Cram101 Inc.
—Outlines & Highlights for Art History: Medieval Art by Marilyn Stokstad, ISBN. 2011. 146p. pap. 29.95 ***(978-1-61812-558-3(3))*** Cram101 Inc.
—Outlines & Highlights for Art History Portable Edition: Book 5. 2011. 102p. pap. 27.95 ***(978-1-61812-554-5(0))*** Cram101 Inc.
—Outlines & Highlights for Art History Portable Edition Book: 14th - 17th Century Art, Vol. 3 by Marilyn Stokstad, ISBN. 2011. 158p. pap. 29.95 ***(978-1-61812-555-2(9))*** Cram101 Inc.
—Outlines & Highlights for Art History Portable Edition, Book: A View of the World by Marilyn Stokstad, ISBN. 2011. 106p. pap. 28.95 ***(978-1-61812-552-1(4))*** Cram101 Inc.
—Outlines & Highlights for Art History Volume 2 by Stokstad, Isbn: 0130913504 0131059122. 2011. 408p. pap. 35.95 ***(978-1-61812-838-6(8))*** Cram101 Inc.
—Outlines & Highlights for Art in Renaissance Italy by Paoletti & Radke, Isbn: 013091830x. 2011. 310p. pap. 32.95 ***(978-1-61812-926-0(0))*** Cram101 Inc.
—Outlines & Highlights for Art since 1900 V2: 9780500285350 0500285357. 2011. 290p. pap. 32.95 ***(978-1-61812-557-6(5))*** Cram101 Inc.
—Outlines & Highlights for Baroque & Rococo: Art & Culture by Minor. 2011. 266p. pap. 31.95 ***(978-1-61812-932-1(5))*** Cram101 Inc.
—Outlines & Highlights for Greek Art & Archaeology by John G Pedley, Isbn: 9780132409346. 2010. 126p. pap. 28.95 *(978-1-61698-096-2(6))* Cram101 Inc.
—Outlines & Highlights for Italian Renaissance Art by Laurie Schneider Adams, Isbn: 9780813336916. 2010. 160p. pap. 29.95 *(978-1-61654-064-7(5))* Cram101 Inc.
—Outlines & Highlights for Materials for Conservation by C V Horie, Isbn: 9780750669054. 2011. 180p. pap. 29.95 ***(978-1-4288-0440-1(4))*** Cram101 Inc.
—Outlines & Highlights for the Visual Arts: A History by Honour & Fleming, ISBN. 2011. 698p. pap. 42.95 ***(978-1-61812-702-0(0))*** Cram101 Inc.
Cram101 Textbook Reviews & Cram101 Textbook Reviews. Outlines & Highlights for a World of Art by Henry M Sayre, Isbn: 9780205677207 0205677207. 2011. 478p. pap. 37.95 ***(978-1-61812-044-1(1))*** Cram101 Inc.
—Outlines & Highlights for Art: A Brief History by Marilyn Stokstad, ISBN. 2011. 532p. pap. 38.95 ***(978-1-61812-038-0(7))*** Cram101 Inc.
—Outlines & Highlights for Understanding Art by James W Kalat. 2011. 406p. pap. 35.95 ***(978-1-61830-724-8(X))*** Cram101 Inc.

Cram101 Textbook Reviews Staff. Outlines & Highlights for Art Across Time, Volume II by Laurie Schneider Adams, Isbn: 9780072969740. 2009. 184p. pap. 29.95 *(978-1-4288-9505-8(1))* Cram101 Inc.

—Outlines & Highlights for Art History: 18th - 21st Century by Marilyn Stokstad, ISBN. 2009. 58p. pap. 26.95 *(978-1-4288-9102-9(1))* Cram101 Inc.

—Outlines & Highlights for Art History: A View of the West, Combined by Marilyn Stokstad, Patrick Frank, D. Fairchild Ruggles, ISBN. 2009. 140p. pap. 28.95 *(978-1-4288-9214-9(1))* Cram101 Inc.

—Outlines & Highlights for Art History, Combined by Marilyn Stokstad, Isbn: 9780132368544. 2009. 212p. pap. 30.95 *(978-1-4288-9223-1(0))* Cram101 Inc.

—Outlines & Highlights for Art History, Volume One by Marilyn Stokstad, Isbn: 9780131743205. 2009. 94p. pap. 27.95 *(978-1-4288-9558-4(2))* Cram101 Inc.

—Outlines & Highlights for Art History, Volume Two by Marilyn Stokstad, Isbn: 9780131991408. 2009. 118p. pap. 28.95 *(978-1-4288-9500-3(0))* Cram101 Inc.

—Outlines & Highlights for Art Past Art Present by David G Wilkins, Bernard Schultz, Katheryn M Linduff, Isbn: 9780136011002. 2009. 108p. pap. 28.95 *(978-1-4288-9168-5(4))* Cram101 Inc.

—Outlines & Highlights for Art Past, Art Present by David G Wilkins, Isbn: 9780132357166. 2009. 126p. pap. 28.95 *(978-1-4288-9472-3(1))* Cram101 Inc.

—Outlines & Highlights for Artforms: An Introduction to the Visual Arts by Patrick Frank, ISBN. 2009. 144p. pap. 28.95 *(978-1-4288-9605-5(8))* Cram101 Inc.

—Outlines & Highlights for Gardners Art Through the Ages: A Concise Global History (with ArtStudy Online Printed Access Card & Timeline) by Fred S. Kle. 2009. 148p. pap. 29.95 *(978-1-4288-9126-5(9))* Cram101 Inc.

—Outlines & Highlights for Gardners Art Through the Ages: A Global History by Fred S. Kleiner, ISBN. 2009. 214p. pap. 30.95 *(978-1-4288-9401-3(2))* Cram101 Inc.

—Outlines & Highlights for Gardners Art Through the Ages: A Global History, Vol. 1 by Fred S. Kleiner, ISBN. 2009. 106p. pap. 28.95 *(978-1-4288-9402-0(0))* Cram101 Inc.

—Outlines & Highlights for Gardners Art Through the Ages: A Global History, Vol. 2 by Fred S. Kleiner, ISBN. 2009. 144p. pap. 28.95 *(978-1-4288-9403-7(9))* Cram101 Inc.

—Outlines & Highlights for Gardners Art Through the Ages: The Western Perspective (with Art Study & Timeline Printed Access Card) by Fred S. Kleiner, 2009. 186p. pap. 30.95 *(978-1-4288-9219-4(2))* Cram101 Inc.

—Outlines & Highlights for Gardners Art Through the Ages, Volume I, Chapters 1-18 (with Artstudy Stud by Fred S Kleiner, Christin J Mamiya, Isbn: 978. 2009. 82p. pap. 27.95 *(978-1-4288-9136-4(6))* Cram101 Inc.

—Outlines & Highlights for History of Art: Western Tradition, Volume I by Penelope J. E. Davies, ISBN. 2009. 64p. pap. 27.95 *(978-1-4288-9495-2(0))* Cram101 Inc.

—Outlines & Highlights for History of Far Eastern Art by Sherman Lee, Isbn: 9780131830639. 2009. 126p. pap. 28.95 *(978-1-4288-9812-7(3))* Cram101 Inc.

—Outlines & Highlights for History of Modern Art by H H Arnason, Isbn: 9780131840690. 2009. 188p. pap. 30.95 *(978-1-4288-9537-9(X))* Cram101 Inc.

—Outlines & Highlights for Nineteenth-Century European Art by Petra Ten-Doesschate Chu, Isbn: 9780131886438. 2009. 106p. pap. 28.95 *(978-1-4288-9711-3(9))* Cram101 Inc.

Hirn, Yrjo. The Origins of Art: A Psychological & Sociological Inquiry. 2007. (ENG.). 344p. per. 31.95 *(978-1-4325-0438-0(X))* Kessinger Publishing, LLC.

Lovell, Nadine. Art Activities (Creative Corners) (Illus.). 56p. pap. 8.95 *(978-1-56861-016-0(5))* Swift Learning Resources.

ART—PERIODICALS

Allen, Gwen. Artists' Magazines: An Alternative Space for Art. 2011. (ENG., Illus.). 376p. (gr. 17). 37.95 *(978-0-262-01519-6(6))* MIT Pr.

Attaboy. Hi-Fructose Collected Edition Volume 2 Special Edition Box Set: Under-the-Counter Culture. Owens, Annie, ed. 2010. (ENG.). 300p. 60.00 *(978-0-86719-745-7(5))* Last Gasp of San Francisco.

Cattelan, Maurizio & Ferrari, Pierpaolo, eds. Toilet Paper: Issue 2. 2011. (ENG., Illus.). 40p. pap. 12.00 ***(978-1-935202-59-2(6))*** Deste Foundation GRC. Dist: D.A.P./Distributed Art Pubs.

D&AD. D&AD 2011. 2011. (ENG, FRE & GER., Illus.). 592p. 59.99 ***(978-3-8365-2884-9(3))*** TASCHEN DEU. Dist: Ingram Pub. Services.

East on Central (2007) A Journal of Arts & Letters from Highland Park, Il. 2007. per. 10.00 *(978-0-9725761-6-1(9))* East on Central Assn.

Fairey, Shepard & Gastman, Roger, eds. Swindle: Faile. 2007. 144p. 14.95 *(978-0-9791621-3-8(0),* Swindle Quarterly) R. Rock Enterprises.

—Swindle: Germs. 2007. 144p. 14.95 *(978-0-9791621-4-5(9),* Swindle Quarterly) R. Rock Enterprises.

Farimani: Art Critical/Aesthetic Theory Music, No.1. 2008. (Illus.). 224p. *(978-0-9801508-0-3(9))* Farimani.

Fiell, Charlotte & Peter, ed. Domus, 1970-1974, Vol. 7. 2009. (Domus Ser.). (ITA & ENG., Illus.). 580p. 69.99 *(978-3-8365-0957-2(1))* TASCHEN DEU. Dist: Ingram Pub. Services.

—Domus, 1975-1979, Vol. 8. 2009. (Domus Ser.). (ITA, ENG & FRE., Illus.). 580p. 69.99 *(978-3-8365-0958-9(X))* TASCHEN DEU. Dist: Ingram Pub. Services.

—Domus, 1980-1984, Vol. 9. 2009. (Domus Ser.). (ITA & ENG., Illus.). 580p. 69.99 *(978-3-8365-0959-6(8))* TASCHEN DEU. Dist: Ingram Pub. Services.

Foss, Paul, et al. The &-Files: Art & Text, 1981-2002. 2009. (ENG., Illus.). 116p. pap. 18.95 *(978-0-9799752-1-9(2))* Whale & Star Pr.

Foulon, Anne-Cecile. De l'Art pour Tous: Les Editions F. Bruckmann et leurs Revues d'Art dans Munich Ville d'Art vers 1900. (Munchener Studien zur Literarischen Kultur in Deutschland: Vol. 36). (FRE., Illus.). 448p. 57.95 *(978-3-631-50157-3(9))* Lang, Peter Publishing, Inc.

Gaehtgens, Thomas W. & Zelljadt, Katja, eds. Getty Research Journal. (Getty Research Journal Ser.). (ENG., No. 2. 2010. Illus.). 228p. pap. 50.00 *(978-1-60606-017-9(1))*No. 3. 2011. 234p. pap. 50.00 *(978-1-60606-063-6(5))* Getty Pubns. (Getty Research Institute).

Graphis Staff. Graphis Annual Reports 2009. 2009. (Illus.). 256p. pap. 70.00 *(978-1-932026-51-1(7))* HarperCollins Pubs.

Griffith, Terri, et al, eds. The Essential New Art Examiner. 2011. (ENG.). 350p. pap. 22.50 ***(978-0-87580-662-4(7))*** Northern Illinois Univ. Pr.

Jackson, Jeffrey B. & Jemison, Dana L. The Dome: Complete Index, 1897-1900. 2007. 84p. 15.00 *(978-0-9798359-2-6(5))* Quat'z'Arts Pr.

Kadour, Ric Kasini, ed. Vermont Contemporary Art Annual 2008. 2008. pap. 25.00 *(978-0-9771397-5-0(1))* Kasini Hse.

Lidinsky, Richard, ed. DADDY Number 6. 2008. (Illus.). pap. 15.00 *(978-0-9778819-6-3(2))* Peres Projects, Los Angeles Berlin.

Lyne-Winkler, Layla, ed. Plastic Antinomy Number 3: Blue/Green Issue. 2009. 48p. pap. 8.00 *(978-0-86719-728-0(5))* Last Gasp of San Francisco.

Mather Jr, Frank Jewett. Art Studies: Medieval, Renaissance & Modern. Mather Jr., Frank Jewett et al, eds. 2011. 174p. 42.95 ***(978-1-258-06361-0(1))*** Literary Licensing, LLC.

McGonigal, Mike, ed. Yeti 11. 2011. (ENG.). 192p. 11.95 *(978-0-9829819-1-7(0),* Yeti Publishing) Verse Chorus Pr.

McGonigal, Mike, ed. Yeti 12: Includes 7 Vinyl Record. 2012. (ENG.). 192p. pap. 14.95 ***(978-0-9829819-2-4(9),*** Yeti Publishing) Verse Chorus Pr.

Moure, Nancy Dustin Wall. Historical Collections Council Newsletters, January 1999-May 2006 & Miscellaneous Articles. 2006. (Publications in Southern California Art: 9). 741p. 80.00 *(978-0-9614622-9-1(9))* Dustin Pubns.

Najafi, Sina, ed. Shame: A Quarterly of Art & Culture. 2008. (ENG., Illus.). 112p. pap. 12.00 *(978-1-932698-29-9(9))* Cabinet.

Needlecraft Practical Journal No. 175. 2007. 9.95 *(978-1-934268-13-1(5))* Bramcost Pubns., LLC.

Owens, Annie & Attaboy, eds. Hi-Fructose Collected Edition Volume 2: Under-the-Counter Culture. 2010. (ENG., Illus.). 300p. 39.95 *(978-0-86719-744-0(7))* Last Gasp of San Francisco.

Owens, Annie & Attaboy! Hi-Fructose Collected Edition Hardcover. 2009. (Illus.). 250p. 35.00 *(978-0-86719-713-6(7))* Last Gasp of San Francisco.

Pace, Brian & Killion, Stephen, eds. GIUe: Ball State Department of Architecture Student Journal. 8th ed. 2007. per. 16.00 *(978-0-9707701-5-8(4))* Ball State Univ.

Parkett, compiled by. Art Works - 25 Years: The 200 Editions Made for Parkett since 1984. 2009. (ENG., Illus.). 517p. pap. 45.00 *(978-3-907582-25-1(X))* Parkett Verlag AG CHE. Dist: D.A.P./Distributed Art Pubs.

Pedersen, B. Martin. 100 Best Advertising Annual 2011, 1 vol. 2010. (ENG., Illus.). 237p. 70.00 *(978-1-932026-62-7(2))* Graphis, U.S., Inc.

Petrovich, Dushko & White, Roger, eds. Paper Monument. 2007. 100p. per. 10.00 *(978-0-9797575-0-1(9))* Paper Monument.

Porter, Arthur Kingsley. Art Studies: Medieval, Renaissance & Modern. Porter, Arthur Kingsley et al, eds. 2011. 542p. 62.95 ***(978-1-258-06770-0(6))*** Literary Licensing, LLC.

Rudge, William Edwin & Rollins, Carl P. Print: A Quarterly Journal of the Graphic Arts, V3, No. 4, Fall 1945. 2011. 92p. 38.95 ***(978-1-258-09139-2(9))*** Literary Licensing, LLC.

Sartain's Union Magazine of Literature & Art, Set, Vols. 1-11. reprint ed. lib. bdg. 525.00 *(978-0-404-19550-2(4))* AMS Pr., Inc.

Scheffer, Charlotte, et al, eds. Opuscula Atheniensia 30: Annual of the Swedish Institute in Rome. 2006. (Illus.). 221p. pap. 177.50 *(978-91-7916-054-8(9))* Astroms, Paul Forlag SWE. Dist: Coronet Bks.

—Opuscula Romana 30: Annual of the Swedish Institute in Rome. 2006. (Illus.). 133p. pap. 175.00 *(978-91-7042-173-0(0))* Astroms, Paul Forlag SWE. Dist: Coronet Bks.

Slanted Light Press Staff, ed. Fresh 3: Cutting Edge Illustrations in the Press, 1 vol. 2011. (ENG., Illus.). 352p. 65.00 *(978-3-942597-04-3(7))* DAAB Media Gmbh DEU. Dist: Innovative Logistics.

SLC Visual Art Review. Sarah Lawrence Visual Art Review. 2010. pap. 14.99 *(978-0-578-05594-7(5))* SLCVAR.

Steele, Valerie, ed. Fashion Theory Vol. 11: The Journal of Dress, Body & Culture. 2007. (Fashion Theory Ser.). (ENG., Illus.). 128p. pap. 29.95 *(978-1-84520-604-8(5))* Berg Pubs. GBR. Dist: Macmillan.

Steele, Valerie & Palmer, Alexandra, eds. Fashion Theory Vol. 4: The Journal of Dress, Body & Culture. 2008. (Fashion Theory Ser.: Vol. 13, Issue 1). (ENG., Illus.). 128p. pap. 34.95 *(978-1-84520-837-0(4))* Berg Pubs. GBR. Dist: Macmillan.

Swindle #11. 2007. pap. 14.95 *(978-0-9791621-2-1(2),* Swindle Quarterly) R. Rock Enterprises.

Swindle Magazine. Swindle 14. 2007. (Illus.). 136p. pap. 14.95 *(978-0-9791621-6-9(5),* Swindle Quarterly) R. Rock Enterprises.

Swindle Magazine Staff. Swindle Icons 2. 2007. (Illus.). 160p. pap. 15.95 *(978-0-9791621-5-2(7),* Swindle Quarterly) R. Rock Enterprises.

Taschen, et al. D&AD 2010. The Best Advertising & Design in the World. 2010. (FRE, GER & ENG., Illus.). 576p. 59.99 *(978-3-8365-2499-5(6))* TASCHEN DEU. Dist: Ingram Pub. Services.

Taschen Publishing Staff. Domus, 1955-1959, Vol. 4. Volk, Annick et al, eds. 2008. (ITA & ENG., Illus.). 580p. 69.99 *(978-3-8365-0954-1(7))* TASCHEN DEU. Dist: Ingram Pub. Services.

—Domus, 1960-1964, Vol. 5. Volk, Annick et al, eds. 2008. (ITA & ENG., Illus.). 580p. 69.99 *(978-3-8365-0955-8(5))* TASCHEN DEU. Dist: Ingram Pub. Services.

—Domus, 1965-1969, Vol. 6. Volk, Annick et al, eds. 2008. (ITA & ENG., Illus.). 580p. 69.99 *(978-3-8365-0956-5(3))* TASCHEN DEU. Dist: Ingram Pub. Services.

Tong, Darlene. Contemporary Art Periodicals by Artists: Documentation & Index for the Decade of the Seventies. (Contemporary Documents Ser.). (Illus.). 400p. pap. *(978-0-931818-03-5(6))* Contemporary Arts Pr.

ART—PHILOSOPHY

Adams, Laurie Schneider. The Making & Meaning of Art. 2007. (ENG.). 192p. (C). pap. 20.20 *(978-0-13-142836-2(5),* Prentice Hall) Prentice Hall PTR.

Adams, Laurie Schneider & Laurence King Publishing Limited Staff. The Making & Meaning of Art. 2006. (ENG., Illus.). 592p. (C). per. 152.67 *(978-0-13-177919-8(2),* Prentice Hall) Prentice Hall PTR.

Agamben, Giorgio. Profanations. Fort, Jeff, tr. from ITA. 2007. (ENG., Illus.). 99p. (gr. 17). 25.95 *(978-1-890951-82-5(X))* Zone Bks.

Allen, Barry. Artifice & Design: Art & Technology in Human Experience. 2008. (Illus.). 264p. 36.95 *(978-0-8014-4682-5(1))* Cornell Univ. Pr.

Amey, Claude. Arts et Pouvoir: Séminaire Interarts de Paris, 2005-2006. 2007. (FRE.). 264p. (C). pap. 29.00 ***(978-2-252-03642-6(7))*** Klincksieck, Editions FRA. Dist: ISD.

Arnheim, Rudolf. Entropy & Art: An Essay on Disorder & Order. 2nd anniv. ed. 2010. (ENG., Illus.). 80p. pap. 18.95 *(978-0-520-26600-1(5))* Univ. of California Pr.

Art & Architecture, Set. 2008. 342p. 200.00 *(978-0-415-46403-1(X))* Routledge.

Auxier, Randall E. & Hahn, Lewis Edwin, eds. The Philosophy of Arthur C. Danto, Vol. 33. 2012. (Library of Living Philosophers Ser.). (ENG.). 816p. 99.95 *(978-0-8126-9732-2(4))* Open Court Publishing Co.

Avital, Tsion. Art versus Nonart: Art out of Mind. Harries, John G., tr. from HEB. 2010. (Contemporary Artists & their Critics Ser.). (ENG.). 461p. pap. 55.00 *(978-0-521-15480-2(4))* Cambridge Univ. Pr.

Bateman, Chris. Imaginary Games. 2011. (ENG.). 334p. pap. 26.95 ***(978-1-84694-941-8(6))*** O Bks.,John Hunt.

Bauer, Matthias, et al. Kunst und Kognition: Interdisziplinäre Studien zur Erzeugung von Bildsinn. 2008. (Illus.). 305p. pap. *(978-3-7705-4451-6(X))* Wilhelm/Fink#GmbH & Co. Verlags-KG.

Beech, Dave. Beauty. 2009. (Documents of Contemporary Art Ser.). (ENG., Illus.). 239p. (gr. 17). pap. 24.95 *(978-0-262-51238-1(6))* MIT Pr.

Berger, John. Bento's Sketchbook. 2011. (ENG., Illus.). 176p. 28.95 *(978-0-307-37995-5(7),* Pantheon) Knopf Doubleday Publishing Group.

Berman, Eleanor Davidson. Thomas Jefferson among the Arts: An Essay in Early American Esthetics. 2011. 342p. 51.95 ***(978-1-258-05798-5(0))*** Literary Licensing, LLC.

berning, stan. About Art. 2009. 132p. pap. 15.00 *(978-0-578-00623-9(5))* Berning, Stan.

Beuys, Joseph. Joseph Beuys: Das Ende des 20. Jahrhunderts/the End of the 20th Century. Willisch, Susanne & Heimberg, Bruno, eds. 2007. (GER & ENG., Illus.). 394p. 99.95 *(978-3-8296-0287-7(1))* Schirmer/Mosel Verlag GmbH DEU. Dist: Prestel Publishing.

Bianchini, Paola. Interruptio. 2010. (ITA., Illus.). 157p. *(978-88-89298-99-2(5))* Effe.

Blom, Ina. On the Style Site. 2007. (Illus.). 264p. pap. 29.95 *(978-1-933128-30-6(5))* Sternberg Pr.

Boulting, Noel E. On Interpretative Activity: A Peircian Approach to the Interpretation of Science, Technology & the Arts. 2006. (Philosophy of History & Culture Ser.: Vol. 24). xi, 177p. *(978-90-04-15409-4(4))* BRILL.

Bray, William E. Defining Art: Messages from God. 2007. 132p. per. 13.95 *(978-0-595-42718-5(9))* iUniverse, Inc.

Broadhurst, Susan. Digital Practices: Aesthetic & Neuroesthetic Approaches to Performance & Technology. 2007. (ENG., Illus.). 232p. 100.00 *(978-0-230-55313-2(3))* Palgrave Macmillan.

Burda, Hubert. The Digital Wunderkammer: 10 Chapters on the Iconic Turn, 1 vol. 2011. (ENG., Illus.). 202p. 45.00 ***(978-3-7705-5193-4(1))*** Wilhelm/Fink#GmbH & Co. Verlags-KG DEU. Dist: D.A.P./Distributed Art Pubs.

Burgin, Victor. Parallel Texts: Interviews & Interventions about Art. 2011. (ENG., Illus.). 248p. pap. 35.00 *(978-1-86189-813-5(4))* Reaktion Bks., Ltd. GBR. Dist: Chicago Distribution Ctr.

Cannatella, Howard. Creating a Better Place to Live: The Argument for Craft Education. 2011. 184p. pap. ***(978-1-86335-971-9(0))*** Common Ground Publishing Pty, Ltd.

Carey, John. What Good Are the Arts?, 1 vol. 2010. (ENG.). 304p. pap. 17.95 *(978-0-19-973597-6(2))* Oxford Univ. Pr., Inc.

Carr, Paul H. Beauty in Science & Spirit. 2007. (Illus.). xxiii, 171p. per. 18.00 *(978-0-9776514-7-4(9)); (978-0-9793778-5-3(4))* Beech River Bks.

Carroll, Noël. Art in Three Dimensions. 2010. 536p. 74.00 *(978-0-19-955931-2(7))* Oxford Univ. Pr., Inc.

Carroll, Noel. Art in Three Dimensions. 2012. (ENG.). 548p. pap. 45.00 ***(978-0-19-965592-2(8))*** Oxford Univ. Pr., Inc.

Carson, Juli, ed. & text. Exile of the Imaginary: Politics Aesthetics Love, 1 vol. 2007. (ENG., Illus.). 184p. pap. 29.00 *(978-3-86560-211-4(8))* Verlag der Buchhandlung Walther Konig DEU. Dist: D.A.P./Distributed Art Pubs.

Carter, Michael. Framing Art: Introducing Theory & the Visual Image. (Illus.). 211p. pap. *(978-0-86806-355-3(X),* Hale & Iremonger) GHR Pr., The.

Chamberland, Rev. Sylvain, Nyudo. Artist - Bodhisattva - A Manifesto. 2008. 104p. pap. 17.50 *(978-1-4357-2320-7(1))* Lulu Enterprises Inc.

Cheetham, Mark A. Kant, Art, & Art History: Moments of Discipline. 2009. (ENG., Illus.). 236p. pap. 34.99 *(978-0-521-10756-3(3))* Cambridge Univ. Pr.

Cianfanelli, Elisabetta, et al. Rights through Making: Wearing Quality. 2009. (Ethics in Design Ser.). (Illus.). 96p. (C). pap. 23.00 *(978-88-596-0525-6(3))* Edizioni Polistampa ITA. Dist: Brown, David Bk. Co., The.

Clement, Page. Knowledge & Understanding in Art. Date not set. (Illus.). 111p. pap. *(978-0-05-005086-6(9))* Addison-Wesley Longman, Inc.

Coles, Alex, ed. Design & Art. 2007. (Documents of Contemporary Art Ser.). (ENG.). 208p. (gr. 17). pap. 24.95 *(978-0-262-53289-1(1))* MIT Pr.

Comfort, Kelly. Art & Life in Aestheticism: De-Humanizing & Re-Humanizing Art, the Artist & the Artistic Receptor. Comfort, Kelly, ed. 2008. (ENG., Illus.). 248p. 84.00 *(978-0-230-55116-9(5))* Palgrave Macmillan.

Coomaraswamy, Ananda K. Is Art a Superstition, or a Way of Life? 2011. 28p. 35.95 ***(978-1-258-02502-1(7))*** Literary Licensing, LLC.

Coomaraswamy, Ananda Kentish. Christian & Oriental Philosophy of Art. 2011. (ENG., Illus.). 160p. pap. 7.95 *(978-0-486-20378-2(6))* Dover Pubns., Inc.

Corse, Sandra. Craft Objects, Aesthetic Contexts: Kant, Heidegger, & Adorno on Craft. 2008. (ENG.). 110p. pap. 26.50 *(978-0-7618-4287-3(X))* Univ. Pr. of America, Inc.

Costello, Diarmuid & Willsdon, Dominic, eds. The Life & Death of Images. 2008. (Illus.). 256p. 76.95 *(978-0-8014-4698-6(8))* Cornell Univ. Pr.

—The Life & Death of Images: Ethics & Aesthetics. 2008. (Illus.). 255p. pap. 24.95 *(978-0-8014-7455-2(8))* Cornell Univ. Pr.

Cousins, James H. Work & Worship. 2006. 172p. per. *(978-1-4067-2937-5(X),* Hesperides Pr.) Read Bks.

Crowther, Paul. Defining Art, Creating the Canon: Artistic Value in an Era of Doubt. (ENG.). 2012. 276p. pap. 35.00 ***(978-0-19-969858-5(9))*** 2007. 288p. 85.00 *(978-0-19-921068-8(3))* Oxford Univ. Pr., Inc.

—The Phenomenology of Modern Art: Exploding Deleuze, Illuminating Style. 2012. (ENG., Illus.). 296p. 140.00 ***(978-1-4411-3091-4(8))***; pap. 44.95 ***(978-1-4411-4258-0(4))*** Continuum International Publishing Group, Ltd. GBR. Dist: National Bk. Network.

—Phenomenology of the Visual Arts (Even the Frame) 2009. (ENG., Illus.). 264p. 55.00 *(978-0-8047-6214-4(7))* Stanford Univ. Pr.

—Phenomenology of Visual Arts. 2010. (ENG., Illus.). 264p. pap. 22.95 *(978-0-8047-7602-8(4))* Stanford Univ. Pr.

Dahnke, Michael D. Film, Art, & Filmart: An Introduction to Aesthetics Through Film. 2007. (ENG., Illus.). 140p. per. 29.50 *(978-0-7618-3721-3(3))* Univ. Pr. of America, Inc.

D'Alleva, Anne. Methods & Theories of Art History. 2009. (ENG., Illus.). 192p. pap. 18.95 *(978-1-85669-417-9(8))* King, Laurence Publishing GBR. Dist: Hachette Bk. Group.

Dasilva, Fabio B. & Bompadre, Viviana A. How Does Language Communicate Through Drama: Television, Film, & Theater as Distinct Discourse Types. 204p. 109.95 *(978-0-7734-5156-8(0))* Mellen, Edwin Pr., The.

Daverio, Philippe. The Ideal Museum. 2012. (ENG., Illus.). 288p. 50.00 ***(978-0-8478-3755-7(6))*** Rizzoli International Pubns., Inc.

Davies, Stephen. Philosophical Perspectives on Art. (ENG.). 288p. 2010. pap. 35.00 *(978-0-19-920243-0(5))* 2007. 85.00 *(978-0-19-920242-3(7))* Oxford Univ. Pr., Inc.

Deleuze, Gilles & Deleuze. Francis Bacon: The Logic of Sensation. (Illus.). 228p. 90.00 *(978-0-8264-6647-1(8))* Continuum International Publishing Group, Ltd. GBR. Dist: National Bk. Network.

Denham, Alison, ed. Plato on Art & Beauty. 2012. (Philosophers in Depth Ser.). (ENG., Illus.). 264p. 85.00 ***(978-0-230-31440-5(6))*** Palgrave Macmillan.

Dewey, John. The Later Works of John Dewey Vol. 9: Essays, Reviews, Miscellany, & a Common Faith. Boydston, Jo Ann, ed. 2008. (Collected Works of John Dewey Ser.). (ENG.). 534p. pap. 40.00 *(978-0-8093-2819-2(4))* Southern Illinois Univ. Pr.

Diederichsen, Diedrich. On (Surplus) Value in Art. 2008. (DUT & GER.). 98p. pap. 19.95 *(978-1-933128-50-4(X))* Sternberg Pr.

Durston, Diane. Wabi Sabi: The Art of Everyday Life. 2006. (ENG., Illus.). 368p. pap. 8.95 *(978-1-58017-628-6(3),* 1580176283) Storey Publishing, LLC.

Dutton, Denis. The Art Instinct: Beauty, Pleasure, & Human Evolution. (ENG.). 288p. 2010. pap. 15.00 *(978-1-60819-055-3(2))* 2008. 25.00 *(978-1-59691-401-8(7))* Bloomsbury Publishing.

Eco, Umberto. On Ugliness. McEwen, Alastair, tr. from ITA. Tr. of Storia della Bruttezza. (Illus.). 456p. 2011. (ENG.). pap. 29.95 *(978-0-8478-3723-6(8))* 2007. 45.00 *(978-0-8478-2966-8(3))* Rizzoli International Pubns., Inc.

Eco, Umberto, ed. History of Beauty. 2010. (ENG., Illus.). 440p. pap. 29.95 *(978-0-8478-3530-0(8))* Rizzoli International Pubns., Inc.

—History of Beauty & on Ugliness, Set. 2008. (ENG., Illus.). 888p. 90.00 *(978-0-8478-3176-0(0))* Rizzoli International Pubns., Inc.

Eldib, Ken / Omar. Criticizing Ben Franklin: Quips, Quotes & Quandaries. 2010. (ENG., Illus.). 197p. pap. 19.95 *(978-0-9665598-3-5(5))* GTC Pr. Co.

Elkins, James. Chinese Landscape Painting as Western Art History. 2010. (ENG., Illus.). 208p. (gr. 17). 45.00 *(978-962-209-000-2(1))* Hong Kong Univ. Pr. HKG. Dist: Columbia Univ. Pr.

—Chinese Landscape Painting As Western Art History. 2010. 208p. *(978-9971-69-523-1(5))* Hong Kong Univ. Pr.

Elkins, Naef. What Is an Image? Elkins, James & Naef, Maja, eds. 2011. (Stone Art Theory Institutes Ser.). (ENG., Illus.). 264p. 84.95 ***(978-0-271-05064-5(0))*** Pennsylvania State Univ. Pr.

Elliott, Paul. Guattari Reframed: Interpreting Key Thinkers for the Arts. 2012. (Contemporary Thinkers Reframed Ser.). (ENG., Illus.). 160p. pap. 26.00 ***(978-1-78076-233-3(X))*** I. B. Tauris & Co., Ltd. GBR. Dist: Macmillan.

Febres, Carlos. Nindo Ryu Gendai Ninjutsu: Introduction to Theories & Applications in the Modern Art of Perseverance. Date not set. (Illus.). 90p. pap. 13.95 *(978-0-7392-0143-5(3),* P03078) Morris Publishing.

Fenner, David E. W. Art in Context: Understanding Aesthetic Value. 2008. (ENG.). 368p. 59.95 *(978-0-8040-1104-4(4));* per. 29.95 *(978-0-8040-1105-1(2))* Swallow Pr.

Fichner-Rathus, Lois. Foundations of Art & Design. 2011. (ENG., Illus.). 360p. (C). spiral bd. 98.95 *(978-1-111-77145-4(6))* Wadsworth.

Finkelstein, Louis. The Unpicturelikeness of Pollock, Soutine, & Others: Selected Writings & Talks. 2008. (Illus.). xii, 187p. pap. *(978-1-877675-67-6(9))* Midmarch Arts Pr.

Fischer, Ernst. The Necessity of Art. Bostock, Anna, tr. from GER. 2nd ed. 2010. (ENG.). 272p. pap. 21.95 *(978-1-84467-593-7(9),* 844593) Verso Bks. GBR. Dist: Norton, W. W. & Co., Inc.

FitzGerald, Mary. Mary FitzGerald: Afterlife. 2009. (Illus.). 36p. 55.00 *(978-1-84682-199-8(1))* Four Courts Pr. IRL. Dist: International Specialized Bk. Services.

Fløistad, Guttorm, ed. Volume 9: Aesthetics & Philosophy of Art: Aesthetics & Philosophy of Art. 2010. (Contemporary Philosophy: A New Survey Ser.). (GER & FRE.). viii, 416p. pap. 239.00 *(978-90-481-7273-3(X),* 904817273X) Springer.

Floistad, Guttorm, ed. Aesthetics & Philosophy of Art. 2007. (Contemporary Philosophy: A New Survey Ser.). viii, 416p. 239.00 *(978-1-4020-5068-8(2),* 1402050682) Springer.

Foucault, Michel. Manet & the Object of Painting. 2010. (ENG., Illus.). 80p. 21.95 *(978-1-85437-845-3(7))* Tate Publishing, Ltd. GBR. Dist: Hachette Bk. Group.

—This Is Not a Pipe. Harkness, James, ed. 2nd anniv. ed. 2008. (Quantum Bks.). (Illus.). 104p. pap. 17.95 *(978-0-520-23694-3(7))* Univ. of California Pr.

Frattarolo, Eleonora & Cremonini, Leonardo. La Necessità Dell'arte Oggi: Rappresentare o Presentare?: Atti Del Convegno. 2010. (ITA.). 95p. *(978-88-8016-988-8(2))* De Luca Editori d'Arte.

Freeland, Cynthia A. Art Theory. 2007. (Very Short Introductions Ser.). (ENG., Illus.). 184p. pap. 11.95 *(978-0-19-280463-1(4))* Oxford Univ. Pr., Inc.

Fried, Michael. Why Photography Matters As Art As Never Before. 2008. (ENG., Illus.). 410p. 55.00 *(978-0-300-13684-5(6))* Yale Univ. Pr.

Friedlander, Jennifer. Feminine Look: Sexuation, Spectatorship, Subversion. 2009. (SUNY Series in Psychoanalysis & Culture). 149p. pap. 24.95 *(978-0-7914-7296-5(5))* State Univ. of New York Pr.

Frothingham, A. L. The Philosophy of Art. 2009. pap. 20.44 *(978-1-60724-500-1(0))* Gorgias Pr., LLC.

Gage, John. Color in Art. 2006. (World of Art Ser.). (ENG., Illus.). 224p. pap. 18.95 *(978-0-500-20394-1(6))* Thames & Hudson.

Gaut, Berys, ed. Thinking about Art: Classic & Contemporary Philosophical Readings. 2009. 560p. 34.00 *(978-0-415-40576-6(9));* 122.00 *(978-0-415-40575-1(0))* Routledge.

Gaut, Berys & Livingston, Paisley, eds. The Creation of Art: New Essays in Philosophical Aesthetics. 2007. (ENG., Illus.). 304p. pap. 63.00 *(978-0-521-03779-2(4))* Cambridge Univ. Pr.

Goldblatt, David & Brown, Lee. Aesthetics. 3rd ed. 2010. (ENG., Illus.). 480p. (C). pap. 84.00 *(978-0-205-01703-4(7),* Prentice Hall) Prentice Hall PTR.

Goldie, Peter & Schellekens, Elisabeth, eds. Philosophy & Conceptual Art. 2009. (ENG., Illus.). 312p. pap. 45.00 *(978-0-19-956825-3(1))* Oxford Univ. Pr., Inc.

Gracia, Jorge J. E. Painting Borges: Philosophy Interpreting Art Interpreting Literature. 2012. (SUNY series in Latin American & Iberian Thought & Culture Ser.). (ENG.). 288p. 90.00 ***(978-1-4384-4177-1(0));*** pap. 25.95 ***(978-1-4384-4178-8(9))*** State Univ. of New York Pr.

Gracyk, Theodore. The Philosophy of Art: An Introduction. 2011. (ENG.). 284p. 69.95 ***(978-0-7456-4915-3(7));*** pap. 24.95 ***(978-0-7456-4916-0(5))*** Polity Pr. GBR. Dist: Wiley, John & Sons, Inc.

Graham, Gordon. The Re-enchantment of the World: Art versus Religion. 2010. (ENG.). 224p. pap. 29.95 *(978-0-19-958137-5(1))* Oxford Univ. Pr., Inc.

—The Re-Enchantment of the World: Art Versus Religion. 2007. (ENG.). 176p. 75.00 *(978-0-19-926596-1(8))* Oxford Univ. Pr., Inc.

Grammel, Soren & Kunstverein, Grazer, eds. Der Symbolische Auftraggeber/the Symbolic Commissioner. 2011. (ENG & GER., Illus.). 224p. 34.00 ***(978-1-934105-35-1(X))*** Sternberg Pr.

Grave, Johannes, et al. Der Körper der Kunst: Konstruktionen der Totalität Im Kunstdiskurs Um 1800. 2007. (Asthetik Um 1800 Ser.). (GER., Illus.). 230p. (C). 41.00 *(978-3-525-47504-1(7))* Vandenhoeck & Ruprecht GmbH & Co. KG DEU. Dist: ISD.

Graves, David. The New Institutional Theory of Art. 2010. pap. *(978-1-86335-721-0(1))* Common Ground Publishing Pty, Ltd.

Groys, Boris. Boris Groys: Going Public. 2011. (E-Flux Journal Ser.). (ENG., Illus.). 168p. pap. 15.00 ***(978-1-934105-30-6(9))*** Sternberg Pr.

—Under Suspicion: A Phenomenology of Media. Strathausen, Carsten, tr. from GER. 2012. (Columbia Themes in Philosophy, Social Criticism, & the Arts Ser.). (ENG., Illus.). 232p. (gr. 17). 50.00 ***(978-0-231-14618-0(3))*** Columbia Univ. Pr.

Grundberg, Andy. Crisis of the Real: Writings on Photography. 3rd ed. 2010. (ENG., Illus.). 292p. pap. 19.95 *(978-1-59711-140-9(6))* Aperture Foundation, Inc.

Grundy, Gordy. Fortuna Now. 2007. 80p. pap. 74.85 *(978-1-4303-2126-2(1))* Lulu Enterprises Inc.

Guillon, Roland. Harmonie, Rythme et Sociétés: Genèse de L'art Contemporain. 2010. (FRE.). 199p. pap. *(978-2-296-13086-9(0))* Harmattan Pr.

Guston, Philip. Philip Guston: Collected Writings, Lectures, & Conversations. coolidge, clark, ed. 2010. (Documents of Twentieth-Century Art Ser.). (ENG., Illus.). 352p. pap. 29.95 *(978-0-520-25716-0(2))* Univ. of California Pr.

Hagberg, Garry L., ed. Art & Ethical Criticism. 2008. (New Directions in Aesthetics Ser.: 11). (ENG., Illus.). 304p. 104.95 *(978-1-4051-3483-5(6),* Wiley-Blackwell) Wiley, John & Sons, Inc.

—Art & Ethical Criticism. 2010. (New Directions in Aesthetics Ser.: 19). (ENG.). 304p. pap. 34.95 *(978-1-4443-3787-7(4),* Wiley-Blackwell) Wiley, John & Sons, Inc.

Halsall, Francis. Systems of Art: Art, History & Systems Theory. 2008. (Illus.). 253p. pap. 70.95 *(978-3-03911-073-5(X))* Lang, Peter AG GBR. Dist: Lang, Peter.

Halsall, Francis, et al. Rediscovering Aesthetics: Transdisciplinary Voices from Art History, Philosophy, & Art Practice. Halsall, Francis et al, eds. 2008. (ENG.). 336p. 65.00 *(978-0-8047-5990-8(1));* pap. 24.95 *(978-0-8047-5991-5(X))* Stanford Univ. Pr.

Harries, K. Art Matters: A Critical Commentary on Heidegger's - the Origin of the Work of Art. 2009. (Contributions to Phenomenology Ser.). xii, 204p. 179.00 *(978-1-4020-9988-5(6),* 1402099886) Springer.

Harris, Roy. The Great Debate about Art. 2010. 130p. pap. 12.95 *(978-0-9842010-0-6(9))* Prickly Paradigm Pr., LLC.

Harrison, Charles. Since 1950: Art & Its Criticism. 2009. (ENG., Illus.). 272p. 45.00 *(978-0-300-15186-2(1))* Yale Univ. Pr.

Häussler, Harriet. Aus Künstlersicht. 13 Fragen - 51 Interviews. 2010. (GER & ENG., Illus.). 244p. 37.50 *(978-3-86678-363-8(9))* Kerber Verlag DEU. Dist: D.A.P./Distributed Art Pubs.

Haynes, Deborah J. Bakhtin & the Visual Arts. 2008. (Cambridge Studies in New Art History & Criticism Ser.). (ENG., Illus.). 240p. pap. 36.99 *(978-0-521-06604-4(2))* Cambridge Univ. Pr.

Hegel, Georg Wilhelm Friedrich. The Introduction to Hegel's Philosophy of Fine Art. Bosanquet, Bernard, tr. 2007. (ENG.). 308p. 43.95 *(978-0-548-12927-2(4))* Kessinger Publishing, LLC.

Heidegger, Martin. Arte y Poesia. (Breviarios Ser.).Tr. of Ursprung des Kunstwerkes. (SPA.). 9.95 *(978-968-16-0040-2(1))* Fondo de Cultura Economica USA.

Heikkilä, Martta. At the Limits of Presentation: Coming-into-Presence & its Aesthetic Relevance in Jean-Luc Nancy's Philosophy. 2008. (Europäische Hochschulschriften. Reihe 20: Philosophie Ser.). 312p. pap. 74.95 *(978-3-631-58105-6(X))* Lang, Peter GmbH, Europaischer Verlag der Wissenschaften DEU. Dist: Lang, Peter.

Heussenstamm, Paul. Divine Forces: Art That Awakens the Soul. 2009. pap. 24.95 *(978-1-61584-681-8(6))* Independent Pub.

Hick, Darren Hudson. Introducing Aesthetics & the Philosophy of Art. 2012. (ENG., Illus.). 248p. 110.00 ***(978-1-4411-9820-4(2));*** pap. 32.95 ***(978-1-4411-7103-0(7))*** Continuum International Publishing Group, Ltd. GBR. Dist: National Bk. Network.

Hickey, Dave. The Invisible Dragon: Essays on Beauty. rev. exp. ed. 2009. (ENG., Illus.). 152p. 22.00 *(978-0-226-33318-2(3))* Univ. of Chicago Pr.

Holder, Will, ed. For the Blind Man in the Dark Room Looking for the Black Cat That Isn't There. 2009. (ENG., Illus.). 176p. pap. 40.00 *(978-0-9777528-6-7(0))* Contemporary Art Museum St. Louis.

Holly, Michael Ann & Smith, Marquard, eds. What Is Research in the Visual Arts? Obsession, Archive, Encounter. 2009. (Clark Studies in the Visual Arts Ser.). (ENG., Illus.). 246p. pap. 24.95 *(978-0-300-13413-1(4))* Yale Univ. Pr.

Hub, Berthold. Die Perspektive der Antike: Archäologie einer symbolischen Form. 2008. (Europäische Hochschulschriften. Reihe 20: Philosophie Ser.). (GER.). 410p. pap. 99.95 *(978-3-631-57559-8(9))* Lang, Peter GmbH, Europaischer Verlag der Wissenschaften DEU. Dist: Lang, Peter.

Hulme, Thomas E. Speculations. (Des Imagistes). reprint ed. 24.00 *(978-0-404-17115-5(X))* AMS Pr., Inc.

Iliescu, Sanda, ed. The Hand & the Soul: Aesthetics & Ethics in Architecture & Art. 2009. (ENG., Illus.). 320p. (gr. 17). 55.00 *(978-0-8139-2760-2(9))* Univ. Pr. of Virginia.

Iversen, Margaret & Melville, Stephen W. Writing Art History: Disciplinary Departures. 2010. (ENG., Illus.). 256p. 85.00 *(978-0-226-38825-0(5));* pap. 30.00 *(978-0-226-38826-7(3))* Univ. of Chicago Pr.

Jacob, M. J. Learning Mind: Experience into Art. Baas, Jacquelynn & Jacob, Mary Jane, eds. 2010. (ENG., Illus.). 288p. 49.95 *(978-0-520-26076-4(7))* Univ. of California Pr.

jagodzinski, jan. Visual Art & Education in an Era of Designer Capitalism. 2011. (Education, Psychoanalysis, Social Transformation Ser.). (ENG.). 256p. pap. 30.00 ***(978-0-230-61880-0(4))*** Palgrave Macmillan.

Jagodzinski, Jan. Visual Art & Education in an Era of Designer Capitalism: Deconstructing the Oral Eye. 2010. (Education, Psychoanalysis, Social Transformation Ser.). (ENG., Illus.). 268p. 89.00 *(978-0-230-61879-4(0))* Palgrave Macmillan.

Jinarajadasa, C. Art As Will & Idea. 2006. pap. 24.95 *(978-1-4286-4918-7(2))* Kessinger Publishing, LLC.

Judovitz, Dalia & Duchamp, Marcel. Drawing on Art: Duchamp & Company. 2010. (Illus.). 288p. 75.00 *(978-0-8166-6529-7(X));* (ENG., pap. 24.95 *(978-0-8166-6530-3(3))* Univ. of Minnesota Pr.

Kagan, Sacha. Art & Sustainability: Connecting Patterns for a Culture of Complexity. 2011. (ENG & GER., Illus.). 476p. pap. 54.95 ***(978-3-8376-1803-7(X))*** Transcript Verlag DEU. Dist: Transaction Pubs.

Kelehear, Zach. Instructional Leadership as Art: Connecting ISLLC & Aesthetic Inspiration. 2008. (ENG., Illus.). 158p. 74.95 *(978-1-57886-751-6(7))* Rowman & Littlefield Education.

Kemal, Salim & Gaskell, Ivan, eds. Politics & Aesthetics in the Arts. 2010. (Cambridge Studies in Philosophy & the Arts Ser.). (ENG., Illus.). 284p. (C). pap. 30.99 *(978-0-521-14196-3(6))* Cambridge Univ. Pr.

Kester, Grant H. The One & the Many: Contemporary Collaborative Art in a Global Context. 2011. (ENG., Illus.). 320p. 89.95 *(978-0-8223-4972-3(8));* pap. 24.95 *(978-0-8223-4987-7(6))* Duke Univ. Pr.

Killiam, Marie-Therese. The End of Art: A Comparative Analysis of French Postmodern Art Theorists. 2011. x, 89p. pap. *(978-1-86335-894-1(3))* Common Ground Publishing Pty, Ltd.

Klein, Alex, ed. Words Without Pictures. 2010. (ENG., Illus.). 510p. pap. 24.95 *(978-1-59711-142-3(2))* Aperture Foundation, Inc.

Kokoli, Alexandra, ed. Susan Hiller: the Provisional Texture of Reality. 2008. (ENG., Illus.). 160p. pap. 22.00 *(978-3-905829-56-3(8))* JRP Ringier Kunstverlag AG CHE. Dist: D.A.P./Distributed Art Pubs.

Kubler, George. The Shape of Time: Remarks on the History of Things. 2008. (ENG., Illus.). 144p. per. 17.00 *(978-0-300-10061-7(2))* Yale Univ. Pr.

Kul-Want, Christopher, ed. Philosophers on Art from Kant to the Postmodernists: A Critical Reader. 2010. (ENG., Illus.). 376p. (gr. 17). 89.50 *(978-0-231-14094-2(0));* pap. 29.50 *(978-0-231-14095-9(9))* Columbia Univ. Pr.

Kulvicki, John V. On Images. 2006. (ENG., Illus.). 272p. 60.00 *(978-0-19-929075-8(X))* Oxford Univ. Pr., Inc.

Leclercq, J., ed. La raison par quatre Chemins: En hommage a Claude Troisfontaines. 2007. (Bibliotheque Philosophique de Louvain Ser.). (FRE.). 532p. (C). pap. 70.00 *(978-90-429-1970-9(1))* Peeters Pubs. & Booksellers BEL. Dist: Brown, David Bk. Co., The.

Lehrer, Keith. Art, Self & Knowledge, 1 vol. 2011. (ENG., Illus.). 224p. pap. 24.95 ***(978-0-19-530499-2(3))*** Oxford Univ. Pr., Inc.

Leibowitz, J. R. Hidden Harmony: The Connected Worlds of Physics & Art. 2008. (ENG., Illus.). 160p. 28.00 *(978-0-8018-8866-3(2))* Johns Hopkins Univ. Pr.

Levi, Carlo. Fear of Freedom. Pugliese, Stanislao G., ed. Gourevitch, Adolphe, tr. from ITA. 2008. (ENG., Illus.). 176p. (gr. 17). 75.00 *(978-0-231-13996-0(9))* Columbia Univ. Pr.

—Fear of Freedom. Pugliese, Stanislao G., ed. & tr. by. from ITA. Gourevitch, Adolphe, tr. from ITA. 2008. (ENG., Illus.). 176p. (gr. 17). pap. 24.00 *(978-0-231-13997-7(7))* Columbia Univ. Pr.

Levinson, Jerrold. Contemplating Art. 2006. 432p. 165.00 *(978-0-19-920618-6(X))* Oxford Univ. Pr., Inc.

—Contemplating Art: Essays in Aesthetics. 2006. (ENG.). 432p. per. 55.00 *(978-0-19-920617-9(1))* Oxford Univ. Pr., Inc.

Lewis, Wyndham. Time & Western Man. (Des Imagistes). reprint ed. 36.00 *(978-0-404-17125-4(7))* AMS Pr., Inc.

Livingston, Ray. The Traditional Theory of Literature. 2009. (ENG.). 200p. pap. 50.00 *(978-0-8166-5819-0(6))* Univ. of Minnesota Pr.

Locke, Michael H. Insights in Light: Photographic Art & Philosophy. 2009. 134p. pap. 45.99 *(978-1-4490-0143-8(2))* AuthorHouse.

Lopes, Dominic. A Philosophy of Computer Art. 2009. (ENG., Illus.). 160p. (C). 39.95 *(978-0-415-54762-8(8))* Routledge.

Lotringer, Sylvère. Overexposed: Perverting Perversions. 2007. (Foreign Agents Ser.). (ENG.). 216p. (gr. 17). per. 14.95 *(978-1-58435-045-3(8))* Semiotexte/Smart Art.

Lough, James & Herron, Patricia, eds. Spheres of Awareness: A Wilberian Integral Approach to Literature, Philosophy, Psychology, & Art. 2009. (ENG.). 208p. pap. 33.99 *(978-0-7618-4804-2(5))* Univ. Pr. of America, Inc.

Lyotard, Jean-Francois. Discourse, Figure. 2011. (Illus.). xxiii, 516p. pap. ***(978-0-8166-4566-4(3))*** Univ. of Minnesota Pr.

MacIver, Roderick. Art as a Way of Life. 2009. (ENG., Illus.). 96p. pap. 16.95 *(978-1-55643-920-9(2))* North Atlantic Bks.

Macleod, Katy & Holdridge, Lin, eds. Thinking Through Art. 2009. (Illus.). 256p. pap. 39.95 *(978-0-415-57633-8(4))* Routledge.

Marcuse, Herbert. Art & Liberation, Vol. 4. Kellner, Douglas, ed. 2006. (Collected Papers of Herbert Marcuse Ser.: Vol. 4). 264p. 99.95 *(978-0-415-13763-6(7),* RU14576) Routledge.

Margolis, Joseph. The Arts & the Definition of the Human: Toward a Philosophical Anthropology. 2008. (ENG.). 200p. 60.00 *(978-0-8047-5953-3(7));* pap. 24.95 *(978-0-8047-5954-0(5))* Stanford Univ. Pr.

—The Cultural Space of the Arts & the Infelicities of Reductionism. 2010. (Columbia Themes in Philosophy, Social Criticism, & the Arts Ser.). (ENG., Illus.). 232p. (gr. 17). 24.50 *(978-0-231-14728-6(7))* Columbia Univ. Pr.

Margolis, Joseph. Philosophy Looks at the Arts: Contemporary Readings in Aesthetics. 2011. 250p. 46.95 ***(978-1-258-03566-2(9))*** Literary Licensing, LLC.

Maritain, Jacques. Art & Scholasticism with Other Essays. 2007. 124p. 19.99 *(978-1-59986-731-1(1));* pap. 16.99 *(978-1-59986-847-9(4),* FQ Classics) Filiquarian Publishing, LLC.

Mattick, Jr, Paul, Paul, ed. Eighteenth-Century Aesthetics & the Reconstruction of Art. 2008. (ENG.). 268p. pap. 37.99 *(978-0-521-06683-9(2))* Cambridge Univ. Pr.

Mayo, Nuria Enguita. Afterall: Spring 2011, Issue 26. Lafuente, Pablo & Roelstraete, Dieter, eds. 2011. (Illus.). 130p. pap. 10.00 *(978-1-84638-075-4(8))* Univ. of Chicago Pr.

McNamara, Andrew. An Apprehensive Aesthetic: The Legacy of Modernist Culture. 2009. (Illus.). 293p. pap. *(978-3-03911-720-8(3))* Lang, Peter.

Medley, Stuart. The Picture in Design: What Graphic Designers, Art Directors & Illustrators Should Know about Communicating with Pictures. 2012. pap. ***(978-1-61229-050-8(7))*** Common Ground Publishing Pty, Ltd.

Miah, Andy. Human Futures: Art in an Age of Uncertainty. Miah, Andy, ed. 2009. (ENG., Illus.). 352p. 59.95 *(978-1-84631-181-9(0))* Liverpool Univ. Pr. GBR. Dist: Chicago Distribution Ctr.

Miller, Jonathan, et al. On Reflection. (Illus.). 224p. *(978-1-85709-237-0(6))* National Gallery Pubns., Ltd.

Mitchell, Andrew J. Heidegger among the Sculptors: Body, Space, & the Art of Dwelling. 2010. (ENG., Illus.). 144p. 50.00 *(978-0-8047-7022-4(0));* pap. 17.95 *(978-0-8047-7023-1(9))* Stanford Univ. Pr.

Moggach, Douglas, ed. Politics, Religion, & Art: Hegelian Debates. 2011. (Topics in Historical Philosophy Ser.). (ENG.). 368p. 89.95 *(978-0-8101-2729-5(6))* Northwestern Univ. Pr.

Moineau, Jean-Claude. Retour du Futur: L'art à Contre-Courant. 2010. (FRE.). 367p. *(978-2-915453-59-1(4),* Spotlight Poets) Ere.

Munro, Thomas. Toward Science in Aesthetics. 2011. 384p. 53.95 ***(978-1-258-05800-5(6))*** Literary Licensing, LLC.

Murphy, Sinead. The Art Kettle. 2012. (ENG.). 86p. pap. 14.95 ***(978-1-84694-984-5(X))*** Hunt, John Publishing Ltd. GBR. Dist: National Bk. Network.

Musgrave, Lisa Ryan, ed. Feminist Aesthetics & Philosophy of Art: the Power of Critical Visions & Creative Engagement: The Power of Critical Visions & Creative Engagement. 2010. (ENG., Illus.). 290p. 189.00 *(978-1-4020-6836-2(0))* Springer.

Nehamas, A. Only A Promise of Happiness - the Place of Beauty in A World. 2010. (ENG., Illus.). 208p. pap. 24.95 *(978-0-691-14865-6(1))* Princeton Univ. Pr.

Neill, Alex & Ridley, Aaron, eds. Arguing about Art: Contemporary Philosophical Debates. 3rd rev. ed. 2007. (Arguing about Philosophy Ser.). (ENG., Illus.). 504p. (C). 150.00 *(978-0-415-42450-9(X));* per. 41.95 *(978-0-415-42451-6(8))* Routledge.

Newall, Michael. What Is a Picture? Depiction, Realism, Abstraction. 2011. (ENG., Illus.). 288p. 85.00 *(978-0-230-27655-0(5))* Palgrave Macmillan.

Noé, Luis Felipe. Noescritos/ No-writings about that Thing Called Art: Sobre eso que se llama arte. 2007. (SPA.). 507p. pap. *(978-987-1156-74-0(X))* Hidalgo, Adriana Editora S.A.

O'Hear, Anthony. The Landscape of Humanity: Art, Culture & Society. 2008. (St. Andrews Studies in Philosophy & Public Affairs Ser.). (ENG.). 242p. 80.00 *(978-1-84540-145-0(X))* Imprint Academic GBR. Dist: Ingram Pub. Services.

Olivier, Bert. Philosophy & Art: Collected Essays. 2009. 255p. 49.95 *(978-3-03911-903-5(6))* Lang, Peter AG GBR. Dist: Lang, Peter.

Osborne, Richard & Sturgis, Dan. Art Theory for Beginners. 2009. (For Beginners Ser.). (ENG., Illus.). 192p. pap. 14.99 *(978-1-934389-47-8(1),* For Beginners) Steerforth Pr.

O'Sullivan, Simon. Art Encounters Deleuze & Guattari: Thought Beyond Representation. 2008. (Renewing Philosophy Ser.). (ENG.). 256p. pap. 33.00 *(978-0-230-57373-4(8))* Palgrave Macmillan.

P. S. 1 Symposium: A Practical Avant-Garde. 2007. 6.00 *(978-0-9760503-9-1(0))* n+1 Research.

Palmer, Michael. Paul Tillich's Philosophy of Art. (Theologische Bibliothek Töpelmann Ser.). (ENG.). XXII, 217p. 195.00 ***(978-3-11-177692-7(1))*** De Gruyter, Walter Inc.

Papapetros, Spyros. On the Animation of the Inorganic: Art, Architecture, & the Extension of Life. 2012. (ENG., Illus.). 440p. 45.00 ***(978-0-226-64568-1(1))*** Univ. of Chicago Pr.

Parker, De Witt. The Analysis of Art. reprint ed. 39.50 *(978-0-404-59289-9(9))* AMS Pr., Inc.

Parry, Ben, ed. Cultural Hijack: Rethinking Intervention. 2012. (ENG., Illus.). 288p. pap. 45.00 ***(978-1-84631-751-4(7))*** Liverpool Univ. Pr. GBR. Dist: Chicago Distribution Ctr.

Paskow, Alan. The Paradoxes of Art: A Phenomenological Investigation. 2008. (ENG., Illus.). 272p. (C). pap. 34.99 *(978-0-521-73318-2(9))* Cambridge Univ. Pr.

Pekáry, Thomas. Phidias in Rom: Beiträge Zum Spätantiken Kunstverständnis. 2007. (Philippika - marburger altertumskundliche Abhandlungen Ser.). (GER., Illus.). 173p. pap. 72.00 *(978-3-447-05516-1(2))* Harrassowitz, Otto Verlag DEU. Dist: ISD.

Penser L'art: Séminaire Interarts de Paris. 2009. (FRE.). 320p. (C). pap. 44.00 ***(978-2-252-03739-3(3))*** Klincksieck, Editions FRA. Dist: ISD.

Pericolo, Lorenzo & Nagel, Alexander. Subject as Aporia in Early Modern Art. 2010. (Illus.). 274p. 119.95 *(978-0-7546-6493-2(7))* Ashgate Publishing Co.

Pessler, Monika. UNDISZIPLINIERT / UNDISCIPLINED: Das Phänomen Raum in Kunst, Architektur und Design / The Phenomenon of Space in Art, Architecture & Design. Bast, Gerald, ed. 2008. (ENG & GER., Illus.). 159p. pap. *(978-3-211-09411-2(3),* 321094113) Actar Birkhauser Distribution.

Petry, Michael. The Art of Not Making: The New Artist/Artisan Relationship. 2012. (ENG., Illus.). 208p. pap. 34.95 ***(978-0-500-29026-2(1),*** 529026) Thames & Hudson.

Piper, Raymond Frank. The Hungry Eye: An Introduction to Cosmic Art. 2011. 142p. 40.95 ***(978-1-258-04573-9(7))*** Literary Licensing, LLC.

Pistoletto, Michelangelo. The Third Paradise. 2010. (ENG., Illus.). 96p. 24.95 *(978-88-317-0649-0(7))* Marsilio Editori spa ITA. Dist: Random Hse., Inc.

Pope Pius Xii & Pizzardo, Joseph. The Function of Art, Addresses of Pope Pius Xii: On Sacred Art, Instruction of the Supreme Sacred Congregation of the Holy Office. 2011. 12p. pap. 35.95 **(978-1-258-04844-0(2))** Literary Licensing, LLC.

Preimesberger, Rudolf. Paragons & Paragone: Van Eyck Raphael Michelangelo Caravaggio Bernini. 2011. (ENG., Illus.). 158p. 40.00 *(978-0-89236-964-5(7),* Getty Research Institute) Getty Pubns.

Preziosi, Donald & Farago, Claire. Art Is Not What You Think It Is. 2012. (Blackwell Manifestos Ser.: 60). (ENG., Illus.). 192p. pap. 26.95 **(978-1-4051-9239-2(9))**; 79.95 **(978-1-4051-9240-8(2))** Wiley, John & Sons, Inc. (Wiley-Blackwell).

Puolakka, Kalle. Relativism & Intentionalism in Interpretation: Davidson, Hermeneutics, & Pragmatism. 2011. (ENG.). 200p. 60.00 *(978-0-7391-5080-1(4))* Lexington Bks.

Rackauskas, Janice Evon. Season's Blessed. 2009. 120p. pap. 35.00 *(978-1-4269-0130-0(5))* Trafford Publishing.

Rancière, Jacques. The Future of the Image. Elliott, Gregory, tr. from FRE. 2009. (ENG.). 160p. pap. 17.95 *(978-1-84467-297-4(2),* 844297) Verso Bks. GBR. Dist: Norton, W. W. & Co., Inc.

Reichert, Marcus, frwd. Art Without Art: Selected Writing from the World of Blunt Edge. 2008. (Illus.). 137p. pap. 29.50 *(978-0-9546656-6-1(X))* Ziggurat Bks. GBR. Dist: Trans-Atlantic Pubns., Inc.

Ridley, Aaron. Routledge Philosophy Guidebook to Nietzshe on Art. 2007. (Routledge Philosophy Guidebooks Ser.). (ENG.). 208p. (C). 105.00 *(978-0-415-31590-6(5))* Routledge.

Riverin. Modern Impressions Book 3. 2011. 196p. pap. 51.08 **(978-1-4634-0727-8(0))** AuthorHouse.

Rochlitz, Rainer. Subversion & Subsidy: Contemporary Art & Aesthetics. Roberts, Dafydd, tr. from FRE. 2008. (SB-the French List Ser.). (ENG.). 240p. 99.95 *(978-1-905422-70-8(9))*; pap. 29.95 *(978-1-905422-71-5(7))* Seagull Bks. GBR. Dist: Chicago Distribution Ctr.

Ross, Bruce. Venturing upon Dizzy Heights: Lectures & Essays on Philosophy, Literature, & the Arts. 2008. (Illus.). 130p. (C). 59.95 *(978-1-4331-0287-5(0))* Lang, Peter Publishing, Inc.

Ruffini, Marco. Art Without an Author: Vasari's Lives & Michelangelo's Death. 2011. (Modern Language Initiative Ser.). (ENG., Illus.). 208p. 80.00 *(978-0-8232-3455-4(X))*; pap. 26.00 *(978-0-8232-3456-1(8))* Fordham Univ. Pr.

Sala, Nicoletta, ed. Chaos & Complexity in Arts & Architecture. 2006. 178p. (C). 39.00 *(978-1-60021-232-1(8))* Nova Science Pubs., Inc.

Sallis, John. Transfigurements: On the True Sense of Art. 204p. 2011. pap. 20.00 *(978-0-226-73418-7(8))* 2008. (ENG.). 25.00 *(978-0-226-73422-4(6))* Univ. of Chicago Pr.

Saorsa, Jac. Narrating the Catastrophe: An Artist's Dialogue with Deleuze & Ricoeur. 2011. (ENG., Illus.). 222p. 60.00 *(978-1-84150-460-5(2))* Intellect, Ltd. GBR. Dist: Chicago Distribution Ctr.

Schachter, Judith & Brockmann, Stephen. (Im)permanence: Cultures In/Out of Time. 2008. (Illus.). 284p. *(978-0-9797664-0-4(0))* Ctr. for the Arts in Society.

Schaeffer, Jean-Marie. Art of the Modern Age: Philosophy of Art from Kant to Heidegger. Rendall, Steven, tr. 2009. (New French Thought Ser.). (ENG., Illus.). 376p. (C). pap. 30.95 *(978-0-691-14436-8(2))* Princeton Univ. Pr.

Scharfstein, Ben-Ami. Art Without Borders: A Philosophical Exploration of Art & Humanity. 2009. (ENG., Illus.). 558p. 35.00 *(978-0-226-73609-9(1))* Univ. of Chicago Pr.

Schavemaker, Margriet, et al, eds. Now Is the Time. 2010. (ENG., Illus.). 192p. pap. 40.00 *(978-90-5662-721-8(X))* NAi Uitgevers / Publishers Stichting NLD. Dist: D.A.P./Distributed Art Pubs.

Schavemaker, Margriet & Rakier, Mischa. Right about Now: Art & Theory since the 1990s, 1 vol. 2008. (ENG., Illus.). 184p. pap. 29.95 *(978-90-78088-17-2(6))* Valiz NLD. Dist: D.A.P./Distributed Art Pubs.

Schellekens, Elisabeth, ed. Philosophy & Conceptual Art. 2007. (ENG., Illus.). 312p. 99.00 *(978-0-19-928555-6(1))* Oxford Univ. Pr., Inc.

Schellekens, Elisabeth & Goldie, Peter, eds. The Aesthetic Mind: Philosophy & Psychology. 2012. (ENG., Illus.). 420p. 99.00 **(978-0-19-969151-7(2))** Oxford Univ. Pr., Inc.

Schier, Flint. Deeper into Pictures: An Essay on Pictorial Representation. 2009. (Cambridge Studies in Philosophy Ser.). (ENG.). 240p. pap. 34.99 *(978-0-521-10940-6(X))* Cambridge Univ. Pr.

Schinzel, Hiltrud. Touching Vision: Essays on Restoration Theory & the Perception of Art. 2008. (ENG., Illus.). 262p. pap. 28.95 *(978-90-5487-352-5(3))* VUB Univ. Pr. BEL. Dist: Independent Pubs. Group.

Schultz, Deborah. Marcel Broodthaers: Strategy & Dialogue. 2007. (Illus.). 306p. pap. *(978-3-03910-918-0(9))* Lang, Peter AG.

Schuon, Frithjof. Art from the Sacred to the Profane: East & West. Schuon, Catherine, ed. 2007. (Writings of Frithjof Schuon Ser.). (ENG., Illus.). 160p. per. 24.95 *(978-1-933316-35-2(7))* World Wisdom, Inc.

Schwartzman, Madeline. See Yourself Sensing: Redefining Human Perception. 2011. (ENG., Illus.). 192p. pap. 45.00 *(978-1-907317-29-3(5))* Black Dog Publishing Ltd. GBR. Dist: Perseus Distribution.

Scully, Sean. Sean Scully: Resistance & Persistence: Selected Writings. Ingleby, Florence, ed. 2006. (ENG., Illus.). 192p. 29.95 *(978-1-85894-351-0(5))* Merrell Pubs. Ltd. GBR. Dist: Perseus Distribution.

Shaw, Devin Zane. Freedom & Nature in Schelling's Philosophy of Art. 2011. (Continuum Studies in Philosophy Ser.). (ENG.). 192p. 120.00 *(978-1-4411-5624-2(0))* Continuum International Publishing Group, Ltd. GBR. Dist: National Bk. Network.

Shaw, Theodore L. Art Reconstructed: A New Theory of Aesthetics. 2011. 286p. 48.95 **(978-1-258-07199-8(1))** Literary Licensing, LLC.

Shlain, Leonard. Art & Physics: Parallel Visions in Space, Time, & Light. 2007. (P. S. Ser.). (ENG., Illus.). 496p. pap. 16.99 *(978-0-06-122797-4(8),* William Morrow Paperbacks) HarperCollins Pubs.

Shore, Stephen. The Nature of Photographs. 2nd ed. 2010. (ENG., Illus.). 136p. pap. 19.95 *(978-0-7148-5904-0(4))* Phaidon Pr., Inc.

Silverman, Kaja. Flesh of My Flesh. 2009. (ENG., Illus.). 304p. 60.00 *(978-0-8047-6207-6(4))*; pap. 21.95 *(978-0-8047-6208-3(2))* Stanford Univ. Pr.

Sinclair, Mark. Heidegger, Aristotle & the Work of Art: Poiesis in Being. annot. ed. 2007. (ENG.). 256p. 100.00 *(978-1-4039-8978-9(8))* Palgrave Macmillan.

Sitte, Camillo, et al. Schriften Zu Kunstkritik und Kunstgewerbe. 2008. (GER., Illus.). 642p. *(978-3-205-77581-2(3))* Bohlau Verlag Gmbh & Cie.

Sleeth, D. B. The Integral Ego: A New Understanding of the Whole Person That Includes All Ideas on the Nature of God. 2008. (ENG., Illus.). 234p. pap. 39.99 *(978-0-7618-4310-8(8))* Univ. Pr. of America, Inc.

Smith, Ann Kennedy. Painted Poetry: Colour in Baudelaire's Art Criticism. 2011. (Illus.). 248p. pap. 55.95 *(978-3-03911-094-0(2))* Lang, Peter AG GBR. Dist: Lang, Peter.

Smith, Paul & Wilde, Carolyn, eds. A Companion to Art Theory. 2007. (Blackwell Companions in Cultural Studies: 21). (ENG., Illus.). 552p. 209.95 *(978-0-631-20762-7(7),* Wiley-Blackwell) Wiley, John & Sons, Inc.

Smith, Terry. What Is Contemporary Art? 2009. (Illus.). 300p. 66.66 *(978-0-226-76430-6(3))*; (ENG., 344p. pap. 25.00 *(978-0-226-76431-3(1))* Univ. of Chicago Pr.

Springgay, S., et al, eds. Being with A/R/Tography. 2007. 320p. per. *(978-90-8790-262-9(X))* Sense Pubs.

Stafford, Barbara Maria. Echo Objects: The Cognitive Work of Images. 2007. (ENG., Illus.). 296p. 47.50 *(978-0-226-77051-2(6))* Univ. of Chicago Pr.

Stecker, Robert. Aesthetics. Gracyk, Ted, ed. 2010. (Elements of Philosophy Ser.). (ENG.). 422p. 99.00 *(978-0-7425-6436-7(3))* Rowman & Littlefield Publishers, Inc.

—Aesthetics. Gracyk, Theodore, ed. 2010. (Elements of Philosophy Ser.). (ENG.). 422p. pap. 70.00 *(978-0-7425-6437-4(1))* Rowman & Littlefield Publishers, Inc.

—Aesthetics & the Philosophy of Art. 2nd ed. 2010. (Elements of Philosophy Ser.). (ENG.). 328p. 90.00 *(978-0-7425-6410-7(X))*; pap. 39.95 *(978-0-7425-6411-4(8))* Rowman & Littlefield Publishers, Inc.

Steiner, Rudolf. Art in the Light of Mystery Wisdom. 2011. 206p. 44.95 **(978-1-258-00161-2(6))** Literary Licensing, LLC.

Sutton, Tiffany. The Classification of Visual Art: A Philosophical Myth & its History. 2007. (ENG., Illus.). 200p. pap. 41.00 *(978-0-521-03974-1(6))* Cambridge Univ. Pr.

Tagg, John. The Disciplinary Frame: Photographic Truths & the Capture of Meaning. 2009. (Illus.). 392p. 82.50 *(978-0-8166-4287-8(7))* Univ. of Minnesota Pr.

Taine, Hippolyte A. Lectures on Art, 2 vols. (Illus.). reprint ed. 115.00 *(978-0-404-06333-7(0))* AMS Pr., Inc.

Tamme, Anne Mary. A Critique of John Dewey's Theory of Fine Art in the Light of the Principles of Thomism. 2011. 148p. 40.95 **(978-1-258-01282-3(0))** Literary Licensing, LLC.

Tanke, Joseph J. Foucault Philosophy of Art: A Genealogy of Modernity. 2009. (Philosophy, Aesthetics & Cultural Theory Ser.). (ENG., Illus.). 240p. 150.00 *(978-1-84706-484-4(1))* Continuum International Publishing Group, Ltd. GBR. Dist: National Bk. Network.

—Philosophy of Art: A Genealogy of Modernity. 2009. (Philosophy, Aesthetics & Cultural Theory Ser.). (ENG., Illus.). 240p. 34.95 *(978-1-84706-485-1(X))* Continuum International Publishing Group, Ltd. GBR. Dist: National Bk. Network.

Taylor, Mark C. Refiguring the Spiritual: Beuys, Barney, Turrell, Goldsworthy. 2012. (Religion, Culture, & Public Life Ser.). (ENG., Illus.). 244p. (gr. 17). 27.50 **(978-0-231-15766-7(5))** Columbia Univ. Pr.

Tymieniecka, A-T., ed. Metamorphosis: Creative Imagination in Fine Arts Between Life-Projects & Human Aesthetic Aspirations. 2010. (Analecta Husserliana Ser.). xvi, 428p. pap. 319.00 *(978-90-481-6463-9(X),* 904816463X) Springer.

Vaillant, Alexis, et al. Options with Nostrils. 2011. (ENG., Illus.). pap. 18.00 **(978-1-934105-16-0(3))** Sternberg Pr.

Van De Vall, Renee & Vall, Renée van de. At the Edges of Vision: A Phenomenological Aesthetics of Contemporary Spectatorship. 2008. (Histories of Vision Ser.). (Illus.). 190p. 114.95 *(978-0-7546-4073-8(6))* Ashgate Publishing Co.

Van den Braembussche, Antoon. Thinking Art. 2009. (ENG., Illus.). xxi, 326p. 109.00 *(978-1-4020-5637-6(0),* 1402056370) Springer.

Velasquez, Manuel. Art & Meaning Enrichment Chapter for Velasquez's Philosophy: A Text with Readings, 11th. 11th ed. 2010. (ENG.). 16p. (C). pap. 16.95 *(978-0-8400-3325-3(7))* Wadsworth.

Verwoert, Jan. Tell Me What You Want, What You Really, Really Want. Ohlraun, Vanessa, ed. 2011. (ENG., Illus.). 312p. 22.00 **(978-1-934105-14-6(7))** Sternberg Pr.

Vickery, Jonathan & Costello, Diarmuid, eds. Art: Key Contemporary Thinkers. 2007. (ENG.). 256p. pap. 26.95 *(978-1-84520-320-7(8))* Berg Pubs. GBR. Dist: Macmillan.

—Art: Key Contemporary Thinkers. 2007. (ENG.). 1p. 99.95 *(978-1-84520-319-1(4))* Berg Pubs. GBR. Dist: Macmillan.

Walker, Deborah. Giorgio de Chirico & the Real. 2008. 84p. pap. *(978-3-639-04201-6(8))* VDM Verlag Dr. Mueller e.K.

Walton, Kendall L. Marvelous Images: On Values & the Arts. 2008. (ENG., Illus.). 256p. 99.00 *(978-0-19-517794-7(0))*; pap. 24.95 *(978-0-19-517795-4(9))* Oxford Univ. Pr., Inc.

Warner, Marina. Phantasmagoria: Spirit Visions, Metaphors, & Media into the Twenty-First Century. 2008. (ENG., Illus.). 496p. pap. 37.95 *(978-0-19-923923-8(1))* Oxford Univ. Pr., Inc.

Wartenberg, Thomas E. The Nature of Art: An Anthology. 3rd ed. 2011. (ENG.). 368p. (C). pap. 113.95 *(978-1-111-18652-4(9))* Wadsworth.

Watson, Gray. Art & Sex. 2008. (Art and... Ser.). (ENG., Illus.). 168p. 79.00 *(978-1-84511-664-4(X))*; pap. 28.00 *(978-1-84511-665-1(8))* I. B. Tauris & Co., Ltd. GBR. Dist: Macmillan.

Wiesing, Lambert. Artificial Presence: Philosophical Studies in Image Theory. Schott, Nils, tr. from GER. 2009. (Cultural Memory in the Present Ser.). (ENG., Illus.). 168p. 60.00 *(978-0-8047-5940-3(5))*; pap. 21.95 *(978-0-8047-5941-0(3))* Stanford Univ. Pr.

Willis, Gary. Art As Mime. 2010. 232p. pap. *(978-3-8383-1920-9(6))* Lambert Academic Publishing.

Wolf, Norbert & Schneider, Norbert. Still Life. 25th ed. 2009. (ENG., Illus.). 216p. 14.99 *(978-3-8365-1018-9(9))* TASCHEN DEU. Dist: Ingram Pub. Services.

Wolff, Janet. The Aesthetics of Uncertainty. 2008. (Columbia Themes in Philosophy, Social Criticism, & the Arts Ser.). (ENG., Illus.). 200p. (gr. 17). 40.00 *(978-0-231-14096-6(7))* Columbia Univ. Pr.

Zangwill, Nick. Aesthetic Creation. (ENG.). 2012. 200p. pap. 29.95 **(978-0-19-964530-5(2))** 2007. 192p. 65.00 *(978-0-19-926187-1(3))* Oxford Univ. Pr., Inc.

Zepke, Stephen. Art As Abstract Machine. 2011. (ENG., Illus.). 318p. pap. 39.95 **(978-0-415-89006-9(3))** Routledge.

Zepke, Stephen & O'Sullivan, Simon, eds. Deleuze & Contemporary Art. 2010. (Deleuze Connections Ser.). (ENG., Illus.). 280p. (gr. 17). 115.00 *(978-0-7486-3837-6(7))*; pap. 35.00 *(978-0-7486-3838-3(5))* Edinburgh Univ. Pr. GBR. Dist: Columbia Univ. Pr.

Zijlmans, Kitty & van Damme, Wilfried, eds. World Art Studies. 2008. (ENG., Illus.). 464p. (C). pap. 39.95 *(978-90-78088-22-6(2))* Valiz NLD. Dist: D.A.P./Distributed Art Pubs.

Zucker, Paul. A Platonic Discourse about Some Philosophical Problems of Art, X: Between A Young Man, the Student, Y, & Paul Zucker, the Author, Z. 2011. 44p. 35.95 **(978-1-258-00960-1(9))** Literary Licensing, LLC.

ART—POLITICAL ASPECTS

Adang, Marc. Voor Sociaal-Democratie, Smaakopvoeding en Verheffend Genot: De Amsterdamse Vereniging Kunst Aan Het Volk, 1903-1928. 2008. (DUT., Illus.). 766p. 57.50 **(978-90-5260-314-8(6))** Aksant Academic Pubs. NLD. Dist: Amsterdam Univ. Pr.

Adlington, Robert. Sound Commitments: Avant-Garde Music & the Sixties. 2009. (ENG., Illus.). 336p. 99.00 *(978-0-19-533664-1(X))* Oxford Univ. Pr., Inc.

Alexander, Jeffrey C. The Performance of Politics: Obama's Victory & the Democratic Struggle for Power, 1 vol. 2010. (ENG., Illus.). 336p. 29.95 *(978-0-19-974446-6(7))* Oxford Univ. Pr., Inc.

Amey, Claude. Arts et Pouvoir: Séminaire Interarts de Paris, 2005-2006. 2007. (FRE.). 264p. (C). pap. 29.00 **(978-2-252-03642-6(7))** Klincksieck, Editions FRA. Dist: ISD.

Anastasio, Andrea. Fingerprint. 2009. (ENG., Illus.). 104p. 29.95 *(978-81-906756-2-8(1))* Tara Publishing IND. Dist: Perseus-PGW.

Antliff, Allan. Anarchy & Art: From the Paris Commune to the Fall of the Berlin Wall. 2007. (ENG., Illus.). 224p. pap. 23.95 *(978-1-55152-218-0(7))* Arsenal Pulp Pr. CAN. Dist: Consortium Bk. Sales & Distribution.

Araeen. Third Text. 2007. 49.95 *(978-0-415-44118-6(8))* Taylor & Francis Group.

Araeen, Rasheed & Sardar, Ziauddin, eds. Third Text. 2007. (ENG.). 10p. 49.95 *(978-0-415-44120-9(X),* Taylor & Francis) Taylor & Francis Group GBR. Dist: Taylor & Francis Group.

Atkinson, Dennis. Art, Equality & Learning: Pedagogies Against the State. 2011. 194p. **(978-94-6091-453-9(5))**; pap. **(978-94-6091-452-2(7))** Sense Pubs.

Bal, Mieke. Of What One Cannot Speak: Doris Salcedo's Political Art. 2011. (ENG., Illus.). 296p. 45.00 *(978-0-226-03578-9(6))* Univ. of Chicago Pr.

Baladran, Zbynek & Havranek, Vit, eds. Atlas of Transformation. 2011. (ENG., Illus.). 724p. pap. 45.00 *(978-3-03764-147-7(9))* JRP Ringier Kunstverlag AG CHE. Dist: D.A.P./Distributed Art Pubs.

Bang, Larsen La, ed. Nomeda & Gediminas/Devices for Action. 2008. 188p. pap. *(978-84-89771-65-9(0))* Actar Birkhauser Distribution.

Barrett, Lindsay. The Prime Minister's Christmas Card: Blue Poles & Cultural Politics in the Whitlam Era. 2011. (ENG.). 264p. (C). pap. 26.95 *(978-1-86487-275-0(6))* Power Pubns. AUS. Dist: Univ. of Washington Pr.

Barron, Stephanie, et al. Art of Two Germanys - Cold War Cultures. 2009. (Illus.). 460p. *(978-0-8109-7647-4(1))* Abrams.

Baukol, Bard. William Prynne & the Politics of Reaction. 2008. 372p. pap. *(978-3-8364-7122-0(1))* VDM Verlag Dr. Mueller e.K.

Berlin, Isaiah. The Soviet Mind: Russian Culture under Communism. Hardy, Henry, ed. 2011. (ENG.). 242p. pap. 20.95 *(978-0-8157-2155-0(2))* Brookings Institution Pr.

Bernstein, Lee. America Is the Prison: Arts & Politics in Prison in The 1970s. 2010. (ENG., Illus.). 240p. 35.00 *(978-0-8078-3387-2(8))* Univ. of North Carolina Pr.

—America Is the Prison: Arts & Politics in Prison in the 1970s. 2010. (Illus.). xi, 244p. pap. *(978-0-8078-7117-1(6))* Univ. of North Carolina Pr.

Bishop, Claire & Dziewanska, Marta, eds. 1968-1989. Political Upheaval & Artistic Change. 2011. (ENG & POL., Illus.). 504p. pap. 25.00 **(978-83-924044-0-8(8))** Muzeum Sztuki Nowoczesnej w Warszawie POL. Dist: Chicago Distribution Ctr.

Block, Herbert. Herblock: The Life & Work of the Great Political Cartoonist. Katz, Harry, ed. 2009. (ENG., Illus.). 304p. 35.00 *(978-0-393-06772-9(6),* 6772) Norton, W. W. & Co., Inc.

Bodleian Library Staff, ed. Postcards from Utopia: The Art of Political Propaganda. 2009. (Bodleian Library - Postcards From Ser.). (ENG., Illus.). 112p. 20.00 *(978-1-85124-337-2(2))* Bodleian Library GBR. Dist: Chicago Distribution Ctr.

—Postcards of Lost Royals. 2009. (Bodleian Library - Postcards From Ser.). (ENG., Illus.). 112p. 20.00 *(978-1-85124-332-7(1))* Bodleian Library GBR. Dist: Chicago Distribution Ctr.

Bowers, Andrea. Nothing Is Neutral: Andrea Bowers. 2006. (ENG., Illus.). 151p. pap. 30.00 *(978-0-9749831-4-1(4))* California Institute of the Arts.

Brown, Courtney. Politics in Music: Music & Political Transformation from Beethoven to Hip-Hop. 2007. 260p. per. 24.95 *(978-0-9766762-3-2(0))* Farsight Pr.

Bruce, Katie & Hollows, Victoria. Towards an Engaged Gallery: Contemporary art & human Rights. 2007. (Illus.). 96p. per. *(978-0-902752-88-7(X))* Glasgow Museums.

Bryan-Wilson, Julia. Art Workers: Radical Practice in the Vietnam War Era. (Illus.). 2011. 295p. pap. 29.95 *(978-0-520-26975-0(6))* 2009. (ENG., 256p. 60.00 *(978-0-520-25728-3(6))* Univ. of California Pr.

Cameron. Peter Saul. 2008. (ENG., Illus.). 160p. 55.00 *(978-3-7757-2204-9(1))* Hatje Cantz Verlag GmbH & Co KG DEU. Dist: D.A.P./Distributed Art Pubs.

Campens, Angelique, et al. For Reasons of State. 2009. (Independent Study Program Ser.). (ENG., Illus.). 48p. pap. 16.95 *(978-0-300-14694-3(9))* Yale Univ. Pr.

Carlisle, Janice. Picturing Reform in Victorian Britain. 2012. (Cambridge Studies in Nineteenth-Century Literature & Culture Ser.: 79). (ENG., Illus.). 320p. 99.00 **(978-0-521-86836-5(X))** Cambridge Univ. Pr.

Cassidy. Politics & Civil Ideals in Italian Sculpture, C. 1250-1400 Volume 46. 2007. (Studies in Medieval & Early Renaissance Art History Ser.). (Illus.). 314p. (C). 174.00 *(978-1-905375-01-1(8))* Miller, Harvey Pubs. GBR. Dist: Brown, David Bk. Co., The.

Chung, Anita, ed. Chinese Art in an Age of Revolution: Fu Baoshi (1904-1965) 2012. (ENG., Illus.). 256p. pap. 50.00 *(978-0-300-16974-4(4))* Yale Univ. Pr.

Cole, Michael W. Ambitious Form: Giambologna, Ammanati, & Danti in Florence. 2010. (ENG., Illus.). 372p. (C). 49.50 *(978-0-691-14744-4(2))* Princeton Univ. Pr.

Conal, Robbie. Not Your Typical Political Animal: Animal Drawings & Paintings by Guerrilla Poster Artist Robbie Conal. 2009. (Illus.). 80p. (YA). pap. 24.95 *(978-0-615-32667-2(6))* ArtAttack Pr.

Cooke, Miriam. Dissident Syria: Making Oppositional Arts Official. 2007. (ENG., Illus.). 208p. 79.95 *(978-0-8223-4016-4(X))*; per. 22.95 *(978-0-8223-4035-5(6))* Duke Univ. Pr.

Craven, David. Art & Revolution in Latin America, 1910-1990. 2006. (ENG., Illus.). 240p. pap. 38.00 *(978-0-300-12046-2(X))* Yale Univ. Pr.

Cronin, J. Keri & Robertson, Kirsty, eds. Imagining Resistance: Visual Culture & Activism in Canada. 2010. (Cultural Studies). (ENG., Illus.). 294p. (C). pap. 39.95 *(978-1-55458-257-0(1))* Wilfrid Laurier Univ. Pr. CAN. Dist: Univ. of Toronto Pr.

Crowley, David & Pavitt, Jane. Cold War Modern: Design 1945-1970. Crowley, David & Pavitt, Jane, eds. 2008. (ENG., Illus.). 320p. 80.00 *(978-1-85177-543-9(9))* V & A Pubns. GBR. Dist: Hachette Bk. Group.

Cullen, Fintan. Ireland on Show: Art Union & Nationhood. 2012. (Illus.). 124.95 **(978-1-4094-3109-1(6))** Ashgate Publishing Co.

Cuno, James. Who Owns Antiquity? Museums & the Battle over Our Ancient Heritage. 2008. (ENG., Illus.). 272p. 24.95 *(978-0-691-13712-4(9))* Princeton Univ. Pr.

Davis, Walter A. Art & Politics: Psychoanalysis, Ideology, Theatre. 2006. (ENG.). 192p. 100.00 *(978-0-7453-2648-1(X))*; per. 28.95 *(978-0-7453-2647-4(1))* Pluto Pr. GBR. Dist: Macmillan.

De Roo, Ruben & Vanhaesebrouck, Karel, eds. Art & Activism in the Age of Globalization. 2011. (ENG., Illus.). 334p. pap. 35.00 *(978-90-5662-779-9(1))* NAi Uitgevers / Publishers Stichting NLD. Dist: D.A.P./Distributed Art Pubs.

Derksen, Jeff. Annihilated Time: Poetry & Other Politics. 2009. (ENG.). 304p. pap. 29.95 *(978-0-88922-612-8(1))* Talonbooks, Ltd. CAN. Dist: Consortium Bk. Sales & Distribution.

Dorléac, Laurence Bertrand, et al. Art of the Defeat: France, 1940-1944. Todd, Jane Marie, tr. from FRE. 2009. (ENG., Illus.). 416p. 45.00 *(978-0-89236-891-4(8))* Oxford Univ. Pr., Inc.

Douglas, Stan, ed. Vancouver Anthology. 2nd rev. ed. 2009. (ENG.). 368p. 35.00 **(978-0-88922-614-2(8))** Talonbooks, Ltd. CAN. Dist: Consortium Bk. Sales & Distribution.

Dressler, Iris & Christ, Hans, eds. Postcapital Archive (1989-2001) Technologies To The People. 2011. (ENG., Illus.). 320p. 55.00 **(978-3-7757-3170-6(9))** Hatje Cantz Verlag GmbH & Co KG DEU. Dist: D.A.P./Distributed Art Pubs.

Dressler, Iris & Christ, Hans, eds. Subversive Praktiken: Kunst unter Bedingungen politischer Repression 60er-80er / Südamerika / Europa. 2011. (ENG., Illus.). 584p. 60.00 *(978-3-7757-2755-6(8))* Hatje Cantz Verlag GmbH & Co KG DEU. Dist: D.A.P./Distributed Art Pubs.

Dunn, Alec & MacPhee, Josh, eds. A Journal of International Political Graphics. 2010. (Signal Ser.). (ENG & ABK.). 128p. pap. 14.95 *(978-1-60486-091-7(X))* PM Pr.

Eckmann, Sabine. Precarious Worlds: Contemporary Art from Germany. 2012. (ENG., Illus.). 72p. 30.00 **(978-0-936316-34-5(9))** Washington Univ., Mildred Lane Kemper Art Museum.

Eisenman, Stephen F. The Abu Ghraib Effect. 2010. (ENG., Illus.). 128p. pap. 14.95 *(978-1-86189-646-9(8))* Reaktion Bks., Ltd. GBR. Dist: Chicago Distribution Ctr.

Elliott, Jeannette Shambaugh. The Odyssey of China's Imperial Art Treasures. 2007. (Samuel & Althea Stroum Bks.). (ENG., Illus.). 192p. per. 19.95 *(978-0-295-98588-3(3))* Univ. of Washington Pr.

Esche, Charles, et al, eds. Citizens & Subjects: The Netherlands, for Example, 1 vol. 2007. (ENG., Illus.). 336p. pap. 29.00 *(978-3-905770-73-5(3))* JRP Ringier Kunstverlag AG CHE. Dist: D.A.P./Distributed Art Pubs.

Esche, Charles & Lewis, Mark. Art & Social Change: A Critical Reader. Bradley, Will, ed. 2008. (ENG., Illus.). 480p. pap. 39.95 *(978-1-85437-626-8(8))* Tate Publishing, Ltd. GBR. Dist: Hachette Bk. Group.

Ferrell, Robyn. Sacred Exchanges: Images in Global Context. 2012. (Columbia Themes in Philosophy, Social Criticism, & the Arts Ser.). (ENG., Illus.). 192p. (gr. 17). 50.00 ***(978-0-231-14880-1(1))*** Columbia Univ. Pr.

Fleck, Cathleen A. The Clement Bible at the Medieval Courts of Naples & Avignon: A Story of Papal Power Royal Prestige & Patronage. 2010. (Illus.). 370p. 124.95 *(978-0-7546-6980-7(7))* Ashgate Publishing Co.

Fordham, Douglas. British Art & the Seven Years' War: Allegiance & Autonomy. 2010. (Illus.). 352p. (C). 65.00 *(978-0-8122-4243-0(2))* Univ. of Pennsylvania Pr.

Francis Alÿs: Sometimes Doing Something Poetic Can Become Political & Sometimes Doing Something Political Can Become Poetic. 2007. per. 20.00 *(978-0-9769136-7-2(4))* Zwirner, David Inc.

Freire, Cristina & Longoni, Ana. Conceitualismos Do Sul/Sur: Conceptualismos Del Sur. 2009. (POR & SPA., Illus.). 361p. *(978-85-7419-957-3(5))* Annablume Editora Comunicacao Ltda.

Gaughan, Martin Ignatius. German Art 1907-1937: Modernism & Modernisation. (Illus.). 351p. pap. 89.95 *(978-3-03910-900-5(6))* Lang, Peter CHE. Dist: Lang, Peter Publishing, Inc.

Gennaro, I. de, et al. Artists & Intellectuals & the Requests of Power. 2009. (Studies on the Interaction of Art, Thought & Power). (Illus.). 224p. *(978-90-04-17213-5(0))* BRILL.

Genter, Robert. Late Modernism: Art, Culture, & Politics in Cold War America. 2010. (Arts & Intellectual Life in Modern America Ser.). 384p. (C). 49.95 *(978-0-8122-4264-5(5))* Univ. of Pennsylvania Pr.

Georgiou, Danielle. The Politics of State Public Arts Funding: Examining the Factors & Changes in State-Level Funding for the Arts. 2008. 192p. pap. *(978-3-639-09583-8(9))* VDM Verlag Dr. Mueller e.K.

Giunta, Andrea. Avant-Garde, Internationalism, & Politics: Argentine Art in the Sixties. Kahn, Peter, tr. from SPA. 2007. (Latin America Otherwise Ser.). (ENG., Illus.). 432p. per. 27.95 *(978-0-8223-3893-2(9))*; 99.95 *(978-0-8223-3877-2(7))* Duke Univ. Pr.

Goede, Don. Abraham Obama: A Guerilla Tour Through Art & Politics. 2009. (Illus.). 288p. pap. 19.95 *(978-0-86719-722-8(6))* Last Gasp of San Francisco.

Gomez-Barris, Macarena. Where Memory Dwells: Culture & State Violence in Chile. 2008. (Illus.). 224p. 60.00 *(978-0-520-25583-8(6))*; 240p. pap. 26.95 *(978-0-520-25584-5(4))* Univ. of California Pr.

Greeley, Robin Adele. Surrealism & the Spanish Civil War. 2006. (ENG., Illus.). 240p. 65.00 *(978-0-300-11295-5(5))* Yale Univ. Pr.

Groys, Boris. Art Power. 2008. (ENG.). 200p. (gr. 17). 25.95 *(978-0-262-07292-2(0))* MIT Pr.

Groys, Boris. Boris Groys: Going Public. 2011. (E-Flux Journal Ser.). (ENG., Illus.). 168p. pap. 15.00 ***(978-1-934105-30-6(9))*** Sternberg Pr.

Guilbaut, Serge, contrib. by. Be-Bomb: The Transatlantic War of Images & All That Jazz. 1946-1956. 2008. (Illus.). 774p. pap. *(978-84-89771-47-5(2))* Museu d'Art Contemporani de Barcelona.

Haas, Gilda, et al, eds. We Shall Not Be Moved: Posters & the Fight Against Displacement in L. A.'s Figueroa Corridor. 2008. (FM Press Ser.). (ENG., Illus.). 51p. pap. 15.00 *(978-1-60486-038-2(3))* PM Pr.

Harris, Jonathan. Identity Theft: The Cultural Colonization of Contemporary Art. Harris, Jonathan, ed. 2009. (ENG., Illus.). 272p. 85.00 *(978-1-84631-103-1(9))* Liverpool Univ. Pr. GBR. Dist: Chicago Distribution Ctr.

Harris, Jonathan, ed. Identity Theft: The Cultural Colonisation & Contemporary Art. 2009. (Liverpool University Press - Tate Liverpool Critical Forum Ser.). (ENG., Illus.). 272p. pap. 39.95 *(978-1-84631-102-4(0))* Liverpool Univ. Pr. GBR. Dist: Chicago Distribution Ctr.

Hebel, Udo J. & Wagner, Christoph, eds. Pictorial Cultures & Political Iconographies: Approaches, Perspectives, Case Studies from Europe & America. 2011. (ENG., Illus.). 445p. 210.00 ***(978-3-11-219088-3(2))***; 140.00 ***(978-3-11-023785-6(7))*** De Gruyter, Walter Inc.

Hegyi, Lorand. Passage to Europe: Realities, References, Reflections. 2008. (ENG., Illus.). 160p. pap. 29.95 *(978-88-7439-168-4(4))* 5 Continents ITA. Dist: Hachette Bk. Group.

Hinderliter, Beth, et al, eds. Communities of Sense: Rethinking Aesthetics & Politics. 2009. (ENG., Illus.). 384p. 94.95 *(978-0-8223-4497-1(1))*; pap. 26.95 *(978-0-8223-4513-8(7))* Duke Univ. Pr.

Hite, Katherine. Politics & the Art of Commemoration. 2011. (Interventions Ser.). (ENG., Illus.). 160p. (C). 130.00 *(978-0-415-78071-1(3))* Routledge.

Hung, Chang-tai. Mao's New World: Political Culture in the Early People's Republic. 2010. (Illus.). 328p. 39.95 *(978-0-8014-4934-5(0))* Cornell Univ. Pr.

Jaar, Alfredo, illus. Alfredo Jaar: la Politique des Images. 2008. (FRE & ENG.). 160p. per. 49.00 *(978-3-905770-48-3(2))* JRP Ringier Kunstverlag AG CHE. Dist: D.A.P./Distributed Art Pubs.

Jachec, Nancy. Politics & Painting at the Venice Biennale, 1948-1964: Italy & the Idea of Europe. 2008. (Critical Perspectives in Art History Ser.). (ENG., Illus.). 224p. 84.00 *(978-0-7190-6896-6(7))* Manchester Univ. Pr. GBR. Dist: Macmillan.

Kaneff, Deema & Kapferer, Judith. The State & the Arts: Articulating Power & Subversion. 2008. (Illus.). 240p. 27.95 *(978-1-84545-578-1(9))* Berghahn Bks., Inc.

Karaba, Elpida & Yiakoumaki, Nayia. FeedBack: Ideas That Inform, Construct & Concern the Production of Exhibitions & Events. Karaba, E. & Yiakoumaki, N., eds. 2007. (Illus.). 180p. per. *(978-0-9554796-8-7(1))* Nute Publishing, Ltd.

Kelly, Elaine & Wlodarski, Amy, eds. Art Outside the Lines: New Perspectives on GDR Art Culture. 2011. (Illus.). 298p. pap. 8400.00 *(978-90-420-3341-2(X))* Rodopi.

Kidd, Dustin. Legislating Creativity: The Intersection of Art & Politics. 2009. (Routledge Advances in Sociology Ser.). (ENG., Illus.). 190p. 125.00 *(978-0-415-87119-8(0))* Routledge.

—Legislating Creativity: The Intersections of Art & Politics. 2009. (Illus.). xvi, 174p. 95.00 *(978-0-203-85979-7(0))* Routledge.

King, David. Red Star over Russia: A Visual History of the Soviet Union from the Revolution to the Death of Stalin. 2009. (ENG., Illus.). 352p. 50.00 *(978-0-8109-8279-6(X))* Abrams.

Klanten, R., et al, eds. Art & Agenda: Political Art & Activism. 2011. (Illus.). 288p. *(978-3-89955-342-0(X))* Die Gestalten Verlag.

Klin, Richard. Something to Say: Thoughts on Art & Politics in America. 2011. (ENG., Illus.). 168p. pap. 14.95 ***(978-1-935248-19-4(7))*** Leapfrog Pr.

Kohle, Hubertus & Reichardt, Rolf. Visualising the Revolution: Politics & Pictorial Arts in Late Eighteenth-Century France. 2008. (Reaktion Books - Picturing History Ser.). (ENG., Illus.). 240p. 45.00 *(978-1-86189-312-3(4))* Reaktion Bks., Ltd. GBR. Dist: Chicago Distribution Ctr.

Kutuzova, Anna. An Imperialist Hawk. 2008. 76p. pap. *(978-3-639-08514-3(0))* VDM Verlag Dr. Mueller e.K.

Lacy, Suzanne. Leaving Art: Writings on Performance, Politics, & Publics, 1974-2007. 2010. (ENG., Illus.). 424p. 99.95 *(978-0-8223-4552-7(8))*; pap. 27.95 *(978-0-8223-4569-5(2))* Duke Univ. Pr.

Latorre, Guisela. Walls of Empowerment: Chicana/o Indigenist Murals of California. 2008. (ENG., Illus.). 324p. 60.00 *(978-0-292-71883-8(7))*; pap. 27.95 *(978-0-292-71906-4(X))* Univ. of Texas Pr.

Leger, Marc James. Brave New Avant Garde: Essays on Contemporary Art & Politics. 2012. (ENG., Illus.). 208p. pap. 22.95 ***(978-1-78099-050-7(2))*** Hunt, John Publishing Ltd. GBR. Dist: National Bk. Network.

Lindquist, Sherry. Agency Visuality & Society at the Chartreuse de Champmol. 2008. (Illus.). 282p. 124.95 *(978-0-7546-6046-0(X))* Ashgate Publishing Co.

MacPhee, Josh, ed. Paper Politics: Socially Engaged Printmaking Today. 2009. (ENG.). 144p. pap. 24.95 *(978-1-60486-090-0(1))* PM Pr.

MacPhee, Josh & Reuland, Erik, eds. Realizing the Impossible: Art Against Authority. 2007. (ENG., Illus.). 225p. per. 23.95 *(978-1-904859-32-1(1))* AK Pr. GBR. Dist: Consortium Bk. Sales & Distribution.

Maguire, Henry & Nelson, Robert S., eds. San Marco, Byzantium, & the Myths of Venice. 2010. (Dumbarton Oaks Byzantine Symposia & Colloquia Ser.). (ENG., Illus.). 304p. 60.00 *(978-0-88402-360-9(5))* Dumbarton Oaks.

Marman, Jennifer & Borins, Daniel. Jennifer Marman & Daniel Borins: Project for a New American Century. 2009. (ENG., Illus.). 64p. *(978-0-921972-55-6(5))* Art Gallery of York Univ.

Martin, Jean-Hubert. Arte Religione Politica: Art, Religion, Politics. 2008. (ENG., Illus.). 104p. 19.95 *(978-88-7439-236-0(2))* 5 Continents ITA. Dist: Hachette Bk. Group.

Mazloomi, Carolyn L. Journey of Hope: Quilts Inspired by President Barack Obama. 2010. (ENG., Illus.). 216p. 24.99 *(978-0-7603-3935-0(X),* 076033935X, Voyageur Pr) MBI Publishing Co. LLC.

McCaughan, Edward J. Art & Social Movements: Cultural Politics in Mexico & Aztlán. 2012. (ENG., Illus.). 240p. pap. 23.95 ***(978-0-8223-5182-5(X))*** Duke Univ. Pr.

—Artists & Social Movements: Cultural Politics in Mexico & Aztlán. 2012. (ENG., Illus.). 240p. 84.95 ***(978-0-8223-5168-9(4))*** Duke Univ. Pr.

McInnis, Maurie D. & Nelson, Louis P., eds. Shaping the Body Politic: Art & Political Formation in Early America. 2011. (Thomas Jefferson Foundation Distinguished Lecture Ser.). (ENG., Illus.). 336p. (gr. 17). 45.00 *(978-0-8139-3102-9(9))* Univ. Pr. of Virginia.

McWilliam, Neil, ed. Lines of Attack: Conflicts in Caricature. 2010. (ENG., Illus.). 96p. pap. 18.95 *(978-0-938989-32-5(4))* Duke Univ. Pr.

Michalski, Sergiusz. Public Monuments: Art in Political Bondage 1870-1997. 2006. 236p. reprint ed. pap. 25.00 *(978-1-4223-5342-4(7))* DIANE Publishing Co.

Mitchell, John. Out of the Dark Ages. 2008. (Illus.). 192p. pap. 27.00 *(978-0-7156-3685-5(5))* Duckworth Publishers GBR. Dist: International Publishers Marketing.

Mittler, Barbara. A Continuous Revolution: Making Sense of Cultural Revolution Culture. 2012. (Harvard East Asian Monographs: 343). (ENG., Illus.). 500p. 59.95 ***(978-0-674-06581-9(6))*** Harvard Univ., Asia Ctr.

Moore, Alan. Art Gangs: Postmodern Artists - Collectives in New York City. 2011. 256p. pap. 17.95 ***(978-1-57027-237-0(9))*** Autonomedia.

Moore, Colin. Propaganda Prints: A History of Art in the Service of Social & Political Change. 2011. (ENG., Illus.). 200p. 55.00 *(978-1-4081-0591-7(8))* A & C Black GBR. Dist: Macmillan.

Murphy, Sinead. The Art Kettle. 2012. (ENG.). 86p. pap. 14.95 ***(978-1-84694-984-5(X))*** Hunt, John Publishing Ltd. GBR. Dist: National Bk. Network.

Murray, Julia K. Mirror of Morality: Chinese Narrative Illustration & Confucian Ideology. 2007. (Illus.). 194p. 60.00 *(978-0-8248-3001-4(6))* Univ. of Hawaii Pr.

Noorthoorn, Victoria, ed. Beginning with a Bang! From Confrontation to Intimacy. 2008. (David Rockefeller Center for Latin American Studies, Art Cat Ser.). (Illus.). 108p. pap. 22.95 *(978-1-879128-34-7(9))* Americas Society.

Oliver-Smith, Kerry, et al. Project Europa: Imagining the (Im)possible. 2010. (ENG., Illus.). 116p. pap. 29.95 *(978-0-9762552-9-1(4))* Univ. Pr. of Florida.

Ostertag, Bob. Creative Life: Music, Politics, People, & Machines. 2009. (ENG., Illus.). 208p. 65.00 *(978-0-252-03451-0(1))*; pap. 20.00 *(978-0-252-07646-6(X))* Univ. of Illinois Pr.

Zden Firat, Begüm & Kuryel, Aylin, eds. Cultural Activism: Practices, Dilemmas, & Possibilities. 2011 (ENG., Illus.). 261p. pap. 73.00 *(978-90-420-2981-1(1))* Rodopi.

Pavitt, Jane. Fear & Fashion in the Cold War. 2008. (ENG., Illus.). 128p. pap. 37.50 *(978-1-85177-544-6(7))* V & A Pubns. GBR. Dist: Hachette Bk. Group.

Perucci, Tony. Paul Robeson & the Cold War Performance Complex: Race, Madness, Activism. 2012. E-Book ***(978-0-472-02820-7(0))***; (ENG.). 232p. 75.00 ***(978-0-472-07168-5(8))***; (ENG.). 232p. pap. 28.95 ***(978-0-472-05168-7(7))*** Univ. of Michigan Pr.

Philipsen, Lotte. Globalizing Art. Place, Identity & Transformation. Stavning Thomsen, Bodil Marie & Ørjasæter, Kristin, eds. 2011. (ENG., Illus.). 296p. (C). pap. 48.00 ***(978-87-7934-572-0(7))*** Aarhus Universitetsforlag DNK. Dist: ISD.

Piotrowski, Piotr. In the Shadow of Yalta: Art & the Avant-garde in Eastern Europe, 1945-1989. 2011. (Illus.). 488p. pap. 30.00 *(978-1-86189-863-0(0))* Reaktion Bks., Ltd. GBR. Dist: Chicago Distribution Ctr.

—In the Shadow of Yalta: Art & the Avant-Garde in Eastern Europe, 1945-1989. Piotrowski, Piotr, tr. from POL. 2009. (ENG., Illus.). 498p. 55.00 *(978-1-86189-438-0(4))* Reaktion Bks., Ltd. GBR. Dist: Chicago Distribution Ctr.

Preziosi, Donald. Art Religion & Amnesia. 2012. (ENG.). 224p. (C). pap. 39.95 ***(978-0-415-77861-9(1))*** Routledge.

Ranciere, Jacques. Aesthetics & Its Discontents. 2009. (ENG.). 176p. 64.95 *(978-0-7456-4630-5(1))*; pap. 19.95 *(978-0-7456-4631-2(X))* Polity Pr. GBR. Dist: Wiley, John & Sons, Inc.

Rancière, Jacques. The Future of the Image. Elliott, Gregory, tr. from FRE. 2009. (ENG.). 160p. pap. 17.95 *(978-1-84467-297-4(2),* 844297) Verso Bks. GBR. Dist: Norton, W. W. & Co., Inc.

Rieff, David & Ribas, Joao. Rirkrit Tiravanija: Demonstration Drawings. 2008. (Drawing Papers). pap. 15.00 *(978-0-942324-25-9(0))* Drawing Ctr.

Robinson, Hilary. Reading Art, Reading Irigaray: The Politics of Art by Women. 2006. (ENG., Illus.). 192p. pap. 31.00 *(978-1-86064-953-0(X))* I. B. Tauris & Co., Ltd. GBR. Dist: Macmillan.

Rogers, Molly & Blight, David. Delia's Tears: Race, Science, & Photography in Nineteenth-Century America. 2010. (Illus.). 384p. 37.50 *(978-0-300-11548-2(2))* Yale Univ. Pr.

Roslak, Robyn. Neo-Impressionism & Anarchism Politics in Fin-de-Siecle France: Painting Politics & Landscape. 2007. (Illus.). 232p. 124.95 *(978-0-7546-5711-8(6))* Ashgate Publishing Co.

Ruskin, John. The Complete Works of John Ruskin, 39 vols., Set. Incl. Bible of Amiens, Valle Crucis, the Art of Enland, the Pleasurers of England. reprint ed. lib. bdg. 98.00 *(978-1-58201-373-2(X))*; Bibliography, Catalogue of Ruskin's Drawings, Addena et Corrigenda. reprint ed. lib. bdg. 98.00 *(978-1-58201-378-7(0))*; Bibliotheca Pastorum, the Economist of Xenophon, Rock Honeycomb. reprint ed. lib. bdg. 98.00 *(978-1-58201-371-8(3))*; Cestus of Aglaia, the Queen of the Air. reprint ed. lib. bdg. 98.00 *(978-1-58201-359-6(4))*; Deucalion & Other Studies in Rocks & Stones. reprint ed. lib. bdg. 98.00 *(978-1-58201-366-4(7))*; Early Prose Writings 1834-1843. 550p. reprint ed. lib. bdg. 98.00 *(978-1-58201-341-1(1))*; General Index. reprint ed. lib. bdg. 98.00 *(978-1-58201-379-4(9))*; Giotto, His Works in Padua, The Cavalli Monuments, Guide to the Academy, St. Mark's Rest. reprint ed. lib. bdg. 98.00 *(978-1-58201-364-0(0))*; Guild & Museum of St. George. reprint ed. lib. bdg. 98.00 *(978-1-58201-370-1(5))*; Harbours of England. 646p. reprint ed. lib. bdg. 98.00 *(978-1-58201-353-4(5))*; Joy Forever. 487p. reprint ed. lib. bdg. 98.00 *(978-1-58201-356-5(X))*; Lectures on Architecture & Painting. 603p. reprint ed. lib. bdg. 98.00 *(978-1-58201-352-7(7))*; Lectures on Art, Artra Pentelici. reprint ed. lib. bdg. 98.00 *(978-1-58201-360-2(8))*; Love's Meinie & Proserpina. reprint ed. lib. bdg. 98.00 *(978-1-58201-365-7(9))*; Notes on Prout & Hunt & Other Art Criticisms. 499p. reprint ed. lib. bdg. 98.00 *(978-1-58201-354-1(3))*; Poems. 541p. reprint ed. lib. bdg. 98.00 *(978-1-58201-342-8(X))*; Praeterita & Dilecta. reprint ed. lib. bdg. 98.00 *(978-1-58201-375-6(6))*; Ruskin Art Collection at Oxford. reprint ed. lib. bdg. 98.00 *(978-1-58201-361-9(6))*; Seven Lamps of Architecture. lib. bdg. 98.00 *(978-1-58201-348-0(9))*; Stones of Venice. lib. bdg. 98.00 *(978-1-58201-349-7(7))*; Storm-Cloud of the Nineteenth Century; On the Old Road; Arrows of the Chace; Ruskiniana. reprint ed. lib. bdg. 98.00 *(978-1-58201-374-9(8))*; Studies of Peasant Life, the Story of Ida, Roadside, Songs of Tuscany. reprint ed. lib. bdg. 98.00 *(978-1-58201-372-5(1))*; Unto This Last Munera Pulveris Time & Tide. 565p. reprint ed. lib. bdg. 98.00 *(978-1-58201-357-2(8))*; Val d'Arno, the Schools of Florence, Mornings in Florence, the Shepherd's Tower. reprint ed. lib. bdg. 98.00 *(978-1-58201-363-3(2))*; Pt. 1. Fors Clavigera Letters, 1-36. reprint ed. lib. bdg. 98.00 *(978-1-58201-367-1(5))*; Pt. 1. Letters of John Ruskin, 1827-1869. reprint ed. lib. bdg. 98.00 *(978-1-58201-376-3(4))*; Pt. 1. Modern Painters. 607p. reprint ed. lib. bdg. 98.00 *(978-1-58201-343-5(8))*; Pt. 2. Fors Clavigera Letters, 37-72. reprint ed. lib. bdg. 98.00 *(978-1-58201-368-8(3))*; Pt. 2. Letters of John Ruskin, 1870-1889. reprint ed. lib. bdg. 98.00 *(978-1-58201-377-0(2))*; Pt. 2. Modern Painters. 399p. reprint ed. lib. bdg. 98.00 *(978-1-58201-344-2(6))*; Pt. 2. Stones of Venice. 470p. reprint ed. lib. bdg. 98.00 *(978-1-58201-350-3(0))*; Pt. 3. Fors Clavigera Letters, 73-96. reprint ed. lib. bdg. 98.00 *(978-1-58201-369-5(1))*; Pt. 3. Modern Painters. 439p. reprint ed. lib. bdg. 98.00 *(978-1-58201-345-9(4))*; Pt. 3. Stones of Venice. 436p. reprint ed. lib. bdg. 98.00 *(978-1-58201-351-0(9))*; Pt. 4. Modern Painters. 407p. reprint ed. lib. bdg. 98.00 *(978-1-58201-346-6(2))*; Pt. 5. Modern Painters. 495p. reprint ed. lib. bdg. 98.00 *(978-1-58201-347-3(0))*; 1999. Set lib. bdg. 3822.00 o.p. *(978-1-58201-340-4(3))* Classic Bks.

—A Joy for Ever: (and Its Price in the Market) 2007. (ENG.). 138p. pap. 18.99 *(978-1-4346-3450-4(7))*; 152p. pap. 21.99 *(978-1-4346-3451-1(5))* BiblioBazaar.

Saehrendt, Christian. Kunst als Botschafter einer künstlichen Nation: Pallas Athene - 27. Studien zur Rolle der bildenden Kunst in der Auswärtigen Kulturpolitik der DDR. 2009. (Pallas Athene. Beitrage zur Universitats- und Wissenschaftsgeschichte Ser.). (GER., Illus.). 197p. (C). 52.00 *(978-3-515-09227-2(7))* Steiner, Franz Verlag Wiesbaden GmbH DEU. Dist: Brown, David Bk. Co., The.

Sardar, Ziauddin & Rasheed, Araeen, eds. Third Text: Critical Perspectives on Contemporary Art & Culture. 2007. (Illus.). 112p. per. 49.95 *(978-0-415-44117-9(X))* Taylor & Francis Group.

Sartwell, Crispin. Political Aesthetics. 2010. 272p. 35.00 *(978-0-8014-4890-4(5))* Cornell Univ. Pr.

Saxenhuber, Hedwig. Kunst + Politik / Art + Politics. 2008. (GER & ENG., Illus.). 251p. pap. 39.95 *(978-3-211-09450-0(1))* Springer Wien AUT. Dist: Actar Birkhauser Distribution.

Schmelz, Peter John. Such Freedom, If Only Musical: Unofficial Soviet Music During the Thaw. 2009. (ENG., Illus.). 432p. 65.00 *(978-0-19-534193-5(7))* Oxford Univ. Pr., Inc.

Schrank, Sarah. Art & the City: Civic Imagination & Cultural Authority in Los Angeles. (Illus.). 224p. (C). 2011. pap. 24.95 *(978-0-8122-2153-4(2))* 2008. 55.00 *(978-0-8122-4117-4(7))* Univ. of Pennsylvania Pr.

Segal, Lauren, et al. Mapping Memory: Former Prisoners Tell Their Stories. 2007. (Illus.). 136p. pap. *(978-0-620-36819-3(5))* Krut, David Publishing.

Seidel, Max & Silva, Romano. The Power of Images, the Images of Power: Lucca as an Imperial City - Political Iconography. 2008. (ENG.). 408p. 148.00 *(978-3-422-06716-5(7))* Deutscher Kunstverlag GmbH DEU. Dist: Independent Pubs. Group.

Seijdel, Jorinde & Melis, Liesbeth, eds. Open 18: 2030 War Zone Amsterdam. 2010. (ENG., Illus.). 160p. pap. 30.00 *(978-90-5662-710-2(4))* NAi Uitgevers / Publishers Stichting NLD. Dist: D.A.P./Distributed Art Pubs.

Shapiro, Michael J. Deforming American Political Thought: Ethnicity, Facticity, & Genre. 2006. (ENG., Illus.). 272p. 40.00 *(978-0-8131-2412-4(3))* Univ. Pr. of Kentucky.

Siegfried, Susan L., et al. Staging Empire: Napoleon, Ingres, & David. 2007. (ENG., Illus.). 272p. 56.95 *(978-0-271-02858-3(0))* Pennsylvania State Univ. Pr.

Silver, Larry. Marketing Maximilian: The Visual Ideology of a Holy Roman Emperor. 2008. (ENG., Illus.). 352p. (C). 59.95 *(978-0-691-13019-4(1))* Princeton Univ. Pr.

Siraganian, Lisa. Modernism's Other Work: The Art Object's Political Life, 1 vol. 2012. (ENG., Illus.). 304p. 65.00 ***(978-0-19-979655-7(6))*** Oxford Univ. Pr., Inc.

Speer, George V. Things of the Spirit: Art & Healing in the American Body Politic, 1929-1941. 2012. 258p. (C). 83.95 ***(978-1-4331-1568-4(9))*** Lang, Peter Publishing, Inc.

Steinhoff, Judith & Smith, Timothy B. Art as Politics in Late Medieval & Renaissance Siena. 2012. (Illus.). 250p. ***(978-1-4094-0066-0(2))*** Ashgate Publishing Co.

Sylvester, Christine. Art/Museums: International Relations Where We Least Expect It. 2009. (Media & Power Ser.). (Illus.). 240p. pap. 36.95 *(978-1-59451-465-4(8))* Paradigm Pubs.

Thompson, Nato. Seeing Power: Art & Activism in the Age of Cultural Production. 2012. (ENG., Illus.). 176p. pap. 21.95 *(978-1-61219-044-0(8))* Melville Hse. Publishing.

Tite, Catherine. Portraiture, Dynasty, & Power: Art Patronage in Hanoverian Britain, 1714-1759. 2010. *(978-1-60497-678-6(0))* Cambria Pr.

Truettner, William H. Painting Indians & Building Empires in North America, 1710-1840. 2010. (ENG., Illus.). 176p. 39.95 *(978-0-520-26631-5(5))* Univ. of California Pr.

Tucker, Daniel, footn. Visions for Chicago. 2011. 143p. pap. 10.00 ***(978-1-4507-7523-6(3))*** Green Lantern Pr.

Tucker, Kenneth H., Jr. Workers of the World, Enjoy! Aethetic Politics from Revolutionary Syndicalism to the Global Justice Movement. 2010. (Politics History & Social Chan Ser.). (ENG.). 224p. 61.50 *(978-1-59213-764-0(4))* Temple Univ. Pr.

Unger, Daniel M. Guercino's Piantings & His Patrons' Politics in Early Modern Italy. 2010. (Visual Culture in Early Modernity Ser.). (Illus.). 212p. 124.95 *(978-0-7546-6909-8(2))* Ashgate Publishing Co.

Van Dijk, Maite, et al. Sculptuur Studies 2006. 2007. (ENG., Illus.). 160p. pap. 30.00 *(978-90-400-8258-0(8))* Waanders B.V., Uitgeverij NLD. Dist: National Bk. Network.

Virilio, Paul. Art as Far as the Eye Can See. Rose, Julie, tr. from FRE. 2010. (ENG.). 1p. pap. 18.95 *(978-1-84788-540-1(3))* Berg Pubs. GBR. Dist: Macmillan.

Volk, Gregory & Russ, Sabine, texts. Carnival Within. An Exhibition Made in America: Discover Us! 2010. (ENG., Illus.). 298p. pap. 42.00 *(978-3-941185-20-3(9))* Verlag fur Moderne Kunst DEU. Dist: D.A.P./Distributed Art Pubs.

Wells, Rachel. Scale in Contemporary Sculpture: Enlargement, Miniaturisation & the Life-Size. 2012. (Illus.). 208p. ***(978-1-4094-3194-7(0))*** Ashgate Publishing, Ltd.

Williams, Gregory H. Permission to Laugh: Humor & Politics in Contemporary German Art. 2012. (ENG., Illus.). 248p. 49.00 ***(978-0-226-89895-7(4))*** Univ. of Chicago Pr.

Williams, Raymond. Politics of Modernism: Against the New Conformists. 2007. (Radical Thinkers Ser.: Vol. 23). (ENG.). 208p. per. 12.95 *(978-1-84467-580-7(7)*, 844580) Verso Bks. GBR. Dist: Norton, W. W. & Co., Inc.

Winegar, Jessica. Creative Reckonings: The Politics of Art & Culture in Contemporary Egypt. 2006. (Stanford Studies in Middle Eastern & Islamic Societies & Cultures). (ENG., Illus.). 416p. 70.00 *(978-0-8047-5476-7(4))*; per. 26.95 *(978-0-8047-5477-4(2))* Stanford Univ. Pr.

Wylie, Diana. Art & Revolution: The Life & Death of Thami Mnyele, South African Artist. 2008. (Reconsiderations in Southern African History Ser.). (ENG., Illus.). 264p. (C). (gr. 13-17). pap. 25.00 *(978-0-8139-2764-0(1))* Univ. Pr. of Virginia.

Yonan, Michael Elia. Empress Maria Theresa & the Politics of Habsburg Imperial Art. 2011. (ENG., Illus.). 232p. 90.00 *(978-0-271-03722-6(9))* Pennsylvania State Univ. Pr.

Zarobell, John. Empire of Landscape: Space & Ideology in French Colonial Algeria. 2009. (ENG., Illus.). 240p. 95.00 *(978-0-271-03443-0(2))* Pennsylvania State Univ. Pr.

ART—PRICES

see also Art—Catalogs; Art As an Investment; Prices
also Painting—Prices, and similar headings

Diederichsen, Diedrich, text. On Surplus Value. 2008. (ENG., Illus.). 128p. pap. 10.00 *(978-90-73362-81-9(4))* Witte De With Centre for Contemporary Art NLD. Dist: D.A.P./Distributed Art Pubs.

Findlay, Michael. The Value of Art: Money, Power, Beauty. 2012. (Illus.). 208p. 29.95 ***(978-3-7913-4638-0(5))*** Prestel Publishing.

ART—PRIVATE COLLECTIONS

Abaza, Mona. Collecting Modern Egyptian Art: Sherwet Shafei & the Pioneer Painters of the Twentieth Century. 2011. (ENG.). 208p. 49.50 *(978-977-416-394-4(X))* American Univ. in Cairo Pr. EGY. Dist: Oxford Univ. Pr., Inc.

Ackley, Clifford, et al, texts. Splendor & Elegance. 2009. (ENG., Illus.). 160p. 55.00 *(978-0-87846-738-9(6))* Museum of Fine Arts, Boston.

Allen, Brian, et al. Paul Mellon's Legacy: A Passion for British Art. 2007. (ENG., Illus.). 348p. 65.00 *(978-0-300-11746-2(9))* Yale Univ. Pr.

American Art Association. Gothic & Renaissance Art: The Collection of the Late Thomas Fortune Ryan. 2011. 38p. 35.95 ***(978-1-258-02381-2(4))*** Literary Licensing, LLC.

Andera, Margaret & Stone, Lisa. Accidental Genius: Art from the Anthony Petullo Collection. 2012. ***(978-0-944110-97-3(5))***; (Illus.). 215p. pap. ***(978-3-7913-6405-6(7))*** Milwaukee Art Museum.

Anspach, Isabelle, contrib. by. Museum & Gardens van Buuren. 2012. (ENG., Illus.). 128p. 34.00 *(978-90-6153-771-7(1))* Mercatorfonds N. V. BEL. Dist: D.A.P./Distributed Art Pubs.

Antille, Emmanuelle, et al. Swiss Made: The Art of Falling Apart. 2006. (ENG & DUT., Illus.). 96p. pap. 35.00 *(978-90-400-9078-3(5))* Waanders B.V., Uitgeverij NLD. Dist: National Bk. Network.

Art Works. 2011. (ENG., Illus.). 256p. pap. 55.00 ***(978-3-7757-2777-8(9))*** Hatje Cantz Verlag GmbH & Co KG DEU. Dist: D.A.P./Distributed Art Pubs.

Austin, Reid. Alberto Vargas: Works from the Max Vargas Collection. 2006. (ENG., Illus.). 144p. 45.00 *(978-0-8212-5792-0(7))* Bulfinch.

Avril, Ellen. Ancient Artistry: Pre-Chinese Ceramics & Jades from the Shatzman Collection. 2006. (Illus.). 55p. pap. 15.00 *(978-0-9646042-2-3(1))* Cornell Univ., Herbert F. Johnson Museum of Art.

Bailey, Sheldon. 180. 2008. pap. *(978-0-9792142-1-9(1))* BE-YOU-tiful MYnd Pubns.

Baillio, Joseph. The Odyssey Continues: Masterworks from the New Orleans Museum of Art & from provate New Orleans Collections. 2006. per. 45.00 *(978-0-9657856-3-1(7))* Wildenstein & Co., Inc.

Baldessari, John. John Baldessari: A Print Retrospective from the Collections of Jordan D. Schnitzer & his Family Foundation. 2010. (ENG., Illus.). 160p. 59.95 *(978-1-935202-10-3(3))* D.A.P./Distributed Art Pubs.

Bargna, Ivan & Parodi da Passano, M. Giovanna. L'Africa Delle Meraviglie: Arti Africane Nelle Collezioni Italiane = the Wonders of Africa: African Arts in Italian Collections. 2011. (ITA & ENG., Illus.). 204p. pap. 60.00 ***(978-88-366-1949-8(5))*** Silvana ITA. Dist: D.A.P./Distributed Art Pubs.

Barilleaux, Rene Paul. Tom Slick: International Art Collector: An Exhibition. 2009. *(978-0-916677-53-4(2))* McNay, Marion Koogler Art Museum.

Baskett, John. Paul Mellon's Legacy: A Passion for British Art Masterpieces from the Yale Center for British Art. 2007. *(978-0-9790378-0-1(8))*; pap. *(978-1-905711-02-4(6))* Yale Ctr. for British Art.

Bear, Jordan, et al. Mannerism & Modernism: The Kasper Collection. 2011. *(978-0-87598-156-7(9))* Giles, D. Ltd.

Belli, Gabriella & Panza di Biumo, Giuseppe, texts. Conceptual Art. 2011. (ITA & ENG., Illus.). 144p. pap. 50.00 *(978-88-366-1820-0(0))* Silvana ITA. Dist: D.A.P./Distributed Art Pubs.

Birnie, Annabelle. Art in the Office. 2007. (ENG., Illus.). 240p. 45.00 *(978-90-400-8255-9(3))* Waanders B.V., Uitgeverij NLD. Dist: National Bk. Network.

Bonami, Francesco. Spirit & Space: Sandretto Re Rebaudengo Collection. 2011. (ENG., Illus.). 200p. pap. 43.00 ***(978-84-92441-36-5(4))*** T.F. Editores ESP. Dist: National Bk. Network.

Borchardt-Hume, Achim, text. Keeping It Real: From the Ready-Made to the Everyday. 2011. (ENG., Illus.). 132p. pap. 35.00 *(978-0-85488-181-9(6))* Whitechapel Art Gallery GBR. Dist: D.A.P./Distributed Art Pubs.

Brettell, Richard R. & Dickerson, C. D., III. From the Private Collections of Texas: European Art, Ancient to Modern. 2010. (Illus.). 456p. 65.00 *(978-0-300-14494-9(6))* Kimbell Art Museum.

Brettell, Richard R. & Dickerson, C. D. From the Private Collections of Texas: European Art, Ancient to Modern. 2009. (Illus.). xv, 455p. pap. *(978-0-912804-51-4(3))* Kimbell Art Museum.

Brettell, Richard R., et al. The Metropolitan Museum of Art Vol. 3: Nineteenth - And Twentieth - Century Paintings. 2010. (ENG., Illus.). 496p. (C). 125.00 *(978-0-691-14536-5(9))* Princeton Univ. Pr.

Brock, Charles, et al. American Modernism: The Shein Collection. 2010. *(978-0-89468-365-7(9))* National Gallery of Art.

Brown, Kendall H. Deco Japan: Shaping Art & Culture, 1920-1945. 2012. ***(978-0-88397-157-4(7))*** Art Services International.

Brusic, Robert M. & Evenrud, Jerry. And Grace Will Lead Me Home: The Jerry Evenrud Collection of Images of the Parable of the Prodigal Son. 2007. (ENG., Illus.). 200p. 40.00 *(978-1-932688-18-4(8)*, Lutheran Univ. Pr.) Kirk Hse. Pubs.

Burns, James D. Celestial Gardens: Nature, Art & the Textiles of Persia. 2011. (ENG., Illus.). 383p. 225.00 ***(978-1-884167-23-2(3))*** Umbrage Editions.

Buvelot, Quentin. Made in Holland: Highlights from the Collection of Eijk & Rose-Marie de Mol Van Otterloo. 2011. 152p. pap. 50.00 *(978-90-400-7744-9(4))* Waanders B.V., Uitgeverij NLD. Dist: National Bk. Network.

Cameron, Dan, et al. ArtWorks: The Progressive Collection, 1 vol. 2007. (ENG., Illus.). 292p. 55.00 *(978-1-933045-72-6(8))* D.A.P./Distributed Art Pubs.

Campbell, Sara. Collector without Walls: Norton Simon & His Hunt for the Best. 2010. (Illus.). 260p. 65.00 *(978-0-9726681-8-7(7))* Norton Simon Museum.

Campbell, Thomas P. Henry VIII & the Art of Majesty: Tapestries at the Tudor Court. 2007. (ENG., Illus.). 440p. 75.00 *(978-0-300-12234-3(9))* Yale Univ. Pr.

Cantini, Lorenzo & Michelli, Carla. La Raccolta D'arte Esso: 1949-1983. 2007. (ITA & ENG., Illus.). 299p. 75.00 *(978-88-370-5687-2(7))* Electa ITA. Dist: Trans-Atlantic Pubns., Inc.

Carlano, Annie. Contemporary British Studio Ceramics. 2010. (ENG., Illus.). 224p. 60.00 *(978-0-300-16719-1(9))* Yale Univ. Pr.

Carrillo, Charles M. & Steele, Thomas J. A Century of Retablos: The Janis & Dennis Lyon Collection of New Mexican Santos, 1780-1880. 2007. (ENG., Illus.). 242p. 60.00 *(978-1-55595-273-0(9))* Hudson Hills Pr. LLC.

Cartwright, Derrick R. & Brown, Bill. Personal Views: Regarding Private Collections in San Diego. 2006. *(978-0-937108-39-0(1))* San Diego Museum of Art.

Casper, Jens & Shryen, Annette, texts. Boros Collection. 2010. (ENG., Illus.). 198p. 75.00 *(978-3-7757-2478-4(8))* Hatje Cantz Verlag GmbH & Co KG DEU. Dist: D.A.P./Distributed Art Pubs.

Chicuri, Abelardo Mena, et al. Cuba Avant-Garde: Contemporary Cuban Art from the Farber Collection / Arte Contemporaneo Cubano de la Coleccion Farber. Delson, Susan, ed. Lizarraga, Felix, tr. 2007. (SPA & ENG., Illus.). 188p. pap. 29.95 *(978-0-9762552-5-3(1))* Univ. Pr. of Florida.

—Cuba Avant-Garde: Contemporary Cuban Art from the Farber Collection /Arte Contemporaneo Cubano de la Coleccion Farber. Delson, Susan, ed. Lizarraga, Felix, tr. 2007. (SPA & ENG., Illus.). 188p. 59.95 *(978-0-9762552-4-6(3))* Univ. Pr. of Florida.

Chong, Alan & Murai, Noriko. Journeys East: Isabella Stewart Gardner & Asia. 2009. (Illus.). 420p. pap. 75.00 *(978-1-934772-75-1(5))* Periscope Publishing.

Clifton, James & Scatone, Leslie M. The Plains of Mars: European War Prints, 1500-1825, from the Collection of the Sarah Campbell Blaffer Foundation. 2009. pap. *(978-0-89090-167-0(8))* Yale Univ. Pr.

Coetzee, Mark & Lagos, Luisa. Memorials of Identity: New Media from the Rubell Family Collection. 2009. (ENG., Illus.). 175p. 30.00 *(978-0-9716341-8-3(1))* Rubell Family Collection.

Cork, Richard & Martin, Elliott Zooey. End Game: British Contemporary Art from the Chaney Family Collection. 2008. (ENG., Illus.). 80p. pap. 14.95 *(978-0-300-14201-3(3))* Museum of Fine Arts, Houston.

Critchley, Simon, et al, texts. The Luminous Interval. 2011. (ENG., Illus.). 207p. 49.95 *(978-0-89207-412-9(4))* Guggenheim, Solomon R. Museum.

Cunningham, C. c. Religious Art of the Middle Ages & Renaissance. 2011. 50p. 35.95 ***(978-1-258-03699-7(1))*** Literary Licensing, LLC.

De Long, David G., ed. Sunnylands: Art & Architecture of the Annenberg Estate in Rancho Mirage, California. 2009. (Illus.). 200p. 34.95 *(978-0-8122-4161-7(4))* Univ. of Pennsylvania Pr.

De Montclos, Brigitte. Moscow: Splendours of the Romanovs. 2009. (ENG., Illus.). 304p. 50.00 *(978-88-572-0256-3(9))* Skira Editore ITA. Dist: Random Hse., Inc.

De Nicolay-Mazery, Christiane. The Yves Saint Laurent-Pierre Berge Collection: The Sale of the Century. 2009. (ENG., Illus.). 320p. 95.00 *(978-2-08-030130-7(6))* Flammarion et Cie FRA. Dist: Random Hse., Inc.

De Pillis, Mario S. & Goodwillie, Christian. Gather up the Fragments: The Andrews Shaker Collection. 2008. (ENG., Illus.). 400p. 75.00 *(978-0-300-13760-6(5))* Yale Univ. Pr.

de Waal, Edmund. A Hare with Amber Eyes: A Family's Century of Art & Loss. 2010. (ENG., Illus.). 368p. 26.00 *(978-0-374-10597-6(9))* Farrar, Straus & Giroux.

—The Hare with Amber Eyes: A Hidden Inheritance. 2011. (ENG., Illus.). 368p. pap. 16.00 *(978-0-312-56937-2(8))* Picador.

Dehan, Amy Miller. Outside the Ordinary: Contemporary Art in Glass, Wood, & Ceramics from the Wolf Collection. 2009. (ENG.). 176p. pap. 30.00 *(978-0-8214-1861-1(0))* Ohio Univ. Pr.

Denver Museum of Art Staff, ed. Sweet on the West: How Candy Built a Colorado Treasure. 2008. (ENG.). 80p. pap. 10.95 *(978-0-8061-9969-6(5))* Denver Art Museum.

Dervaux, Isabelle & Flavin, Dan. Dan Flavin: Drawing. 2012. ***(978-0-87598-162-8(3))*** Giles, D. Ltd.

Diaz de León, Francisco. Francisco Díaz de León. 2011. (ENG., Illus.). 160p. 45.00 *(978-84-936123-6-8(7))* RM Verlag, S.L. ESP. Dist: D.A.P./Distributed Art Pubs.

Dolkart, Judith F., et al. Masterworks - The Barnes Foundation. 2012. (ENG., Illus.). 374p. 40.00 ***(978-0-8478-3806-6(4)***, Skira) Rizzoli International Pubns., Inc.

Dorigato, Attilia. Murano: Island of Glass. 2006. (ENG., Illus.). 60.00 *(978-88-7743-293-3(4))* Arsenale Editrice SRL ITA. Dist: Antique Collectors' Club.

Dubois, Hughes, photos by. Solomon Islands Art: The Conru Collection. 2008. (ENG., Illus.). 256p. 125.00 *(978-88-7439-493-7(4))* 5 Continents ITA. Dist: Hachette Bk. Group.

Dunkley, Tina Maria & Cullum, Jerry. In the Eye of the Muses: Selections from the Clark Atlanta University Art Collection. 2012. ***(978-0-615-59005-9(5))*** Massachusetts College of Art.

Duparc, Frederik J., et al. Golden: Dutch & Flemish Masterworks from the Rose-Marie & Eijk Van Otterloo Collection. 2011. (Illus.). 404p. ***(978-0-87577-222-6(6))*** Peabody Essex Museum.

Ebrey, Patricia Buckley. Accumulating Culture: The Collections of Emperor Huizong. 2008. (ENG., Illus.). 576p. 65.00 *(978-0-295-98778-1(2))* Univ. of Washington Pr.

Eccles, Tom, frwd. At Home/Not at Home. 2010. (ENG., Illus.). 168p. 40.00 *(978-1-936192-07-6(1))* Ctr. for Curatorial Studies, The.

Eitel, Rhoda, intro. The Thaw Collection of Master Drawings: Acquisitions since 2002. 2009. *(978-0-87598-153-6(4))* Pierpont Morgan Library.

Eshoo, Amy, ed. 560 Broadway: A New York Drawing Collection at Work, 1991-2006. 2008. (ENG., Illus.). 200p. 45.00 *(978-0-300-13539-8(4))* Yale Univ. Pr.

Farrell, Jennifer. Get There First, Decide Promptly: The Richard Brown Baker Collection of Postwar Art. 2012. (ENG., Illus.). 372p. 50.00 *(978-0-300-15302-6(3))* Yale Univ. Art Gallery.

Frederick R. Weisman Art Foundation Collection. 2007. *(978-0-9740908-1-8(6))* Weisman, Frederick R. Philanthropic Foundation.

Gasparri, Carlo, ed. Le Sculture Farnese. 2010. (ITA.). 368p. 135.00 *(978-88-510-0607-5(5))* Electa ITA. Dist: Trans-Atlantic Pubns., Inc.

Gingeras, Alison M. Sequence 1: Painting & Sculpture from the François Pinault Collection. 2008. (FRE, ITA & ENG., Illus.). 328p. 75.00 *(978-88-6130-206-8(8))* Skira Editore ITA. Dist: Random Hse., Inc.

Gordon-Levitt, Joseph. The Tiny Book of Tiny Stories, Vol. 1. 2011. (Tiny Book of Tiny Stories Ser.: Vol. 1). (ENG.). 64p. 14.99 ***(978-0-06-212166-0(9))*** HarperCollins Pubs.

Green, Nancy E. Joie de Vivre: Art Nouveau & Art Deco Ceramics from the Shatzman Collection. 2009. (Illus.). 71p. *(978-1-934260-10-4(X))* Cornell Univ., Herbert F. Johnson Museum of Art.

Gunn, Michael, contrib. by. From the South Seas: Oceanic Art from the Teel Collection, 1 vol. 2006. (ENG., Illus.). 192p. (gr. 13-18). 50.00 *(978-0-87846-697-9(5))* Museum of Fine Arts, Boston.

Gurney, George. Variations on America: Masterworks of the American Art Forum, Smithsonian American Art Museum. 2008. *(978-0-9790678-0-8(4))* Smithsonian American Art Museum.

Gurney, George, et al. Variations on America: Masterworks from American Art Forum Collections. 2006. (ENG., Illus.). 192p. 30.00 *(978-1-904832-42-3(3))* Giles, D. Ltd. GBR. Dist: Antique Collectors' Club.

Haase, Claus-Peter. A Collector's Fortune, Islamic Art. 2007. 132p. 49.00 *(978-3-7774-4085-9(X))* Hirmer Verlag GmbH DEU. Dist: Chicago Distribution Ctr.

Haniel, Franz, ed. The Haniel Collection. 2011. (ENG., Illus.). 320p. 89.00 ***(978-3-8030-3351-2(9))*** Wasmuth, Ernst J. Verlag GmbH & Co. DEU. Dist: D.A.P./Distributed Art Pubs.

Hanzal, Carla M. Contemporary, Cool & Collected. 2007. *(978-0-9762300-3-8(8))* Mint Museum, The.

Hargraves, Matthew & Ryskamp, Charles. Varieties of Romantic Experience: Drawings from the Collection of Charles Ryskamp. 2010. (ENG., Illus.). 344p. 75.00 *(978-0-300-15292-0(2))* Yale Ctr. for British Art.

Hartop, Christopher. A Noble Pursuit: English Silver from the Rita Gans Collection at the Virginia Museum of Fine Arts. 2011. (ENG., Illus.). 88p. (gr. 17). pap. 25.00 *(978-0-917046-90-2(0))* Univ. Pr. of Virginia.

—A Noble Pursuit: English Silver from the Rita Gans Collection at the Virginia Museum of Fine Arts. 2010. *(978-0-917046-91-9(9))* Virginia Museum of Fine Arts.

Hayward, Maria. The 1542 Inventory of Whitehall: The Palace & Its Keeper, 2 vols. 2006. (ENG., Illus.). 624p. (C). 320.00 *(978-0-9547916-0-5(6))* Illuminata Publishers GBR. Dist: Brown, David Bk. Co., The.

Hellandsjo, Karin. The Erling Neby Collection. 2011. (ENG., Illus.). 240p. 80.00 *(978-88-572-0862-6(1))* Skira Editore ITA. Dist: Random Hse., Inc.

Heller, Ena. Icons or Portraits. 2007. (Illus.). 283p. 60.00 *(978-1-58516-682-4(0))* American Bible Society.

Hess, Donald & Steiner, Myrtha, texts. Hess Art Collection. 2010. (ENG., Illus.). 372p. 60.00 *(978-3-7757-2139-4(8))* Hatje Cantz Verlag GmbH & Co KG DEU. Dist: D.A.P./Distributed Art Pubs.

Hicks, Alistar. Contemporary Art at Deutsche Bank. (Illus.). 167p. 39.95 *(978-3-89322-825-6(X))* Edition Cantz DEU. Dist: D.A.P./Distributed Art Pubs.

Higonnet, Anne. A Musem of One's Own: Private Collecting, Public Gift. 2010. (Illus.). 260p. 49.95 *(978-1-934772-92-8(5))* Periscope Publishing.

Hinrichs, Kit & Hirasuna, Delphine. 100 American Flags: A Unique Collection of Old Glory Memorabilia. 2008. (ENG., Illus.). 112p. 19.95 *(978-1-58008-920-3(8))* Ten Speed Pr.

Hinton, Jack. The Art of German Stoneware, 1300-1900, from the Charles W. Nichols Collection & the Philadelphia Museum of Art. 2012. ***(978-0-87633-236-8(X))*** Philadelphia Museum of Art.

Hirschland, Ellen B. & Ramage, Nancy. The Cone Sisters of Baltimore: Collecting at Full Tilt. 2008. (ENG., Illus.). 352p. 34.95 *(978-0-8101-2481-3(5))* Northwestern Univ. Pr.

Hofer, Candida. Candida Hofer: on Kawara, Date Paintings in Private Collections. 2009. (ENG., Illus.). 256p. 95.00 *(978-3-86560-530-6(3))* Verlag der Buchhandlung Walther Konig DEU. Dist: D.A.P./Distributed Art Pubs.

Hughes, Eleanor & Trumble, Angus. The Independent Eye: Contemporary British Art from the Collection of Samuel & Gabrielle Lurie. 2010. (Illus.). 144p. 65.00 *(978-0-300-17139-6(0))* Yale Ctr. for British Art.

Humphries, Lund, et al. Collectors in St Petersburg. 2007. (Illus.). 128p. 40.00 *(978-0-85331-960-3(X)*, Lund Humphries Pubs.) Ashgate Publishing, Ltd. GBR. Dist: Ashgate Publishing Co.

Imperato, Gavin H. & Imperato, Pascal James. Bundu, Sowei Headpieces of the Sande Society of West Africa: The Imperato Family Collection. 2012. ***(978-1-936658-10-7(0))*** Kilima Hse. Pubs.

Inselmann, Andrea. A Private Eye: Dada, Surrealism, & More from the Brandt Collection. 2006. (Illus.). 160p. pap. 25.00 *(978-0-9646042-3-0(X))* Cornell Univ., Herbert F. Johnson Museum of Art.

The James T. Bialac Collection: Selected Works. 2012. ***(978-0-8061-4299-9(5))***; pap. ***(978-0-8061-4304-0(5))*** Univ. of Oklahoma Pr.

Joralemon, Peter David, et al. At the Heart of Precolumbian America. 2008. (ENG., Illus.). 264p. 65.00 *(978-88-7439-064-9(5))* 5 Continents ITA. Dist: Hachette Bk. Group.

Joyner, Brooks. Legends of the West: The Foxley Collection. 2006. *(978-0-936364-34-6(3))* Joslyn Art Museum.

Kaeppler, Adrienne L. & Kaeppler, Adrienne Lois. Polynesia: The Mark & Carolyn Blackburn Collection of Polynesian Art. 2010. (Illus.). xxxv, 410p. ***(978-1-883528-38-6(0))*** Ai Pohaku Pr.

Kaeppler, Adrienne Lois. Polynesia: The Mark & Carolyn Blackburn Collection of Polynesian Art. 2010. (Illus.). xxxv, 410p. ***(978-1-883528-40-9(2))*** Ai Pohaku Pr.

Kelley, Jeff. Half-Life of a Dream: Contemporary Chinese Art from the Logan Collection. 2008. (Illus.). 144p. 40.00 *(978-0-520-25779-5(0))* Univ. of California Pr.

Kerin, Melissa R. Artful Beneficence: Materials & Meanings of Himalayan Art: Selections from the David Nalin Himalayan Art Collection. 2009. *(978-0-9772131-5-3(3))* Serindia Pubns., Inc.

Kerkhoven, Ronald A. R. & Museum van der Togt, contrib. by. Beauties, Beasts, & Birds: Corneille & His Collection of African Art. (Illus.). 103p. *(978-90-6825-222-4(4))* Uniepers B.V./Denis.

Kinsey, Bernard W. & Kinsey, Shirley Pooler. The Kinsey Collection, Collectors Edition: Shared Treasures of Bernard & Shirley Kinsey: Where Art & History Intersect. 2010. (Illus.). 160p. 99.95 *(978-0-9826225-1-3(1))* Allen, Charles Imaging Experts.

Koella, Rudolf, et al, texts. The Arthur & Hedy Hahnloser Collection: An Eye for Art Shared with Artists. 2011. (ENG., Illus.). 384p. 75.00 ***(978-1-935202-63-9(4))*** D.A.P./Distributed Art Pubs.

Koons, Jeff, ed. Skin Fruit: A View of a Collection. 2012. (ENG., Illus.). 92p. pap. 25.00 ***(978-1-935202-77-6(4))*** Deste Foundation GRC. Dist: D.A.P./Distributed Art Pubs.

Kürti, Emese. Bukarest-Budapest Híd: Kortárs Román és Magyar Muvészet: Hunya Gábor Gyujteménye. 2010. (HUN & ENG., Illus.). 216p. 24.95 ***(978-963-9731-89-9(7))*** Vince Kiado Kft HUN. Dist: Independent Pubs. Group.

Lange, Christiane, text. Ludwig Mies Van der Rohe & Lilly Reich: Furniture & Interiors, 1 vol. 2007. (ENG., Illus.). 208p. 55.00 *(978-3-7757-1921-6(0))* Hatje Cantz Verlag GmbH & Co KG DEU. Dist: D.A.P./Distributed Art Pubs.

Lange, Christiane & Diederen, Roger, eds. Das Ewige Auge: Von Rembrandt bis Picasso. Meisterwerke der Sammlung Jan Krugier und Marie-Anne Krugier-Poniatowski. 2007. (GER., Illus.). 511p. (C). 56.00 *(978-3-7774-3695-1(X))* Hirmer Verlag GmbH DEU. Dist: Brown, David Bk. Co., The.

Leber, Christina. Kunstsammlungen in deutschen Wirtschaftsunternehmen im Zeitraum zwischen 1965 Und 2000: Eine Untersuchung der Sammlungsmodelle der HERTA GmbH, der Tetra Pak Rausing & Co. KG, der Deutsche Bank AG, der Adolf Würth GmbH & Co. KG sowie der DG BANK

Deutsche Genossenschaftsbank AG. 2008. (Europäische Hochschulschriften. Reihe 28: Kunstgeschichte Ser.). (GER.). 408p. pap. 99.95 *(978-3-631-55431-9(1))* Lang, Peter GmbH, Europäischer Verlag der Wissenschaften DEU. Dist: Lang, Peter.

Lynch, K. Kachina Carvings: My Personal Collection. 2009. (Illus.). 102p. pap. 38.95 *(978-1-4327-4695-7(2))* Outskirts Pr., Inc.

MacAdam, Barbara J., ed. Embracing Elegance, 1885-1920: American Art from the Huber Family Collection. 2011. (Illus.). 116p. pap. 24.95 *(978-0-944722-41-1(5))* Hood Museum of Art.

Manoguerra, Paul, et al, contrib. by. Amazing Grace: Self-Taught Artists from the Mullis Collection. 2007. (ENG.). 162p. 48.00 *(978-0-915977-63-5(X))* Univ. of Georgia, Georgia Museum of Art.

Markin, Tracy Kamenstein. The Markin Collection. 2007. (Illus.). 443p. *(978-0-9793194-0-2(4))* ToTo The Outsider Pub.

McClusky, Pamela. Ancestral Modern: Australian Aboriginal Art. 2012. (ENG., Illus.). 176p. 50.00 ***(978-0-300-18003-9(9))*** Yale Univ. Pr.

McCombs, W. Douglas, ed. Horsing Around: 19th Century Cast Iron Hitching Posts. 2008. (Albany Institute of History & Art Ser.). (Illus.). 76p. pap. 26.95 *(978-0-939072-17-0(3),* Suny Pr.) State Univ. of New York Pr.

McCullagh, Suzanne Folds, ed. Gray Collection: Seven Centuries of Art. 2010. (Illus.). 224p. 50.00 *(978-0-300-16626-2(5))* Art Institute of Chicago.

Melissa Richardson Banks Staff, ed. Papel Chicano: Works on Paper from the Collection of Cheech Marin. 2007. 96p. 24.99 *(978-0-9724735-5-2(6))* La Mano Pr.

Mentasti, Rosa Barovier, ed. Exquisite Glass Ornaments: The Nineteenth-Century Glass Revival. 2011. (ENG., Illus.). 124p. 39.50 *(978-88-317-0650-6(0))* Marsilio Editori spa ITA. Dist: Random Hse., Inc.

Miniaturensammlung Tansey, ed. Miniaturen des Rokoko aus der Sammlung Tansey. 2008. (GER., Illus.). 428p. (C). 119.00 *(978-3-7774-4335-5(2))* Hirmer Verlag GmbH DEU. Dist: Brown, David Bk. Co., The.

Minimalism and After Staff. Minimalism & After: Tradition und Tendenzen minimalistischer Kunst von 1950 bis heute. Wiehager, Renate, ed. 2010. (ENG., Illus.). 632p. 95.00 *(978-3-7757-2386-2(2))* Hatje Cantz Verlag GmbH & Co KG DEU. Dist: D.A.P./Distributed Art Pubs.

Morton, Mary, ed. Oudry's Painted Menagerie: Portraits of Exotic Animals in Eighteenth-Century France. 2007. 192p. (ENG.). 60.00 *(978-0-89236-879-2(9));* (Illus.). pap. 40.00 *(978-0-89236-889-1(6))* Oxford Univ. Pr., Inc.

Mossinger, Ingrid & Drechsel, Kerstin, eds. Wolfgang Mattheuer: The Prints-the Hartmut Koch Donation. 2010. (ENG., Illus.). 256p. 78.00 ***(978-3-86832-034-3(2))*** Wienand GmbH, Druck- & Verlagshaus DEU. Dist: Independent Pubs. Group.

Muntean, Marcus & Rosenblum, Adi. Muntean/Rosenblum: Make Death Listen, 1 vol. Bovier, Lionel, ed. 2007. (ENG., Illus.). 182p. pap. 45.00 *(978-3-905701-98-2(7))* JRP Ringier Kunstverlag AG CHE. Dist: D.A.P./Distributed Art Pubs.

Newbery, Timothy. The Robert Lehman Collection XIII: Frames. 2007. (ENG., Illus.). 520p. (C). 125.00 *(978-0-691-13483-3(9))* Princeton Univ. Pr.

Nisbet, Peter & Feininger, Lyonel. Lyonel Feininger: Drawings & Watercolors from the William S. Lieberman Bequest to the Busch-Reisinger Museum. 2011. *(978-1-891771-54-5(X))* Hatje Cantz Verlag GmbH & Co KG.

—Lyonel Feininger: Drawings & Watercolors from the William S. Lieberman Bequest to the Busch-Reisinger Museum. 2011. (ENG., Illus.). 144p. 45.00 *(978-3-7757-2787-7(6))* Hatje Cantz Verlag GmbH & Co KG DEU. Dist: D.A.P./Distributed Art Pubs.

Noelle, Alexander J., ed. American Reflections: The Collection of Dr. Timothy Mclaughlin. 2011. (Illus.). 80p. pap. 19.95 *(978-0-9724497-0-0(1))* New Britain Museum of American Art.

Oetker, Brigitte & Oetker, Arend, eds. The Collection of Brigitte & Arend Oetker. 2009. (ENG., Illus.). 176p. 59.95 *(978-3-86560-525-2(7))* Verlag der Buchhandlung Walther Konig DEU. Dist: D.A.P./Distributed Art Pubs.

Oettinger, Marion, Jr. Folk Treasures of Mexico: The Nelson A. Rockefeller Collection. rev. ed. 2010. 224p. 39.95 *(978-1-55885-595-3(5))* Arte Publico Pr.

Okada, Koichiro, et al. Masters of Bamboo: Artistic Lineages in the Lloyd Cotsen Japanese Basket Collection. 2008. (ENG., Illus.). 144p. pap. 25.00 *(978-0-939117-40-6(1))* Asian Art Museum of San Francisco.

Parr, Martin & Weski, Thomas. Parrworld, 2 vols. 2008. (Illus.). *(978-1-57110-593-3(6))* Aperture Foundation, Inc.

Passion Bild: Russische Kunst seit 1970. 2010. (Illus.). 280p. 171.00 ***(978-3-85881-199-8(8))*** Scheidegger und Spiess AG, Verlag CHE. Dist: Antique Collectors' Club.

Paul, Carole. The Borghese Collections & the Display of Art in the Age of the Grand Tour. 2008. (Illus.). 358p. 134.95 *(978-0-7546-6134-4(2))* Ashgate Publishing Co.

Petullo, Anthony. Art Without Category: British & Irish Art from the Anthony Petullo Collection. 2009. (Illus.). 84p. *(978-1-60743-122-0(X))* Independent Pub.

Phillips, Lisa, text. Skin Fruit. 2010. (ENG., Illus.). 208p. pap. 45.00 *(978-1-935202-19-6(7))* New Museum of Contemporary Art, The.

Powell, Katie Tierney. Capturing the Sublime: Italian Drawings of the Renaissance & Baroque. McCullagh, Suzanne Folds, ed. 2012. (ENG., Illus.). 312p. 65.00 ***(978-0-300-17970-5(7))*** Art Institute of Chicago.

Proud, Hayden. Revisions+ Expanding the Narrative of South African Art - The Campbell Smith Collection. 2nd ed. 2008. (Illus.). 104p. pap. 43.00 *(978-1-874817-36-9(7))* Unisa Press / Uitgewers GBR. Dist: International Specialized Bk. Services.

Quintanilla, Faustino. A Life for Art: The Jaime Andrade Collection. 2011. ***(978-1-936658-07-7(0))*** QCC Art Gallery.

Reents-Budet, Dorie. Passionate Journey: The Grice Collection of Native American Art. 2009. *(978-0-9762300-6-9(2))* Mint Museum, The.

Rennert, Jack. Posters of the Belle Epoque: The Wine Spectator Collection. 2007. (ENG., Illus.). 222p. 75.00 *(978-0-7570-0064-5(9))* Square One Pubs.

Rewald, Sabine & Dabrowski, Magdalena. The American Matisse: The Dealer, His Artists, His Collection. 2010. (ENG., Illus.). 208p. 60.00 *(978-0-300-15510-5(7))* Yale Univ. Pr.

Rhie, Marylin & Thurman, Robert. A Shrine for Tibet: The Alice S. Kandell Collection of Tibetan Sacred Art. 2010. (ENG.). 336p. (gr. 12). 60.00 *(978-1-59020-310-1(0))* Overlook Pr., The.

Rhie, Marylin M. & Thurman, Robert A. F. A Shrine for Tibet: The Alice S. Kandell Collection. 2009. *(978-0-9670115-7-8(4))* Overlook Pr., The.

River, Glen. Art Migration to New Media. 2009. 48p. pap. 24.95 *(978-1-4357-4929-0(4))* Lulu Enterprises Inc.

Roberts, Jane. George III & Queen Charlotte: Patronage, Collecting & Court Taste. 2006. (Illus.). 65.00 *(978-1-902163-73-4(7))* Royal Collection Enterprises Ltd. GBR. Dist: Antique Collectors' Club.

Robson, Samantha. The Artistic Collection. 2009. 73p. pap. 42.50 *(978-1-4452-1858-8(5))* Lulu Enterprises Inc.

Román, Dulce María & Oliver-Smith, Kerry. Paradigms & the Unexpected: Modern & Contemporary Art from the Shey Collection. 2007. *(978-0-9762552-6-0(X));* pap. *(978-0-9762552-7-7(8))* Harn Museum of Art.

Rondeau, James. Contemporary Collecting: The Donna & Howard Stone Collection. 2010. (Contemporary Collecting Ser.). (ENG., Illus.). 160p. 50.00 *(978-0-300-16548-7(X))* Art Institute of Chicago.

—Judith Neisser Collection: Minimal & Postminimal Innovation. 2011. (Contemporary Collecting Ser.). (ENG., Illus.). 160p. 35.00 *(978-0-300-17024-5(6))* Art Institute of Chicago.

Rooney, Dawn F. Khmer Ceramics: Beauty & Meaning. 2010. (ENG., Illus.). 216p. *(978-974-9863-88-6(7),* River Bks. Pr. Dist A C) Antique Collectors' Club.

Roselione-Valadez, Juan, ed. Beg Borrow & Steal: Rubell Family Collection. 2011. (ENG., Illus.). 272p. pap. 49.95 *(978-0-9821195-2-5(6))* Rubell Family Collection.

Ross, Mickey, text. Razzia: 25 Years of Poster Art. 2007. (ENG., Illus.). 222p. 60.00 *(978-0-7570-0070-6(3))* Square One Pubs.

Roth, Linda H. & Kornhauser, Elizabeth Mankin, eds. At Home with Gustav Stickley: Arts & Crafts from the Stephen Gray Collection. 2008. (ENG., Illus.). 120p. 50.00 *(978-0-918333-24-7(5))* Wadsworth Atheneum.

San Francisco Museum of Modern Art Staff, contrib. by. Calder to Warhol: Introducing the Fisher Collection. 2010. *(978-0-918471-85-7(0))* San Francisco Museum of Modern Art.

Sasse, Julie R. An Eclectic Eye: Selections from the Dan Leach Collection. 2007. (Illus.). 180p. pap. 30.00 *(978-0-911611-34-2(7))* Tucson Museum of Art.

Schipsi, Laureen, ed. Art & Activism: Projects of John & Dominique de Menil. 2010. (Illus.). 344p. 65.00 *(978-0-300-12377-7(9))* Yale Univ. Pr.

Scholten, Frits. The Robert Lehman Collection. 2011. (Illus.). xiii, 274p. ***(978-1-58839-441-5(7))*** Metropolitan Museum of Art, The.

—The Robert Lehman Collection at the Metropolitan Museum of Art V12 - European Sculpture & Metalwork. 2012. (ENG., Illus.). 268p. (C). 75.00 ***(978-0-691-15489-3(9))*** Princeton Univ. Pr.

Seattle Art Museum Staff, contrib. by. Ancestral Modern: Australian Aboriginal Art: Kaplan & Levi Collection. 2012. ***(978-0-932216-67-0(6))*** Yale Univ. Pr.

Sframeli, Maria & Nitti, Patrizia. Trésor des Médicis. 2010. (FRE., Illus.). 271p. *(978-2-08-124505-1(1))* Editions Flammarion.

Sherer, Scott A. The Lam Collection of Aboriginal Art. 2008. 79p. *(978-1-933979-19-9(4))* Bright Sky Pr.

Shoemaker, Innis H. & Ittmann, John W. Adventures in Modern Art: The Charles K. Williams II Collection. 2009. (Illus.). 336p. *(978-0-87633-216-0(5));* *(978-0-87633-215-3(7))* Philadelphia Museum of Art.

Shoemaker, Innis Howe. Adventures in Modern Art: The Charles K. Williams II Collection. 2009. (ENG., Illus.). 336p. 60.00 *(978-0-300-14978-4(6))* Yale Univ. Pr.

Sicca, Cinzia M., ed. John Talman: An Early Eighteenth-Century Connoisseur. 2009. (Studies in British Art Ser.). (ENG., Illus.). 330p. 75.00 *(978-0-300-12335-7(3))* Yale Univ. Pr.

Sidorenko, Irina. Private Art Collecting in St Petersburg Around 1900. 2008. 104p. pap. *(978-3-639-03017-4(6))* VDM Verlag Dr. Mueller e.K.

Sieveking, Hinrich, et al. German Master Drawings: From the Wolfgang Ratjen Collection, 1580-1900. 2010. (ENG., Illus.). 320p. 65.00 *(978-1-907372-06-3(7))* Holberton, Paul Publishing GBR. Dist: Univ. of Washington Pr.

Srp, Karel, et al. New Formations: Czech Avant-Garde Art & Modern Glass from the Roy & Mary Cullen Collection. 2011. (ENG., Illus.). 320p. 75.00 *(978-0-300-16996-6(5))* Museum of Fine Arts, Houston.

St. Andrew's Episcopal Cathedral, compiled by. All Things Good: Palates & Palettes of the Cathedral Parish of Saint Andrew. 2007. 26.95 *(978-0-9800152-0-1(0))* St. Andrew's Episcopal Cathedral.

Starkman, Christine. Unrivalled Splendor: The Kimiko & John Powers Collection of Japanese Art. 2012. (ENG., Illus.). 272p. 65.00 ***(978-0-300-17962-0(6))*** Museum of Fine Arts, Houston.

Steiner, Barbara, ed. The Captured Museum. 2011. (ENG., Illus.). 256p. pap. 40.00 *(978-3-86859-059-3(5))* Jovis Verlag GmbH DEU. Dist: D.A.P./Distributed Art Pubs.

Stiver, David J. The Art & Image of the Cross. 2007. (Illus.). 125p. pap. *(978-0-9794266-2-9(6))* 23rd Street Pr.

Stone, Lisa. Accidenta Genius: Art from the Anthony Petullo Collection. 2012. (Illus.). 240p. 60.00 ***(978-3-7913-5200-8(8))*** Prestel Publishing.

Stoschek, Julia Stoschek Collection No. 1: Destroy She Said. 2008. (ENG., Illus.). 304p. 70.00 *(978-3-7757-2231-5(9))* Hatje Cantz Verlag GmbH & Co KG DEU. Dist: D.A.P./Distributed Art Pubs.

Stringer, John, et al. Closet Circus: The Lloyd & Elizabeth Horn Collection of Contemporary Western Australian Art. 2008. 224p. pap. 49.95 *(978-1-921361-27-2(1))* Fremantle Pr. AUS. Dist: Independent Pubs. Group.

Tinterow, Gary, et al. Abstract Expressionism & Other Modern Works: The Muriel Kallis Steinberg Newman Collection in the Metropolitan Museum of Art. 2007. (Illus.). x, 214p. 29.95 *(978-1-58839-274-9(0))* Metropolitan Museum of Art, The.

Urbaschek, Stephan, ed. Fast Forward: Media Art - the Goetz Collection, 1 vol. 2006. (GER & ENG., Illus.). 532p. 60.00 *(978-3-7757-1865-3(6))* Hatje Cantz Verlag GmbH & Co KG DEU. Dist: D.A.P./Distributed Art Pubs.

Ursprung, Philip, text. Jürgen Mayer H. Wirrwarr. 2011. (ENG., Illus.). 216p. 300.00 *(978-3-7757-2779-2(5))* Hatje Cantz Verlag GmbH & Co KG DEU. Dist: D.A.P./Distributed Art Pubs.

Van Den Abeele, Lieven, et al. Disorder in the House: Vanhaerents Art Collection. 2010. (ENG & DUT., Illus.). 144p. 45.00 *(978-90-209-9105-5(1),* Lannoo Pubs. (Acc)) Antique Collectors' Club GBR. Dist: National Bk. Network.

Van der Sman, Gert Jan. Lorenzo & Giovanna: Life & Art in Renaissance Florence. 2011. (ENG., Illus.). 160p. pap. 25.00 *(978-88-7461-128-7(5))* Mandragora ITA. Dist: Antique Collectors' Club.

Venet, Diane, ed. From Picasso to Jeff Koons - The Artist As Jeweler. 2011. (ENG., Illus.). 240p. 70.00 ***(978-88-572-1156-5(8))*** Skira Editore ITA. Dist: Random Hse., Inc.

Virginia Museum of Fine Arts Staff, contrib. by. Making History: 20th-Century African American Art. 2012. ***(978-1-934351-00-0(8))*** Virginia Museum of Fine Arts.

Walker, John, intro. Painting & Sculpture from the Samuel H. Kress Collections. *(978-0-89468-019-9(6))* National Gallery of Art.

Warren, Jeremy. Beauty & Power: Renaissance & Baroque Bronzes from the Collection of Peter Marino. 2010. (ENG., Illus.). 288p. 90.00 *(978-0-900785-77-1(2))* Holberton, Paul Publishing GBR. Dist: Univ. of Washington Pr.

Weininger, Andor, et al. Andor Weininger: Works in the Busch-Reisinger Museum. 2006. (ENG., Illus.). 75p. pap. 10.00 *(978-1-891771-14-9(0),* Harvard Art Museum (Acc)) Antique Collectors' Club GBR. Dist: National Bk. Network.

Weislogel, Andrew C., text. Studied Elegance: Italian Master Drawings from the Askin Collection. 2007. (Illus.). 56p. per. *(978-1-934260-01-2(0))* Cornell Univ., Herbert F. Johnson Museum of Art.

Wenley, Robert. French Bronzes in the Wallace Collection. 2006. (ENG., Illus.). 112p. pap. 24.95 *(978-0-900785-78-8(0))* Wallace Collection GBR. Dist: National Bk. Network.

Wiehager, Renate, ed. Art & Stars & Cars. 2011. (ENG., Illus.). 216p. pap. 50.00 ***(978-3-7757-3185-0(7))*** Hatje Cantz Verlag GmbH & Co KG DEU. Dist: D.A.P./Distributed Art Pubs.

Wiehager, Renate, ed. Blitzen-Benz BANG. Daimler Art Collection: Mixed Media, Sculptures, Commissioned Works. 2009. (ENG., Illus.). 520p. 75.00 *(978-3-7757-2310-7(2))* Hatje Cantz Verlag GmbH & Co KG DEU. Dist: D.A.P./Distributed Art Pubs.

Wolk-Simon, Linda & Bambach, Carmen. An Italian Journey: Drawings from the Tobey Collection: Correggio to Tiepolo. 2010. (Illus.). xi, 256p. 50.00 *(978-1-58839-379-1(8))* Metropolitan Museum of Art, The.

Wolk-Simon, Linda & Bambach, Carmen C. An Italian Journey: Drawings from the Tobey Collection: Correggio to Tiepolo. 2010. (Illus.). 268p. 50.00 *(978-0-300-15524-2(7))* Yale Univ. Pr.

Woodward, Hiram W. The Sacred Sculpture of Thailand: The Alexander B. Griswold Collection, the Walters Art Gallery. (Illus.). 328p. *(978-0-500-97457-5(8))* Thames & Hudson.

Yount, Sylvia. Private Passion, Public Promise: The James W. & Frances G. Mcglothlin Collection of American Art. 2010. (ENG., Illus.). 96p. (gr. 17). 30.00 *(978-0-917046-95-7(1))* Univ. Pr. of Virginia.

ART—PSYCHOLOGY

Adam, Ken, et al. Style & Scale: Or, Do You Have Anxiety?: A Conversation With. 2009. (GER & ENG., Illus.). 120p. pap. 39.95 *(978-3-211-99215-9(4))* Springer Wien AUT. Dist: Actar Birkhauser Distribution.

Arnheim, Rudolf. Toward a Psychology of Art. 2nd anniv. ed. 2010. (ENG., Illus.). 378p. pap. 24.95 *(978-0-520-26601-8(3))* Univ. of California Pr.

Brill, Dorothee. Shock & the Senseless in Dada & Fluxus. 2010. (Interfaces: Studies in Visual Culture Ser.). (Illus.). 256p. (C). 85.00 *(978-1-58465-902-0(5));* pap. 29.95 *(978-1-58465-917-4(3))* Univ. Pr. of New England. (Dartmouth College Press).

Byrne, David. Arboretum. 2006. (ENG., Illus.). 192p. 25.00 *(978-1-932416-57-2(9))* McSweeney's Publishing.

Campanaro, Judith. Art for the Soul: The Healing Power of Creativity. 2006. (Illus.). 136p. per. 19.95 *(978-0-9749610-6-4(X),* Creative Minds Pr.) Beagle Bay Bks.

Carter, Michael. Framing Art: Introducing Theory & the Visual Image. (Illus.). 211p. pap. *(978-0-86806-355-3(X),* Hale & Iremonger) GHR Pr., The.

Clark, T. J. The Sight of Death: An Experiment in Art Writing. 2008. (ENG., Illus.). 272p. per. 22.00 *(978-0-300-13758-3(3))* Yale Univ. Pr.

Corrie, Sarah. The Art of Inspired Living: Coach Yourself with Positive Psychology. 2009. (Professional Coaching Ser.). 336p. pap. 39.95 *(978-1-85575-571-7(4))* Karnac Bks. GBR. Dist: Stylus Publishing, LLC.

DiEdwardo, Maryann & Pasda, Patricia. The Horse Keeper: The Healing Gifts of Painting & Writing about Horses. 2008. 171p. pap. 14.95 *(978-0-7414-4659-6(6))* Infinity Publishing.

Doh, Jenny. Art Saves: Stories, Inspiration & Prompts Sharing the Power of Art. 2011. (ENG., Illus.). 144p. pap. 24.99 *(978-1-4403-0906-9(X),* North Light Bks.) F&W Media, Inc.

Freeman-Zachery, Rice. Creative Time & Space: Making Room for Making Art. 2009. (ENG., Illus.). 144p. pap. 22.99 *(978-1-60061-322-7(5),* North Light Bks.) F&W Media, Inc.

Freud, Sigmund & Brill, A. A. Leonardo Da Vinci: A Psychosexual Study of an Infantile Reminiscence. 2009. *(978-1-57898-819-8(5));* pap. *(978-1-57898-820-4(9))* Martino Publishing.

Gilbert, Douglas. Art & Soul. 2007. 72p. per. 10.95 *(978-1-4327-0871-9(6))* Outskirts Pr., Inc.

Glaser, Milton. Drawing Is Thinking. 2008. (Illus.). (ENG.). 208p. (gr. 12). 45.00 *(978-1-58567-994-2(1));* 223p. *(978-0-7156-3834-7(3))* Overlook Pr., The.

Glynn, Eugene. Desperate Necessity: Writings on Art & Creativity in Psychoanalytic Theory. 2008. (Illus.). 104p. 20.00 *(978-1-934772-88-1(7))* Periscope Publishing.

Hagman. The Artist's Mind: A Psychoanalytic Perspective on Creativity, Modern Art & Modern Artists. 2010. (ENG.). 192p. (C). 90.00 *(978-0-415-46705-6(5))* Routledge.

Hagman, George. The Artist's Mind: A Psychoanalytic Perspective on Creativity, Modern Art & Modern Artists. 2010. (ENG.). 192p. (C). pap. 34.95 *(978-0-415-46706-3(3))* Routledge.

Herndon-Consagra, Francesca & Norton, Sydney Jane, eds. Dreamscapes. 2011. (Illus.). 40p. pap. 0.00 *(978-0-9823347-2-0(9))* Pulitzer Foundation For The Arts.

hler, Martin. Grenzen der Katharsis in den modernen Künsten: Transformationen des aristotelischen Modells seit Bernays, Nietzsche und Freud. Vöhler, Martin & Linck, Dirck, eds. 2009.Tr. of Boundaries of Catharsis in the Modern Arts. (GER., Illus.). XIV, 391p. 109.00 *(978-3-11-020624-1(2))* De Gruyter, Walter Inc.

Iversen, Margaret. Beyond Pleasure: Freud, Lacan, Barthes. 2007. (Refiguring Modernism Ser.). (ENG., Illus.). 272p. 40.00 *(978-0-271-02971-9(4))* Pennsylvania State Univ. Pr.

Jinarajadasa, C. Art As Will & Idea. 2006. pap. 24.95 *(978-1-4286-4918-7(2))* Kessinger Publishing, LLC.

Joselit, David. States of Form - the Object in Networks. 2012. (POINT: Essays on Architecture Ser.). (ENG.). 152p. (C). 19.95 ***(978-0-691-15044-4(3))*** Princeton Univ. Pr.

Kimmelman, Michael. The Accidental Masterpiece: On the Art of Life & Vice Versa. 2006. (ENG., Illus.). 256p. (gr. 12-18). 15.00 *(978-0-14-303733-0(1),* Penguin (Non-Classics)) Penguin Group (USA) Inc.

Krauss, Rosalind E. Under Blue Cup. 2011. (ENG., Illus.). 152p. (gr. 17). 24.95 *(978-0-262-01613-1(3))* MIT Pr.

Kris, Ernst. Psychoanalytic Explorations in Art. Date not set. (Illus.). 377p. 55.00 *(978-0-8236-4440-7(5),* 04440) International Universities Pr., Inc.

Kuppers, Petra. The Scar of Visibility: Medical Performances & Contemporary Art. 2007. (Illus.). 360p. 90.00 *(978-0-8166-4652-4(X));* per. 29.95 *(978-0-8166-4653-1(8))* Univ. of Minnesota Pr.

Kuri, Erin L. Helping to Make Them See. 2008. 80p. pap. *(978-3-639-03411-0(2))* VDM Verlag Dr. Mueller e.K.

Manzotti, Riccardo. Situated Aesthetics: Art Beyond the Skin. 2011. (ENG., Illus.). 250p. pap. 34.90 *(978-1-84540-238-9(3))* Imprint Academic GBR. Dist: Ingram Pub. Services.

Milbrath, Constance. Patterns of Artistic Development in Children: Comparative Studies of Talent. 2010. (ENG.). 438p. pap. 39.99 *(978-0-521-15562-5(2))* Cambridge Univ. Pr.

Milbrath, Constance & Trautner, Hanns M., eds. Children's Understanding & Production of Pictures, Drawings, & Art: Theoretical & Empirical Approaches. 2007. (Illus.). 352p. pap. 44.00 *(978-0-88937-350-1(7))* Hogrefe Publishing.

Müller, Marcus & Kluwe, Sandra, eds. Identitätsentwürfe in der Kunstkommunikation: Studien Zur Praxis der Sprachlichen und Multimodalen Positionierung Im Interaktionsraum ,Kunst' 2012. (Sprache und Wissen Ser.). (GER., Illus.). X, 358p. (gr. 17). 168.00 ***(978-3-11-027831-6(6))*** De Gruyter, Walter Inc.

Novick, Linda. The Painting Path: Embodying Spiritual Discovery Through Yoga, Brush & Color. 2007. (Illus.). 199p. per. 18.99 *(978-1-59473-226-3(4),* SkyLight Paths Publishing.

Pardee, Alex. Awful/Homesick. 2008. (Illus.). 96p. 19.95 *(978-1-934991-00-8(7))* Upper Playground Pubng.

Pinna, Baignio, ed. Art & Perception. Towards a Visual Science of Art, Part 2. 2008. 428p. (C). *(978-90-04-16630-1(0))* BRILL.

Pinna, Baingio. Art & Perception. Towards a Visual Science of Art, Part 1. 2008. 308p. *(978-90-04-16629-5(7))* BRILL.

Porter, Tom. Will Alsop. 2010. (ENG., Illus.). 176p. pap. 53.95 *(978-0-415-54961-5(2))* Routledge.

Richmond, Wendy. Art Without Compromise. 2009. (ENG.). 256p. pap. 24.95 *(978-1-58115-666-9(9),* 115666, Allworth Pr.) Skyhorse Publishing Co., Inc.

Serig, Daniel. Visual Metaphor & the Contemporary Artist. 2008. 172p. pap. *(978-3-8364-7091-9(8))* VDM Verlag Dr. Mueller e.K.

Stanway, Penny. Free Your Inner Artist: Using your feelings, courage & Imagination. 2010. (ENG., Illus.). 156p. (C). pap. 29.95 *(978-0-85442-181-7(5))* Stobart Davies, Ltd. GBR. Dist: Brown, David Bk. Co., The.

Turner, Mark, ed. The Artful Mind: Cognitive Science & the Riddle of Human Creativity. 2006. (ENG., Illus.). 336p. 39.99 *(978-0-19-530636-1(8))* Oxford Univ. Pr., Inc.

Updike, John. Always Looking: Essays on Art. Carduff, Christopher, ed. 2012. (ENG., Illus.). 224p. 45.00 ***(978-0-307-95730-6(6)***, Knopf) Knopf Doubleday Publishing Group.

Warren, Frank. My Secret. 2006. (ENG., Illus.). 125p. 21.99 *(978-0-06-119668-3(1)*, Morrow, William & Co.) HarperCollins Pubs.

—PostSecret: Confessions on Life, Death, & God. 2009. (ENG.). 288p. 22.99 *(978-0-06-185933-5(8)*, Morrow, William & Co.) HarperCollins Pubs.

—The Secret Lives of Men & Women: A PostSecret Book. 2007. (ENG., Illus.). 125p. 21.99 *(978-0-06-119875-5(7)*, Morrow, William & Co.) HarperCollins Pubs.

Westfall, Patricia. The Designing Editor: Visual Communication for Verbal Communicators. 2007. cd-rom 19.95 *(978-0-9778102-8-4(3))* Zip Publishing.

White, Jack. Messages of Effusion. 2010. 231p. pap. 29.95 *(978-0-557-33689-0(9))* Lulu Enterprises Inc.

Wolfe, Tom. The Painted Word. 2008. (ENG., Illus.). 112p. pap. 14.00 *(978-0-312-42758-0(1))* Picador.

Wolfson, Rutger, ed. This Is the Flow: the Museum as a Space for Ideas. 2009. (ENG., Illus.). 260p. pap. 32.50 *(978-90-78088-24-0(9))* Valiz NLD. Dist: D.A.P./Distributed Art Pubs.

Zock, T. H., ed. At the Crossroads of Art & Religion: Imagination, Commitment, Transcendence. 2008. (Groningen Studies in Cultural Change Ser.). (ENG.). 206p. (C). 70.00 *(978-90-429-2173-3(0))* Peeters Pubs. & Booksellers BEL. Dist: Brown, David Bk. Co., The.

ART—REPRODUCTION

see also Copy Art; Imitation in Art

Allen, Nancy. Art Museum Images in Scholarly Publishing. 2009. pap. *(978-0-89263-021-9(3))* Rice Univ. Pr.

Bartsch, Tatjana, et al, eds. Das Originale der Kopie: Kopien als Produkte und Medien der Transformation von Antike. 2010. (Transformationen der Antike Ser.).Tr. of Originality of Copies. (GER., Illus.). VIII, 349p. 112.00 *(978-3-11-022544-0(1))* De Gruyter, Walter Inc.

Gaudio, Michael. Engraving the Savage: The New World & Techniques of Civilization. 2008. (Illus.). 240p. 75.00 *(978-0-8166-4846-7(8))*; per. 25.00 *(978-0-8166-4847-4(6))* Univ. of Minnesota Pr.

Hattori, Cordélia. D'après les Maîtres: Léonard de Vinci, Raphaël, Watteau, Goya, Courbet —: La Gravure D'interprétation D'Alphonse Leroy (1820-1902) à Omer Bouchery (1882-1962) 2008. (FRE & ENG., Illus.). 112p. pap. 40.00 *(978-2-35340-017-1(5))* Gourcuff Gradenigo FRA. Dist: National Bk. Network.

Hickson, Sally Anne & Gregory, Sharon, eds. Inganno-The Art of Deception: Imitation Reception & Deceit in Early Modern Art. 2012. (Visual Culture in Early Modernity Ser.). (Illus.). 200p. 104.95 ***(978-1-4094-3149-7(5))*** Ashgate Publishing Co.

Ruf, Beatrix, ed. Josh Smith. 2009. (ENG., Illus.). 268p. pap. 45.00 *(978-3-03764-035-7(9))* JRP Ringier Kunstverlag AG CHE. Dist: D.A.P./Distributed Art Pubs.

Verhoogt, Robert. Art in Reproduction: Nineteenth-Century Prints after Lawrence Alma-Tadema, Jozef Israels & Ary Scheffer. 2007. (Illus.). 736p. 65.00 *(978-90-5356-913-9(8)*, Leiden Univ. Pr.) Amsterdam Univ. Pr. NLD. Dist: Chicago Distribution Ctr.

ART—RHYTHM

see Proportion (Art)

ART—STUDY AND TEACHING

see also Art Schools

also subdivision Study and Teaching or Technique under various types of art, e.g. Painting—Study and Teaching; Sculpture—Technique

Alexenberg, Mel, ed. Educating Artists in a Digital Age: Learning at the Intersections of Art, Science, Technology, & Culture. 2008. (ENG., Illus.). 192p. 60.00 *(978-1-84150-191-8(3))* Intellect, Ltd. GBR. Dist: Chicago Distribution Ctr.

Armleder, John & Marks, Lisa. Piero Golia: Desert Interviews or How to Jump off the Roof & Not Hit the Ground. 2011. (ENG., Illus.). 100p. pap. 28.00 *(978-3-03764-106-4(1))* JRP Ringier Kunstverlag AG CHE. Dist: D.A.P./Distributed Art Pubs.

Art History. tchr. ed. 41.95 *(978-0-382-40657-7(5))* Cobblestone Publishing Co.

Aziz, Seemi. Teaching Islamic Art for Understanding of Islamic Culture. 2008. 204p. pap. *(978-3-639-09564-7(2))* VDM Verlag Dr. Mueller e.K.

Beaufort, Matthew, ed. Consciousness-Based Education: Volume VII: Art: A Foundation for Teaching & Learning in the Academic Disciplines, 12, 7. 2010. (Illus.). 524p. pap. *(978-0-923569-30-3(8))* Maharishi Univ. of Management Pr.

Benzel, Kim. Art of the Ancient Near East: A Resource for Educators. 2010. (Illus.). 134p. 79.95 *(978-1-58839-358-6(5))* Metropolitan Museum of Art, The.

Berenato, Carolyn. John Dewey's Educational Philosophy & the Barnes Foundation. 2010. 152p. pap. *(978-3-8383-4974-9(1))* Lambert Academic Publishing.

Bey, Sharif. Aaron Douglas & Hale Woodruff: The Social Responsibility & Expanded Pedagogy of the Black Artist. 2008. 236p. pap. *(978-3-639-10274-1(6))* VDM Verlag Dr. Mueller e.K.

Biefer, Marilyn & Fiedor, Marianna. Could It Be? 2010. 24p. 14.99 *(978-1-4490-8911-5(9))* AuthorHouse.

Birnbaum, Daniel. Teaching Art. 2008. (ENG., Illus.). 376p. pap. 48.00 *(978-3-86560-339-5(4))* Verlag der Buchhandlung Walther Konig DEU. Dist: D.A.P./Distributed Art Pubs.

Blalock, Ashley V. Studies in Art: Institutions, Form, Materials, & Meaning. rev. ed. 2010. (ENG.). 312p. pap. 62.19 *(978-0-7575-5036-2(3))* Kendall Hunt Publishing Co.

Bodilly, Susan & Augustine, Catherine H. Revitalizing Arts Education Through Community-Wide Coordination. 2008. 108p. pap. 20.00 *(978-0-8330-4306-1(4)*, MG-702) RAND Corp., The.

Bolles, Ron & Bolles, Reina. Learning That Lasts A Lifetime: The Transforming Power of the Arts in the Lives of Children. 2011. (ENG.). 353p. pap. 17.95 ***(978-1-4327-7592-6(8))*** Outskirts Pr., Inc.

Brockless, Adrian. Philosophical Notes: an Outlook. 2009. 240p. pap. 21.50 *(978-1-4452-0931-9(4))* Lulu Enterprises Inc.

Burnham, Rika & Kai-Kee, Elliott. Teaching in the Art Museum: Interpretation As Experience. 2011. (ENG., Illus.). 192p. pap. 30.00 *(978-1-60606-058-2(9)*, J. Paul Getty Museum) Getty Pubns.

Campana, D. M. Teacher of Geometrical Drawing. 16.95 *(978-0-939608-26-3(X))* Campana Art Co.

—Teacher of Linoleum Block Painting. 7.50 *(978-0-939608-25-6(1))* Campana Art Co.

Chin, Chong-Hwa. Conversation In-Between Identities: A Reflective Journey of Becoming An Art Teacher. 2008. 80p. pap. *(978-3-639-10118-8(9))* VDM Verlag Dr. Mueller e.K.

Chung, Sheng Kuan. Social Reconstructionism in Art Education. 2008. 200p. pap. *(978-3-639-05192-6(0))* VDM Verlag Dr. Mueller e.K.

Clough, Peter. Sculptural Materials in the Classroom. 2007. (ENG., Illus.). 96p. pap. 24.95 *(978-0-7136-8829-0(7))* A & C Black GBR. Dist: Macmillan.

Colbert, Cynthia. Connections in Art Kindergarten. (Illus.). *(978-0-87192-545-9(1))* Davis Pubns., Inc.

Conlin, Janet Louise. A Work of Heart: A Year of Kindergarten Art Lessons. 2007. (Illus.). 64p. pap. 24.99 *(978-0-9795406-0-8(7))* btcpubns.

Cooper, Mark & Sjostrom, Lisa. Making Art Together: How Collaborative Art-Making Can Transform Kids, Classrooms, & Communities. 2007. (ENG., Illus.). 160p. per. 18.00 *(978-0-8070-6619-5(2))* Beacon Pr.

Cornett, Claudia E. Creating Meaning Through Literature & the Arts: An Integration Resource for Classroom Teachers. 3rd rev. ed. 2006. (ENG., Illus.). 448p. (C). per. 83.40 *(978-0-13-171878-4(9)*, Prentice Hall) Prentice Hall PTR.

Costantino, Tracie & White, Boyd, eds. Essays on Aesthetic Education for the 21st Century. 2010. 228p. *(978-94-6091-121-7(8))*; pap. *(978-94-6091-120-0(X))* Sense Pubs.

Cram101 Textbook Reviews. Outlines & Highlights for Art & Creative Development for Young Children by Robert Schirmacher, Isbn: 9781428359208. 2010. 96p. pap. 27.95 *(978-1-61698-049-8(4))* Cram101 Inc.

Daichendt, G. James. Artist Scholar: Reflections on Writing & Research. 2011. (ENG., Illus.). 161p. pap. 25.00 *(978-1-84150-487-2(4))* Intellect, Ltd. GBR. Dist: Chicago Distribution Ctr.

Davis, Jessica Hoffmann & Hoffmann Davis, Jessica. Why Our Schools Need the Arts. 2007. (ENG., Illus.). 160p. pap. 22.95 *(978-0-8077-4834-3(X))* Teachers College Pr., Teachers College, Columbia Univ.

De Long, Ron, et al. Dream-Makers After-School: Art & after-School Lessons. De Long, Ron et al, eds. 2007. (Illus.). 104p. spiral bd. 9.99 *(978-0-86696-326-8(X))* Binney & Smith, Inc.

—Dream-Makers Language Arts: Art & Language. De Long, Ron et al, eds. 2007. (Illus.). 104p. spiral bd. 9.99 *(978-0-86696-325-1(1))* Binney & Smith, Inc.

—Dream-Makers Social Studies: Art andSocial Studies. De Long, Ron et al, eds. 2007. (Illus.). 104p. spiral bd. 9.99 *(978-0-86696-324-4(3))* Binney & Smith, Inc.

Desai, Dipti, et al. History As Art, Art As History: Contemporary Art & Social Studies Education. 2009. (ENG., Illus.). 288p. 150.00 *(978-0-415-99375-3(X))* Routledge.

DeSantis, Charles. Smart, Beautiful & Important: Teaching Art to AIDS-affected Orphans in Africa's Largest Slum. 2010. (Illus.). 132p. 42.00 *(978-0-9828061-1-1(6)*, Scarith) New Academia Publishing, LLC.

Donahue, David M. & Stuart, Jennifer, eds. Artful Teaching: Integrating the Arts for Understanding Across the Curriculum. 2010. (ENG., Illus.). 192p. pap. 24.95 *(978-0-8077-5080-3(8))*; 57.00 *(978-0-8077-5081-0(6))* Teachers College Pr., Teachers College, Columbia Univ.

Drews, Juliane. The Educational Situation of Roma in Bulgari. 2008. 100p. pap. *(978-3-639-03436-3(8))* VDM Verlag Dr. Mueller e.K.

Duffus, Robert L. American Renaissance. reprint ed. 34.50 *(978-0-404-02214-3(6))* AMS Pr., Inc.

Eckert, Carol. Conversing in Art: Learning the Language of the Visual Arts. rev. ed. 2010. (ENG.). 260p. spiral bd. 118.55 *(978-0-7575-7660-7(5))* Kendall Hunt Publishing Co.

Educacion y Accion Cultural Musac, ed. Working from Diversity: Learning Experiences through Art of the Present, Educacion y Accion Cultural MUSAC. 2010. 148p. pap. *(978-84-92861-34-7(7))* Actar Birkhauser Distribution.

Education in Art: Future Building. pap. *(978-0-89236-410-7(6))* Getty Pubns.

Faulkner, Barbara. A Way of Seeing & the Spiritual Search for Visual Truth in Painting. 2007. 172p. per. *(978-3-8364-2978-8(0))* VDM Verlag Dr. Mueller e.K.

Fichner-Rathus, Lois. Foundations of Art & Design. 2007. (ENG.). (C). 360p. pap. 103.95 *(978-0-534-61338-9(1))*; (Illus.). 368p. per. 103.95 *(978-0-495-10262-5(8))* Wadsworth.

Flick, Gert-Rudolf. Masters & Pupils: The Artistic Succession from Perugino to Manet, 1480-1880. 2008. (Hogarth Arts Ser.). (Illus.). 400p. 100.00 *(978-0-9554063-2-4(3))* Holberton, Paul Publishing GBR. Dist: Casemate Pubs. & Bk. Distributors, LLC.

Flora, Sherrill B. Cut, Color, Trace, & Paste: Reproducible Activities for Learning & Practicing a Variety of Fine Motor Skills. 2010. (ENG., Illus.). 64p. pap. 11.99 *(978-1-60268-079-1(5)*, Key Education Publishing Company, LLC) Carson-Dellosa Publishing, LLC.

Freeman-Zachery, Rice. Destination Creativity: The Life-Altering Journey of the Art Retreat. 2011. (ENG.). 144p. pap. 24.99 *(978-1-4403-0869-7(1)*, North Light Bks.) F&W Media, Inc.

Gnanadesikan, Mrudulla. Art & Techniques of Simulation, Grades 7-12. pap., tchr. ed. 18.50 *(978-0-86651-337-1(X)*, DSO1706) Globe Fearon Educational Publishing.

Goodridge, Paula. 100+ Fun Ideas for Art Activities That Are Easy to Prepare & That Children Will Love. 2009. (Illus.). 128p. pap. *(978-1-905780-33-4(8))* Brilliant Pubns.

Griffiths, Fleur. Supporting Children's Creativity Through Music, Dance, Drama & Art: Creative Conversations in the Early Years. 2010. (ENG., Illus.). 140p. 120.00 *(978-0-415-48965-2(2))*; pap. 37.95 *(978-0-415-48966-9(0))* Fulton, David Pubs. GBR. Dist: Taylor & Francis Group.

Gura, Mark. Visual Arts Units for All Levels. 2008. vi, 320p. pap. 44.95 *(978-1-56484-242-8(8))* International Society for Technology in Education.

Hardy, Tom, ed. Art Education in a Postmodern World. 2010. (Intellect Books - Readings in Art & Design Education Ser.). (Illus.). 164p. pap. 35.00 *(978-1-84150-302-8(9))* Intellect, Ltd. GBR. Dist: Chicago Distribution Ctr.

Hayhoe, Simon. Arts, Culture, & Blindness: A Study of Blind Students in the Visual Arts. 2008. (Illus.). 212p. pap. 30.00 *(978-1-934844-07-6(1))* Teneo Pr.

Hendrick, Becky. About & Through the Arts: Lessons & Activities for Creative Teaching & Learning. 2nd rev. ed. 2012. (ENG.). 192p. pap. 56.00 ***(978-0-7575-9232-4(5))*** Kendall Hunt Publishing Co.

Herne, Steve, et al, eds. Readings in Primary Art Education. 2009. (Intellect Books - Readings in Art & Design Education Ser.). (ENG., Illus.). 256p. pap. 40.00 *(978-1-84150-242-7(1))* Intellect, Ltd. GBR. Dist: Chicago Distribution Ctr.

Hetland, Lois, et al. Studio Thinking: The Real Benefits of Arts Education. 2007. 128p. 31.95 *(978-0-8077-4819-0(6))* Teachers College Pr., Teachers College, Columbia Univ.

—Studio Thinking: The Real Benefits of Visual Arts Education. 2007. (ENG., Illus.). 128p. pap. 26.95 *(978-0-8077-4818-3(8))* Teachers College Pr., Teachers College, Columbia Univ.

Hickey-Moody, Anna. Youth Arts & Education. 2012. (Routledge Advances in Sociology Ser.). (ENG., Illus.). 208p. (C). 135.00 ***(978-0-415-57264-4(9))*** Routledge.

Hickman, Richard. Why We Make Art: And Why It Is Taught. 2nd ed. 2010. (ENG., Illus.). 195p. pap. 25.00 *(978-1-84150-378-3(9))* Intellect, Ltd. GBR. Dist: Chicago Distribution Ctr.

Hickman, Richard, ed. Critical Studies in Art & Design Education. 2010. (Intellect Books - Readings in Art & Design Education Ser.). (ENG., Illus.). 224p. pap. 30.00 *(978-1-84150-205-2(7))* Intellect, Ltd. GBR. Dist: Chicago Distribution Ctr.

—Research in Art & Design Education: Issues & Exemplars. 2008. (ENG.). 208p. 50.00 *(978-1-84150-199-4(9))* Intellect, Ltd. GBR. Dist: Chicago Distribution Ctr.

Hollingworth, Patricia & Hollingsworth, Peter. Smart Art: Learning to Classify & Critique Art. 2008. (ENG.). 112p. (gr. 2-10). pap. 19.95 *(978-1-59363-341-7(6))* Prufrock Pr.

Houseley, Laura. The Independent Design Guide: Innovative Products from the New Generation. 2009. (ENG., Illus.). 352p. 45.00 *(978-0-500-51457-3(7)*, 551457) Thames & Hudson.

Hume, Helen D. The Art Teacher's Survival Guide for Elementary & Middle Schools. 2nd ed. 2008. (J-B Ed: Survival Guides: 31). (ENG., Illus.). 512p. pap. 34.95 *(978-0-470-18302-1(0)*, Jossey-Bass) Wiley, John & Sons, Inc.

Hutzel, Karen, et al, eds. Transforming City Schools Through Art: Approaches to Meaningful K-12 Learning. 2012. (ENG., Illus.). 192p. 64.00 ***(978-0-8077-5293-7(2))***; pap. 29.95 ***(978-0-8077-5292-0(4))*** Teachers College Pr., Teachers College, Columbia Univ.

Johnt, Marlene Nall. A Retired Art Teacher Tells All: One Hundred Simple Tips to Help Teachers Become Efficient, Inspiring, & Happy Educators. 2010. 320p. 32.95 *(978-1-4502-4978-2(7))*; pap. 22.95 *(978-1-4502-4976-8(0))* iUniverse, Inc.

Kehl, Richard & Laliberte, Norman, creators. 100 Ways to Have Fun with an Alligator: Plus 100 Other Involving Art Projects. 2011. (ENG., Illus.). 48p. pap. 17.95 *(978-1-59583-447-8(8)*, Darling & Co.) Laughing Elephant.

Keifer-Boyd, Karen & Maitland-Gholson, Jane. Engaging Visual Culture. Stewart, Marilyn, ed. 2007. (Art Education in Practice Ser.). (ENG.). 162p. pap. 24.95 *(978-0-87192-775-0(6))* Davis Pubns., Inc.

Kleiner, Fred S. Gardner's Art Through the Ages Bk. B: A Global History. 13th ed. 2009. (ENG.). 224p. (C). pap. 79.95 *(978-0-495-79451-6(1))* Wadsworth.

Kohle, Hubertus. Kunstgeschichte Digital: Eine Einfuehrung fuer Praktiker & Studierende. (GER., Illus.). 216p. *(978-3-496-01163-7(7))* Reimer, Dietrich.

Koster, Joan Bouza. Growing Artists: Teaching the Arts to Young Children. 5th ed. 2011. (Whatrsquo;s New in Early Childhood Ser.). (ENG.). 464p. (C). pap. 150.95 *(978-1-111-30274-0(X))* Wadsworth.

Kuffler-Yair, Miki. Developing Visual Spatial Perception Through Drawing Human Figure. 2010. 372p. pap. *(978-3-639-24108-2(8))* VDM Verlag Dr. Mueller e.K.

Kuri, Erin L. Helping to Make Them See. 2008. 80p. pap. *(978-3-639-03411-0(2))* VDM Verlag Dr. Mueller e.K.

Largo, Marissa. From the Pearl of the Orient to Uptown. 2008. 60p. pap. *(978-3-639-06595-4(6))* VDM Verlag Dr. Mueller e.K.

Lawton, Pamela Harris. Artstories. 2008. 216p. pap. *(978-3-639-04898-8(9))* VDM Verlag Dr. Mueller e.K.

Lewis, Richard L. & Lewis, Susan Ingalls. The Power of Art. 2nd ed. 2008. (ENG.). 528p. (C). pap. 113.95 *(978-0-534-64103-0(2))* Wadsworth.

Linerode, Darla. Let's Look at Art, 9 vols., Set. (Illus.). 168p. (Orig.). pap. 410.00 *(978-1-56762-044-3(2))* Modern Learning Pr.

Liu, Kuang-Hsia. Teaching Digital Art in Art Teacher Education. 2008. 208p. pap. *(978-3-639-07246-4(4))* VDM Verlag Dr. Mueller e.K.

Ludden, Ken. Mfab Catalog 2011-2012. 2011. 260p. pap. 24.95 ***(978-1-257-05377-3(9))*** Lulu Enterprises Inc.

Madoff, Steven Henry. Art School: Propositions for the 21st Century. Madoff, Steven Henry, ed. 2009. (ENG., Illus.). 392p. (gr. 17). pap. 34.95 ***(978-0-262-13493-4(4))*** MIT Pr.

Main, Marisa Jones. The Language of Art. 2008. 92p. pap. *(978-3-8364-2721-0(4))* VDM Verlag Dr. Mueller e.K.

Mantle, Eric. A Visual Guide to Classical Art Theory for Drawing & Painting Students. 2009. (ENG.). 160p. pap. 22.50 *(978-1-935166-12-2(3))* Parkhurst Brothers, Inc., Pubs.

Mason, Rachel & Eca, Teresa, eds. International Dialogues about Visual Culture, Education & Art. 2008. (Illus.). 256p. pap. 40.00 *(978-1-84150-167-3(0))* Intellect, Ltd. GBR. Dist: Chicago Distribution Ctr.

Mayo, Sherry. Artists at the Human-Computer Interface. 2009. 204p. pap. *(978-3-639-15984-4(5))* VDM Verlag Dr. Mueller e.K.

McCormick, Ed, et al. Lesson Plans That Wow! Twelve Standards-Based Lessons for Classroom & Art Teacher K-12. 2007. (Illus.). 112p. per. 24.95 *(978-0-9759564-6-5(9)*, Creative Companions) ArtMolds Productions.

McElheny, Josiah. Josiah Mcelheny:A Space for an Island Universe. Cooke, Lynne & McElheny, Josiah, eds. 2009. (ENG., Illus.). 136p. 30.00 *(978-84-7506-884-8(7))* Turner, Ediciones S.A. ESP. Dist: D.A.P./Distributed Art Pubs.

Meyer, Connie L. Behold the Beauty: Art Curriculum for Elementary Christian Education; Kindergarten & Grade 1. 2007. (ENG., Illus.). 179p. spiral bd. 29.95 *(978-0-916206-89-5(0))* Reformed Free Publishing Assn.

Mirzoeff, Nicholas. The Right to Look: A Counterhistory of Visuality. 2011. (ENG., Illus.). 408p. 89.95 *(978-0-8223-4895-5(0))* Duke Univ. Pr.

Mulcahey, Christine. The Story in the Picture: Inquiry & Artmaking with Young Children. 2010. (Early Childhood Education Ser.). (ENG.). 120p. pap. 19.95 *(978-0-8077-5007-0(7))*; (Illus.). 42.00 *(978-0-8077-5008-7(5))* Teachers College Pr., Teachers College, Columbia Univ.

Ngara, Constantine & Porath, Marion. Conceptions of Giftedness & Creativity from Afric. 2010. 124p. pap. *(978-3-639-24538-7(5))* VDM Verlag Dr. Mueller e.K.

Nicholson, Helen. Theatre & Education. 2009. (Theatre & Ser.). (ENG.). 80p. pap. 9.00 *(978-0-230-21857-4(1))* Palgrave Macmillan.

Norris, Michael. Medieval Art: A Resource for Educators. 2006. (Metropolitan Museum of Art Ser.). (ENG., Illus.). 199p. 79.95 *(978-0-300-10196-6(1))* Yale Univ. Pr.

Orr, Penelope & Dorn, Charles M. Art Education in a Climate of Reform: The Need for Measurable Goals in Art Instruction. 2008. (ENG., Illus.). 136p. 70.00 *(978-1-57886-788-2(6))*; pap. 32.95 *(978-1-57886-789-9(4))* Rowman & Littlefield Education.

Ose, Meredith. Art History. 2010. (Daily Warm-Ups Ser.). 223p. pap. 18.99 incl. cd-rom *(978-0-8251-6589-4(X))* Walch Education.

P. S. 1 Symposium: A Practical Avant-Garde. 2007. 6.00 *(978-0-9760503-9-1(0))* n+1 Research.

Patterson, Pam. Enacting Learning. 2010. 228p. pap. *(978-3-8383-8441-2(5))* Lambert Academic Publishing.

Pearse, Harold. From Drawing to Visual Culture: A History of Art Education in Canada. 2006. (ENG., Illus.). 318p. (C). *(978-0-7735-3070-6(3))* McGill-Queen's Univ. Pr.

Pearson Teacher Education Staff & Pearson Evaluation Systems Staff. Visual Arts (Grades 5-12) 2012. (ENG.). (C). 19.93 ***(978-0-13-300771-8(5))*** Allyn & Bacon, Inc.

Pelo, Ann. The Language of Art: Inquiry-Based Studio Practices in Early Childhood Settings. 2007. (ENG., Illus.). 160p. (J). pap. 29.95 *(978-1-929610-99-0(8))* Redleaf Pr.

Prince, Eileen S. Art Is Fundamental: Teaching the Elements & Principles of Art in Elementary School. 2008. (ENG., Illus.). 200p. pap. 19.95 *(978-1-56976-216-5(3)*, Zephyr Pr.) Chicago Review Pr., Inc.

Quinn, Therese M., et al, eds. Art & Social Justice Education. 2011. (ENG., Illus.). 248p. 140.00 ***(978-0-415-87906-4(X))***; pap., pap. 49.95 ***(978-0-415-87907-1(8))*** Routledge.

Reid, Natasha. Developing Gallery Outreach Policy. 2008. 76p. pap. *(978-3-639-03229-1(2))* VDM Verlag Dr. Mueller e.K.

Rooster Springs Elementary. The Elementary Adventures of Charlie & Dino. 2009. (Illus.). 92p. pap. 27.49 *(978-1-4389-9724-7(8))* AuthorHouse.

Rose, Karel & Kincheloe, Joe L. Art, Culture, & Education: Artful Teaching in a Fractured Landscape. (Counterpoints Ser.). xiii, 162p. pap. 31.95 *(978-0-8204-5745-1(0))* Lang, Peter Publishing, Inc.

Rosenberg, Martin & Thurber, Francis Beatty. Gender Matters in Art Education. 2007. (ENG., Illus.). 155p. pap. 24.95 *(978-0-87192-745-3(4))* Davis Pubns., Inc.

Ruffini, Marco. Art Without an Author: Vasari's Lives & Michelangelo's Death. 2011. (Modern Language Initiative Ser.). (ENG., Illus.). 208p. 80.00 *(978-0-8232-3455-4(X))*; pap. 26.00 *(978-0-8232-3456-1(8))* Fordham Univ. Pr.

Salzman, Marshall. How Shapes Function Within a Frame: Art Teachers, Art Students & Artists. 2009. 108p. pap., wbk. ed. 9.95 *(978-1-4327-2992-9(6))* Outskirts Pr., Inc.
Schirrmacher, Robert & Fox, J. Englebright. Art & Creative Development for Young Children. 6th ed. 2008. (ENG., Illus.). 416p. (C). per. 128.95 *(978-1-4283-5920-8(6))* Delmar Cengage Learning.
—Art & Creative Development for Young Children. 7th ed. 2011. (Whatrsquo;s New in Early Childhood Ser.). (ENG.). 368p. (C). pap. 134.95 *(978-0-495-91312-2(X))* Wadsworth.
Schork, Gretchen A. L. The Teaching Spells. 2009. 204p. pap. 24.96 *(978-0-557-06964-4(5))* Lulu Enterprises Inc.
Schultz, Jeffrey. Nice but Not Necessary. 2010. 120p. pap. *(978-3-8383-4743-1(9))* Lambert Academic Publishing.
Schwarz, Hans-Peter & Schlesser, Giaco, prefs. Bekanntmachungen, 1 vol. 2007. (GER & ENG., Illus.). 256p. per. 28.00 *(978-3-905701-84-5(7))* JRP Ringier Kunstverlag AG CHE. Dist: D.A.P./Distributed Art Pubs.
Sellen, Betty-Carol. Art Centers: American Studios & Galleries for Artists with Developmental or Mental Disabilities. 2008. (ENG., Illus.). 212p. pap. 49.95 *(978-0-7864-4140-2(2))* McFarland & Co., Inc. Pubs.
Sidaway, Ian & Seligman, Patricia. Be an Artist in 10 Steps. 2009. (ENG., Illus.). 416p. 30.00 *(978-0-600-61856-0(0),* Hamlyn) Octopus Publishing Group GBR. Dist: Hachette Bk. Group.
Sitte, Camillo, et al. Camillo Sitte Gesamtausgabe 04: Schriften zu Pädagogik und Schulwesen. 2008. (GER., Illus.). 458p. *(978-3-205-77177-7(X))* Bohlau Verlag GmbH u. Co. KG.
Smith, Walter. Art Education, Scholastic & Industrial by Walter Smith. 2006. 484p. per. 29.99 *(978-1-4255-5314-2(1))* MPublishing.
Smyth, Sandy. The Creative Process of Children: The Open Studio. 2010. 104p. pap. 10.99 *(978-1-60957-311-9(0))* Xulon Pr., Inc.
Soganci, Ismail Ozgur. An Interdisciplinary Study of Problematizing a Curricular Muteness. 2010. 352p. pap. *(978-3-8383-5682-2(9))* Lambert Academic Publishing.
Springgay, S., et al, eds. Being with A/R/Tography. 2007. 320p. per. *(978-90-8790-262-9(X))* Sense Pubs.
Stewart, Marilyn G. & Katter, Eldon. Explorations in Art - A Community Connection SE. 2nd ed. 2008. (ENG., Illus.). 334p. stu. ed. 61.95 *(978-0-87192-882-5(5))* Davis Pubns., Inc.
—Explorations in Art - A Community Connection TE. 2nd ed. 2008. (ENG., Illus.). 334p. pap., tchr. ed. 85.95 *(978-0-87192-896-2(5))* Davis Pubns., Inc.
—Explorations in Art - A Global Pursuit SE. 2nd ed. 2008. (Explorations in Art Ser.). (ENG., Illus.). 344p. stu. ed. 61.95 *(978-0-87192-881-8(7))* Davis Pubns., Inc.
—Explorations in Art - A Global Pursuit TE. 2nd ed. 2008. (Explorations in Art Ser.). (ENG., Illus.). 344p. pap., tchr. ed. 85.95 *(978-0-87192-895-5(7))* Davis Pubns., Inc.
Sullivan, Graeme. Art Practice as Research: Inquiry in Visual Arts. 2nd ed. 2009. (Illus.). 312p. (C). pap. 70.00 *(978-1-4129-7451-6(8),* B74516P) SAGE Pubns., Inc.
Swan, Ann. Botanical Portraits with Colored Pencils. 2010. (ENG.). 128p. 18.99 *(978-0-7641-6974-8(2))* Barron's Educational Series, Inc.
Szekely. Art Teaching. 2011. (ENG., Illus.). 456p. 160.00 *(978-0-415-99057-8(2))* Routledge.
Urbino, L. B. & Day, Henry. Art Recreations. 2009. 344p. 36.95 *(978-1-4357-5590-1(1))* Lulu Enterprises Inc.
Vecchi, Vea. Art & Creativity in Reggio Emilia: Exploring the Role & Potential of Ateliers in Early Childhood Education. 2010. (Contesting Early Childhood Ser.). (ENG., Illus.). 224p. 140.00 *(978-0-415-46877-0(9))*; pap. 45.95 *(978-0-415-46878-7(7))* Routledge.
Waldorf, Lynn A. Dynamics of a Teaching Artist Residency. 2010. 228p. pap. *(978-3-639-26591-8(3))* VDM Verlag Dr. Mueller e.K.
Walter, Ofra. The Art of Movement; Alternative Ways to Conceptualize Concepts. 2011. 320p. pap. ***(978-3-8454-2058-5(8))*** Lambert Academic Publishing.
Wexler, Alice & Wexler, Alice J. Art & Disability: The Social & Political Struggles Facing Education. 2009. (ENG., Illus.). 272p. 89.00 *(978-0-230-60629-6(6))* Palgrave Macmillan.
Wexler, Alice J. Art & Disability: The Social & Political Struggles Facing Education. 2011. (ENG., Illus.). 266p. pap. 28.00 *(978-0-230-11485-2(7))* Palgrave Macmillan.
Wexler, Alice J. Reframing Art Education Beyond the Classroom: Pondering the Outsider & Other Sites of Learning. 2012. (ENG., Illus.). 223p. 85.00 ***(978-0-230-11430-2(X))*** Palgrave Macmillan.
Why Art Education? *(978-0-937652-29-9(6))* National Art Education Assn.
Wynne, Sharon. Praxis Art Sample Test 10133. 2008. (Xam Praxis Ser.). (ENG.). 76p. pap., pupil's gde. ed. 21.95 *(978-1-60787-043-2(6))* XAMonline, Inc.
Youth Arts & Education. 2012. (C). 125.00 ***(978-0-203-85582-9(5))*** Routledge.

ART—STUDY AND TEACHING—GREAT BRITAIN

Addison, Nicholas & Burgess, Lesley, eds. Debates in Art & Design Teaching. 2012. (Debates in Subjects Teaching Ser.). (ENG., Illus.). 240p. (C). 155.00 *(978-0-415-61886-1(X))*; pap. 40.95 *(978-0-415-61887-8(8))* Routledge.
Atkinson, Dennis. Art, Equality & Learning: Pedagogies Against the State. 2011. 194p. ***(978-94-6091-453-9(5))***; pap. ***(978-94-6091-452-2(7))*** Sense Pubs.
Churchill Dower, Ruth. Cultural Entitlement in a Nutshell. 2009. 35p. pap. 25.50 *(978-1-4092-8587-8(1))* Lulu Enterprises Inc.
Cox. Teaching Art & Design 3-11. Watts, Robert, ed. 2007. (Reaching the Standard Ser.). (ENG., Illus.). 208p. 44.95 *(978-0-8264-5110-1(1))* Continuum International Publishing Group, Ltd. GBR. Dist: National Bk. Network.
Dash, P. African Caribbean Pupils in Art Education. 2010. 242p. *(978-94-6091-049-4(1))*; (Illus.). pap. *(978-94-6091-048-7(3))* Sense Pubs.
Key, Paul & Stillman, Jane. Teaching Primary Art & Design. 2009. (Illus.). 162p. pap. *(978-1-84445-254-5(9))* Learning Matters Ltd.
May, Markham & Warr, Sue. Teaching Creative & Media 14+ 2011. (ENG.). 152p. (C). pap. 43.00 ***(978-0-335-23752-4(5),*** 0335237525) McGraw-Hill Education GBR. Dist: McGraw-Hill Cos., The.
May, Markham & Warr, Sue. Teaching Creative Arts & Media 14+ 2011. (ENG.). 152p. (C). 120.00 *(978-0-335-23751-7(7),* 0335237517) McGraw-Hill Education GBR. Dist: McGraw-Hill Cos., The.
Rayment, Trevor, ed. The Problem of Assessment in Art & Design. 2007. (Readings in Art & Design Education Ser.). (Illus.). 128p. 50.00 *(978-1-84150-145-1(X))* Intellect, Ltd. GBR. Dist: Chicago Distribution Ctr.

ART—STUDY AND TEACHING (ELEMENTARY)

Alexander, Kay. Art Activities with Paper, Clay, Fibers, & Printmaking: Using Masterworks As Inspiration. 2011. ***(978-1-56290-652-7(3))*** Crystal Productions.
Benbow, Elaine. The Really Useful Art Book. 2012. (Really Useful Ser.). (ENG.). 144p. (C). pap. 44.95 *(978-0-415-67835-3(8))* Routledge.
Cataldo, Jude. Hands-on Art Activities for the Elementary Classroom: Seasonal, Holiday, & Design Activities for Grades K-5. 2006. (ENG., Illus.). 240p. pap. 29.95 *(978-0-471-56339-6(0),* Jossey-Bass) Wiley John & Sons, Inc.
Clements, Robert D. & Wachowiak, Frank. Emphasis Art: A Qualitative Art Program for Elementary & Middle Schools. 9th ed. 2009. (ENG.). 432p. (C). 141.60 *(978-0-13-714582-9(9))*; 148.27 *(978-0-13-610105-5(4))* Allyn & Bacon, Inc.
Colbert, Cynthia. Connections in Art: Level One. (Illus.) *(978-0-87192-417-9(X))* Davis Pubns., Inc.
Corbett, H. Dickson, et al. Creating & Sustaining Arts-Based School Reform: The A+ Schools Program. 2008. CXCVIII, 10p. 145.00 *(978-0-8058-6130-1(5))* Erlbaum, Lawrence Assocs., Inc.
Day, Michael & Hurwitz, Al. Children & Their Art: Art Education for Elementary & Middle Schools. 9th ed. 2011. (ENG.). 432p. (C). 196.95 *(978-0-495-91357-3(X))* Wadsworth.
Desmet, Anne. Primary Prints. 2011. (ENG., Illus.). 144p. pap. 25.95 *(978-1-4081-1143-7(8))* A & C Black GBR. Dist: Macmillan.
Doster, Jennifer. Bringing History Alive with Art Education. 2008. 452p. pap. *(978-3-639-01650-5(5))* VDM Verlag Dr. Mueller e.K.
Douglas, Katherine M. & Jaquith, Diane B. Engaging Learners Through Artmaking: Choice-Based Art Education in the Classroom. 2009. (ENG.). 128p. pap. 21.95 *(978-0-8077-4976-0(1))* Teachers College Pr., Teachers College, Columbia Univ.
Eder, Michael, et al. Portraying Identity Through Art: A Sourcebook for Middle-Grade Visual Arts Teachers. Cunningham, Jennifer & Rothman, Michael, eds. 2008. (Wisdom of Educators Ser.). (ENG., Illus.). 117p. spiral bd. *(978-0-9763600-5-6(5))* Neighborhood Hse. Charter Schl.
Gutteridge, Daphne & Smith, Vivien. Creating an Emotionally Healthy Classroom: Practical & Creative Literacy & Art Resources for Key Stage 2. 2009. (ENG., Illus.). 114p. pap. 35.95 *(978-0-415-49728-2(0))* Fulton, David Pubs. GBR. Dist: Taylor & Francis Group.
—Creating an Emotionally Healthy Classroom: Practical & Creative Pshe Literacy & Poetry Resource for Key Stage 2. 2009. (ENG., Illus.). 128p. 105.00 *(978-0-415-49729-9(9))* Fulton, David Pubs. GBR. Dist: Taylor & Francis Group.
Herz, Rebecca Shulman. Looking at Art in the Classroom: Art Investigations From the Guggenheim Museum. 2010. (ENG., Illus.). 160p. pap. 23.95 *(978-0-8077-5047-6(5))* Teachers College Pr., Teachers College, Columbia Univ.
Key, Paul & Stillman, Jane. Teaching Primary Art & Design. 2009. (Illus.). 162p. pap. *(978-1-84445-254-5(9))* Learning Matters Ltd.
Kohl, MaryAnn F. Art with Anything: 52 Weeks of Fun with Everyday Stuff. 2010. (ENG., Illus.). 128p. pap. 19.95 *(978-0-87659-085-0(7))* Gryphon Hse., Inc.
Prince, Eileen S. Art Is Every Day: Activities for the Home, Park, Museum, & City. 2012. (ENG.). 224p. (gr. -1). pap. 16.95 ***(978-1-56976-715-3(7),*** Zephyr Pr.) Chicago Review Pr., Inc.
Reilly, Mary Anne & Gangi, Jane M. Deepening Literacy Learning: Art & Literature in K-8 Classrooms. 2010. E-Book *(978-1-60752-459-5(7))*; (Illus.). xviii, 392p. pap. *(978-1-60752-458-8(9))*; (Illus.). xviii, 392p. pap. *(978-1-60752-457-1(0))* Information Age Publishing, Inc.
Saccardi, Marianne C. Art in Story: Teaching Art History to Elementary School Children, 1 vol. 2nd ed. 2006. (Illus.). 484p. pap. 35.00 *(978-1-59158-359-2(4),* LU3594, Teacher Ideas Pr.) Libraries Unlimited, Inc.
Siebert, Nicole. Innovative Art Projects for Children. 2010. (ENG.). 88p. (J). spiral bd. 19.95 *(978-1-56290-669-5(0))* Crystal Productions.
Stivers, Janet B. & Schudel, Donna. Dream-Makers Early Childhood: Building Creativity & Confidence. Stivers, Janet B. & Schudel, Donna, eds. 2008. 104p. spiral bd. 19.99 *(978-0-86696-331-2(6))* Binney & Smith, Inc.
Szekely. Art Teaching. 2011. (ENG., Illus.). 456p. pap. 89.95 *(978-0-415-99058-5(0))* Routledge.

ART—STUDY AND TEACHING (SECONDARY)

Addison, Nicholas & Burgess, Lesley. Learning to Teach Art & Design in the Secondary School: A Companion to School Experience. Addison, Nicholas & Burgess, Lesley, eds. 2nd rev. ed. 2008. (Learning to Teach Subjects in the Secondary School Ser.). (Illus.). CCCLX, 24p. pap. 45.95 *(978-0-415-37773-7(0))* Routledge.
Addison, Nicholas & Burgess, Lesley, eds. Debates in Art & Design Teaching. 2012. (Debates in Subjects Teaching Ser.). (ENG., Illus.). 240p. (C). 155.00 *(978-0-415-61886-1(X))*; pap. 40.95 *(978-0-415-61887-8(8))* Routledge.
Albers, Peggy. Finding the Artist Within: Creating & Reading Visual Texts in the English Language Arts Classroom. 2007. 288p. 32.95 *(978-0-87207-613-6(X))* International Reading Assn.
Churchill Dower, Ruth. Cultural Entitlement in a Nutshell. 2009. 35p. pap. 25.50 *(978-1-4092-8587-8(1))* Lulu Enterprises Inc.
Clements, Robert D. & Wachowiak, Frank. Emphasis Art: A Qualitative Art Program for Elementary & Middle Schools. 9th ed. 2009. (ENG.). 432p. (C). 141.60 *(978-0-13-714582-9(9))* Allyn & Bacon, Inc.
Colbert. Connections in Art. 179.95 *(978-0-87192-414-8(5))*; Vol. 2. 179.95 *(978-0-87192-422-3(6))*; Vol. 3. 179.95 *(978-0-87192-430-8(7))*; Vol. 4. 179.95 *(978-0-87192-438-4(2))*; Vol. 5. 179.95 *(978-0-87192-446-9(3))* Davis Pubns., Inc.
Doster, Jennifer. Bringing History Alive with Art Education. 2008. 452p. pap. *(978-3-639-01650-5(5))* VDM Verlag Dr. Mueller e.K.
Douglas, Katherine M. & Jaquith, Diane B. Engaging Learners Through Artmaking: Choice-Based Art Education in the Classroom. 2009. (ENG.). 128p. pap. 21.95 *(978-0-8077-4976-0(1))* Teachers College Pr., Teachers College, Columbia Univ.
Greenberg, Barbara R. & Patterson, Dianne. Art in Chemistry, Chemistry in Art, 1 vol. 2nd rev. ed. 2007. (Illus.). 412p. per. 35.00 *(978-1-59158-309-7(8),* LU3098, Teacher Ideas Pr.) Libraries Unlimited, Inc.
Hobbs, Richard. Visual Experience. 2010. (ENG., Illus.). ix, 241p. pap. *(978-0-87192-983-9(X))* Davis Pubns., Inc.
Hodge, Susie. The Art & Design Teacher's Handbook. 2010. (Continuum Education Handbooks Ser.). (ENG., Illus.). 176p. 34.95 *(978-1-84706-150-8(8))* Continuum International Publishing Group, Ltd. GBR. Dist: National Bk. Network.
Katter, Eldon & Stewart, Marilyn G. Art: A Community Connection E-Gallery. cd-rom *(978-0-87192-503-9(6))* Davis Pubns., Inc.
—Art: A Community Connection Student Art Gallery. cd-rom *(978-0-87192-504-6(4))* Davis Pubns., Inc.
—Art & the Human Experience: A Personal Journey Teachers Resource Binder. pap., tchr. ed. *(978-0-87192-560-2(5))* Davis Pubns., Inc.
Levin, Freddie. Draw Plus Science: Enhance Science Learning Through Art Activities! 2012. pap. ***(978-0-939217-91-5(0))*** Peel Productions, Inc.
May, Markham & Warr, Sue. Teaching Creative & Media 14+ 2011. (ENG.). 152p. (C). pap. 43.00 ***(978-0-335-23752-4(5),*** 0335237525) McGraw-Hill Education GBR. Dist: McGraw-Hill Cos., The.
May, Markham & Warr, Sue. Teaching Creative Arts & Media 14+ 2011. (ENG.). 152p. (C). 120.00 *(978-0-335-23751-7(7),* 0335237517) McGraw-Hill Education GBR. Dist: McGraw-Hill Cos., The.
New Museum of Contemporary Art Staff. Rethinking Contemporary Art & Multicultural Education. Cahan, Susan & Kocur, Zoya, eds. 2nd rev. ed. 2010. (ENG.). 448p. 150.00 *(978-0-415-88346-7(6))* Routledge.
New Museum Staff. Rethinking Contemporary Art & Multicultural Education. Joo, Eungie et al, eds. 2nd rev. ed. 2010. (ENG.). 448p. pap. 54.95 *(978-0-415-96085-4(1))* Routledge.
Reilly, Mary Anne & Gangi, Jane M. Deepening Literacy Learning: Art & Literature in K-8 Classrooms. 2010. E-Book *(978-1-60752-459-5(7))*; (Illus.). xviii, 392p. pap. *(978-1-60752-458-8(9))*; (Illus.). xviii, 392p. pap. *(978-1-60752-457-1(0))* Information Age Publishing, Inc.
Rossi, Antony. Who Am I? (Shorewood Art Programs for Education Ser.). 8p. tchr. ed. 107.00 *(978-0-88185-023-9(3))* Shorewood Fine Art Bks., Inc.

ART—STUDY AND TEACHING (HIGHER)

Beattie, Mary, ed. The Quest for Meaning: Narratives of Teaching, Learning & the Arts. 2009. 284p. *(978-94-6091-036-4(X))*; pap. *(978-94-6091-035-7(1))* Sense Pubs.
Buckley, Brad & Conomos, John, eds. Rethinking the Contemporary Art School: The Artist, the PhD, & the Academy. 2010. (ENG.). 237p. pap. 25.00 *(978-0-919616-49-3(6))* Press of the Nova Scotia College of Art & Design CAN. Dist: D.A.P./Distributed Art Pubs.
Buster, Kendall & Crawford, Paula. The Critique Handbook: The Student's Sourcebook & Survival Guide. 2nd ed. 2009. (ENG.). 160p. (C). pap. 23.80 *(978-0-205-70811-6(0),* Prentice Hall) Prentice Hall PTR.
Cram101 Textbook Reviews. Outlines & Highlights for Look! Fundamentals of Art History by Anne DAlleva, ISBN. 2011. 94p. pap. 27.95 ***(978-1-61812-450-0(1))*** Cram101 Inc.
D'Alleva, Anne. Look! Art History Fundamentals. 3rd ed. 2010. (ENG.). 164p. (C). pap. 38.20 *(978-0-205-76871-4(7),* Prentice Hall) Prentice Hall PTR.
Elkins, James, ed. Artists with Phds: On the New Doctoral Degree in Studio Art. 2009. (Illus.). 300p. pap. 28.00 *(978-0-9818654-5-4(3))* New Academia Publishing, LLC.
HiArt. HiArt No. 5: Higher Italian Education in Art & Music. 2011. (ITA & ENG., Illus.). 96p. pap. 21.95 ***(978-88-492-2181-7(9))*** Gangemi ITA. Dist: International Publishers Marketing.
Kennedy, Garry Neill. The Last Art College: Nova Scotia College of Art & Design, 1968-1978. 2012. (ENG., Illus.). 480p. (gr. 17). 60.00 ***(978-0-262-01690-2(7))*** MIT Pr.
Kook-Anderson, Grace, et al. Best Kept Secret: UCI & the Development of Contemporary Art in Southern California, 1964-1971. 2011. ***(978-0-940872-37-0(4))*** Laguna Art Museum Store.
Mann, Stewart. Study Skills for Art, Design & Media Students. 2011. (ENG., Illus.). 315p. pap. 37.50 *(978-0-273-72272-4(7))* Pearson Education, Ltd. GBR. Dist: Trans-Atlantic Pubns., Inc.
Peterson's Guides Staff. College Guide for Visual Arts Majors 2008: Real-World Admission Guide for All Fine Arts, Design, & Media Majors. Seghers, Linda, ed. 2007. (ENG., Illus.). 416p. pap. 24.00 *(978-0-7689-2423-7(5))* Peterson's.
Whitney Museum of American Art Staff, contrib. by. Independent Study Program: 40 Years: Whitney Museum of American Art, 1968-2008. 2008. pap. *(978-0-87427-158-4(4))* Whitney Museum of American Art.
Witham, Larry. Art Schooled: A Year among Prodigies, Rebels, & Visionaries at a World-Class Art College. 2012. (ENG., Illus.). 344p. 27.95 *(978-1-61168-007-2(7))* Univ. Pr. of New England.
Wu, Carin. How Computer Technology Influences Art & Design Programs. 2008. 220p. pap. *(978-3-639-06940-2(4))* VDM Verlag Dr. Mueller e.K.

ART—SUBJECTS

see Art—Themes, Motives, etc.

ART—TECHNIQUE

see also subdivision Technique under painting, sculpture and similar headings
Aguilera, Steven. A New Perspective #8213; Universal Edition. 2008. 188p. pap. 29.95 *(978-0-578-00038-1(5))* Artistech Bks.
Angell, Tony. Puget Sound Through an Artist's Eye. 2009. (ENG., Illus.). 140p. 35.00 *(978-0-295-98927-3(0))* Univ. of Washington Pr.
Bacon, Richard M. Forgotten Arts, Vol. 3. (Illus.). 64p. reprint ed. pap. 6.95 *(978-0-911658-71-2(8),* 30-250-4) Rodale Pr., Inc.
Bain, Christina. Pixels Are Not Paint. 2010. 252p. pap. *(978-3-639-13284-7(X))* VDM Verlag Dr. Mueller e.K.
Barbara, O. Roberts, ed. First Aid for Art: Essential Salvage Techniques. 2006. (Illus.). 108p. 19.95 *(978-1-889097-69-5(1))* Hard Pr. Editions.
Barzel, Amnon. Light Art: Targetti Light Art Collection. 2006. (ENG., Illus.). 272p. 40.00 *(978-88-7624-633-3(9))* Skira Editore ITA. Dist: Random Hse., Inc.
Bellemare, Sarah Ahearn. Painted Pages: Fueling Creativity with Sketchbooks & Mixed Media. 2011. (ENG., Illus.). 128p. pap. 24.99 *(978-1-59253-686-3(7),* 1592536867, Fair Winds Press) Quayside.
Berlyn, Ineke. The Quilted Object: Making Things with Quilt Art Techniques. 2009. (ENG., Illus.). 128p. 27.95 *(978-1-906388-23-2(7),* Batsford, B. T. Ltd.) Anova Bks. GBR. Dist: Sterling Publishing Co., Inc.
Beylerian, George & Dent, Andrew. Ultra Materials: How Materials Innovation Is Changing the World. Quinn, Bradley, ed. 2007. (ENG., Illus.). 288p. 75.00 *(978-0-500-51382-8(1),* 551382) Thames & Hudson.
Brereton, Richard. The Hidden Art of Designers, Illustrators & Creatives. 2009. (ENG., Illus.). 240p. 30.00 *(978-1-85669-582-4(4))* King, Laurence Publishing GBR. Dist: Hachette Bk. Group.
Britt, Salvesen & Stratis, Harriet K., eds. The Broad Spectrum: Studies in the Materials, Techniques, & Conservation of Color on Paper. 2006. (Conservation of Color on Paper Ser.). (ENG., Illus.). 264p. 160.00 *(978-1-873132-57-9(3))* Archetype Pubns. GBR. Dist: National Bk. Network.
Brunetti, Ivan. Cartooning: Philosophy & Practice. 2011. (Illus.). 88p. pap. 13.00 *(978-0-300-17099-3(8))* Yale Univ. Pr.
Burnett, Chris. Sprawl Code. 2007. *(978-0-9767490-5-9(X))* Preacher's Biscuit Bks.
Camp, Jeffery & Kirk, Joanna. Almanac. 2010. (ENG., Illus.). 256p. 50.00 *(978-1-905711-64-2(6))* Royal Academy of Arts GBR. Dist: Hachette Bk. Group.
Carr, Peter. Port of Culture: Liverpool Through the Photography of Pete Carr. 2008. (ENG., Illus.). 112p. 34.95 *(978-1-84631-170-3(5))* Liverpool Univ. Pr. GBR. Dist: Chicago Distribution Ctr.
Carriker, Pam. Art at the Speed of Life: Motivation & Inspiration for Making Mixed-Media Art Every Day. 2011. (ENG., Illus.). 144p. pap. 22.95 *(978-1-59668-261-0(2))* Interweave Pr., LLC.
Castonguay, Sophie. Unleash Your Inner Florist: How to Make Wedding & Special Event Flowers. 2008. 124p. pap. 36.99 *(978-1-4389-1757-3(0))* AuthorHouse.
Cherry, Deborah & Cullen, Fintan, eds. Location. 2007. (Art History Special Issues Ser.: 2). (ENG., Illus.). 240p. per. 32.95 *(978-1-4051-4694-4(X),* Wiley-Blackwell) Wiley, John & Sons, Inc.
Chilakamarri, Rambob Chary. India Nail Art. 2008. 50p. pap. 16.95 *(978-1-60474-491-0(X))* PublishAmerica, Inc.
Clarke, Mark. The Art of All Colours: Mediaeval Recipe Books for Painters & Illuminators. 2007. (ENG., Illus.). 152p. pap. 50.00 *(978-1-873132-72-2(7))* Archetype Pubns. GBR. Dist: National Bk. Network.
Coaker, Randy M. A Pocket Book Guide on How to Take Better Holiday Photos. 2010. (Illus.). 100p. pap. 32.99 *(978-1-4520-2840-8(0))* AuthorHouse.
Cora, Bruno. Nakis Panayotidis: Thief of Light. 2006. (ENG.). 239p. pap. 55.00 *(978-3-7165-1419-1(5),* Benteli Verlags Ag Dist) Antique Collectors' Club GBR. Dist: National Bk. Network.
Coster, Bill, photos by. Creative Nature Photography: Essential Tips & Techniques, 1 vol. 2011. (ENG., Illus.). 160p. pap. 18.95 *(978-1-55365-847-4(7),* Greystone Bks.) D&M Pubs. Inc. CAN. Dist: Perseus-PGW.
Covey, Sylvie. Photoshop for Artists: A Complete Guide for Fine Artists, Photographers, & Printmakers. 2012. (ENG., Illus.). 304p. pap. 35.00 ***(978-0-8230-0671-7(9))*** Watson-Guptill Pubns., Inc.
Crilley, Mark. Mastering Manga with Mark Crilley: 30 drawing lessons from the creator of Akiko. 2012. (ENG., Illus.). 128p. pap. 22.99 ***(978-1-4403-0931-1(0),*** Impact) F&W Media, Inc.
Cyr, Lisa. Art Revolution: Alternative Approaches for Fine Artists & Illustrators. 2009. (ENG., Illus.). 160p. pap. 26.99 *(978-1-60061-149-0(4),* North Light Bks.) F&W Media, Inc.

Darvas, Lou. You Can Draw Cartoons. 2011. 160p. 41.95 ***(978-1-258-09774-5(5))*** Literary Licensing, LLC.

Davis, Alexander J. Sketches of Montgomery Place. (Illus.). 9.95 *(978-0-912882-74-1(3))* Sleepy Hollow Pr.

Day, Shirley E. Theorem Painting: The Fine Art of Stenciling. 32p. pap. 12.95 *(978-1-931227-03-2(9))* Crafter's Corner, Inc.

Delamare, François. Blue Pigments: From Art to Industry. 2012. (ENG.). 400p. pap. 90.00 *(978-1-904982-37-1(9))* Archetype Pubns. GBR. Dist: National Bk. Network.

Di Leito, Darren. Mail Me Art: Going Postal with the World's Best Illustrators & Designers. 2009. (ENG., Illus.). 224p. pap. 30.00 *(978-1-60061-103-2(6)*, HOW Bks.) F&W Media, Inc.

DiEdwardo, Maryann & Pasda, Patricia. The Horse Keeper: The Healing Gifts of Painting & Writing about Horses. 2008. 171p. pap. 14.95 *(978-0-7414-4659-6(6))* Infinity Publishing.

Disney Editions Staff. The Art of Disney Epic Mickey. 2011. (ENG., Illus.). 160p. 40.00 *(978-1-4231-4826-5(6)*, Disney Editions) Disney Pr.

Doh, Jenny. Creative Pilgrimage: An Exploration of Artful Gatherings & Discovery of Innovative Art Techniques. 2012. (ENG., Illus.). 152p. pap. 24.99 *(978-1-59253-753-2(7)*, 1592537537) Quayside.

Dunphy, Niamh. This Dreaded Sight Twice Seen. 2009. (Illus.). 76p. pap. *(978-3-639-12816-1(8))* VDM Verlag Dr. Mueller e.K.

Eckert, Monika. Lace: Filigrane Tücher. 2010. 102p. pap. 34.90 *(978-3-8391-6722-9(1))* Bks. on Demand.

Faigin, Gary. The Artist's Complete Guide to Facial Expression. 2nd ed. 2008. (ENG., Illus.). 288p. pap. 24.95 *(978-0-8230-0432-4(5))* Watson-Guptill Pubns., Inc.

Ferre´, Whitney. The Artist Within: A Guide to Becoming Creatively Fit. 2008. (ENG.). 236p. pap. 15.95 *(978-1-59652-407-1(3))* Turner Publishing Co.

Fiero, Gloria & Adams, Laurie. Art Across Time Vol. 1: Prehistory to the Fourteenth Century. 4th ed. 2010. (ENG., Illus.). 544p. (C). pap. 142.67 *(978-0-07-735373-5(0)*, 0077353730) McGraw-Hill Cos., The.

Fuga, Antonella. Artists' Techniques & Materials. 2006. (Guide to Imagery Ser.). (Illus.). 384p. pap. 24.95 *(978-0-89236-860-0(8))* Oxford Univ. Pr., Inc.

Gatto, Joseph A., et al. Exploring Visual Design. 3rd ed. (Illus.). 97.50 *(978-0-87192-466-7(8))*; *(978-0-87192-383-7(1))* Davis Pubns., Inc.

Gatto, Joseph A., et al. Exploring Visual Design 4th Ed. TE on CD. 4th ed. 2011. cd-rom ***(978-1-61528-119-0(3))*** Davis Pubns., Inc.

Getha, Patricia. The Art of Drawing & Painting Horses. 2012. ***(978-1-936309-98-6(X))*** Foster, Walter Publishing, Inc.

Gilbert, Colin, et al. The Daily Book of Art: 365 readings that teach, inspire & Entertain. 2009. (ENG., Illus.). 376p. 22.95 *(978-1-60058-131-1(5)*, 1600581315) Foster, Walter Publishing, Inc.

Glitschka, Von. Crumble - Crackle - Burn: 120 Stunning Textures for Design & Illustration. 2007. (ENG., Illus.). 128p. 35.00 *(978-1-58180-958-9(1)*, HOW Bks.) F&W Media, Inc.

—Drip Dot Swirl: 94 Incredible Patterns for Design & Illustration. 2009. (ENG., Illus.). 112p. 35.00 *(978-1-60061-134-6(6)*, HOW Bks.) F&W Media, Inc.

Glorieux-Desouche, Isabelle. How to Talk to Children about World Art. 2010. (ENG., Illus.). 176p. pap. 19.95 *(978-0-7112-3091-0(9))* Lincoln, Frances Ltd. GBR. Dist: Perseus-PGW.

Goodridge, Paula. 100+ Fun Ideas for Art Activities That Are Easy to Prepare & That Children Will Love. 2009. (Illus.). 128p. pap. *(978-1-905780-33-4(8))* Brilliant Pubns.

Grace, Chrissie. Sharing Stitches: Exchanging Fabric & Inspiration to Sew One-of-a-Kind Projects. 2010. (ENG., Illus.). 144p. pap. 24.99 *(978-1-60061-943-4(6)*, North Light Bks.) F&W Media, Inc.

Gurney, James. Color & Light: A Guide for the Realist Painter. 2010. (ENG., Illus.). 224p. pap. 24.99 *(978-0-7407-9771-2(9))* Andrews McMeel Publishing.

Hammonds, Hollis. Drawing Structure: Conceptual & Observational Techniques. rev. ed. 2011. (ENG.). 154p. pap. 53.00 *(978-0-7575-6310-2(4))* Kendall Hunt Publishing Co.

Harrison, Birge. Landscape Painting. 2009. 320p. 25.99 *(978-1-103-09105-8(0))*; pap. 19.99 *(978-1-103-09103-4(4))* BiblioBazaar.

—Landscape Painting. 2008. 316p. pap. *(978-1-4437-0651-3(5))* Read Bks.

—Landscape Painting. 2008. 140p. pap. 14.95 *(978-0-9800454-2-0(8))* Velatura Pr., LLC.

Hartung, Ruthanne. Fraktur: Tips, Tools, & Techniques for Learning the Craft. 2008. (Heritage Crafts Today Ser.). (ENG., Illus.). 128p. 24.95 *(978-0-8117-3415-8(3))* Stackpole Bks.

Hawes, William & Olson, Beth M. The Performer in Mass Media: Connecting with Television & Online Audiences. 2nd ed. 2010. *(978-1-890871-99-4(0))* Holcomb Hathaway, Inc.

Hedley, Gwen. Drawn to Stitch: Line, Drawing, & Mark-Making in Textile Art. 2010. (ENG., Illus.). 144p. pap. 29.95 *(978-1-59668-233-7(7))* Interweave Pr., LLC.

Hemphill, Brian K. The Elements of Creative & Expressive Artistry: A Philosophy for Creating Everything Artistic. 2011. 600p. 43.95 ***(978-1-4620-0584-0(5))*** iUniverse, Inc.

Henson, H. D. Reaching Beyond the Hedges. 2009. 116p. pap. 39.49 *(978-1-4389-1951-5(4))* AuthorHouse.

Hermens, Erma & Townsend, Joyce. Sources & Serendipity: Testimonies of Artists' Practice. 2010. (ENG., Illus.). 208p. pap. 75.00 *(978-1-904982-52-4(2))* Archetype Pubns. GBR. Dist: National Bk. Network.

Hershberger, Carlynne & Huff, Kelli Money. Creative Colored Pencil Workshop: 52 Exercises for Combining Colored Pencil with Your Favorite Mediums. 2007. (ENG., Illus.). 144p. 29.99 *(978-1-58180-818-6(6)*, North Light Bks.) F&W Media, Inc.

Hissey, Ivan, et al. The Complete Step-by-Step Guide to Drawing Cartoons, Manga & Anime: Expert Techniques & Projects, Shown in More Than 2000 Illustrations. 2012. (ENG., Illus.). 512p. 29.99 ***(978-0-7548-2373-5(3))*** Anness Publishing GBR. Dist: National Bk. Network.

Hitch, Bryan. Ultimate Comics Studio. 2010. (ENG., Illus.). 128p. pap. 24.99 *(978-1-60061-327-2(6)*, Impact) F&W Media, Inc.

Hollahan, Lee. How to Use, Adapt, & Design Sewing Patterns: From Store-Bought Patterns to Drafting Your Own - Fashion Sewing with Confidence. 2010. (ENG., Illus.). 144p. pap., instr.'s gde. ed. 21.99 *(978-0-7641-4425-7(1))* Barron's Educational Series, Inc.

Hollingworth, Patricia & Hollingsworth, Peter. Smart Art: Learning to Classify & Critique Art. 2008. (ENG.). 112p. (gr. 2-10). pap. 19.95 *(978-1-59363-341-7(6))* Prufrock Pr.

Horovitz, Ellen G. Digital Photographer's Guide to Alternative & Mixed Media Art. 2011. (ENG., Illus.). 160p. pap. 24.95 *(978-1-60059-535-6(9)*, Pixiq) Sterling Publishing Co., Inc.

Jenny, Peter. The Artist's Eye. 2012. (ENG., Illus.). 216p. pap. 12.00 ***(978-1-61689-056-8(8))*** Princeton Architectural Pr.

Johnson, Cathy. Artist's Journal Workshop: Creating Your Life in Words & Pictures. 2011. (ENG., Illus.). 144p. pap. 22.99 *(978-1-4403-0868-0(3)*, North Light Bks.) F&W Media, Inc.

Johnson, Roni & Johnson. Collage & Altered Art. 2009. (Teach Yourself VISUALLY Consumer Ser.: 18). (ENG., Illus.). 224p. pap. 21.99 *(978-0-470-44719-2(2)*, Visual) Wiley, John & Sons, Inc.

Johnt, Marlene Nall. A Retired Art Teacher Tells All: One Hundred Simple Tips to Help Teachers Become Efficient, Inspiring, & Happy Educators. 2010. 320p. 32.95 *(978-1-4502-4978-2(7))*; pap. 22.95 *(978-1-4502-4976-8(0))* iUniverse, Inc.

Kent, Corita & Steward, Jan. Learning by Heart: Teaching to Free the Creative Spirit. 2nd ed. 2008. (ENG., Illus.). 232p. pap. 24.95 *(978-1-58115-647-8(2)*, 115647, Allworth Pr.) Skyhorse Publishing Co., Inc.

Kipnis, Lois, et al. Together We Can Improvise, Vol 1: Three Units Based on Stories & Themes for Teachers K-3 & Teaching Artists, Book & CD. 2011. (ENG.). 92p. pap. 26.99 ***(978-0-7390-7360-5(5))*** Alfred Publishing Co., Inc.

Kroustallis, Stefanos. Art Technology: Sources & Methods: Proceedings of the Second Symposium of the Art Technological Source Research Working Group. 2008. (SPA & ENG., Illus.). 184p. pap. 75.00 *(978-1-904982-29-6(8))* Archetype Pubns. GBR. Dist: National Bk. Network.

Kuentz, Stephan Levy. Biomannerism. (Illus.). 104p. pap. 47.00 *(978-4-8457-1121-5(4))* Libro Port JPN. Dist: RAM Pubns. & Distribution.

Kuffler-Yair, Miki. Developing Visual Spatial Perception Through Drawing Human Figure. 2010. 372p. pap. *(978-3-639-24108-2(8))* VDM Verlag Dr. Mueller e.K.

Le Glatin Keis, Mari, illus. & text. The Art of Travel with a Sketchbook: Six Tips to Get Started. 2007. (ENG.). 100p. pap. 24.99 *(978-1-57421-618-9(X))* Design Originals.

Leland, Nita. The New Creative Artist: A Guide to Developing Your Creative Spirit. rev. exp. ed. 2006. (ENG., Illus.). 176p. 29.99 *(978-1-58180-756-1(2)*, 33423) F&W Media, Inc.

Let's Face It. 2007. spiral bd. *(978-0-9767481-3-7(4))* Digital or Not.

Library Association, American Mutual. Ladies' Manual of Art. 2009. 300p. 34.95 *(978-1-4357-5539-0(1))* Lulu Enterprises Inc.

Lieser, Wolf. The World of Digital Art. 2010. 276p. 59.99 *(978-0-8416-7164-5(8))* Langenscheidt Publishing Group.

Ligon, Scott. Digital Art Revolution: Creating Fine Art with Photoshop. 2010. (ENG., Illus.). 256p. pap. 29.99 *(978-0-8230-9536-0(3))* Watson-Guptill Pubns., Inc.

Lippincott, Gary A. The Fantasy Illustrator's Technique Book. 2007. (ENG., Illus.). 128p. pap. 21.99 *(978-0-7641-3574-3(0))* Barron's Educational Series, Inc.

Lombardi, Thomas. The Classification of Style in Painting. 2008. 116p. pap. *(978-3-639-02758-7(2))* VDM Verlag Dr. Mueller e.K.

Mann, Lindsey. Coloured Aluminium Jewellery. 2010. (ENG., Illus.). 128p. pap. 24.95 *(978-1-4081-0629-7(9))* A & C Black GBR. Dist: Macmillan.

Markovitz, Mitch. How to Draw & Paint Trains Like a Pro. 2009. (Motorbooks Studio Ser.). (ENG., Illus.). 128p. pap. 19.99 *(978-0-7603-2927-6(3)*, 0760329273, Voyageur Pr) MBI Publishing Co. LLC.

Marsh, Gail. 19th Century Embroidery Techniques. 2009. (ENG., Illus.). 192p. 24.95 *(978-1-86108-561-0(3))* Guild of Master Craftsman Pubns., Ltd. GBR. Dist: Sterling Publishing Co., Inc.

Martinez, Scape. Graff: The Art & Technique of Graffiti. 2009. (ENG., Illus.). 128p. pap. 22.99 *(978-1-60061-071-4(4)*, Impact) F&W Media, Inc.

Mawn, Misty. Unfurling, a Mixed-Media Workshop with Misty Mawn: Inspiration & Techniques for Self-Expression Through Art. 2011. (ENG., Illus.). 128p. pap. 24.99 *(978-1-59253-688-7(3)*, 1592536883) Quayside.

McNulty, Mark. Pop Cultured: The Photography of Mark Mcnulty. 2008. (ENG., Illus.). 208p. 34.95 *(978-1-84631-168-0(3))* Liverpool Univ. Pr. GBR. Dist: Chicago Distribution Ctr.

Mehigan, Janet. Mastering the Art of Calligraphy. 2012. (ENG., Illus.). 264p. 19.99 *(978-0-7548-2178-6(1))* Anness Publishing GBR. Dist: National Bk. Network.

Miller, Steve. Beasts! How to Draw Fantastic Predators, Creepy Crawlies, & Cryptids. 2008. (ENG., Illus.). 144p. pap. 19.95 *(978-0-8230-1668-6(4))* Watson-Guptill Pubns., Inc.

Miyazaki, Hayao. The Art of Ponyo. 2009. (Ponyo on the Cliff by the Sea Ser.). (ENG., Illus.). 268p. pap. 34.99 *(978-1-4215-3064-2(3))* Viz Media.

Moser, Thomas E., Jr. Surfer in the Sky. 2010. 112p. 24.99 *(978-0-9843793-0-9(4))* Graphcom, Inc.

Muther, Richard. The History of Modern Painting. 2010. 432p. pap. 33.45 *(978-1-4455-6485-2(8))* Audubon Pr. & Christian Bk. Service.

Nimmer, Dean. Art from Intuition: Overcoming your Fears & Obstacles to Making Art. 2008. (ENG., Illus.). 160p. pap. 25.95 *(978-0-8230-9750-0(1))* Watson-Guptill Pubns., Inc.

North Light Books Staff. Drawing & Painting Animals: The Essential Guide. 2008. (ENG.). 192p. pap. 19.99 *(978-1-60061-110-0(9)*, North Light Bks.) F&W Media, Inc.

—Sketchbook Confidential: Secrets from the private sketches of over 40 master Artists. 2010. (ENG., Illus.). 176p. pap. 24.99 *(978-1-4403-0859-8(4)*, North Light Bks.) F&W Media, Inc.

Novick, Linda. The Painting Path: Embodying Spiritual Discovery Through Yoga, Brush & Color. 2007. (Illus.). 199p. per. 18.99 *(978-1-59473-226-3(4))* SkyLight Paths Publishing.

Ocvirk, Otto, et al. Art Fundamentals: Theory & Practice. 11th ed. 2008. (ENG., Illus.). 336p. (C). pap. 116.67 *(978-0-07-352652-2(5)*, 0073526525) McGraw-Hill Cos., The.

Ocvirk, Otto G. Art Fundamentals: Theory & Practice. 12th ed. 2012. pap. ***(978-0-07-337927-2(1))*** McGraw-Hill Cos., The.

O'Donnell, Timothy. Sketchbook: Conceptual Drawings from the World's Most Influential Designers. 2009. (ENG., Illus.). 192p. 40.00 *(978-1-59253-521-7(6)*, 1592535216) Quayside.

Olwin, Anne. Color Quick Reference Guide. 2007. 5.95 *(978-1-934396-01-8(X))* Creativity Pr.

—Create Exciting Art. 2007. 5.95 *(978-1-934396-06-3(0))* Creativity Pr.

—Insider Tips & Wisdom. 2007. 5.95 *(978-1-934396-07-0(9))* Creativity Pr.

Rheaume, John. How to Draw Wizards: Discover the Secrets to Drawing, Painting, & Illustrating a World of Sorcery. 2011. (Fantasy Underground Ser.). 128p. (YA). (gr. 9-12). 48.95 *(978-1-936309-65-8(3))* Foster, Walter Publishing, Inc.

Rivers, Charlotte. Little Book of Letterpress. 2010. (ENG.). 192p. 24.95 *(978-0-8118-7507-3(5))* Chronicle Bks. LLC.

Robert, Monique. Papier Mâché Design: With Advanced Techniques. 2009. 136p. pap. 42.50 *(978-1-4389-9320-1(X))* AuthorHouse.

Robinson, Robert H. You Kan Do a Kandinsky: Enter the Wonderful World of Kandinsky. (Illus.). 62p. 20.00 *(978-0-911145-00-7(1))* Sussex Countian, Inc.

Roy, Ashok. National Gallery Technical Bulletin, Vol. 28. 2007. (National Gallery Technical Bulletin Ser.). (ENG., Illus.). 96p. pap. 70.00 *(978-1-85709-372-8(0))* Yale Univ. Pr.

Roy, Ashok, ed. The National Gallery Technical Bulletin, Vol. 29. 2009. (ENG., Illus.). 80p. pap. 70.00 *(978-1-85709-419-0(0))* Yale Univ. Pr.

Rugg, Judith & Sedgwick, Michele, eds. Issues in Curating Contemporary Art & Performance. 2008. (Illus.). 272p. 60.00 *(978-1-84150-162-8(X))* Intellect, Ltd. GBR. Dist: Chicago Distribution Ctr.

Samulak, Michael I. A Is for Africa: Coloring Book. 2010. 48p. pap. 9.99 *(978-1-4269-4097-2(1))* Trafford Publishing.

Schenck, Walter Joseph. World's Greatest Artists. 2011. 80p. pap. 10.95 *(978-1-4620-0734-9(1))* iUniverse, Inc.

Schneider, Fredric T. The Art of Japanese Cloisonne Enamel: History, Techniques & Artists, 1600 to the Present. 2010. (ENG., Illus.). 372p. 95.00 *(978-0-7864-4732-9(X))* McFarland & Co., Inc. Pubs.

Serrats, Marta. Point of Purchase. 2006. (Illus.). 256p. 45.00 *(978-0-06-089351-4(6)*, Collins Design) HarperCollins Pubs.

Sidaway, Ian & Seligman, Patricia. Be an Artist in 10 Steps. 2009. (ENG., Illus.). 416p. 30.00 *(978-0-600-61856-0(0)*, Hamlyn) Octopus Publishing Group GBR. Dist: Hachette Bk. Group.

Sigurdson, Trudy. Tantalizing Textures: Ideas & Techniques for Scrapbookers. 2007. (ENG., Illus.). 128p. pap. 22.99 *(978-1-59963-005-2(2)*, Memory Makers Bks.) F&W Media, Inc.

Simanaitis, Suzanne. Kaleidoscope: Projects & Ideas to Spark Your Creativity. 2007. (ENG., Illus.). 144p. pap. 24.99 *(978-1-58180-879-7(8)*, North Light Bks.) F&W Media, Inc.

Smith, Ray & Dorling Kindersley Publishing Staff. Artist's Handbook. 3rd ed. 2009. (ENG.). 384p. pap. 21.95 *(978-0-7566-5722-2(9))* Dorling Kindersley Publishing, Inc.

Stevens, Jim. Advanced Scrimshaw Techniques. 2008. (Illus.). 64p. pap. 14.99 *(978-0-7643-3017-9(9))* Schiffer Publishing, Ltd.

Stikker, Carolien & Hoegen, Philippine. Super Structure. 2009. (Samuel Dorsky Museum of Art Ser.). (Illus.). 144p. pap. 14.00 *(978-0-615-29286-1(0)*, Suny Pr.) State Univ. of New York Pr.

Strickland, Carol. The Illustrated Timeline of Art History: A Crash Course in Words & Pictures. 2006. (ENG., Illus.). 128p. 12.95 *(978-1-4027-3603-2(7))* Sterling Publishing Co., Inc.

Stroud, Betsy Dillard. The Artist's Muse: Unlock the Door to Your Creativity. 2006. (ENG., Illus.). 96p. pap. 26.99 *(978-1-58180-875-9(5)*, North Light Bks.) F&W Media, Inc.

Sutton, Jeremy. Painter X Creativity: Digital Artist's Handbook. 2007. (ENG., Illus.). 320p. pap. 49.95 *(978-0-240-80929-8(7)*, Focal Pr.) Elsevier Science & Technology Bks.

Tanemura, Arina. The Art of Full Moon. 2008. (Art of Full Moon Ser.). (ENG.). 68p. pap. 19.99 *(978-1-4215-1885-5(6))* Viz Media.

Thomas, Vernada. Therapeutic Art Activities for Alzheimer's/Dementia Patients. 2008. 124p. 29.99 *(978-1-4363-8416-2(8))*; pap. 19.99 *(978-1-4363-8415-5(X))* Xlibris Corp.

Thunfors, Jacquelyn. Paint Your Life. 2009. (Illus.). 127p. *(978-1-60643-958-6(8))* Riverside Publishing Co.

Urbino, L. B. (Levina Buoncuore). Art Recreations: Being A Complete Guide to Pencil Drawing, Oil Painting ... Moss Work, Papier Mache ... Wax Work, Shell Work ... Enamel Painting, Etc. 2006. 340p. per. 23.99 *(978-1-4255-3415-8(5))* MPublishing.

van den Brink, Peter. ArtMatters: Netherlands Technical Studies in Art. 2006. (Illus.). 128p. (C). 75.00 *(978-90-400-8728-8(8))* Waanders B.V., Uitgeverij NLD. Dist: Antique Collectors' Club.

Ward, Gerald W. R. The Grove Encyclopedia of Materials & Techniques in Art. 2008. (ENG., Illus.). 864p. 160.00 *(978-0-19-531391-8(7))* Oxford Univ. Pr., Inc.

Warshaw, Josie. Pottery Masterclass: Handbuilding. 2010. (ENG., Illus.). 128p. pap. 17.99 *(978-1-84476-817-2(1))* Anness Publishing GBR. Dist: National Bk. Network.

—The Practical Potter. 2012. (ENG., Illus.). 256p. pap. 24.99 *(978-1-84476-905-6(4))* Anness Publishing GBR. Dist: National Bk. Network.

Watase, Yuu. The Art of Fushigi Yugi: The Mysterious Play. 2006. (Fushigi Yugi Ser.). (ENG., Illus.). 96p. 19.99 *(978-1-4215-0715-6(3))* Viz Media.

Watson, Neil. Visual Principles - A Guide to Drawing & Painting Architecture. Date not set. *(978-0-393-73011-1(5))* Norton, W. W. & Co., Inc.

Wigan, Mark. Thinking Visually. 2007. (Basics Illustration Ser.). (ENG., Illus.). 176p. pap. 34.50 *(978-2-940373-15-4(9))* AVA Publishing GBR. Dist: Ingram Pub. Services.

Williamson, Al. Al Williamson Archives Volume Two. 2011. (ENG., Illus.). 64p. pap. 19.95 ***(978-1-933865-34-8(2))*** Flesk Pubns.

Wolffe, Dave. Autoeroticasphyxium. 2011. 242p. pap. 19.99 ***(978-1-4568-8590-8(1))*** Xlibris Corp.

Woods, Kim W., ed. Making Renaissance Art. 2007. (Renaissance Art Reconsidered Ser.). (ENG., Illus.). 352p. (C). pap. 35.00 *(978-0-300-12189-6(X))* Yale Univ. Pr.

Wright-Correll, Arlene. How to Create Art Without Knowing How to Draw a Straight Line. 2007. 94p. pap. 39.95 *(978-0-615-15184-7(1))* Trade Resources Unlimited.

Zelanski, Paul & Fisher, Mary Pat. The Art of Seeing. 8th ed. 2010. (ENG., Illus.). 560p. (C). pap. 152.67 *(978-0-205-74834-1(1)*, Prentice Hall) Prentice Hall PTR.

Zhao, Jianlei, et al. Zhongguo Min Jian ni Su Ji Fa. 2009. (CHI., Illus.). 166p. *(978-7-5045-8022-1(8))* China Labour and Social Security Publishing Hse.

ART—THEFTS

see Art Thefts

ART—THEMES, MOTIVES, ETC.

Alderete, Jorge. Graficos Mexicanos. 2011. (ENG.). 256p. 44.95 *(978-1-907621-02-4(4))* Korero Books LLP GBR. Dist: Independent Pubs. Group.

Alexander, Darsie, et al, texts. The Spectacular of Vernacular. 2011. (ENG., Illus.). 128p. pap. 19.99 *(978-0-935640-99-1(1))* Walker Art Ctr.

Allen, Terry. Terry Allen. 2010. (ENG., Illus.). 312p. 65.00 *(978-0-292-72246-0(X))* Univ. of Texas Pr.

Amer, Ghada. Ghada Amer. 2010. (ENG., Illus.). 304p. 70.00 *(978-0-9800242-0-3(X))* Miller, Gregory & Co.

Anderson, Kim & Carson, Jenny. Art 101: Understanding Visual Artforms in Our World Workbook. rev. ed. 2010. (ENG.). 38p. spiral bd. 28.50 *(978-0-7575-7460-3(2))* Kendall Hunt Publishing Co.

Anfam, David & Pousette-Dart, Richard. Pousette-Dart: Predominantly White Paintings, 1 vol. 2010. (ENG.). 64p. pap. 24.95 *(978-0-943044-36-1(7))* Phillips Collection, The.

Arastu, Salma. The Lyrical Line: Embracing All & Flowing. Hinh, Angie, ed. 2008. (Illus.). 104p. 45.00 *(978-0-9719552-9-5(8)*, Half Full Pr.) Source Bk. Pubns.

Arweiler, Alexander H. Machtfragen: Zur kulturellen Repräsentation und Konstruktion von Macht in Antike, Mittelalter und Neuzeit. Arweiler, Alexander & Gauly, Bardo M., eds. 2008. (GER., Illus.). 303p. (C). 74.00 *(978-3-515-09295-1(1))* Steiner, Franz Verlag Wiesbaden GmbH DEU. Dist: Brown, David Bk. Co., The.

Avery, Kevin J., et al. Alexis Rockman: A Fable for Tomorrow. 2011. (ENG., Illus.). 176p. 49.95 *(978-1-904832-86-7(5))* Giles, D. Ltd. GBR. Dist: National Bk. Network.

Bü & che, Wolfgang. Lyonel Feininger: Die Halle-Bilder. Buche, Wolfgang, ed. 2010. (GER., Illus.). 175p. (C). 56.00 *(978-3-7774-2241-1(X))* Hirmer Verlag GmbH DEU. Dist: Brown, David Bk. Co., The.

B.A.I. Staff, ed. Delvaux: and the Antiquity, 1 vol. 2010. (ENG.). 189p. pap. 40.00 *(978-90-8586-541-4(7))* Exhibitions International BEL. Dist: Innovative Logistics.

Baker, Ian. Goddesses of the Celestial Gallery. 2011. (ENG., Illus.). 64p. 24.95 *(978-1-60887-022-6(7))* Palace Pr. International.

Balazs, Harold. Harold Balazs. 2010. (Thomas T. Wilson Ser.). (ENG., Illus.). 160p. 60.00 *(978-0-295-99059-0(7))* Univ. of Washington Pr.

Bartholomew, Terese Tse & Tsuruta, Kaz. Hidden Meanings in Chinese Art. 2012. (ENG., Illus.). 352p. pap. 45.00 ***(978-0-939117-37-6(1))*** Asian Art Museum of San Francisco.

Basting, Anne Davis. Hiding Places: Memory in the Arts. 2011. ***(978-0-9710703-3-2(4))*** Kohler, John Michael Arts Ctr.

Batchen, Geoffrey. What of Shoes? Van Gogh & Art History. 2009. (ENG.). 48p. pap. 14.95 *(978-3-86502-218-9(9)*, Art Stock Bks. Ltd/Csi) Continental Sales, Inc.

Batino, Sabrina. Itinerari Del Sacro Nelle Forme Del Bere: Articolazioni Morfologiche e Funzionali Della Ceramica Greca Ad Uso Potorio in Ambito Rituale. 2009. (ITA & ENG., Illus.). 313p. (C). pap. 125.00 (978-1-4073-0457-1(7)) British Archaeological Reports Ltd. GBR. Dist: Brown, David Bk. Co., The.

Bercht, Fatima. Viva David Tineo: A Retrospective of Tucson's Muralist & Art Educator. 2010. (Illus.). 64p. pap. 20.00 (978-0-911611-38-0(X)) Tucson Museum of Art.

Bills, Mark, et al. Dickens & the Artists. 2012. (ENG., Illus.). 200p. 55.00 **(978-0-300-17602-5(3))** Yale Univ. Pr.

Birdsall, Byron & Garvey, Mike. People of the Saltchuk: Paintings by Byron Birdsall. 2009. (978-1-933245-17-1(4)) Documentary Media LLC.

Blache, Gustave. Leah Chase: Paintings by Gustave Blache III. 2012. (ENG.). 84p. 40.00 **(978-1-55595-378-2(6))** Hudson Hills Pr. LLC.

Blish, Carolyn. Drawing Closer. 2010. 29.95 (978-0-578-05105-5(2)) Blish, Carolyn Studio.

Blum, Shirley Neilsen. Henri Matisse: Rooms with a View. 2010. (ENG., Illus.). 192p. 60.00 (978-1-58093-295-0(9)) Monacelli Pr., Inc.

Boeckl, Christine M. Images of Leprosy: Disease, Religion, & Politics in European Art. 2011. (Illus.). 248p. 48.00 (978-1-935503-14-9(6)); pap. 30.00 (978-1-935503-15-6(4)) Truman State Univ. Pr.

Boellert, Arvid. Drei Farben, Weiss: Three Colours, White. 2007. (GER & ENG., Illus.). 125p. (978-3-89930-199-1(4)) Schiler, Hans.

Bonin, Cosima von, et al. Dressing the Message: Transformationen Von Kunst und Mode. 2008. (Illus.). 120p. (978-3-89169-208-0(0)) Sprengel Museum.

Bradfield, Geoffrey. Geoffrey Bradfield: Ex Arte. 2009. (ENG., Illus.). 360p. 50.00 (978-1-933415-78-9(9)) Panache Partners, LLC.

Brady, Joan B. & Scott, Sue. Between Brushstrokes: Paintings, Poetry & Prose. 2008. (ENG., Illus.). 180p. 50.00 (978-1-55595-301-0(8)) Hudson Hills Pr. LLC.

Brenk, Beat. Medieval Image-Concepts & the Meaning of Visual Programs. 2013. (ENG., Illus.). 560p. (C). 300.00 (978-1-899828-73-9(7)) Pindar Pr. GBR. Dist: Brown, David Bk. Co., The.

Brettell, Richard R. Pissarro's People. 2011. (Illus.). 304p. 65.00 (978-3-7913-5118-6(4)) Prestel Publishing.

Brown, Kathryn. Women Readers in French Painting 1870-1890: A Space for the Imagination. 2012. (Illus.). 272p. 124.95 **(978-1-4094-0875-8(2))** Ashgate Publishing Co.

Buscema, John & Soltero, Emilio. John Buscema: A Life in Sketches. 2008. (Illus.). 104p. (978-0-9741332-3-2(X)) Pearl Pr.

Campos, Cristian & Ruiz, Daniel Cruz. MANDALA DESIGN HANDBOOK: MANUEL DE DESIGN DE MANDALA / LEITFADEN FÜR MANDALA-DESIGNS / ONTWERPHANDBOEK VOOR MANDALA'S, 1 vol. 2010. (FRE, DUT, GER & ENG., Illus.). 559p. pap. 19.95 (978-94-6065-038-3(4)) booQs Publishers bvba BEL. Dist: Innovative Logistics.

Cattelan, Maurizio, ed. Maurizio Cattelan: All. 2011. (ENG., Illus.). 255p. 45.00 **(978-0-89207-416-7(7))** Guggenheim, Solomon R. Museum.

Chagall, Marc, et al. Marc Chagall: Der Maler Am Fenster. 2009. (GER., Illus.). 167p. (C). 45.00 (978-3-7774-6025-3(7)) Hirmer Verlag GmbH DEU. Dist: Brown, David Bk. Co., The.

Charing, Howard G. The Ayahuasca Visions of Pablo Amaringo. 2011. (ENG.). 1p. 40.00 (978-1-59477-345-7(9)) Inner Traditions International, Ltd.

Cheshire, Jim, et al. Tennyson Transformed: Alfred Lord Tennyson & Visual Culture. 2009. (Illus.). 160p. 80.00 (978-1-84822-003-4(0), Lund Humphries Pubs.) Ashgate Publishing, Ltd. GBR. Dist: Ashgate Publishing Co.

Chiesi, Benedetta & Ruffini, Mario, eds. Musiche di legni in riva D'Arno: Le sculture di Giuseppe Gavazzi dal Canottieri a Ponte Vecchio. 2011. (ITA., Illus.). 108p. (C). pap. 50.00 **(978-88-596-0941-4(0))** Polistampa ITA. Dist: Brown, David Bk. Co., The.

Choi, Justine & Barletta, Destiny, eds. A Force of Nature: The Ceramic Art of Randy Johnston. 2011. (Illus.). 104p. 50.00 **(978-1-879985-23-0(3))** Pucker Gallery.

Chronicle Books Staff. American Trademarks: From the Roaring '20s to the Swinging '60s. Baker, Eric & Blik, Tyler, eds. 2010. (ENG., Illus.). 256p. pap. 29.95 (978-0-8118-7220-1(3)) Chronicle Bks. LLC.

Clark-Langager, Sarah & Dietrich, William, eds. Critical Messages: Contemporary Northwest Artists on the Environment. 2010. (ENG., Illus.). 80p. pap. 24.95 (978-1-878237-07-1(1)) Western Washington Univ., Western Gallery.

Clarke, Jay A. Becoming Edvard Munch: Influence, Anxiety, & Myth. 2009. (ENG., Illus.). 232p. 50.00 (978-0-300-11950-3(X)) Art Institute of Chicago.

Clarke, Jay A. y. Becoming Edvard Munch: Influence, Anxiety, & Myth. 2009. (Illus.). 231p. pap. (978-0-86559-228-5(4)) Art Institute of Chicago.

Codell, Julie F., ed. Transculturation in British Art, 1770-1930. 2012. (British Art: Global Contexts Ser.). (Illus.). 312 + 4 lourp. 119.95 **(978-1-4094-0977-9(5))** Ashgate Publishing Co.

Cohen, Ada. Art in the Era of Alexander the Great: Paradigms of Manhood & Their Cultural Traditions. 2010. (ENG., Illus.). 422p. (C). 95.00 (978-0-521-76904-4(3)) Cambridge Univ. Pr.

Coleman, Brian. Barry Dixon Inspirations, 1 vol. 2011. (ENG., Illus.). 224p. 40.00 (978-1-4236-0751-9(1)) Gibbs Smith, Publisher.

Collins, Don. Traces of Forgotten Places: An Artist's Thirty-Year Exploration & Celebration of Texas as It Was. Baker, T. Lindsay, ed. 2008. (ENG., Illus.). 176p. pap. 19.95 (978-0-87565-361-7(8)) Texas Christian Univ. Pr.

Connors, John Emmett & Grasso, Vito. John Connors: Artist from Troy. 2012. **(978-1-4384-4461-1(3))**; (ENG.). 128p. pap. 29.95 **(978-1-4384-4462-8(1))** State Univ. of New York Pr.

Cook, Brian. Brian Cook's Landscapes of Britain. 2011. (ENG., Illus.). 144p. 29.95 (978-1-906388-78-2(4), Batsford, B. T. Ltd.) Anova Bks. GBR. Dist: Sterling Publishing Co., Inc.

Corbett, David Peters & Monks, Sarah, eds. Anglo-American: Artistic Exchange between Britain & the USA. 2012. (Art History Special Issues Ser.: 9). (ENG.). 264p. pap. 39.95 **(978-1-4443-5143-9(5)**, Wiley-Blackwell) Wiley, John & Sons, Inc.

Cox, Caroline. Seduction: A Celebration of Sensual Style. 2006. (Illus.). 192p. 35.00 (978-0-06-113815-7(0), Collins Design) HarperCollins Pubs.

Cram101 Textbook Reviews. Outlines & Highlights for Exploring Art: Global, Thematic Approach by Margaret Lazzari. 2011. 292p. pap. 32.95 **(978-1-61490-939-2(3))** Cram101 Inc.

Cram101 Textbook Reviews & Cram101 Textbook Reviews. Outlines & Highlights for Exploring Art by Margaret Lazzari, Isbn: 0495102555 9780495102557. 2011. 422p. pap. 35.95 **(978-1-61812-040-3(9))** Cram101 Inc.

Crumb, Sophie & Crumb, R. Sophie Crumb: Evolution of a Crazy Artist. Kominsky-Crumb, Aline, ed. 2010. (ENG., Illus.). 304p. 350.00 (978-0-393-08014-8(5), 8014) Norton, W. W. & Co., Inc.

Crumb, Sophie & Crumb, Robert. Sophie Crumb: Evolution of a Crazy Artist. Kominsky-Crumb, Aline, ed. 2010. (ENG., Illus.). 272p. 27.95 (978-0-393-07996-8(1), 7996) Norton, W. W. & Co., Inc.

Cruzvillegas, Abraham, et al, texts. Melanie Smith: Parres. 2008. (ENG., Illus.). 105p. 45.00 (978-968-9056-34-8(4)) Turner, Ediciones S.A. ESP. Dist: D.A.P./Distributed Art Pubs.

Curtan, Patricia. Menus for Chez Panisse: The Art & Letterpress of Patricia Curtan. 2011. (ENG., Illus.). 184p. 40.00 (978-1-61689-029-2(0)) Princeton Architectural Pr.

Dai, Dunbang, illus. 56 Ethnic Groups in China: Paintings by Dai Dunbang. 2010. (Discovering China Ser.). (ENG.). 134p. 14.95 (978-1-60652-157-1(8)) Reader's Digest Assn., Inc., The.

Danzker, Jo-Anne Birnie & Bott, Gian Casper, eds. Seance: Albert Von Keller & the Occult. 2010. (ENG., Illus.). 104p. 30.00 (978-0-295-99082-8(1)) Frye Art Museum.

Darling, Michael, ed. & text. Target Practice: Painting under Attack, 1949-78. 2009. (ENG., Illus.). 156p. 50.00 (978-0-932216-64-9(1)) Seattle Art Museum.

Deneulin, Luc & Swinnen, Johan. Raoul Servais: The Wizard of Ostend: Commitment, Challenge, Recognition. 2009. (ENG, DUT & FRE., Illus.). 320p. pap. 54.00 (978-90-5487-480-5(5)) VUB Univ. Pr. BEL. Dist: Independent Pubs. Group.

Deutscher Verein Fur Kuns Staff. Matthias Grünewald: Die Zeichnungen / The Drawings / Les Dessins. 2008. (ENG., Illus.). 184p. 300.00 (978-3-7757-2141-7(X)) Hatje Cantz Verlag GmbH & Co KG DEU. Dist: D.A.P./Distributed Art Pubs.

Deyber, Robert & Gladstone, Valerie. Robert Deyber: A Language All His Own. 2008. (Illus.). 126p. (978-0-9814577-2-7(X)) Wellspring Communications, Inc.

Dial, Thornton & Herman, Bernard L. Thornton Dial: Thoughts on Paper. 2012. (ENG., Illus.). 224p. 45.00 **(978-0-8078-3529-6(3))** Univ. of North Carolina Pr.

Dillon, Sheila & Welch, Katherine E., eds. Representations of War in Ancient Rome. 2009. (ENG., Illus.). 380p. (C). pap. 40.99 (978-0-521-13063-7(2)) Cambridge Univ. Pr.

Dintenfass, Marylyn, et al. Paintings. 2007. (ENG., Illus.). 144p. 50.00 (978-1-55595-279-2(8)) Hudson Hills Pr. LLC.

Dobkins, Rebecca J., et al. Joe Feddersen: Vital Signs. 2008. (ENG., Illus.). 128p. pap. 29.95 (978-0-295-98860-3(6)) Univ. of Washington Pr.

Donovan, Art. The Art of Steampunk: Extraordinary Devices & Ingenious Contraptions from the Leading Artists of the Steampunk Movement. 2011. (ENG., Illus.). 128p. pap. 19.95 (978-1-56523-573-1(8)) Fox Chapel Publishing Co., Inc.

Donovan, Tara. Tara Donovan. 2008. (ENG., Illus.). 160p. 45.00 (978-1-58093-213-4(4)) Monacelli Pr., Inc.

Dougherty, Patrick. Stickwork. 2010. (ENG., Illus.). 208p. pap. 34.95 (978-1-56898-976-1(8)) Princeton Architectural Pr.

Drake, James. James Drake. 2008. (M. Georgia Hegarty Dunkerley Series in Contemporary Art). (ENG., Illus.). 256p. 55.00 (978-0-292-71860-9(8)) Univ. of Texas Pr.

Dubin, Lois. Adornment: The Necklaces of Barbara Natoli Witt. 2011. (Illus.). 162p. 50.00 (978-1-55595-334-8(4)) Hudson Hills Pr. LLC.

Eckhard Schulze-Fielitz: Metasprache des Raums / Metalanguage of Space. 2009. 536p. 59.95 (978-3-211-99197-8(2)) Springer Wien AUT. Dist: Actar Birkhauser Distribution.

Eden, Xandra, et al. The Lining of Forgetting: Internal & External memory in Art. 2008. (Illus.). 135p. lib. bdg. 35.00 (978-1-890949-11-2(6)) Univ. of North Carolina at Greensboro, Weatherspoon Art Museum.

Edwards, Janet & Edwards, Fred. Palms to Peaks: The Art of Janet Edwards. 2011. (ENG., Illus.). 176p. 49.95 (978-1-58948-285-2(9), ESRI Pr.) ESRI, Inc.

El-Shahawy, Abeer. Recherche sur la decoration des tombes thebaines du Nouvel Empire: Originalites iconographiques et Innovations. 2010. (Internet-Beitrage Zur Agyptologie und Sudanarchaologie Ser.: XIII). (FRE.). 400p. (C). pap. 80.00 (978-1-906137-19-9(6)) Golden Hse. Pubns. GBR. Dist: Brown, David Bk. Co., The.

Eleey, Peter, et al, texts. Now You See It. 2009. (ENG., Illus.). 72p. 35.00 (978-0-934324-47-2(6)) Aspen Art Museum.

Elliott, David & Ozaki, Tetsuya. Bye Bye Kitty!!! Between Heaven & Hell in Contemporary Japanese Art. 2011. (ENG., Illus.). 136p. pap. 35.00 (978-0-300-16690-3(7)) Yale Univ. Pr.

Ensminger, David A. Visual Vitriol: The Street Art & Subcultures of the Punk & Hardcore Generation. 2011. (ENG., Illus.). 336p. 70.00 (978-1-60473-968-8(1)) Univ. Pr. of Mississippi.

Ernst, Rudy. Sculptomania: 25 Years of Sculpting. 2nd ed. 2011. **(978-1-936658-05-3(4))** QCC Art Gallery.

Evans, Henry. Botanical Prints. 2011. (ENG., Illus.). 96p. pap. 24.95 (978-1-58243-637-1(1), Counterpoint) Counterpoint LLC.

Fairey, Shepard. Obey: Supply & Demand: The Art of Shepard Fairey. 20th ed. 2009. (Illus.). 439p. 59.95 (978-1-58423-349-7(4)) Gingko Pr., Inc.

Feige, Daniel Martin & Köppe, Tilmann, eds. Funktionen von Kunst. 2009. (GER & ENG.). 224p. pap. 56.95 (978-3-631-57838-4(5)) Lang, Peter GmbH, Europaischer Verlag der Wissenschaften DEU. Dist: Lang, Peter.

Fili, Louise. Elegantissima: The Design & Typography of Louise Fili. 2012. (ENG.). 256p. 40.00 **(978-1-61689-097-1(5))** Princeton Architectural Pr.

Fisher, Vernon & Auping, Michael. Vernon Fisher. 2010. (ENG., Illus.). 256p. 55.00 (978-0-292-72323-8(7)) Univ. of Texas Pr.

Focke, Anne, ed. Trimpin: Contraptions for Art & Sound. 2011. (ENG., Illus.). 208p. 40.00 (978-0-295-99109-2(7)) Marquand Bks., Inc.

Fort, Ilene Susan, et al, contrib. by. In Wonderland: The Surrealist Adventures of Women Artists in Mexico & the United States. 2012. (ENG., Illus.). 256p. 60.00 **(978-3-7913-5141-4(9))** Prestel Publishing.

Foster, Fredericka. Waterway. 2009. (Illus.). 22p. (978-1-891848-15-5(1)) Fischbach Gallery.

Frank, Nance & Sanchez, Mario. Mario Sanchez: Better Than Ever. 2010. (ENG.). 96p. pap. 20.00 (978-1-56164-476-6(5)) Pineapple Pr., Inc.

Freedman, Luba. Classical Myths in Italian Renaissance Painting. 2011. (ENG., Illus.). 308p. 95.00 (978-1-107-00119-0(6)) Cambridge Univ. Pr.

—The Revival of the Olympian Gods in Renaissance Art. 2010. (ENG., Illus.). 320p. (C). pap. 44.00 (978-0-521-18103-7(8)) Cambridge Univ. Pr.

Friedman, Drew. Drew Friedman's Sideshow Freaks. 2011. (ENG., Illus.). 112p. 19.95 (978-0-922233-36-6(5)) Blast Bks.

Friedrich, Julia & KtxFBnig, Kasper, eds. Wüste, Meer und Sterne: Desert, Sea & Stars. 2011. (GER & ENG., Illus.). 152p. 55.00 **(978-3-86560-971-7(6))** Verlag der Buchhandlung Walther Konig DEU. Dist: D.A.P./Distributed Art Pubs.

Furnas, Barnaby & Dunham, Carroll. Barnaby Furnas. 2009. (ENG., Illus.). 160p. 50.00 (978-0-8109-9625-0(1)) Abrams.

Gao, Minglu. Total Modernity & the Avant-Garde in Twentieth-Century Chinese Art. 2011. (ENG., Illus.). 424p. (gr. 17). 39.95 (978-0-262-01494-6(7)) MIT Pr.

Gaudaire-Thor, Jean. Trafiquer dans L'inconnu... Arthur Rimbaud. 2008. (ENG.). 224p. pap. 60.00 (978-2-35340-023-2(X)) Gourcuff Gradenigo FRA. Dist: National Bk. Network.

German, Andrew. John Stobart: The Grandeur of America's Age of Sail. 2009. 168p. 34.95 (978-0-9635775-4-2(9)); (ENG.). pap. 24.95 (978-0-9635775-5-9(7)) Osmington Hse. Publishing.

Getsy, David. From Diversion to Subversion: Games, Play, & Twentieth-Century Art. 2011. (Refiguring Modernism Ser.). (ENG.). 240p. pap. 74.95 (978-0-271-03703-5(2)) Pennsylvania State Univ. Pr.

Geysen, Leopold & Derez, M. Leuven: Een serie Aquarellen. 2007. (ENG.). 93p. (C). 33.00 (978-90-429-1844-3(6)) Peeters Pubs. & Booksellers BEL. Dist: Brown, David Bk. Co., The.

Gillespie, Spike. Quilting Art: Inspiration, Ideas & Innovative Works from 20 Contemporary Quilters. 2009. (ENG., Illus.). 160p. 35.00 (978-0-7603-3526-0(5), 0760335265, Voyageur Pr) MBI Publishing Co. LLC.

Glen, Thistlewood & Thistlewood, Stephen. Carnival Glass: The Magic & the Mystery. 2nd rev. ed. 2008. (Illus.). 224p. 49.99 (978-0-7643-2989-0(8)) Schiffer Publishing, Ltd.

Glier, Mike, et al. Mike Glier: Along a Long Line. 2009. (ENG., Illus.). 200p. 60.00 (978-1-55595-319-5(0)) Hudson Hills Pr. LLC.

González, José Gamaliel. Bringing Aztlan to Chicago: My Life, My Work & My Art. Zimmerman, Marc, ed. 2010. (Latinos in Chicago & Midwest Ser.). (ENG.). 216p. pap. 30.00 (978-0-252-07735-7(0)) Univ. of Illinois Pr.

—Bringing Aztlan to Mexican Chicago: My Life, My Work & My Art. Zimmerman, Marc, ed. 2010. (Latinos in Chicago & Midwest Ser.). (ENG., Illus.). 216p. 65.00 (978-0-252-03538-8(0)) Univ. of Illinois Pr.

Gorringe, Timothy J. Earthly Visions: Theology & the Challenge of Art. 2011. (ENG., Illus.). 264p. 45.00 (978-0-300-16280-6(4)) Yale Univ. Pr.

Govier, Louise. Hogarth to Turner: British Painting. 2010. (ENG., Illus.). 72p. pap. 15.00 (978-1-85709-487-9(5)) Yale Univ. Pr.

Groebner, Valentin. Defaced: The Visual Culture of Violence in the Late Middle Ages. Selwyn, Pamela, tr. from GER. 2009. (ENG., Illus.). 217p. (gr. 17). pap. 22.95 (978-1-890951-38-2(2)) Zone Bks.

Guile, Carolyn C., et al. Reading Space: The Art of Xu Bing. Guile, Carolyn C., ed. 2009. (Illus.). 68p. pap. 25.00 (978-0-9819530-0-7(X)) Colgate University — Clifford Gallery.

Guston, P. Writing & Talking. 2010. (Documents of Twentieth-Century Art Ser.). (Illus.). 352p. 65.00 (978-0-520-23509-0(6)) Univ. of California Pr.

Guttmann, Allen. Sports & American Art from Benjamin West to Andy Warhol. 2011. (Illus.). 336p. 39.95 (978-1-55849-874-7(5)) Univ. of Massachusetts Pr.

Hackett, Regina. I Surprise Myself: The Art of Elizabeth Sandvig. 2007. (ENG., Illus.). 64p. 27.95 (978-0-295-98710-1(3)) Univ. of Washington Pr.

Hampton, Alexa. The Language of Interior Design. 2010. (ENG., Illus.). 256p. 50.00 (978-0-307-46053-0(3), Clarkson Potter) Crown Publishing Group.

Hans Wolfsbauer-Schönau Salzburg: Gemälde und Grafiken Paintings & Drawings. 2009. 208p. 49.95 (978-3-211-98121-4(7)) Springer Wien AUT. Dist: Actar Birkhauser Distribution.

Harrison, Charles. Painting the Difference: Sex & Spectator in Modern Art. 2008. (ENG., Illus.). 312p. pap. 45.00 (978-0-226-31798-4(6)) Univ. of Chicago Pr.

Hayes, Paula & Marshall, Richard D. Paula Hayes. 2012. (ENG., Illus.). 240p. 50.00 **(978-1-58093-329-2(7))** Monacelli Pr., Inc.

Heartney, Eleanor & DeMonte, Claudia. Claudia Demonte. 2009. 112p. 29.95 (978-0-7649-5097-1(5)) Pomegranate Communications, Inc.

Heil, Axel & Schoppmann, Wolfgang, eds. Peter Zimmerman: Epoxiology, 1 vol. 2007. (FRE, GER & ENG., Illus.). 148p. 60.00 (978-3-86560-179-7(0)) Verlag der Buchhandlung Walther Konig DEU. Dist: D.A.P./Distributed Art Pubs.

Hein, Laura & Jennison, Rebecca, eds. Imagination Without Borders: Feminist Artist Tomiyama Taeko & Social Responsibility. 2010. (Illus.). 164p. 60.00 (978-1-929280-62-9(9)) Univ. of Michigan, Ctr. for Japanese Studies.

—Imagination Without Borders: Feminist Artist Tomiyama Taeko & Social Responsibility. 2010. (Illus.). 164p. pap. 24.00 (978-1-929280-63-6(7)) Univ. of Michigan, Ctr. for Japanese Studies.

Hemer, Irene. Siqueiros: Landscape Painter. 2011. (ENG., Illus.). 236p. 50.00 (978-84-92480-96-8(3)) RM Verlag, S.L. ESP. Dist: D.A.P./Distributed Art Pubs.

Himmelsbach, Sabine & Eppeneder, Ralf, eds. Gateways: Kunst und vernetzte Kultur. 2011. (GER & ENG., Illus.). 240p. pap. 55.00 **(978-3-7757-2796-9(5))** Hatje Cantz Verlag GmbH & Co KG DEU. Dist: D.A.P./Distributed Art Pubs.

Hinrichs, Ernst & Zernack, Klaus, eds. Daniel Chodowiecki (1726-1801) Kupferstecher, Illustrator, Kaufmann. (Wolfenbatteler Studien zur Aufklärung Ser.).Tr. of Daniel Chodowiecki (1726-1801). Engraver, genre painter Merchant. (GER.). X, 265p. 165.00 **(978-3-11-179461-7(X))** De Gruyter, Walter Inc.

Hirondelle, Anne, et al. Anne Hirondelle: Ceramic Art, 1 vol. 2012. (ENG., Illus.). 88p. 29.95 **(978-0-295-99151-1(8))** Univ. of Washington Pr.

Hirsh, Jennie & Wallace, Isabelle Loring. Contemporary Art & Classical Myth. 2011. (Illus.). 410p. 124.95 (978-0-7546-6974-6(2)) Ashgate Publishing Co.

Hough, Jessica & Ramirez-Montagut, Monica, eds. Revisiting the Glass House: Contemporary Art & Modern Architecture. 2008. (ENG., Illus.). 134p. pap. 39.95 (978-0-300-13587-9(4)) Yale Univ. Pr.

Hourihane, Colum. Looking Beyond: Visions, Dreams & Insights in Medieval Art & Thought. 2010. (Index of Christian Art: Occasional Papers Ser.). (ENG., Illus.). 400p. pap. 35.00 (978-0-9768202-8-4(5)) Index of Christian Art, Princeton Univ., The.

Huang, Teresa, tr. Poetic License-the Art of Joan Schulze. 2010. (ENG & CHI., Illus.). 168p. (978-0-9744196-2-6(1)) Schulze, Joan.

—Poetic License-the Art of Joan Schulze. 2010. (ENG & CHI.). pap. 42.00 (978-0-9744196-3-3(X)) Schulze, Joan.

Humphrey, Joanne Fenton. Ameen. 2009. (Illus.). 121p. 49.95 (978-0-615-29130-7(9)) Windjammer Adventure Publishing.

Hustvedt, Siri. Mysteries of the Rectangle: Essays on Painting. 2006. (ENG., Illus.). 204p. pap. 24.95 (978-1-56898-618-0(1)) Princeton Architectural Pr.

Inselmann, Andrea. Dangerous Waters. 2007. 20.00 net. (978-1-934260-00-5(2)) Cornell Univ., Herbert F. Johnson Museum of Art.

Irwin, Robert & Simms, Matthew. Notes Toward a Conditional Art. 2011. (ENG., Illus.). 352p. 35.00 (978-1-60606-075-9(9), J. Paul Getty Museum) Getty Pubns.

Ishkanian, Hagop. Hagop Ishkanian: Works, 1962-2008. 2008. (ARM & ENG., Illus.). 160p. pap. (978-1-60725-611-3(8)) Kan sasana Printer.

Jamal, Ashraf, et al. Lien Botha. (TAXI Art Bks.: Bk. 5). (Illus.). 16p. (C). pap., tchr. ed., suppl. ed. (978-0-9584496-2-5(7)) Krut, David Publishing.

Jankovics, Marcell & Méry, Gábor. A Locsei Szent Jakab Templom Szárnyasoltárai. 2007. (HUN., Illus.). 114p. (978-80-89286-00-3(3)) Mery, Gabriel, Mery Ratio.

Johnson, Janis. The Artist's Eye: Vernon P. Johnson's Watercolors of 1950s Small Town America. 2010. (Illus.). 136p. (C). 34.95 (978-0-615-37465-9(4)) Knox County Historical Society.

Johung, Jennifer. Replacing Home: From Primordial Hut to Digital Network in Contemporary Art. 2011. (ENG., Illus.). 232p. 75.00 **(978-0-8166-7287-5(3))**; pap. 25.00 **(978-0-8166-7288-2(1))** Univ. of Minnesota Pr.

Jones, Malcolm. The Print in Early Modern England: An Historical Oversight. 2010. (ENG., Illus.). 352p. 95.00 (978-0-300-13697-5(8)) Yale Univ. Pr.

Kaal, Anneke. From Beginning to End: Painting Creation, the Ten Commandments, the Apostles' Creed, & Apocalypse. 2006. (Illus.). 88p. (978-1-903689-39-4(2)) Piquant Editions Ltd.

Kaill, Susie. Alexandre Hogue: An American Visionary — Paintings & Works on Paper. 2010. (Tarleton State University Southwestern Studies in the Humanities Ser.). (Illus.). 232p. 35.00 (978-1-60344-214-5(6)) Texas A&M Univ. Pr.

Kandinsky, Wassily. Concerning the Spiritual in Art. 2008. 80p. pap. (978-1-4068-7576-8(7)) Echo Library.

—Concerning the Spiritual in Art. 2010. (Illus.). 52p. pap. 20.00 (978-1-153-59686-2(5)) General Bks. LLC.

—Concerning the Spiritual in Art. 2011. 94p. pap. 16.95 (978-1-60444-270-0(0)) IndoEuropeanPublishing.com.

—Concerning the Spiritual in Art. 2010. (ENG., Illus.). 84p. pap. 8.95 (978-1-60942-001-7(2)) International Alliance Pro-Publishing, LLC.

—Concerning the Spiritual in Art. 2010. 68p. pap. 13.56 (978-1-162-65829-5(2)); 31.95 (978-1-161-42693-9(0)) Kessinger Publishing, LLC.

—Concerning the Spiritual in Art. 2008. (ENG.). 80p. pap. 8.95 (978-1-60597-829-1(9), Book Jungle) Standard Pubns., Inc.

Kanzaka, Sekka & Marks, Andreas. Kamisaka Sekka: Rinpa Traditionalist, Modern Designer. 2012. 192p. ***(978-0-7649-6175-5(6))*** Pomegranate Communications, Inc.

Kastner, Jeffrey. Nature. 2012. (Whitechapel: Documents of Contemporary Art Ser.). (ENG.). 240p. (gr. 17). pap. 24.95 ***(978-0-262-51766-9(3))*** MIT Pr.

Kelly, Daniel. Daniel Kelly: An American Artist in Japan, 1 vol. 2010. (ENG., Illus.). 128p. 45.00 *(978-4-7700-3133-4(5))* Kodansha America, Inc.

Ken Davies American Realist. aut. ed. 2009. (Illus.). 224p. 60.00 *(978-0-615-29534-3(7))* Ken & Maryann Davies.

Kessler, Herbert L. & Nirenberg, David, eds. Judaism & Christian Art: Aesthetic Anxieties from the Catacombs to Colonialism. 2011. (Illus.). 456p. (C). 69.95 *(978-0-8122-4285-0(8))* Univ. of Pennsylvania Pr.

Kibuuka, David. Modern Batik Art. 2009. 108p. pap. 61.99 *(978-1-4363-5178-2(2))* Xlibris Corp.

Kiely, Robert. Blessed & Beautiful: Picturing the Saints. 2010. (Illus.). 288p. 40.00 *(978-0-300-16277-6(4))* Yale Univ. Pr.

Kitchen, Denis, et al. The Oddly Compelling Art of Denis Kitchen. 2010. (Illus.). 200p. 34.99 *(978-1-59582-360-1(3))* Dark Horse Comics.

Kleuver, Beatrix. Country Chic. 2011. (ENG., Illus.). 160p. 50.00 ***(978-90-8989-475-5(6))*** Lannoo Pubs./Racine.

Kogan, Simon. Simon Kogan: Sculptor. 2008. (Illus.). *(978-0-9798608-0-5(6))* Kan sasana Printer.

Kondoleon, Christine, text. Aphrodite & the Gods of Love. 2011. (ENG., Illus.). 256p. 55.00 *(978-0-87846-756-3(4))* Museum of Fine Arts, Boston.

Korero Books Staff & Strongman, Jay. Steampunk: The Art of Victorian Futurism. 2011. (ENG.). 176p. 35.00 *(978-1-907621-03-1(2))* Korero Books LLP GBR. Dist: Independent Pubs. Group.

Korn, Irene. Great Masterpieces of the World. 2nd rev. ed. 2009. 128p. 17.95 *(978-1-59764-122-7(7))* New Line Bks.

Kristeva, Julia. The Severed Head: Capital Visions. Gladding, Jody, tr. from FRE. 2011. (European Perspectives: a Series in Social Thought & Cultural Criticism Ser.). (ENG., Illus.). 176p. (gr. 17). 34.50 ***(978-0-231-15720-9(7))*** Columbia Univ. Pr.

Krols, Birgit. 3D Street Art, 1 vol. 2011. (ENG., Illus.). 192p. pap. 39.95 *(978-90-79761-29-6(X))* Tectum B.V.B.A. BEL. Dist: Innovative Logistics.

Kubo, Tite. Bleach Masked - Official Character, Bk. 2. 2012. (Bleach MASKED: Official Character Book 2 Ser.). (ENG.). 200p. pap. 14.99 ***(978-1-4215-4230-0(7))*** Viz Media.

Kunz, Sabine, ed. Observing Beast, Time, Evolution: Art & Natural Science. 2009. (ENG., Illus.). 128p. pap. 28.50 *(978-3-86678-206-8(3))* Kerber Verlag DEU. Dist: D.A.P./Distributed Art Pubs.

Lachman, Charles. The Ten Symbols of Longevity. 2006. (Collection in Context). (ENG., Illus.). 56p. per. 19.95 *(978-0-295-98657-9(3))* Univ. of Washington Pr.

Lamboy, Stephen, et al. Giancarlo & Stefano Pedretti: Maestri Incisori = Master Engravers. 2010. (Illus.). 256p. ***(978-1-886768-97-0(8))*** Blue Bk. Pubns., Inc.

Langer, Lawrence L., et al. Icons of Loss: The Art of Samuel Bak. 2011. *(978-1-936658-02-2(X))* QCC Art Gallery.

Lascault, Gilbert. In Folio: Gouaches et Aquarelles de Candida Romero. 2012. (FRE & ENG., Illus.). 112p. pap. 30.00 *(978-2-35340-025-6(6))* Gourcuff Gradenigo FRA. Dist: National Bk. Network.

Lazzari, Margaret & Schlesier, Dona. Exploring Art: A Global, Thematic Approach. 4th ed. 2011. (ENG.). 512p. (C). pap. 168.95 *(978-1-111-34379-8(9))*; pap. 160.95 *(978-1-111-34378-1(0))* Brooks/Cole.

Lim, C. J. & Liu, Ed. Short Stories: London in Two-and-a-half Dimensions. 2011. (ENG., Illus.). 240p. 155.00 *(978-0-415-66889-7(1))* Routledge.

Lindey, Christine. Keywords of Nineteenth-Century Art. 2007. (ENG.). 240p. 35.00 *(978-0-9532609-3-5(3))*; (Illus.). pap. 19.95 *(978-0-9532609-1-1(7))* Antique Collectors' Club GBR. (Sansom (Acc)). Dist: National Bk. Network.

Lucas, Charlie & Windham, Ben. Tin Man. 2nd ed. 2009. (ENG., Illus.). 192p. 49.95 *(978-0-8173-1681-5(7))* Univ. of Alabama Pr.

Luce, Stephen. Studies of the Exploits of Heracles on Vases. 2009. pap. 19.60 *(978-1-60724-455-4(1))* Gorgias Pr., LLC.

Mahler, Carol. Guy Labree: Barefoot Artist of the Florida Seminoles. 2010. (ENG., Illus.). 152p. 34.95 *(978-0-8130-3430-0(2))* Univ. Pr. of Florida.

Marchesi, Robin. Barry Flanagan: Poet of the Building Site. 2012. (ENG., Illus.). 64p. pap. 22.95 ***(978-88-8158-824-4(2))*** Charta ITA. Dist: D.A.P./Distributed Art Pubs.

Marcos, Marcos A., et al. Marguerite Nakhla: Legacy to Modern Egyptian Art. 2009. (ENG., Illus.). 141p. (C). pap. 39.95 *(978-0-9812726-0-3(6))* Brown, David Bk. Co., The.

Marepe, et al. Marepe. 2008. (POR & ENG., Illus.). 192p. 69.00 *(978-3-935567-40-4(5))* Holzwarth Pubns. DEU. Dist: D.A.P./Distributed Art Pubs.

Markus, Csaba. Artist & Muses: The Life & Art of Csaba Markus. 2007. (Illus.). *(978-0-9746635-1-7(4))* Dreaming Muse Fine Art Books & DVDs.

Marsh, Joanna & Rockman, Alexis. Alexis Rockman: A Fable for Tomorrow. 2010. (Illus.). 176p. *(978-0-9790678-8-4(X))* Smithsonian American Art Museum.

Martin, David F. The Art of Richard Bennett. 2010. (ENG., Illus.). 80p. pap. 24.95 *(978-0-939806-07-2(X))* Historical Society of Seattle & King County/Museum of History & Industry.

Massey, Richard J., intro. The Last Supper: A Yigal Ozeri exhibit from the Richard J. Massey Collection. 2010. (ENG.). 50.00 *(978-0-615-39882-2(0))* Massey, Richard.

Massing, Jean-Michel. Studies in Imagery. 2007. (FRE & ENG., Illus.). 446p. (C). 300.00 *(978-1-899828-98-2(2))* Pindar Pr. GBR. Dist: Brown, David Bk. Co., The.

MCD. The Land of the Number Zero: Art & Text. 2007. (Illus.). 141p. 54.99 *(978-1-4363-1566-1(2))* Xlibris Corp.

McKenzie, Janet. Holiness & the Feminine Spirit: The Art of Janet Mckenzie. 2009. (Illus.). 144p. 28.00 *(978-1-57075-844-7(1))* Orbis Bks.

Mecklenburg, Virginia & McCarthy, Todd. Telling Stories: Norman Rockwell from the Collections of George Lucas & Steven Spielberg. 2010. (ENG., Illus.). 256p. 65.00 *(978-0-8109-9651-9(0))* Abrams.

Meltzoff, Stanley & Rivkin, Mike. Stanley Meltzoff: Picture Maker. 2010. (Illus.). 182p. *(978-0-935217-99-5(1))* International Game Fish Assn.

Mercurio, Gianni, et al. Tony Oursler: Open Obscura. 2011. (ITA & ENG., Illus.). 176p. 55.00 *(978-88-7179-663-5(2))* Antique Collectors' Club.

Meret, Sasha. Lost & Found Appointments. 2012. ***(978-0-923389-03-1(2))*** Spuyten Duyvil.

Micheli-Lamboy, Elena, et al. Firmo Fracassi: Maestro Incisore = Master Engraver. 2008. (Illus.). 236p. ***(978-1-886768-83-3(8))*** Blue Bk. Pubns., Inc.

Mignonneau, Laurent. Christa Sommerer & Laurent Mignonneau: Interactive Art Research. Stocker, Gerfried & Sommerer, Christa, eds. 2009. (ENG., Illus.). 232p. 59.95 *(978-3-211-99015-5(1)*, 3211990151) Springer.

Millett-Gallant, Ann. The Disabled Body in Contemporary Art. (ENG., Illus.). 2012. 188p. pap. 27.00 ***(978-0-230-34142-5(X))*** 2010. 192p. 79.00 *(978-0-230-10406-8(1))* Palgrave Macmillan.

Millos, Elias Ioannes, intro. John of Mosul's Book of Beautiful Guidance. 2010. (SYR.). 116.00 *(978-1-60724-878-1(6))* Gorgias Pr., LLC.

Minsky, Richard. The Book Art of Richard Minsky. 2011. (ENG., Illus.). 148p. 34.95 *(978-0-8076-1606-2(0)*, 761606) Braziller, George Inc.

Mishori, Efrat. Mika Rottenberg. 2011. (ENG., Illus.). 204p. 45.00 *(978-0-9826813-0-5(5))* Miller, Gregory & Co.

Mistretta, Andrea. Mardi Gras Parade of Posters, 1 vol. 2009. (ENG., Illus.). 96p. 19.95 *(978-1-58980-778-5(2))* Pelican Publishing Co., Inc.

Monet, Claude. Monet's Impressions: Words & Pictures. 2009. (Illus.). *(978-1-58889-806-7(7))* Chronicle Bks. LLC.

Montoya, Juan. Juan Montoya. 2009. (ENG., Illus.). 304p. 75.00 *(978-1-58093-244-8(4))* Monacelli Pr., Inc.

Morano, Cohen. Rest Is up to You: A Boy Named Cohen Morano, 118 Artists, & a Watercolor Revolution. 2009. (ENG., Illus.). 176p. (J). (gr. -1-17). pap. 24.95 *(978-0-8118-6859-4(1))* Chronicle Bks. LLC.

Morden, Barbara. John Martin: Apocalypse Now! 2011. (ENG., Illus.). 150p. 49.95 *(978-1-904794-99-8(8))* Northumbria University Press GBR. Dist: Independent Pubs. Group.

Morelli, Angela. Roman Britain & Classical Deities. 2009. (ENG., Illus.). 75p. (C). pap. 67.50 *(978-1-4073-0427-4(5))* British Archaeological Reports Ltd. GBR. Dist: Brown, David Bk. Co., The.

Morgan, Robert C., et al. Marcia Gygli King: Forty Years. Sherer, Scott A., ed. 2008. (Illus.). 60p. pap. 15.00 *(978-1-883502-17-1(9))* San Antonio Museum of Art.

Moseneder, Karl. Streit Um Bilder. (GER., Illus.). xxxvii, 235p. *(978-3-496-01169-9(6))* Reimer, Dietrich.

Mozzati, Luca. Islamic Art. 2010. (Illus.). 320p. 85.00 *(978-3-7913-4455-3(2))* Prestel Publishing.

Murray, Patricia. Hawaiian Quilt Inspirations. 2009. 80p. pap. 9.95 *(978-1-56647-918-9(5))* Mutual Publishing LLC.

Naylor, David. Old World Interiors: A Modern Interpretation, 1 vol. 2008. (ENG., Illus.). 184p. 40.00 *(978-1-4236-0116-6(5))* Gibbs Smith, Publisher.

Nelson, Maggie. The Art of Cruelty: A Reckoning. 2011. (ENG.). 304p. 24.95 *(978-0-393-07215-0(0)*, 7215) Norton, W. W. & Co., Inc.

Nieman, John. Art of More Lists. 2009. (Illus.). 95p. 42.99 *(978-1-4415-5838-1(1))* Xlibris Corp.

Nolen-Weathington, Eric. Nick Cardy: Behind the Art. 2008. 128p. 34.95 *(978-1-893905-99-3(3))* TwoMorrows Publishing.

Nova, Alessandro. The Book of the Wind: The Representation of the Invisible. 2011. (ENG., Illus.). 224p. (C). *(978-0-7735-3833-7(X))* McGill-Queen's Univ. Pr.

Ochiauri, Gogi, ed. The Sculptures & Art of Gogi Ochiauri: an Album with Text. 2010. (Focus on Civilizations & Cultures - Painting & Sculpture Ser.). 89.00 *(978-1-61668-304-7(X))* Nova Science Pubs., Inc.

Osthoff, Simone. Performing the Archive: The transformation of the archive in Contemporary art from repository of documents to art Medium. Schirmacher, Wolfgang, ed. 2009. (Illus.). 208p. pap. 21.95 *(978-0-9825309-0-0(0))* Atropos Pr.

Padiyar, Satish. Chains: David, Canova, & the Fall of the Public Hero in Postrevolutionary France. 2007. (ENG., Illus.). 224p. 60.00 *(978-0-271-02963-4(3))* Pennsylvania State Univ. Pr.

Parrish, Maxfield. Worlds of Enchantment: The Art of Maxfield Parrish. 2010. (Dover Fine Art, History of Art Ser.). (ENG., Illus.). 96p. pap. 14.95 *(978-0-486-47306-2(6))* Dover Pubns., Inc.

Parron, Suzi & Groves, Donna Sue. Barn Quilts & the American Quilt Trail Movement. 2012. (ENG., Illus.). 240p. pap. 29.95 ***(978-0-8040-1138-9(9))*** Swallow Pr.

Pawson, John. A Visual Inventory. 2012. (ENG., Illus.). 320p. 49.95 ***(978-0-7148-6350-4(5))*** Phaidon Pr., Inc.

Payne, Alina. From Ornament to Object: Genealogies of Architectural Modernism. 2012. (ENG., Illus.). 360p. 65.00 ***(978-0-300-17533-2(7))*** Yale Univ. Pr.

Pericoli, Matteo. The City Out My Window: 63 Views on New York. 2009. (ENG., Illus.). 144p. 21.99 *(978-1-4165-6990-9(1))* Simon & Schuster.

Perron, Suzanne. Designing in Ivory & White: Suzanne Perron Gowns from the Inside Out. 2012. (Illus.). 152p. 55.00 ***(978-0-8071-4370-4(7))*** Louisiana State Univ. Pr.

Perry, Claire. The Great American Hall of Wonders: Art, Science, & Invention in the Nineteenth Century. 2011. (ENG., Illus.). 256p. 65.00 *(978-1-904832-97-3(0))* Giles, D. Ltd. GBR. Dist: Antique Collectors' Club.

—The Great American Hall of Wonders: Art, Science, & Invention in the Nineteenth Century. 2011. *(978-0-9790678-9-1(8))* Smithsonian American Art Museum.

Phaidon Press Editors. The Art Book. 2006. (SPA.). pap. 24.95 *(978-0-7148-9854-4(6))* Phaidon Pr., Inc.

Phillips, Gary & Fewell, Danna. Icon of Loss: The Haunting Child of Samuel Bak. Barletta, Destiny, ed. 2009. 50.00 *(978-1-879985-21-6(7))* Pucker Gallery.

Philosophy of Time Travel. 2007. per. *(978-0-942949-33-9(1))* Studio Museum in Harlem, The.

Podwal, Mark. Doctored Drawings. 2007. (ENG., Illus.). 80p. 22.00 *(978-1-934137-02-4(2))* Bellevue Literary Pr.

Post, Melissa G. Preston Singletary: Echoes, Fire, & Shadows. 2009. (ENG., Illus.). 152p. 45.00 *(978-0-295-98918-1(1))* Univ. of Washington Pr.

Preimesberger, Rudolf. Paragons & Paragone: Van Eyck Raphael Michelangelo Caravaggio Bernini. 2011. (ENG., Illus.). 158p. 40.00 *(978-0-89236-964-5(7)*, Getty Research Institute) Getty Pubns.

Pruitt, Rob. Pop Touched Me: The Art of Rob Pruitt. 2010. (ENG., Illus.). 224p. 50.00 *(978-0-8109-5432-8(X))* Abrams.

Rabottini, Alessandro, ed. Permanent Mimesis: An Exhibition about Simulation & Realism. 2010. 112p. 47.50 *(978-88-370-7793-8(9))* Electa ITA. Dist: Trans-Atlantic Pubns., Inc.

Rachlin, Harvey. Scandals, Vandals, & Da Vincis: A Gallery of Remarkable Art Tales. 2007. (ENG., Illus.). 368p. (gr. 12-18). 15.00 *(978-0-14-303835-1(4)*, Penguin (Non-Classics)) Penguin Group (USA) Inc.

Reifenscheid, Beate, ed. The Final Freedom: from the Pioneers of Land Art. 2011. (GER & ENG., Illus.). 192p. pap. 40.00 ***(978-88-366-2002-9(7))*** Silvana ITA. Dist: D.A.P./Distributed Art Pubs.

Reuter, Laurel & Mojsilov, Zoran. Zoran Mojsilov. 2009. (Illus.). 91p. *(978-0-943107-20-2(2))* North Dakota Museum of Art.

Rewald, Sabine. Rooms with a View: The Open Window in the 19th Century. 2011. (Illus.). 204p. pap. 30.00 *(978-0-300-16977-5(9))* Yale Univ. Pr.

Roberts, Holly. Holly Roberts: Works 2000 to 2009. 2010. (Illus.). 70p. ***(978-1-59005-258-7(7))*** Nazraeli Pr.

Rockwell, Norman. Norman Rockwell's Spirit of America. 2011. (ENG., Illus.). 224p. 24.95 *(978-1-4197-0065-1(0))* Abrams.

Roper, Lyndal. The Witch in the Western Imagination. 2012. E-Book ***(978-0-8139-3300-9(5))***; (ENG., Illus.). 248p. (gr. 17). 39.50 ***(978-0-8139-3297-2(1))*** Univ. Pr. of Virginia.

Rosen, Jo-Anne, ed. Transformations: The Sculpture & Paintings of Harriet Grannis Moore. 2008. (Illus.). 138p. pap. 30.00 *(978-1-931002-70-7(3)*, Wordrunner Pr.) Wordrunner Chapbooks.

Ross, Alex. Rough Justice. Kidd, Chip, ed. 2010. (ENG., Illus.). 224p. 30.00 *(978-0-375-71490-0(1)*, Pantheon) Knopf Doubleday Publishing Group.

Ross, Alex. Rough Justice: The DC Comics Sketches of Alex Ross. Kidd, Chip, ed. 2012. (ENG., Illus.). 224p. pap. 24.95 ***(978-0-307-37878-1(0)***, Pantheon) Knopf Doubleday Publishing Group.

Ryan, Jay. 100 Posters / 134 Squirrels: A Decade of Hot Dogs, Large Mammals, & Independent Rock: the Handcrafted Art of Jay Ryan. 2010. (ENG., Illus.). 120p. pap. 22.95 ***(978-1-936070-68-8(5))*** Akashic Bks.

Ryman, Robert. Robert Ryman: Variations & Improvisations, 1 vol. 2010. (ENG.). 32p. pap. 15.95 *(978-0-943044-35-4(9))* Phillips Collection, The.

Samaras, Isabel. On Tender Hooks. 2009. (ENG.). 160p. 250.00 *(978-0-8118-7087-0(1))*; (Illus.). 35.00 *(978-0-8118-6604-0(1))* Chronicle Bks. LLC.

Sarram, M. Persian Painting at Its Best: The Life & the Work of Colonel M. Sarram. 2009. 276p. pap. 74.95 *(978-1-4389-3279-8(0))* AuthorHouse.

Scala, Mark W., ed. Fairy Tales, Monsters, & the Genetic Imagination. 2012. (Frist Center for the Visual Arts Title Ser.). (ENG., Illus.). 160p. pap. 29.95 *(978-0-8265-1814-9(1))* Vanderbilt Univ. Pr.

Scheicher, Harald & Biller, Barbara. Macht des Bildes - Visionen des Göttliche: Kunst und Transzendent in Österreich im 20. Jahrhundert. Katalogbuch zur Ausstellung in Bleiburg, 26.04.2009-08.11.2009, Werner Berg Museum Bleiburg. 2009. (Illus.). 383p. *(978-3-7774-8055-8(X))* Hirmer Verlag GmbH.

Scher, Paula. MAPS. 2011. (ENG., Illus.). 144p. 50.00 ***(978-1-61689-033-9(9))*** Princeton Architectural Pr.

Scholten, Frits. Judith Pfaeltzer: The Sculpture as Landscape. 2008. (DUT & ENG., Illus.). 112p. pap. 55.00 *(978-90-400-8387-7(8))* Waanders B.V., Uitgeverij NLD. Dist: National Bk. Network.

Schulte, Jessica. Can You Find It Inside? Search & Discover for Young Art Lovers. 2009. (ENG.). 27p. (J). 13.00 *(978-1-4379-6650-3(0))* DIANE Publishing Co.

Schultz, Deborah. Pictorial Narrative in the Nazi Period: Felix Nussbaum, Charlotte Salomon & Arnold Daghani. 2009. (ENG., Illus.). 148p. (C). 125.00 *(978-0-415-49095-5(2))* Routledge.

Seidenberg, Jean. Jean Seidenberg: Paintings, Drawings, Sculpture. 2009. (ENG.). 144p. 40.00 *(978-0-9627757-1-0(1))* Silkmont/Count.

Shelton, Barrie. Learning from the Japanese City: Looking East in Urban Design. 2nd rev. ed. (Planning, History & Environment Ser.). (ENG., Illus.). 208p. (C). 2013. pap. 62.95 *(978-0-415-55440-4(3))* 2012. 165.00 *(978-0-415-55439-8(X))* Routledge.

Sheriff, Mary D., ed. Cultural Contact & the Making of European Art since the Age of Exploration. 2010. (Bettie Allison Rand Lectures in Art History Ser.). (ENG., Illus.). 248p. 35.00 *(978-0-8078-3366-7(5))* Univ. of North Carolina Pr.

Shore, Stephen. The Nature of Photographs. 2nd ed. 2010. (ENG., Illus.). 136p. pap. 19.95 *(978-0-7148-5904-0(4))* Phaidon Pr., Inc.

Showers, Jan. Glamorous Rooms. 2009. (ENG., Illus.). 208p. 50.00 *(978-0-8109-4974-4(1))* Abrams.

silvertoons. Passion for Life. 2009. (Illus.). 200p. 40.00 *(978-0-9745701-3-6(3))* silvertoons.

Simon, Joan & Faxon, Susan C. Sheila Hicks: 50 Years. 2010. (ENG., Illus.). 256p. 65.00 *(978-0-300-12164-3(4))* Yale Univ. Pr.

Sims, Martin. Sonic Forms & Acoustic Matter - an Investigation into the Sculptural Possibilities for Conjunctions of Sound & Materiality. 2008. 60p. pap. *(978-3-639-10664-0(4))* VDM Verlag Dr. Mueller e.K.

Smith, Amy Claire. Polis & Personification in Classical Athenian Art. 2011. (Illus.). xlv, 202p. ***(978-90-04-19417-5(7))*** BRILL.

Sparagana, John & Bal, Mieke. Sleeping Beauty: A One-Artist Dictionary. 2008. (Project Tango Ser.). (Illus.). 136p. 35.00 *(978-0-226-03552-9(2))* Univ. of Chicago Pr.

Spring, Christopher. African Art in Detail. 2010. (Art in Detail Ser.). (Illus.). 144p. 22.95 *(978-0-674-03622-2(0))* Harvard Univ. Pr.

Stack, Gael. Gael Stack. 2011. (ENG., Illus.). 216p. 60.00 *(978-0-292-72854-7(9))* Univ. of Texas Pr.

Staninger, Hildegarde. Portals to Destiny. 2011. 44p. pap. 19.99 ***(978-1-61215-857-0(9))*** Xulon Pr., Inc.

Stavitsky, Gail & Warhol, Andy. Warhol & Cars: American Icons. 2011. *(978-0-615-41922-0(4))* Montclair Art Museum.

Stebbing, Peter. The Goetheanum Cupola Motifs of Rudolf Steiner: Paintings by Gerard Wagner. 2011. (Illus.). 248p. *(978-0-88010-737-2(5))* SteinerBooks, Inc.

Steiner, Wendy. The Real Real Thing: The Model in the Mirror of Art. 2010. (Illus.). 240p. 32.50 *(978-0-226-77219-6(5))* Univ. of Chicago Pr.

Strauber, Susan, et al. Women in Impressionism: From Mythical Feminine to Modern Woman. Sondergaard, Sidsel Maria, ed. 2007. (ENG., Illus.). 288p. 55.00 *(978-88-7624-787-3(4))* Skira Editore ITA. Dist: Random Hse., Inc.

Szulakowska, Urszula. Alchemy in Contemporary Art. 2011. (Illus.). 236p. 114.95 *(978-0-7546-6736-0(7))* Ashgate Publishing Co.

The Mailbox Books Staff. Arts & Crafts for Favorite Themes: PreK-1. 2010. (Illus.). 144p. 19.95 *(978-1-56234-935-6(X)*, Mailbox Bks., The) Education Ctr., Inc.

Thomsen, Arne. Die Wirkung der Götter: Bilder Mit Flügelfiguren auf Griechischen Vasen des 6. und 5. Jahrhunderts V. Chr. (Image & Context Ser.).Tr. of Impact of the Gods. (GER.). XII, 506p. 2012. (gr. 17). E-Book 210.00 ***(978-3-11-219164-4(1))*** 2011. (Illus.). 140.00 ***(978-3-11-023898-3(5))*** De Gruyter, Walter Inc.

Tompkins, Robert David, et al. The Life & Art of Ralph Ray, Jr. 2009. (Illus.). 124p. 71.99 *(978-1-4415-2914-5(4))* Xlibris Corp.

Tove, Siv & Walker, Kulbrandstad. Sense & the Senses in Early Modern Art & Cultural Practice. Sanger, Alice E., ed. 2012. (Visual Culture in Early Modernity Ser.). (Illus.). 230p. 124.95 ***(978-1-4094-0004-2(2))*** Ashgate Publishing Co.

Tsao, Hsingyuan & Ames, Roger T., eds. Xu Bing & Contemporary Chinese Art: Cultural & Philosophical Reflections. 2011. (SUNY series in Chinese Philosophy & Culture Ser.). (Illus.). 240p. 75.00 *(978-1-4384-3791-0(9))*; pap. 24.95 *(978-1-4384-3790-3(0))* State Univ. of New York Pr.

Udall, Sharyn R. Dance & American Art: A Long Embrace. 2012. (ENG., Illus.). 456p. 60.00 ***(978-0-299-28800-6(5))*** Univ. of Wisconsin Pr.

Udall, Sharyn Rohlfsen. Dance & American Art: A Long Embrace. 2012. E-Book ***(978-0-299-28803-7(X))*** Univ. of Wisconsin Pr.

van Bogaert, Emily & Brothers, Stephanie. Bryce Hudson: Explorations in the Shadow of Pop Culture. 2009. 56p. 19.95 *(978-0-9797006-1-3(2))* Holland Brown.

Vanhaelen, Angela. The Wake of Iconoclasm: Painting the Church in the Dutch Republic. 2012. (ENG.). 240p. ***(978-0-271-05061-4(6))*** Pennsylvania State Univ. Pr.

Vasquez, Jaime, et al. The Metaphorical Dream: The Art of Jaime Vasquez. 2011. ***(978-1-936658-03-9(8))*** QCC Art Gallery.

Veen, Henk Th. van. The Translation of Raphael's Roman Style. van Veen, H. Th., ed. 2007. (Groningen Studies in Cultural Change Ser.). (ENG.). 138p. (C). 66.00 *(978-90-429-1855-9(1))* Peeters Pubs. & Booksellers BEL. Dist: Brown, David Bk. Co., The.

Viatte, Germain. Yves Lévêque, à Fleur de Terre, 1962-2007: Quarante Cinq Ans de Peinture. 2008. (FRE & ENG., Illus.). 224p. 125.00 *(978-2-35340-035-5(3))* Gourcuff Gradenigo FRA. Dist: National Bk. Network.

Victore, James & Bierut, Michael. Victore or, Who Died & Made You Boss? 2010. (ENG., Illus.). 208p. 40.00 *(978-0-8109-9591-8(3))* Abrams.

Vine, Richard & Gaillard, Christopher. William Steiger: Transport. 2011. (ENG., Illus.). 180p. 60.00 *(978-1-55595-358-4(1))* Hudson Hills Pr. LLC.

Vogt, Ernst. Das Leipziger Antikenmuseum und die griechische Literatur. (Lectiones Teubnerianae (LT) Ser.). (GER.). 58p. 210.00 ***(978-3-11-181303-5(7))*** De Gruyter, Walter Inc.

Wagner, Anne Middleton. A House Divided: American Art since 1955. 2012. (ENG., Illus.). 240p. 70.00 *(978-0-520-26847-0(4))*; pap. 34.95 *(978-0-520-27097-8(5))* Univ. of California Pr.

Weiss, Rachel. To & from Utopia in the New Cuban Art. 2011. (ENG., Illus.). 368p. pap. 34.95 *(978-0-8166-6515-0(X))* Univ. of Minnesota Pr.

Weller, Alan. Mehndi Tattoo Flash CD-ROM & Book. 2011. (Dover Electronic Clip Art Ser.). (ENG., Illus.). 48p. pap. 19.95 *(978-0-486-99093-4(1))* Dover Pubns., Inc.

Wetzel, Craig & Tambellini, Mary L. Come Home & Remember. 2010. *(978-1-933197-73-9(0))* Orange Frazer Pr.

Whyte, Mary. Working South: Paintings & Sketches. 2011. (Illus.). 128p. 49.95 *(978-1-57003-966-9(6))*; pap. 29.95 *(978-1-57003-967-6(4))* Univ. of South Carolina Pr.
Wierich, Jochen. Grand Themes: Emanuel Leutze, Washington Crossing the Delaware, & American History Painting. 2012. (Illus.). 224p. 69.95 ***(978-0-271-05032-4(2))*** Pennsylvania State Univ. Pr.
Williams, Terry Tempest, et al. Island: Paintings by Tom Curry. 2012. (ENG., Illus.). 80p. 19.95 ***(978-1-60893-003-6(3))*** Down East Bks.
Wingate, Carl Edmond. A Heavenly Hobo, Painting Shirts along the Way. 2009. (Illus.). 100p. pap. 24.95 *(978-0-615-25659-7(7))* Photosensography.
Wolf, Rachel Rubin. Strokes of Genius: The Best of Drawing. 2007. (Strokes of Genius Ser.). (ENG., Illus.). 144p. 32.99 *(978-1-58180-861-2(5))*, North Light Bks.) F&W Media, Inc.
—Strokes of Genius 2: Light & Shadow. 2009. (Strokes of Genius Ser.). (ENG., Illus.). 144p. 32.99 *(978-1-60061-158-2(3))*, North Light Bks.) F&W Media, Inc.
Wolf, Vicente. Lifting the Curtain on Design. 2010. (ENG., Illus.). 224p. 50.00 *(978-1-58093-267-7(3))* Monacelli Pr., Inc.
Wyeth, Jamie. Jamie Wyeth: Seven Deadly Sins. 2009. (Illus.). 51p. *(978-0-918749-26-0(3))* Farnsworth, W.A. Library & Art Museum.
Wyeth, N. C. Great Illustrations by N. C. Wyeth. Menges, Jeff A., ed. & intro. by. 2011. (Dover Fine Art, History of Art Ser.). (ENG., Illus.). 128p. pap. 19.95 *(978-0-486-47295-9(7))* Dover Pubns., Inc.
Xingjian, Qian & Xiaoyan, He. Famous Flowers in China. 2010. (Discovering China Ser.). (ENG., Illus.). 112p. 14.95 *(978-1-60652-156-4(X))* Reader's Digest Assn., Inc., The.
Yekani, Elahe Haschemi. The Privilege of Crisis: Narratives of Masculinities in Colonial & Postcolonial Literature, Photography, & Film. 2011. (ENG.). 320p. pap. 49.00 *(978-3-593-39399-5(9))* Campus Verlag GmbH DEU. Dist: Chicago Distribution Ctr.
Yu, Chifu. Chifu Yu: Faces. 2012. (ENG., Illus.). 180p. 39.95 ***(978-0-8351-0018-2(9))*** Long River Pr.
Zanfi, Claudia, ed. Lois & Franziska Weinberger: the Mobile Gardens. 2009. (ENG., Illus.). 80p. pap. 20.00 *(978-88-6208-102-3(2))* Damiani ITA. Dist: D.A.P./Distributed Art Pubs.
Zelevansky, Lynn & Sussman, Elisabeth, eds. Paul Thek: Diver, A Retrospective. 2010. (ENG., Illus.). 304p. 65.00 *(978-0-300-16595-1(1))* Yale Univ. Pr.

ART—THERAPEUTIC USE
see Art Therapy

ART—TRADE
see Art Industries and Trade

ART—VOCATIONAL GUIDANCE
see also Commercial Art—Vocational Guidance

Benson, Barb. The ArtSlut's Guide to Makin' It ~As a Visual Artist. 2007. (ArtSlut's Easy Guides). 128p. per. 14.95 *(978-0-9758655-0-7(1))* Goody Good Deeds Inc.
Bhandari, Heather Darcy & Melber, Jonathan. ArtWork: Everything You Need to Know (And Do) As You Pursue Your Art Career. 2009. (ENG., Illus.). 304p. pap. 16.95 *(978-1-4165-7233-6(3))*, Free Pr.) Free Pr.
Branagan, Alison. Business for Artists & Designers. 2011. (ENG., Illus.). 256p. pap., instr.'s gde. ed. 25.95 *(978-1-4081-1903-7(X))* A & C Black GBR. Dist: Macmillan.
Carey, Brainard. Making It in the Art World: New Approaches to Galleries, Shows, & Raising Money. 2011. (ENG.). 256p. pap. 19.95 *(978-1-58115-868-7(8))*, 115868, Allworth Pr.) Skyhorse Publishing Co., Inc.
Carter, Katharine T. Accelerating on the Curves: The Artist's Roadmap to Success. 2011. pap. 95.00 ***(978-0-9845453-0-8(1))*** Carter, Katharine T. & Assocs.
Cho, Joy Deangdeelert. Creative, Inc: The Ultimate Guide to Running a Successful Freelance Business. 2010. (ENG., Illus.). 184p. pap. 16.95 *(978-0-8118-7161-7(4))* Chronicle Bks. LLC.
Clement, Page. Investigating & Making It in Art. Date not set. (Illus.). 220p. pap. *(978-0-05-005085-9(0))* Addison-Wesley Longman, Inc.
Colston, Valerie. 200 Projects to Strengthen Your Art Skills. 2008. (Aspire Ser.). (ENG., Illus.). 128p. pap. 21.99 *(978-0-7641-3811-9(1))* Barron's Educational Series, Inc.
Eberts, Marjorie & Gisler, Margaret. Careers for Culture Lovers & Other Artsy Types. 3rd ed. 2006. (Careers for You Ser.). (ENG.). 167p. 25.70 *(978-1-4177-6232-3(2))*, Turtleback) Turtleback Bks.
Frank, Patrick L. & Preble, Sarah. Prebles' Artforms. 10th ed. 2011. (ENG.). (C). ring bd. 104.67 *(978-0-205-21822-6(9))*, Prentice Hall) Prentice Hall PTR.
Frank, Patrick L., et al. Prebles' Artforms, Books a la Carte Plus MyArtsLab. 10th ed. 2011. (ENG.). (C). ring bd. 104.67 *(978-0-205-20938-5(6))*, Prentice Hall) Prentice Hall PTR.
Grant, Daniel. The Business of Being an Artist. 4th ed. 2010. (ENG.). 448p. pap. 27.50 *(978-1-58115-673-7(1))*, 115673, Allworth Pr.) Skyhorse Publishing Co., Inc.
Levine, Steven. Lacan Reframed: Interpreting Key Thinkers for the Arts. 2008. (Contemporary Thinkers Reframed Ser.). (ENG., Illus.). 160p. pap. 26.00 *(978-1-84511-548-7(1))* I. B. Tauris & Co., Ltd. GBR. Dist: Macmillan.
Longson, Sally. Life after... Art & Design: A Practical Guide to Life after Your Degree. 2006. (Illus.). 178p. per. 21.95 *(978-0-415-37590-0(8))* Routledge.
Loveland, Elaina. Creative Careers: Paths for Aspiring Actors, Artists, Dancers, Musicians & Writers. 2nd ed. 2009. (ENG.). 352p. pap. 17.95 *(978-1-932662-34-4(0))* SuperCollege LLC.
Martin-Jones, David & Sutton, Damian. Deleuze Reframed: Interpreting Key Thinkers for the Arts. 2008. (Contemporary Thinkers Reframed Ser.). (ENG., Illus.). 160p. pap. 26.00 *(978-1-84511-547-0(3))* I. B. Tauris & Co., Ltd. GBR. Dist: Macmillan.
Matters, Print & Stratford, S. J. Arts & Entertainment. 2009. (Field Guides to Finding a New Career Ser.). 216p. (C). (gr. 9-18). pap. 16.95 *(978-0-8160-7619-2(7))*, Checkmark Bks.); 39.95 *(978-0-8160-7595-9(6))*, Ferguson Publishing Co.) Facts On File, Inc.
Michels, Caroll. How to Survive & Prosper As an Artist: Selling Yourself Without Selling Your Soul. 6th ed. 2009. (ENG.). 400p. pap. 21.99 *(978-0-8050-8848-9(2))*, Owl Bks.) Holt, Henry & Co.
Miller, Stacy & Wojak, Angie. Starting Your Career as an Artist: A Guide for Painters, Sculptors, Photographers, & Other Visual Artists. 2011. (Starting Your Career Ser.). (ENG.). 256p. pap. 19.95 *(978-1-58115-853-3(X))*, 115853, Allworth Pr.) Skyhorse Publishing Co., Inc.
Pierre, Summer. The Artist in the Office: How to Creatively Survive & Thrive Seven Days a Week. 2010. (ENG., Illus.). 128p. (gr. 12-18). 13.95 *(978-0-399-53564-2(0))*, Perigee Trade) Penguin Group (USA) Inc.
Richards, K. Malcolm & Richards, K. M. Derrida Reframed: Interpreting Key Thinkers for the Arts. 2008. (Contemporary Thinkers Reframed Ser.). (ENG., Illus.). 160p. pap. 26.00 *(978-1-84511-546-3(5))* I. B. Tauris & Co., Ltd. GBR. Dist: Macmillan.
Salmon, Mark. Opportunities in Visual Arts Careers. 3rd ed. 2008. (ENG.). 160p. pap. 14.95 *(978-0-07-154529-7(8))*, 0071545298) McGraw-Hill Cos., The.

ART—YEARBOOKS

Brown, Brice & Winkfield, Trevor, eds. The Sienese Shredder, 1 vol. 2007. (ENG., Illus.). 252p. pap. 25.00 *(978-0-9787108-0-4(0))* Sienese Shredder Editions.
Society of Illustrators Staff. Illustrators 50. 50th ed. 2009. (Illus.). 608p. pap. 45.00 *(978-0-06-158278-3(6))*, Collins Design) HarperCollins Pubs.

ART, ABORIGINAL AUSTRALIAN
see also Painting, Aboriginal Australian

Allen, Lindy & Lakic, Mira. Women's Work: Aboriginal Women's Artefacts in the Museum of Victoria. 2007. (ENG., Illus.). 72p. pap. 19.95 *(978-0-7306-8711-5(2))* Museum Victoria Publishing AUS. Dist: National Bk. Network.
Brown, Penny. Aboriginal Designs. 2007. (Design Source Bks.). (ENG., Illus.). 32p. pap. 9.95 *(978-1-84448-253-5(7))* Search Pr., Ltd. GBR. Dist: Independent Pubs. Group.
Croft, Brenda L. Culture Warriors: National Indigenous Art Triennial '07. Clark, Deborah & Jenkins, Susan, eds. 2008. (Illus.). 218p. pap. *(978-0-642-54133-8(7))* National Gallery of Australia.
Demin. Once in Broome. 2007. pap. *(978-1-921248-06-1(8))* Magabala Bks.
Gellatly, Kelly. Gordon Bennett. 2008. (ENG., Illus.). 135p. pap. 29.95 *(978-0-7241-0290-7(6))* National Gallery of Victoria AUS. Dist: National Bk. Network.
Johnson, Vivien. Clifford Possum Tjapaltjarri. 2007. (Illus.). 256p. 55.00 *(978-0-7308-3053-5(5))* Art Gallery of South Australia AUS. Dist: Antique Collectors' Club.
König, Kasper, et al. Remembering Forward: Australian Aboriginal Painting since 1960. 2011. (ENG., Illus.). 188p. (C). 50.00 *(978-1-907372-14-8(8))* Holberton, Paul Publishing GBR. Dist: Univ. of Washington Pr.
McClusky, Pamela. Ancestral Modern: Australian Aboriginal Art. 2012. (ENG., Illus.). 176p. 50.00 ***(978-0-300-18003-9(9))*** Yale Univ. Pr.
McGregor, Ken. Artists of the Western Desert: Portraits, 2006-11. 2011. (ENG., Illus.). 200p. (C). pap. 79.95 ***(978-1-921394-64-5(1))*** Macmillan Art Publishing AUS. Dist: Brown, David Bk. Co., The.
McLean, Ian. White Aborigines: Identity Politics in Australian Art. 2009. (ENG., Illus.). 216p. (C). pap. 33.99 *(978-0-521-12067-8(5))* Cambridge Univ. Pr.
McLean, Ian, ed. How Aborigines Invented the Idea of Contemporary Art: Writings on Aboriginal Contemporary Art. 2011. (ENG., Illus.). 360p. (C). pap. 49.95 *(978-0-909952-37-2(X))* Power Pubns. AUS. Dist: Univ. of Washington Pr.
Michael, Linda, ed. They are Meditating: Bark Paintings from the MCA's Arnott's Collection. 2008. (Illus.). 200p. pap. *(978-1-921034-23-7(8))* Museum of Contemporary Art - Sydney.
Morphy, Howard. Becoming Art: Exploring Cross-Cultural Categories. 2007. (ENG., Illus.). 1p. 104.95 *(978-1-84520-656-7(8))*; 288p. pap. 29.95 *(978-1-84520-657-4(6))* Berg Pubs. GBR. Dist: Macmillan.
Perkins, Hetti, et al, eds. One Sun One Moon: Aboriginal Art in Australia. 2007. (Illus.). 368p. 85.00 *(978-0-7913-3771-5(8))* Prestel Publishing.
Seattle Art Museum Staff, contrib. by. Ancestral Modern: Australian Aboriginal Art: Kaplan & Levi Collection. 2012. ***(978-0-932216-67-0(6))*** Yale Univ. Pr.
Sherer, Scott A. The Lam Collection of Aboriginal Art. 2008. 79p. *(978-1-933979-19-9(4))* Bright Sky Pr.
West, Margie, ed. Yalangbara: Art of the Djang'kawa. 2008. pap. *(978-0-9803846-7-3(2))* Darwin, Charles Univ. Pr.

ART, ABSTRACT
see also Concrete Art; Minimal Art

Adams, Henry. Vincent Campanella: Classical Abstractionist. 2007. (Illus.). 60p. per. 10.00 *(978-0-9615372-8-9(0))* Albrecht-Kemper Museum of Art.
Amalfitano, Lelia & Fox, Judith Hoos. The Strange Life of Objects: The Art of Annette Lemieux. 2011. (ENG., Illus.). 232p. 49.00 *(978-1-883015-45-9(6))* Krannert Art Museum.
Antcliffe, Mark & Greene, Vivien, eds. The Vorticists. 2010. (ENG., Illus.). 192p. pap. 39.95 *(978-1-85437-885-9(6))* Tate Publishing, Ltd. GBR. Dist: Hachette Bk. Group.
Balkema, Annette, text. Li Lei: Chinese Abstractionist. 2010. (ENG., Illus.). 200p. 75.00 *(978-3-7757-2497-5(4))* Hatje Cantz Verlag GmbH & Co KG DEU. Dist: D.A.P./Distributed Art Pubs.
Balken, Debra Bricker. John Storrs: Machine-Age Modernist. 2010. (ENG., Illus.). 112p. pap. 29.95 *(978-0-934552-79-0(7))* Boston Athenaeum Library.
Barzel, Amnon. Hans Hartung. 2007. (FRE & ENG., Illus.). 296p. *(978-88-7439-395-4(4))* 5 Continents.
Bätschmann, Oskar. Pia Fries: Krapprhizom Luisenkupfer. 2011. (ENG., Illus.). 208p. 60.00 ***(978-3-941263-29-1(3))*** Richter Verlag DEU. Dist: D.A.P./Distributed Art Pubs.
Bedford, Christopher & Walker, Hamza. Mark Bradford. 2010. (Illus.). 256p. 65.00 *(978-0-300-16358-2(4))* Yale Univ. Pr.
Beltei, Nadia. Abstract Art by NADIA BELTEI. 2009. 68p. pap. 28.99 *(978-0-557-08551-4(9))* Lulu Enterprises Inc.
Berry Jr., Artist/Artrepreneur Robert L. Art of JazzXpressions. 2008. 64p. pap. 33.35 *(978-1-4357-0813-6(X))* Lulu Enterprises Inc.
Berry, Robert L., Jr. The Jazz in Abstract Art. 2008. 108p. 29.32 *(978-1-4303-1805-7(8))* Lulu Enterprises Inc.
Bessa, Antonio Sergio. Öyvind Fahlström: The Art of Writing. 2008. (Avant-Garde & Modernism Studies). (ENG., Illus.). 192p. pap. 29.95 *(978-0-8101-2298-7(7))* Northwestern Univ. Pr.
Black, Karla. Karla Black: It's Proof That Counts. 2010. (ENG & GER., Illus.). 192p. 55.00 *(978-3-03764-084-5(7))* JRP Ringier Kunstverlag AG CHE. Dist: D.A.P./Distributed Art Pubs.
Bohn, Kendall, illus. Abstract Adventure III: A Kaleidoscopia Coloring Book. 2007. 56p. 8.95 *(978-0-929636-81-8(3))* Syren Bk. Co.
Breuer, Marco. Marco Breuer: Early Recordings, 1 vol. 2007. (ENG., Illus.). 96p. 65.00 *(978-1-59711-033-4(7))* Aperture Foundation, Inc.
Carrier, David. Sean Scully. 2006. (ENG., Illus.). 224p. pap. 34.95 *(978-0-500-28626-5(4))* Thames & Hudson.
Castagno, John. Abstract Artists: Signatures & Monograms, an International Directory. 2007. (ENG., Illus.). 496p. 275.00 *(978-0-8108-5897-8(5))*, Scarecrow Pr., Inc.
Comunale Casa Rusca, Locarno Pinacoteca, et al. Wilfrid Moser: Milestones - Oeuvre, 1934-1997. Museum of Fine Arts Bern Staff, ed. 2009. (Illus.). 300p. 110.00 *(978-3-85881-716-7(3))* Scheidegger und Spiess AG, Verlag CHE. Dist: Antique Collectors' Club.
Cramer, Charles A. Abstraction & the Classical Ideal, 1760-1920. 2006. (University of Delaware Press Studies in 17th- & 18th- Century Art & Culture). (Illus.). 182p. 59.50 *(978-0-87413-935-8(X))* Univ. of Delaware Pr.
Crowther, Paul & Wansche, Isabel, eds. Meanings of Abstract Art: Between Nature & Theory. 2012. (Routledge Advances in Visual Studies). (ENG., Illus.). 314p. (C). 125.00 ***(978-0-415-89993-2(1))*** Routledge.
Di Ozesanmuseum Bamberg, et al, eds. Neogeo: A New Edge to Abstraction. 2007. (Illus.). 191p. per. 59.00 *(978-3-89995-194-5(X))* Die Gestalten Verlag DEU. Dist: Prestel Publishing.
Diederichsen, Diedrich, text. On Surplus Value. 2008. (ENG., Illus.). 128p. pap. 10.00 *(978-90-73362-81-9(4))* Witte De With Centre for Contemporary Art NLD. Dist: D.A.P./Distributed Art Pubs.
d'Orgeval, Domitille, et al. Geometry Beyond Limits: Latin American Contemporary Art. 2010. (ENG & FRE., Illus.). 246p. 60.00 *(978-88-7439-542-2(6))*, 5 Continents ITA. Dist: Hachette Bk. Group.
Dunne, Aidan. Patrick Scott. 2008. (ENG.). 256p. 249.95 *(978-1-905483-53-2(8))* Liberties Pr. IRL. Dist: Dufour Editions, Inc.
Ebony, David. Emily Mason: The Fifth Element. 2007. (Illus.). 128p. 39.95 *(978-0-8076-1570-6(6))* Braziller, George Inc.
Elger, Dietmar. Abstract Art. 2008. (ENG., Illus.). 96p. pap. 9.99 *(978-3-8228-5620-8(7))* TASCHEN DEU. Dist: Ingram Pub. Services.
Fajardo-Hill, Cecilia, ed. Fortunate Objects/Objetos Afortunados. 2008. (ENG., Illus.). 160p. per. 49.95 *(978-88-8158-662-2(2))* Charta ITA. Dist: D.A.P./Distributed Art Pubs.
Franciolli, Marco, et al, eds. Gutai. 2011. (ENG & ITA., Illus.). 264p. pap. 49.95 *(978-88-366-1815-6(4))* Silvana ITA. Dist: D.A.P./Distributed Art Pubs.
Gassner, Hubertus, et al, eds. Mark Rothko: Retrospektive. 2008. (GER., Illus.). 200p. (C). pap. 68.00 *(978-3-7774-3935-8(5))* Hirmer Verlag GmbH DEU. Dist: Brown, David Bk. Co., The.
Godfrey, Mark. Abstraction & the Holocaust. 2007. (ENG., Illus.). 304p. 55.00 *(978-0-300-12676-1(X))* Yale Univ. Pr.
—The Memory of Modernism: Abstract Art & the Holocaust. 2006. (ENG.). 30.00 *(978-0-300-11090-6(1))* Yale Univ. Pr.
Gray, Sarah Willard. Abstracting from the Cultural Landscape. 2010. 72p. pap. *(978-3-8383-8719-2(8))* Lambert Academic Publishing.
Groos, Ulrike. Palermo. 2007. (Illus.). 280p. pap. 60.00 *(978-3-8321-9015-6(5))* Merrell Pubs. Ltd. GBR. Dist: Perseus Distribution.
Gunn, Ann V. The Prints of Wilhelmina Barns-Graham: A Complete Catalogue. 2007. (Illus.). 160p. 80.00 *(978-0-85331-969-6(3))*, Lund Humphries Pubs.) Ashgate Publishing, Ltd. GBR. Dist: Ashgate Publishing Co.
Janssen, Hans, et al. Mondrian, 1892-1914: The Path to Abstraction. 2006. (Illus.). 224p. 65.00 *(978-90-400-8708-0(3))* Waanders B.V., Uitgeverij NLD. Dist: Antique Collectors' Club.
Jimenez, Ariel. A Constructive Vision. 2010. (ENG., Illus.). 344p. 65.00 *(978-0-9823544-0-7(1))* Fundacion Cisneros.
Kelly, Wendy. Abstraction & Its Processes. 2011. 200p. pap. ***(978-3-8443-8110-8(4))*** Lambert Academic Publishing.
Kiblitsky, Alexander. Sheila Isham. 2006. (ENG.). 224p. 50.00 *(978-3-935298-99-5(4))* Kiblitsky, Joseph Palace Editions DEU. Dist: National Bk. Network.
Kieser, Ronald. See What You Believe. 2010. 105p. pap. 38.00 *(978-0-557-32179-7(4))* Lulu Enterprises Inc.
—See What You Believe II - A Space Oddity. 2010. 103p. pap. 38.00 *(978-0-557-33523-7(X))* Lulu Enterprises Inc.
Kimes, Beverly Rae. Otis Chandler: The Pursuit of Uncommon Excellence. Wilkins, Amy, ed. 2007. *(978-0-9618705-1-5(6))* Art Ctr. College of Design.
Knöller, Paco. Paco Kn#xF6;ller: K#xFC;nstliche Paradiese. 2011. (ENG., Illus.). 56p. 25.00 ***(978-3-941263-31-4(5))*** Richter Verlag DEU. Dist: D.A.P./Distributed Art Pubs.
Ledezma, Juan. The Sites of Latin American Abstraction/Los Sitios de la Abstraccion Lationoamericana. 2008. (ENG., Illus.). 248p. 75.00 *(978-88-8158-664-6(9))* Charta ITA. Dist: D.A.P./Distributed Art Pubs.
Lewis, Wyndham. Blast 1. 2009. *(978-1-58423-342-8(7))* Gingko Pr., Inc.
Libin, Liu, et al, eds. Visible/Invisible, 1 vol. 2008. (ENG., Illus.). 240p. 80.00 *(978-988-99265-7-1(1))* Timezone 8 Ltd. HKG. Dist: D.A.P./Distributed Art Pubs.
Magnaguagno, Guido & Omlin, Sibylle. Klaus Born - Malerei. 2008. (Illus.). 124p. 50.00 *(978-3-85881-226-1(9))* Scheidegger und Spiess AG, Verlag CHE. Dist: Antique Collectors' Club.
Maloon, Terence, ed. Paths to Abstraction 1867-1917. 2011. (Illus.). 295p. 65.00 *(978-3-7913-5091-2(9))* Prestel Publishing.
Marcoci, Roxana. Comic Abstraction: Image-Breaking, Image-Making, 1 vol. 2007. (ENG., Illus.). 160p. 39.95 *(978-0-87070-709-4(4))* Museum of Modern Art.
Matter, Mercedes. Mercedes Matter. 2010. (ENG., Illus.). 276p. 55.00 *(978-0-615-30990-3(9))* Borghi, Mark Fine Art.
McGarry, Susan Hallsten & Tobey, Rebecca. Partners in Art: Gene & Rebecca Tobey. 2007. (ENG., Illus.). 360p. 75.00 *(978-1-934491-02-7(0))* Fresco Fine Art Pubns., LLC.
Mecklenburg, Virginia M. Modern Masters: American Abstraction at Midcentury. 2009. (ENG., Illus.). 272p. 65.00 *(978-1-904832-59-1(8))* Giles, D. Ltd. GBR. Dist: Antique Collectors' Club.
Mercer, Kobena, ed. Discrepant Abstraction. 2006. (Annotating Art's Histories Ser.: Vol. 2). (ENG., Illus.). 224p. (gr. 17). pap. 27.00 *(978-0-262-63337-6(X))* MIT Pr.
Minimalism and After Staff. Minimalism & After: Tradition und Tendenzen minimalistischer Kunst von 1950 bis heute. Wiehager, Renate, ed. 2010. (ENG., Illus.). 632p. 95.00 *(978-3-7757-2386-2(2))* Hatje Cantz Verlag GmbH & Co KG DEU. Dist: D.A.P./Distributed Art Pubs.
Mondrian, Piet & Léal, Brigitte. Mondrian. 2010. (FRE., Illus.). 357p. *(978-2-84426-451-0(4))* Centre National d'Art et de Culture Georges Pompidou.
Morris, Sarah. On Architecture, Film & Art: A Conversation Between Sarah Morris & Hans Ulrich Obrist. Bechtler, Cristine & Obrist, Hans Ulrich, eds. 2012. (Art & Architecture in Discussion Ser.). (ENG., Illus.). 110p. pap. 39.95 ***(978-3-7091-1031-7(9)***, 3709110319) Springer Wien AUT. Dist: Springer.
Motherwell, Robert. Open. 2010. (ENG., Illus.). 183p. 65.00 *(978-1-901785-12-8(2))* 21 Publishing GBR. Dist: D.A.P./Distributed Art Pubs.
Museum Bellerive Zürich Staff & State Collection of Prints and Drawings Staff, eds. Hermann Obrist: Skulptur, Raum, Abstraktion um 1900. 2009. (ENG., Illus.). 240p. 75.00 *(978-3-85881-239-1(0))* Scheidegger und Spiess AG, Verlag CHE. Dist: Antique Collectors' Club.
Nachtigaller, Roland, et al, texts. Olaf Quantius - Scheunentod. 2011. (ENG., Illus.). 96p. 40.00 *(978-3-86678-410-9(4))* Kerber Verlag DEU. Dist: D.A.P./Distributed Art Pubs.
O'Hare, Mary Kate. Constructive Spirit: Abstract Art in South & North America, 1920s-50s. 2010. 196p. 39.95 *(978-0-7649-5274-6(9))* Pomegranate Communications, Inc.
Parkstone Press Staff, creator. Malevich. 2008. (Illus.). 39.95 *(978-1-85995-690-8(4))* Parkstone Pr. USA, Ltd.
Perlman, Joan, illus. Joan Perlman: Element/Frumkraftur, 1 vol. 2008. (ENG.). 36p. per. 24.95 *(978-0-9703407-6-4(1))* Future Studio.
Petrova, E. A. & Petrova, Yevgenia, eds. Abstraction in Russia, 2 vols. 2006. (ENG., Illus.). pap. 160.00 *(978-3-935298-50-6(1))*, Palace Editions) Mandala Publishing.
Pritchard, Sue, text. The Fifties, 4 vols. 2009. (ENG., Illus.). 80p. 12.95 *(978-1-85177-585-9(4))* V & A Pubns. GBR. Dist: Hachette Bk. Group.
Rabottini, Alessandro. Aaron Curry: Bad Dimension. 2010. (ENG., Illus.). 180p. pap. 49.95 *(978-3-86560-745-4(4))*, Verlag der Buchhandlung Walther Konig DEU. Dist: D.A.P./Distributed Art Pubs.
Raymond, Yasmil, et al, texts. Abstract Resistance. 2010. (ENG., Illus.). 96p. pap. 9.99 *(978-0-935640-95-3(9))* Walker Art Ctr.
Robinson, Robert H. You Kan Do a Kandinsky: Enter the Wonderful World of Kandinsky. (Illus.). 62p. 20.00 *(978-0-911145-00-7(1))* Sussex Countian, Inc.
Scheibitz, Thomas. Film, Music & Novel. Beard, Jason, ed. 2008. (ENG., 256p. Illus.). 100.00 *(978-1-904212-11-9(5))*; 155.00 *(978-1-904212-35-5(2))* Other Criteria GBR. Dist: Hachette Bk. Group.
Sheldon Museum of Art. The Geometric Unconscious: A Century of Abstraction. Veneciano, Jorge Daniel, ed. 2012. (American Transnationalism: Perspectives from the Sheldon Museum of Art Ser.). (ENG., Illus.). 208p. pap. 50.00 ***(978-0-8032-4092-5(9))*** Univ. of Nebraska Pr.
Slobodkina, Esphyr, et al. Rediscovering Slobodkina: A Pioneer of American Abstraction. 2009. (ENG., Illus.). 184p. 60.00 *(978-1-55595-312-6(3))* Hudson Hills Pr. LLC.
Souter, Gerry. Malevich. 2008. (Temporis Ser.). (ENG., Illus.). 255p. 39.95 *(978-1-85995-684-7(X))* Parkstone Pr. USA, Ltd.

St. John, Sue. Journeys to Abstraction: 100 Paintings & Their Secrets Revealed. 2012. (ENG., Illus.). 192p. 29.99 (978-1-4403-1143-7(9), North Light Bks.) F&W Media, Inc.

Strayer, Jeffrey. Subjects & Objects: Art, Essentialism, & Abstraction. 2007. (Philosophy of History & Culture Ser.). 388p. (978-90-04-15714-9(X)) BRILL.

Suarez, Osbel, text. Cold America. 2011. 504p. 85.00 (978-84-7075-588-0(9)) Fundacion Juan March ESP. Dist: Actar Birkhauser Distribution.

Temkin, Ann, text. Abstract Expressionism at the Museum of Modern Art. 2010. (ENG., Illus.). 124p. 29.95 (978-0-87070-793-3(0)) Museum of Modern Art.

Thomas, David. Walters: Art of Realism & Abstraction. 2010. (Illus.). 184p. (C). 99.00 (978-1-921394-06-5(4)) Macmillan Art Publishing AUS. Dist: Brown, David Bk. Co., The.

Turner, Beth. Georgia O'Keeffe: Abstraction. Haskell, Barbara, ed. 2009. (ENG., Illus.). 256p. 65.00 (978-0-300-14817-6(8)) Yale Univ. Pr.

Varnedoe, Kirk. Pictures of Nothing: Abstract Art since Pollock. 2006. (Bollingen Ser.: Vol. 2003). (ENG., Illus.). 304p. 49.95 (978-0-691-12678-4(X)) Princeton Univ. Pr.

Voigt, Jorinde. Jorinde Voigt: Nexus. 2011. (ENG., Illus.). 144p. pap. 55.00 (978-3-7757-2823-2(6)) Hatje Cantz Verlag GmbH & Co KG DEU. Dist: D.A.P./Distributed Art Pubs.

Von Drathen, Doris. Rui Chafes. 2008. (ENG., Illus.). 152p. 59.95 (978-88-8158-657-8(6)) Charta ITA. Dist: D.A.P./Distributed Art Pubs.

Warhol, Andy. Andy Warhol: Ladies & Gentlemen. 2010. (ENG., Illus.). 80p. 30.00 (978-1-61623-717-2(1)) Skarstedt Fine Art.

Weller, Alan. Photoshop Brushes & Creative Tools: Calligraphic & Abstract Designs. 2010. (Electronic Clip Art Photoshop Brushes Ser.). (ENG.). 48p. pap. 19.95 (978-0-486-99101-6(6)) Dover Pubns., Inc.

Wiehager, Renate, ed. Discourses in Painting: Painting, Prints, & Object Art from the Daimler Art Collection, 1908-2010. 2011. (ENG., Illus.). 360p. pap. 75.00 (978-3-7757-2730-3(2)) Hatje Cantz Verlag GmbH & Co KG DEU. Dist: D.A.P./Distributed Art Pubs.

ART, AFGHANISTAN

Abdul, Lisa & Caragliano, Renata. Lisa Abdul. 2009. (ITA & ENG., Illus.). 172p. 45.00 (978-88-7757-223-3(X)) Hopefulmonster Editore ITA. Dist: D.A.P./Distributed Art Pubs.

Aruz, Joan & Fino, Elisabetta Valtz, eds. Afghanistan: Forging Civilizations along the Silk Road. 2012. (ENG., Illus.). 144p. pap. 35.00 (978-0-300-17954-5(5)) Yale Univ. Pr.

Ball, Warwick. The Monuments of Afghanistan: History, Archaeology & Architecture. 2008. (ENG., Illus.). 384p. 116.00 (978-1-85043-436-8(0)) I. B. Tauris & Co., Ltd. GBR. Dist: Macmillan.

Boetti, Alighiero, et al. Order & Disorder: Alighiero Boetti by Afghan Women. 2012. (ENG., Illus.). 132p. pap. 25.00 (978-0-9778344-8-8(4)) Univ. of California, Los Angeles, Fowler Museum of Cultural History.

Hiebert, Fredrik. Afghanistan: Hidden Treasures from the National Museum, Kabul. Cambon, Pierre, ed. 2008. (ENG., Illus.). 304p. pap. 30.00 (978-1-4262-0295-7(4)) National Geographic Society.

Hiebert, Fredrik T. & Cambon, Pierre. Afghanistan: Hidden Treasures from the National Museum, Kabul. 2008. (Illus.). 303p. (978-1-4262-0374-9(8)) National Geographic Society.

Krieken-Pieters, Juliette van. Art & Archaeology of Afghanistan: Its Fall & Survival: A Multi-Disciplinary Approach. 2006. (Handbook of Oriental Studies. Section Eight. Central Asia Ser.). (Illus.). 412p. (978-90-04-15182-6(6)) BRILL.

Mascelloni, Enrico. War Rugs: The Nightmare of Modernism. 2009. (ENG., Illus.). 208p. pap. 42.00 (978-88-6130-866-4(X)) Skira Editore ITA. Dist: Random Hse., Inc.

Paine, Sheila. Embroidery from Afghanistan. 2007. (Fabric Folios Ser.). (ENG., Illus.). 88p. pap. 22.50 (978-0-295-98661-6(1)) Univ. of Washington Pr.

ART, AFRICAN

Adjaye, David & Bouttiaux, Anne-Marie, eds. Geo-Graphics: A Map of Art Practices, Past & Present, 1 vol. 2010. (ENG.). 384p. pap. 55.00 (978-88-366-1658-9(5)) Silvana ITA. Dist: D.A.P./Distributed Art Pubs.

Africa Comics. 2006. per. 44.95 (978-0-942949-32-2(3)) Studio Museum in Harlem, The.

Arnold, Marion, ed. Art in Eastern Africa. 2007. (Illus.). 199p. (C). (978-9987-449-13-2(1)) Mkuki na Nyoka Pubs. TZA. Dist: Michigan State Univ. Pr.

Aronson, Lisa & Weber, John S. Environment & Object: Recent African Art. 2011. (978-0-9821486-6-2(6)); (978-3-7913-5209-1(1)) Tang, Frances Young Teaching Museum & Art Gallery at Skidmore College, The.

Barbatti, Bruno. Berber Carpets of Morocco: The Symbols Origin & Meaning. 2009. (ENG., Illus.). 344p. 120.00 (978-2-86770-184-9(8)) ACR Edition FRA. Dist: Antique Collectors' Club.

Bargna, Ivan. Africa. 2009. (Dictionaries of Civilization Ser.). (ENG., Illus.). 388p. pap. 26.95 (978-0-520-25974-4(2)) Univ. of California Pr.

Bargna, Ivan & Parodi da Passano, M. Giovanna. L'Africa Delle Meraviglie: Arti Africane Nelle Collezioni Italiane = the Wonders of Africa: African Arts in Italian Collections. 2011. (ITA & ENG., Illus.). 204p. pap. 60.00 (978-88-366-1949-8(5)) Silvana ITA. Dist: D.A.P./Distributed Art Pubs.

Bassani, Ezio. African Art. 2012. (ENG., Illus.). 380p. 80.00 (978-88-572-0869-5(9)) Skira Editore ITA. Dist: Random Hse., Inc.

Beckwith, Carol & Fisher, Angela. Painted Bodies: African Body Painting, Tattoos, & Scarification. 2012. (ENG., Illus.). 288p. 100.00 (978-0-8478-3405-1(0)) Rizzoli International Pubns., Inc.

Bernasek, Lisa. Artistry of the Everyday: Beauty & Craftsmanship in Berber Art. 2008. (Peabody Museum Collections Ser.). (Illus.). 128p. pap. 21.95 (978-0-87365-405-0(6)) Peabody Museum of Archaeology & Ethnology, Harvard Univ., Pubns. Dept.

Berzock, Kathleen Bickford & Clarke, Christa, eds. Representing Africa in American Art Museums: A Century of Collecting & Display. 2010. (Mclellan Book Ser.). (ENG., Illus.). 320p. pap. 40.00 (978-0-295-98961-7(0)) Univ. of Washington Pr.

Bester, Rory. Claudette Schreuders. 2011. (Illus.). 240p. 49.95 (978-3-7913-5110-0(9)) Prestel Publishing.

Bickford-Berzock, Kathleen. Benin: Royal Arts of a West African Kingdom. 2008. (ENG., Illus.). 36p. pap. 9.95 (978-0-300-13677-7(3)) Art Institute of Chicago.

Bognolo, Daniela. Lobi: Visions of Africa. 2008. (Visions of Africa Ser.). (ENG., Illus.). 160p. 34.95 (978-88-7439-350-3(4)) 5 Continents ITA. Dist: Hachette Bk. Group.

Bortolot, Alexander Ives. Revolutions: A Century of Makonde Masquerade in Mozambique. 2007. (Illus.). 72p. (978-1-884919-20-6(0)) Columbia Univ., The Miriam & Ira D. Wallach Art Gallery.

Bouttiaux, Anne-Marie. Persona: Masks of Africa - Identities Hidden & Revealed. 2009. (ENG., Illus.). 304p. 50.00 (978-88-7439-513-2(2)) 5 Continents ITA. Dist: Hachette Bk. Group.

Boyer, Alain-Michel. Baule: Visions of Africa. 2008. (ENG., Illus.). 160p. pap. 34.95 (978-88-7439-386-2(5)) 5 Continents ITA. Dist: Hachette Bk. Group.

Brennan, Jonathan, tr. Miquel Barcelo: the African Work. 2009. (ENG., Illus.). 264p. pap. 50.00 (978-84-7506-831-2(6)) Turner, Ediciones S.A. ESP. Dist: D.A.P./Distributed Art Pubs.

Castagno, John. African, Asian & Middle Eastern Artists: Signatures & Monograms From 1800. 2008. (ENG., Illus.). 150p. 125.00 (978-0-8108-6357-6(X)) Scarecrow Pr., Inc.

Chikukwa, Raphael. Seeing Ourselves. 2012. (ENG., Illus.). 76p. pap. 24.95 (978-88-8158-823-7(4)) Charta ITA. Dist: D.A.P./Distributed Art Pubs.

Clarke, Christa. The Art of Africa: A Resource for Educators. 2007. (Metropolitan Museum of Art Publications). (ENG., Illus.). 216p. 79.95 (978-0-300-12312-8(4)) Yale Univ. Pr.

Cole, Ernest. The Photographer. 2010. (ENG., Illus.). 256p. 56.00 (978-3-86930-137-2(6)) Steidl, Gerhard Druckerei und Verlag DEU. Dist: Innovative Logistics.

Colleyn, Jean-Paul. Bamana. 2008. (ENG., Illus.). 144p. pap. 34.95 (978-88-7439-348-0(2)) 5 Continents ITA. Dist: Hachette Bk. Group.

Colleyn, Jean-Paul, et al. Boli. 2010. (FRE & ENG., Illus.). 176p. 50.00 (978-2-35340-075-1(2)) Gourcuff Gradenigo FRA. Dist: National Bk. Network.

Cossa, Egidio & Schlinkert, Guido. IbridAAfricA: Hybrid 3. 2010. 144p. pap. 29.95 (978-88-492-0268-7(7)) Gangemi ITA. Dist: International Publishers Marketing.

Cram101 Textbook Reviews. Outlines & Highlights for a History of Art in Africa by Visona, et Al , Isbn: 0134421876. 2011. 338p. pap. 33.95 (978-1-61812-869-0(8)) Cram101 Inc.

Cremin, Mary. Romuald Hazoume. 2011. (ENG., Illus.). 160p. pap. 40.00 (978-1-907020-52-0(7)) Irish Museum of Modern Art IRL. Dist: D.A.P./Distributed Art Pubs.

Darish, Patricia & Binkley, David A. Kuba. 2010. (Visions of Africa Ser.). (ENG., Illus.). 144p. pap. 34.95 (978-88-7439-404-3(7)) 5 Continents ITA. Dist: Hachette Bk. Group.

Delafosse, Maurice. African Art. 2012. (Temporis Ser.). (ENG., Illus.). 256p. 39.95 (978-1-84484-897-3(3)) Parkstone Pr. USA, Ltd.

Doris, David T. Vigilant Things: On Thieves, Yoruba Anti-Aesthetics, & the Strange Fates of Ordinary Objects in Nigeria. 2011. (ENG., Illus.). 416p. 60.00 (978-0-295-99073-6(2)) Univ. of Washington Pr.

Drewal, Henry John. Sacred Waters: Arts for Mami Wata & Other Divinities in Africa & the Diaspora. Drewal, Henry John, ed. 2008. (African Expressive Cultures Ser.). (ENG., Illus.). 708p. 75.00 (978-0-253-35156-2(1), 0253351561) Indiana Univ. Pr.

Drewal, Henry John & Drewal et al., Henry John. Mami Wata: Arts for Water Spirits in Africa & Its Diasporas. 2008. (ENG., Illus.). 228p. pap. (978-0-9748729-9-5(7)) Univ. of California, Los Angeles, Fowler Museum of Cultural History.

Dube, Prince Mbusi & Dube, Prince, eds. Dumile Feni Retrospective: Johannesburg Art Gallery. 2007. (ENG., Illus.). 250p. 79.95 (978-1-86814-442-6(9)) Witwatersrand Univ. Pr. Pubns. ZAF. Dist: Transaction Pubs.

Eisenhofer, Stefan. African Art. Wolf, Norbert, ed. 2010. (ENG., Illus.). 96p. pap. 9.99 (978-3-8228-5576-8(6)) TASCHEN DEU. Dist: Ingram Pub. Services.

Enwezor, Okwui. Events of the Self: Portraiture & Social Identity - Contemporary African Photography from the Walther Collection, 1 vol. 2010. (ENG & GER., Illus.). 352p. 88.00 (978-3-86930-157-0(0)) Steidl, Gerhard Druckerei und Verlag DEU. Dist: Innovative Logistics.

Enwezor, Okwui & Okeke-Agulu, Chika, eds. Contemporary African Art Since 1980. 2009. (ENG., Illus.). 366p. pap. 60.00 (978-88-6208-092-7(1)) Damiani ITA. Dist: D.A.P./Distributed Art Pubs.

Faber, Paul. Africa at the Tropenmuseum: Collections at the Tropenmuseum. 2012. (Illus.). 168p. 50.00 (978-94-6022-119-4(X)) Royal Tropical Institute Pr. (KIT (Koninklijk Instituut voor de Tropen) NLD. Dist: Stylus Publishing, LLC.

Fagaly, William A., ed. Ancestors of Congo Square: African Art in the New Orleans Museum of Art. 2011. (Illus.). 376p. 75.00 (978-1-85759-698-4(6)) Scala, Editions FRA. Dist: National Bk. Network.

Fini, Claudia, et al, eds. Contemporary Photography from Africa & Middle East: Breaking News. 2011. (Illus.). 208p. 55.00 (978-88-572-0645-5(9)) Skira Editore ITA. Dist: Random Hse., Inc.

Fosso, Samuel. Samuel Fosso: PHotoBolsillo International. 2011. (ENG & SPA., Illus.). 112p. pap. 20.00 (978-84-92841-62-2(1)) La Fabrica ESP. Dist: D.A.P./Distributed Art Pubs.

Foundry, Wargame. Foundry Miniatures Compendium. 2008. (Illus.). 96p. pap. 32.00 (978-1-901543-16-2(1)) Foundry Bks. GBR. Dist: Casemate Pubs. & Bk. Distributors, LLC.

Geary, Christraud M. & Xatart, Stephanie. Material Journey: Collecting African & Oceanic Art, 1945-2000, 1 vol. 2007. (ENG., Illus.). 250p. pap. 35.00 (978-0-87846-715-0(7)) Museum of Fine Arts, Boston.

Gerdes, Paulus. Lunda Geometry: Mirror Curves, Designs, Knots, Polyominoes, Patterns, Symmetries. 2008. 202p. pap. 18.95 (978-1-4357-2629-1(4)) Lulu Enterprises Inc.

Harney, Elizabeth, et al. Inscribing Meaning: Writing & Graphic Systems in African Art. 2008. (ENG., Illus.). 256p. per. 55.00 (978-88-7439-377-0(6)) 5 Continents ITA. Dist: Hachette Bk. Group.

Hazoume, Romuald. Romuald Hazoumé: My Paradise - Made in Porto-Novo. 2010. (ENG., Illus.). 144p. 40.00 (978-3-7757-2645-0(4)) Hatje Cantz Verlag GmbH & Co KG DEU. Dist: D.A.P./Distributed Art Pubs.

Hetherington, Tim, photos by. Long Story Bit by Bit: Liberia Retold. 2009. (ENG., Illus.). 140p. 45.00 (978-1-884167-73-7(X)) Umbrage Editions.

Holm, Michael, ed. Candice Breitz. 2008. (ENG., Illus.). 48p. 30.00 (978-87-91607-22-6(1)) Louisana DNK. Dist: D.A.P./Distributed Art Pubs.

Hug, Alfons, et al. The Tropics: Views from the Middle of the Globe. 2009. (ENG., Illus.). 344p. 69.00 (978-3-86678-166-5(0)) Kerber Verlag DEU. Dist: D.A.P./Distributed Art Pubs.

Hurault, Jean. Africains de Guyane: La vie matérielle et l'art des Noirs Réfugiés de Guyane. (Art in its Context . Studies in Ethno-Aesthetics / Field Reports). (FRE.). 224p. 135.00 (978-3-11-125130-1(6)) De Gruyter, Mouton DEU. Dist: de Gruyter, Walter GmbH & Co. KG.

Jaar, Alfredo, et al, contrib. by. Emergency. 2006. (Illus.). 261p. (gr. 13-18). 29.95 (978-84-95951-90-8(8)) D.A.P./Distributed Art Pubs.

Kaabi-Linke, Nadia, ed. Nadia Kaabi-Linke: Tatort. 2011. (ENG., Illus.). 88p. 40.00 (978-3-86678-459-8(7)) Kerber Verlag DEU. Dist: D.A.P./Distributed Art Pubs.

Kahan, Leonard, et al, eds. Surfaces: Color, Substances, & Ritual Applications on African Sculpture. 2009. (African Expressive Cultures Ser.). (ENG., Illus.). 536p. 75.00 (978-0-253-35251-4(7), 0253352517) Indiana Univ. Pr.

Kasfir, Sidney Littlefield & Kasfir, Sidney L. African Art & the Colonial Encounter: Inventing a Global Commodity. 2007. (ENG., Illus.). 408p. 75.00 (978-0-253-34892-0(7)); pap. 27.95 (978-0-253-21922-0(1), 0253219221) Indiana Univ. Pr.

Kittelmann, Udo, et al, eds. Who Knows Tomorrow. Afrika. SMB. Hamburger Bahnhof. 2011. (GER & ENG., Illus.). 632p. 75.00 (978-3-86560-789-8(6)) Verlag der Buchhandlung Walther Konig DEU. Dist: D.A.P./Distributed Art Pubs.

Klopper, Sandra, et al. The Art of Southeast Africa. 2008. (ENG., Illus.). 224p. 55.00 (978-88-7439-001-4(7)) 5 Continents ITA. Dist: Hachette Bk. Group.

Kreamer, Christine Mullen. African Vision: The Walt Disney-Tishman African Art Collection. 2007. (Illus.). xvii, 235p. (978-3-7913-6114-7(7)) Prestel Verlag GmbH & Co KG.

Kwami, Atta. Kumasi Realism, 1951-2007: An African Modernism. 2012. (Columbia/Hurst Ser.). (ENG., Illus.). 176p. (gr. 17). 40.00 (978-0-231-70242-3(6)) Columbia Univ. Pr.

Kwami, Atta. Kumasi Realism 1951-2007: An African Modernism. 2011. (978-0-231-80010-5(X)) Columbia Univ. Pr.

LaDuke, Betty. Africa: Women's Art, Women's Lives. (Illus.). 187p. 18.95 (978-0-86543-435-6(2)) Africa World Pr.

Lamp, Frederick John, et al, contrib. by. Accumulating Histories: African Art from the Charles B. Benenson Collection at the Yale University Art Gallery. 2012. (ENG., Illus.). 328p. 75.00 (978-0-300-16992-8(2)) Yale Univ. Art Gallery.

Lawal, Babatunde & Petridis, Constantine. Yoruba: Visions of Africa Series. 2012. (Visions of Africa Ser.). (Illus.). 160p. pap. 34.95 (978-88-7439-587-3(6)) 5 Continents ITA. Dist: Abrams.

Losambe, Lokangaka & Eke, Maureen N. Literature, the Visual Arts, & Globalization in Africa & Its Diaspora. 2011. (Illus.). xvii, 242p. (978-1-59221-817-2(2)); 340p. pap. (978-1-59221-810-3(5)) Africa World Pr.

Mack, John. Preserving the Cultural Heritage of Africa: Crisis or Renaissance? Yoshida, Kenji, ed. 2010. (Illus.). 224p. pap. 29.95 (978-0-85255-982-6(8), Currey, James) Boydell & Brewer, Ltd. GBR. Dist: Boydell & Brewer, Inc.

Magliani, Mauro, photos by. African Costumes & Textiles: From the Berbers to the Zulus. 2008. (ENG., Illus.). 320p. 85.00 (978-88-7439-476-0(4)) 5 Continents ITA. Dist: Hachette Bk. Group.

Magnin, André & Magnin, Andre. African Art Now: Masterpieces from the Jean Pigozzi Collection. (Illus.). 224p. (978-1-85894-289-6(6)) Merrell Pubs. Ltd.

Mas. Life & death in precolombian America: The Collection Janssens, 1 vol. 2012. (ENG.). 160p. 54.00 (978-90-8586-579-7(4)) Exhibitions International BEL. Dist: Innovative Logistics.

Mason, Andy. What's So Funny? Under the Skin of South African Cartooning. 2009. 224p. pap. 24.95 (978-1-919930-74-9(4)) Double Storey Bks. ZAF. Dist: International Publishers Marketing.

Mattet, Laurence. Arts & Cultures. (ENG.). No. 8. 8th ed. 2009. 360p. pap. 39.00 (978-2-7572-0070-4(4))No. 9. 9th ed. 2008. 340p. pap. 39.00 (978-2-7572-0164-0(6)) Continental Sales, Inc. (Art Stock Bks. Ltd/Csi).

Melo, Dilma de & Calaça, Maria Cecília Felix. Arte Africana e Afro-Brasileira. 2nd ed. 2007. (POR., Illus.). 90p. (978-85-87769-73-2(1)) Imprensa Oficial do Estado S/A Imesp.

Mercer, Sunni. The Measure of My Strength: Lizinga Lemandla Ami. 2011. pap. 34.99 (978-1-61739-633-5(8)) Tate Publishing & Enterprises, LLC.

Meyer, Laure. Art & Craft in Africa. 2008. (Illus.). 256p. pap. 23.50 (978-2-87939-337-7(X)) Terrail, Pierre Editions FRA. Dist: Wybel Marketing Group.

—Black Africa: Masks, Sculptures, Jewelry. 2007. (Illus.). 255p. pap. 23.50 (978-2-87939-320-9(5)) Terrail, Pierre Editions FRA. Dist: Perseus-PGW.

Mezian, Nadia, et al. Tamy Tazi - Caftans. 2011. (ENG & FRE., Illus.). 192p. 75.00 (978-88-572-0323-2(9)) Skira Editore ITA. Dist: Random Hse., Inc.

Mitchell, Peter & Smith, Benjamin, eds. The Eland's People: New Perspectives in the Rock Art of the Maloti-Drakensberg Bushmen. 2011. (ENG., Illus.). 256p. pap. 60.00 (978-1-86814-498-3(4)) Witwatersrand Univ. Pr. Pubns. ZAF. Dist: Transaction Pubs.

Muholi, Zanele. Faces & Phases. 2010. (Illus.). 96p. 35.00 (978-3-7913-4495-9(1)) Prestel Publishing.

Ngara, Constantine & Porath, Marion. Conceptions of Giftedness & Creativity from Afric. 2010. 124p. pap. (978-3-639-24538-7(5)) VDM Verlag Dr. Mueller e.K.

Njogu, Kimani. Getting Heard: (Re)claiming Performance Space in Kenya. 2008. 204p. pap. (978-9966-7244-3-4(5)) Twaweza Communications, Ltd. KEN. Dist: Michigan State Univ. Pr.

Ogbechie, Sylvester Okwunodu. Ben Enwonwu: The Making of an African Modernist. 2008. (Rochester Studies in African History & the Diaspora Ser.: Volume 37). (Illus.). 333p. 75.00 (978-1-58046-235-8(9)) Univ. of Rochester Pr.

Okediji, Moyo. Western Frontiers of African Art. 2011. (Rochester Studies in African History & the Diaspora Ser.: Volume 53). (Illus.). 354p. 85.00 (978-1-58046-370-6(3)) Univ. of Rochester Pr.

Okwunodu Ogbechie, Sylvester. Making History: African Colllectors & the Canon of African Art. 2012. (ENG., Illus.). 256p. 70.00 (978-88-7439-571-2(X)) 5 Continents ITA. Dist: Abrams.

Owusu, Heike. African Symbols. 2007. (ENG., Illus.). 320p. per. 12.95 (978-1-4027-4622-2(9)) Sterling Publishing Co., Inc.

Pemberton, John, 3rd. African Beaded Art: Power & Adornment. 2008. (Illus.). 224p. pap. (978-0-87391-058-3(3)) Smith College Pubns.

Perrois, Louis. Fang. 2008. (ENG., Illus.). 156p. pap. 29.00 (978-88-7439-295-7(8)) 5 Continents ITA. Dist: Hachette Bk. Group.

Perrois, Louis & Grand-Dufay, Charlotte. Punu: Visions of Africa. 2008. (ENG., Illus.). 160p. pap. 34.95 (978-88-7439-401-2(2)) 5 Continents ITA. Dist: Hachette Bk. Group.

Phillips, Tom. A Humument: A Treated Victorian Novel. 5th ed. 2012. (ENG., Illus.). 384p. pap. 26.95 (978-0-500-28999-0(9), 528999) Thames & Hudson.

Picton, John, et al, eds. The Poetics of Cloth: African Textiles/Recent Art. 2009. (ENG., Illus.). 112p. pap. 25.00 (978-0-615-22083-3(5)) Grey Art Gallery & Study Ctr., New York Univ.

Pieprzak, Katarzyna. Imagined Museums: Art & Modernity in Postcolonial Morocco. 2010. (Illus.). 280p. 75.00 (978-0-8166-6518-1(4)); (ENG., pap. 25.00 (978-0-8166-6519-8(2)) Univ. of Minnesota Pr.

Plissart, Marie-Françoise. Kinshasa: Tales of the Invisible City. 2006. (Illus.). 288p. 30.00 (978-90-5544-554-7(1)) Ludion BEL. Dist: D.A.P./Distributed Art Pubs.

Postcard Books Staff. Afrikanishe Kunst African Art. 4.95 (978-3-7913-1817-2(9)) Prestel Publishing.

Rosengarten, Dale, et al. Grass Roots: African Origins of an American Art. 2008. (Illus.). 269p. 60.00 (978-0-945802-50-1(1)); pap. 35.00 (978-0-945802-51-8(X)) Museum for African Art.

Samulak, Michael I. A Is for Africa: Coloring Book. 2010. 48p. pap. 9.99 (978-1-4269-4097-2(1)) Trafford Publishing.

Schmidt, A. M. & Westerdijk, P. The Cutting Edge: West Central African 19th Century Throwing Knives in the National Museum of Ethnology Leiden. 2010. (Illus.). 112p. 44.00 (978-90-5450-007-0(7)) KITLV Pr. NLD. Dist: Univ. of Hawaii Pr.

Scott, Monique. Rethinking Evolution in the Museum: Envisioning African Origins. 2007. (Museum Meanings Ser.). (ENG., Illus.). 208p. (C). per. 41.95 (978-0-415-40540-9(8)) Routledge.

Scott, Monique Gilmonre. Up from Africa. 2007. (Museum Meanings Ser.). (ENG., Illus.). 208p. (C). 130.00 (978-0-415-40539-3(4)) Routledge.

Shein. Theatrical Exhibitions. 197p. (978-0-88978-006-4(4)) Arsenal Pulp Pr.

Shepard-Stewart, Lisa. African Accents on the GO! Designing Accessories with Cultural Style. 2007. (Illus.). 80p. per. 21.95 (978-0-9787404-0-5(8)) Cultured Expressions, Inc.

Siegmann, William. African Art: A Century at the Brooklyn Museum. 2009. (Illus.). 296p. pap. (978-0-87273-163-9(4)) Brooklyn Museum, The.

—African Art: A Century at the Brooklyn Museum. 2009. (Illus.). 304p. (978-3-7913-4321-1(1)) Prestel Verlag GmbH & Co KG.

Silvester, Hans. Natural Fashion: Tribal Decoration from Africa. 2008. (ENG., Illus.). 168p. 45.00 (978-0-500-54358-0(5)) Thames & Hudson.

Simonetti, Marie-Agathe. A Journey from Renaissance to Contemporary Art. 2011. 96p. pap. (978-3-8443-3272-8(3)) Lambert Academic Publishing.

Sims, Lowery Stokes & King-Hammond, Leslie, eds. Global Africa Project. 2010. (Illus.). 224p. 45.00 (978-3-7913-5084-4(6)) Prestel Publishing.

Skotnes, Pippa. Unconquerable Spirit: George Stow's History Paintings of the San. 2009. (ENG., Illus.). 216p. 44.95 (978-0-8214-1869-7(6)) Ohio Univ. Pr.

Sleigh, Mary. African Inspirations in Embroidery. 2009. (ENG., Illus.). 128p. pap. 21.95 (978-1-906388-32-4(6), Batsford, B. T. Ltd.) Anova Bks. GBR. Dist: Sterling Publishing Co., Inc.

Soan, Hazel. Haze Soans African Watercolours. 2008. (ENG., Illus.). 128p. pap. 24.95 *(978-0-00-727343-0(6))* HarperCollins Pubs. Ltd. GBR. Dist: Independent Pubs. Group.

Spring, Christopher. African Art in Detail. 2010. (Art in Detail Ser.). (Illus.). 144p. 22.95 *(978-0-674-03622-2(0))* Harvard Univ. Pr.

—Angaza Afrika: African Art Now. 2008. (ENG., Illus.). 336p. pap. 40.00 *(978-1-85669-548-0(4))* King, Laurence Publishing GBR. Dist: Hachette Bk. Group.

Stepan, Peter. Picasso's Collection of African & Oceanic Art: Masters of Metamorphosis. 2006. (Illus.). 136p. 85.00 *(978-3-7913-3691-6(6))* Prestel Publishing.

Vajda, Lazlo, et al. African Masks: The Barbier-Mueller Collection. 2007. (Illus.). 287p. pap. 19.95 *(978-3-7913-3807-1(2))* Prestel Publishing.

van Cutsem-Vanderstraete, Anne. Powerful Headdresses: Africa & Asia. 2010. (ENG., Illus.). 200p. 85.00 *(978-88-7439-551-4(5))* 5 Continents ITA. Dist: Hachette Bk. Group.

Van Dyke, Kristina. African Art: From the Menil Collection. 2008. (Illus.). 239p. pap. *(978-0-939594-64-1(1))* Menil Foundation.

—African Art, from the Menil Collection. Van Dyke, Kristina, ed. 2008. (ENG., Illus.). 240p. 65.00 *(978-0-300-12376-0(0))* Yale Univ. Pr.

Vinnicombe, Patricia. People of the Eland: Rock Paintings of the Drakensberg Bushmen as a Reflection of their Life & Thought. 2011. (ENG.). 400p. pap. 89.95 *(978-1-86814-497-6(6))* Witwatersrand Univ. Pr. Pubns. ZAF. Dist: Transaction Pubs.

Visona, Monica Blackmun. Constructing African Art Histories for the Lagoons of Cote D'Ivoire. 2010. (Illus.). 216p. 109.95 *(978-1-4094-0440-8(4))* Ashgate Publishing Co.

von Lintig, Bettina. African Impressions. 2011. (ENG., Illus.). 288p. 68.00 *(978-88-7439-597-2(3))* 5 Continents ITA. Dist: Hachette Bk. Group.

Vormese, Francine & Braun, Annette. Mickael Kra: Jewellery Between Paris Glamour & African Tradition. 2006. (FRE & ENG., Illus.). 192p. 60.00 *(978-3-89790-226-8(5))* Arnoldsche Art Pubs. DEU. Dist: Antique Collectors' Club.

Walker, Roslyn Adele. The Arts of Africa at the Dallas Museum of Art. 2010. (ENG., Illus.). 304p. 75.00 *(978-0-300-13895-5(4))* Dallas Museum of Art.

Williamson, Jenny & Parker, Pat. Quilt the Beloved Country. 2009. (ENG., Illus.). 113p. 26.95 *(978-1-57432-989-6(8))*, 1574329898, American Quilter's Society) Collector Bks.

Wright, Kristina Dziedzic. Art, Culture, & Tourism on an Indian Ocean Island: An Ethnographic Study of Jua Kali Lamu. 2009. (Illus.). 252p. 109.95 *(978-0-7734-3874-3(2))* Mellen, Edwin Pr., The.

ART, AFRICAN AMERICAN

see African American Art

ART, AMERICAN

see also African American Art; Art, Pennsylvania Dutch; Hispanic American Art

Adams, Henry. The Beauty of Damage: The World of Christopher Pekoc. 2008. (Illus.). pap. 19.95 *(978-0-9758843-9-3(5))* Green Panda Pr.

—What's American about American Art? 2009. 148p. pap. 35.00 *(978-1-55595-403-1(0))* Hudson Hills Pr. LLC.

—What's American about American Art? A Gallery Tour in the Cleveland Museum of Art. 2008. (Illus.). 146p. *(978-0-940717-97-8(2))* Cleveland Museum of Art.

Adams, Marina. Marina Adams. 2008. pap. 0.00 *(978-0-9797964-9-4(0))* CUE Art Foundation.

Adams, Robert. What Can We Believe Where? Photographs of the American West. 2010. (Illus.). 128p. pap. 25.00 *(978-0-300-15247-9(2))* Yale Univ. Art Gallery.

Adams, Shelby Lee, photos by. Shelby Lee Adams: Salt & Truth. 2011. (ENG., Illus.). 120p. 60.00 ***(978-0-9845739-1-2(7))*** Candela Bks.

Adamson, Glenn, et al, contrib. by. Hot House: Expanding the Field of Fiber at Cranbrook, 1970-2007. 2007. 96p. pap. *(978-0-9668577-6-4(3))* Cranbrook Art Museum.

Ades, Dawn, et al. Surrealism in Latin America: Vivísimo Muerto. 2012. ***(978-1-60606-117-6(8))*** Getty Pubns.

Adi Da Samraj. Transcendental Realism: The Image-Art of Egoless Coincidence with Reality Itself. 2nd ed. 2010. (Illus.). 265p. ***(978-1-57097-285-0(0))*** Dawn Horse Pr.

Adler, Dan. Hanne Darboven: Cultural History, 1880-1983. 2009. (One Work Ser.). (ENG., Illus.). 112p. (gr. 17). 35.00 *(978-1-84638-051-8(0))*; pap. 16.00 *(978-1-84638-050-1(2))* Afterall Publishing GBR. Dist: MIT Pr.

Adnan, Etel. Etel Adnan: Der Preis der Liebe, den wir nicht zahlen wollen. 2011. (ENG., Illus.). 32p. pap. 10.00 ***(978-3-7757-2855-3(4))*** Hatje Cantz Verlag GmbH & Co KG DEU. Dist: D.A.P./Distributed Art Pubs.

Agee, William C. & Faxon, Susan C. Coming of Age: American Art, 1850s to 1950s. 2006. (Illus.). 136p. pap. *(978-1-885444-33-2(8))* American Federation of Arts, The.

—Coming of Age: American Art, 1850s To 1950s. 2006. (ENG., Illus.). 136p. 55.00 *(978-0-300-11523-9(7))* Yale Univ. Pr.

Agee, William C., et al. American Vanguards: Graham, Davis, Gorky, de Kooning, & Their Circle, 1927-1942. 2011. (ENG., Illus.). 256p. 65.00 *(978-0-300-12167-4(9))* Yale Univ. Pr.

Aitken, Doug. Doug Aitken: the Idea of the West, 1 vol. 2010. (ENG., Illus.). 160p. 55.00 *(978-1-935202-51-6(0))* D.A.P./Distributed Art Pubs.

—Sleepwalkers: A Future Time Capsule. 2012. (ENG.). 96p. 300.00 *(978-1-56898-871-9(0))* Princeton Architectural Pr.

Alberti, Donald & Hentschel, Martin. Alan Uglow. 2010. (GER & ENG., Illus.). 144p. 55.00 *(978-3-86678-385-0(X))* Kerber Verlag DEU. Dist: D.A.P./Distributed Art Pubs.

Albrecht, Donald, ed. Paris-New York: Design Fashion Culture, 1925-1940. 2008. (ENG., Illus.). 240p. 50.00 *(978-1-58093-211-0(8))* Monacelli Pr., Inc.

Alexander, Darsie, et al, texts. The Spectacular of Vernacular. 2011. (ENG., Illus.). 128p. pap. 19.99 *(978-0-935640-99-1(1))* Walker Art Ctr.

Alexander, Peter. Peter Alexander: Resin Work 1965-2009. 2012. (ENG., Illus.). 40p. pap. 35.00 *(978-1-934171-12-7(3))* Foundation 2021.

Alexander, Thomas E. Stanley Marcus: The Relentless Reign of a Merchant Prince. 2009. (Illus.). 261p. pap. 19.95 *(978-1-934645-94-9(X)*, Eakin Pr.) Eakin Pr.

Alexanian, Nubar. NONFICTION Photographs by Nubar Alexanian from the Film Sets of Errol Morris. 2008. (Illus.). 96p. 60.00 *(978-0-9669733-0-3(5))* Walker Creek Pr.

Allen, Stuart & Lane, Allison Hays. Stuart Allen: 2926'14" N 9828'55" W: Mapping Daylight. 2007. *(978-1-883502-16-4(0))* San Antonio Museum of Art.

Allen, Terry. Jim Roche: Glory Roads, 1 vol. 2011. (ENG., Illus.). 88p. pap. 22.50 ***(978-1-889282-23-7(5))*** Florida State Univ., Museum of Fine Arts.

Alpern, Andrew. Catalogue of the Andrew Alpern Collection of Drawing Instruments: At the Avery Architectural & Fine Arts Library, New York City. Fabian, Carole Ann, ed. 2010. (ENG., Illus.). 160p. 60.00 *(978-0-9789037-3-2(0)*, 890373, Avery Architectural & Fine Arts Library) Avery Architectural & Fine Arts Library.

Altshuler, Bruce. Collecting the New: Museums & Contemporary Art. 2007. (ENG., Illus.). 208p. (C). per. 21.95 *(978-0-691-13373-7(5))* Princeton Univ. Pr.

Ambrosino, Giancarlo, et al, eds. David Wojnarowicz: A Definitive History of Five or Six Years on the Lower East Side. 2006. (Semiotext(e) / Native Agents Ser.). (ENG., Illus.). 220p. (gr. 17). 29.95 *(978-1-58435-035-4(0))* Semiotexte/Smart Art.

American Art, nos. 3 & 4. Vol. 8. pap. 15.00 *(978-0-937311-18-9(9))* Vol. 10. pap. 15.00 *(978-0-937311-29-5(4))* Smithsonian American Art Museum.

American Art Vol. 9, No. 2: Summer. (Illus.). 128p. pap. 15.00 *(978-0-937311-22-6(7))* Smithsonian American Art Museum.

American Art Vol. 9, No. 3: Fall. (Illus.). 128p. pap. 15.00 *(978-0-937311-23-3(5))* Smithsonian American Art Museum.

American Quilter's Society Staff, contrib. by. Best of Show Quilts, 1985-2009: AQS Quilt Show & Contest. 2009. *(978-1-57432-986-5(3)*, American Quilter's Society) Collector Bks.

Amilus Inc., compiled by. American Illustration 27. 2009. (ENG., Illus.). 400p. 75.00 *(978-1-886212-29-9(5))* Amilus Inc.

—American Illustration 28. 2010. (ENG., Illus.). 416p. 75.00 *(978-1-886212-31-2(7))* Amilus Inc.

—American Photography 24. 2009. (ENG., Illus.). 402p. 75.00 *(978-1-886212-30-5(9))* Amilus Inc.

—American Photography 25. 2010. (ENG., Illus.). 416p. 75.00 *(978-1-886212-32-9(5))* Amilus Inc.

Anastas, Ayreen & Gabri, Rene, contrib. by. Paul Ryan: Zwei ist keine Zahl. Ein Gespräch mit Ayreen Anastas & Rene Gabri. 2011. (ENG., Illus.). 48p. pap. 10.00 ***(978-3-7757-2864-5(3))*** Hatje Cantz Verlag GmbH & Co KG DEU. Dist: D.A.P./Distributed Art Pubs.

Andera, Margaret & Stone, Lisa. Accidental Genius: Art from the Anthony Petullo Collection. 2012. ***(978-0-944110-97-3(5))*** Milwaukee Art Museum.

Andersen, Wayne. Marcel Duchamp: The Failed Messiah. 2010. 402p. 45.00 *(978-0-9725573-4-4(2))* Fabriart Editions, Ltd.

Anderson, Laurie. Laurie Anderson: Nothing in My Pockets. 2009. (ENG., Illus.). 62p. pap. 45.00 *(978-2-914563-43-7(4))* Dis Voir Editions FRA. Dist: D.A.P./Distributed Art Pubs.

Anderson, Susan M. Collecting California: Selections from Laguna Art Museum. 2009. *(978-0-940872-36-3(6))* Laguna Art Museum Store.

Andrade, Edna & Paschall, Douglas. Sensational: Edna Andrade's Drawings: Woodmere Art Museum, March 25-June 24, 2007. 2007. (Illus.). 32p. *(978-1-888008-19-7(9))* Woodmere Art Museum, Inc.

Andre, Carl. Carl Andre. 2011. (ENG., Illus.). 152p. pap. 55.00 ***(978-3-86560-999-1(6))*** Verlag der Buchhandlung Walther Konig DEU. Dist: D.A.P./Distributed Art Pubs.

Antin, David. Radical Coherency: Selected Essays on Art & Literature 1966 to 2005. 2011. (ENG.). 384p. 75.00 *(978-0-226-02096-9(7))*; pap. 25.00 *(978-0-226-02097-6(5))* Univ. of Chicago Pr.

Anton, Alina-Elena. Reading the Modern American City: The Urban Space in Fiction - from Dreiser to Bellow to Amy Tan. 2011. 60p. pap. ***(978-3-639-31596-7(0))*** VDM Verlag Dr. Mueller e.K.

Aquin, Stephane, ed. Tom Wesselmann. 2012. (Illus.). 208p. 65.00 ***(978-3-7913-5202-2(4))*** Prestel Publishing.

Arbitman, Kahren Jones & Gallo, Susan M. Picturing Florida: From the First Coast to the Space Coast. 2008. (ENG., Illus.). 223p. 75.00 *(978-1-934491-09-6(8))* Fresco Fine Art Pubns., LLC.

Arnold, Sara C., ed. The Life & Art of Alfred Hutty: Woodstock to Charleston. 2011. 224p. 49.95 ***(978-1-61117-041-2(9))***; pap. 24.95 ***(978-1-61117-042-9(7))*** Univ. of South Carolina Pr.

Aronson, Julie. Bessie Potter Vonnoh: Sculptor of Women. 2008. (ENG., Illus.). 308p. 60.00 *(978-0-8214-1800-0(9))*; pap. 39.95 *(978-0-8214-1801-7(7))* Ohio Univ. Pr.

Arrhenius, Sara, et al. Tomás Saraceno: 14 Billions. 2012. (SWE & ENG., Illus.). 192p. 75.00 *(978-88-572-0857-2(5))* Skira Editore ITA. Dist: Random Hse., Inc.

Art Institute of Chicago Staff, contrib. by. The Essential Guide. 3rd ed. 2009. (Illus.). 336p. pap. *(978-0-86559-229-2(2))* Art Institute of Chicago.

Art, Momenta. Untreated Strangeness. 2010. 19p. 14.95 *(978-0-557-17349-5(3))* Lulu Enterprises Inc.

The Art of Mary Beth Edelson. (Illus.). 200p. 65.00 *(978-0-9604650-7-1(3))*; pap. *(978-0-9604650-6-4(5))* Seven Cycles.

The Art of Milford Zornes: From Private Collections. 2010. (Illus.). 96p. pap. 23.95 *(978-0-9842797-0-8(9))* Sasse, Gene.

Artzybasheff, Boris. As I See: The Fantastic World of Boris Artzybasheff. 2008. (ENG., Illus.). 96p. 19.95 *(978-1-84576-767-9(5)*, Titan Bks.) Titan Bks. Ltd. GBR. Dist: Random Hse., Inc.

Asoma, Yayoi. Yayoi Asoma. 2008. pap. 0.00 *(978-0-9797964-8-7(2))* CUE Art Foundation.

Ater, Renée & Fuller, Meta Warrick. Remaking Race & History: The Sculpture of Meta Warrick Fuller. 2011. (ENG., Illus.). 208p. 49.95 *(978-0-520-25212-6(3))* Univ. of California Pr.

Attoe, Dan. Dan Attoe: I Made Most of This Shit Up. 2010. (ENG., Illus.). 216p. pap. 75.00 *(978-0-9817658-6-0(6))* Peres Projects, Los Angeles Berlin.

Auerbach, Ruth, et al. 3 Perspectives: Eugenio Espinoza, Alvaro Oyarzún, José Alejandro Restrepo: Cisneros Fontanals Art Foundation 2007 Commissions Program Exhibition. 2007. (SPA & ENG., Illus.). 60p. ***(978-0-9774079-5-8(0))*** Cisneros Fontanals Art Foundation.

Auerbach, Tauba. How to Spell the Alphabet, 1 vol. 2007. (ENG., Illus.) 112p. 30.00 *(978-0-9778686-0-5(5))* Deitch, Jeffrey Inc.

Aupetitallot, Yves, ed. Kelley Walker. 2008. (ENG., Illus.). 160p. pap. 49.00 *(978-3-905770-68-1(7))* JRP Ringier Kunstverlag AG CHE. Dist: D.A.P./Distributed Art Pubs.

Auther, Elissa. String, Felt, Thread: The Hierarchy of Art & Craft in American Art. 2009. (Illus.). 280p. 90.00 *(978-0-8166-5608-0(8))*; (ENG., pap. 29.95 *(978-0-8166-5609-7(6))* Univ. of Minnesota Pr.

Avery, Kevin J., et al. Alexis Rockman: A Fable for Tomorrow. 2011. (ENG., Illus.). 176p. 49.95 *(978-1-904832-86-7(5))* Giles, D. Ltd. GBR. Dist: National Bk. Network.

Avril, Ellen. Ancient Artistry: Pre-Chinese Ceramics & Jades from the Shatzman Collection. 2006. (Illus.). 55p. pap. 15.00 *(978-0-9646042-2-3(1))* Cornell Univ., Herbert F. Johnson Museum of Art.

Axsom, Richard H. 100 Years, 100 Works of Art: Introduction to the Collection of the Grand Rapids Art Museum. 2010. *(978-0-615-39126-7(5))* Yale Univ. Pr.

Ayers, Joyce. My Views As Seen Thru This Camer. 2009. 64p. pap. 38.49 *(978-1-4389-8627-2(0))* AuthorHouse.

Baechler, Donald. Donald Baechler: XL + XS. 2010. (ENG., Illus.). 144p. 45.00 *(978-88-366-1536-0(8))* Silvana ITA. Dist: D.A.P./Distributed Art Pubs.

Bagnoli, Martina, et al, eds. Treasures of Heaven: Saints, Relics, & Devotion in Medieval Europe. 2010. (Illus.). 278p. 65.00 *(978-0-300-16827-3(6))* Yale Univ. Pr.

Bagnoli, Martina & Gerry, Kathryn B. The Medieval World: The Walters Art Museum. 2011. (Illus.). 216p. pap. ***(978-0-911886-75-7(3))*** Walters Art Museum, US.

Baigell, Matthew. Jewish Art in America: An Introduction. 2006. (ENG., Illus.). 280p. 96.00 *(978-0-7425-4640-0(3))*; pap. 29.95 *(978-0-7425-4641-7(1))* Rowman & Littlefield Publishers, Inc.

Baillio, Joseph. The Odyssey Continues: Masterworks from the New Orleans Museum of Art & from provate New Orleans Collections. 2006. per. 45.00 *(978-0-9657856-3-1(7))* Wildenstein & Co., Inc.

Baker, Kenneth. The Lightning Field. 2008. (Illus.). 160p. 35.00 *(978-0-300-13894-8(6))* Yale Univ. Pr.

Bakker, Conrad. Conrad Bakker: Objects & Economies: Untitled Projects 1997-2007. 2009. (ENG., Illus.). 80p. pap. 8.95 *(978-1-879003-51-4(1))* Des Moines Art Ctr.

Balazs, Harold. Harold Balazs. 2010. (Thomas T. Wilson Ser.). (ENG., Illus.). 160p. 60.00 *(978-0-295-99059-0(7))* Univ. of Washington Pr.

Baldessari, John. John Baldessari: A Print Retrospective from the Collections of Jordan D. Schnitzer & his Family Foundation. 2010. (ENG., Illus.). 160p. 59.95 *(978-1-935202-10-3(3))* D.A.P./Distributed Art Pubs.

—John Baldessari: Parse. 2010. (ENG., Illus.). 312p. 95.00 *(978-3-03764-117-0(7))* JRP Ringier Kunstverlag AG CHE. Dist: D.A.P./Distributed Art Pubs.

Balken, Debra Bricker. John Marin: Modernism at Midcentury. 2011. (ENG., Illus.). 120p. 40.00 *(978-0-300-14993-7(X))* Yale Univ. Pr.

Ball, David M. & Kuhlman, Martha B., eds. The Comics of Chris Ware. 2010. (ENG., Illus.). 288p. 55.00 *(978-1-60473-442-3(6))* Univ. Pr. of Mississippi.

Ballester Moreno, Antonio. Antonio Ballester Moreno. 2008. (Illus.). pap. 20.00 *(978-0-9778819-7-0(0))* Peres Projects, Los Angeles Berlin.

Bama, James. James Bama Sketchbook: A Seventy Year Journey, Traveling from the Far East to the Old West. 2010. 144p. pap. 24.95 *(978-1-933865-24-9(5))* Flesk Pubns.

Bancroft, Sarah C. Two Schools of Cool. 2012. (Illus.). 112p. pap. 29.95 ***(978-3-7913-5188-9(5))*** Prestel Publishing.

Bancroft, Sarah C. 2010 California Biennial: Orange County Museum of Art. 2011. (Illus.). 208p. pap. 39.95 *(978-3-7913-5119-3(2))* Prestel Publishing.

Banks, Eric. Christopher Wool. Holzwarth, Hans Werner, ed. 2012. (ENG, FRE & GER., Illus.). 432p. 69.99 ***(978-3-8365-3562-5(9))*** TASCHEN DEU. Dist: Ingram Pub. Services.

Bannon, Anthony & Wells, Benedict. Roger Eberhard. Wilted Country. Keller, Walter, ed. 2010. (GER & ENG., Illus.). 80p. 55.00 *(978-3-85881-306-0(0))* Scheidegger und Spiess AG, Verlag CHE. Dist: Antique Collectors' Club.

Barilleaux, Rene Paul. Tom Slick: International Art Collector: An Exhibition. 2009. *(978-0-916677-53-4(2))* McNay, Marion Koogler Art Museum.

Barker, Scott Grant & Myers, Jane. Intimate Modernism: Fort Worth Circle Artists in The 1940s. 2008. (ENG., Illus.). 208p. 39.95 *(978-0-88360-103-7(6)*, Amon Carter Museum.

Barnes, Lucinda & Baas, Jacquelynn. Measure of Time, 1 vol. 2007. (ENG., Illus.). 176p. pap. 25.00 *(978-0-9719397-6-9(4))* Univ. of California, Berkeley Art Museum & Pacific Film Archive.

Barney, Tina. Players, 1 vol. Kidd, Chip, ed. 2011. (ENG., Illus.). 96p. 49.95 *(978-3-86521-995-4(0))* Steidl, Gerhard Druckerei und Verlag DEU. Dist: Innovative Logistics.

Barratt, Carrie Rebora & Zabar, Lori. American Portrait Miniatures in the Metropolitan Museum of Art. 2010. (Illus.). 328p. 65.00 *(978-0-300-14895-4(X))* Yale Univ. Pr.

—American Portrait Miniatures in the Metropolitan Museum of Art. 2010. (Illus.). xi, 316p. 65.00 *(978-1-58839-357-9(7))* Metropolitan Museum of Art, The.

Barrett & Barrett, Terry. Criticizing Art: Understanding the Contemporary. 3rd ed. 2011. (ENG., Illus.). 256p. (C). pap. 55.33 *(978-0-07-337919-7(0)*, 0073379190) McGraw-Hill Cos., The.

Barriault, Anne B. Selections from the Virginia Museum of Fine Arts. 2nd rev. ed. 2007. (ENG., Illus.). 376p. 45.00 *(978-0-917046-82-7(X))* Virginia Museum of Fine Arts.

Barriault, Anne B. & Davidson, Kay M. Selections from the Virginia Museum of Fine Arts. 2007. (Illus.). xix, 355p. pap. *(978-0-917046-81-0(1))* United States Holocaust Memorial Museum.

Barringer, T. J. Object Lessons. 2007. *(978-0-89467-967-4(8))* Yale Univ. Art Gallery.

Barry, Robert, photos by. Robert Barry: Real … … Personal, 5 vols. 2008. (ITA & ENG., Illus.). 56p. 15.00 *(978-3-905701-48-7(0))* JRP Ringier Kunstverlag AG CHE. Dist: D.A.P./Distributed Art Pubs.

Barry X Ball. pap. 25.00 *(978-2-903004-12-5(9))* Galerie Isy Brachot FRA. Dist: D.A.P./Distributed Art Pubs.

Barryte, Bernard, ed. Rodin & America. 2011. (ENG., Illus.). 384p. 75.00 ***(978-88-366-2000-5(0))*** Silvana ITA. Dist: D.A.P./Distributed Art Pubs.

Basa, Lynn. The Artist's Guide to Public Art: How to Find & Win Commissions. 2008. (ENG., Illus.). 240p. pap. 19.95 *(978-1-58115-501-3(8)*, 115501, Allworth Pr.) Skyhorse Publishing Co., Inc.

Basualdo, C. Bruce Nauman: Topological Gardens. Basualdo, Carlos, ed. & contrib. by by. Taylor, Michael R. et al, contrib. by. 2009. (ENG & ITA., Illus.). 240p. 40.00 *(978-0-300-14981-4(6))* Yale Univ. Pr.

Basualdo, Carlos & Battle, Erica F., eds. Bruce Nauman: Topological Gardens - Installation Views. 2010. (Illus.). 60p. pap. 12.00 *(978-0-300-16463-3(7))* Yale Univ. Pr.

Basualdo, Carlos, et al. Bruce Nauman: Topological Gardens. 2009. (ITA & ENG., Illus.). 240p. *(978-0-87633-217-7(3))* Philadelphia Museum of Art.

Bauermeister, Mary, et al. Welten in der Schachtel / Worlds in a Box: Mary Bauermeister und die experimentelle Kunst der 1960er Jahre / Mary Bauermeister & the Experimental Art of the Sixties. 2011. (GER & ENG., Illus.). 176p. 55.00 *(978-3-86678-449-9(X))* Kerber Verlag DEU. Dist: D.A.P./Distributed Art Pubs.

Baumann, Daniel & Bellini, Andrea, eds. John Mccracken. 2011. (ENG., Illus.). 262p. 65.00 *(978-88-572-0776-6(5))* Skira Editore ITA. Dist: Random Hse., Inc.

Baume, Nicholas, ed. Sol Lewitt: Structures, 1965-2006. 2012. (ENG., Illus.). 192p. 50.00 *(978-0-300-17861-6(1))* Yale Univ. Pr.

Baume, Nicholas, intro. Double Take. 2010. (ENG., Illus.). 48p. pap. 9.95 *(978-0-9608488-6-7(X))* Public Art Fund.

Bayri, Gaye. Paradoxical Nature of American Art During the Great Depression. 2011. 84p. pap. ***(978-3-8433-9053-8(3))*** Lambert Academic Publishing.

Bazzano-Nelson, Florencia & Porter, Liliana. Liliana Porter & the Art of Simulation. 2008. (Illus.). 184p. 114.95 *(978-0-7546-6465-9(1))* Ashgate Publishing Co.

Beal, Graham William John & Mancoff, Debra N. Treasures of the DIA: The Detroit Institute of Arts. 2007. *(978-0-89558-160-0(4))* Detroit Institute of Arts.

Bear, Jordan, et al. Mannerism & Modernism: The Kasper Collection. 2011. *(978-0-87598-156-7(9))* Giles, D. Ltd.

Beard, Rick, et al. Packaging Presidents: A Book Illustrating the Merrill C. Berman Collection. 2008. (Illus.). 200p. pap. *(978-0-9799182-1-6(9))* Abraham Lincoln Presidential Library Foundation.

Bearden, Romare. Romare Bearden, American Modernist. Fine, Ruth & Francis, Jacqueline, eds. 2011. (Studies in the History of Art Ser.). (ENG., Illus.). 304p. 70.00 *(978-0-300-12161-2(X))* National Gallery of Art.

Becker, Cynthia & Loughran, Kristyne, contrib. by. Desert Jewels: North African Jewelry & Photography from the Xavier Guerrand-Hermes Collection. 2009. (Illus.). 95p. pap. 19.95 *(978-0-945802-52-5(8))* Museum for African Art.

Becket-Griffith, Jasmine. Portfolio One. 2010. 64p. pap. 29.50 *(978-0-557-60586-6(5))* Lulu Enterprises Inc.

Behrendt, Kurt A. The Art of Gandhara in the Metropolitan Museum of Art. 2007. 24.95 *(978-1-58839-224-4(4))* Metropolitan Museum of Art, The.

Bell, Nicholas. A Revolution in Wood: The Bresler Collection. 2010. (ENG., Illus.). 152p. 45.00 *(978-1-58834-304-8(9))* Smithsonian Institution Pr.

Ben-Haim, Tsipi. Urban Stories: New York City Kids Paint Murals. 2010. (ENG.). 111p. pap. 40.00 *(978-1-884167-74-4(8))* Umbrage Editions.

Benjamin, Robert, photos by. Robert Benjamin: Notes from a Quiet Life. 2012. (ENG., Illus.). 72p. 45.00 ***(978-1-934435-37-3(6))*** Radius Bks.

Benson, Richard, photos by. & text. North South East West. 2011. (ENG., Illus.). 128p. 35.00 ***(978-0-87070-816-9(3))*** Museum of Modern Art.

Berardi, Marianne & Adams, Henry. Discovering Margot Peet: The Artist & the Art World of Kansas City. 2008. *(978-1-889274-32-4(1))* Posterity Pr.

Bercht, Fatima. Viva David Tineo: A Retrospective of Tucson's Muralist & Art Educator. 2010. (Illus.). 64p. pap. 20.00 (978-0-911611-38-0(X)) Tucson Museum of Art.

Beresford, Laura. Folk Art from the American Museum in Britain. 2011. (ENG., Illus.). 128p. pap. 35.00 (978-1-85759-676-2(5)) Scala, Editions FRA. Dist: National Bk. Network.

Berger, Maurice, ed. The 1980s: A Virtual Discussion, 1 vol. 2006. (ENG., Illus.). 240p. pap. 14.95 (978-1-890761-09-7(5)) Univ. of Maryland Baltimore County, Fine Arts Gallery.

Bergh, Susan. Wari: Lords of the Ancient Andes. 2012. (ENG., Illus.). 304p. 60.00 **(978-0-500-51656-0(1)**, 551656) Thames & Hudson.

Berman, Avis, text. Bill Scott: Looking Through. 2007. pap. (978-0-9759954-8-8(0)) Taggart, Hollis Galleries.

Berman, Eleanor Davidson. Thomas Jefferson among the Arts: An Essay in Early American Esthetics. 2011. 342p. 51.95 **(978-1-258-05798-5(0))** Literary Licensing, LLC.

Bernstein, Lee. America Is the Prison: Arts & Politics in Prison in The 1970s. 2010. (ENG., Illus.). 240p. 35.00 (978-0-8078-3387-2(8)) Univ. of North Carolina Pr.

Berry, Ian, ed. Tim Rollins & K. O. S. 2009. (ENG., Illus.). 220p. (gr. 17). 39.95 (978-0-262-01355-0(X)) MIT Pr.

Berry, Ian & Lewis, Tom, eds. Lives of the Hudson. 2010. (Illus.). 224p. 49.95 (978-3-7913-5047-9(1)) Prestel Publishing.

Berry, Ian & Zuckermann Jacobsen, Heidi. Fred Tomaselli. 2009. (Illus.). 272p. 60.00 (978-3-7913-4392-1(0)) Prestel Publishing.

Berry, Ian, et al. Joseph Grigely: St. Cecilia. 2007. (Opener Ser.: Vol. 13). (Illus.). 127p. (978-0-9765723-4-3(6)) Tang, Frances Young Teaching Museum & Art Gallery at Skidmore College, The.

Bhandari, Heather Darcy & Melber, Jonathan. ArtWork: Everything You Need to Know (And Do) As You Pursue Your Art Career. 2009. (ENG., Illus.). 304p. pap. 16.95 (978-1-4165-7233-6(3), Free Pr.) Free Pr.

Bianchedi, Remo. Yo No Es Otro: Remo Bianchedi. 2010. (SPA., Illus.). 183p. (978-987-23991-3-9(1)); pap. (978-987-23991-4-6(X)) Fundacion Mundo Nuevo.

Bianco, Juliette M., et al, contrib. by. Wenda Gu at Dartmouth: The Art of Installation. 2008. (Illus.). 160p. pap. 35.00 (978-1-58465-707-1(3)) Hood Museum of Art & Univ. Pr. of New England.

Bickerton, Ashley & Oosterhof, Gosse. Horn of Plenty: 16 Artists from NYC. (GER & ENG., Illus.). 103p. 29.50 (978-90-5006-026-4(9)) Stedelijk Museum NLD. Dist: D.A.P./Distributed Art Pubs.

Biedenharn Jones, Ann. Ann Biedenharn Jones: Life & Art. 2010. (Illus.). 128p. 29.95 (978-0-615-38967-7(8)) Blue Lake Pr. LLC.

Biesenbach, Klaus. Henry Darger. 2009. (Illus.). 304p. 85.00 (978-3-7913-4210-8(X)) Prestel Publishing.

Biesenbach, Klaus, et al, texts. Greater New York 2010, 1 vol. 2010. (ENG.). 250p. pap. 19.00 (978-0-9841776-2-2(0)) P.S.1 Contemporary Art Ctr.

Bilney, Marie & Clark, Christina. Bits & Pieces of Cragsmoor: Including a History of the Carroll Butler Brown House. 2010. 296p. pap. 23.99 (978-1-4520-6195-5(5)) AuthorHouse.

Birge, Debra L. The World of My Little Pony (r): An Unauthorized Guide for Collectors. 2nd rev. exp. ed. 2008. (Schiffer Book for Collectors Ser.). (Illus.). 128p. pap. 24.95 (978-0-7643-2878-7(6)) Schiffer Publishing, Ltd.

Birk, Sandow. The Depravities of War - Sandow Birk. 2007. per. 22.95 (978-0-9771696-9-6(3)) Grand Central Pr.

Birky Greene, Stacie. Junk Mail Takes Flight. 2009. 34p. pap. 16.95 (978-0-557-04469-6(3)) Lulu Enterprises Inc.

Blache, Gustave. Leah Chase: Paintings by Gustave Blache III. 2012. (ENG.). 84p. 40.00 **(978-1-55595-378-2(6))** Hudson Hills Pr. LLC.

Black, Patti Carr. The Mississippi Story. Dietrick, Robin C., ed. 2007. (ENG., Illus.). 132p. 29.95 (978-1-887422-14-7(5)) Univ. Pr. of Mississippi.

Bland, Bartholomew. Red Grooms: In the Studio. 2008. (Illus.). 32p. 9.99 net. (978-0-943651-36-1(0)) Hudson River Museum.

Bland, Bartholomew F. I WANT Candy: The Sweet Stuff in American Art. 2007. (Illus.). 50p. per. 9.99 (978-0-943651-34-7(4)) Hudson River Museum.

Blaut, Julia, et al. Glorious Sky: Herbert Katzman's New York. 2010. (ENG., Illus.). 144p. 45.00 (978-1-904832-83-6(0)) Giles, D. Ltd. GBR. Dist: Antique Collectors' Club.

Blauvelt, Andrew. Worlds Away: New Suburban Landscapes. 2008. (ENG., Illus.). 336p. pap. 34.95 (978-0-935640-90-8(8)) Walker Art Ctr.

Bleckner, Ross. Ross Bleckner: My Life in the New York Times. 2011. (ENG., Illus.). 96p. pap. 24.95 (978-1-893207-27-1(7)) Edgewise Pr.

Bleckner, Ross, et al. John Newsom: Allegories of Naturalism. 2011. (ENG., Illus.). 136p. 55.00 (978-88-8158-801-5(3)) Charta ITA. Dist: D.A.P./Distributed Art Pubs.

Block, Gay, photos by. Gay Block: about Love. 2011. (ENG., Illus.). 312p. 65.00 (978-1-934435-32-8(5)) Radius Bks.

Blomberg, Nancy J. [Re]inventing the Wheel: Advancing the Dialogue on Contemporary American Indian Art. 2008. pap. (978-0-914738-59-6(3)) Denver Art Museum.

Blum, Sylvie, photos by. Naked Beauty. 2011. (ENG, GER, FRE, SPA & ITA., Illus.). 160p. 95.00 **(978-3-8327-9579-5(0))** teNeues Publishing Co.

Bochner, Jay. An American Lens: Scenes from Alfred Stieglitz's New York Secession. 2008. (ENG., Illus.). 389p. (gr. 17). pap. 19.95 (978-0-262-52488-9(0)) MIT Pr.

Bogart, Michele H. The Politics of Urban Beauty: New York & Its Art Commission. 2006. (Illus.). 352p. 60.00 (978-0-226-06305-8(4)) Univ. of Chicago Pr.

Bois. Leger Paris-Newyork. 2008. (ENG., Illus.). 208p. 75.00 (978-3-7757-2161-5(4)) Hatje Cantz Verlag GmbH & Co KG DEU. Dist: D.A.P./Distributed Art Pubs.

Bois, Yve-Alain & Ruscha, Edward. Edward Ruscha Vol. I: Catalogue Raisonné of the Paintings, 1 vol. 2008. (ENG., Illus.). 469p. (gr. 13-18). 200.00 (978-3-88243-972-4(6)) Steidl, Gerhard Druckerei und Verlag DEU. Dist: Innovative Logistics.

Bolton King, Michelle, ed. Phantasmania. 2008. (ENG., Illus.). 96p. 29.95 (978-1-891246-15-9(1)) Kemper Museum of Contemporary Art & Design.

Bonami, Francesco. 2010: Whitney Biennial. Carrion-Muryari, Gary, ed. 2010. (Illus.). 264p. pap. 45.00 (978-0-300-16242-4(1)) Yale Univ. Pr.

Bonansinga, Kate. Enrique Jezik Lines of Division. 2011. (Illus.). 56p. pap. 10.00 **(978-0-9818033-4-0(2))** Univ. of Texas at El Paso, The Dept. of Art.

Bonet, Eugeni. Parallel: Benet Rossell. 2010. 256p. pap. 54.95 (978-84-92505-42-5(7)) Museu d'Art Contemporani de Barcelona ESP. Dist: Actar Birkhauser Distribution.

Bonetti, David & Dreishpoon, Douglas. The Panza Collection: An Experience of Color & Light. 2007. (Illus.). 119p. (978-1-887457-08-8(9)) Buffalo Fine Arts/Albright-Knox Art Gallery.

Borchardt-Hume, Walid Raad: Miraculous Beginnings. 2011. (ENG., Illus.). 144p. pap. 37.95 (978-0-85488-185-7(9)) Whitechapel Art Gallery GBR. Dist: D.A.P./Distributed Art Pubs.

Boris, Staci. The New Authentics: Artists of the Post-Jewish Generation. 2008. (ENG., Illus.). 144p. per. 29.95 (978-0-935982-65-7(5)) Spertus College of Judaica Pr., The.

Bottoms, Greg. The Colorful Apocalypse: Journeys in Outsider Art. 2007. xv, 182p. pap. (978-0-226-06687-5(8)); 200p. 20.00 (978-0-226-06685-1(1)) Univ. of Chicago Pr.

Bouguereau, William Adolphe & Zafran, Eric. In the Studios of Paris: William Bouguereau & His American Students: Exhibition. 2006. (Illus.). 211p. pap. (978-0-86659-028-0(5)) Yale Univ. Pr.

Bovier, Lionel, ed. Michael Cline. 2010. (ENG., Illus.). 64p. 35.00 (978-3-03764-052-4(9)) JRP Ringier Kunstverlag AG CHE. Dist: D.A.P./Distributed Art Pubs.

—Troy Brauntuch. 2010. (ENG., Illus.). 144p. 80.00 (978-3-905770-81-0(4)) JRP Ringier Kunstverlag AG CHE. Dist: D.A.P./Distributed Art Pubs.

Bovier, Lionel & Taylor, Kelly, eds. Jonathan Horowitz: And/or. 2009. (ENG., Illus.). 192p. pap. 55.00 (978-3-03764-018-0(9)) JRP Ringier Kunstverlag AG CHE. Dist: D.A.P./Distributed Art Pubs.

Bowles, John Parish. Adrian Piper: Race, Gender, & Embodiment. 2011. (ENG., Illus.). 352p. 94.95 (978-0-8223-4896-2(9)); pap. 25.95 (978-0-8223-4920-4(5)) Duke Univ. Pr.

Bradford, Mark. Mark Bradford: Merchant Posters. 2010. (ENG., Illus.). 160p. 50.00 (978-0-9800242-2-7(6)) Miller, Gregory & Co.

Bradley, Joe, text. Joe Bradley: Drawings. 2012. (ENG., Illus.). 124p. pap. 29.95 **(978-0-9845892-9-6(5))** PictureBox, Inc.

Brainard, Joe. The Nancy Book. 2008. (ENG., Illus.). 144p. 39.50 (978-0-9799562-0-1(X)) Siglio Pr.

Brennan, Marcia. Modernism's Masculine Subjects: Matisse, the New York School, & Post-Painterly Abstraction. 2006. (ENG., Illus.). 240p. (gr. 17). per. 14.95 (978-0-262-52468-1(6)) MIT Pr.

Brenneman, David. Toulouse-Lautrec & Friends: The Irene & Howard Stein Collection. 2010. 30.00 (978-1-932543-41-4(4)) High Museum of Art.

Bresenhan, Karey & Puentes, Nancy O'Bryant. Lone Stars III: Texas Quilts Today. 2011. (Illus.). 400p. E-Book **(978-0-292-73556-9(1))** Univ. of Texas Pr.

Bresenhan, Karoline Patterson & Puentes, Nancy O'Bryant. Lone Stars III: A Legacy of Texas Quilts, 1986-2011. 2011. (ENG., Illus.). 400p. 50.00 (978-0-292-72699-4(6)); pap. 29.95 (978-0-292-72940-7(5)) Univ. of Texas Pr.

Brettell, Richard R. James Magee: The Hill. 2010. (Illus.). 200p. 40.00 (978-3-7913-5079-0(X)) Prestel Publishing.

Brettell, Richard R. & Dickerson, C. D., III. From the Private Collections of Texas: European Art, Ancient to Modern. 2010. (Illus.). 456p. 65.00 (978-0-300-14494-9(6)) Kimbell Art Museum.

Brettell, Richard R., et al. The Metropolitan Museum of Art Vol. 3: Nineteenth - And Twentieth - Century Paintings. 2010. (ENG., Illus.). 496p. (C). 125.00 (978-0-691-14536-5(9)) Princeton Univ. Pr.

Brewster, Anna Richards. Anna Richards Brewster, American Impressionist. Maxwell, Judith Kafka, ed. 2008. (Illus.). 216p. 45.00 (978-0-520-25749-8(9)) Univ. of California Pr.

Bright, Damien, et al. Osvaldo Romberg +/- 70, Even. 2010. 208p. pap. 24.95 (978-1-58177-108-4(8)) Barrytown/Station Hill Pr.

Brilliant, Virginia. The John & Mable Ringling Museum of Art. 2011. (ENG., Illus.). 64p. pap. 7.95 **(978-1-85759-694-6(3))** Scala, Editions FRA. Dist: National Bk. Network.

Briney, S. Self Portrait. 2010. 192p. pap. 15.99 (978-1-4490-6161-6(3)) AuthorHouse.

Briseño, Rolando & Cantú, Norma E. Moctezuma's Table: Rolando Briseño's Mexican & Chicano Tablescapes. 2010. (Rio Grande/Rio Bravo: Borderlands Culture & Traditions Ser.). (ENG., Illus.). 200p. 42.00 (978-1-60344-183-4(2)) Texas A&M Univ. Pr.

Brittin, Charles. Charles Brittin: West & South. 2011. (ENG., Illus.). 216p. 60.00 (978-3-7757-2836-2(8)) Hatje Cantz Verlag GmbH & Co KG DEU. Dist: D.A.P./Distributed Art Pubs.

Brock, Charles, et al. American Modernism: The Shein Collection. 2010. (978-0-89468-365-7(9)) National Gallery of Art.

Broderick, Mosette. Triumvirate: McKim, Mead & White: Art, Architecture, Scandal, & Class in America's Gilded Age. 2010. (ENG., Illus.). 608p. 40.00 (978-0-394-53662-0(2), Knopf) Knopf Doubleday Publishing Group.

Brougher, Kerry, et al, texts. The Panza Collection. 2009. (ENG., Illus.). 96p. pap. 25.00 (978-0-9789603-1-3(4)) Hirshhorn Museum & Sculpture Garden.

Brown, Amy & de Lint, Charles. The Art of Amy Brown, Bk. 1. 2010. (Illus.). 160p. 30.00 (978-0-9744612-1-2(0)) Chimera Publishing.

Brown, Amy & Pierce, Tamora. The Art of Amy Brown, Vol. 2. 2010. 160p. 35.00 (978-0-9744612-5-0(3)) Chimera Publishing.

Brown, Betty Ann & White, John M., contrib. by. Lifelines: John M. White: A Retrospective Exhibition of Performance, Installation, Sculpture, Painting & Drawing. 2011. (ENG., Illus.). 56p. pap. 25.00 **(978-0-9833385-0-5(7))** Armory Ctr. for the Arts.

Brown, Elizabeth. Kiki Smith: Photographs. 2010. (Illus.). 208p. 49.95 (978-3-7913-4465-2(X)) Prestel Publishing.

Brown, Harrison Bird & Routhier, Jessica Skwire. Vividly True to Nature: Harrison Bird Brown, 1831-1915. 2007. (Illus.). 32p. pap. (978-0-916857-45-5(X)) Portland Museum of Art.

Brown, Iona Rozeal. Iona Rozeal Brown. 2010. (ENG., Illus.). 96p. 45.00 (978-3-7757-2601-6(2)) Hatje Cantz Verlag GmbH & Co KG DEU. Dist: D.A.P./Distributed Art Pubs.

Brush, Daniel. 30 Years Work Bk. 1: "Animals", 3 vols. 2008. (ENG., Illus.). 320p. 85.00 (978-3-86521-476-8(2)) Steidl, Gerhard Druckerei und Verlag DEU. Dist: Innovative Logistics.

Brusic, Robert M. & Evenrud, Jerry. And Grace Will Lead Me Home: The Jerry Evenrud Collection of Images of the Parable of the Prodigal Son. 2007. (ENG., Illus.). 200p. 40.00 (978-1-932688-18-4(8), Lutheran Univ. Pr.) Kirk Hse. Pubs.

Bryan-Wilson, Julia. Art Workers: Radical Practice in the Vietnam War Era. 2011. (Illus.). 295p. pap. 29.95 (978-0-520-26975-0(6)) Univ. of California Pr.

Bühl, Gudrun, ed. Dumbarton Oaks: The Collections. 2008. (Dumbarton Oaks Collection Ser.). (Illus.). 384p. pap. 24.95 (978-0-88402-354-8(0)) Dumbarton Oaks.

Buhle, Paul, ed. Jews & American Comics: An Illustrated History of an American Art Form. 2008. (ENG., Illus.). 198p. 29.95 (978-1-59558-331-4(9)) New Pr., The.

Buick, Kirsten. Child of the Fire: Mary Edmonia Lewis & the Problem of Art History's Black & Indian Subject. 2010. (ENG., Illus.). 344p. 94.95 (978-0-8223-4247-2(2)); pap. 25.95 (978-0-8223-4266-3(9)) Duke Univ. Pr.

Burgard, Timothy Anglin. Matter & Spirit: Stephen de Staebler. 2012. (ENG., Illus.). 224p. 65.00 **(978-0-520-27230-9(7))** Univ. of California Pr.

—Matter & Spirit - Stephen de Staebler. 2012. (ENG., Illus.). 224p. pap. 34.95 **(978-0-520-27231-6(5))** Univ. of California Pr.

Burke, Gregory, ed. Lawrence Weiner: the Other Side of A Cul-de-Sac. 2009. (ENG., Illus.). 48p. 35.00 (978-1-894212-25-0(8)) Power Plant, The CAN. Dist: D.A.P./Distributed Art Pubs.

Burnet, Mary Q. Art & Artists in Indiana. (Illus.). 448p. reprint ed. lib. bdg. 98.00 (978-0-7222-0857-1(X)) Library Reprints, Inc.

Burns-Clair, Pam, et al. Walt Disney's First Lady of Imagineering, Harriet Burns. 2010. (978-1-57864-600-5(6)) Donning Co. Pubs.

Burns, Sarah. American Art to 1900: A Documentary History. Davis, John, ed. 2009. (ENG., Illus.). 988p. 70.00 (978-0-520-24526-6(1)); pap. 36.95 (978-0-520-25756-6(1)) Univ. of California Pr.

Burr, Tom. Tom Burr: Moods. 2008. (ENG., Illus.). 64p. pap. 29.95 (978-3-86560-275-6(4)) Verlag der Buchhandlung Walther Konig DEU. Dist: D.A.P./Distributed Art Pubs.

—Tom Burr: Extrospective: Works 1994-2006, 1 vol. Derieux, Florence, ed. 2006. (FRE & ENG., Illus.). 160p. pap. 45.00 (978-3-905701-82-1(0)) JRP Ringier Kunstverlag AG CHE. Dist: D.A.P./Distributed Art Pubs.

Burris, Jennifer, et al. Fore - Closed Between Crisis & PoS - Sibility. 2012. (ENG., Illus.). 152p. pap. 16.95 **(978-0-300-17867-8(0))** Yale Univ. Pr.

Burton, Johanna. Pop Art: Contemporary Perspectives: Princeton University Art Museum. 2007. (Illus.). 159p. (978-0-943012-44-5(9)) Princeton Univ. Art Museum.

Burton, Johanna, et al. Sherrie Levine: Mayhem. 2012. (ENG., Illus.). 216p. 60.00 (978-0-300-17596-7(5)) Yale Univ. Pr.

Busch, Jason, ed. & text. Carnegie Museum of Art: Decorative Arts & Design. 2010. (ENG., Illus.). 224p. pap. 19.95 (978-0-88039-052-1(2)) Carnegie Museum of Art, The.

Butler, Jon & Cooper, Helen A. Life, Liberty, & the Pursuit of Happiness: Art & the American Experience, 1660-1900. 2008. pap. (978-0-89467-966-7(X)) Yale Univ. Pr.

Butts, Porter. Art in Wisconsin. (Illus.). 213p. reprint ed. lib. bdg. 98.00 (978-0-7222-0329-3(2)); lib. bdg. 98.00 (978-0-7222-0383-5(7)) Library Reprints, Inc.

Cadigan, Glen. The Titans Companion Volume 2, Vol. 2. 2008. 224p. pap. 26.95 (978-1-893905-87-0(X)) TwoMorrows Publishing.

Cadou, Carol Borchert. The George Washington Collection: Fine & Decorative Arts at Mount Vernon. 2006. (ENG., Illus.). 254p. 60.00 (978-1-55595-268-6(2)) Hudson Hills Pr. LLC.

Cage, John. The Anarchy of Silence: John Cage & Experimental Art. 2010. (Illus.). 295p. pap. 59.95 (978-84-92505-14-2(1)) Museu d'Art Contemporani de Barcelona ESP. Dist: Actar Birkhauser Distribution.

—Every Day Is a Good Day: the Visual Art of John Cage. 2010. (ENG., Illus.). 160p. pap. 30.00 (978-1-85332-283-9(0)) Hayward Gallery Publishing GBR. Dist: D.A.P./Distributed Art Pubs.

Calit2, Gallery. Overheard. 2010. 48p. pap. 28.51 (978-0-578-05311-0(X)) gallery@calit2.

—Tijuana/San Diego: Cooperation & Confrontation at the Interface. 2010. 100p. pap. 44.00 (978-0-578-04780-5(2)) gallery@calit2.

Calvin, Paula E. & Deacon, Deborah A. American Women Artists in Wartime, 1776-2010. 2011. (ENG.). 222p. pap. 49.95 (978-0-7864-4987-3(X)) McFarland & Co., Inc. Pubs.

Cameron. Peter Saul. 2008. (ENG., Illus.). 160p. 55.00 (978-3-7757-2204-9(1)) Hatje Cantz Verlag GmbH & Co KG DEU. Dist: D.A.P./Distributed Art Pubs.

Campbell, Jim. Jim Campbell. 2010. (ENG., Illus.). 168p. 55.00 (978-3-7757-2542-2(3)) Hatje Cantz Verlag GmbH & Co KG DEU. Dist: D.A.P./Distributed Art Pubs.

Campbell, Thomas P. The Metropolitan Museum of Art Guide. 2012. (ENG., Illus.). 456p. pap. 24.95 **(978-0-300-17949-1(9))** Yale Univ. Pr.

Candida Smith, Richard. The Modern Moves West: California Artists & Democratic Culture in the Twentieth Century. 2009. (Arts & Intellectual Life in Modern America Ser.). (Illus.). 264p. (C). 39.95 (978-0-8122-4188-4(6)) Univ. of Pennsylvania Pr.

Canwell, Bruce & Mullaney, Dean. Genius, Illustrated: the Life & Art of Alex Toth: The Life & Art of Alex Toth. 2012. (Illus.). 288p. 49.99 **(978-1-61377-024-5(3))** Idea & Design Works, LLC.

Caplin, Abbie. Harvey Caplin's Real Cowboys & the Old West. 2010. (Illus.). 160p. 39.99 (978-0-7643-3434-4(4)) Schiffer Publishing, Ltd.

Carbone, Teresa A., ed. Youth & Beauty: Art of the American Twenties. 2011. (ENG., Illus.). 213p. 60.00 (978-0-8478-3725-0(4), Skira) Rizzoli International Pubns., Inc.

Carder, James N., ed. A Home of the Humanities: The Collecting & Patronage of Mildred & Robert Woods Bliss. 2011. (Dumbarton Oaks Collection Ser.). (ENG., Illus.). 200p. 65.00 (978-0-88402-365-4(6)) Dumbarton Oaks.

Carfagna, Dante & Davis, Josh, eds. See Label for Contents: A Survey of 45 RPM Label Art in America, 1955-1980. 2010. (ENG., Illus.). 288p. pap. 29.95 (978-0-9798110-4-3(X)) Wax Poetics, Inc.

Caricature Carvers of America Staff. Carving an 1880s Western Train: Its Passengers & Crew. 2009. (Illus.). 64p. pap. 16.99 (978-0-7643-3381-1(X)) Schiffer Publishing, Ltd.

Carlano, Annie. Contemporary British Studio Ceramics. 2010. (ENG., Illus.). 224p. 60.00 (978-0-300-16719-1(9)) Yale Univ. Pr.

Carlson, Ann & Strom, Mary Ellen. Carlson/Strom: New Performance Video. 2009. (Illus.). 48p. (978-0-945506-60-7(0)) DeCordova Museum & Sculpture Park.

Carpenter, John T. The Artist's Touch, the Craftsman's Hand: Three Centuries of Japanese Prints in the Portland Art Museum, 1 vol. Graybill, Maribeth, ed. 2011. (ENG., Illus.). 348p. 45.00 **(978-1-883124-32-8(8))** Portland Art Museum.

Carrillo, Charles M. & Steele, Thomas J. A Century of Retablos: The Janis & Dennis Lyon Collection of New Mexican Santos, 1780-1880. 2007. (ENG., Illus.). 242p. 60.00 (978-1-55595-273-0(9)) Hudson Hills Pr. LLC.

Carroll, Mary Ellen. Mary Ellen Carroll: Causes, Place, Mistakes, Boredom, Lies, Resemblance, Pleasure, Nothing, Temporality, Affect, Inscription, Envy/Imitation, Utilitarianism, Disappearance, Literalness, Thingness, 1 vol. 2010. (ENG., Illus.). 360p. pap. 50.00 (978-3-86521-618-2(8)) Steidl, Gerhard Druckerei und Verlag DEU. Dist: Innovative Logistics.

Carson, David & Blackwell, Lewis. The End of Print: The Grafik Design of David Carson. 2nd rev. ed. 2012. (ENG., Illus.). 192p. 45.00 **(978-1-85669-888-7(2))** King, Laurence Publishing GBR. Dist: Hachette Bk. Group.

Carson, Juli, ed. MFA Thesis Exhibitions 2007. 2007. per. (978-1-884355-08-0(0)) Univ. of California, Irvine, Univ. Art Gallery.

Carter, Christopher. Stalwart: The Art of Christopher Carter. 2009. (ENG., Illus.). 44p. 19.95 (978-0-9773399-5-2(5)) Channel Photographics.

Carter, David E. & Stephens, Suzanna Mw. American Graphic Design & Advertising 25. 2010. (ENG.). 336p. 55.00 (978-0-06-183689-3(3), Collins Design) HarperCollins Pubs.

Carton, Laura & Manchanda, Catharina. Stripped. 2010. (Illus.). (978-1-59005-249-5(8)) Nazraeli Pr.

Carver, Jon & Shukman, Henry. Kora: Ricardo Mazal. 2010. (ENG., Illus.). 104p. 50.00 (978-1-934491-29-4(2)) Fresco Fine Art Pubns., LLC.

Casarosa, Enrico, et al. Three Trees Make a Forest. 2006. (Illus.). 84p. 24.95 (978-1-58423-226-1(9)) Gingko Pr., Inc.

Castle, James & Percy, Ann. James Castle: A Retrospective. 2008. (978-0-87633-206-1(8)); (978-0-87633-207-8(6)) Philadelphia Museum of Art.

Catalani, Stefano, et al. Knitted, Knotted, Twisted, & Twined: The Jewelry of Mary Lee Hu, 1 vol. 2012. (ENG., Illus.). 128p. 34.95 **(978-0-615-56156-1(X))** Bellevue Arts Museum.

Catalogue Entries by the Curators of Birmingham Museum of Art Staff. Birmingham Museum of Art: Guide to the Collection. 2011. (ENG., Illus.). 272p. pap. 35.00 (978-1-904832-77-5(6)) Giles, D. Ltd. GBR. Dist: Antique Collectors' Club.

Causey, Gregory, ed. Denizens of the Desert: AMARC Photographs by Danny Causey. 2008. 124p. pap. 28.99 (978-1-934446-15-7(7)) Romance Divine LLC.

Cavalieri, Paul & Lange, Tod. Truck Art: A Decade of Graffiti. 2010. (Illus.). 160p. pap. 29.99 (978-0-7643-3493-1(X)) Schiffer Publishing, Ltd.

Celant, Germano. The American Tornado: Art in Power, 1949-2008. 2008. (ENG., Illus.). 448p. pap. 55.00 (978-88-6130-068-2(5)) Skira Editore ITA. Dist: Random Hse., Inc.

Celaya, Enrique Martinez. Nomad: Miami Art Museum November 2, 2007 - January 13 2008. 2007. (ENG., Illus.). 128p. 35.00 *(978-0-9673608-9-8(7))* Whale & Star Pr.
Central Washington University Staff, contrib. by. Crossroads & Connections: Central Washington University Art Alumni Exhibition. 2008. (Illus.). 128p. pap. 29.95 *(978-0-87422-300-2(8))* Washington State Univ. Pr.
Cerizza, Luca, ed. Maps & Legends. 2009. (ENG., Illus.). 280p. 27.00 *(978-3-905829-13-6(4))* JRP Ringier Kunstverlag AG CHE. Dist: D.A.P./Distributed Art Pubs.
Cézanne, Paul, et al. Cezanne & American Modernism. 2009. pap. *(978-0-9824716-0-9(2))* Montclair Art Museum.
Chanse, Samantha. Activist Imagination: Is an Exhibition & Series of Discussions Investigating, Exploring, & Imagining the Past, Present, & Future of Activism: Artists, Bob Hsiang, Donna Keiko Ozawa, Christine Wong Yap. 2008. (Illus.). 72p. *(978-0-9797707-2-2(6))* Kearny Street Workshop.
Chaplin, Beth. The Acting Biz: A Career Guide to the Twin Cities. Chaplin, Beth, ed. 2009. (ENG.). 354p. pap. 35.00 *(978-1-933794-17-4(8))* Kirk Hse. Pubs.
Charles R. Mack. European Art in the Columbia Museum of Art, Including the Samuel H. Kress Collection, Volume One: The Thirteenth through the Sixteenth Century. 2009. (ENG.). 304p. pap. 29.95 *(978-1-57003-806-8(6))* Univ. of South Carolina Pr.
Chen, Katherine K. Enabling Creative Chaos: The Organization Behind the Burning Man Event. 2009. (ENG., Illus.). 272p. 75.00 *(978-0-226-10237-5(8))*; pap. 25.00 *(978-0-226-10238-2(6))* Univ. of Chicago Pr.
Cheney, Liana De Girolami, et al. Self-portraits by women Painters. 2nd ed. 2009. (ENG., Illus.). 296p. pap. 28.00 ***(978-0-9823867-3-6(7))*** New Academia Publishing, LLC.
Chihuly Bellagio, 1 Disc with Book. 2nd rev. ed. 2007. (Illus.). 78p. 25.00 *(978-1-57684-160-0(X))* Portland Pr., Inc.
Chihuly, Dale, illus. Dale Chihuly: A Celebration. 2011. (ENG.). 128p. 19.95 *(978-1-4197-0000-2(6))* Abrams.
Chihuly, Dale & Belcovson, Joe. Chihuly at the Salk. 2010. (Illus.). ***(978-1-57684-186-0(3))*** Portland Pr., Inc.
Children, The Destiny. New York City Graffiti: The Destiny Children. 2011. (Illus.). 344p. 50.00 ***(978-0-7643-3720-8(3)***, Schiffer Publishing Ltd) Schiffer Publishing, Ltd.
Chock, Eric & Lum, Darrell H. Y., eds. Bamboo Ridge No. 98. 2011. 256p. pap. 18.00 ***(978-0-910043-84-7(1))*** Bamboo Ridge Pr.
Chow, Brian G. & Sun, Seunghye. The Lure of Painted Poetry: Japanese & Korean Art. 2011. (Illus.). 120p. 50.00 *(978-1-55595-364-5(6))* Hudson Hills Pr. LLC.
Chowdhry, Pritika. Visceral Mappings: Transdiasporic Art Practices. 2007. (Illus.). 50p. pap. 24.95 *(978-0-9797340-0-7(2))* Chowdhry, Pritika.
Christensen, James C. & Horowitz, Kate. Men & Angels: The Art of James C. Christensen. 2008. (ENG., Illus.). 256p. 85.00 *(978-0-86713-102-4(0)*, 0867131020) Greenwich Workshop Pr.
Christo & Jeanne Claude. Christo & Jeanne-Claude: Early Works 1958-64. 2010. (ENG & GER., Illus.). 192p. pap. 35.00 *(978-3-941100-79-4(3))* DruckVerlag Kettler GmbH DEU. Dist: D.A.P./Distributed Art Pubs.
Cikovsky, Nicolai, ed. Winslow Homer Watercolors. 2009. (ENG., Illus.). 120p. 35.00 *(978-0-7893-9955-7(5))* Universe Publishing.
Cirincione, Janine, intro. Feng Zhengjie. 2007. (Illus.). 32p. 10.00 *(978-0-9798486-0-5(1))* Tilton Gallery.
Clark, Carol & Deas, Charles. Charles Deas & 1840s America. 2009. (Charles M. Russell Center on Art & Photography of the American West Ser.). (ENG.). 248p. (C). 39.95 *(978-0-8061-4030-8(5))*; pap. *(978-0-8061-4048-3(8))* Univ. of Oklahoma Pr.
Clark, Garth. Ian Ingram: Divining. 2010. (Illus.). 40p. 30.00 *(978-0-9826397-0-2(8))* Friedman, Barry Ltd.
Clark, Kirk. Celebration of Spirit. 2007.Tr. of Celebracion de Espiritu. (Illus.). 144p. 40.00 *(978-0-9774935-0-0(4))* Clark, Kirk.
Clark-Langager, Sarah & Dietrich, William, eds. Critical Messages: Contemporary Northwest Artists on the Environment. 2010. (ENG., Illus.). 80p. pap. 24.95 *(978-1-878237-07-1(1))* Western Washington Univ., Western Gallery.
Clark, Michael. Exposed: Inside the Life & Images of a Pro Photographer. 2012. (Voices That Matter Ser.). (ENG.). 288p. pap. 49.99 ***(978-0-321-81123-3(2))*** New Riders Publishing.
Clark, Robin Lee. Phenomenal: California Light, Space, Surface. 2011. (ENG.). 240p. 39.95 *(978-0-520-27060-2(6))* Univ. of California Pr.
Clark, Vicky A. Popular Salon of the People: Associated Artists of Pittsburgh, 1910-2006. 2007. (Illus.). 164p. *(978-0-88039-050-7(6))* Carnegie Museum of Art, The.
Clemence, Paul & Davidow, Julie. Miami: Contemporary Artists. 2007. (Illus.). 288p. pap. 49.95 *(978-0-7643-2647-9(3))* Schiffer Publishing, Ltd.
Cleveland, David Adams. A History of American Tonalism, 1880-1920. 2010. (ENG., Illus.). 640p. 75.00 *(978-1-55595-302-7(6))* Hudson Hills Pr. LLC.
Coetzee, Mark & Lagos, Luisa. Memorials of Identity: New Media from the Rubell Family Collection. 2009. (ENG., Illus.). 175p. 30.00 *(978-0-9716341-8-3(1))* Rubell Family Collection.
Colangelo, Carmon, et al. On the Margins. 2008. (Illus.). 64p. 30.00 *(978-0-936316-25-3(X))* Washington Univ., Mildred Lane Kemper Art Museum.
Colbert, Charles. Haunted Visions: Spiritualism & American Art. 2011. (Arts & Intellectual Life in Modern America Ser.). (Illus.). 336p. (C). 49.95 *(978-0-8122-4325-3(0))* Univ. of Pennsylvania Pr.
Coleman, Robert Randolf & Bohn, Babette. The Art of Disegno: Italian Prints & Drawings from the Georgia Museum of Art. 2007. *(978-0-915977-62-8(1))* Univ. of Georgia, Georgia Museum of Art.
Colley, Robert, et al, eds. Stone Canoe, Number 4: A Journal of Arts & Ideas from Upstate New York. 2010. (Stone Canoe Ser.). (Illus.). 327p. pap. *(978-0-9791944-3-6(1))* Syracuse Univ. Pr.
Condo, George. Mental States. 2011. (ENG., Illus.). 168p. 50.00 *(978-1-85332-289-1(X))* Hayward Gallery Publishing GBR. Dist: D.A.P./Distributed Art Pubs.
Conley, Cort. Idaho Artists. 2011. pap. 29.95 ***(978-0-932129-48-2(X)***, Idaho Ctr. for the Bk.) Hemingway Western Studies Ctr.
Conrod, Suzanne & Conrod, Hugh. Rug Art - Rescued from Oblivion. 2010. 216p. pap. 19.95 *(978-1-4520-0237-8(1))* AuthorHouse.
—Rug Art - Rescued from Oblivion: A Hooked Rug Museum of North America Research Project. 2010. 216p. 26.95 *(978-1-4520-0238-5(X))* AuthorHouse.
Contreras Gómez, Carmen, text. Ryan Mcginness: Studio Franchise. 2010. (ENG.). 196p. 35.00 *(978-84-96917-63-7(0))* Caja de Madrid ESP. Dist: Actar Birkhauser Distribution.
Cook, Colin & Shambaugh, Bill. Colin Cook und Bill Shambaugh: Drawings with Bill. 2009. (ENG.). 64p. 30.00 *(978-3-86828-069-2(3))* Kehrer Verlag Heidelberg, Klaus Kehrer DEU. Dist: Consortium Bk. Sales & Distribution.
Cooke, Lynne & Crimp, Douglas, eds. Mixed Use, Manhattan: Photography & Related Practices, 1970s to the Present. 2010. (ENG., Illus.). 303p. (gr. 17). 49.95 *(978-0-262-01482-3(3))* MIT Pr.
Cooke, Lynne & Vila-Matas, Enrique, texts. Dominique Gonzalez-Foerster: Chronotopes & Dioramas. 2010. (ENG., Illus.). 128p. 25.00 *(978-0-944521-57-1(6))* Dia Ctr. for the Arts.
Cooper, Chris. Idle Hands: The Art of Coop. 2011. (ENG., Illus.). 208p. 50.00 ***(978-1-61404-002-6(8))*** Baby Tattoo Bks.
Cooper, Martha. Remembering 9/11. 2011. (JPN, ARA, HIN, SPA & ENG., Illus.). 80p. pap. 10.95 *(978-1-935613-09-1(X))* Batty, Mark Pub., LLC.
Cooper, Martha, photos by. Tag Town: The Evolution of New York Graffiti Writing. 2007. (ENG., Illus.). 112p. 24.95 *(978-91-85639-05-2(2))* Dokument forlag, Fotograf Malcolm Jacobsson SWE. Dist: SCB Distributors.
Corbett, David Peters & Monks, Sarah, eds. Anglo-American: Artistic Exchange between Britain & the USA. 2012. (Art History Special Issues Ser.: 9). (ENG.). 264p. pap. 39.95 ***(978-1-4443-5143-9(5)***, Wiley-Blackwell) Wiley, John & Sons, Inc.
Corbett, William. Albert York. 2010. 94p. pap. 17.50 *(978-0-9824100-5-9(0))* Pressed Wafer Pr.
Corral, María de & Lane, John R., eds. Fast Forward: Contemporary Collections for the Dallas Museum of Art. 2007. (ENG., Illus.). 328p. 65.00 *(978-0-300-12291-6(8))* Dallas Museum of Art.
Cossons, Malcolm & Phillips, Jocelyn. Collect Contemporary Photography. 2012. (ENG., Illus.). 208p. pap. 21.95 ***(978-0-500-28854-2(2)***, 528854) Thames & Hudson.
Costa, Guido. Nan Goldin. 2010. (ENG., Illus.). 128p. 12.95 *(978-0-7148-5945-3(1))* Phaidon Pr., Inc.
Cox, Julian. Robert Weingarten: The Portrait Unbound. 2010. (ENG., Illus.). 120p. 35.00 *(978-1-932543-33-9(3))* High Museum of Art.
Coxon, Ann. Louise Bourgeois. 2010. (ENG., Illus.). 540p. pap. 27.50 *(978-1-85437-882-8(1))* Tate Publishing, Ltd. GBR. Dist: Hachette Bk. Group.
Coyne, Petah & Lloyd, Ann Wilson. Petah Coyne: Vermilion Fog. 2008. (ENG., Illus.). 88p. 39.95 *(978-88-8158-684-4(3))* Charta ITA. Dist: D.A.P./Distributed Art Pubs.
Crabapple, Molly. Art of Molly Crabapple Volume 1: Week in Hell: Week in Hell. 2012. (Illus.). 48p. (YA). pap. 9.99 ***(978-1-61377-154-9(1))*** Idea & Design Works, LLC.
Craig, James A. Fitz H. Lane: An Artist's Voyage Through Nineteenth-Century America. 2006. (Illus.). 222p. pap., per. 32.99 *(978-1-59629-090-7(0))* History Pr., The.
Cram101 Textbook Reviews. Outlines & Highlights for Framing Americ: A Social History of American Art by Frances K. Pohl, ISBN. 2011. 384p. pap. 34.95 ***(978-1-61812-561-3(3))*** Cram101 Inc.
Crawford, Ralston, illus. Ralston Crawford & Jazz. 2011. 262p. pap. 24.95 ***(978-1-891442-77-3(5))*** Virginia Publishing Corp.
Crawley, Susan. Bill Traylor: Drawings from the Collections of the High Museum of Art & the Montgomery Museum of Fine Arts. 2012. (Illus.). 104p. 29.95 ***(978-3-7913-5199-5(0))*** Prestel Publishing.
Crosman, Christopher B. & Shapiro, Emily D. Celebrating the American Spirit: Masterworks from Crystal Bridges Museum of American Art. 2011. (ENG., Illus.). 356p. 60.00 ***(978-1-55595-371-3(9))*** Hudson Hills Pr. LLC.
Cross, Susan M. & Markonish, Denise, eds. Sol Lewitt: 100 Views. 2009. (ENG., Illus.). 272p. pap. 45.00 *(978-0-300-15282-1(5))* Yale Univ. Pr.
Crow, Nancy. Crossroads: Constructions, Markings, & Structures. 2008. (ENG., Illus.). 64p. per. 22.95 *(978-1-933308-19-7(2))* Breckling Pr.
Crowell, Aron & Worl, Rosita, eds. Living Our Cultures, Sharing Our Heritage: The First Peoples of Alaska. 2010. (ENG., Illus.). 312p. 50.00 *(978-1-58834-270-6(0))* Smithsonian Institution Pr.
Crown, Carol & Russel, Charles, eds. Sacred & Profane: Voice & Vision in Southern Self-Taught Art. 2007. (ENG., Illus.). 286p. 50.00 *(978-1-57806-916-3(5))* Univ. Pr. of Mississippi.
Crown Foundation, The. Jaume Plensa. 2008. (ENG., Illus.). 240p. 60.00 *(978-3-7757-2080-9(4))* Hatje Cantz Verlag GmbH & Co KG DEU. Dist: D.A.P./Distributed Art Pubs.
Crumb, R. & Obrist, Hans Ulrich, texts. Crumb/Obrist, 1 vol. 2007. (ENG.). 47p. pap. 16.00 *(978-3-88375-948-7(1))* Verlag der Buchhandlung Walther Konig DEU. Dist: D.A.P./Distributed Art Pubs.
Cubbs, Joanne & Metcalf, Eugene W., eds. Hard Truths: The Art of Thornton Dial. 2011. (Illus.). 240p. 45.00 *(978-3-7913-5058-5(7))* Prestel Publishing.
Cupola Bobber. 2007. 8.00 *(978-0-9776417-9-6(1))* CUE Art Foundation.
Curtan, Patricia. Menus for Chez Panisse: The Art & Letterpress of Patricia Curtan. 2011. (ENG., Illus.). 184p. 40.00 *(978-1-61689-029-2(0))* Princeton Architectural Pr.
Curto, Guido & Gambari, Olga, eds. Contemporary Mithologies. 2009. (ENG & ITA., Illus.). 200p. 45.00 *(978-88-7757-235-6(3))* Hopefulmonster Editore ITA. Dist: D.A.P./Distributed Art Pubs.
Cushing, Stanley Ellis & Dearinger, David B. Acquired Tastes: 200 Years of Collecting for the Boston Athenaeum. 2007. (Illus.). 388p. 65.00 *(978-0-934552-73-8(8))* Boston Athenaeum Library.
Cutler, Amy. Amy Cutler: Turtle Fur, 1 vol. 2011. (ENG., Illus.). 160p. 60.00 *(978-3-7757-2809-6(0))* Hatje Cantz Verlag GmbH & Co KG DEU. Dist: D.A.P./Distributed Art Pubs.
Czestochowski, Joseph S. & Swann, James. James Swann Prints: A Catalogue Raisonne. 2009. *(978-0-9716408-4-9(X))* International Arts.
Czestochowski, Joseph S., et al. Associated American Artists: Catalogue Raisonne, 1934-2000. 2010. *(978-0-9716408-6-3(6))* International Arts.
Dabakis, Melissa. Visualizing Labor in American Sculpture: Monuments, Manliness, & the Work Ethic, 1880-1935. 2011. (Cambridge Studies in American Visual Culture Ser.). (ENG.). 314p. pap. 60.00 *(978-0-521-28327-4(2))* Cambridge Univ. Pr.
Dailey, Victoria, et al. Behold the Da: The Color Block Prints of Frances Gearhart. 2009. pap. 29.95 *(978-1-61623-538-3(1))* Independent Pub.
Dameron, Meg, et al, compiled by. Our Fondest Dreams & Hopes: Commemorating the Seventy-Fifth Anniversary of the Washington County Museum of Fine Arts. 2006. per. *(978-0-9753285-8-3(1))* H.B.P., Inc.
Danilowitz, Brenda & Weber, Nicolas Fox. The Prints of Josef Albers: A Catalogue Raisonné, 1915-1976. 2010. (ENG., Illus.). 240p. 95.00 *(978-1-55595-324-9(7))* Hudson Hills Pr. LLC.
Danto, Arthur C. Andy Warhol. 2010. (Icons of America Ser.). (ENG., Illus.). 192p. pap. 16.00 *(978-0-300-16908-9(6))* Yale Univ. Pr.
David, Hickey. Primary Atmospheres: Works from California, 1960-1970, 1 vol. 2010. (ENG., Illus.). 100p. 68.00 *(978-3-86930-147-1(3))* Steidl, Gerhard Druckerei und Verlag DEU. Dist: Innovative Logistics.
Davies, Glen C. Stranger in Paradise: The Works of Reverend Howard Finster. 2010. (Illus.). 152p. 40.00 *(978-1-883015-44-2(8))* Univ. of Washington Pr.
Davila, Arlene. Culture Works: Space, Value, & Mobility Across the Neoliberal Americas. 2012. (ENG.). 256p. 70.00 ***(978-0-8147-4429-1(X))***; pap. 22.00 ***(978-0-8147-4430-7(3))*** New York Univ. Pr.
Dávila, Arlene M. Culture Works: Space, Value, & Mobility Across the Neoliberal Americas. 2012. E-Book ***(978-0-8147-4431-4(1))***; E-Book ***(978-0-8147-4432-1(X))*** New York Univ. Pr.
Davis, Anita Price. New Deal Art in North Carolina: The Murals, Sculptures, Reliefs, Paintings, Oils & Frescoes & Their Creators. 2008. (ENG., Illus.). 254p. pap. 45.00 *(978-0-7864-3779-5(0))* McFarland & Co., Inc. Pubs.
Davis, James W. Image as Idea: The Arts in Global Cultures. 2007. 288p. pap. 67.61 *(978-0-7575-4190-2(9))* Kendall Hunt Publishing Co.
Davis, Jessica Hoffmann & Hoffmann Davis, Jessica. Why Our Schools Need the Arts. 2007. (ENG., Illus.). 160p. pap. 22.95 *(978-0-8077-4834-3(X))* Teachers College Pr., Teachers College, Columbia Univ.
Davis, Keith F. The Origins of American Photography 1839-1885: From Daguerreotype to Dry-Plate - The Hallmark Photographic Collection at the Nelson-Atkins Museum of Art. 2007. (ENG., Illus.). 360p. 65.00 *(978-0-300-12286-2(1))* Yale Univ. Pr.
Davy, Jennifer, et al. Material Culture: 16 February/6 April 2008, Fort Worth Contemporary Arts. 2010. (ENG., Illus.). 48p. pap. 19.95 *(978-0-9801617-0-0(3))* Texas Christian Univ. Pr.
De Balincourt, Jules. Jules de Balincourt: Malpais. 2009. (ENG., Illus.). 48p. pap. 30.00 *(978-2-910055-32-5(9))* Galerie Thaddaeus Ropac FRA. Dist: D.A.P./Distributed Art Pubs.
De Berardinis, Olivia. The Art of Olivia Limited Edition Book Set. 240p. 100.00 *(978-0-929643-08-3(9))* Ozone Productions, Ltd.
de Lint, Charles. The Art of Amy Brown, Bk. 1. 2010. (ENG., Illus.). 168p. pap. 20.00 *(978-0-9744612-2-9(9))* Chimera Publishing.
De Long, David G., ed. Sunnylands: Art & Architecture of the Annenberg Estate in Rancho Mirage, California. 2009. (Illus.). 200p. 34.95 *(978-0-8122-4161-7(4))* Univ. of Pennsylvania Pr.
de Sève, Peter. A Sketchy Past: The Art of Peter de SèVe. 2010. 240p. 54.95 *(978-2-35574-099-2(2))* Editions Akileos FRA. Dist: SCB Distributors.
Deaner, Joshua. I Sell Fish. 2009. *(978-1-61584-079-3(6))* Independent Pub.
Dearden, Venetia. Eight Days. 2012. (ENG., Illus.). 80p. pap. 45.00 ***(978-3-86828-254-2(8))*** Kehrer Verlag Heidelberg, Klaus Kehrer DEU. Dist: Consortium Bk. Sales & Distribution.
Debra, Singer & Matthew, Lyons. Just kick it till it Breaks. 2007. (Illus.). 50p. 10.00 *(978-0-9793368-0-5(5))* Kitchen, The.
DeLong, Lea Rosson. Christian Petersen: Urban Artist, 1900-1934. 2007. (Illus.). 208p. 20.00 *(978-0-9777494-1-6(X))* Iowa State Univ., College of Design.
DeMarinis, Paul, et al. Paul DeMarinis: Buried in Noise. 2011. (GER & ENG., Illus.). 208p. 48.00 ***(978-3-86828-141-5(X))*** Kehrer Verlag Heidelberg, Klaus Kehrer DEU. Dist: Consortium Bk. Sales & Distribution.
Demos, T. J. Dara Birnbaum: Technology - Transformation - Wonder Woman. 2010. (One Work Ser.). (ENG., Illus.). 118p. (gr. 17). 35.00 *(978-1-84638-066-2(9))*; pap. 16.00 *(978-1-84638-067-9(7))* Afterall Publishing GBR. Dist: MIT Pr.
Denes, Agnes & Denes. The Human Argument: The Writings of Agnes Denes. Ottman, Klaus, ed. 2008. (ENG.). 300p. pap. 25.00 *(978-0-88214-569-3(X))* Spring Pubns., Inc.
Denning, Michael. The Cultural Front: The Laboring of American Culture in the Twentieth Century. 2nd ed. 2011. (ENG., Illus.). 576p. pap. 29.95 *(978-1-84467-464-0(9)*, 844464) Verso Bks. GBR. Dist: Norton, W. W. & Co., Inc.
Denton, Karl. My Blue Jean Jacket. 2010. 162p. pap. 62.95 *(978-0-557-31867-4(X))* Lulu Enterprises Inc.
Denver Museum of Art Staff, ed. Heart of the West: New Painting & Sculpture of the American West. 2008. (ENG.). 64p. pap. 10.95 *(978-0-8061-9971-9(7))* Denver Art Museum.
—Redrawing Boundaries: Perspectives on Western American Art. 2008. (ENG.). 80p. pap. 10.95 *(978-0-8061-9970-2(9))* Denver Art Museum.
—Sweet on the West: How Candy Built a Colorado Treasure. 2008. (ENG.). 80p. pap. 10.95 *(978-0-8061-9969-6(5))* Denver Art Museum.
—West Point Points West. 2008. (ENG.). 80p. pap. 10.95 *(978-0-8061-9968-9(7))* Denver Art Museum.
Dervaux, Isabelle & Flavin, Dan. Dan Flavin: Drawing. 2012. ***(978-0-87598-162-8(3))*** Giles, D. Ltd.
Devon, Marjorie. Migrations: New Directions in Native American Art. 2006. (ENG., Illus.). 143p. pap. 29.95 *(978-0-8263-3769-6(4))* Univ. of New Mexico Pr.
DeWolf, Holly. Breaking into Freelance Illustration: A Guide for Artists, Designers & Illustrators. 2009. (ENG.). 272p. pap. 19.99 ***(978-1-60061-197-1(4)***, HOW Bks.) F&W Media, Inc.
Dial, Thornton & Herman, Bernard L. Thornton Dial: Thoughts on Paper. 2012. (ENG., Illus.). 224p. 45.00 ***(978-0-8078-3529-6(3))*** Univ. of North Carolina Pr.
Diaz, Daniel Martin. Anatomy of Sorrow: the Artwork of Daniel Martin Diaz. 2011. (ENG., Illus.). 128p. 35.00 ***(978-0-86719-768-6(4))*** Last Gasp of San Francisco.
DiazCasas, Rafael, et al. Hard Light: The Work of Emilio Sanchez. 2011. (ENG., Illus.). 192p. 45.00 ***(978-3-7913-5131-5(1))*** Prestel Publishing.
Dick, R. H. My Time There: The Art Colonies of Santa Fe & Taos, New Mexico, 1956-2006. 2007. (ENG., Illus.). 127p. (gr. 9). 44.95 *(978-0-9639804-3-9(3))* St. Louis Mercantile Library Assn.
Dickey, Tina. Color Creates Light: Studies with Hans Hofmann. 2010. (ENG., Illus.). 400p. 49.95 *(978-0-520-25744-3(8))* Univ. of California Pr.
Dijkstra, Bram. Naked: The Nude in America. 2010. (ENG., Illus.). 476p. 75.00 *(978-0-8478-3366-5(6))* Rizzoli International Pubns., Inc.
Dika, Vera. The (Moving) Pictures Generation: The Cinematic Impulse in Downtown New York Art & Film. 2012. (ENG., Illus.). 266p. 90.00 ***(978-0-230-34144-9(6))*** Palgrave Macmillan.
Dillon, Brian, et al, texts. Walking in My Mind. 2009. (ENG., Illus.). 160p. pap. 40.00 *(978-1-85332-277-8(6))* Hayward Gallery Publishing GBR. Dist: D.A.P./Distributed Art Pubs.
Dine, Jim. Jim Dine: Aldo et Moi, 1 vol. 2008. (ENG., Illus.). 224p. 50.00 *(978-3-86521-461-4(4))* Steidl, Gerhard Druckerei und Verlag DEU. Dist: Innovative Logistics.
—Old Me, Now, 1 vol. 2010. (ENG., Illus.). 64p. pap. 19.95 *(978-3-86930-038-2(8))* Steidl, Gerhard Druckerei und Verlag DEU. Dist: Innovative Logistics.
Dion, Mark. Mark Dion. 2008. (ENG., Illus.). 160p. 60.00 *(978-3-7757-2197-4(5))* Hatje Cantz Verlag GmbH & Co KG DEU. Dist: D.A.P./Distributed Art Pubs.
Dion, Mark & Courtney, Julie. Travels of William Bartram Reconsidered. 2010. (Illus.). 111p. 35.00 *(978-0-615-25748-8(8))* Bartram, John Assn.
Dolkart, Judith F., et al. Masterworks - The Barnes Foundation. 2012. (ENG., Illus.). 374p. 40.00 ***(978-0-8478-3806-6(4)***, Skira) Rizzoli International Pubns., Inc.
Donahue, David M. & Stuart, Jennifer, eds. Artful Teaching: Integrating the Arts for Understanding Across the Curriculum. 2010. (ENG., Illus.). 192p. pap. 24.95 *(978-0-8077-5080-3(8))*; 57.00 *(978-0-8077-5081-0(6))* Teachers College Pr., Teachers College, Columbia Univ.
Donovan, Tara. Tara Donovan. 2008. (ENG., Illus.). 160p. 45.00 *(978-1-58093-213-4(4))* Monacelli Pr., Inc.
Doris, Sara. Pop Art & the Contest over American Culture. 2006. (ENG., Illus.). 316p. 106.99 *(978-0-521-83658-6(1))* Cambridge Univ. Pr.
Dorrill, Lisa. Seven Lively Artsts: Fifty Years of ARt. 2006. 47p. lib. bdg. 10.00 *(978-0-9785645-0-6(2))* Cumberland County Historical Society.
Doshi, Balkrishna, et al. Scapes: Laura de Santillana & Alessandro Diaz de Santillana, 1 vol. 2012. (ENG., Illus.). 128p. 55.00 ***(978-0-295-99188-7(7))*** Univ. of Washington Pr.
Doster, Jennifer. Bringing History Alive with Art Education. 2008. 452p. pap. *(978-3-639-01650-5(5))* VDM Verlag Dr. Mueller e.K.
Dougherty, Patrick. Stickwork. 2010. (ENG., Illus.). 208p. pap. 34.95 *(978-1-56898-976-1(8))* Princeton Architectural Pr.
Douglas, aka Elbow Toe, By Brian Adam. Paper Cuts. 2011. (ENG.). 80p. 50.00 ***(978-88-88493-77-0(8))*** Drago Arts & Communication ITA. Dist: SCB Distributors.
Dover. Maxfield Parrish: Postcards. 2010. (Dover Postcards Ser.). (ENG., Illus.). 24p. pap. 6.95 *(978-0-486-48068-8(2))* Dover Pubns., Inc.
Dover Publications Inc. Staff. 120 Great Paintings of the American West. Grafton, Carol Belanger, ed. 2008. (Dover Electronic Clip Art Ser.). (ENG., Illus.). 128p. pap. 34.95 *(978-0-486-99898-5(3))* Dover Pubns., Inc.

Dower, Darwin. The Wood Sculpturing of Darwin Dower: Sculptured stories of the past through incredible Detail. 2006. (Illus.). 80p. lib. bdg. *(978-0-9754460-3-4(7))* Publisher's Place.

Drain, Jim & Peterson, Ara. Hypnogooogia. 2007. (Illus.). 30p. per. *(978-0-9778686-2-9(1))* Deitch, Jeffrey Inc.

Draper, James David. Cameo Appearances. 2008. (ENG., Illus.). 56p. pap. 19.95 *(978-0-300-14145-0(9))* Yale Univ. Pr.

Dreishpoon, Douglas, et al, texts. Guillermo Kuitca Everything: Everything - Paintings & Works on Paper, 1980-2008. 2009. (ENG., Illus.). 228p. 49.95 *(978-1-85759-596-3(3))* Scala Bks.

Dressler, Iris & Christ, Hans, eds. Subversive Praktiken: Kunst unter Bedingungen politischer Repression 60er-80er / Südamerika / Europa. 2011. (ENG., Illus.). 584p. 60.00 *(978-3-7757-2755-6(8))* Hatje Cantz Verlag GmbH & Co KG DEU. Dist: D.A.P./Distributed Art Pubs.

Drexler, J. Lee & Cohen, James R. Fabulous Finds: How Expert Appraiser Lee Drexler Sold Wall Street's Charging Bull, Found Hidden Treasures & Mingled with the Rich & Famous. 2011. (ENG.). 178p. pap. 16.95 *(978-1-61035-013-6(8))* Linden Publishing Co., Inc.

Droz, Dwight. The Art of the Midnight Poet. 2007. 152p. pap. 24.95 *(978-0-9706357-9-2(6))* Scandia Patch Pr.

Drutt, Matthew. 2005 Artpace Residencies & Exhibitions: Ricky Armendariz, Rae Culbert, Trisha Donnelly ... 2009. *(978-1-888302-02-8(X))* Artpace San Antonio.

—2006 Artpace Residencies & Exhibitions: Chiho Aoshima, Edgar Arceneaux, Andrea Bowers ... 2009. *(978-1-888302-03-5(8))* Artpace San Antonio.

Duffus, Robert L. American Renaissance. reprint ed. 34.50 *(978-0-404-02214-3(6))* AMS Pr., Inc.

Duke, Marc. The Art Festival Handbook. 2008. 276p. 24.95 *(978-0-615-19813-2(9))*; (ENG.). pap. 16.95 *(978-0-615-19814-9(7))* Virtualbookworm.com Publishing, Inc.

Dulce, Román, et al. American Selections from the Samuel P. Harn Museum of Art. 2009. (ENG., Illus.). 160p. pap. 29.95 *(978-0-9762552-8-4(6))* Univ. Pr. of Florida.

Dunbar, Elizabeth & Berry, Ian. Dario Robleto: Alloy of Love. 2008. (Illus.). 296p. *(978-0-9765723-6-7(2))* Tang, Frances Young Teaching Museum & Art Gallery at Skidmore College, The.

Duncan, Michael, et al. Charles Garabedian: A Retrospective. 2011. *(978-0-89951-111-5(2))* Santa Barbara Museum of Art.

Dunlap, Sarah & Buck, Stephanie. Fitz Henry Lane: Family & Friends. 2007. (Illus.). 185p. pap. 18.95 *(978-0-615-15729-0(7))* Church & Mason Publishing.

Durant, Sam & Ketchum-Heap of Birds, Shanna. Sam Durant: Scenes from the Pilgrim Story: Myths, Massacres, & Monuments. 2007. (Illus.). 76p. *(978-0-9771419-3-7(4))* Massachusetts College of Art.

Durham, Jimmie. Jimmie Durham: Amoxohtli: A Road Book. 2011. (ENG., Illus.). 228p. pap. 55.00 ***(978-3-86560-920-5(1))*** Verlag der Buchhandlung Walther Konig DEU. Dist: D.A.P./Distributed Art Pubs.

Duty, Michael & McGarry, Susan Hallsten. Texas Traditions: Contemporary Artists of the Lone Star State. 2010. (ENG., Illus.). 240p. 85.00 *(978-1-934491-24-9(1))* Fresco Fine Art Pubns., LLC.

Dziewior, Yilmaz, ed. Roni Horn: Well & Truly. 2010. (ENG & GER., Illus.). 96p. 55.00 *(978-3-86560-816-1(7))* Kunsthaus Bregenz AUT. Dist: D.A.P./Distributed Art Pubs.

Dzine. The Beautiful Struggle: The Art of Dzine. 2011. (Illus.). 224p. *(978-3-89955-329-1(2))* Die Gestalten Verlag.

Earle, Peggy. Legacy: Walter Chrysler Jr. & the Untold Story of Norfolk's Chrysler Museum of Art. 2008. (ENG.). 216p. 22.95 *(978-0-8139-2718-3(8))* Univ. Pr. of Virginia.

Eberle, Todd, photos by. Todd Eberle: Empire of Space. 2011. (ENG., Illus.). 300p. 85.00 *(978-0-8478-3502-7(2))* Rizzoli International Pubns., Inc.

Ebling, Bethany. BeautyScapes Natural Landscapes in a Beautiful World. 2010. 42p. pap. 23.00 *(978-0-557-39051-9(6))* Lulu Enterprises Inc.

Ebony, David. Emily Mason: The Fifth Element. 2nd ed. 2009. (Illus.). 128p. 39.95 *(978-0-9777571-5-2(3))* Findlay, David Jr., Inc.

Eckmann, Sabine. Sharon Lockhart: Lunch Break. 2010. (Illus.). 160p. pap. 40.00 *(978-0-936316-29-1(2))* Washington Univ., Mildred Lane Kemper Art Museum.

Edelman, Aliza, et al. Marylyn Dintenfass: Parallel Park. 2011. (ENG., Illus.). 140p. 50.00 ***(978-1-55595-346-1(8))*** Hudson Hills Pr. LLC.

Edwards, Janet & Edwards, Fred. Palms to Peaks: The Art of Janet Edwards. 2011. (ENG., Illus.). 176p. 49.95 *(978-1-58948-285-2(9)*, ESRI Pr.) ESRI, Inc.

Edwards, Steve. Martha Rosler: The Bowery in Two Inadequate Descriptive Systems. 2012. (Afterall Ser.). (ENG., Illus.). 112p. (gr. 17). 35.00 ***(978-1-84638-083-9(9))***; pap. 16.00 ***(978-1-84638-084-6(7))*** MIT Pr.

Eisenhauer, Paul & Farrington, Lynne, eds. Wharton Esherick & the Birth of the American Modern. 2011. (Illus.). 160p. 29.99 *(978-0-7643-3788-8(2))* Schiffer Publishing, Ltd.

Eitel, Rhoda, intro. The Thaw Collection of Master Drawings: Acquisitions since 2002. 2009. *(978-0-87598-153-6(4))* Pierpont Morgan Library.

Ekhtiar, Maryam. Masterpieces from the Department of Islamic Art in the Metropolitan Museum of Art. 2011. (Illus.). xiii, 431p. ***(978-1-58839-434-7(4))***; pap. ***(978-1-58839-435-4(2))*** Metropolitan Museum of Art, The.

Eklund, Douglas. The Pictures Generation, 1974-1984. 2009. 40.00 *(978-1-58839-315-9(1))*; 60.00 *(978-1-58839-314-2(3))* Metropolitan Museum of Art, The.

—The Pictures Generation, 1974-1984. 2009. (ENG., Illus.). 352p. 60.00 *(978-0-300-14892-3(5))* Yale Univ. Pr.

Elaine, James, et al, texts. Hammer Projects. 2009. (ENG., Illus.). 432p. 60.00 *(978-0-943739-35-9(7))* Hammer Museum.

Elderfield, John, ed. & text. Willem de Kooning: A Retrospective. 2011. (ENG., Illus.). 504p. 75.00 ***(978-0-87070-797-1(3))*** Museum of Modern Art.

Eliasoph, Philip. Robert Vickrey: The Magic of Realism. 2009. (ENG., Illus.). 240p. 75.00 *(978-1-55595-292-1(5))* Hudson Hills Pr. LLC.

Elwood, Marie B. The Egyptian Album of John Elliott Woolford: Original Watercolours by John Elliott Woolford & with Maps by the Ninth Earl of Dalhousie. 2009. (Illus.). 202p. 149.95 *(978-0-7734-3880-4(7))* Mellen, Edwin Pr., The.

Engberg, Sri, ed. From Here to There: Alec Soth's America. 2010. (ENG., Illus.). 288p. 60.00 *(978-0-935640-96-0(7))* Walker Art Ctr.

Engelbach, Barbara, et al, texts. Looking for Mushrooms: Beat Poets, Hippies, Funk, Minimal Art. 2009. (GER & ENG., Illus.). 240p. pap. 59.95 *(978-3-86560-548-1(6))* Verlag der Buchhandlung Walther Konig DEU. Dist: D.A.P./Distributed Art Pubs.

English, Ron. Son of Pop: Ron English Paints His Progeny. 2007. (Illus.). 96p. 24.95 incl. cd-rom *(978-0-9766325-1-1(9))* 9mm Bks.

Epstein, Mitch, photos by. Mitch Epstein Recreation: American Photographs 1973-1988, 1 vol. 2009. (ENG., Illus.). 144p. 75.00 *(978-3-86521-084-5(8))* Steidl, Gerhard Druckerei und Verlag DEU. Dist: Innovative Logistics.

Erdosi, Aniko, et al, texts. Alina & Jeff Bliumis, Receiving the Stranger. 2007. (Illus.). 112p. pap. 25.00 *(978-0-9797248-0-0(5))* CheckOff Art Pr.

Erik Abel, Klutch & Michael Fields, David Stein. Invision: A Collection of Visual Art in Portland + Beyond. 2008. 80p. pap. 22.00 *(978-0-9776051-7-0(5))* Another Sky Pr.

Ernst, Rudy. Sculptomania: 25 Years of Sculpting. 2nd ed. 2011. ***(978-1-936658-05-3(4))*** QCC Art Gallery.

Esau, Erika. Images of the Pacific Rim: Australia & California, 1850-1935. 2011. (ENG., Illus.). 368p. pap. 59.95 *(978-0-909952-39-6(6))* Power Pubns. AUS. Dist: Univ. of Washington Pr.

Esche, Charles, et al, eds. Heartland. 2009. (Illus.). 176p. pap. 30.00 *(978-0-935573-47-3(X))* Univ. of Chicago, David & Alfred Smart Museum.

Eshun, Kodwo. Dan Graham: Rock My Religion. 2012. (Afterall Ser.). (ENG., Illus.). 112p. (gr. 17). 35.00 ***(978-1-84638-085-3(5))***; pap. 16.00 ***(978-1-84638-086-0(3))*** MIT Pr.

Ethridge, Roe & Thompson, Cheyney. Roe Ethridge & Cheyney Thompson: Lynn Valley 6. 2011. (ENG., Illus.). 100p. pap. 32.00 *(978-0-920293-76-8(X))* Walther König/Bywater Bros. Ed./Presentation Hse.

Evans, Cerith Wyn. Parkett No. 87: Cerith Wyn Evans, Katarina Fritsch, Annette Kelm, Kelly Walker. 2010. (ENG., Illus.). 300p. pap. 32.00 *(978-3-907582-47-3(0))* Parkett Verlag AG CHE. Dist: D.A.P./Distributed Art Pubs.

EXORB - Laurie Hassold. 2006. per. 0.00 *(978-0-9771696-3-4(4))* Grand Central Pr.

Exploring Nirvana: The Art of Jessica Park. 2008. (Illus.). 96p. pap. 19.95 *(978-0-9814732-0-8(2))* Massachusetts College of Liberal Arts.

Fahey, Valerie, text. Pam Glover: A Life in Art. 2011. (Illus.). 24p. pap. 9.95 ***(978-1-886091-01-6(3))*** Hearst Art Gallery, Saint Mary's College.

Fahlman, Betsy. New Deal Art in Arizona. 2009. (ENG., Illus.). 222p. 49.95 *(978-0-8165-2292-7(8))* Univ. of Arizona Pr.

—Wonders of Work & Labor: The Steidle Collection of American Industrial Art. 2008. (Illus.). 176p. 50.00 *(978-0-615-23428-1(3))* Earth & Mineral Sciences Museum & Art Gallery.

Faile. Faile. 2010. (Illus.). 224p. *(978-3-89955-292-8(X))* Die Gestalten Verlag.

Fair, Susan W. Alaska Native Art: Tradition, Innovation, Continuity. Blodgett, Jean, ed. 2007. (ENG., Illus.). 312p. 65.00 *(978-1-889963-79-2(8))*; pap. 32.95 *(978-1-889963-82-2(8))* Univ. of Alaska Pr.

Fairey, Shepard. May Day. 2011. (Illus.). 133p. *(978-1-58423-428-9(8))* Gingko Pr., Inc.

—Obey: Supply & Demand: The Art of Shepard Fairey. 20th ed. 2009. (Illus.). 439p. 59.95 *(978-1-58423-349-7(4))* Gingko Pr., Inc.

Falberg, Bill, ed. United States Multiple Advertising & Discount Postal Cards: A Handbook Originally in 1982 by David G. Nussmann, Charles A. Fricke & George S. Norton. 2007. (Illus.). 180p. *(978-0-9800112-0-3(5))* United Postal Stationery Society.

Fang, Hu, et al, texts. The Work of Glenn Kaino: Communicating Rooks. 2009. (ENG., Illus.). 144p. 55.00 *(978-3-7757-2304-6(8))* Hatje Cantz Verlag GmbH & Co KG DEU. Dist: D.A.P./Distributed Art Pubs.

Fang, Jing Pei, et al. Elegance of the Qing Court: Reflections of a Dynasty Through Its Art. 2008. *(978-0-936364-35-3(1))* Joslyn Art Museum.

Feinstein, Roni. Circa 1958: Breaking Ground in American Art. 2008. (Distributed for the Ackland Art Museum Ser.). (ENG., Illus.). 160p. pap. 34.00 *(978-0-8078-5949-0(4))* Univ. of North Carolina Pr.

Fennimore, Donald L. Delaware Silver: The Col. Kenneth P. & Regina I. Brown Collection. 2008. *(978-1-893287-10-5(6))*; pap. *(978-1-893287-11-2(4))* Biggs, Sewell C. Museum of American Art.

—Iron at Winterthur. 2010. (ENG.). 428p. 45.00 *(978-1-4379-7079-1(6))* DIANE Publishing Co.

Ferguson, Russell. Larry Johnson. 2009. (Illus.). 120p. 45.00 *(978-3-7913-4391-4(2))* Prestel Publishing.

Ferguson, Russell, et al. Larry Johnson. 2009. *(978-0-943739-38-0(1))* Yale Univ. Pr.

Fern, Alan, et al. One Hundred Stories: Highlights from the Washington County Museum of Fine Arts. 2008. (Illus.). 232p. pap. 29.95 *(978-0-914495-02-4(X))* Washington County Museum of Fine Arts.

Ferrar, Alexander. Variety Is the Spice: The art of Alexander Ferrar. 2011. (ENG.). 72p. pap. 19.95 ***(978-1-4537-8419-8(5))*** CreateSpace.

Fields, Jill, ed. Entering the Picture: Judy Chicago, the Fresno Feminist Art Program, & the Collective Visions of Women Artists. 2011. (New Directions in American History Ser.). (ENG., Illus.). 336p. (C). 150.00 *(978-0-415-88768-7(2))*; pap. 42.95 *(978-0-415-88769-4(0))* Routledge.

Fili, Louise. Elegantissima: The Design & Typography of Louise Fili. 2012. (ENG.). 256p. 40.00 ***(978-1-61689-097-1(5))*** Princeton Architectural Pr.

Finch, Elizabeth, et al. Art at Colby. Corwin, Sharon, ed. 2009. (ENG., Illus.). 376p. 50.00 *(978-0-9822922-1-1(X))* Colby College Museum of Art.

Fink, Lois Marie & Staiti, Paul, contrib. by. American Artists & the Louvre. 2007. (Illus.). 147p. pap. 49.95 *(978-2-7541-0097-7(0))* Hazan, Fernand, Editeur FRA. Dist: Gingko Pr., Inc.

Firmin, Sandra. Artpark: 1974-1984. 2011. *(978-0-9842518-1-0(2))* Princeton Architectural Pr.

Fishback, Kurt Edward. Portrait of an Artist. 2010. 62p. pap. 32.80 *(978-1-4357-5429-4(8))* Lulu Enterprises Inc.

Fisher, Harrison. American Beauties: The Artwork of Harrison Fisher. 2012. (Dover Fine Art, History of Art Ser.). (ENG.). 160p. pap. 19.95 ***(978-0-486-48910-0(8))*** Dover Pubns., Inc.

Fisher, Mark. Michael Wilkinson: 1979. 2012. (ENG.). 192p. pap. 29.95 *(978-1-907317-43-9(0))* Black Dog Publishing Ltd. GBR. Dist: Perseus Distribution.

Fisher, Vernon & Auping, Michael. Vernon Fisher. 2010. (ENG., Illus.). 256p. 55.00 *(978-0-292-72323-8(7))* Univ. of Texas Pr.

FitzGerald, Michael. Picasso & American Art. 2006. (ENG., Illus.). 400p. 65.00 *(978-0-300-11452-2(4))* Yale Univ. Pr.

FitzGerald, Michael C. & Boddewyn, Julia May. Picasso & American Art. 2006. (Illus.). 400p. pap. *(978-0-87427-154-6(1))* Whitney Museum of American Art.

Fitzgerald, Oscar P. Studio Furniture of the Renwick Gallery: Smithsonian American Art Museum. 2008. (ENG., Illus.). 223p. pap. 35.00 *(978-1-56523-367-6(0))* Fox Chapel Publishing Co., Inc.

Flavin, Dan. Dan Flavin: Icons. 2009. (Illus.). 80p. *(978-3-8296-0405-5(X))* Schirmer/Mosel Verlag GmbH.

Fleming, Geoffrey K., text. Irving Ramsey Wiles N. A 1861-1948: Portraits & Paintings, 1910-1948. 2011. (ENG., Illus.). 308p. 50.00 *(978-1-55595-359-1(X))* Hudson Hills Pr. LLC.

Fleming, Jennie A. Out of Place. 2007. (Illus.). 48p. *(978-0-937123-45-4(5))* Univ. of Maryland, Art Gallery, The.

—Trajectories: Marking Time in Contemporary Art. 2008. (Illus.). 51p. *(978-0-937123-46-1(3))* Univ. of Maryland, Art Gallery, The.

Flores, Samuel. Samuel Flores: Upper Playground. 2006. (Illus.). 90p. 19.95 *(978-0-9778854-4-2(5))* Upper Playground Pubng.

Folie, Sabine, ed. & text. Ree Morton: Works 1971-1977. 2009. (ENG., Illus.). 208p. pap. 60.00 *(978-3-941185-30-2(6))* Verlag fur Moderne Kunst DEU. Dist: D.A.P./Distributed Art Pubs.

Fontana, Blaine. Sedimental Promises: The Art of Blaine Fontana. 2006. (Illus.). 92p. 19.95 *(978-0-9778854-1-1(0))* Upper Playground Pubng.

Forsyth, William. Art in Indiana. (Illus.). 39p. reprint ed. lib. bdg. 88.00 *(978-0-7222-0837-3(5))* Library Reprints, Inc.

Fort, Ilene Susan, et al, contrib. by. In Wonderland: The Surrealist Adventures of Women Artists in Mexico & the United States. 2012. (ENG., Illus.). 256p. 60.00 ***(978-3-7913-5141-4(9))*** Prestel Publishing.

Foshay, Ella M. & Orcutt, Kimberly. Making American Taste: Narrative Art for a New Democracy. Gallati, Barbara Dayer, ed. 2011. (ENG., Illus.). 324p. 65.00 *(978-1-904832-76-8(8))* Giles, D. Ltd. GBR. Dist: Antique Collectors' Club.

Foster, Carter E. & Sirmans, Franklin. Steve Wolfe on Paper. 2009. (ENG., Illus.). 102p. 19.95 *(978-0-300-15898-4(X))* Yale Univ. Pr.

Foster, Kathleen A. Thomas Chambers: American Marine & Landscape Painter, 1808-1869. 2008. (Illus.). xi, 171p. *(978-0-87633-205-4(X))*; *(978-0-87633-204-7(1))* Philadelphia Museum of Art.

Francis, Doris, ed. Faith & Transformation: Votive Offerings & Amulets from the Alexander Girard Collection. 2007. (ENG., Illus.). 160p. pap. 29.95 *(978-0-89013-504-4(5))* Museum of New Mexico Pr.

Franco, James. James Franco: Dangerous Book Four Boys. Heiss, Alanna, ed. 2012. (ENG., Illus.). 208p. 50.00 ***(978-0-8478-3813-4(7)***, Skira) Rizzoli International Pubns., Inc.

Frank, Michael & Reilly Sacco, Louise. The Museum of Bad Art: Masterworks. 2008. (ENG., Illus.). 128p. 14.95 *(978-1-58008-911-1(9))* Ten Speed Pr.

Frank, Susan Behrends. David Smith Invents. 2011. (ENG., Illus.). 112p. 30.00 *(978-0-300-16965-2(5))* Yale Univ. Pr.

Franklin, F. Abron & Blake, Joseph P. Personal Renaissance. 2011. pap. 25.00 ***(978-1-4276-5254-6(6))*** Aardvark Global Publishing.

Franks, Pamela & Steele, Robert E. Embodied: Black Identities in American Art from the Yale University Art Gallery. 2010. *(978-0-89467-977-3(5))* Yale Univ. Art Gallery.

Fred Jones Jr. Museum of Art Staff, et al, contrib. by. The Eugene B. Adkins Collection: Selected Works. 2011. (ENG., Illus.). 304p. 60.00 *(978-0-8061-4100-8(X))*; pap. 29.95 *(978-0-8061-4101-5(8))* Univ. of Oklahoma Pr.

Frederick R. Weisman Art Foundation Collection. 2007. *(978-0-9740908-1-8(6))* Weisman, Frederick R. Philanthropic Foundation.

Fredericks, Stephen & Jetter, Frances, texts. The Art of Persuasion. 2007. *(978-0-9728613-9-7(4))* New York Society of Etchers, Inc., The.

Fredericks, Stephen A. The New York Etching Club Minutes: November 12, 1877, Through December 8, 1893. 2008. *(978-0-89263-011-0(6))*; *(978-0-89263-010-3(8))* Rice Univ. Pr.

Freiman, Lisa D., et al. Gloria: Allora & Calzadilla. 2011. (ENG., Illus.). 160p. 45.00 ***(978-3-7913-5137-7(0))*** Prestel Publishing.

Friede, John, et al, eds. New Guinea Highlands: Art from the Jolika Collection. 2011. (Illus.). 672p. 120.00 *(978-3-7913-5055-4(2))* Prestel Publishing.

Friedlander, Lee, afterword by. Raoul Hague: His Work & Place: A Memoir. 2009. (Illus.). 100p. *(978-1-59005-243-3(9))* Nazraeli Pr.

Friedrich, Julia & K#xF6;nig, Kasper, eds. Wüste, Meer und Sterne: Desert, Sea & Stars. 2011. (GER & ENG., Illus.). 152p. 55.00 ***(978-3-86560-971-7(6))*** Verlag der Buchhandlung Walther Konig DEU. Dist: D.A.P./Distributed Art Pubs.

Front Forty Press, ed. Graffitecture: Chicago Graffiti Artists Attack Photographic Spaces. 2007. (Illus.). 120p. pap. 20.00 *(978-0-9778689-7-1(4))* Front Forty Pr.

Frye, Michael. Digital Landscape Photography: in the Footsteps of Ansel Adams & the Masters. 2010. (ENG., Illus.). 192p. pap. 24.95 *(978-0-240-81243-4(3)*, Focal Pr.) Elsevier Science & Technology Bks.

Fukumoto, Jodi. The Guide to American Money Folds. 2010. (ENG.). 112p. *(978-1-59700-754-2(4))* Island Heritage Publishing.

Funcke, Bettina & Ruf, Beatrix, eds. Guyton, Price, Smith, Walker, 1 vol. 2011. (ENG., Illus.). 192p. pap. 35.00 *(978-3-905770-30-8(X))* JRP Ringier Kunstverlag AG CHE. Dist: D.A.P./Distributed Art Pubs.

Fundacio Joan Miro, creator. Modernitat Americana: Obres de la Corcoran Gallery of Art: 1 Novembre 2008-25 Gener 2009. 2009. (ENG, FRE & SPA., Illus.). 172p. *(978-84-934730-8-2(1))* Fundacio Joan Miro.

Furnas, Barnaby. Barnaby Furnas: Floods. 2010. (ENG., Illus.). 54p. 13.95 *(978-1-931867-16-0(X))* Museum of Contemporary Art, Denver.

Gaehtgens, Thomas W. & Zelljadt, Katja, eds. Getty Research Journal. (Getty Research Journal Ser.). (ENG., No. 2. 2010. Illus.). 228p. pap. 50.00 *(978-1-60606-017-9(1))*No. 3. 2011. 234p. pap. 50.00 *(978-1-60606-063-6(5))* Getty Pubns. (Getty Research Institute).

Gagosian Gallery Staff, et al, contrib. by. Ferus. 2nd ed. 2009. (Illus.). 146p. 55.00 *(978-0-8478-3234-7(1))* Rizzoli International Pubns., Inc.

Gallery, David Klein. Bo Bartlett. 2009. pap. *(978-1-61623-737-0(6))* Independent Pub.

Gallery, Simpson Gallagher. T. D. Kelsey & Julie Oriet Unplugged & Unleashed. 2009. pap. *(978-1-61623-068-5(1))* Independent Pub.

Garnwell, Lynn. Color & Form: The Geometric Sculptures of Morton C. Bradley, Jr. 2012. (ENG., Illus.). 160p. 30.00 ***(978-0-253-00610-3(4)***, 0253006104) Indiana Univ. Pr.

Gangitano, Lia, ed. Dead Flowers. 2011. (ENG., Illus.). 260p. pap. 40.00 ***(978-0-9802324-2-4(2))*** Participant Pr.

Ganz, James A. Artistic San Francisco. 2011. 76p. 24.95 ***(978-0-7649-5989-9(1))*** Fine Arts Museums of San Francisco.

Garcia, Camille Rose. Mirror, Black Mirror: The Art of Camille Rose Garcia. 2012. (ENG., Illus.). 136p. 45.00 ***(978-0-86719-765-5(X))*** Last Gasp of San Francisco.

Garibaldi Frick, Mike. Dialogue Project: A Provocative Public Art Adventure Across the United States Featuring Thousands of Inspiring Quotations, Vol. 3. 2007. 219p. per. 24.95 *(978-0-615-13384-3(3))* Evolve Arts, Inc.

Garrels, Gary, contrib. by. Eden's Edge: Fifteen la Artists, 1 vol. 2007. (ENG., Illus.). 144p. 35.00 *(978-0-943739-31-1(4))* Hammer Museum.

Gass, Alison & Zimbardo, Tanya. Fifty Years of Bay Area Art: The SECA Awards. 2011. (Illus.). 168p. ***(978-0-918471-89-5(3))*** San Francisco Museum of Modern Art.

Gatewood, Charles, photos by. Tattoo Special: Goliath Wallpaper of Fame - Issue 01. 2011. (ENG., Illus.). 44p. pap. 24.95 ***(978-3-936709-60-5(2))*** Goliath DEU. Dist: SCB Distributors.

Gehry, Frank, frwd. Charles Arnoldi, 1972-2008. 2008. (ENG., Illus.). 360p. 65.00 *(978-1-934435-07-6(4))* Radius Bks.

Genter, Robert. Late Modernism: Art, Culture, & Politics in Cold War America. 2010. (Arts & Intellectual Life in Modern America Ser.). 384p. (C). 49.95 *(978-0-8122-4264-5(5))* Univ. of Pennsylvania Pr.

Georgia Museum of Art Staff. A Colorful Past: Decorative Arts of Georgia. Callahan, Ashley, ed. 2010. (ENG., Illus.). 152p. pap. 35.00 *(978-0-915977-72-7(9))* Univ. of Georgia, Georgia Museum of Art.

Gero, Jan. My Drawing. 2011. 428p. pap. 37.95 ***(978-1-4620-5785-6(3))*** iUniverse, Inc.

Geter, Gene. Unedited: New York Modeling & Designs of Reality. 2009. 49p. pap. 10.50 *(978-0-615-26269-7(4))* Geter, Gene.

Giancola, Donato. Middle-Earth: Visions of a Modern Myth. 2010. (ENG., Illus.). 88p. 25.00 *(978-1-59929-047-8(2))* Underwood Books.

Gidley, Mick & Lawson-Peebles, Robert, eds. Views of American Landscapes. 2007. (ENG.). 252p. pap. 56.00 *(978-0-521-03393-0(4))* Cambridge Univ. Pr.

Gilden, Bruce, photos by. Stern Portfolio 64 Bruce Gilden. 2011. (ENG & GER., Illus.). 96p. 45.00 ***(978-3-652-00005-5(6))*** teNeues Publishing Co.

Gill, Bob. Bob Gill, So Far. 2011. (ENG., Illus.). 304p. 50.00 ***(978-1-85669-819-1(X))*** King, Laurence Publishing GBR. Dist: Hachette Bk. Group.

Gillespie, Spike. Quilting Art: Inspiration, Ideas & Innovative Works from 20 Contemporary Quilters. 2009. (ENG., Illus.). 160p. 35.00 *(978-0-7603-3526-0(5)*, 0760335265, Voyageur Pr) MBI Publishing Co. LLC.

Ginsberg, Mimi & Pensler, Alan. Abraham Manievich. 2012. (ENG., Illus.). 192p. 60.00 ***(978-1-55595-345-4(X))*** Hudson Hills Pr. LLC.

Gleissner, Stephen. Sue Jean Covacovich: Pioneer Kansas Abstract Artist. 2006. (Illus.). 36p. 15.00 *(978-0-939324-52-1(0))* Wichita Art Museum.

Glier, Mike, et al. Mike Glier: Along a Long Line. 2009. (ENG., Illus.). 200p. 60.00 (978-1-55595-319-5(0)) Hudson Hills Pr. LLC.

Glimcher, Mildred L. Happenings: New York, 1958-1963. 2012. (ENG., Illus.). 320p. 65.00 (978-1-58093-307-0(6)) Monacelli Pr., Inc.

Goede, Don. Abraham Obama: A Guerilla Tour Through Art & Politics. 2009. (Illus.). 288p. pap. 19.95 (978-0-86719-722-8(6)) Last Gasp of San Francisco.

Goetzmann, William H. & Goetzmann, William N. The West of the Imagination. 2nd rev. ed. 2009. (ENG., Illus.). 640p. 65.00 (978-0-8061-3533-5(6)) Univ. of Oklahoma Pr.

Goff, Robert & Rosenthal, Cassie, eds. Ahmed Alsoudani. 2009. (GER & ENG., Illus.). 96p. 55.00 (978-3-7757-2358-9(7)) Hatje Cantz Verlag GmbH & Co KG DEU. Dist: D.A.P./Distributed Art Pubs.

Goines, David Lance. The Poster Art of David Lance Goines: A 40-Year Retrospective, 1968-2009. 2010. (Dover Fine Art, History of Art Ser.). (ENG., Illus.). 160p. pap. 24.95 (978-0-486-47875-3(0)) Dover Pubns., Inc.

Goldberg, Joseph, et al. Joseph Goldberg: Jeweled Earth. 2008. (Thomas T. Wilson Ser.). (ENG., Illus.). 80p. 29.95 (978-0-295-98767-5(7)) Univ. of Washington Pr.

Goldman, Stephen & Swindler, Rebecca, eds. Barsamian: 20 Years-Searching for the Answer. 2011. 20p. (978-0-9845213-1-9(3)) Holocaust Memorial Ctr.

Goldstein, Ann, et al. This Is Not to Be Looked At: Highlights from the Permanent Collection of the Museum of Contemporary Art, Los Angeles. 2008. (ENG., Illus.). 384p. 59.95 (978-1-933751-07-8(X)) Museum of Contemporary Art, Los Angeles.

Goldstein, Jesse & Chen, Mary, compiled by. Space 1026 Volume One: Pulling Teeth. 2000th ltd. ed. 2006. (Illus.). 128p. 25.00 (978-0-9776523-0-3(0)) Tonearm/Lawrence Pubns.

Goldston, Bill, intro. Tatyana Grosman: A Scrapbook by Riva Castleman. 2009. (ENG., Illus.). 150p. 125.00 (978-0-9818293-0-2(9)) Universal Ltd. Art Editions, Inc.

Gomez, Edward Madrid, text. Sam Glankoff: Print-Paintings. 2007. (Illus.). 23p. (978-0-9777686-7-7(8)) Carberry, Valerie Gallery, Inc.

Gonzalez, Jennifer A. Subject to Display: Reframing Race in Contemporary Installation Art. 2008. (ENG., Illus.). 320p. (gr. 17). 31.95 (978-0-262-07286-1(6)) MIT Pr.

González, Jennifer A. Subject to Display: Reframing Race in Contemporary Installation Art. 2011. (ENG., Illus.). 320p. (gr. 17). pap. 17.95 (978-0-262-51602-0(0)) MIT Pr.

Gonzalez, Mark. Solid-Colored Dinnerware: Depression to Mid-Century. 2008. (Schiffer Book for Collectors Ser.). (Illus.). 160p. pap. 29.95 (978-0-7643-2846-6(8)) Schiffer Publishing, Ltd.

Gorbaty, Norman. Norman Gorbaty: Works of a Modern Master. 2009. (978-0-9764756-7-5(7)) QCC Art Gallery.

Gordon Jr., Steve, et al. 100 Habits of Successful Freelance Designers: Insider Secrets for Working Smart & Staying Creative. 2009. (100 Habits Ser.). (ENG., Illus.). 192p. 40.00 (978-1-59253-512-5(7), 1592535127, Rockport Publishers) Quayside.

Görner, Veit & Moll, Frank-Thorsten, eds. Compeshitstem: The New Deal. 2010. (ENG.). 114p. 35.00 (978-3-86828-087-6(1)) Kehrer Verlag Heidelberg, Klaus Kehrer DEU. Dist: Consortium Bk. Sales & Distribution.

Grafton, Carol Belanger. 60 Great American Art Nouveau Posters Platinum DVD & Book. 2011. (Dover Electronic Clip Art Ser.). (ENG., Illus.). 64p. pap. 19.95 (978-0-486-99154-2(7)) Dover Pubns., Inc.

Graham, Dan. Dan Graham. Kitnick, Alex, ed. 2011. (October Files Ser.). (ENG., Illus.). 232p. (gr. 17). 35.00 (978-0-262-01528-8(5)); pap. 19.95 (978-0-262-51577-1(6)) MIT Pr.

Grassi, Francesca, ed. Rirkrit Tiravanija: A Retrospective: Tomorrow Is Another Fine Day, 1 vol. 2007. (ENG., Illus.). 218p. 75.00 (978-3-905770-32-2(6)) JRP Ringier Kunstverlag AG CHE. Dist: D.A.P./Distributed Art Pubs.

Grassi, Neysa. Neysa Grassi: Rose Gatherer, 2001-2011. 2011. (Illus.). 50p. pap. 20.00 (978-1-879173-79-8(4)) Locks Art Pubns.

Green, Renée. Renee Green: Endless Dreams & Time-Based Streams. 2011. (ENG., Illus.). 144p. pap. 35.00 (978-0-9826789-0-9(8)) Yerba Buena Ctr. for the Arts.

Greenberg, Stanley. Stanley Greenberg: Time Machines. 2011. (Illus.). 131p. 59.95 (978-3-7774-4041-5(8)) Hirmer Verlag GmbH DEU. Dist: Chicago Distribution Ctr.

Greene, Balcomb & Peters, Lisa N. Balcomb Greene, 1904-1990: A Retrospective: November 20, 2008-January 3, 2009. 2008. (Illus.). 24p. pap. (978-0-945936-94-7(X)) Spanierman Gallery.

Greene, Candace S. & Thornton, Russell, eds. The Year the Stars Fell: Lakota Winter Counts at the Smithsonian. 2007. (ENG., Illus.). 377p. 45.00 (978-0-8032-2211-3(4)) Univ. of Nebraska Pr.

Greenwood, Tim & Vardanyan, Edda. Hakob's Gospels: The Life & Work of an Armenian Artist of the Sixteenth Century. 2006. (Sam Fogg Ser.). (ENG., Illus.). 80p. pap. 35.00 (978-0-9549014-7-9(9)) Sam, Fogg Rare Books GBR. Dist: Univ. of Washington Pr.

Griffin, Gillet, intro. Ancient American Art: Masterworks of the Pre-Columbian Era, 3500 BC - 1532 AD. 2011. (ENG., Illus.). 392p. 90.00 (978-88-7439-554-5(X)) 5 Continents ITA. Dist: Hachette Bk. Group.

Grimonprez, Johan. Johan Grimonprez: It's a Poor Sort of Memory that Only Works Backwards. 2011. (ENG., Illus.). 352p. 45.00 (978-3-7757-3130-0(X)) Hatje Cantz Verlag GmbH & Co KG DEU. Dist: D.A.P./Distributed Art Pubs.

Grooms, Red. Red Grooms - Charlie Chaplin. (Illus.). 18p. pap. 19.50 (978-1-56762-051-1(5)) Modern Learning Pr.

—Red Grooms - Double-Decker Bus. (Illus.). 18p. pap. 19.50 (978-1-56762-053-5(1)) Modern Learning Pr.

—Red Grooms - Fats Domino. (Illus.). 18p. pap. 17.50 (978-1-56762-052-8(3)) Modern Learning Pr.

Groseclose, Barbara S. & Wierich, Jochen. Internationalizing the History of American Art: Views. 2009. (Illus.). 240p. 70.00 (978-0-271-03200-9(6)) Pennsylvania State Univ. Pr.

Gross, Frederick. Diane Arbus's 1960s: Auguries of Experience. 2012. 248p. 75.00 (978-0-8166-7011-6(0)); pap. 24.95 (978-0-8166-7012-3(9)) Univ. of Minnesota Pr.

Gurney, George. Variations on America: Masterworks of the American Art Forum, Smithsonian American Art Museum. 2008. (978-0-9790678-0-8(4)) Smithsonian American Art Museum.

Gurney, George, et al. Variations on America: Masterworks from American Art Forum Collections. 2006. (ENG., Illus.). 192p. 30.00 (978-1-904832-42-3(3)) Giles, D. Ltd. GBR. Dist: Antique Collectors' Club.

Gustafson, Donna, ed. Images from the World Between: The Circus in Twentieth-Century American Art. 2007. (ENG., Illus.). 184p. (gr. 17). pap. 19.95 (978-0-262-57241-5(9)) MIT Pr.

Guttmann, Allen. Sports & American Art from Benjamin West to Andy Warhol. 2011. (Illus.). 336p. 39.95 (978-1-55849-874-7(5)) Univ. of Massachusetts Pr.

Guyton, Wade. Wade Guyton: Zeichnungen FüR ein Kleines Zimmer. 2011. (ENG., Illus.). 130p. pap. 49.95 (978-3-86560-988-5(0)) Verlag der Buchhandlung Walther Konig DEU. Dist: D.A.P./Distributed Art Pubs.

Gygax, Raphael, ed. Deterioration, They Said. 2010. (ENG., Illus.). 92p. 35.00 (978-3-03764-076-0(6)) JRP Ringier Kunstverlag AG CHE. Dist: D.A.P./Distributed Art Pubs.

Gygax, Raphael & Munder, Heike, eds. Alex Bag. 2011. (ENG., Illus.). 230p. 55.00 (978-3-03764-220-7(3)) JRP Ringier Kunstverlag AG CHE. Dist: D.A.P./Distributed Art Pubs.

Haas, Philip & Warner Malcolm. Butchers, Dragons, Gods & Skeletons: Film Installations by Philip Haas. 2009. (Illus.). ix, 94p. (978-0-912804-50-7(5)) Kimbell Art Museum.

Hainley, Bruce, intro. Jay Defeo: Works from the Estate of Jay Defeo. 2007. (Illus.). 48p. per. 20.00 (978-0-9713548-3-8(9)) Nielsen Gallery.

Hall, Grace Cynthia. The Wadsworth Trail. 2007. (YA). pap. 10.95 (978-0-9792509-0-3(0)) Stevens County Historical Society & Museum.

Hall, Sarah J. & McPherson, Craig. Steel: Pittsburgh Drawings by Craig Mcpherson. 2008. (Illus.). 48p. pap. 14.95 (978-0-9703425-9-1(4)) Frick Art & Historical Ctr.,The.

Hallmark, Kara Kelley. Encyclopedia of Asian American Artists, 1 vol. 2007. (Artists of the American Mosaic Ser.). (Illus.). 312p. 85.00 (978-0-313-33451-1(X), GR3451, Greenwood Pr.) Greenwood Publishing Group, Inc.

Halsey, William & Blackman, Lynne. William Halsey: Mastery of the Modern. 2006. (978-0-9785365-1-0(7)) Charleston Renaissance Gallery, The.

Han, Heng-Gil & Ho, Christopher K. Jamaica Flux: Workspaces & Windows 2010: Art As Action, April 10, 2010-June 12, 2010. 2010. (978-0-9762853-7-3(1)) Jamaica Ctr. for Arts & Learning.

Han, Heng-Gil & Ortiz, Lori. 2011 Studio LLC. 2012. (978-0-9762853-9-7(8)) Jamaica Ctr. for Arts & Learning.

Hanzal, Carla M. Contemporary, Cool & Collected. 2007. (978-0-9762300-3-8(8)) Mint Museum, The.

Hardy, Ed. Beyond Skin. 2009. (FRE, GER & ENG., Illus.). 240p. 98.00 (978-3-8327-9352-4(6)) teNeues Publishing Co.

—Ed Hardy Beyond Skin Collector's Edition. 2009. 240p. 3250.00 (978-3-8327-9119-3(1)) teNeues Publishing Co.

Hardy, Joanna, ed. Collect Contemporary - Jewelry. 2012. (ENG., Illus.). 208p. pap. 21.95 (978-0-500-28855-9(0), 528855) Thames & Hudson.

Harper, Charley. Birds & Words. 2008. (ENG., Illus.). 152p. 50.00 (978-1-934429-17-4(1)); 151p. 50.00 (978-1-934429-20-4(1)) AMMO Bks., LLC.

Harris, Adam Duncan. Wildlife in American Art: Masterworks from the National Museum of Wildlife Art. 2009. (ENG.). 320p. (C). 55.00 (978-0-8061-4015-5(1)) Univ. of Oklahoma Pr.

—Wildlife in American Art: Masterworks from the National Museum of Wildlife Art. 2009. (ENG.). 320p. pap. 35.00 (978-0-8061-4099-5(2)) Univ. of Oklahoma Pr.

Harris, Adam Duncan & Kuhn, Bob. Bob Kuhn: Drawing on Instinct. 2012. (978-0-8061-4300-2(2)); pap. (978-0-8061-4301-9(0)) Univ. of Oklahoma Pr.

Harris, Susan & Howard, Jan. Pat Steir: Drawing Out of Line. 2010. pap. 35.00 (978-0-615-34382-2(1)) RISD Museum.

Harrison, Jeff, et al. Collecting with Vision: Treasures from the Chrysler Museum of Art. 2007. (ENG., Illus.). 160p. 35.00 (978-1-904832-33-1(4)) Giles, D. Ltd. GBR. Dist: Antique Collectors' Club.

Harrison, Rachel. Rachel Harrison: Museum with Walls. 2010. (ENG., Illus.). 272p. 65.00 (978-1-936192-03-8(9), Ctr. for Curatorial Studies) Bard College Pubns. Office.

Harrison, Stephen, et al. Artistic Luxury: Fabergé Tiffany Lalique. 2008. (Illus.). xii, 358p. (978-0-940717-99-2(9)); (978-0-940717-98-5(0)) Yale Univ. Pr.

Harthorn, Sandy. Devorah Sperber: Threads of Perception. 2010. (ENG., Illus.). 56p. pap. 22.50 (978-0-295-98960-0(2)) Univ. of Washington Pr.

Hartley, Keith. Andy Warhol: A Celebration of Life & Death. 2008. (ENG., Illus.). 112p. pap. (978-1-903278-99-4(6)) National Galleries of Scotland.

Harvey, Doug & Fernandez, Veronica. Sean Duffy. 2011. (Front Forty Press - Front Forty Profiles Ser.). (Illus.). 122p. pap. 25.00 (978-0-615-40146-1(5)) Front Forty Pr.

Haskell, Barbara, ed. Lyonel Feininger: At the Edge of the World. 2011. (ENG., Illus.). 288p. 65.00 (978-0-300-16846-4(2)) Yale Univ. Pr.

Hassrick, Peter H., et al, contrib. by. A Century of Sanctuary: The Art of Zion National Park. 2008. (ENG.). 61p. (978-0-915630-47-9(8)); pap. (978-0-915630-48-6(6)) Zion Natural History Assn.

Hatch, Kevin & Conner, Bruce. Looking for Bruce Conner. 2012. (October Bks.). (ENG., Illus.). 352p. (gr. 17). 29.95 (978-0-262-01681-0(8)) MIT Pr.

Hathaway, Norman & Salisbury, Mike. Overspray: Riding High with the Kings of California Airbrush Art, 1 vol. Nadel, Dan, ed. 2008. (ENG., Illus.). 226p. 50.00 (978-0-9794153-0-2(6)) PictureBox, Inc.

HC Porter Fine Art Book: Backyards & Beyond: Mississippians & Their Stories. 2008. (Illus.). 200p. 45.00 (978-0-9818499-0-4(3)) Backyards & Beyond.

Healy, Patrick. Virgil Grotfeldt. 2007. 208p. (978-2-87909-818-0(1)); (Illus.). (978-3-87909-818-7(2)) Wienand GmbH, Druck- & Verlagshaus.

Heartney, Eleanor. Roxy Paine. 2009. (Illus.). 256p. 75.00 (978-3-7913-4137-8(5)) Prestel Publishing.

Heartney, Eleanor & DeMonte, Claudia. Claudia Demonte. 2009. 112p. 29.95 (978-0-7649-5097-1(5)) Pomegranate Communications, Inc.

Heckscher, Morrison H. The American Wing at the Metropolitan Museum of Art: A Walking Guide. 2012. (ENG., Illus.). 96p. pap. 9.95 (978-1-85759-742-4(7)) Scala, Editions FRA. Dist: National Bk. Network.

Heffernan, Maureen. Fairy Houses of the Maine Coast. 2010. (ENG.). 72p. 14.95 (978-0-89272-787-2(X)) Down East Bks.

Hegarty, Antony & Johnsons, Antony. Antony & the Johnsons: Swanlights. 2010. (ENG., Illus.). 144p. 35.00 (978-0-8109-9680-9(4), Abrams Image) Abrams.

Held, Peter, ed. The Art of Toshiko Takaezu: In the Language of Silence. 2011. (ENG., Illus.). 160p. 40.00 (978-0-8078-3482-4(3)) Univ. of North Carolina Pr.

Helsinger, Elizabeth K. The Writing of Modern Life: The Etching Revival in France, Britain, & the U. S., 1850-1940. 2009. (Illus.). 104p. pap. 20.00 (978-0-935573-45-9(3)) Univ. of Chicago, David & Alfred Smart Museum.

Helwein, Mercedes, illus. Walk the Floor. 2010. (ENG.). 40p. 33.00 (978-88-88493-65-7(4)) Drago Arts & Communication ITA. Dist: SCB Distributors.

Henderikse, Jan. Images & Other Pictures. 14.95 (978-0-932455-00-0(X)) Henderikse.

Henderson, James D., Jr. Royal Austria Porcelain. 2008. (Illus.). 272p. bds. 59.95 (978-0-7643-2820-6(4)) Schiffer Publishing, Ltd.

Henderson, Wyntoun Xavier. Common Threads of Freedom Compounding. 2007. 340p. pap. 23.95 (978-1-59299-254-6(4)) Inkwater Pr.

Henson, H. D. Reaching Beyond the Hedges. 2009. 116p. pap. 39.49 (978-1-4389-1951-5(4)) AuthorHouse.

Hentschel, Martin & Stange, Raimar, eds. Allora & Calzadilla. 2010. (GER & ENG., Illus.). 128p. 50.00 (978-3-941185-62-3(4)) Verlag fur Moderne Kunst DEU. Dist: D.A.P./Distributed Art Pubs.

Heon, Laura, text. Barry X Ball, 1 vol. 2007. (ENG., Illus.). 80p. 20.00 (978-0-9764492-4-9(2)) Site Santa Fe.

Hertz, Richard. The Beat & the Buzz: Inside the L.A. Art World. 2009. 354p. pap. (978-0-9640165-6-9(7)) Minneola Pr.

Hess, Donald & Steiner, Myrtha, texts. Hess Art Collection. 2010. (ENG., Illus.). 372p. 60.00 (978-3-7757-2139-4(8)) Hatje Cantz Verlag GmbH & Co KG DEU. Dist: D.A.P./Distributed Art Pubs.

Hess, Lowell. The Art of Lowell Hess: Edited & with an introduction by Lowell Hess. 2011. 152p. 45.00 (978-1-4575-0022-0(1)) Dog Ear Publishing, LLC.

Hetland, Lois, et al. Studio Thinking: The Real Benefits of Arts Education. 2007. 128p. 31.95 (978-0-8077-4819-0(6)) Teachers College Pr., Teachers College, Columbia Univ.

—Studio Thinking: The Real Benefits of Visual Arts Education. 2007. (ENG., Illus.). 128p. pap. 26.95 (978-0-8077-4818-3(8)) Teachers College Pr., Teachers College, Columbia Univ.

Heuer, Elizabeth. Eugene Savage: The Seminole Paintings. 2011. (ENG., Illus.). 64p. pap. 12.95 (978-1-904832-99-7(7)) Giles, D. Ltd. GBR. Dist: Antique Collectors' Club.

Heynen, Julian. Joe Scanlan. 2008. (ENG., Illus.). 112p. 38.00 (978-3-86678-062-0(1)) Kerber Verlag DEU. Dist: D.A.P./Distributed Art Pubs.

Hickey, Dave, et al. James Hayward: Works 1975-2007. 2007. 45.00 (978-0-9761509-3-0(X)) Modernism, Inc.

Higgs, Matthew & Fletcher, Harrell, texts. Michael Patterson-Carver: Free Speech Zone. 2011. (ENG., Illus.). 80p. 19.95 (978-0-9561928-2-0(3)) Four Corners Bks. GBR. Dist: D.A.P./Distributed Art Pubs.

Hill, Carolyn, et al. Tempests & Romantic Visionaries: Images of Storms in European & American Art. George, Hardy S. & Pavelka, Jeffrey J., eds. 2006. (ENG., Illus.). 136p. per. 25.00 (978-0-911919-04-2(X)) Oklahoma City Museum of Art.

Hills, Patricia, et al, contrib. by. Perfectly American: The Art-Union & Its Artists. 2011. (ENG., Illus.). 200p. 39.95 (978-0-9819799-2-2(0)); pap. 24.95 (978-0-9819799-3-9(9)) Gilcrease Museum.

Hine, Thomas. The Great Funk: Styles of the Shaggy, Sexy, Shameless 1970s. 2009. (ENG., Illus.). 256p. pap. 16.00 (978-0-374-53167-6(6)) Farrar, Straus & Giroux.

Hinrichs, Kit & Hirasuna, Delphine. 100 American Flags: A Unique Collection of Old Glory Memorabilia. 2008. (ENG., Illus.). 112p. 19.95 (978-1-58008-920-3(8)) Ten Speed Pr.

Hirondelle, Anne, et al. Anne Hirondelle: Ceramic Art, 1 vol. 2012. (ENG., Illus.). 88p. 29.95 (978-0-295-99151-1(8)) Univ. of Washington Pr.

Hirtle, John. Arti-Sands at Hampton Beach. 2010. 56p. pap. 11.95 (978-0-557-45892-9(7)) Lulu Enterprises Inc.

Hobbs, Robert. André Ethier: André Ethier's Knowing Naiveté. 2007. (Illus.). 48p. pap. 25.00 (978-0-9779002-1-3(5)) Derek Eller Gallery, Inc.

Hofer, Margaret K., et al. Stories in Sterling: Four Centuries of Silver in New York. 2011. (ENG., Illus.). 352p. 69.95 (978-1-904832-65-2(2)) Giles, D. Ltd. GBR. Dist: Antique Collectors' Club.

Hoffman, Jens & Mercer, Kobena. Hew Locke: Stranger in Paradise. 2011. (ENG., Illus.). 144p. pap. 45.00 (978-1-907317-38-5(4)) Black Dog Publishing Ltd. GBR. Dist: Perseus Distribution.

Holland, Hugh. Locals Only. Crist, Steve, ed. 2010. (ENG., Illus.). 76p. 39.95 (978-1-934429-47-1(3)) AMMO Bks., LLC.

Hollein, Max. Julian Schnabel. Moos, David & Schnabel, Julian, eds. 2009. (ENG., Illus.). 432p. 90.00 (978-88-6130-317-1(X)) Skira Editore ITA. Dist: Random Hse., Inc.

Holzwarth, Hans Werner, ed. Jeff Koons. 2009. (ENG., Illus.). 591p. 69.99 (978-3-8365-0328-0(X)) TASCHEN DEU. Dist: Ingram Pub. Services.

Hooper, Rachel & Coolquitt, Andy. Andy Coolquitt. 2012. (ENG.). 185p. 50.00 (978-0-292-73894-2(3)) Univ. of Texas Pr.

Hopper, Kippra D. & Churchill, Laurie J. Art of West Texas Women: A Celebration. 2010. (Illus.). 224p. pap. 29.95 (978-0-89672-669-7(X)) Texas Tech Univ. Pr.

Horn, Roni. Roni Horn. 2011. (ENG., Illus.). 135p. 50.00 (978-89-92233-43-9(4)) Kukje Gallery Inc. KOR. Dist: D.A.P./Distributed Art Pubs.

Houk, Rose. Guide to American Indian Beadwork Southwest. 2008. 48p. pap. 5.95 (978-1-58369-109-0(X)) Western National Parks Assn.

Houston, David. George Dunbar: Southern Masters Series. 2007. (Illus.). pap. 19.95 (978-0-9772544-2-2(9)) Ogden Museum of Southern Art, The.

Howard, Judy. Heavenly Patchwork II: Quilt Stories to Warm Your Heart. 2007. (Illus.). 182p. 14.95 (978-0-9762375-2-5(0)) Dorcas Publishing.

Howarth, Crispin. Varilaku: Pacific Arts from the Solomon Islands. 2011. (ENG., Illus.). 128p. (C). pap. 34.95 (978-0-642-33420-6(X)) National Gallery of Australia AUS. Dist: Univ. of Washington Pr.

Howell, Andy. Art, Skateboarding & Life. 2007. (Illus.). pap. 29.95 (978-1-58423-261-2(7)) Gingko Pr., Inc.

Huang, Teresa, tr. Poetic License-the Art of Joan Schulze. 2010. (ENG & CHI., Illus.). 168p. (978-0-9744196-2-6(1)) Schulze, Joan.

—Poetic License-the Art of Joan Schulze. 2010. (ENG & CHI.). pap. 42.00 (978-0-9744196-3-3(X)) Schulze, Joan.

Hughes, Amanda M. & Wood, Carolyn H. A Place for Meaning: Art, Faith, & Museum Culture. 2010. (Distributed for the Ackland Art Museum Ser.). (ENG., Illus.). 245p. pap. 30.00 (978-0-9743656-3-3(7)) Univ. of North Carolina Pr.

Huldisch, Henriette & Momin, Shamim M. Whitney Biennial 2008. 2008. (ENG., Illus.). 288p. pap. 45.00 (978-0-300-13689-0(7)) Yale Univ. Pr.

Hurowitz, Sharon Coplan. The Prints of John Baldessari: A Catalogue Raisonné, 1971-2007. 2010. (ENG., Illus.). 408p. 125.00 (978-1-55595-290-7(9)) Hudson Hills Pr. LLC.

Hushka, Rock. The Eloquent Silver Curve: The Jewelry of Flora Book. 2011. pap. (978-0-924335-34-1(3)) Tacoma Art Museum.

Hushka, Rock & Adams, Victoria. Where Sky Meets Earth: The Luminous Landscapes of Victoria Adams. 2010. (ENG., Illus.). 80p. pap. 21.95 (978-0-924335-30-3(0)) Tacoma Art Museum.

IDB Cultural Center Staff, et al, contrib. by. 50 Años, 50 Obras: Obras Sobresalientes Del Arte de América Latina y el Caribe Del Siglo XX. 2009. (ENG & SPA., Illus.). 89p. (978-1-59782-088-2(1)) Inter-American Development Bank.

Ikegami, Hiroko & Rauschenberg, Robert. The Great Migrator: Robert Rauschenberg & the Global Rise of American Art. 2010. (ENG., Illus.). 296p. (gr. 17). 29.95 (978-0-262-01425-0(4)) MIT Pr.

Iles, Chrissie. Paul Mccarthy: Central Symmetrical Rotation Movement: Three Installations, Two Films. 2008. (Illus.). 72p. 18.95 (978-0-300-14138-2(6)) Yale Univ. Pr.

Iles, Chrissie, et al. A Decade in Conversation: A Ten-Year Celebration of the Bucksbaum Award, 2000-2010 - With Interviews with Paul Pfeiffer, Irit Batsry, Raymond Pettibon, Mark Bradford, & Omer Fast. 2010. (Illus.). 88p. 19.95 (978-0-300-16755-9(5)) Yale Univ. Pr.

Indiana, Gary. Andy Warhol & the Can That Sold the World. 2010. (ENG.). 192p. 22.00 (978-0-465-00233-7(1)) Basic Bks.

Inglot, Joanna. Warm: A Feminist Art Collective in Minnesota. 2007. (Illus.). 224p. pap. 34.95 (978-0-8166-5038-5(1)) Univ. of Minnesota Pr.

Ingrid Sanclement, Anna Sanclement. Taylor Bell, the Traveling Kitten: Volume One. 2010. 24p. pap. 14.93 (978-1-4269-2567-2(0)) Trafford Publishing.

Inselmann, Andrea. A Private Eye: Dada, Surrealism, & More from the Brandt Collection. 2006. (Illus.). 160p. pap. 25.00 (978-0-9646042-3-0(X)) Cornell Univ., Herbert F. Johnson Museum of Art.

Inselmann, Andrea & Arning, Bill. Marc Swanson: Hurry on Sundown. 2009. (Illus.). 96p. pap. (978-1-934260-09-8(6)) Cornell Univ., Herbert F. Johnson Museum of Art.

Inspirationals: A Collection of Photography & Writings by Marian Kraus. 2007. (Illus.). 98p. pap. 24.95 (978-0-615-17913-1(4)) Kraus, Marian Photography, Inc.

Interact, W. K. WK Interact - 2. 5: Language of New York Street Life. 2009. 96p. pap. 29.00 (978-88-88493-44-2(1)) Drago Arts & Communication ITA. Dist: SCB Distributors.

Iowa City Press-Citizen. In Situ: A collection of literary & visual arts from the Iowa City Area. 2007. (Illus.). 200p. per. (978-0-9712727-2-9(7)) Iowa City Pr.-Citizen.

Irving, Christopher. Comics Introspective Volume 1: Peter Bagge, Vol. 1. 2007. (Comics Introspective Ser.). (Illus.). 128p. pap. 16.95 (978-1-893905-83-2(7)) TwoMorrows Publishing.

—Comics Introspective Volume Two: Dean Haspiel. 2008. 128p. pap. 16.95 *(978-1-893905-90-0(X))* TwoMorrows Publishing.

Irwin, Robert & Simms, Matthew. Notes Toward a Conditional Art. 2011. (ENG., Illus.). 352p. 35.00 *(978-1-60606-075-9(9)*, J. Paul Getty Museum) Getty Pubns.

Israel, Mei-Ling. The World as Light: An Introduction to the Art of Adi Da Samraj. 2007. (Illus.). 127p. per. *(978-1-57097-230-0(3))* Dawn Horse Pr.

Israel, Nico. Meg Cranston. 2008. (ENG., Illus.). 202p. pap. 49.00 *(978-3-905829-34-1(7))* JRP Ringier Kunstverlag AG CHE. Dist: D.A.P./Distributed Art Pubs.

Ivey, Paul Eli, et al. Barbara Rogers: The Imperative of Beauty. 2012. (ENG., Illus.). 224p. 60.00 ***(978-1-55595-347-8(6))*** Hudson Hills Pr. LLC.

J Paul Getty Museum. The J. Paul Getty Museum Handbook of the Collections. 7th ed. 2007. (Illus.). 336p. 26.95 *(978-0-89236-886-0(1))*; pap. 16.95 *(978-0-89236-887-7(X))* Oxford Univ. Pr., Inc.

Jaar, Alfredo, illus. Alfredo Jaar: la Politique des Images. 2008. (FRE & ENG.). 160p. per. 49.00 *(978-3-905770-48-3(2))* JRP Ringier Kunstverlag AG CHE. Dist: D.A.P./Distributed Art Pubs.

Jackson, Cassandra. Violence Visual Culture & the Black Male Body. 2010. (Routledge Research in Cultural & Media Studies). (ENG., Illus.). 152p. (C). 125.00 *(978-0-415-88042-8(4))* Routledge.

Jacob, John P., ed. Kodak Girl, 1 vol. 2012. (ENG., Illus.). 328p. 78.00 ***(978-3-86930-324-6(7))*** Steidl, Gerhard Druckerei und Verlag DEU. Dist: Innovative Logistics.

Jacobson, Heidi Zuckerman & Deller, Jeremy. "Marlon Brando, Pocahontas, & Me" 2009. (ENG., Illus.). 72p. 35.00 *(978-0-934324-43-4(3))* Aspen Art Museum.

Jaffee, Barbara. The New Art Examiner: Chicago's Independent Voice of the Visual Arts 1973-2002. 2011. (Illus.). 24p. pap. 10.00 ***(978-0-9823852-4-1(2))*** Northern Illinois University Art Museum.

The James T. Bialac Collection: Selected Works. 2012. ***(978-0-8061-4299-9(5))***; pap. ***(978-0-8061-4304-0(5))*** Univ. of Oklahoma Pr.

Jane, Xylor. Xylor Jane. 2010. (ENG., Illus.). 64p. pap. 20.00 *(978-0-9820947-8-5(7))* PictureBox, Inc.

Jansen, Gregor, et al, texts. Friedrich Kunath: Rising vs. Setting. 2009. (ENG., Illus.). 200p. pap. 39.99 *(978-0-934324-44-1(1))* Aspen Art Museum.

Janzen, John M. A Carved Loango Tusk: Local Images & Global Connections. 2009. (Illus.). 69p. *(978-0-938332-24-4(4))* Univ. of Kansas Pubns.

Jean, James. Rift. 2010. (ENG., Illus.). 18p. 12.95 *(978-0-8118-7117-4(7))* Chronicle Bks. LLC.

Jeffri, Joan & Ding, Yu. Respect for Art: Visual Arts Administration & Management in China & the United States. 2007. 327p. per. *(978-7-80198-664-1(4))* Intellectual Property Publishing Hse.

Jenkins, Bruce. Gordon Matta-Clark: Conical Intersect. 2011. (Afterall Ser.). (ENG., Illus.). 112p. (gr. 17). pap. 16.00 *(978-1-84638-073-0(1))* Afterall Publishing GBR. Dist: MIT Pr.

—Gordon Matta-Clark: Conical Intersect. 2011. (Afterall Ser.). (ENG., Illus.). 112p. 35.00 *(978-1-84638-072-3(3))* MIT Pr.

Jeroen Kooijmans: New York Is Eating Me & the Cactus Dance. 2006. (Illus.). (gr. 13-18). 22.00 *(978-90-8546-064-0(6))* Artimo Foundation NLD. Dist: D.A.P./Distributed Art Pubs.

Jimenez, Ariel, ed. Alfredo Boulton & His Contemporaries: Critical Dialogues in Venezuelan Art, 1912-1974. 2008. (ENG., Illus.). 376p. (C). pap. 35.00 *(978-0-87070-710-0(8))* Museum of Modern Art.

Jo, Jeanne & Schopen, Mac. The Wrong Side of Reno: Three Decades of Punk & Hardcore in the Biggest Little City. 2010. 192p. pap. 61.60 *(978-0-557-58700-1(X))* Lulu Enterprises Inc.

Johanson, George. Equivalents: Portraits of Oregon Artists. pap. *(978-1-883124-13-7(1))* Portland Art Museum.

Johns, Elizabeth, et al. One Hundred Stories: Highlights from the Washington County Museum of Fine Arts. 2008. (ENG., Illus.). 232p. 49.95 *(978-1-904832-54-6(7))* Giles, D. Ltd. GBR. Dist: Antique Collectors' Club.

Johnson, Jacqueline. Classic Perfume Advertising: 1920-1970. 2007. (Illus.). 192p. pap. 39.95 *(978-0-7643-2741-4(0))* Schiffer Publishing, Ltd.

Johnson, Janis. The Artist's Eye: Vernon P. Johnson's Watercolors of 1950s Small Town America. 2010. (Illus.). 136p. (C). 34.95 *(978-0-615-37465-9(4))* Knox County Historical Society.

Johnson, Mark Dean, et al. Asian American Modern Art: Shifting Currents, 1900-1970. Cornell, Daniel & Johnson, Mark Dean, eds. 2008. (ENG., Illus.). 168p. 50.00 *(978-0-520-25864-8(9))* Univ. of California Pr.

Johnson, Pamela, ed. Peter Seitz, Desiging a Life. deluxe ed. 2007. pap. 35.00 *(978-0-9800893-0-1(1))* Minneapolis College of Art & Design.

Jon, Dennis Michael, ed. Vermillion Editions Limited: A History & Catalogue, 1977-1992. ltd. ed. 2006. (Illus.). 352p. 54.95 *(978-0-8166-4972-3(3))* Univ. of Minnesota Pr.

Jones, Amelia, et al, texts. ASCO: Elite of the Obscure. 2011. (ENG., Illus.). 432p. 60.00 ***(978-3-7757-3003-7(6))*** Hatje Cantz Verlag GmbH & Co KG DEU. Dist: D.A.P./Distributed Art Pubs.

Jones, Ben. Ben Jones: Men's Group Black Math. 2011. (ENG., Illus.). 80p. 24.95 *(978-0-9820947-9-2(5))* PictureBox, Inc.

Jones, Jeffrey. Jeffrey Jones: A Life in Art. 2011. (Illus.). 256p. 49.99 *(978-1-60010-737-5(0))* Idea & Design Works, LLC.

Jones, Kellie. Now Dig This! Art & Black Los Angeles, 1960-1980. 2011. (ENG., Illus.). 352p. 60.00 ***(978-3-7913-5136-0(2))*** Prestel Publishing.

Jones, Lisa, et al. EyeMinded: Living & Writing Contemporary Art. 2011. (ENG., Illus.). 528p. 99.95 *(978-0-8223-4861-0(6))*; pap. 27.95 *(978-0-8223-4873-3(X))* Duke Univ. Pr.

Jones, William B. Classics Illustrated: A Cultural History 2d Ed. 2nd rev. ed. 2011. (ENG., Illus.). 409p. 55.00 *(978-0-7864-3840-2(1))* McFarland & Co., Inc. Pubs.

Jones, William E. Tearoom. 2008. (Illus.). 43p. 14.00 *(978-0-9786830-8-5(0))* 2nd Cannons Pubns.

Joshua Cooper, Thomas, et al, photos by. Thomas Joshua Cooper & Timothy O'Sullivan: Shoshone Falls. 2010. (ENG., Illus.). 48p. pap. 50.00 *(978-1-934435-25-0(2))* Radius Bks.

Joyce, Julie. Pasadena to Santa Barbara: A Selected History of Art in Southern California, 1951-1969. 2012. ***(978-0-89951-113-9(9))*** Santa Barbara Museum of Art.

Joyner, Brooks. Legends of the West: The Foxley Collection. 2006. *(978-0-936364-34-6(3))* Joslyn Art Museum.

Judy Collischan. Made in the U S A: Modern/Contemporary Art in America. 2010. 560p. pap. 44.95 *(978-1-4401-9854-0(3))* iUniverse, Inc.

K#xFC;ng, Moritz, ed. Peter Downsbrough: the Books, 1968-2010. 2011. (ENG., Illus.). 332p. 45.00 ***(978-3-7757-2833-1(3))*** Hatje Cantz Verlag GmbH & Co KG DEU. Dist: D.A.P./Distributed Art Pubs.

Kachur, Lewis. Past Pop: Robert Rauschenberg & James rosenquist Graphics of The 1970s. 2009. pap. *(978-1-61584-017-5(6))* Independent Pub.

Kadour, Ric Kasini. Women. 2008. (Illus.). 50p. pap. 20.00 *(978-0-9771397-4-3(3))* Kasini Hse.

Kadour, Ric Kasini, afterword by. 2007 Art's Alive Festival of Fine Art Festival Catalog. 2007. per. 25.00 *(978-0-9771397-2-9(7))* Kasini Hse.

Kadour, Ric Kasini, ed. Vermont Contemporary Art Annual 2008. 2008. pap. 25.00 *(978-0-9771397-5-0(1))* Kasini Hse.

Kahn, Tobi, et al. Tobi Kahn: Sacred Spaces for the 21st Century. Heller, Ena Giurescu, ed. 2009. (ENG., Illus.). 112p. 39.95 *(978-1-904832-64-5(4))* Giles, D. Ltd. GBR. Dist: Antique Collectors' Club.

Kalil, Susie. Alexandre Hogue: An American Visionary — Paintings & Works on Paper. 2010. (Tarleton State University Southwestern Studies in the Humanities Ser.). (Illus.). 232p. 35.00 *(978-1-60344-214-5(6))* Texas A&M Univ. Pr.

Kamehiro, Stacy L. The Arts of Kingship: Hawaiian Art & National Culture of the Kalakaua ERA. 2009. (Illus.). xii, 266p. (C). 60.00 *(978-0-8248-3263-6(9))*; pap. 24.00 *(978-0-8248-3358-9(9))* Univ. of Hawaii Pr.

Kammen, Michael. Meadows of Memory: Images of Time & Tradition in American Art & Culture. 2012. (ENG., Illus.). 220p. pap. 25.00 ***(978-0-292-74232-1(0))*** Univ. of Texas Pr.

Kammen, Michael G. Visual Shock: A History of Art Controversies in American Culture. 2007. (Vintage Ser.). (ENG., Illus.). 480p. pap. 18.00 *(978-1-4000-3464-2(7)*, Vintage) Knopf Doubleday Publishing Group.

Kamps, Toby. Art of Our Time: Selections from the Ulrich Museum of Art, Wichita State University. McDonnell, Patricia & Stamey, Emily, eds. 2010. (ENG., Illus.). 168p. 49.95 *(978-0-295-99024-8(4))*; pap. 29.95 *(978-0-295-99025-5(2))* Wichita State Univ., Ulrich Museum of Art.

Kanjo, Kathryn. Lasting Impressions. 2008. 40p. pap. 12.00 *(978-0-942006-74-2(7))* Univ. of California, Santa Barbara, Art Museum.

Karbo, Karen. How Georgia Became O'Keefe: Lessons on the Art of Living. 2011. (ENG., Illus.). 240p. 21.95 *(978-0-7627-7131-8(3)*, skirt!) Globe Pequot Pr., The.

Kargl, Georg, ed. Carter - an Arm with Hair: (the Vienna Catalogue, 1973) 2008. (Illus.). 176p. 29.95 *(978-3-7082-3254-6(2))* Skarabaeus AUT. Dist: SCB Distributors.

Karmel, Pepe, ed. & text. New York Cool: Painting & Sculpture from the NYU Art Collection. 2009. (ENG., Illus.). 208p. pap. 40.00 *(978-0-615-18105-9(8))* Grey Art Gallery & Study Ctr., New York Univ.

Kasner, Stephen. Stephen Kasner: Works: 1993-2006. 2007. (Illus.). 160p. pap. 29.95 *(978-0-9764035-6-2(0))* Scapegoat Publishing.

Kasner, Stephen & Hellion, Dwid. Stephen Kasner: Works 1993-2006. 160p. 39.95 *(978-0-9764035-5-5(2))* Scapegoat Publishing.

Katlan, Alexander. The Black & White Exhibitions of the Salmagundi Sketch Club 1878 to 1887: A Guide to Etchings, Engravings, Drawings, Sculpture, Ceramics, Oils, & Monotypes. 2007. (Illus.). 273p. *(978-0-9791290-0-1(1))* Katlan, Alexander Conservator, Inc.

katlan, Alexander/w., Sr. The Salmagundi Club Painting Exhibition Records 1889 To 1939: A Guide to the Annual Exhibition of Oil Paintings & the Annual Exhibition & Auction Sale of Pictures. 2008. (Illus.). 480p. 65.00 *(978-0-9791290-1-8(X))* Katlan, Alexander Conservator, Inc.

Katz, Alex. Alex Katz. 2008. (ENG., Illus.). 88p. 15.00 *(978-3-905770-79-7(2))* JRP Ringier Kunstverlag AG CHE. Dist: D.A.P./Distributed Art Pubs.

—Alex Katz: Prints. 2010. (ENG., Illus.). 240p. 60.00 *(978-3-7757-2585-9(7))* Hatje Cantz Verlag GmbH & Co KG DEU. Dist: D.A.P./Distributed Art Pubs.

Katz, Jonathan D. & Ward, David C. Hide/Seek: Difference & Desire in American Portraiture. 2010. (ENG., Illus.). 296p. 45.00 *(978-1-58834-299-7(9))* Smithsonian Institution Pr.

Katzman, Laura & Brannan, Beverly W. Re-viewing Documentary: The Photographic Life of Louise Rosskam. 2011. (ENG.). 128p. pap. 39.95 ***(978-1-879383-77-7(2))*** Pennsylvania State Univ. Pr.

Kazmierczak, Elka, ed. & des. Art of Survival: Women, Healing, & the Arts. 1600th ed. 2006. (Illus.). 32p. 12.95 *(978-0-9778478-0-8(2))* Elka Bks.

Keegan, Matt & Rafferty, Sara, eds. North Drive Press: NDP No. 4, 1 vol. 2008. (ENG., Illus.). 50.00 *(978-1-933045-71-9(X))* D.A.P./Distributed Art Pubs.

Keeler, Nancy, text. Gardens in Perpetual Bloom. 2010. (ENG., Illus.). 136p. pap. 24.95 *(978-0-87846-749-5(1))* Museum of Fine Arts, Boston.

Kehr, Walter, photos by. Walter Kehr: Photographs 1995-2005. 2010. (ENG., Illus.). 160p. 50.00 *(978-3-86828-093-7(6))* Kehrer Verlag Heidelberg, Klaus Kehrer DEU. Dist: Consortium Bk. Sales & Distribution.

Kelby, William. Notes on American Artists, 1754-1820. 2009. 100p. pap. 18.95 *(978-1-120-65684-1(2))* Kessinger Publishing, LLC.

Kelker, Nancy L. & Bruhns, Karen O. Faking Ancient Mesoamerica. 2009. (ENG., Illus.). 256p. pap. 29.95 *(978-1-59874-149-0(7))*; lib. bdg. 89.00 *(978-1-59874-150-6(0))* Left Coast Pr., Inc.

Kelleher, Diane Elizabeth. How to Research, Write & Publish an Art History Book in American Art. 2011. 48p. pap. 10.95 ***(978-1-4634-6799-9(0))*** AuthorHouse.

Keller, Jan. Pieces from My Crazy Quilt. Roberts, Janetta & Holzworth, Amy, eds. Date not set. (Illus.). 128p. pap. 12.95 *(978-1-889579-00-9(9))* Black Sheep Bks. & Publishing.

Kelley, Jeff. Childsplay: The Art of Allan Kaprow. 2007. (Illus.). 249p. per. 27.95 *(978-0-520-25388-9(4))* Univ. of California Pr.

Kelley, Kitty. Capturing Camelot: Stanley Tretick's Iconic Images of the Kennedys. 2012. (ENG., Illus.). 192p. 29.99 ***(978-0-312-64342-3(X)***, Dunne, Thomas Bks.) St. Martin's Pr.

Kelly, Sarah E., et al. The Age of American Impressionism: Masterpieces from the Art Institute of Chicago. Barter, Judith A., ed. 2011. (Contemporary Collecting Ser.). (ENG., Illus.). 160p. 50.00 *(978-0-300-17574-5(4))* Art Institute of Chicago.

Ken Davies American Realist. aut. ed. 2009. (Illus.). 224p. 60.00 *(978-0-615-29534-3(7))* Ken & Maryann Davies.

Ken Gonzales-Day. 2006. 8.00 *(978-0-9774617-4-1(0))* CUE Art Foundation.

Kennedy, Brian & Burke, Emily Shubert, eds. Modern & Contemporary Art at Dartmouth: Highlights from the Hood Museum of Art. 2009. (Illus.). 240p. pap. 40.00 *(978-1-58465-787-3(1))* Hood Museum of Art.

Kennedy, Roger G. When Art Worked: The New Deal, Art, & Democracy. 2009. (Illus.). 368p. 75.00 *(978-0-8478-3089-3(6))* Rizzoli International Pubns., Inc.

Kenney, Marcus, illus. Marcus Kenney, 1 vol. 2008. (ENG.). 80p. per. 35.00 *(978-0-9797440-2-0(4))* D.A.P./Distributed Art Pubs.

Kerin, Melissa R. Artful Beneficence: Materials & Meanings of Himalayan Art: Selections from the David Nalin Himalayan Art Collection. 2009. *(978-0-9772131-5-3(3))* Serindia Pubns., Inc.

Kerr, Kavar, selected by. The Heart of a Collection: National Museum of Wildlife Art: Highlights of the NMWA Collection. 2012. ***(978-1-57864-707-1(X))*** Donning Co. Pubs.

Kertess, Klaus. Seen, Written. 2011. (ENG., Illus.). 220p. pap. 25.00 *(978-0-9800242-9-6(3))* Miller, Gregory & Co.

Kienholz, Lyn. L. A. Rising: SoCal Artists Before 1980. Betinski, Elizabeta & Nelson, Corinne, eds. 2011. (Illus.). 516p. 75.00 net. *(978-0-917571-13-8(4))* California/International Arts Foundation.

Kim, Hee-Young. The Vestige of Resistance. 2009. 196p. pap. *(978-3-639-19544-6(2))* VDM Verlag Dr. Mueller e.K.

Kim, Sojin. Chicano Graffiti & Murals: The Neighborhood Art of Peter Quezada. 2010. (Folk Art & Artists Ser.). (ENG.). 72p. (C). pap. 30.00 *(978-1-61703-066-6(X))* Univ. Pr. of Mississippi.

Kimball, Roger. Counterpoints: 25 Years of the New Criterion on Culture & the Arts. 2008. (ENG.). 512p. pap. 22.50 *(978-1-56663-805-0(4))* Dee, Ivan R. Pub.

Kimes, Beverly Rae. Otis Chandler: The Pursuit of Uncommon Excellence. Wilkins, Amy, ed. 2007. *(978-0-9618705-1-5(6))* Art Ctr. College of Design.

King-Hammond, Leslie & Lee-Smith, Hughie. Hughie Lee-Smith. 2010. (David C. Driskell Ser. of African American Art Ser.: Vol. 8). (Illus.). 124p. 35.00 *(978-0-7649-5351-4(6))* Pomegranate Communications, Inc.

Kinsey, Bernard W. & Kinsey, Shirley Pooler. The Kinsey Collection, Collectors Edition: Shared Treasures of Bernard & Shirley Kinsey: Where Art & History Intersect. 2010. (Illus.). 160p. 99.95 *(978-0-9826225-1-3(1))* Allen, Charles Imaging Experts.

Kirkpatrick, Diane & Sheridan, Sonia Landy. The Art of Sonia Landy Sheridan. 2009. (Illus.). 72p. pap. 24.95 *(978-0-944722-38-1(5))* Hood Museum of Art.

Kirwin, Liza & Lord, Joan. Artists in Their Studios: Images from the Smithsonian's Archives of American Art. 2007. (Illus.). 192p. 35.00 *(978-0-06-115012-8(6)*, Collins Design) HarperCollins Pubs.

KIT Publishers. Betsabee Romero: Cars & Traces. 2010. 160p. pap. 30.00 *(978-94-6022-123-1(8))* Royal Tropical Institute Pr. (KIT (Koninklijk Instituut voor de Tropen) NLD. Dist: Stylus Publishing, LLC.

Kittelmann, Udo, ed. Elaine Sturtevant: Author of the Quixote. 2009. (ENG., Illus.). 48p. 45.00 *(978-3-86560-472-9(2))* Verlag der Buchhandlung Walther Konig DEU. Dist: D.A.P./Distributed Art Pubs.

Kittelmann, Udo & Schmitz, Britta, eds. Paul Pfeiffer: The Saints. 2010. (ENG., Illus.). 232p. pap. 45.00 ***(978-3-86828-102-6(9))*** Kehrer Verlag Heidelberg, Klaus Kehrer DEU. Dist: Consortium Bk. Sales & Distribution.

Kjellgren, Eric. Oceania: Art of the Pacific Islands in the Metropolitan Museum of Art. 2007. 24.95 *(978-1-58839-238-1(4))*; 45.00 *(978-1-58839-237-4(6))* Metropolitan Museum of Art, The.

Klant, Michael. Art Brands: Wenn Hunde Beuys Fressen/When Dogs Eat Beuys. 2008. (GER & ENG., Illus.). 120p. pap. 30.00 *(978-3-7757-2116-5(9))* Hatje Cantz Verlag GmbH & Co KG DEU. Dist: D.A.P./Distributed Art Pubs.

Kleeblatt, Norman L. Action/Abstraction: Pollock, de Kooning, & American Art, 1940-1976. Kleeblatt, Norman L., ed. 2009. (ENG., Illus.). 344p. pap. 50.00 *(978-0-300-13920-4(9))* Yale Univ. Pr.

Klein, Mason & Evans, Catherine. The Radical Camera: New York's Photo League, 1936-1951. 2011. (ENG., Illus.). 248p. 50.00 *(978-0-300-14687-5(6))* Yale Univ. Pr.

Klein, Yves. Yves Klein: USA. 2010. (ENG., Illus.). 204p. 32.00 *(978-2-916275-64-2(9))* Dilecta, Editions FRA. Dist: D.A.P./Distributed Art Pubs.

Klein, Yves & Klein. Overcoming the Problems of Art: The Writings of Yves Klein. Ottmann, Klaus, tr. from FRE. 2007. (ENG., Illus.). 300p. pap. 22.00 *(978-0-88214-568-6(1))* Spring Pubns., Inc.

Klett, Mark, photos by. Mark Klett: Wendover: The Half-Life of History. 2011. (ENG., Illus.). 160p. 55.00 ***(978-1-934435-39-7(2))*** Radius Bks.

Kloss, William. Masterworks of American Art. 2008. pap. 25.00 *(978-1-59803-500-1(2))* Teaching Co., LLC, The.

Koeppe, Wolfram, et al. The Robert Lehman Collection at the Metropolitan Museum of Art V15 - European & Asian Decorative Arts. 2012. (ENG., Illus.). 400p. (C). 95.00 ***(978-0-691-15490-9(2))*** Princeton Univ. Pr.

Koestenbaum, Robert, et al, texts. Lari Pittman. 2011. (Illus.). 276p. 75.00 *(978-0-8478-3576-8(6)*, Skira) Rizzoli International Pubns., Inc.

Koestenbaum, Wayne, et al. Jack Pierson: Angel Youth. 2008. (ENG., Illus.). 436p. pap. 59.95 *(978-88-8158-677-6(0))* Charta ITA. Dist: D.A.P./Distributed Art Pubs.

Kohler, Ruth. Sublime Spaces & Visionary Worlds: Built Environments of Vernacular Artists. 2007. (Illus.). 427p. pap. *(978-0-9710703-5-6(0))* Princeton Architectural Pr.

Kondoleon, Christine, et al. Classical Art. 2008. (ENG., Illus.). 240p. pap. 22.50 *(978-0-87846-728-0(9))* Museum of Fine Arts, Boston.

Kook-Anderson, Grace, et al. Best Kept Secret: UCI & the Development of Contemporary Art in Southern California, 1964-1971. 2011. ***(978-0-940872-37-0(4))*** Laguna Art Museum Store.

Koons, Jeff. Jeff Koons. 2010. (ENG & GER., Illus.). 36p. 40.00 *(978-3-935567-49-7(9))* Holzwarth Pubns. DEU. Dist: D.A.P./Distributed Art Pubs.

Korine, Harmony. Harmony Korine: Pigxote. 2009. (ENG., Illus.). 96p. pap. 28.00 *(978-3-905714-62-3(0))* Nieves CHE. Dist: D.A.P./Distributed Art Pubs.

Korshak, Stephen & Spurlock, J. David. Paintings of J. Allen St. John, 1 vol. 2008. (ENG., Illus.). 168p. pap. 24.95 *(978-1-887591-87-4(7))* Vanguard Productions.

Kozloff, Joyce. China Is Near, 1 vol. 2010. (ENG., Illus.). 96p. pap. 37.50 *(978-88-8158-787-2(4))* Charta ITA. Dist: D.A.P./Distributed Art Pubs.

Kraler-Bergmann, Doris. Sylvia Plathaes Lyrical Responses to Works of Art. 2008. 96p. pap. *(978-3-639-03464-6(3))* VDM Verlag Dr. Mueller e.K.

Kren, Thomas. Illuminated Manuscripts of Belgium & the Netherlands. 2010. (Illus.). 96p. pap. 19.95 *(978-1-60606-014-8(7))* Getty Pubns.

Krody, Sumru Belger & Çakmut, Feza. Colors of the Oasis: Central Asian Ikats. 2010. *(978-0-87405-033-2(2))*; pap. *(978-0-87405-034-9(0))* Textile Museum.

Kroiz, Lauren. Creative Composites: Modernism, Race, & the Stieglitz Circle. 2012. (Phillips Book Prize Ser.). (ENG.). 271p. 49.95 ***(978-0-520-27249-1(8))*** Univ. of California Pr.

Kuh, Katharine. My Love Affair with Modern Art: Behind the Scenes with a Legendary Curator. Berman, Avis, ed. 2012. (ENG.). 336p. pap. 14.95 ***(978-1-61145-506-9(5)***, 611506, Arcade Publishing) Skyhorse Publishing Co., Inc.

Kuniholm, Peter I., et al. A Guide to the Classical Collections of Cornell University. Terrell, Jane S., ed. 2nd ed. 2011. (Published by the Herbert F. Johnson Museum of Art, Cornell University Press, & Archaeology & Art Publications Ser.). (Illus.). 80p. reprint ed. pap. 19.95 *(978-1-934260-08-1(8))* Cornell Univ., Herbert F. Johnson Museum of Art.

Kuo, Andrew. Andrew Kuo: What Me Worry. 2011. (ENG., Illus.). 208p. 49.95 *(978-88-6208-153-5(7))* Damiani ITA. Dist: D.A.P./Distributed Art Pubs.

Kushner, Marilyn. Donald Saff: Art in Collaboration. 2010. (Illus.). 208p. 49.95 *(978-3-7913-4205-4(3))* Prestel Publishing.

Lacoste, compiled by. Visionaire No. 54: Sport No. 1, Knight / Lagerfeld / Stipe. 2008. (ENG., Illus.). bds. 250.00 *(978-1-888645-70-5(9))* Visionaire Publishing.

Laguna Art Museum. In the Land of Retinal Delights. 2008. (Illus.). 160p. *(978-1-58423-317-6(6))* Laguna Art Museum Store.

Laichas, William D., ed. New Mexico Millennium Collection: A Twenty-First Century Celebration of Fine Art in New Mexico. 2007. (ENG., Illus.). 160p. 45.00 *(978-0-9679034-0-8(8))* New Mexico Millennium Collection, LLC.

Lake, Prince Dav, ed. Winslow Homers Empire State. 2010. (Illus.). 84p. pap. 19.99 *(978-0-8156-8155-7(0))* Syracuse Univ. Pr.

Lambert-Beatty, Carrie. Being Watched: Yvonne Rainer & The 1960s. 2011. (October Bks.). (ENG., Illus.). 384p. (gr. 17). pap. 19.95 *(978-0-262-51607-5(1))* MIT Pr.

Lambrecht, Laurie. Roy Lichtenstein in His Studio. 2011. (ENG., Illus.). 128p. 35.00 *(978-1-58093-318-6(1))* Monacelli Pr., Inc.

Landers, Sean. Sean Landers: 1991-1994, Improbable History. 2011. (ENG., Illus.). 388p. 95.00 ***(978-3-03764-178-1(9))*** JRP Ringier Kunstverlag AG CHE. Dist: D.A.P./Distributed Art Pubs.

Lapatin, Kenneth & Wight, Karol, eds. The Antiquities Collection. 2nd rev. ed. 2010. (Illus.). 264p. pap., instr.'s hndbk. ed. 19.95 *(978-0-89236-998-0(1)*, J. Paul Getty Museum) Getty Pubns.

Lapthisophon, Stephen. Writing Art Cinema 1988-2010. 2011. 103p. pap. 12.00 *(978-1-4507-4210-8(6))* Green Lantern Pr.

Lark Books. Quilt National 2011. 2011. (Quilt National Ser.). (ENG., Illus.). 112p. 27.95 *(978-1-60059-799-2(8))* Lark Bks.

Lash, Miranda. The Sydney & Walda Besthoff Sculpture Garden at the New Orleans Museum of Art. 2012. (ENG., Illus.). 176p. 49.95 **(978-1-85759-739-4(7))** Scala, Editions FRA. Dist: National Bk. Network.

LaVella, Mike, ed. The Rock 'n Roll Monster Art of Dirty Donny: A Decade of Freelance on the Canvas Highway. 2008. (ENG.). 152p. pap. 24.95 *(978-0-9795132-3-7(5))* Scapegoat Publishing.

Lavin, Maud. Push Comes to Shove: New Images of Aggressive Women. 2010. (ENG., Illus.). 312p. (gr. 17). 27.95 *(978-0-262-12309-9(6))* MIT Pr.

Lawing, Douglas, et al. The Spirit of Modernism: The John R. Eckel, Jr. Foundation Gift to the Museum of Fine Arts, Houston. 2011. pap. **(978-0-89090-175-5(9))** Museum of Fine Arts, Houston.

Lawrence, James & Richardson, John. Robert Rauschenberg. 2011. (Illus.). 256p. 75.00 *(978-3-7913-4557-4(5))* Prestel Publishing.

Lazarus, Marvin. Perfect Timing: Artists in New York, 19581962. 2010. (ENG.). 144p. 39.95 *(978-0-9794727-7-0(6))* Five Ties Publishing.

Leaders of American Impressionism: Mary Cassatt, Childe Hassam, John H. Twachtman & J. Alden Weit. (Brooklyn Museum Publications in Reprint). 13.95 *(978-0-405-18863-3(3), 19595)* Ayer Co. Pubs., Inc.

Leavitt, William, et al. William Leavitt: Theater Objects. 2011. (ENG., Illus.). 144p. pap. 40.00 *(978-1-933751-18-4(5))* Museum of Contemporary Art, Los Angeles.

Lecercle, Jean-Jacques & Kral, Françoise. Architecture & Philosophy: New Perspectives on the Work of Arakawa & Madeline Gins. 2010. (Illus.). 233p. pap. 64.00 *(978-90-420-3189-0(1))* Rodopi.

Lee, Anthony W. Picturing Chinatown: Art & Orientalism in San Francisco. 2008. (ENG.). 347p. 45.00 *(978-1-4223-9266-9(X))* DIANE Publishing Co.

Lee, Jim & Baker, Bill. Icons: The DC Comics & Wildstorm Art of Jim Lee. 2010. (Illus.). 296p. 39.95 *(978-1-84576-519-4(2)*, Titan Bks.) Titan Bks. Ltd. GBR. Dist: Random Hse., Inc.

Leeds, Valerie Ann. 101 Masterpieces of New York City: Must-See Works of Art & Architecture in the New York Metropolitan Area. 2009. (ENG., Illus.). 232p. pap. 15.95 *(978-1-59350-098-6(X))* Alyson Pubns.

Lehmbeck, Leah Rosenblatt. Proof: The Rise of Printmaking in Southern California. Lehmbeck, Leah, ed. 2011. (Illus.). 256p. **(978-1-60606-093-3(7))** Getty Pubns.

LEISSRING, Jack. Jerrold Ballaine, Winter Landscapes. 2010. 55p. pap. 20.50 *(978-0-557-39087-8(7))* Lulu Enterprises Inc.

Leja, Michael. Looking Askance: Skepticism & American Art from Eakins to Duchamp. 2007. (Illus.). 300p. pap. 37.95 *(978-0-520-24996-7(8))* Univ. of California Pr.

Lenkowsky, Kate & Lenkowsky, Kathleen. Contemporary Quilt Art: An Introduction & Guide. 2008. (ENG., Illus.). 304p. 34.95 *(978-0-253-35124-1(3), 0253351243)* Indiana Univ. Pr.

LePere, Gene Hirshhorn. Little Man in a Big Hurry. 2009. (ENG.). 271p. 26.95 *(978-0-533-16079-2(0))* Vantage Pr., Inc.

Lerner, Leslie, et al. Under the Radar: Leslie Lerner. 2008. (Illus.). 31p. *(978-0-915171-75-0(9))* Katonah Gallery.

Letscher, Lance. Lance Letscher: Collage. collector's ed. 2010. (ENG., Illus.). 224p. 250.00 *(978-0-292-72395-5(4))* Univ. of Texas Pr.

Levenson, Michael. Modernism. 2011. (ENG., Illus.). 336p. 40.00 *(978-0-300-11173-6(8))* Yale Univ. Pr.

Levin, Eli. Santa Fe Bohemia: The Art Colony, 1964-1980. 2007. (ENG.). 320p. 29.95 *(978-0-86534-512-6(0))*; per. 24.95 *(978-0-86534-513-3(9))* Sunstone Pr.

Levithan, David. We Are Quiet We Are Loud. 2008. (Best Young Writers & Artists in Americ Ser.). (ENG., Illus.). 368p. (J). (gr. 7). pap. 8.99 *(978-0-545-03399-2(3)*, PUSH) Scholastic, Inc.

Levy, Ellen. Criminal Ingenuity: Moore, Cornell, Ashbery, & the Struggle Between the Arts, 1 vol. 2011. (Modernist Literature & Culture Ser.). (ENG., Illus.). 304p. 49.95 *(978-0-19-974635-4(4))* Oxford Univ. Pr., Inc.

Lewallen, Constance M., et al. State of Mind: New California Art Circa 1970. 2011. (ENG., Illus.). 296p. 39.95 *(978-0-520-27061-9(4))* Univ. of California Pr.

Lidtke, Thomas, frwd. A Corner of the World: The Art of Lois Ireland Zwettler. 2007. (Illus.). 24p. per. *(978-0-9710228-0-5(1))* Museum of Wisconsin Art.

Lier, Alexandra. Speedseekers. 2008. 274p. *(978-1-58423-315-2(X))*; (Illus.). *(978-1-58423-314-5(1))* Gingko Pr., Inc.

Light, Michael, photos by. Michael Light: la Day, la Night. 2011. (ENG., Illus.). 72p. 60.00 *(978-1-934435-30-4(9))* Radius Bks.

Lin, Maya. Boundaries. 2006. (ENG., Illus.). 224p. pap. 25.00 *(978-0-7432-9959-6(0))* Simon & Schuster.

Lingad, Ken & Deats, Suzanne. Contemporary Native American Artists, 1 vol. 2012. (ENG., Illus.). 184p. 50.00 *(978-1-4236-0559-1(4))* Gibbs Smith, Publisher.

Linton, Meg, text. Gary Lang: Hybrid Variations. 2008. (Illus.). 72p. per. 20.00 *(978-0-9800962-0-0(0))* Cella, Edward Art+Architecture.

Lippard, Lucy & Fox, William, texts. Land/Art: New Mexico. 2010. (ENG., Illus.). 196p. 45.00 *(978-1-934435-17-5(1))* Radius Bks.

Lippard, Lucy, et al. Ree Morton: At the Still Point of the Turning World. 2009. (Illus.). 118p. pap. 20.00 *(978-0-942324-48-8(X))* Drawing Ctr.

Lippincott, Louise & Avinoff, Andrey. Andrey Avinoff: In Pursuit of Beauty. 2011. (ENG., Illus.). 104p. pap. 24.95 *(978-0-88039-053-8(0))* Carnegie Museum of Art, The.

Little, Carl & Hartgen, David /Thomas. Vincent Andrew Hartgen: His Art & Legacy. 2008. (Illus.). 250p. 55.00 *(978-0-9778232-1-5(0))* Hartgen, Stephen.

Livingston, Jane & Alexander, John. John Alexander: A Retrospective. 2007. pap. *(978-0-89090-154-0(6))* Museum of Fine Arts, Houston.

Loendorf, Lawrence L. Thunder & Herds: Rock Art of the High Plains. 2008. (ENG., Illus.). 254p. 94.00 *(978-1-59874-152-0(7))*; pap. 32.95 *(978-1-59874-151-3(9))* Left Coast Pr., Inc.

Longari, Elisabetta & Honnef, Klaus. Linda Salerno. 2010. (ENG., Illus.). 120p. pap. 45.00 *(978-88-8158-782-7(3))* Charta ITA. Dist: D.A.P./Distributed Art Pubs.

Longwell, Alicia G., intro. First Impressions: Nineteenth-Century American Master Prints. 2010. (Illus.). 96p. *(978-0-943526-55-3(8))* Parrish Art Museum, The.

Longwell, Alicia Grant. First Impressions: Nineteenth-Century American Master Prints. 2010. (ENG., Illus.). 96p. 39.95 *(978-1-904832-75-1(X))* Giles, D. Ltd. GBR. Dist: Antique Collectors' Club.

Lopes, Marilyn/Jansen, creator. Maui Hawaiian Quilt Patterns: A Collection of Hawaiian Quilt Patterns. 2007. per. 6.00 *(978-0-9761070-3-3(1))* Jansen, Marilyn.

Lorz, Julienne, ed. Stop, Repair, Prepare. 2009. (GER & ENG., Illus.). 80p. 49.95 *(978-3-86560-474-3(9))* Verlag der Buchhandlung Walther Konig DEU. Dist: D.A.P./Distributed Art Pubs.

Losty, Jeremiah P. Indian Miniatures from the James Ivory Collection. 2011. (Illus.). 220p. pap. 65.00 *(978-0-9553306-7-4(X)*, Francesco Galloway (Acc)) Antique Collectors' Club GBR. Dist: National Bk. Network.

Lovell, Margaretta M. Art in a Season of Revolution: Painters, Artisans, & Patrons in Early America. 2007. (Early American Studies). (Illus.). 360p. (C). per. 29.95 *(978-0-8122-1991-3(0))* Univ. of Pennsylvania Pr.

Lovell, Whitfield. Mercy, Patience & Destiny: the Women of Whitfield Lovell's Tableaux. 2010. (ENG., Illus.). 58p. pap. 20.00 *(978-0-615-22202-8(1))* Savannah College of Art & Design Exhibitions.

Lovenheim, Barbara & Smith, Paul J. Breaking Ground: A Century of Craft Art in Western New York. 2010. (ENG., Illus.). 156p. 50.00 *(978-1-55595-354-6(9))* Hudson Hills Pr. LLC.

Lowrey, Carol & Lever, Hayley. Hayley Lever & the Modern Spirit. 2010. (Illus.). 48p. pap. **(978-1-935617-05-1(2))** Spanierman Gallery.

Lowry, Carol. A Legacy of Art: Paintings & Sculptures by Artist Life Members of the National Arts Club. 2008. (ENG., Illus.). 216p. 60.00 *(978-0-615-15499-2(9))* Hudson Hills Pr. LLC.

Lowry, Glenn, text. The Museum of Modern Art in This Century. 2009. (ENG., Illus.) 50p. pap. 9.95 *(978-0-87070-764-3(7))* Museum of Modern Art.

Luc, Dinh Viet & Jones, Charles D., illus. Bear Went over the Mountain. 2011. 86p. 525.00 **(978-1-936205-25-7(4))** Austin, Stephen F. State Univ. Pr.

Lucas, Renata, et al. Renata Lucas. 2007. 25.00 *(978-0-9749831-7-2(9))* California Institute of the Arts.

Luie-Smith, Edward. Margaret Evageline. 2010. pap. 25.00 *(978-0-578-05783-5(2))* Evangeline Studio.

Lyle, Val. The Truths: The brutal tenderness of Appalachia. 2009. pap. *(978-1-61584-019-9(2))* Independent Pub.

Lynch, David, photos by. David Lynch: Dark Splendor. 2010. (ENG., Illus.). 352p. 85.00 *(978-3-7757-2644-3(6))* Hatje Cantz Verlag GmbH & Co KG DEU. Dist: D.A.P./Distributed Art Pubs.

Lyne-Winkler, Layla, ed. Plastic Antinomy Number 3: Blue/Green Issue. 2009. 48p. pap. 8.00 *(978-0-86719-728-0(5))* Last Gasp of San Francisco.

Lynes, Barbara Buhler & O'Keeffe, Georgia. The Georgia O'Keeffe Museum Collections. 2007. (ENG., Illus.). 352p. 70.00 *(978-0-8109-0957-1(X))* Abrams.

Lynes, Barbara Buhler & Weinberg, Jonathan. Shared Intelligence: American Painting & the Photograph. 2011. (ENG., Illus.). 274p. 39.95 *(978-0-520-26906-4(3))* Univ. of California Pr.

Lyon, Christopher. Nancy Spero: The Work. 2010. (Illus.). 312p. 85.00 *(978-3-7913-4416-4(1))* Prestel Publishing.

Muller-Westermann, Iris, ed. & text. Jutta Koether. 2011. (ENG & SWE., Illus.). 96p. pap. 34.95 **(978-3-86560-981-6(3))** Verlag der Buchhandlung Walther Konig DEU. Dist: D.A.P./Distributed Art Pubs.

MacAdam, Barbara J. American Art at Dartmouth: Highlights from the Hood Museum of Art. 2007. (Illus.). ix, 244p. *(978-1-58465-667-8(0))* Hood Museum of Art.

—American Art at Dartmouth: Highlights from the Hood Museum of Art. 2007. (ENG., Illus.). 256p. pap. 40.00 *(978-1-58465-668-5(9))* Hood Museum of Art.

MacAdam, Barbara J., ed. Embracing Elegance, 1885-1920: American Art from the Huber Family Collection. 2011. (Illus.). 116p. pap. 24.95 *(978-0-944722-41-1(5))* Hood Museum of Art.

Mack, Angela D. & Hoffius, Stephen G., eds. Landscape of Slavery: The Plantation in American Art. 2008. (Illus.). 166p. 49.95 *(978-1-57003-719-1(1))*; pap. 24.95 *(978-1-57003-720-7(5))* Univ. of South Carolina Pr.

Mackenzie, Colin. Masterworks of Chinese Art: The Nelson-Atkins Museum of Art, 1 vol. 2011. (ENG., Illus.). 104p. 24.95 **(978-0-615-48882-0(X))** Nelson-Atkins Museum of Art, The.

MacPhee, Josh. Signs of Change: Social Movement Cultures, 1960s to Now. 2010. (ENG., Illus.). 178p. pap. 28.95 *(978-1-84935-027-3(2))* AK Pr. GBR. Dist: Consortium Bk. Sales & Distribution.

MacPherson, Mark & Fam, Max, eds. Hijacked Volume One: Australia & America. 2011. (ENG., Illus.). 288p. 50.00 **(978-3-86828-125-5(8))** Kehrer Verlag Heidelberg, Klaus Kehrer DEU. Dist: Consortium Bk. Sales & Distribution.

Madden, David, et al. Richard Anuskiewicz: Paintings & Sculptures 1945-2001. 2011. (ENG., Illus.). 272p. 85.00 *(978-88-7038-483-3(7))* Centro Di ITA. Dist: Antique Collectors' Club.

*Made in Pennsylvania: A Folk Art Tradition. 2007. 29.95 *(978-0-931241-35-2(9))* Antique Collectors' Club.

Madson, Jerry. Bog Walk Pitcher Plants Meet Implicate Polysynthesis. 2007. 100p. pap. 44.50 *(978-1-4303-2883-4(5))* Lulu Enterprises Inc.

Maguire, Gregory. Making Mischief: A Maurice Sendak Appreciation. 2009. (ENG., Illus.) 208p. 27.50 *(978-0-06-168916-1(5)*, Morrow, William & Co.) HarperCollins Pubs.

Malik, Anne E. A New & Native Beauty: The Art & Craft of Greene & Greene. Bosley, Edward R., ed. 2008. (Illus.). 272p. 75.00 *(978-1-85894-452-4(X))* Merrell Pubs. Ltd. GBR. Dist: Perseus Distribution.

Mallett, Renee. Fairies, Mermaids, & Other Mystical Creatures: Artist Trading Cards. 2008. (Illus.). 160p. pap. 29.95 *(978-0-7643-2803-9(4))* Schiffer Publishing, Ltd.

Malone, Meredith. Tomas Saraceno: Cloud-Specific. Marjanovic, Igor, ed. 2012. (ENG., Illus.). 120p. pap. 30.00 **(978-0-936316-35-2(7))** Washington Univ., Mildred Lane Kemper Art Museum.

Mangold, Robert & Dreishpoon, Douglas. Beyond the Line: Paintings & Project, 2000-2008. 2009. (ENG., Illus.). 128p. 150.00 *(978-0-8109-5487-8(7))* Abrams.

Mann, Sally. Sally Mann? The Flesh & the Spirit. 2010. (ENG., Illus.). 204p. 55.00 *(978-1-59711-162-1(7))* Aperture Foundation, Inc.

Mann, Sally, photos by. Proud Flesh. 2009. (ENG., Illus.). 64p. 80.00 *(978-1-59711-135-5(X))* Aperture Foundation, Inc.

Manoguerra, Paul, et al., contrib. by. Amazing Grace: Self-Taught Artists from the Mullis Collection. 2007. (ENG.). 162p. 48.00 *(978-0-915977-63-5(X))* Univ. of Georgia, Georgia Museum of Art.

Marcoci, Roxana & Eagleton, Terry, texts. Sanja Ivekovic? Sweet Violence. 2011. (ENG., Illus.). 192p. 50.00 **(978-0-87070-811-4(2))** Museum of Modern Art.

Marien, Mary Warner. Photography & its Critics: A Cultural History, 1839-1900. 2011. (Perspectives on Photography Ser.). (ENG., Illus.). 242p. pap. 31.99 **(978-1-107-40338-3(3))** Cambridge Univ. Pr.

Marion, Larry. The Lost Beatles Photographs: The Bob Bonis Archive, 1964-1966. 2011. (ENG., Illus.). 192p. 29.99 *(978-0-06-196078-9(0))* HarperCollins Pubs.

—The Lost Rolling Stones Photographs: The Bob Bonis Archive, 1964-1966. 2010. (ENG., Illus.). 288p. 29.99 *(978-0-06-196079-6(9))* HarperCollins Pubs.

Mark Dagley - Shaped Canvas. 2008. (Illus.). 16p. pap. 15.00 *(978-0-9677326-9-5(7))* Abaton Bk. Co.

Mark, Lisa, ed. Sterling Ruby: MOCA Focus. 2008. (ENG., Illus.). 152p. pap. 24.95 *(978-1-933751-10-8(X))* Museum of Contemporary Art, Los Angeles.

Markonish, Denise. Petah Coyne: Everything That Rises Must Converge. 2010. (ENG., Illus.). 128p. pap. 25.00 *(978-0-300-16770-2(9))* Yale Univ. Pr.

Marley, Christopher. Pheromone: The Insect Artwork of Christopher Marley. 2008. (Illus.). 256p. 75.00 *(978-0-7649-4619-6(6))* Pomegranate Communications, Inc.

Marquis. American Art Directory 2007-2008. 61st ed. 2006. 1046p. 299.00 *(978-0-87217-843-4(9))* National Register Publishing.

Marquis Who's Who Staff. Who's Who in American Art 2008. 28th ed. 2007. 1512p. 297.00 *(978-0-8379-6307-5(9))* Marquis Who's Who, LLC.

Mars-1, et al, contrib. by. Further. 2010. (Illus.). 353p. pap. 39.95 *(978-1-58423-406-7(7))* Gingko Pr., Inc.

Marsh, Joanna & Rockman, Alexis. Alexis Rockman: A Fable for Tomorrow. 2010. (Illus.). 176p. *(978-0-9790678-8-4(X))* Smithsonian American Art Museum.

Marter, Joan. The Grove Encyclopedia of American Art, 5 vols., Set. 2011. (ENG., Illus.). 2608p. 1045.00 *(978-0-19-533579-8(1))* Oxford Univ. Pr., Inc.

Marter, Joan, ed. Abstract Expressionism: The International Context. 2007. (Na Ser.). (ENG., Illus.). 320p. pap. 29.95 *(978-0-8135-3975-1(7))* Rutgers Univ. Pr.

Marter, Joan M. The Grove Encyclopedia of American Art. 2011. (Illus.). E-Book **(978-0-19-973926-4(9))** Oxford Univ. Pr., Inc.

Marti, Virgil. Set Pieces: Curated by Virgil Marti from the Collection of the Philadelphia Museum of Art. 2011. (ENG., Illus.). 64p. pap. 20.00 *(978-0-88454-119-6(3))* Univ. of Pennsylvania, Institute of Contemporary Art.

Martin, Daria. Daria Martin, 1 vol. 2006. (ENG., Illus.). 96p. 29.00 *(978-3-905701-54-8(5))* JRP Ringier Kunstverlag AG CHE. Dist: D.A.P./Distributed Art Pubs.

Martin, David F. The Art of Richard Bennett. 2010. (ENG., Illus.). 80p. pap. 24.95 *(978-0-939806-07-2(X))* Historical Society of Seattle & King County/Museum of History & Industry.

—Evergreen Muse: The Art of Elizabeth Colborne. 2011. (ENG., Illus.). 96p. (C). pap. 25.00 *(978-0-295-99142-9(9))* Whatcom Museum of History & Art.

Martin, Mary L. & Skinner, Tina. The Ultimate Collector's Guide to Surfing Postcards. 2008. (Illus.). 160p. pap. 29.95 *(978-0-7643-2909-8(X))* Schiffer Publishing, Ltd.

Martinez, Daniel Joseph, contrib. by. Capitalism in Question (Because It Is) Ian Arenas, Matthew Brandt, James Melinat, Gabie Strong, Kara Tanaka, Grant Vetter. 2010. (ENG.). pap. *(978-0-615-31623-9(9))* Pitzer College Art Galleries.

Maryann Pasda Diedwardo. Pennsylvania Voices Book Viii: The Artist's Journal, Art for a Cause. 2009. 156p. pap. 13.99 *(978-1-4389-4256-8(7))* AuthorHouse.

Marzio, Peter C. American Art & Philanthropy: Twenty Years of Collecting at the Museum of Fine Arts, Houston. 2010. (ENG., Illus.). 388p. 75.00 *(978-0-300-16756-6(3))* Museum of Fine Arts, Houston.

Matt, Gerald, et al, eds. Andro Wekua: Pink Wave Hunter, 3 Volumes. 2011. (ENG., Illus.). 388p. pap. 49.95 **(978-3-86560-961-8(9))** Verlag der Buchhandlung Walther Konig DEU. Dist: D.A.P./Distributed Art Pubs.

Matt, Gerald & Genzmer, Synne, texts. Clifton Childree: Fuck that Chicken from Popeyes. 2011. (ENG., Illus.). 120p. pap. 30.00 **(978-3-86984-201-1(3))** Verlag fur Moderne Kunst DEU. Dist: D.A.P./Distributed Art Pubs.

Matta-Clark, Gordon & Moure, Gloria. Gordon Matta-Clark: Works & Collected Writings, 1 vol. 2006. (ENG., Illus.). 304p. 75.00 *(978-84-343-1109-1(7))* Poligrafa, Ediciones, S. A. ESP. Dist: D.A.P./Distributed Art Pubs.

Matta-Clark, Gordon & Sussman, Elisabeth. Gordon Matta-Clark "You Are the Measure" 2007. (Illus.). 239p. *(978-0-87427-156-0(8))* Whitney Museum of American Art.

Mattet, Laurence. Arts & Cultures. (ENG.). No. 8. 8th ed. 2009. 360p. pap. 39.00 *(978-2-7572-0070-4(4))*No. 9. 9th ed. 2008. 340p. pap. 39.00 *(978-2-7572-0164-0(6))* Continental Sales, Inc. (Art Stock Bks. Ltd/Cs).

Matthews, Nancy Mowll & Kennedy, Elizabeth, eds. Prendergast in Italy. 2009. (Illus.). 192p. 55.00 *(978-1-85894-483-8(X))* Merrell Pubs. Ltd. GBR. Dist: Perseus Distribution.

Mazow, Leo G. & Murphy, Kevin M. Taxing Visions: Financial Episodes in Late Nineteenth-Century American Art. 2010. (ENG.). 80p. pap. 24.95 *(978-0-911209-68-6(9))* Pennsylvania State Univ. Pr.

McBride, Rita. Rita Mcbride. 2010. (ENG & GER., Illus.). 144p. 60.00 *(978-3-941263-14-7(5))* Richter Verlag DEU. Dist: D.A.P./Distributed Art Pubs.

McCallum, Bradley & Tarry, Jacqueline, illus. Whitewash, 1 vol. 2007. (ENG.). 77p. 30.00 *(978-988-99264-1-0(5))* Timezone 8 Ltd. HKG. Dist: D.A.P./Distributed Art Pubs.

McCarthy, Paul. Head Shop/Shop Head: Works, 1966-2006, 1 vol. 2008. (ENG., Illus.). 688p. pap. 50.00 *(978-3-86521-300-6(6))* Steidl, Gerhard Druckerei und Verlag DEU. Dist: Innovative Logistics.

—Paul Mccarthy's Low Life Slow Life. 2010. (ENG., Illus.). 640p. pap. 75.00 *(978-3-7757-2573-6(3))* Hatje Cantz Verlag GmbH & Co KG DEU. Dist: D.A.P./Distributed Art Pubs.

McCarthy, Paul, et al, texts. Paul Mccarthy Three Sculptures/Hummel, 2 vols. 2010. (Illus.). 48p. pap. 100.00 *(978-0-9790942-9-3(1))* L & M Arts.

McCombs, W. Douglas, ed. Horsing Around: 19th Century Cast Iron Hitching Posts. 2008. (Albany Institute of History & Art Ser.). (Illus.). 76p. pap. 26.95 *(978-0-939072-17-0(3)*, Suny Pr.) State Univ. of New York Pr.

McCorquodale, Duncan, ed. Krzysztof Wodiczko. 2011. (ENG., Illus.). 352p. 59.95 *(978-1-907317-13-2(9))* Black Dog Publishing Ltd. GBR. Dist: Perseus Distribution.

McCracken, John. John Mccracken: Sketchbook. 2008. (ENG., Illus.). 168p. 65.00 *(978-1-934435-12-0(0))* Radius Bks.

McDaniel, Lynda. Contemporary Hawaii Woodworkers: The Wood, the Art, the Aloha. 2009. (Illus.). 224p. 44.95 *(978-0-615-29944-0(X))* Contemporary Pubns.

McDonald, Christie, et al. Painting My World: The Art of Dorothy Eisner. McDonald, Christie, ed. 2008. (ENG., Illus.). 128p. *(978-1-85149-585-6(1)*, Antique Collectors Club Dist) Antique Collectors' Club.

McDonnell, Patricia. Marsden Hartley: American Modern. 2007. (ENG., Illus.). 84p. per. 27.95 *(978-1-885116-12-3(8))* Weisman, Frederick R. Art Museum.

McDonough, Tom, et al, texts. Adel Abdessemed: Situation & Practice. 2009. (ENG., Illus.). 128p. pap. 40.00 *(978-0-938437-70-3(4))* Massachusetts Institute of Technology, List Visual Arts Ctr.

McGarry, Susan Hallsten. Freedom of Expression: The Art of Charles W. Thwaites. 2008. (ENG., Illus.). 119p. pap. 35.00 *(978-1-934491-08-9(X))* Fresco Fine Art Pubns., LLC.

McGarry, Susan Hallsten & Palmore, Thomas. Earthlings: The Paintings of Tom Palmore. 2008. (ENG., Illus.). 120p. (C). 45.00 *(978-1-934397-05-3(9)*, Quaid Publishing.

McGarry, Susan Hallsten & Tobey, Rebecca. Partners in Art: Gene & Rebecca Tobey. 2007. (ENG., Illus.). 360p. 75.00 *(978-1-934491-02-7(0))* Fresco Fine Art Pubns., LLC.

McGee, Barry. Barry McGee. 2010. (ENG., Illus.). 176p. 49.95 *(978-88-6208-096-5(4))* Damiani ITA. Dist: D.A.P./Distributed Art Pubs.

McGee, Micki, ed. Yaddo: Making American Culture. 2008. (ENG., Illus.). 184p. (gr. 17). 90.00 *(978-0-231-14736-1(8))*; pap. 29.95 *(978-0-231-14737-8(6))* Columbia Univ. Pr.

McGinnis, Mark & Vinti, Carlo. Front Forty Profiles, No. 1. 2010. (Front Forty Press - Front Forty Profiles Ser.). (ITA & ENG., Illus.). 144p. pap. 20.00 *(978-0-9825458-0-5(0))* Front Forty Pr.

McInnis, Maurie D. & Nelson, Louis P., eds. Shaping the Body Politic: Art & Political Formation in Early America. 2011. (Thomas Jefferson Foundation Distinguished Lecture Ser.). (ENG., Illus.). 336p. (gr. 17). 45.00 *(978-0-8139-3102-9(9))* Univ. Pr. of Virginia.

McLaughlin, Judith. The Sacred Feminine: Images of the Southwest: The Development of the Feminine Principle in New Mexican Folkloric Art. 2009. pap. *(978-1-890689-27-8(0)*, Rio Grande Bks.) LPD Pr.

McManus, Michael. Michael Knowlton: Blackwater Babylon. 2008. (Illus.). 48p. per. 15.00 *(978-0-9771696-8-9(5)*, Grand Central Pr.

McMillen, Michael C., et al. Michael C. McMillen: Train of Thought. 2011. (Illus.). 192p. *(978-3-7913-5125-4(7))* Oakland Museum.

McNutt, Jennifer Complo & Holland, Ashley. Art Quantum: The Eiteljorg Fellowship for Native American Fine Art 2009. Nottage, James, ed. 2010. (ENG., Illus.). 96p. pap. 26.95 *(978-0-295-98996-9(3))* Univ. of Washington Pr.

McPheron, Marilyn Turner. Oh no! more Snow! 2011. 44p. (gr. -1). pap. 17.44 **(978-1-4269-6935-5(X))** Trafford Publishing.

McPherson, Tara. Lost Constellations: The Art of Tara McPherson. 2011. (Illus.). 112p. 22.99 *(978-1-59582-222-2(4))* Dark Horse Comics.

McWilliam, Neil, ed. Lines of Attack: Conflicts in Caricature. 2010. (ENG., Illus.). 96p. pap. 18.95 *(978-0-938989-32-5(4))* Duke Univ. Pr.

Mead Art Museum, et al. Orra White Hitchcock (1796-1863) An Amherst Woman of Art & Science. 2011. (ENG., Illus.). 114p. pap. 39.95 (978-0-914337-23-2(8)) Amherst College, Mead Art Museum.

Meatyard, Ralph Eugene, photos by. Ralph Eugene Meatyard. 2011. (ENG., Illus.). 129p. 60.00 (978-1-934435-33-5(3)) Radius Bks.

Mecklenburg, Virginia M. Modern Masters: American Abstraction at Midcentury. 2009. (ENG., Illus.). 272p. 65.00 (978-1-904832-59-1(8)) Giles, D. Ltd. GBR. Dist: Antique Collectors' Club.

Meecham, Pam & Sheldon, Julie. Making American Art: A Critical Introduction. 2008. (ENG., Illus.). 280p. (C). pap. 39.95 (978-0-415-42070-9(9)) Routledge.

McGraw, Richard. Confronting Modernity: Art & Society in Louisiana. 2008. (ENG., Illus.). 304p. 55.00 (978-1-57806-417-5(1)) Univ. Pr. of Mississippi.

Mehretu, Julie, contrib. by. Huma Bhabha, 1 vol. 2011. (ENG.). 140p. 75.00 (978-0-935875-25-6(5)) Blum, Peter Edition.

Meier, Margaret. Vintage Textured Barkcloth. 2007. (Schiffer Book for Collectors Ser.). (Illus.). 160p. pap. 29.95 (978-0-7643-2663-9(5)) Schiffer Publishing, Ltd.

Mera, H. P. The Rain Bird: A Study in Pueblo Design. 2011. 122p. 40.95 **(978-1-258-09805-6(9))** Literary Licensing, LLC.

Merali, Shaheen. New York States of Mind: Art in the City. Merali, Shaheen, ed. 2007. (ENG., Illus.). 320p. 29.95 (978-0-86356-681-3(2)) Saqi Bks. GBR. Dist: Consortium Bk. Sales & Distribution.

Mercurio, Gianni. Roy Lichtenstein: Meditations on Art. 2010. (Illus.). 372p. 100.00 (978-88-572-0460-4(X)) Skira Editore ITA. Dist: Random Hse., Inc.

Mercurio, Gianni, et al. Tony Oursler: Open Obscura. 2011. (ITA & ENG., Illus.). 176p. 55.00 (978-88-7179-663-5(2)) Antique Collectors' Club.

Merrill, Linda, et al. Picturing America: Teachers Resource Book. 2008. (978-0-615-20793-3(6)) National Endowment for the Humanities.

Messinger, Lisa Mintz & Dabrowski, Magdalena. Stieglitz & His Artists: Matisse to O'Keeffe: The Alfred Stieglitz Collection in the Metropolitan Museum of Art. 2011. 65.00 **(978-1-58839-433-0(6))** Metropolitan Museum of Art, The.

Metropolitan Museum of Art (New York, N.Y.) Staff, contrib. by. The Metropolitan Museum of Art Guide. 2012. **(978-1-58839-455-2(7))** Metropolitan Museum of Art, The.

Meyers, Amy R. W. & Ford, Lisa L. Knowing Nature: Art & Science in Philadelphia, 1740-1840. Meyers, Amy R. W., ed. 2006. (ENG., Illus.). 432p. 65.00 (978-0-300-11104-0(5)) Yale Univ. Pr.

Michael Hurson: Paintings, Drawings & Sculpture. 2008. (Illus.). 112p. 40.00 (978-0-9760250-9-2(4), Plain Paper Pr.) Plain White Pr., LLC.

Middlebrook, Jason & Lombino, Mary-Kay. Jason Middlebrook: Live with Less. 2009. (Illus.). 56p. pap. (978-0-910763-37-0(2)) Univ. at Albany, Univ. Art Museum.

Miguel Luciano. 2007. 8.00 (978-0-9776417-8-9(3)) CUE Art Foundation.

Milchan, Elinor. Elinor Milchan: Seven. 2008. (ENG., Illus.). 132p. pap. 47.95 (978-88-8158-701-8(7)) Charta ITA. Dist: D.A.P./Distributed Art Pubs.

Miller, Dan, des. Richard Phillips. 2007. (Illus.). 61p. 80.00 (978-1-932598-48-3(0)) Gagosian Gallery.

Miller, Dana, ed. Legacy: The Emily Fisher Landau Collection. 2011. (ENG., Illus.). 388p. 75.00 (978-0-300-17108-2(0)) Yale Univ. Pr.

Miller, David Lee & Levine, Nina, eds. A Touch More Rare: Harry Berger, Jr. , & the Arts of Interpretation. 2009. (ENG., Illus.). 336p. 65.00 (978-0-8232-3030-3(9)) Fordham Univ. Pr.

Miller, Francine Koslow. Metaphysical Dreamweaver: The Art of Enrico V. Pinardi. Barletta, Destiny, ed. 2011. (Illus.). lib. bdg. 50.00 (978-1-879985-22-3(5)) Pucker Gallery.

Miller, John. John Miller: the Ruin of Exchange. Alberro, Alexander, ed. & text by. 2012. (ENG., Illus.). 256p. pap. 24.95 **(978-3-03764-194-1(0))** JRP Ringier Kunstverlag AG CHE. Dist: D.A.P./Distributed Art Pubs.

Million Dollar Vandal: The Life & Crimes of Desa. ltd. ed. 2006. (Illus.). 192p. 39.95 (978-0-9768516-3-9(6)) AKA Projects.

Mills, Cynthia, et al. East-West Interchanges in American Art: "A Long & Tumultuous Relationship" 2011. **(978-1-935623-08-3(7))** Smithsonian Institution Scholarly Pr.

Minskey, Robert & Minsky, Richard, eds. The Art of American Book Covers: 1875-1930. 2010. (ENG., Illus.). 136p. 34.95 (978-0-8076-1602-4(8), 761602) Braziller, George Inc.

Minsky, Richard. The Book Art of Richard Minsky. 2011. (ENG., Illus.). 148p. 34.95 (978-0-8076-1606-2(0), 761606) Braziller, George Inc.

Mintz, Robert. Japanese Cloisonné Enamels: The Stephen W. Fisher Collection. 2009. pap. (978-0-911886-71-9(0)) Walters Art Museum, US.

Mobley, Amanda. The Canopy Overhead: The Later Years of Dwight Kirsch. 2008. (ENG., Illus.). 28p. 10.00 (978-0-938932-18-5(7)) Univ. of Nebraska, Ctr. for Great Plains Studies.

Molderings, Herbert. Duchamp & the Aesthetics of Chance: Art as Experiment. Brogden, John V., tr. from GER. 2010. (Columbia Themes in Philosophy, Social Criticism, & the Arts Ser.). (ENG., Illus.). 240p. (gr. 17). 27.50 (978-0-231-14762-0(7)) Columbia Univ. Pr.

Moles, Kathleen & Arnaud, Jean-Pierre. John Franklin Koenig: Northwest Master, Home & Away. 2008. (Illus.). 74p. pap. 20.00 (978-0-938506-13-3(7)) Whatcom Museum of History & Art.

Molesworth, Helen. Solitaire: Lee Lozano, Sylvia Plimack Mangold, Joan Semmel. Molesworth, Helen, ed. 2008. (ENG., Illus.). 164p. pap. 24.95 (978-0-300-12529-0(1)) Yale Univ. Pr.

Molesworth, Helen, ed. Catherine Opie: Empty & Full. 2011. (ENG., Illus.). 96p. 40.00 (978-3-7757-3015-0(X)) Hatje Cantz Verlag GmbH & Co KG DEU. Dist: D.A.P./Distributed Art Pubs.

Monroe, Gary. The Highwaymen Murals: Al Black's Concrete Dreams. 2009. (ENG., Illus.). 160p. 39.95 (978-0-8130-3359-4(4)) Univ. Pr. of Florida.

Moore, Alan. Art Gangs: Postmodern Artists - Collectives in New York City. 2011. 256p. pap. 17.95 **(978-1-57027-237-0(9))** Autonomedia.

Moore, Kevin, ed. & text. Starburst: Color Photography in America 1970-1980. 2010. (ENG., Illus.). 272p. 75.00 (978-3-7757-2490-6(7)) Hatje Cantz Verlag GmbH & Co KG DEU. Dist: D.A.P./Distributed Art Pubs.

Moore, Thurston, ed. James Hamilton: You Should Have Heard Just What I Seen. 2010. (ENG., Illus.). 304p. 75.00 (978-1-61623-495-9(4)) Independent Pub.

Morgan, Anne Lee. Oxford Dictionary of American Art & Artists. 2008. (Oxford Paperback Reference Ser.). (ENG.). 560p. pap. 17.95 (978-0-19-537321-9(9)) Oxford Univ. Pr., Inc.

Morgan, Robert C., ed. Bruce Nauman. 2011. (Art + Performance Ser.). (ENG., Illus.). 396p. pap. 22.95 **(978-1-55554-155-2(0))** PAJ Pubns.

Morris, Ann, et al. Sculpture Woods: Studio Grounds of Ann Morris. 2008. (ENG., Illus.). 164p. (978-0-295-98827-6(4)) Museum of Northwest Art.

Morrow, John. Kirby Five-Oh! Celebrating 50 Years of the King of Comics. 2008. (Illus.). 168p. pap. 19.95 (978-1-893905-89-4(6)) TwoMorrows Publishing.

Mossaed, Mahvash. Dear Dr. B. Encounters of a Volunteer at a County Hospital. 2007. (978-0-9796912-1-8(4)) Zodeak G42nd Publishing.

Mosset, Olivier, et al, texts. Born To Be Wild. Homage to Steven Parrino. 2010. (ENG., Illus.). 96p. pap. 40.00 (978-3-941185-55-5(1)) Verlag fur Moderne Kunst DEU. Dist: D.A.P./Distributed Art Pubs.

Motherwell, Robert. Open. 2010. (ENG., Illus.). 183p. 65.00 (978-1-901785-12-8(2)) 21 Publishing GBR. Dist: D.A.P./Distributed Art Pubs.

Motian-Meadows, Mary & Garnsey, Georgia. The Murals of Colorado: Walls That Speak. 2012. 29.95 (978-1-55566-438-1(5)) Johnson Bks.

Muller, Christopher & Van Duyn, Edna, eds. Richard Hawkins: of Two Minds, Simultaneously. 2009. (ENG., Illus.). 162p. pap. 59.95 (978-3-86560-425-5(0)) Verlag der Buchhandlung Walther Konig DEU. Dist: D.A.P./Distributed Art Pubs.

Munder, Heike & Seifermann, Ellen, eds. Rachel Harrison: If I Did It. 2008. (GER & ENG., Illus.). 144p. per. 49.00 (978-3-905770-56-8(3)) JRP Ringier Kunstverlag AG CHE. Dist: D.A.P./Distributed Art Pubs.

Munroe, Alexandra. The Third Mind: American Artists Contemplate Asia, 1860-1969, 1 vol. Munroe, Alexandra, ed. 2009. (ENG., Illus.). 440p. 85.00 (978-0-89207-383-2(7)) Guggenheim, Solomon R. Museum.

MURPHY, David Richard. Gold. 2008. 33p. 36.97 (978-1-4357-6054-7(9)) Lulu Enterprises Inc.

Murphy, Kevin, et al. Three Fragments of a Lost Tale - Sculpture & Story by John Frame. 2011. (ENG.). 112p. pap. 24.95 (978-0-87328-245-1(0)) Huntington Library Pr.

Murray, James T. & Murray, Karla L. Broken Windows: Graffiti NYC. 2009. (Illus.). 249p. 39.95 (978-1-58423-376-3(1)) Gingko Pr., Inc.

Murray, Mary E., et al. Auspicious Vision: Edward Wales Root & American Modernism. 2008. (978-0-915895-34-2(X)) Munson-Williams-Proctor Institute.

MUSAC, creator. End: Marina Nunez. 2009. (Illus.). (978-84-96540-30-9(8)) Charta.

Museum of Arts and Design. Crafting Modernism: Midcentury American Art & Design. 2011. (ENG., Illus.). 368p. 65.00 (978-0-8109-8480-6(6)) Abrams.

Museum of Fine Arts, Houston Staff, contrib. by. Core: Artists & Critics in Residence. 2008. (Illus.). 206p. (978-0-89090-162-5(7)) Museum of Fine Arts, Houston.

—Looking at Art: An Art History Survey at the Museum of Fine Arts, Houston. 2009. pap. (978-0-89090-169-4(4)) Museum of Fine Arts, Houston.

—Masterpieces from the Museum of Fine Arts, Houston: Director's Choice. 2010. (Illus.). 208p. 50.00 (978-0-300-16372-8(X)) Museum of Fine Arts, Houston.

Museyon Guides, ed. Art + NYC: A Complete Guide to New York City Art & Artists. 2011. (Art+ Ser.). (ENG., Illus.). 304p. pap. 19.95 (978-0-9822320-8-8(X)) Museyon Inc.

Najafi, Sina, ed. Cabinet 37: Bubbles. 2010. (ENG., Illus.). 112p. pap. 12.00 (978-1-932698-35-0(3)) Cabinet.

Nakashima, Tom, et al. Tom Nakashima: Two Decades. 2007. (Illus.). 44p. pap. (978-1-890021-20-7(2)) Morris Museum of Art.

Nassau County Museum of Art Staff, contrib. by. Long Island Collects: Cézanne, Degas, Renoir & Chagall Come to Long Island. 2009. (Illus.). 28p. (978-0-9815644-3-2(7)) Nassau County Museum of Art.

National Museum of the American Indian (U.S.), George Gustav Heye Center Staff, contrib. by. Off the Map: Landscape in the Native Imagination. 2007. (Illus.). 88p. (978-1-933565-08-8(X)) Smithsonian National Museum of the American Indian.

National Museum of the American Indian (U.S.) Staff, contrib. by. Essays on Native Modernism: Complexity & Contradiction in American Indian Art. 2006. (NMAI Editions Ser.). (Illus.). 112p. (978-1-933565-02-6(0)) Smithsonian National Museum of the American Indian.

National Register Publishing, creator. American Art Directory. 63rd ed. 2008. (American Art Directory Ser.). 1035p. 371.25 (978-0-87217-755-0(6)) National Register Publishing.

National Register Publishing Co. Staff. American Art Directory. 65th ed. 2011. 1086p. 297.00 (978-0-87217-764-2(5)) National Register Publishing.

Nauman, Bruce. Bruce Nauman: Live or Die. 2010. (ENG., Illus.). 240p. 59.95 (978-3-8321-9284-6(0)) DuMont DEU. Dist: D.A.P./Distributed Art Pubs.

Neff, Emily Ballew. The Modern West: American Landscapes, 1890-1950. 2006. (Illus.). (ENG.). 315p. 65.00 (978-0-300-11448-5(6)); xix, 315p. pap. (978-0-89090-145-8(7)) Yale Univ. Pr.

Neff, John H. & Silverman, Lanny. Karl Wirsum: Winsome Works(some) 2007. (Illus.). 68p. pap. 25.00 (978-0-938903-40-6(3)) City of Chicago, Dept. of Cultural Affairs.

Nelson-Atkins Museum of Art Staff, contrib. by. The Nelson-Atkins Museum of Art: A Handbook of the Collection. 7th ed. 2008. (978-0-942614-38-1(0)); pap. (978-0-942614-39-8(9)) Nelson-Atkins Museum of Art, The.

Nelson, Harold. The House That Sam Built: Sam Maloof & Art in the Pomona Valley, 1945-1985. 2011. (ENG.). 160p. pap. 29.95 **(978-0-87328-248-2(5))** Huntington Library Pr.

—The House That Sam Built: Sam Maloof & Art in the Pomona Valley, 1945-1985. 2011. (ENG.). 192p. 39.95 **(978-0-87328-246-8(9))** Huntington Library Pr.

Nemerov, Alexander. To Make a World: George Ault & 1940s America. 2011. (ENG., Illus.). 152p. 45.00 (978-0-300-17239-3(7)) Yale Univ. Pr.

Nemmers, Laura K., et al, eds. Samuel P. Harn Museum of Art: Twenty Years - The Collection Catalogue. 2010. (ENG., Illus.). 288p. 50.00 (978-0-8130-3513-0(9)) Univ. Pr. of Florida.

Neto, Ernesto, contrib. by. Ernesto Neto: from Sebastian to Olivia (BAD ISBN DNU) 2008. (ENG., Illus.). 120p. 69.00 (978-3-935567-45-9(6)) Holzwarth Pubns. DEU. Dist: D.A.P./Distributed Art Pubs.

New York Festivals. New York Festivals 15. 2007. (Illus.). 584p. 65.00 (978-0-9774930-1-2(6)) HarperCollins Pubs.

New York Festivals Staff. New York Festivals 16. 2008. (Illus.). 256p. 65.00 (978-0-9774930-2-9(4), Collins Design) HarperCollins Pubs.

New-York Historical Society. Museum and. Catalogue of the Museum & Gallery of Art of the New York Historical Society 1873. 2006. 156p. per. 18.99 (978-1-4255-1162-3(7)) MPublishing.

Newbery, Timothy J. The Robert Lehman Collection. 2007. (Illus.). xiii, 465p. 100.00 (978-1-58839-269-5(4)) Metropolitan Museum of Art, The.

Nicosia, Nic. Nic Nicosia. 2012. (ENG., Illus.). 264p. 75.00 **(978-0-292-74369-4(6))** Univ. of Texas Pr.

Nieman, John. Art of More Lists. 2009. (Illus.). 95p. 42.99 (978-1-4415-5838-1(1)) Xlibris Corp.

Nisbet, Peter. The Busch-Reisinger Museum: Harvard University Art Museums. 2007. (Illus.). 277p. pap. (978-1-891771-45-3(0)); pap. (978-1-85759-489-8(4)) Harvard Univ. Art Museums.

Nittve, Lars, text. Time & Place Vol. 3: Los Angeles 1957-1968, Vol. 3. 2008. (ENG., Illus.). 142p. pap. 50.00 (978-3-86521-640-3(4)) Steidl, Gerhard Druckerei und Verlag DEU. Dist: D.A.P./Distributed Art Pubs.

Noble, Nancy & Buckberrough, Sherry. Women Artists @ New Britain Museum. 2011. (Illus.). 96p. pap. 25.00 (978-0-9724497-2-4(8)) New Britain Museum of American Art.

Noelle, Alexander J., ed. American Reflections: The Collection of Dr. Timothy Mclaughlin. 2011. (Illus.). 80p. pap. 19.95 (978-0-9724497-0-0(1)) New Britain Museum of American Art.

Nolen-Weathington, Eric. Modern Masters Volume 14: Frank Cho, Vol. 14. 2010. (Modern Masters Ser.). (Illus.). 120p. pap. 15.95 (978-1-893905-84-9(5)) TwoMorrows Publishing.

—Modern Masters Volume 15: Mark Schultz. 2008. (Modern Masters Ser.: Vol. 15). (Illus.). 128p. pap. 14.95 (978-1-893905-85-6(3)) TwoMorrows Publishing.

—Modern Masters Volume 16: Mike Allred. 2008. (Modern Masters Ser.). (Illus.). 120p. pap. 14.95 (978-1-893905-86-3(1)) TwoMorrows Publishing.

Noorthoorn, Victoria, ed. Beginning with a Bang! From Confrontation to Intimacy. 2008. (David Rockefeller Center for Latin American Studies, Art Cat Ser.). (Illus.). 108p. pap. 22.95 (978-1-879128-34-7(9)) Americas Society.

Norman Rockwell Museum, et al. American Chronicles: The Art of Norman Rockwell. 2007. (Illus.). 275p. 45.00 (978-0-9615273-2-7(3)) Rockwell, Norman Museum.

Norr, David, ed. & text. Teresita Fernandez: Blind Landscape. 2010. (ENG., Illus.). 160p. pap. 55.00 (978-3-03764-049-4(9)) JRP Ringier Kunstverlag AG CHE. Dist: D.A.P./Distributed Art Pubs.

North Carolina Museum of Art Staff, contrib. by. North Carolina Museum of Art: Handbook of the Collections. 2010. pap. (978-0-88259-992-2(5)) North Carolina Museum of Art.

Nottage, James H. Diversity & Dialogue: The Eiteljorg Fellowship for Native American Fine Art 2007. Nottage, James H., ed. 2008. (ENG., Illus.). 120p. (978-0-295-98781-1(2)) Eiteljorg Museum of American Indians & Western Art.

O'Brien, Donald C. Amos Doolittle: Engraver of the New Republic. 2007. 65.00 (978-1-58456-206-1(4)) Oak Knoll Pr.

Obrist, Hans Ulrich, ed. Hans Ulrich Obrist & Rirkrit Tiravanija: the Conversation Series. 2011. (ENG., Illus.). 150p. pap. 29.00 (978-3-86560-654-9(7)) Verlag der Buchhandlung Walther Konig DEU. Dist: D.A.P./Distributed Art Pubs.

—Hans Ulrich Obrist & Yoko Ono: the Conversation Series. 2010. (ENG., Illus.). 96p. pap. 27.00 (978-3-86560-652-5(0)) Verlag der Buchhandlung Walther Konig DEU. Dist: D.A.P./Distributed Art Pubs.

—Jeff Koons: Popeye Series, 1 vol. 2009. (ENG., Illus.). 88p. pap. 39.95 (978-3-86560-666-2(0)) Verlag der Buchhandlung Walther Konig DEU. Dist: D.A.P./Distributed Art Pubs.

O'Connor, Mallory McCane & Monroe, Gary. Florida's American Heritage River: Images from the St. Johns Region. 2009. (ENG., Illus.). 384p. 44.95 (978-0-8130-3352-5(7)) Univ. Pr. of Florida.

of California, Phranc. Phranc: The Cardboard Cobbler. 2007. pap. 8.00 (978-0-9797964-0-1(7)) CUE Art Foundation.

O'Hare, Mary Kate. Constructive Spirit: Abstract Art in South & North America, 1920s-50s. 2010. 196p. 39.95 (978-0-7649-5274-6(9)) Pomegranate Communications, Inc.

Okediji, Moyo. Western Frontiers of African Art. 2011. (Rochester Studies in African History & the Diaspora Ser.: Volume 53). (Illus.). 354p. 85.00 (978-1-58046-370-6(3)) Univ. of Rochester Pr.

Okeefe, Raven. Raven's L'il Critters. 2008. 60p. pap. 12.95 (978-1-934543-62-7(4)) HollywoodComics.com, LLC.

Oklahoma City Museum of Art, et al. Breaking the Mold: Selections from the Washington Gallery of Modern Art, 1961-1968. George, Hardy S. & Pavelka, Jeffrey J., eds. 2008. (Illus.). 144p. pap. 25.00 (978-0-911919-05-9(8)) Oklahoma City Museum of Art.

Okon, Yoshua. Yoshua Okon: US. 2011. (ENG., Illus.). 198p. pap. 25.00 (978-0-9826789-1-6(6)) Yerba Buena Ctr. for the Arts.

Olaf, Hajek. Flowerhead: The Illustrations of Olaf Hajek. 2010. (Illus.). 144p. 60.00 (978-3-89955-281-2(4)) Die Gestalten Verlag DEU. Dist: Prestel Publishing.

Oldham, Todd, ed. Maybe Now I'll Get the Respect I So Richly Deserve. 2009. (ENG., Illus.). 432p. 2nd ed. 300.00 (978-1-934429-31-0(7)) 3rd ed. 300.00 (978-1-934429-32-7(5)) AMMO Bks., LLC.

—Wayne White: Maybe Now I'll Get the Respect I So Richly Deserve. 4th ed. 2009. (ENG., Illus.). 432p. 300.00 (978-1-934429-33-4(3)) AMMO Bks., LLC.

O'Leary, Elizabeth, et al. American Art at the Virginia Museum of Fine Arts. 2010. (ENG., Illus.). 432p. (gr. 17). 50.00 (978-0-917046-94-0(3)) Univ. Pr. of Virginia.

O'Leary, Elizabeth L. American Art at the Virginia Museum of Fine Arts. 2010. (Illus.). ix, 422p. pap. (978-0-917046-93-3(5)) Virginia Museum of Fine Arts.

Oliver, Valerie Cassel, et al. Donald Moffett: The Extravagant Vein. 2011. (ENG., Illus.). 224p. 65.00 (978-0-8478-3727-4(0), Skira) Rizzoli International Pubns., Inc.

One Club Staff, ed. One Show Boxed Set / 2008 Awards. 2009. (One Show Ser.). (ENG., Illus.). 928p. 150.00 (978-0-929837-39-0(8), 0929837398) Quayside.

O'Neil, Robyn. Robyn O'Neil: the World has Won. A Final Bow Was Taken. 2010. (ENG., Illus.). 68p. pap. 25.00 (978-1-879003-57-6(0)) Des Moines Art Ctr.

O'Neill, Amy, illus. Amy O'Neill: Suburban Imagination. 2008. (ENG.). 80p. 35.00 (978-3-905829-20-4(7)) JRP Ringier Kunstverlag AG CHE. Dist: D.A.P./Distributed Art Pubs.

Ono, Yoko. An Invisible Flower. 2012. (ENG., Illus.). 48p. 16.95 **(978-1-4521-0911-4(7))** Chronicle Bks. LLC.

Orcutt, Kimberly. John Rogers: American Stories. 2010. (ENG., Illus.). 224p. 50.00 (978-0-85667-689-5(6)) Wilson, Philip Pubs., Ltd. GBR. Dist: Macmillan.

Orr, Penelope & Dorn, Charles M. Art Education in a Climate of Reform: The Need for Measurable Goals in Art Instruction. 2008. (ENG., Illus.). 136p. 70.00 (978-1-57886-788-2(6)); pap. 32.95 (978-1-57886-789-9(4)) Rowman & Littlefield Education.

Orsillo, Artist Bob. The Sequence. 2007. 69p. pap. 27.50 (978-0-615-17524-9(4)) North River Editions.

O'Toole, Judith. Different Views in Hudson River School Painting. 2008. (ENG.). 160p. (gr. 17). pap. 27.95 (978-0-231-13821-5(0)) Columbia Univ. Pr.

Otsuka, Ronald. Asia & Spanish America: Trans-Pacific Artistic & Cultural Exchange, 1500-1850. Pierce, Donna, ed. 2009. (ENG.). 208p. (C). pap. 39.95 (978-0-8061-9973-3(3)) Denver Art Museum.

Oursler, Tony. Tony Oursler: Lock 2, 4, 6. 2010. (ENG & GER., Illus.). 160p. 68.00 (978-3-86560-719-5(5)) Kunsthaus Bregenz AUT. Dist: D.A.P./Distributed Art Pubs.

—Tony Oursler: Thinking Gaze. 2009. (ENG & SPA., Illus.). 198p. 40.00 (978-84-7506-834-3(0)) Turner, Ediciones S.A. ESP. Dist: D.A.P./Distributed Art Pubs.

Pace, Stephen. Stephen Pace: Abstract Expressionist. 2011. (Illus.). 32p. **(978-1-935617-11-2(7)**, Orbit Books) Spanierman Gallery.

Paglia, Michael & Chandler, Mary Voetz. Colorado Abstract: Paintings & Sculpture. 2009. (ENG., Illus.). 319p. 85.00 (978-1-934491-12-6(8)) Fresco Fine Art Pubns., LLC.

Paik, Nam June. Nam June Paik. Lee, Sook-Kyung & Rennert, Susanne, eds. 2011. (ENG., Illus.). 208p. 45.00 (978-1-85437-924-5(0)) Tate Publishing, Ltd. GBR. Dist: Hachette Bk. Group.

Paiva, Troy. Night Vision: The Art of Urban Exploration. 2008. (ENG., Illus.). 144p. pap. 24.95 (978-0-8118-6338-4(7)) Chronicle Bks. LLC.

Palermo, et al. Blinky Palermo: To the People of New York. 2009. (ENG., Illus.). 208p. 60.00 (978-3-937572-52-9(X)) Richter Verlag DEU. Dist: D.A.P./Distributed Art Pubs.

Paloscia, Pax. Let the Kids Play. 2007. (ENG., Illus.). 96p. pap. 29.00 (978-88-88493-20-6(4)) Drago Arts & Communication ITA. Dist: SCB Distributors.

Paned Expressions Studios. BeBeveled. 2007. (Illus.). 60p. cd-rom 39.00 (978-0-9773697-7-5(3)) Paned Expressions Studios, Inc.

Panter, Gary, intro. Matt Leines: You Are Forgiven. 2008. (ENG., Illus.). 144p. 45.00 (978-0-9776523-5-8(1)) Heartworm Pr.

Pardo, Jorge. Jorge Pardo. 2011. (ENG., Illus.). 144p. 70.00 (978-3-941263-03-1(X)) Richter Verlag DEU. Dist: D.A.P./Distributed Art Pubs.

Pardo, Patrick, et al. John Baldessari Catalogue Raisonne: Volume One: 1956-1974. 2012. (ENG., Illus.). 472p. 200.00 **(978-0-300-17448-9(9))** Yale Univ. Pr.

Park, Joe. I Am Yours. 2011. (ENG.). 30p. pap. 9.95 (978-0-8118-7927-9(5)) Chronicle Bks. LLC.

Parliament, Ian C. & Cadafalch, Antonio. Day of the Dead: Celebrating the Dia de Los Muertos in pop art, graphics & Installations. Alderete, ed. 2011. (ENG., Illus.). 176p. 35.00 (978-1-907621-01-7(6)) Korero Books LLP GBR. Dist: Independent Pubs. Group.

Pasquine, Ruth. Emil Bisttram: American Painter, Vol. 1. 2010. 380p. pap. (978-3-8383-7709-4(5)) Lambert Academic Publishing.

—Emil Bisttram: American Painter, Vol. 2. 2010. 332p. pap. (978-3-8383-7711-7(7)) Lambert Academic Publishing.

Pat Musick. No New Thing under the Sun: One Artist's Chosen Journey. 2009. (Illus.). 144p. pap. 39.44 (978-1-4251-9213-6(0)) Trafford Publishing.

Pearson, Joshua T. Alphabhetto. 2011. 56p. pap. 25.95 **(978-1-4634-0772-8(6))** AuthorHouse.

Peck, Amelia. American Quilts & Coverlets in the Metropolitan Museum of Art. 2009. (ENG., Illus.). 320p. 29.95 (978-0-300-15903-5(X)) Yale Univ. Pr.

Pelkonen, Eeva-Liisa. Kevin Roche: Architecture as Environment. 2011. (ENG., Illus.). 280p. 65.00 (978-0-300-15223-4(X)) Yale Univ. Pr.

Pencil, Imaginative. Visionary Landscapes. 2008. 160p. pap. 60.00 (978-1-4116-7843-9(5)) Lulu Enterprises Inc.

Pepall, Rosalind. Tiffany Glass: A Passion for Color. 2010. (ENG., Illus.). 264p. 60.00 (978-0-8478-3426-6(3)) Rizzoli International Pubns., Inc.

Perl, Jed. A Culture in the Making: New York & San Francisco in the 1950s And '60s. 2006. (Illus.). 124p. 30.00 (978-1-933399-11-9(2)) Hackett-Freedman Gallery, Inc.

—New Art City: Manhattan at Mid-Century. 2007. (Vintage Ser.). (ENG., Illus.). 656p. pap. 18.95 (978-1-4000-3465-9(5), Vintage) Knopf Doubleday Publishing Group.

Pero, Linda Szekeley, et al. American Chronicles: The Art of Norman Rockwell. 2009. (ENG., Illus.). 276p. pap. 30.00 (978-0-9615273-3-4(1)) Rockwell, Norman Museum.

Perron, Suzanne. Designing in Ivory & White: Suzanne Perron Gowns from the Inside Out. 2012. (Illus.). 152p. 55.00 **(978-0-8071-4370-4(7))** Louisiana State Univ. Pr.

Perry, Claire. The Great American Hall of Wonders: Art, Science, & Invention in the Nineteenth Century. 2011. (ENG., Illus.). 256p. 65.00 (978-1-904832-97-3(0)) Giles, D. Ltd. GBR. Dist: Antique Collectors' Club.

—The Great American Hall of Wonders: Art, Science, & Invention in the Nineteenth Century. 2011. (978-0-9790678-9-1(8)) Smithsonian American Art Museum.

—Young America: Childhood in Nineteenth-Century Art & Culture. 2006. (Illus.). xii, 236p. pap. (978-0-937031-27-8(5)) Cantor, Iris & B. Gerald Ctr. for Visual Arts at Stanford Univ.

Perry, Mike. Wondering Around Wandering: Work-So-Far by Mike Perry. 2012. (ENG., Illus.). 248p. 39.95 **(978-0-8478-5803-3(0))** Rizzoli International Pubns., Inc.

Perucci, Tony. Paul Robeson & the Cold War Performance Complex: Race, Madness, Activism. 2012. E-Book **(978-0-472-02820-7(0))**; (ENG.). 232p. 75.00 **(978-0-472-07168-5(8))**; (ENG.). 232p. pap. 28.95 **(978-0-472-05168-7(7))** Univ. of Michigan Pr.

Peterson, Larry Len. The Call of the Mountains: The Artists of Glacier National Park. (Illus.). 156p. pap. 32.95 (978-0-9635642-7-6(7), 1367) Settlers West Galleries, Inc.

Petrovich, Dushko & White, Roger, eds. Paper Monument. 2007. 100p. per. 10.00 (978-0-9797575-0-1(9)) Paper Monument.

Pettibon, Raymond. Raymond Pettibon. Rugoff, Ralph, ed. 2012. (ENG., Illus.). 384p. 135.00 (978-0-8478-3500-3(6)) Rizzoli International Pubns., Inc.

Pettibon, Raymond. Raymond Pettibon: Looker-Upper. 2011. (ENG., Illus.). 48p. pap. 34.95 **(978-3-931355-70-8(5))** Verlag der Buchhandlung Walther Konig DEU. Dist: D.A.P./Distributed Art Pubs.

Phagan, Patricia. A Taste for the Modern: Gifts from Blanchette Hooker Rockefeller, Edna Bryner Schwab, & Virginia Herrick Deknatel. 2011. pap. **(978-0-9820606-3-6(7))** Loeb, Frances Lehman Art Ctr., Vassar Coll., The.

Phelan, Peggy, ed. Live Art in La. 2012. (ENG., Illus.). 256p. 125.00 **(978-0-415-68422-4(6))**; pap. 39.95 **(978-0-415-68423-1(4))** Routledge.

Philippi, Michael & Westheider, Otrud. Modern Life. Edward Hopper & His Time. 2009. (ENG.). 240p. 59.95 (978-3-7774-2001-1(8), Art Stock Bks. Ltd/Csi) Continental Sales, Inc.

Phillips, Glenn. California Video: Artists & Histories. 2008. pap. (978-0-89236-923-2(X)) Getty Pubns.

Phillips, Glenn, et al. California Video: Artists & Histories. 2008. (Illus.). 320p. 39.95 (978-0-89236-922-5(1)) Oxford Univ. Pr., Inc.

Philosophy of Time Travel. 2007. per. (978-0-942949-33-9(1)) Studio Museum in Harlem, The.

Pidcock, Stephen W. Faces of the Susquehanna: A Photographic Study of Natural Reflections. 2012. (Illus.). 128p. 29.99 **(978-0-7643-3931-8(1)**, Schiffer Publishing Ltd) Schiffer Publishing, Ltd.

Pierce, Donna, ed. The Arts of South America, 1492-1850. 2010. (ENG.). 224p. (C). pap. 39.95 (978-0-8061-9976-4(8)) Denver Art Museum.

Pierson, Jack, photos by. Jack Pierson: Night. 2011. (ENG., Illus.). 92p. 40.00 (978-89-92233-40-8(X)) Kukje Gallery Inc. KOR. Dist: D.A.P./Distributed Art Pubs.

Pirtle, Jim. Jim Pirtle. 2008. pap. 0.00 (978-0-9797964-7-0(4)) CUE Art Foundation.

Pitman, Bonnie. Dallas Museum of Art: A Guide to the Collection. 2012. (ENG., Illus.). 368p. pap. 24.95 **(978-0-300-17963-7(4))** Dallas Museum of Art.

Pogue, Stephanie E., et al. Arabesque: The Art of Stephanie E. Pogue. 2008. (Illus.). 48p. pap. (978-0-9819093-0-1(2)) Univ. of Maryland, David C. Driskell Ctr.

Pohl, Frances K. Framing America: A Social History of American Art. 3rd ed. 2012. (ENG., Illus.). 616p. (C). pap. 70.00 net. **(978-0-500-28983-9(2)**, 528983) Thames & Hudson.

Pollard, Robert. Town of Mirrors: The Reassembled Imagery of Robert Pollard. 2008. (ENG., Illus.). 136p. 29.99 (978-1-56097-924-1(0), 56924) Fantagraphics Bks.

Powers, John S. Temporary Art & Public Place: Comparing Berlin with Los Angeles. 2009. (Europäische Hochschulschriften. Reihe 28: Kunstgeschichte Ser.). (Illus.). 404p. pap. 99.95 (978-3-631-56430-1(9)) Lang, Peter GmbH, Europaischer Verlag der Wissenschaften DEU. Dist: Lang, Peter.

Preston, Jerry D. & Emery, John C. Windows of Enduring Color: Stained Glass. 2008. (ENG., Illus.). 80p. pap. 23.95 (978-0-919985-57-5(2)) Wardell Pubns., Inc.

Preziosi, Donald. Classic American Diners: Collectible Postcards & Matchcovers. 2007. (Schiffer Book Ser.). (Illus.). 176p. 39.95 (978-0-7643-2610-3(4)) Schiffer Publishing, Ltd.

Price, Marshall N., et al. Martin Kline: Romantic Nature. 2012. (ENG., Illus.). 160p. 50.00 **(978-1-55595-348-5(4))** Hudson Hills Pr. LLC.

Price, S. W. The Old Masters of the Bluegrass. (Illus.). 181p. reprint ed. lib. bdg. 88.00 (978-0-7222-4935-2(7)) Library Reprints, Inc.

Priddy, Bob & Ball, Jeffrey. The Art of the Missouri Capitol: History in Canvas, Bronze, & Stone. 2011. (ENG., Illus.). 416p. (gr. 7). 49.95 (978-0-8262-1921-3(7)) Univ. of Missouri Pr.

Prieto, Rosi. A Concise History of Art: The Western World. rev. ed. 2009. (ENG.). 268p. pap. 112.19 (978-0-7575-6621-9(9)) Kendall Hunt Publishing Co.

Primordial Images of a Modern Mystic - Myron Conan Dyal. 2007. per. 24.95 (978-0-9771696-5-8(0)) Grand Central Pr.

Prince, Eileen S. Art Is Fundamental: Teaching the Elements & Principles of Art in Elementary School. 2008. (ENG., Illus.). 200p. pap. 19.95 (978-1-56976-216-5(3), Zephyr Pr.) Chicago Review Pr., Inc.

Prince, Richard. Richard Prince: 3rd Place. 2008. (ENG., Illus.). 82p. pap. 30.00 (978-3-86560-492-7(7)) Verlag der Buchhandlung Walther Konig DEU. Dist: D.A.P./Distributed Art Pubs.

—Richard Prince Four Cowboys. 2010. (ENG., Illus.). 20p. pap. 90.00 (978-1-906957-02-5(9)) Abrams.

Princenthal, Nancy, ed. Joyce Kozloff: Co-Ordinates. 2009. (ENG., Illus.). 132p. 45.00 (978-0-9763488-8-2(0)) Dickinson College, The Trout Gallery.

Progress, Michael Davis & Stephen Moore. 2006. per. 24.95 (978-0-9771696-2-7(6)) Grand Central Pr.

Quackenbush, Liz, et al, contrib. by. Esme Thompson: The Alchemy of Deisgn. 2011. (Illus.). 84p. pap. 19.95 (978-0-944722-40-4(7)) Hood Museum of Art.

Quang, Bright. Vietnamese American Arts. 2011. 108p. pap. 33.48 **(978-1-4634-0440-6(9))** AuthorHouse.

Quillman, Catherine. 100 Artists of the Brandywine Valley. 2011. (Illus.). 240p. 45.00 (978-0-7643-3674-4(6)) Schiffer Publishing, Ltd.

Quintanilla, Faustino. A Life for Art: The Jaime Andrade Collection. 2011. **(978-1-936658-07-7(0))** QCC Art Gallery.

Raby, Julian, intro. Ideals of Beauty: Asian & American Art in the Freer & Sackler Galleries. 2010. (World of Art Ser.). (ENG., Illus.). 192p. pap. 19.95 (978-0-500-20403-0(9), 520403) Thames & Hudson.

Racz, Imogen, . Imogen. Contemporary Crafts. 2009. (ENG., Illus.). 1p. pap. 34.95 (978-1-84520-305-2(7)) Berg Pubs. GBR. Dist: Macmillan.

Radical Structures. 2007. (Illus.). pap. 10.00 (978-0-9677326-8-8(9)) Abaton Bk. Co.

Ragnar. Symptomatica. 2008. (ENG., Illus.). 80p. pap. 24.95 (978-0-9793307-9-7(3)) Baby Tattoo Bks.

Ramírez, Mari Carmen & Olea, Hector. Carlos Cruz-Diez: Color in Space & Time. 2011. (ENG., Illus.). 512p. 75.00 (978-0-300-16994-2(9)) Museum of Fine Arts, Houston.

Ramírez-Montagut, Mónica. Kaws. 2010. (ENG., Illus.). 256p. 45.00 (978-0-8478-3434-1(4), Skira) Rizzoli International Pubns., Inc.

Ramos, Mel, et al. Mel Ramos: 100+ Zeichnungen. 2011. (GER & ENG., Illus.). 128p. 39.95 **(978-3-86678-444-4(9))** Kerber Verlag DEU. Dist: D.A.P./Distributed Art Pubs.

Rapoport, Sonya, et al. Pairing of Polarities: The Life & Art of Sonya Rapoport. 2012. pap. **(978-1-59714-187-1(9))** Heyday.

Raskin, David. Donald Judd. 2010. (Illus.). 220p. 55.00 (978-0-300-16276-9(6)) Yale Univ. Pr.

Raspail, Thierry, et al. Marlène Mocquet. 2010. (ENG & FRE., Illus.). 112p. 34.95 (978-88-7439-522-4(1)) 5 Continents ITA. Dist: Hachette Bk. Group.

Ratcliff, Carter & Paley, Albert. Albert Paley in the 21st Century. Gribauco, Paola, ed. 2010. (978-0-615-35392-0(4)) Paley Studios Ltd.

Rattemeyer, Christian, et al, eds. Alighiero Boetti: Game Plan. 2011. (ENG., Illus.). 290p. 50.00 **(978-0-87070-819-0(8))** Museum of Modern Art.

Rauschenberg, Robert. Robert Rauschenberg. 2010. (ENG., Illus.). 48p. pap. 9.95 (978-0-87070-767-4(1)) Museum of Modern Art.

Ravenal, John B. Modern & Contemporary Art at the Virginia Museum of Fine Arts. 2007. (ENG., Illus.). 252p. 19.50 (978-0-917046-80-3(3)) Virginia Museum of Fine Arts.

Ray, Rex. Rex Ray: Art + Design. 2007. (ENG., Illus.). 160p. 35.00 (978-0-8118-5975-2(4)) Chronicle Bks. LLC.

Reaves, Wendy Wick. Reflections/Refractions: Self-Portraiture in the Twentieth Century. 2009. (ENG.). 224p. 49.95 (978-0-9788460-2-2(8)) Smithsonian Institution Scholarly Pr.

Rebay, Hilla. Museum of Non-Objective Painting. Vail, Karole, ed. 2009. (ENG., Illus.). 352p. 45.00 (978-0-89207-393-1(4)) Guggenheim, Solomon R. Museum.

Reich, Sue. World War II Quilts. 2010. (Illus.). 192p. 39.99 (978-0-7643-3451-1(4)) Schiffer Publishing, Ltd.

Reid, Sheila. Art Memories: The Life & Works of Sheila Reid. ltd. ed. 2010. (Illus.). 128p. (978-0-9646268-4-3(5)) Rush Editions.

Reilly, Maura & Gerdts, William H. Patricia Cronin: Harriet Hosmer - Lost & Found. 2009. (ENG., Illus.). 104p. 39.95 (978-88-8158-732-2(7)) Charta ITA. Dist: D.A.P./Distributed Art Pubs.

Remington, R. Roger. Will Burtin & the Display of Visual Knowledge, 3, Volume 3. 2009. (ENG., Illus.). pap. 15.99 (978-1-933360-36-2(4)) Rochester Institute of Technology, Cary Graphic Arts Pr.

Renoir, Auguste & House, John. The Genius of Renoir: Paintings from the Clark. 2011. (Illus.). 140p. 39.95 (978-0-300-11105-7(3)) Yale Univ. Pr.

Ressler, Susan R., ed. Women Artists of the American West. alt. ed. 2010. (ENG., Illus.). 397p. pap. 45.00 (978-0-7864-6438-8(0)) McFarland & Co., Inc. Pubs.

Rexer, Lyle, text. The Drawings of the Electric Pencil. 2011. (ENG., Illus.). 160p. 59.95 (978-0-578-06832-9(X)) Electric Pencil Pr.

Reyes Taubman, Julie, photos by. Julie Reyes Taubman: Detroit: 138 Square Miles. 1 vol. 2011. (ENG.). 480p. 65.00 **(978-0-9823896-0-7(4))** Museum of Contemporary Art Detroit.

Reynolds, Andi Milam. Collection of the National Quilt Museum. 2009. (978-1-57432-987-2(1), American Quilter's Society) Collector Bks.

Reynolds, Sarah C. Houston Reflections: Art in the City, 1950s, 60s, & 70s. 2008. (978-0-89263-005-9(1)) Rice Univ. Pr.

Rhie, Marylin & Thurman, Robert. A Shrine for Tibet: The Alice S. Kandell Collection of Tibetan Sacred Art. 2010. (ENG.). 336p. (gr. 12). 60.00 (978-1-59020-310-1(0)) Overlook Pr., The.

Ribas, Joao. Matt Mullican: A Drawing Translates the Way of Thinking. 2008. (Illus.). pap. 18.00 (978-0-942324-03-7(X)) Drawing Ctr.

Ribas, Joao, ed. Frances Stark: This Could Become a Gimick [sic] or an Honest Articulation of the Workings of the Mind. 2011. (ENG., Illus.). 200p. pap. 20.00 (978-0-938437-75-E(5)) Massachusetts Institute of Technology, List Visual Arts Ctr.

Richards, Melanie. A Call to Arts: How Artistic Living Can Redeem Us. 2010. 98p. pap. 13.98 (978-0-557-27291-4(2)) Lulu Enterprises Inc.

Richardson, Keith. Doorways to Heaven: A Spiritual Journey Guided by Angels, Miracles & the Art of Andy Lakey. 2010. 256p. pap. 16.95 (978-1-4327-6080-9(7)) Outskirts Pr., Inc.

Rider, Alistair. Carl Andre: Things in Their Elements. 2011. (ENG., Illus.). 272p. 75.00 (978-0-7148-4922-5(7)) Phaidon Pr., Inc.

Rinder, Lawrence, et al. Create. 2011. (ENG., Illus.). 179p. pap. 27.50 (978-0-9719397-9-0(9)) Univ. of California, Berkeley Art Museum & Pacific Film Archive.

Rivera-Servera, Ramón H. & Young, Harvey, eds. Performance in the Borderlands. 2010. (Performance Interventions Ser.). (ENG.). 312p. 89.00 (978-0-230-57460-1(2)) Palgrave Macmillan.

Robert Hull Fleming Museum. Material Pursuits. 2007. (978-0-934658-00-3(5)) Fleming, Robert Hull Museum.

Robertson, Edna, et al. Artists of the Canyons & Caminos: Santa Fe: Early Twentieth Century, 1 vol. 2006. (ENG., Illus.). 176p. per. 19.95 (978-1-4236-0114-2(9)) Gibbs Smith, Publisher.

Robinson, Greg, et al, eds. Miné Okubo: Following Her Own Road. 2008. (ENG., Illus.). 224p. pap. 26.95 (978-0-295-98774-3(X)) Univ. of Washington Pr.

Robinson, J. Dennis. Maritime Portsmouth: The Sawtelle Collection. Candee, Richard M., ed. 2011. (Illus.). 212p. 35.00 **(978-0-915819-38-6(4))** Portsmouth Marine Society, The.

Roblin, Kimberly, et al, contrib. by. Forging a Nation: The American History Collection at Gilcrease Museum. 2011. (ENG.). 250p. (C). 39.95 (978-0-9725657-9-0(5)) Gilcrease Museum.

Roche, Catherine. Fleeting Beauty: Japanese Woodblock Prints. 2010. (978-0-932216-66-3(8), Seattle Art Museum.

Rodari, Florian. Kosta Alex. 2011. (ENG., Illus.). 180p. 65.00 (978-0-300-17665-0(1), Yale Univ. Pr.

Rodrigue, George. George Rodrigue Prints: A Catalogue Raisonné 1970-2007. 2008. (ENG., Illus.). 256p. 55.00 (978-0-8109-9517-8(4)) Abrams.

Rojas, Clare, photos by. Everything Flowers. 2011. (ENG., Illus.). 96p. 22.95 (978-0-8118-7151-8(7)) Chronicle Bks. LLC.

Rolling, James H. Cinderella Story: A Scholarly Sketchbook about Race, Identity, Barack Obama, the Human Spirit, & Other Stuff That Matters. 2010. (Crossroads in Qualitative Inquiry Ser.). (ENG., Illus.). 228p. 75.00 (978-0-7591-1176-9(6)) AltaMira Pr.

Ron, Linden. Ron Linden. 2007. pap. 8.00 (978-0-9791843-9-0(8)) CUE Art Foundation.

Ronda, Bruce A. Reading the Old Man: John Brown in American Culture. 2008. (ENG., Illus.). 218p. 39.95 (978-1-57233-620-9(X)) Univ. of Tennessee Pr.

Rondeau, James. Judith Nesser Collection: Minimal & Postminimal Innovation. 2011. (Contemporary Collecting Ser.). (ENG., Illus.). 160p. 35.00 (978-0-300-17024-5(6)) Art Institute of Chicago.

Roof, Katherine Metcalf. The Life & Art of William Merritt Chase. 2010. 414p. pap. 32.95 (978-1-4455-6405-0(X)) Audubon Pr. & Christian Bk. Service.

Rooney, E. Ashley. 100 Artists of New England. 2011. (Illus.). 224p. 45.00 (978-0-7643-3665-2(7)) Schiffer Publishing, Ltd.

Rosand, David. Edward Koren: The Capricious Line. 2010. (ENG., Illus.). 136p. pap. 30.00 (978-1-884919-26-8(X)) Columbia Univ., The Miriam & Ira D. Wallach Art Gallery.

Rosenbaum, Julia B. Visions of Belonging: New England Art & the Making of American Identity. 2006. (Illus.). 233p. 32.95 (978-0-8014-4470-8(5), Comstock Publishing Assocs.) Cornell Univ. Pr.

Rosolowski, Tacey. Sculpture to Wear: The Jewelry of Marjorie Schick. 2007. (Contemporary Jewellery Ser.). (ENG., Illus.). 240p. 75.00 (978-3-89790-258-9(3)) Arnoldsche Art Pubs. DEU. Dist: Antique Collectors' Club.

Ross, Alex. Rough Justice. Kidd, Chip, ed. 2010. (ENG., Illus.). 224p. 30.00 (978-0-375-71490-0(1), Pantheon) Knopf Doubleday Publishing Group.

Ross, Elliot. Animal. 2010. (ENG., Illus.). 112p. 70.00 (978-90-5330-730-4(3)) Mets en Schilt Uitgevers NLD. Dist: Ingram Pub. Services.

Rothkopf, Scott. Glenn Ligon: America. 2011. (ENG., Illus.). 304p. 65.00 (978-0-300-16847-1(0)) Yale Univ. Pr.

—Jeff Koons: Hulk Elvis. 2010. (ENG., Illus.). 140p. 80.00 (978-0-8478-3359-7(3)) Rizzoli International Pubns., Inc.

—The Other Sixties: The Return of Surrealism in American Art Criticism. 2010. (ENG.). 192p. 45.00 (978-0-300-09349-0(7)) Yale Univ. Pr.

Rotman, Steve. Bay Area Graffiti. 2011. (Illus.). 208p. pap. 35.00 (978-1-935613-32-9(4)) Batty, Mark Pub., LLC.

Rubell Family Collection Staff, contrib. by. Red Eye: L.A. Artists from the Rubell Family Collection, December 6, 2006-May 31, 2007. 2008. (ENG., Illus.). 218p. 40.00 (978-0-9789888-7-6(6)) Rubell Family Collection.

Rubin, David S. Waterflow. Rubin, David S., ed. 2009. (Illus.). 24p. (YA). pap. 8.00 (978-1-883502-20-1(9)) San Antonio Museum of Art.

Rubio, Agustín, ed. Terence Koh: 1980-2008. 2009. (ENG., Illus.). 208p. 55.00 (978-3-7757-2308-4(0)) Hatje Cantz Verlag GmbH & Co KG DEU. Dist: D.A.P./Distributed Art Pubs.

Rudolph, William Keyse & Kirtley, Alexandra Alevizatos. Treasures of American & English Painting & Decorative Arts: From the Julian Wood Glass Jr. Collection. 2011. (Illus.). 248p. 50.00 (978-0-8478-3626-0(6), Skira) Rizzoli International Pubns., Inc.

Ruf, Beatrix, ed. Jennifer Allora & Guillermo Calzadilla. 2010. (ENG., Illus.). 156p. 55.00 (978-3-03764-027-2(8)) JRP Ringier Kunstverlag AG CHE. Dist: D.A.P./Distributed Art Pubs.

Ruiz, Maximiliano. Graffiti Argentina. (Illus.). 152p. 2009. (ENG.). pap. 24.95 (978-0-500-28762-0(7), 528762) 2008. **(978-0-500-51441-2(0))** Thames & Hudson.

Ruscha, Paul, photos by. Paul Ruscha's Full Moon, 1 vol. 2008. (ENG., Illus.). 184p. pap. 20.00 (978-3-86521-251-3(X)) Steidl, Gerhard Druckerei und Verlag DEU. Dist: Innovative Logistics.

Rush, Michael. The Rose Art Museum Collection. 2009. (ENG., Illus.). 288p. 60.00 (978-0-8109-5574-5(1)) Abrams.

Rutherford, Brett. Things Seen in Graveyards: Photos & Digital Art. 2007. (Illus.). 48p. pap. 17.00 (978-0-922558-26-5(0), Grim Reaper Bks.) Poet's Pr., The.

Rutledge, Anna Wells. Artists in the Life of Charleston: Through Colony & State from Restoration to Reconstruction. 2011. 164p. 41.95 **(978-1-258-01981-5(7))** Literary Licensing, LLC.

Ryan, Jay. Animals & Objects in & Out of Water: Posters by Jay Ryan, 20052008. 2009. (ENG., Illus.). 150p. pap. 22.95 (978-1-933354-92-7(5)) Akashic Bks.

Ryden, Mark. Mark Ryden, Pinxit. collector's ed. 2011. (ENG., Illus.). 300p. 1000.00 **(978-3-8365-2066-9(4))** TASCHEN DEU. Dist: Ingram Pub. Services.

Saab, A. Joan. For the Millions: American Art & Culture Between the Wars. 2009. (Arts & Intellectual Life in Modern America Ser.). 240p. (C). pap. 24.95 (978-0-8122-2069-8(2)) Univ. of Pennsylvania Pr.

Sachs, Tom. Islandia: Tom Sachs, 1 vol. 2007. (ENG., Illus.). 68p. pap. 30.00 (978-0-9790499-1-0(1)) Sachs, Tom.

Sachs, Tom, et al, contrib. by. Tom Sachs: Space Program. 2009. (ENG., Illus.). 280p. pap. 65.00 (978-0-8478-3226-2(0)) Rizzoli International Pubns., Inc.

Saint, Felipe. Dibujos Que Hablan Al Corazon.Tr. of Drawings That Speak to the Heart. (SPA.). (978-84-7645-395-7(7), 223519) Clie, Editorial.

Saleem, Samia. Degrees of Separation. 2007. (ENG., Illus.). 72p. 24.95 (978-0-9771992-2-8(3)) Featherproof Bks.

Salmagundi Club Painting Exhibition Records 1940-1951 & Water Color Exhibition Records 1900-1951. 2009. (Illus.). 623p. 65.00 (978-0-9791290-2-5(8), Katlan, Alexander Conservator, Inc.

Salvesen, Britt & Davis, Keith, texts. At the Crossroads of American Photography. 2009. (ENG., Illus.). 152p. 55.00 (978-1-934435-15-1(5)) Radius Bks.

Samuel Dorsky Museum of Art Staff. Eva Watson-Schutze. 2009. (Samuel Dorsky Museum of Art Ser.). (Illus.). 60p. pap. 18.00 (978-0-615-25832-4(8), Suny Pr.) State Univ. of New York Pr.

—Taking A Different T. 2009. (Samuel Dorsky Museum of Art Ser.). (Illus.). 64p. pap. 20.00 (978-0-615-25333-1(6), Suny Pr.) State Univ. of New York Pr.

Samuel Dorsky Museum of Art Staff & Schneemann, Carolee. Carolee Schneemann: Within & Beyond the Premises. 2010. (Illus.). 84p. pap. 16.00 (978-0-615-34823-0(8), Suny Pr.) State Univ. of New York Pr.

San Francisco Museum of Modern Art Staff, contrib. by. Calder to Warhol: Introducing the Fisher Collection. 2010. (978-0-918471-85-7(0)) San Francisco Museum of Modern Art.

Sanders, Terrence, ed. The Saratoga Collection. 2011. (ENG., Illus.). 104p. pap. 40.00 **(978-1-60801-061-5(9))** Univ Of New Orleans Pr.

Sandler, Irving. From Avant-Garde to Pluralism: An on-the-Spot History. 2008. 292p. 30.00 (978-1-889097-68-8(3)) Hard Pr. Editions.

Sangster, Gary. Lead Pencil Studio: Annie Han + Daniel Mihalyo: After. 2009. (ENG., Illus.). 56p. pap. 22.50 (978-0-295-98934-1(3)) Univ. of Washington Pr.

Sante, Luc. Folk Photography: The American Real-Photo Postcard, 1905-1930. 2010. (ENG.). 160p. pap. 24.95 (978-1-891241-55-0(9)) Verse Chorus Pr.

Sasse, Julie R. An Eclectic Eye: Selections from the Dan leach Collection. 2007. (Illus.). 180p. pap. 30.00 (978-0-911611-34-2(7)) Tucson Museum of Art.

Scher, Paula. MAPS. 2011. (ENG., Illus.). 144p. 50.00 (978-1-61689-033-9(9)) Princeton Architectural Pr.

Schimmel, Paul. Under the Big Black Sun: California Art, 1974-1981. 2011. (ENG., Illus.). 320p. 60.00 (978-3-7913-5139-1(7)) Prestel Publishing.

Schmidt-Burkhardt, Astrit, ed. Maciunas' Learning Machines: From Art History to a Chronology of Fluxus. 2nd ed. 2011. Orig. Title: Maciunas' Learning Machines. (ENG., Illus.). 216p. pap. 59.95 (978-3-7091-0479-8(3), 3709104793) Springer Wien AUT. Dist: Springer.

Schmitz, Jerry. The Art of Shrek Forever After. 2010. (ENG., Illus.). 144p. 24.95 (978-1-60887-002-8(2)) Palace Pr. International.

Schmuckli, Claudia & Weiss, Allen S. Leonardo Drew: Existed. Schmuckli, Claudia, ed. 2009. (ENG., Illus.). 208p. 59.95 (978-1-904832-58-4(X)) Giles, D. Ltd. GBR. Dist: Antique Collectors' Club.

Schneider, Rebecca, et al, texts. Mark Tribe: the Port Huron Project. 2010. (ENG., Illus.). 72p. pap. 27.50 (978-88-8158-762-9(9)) Charta ITA. Dist: D.A.P./Distributed Art Pubs.

Schon, Billy. Fresh Paint: NYC. 2010. (Illus.). 176p. 34.99 (978-0-7643-3495-5(6)) Schiffer Publishing, Ltd.

Schönhuth, Friederik. Jason Dodge: I Woke Up, There Was a Note in My Pocket Explaining What Had Happened. 2010. (ENG., Illus.). 216p. pap. 45.00 (978-3-7757-2618-4(7)) Hatje Cantz Verlag GmbH & Co KG DEU. Dist: D.A.P./Distributed Art Pubs.

Schor, Mira. A Decade of Negative Thinking: Essays on Art, Politics, & Daily Life. 2010. (ENG., Illus.). 336p. 89.95 (978-0-8223-4584-8(6)); pap. 24.95 (978-0-8223-4602-9(8)) Duke Univ. Pr.

Schorr, Todd. American Surreal. 2009. (Illus.). 100p. 39.95 (978-0-86719-709-9(9)) Last Gasp of San Francisco.

Schrank, Sarah. Art & the City: Civic Imagination & Cultural Authority in Los Angeles. 2008. (Illus.). 224p. (C). 55.00 (978-0-8122-4117-4(7)) Univ. of Pennsylvania Pr.

Schretlen, Helen. Loving Art: The William & Anna Singer Collection. 2007. (ENG., Illus.). 224p. 60.00 (978-90-400-8234-4(0)) Allemandi, Umberto & Co. GBR. Dist: National Bk. Network.

Schulz, Regine & Seidel, Matthias. Egyptian Art. 2009. pap. (978-0-911886-70-2(2)) Walters Art Museum, US.

Schumacher, Rainald, et al, eds. Mike Kelley: Goetz Collection. 2009. (ENG., Illus.). 272p. 50.00 (978-3-939894-11-7(7)) Goetz, Ingvild, Kunstverlag, GmbH DEU. Dist: D.A.P./Distributed Art Pubs.

Schutz, Dana. Dana Schutz: If It Appears in the Desert. 2009. (ENG., Illus.). 40p. pap. 60.00 (978-3-931355-48-7(9)) Verlag der Buchhandlung Walther Konig DEU. Dist: D.A.P./Distributed Art Pubs.

Schwabsky, Barry, text. Chloe Piene. 2008. (ENG., Illus.). 104p. 45.00 (978-2-907650-33-5(5)) Carre d'Art FRA. Dist: D.A.P./Distributed Art Pubs.

Schwabsky, Barry, et al. Suzanne McClelland: Rock & Shift. 2010. (ENG., Illus.). 86p. 39.95 (978-1-889097-75-6(6)) Hard Pr. Editions.

Schwain, Kristin. Signs of Grace: Religion & American Art in the Gilded Age. 2007. (Illus.). 172p. 29.95 (978-0-8014-4577-4(9)) Cornell Univ. Pr.

Schwartz, Constance. The Sea Around Us. 2010. (Illus.). 28p. pap. (978-0-9815644-8-7(8)) Nassau County Museum of Art.

Schwendener, Martha & Dumbadze, Alexander, texts. Cameron Martin: Analogue. 2009. (ENG., Illus.). 144p. 40.00 (978-0-9716702-3-5(4)) GHava{Press}.

Scott, A. O. Sanctuary. 2010. (ENG., Illus.). 96p. 60.00 (978-0-8109-9199-6(3)) Abrams.

Scott, Bill & Coyle, Heather Campbell. Painted Poetry: The Art of Mary Page Evans. 2012. (ENG., Illus.). 96p. 45.00 (978-1-55595-374-4(3)) Hudson Hills Pr. LLC.

Seaton, Elizabeth G., ed. Paths to the Press: Printmaking & American Women Artists, 1910-1960. 2006. (Illus.). 261p. pap. 40.00 (978-1-890751-13-5(8)) Kansas State Univ., Marianna Kistler Beach Museum of Art, The.

Secrest, Tom. Tom Secrest. 2007. pap. 8.00 (978-0-9797964-2-5(3)) CUE Art Foundation.

Sedley, Jeremy, et al, eds. New Art International, Volume 12: A Compendium of Recent Works by World Contemporary Artists. 2008. (New Art International Ser.). (Illus.). 179p. 26.00 (978-0-9773540-4-7(0)) A.R.T. Pr.

See, Sarita Echavez. The Decolonized Eye: Filipino American Art & Performance. 2009. (ENG., Illus.). 232p. 75.00 (978-0-8166-5318-8(6)) Univ. of Minnesota Pr.

Segal, Richard D. & Segal, Monica M. Contemporary Realism: The Seavest Collection. 2007. (Illus.). 192p. (978-1-933112-37-4(9)) Collectors Pr., Inc.

Seidenberg, Jean. Jean Seidenberg: Paintings, Drawings, Sculpture. 2009. (ENG.). 144p. 40.00 (978-0-9627757-1-0(1)) Silkmont/Count.

Seimons, Mark & Weiwei, Ai. Ai Weiwei. 2009. (ENG & GER., Illus.). 120p. pap. 29.95 (978-3-7913-5014-1(5)) Prestel Publishing.

Seims, A. J. Yarns of Alaska: The Ballads of Moose Jaw Seims. 2011. 48p. pap. 16.95 (978-1-57833-535-0(3)) Todd Communications.

Seligman, Rachel, ed. Union College Senior Invitational. 2008. (Illus.). per. (978-0-9763207-7-7(0)) Union College, Mandeville Gallery.

Semedo, Joan. From Crayons to Oils: A Dialogue of Joan Semedo's Art Career. 2008. (Illus.). 15.99 (978-1-4257-8044-9(X)) Xlibris Corp.

Semelka, Richard. Clyde Jones Penguins, Giraffes & Other Critters His Joyous Vision. 2010. 93p. pap. 33.81 (978-0-557-18317-3(0)) Lulu Enterprises Inc.

Shaft. 2008. (Illus.). 64p. pap. 25.00 (978-0-9790862-8-1(0)) Upper Playground Pubng.

Shannon, Joshua. The Disappearance of Objects: New York Art & the Rise of the Postmodern City. 2009. (ENG., Illus.). 232p. 60.00 (978-0-300-13706-4(0)) Yale Univ. Pr.

Shark, Bud. The Legend of Bud Shark & His Indelible Ink. 2010. (ENG., Illus.). 228p. 60.00 (978-0-945367-37-6(6)) Hardy Marks Pubns.

Shawah, Henry. Henry Shawah: Goldsmith & Sculptor. 2009. (ENG., Illus.). 132p. 65.00 (978-1-55595-321-8(2)) Hudson Hills Pr. LLC.

Shearer, Christine Fowler & Robinson, William H. Cral Gaertner & the American Scene. Korneitchuck, Ursula, ed. (Illus.). pap. (978-0-9639562-7-9(2)) Cleveland Artists Foundation.

Shelley, Donald A. The Fraktur-Writings or Illuminated Manuscripts of the Pennsylvania Germans. 2011. 398p. 54.95 (978-1-258-04755-9(1)) Literary Licensing, LLC.

Shields, Scott A., et al. The Crocker Art Museum Collection: Unveiled. Shields, Scott A., ed. 2010. (Illus.). 544p. (978-1-884038-19-8(0)) Crocker Art Museum.

Shiff, Richard. Doubt. 2007. (Theories of Modernism & Postmodernism in the Visual Arts Ser.). (ENG., Illus.). 216p. 125.00 (978-0-415-97308-3(2)); per. 29.95 (978-0-415-97309-0(0)) Routledge.

Shoemaker, Innis H. & Ittmann, John W. Adventures in Modern Art: The Charles K. Williams II Collection. 2009. (Illus.). 336p. (978-0-87633-216-0(5)); (978-0-87633-215-3(7)) Philadelphia Museum of Art.

Shoemaker, Innis Howe. Adventures in Modern Art: The Charles K. Williams II Collection. 2009. (ENG., Illus.). 336p. 60.00 (978-0-300-14978-4(6)) Yale Univ. Pr.

Shone, Richard & Stonard, John-Paul. The Books That Shaped Art History: From Gombrich & Greenberg to Alpers & Krauss. 2012. (ENG., Illus.). 208p. 34.95 (978-0-500-23895-0(2), 523895) Thames & Hudson.

Shopsin, Tamara. Tamara Shopsin: C'est le Pied II. 2009. (ENG., Illus.). 96p. pap. 14.95 (978-0-9823653-0-4(6)) Ice Plant, The.

Shore, Jim & Shore, Jan. Jim & Jan Shore's Passion for Quilts: 24 Art-Inspired Projects. 2009. (ENG.). 182p. 34.95 (978-0-9819762-0-4(4), 0981976204) All American Crafts.

Shortcut Books LLC, compiled by. Director's Dozen: 12 lasting impressions from the Detroit Institute of Arts. 2007. (Illus.). 24p. per. 4.95 (978-0-9779962-2-3(0)) Shortcut Bks. LLC.

Showers, Jan. Glamorous Rooms. 2009. (ENG., Illus.). 208p. 50.00 (978-0-8109-4974-4(1)) Abrams.

Siedell, Daniel A. Martinez Celaya: Early Work. 2007. (ENG., Illus.). 392p. 69.00 (978-0-9673608-6-7(2)) Whale & Star Pr.

Siegmann, William. African Art: A Century at the Brooklyn Museum. 2009. (Illus.). 304p. (978-3-7913-4321-1(1)) Prestel Verlag GmbH & Co KG.

Silber, Mark & Nels, Nelson, photos by. Portraits & Voices: Workers of Seven Mills. 2007. (Illus.). 56p. pap. 14.00 (978-0-9799307-0-6(7)) Museum L-A.

Silber, Mark & Nelson, Nels, photos by. Portraits & Voices: Workers of Seven Mills. 2007. (Illus.). 56p. pap. 24.00 incl. DVD (978-0-9799307-1-3(5)) Museum L-A.

Silbergeld, Jerome & Ching, Dora C. Articulations - Undefining Chinese Contemporary Art. 2010. (Publications of the Department of Art & Archaeology, Princeton University Ser.). (ENG., Illus.). 320p. (C). pap. 29.95 (978-0-691-14860-1(0)) Princeton Univ. Pr.

Silke, Jim. Bettie Page Rules! The Pin-Up Battles of the Classic Beauties & Bombshells of the 1950's in over 300 Rare Photographs & Original Artwork. Gore, Shawna, ed. 2007. (Illus.). 128p. pap. 22.95 (978-1-59307-756-3(4)) Dark Horse Comics.

Simon, Amy, photos by. Amy Simon: A Different State of Mind. 2010. (ENG., Illus.). 80p. 45.00 (978-3-7757-2622-1(5)) Hatje Cantz Verlag GmbH & Co KG DEU. Dist: D.A.P./Distributed Art Pubs.

Simpson, Bennett & Iles, Chrissie, eds. Dan Graham: Beyond. 2009. (ENG., Illus.). 348p. (gr. 17). pap. 44.95 (978-1-933751-12-2(6)) MIT Pr.

Sims, Lowery Stokes, text. The Persistence of Geometry: Form, Content, & Culture in the Collection of the Cleveland Museum of Art. 2007. (ENG., Illus.). 128p. pap. 22.50 (978-0-940717-86-2(7)) Cleveland Museum of Art.

Singerman, Howard. Art History, after Sherrie Levine. 2011. (ENG., Illus.). 304p. 65.00 (978-0-520-26721-3(4)); pap. 24.95 (978-0-520-26722-0(2)) Univ. of California Pr.

Sinnreich, Ursula, ed. James Turrell: Geometrie des Lichts. 2009. (ENG & GER., Illus.). 128p. 55.00 (978-3-7757-2369-5(2)) Hatje Cantz Verlag GmbH & Co KG DEU. Dist: D.A.P./Distributed Art Pubs.

Sinsheimer, Karen & Ferri, Rita A. Made in Santa Barbara: Contemporary Photographs: Santa Barbara Museum of Art, July 1-October 7, 2007. 2007. (CAT., Illus.). 57p. pap. (978-0-89951-109-2(0)) Santa Barbara Museum of Art.

Siracusano, Gabriela. Pigments & Power in the Andes: From the Material to the Symbolic in Andean Cultural Practices, 1500-1800. 2011. (ENG., Illus.). 256p. pap. 70.00 (978-1-904982-56-2(5)) Archetype Pubns. GBR. Dist: National Bk. Network.

Sisley, Logan. Richard Tuttle: Triumphs. 2012. (ENG., Illus.). 102p. pap. 45.00 (978-1-901702-37-8(5)) Lane, Hugh Gallery IRL. Dist: D.A.P./Distributed Art Pubs.

Skinner, Tina. Found Object Art II. 2009. (Illus.). 176p. bds. 49.99 (978-0-7643-3162-6(0)) Schiffer Publishing, Ltd.

Slade, Kathy, ed. Kota Ezawa: Odessa Staircase Redux. 2010. (ENG., Illus.). 168p. pap. 35.00 (978-3-03764-083-8(9)) JRP Ringier Kunstverlag AG CHE. Dist: D.A.P./Distributed Art Pubs.

Slay, David Henson. Georgia Civil War Manuscripts Collections: An Annotated Bibliography. 2011. (978-0-8173-8570-5(3)) Univ. of Alabama Pr.

SLC Visual Art Review. Sarah Lawrence Visual Art Review. 2010. pap. 14.99 (978-0-578-05594-7(5)) SLCVAR.

Sloan, Mark, ed. Aldwyth: Collage & Assemblage 1991-2009. 2010. (ENG., Illus.). 112p. pap. 29.95 (978-0-615-26885-9(4)) Halsey Institute of Contemporary Art.

Slobodkina Foundation. Esphyr Slobodkina: Rediscovering a Pioneer of American Abstraction. 2008. pap. (978-0-9793620-0-2(8)) Slobodkina Foundation, The.

Smith, Allison. Allison Smith: Needle Work. 2010. (Illus.). 64p. pap. 15.00 (978-0-936316-30-7(6)) Washington Univ., Mildred Lane Kemper Art Museum.

Smith, Edward Lucie & Nahas, Dominique. Margaret Evangeline. 2011. (ENG., Illus.). 160p. 47.50 (978-88-8158-808-4(0)) Charta ITA. Dist: D.A.P./Distributed Art Pubs.

Smith, Jeffrey Chipps. The Art of the Goldsmith in Late Fifteenth-Century Germany: The Kimbell Virgin & Her Bishop. 2006. (Kimbell Masterpiece Ser.). (ENG., Illus.). 86p. pap. 16.95 (978-0-300-11736-3(1)) Kimbell Art Museum.

—The Kimbell Virgin & Her Bishop: The Art of the Goldsmith in Late Fifteenth-Century Germany. 2006. (Kimbell Masterpiece Ser.). (Illus.). vii, 86p. (978-0-912804-45-3(9)) Kimbell Art Museum.

Smith, Jessica Todd & Murphy, Kevin M. Pressed in Time: American Prints, 1905-1950. 2008. (Illus.). 88p. pap. 19.95 (978-0-87328-234-5(5)) Huntington Library Pr.

Smith, Katharine & Schiller, Joyce. Illustrating Her World: Ellen B. T. Pyle. 2009. pap. (978-0-9771644-0-0(3)) Delaware Art Museum, The.

Smith, Michael. Baby Ikki at the Museum. 2012. (ENG., Illus.). 26p. 9.95 (978-0-300-18104-3(3)) Yale Univ. Pr.

Smith, Patti, photos by. Patti Smith: Camera Solo. 2011. (ENG., Illus.). 96p. pap. (978-0-918333-11-7(3)) Wadsworth Atheneum.

Smith, Richard G. Lee Bontecou: A Retrospective. Smith, Elizabeth A. T., ed. & contrib. by by. Storr, Robert, contrib. by. 2008. (ENG., Illus.). 240p. pap. 50.00 (978-0-300-13746-0(X)) Yale Univ. Pr.

Smith, Thomas Brent. A Place of Refuge: Maynard Dixon's Arizona. 2008. (ENG.). 160p. (C). 49.95 (978-0-911611-36-6(3)) Tucson Museum of Art.

Smith, Valerie, et al, texts. Juan Downey: the Invisible Architect. 2011. (ENG., Illus.). 200p. pap. 35.00 (978-0-938437-76-5(3)) Massachusetts Institute of Technology, List Visual Arts Ctr.

Sneyd, Doug & Johnson, Lynn. The Art of Doug Sneyd. 2011. (Illus.). 248p. 39.99 (978-1-59582-725-8(0)) Dark Horse Comics.

Sollins, Marybeth, ed. Art21: Art in the Twenty-First Century 5, 5 vols., Vol. 5. 2009. (Illus.). 224p. 45.00 (978-0-615-30836-4(8)) Art21, Incorporated.

Sorel, Edward. The Mural at the Waverly Inn: A Portrait of Greenwich Village Bohemians. 2008. (Illus.). 56p. 15.95 (978-0-307-37731-9(8), Pantheon) Knopf Doubleday Publishing Group.

South Carolina State Museum. Edmund Yaghjian: A Retrospective. 2011. (Distributed for the South Carolina State Museum Ser.). 88p. 19.95 (978-0-9836794-2-4(8)) Univ. of South Carolina Pr.

—New Deal Art in South Carolina: Government-Supported Images from the Great Depression. 2011. (Distributed for the South Carolina State Museum Ser.). 86p. pap. 14.95 (978-0-9836794-0-0(1)) Univ. of South Carolina Pr.

—South Carolina Art: Selections from the South Carolina State Musuem. 2011. (Distributed for the South Carolina State Museum Ser.). 92p. pap. 14.95 (978-0-9836794-1-7(X)) Univ. of South Carolina Pr.

Spanierman Gallery Staff, contrib. by. American Works on Paper: 1800 to the Present. 2010. (Illus.). 56p. (978-1-935617-02-0(8)) Spanierman Gallery.

Sparagana, John & Bal, Mieke. Sleeping Beauty: A One-Artist Dictionary. 2008. (Project Tango Ser.). (Illus.). 136p. 35.00 (978-0-226-03552-9(2)) Univ. of Chicago Pr.

Spark, Nick T. Spoons West! Fred Harvey, the Navajo, & the Souvenir Spoons of the Southwest 1890-1941. 2007. 60p. pap. 29.95 (978-1-4357-0211-0(5)) Lulu Enterprises Inc.

Spector, Nancy. Pierre Huyghe. 2009. 160p. 49.95 (978-0-7148-4582-1(5)) Phaidon Pr., Inc.

Spector, Nancy, ed. Richard Prince, 1 vol. 2007. (ENG., Illus.). 368p. 60.00 (978-0-89207-363-4(2)) Guggenheim, Solomon R. Museum.

Spector, Nancy & Prince, Richard. Richard Prince. 2007. (Illus.). 371p. (978-0-89207-364-1(0)) Guggenheim, Solomon R. Museum.

Speed, Julie. Speed Art, 2003-2009. 2009. (ENG., Illus.). 188p. 55.00 (978-0-292-71994-1(9)) Univ. of Texas Pr.

Speer, George V. Things of the Spirit: Art & Healing in the American Body Politic, 1929-1941. 2012. 258p. (C). 83.95 (978-1-4331-1568-4(9)) Lang, Peter Publishing, Inc.

Spiegelman, Art. Be a Nose!, 3 vols. 2009. (ENG., Illus.). 192p. 29.00 (978-1-934781-14-2(2)) McSweeney's Publishing.

Springfield Library and Museums Association. The Legacy of Currier. 2010. pap. 19.95 (978-0-916746-00-1(3)) Springfield Library & Museum Assn.

Squires, William Tolliver. Art, Experience & Faith. 2010. (Illus.). 108p. pap. 11.95 (978-1-4327-4419-9(4)) Outskirts Pr., Inc.

St. Gaudens, Homer. The American Artist & His Times. 2011. 414p. 54.95 (978-1-258-10519-8(5)) Literary Licensing, LLC.

Stack, Gael. Gael Stack. 2011. (ENG., Illus.). 216p. 60.00 (978-0-292-72854-7(9)) Univ. of Texas Pr.

Stavitsky, Gail & Rothkopf, Katherine. Cezanne & American Modernism. 2009. (ENG., Illus.). 376p. 65.00 (978-0-300-14715-5(5)) Yale Univ. Pr.

Stavitsky, Gail & Warhol, Andy. Warhol & Cars: American Icons. 2011. (978-0-615-41922-0(4)) Montclair Art Museum.

Stegmann, Markus, ed. Ulrich Meister. 2010. (ENG., Illus.). 168p. 55.00 (978-3-7757-2475-3(3)) Hatje Cantz Verlag GmbH & Co KG DEU. Dist: D.A.P./Distributed Art Pubs.

Stelmach, Augelina. Crossing Boundaries: The Art of Lee Waisler. 2006. (ENG., Illus.). 144p. 50.00 (978-1-890206-34-5(2)) Mapin Publishing Pvt. Ltd IND. Dist: National Bk. Network.

Stern, David, et al. Chosen: Philadelphia's Great Hebraica. 2007. (Illus.). 80p. pap. (978-0-939084-36-4(8)) Rosenbach Museum & Library, The.

Stern, Jean & Farrington, Lisa E., texts. Timothy J. Clark. 2008. (Illus.). 144p. 39.95 (978-0-7649-4352-2(9)) Pomegranate Communications, Inc.

Stettinius, Gordon, text. Gita Lenz: Photographs. 2011. (ENG., Illus.). 100p. 50.00 (978-0-9845739-0-5(9)) Candela Bks.

Stevens, D. J. On a Broader Canvas: Creating Style with Wall Murals & Art Finishes. 2009. 148p. pap. 45.00 (978-1-4389-4306-0(7)) AuthorHouse.

Stevens, Dave. Brush with Passion: The Art & Life of Dave Stevens. Fenner, Arnie & Fenner, Cathy, eds. 2008. (ENG., Illus.). 288p. 39.95 (978-1-59929-010-2(3)) Underwood Books.

Stockebrand, Marianne, ed. Chinati: The Vision of Donald Judd. 2010. (ENG., Illus.). 328p. 65.00 (978-0-300-16939-3(6)) Yale Univ. Pr.

Stormes, Chuck & Reeves, Don. Luis Ortega's Rawhide Artistry: Braiding in the California Tradition. 2010. (Western Legacies Ser.). (ENG., Illus.). 160p. (C). pap. 29.95 (978-0-8061-4091-9(7)) Univ. of Oklahoma Pr.

Storr, Robert. Paul Mccarthy: Vol. 1: Piccadilly Circus / Vol. 2: Bunker Basement, 2 vols. 2009. (ENG., Illus.). 348p. 120.00 (978-3-86521-626-7(9)) Steidl, Gerhard Druckerei und Verlag DEU. Dist: Innovative Logistics.

Stoute, Ryan. The Godminds. 2011. 28p. pap. 16.16 (978-1-4269-6559-3(1)) Trafford Publishing.

Strick, Jeremy. Public Notice 3: Jitish Kallat at the Art Institute of Chicago. Ghose, Madhuvanti, ed. 2011. (ENG., Illus.). 96p. 25.00 (978-0-300-17158-7(7)) Art Institute of Chicago.

Strong, Lisa Maria. Sentimental Journey: The Art of Alfred Jacob Miller. 2008. (ENG.). 238p. (C). 45.00 (978-0-88360-105-1(2)) Amon Carter Museum of American Art.

Stroun, Fabrice & Bovier, Lionel, eds. Jim Shaw: My Mirage. 2011. (ENG., Illus.). 240p. pap. 55.00 (978-3-03764-187-3(8)) JRP Ringier Kunstverlag AG CHE. Dist: D.A.P./Distributed Art Pubs.

Studio on Fire. Studio on Fire: Iron Beasts Make Great Beauty. 2011. (ENG., Illus.). 144p. 30.00 (978-3-89955-381-9(0)) Die Gestalten Verlag DEU. Dist: Prestel Publishing.

Sturtevant, Elaine. Elaine Sturtevant: the Razzle Dazzle of Thinking. 2010. (ENG., Illus.). 304p. 55.00 (978-3-03764-090-6(1)) JRP Ringier Kunstverlag AG CHE. Dist: D.A.P./Distributed Art Pubs.

StyleEase Software. StyleEase 5. 0 for Chicago/Turabian Style: (cardboard Sleeve) 2011. (C). cd-rom 40.00 (978-0-9835424-4-5(9)) StyleEase Software, LLC.

—StyleEase 5. 0 for Chicago/Turabian Style: (DVD Case) 2011. (C). cd-rom 45.00 (978-0-9835424-5-2(7)) StyleEase Software, LLC.

Subotnick, Ali, text. Nine Live: Visionary Artists from L. A. 2009. (ENG., Illus.). 200p. 30.00 (978-0-943739-36-6(5)) Hammer Museum.

Superstar, Jocelyn & SFaustina. Bay Area Graffiti: '80s - '90s - Early Bombing. 2011. (ENG., Illus.). 208p. 50.00 (978-1-935613-17-6(0)) Batty, Mark Pub., LLC.

Sussman, Elisabeth & Wilson, Jane. Jane Wilson: Horizons. 2009. (Illus.). 192p. (978-1-85894-488-3(0)) Merrell Pubs. Ltd.

Sussman, Elisabeth, et al. Whitney Biennial 2012. 2012. (ENG., Illus.). 400p. pap. 45.00 (978-0-300-18036-7(5)) Yale Univ. Pr.

Swartz, Anne. Pattern & Decoration: An Ideal Vision in American Art. 2007. (Illus.). 120p. per. 19.99 (978-0-943651-35-4(2)) Hudson River Museum.

Swoon. Swoon, 1 vol. 2008. (ENG., Illus.). 64p. per. 25.00 (978-0-9778686-6-7(4)) Deitch, Jeffrey Inc.

Symmes, Marilyn F. Pop Art & After: Prints+popular Culture. 2008. (Illus.). 131p. (978-0-9769030-9-3(1)) Zimmerli, Jane Voorhees Art Museum.

Szperling, Severin. A Catalog of Holocaust Medals: A History Etched in Metal. 2010. pap. 98.95 (978-1-60494-421-1(8)) Wheatmark.

Taaffe, Philip, et al. Philip Taaffe: Anima Mundi. 2011. (ENG., Illus.). 126p. pap. 40.00 (978-1-907020-60-5(8)) Irish Museum of Modern Art IRL. Dist: D.A.P./Distributed Art Pubs.

Takeover. 2007. pap. (978-0-9778084-1-0(6)) Hyde Park Art Center, The.

Tam, Karen. Karen Tam. 2007. pap. 8.00 (978-0-9797964-1-8(5)) CUE Art Foundation.

Tamaki, Jillian. Indoor Voice. 2010. (ENG., Illus.). 64p. pap. 19.95 (978-1-77046-014-0(4)) Drawn & Quarterly Pubns. CAN. Dist: Macmillan.

Tanguy, Sarah. Mapping: Memory & Motion in Contemporary Art. 2010. (Illus.). 52p. (978-0-915171-80-4(5)) Katonah Gallery.

Tatham, David & Prince, David Lake. Winslow Homer's Empire State: Houghton Farm & Beyond. 2010. (Illus.). 84p. (978-0-8156-8179-3(8)) Syracuse Univ. Pr.

Taylor, Chris & Gilbert, Bill. Land Arts of the American West. 2009. (ENG., Illus.). 384p. 60.00 (978-0-292-71672-8(9)) Univ. of Texas Pr.

Taylor, Michael & Chimes, Thomas. Thomas Chimes: Adventures in Pataphysics. 2007. (Illus.). xi, 255p. (978-0-87633-253-5(X)); (978-0-87633-252-8(1)) Philadelphia Museum of Art.

Taylor, Michael R. Marcel Duchamp: Étant Donnés. 2009. (978-0-87633-211-5(4)); (978-0-87633-210-8(6)) Philadelphia Museum of Art.

Tedeschi, Martha & Dahm, Kristi. John Marin's Watercolors: A Medium for Modernism. 2011. (ENG., Illus.). 192p. 50.00 (978-0-300-16637-8(0)) Art Institute of Chicago.

Telfair Museum of Art & Sammons, Tania June. The Owens-Thomas House. 2008. (ENG., Illus.). 64p. 12.95 *(978-0-933075-10-8(3))* Telfair Museum of Art.

—The Story of Silver in Savannah: Creating & Collecting since the 18th Century. 2010. (ENG., Illus.). 128p. 24.95 *(978-0-933075-13-9(8))* Telfair Museum of Art.

Templeton, Ed. Deformer. ltd. ed. 2008. (ENG., Illus.). 176p. 600.00 *(978-88-6208-060-6(3))* Damiani ITA. Dist: D.A.P./Distributed Art Pubs.

Templeton, Ed, photos by. Ed Templeton: the Cemetery of Reason. 2010. (ENG., Illus.). 160p. pap. 39.95 *(978-90-75679-34-2(3))* Vereniging voor het Museum van Hedendaagse Kunst BEL. Dist: D.A.P./Distributed Art Pubs.

Templeton, Edith. Deformer. 2008. (ENG., Illus.). 170p. 55.00 *(978-88-6208-050-7(6))* Damiani ITA. Dist: D.A.P./Distributed Art Pubs.

The Tender among Us: Project Series 32: Liat Yossifor. 2007. (Illus.). 24p. pap. 10.00 *(978-0-9786996-3-5(7))* Pomona College Museum of Art.

teNeues. AAD New York: Art Architecture Design. 2010. (Illus.). 168p. pap. 12.95 *(978-3-8327-9435-4(2))* teNeues Publishing Co.

Terjanian, Pierre. Princely Armor in the Age of Durer: A Renaissance Masterpiece in the Philadelphia Museum of Art. 2012. (ENG., Illus.). 56p. pap. 18.00 *(978-0-300-17531-5(7))* Yale Univ. Pr.

The Pace Gallery, prod. Kiki Smith: Lodestar. 2010. (Illus.). 44p. 40.00 *(978-1-935410-10-2(5))* Pace Gallery, The.

—Robert Mangold: Ring Paintings. 2011. (Illus.). 30p. pap. 30.00 *(978-1-935410-18-8(0))* Pace Gallery, The.

Thomas, Elizabeth, ed. Matrix: Berkeley. 2009. (ENG., Illus.). 560p. pap. 35.00 *(978-0-9719397-8-3(0))* Univ. of California, Berkeley Art Museum & Pacific Film Archive.

Thomas, Roy & Amash, Jim. John Romita... & All That Jazz! 2007. 208p. 44.95 *(978-1-893905-76-4(4))* TwoMorrows Publishing.

Thompson, Carol. Radcliffe Bailey: Memory as Medicine. 2011. 160p. 45.00 *(978-1-932543-42-1(2))* High Museum of Art.

Thompson, Mimi. Robert Rauschenberg: Prints from Universal Limited Art Editions, 1962-2008. 2011. (Illus.). 120p. pap. *(978-0-9717187-8-4(4))* Jones Jr., Fred Museum of Art.

Thrasher Magazine. Thrasher: Maximum Rad. 2012. (ENG., Illus.). 256p. 35.00 ***(978-0-7893-2432-0(6))*** Universe Publishing.

Thurber, T. Barton. European Art at Dartmouth: Highlights from the Hood Museum of Art. 2008. (Illus.). ix, 222p. *(978-1-58465-738-5(3))*; (ENG., 232p. pap. 40.00 *(978-1-58465-724-8(3))* Hood Museum of Art.

Tierney, Tom. Famous Texas Men: Paper Dolls. 2008. (Illus.). 40p. pap. 9.95 *(978-0-7643-2901-2(4))* Schiffer Publishing, Ltd.

Tinterow, Gary, et al. Abstract Expressionism & Other Modern Works: The Muriel Kallis Steinberg Newman Collection in the Metropolitan Museum of Art. 2007. (Illus.). x, 214p. 29.95 *(978-1-58839-274-9(0))* Metropolitan Museum of Art, The.

Tokar Miller, Nancy. Nancy Tokar Miller... in Retrospect. 2009. (ENG., Illus.). 140p. pap. *(978-0-9814840-4-4(2))* Univ. of Arizona Museum of Art.

Toth, Alex, et al. Genius, Isolated: the Life & Art of Alex Toth: The Life & Art of Alex Toth. 2011. (Illus.). 328p. 49.99 *(978-1-60010-828-0(8))* Idea & Design Works, LLC.

Touchie, Rodger D. Edward S. Curtis above the Medicine Line: Portraits of Aboriginal Life in the Canadian West, 1 vol. 2010. (ENG., Illus.). 192p. *(978-1-926613-77-2(5))* Heritage Hse.

Tracy, Kathleen. Remembering Adelia: Quilts Inspired by Her Diary. 2009. (ENG., Illus.). 96p. pap. *(978-1-56477-865-9(7))* Martingale & Co.

Tragatschnig, Ulrich. Konzeptuelle Kunst: Interpretationsparadigmen: Ein Propaedeutikum. (GER.). 194p. *(978-3-496-01187-3(4))* Reimer, Dietrich.

Traugott, Joseph. Sole Mates: Cowboy Boots & Art. 2010. (ENG.). 124p. *(978-0-89013-555-5(7))* Museum of New Mexico Pr.

Traugott, Joseph & TRAUGOTT, Joseph. The Art of New Mexico: How the West Is One. 2007. (ENG., Illus.). 225p. 55.00 *(978-0-89013-497-9(9))* Museum of New Mexico Pr.

Tretiack, Philippe. Warhol's America. 2008. pap. *(978-2-7594-0312-7(2))* Assouline.

Troll, Ray. Something Fishy This Way Comes: The Artwork of Ray Troll. 2010. (ENG., Illus.). 128p. pap. 19.95 *(978-1-57061-682-2(5))* Sasquatch Bks.

Truck, Fred. 10 Year Sandwich. 2008. (Illus.). 146p. 99.95 *(978-0-938236-13-9(X))*; (ENG., 119.95 *(978-0-938236-14-6(8))* Electric Bank, The.

Truman, Vincent. This Is My First Time So Please Be Brutal. 2008. (Illus.). 224p. pap. 12.98 *(978-1-4357-0685-9(4))* Lulu Enterprises Inc.

Tsai, Eugenie & Biggers, Sanford. Sanford Biggers: Sweet Funk — an Introspective. 2011. ***(978-0-87273-169-1(3))*** Brooklyn Museum, The.

Tucker, Thomas Deane. Derridada: Duchamp as Readymade Deconstruction. 2010. (ENG.). 110p. pap. 24.50 *(978-0-7391-1623-4(1))* Lexington Bks.

Tung, Lisa & Zaug, Chloé. "Crafty" Elaine Bradford, Nick Cave, Rob Conger ... 2007. (Illus.). 75p. *(978-0-9771419-2-0(6))* Massachusetts College of Art.

Turbeville, Deborah. Deborah Turbeville - The Fashion Pictures. 2011. (ENG., Illus.). 304p. 85.00 *(978-0-8478-3479-2(4))* Rizzoli International Pubns., Inc.

Turgeon, Mark. Mark Turgeon. 2007. 8.00 *(978-0-9791843-7-6(1))* CUE Art Foundation.

Turrell, James. James Turrell: The Wolfsburg Project. 2010. (ENG & GER., Illus.). 184p. 60.00 *(978-3-7757-2455-5(9))* Hatje Cantz Verlag GmbH & Co KG DEU. Dist: D.A.P./Distributed Art Pubs.

Twombly, Cy. States of Mind. Catalog MUMOK, Vienna. 2009. (Illus.). 160p. *(978-3-8296-0445-1(9))* Schirmer/Mosel Verlag GmbH.

Uchill, Rebecca, et al. On Procession: Art on Parade. Uchill, Rebecca, ed. 2009. (Illus.). 120p. pap. 24.95 *(978-0-936260-87-7(4))* Indianapolis Museum of Art.

Udall, Sharyn R. Dance & American Art: A Long Embrace. 2012. (ENG., Illus.). 456p. 60.00 ***(978-0-299-28800-6(5))*** Univ. of Wisconsin Pr.

Udall, Sharyn R. & Weekly, Nancy. Sensory Crossovers: Synesthesia in American Art. Hall, Dawn, ed. 2010. (Illus.). 111p. pap. 37.00 *(978-0-9779910-5-1(9))* Albuquerque Museum of Art and History.

Udall, Sharyn Rohlfsen. Dance & American Art: A Long Embrace. 2012. E-Book ***(978-0-299-28803-7(X))*** Univ. of Wisconsin Pr.

Umberger, Leslie, ed. Sublime Spaces & Visionary Worlds: Built Environments of Vernacular Artists. 2007. (ENG., Illus.). 416p. 65.00 *(978-1-56898-728-6(5))* Princeton Architectural Pr.

Umberger, Leslie & Chaloupka, Amy. American Story. 2009. *(978-0-9710703-8-7(5))* Kohler, John Michael Arts Ctr.

Underground Pop. 2010. (Illus.). 50p. pap. 25.00 *(978-0-943526-47-8(7))* Parrish Art Museum, The.

Underwood, Sandra L. Art in Savannah: A Guide to the Monuments, Museums, Galleries, & Other Places. 2007. (Illus.). 144p. pap. 14.95 *(978-0-7643-2649-3(X))* Schiffer Publishing, Ltd.

Unruh, Allison, ed. Robert Indiana: New Perspectives. 2012. (ENG., Illus.). 240p. 70.00 ***(978-3-7757-3135-5(0))*** Hatje Cantz Verlag GmbH & Co KG DEU. Dist: D.A.P./Distributed Art Pubs.

Updike, Robin & Dailey, Michael. Michael Dailey: Color, Light, Time, & Place - Selected Works, 1965-2007. 2008. (ENG., Illus.). 48p. *(978-0-295-98830-6(4))* Univ. of Washington Pr.

Vaina, John Thomas. Art Unseen: The Sculptures, Inventions, & Scale Models of Sebastian Thomas Vaina. 2009. 40p. pap. 21.99 *(978-1-4415-7375-9(5))* Xlibris Corp.

Vallejo, Boris & Bell, Julie. Imaginistix: The Art of Boris Vallejo & Julie Bell. 2007. (ENG., Illus.). 192p. 29.95 *(978-0-06-113846-1(0)*, Collins Design) HarperCollins Pubs.

van Bogaert, Emily & Brothers, Stephanie. Bryce Hudson: Explorations in the Shadow of Pop Culture. 2009. 56p. 19.95 *(978-0-9797006-1-3(2))* Holland Brown.

van Duyn, Edna, ed. Michael Borremans: Weight. 2008. (ENG., Illus.). 88p. 45.00 *(978-3-7757-2130-1(4))* Hatje Cantz Verlag GmbH & Co KG DEU. Dist: D.A.P./Distributed Art Pubs.

Van Dyke, Nella, contrib. by. Art & Context: The '50s And '60s. 2006. (Illus.). 78p. *(978-0-9755662-2-0(9))* Museum of Art, Washington State Univ.

Van Hoesen, Beth, et al. 5,000 Years of Chinese Jade: Featuring Selections from the National Museum of History, Taiwan, & the Arthur M. Sackler Gallery, Smithsonian Institution, 1 vol. 2011. (ENG., Illus.). 130p. pap. 29.95 ***(978-0-615-47180-8(3))*** San Antonio Museum of Art.

Vardi, David, ed. Supermix: The Union of Diverse Contemporary Art in Miami. 2008. (ENG & SPA., Illus.). 303p. lib. bdg. 20.00 *(978-0-9778621-3-9(5))* Edge Zones, Inc.

Various Authors. Contraluz: Juan Gatti. 2012. (ENG & SPA., Illus.). 168p. 90.00 ***(978-84-15253-34-1(6))*** T.F. Editores ESP. Dist: National Bk. Network.

—Rubell Family Collection: Paintings. 2012. (ENG., Illus.). 240p. pap. 43.00 ***(978-84-15253-35-8(4))*** T.F. Editores ESP. Dist: National Bk. Network.

Varnedoe, Kirk. Pictures of Nothing: Abstract Art since Pollock. 2006. (Bollingen Ser.: Vol. 2003). (ENG., Illus.). 304p. 49.95 *(978-0-691-12678-4(X))* Princeton Univ. Pr.

Vasquez, Jaime, et al. The Metaphorical Dream: The Art of Jaime Vasquez. 2011. ***(978-1-936658-03-9(8))*** QCC Art Gallery.

Vess, Charles. Drawing down the Moon: The Art of Charles Vess. 2011. 212p. pap. 29.99 ***(978-1-59582-765-4(X))*** Dark Horse Comics.

Vicario, Gilbert, et al, texts. Daniel Joseph Martinez. 2009. (ENG., Illus.). 248p. 60.00 *(978-3-7757-2305-3(6))* Hatje Cantz Verlag GmbH & Co KG DEU. Dist: D.A.P./Distributed Art Pubs.

Villareal, Leo. Leo Villareal. 2010. (ENG., Illus.). 192p. 55.00 *(978-3-7757-2656-5(X))* Hatje Cantz Verlag GmbH & Co KG DEU. Dist: D.A.P./Distributed Art Pubs.

Vine, Richard & Gaillard, Christopher. William Steiger: Transport. 2011. (ENG., Illus.). 180p. 60.00 *(978-1-55595-358-4(1))* Hudson Hills Pr. LLC.

Violette, Robert, ed. Carnal Knowledge. 2011. (ENG., Illus.). 144p. 75.00 *(978-1-900828-30-7(8))* Violette Editions GBR. Dist: D.A.P./Distributed Art Pubs.

Visocky O'Grady, Jennifer & O'Grady, Ken. A Designer's Research Manual: Succeed in Design by Knowing Your Clients & What They Really Need. 2009. (Design Field Guide Ser.). (ENG., Illus.). 192p. pap. 25.00 *(978-1-59253-557-6(7)*, 159253557) Quayside.

Volk, Gregory & Russ, Sabine, texts. Carnival Within. An Exhibition Made in America: Discover Us! 2010. (ENG., Illus.). 298p. pap. 42.00 *(978-3-941185-20-3(9))* Verlag fur Moderne Kunst DEU. Dist: D.A.P./Distributed Art Pubs.

Volla, Matt. Matt Volla's Unruly Drawings. 2007. (Illus.). 224p. pap. 20.00 *(978-0-9778689-1-9(5))* Front Forty Pr.

von Amelunxen, Hubertus, et al, eds. Gordon Matta-Clark: Moment to Moment: Space. 2012. (ENG., Illus.). 224p. pap. 60.00 ***(978-3-86984-138-0(9))*** Verlag fur Moderne Kunst DEU. Dist: D.A.P./Distributed Art Pubs.

Vossia. 2007. (Illus.). 96p. 19.95 *(978-0-9778854-5-9(3))* Upper Playground Pubng.

Wagner, Anne Middleton. A House Divided: American Art since 1955. 2012. (ENG., Illus.). 240p. 70.00 *(978-0-520-26847-0(4))*; pap. 34.95 *(978-0-520-27097-8(5))* Univ. of California Pr.

Wagner, David J. American Wildlife Art. 2008. *(978-0-9778028-6-9(8))* Marquand Bks., Inc.

Wainwright, Lisa. Things of Nature & the Nature of Things: John Wilde in the Mcclain Collection. 2007. (Chazen Museum of Art Catalogs Ser.). (Illus.). 46p. pap. 29.95 *(978-0-932900-98-2(4))* Univ. of Wisconsin-Madison, Chazen Museum of Art.

Walker, Andrew & Turk, Janeen. Joe Jones: Radical Painter of the American Scene. 2010. (ENG., Illus.). 224p. 60.00 *(978-0-89178-094-6(7))* St. Louis Art Museum.

Walker, Hamza, et al, texts. Restless Empathy. 2010. (ENG., Illus.). 192p. pap. 40.00 *(978-0-934324-49-6(2))* Aspen Art Museum.

Walker, Hollis. Zink: The Language of Enchantment. 2006. (New Mexico Magazine Artist Ser.: No. 6). (ENG., Illus.). 96p. 19.95 *(978-0-937206-90-4(3))* New Mexico Magazine.

Walker, Stephen. Gordon Matta-Clark: Art, Architecture & the Attack on Modernism. 2009. (ENG., Illus.). 224p. pap. 31.00 *(978-1-84511-966-9(5))* I. B. Tauris & Co., Ltd. GBR. Dist: Macmillan.

Wallace, Kevin. River of Destiny: The Life & Work of Binh Pho. 2006. pap. 35.00 *(978-0-9712772-6-7(5))* Long Beach Museum of Art.

Ward, Gerald W. R., et al. contrib. by. American Decorative Arts: MFA Highlights, 1 vol. 2006. (ENG., Illus.). 224p. (gr. 13-18). pap. 19.95 *(978-0-87846-698-6(3))* Museum of Fine Arts, Boston.

Ward, Joseph. American Silences: The Realism of James Agee, Walker Evans, & Edward Hopper. 2010. (ENG., Illus.). 235p. pap. 29.95 *(978-1-4128-1097-5(3))* Transaction Pubs.

Ware, Chris. Uninked: Paintings, Sculpture & Graphic Works by Five Cartoonists. 2007. *(978-0-910407-59-5(2))* Phoenix Art Museum.

Warhol, Andy. Andy Warhol: Strange World. 2009. (ENG., Illus.). 78p. pap. 40.00 *(978-0-9794164-3-9(4))* Kasmin, Paul Gallery.

Warhol, Andy, et al. Warhol from the Sonnabend Collection. 2009. (ENG., Illus.). 180p. 85.00 *(978-0-8478-3277-4(5))* Rizzoli International Pubns., Inc.

Wark, Jayne. Radical Gestures: Feminism & Performance Art in North America. 2006. (ENG., Illus.). 304p. (C). *(978-0-7735-2956-4(X))*; per. *(978-0-7735-3066-9(5))* McGill-Queen's Univ. Pr.

Warren, Isensee. Warren Isensee. 2008. (Illus.). 34p. per. *(978-0-9795501-2-6(2))* Danese.

Warren, Lynne. Chicago Imagists. 2011. ***(978-0-913883-36-5(0))*** Madison Art Ctr., Inc.

Warren, Lynne. Jim Nutt: Coming into Character. 2011. (ENG., Illus.). 136p. 35.00 *(978-0-300-17238-6(3))* Yale Univ. Pr.

Warren, Lynne, ed. Alexander Calder & Contemporary Art: Form - Balance - Joy. 2010. (ENG., Illus.). 176p. 45.00 *(978-0-500-51523-5(9)*, 551523) Thames & Hudson.

Waschek, Matthias & Mani, Camran, eds. Dan Flavin: Constructed Light. 2008. 0.00 *(978-0-9714648-7-2(1))* Pulitzer Foundation For The Arts.

Webb, Alex, photos by. Alex Webb: the Suffering of Light. 2011. (ENG., Illus.). 204p. 65.00 *(978-1-59711-173-7(2))* Aperture Foundation, Inc.

Weber, Bruce. All-American VI: Larger Than Life. 2006. (Illus.). 192p. mass mkt. 155.00 net. *(978-0-9787124-1-9(2)*, Little Bear Pr.) Little Bear, Inc.

—All-American VII: An Anthem for the South: 'till I Get It Right. 2007. 192p. pap. *(978-0-9787124-2-6(0)*, Little Bear Pr.) Little Bear, Inc.

Webster, Kyle T. Deadline Drawings: Volume 1. 2007. 78p. pap. 29.95 *(978-0-615-17063-3(3))* Webster, Kyle T.

Webster, Sue & Noble, Tim. British Rubbish. 2011. (ENG., Illus.). 240p. 65.00 *(978-0-8478-3694-9(0))* Rizzoli International Pubns., Inc.

Weibel, Peter & Blase, Christoph, eds. Record Again! 40jahrevideokunst.de - Teil 2. 2011. (ENG., Illus.). 536p. pap. 55.00 ***(978-3-7757-2522-4(9))*** Hatje Cantz Verlag GmbH & Co KG DEU. Dist: D.A.P./Distributed Art Pubs.

Weinberg, Adam D., frwd. Whitney Museum of American Art at Altria: 25 Years. 2008. (Illus.). 192p. 45.00 *(978-0-300-13933-4(0))* Yale Univ. Pr.

Weiner, Lawrence. Lawrence Weiner: If in Fact There Is A Context. 2011. (ENG., Illus.). 24p. pap. 10.00 ***(978-3-7757-2857-7(0))*** Hatje Cantz Verlag GmbH & Co KG DEU. Dist: D.A.P./Distributed Art Pubs.

Weiss, Jeffrey, ed. Dan Flavin: New Light. 2006. (ENG., Illus.). 176p. pap. 27.00 *(978-0-300-11409-6(5))* Yale Univ. Pr.

Westheider, Ortrud & Muller, Karsten, eds. Neue Welt: Die Erfindung der amerikanischen Malerei. 2007. (GER., Illus.). 240p. (C). 52.50 *(978-3-7774-3415-5(9))* Hirmer Verlag GmbH DEU. Dist: Brown, David Bk. Co., The.

White, Doug. Drawing & Rendering the Figure in Black & White & Colour: A Student Guide. 2011. pap. 24.95 ***(978-0-533-16495-0(8))*** Vantage Pr., Inc.

White, Lauralynn. Chautauqua Sketchbook 2009. 2010. 148p. pap. 19.99 *(978-0-557-54838-5(1))* Lulu Enterprises Inc.

Whitehouse, David. Islamic Glass in the Corning Museum of Glass. 2010. (Illus.). *(978-0-87290-175-9(0))* Corning Museum of Glass.

Whitney. Christian Marclay - Festival, 3 vols. 2010. (Illus.). 200p. pap. *(978-0-300-16900-3(0))* Yale Univ. Pr.

Whitney Gallery of Western Art Staff, contrib. by. Timeless Treasures: 50 Favorites from the Whitney Gallery of Western Art. 2008. pap. *(978-0-931618-68-0(1))* Buffalo Bill Historical Ctr.

Whitney Museum of American Art Staff, contrib. by. Independent Study Program: 40 Years: Whitney Museum of American Art, 1968-2008. 2008. pap. *(978-0-87427-158-4(4))* Whitney Museum of American Art.

Whyte, Mary. Working South: Paintings & Sketches. 2011. (Illus.). 128p. 49.95 *(978-1-57003-966-9(6))*; pap. 29.95 *(978-1-57003-967-6(4))* Univ. of South Carolina Pr.

Wiggins, Colin & de Wildt, Annemarie. The Hoerengracht: Kienholz. 2010. (ENG., Illus.). 56p. pap. 15.00 *(978-1-85709-453-4(0))* Yale Univ. Pr.

wildermuth, nick. Art by Nick Wildermuth. 2010. 76p. pap. 25.80 *(978-0-557-52662-8(0))* Lulu Enterprises Inc.

Willers, Karl. Milton Avery & the End of Modernism. 2011. 80p. pap. 20.00 ***(978-0-615-40181-2(3)***, Suny Pr.) State Univ. of New York Pr.

Williams, Charlotte & Williams, Evelyn A., eds. Denis Williams: New & Collected Essays.: A Life in Works. 2010. (ENG., Illus.). 262p. 75.00 *(978-90-420-2791-6(6))* Rodopi.

Williams, Christopher, et al. Christopher Williams. For Example: Dix-Huit Leçons Sur La Société Industrielle (Revision 11) Kunsthalle Baden-Baden. 2011. (ENG & GER., Illus.). 208p. pap. 35.00 *(978-3-86560-844-4(2))* Verlag der Buchhandlung Walther Konig DEU. Dist: D.A.P./Distributed Art Pubs.

Williams, Emmett. A Flexible History of Fluxus Facts & Fictions. 2007. (ENG., Illus.). 152p. 45.00 *(978-0-500-97664-7(3))* Thames & Hudson.

Wills, David. Audrey in The 60s. 2012. (ENG.). 256p. 40.00 ***(978-0-06-220901-6(9))*** HarperCollins Pubs.

Wilmerding, John. Tom Wesselmann: His Voice & Vision. 2008. (ENG., Illus.). 288p. 60.00 *(978-0-8478-3085-5(3))* Rizzoli International Pubns., Inc.

Wilmerding, John & Komanecky, Michael K., contrib. by. Robert Indiana & the Star of Hope. 2009. (ENG., Illus.). 128p. 45.00 *(978-0-300-15470-2(4))* Yale Univ. Pr.

Wilson, Janet. South American Parchment Craft. 2006. (Passion for Paper Ser.). (ENG., Illus.). 80p. pap. 19.95 *(978-1-84448-065-4(8))* Search Pr., Ltd. GBR. Dist: Independent Pubs. Group.

Wilson, Kristina. The Modern Eye: Stieglitz, Moma & the Art of the Exhibition, 1925-1934. 2009. (ENG., Illus.). 256p. 50.00 *(978-0-300-14916-6(6))* Yale Univ. Pr.

Wilson, Michael. Contemporary Art in North America: Artworld. Black Dog Publishing Staff, ed. 2011. (Artworld Ser.). (ENG., Illus.). 240p. 49.95 *(978-1-907317-23-1(6))* Black Dog Publishing Ltd. GBR. Dist: Perseus Distribution.

Witkovsky, Matthew S., ed. Dawoud Bey: Harlem U. S. A. 2012. (ENG., Illus.). 88p. 25.00 ***(978-0-300-18126-5(4))*** Art Institute of Chicago.

Wolfe, Ann M. Suburban Escape: The Art of California Sprawl. 2006. (Illus.). 132p. pap. 35.00 *(978-1-930066-54-0(6))* Ctr. for American Places, Inc.

Wolfe, Gregory. Sacred Passion: The Art of William Schickel, Second Edition. 2nd ed. 2010. (ENG., Illus.). 240p. 75.00 *(978-0-268-04417-6(1))* Univ. of Notre Dame Pr.

Wolk-Simon, Linda. Raphael at the Metropolitan: The Colonna Altarpiece. 2006. (ENG., Illus.). 76p. per. 19.95 *(978-0-300-11790-5(6))* Yale Univ. Pr.

Woodall, Joanna. Amor, Mors, Memoria: The Mimetic Art of Antonis Mor. 2007. (ENG.). 272p. 60.00 *(978-0-300-11122-4(3))* Yale Univ. Pr.

Woodward, Fred, text. Listen. 2010. (ENG., Illus.). 200p. 75.00 *(978-0-8478-3464-8(6))* Rizzoli International Pubns., Inc.

Wool, Christopher, photos by. Christopher Wool. 2008. (ENG., Illus.). 40p. 50.00 *(978-3-935567-42-8(1))* Holzwarth Pubns. DEU. Dist: D.A.P./Distributed Art Pubs.

—Christopher Wool: Pattern Paintings 1987-2000. 2008. (ENG., Illus.). 48p. pap. 25.00 *(978-0-9709090-7-7(1))* Skarstedt Fine Art.

Wyatt, Gary. Susan Point. (Illus.). pap. 39.95 *(978-1-55054-810-5(7))* D&M Pubs. Inc. CAN. Dist: Perseus-PGW.

Wylie, Charles, et al, texts. On Kawara: 10 Tableaux & 16,952 Pages. 2008. (ENG., Illus.). 192p. 50.00 *(978-0-300-13734-7(6))* Dallas Museum of Art.

Wyman, Jessica, ed. Pro Forma: Language, Text, Visual Art. 2007. (ENG., Illus.). 64p. pap. 12.95 *(978-0-920397-38-1(7))* Y Y Z Artists Outlet CAN. Dist: LitDistCo.

—Pro Forma Vol. 2: Language/text/visual Art. 2007. (ENG., Illus.). 96p. pap. 14.95 *(978-0-920397-39-8(5))* Y Y Z Artists Outlet CAN. Dist: LitDistCo.

—Pro Forma Vol. 3: Language/text/visual Art. 2007. (ENG., Illus.). 62p. pap. 14.95 *(978-0-920397-40-4(9))* Y Y Z Artists Outlet CAN. Dist: LitDistCo.

Wynne, Rob. Rob Wynne: In cog Nito. 2011. (Illus.). 60p. pap. 20.00 ***(978-1-879173-78-1(6))*** Locks Art Pubns.

Xandra Eden & Gary Indiana. Dike Blair: Now & Again. 2010. (ENG., Illus.). 96p. pap. 35.00 *(978-1-890949-12-9(4))* Univ. of North Carolina at Greensboro Weatherspoon Art Museum.

Yale University, Art Gallery Staff, contrib. by. Art for Yale: Collecting for a New Century: Celebrating the Yale University Art Gallery's 175th Anniversary & the Centennial of Paul Mellon's Birth. 2007. *(978-0-89467-969-8(4))* Yale Univ. Art Gallery.

—From Any Angle: Photographs from the Collection of Doris Bry. 2008. *(978-0-89467-972-8(4))* Yale Univ. Art Gallery.

Yaniger, Derek. Wildsville: The Art of Derek Yaniger. 2008. (Masters of Lowbrow Ser.). (ENG., Illus.). 112p. 27.95 *(978-0-9558336-3-2(9))* Korero Books LLP GBR. Dist: Independent Pubs. Group.

Yoe, Craig. Krazy Kat & the Art of George Herriman: A Celebration. 2011. (ENG., Illus.). 224p. 29.95 *(978-0-8109-9594-9(8))* Abrams.

Young, Aaron. Aaron Young: Repeat Offender. 2011. (ENG., Illus.). 67p. 35.00 *(978-89-92233-42-2(6))* Kukje Gallery Inc. KOR. Dist: D.A.P./Distributed Art Pubs.

Yount, Sylvia. Private Passion, Public Promise: The James W. & Frances G. Mcglothlin Collection of American Art. 2010. (ENG., Illus.). 96p. (gr. 17). 30.00 *(978-0-917046-95-7(1))* Univ. Pr. of Virginia.

A

Zakheim, Masha. Coit Tower, San Francisco: Its History & Art. 2009. *(978-1-884244-32-2(7))* volcano pr.

Zauith, Guilherme & Fox-Tucker, Matt. Textura Dos: Buenos Aires Street Art. 2010. (ENG & SPA., Illus.). 160p. 35.00 *(978-1-935613-03-9(0))* Batty, Mark Pub., LLC.

Zehnder, Amanda, text. Impressionism & Post-Impressionism Collection Highlights: Carnegie Museum of Art. 2012. (ENG., Illus.). 176p. pap. 19.95 ***(978-0-88039-054-5(9))*** Carnegie Museum of Art, The.

Zinn, Howard, et al. Eleanor Rubin Dreams of Despair. 2011. (ENG., Illus.). 64p. pap. 24.95 *(978-88-8158-788-9(2))* Charta ITA. Dist: D.A.P./Distributed Art Pubs.

Zuber, Ed. Scrambled & Colored Eggs. 2010. 128p. pap. 38.49 *(978-1-4389-5517-9(0))* AuthorHouse.

Zurier, Rebecca. Picturing the City: Urban Vision & the Ashcan School. 2006. (Illus.). 407p. 55.00 *(978-0-520-22018-8(8))* Univ. of California Pr.

2007 Portland Museum of Art Biennial. 2007. per. 13.95 *(978-0-916857-44-8(1))* Portland Museum of Art.

ART, AMERICAN—BIBLIOGRAPHY

Fox, Ron. Cow Parade West Hartford: Around the World & Home Again. 2007. pap. 22.00 *(978-1-933197-42-5(0))* Orange Frazer Pr.

Schimmelman, Janice Gayle. Books on Art in Early America: Books on Art, Aesthetics & Instruction Available in American Libraries & Bookstores Through 1815. 2007. (ENG.). 292p. 65.00 *(978-1-58456-214-6(5))* Oak Knoll Pr.

ART, AMERICAN—HISTORY

Bach, Jonathan, et al. In the Future... Entertainment Design at Art Center College of Design. 2006. (ENG., Illus.). 175p. 39.95 *(978-1-933492-18-6(X))* Design Studio Pr.

Beauchamp, Monte & North, Bill. Blab World Number 1. 2010. (ENG., Illus.). 128p. 24.95 *(978-0-86719-746-4(3))* Last Gasp of San Francisco.

Becker, Stephen, ed. Theodore Wores in the Southwest. 2007. (California Historical Society Ser.). (Illus.). 98p. per. 24.95 *(978-1-59714-047-8(3))* Heyday.

Braddock, Alan C. & Irmscher, Christoph, eds. A Keener Perception: Ecocritical Studies in American Art History. 2009. (ENG., Illus.). 304p. 60.00 *(978-0-8173-1668-6(X))*; pap. 29.95 *(978-0-8173-5551-7(0))* Univ. of Alabama Pr.

Bruhn, Thomas P. & Sternway, Kate. The American Print: Originality & Experimentation 1790-1890. Date not set. (Illus.). 128p. (Orig.). pap. 14.95 *(978-0-918386-44-1(6))* William Benton Museum of Art.

Cadge Moore, Catie. Cultural Diversity in American Art History: An Introduction to Intercultural Studies Through Visual Arts. rev. ed. 2009. (ENG.). 164p. pap. 44.35 *(978-0-7575-6980-7(3))* Kendall Hunt Publishing Co.

Carder, James N. American Art at Dumbarton Oaks. 2011. (Dumbarton Oaks Collection Ser.). (ENG., Illus.). 136p. pap. 20.95 *(978-0-88402-366-1(4))* Dumbarton Oaks.

Champney, Benjamin. Sixty Years' Memories of Art & Artists. 2010. 224p. pap. 25.75 *(978-1-178-07509-0(5))* BiblioBazaar.

—Sixty Years' Memories of Art & Artists. 2010. 68p. pap. 20.00 *(978-1-151-81929-1(8))* General Bks. LLC.

Charwood, Lindsay & Tilton, Connie Rogers, eds. L. A. Object & David Hammons Body Prints. 2011. (ENG., Illus.). 424p. 65.00 *(978-1-4276-1374-5(5))* Tilton Gallery.

Cooper, James Fenimore. Knights of the Brush: The Hudson River School & the Moral Landscape. 2008. (ENG., Illus.). 112p. 35.00 *(978-0-9818663-0-7(1))* Newington Cropsey Cultural Studies Ctr.

Cox, Kenyon. The Classic Point of View. 2009. 74p. pap. *(978-1-151-54766-8(2))* Books LLC.

Crump, Robert L. Minnesota Prints & Printmakers, 1900-1945. 2009. (ENG., Illus.). 208p. 49.95 *(978-0-87351-635-8(4))* Minnesota Historical Society Pr.

Cuba, Nan & Robinson, Riley. Art at Our Doorstep: San Antonio Writers & Artists. 2008. (ENG., Illus.). 224p. pap. 29.95 *(978-1-59534-049-8(1))* Trinity Univ. Pr.

Curtis, Judith A. Rocky Neck Art Colony, 1850-1950. 2008. (Illus.). 160p. 34.95 *(978-0-9794505-0-1(0))* Rocky Neck Art Colony, Inc., The.

Curtis, Shelley, ed. This Bountiful Place: Art about Agriculture: the Permanent Collection. 2007. (Illus.). 256p. per. 26.00 *(978-0-87595-303-8(4))* Oregon Historical Society Pr.

Dana, John Cotton. American Art. 31p. reprint ed. lib. bdg. 88.00 *(978-0-7222-0270-8(9))* Library Reprints, Inc.

Davidson, Susan, ed. Art in America: 300 Years of Innovation. 2007. (ENG., Illus.). 351p. 69.95 *(978-1-85894-394-7(9))* Merrell Pubs. Ltd. GBR. Dist: Perseus Distribution.

Drohojowska-Philp, Hunter. Rebels in Paradise: The Los Angeles Art Scene & The 1960s. 2011. (ENG., Illus.). 288p. 32.50 *(978-0-8050-8836-6(9))* Holt, Henry & Co.

Dunlap, William & Bayley, Frank W. A History of the Rise & Progress of the Arts of Design in the United States, 3 vols. (Illus.). reprint ed. lib. bdg. 375.00 *(978-0-7222-4674-0(9))* Library Reprints, Inc.

Flammarion Staff. Flammarion Fall 2004 Catalog. (Illus.). *(978-2-08-114378-4(X))* Flammarion et Cie FRA. Dist: Macmillan.

Fletcher, William D., frwd. Clare Leighton an Exhibition: American Sheaves English Seed Corn. (Illus.). pap. 3.00 *(978-0-89073-098-0(9)*, 180) Boston Public Library.

Flora, Jim. The Sweetly Diabolic Art of Jim Flora. Chusid, Irwin & Economon, Barbara, eds. 2009. (ENG., Illus.). 180p. pap. 34.99 *(978-1-60699-159-6(0)*, 699159) Fantagraphics Bks.

Groseclose & Wierich. Internationalizing Hist American Art. pap. 35.00 *(978-0-271-03088-3(7))* Pennsylvania State Univ. Pr.

Guilbaut, Serge, contrib. by. Be-Bomb: The Transatlantic War of Images & All That Jazz. 1946-1956. 2008. (Illus.). 774p. pap. *(978-84-89771-47-5(2))* Museu d'Art Contemporani de Barcelona.

Hale, Sondra & Wolverton, Terry, eds. From Site to Vision: The Woman's Building in Contemporary Culture. 2011. pap. 27.59 ***(978-0-930209-24-7(9))*** Maltz, Ben Gallery, Otis College of Art & Design.

Hernandez, Jo Farb. Gerald Walburg. ltd. ed. 2007. 184p. 49.95 *(978-0-9721984-1-7(5))* Thompson, Natalie & James Art Gallery,San Jose State University.

Horse Capture, Joe D., et al, contrib. by. Native American Art at Dartmouth: Highlights from the Hood Museum of Art. 2011. (Illus.). 216p. pap. 40.00 *(978-1-61168-033-1(6))* Hood Museum of Art & Univ. Pr. of New England.

Joan Stuhr, ed. Ritual Beauty: Art of the Ancient Americas. 2009. (ENG., Illus.). 168p. 75.00 *(978-0-9814840-2-0(6))* Univ. of Arizona Museum of Art.

Keiter, Ellen J., et al. Shattering Glass: New Perspectives: November 11, 2007-February 24, 2008, Katonah Museum of Art. 2007. (Illus.). 40p. pap. *(978-0-915171-73-6(2))* Katonah Gallery.

Koch, Polly. The Old, Weird America, 1 vol. 2008. (ENG., Illus.). 160p. 34.99 *(978-1-933619-12-5(0))* Contemporary Arts Museum, Houston.

Koplos, Janet & Metcalf, Bruce. Makers: A History of American Studio Craft. 2010. (ENG., Illus.). 544p. 65.00 *(978-0-8078-3413-8(0))* Univ. of North Carolina Pr.

Landauer, Susan, frwd. Grillo: Abstract Expressionism: the Formative Years 1946-1948. 2010. (ENG.). 134p. 50.00 *(978-0-9823196-6-6(5))* Fields Publishing.

Lark Books Staff. Quilt National 2009: The Best of Contemporary Quilts - More Than 80 Inspiring Creations. 2009. (Quilt National Ser.). (ENG., Illus.). 112p. 24.95 *(978-1-60059-423-6(9))* Lark Bks.

LeBlanc, Steven A. & Henderson, Lucia R. Symbols in Clay: Seeking Artists' Identities in Hopi Yellow Ware Bowls. 2009. (Papers of the Peabody Museum Ser.: 84). (Illus.). 184p. pap. 35.00 *(978-0-87365-212-4(6))* Peabody Museum of Archaeology & Ethnology, Harvard Univ., Pubns. Dept.

Loebl, Suzanne. America's Medicis: The Rockefellers & Their Astonishing Cultural Legacy. 2010. (ENG.). 448p. 34.99 *(978-0-06-123722-5(1))* HarperCollins Pubs.

Malia, Peter J. Flying Horses: The Golden Age of American Carousel Art, 1870-1930. ltd. aut. num. ed. 2010. (ENG., Illus.). 200p. 49.50 *(978-0-9825468-2-6(3))* Connecticut Pr., The.

Markonish, Denise, ed. Badlands: New Horizons in Landscape. 2008. (ENG., Illus.). 232p. (gr. 17). pap. 26.95 *(978-0-262-63366-6(3))* MIT Pr.

McElheny, Josiah. Josiah Mcelheny:A Space for an Island Universe. Cooke, Lynne & McElheny, Josiah, eds. 2009. (ENG., Illus.). 136p. 30.00 *(978-84-7506-884-8(7))* Turner, Ediciones S.A. ESP. Dist: D.A.P./Distributed Art Pubs.

Moure, Nancy Dustin Wall. Historical Collections Council Newsletters, January 1999-May 2006 & Miscellaneous Articles. 2006. (Publications in Southern California Art: 9). 741p. 80.00 *(978-0-9614622-9-1(9))* Dustin Pubns.

—Index to Articles on California Art & Artists found in Newspapers published in Laguna Beach (C. 1920-1945), Hollywood (C. 1911-1936) & Pasadena (C. 1900-1940) 2006. (Publications in Southern California Art: 8). 735p. 80.00 *(978-0-9614622-8-4(0))* Dustin Pubns.

Mumford, Robert & Mumford, Lewis. Mumford on Modern Art in The 1930s. Wojtowicz, Robert, ed. 2008. (Illus.). 288p. pap. 22.95 *(978-0-520-25808-2(8))* Univ. of California Pr.

Nittve, Lars, et al, texts. Time & Place, 3 vols. 2009. (ENG., Illus.). 430p. 100.00 *(978-3-86521-641-0(2))* Steidl, Gerhard Druckerei und Verlag DEU. Dist: D.A.P./Distributed Art Pubs.

O'Mahony, Mike. American Art. 2010. (Todo Arte Ser.). (SPA.). 384p. pap. 19.00 *(978-84-9764-733-5(5))* Edimat Libros, S. A. ESP. Dist: Independent Pubs. Group.

Otis College of Art and Design. Doin' It in Public: Feminism & Art at the Woman's Building. Maberry, Sue, ed. 2011. (Illus.). 192p. pap. 30.00 ***(978-0-930209-22-3(2))*** Maltz, Ben Gallery, Otis College of Art & Design.

Pritchard, Gayle A. Uncommon Threads: Ohio's Art Quilt Revolution. 2006. (Ohio Quilt Ser.). (Illus.). 144p. per. 22.95 *(978-0-8214-1706-5(1))* Ohio Univ. Pr.

Robinson, Riley & Cuba, Nan, eds. Art at Our Doorstep: San Antonio Writers & Artists. 2008. (ENG., Illus.). 224p. 50.00 *(978-1-59534-039-9(4))* Trinity Univ. Pr.

Román, Dulce María & Oliver-Smith, Kerry. Paradigms & the Unexpected: Modern & Contemporary Art from the Shey Collection. 2007. *(978-0-9762552-6-0(X))*; pap. *(978-0-9762552-7-7(8))* Harn Museum of Art.

Schebler Roberts, Elise. The Quilt: A History & Celebration of an American Art Form. (ENG., Illus.). 348p. 2010. pap. 24.99 *(978-0-7603-3785-1(3)*, 0760337853) 2007. 50.00 *(978-0-7603-2688-6(6)*, 0760326886) MBI Publishing Co. LLC. (Voyageur Pr).

Sharpe, W. C. & Sharpe, William. New York Nocturne: The City after Dark in Literature, Painting, & Photography, 1850-1950. 2008. (ENG., Illus.). 456p. (C). 39.95 *(978-0-691-13324-9(7))* Princeton Univ. Pr.

Siegel, Katy. Since '45: America & the Making of Contemporary Art. 2011. (ENG., Illus.). 224p. 29.00 *(978-1-86189-773-2(1))* Reaktion Bks., Ltd. GBR. Dist: Chicago Distribution Ctr.

Sielman, Martha & Hemachandra, Ray. Art Quilts: Major Works by Leading Artists. 2008. (Masters Ser.). (ENG., Illus.). 416p. pap. 24.95 *(978-1-60059-107-5(8))* Lark Bks.

Skinner, Tina. 100 Artists of the West Coast II. 2009. (Illus.). 224p. bds. 39.99 *(978-0-7643-3271-5(6))* Schiffer Publishing, Ltd.

Sladen, Mark & Yedgar, Ariella. Panic Attack! Art in the Punk Years. 2007. (ENG., Illus.). 224p. 44.95 *(978-1-85894-403-6(1))* Merrell Pubs. Ltd. GBR. Dist: Perseus Distribution.

South, Will, et al. A Seed of Modernism: The Art Students League of Los Angeles, 1906-1953. 2008. (Illus.). 149p. pap. *(978-1-59714-076-8(7))* Heyday.

Updike, John & Robinson, Greg. A Tragedy of Democracy: Japanese Confinement in North America. 2009. (ENG.). 408p. (gr. 17). 29.95 *(978-0-231-12922-0(X))* Columbia Univ. Pr.

Vincent, Adrian. A Companion to Victorian & Edwardian Artists. (Illus.). 352p. pap. *(978-0-7153-0174-6(8))* David & Charles Pubs. GBR. Dist: David & Charles Pubs.

Weir, David. Decadent Culture in the United States: Art & Literature Against the American Grain, 1890-1926. 2007. (SUNY Series, Studies in the Long Nineteenth Century). (Illus.). 233p. 75.00 *(978-0-7914-7277-4(9))* State Univ. of New York Pr.

—Decadent Culture in the United States: Art & Literature against the American Grain, 1890-1926. 2009. (SUNY Series, Studies in the Long Nineteenth Century). 256p. pap. 29.95 *(978-0-7914-7278-1(7))* State Univ. of New York Pr.

Zehnder, Amanda, ed. Modern Japanese Prints. 2009. (ENG., Illus.). 200p. pap. 34.95 *(978-0-88039-049-1(2))* Carnegie Museum of Art, The.

ART, AMERICAN—ITALIAN INFLUENCES

Dini, Jane, et al. Sargent & Italy. Robertson, Bruce, ed. 2008. (ENG., Illus.). 208p. pap. 40.00 *(978-0-691-13944-9(X))* Princeton Univ. Pr.

Frantz, Susanne K. & Kangas, Matthew. Viva Vetro! Glass Alive!: Venice & America. 2008. (ENG., Illus.). 202p. pap. 29.95 *(978-0-88039-048-4(4))* Carnegie Museum of Art, The.

ART, ANCIENT

see also Classical Antiquities; Seven Wonders of the World

also Art, Greek; Art, Roman; and similar headings

Albersmeier, Sabine. The Art of Ancient Greece. 2007. (Illus.). 206p. pap. *(978-0-911886-69-6(9))* Walters Art Museum, US.

Aoyama, Kazuo. Elite Craft Producers, Artists, & Warriors at Aguateca: Lithic Analysis. 2009. (ENG., Illus.). 224p. 60.00 *(978-0-87480-959-6(2))* Univ. of Utah Pr.

The Art & History of Paestum. 80p. pap. *(978-88-8029-077-3(0))* Casa Editrice Bonechi.

Aruz, Joan, et al, eds. Beyond Babylon: Art, Trade, & Diplomacy in the Second Millennium B. C. 2008. (ENG., Illus.). 548p. 75.00 *(978-0-300-14143-6(2))* Yale Univ. Pr.

Aruz, Joan & Fino, Elisabetta Valtz, eds. Afghanistan: Forging Civilizations along the Silk Road. 2012. (ENG., Illus.). 144p. pap. 35.00 ***(978-0-300-17954-5(5))*** Yale Univ. Pr.

Aruz, Joan, et al. Beyond Babylon: Art, Trade, & Diplomacy in the Second Millennium B.C. 2008. (Illus.). xxiii, 524p. 75.00 *(978-1-58839-295-4(3))* Metropolitan Museum of Art, The.

Bailey, Paul. Censoring Sexuality. 2007. (ENG., Illus.). 112p. 20.00 *(978-1-905422-56-2(3))* Seagull Bks. GBR. Dist: Chicago Distribution Ctr.

Benzel, Kim. Art of the Ancient Near East: A Resource for Educators. 2010. (Illus.). 134p. 79.95 *(978-1-58839-358-6(5))* Metropolitan Museum of Art, The.

Benzel, Kim, et al. Art of the Ancient near East: A Resource for Educators. 2010. (ENG., Illus.). 140p. 79.95 *(978-0-300-16708-5(3))* Yale Univ. Pr.

Bernet Kempers, A. J. Ancient Indonesian Art. 22.50 *(978-0-674-03350-4(7))* Harvard Univ. Pr.

Bonechi, Casa. Pompeii. (Illus.). 128p. pap. *(978-88-7009-454-1(5))* Casa Editrice Bonechi.

Brettell, Richard R. & Dickerson, C. D., III. From the Private Collections of Texas: European Art, Ancient to Modern. 2010. (Illus.). 456p. 65.00 *(978-0-300-14494-9(6))* Kimbell Art Museum.

Butovski, Viktor & Orlova, Maria. The Russian Ornament Sourcebook, 1 vol. 2011. (ENG., Illus.). 336p. 39.95 *(978-1-908126-02-3(7))* Vivays Pubng. Ltd. GBR. Dist: Innovative Logistics.

Cuno, James. Who Owns Antiquity? Museums & the Battle over Our Ancient Heritage. 2008. (ENG., Illus.). 272p. 24.95 *(978-0-691-13712-4(9))* Princeton Univ. Pr.

Deger-Jalkotzy, Sigrid & Schindel, Nikolaus, eds. Gold: Tagung anlasslich der Grundung des Zentrums Archaologie und Altertumswissenschaften an der Osterreichischen Akademie der Wissenschaften, 19. 20. April 2007. 2009. (Denkschriften der Phil. -Hist. Klasse Ser.). (GER., Illus.). 206p. (C). pap. 102.00 *(978-3-7001-6547-7(1))* Austrian Academy of Sciences Press AUT. Dist: Brown, David Bk. Co., The.

Donohue, A. A. & Fullerton, Mark D., eds. Ancient Art & its Historiography. 2011. (ENG., Illus.). 224p. pap. 45.00 *(978-0-521-29259-7(X))* Cambridge Univ. Pr.

Ergin, N. & Redford, S., eds. Perceptions of the Past in the Turkish Republic: Classical & Byzantine Periods. 2010. (Ancient near Eastern Studies Supplement Ser.). (ENG., Illus.). 236p. (C). 115.00 *(978-90-429-2264-8(8))* Peeters Pubs. & Booksellers BEL. Dist: Brown, David Bk. Co., The.

Evans, Linda. Animal Behaviour in Egyptian Art: Representations of the Natural World in Memphite Tomb Scenes. 2010. (ACE Studies). (ENG., Illus.). 350p. (C). pap. 130.00 *(978-0-85668-826-3(6))* Australian Ctr. for Egyptology AUS. Dist: Brown, David Bk. Co., The.

Faure, Élie, et al. Ancient Art. 2010. 256p. *(978-1-84484-682-5(2))* Parkstone International.

Finamore, Daniel & Houston, Stephen, eds. Fiery Pool: The Maya & the Mythic Sea. 2010. (ENG., Illus.). 328p. 65.00 *(978-0-300-16137-3(9))* Yale Univ. Pr.

Frape, Christopher J. Burnished Beauty: The Art of Stone in Early Southeast Asia. 2006. (ENG., Illus.). 58.00 *(978-974-8304-88-5(4))* Orchid Pr. THA. Dist: National Bk. Network.

Frederiksen, Rune & Marchand, Eckart, eds. Plaster Casts: Making, Collecting & Displaying from Classical Antiquity to the Present. (Transformationen der Antike Ser.). (ENG., Illus.). XII, 752p. 2011. 280.00 ***(978-3-11-173105-6(7))*** 2010. 182.00 *(978-3-11-020856-6(3))* De Gruyter, Walter Inc.

Georganteli, Eurydice, et al. Sacred & Profane. 2010. (ENG., Illus.). 128p. 40.00 *(978-1-904832-80-5(6))* Giles, D. Ltd. GBR. Dist: Antique Collectors' Club.

Griffin, Gillet, intro. Ancient American Art: Masterworks of the Pre-Columbian Era, 3500 BC - 1532 AD. 2011. (ENG., Illus.). 392p. 90.00 *(978-88-7439-554-5(X))* 5 Continents ITA. Dist: Hachette Bk. Group.

Gunter, Ann. Greek Art & the Orient. 2009. (ENG., Illus.). 272p. 92.00 *(978-0-521-83257-1(8))* Cambridge Univ. Pr.

Gunter, Ann C. Greek Art & the Orient. 2012. (ENG., Illus.). 272p. (C). pap. 32.99 ***(978-0-521-18299-7(9))*** Cambridge Univ. Pr.

Harrison, Jane E. Ancient Art & Ritual. 2007. 134p. pap. 18.99 *(978-1-4346-0710-2(0))*; (ENG.). 148p. pap. 19.99 *(978-1-4346-0770-6(4))* BiblioBazaar.

Hayes, Elizabeth R. The Evolution of Visual, Literary, & Performing Arts from Tribal Cultures Through the Middle Ages. 2009. (Illus.). xii, 226p. pap. *(978-0-7409-3153-6(9)*, Ohio Univ. Ctr. for International Studies) Paper House Productions.

Hemingway, Séan A. & De Puma, Richard Daniel. Art of the Classical World in the Metropolitan Museum of Art: Greece, Cyprus, Etruria, Rome. 2007. 45.00 *(978-1-58839-219-0(8))*; 60.00 *(978-1-58839-217-6(1))* Metropolitan Museum of Art, The.

Hub, Berthold. Die Perspektive der Antike: Archäologie einer symbolischen Form. 2008. (Europäische Hochschulschriften. Reihe 20: Philosophie Ser.). (GER.). 410p. pap. 99.95 *(978-3-631-57559-8(9))* Lang, Peter GmbH, Europaischer Verlag der Wissenschaften DEU. Dist: Lang, Peter.

Johnson, Robert Bowie. Noah in Ancient Greek Art. 2007. (ENG.). 112p. pap. 11.95 *(978-0-9705438-4-4(0))* Solving Light Bks.

Jones, David M. The Art & Architecture of the Incas. 2012. (ENG., Illus.). 128p. pap. 16.99 ***(978-1-78019-138-6(3))*** Anness Publishing GBR. Dist: National Bk. Network.

Junker, Klaus. Interpreting the Images of Greek Myths: An Introduction. 2011. (ENG., Illus.). 240p. (C). 95.00 ***(978-0-521-89582-8(0))*** Cambridge Univ. Pr.

Knight, Richard Payne. Bacchus & Ariadne According to Ancient Art & Mythology - 2006. pap. 12.95 *(978-1-4304-0327-2(6))* Kessinger Publishing, LLC.

—The Good & Evil Principles According to Ancient Art & Mythology. 2006. pap. 9.95 *(978-1-4304-0320-3(9))* Kessinger Publishing, LLC.

—An Inquiry into the Symbolical Language of Ancient Art & Mythology. 2011. (Cambridge Library Collection - Spiritualism & Esoteric Knowlege Ser.). (ENG.). 210p. pap. 22.99 *(978-1-108-02810-3(1))* Cambridge Univ. Pr.

—The Myrtle & Other Emblems According to Ancient Art And. 2006. pap. 9.95 *(978-1-4304-0324-1(1))* Kessinger Publishing, LLC.

Kraus, Chris, et al, eds. Visualizing the Tragic: Drama, Myth, & Ritual in Greek Art & Literature; Essays in Honour of Froma Zeitlin. 2007. (ENG., Illus.). 480p. 175.00 *(978-0-19-927602-8(1))* Oxford Univ. Pr., Inc.

Künzl-Snodgrass, Annemarie & Snodgrass, Anthony, trs. from GER. Interpreting the Images of Greek Myths: An Introduction. 2011. (ENG., Illus.). 240p. (C). pap. 32.99 ***(978-0-521-72007-6(9))*** Cambridge Univ. Pr.

Mertens, Joan R. How to Read Greek Vases. 2011. (ENG., Illus.). 176p. pap. 25.00 *(978-0-300-15523-5(9))* Yale Univ. Pr.

Mesia Montenegro, Christian, ed. The Art of Precolumbian Ecuador. 2012. (Illus.). 360p. pap. 60.00 *(978-88-7439-596-5(5))* 5 Continents ITA. Dist: Abrams.

Miksic, John. Old Javanese Gold: The Hunter Thompson Collection at the Yale University Art Gallery. 2nd ed. 2011. (ENG., Illus.). 284p. 60.00 *(978-0-300-16910-2(8))* Yale Univ. Art Gallery.

Montenegro, Christian Mesía, frwd. Charms in Pre-Columbian Ecuador. 2011. (ENG., Illus.). 148p. pap. 34.95 *(978-88-7439-591-0(4))* 5 Continents ITA. Dist: Hachette Bk. Group.

Musée du Louvre, contrib. by. The Louvre & the Ancient World: Greek, Etruscan, Roman, Egyptian, & near Eastern Antiquities from the Musée du Louvre. 2007. 35.00 *(978-1-932543-19-3(8))* High Museum of Art.

Nardo, Don, ed. Ancient Egyptian Art & Architecture. 2011. (Eye on Art Ser.). (Illus.). 128p. (YA). (gr. 7-12). 33.45 *(978-1-4205-0674-7(9))* Cengage Gale.

Newby, Zahra & Leader-Newby, Ruth, eds. Art & Inscriptions in the Ancient World. 2006. (ENG., Illus.). 322p. 159.00 *(978-0-521-86851-8(3))* Cambridge Univ. Pr.

Novacek, Gabriella V. Ancient Israel: Highlights from the Collection of the Oriental Institute of the University of Chicago. 2011. (Oriental Institute Museum Publications). (ENG., Illus.). 130p. (C). pap. 41.95 *(978-1-885923-65-3(1))* Oriental Institute of the Univ. of Chicago, The.

Patch, Diana. Dawn of Egyptian Art. 2012. (ENG., Illus.). 288p. 60.00 ***(978-0-300-17952-1(9))*** Yale Univ. Pr.

Phillips, Sam. The Art Lovers' Guide - London: The Finest Art in London by Museum, Artist, or Period. 2011. (Illus.). 240p. pap. 19.95 *(978-0-8478-3628-4(2))*, Skira) Rizzoli International Pubns., Inc.

Piggott, Stuart & Daniel, Glyn E. A Picture Book of Ancient British Art. 2011. (ENG., Illus.). 90p. pap. 21.99 *(978-0-521-17640-8(9))* Cambridge Univ. Pr.

Quette, Béatrice, ed. Cloisonne: Chinese Enamels from the Yuan, Ming & Qing Dynasties. 2011. (ENG., Illus.). 368p. 80.00 *(978-0-300-16720-7(2))* Yale Univ. Pr.

Reber, Franz Von. History of Ancient Art. Clarke, Joseph Thacher, tr. 2007. (ENG.). 500p. 53.95 *(978-0-548-15060-3(5))*; 504p. per. 38.95 *(978-1-4304-4397-1(9))* Kessinger Publishing, LLC.

Richardson, Rufus. Pirene. 2009. pap. 20.32 *(978-1-60724-490-5(X))* Gorgias Pr., LLC.

Rocheleau, Caroline M. Ancient Egyptian Art: Systematic Catalogue of the Collection, North Carolina Museum of Art, Raleigh. 2012. ***(978-0-88259-996-0(8))*** North Carolina Museum of Art.

Schatz, Florence. Ancient Egyptian Art - the Fun Way. 2008. 104p. pap. 33.49 *(978-1-4389-1469-5(5))* AuthorHouse.

Schmandt-Besserat, Denise. When Writing Met Art: From Symbol to Story. 2007. (ENG., Illus.). 144p. 45.00 *(978-0-292-71334-5(7))* Univ. of Texas Pr.

Scholl, Andreas, et al. Greek Vases: Gods, Heroes & Mortals. 2010. (ENG., Illus.). 128p. pap. 29.95 *(978-1-85759-606-9(4))* Scala, Editions FRA. Dist: National Bk. Network.

Smith, Tyler Jo. Komast Dancers in Archaic Greek Art. 2010. (Oxford Monographs on Classical Archaeology Ser.). (ENG., Illus.). 360p. 120.00 *(978-0-19-957865-8(6))* Oxford Univ. Pr., Inc.

Snodgrass, Anthony M. Narration & Allusion in Archaic Greek Art. (ENG., Illus.). 23p. (C). pap. 7.00 *(978-0-904920-08-6(9))* Brown, David Bk. Co., The.

Spier, Jeffrey. Treasures of the Ferrell Collection. 2010. (ENG., Illus.). 340p. (C). 150.00 *(978-3-89500-795-8(1))* Reichert, Ludwig Dr. DEU. Dist: Brown, David Bk. Co., The.

Stewart, Andrew. Classical Greece & the Birth of Western Art. 2008. (ENG., Illus.). 376p. (C). 90.00 *(978-0-521-85321-7(4))* Cambridge Univ. Pr.

Stewart, Andrew & Stewart, Andrew F. Classical Greece & the Birth of Western Art. 2008. (ENG., Illus.). 376p. (C). pap. 28.99 *(978-0-521-61835-9(5))* Cambridge Univ. Pr.

Stokstad, Marilyn & Cothren, Michael. Art History Portable Book 1: Ancient Art. 4th ed. 2010. (ENG.). 272p. (C). pap. 80.00 *(978-0-205-79091-3(7), Prentice Hall)* Prentice Hall PTR.

Török, László. Hellenizing Art in Ancient Nubia, 300 BC-AD 250, & Its Egyptian Models: A Study in "Acculturation" 2011. (Culture & History of the Ancient near East Ser.). (Illus.). XXVI, 486p. ***(978-90-04-21128-5(4))*** BRILL.

Watt, James C. Y. ed. The World of Khubilai Khan: Chinese Art in the Yuan Dynasty. 2010. (ENG., Illus.). 360p. 65.00 *(978-0-300-16656-9(7))* Yale Univ. Pr.

Waxman, Sharon. Loot: The Battle over the Stolen Treasures of the Ancient World. (ENG., Illus.). 432p. 2009. pap. 18.00 *(978-0-8050-9088-8(6))* 2008. 30.00 *(978-0-8050-8653-9(6))* Holt, Henry & Co. (Times Bks.).

Winckelmann. Schriften und Nachlass / Monumenti antichi inediti spiegati ed illustrati. Roma 1767. Borbein & Kunze, eds. 2011. (Schriften und Nachlass Ser.). (GER & ITA., Illus.). 622p. (C). 123.00 ***(978-3-8053-4193-6(8))*** Zabern, Philipp von Verlag, GmbH DEU. Dist: Brown, David Bk. Co., The.

Winter, Irene. On the Art in the Ancient Near East, 2 vols. 2009. (Illus.). *(978-90-04-17500-6(8))*; *(978-90-04-17237-1(8))* BRILL.

Winter, Irene, et al. Ancient near Eastern Art in Context: Studies in Honor of Irene J. Winter by Her Students. 2007. (Culture & History of the Ancient near East Ser.). (Illus.). 536p. *(978-90-04-15702-6(6))* BRILL.

Winter, Irene J. & Winter, Irene. On the Art in the Ancient Near East, 2 vols. 2009. (Illus.). *(978-90-04-17499-3(0))* BRILL.

ART, ANGLO-SAXON

Cramp, Rosemary, et al. Aedificia Nova: Studies in Honor of Rosemary Cramp. 2008. (Illus.). xv, 427p. 80.00 *(978-1-58044-110-0(6))* Medieval Institute Pubns.

Crawford, Sally, et al. Form & Order in the Anglo-Saxon World, AD 600-1100. 2009. (Anglo-Saxon Studies in Archaeology & History Ser.). (Illus.). 128p. (C). pap. 70.00 *(978-1-905905-13-3(0))* Oxford Univ. Pr. GBR. Dist: Brown, David Bk. Co., The.

Deshman, Robert & Cohen, Adam S. Eye & Mind: Collected Essays in Anglo-Saxon & Early Medieval Art. 2009. *(978-1-58044-122-3(X))*; *(978-1-58044-121-6(1))* Medieval Institute Pubns.

Karkov, Catherine E. The Art of Anglo-Saxon England. 2011. (Boydell Studies in Medieval Art & Architecture Ser.: Volume 1). (Illus.). 348p. 80.00 *(978-1-84383-628-5(9), Boydell Press)* Boydell & Brewer, Ltd. GBR. Dist: Boydell & Brewer, Inc.

Muir, Bernard J., ed. A Digital Facsimile of Oxford, Bodleian Library, MS Junius 11. 2007. cd-rom 395.00 *(978-1-85124-330-3(5))* Bodleian Library GBR. Dist: Chicago Distribution Ctr.

Pollington, Stephen. Anglo-Saxon Art, Myth & Material Culture from the 4th to 7th Century: Wayland's Work. 2010. (ENG., Illus.). 542p. (C). 170.00 *(978-1-898281-56-6(4))* Anglo-Saxon Bks. GBR. Dist: Brown, David Bk. Co., The.

Raw, Barbara Catherine. Anglo-Saxon Crucifixion Iconography & the Art of the Monastic Revival. 2009. (Cambridge Studies in Anglo-Saxon England Ser.). (ENG., Illus.). 328p. (C). pap. 42.00 *(978-0-521-09308-8(2))* Cambridge Univ. Pr.

Webster, Leslie. Anglo-Saxon Art. 2011. 256p. pap. 29.95 ***(978-0-8014-7766-9(2))*** Cornell Univ. Pr.

Westwood, J. O. Celtic & Anglo-Saxon Art & Ornament. 2007. (Dover Pictorial Archives Ser.). (ENG., Illus.). 64p. per. 14.95 *(978-0-486-45816-8(4))* Dover Pubns., Inc.

—Celtic & Anglo-Saxon Art & Ornament in Full Color CD-ROM & Book. 2008. (Dover Electronic Clip Art Ser.). (ENG., Illus.). 48p. pap. 22.95 *(978-0-486-99723-0(5))* Dover Pubns., Inc.

ART, APOCALYPTIC

see Apocalyptic Art

ART, APPLIED

see Art Industries and Trade

ART, ARAB

see Islamic Art

ART, ARMENIAN

Der Nessessian, Sirarpie. The Date of the Initial Miniatures of the Etchmiadzin Gospel. 2010. 84.20 *(978-1-61143-263-3(4))* Gorgias Pr., LLC.

Halajian, John. Armenian Church Architecture: From Dormancy to Revival. 2006. (Illus.). 214p. per. 16.95 *(978-1-59886-090-0(9))* Tete Publishing & Enterprises, LLC.

Karapetian, Vartan, et al. Armenia: Imprints of a Civilization. 2012. (ENG., Illus.). 408p. 75.00 ***(978-88-572-1244-9(0))*** Skira Editore ITA. Dist: Random Hse., Inc.

Kouymjian, Dickran. Between Paris & Fresno: Armenian Studies in Honor of Dickran Kouymjian. 2008. (Armenian Studies). (C). *(978-1-56859-168-1(3))* Mazda Pubs., Inc.

Kurkjian, Vahan M. A History of Armeni. 2011. 564p. 63.95 ***(978-1-258-06149-4(X))*** Literary Licensing, LLC.

Nersessian, Vrej. A Catalogue of the Armenian Manuscripts in the British Library & Other Libraries in the United Kingdom. 2012. (Illus.). 1352p. 250.00 *(978-0-7123-4905-5(7))* British Library, The GBR. Dist: Chicago Distribution Ctr.

ART, ASIAN

Abels, Birgit, ed. Austronesian Soundscapes: Performing Arts in Oceania & Southeast Asia. 2011. (IIAS Publications Ser.). (ENG., Illus.). 336p. pap. *(978-90-8964-085-7(1))* Amsterdam Univ. Pr.

All Rights Reserved, creator. Hkda Awards, Volume 2: Design. No Junkfood. Wrap up Your Freshstuff Now. 2007. (CHI & ENG., Illus.). 367p. 59.95 *(978-988-99001-6-8(5))* All Rights Reserved Ltd. HKG. Dist: Gingko Pr., Inc.

Allan, James W. Art & Architecture of Twelver Shi'ism. 2012. (ENG.). 182p. (C). 60.00 ***(978-1-898592-29-7(2))*** Azimuth Editions GBR. Dist: Brown, David Bk. Co., The.

Assemani, Stephen Evodius & Assemani, Joseph Simon. Catalog of Syriac & Garshuni Manuscripts in the Vatican Library. 2010. (LAT.). 303.76 *(978-1-60724-904-7(9))*; 303.76 *(978-1-60724-905-4(7))* Gorgias Pr., LLC.

Auad, Manuel, ed. The Art of Alex Niño. 2008. (Illus.). 160p. pap. 24.95 *(978-0-9669381-6-6(X))* Auad Publishing.

—The Art of Alex niño, Signed Limited Edition. 2008. 160p. 34.95 *(978-0-9669381-8-0(6))* Auad Publishing.

BAI Staff, ed. A Passage to Asia: 35 Centuries of Exchange Between Asia & Europe, 1 vol. 2010. (ENG.). 271p. 60.00 *(978-90-8586-565-0(4))* Exhibitions International BEL. Dist: Innovative Logistics.

Beltran, Orlando A. Symbolism of Oriental Religious Art. 2011. 234p. 46.95 ***(978-1-258-04376-6(9))*** Literary Licensing, LLC.

Bhatt, Shaila. Translating Museums: A Counterhistory of South Asian Museology. 2012. (Critical Cultural Heritage Ser.). (ENG.). 320p. pap. 37.95 ***(978-1-61132-145-6(X))***; (Illus.). 94.00 ***(978-1-61132-144-9(1))*** Left Coast Pr., Inc.

Blanc, Dominique, et al. Masks of the Himalayas. 2009. (ENG., Illus.). 160p. 45.00 *(978-88-7439-519-4(1))* 5 Continents ITA. Dist: Hachette Bk. Group.

Brand, Heather, ed. Red Hot: Asian Art Today from the Chaney Family Collection. 2008. (ENG., Illus.). 208p. pap. 39.95 *(978-0-300-13889-4(X))* Museum of Fine Arts, Houston.

Brown, Rebecca M. & Hutton, Deborah S., eds. A Companion to Asian Art & Architecture. 201‥. (Blackwell Companions to Art History Ser.: 9). (ENG., Illus.). 688p. 199.95 *(978-1-4051-8537-0(6), Wiley-Blackwell)* Wiley, John & Sons, Inc.

Bucarelli, Angelo. Il Drago e la Farfalla: Arte Contemporanea in Vietnam Ròng Và Bm. 2010. (ITA & ENG., Illus.). 144p. pap. 23.95 *(978-88-492-1015-6(9))* Gangemi ITA. Dist: International Publishers Marketing.

Bunker, Emma C. & Latchford, Douglas. Khmer Bronzes: New Interpretations of the Past. 2011. ***(978-1-58886-111-5(2))*** Art Media Resources, Inc.

Burckhardt, Titus. Foundations of Oriental Art & Symbolism. 2009. (ENG., Illus.). 148p. pap. 22.95 *(978-1-933316-72-7(1))* World Wisdom, Inc.

Cader, Muhanned, ed. The One Year Drawing Project: May 2005 - October 2007. 2008. (Illus.). 416p. pap. *(978-0-9556674-1-1(0))* Actar Birkhauser Distribution.

Castagno, John. African, Asian & Middle Eastern Artists: Signatures & Monograms From 1800. 2008. (ENG., Illus.). 150p. 125.00 *(978-0-8108-6357-6(X))* Scarecrow Pr., Inc.

Chiu, Melissa & Genocchio, Benjamin. Contemporary Art in Asia: A Critical Reader. 2011. (Illus.). ix, 430p. *(978-0-262-01491-5(2))* MIT Pr.

Chiu, Melissa & Genocchio, Benjamin, eds. Contemporary Art in Asia: A Critical Reader. 2011. (ENG., Illus.). 440p. (gr. 17). pap. 29.95 *(978-0-262-51623-5(3))* MIT Pr.

Cort, Louise Allison & Jett, Paul, eds. Gods of Angkor: Bronzes from the National Museum of Cambodia. 2010. (ENG., Illus.). 160p. pap. 40.00 *(978-0-295-99042-2(2))* Sackler, Arthur M. Foundation, The.

Cotter, Suzanne, ed. Out of Beirut, 1 vol. 2007. (ENG., Illus.). 112p. pap. 27.00 *(978-3-905701-90-6(1))* JRP Ringier Kunstverlag AG CHE. Dist: D.A.P./Distributed Art Pubs.

Curtis, John. Oxus Treasure. 2012. (Objects in Focus Ser.). (ENG., Illus.). 64p. (C). pap. 10.00 *(978-0-7141-5079-6(7))* British Museum Pr. GBR. Dist: Brown, David Bk. Co., The.

Dadi, Iftikhar. Modernism & the Art of Muslim South Asia. 2010. (Islamic Civilization & Muslim Networks Ser.). (ENG., Illus.). 360p. 39.95 *(978-0-8078-3358-2(4))* Univ. of North Carolina Pr.

Dalmia, Yashodhara & Hashmi, Salima. Memory, Metaphor, Mutations: The Contemporary Art of India & Pakistan. 2007. (ENG., Illus.). 239p. 199.00 *(978-0-19-567347-0(6))* Oxford Univ. Pr., Inc.

David, Catherine, ed. Hassan Sharif: Works 1973-2010. 2011. (ENG., Illus.). 320p. pap. 60.00 ***(978-3-7757-2824-9(4))*** Hatje Cantz Verlag GmbH & Co KG DEU. Dist: D.A.P./Distributed Art Pubs.

Desai, Vishakha N. Asian Art History in the Twenty-First Century. 2007. (Clark Studies in the Visual Arts). (Illus.). xiii, 253p. *(978-0-931102-73-8(1))* Clark, Sterling & Francine Art Institute.

Desai, Vishakha N., ed. Asian Art History in the Twenty-First Century. 2008. (Clark Studies in the Visual Arts). (ENG., Illus.). 272p. (C). pap. 24.95 *(978-0-300-12553-5(4))* Yale Univ. Pr.

Dopp, Hans-Jurgen. Forbidden Asia. 2012. (Mega Square Ser.). (ENG., Illus.). 256p. 12.95 ***(978-1-906981-44-0(2))*** Parkstone Pr. USA, Ltd.

Douglas, Janet G., et al, told to. Scientific Research in the Field of Asian Art: Proceedings of the First Forbes Symposium at the Freer Gallery of Art. 2007. (ENG., Illus.). 208p. 120.00 *(978-1-873132-38-8(7))* Archetype Pubns. GBR. Dist: National Bk. Network.

DuBasky, Valentina. The Cambodian Journal: Drawings 1994-1998. 2009. (Illus.). 68p. pap. 25.00 *(978-0-9823480-1-7(0), Abingdon Square)* Abingdon Square Publishing, Ltd.

Frape, Christopher J. Burnished Beauty: The Art of Stone in Early Southeast Asia. 2006. (ENG., Illus.). 58.00 *(978-974-8304-88-5(4))* Orchid Pr. THA. Dist: National Bk. Network.

Ganguli, Milada. Naga Art. (Illus.). 96p. (C). 54.00 *(978-1-881570-19-6(3))* Science Pubs.

Gilbert, Helen & Lo, Jacqueline. Performance & Cosmopolitics: Cross-Cultural Transactions in Australasia. 2009. (Studies in International Performance Ser.). (ENG., Illus.). 256p. pap. 32.00 *(978-0-230-23402-4(X))* Palgrave Macmillan.

Grabar, Oleg. Ars Orientalis V3: The Arts of Islam & the East. Grabar, Oleg & Loehr, Max, eds. 2011. 406p. 54.95 ***(978-1-258-06707-6(2))*** Literary Licensing, LLC.

Hagedorn, Annette, ed. The Phenomenon of Foreign in Oriental Art. 2006. (ENG., Illus.). 204p. (C). 150.00 *(978-3-89500-476-6(6))* Reichert, Ludwig Dr. DEU. Dist: Brown, David Bk. Co., The.

Hannes, Nick. Red Journey. 2010. (ENG., Illus.). 144p. 50.00 *(978-90-209-8402-6(0))* Lannoo Pubs./Racine.

Harris, Kristy. Scrapbook Asian Style! Create One-of-a-Kind Projects with Asian-Inspired Materials, Colors & Motifs. 2008. (ENG., Illus.). 192p. pap. 24.95 *(978-0-8048-3933-4(6))* Tuttle Publishing.

Hashmi, Salima & Hamid, Mohsin. Hanging Fire: Contemporary Art from Pakistan. 2009. (ENG., Illus.). 160p. 49.95 *(978-0-300-15418-4(6))* Yale Univ. Pr.

Immerzeel, M. Identity Puzzles: Medieval Christian Art in Syria & Lebanon. 2009. (Orientalia Lovaniensia Analecta Ser.). (ENG.). 334p. (C). 116.00 *(978-90-429-2149-8(8))* Peeters Pubs. & Booksellers BEL. Dist: Brown, David Bk. Co., The.

Jahan, Shahnaj Husne. Abhijñan: Studies in South Asian Archaeology & Art History of Artefacts. 2009. (Bar S Ser.). (ENG., Illus.). 167p. (C). pap. 110.00 *(978-1-4073-0456-8(5))* British Archaeological Reports Ltd. GBR. Dist: Brown, David Bk. Co., The.

Kataoka, Mami & Harding, Allison. Phantoms of Asia: Contemporary Awakens the Past. 2012. (ENG., Illus.). 256p. 35.00 ***(978-0-939117-59-8(2))*** Asian Art Museum of San Francisco.

Kemp, Hans, ed. Doors. 2008. (Illus.). 200p. 16.95 *(978-962-85637-7-7(7))* Visionary World, Ltd. HKG. Dist: AtlasBooks Distribution.

Khemir, Sabiha, et al. From Cordoba to Samarqand: Masterpieces from the New Islamic Art Museum in Doha. 2008. (ENG., Illus.). 224p. 50.00 *(978-88-7439-316-9(4))* 5 Continents ITA. Dist: Hachette Bk. Group.

Khushik, Faheem. Aesthetic & Home Decoration. 2011. 104p. pap. ***(978-3-8443-0921-8(7))*** Lambert Academic Publishing.

Knight, Michael, ed. Collector's Choice, Collector's Voice. 2011. (ENG., Illus.). 64p. pap. 12.95 *(978-0-939117-49-9(5))* Asian Art Museum of San Francisco.

Kumar, Abhishek. Expression of Cultural Identity Through Arts. 2010. 72p. pap. *(978-3-639-24337-6(4))* VDM Verlag Dr. Mueller e.K.

Kunst- und Ausstellungshalle der Bundesrepublik De, ed. Gandhara: Das buddhistische Erbe Pakistans. Legenden, Klöster und Paradiese. 2008. (Illus.). 384p. (C). 68.00 *(978-3-8053-3916-2(X))* Zabern, Philipp von Verlag, GmbH DEU. Dist: Brown, David Bk. Co., The.

Lee-Kalisch, Jeong-hee, et al, eds. Long Life Festschrift in Honour of Roger Goepper. 2006. (Illus.). 289p. pap. *(978-0-8204-9855-3(6))* Lang, Peter AG.

Lent, John A., ed. Southeast Asian Cartooning. 2012. (ENG., Illus.). 304p. pap. 38.95 ***(978-0-87580-678-5(3))*** Northern Illinois Univ. Pr.

Lung, Haha. Mind Fist: The Asian Art of the Ninja Masters. 2008. (ENG.) 240p. 12.95 *(978-0-8065-3062-8(6), Citadel Pr.)* Kensington Publishing Corp.

Magliani, Mauro & Piovan, Barbara, photos by. Kris Hilts: Masterpieces of Southeast Asian Art. 2011. (ENG., Illus.). 160p. 48.00 *(978-88-7439-585-9(X))* 5 Continents ITA. Dist: Hachette Bk. Group.

Marsh, Kevin R. Drawing Lines in the Forest: Creating Wilderness Areas in the Pacific Northwest. 2010. (Weyerhaeuser Environmental Bks.). (ENG.) 256p. pap. 24.95 *(978-0-295-99011-8(2))* Univ. of Washington Pr.

Masselos, Jim, ed. The Great Empires of Asia. 2010. (ENG.). 240p. 34.95 *(978-0-520-26859-3(8))* Univ. of California Pr.

Mattet, Laurence. Arts & Cultures. (ENG.). No. 8. 8th ed. 2009. 360p. pap. 39.00 *(978-2-7572-0070-4(4))*No. 9. 9th ed. 2008. 340p. pap. 39.00 *(978-2-7572-0164-0(6)*, Continental Sales, Inc. (Art Stock Bks. Ltd/Csi).

Melissa, Chiu & Benjamin, Genocchio. Asian Art Now. 2010. (ENG., Illus.). 256p. 60.00 *(978-1-58093-296-1(3))* Monacelli Pr., Inc.

Menzies, Jackie, et al. Asian Collections: The Art Gallery of New South Wales. (Illus.). 352p. pap. 39.95 *(978-0-7347-6351-8(4))* Art Media Resources, Inc.

Merali, Shaheen, ed. Re-Imagining Asia: A Thousand Years of Separation. 2008. (ENG., Illus.). 364p. pap. 29.95 *(978-0-86356-653-0(7))* Saqi Bks. GBR. Dist: Consortium Bk. Sales & Distribution.

Mills, Cynthia, et al. East-West Interchanges in American Art: "A Long & Tumultuous Relationship" 2011. ***(978-1-935623-08-3(7))*** Smithsonian Institution Scholarly Pr.

Mingana, Alphonse, ed. Job of Edessa's Book of Treasures. 2010. 143.36 *(978-1-60724-909-2(X))* Gorgias Pr., LLC.

Morgan, Michelle J. 100 Treasures: The Museum of East Asian Art. (Illus.). 88p. pap. 22.50 *(978-1-897734-11-7(5))* Museum of East Asian Art GBR. Dist: Art Media Resources, Inc.

Moss, Peter & Banks, Anthony. Asian Furniture: A Directory & Sourcebook. Moss, Peter, ed. 2007. (ENG., Illus.). 308p. 70.00 *(978-0-500-51378-1(3))* Thames & Hudson.

Naqvi, Akbar. Image & Identity. 2nd ed. 2011. (Illus.). 302p. pap. 75.00 *(978-0-19-547172-4(5))* Oxford Univ. Pr., Inc.

Neva, Elena. Jewelry of Central Asia. 2008. (Illus.). 144p. pap. *(978-1-934881-11-8(2), M-Graphics)* M-Graphics Publishing.

—Tajik Jewelry. 2010. (ENG & RUS., Illus.). 216p. pap. *(978-1-934881-30-9(9), M-Graphics)* M-Graphics Publishing.

Nietupski, Paul K. Reading Asian Art & Artifacts: Windows to Asia on American College Campuses. 2011. (ENG.). 240p. pap. 32.95 *(978-1-61146-071-1(9))* Lehigh Univ. Pr.

Nietupski, Paul K. & O'Mara, Joan. Reading Asian Art & Artifacts: Windows to Asia on American College Campuses. 2011. (ENG.). 240p. 80.00 *(978-1-61146-070-4(0))* Lehigh Univ. Pr.

North, Michael, ed. Artistic & Cultural Exchanges Between Europe & Asia, 1400-1900: Rethinking Markets, Workshops & Collections. 2010. (Illus.). 216p. 124.95 *(978-0-7546-6937-1(8))* Ashgate Publishing Co.

Otsuka, Ronald. Asia & Spanish America: Trans-Pacific Artistic & Cultural Exchange, 1500-1850. Pierce, Donna, ed. 2009. (ENG.). 208p. (C). pap. 39.95 *(978-0-8061-9973-3(3))* Denver Art Museum.

Pal, Pratapaditya. East Meets West. 2010. (Illus.). 196p. 45.00 *(978-93-80581-00-2(9))* Marg Pubns. IND. Dist: National Bk. Network.

Peleggi, Maurizio, et al, eds. Eye of the Beholder: Reception, Audience, & Practice of Modern Asian Art. 2007. (University of Sydney East Asian Ser.: Vol. 15). (Illus.). 324p. per. *(978-1-876957-10-0(7))* Wild Peony Bk. Pubs. Pty., Ltd.

Pinder, Polly. Handmade Oriental Cards. 2007. (Simple & Stunning Ser.). (ENG., Illus.). 48p. pap. 13.95 *(978-1-84448-210-8(3))* Search Pr., Ltd. GBR. Dist: Independent Pubs. Group.

Proser, Adriana, ed. Pilgrimage & Buddhist Art. 2010. (Illus.). 224p. 65.00 *(978-0-300-15566-2(2))* Yale Univ. Pr.

Raby, Julian, intro. Ideals of Beauty: Asian & American Art in the Freer & Sackler Galleries. 2010. (World of Art Ser.). (ENG., Illus.). 192p. pap. 19.95 *(978-0-500-20403-0(9), 520403)* Thames & Hudson.

Rhie. Early Buddhist Art of China & Central Asia, Volume III: The Western Ch'in in Kansu in the Sixteen Kingdoms Period & Inter-relationships with the Buddhist Art of GandhÀra. 2010. (Handbook of Oriental Studies. Section 4 China Ser.). 1032p. *(978-90-04-18400-8(7))* BRILL.

Rhie, Marylin M. Early Buddhist Art of China & Central Asia. 2007. *(978-90-04-16137-5(6))* BRILL.

Search Press. Oriental Papers: 24 Perforated Papers. 2006. (Crafter's Paper Library). (ENG., Illus.). 48p. pap. 11.95 *(978-1-84448-223-8(5))* Search Pr., Ltd. GBR. Dist: Independent Pubs. Group.

Shashibala & Shashibala. Divine Art. 2007. (ENG., Illus.). 143p. 19.95 *(978-81-7436-321-3(1))* Roli Bks. Private, Ltd. IND. Dist: Ingram Pub. Services.

Skinner, Margarita & Kawar, Widad. Palestinian Embroidery Motifs: A Treasury of Stitches 1850-1950. 2010. (Illus.) 210p. pap. 34.95 *(978-1-901764-47-5(8))* International Publishers Marketing.

Skira Books Staff & Geoffroy-Schneiter, Bérénice. Asian Jewellery: Ethnic Rings, Bracelets, Necklaces, Earrings, Belts, Head Ornaments. 2012. (ENG., Illus.). 312p. pap. 45.00 *(978-88-572-0670-1(2))* Skira Editore ITA. Dist: Random Hse., Inc.

Snyder, Jeffrey B. Asian Ivory. 2007. (Illus.). 288p. pap. 79.95 *(978-0-7643-2728-5(3))* Schiffer Publishing, Ltd.

Srinivasan, Doris M., ed. On the Cusp of an Era: Art in the Pre-Kusana World. 2006. (Brill's Inner Asian Library). (Illus.). 402p. *(978-90-04-15451-3(5))*, BRILL.

Stoute, Ryan. Vigil of the Violentflies. 2011. 36p. pap. 18.41 *(978-1-4269-6224-0(X))* Trafford Publishing.

Sze, Sarah. Sarah Sze: Infinite Line. 2011. (ENG., Illus.). 144p. 55.00 ***(978-0-87848-113-2(3))*** Yale Univ. Pr. GBR. Dist: D.A.P./Distributed Art Pubs.

Taylor, Paul Michael, et al. Turkmenistan: Ancient Arts Today. 2011. pap. 14.95 ***(978-0-9724557-9-4(5))***; (Illus.). 71p. pap. 14.95 ***(978-0-9724557-8-7(7))*** Smithsonian Institution, Asian Cultural History Program.

Teng, Nee Cheong. Nee Cheong: Those the Gods Love Grow Mightier. 2011. (Illus.). 136p. 70.00 **(978-981-08-6053-0(6))** Artpostasia Inc. PHL. Dist: National Bk. Network.

Tingley, Nancy. Arts of Ancient Vietnam: From River Plain to Open Sea. 2009. (ENG., Illus.). 368p. 60.00 *(978-0-300-14696-7(5))* Museum of Fine Arts, Houston.

—Buddhas. 2009. 120p. 29.95 *(978-0-7649-4800-8(8))* Pomegranate Communications, Inc.

Toufic, Jalal. Jalal Toufic: Poes »Das Ovale Porträt«, mit den Augen eines Engels gelesen und umgeschrieben. 2011. (ENG., Illus.). 24p. pap. 10.00 **(978-3-7757-2860-7(0))** Hatje Cantz Verlag GmbH & Co KG DEU. Dist: D.A.P./Distributed Art Pubs.

Tri Postal (Organization: Lille, France) Staff, contrib. by. La Route de la Soie: The Silk Road: Lille3000, Saatchi Gallery. 2010. (FRE & ENG., Illus.). 96p. *(978-2-84278-806-3(0))* Beaux Arts.

Tuli, Neville. Osian's Masterpieces & Museum-Quality Series-VII: Null, Vol. 4. 2012. (ENG., Illus.). 65.00 *(978-1-890206-77-2(6))* Mapin Publishing Pvt. Ltd IND. Dist: National Bk. Network.

Unterholzner, Daniela. Southeast-Asian Fans in Habsburg Collections. 2010. 140p. pap. *(978-3-639-23912-6(1))* VDM Verlag Dr. Mueller e.K.

Vainker, Shelagh & Lin, James C. S. Pu Quan & His Generation: Imperial Painters from Twentieth-Century China. 2006. (ENG & CHI., Illus.). 96p. pap. 19.95 *(978-1-85444-204-8(X))* Ashmolean Museum GBR. Dist: National Bk. Network.

van Cutsem-Vanderstraete, Anne. Powerful Headdresses: Africa & Asia. 2010. (ENG., Illus.). 200p. 85.00 *(978-88-7439-551-4(5))* 5 Continents ITA. Dist: Hachette Bk. Group.

Vo, Nghia M., et al. The Men of Vietnam. 2008. 256p. pap. 17.95 *(978-1-4327-3782-5(1))* Outskirts Pr., Inc.

Weir, Shelagh. Embroidery from Palestine. 2007. (Fabric Folios Ser.). (ENG., Illus.). 88p. pap. 22.50 *(978-0-295-98660-9(3))* Univ. of Washington Pr.

Weller, Alan. Asian Tattoo Flash CD-ROM & Book. 2009. (Dover Electronic Clip Art Ser.). (ENG., Illus.). 48p. pap. 22.95 *(978-0-486-99015-6(X))* Dover Pubns., Inc.

Wilcken, Lane. Filipino Tattoos: Ancient to Modern. 2010. (Illus.). 176p. 39.99 *(978-0-7643-3602-7(9))* Schiffer Publishing, Ltd.

Winter, John, ed. Scientific Research on the Pictorial Arts of Asia: Proceedings of the Second Forbes Symposium at the Freer Gallery of Art. 2007. (ENG., Illus.). 166p. 120.00 *(978-1-873132-74-6(3))* Archetype Pubns. GBR. Dist: National Bk. Network.

Youngman, Robert P., et al. The Youngman Collection: Chinese Jades from Neolithic to Qing. 2008. *(978-1-58886-098-9(1))* Art Media Resources, Inc.

Yuferova, I. P. Fine Arts of Soviet Kazakhstan: Companies-Products-Services. Zhangeldin, E. T., ed. (Illus.). 263p. 49.95 *(978-0-934393-14-0(1))* Rector Pr., Ltd.

Yunus, Noor Azlina. Malaysian Batik: Reinventing a Tradition. 2012. (ENG., Illus.). 176p. 34.95 **(978-0-8048-4264-8(7))** Tuttle Publishing.

Zhenqing, Gu, ed. Two Asias, Two Europes: An International Exhibition of Contemporary Art, 1 vol. 2008. (ENG., Illus.). 215p. pap. 48.00 *(978-988-99609-4-0(X))* Timezone 8 Ltd. HKG. Dist: D.A.P./Distributed Art Pubs.

ART, ASIAN AMERICAN

see Asian American Art

ART, ASSYRO-BABYLONIAN

Atac, Mehmet Ali. The Mythology of Kingship in Neo-Assyrian Art. 2010. (ENG., Illus.). 300p. (C). 99.00 *(978-0-521-51790-4(7))* Cambridge Univ. Pr.

Gunter, Ann. Greek Art & the Orient. 2009. (ENG., Illus.). 272p. 92.00 *(978-0-521-83257-1(8))* Cambridge Univ. Pr.

Gunter, Ann C. Greek Art & the Orient. 2012. (ENG., Illus.). 272p. (C). pap. 32.99 **(978-0-521-18299-7(9))** Cambridge Univ. Pr.

Rizza, Alfredo. Assyrians & Babylonians: History & Treasures of an Ancient Civilization. 2010. (ENG.). 19.98 *(978-88-544-0457-1(8))* White Star ITA. Dist: Random Hse., Inc.

Steymans, Hans Ulrich, ed. Gilgamesch: Ikonographie eines Helden. 2011. (Orbis Biblicus et Orientalis Ser.). (GER., Illus.). 462p. (C). 158.00 *(978-3-525-54366-5(2))* Vandenhoeck & Ruprecht GmbH & Co. KG DEU. Dist: ISD.

ART, AUSTRALIAN

Anderson, Jaynie. The Cambridge Companion to Australian Art. 2011. (ENG.). 398p. 125.00 **(978-0-521-19700-7(7))**; pap. 55.00 **(978-1-107-60158-1(4))** Cambridge Univ. Pr.

Asmodelle, Estelle. Transience. 2010. 78p. pap. 29.95 *(978-1-4461-5046-7(1))* Lulu Enterprises Inc.

Bunbury, Alisa. Arid Arcadia: Art of the Flinders Ranges. 2007. (Illus.). 108p. 45.00 *(978-0-7308-3021-4(7))* Art Gallery of South Australia AUS. Dist: Antique Collectors' Club.

Cassidy, S. Bleed Bled Said: Adam Geczy & Mike Parr. Storer, Russell, ed. 2011. (ENG.). 52p. (C). pap. 21.95 *(978-1-86487-553-9(4))* Power Pubns. AUS. Dist: Univ. of Washington Pr.

Coyle, Rebecca & Hayward, Philip. Apparition: Holographic Art in Australia. 2011. (ENG.). 144p. (C). pap. 26.95 *(978-0-909952-27-3(2))* Power Pubns. AUS. Dist: Univ. of Washington Pr.

Defenestrate-Bascule, Orryelle. Conjunctio: A Graphic Grimoire. Ansell, Robert, ed. 2008. (Illus.). 64.95 *(978-0-9558130-1-6(8))* Fulgur Ltd. GBR. Dist: Holmes Publishing Group, LLC.

Delany, Max, frwd. Brook Andrew: Eye to Eye. 2007. (Illus.). 86p. *(978-0-9775782-3-8(2))* Monash Univ. Museum of Art.

Dew, Christine. Uncommissioned Art: An A-Z of Australian Graffiti. 2008. (ENG.). 280p. pap. 31.00 *(978-0-522-85506-7(7))* Melbourne Univ. Publishing AUS. Dist: Independent Pubs. Group.

Esau, Erika. Images of the Pacific Rim: Australia & California, 1850-1935. 2011. (ENG., Illus.). 368p. pap. 59.95 *(978-0-909952-39-6(6))* Power Pubns. AUS. Dist: Univ. of Washington Pr.

Gellatly, Kelly. Rosalie Gascoigne. 2009. (ENG.). 128p. pap. 29.95 *(978-0-7241-0302-7(3))* National Gallery of Victoria AUS. Dist: National Bk. Network.

Haddon, A. C. & Rivers, W. H. R. Reports of the Cambridge Anthropological Expedition to Torres Straits: Volume 4, Arts & Crafts, 6 vols. 2011. (ENG., Illus.). 517p. pap. 60.00 *(978-0-521-17988-1(2))* Cambridge Univ. Pr.

Heartney, Eleanor, ed. Andrew Rogers: Geoglyphs, Rhythms of Life. 2009. (ENG., Illus.). 646p. (C). 225.00 *(978-88-8158-712-4(2))* Macmillan Art Publishing AUS. Dist: Brown, David Bk. Co., The.

Henderson, Sue, et al, texts. Space Antics Sue Henderson, David Marsden, Penny Mason. 2011. (Illus.). 4p. mass mkt. **(978-0-9808003-5-7(8))** Burnie Regional Art Gallery.

Higgie, Jennifer, text. Scenes. 2010. (ENG., Illus.). 64p. 39.95 *(978-3-03764-029-6(4))* JRP Ringier Kunstverlag AG CHE. Dist: D.A.P./Distributed Art Pubs.

Jenkins, Susan. It's a Power. 2010. 404p. pap. *(978-3-8383-2468-5(4))* Lambert Academic Publishing.

John Young: Silhouettes & Polychromes. pap. *(978-1-86395-399-3(X))* Bookman Pr.

Jones, Stephen. Synthetics: Aspects of Art & Technology in Australia, 1956-1975. 2011. (Leonardo Bks.). (ENG., Illus.). 416p. (gr. 17). 40.00 *(978-0-262-01496-0(3))* MIT Pr.

Kastner, Jeffrey, text. Jeff Gibson: Sarsaparilla to Sorcery, 1 vol. 2007. (ENG., Illus.). 72p. (C). 24.95 *(978-0-9779789-1-5(5))* Binghamton Univ., Art Museum, State Univ. of New York.

Keys, Melissa & text. The Weight of History. 2007. (Illus.). 4p. *(978-0-9775782-4-5(0))* Monash Univ. Museum of Art.

Larsen, Pia. Discourse & Configurations of Gender - Reconfiguring Gender Conceptions. 2008. 72p. pap. *(978-3-8364-5102-4(6))* VDM Verlag Dr. Mueller e.K.

Lewis, C. J. Eternity Series. 2008. 40p. pap. 21.95 *(978-1-4092-2306-1(X))* Lulu Enterprises Inc.

Lycett, Joseph & McPhee, John. Joseph Lycett: Convict Artist. 2008. (ENG., Illus.). 285p. 69.95 *(978-1-876991-21-0(6))* Historic Houses Trust of New South Wales AUS. Dist: National Bk. Network.

Lynn, Victoria. Double Take: Anne Landa Award for Video & New Media Arts 2009. 2009. (Illus.). 54p. pap. *(978-1-74174-043-1(6))* Art Gallery of New South Wales.

Lynne, Victoria & Hage, Ghassan, texts. Regarding Fear & Hope. 2007. (Illus.). 55p. *(978-0-9775782-5-2(9))* Monash Univ. Museum of Art.

MacPherson, Mark & Pam, Max, eds. Hijacked Volume One: Australia & America. 2011. (ENG., Illus.). 288p. 50.00 **(978-3-86828-125-5(8))** Kehrer Verlag Heidelberg, Klaus Kehrer DEU. Dist: Consortium Bk. Sales & Distribution.

Matt, Gerald & Renier, Ricky, eds. Ricky Swallow: Younger Than Yesterday. 2008. (ENG., Illus.). 84p. pap. 25.00 *(978-3-939738-89-3(1))* Verlag fur Moderne Kunst DEU. Dist: D.A.P./Distributed Art Pubs.

McAuliffe, Chris. Jon Cattapan: Possible Histories. 2008. (ENG., Illus.). 240p. 41.00 *(978-0-522-85498-5(2))* Melbourne Univ. Publishing AUS. Dist: Independent Pubs. Group.

Michael, Linda. 21st Century Modern: 2006 Adelaide Biennial of Australian Art. 2006. (Illus.). 88p. 24.95 *(978-0-7308-3038-2(1))* Art Gallery of South Australia AUS. Dist: Antique Collectors' Club.

Neri, Louise. Marc Newson. 2007. (Illus.). 84p. 80.00 *(978-1-932598-43-8(X))* Gagosian Gallery.

Newton, Helmut, photos by. Helmut Newton - Polaroids. 2011. (ENG.). 256p. 59.99 **(978-3-8365-2886-3(X))** TASCHEN DEU. Dist: Ingram Pub. Services, Taschen America, LLC.

Orlando, Mardi. The Life Expectancy of Wind. 2009. 176p. pap. 16.25 *(978-1-4269-1545-1(4))* Trafford Publishing.

Price-Jones, Humphrey. Spirit of the Wedge-Tailed Eagle: The Art og Humphrey Price-Jones. 2008. 96p. 43.00 *(978-0-643-09433-8(4))* CSIRO Publishing AUS. Dist: Stylus Publishing, LLC.

Roberts, Claire, ed. Other Histories: Guan Wei's Fable for a Contemporary World; Documentation of an Exhibition. 2009. (Illus.). 165p. pap. 45.00 *(978-1-876957-13-1(1))* Univ. of Hawaii Pr.

Ryan, Judith. Across the Desert: Aboriginal Batik from Central Australia. 2009. (ENG., Illus.). 168p. pap. 37.50 *(978-0-7241-0299-0(X))* National Gallery of Victoria AUS. Dist: National Bk. Network.

Sheldon, George F. Hugh Williamson: Physician, Patriot & Founding Father. 2009. (ENG., Illus.). 340p. pap. 39.00 *(978-1-59102-770-6(5),* Humanity Bks.) Prometheus Bks., Pubs.

Slicer-Smith, Jane. Swing, Swagger, Drape: Knit the Colors of Australia. 2009. (ENG., Illus.). 208p. pap. 24.95 *(978-1-933064-17-8(X),* XRX Bks.) XRX, Inc.

Smallman, Jake & Nyman, Carl. Stencil Graffiti Capital - Melbourne. 2011. (Illus.). 160p. pap. 21.95 *(978-1-935613-31-2(6))* Batty, Mark Pub., LLC.

Smith, Geoffrey. Charles Blackman. 2009. (ENG.). 144p. 34.95 *(978-0-7241-0274-7(4))* National Gallery of Victoria AUS. Dist: National Bk. Network.

Smith, Geoffrey & St John Moore, Felicity. Charles Blackman: Alice in Wonderland. 2007. (ENG., Illus.). 144p. pap. 26.50 *(978-0-7241-0272-3(8))* National Gallery of Victoria AUS. Dist: National Bk. Network.

Smith, Terry. What Is Contemporary Art? 2009. (Illus.). 300p. 66.66 *(978-0-226-76430-6(3))*; (ENG., 344p. pap. 25.00 *(978-0-226-76431-3(1))* Univ. of Chicago Pr.

Smith, Tracey. Creative Relationships. 2009. 77p. pap. 24.96 *(978-1-4092-7946-4(4))* Lulu Enterprises Inc.

Stringer, John, et al. Closet Circus: The Lloyd & Elizabeth Horn Collection of Contemporary Western Australian Art. 2008. 224p. pap. 49.95 *(978-1-921361-27-2(1))* Fremantle Pr. AUS. Dist: Independent Pubs. Group.

Taylor, Elena. Grace Crowley: Being Modern. 2007. (ENG., Illus.). 64p. pap. *(978-0-642-54192-5(2))* National Gallery of Australia.

Victoria, Curators Natl Gall. Light Sensitivity. 2007. (ENG., Illus.). 112p. pap. 26.50 *(978-0-7241-0276-1(0))* National Gallery of Victoria AUS. Dist: National Bk. Network.

Vivian, Helen, ed. When You Think About Art: The Ewing & George Paton Gallery, 1971-2008. 2008. (Illus.). 288p. (C). 80.00 *(978-1-921394-02-7(1))* Macmillan Art Publishing AUS. Dist: Brown, David Bk. Co., The.

Volkenandt, Claus & Kaufmann, Christian, eds. Between Indigenous Australia & Europe: John Mawurndjul. 2009. (ENG.). 240p. pap. 59.95 *(978-3-496-02809-3(2),* Art Stock Bks. Ltd/Csi) Continental Sales, Inc.

Were, Graeme. Lines That Connect. 2010. 224p. 38.00 *(978-0-8248-3384-8(8))* Univ. of Hawaii Pr.

West, Franz. Franz West: White Elephant. 2010. (ENG., Illus.). 64p. 30.00 *(978-84-92480-80-7(7))* RM Verlag, S.L. ESP. Dist: D.A.P./Distributed Art Pubs.

Wood Street Galleries, prod. Workin' down Under. 2007. pap. *(978-0-9760949-2-0(4))* Wood Street Galleries.

ART, AUSTRALIAN ABORIGINAL

see Art, Aboriginal Australian

ART, AUSTRIAN

Aigner, Silvie, ed. Emanzipation und Konfrontation / Emancipation & Confrontation / Emancipacija in konfrontacija: Kunst aus Kärnten von 1945 bis heute. Architektur aus Kärnten seit 1945 und Kunst im öffentlichen Raum heute., 3 vols. 2008. (GER, SLV & ENG., Illus.). 1010p. *(978-3-211-75622-5(1),* 3211756221) Actar Birkhauser Distribution.

Ankele, Gudrun & Zyman, Daniela, eds. Los Carpinteros: Handwork, Constructing the World. 2011. (ENG., Illus.). 380p. 190.00 *(978-1-935202-67-7(7))* Thyssen-Bornemisza Art Contemporary AUT. Dist: D.A.P./Distributed Art Pubs.

Asenbaum, Paul, et al. Glanzstucke: Emilie Flöge und der Schmuck der Wiener Werkstätte. 2009. (GER & ENG., Illus.). 152p. 70.00 *(978-3-89790-298-5(2))* Arnoldsche Art Pubs. DEU. Dist: Antique Collectors' Club.

Bast, Gerald, ed. Mit Eigenen Augen/with Their Own Eyes: KunstlerInnen Aus der Ehemaligen Meisterklasse Maria Lassnig/Former Students of Maria Lassnig. 2008. (GER & ENG., Illus.). 176p. pap. *(978-3-211-77840-1(3),* 3211778403) Actar Birkhauser Distribution.

Baudin-Renau, Katia, ed. Franz West. 2010. 350p. 72.50 *(978-88-370-7466-1(2))* Electa ITA. Dist: Trans-Atlantic Pubns., Inc.

Beethoven-Haus (Bonn, Germany) Staff & Brandstatter, Christian, eds. Vienna 1900: Art, Life & Culture. 2006. (ENG., Illus.). 400p. 50.00 *(978-0-86565-175-3(2))* Vendome Pr., The.

Bitesnich, Andreas H., photos by. Erotic. 2011. 96p. 65.00 *(978-3-8327-9479-8(4))* teNeues Publishing Co.

Blaas-Pratscher, Katharina. Öffentliche Kunst, Kunst im öffentlichen Raum Niederösterreich, Band 9: / Public Art Lower Austria, Volume 9. 2009. (GER & ENG., Illus.). 256p. 59.95 *(978-3-211-99013-1(5))* Springer Wien AUT. Dist: Actar Birkhauser Distribution.

Blaas-Pratscher, Katharina, ed. Öffentliche Kunst, Kunst im öffentlichen Raum Niederösterreich, Band 10: / Public Art Lower Austria, Volume 10. 2012. (Public Art Lower Austria Ser.). (ENG & GER., Illus.). 224p. 49.95 **(978-3-7091-0780-5(6))** Springer Wien AUT. Dist: Actar Birkhauser Distribution.

Blanz, Hubert. Slideshow. 2009. (GER., Illus.). 176p. 39.95 *(978-3-211-85781-6(8))* Springer Wien AUT. Dist: Actar Birkhauser Distribution.

Bollmann, Karl & Schrage, Dieter. Elisabeth Defner: Man - Nature - Cosmos Jewellery & Objects. 2012. (ENG & GER., Illus.). 248p. 85.00 **(978-3-89790-353-1(9))** Arnoldsche Art Pubs. DEU. Dist: National Bk. Network.

Carl, Klaus H. & Charles, Victoria. Viennese Secession. 2011. (Art of Century Ser.). (ENG., Illus.). 200p. 19.95 *(978-1-84484-845-4(0))* Parkstone Pr. USA, Ltd.

Dellenbaugh, Virginia. Markus Schinwald. 2008. (GER & ENG., Illus.). 208p. 39.00 *(978-3-905829-22-8(3))* JRP Ringier Kunstverlag AG CHE. Dist: D.A.P./Distributed Art Pubs.

Ecker, Berthold & Hilger, Wolfgang, eds. Die fünfziger Jahre: Kunst und Kunstverständnis in Wien. 2009. (ENG & GER., Illus.). 432p. 49.95 *(978-3-7091-0051-6(8))* Springer Wien AUT. Dist: Actar Birkhauser Distribution.

Ecker, Berthold, et al. stark bewölkt / Clouds up High: flüchtige Erscheinungen des Himmels / Fleeting Figures in the Sky. 2009. (GER & ENG., Illus.). 224p. 39.95 *(978-3-211-89113-1(7))* Springer Wien AUT. Dist: Actar Birkhauser Distribution.

Estermann, Lorenz. Lorenz Estermann: Public Hyperbindings. 2010. (ENG., Illus.). 104p. 55.00 *(978-3-7757-2609-2(8))* Hatje Cantz Verlag GmbH & Co KG DEU. Dist: D.A.P./Distributed Art Pubs.

Export, Valie. VALIE EXPORT Zeit und Gegenzeit. Time & Countertime. 2011. (ENG & GER., Illus.). 304p. 59.95 *(978-3-86560-874-1(4))* Verlag der Buchhandlung Walther Konig DEU. Dist: D.A.P./Distributed Art Pubs.

Farocki, Harun. Harun Farocki: Nebeneinander. 2008. (ENG., Illus.). 130p. pap. 48.00 *(978-3-86560-286-2(X))* Verlag der Buchhandlung Walther Konig DEU. Dist: D.A.P./Distributed Art Pubs.

Fenz, Werner, et al, eds. Kunst im öffentlichen Raum Steiermark. Art in Public Space Styria: Projekte / Projects 2007-2008. 2010. 344p. pap. *(978-3-7091-0118-6(2))* Actar Birkhauser Distribution.

Fleck, Robert & Fuchs, Rainer. Erwin Wurm, 1 vol. 2007. (ENG., Illus.). 304p. 60.00 *(978-3-7757-1866-0(4))* Hatje Cantz Verlag GmbH & Co KG DEU. Dist: D.A.P./Distributed Art Pubs.

Haas, Ernst. Ernst Haas: Colour Correction. Ewing, William A., ed. 2011. (ENG., Illus.). 200p. 65.00 *(978-3-86930-136-5(8))* Steidl, Gerhard Druckerei und Verlag DEU. Dist: Innovative Logistics.

Heilingsetzer, Semirah, ed. Thage: Malerei zwischen Konvention und Avantgarde. 2009. (GER.). 159p. 47.95 *(978-3-631-58203-9(X))* Lang, Peter GmbH, Europaischer Verlag der Wissenschaften DEU. Dist: Lang, Peter.

Hoeller, Silvia. Lois & Franziska Weinberger: Feldarbeit / Field Work. Bertsch, Christoph, ed. 2008. (Illus.). 272p. 34.95 *(978-3-7082-3225-6(9))* Skarabaeus AUT. Dist: SCB Distributors.

Holler, Carsten. Carsten Holler. 2011. (ENG., Illus.). 288p. 75.00 *(978-3-7757-2395-4(1))* Hatje Cantz Verlag GmbH & Co KG DEU. Dist: D.A.P./Distributed Art Pubs.

Hurlston, David. Ron Mueck. 2011. (Illus.). 192p. pap. 30.00 *(978-0-300-17683-4(X))* Yale Univ. Pr.

Husslein-Arco, Agnes. Prince Eugene: Commander Philosopher. 2010. (ENG.). 360p. 75.00 *(978-3-7774-2551-1(6),* Art Stock Bks. Ltd/Csi) Continental Sales, Inc.

Husslein-Arco, Agnes, ed. Gustav Klimt/Josef Hoffmann: Pioneers of Modernism. 2012. (GER., Illus.). 332p. 49.95 **(978-3-7913-5149-0(4))** Prestel Publishing.

Husslein-Arco, Agnes & Koja, Stephan, eds. Rodin & Vienna. 2011. (Illus.). 175p. 49.95 *(978-3-7774-3311-0(X))* Hirmer Verlag GmbH DEU. Dist: Chicago Distribution Ctr.

Jelinek, Robert, ed. OFFSHORE CENSUS: The Citizens of the State of Sabotage. 2011. (GER., Illus.). 410p. 59.95 *(978-3-7091-0533-7(1),* 3709105331) Springer Wien AUT. Dist: Springer.

Kargl, Georg. Georg Kargl, Fine Arts Since 1998: Box Since 2005, 1 vol. 2006. (ENG., Illus.). 328p. per. 35.00 *(978-3-86560-063-9(8))* Verlag der Buchhandlung Walther Konig DEU. Dist: D.A.P./Distributed Art Pubs.

Katz, Alex. Alex Katz: Prints & Works in Editions 1947-2010. 2011. (ENG., Illus.). 208p. 120.00 **(978-3-7757-2766-2(3))** Hatje Cantz Verlag GmbH & Co KG DEU. Dist: D.A.P./Distributed Art Pubs.

Koeppe, Wolfram. Vienna Circa 1780: An Imperial Silver Service Rediscovered. 2010. (Illus.). 124p. 35.00 *(978-0-300-15518-1(2))* Yale Univ. Pr.

Koschatzky-Elias, Gabriela & Aigner, Carl. Fritz Maierhofer: Jewellery & More! 2007. (GER & ENG., Illus.). 200p. 75.00 *(978-3-89790-245-9(1))* Arnoldsche Art Pubs. DEU. Dist: Antique Collectors' Club.

Kueng, Moritz, ed. Heimo Zobernig: Stellproblemen. 2009. (ENG., Illus.). 144p. pap. 48.00 *(978-3-86560-567-2(2))* Verlag der Buchhandlung Walther Konig DEU. Dist: D.A.P./Distributed Art Pubs.

Lackner, Franz. Katalog der Mittelalterlichen Handschriften Bis Zum Ende des 16. Jahrhunderts in der Zentralbibliothek der Wiener Franziskanerprovinz in Graz. 2006. (Veroffentlichungen der Kommission fur Schrift- und Buchwesen des Mittelalters, Reihe II Ser.). (GER., Illus.). 218p. (C). 108.00 *(978-3-7001-3614-9(5))* Austrian Academy of Sciences Press AUT. Dist: Brown, David Bk. Co., The.

Lamb-Faffelberger, Margarete. Staging Export: Valie zu Ehren. 2010. (Austrian Culture Ser.). (GER.). 240p. (C). 75.95 *(978-1-4331-1061-0(X))* Lang, Peter Publishing, Inc.

Lang, Helmut. Alles Gleich Schwer. 2009. (ENG., Illus.). 122p. pap. 45.00 *(978-3-86560-541-2(9))* Verlag der Buchhandlung Walther Konig DEU. Dist: D.A.P./Distributed Art Pubs.

Levy, Aaron, intro. Blood Orgies: Hermann Nitsch in America. 2008. 229p. pap. *(978-0-9815409-0-0(2))* Slought Foundation.

Maderna, Marianne, ed. Marianne Maderna: Historysteria. 2008. (ENG & GER., Illus.). 304p. *(978-3-211-75582-2(9),* 3211755829) Actar Birkhauser Distribution.

Meyer, Christian, text. Vienna 1900. 2011. (ENG., Illus.). 272p. 75.00 *(978-3-7757-2685-6(3))* Hatje Cantz Verlag GmbH & Co KG DEU. Dist: D.A.P./Distributed Art Pubs.

Mignonneau, Laurent. Christa Sommerer & Laurent Mignonneau: Interactive Art Research. Stocker, Gerfried & Sommerer, Christa, eds. 2009. (ENG., Illus.). 232p. 59.95 *(978-3-211-99015-5(1),* 3211990151) Springer.

Nachtigaller, Roland, et al, texts. Martin Walde: A Second Home for Schrödinger's Cat. 2010. (ENG., Illus.). 232p. pap. 50.00 *(978-3-7757-2623-8(3))* Hatje Cantz Verlag GmbH & Co KG DEU. Dist: D.A.P./Distributed Art Pubs.

Natter, Tobias G. Ansichten: Frühe Fotografie Aus Vorarlberg. 2008. (Illus.). 187p. *(978-3-901802-29-4(0))* Vorarlberger Landesmuseum, VLM, Landesmuseumsverein.

Noever, Peter, ed. Eva Schlegel: In Between. 2011. (GER & ENG., Illus.). 200p. pap. 60.00 ***(978-3-86984-174-8(5))*** Verlag fur Moderne Kunst DEU. Dist: D.A.P./Distributed Art Pubs.

Noever, Peter, ed. & text. 20/21: MAK Collection of Contemporary Art. 2010. (ENG., Illus.). 244p. pap. 40.00 *(978-3-941185-29-5(2))* Verlag fur Moderne Kunst DEU. Dist: D.A.P./Distributed Art Pubs.

Oberhuber, Oswald & Ettl, Stephan. Oberhuber: Plakate Plakate Plakate. Posters Posters Posters. Werkverzeichnis Catalogue Raisonné. 2009. (GER & ENG., Illus.). 520p. 69.95 *(978-3-211-89111-7(0))* Springer Wien AUT. Dist: Actar Birkhauser Distribution.

Parcerisas, Pila, ed. Viennese Actionism. 2008. 440p. pap. *(978-84-96954-44-1(7))* Actar Birkhauser Distribution.

Platzer, Monika. Wiener Kinetismus: eine bewegte ModerneViennese Kineticism: Modernism in Motion: Eine Bewegte Moderne Viennese Kineticism: Modernism in Motion. Bast, Gerald, ed. 2011. (ENG.). 256p. 69.95 *(978-3-211-99143-5(3))* Springer Wien AUT. Dist: Actar Birkhauser Distribution.

Pongratz, Peter. Sweet Home Vienna: Neue Arbeiten: Recent Work 1998-2006. 2006. (Illus.). 191p. *(978-3-211-32791-3(6)*, 3211327916) Actar Birkhauser Distribution.

Radford, Rod. Island to Empire: 300 Years of British Art 1550-1850. 2007. (Illus.). 336p. 60.00 *(978-0-7308-3014-6(4))* Art Gallery of South Australia AUS. Dist: Antique Collectors' Club.

Rainer, Arnulf. Arnulf Rainer. Visages. 2011. (GER & ENG., Illus.). 132p. 59.95 ***(978-3-8321-9370-6(7))*** DuMont DEU. Dist: D.A.P./Distributed Art Pubs.

Rainer, Arnulf, photos by & text. Arnulf Rainer: Cross 1956-2009. 2010. (ENG., Illus.). 216p. 130.00 *(978-3-86984-000-0(5))* Verlag der Buchhandlung Walther Konig DEU. Dist: D.A.P./Distributed Art Pubs.

Reilly, Maura, et al. Richard Bell: Uz vs. Them. 2011. (Illus.). 80p. pap. *(978-1-885444-40-0(0))* American Federation of Arts, The.

—Richard Bell: Uz vs. Them. 2011. (ENG., Illus.). 80p. 35.00 *(978-1-904832-95-9(4))* Giles, D. Ltd. GBR. Dist: Antique Collectors' Club.

Roitmeister, Carl, et al. Carrousel. 2008. (GER & ENG., Illus.). 128p. 50.00 *(978-3-86560-417-0(X))* Kunsthaus Bregenz AUT. Dist: D.A.P./Distributed Art Pubs.

Rosenblum, Adi & Muntean, Markus. Muntean / Rosenblum. 2009. (ENG, MUL & GER., Illus.). 84p. 49.00 *(978-3-86678-167-2(9))* Kerber Verlag DEU. Dist: D.A.P./Distributed Art Pubs.

Saxenhuber, Hedwig. Kunst + Politik / Art + Politics. 2008. (GER & ENG., Illus.). 251p. pap. 39.95 *(978-3-211-09460-0(1))* Springer Wien AUT. Dist: Actar Birkhauser Distribution.

Scheicher, Harald & Biller, Barbara. Macht des Bildes - Visionen des Göttliche: Kunst und Transzendent in Österreich im 20. Jahrhundert. Katalogbuch zur Ausstellung in Bleiburg, 26.04.2009-08.11.2009, Werner Berg Museum Bleiburg. 2009. (Illus.). 383p. *(978-3-7774-8055-8(X))* Hirmer Verlag GmbH.

Schick, Karin. Man darf auch weben was man nicht sieht: Die Teppiche von Dieter Roth und Ingrid Wiener. 2008. (ENG & GER., Illus.). 248p. 75.00 *(978-3-86678-104-7(0))* Kerber Verlag DEU. Dist: D.A.P./Distributed Art Pubs.

Schneider, Eckhard, ed. Michael Craig-Martin: Signs of Life, 1 vol. 2006. (ENG., Illus.). 128p. 65.00 *(978-3-86560-085-1(9))* Kunsthaus Bregenz AUT. Dist: D.A.P./Distributed Art Pubs.

Schneider, Eckhard, ed. & intro. Gottfried Bechtold: Reine und Gemischte Zustande, 1 vol. 2007. (ENG., Illus.). 160p. pap. 62.00 *(978-3-902525-45-1(2))* Kunsthaus Bregenz AUT. Dist: D.A.P./Distributed Art Pubs.

Schneider, Eckhard, text. Markus Schinwald. Vanishing Lessons. 2009. (ENG & GER., Illus.). 144p. 57.00 *(978-3-86560-536-8(2))* Kunsthaus Bregenz AUT. Dist: D.A.P./Distributed Art Pubs.

Schneider, Ula & Zobl, Beatrix, eds. Soho in Ottakring: What's up? Was ist Hier Los? 2008. (ENG & GER., Illus.). 152p. pap. *(978-3-211-78587-4(6)*, 3211785876) Actar Birkhauser Distribution.

Schröder, Klaus Albrecht. Monet to Picasso, the Batliner Collection. 2008. 420p. 70.00 *(978-3-86568-319-9(3))* Imhof, Michael Verlag GmbH & Co. KG DEU. Dist: Independent Pubs. Group.

Sekler, Eduard F., contrib. by. Yearning for Beauty: The Wiener Werkstatte & the Stoclet House, 1 vol. 2006. (ENG., Illus.). 452p. 95.00 *(978-3-7757-1778-6(1))* Hatje Cantz Verlag GmbH & Co KG DEU. Dist: D.A.P./Distributed Art Pubs.

Sonvilla-Weiss, Stefan. Synthesis & Nullification: Works, 1991-2011. 2012. (ENG.). 224p. pap. 49.95 ***(978-3-7091-1028-7(9)***, 3709110289) Springer Wien AUT. Dist: Springer.

Soussloff, Catherine M. The Subject in Art: Portraiture & the Birth of the Modern. 2006. (ENG., Illus.). 192p. 79.95 *(978-0-8223-3658-7(8))*; per. 22.95 *(978-0-8223-3670-9(7))* Duke Univ. Pr.

Steinhauer, Harry. Hungering Artist or Artist in Hungering: Kafka's A Hunger Artist. 2011. 20p. 35.95 ***(978-1-258-01133-8(6))*** Literary Licensing, LLC.

Stimm, Thomas. Thomas Stimm: Terra. 2011. (ENG., Illus.). 144p. pap. 55.00 ***(978-3-86560-937-3(6))*** Verlag der Buchhandlung Walther Konig DEU. Dist: D.A.P./Distributed Art Pubs.

teNeues. AAD Vienna: Art Architecture Design. 2010. (Illus.). 168p. pap. 12.95 *(978-3-8327-9434-7(4))* teNeues Publishing Co.

Toman, Rolf, ed. Vienna: Art & Architecture. 2008. (Art & Architecture Ser.). (Illus.). 452p. pap. 24.95 *(978-0-8416-0290-8(5))* American Map Corp.

Ullrich, Wolfgang. G. R. A. M.: Reenactments 1998-2011. 2012. (ENG & GER., Illus.). 144p. 45.00 ***(978-84-343-1294-4(8))*** Polígrafa, Ediciones, S. A. ESP. Dist: D.A.P./Distributed Art Pubs.

Witt-Dorring, Christian, text. Josef Hoffmann: Interiors 1902-1913. 2009. (ENG., Illus.). 88p. 45.00 *(978-1-931794-20-6(0))* Neue Galerie New York.

ART, AZTEC

see Aztec Art

ART, BALINESE

Couteau, Ph.D., Jean. Bali Inspires: The Rudana Art Collection. 2011. (ENG., Illus.). 310p. 49.95 *(978-602-95704-1-0(2))* Tuttle Publishing.

Sedana, I. Nyoman & Rubin, Leon. Performance in Bali. 2007. (Theatres of the World Ser.). (Illus.). 159p. 120.00 *(978-0-415-33131-9(5))* Routledge.

Vickers, Adrian. Balinese Art: Paintings & Drawings of Bali, 1800-2010. 2012. (ENG., Illus.). 256p. 49.95 ***(978-0-8048-4248-8(5))*** Tuttle Publishing.

ART, BAROQUE

see also Painting, Baroque

Avery, Charles. Bernini: Genius of the Baroque. 2006. (ENG., Illus.). 288p. pap. 44.95 *(978-0-500-28633-3(7))* Thames & Hudson.

Babelon, Jean. Histoire de l'Art Vol. 3: Renaissance, Baroque, Romantisme. (FRE.). 1704p. *(978-0-8288-7602-5(9))* French & European Pubns., Inc.

Bailey, Gauvin A. Between Renaissance & Baroque: Jesuit Art in Rome, 1565-1610. 2009. (ENG., Illus.). 552p. pap. *(978-1-4426-1030-9(1))* Univ. of Toronto Pr.

Bailey, Gauvin Alexander. Baroque & Rococo. 2012. (ENG., Illus.). 448p. pap. 29.95 ***(978-0-7148-5742-8(4))*** Phaidon Pr., Inc.

Bussagli, Marco & Reiche, Mattia. Baroque & Rococo. 2009. (ENG., Illus.). 192p. pap. 14.95 *(978-1-4027-5925-3(8))* Sterling Publishing Co., Inc.

Campbell, Thomas P. & Cleland, Elizabeth A. H., eds. Tapestry in the Baroque: New Aspects of Production & Patronage. 2011. (ENG., Illus.). 368p. pap. 40.00 *(978-0-300-15514-3(X))* Yale Univ. Pr.

Carl, Klaus H. & Charles, Victoria. Baroque Art. 2009. (Art of Century Ser.). (ENG., Illus.). 200p. 19.95 *(978-1-84484-621-4(0))* Parkstone International GBR. Dist: Ingram Pub. Services.

Carrillo Azpéitia, Rafael. El Arte Barroco en Mexico. (Panorama of Mexico Ser.). (SPA., Illus.). 162p. 10.95 *(978-968-38-0062-6(9)*, PN629) Panorama Editorial MEX. Dist: Continental Bk. Co., Inc.

Castelnuovo, Enrico & Barberis, Walter. La reggia di Venaria e i Savoia. Arte, magnificenza e storia di una corte europea. Catalogo della mostra (12 ottobre 2007-30 marzo 2008), 2 vols. 2008. (ITA & ENG., Illus.). 680p. pap. 90.00 *(978-88-422-1585-1(6))* Allemandi, Umberto & Co. GBR. Dist: National Bk. Network.

Cram101 Textbook Reviews. Outlines & Highlights for Baroque & Rococo: Art & Culture by Minor. 2011. 266p. pap. 31.95 ***(978-1-61812-932-1(5))*** Cram101 Inc.

Dallett, Joseph B., et al. Romeyn de Hooghe: Virtuoso Etcher. 2009. (Illus.). 96p. pap. *(978-1-934260-11-1(8))* Cornell Univ., Herbert F. Johnson Museum of Art.

Deleuze, Gilles. The Fold: Leibniz & Baroq. Conley, Tom, tr. from FRE. (Illus.). 192p. *(978-0-485-11421-8(6))* Continuum International Publishing Group, Ltd.

—The Fold: Leibniz & the Baroque. (Illus.). 192p. pap. *(978-0-485-12087-5(9))* Continuum International Publishing Group, Ltd.

Dixon, Susan M., ed. Italian Baroque Art. 2008. (Blackwell Anthologies in Art History Ser.). (ENG., Illus.). 416p. 120.95 *(978-1-4051-3966-3(8)*, Wiley-Blackwell) Wiley, John & Sons, Inc.

—Italian Baroque Art. 2008. (Blackwell Anthologies in Art History Ser.: 3). (ENG., Illus.). 416p. pap. 54.95 *(978-1-4051-3967-0(6)*, Wiley-Blackwell) Wiley, John & Sons, Inc.

Freund, Philip. Laughter & Grandeur: Theatre in the Age of Baroque. 2008. (Stage by Stage Ser.). (ENG.). 350p. 55.00 *(978-0-7206-1298-1(5))* Owen, Peter Ltd. GBR. Dist: Independent Pubs. Group.

Gal, Ofer & Chen-Morris, Raz D. Baroque Science. 2012. (Illus.). 320p. 45.00 ***(978-0-226-92398-7(3))*** Univ. of Chicago Pr.

Hills, Helen, ed. Rethinking the Baroque. 2011. (Illus.). 286p. 124.95 *(978-0-7546-6685-1(9))* Ashgate Publishing Co.

Husslein-Arco, Agnes. Prince Eugene: Commander Philosopher. 2010. (ENG.). 360p. 75.00 *(978-3-7774-2551-1(6)*, Art Stock Bks. Ltd/Csi) Continental Sales, Inc.

Leone, Stephanie C., ed. The Pamphilj & the Arts: Patronage & Consumption in Baroque Rome. 2011. (ENG & ITA., Illus.). 200p. pap. 45.00 *(978-1-892850-17-1(6))* McMullen Museum of Art, Boston College.

Liebergen, Patrick M. Singer's Library of Arias: Low Voice, Book & CD. 2008. (ENG.). 120p. pap. 24.95 *(978-0-7390-5142-9(3))* Alfred Publishing Co., Inc.

Lombaerde. Innovation & Experience in Early Baroque in the Southern Netherlands the Case of the Jesuit Church in Antwerp. 2008. (Architectura Moderna Ser.). (ENG., Illus.). 266p. (C). pap. 138.00 *(978-2-503-52388-0(9))* Brepols Pubs. BEL. Dist: ISD.

Maiorino, Giancarlo. The Cornucopian Mind & the Baroque Unity of the Arts. 2008. pap. 24.95 *(978-0-271-02790-6(8))* Pennsylvania State Univ. Pr.

Matthews, Roy, et al. The Humanistic Tradition Bk. 4: Faith, Reason, & Power in the Early Modern World. 6th ed. 2010. (ENG., Illus.). 192p. (C). pap. 45.67 *(978-0-07-734626-3(2)*, 0077346262) McGraw-Hill Cos., The.

Mcnair, Trudy. A History of Art & Civilization: The Renaissance & Baroque Periods. rev. ed. 2011. (ENG.). 218p. pap. 90.00 ***(978-0-7575-8975-1(8))*** Kendall Hunt Publishing Co.

Multiple. Boettger Stoneware: Johann Friedrich Boettger & Treasury Art. 2009. (ENG.). 168p. pap. 34.95 *(978-3-422-06900-8(3))* Deutscher Kunstverlag GmbH DEU. Dist: Independent Pubs. Group.

Petican, Laura. Arte Povera & the Baroque: Building an International Identity. 2011. 275p. pap. ***(978-3-0343-0477-1(3))*** Lang, Peter.

Porters, Pieter. Elegance & Decadence: The Luxurious, Baroque Interiors of Pieter Porters. 2010. (FRE, DUT, GER & ENG., Illus.). 272p. 120.00 *(978-90-209-8424-8(1))* Lannoo Pubs./Racine.

Powell, Katie Tierney. Capturing the Sublime: Italian Drawings of the Renaissance & Baroque. McCullagh, Suzanne Folds, ed. 2012. (ENG., Illus.). 312p. 65.00 ***(978-0-300-17970-5(7))*** Art Institute of Chicago.

Riegl, Alois, et al. The Origins of Baroque Art in Rome. Hopkins, Andrew & Witte, Arnold Alexander, eds. 2010. (Texts & Documents Ser.). (ENG., Illus.). 292p. pap. 50.00 *(978-1-60606-041-4(4)*, Getty Research Institute) Getty Pubns.

Scott, W. B. Treasury of Baroque & Rococo Designs. Belanger Grafton, Carol, ed. 2010. (Dover Pictorial Archive Ser.). (ENG., Illus.). 144p. pap. 19.95 *(978-0-486-47043-6(1))* Dover Pubns., Inc.

Syndram, Dirk, et al. The Baroque Treasury at the Grunes Gewolbe Dresden. 2007. (Masterpieces (Staatliche Kunstsammlungen Dresden) Ser.). (ENG., Illus.). 180p. pap. 39.95 *(978-3-422-06644-1(6))* Deutscher Kunstverlag GmbH DEU. Dist: Independent Pubs. Group.

Tarabra, Daniela. European Art of the Eighteenth Century. 2008. (Illus.). 384p. pap. 24.95 *(978-0-89236-921-8(3))* Oxford Univ. Pr., Inc.

Toman, Rolf, ed. Baroque: Architecture - Sculpture - Painting, 1 vol. 2011. (ENG.). 500p. 19.99 ***(978-3-8331-6001-1(2))*** h.f.ullmann DEU. Dist: Innovative Logistics.

Toman, Rolf, ed. Baroque: Architecture, Sculpting, Painting. 2008. (Architecture Sculpture Painting Ser.). (Illus.). 500p. per. 24.95 *(978-0-8416-0058-4(9))* American Map Corp.

Torres Olleta, M. Gabriela. Redes Iconográficas: San Francisco Javier en la Cultura Visual Del Barroco. 2009. (SPA., Illus.). 869p. pap. 168.00 *(978-84-8489-453-7(3))* Iberoamericana Vervuert Publishing Corp.

Van der Stighelen, Katlijne & Watteeuw, Bert, eds. Pokerfaced: Flemish & Dutch Baroque Faces Unveiled. 2011. (Museum at the Crossroads Ser.). (DUT, ENG & GER., Illus.). 277p. (C). pap. 109.00 *(978-2-503-52564-8(4))* Brepols Pubs. BEL. Dist: ISD.

Whitfield, Clovis. Caravaggio's Eye. 2011. (ENG., Illus.). 264p. 65.00 *(978-1-907372-10-0(5))* Holberton, Paul Publishing GBR. Dist: Univ. of Washington Pr.

Zamora, Lois Parkinson. The Inordinate Eye: New World Baroque & Latin American Fiction. 2006. (Illus.). 424p. 55.00 *(978-0-226-97856-7(7))* Univ. of Chicago Pr.

Zirpolo, Lilian H. Historical Dictionary of Baroque Art & Architecture. 2010. (Historical Dictionaries of Literature & the Arts Ser.). (ENG., Illus.). 642p. 140.00 *(978-0-8108-6155-8(0))* Scarecrow Pr., Inc.

ART, BELGIAN

Acconci, Vito & Buchloh, B. H. D. A Bit of Matter & a Little Bit More: The Collection & the Archives of Herman & Nicole Daled. Wilmes, Ulrich, ed. 2011. (ENG., Illus.). 456p. pap. 95.00 *(978-3-86560-763-8(2))* Verlag der Buchhandlung Walther Konig DEU. Dist: D.A.P./Distributed Art Pubs.

Allegaert, Patrick. Johan Tahon: Makes Arche. 2010. (ENG., Illus.). 96p. pap. *(978-90-209-8866-6(2)*, Lannoo Pubs. (Acc)) Antique Collectors' Club.

Allegaert, Sophie & Mestdagh, Chris. Colorful Retreats: By Chris Mestdagh. 2010. (ENG., Illus.). 192p. pap. *(978-90-5856-336-1(7)*, Stichting Kunstboak (Acc)) Antique Collectors' Club.

Anspach, Isabelle, contrib. by. Museum & Gardens van Buuren. 2012. (ENG., Illus.). 128p. 34.00 *(978-90-6153-771-7(1))* Mercatorfonds N. V. BEL. Dist: D.A.P./Distributed Art Pubs.

Bellour, Raymond. David Claerbout. 2008. (ENG., Illus.). 160p. pap. 49.00 *(978-3-905829-38-9(X))* JRP Ringier Kunstverlag AG CHE. Dist: D.A.P./Distributed Art Pubs.

Bonnier, Bernadette & Carpiaux, Vronique. Museum Félicien Rops. 2010. (ENG., Illus.). 96p. pap., instr.'s gde. ed. *(978-90-5856-334-7(0)*, Stichting Kunstboak (Acc)) Antique Collectors' Club.

Borka, Max. Art of the Loom, 1 vol. 2011. (ENG., Illus.). 160p. 92.50 ***(978-94-90693-09-1(X))*** Exhibitions International BEL. Dist: Innovative Logistics.

Broodthaers, Marcel. Marcel Broodthaers heute. Von realer Gegenwart. 2011. (ENG., Illus.). 228p. pap. 45.00 *(978-3-86560-891-8(4))* Verlag der Buchhandlung Walther Konig DEU. Dist: D.A.P./Distributed Art Pubs.

Buggenhout, Peter. Peter Buggenhout: It's a Strange, Strange World, Sally. 2010. (ENG., Illus.). 208p. pap. *(978-90-209-8476-7(4)*, Lannoo Pubs. (Acc)) Antique Collectors' Club.

Canonne, Xavier, et al. Beyond the Document. 2012. (FRE, DUT & ENG., Illus.). 240p. 60.00 *(978-90-209-9493-3(X))* Lannoo Pubs./Racine.

Charney, Noah. Stealing the Mystic Lamb: The True Story of the World's Most Coveted Masterpiece. 2010. (ENG., Illus.). 336p. 27.95 *(978-1-58648-800-0(7))* PublicAffairs.

Clifton, James, et al, contrib. by. Scripture for the Eyes: Bible Illustration in Netherlandish Prints of the Sixteenth Century. 2009. (Illus.). 224p. pap. 49.95 *(978-0-9777839-3-9(6))* Museum of Biblical Art.

Cock, Jan de. Denkmal III, 5 vols. 2008. (Illus.). 650p. *(978-90-808424-3-4(5))* Atelier Jan de Cock.

Collas, I. Hans & Schandel, P., eds. Manuscrits de Louis de Bruges. 2010. (Manuscrits enlumines des anciens Pays-Bas Meridionaux Ser.). (FRE., Illus.). 347p. (C). 218.00 *(978-2-7177-2396-0(X))* Brepols Pubs. BEL. Dist: ISD.

Cornyn, Christine. Marie-Antoinette: La Douceur de l'Ignorance. 2010. (ENG., Illus.). 96p. *(978-90-209-9084-3(5)*, Lannoo Pubs. (Acc)) Antique Collectors' Club.

D'Alessandro, Jill & De Borchgrave, Isabelle. Pulp Fashion: The Art of Isabelle de Borchgrave. 2011. (Illus.). 104p. *(978-3-7913-5105-6(2))* Fine Arts Museums of San Francisco.

De Maeyer, Jan, ed. The Revival of Medieval Illumination: Nineteenth-Century Belgium Manuscripts & Illuminations from a European Perspective. 2008. (KADOC Artes Ser.). (FRE & ENG., Illus.). 336p. 89.95 *(978-90-5867-591-0(2))* Leuven Univ. Pr. BEL. Dist: Cornell Univ. Pr.

De Oliveira, Nicolas, et al. Hans Op de Beeck: On Vanishing, 1 vol. 2008. (ENG., Illus.). 368p. 115.00 *(978-90-6153-711-3(8))* Exhibitions International N.V. BEL. Dist: D.A.P./Distributed Art Pubs.

Decan, Liesbeth. Axelleration: Evelyne Axel,1964-1972. 2012. (ENG & GER., Illus.). 112p. pap. 40.00 ***(978-90-209-9947-1(8))*** Lannoo Pubs./Racine.

Dejonghe, Kaat. In the Margin: Belgian Documentary Photography. 2011. (ENG, FRE & DUT., Illus.). 160p. 50.00 *(978-90-209-9627-2(4))* Lannoo Pubs./Racine.

Deoldere, Luc. Tlc - The Low Countries 17: Arts & Society in Flanders & the Netherlands. 2011. (ENG., Illus.). 320p. pap. 65.00 *(978-90-79705-00-9(4))* Lannoo Pubs./Racine.

—TLC - The Low Countries 18: Arts & Society in Flanders & the Netherlands. 2011. (ENG., Illus.). 316p. pap. 65.00 *(978-90-79705-05-4(5))* Lannoo Pubs./Racine.

Dewulf, Bernard, ed. Raoul De Keyser: Replay Gemälde 1964-2008. 2010. (ENG., Illus.). 160p. 55.00 *(978-3-7757-2489-0(3))* Hatje Cantz Verlag GmbH & Co KG DEU. Dist: D.A.P./Distributed Art Pubs.

Elias, Willem. Aspects of Belgian Art after 1945, 2 vols., Pts. 1 & 2. 2010. (ENG., Illus.). 280p. 75.00 *(978-1-55595-350-8(6))* Hudson Hills Pr. LLC.

Fabre, Jan. Jan Fabre: Hortus Corpus. 2011. (ENG., Illus.). 224p. 50.00 ***(978-90-5662-816-1(X))*** NAi Uitgevers / Publishers Stichting NLD. Dist: D.A.P./Distributed Art Pubs.

Fabre, Jan & Di Pietrantonio, Giacinto. Jan Fabre: Homo Faber: Drawings, Performances, Photoworks, Films, Sculptures & Installations. 2009. (ENG., Illus.). 400p. 100.00 *(978-90-6153-649-9(9))* Mercatorfonds N. V. BEL. Dist: D.A.P./Distributed Art Pubs.

Ferguson, Russell & Alÿs, Francis. Francis Alÿs: Politics of Rehearsal. 2007. (SPA & ENG., Illus.). 142p. *(978-0-943739-32-8(2))* Yale Univ. Pr.

Foulon, Francoise, et al. Charles Kaisin: Design in Motion. 2009. (ENG & FRE., Illus.). 128p. 55.00 *(978-90-5856-312-5(X))* Stichting Kunstboek Bvba BEL. Dist: Antique Collectors' Club.

Geest, Joost de & Vekemans, Bruno. Bruno Vekemans: Kinshasa Congo. 2009. (FRE, DUT, GER & ENG., Illus.). 112p. 45.00 *(978-90-77207-19-2(8)*, Art Stock Bks. Ltd/Csi) Continental Sales, Inc.

Gibson, Walter S. Figures of Speech: Picturing Proverbs in Renaissance Netherlands. 2010. (ENG., Illus.). 256p. 49.95 *(978-0-520-25954-6(8))* Univ. of California Pr.

Goddin, Philippe. The Art of Herge, Inventor of Tintin, 1937-1949, Vol. 2. Farr, Michael, tr. 2010. (Illus.). 208p. 39.95 *(978-0-86719-724-2(2))* Last Gasp of San Francisco.

Gruyaert, Harry, photos by. Edges. 2010. (ENG., Illus.). 104p. 100.00 *(978-90-5330-616-1(1))* Mets en Schilt Uitgevers NLD. Dist: Ingram Pub. Services.

Haidu, Rachel. The Absence of Work: Marcel Broodthaers, 1964-1976. 2010. (October Bks.). (ENG., Illus.). 400p. (gr. 17). 36.95 *(978-0-262-01450-2(5))* MIT Pr.

Hlavajova, Maria, et al, eds. Open 16: the Art Biennial as a Global Phenomenon. 2009. (ENG., Illus.). 112p. pap. 30.00 *(978-90-5662-667-9(1))* NAi Uitgevers / Publishers Stichting NLD. Dist: D.A.P./Distributed Art Pubs.

Howe, Jeffery, ed. A New Key: Modern Belgian Art from the Simon Collection. 2007. (Illus.). 233p. per. 50.00 *(978-1-892850-12-6(5))* McMullen Museum of Art, Boston College.

Jacobs, Lynn F. Opening Doors: The Early Netherlandish Triptych Reinterpreted. 2011. (ENG.). 408p. 94.95 *(978-0-271-04840-6(9))* Pennsylvania State Univ. Pr.

Judah, Hettie & Pouillard, Véronique. Delvaux: 180 years of Belgian Luxury. 2010. (ENG., Illus.). 224p. 60.00 *(978-90-209-8599-3(X)*, Lannoo Pubs. (Acc)) Antique Collectors' Club GBR. Dist: National Bk. Network.

Kamagurka. The Holy Kamal 2012. (ENG., Illus.). 896p. 55.00 ***(978-90-5856-386-6(3))*** Stichting Kunstboek Bvba BEL. Dist: National Bk. Network.

Kittelmann, Udo. Michel Majerus. 2008. (GER & ENG., Illus.). 120p. pap. 49.00 *(978-3-905770-85-8(7))* JRP Ringier Kunstverlag AG CHE. Dist: D.A.P./Distributed Art Pubs.

Kung, Moritz, ed. Tropicalisation, 1 vol. 2007. (ENG., Illus.). 34p. pap. 9.00 *(978-2-940271-49-8(6))* JRP Ringier Kunstverlag AG CHE. Dist: D.A.P./Distributed Art Pubs.

Matthys, Daniël. Danny Matthy's: Monograph. (DUT., Illus.). 321p. *(978-90-72191-08-3(0))* Imschoot.

Mayne, Kate, text. Luc Tuymans: Dead Skull, 1 vol. 2012. (ENG., Illus.). 240p. 4000.00 *(978-90-5544-848-7(6))* Ludion BEL. Dist: D.A.P./Distributed Art Pubs.

Neubauer, Susanne, ed. Anne-Mie van Kerckhoven: Nothing More Natural. 2009. (DUT, FRE, GER & ENG., Illus.). 272p. pap. 69.95 *(978-3-86560-528-3(1))* Verlag der Buchhandlung Walther Konig DEU. Dist: D.A.P./Distributed Art Pubs.

Pluvinge, Gonzague. Expo 58: Between Utopia & Reality. 2008. (ENG., Illus.). 208p. pap. *(978-2-87386-541-2(5)*, Lannoo Pubs. (Acc)) Antique Collectors' Club.

Quinze, Arne. Arne Quinze: Modern Contemporary. 2011. (ENG., Illus.). 300p. 70.00 *(978-3-7757-2693-1(4))* Hatje Cantz Verlag GmbH & Co KG DEU. Dist: D.A.P./Distributed Art Pubs.

Roelstraete, Dieter, et al, trs. from DUT. Luc Tuymans: I Don't Get It, 1 vol. 2008. (ENG., Illus.). 199p. 65.00 *(978-90-5544-690-2(4))* Ludion BEL. Dist: D.A.P./Distributed Art Pubs.

Schafhausen, Nicolaus, et al, eds. Edith Dekyndt: Source Book 8. 2011. (ENG., Illus.). 112p. pap. 15.00 *(978-90-73362-90-1(3))* Witte De With Centre for Contemporary Art NLD. Dist: D.A.P./Distributed Art Pubs.

Schmid, Marion. Chantal Akerman. 2011. (French Film Directors Ser.). (ENG., Illus.). 208p. 75.95 *(978-0-7190-7716-6(8))* Manchester Univ. Pr. GBR. Dist: Macmillan.

Schmidt, Johann-Karl, ed. Jan Fabre: The Lime-Twig Man. (ENG & GER., Illus.). 224p. 39.95 *(978-3-89322-751-8(2))* Edition Cantz DEU. Dist: D.A.P./Distributed Art Pubs.

Schmitz-Von Ledebur, Katja. Habsburg Treasures: Renaissance Tapestries from the Kunsthistorisches Museum, Vienna. 2010. *(978-0-9767102-8-8(5))* International Arts & Artists.

Smerling, Walter. Doing It My Way: Perspectives on Belgian Art. 2008. (GER & ENG., Illus.). 104p. pap. 49.00 *(978-3-87909-954-2(5)*, Art Stock Bks. Ltd/Csi) Continental Sales, Inc.

Sultan, Terrie, ed. Chantal Akerman: Moving Through Time & Space, 1 vol. 2008. (ENG., Illus.). 72p. 24.95 *(978-0-9778028-5-2(X))* Blaffer Art Museum.

Thalen, Rob, et al. Curves: Thalen & Thalen. 2011. (FRE, DUT, GER & ENG., Illus.). 240p. *(978-90-5856-358-3(8)*, Stichting Kunstboak (Acc)) Antique Collectors' Club.

Tuymans, Luc. Against the Day, 1 vol. 2010. (ENG., Illus.). 96p. 55.00 *(978-3-86930-047-4(7))* Steidl, Gerhard Druckerei und Verlag DEU. Dist: Innovative Logistics.

—Is It Safe? 2010. (ENG., Illus.). 224p. 69.95 *(978-0-7148-5603-2(7))* Phaidon Pr., Inc.

Tuymans, Luc & Hui, Yu, contrib. by. The Forbidden Empire: Visions of the World by Chinese & Flemish Masters, 1 vol. 2008. (ENG., Illus.). 208p. 86.00 *(978-90-6153-715-1(0))* Exhibitions International N.V. BEL. Dist: D.A.P./Distributed Art Pubs.

Tuymans, Luc & Weiwei, Ai, eds. The State of Things - Brussels/Beijing. 2010. (ENG., Illus.). 256p. *(978-90-209-8683-9(X)*, Lannoo Pubs. (Acc)) Antique Collectors' Club.

Van Beirendonck, Walter. Walter Van Beirendonck: Dream the World Awake. 2012. (ENG., Illus.). 240p. 90.00 ***(978-90-209-6112-6(8))*** Lannoo Pubs./Racine.

Van Den Abeele, Lieven, et al. Disorder in the House: Vanhaerents Art Collection. 2010. (ENG & DUT., Illus.). 144p. 45.00 *(978-90-209-9105-5(1)*, Lannoo Pubs. (Acc)) Antique Collectors' Club GBR. Dist: National Bk. Network.

Van Gelder, Hilde, ed. Collective Inventions: Surrealism in Belgium. 2008. (Lieven Gevaert Ser.). (Illus.). 247p. pap. 29.95 *(978-90-5867-592-7(0))* Leuven Univ. Pr. BEL. Dist: Cornell Univ. Pr.

Van Tieghem, Jean-Pierre. Ghysels: The Beauty of Space. 2008. (ENG., Illus.). 180p. 75.00 *(978-88-7439-418-0(7))* 5 Continents ITA. Dist: Hachette Bk. Group.

Walker, Hamzah. Anne-Mie Van Kerckhoven. 2012. (ENG., Illus.). 216p. 95.00 ***(978-90-209-9937-2(0))*** Lannoo Pubs./Racine.

Willingham, et al. Silver Stained Roundels & Unipartite Panels Before the French Revolution Flanders Vol. 1: The Province of Antwerp. 2007. (Corpus vitrearum, belgium, Checklists Ser.). (Illus.). 464p. 138.00 *(978-1-905375-25-7(5))* Brepols Pubs. BEL. Dist: Brown, David Bk. Co., The.

ART, BLACK

Douglas, Robert L. Resistance, Insurgence, & Identity: The Art of Mari Evans, Nelson Stevens, & the Black Arts Movement. 2008. *(978-1-59221-564-5(5))*; 376p. pap. *(978-1-59221-565-2(3))* Africa World Pr.

Falola, Toyin, et al. Migrations & Creative Expressions in Africa & the African Diaspora. 2008. 510p. pap. 55.00 *(978-1-59460-460-7(6))* Carolina Academic Pr.

Gorschlüter, Peter. Afro Modern: Journeys Through the Black Atlantic. Barson, Tanya, ed. 2010. (ENG., Illus.). 208p. 32.50 *(978-1-85437-923-8(2))* Tate Publishing, Ltd. GBR. Dist: Hachette Bk. Group.

Kreamer, Christine Mullen. African Vision: The Walt Disney-Tishman African Art Collection. 2007. (Illus.). xvii, 235p. *(978-3-7913-6114-7(7))* Prestel Verlag GmbH & Co KG.

Meyer, Laure. Art & Craft in Africa. 2008. (Illus.). 256p. pap. 23.50 *(978-2-87939-337-7(X))* Terrail, Pierre Editions FRA. Dist: Wybel Marketing Group.

Peffer, John. Art & the End of Apartheid. 2009. (ENG., Illus.). 352p. 90.00 *(978-0-8166-5001-9(2))*; pap. 29.95 *(978-0-8166-5002-6(0))* Univ. of Minnesota Pr.

Proud, Hayden. Revisions+ Expanding the Narrative of South African Art - The Campbell Smith Collection. 2nd ed. 2008. (Illus.). 104p. pap. 43.00 *(978-1-874817-36-9(7))* Unisa Press / Uitgewers GBR. Dist: International Specialized Bk. Services.

Szok, Peter. Wolf Tracks: Popular Art & Re-Africanization in Twentieth-Century Panama. 2012. (Caribbean Studies Ser.). (ENG.). 320p. 55.00 ***(978-1-61703-243-1(3))*** Univ. Pr. of Mississippi.

Williamson, Sue. Resistance Art in South Africa 2005. 2010. (Illus.). 160p. pap. 47.95 *(978-1-919930-69-5(8))* Double Storey Bks. ZAF. Dist: International Publishers Marketing.

ART, BODY

see Body Art

ART, BRAZILIAN

Brett, Guy, ed. & text. Cildo Meireles. 2009. (ENG., Illus.). 192p. 45.00 *(978-1-933045-91-7(4))* D.A.P./Distributed Art Pubs.

Britto, Romero. Happy! 2010. (ENG., Illus.). 54p. 19.95 *(978-0-7893-2068-1(1))* Universe Publishing.

Calirman, Claudia. Brazilian Art under Dictatorship: Antonio Manuel, Artur Barrio, & Cildo Meireles. 2012. (ENG., Illus.). 264p. 89.95 ***(978-0-8223-5139-9(0))***; pap. 24.95 ***(978-0-8223-5153-5(6))*** Duke Univ. Pr.

Capoeira, Nestor. The Little Capoeira Book, Revised Edition. Ladd, Alex, tr. from POR. 3rd rev. ed. 2007. (ENG., Illus.). 240p. pap. 18.95 *(978-1-58394-198-0(3)*, Blue Snake Bks.) North Atlantic Bks.

Chastanet, Francois. Pixacao: Sao Paulo Signature. 2007. (Illus.). 279p. 45.00 *(978-2-9528097-1-9(2))* Gingko Pr., Inc.

Chhangur, Emelie & Zaccagnini, Carla. Carla Zaccagnini: No. It Is Opposition. Maranda, Michael, ed. 2010. (POR, SPA & ENG., Illus.). 112p. pap. 25.00 *(978-0-921972-57-0(1))* Art Gallery of York Univ. CAN. Dist: D.A.P./Distributed Art Pubs.

Elderfield, John & Monrad, Kasper. Bob Dylan: The Brazil Series. 2010. (Illus.). 192p. 49.95 *(978-3-7913-5098-1(6))* Prestel Publishing.

Falconi, José Luis & Rangel, Gabriela, eds. Emancipatory Action: Paula Trope & the Meninos. 2008. (David Rockefeller Center for Latin American Studies, Art Catalogs Ser.). (Illus.). 146p. pap. 17.95 *(978-0-674-02518-9(0))* Harvard Univ. Pr.

Farias, Agnaldo, text. Delson Uchoa. 2010. (ENG., Illus.). 120p. 49.95 *(978-88-8158-746-9(7))* Charta ITA. Dist: D.A.P./Distributed Art Pubs.

Garramuño, Florencia. Modernidades Primitivas: Tango, Samba y Nación. 2007. (Tierra Firme Ser.). (SPA., Illus.). 269p. pap. 13.95 *(978-950-557-701-9(X))* Fondo de Cultura Economica USA.

Gruenhaeuser, Amber. How&Nosm: The Brazil Diaries. 2011. (On the Run Bks.). (ENG., Illus.). 128p. 19.95 ***(978-3-937946-32-0(2))***; pap. 14.95 ***(978-3-937946-31-3(4))*** From Here To Fame GmbH DEU. Dist: SCB Distributors.

Laufer, Berthold. The Decorative Art of the Amur Tribes. 2010. 78p. pap. 13.69 *(978-1-151-88219-6(4))* General Bks. LLC.

—The Decorative Art of the Amur Tribes. 2008. 156p. 36.95 *(978-0-548-94890-3(9))* 2007. (ENG.). 160p. per. 21.95 *(978-0-548-62374-9(0))* Kessinger Publishing, LLC.

Lockmiller, Alice. Teacher's Guide for Tiago, Explorer of Brazil. 2010. 56p. pap. 13.95 *(978-0-557-36740-5(9))* Lulu Enterprises Inc.

Lucas, Renata & Christov-Bakargiev, Carolyn. Renata Lucas: Postpone the End. 2009. (FRE & ENG., Illus.). 115p. *(978-88-366-1576-6(7))* Silvana.

Luduvico, Rosilene. Rosilene Luduvico: See it Coming. 2008. (ENG., Illus.). 136p. pap. 55.00 *(978-3-938821-64-0(7))* Verlag fur Moderne Kunst DEU. Dist: D.A.P./Distributed Art Pubs.

Machado, Arlindo, et al, texts. Regina Silveira. 2011. (ENG., Illus.). 200p. 55.00 *(978-88-8158-799-5(8))* Charta ITA. Dist: D.A.P./Distributed Art Pubs.

Marepe, et al. Marepe. 2008. (POR & ENG., Illus.). 192p. 69.00 *(978-3-935567-40-4(5))* Holzwarth Pubns. DEU. Dist: D.A.P./Distributed Art Pubs.

Melo, Dilma de & Calaça, Maria Cecília Felix. Arte Africana e Afro-Brasileira. 2nd ed. 2007. (POR., Illus.). 90p. *(978-85-87769-73-2(1))* Imprensa Oficial do Estado S/A Imesp.

Meurs, Paul, et al, eds. Brazil Contemporary. 2009. (ENG., Illus.). 318p. pap. 45.00 *(978-90-5662-677-8(9))* NAi Uitgevers / Publishers Stichting NLD. Dist: D.A.P./Distributed Art Pubs.

Mondadori Electa. Beatriz Milhazes: Art Compilation. 2012. (ENG., Illus.). 192p. 70.00 ***(978-88-370-8756-2(X))*** Electa ITA. Dist: National Bk. Network.

Muniz, Vik & text. Vik Muniz: Verso. 2009. (ENG., Illus.). 76p. pap. 34.95 *(978-88-8158-723-0(8))* Charta ITA. Dist: D.A.P./Distributed Art Pubs.

Nair, Parvati. A Different Light: The Photography of Sebastião Salgado. 2012. (ENG., Illus.). 376p. 99.95 ***(978-0-8223-5031-6(9))***; pap. 29.95 ***(978-0-8223-5048-4(3))*** Duke Univ. Pr.

Neto, Ernesto. Ernesto Neto: The Edges of the World. 2010. (ENG., Illus.). 154p. pap. 40.00 *(978-1-85332-284-6(9))* Hayward Gallery Publishing GBR. Dist: D.A.P./Distributed Art Pubs.

Neuenschwander, Rivane. Rivane Neuenschwander: A Day Like Any Other, 1 vol. 2011. (ENG & POR., Illus.). 244p. pap. 49.95 *(978-0-915557-93-6(2))* New Museum of Contemporary Art, The.

Nittve, Lars, et al, texts. Time & Place, 3 vols. 2009. (ENG., Illus.). 430p. 100.00 *(978-3-86521-641-0(2))* Steidl, Gerhard Druckerei und Verlag DEU. Dist: D.A.P./Distributed Art Pubs.

Noever, Peter, ed. Thomas Feichtner - Edge to Edge: Experimentelles Design / Experimentelle Gestaltung. 2010. (ENG & GER., Illus.). 200p. pap. 59.95 *(978-3-0346-0342-3(8))* Birkhauser Verlag AG CHE. Dist: Actar Birkhauser Distribution.

Olea, Hector, et al. Building on a Construct: The Adolpho Leirner Collection of Brazilian Constructive Art at the Museum of Fine Arts, Houston. 2010. (ENG., Illus.). 408p. 70.00 *(978-0-300-14698-1(1))* Museum of Fine Arts, Houston.

Parr, Martin, et al, photos by. Visual Correspondences. 2010. (ENG & SPA., Illus.). 336p. pap. 39.95 *(978-950-889-183-9(1))* La Marca ARG. Dist: D.A.P./Distributed Art Pubs.

Perez-Oramas, Luis. Carlito Carvalhosa: Nice to Meet You. 2011. (ENG., Illus.). 280p. 55.00 ***(978-88-8158-815-2(3))*** Charta ITA. Dist: D.A.P./Distributed Art Pubs.

Ponchianinho, Mastre. Essential Capoeira: The Guide to Mastering the Art. 2008. (Martial Arts Ser.). (ENG., Illus.). 128p. per. 19.95 *(978-1-58394-196-6(7)*, Blue Snake Bks.) North Atlantic Bks.

Reis, Manuel Joaquim. A Crítica de Arte No ABC. 2009. (POR.). 364p. *(978-85-7921-028-0(3))* Terceira Margem Editora Didatica Ltda.

Roosevelt, José. Roosevelt. 2012. (ENG.). 208p. 69.95 *(978-87-992147-9-2(2))* Fantasmus-Art DNK. Dist: Independent Pubs. Group.

Roza, Greg. Brazilian Jiu-Jitsu. 2012. (Mixed Martial Arts Ser.). (ENG.). 48p. (YA). (gr. 5-8). lib. bdg. 27.95 ***(978-1-4488-6965-7(X)***, Rosen Central) Rosen Publishing Group, Inc., The.

Sansi & Sansi-Roca, Roger. Fetishes & Monuments: Afro-Brazilian Art & Culture in the Twentieth Century. 2007. (Remapping Cultural History Ser.: Vol. 6). (Illus.). 224p. 90.00 *(978-1-84545-363-3(8))* Berghahn Bks., Inc.

Sansi, Roger. Fetishes & Monuments: Afro-Brazilian Art & Culture in the 20th Century. 2009. (Illus.). 224p. 24.50 *(978-1-84545-711-2(0))* Berghahn Bks., Inc.

Shaw, Lisa & Dennison, Stephanie. Brazilian National Cinema. 2007. (National Cinemas Ser.). (Illus.). 223p. 140.00 *(978-0-415-33815-8(8))*; per. 33.95 *(978-0-415-33816-5(6))* Routledge.

Soares, Valeska, et al. Seducoes, 1 vol. 2007. (ENG & SPA., Illus.). 200p. 55.00 *(978-3-7757-1884-4(2))* Hatje Cantz Verlag GmbH & Co KG DEU. Dist: D.A.P./Distributed Art Pubs.

Tatay, Helena, ed. Anna Maria Maiolino. 2011. (ENG., Illus.). 256p. 45.00 *(978-3-86560-913-7(9))* Verlag der Buchhandlung Walther Konig DEU. Dist: D.A.P./Distributed Art Pubs.

Venancio Filho, Paulo. Rio de Janeiro 1956-1964: Time & Place. 2008. (ENG., Illus.). 112p. pap. 40.00 *(978-3-86521-638-0(2))* Steidl, Gerhard Druckerei und Verlag DEU. Dist: Innovative Logistics.

Watson, Richard. Capoflex. 2009. pap. *(978-1-61584-927-7(0))* Independent Pub.

ART, BRITISH

see also Aesthetic Movement (Art)

AA Publishing. British Wildlife Photography Awards. 2010. (ENG., Illus.). 224p. 45.00 *(978-0-7495-6649-4(3))* Automobile Assn. GBR. Dist: Independent Pubs. Group.

Ackley, Clifford, ed. Rhythms of Modern Life: British Prints 1914-1939. 2008. (ENG., Illus.). 224p. 60.00 *(978-0-87846-724-2(6))* Museum of Fine Arts, Boston.

Ackley, Clifford S., ed. Rhythms of Modern Life: British Prints, 1914-1939. 2008. 223p. pap. 37.50 *(978-0-87846-725-9(4))* Museum of Fine Arts, Boston.

Adams, Hazard. William Blake on His Poetry & Painting: A Study of A Descriptive Catalogue, Other Prose Writings & Jerusalem. 2010. (ENG., Illus.). 199p. pap. 55.00 *(978-0-7864-4986-6(1))* McFarland & Co., Inc. Pubs.

Adler, Phoebe, ed. Contemporary Art in the United Kingdom. 2012. (Artworld Ser.). (ENG., Illus.). 240p. pap. 29.95 ***(978-1-907317-68-2(6))*** Black Dog Publishing Ltd. GBR. Dist: Perseus Distribution.

Ager, Barry & Williams, Gareth. The Vale of York Hoard. 2010. (Objects in Focus Ser.). (ENG., Illus.). 48p. (C). pap. 10.00 *(978-0-7141-1818-5(4))* British Museum Pr. GBR. Dist: Brown, David Bk. Co., The.

Airside. Airside. 2009. (JPN & ENG., Illus.). 294p. pap. 60.00 *(978-3-89955-244-7(X))* Die Gestalten Verlag DEU. Dist: Prestel Publishing.

Albinson, Cassandra, et al. Thomas Lawrence: Regency Power & Brilliance. 2011. (Illus.). 280p. 70.00 *(978-0-300-16718-4(0))* Yale Ctr. for British Art.

Allemand-Cosneau, Claude, et al. Henry Moore: From the Inside Out. 2009. (Illus.). 200p. pap. 19.95 *(978-3-7913-4176-7(6))* Prestel Publishing.

Allen, Brian, et al. Paul Mellon's Legacy: A Passion for British Art. 2007. (ENG., Illus.). 348p. 65.00 *(978-0-300-11746-2(9))* Yale Univ. Pr.

Ansell, Robert, ed. & frwd. The valley of Fear. 2008. (ENG., Illus.). 84.95 *(978-0-9558130-0-9(X))* Fulgur Ltd. GBR. Dist: Holmes Publishing Group, LLC.

Archer, Jayne Elisabeth, et al, eds. The Intellectual & Cultural World of the Early Modern Inns of Court. 2011. (ENG., Illus.). 336p. 89.95 *(978-0-7190-8236-8(6))* Manchester Univ. Pr. GBR. Dist: Macmillan.

Artmonsky, Ruth. Art for Everyone: Contemporary Lithographs Ltd. 2010. (ENG., Illus.). 118p. *(978-1-85149-627-3(0)*, Antique Collectors Club Dist) Antique Collectors' Club.

—The School Prints: A Romantic Project. 2010. (ENG., Illus.). 126p. *(978-1-85149-628-0(9)*, Antique Collectors Club Dist) Antique Collectors' Club.

Ashery, Oreet & Sansour, Larissa. The Novel of Nonel & Vovel. 2009. (ENG., Illus.). 188p. pap. 39.95 *(978-88-8158-733-9(5))* Charta ITA. Dist: D.A.P./Distributed Art Pubs.

Asprey, Ronald. The Statues of London. 2008. (Illus.). 256p. 89.95 *(978-1-85894-472-2(4))* Merrell Pubs. Ltd. GBR. Dist: Perseus Distribution.

Austen, Jane. Sense & Sensibility & Persuasion. 2008. 520p. 55.95 *(978-0-548-94320-5(6))* Kessinger Publishing, LLC.

—Sense & Sensibility, & Persuasion. 2007. 524p. per. 40.95 *(978-0-548-59923-5(8))* Kessinger Publishing, LLC.

Bacon, Francis & Hirst, Damien, illus. Triptychs & a Thousand Years: Francis Bacon & Damien Hirst. 2008. (ENG.). 104p. 180.00 *(978-1-904212-49-2(2))* Other Criteria GBR. Dist: Abrams.

Bagshaw, Stuart & Oates, David. Brighton Graffiti. 2008. (Illus.). 144p. pap. 29.95 *(978-3-7913-3965-8(6))* Prestel Publishing.

Bailey, David, photos by. David Bailey, NY JS DB 62, 1 vol. 2008. (ENG., Illus.). 66p. 50.00 *(978-3-86521-414-0(2))* Steidl, Gerhard Druckerei und Verlag DEU. Dist: Innovative Logistics.

Baker, Christoper. English Drawings & Watercolours 1600-1900. 2011. (ENG., Illus.). 495p. ***(978-1-906270-35-3(X))*** National Galleries of Scotland.

Barber, Martyn. A History of Aerial Photography & Archaeology: Mata Hari's Glass Eye & Other Tales. 2012. (ENG., Illus.). 256p. 50.00 ***(978-1-84802-036-8(8))*** English Heritage GBR. Dist: Brown, David Bk. Co., The.

Barnett, Tertia & Sharpe, K., eds. Carving a Future for British Rock Art: New Directions for Research, Management & Presentation. 2010. (ENG., Illus.). 191p. (C). 130.00 *(978-1-84217-364-0(2))* Oxbow Bks., Ltd. GBR. Dist: Brown, David Bk. Co., The.

Barringer, Tim, intro. Paintings from the Reign of Victoria: The Royal Holloway Collection, London. 2008. (ENG., Illus.). 256p. 75.00 *(978-0-7112-2927-3(9))* Lincoln, Frances Ltd. GBR. Dist: Perseus-PGW.

Baskett, John. Paul Mellon's Legacy: A Passion for British Art Masterpieces from the Yale Center for British Art. 2007. *(978-0-9790378-0-1(8))*; pap. *(978-1-905711-02-4(6))* Yale Ctr. for British Art.

Beard, Steve. Voodoo Science Park. Rushdy, Hatem, ed. 2011. (ENG., Illus.). 115p. pap. 14.95 *(978-1-84694-527-4(5))* O Bks. John Hunt.

Beaumont, Mary Rose. Albert Irvin: The Complete Prints. ltd. ed. 2010. (Illus.). 136p. 600.00 *(978-1-84822-055-3(3)*, Lund Humphries Pubs.) Ashgate Publishing, Ltd. GBR. Dist: Ashgate Publishing Co.

Beechey, James & Stephens, Chris, eds. Picasso & Modern British Art. 2012. (ENG., Illus.). 240p. pap. 35.00 ***(978-1-85437-890-3(2))*** Tate Publishing, Ltd. GBR. Dist: Hachette Bk. Group.

Behr, Shulamith, et al. Forced Journeys: Artists in Exile in Britain C. 1933-45. 2009. (Illus.). 112p. 70.00 *(978-0-900157-13-4(5)*, Lund Humphries Pubs.) Ashgate Publishing, Ltd. GBR. Dist: Ashgate Publishing Co.

Bertola, Chiara, ed. & text. Mona Hatoum: Interior Landscape. 2009. (ENG & ITA., Illus.). 168p. pap. 39.95 *(978-88-8158-735-3(1))* Charta ITA. Dist: D.A.P./Distributed Art Pubs.

Beshty, Walead. Walead Beshty: Selected Correspondences 2001-2009. 2010. (ENG., Illus.). 128p. pap. 50.00 *(978-88-6208-135-1(9))* Damiani ITA. Dist: D.A.P./Distributed Art Pubs.

Biggs, Bryan, ed. Art in a City Revisited. 2009. (ENG., Illus.). 256p. pap. 34.95 *(978-1-84631-083-6(0))* Liverpool Univ. Pr. GBR. Dist: Chicago Distribution Ctr.

Bills, Mark. An Artists' Village: G. F. Watts & Mary Watts in Compton. 2011. (ENG., Illus.). 176p. pap. 35.00 *(978-0-85667-696-3(9))* Wilson, Philip Pubs., Ltd. GBR. Dist: Macmillan.

Bills, Mark, et al. Dickens & the Artists. 2012. (ENG., Illus.). 200p. 55.00 ***(978-0-300-17602-5(3))*** Yale Univ. Pr.

Bird, Michael. The St Ives Artists: A Cultural Biography 1939-64. 2008. (Illus.). 192p. pap. 40.00 *(978-0-85331-956-6(1)*, Lund Humphries Pubs.) Ashgate Publishing, Ltd. GBR. Dist: Ashgate Publishing Co.

Birkenstock, Eva, et al, eds. Tris Vonna-Michell. 2011. (ENG., Illus.). 80p. pap. 39.95 ***(978-3-03764-170-5(3))*** JRP Ringier Kunstverlag AG CHE. Dist: D.A.P./Distributed Art Pubs.

Black, Jonathan. The Face of Courage: Eric Kennington, Portraiture & the Second World War. 2011. (ENG., Illus.). 160p. pap. 35.00 *(978-0-85667-705-2(1))* Wilson, Philip Pubs., Ltd. GBR. Dist: Macmillan.

Blake, Peter. Venice Fantasies. Livingstone, Marco, ed. 2010. (ENG., Illus.). 96p. 47.95 *(978-1-904634-92-8(3))* Enitharmon Pr. GBR. Dist: Dufour Editions, Inc.

Blazwick, Iwona & Yiakoumaki, Nayia, frwds. This Is Tomorrow. 2011. (ENG., Illus.). 132p. spiral bd. 24.95 *(978-0-85488-186-4(7))* Whitechapel Art Gallery GBR. Dist: D.A.P./Distributed Art Pubs.

Blish, Carolyn. Drawing Closer. 2010. 29.95 *(978-0-578-05105-5(2))* Blish, Carolyn Studio.

Bolton, Andrew. AngloMania: Tradition & Transgression in British Fashion. 2006. (Illus.). 160p. 29.95 *(978-1-58839-206-0(6))* Metropolitan Museum of Art, The.

Bolton, Andrew & Koda, Harold. Anglomania: Tradition & Transgression in British Fashion. 2007. (ENG., Illus.). 160p. 29.95 *(978-0-300-11785-1(X))* Yale Univ. Pr.

Bonaventura, Paul. The Art & Craft of Richard Woods. 2012. (Illus.). 250p. 80.00 ***(978-1-84822-108-6(8)***, Lund Humphries Pubs.) Ashgate Publishing, Ltd. GBR. Dist: Ashgate Publishing Co.

Borthwick, Mark. Not in Fashion. 2009. (ENG., Illus.). 272p. 50.00 *(978-0-8478-3149-4(3))* Rizzoli International Pubns., Inc.

Bown, Jane. Exposures. 2010. (ENG., Illus.). 224p. 50.00 *(978-0-85265-141-4(4))* Random Hse. GBR. Dist: Independent Pubs. Group.

Bown, Nicola, et al. The Victorian Supernatural. Bown, Nicola et al, eds. 2009. (Cambridge Studies in Nineteenth-Century Literature & Culture Ser.). (ENG., Illus.). 328p. pap. 46.00 *(978-0-521-11464-6(0))* Cambridge Univ. Pr.

Bracewell, Michael, text. Gilbert & George: Jack Freak Pictures. 2010. (ENG., Illus.). 176p. 45.00 *(978-3-7757-2505-7(9))* Hatje Cantz Verlag GmbH & Co KG DEU. Dist: D.A.P./Distributed Art Pubs.

Bremmer, Rolf H., et al, eds. Foundations of Learning: The Transfer of Encyclopaedic Knowledge in the Early Middle Ages. 2007. (Mediaevalia Groningana New Ser.). (ENG., Illus.). 393p. (C). pap. 101.00 *(978-90-429-1979-2(5))* Peeters Pubs. & Booksellers BEL. Dist: Brown, David Bk. Co., The.

Brockington, Grace. Internationalism & the Arts in Britain & Europe at the Fin de Siècle. 2009. (Illus.). 368p. 68.95 *(978-3-03911-128-2(0))* Lang, Peter AG GBR. Dist: Lang, Peter.

Brown, Paul, et al, eds. White Heat Cold Logic: British Computer Art, 1960-1980. 2009. (Leonardo Bks.). (ENG., Illus.). 464p. (gr. 17). 44.95 (978-0-262-02653-6(8)) MIT Pr.

Brown, Peter O. Walter Goodman's the Printseller's Window. 2009. pap. 15.00 net. (978-0-918098-12-2(2)) Memorial Art Gallery of the Univ. of Rochester.

Buckland, Gail. UFO. 2010. (ENG., Illus.). 408p. 135.00 (978-0-8109-9696-0(0)) Abrams.

Buhrs, Michael & Brandlhuber, Margot Th., eds. Frederic Lord Leighton: A Princley Painter of the Victorian Age. 2009. (Illus.). 208p. 35.00 (978-3-7913-4383-9(1)) Prestel Publishing.

Capwell, Tobias. Noble Art of the Sword. 2012. (Illus.). 264p. pap. 65.00 (978-0-900785-43-6(8)) Holberton, Paul Publishing GBR. Dist: Casemate Pubs. & Bk. Distributors, LLC.

Carey-Thomas, Lizzie & Stout, Katharine. The Turner Prize & British Art. 2008. (ENG., Illus.). 112p. pap. 27.50 (978-1-85437-742-5(6)) Tate Publishing, Ltd. GBR. Dist: Hachette Bk. Group.

Carlisle, Janice. Picturing Reform in Victorian Britain. 2012. (Cambridge Studies in Nineteenth-Century Literature & Culture Ser.: 79). (ENG., Illus.). 320p. 99.00 (978-0-521-86836-5(X)) Cambridge Univ. Pr.

Carr, Peter. Port of Culture: Liverpool Through the Photography of Pete Carr. 2008. (ENG., Illus.). 112p. 34.95 (978-1-84631-170-3(5)) Liverpool Univ. Pr. GBR. Dist: Chicago Distribution Ctr.

Carrington, Leonora. Leonora Carrington: What She Might Be. 2008. (Illus.). 100p. pap. (978-0-936227-29-0(X)) Dallas Museum of Art.

Castello, Joe. The Joe Public Guide to Being English. 2nd ed. 2007. 132p. per. (978-1-84401-906-9(3)) Athena Pr.

Chapman, Jake & Chapman, Dinos. Flogging a Dead Horse: The Life & Works of Jake & Dinos Chapman. Fuel Staff, ed. 2011. (ENG., Illus.). 336p. 85.00 (978-0-8478-3478-5(6)) Rizzoli International Pubns., Inc.

Chapman, Jake & Chapman, Dinos, texts. Jake & Dinos Chapman: Insult to Injury, 1 vol. 2008. (ENG., Illus.). 176p. 70.00 (978-3-88243-957-1(2)) Steidl, Gerhard Druckerei und Verlag DEU. Dist: Innovative Logistics.

Cherry, John. Holy Thorn Reliquary. 2010. (Objects in Focus Ser.). (ENG., Illus.). 56p. (C). pap. 10.00 (978-0-7141-2820-7(1)) British Museum Pr. GBR. Dist: Brown, David Bk. Co., The.

Cheshire, Jim, et al. Tennyson Transformed: Alfred Lord Tennyson & Visual Culture. 2009. (Illus.). 160p. 80.00 (978-1-84822-003-4(0), Lund Humphries Pubs.) Ashgate Publishing, Ltd. GBR. Dist: Ashgate Publishing Co.

Chung, Minh. Korean Treasures: Rare Books, Manuscripts & Artefacts in the Bodleian Libraries & Museums of Oxford University. Riley, Ha Yea, tr. 2012. (Illus.). 160p. 60.00 (978-1-85124-287-0(2)) Bodleian Library GBR. Dist: Chicago Distribution Ctr.

Clark, Adrian. British & Irish Art, 1945-1951: From War to Festival. 2010. (Illus.). 272p. 50.00 (978-0-9554063-4-8(X)) Holberton, Paul Publishing GBR. Dist: Casemate Pubs. & Bk. Distributors, LLC.

Clarke, Brian. Brian Clarke: Work: Work, 1 vol. 2009. (ENG., Illus.). 1006p. 249.90 (978-3-86521-633-5(1)) Steidl, Gerhard Druckerei und Verlag DEU. Dist: Innovative Logistics.

Clarke, Robert. Seven Years with Banksy. 2012. (ENG., Illus.). 224p. pap. 19.95 (978-1-84317-865-1(6)) O'Mara, Michael Bks., Ltd. GBR. Dist: Independent Pubs. Group.

Clayton, Timothy. Colnaghi: The History. 2010. (ENG., Illus.). 68p. pap. 40.00 (978-1-907372-07-0(5)) Holberton, Paul Publishing GBR. Dist: Univ. of Washington Pr.

Codell, Julie F., ed. Transculturation in British Art, 1770-1930. 2012. (British Art: Global Contexts Ser.). (Illus.). 312 + 4 lourp. 119.95 (978-1-4094-0977-9(5)) Ashgate Publishing Co.

Coldwell, Paul. Morandi's Legacy: Influences on British Art. 2006. (ENG., Illus.). 80p. 42.00 (978-0-85667-620-8(9)) Wilson, Philip Pubs., Ltd. GBR. Dist: Macmillan.

Coleman, Priscilla & Cheston, Paul. Court Scenes: The Court Art of Priscilla Coleman. 2010. (Illus.). 64p. 34.00 (978-0-85490-039-8(X)) Gaunt, Inc.

Cook, Beryl. Happy Days. (Illus.). 64p. pap. 22.95 (978-0-575-06651-9(2)) Gollancz, Victor Ltd. GBR. Dist: Trafalgar Square Publishing.

Cook, Brian. Brian Cook's Landscapes of Britain. (ENG., Illus.). 2012. 128p. 14.95 (978-1-84994-036-8(3)) 2011. 144p. 29.95 (978-1-906388-78-2(4)) Anova Bks. GBR. (Batsford, B. T. Ltd.). Dist: Sterling Publishing Co., Inc.

Cook, Dutton. Art in England. 2008. 260p. 28.99 (978-0-554-26976-4(7)); 25.99 (978-0-554-36279-3(1)) BiblioBazaar.

—Art in England: Notes & Studies. 2007. (ENG.). 232p. per. 20.99 (978-1-4346-2272-3(X)); 260p. per. 23.99 (978-1-4346-2330-0(0)) BiblioBazaar.

Cooper, Jeremy. Growing Up: The Young British Artists At 50. 2012. 176p. 39.95 (978-3-7913-4702-8(0)) Prestel Publishing.

Corbett, David Peters & Monks, Sarah, eds. Anglo-American: Artistic Exchange between Britain & the USA. 2012. (Art History Special Issues Ser.: 9). (ENG.). 264p. pap. 39.95 (978-1-4443-5143-9(5), Wiley-Blackwell) Wiley, John & Sons, Inc.

Cork, Richard & Martin, Elliott Zooey. End Game: British Contemporary Art from the Chaney Family Collection. 2008. (ENG., Illus.). 80p. pap. 14.95 (978-0-300-14201-3(3)) Museum of Fine Arts, Houston.

Cork, Richard & Sewell, Brian, contrib. by. History of the Saatchi Gallery. 2nd ed. 2011. (ENG., Illus.). 1008p. 125.00 (978-1-86154-315-8(8)) Booth-Clibborn Editions GBR. Dist: Hachette Bk. Group.

Cosh, Stephen R. & Neal, David S. Roman Mosaics of Britain Vol. 4: West Britain, Incorporating Wales, 4 vols. 2010. (ENG., Illus.). 470p. (C). 320.00 (978-0-85431-294-8(3)) Society of Antiquaries of London GBR. Dist: Brown, David Bk. Co., The.

Costello, Leo. J. M. W. Turner & the Subject of History. 2012. (Illus.). 280p. 119.95 (978-0-7546-6922-7(X)) Ashgate Publishing Co.

Craft, Stephen. Robyn Beeche: Visage to Vraj. 2009. (ENG., Illus.). 224p. 75.00 (978-1-86470-312-2(1)) Images Publishing Group AUS. Dist: National Bk. Network.

Cragg, Tony & Loyrette, Henri. Tony Cragg: Figure out Figure In. 2011. (ENG., Illus.). 102p. 39.95 (978-2-916275-87-1(8)) Verlag der Buchhandlung Walther Konig DEU. Dist: D.A.P./Distributed Art Pubs.

Creed, Martin. Martin Creed, Complete Works. (Illus.). 600p. pap. 65.00 (978-3-86521-408-9(8)) Steidl, Gerhard Druckerei und Verlag DEU. Dist: D.A.P./Distributed Art Pubs.

Crehan, Kate. Community Art: An Anthropological Perspective. 2012. (ENG., Illus.). 224p. 99.95 (978-1-84788-834-1(8)); pap. 34.95 (978-1-84788-833-4(X)) Berg Pubs. GBR. Dist: Macmillan.

Crowley, John E. Imperial Landscapes: Britain's Global Visual Culture, 1745-1820. 2011. (Paul Mellon Centre for Studies in Britis Ser.). (ENG., Illus.). 320p. 85.00 (978-0-300-17050-4(5)) Yale Univ. Pr.

Cunchillos Jaime, Carmelo, ed. Wyndham Lewis the Radical: Essays on Literature & Modernity. 2007. 278p. pap. 61.95 (978-3-03911-200-5(7)) Lang, Peter Publishing, Inc.

Curators of the The Royal Collection Staff. Treasures: The Royal Collection. Roberts, Jane, ed. 2010. (Illus.). 256p. 30.00 (978-1-905686-05-6(6)) Royal Collection Enterprises Ltd. GBR. Dist: Chicago Distribution Ctr.

—Treasures: The Royal Collection. 2008. (ENG.). 256p. 50.00 (978-1-85759-568-0(8)) Scala, Editions FRA. Dist: National Bk. Network.

Curtin, Gemma, et al, eds. Kenneth Grange: Making Britain Modern. 2011. (ENG., Illus.). 192p. pap. 29.95 (978-1-907317-54-5(6)) Black Dog Publishing Ltd. GBR. Dist: Perseus Distribution.

Cuss, Terence Camerer. The English Watch: 1585-1970 A Unique Alliance of Art, Design & Inventive Genius. 2008. (ENG., Illus.). 504p. (978-1-85149-588-7(6), Antique Collectors Club Dist) Antique Collectors' Club.

Dadd, Richard. Richard Dadd: the Artist & the Asylum. 2011. (ENG., Illus.). 208p. 50.00 (978-1-935202-68-4(5)) D.A.P./Distributed Art Pubs.

Davenport, Cyril James Humphries. English Embroidered Bookbindings. 2007. (Illus.). 92p. pap. (978-1-84830-023-1(9), Wildhern Pr.) Echo Library.

David, Enrico. Enrico David. 2009. (ENG., Illus.). 84p. 62.00 (978-3-86560-580-1(X)) Verlag der Buchhandlung Walther Konig DEU. Dist: D.A.P./Distributed Art Pubs.

Dawson, Aileen. English & Irish Delftware 1570-1840. 2010. (ENG., Illus.). 320p. (C). 70.00 (978-0-7141-2810-8(4)) British Museum Pr. GBR. Dist: Brown, David Bk. Co., The.

De Cruz, Gemma, frwd. Ant Noises at the Saatchi Gallery. (Illus.). 56p. pap. 20.00 (978-0-9538587-0-5(7), A20007) Saatchi Gallery GBR. Dist: D.A.P./Distributed Art Pubs.

de Guitaut, Caroline. Fabergé's Animals: A Royal Farm in Miniature. 2010. (Illus.). 119p. 24.95 (978-1-905686-12-4(9)) Royal Collection Enterprises Ltd. GBR. Dist: Chicago Distribution Ctr.

De Hamel, Christopher & Lovett, Patricia, intros. The Macclesfield Alphabet: A Facsimile. 2010. (ENG., Illus.). 128p. (C). 60.00 (978-0-7123-5804-0(8)) British Library, The GBR. Dist: Brown, David Bk. Co., The.

Dean, Tacita. Seven Books Grey, 7 vols. 2011. (ENG & GER., Illus.). 976p. pap. 98.00 (978-3-86930-299-7(2)) Steidl, Gerhard Druckerei und Verlag DEU. Dist: Innovative Logistics.

Deller, Jeremy. It Is What It Is. 2012. (ENG., Illus.). 180p. pap. 39.95 (978-1-928570-13-4(5)) Creative Time.

Derieux, Florence, ed. Dexter Dalwood. 2010. (ENG., Illus.). 160p. pap. 55.00 (978-3-03764-126-2(6)) JRP Ringier Kunstverlag AG CHE. Dist: D.A.P./Distributed Art Pubs.

Desmarais, Jane. Model & Supermodel: The Artist's Model in British Art & Culture. Desmarais, Jane et al, eds. 2007. (Barber Institute's Critical Perspectives Ser.). (ENG., Illus.). 192p. 94.00 (978-0-7190-6662-7(X)) Manchester Univ. Pr. GBR. Dist: Macmillan.

Dmitrieva, Olga & Abramova, Natalya, eds. Britannia & Muscovy: English Silver at the Court of the Tsars. 2006. (ENG., Illus.). 304p. 85.00 (978-0-300-11676-6(0)) Yale Univ. Pr.

Dodwell, C. R. The Canterbury School of Illumination 1066-1200. 2011. (ENG.). 230p. pap. 31.99 (978-0-521-18059-7(7)) Cambridge Univ. Pr.

Donald, Diana. Picturing Animals in Britain. 2008. (ENG., Illus.). 256p. 65.00 (978-0-300-12679-2(4)) Yale Univ. Pr.

Dorment, Richard, et al. Art, Power, Diplomacy: The Untold Story of the Government Art Collection. 2011. (ENG., Illus.). 192p. pap. 35.00 (978-1-85759-694-5(9)) Scala, Editions FRA. Dist: National Bk. Network.

Dover, Rackham. 2010. (Dover Postcards Ser.). (ENG., Illus.). 24p. pap. 6.95 (978-0-486-48019-0(4)) Dover Pubns., Inc.

Duffy, Chris. Duffy. 2011. (ENG., Illus.). 256p. 85.00 (978-1-85149-657-0(2)) Antique Collectors' Club.

Duffy, Stephen & Vogtherr, Christoph Martin. Miniatures in the Wallace Collection. 2010. (ENG., Illus.). 154p. (C). pap. 50.00 (978-0-900785-83-2(7)) Holberton, Paul Publishing GBR. Dist: Univ. of Washington Pr.

Eatock, Daniel. Imprint: Works, 1975-2007. 2008. (ENG., Illus.). 224p. 60.00 (978-1-56898-788-0(9)) Princeton Architectural Pr.

Eccher, Danilo. Marc Quinn: Myth. 2009. (ENG & ITA., Illus.). 120p. 49.95 (978-88-8158-725-4(4)) Charta ITA. Dist: D.A.P./Distributed Art Pubs.

Elam, Caroline. Roger Fry's Journey from Primitives to the Post-Impressionists. 2011. (ENG., Illus.). 48p. (978-1-906270-11-7(2)) National Galleries of Scotland.

Ellis, Patricia, contrib. by. New Labour. (Illus.). 64p. pap. 32.00 (978-0-9538587-2-9(3)) Saatchi Gallery GBR. Dist: D.A.P./Distributed Art Pubs.

Ellis, Patricia, frwd. Newspeak. 2010. (ENG., Illus.). 368p. pap. 55.00 (978-1-86154-314-1(X)) Booth-Clibborn Editions GBR. Dist: Hachette Bk. Group.

Emin, Tracey. One Thousand Drawings. 2009. (ENG., Illus.). 2016p. 75.00 (978-0-8478-3202-6(3)) Rizzoli International Pubns., Inc.

Emin, Tracey. Tracey Emin: Love Is What You Want. 2011. (ENG., Illus.). 260p. pap. 45.00 (978-1-85332-293-8(8)) Hayward Gallery Publishing GBR. Dist: D.A.P./Distributed Art Pubs.

Evans, Cerith Wyn. Parkett No. 87: Cerith Wyn Evans, Katarina Fritsch, Annette Kelm, Kelly Walker. 2010. (ENG., Illus.). 300p. pap. 32.00 (978-3-907582-47-3(0)) Parkett Verlag AG CHE. Dist: D.A.P./Distributed Art Pubs.

Ferguson, Russell, et al, contrib. by. Richard Wright. 2010. (ENG., Illus.). 144p. 80.00 (978-0-8478-3504-1(9)) Rizzoli International Pubns., Inc.

Fletcher, Helmreich. Rise of Modern Art Market in London: The Rise of the Modern Art Market in London. Fletcher, Pamela & Helmreich, Anne, eds. 2012. (ENG., Illus.). 336p. 100.00 (978-0-7190-8460-7(1)) Manchester Univ. Pr. GBR. Dist: Macmillan.

Flood, Catherine. British Posters: Advertising, Art & Activism. 2012. (ENG., Illus.). 128p. pap. 35.00 (978-1-85177-676-4(1)) V & A Pubns. GBR. Dist: Hachette Bk. Group.

Fornieles, Eloise. Eloise Fornieles. Beard, Jason, ed. 2009. (ENG., Illus.). 32p. pap. 35.00 (978-1-904212-63-8(8)) Other Criteria GBR. Dist: Hachette Bk. Group.

Forrester, Gillian, ed. Rebecca Salter: Into the Light of Things. 2011. (ENG., Illus.). 282p. 60.00 (978-0-300-17042-9(4)) Yale Univ. Pr.

Foster, Kathleen A. Thomas Chambers: American Marine & Landscape Painter, 1808-1869. 2008. (ENG., Illus.). 184p. 50.00 (978-0-300-14105-4(X)) Yale Univ. Pr.

Foster, Norman & text. Norman Foster Set: Drawings, 1958-2008, 2 vols. 2011. (ENG., Illus.). 232p. 150.00 (978-0-9564339-2-3(8)) Ivory Pr. ESP. Dist: D.A.P./Distributed Art Pubs.

Frye, Susan. Pens & Needles: Women's Textualities in Early Modern England. 2010. (Material Texts). (Illus.). 344p. (C). 65.00 (978-0-8122-4238-6(6)) Univ. of Pennsylvania Pr.

Gagosian Gallery Staff, compiled by. Glenn Brown. 2010. (ENG., Illus.). 148p. 100.00 (978-0-8478-3488-4(3)) Rizzoli International Pubns., Inc.

Games Design Workshop Staff. Blood & Iron. (Illus.). 224p. (978-1-85585-008-2(1), Collins & Brown) Anova Bks.

Georganteli, Eurydice, et al. Sacred & Profane. 2010. (ENG., Illus.). 128p. 40.00 (978-1-904832-80-5(6)) Giles, D. Ltd. GBR. Dist: Antique Collectors' Club.

German, Andrew. John Stobart: The Grandeur of America's Age of Sail. 2009. 163p. 34.95 (978-0-9635775-4-2(9)); (ENG.). pap. 24.95 (978-0-9635775-5-9(7)) Osmington Hse. Publishing.

Gilbert, et al, contrib. by. Gilbert & George: 4 Octobre 1997-4 Janvier 1998, Musee d'Art Moderne de la Ville de Paris. (Illus.). 432p. (978-2-87900-360-3(1)) Paris-Musées, Association.

Gillick, Liam, photos by. Liam Gillick: Woven/Intersected/Revised, 5 vols. 2008. (ITA & ENG., Illus.). 72p. 15.00 (978-3-905701-47-0(2)) JRP Ringier Kunstverlag AG CHE. Dist: D.A.P./Distributed Art Pubs.

Goble, Warwick. Goble's Fairy Tale Illustrations: 86 Full-Color Plates. Menges, Jeff A., ed. 2008. (Dover Fine Art, History of Art Ser.). (ENG., Illus.). 96p. pap. 14.95 (978-0-486-46521-0(7)) Dover Pubns., Inc.

Goldhill, Simon. Victorian Culture & Classical Antiquity: Art, Opera, Fiction, & the Proclamation of Modernity. 2011. (Martin Classical Lectures). (ENG., Illus.). 368p. (C). 45.00 (978-0-691-14994-4(4)) Princeton Univ. Pr.

Goring, E., et al. Kevin Coates: A Hidden Alchemy - Goldsmithing - Jewels & Tablepieces. 2008. (ENG., Illus.). 312p. 75.00 (978-3-89790-284-8(2)) Arnoldsche Art Pubs. DEU. Dist: Antique Collectors' Club.

Gormley, Antony. One & Other. 2010. (ENG., Illus.). 700p. 59.95 (978-0-224-09078-0(X), Jonathan Cape) Random Hse. GBR. Dist: Independent Pubs. Group.

Gott. Modern Britain 1900-1960. 2008. (ENG., Illus.). 308p. pap. 39.95 (978-0-7241-0292-1(2)) National Gallery of Victoria AUS. Dist: National Bk. Network.

Gray, Colin. In Sickness & Health, 1 vol. 2011. (ENG., Illus.). 96p. 39.00 (978-3-86521-940-4(3)) Steidl, Gerhard Druckerei und Verlag DEU. Dist: Innovative Logistics.

Grunenberg, Christoph. Peter Blake. Sillars, Laurence, ed. 2007. (ENG., Illus.). 216p. pap. 49.95 (978-1-85437-717-3(5)) Tate Publishing, Ltd. GBR. Dist: Hachette Bk. Group.

Gudenrath, William, et al. Roman Cameo Glass in the British Museum. 2010. (ENG., Illus.). 110p. (C). pap. 60.00 (978-0-7141-2267-0(X)) British Museum Pr. GBR. Dist: Brown, David Bk. Co., The.

Gunn, Ann V. The Prints of Wilhelmina Barns-Graham: A Complete Catalogue. 2007. (Illus.). 160p. 80.00 (978-0-85331-969-6(3), Lund Humphries Pubs.) Ashgate Publishing, Ltd. GBR. Dist: Ashgate Publishing Co.

Gwilt, Joanna. French Porcelain for English Palaces: Sèvres from the Royal Collection. 2010. (Illus.). 200p. pap. 25.00 (978-1-905686-14-8(5)) Royal Collection Enterprises Ltd. GBR. Dist: Chicago Distribution Ctr.

Gygax, Raphael & Munder, Heike, eds. Dawn Mellor. 2009. (ENG & GER., Illus.). 64p. 35.00 (978-3-905829-98-3(3)) JRP Ringier Kunstverlag AG CHE. Dist: D.A.P./Distributed Art Pubs.

—Giotto's Play/Giottos Schauspiel. 2008. (ENG., Illus.). 296p. per. 65.00 (978-3-905770-82-7(2)) JRP Ringier Kunstverlag AG CHE. Dist: D.A.P./Distributed Art Pubs.

Hack, Jefferson. Dazed & Confused: Making It up As We Go Along. Rankin, Angela & Furniss, Jo-Ann, eds. 2011. (ENG., Illus.). 336p. 60.00 (978-0-8478-3692-5(4)) Rizzoli International Pubns., Inc.

Hackworth, Nick. Jake & Dinos Chapman. 2008. (Tate Modern Artists Ser.). (ENG., Illus.). 128p. pap. 27.50 (978-1-85437-664-0(0)) Tate Publishing, Ltd. GBR. Dist: Abrams.

Hamilton, Frederick W. A Brief History of Printing in England: a Short History of Printing In. 2007. (ENG.). 84p. per. 17.95 (978-1-4304-4378-0(2)) Kessinger Publishing, LLC.

Hamilton, Richard. Richard Hamilton: Modern Moral Matters, 1 vol. 2010. (ENG., Illus.). 96p. pap. 45.00 (978-3-86560-751-5(9)) Verlag der Buchhandlung Walther Konig DEU. Dist: D.A.P./Distributed Art Pubs.

Hamling, Tara. Decorating the "Godly" Household: Religious Art in Post-Reformation Britain. 2011. (Paul Mellon Centre for Studies in Britis Ser.). (ENG., Illus.). 256p. 75.00 (978-0-300-16282-0(0)) Yale Univ. Pr.

Harding, Mike. A Little Book of Devils & Demons. 2008. (Little Bks.). (ENG.). 96p. 12.95 (978-1-84513-307-8(2)) Aurum Pr., Ltd. GBR. Dist: Independent Pubs. Group.

Harris, Jonathan, ed. Inside the Death Drive: Excess & Apocalypse in the World of the Chapman Brothers. 2010. (Liverpool University Press - Tate Liverpool Critical Forum Ser.). (ENG., Illus.). 240p. pap. 49.95 (978-1-84631-192-5(6)) Liverpool Univ. Pr. GBR. Dist: Chicago Distribution Ctr.

Hartop, Christopher. British & Irish Silver in the Fogg Art Museum, Harvard University Art Museums. 2007. (Harvard University Art Museums Ser.). (ENG., Illus.). 264p. 75.00 (978-0-300-11770-7(1)) Yale Univ. Pr.

—A Noble Pursuit: English Silver from the Rita Gans Collection at the Virginia Museum of Fine Arts. 2011. (ENG., Illus.). 88p. (gr. 17). pap. 25.00 (978-0-917046-90-2(0)) Univ. Pr. of Virginia.

—A Noble Pursuit: English Silver from the Rita Gans Collection at the Virginia Museum of Fine Arts. 2010. (978-0-917046-91-9(9)) Virginia Museum of Fine Arts.

Harvey, Marcus & Beard, Jason. Marcus Harvey. 2009. (Illus.). 208p. 140.00 (978-1-904212-62-1(X)) Other Criteria GBR. Dist: Abrams.

Haskins, Katherine. The Art-Journal & Fine Art Publishing in Victorian England, 1850-1880. 2012. (Illus.). 232p. 119.95 (978-1-4094-1810-8(3)) Ashgate Publishing Co.

Hawkes, Jason. London at Night. 2010. (ENG., Illus.). 160p. 45.00 (978-1-85894-517-0(8), Merrell Pubs. Ltd. GBR. Dist: Perseus Distribution.

Haynes, Clare. Pictures & Popery: Art & Religion in England 1660-1760. 2006. (Illus.). 238p. 130.00 (978-0-7546-5506-0(7)) Ashgate Publishing Co.

Hebgin-Barnes, Penny. The Medieval Stained Glass of Cheshire. 2010. (ENG., Illus.). 642p. 210.00 (978-0-19-726469-0(7)) Oxford Univ. Pr., Inc.

Helland, Janice. British & Irish Home Arts & Industries 1880-1914: Marketing Craft, Making Fashion. 2007. (Illus.). 219p. (C). pap. 32.50 (978-0-7165-2891-3(6)) Irish Academic Pr. IRL. Dist: International Specialized Bk. Services.

—British & Irish Home Arts & Industries, 1880-1914: Marketing Craft, Making Fashion. 2007. (Illus.). 219p. (C). 75.00 (978-0-7165-2890-6(8)) Irish Academic Pr. IRL. Dist: International Specialized Bk. Services.

Hemsworth, Gerard. Hidden Agenda, 1 vol. 2010. (GER & ENG., Illus.). 84p. 45.00 (978-3-941185-89-0(6)) Verlag fur Moderne Kunst DEU. Dist: D.A.P./Distributed Art Pubs.

Herbert, James. Creating the AHRC: An Arts & Humanities Research Council for the United Kingdom in the Twenty-first Century. 2008. (ENG., Illus.). 100p. pap. 24.95 (978-0-19-726429-4(8)) Oxford Univ. Pr., Inc.

Hicks, Alistar. Contemporary Art at Deutsche Bank. (Illus.). 167p. 39.95 (978-3-89322-825-6(X)) Edition Cantz DEU. Dist: D.A.P./Distributed Art Pubs.

Higgie, Jennifer, text. Scenes. 2010. (ENG., Illus.). 64p. 39.95 (978-3-03764-029-6(4)) JRP Ringier Kunstverlag AG CHE. Dist: D.A.P./Distributed Art Pubs.

Hiller, Susan & Gallagher, Ann. Susan Hiller. 2011. (ENG., Illus.). 192p. pap. 39.95 (978-1-85437-888-0(0)) Tate Publishing, Ltd. GBR. Dist: Hachette Bk. Group.

Hirst, Damien. The Complete Vitrines. 2012. (Illus.). 180p. 150.00 (978-1-906967-43-7(1)) Other Criteria GBR. Dist: Abrams.

—Cornucopia. 2010. (ENG.). 160p. 240.00 (978-1-906967-32-1(6)); (Illus.). 85.00 (978-1-906967-31-4(8)) Other Criteria GBR. Dist: Abrams, Hachette Bk. Group.

—Dark Trees. 2010. (ENG.). 80p. 210.00 (978-1-906967-28-4(8)); (Illus.). 70.00 (978-1-906967-27-7(X)) Other Criteria GBR. Dist: Abrams, Hachette Bk. Group.

—No Love Lost. 2010. (ENG., Illus.). 64p. 40.00 (978-1-906967-22-2(9)); 200.00 (978-1-906967-23-9(7)) Other Criteria GBR. Dist: Hachette Bk. Group.

—Nothing Matters. 2010. (ENG., Illus.). 120p. 80.00 (978-1-906967-19-2(9)); 72p. 240.00 (978-1-906967-20-8(2)) Other Criteria GBR. Dist: Hachette Bk. Group.

—Poisons + Remedies. aut. ltd. ed. 2011. (ENG.). 88p. pap. 265.00 (978-1-906967-45-1(8)) Abrams.

—Romance in the Age of Uncertainty. Beard, Jason, ed. 2008. (ENG., Illus.). 144p. pap. 90.00 (978-0-9542363-7-3(8)) Other Criteria GBR. Dist: Hachette Bk. Group.

—8 Minutes, 1 vol. 2009. (ENG., Illus.). 264p. 68.00 *(978-3-86521-864-3(4))* Steidl, Gerhard Druckerei und Verlag DEU. Dist: Innovative Logistics.

Hirst, Damien & Beard, Jason, eds. Requiem I & II: Text in English & Ukrainian. aut. ed. 2009. (ENG., Illus.). 326p. 675.00 *(978-1-906967-07-9(5))* Other Criteria GBR. Dist: Hachette Bk. Group.

Hirst, Damien & Brown, Gordon. The Complete Spot Paintings, 1986-2011. 2012. (Illus.). 1024p. 280.00 ***(978-1-906967-48-2(2))*** Other Criteria GBR. Dist: Abrams.

Hoptman, Laura, ed. Brion Gysin. 2010. (ENG., Illus.). 192p. 39.95 *(978-1-85894-521-7(6))* Merrell Pubs. Ltd. GBR. Dist: Perseus Distribution.

Hourihane, Colum, ed. Insular & Anglo-Saxon Art & Thought in the Early Medieval Period. 2011. (Illus.). 360p. pap. 35.00 ***(978-0-9837537-0-4(9))*** Index of Christian Art, Princeton Univ., The.

Howard, Helen. Pigments of English Medieval Wall Painting. 2007. (ENG., Illus.). 314p. 130.00 *(978-1-873132-48-7(4))* Archetype Pubns. GBR. Dist: National Bk. Network.

Hubbard, Sue. Adventures in Art: Selected Writings, 1990-2010. 2010. (ENG., Illus.). 302p. pap. 37.50 *(978-1-906967-21-5(0))* Other Criteria GBR. Dist: Hachette Bk. Group.

Hughes, Eleanor & Trumble, Angus. The Independent Eye: Contemporary British Art from the Collection of Samuel & Gabrielle Lurie. 2010. (Illus.). 144p. 65.00 *(978-0-300-17139-6(0))* Yale Ctr. for British Art.

Huijts, Stijn, intro. Stanley Donwood: Red Maze. 2011. (ENG., Illus.). 160p. 59.95 *(978-94-90624-03-3(9))* Schunck NLD. Dist: D.A.P./Distributed Art Pubs.

Hunt, Ian, et al. The Self as a Stranger: Simon Lewty. 2010. (ENG., Illus.). 192p. 49.95 *(978-1-907317-07-1(4))* Black Dog Publishing Ltd. GBR. Dist: Perseus Distribution.

Hunter, Michael. Printed Images in Early Modern Britain: Essays in Interpretation. 2010. (Illus.). 396p. 124.95 *(978-0-7546-6654-7(9))* Ashgate Publishing Co.

Inankur, Zeynep, et al, eds. The Poetics & Politics of Place: Ottoman Istanbul & British Orientalism. 2010. (ENG., Illus.). 288p. (C). pap. 60.00 *(978-0-295-99110-8(0))* Univ. of Washington Pr.

Inskip, Peter & Gee, Stephen. Louis I. Kahn & the Yale Center for British Art: A Conservation Plan. 2012. (ENG., Illus.). 200p. 50.00 *(978-0-300-17164-8(1))* Yale Ctr. for British Art.

Jacques, David. Por Convencion Ferrer: The Northwest of England, Anarchosyndicalism & Time Travel. 2009. (ENG., Illus.). 128p. 39.95 *(978-1-84631-206-9(X))* Liverpool Univ. Pr. GBR. Dist: Chicago Distribution Ctr.

James, M. R. Lists of Manuscripts Formerly in Peterborough Abbey Library. 2010. (Cambridge Library Collection - History Ser.). (ENG.). 110p. pap. 19.99 *(978-1-108-01135-8(7))* Cambridge Univ. Pr.

James, Russell. The Pocket Guide to Victorian Artists & Their Models. 2011. (Illus.). 240p. pap. 19.95 *(978-1-84468-095-5(9))* Pen & Sword Bks. Ltd. GBR. Dist: Casemate Pubs. & Bk. Distributors, LLC.

Jarvis, James. James Jarvis: de Profundis. 2011. (ENG., Illus.). 64p. 19.95 ***(978-0-9845892-3-4(6))*** PictureBox, Inc.

Jenkins, David Fraser. Paul Nash: The Elements. 2010. (ENG., Illus.). 168p. pap. 39.95 *(978-1-85759-619-9(6))* Scala, Editions FRA. Dist: National Bk. Network.

Jeremiah, David. Representations of British Motoring. 2007. (Studies in Design & Material Culture Ser.). (ENG., Illus.). 264p. 89.00 *(978-0-7190-7540-7(8))* Manchester Univ. Pr. GBR. Dist: Macmillan.

Jerome, Jerome K. Three Men in a Boat. 2011. (Campfire Graphic Novels Ser.). (ENG., Illus.). 72p. pap. 9.99 *(978-93-80741-07-9(3)*, Campfire) Kalyani Navyug Media Pty. Ltd. IND. Dist: Random Hse., Inc.

John Hinde International Staff, contrib. by. Our True Intent Is All for Your Delight: The John Hinde Butlin's Photographs. 2011. (ENG., Illus.). 128p. 29.95 ***(978-1-905712-20-5(0))*** Boot, Chris GBR. Dist: D.A.P./Distributed Art Pubs.

Johnson, Alfred Edwin. Frank Reynolds, R I. 2007. (Illus.). 56p. per. *(978-1-4065-3478-8(1))* Dodo Pr.

Johnson, Nora. The Actor as Playwright in Early Modern Drama. 2009. (ENG., Illus.). 220p. pap. 33.99 *(978-0-521-11737-1(2))* Cambridge Univ. Pr.

Jolivette, Catherine. Landscape, Art & Identity in 1950s Britain. 2009. (Illus.). 190p. 114.95 *(978-0-7546-6363-8(9))* Ashgate Publishing Co.

Jones, Allen. Allen Jones: Showtime. 2010. (ENG., Illus.). 92p. 40.00 *(978-3-86678-352-2(3))* Kerber Verlag DEU. Dist: D.A.P./Distributed Art Pubs.

Jones, Laura K., ed. A Hedonist's Guide to Art. 2010. (Hedonist's Guide To... Ser.). (ENG., Illus.). 240p. 20.00 *(978-1-905428-50-2(2)*, HG2) Filmer Ltd. GBR. Dist: Perseus-PGW.

Jones, Stanley. Stanley Jones & the Curwen Studio. 2010. (ENG., Illus.). 160p. 55.00 *(978-1-4081-0286-2(2))* A & C Black GBR. Dist: Macmillan.

Kapoor, Anish. Anish Kapoor: Flashback. 2011. (ENG., Illus.). 96p. 35.00 *(978-1-85332-288-4(1))* Hayward Gallery Publishing GBR. Dist: D.A.P./Distributed Art Pubs.

—Architecture Projects, 1 vol. 2011. (ENG., Illus.). 300p. 85.00 *(978-3-86521-999-2(3))* Steidl, Gerhard Druckerei und Verlag DEU. Dist: Innovative Logistics.

Kaspar, Tobias, ed. Jonathan Monk: Studio Visit. 2010. (ENG., Illus.). 154p. pap. 22.00 *(978-3-03764-065-4(0))* JRP Ringier Kunstverlag AG CHE. Dist: D.A.P./Distributed Art Pubs.

Kelly, Jason M. The Society of Dilettanti: Archaeology & Identity in the British Enlightenment. 2010. (Paul Mellon Centre for Studies in Britis Ser.). (ENG., Illus.). 366p. 75.00 *(978-0-300-15219-7(1))* Yale Univ. Pr.

Kemp, Dominic, et al. Terry Frost Prints: A Catalogue Raisonne. 2010. (Illus.). 304p. 90.00 *(978-1-84822-035-5(9)*, Lund Humphries Pubs.) Ashgate Publishing, Ltd. GBR. Dist: Ashgate Publishing Co.

Khan, Farah. The First British Book of Henna Art. 2008. (Illus.). 64p. pap. 25.49 *(978-1-4343-6759-4(2))* AuthorHouse.

Kinley, Catherine. Peter Kinley. 2010. (Illus.). 128p. 70.00 *(978-1-84822-005-8(7)*, Lund Humphries Pubs.) Ashgate Publishing, Ltd. GBR. Dist: Ashgate Publishing Co.

Kirk, Joanna. Joanna Kirk. 2010. (ENG., Illus.). 32p. 35.00 *(978-1-906957-08-7(8))*; 60.00 *(978-1-906957-09-4(6))* Murderme GBR. Dist: Hachette Bk. Group.

Kitson, Clare. British Animation: The Channel 4 Factor. 2009. (ENG., Illus.). 248p. pap. 29.95 *(978-0-253-22096-7(3)*, 0253220963) Indiana Univ. Pr.

Korero Books Staff, et al. Burlesque Poster Design: The Art of Tease. 2009. (ENG., Illus.). 178p. 39.95 *(978-0-9553398-2-0(0))* Korero Books LLP GBR. Dist: Independent Pubs. Group.

Kraut, Gretchen. History of German Porn. 2009. (Illus.). 256p. 29.95 *(978-3-936709-37-7(8))* Goliath DEU. Dist: SCB Distributors.

Kriz, Kay Dian. Slavery, Sugar, & the Culture of Refinement: Picturing the British West Indies, 1700-1840. 2008. (ENG., Illus.). 288p. 75.00 *(978-0-300-14062-0(2))* Yale Univ. Pr.

Kumar, Abhishek. Expression of Cultural Identity Through Arts. 2010. 72p. pap. *(978-3-639-24337-6(4))* VDM Verlag Dr. Mueller e.K.

Lambirth, Andrew. John Hoyland Ra. 2010. (ENG., Illus.). 160p. 65.00 *(978-1-906509-07-1(7))* Unicorn Pr., London GBR. Dist: National Bk. Network.

—Margaret Mellis. 2010. (Illus.). 200p. 80.00 *(978-1-84822-048-5(0)*, Lund Humphries Pubs.) Ashgate Publishing, Ltd. GBR. Dist: Ashgate Publishing Co.

Lambirth, Andrew & Sevenson, Jane. Edward Burra. Martin, Simon, ed. 2011. (Illus.). 176p. 70.00 ***(978-1-84822-090-4(1)***, Lund Humphries Pubs.) Ashgate Publishing, Ltd. GBR. Dist: Ashgate Publishing Co.

Lambourne, Lionel. The Aesthetic Movement. 2011. (ENG., Illus.). 240p. pap. 39.95 ***(978-0-7148-6319-1(X))*** Phaidon Pr., Inc.

Langford, Jon. Skull Orchard Revisited: Art, Words, & Music. 2011. (ENG., Illus.). 96p. 19.95 *(978-1-891241-30-7(3))* Verse Chorus Pr.

Le Feuvre, Lisa & Morton, Tom. British Art Show 7: In the Days of the Comet. 2011. (ENG., Illus.). 192p. pap. 35.00 *(978-1-85332-286-0(5))* Hayward Gallery Publishing GBR. Dist: D.A.P./Distributed Art Pubs.

Le Restif, Claire, et al. Blaise Drummond. 2010. (GER & ENG., Illus.). 112p. 40.00 *(978-3-86678-377-5(9))* Kerber Verlag DEU. Dist: D.A.P./Distributed Art Pubs.

Leca, Benedict, ed. Thomas Gainsborough & the Modern Woman. 2010. (Illus.). 196p. pap. *(978-0-931537-37-0(1))* Cincinnati Art Museum.

Lee, Paul. Paul Lee. 2008. (Illus.). pap. 40.00 *(978-0-9778819-8-7(9))* Peres Projects, Los Angeles Berlin.

Lester, Richard. Photographing Fashion: British Style in the Sixties. 2009. (ENG., Illus.). 192p. *(978-1-85149-600-6(9)*, Antique Collectors Club Dist) Antique Collectors' Club.

Levinson, Orde & Jenkins, David Fraser. The Prints of John Piper: Quality & Experiment - A Catalogue Raisonné, 1923-91. Levinson, Orde, ed. 3rd rev. exp. ed. 2010. (Illus.). 232p. 250.00 *(978-1-84822-063-8(4)*, Lund Humphries Pubs.) Ashgate Publishing, Ltd. GBR. Dist: Ashgate Publishing Co.

Lewis, Wyndham. Blast 1. 2009. *(978-1-58423-342-8(7))* Gingko Pr., Inc.

Lim, C. J. & Liu, Ed. Short Stories: London in Two-and-a-half Dimensions. 2011. (ENG., Illus.). 240p. 155.00 *(978-0-415-66889-7(1))* Routledge.

Lindbergh, Peter, photos by. Anish Kapoor: Monumenta 2011. 2011. (ENG., Illus.). 96p. pap. 20.00 ***(978-2-7118-5817-0(0))*** Editions de la Reunion des Musees nationaux FRA. Dist: D.A.P./Distributed Art Pubs.

Linnell, David. Blake, Palmer, Linnell & Co. Life of John Linnell. 2010. (ENG., Illus.). 416p. 60.00 *(978-0-86332-917-3(9))* Antique Collectors' Club.

Liversidge, Peter. Proposals for Liverpool. 2009. (ENG.). 142p. pap. 29.95 *(978-1-84631-205-2(1))* Liverpool Univ. Pr. GBR. Dist: Chicago Distribution Ctr.

Livingstone, Marco. Peter Blake: One Man Show. (Illus.). 240p. 2011. pap. 50.00 *(978-1-84822-015-7(4))* 2009. 1000.00 *(978-1-84822-039-3(1))* Ashgate Publishing, Ltd. GBR. (Lund Humphries Pubs.). Dist: Ashgate Publishing Co.

Long, Richard & Tufnell, Ben. Selected Statements And: R Long. 2009. (ENG., Illus.). 128p. pap. 35.00 *(978-1-905620-15-9(2))* Haunch of Venison GBR. Dist: D.A.P./Distributed Art Pubs.

Lubbock, Tom. English Graphic. 2012. (ENG., Illus.). 208p. 29.95 ***(978-0-7112-3370-6(5))*** Lincoln, Frances Ltd. GBR. Dist: Perseus-PGW.

Lucas, Sarah & Garbay, Olivier, photos by. The MUG. 2009. (ENG., Illus.). 640p. 125.00 *(978-1-904212-51-5(4))* Other Criteria GBR. Dist: Hachette Bk. Group.

Lyden, Anne M. & Kingsley, Hope. The Photographs of Frederick H. Evans. 2010. (Illus.). 184p. 50.00 *(978-0-89236-988-1(4))* Oxford Univ. Pr., Inc.

MacNaughton, Alex. London Street Art. 2006. (Illus.). 96p. 14.95 *(978-3-7913-3674-9(6))* Prestel Publishing.

Macnaughton, Alex. London Street Art 2. 2007. (Illus.). 96p. 14.95 *(978-3-7913-3858-3(7))* Prestel Publishing.

Malek, Jaromir & Málek, Jaromír. ABC of Egyptian Hieroglyphs. 2011. (ENG., Illus.). 48p. pap. 10.00 *(978-1-85444-247-5(3))* Ashmolean Museum GBR. Dist: Antique Collectors' Club.

Malik, Amna & Malik, A. Sarah Lucas: Au Naturel. 2009. (One Work Ser.). (ENG., Illus.). 112p. (gr. 17). pap. 16.00 *(978-1-84638-054-9(5))* Afterall Publishing GBR. Dist: MIT Pr.

Malpas, William. Andy Goldsworthy: Pocket Guide. 2007. (Sculptors Ser.). (Illus.). 288p. pap. 24.00 *(978-1-86171-184-7(0))* Crescent Moon Publishing GBR. Dist: Gardners Bks. Ltd.

—Andy Goldsworthy in America. 2nd ed. 2010. (Sculptors Ser.). (Illus.). 336p. pap. 40.00 *(978-1-86171-304-9(5))* Crescent Moon Publishing GBR. Dist: NACSCORP, Inc.

—Andy goldsworthy in Close-up. 4th ed. 2010. (Sculptors Ser.). (Illus.). 292p. pap. 40.00 *(978-1-86171-293-6(6))* Crescent Moon Publishing GBR. Dist: NACSCORP, Inc.

—Land art in the U. K. A Complete Guide to Landscape, Environmental, Earthworks, Nature, Sculpture & Installation Art in the United Kingdom. 2007. (Sculptors Ser.). (Illus.). 386p. 60.00 *(978-1-86171-095-6(X))*; pap. 40.00 *(978-1-86171-090-1(9))* Crescent Moon Publishing GBR. Dist: NACSCORP, Inc.

Manson, David. Willy Tirr (1915 - 1991) Figure in a Landscape. 2010. (Illus.). 116p. pap. 35.49 *(978-1-4520-0506-5(0))* AuthorHouse.

Maranda, Michael, ed. The Saskia Olde Wolbers Files: And While I Have Been Lying Here Perfectly Still. 2009. (ENG., Illus.). 136p. pap. 20.00 *(978-0-921972-53-2(9))* Art Gallery of York Univ. CAN. Dist: D.A.P./Distributed Art Pubs.

Marshall, Nancy Rose. City of Gold & Mud: Painting Victorian London. 2012. (Paul Mellon Centre for Studies in British Art Ser.). (ENG., Illus.). 320p. 75.00 ***(978-0-300-17446-5(2))*** Yale Univ. Pr.

Martin, Alan C. The Cream of Tank Girl. 2008. (ENG., Illus.). 208p. 29.95 *(978-1-84576-942-0(2)*, Titan Bks.) Titan Bks. Ltd. GBR. Dist: Random Hse., Inc.

Martiniz-Ruiz, Barbaro. Art & Emancipation in Jamaica: Isaac Mendes Belisario & His Worlds. Barringer, Tim & Forrester, Gillian, eds. 2007. (Illus.). 612p. 75.00 *(978-0-300-11661-8(6))* Yale Ctr. for British Art.

Martins, Edgar, photos by. Edgar Martins: Topologies, 1 vol. 2008. (ENG., Illus.). 128p. 50.00 *(978-1-59711-057-0(4))* Aperture Foundation, Inc.

Massey, Ian & Procktor, Patrick. Patrick Procktor: Art & Life. 2010. (ENG., Illus.). 224p. 70.00 *(978-1-906509-09-5(3))* Unicorn Pr., London GBR. Dist: National Bk. Network.

Mazel, Aron, et al, eds. Art as Metaphor: The Prehistoric Rock-Art of Britain. 2007. (ENG., Illus.). 256p. (C). pap. 39.95 *(978-1-905739-16-5(8))* Archaeopress GBR. Dist: Brown, David Bk. Co., The.

McElney, Brian S. Inaugural Exhibition Catalog of the Museum of East Asian Art. (Illus.). 281p. 75.00 *(978-1-897734-00-1(X))* Museum of East Asian Art GBR. Dist: Art Media Resources, Inc.

McInnis, Maurie D. Slaves Waiting for Sale: Abolitionist Art & the American Slave Trade. 2011. (ENG., Illus.). 280p. 40.00 *(978-0-226-55933-9(5))* Univ. of Chicago Pr.

McKell, Iain, photos by. The New Gypsies. 2011. (Illus.). 128p. 39.95 *(978-3-7913-4519-2(2))* Prestel Publishing.

Mentasti, Rosa Barovier, ed. Exquisite Glass Ornaments: The Nineteenth-Century Glass Revival. 2011. (ENG., Illus.). 124p. 39.50 *(978-88-317-0650-6(0))* Marsilio Editori spa ITA. Dist: Random Hse., Inc.

Merrick, Jay. Firstsite: Art Spaces. 2012. (ENG., Illus.). 64p. pap. 7.95 ***(978-1-85759-755-4(9))*** Scala, Editions FRA. Dist: National Bk. Network.

Miglietti, Francesca Alfano. Franko B: I Still Love. 2011. (ITA & ENG., Illus.). 168p. 55.00 *(978-88-7179-656-7(X)*, Ore Cultura Srl (Acc)) Antique Collectors' Club GBR. Dist: National Bk. Network.

Miller, James. The Work of a Master Goldsmith: A Unique Collection. 2009. (ENG., Illus.). 160p. 100.00 *(978-0-7198-0102-0(8))* Hale, Robert Ltd. GBR. Dist: Independent Pubs. Group.

Mitchinson, David. Celebrating Moore: Works from the Collection of the Henry Moore Foundation. rev. ed. 2006. (Illus.). 360p. pap. 40.00 *(978-0-85331-944-3(8)*, Lund Humphries Pubs.) Ashgate Publishing, Ltd. GBR. Dist: Ashgate Publishing Co.

Muir, Gregor, ed. Henry Moore: Ideas for Sculpture. 2010. (ENG., Illus.). 164p. 85.00 *(978-3-03764-073-9(1))* JRP Ringier Kunstverlag AG CHE. Dist: D.A.P./Distributed Art Pubs.

Nakajima, Toshiro, ed. Nakajima: Mario Praz: a Symposium of Literature, History & Arts. 2008. (ENG.). 2700p. 990.00 *(978-4-902454-19-2(X))* Synapse, Edition JPN. Dist: Taylor & Francis Group.

Nelson, Mike. Mike Nelson: A Psychic Vacuum. 2010. (ENG., Illus.). 196p. 39.95 *(978-1-928570-11-0(9))* Creative Time.

Nelson, Zed, photos by. Love Me. 2009. (ENG., Illus.). 192p. 45.00 *(978-88-6965-165-6(7))* Contrasto DUE ITA. Dist: Consortium Bk. Sales & Distribution.

Noton, David. Photography Essentials Full Frame Photography: Full Frame Photography. 2010. (ENG., Illus.). 192p. pap. 26.99 *(978-0-7153-3615-1(0))* David & Charles Pubs. GBR. Dist: F&W Media, Inc.

Official Catalogue of the Great Exhibition of the Works of Industry of All Nations 1851. 2011. (Cambridge Library Collection - History Ser.). (ENG.). 342p. pap. 28.99 *(978-1-108-02999-5(X))* Cambridge Univ. Pr.

Ofili, Chris. Chris Ofili. 2009. (ENG., Illus.). 272p. 85.00 *(978-0-8478-3215-6(5))* Rizzoli International Pubns., Inc.

Ogg, Kirsty, ed. & text. Claire Barclay: Shadow Spans. 2012. (ENG., Illus.). 56p. pap. 19.95 ***(978-0-85488-191-8(3))*** Whitechapel Art Gallery GBR. Dist: D.A.P./Distributed Art Pubs.

Oleksijczuk, Denise Blake. The First Panoramas: Visions of British Imperialism. 2011. (Illus.). 264p. 90.00 *(978-0-8166-4860-3(3))*; pap. 29.95 *(978-0-8166-4861-0(1))* Univ. of Minnesota Pr.

O'Neill, Morna. Walter Crane: The Arts & Crafts, Painting, & Politics. 2011. (Paul Mellon Centre for Studies in Britis Ser.). (Illus.). 320p. 75.00 *(978-0-300-16768-9(7))* Yale Univ. Pr.

O'Reilly, Sally, ed. Brian Griffiths: Crummy Love. 2011. (ENG., Illus.). 208p. 55.00 ***(978-3-86560-957-1(0))*** Verlag der Buchhandlung Walther Konig DEU. Dist: D.A.P./Distributed Art Pubs.

Orr, Chris. Chris Orr: The Multitude Diaries. 2008. (ENG., Illus.). 240p. 19.95 *(978-1-905711-35-2(2))* Royal Academy of Arts GBR. Dist: Hachette Bk. Group.

Owens, Susan, et al. Amazing Rare Things: The Art of Natural History in the Age of Discovery. 2009. (ENG., Illus.). 224p. pap. 24.95 *(978-0-9798456-2-8(9)*, 979842) Kales Pr.

Page, John R. & Bayer, Thomas M. The Development of the Art Market in England: Money as Muse, 1730-1900, 1 vol. 2011. (Financial History Ser.). (ENG., Illus.). 288p. 99.00 *(978-1-84893-043-8(7))* Pickering & Chatto Pubs., Ltd. GBR. Dist: Ashgate Publishing Co.

Panayotova, Stella. The Macclesfield Psalter. Panayotova, Stella, ed. 2008. (LAT & ENG., Illus.). 352p. 125.00 *(978-0-500-23852-3(9)*, 523852) Thames & Hudson.

Paolozzi, Eduardo. Eduardo Paolozzi: the Jet Age Compendium. 2010. (ENG., Illus.). 108p. pap. 19.95 *(978-0-9545025-8-4(2))* Four Corners Bks. GBR. Dist: D.A.P./Distributed Art Pubs.

Parr, Martin, et al, photos by. Visual Correspondences. 2010. (ENG & SPA., Illus.). 336p. pap. 39.95 *(978-950-889-183-9(1))* La Marca ARG. Dist: D.A.P./Distributed Art Pubs.

Parr, Martin & Weski, Thomas. Parrworld, 2 vols. 2008. (Illus.). *(978-1-57110-693-3(6))* Aperture Foundation, Inc.

Payne, Oliver & Relph, Nick. Oliver Payne & Nick Relph, 1 vol. 2006. (ENG., Illus.). 196p. 38.00 *(978-3-905701-45-6(6))* JRP Ringier Kunstverlag AG CHE. Dist: D.A.P./Distributed Art Pubs.

Pearson, Lynn F. Public Art Since 1950. 2008. (Shire Library). (ENG., Illus.). 64p. per. 12.95 *(978-0-7478-0642-4(X))* Shire Pubns., Ltd. GBR. Dist: Random Hse., Inc.

Pergam, Elizabeth A. The Manchester Art Treasures Exhibition of 1857: Entrepreneurs, Connoisseurs & the Public. 2011. (Illus.). 396p. 124.95 *(978-1-4094-1830-6(8))* Ashgate Publishing Co.

Pericoli, Matteo. London Unfurled. 2012. (ENG., Illus.). 60p. 35.00 ***(978-0-330-51782-9(1))*** Macmillan Pubs., Ltd. GBR. Dist: Independent Pubs. Group.

Perridge, Madeleine. Decorative Indi. 2010. 72p. pap. *(978-3-8383-3378-6(0))* Lambert Academic Publishing.

Petullo, Anthony. Art Without Category: British & Irish Art from the Anthony Petullo Collection. 2009. (Illus.). 84p. *(978-1-60743-122-0(X))* Independent Pub.

Phagan, Patricia, et al. Thomas Rowlandson: Pleasures & Pursuits in Georgian England. 2011. (ENG., Illus.). 184p. 59.95 *(978-1-904832-78-2(4))* Giles, D. Ltd. GBR. Dist: Antique Collectors' Club.

—Thomas Rowlandson: Pleasures & Pursuits in Georgian England. 2011. (Illus.). 184p. *(978-0-9820606-1-2(0))* Loeb, Frances Lehman Art Ctr., Vassar Coll., The.

Phillips, Sam. Frieze Art Fair Yearbook 2011 - 12. 2011. (ENG., Illus.). 530p. pap. 35.00 ***(978-0-9553201-7-0(8))*** Frieze GBR. Dist: D.A.P./Distributed Art Pubs.

Potter, Matthew. The Inspirational Genius of Germany. 2012. (ENG., Illus.). 320p. 95.00 ***(978-0-7190-8712-7(0))*** Manchester Univ. Pr. GBR. Dist: Macmillan.

Prown, Jules David. The Architecture of the Yale Center for British Art. 2009. (ENG., Illus.). 72p. 35.00 *(978-0-300-14964-7(6))* Yale Ctr. for British Art.

Quilley, Geoff. Empire to Nation: Art, History & the Visualization of Maritime Britain, 1768-1829. 2011. (ENG., Illus.). 304p. 80.00 *(978-0-300-17568-4(X))* Yale Univ. Pr.

Rackham, Arthur. Rackham's Fairies, Elves & Goblins: More Than 80 Full-Color Illustrations. Menges, Jeff A., ed. 2007. (Dover Fine Art, History of Art Ser.). (ENG., Illus.). 96p. pap. 14.95 *(978-0-486-46023-9(1))* Dover Pubns., Inc.

Racz, Imogen, , Imogen. Contemporary Crafts. 2009. (ENG., Illus.). 1p. pap. 34.95 *(978-1-84520-309-2(7))* Berg Pubs. GBR. Dist: Macmillan.

Radford, Rod. Island to Empire: 300 Years of British Art 1550-1850. 2007. (Illus.). 336p. 60.00 *(978-0-7308-3014-6(4))* Art Gallery of South Australia AUS. Dist: Antique Collectors' Club.

Rankin, Photographer & Hirst, Damien. Myths, Monsters & Legends. 2011. (ENG.). 72p. 60.00 ***(978-0-9567794-6-5(8))*** Rankin Photography GBR. Dist: SCB Distributors.

Rauser, Amelia F. Caricature Unmasked: Irony, Authenticity, & Individualism in Eighteenth-Century English Prints. 2008. (ENG., Illus.). 60.00 *(978-1-61149-323-8(4))* Univ. of Delaware Pr.

Read, Charles Hercules & Dalton, O. M. Antiquities from the City of Benin & from Other Parts of West Africa in the British Museum. 2008. (Illus.). 95.00 *(978-1-57898-701-6(6))* Martino Publishing.

Redington, Ginny, et al. Georgian Jewellery, 1714-1830. 2007. (ENG., Illus.). 200p. *(978-1-85149-539-9(8)*, Antique Collectors Club Dist) Antique Collectors' Club.

Riley, Andrew. Let us Face the Future: British Art 1945-1968. 2011. (ENG & SPA.). 283p. 54.95 *(978-84-937610-8-0(7))* Fundacio Joan Miro ESP. Dist: Actar Birkhauser Distribution.

Robins, Anna Gruetzner. A Fragile Modernism: Whistler & His Impressionist Followers. 2008. (ENG., Illus.). 256p. 60.00 *(978-0-300-13545-9(9))* Yale Univ. Pr.

Robinson, Alistair & Lambton, Lucinda. David Harrison. 2010. (ENG., Illus.). 128p. 50.00 *(978-0-85667-671-0(3))* Wilson, Philip Pubs., Ltd. GBR. Dist: Macmillan.

Robinson, James. Masterpieces Medieval Art. 2008. (ENG., Illus.). 320p. 39.95 *(978-0-7141-2815-3(5))* British Museum Pr. GBR. Dist: Brown, David Bk. Co., The.

Robinson, Joseph Armitage & James, M. R. The Manuscripts of Westminster Abbey. 2011. (Cambridge Library Collection - History Ser.). (ENG.). 122p. pap. 19.99 *(978-1-108-02787-8(3))* Cambridge Univ. Pr.

Robinson, Michael. Turner: His life & works in 500 Images. 2010. (ENG., Illus.). 256p. 35.00 *(978-0-7548-2084-0(X))* Anness Publishing GBR. Dist: National Bk. Network.

Roelstraete, Dieter. Richard Long: A Line Made by Walking. 2010. (One Work Ser.). (ENG., Illus.). 112p. (gr. 17). pap. 16.00 *(978-1-84638-058-7(8))* Afterall Publishing GBR. Dist: MIT Pr.

Rosenberg, Angela, et al, texts. Simon Starling: under Lime. 2009. (GER & ENG., Illus.). 128p. pap. 46.00 *(978-3-86560-597-9(4))* Verlag der Buchhandlung Walther Konig DEU. Dist: D.A.P./Distributed Art Pubs.

Rosewell, Roger. Stained Glass. 2012. (Shire Library). (ENG., Illus.). 96p. pap. 12.95 ***(978-0-7478-1147-3(4))*** Shire Pubns., Ltd. GBR. Dist: Random Hse., Inc.

Rudolph, William Keyse & Kirtley, Alexandra Alevizatos. Treasures of American & English Painting & Decorative Arts: From the Julian Wood Glass Jr. Collection. 2011. (Illus.). 248p. 50.00 *(978-0-8478-3626-0(6)*, Skira) Rizzoli International Pubns., Inc.

Ruskin, John. Art of England. 2007. 300p. 43.95 *(978-0-548-11229-8(0))* Kessinger Publishing, LLC.

—Mornings in Florence & the Two Paths. 2008. 292p. 25.99 *(978-0-554-35770-6(4))* 2008. 292p. 28.99 *(978-0-554-26467-7(6))* 2007. (ENG.). 258p. pap. 21.99 *(978-1-4346-1177-2(9))* 2007. (ENG.). 290p. pap. 23.99 *(978-1-4346-1248-9(1))* BiblioBazaar.

Rutherford, Emma. Silhouette: The Art of the Shadow. 2009. (ENG., Illus.). 256p. 65.00 *(978-0-8478-3077-0(2))* Rizzoli International Pubns., Inc.

Safer, Samantha Erin. Textile Revolution: Medals, Wiggles & Pop, 1961-1971. 2010. (ENG., Illus.). 264p. pap. *(978-1-85149-648-8(3)*, Antique Collectors Club Dist) Antique Collectors' Club.

Salisbury, Martin. Artists at the Fry: A Guide to the Works in the Fry Art Gallery. 2008. (ENG., Illus.). 96p. pap. *(978-0-9537810-2-7(X)*, Frye Art Gallery The) Antique Collectors' Club.

Saul, Nigel. English Church Monuments in the Middle Ages: History & Representation. (ENG., Illus.). 2011. 432p. pap. 45.00 *(978-0-19-960613-9(7))* 2009. 400p. 150.00 *(978-0-19-921598-0(7))* Oxford Univ. Pr., Inc.

Saunders, David. British Museum Technical Research Bulletin, Volume 4. 2011. (ENG., Illus.). 156p. pap. 40.00 *(978-1-904982-55-5(7))* Archetype Pubns. GBR. Dist: National Bk. Network.

Scheuerle, William H. George Baxter, the First Color Printing from Metal Plates & Wood Blocks: Portraying Victorian Values of England's Rising Middle Class. 2011. (Illus.). 180p. 129.95 ***(978-0-7734-3920-7(X))*** Mellen, Edwin Pr., The.

Schneider, Gregor. Die Familie Schneider, 1 vol. 2008. (ENG., Illus.). 184p. 35.00 *(978-3-86521-236-8(0))* Steidl, Gerhard Druckerei und Verlag DEU. Dist: Innovative Logistics.

Schroder, Timothy. Renaissance Silver in the Schroder Collection. 2007. (Schroder Collection). (ENG., Illus.). 176p. pap. 50.00 *(978-0-900785-96-2(9))* Holberton, Paul Publishing GBR. Dist: Casemate Pubs. & Bk. Distributors, LLC.

Scott, Kathleen L. An Index of Images in English Manusripts from Chaucer to Henry VIII: The British Library. the Additional & Egerton Collection. 2011. (Index of images in english Manuscripts). (Illus.). 500p. (C). pap. 174.00 *(978-1-905375-63-9(8))* Miller, Harvey Pubs. GBR. Dist: Brown, David Bk. Co., The.

Seewald, Jan. Theatrical Sculpture: Skulptiere Bildnisse Berühmter Englischer Schauspieler, 1750-1850, Insbesondere David Garrick und Sarah Siddons. 2007. (GER., Illus.). 241p. *(978-3-8316-0671-9(4))* Utz, Herbert Verlag GmbH.

Shanes, Eric. Turner: Life & Masterworks. 2008. (Temporis Ser.). (ENG., Illus.). 255p. 39.95 *(978-1-85995-681-6(5))* Parkstone International GBR. Dist: Ingram Pub. Services.

Shave, Stuart, ed. Nigel Cooke. 2011. (ENG., Illus.). 112p. 65.00 *(978-3-86560-911-3(2))* Verlag der Buchhandlung Walther Konig DEU. Dist: D.A.P./Distributed Art Pubs.

Sherwood, Shirley & Rix, Martyn. Treasures of Botanical Art: Icons from the Shirley Sherwood & Kew Collections. 2009. (ENG., Illus.). 272p. pap. *(978-1-84246-221-8(0)*, Royal Botanic Gardens Edinburg) Antique Collectors' Club.

Shrigley, David & Chronicle Books Staff. Red Book. 2010. (ENG., Illus.). 240p. pap. 16.95 *(978-0-8118-7430-4(3))* Chronicle Bks. LLC.

Sicca, Cinzia Maria, et al. The Anglo-Florentine Renaissance: Art for the Early Tudors. 2012. (Studies in British Art Ser.). (ENG., Illus.). 424p. 75.00 *(978-0-300-17608-7(2)*, Yale Ctr. for British Art.

silvertoons. Passion for Life. 2009. (Illus.). 200p. 40.00 *(978-0-9745701-3-6(3))* silvertoons.

Simon, Robin, text. Hogarth, France & British Art. 2007. (ENG., Illus.). 400p. pap. 45.00 *(978-0-9554063-0-0(7))* Holberton, Paul Publishing GBR. Dist: Casemate Pubs. & Bk. Distributors, LLC.

Simpson, James. Under the Hammer: Iconoclasm in the Anglo-American Tradition. 2011. (Clarendon Lectures in English Literature Ser.). (ENG., Illus.). 208p. 45.00 *(978-0-19-959165-7(2))* Oxford Univ. Pr., Inc.

Smerling, Walter. Anthony Cragg: Dinge im Kopf / Things on the Mind. Skulpturen, Zeichnungen, Grafiken / Sculptures, Drawings, Graphic Art. Smerling, Walter, ed. 2011. (ENG & GER., Illus.). 136p. pap. 58.95 ***(978-3-86832-052-7(0))*** Wienand GmbH, Druck- & Verlagshaus DEU. Dist: Independent Pubs. Group.

Smith, Alison. Watercolour. 2011. (ENG., Illus.). 208p. pap. 39.95 *(978-1-85437-913-9(5))* Tate Publishing, Ltd. GBR. Dist: Hachette Bk. Group.

Solkin, David H. Painting Out of the Ordinary: Modernity & the Art of Everday Life in Early Nineteenth-Century England. 2008. (Paul Mellon Centre for Studies in British Art). (ENG., Illus.). 288p. 75.00 *(978-0-300-14061-3(4))* Yale Univ. Pr.

Spalding, Frances. Prunella Clough: Seeing the World Sideways. 2012. (Illus.). 240p. 70.00 ***(978-1-84822-011-9(1)***, Lund Humphries Pubs.) Ashgate Publishing, Ltd. GBR. Dist: Ashgate Publishing Co.

Stallabrass, Julian. High Art Lite: The Rise & Fall of young british Art. rev. exp. ed. 2006. (ENG., Illus.). 356p. pap. 24.95 *(978-1-84467-085-7(6)*, 844085) Verso Bks. GBR. Dist: Norton, W. W. & Co., Inc.

Starling, Simon, illus. Simon Starling: Nachbau, 1 vol. 2008. (ENG.). 160p. pap. 24.00 *(978-3-86521-470-6(3))* Steidl, Gerhard Druckerei und Verlag DEU. Dist: Innovative Logistics.

Stemp, Sinty. Jean Muir: Beyond Fashion. 2009. (ENG., Illus.). 176p. *(978-1-85149-621-1(1)*, Antique Collectors Club Dist) Antique Collectors' Club.

Stiletto, Johnny. Vintage 80s: London Street Photography. 2011. (ENG., Illus.). 176p. pap. 19.95 *(978-0-7112-3251-8(2))* Lincoln, Frances Ltd. GBR. Dist: Perseus-PGW.

Stourton, James & Sebag-Montefiore, Charles. The British As Art Collectors: From the Tudors to the Present. 2012. (ENG., Illus.). 400p. 100.00 ***(978-1-85759-749-3(4))*** Scala, Editions FRA. Dist: National Bk. Network.

String, Tatiana C. Art & Communication in The Reign of Henry VIII. 2008. (Illus.). 170p. 104.95 *(978-0-7546-6305-8(1))* Ashgate Publishing Co.

Strong, Roy. Elizabethan Image-Painting in England 1540-1620. (Tate Gallery Publications). reprint ed. 7.50 *(978-0-405-00225-0(4))* Ayer Co. Pubs., Inc.

Stubbs, Mike & Newman, Karen, eds. We Are the Real-Time Experiment: 20 Years of FACT. 2010. (Liverpool University Press - Foundation for Art Creative Technology Ser.). (ENG., Illus.). 208p. 29.95 *(978-1-84631-229-8(9))* Liverpool Univ. Pr. GBR. Dist: Chicago Distribution Ctr.

Sumner, Ann. The Barber Institute of Fine Arts: Director's Choice. 2011. (ENG., Illus.). 80p. pap. 12.95 *(978-1-85759-652-6(8))* Scala, Editions FRA. Dist: National Bk. Network.

Sumner, Ann, ed. Court on Canvas: Tennis in Art. 2011. (ENG., Illus.). 176p. pap. 35.00 *(978-0-85667-706-9(X))* Wilson, Philip Pubs., Ltd. GBR. Dist: Macmillan.

Sutcliffe, Prudence, et al. Unfolding Pictures: Fans in the Royal Collection. 2010. (ENG., Illus.). 232p. 45.00 *(978-1-902163-16-1(8))* Royal Collection Enterprises Ltd. GBR. Dist: Chicago Distribution Ctr.

Taylor, Roger. Impressed by Light: British Photographs from Paper Negatives, 1840-1860. 2007. (ENG., Illus.). 452p. 75.00 *(978-0-300-12405-7(8))* Yale Univ. Pr.

Taylor-Wood, Sam, photos by. Birth of a Clown, 1 vol. 2011. (ENG., Illus.). 112p. 95.00 *(978-3-86521-853-7(9))* Steidl, Gerhard Druckerei und Verlag DEU. Dist: Innovative Logistics.

Tillyer, William. William Tillyer: Watercolours. 2010. (ENG., Illus.). 272p. 55.00 *(978-1-901785-13-5(0))* 21 Publishing GBR. Dist: D.A.P./Distributed Art Pubs.

Tilson, Joe & Di Martino, Enzo. Tilson: The Printed Works, 1963-2009. 2010. (ITA & ENG., Illus.). 216p. pap. 55.00 *(978-1-905711-82-6(4))* Royal Academy of Arts GBR. Dist: Hachette Bk. Group.

Tovey, David. Sea Change: Fine & Decorative Art in St Ives 1914-1930. 2010. (Illus.). 302p. pap. *(978-0-9538363-8-3(X))* American Teilhard Assn

Townsend, Chris. New Art from London. 2006. (ENG., Illus.). 216p. pap. 29.95 *(978-0-500-28606-7(X))* Thames & Hudson.

Trench, Lucy. The Victoria & Albert Museum: The World's Greatest Museum of Art & Design. 2010. (ENG., Illus.). 144p. 35.00 *(978-1-85177-508-8(0))* V & A Pubns. GBR. Dist: Hachette Bk. Group.

Treuherz, Julian. Ford Madox Brown: Pre-Raphaelite Pioneer. 2011. (ENG., Illus.). 336p. 55.00 ***(978-0-85667-700-7(0))*** Wilson, Philip Pubs., Ltd. GBR. Dist: Macmillan.

Tri Postal (Organization: Lille, France) Staff, contrib. by. La Route de la Soie: The Silk Road: Lille3000, Saatchi Gallery. 2010. (FRE & ENG., Illus.). 96p. *(978-2-84278-806-3(0))* Beaux Arts.

Trümpler, Stefan & Clarke, Brian. Brian Clarke. Life & Death. 2011. (ENG., Illus.). 80p. 45.00 *(978-3-7165-1671-3(6))* Benteli Verlag CHE. Dist: Antique Collectors' Club.

Tucker, David, ed. British Social Realism in the Arts Since 1940. 2011. (ENG., Illus.). 240p. 85.00 *(978-0-230-24245-6(6))* Palgrave Macmillan.

Turner, Silvie. Julian Trevelyan Catalogue Raisonne of Prints: Revised Reprint. rev. ed. 2010. (Illus.). 184p. 170.00 *(978-1-84822-077-5(4)*, Lund Humphries Pubs.) Ashgate Publishing, Ltd. GBR. Dist: Ashgate Publishing Co.

Victoria and Albert Museum Staff. The Victoria & Albert Museum: Pocket Address Book 2008. 2007. (Illus.). 112p. 9.95 *(978-0-7112-2794-1(2))* Lincoln, Frances Ltd. GBR. Dist: Perseus-PGW.

Victoria and Albert Museum Staff, et al. A Grand Design: The Art of the Victoria & Albert Museum. (Illus.). 431p. *(978-1-85177-217-9(0))* V & A Pubns.

Vogtherr, Christoph. The Wallace Collection: Director's Choice. 2012. (ENG., Illus.). 80p. pap. 14.95 ***(978-1-85759-770-7(2))*** Scala, Editions FRA. Dist: National Bk. Network.

Voss, Roy, text. Daniel Sturgis: Don't Argue, 2007- exhibition catalog with an essay by Roy Voss. 2007. (Illus.). per. *(978-0-9774221-1-1(9))* Broar, Cynthia Gallery.

Wade, Stephen. Rowlandson Project. 2011. (Illus.). 160p. pap. 19.95 ***(978-1-84868-233-7(6))*** Amberley Publishing GBR. Dist: Casemate Pubs. & Bk. Distributors, LLC.

Waggoner, Diane, et al. The Pre-Raphaelite Lens: British Photography & Painting, 1848-1875. 2010. (Illus.). 240p. 65.00 *(978-1-84822-067-6(7)*, Lund Humphries Pubs.) Ashgate Publishing, Ltd. GBR. Dist: Ashgate Publishing Co.

Walker, Ian. So Exotic, So Homemade: Surrealism, Englishness & Documentary Photography. 2008. (Critical Image Ser.). (ENG., Illus.). 288p. 89.00 *(978-0-7190-7340-3(5))* Manchester Univ. Pr. GBR. Dist: Macmillan.

Wallinger, Mark & text. Mark Wallinger: the Russian Linesman. 2009. (ENG., Illus.). 144p. pap. 40.00 *(978-1-85332-272-3(5))* Hayward Gallery Publishing GBR. Dist: D.A.P./Distributed Art Pubs.

Walsh, Michael J. K., ed. London, Modernism, And 1914. 2010. (ENG., Illus.). 314p. 89.00 *(978-0-521-19580-5(2))* Cambridge Univ. Pr.

Warner, Carl. Carl Warner's Food Landscapes. 2010. (ENG., Illus.). 128p. 22.50 *(978-0-8109-8993-1(X)*, Abrams Image) Abrams.

Waterfield, Hermione & King, J. C. H. Provenance: Twelve Collectors of Ethnographic Art in England 1760-1990. 2010. (Illus.). 176p. pap. 45.00 *(978-1-903470-96-1(X))* Univ. of Washington Pr.

Webb, Brian & Artmonsky, Ruth. FHK Henrion. 2011. (ENG., Illus.). 96p. 19.95 *(978-1-85149-632-7(7))* Antique Collectors' Club.

Webb, Brian & Skipwith, Peyton. Peter Blake. 2010. (ENG., Illus.). 96p. *(978-1-85149-618-1(1)*, Antique Collectors Club Dist) Antique Collectors' Club.

Weller, Alan. Victorian Vector Designs. 2009. (Dover Pictura Electronic Clip Art Ser.). (ENG., Illus.). 128p. pap. 49.95 *(978-0-486-99025-5(7))* Dover Pubns., Inc.

Whitford, Frank, text. Royal Academy Illustrated 2009: A Selection from the 241st Summer Exhibition. 2009. (ENG., Illus.). 200p. pap. 35.00 *(978-1-905711-43-7(3))* Royal Academy of Arts GBR. Dist: Hachette Bk. Group.

Wilcox, Claire, ed. The Golden Age of Couture: Paris & London 1947-1957. 2007. (ENG., Illus.). 224p. 55.00 *(978-1-85177-520-0(X))* V & A Pubns. GBR. Dist: Hachette Bk. Group.

Wilcox, Timothy. Constable & Salisbury: The Soul of Landscape. 2011. (ENG., Illus.). 196p. pap. 39.95 *(978-1-85759-678-6(1))* Scala, Editions FRA. Dist: National Bk. Network.

—Laura Knight at the Theatre. 2008. (ENG., Illus.). 128p. pap. 45.00 *(978-0-906290-91-0(0))* Unicorn Pr., London GBR. Dist: National Bk. Network.

Willett, John. Art in a City. rev. ed. 2007. (ENG., Illus.). 256p. pap. 35.00 *(978-1-84631-082-9(2))* Liverpool Univ. Pr. GBR. Dist: Chicago Distribution Ctr.

Wilson, Andrew. Richard Hamilton - Swingeing London 67. 2011. (Afterall Ser.) (ENG., Illus.). 120p. (gr. 17). pap. 16.00 ***(978-1-84638-077-8(4))*** Afterall Publishing GBR. Dist: MIT Pr.

Woodford, Annie. Ice: Tracing the Line of Existence. 2010. (Illus.). 55p. *(978-0-9565536-0-7(5))* Timeforce Pr.

Wootton, David & Nickerson, Fiona. The Definitive Thelwell. 2010. (ENG., Illus.). 104p. pap. *(978-1-905738-14-4(5))* Beetles, Chris Ltd.

Wright, Barnaby, ed. Walter Sickert: The Camden Town Nudes. 2008. (Illus.). 111p. 50.00 *(978-1-903470-59-6(5))* Holberton, Paul Publishing GBR. Dist: Univ. of Washington Pr.

Wright, Rick. On the Line HC. 2011. (Illus.). 48p. (YA). 12.99 *(978-1-60706-346-9(8))* Image Comics.

Wright, Steve. Banksy's Bristol: Home Sweet Home. 2009. 112p. 24.95 *(978-0-86719-708-2(0))* Last Gasp of San Francisco.

Yamada, Akihiro. Secrets of the Printed Page in the Age of Shakespeare: Bibliographical Studies in the Plays of Beaumont, Chapman, Dekker, Fletcher, Ford, Marston, Shakespeare, Shirley, & in the Text of King James I's the True Lawe of Free Monarchies: With an Edition of Arcadia Restored, Egerton MS 1994, Folios 212-23 in the British Library. 2010. (Illus.). xxii, 290p. *(978-0-404-62346-3(8)*, AMS Pr., Inc.

Zybok, Oliver, ed. Lothar Götz, Works - 2011. 2011. (ENG., Illus.). 231p. 60.00 ***(978-3-7757-3002-0(8))*** Hatje Cantz Verlag GmbH & Co KG DEU. Dist: D.A.P./Distributed Art Pubs.

ART, BRITISH—HISTORY

Altholz, Josef L., ed. The Mind & Art of Victorian England. 2009. (ENG.). 206p. pap. 50.00 *(978-0-8166-5693-6(2))* Univ. of Minnesota Pr.

Armstrong, Walter. Art in Great Britain & Ireland. 2009. 194p. pap. *(978-1-151-73668-0(6))* Books LLC.

—Art in Great Britain & Ireland. 2008. 368p. 48.95 *(978-1-4369-8455-3(6))*; pap. 33.95 *(978-1-4367-8158-9(2))* Kessinger Publishing, LLC.

Barringer, Tim. Art & the British Empire. Quilley, Geoff et al, eds. 2007. (ENG., Illus.). 464p. 94.00 *(978-0-7190-7392-2(8))* Manchester Univ. Pr. GBR. Dist: Macmillan.

Bindman, David, ed. The History of British Art, 3 vols. 2008. (Illus.). 832p. 150.00 *(978-0-300-14304-1(4))* Yale Univ. Pr.

—The History of British Art, Volume 2: 1600-1870. 2009. (ENG., Illus.). 248p. 50.00 *(978-0-300-11671-7(3))* Yale Ctr. for British Art.

Bindman, David & Ayers, Tim, eds. The History of British Art, Volume 1: 600-1600. 2009. (ENG., Illus.). 296p. 50.00 *(978-0-300-11670-0(5))* Yale Ctr. for British Art.

Bindman, David & Stephens, Chris, eds. The History of British Art, Volume 3: 1870-Now. 2009. (ENG., Illus.). 256p. 50.00 *(978-0-300-11672-4(1))* Yale Ctr. for British Art.

Bosman, Suzanne. The National Gallery in Wartime. 2008. (ENG., Illus.). 128p. pap. 24.95 *(978-1-85709-424-4(7))* Yale Univ. Pr.

Brooke, Iris & Landes, William-Alan. English Costume of the Baroque Age, Seventeenth Century: With Select Patterns. 3rd ed. 2008. *(978-0-88734-948-5(X))* Players Pr., Inc.

Claire Gittings, et al. The National Portrait Gallery Book of Elizabeth I. 2006. (4-Fold Ser.) (ENG., Illus.). 9.95 *(978-1-85759-429-4(0))* Scala, Editions FRA. Dist: National Bk. Network.

Crosskey, Gordon. Old Sheffield Plate: A History of the 18th Century Plated Trade. 2012. (Illus.). 454p. ***(978-0-9568003-0-5(0))*** Antique Collectors' Club.

Edwards, Steve. The Making of English Photography: Allegories. 2006. (ENG., Illus.). 368p. 100.95 *(978-0-271-02713-5(4))* Pennsylvania State Univ. Pr.

Fordham, Douglas. British Art & the Seven Years' War: Allegiance & Autonomy. 2010. (Illus.). 352p. (C). 65.00 *(978-0-8122-4243-0(2))* Univ. of Pennsylvania Pr.

Frayling, Christopher. Art & Design: 100 Years at the Royal College of Art. 2006. (ENG., Illus.) 320p. 45.00 *(978-1-85585-725-4(1)*, Richard Dennis Pubns. Dl) Antique Collectors' Club GBR. Dist: National Bk. Network.

Gittings, Claire & Gittings, Clare. The Tudors. 2006. (ENG., Illus.). 9.95 *(978-1-85759-430-0(4))* Scala, Editions FRA. Dist: National Bk. Network

Grafton, Carol Belanger, ed. Victorian Design from the Crystal Palace Exhibition. 2010. (Dover Pictorial Archive Ser.). (ENG., Illus.). 128p. pap. 19.95 *(978-0-486-47219-5(1))* Dover Pubns., Inc.

Grunenberg, Christoph. Centre of the Creative Universe Liverpool & the Avant-Garde. Knifton, Robert, ed. 2007. (ENG., Illus.). 288p. 75.00 *(978-1-84631-089-8(X))* Liverpool Univ. Pr. GBR. Dist: Chicago Distribution Ctr.

A History of the Stained Glass of St George's Chapel, Windsor Castle. 2006. (Historical Monographs Relating to St George's Chapel, Windso Ser.). (Illus.). 263p. pap. 60.00 *(978-0-9539676-3-6(8))* Dean & Canons of Windsor GBR. Dist: Brown, David Bk. Co., The.

James, Susan E. & James, Susan. The Feminine Dynamic in English Art, 1485-1603: Women As Consumers, Patrons & Painters. 2009. (Illus.). 376p. 124.95 *(978-0-7546-6381-2(7))* Ashgate Publishing Co.

Jones, Malcolm. The Print in Early Modern England: An Historical Oversight. 2010. (ENG., Illus.). 352p. 95.00 *(978-0-300-13697-5(8))* Yale Univ. Pr.

Kepetzis, Ekaterini. Vergegenwärtigte Antike: Studien zur Gattungsüberschreitung in der französischen und englischen Malerei (1840-1914) 2009. (GRE & GER., Illus.). 378p. pap. 81.95 *(978-3-631-58124-7(6))* Lang, Peter GmbH, Europaischer Verlag der Wissenschaften DEU. Dist: Lang, Peter.

Knifton, Robert, ed. Centre of the Creative Universe: Liverpool & the Avant-Garde. 2007. (ENG., Illus.). 288p. per. 30.00 *(978-1-84631-081-2(4))* Liverpool Univ. Pr. GBR. Dist: Chicago Distribution Ctr.

Litchfield, R. B. Tom Wedgwood the First Photographer an A. 2006. pap. 30.95 *(978-1-4286-5615-4(4))* Kessinger Publishing, LLC.

Muir, Gregor. Lucky Kunst: The Rise & Fall of Young British Art. 2011. (ENG., Illus.). 250p. pap. 15.95 *(978-1-84513-528-7(8))* Aurum Pr., Ltd. GBR. Dist: Independent Pubs. Group.

Palgrave, Francis Turner. Essays on Art. 2009. 328p. 25.99 *(978-1-103-23859-0(0))*; pap. 19.99 *(978-1-103-23856-9(6))* BiblioBazaar.

—Essays on Art. 2009. 178p. pap. *(978-1-4590-4790-7(7))*; 170p. pap. *(978-0-217-47289-0(3))* Books LLC.

—Essays on Art. 2007. (ENG.). 322p. 45.95 *(978-0-548-01997-9(5))* Kessinger Publishing, LLC.

Paraskos, Michael. Reading Read: New Views on Herbert Read. 2008. (Illus.) 237p. pap. 36.95 *(978-1-904491-08-8(1))* Freedom Pr. GBR. Dist: AK Pr. Distribution.

Platman, Lara. Art Workers Guild 125 Years. 2010. (ENG.). 320p. pap. 29.95 *(978-1-906509-05-7(0))* Unicorn Pr., London GBR. Dist: National Bk. Network.

Pooke, Grant. Contemporary British Art: An Introduction. 2010. (ENG., Illus.). 304p. 39.95 *(978-0-415-38974-7(7))*; 131.00 *(978-0-415-38973-0(9))* Routledge.

Quilley, Barringer. Art & the British Empire. Barringer, Timothy et al, eds. 2009. (ENG., Illus.). 464p. pap. 50.00 *(978-0-7190-8193-4(9))* Manchester Univ. Pr. GBR. Dist: Macmillan.

Redford, Bruce. Dilettanti: The Antic & the Antique in Eighteenth-Century England. 2008. (ENG., Illus.). 236p. 50.00 *(978-0-89236-924-9(8))* Oxford Univ. Pr., Inc.

Rennie, Paul. Modern British Posters: Art, Design & Communication. 2010. (ENG., Illus.). 192p. 49.95 *(978-1-906155-97-1(6))* Black Dog Publishing Ltd. GBR. Dist: Perseus Distribution.

Riley, Richard. Metamorphosis: British Art of the Sixties. 2006. (ENG., Illus.). 112p. 48.00 *(978-88-422-1360-4(8))* Allemandi, Umberto & Co. GBR. Dist: Antique Collectors' Club.

Rosoman, Treve. London Wallpapers: Their Manufacture & Use 1690-1840 (Revised Edition) 2nd rev. ed. 2009. (ENG., Illus.). 76p. pap. 40.00 *(978-1-84802-048-1(1))* English Heritage GBR. Dist: Brown, David Bk. Co., The.

Sladen, Mark & Yedgar, Ariella. Panic Attack! Art in the Punk Years. 2007. (ENG., Illus.). 224p. 44.95 *(978-1-85894-403-6(1))* Merrell Pubs. Ltd. GBR. Dist: Perseus Distribution.

Strobel, Heidi A. The Artistic Matronage of Queen Charlotte (1744-1818) How a Queen Promoted Both Art & Female Artists in English Society. 2011. (Illus.). 412p. 159.95 ***(978-0-7734-1579-9(3))*** Mellen, Edwin Pr., The.

Tite, Catherine. Portraiture, Dynasty, & Power: Art Patronage in Hanoverian Britain, 1714-1759. 2010. *(978-1-60497-678-6(0))* Cambria Pr.

Whitehead, Christopher. Museums & the Construction of Disciplines: Art & Archaeology in Nineteenth-Century Britain. 2009. (Duckworth Archaeology

Ser.). (Illus.). 144p. pap. 24.95 (978-0-7156-3508-7(5)) Duckworth Publishers GBR. Dist: International Publishers Marketing.

ART, BUDDHIST
see Buddhist Art

ART, BULGARIAN
Berg, Stephan & Solakov, Nedko. Emotions. 2008. (GER & ENG., Illus.). 224p. 60.00 (978-3-7757-2211-7(4)) Hatje Cantz Verlag GmbH & Co KG DEU. Dist: D.A.P./Distributed Art Pubs.

Boettger, Suzaan & Solakov, Nedko. 99 Fears. 2008. (ENG., Illus.). 112p. 29.95 (978-0-7148-4888-4(3)) Phaidon Pr., Inc.

Boubnova, Iara, ed. Ivan Moudov: Trick or Treat. 2009. (ENG., Illus.). 144p. pap. 37.50 (978-3-86560-600-6(8)) Verlag der Buchhandlung Walther Konig DEU. Dist: D.A.P./Distributed Art Pubs.

Dejanoff, Plamen, photos by. Dejanoff. 2008. (ENG., Illus.). 160p. pap. 49.00 (978-3-905701-58-6(8)) JRP Ringier Kunstverlag AG CHE. Dist: D.A.P./Distributed Art Pubs.

Drews, Juliane. The Educational Situation of Roma in Bulgari. 2008. 100p. pap. (978-3-639-03436-3(8)) VDM Verlag Dr. Mueller e.K.

Fleck, Robert, text. Oda Jaune: First Water. 2011. (ENG., Illus.). 240p. 85.00 (978-3-7757-2677-1(2)) Hatje Cantz Verlag GmbH & Co KG DEU. Dist: D.A.P./Distributed Art Pubs.

Gierstberg, Frits, ed. Vesselina Nikolaeva: Simply a Line. 2010. (ENG., Illus.). 144p. 60.00 (978-90-5662-699-0(X)) NAi Uitgevers / Publishers Stichting NLD. Dist: D.A.P./Distributed Art Pubs.

Goldberger, Paul & Christo, Jeanne-Claude. Christo & Jeanne-Claude: The complete life & work of Christo & Jeanne-Claude. 2010. (ENG., Illus.). 700p. 1500.00 (978-3-8365-0664-9(5)) TASCHEN DEU. Dist: Ingram Pub. Services.

Mortcheva, Aglaia. Aglaia Mortcheva, Art Book, Volume 1. 2009. 34p. pap. 22.00 (978-0-557-07904-9(7)) Lulu Enterprises Inc.

Solakov, Nedko. Nedko Solakov: Emotions (without masks) 2010. (ENG., Illus.). 278p. pap. 25.00 (978-3-7757-2565-1(2)) Hatje Cantz Verlag GmbH & Co KG DEU. Dist: D.A.P./Distributed Art Pubs.

Solakov, Nedko. Nedko Solakov: All in Order, with Exceptions. 2011. (ENG., Illus.). 400p. 60.00 (978-3-7757-3172-0(5)) Hatje Cantz Verlag GmbH & Co KG DEU. Dist: D.A.P./Distributed Art Pubs.

Triossi, Amanda. Bvlgari, 1884-2009: Tra Eternità E Storia, 1884-2009 - 125 Anni Di Gioielli Italiani. 2009. (ENG., Illus.). 376p. 80.00 (978-88-572-0048-4(5)) Skira Editore ITA. Dist: Random Hse., Inc.

ART, BURMESE
McGill, Forrest & Chirapravati, M. L. Pattaratorn. Emerald Cities: Arts of Siam & Burma 1775-1950. 2009. (ENG., Illus.). 224p. 49.00 (978-0-939117-50-5(9)) Asian Art Museum of San Francisco.

Myint-U, Thant & Myintu, Thant. River of Lost Footsteps: A Personal History of Burma. 2008. (ENG., Illus.). 400p. pap. 15.00 (978-0-374-53116-4(1)) Farrar, Straus & Giroux.

Ranard, Andrew. Burmese Painting: A Linear & Lateral History. 2009. (ENG., Illus.). 378p. 100.00 (978-974-9511-76-3(X)) Silkworm Bks. THA. Dist: Univ. of Washington Pr.

Roveda, Vittorio & Clark, Joyce. Bayon Reconsidered. 2007. (Illus.). 256p. 85.00 (978-974-9863-05-3(4)) River Bks. THA. Dist: Antique Collectors' Club.

ART, BYZANTINE
Adams, Noel & Entwistle, Chris, eds. 'Intelligible Beauty' Recent Research on Byzantine Jewellery. 2010. (British Museum Research Publication). (ENG., Illus.). 245p. (C). pap. 90.00 (978-0-86159-178-7(X)) British Museum Pr. GBR. Dist: Brown, David Bk. Co., The.

Alchermes, et al, eds. Anaohmata Eoptika. 2010. (ENG., Illus.). 346p. (C). 135.00 (978-3-8053-4101-1(6)) Zabern, Philipp von Verlag, GmbH DEU. Dist: Brown, David Bk. Co., The.

Armstrong, Pamela, ed. Ritual & Art: Byzantine Essays for Christopher Walter. 2006. (FRE, GEC & ENG., Illus.). v, 307p. (C). 150.00 (978-1-899828-62-3(1)) Pindar Pr. GBR. Dist: Brown, David Bk. Co., The.

Bayet, Charles. Byzantine Art. 2009. (Art of Century Ser.). (ENG, FRE & GER., Illus.). 200p. 19.95 (978-1-84484-620-7(2)) Parkstone International GBR. Dist: Ingram Pub. Services.

Beckett, Sr. Wendy. Real Presence: Sr. Wendy on the Earliest Icons. 2010. (Illus.). 128p. 25.00 (978-1-57075-898-0(0)) Orbis Bks.

Brenk, Beat. The Apse, the Image & the Icon: An Historical Perspective of the Apse As a Space for Images. 2010. (Spatantike-Fruhes Christentum-Byzanz Ser.). (ENG., Illus.). 220p. (C). 50.00 (978-3-89500-703-3(X)) Reichert, Ludwig Dr. DEU. Dist: Brown, David Bk. Co., The.

Brooks, Sarah T. Byzantium, Faith, & Power (1261-1557) Perspectives on Late Byzantine Art & Culture. 2007. (Metropolitan Museum of Art Symposia Ser.). (Illus.). xi, 201p. 75.00 (978-1-58839-208-4(2)) Metropolitan Museum of Art, The.

Brooks, Sarah T., ed. Byzantium: Faith & Power (1261-1557) Perspectives on Late Byzantine Art & Culture - The Metropolitan Museum of Art Symposia. 2007. (Metropolitan Museum of Art Ser.). (ENG., Illus.). 216p. pap. 29.95 (978-0-300-11141-5(X)) Yale Univ. Pr.

Brubaker, Leslie & Cunningham, Mary. The Cult of the Mother of God in Byzantium. 2011. (Birmingham Byzantine & Ottoman Studies). (Illus.). 328p. 124.95 (978-0-7546-6266-2(7)) Ashgate Publishing Co.

Bryer, Anthony. The Byzantine Monuments & Topography of the Pontos. 2008. 188p. pap. 45.00 (978-1-59740-635-2(X)) ACLS Humanities E-Book.

Buhl, Gudrun, et al, eds. Spatantike und byzantinische Elfenbeinbildwerke im Diskurs. 2008. (Spatantike-Fruhes Christentum-Byzanz Ser.). (GER, ENG & FRE., Illus.). 320p. (C). 199.00 (978-3-89500-497-1(9)) Reichert, Ludwig Dr. DEU. Dist: Brown, David Bk. Co., The.

Cavarnos, Constantine. Byzantine Sacred Art. 2011. 132p. 40.95 (978-1-258-06676-5(9)) Literary Licensing, LLC.

Cormack, Robin & Vassilaki, Maria. Byzantium, 330-1453. 2008. (ENG., Illus.). 496p. 115.00 (978-1-905711-26-0(3)) Royal Academy of Arts GBR. Dist: Hachette Bk. Group.

Curcic, Slobodan & Hadjitryphonos, Evangelia. Architecture as Icon: Perception & Representation of Architecture in Byzantine Art. 2010. (ENG., Illus.). 376p. pap. 60.00 (978-0-300-12211-4(X)) Yale Univ. Pr.

Cutler, Anthony. Image Making in Byzantium, Sasanian Persia & the Early Muslim World: Images & Cultural Relations. 2009. (Variorum Collected Studies). (Illus.). 322p. 170.00 (978-0-7546-5949-5(6)) Ashgate Publishing Co.

Demus, Otto. Byzantine Mosaic Decoration: Aspects of Monumental Art in Byzantium. 2008. 184p. pap. 18.00 (978-1-59740-639-0(2)) ACLS Humanities E-Book.

Dennison, Walter. Studies in East Christian & Roman Art. 2010. 124p. pap. 21.42 (978-1-152-61902-9(0)) General Bks. LLC.

Dennison, Walter, et al. Studies in East Christian & Roman Art. 2010. 348p. pap. 32.75 (978-1-177-69814-6(5)) BiblioBazaar.

Drewer, Lois & Hourihane, Colum. Byzantine Art:: Recent Studies: Essays in Honor of Lois Drewer. 2009. (Illus.). xx, 197p. (978-0-86698-426-3(7)) Arizona State Univ., Arizona Ctr. for Medieval & Renaissance Studies.

Eichner, Ina & Tsamakda, Vasiliki, eds. Syrien und seine Nachbarn von der Spatantike bis in die islamische Zeit. 2009. (Spatantike-Fruhes Christentum-Byzanz Ser.). (GER., Illus.). 308p. (C). 168.00 (978-3-89500-674-6(2)) Reichert, Ludwig Dr. DEU. Dist: Brown, David Bk. Co., The.

Epstein, William M. & Pentcheva, Bissera V. The Sensual Icon: Space, Ritual, & the Senses in Byzantium. 2010. (ENG.). 320p. 84.95 (978-0-271-03584-0(6)) Pennsylvania State Univ. Pr.

Evans, Helen C., ed. Byzantium & Islam: Age of Transition. 2012. (ENG., Illus.). 352p. 65.00 (978-0-300-17950-7(2)) Yale Univ. Pr.

Frothingham, Arthur. Notes on Byzantine Art & Culture in Italy & Especially in Rome. 2009. pap. 23.20 (978-1-60724-484-4(5)) Gorgias Pr., LLC.

Galavaris, George. Colours, Symbols, Worship: The Mission of the Byzantine Artist. 2012. (ENG.). 440p. (C). 300.00 (978-1-899828-68-5(0)) Pindar Pr. GBR. Dist: Brown, David Bk. Co., The.

Grotowski, Piotr, ed. Arms & Armour of the Warrior Saints: Tradition & Innovation in Byzantine Iconography (843-1261) Brzezinski, Richard, tr. 2010. (Medieval Mediterranean Ser.). (Illus.). 704p. (978-90-04-18548-7(8)) BRILL.

Hayman, Richard. The Green Man. 2010. (Shire Library). (ENG., Illus.). 56p. pap. 12.95 (978-0-7478-0784-1(1)) Shire Pubns., Ltd. GBR. Dist: Random Hse., Inc.

Hetherington, Paul. Enamels, Crowns, Relics & Icons: Studies on Luxury Arts in Byzantium. 2008. (Variorum Collected Studies). (Illus.). 328p. 170.00 (978-0-7546-5950-1(X)) Ashgate Publishing Co.

Hutton, William Holden. The Church of the Sixth Century: Six Chapters In Ecclesiastical History. 2006. (ENG.). 344p. per. 31.95 (978-1-4286-4141-9(6)) Kessinger Publishing, LLC.

James, Elizabeth, ed. Art & Text in Byzantine Culture. 2010. (ENG.). 246p. (C). pap. 36.99 (978-0-521-16876-2(7)) Cambridge Univ. Pr.

Koenen, Ulrike & Muller-Wiener, Martina, eds. Grenzgange im ostlichen Mittelmeerraum: Byzanz und die Islamische Welt vom 9. -13. Jahrhundert. 2008. (GER., Illus.). 288p. (C). 99.00 (978-3-89500-403-2(0)) Reichert, Ludwig Dr. DEU. Dist: Brown, David Bk. Co., The.

Kordis, George. Icon As Communion: The Ideals & Compositional Principles of Icon Painting. 2010. (978-1-935317-09-8(1)) Holy Cross Orthodox Pr.

Lazaris, Stavros. Art et Science Vétérinaire à Byzance: Formes et Fonctions de L'image Hippiatrique. 2010. (FRE., Illus.). 288p. (978-2-503-53446-6(5)) Brepols Pubs.

Lightfoot, Mücahide & Lightfoot, Chris. Amorium: A Byzantine City in Anatolia. 2007. (Homer Archaeological Guides). (ENG., Illus.). 180p. (C). pap. 36.00 (978-975-8293-80-3(X)) Homer Kitabevi TUR. Dist: Brown, David Bk. Co., The.

Lowden, John. The Jaharis Gospel Lectionary: The Story of a Byzantine Book. 2009. (ENG., Illus.). 144p. 30.00 (978-0-300-14899-2(2)) Yale Univ. Pr.

Lymberopoulou, Angeliki. Images of the Byzantine World: Visions Messages & Meanings. 2011. (Illus.). 272p. 124.95 (978-1-4094-0776-8(4)) Ashgate Publishing Co.

Maguire, Eunice Dauterman & Maguire, Henry. Other Icons: Art & Power in Byzantine Secular Culture. 2006. (ENG., Illus.). 232p. (C). 62.95 (978-0-691-12564-0(3)) Princeton Univ. Pr.

Maguire, Henry. Image & Imagination in Byzantine Art. 2007. (Variorum Collected Studies Series: CS866 Ser.). (Illus.). 368p. 170.00 (978-0-7546-5907-5(0)) Ashgate Publishing Co.

Maguire, Henry & Nelson, Robert S., eds. San Marco, Byzantium, & the Myths of Venice. 2010. (Dumbarton Oaks Byzantine Symposia & Colloquia Ser.). (ENG., Illus.). 304p. 60.00 (978-0-88402-360-9(5)) Dumbarton Oaks.

Meyer, Mati. An Obscure Portrait: Imaging Women's Reality in Byzantine Art. 2009. (ENG., Illus.). 575p. (C). 300.00 (978-1-904597-32-2(7)) Pindar Pr. GBR. Dist: Brown, David Bk. Co., The.

Nelson, Robert S. Later Byzantine Painting: Art Agency & Appreciation. 2007. (Variorum Collected Studies). (Illus.). 430p. 190.00 (978-0-86078-997-0(7)) Ashgate Publishing Co.

Nelson, Robert S. & Collins, Kristen M., eds. Holy Image, Hallowed Ground: Icons from Sinai. 2007. (Illus.). 320p. 75.00 (978-0-89236-855-6(1)); pap. 50.00 (978-0-89236-856-3(X)) Oxford Univ. Pr., Inc.

Noga-Banai, Galit. The Trophies of the Martyrs: An Art Historical Study of Early Christian Silver Reliquaries. 2008. (Oxford Studies in Byzantium Ser.). (ENG., Illus.). 300p. 170.00 (978-0-19-921774-8(2)) Oxford Univ. Pr., Inc.

Osborne, John. Medieval Rome: A History in Art. 2013. (ENG., Illus.). 620p. (C). 300.00 (978-1-904597-41-4(6)) Pindar Pr. GBR. Dist: Brown, David Bk. Co., The.

Pekáry, Thomas. Phidias in Rom: Beiträge Zum Spätantiken Kunstverständnis. 2007. (Philippika - marburger altertumskundliche Abhandlungen Ser.). (GER., Illus.). 173p. pap. 72.00 (978-3-447-05516-1(2)) Harrassowitz, Otto Verlag DEU. Dist: ISD.

Piltz, Elisabeth. From Constantine the Great to Kandinsky: Studies in Byzantine & Post-Byzantine Art & Architecture. 2007. (Bar S Ser.). (Illus.). 75p. (C). pap. 65.00 (978-1-4073-0104-4(7)) British Archaeological Reports Ltd. GBR. Dist: Brown, David Bk. Co., The.

Talbot, A. M. Dumbarton Oaks Papers, Vol. 62. Talbot, Alice-Mary, ed. 2010. (Dumbarton Oaks Papers). (Illus.). 400p. 125.00 (978-0-88402-355-5(9)) Dumbarton Oaks.

Talbot, Alice-Mary & Whitehouse, David, eds. Dumbarton Oaks Papers, Vol. 59. 2007. (Dumbarton Oaks Papers). (Illus.). 400p. 125.00 (978-0-88402-312-8(5)) Dumbarton Oaks.

Vaboulis, Peter. Byzantine Decorative Art. (Illus.). 250p. 200.00 (978-0-89241-035-4(3), D139) Caratzas, Aristide D. Pub.

Vikan, Gary. Early Byzantine Pilgrimage Art. 2nd rev. ed. 2011. (Dumbarton Oaks Byzantine Collection Publications: 5). (Illus.). 118p. pap. 29.95 (978-0-88402-358-6(3)) Dumbarton Oaks.

Walker, Alicia. The Emperor & the World: Exotic Elements in the Imagining of Middle Byzantine Imperial Power. 2012. (ENG., Illus.). 400p. 95.00 (978-1-107-00477-1(2)) Cambridge Univ. Pr.

Wollesen, Jens. The Frescoes in the Royal Chapel at Pyrga on Cyprus: New Evidence & Datings. 2010. (Studies & Texts). (ENG., Illus.). 194p. 95.00 (978-0-88844-169-0(X)) Pontifical Institute of Mediaeval Studies, Dept. of Pubns. CAN. Dist: Univ. of Toronto Pr.

Woodfin, Warren T. The Embodied Icon: Liturgical Vestments & Sacramental Power in Byzantium. 2012. (Oxford Studies in Byzantium Ser.). (ENG., Illus.). 368p. 125.00 (978-0-19-959209-8(8)) Oxford Univ. Pr., Inc.

ART, CAMEROON
Geary, Christraud M. Bamum: Visions of Africa Series. 2011. (Visions of Africa Ser.). (ENG., Illus.). 160p. pap. 34.95 (978-88-7439-573-6(6)) 5 Continents ITA. Dist: Hachette Bk. Group.

Notue, Jean-Paul & Triaca, Bianca. Mankon: Arts, Heritage & Culture from the Mankon Kingdom (Western Cameroon) 2008. (ENG., Illus.). 336p. pap. 35.00 (978-88-7439-200-1(1)) 5 Continents ITA. Dist: Hachette Bk. Group.

ART, CANADIAN
About 1865: Tony Scherman. 2007. (978-0-9793336-0-6(1)) Winston Wächter Fine Art.

Ackerman, Marianne. Minority Report: An Alternative History of English-Language Arts in Quebec. Rodgers, Guy & Nasrallah, Dimitri, eds. 2011. (Essay Ser.). (ENG.). 156p. 20.00 (978-1-55071-355-8(8)) Guernica Editions, Inc. CAN. Dist: Univ. of Toronto Pr.

Adamson, Jeremy. Canadian Paintings in the Thomson Collection. 2008. (Illus.). 144p. pap. 50.00 (978-1-903470-83-1(8)) Holberton, Paul Publishing GBR. Dist: Casemate Pubs. & Bk. Distributors, LLC.

Ainslie, Patricia & LaViolette, Mary-Beth. Alberta Art & Artists: An Overview, 1 vol. 2007. (ENG., Illus.). 160p. 39.95 (978-1-894856-61-4(9)) Fitzhenry & Whiteside, Ltd. CAN. Dist: Ingram Pub. Services.

Amos, Robert. Artists in Their Studios: Where Art Is Born, 1 vol. 2007. (ENG., Illus.). 160p. (978-1-894898-58-4(3)) TouchWood Editions.

Appleby, Dee. From Land & Sea: Nova Scotia's Contemporary Landscape Artists. 2010. (ENG., Illus.). 156p. 35.00 (978-1-55109-729-9(X)) Down East Bks.

Archbold, Rick. Natural Worlds. 2010. (ENG., Illus.). 192p. 40.00 (978-1-897330-47-0(2)) Madison Pr. Bks. CAN. Dist: Independent Pubs. Group.

Arnold, Grant & Henry, Karen, eds. Traffic: Conceptual Art in Canada 1965-1980, 1 vol. 2012. (ENG., Illus.). 176p. 59.00 (978-1-895442-88-5(5)) D&M Pubs. Inc. CAN. Dist: Perseus-PGW.

Arnold, Grant & Thom, Ian M. Shore, Forest & Beyond: Art from the Audain Collection, 1 vol. 2012. (ENG., Illus.). 144p. 55.00 (978-1-55365-929-7(5)) D&M Pubs. Inc. CAN. Dist: Perseus-PGW.

Arnold, Grant, et al. Ken Lum, 1 vol. 2011. (ENG., Illus.). 144p. 55.00 (978-1-55365-498-8(6)) D&M Pubs. Inc. CAN. Dist: Perseus-PGW.

Beltei, Nadia. Abstract Art by NADIA BELTEI. 2009. 68p. pap. 28.99 (978-0-557-08551-4(9)) Lulu Enterprises Inc.

Bonnet, Frédéric, ed. General Idea: A Retrospective 1969-1994. 2011. (ENG., Illus.). 224p. 39.95 (978-3-03764-162-0(2)) JRP Ringier Kunstverlag AG CHE. Dist: D.A.P./Distributed Art Pubs.

Brandis, Gerard Brender à. A Wood Engraver's Alphabet. 2008. (ENG., Illus.). 64p. pap. 16.95 (978-0-88984-311-0(2)) Porcupine's Quill, Inc. CAN. Dist: Univ. of Toronto Pr.

Brehm, Meike, ed. Habitat. 2009. (ENG., Illus.). 176p. pap. 54.00 (978-3-86560-579-5(6)) Verlag der Buchhandlung Walther Konig DEU. Dist: D.A.P./Distributed Art Pubs.

Bryce, Alan D. Art Smart: The Intelligent Guide to Investing in the Canadian Art Market. 2007. (ENG., Illus.). 176p. pap. 24.99 (978-1-55002-676-4(3), Dundurn Pr.) Dundurn CAN. Dist: Ingram Pub. Services.

Bulloch, Angela. Angela Bulloch: Time & Line. 2012. (ENG & GER., Illus.). 112p. 45.00 (978-3-7757-3171-3(7)) Hatje Cantz Verlag GmbH & Co KG DEU. Dist: D.A.P./Distributed Art Pubs.

Burke, Gregory, text. Universal Code: Art & Cosmology in the Information Age. 2010. (ENG., Illus.). 136p. 58.00 (978-1-894212-28-1(2)) Power Plant, The CAN. Dist: D.A.P./Distributed Art Pubs.

Burke, Gregory, et al, texts. Scott Lyall: the Color Ball. 2010. (ENG., Illus.). 96p. 42.50 (978-1-894212-27-4(4)) Power Plant, The CAN. Dist: D.A.P./Distributed Art Pubs.

Butlin, Susan. The Practice of Her Profession: Florence Carlyle, Canadian Painter in the Age of Impressionism. 2009. (McGill-Queen's/Beaverbrook Canadian Foundation Studies in Art History Ser.). (ENG., Illus.). 352p. (C). (978-0-7735-3509-1(8)) McGill-Queen's Univ. Pr.

Campany, David. Jeff Wall: Picture for Women. 2011. (Afterall Ser.). (ENG., Illus.). 118p. (gr. 17). pap. 16.00 (978-1-84638-071-6(5)) Afterall Publishing GBR. Dist: MIT Pr.

Carr, Emily & Heritage House Publishing Co. Ltd. Staff. Studio Billie's Calendar: A Perpetual Calendar, 1 vol. 2011. (ENG., Illus.). 16p. pap. 14.95 (978-0-7726-6284-2(3)) Heritage Hse. CAN. Dist: TNT Media Group, Inc.

Carson, Andrea, frwd. Flash Forward 2008: Emerging Photographers from Canada, the United Kingdom & the United States. 2008. (ENG.). 192p. 30.00 (978-0-9739739-6-9(X)) Magenta Publishing for the Arts CAN. Dist: Consortium Bk. Sales & Distribution.

Cheetham, Mark A. & Hutcheon, Linda. Remembering Postmodernism: Trends in Canadian Art, 1970-1990. 2nd ed. 2012. (ENG., Illus.). 176p. pap. 35.00 (978-0-19-544879-5(0)) Oxford Univ. Pr., Inc.

Chenoweth, Lynda Salter. Philena's Friendship Quilt: A Quaker Farewell to Ohio. 2009. (Ohio Quilt Ser.). (ENG., Illus.). 104p. pap. 22.95 (978-0-8214-1858-1(0)) Ohio Univ. Pr.

Chhangur, Emelie, et al. FastwÜrms: Donky Ninja Witch: A Living Retrospective. 2011. (ENG., Illus.). 112p. (978-0-921972-60-0(1)) Art Gallery of York Univ.

Chiasson, Hermenegilde. Anecdotes & Enigmas (Anecdotes et Enigmes) The Marion McCain Atlantic Art Exhibition 1994. (Illus.). 64p. pap. 7.95 (978-0-920674-40-6(2)) Beaverbrook Art Gallery CAN. Dist: Goose Lane Editions.

Clark-Langager, Sarah & Dietrich, William, eds. Critical Messages: Contemporary Northwest Artists on the Environment. 2010. (ENG., Illus.). 80p. pap. 24.95 (978-1-878237-07-1(1)) Western Washington Univ., Western Gallery.

Clarkson, Adrienne, frwd. Celebrating Inuit Art. rev. ed. 2007. (ENG., Illus.). 192p. pap. 26.95 (978-1-55263-803-3(0)) Key Porter Bks. CAN. Dist: Perseus-PGW.

Collins, Curtis J., et al. A New Brunswick Trilogy: Philip Iverson, Francis Coutellier, Sarah Maloney, 3 vols. (FRE & ENG., Illus.). pap. 12.95 (978-0-920674-45-1(3)) Beaverbrook Art Gallery CAN. Dist: Goose Lane Editions.

Corcoran, Frank & Rabinovitch, Victor. Treasures from the Canadian Museum of Civilization & the Canadian War Museum. 2011. (ENG., Illus.). 200p. (C). pap. 49.95 (978-0-660-19915-3(7)) Canadian Museum of Civilization/Musee Canadien des Civilisations CAN. Dist: Univ. of Washington Pr.

Coughlin, Linda Rae. Modern Hooked Rugs. 2007. (Illus.). 176p. pap. 29.95 (978-0-7643-2631-8(7)) Schiffer Publishing, Ltd.

Coulis, Michael, et al. Journeys Beyond the Neatline: Expanding the Boundaries of Cartography. 2010. (ENG., Illus.). 90p. pap. (978-1-55195-258-1(0)) Univ. of Alberta Pr. CAN. Dist: Michigan State Univ. Pr.

Crane, Walter, illus. The Marquis of Carabas Picture Book. 2008. 36p. pap. (978-1-84830-913-5(9), Wildhern Pr.) Echo Library.

Dawn, Leslie. National Visions, National Blindness: Canadian Art & Identities in The 1920s, 1 vol. 2007. (ENG., Illus.). 456p. pap. 29.95 (978-0-7748-1218-4(4)) UBC Pr. CAN. Dist: Univ. of Washington Pr.

De Wolf, Hans, ed. Jeff Wall: the Crooked Path. 2011. (ENG., Illus.). 255p. 50.00 (978-90-5544-862-3(1)) Lundion, Uitgeverij NLD. Dist: D.A.P./Distributed Art Pubs.

Des Rochers, Jacques, ed. Quebec & Canadian Art: The Montreal Museum of Fine Arts' Collection: Volume I. 2012. (ENG., Illus.). 400p. 55.00 (978-2-89192-355-2(3)) Abrams.

Diviney, David. David Askevold: Once upon a Time in the East. 2011. (ENG.). 160p. 50.00 (978-0-86492-659-3(6)) Goose Lane Editions CAN. Dist: Univ. of Toronto Pr.

Douglas, Stan, ed. Vancouver Anthology. 2nd rev. ed. 2009. (ENG.). 368p. 35.00 (978-0-88922-614-2(8)) Talonbooks, Ltd. CAN. Dist: Consortium Bk. Sales & Distribution.

Duncan, Alastair. High Style: Masterworks from the Bernard & Sylvia Ostry Collection in the Royal Ontario Museum. 2006. (ENG., Illus.). 148p. (978-0-88854-446-9(4)) Royal Ontario Museum.

Dzama, Marcel. Marcel Dzama: the Infidels, 1 vol. 2010. (ENG.). 152p. 79.95 (978-3-941100-88-6(2)) DruckVerlag Kettler GmbH DEU. Dist: D.A.P./Distributed Art Pubs.

Fillmore, Sarah. Jacques Hurtubise: Catalogue Raisonné. 2011. (FRE & ENG., Illus.). 256p. 60.00 (978-0-86492-662-3(6)) Goose Lane Editions CAN. Dist: Univ. of Toronto Pr.

Fisher, Jennifer, ed. Technologies of Intuition. 2007. (ENG., Illus.). 288p. pap. 26.95 (978-0-920397-43-5(3)) Y Y Z Artists Outlet CAN. Dist: LitDistCo.

Gale, Peggy, et al. Art at Work/L'Art Au Travail: rt Bank of the Canada Council of the Arts/ le Banque d'Oeuvres d'Art du Conseil des Arts du Canada. Henry, Victoria, ed. 2007. (ENG & FRE., Illus.). 144p. pap. 45.00 *(978-0-86492-429-2(1))* Goose Lane Editions CAN. Dist: Univ. of Toronto Pr.

Gibson, Bethany. Roadsworth. 2011. (ENG., Illus.). 208p. pap. 29.95 ***(978-0-86492-638-8(3))*** Goose Lane Editions CAN. Dist: Univ. of Toronto Pr.

Grace, Sherrill. On the Art of Being Canadian. 2010. (ENG., Illus.). 224p. pap. 35.95 *(978-0-7748-1579-6(5))* UBC Pr. CAN. Dist: Univ. of Washington Pr.

Graham, Rodney. Rodney Graham: Through the Forest, 1 vol. 2010. (ENG.). 168p. pap. 55.00 *(978-3-7757-2577-4(6))* Hatje Cantz Verlag GmbH & Co KG DEU. Dist: D.A.P./Distributed Art Pubs.

Gray, Zoe, et al. Geoffrey Farmer. 2008. (ENG., Illus.). 96p. pap. 15.00 *(978-90-73362-79-6(2))* Witte De With Centre for Contemporary Art NLD. Dist: D.A.P./Distributed Art Pubs.

Grenville, Bruce & Steedman, Scott, eds. Visions of British Columbia: A Landscape Manual, 1 vol. 2010. (ENG., Illus.). 256p. pap. 35.00 *(978-1-55365-500-8(1))* D&M Pubs. Inc. CAN. Dist: Perseus-PGW.

Hanshew, Annie. Border to Border: Historic Quilts & Quiltmakers of Montana. 2010. (ENG., Illus.). 240p. pap. 24.95 *(978-0-9759196-2-0(8))* Montana Historical Society Pr.

Herbert, Elizabeth & Snow, John. Art of John Snow. 2010. (Illus.). 220p. pap. 49.95 *(978-1-55238-516-6(7))* Univ. of Calgary Pr. CAN. Dist: Michigan State Univ. Pr.

Hermant, Sydney, et al. Aunt Maud's Scrapbook, 1 vol. 2007. (ENG., Illus.). 112p. pap. 29.00 *(978-3-905770-03-2(2))* JRP Ringier Kunstverlag AG CHE. Dist: D.A.P./Distributed Art Pubs.

Herzog, Fred, photos by. Fred Herzog: Photographs, 1 vol. 2011. (ENG., Illus.). 192p. 45.00 *(978-3-7757-2811-9(2))* Hatje Cantz Verlag GmbH & Co KG DEU. Dist: D.A.P./Distributed Art Pubs.

Hopkins, Candice & Swanson, Kerry. Shapeshifters, Time Travellers, & Storytellers. 2009. (ENG., Illus.). 192p. 19.99 *(978-0-88854-455-1(3))* Royal Ontario Museum CAN. Dist: Univ. of Toronto Pr.

Huneault, Kristina & Anderson, Janice. Rethinking Professionalism: Women & Art in Canada, 1850-1970. 2012. (McGill-Queen's/Beaverbrook Canadian Foundation Studies in Art History Ser.). (ENG., Illus.). 472p. (C). ***(978-0-7735-3966-2(2))*** McGill-Queen's Univ. Pr.

Kaiser, Philipp. Jack Goldstein X 10,000. 2012. (Illus.). 240p. pap. 49.95 ***(978-3-7913-5193-3(1))*** Prestel Publishing.

Kellman, Tila L. Figuring Redemption: Resighting My Self in the Art of Michael Snow. 2010. (ENG.). 222p. (C). pap. 39.95 *(978-1-55458-249-5(0))* Wilfrid Laurier Univ. Pr. CAN. Dist: Univ. of Toronto Pr.

King, Ross. Defiant Spirits: The Modernist Revolution of the Group of Seven, 1 vol. 2011. (ENG., Illus.). 504p. pap. 24.95 *(978-1-55365-882-5(5))* D&M Pubs Inc. CAN. Dist: Perseus-PGW.

Kramer, Jennifer. Kesu' The Art & Life of Doug Cranmer, 1 vol. 2012. (ENG., Illus.). 160p. pap. 34.95 ***(978-0-295-99144-3(5))*** Univ. of Washington Pr.

Laliberte, Mark. Brickbrickbrick. 2010. (ENG., Illus.). 128p. pap. 18.00 *(978-1-897388-57-0(8))* BookThug CAN. Dist: SPD-Small Pr. Distribution.

Ledwell, Frank. Dip & Veer: Reflections on the Art of Alex Colville. 64p. pap. 12.95 *(978-0-9698606-2-4(5))* Acorn Pr., The CAN. Dist: Goose Lane Editions.

Lee, Tim, et al. Modern Optical Experiements in Typography: Univers Ultra Light Oblique (1968), 1 vol. 2007. (ENG., Illus.). 1028p. pap. 29.00 *(978-3-905770-04-9(0))* JRP Ringier Kunstverlag AG CHE. Dist: D.A.P./Distributed Art Pubs.

Lexier, Micah. Micah Lexier: I'm Thinking of a Number. 2010. (ENG., Illus.). 300p. 50.00 *(978-0-919616-50-9(X))* Press of the Nova Scotia College of Art & Design CAN. Dist: D.A.P./Distributed Art Pubs.

Lister, Ken, ed. Canada Collects: The Passionate Eye, 1 vol. 2007. (ENG., Illus.). 192p. 24.99 *(978-0-88854-453-7(7))* Royal Ontario Museum CAN. Dist: Univ. of Toronto Pr.

Lochnan, Katharine. Black Ice: David Blackwood's Prints of Newfoundland, 1 vol. 2011. (ENG., Illus.). 224p. pap. 40.00 *(978-1-55365-779-8(9))* D&M Pubs. Inc. CAN. Dist: Perseus-PGW.

MacDonald, Rory & Irwin, Kathleen, eds. Sighting, Citing, Siting: Crossfiring/Mama Wetotan: Theorising Practice. 2009. (University of Regina Publications (UR) Ser.). (ENG., Illus.). 208p. mass mkt. 40.00 *(978-0-88977-228-1(2))* Canadian Plains Research Ctr. CAN. Dist: Univ. of Toronto Pr.

Macnair, Peter L., et al. The Legacy: Tradition & Innovation in Northwest Coast Indian Art, 1 vol. 2007. (Royal BC Museum Ser.). (ENG., Illus.). 196p. pap. 36.95 *(978-0-7726-5509-4(6))* UBC Pr. CAN. Dist: Univ. of Washington Pr.

Marman, Jennifer & Borins, Daniel. Jennifer Marman & Daniel Borins: Project for a New American Century. 2009. (ENG., Illus.). 64p. *(978-0-921972-55-6(5))* Art Gallery of York Univ.

Mason, Roger B. Franz Johnston. Date not set. 19.95 *(978-1-55082-179-6(2))* Quarry Pr. CAN. Dist: LPC/InBook.

McCallum, Pamela. Cultural Memories & Imagined Futures: The Art of Jane Ash Poitras. 2009. (Art in Profile Ser.). (ENG., Illus.). 128p. pap. 41.95 *(978-1-55238-271-4(0))* Univ. of Calgary Pr. CAN. Dist: Chicago Distribution Ctr.

McKay, Marylin J. Picturing the Land: Narrating Territories in Canadian Landscape Art, 1500-1950. 2011. (McGill-Queen's/Beaverbrook Canadian Foundation Studies in Art History Ser.). (ENG., Illus.). 384p. (C). pap. *(978-0-7735-3817-7(8))* McGill-Queen's Univ. Pr.

McNutt, Jennifer Complo & Holland, Ashley. Art Quantum: The Eiteljorg Fellowship for Native American Fine Art 2009. Nottage, James, ed. 2010. (ENG., Illus.). 96p. pap. 26.95 *(978-0-295-98996-9(3))* Univ. of Washington Pr.

McRobert, Laurie. Char Davies' Immersive Virtual Art & the Essence of Spatiality. 2007. (ENG., Illus.). 290p. *(978-0-8020-9094-2(X))* Univ. of Toronto Pr.

Moos, David, et al. Iain Baxterand & Works, 1958-2011. Moos, David, ed. 2012. (ENG., Illus.). 220p. pap. 45.00 ***(978-0-86492-646-3(4))*** Goose Lane Editions CAN. Dist: Univ. of Toronto Pr.

Moray, Gerta. Unsettling Encounters: First Nations Imagery in the Art of Emily Carr. 2006. (Illus.). 386p. 75.00 *(978-0-295-98608-1(5))* Univ. of Washington Pr.

Müller, Vanessa Joan, et al, eds. Ian Wallace: A Literary of Images. 2008. (Illus.). 220p. 49.95 *(978-1-933128-51-1(8))* Sternberg Pr.

Nasby, Judith, et al. Will Gorlitz: Nowhere If Not Here. 2009. (ENG., Illus.). 120p. pap. 38.95 *(978-1-55458-049-1(8))* Wilfrid Laurier Univ. Pr. CAN. Dist: Univ. of Toronto Pr.

National Museum of the American Indian (U.S.) Staff, contrib. by. Essays on Native Modernism: Complexity & Contradiction in American Indian Art. 2006. (NMAI Editions Ser.). (Illus.). 112p. *(978-1-933565-02-6(0))* Smithsonian National Museum of the American Indian.

Nevitt, Richard B. & Nevitt, Richard. A Caledon Sketchbook. 2008. (ENG., Illus.). 128p. pap. 18.95 *(978-0-88984-310-3(4))* Porcupine's Quill, Inc. CAN. Dist: Univ. of Toronto Pr.

O'Brian, Melanie. Vancouver Art & Economies. O'Brian, Melanie, ed. 2007. (ENG., Illus.). 300p. pap. 24.95 *(978-1-55152-214-2(4))* Arsenal Pulp Pr. CAN. Dist: Consortium Bk. Sales & Distribution.

Pageot, Edith-Anne & Falvey, Emily. Jinny Yu. 2008. (FRE & ENG., Illus.). 60p. (gr. 10-12). pap. 30.00 *(978-2-923243-01-6(3))* Art mur, Editions CAN. Dist: Univ. of Ottawa Pr./Presses de l'Universite d'Ottawa.

Parron, Suzi & Groves, Donna Sue. Barn Quilts & the American Quilt Trail Movement. 2012. (ENG., Illus.). 240p. pap. 29.95 ***(978-0-8040-1138-9(3))*** Swallow Pr.

Paterson, James. Jim's Grandiose Big Bible Picture Book. 2007. (ENG., Illus.). 96p. 35.00 *(978-0-9782221-4-7(8))* ECW Pr. CAN. Dist: Independent Pubs. Group.

Pearse, Harold. From Drawing to Visual Culture: A History of Art Education in Canada. 2006. (ENG., Illus.). 318p. (C). *(978-0-7735-3070-6(3))* McGill-Queen's Univ. Pr.

Penny, Evan. Evan Penny: Rendering Realities. 2011. (ITA, GER & ENG., Illus.). 160p. 45.00 ***(978-3-86560-990-8(2))*** Verlag der Buchhandlung Walther Konig DEU. Dist: D.A.P./Distributed Art Pubs.

Perry, Lorne. Drawing from the Mountain: An Illustrated Journey, 1 vol. 2010. (ENG., Illus.). 144p. *(978-1-894765-81-7(8))* Rocky Mountain Bks.

Plesch, Veronique. The Wisdom of the Imagination: The Livres d'Artiste of Lucie Lambert. Martineau, Sheila, ed. 2012. (ENG., Illus.). 64p. 24.95 *(978-1-897476-27-7(2))* Simply Read Bks. CAN. Dist: Perseus-PGW.

Polidori, Robert. Points Between... up till Now, 1 vol. 2010. (ENG., Illus.). 192p. pap. 45.00 *(978-3-86521-994-7(2))* Steidl, Gerhard Druckerei und Verlag DEU. Dist: Innovative Logistics.

Prakash, A. K. Independent Spirit: Early Canadian Women Artists. 2008. (ENG., Illus.). 408p. 75.00 *(978-1-55407-417-4(7))* Firefly Bks., Ltd.

Rabinowitch, David. Birth of Romanticism Drawings, 1 vol. 2011. (ENG.). 82p. 55.00 *(978-0-935875-24-9(7))* Blum, Peter Edition.

Randell, Roy. Spiritual Art. 2010. 125p. pap. 44.80 *(978-0-557-39643-6(3))* Lulu Enterprises Inc.

Reid, Dennis, ed. Jack Chambers: Light, Spirit, Time, Place, & Life. 2011. (ENG., Illus.). 240p. pap. 45.00 ***(978-0-86492-645-6(6))*** Goose Lane Editions CAN. Dist: Univ. of Toronto Pr.

Robertson, Clive. Policy Matters: Administrations of Art & Culture. 2006. (ENG., Illus.). 288p. per. 19.95 *(978-0-920397-36-7(0))* Y Y Z Artists Outlet CAN. Dist: LitDistCo.

Robinson, Chris J. & Robinson, Chris. Canadian Animation: Looking for a Place to Happen. 2008. (ENG., Illus.). 300p. pap. 27.95 *(978-0-86196-688-2(0),* 0861966880) Libbey, John & Co., Ltd. AUS. Dist: Indiana Univ. Pr.

Roth, Paul, ed. Oil, 1 vol. 2011. (ENG., Illus.). 216p. 128.00 *(978-3-86521-943-5(8))* Steidl, Gerhard Druckerei und Verlag DEU. Dist: Innovative Logistics.

Samwald, Odilie. Odilie - the adventure Continues. 2010. 84p. pap. 29.20 *(978-0-557-51933-0(0))* Lulu Enterprises Inc.

Schmuckli, Claudia, et al. Jon Pylypchuk. 2010. (ENG., Illus.). 96p. 39.95 *(978-0-941193-45-0(4))* Blaffer Art Museum.

Shapton, Leanne. Toronto, 1 vol. 2007. (ENG., Illus.). 112p. pap. 30.00 *(978-0-9701656-8-8(4))* J&L Bks., Inc.

Shields, Conal. Kenneth Thomson the Collector. 2009. (Illus.). 128p. pap. 50.00 ***(978-1-903470-79-4(X))*** Holberton, Paul Publishing GBR. Dist: Casemate Pubs. & Bk. Distributors, LLC.

Shink, Diane & Neary, Karen. Canadian Heritage Quilting: Quick Creative Designs. 2008. (ENG., Illus.). 128p. pap. 22.95 *(978-0-88780-753-4(4))* Formac Publishing Co., Ltd. CAN. Dist: Casemate Pubs. & Bk. Distributors, LLC.

Simmonds, Charles, et al. Landscape Body Dwelling: Charles Simonds at Dumbarton Oaks. 2012. (ENG., Illus.). 116p. pap. 40.00 *(978-0-88402-371-5(0))* Dumbarton Oaks.

Simoens, Tommy, ed. Stan Douglas: Midcentury Studio. 2011. (ENG., Illus.). 116p. 40.00 ***(978-90-5544-879-1(6))*** Lundion, Uitgeverij NLD. Dist: D.A.P./Distributed Art Pubs.

Smart, Tom. Immolation: Recent Figuration by Graham Metson. (Illus.). 48p. pap. 5.00 *(978-0-920674-30-7(5))* Beaverbrook Art Gallery CAN. Dist: Goose Lane Editions.

Townsend-Gault & Duffek, K. Bill Reid & Beyond, 1 vol. (ENG., Illus.). 320p. pap. 27.95 *(978-1-55365-094-2(8))* D&M Pubs. Inc. CAN. Dist: Perseus-PGW.

Trier, Walter & Schmitz, Walter. Walter Trier und Die Bilderwelt der Kinder. 2007. (GER., Illus.). 333p. *(978-3-937672-53-3(2))* w.e.b. Universitatsverlag/Buchhandel Eckhard Richter & Co. oHG.

Urquhart, Tony. Off the Wall. 2008. (ENG., Illus.). 224p. pap. 27.95 *(978-0-88984-302-8(3))* Porcupine's Quill, Inc. CAN. Dist: Univ. of Toronto Pr.

Vallières, Nicole & Cooper, Cynthia. 90 Treasures, 90 Stories, 90 Years. 2012. (Illus.). 268p. (C). pap. ***(978-1-895615-16-6(X))*** McGill-Queen's Univ. Pr.

Von Szombathy, Chris. Fire Away. 2008. (ENG., Illus.). 96p. pap. *(978-1-897299-49-4(4))* Drawn & Quarterly Pubns.

Vorano, Norman, et al. Inuit Prints, Japanese Inspiration: Early Printmaking in the Canadian Arctic. 2011. (ENG., Illus.). 100p. (C). pap. 29.95 *(978-0-660-19970-2(X))* Canadian Museum of Civilization/Musee Canadien des Civilisations CAN. Dist: Univ. of Washington Pr.

Wallace, Ian. Ian Wallace: Die erste documenta 1955. 2011. (ENG., Illus.). 40p. pap. 10.00 ***(978-3-7757-2851-5(1))*** Hatje Cantz Verlag GmbH & Co KG DEU. Dist: D.A.P./Distributed Art Pubs.

Wark, Jayne. Radical Gestures: Feminism & Performance Art in North America. 2006. (ENG., Illus.). 304p. (C). *(978-0-7735-2956-4(X))*; per. *(978-0-7735-3066-9(5))* McGill-Queen's Univ. Pr.

Webb, Brian, ed. Ode au Corps: Une Histoire de Danse. (FRE & ENG., Illus.). 128p. pap. 14.95 *(978-0-920159-98-9(2))* Banff Centre Pr. CAN. Dist: Literary Pr. Group of Canada.

Whitelaw, Anne, et al, eds. The Visual Arts in Canada: The Twentieth Century. (ENG., Illus.). 496p. 2011. pap. 59.95 *(978-0-19-543459-0(5))* 2010. 89.95 *(978-0-19-542125-5(6))* Oxford Univ. Pr., Inc.

Williams, Barbara. A Gentlewoman in Upper Canada: The Journals, Letters & Art of Anne Langton. 2008. (ENG., Illus.). 384p. *(978-0-8020-3549-3(3))* Univ. of Toronto Pr.

Wilson, Michael. Contemporary Art in North America: Artworld. Black Dog Publishing Staff, ed. 2011. (Artworld Ser.). (ENG., Illus.). 240p. 49.95 *(978-1-907317-23-1(6))* Black Dog Publishing Ltd. GBR. Dist: Perseus Distribution.

Wood, Brian & Pearce, Shelley. Brian Wood: 2009-2010 Dr. Roy E. Morgan Exhibition, January 18-March 14, 2010. 2009. (Illus.). 28p. *(978-0-942945-31-7(X))* Wilkes College, Sordoni Art Gallery.

Wood, Wilma. The Vanishing Landscape. 2007. pap. 27.95 *(978-1-55059-340-2(4))* Detselig Enterprises, Ltd. CAN. Dist: Temeron Bks., Inc.

Wyatt, Gary R. Mythic Beings: Spirit Art of the Northwest Coast, 1 vol. (ENG.). 144p. pap. 28.95 *(978-1-55054-639-2(2))* D&M Pubs. Inc. CAN. Dist: Perseus-PGW.

Wyman, Jessica, ed. Pro Forma: Language, Text, Visual Art. 2007. (ENG., Illus.). 64p. pap. 12.95 *(978-0-920397-38-1(7))* Y Y Z Artists Outlet CAN. Dist: LitDistCo.

—Pro Forma Vol. 2: Language/text/visual Art. 2007. (ENG., Illus.). 96p. pap 14.95 *(978-0-920397-39-8(5))* Y Y Z Artists Outlet CAN. Dist: LitDistCo.

—Pro Forma Vol. 3: Language/text/visual Art. 2007. (ENG., Illus.). 62p. pap 14.95 *(978-0-920397-40-4(9))* Y Y Z Artists Outlet CAN. Dist: LitDistCo.

ART, CARIBBEAN

Alex, Webb. Caribbean. 2010. 136p. *(978-1-907112-18-8(9))* Trolley.

Bickerton, Derek, et al. Ashley Bickerton. 2011. (Illus.). 400p. 375.00 *(978-1-906967-38-3(5))* Other Criteria GBR. Dist: Abrams.

Cullen, Deborah & Fuentes, Elvis, eds. Caribbean: Art at the Crossroads of the World. 2012. (ENG., Illus.). 496p. 65.00 ***(978-0-300-17854-8(9))*** Yale Univ. Pr.

Dash, P. African Caribbean Pupils in Art Education. 2010. 242p. *(978-94-6091-049-4(1))*; (Illus.). pap. *(978-94-6091-048-7(3))* Sense Pubs.

IDB Cultural Center Staff, et al, contrib. by. 50 Años, 50 Obras: Obras Sobresalientes Del Arte de América Latina y el Caribe Del Siglo XX. 2009. (ENG & SPA., Illus.). 89p. ***(978-1-59782-088-2(1))*** Inter-American Development Bank.

Mosaka, Tumelo. Infinite Island: Contemporary Caribbean Art. 2007. (ENG., Illus.). 224p. 58.00 *(978-0-85667-641-3(1))* Wilson, Philip Pubs., Ltd. GBR. Dist: Macmillan.

Mosaka, Tumelo, et al. Infinite Island: Contemporary Caribbean Art. 2007. pap. *(978-0-87273-158-5(8))* Brooklyn Museum, The.

Shipp, Steve. Latin American & Caribbean Artists of the Modern Era: A Biographical Dictionary of More Than 12,700 Persons, 2 vols. alt. ed. 2012. (ENG., Illus.). 916p. pap. 75.00 *(978-0-7864-6626-9(X))* McFarland & Co., Inc. Pubs.

Sims, Lowery Stokes, frwd. Llewellyn Xavier: His Life & Work. 2007. (ENG., Illus.). 224p. *(978-1-4050-8649-3(1))* Macmillan Caribbean.

Smit, Jennifer & de Rooy, Felix. Curaçao Classics: Visual Arts from the 20th Century & Onwards. 2012. 160p. 49.50 ***(978-94-6022-158-3(0))*** Royal Tropical Institute Pr. (KIT (Koninklijk Instituut voor de Tropen) NLD. Dist: Stylus Publishing, LLC.

Wainwright, Leon. Timed Out: Art & the Transnational Caribbean. 2012. (Rethinking Art's Histories Ser.). (ENG., Illus.). 208p. pap. 30.95 ***(978-0-7190-8594-9(2))*** Manchester Univ. Pr. GBR. Dist: Macmillan.

—Timed Out: rt & the Transnational Caribbean. 2012. (Rethinking Art's Histories Ser.). (ENG., Illus.). 208p. 95.00 ***(978-0-7190-8484-3(9))*** Manchester Univ. Pr. GBR. Dist: Macmillan.

Williams, Evelyn A. The Art of Denis Williams. 2012. (ENG., Illus.). 174p. pap. 54.95 ***(978-1-84523-193-4(7))*** Peepal Tree Pr., Ltd. GBR. Dist: Independent Pubs. Group.

ART, CARLOVINGIAN

see Art, Carolingian

ART, CAROLINGIAN

Chazelle, Celia. The Crucified God in the Carolingian Era: Theology & Art of Christ's Passion. 2007. (ENG., Illus.). 356p. per. 74.00 *(978-0-521-03945-1(2))* Cambridge Univ. Pr.

McKitterick, Rosamond. Charlemagne: The Formation of Carolingian Identity. 2008. (ENG., Illus.). 478p. (C). 88.00 *(978-0-521-88672-7(4))* Cambridge Univ. Pr.

Wormald, Patrick & Nelson, Janet L., eds. Lay Intellectuals in the Carolingian World. 2011. (ENG.). 278p. pap. 36.99 *(978-0-521-17409-1(0))* Cambridge Univ. Pr.

ART, CELTIC

Alfred Publishing Staff. The Greatest Journey Essential Collection: Piano/Vocal/Chords. 2009. (ENG.). 112p. pap. 21.95 *(978-0-7390-6063-6(5))* Alfred Publishing Co., Inc.

Allen, J. Romilly. Celtic Art in Pagan & Christian Times. 2010. 414p. 39.96 *(978-1-169-33887-6(9))*; 49.95 *(978-1-161-60727-7(7))* Kessinger Publishing, LLC.

—Celtic Art in Pagan & Christian Times. 2008. (ENG.). 424p. per. *(978-1-4086-5308-1(7))* Read Bks.

Brown, Penny. Celtic Designs. 2012. (Design Library). (ENG., Illus.). 64p. pap. 12.95 ***(978-1-84448-725-7(3))*** Search Pr., Ltd. GBR. Dist: Independent Pubs. Group.

Combs, Karen. Celtic Pieced Illusions. 2006. (ENG., Illus.). 112p. per. 24.95 *(978-1-57432-916-2(2),* 1574329162, American Quilter's Society) Collector Bks.

Davis, Courtney, et al. Compendium of Celtic Crafts. 2009. (ENG., Illus.). 192p. pap. 19.95 *(978-1-84448-355-6(X))* Search Pr., Ltd. GBR. Dist: Independent Pubs. Group.

Garrow, Duncan, et al, eds. Rethinking Celtic Art. 2008. (ENG., Illus.). 208p. (C). pap. 70.00 *(978-1-84217-318-3(9))* Oxbow Bks., Ltd. GBR. Dist: Brown, David Bk. Co., The.

Garrow, Duncan & Gosden, Chris. Technologies of Enchantment? Exploring Celtic Art: 400 BC to AD 100. 2012. (ENG., Illus.). 408p. 150.00 ***(978-0-19-954806-4(4))*** Oxford Univ. Pr., Inc.

Graham-Flynn, Fiona. The Simple Art of Celtic Calligraphy. 2008. (ENG., Illus.). 128p. pap. 19.95 *(978-1-906094-91-1(8))* CICO Bks. GBR. Dist: Ryland Peters & Small.

Harding, D. W. The Archaeology of Celtic Art. 2007. (Illus.). 301p. 125.00 *(978-0-415-35177-5(4))* Routledge.

Harding, Derek William. The Archaeology of Celtic Art. 2007. (ENG., Illus.). 336p. per. 45.95 *(978-0-415-42866-8(1))* Routledge.

Highfill, Page. Thin Places & Five Clues in Their Architecture. 2009. 152p. pap. 19.95 *(978-0-578-03158-3(2))* EnterPaths, LLC.

Jammula, S. R. Vector Designs: Celtic Frames & Borders (Paperback) 2008. (Illus.). 160p. pap. 14.95 *(978-0-9742408-0-0(X))* Xlicons, Inc.

—Vector Designs - Celtic Frames & Borders (CD-ROM) 2008. (Illus.). cd-rom 24.95 *(978-0-9742408-2-4(6))* Xlicons, Inc.

Laing, Lloyd. European Influence on Celtic Art: Patrons & Artists. 2010. (Illus.). 256p. 70.00 *(978-1-84682-175-2(4))* Four Courts Pr. IRL. Dist: International Specialized Bk. Services.

Littlejohn, Stuart. Celtic Fantasy in Watercolour. 2008. (Fantasy Art Ser.). (ENG., Illus.). 48p. pap. 15.95 *(978-1-84448-292-4(8))* Search Pr., Ltd. GBR. Dist: Independent Pubs. Group.

Müller, Felix, ed. Art of the Celts: 700 B. C. to A. D. 700. 2009. (Illus.). 304p. 70.00 *(978-0-8014-4869-0(7))* Cornell Univ. Pr.

Noble, Marty. Celtic Crosses Tattoos. 2006. (Dover Tattoos Ser.). (ENG., Illus.). 2p. (gr. -1-3). pap. 1.50 *(978-0-486-45208-1(5))* Dover Pubns., Inc.

O'Brien, Sarah. Celtic Tattoos: Includes Trinity Pendant Necklace. 2010. (ENG.). 72p. pap. 6.95 *(978-0-7624-3751-1(0))* Running Pr. Bk. Pubs.

Piggott, Stuart. Early Celtic Art: From Its Origins to Its Aftermath. 2008. (ENG., Illus.). 77p. pap. 39.95 *(978-0-202-36186-4(1))* Aldine Transaction.

Search Press. Celtic Papers: 24 Perforated Papers. 2006. (Crafter's Paper Library). (ENG., Illus.). 48p. pap. 11.95 *(978-1-84448-222-1(7))* Search Pr., Ltd. GBR. Dist: Independent Pubs. Group.

Stegenga, Wil. Geometric Motifs. 2007. (Dover Electronic Clip Art Ser.). (ENG., Illus.). 56p. pap. 14.95 *(978-0-486-99833-6(9))* Dover Pubns., Inc.

Taylor, Joules. The Book of Celtic Symbols: Symbols, Stories & Blessings for Everyday Living. 2007. (ENG., Illus.). 160p. *(978-1-906094-19-5(5))* Ryland Peters & Small.

Weller, Alan. Celtic Vector Designs. 2008. (Dover Pictura Electronic Clip Art Ser.). (ENG.). 128p. pap. 49.95 *(978-0-486-99022-4(2))* Dover Pubns., Inc.

—Celtic Vector Motifs. 2010. (Dover Electronic Clip Art Ser.). (ENG., Illus.). 48p. pap. 19.95 *(978-0-486-99109-2(1))* Dover Pubns., Inc.

Westwood, J. O. Celtic & Anglo-Saxon Art & Ornament. 2007. (Dover Pictorial Archives Ser.). (ENG., Illus.). 64p. per. 14.95 *(978-0-486-45816-8(4))* Dover Pubns., Inc.

—Celtic & Anglo-Saxon Art & Ornament in Full Color CD-ROM & Book. 2008. (Dover Electronic Clip Art Ser.). (ENG., Illus.). 48p. pap. 22.95 *(978-0-486-99723-0(5))* Dover Pubns., Inc.

Whitfield, Niamh. Design & Techniques in Early Medieval Celtic Metalwork. 2013. (ENG., Illus.). 580p. (C). 300.00 (978-1-904597-33-9(5)) Pindar Pr. GBR. Dist: Brown, David Bk. Co., The.

ART, CHILEAN

Alys, Francis. Francis Alys: A Story of Deception. 2010. (ENG., Illus.). 192p. pap. 35.00 (978-0-87070-790-2(6)) Museum of Modern Art.

Auerbach, Ruth, et al. 3 Perspectives: Eugenio Espinoza, Alvaro Oyarzún, José Alejandro Restrepo: Cisneros Fontanals Art Foundation 2007 Commissions Program Exhibition. 2007. (SPA & ENG., Illus.). 60p. (978-0-9774079-5-8(0)) Cisneros Fontanals Art Foundation.

Buchmann, Sabeth, text. Cristobal Lehyt: Drama Projection. 2010. (ENG & GER., Illus.). 180p. pap. 45.00 (978-3-03764-019-7(7)) JRP Ringier Kunstverlag AG CHE. Dist: D.A.P./Distributed Art Pubs.

Ellegood, Anne, et al, texts. Ivan Navarro: Threshold. 2009. (ENG., Illus.). 80p. pap. 37.95 (978-88-8158-728-5(9)) Charta ITA. Dist: D.A.P./Distributed Art Pubs.

Lazzara, Michael J. Chile in Transition: The Poetics & Politics of Memory. 2006. (ENG., Illus.). 224p. 59.95 (978-0-8130-3008-1(0)) Univ. Pr. of Florida.

Palmer, Rod. Street Art Chile. 2008. (Illus.). 144p. pap. 24.95 (978-1-58423-300-8(1)) Gingko Pr., Inc.

Vasquez de la Horra, Sandra. Sandra Vásquez de la Horra. 2010. (ENG., Illus.). 184p. 60.00 (978-3-7757-2655-9(1)) Hatje Cantz Verlag GmbH & Co KG DEU. Dist: D.A.P./Distributed Art Pubs.

ART, CHINESE

Agi-New Voice, Agi New Member 04/05. 2009. 276p. pap. (978-3-9810544-5-3(8)) Page One Publishing.

Ahuja, Shilpa. Designing a Chinese Cultural Center in Indi. 2010. 136p. pap. (978-3-8383-5919-9(4)) Lambert Academic Publishing.

Ai, Weiwei & Meile, Urs. Ai Weiwei Works, 2004-2007. 2008. (ENG., Illus.). 219p. pap. 39.00 (978-3-905829-27-3(4)) JRP Ringier Kunstverlag AG CHE. Dist: D.A.P./Distributed Art Pubs.

Alexander, Mary & Alexander, Frances. A Handbook on Chinese Art Symbols. 2011. 84p. 37.95 (978-1-258-01098-0(4)) Literary Licensing, LLC.

Ambrozy, Lee & Weiwei, Ai. Ai Weiwei's Blog: Writings, Interviews, & Digital Rants, 2006-2009. Ambrozy, Lee, ed. & tr. by. from CHI. 2011. (Writing Art Ser.). (ENG., Illus.). 336p. (gr. 17). pap. 24.95 (978-0-262-01521-9(8)) MIT Pr.

Ashton, Leigh. Chinese Art. 2006. 176p. per. (978-1-4067-9676-6(X), Hesperides Pr.) Read Bks.

Avril, Ellen. Ancient Artistry: Pre-Chinese Ceramics & Jades from the Shatzman Collection. 2006. (Illus.). 55p. pap. 15.00 (978-0-9646042-2-3(1)) Cornell Univ., Herbert F. Johnson Museum of Art.

Bachhofer, Ludwig. A Short History of Chinese Art. reprint ed. 47.50 (978-0-404-20014-5(1)) AMS Pr., Inc.

—A Short History of Chinese Art. 2010. 226p. 31.96 (978-1-169-74036-5(7)) 2010. 224p. pap. 19.96 (978-1-163-17377-0(0)) 2010. 226p. 39.95 (978-1-161-63856-1(3)) 2007. (ENG.). 224p. per. 24.95 (978-1-4325-4728-8(3)) Kessinger Publishing, LLC.

Balkema, Annette, text. Li Lei: Chinese Abstractionist. 2010. (ENG., Illus.). 200p. 75.00 (978-3-7757-2497-5(4)) Hatje Cantz Verlag GmbH & Co KG DEU. Dist: D.A.P./Distributed Art Pubs.

Banca della Svizzera italiana Staff, contrib. by. Free Zone - China. 2008. (ITA & ENG., Illus.). 174p. 22.00 (978-3-905829-61-7(4)) JRP Ringier Kunstverlag AG CHE. Dist: D.A.P./Distributed Art Pubs.

Bao, Yuheng. A Handbook of Chinese Art, Crafts, & Culture. 2009. (Illus.). 436p. 129.95 (978-0-7734-4897-1(7)) Mellen, Edwin Pr., The.

Bartholomew, Terese, et al. Later Chinese Jades: Ming Dynasty to Early Twentieth Century. 2007. (ENG.). 368p. 95.00 (978-0-939117-41-3(X)) Asian Art Museum of San Francisco.

Bartholomew, Terese Tse & Tsuruta, Kaz. Hidden Meanings in Chinese Art. 2012. (ENG., Illus.). 352p. pap. 45.00 (978-0-939117-37-6(1)) Asian Art Museum of San Francisco.

Beevers, David, ed. Chinese Whispers: Chinoiserie in Britain 1650-1930. 2009. (ENG., Illus.). 144p. pap. (978-0-948723-71-1(8), Royal Pavilion Libraries & Mus) Antique Collectors' Club.

Berghuis, Thomas J. Performance Art in China, 1 vol. 2007. (ENG., Illus.). 320p. 40.00 (978-988-99265-9-5(8)) Timezone 8 Ltd. HKG. Dist: D.A.P./Distributed Art Pubs.

—Writing on the Wall: Chinese New Realism & Avant-Garde in the Eighties & Nineties. 2008. (ENG., Illus.). 152p. pap. 40.00 (978-90-5662-542-9(X)) NAi Uitgevers / Publishers Stichting NLD. Dist: D.A.P./Distributed Art Pubs.

Bertholet, Ferdinand M. Concubines & Courtesans: Women in Chinese Erotic Art. 2011. (ENG., Illus.). 208p. 60.00 (978-3-7913-4629-8(6)) Prestel Publishing.

Biderman, Stan. Bullet Trains to Yaks: Glimpses into Art, Politics, & Culture in China & Tibet. 2011. 144p. pap. 24.95 (978-0-9832636-0-9(4)) Irony Pr.

Bing, Xu. Xu Bing, 1 vol. 2012. (ENG., Illus.). 280p. 85.00 (978-0-9568670-0-1(6)) Albion Editions GBR. Dist: D.A.P./Distributed Art Pubs.

Boisseau, Sylvie & Westermeyer, Frank. Sylvie Boisseau, Frank Westermeyer: Chinesisch von Vorteil. 2010. (ENG., Illus.). 80p. pap. 30.00 (978-3-86678-305-8(1)) Kerber Verlag DEU. Dist: D.A.P./Distributed Art Pubs.

Burnett, Katharine P. Dimensions of Originality: Essays on Seventeenth-century Chinese Art Criticism. 2011. (ENG., Illus.). 450p. (gr. 17). 60.00 (978-962-996-456-6(2)) Chinese Univ. of Hong Kong, The HKG. Dist: Columbia Univ. Pr.

Burris, Jon. At Work: Portraits of 25 Contemporary Chinese Artists. 2011. (ENG.). 240p. 45.00 (978-1-59265-085-9(6)) Long River Pr.

Bushell, Stephan W. Chinese Art. 2009. (Temporis Ser.). (ENG., Illus.). 255p. 39.95 (978-1-84484-559-0(1)) Parkstone International GBR. Dist: Ingram Pub. Services.

Carter, Dagny. China Magnificent: Five Thousand Years of Chinese Art. 236p. 2010. pap. 21.56 (978-1-163-16325-2(2)) 2008. 41.95 (978-1-4366-9271-7(7)) 2007. (ENG.). per. 26.95 (978-1-4325-6411-7(0)) Kessinger Publishing, LLC.

Chen, Xhingyu. Chinese Artists: New Media, 1990-2010. 2011. (Illus.). 176p. 50.00 (978-0-7643-3675-1(4)) Schiffer Publishing, Ltd.

Chin-Hsiung, Hsu. The Menzies Collection of Shange Dynasty Oracle Bones Vol. I: A Catalogue. (Illus.). 1474p. (978-0-88854-022-5(1)) BRILL.

—The Menzies Collection of Shange Dynasty Oracle Bones Vol. II: The Text. (Illus.). 1588p. (978-0-88854-023-2(X)) BRILL.

Chinese Arts Auction Records 2000: 2000 Fine Arts 1/1/99 - 12/31/99. (Illus.). 500p. pap. 59.95 (978-957-99189-9-2(6)) Chinese Art Bks. Cultural Enterprise Co., Ltd. TWN. Dist: Art Media Resources, Inc.

Chinese Arts Auction Records 2000: Antiques 1/1/99 - 12/31/99. (Illus.). 500p. pap. 59.95 (978-957-99189-8-5(8)) Chinese Art Bks. Cultural Enterprise Co., Ltd. TWN. Dist: Art Media Resources, Inc.

Chinese Paper Cutting. 2006. 103p. 14.99 (978-7-5085-0416-2(X), CHPACU) China Intercontinental Communication Ctr. CHN. Dist: China Bks. & Periodicals, Inc.

Chiu, Melissa. Chinese Contemporary Art 7 Things You Should Know. 2008. (Illus.). 112p. (978-0-9785764-3-1(8)) Art Issue Editions, AW Asia.

Chiu, Melissa, text. Breakout: Chinese Art Outside China, 1 vol. 2007. (ENG., Illus.). 256p. pap. 45.00 (978-88-8158-639-4(8)) Charta ITA. Dist: D.A.P./Distributed Art Pubs.

Chiu, Melissa & Zheng, Shengtian. Art & China's Revolution. 2008. (Illus.). 280p. 65.00 (978-0-300-14064-4(9)) Yale Univ. Pr.

Chiu, Melissa & Zheng, Shengtian. Art & China's Revolution. 2008. pap. (978-0-87848-108-8(7)) Yale Univ. Pr.

Chow, Roger & Youguang, Huo. Sparkling Splendours: The Art of Ancient Chinese Carving on Rock Crystal & Agate, The Taoshi Zhai Collection. (Illus.). 285p. 95.00 (978-962-7101-49-9(4)) Art Museum Chinese Univ. of Hong Kong DEU. Dist: Art Media Resources, Inc.

Christensen, Karen, adapted by. Kailun Zodiac Collection: Designs from China for the Year of the Snake. 2007. pap. 12.95 (978-1-933782-27-0(7)) Berkshire Publishing Group.

Chuang, Yu-Cheng. The Chinese Jingjie & the 18th-Century Western Picturesque. 2010. 268p. pap. (978-3-8383-4390-7(5)) Lambert Academic Publishing.

Chun, Ouyang. Ouyang Chun: Whales, Pirates & Good Intentions. 2011. (ENG., Illus.). 78p. 100.00 (978-988-18816-2-5(5)) Timezone 8 Ltd. HKG. Dist: D.A.P./Distributed Art Pubs.

Cindy Ho & Christine Mathieu, eds. Quentin Roosevelt's China: Ancestral Realms of the Naxi: 2011. (Illus.). 200p. 75.00 (978-0-9845190-1-9(7)) Rubin Museum of Art.

Clark, John. Asian Modernities: Chinese & Thai Art Compared, 1980-1999. 2011. (ENG., Illus.). 288p. (C). pap. 59.95 (978-0-909952-38-9(8)) Power Pubns. AUS. Dist: Univ. of Washington Pr.

—Modernities of Chinese Art. 2009. (Illus.). (978-90-04-17750-5(7)) BRILL.

Clark, Paul. The Chinese Cultural Revolution: A History. 2008. (ENG., Illus.). 368p. 85.00 (978-0-521-87515-8(3)); pap. 24.99 (978-0-521-69786-6(7)) Cambridge Univ. Pr.

Clarke, David. Chinese Art & Its Encounter with the World. 2011. 272p. (978-988-8053-84-1(1)) Hong Kong Univ. Pr.

Clarke, David. Chinese Art & Its Encounter with the World: Negotiating Alterity in Art & Its Historical Interpretation. 2011. (ENG., Illus.). 272p. (gr. 17). 40.00 (978-988-8083-06-0(6)) Hong Kong Univ. Pr. HKG. Dist: Columbia Univ. Pr.

Clunas, Craig. Art in China. 2nd ed. 2009. (Oxford History of Art Ser.). (ENG., Illus.). 272p. pap. 27.95 (978-0-19-921734-2(3)) Oxford Univ. Pr., Inc.

—Empire of Great Brightness: Visual & Material Cultures of Ming China, 1368-1644. 2012. (ENG., Illus.). 256p. pap. 55.00 (978-1-86189-360-4(4)) Reaktion Bks., Ltd. GBR. Dist: Chicago Distribution Ctr.

—Empire of Great Brightness: Visual & Material Cultures of Ming China, 1368-1644. 2007. (Illus.). 288p. 61.00 (978-0-8248-3149-3(7)) Univ. of Hawaii Pr.

Costa, Xavier, ed. Ai wei Wei: With Milk, find something everybody can Use. 2010. 40p. pap. 19.95 (978-84-92861-46-0(0)) Fundacio Mies Van Der Rohe ESP. Dist: Actar Birkhauser Distribution.

Croissant, Doris & Mostow, Joshua S., eds. Performing "Nation" Gender Politics in Literature, Theater, & the Visual Arts of China & Japan, 1880-1940. 2008. (Sinica Leidensia Ser.). (Illus.). xxxii, 448p. (978-90-04-17019-3(7)) BRILL.

Desroches, Jean-Paul, et al. Fils du Ciel. 2009. (FRE., Illus.). 231p. (978-90-6153-887-5(4)); (978-90-6153-886-8(6)) Mercatorfonds N. V.

Di'an, Fan & Ga, Zhang, eds. Synthetic Times: Media Art China 2008. 2009. (ENG., Illus.). 358p. (gr. 17). pap. 44.95 (978-0-262-51226-8(2)) MIT Pr.

Dong, Song. Song Dong: Dad & Mom, Don't Worry about Us, We Are All Well. 2011. (ENG., Illus.). 144p. 35.00 (978-0-9826789-2-3(4)) Yerba Buena Ctr. for the Arts.

Duda, Margaret B. Traditional Chinese Toggles. 2011. (ENG.). 272p. 95.00 (978-981-4260-61-9(4), Didier Millet,Csi) Continental Sales, Inc.

Eikelmann, Renate, ed. Die Wittelsbacher und das Reich der Mitte: 400 Jahre China und Bayern. Katalogbuch zur Ausstellung in München, 27.03.2009-26.07.2009, Bayerisches Nationalmuseum. 2009. (GER., Illus.). 592p. (C). 65.00 (978-3-7774-9045-8(8)) Hirmer Verlag GmbH DEU. Dist: Brown, David Bk. Co., The.

Elliott, Jeannette Shambaugh. The Odyssey of China's Imperial Art Treasures. 2007. (Samuel & Althea Stroum Bks.). (ENG., Illus.). 192p. per. 19.95 (978-0-295-98688-3(3)) Univ. of Washington Pr.

Fang, Chung-Yu. Contemporary Art in Taiwan After 1987. 2010. 88p. pap. (978-3-8383-5759-1(0)) Lambert Academic Publishing.

Fang, Jing Pei, et al. Elegance of the Qing Court: Reflections of a Dynasty Through Its Art. 2008. (978-0-936364-35-3(1)) Joslyn Art Museum.

Fang, Natalia S. Y. Empress Dowager Cixi: Images, Ideas & Reality. 2008. 304p. pap. (978-3-639-10964-1(3)) VDM Verlag Dr. Mueller e.K.

Feireiss, Kristin, et al. And: Interdisciplinary Creative Arts from China. 2007. (GER & ENG., Illus.). 71p. (978-3-937093-83-3(4)) Commerell, Hans-Jurgen, Aedes Pubs.

Feng, Shaoxie & Zhu, Xiaodan. Bai Nian Guangzhou: Feng Shaoxie You Hua Ji = Guangzhou Impression: Canton's Splendor over 200 Years: Feng Shaoxie Oil Paintings. 2010. (CHI & ENG., Illus.). 90p. (978-0-9844493-3-0(7)) International Publishing Hse. for China's Culture.

Fenollosa, Ernest F., ed. Epochs of Chinese & Japanese Art: An Outline History of East Asiatic Design, 2 vols. 2007. (Stone Bridge Classics Ser.). (ENG., Illus.). 676p. per. 18.95 (978-1-933330-26-6(0)) Stone Bridge Pr.

Fogel, Joshua. The Role of Japan in Modern Chinese Art. 2011. (ENG.). 384p. pap. 96.95 (978-0-9845909-7-1(8)) Institute for International Studies, Univ. of California, Berkeley.

Foster, Elena & Obrist, Hans Ulrich, eds. Ways Beyond Art: Ai Weiwei. 2009. (SPA & ENG., Illus.). 133p. (978-0-9559613-2-8(7)) Ivory Pr.

Fraser, Stewart E. 100 Great Chinese Posters. Date not set. 112p. 30.00 (978-0-9664202-4-1(1)) Square One Pubs.

Fuchs, Rainer, et al, texts. China: Facing Reality. 2008. (GER & ENG., Illus.). 206p. 80.00 (978-3-939738-87-9(5)) Verlag fur Moderne Kunst DEU. Dist: D.A.P./Distributed Art Pubs.

Fürlus, Eckhard, ed. Variantology 3. 2008. (ENG., Illus.). 478p. pap. 98.00 (978-3-86560-366-1(1)) Verlag der Buchhandlung Walther Konig DEU. Dist: D.A.P./Distributed Art Pubs.

Gao, Minglu. Total Modernity & the Avant-Garde in Twentieth-Century Chinese Art. 2011. (ENG., Illus.). 424p. (gr. 17). 39.95 (978-0-262-01494-6(7)) MIT Pr.

Geuna, Elena. Zhang Huan: Ashman. 2011. (ENG., Illus.). 160p. 55.00 (978-88-7179-642-0(X), Ore Cultura Srl (Acc)) Antique Collectors' Club GBR. Dist: National Bk. Network.

Groom, Simon, et al, eds. The Real Thing: Contemporary Art from China. 2008. (ENG., Illus.). 208p. pap. 40.00 (978-1-85437-713-5(2)) Tate Publishing, Ltd. GBR. Dist: Hachette Bk. Group.

Grosenick, Uta & Ochs, Alexander, eds. Yang Shaobin. 2010. (ENG, POR & GER., Illus.). 116p. 44.95 (978-3-8321-9265-5(4)) DuMont DEU. Dist: D.A.P./Distributed Art Pubs.

Grosenick, Uta & Schubbe, Caspar H., eds. China Art Book. 2010. (ENG., Illus.). 670p. per. 59.95 (978-3-8321-7769-0(8)) DuMont DEU. Dist: D.A.P./Distributed Art Pubs.

Grousset, Rene. Chinese Art & Culture. 2009. 514p. 55.95 (978-1-104-85208-5(X)) 2007. (ENG.). 512p. per. 40.95 (978-0-548-39185-3(8)) Kessinger Publishing, LLC.

Guo li gu gong bo wu yuan Staff & Guo li gu gong bo wu yuan bian ji wei yuan hui Staff, contrib. by. A Collection of the Best in Chinese Art. (CHI., Illus.). 366p. (978-957-562-197-1(2)) National Palace Museum.

Guo-Qiang, Cai. Cai Guo-Qiang: Fallen Blossoms. 2010. (ENG., Illus.). 208p. 55.00 (978-0-9724556-5-7(5)) Fabric Workshop, Inc.

Haifeng, Ni. Ni Haifeng: Para-Production. 2009. (ENG., Illus.). 112p. pap. 20.00 (978-988-18033-5-1(7)) Timezone 8 Ltd. HKG. Dist: D.A.P./Distributed Art Pubs.

—Ni Haifeng: the Return of the Shreds. 2008. (ENG., Illus.). 80p. pap. 29.95 (978-90-71655-22-7(9)) Valiz NLD. Dist: D.A.P./Distributed Art Pubs.

Han, Xin. Zi Jin Cheng Jian Zheng, 2 vols. 2009. (CHI., Illus.). 434p. (978-7-80168-490-5(7)) Study Publishing Hse.

Hang, Jian & Guo, Qiuhui. Chinese Arts & Crafts. 3rd ed. 2012. (Introductions to Chinese Culture Ser.). (ENG., Illus.). 202p. pap. 19.99 (978-0-521-18655-1(2)) Cambridge Univ. Pr.

Hannes, Nick. Red Journey. 2010. (ENG., Illus.). 144p. 50.00 (978-90-209-8402-6(0)) Lannoo Pubs./Racine.

Hanru, Hou, contrib. by. China Onward: The Estella Collection: Chinese Contemporary Art, 1996-2006, 1 vol. 2007. (ENG., Illus.). 468p. 85.00 (978-87-91607-38-7(8)) Louisana DNK. Dist: D.A.P./Distributed Art Pubs.

Hao, Lu, ed. See a World in Grain of Sand. 2010. (ENG., Illus.). 168p. 50.00 (978-7-5006-8730-6(3)) China Youth Publishing Hse. CHN. Dist: D.A.P./Distributed Art Pubs.

Heathfield, Adrian, et al. Out of Now: The Lifeworks of Tehching Hsieh. 2008. (ENG., Illus.). 384p. (gr. 17). 49.95 (978-0-262-01255-3(3)) MIT Pr.

Holding, Julie. Hau Pei Jen: Bold Horizons in Ink & Color. 2010. 96p. pap. 32.50 (978-1-4490-9679-3(4)) AuthorHouse.

Hu, Philip K. Later Chinese Bronzes: The Saint Louis Art Museum & Robert E. Kresko Collections. 2008. (Illus.). 208p. 59.95 (978-0-89178-091-5(2)) St. Louis Art Museum.

—Later Chinese Bronzes: The Saint Louis Art Museum & Robert E. Kresko Collections. Steiner, Mary Ann, ed. 2008. (ENG & CHI., Illus.). 208p. pap. 39.95 (978-0-89178-092-2(0)) St. Louis Art Museum.

Huang, Quanxin. Sourcebook of Chinese Art & Design Motifs. 2012. (ENG.). 250p. pap. 24.95 (978-1-59265-094-1(5)) Long River Pr.

Huang, Wenya & Cui, Kaixuan. 798: Inside China's Art Zone. 2010. (ENG.). 260p. pap. 24.95 (978-1-59265-084-2(8)) Long River Pr.

Huber, Jorg & Zhao, Chuan. A New Thoughtfulness in Contemporary China: Critical Voices in Art & Aesthetics. 2011. (ENG., Illus.). 232p. pap. 39.95 (978-3-8376-1665-1(7)) Transcript Verlag DEU. Dist: Transaction Pubs.

Huber, Jorg Huber & Zhao, Chuan, eds. A New Thoughtfulness in Contemporary China: Critical Voices in Art & Aesthetics. 2011. 250p. pap. (978-988-8083-37-4(6)) Hong Kong Univ. Pr.

Hung, Wu. Displacement: The Three Gorges Dam & Contemporary Chinese Art. 2008. (Illus.). 160p. pap. 30.00 (978-0-935573-46-6(1)) Univ. of Chicago, David & Alfred Smart Museum.

Hung, Wu, ed. Re-Imagining the Real. 2011. (ENG., Illus.). 224p. pap. 40.00 (978-988-18816-1-8(7)) Timezone 8 Ltd. HKG. Dist: D.A.P./Distributed Art Pubs.

Hung, Wu, ed. & text. Hung Liu: Great Granary. 2011. (ENG., Illus.). 220p. 50.00 (978-988-18907-3-3(X)) Timezone 8 Ltd. HKG. Dist: D.A.P./Distributed Art Pubs.

Hung, Wu, text. Making History: Wu Hung on Contemporary Art. 2009. (ENG., Illus.). 278p. 50.00 (978-988-99617-0-1(9)) Timezone 8 Ltd. HKG. Dist: D.A.P./Distributed Art Pubs.

Hung, Wu & Wang, Peggy, eds. Contemporary Chinese Art: Primary Documents. 2010. (ENG., Illus.). 464p. pap. 40.00 (978-0-8223-4943-3(4)) Duke Univ. Pr.

Hungs, Wu. Stroy of Ruins - Presence & Absence in Chinese Visual Art. 2012. (ENG., Illus.). 296p. (C). 60.00 (978-0-691-15502-9(X)) Princeton Univ. Pr.

Jeffri, Joan & Ding, Yu. Respect for Art: Visual Arts Administration & Management in China & the United States. 2007. 327p. per. (978-7-80198-664-1(4)) Intellectual Property Publishing Hse.

Jiagang, Chen, photos by. Chen Jiagang: the Great Third Front. 2009. (ENG., Illus.). 182p. 75.00 (978-988-17522-2-2(1)) Timezone 8 Ltd. HKG. Dist: D.A.P./Distributed Art Pubs.

Jiang, Joshua, ed. Burden or Legacy: From the Chinese Cultural Revolution to Contemporary Art. 2007. (ENG., Illus.). 172p. (gr. 17). 70.00 (978-962-209-869-5(X)); per. 45.00 (978-962-209-870-1(3)) Hong Kong Univ. Pr. HKG. Dist: Columbia Univ. Pr.

Jiehong, Jiang H. Red: China's Cultural Revolution. 2011. (ENG., Illus.). 252p. 59.95 (978-0-224-08781-0(9)) Random Hse. GBR. Dist: Independent Pubs. Group.

Kang, Yuan. Taiwan Bo Li Xin Jing Jie: Tai Ming Jiang Yu Taiwan Bo Li Guan. 2010. (CHI., Illus.). 183p. (978-986-177-346-9(0)) How Do Publishing Inc.

Ke, Chen. Chen Ke: Hard-Boiled Wonderland & the End of the World. 2011. (ENG., Illus.). 108p. pap. 30.00 (978-988-18906-6-5(7)) Timezone 8 Ltd. HKG. Dist: D.A.P./Distributed Art Pubs.

Kelley, Jeff. Half-Life of a Dream: Contemporary Chinese Art from the Logan Collection. 2008. (Illus.). 144p. 40.00 (978-0-520-25779-5(0)) Univ. of California Pr.

Kelley, Jeff & Tsuruta, Kaz. Rocks into Gold: Zhan Wang - Sculptures from the Sierra. 2008. (ENG.). 88p. pap. 24.95 (978-0-939117-45-1(2)) Asian Art Museum of San Francisco.

Kikuchi, Yuko. Refracted Modernity: Visual Culture & Identity in Colonial Taiwan. 2007. (Illus.). 285p. 62.00 (978-0-8248-3050-2(4)) Univ. of Hawaii Pr.

King, Richard, ed. Art in Turmoil: The Chinese Cultural Revolution, 1966-76. 2010. (ENG., Illus.). 318p. pap. 35.95 (978-0-7748-1543-7(4)) UBC Pr. CAN. Dist: Univ. of Washington Pr.

Knight, Michael & Chan, Dany. Shanghai: Art of the City. 2010. (ENG., Illus.). 300p. 49.00 (978-0-939117-52-9(5)) Asian Art Museum of San Francisco.

Kovskaya, Maya, ed. & intro. China under Construction: Contemporary Art from the People's Republic, 1 vol. 2008. (ENG., Illus.). 140p. pap. 42.00 (978-0-9798109-1-6(4)) Futurista Arts.

Kuo, Jason C. Perspectives on Connoisseurship of Chinese Painting. 2008. 236p. 34.00 (978-0-9800814-7-3(5)) New Academia Publishing, LLC.

Landsberger, Stefan. Chinese Posters: The Iish-Landsberger Collection. 2009. (Illus.). 286p. pap. 24.95 (978-3-7913-4389-1(0)) Prestel Publishing.

Lange, Amanda E. Chinese Export Art at Historic Deerfield. 2006. (ENG., Illus.). 272p. 65.00 (978-0-9666769-4-5(7)) Historic Deerfield Inc.

Lee, Hui-Shu. Empresses, Art, & Agency in Song Dynasty China. 2010. (ENG., Illus.). 336p. 65.00 (978-0-295-98963-1(7)) Univ. of Washington Pr.

Lee, Sonya S. Surviving Nirvana: Death of the Buddha in Chinese Visual Culture. 2010. (CHI., Illus.). 372p. (978-988-220-744-8(8)) Hong Kong Univ. Pr.

—Surviving Nirvana: Death of the Buddha in Chinese Visual Culture. 2010. (ENG., Illus.). 372p. (gr. 17). 55.00 (978-962-209-125-2(3)) Hong Kong Univ. Pr. HKG. Dist: Columbia Univ. Pr.

Lei, Han, photos by. Han Lei: in Between. 2011. (ENG., Illus.). 100p. 40.00 (978-988-18907-4-0(8)) Timezone 8 Ltd. HKG. Dist: D.A.P./Distributed Art Pubs.

Lei, Hong, illus. Hong Lei: Chinese Artists of Today: The Red Should Languish & Green Must Grow, 1 vol. 2008. (ENG.). 213p. 90.00 (978-7-5410-2991-2(2)) Timezone 8 Ltd. HKG. Dist: D.A.P./Distributed Art Pubs.

Lei Lei, Qu. The Simple Art of Chinese Brush Painting: Create Your Own Oriental Flowers, Plants, & Birds for Joy & Harmony. 2008. (ENG., Illus.). 128p. pap. 14.95 (978-1-4027-5391-6(8)) Sterling Publishing Co., Inc.

Leung, Angela Ki Che. Leprosy in China: A History. 2008. (Studies of the Weatherhead East Asian Institute, Columbia University Ser.). (ENG., Illus.). 392p. (gr. 17). 55.00 (978-0-231-12300-6(0)) Columbia Univ. Pr.

Li, Qiang. Sha Hai Xie Ying. 2009. (CHI., Illus.). 188p. (978-7-5601-4590-7(6)) Jilin Univ. Pr.

Li, Shan. Reading. Yu, Yu Christina, tr. 2006. (Illus.). 125p. pap. 20.00 (978-0-9787666-1-0(X)) Chambers Fine Art LLC.

Li, Song. Chinese Bronze Ware. 3rd ed. 2011. (Introductions to Chinese Culture Ser.). (ENG., Illus.). 164p. pap. 19.99 *(978-0-521-18685-8(4))* Cambridge Univ. Pr.

Liang, Jiang. Zhongguo Mei Shu Jian Cang Shi Gao: Aoutline [sic] History of the Chinese Art Appreciation & Collection. 2009. (CHI., Illus.). 339p. *(978-7-5010-2904-4(0))* Cultural Relics Publishing Hse.

Libin, Liu, et al, eds. Visible/Invisible, 1 vol. 2008. (ENG., Illus.). 240p. 80.00 *(978-988-99265-7-1(1))* Timezone 8 Ltd. HKG. Dist: D.A.P./Distributed Art Pubs.

Lin, Xiaoping. Children of Marx & Coca-Cola: Chinese Avant-Garde Art & Independent Cinema. 2009. (Illus.). 312p. (C). 47.00 *(978-0-8248-3336-7(8))* Univ. of Hawaii Pr.

Ling, Jian. Ling Jian: Moon in Glass. 2011. (ENG., Illus.). 104p. pap. 30.00 ***(978-988-19912-5-6(0))*** Timezone 8 Ltd. HKG. Dist: D.A.P./Distributed Art Pubs.

Liu, Cary Y. & Richard, Naomi Noble, eds. Rethinking the Wu Family Shrines & Han China: Ideals, Practices, & Problems. 2008. (Illus.). 448p. pap. 35.00 *(978-0-943012-48-3(1))* Princeton Univ. Art Museum.

Liu, Cary Y., et al. Rethinking Recarving: Ideals, Practices, & Problems of the Wu Family Shrines & Han China. 2008. (ENG., Illus.). 384p. pap. 60.00 *(978-0-300-13704-0(4))* Yale Univ. Pr.

Liu, Yang, ed. Thunderbolt Illustration. 2009. (ENG., Illus.). 340p. pap. 65.00 *(978-988-18078-1-6(5))* Azur Corp. JPN. Dist: Antique Collectors' Club.

Lonergan, Lei-Seu. The Great Paper Toy Book. 2009. (Illus.). 161p. 91.99 *(978-1-4363-9147-4(4))* Xlibris Corp.

Lü, Peng. Zhongguo Dang Dai Yi Shu de Li Shi Jin Cheng Yu Shi Chang Hua Qu Shi. 2010. (CHI.). *(978-7-301-16243-9(X))* Beijing University Pr.

Lu, Shengzhong. Square Earth, Round Heaven. 2007. (CHI & ENG., Illus.). 128p. pap. 40.00 *(978-0-9787666-4-1(4))* Chambers Fine Art LLC.

Lu, Wensheng & Murray, Julia K. Confucius. Lee Barrett, J. May, ed. 2010. (Illus.). 200p. pap. *(978-0-9774054-5-9(1))* China Institute Gallery, China Institute in America.

Mackenzie, Colin. Masterworks of Chinese Art: The Nelson-Atkins Museum of Art, 1 vol. 2011. (ENG., Illus.). 104p. 24.95 ***(978-0-615-49882-0(X))*** Nelson-Atkins Museum of Art, The.

Mao, Christophe, frwd. The Rock Touring Around Great Britain. 2007. (CHI & ENG., Illus.). 64p. pap. 20.00 *(978-0-9787666-7-2(9))* Chambers Fine Art LLC.

Martynova, Tamara & Xu, Mingtang. Zhong Yuan Qigong: First stage of Ascent. 2009. 484p. pap. 29.95 *(978-0-595-46628-3(1))* iUniverse, Inc.

Mason, Charles. Spinach Green & Mutton-fat White: Chinese Jades of the Qing Dynasty (1644-1911) 2006. per. 24.95 *(978-0-9762552-1-5(9))* Harn Museum of Art.

Maudsley, Catherine. Art & Imitation in China. 2006. (ENG.). 350p. (gr. 17). 75.00 ***(978-962-7287-51-3(2))*** Hong Kong Univ. Pr. HKG. Dist: Columbia Univ. Pr.

McElney, Brian S. Inaugural Exhibition Catalog of the Museum of East Asian Art. (Illus.). 281p. 75.00 *(978-1-897734-00-1(X))* Museum of East Asian Art GBR. Dist: Art Media Resources, Inc.

Meier, Simon. Chinese Youth Identities in Cao Fei's Storage Box , Fresh & Cosplayers. 2011. 60p. pap. ***(978-3-640-64098-0(5))*** Hammer, Patrick, Tanja Hammer, Matthias Knoop, Julius Mittenzwei, Georg Steinbach u. Michael Teltscher. GRIN Verlag GbR.

Metrick-Chen, Lenore. Collecting Objects/Excluding People: Chinese Subjects & American Visual Culture, 1830-1900. 2012. (ENG.). 320p. 85.00 ***(978-1-4384-4325-6(0))*** State Univ. of New York Pr.

Michaelson, Carol & Portal, Jane. Chinese Art in Detail. 2006. (Art in Detail Ser.). (Illus.). 144p. 22.95 *(978-0-674-02389-5(7))* Harvard Univ. Pr.

Min, Anchee, et al. Chinese Propaganda Posters: 25 Jahre TASCHEN. 2011. (25 Ser.). (ENG., Illus.). 320p. 14.99 ***(978-3-8365-3108-5(9))*** TASCHEN DEU. Dist: Ingram Pub. Services.

Minick, Scott & Ping, Jiao. Chinese Graphic Design in the Twentieth Century. 2010. (ENG., Illus.). 160p. pap. 19.95 *(978-0-500-28873-3(9)*, 528873) Thames & Hudson.

Morin, France & Farmer, John, eds. The Quiet in the Land: Luang Prabang, Laos. 2010. (ENG., Illus.). 240p. 45.00 *(978-0-9841667-0-1(X))* Quiet in the Land Inc., The.

Mukerji, Betty-Lou. Chinese Sewing Baskets. 2008. 212p. pap. 54.49 *(978-1-4389-1523-4(3))* AuthorHouse.

Munsterberg, Hugo. A Short History of Chinese Art. *(978-0-8022-1170-5(4))* Philosophical Library, Inc.

Neo Chinese Art. 2009. 255p. *(978-7-5381-5454-2(X))* Page One Publishing.

Noe, Christoph, et al. Young Chinese Artists: The Next Generation. 2nd ed. 2010. (Illus.). 296p. pap. 29.95 *(978-3-7913-5060-8(9))* Prestel Publishing.

Obrist, Hans Ulrich, text. No Snow on the Broken Bridge Film & Video Installations, 1 vol. 2007. (ENG., Illus.). 180p. pap. 35.00 *(978-3-905701-85-2(5))* JRP Ringier Kunstverlag AG CHE. Dist: D.A.P./Distributed Art Pubs.

Osselt, Estelle Niklès Van. Five Blessings: Coded Messages in Chinese Art. 2011. (ENG., Illus.). 224p. pap. 55.00 *(978-88-7439-557-6(4))* 5 Continents ITA. Dist: Hachette Bk. Group.

Pakesch, Peter. China Welcomes You. 2008. (GER & ENG., Illus.). 175p. pap. 49.95 *(978-3-86560-271-8(1))* Verlag der Buchhandlung Walther Konig DEU. Dist: D.A.P./Distributed Art Pubs.

Pan, An-Yi. Painting Faith: Li Gonglin & Northern Song Buddhist Culture. 2007. (Sinica Leidensia Ser.). (Illus.). 396p. *(978-90-04-16061-3(2))* BRILL.

Pan, Lynn. Shanghai Style: Art & Design Between the Wars. 2008. (ENG.). 312p. pap. 24.95 *(978-1-59265-078-1(3))* Long River Pr.

Pang, Laikwan. The Distorting Mirror: Visual Modernity in China. 2007. (Illus.). 280p. 57.00 *(978-0-8248-3093-9(8))* Univ. of Hawaii Pr.

Pearce, Nicholas & Steuber, Jason, eds. Original Intentions: Essays on Production, Reproduction, & Interpretation in the Arts of China. 2012. (ENG., Illus.). 320p. 60.00 ***(978-0-8130-3972-5(X))*** Univ. Pr. of Florida.

Peili, Zhang. Zhang Peili: Chinese Contemporary Art Awards 2010. 2012. (ENG., Illus.). 160p. 40.00 ***(978-988-19912-7-0(7))*** Timezone 8 Ltd. HKG. Dist: D.A.P./Distributed Art Pubs.

Peng, Chi, photos by. Chi Peng: Me, Myself & I. 2011. (ENG., Illus.). 152p. 55.00 ***(978-3-7757-3132-4(6))*** Hatje Cantz Verlag GmbH & Co KG DEU. Dist: D.A.P./Distributed Art Pubs.

Peng, Lu. From San Servolo to Amalfi: Notes of a Chinese Curator in Venice. 2011. (CHI & ENG., Illus.). 144p. pap. 34.95 ***(978-88-8158-818-3(8))*** Charta ITA. Dist: D.A.P./Distributed Art Pubs.

—A History of Art in 20th Century China. 2010. (ENG., Illus.). 1288p. 180.00 *(978-88-8158-779-7(3))* Charta ITA. Dist: D.A.P./Distributed Art Pubs.

—A Pocket History of 20th-Century Chinese Art. 2011. (ENG., Illus.). 1124p. pap. 59.95 *(978-88-8158-796-4(3))* Charta ITA. Dist: D.A.P./Distributed Art Pubs.

Peng, Lu. Pure Views: Remote from Streams & Mountains: New Painting from China. 2011. (ENG., Illus.). 208p. pap. 55.00 ***(978-88-8158-821-3(8))*** Charta ITA. Dist: D.A.P./Distributed Art Pubs.

Peng, Min. Fluid Bridge. 2008. 100p. pap. *(978-3-639-08185-5(4))* VDM Verlag Dr. Mueller e.K.

Phillips, Christopher. Shanghai Kaleidoscope. 2008. (ENG., Illus.). 144p. 59.99 *(978-0-88854-460-5(X))*; pap. 34.99 *(978-0-88854-461-2(8))* Royal Ontario Museum CAN. Dist: Univ. of Toronto Pr.

Piccus, Robert Peter. Sacred & Secular: The Piccus Collection of Tibetan Rugs. 2011. ***(978-1-932476-55-2(5))*** Serindia Pubns., Inc.

Pollack, Barbara, text. The Wild, Wild East: an American Art Critic's Adventures in China. 2010. (ENG., Illus.). 208p. pap. 24.95 *(978-988-18034-9-8(7))* Timezone 8 Ltd. HKG. Dist: D.A.P./Distributed Art Pubs.

Powers, Martin J. Pattern & Person: Ornament, Society, & Self in Classical China. 2006. (Harvard East Asian Monographs: 262). (Illus.). 424p. 49.95 *(978-0-674-02139-6(8))* Harvard Univ., Asia Ctr.

Qi, Zhu & Lei, Cheng, eds. Beijing 798 Now: Changing Art, Architecture & Society in China. 2009. (CHI & ENG., Illus.). 400p. pap. 60.00 *(978-988-17521-9-2(1))* Timezone 8 Ltd. HKG. Dist: D.A.P./Distributed Art Pubs.

Quette, Béatrice, ed. Cloisonne: Chinese Enamels from the Yuan, Ming & Qing Dynasties. 2011. (ENG., Illus.). 368p. 80.00 *(978-0-300-16720-7(2))*, Yale Univ. Pr.

Randall, Christopher. The Brush & the Stone: The Dr. Dean Edell Collection of Chinese Art. (Illus.). 142p. 85.00 *(978-1-878529-54-1(4))* Art Media Resources, Inc.

Ravenal, John B., et al. Xu Bing: Tobacco Project, Duke/Shanghai/Virginia, 1999-2011. Tomii, Reiko, ed. 2011. (ENG., Illus.). 144p. (C). (gr. 13-17). pap. 35.00 *(978-0-917046-96-4(X))* Univ. Pr. of Virginia.

Reifenscheid, Beate, ed. China's Revision: Focus Beijing. 2009. (CHI, GER & ENG., Illus.). 144p. 39.95 *(978-3-7913-4274-0(6))* Prestel Publishing.

Ren, David. The Imperial Rocks. (Illus.). 299p. 110.00 *(978-7-108-01237-1(5))* SDX Joint Publishing, Co. CHN. Dist: Art Media Resources, Inc.

Ren, Liu, Illus. Liu Ren's Photographs, 1 vol. 2008. (ENG.). 48p. pap. 16.00 *(978-988-99609-1-9(5))* Timezone 8 Ltd. HKG. Dist: D.A.P./Distributed Art Pubs.

Rhie. Early Buddhist Art of China & Central Asia, Volume III: The Western Ch'in in Kansu in the Sixteen Kingdoms Period & Inter-relationships with the Buddhist Art of Gandhāra. 2010. (Handbook of Oriental Studies. Section 4 China Ser.). 1032p. *(978-90-04-18400-8(7))* BRILL.

Ribas, Joao & Vine, Richard. Sun Xun: Shock of Time. 2009. pap. 10.00 *(978-0-942324-45-7(5))* Drawing Ctr.

Roberts, Claire. Photography & China. 2012. (Reaktion Books - Exposures Ser.). (Illus.). 192p. pap. 29.95 ***(978-1-86189-911-8(4))*** Reaktion Bks., Ltd. GBR. Dist: Chicago Distribution Ctr.

Rujivacharakul, Vimalin. Collecting China: The World, China, & a Short History of Collecting. (Illus.). 2011. (ENG.). 240p. 65.00 *(978-1-61149-006-0(5))* 2010. 210p. *(978-0-87413-096-6(4))* Univ. of Delaware Pr.

Saatchi Gallery Staff. The Revolution Continues: New Art from China. 2008. (ENG., Illus.). 272p. 29.95 *(978-0-8478-3206-4(6))* Rizzoli International Pubns., Inc.

Sabattini, Mario & Celli, Nicoletta. The Treasures of Imperial Beijing. 2007. (ENG., Illus.). 312p. 45.00 *(978-88-544-0234-8(6)*, White Star) Rizzoli International Pubns., Inc.

Salmony, Alfred. Sino-Siberian Art in the Collection of C. T. Loo. 2006. (ENG., Illus.). 119p. 70.00 *(978-1-878529-36-7(6))* Orchid Pr. THA. Dist: National Bk. Network.

Sans, Jérôme, ed. Art China Now: And Tomorrow. 2012. (ENG., Illus.). 528p. pap. 50.00 ***(978-988-19912-1-8(8))*** Timezone 8 Ltd. HKG. Dist: D.A.P./Distributed Art Pubs.

Sans, Jerome, text. Breaking Forecast. 2011. (ENG., Illus.). 226p. pap. 35.00 *(978-988-18816-7-0(6))* Timezone 8 Ltd. HKG. Dist: D.A.P./Distributed Art Pubs.

Sen, He. He Sen: Paintings. 2010. (ENG., Illus.). 160p. 50.00 *(978-88-6208-137-5(5))* Damiani ITA. Dist: D.A.P./Distributed Art Pubs.

Sensabaugh, David Ake. The Scholar as Collector: Chinese Art at Yale. 2006. (ENG., Illus.). 48p. pap. 18.50 *(978-0-89467-958-2(9))* Yale Univ. Art Gallery.

Shao, Xuehai. Xian Qin Yi Shu Shi. 2010. (Illus.). *(978-7-80713-881-5(5))* Shandong Pictorial Publishing Hse.

Shen, Jiawei. Lan Wang. 2010. 350p. 85.00 *(978-1-876957-14-8(X))* Wild Peony Bk. Pubs. Pty., Ltd. AUS. Dist: Univ. of Hawaii Pr.

Shi, Jinsong. Ne Zha 2008: A Child Boutique. 2008. (CHI., Illus.). 102p. pap. 30.00 *(978-0-9787666-9-6(5))* Chambers Fine Art LLC.

Shiming, Gao. Liu Wei: 2006-2007. Boers, Waling, ed. 2009. (ENG., Illus.). 139p. 50.00 *(978-988-17143-2-9(X))* Timezone 8 Ltd. HKG. Dist: D.A.P./Distributed Art Pubs.

Silbergeld, Jerome & Ching, Dora C. Articulations - Undefining Chinese Contemporary Art. 2010. (Publications of the Department of Art & Archaeology, Princeton University Ser.). (ENG., Illus.). 320p. (C). pap. 29.95 *(978-0-691-14860-1(0))* Princeton Univ. Pr.

Silbergeld, Jerome, et al. Outside In: Chinese x American x Contemporary Art. 2009. (ENG., Illus.). 304p. 60.00 *(978-0-300-12208-4(X))* Yale Univ. Pr.

Silvrants, Els, ed. Jean Bernard Koeman: Everything Beautiful Is Far Away. 2009. (ENG., Illus.). 144p. 45.00 *(978-988-17144-9-7(4))* Timezone 8 Ltd. HKG. Dist: D.A.P./Distributed Art Pubs.

Smith, Karen. Nine Lives: The Birth of Avant-Garde Art in New China: the Updated Edition. 2008. (Illus.). 449p. pap. 50.00 *(978-0-9785764-4-8(6))* Art Issue Editions, AW Asia.

Smith, Karen, ed. Nine Lives: the Birth of Avant-Garde Art in New China. 2008. (ENG., Illus.). 473p. pap. 50.00 *(978-988-17143-3-6(8))* Timezone 8 Ltd. HKG. Dist: D.A.P./Distributed Art Pubs.

Starr, Kenneth. Black Tigers: A Grammar of Chinese Rubbings. 2008. (ENG., Illus.). 320p. pap. 40.00 *(978-0-295-98811-5(8))* Univ. of Washington Pr.

Steuber, Jason, ed. China: 3000 Years of Art & Literature. 2008. (ENG., Illus.). 240p. 60.00 *(978-1-59962-030-5(8)*, Welcome Bks.) Welcome Enterprises, Inc.

Strober, Eva. Symbols on Chinese Porcelain: 10,000 x Happiness. 2011. (ENG., Illus.). 240p. 95.00 *(978-3-89790-350-0(4))* Arnoldsche Art Pubs. DEU. Dist: Antique Collectors' Club.

Sullivan, Michael. The Arts of China. 5th rev. exp. ed. 2009. (Illus.). 352p. pap. 39.95 *(978-0-520-25569-2(0))* Univ. of California Pr.

Sun, Dingpu, et al. Zi You Sui Jing: Dingpu Zi Sha Hu Zuo Pin Ji. 2008. (CHI., Illus.). 27p. *(978-7-5410-3577-7(7))* Sichuan Fine Arts Publishing Hse.

Sun, Xiaogang. Wenshu Pu Sa Tu Xiang Xue Yan Jiu: A Bodhisattva of Wisdom: Iconography Study. 2007. (CHI., Illus.). 264p. *(978-7-80588-590-2(7))* Gansu People's Fine Arts Publishing Hse.

Tamayo, Museo. Felicidad Indecible. 2006. 83p. pap. 37.00 *(978-968-5979-09-2(X))* Trucatriche.

Tambling, Jeremy & Lo, Louis. Walking Macao, Reading the Baroque. 2009. (ENG., Illus.). 272p. (gr. 17). 60.00 *(978-962-209-937-1(8))*; pap. 28.00 *(978-962-209-938-8(6))* Hong Kong Univ. Pr. HKG. Dist: Columbia Univ. Pr.

Thomas Cole. Patterns of Life: The Art of Tibetan Carpets. 2011. 40.00 *(978-0-9845190-0-2(9))* Rubin Museum of Art.

Tinari, Philip. Artists in China. 2011. (Illus.). 448p. 50.00 ***(978-1-905216-38-3(6))*** Verbavolantedizioni ITA. Dist: Ingram Pub. Services.

Tongcheng Shi bo wu guan Staff & Tongcheng Shi wen wu guan li suo Staff, contrib. by. Tongcheng Wen Wu Jing Hua, 2 vols. 2009. (CHI., Illus.). 371p. *(978-7-5398-1292-2(3))* Anhui Fine Arts Publishing Hse.

Tsao, Hsingyuan & Ames, Roger T., eds. Xu Bing & Contemporary Chinese Art: Cultural & Philosophical Reflections. 2011. (SUNY series in Chinese Philosophy & Culture Ser.). (Illus.). 240p. 75.00 *(978-1-4384-3791-0(9,)*; pap. 24.95 *(978-1-4384-3790-3(0))* State Univ. of New York Pr.

Tseng, Lillian Lan-ying. Picturing Heaven in Early China. 2011. (Harvard East Asian Monographs). (ENG., Illus.). 480p. 69.95 *(978-0-674-06069-2(5))* Harvard Univ., Asia Ctr.

Tuymans, Luc & Weiwei, Ai, eds. The State of Things - Brussels/Beijing. 2010. (ENG., Illus.). 256p. *(978-90-209-8683-9(X)*, Lannoo Pubs. (Acc)) Antique Collectors' Club.

Uhlig, Helmut. On the Path to Enlightenment: The Berti Aschmann Foundation of Tibetan Art at the Museum Rietberg Zürich. 2011. (ENG., Illus.). 226p. (C). 50.00 *(978-3-907070-60-4(7))* Holberton, Paul Publishing GBR. Dist: Univ. of Washington Pr.

Van Assche, Annie, ed. The Monk & the Demon: Contemporary Chinese Art. 2008. (ENG., Illus.). 184p. 39.00 *(978-88-7439-151-6(X))* 5 Continents ITA. Dist: Hachette Bk. Group.

Van Gulik, Robert H., tr. Mi Fu on Ink-Stones. 2006. (CHI & ENG., Illus.). 84p. 35.00 *(978-974-524-083-4(4))* Orchid Pr. THA. Dist: National Bk. Network.

Verlag, Hirmer & Hirmer Verlag. Tibet: Kloester oeffnen ihre Schatzkammern. 2006. (GER., Illus.). 664p. (C). pap. 63.00 *(978-3-7774-3115-4(X))* Hirmer Verlag GmbH DEU. Dist: Brown, David Bk. Co., The.

Vigneron, Frank. I Like Hong Kong... Art & Deterritorialization. 2010. (ENG., Illus.). 528p. (gr. 17). 60.00 *(978-962-996-431-3(7))* Chinese Univ. of Hong Kong, The HKG. Dist: Columbia Univ. Pr.

Vine, Richard. New China, New Art: (Revised & Expanded Edition) 2nd rev. ed. 2011. (ENG., Illus.). 256p. pap. 39.95 ***(978-3-7913-4550-5(8))*** Prestel Publishing.

Vine, Richard. New China New Art: Zhongguo Dang Dai Yi Shu. 2008. (Illus.). 256p. 60.00 *(978-3-7913-3942-9(7))* Prestel Publishing.

Wang, Jianwei. Dilemma- Three Way Fork in the Road. 2007. (ENG & CHI., Illus.). 125p. pap. 40.00 *(978-0-9787666-5-8(2))* Chambers Fine Art LLC.

Wang, Tianhua. Qiang Xiu Jing Pin Tu Yang Ji = Qiang Embroidery. 2009. (Illus.). 207p. *(978-7-5410-3848-8(2))* Sichuan Fine Arts Publishing Hse.

Wang, Ziyi. Zhong Ri Tao Ci Cha Qi Wen Hua Bi Jiao Yan Jiu: Comparative Study of Ceramic Tea Ware Culture in China & Japan. 2010. (CHI., Illus.). *(978-7-01-008507-4(2))* People's Publishing Hse., The.

Watt, James C. Y. The World of Khubilai Khan: Chinese Art in the Yuan Dynasty. 2010. (Illus.). xviii, 342p. 65.00 ***(978-1-58839-402-6(6))*** Metropolitan Museum of Art, The.

Watt, James C. Y., ed. The World of Khubilai Khan: Chinese Art in the Yuan Dynasty. 2010. (ENG., Illus.). 360p. 65.00 *(978-0-300-16656-9(7))* Yale Univ. Pr.

Weidu, Ma. Classical Chinese Doors & Windows. 2006. (Illus.). 386p. 195.00 *(978-3-211-32191-1(8)*, 3211321918) Springer Wien AUT. Dist: Springer.

Weiwei, Ai & Li, Pi, eds. In Production Mode, Contemporary Art in China. 2009. (ENG., Illus.). 276p. pap. 50.00 *(978-988-17522-9-1(9))* Timezone 8 Ltd. HKG. Dist: D.A.P./Distributed Art Pubs.

Weiwei, Ai & Obrist, Hans Ulrich. Ai Weiwei Speaks. 2011. (ENG., Illus.). 112p. pap. 9.99 ***(978-0-241-95754-7(0)***, Penguin Global) Penguin Group (USA) Inc.

Weiwei, Ai, et al. Art & Cultural Policy in China: A Conversation between Ai Weiwei, Uli Sigg & Yung Ho Chang, moderated by Peter Pakesch. 2009. (GER & ENG., Illus.). 132p. pap. 39.95 *(978-3-211-89240-4(0))* Springer Wien AUT. Dist: Actar Birkhauser Distribution.

Welch, Patricia Bjaaland. Chinese Art: A Guide to Motifs & Visual Imagery. 2008. (ENG., Illus.). 320p. 49.95 *(978-0-8048-3864-1(X))* Tuttle Publishing.

Weller, Alan. Chinese Vector Designs. 2009. (Dover Pictura Electronic Clip Art Ser.). (ENG.). 128p. pap. 49.95 *(978-0-486-99043-9(5))* Dover Pubns., Inc.

Wen, Zhu. Chinese Style: Interiors, Furniture, Details. 2011. (ENG., Illus.). 192p. 29.95 *(978-1-60220-007-4(6))* BetterLink Pr., Inc.

Wenbo, Chen. Chen Wenbo: Urban Verses. 2009. (ENG., Illus.). 232p. 60.00 *(978-988-17522-1-5(3))* Timezone 8 Ltd. HKG. Dist: D.A.P./Distributed Art Pubs.

Wenjun, Zhang. The Henan Museum. 2010. (ENG., Illus.). 192p. pap. 35.00 *(978-1-85759-633-5(1))* Scala, Editions FRA. Dist: National Bk. Network.

Wilson, Mark, et al. New World Order: Contemporary Installation Art & Photography from China. 2008. (ENG., Illus.). 200p. pap. 40.00 *(978-90-5662-251-0(X)*, NAi Uitgevers / Publishers Stichting NLD. Dist: D.A.P./Distributed Art Pubs.

Wroblewski, Chris. China Tattoo. 2008. (ENG., Illus.). 140p. 29.95 *(978-0-86719-698-6(X)*, Last Gasp of San Francisco.

Xia, Jifeng, frwd. Sun Jianchun: China 2006. 2011. (ENG., Illus.). 416p. pap. 20.00 *(978-988-18816-4-9(1))* Timezone 8 Ltd. HKG. Dist: D.A.P./Distributed Art Pubs.

Xi'an. Unter der gelben Erde. 2007. (GER., Illus.). 224p. (C). 34.00 ***(978-3-8053-3604-8(7))*** Zabern, Philipp von Verlag, GmbH DEU. Dist: Brown, David Bk. Co., The.

Xiaochun, Miao. Miao Xiaochun 2009 - 1999. 2010. (ENG & GER., Illus.). 198p. 55.00 *(978-3-8321-9285-3(9))* DuMont DEU. Dist: D.A.P./Distributed Art Pubs.

—Miao Xiaochun: Macromania. 2011. (ENG., Illus.). 164p. 25.00 *(978-988-18907-0-2(5))* Timezone 8 Ltd. HKG. Dist: D.A.P./Distributed Art Pubs.

Yang, Shu, ed. The Road Map of Painting. 1 vol. 2007. (ENG., Illus.). 159p. pap. 30.00 *(978-988-99264-3-9(2))* Timezone 8 Ltd. HKG. Dist: D.A.P./Distributed Art Pubs.

Yihan, Wang, ed. China International Gallery Exposition 2006, 1 vol. 2007. (ENG., Illus.). 429p. pap. 46.00 *(978-988-99015-6-1(0))* Timezone 8 Ltd. HKG. Dist: D.A.P./Distributed Art Pubs.

Yin, Wang & Zuo, Jing. Wang Yin. 2011. (ENG., Illus.). 136p. 40.00 *(978-988-18816-3-2(3))*, Timezone 8 Ltd. HKG. Dist: D.A.P./Distributed Art Pubs.

Yu, Chitfu. Chitfu Yu: Faces. 2012. (ENG., Illus.). 180p. 39.95 ***(978-0-8351-0018-2(9))***, Long River Pr.

Yu, Miao. Imagining & Inventing Shanghai. 2008. 88p. pap. *(978-3-639-05519-1(5))*, VDM Verlag Dr. Mueller e.K.

Yu, Ming. Chinese Jade. 3rd ed. 2011. (Introductions to Chinese Culture Ser.). (ENG., Illus.). 152p. pap. 19.99 ***(978-0-521-18684-1(6))*** Cambridge Univ. Pr.

Yutang, Lin. Chinese Theory of Art: Translations from the Masters of Chinese Art. 2010. (ENG.). 256p. pap. 24.95 *(978-1-84368-032-1(7))* Pallas Athene GBR. Dist: Independent Pubs. Group.

Zehou, Li. The Chinese Aesthetic Tradition. Samei, Majia Bell, tr. from CHI. 2009. 257p. *(978-0-8248-3307-7(4))* Univ. of Hawaii Pr.

Zhan, Wang. Garden Utopia. 2008. (CHI & ENG.). *(978-0-9801179-0-5(9))* Long March Space Corp.

Zhenqing, Gu, et al, eds. To Each His Own, 1 vol. Yu, Xu, tr. 2008. (ENG., Illus.). 151p. pap. 40.00 *(978-988-99264-3-4(1))* Timezone 8 Ltd. HKG. Dist: D.A.P./Distributed Art Pubs.

Zhong Biao: American Debut. 2007. pap. 20.00 *(978-0-9795141-1-1(8))* Norris, Frey Gallery.

Zhu, Zhu, et al, eds. Thirty Years of Adventures: Art & Artists From 1979. 2011. (ENG., Illus.). 792p. 75.00 ***(978-988-19912-4-9(2))*** Timezone 8 Ltd. HKG. Dist: D.A.P./Distributed Art Pubs.

Zou, Yueqin & Yan, Changyuan, compiled by. 60 Years of Chinese Art: Contemporary Art in the People's Republic of China (1949-2009) 2012. (ENG., Illus.). 280p. pap. 59.95 ***(978-1-59265-110-8(0))*** Long River Pr.

ART, CHRISTIAN

see Christian Art and Symbolism

ART, CISTERCIAN

see Cistercian Art

ART, CIVIC

see Art, Municipal; Public Art

ART, COMMERCIAL
see Commercial Art

ART, COMPUTER
see Computer Art

ART, CONCEPTUAL
see Conceptual Art

ART, CONCRETE
see Concrete Art

ART, COPTIC

Bosson, N. & Boud'hors, A., eds. Actes du huitième congrès international d'études Coptes: Paris, 28 juin - 3 Juillet 2004, 2 vols. 2007. (Orientalia Lovaniensia Analecta Ser.). (ENG.). 920p. (C). 232.00 *(978-90-429-1909-9(4))* Peeters Pubs. & Booksellers BEL. Dist: Brown, David Bk. Co., The.

Cooney, John. Late Egyptian & Coptic Art: An Introduction to the Collections in the Brooklyn Museum. 2011. 82p. 37.95 ***(978-1-258-09289-4(1))*** Literary Licensing, LLC.

Cooney, John D. & Riefstahl, Elizabeth. Pagan & Christian Egypt: Egyptian Art from the First to the Tenth Century. 2011. 198p. 42.95 ***(978-1-258-03750-5(5))*** Literary Licensing, LLC.

Eaton-Krauss, M., et al, eds. Egypt 1350 BC to Ad 1800: Art Historical & Archaeological Studies for Gawdat Gabra. 2011. (Sprachen und Kulturen des Christlichen Orients Ser.). (ENG., Illus.). 176p. (C). 100.00 ***(978-3-89500-820-7(6))*** Reichert, Ludwig Dr. DEU. Dist: Brown, David Bk. Co., The.

Gabra, Gawdat & Eaton-Krauss, Marianne. The Treasures of Coptic Art: In the Coptic Museum & Churches of Old Cairo. 2007. (ENG., Illus.). 240p. 59.95 *(978-977-424-933-4(X))* American Univ. in Cairo Pr. EGY. Dist: Oxford Univ. Pr., Inc.

Guirguis, Magdi. An Armenian Artist in Ottoman Egypt: Yuhanna Al-Armani & His Coptic Icons. 2008. (ENG., Illus.). 144p. 27.95 *(978-977-416-152-0(1))* American Univ. in Cairo Pr. EGY. Dist: Oxford Univ. Pr., Inc.

Hatch, William H. P. Three Coptic Fragments from Nitri: The Annual of the American Schools of Oriental Research V6, 1924-1925. 2011. 8p. pap. 35.95 ***(978-1-258-06071-8(X))*** Literary Licensing, LLC.

ART, COPY
see Copy Art

ART, CRETAN

Andreadaki-Vlazaki, Maria, et al, eds. From the Land of the Labyrinth: Minoan Crete, 3000-1100 B. C., 2 vols. 2008. (ENG.). 470p. (C). pap. 45.00 *(978-0-9776598-2-1(8))* Onassis, Alexander S. Public Benefit Foundation (US).

Iozzo, Mario, text. Crete. (Illus.). 160p. pap. *(978-88-8029-424-5(5))* Casa Editrice Bonechi.

ART, CUBAN

Alonso, Alejandro G. Havana Deco. 2007. 39.95 *(978-0-7937-3232-6(8))* Norton, W. W. & Co., Inc.

Alonso, Alejandro G., et al. Havana Deco. 2007. (ENG., Illus.). 192p. 39.95 *(978-0-393-73232-0(0), 73232)* Norton, W. W. & Co., Inc.

Bedia, José. Jose Bedia: A Monograph, 1 vol. Power, Kevin, ed. 2007. (SPA & ENG., Illus.). 256p. (gr. 13-18). 75.00 *(978-84-7506-615-8(1))* Turner, Ediciones S.A. ESP. Dist: D.A.P./Distributed Art Pubs.

Bettelheim, Judith & Berlo, Janet Catherine. Transcultural Pilgrim: Three Decades of Work by José Bedia, 1 vol. 2011. (ENG., Illus.). 216p. pap. 35.00 ***(978-0-9778344-7-1(6))*** Univ. of California, Los Angeles, Fowler Museum of Cultural History.

Bondil, Nathalie, ed. Cuba: Art & History from 1868 to Today. 2009. (Illus.). 368p. pap. 49.95 *(978-3-7913-4394-5(7))* Prestel Publishing.

Bronx Museum of the Arts Staff. Quisqueya Henriquez: The WORLD OUTSIDE A Survey Exhibition 1991-2007. 2007. (Illus.). 65p. per. 32.00 *(978-0-917535-00-0(6))* Bronx Museum of the Arts, The.

Campos-Pons, Maria Magdalena, et al. Maria Magdalena Campos-Pons: Everything Is Separated by Water. 2007. (ENG., Illus.). 184p. 45.00 *(978-0-300-12345-6(0))* Yale Univ. Pr.

Chicuri, Abelardo Mena, et al. Cuba Avant-Garde: Contemporary Cuban Art from the Farber Collection / Arte Contemporaneo Cubano de la Coleccion Farber. Delson, Susan, ed. Lizarraga, Felix, tr. 2007. (SPA & ENG., Illus.). 188p. pap. 29.95 *(978-0-9762552-5-3(1))* Univ. Pr. of Florida.

—Cuba Avant-Garde: Contemporary Cuban Art from the Farber Collection /Arte Contemporaneo Cubano de la Coleccion Farber. Delson, Susan, ed. Lizarraga, Felix, tr. 2007. (SPA & ENG., Illus.). 188p. 59.95 *(978-0-9762552-4-6(3))* Univ. Pr. of Florida.

Cordero, Raul. Raul Cordero. 2011. (SPA & ENG., Illus.). 220p. pap. 30.00 *(978-84-7506-842-8(1))* Turner, Ediciones S.A. ESP. Dist: D.A.P./Distributed Art Pubs.

D'Agati, Mauro. Alamar: Habana - Cuba, 1 vol. 2010. (ENG & SPA., Illus.). 156p. 75.00 *(978-3-86521-954-1(3))* Steidl, Gerhard Druckerei und Verlag DEU. Dist: Innovative Logistics.

de la Fuente, Alejandro, ed. Queloides: Race & Racism in Cuban Contemporary Art. 2011. (ENG & SPA., Illus.). 164p. pap. 40.00 *(978-0-8229-6152-9(0))* Univ. of Pittsburgh Pr.

Enwezor, Okuwi, et al. Overlapping. 2010. (ENG., Illus.). 288p. 75.00 *(978-88-8158-784-1(X))* Charta ITA. Dist: D.A.P./Distributed Art Pubs.

Esteban, Angel, ed. Madrid Habanece: Cuba y España en el Punto de Mira Transatlántico. 2011. pap. 29.80 ***(978-84-8489-576-3(9))*** Iberoamericana Vervuert Publishing Corp.

Fernandes, Sujatha. Cuba Represent! Cuban Arts, State Power, & the Making of New Revolutionary Cultures. 2006. (ENG., Illus.). 240p. 79.95 *(978-0-8223-3859-8(9))*; per. 22.95 *(978-0-8223-3891-8(2))* Duke Univ. Pr.

Gelburd, Gail. Ajiaco: Stirrings of the Cuban Soul. 2010. (ENG., Illus.). 112p. pap. 29.95 *(978-1-58465-847-4(9))* Univ. Pr. of New England.

Gracia, Jorge J. E. Identity, Memory, & Diaspora: Voices of Cuban-American Artists, Writers, & Philosophers. Bosch, Lynette M. F. & Borland, Isabel Alvarez, eds. 2009. 296p. pap. 29.95 *(978-0-7914-7318-4(X))* State Univ. of New York Pr.

—Images of Thought: Philosophical Interpretations of Carlos Estevez's Art. 2009. (SUNY series in Latin American & Iberian Thought & Culture Ser.). (Illus.). 224p. 74.50 *(978-0-7914-9379-3(2))* State Univ. of New York Pr.

Gracia, Jorge J. E., et al. Images of Thought: Philosophical Interpretations of Carlos Estevez's Art. 2009. (SUNY Series in Latin American & Iberian Thought & Culture). (Illus.). 224p. pap. 29.95 *(978-0-7914-9380-9(6))* State Univ. of New York Pr.

Hernandez, Django. Diango Hernandez: Diamonds & Stones. 2009. (ENG., Illus.). 320p. 40.00 *(978-88-6208-080-4(8))* Damiani ITA. Dist: D.A.P./Distributed Art Pubs.

Herrera, Andrea O'Reilly. Cuban Artists Across the Diaspora: Setting the Tent Against the House. 2011. (ENG., Illus.). 272p. 60.00 *(978-0-292-72392-4(X))*; pap. 24.95 *(978-0-292-72695-6(3))* Univ. of Texas Pr.

Lorz, Julienne, ed. Stop, Repair, Prepare. 2009. (GER & ENG., Illus.). 80p. 49.95 *(978-3-86560-474-3(9))* Verlag der Buchhandlung Walther Konig DEU. Dist: D.A.P./Distributed Art Pubs.

Los Carpinteros. Los Carpinteros Handwork: Constructing the World. 2011. (ENG., Illus.). 380p. 79.00 *(978-3-86560-808-6(6))* Verlag der Buchhandlung Walther Konig DEU. Dist: D.A.P./Distributed Art Pubs.

Martinez, Juan A. Maria Brito. (Ver Ser.). (Illus.). 128p. 2009. pap. 24.95 *(978-0-89551-109-6(6))* 2007. 60.00 *(978-0-89551-108-9(8))* Univ. of Minnesota Pr.

Milstein, Jeffrey. Cuba. 2010. (ENG., Illus.). 128p. 25.00 *(978-1-58093-275-2(4))* Monacelli Pr., Inc.

Mosquera, Gerardo, et al. Tania Bruguera on the Political Imaginary. 2010. (ENG., Illus.). 144p. pap. 39.95 *(978-88-8158-764-3(5))* Charta ITA. Dist: D.A.P./Distributed Art Pubs.

Ochoa Foster, Elena, ed. Drama Turquesa: Los Carpinteros. 2010. (SPA & ENG., Illus.). 166p. pap. 39.95 *(978-0-9564339-1-6(X))* Ivory Pr. ESP. Dist: Actar Birkhauser Distribution.

Petrova, Yevgenia, ed. Art from Cuba: The Ludwig Collection. 2006. (MUL & ENG., Illus.). 242p. 80.00 *(978-3-935298-27-8(7))*, Palace Editions) Mandala Publishing.

Remba, Natania. Surrounded by Water: Expressions of Freedom & Isolation in Contemporary Cuban Art. 2008. (Illus.). 64p. pap. 15.00 *(978-1-881450-28-3(7))* Boston Univ., Art Gallery.

Roca, Octavio. Cuban Ballet, 1 vol. 2010. (ENG., Illus.). 240p. 40.00 *(978-1-4236-0758-8(9))* Gibbs Smith, Publisher.

Rosado, Jesus & Schweigert, Scott A. Carlos Luna: Personal Histories. 2006. (ENG & SPA., Illus.). 154p. 50.00 *(978-0-9791753-0-5(5))* Arnold, Suzanne H. Art Gallery.

Unbroken Ties: Dialogues in Cuban Art. 2008. (ENG & SPA., Illus.). 81p. pap. 24.95 *(978-0-9678056-6-5(X))* Nova Southeastern Univ., Museum of Art Fort Lauderdale.

Vives, Cristina, ed. & text. Belkis Ayon: Kname. 2010. (ENG., Illus.). 312p. 55.00 *(978-84-7506-916-6(9))* Turner, Ediciones S.A. ESP. Dist: D.A.P./Distributed Art Pubs.

Weiss, Rachel. To & from Utopia in the New Cuban Art. 2011. (ENG., Illus.). 368p. pap. 34.95 *(978-0-8166-6515-0(X))* Univ. of Minnesota Pr.

ART, CYCLADIC

Stampolidis, Nicholas & Sotirakopoulou, Peggy. Aegean Waves: Artworks of the Early Cycladic Culture in the Museum of Cycladic Art. Hardy, David, tr. 2008. (ENG., Illus.). 224p. 65.00 *(978-88-6130-346-1(3))* Rizzoli International Pubns., Inc.

Uhl, Jason. A Brief Introduction to Ancient Aegean Art: Cycladic, Minoan, & Mycenaean Art & Architecture. 2007. 76p. per. 16.95 *(978-1-4241-8204-6(2))* PublishAmerica, Inc.

ART, CZECH

Baldwin, Gary D. Moser Glass: The Klabin Collection. 2007. (ENG.). 132p. 69.95 *(978-0-9647080-9-9(4))* Healing Wisdom Pubns.

Bovier, Lionel & Caratsch, Andrea, eds. Milan Kunc: Sculpture. 2010. (ENG., Illus.). 96p. 35.00 *(978-3-03764-062-3(6))* JRP Ringier Kunstverlag AG CHE. Dist: D.A.P./Distributed Art Pubs.

Glushko, Elena. Medieval Challenges Modern. 2008. 92p. pap. *(978-3-639-05038-7(X))* VDM Verlag Dr. Mueller e.K.

Havranek, Vit, ed. Katerina Seda: for Every Dog a Different Master. 2008. (ENG., Illus.). 200p. pap. 39.00 *(978-3-905829-66-2(5))* JRP Ringier Kunstverlag AG CHE. Dist: D.A.P./Distributed Art Pubs.

Henderson, James D., Jr. Royal Austria Porcelain. 2008. (Illus.). 272p. bds. 59.95 *(978-0-7643-2820-6(4))* Schiffer Publishing, Ltd.

Kicken, Rudolf & Kicken, Annette, eds. Frantisek Drtikol. 2012. (ENG & GER., Illus.). 101p. 55.00 *(978-3-7757-2600-9(4))* Hatje Cantz Verlag GmbH & Co KG DEU. Dist: D.A.P./Distributed Art Pubs.

Kolar, Viktor, photos by. Ostrava. 2011. (ENG., Illus.). 204p. 75.00 *(978-80-7437-030-4(5))* Kant CZE. Dist: D.A.P./Distributed Art Pubs.

Koudelka, Josef, photos by. Chaos. 2008. (ENG.). 79.95 *(978-0-7148-4594-4(9))* Phaidon Pr., Inc.

MacDonald, Deanna. Art for Travellers Prague: The Essential Guide to Viewing Art in Prague. 2006. (Art for Travellers Ser.). (ENG., Illus.). 304p. pap. 20.00 *(978-1-56656-622-3(3))* Interlink Publishing Group, Inc.

Matt, Gerald & Blickle, Ursula, eds. The Cabinet of Jan Svankmajer: The Pendulum, the Pit, & Other Peculiarities. 2012. (ENG & GER., Illus.). 240p. 55.00 ***(978-3-86984-256-1(3))*** Verlag fur Moderne Kunst DEU. Dist: D.A.P./Distributed Art Pubs.

Neslehova, Mahulena. Jan Koblasa: Intaglio Prints. 2011. (ENG., Illus.). 262p. pap. 40.00 *(978-80-246-1811-1(7))* Karolinum, nakladatelstvi Univerzity Karlovy CZE. Dist: Chicago Distribution Ctr.

Sedá, Katerina. Katerina Sedá *1977. 2008. (CZE & ENG., Illus.). 160p. 48.00 *(978-3-905770-95-7(4))* JRP Ringier Kunstverlag AG CHE. Dist: D.A.P./Distributed Art Pubs.

Seda, Katerina. Katerina Seda: over & Over. 2010. (ENG., Illus.). 312p. 45.00 *(978-3-03764-111-8(8))* JRP Ringier Kunstverlag AG CHE. Dist: D.A.P./Distributed Art Pubs.

Srp, Karel, et al. New Formations: Czech Avant-Garde Art & Modern Glass from the Roy & Mary Cullen Collection. 2011. (ENG., Illus.). 320p. 75.00 *(978-0-300-16996-6(5))* Museum of Fine Arts, Houston.

Urban, Otto. Decadence - In Morbid Colours Bohemia: Art & the Idea of Decadence in the Bohemian Lands, 1880-1914. 2011. (ENG., Illus.). 410p. 85.00 *(978-80-86300-84-9(6))* Nakladatelstvi Arbor vitae CZE. Dist: D.A.P./Distributed Art Pubs.

Virgin Forest Mon I. 2011. (ENG., Illus.). 248p. 75.00 *(978-80-86970-91-2(4))* Kant CZE. Dist: D.A.P./Distributed Art Pubs.

ART, DECORATIVE

see also Bronzes; Decoration and Ornament; Design, Decorative; Embroidery; Enamel and Enameling; Furniture; Illustration of Books; Mosaics; Mural Painting and Decoration; Needlework; Pottery; Screens; Tapestry; Textile Design; Vase Painting

also Art, African; Art, Byzantine, and similar headings

Adamson, Glenn, ed. The Craft Reader. 2010. (ENG., Illus.). 1p. 129.95 *(978-1-84788-304-9(4))*; 672p. pap. 39.95 *(978-1-84788-303-2(6))* Berg Pubs. GBR. Dist: Macmillan.

Adamson, Glenn, et al, eds. The Journal of Modern Craft Volume 2 Issue 3. 2009. (ENG.). 1p. pap. 34.95 *(978-1-84788-529-6(2))* Berg Pubs. GBR. Dist: Macmillan.

Addison, Julia de Wolf Gl. Arts & Crafts in the Middle Ages. 2008. 308p. 28.99 *(978-0-554-33203-1(5))* 2008. 308p. 29.99 *(978-0-554-23900-2(0))* 2006. (ENG.). 272p. pap. 21.99 *(978-1-4264-5135-5(0))* 2006. (ENG.). 304p. pap. 24.99 *(978-1-4264-5436-3(8))* BiblioBazaar.

Alfoldy, Sandra. The Allied Arts: Architecture & Craft in Postwar Canada. 2012. (McGill-Queen's/Beaverbrook Canadian Foundation Studies in Art History Ser.). (ENG., Illus.). 264p. (C). ***(978-0-7735-3960-0(3))***; pap. ***(978-0-7735-4003-3(2))*** McGill-Queen's Univ. Pr.

American Bounty. 2006. 44p. 10.95 *(978-1-60140-101-4(9))* Leisure Arts, Inc.

Andrews, Lynne. Christmas Blessings. 2007. (Illus.). 36p. 12.95 *(978-1-934539-02-6(3))* Viking Woodcrafts, Inc.

Anisimova, Elena, et al. Art Nouveau During the Reign of the Last Tsars. 2008. (Illus.). 128p. 40.00 *(978-0-85331-987-0(1)*, Lund Humphries Pubs.) Ashgate Publishing, Ltd. GBR. Dist: Ashgate Publishing Co.

Artie, East Coast. Pro Pinstripe Techniques. 2011. (ENG., Illus.). 144p. pap. 27.95 *(978-1-929133-92-5(8)*, 1929133928, ArtKulture) Wolfgang Pubns., Inc.

Ave, Joop, et al. Indonesian Arts & Crafts. 2009. (ENG., Illus.). 228p. 49.95 *(978-979-8926-27-3(7))* Archipelago Pr IDN. Dist: Tuttle Publishing.

Bar, Noma. Guess Who? The Many Faces of Noma Bar. 2007. (ENG., Illus.). 128p. pap. 19.95 *(978-0-9779850-7-4(5))* Batty, Mark Pub., LLC.

Bartoletti, Laurence. Creation en France: Arts decoratifs 1945-1965: Repertoire Alphabetique. 2010. (ENG.). 388p. pap. 95.00 *(978-2-35340-019-5(1))* Gourcuff Gradenigo FRA. Dist: National Bk. Network.

Beevers, David, ed. Chinese Whispers: Chinoiserie in Britain 1650-1930. 2009. (ENG., Illus.). 144p. pap. *(978-0-948723-71-1(8)*, Royal Pavilion Libraries & Mus) Antique Collectors' Club.

Bell, Nicholas R., et al. History in the Making: Renwick Craft Invitational 2011. 2011. (ENG., Illus.). 104p. pap. 24.95 *(978-1-85759-703-5(6))* Scala, Editions FRA. Dist: National Bk. Network.

Best, Laura. Memories in Time: Legacy. 2008. (Illus.). 57p. pap. 14.95 *(978-0-9770886-0-7(X))* Echoroad Inc.

Birkhauser creator. Form 211. 2007. (Zeitschrift Form Ser.). (Illus.). 106p. per. 19.95 *(978-3-936560-38-1(2)*, 3936560382) Birkhauser Verlag GmbH DEU. Dist: Springer.

Bloom, Jonathan M. Arts of the City Victorious: Islamic Art & Architecture in Fatimid North Africa & Egypt. 2008. (ENG., Illus.). 256p. 75.00 *(978-0-300-13542-8(4))* Yale Univ. Pr.

Bomford, David. Seeing the Collections at the Getty Center. 2009. (Illus.). 64p. pap. 10.95 *(978-0-89236-962-1(0))* Oxford Univ. Pr., Inc.

Bonansinga, Kate. Staged Stories: Renwick Craft Invitational 2009. 2009. (ENG., Illus.). 84p. pap. 24.95 *(978-1-85759-617-5(X))* Scala, Editions FRA. Dist: National Bk. Network.

Boyer, Marie-France. The Private Realm of Marie Antoinette. 2006. (ENG., Illus.). 112p. pap. 19.95 *(978-0-500-28632-6(9))* Thames & Hudson.

Bresco, Jose L. Encyclopedie Pratique du Desin et des Arts Decoratifs. (FRE.). 75.00 *(978-0-7859-0734-3(3)*, M6046) French & European Pubns., Inc.

Bryce, James. South America. reprint ed. lib. bdg. 48.00 *(978-0-7426-1229-7(5))* Classic Bks.

Bucquoye, Moniek, et al, texts. Design Art, 1 vol. ltd. ed. 2011. (ENG., Illus.). 240p. 85.00 *(978-90-5856-300-2(6))* Stichting Kunstboek Bvba BEL. Dist: Antique Collectors' Club.

Busch, Jason, ed. & text. Carnegie Museum of Art: Decorative Arts & Design. 2010. (ENG., Illus.). 224p. pap. 19.95 *(978-0-88039-052-1(2))* Carnegie Museum of Art, The.

Busch, Jason T. & Futter, Catherine L. Inventing the Modern World: Decorative Arts at the World's Fairs, 1851-1939. 2012. (ENG., Illus.). 304p. 75.00 ***(978-0-8478-3809-7(9)***, Skira) Rizzoli International Pubns., Inc.

Cadou, Carol Borchert. The George Washington Collection: Fine & Decorative Arts at Mount Vernon. 2006. (ENG., Illus.). 254p. 60.00 *(978-1-55595-268-6(2))* Hudson Hills Pr. LLC.

Campana, D. M. The Artist & the Decorator. (Illus.). 14.95 *(978-0-939608-16-4(2))* Campana Art Co.

—Decorative Designs. (Illus.). No. 1. 10.50 *(978-0-939608-20-1(0))*No. 6. 10.50 *(978-0-939608-24-9(3))*No. 7. 17.50 *(978-0-939608-19-5(7))* Campana Art Co.

Campbell, Gordon. The Grove Encyclopedia of Decorative Arts, 2 vols., Set. 2006. (ENG., Illus.). 1290p. 315.00 *(978-0-19-518948-3(5))* Oxford Univ. Pr., Inc.

Cannatella, Howard. Creating a Better Place to Live: The Argument for Craft Education. 2011. 184p. pap. ***(978-1-86335-971-9(0))*** Common Ground Publishing Pty, Ltd.

Chambers, Ruth, et al, eds. Utopic Impulses: Contemporary Ceramics Practice. 2008. (ENG., Illus.). 316p. per. *(978-1-55380-051-4(6))* Ronsdale Pr.

Cohen, David & Anderson, Scott. A Visual Language: Elements of Design. 2006. (ENG., Illus.). 112p. pap. 32.95 *(978-0-7136-6773-8(7))* A & C Black GBR. Dist: Macmillan.

Cole, Arthur Harrison & Watts, George Byron. The Handicrafts of France: As Recorced in the Descriptions des Arts et Metiers, 1761-1788. 2011. 50p. 36.95 ***(978-1-258-10329-3(X))*** Literary Licensing, LLC.

Conway, Moncure Daniel. Travels in South Kensington. 2009. 60p. pap. *(978-0-217-41109-7(6))* Books LLC.

Cooke, Edward S., Jr., et al, eds. The Journal of Modern Craft Volume 2 Issue 2. 2009. (Journal of Modern Craft Ser.). (ENG., Illus.). 128p. pap. 34.95 *(978-1-84788-528-9(4))* Berg Pubs. GBR. Dist: Macmillan.

Couch, Dale L. Neighboring Voices: The Decorative Culture of Our Southern Cousins: The Fifth Henry D. Green Symposium of the Decorative Arts: Georgia Museum of Art, Athens, Georgia, January 29 & 30, 2010. 2011. ***(978-0-915977-76-5(1))*** Univ. of Georgia, Georgia Museum of Art.

Cowen, Pamela. A Fanfare for the Sun King: Unfolding Fans for Louis XIV. 2006. (ENG., Illus.). per. 45.00 *(978-1-903942-20-8(9)*, Third Millenium Pub Ltd) Antique Collectors' Club GBR. Dist: National Bk. Network.

Crane, Lucy. Art & the Formation of Taste. 2009. 324p. 25.99 *(978-1-103-29026-0(6))*; pap. 19.99 *(978-1-103-29023-9(1))* BiblioBazaar.

—Art & the Formation of Taste. 2009. 94p. pap. 14.14 *(978-1-151-59185-2(8))* General Bks. LLC.

Crochet, Treena M. Designer's Guide to Decorative Accessories. 2008. (ENG., Illus.). 304p. (C). 47.20 *(978-0-13-233114-2(4)*, Prentice Hall) Prentice Hall PTR.

Danto, Arthur C. & Simon, Joan. Sheila Hicks: Weaving as Metaphor. Stritzler-Levine, Nina, ed. 2006. (Bard Graduate Center for Studies in the Decorative Arts, Design & Culture). (ENG., Illus.). 416p. 80.00 *(978-0-300-11685-4(3))* Yale Univ. Pr.

De Giorgio, Cynthia. St. John's Co-Cathedral, Valletta. 2007. (ENG.). 56p. (C). pap. 9.95 *(978-99932-7-171-0(3))* Midsea Bks. Ltd. MLT. Dist: Brown, David Bk. Co., The.

Dehejia, Vicya. Delight in Design: Indian Silver for the Raj. 2008. (ENG., Illus.). 200p. 65.00 *(978-0-944142-43-1(5))* Mapin Publishing Pvt. Ltd IND. Dist: National Bk. Network.

Detroit Institute Of Arts. Decorative Arts of the Italian Renaissance, 1400-1600. 2011. 182p. 42.95 ***(978-1-258-01796-5(2))*** Literary Licensing, LLC.

Dmitrieva, Olga & Abramova, Natalya, eds. Britannia & Muscovy: English Silver at the Court of the Tsars. 2006. (ENG., Illus.). 304p. 85.00 *(978-0-300-11678-6(0))* Yale Univ. Pr.

Dover Publications Inc. Staff & Grafton, Carol Belanger. Japanese Vector Designs. Weller, Alan, ed. 2008. (Dover Pictura Electronic Clip Art Ser.). (ENG.). 128p. pap. 49.95 *(978-0-486-99023-1(0))* Dover Pubns., Inc.

Droth, Marina, et al. Taking Shape: Finding Sculpture in the Decorative Arts. 2009. (Illus.). 176p. 40.00 *(978-0-89236-963-8(9))* Oxford Univ. Pr., Inc.

Duncan, Alastair. High Style: Masterworks from the Bernard & Sylvia Ostry Collection in the Royal Ontario Museum. 2006. (ENG., Illus.). 148p. *(978-0-88854-446-9(4))* Royal Ontario Museum.

Edwards, Jason & Hart, Imogen. Rethinking the Interior, C.1867-1896: Aestheticism & Arts & Crafts. 2010. (Illus.). 294p. 124.95 *(978-0-7546-6817-6(7))* Ashgate Publishing Co.

Eisler, Max. Dagobert Peche (1887-1923) Artist of the Wiener Werkstatte. (GER, ENG & FRE., Illus.). 160p. 95.00 *(978-3-925369-13-1(9))* Arnoldsche Art Pubs. DEU. Dist: Antique Collectors' Club.

Euler, Laura. The Glasgow Style: Artists in the Decorative Arts, Circa 1900. 2008. (Illus.). 272p. 69.99 *(978-0-7643-3044-5(6))* Schiffer Publishing, Ltd.

Fang, Jing Pei, et al. Elegance of the Qing Court: Reflections of a Dynasty Through Its Art. 2008. *(978-0-936364-35-3(1))* Joslyn Art Museum.

Farmer, Will. Clarice Cliff. 2010. (Shire Library). (ENG., Illus.). 64p. pap. 12.95 *(978-0-7478-0774-2(4))* Shire Pubns., Ltd. GBR. Dist: Random Hse., Inc.

Farnham, T. C., 8th. Catalogue of Stamping Patterns Embracing All of the Latest & Choicest Designs Used in Connection with the Illustrated Catalogue Home Beautiful, A Treatise of Decorative Art Needlework & Embroider Materials. 2007. (Illus.). 212p. (C). pap. 45.00 (978-0-944311-22-6(9)) Michigan State Univ. Museum.

Fiell, Charlotte & Fiell, Peter. Decorative Arts 70's. 2006. (ENG, FRE & GER., Illus.). 575p. pap. 14.99 (978-3-8228-5043-5(8)) TASCHEN DEU. Dist: Ingram Pub. Services.

Fiell, Charlotte & Fiell, Peter, eds. Decorative Art 70s. 2006. (ITA, POR & SPA.). 576p. pap. 12.99 (978-3-8228-5044-2(6)) Taschen America, LLC.

Fischer, Barbara Morris, ed. The Sunlit Path. Date not set. (Illus.). 72p. lib. bdg. 37.95 (978-0-912658-22-3(3)) Mark, J. Pr.

French. Americana... from Our Hearts. 2007. 12.95 (978-1-934539-00-2(7)) Viking Woodcrafts, Inc.

Gaehtgens, Thomas W. & Zelljadt, Katja, eds. Getty Research Journal, No. 1. 2009. (Getty Research Journal Ser.). (ENG., Illus.). 228p. pap. 50.00 (978-0-89236-970-6(1), Getty Research Institute) Getty Pubns.

Gaunt, Pamela. Decorative Art in the Twentieth Century. 2010. 156p. pap. (978-3-639-22348-4(9)) VDM Verlag Dr. Mueller e.K.

Georgia Museum of Art. Decorative Arts in Georgia: Historic Sites, Historic Contexts - The Third Henry D. Green Symposium of the Decorative Arts. Callahan, Ashley, ed. 2008. (ENG.). 158p. pap. 25.00 (978-0-915977-66-6(4)) Univ. of Georgia, Georgia Museum of Art.

Georgia Museum of Art Staff. A Colorful Past: Decorative Arts of Georgia. Callahan, Ashley, ed. 2010. (ENG., Illus.). 152p. pap. 35.00 (978-0-915977-72-7(9)) Univ. of Georgia, Georgia Museum of Art.

Gordon, John Stuart. A Modern World: American Design from the Yale University Art Gallery, 1920-1950. 2011. (ENG., Illus.). 438p. 75.00 (978-0-300-15301-9(5)) Yale Univ. Pr.

Greenhalgh, Paul, ed. The Persistence of Craft. 2009. (ENG., Illus.). 224p. 49.95 (978-0-7136-5001-3(X)) A & C Black GBR. Dist: Macmillan.

Haglund, Jill. Seasons & Celebrations. 2008. (ENG.). 116p. pap. 21.95 (978-1-891898-18-1(3)) Tweety Jill Pubns.

Hang, Jian & Guo, Qiuhui. Chinese Arts & Crafts. 3rd ed. 2012. (Introductions to Chinese Culture Ser.). (ENG., Illus.). 202p. pap. 19.99 **(978-0-521-18655-1(2))** Cambridge Univ. Pr.

Harris, John. Moving Rooms: The Trade in Architectural Salvages. 2007. (ENG., Illus.). 240p. 65.00 (978-0-300-12420-0(1)) Yale Univ. Pr.

Harrison, Stephen, et al. Artistic Luxury: Faberge, Tiffany, Lalique. 2008. (ENG., Illus.). 372p. 60.00 (978-0-300-14224-2(2)) Yale Univ. Pr.

Hart, Imogen. Arts & Crafts Objects. 2010. (Studies in Design & Material Culture Ser.). (ENG., Illus.). 288p. 89.95 (978-0-7190-7971-9(3)); pap. 34.95 (978-0-7190-7972-6(1)) Manchester Univ. Pr. GBR. Dist: Macmillan.

Hay, Jonathan. Sensuous Surfaces: The Decorative Object in Early Modern China. 2010. 272p. (C). 63.00 (978-0-8248-3361-9(9)) Univ. of Hawaii Pr.

Hiesinger, Kathryn B. Collecting Modern: Design at the Philadelphia Museum of Art since 1876. 2011. (Illus.). 304p. (978-0-87633-221-4(1)) Philadelphia Museum of Art.

Hildebrand, Grant. Elegant Explorations: The Designs of Philip Jacobson. 2007. (ENG., Illus.). 80p. pap. 25.00 (978-0-295-98719-4(7)) Univ. of Washington Pr.

Hillenbrand, Robert. Studies in the Islamic Decorative Arts. 2011. (ENG., Illus.). 574p. (C). 300.00 (978-1-904597-50-6(5)) Pindar Pr. GBR. Dist: Brown, David Bk. Co., The.

Hu, Chunsheng & Hu, Hua. Wenzhou Hua Ban, Tong Pi. 2008. (Illus.). 231p. (978-7-80686-636-8(1)) Zhejiang Photographic Pr.

Hughes, Angie. Stitch, Cloth, Paper & Paint: Mixed Media Ideas & Inspiration. (ENG., Illus.). 96p. 2011. pap. 19.95 (978-1-84448-733-2(4)) 2009. 29.95 (978-1-84448-233-7(2)) Search Pr., Ltd. GBR. Dist: Independent Pubs. Group.

Hull, Brent & Franck, Christine G. H. Traditional American Rooms: Celebrating Style, Craftsmanship, & Historic Woodwork. 2008. (Illus.). 179p. (978-1-56523-445-1(6)) Fox Chapel Publishing Co., Inc.

Hunt, Elizabeth Moore. Illuminating the Borders of Northern French & Flemish Manuscripts, 1270-1310. 2006. (Studies in Medieval History & Culture). (Illus.). 241p. 131.00 (978-0-415-97760-9(6)) Routledge.

Hunter, Anne. Finishing Touches III. 2007. (Illus.). 40p. 12.95 (978-0-9786331-9-6(9)) Viking Woodcrafts, Inc.

Jacquemart, Albert. Decorative Art. 2012. (Temporis Ser.). (ENG., Illus.). 256p. 39.95 (978-1-84484-899-7(X)) Parkstone Pr. USA, Ltd.

Jaffer, Amin. Made for Maharajas: A Design Diary of Princely India. Singh, Martand, ed. 2006. (ENG., Illus.). 276p. 65.00 (978-0-86565-174-6(4)) Vendome Pr., The.

Jammula, S. R. Vector Designs: Decorative Frames & Borders (Paperback) 2008. (Illus.). 160p. pap. 14.95 (978-0-9742408-1-7(8)) Xlicons, Inc.

—Vector Designs - Decorative Frames & Borders (CD-ROM) 2008. (Illus.). cd-rom 24.95 (978-0-9742408-3-1(4)) Xlicons, Inc.

Jirka-Schmitz, Patrizia. Netsuke Vol. 2: Four Centuries of Masterpieces. 2007. (ENG., Illus.). 416p. 135.00 (978-3-925369-90-2(2)) Arnoldsche Art Pubs. DEU. Dist: Antique Collectors' Club.

Johnson, Donald-Brian & Pina, Leslie. Deco Decor: Porcelain, Glass, & Metal Accessories for the Home. 2009. (Illus.). 240p. bds. 69.99 (978-0-7643-3178-7(7)) Schiffer Publishing, Ltd.

Kaplin, David L. California Design, 1930-1965: Living in a Modern Way. Kaplan, Wendy, ed. 2011. (ENG., Illus.). 360p. (gr. 17). 60.00 **(978-0-262-01607-0(9))** MIT Pr.

Karper, Diane. A Walk in My Shoes: Our Lives of Hope: An Oral History of the Artists of the "Made in Honduras Craft Co-Op," Trujillo, Honduras. 2010. pap. (978-0-911469-35-6(4)) Hood, Alan C. & Co., Inc.

Kelly, Annie. Casa San Miguel: Inspired Design & Decoration. 2008. (ENG., Illus.). 240p. 55.00 (978-0-8478-3044-2(6)) Rizzoli International Pubns., Inc.

Kidston, Cath. Make! Over 40 Fantastic Projects with 16 Exclusive Designs. 2010. (ENG., Illus.). 176p. pap. 24.99 (978-0-312-59686-6(3), St. Martin's Griffin) St. Martin's Pr.

Kirsten, Sven A. Tiki Modern: And the Wild World of Witco. 2007. (FRE, GER & ENG., Illus.). 335p. 39.99 (978-3-8228-4717-6(8)) TASCHEN DEU. Dist: Ingram Pub. Services.

Kisluk-Grosheide, Danielle O. & Munger, Jeffrey H. The Wrightsman Galleries for French Decorative Arts, the Metropolitan Museum of Art. 2010. (Illus.). xii, 259p. 40.00 (978-1-58839-366-1(6)) Metropolitan Museum of Art, The.

Klich, Lynda & Mogul, Jonathan, eds. The Journal of Decorative & Propaganda Arts: Mexico Theme Issue, Issue 26. 2010. 304p. pap. 50.00 (978-1-930776-18-0(7)) Wolfson Foundation of Decorative & Propaganda Arts, Inc., The.

Koeppe, Wolfram, et al. The Robert Lehman Collection at the Metropolitan Museum of Art V15 - European & Asian Decorative Arts. 2012. (ENG., Illus.). 400p. (C). 95.00 **(978-0-691-15490-9(2))** Princeton Univ. Pr.

Koplos, Janet & Metcalf, Bruce. Makers: A History of American Studio Craft. 2010. (ENG., Illus.). 544p. 65.00 (978-0-8078-3413-8(0)) Univ. of North Carolina Pr.

Kosek, Joanna M. Conservation Mounting for Prints & Drawings: A Manual Based on Current Practice at the British Museum. 2006. (ENG., Illus.). 185p. 90.00 (978-1-873132-59-3(X)) Archetype Pubns. GBR. Dist: National Bk. Network.

Krill, Rosemary Troy. Early American Decorative Arts, 1620-1860: A Handbook for Interpreters. 2010. (American Association for State & Local History Ser.). (ENG.). 278p. 100.00 incl. cd-rom (978-0-7591-1944-4(9)); pap. 49.95 incl. cd-rom (978-0-7591-1945-1(7)) AltaMira Pr.

Lange, Amanda Elizabeth. Delftware at Historic Deerfield, 1600-1800. 2006. (ENG., Illus.). 50.00 (978-0-9666769-1-4(2)) Historic Deerfield Inc.

Laquidara, Judy. 60 Pieced Quilt Borders: Mix & Match. 2012. (ENG., Illus.). 120p. pap. 26.95 **(978-1-60460-012-4(8)**, 1604600128, American Quilter's Society) Collector Bks.

Lauria, Jo & Fenton, Steve. Craft in America: Celebrating Two Centuries of Artists & Objects. 2007. (ENG., Illus.). 320p. 60.00 (978-0-307-34647-6(1), Clarkson Potter) Crown Publishing Group.

Le Chevallier, Jacques & Archieri, Jean-François. Jacques Le Chevallier, 1896-1987: La Lumière Moderne. 2008. (FRE & ENG., Illus.). 248p. pap. 65.00 (978-2-35340-021-8(3)) Gourcuff Gradenigo FRA. Dist: National Bk. Network.

Loring, John. Tiffany Style: 170 Years of Design. 2008. (ENG., Illus.). 304p. 50.00 (978-0-8109-7293-3(X)) Abrams.

Lovenheim, Barbara & Smith, Paul J. Breaking Ground: A Century of Craft Art in Western New York. 2010. (ENG., Illus.). 156p. 50.00 (978-1-55595-354-6(9)) Hudson Hills Pr. LLC.

Lover, Linda. Brushtiques Vol 2. 2007. (Illus.). 44p. 12.95 (978-1-934539-01-9(5)) Viking Woodcrafts, Inc.

MacGonagle, Elizabeth. Crafting Identity in Zimbabwe & Mozambique. 2007. (Rochester Studies in African History & the Diaspora Ser.: Volume 30). (Illus.). 205p. 80.00 (978-1-58046-257-0(X)) Univ. of Rochester Pr.

Maguire, Eunice Dauterman & Maguire, Henry. Other Icons: Art & Power in Byzantine Secular Culture. 2006. (ENG., Illus.). 232p. (C). 62.95 (978-0-691-12564-0(3)) Princeton Univ. Pr.

Maisonette, des. I Colour Book: Abstract Designs. 2007. (ENG., Illus.). 48p (978-0-7134-9032-9(2), Batsford, B. T. Ltd.) Anova Bks. GBR. Dist: Sterling Publishing Co., Inc.

Marcus, Neiman. Neiman Marcus: Over the Top. 2010. (ENG., Illus.). 160p. 50.00 (978-2-7594-0469-8(2)) Assouline FRA. Dist: Perseus Distribution.

Marston, Gwen. Liberated Medallion Quilts. 2012. (ENG., Illus.). 112p. pap. 24.95 **(978-1-60460-028-5(4)**, 1604600284, American Quilter's Society) Collector Bks.

Matsuo, Mikio, photos by. Zuancho in Kyoto: Textile Design Books for the Kimono Trade. 2008. (Illus.). 34p. (978-0-911221-41-1(7)) Stanford Univ. Libraries.

McCallum, Graham Leslie & McCallum, Graham. 4000 Alphabet & Letter Motifs: A Sourcebook. 2009. (ENG., Illus.). 400p. 17.95 (978-0-7134-9060-2(8), Batsford, B. T. Ltd.) Anova Bks. GBR. Dist: Sterling Publishing Co., Inc.

McNaughton, Phoebe. Perspective & Other Optical Illusions. 2007. (Wooden Bks.). (ENG., Illus.). 64p. 12.00 (978-0-8027-1633-0(4)) Walker & Co.

Mellins, Thomas & Albrecht, Donald. The American Style. 2011. (ENG., Illus.). 224p. 50.00 (978-1-58093-285-1(1)) Monacelli Pr., Inc.

Menz, Christopher. Morris & Co. 2007. (Illus.). 188p. 55.00 (978-0-7308-3029-0(2)) Art Gallery of South Australia AUS. Dist: Antique Collectors' Club.

Miller, Judith. Decorative Arts: Style & Design from Classical to Contemporary. 2007. 76p. (C). 66.67 (978-0-13-208130-6(X)) Prentice Hall Higher Education.

Milosch, Jane & Frantz, Susanne K. From the Ground Up: Renwick Craft Invitational 2007. 2007. pap. (978-0-9790678-1-5(2)) Smithsonian American Art Museum.

Mornement, Caroline, ed. & compiled by. Craft Galleries Guide: 2009/10. 10th ed. 2009. (ENG., Illus.). 356p. pap. 28.95 (978-0-9550026-7-0(2)) BCF Bks. GBR. Dist: Macmillan.

Mostek, Pamela. Blended Borders: Quilts with a Creative Edge. 2009. (ENG., Illus.). 48p. pap. (978-1-56477-930-4(0)) Martingale & Co.

Mundt, Barbara. Der Pommersche Kunstschrank: des Augsburger Unternehmers Hainhofer für den gelehrten Herzog vom Pommern. 2009. (GER., Illus.). 447p. (978-3-7774-8045-9(2)) Hirmer Verlag GmbH.

Museum of Arts and Design. Crafting Modernism: Midcentury American Art & Design. 2011. (ENG., Illus.). 368p. 65.00 (978-0-8109-8480-6(6)) Abrams.

Nokes, Jill. Yard Art & Handmade Places: Extraordinary Expressions of Home. 2007. (ENG., Illus.). 188p. 29.95 (978-0-292-71679-7(6)) Univ. of Texas Pr.

Official Catalogue of the Great Exhibition of the Works of Industry of All Nations 1851. 2011. (Cambridge Library Collection - History Ser.). (ENG.). 342p. pap. 28.99 (978-1-108-02999-5(X)) Cambridge Univ. Pr.

Payne, Alina. From Ornament to Object: Genealogies of Architectural Modernism. 2012. (ENG., Illus.). 360p. 65.00 **(978-0-300-17533-2(7))** Yale Univ. Pr.

Peirce, Donald. Art & Enterprise: American Decorative Art 1825-1917 - The Virginia Carroll Crawford Collection. 2006. (ENG., Illus.). 464p. 60.00 (978-0-939802-87-6(2)) High Museum of Art.

Pepin Press. Graphics 1900. 2011. (MUL & ENG., Illus.). 168p. pap. 24.99 incl. cd-rom (978-90-5768-155-4(2)) Pepin Pr. NLD. Dist: National Bk. Network.

Pool, Mary Jane & Howard, Linn. The Angel Tree: Celebrating Christmas at the Metropolitan Museum of Art. 2011. (ENG., Illus.). 128p. 24.95 (978-0-8109-9692-2(8)) Abrams.

Potvin, John & Myzelev, Alla, eds. Material Cultures, 1740-1920: The Meanings & Pleasures of Collecting. 2009. (Illus.). 250p. 124.95 (978-0-7546-6144-3(X)) Ashgate Publishing Co.

Preserving the American Spirit in the DAR Museum. 2006. (Illus.). 64p (978-1-57864-356-1(2)) Donning Co. Pubs.

Pricco, Evan. Juxtapoz Handmade. Revelli, M., ed. 2010. (Illus.). 207p. 29.95 (978-1-58423-396-1(6)) Gingko Pr., Inc.

Price, Noa. Interchanging Influences on the Road. 2010. 80p. pap. (978-3-639-22565-5(1)) VDM Verlag Dr. Mueller e.K.

Ranjan, Aditi & Ranjan, M. P. Handmade in India: Crafts of India. 2010. 95.00 (978-1-890206-85-7(7)) Grantha Corp.

Ranjan, Aditi & Ranjan, M. P., eds. Handmade in India: A Geographic Encyclopedia of India Handicrafts. 2009. (ENG., Illus.). 579p. 65.00 (978-0-7892-1047-0(9)) Abbeville Pr., Inc.

Robach, Cilla. Formens Frigörelse: Konsthantverk Och Design under Debatt I 1960-Talets Sverige. 2010. (SWE., Illus.). 373p. (978-91-85689-32-3(7)) Arvinius Forlag.

Roberts, Phillip. Waikiki Tiki. 2010. 264p. 22.95 (978-1-57306-311-1(8)) Bess Pr., Inc.

Rousmaniere, Nicole, ed. Crafting Beauty in Modern Japan: Celebrating Fifty Years of the Japan Traditional Art Crafts Exhibition. 2007. (ENG., Illus.). 208p. pap. 45.00 (978-0-295-98733-0(2)) Univ. of Washington Pr.

Rowland, Jen & Stowe, Tori. Catalogue of Eastern Cape Craft. 2006. (Illus.). 96p. (978-1-920033-02-6(5)) NISC (Pty) Ltd.

Ruskin, John. The Nature of Gothic. 2007. (ENG.). 108p. 34.95 (978-0-548-12301-0(2)) Kessinger Publishing, LLC.

Schapper, Linda P. The Complete Book of Crochet Border Designs: Hundreds of Classic & Original Patterns. 2008. (ENG., Illus.). 256p. 29.95 (978-1-57990-914-7(0)) Lark Bks.

Schmidt, Petra, et al, eds. Patterns. Muster in Design, Kunst und Architektur. 2006. (Illus.). 332p. 82.95 (978-3-7643-7185-2(4), 3764371854) Birkhauser Verlag AG CHE. Dist: Springer.

Sekler, Eduard F., contrib. by. Yearning for Beauty: The Wiener Werkstatte & the Stoclet House, 1 vol. 2006. (ENG., Illus.). 452p. 95.00 (978-3-7757-1778-6(1)) Hatje Cantz Verlag GmbH & Co KG DEU. Dist: D.A.P./Distributed Art Pubs.

Shannon, Sharon. Timeless Treasures. 2007. (Illus.). 12.95 (978-0-9786331-8-9(0)) Viking Woodcrafts, Inc.

Shipway, Verna Cook & Shipway, Warren. Mexican Interiors. 3rd ed. 2007. 39.95 (978-0-940512-48-1(3)) Hennessey & Ingalls, Inc.

Sitte, Camillo, et al. Camillo Sitte Gesamtausgabe 04: Schriften zu Pädagogik und Schulwesen. 2008. (GER., Illus.). 458p. (978-3-205-77177-7(X)) Bohlau Verlag GmbH u. Co. KG.

Smith, Gibbs. The Art of Adornment: Design - Fashion - Art. 2011. (ENG., Illus.). 80p. 12.99 (978-1-4236-2345-8(2)) Gibbs Smith, Publisher.

Standard Publishing Staff. Art & Decorating. 2009. (Children's Ministry Helps Ser.). (ENG.). (J). cd-rom 19.99 (978-0-7847-2289-3(7)) Standard Publishing.

Sutcliffe, Prudence, et al. Unfolding Pictures: Fans in the Royal Collection. 2010. (ENG., Illus.). 232p. 45.00 (978-1-902163-16-1(8)) Royal Collection Enterprises Ltd. GBR. Dist: Chicago Distribution Ctr.

Suzuki, Howard K. Soap Carving Creatures from the Oceans & Coral Reefs. 2007. (Illus.). 64p. pap. 12.95 (978-0-7643-2754-4(2)) Schiffer Publishing, Ltd.

Swartz, Anne. Pattern & Decoration: An Ideal Vision in American Art. 2007. (Illus.). 120p. per. 19.99 (978-0-943651-35-4(2)) Hudson River Museum.

Swift, Ellen. Style & Function in Roman Decoration: Living with Objects & Interiors. 2009. (Illus.). 264p. 124.95 (978-0-7546-6563-2(1)) Ashgate Publishing Co.

Syndram, Dirk. Juwelenkunst des Barock: Johann Melchior Dinglinger im Grünen Gewölbe. 2008. (Illus.). 240p. (C). 47.00 (978-3-7774-4445-1(6)) Hirmer Verlag GmbH DEU. Dist: Brown, David Bk. Co., The.

Teitelbaum, James. Tiki Road Trip: A Guide to Tiki Culture in North America. 2nd ed. 2007. (ENG., Illus.). 312p. per. 16.95 (978-1-59580-019-0(0)) Santa Monica Pr.

Vaboulis, Peter. Byzantine Decorative Art. (Illus.). 250p. 200.00 (978-0-89241-035-4(3), D139) Caratzas, Aristide D. Pub.

Vassos, John. Phobia: An Art Deco Graphic Masterpiece. 2009. (Dover Fine Art, History of Art Ser.). (ENG., Illus.). 112p. pap. 14.95 (978-0-486-47032-0(6)) Dover Pubns., Inc.

Wang, Xizhi. Jin Wang Xizhi Chuan Shi Mo Ji Xuan. 2010. (CHI.). 38p. (978-7-5010-2933-4(4)) Cultural Relics Publishing Hse.

Ward, Gerald W. R., et al. Shy Boy, She Devil & Isis: The Art of Conceptual Craft. 2007. 183p. pap. 35.00 (978-0-87846-720-4(3)) Museum of Fine Arts, Boston.

Webster, Polly. Antique Collectors Guide to New England: Antique Shops, Auction Houses, Museums & Historic Homes. 2011. 182p. 42.95 **(978-1-258-06763-2(3))** Literary Licensing, LLC.

Weightman, Stephanie. Decorative Painting: 15 Step-by-Step Projects - Simple to Make, Stunning Results. 2008. (Quick & Easy Crafts Ser.). (ENG., Illus.). 80p. pap. (978-1-84773-278-1(X)) New Holland Pubs., Ltd. GBR. Dist: Sterling Publishing Co., Inc.

Weller, Alan. Repeatable Backgrounds: Geometric & Abstract Patterns. 2009. (Dover Electronic Clip Art Ser.). (ENG., Illus.). 48p. pap. 19.95 (978-0-486-99020-0(6)) Dover Pubns., Inc.

Yaguchi, Kanako & Kamako, Yaguchi. The Art of Decorative Paper Stencils: Fold, Cut, & Open. 2008. (ENG., Illus.). 96p. pap. 17.99 (978-1-59253-440-1(6), 1592534406, Quarry Books) Quayside.

ART, DECORATIVE—EXHIBITIONS

Ayazi, Souri. Luristan Bronze Disc-Headed Pins. 2008. 260p. 130.00 (978-3-932942-27-3(2)) Legat-Verlag GmbH & Company KG DEU. Dist: Independent Pubs. Group.

Bath, Michael. Renaissance Decorative Painting in Scotland. 2006. (ENG., Illus.). 226p. pap. 49.95 (978-1-901663-60-0(4), 3064) NMS Enterprises Ltd. - Publishing GBR. Dist: National Bk. Network.

Bell, Robert. Transformations: The Language of Craft. 2006. (ENG., Illus.). 144p. pap. 30.00 (978-0-642-54138-3(8)) National Gallery of Australia AUS. Dist: Univ. of Washington Pr.

Berenson, Kathryn. Marseille. 2010. (ENG., Illus.). 128p. pap. 29.95 **(978-0-9814582-4-3(6)**, Int'l Quilt Study Ctr. & Museum at UNL) International Quilt Study Ctr. & Museu.

Bieber, Susanneh. Off-Site: Four site-specific art projects: Amy Balkin, Jeff Knwolton & Naomi Spellman, Ed Osborn, Claudia Tennyson. 2006. 5.00 net. (978-0-9790112-1-4(3)) Fresno Metropolitan Museum.

Bonansinga, Kate. Staged Stories: Renwick Craft Invitational 2009. 2009. (ENG., Illus.). 84p. pap. 24.95 (978-1-85759-617-5(X)) Scala, Editions FRA. Dist: National Bk. Network.

Boysson, Bernad. Museum of Decorative Arts of Brodeaux. 2006. 128p. (978-2-85056-932-6(1)) Somogy Editions d'Art.

Calder, Alexander, et al. Calder Jewelry. 2007. (978-0-300-13674-6(9)) Yale Univ. Pr.

Dal Co, Francesco, ed. SOM Journal 6. 2010. (ENG., Illus.). 208p. pap. 30.00 (978-3-7757-2637-5(3)) Hatje Cantz Verlag GmbH & Co KG DEU. Dist: D.A.P./Distributed Art Pubs.

Dehan, Amy Miller. Outside the Ordinary: Contemporary Art in Glass, Wood, & Ceramics from the Wolf Collection. 2009. (ENG.). 176p. pap. 30.00 (978-0-8214-1861-1(0)) Ohio Univ. Pr.

Farnsworth, Donald & Farnsworth, Era. Donald & Era Farnsworth: The Magnolia Tapestry Project. 2007. (Illus.). 40p. 42.00 (978-0-9799164-4-1(5)) Magnolia Editions.

Farnsworth, Donald & Nava, John, photos by. Chuck Close: The Magnolia Tapestry Project. 2007. (Illus.). 40p. 42.00 (978-0-9799164-1-0(0)) Magnolia Editions.

Feldman, Anita & Prichard, Sue. Henry Moore Textiles. 2009. (Illus.). 160p. pap. 40.00 (978-1-84822-052-2(9), Lund Humphries Pubs.) Ashgate Publishing, Ltd. GBR. Dist: Ashgate Publishing Co.

Fischer, Felice. The Art of Japanese Craft: 1875 to the Present. 2008. (978-0-87633-202-3(5)) Philadelphia Museum of Art.

Haase, Claus-Peter. A Collector's Fortune, Islamic Art. 2007. 132p. 49.00 (978-3-7774-4085-9(X)) Hirmer Verlag GmbH DEU. Dist: Chicago Distribution Ctr.

Harrison, Stephen, et al. Artistic Luxury: Fabergé Tiffany Lalique. 2008. (Illus.). xii, 358p. (978-0-940717-99-2(9)); (978-0-940717-98-5(0)) Yale Univ. Pr.

Heyse-Moore, Dominique, et al. The Walls Are Talking: Wallpaper, Art & Culture. 2010. (ENG., Illus.). 128p. 50.00 (978-0-9842260-0-9(1)) KWS Pubs.

Johnson, Marilynn A., et al. Louis Comfort Tiffany: Artist for the Ages. 2006. (ENG., Illus.). 240p. 49.95 (978-1-85759-384-6(7)) Scala, Editions FRA. Dist: National Bk. Network.

Laufer, Marilyn, et al. Real Western Wear: Beaded Gauntlets from the William Healey Collection: September 29, 2007-January 6, 2008. 2007. (978-0-915977-65-9(6)) Univ. of Georgia, Georgia Museum of Art.

Le Chevallier, Jacques & Archieri, Jean-François. Jacques Le Chevallier, 1896-1987: La Lumière Moderne. 2008. (FRE & ENG., Illus.). 248p. pap. 65.00 (978-2-35340-021-8(3)) Gourcuff Gradenigo FRA. Dist: National Bk. Network.

McElney, Brian S. Inaugural Exhibition Catalog of the Museum of East Asian Art. (Illus.). 281p. 75.00 (978-1-897734-00-1(X)) Museum of East Asian Art GBR. Dist: Art Media Resources, Inc.

Miller, Tony & Hui, Humphrey K. F. Elegance in Relief: Carved Porcelain from Jingdezhen of the 19th to early 20th Centuries. (CHI & ENG., Illus.). 358p. 55.00 (978-962-7101-75-8(3)) Art Media Resources, Inc.

Pal, Pratapaditya, ed. The Arts of Kashmir. 2008. (ENG., Illus.). 224p. pap. 55.00 (978-88-7439-408-1(X)) 5 Continents ITA. Dist: Hachette Bk. Group.

Piña, Leslie. Mexican Silver Jewelry Details. 2008. (Illus.). 304p. bds. 89.99 (978-0-7643-3081-0(0)) Schiffer Publishing, Ltd.

Schick, Marjorie. Sculpture Transformed: The Work of Marjorie Schick. 2007. *(978-0-9767102-2-6(6))* International Arts & Artists.

Schroder, Timothy. Renaissance Silver in the Schroder Collection. 2007. (Schroder Collection). (ENG., Illus.). 176p. pap. 50.00 *(978-0-900785-96-2(9))* Holberton, Paul Publishing GBR. Dist: Casemate Pubs. & Bk. Distributors, LLC.

Stevenson, John, intro. The Elephant & the Lotus: Vietnamese Ceramics in the Museum of Fine Arts, Boston, 1 vol. 2008. (ENG., Illus.). 272p. 85.00 *(978-0-87846-717-4(3))* Museum of Fine Arts, Boston.

Walpole, Lois. Urban Baskets: Tradition Recycled. 2010. (Illus.). 60p. pap. *(978-0-9565217-1-2(1))* Kan sasana Printer.

Ward, Gerald W. R. & Muniz, Julie M., eds. Shy Boy, She Devil, & Isis: The Art of Conceptual Craft; Selections from the Wornick Collection, 1 vol. 2007. (ENG., Illus.). 256p. 55.00 *(978-0-87846-718-1(1))* Museum of Fine Arts, Boston.

ART, DUTCH

see also De Stijl (Art Movement)

Adang, Marc. Voor Sociaal-Democratie, Smaakopvoeding en Verheffend Genot: De Amsterdamse Vereniging Kunst Aan Het Volk, 1903-1928. 2008. (DUT., Illus.). 766p. 57.50 ***(978-90-5260-314-8(6))*** Aksant Academic Pubs. NLD. Dist: Amsterdam Univ. Pr.

Alexander-Skipnes & Alexander-Skipnes, Ingrid. Cultural Exchange Between the Low Countries & Italy (1400-1600) 2007. (Museums at the Crossroads Ser.). (ENG., Illus.). 292p. (C). pap. 116.00 *(978-2-503-51838-1(9))* Brepols Pubs. BEL. Dist: ISD.

Bastiaans, Christiaan & text. Christiaan Bastiaans: Club Mama Gemutlich. 2010. (ENG., Illus.). 192p. 55.00 *(978-3-86678-287-7(X))* Kerber Verlag DEU. Dist: D.A.P./Distributed Art Pubs.

Beek, Wim Van Der. Jos Dirix: Sculptures Cyclical Life. 2009. (DUT & ENG., Illus.). 120p. *(978-90-78964-29-2(4),* Thieme Art (Acc)) Antique Collectors' Club.

Belkin, Kristin Lohse. Copies & Adaptations from Renaissance & Later Artists: German & Netherlandish Artists, 2 vols. 2009. (Corpus Rubenianum Ludwig Burchard Ser.). (ENG., Illus.). 600p. (C). 276.00 *(978-1-905375-38-7(7))* Miller, Harvey Pubs. GBR. Dist: Brown, David Bk. Co., The.

Beumer, Marjolein. Capturing Museum Knowledge: A Twenty Year Evolution in Digitally Recording the Tropenmuseum Collection. 2009. (Bulletins of the Royal Tropical Institute Ser.). 112p. pap. 35.00 *(978-90-6832-749-6(6))* Royal Tropical Institute Pr. (KIT (Koninklijk Instituut voor de Tropen) NLD. Dist: Stylus Publishing, LLC.

Bikker, Jonathan, et al. Dutch Paintings of the Seventeenth Century in the Rijksmuseum Amsterdam Vol. 1: Artists Born Between 1570 & 1600, 2 vols. 2008. (ENG., Illus.). 584p. 500.00 *(978-90-8689-027-9(X))* Yale Univ. Pr.

BIS Publishers Staff. Dutch Design 2008-2009, 2 vols. 2009. (DUT & ENG., Illus.). 856p. 59.00 *(978-90-6369-180-6(7))* Bis B.V., Uitgeverij(BIS Publishers) NLD. Dist: Consortium Bk. Sales & Distribution.

Clifton, James, et al, contrib. by. Scripture for the Eyes: Bible Illustration in Netherlandish Prints of the Sixteenth Century. 2009. (Illus.). 224p. pap. 49.95 *(978-0-9777839-3-9(6))* Museum of Biblical Art.

Curd, Mary Bryan H. Flemish & Dutch Artists in Early Modern England: Collaboration & Competition, 1460-1680. 2010. (Visual Culture in Early Modernity Ser.). (Illus.). 256p. 119.95 *(978-0-7546-6712-4(X))* Ashgate Publishing Co.

Dadi, Iftikhar, et al, texts. 6(0) Ways. 2010. (ENG., Illus.). 208p. pap. 40.00 *(978-90-5662-684-6(1))* NAi Uitgevers / Publishers Stichting NLD. Dist: D.A.P./Distributed Art Pubs.

De Bruijne, Ellen, ed. L. A. Raeven. 2011. (ENG., Illus.). 220p. pap. 60.00 *(978-3-7757-2706-8(X))* Hatje Cantz Verlag GmbH & Co KG DEU. Dist: D.A.P./Distributed Art Pubs.

den Hollander, A. A. Virtuelle Vergangenheit: Die Textrekonstruktion einer verlorenen mittelniederlandischen Evangelienharmonie. Die Handschrift Utrecht Universitatsbibliothek 1009. 2007. (Bibliotheca Ephemeridum Theologicarum Lovaniensium Ser.). (GER.). 168p. (C). pap. 85.00 *(978-90-429-1989-1(2))* Peeters Pubs. & Booksellers BEL. Dist: Brown, David Bk. Co., The.

Denderen, Ad Van. So Blue, So Blue: Edges of the Mediterranean, 1 vol. 2008. (ENG., Illus.). 272p. pap. 45.00 *(978-3-86521-734-9(6))* Steidl, Gerhard Druckerei und Verlag DEU. Dist: Innovative Logistics.

Deoldere, Luc. TLC - The Low Countries 16: Arts & Society in Flanders & the Netherlands. 2011. (Illus.). 320p. pap. *(978-90-75862-95-9(4),* Lannoo Pubs. (Acc)) Antique Collectors' Club.

—Tlc - The Low Countries 17: Arts & Society in Flanders & the Netherlands. 2011. (ENG., Illus.). 320p. pap. 65.00 *(978-90-79705-00-9(4))* Lannoo Pubs./Racine.

—TLC - The Low Countries 18: Arts & Society in Flanders & the Netherlands. 2011. (ENG., Illus.). 316p. pap. 65.00 *(978-90-79705-05-4(5))* Lannoo Pubs./Racine.

Dückers, Rob & Roelofs, Pieter. The Limbourg Brothers: Reflections on the Origins & the Legacy of Three Illuminators from Nijmegen. 2009. *(978-90-04-17512-9(1))* BRILL.

Dumas, Charlotte. Paradis, 1 vol. 2010. (ENG.). 76p. 56.00 *(978-90-8910-136-5(5))* Exhibitions International BEL. Dist: Innovative Logistics.

Duyves, Mattias & Put, Roos van. Ton of Holland: Contemporary Embroidery. 2013. (ENG., Illus.). 240p. 75.00 *(978-90-78964-47-6(2))* Thieme Art NLD. Dist: National Bk. Network.

Eliens, Titus M. Modern Glass in the Netherlands: 1880-1940. 2006. (DUT & ENG., Illus.). 164p. (C). 50.00 *(978-90-400-8671-7(0))* Waanders B.V., Uitgeverij NLD. Dist: Antique Collectors' Club.

Enke, Dieter. Andries Dirk Copier: Ideas in glass. Unica & more. 2010. (ENG., Illus.). 200p. 70.00 incl. cd-rom *(978-3-89790-299-2(0))* Arnoldsche Art Pubs. DEU. Dist: Antique Collectors' Club.

Esche, Charles, et al, eds. Citizens & Subjects: The Netherlands, for Example, 1 vol. 2007. (ENG., Illus.). 336p. pap. 29.00 *(978-3-905770-73-5(3))* JRP Ringier Kunstverlag AG CHE. Dist: D.A.P./Distributed Art Pubs.

Evans & Frankel, Susannah. The House of Viktor & Rolf. 2008. (Illus.). 256p. 59.95 *(978-1-85894-460-9(0))* Merrell Pubs. Ltd. GBR. Dist: Perseus Distribution.

Folie, Sabine, text. Rob Voerman: Aftermath. 2010. (ENG., Illus.). 160p. pap. 40.00 *(978-90-78088-40-0(0))* Valiz NLD. Dist: D.A.P./Distributed Art Pubs.

Garfik, Clare & Kuiper, Sybren, contrib. by. Cuny Janssen: Finding Thoughts. 2006. (Illus.). 80p. (gr. 13-18). 42.00 *(978-90-8546-053-4(0))* Veenman Pubs. NLD. Dist: D.A.P./Distributed Art Pubs.

Gibson, Walter S. Figures of Speech: Picturing Proverbs in Renaissance Netherlands. 2010. (ENG., Illus.). 256p. 49.95 *(978-0-520-25954-6(8))* Univ. of California Pr.

Golahny, A., et al, eds. In His Milieu: Essays on Netherlandish Art in Memory of John Michael Montias. 2007. (Illus.). 640p. pap. *(978-90-5356-933-7(2),* Leiden Univ. Pr.) Amsterdam Univ. Pr.

Gordon, Rivca & Gordon, Hayim. Hobbema & Heidegger: On Truth & Beauty. 2008. 150p. (C). 60.95 *(978-0-8204-8168-5(8))* Lang, Peter Publishing, Inc.

Graafland, Scarlett Hooft. Soft Horizons. 2012. (ENG., Illus.). 122p. pap. 50.00 ***(978-3-86828-223-8(8))*** Kehrer Verlag Heidelberg, Klaus Kehrer DEU. Dist: Consortium Bk. Sales & Distribution.

Henderikse, Jan. Jan Henderikse: Acheiropoieta Bilder, nicht von Menschenhand gemacht 1957-2010. 2010. (ENG., Illus.). 216p. 75.00 *(978-3-7757-2597-2(0))* Hatje Cantz Verlag GmbH & Co KG DEU. Dist: D.A.P./Distributed Art Pubs.

Huizing, Colin & Visser, Tijs. Nul = 0: The Dutch Nul Group in an International Context. 2012. (ENG., Illus.). 192p. pap. 45.00 ***(978-90-5662-838-3(0))*** NAi Uitgevers / Publishers Stichting NLD. Dist: D.A.P./Distributed Art Pubs.

Husband, Timothy Bates & Husband, Timothy. The Art of Illumination: The Limbourg Brothers & the Belles Heures of Jean de France, Duc de Berry. 2009. (ENG., Illus.). 388p. 65.00 *(978-0-300-13671-5(4))* Yale Univ. Pr.

Jong, Jan de. Rubens & the Netherlands (Rubens en de Nederlanden) Ramakers, Bart et al, eds. 2006. (Netherlands Yearbook for History of Art Ser.). (ENG., Illus.). 336p. 200.00 *(978-90-400-9109-4(9))* Waanders B.V., Uitgeverij NLD. Dist: National Bk. Network.

Jongh, E. de, et al, contrib. by. Mirror of Everyday Life: Genreprints in the Netherlands, 1550-1700. (Illus.). 399p. *(978-90-5349-237-6(2))* Snoeck-Ducaju en Zoon, N.V.

K#xFC;ng, Moritz, ed. Bas Princen: Reservoir. 2011. (ENG., Illus.). 60p. pap. 45.00 ***(978-3-7757-2832-4(5))*** Hatje Cantz Verlag GmbH & Co KG DEU. Dist: D.A.P./Distributed Art Pubs.

Knol, Meta, et al, eds. Beyond the Dutch: Indonesia, the Netherlands & the Arts from 1990 to Date. 2010. 200p. 39.00 *(978-94-6022-059-3(2))* Royal Tropical Institute Pr. (KIT (Koninklijk Instituut voor de Tropen) NLD. Dist: Stylus Publishing, LLC.

Koekebakker, Olof, text. PrixdeRome. NL 2010. 2010. (ENG., Illus.). 120p. pap. 35.00 *(978-90-5662-753-9(8))* NAi Uitgevers / Publishers Stichting NLD. Dist: D.A.P./Distributed Art Pubs.

Lehmann, Ann-Sophie. In the Flesh: Jan van Eyck's Adam & Eve - Panels & the Making of the Northern Nude. 2012. (ENG., Illus.). 288p. 130.00 *(978-90-400-8378-5(9))* Waanders B.V., Uitgeverij NLD. Dist: National Bk. Network.

Lewis-Anthony, Justin. Circles of Thorns: Hieronymus Bosch & Being Human. 2009. (ENG., Illus.). 200p. 27.95 *(978-1-906286-21-7(3))* Mowbray, A. R. & Co., Ltd. GBR. Dist: National Bk. Network.

LeZotte, Annette. The Home Setting in Early Netherlands Paintings: A Statistical & Iconographical Analysis of Fifteenth- & Early Sixteenth-Century Domestic Imagery. 2008. 196p. *(978-0-7734-5093-6(9))* Mellen, Edwin Pr., The.

Lucas, Edward Verrall. A Wanderer in Holland. 2008. (Illus.). 316p. 28.99 *(978-0-554-34457-7(2))* 2008. (Illus.). 316p. 29.99 *(978-0-554-25154-7(X))* 2007. (ENG.). 282p. pap. 21.99 *(978-1-4264-8278-6(7))* 2007. (ENG.). 312p. pap. 24.99 *(978-1-4264-8315-8(5))* BiblioBazaar.

—A Wanderer in Holland. 2008. 436p. 51.95 *(978-1-4369-9935-9(9));* pap. 36.95 *(978-1-4367-5766-9(5))* Kessinger Publishing, LLC.

Marchant, Nancy. Knitting Brioche: The Essential Guide to the Brioche Stitch. 2010. (ENG., Illus.). 256p. pap. 27.99 *(978-1-60061-301-2(2),* North Light Bks.) F&W Media, Inc.

Melion, Walter S. Scripture for the Eyes: Bible Illustration in Netherlandish Prints of the Sixteenth Century. Clifton, James, ed. 2009. (ENG., Illus.). 224p. 65.00 *(978-1-904832-66-9(0))* Giles, D. Ltd. GBR. Dist: Antique Collectors' Club.

Morris, Stuart. Vincent Van Gogh: Visionary Landscapes. 2nd ed. 2008. (Painters Ser.). (Illus.). 132p. pap. *(978-1-86171-185-4(9))* Crescent Moon Publishing.

Netherlands Art, Architecture & Landscape. Date not set. (Illus.). 400p. 19.95 *(978-3-8290-6471-2(3),* 521653) Konemann.

Oltheten, Paulien, photos by. Theorie Van de Straat/Theory of the Street. 2008. (ENG., Illus.). 176p. pap. 39.95 *(978-90-5662-597-9(7))* NAi Uitgevers / Publishers Stichting NLD. Dist: D.A.P./Distributed Art Pubs.

Ornstein-Van Slooten, Eva. The Rembrandt House: A Catalogue of Rembrandt Etchings. Van Der Veen, Jaap, ed. 2006. (ENG., Illus.). 176p. pap. 19.95 *(978-90-400-8851-3(9))* Waanders B.V., Uitgeverij NLD. Dist: National Bk. Network.

Ploeg, Peter van der, et al, contrib. by. Princely Patrons: The Collection of Frederick Henry of Orange & Amalia of Solms in the Hague. (Illus.). 276p. *(978-90-400-9193-3(5))* Waanders B.V., Uitgeverij.

Priem, Ruud. Rembrandt & the Golden Age of Dutch Art: Treasures from the Rijksmuseum, Amsterdam. Hunter-Stiebel, Penelope, ed. 2007. (ENG., Illus.). 144p. 29.95 *(978-1-883124-23-6(9))* Portland Art Museum.

—Vermeer, Rembrandt & the Golden Age of Dutch Art: Masterpieces of the Rijksmuseum, 1 vol. 2009. (ENG., Illus.). 240p. pap. 39.95 *(978-1-55365-471-1(4))* D&M Pubs. Inc. CAN. Dist: Perseus-PGW.

Ricchi, Daria, et al, texts. Giny Vos: Singing in the Dark. 2011. (ENG., Illus.). 192p. pap. 45.00 *(978-90-78088-33-2(8))* Valiz NLD. Dist: D.A.P./Distributed Art Pubs.

Rorimer, Anne, et al. Ger Van Elk: Monograph. 2009. (DUT & ENG., Illus.). 304p. pap. *(978-90-78964-28-5(6),* Thieme Art (Acc)) Antique Collectors' Club.

Royalton-Kisch, Martin. Rembrandt as Printmaker, 1 vol. 2006. (ENG., Illus.). 96p. pap. 25.00 *(978-1-85332-255-6(5))* Hayward Gallery Publishing GBR. Dist: D.A.P./Distributed Art Pubs.

Sakamoto, Tomoko & Prat, Ramon, eds. Super Holland Design: New Graphics. 2008. (Illus.). 431p. *(978-84-96954-19-9(6))* Actar Birkhauser Distribution.

Sassen, Vivianne, et al, photos by. Dutch Dare: Contemporary Photography from the Netherlands, 1 vol. 2007. (ENG., Illus.). 136p. pap. 24.00 *(978-90-5662-548-1(9))* NAi Uitgevers / Publishers Stichting NLD. Dist: D.A.P./Distributed Art Pubs.

Seaman, Natasha T. The Religious Paintings of Hendrick Ter Brugghen: Reinventing Christian Painting after the Reformation in Utrecht. 2012. (Visual Culture in Early Modernity Ser.). (Illus.). 200p. 104.95 ***(978-1-4094-3495-5(8))*** Ashgate Publishing Co.

Sellin, Christine Petra. Fractured Families & Rebel Maidservants: The Biblical Hagar in Seventeenth-Century Dutch Art & Literature. 2006. (ENG., Illus.). 208p. pap. 39.95 *(978-0-567-02901-0(8),* T&T Clark Int'l) Continuum International Publishing Group, Ltd. GBR. Dist: National Bk. Network.

Shorto, Russell. Exploring Historic Dutch New York: New York City * the Hudson Valley * New Jersey * Delaware. Scheltema, Gajus & Westerhuijs, Heleen, eds. 2011. (New York City Ser.). (ENG.). 256p. pap. 19.95 ***(978-0-486-48637-6(0))*** Dover Pubns., Inc.

Sluijter, Eric Jan. Rembrandt & the Female Nude. 2007. (Amsterdam Studies in the Dutch Golden Age Ser.). (ENG., Illus.). 448p. pap. *(978-90-5356-837-8(9),* Leiden Univ. Pr.) Amsterdam Univ. Pr.

Sluijter, Kim. Locating 'Realism' in Seventeenth-Century Dutch Art. 2011. 80p. pap. ***(978-3-8443-2310-8(4))*** Lambert Academic Publishing.

Sluijter-Seijffert, Nicolette C., et al. Aemulatio. Coutré, Jacquelyn N., ed. 2011. (Illus.). 512p. 135.00 ***(978-90-400-7801-9(7))*** Waanders B.V., Uitgeverij NLD. Dist: National Bk. Network.

Smits, Lisette, ed. Barbara Visser Is Er Niet: Works 1990-2006, 1 vol. 2007. (ENG., Illus.). 240p. 45.00 *(978-3-905770-25-4(3))* JRP Ringier Kunstverlag AG CHE. Dist: D.A.P./Distributed Art Pubs.

Stedelijk Museum: Survey. pap. 19.95 *(978-90-5006-032-5(3))* Stedelijk Museum NLD. Dist: D.A.P./Distributed Art Pubs.

Suh, H. Anna. Van Gogh's Letters: The Mind of the Artist in Paintings, Drawings, & Words, 1875-1890. 2010. (ENG., Illus.). 320p. pap. 19.95 *(978-1-57912-859-3(9),* 1579128599) Black Dog & Leventhal Pubs., Inc.

Timmer, Nicole, text. PrixdeRome. NL 2011. 2011. (ENG., Illus.). 112p. pap. 35.00 ***(978-90-5662-812-3(7))*** NAi Uitgevers / Publishers Stichting NLD. Dist: D.A.P./Distributed Art Pubs.

Tompkins Rivas, Pilar, et al, contrib. by. Bas Jan Ader. 2010. (ENG., Illus.). 69p. pap. 7.95 *(978-0-9829956-0-0(1))* Pitzer College Art Galleries.

Tromp, Henk. A Real Van Gogh: How the Art World Struggles with Truth. 2010. (Illus.). 351p. pap. *(978-90-8964-176-2(9))* Amsterdam Univ. Pr.

van Bommel, Maarten, et al, eds. Inside Out Victory Boogie Woogie: A Material History of Mondrian's Masterpiece. 2012. (RCE Publications). (ENG., Illus.). 320p. pap. ***(978-90-8964-373-5(7))*** Amsterdam Univ. Pr.

Van Buhren, Ralf. Die Werke der Barmherzigkeit in der Kunst des 12.-18. Jahrhunderts. Date not set. (Studien zur Kunstgeschichte Ser.: Bd. 115). (GER., Illus.). 424p. *(978-3-487-10319-8(2))* Olms, Georg Verlag AG.

Van de Velde, C., ed. Classical Mythology in the Netherlands in the Age of Renaissance & Baroque - la mythologie classique aux temps de la Renaissance et du Baroque dans les Pays-Bas: Proceedings of the International Conference Antwerp, 19-21 May 2005 - Actes du Colloque international Anvers, 19-21 Mai 2005. 2009. (Travaux de la Renaissance et de L'Humanisme Ser.). (ENG & FRE., Illus.). 394p. (C). pap. 95.00 *(978-90-429-2052-1(1))* Peeters Pubs. & Booksellers BEL. Dist: Brown, David Bk. Co., The.

van den Heuvel, Maartje, ed. Nature as Artifice. 2008. (ENG.). 288p. 80.00 *(978-90-5662-028-8(2))* NAi Uitgevers / Publishers Stichting NLD. Dist: D.A.P./Distributed Art Pubs.

Van der Stighelen, K., ed. The Nude & the Norm in the Early Modern Low Countries. 2011. (Museums at the Crossroads Ser.). (ENG., Illus.). 220p. (C). pap. 94.00 *(978-2-503-53569-2(0))* Brepols Pubs. BEL. Dist: ISD.

Van der Vinde, Lea. Children in the Mauritshuis. 2008. (ENG., Illus.). 72p. 29.95 *(978-90-400-8430-0(0))* Waanders B.V., Uitgeverij NLD. Dist: National Bk. Network.

van Dijk, Janneke & Legêne, Susan. The Netherlands East Indies at the Tropenmuseum. 2011. (Collections at the Tropenmuseum Ser.). 200p. 45.00 *(978-90-6832-751-9(8))* Royal Tropical Institute Pr. (KIT (Koninklijk Instituut voor de Tropen) NLD. Dist: Stylus Publishing, LLC.

van Gelder, Esther. Tussen hof en Keizerskroon: Carolus Clusius en de ontwikkeling van de botanie aan Midden-Europese Hoven (1573-1593) 2011. (LUP Dissertaties Ser.). (DUT.). 444p. pap. ***(978-90-8728-131-1(5),*** Leiden Univ. Pr.) Amsterdam Univ. Pr.

Vanstiphout, Wouter & van den Boogerd, Dominic, texts. Jeroen Doorenweerd. 2009. (ENG & DUT., Illus.). 208p. pap. 45.00 *(978-90-5662-676-1(0))* NAi Uitgevers / Publishers Stichting NLD. Dist: D.A.P./Distributed Art Pubs.

Waanders Editors. Black Is Beautiful: Rubens to Dumas. 2008. (ENG., Illus.). 336p. 45.00 *(978-90-400-8497-3(1))* Waanders B.V., Uitgeverij NLD. Dist: National Bk. Network.

—Body & Embodiment: In Dutch Expressive Arts, 1450-1700. 2009. (ENG., Illus.). 336p. 195.00 *(978-90-400-8418-8(1))* Waanders B.V., Uitgeverij NLD. Dist: National Bk. Network.

—Envisioning the Artist: In the Early Modern Netherlands. 2010. (ENG., Illus.). 344p. 195.00 *(978-90-400-7683-1(9))* Waanders B.V., Uitgeverij NLD. Dist: National Bk. Network.

Walther, Ingo F. & Metzger, Rainer. Van Gogh - the Complete Paintings. 2006. 736p. (DUT.). pap. 12.99 *(978-3-8228-5137-1(X));* (FRE.). pap. 12.99 *(978-3-8228-5067-1(5));* (SPA.). pap. 12.99 *(978-3-8228-5066-4(7));* (POR.). pap. 12.99 *(978-3-8228-5219-4(8));* (ITA.). pap. 12.99 *(978-3-8228-5218-7(X));* (GER.). pap. 12.99 *(978-3-8228-5065-7(9))* Taschen America, LLC.

—Van Gogh - the Complete Paintings. 2006. (JPN.). 736p. pap. *(978-4-88783-292-3(3))* Taschen Japan.

Weller, Dennis P., et al, contrib. by. Rembrandt in America: Collecting & Connoisseurship. 2011. (ENG., Illus.). 224p. pap. 60.00 *(978-0-8478-3685-7(1),* Skira) Rizzoli International Pubns., Inc.

Weller, Dennis P., intro. & text. Rembrandt: Paintings in America. 2011. (Illus.). 224p. pap. 50.00 *(978-0-8478-3687-1(8),* Skira) Rizzoli International Pubns., Inc.

Weststeijn, Thijs. The Visible World: Samuel van Hoogstraten's Art Theory & the Legitimation of Painting in the Dutch Golden Age. 2009. (Amsterdam Studies in the Dutch Golden Age Ser.). (Illus.). 512p. pap. *(978-90-8964-027-7(4),* Leiden Univ. Pr.) Amsterdam Univ. Pr.

Wheelock, Arthur K., Jr., et al. Jan Lievens: A Dutch Master Rediscovered. 2008. (ENG., Illus.). 320p. (C). 65.00 *(978-0-300-14213-6(7))* Yale Univ. Pr.

World Press Photo Foundation Staff & World, Press. World Press Photo 2008. 2008. (ENG., Illus.). 140p. pap. 24.95 *(978-0-500-97677-7(5))* Thames & Hudson.

Wouda, Raimond. School. 2009. (Illus.). 52p. *(978-1-59005-241-9(2))* Nazraeli Pr.

Zandvliet, Kees. The Dutch Encounter with Asia: 1600-1950. 2006. (Illus.). 464p. (C). 50.00 *(978-90-400-8717-2(2))* Waanders B.V., Uitgeverij NLD. Dist: Antique Collectors' Club.

ART, EARLY CHRISTIAN

see Christian Art and Symbolism

ART, EAST ASIAN

Ching, Dora C. & Smith, Judith. Bridges to Heaven: Essays on East Asian Art in Honor of Professor Wen C. Fong, 2 vols. 2011. (Publications of the Department of Art & Archaeology, Princeton University Ser.). (ENG., Illus.). 992p. (C). 175.00 ***(978-0-691-15298-1(5))*** Princeton Univ. Pr.

Coomaraswamy, Ananda Kentish. Introduction to the Art of Eastern Asi. 2011. 48p. 35.95 ***(978-1-258-02454-3(3))*** Literary Licensing, LLC.

Cram101 Textbook Reviews. Outlines & Highlights for a History of Far Eastern Art by Lee, Isbn: 0810934140 0133933989. 2011. 402p. pap. 35.95 ***(978-1-61812-674-0(1))*** Cram101 Inc.

Cram101 Textbook Reviews Staff. Outlines & Highlights for History of Far Eastern Art by Sherman Lee, Isbn: 9780131830639. 2009. 126p. pap. 28.95 *(978-1-4288-9812-7(3))* Cram101 Inc.

FAHR BECKER, Gabriele. The art of east Asia, 1 vol. 2011. (ENG.). 740p. 49.99 *(978-3-8331-6098-1(5))* h.f.ullmann DEU. Dist: Innovative Logistics.

Fahr-Becker, Gabriele, ed. The Art of East Asia. 2008. (Art & Architecture Ser.). (Illus.). 739p. 69.95 *(978-0-8416-0093-5(7))* American Map Corp.

Hou, Cuixing. Chou Xiang Xin Jing. 2007. (CHI & ENG., Illus.). 191p. *(978-986-00-9516-6(7))* Academia Sinica.

Jungmann, Burglind, et al, eds. Shifting Paradigms in East Asian Visual Culture: A Festschrift in Honour of Lothar Ledderose. 2012. (ENG.). 400p. 89.00 *(978-3-496-01440-9(7))* Reimer, Dietrich DEU. Dist: Independent Pubs. Group.

Maggia, Filippo & Lazzarini, Francesca. Contemporary Photography from the Far East: Asian Dub Photography. Maggia, Filippo & Lazzarini, Francesca, eds. 2009. (ENG., Illus.). 240p. 50.00 *(978-88-572-0067-5(1))* Skira Editore ITA. Dist: Random Hse., Inc.

Marella, Primo & Battiston, Eleonora, eds. Post-Tsunami Art. 2009. (ENG., Illus.). 168p. 45.00 *(978-88-6208-090-3(5))* Damiani ITA. Dist: D.A.P./Distributed Art Pubs.

ART, ECCLESIASTICAL

see Christian Art and Symbolism

ART, EFFECT OF

see Art Therapy

ART, EGYPTIAN

Abaza, Mona. Collecting Modern Egyptian Art: Sherwet Shafei & the Pioneer Painters of the Twentieth Century. 2011. (ENG.). 208p. 49.50 *(978-977-416-394-4(X))* American Univ. in Cairo Pr. EGY. Dist: Oxford Univ. Pr., Inc.

Amer, Ghada. Ghada Amer. 2010. (ENG., Illus.). 304p. 70.00 *(978-0-9800242-0-3(X))* Miller, Gregory & Co.

Andreae, Bernard. Kleopatra und die Caesaren: Katalogband zur Ausstellung im Bucerius Kunst Forum, Hamburg. 2006. (GER., Illus.). 264p. (C). pap. 42.00 *(978-3-7774-3245-8(8))* Hirmer Verlag GmbH DEU. Dist: Brown, David Bk. Co., The.

Aufrere, Sydney H. Description de l'Egypte Published by Order of Napoleon Bonaparte. (ENG & FRE., Illus.). 552p. 75.00 *(978-2-909808-49-9(1))* Inter-Livres-Bibliotheque de l'image FRA. Dist: Weatherhill, Inc.

Avedissian, Chant. Patterns, Costumes & Stencils. 2009. (ENG.). 128p. pap. 19.95 *(978-0-86356-679-0(0))* Saqi Bks. GBR. Dist: Consortium Bk. Sales & Distribution.

Bárta, Miroslav & Barta, Miroslav, eds. Old Kingdom Art & Archaeology: Proceedings of a Conference, Prague 2004. 2006. (ENG.). 300p. (C). 100.00 *(978-80-200-1465-8(9))* Czech Institute of Egyptology CZE. Dist: Brown, David Bk. Co., The.

Ben-Tor, Daphna. Scarabs, Chronology, & Interconnections: Egypt & Palestine in the Second Intermediate Period. 2007. (Orbis Biblicus et Orientalis. Series Archaeologica Ser.). (GER & ENG., Illus.). 442p. (C). 144.00 *(978-3-525-53204-1(0))* Vandenhoeck & Ruprecht GmbH & Co. KG DEU. Dist: ISD.

Bernhauer, Edith. Innovationen in der Privatplastik: Die 18. Dynastie und ihre Entwicklung. 2010. (Philippika Ser.). (GER.). 341p. (C). pap. 102.00 *(978-3-447-05712-7(2))* Harrassowitz, Otto Verlag DEU. Dist: ISD.

Bietak, Manfred & Maguire, Louise C. Tell el-Dab'a XXI. 2009. (Denkschriften der Gesamtakademie Ser.). (ENG.). 260p. (C). pap. 142.50 *(978-3-7001-6585-9(4))* Austrian Academy of Sciences Press AUT. Dist: Brown, David Bk. Co., The.

Bleiberg, Edward. To Live Forever: Egyptian Treasures from the Brooklyn Museum. 2008. (Illus.). 152p. pap. *(978-0-87273-159-2(6))* Brooklyn Museum, The.

Bleiberg, Edward & Cooney, Kathlyn M. To Live Forever: Egyptian Treasures from the Brooklyn Museum. 2008. (ENG., Illus.). 152p. 39.95 *(978-1-904832-52-2(0))* Giles, D. Ltd. GBR. Dist: Antique Collectors' Club.

Bongioann, Alessandro & Croce, Maria Sole, eds. The Treasures of Ancient Egypt: The Collection of the Egyptian Museum in Cairo. Milan, C T M, tr. 2007. (Illus.). 631p. pap. 12.99 *(978-88-540-0834-2(6))* White Star ITA. Dist: Book Sales, Inc.

Capart, Jean. Lectures on Egyptian Art. 2007. (ENG.). 320p. 45.95 *(978-0-548-09245-3(1))* Kessinger Publishing, LLC.

Cooney, John. Late Egyptian & Coptic Art: An Introduction to the Collections in the Brooklyn Museum. 2011. 82p. 37.95 ***(978-1-258-09289-4(1))*** Literary Licensing, LLC.

Cooney, John D. & Riefstahl, Elizabeth. Pagan & Christian Egypt: Egyptian Art from the First to the Tenth Century. 2011. 198p. 42.95 ***(978-1-258-03750-5(5))*** Literary Licensing, LLC.

D'Auria, Sue & Fazzini, Richard A. Servant of Mut: Studies in Honor of Richard A. Fazzini. 2007. (Illus.). xxiv, 267p. *(978-90-04-15857-3(X))* BRILL.

D'Avennes, Prisse. Atlas of Egyptian Art. 2008. (ENG., Illus.). 128p. pap. 24.95 *(978-977-416-120-9(3))* American Univ. in Cairo Pr. EGY. Dist: Oxford Univ. Pr., Inc.

Deger-Jalkotzy, Sigrid & Schindel, Nikolaus, eds. Gold: Tagung anlasslich der Grundung des Zentrums Archaologie und Altertumswissenschaften an der Osterreichischen Akademie der Wissenschaften, 19. 20. April 2007. 2009. (Denkschriften der Phil. -Hist. Klasse Ser.). (GER., Illus.). 206p. (C). pap. 102.00 *(978-3-7001-6547-7(1))* Austrian Academy of Sciences Press AUT. Dist: Brown, David Bk. Co., The.

Dover. Egyptian Motifs in the Art Deco Style. 2011. (Dover Pictorial Archive Ser.). (ENG., Illus.). 80p. pap. 16.95 ***(978-0-486-48446-4(7))*** Dover Pubns., Inc.

Dover Publications Inc. Staff, creator. Ancient Egyptian Design. 2007. (Dover Pictura Electronic Clip Art Ser.). (ENG., Illus.). 128p. pap. 39.95 *(978-0-486-99806-0(1))* Dover Pubns., Inc.

Evans, Linda. Animal Behaviour in Egyptian Art: Representations of the Natural World in Memphite Tomb Scenes. 2010. (ACE Studies). (ENG., Illus.). 350p. (C). pap. 130.00 *(978-0-85668-826-3(6))* Australian Ctr. for Egyptology AUS. Dist: Brown, David Bk. Co., The.

Freed, Rita. The secrets of Tomb 10A: Egypt 2000 BC. 2009. 224p. pap. 40.00 *(978-0-87846-748-8(3))* Museum of Fine Arts, Boston.

Freed, Rita, et al, texts. The Secrets of Tomb 10A. 2009. (ENG., Illus.). 208p. 60.00 *(978-0-87846-747-1(5))* Museum of Fine Arts, Boston.

Georganteli, Eurydice, et al. Sacred & Profane. 2010. (ENG., Illus.). 128p. 40.00 *(978-1-904832-80-5(6))* Giles, D. Ltd. GBR. Dist: Antique Collectors' Club.

Hagen, Rose-Marie. Egyptian Art. Wolf, Norbert, ed. 2007. (Basic Art Ser.). (ENG., Illus.). 94p. pap. 9.99 *(978-3-8228-5458-7(1))* TASCHEN DEU. Dist: Ingram Pub. Services.

Hagen, Rose-Marie & Hagen, Rainer. Egypt: People, Gods, Pharaohs. 25th ed. 2006. (ENG., Illus.). 240p. 14.99 *(978-3-8228-4767-1(4))* TASCHEN DEU. Dist: Ingram Pub. Services.

Humbert, Jean-Marcel & Price, Clifford, eds. Imhotep Today: Egyptianizing Architecture. 2007. (Encounters with Ancient Egypt series, University College London Institute of Archaeology Publications). (ENG., Illus.). 340p. pap. 34.95 *(978-1-59874-201-5(9))* Left Coast Pr., Inc.

Kamrin, Janice. The Illustrated Guide to the Luxor Museum of Ancient Art & the Nubia Museum of Aswan: With the Luxor Mummification Museum & the Kom Ombo Crocodile Museum. 2012. (ENG.). 308p. 29.95 *(978-977-416-344-9(3))* American Univ. in Cairo Pr. EGY. Dist: Oxford Univ. Pr., Inc.

Mahnke, Charis. Alexandrinische Mosaikglaseinlagen: Die Typologie, Systematik und Herstellung Von Gesichterdarstellungen in der Ptolemäischen Glaskunst. 2008. (Philippika Ser.). (GER., Illus.). 200p. (C). pap. 87.00 *(978-3-447-05633-5(9))* Harrassowitz, Otto Verlag DEU. Dist: ISD.

Malek, Jaromir & Málek, Jaromír. ABC of Egyptian Hieroglyphs. 2011. (ENG., Illus.). 48p. pap. 10.00 *(978-1-85444-247-5(3))* Ashmolean Museum GBR. Dist: Antique Collectors' Club.

Manley, Bill. Egyptian Treasures. 2010. (ENG., Illus.). 176p. 29.95 *(978-1-905267-17-0(7))* NMS Enterprises Ltd. - Publishing GBR. Dist: National Bk. Network.

Marcos, Marcos A., et al. Marguerite Nakhla: Legacy to Modern Egyptian Art. 2009. (ENG., Illus.). 141p. (C). pap. 39.95 *(978-0-9312726-0-3(6))* Brown, David Bk. Co., The.

Maspero, Gaston. Manual of Egyptian Archaeology & Guide to the Study of Antiquities in Egypt. 2008. 368p. 29.99 *(978-0-554-35927-4(8))* 2008. 368p. 31.99 *(978-0-554-26624-4(5))* 2007. (ENG.). 344p. pap. 23.99 *(978-1-4346-1480-3(8))* 2007. (ENG.). 364p. pap. 26.99 *(978-1-4346-1574-9(X))* BiblioBazaar.

—Manual of Egyptian Archaeology & Guide to the Study of Antiquities in Egypt: For the Use of Students & Travellers. Edwards, Amelia B., tr. from FRE. 5th ed. 2010. (Cambridge Library Collection - Archaeology Ser.). (Illus.). 424p. pap. 31.99 *(978-1-108-01763-3(0))* Cambridge Univ. Pr.

Meijer, W. Arnold & Dijk, Jacobus van. Objects for Eternity: Egyptian Antiquities from the W. Arnold Meijer Collection. 2006. (Illus.). 280p. 45.00 *(978-3-8053-3651-2(9))* Zabern, Philipp von Verlag GmbH DEU. Dist: Brown, David Bk. Co., The.

Nabil. I Won't Let You Die. 2009. (ENG., Illus.). 272p. 60.00 *(978-3-7757-2306-0(4))* Hatje Cantz Verlag GmbH & Co KG DEU. Dist: D.A.P./Distributed Art Pubs.

Nardo, Don, ed. Ancient Egyptian Art & Architecture. 2011. (Eye on Art Ser.). (Illus.). 128p. (YA). (gr. 7-12). 33.45 *(978-1-4205-0674-7(9))* Cengage Gale.

Nicholls, Dale Reeves, et al. Egyptian Revival Jewelry & Design. 2006. (Illus.). 176p. 39.95 *(978-0-7643-2540-3(X))* Schiffer Publishing, Ltd.

Nilsson, Maria. Crown of Arsinoe II: The Creation of an Image of Authority. 2012. (ENG., Illus.). 272p. (C). 110.00 ***(978-1-84217-492-0(4))*** Oxbow Bks., Ltd. GBR. Dist: Brown, David Bk. Co., The.

Obrist, Hans Ulrich, ed. Susan Hefuna: Pars Pro Toto. 2009. (ARA & ENG., Illus.). 256p. pap. 90.00 *(978-3-939583-76-9(6))* Kehrer Verlag Heidelberg, Klaus Kehrer DEU. Dist: Consortium Bk. Sales & Distribution.

O'Kane, Bernard. The Illustrated Guide to the Museum of Islamic Art in Cairo: With the Museums of Islamic Ceramics & Islamic Textiles. 2012. (ENG.) 416p. 29.95 *(978-977-416-338-8(9))* American Univ. in Cairo Pr. EGY. Dist: Oxford Univ. Pr., Inc.

Owusu, Heike. Egyptian Symbols. 2008. (ENG., Illus.). 304p. pap. 12.95 *(978-1-4027-4623-9(7))* Sterling Publishing Co., Inc.

Patch, Diana. Dawn of Egyptian Art. 2012. (ENG., Illus.). 288p. 60.00 ***(978-0-300-17952-1(9))*** Yale Univ. Pr.

Quibell, A. A. Egyptian History & Art 1923. 2007. (ENG.). 206p. 39.95 *(978-0-548-05406-2(1))* Kessinger Publishing, LLC.

Radwan, Ali, ed. Ancient Egypt at the Cairo Museum. 2011. (Illus.). 214p. pap. ***(978-977-437-926-0(8))*** American Univ. in Cairo Pr.

Regine, Schulz. Art & Architecture Egypt. 2010. (Art & Architecture Pocket Ser.). 68p. pap. 16.99 *(978-0-8416-7158-4(3))* Langenscheidt Publishing Group.

Roberts, David, illus. The Pyramids Portfolio. 2011. 19.95 *(978-977-416-429-3(6))* Oxford Univ. Pr., Inc.

Robins, Gay. The Art of Ancient Egypt. 2nd rev. ed. 2008. (Illus.). 272p. pap. 30.50 *(978-0-674-03065-7(6))* Harvard Univ. Pr.

Rocheleau, Caroline M. Ancient Egyptian Art: Systematic Catalogue of the Collection, North Carolina Museum of Art, Raleigh. 2012. ***(978-0-88259-996-0(8))*** North Carolina Museum of Art.

Roques, K. A. V. Contemporary Art from Egypt. 2008. (ENG.). 200p. 59.00 *(978-3-87909-938-2(3))* Wienand GmbH, Druck- & Verlagshaus DEU. Dist: Independent Pubs. Group.

Russmann, Edna R. Unearthing the Truth: Egypt's Pagan & Coptic Sculpture. 2009. *(978-0-87273-162-2(6))* Brooklyn Museum, The.

Schatz, Florence. Ancient Egyptian Art - the Fun Way. 2008. 104p. pap. 33.49 *(978-1-4389-1469-5(5))* AuthorHouse.

Schulz, Regine & Seidel, Matthias. Egyptian Art. 2009. pap. *(978-0-911886-70-2(2))* Walters Art Museum, US.

Seidel, Matthias & Schulz, Regine. Egypt. 2008. (Art & Architecture Ser.). (Illus.). 608p. 19.95 *(978-0-8416-0147-5(X))* American Map Corp.

—Egypt, 1 vol. 2010. (ENG., Illus.). 608p. pap. 9.99 *(978-3-8331-5281-8(8))* h.f.ullmann DEU. Dist: Innovative Logistics.

Seidel, Matthias, et al. Egyptian Art: The Walters Art Museum. 2009. (ENG., Illus.). 192p. 45.00 *(978-1-904832-57-7(1))* Giles, D. Ltd. GBR. Dist: Antique Collectors' Club.

Stamm, Rainer, ed. Paula Modersohn-Becker und die Mumienportraits: Eine Hommage zum 100. Todestag der Künstlerin. Katalogbuch zur Ausstellung: Bremen, 14.10.2007-24.02.2008, Kunstsammlung Böttcherstraße. 2007. (GER., Illus.). 220p. (C). pap. 53.00 *(978-3-7774-3735-4(2))* Hirmer Verlag GmbH DEU. Dist: Brown, David Bk. Co., The.

Strudwick, Helen & Strudwick, Nigel, eds. Old Kingdom, New Perspectives: Egyptian Art & Archaeology 2750-2150 BC. 2011. (ENG., Illus.). 344p. (C). 120.00 *(978-1-84217-430-2(4))* Oxbow Bks., Ltd. GBR. Dist: Brown, David Bk. Co., The.

Strudwick, Nigel. Masterpieces of Ancient Egypt. 2006. (ENG., Illus.). 352p. 35.00 *(978-0-292-71662-9(1))* Univ. of Texas Pr.

Supreme Council of Antiquities, ed. Bulletin of the Egyptian Museum: Volume 6. 2011. (ENG.). 88p. pap. 24.50 ***(978-977-479-535-0(0))*** American Univ. in Cairo Pr. EGY. Dist: Oxford Univ. Pr., Inc.

Taschen, creator. Description de L'Egypte. 25th ed. 2007. (ENG, FRE & GER., Illus.). 752p. pap. 14.99 *(978-3-8228-3775-7(X))* TASCHEN DEU. Dist: Ingram Pub. Services.

Tiradritti, Francesco. Egyptian Wall Painting. 2008. (ENG., Illus.). 392p. 175.00 *(978-0-7892-1008-1(8))* Abbeville Pr., Inc.

Tiradritti, Francesco & Vannini, Sandro. Egyptian Wall Painting, deluxe ed. 2008. (ENG., Illus.). 391p. 150.00 *(978-0-7892-1005-0(3))* Abbeville Pr., Inc.

Török, László. Hellenizing Art in Ancient Nubia, 300 BC-AD 250, & Its Egyptian Models: A Study in "Acculturation" 2011. (Culture & History of the Ancient near East Ser.). (Illus.). XXVI, 486p. ***(978-90-04-21128-5(4))*** BRILL.

Vassilika, Eleni. Art Treasures from the Museo Egizio. 2006. (ENG.). 160p. pap. 16.95 *(978-88-422-1417-5(5))* Allemandi, Umberto & Co. GBR. Dist: Antique Collectors' Club.

Walsem, René van & van Walsem, Renee. Iconography of Old Kingdom Elite Tombs: Analysis & Interpretation. 2006. (Mededelingen en Verhandelingen Van Het Vooraziatisch-Egyptisch Genootschap "Ex Oriente Lux" Ser.: Vol. 35). (ENG., Illus.). 142p. (C). pap. 22.00 *(978-90-429-1715-6(6))* Peeters Pubs. & Booksellers BEL. Dist: Brown, David Bk. Co., The.

Weller, Alan. Egyptian Vector Motifs. 2011. (Dover Electronic Clip Art Ser.). (ENG.). 48p. pap. 19.95 *(978-0-486-99162-7(8))* Dover Pubns., Inc.

Whitehouse, Helen & Brown, C. Ancient Egypt & Nubia. 2009. (ENG., Illus.). 128p. pap. 22.50 *(978-1-85444-202-4(3))* Ashmolean Museum GBR. Dist: Antique Collectors' Club.

Ziegler, Christiane. Queens of Egypt. Somogy Edition D'Art Staff, ed. 2008. (ENG.). 368p. 89.00 *(978-2-7572-0190-9(5))*, Art Stock Bks. Ltd/Csi) Continental Sales, Inc.

ART, ENGLISH

see Art, British

ART, ESKIMO

see Eskimos—Art

ART, ETHIOPIAN

Di Salvo, Mario. Crosses of Ethiopia: The Sign of Faith. Evolution & Form. 2006. (ENG., Illus.). 176p. 65.00 *(978-88-7624-256-4(2))* Skira Editore ITA. Dist: Random Hse., Inc.

Horowitz, Deborah E., et al. Ethiopian Art. 2006. (ENG., Illus.). 30.00 *(978-1-903942-02-4(0))* Third Millenium Publishing GBR. Dist: National Bk. Network.

Marx, Annegret, et al. Arise & Go Toward the South: 2000 Years of Christianity in Ethiopia. 2009. (GER & ENG., Illus.). 368p. 59.00 *(978-3-932942-28-0(0))* Legat-Verlag GmbH & Company KG DEU. Dist: Independent Pubs. Group.

Samuel P. Harn Museum of Art Staff, contrib. by. Continuity & Change: Three Generations of Ethiopian Artists. 2007. (Illus.). 124p. *(978-0-9762552-3-9(5))* Harn Museum of Art.

Zegeye, Abebe. Zerihun Yetmgeta: The Magical Universe of Art. 2008. (Illus.). 76p. pap. 22.50 *(978-1-86888-500-8(3))* Unisa Press / Uitgewers GBR. Dist: International Specialized Bk. Services.

ART, ETHNIC

see Ethnic Art

ART, ETRUSCAN

Iczzo, Mario, ed. The Chimaera of Arezzo. 2009. (Illus.). 52p. (C). (ENG.). pap. 15.00 *(978-88-596-0628-4(4))*; (ITA., pap. 15.00 *(978-88-596-0627-7(6))* Polistampa ITA. Dist: Brown, David Bk. Co., The.

Lawrence, D. H. Etruscan Places. 2007. (ENG.). 216p. per. *(978-1-4067-0400-6(8))* Read Bks.

Lowenstam, Steven. As Witnessed by Images: The Trojan War Tradition in Greek & Etruscan Art. 2008. (ENG., Illus.). 248p. (gr. 17). 52.00 *(978-0-8018-8775-8(5))* Johns Hopkins Univ. Pr.

Shepard, Katharine. The Fish-Tailed Monster in Greek & Etruscan Art. 2011. 156p. pap. 24.95 ***(978-1-61646-074-7(1))*** Coachwhip Pubns.

Steingraber, Stephan. Abundance of Life: Etruscan Wall Painting. Stockman, Russell, tr. from ITA. 2006. (Illus.). 320p. 150.00 *(978-0-89236-865-5(9))* Oxford Univ. Pr., Inc.

Torelli, Mario & Sgubini Moretti, Anna Maria. Etruschi: Le Antiche Metropoli Del Lazio. Torelli, Mario & Moretti, Anna Maria, eds. 2009. (ITA., Illus.). 304p. 77.50 *(978-88-370-6620-8(1))* Electa ITA. Dist: Trans-Atlantic Pubns., Inc.

Winter, Nancy A. Symbols of Wealth & Power: Architectural Terracotta Decoration in Etruria & Central Italy, 640-510 B. C. 2009. (Supplements to the Memoirs of the American Academy in Rome Ser.). (ENG., Illus.). 728p. 95.00 *(978-0-472-11665-2(7))* Univ. of Michigan Pr.

ART, EUROPEAN

Abelovsky, Jan & Bajcurova, Katarina. Art in Changing Times: Painting & Sculpture in Slovakia 1890-1949. 2007. (Illus.). 384p. 100.00 *(978-80-7145-412-0(5))* Slovart, Vydavateľstvo, spol. s.r.o, SVK. Dist: Independent Pubs. Group.

Ackley, Clifford, et al, texts. Splendor & Elegance. 2009. (ENG., Illus.). 160p. 55.00 *(978-0-87846-738-9(6))* Museum of Fine Arts, Boston.

Adamson, Walter L. Embattled Avant-Gardes: Modernism's Resistance to Commodity Culture in Europe. 2009. (ENG.). 448p. pap. 31.95 *(978-0-520-26153-2(4))* Univ. of California Pr.

Adlam, Carol & Simpson, Juliet, eds. Critical Exchange: Art Criticism of the Eighteenth & Nineteenth Centuries in Russia & Western Europe. 2009. (Cultural Interactions: Studies in the Relationship between the Arts Ser.). (ENG.). 420p. pap. 92.95 *(978-3-03911-556-3(1))* Lang, Peter GmbH, Europaischer Verlag der Wissenschaften DEU. Dist: Lang, Peter.

Alofsin, Anthony & Wright, Frank Lloyd. Frank Lloyd Wright, Art Collector: Secessionist Prints from the Turn of the Century. 2012. E-Book ***(978-0-292-73722-8(X))*** Univ. of Texas Pr.

Alpern, Andrew. Catalogue of the Andrew Alpern Collection of Drawing Instruments: At the Avery Architectural & Fine Arts Library, New York City. Fabian, Carole Ann, ed. 2010. (ENG., Illus.). 160p. 60.00 *(978-0-9789037-3-2(0))*, 890373, Avery Architectural & Fine Arts Library) Avery Architectural & Fine Arts Library.

Amsellem, Patrick. Jesper Just: Romantic Delusions. 2008. *(978-0-87273-160-8(X))* Brooklyn Museum, The.

Antonas, Aristide, et al, texts. FACE, Investigations of a Dog. 2011. (ENG., Illus.). 160p. pap. 15.00 ***(978-3-03764-171-2(1))*** JRP Ringier Kunstverlag AG CHE. Dist: D.A.P./Distributed Art Pubs.

Areford, David. The View & the Printed Image in Late Medieval Europe. 2010. (Visual Culture in Early Modernity Ser.). (Illus.). 346p. 124.95 *(978-0-7546-6762-9(6))* Ashgate Publishing Co.

Art Guide 2009 Staff. Contemporary Europe Art Guide 2009. 2009. (ENG., Illus.). 368p. pap. 45.00 *(978-3-7757-2336-7(6))* Hatje Cantz Verlag GmbH & Co KG DEU. Dist: D.A.P./Distributed Art Pubs.

Art Institute of Chicago, creator. Old Masters at the Art Institute of Chicago. 2006. (Museum Studies). (ENG., Illus.). 96p. pap. 16.95 *(978-0-300-11951-0(8))* Art Institute of Chicago.

Babelon, Jean. Histoire de l'Art Vol. 2: L'Europe Medievale. (FRE.). 1748p. *(978-0-8288-7601-8(0))* French & European Pubns., Inc.

Bagnoli, Martina. Treasures of Heaven: Saints, Relics, & Devotion in Medieval Europe. 2010. (Illus.). xviii, 259p. pap. *(978-0-911886-74-0(5))* Cleveland Museum of Art.

Bagnoli, Martina, et al, eds. Treasures of Heaven: Saints, Relics, & Devotion in Medieval Europe. 2010. (Illus.). 278p. 65.00 *(978-0-300-16827-3(6))* Yale Univ. Pr.

Bailey, Gauvin Alexander. Baroque & Rococo. 2012. (ENG., Illus.). 448p. pap. 29.95 ***(978-0-7148-5742-8(4))*** Phaidon Pr., Inc.

Baladran, Zbynek & Havranek, Vit, eds. Atlas of Transformation. 2011. (ENG., Illus.). 724p. pap. 45.00 *(978-3-03764-147-7(9))* JRP Ringier Kunstverlag AG CHE. Dist: D.A.P./Distributed Art Pubs.

Balsells, David, ed. & text. Praha, Paris, Barcelona. 2010. (ENG., Illus.). 250p. 70.00 *(978-84-92841-02-8(8))* Museu Nacional d'Art de Catalunya ESP. Dist: D.A.P./Distributed Art Pubs.

Bang, Larsen La, ed. Nomeda & Gediminas/Devices for Action. 2008. 188p. pap. *(978-84-89771-65-9(0))* Actar Birkhauser Distribution.

Baragli, Sandra. European Art of the Fourteenth Century. Phillips, Brian D., tr. from ITA. 2007. (Art Through the Centuries Ser.). (Illus.). 384p. pap. 24.95 *(978-0-89236-859-4(4))* Oxford Univ. Pr., Inc.

Bardazzi, Francesca, et al. Cézanne in Florence: Two Collectors & the 1910 Exhibition of Impressionism. 2007. (Illus.). 272p. pap. *(978-88-370-4971-3(4))* Electa.

Barrett, Brian Dudley. Artists on the Edge: The Rise of Coastal Artist's Colonies, 1880-1920. 2011. (Illus.). 408p. pap. *(978-90-8964-251-6(X))* Amsterdam Univ. Pr.

Basile, Matteo, photos by. Thishumanity. 2011. (ENG., Illus.). 167p. 40.00 *(978-88-6208-163-4(4))* Damiani ITA. Dist: D.A.P./Distributed Art Pubs.

Baskins, Cristelle & Rosenthal, Lisa, eds. Allegory in Early Modern Visual Culture: Embodying Meaning. 2007. (Illus.). 316p. 134.95 *(978-0-7546-5760-6(4))* Ashgate Publishing Co.

Bauer, W. O. Europäisches Besteck-Design 1945-2000: Design-Sammlung Bauer. 2008. (ENG., Illus.). 176p. 60.00 *(978-3-89790-246-6(X))* Arnoldsche Art Pubs. DEU. Dist: Antique Collectors' Club.

Baumann, Leonie, et al, eds. Crosskick: European Art Academies as Guests in German Kunstvereine. 2009. (ENG., Illus.). 210p. pap. 39.95 *(978-3-86560-518-4(4))* Verlag der Buchhandlung Walther Konig DEU. Dist: D.A.P./Distributed Art Pubs.

Baumann, Uwe, et al. Streitkultur: Okzidentale Traditionen des Streitens in Literatur, Geschichte und Kunst. Super alta perennis. Studien zur Wirkung der Klassischen Antike 2. 2008. (Super alta perennis. Studien zur Wirkung der Klassischen Antike Ser.). (GER & ENG., Illus.). 394p. (C). 88.00 *(978-3-89971-465-4(2))* Vandenhoeck & Ruprecht GmbH & Co. KG DEU. Dist: ISD.

Berger, Stefan, et al. Narrating the Nation: Representations in History, Media, & the Arts. 2008. (Illus.). 352p. 95.00 *(978-1-84545-424-1(3))* Berghahn Bks., Inc.

Bernabei, Roberta, , Roberta. Contemporary Jewellers: Interviews with European Artists. 2011. (ENG., Illus.). 256p. 99.95 *(978-1-84520-769-4(6))*; pap. 34.95 *(978-1-84520-770-0(X))* Berg Pubs. GBR. Dist: Macmillan.

Besten, Liesbeth Den. On Jewellery: A Compendium of International Contemporary Art Jewellery. 2012. (ENG., Illus.). 240p. 50.00 *(978-3-89790-349-4(0))* Arnoldsche Art Pubs. DEU. Dist: Antique Collectors' Club.

Biesenbach, Klaus. Marina Abramovic: The Artist Is Present. 2010. (ENG., Illus.). 224p. 50.00 *(978-0-87070-747-6(7))* Museum of Modern Art.

Birnbaum, Daniel & Starling, Simon, texts. Guillermo Faivovich & Nicolas Goldberg: the Campo del Cielo Meteorites. 2011. (ENG., Illus.). 184p. 60.00 *(978-3-7757-2717-4(5))* Hatje Cantz Verlag GmbH & Co KG DEU. Dist: D.A.P./Distributed Art Pubs.

BIS Publishers Staff, et al. The Daily Gorilla. 2008. (ENG., Illus.). 176p. 25.00 *(978-90-6369-191-2(2))* Bis B.V., Uitgeverij(BIS Publishers) NLD. Dist: Consortium Bk. Sales & Distribution.

BIS Publishers Staff, et al. Performative Geometries: Transforming Textile Techniques. 2011. (ENG., Illus.). 160p. pap. 28.00 ***(978-90-6369-250-6(1))*** Bis B.V., Uitgeverij(BIS Publishers) NLD. Dist: Consortium Bk. Sales & Distribution.

Bishop, Claire & Dziewanska, Marta, eds. 1968-1989. Political Upheaval & Artistic Change. 2011. (ENG & POL., Illus.). 504p. pap. 25.00 ***(978-83-924044-0-8(8))*** Muzeum Sztuki Nowoczesnej w Warszawie POL. Dist: Chicago Distribution Ctr.

Blanc, J. & Maes, G., eds. Echanges artistiques entre les anciens Pays-Bas et la France. 2010. (Museums at the Crossroads Ser.). (DUT, ENG & FRE., Illus.). 365p. (C). pap. 109.00 *(978-2-503-53095-6(8))* Brepols Pubs. BEL. Dist: Brown, David Bk. Co., The.

Boado, Felipe Criado, et al, eds. Representations & Communications: Creating an Archaeological Matrix of Late Prehistoric Rock Art. 2010. (ENG., Illus.). 167p. (C). pap. 50.00 *(978-1-84217-397-8(9))* Oxbow Bks., Ltd. GBR. Dist: Brown, David Bk. Co., The.

Bodleian Library Staff, ed. Postcards from Utopia: The Art of Political Propaganda. 2009. (Bodleian Library - Postcards From Ser.). (ENG., Illus.). 112p. 20.00 *(978-1-85124-337-2(2))* Bodleian Library GBR. Dist: Chicago Distribution Ctr.

Boeckl, Christine M. Images of Leprosy: Disease, Religion, & Politics in European Art. 2011. (Illus.). 248p. 48.00 *(978-1-935503-14-9(6))*; pap. 30.00 *(978-1-935503-15-6(4))* Truman State Univ. Pr.

Boellert, Arvid. Drei Farben, Weiss: Three Colours, White. 2007. (GER & ENG., Illus.). 125p. *(978-3-89930-199-1(4))* Schiler, Hans.

Boime, Albert. Art in an Age of Civil Struggle, 1848-1871. 2008. (Social History of Modern Art Ser.). (Illus.). 784p. 65.00 *(978-0-226-06328-7(3))* Univ. of Chicago Pr.

Bollmann, Karl. Castle in the Air: õhuLoss: Jewellery from Estonia. 2011. (ENG & EST., Illus.). 296p. 85.00 ***(978-3-89790-359-3(8))*** Arnoldsche Art Pubs. DEU. Dist: Antique Collectors' Club.

Bondil, Nathalie & Bouthours, Jean-Michel, eds. Van Dongen. 2009. (Illus.). 351p. *(978-2-7541-0326-8(0))* Hazan, Fernand, Editeur.

Bonin, Cosima von, et al. Dressing the Message: Transformationen Von Kunst und Mode. 2008. (Illus.). 120p. *(978-3-89169-208-0(0))* Sprengel Museum.

Bonsai Art Europe 1. *(978-0-9532287-0-6(3))* Moyogi Bks. GBR. Dist: Vine Hse. Distribution.

Book Industry Services Publishers Staff. European Business Design, No. 1. 2009. (ENG.). 216p. 39.00 *(978-90-6369-172-1(6))* Bis B.V., Uitgeverij(BIS Publishers) NLD. Dist: Consortium Bk. Sales & Distribution.

Book Industry Services Publishers Staff & Bolger, MaryAnn. Design Factory: On the Edge of Europe. 2009. (ENG., Illus.). 240p. 65.00 *(978-90-6369-185-1(8))* Bis B.V., Uitgeverij(BIS Publishers) NLD. Dist: Consortium Bk. Sales & Distribution.

Borchardt-Hume, Achim, ed. Per Kirkeby. 2009. (ENG., Illus.). 176p. pap. 26.95 *(978-1-85437-821-7(X))* Tate Publishing, Ltd. GBR. Dist: Hachette Bk. Group.

Bouvry, Florence. Une Anthropologie des Manifestations Esthetiques Du Mesolithique Europeen De la Fin Du Tardiglaciaire et Durant le Postglaciaire. 2008. (Bar S Ser.). (FRE., Illus.). 643 p. (C). 175.00 *(978-1-4073-0255-3(8))* British Archaeological Reports Ltd. GBR. Dist: Brown, David Bk. Co., The.

Boyle-Turner, Caroline, et al. Current Issues in 19th-Century Art. 2008. (Van Gogh Studies). (ENG., Illus.). 208p. 75.00 *(978-90-400-8350-1(9))* Waanders B.V., Uitgeverij NLD. Dist: National Bk. Network.

Brenske, Stefan. Modern Icons. 2007. (ENG & GER., Illus.). 120p. 90.00 *(978-3-7954-1680-5(9))* Schnell und Steiner GmbH, Verlag DEU. Dist: Independent Pubs. Group.

Brettell, Richard R. & Dickerson, C. D. From the Private Collections of Texas: European Art, Ancient to Modern. 2009. (Illus.). xv, 455p. pap. *(978-0-912804-51-4(3))* Kimbell Art Museum.

Brettell, Richard R. & Dickerson, C. D., III. From the Private Collections of Texas: European Art, Ancient to Modern. 2010. (Illus.). 456p. 65.00 *(978-0-300-14494-9(6))* Kimbell Art Museum.

Brill, Dorothee. Shock & the Senseless in Dada & Fluxus. 2010. (Interfaces: Studies in Visual Culture Ser.). (Illus.). 256p. (C). 85.00 *(978-1-58465-902-0(5))*; pap. 29.95 *(978-1-58465-917-4(3))* Univ. Pr. of New England. (Dartmouth College Press).

Brockington, Grace. Internationalism & the Arts in Britain & Europe at the Fin de Siècle. 2009. (Illus.). 368p. 68.95 *(978-3-03911-128-2(0))* Lang, Peter AG GBR. Dist: Lang, Peter.

Bruijnen, Y. Jan van Rillaer Louvain City Painters. 2011. (Ars Nova Ser.). (ENG.). 312p. (C). 174.00 *(978-2-503-52569-3(5))* Brepols Pubs. BEL. Dist: ISD.

Bryzgel, Amy. Performing the East: Performance Art in Russia, Latvia & Poland since 1980. 2012. (ENG., Illus.). 256p. 92.00 ***(978-1-84885-948-7(1))*** I. B. Tauris & Co., Ltd. GBR. Dist: Macmillan.

Buchanan, I. Hapsburg Tapestries. 2012. (Studies in Western Tapestry Ser.). (ENG., Illus.). 250p. (C). 145.00 *(978-2-503-51670-7(X))* Brepols Pubs. BEL. Dist: ISD.

Buck, Stephanie & Hohenstatt, Peter. Raffaello Santi, Known as Raphael: 1483-1520. 2008. (Masters of Italian Art Ser.). (Illus.). 120p. per. 9.95 *(978-0-8416-0083-6(X))* American Map Corp.

Buhagiar, Mario. Essays on the Knights & Art & Architecture in Malta 1500-1798. 2009. (Maltese social studies Ser.). (ENG., Illus.). 350p. (C). 65.00 *(978-99932-7-246-5(9))* Midsea Bks. Ltd. MLT. Dist: Brown, David Bk. Co., The.

Buhr, Elke. Begegnung Bauhaus: Kurt Schmidt und Künstler der Avantgarde Von Kandinsky Bis Vasarely: Kunstsammlung Gera, 25. März Bis 28. Juni 2009. 2009. (Illus.). 159p. pap. *(978-3-910051-52-2(9))* Glaux Verlag Christine Jager KG.

Buren, Anne Van. Illuminating Fashion: Dress in the Art of Medieval France & the Netherlands, 1325-1515. Wieck, Roger S., ed. 2011. (ENG., Illus.). 448p. 95.00 *(978-1-904832-90-4(3))* Giles, D. Ltd. GBR. Dist: National Bk. Network.

Buric, Anka. Problemi U Crnogorskoj Savremenoj Likovnoj Umjetnosti: Radovi Sa Okruglog Stola, Podgorica, 12. Jun 2008. Godine. 2009. (Illus.). 102p. *(978-86-7215-217-3(4))* Crnogorska akademija nauka i umjetnosti.

Burucúa, José E. La Imagen y la Risa: Las Pathosformeln de lo Cómico en el Grabado Europeo de la Modernidad Temprana. 2007. (Pequenos Tratados Ser.). (SPA., Illus.). 144p. pap. 18.95 ***(978-84-934746-9-0(X))*** Editorial Periferica ESP. Dist: Independent Pubs. Group.

Bury, Stephen. Breaking the Rules: The Printed Face of the European Avant Garde 1900-1937. 2008. (ENG., Illus.). 176p. 60.00 *(978-0-7123-0975-2(6))* British Library, The GBR. Dist: Chicago Distribution Ctr.

—Breaking the Rules: The Printed Face of the European Avant Garde 1900-1937. 2008. (ENG., Illus.). 128p. pap. 30.00 *(978-0-7123-0980-6(2))* British Library, The GBR. Dist: Chicago Distribution Ctr.

Camara, Eva M. & Minguet, Eva. European Illustrators. Minguet, Josep M. & Monsa, eds. 2011. (ENG & SPA., Illus.). 96p. pap. 24.00 *(978-84-15223-00-9(5))* Instituto Monsa de Ediciones, S.A. ESP. Dist: Trans-Atlantic Pubns., Inc.

Campbell, Gordon. The Grove Encyclopedia of Northern Renaissance Art, 3 vols., Set. 2009. (ENG., Illus.). 2114p. 415.00 *(978-0-19-533466-1(3))* Oxford Univ. Pr., Inc.

Campbell, Thomas P., ed. Tapestry in the Baroque: Threads of Splendor. 2007. (ENG., Illus.). 576p. 75.00 *(978-0-300-12407-1(4))* Yale Univ. Pr.

Campbell, Thomas P., et al. Tapestry in the Baroque: Threads of Splendor. 2007. 35.00 *(978-1-58839-230-5(9))*; 75.00 *(978-1-58839-229-9(5))* Metropolitan Museum of Art, The.

Cárcova, Ernesto de la. Cuadros de Viaje: Artistas Argentinos en Europa y Estados Unidos, 1880-1910. 2008. (Tierra Firme Ser.). (SPA., Illus.). 383p. pap. 30.99 *(978-950-557-779-8(6))* Fondo de Cultura Económcia.

Castagno, John. European Artists III: Signatures & Monograms From 1800. 2008. (ENG.). 308p. 200.00 *(978-0-8108-6208-1(5))* Scarecrow Pr., Inc.

Castelnuovo, Enrico & Barberis, Walter. La reggia di Venaria e i Savoia. Arte, magnificenza e storia di una corte europea. Catalogo della mostra (12 ottobre 2007-30 marzo 2008), 2 vols. 2008. (ITA & ENG., Illus.). 680p. pap. 90.00 *(978-88-422-1585-1(6))* Allemandi, Umberto & Co. GBR. Dist: National Bk. Network.

Cerizza, Luca, ed. Maps & Legends. 2009. (ENG., Illus.). 280p. 27.00 *(978-3-905829-13-6(4))* JRP Ringier Kunstverlag AG CHE. Dist: D.A.P./Distributed Art Pubs.

—Town Hidden under Concrete - Passageway, 1 vol. 2007. (SPA & ENG., Illus.). 80p. 15.00 *(978-3-905701-92-0(8))* JRP Ringier Kunstverlag AG CHE. Dist: D.A.P./Distributed Art Pubs.

Chapuis, Julien, ed. Invention: Northern Renaissance Studies in Honor of Molly Faries. 2008. (Me Fecit Ser.). (ENG., Illus.). 231p. (C). 116.00 *(978-2-503-52768-0(X))* Brepols Pubs. BEL. Dist: ISD.

Charles R. Mack. European Art in the Columbia Museum of Art, Including the Samuel H. Kress Collection, Volume One: The Thirteenth through the Sixteenth Century. 2009. (ENG.). 304p. pap. 29.95 *(978-1-57003-806-8(6))* Univ. of South Carolina Pr.

Charles, Victoria. Renaissance Art. 2007. (Art of Century Ser.). (ENG., Illus.). 199p. pap. 19.95 *(978-1-85995-676-2(9))* Parkstone International GBR. Dist: Ingram Pub. Services.

Charles, Victoria & Carl, Klaus H. Gothic Art. 2008. (Art of Century Ser.). (ENG., Illus.). 199p. 19.95 *(978-1-84484-461-6(7))* Parkstone International GBR. Dist: Ingram Pub. Services.

—Medieval Art in Europe from 987 To 1489. 2012. (Must Ser.). (ENG.). 400p. 49.95 *(978-1-906981-03-7(5))* Parkstone Pr. USA, Ltd.

Cheney, Liana De Girolami, et al. Self-portraits by women Painters. 2nd ed. 2009. (ENG., Illus.). 296p. pap. 28.00 *(978-0-9823867-3-6(7))* New Academia Publishing, LLC.

Chu, Petra ten-Doesschate. Nineteenth-Century European Art. 3rd rev. ed. 2010. (ENG., Illus.). 560p. (C). pap. 116.80 *(978-0-205-70799-7(8)*, Prentice Hall) Prentice Hall PTR.

Clarke, Jay A. Becoming Edvard Munch: Influence, Anxiety, & Myth. 2009. (ENG., Illus.). 232p. 50.00 *(978-0-300-11950-3(X))* Art Institute of Chicago.

Clarke, Jay A. y. Becoming Edvard Munch: Influence, Anxiety, & Myth. 2009. (Illus.). 231p. pap. *(978-0-86559-228-5(4))* Art Institute of Chicago.

Clarke, Michael, et al. Inspiring Impressionism: The Impressionists & the Art of the Past. Dumas, Ann, ed. 2007. (ENG., Illus.). 280p. 65.00 *(978-0-300-13132-1(1))* Yale Univ. Pr.

Clottes, Jean. Cave Art. 2010. (ENG., Illus.). 336p. pap. 39.95 *(978-0-7148-5723-7(8))* Phaidon Pr., Inc.

Colegio de Arquitectos de Cataluña Staff, contrib. by. Landscape: Product/Production. 2008. (SPA & ENG., Illus.). 336p. pap. *(978-84-96842-33-5(9))* Actar Birkhauser Distribution.

Collins, Emlyn. Deciphering Mediterranean Scripts. 2010. 256p. pap. *(978-3-8383-6876-4(2))* Lambert Academic Publishing.

Cossons, Malcolm & Phillips, Jocelyn. Collect Contemporary Photography. 2012. (ENG., Illus.). 208p. pap. 21.95 ***(978-0-500-28854-2(2)***, 528854) Thames & Hudson.

Costa, José Manuel. Sound Art. 2010. 330p. pap. 34.95 *(978-84-96917-69-9(X))* Caja de Madrid ESP. Dist: Actar Birkhauser Distribution.

Cram101 Textbook Reviews. Outlines & Highlights for Baroque & Rococo: Art & Culture by Minor. 2011. 266p. pap. 31.95 ***(978-1-61812-932-1(5))*** Cram101 Inc.

Cram101 Textbook Reviews & Cram101 Textbook Reviews. Outlines & Highlights for Art in an Age of Civil Struggle, 1848-1871 by Albert Boime, Isbn: 9780226063287. 2011. 268p. pap. 31.95 ***(978-1-61461-825-6(9))*** Cram101 Inc.

Cram101 Textbook Reviews Staff. Outlines & Highlights for Nineteenth-Century European Art by Petra Ten-Doesschate Chu, Isbn: 9780131886438. 2009. 106p. pap. 28.95 *(978-1-4288-9711-3(9))* Cram101 Inc.

—Outlines & Highlights for Seventeenth Century Art & Architecture by Ann Sutherland Harris, Isbn: 9780136033721. 2009. 64p. pap. 27.95 *(978-1-4288-9217-0(6))* Cram101 Inc.

Cuir, Raphael. The Development of the Study of Anatomy from the Renaissance to Cartesianism: Da Carpi, Vesalius, Estienne, Bidloo. 2009. (Illus.). 278p. 109.95 *(978-0-7734-4657-1(5))* Mellen, Edwin Pr., The.

David, Caroline, ed. Frontières Invisibles - Invisible Borders. 2009. (FRE & ENG., Illus.). 224p. pap. *(978-90-5856-315-6(4)*, Stichting Kunstboek (Acc)) Antique Collectors' Club.

de Girolamo, Domenico. Subway Player: Blackbook Cult Series 2: Mser. 2011. (ENG.). 88p. 29.95 ***(978-88-904178-8-7(9))*** Whole Train Pr. ITA. Dist: SCB Distributors.

De Luisi, Stefano. Blacno. 2010. (Illus.). 128p. pap. *(978-1-907112-14-0(6))* Trolley.

De Montclos, Brigitte. Moscow: Splendours of the Romanovs. 2009. (ENG., Illus.). 304p. 50.00 *(978-88-572-0256-3(9))* Skira Editore ITA. Dist: Random Hse., Inc.

de Zegher, Catherine & Pollock, Griselda. Bracha l ettinger art as Compassion, 1 vol. 2011. (ENG., Illus.). 320p. 68.00 ***(978-94-6117-008-8(4))*** Exhibitions International BEL. Dist: Innovative Logistics.

Debono, Sandro, ed. Art Nouveau & Malta: An Introduction. 2011. (ENG., Illus.). 96p. (C). pap. 35.00 *(978-99932-7-335-6(X))* Midsea Bks. Ltd. MLT. Dist: Brown, David Bk. Co., The.

Debono, Sandro & Scicluna, Bernadine. The Busuttil Family: A Legacy of Three Generations. 2010. (Illus.). 136p. pap. 52.00 *(978-99932-7-305-9(8))* Midsea Bks. Ltd. MLT. Dist: Brown, David Bk. Co., The.

Dietrich, Nikola & Fabricius, Jacob, eds. Henrik Olesen, 1 vol. 2011. (ENG.). 224p. 60.00 *(978-3-7757-2842-3(2))* Hatje Cantz Verlag GmbH & Co KG DEU. Dist: D.A.P./Distributed Art Pubs.

Dover. Renaissance & Baroque Ceiling Masterpieces. 2008. (Dover Pictorial Archive Ser.). (ENG., Illus.). 80p. pap. 17.95 *(978-0-486-46529-6(2))* Dover Pubns., Inc.

Dover & Postcards. Alice in Wonderland Postcards. 2012. (Dover Postcards Ser.). (ENG., Illus.). 24p. pap. 6.95 ***(978-0-486-48884-4(5))*** Dover Pubns., Inc.

Dover & Weller, Alan. Pre-Columbian Design. 2008. (Dover Pictura Electronic Clip Art Ser.). (ENG., Illus.). 128p. pap. 39.95 *(978-0-486-99751-3(0))* Dover Pubns., Inc.

Dragset, Ingar & Elmgreen, Michael & Dragset, Ingar. Elmgreen & Dragset: Home Is the Place You Left. 2008. (ENG., Illus.). 196p. pap. 52.00 *(978-3-86560-473-6(0))* Verlag der Buchhandlung Walther Konig DEU. Dist: D.A.P./Distributed Art Pubs.

Dressler, Iris & Christ, Hans, eds. Subversive Praktiken: Kunst unter Bedingungen politischer Repression 60er-80er / Südamerika / Europa. 2011. (ENG., Illus.). 584p. 60.00 *(978-3-7757-2755-6(8))* Hatje Cantz Verlag GmbH & Co KG DEU. Dist: D.A.P./Distributed Art Pubs.

Driver, Martha W. & Orr, Michael T. An Index of Images in English Manuscripts: From the Time of Chaucer to Henry VIII, C. 1380-C. 1509. 2007. (Index of Images in English Manuscripts from Chaucer to Henry Ser.). (Illus.). 176p. pap. 81.00 *(978-1-905375-22-6(0))* Miller, Harvey Pubs. GBR. Dist: Brown, David Bk. Co., The.

Dumas, Ann & Bray, Xavier, intros. Inspiring Impressionism: The Impressionists & the Art of the Past. 2007. *(978-0-914738-58-9(5))*; pap. *(978-0-914738-57-2(7))* Denver Art Museum.

Eamon, Christopher. Rearview Mirror: New Art from Central & Eastern Europe. 2012. (ENG., Illus.). 100p. 45.00 ***(978-0-88950-160-7(2))*** Art Gallery of Alberta CAN. Dist: D.A.P./Distributed Art Pubs.

Eeden, Marcel van. Marcel van Eeden. Schritte ins Reich der Kunst. 2011. (GER & ENG., Illus.). 104p. pap. 27.50 ***(978-3-86560-931-1(7))*** Verlag der Buchhandlung Walther Konig DEU. Dist: D.A.P./Distributed Art Pubs.

Eichler, Dominic, et al. Wilhelm Sasnal. 2011. (ENG., Illus.). 160p. pap. 45.00 ***(978-0-7148-6079-4(4))*** Phaidon Pr., Inc.

Eikelmann, Renate, ed. Die Wittelsbacher und das Reich der Mitte: 400 Jahre China und Bayern. Katalogbuch zur Ausstellung in München, 27.03.2009-26.07.2009, Bayerisches Nationalmuseum. 2009. (GER., Illus.). 592p. (C). 65.00 *(978-3-7774-9045-8(8))* Hirmer Verlag GmbH DEU. Dist: Brown, David Bk. Co., The.

Ekserdjian, David, ed. Treasures from Budapest: European Masterpieces from Leonardo to Schiele. 2011. (ENG., Illus.). 288p. 60.00 *(978-1-905711-80-2(8))* Royal Academy of Arts GBR. Dist: Hachette Bk. Group.

Elliott, David, et al, texts. A Building Is Not a Building. 2009. (ENG., Illus.). 132p. 85.00 *(978-3-7757-2366-4(8))* Hatje Cantz Verlag GmbH & Co KG DEU. Dist: D.A.P./Distributed Art Pubs.

Ensor, James. Doctrinal Nourishment: Art & Anarchism in the Time of James Ensor. 2009. (ENG., Illus.). 88p. pap. 20.00 *(978-0-87587-199-8(2))* Los Angeles County Museum of Art.

Epica. Epica Bk. 24: Europe's Best Advertising. 2011. (ENG., Illus.). 400p. 65.00 ***(978-2-88479-109-0(4))*** Ava Publishing SA CHE. Dist: Ingram Pub. Services.

Epica, compiled by. Epica Bk. 22: Europe's Best Advertising. 2009. (Epica: Europe's Best Advertising Ser.). (ENG., Illus.). 400p. 65.00 *(978-2-88479-107-6(8))* Ava Publishing SA CHE. Dist: Ingram Pub. Services.

Fakso, Alex. Alex Fakso Heavy Metal, 1 vol. 2007. (ENG., Illus.). 164p. 35.00 *(978-88-89431-49-8(0))* Damiani ITA. Dist: D.A.P./Distributed Art Pubs.

Farago, Claire. Re-Reading Leonardo: The Treatise on Painting Across Europe, 1550-1900. 2009. (Illus.). 652p. 139.95 *(978-0-7546-6532-8(1))* Ashgate Publishing Co.

The Feast in the House of Simon: Veronese. (Illus.). 172p. 45.00 *(978-2-909838-26-7(9))* de Gourcuff, Alain Editeur FRA. Dist: Antique Collectors' Club.

Felderer, Brigitte, et al, texts. Christian Ruschitzka: Leitmotive. 2011. (ENG., Illus.). 192p. 55.00 ***(978-3-7757-3183-6(0))*** Hatje Cantz Verlag GmbH & Co KG DEU. Dist: D.A.P./Distributed Art Pubs.

Fisher, Celia. Flowers of the Renaissance. 2011. (ENG., Illus.). 160p. 39.95 *(978-1-60606-062-9(7)*, J. Paul Getty Museum) Getty Pubns.

Fleckner, Uwe. The Invention of the 20th Century: Carl Einstein & the Avant-Gardes. 2009. 324p. pap. 65.00 *(978-84-8026-386-3(5))* Museo Nacional Centro de Arte Reina Sofia ESP. Dist: Actar Birkhauser Distribution.

Folga-Januszewska, Dorota & Majewski, Lech. The Mystic Middle Ages. 2008. 160p. 50.00 *(978-83-87730-59-8(9))* Bosz, Szymanik i wspolnicy POL. Dist: Independent Pubs. Group.

Fornsgaard, Jes & Thau, Carsten. Jes Fornsgaard: Incorporating Architecture. 2009. (DAN, MUL & ENG., Illus.). 116p. *(978-87-92420-05-3(2))* Bogvaerket.

Frangenberg, Thomas & Williams, Robert, eds. The Beholder: The Experience of Art in Early Modern Europe. 2006. (Histories of Vision Ser.). (Illus.). 244p. 130.00 *(978-0-7546-0679-6(1))* Ashgate Publishing Co.

Frederiksen, Jens & Harden, Trine, photos by. The Most Beautiful Museum in the World. 2012. (ENG., Illus.). 144p. 40.00 *(978-3-7757-2342-8(0))* Hatje Cantz Verlag GmbH & Co KG DEU. Dist: D.A.P./Distributed Art Pubs.

French, Anne. Art Treasures in the North: Northern Families on the Grand Tour. 2010. (ENG., Illus.). 96p. 55.00 *(978-0-906290-36-1(8))* Unicorn Pr., London GBR. Dist: National Bk. Network.

Friedman, Julia. Beyond Symbolism & Surrealism: Alexei Remizov's Synthetic Art. 2011. (ENG., Illus.). 286p. 69.95 *(978-0-8101-2617-6(6))* Northwestern Univ. Pr.

Frits, Giertsberg. The Dutch Photobook: A Thematic Selection from 1945 Onwards, 1 vol. 2012. (ENG., Illus.). 240p. 75.00 ***(978-1-59711-200-0(3))*** Aperture Foundation, Inc.

García Lorca, Federico. In Search of Duende. Maurer, Christopher, ed. Di Giovanni, tr. from SPA. 2nd ed. 2010. (New Directions Bibelot Ser.). (ENG.). 100p. pap. 9.95 *(978-0-8112-1855-9(4)*, 21855) New Directions Publishing Corp.

Gertsman, E. The Dance of Death in the Middle Ages: Image, Text, Performance. 2010. (Studies in the Visual Cultures of the Middle Ages Ser.). (ENG., Illus.). 356p. (C). 123.00 *(978-2-503-53063-5(X))* Brepols Pubs. BEL. Dist: ISD.

Gierstberg, Frits, ed. Reinier Gerritsen: Wall Street Stop. 2011. (ENG., Illus.). 120p. 45.00 *(978-3-7757-2720-4(5))* Hatje Cantz Verlag GmbH & Co KG DEU. Dist: D.A.P./Distributed Art Pubs.

Giorgi, Rosa. European Art of the Seventeenth Century. 2008. (Illus.). 384p. pap. 24.95 *(978-0-89236-934-8(5))* Oxford Univ. Pr., Inc.

Giusti, Annamaria & Koeppe, Wolfram, eds. Art of the Royal Court: Treasures in Pietre Dure from the Palaces of Europe. 2008. (ENG., Illus.). 428p. 65.00 *(978-0-300-13672-2(2))* Yale Univ. Pr.

Gohr. On Per Kirkeby. 2009. (ENG., Illus.). 128p. 40.00 *(978-3-7757-2321-3(8))* Hatje Cantz Verlag GmbH & Co KG DEU. Dist: D.A.P./Distributed Art Pubs.

Golan, Romy. Muralnomad: The Paradox of Wall Painting, Europe, 1927-1957. 2009. (ENG., Illus.). 256p. 70.00 *(978-0-300-14153-5(X))* Yale Univ. Pr.

Gorringe, Timothy J. Earthly Visions: Theology & the Challenge of Art. 2011. (ENG., Illus.). 264p. 45.00 *(978-0-300-16280-6(4))* Yale Univ. Pr.

Goulart, Ron. Good Girl Art Around the World. 2012. (Illus.). 176p. 49.99 *(978-1-932563-10-8(5))* Hermes Pr.

Grabowska-Konwent, Anna. Zoografika: Gnieznienskie Spotkania Z Plakatem: Spotkanie 8: Plakat, Grafika, Druki Ze Zbiorów Muzeum Narodowego W Poznaniu. 2009. (POL., Illus.). 189p. *(978-83-61391-16-6(9))* Muzeum Poczatkow Panstwa Polskiego w Gnieznie.

Green, Christopher, et al. Modern Antiquity: Picasso, de Chirico, Léger, Picabia. 2011. (ENG., Illus.). 176p. 39.95 *(978-0-89236-977-5(9)*, J. Paul Getty Museum) Getty Pubns.

Gregory, Jarrett & Valdez, Sarah, eds. Ostalgia. 2011. (ENG., Illus.). 120p. pap. 35.00 ***(978-0-915557-96-7(7))*** New Museum of Contemporary Art, The.

Grootenboer, Hanneke. Treasuring the Gaze. 2012. (Illus.). 240p. 45.00 ***(978-0-226-30966-8(5))*** Univ. of Chicago Pr.

—Treasuring the Gaze: Intimate Vision in Late Eighteenth-Century Eye Miniatures. 2012. (Illus.). E-Book ***(978-0-226-30971-2(1))*** Univ. of Chicago Pr.

Gunckel, Colin, ed. The Oscar Castillo Papers & Photograph Collection. 2011. (ENG., Illus.). 208p. (C). pap. 19.95 *(978-0-89551-140-9(1))* UCLA Chicano Studies Research Ctr. Pr.

Handberg, Mette N. Norwegian Patterns for Knitting: Classic Sweaters, Hats, Vests, & Mittens. 2010. (ENG.). 121p. 24.95 *(978-1-57076-448-6(4))* Trafalgar Square Bks.

Hannes, Nick. Red Journey. 2010. (ENG., Illus.). 144p. 50.00 *(978-90-209-8402-6(0))* Lannoo Pubs./Racine.

Hanru, Hou. Global Multitude. Hanru, Hou, ed. 2008. 160p. pap. *(978-84-935844-4-3(4))* Actar Birkhauser Distribution.

Harding, Mike. A Little Book of Devils & Demons. 2008. (Little Bks.). (ENG.). 96p. 12.95 *(978-1-84513-307-8(2))* Aurum Pr., Ltd. GBR. Dist: Independent Pubs. Group.

Hardwick, P, ed. The Playful Middle Ages: Essays in Memory of Elaine C. Block. 2011. (Medieval Texts & Cultures of Northern Europe Ser.). (ENG & FRE., Illus.). 247p. (C). 123.00 *(978-2-503-52880-9(5))* Brepols Pubs. BEL. Dist: ISD.

Hardy, Joanna, ed. Collect Contemporary - Jewelry. 2012. (ENG., Illus.). 208p. pap. 21.95 ***(978-0-500-28855-9(0)***, 528855) Thames & Hudson.

Harrison, Stephen, et al. Artistic Luxury: Fabergé Tiffany Lalique. 2008. (Illus.). xii, 358p. *(978-0-940717-99-2(9))*; *(978-0-940717-98-5(0))* Yale Univ. Pr.

Hatoum, Mona. Mona Hatoum: Unhomely. 2009. (ENG., Illus.). 104p. 50.00 *(978-3-935567-46-6(4))* Holzwarth Pubns. DEU. Dist: D.A.P./Distributed Art Pubs.

Heartney, Eleanor & Gasimov, Khanlar. Khanlar Gasimov. 2011. (ENG., Illus.). 48p. pap. 16.95 ***(978-88-8158-819-0(6))*** Charta ITA. Dist: D.A.P./Distributed Art Pubs.

Hegyi, Lorand. Passage to Europe: Realities, References, Reflections. 2008. (ENG., Illus.). 160p. pap. 29.95 *(978-88-7439-168-4(4))* 5 Continents ITA. Dist: Hachette Bk. Group.

Herd, Kerstin. Walt Disneys Bildwelten in der zeitgenössischen Kunst: und ihr Ursprung in der Malerei des 18. bis 20. Jahrhunderts. 2010. 112p. pap. *(978-3-639-26640-5(4))* VDM Verlag Dr. Mueller e.K.

Hernando, Maral Kekejian, ed. Are 41 creators from the new Madrid scene Mistaken? 2010. 82p. pap. 24.95 *(978-84-96917-70-5(3))* Caja de Madrid ESP. Dist: Actar Birkhauser Distribution.

Heß, Gilbert, et al, eds. Raffael als Paradigma: Rezeption, Imagination und Kult im 19. Jahrhundert. 2011.Tr. of Raphael as Paradigm. (GER., Illus.). XXIX, 426p. 168.00 ***(978-3-11-025562-1(6))*** De Gruyter, Walter Inc.

Hill, Carolyn, et al. Tempests & Romantic Visionaries: Images of Storms in European & American Art. George, Hardy S. & Pavelka, Jeffrey J., eds. 2006. (ENG., Illus.). 136p. per. 25.00 *(978-0-911919-04-2(X))* Oklahoma City Museum of Art.

Hirakawa, Kayo. The Pictorialization of Dürer's Drawings in Northern Europe in the Sixteenth & Seventh Centuries. 2009. (Illus.). 178p. pap. *(978-3-03911-725-3(4))* Lang, Peter.

Hoger, Hans, contrib. by. Zurich-Milano. 2007. (Poster Collection: Vol. 14). (Illus.). 95p. pap. 29.95 *(978-3-03778-079-4(7)*, 3037780797) Lars Muller Pubs. CHE. Dist: Springer.

Hopkins, David, ed. Neo-avant-garde. 2006. (Avant Garde Critical Studies: 20). (Illus.). 464p. *(978-90-420-2125-9(X))* Rodopi.

Hovens, Pieter. The American Indian Material Culture: Ten Kate Collection, 1882-1888. 2010. (ENG., Illus.). 282p. pap. 39.00 *(978-3-9811620-1-1(3))* ZKF Pubs. DEU. Dist: Univ. of Nebraska Pr.

Hübner, Helga & Regtmeier, Eva. Maria de' Medici: Eine Fremde. Florenz - Paris - Brüssel - London - Köln. 2010. (Dialoghi / Dialogues. Literatur und Kultur Italiens und Frankreichs Ser.). (GER.). 258p. 67.95 *(978-3-631-60118-1(2))* Lang, Peter GmbH, Europaischer Verlag der Wissenschaften DEU. Dist: Lang, Peter.

Hults, Linda C. The Witch as Muse: Art, Gender, & Power in Early Modern Europe. 2011. (Illus.). 360p. (C). pap. 26.50 *(978-0-8122-2145-9(1))* Univ. of Pennsylvania Pr.

Husslein-Arco, Agnes. Barock: Meisterwerke Im Belvedere. 2008. (GER., Illus.). 367p. *(978-3-901508-43-1(0))* Bibliothek der Provinz, Verlag fur Literatur Kunst & Musikalien.

Ilg, Ulrike. Text und Bild in Reiseberichten des 16. Jahrhunderts: Westliche Zeugnisse über Amerika und das Osmanische Reich. 2009. (ENG.). 324p. pap. 38.00 *(978-3-422-06871-1(6)*, Art Stock Bks. Ltd/Csi) Continental Sales, Inc.

Index Books Editors, ed. Select H: Graphic Design from Spain, 1 vol. 2009. (ENG.). 752p. 39.95 *(978-84-92643-22-6(6))* Index Bks., Spain ESP. Dist: Innovative Logistics

Indij, Guido, ed. 1000 Stencils: Argentina Graffiti, 1 vol. 2007. (ENG., Illus.). 240p. per. 25.00 *(978-950-889-164-8(5))* La Marca ARG. Dist: D.A.P./Distributed Art Pubs.

Jennings, Oscar. Early Woodcut Initials: Containing over Thirteen Hundred Reproductions of Ornamental Letters of the Fifteenth & Sixteenth Centuries. 2007. (Illus.). 288p. 75.00 *(978-1-57898-621-7(4))* Martino Publishing.

Jongerius, Hella & Schouwenberg, Louise. Hella Jongerius - Misfit. 2011. (ENG., Illus.). 308p. 49.95 *(978-0-7148-5987-3(7))* Phaidon Pr., Inc.

Jungblut, Marie-Paul. Looted! Current Questions Regarding the Cultural Looting by the National Socialists in Europe. 2008. (ENG.). 164p. pap. 38.00 *(978-3-422-06814-8(7)*, Art Stock Bks. Ltd/Csi) Continental Sales, Inc.

Kaminski, Marion. Titian: Tiziano Vecellio: 1488/1490-1576. 2008. (Masters of Italian Art Ser.). (Illus.). 140p. pap. 9.95 *(978-0-8415-0084-3(8))* American Map Corp.

Keeble, K. Corey. European Bronzes in the Royal Ontario Museum. (Illus.). 1276p. *(978-0-88854-277-9(1))* BRILL.

Keeler, Nancy, text. Gardens in Perpetual Bloom. 2010. (ENG., Illus.). 136p. pap. 24.95 *(978-0-87846-749-5(1))* Museum of Fine Arts, Boston.

Keller, Christoph, ed. Gitte Villesen: the Story Is Not All Mine, nor Is it Told by Me Alone. 2011. (ENG., Illus.). 192p. pap. 45.00 *(978-3-03764-005-0(7))* JRP Ringier Kunstverlag AG CHE. Dist: D.A.P./Distributed Art Pubs.

Kesselskramer. A New Kilo of KesselsKramer. 2010. (ENG & JPN., Illus.). 428p. pap. 34.50 *(978-4-89444-860-5(2)*, PIE Bks.) Rizzoli International Pubns., Inc.

Kessler, Herbert L. & Nirenberg, David, eds. Judaism & Christian Art: Aesthetic Anxieties from the Catacombs to Colonialism. 2011. (Illus.). 456p. (C). 69.95 *(978-0-8122-4285-0(8))* Univ. of Pennsylvania Pr.

Keurs, Pieter ter. Colonial Collections Revisited. 2011. (CNWS Publications). (Illus.). viii, 269p. *(978-90-5789-152-6(2)*, Leiden Univ. Pr.) Amsterdam Univ. Pr.

Kharibian, Leah, intro. National Gallery Pocket Collection. 2009. (ENG., Illus.). 240p. 15.00 *(978-1-85709-447-3(6))* Yale Univ. Pr.

Koeppe, Wolfram, et al. Art of the Royal Court: Treasures in Pietre Dure from the Palaces of Europe. 2008. (Illus.). xvi, 412p. 65.00 *(978-1-58839-288-6(0))* Metropolitan Museum of Art, The.

Kotnik, Vlado. Opera, Power & Ideology: Anthropological Study of a National Art in Slovenia. 2010. 210p. 50.95 *(978-3-631-59628-9(6))* Lang, Peter GmbH, Europaischer Verlag der Wissenschaften DEU. Dist: Lang, Peter.

Kotsopoulos, Nikolaos, ed. Contemporary Art in Eastern Europe: Artworld. 2010. (Artworld Ser.). (ENG., Illus.). 240p. 49.95 *(978-1-906155-84-1(4))* Black Dog Publishing Ltd. GBR. Dist: Perseus Distribution.

Kramer, F. & Hollein, M. Johann Wilhelm Schirmer: Vom Rheinland in die Welt. Band 2 / Autobiographische Schriften. 2010. 260p. *(978-3-86568-544-5(7))* Imhof, Michael Verlag GmbH & Co. KG.

Krause, Jargen. Märtyrer und Prophet: Studien zum Nietzsche-Kult in der bildenden Kunst der Jahrhundertwende. (Monographien und Texte zur Nietzsche-Forschung Ser.). (GER., Illus.). XII, 291p. 300.00 ***(978-3-11-175718-6(8))*** De Gruyter, Walter Inc.

Kren, Thomas. Illuminated Manuscripts of Belgium & the Netherlands. 2010. (Illus.). 96p. pap. 19.95 *(978-1-60606-014-8(7))* Getty Pubns.

Kristeva, Julia. The Severed Head: Capital Visions. Gladding, Jody, tr. from FRE. 2011. (European Perspectives: a Series in Social Thought & Cultural Criticism Ser.). (ENG., Illus.). 176p. (gr. 17). 34.50 ***(978-0-231-15720-9(7))*** Columbia Univ. Pr.

Kroesen, J. E. A. & Schmidt, Victor M., eds. The Altar & Its Environment. 2010. (Studies in the Visual Cultures of the Middle Ages Ser.). (ENG & FRE., Illus.). 314p. (C). pap. 138.00 *(978-2-503-53044-4(3))* Brepols Pubs. BEL. Dist: ISD.

Lachowicz, Andrzej, et al. Andrzej Lachowicz: Obserwacje I Notacje = Observations & Notations. 2008. (POL & ENG.). 154p. *(978-83-61156-03-1(8))* Centre for Contemporary Art Ujazdowski.

Lahuerta, Juan Jose. Dalí, Lorca y la Residencia de Estudiantes, 2 vols. 2010. (Illus.). (SPA.). *(978-84-92827-85-5(8))*; (ENG & SPA., *(978-84-92827-89-3(0))*; (ENG & SPA., *(978-84-92827-90-9(4))* Sociedad Estatal de Conmemoraciones Culturales.

Laing, Lloyd. European Influence on Celtic Art: Patrons & Artists. 2010. (Illus.). 256p. 70.00 *(978-1-84682-175-2(4))* Four Courts Pr. IRL. Dist: International Specialized Bk. Services.

Lartillot, Francoise & Gellhaus, Axel, eds. Années vingt - Années soixante, Réseaux du sens - Réseaux des sens/Zwanziger Jahre - Sechziger Jahre, Netzwerk des Sinns - Netzwerke der Sinne: Quels paradigmes pour une analyse de l'histoire culturelle dans les pays de langue Allemande? 2009. (Convergences Ser.). (GER & FRE.). 267p. pap. *(978-3-0343-0047-6(6))* Lang, Peter.

Laser 3.14. Are you reading Me?, 300 vols. 2011. (ENG.). 160p. pap. 25.95 *(978-90-488-0188-6(5))* Lebowski NLD. Dist: SCB Distributors.

Lauckaite, Laima. Art in Vilnius. 2009. (ENG.). 200p. 69.00 *(978-9955-23-183-7(1)*, Art Stock Bks. Ltd/Csi) Continental Sales, Inc.

Legrand-Pineau, Alexandra, et al, eds. Ancient & Modern Bone Artefacts from America to Russia. 2010. (Bar S Ser.). (ENG., Illus.). 324p. (C). pap. 132.50 *(978-1-4073-0677-3(4))* British Archaeological Reports Ltd. GBR. Dist: Brown, David Bk. Co., The.

Lermer, Andrea & Shalem, Avinoam, eds. After One Hundred Years: The 1910 Exhibition Meisterwerke muhammedanischer Kunst Reconsidered. 2010. (Islamic History & Civilization Ser.). (GER & ENG., Illus.). 440p. *(978-90-04-19001-6(5))* BRILL.

Levine, David A. & Freiberg, Jack, eds. Medieval Renaissance Baroque: A Cat's Cradle for Marilyn Aronberg Lavin. 2009. (Illus.). 230p. pap. 30.00 *(978-1-59910-130-9(0))* Italica Pr.

Lindemann, Wilhelm & Lindemann, W., eds. Bengel Art Déco-Schmuck: Der Schmuck und das Industrie-Denkmal in Idar-Oberstein. 2007. (ENG., Illus.). 200p. 85.00 *(978-3-89790-271-8(0))* Arnoldsche Art Pubs. DEU. Dist: Antique Collectors' Club.

Lingo, Estelle. Francois Duquesnoy & the Greek Ideal. 2007. (Illus.). 240p. 75.00 *(978-0-300-12483-5(X))* Yale Univ. Pr.

Lista, Giovanni. Arte Povera. 2008. (Gallery of the Arts Ser.). (ENG., Illus.). 112p. 18.95 *(978-88-7439-215-5(X))* 5 Continents ITA. Dist: Hachette Bk. Group.

Llorens, Tomàs, et al. Portraits of the Belle Époque. 2012. (ENG., Illus.). 272p. 85.00 ***(978-1-55595-349-2(2))*** Hudson Hills Pr. LLC.

Lodoen, Trond & Mandt, Gro. The Rock Art of Norway. 2010. (ENG., Illus.) 344p. pap. 60.00 *(978-1-905119-28-8(3))* Windgather Pr. GBR. Dist: Brown, David Bk. Co., The.

Macel, Christine, ed. Promises of the Past. 2010. (ENG., Illus.). 256p. pap. 65.00 *(978-3-03764-099-9(5))* JRP Ringier Kunstverlag AG CHE. Dist: D.A.P./Distributed Art Pubs.

MacGregor, Arthur. The Ashmolean Museum: A History of the Museum & Its Collections. 2006. (Ashmolean Handbooks). (ENG., Illus.). 80p. 22.95 *(978-1-85444-149-2(3)*, 1493); pap. 15.95 *(978-1-85444-146-5(5)*, 1469X) Ashmolean Museum GBR. Dist: Antique Collectors' Club.

MacInnes, M. J. Nature to Advantage Dress'd. spiral bd. 3.75 *(978-0-87018-043-9(6))* Ross & Haines Old Bks. Co.

Manifesta 8. 2010. (ENG., Illus.). 384p. pap. 50.00 *(978-88-366-1697-8(6))* Silvana ITA. Dist: D.A.P./Distributed Art Pubs.

Marien, Mary Warner. Photography & Its Critics: A Cultural History, 1839-1900. 2011. (Perspectives on Photography Ser.). (ENG., Illus.). 242p. pap. 31.99 ***(978-1-107-40338-3(3))*** Cambridge Univ. Pr.

Masotta, Carlos, ed. Landscapes in Early 1900s/Paisajes en Las Primeras: Argentine Photo Postcards/Fotograficas Argentinas Del, 1 vol. 2007. (ENG., Illus.). 120p. per. 15.00 *(978-950-889-161-7(0))* La Marca ARG. Dist: D.A.P./Distributed Art Pubs.

Maxwell, Susan. The Court Art of Friedrich Sustris: Patronage in Late Renaissance Bavaria. 2011. (Visual Culture in Early Modernity Ser.). (Illus.). 250p. 109.95 *(978-0-7546-6887-9(8))* Ashgate Publishing Co.

Medved, Andrej, et al. Rojstvo Modernizma: Prelomnica V Slikarstvu 1976-1980: Tomo Podgornik & Emerik Bernard. 2009. (SLV., Illus.). 139p. *(978-961-6394-15-4(0))* Hyperion Pr.

Melano, Ingrid. The Powers Behind Contemporary Art Exhibitions in European Museums. 2011. 144p. pap. ***(978-3-8443-3440-1(8))*** Lambert Academic Publishing.

Mertins, Detlef & Jennings, Michael William. G: An Avant-Garde Journal of Art, Architecture, Design, & Film, 1923-1926. 2010. (ENG.). 280p. 40.00 *(978-1-60606-039-1(2))* Getty Pubns.

Meschede, Friedrich & Husch, Anette, texts. Ars Viva 10/11: Labor, Laboratory. 2011. (ENG., Illus.). 176p. pap. 45.00 *(978-3-7757-2778-5(7))* Hatje Cantz Verlag GmbH & Co KG DEU. Dist: D.A.P./Distributed Art Pubs.

Messinger, Lisa Mintz & Dabrowski, Magdalena. Stieglitz & His Artists: Matisse to O'Keeffe: The Alfred Stieglitz Collection in the Metropolitan Museum of Art. 2011. 65.00 ***(978-1-58839-433-0(6))*** Metropolitan Museum of Art, The.

Miller, Lesley, ed. Princely Treasures: European Masterpieces 1600-1800, from the Victoria & Albert Museum. 2011. (ENG., Illus.). 192p. 30.00 *(978-1-85177-633-7(8))* V & A Pubns. GBR. Dist: Hachette Bk. Group

Mirabella, M. Bella, intro. Ornamentalism: The Art of Renaissance Accessories. 2012. pap. ***(978-0-472-05117-5(2))***; (Illus.). 342p. E-Book ***(978-0-472-02800-9(6))*** Univ. of Michigan Pr.

Mitchell, John. Out of the Dark Ages. 2008. (Illus.). 192p. pap. 27.00 *(978-0-7156-3685-5(5))* Duckworth Publishers GBR. Dist: International Publishers Marketing.

Mlcoch, Jan & Birgus, Vladimir, eds. Czech Photography of the 20th Century. 2011. (ENG., Illus.). 396p. 85.00 *(978-80-7437-027-4(5))* Kant CZE. Dist: D.A.P./Distributed Art Pubs.

Moffitt, John F. Our Lady of Guadalupe: The Painting, the Legend & the Reality. 2006. (ENG., Illus.). 271p. per. 39.95 *(978-0-7864-2667-6(5))* McFarland & Co., Inc. Pubs.

Moller, Simon Dybbroe. Like Origami Gone Wrong, 1 vol. 2007. (ENG., Illus.). 100p. 29.00 *(978-3-905770-33-9(4))* JRP Ringier Kunstverlag AG CHE. Dist: D.A.P./Distributed Art Pubs.

Mondrian, Piet. MondrianDe Stijl. 2011. (GER & ENG., Illus.). 304p. 60.00 ***(978-3-7757-3023-5(0))*** Hatje Cantz Verlag GmbH & Co KG DEU. Dist: D.A.P./Distributed Art Pubs.

Mondrian, Piet & Léal, Brigitte. Mondrian. 2010. (FRE., Illus.). 357p. *(978-2-84426-451-0(4))* Centre National d'Art et de Culture Georges Pompidou.

Monrad, Kasper. Hammershoi & Europe. 2012. (Illus.). 272p. 49.95 ***(978-3-7913-5174-2(5))*** Prestel Publishing.

Mossinger, Ingrid & Ritter, Beate. Björn Nörgaard: Mythos und Morphologie. 2010. (ENG.). 128p. 58.00 *(978-3-86832-001-5(6)*, Art Stock Bks. Ltd/Csi) Continental Sales, Inc.

Muller, Melissa & Tatzkow, Monika. Lost Lives, Lost Art: Jewish Collectors, Nazi Art Theft, & the Quest for Justice. 2010. (ENG., Illus.). 248p. 40.00 *(978-0-86565-263-7(5))* Vendome Pr., The.

Muller, Richard, photos by. Enter. 2010. (Illus.). 212p. 99.00 *(978-80-556-0298-1(0))* Slovart, Vydavatel'stvo, spol. s.r.o. SVK. Dist: Independent Pubs. Group.

Museu Calouste Gulbenkian Staff, contrib. by. European Illuminated Manuscripts: In the Calouste Gulbenkian Collection. 2007. (Illus.). 512p. 190.00 ***(978-1-85759-503-1(3))*** Scala Pubs., Ltd. GBR. Dist: Antique Collectors' Club.

Museyon Guides, ed. Art + Travel Europe: Step into the Lives of Five Famous Painters. 2010. (Art+ Ser.). (ENG., Illus.). 208p. pap. 17.95 *(978-0-9822320-5-7(5))* Museyon Inc.

Nash, Susie. Northern Renaissance Art. 2009. (Oxford History of Art Ser.). (ENG., Illus.). 384p. pap. 29.95 *(978-0-19-284269-5(2))* Oxford Univ. Pr., Inc.

Neverov, Olegs Yakovlevichs. The Hermitage Collections: Volume I: Treasures of World Art; Volume II: from the Age of Enlightenment to the Present Day. 2010. (Illus.). 656p. 95.00 *(978-0-8478-3503-4(0))* Rizzoli International Pubns., Inc.

Nichol, John. European History, Literature, & Art, from A.d. 200 to 1888, & of American History, Literature, & Art. reprint ed. 150.00 *(978-0-7222-7265-7(0))* Library Reprints, Inc.

Nichols, Tom. The Art of Poverty: Irony & Ideal in Sixteenth-Century Beggar Imagery. 2008. (ENG., Illus.). 304p. 100.00 *(978-0-7190-7582-7(3))* Manchester Univ. Pr. GBR. Dist: Macmillan.

Nichols, Tom, ed. Others & Outcasts in Early Modern Europe: Picturing the Social Margins. 2007. (Illus.). 288p. 124.95 *(978-0-7546-5557-2(1))* Ashgate Publishing Co.

North, Michael, ed. Artistic & Cultural Exchanges Between Europe & Asia, 1400-1900: Rethinking Markets, Workshops & Collections. 2010. (Illus.). 216p. 124.95 *(978-0-7546-6937-1(8))* Ashgate Publishing Co.

Norwich, John Julius, intro. Croatia: Aspects of Art, Architecture & Cultural Heritage. 2009. (ENG., Illus.). 224p. 65.00 *(978-0-7112-2921-1(X))* Lincoln, Frances Ltd. GBR. Dist: Perseus-PGW.

Novero, Cecilia. Antidiets of the Avant-Garde: From Futurist Cooking to Eat Art. 2010. (ENG., Illus.). 368p. pap. 27.50 *(978-0-8166-4601-2(5))* Univ. of Minnesota Pr.

Okediji, Moyo. Western Frontiers of African Art. 2011. (Rochester Studies in African History & the Diaspora Ser.: Volume 53). (Illus.). 354p. 85.00 *(978-1-58046-370-6(3))* Univ. of Rochester Pr.

Oliver-Smith, Kerry, et al. Project Europa: Imagining the (Im)possible. 2010 (ENG., Illus.). 116p. pap. 29.95 *(978-0-9762552-9-1(4))* Univ. Pr. of Florida.

Ondak, Roman. Roman Ondak: Measuring the Universe. 2009. (ENG., Illus.). 168p. 35.00 *(978-3-03764-024-1(3))* JRP Ringier Kunstverlag AG CHE. Dist: D.A.P./Distributed Art Pubs.

O'Neill, Paul, ed. Locating the Producers. 2011. (ENG., Illus.). 412p. pap. 27.50 *(978-90-78088-51-6(6))* Valiz NLD. Dist: D.A.P./Distributed Art Pubs.

O'Neill, Paul, ed. & text. Neighbourhood Secrets. 2010. (ENG. Illus.). 384p. pap. 60.00 *(978-82-7547-349-1(7))* Pr., Forlaget NOR. Dist: D.A.P./Distributed Art Pubs.

Orachev, Atanas & Handjiyski, Antoniy. Bulgaria: The Land of Treasures. 2006. (Illus.). 143p. 57.50 *(978-954-500-164-2(X))* Borina BGR. Dist: Coronet Bks.

Os, H. W. Van, et al. Dreaming of Italy. 2007. (ENG., Illus.). 128p. 39.50 *(978-90-400-8222-1(7))* Waanders B.V., Uitgeverij NLD. Dist: National Bk. Network.

Pabedinskas, Tomas. Contemporary Lithuanian Photography. 2010. 172p. pap. *(978-3-8383-4312-9(3))* Lambert Academic Publishing.

Pabijanek, Katarzyna. Representation of the Body in Polish Art after 1989: Towards a history of Polish art after 1989. 2008. 88p. pap. *(978-3-639-10610-7(5))* VDM Verlag Dr. Mueller e.K.

Pal, Pratapaditya. East Meets West. 2010. (Illus.). 196p. 45.00 *(978-93-80581-00-2(9))* Marg Pubns. IND. Dist: National Bk. Network.

Parshall, Peter, ed. The Woodcut in Fifteenth-Century Europe. 2009. (Studies in the History of Art Ser.). (ENG., Illus.). 352p. 70.00 *(978-0-300-12163-6(6))* National Gallery of Art.

Pejic, Bojana, ed. Gender Check: A Reader. 2011. (ENG.). 380p. pap. 39.95 *(978-3-86560-883-3(3))* Verlag der Buchhandlung Walther Konig DEU. Dist: D.A.P./Distributed Art Pubs.

Petersen, Stephen. Space-Age Aesthetics: Lucio Fontana, Yves Klein, & the Postwar European Avant-Garde. 2009. (Refiguring Modernism Ser.). (ENG.). 320p. pap. 75.00 *(978-0-271-03342-5(8))* Pennsylvania State Univ. Pr.

Pijzel-Domisse, Jet & M. Eliëns, Titus. Glinsterend Glas: 1500 Jaar Europese Glaskunst. 2009. (DUT & ENG., Illus.). 352p. 85.00 *(978-90-400-8606-9(0))* Waanders B.V., Uitgeverij NLD. Dist: National Bk. Network.

Piotrowski, Piotr. In the Shadow of Yalta: Art & the Avant-garde in Eastern Europe, 1945-1989. 2011. (Illus.). 488p. pap. 30.00 *(978-1-86189-863-0(0))* Reaktion Bks., Ltd. GBR. Dist: Chicago Distribution Ctr.

—In the Shadow of Yalta: Art & the Avant-Garde in Eastern Europe, 1945-1989. Piotrowski, Piotr, tr. from POL. 2009. (ENG., Illus.). 498p. 55.00 *(978-1-86189-438-0(4))* Reaktion Bks., Ltd. GBR. Dist: Chicago Distribution Ctr.

Piotrowski, Piotr, tr. Art & Democracy in Post-Communist Europe. 2012. (Illus.). 272p. pap. 32.00 ***(978-1-86189-895-1(9))*** Reaktion Bks., Ltd. GBR. Dist: Chicago Distribution Ctr.

Ponciroli, Virginia, ed. Nunziante Opere 1995-2010: [in English & Italian]. 2010. 208p. 99.50 ***(978-88-370-7790-7(4))*** Electa ITA. Dist: Trans-Atlantic Pubns., Inc.

Prieto, Rosi. A Concise History of Art: The Western World. rev. ed. 2009. (ENG.). 268p. pap. 112.19 *(978-0-7575-6621-9(9))* Kendall Hunt Publishing Co.

Ramirez, Mari Carmen & Crespin, Ester. Untangling the Web: Gego's Reticularea, an Anthology of Critical Response. Huizi, María Elena, ed. 2012. (ENG & SPA., Illus.). 304p. 50.00 *(978-0-300-16613-2(3))* Museum of Fine Arts, Houston.

Ramson, Sidsel. Sidsel Ramson: A Photographic Odyssey. 2011. (ENG., Illus.). 360p. 80.00 *(978-2-7022-0937-0(8))* Cercle d'Art, Editions FRA. Dist: National Bk. Network.

Rattemeyer, Christian, ed. Exhibiting the New Art: 'Op Losse Schroeven' & 'When Attitudes Become Form' 1969. 2011. (ENG., Illus.). 280p. pap. 27.50 *(978-3-86560-859-8(0))* Verlag der Buchhandlung Walther Konig DEU. Dist: D.A.P./Distributed Art Pubs.

Reaulx, Dominique de Fornt. Artist's Studio. 2008. (Photography at the Mus?e D'Orsay Ser.). (ENG., Illus.). 96p. pap. 10.00 *(978-88-7439-219-3(2))* 5 Continents ITA. Dist: Hachette Bk. Group.

Rewald, Sabine. Rooms with a View: The Open Window in the 19th Century. 2011. (Illus.). xiii, 190p. pap. 30.00 ***(978-1-58839-413-2(1))*** Metropolitan Museum of Art, The.

Richardson, Carol M., ed. Locating Renaissance Art. 2007. (Renaissance Art Reconsidered Ser.). (ENG., Illus.). 352p. pap. 35.00 (978-0-300-12188-9(1)) Yale Univ. Pr.

Robinson, Julia, ed. New Realisms, 1957-1962: Object Strategies Between Readymade & Spectacle. 2010. (ENG., Illus.). 294p. (gr. 17). pap. 44.95 (978-0-262-51522-1(9)) MIT Pr.

Rodriguez, Maria Ines. Modernidad Tropical. 2010. 160p. pap. (978-84-92861-30-9(4)) Actar Birkhauser Distribution.

Rosenthal, Leon. Romanticism. 2008. (Art of Century Ser.). (ENG., Illus.). 199p. 19.95 (978-1-84484-458-6(7)) Parkstone International GBR. Dist: Ingram Pub. Services.

San Juan, Rose Marie. Vertiginous Mirrors. 2011. (Rethinking Art's Histories Ser.). (ENG., Illus.). 240p. 95.00 (978-0-7190-8481-2(4)) Manchester Univ. Pr. GBR. Dist: Macmillan.

Saxgren, Henrik, photos by. Henrik Saxgren: Unintended Sculptures. 2010. (ENG., Illus.). 112p. 70.00 (978-3-7757-2501-9(6)) Hatje Cantz Verlag GmbH & Co KG DEU. Dist: D.A.P./Distributed Art Pubs.

Scallen, Catherine B. Art of the Northern Renaissance. 2007. per. 49.95 (978-1-59803-333-5(6)) Teaching Co., LLC, The.

Scholz, Dieter. Pinsel & Dolch: Anarchistische Ideen in Kunst & Kunsttheorie 1840-1920. (GER., Illus.). 477p. (978-3-496-01199-6(8)) Reimer, Dietrich.

Sciberras, Keith. Baroque Painting in Malta. 2009. (ENG., Illus.). 450p. (C). 148.00 (978-99932-7-249-6(3)) Midsea Bks. Ltd. MLT. Dist: Brown, David Bk. Co., The.

Sedley, Jeremy, et al, eds. New Art International, Volume 12: A Compendium of Recent Works by World Contemporary Artists. 2008. (New Art International Ser.). (Illus.). 179p. 26.00 (978-0-9773540-4-7(0)) A.R.T. Pr.

Sheriff, Mary D., ed. Cultural Contact & the Making of European Art since the Age of Exploration. 2010. (Bettie Allison Rand Lectures in Art History Ser.). (ENG., Illus.). 248p. 35.00 (978-0-8078-3366-7(5)) Univ. of North Carolina Pr.

Shoemaker, Innis H. & Ittmann, John W. Adventures in Modern Art: The Charles K. Williams II Collection. 2009. (Illus.). 336p. (978-0-87633-215-3(7)); (978-0-87633-216-0(5)) Philadelphia Museum of Art.

Shoemaker, Innis Howe. Adventures in Modern Art: The Charles K. Williams II Collection. 2009. (ENG., Illus.). 336p. 60.00 (978-0-300-14978-4(6)) Yale Univ. Pr.

Silver, Larry & Wyckoff, Elizabeth, eds. Grand Scale: Monumental Prints in the Age of Dürer & Titian. 2008. (Illus.). 176p. 50.00 (978-0-300-13879-5(2)) Yale Univ. Pr.

Simonson, Karina. Creation of Fictional Community. 2011. 80p. pap. (978-3-8433-8549-7(1)) Lambert Academic Publishing.

Smash 137. Smash Proof. 2009. (On the Run Ser.). (Illus.). 128p. 19.95 (978-3-937946-57-3(8)); pap. 14.95 (978-3-937946-56-6(X)) From Here To Fame GmbH DEU. Dist: SCB Distributors.

Smith, David R. Parody & Festivity in Early Modern Art: Essays on Comedy As Social Vision. 2012. (Illus.). 230p. 119.95 (978-1-4094-3030-8(8)) Ashgate Publishing Co.

Steves, Rick & Openshaw, Gene. Rick Steves' Europe 101: History & Art for the Traveler. 7th ed. 2007. (Rick Steves Ser.). (ENG., Illus.). 536p. per. 24.95 (978-1-56691-516-8(3)) Avalon Travel Publishing.

Stichting Kunstboek. Bonsai: Noelanders Trophy 10 Years. 2010. (ENG., Illus.). 224p. (978-90-5856-341-5(3), Stichting Kunstboek (Acc)) Antique Collectors' Club.

Sultana, Sharon. The National Museum of Archaeology: The Neolithic Period. 2006. (ENG., Illus.). 40p. (C). pap. 9.95 (978-99932-7-076-8(8)) Midsea Bks. Ltd. MLT. Dist: Brown, David Bk. Co., The.

Supicic, Ivan. Croatia in the Late Middle Ages & the Renaissance: A Cultural Survey. 2009. (ENG., Illus.). 800p. 110.00 (978-0-85667-624-6(1)) Wilson, Philip Pubs., Ltd. GBR. Dist: Macmillan.

Sureda, Joan, photos by. Goya & Italy. 2008. (ENG., Illus.). 310p. pap. 69.00 (978-84-7506-808-4(1)) Turner, Ediciones S.A. ESP. Dist: D.A.P./Distributed Art Pubs.

Szymusiak, Dominique. La donation Alice Teriade: La collection d'un editeur D'art. 2008. (ENG.). 120p. pap. 45.00 (978-2-35340-038-6(8)) Gourcuff Gradenigo FRA. Dist: National Bk. Network.

Tamayo, Museo. La Maquina y el Juglar Coleccion Renault. 2006. 69p. pap. 41.00 (978-968-5979-11-5(1)) Trucatriche.

Tarabra, Daniela. European Art of the Eighteenth Century. 2008. (Illus.). 384p. pap. 24.95 (978-0-89236-921-8(3)) Oxford Univ. Pr., Inc.

Tarasov, Oleg. Framing Russian Art. 2011. (ENG., Illus.). 415p. 70.00 (978-1-86189-762-6(6)) Reaktion Bks., Ltd. GBR. Dist: Chicago Distribution Ctr.

The Curators and Employees of Kelvingrove Art Gallery and Museum. Kelvingrove Art Gallery & Museum: The Curators & employees of Kelvingrove Art Gallery & Museum. 2009. (ENG., Illus.). 128p. pap. 20.00 (978-0-85667-667-3(5)) Wilson, Philip Pubs., Ltd. GBR. Dist: Macmillan.

Thun-Hohenstein, Christoph, pref. East by South West. 2012. (ENG & GER., Illus.). 179p. pap. 40.00 (978-3-86984-224-0(5)) Verlag fur Moderne Kunst DEU. Dist: D.A.P./Distributed Art Pubs.

Thurber, T. Barton. European Art at Dartmouth: Highlights from the Hood Museum of Art. 2008. (Illus.). ix, 222p. (978-1-58465-738-5(3)); (ENG., 232p. pap. 40.00 (978-1-58465-724-8(3)) Hood Museum of Art.

Thyssen-Bornemisza Art Contemporary. Kuba: Journey Against the Current. 2006. (Illus.). 182p. pap. (978-3-211-36513-7(3), 3211365133) Actar Birkhauser Distribution.

Tinterow, Gary, et al. Abstract Expressionism & Other Modern Works: The Muriel Kallis Steinberg Newman Collection in the Metropolitan Museum of Art. 2007. (Illus.). x, 214p. 29.95 (978-1-58839-274-9(0)) Metropolitan Museum of Art, The.

Tojner, Poul Erik & Wilmes, Ulrich, eds. Per Kirkeby: Louisiana 2008. 2009. (ENG., Illus.). 192p. 40.00 (978-87-91607-57-8(4)) Louisana DNK. Dist: D.A.P./Distributed Art Pubs.

Toman, Rolf, ed. Gothic: Architecture, Sculpture, Painting. 2008. (Architecture Sculpture Painting Ser.). (Illus.). 520p. per. 24.95 (978-0-8416-0068-3(6)) American Map Corp.

—Neoclassicism & Romanticism: Architecture, Sculpture, Painting, Drawings: 1750-1848. 2008. (Architecture Sculpture Painting Ser.). (Illus.). 520p. per. 24.95 (978-0-8416-0089-8(9)) American Map Corp.

Tomasso Brothers Fine Art Staff. Scultura III. 2010. (ENG., Illus.). 80p. (C). 50.00 (978-1-907372-15-5(6)) Holberton, Paul Publishing GBR. Dist: Univ. of Washington Pr.

Topfer, Klaus & Wagner, Hilke, texts. Tue Greenfort: Linear Deflection. 2009. (ENG., Illus.). 192p. pap. 35.00 (978-3-86560-526-9(5)) Verlag der Buchhandlung Walther Konig DEU. Dist: D.A.P./Distributed Art Pubs.

Tove, Siv & Walker, Kulbrandstad. Sense & the Senses in Early Modern Art & Cultural Practice. Sanger, Alice E., ed. 2012. (Visual Culture in Early Modernity Ser.). (Illus.). 230p. 124.95 (978-1-4094-0004-2(2)) Ashgate Publishing Co.

Townsend, Eleano & Townsend, Eleanor. Death & Art: Europe, 1200-1530. 2009. (ENG., Illus.). 96p. 22.50 (978-1-85177-583-5(8)) V & A Pubns. GBR. Dist: Hachette Bk. Group.

Tragatschnig, Ulrich. Konzeptuelle Kunst: Interpretationsparadigmen: Ein Propaedeutikum. (GER.). 194p. (978-3-496-01187-3(4)) Reimer, Dietrich.

Tuli, Neville. Osian's A Historical Epic: From Surrender to Revolt, Swaraj to Responsibility. 2006. (ENG., Illus.). 45.00 (978-1-890206-51-2(2)) Mapin Publishing Pvt. Ltd IND. Dist: National Bk. Network.

Turner, Adriana & Warren, Jeremy, eds. Auctions, Agents & Dealers: The Mechanisms of the Art Market 1660-1830. 2008. (Studies in the history of Collections). (ENG., Illus.). 173p. (C). pap. 50.00 (978-1-903767-10-8(5)) Archaeopress GBR. Dist: Brown, David Bk. Co., The.

Turvey, Malcolm. The Filming of Modern Life: European Avant-Garde Film of the 1920s. 2011. (October Bks.). (ENG., Illus.). 232p. (gr. 17). 29.95 (978-0-262-01518-9(8)) MIT Pr.

Tuymans, Luc & Gas, Alison. Luc Tuymans: The Reality of the Lowest Rank - A Vision of Central Europe. 2011. (ENG., Illus.). 300p. 85.00 (978-90-209-8997-7(9)) Lannoo Pubs./Racine.

Unterholzner, Daniela. Southeast-Asian Fans in Habsburg Collections. 2010. 140p. pap. (978-3-639-23912-6(1)) VDM Verlag Dr. Mueller e.K.

Van Rysselbergerghe, Theo, illus. Theo Van Rysselberghe, 1 vol. 2007. (FRE & ENG.). 256p. 80.00 (978-90-5779-080-5(7)) Exhibitions International N.V. BEL. Dist: D.A.P./Distributed Art Pubs.

Vavouranakis, Giorgos, ed. The Seascape in Aegean Prehistory. 2011. (Monographs of the Danish Institute at Athens). (ENG., Illus.). 288p. (C). 50.00 (978-87-7934-571-3(9)) Aarhus Universitetsforlag DNK. Dist: ISD.

Verbruggen, Carin, photos by. Under_Exposed. 2009. (Illus.). 136p. 55.00 (978-90-5330-615-4(3)) Mets en Schilt Uitgevers NLD. Dist: Ingram Pub. Services.

Vickers, Michael. Scythian & Thracian Antiquities in Oxford. 2006. (ENG., Illus.). 80p. 22.95 (978-1-85444-181-2(7)) Ashmolean Museum GBR. Dist: Antique Collectors' Club.

Vilinbachov, George & Olausson, Magnus, eds. Staging Power: Napoleon, Charles John, Alexander. 2010. 424p. 129.50 (978-91-7100-824-4(1)) Moderna Museet SWE. Dist: Coronet Bks.

Vinzent, Jutta, text. Overcoming Dictatorships. 2009. (ENG., Illus.). 96p. pap. 32.00 (978-3-86678-178-8(4)) Kerber Verlag DEU. Dist: D.A.P./Distributed Art Pubs.

von Huene, Stephan. Stephan von Huene: The Song of the Line/Die Zeichnungen 1950-1999. 2010. (ENG., Illus.). 144p. 45.00 (978-3-7757-2642-9(X)) Hatje Cantz Verlag GmbH & Co KG DEU. Dist: D.A.P./Distributed Art Pubs.

Wagner, Wolfgang Eric. Die Liturgische Gegenwart des Abwesenden Königs: Gebetsverbrüderung und Herrscherbild Im Frühen Mittelalter. 2010. (GER & ENG.). 392p. (978-90-04-18923-2(8)) BRILL.

Warren, Jeremy. Beauty & Power: Renaissance & Baroque Bronzes from the Collection of Peter Marino. 2010. (ENG., Illus.). 288p. 90.00 (978-0-900785-77-1(2)) Holberton, Paul Publishing GBR. Dist: Univ. of Washington Pr.

Weislogel, Andrew C. & Iacono, Domenic J. A Changing Landscape: Prints & Drawings 1570-1670 from the Arthur & Arlene Elkind Collection. 2006. (Illus.). 52p. pap. 5.00 (978-0-9646042-1-6(3)) Cornell Univ., Herbert F. Johnson Museum of Art.

Weisswelier, Lilli. Futuristen Auf Europa-Tournee: Zur Vorgeschichte, Konzeption und Rezeption der Ausstellungen Futuristischer Malerei (1911-1913) 2009. (Illus.). 287p. pap. (978-3-8376-1205-9(8)) Transcript Verlag.

Wendelski, Marc, photos by. Marc Wendelski: Nage Libre. 2009. (ENG., Illus.). 120p. 45.00 (978-2-87340-222-8(9)) Yellow now BEL. Dist: D.A.P./Distributed Art Pubs.

West, Shearer, ed. Italian Culture in Northern Europe in the Eighteenth Century. 2011. (Cambridge Studies in Italian History & Culture Ser.). (ENG., Illus.). 288p. pap. 31.00 (978-0-521-18742-8(7)) Cambridge Univ. Pr.

Westheider, Ortrud. Sturz in die Welt: Die Kunst des Manierismus in Europa. Mit Beiträgen von Szilvia Bodnár, Eszter Ágnes Czoma, Anna Ecsedy, Ildikó Ember, Miklós Gálos, Zsuzsa Gonda, Annamária Gosztola, Zoltán Kárpáti, Szilárd Papp, Manga Pattantyús, Michael Philipp, Judit Sebö, Miriam Szöcs, Júlia Tátrai, Vilmos Tátrai, Michael Thimann und Axel Vécsey. Phillip, Michael- & Westheider, Ortrus, eds. 2008. (GER., Illus.). 216p. (C). 55.00 (978-3-7774-4455-0(3)) Hirmer Verlag GmbH DEU. Dist: Brown, David Bk. Co., The.

White, Anthony. Lucio Fontana: Between Utopia & Kitsch. 2011. (October Bks.). (ENG., Illus.). 344p. (gr. 17). 29.95 (978-0-262-01592-9(7)) MIT Pr.

Wiehager, Renate, ed. Discourses in Painting: Painting, Prints, & Object Art from the Daimler Art Collection, 1908-2010. 2011. (ENG., Illus.). 360p. pap. 75.00 (978-3-7757-2730-3(2)) Hatje Cantz Verlag GmbH & Co KG DEU. Dist: D.A.P./Distributed Art Pubs.

Wijsman, H. Luxury Bond: Illustrated Manuscript Production & Noble & Princely Book Ownership in the Burgundian Netherlands (1400-1550) 2010. (Burgundica Ser.). (ENG., Illus.). 717p. (C). 138.00 (978-2-503-52558-7(X)) Brepols Pubs. BEL. Dist: ISD.

Williams, Wes. Monsters & their Meanings in Early Modern Culture: Mighty Magic. 2011. (ENG., Illus.). 320p. 110.00 (978-0-19-957702-6(1)) Oxford Univ. Pr., Inc.

Winters, Laurie, et al. Biedermeier: The Invention of Simplicity. 2006. (978-0-944110-85-0(1)); pap. (978-0-944110-89-8(4)) Milwaukee Art Museum.

Witkovsky, Matthew. Avant-Garde Art in Everyday Life: Early Twentieth-Century European Modernism. 2011. (ENG., Illus.). 160p. 50.00 (978-0-300-16609-5(5)) Art Institute of Chicago.

Wixom, William, et al. The Ronald S. Lauder Collection: Selections from the 3rd Century BC to the 20th Century, 1 vol. 2011. (ENG.). 540p. 75.00 (978-3-7913-5164-3(8)) Prestel Publishing.

Wohl, Hellmut & Montanari, Tommaso, eds. Giovan Pietro Bellori: The Lives of the Modern Painters, Sculptors & Architects. 2009. (ENG., Illus.). 516p. (C). pap. 35.99 (978-0-521-13954-0(6)) Cambridge Univ. Pr.

Xuereb, Paul. Edward Caruana Dingli (1876-1950) Portraits, Views & Folkloristic Scences. 2010. (Illus.). 400p. (C). 148.00 (978-99932-7-303-5(1)) Midsea Bks. Ltd. MLT. Dist: Brown, David Bk. Co., The.

Yoo, Hee-Gwone & Regina, Kristen A., compiled by. Visual Resources from Russia & Eastern Europe in the New York Public Library: A Checklist. 2008. (Illus.). 140.00 (978-0-88354-046-6(0)) Ross Publishing Incorporated.

Zammit, William. The Bellanti Family: Contributions to art & culture in Malta. 2011. (ENG., Illus.). 208p. (C). 98.00 (978-99932-7-331-8(7)) Midsea Bks. Ltd. MLT. Dist: Brown, David Bk. Co., The.

Zeisler, Wilfred & Bouchenot-Déchin, Patricia. The Magnificence & Grandeur of the Royal Houses in Europe. Catherine, Armin & Arminjon, Catherine, eds. 2012. (ENG., Illus.). 368p. 70.00 (978-88-572-1117-6(7)) Skira Editore ITA. Dist: Random Hse., Inc.

Zhenqing, Gu, ed. Two Asias, Two Europes: An International Exhibition of Contemporary Art, 1 vol. 2008. (ENG., Illus.). 215p. pap. 48.00 (978-988-99609-4-0(X)) Timezone 8 Ltd. HKG. Dist: D.A.P./Distributed Art Pubs.

Zika, Charles. The Appearance of Witchcraft. 2009. (Illus.). 320p. 34.95 (978-0-415-56355-0(0)) Routledge.

—The Appearance of Witchcraft: Print & Visual Culture in Sixteenth-Century Europe. 2007. (ENG., Illus.). 320p. 158.00 (978-0-415-08242-6(0)) Routledge.

Zuffi, Stefano. European Art of the Sixteenth Century. Shugaar, Antony, tr. from ITA. 2006. (Art through the Centuries Ser.). (Illus.). 384p. pap. 24.95 (978-0-89236-846-4(2)) Oxford Univ. Pr., Inc.

ART, FAR EASTERN

see Art, East Asian

ART, FINNISH

de Weck, Ziba Ardalan, ed. Eija-Liisa Ahtila: Where Is Where? 2011. (ENG., Illus.). 128p. 59.95 (978-3-86560-759-1(4)) Verlag der Buchhandlung Walther Konig DEU. Dist: D.A.P./Distributed Art Pubs.

Jeu De Paume, Paris. Eija-Liisa Ahtila. 2008. (GER & ENG., Illus.). 192p. pap. 55.00 (978-3-7757-2133-2(9)) Hatje Cantz Verlag GmbH & Co KG DEU. Dist: D.A.P./Distributed Art Pubs.

Kurenniemi, Erkki. Erkki Kurenniemi. 2011. (ENG., Illus.). 48p. pap. 10.00 (978-3-7757-2856-0(2)) Hatje Cantz Verlag GmbH & Co KG DEU. Dist: D.A.P./Distributed Art Pubs.

Persons, Timothy & Hiller, Katrin, texts. The Helsinki School. 2009. (ENG., Illus.). 192p. 60.00 (978-3-7757-2404-3(4)) Hatje Cantz Verlag GmbH & Co KG DEU. Dist: D.A.P./Distributed Art Pubs.

Toikka, Oiva, et al. Birds by Toikka. 2008. (FIN & ENG., Illus.). 159p. pap. (978-951-0-34905-2(4)) Osakeyhtio, Werner Soderstrom.

ART, FLEMISH

Bertone, Carla. Nunziante: Opere 1997-2007: [in English & Italian]. Ponciroli, Virginia, ed. 2008. 202p. pap. 92.50 (978-88-370-6234-7(6)) Electa ITA. Dist: Trans-Atlantic Pubns., Inc.

Collas, I. Hans & Schandel, P., eds. Manuscrits de Louis de Bruges. 2010. (Manuscrits enluminés des anciens Pays-Bas Meridionaux Ser.). (FRE., Illus.). 347p. (C). 218.00 (978-2-7177-2396-0(X)) Brepols Pubs. BEL. Dist: ISD.

Curd, Mary Bryan H. Flemish & Dutch Artists in Early Modern England: Collaboration & Competition, 1460-1680. 2010. (Visual Culture in Early Modernity Ser.). (Illus.). 256p. 119.95 (978-0-7546-6712-4(X)) Ashgate Publishing Co.

De Bunes Ibarra, Miguel Ángel, et al. The Invention of Glory: Afonso V & the Pastrana Tapestries. 2012. (ENG., Illus.). 104p. 65.00 (978-1-55595-375-1(1)) Hudson Hills Pr. LLC.

De Kesel, Wilfried. Flemish 17th Century Lacquers. 2012. (ENG., Illus.). 96p. 47.50 (978-90-5856-373-6(1)) Stichting Kunstboek Bvba BEL. Dist: National Bk. Network.

De Schryver, Antione & Kren, Thomas. The Prayer Book of Charles the Bold: A Study of a Flemish Masterpiece from the Burgundian Court. 2008. (ENG., Illus.). 312p. 60.00 (978-0-89236-943-0(4)) Oxford Univ. Pr., Inc.

Deoldere, Luc. Tlc - The Low Countries 17: Arts & Society in Flanders & the Netherlands. 2011. (ENG., Illus.). 320p. pap. 65.00 (978-90-79705-00-9(4)) Lannoo Pubs./Racine.

—TLC - The Low Countries 18: Arts & Society in Flanders & the Netherlands. 2011. (ENG., Illus.). 316p. pap. 65.00 (978-90-79705-05-4(5)) Lannoo Pubs./Racine.

Diels, A. The Shadow of Rubens: Print Production in Antwerp in the Seventeenth Century. 2009. (print collection of the royal library of Belgium Ser.). (ENG., Illus.). 279p. (C). 167.00 (978-1-905375-50-9(6)) Miller, Harvey Pubs. GBR. Dist: Brown, David Bk. Co., The.

Fryklund, C. Late-Gothic Flemish Wall Painting. 2011. (ENG., Illus.). 435p. (C). 160.00 (978-2-503-51237-2(2)) Brepols Pubs. BEL. Dist: ISD.

Golahny, A., et al, eds. In His Milieu: Essays on Netherlandish Art in Memory of John Michael Montias. 2007. (Illus.). 640p. pap. (978-90-5356-933-7(2), Leiden Univ. Pr.) Amsterdam Univ. Pr.

Howarth, J. Steenwyck Family as Masters of Perspective. 2009. (Pictura Nova Ser.). (Illus.). 571p. (C). 232.00 (978-2-503-51509-0(6)) Miller, Harvey Pubs. GBR. Dist: Brown, David Bk. Co., The.

Hunt, Elizabeth Moore. Illuminating the Borders of Northern French & Flemish Manuscripts, 1270-1310. 2006. (Studies in Medieval History & Culture). (Illus.). 241p. 131.00 (978-0-415-97760-9(6)) Routledge.

Jonckheere, K. Adriaen Thomasz. Key (C. 1545-C. 1589) Portrait of a Calvinist Painter. 2007. (Pictura Nova Ser.). (ENG., Illus.). 396p. (C). 203.00 (978-2-503-52554-9(7)) Brepols Pubs. BEL. Dist: ISD.

Knust, Cornelia. Vorbild der Gerechtigkeit: Jan Provosts Gerichtsbild in Brügge: Mit Einem Katalog Seiner Werke. 2007. (Rekonstruktion der Künste Ser.). (GER., Illus.). 402p. (C). pap. 125.00 (978-3-525-47907-0(7)) Vandenhoeck & Ruprecht GmbH & Co. KG DEU. Dist: ISD.

Koopstra, A. & Weidema, S. Jan Gossart: The Documentary Evidence. 2011. (Studies in Medieval & Early Renaissance Art History Ser.). (ENG., Illus.). 250p. (C). 131.00 (978-1-905375-69-1(7)) Miller, Harvey Pubs. GBR. Dist: Brown, David Bk. Co., The.

Rooses, Max. Art in Flanders. 2010. 378p. pap. 33.75 (978-1-177-79168-7(4)); 366p. pap. 32.75 (978-1-142-12865-4(2)) BiblioBazaar.

—Art in Flanders. 2009. 188p. pap. (978-1-151-73666-6(X)) Books LLC.

—Art in Flanders. 356p. 2010. 37.56 (978-1-165-36184-7(1)) 2009. 46.95 (978-1-104-07211-7(4)) 2009. pap. 31.95 (978-1-104-03622-5(3)) Kessinger Publishing, LLC.

Timmermans, Bert. Patronen Van Patronage in Het Zeventiende-Eeuwse Antwerpen: Een Elite Als Actor Binnen Een Kunstwereld. 2008. (Studies Stadsgeschiedenis Ser.). (DUT., Illus.). 427p. 50.50 (978-90-5260-247-9(6)) Aksant Academic Pubs. NLD. Dist: Amsterdam Univ. Pr.

Tuymans, Luc & Hui, Yu, contrib. by. The Forbidden Empire: Visions of the World by Chinese & Flemish Masters, 1 vol. 2008. (ENG., Illus.). 208p. 86.00 (978-90-6153-715-1(0)) Exhibitions International N.V. BEL. Dist: D.A.P./Distributed Art Pubs.

Van der Stighelen, K., ed. The Nude & the Norm in the Early Modern Low Countries. 2011. (Museums at the Crossroads Ser.). (ENG., Illus.). 220p. (C). pap. 94.00 (978-2-503-53569-2(0)) Brepols Pubs. BEL. Dist: ISD.

Van Suchtelen, Ariane, et al. Rubens & Brueghel: A Working Friendship. Woollett, Anne, ed. 2006. (Illus.). 270p. 65.00 (978-0-89236-847-1(0)) Oxford Univ. Pr., Inc.

Woollett, Anne T., et al. Rubens & Brueghel: A Working Friendship. 2006. (Illus.). 270p. pap. 45.00 (978-0-89236-848-8(9)) Oxford Univ. Pr., Inc.

ART, FOLK

see Folk Art

ART, FRENCH

Acquaviva, Frederic. Gil J. Wolman. I am immortal & Alive. 2010. 184p. pap. 39.95 (978-84-92505-40-1(0)) Museu d'Art Contemporani de Barcelona ESP. Dist: Actar Birkhauser Distribution.

Affron, Matthew, et al. Matisse, Picasso, & Modern Art in Paris: The T. Catesby Jones Collections at the Virginia Museum of Fine Arts & the University of Virginia Art Museum. 2009. (ENG., Illus.). 160p. pap. 39.95 (978-0-917046-88-9(9)) Univ. Pr. of Virginia.

Albrecht, Donald, ed. Paris-New York: Design Fashion Culture, 1925-1940. 2008. (ENG., Illus.). 240p. 50.00 (978-1-58093-211-0(8)) Monacelli Pr., Inc.

Allan, Scott Christopher & Morton, Mary G. Reconsidering Gérôme. 2010. (ENG., Illus.). 168p. pap. 27.50 (978-1-60606-038-4(4), J. Paul Getty Museum) Getty Pubns.

Amado, Antonio. Voiture Minimum: Le Corbusier & the Automobile. 2011. (ENG., Illus.). 368p. (gr. 17). 49.95 (978-0-262-01536-3(6)) MIT Pr.

Aupetitallot, Yves & Prat, Thierry, eds. Kader Attia, 1 vol. 2007. (FRE & ENG., Illus.). 112p. 29.00 (978-2-940271-81-8(X)) JRP Ringier Kunstverlag AG CHE. Dist: D.A.P./Distributed Art Pubs.

Backhaus, Jessica, photos by. One Day in November. 2009. (ENG., Illus.). 128p. 78.00 *(978-3-86828-022-7(7))* Kehrer Verlag Heidelberg, Klaus Kehrer DEU. Dist: Consortium Bk. Sales & Distribution.

Baguley, David. Art & Literature of the Second Empire. 2012. (Durham Modern Languages Ser.). (ENG.). 200p. pap. 24.95 *(978-0-7190-8585-7(3))* Manchester Univ. Pr. GBR. Dist: Macmillan.

Baker, Simon. Surrealism, History & Revolution. 2007. (Illus.). 372p. pap. 99.95 *(978-3-03911-091-9(8))* Lang, Peter Publishing, Inc.

Balducci, Temma, et al. Interior Portraiture & Masculine Identity in France, 1789-1914. 2010. (Illus.). 300p. 119.95 *(978-0-7546-6784-1(7))* Ashgate Publishing Co.

Barikin, Amelia. Parallel Presents: The Art of Pierre Huyghe. 2012. ***(978-0-262-01780-0(6))*** MIT Pr.

Bartz, Gabriele & Konig, Eberhard. Art & Architecture Louvre. 2010. (Art & Architecture Pocket Ser.). 626p. pap. 16.99 *(978-0-8416-7159-1(1))* Langenscheidt Publishing Group.

—Louvre. 2008. (Art & Architecture Ser.). (Illus.). 626p. 19.95 *(978-0-8416-0149-9(6))* American Map Corp.

Baudelaire, Charles. The Mirror of Art, Critical Studies. Mayne, Jonathan, ed. (Illus.). reprint ed. 32.50 *(978-0-404-16303-7(3))* AMS Pr., Inc.

Bennett, Shelley M., et al. French Art of the Eighteenth Century at the Huntington. Bennett, Shelley M. & Sargentson, Carolyn, eds. 2008. (Illus.). 555p. 125.00 *(978-0-300-13594-7(7))* Yale Univ. Pr.

Berenson, Kathryn. Marseille. 2010. (ENG., Illus.). 128p. pap. 29.95 ***(978-0-9814582-4-3(6)***, Int'l Quilt Study Ctr. & Museum at UNL) International Quilt Study Ctr. & Museu.

Bernard, Christian. Claude Lévêque. 2010. (ENG., Illus.). 224p. 75.00 *(978-2-08-030127-7(6))* Flammarion et Cie FRA. Dist: Random Hse., Inc.

Berquet, Gilles & Lugosi, Mirka. Mirka. 2008. (ENG., Illus.). 96p. 49.00 *(978-3-939583-31-8(6))* Kehrer Verlag Heidelberg, Klaus Kehrer DEU. Dist: Consortium Bk. Sales & Distribution.

Binet, Hélène. Composing with Architecture: The Photographs of Helene Binet. 2012. (ENG., Illus.). 224p. 150.00 *(978-0-7148-6119-7(7))* Phaidon Pr., Inc.

Birnbaum, Lillian Birnbaum Transition. 2009. (ENG.). 128p. 45.00 *(978-3-7757-2285-8(8))* Hatje Cantz Verlag GmbH & Co KG DEU. Dist: D.A.P./Distributed Art Pubs.

Birnbaum, Paula J. Women Artists in Interwar France: Framing Femininity's. 2011. (Illus.). 358p. 124.95 *(978-0-7546-6978-4(5))* Ashgate Publishing Co.

Bishop, Janet C., et al. The Steins Collect: Matisse, Picasso, & the Parisian Avant-Garde. 2011. pap. *(978-0-918471-87-1(7))* San Francisco Museum of Modern Art.

Bishop, Michael. Contemporary French Art 2: Gérard Garouste, Colette Deblé, Georges Rousse, Geneviève Asse, Martial Raysse, Christian Jaccard, Joël Kermarrec, Danièle Perronne, Daniel Dezeuze, Philippe Favier, Daniel Nadaud. 2011. (Illus.). 238p. pap. 68.00 ***(978-90-420-3346-7(0))*** Rodopi.

Bishop, Veronica. Contemporary French Art 1: Eleven Studies. 2008. (Illus.). 189p. pap. 57.00 *(978-90-420-2418-2(6))* Rodopi.

Blistene, Bernard, et al. The Museum That Did Not Exist: Daniel Buren. 2010. (Illus.). 352p. 85.00 *(978-3-7913-4499-7(4))* Prestel Publishing.

Blocklehurst, John, et al. Balthus: Works, Interviews. 2008. (ENG., Illus.). 160p. 45.00 *(978-84-343-1165-7(8))* Polígrafa, Ediciones, S. A. ESP. Dist: D.A.P./Distributed Art Pubs.

Bonami, Francesco & Martini, Vittorio. Huang Yong Ping. 2008. (Illus.). 108p. pap. 37.50 *(978-88-370-6075-6(0))* Electa ITA. Dist: Trans-Atlantic Pubns., Inc.

Bourguignon, Katherine M., ed. Impressionist Giverny: A Colony of Artists, 1885-1915. 2007. (Illus.). 224p. pap. 49.00 *(978-0-932171-52-8(4))* Terra Foundation for American Art.

Braun, Emily, et al, texts. Chaos & Classicism: Art in France, Italy, & Germany, 1918-1936. 2011. (ENG., Illus.). 192p. pap. 40.00 *(978-0-89207-405-1(1))* Guggenheim, Solomon R. Museum.

Bremen, Kunsthalle & Bremen, the Kunsthalle, eds. Paula Modersohn-Becker und die Kunst in Paris Um 1900: Von Cezanne bis Picasso. 2007. (GER., Illus.). 359p. (C). pap. 60.00 *(978-3-7774-3535-0(X))* Hirmer Verlag GmbH DEU. Dist: Brown, David Bk. Co., The.

Brenneman, David. Toulouse-Lautrec & Friends: The Irene & Howard Stein Collection. 2010. 30.00 *(978-1-932543-41-4(4))* High Museum of Art.

Bressonneau, Hubert. Paris & Versailles. (Illus.). 208p. pap. 18.95 *(978-88-8029-651-5(5))* Casa Editrice Bonechi ITA. Dist: CPG Publishing, Inc.

Brettell, Richard R. & Pissarro, Joachim. Manet to Matisse: Impressionist Masters from the Marion & Henry Bloch Collection. 2007. pap. *(978-0-942614-36-7(4))* Nelson-Atkins Museum of Art, The.

Brownell, William Crary. French Art: Classic & Contemporary Painting & Sculpture. 2007. 136p. pap. 18.99 *(978-1-4346-0747-8(X))*; (ENG.). 150p. pap. 19.99 *(978-1-4346-0807-9(7))* BiblioBazaar.

Bustamante, Jean-Marc. Jean-Marc Bustamante: A World at a Time. (Illus.). 64p. *(978-3-89322-670-2(2))* Edition Cantz DEU. Dist: D.A.P./Distributed Art Pubs.

Calasso, Roberto. La la Folie Baudelaire, 1 vol. McEwen, Alastair, tr. from ITA. 2012. (ENG., Illus.). 352p. 35.00 ***(978-0-374-18334-9(1))*** Farrar, Straus & Giroux.

Carolyn, Lanchner. Fernand Léger. 2010. (ENG., Illus.). 48p. pap. 9.95 *(978-0-87070-786-5(8))* Museum of Modern Art.

Carpita, Veronica. Dezallier d'Argenville - Muschelkunde. 2009. (ENG, FRE & GER., Illus.). 200p. 39.99 *(978-3-8365-1111-7(8))* TASCHEN DEU. Dist: Ingram Pub. Services.

Carrick, Jill. Nouveau Réalisme, 1960s France, & the Neo-Avant-Garde: Topographies of Chance & Return. 2010. (Illus.). 184p. 104.95 *(978-0-7546-6141-2(5))* Ashgate Publishing Co.

Cass, Claire. The Masters Box Set: Masterpieces of French Art Pottery, 1885-1910 & Clement Massier: Master of Iridescence, 2. 2007. (Illus.). 204p. 75.00 *(978-0-9788371-4-3(2))* Jason Jacques Gallery Pr. The.

Çelik, Zeynep. Empire, Architecture, & the City: French-Ottoman Encounters, 1830-1914. 2008. (ENG., Illus.). 368p. 60.00 *(978-0-295-98779-8(0))* Univ. of Washington Pr.

Cerizza, Luca & Pecoil, Vincent, texts. Ils Sont Peintres. 2009. (ENG & FRE., Illus.). 128p. 22.00 *(978-3-905829-23-5(1))* JRP Ringier Kunstverlag AG CHE. Dist: D.A.P./Distributed Art Pubs.

Cezanne. 2009. *(978-3-8365-1767-6(1))* TASCHEN.

Chagall, Marc & Tériade, E. Chagall et Tériade: L'empreinte D'un Peintre. 2008. (ENG., Illus.). 224p. pap. 60.00 *(978-2-35340-012-6(4))* Gourcuff Gradenigo FRA. Dist: National Bk. Network.

Chaille, Francois & Aliaga, Michel. Cartier: Innovation Through the 20th Century. 2008. (ENG., Illus.). 280p. 65.00 *(978-2-08-030041-6(5))* Flammarion et Cie FRA. Dist: Random Hse., Inc.

Chapin, Mary Weaver. Posters of Paris: Toulouse-Lautrec & his Contemporaries. 2012. (Illus.). 176p. 49.95 ***(978-3-7913-5204-6(0))*** Prestel Publishing.

—Posters of Paris: Toulouse-Lautrec & His Contemporaries. 2012. pap. ***(978-3-7913-6407-0(3))*** Prestel Verlag GmbH & Co KG.

Chartrain, Valerie, ed. Power Chords, 1 vol. 2007. (ENG., Illus.). 168p. pap. 29.00 *(978-3-905770-06-3(7))* JRP Ringier Kunstverlag AG CHE. Dist: D.A.P./Distributed Art Pubs.

Claas. Mathieu Bernard-Reymond. 2008. (ENG., Illus.). 96p. 55.00 *(978-3-7757-2174-5(6))* Hatje Cantz Verlag GmbH & Co KG DEU. Dist: D.A.P./Distributed Art Pubs.

Clancy, Sinead Furlong. The Depiction & Description of the Female Body in Nineteenth-Century French Art, Literature, & Society: Women in the Parks of Paris, 1848-1900. 2011. 277p. 129.95 *(978-0-7734-1451-8(7))* Mellen, Edwin Pr., The.

Closky, Claude & Muracciole, Marie. 02, Claude Closky: Climb at Your Own Risk. 2007. (Illus.). 89p. *(978-88-370-5154-9(9))* Electa.

Connon, Daisy, et al, eds. Aesthetics of Dislocation in French & Francophone Literature & Art: Strategies of Representation. 2009. (FRE & ENG., Illus.). 288p. 109.95 *(978-0-7734-4919-0(1))* Mellen, Edwin Pr., The.

Couturier, Sonia. Drawn to Art: French Artists & Art Lovers in 18th-Century Rome. 2012. (ENG., Illus.). 256p. pap. 45.00 ***(978-88-366-2054-8(X))*** Silvana ITA. Dist: D.A.P./Distributed Art Pubs.

Cowling, E., et al. Picasso: Challenging the Past. 2011. (Illus.). 176p. pap. 25.00 *(978-1-85709-451-0(4))* Yale Univ. Pr.

Criqui, Jean-Pierre, ed. Xavier Veilhan. 2010. (ENG., Illus.). 160p. pap. 55.00 *(978-3-03764-077-7(4))* JRP Ringier Kunstverlag AG CHE. Dist: D.A.P./Distributed Art Pubs.

Cuzin, Jean-Pierre. Fragonard. 2008. (Drawing Gallery Ser.). (ENG., Illus.). 84p. pap. 14.95 *(978-88-7439-079-3(3))* 5 Continents ITA. Dist: Hachette Bk. Group.

D'Alessandro, Stephanie & Elderfield, John. Matisse: Radical Invention, 1913-1917. 2010. (Illus.). 368p. pap. *(978-0-86559-237-7(3))* Art Institute of Chicago.

Damade, Jacques. Jacques-Henri Lartigue. 2010. (Photofile Ser.). (ENG., Illus.). 144p. pap. 15.95 *(978-0-500-41061-5(5)*, 541061) Thames & Hudson.

Damlé, Amaleena & L'Hostis, Aurélie, eds. The Beautiful & the Monstrous: Essays in French Literature, Thought & Culture. 2010. (Modern French Identities Ser.). (Illus.). 237p. pap. 55.95 *(978-3-03911-900-4(1))* Lang, Peter AG GBR. Dist: Lang, Peter.

de Jouy, Manufacture Royale. Toile. 2010. (ENG., Illus.). 80p. 12.99 *(978-1-4236-1692-4(8))* Gibbs Smith, Publisher.

Debailleux, Henri-Francois, et al. Philippe Pasqua: Paradise. 2010. (ENG., Illus.). 160p. 65.00 *(978-88-572-0466-6(9))* Skira Editore ITA. Dist: Random Hse., Inc.

Delteil, Loys, et al. Théodore Géricault. the Graphic Work. L'Oeuvre Gravé. Catalogue Raisonné. Hyman, Alan, ed. 2nd rev. ed. 2010. Orig. Title: Theodore Géricault. le Peintre Graveur Illustré. . (ENG & FRE., Illus.). 280p. 150.00 *(978-1-55660-094-4(1))* Wofsy, Alan Fine Arts.

Derieux, Florence, ed. Marine Hugonnier. 2010. (ENG., Illus.). 160p. pap. 55.00 *(978-3-03764-079-1(0))* JRP Ringier Kunstverlag AG CHE. Dist: D.A.P./Distributed Art Pubs.

Diderot. Salons. (FRE., Illus.). *(978-2-7056-6173-1(5))* Hermann, Editeurs des Sciences & des Arts.

Dion, Mark. Luc Long & Mark Dion: Carnet de Fouilles, Lab Book. 2010. (ENG., Illus.). 136p. 39.95 *(978-2-7427-8609-1(0))* Actes Sud FRA. Dist: D.A.P./Distributed Art Pubs.

Diri#xE9;, Cl#xE9;ment, ed. Isabelle Cornaro. 2012. (ENG., Illus.). 64p. 35.00 ***(978-3-03764-208-5(4))*** JRP Ringier Kunstverlag AG CHE. Dist: D.A.P./Distributed Art Pubs.

Dixon, Annette & Chapin, Mary Weaver. The Dancer: Degas, Forain, Toulouse-Lautrec. 2008. (ENG., Illus.). 256p. 39.95 *(978-1-883124-27-4(1))* Portland Art Museum.

Doolan, Patrick. Recovering the Icon: The Life & Work of Leonid Ouspensky. 2008. (Illus.). 104p. 36.00 *(978-0-88141-270-3(8))* St. Vladimir's Seminary Pr.

Dorléac, Laurence Bertrand, et al. Art of the Defeat: France, 1940-1944. Todd, Jane Marie, tr. from FRE. 2009. (ENG., Illus.). 416p. 45.00 *(978-0-89236-891-4(8))* Oxford Univ. Pr., Inc.

Dover. Barbier Fashion. 2011. (Dover Postcards Ser.). (ENG., Illus.). 24p. pap. 6.95 *(978-0-486-48016-9(X))* Dover Pubns., Inc.

—Seguy. 2010. (Dover Postcards Ser.). (ENG., Illus.). 24p. pap. 6.95 *(978-0-486-48010-7(0))* Dover Pubns., Inc.

Doy, Gen. Claude Cahun: A Sensual Politics of Photography. 2008. (ENG., Illus.). 232p. pap. 29.00 *(978-1-84511-551-7(1))* I. B. Tauris & Co., Ltd. GBR. Dist: Macmillan.

Dubin, Nina L. & Robert, Hubert. Futures & Ruins: Eighteenth-Century Paris & the Art of Hubert Robert. 2010. (ENG., Illus.). 208p. 50.00 *(978-1-60606-023-0(6))* Getty Pubns.

Duchamp, Marcel, et al. Étant Donnés: Manual of Instructions. 2009. (FRE & ENG., Illus.). ***(978-0-87633-212-2(2))*** Philadelphia Museum of Art.

Duchamp, Marcel, et al. Marcel Duchamp: Una Obra Que No Es una Obra "De Arte" 2008. (SPA., Illus.). 358p. *(978-987-21336-7-2(0))* Fundacion Proa.

Dupouy, Alexandre. Erotic French Postcards. 2009. (ENG., Illus.). 144p. 24.95 *(978-2-08-030083-6(0))* Flammarion et Cie FRA. Dist: Random Hse., Inc.

Easton, Elizabeth, et al. Snapshot: Painters & Photography, Bonnard to Vuillard. 2011. (ENG., Illus.). 248p. 50.00 *(978-0-300-17236-2(2))* Yale Univ. Pr.

Eiling, Alexandra, et al, texts. Lumière Noire. Neue Kunst aus Frankreich: New Art from France. 2011. (ENG., Illus.). 232p. pap. 55.00 ***(978-3-86560-996-0(1))*** Verlag der Buchhandlung Walther Konig DEU. Dist: D.A.P./Distributed Art Pubs.

Elffers, Joost, ed. Art Nouveau. 2008. (Gift Paper Ser.). 20p. pap. 9.95 *(978-0-8416-0299-1(9))* American Map Corp.

Engstrom, Barbie & Engstrom, Fred, photos by. Treasure Tours of 278 Masterpieces in the Louvre Museum: For the General Public, with Special Handicapped Tours. 2008. (Illus.). *(978-0-916588-14-4(9))* Kurios Pr.

Faucheur, Jean. Une Nuit. 2007. (FRE & ENG., Illus.). 244p. 28.95 *(978-2-85980-007-9(7))* Kitchen 93 FRA. Dist: SCB Distributors.

Ferretti Bocquillon, Marina, ed. Maximilien Luce: Neo-Impressionist. 2011. (ENG., Illus.). 144p. 39.50 *(978-88-366-1777-7(8))* Silvana ITA. Dist: D.A.P./Distributed Art Pubs.

Folie, Sabine, ed. Un Coup de des: Writing Turned Image, an Alphabet of Pensive Language. 2009. (GER & ENG., Illus.). 250p. pap. 59.95 *(978-3-86560-543-6(5))* Verlag der Buchhandlung Walther Konig DEU. Dist: D.A.P./Distributed Art Pubs.

Foucault, Michel. Manet & the Object of Painting. (ENG., Illus.). 2012. 96p. pap. 14.95 ***(978-1-85437-996-2(8))*** 2010. 80p. 21.95 *(978-1-85437-845-3(7))* Tate Publishing, Ltd. GBR. Dist: Hachette Bk. Group.

Gabardi, Melissa. Jean Després: Jeweler, Maker, & Designer of the Machine Age. 2009. (ENG., Illus.). 224p. 65.00 *(978-0-500-51478-8(X)*, 551478) Thames & Hudson.

Game, Jerome, ed. Porous Boundaries: Texts & Images in Twentieth-Century French Culture. 2007. (Modern French Identities Ser.: Vol. 44). 164p. pap. *(978-0-8204-7595-0(5))* Lang, Peter AG.

Ganz, James A. & Baldus, Édouard. Edouard Baldus at the Château de la Faloise. 2007. (Illus.). 79p. pap. *(978-0-931102-57-8(X))* Clark, Sterling & Francine Art Institute.

Garb, Tamar. Body in Time: Figures of Femininity in Late Nineteenth-Century France. 2008. (ENG., Illus.). 96p. (C). pap. *(978-0-295-98793-4(6))* Univ. of Washington Pr.

Gartner, Peter J. Musee D'Orsay. 2008. (Art & Architecture Ser.). (Illus.). 572p. 19.95 *(978-0-8416-0050-8(3))* American Map Corp.

Gärtner, Peter J. Musée D'Orsay, 1 vol. 2010. (ENG., Illus.). 572p. pap. 9.99 *(978-3-8331-5284-9(2))* h.f.ullmann DEU. Dist: Innovative Logistics.

Gathercole, Patricia M. The Depiction of Clothing in French Medieval Manuscripts. 2008. (Illus.). 116p. *(978-0-7734-5014-1(9))* Mellen, Edwin Pr., The.

Gaudaire-Thor, Jean. Trafiquer dans L'inconnu... Arthur Rimbaud. 2008. (ENG.). 224p. pap. 60.00 *(978-2-35340-023-2(X))* Gourcuff Gradenigo FRA. Dist: National Bk. Network.

George, Hardy S., et al. Paris 1900. George, Hardy S. & Pavelka, Jeffrey J., eds. 2008. (Illus.). 174p. per. 35.00 *(978-0-911919-08-0(2))* Oklahoma City Museum of Art.

Gersh-Ne¿iæ, Beth S. The Demoiselles Revisited. 2007. (Illus.). 44p. per. 25.00 *(978-0-9800556-0-3(1))* Naumann, Francis M. Fine Art, LLC.

Gibson, Michael. Redon. 2011. (ENG., Illus.). 96p. pap. 9.99 *(978-3-8365-3003-3(1))* TASCHEN DEU. Dist: Ingram Pub. Services.

Gierstberg, Frits, et al. Eugène Atget: Paris 1898-1924. 2011. (ENG., Illus.). 320p. 71.00 ***(978-84-15253-03-7(6))*** T.F. Editores ESP. Dist: National Bk. Network.

Giroire, Cécile & Roger, Daniel. Roman Art from the Louvre. 2009. (ENG., Illus.). 280p. pap. 45.00 *(978-1-885444-35-6(4))* Hudson Hills Pr. LLC.

Goddard, Linda. Aesthetic Rivalries: Word & Image in France, 1880-1926. 2012. (Cultural Interactions: Studies in the Relationship between the Arts Ser.). (ENG.). 323p. pap. 69.95 ***(978-3-03911-879-3(X))*** Lang, Peter AG GBR. Dist: Lang, Peter.

Goldstein, Claire. Vaux & Versailles: The Appropriations, Erasures, & Accidents That Made Modern France. 2007. (Illus.). 288p. (C). 59.95 *(978-0-8122-4058-0(8))* Univ. of Pennsylvania Pr.

Goude, Jean-Paul. The Goude Touch: A Ten Year Campaign for Galeries Lafayette. 2010. (ENG., Illus.). 224p. 65.00 *(978-0-500-51486-3(0)*, 551486) Thames & Hudson.

Grancsay, Stephen V., frwd. Master French Gunsmiths' Designs of the Mid-Seventeenth Century. 2011. 48p. 35.95 ***(978-1-258-03180-0(9))*** Literary Licensing, LLC.

Grandena, Florian & Johnston, Cristina. New Queer Images: Representations of Homosexualities in Contemporary Francophone Visual Cultures. 2011. (FRE & ENG.). 230p. pap. 60.95 *(978-3-0343-0182-4(0))* Lang, Peter AG GBR. Dist: Lang, Peter.

Grant, Kim. Surrealism & the Visual Arts: Theory & Reception. 2012. (ENG., Illus.). 416p. pap. 39.99 ***(978-1-107-40334-5(0))*** Cambridge Univ. Pr.

Gualdoni, Flaminio. Impressionism. 2009. (Skira MINI Artbooks Ser.). (ENG., Illus.). 96p. pap. 8.99 *(978-88-6130-738-4(8))* Skira Editore ITA. Dist: Random Hse., Inc.

Guilbaut, Serge, contrib. by. Be-Bomb: The Transatlantic War of Images & All That Jazz. 1946-1956. 2008. (Illus.). 774p. pap. *(978-84-89771-47-5(2))* Museu d'Art Contemporani de Barcelona.

Hale, Rachael. The French Cat. 2011. (ENG., Illus.). 168p. 29.95 *(978-1-58479-950-4(1))* Stewart, Tabori & Chang.

Hamerton, Philip Gilbert. The Sylvan Year. 2009. 190p. pap. *(978-0-217-37384-5(4))*; 202p. pap. *(978-0-217-10853-9(9))* Books LLC.

—The Sylvan Year. 2009. 194p. pap. 19.99 *(978-1-4589-3941-8(3))* General Bks. LLC.

Hanover, Princess Caroline of, frwd. Yinka Shonibare, MBE. 2011. (ENG & FRE., Illus.). 176p. pap. 34.95 *(978-88-7439-564-4(7))* 5 Continents ITA. Dist: Hachette Bk. Group.

Harambourg, Lydia. Helman. 2011. (ENG., Illus.). 64p. 19.95 *(978-2-7022-0944-8(0))* Cercle d'Art, Editions FRA. Dist: National Bk. Network.

Hattori, Cordélia. D'après les Maîtres: Léonard de Vinci, Raphaël, Watteau, Goya, Courbet —: La Gravure D'interprétation D'Alphonse Leroy (1820-1902) à Omer Bouchery (1882-1962) 2008. (FRE & ENG., Illus.). 112p. pap. 40.00 *(978-2-35340-017-1(5))* Gourcuff Gradenigo FRA. Dist: National Bk. Network.

Haworth, Booth & Silvy, Camille. Photographers of Modern Life: Camille Silvy. 2010. (ENG., Illus.). 160p. 40.00 *(978-1-60606-025-4(2))* Getty Pubns.

Hayes, Paul Tucker. Claude Monet: Late Work. 2010. (ENG., Illus.). 216p. 100.00 *(978-0-8478-3603-1(7))* Rizzoli International Pubns., Inc.

He, Jianping, ed. Laboratoires Cccp = Dr. Leche + Melle Rose. 2008. (New Generation of Design Ser.). (Illus.). 215p. pap. *(978-981-245-511-6(6))* Page One Publishing.

Hedeman, Anne D. Translating the Past: Laurent de Premierfait & Boccaccio's de Casibus. 2008. (Illus.). 240p. 60.00 *(978-0-89236-935-5(3))* Oxford Univ. Pr., Inc.

Hegyi, Lorand, et al, contrib. by. From One Century to Another: The Collection of the Musee d'Art Moderne de Saint-Etienne Métropole. 2008. (ENG., Illus.). 272p. 65.00 *(978-88-6130-453-6(2))* Skira Editore ITA. Dist: Random Hse., Inc.

Heilbrun, Francoise & Ooms, Saskia. Maurice Denis. 2008. (Photography at the Mus?e D'Orsay Ser.). (ENG., Illus.). 96p. 10.00 *(978-88-7439-358-9(X))* 5 Continents ITA. Dist: Hachette Bk. Group.

Heraeus, Stefanie. Traumvorstellung & Bildidee: Surreale Strategien in der Franzoesischen Graphik des 19. Jahrhunderts. (GER., Illus.). 228p. *(978-3-496-01177-4(7))* Reimer, Dietrich.

Herz, Ruth. The Art of Justice: The Judge's Perspective. 2012. (ENG., Illus.). 118p. 54.95 ***(978-1-84946-127-6(9))*** Hart Publishing Ltd. GBR. Dist: International Specialized Bk. Services.

Heynickx, Rajesh & De Maeyer, Jan, eds. The Maritain Factor: Taking Religion into Interward Modernism. 2009. (KADOC Studies on Religion, Culture & Society). 240p. pap. 42.50 *(978-90-5867-714-3(1))* Leuven Univ. Pr. BEL. Dist: Cornell Univ. Pr.

Hodge, Susie. Renoir: His Life & Works in 500 Images. 2012. (ENG., Illus.). 256p. 35.00 ***(978-0-7548-2347-6(4))*** Anness Publishing GBR. Dist: National Bk. Network.

Hoobler, Dorothy & Hoobler, Thomas. The Crimes of Paris: A True Story of Murder, Theft, & Detection. 2010. (ENG., Illus.). 400p. pap. 19.95 *(978-0-8032-3432-1(5)*, Bison Bks.) Univ. of Nebraska Pr.

Hooper-Hamersley, Ro. The Hunt after Jeanne-Antoinette de Pompadour: Patronage, Politics, Art, & the French Enlightenment. 2011. (ENG., Illus.). 414p. 85.00 *(978-0-7391-4963-8(6))* Lexington Bks.

Houdouin, Guy. Odon: Sourcier, Sorcier, Magicien. 2010. (FRE & ENG., Illus.). 304p. 110.00 *(978-2-35340-041-6(8))* Gourcuff Gradenigo FRA. Dist: National Bk. Network.

Hunt, Elizabeth Moore. Illuminating the Borders of Northern French & Flemish Manuscripts, 1270-1310. 2006. (Studies in Medieval History & Culture). (Illus.). 241p. 131.00 *(978-0-415-97760-9(6))* Routledge.

Husband, Timothy. The Art of Illumination: The Limbourg Brothers & the Belles Heures of Jean de France, Duc de Berry. 2008. 65.00 *(978-1-58839-294-7(5))* Metropolitan Museum of Art, The.

Jodidio, Philip. Tadao Ando Venice: The Pinault Collection at the Palazzo Grassi & the Punta Della Dogana. 2010. (ENG., Illus.). 160p. 60.00 *(978-0-8478-3410-5(7))* Rizzoli International Pubns., Inc.

Johnson, Dorothy. David to Delacroix: The Rise of Romantic Mythology. 2011. (Bettie Allison Rand Lectures in Art History Ser.). (ENG., Illus.). 272p. 45.00 *(978-0-8078-3451-0(3))* Univ. of North Carolina Pr.

Johnstone, Maren. Desiring Salome. 2008. 72p. pap. *(978-3-639-03157-7(1))* VDM Verlag Dr. Mueller e.K.

Kasmin, Paul, ed. Claude & Francois-Xavier Lalanne: Art. Work. Life. 2012. (ENG., Illus.). 240p. 60.00 ***(978-0-8478-3761-8(0)***, Skira) Rizzoli International Pubns., Inc.

Katz, Robert & Dars, Celestine. The Impressionists: A Comprehensive Visual Reference to One of the Best-Loved Periods of Art History, with over 450 Images. 2012. (ENG., Illus.). 352p. 30.00 ***(978-0-7548-2402-2(0))*** Anness Publishing GBR. Dist: National Bk. Network.

Kear, John & Clarke, Graham, eds. French Art in the 19th Century. (Art in Context Ser.). *(978-1-873403-71-6(2))* Helm Information, Ltd.

Keller, Christoph & Saint-Loubert Bie, Jerome, eds. Yann Serandour: Inside the White Cube. 2010. (ENG., Illus.). 84p. pap. 35.00 *(978-3-03764-042-5(1))* JRP Ringier Kunstverlag AG CHE. Dist: D.A.P./Distributed Art Pubs.

Kepetzis, Ekaterini. Vergegenwärtigte Antike: Studien zur Gattungsüberschreitung in der französischen und englischen Malerei (1840-1914) 2009. (GRE & GER., Illus.). 378p. pap. 81.95 *(978-3-631-58124-7(6))* Lang, Peter GmbH, Europaischer Verlag der Wissenschaften DEU. Dist: Lang, Peter.

Killiam, Marie-Therese. The End of Art: A Comparative Analysis of French Postmodern Art Theorists. 2011. x, 89p. pap. *(978-1-86335-894-1(3))* Common Ground Publishing Pty, Ltd.

Kiraz, George & Ojala, Douglas, eds. Digital Enhancements of Jules Leroy's Album of Illuminated Syriac Manuscripts. 2009. 790.00 *(978-1-60724-422-6(5))*; 790.00 *(978-1-60724-424-0(1))*; 790.00 *(978-1-60724-423-3(3))* Gorgias Pr., LLC.

Kisluk-Grosheide, Danielle O. & Munger, Jeffrey. The Wrightsman Galleries for French Decorative Arts, the Metropolitan Museum of Art. 2010. (Illus.). 272p. 40.00 *(978-0-300-15520-4(4))* Yale Univ. Pr.

Klein, Yves. Yves Klein: Expressing the Immaterial. 2011. (ENG., Illus.). 208p. 31.00 *(978-2-916275-74-1(6))* Dilecta, Editions FRA. Dist: D.A.P./Distributed Art Pubs.

Koda, Harold & Bolton, Andrew. Poiret. 2007. (Illus.). 224p. 65.00 *(978-1-58839-223-7(6))* Metropolitan Museum of Art, The.

Kohle, Hubertus & Reichardt, Rolf. Visualising the Revolution: Politics & Pictorial Arts in Late Eighteenth-Century France. 2008. (Reaktion Books - Picturing History Ser.). (ENG., Illus.). 240p. 45.00 *(978-1-86189-312-3(4))* Reaktion Bks., Ltd. GBR. Dist: Chicago Distribution Ctr.

Konemann Staff. Paris Art & Architecture. Date not set. (Art & Architecture Ser.). (Illus.). 550p. 14.95 *(978-3-8290-4838-5(6)*, 521830) Konemann.

Kostenevich, Albert. French Art at the Hermitage. (Illus.). 472p. *(978-1-86154-136-9(8))* Booth-Clibborn Editions GBR. Dist: Hachette Bk. Group.

—From Russia: French & Russian Master Paintings 1870-1925 from Moscow & St. Petersburg. 2008. (ENG., Illus.). 312p. 90.00 *(978-1-905711-15-4(8))* Royal Academy of Arts GBR. Dist: Abrams.

Koutsomallis, Kyriakos, et al. Henri de Toulouse-Lautrec: Woman as Myth. 2006. (ENG., Illus.). 240p. 75.00 *(978-88-422-1046-7(3))* Allemandi, Umberto & Co. GBR. Dist: Antique Collectors' Club.

Kronberg Frederiksen, Nanna, text. French Art at Ordrupgaard: Complete Catalogue of Paintings, Sculptures, Pastels, Drawings, & Prints. 2011. (ENG., Illus.). 544p. 120.00 *(978-3-7757-2671-9(3))* Hatje Cantz Verlag GmbH & Co KG DEU. Dist: D.A.P./Distributed Art Pubs.

La Niece, Susan, et al, eds. The Heritage of 'Maitre Alpais' An International & Interdisciplinary Examination of Medieval & Associated Limoges Enamel. 2010. (British Museum Occasional Papers). (ENG., Illus.). 62p. (C). pap. 40.00 *(978-0-86159-182-4(8))* British Museum Pr. GBR. Dist: Brown, David Bk. Co., The.

Lachartre, Alain & Lacharte, Alain. Arresting Design: Illustration in the Market Place. 2006. (ENG., Illus.). 260p. 95.00 *(978-2-86656-384-4(0))* Scala Pubs., Ltd. GBR. Dist: Antique Collectors' Club.

Langenscheidt Publishers Staff, contrib. by. French Provincial. 2008. (Joost Elffers Bks.). (Illus.). 20p. per. 9.95 *(978-0-8416-0186-4(0))* American Map Corp.

Larousse Staff. Larousse Dictionnaire du Francais Contemporain Illustre. (FRE.). *(978-0-8288-7855-5(2))* French & European Pubns., Inc.

Leclerc, Franck. L'école de Nice: Paroles D'artistes. 2010. (Illus.). 429p. *(978-2-916954-57-8(0)*, Spotlight Poets) Verlhac Editions.

Leeman, Fred, et al. Odilon Redon & Emile Bernard: Masterpieces from the Andries Bonger Collection. 2009. (ENG., Illus.). 156p. 55.00 *(978-90-400-8589-5(7))* Waanders B.V., Uitgeverij NLD. Dist: National Bk. Network.

Lemonedes, Heather, et al. Paul Gauguin: Durchbruch zur Moderne. 2009. (Illus.). 247p. *(978-2-7427-8695-4(3))*; *(978-90-79310-13-5(1))*; *(978-0-940717-60-2(3))*; *(978-1-935294-00-9(8))*; *(978-3-7757-2426-5(5))*; *(978-3-7757-2533-0(4))* Cleveland Museum of Art.

Lenain, Thierry & Venet, Bernar. Bernar Venet. 2007. (ENG., Illus.). 320p. 75.00 *(978-2-08-030014-0(8))* Flammarion et Cie FRA. Dist: Random Hse., Inc.

Leroy, Jules. Digital Enhancements of Jules Leroy's Album of Illuminated Syriac Manuscripts. 2009. (FRE.). 790.00 *(978-1-60724-425-7(X))* Gorgias Pr., LLC.

L'Estrange, Elizabeth. Holy Motherhood: Gender, Dynasty & Visual Culture in the Later Middle Ages. 2008. (Manchester Medieval Studies). (ENG., Illus.). 320p. 88.00 *(978-0-7190-7543-8(2))* Manchester Univ. Pr. GBR. Dist: Macmillan.

Leutrat, Estelle. Les Débuts de la Gravure Sur Cuivre en France: Lyon 1520-1565. 2007. (FRE., Illus.). 430p. (C). 150.00 *(978-2-600-01096-2(3))* Droz, Librairie CHE. Dist: Brown, David Bk. Co., The.

Lewis, Michael J., et al, eds. New Research on the Bayeux Tapestry: The Proceedings of a Conference at the British Museum. 2011. (ENG., Illus.). 211p. (C). 90.00 *(978-1-84217-976-5(4))* Oxbow Bks., Ltd. GBR. Dist: Brown, David Bk. Co., The.

Linfort, Jean-Michel. Le Périgord des Peintres. 2010. (FRE., Illus.). 295p. *(978-2-86577-270-4(5))* Fanlac, Pierre, Editeur.

Loyrette, Henri. Nineteenth Century French Art: From Romanticism to Impressionism, Post-Impressionism, & Art Nouveau. 2007. (ENG., Illus.). 464p. 100.00 *(978-2-08-030532-9(8))* Flammarion et Cie FRA. Dist: Random Hse., Inc.

Lymbery, Etrenne. Tales of the Paris Bridges: And How the Artists Saw Them. 2006. (Illus.). 68p. reprint ed. pap. 20.00 *(978-1-4223-5876-4(3))* DIANE Publishing Co.

Lyotard, Jean-Francois. Les Transformateurs Duchamp/Duchamp's TRANS/formers. Parret, Herman, ed. 2011. (Jean-François Lyotard: Writings on Contemporary Art & Artists Ser.). 256p. 49.50 *(978-90-5867-790-7(7))* Leuven Univ. Pr. BEL. Dist: Cornell Univ. Pr.

Macel, Christine, ed. Philippe Parreno. 2009. (ENG., Illus.). 256p. 65.00 *(978-3-03764-033-3(2))* JRP Ringier Kunstverlag AG CHE. Dist: D.A.P./Distributed Art Pubs.

Magi, Giovanna. Masterpieces of Louvre. Hollingworth, Michael, tr. 64p. pap. *(978-88-7009-151-9(1))* Casa Editrice Bonechi.

Mansfield, Elizabeth C. The Perfect Foil: FranCois-Andre Vincent & the Revolution in French Painting. 2011. (ENG., Illus.). 320p. 105.00 ***(978-0-8166-7580-7(5))***; pap. 35.00 ***(978-0-8166-7581-4(3))*** Univ. of Minnesota Pr.

Marlowe, Lara. Painted with Words. 2012. (ENG., Illus.). 280p. pap. 44.95 ***(978-1-907593-36-9(5))*** Liberties Pr. IRL. Dist: Dufour Editions, Inc.

Marrinan, Michael. Romantic Paris: Histories of a Cultural Landscape, 1800-1850. 2009. (ENG., Illus.). 488p. 85.00 *(978-0-8047-5062-2(9))*; pap. 35.00 *(978-0-8047-6151-2(5))* Stanford Univ. Pr.

Martina, Padberg. Art & Architecture Paris. 2010. (Art & Architecture Pocket Ser.). 48p. pap. 16.99 *(978-0-8416-7160-7(5))* Langenscheidt Publishing Group.

Martinelli, Roberta & Musée de l'armée France. Mito e Bellezza. Bartolli, Moreno D., ed. 2010. (ITA., Illus.). 336p. pap. 93.50 *(978-88-370-7448-7(4))* Electa ITA. Dist: Trans-Atlantic Pubns., Inc.

Martorelli, Barbara. George Barbier: The Birth of Art Deco. 2009. (ENG.). 176p. 50.00 *(978-88-317-9646-0(1))* Marsilio Editori spa ITA. Dist: Random Hse., Inc.

The Masterpieces of the Grand Louvre. 128p. *(978-88-7009-780-1(3))* Casa Editrice Bonechi.

McAuliffe, Mary. Dawn of the Belle Epoque: The Paris of Monet, Zola, Bernhardt, Eiffel, Debussy, Clemenceau, & Their Friends. 2011. (ENG.). 400p. 26.95 *(978-1-4422-0927-5(5))* Rowman & Littlefield Publishers, Inc.

McDonough, Tom. The Situationists & the City. McDonough, Tom, ed. 2010. (ENG., Illus.). 288p. pap. 26.95 *(978-1-84467-364-3(2)*, 844364) Verso Bks. GBR. Dist: Norton, W. W. & Co., Inc.

McDonough, Tom, ed. The Situationists & the City. 2010. (ENG., Illus.). 288p. 110.00 *(978-1-84467-332-2(4)*, 844332) Verso Bks. GBR. Dist: Norton, W. W. & Co., Inc.

McWilliam, Neil, ed. Lines of Attack: Conflicts in Caricature. 2010. (ENG., Illus.). 96p. pap. 18.95 *(978-0-938989-32-5(4))* Duke Univ. Pr.

Messager, Annette. Annette Messager, the Messengers: The Messengers. 2008. (Illus.). 608p. 85.00 *(978-3-7913-3922-1(2))* Prestel Publishing.

Metropolitan Museum of Art, et al. French Tapestries: Mediaeval, Renaissance & Modern. 2011. 70p. 36.95 ***(978-1-258-02256-3(7))*** Literary Licensing, LLC.

Meylan, Vincent. Boucheron: The Secret Archives. 2011. (ENG., Illus.). 304p. 95.00 ***(978-1-85149-667-9(X))*** Antique Collectors' Club.

Mgle, Emile. The Gothic Image: Religious Art in France in the Thirteenth-Century. 2008. 456p. pap. 41.00 *(978-1-59740-502-7(7))* ACLS Humanities E-Book.

Michaud, Philippe-Alain & Lebovici, Elisabeth. A L'Attaque: Adel Abdessemed, 1 vol. 2007. (FRE & ENG., Illus.). 224p. pap. 29.00 *(978-3-905770-45-2(8))* JRP Ringier Kunstverlag AG CHE. Dist: D.A.P./Distributed Art Pubs.

Miles, Peter, des. Nympheas: Frederic Zaavy. 2007. pap. 40.00 *(978-0-9792277-1-4(2))* de Pury, Phillips & Co.

Millet, Catherine. Contemporary Art in France. 2006. (ENG., Illus.). 384p. 60.00 *(978-2-08-030524-4(7))* Flammarion et Cie FRA. Dist: Random Hse., Inc.

Monet, Claude. Monet Paintings & Drawings. Grafton, Carol Belanger, ed. 2008. (Dover Electronic Clip Art Ser.). (ENG., Illus.). 48p. pap. 22.95 *(978-0-486-99873-2(8))* Dover Pubns., Inc.

Montclos, Jean-Marie Pérouse de, text. Paris: City of Art. exp. ed. 2008. (ENG., Illus.). 730p. 95.00 *(978-0-86565-195-1(7))* Vendome Pr., The.

Morgan, Jessica, ed. TH 2058 - Dominique Gonzalez-Foerster. 2009. (ENG., Illus.). 224p. 29.95 *(978-1-85437-739-5(6))* Tate Publishing, Ltd. GBR. Dist: Hachette Bk. Group.

Morrison, Elizabeth & Hedeman, Anne Dawson. Imagining the Past in France: History in Manuscript Painting, 1250-1500. 2010. (ENG., Illus.). 384p. 80.00 *(978-1-60606-028-5(7))*; pap. 49.95 *(978-1-60606-029-2(5))* Getty Pubns. (J. Paul Getty Museum).

Morton, Mary, ed. Oudry's Painted Menagerie: Portraits of Exotic Animals in Eighteenth-Century France. 2007. 192p. (ENG.). 60.00 *(978-0-89236-879-2(9))*; (Illus.). pap. 40.00 *(978-0-89236-889-1(6))* Oxford Univ. Pr., Inc.

Munder, Heike, ed. & text. Tatiana Trouvé. 2011. (ENG., Illus.). 228p. 75.00 *(978-3-86560-858-1(2))* Verlag der Buchhandlung Walther Konig DEU. Dist: D.A.P./Distributed Art Pubs.

Munter. Mathilde Ter Heijne If It's Me, It's Not Me. 2008. (ENG., Illus.). 144p. 55.00 *(978-3-7757-2250-6(5))* Hatje Cantz Verlag GmbH & Co KG DEU. Dist: D.A.P./Distributed Art Pubs.

Musée des beaux-Arts de Calais Staff, et al, contrib. by. Plaisirs D'Edo: Collections D'estampes Japonaises des Musees de Calais et de Saint-Omer. 2008. (FRE & ENG., Illus.). 128p. pap. 40.00 *(978-2-35340-015-7(9))* Gourcuff Gradenigo FRA. Dist: National Bk. Network.

Napp, Antonia & Röder, Kornelia, eds. Impuls Marcel Duchamp: Where do we go from here? 2011. (ENG & GER., Illus.). 208p. pap. 30.00 ***(978-3-7757-3182-9(2))*** Hatje Cantz Verlag GmbH & Co KG DEU. Dist: D.A.P./Distributed Art Pubs.

Nelson, Christine. Drawing Babar: Early Drafts & Watercolors. 2008. (Illus.). xi, 150p. pap. *(978-0-87598-152-9(6))* Pierpont Morgan Library.

Nickl, Peter & Jeffries, Susan. Gilbert Portanier: Oeuvre 2000-2009. 2009. (ENG., Illus.). 200p. 85.00 *(978-3-89790-289-3(3))* Arnoldsche Art Pubs. DEU. Dist: Antique Collectors' Club.

Noel, William & Weiss, Daniel. Book of Kings: Art, War & the Morgan Library's Medieval Picture Bible. 2006. (ENG., Illus.). 55.00 *(978-1-903942-16-1(0))* Third Millenium Publishing GBR. Dist: National Bk. Network.

N'Ret, Gilles & Arnold, Matthias. Toulouse-Lautrec. Walther, Ingo F., ed. 25th ed. 2009. (ENG., Illus.). 200p. 14.99 *(978-3-8365-1005-9(7))* TASCHEN DEU. Dist: Ingram Pub. Services.

N'Ret, Gilles, et al. Henri Matisse: Cut-Outs - Drawing with Scissors, 2 vols. 2009. (ENG., Illus.). 486p. 200.00 *(978-3-8228-3052-9(6))* TASCHEN DEU. Dist: Ingram Pub. Services.

Obrist, Hans Ulrich & Gonzalez-Foerster, Dominique, texts. Hans Ulrich Obrist & Dominique Gonzalez-Foerster: the Conversation Series. 2008. (ENG., Illus.). 190p. pap. 22.00 *(978-3-86560-334-0(3))* Verlag der Buchhandlung Walther Konig DEU. Dist: D.A.P./Distributed Art Pubs.

O'Neill, Rosemary. Art & Visual Culture on the French Riviera 1956-1971: The Ecole de Nice. 2012. (Illus.). 270p. 119.95 ***(978-0-7546-6471-0(6))*** Ashgate Publishing Co.

Orlan. Fabulous Harlequin: Orlan & the Patchwork Self. Veneciano, Jorge Daniel & Garelick, Rhonda K., eds. 2010. (Life in Performance Ser.). (ENG., Illus.). 176p. pap. 44.95 *(978-0-8032-3475-8(9))* Univ. of Nebraska Pr.

Padiyar, Satish. Chains: David, Canova, & the Fall of the Public Hero in Postrevolutionary France. 2007. (ENG., Illus.). 224p. 60.00 *(978-0-271-02963-4(3))* Pennsylvania State Univ. Pr.

Parkstone Press Staff. Gauguin. 2010. (Mega Square Ser.). (ENG., Illus.). 256p. 12.95 *(978-1-84484-957-4(0))* Parkstone Pr. USA, Ltd.

Parreno, Philippe & Obrist, Hans Ulrich, texts. Hans Ulrich Obrist & Philippe Parreno: the Conversation Series. 2008. (ENG., Illus.). 154p. pap. 22.00 *(978-3-86560-340-1(8))* Verlag der Buchhandlung Walther Konig DEU. Dist: D.A.P./Distributed Art Pubs.

Pearson, Christopher E. M. Designing UNESCO: Art Architecture & International Politics at Mid-Century. 2010. (Illus.). 412p. 134.95 *(978-0-7546-6783-4(9))* Ashgate Publishing Co.

Perell, Josep, ed. Sommerer & Mignonneau: Living Systems. 2011. 96p. pap. *(978-84-92861-79-8(7))* Actar Birkhauser Distribution.

Peter, Gartner. Art & Architecture Musee Dorsay. 2010. (Art & Architecture Pocket Ser.). 572p. pap. 16.99 *(978-0-8416-7152-2(4))* Langenscheidt Publishing Group.

Pettegree, Andrew. The French Book & the European Book World. 2007. (Library of the Written Word Ser.). (Illus.). 336p. *(978-90-04-16187-0(2))* BRILL.

Pie Books Staff. Shop Image Graphics in Paris: Living, Fashion, Food, Service. Takahashi, Kaoru, ed. 2009. (ENG., Illus.). 192p. 75.00 *(978-4-89444-704-2(5)*, PIE Bks.) Rizzoli International Pubns., Inc.

Pie Books Staff, et al. Herve Moran: The Genius of French Poster Art. 2010. (ENG, JPN & FRE., Illus.). 268p. pap. 35.00 *(978-4-89444-840-7(8)*, PIE Bks.) Rizzoli International Pubns., Inc.

Plantu, Jean, frwd. Lovers by Peynet. 2011. (ENG.). 80p. 25.00 *(978-2-7594-0526-8(5))* Assouline FRA. Dist: Perseus Distribution.

Poupard, Didier, ed. Jonvelle: The 100 Best Photographs. 2012. (ENG & FRE., Illus.). 208p. 45.00 ***(978-2-35340-112-3(0))*** Gourcuff Gradenigo FRA. Dist: National Bk. Network.

Prat, Louis-Antoine. Ingres. 2008. (Drawing Gallery Ser.). (ENG., Illus.). 96p. pap. 15.95 *(978-88-7439-099-1(8))* 5 Continents ITA. Dist: Hachette Bk. Group.

Putman, Andree & Bonifassi, Catherine. Andrée Putman: Ambassadrice du Style. 2010. (Illus.). 119p. *(978-2-08-124634-8(1))* Editions Flammarion.

Rabinow, Rebecca A., et al. Cézanne to Picasso: Ambroise Vollard, Patron of the Avant-Garde. 2006. (Metropolitan Museum of Art Publications). (Illus.). 400p. 65.00 *(978-1-58839-195-7(7))* Metropolitan Museum of Art, The.

Reid, Sheila. Art Memories: The Life & Works of Sheila Reid. ltd. ed. 2010. (Illus.). 128p. *(978-0-9646268-4-3(5))* Rush Editions.

Reifenscheid, Beate, ed. Marie Raymond & Yves Klein, 1 vol. 2007. (GER & ENG., Illus.). 240p. 55.00 *(978-3-938025-83-3(2))* Kerber Verlag DEU. Dist: D.A.P./Distributed Art Pubs.

Renoir, Auguste. Renoir in the 20th Century. 2010. (ENG., Illus.). 480p. 85.00 *(978-3-7757-2539-2(3))* Hatje Cantz Verlag GmbH & Co KG DEU. Dist: D.A.P./Distributed Art Pubs.

Riviere, Henri. Thirty-Six Views of the Eiffel Tower: A Turn-of-the-Century Tribute to the City of Light. 2010. (ENG & FRE., Illus.). 108p. 22.95 *(978-0-8118-7698-8(5))* Chronicle Bks. LLC.

Rolf, Toman & Christian, Freigang. Provence. 2010. 4p. pap. 24.99 *(978-0-8416-7166-9(4))* Langenscheidt Publishing Group.

Romney, Émile & Bandou, Mireille. Art Public: Une Collection D'art Contemporain en Guadeloupe. 2010. (FRE, SPA & ENG., Illus.). 175p. *(978-2-08-124504-4(3))* Editions Flammarion.

Rousseau, Pascal, text. Loris Gr#xE9;aud: Cellar Door. 2011. (ENG., Illus.). 392p. 90.00 ***(978-3-03764-167-5(3))*** JRP Ringier Kunstverlag AG CHE. Dist: D.A.P./Distributed Art Pubs.

Rozell, Mary, ed. Clichés-Verre: Radical Images. 2007. pap. 10.00 *(978-0-9746604-3-1(4))* Freeman, Peter Inc.

Sabatier, Gérard. Le Prince et les Arts: Stratégies Figuratives de la Monarchie Française, de la Renaissance Aux Lumières. 2010. (FRE., Illus.). 459p. *(978-2-87673-542-2(3))* Champ Vallon.

Sala, Anri. Why the Lion Roars: Forecasts. 2011. (ENG., Illus.). 1536p. 180.00 *(978-3-86560-779-9(9))* Verlag der Buchhandlung Walther Konig DEU. Dist: D.A.P./Distributed Art Pubs.

Salome, Laurent, ed. A City for Impressionism: Monet, Pissarro & Gauguin in Rouen. 2011. (ENG., Illus.). 400p. 80.00 *(978-88-572-0701-8(3))* Skira Editore ITA. Dist: Random Hse., Inc.

Sauvagnargues, Anne. Deleuze & Art. Sauvagnargues, Anne et al, trs. from FRE. 2013. (Continuum Studies in Continental Philosophy Ser.). (ENG.). 208p. 120.00 ***(978-1-4411-7380-5(3))*** Continuum International Publishing Group, Ltd. GBR. Dist: National Bk. Network.

Sempe, Jean-Jacques. A Little Bit of Paris. 2007. (ENG., Illus.). 128p. 24.95 *(978-0-7893-1571-7(8))* Universe Publishing.

Serres, Michael, et al. Van Cleef & Arpels: The Poetry of Time. 2010. (ENG.). 216p. 85.00 *(978-2-7022-0916-5(5)*, Editions Cercle D'art (Acc)) Antique Collectors' Club GBR. Dist: National Bk. Network.

Serullaz, Arlette & Sérullaz, Arlette. Delacroix. 2008. (Drawing Gallery Ser.). (ENG., Illus.). 96p. pap. 15.95 *(978-88-7439-105-9(6))* 5 Continents ITA. Dist: Hachette Bk. Group.

Silver, Kenneth E. Paris Portraits: Artists, Friends, & Lovers. 2008. (ENG., Illus.). 144p. 50.00 *(978-0-300-14543-4(8))* Yale Univ. Pr.

Simon, Robin, text. Hogarth, France & British Art. 2007. (ENG., Illus.). 400p. pap. 45.00 *(978-0-9554063-0-0(7))* Holberton, Paul Publishing GBR. Dist: Casemate Pubs. & Bk. Distributors, LLC.

Siraudeau, Sébastien. Vintage French Interiors: Inspiration from the Antique Shops & Flea Markets of France. 2008. (ENG., Illus.). 208p. 34.95 *(978-2-08-030054-6(7))* Flammarion et Cie FRA. Dist: Random Hse., Inc.

Sonn, Richard David. Sex, Violence, & the Avant-Garde: Anarchism in Interwar France. 2010. 232p. 65.00 *(978-0-271-03663-2(X))* Pennsylvania State Univ. Pr.

Spence, David. Cezanne. 2009. (Ticktock Essential Artists Ser.). (ENG.). 32p. (J). (gr. 4-7). pap. 6.95 *(978-1-84696-970-6(0))* TickTock Bks. GBR. Dist: Independent Pubs. Group.

—Gauguin. 2009. (Ticktock Essential Artists Ser.). (ENG.). 32p. (J). (gr. 4-7). pap. 6.95 *(978-1-84696-971-3(9))* TickTock Bks. GBR. Dist: Independent Pubs. Group.

—Manet. 2009. (Ticktock Essential Artists Ser.).Tr. of Monet & Impressionism. (ENG.). 32p. (J). (gr. 4-7). pap. 6.95 *(978-1-84696-974-4(3))* TickTock Bks. GBR. Dist: Independent Pubs. Group.

Stein, Susan Alyson, et al. The Annenberg Collection: Masterpieces of Impressionism & Post-Impressionism. 2009. (Illus.). xiv, 338p. 65.00 *(978-1-58839-341-8(0))*; pap. 39.95 *(978-1-58839-342-5(9))* Metropolitan Museum of Art, The.

Sterling, Charles. Peinture Medievale a Paris 1300-1500, 2 vols. (FRE., Illus.). 280p. 200.00 *(978-2-85047-002-8(3))* La Bibliotheque des Arts FRA. Dist: D.A.P./Distributed Art Pubs.

—La Peinture Medievale Pari, 2 vols. (FRE., Illus.). 412p. 200.00 *(978-2-85047-162-9(3))* La Bibliotheque des Arts FRA. Dist: D.A.P./Distributed Art Pubs.

Symons, Arthur. Colour Studies in Paris. 2010. (ENG.). 306p. pap. 29.75 *(978-1-171-60111-1(5))*; 264p. pap. 27.75 *(978-1-178-21960-9(7))*; (ENG.). 306p. pap. 29.75 *(978-1-176-41273-6(6))*; 304p. pap. 29.75 *(978-1-142-80966-9(8))* BiblioBazaar.

—Colour Studies in Paris. 2009. 70p. pap. 14.14 *(978-0-217-79720-7(2))* General Bks. LLC.

—From Toulouse Lautrec to Rodin with Some Personal Impressions. 2007. (ENG., Illus.). 272p. 42.95 *(978-0-548-02201-6(1))* Kessinger Publishing, LLC.

Szekely, Martin. Martin Szekely. 2010. (ENG & FRE., Illus.). 252p. 90.00 *(978-3-03764-098-2(7))* JRP Ringier Kunstverlag AG CHE. Dist: D.A.P./Distributed Art Pubs.

Taylor, Michael & Chagall, Marc. Paris Through the Window: Marc Chagall & His Circle. 2010. *(978-0-87633-230-6(0))* Philadelphia Museum of Art.

Todd, Pamela. The Impressionists at Leisure. 2007. (ENG., Illus.). 176p. 40.00 *(978-0-500-23839-4(1))* Thames & Hudson.

Tucker, Thomas Deane. Derridada: Duchamp as Readymade Deconstruction. 2010. (ENG.). 110p. pap. 24.50 *(978-0-7391-1623-4(1))* Lexington Bks.

Udo, Kittelmann & Silke, Krohn, eds. Hans Bellmer / Louise Bourgeois: Double Sexus. 2010. 160p. 60.00 *(978-3-89955-403-8(5))* Die Gestalten Verlag DEU. Dist: Prestel Publishing.

Vadillo, Monica Ann Walker. Bathsheba in Late Medieval French Manuscript Illumination: Innocent Object of Desire or Agent of Sin? 2008. (Illus.). 132p. 99.95 *(978-0-7734-5243-5(5))* Mellen, Edwin Pr., The.

Vallières, Nicole & Cooper, Cynthia. 90 Treasures, 90 Stories, 90 Years. 2012. (Illus.). 268p. (C). pap. ***(978-1-895615-16-6(X))*** McGill-Queen's Univ. Pr.

Van Claerbergen, Ernst Vegelin & Wright, Barnaby, eds. Renoir at the Theatre: Looking at la Loge. 2008. (Courtauld Institute of Art Gallery Ser.). (Illus.). 128p. pap. 40.00 *(978-1-903470-73-2(0))* Holberton, Paul Publishing GBR. Dist: Casemate Pubs. & Bk. Distributors, LLC.

Vervliet, Hendrik D. L. The Palaeotypography of the French Renaissance: Selected Papers on Sixteenth-Century Typefaces, 2 vols. 2008. (Library of the Written Word Ser.). (Illus.). 294p. *(978-90-04-16982-1(2))* BRILL.

Vervliet, Hendrik D.L. French Renaissance Printing Types: A Conspectus. 2010. (Illus.). 471p. 120.00 *(978-1-58456-271-9(4))* Oak Knoll Pr.

Viatte, Françoise. Baccio Bandinelli: Dessins Italiens du Musée du Louvre. 2011. (ENG., Illus.). 304p. 115.00 *(978-88-89854-63-1(4))* Officina Libraria srl ITA. Dist: Antique Collectors' Club.

Viatte, Germain. Yves Lévêque, à Fleur de Terre, 1962-2007: Quarante Cinq Ans de Peinture. 2008. (FRE & ENG., Illus.). 224p. 125.00 *(978-2-35340-035-5(3))* Gourcuff Gradenigo FRA. Dist: National Bk. Network.

Villet, Jeffrey M. The Complete Prints Maxime Lalanne, Catalogue, Raisonne, Lithographs, & Etchings: Third Edition Expanded. 2010. pap. *(978-1-4507-3423-3(5))* Independent Pub.

Volk, Tina. Transfer und Rezeption des italienischen Futurismus in Frankreich: Kulturtransferprozesse im Bereich der Bildenden Kunst. 2009. 160p. pap. *(978-3-639-22136-7(2))* VDM Verlag Dr. Mueller e.K.

Wakefield, David. French Romantics. 2007. (Illus.). 240p. 50.00 *(978-1-904449-59-1(X))* Pop Art Bks. GBR. Dist: International Publishers Marketing.

Walther, Ingo F. Impressionism, 2 vols. 2010. (25 Ser.). (ENG., Illus.). 712p. 59.99 *(978-3-8365-2286-1(1))* TASCHEN DEU. Dist: Ingram Pub. Services.

Ward, Martha & Leonard, Anne. Looking & Listening in Nineteenth-Century France. 2008. (Illus.). 104p. 24.00 *(978-0-935573-44-2(5))* Univ. of Chicago, David & Alfred Smart Museum.

Waschek, Matthias, et al. The Louvre & the Masterpiece. 2008. 35.00 *(978-1-932543-28-5(7))* High Museum of Art.

Watteau, Antoine & Baetjer, Katharine. Watteau, Music, & Theater. 2009. 35.00 *(978-1-58839-335-7(6))* Metropolitan Museum of Art, The.

Whiteley, Jon & Sonnabend, Martin. Claude Lorrain (C. 1604 - 1682) An Exhibition of Prints, Drawings & Paintings. 2011. (ENG., Illus.). 200p. pap. 45.00 *(978-1-85444-260-4(0))* Ashmolean Museum GBR. Dist: National Bk. Network.

Wiehager, Renate, ed. Zero & Paris 1960: And Today. (FRE & GER., Illus.). 264p. pap. 45.00 *(978-3-89322-931-4(0))* Edition Cantz DEU. Dist: D.A.P./Distributed Art Pubs.

Wilcox, Claire, ed. The Golden Age of Couture: Paris & London 1947-1957. 2007. (ENG., Illus.). 224p. 55.00 *(978-1-85177-520-0(X))* V & A Pubns. GBR. Dist: Hachette Bk. Group.

Wilson, Sarah. Visual World of French Theory: Figurations. 2010. (Illus.). 240p. 65.00 *(978-0-300-16281-3(2))* Yale Univ. Pr.

Wolff, Martha. Kings, Queens, & Courtiers: Art in Early Renaissance France. 2011. (ENG., Illus.). 208p. 60.00 *(978-0-300-17025-2(4))* Art Institute of Chicago.

Wright, Christopher. Poussin: Paintings: A Catalogue Raisonné. 2007. (Illus.). 320p. 75.00 *(978-1-904449-58-4(1))* Chaucer Pr. GBR. Dist: International Publishers Marketing.

YGREC. Kung Fu Panda et la puissance du Croire. 2009. 56p. pap. 16.50 *(978-1-4092-7602-9(3))* Lulu Enterprises Inc.

Yoo, Yae Jin. La Peinture ou les leçons esthétiques chez Marcel Proust. 2011. 160p. (C). 71.95 ***(978-1-4331-1700-8(2))*** Lang, Peter Publishing, Inc.

Zarobell, John. Empire of Landscape: Space & Ideology in French Colonial Algeria. 2009. (ENG., Illus.). 240p. 95.00 *(978-0-271-03443-0(2))* Pennsylvania State Univ. Pr.

Ziskin, Rochelle. Sheltering Art: Collecting & Social Identity in Early Eighteenth-Century Paris. 2012. (ENG.). 360p. ***(978-0-271-03785-1(7))*** Pennsylvania State Univ. Pr.

ART, GERMAN

a Wengen, Stefan & text. Stefan a Wengen: the Mission. 2010. (ENG & GER., Illus.). 176p. 55.00 *(978-3-03764-112-5(6))* JRP Ringier Kunstverlag AG CHE. Dist: D.A.P./Distributed Art Pubs.

Abenstein, Edelgard & Fiedler, Jeannine. Berlin, 1 vol. 2009. (ENG., Illus.). 480p. pap. 9.99 *(978-3-8331-4566-7(8))* h.f.ullmann DEU. Dist: Innovative Logistics.

ADC Verlags GmbH. ADC Deutschland Jahrbuch 2011: Adc Germany Annual. 2011. (ENG.). 550p. 138.00 *(978-3-89986-152-5(3),* Avedition Gmbh,Csi) Continental Sales, Inc.

ADC Verlags GmbH Staff, ed. ADC Germany Yearbook 2010. 2010. (GER & ENG., Illus.). 600p. 130.00 *(978-3-89986-135-8(3),* Avedition Gmbh,Csi) Continental Sales, Inc.

Alciato, Andrea. Held's translation of Alciato's Emblematum Liber (1566) Facsimile Edition Using Glasgow University Library SM 45. Held, Jeremias, ed. 2008. (Imaga Figurata Editions Ser.). (ENG & LAT.). 238p. (C). 109.00 *(978-2-503-52539-6(3))* Brepols Pubs. BEL. Dist: ISD.

Andersen, Wayne. German Artists & Hitler's Mind: Avant-Garde Art in a Turbulent Era. 2007. (ENG., Illus.). 443p. spiral bd. 38.50 *(978-0-9725573-2-0(6))* Fabriart Editions, Ltd.

Arnet, Hélène, et al. Bruno Weber: Die Kraft der Fantasie - ein Lebenswerk. 2011. (GER., Illus.). 240p. (C). 82.00 ***(978-3-7774-3521-3(X))*** Hirmer Verlag GmbH DEU. Dist: Brown, David Bk. Co., The.

Arnoldsche. Fotosommer Stuttgart 2010. 2011. (GER & ENG., Illus.). 148p. 50.00 *(978-3-89790-024-0(6))* Arnoldsche Art Pubs. DEU. Dist: Antique Collectors' Club.

Art Directors Club, ed. ADC Bush 2000: German Art Directors Club Annual. (Illus.). 626p. 89.00 *(978-3-87439-530-4(8))* Universitatsdruckerei & Verlag H. Schmidt GmbH & Co. DEU. Dist: Gingko Pr., Inc.

Art Works. 2011. (ENG., Illus.). 256p. pap. 55.00 ***(978-3-7757-2777-8(9))*** Hatje Cantz Verlag GmbH & Co KG DEU. Dist: D.A.P./Distributed Art Pubs.

Auer, Barbara & Hubl, Michael, texts. Angela Glajcar: Works in Paper & Plastic 2007-2009. 2010. (ENG., Illus.). 96p. pap. 40.00 *(978-3-86678-284-6(5))* Kerber Verlag DEU. Dist: D.A.P./Distributed Art Pubs.

Aurisch, Helga Kessler & Czymmek, Götz. German Impressionist Landscape Painting: Liebermann - Corinth - Slevogt. 2010. (Illus.). 256p. 70.00 ***(978-3-89790-321-0(0))*** Arnoldsche Art Pubs. DEU. Dist: Antique Collectors' Club.

Bü che, Wolfgang. Lyonel Feininger: Die Halle-Bilder. Buche, Wolfgang, ed. 2010. (GER., Illus.). 175p. (C). 56.00 *(978-3-7774-2241-1(X))* Hirmer Verlag GmbH DEU. Dist: Brown, David Bk. Co., The.

Bü, et al. Maler der Brücke: Die Sammlung Hermann Gerlinger in der Auswahl - Katalog. 2009. (GER., Illus.). 119p. *(978-3-89812-618-2(8))* Mitteldeutscher Verlag GmbH, MDV.

Barron, Stephanie, et al. Art of Two Germanys - Cold War Cultures. 2009. (Illus.). (ENG.). 464p. 75.00 *(978-0-8109-8404-2(0))*; 460p. *(978-0-8109-7647-4(1))* Abrams.

Beauchamp, Monte. Krampus: The Devil of Christmas. 2010. (ENG., Illus.). 200p. 18.95 *(978-0-86719-747-1(1))* Last Gasp of San Francisco.

Becker, Katja M. & Podobinski, Stephanie. Young German Design, 2 vols. 2009. (ENG., Illus.). 624p. 119.95 ***(978-3-938666-56-2(0))*** DOM Pubs. DEU. Dist: Innovative Logistics.

Beckmann, Max. Of Truths Impossible to Put in Words: Max Beckmann Contextualized. Long, Rose-Carol Washton & Makela, Maria Martha, eds. 2009. (Illus.). 436p. pap. 68.95 *(978-3-03910-704-9(6))* Lang, Peter AG GBR. Dist: Lang, Peter.

Becksmann, Rü, et al. Die mittelalterlichen Glasmalereien in Freiburg im Breisgau: Corpus Vitrearum Medii Aevi Deutschland 2.2, 2 vols. 2010. (GER., Illus.). *(978-3-87157-226-5(8))* Deutscher Verlag fur Kunstwissenschaft.

Behm, Meike & Werth, Christian, texts. Myriam Holme. 2011. (ENG., Illus.). 88p. 37.50 *(978-3-86678-437-6(6))* Kerber Verlag DEU. Dist: D.A.P./Distributed Art Pubs.

Beletsky, Misha. The Book Jackets of Ismar David: A Calligraphic Legacy. 2011. (Illus.). 48p. pap. 19.95 *(978-1-933360-51-5(8),* RIT Cary Graphic Arts Pr.) Rochester Institute of Technology, Cary Graphic Arts Pr.

Belkin, Kristin Lohse. Copies & Adaptations from Renaissance & Later Artists: German & Netherlandish Artists, 2 vols. 2009. (Corpus Rubenianum Ludwig Burchard Ser.). (ENG., Illus.). 600p. (C). 276.00 *(978-1-905375-38-7(7))* Miller, Harvey Pubs. GBR. Dist: Brown, David Bk. Co., The.

Berg, et al. Julian Rosefeldt: Film Works. 2008. (ENG., Illus.). 176p. 60.00 *(978-3-7757-2171-4(1))* Hatje Cantz Verlag GmbH & Co KG DEU. Dist: D.A.P./Distributed Art Pubs.

Bergdoll, Barry. Bauhaus 1919-1933: Workshops for Modernity. 2009. (ENG., Illus.). 328p. 75.00 *(978-0-87070-758-2(2))* Museum of Modern Art.

Bergmann, Rudolf. Studien zur Glasproduktion seit dem 12. Jahrhundert im ostlichen Westfalen. 2008. (GER., Illus.). 174p. (C). 25.00 *(978-3-8053-3970-4(4))* Zabern, Philipp von Verlag, GmbH DEU. Dist: Brown, David Bk. Co., The.

Berry, Ian, et al, texts. Oliver Herring: TASK. 2012. (ENG., Illus.). 176p. pap. 33.00 ***(978-0-945558-34-7(1))*** Univ. Galleries of Illinois State Univ.

Bertram, Eva, photos by. Eva Bertram: 2 Ein Kind - 2 One Child. 2010. (ENG., Illus.). 160p. 45.00 *(978-3-7757-2621-4(7))* Hatje Cantz Verlag GmbH & Co KG DEU. Dist: D.A.P./Distributed Art Pubs.

Bertsch, von M., et al. Kosmos Runge. Der Morgen der Romantik: Katalog zur Ausstellung in Hamburg; Hamburger Kunsthalle; 3.12.2010-13.03.2011 und in München; Kusthalle der Hypo-Kulturstiftung; 13.05.2011-04.09.2011. Howoldt, J. et al, eds. 2011. (GER., Illus.). 360p. (C). 59.00 *(978-3-7774-3061-4(7))* Hirmer Verlag GmbH DEU. Dist: Brown, David Bk. Co., The.

Bezzenberger, Tilman & Esche, Charles, texts. Maria Eichhorn: Aktiengesellschaft. 2008. (ENG., Illus.). 304p. pap. 49.95 *(978-3-86560-244-2(4))* Verlag der Buchhandlung Walther Konig DEU. Dist: D.A.P./Distributed Art Pubs.

Biller, Maxim. Harlem Holocaust. (GER.). 506p. pap. *(978-3-462-02761-7(1))* Kiepenheuer & Witsch GmbH & Company KG DEU. Dist: International Bk. Import Service, Inc.

Birkhauser, creator. Form 211. 2007. (Zeitschrift Form Ser.). (Illus.). 106p. per. 19.95 *(978-3-936560-38-1(2),* 3936560382) Birkhauser Verlag GmbH DEU. Dist: Springer.

Birnbaum, Daniel. Teaching Art. 2008. (ENG., Illus.). 376p. pap. 48.00 *(978-3-86560-339-5(4))* Verlag der Buchhandlung Walther Konig DEU. Dist: D.A.P./Distributed Art Pubs.

Biro, Matthew. The Dada Cyborg: Visions of the New Human in Weimar Berlin. 2009. (ENG., Illus.). 400p. pap. 29.50 *(978-0-8166-3620-4(6))* Univ. of Minnesota Pr.

Bischoff, Ulrich, et al, texts. Troubled Waters: Zwölf Stilleben aus der Siemens Photography Collection, Pinakothek der Moderne. 2009. (GER & ENG., Illus.). 136p. 59.95 *(978-3-86560-521-4(4))* Verlag der Buchhandlung Walther Konig DEU. Dist: D.A.P./Distributed Art Pubs.

Bitterli, Konrad. Karin Sander. (ENG & GER.). 80p. 29.95 *(978-3-89322-891-1(8))* Edition Cantz DEU. Dist: D.A.P./Distributed Art Pubs.

—Leni Hoffmann: Ubik. (ENG & GER., Illus.). 272p. 45.00 *(978-3-89322-337-4(1))* Edition Cantz DEU. Dist: D.A.P./Distributed Art Pubs.

Blackwell, Kelsey, des. Vera Lutter. 2007. (Illus.). 64p. 60.00 *(978-1-932598-46-9(4))* Gagosian Gallery.

Bluhm, Andreas & Krischel, Roland, eds. Hotel California: Katalog zur Ausstellung, Wallraf-Richartz-Museum & Foundation Corboud, 7.09.2007-18.11.2007. 2007. (GER., Illus.). 95p. (C). 35.00 *(978-3-7774-3855-9(3))* Hirmer Verlag GmbH DEU. Dist: Brown, David Bk. Co., The.

Bock, John. John Bock: Klutterkammer. 2009. (ENG., Illus.). 96p. 49.00 *(978-3-86560-554-2(0))* Verlag der Buchhandlung Walther Konig DEU. Dist: D.A.P./Distributed Art Pubs.

—John Bock. Skipholt. 2012. (ENG., Illus.). 224p. 68.00 *(978-3-86560-380-7(7))* Verlag der Buchhandlung Walther Konig DEU. Dist: D.A.P./Distributed Art Pubs.

Bock, John, illus. John Bock: Maltreated Frigate. 2008. (ENG.). 208p. per. 49.95 *(978-3-86560-252-7(5))* Verlag der Buchhandlung Walther Konig DEU. Dist: D.A.P./Distributed Art Pubs.

Böhm, Florian, ed. Commedia Dell'Arte - Couture Edition. 2010. 320p. 170.00 *(978-3-0346-0544-1(7))* Birkhauser Verlag AG CHE. Dist: Actar Birkhauser Distribution.

Bonechi. Masterpieces of Kunsthistorisc. 64p. *(978-88-7009-500-5(2))* Casa Editrice Bonechi.

Bothe, Rolf, ed. Off to Weimar. (GER., Illus.). 240p. pap. 39.95 *(978-3-89322-868-3(3))* Edition Cantz DEU. Dist: D.A.P./Distributed Art Pubs.

Braun, Bjorn. Björn Braun: Nest. 2010. (ENG., Illus.). 112p. 37.50 *(978-3-86678-369-0(8))* Kerber Verlag DEU. Dist: D.A.P./Distributed Art Pubs.

Braun, Emily, et al, texts. Chaos & Classicism: Art in France, Italy, & Germany, 1918-1936. 2011. (ENG., Illus.). 192p. pap. 40.00 *(978-0-89207-405-1(1))* Guggenheim, Solomon R. Museum.

Bronfen, Elisabeth, text. Julia Stoschek Collection, Number Two. 2009. (ENG., Illus.). 432p. 105.00 *(978-3-7757-2379-4(X))* Hatje Cantz Verlag GmbH & Co KG DEU. Dist: D.A.P./Distributed Art Pubs.

Brush, Kathryn. The Shaping of Art History: Wilhelm Vöge, Adolph Goldschmidt, & the Study of Medieval Art. 2010. (ENG.). 280p. pap. 39.99 *(978-0-521-14762-0(X))* Cambridge Univ. Pr.

Büche, Wolfgang & Gerlinger, Hermann. Painters of the Brücke: Selected from the Collection of Hermann Gerlinger. 2009. (Illus.). 119p. *(978-3-89812-622-9(6))* Mitteldeutscher Verlag GmbH, MDV.

Buchhart, Dieter & Knack, Hartwig, eds. Otto Dix: Zwischen Paradies und Untergang. 2009. (Illus.). 128p. (C). 36.00 *(978-3-7774-2021-9(2))* Hirmer Verlag GmbH DEU. Dist: Brown, David Bk. Co., The.

Budzynski, Scott. Self-Representation in German Art. 2008. 180p. pap. *(978-3-639-02669-6(1))* VDM Verlag Dr. Mueller e.K.

Bujok, Elke & Mueller, Claudius, eds. Weiter als der Horizont: Kunst der Welt. 2008. (GER., Illus.). 288p. (C). pap. 49.00 *(978-3-7774-3895-5(2))* Hirmer Verlag GmbH DEU. Dist: Brown, David Bk. Co., The.

Burke, Peter. Um 1808: Restrukturierung der Wissensarten: Circa 1808: Restructuring Knowledges. 2009. (ENG.). 64p. pap. 24.00 *(978-3-422-06834-6(1),* Art Stock Bks. Ltd/Csi) Continental Sales, Inc.

Campens, Angelique, et al, intros. Based in Berlin. 2011. (ENG., Illus.). 200p. pap. 22.95 ***(978-3-86335-045-1(6))*** Verlag der Buchhandlung Walther Konig DEU. Dist: D.A.P./Distributed Art Pubs.

Casper, Jens & Shryen, Annette, texts. Boros Collection. 2010. (ENG., Illus.). 198p. 75.00 *(978-3-7757-2478-4(8))* Hatje Cantz Verlag GmbH & Co KG DEU. Dist: D.A.P./Distributed Art Pubs.

Caspers, Eva. Ernst Barlach Haus: Stiftung Hermann F. Reemtsma. (Museum Guides). (Illus.). 128p. pap. 14.95 *(978-3-7913-2558-3(2))* Prestel Publishing.

Catsull, Travis. The Heaven Antenna. 2010. 55p. pap. 7.95 *(978-0-557-46210-0(X))* Lulu Enterprises Inc.

Celant, Germano, ed. Roter Sand und ein gefundenes Glück. 2008. (ENG., Illus.). 180p. pap. 94.00 *(978-3-86560-178-0(2))* Fondazione Prada ITA. Dist: D.A.P./Distributed Art Pubs.

Chametzky, Peter. Objects as History in Twentieth-Century German Art: Beckmann to Beuys. 2010. (ENG., Illus.). 304p. 49.95 *(978-0-520-26042-9(2))* Univ. of California Pr.

Christ, Alexa-Beatrice. Frankenthal Porzellan: Der Bestand der Grobherzoglich-Hessischen Porzellansammlung Darmstadt. 2006. (GER & ENG., Illus.). 120p. 60.00 *(978-3-89790-251-0(6))* Arnoldsche Art Pubs. DEU. Dist: Antique Collectors' Club.

Cichocki, Sebastian, et al, texts. Antje Majewski: My Very Gestures. 2009. (ENG & GER., Illus.). 112p. pap. 29.95 *(978-1-933128-56-6(9))* Sternberg Pr.

City Museum Freiburg, Augustiner Museum. Masterpieces from the Middle Ages to the Baroque. 2010. (ENG.). 200p. pap. 28.00 *(978-3-422-06949-7(6),* Art Stock Bks. Ltd/Csi) Continental Sales, Inc.

Coen, Ester, ed. Futurismo 100: Illuminazioni. 2009. (ITA., Illus.). 450p. 142.50 *(978-88-370-6777-9(1))* Electa ITA. Dist: Trans-Atlantic Pubns., Inc.

Czemich, Peter W. Vintage Dita. 2008. (ENG.). 128p. 50.00 *(978-3-03766-590-9(4))* Edition Skylight CHE. Dist: Independent Pubs Group.

Dammann, Martin. Martin Dammann: Fremde Freunde. 2010. (ENG.). 216p. pap. 42.95 *(978-3-7082-3279-9(8))* Skarabaeus AUT. Dist: SCB Distributors.

Dannowski, Hans Werner. Wie schad', dass ich kein Pfaffe bin: Wilhelm Busch und die Religion. 2008. (Illus.). 128p. *(978-3-7859-0980-5(2))* Lutherisches Verlagshaus GmbH.

de Werd, Guido, et al, texts. With a Probability of Being Seen. 2010. (ENG & GER., Illus.). 320p. 95.00 *(978-3-941263-13-0(7))* Richter Verlag DEU. Dist: D.A.P./Distributed Art Pubs.

Descatoire, Christine. Treasures of the Black Death. 2009. (ENG., Illus.). 112p. pap. 40.00 *(978-0-900785-95-5(0))* Holberton, Paul Publishing GBR. Dist: Casemate Pubs. & Bk. Distributors, LLC.

Deshmukh, Marion F., et al, eds. Max Liebermann & International Modernism: An Artist's Career from Empire to Third Reich. 2011. (SGH Ser.). (Illus.). 332p. 39.95 *(978-1-84545-662-7(9))* Berghahn Bks., Inc.

Diederichsen, Diedrich, text. On Surplus Value. 2008. (ENG., Illus.). 128p. pap. 10.00 *(978-90-73362-81-9(4))* Witte De With Centre for Contemporary Art NLD. Dist: D.A.P./Distributed Art Pubs.

Diergarten, Gotz, photos by. Götz Diergarten: Photographs. 2010. (ENG & GER., Illus.). 160p. 55.00 *(978-3-7757-2563-7(6))* Hatje Cantz Verlag GmbH & Co KG DEU. Dist: D.A.P./Distributed Art Pubs.

Documenta. Archive in Motion: 50 Jahre/Years Documenta 1955-2005. (Illus.). 424p. pap. 25.00 *(978-3-86521-398-3(7))* Steidl, Gerhard Druckerei und Verlag DEU. Dist: D.A.P./Distributed Art Pubs.

Domnick, Sabine. Cables, Diamonds, Herringbone: Secrets of Knitting Traditional Fishermen's Sweaters. 2007. (ENG., Illus.). 96p. pap. 19.95 *(978-0-89272-688-2(1))* Down East Bks.

Drechsler, Wolfgang & Leutgeb, Doris, texts. Joseph Beuys, 1 vol. 2007. (ENG., Illus.). 184p. pap. 30.00 *(978-3-938821-72-5(8))* Verlag fur Moderne Kunst DEU. Dist: D.A.P./Distributed Art Pubs.

Drescher, Jürgen, et al. Jürgen Drescher: Arbeiten Bis Heute: Galerie Isabella Czarnowska, Berlin, Mai 36 Galerie Zürich. 2008. (GER & ENG., Illus.). 144p. 64.00 *(978-3-86560-330-2(0))* Verlag der Buchhandlung Walther Konig DEU. Dist: D.A.P./Distributed Art Pubs.

Dufour-Kowalska, Gabrielle. Emil Nolde: L'expressionisme Devant Dieu. 2007. (FRE., Illus.). 216p. (C). pap. 35.00 ***(978-2-252-03623-5(0))*** Klincksieck, Editions FRA. Dist: ISD.

Durner, Jurgen, ed. Jurgen Durner: Disappearance. 2010. (ENG., Illus.). 144p. 58.00 *(978-3-86678-349-2(3))* Kerber Verlag DEU. Dist: D.A.P./Distributed Art Pubs.

Dylla, Sabine. Karin Sander. (Illus.). 48p. 196.95 *(978-3-89322-619-1(2))* Edition Cantz DEU. Dist: D.A.P./Distributed Art Pubs.

Dzama, Marcel. The Berlin Years. 2006. (ENG.). 65p. pap. 42.00 *(978-1-932416-74-9(9))* McSweeney's Publishing.

Dzeiwior, Yilmaz, ed. Cosima von Bonin. The Fatigue Empire. Das Internationale Wollsekretariat 1989 - 2010: The Fatigue Empire. 2011. (ENG., Illus.). 320p. 65.00 *(978-3-86560-817-8(5))* Kunsthaus Bregenz AUT. Dist: D.A.P./Distributed Art Pubs.

Dziewior, Michael Hakimi. 2009. (ENG., Illus.). 138p. pap. 40.00 *(978-3-7757-2268-1(8))* Hatje Cantz Verlag GmbH & Co KG DEU. Dist: D.A.P./Distributed Art Pubs.

Ebert-Schifferer, Sybille & Kieven, Elisabeth, eds. Romisches Jahrbuch der Bibliotheca Hertziana - Band 38. 2010. (Romisches Jahrbuch der Bibliotheca Hertziana Ser.). (GER., Illus.). 240p. (C). 195.00 *(978-3-7774-2311-1(4))* Hirmer Verlag GmbH DEU. Dist: Brown, David Bk. Co., The.

Ecker, Diana. Das Mainzer Dom-Museum: Geschichte und Geschichten. 2008. (GER., Illus.). 238p. *(978-3-935647-42-7(5))* Schmidt, Hermann, Verlag, Mainz GmbH & Co. KG.

Eckmann, Sabine. Precarious Worlds: Contemporary Art from Germany. 2012. (ENG., Illus.). 72p. 30.00 ***(978-0-936316-34-5(9))*** Washington Univ., Mildred Lane Kemper Art Museum.

Eckmann, Sabine, et al. Reality Bites: Making Avant-garde Art in Post-Wall Germany. 2007.Tr. of Reality Bites: Kunst nach dem Mauerfall. (GER.). per. 55.00 *(978-0-936316-21-5(7))* Washington Univ., Mildred Lane Kemper Art Museum.

Eliasson, Olafur. Olafur Eliasson. Innen Stadt Außen. Inner city out. 2010. (ENG & GER., Illus.). 424p. pap. 79.00 *(978-3-86560-765-2(9))* Verlag der Buchhandlung Walther Konig DEU. Dist: D.A.P./Distributed Art Pubs.

Engler, M. D. & Bee, A. Peter Roehr: Ausstellung von 28. November 2009 bis 7. März 2010. 2010. (ENG.). 184p. 60.00 *(978-3-86568-522-3(6),* Art Stock Bks. Ltd/Csi) Continental Sales, Inc.

Eskildsen, Ute, as told by. Photography Collection Museum. 2011. (ENG.). 288p. 45.00 *(978-3-86930-096-2(5))* Steidl, Gerhard Druckerei und Verlag DEU. Dist: Innovative Logistics.

Expanded Original Staff. Cornelia Sollfrank: Expanded Original. 2009. (GER & ENG., Illus.). 144p. pap. 40.00 *(978-3-7757-2390-9(0))* Hatje Cantz Verlag GmbH & Co KG DEU. Dist: D.A.P./Distributed Art Pubs.

Feireiss, Kristin, ed. City & Structure: Photographs by H. G. Esch. 2009. (ENG., Illus.). 256p. 60.00 *(978-3-7757-2281-0(5))* Hatje Cantz Verlag GmbH & Co KG DEU. Dist: D.A.P./Distributed Art Pubs.

Flügge, Matthias. Mark Lammert: Paintings 1997-2010. 2011. (ENG., Illus.). 156p. 45.00 ***(978-3-941263-26-0(9))*** Richter Verlag DEU. Dist: D.A.P./Distributed Art Pubs.

Focke, Anne, ed. Trimpin: Contraptions for Art & Sound. 2011. (ENG., Illus.). 208p. 40.00 *(978-0-295-99109-2(7))* Marquand Bks., Inc.

Fore, Devin. Realism after Modernism: The Rehumanization of Art & Literature. 2012. ***(978-0-262-01771-8(7))*** MIT Pr.

Foulon, Anne-Cecile. De l'Art pour Tous: Les Editions F. Bruckmann et leurs Revues d'Art dans Munich Ville d'Art vers 1900. (Munchener Studien zur Literarischen Kultur in Deutschland: Vol. 36). (FRE., Illus.). 448p. 57.95 *(978-3-631-50157-3(9))* Lang, Peter Publishing, Inc.

Franke, Birgit & Welzel, Barbara. Die Kunst der burgundischen Niederlande: Eine Einführung. (GER., Illus.). 303p. *(978-3-496-01170-5(X))* Reimer, Dietrich.

Frecot. Dada Montages, 1916 - 1933. 2009. (ENG., Illus.). 224p. 60.00 *(978-3-7757-2127-1(4))* Hatje Cantz Verlag GmbH & Co KG DEU. Dist: D.A.P./Distributed Art Pubs.

Friedel, Helmut & Hoberg, Annegret. Kandinsky Complete Prints. 2009. (GER & ENG., Illus.). 296p. 69.00 *(978-3-87909-964-1(2),* Art Stock Bks. Ltd/Csi) Continental Sales, Inc.

Friedel, Helmut & Hoberg, Annegret, eds. The Blue Rider: A Dance in Colour: Watercolours, Drawings & Prints from the Lenbachhaus Munich. 2011. (Illus.). 264p. 65.00 *(978-3-7774-3271-7(7))* Hirmer Verlag GmbH DEU. Dist: Chicago Distribution Ctr.

Friedewald, Boris. Bauhaus: Living Art. 2009. (Illus.). 128p. pap. 14.95 *(978-3-7913-4200-9(2))* Prestel Publishing.

Friese, Peter, ed. Jochen Gerz: The Bremen Questionnaire Sine Somno Nihil, 1990-1995. (ENG & GER., Illus.). 144p. 29.95 *(978-3-89322-788-4(1))* Edition Cantz DEU. Dist: D.A.P./Distributed Art Pubs.

Frischkorn, Holger, et al. Atelier Goldstein Künstler. Schirrmacher, Gabi & Salzer, Christian, eds. 2008. (ENG & GER., Illus.). 240p. pap. 55.00 *(978-3-936314-89-2(6))* Jovis Verlag GmbH DEU. Dist: D.A.P./Distributed Art Pubs.

Fuchs, Rudi. With a Probability of Being Seen: Dorothee & Konrad Fischer: Archives of an Attitude. 2010. 384p. 65.00 *(978-84-92505-43-2(5))* Museu d'Art Contemporani de Barcelona ESP. Dist: Actar Birkhauser Distribution.

Gaensheimer, Susanne & Kramer, Mario, eds. The Lucid Evidence: Fotografie aus der Sammlung des MMK. 2011. (GER & ENG., Illus.). 500p. 85.00 *(978-3-86984-147-2(8))* Verlag fur Moderne Kunst DEU. Dist: D.A.P./Distributed Art Pubs.

Gaspar, Monica & Mazumdar, Pravu. Peter Bauhuis: ABECEDARIUM Schmuck. Gefäß. Gerät. 2012. (ENG., Illus.). 160p. 60.00 ***(978-3-89790-361-6(X))*** Arnoldsche Art Pubs. DEU. Dist: Antique Collectors' Club.

Gaughan, Martin Ignatius. German Art 1907-1937: Modernism & Modernisation. (Illus.). 351p. pap. 89.95 *(978-3-03910-900-5(6))* Lang, Peter CHE. Dist: Lang, Peter Publishing, Inc.

Gefeller, Andreas. Andreas Gefeller: The Japan Series. 2011. (ENG., Illus.). 80p. 60.00 ***(978-3-7757-2994-9(1))*** Hatje Cantz Verlag GmbH & Co KG DEU. Dist: D.A.P./Distributed Art Pubs.

Gierke, Henning von. Henning Von Gierke: Flowing Gold. 2009. (GER & ENG., Illus.). 240p. 75.00 *(978-3-7913-4132-3(4))* Prestel Publishing.

Gorecki, Joachim. Die Fundmünzen der Römischen Zeit in Deutschland: Abteilung IV: Rheinland-Pfalz. Band 1, Nachtrag 1: Stadt Mainz. 2006. (GER., Illus.). 591p. 99.00 *(978-3-8053-3643-7(8))* Zabern, Philipp von Verlag, GmbH DEU. Dist: Brown, David Bk. Co., The.

Gotzkowsky, Bodo & Brosamer, Hans. Die Buchholzschnitte Hans Brosamers in Werken Martin Luthers und Anderen Religiösen Drucken des 16. Jahrhunderts: Ein Bibliographisches Verzeichnis Ihrer Verwendungen. 2009. (GER., Illus.). 495p. *(978-3-87320-363-1(4))* Koerner, Valentin Verlag, GmbH.

Grass, Günter. Günter Grass Vol. 1: Catalogue Raisonné, 1 vol. Ohsoling, Hilke, ed. 2008. (GER & ENG., Illus.). 607p. 125.00 *(978-3-86521-565-9(3))* Steidl, Gerhard Druckerei und Verlag DEU. Dist: Innovative Logistics.

Grave, Johannes. Der "Ideale Kunstkörper" Johann Wolfgang Goethe Als Sammler Von Druckgraphiken und Zeichnungen. 2007. (Asthetik Um 1800 Ser.). (GER., Illus.). 648p. (C). 100.00 *(978-3-525-47503-4(9))* Vandenhoeck & Ruprecht GmbH & Co. KG DEU. Dist: ISD.

Grobe, Jurgen. Urban Art Photography. 2008. (GER & ENG., Illus.). 216p. *(978-3-89955-205-8(9))* Die Gestalten Verlag.

Gronert, Stefan, ed. Daniel Roth. Car Gwyllt. 2009. (ENG., Illus.). 112p. pap. 39.95 *(978-3-86560-577-1(X))* Verlag der Buchhandlung Walther Konig DEU. Dist: D.A.P./Distributed Art Pubs.

Gronert, Stefan, ed. & text. The Dusseldorf School of Photography. 2010. (ENG., Illus.). 320p. 95.00 *(978-1-59711-136-2(8))* Aperture Foundation, Inc.

Gronert, Stefan & Berg, Stephan, eds. Der Westen leuchtet. 2011. (ENG & GER., Illus.). 416p. 65.00 *(978-3-86678-432-1(5))* Kerber Verlag DEU. Dist: D.A.P./Distributed Art Pubs.

Grosse, Katharina. Katharina Grosse: Shadowbox. 2010. (GER & ENG., Illus.). 132p. pap. 46.00 *(978-3-86560-611-2(3))* Verlag der Buchhandlung Walther Konig DEU. Dist: D.A.P./Distributed Art Pubs.

Gualdoni, Flaminio. Bauhaus. 2009. (Skira MINI Artbooks Ser.). (ENG., Illus.). 96p. pap. 8.99 *(978-88-572-0153-5(8))* Skira Editore ITA. Dist: Random Hse., Inc.

Haass, Ulrich, ed. As We Like It: Jewellery & Tableware 1988-2008. 2008. (ENG., Illus.). 320p. 70.00 *(978-3-89790-291-6(5))* Arnoldsche Art Pubs. DEU. Dist: Antique Collectors' Club.

Hahn, Eckart. Grand Ouvert: Diese Publikation erschien anlässlich der Ausstellungen: Kammerspiele, Galerie Rothamel, Frankfurt a. M. 4.September - 17.Oktober 2009, Intimate Play, WAGNER+PARTNER, Berlin 6.November 2009 - 2.Januar 2010. 2010. (ENG., Illus.). 48p. 27.00 *(978-3-86678-343-0(4))* Kerber Verlag DEU. Dist: D.A.P./Distributed Art Pubs.

Haniel, Franz, ed. The Haniel Collection. 2011. (ENG., Illus.). 320p. 89.00 ***(978-3-8030-3351-2(9))*** Wasmuth, Ernst J. Verlag GmbH & Co. DEU. Dist: D.A.P./Distributed Art Pubs.

Hanne Darboven: Briefe aus New York. ltd. ed. 650p. *(978-3-89322-767-9(9))* Edition Cantz DEU. Dist: D.A.P./Distributed Art Pubs.

Harder. Thorsten Brinkmann. 2008. (ENG., Illus.). 168p. 55.00 *(978-3-7757-2205-6(X))* Hatje Cantz Verlag GmbH & Co KG DEU. Dist: D.A.P./Distributed Art Pubs.

Harro, Schweizer. Berlin. 2009. 432p. 59.99 *(978-0-8416-1643-1(4))* American Map Corp.

Haskell, Barbara, ed. Lyonel Feininger: At the Edge of the World. 2011. (ENG., Illus.). 288p. 65.00 *(978-0-300-16846-4(2))* Yale Univ. Pr.

Hatje Cantz, compiled by. Art to Hear: Bauhaus. 2009. (ENG., Illus.). 48p. 30.00 *(978-3-7757-2451-7(6))* Hatje Cantz Verlag GmbH & Co KG DEU. Dist: D.A.P./Distributed Art Pubs.

He, Jianping, ed. Gerwin Schmidt. 2008. (New Generation of Design Ser.). (Illus.). 215p. pap. *(978-981-245-507-9(8))* Page One Publishing.

—Jianping He. 2008. (New Generation of Design Ser.). (Illus.). 215p. pap. *(978-981-245-509-3(4))* Page One Publishing.

Helke, Gun-Dagmar. Deckelterrinen des 18. Jahrhunderts aus Fayence und Zinn: Eine Sammlung auf Gut Hohen Luckow. 2007. (GER., Illus.). 144p. (C). pap. 42.00 *(978-3-7774-3865-8(0))* Hirmer Verlag GmbH DEU. Dist: Brown, David Bk. Co., The.

Heller, Reinhold, text. The Birth of Expressionism, 1905-1913. 2009. (ENG., Illus.). 232p. 55.00 *(978-3-7757-2351-0(X))* Hatje Cantz Verlag GmbH & Co KG DEU. Dist: D.A.P./Distributed Art Pubs.

Hellwig, Karin. Spanien und Deutschland: Kulturtransfer Im 19. Jahrhundert = España y Alemania: Intercambio Cultural en el Siglo XIX. 2007. (MUL, GER & SPA., Illus.). 313p. pap. 56.00 *(978-84-8489-337-0(5))* Iberoamericana Vervuert Publishing Corp.

Hentschel, Martin, ed. Andreas Gursky: Werke 80-08. 2011. (ENG., Illus.). 272p. 60.00 ***(978-3-7757-3022-8(2))*** Hatje Cantz Verlag GmbH & Co KG DEU. Dist: D.A.P./Distributed Art Pubs.

—Herbert Hamak. (ENG & GER., Illus.). 182p. 39.95 *(978-3-89322-850-8(0))* Edition Cantz DEU. Dist: D.A.P./Distributed Art Pubs.

—Stefan Kürten. Black Mirror: Drucke 1991-2009. 2011. (ENG., Illus.). 56p. 34.95 *(978-3-86678-400-0(7))* Kerber Verlag DEU. Dist: D.A.P./Distributed Art Pubs.

Hill, Rachel, et al, trs. Berlin Contemporary: Gallery Guide Berlin. 2008. (ENG., Illus.). 208p. pap. 24.95 *(978-3-939633-77-8(1))* Jovis Verlag GmbH DEU. Dist: D.A.P./Distributed Art Pubs.

Hinrichs, Ernst & Zernack, Klaus, eds. Daniel Chodowiecki (1726-1801) Kupferstecher, Illustrator, Kaufmann. (Wolfenbatteler Studien zur Aufklärung Ser.).Tr. of Daniel Chodowiecki (1726-1801). Engraver, genre painter, Merchant. (GER.). X, 265p. 165.00 ***(978-3-11-179461-7(X))*** De Gruyter, Walter Inc.

Hofer, Candida. Candida Hofer: on Kawara, Date Paintings in Private Collections. 2009. (ENG., Illus.). 256p. 95.00 *(978-3-86560-530-6(3))* Verlag der Buchhandlung Walther Konig DEU. Dist: D.A.P./Distributed Art Pubs.

Hoffmann, Leni. leni hoffmann: RGB: Künstlerbuch. 2010. (GER & ENG., Illus.). 144p. pap. 59.95 *(978-3-8321-9290-7(5))* DuMont DEU. Dist: D.A.P./Distributed Art Pubs.

Hojer, Gerhard. King Ludwig I's Beauty Gallery. 2008. (Illus.). 124p. 24.95 *(978-3-7954-1882-3(8))* Schnell und Steiner GmbH, Verlag DEU. Dist: Independent Pubs. Group.

Hollmann, Eckhard. The Blue Rider. 2011. (Illus.). 192p. pap. 19.95 *(978-3-7913-4528-4(1))* Prestel Publishing.

Holub, Barbara. found, set, appropriated. 2011. (ENG., Illus.). 176p. pap. 50.00 ***(978-3-86984-164-9(8))*** Verlag fur Moderne Kunst DEU. Dist: D.A.P./Distributed Art Pubs.

Homburg, Cornelia, et al. German Art Now. (Illus.). 160p. *(978-1-85894-235-3(7))* Merrell Pubs. Ltd.

Huber, Patrick. Sarah Morris: 1972. 2008. (ENG., Illus.). 64p. 35.00 *(978-3-905829-47-1(9))* JRP Ringier Kunstverlag AG CHE. Dist: D.A.P./Distributed Art Pubs.

Hudson, Suzanne, text. Katja Strunz, 1 vol. 2007. (ENG., Illus.). 140p. 44.00 *(978-3-86560-161-2(8))* Verlag der Buchhandlung Walther Konig DEU. Dist: D.A.P./Distributed Art Pubs.

Huyssen, Andreas. Dada & Photomontage Across Borders. Bathrick, David & Rabinbach, Anson, eds. 2009. (ENG., Illus.). 254p. pap. 14.00 *(978-0-8223-6722-2(X))* Duke Univ. Pr.

Illenberger, Sarah. Sarah Illenberger. 2011. (ENG., Illus.). 128p. 30.00 ***(978-3-89955-385-7(3))*** Die Gestalten Verlag DEU. Dist: Prestel Publishing.

Imhof, Michael. Berlin - Architektur und Kunst - Art & Architecture. 2009. (ENG.). 160p. 24.95 *(978-3-86568-100-3(X)*, Art Stock Bks. Ltd/Csi) Continental Sales, Inc.

Immisch, T. O. The Other Leipzig School: Photography in the GDR. Knorr, Susanne, ed. 2010. (ENG., Illus.). 256p. 55.00 *(978-3-86678-360-7(4))* Kerber Verlag DEU. Dist: D.A.P./Distributed Art Pubs.

International Topsprayer, photos by & text. INTERNATIONAL TOPSPRAYER: MOSES & TAPS. 2011. (Illus.). 288p. ***(978-3-939566-35-9(7))*** Publikat Verlags- und Handels KG.

Jacki, Guenter. Gunter Jacki: Looking for Transmission, 1 vol. 2007. (ENG., Illus.). 224p. 42.00 *(978-3-8030-3203-4(2))* Wasmuth, Ernst J. Verlag GmbH & Co. DEU. Dist: D.A.P./Distributed Art Pubs.

Jádi, Frenec. Kokon Cocoon: Jewellery Objects. 2010. (ENG., Illus.). 160p. pap. 70.00 *(978-3-89790-324-1(5))* Arnoldsche Art Pubs. DEU. Dist: Antique Collectors' Club.

Jager. Wolfgang Tillmans: Lighter. 2008. (GER & ENG., Illus.). 400p. 95.00 *(978-3-7757-2187-5(8))* Hatje Cantz Verlag GmbH & Co KG DEU. Dist: D.A.P./Distributed Art Pubs.

Jager, Joachim & Kittelmann, Udo, eds. Rudolf Stingel: Neue Nationalgalerie Berlin. 2011. (ENG., Illus.). 48p. 45.00 *(978-3-86560-878-9(7))* Verlag der Buchhandlung Walther Konig DEU. Dist: D.A.P./Distributed Art Pubs.

Jankowski, Christian. Christian Jankowski: Briefing. 2009. (ENG., Illus.). 288p. 60.00 *(978-3-7757-2317-6(X))* Hatje Cantz Verlag GmbH & Co KG DEU. Dist: D.A.P./Distributed Art Pubs.

Jansen, Gregor & Thiel, Thomas, eds. Vertrautes Terrain: Aktuelle Kunst in & über Deutschland. 2009. (ENG.). 500p. pap. 45.00 *(978-3-86828-064-7(2))* Kehrer Verlag Heidelberg, Klaus Kehrer DEU. Dist: Consortium Bk. Sales & Distribution.

Jentsch, Ralph. George Grosz: Berlin-New York. 2008. (ENG., Illus.). 288p. 80.00 *(978-88-6130-294-5(7))* Skira Editore ITA. Dist: Random Hse., Inc.

Jepsy & Gruenhaeuser, Amber. Jepsy: The Real Deal. 2010. (ENG., Illus.). 128p. 19.95 *(978-3-937946-67-2(5))*; pap. 14.95 *(978-3-937946-66-5(7))* From Here To Fame GmbH DEU. Dist: SCB Distributors.

Jirka-Schmitz, Patrizia. The World of Netsuke: The Werdelmann Collection at the Museum Kunst. 2007. (ENG., Illus.). 320p. 135.00 *(978-3-89790-209-1(5))* Arnoldsche Art Pubs. DEU. Dist: Antique Collectors' Club.

Jokisch, Christoph & Volz, Peter. Emblems of Eminence: German Renaissance Portrait Medals. 2008. (GER., Illus.). 224p. (C). 154.00 *(978-3-7774-4235-8(6))* Hirmer Verlag GmbH DEU. Dist: Brown, David Bk. Co., The.

Jung, Christine & Heuser, August. Thierry Boissel. 2012. (ENG, FRE & GER., Illus.). 160p. 70.00 ***(978-3-89790-369-2(5))*** Arnoldsche Art Pubs. DEU. Dist: National Bk. Network.

Juul Holm, Michael, ed. German Art in the Louisiana Collection. 2012. (ENG., Illus.). 224p. pap. 35.00 *(978-87-91607-88-2(4))* Louisana DNK. Dist: D.A.P./Distributed Art Pubs.

Kaiser, Fritz. Degenerate Art Exhibition Guide 1937 - Bilingual Edition German/English. von Halasz, Joachim, ed. & tr. by. 2010. 78p. pap. *(978-1-905742-30-1(4))* Foxley Books.

Kalandides, Ares. Berlin Design. 2009. (ENG., Illus.). 262p. pap. 35.00 *(978-3-03768-014-8(8)*, Braun Publish,Csi) Continental Sales, Inc.

Kaltwasser, Martin & Kobberling, Folke. Ressource Stadt - City as a Resource: One man's trash is another man's treasure, 1 vol. 2007. (ENG & GER., Illus.). 128p. pap. 29.95 *(978-3-939633-07-5(0))* Jovis Verlag GmbH DEU. Dist: D.A.P./Distributed Art Pubs.

Kastner, Jeffery, et al, contrib. by. Mountains, 1 vol. 2007. (ENG., Illus.). 112p. pap. 10.00 *(978-1-932698-23-7(X))* Cabinet.

Kelly, Elaine & Wlodarski, Amy, eds. Art Outside the Lines: New Perspectives on GDR Art Culture. 2011. (Illus.). 298p. pap. 8400.00 *(978-90-420-3341-2(X))* Rodopi.

Kennedy, Andrew. Bauhaus. 2009. (Todo Arte Ser.). (ENG.). 384p. pap. 19.00 *(978-84-9794-053-5(9))* Edimat Libros, S. A. ESP. Dist: Independent Pubs. Group.

Kher, Bharti & Tomaselli, Fred. Susan Hefuna - Bharti Kher - Fred Tomaselli: Zwischen den Welten / Between The Worlds. 2011. (ENG., Illus.). 120p. 30.00 ***(978-3-86828-176-7(2))*** Kehrer Verlag Heidelberg, Klaus Kehrer DEU. Dist: Consortium Bk. Sales & Distribution.

Kiecol, Hubert & Melcher, Ralph. Hubert Kiecol: Separee Public. 2010. (FRE, GER & ENG., Illus.). 116p. pap. 48.00 *(978-3-86560-612-9(1))* Verlag der Buchhandlung Walther Konig DEU. Dist: D.A.P./Distributed Art Pubs.

King, Averil. Paula Modersohn-Becker. 2009. (ENG., Illus.). 144p. *(978-1-85149-586-3(X)*, Antique Collectors Club Dist) Antique Collectors' Club.

Kirchner, Ernst Ludwig. Ernst Ludwig Kirchner: Art to Hear. 2010. (ENG., Illus.). 44p. 30.00 *(978-3-7757-2555-2(5))* Hatje Cantz Verlag GmbH & Co KG DEU. Dist: D.A.P./Distributed Art Pubs.

Kittelmann, Udo. Simon Dybbroe Moller: Black, white, gray, cyan, magenta, Yellow. 2010. (GER & ENG., Illus.). 64p. 30.00 *(978-3-86560-571-9(0))* Verlag der Buchhandlung Walther Konig DEU. Dist: D.A.P./Distributed Art Pubs.

Klauke, Jürgen, photos by. Jürgen Klauke: Ästhetische Paranoia. 2010. (ENG., Illus.). 252p. 60.00 *(978-3-7757-2594-1(6))* Hatje Cantz Verlag GmbH & Co KG DEU. Dist: D.A.P./Distributed Art Pubs.

Klaus, Kemp & Keiko, Ueki-Polet, eds. Less & More: The Design Ethos of Dieter Rams. 2010. (GER & ENG., Illus.). 808p. pap. 78.00 *(978-3-89955-277-5(6))* Die Gestalten Verlag DEU. Dist: Prestel Publishing.

Klingsö, et al. Lovis Corinth: Seelenlandschaften. Walchenseebilder und Selbstbildnisse. 2009. (GER., Illus.). 119p. *(978-3-87909-979-5(0))* Wienand GmbH Druck- & Verlagshaus.

Knaus, Bernhard & Honnef, Klaus. Ralf Peters: Fotografie. 2010. (GER & ENG., Illus.). 212p. 60.00 *(978-3-7757-2608-5(X))* Hatje Cantz Verlag GmbH & Co KG DEU. Dist: D.A.P./Distributed Art Pubs.

Knerr, Anne-Barbara. Zeitgeist: 100 Jahre Modeschmuck aus Idar-Oberstein / A Century of Idar-Oberstein Costume Jewellery. 2009. (ENG., Illus.). 192p. 75.00 *(978-3-89790-314-2(8))* Arnoldsche Art Pubs. DEU. Dist: Antique Collectors' Club.

Knoller, Paco, illus. Paco Knöller: Schnitte. Riskante Euphorien, 1 vol. 2008. (ENG.). 96p. 55.00 *(978-3-937572-80-2(5))* Richter Verlag DEU. Dist: D.A.P./Distributed Art Pubs.

Koepnick, Lutz P. Framing Attention: Windows on Modern German Culture. 2006. (Parallax: Re#45;visions of Culture & Society Ser.). (ENG., Illus.). 312p. (gr. 17). 55.00 *(978-0-8018-8489-4(6))* Johns Hopkins Univ. Pr.

Koerner, Joseph Leo. The Reformation of the Image. 2008. 494p. pap. 35.00 *(978-0-226-44837-4(1))* Univ. of Chicago Pr.

Königsmann, Alexandra, et al. Alexandra Königsmann: Only Art. 2009. (GER., Illus.). 144p. *(978-3-7774-7045-0(7))* Hirmer Verlag GmbH.

Konsalik, Heinz G. Das Bernsteinzimmer. (GER.). pap. 20.95 *(978-3-453-04866-9(0))* Verlag Wilhelm Heyne DEU. Dist: Distribooks, Inc.

Kotzur, Hans-Jürgen. Dommuseum Mainz: Führer Durch Die Sammlung. 2008. (GER., Illus.). 148p. (C). 20.00 *(978-3-8053-3871-4(6))* Zabern, Philipp von Verlag, GmbH DEU. Dist: Brown, David Bk. Co., The.

Kraus, Kitty. Kitty Kraus. 2010. (ENG., Illus.). 168p. pap. 40.00 *(978-3-86678-327-0(2))* Kerber Verlag DEU. Dist: D.A.P./Distributed Art Pubs.

Krempel, Ulrich, ed. Eva & Adele: Nota - Light on Weimar. (ENG & GER., Illus.). 64p. pap. *(978-3-89322-244-5(8))* Edition Cantz DEU. Dist: D.A.P./Distributed Art Pubs.

Kruger, Barbara, et al. Barbara Kruger: Circus. 2011. (GER & ENG., Illus.). 64p. pap. 27.50 ***(978-3-86560-945-8(7))*** Verlag der Buchhandlung Walther Konig DEU. Dist: D.A.P./Distributed Art Pubs.

Kuhn, Heinrich, photos by. Heinrich Kuhn: Perfect Photography. 2010. (ENG., Illus.). 280p. 75.00 *(978-3-7757-2569-9(5))* Hatje Cantz Verlag GmbH & Co KG DEU. Dist: D.A.P./Distributed Art Pubs.

Die Kunst (Art) (Schulerduden Ser.). (ENG & GER.). 27.95 *(978-3-411-02200-7(0)*, B2200) Bibliographisches Institut & F. A. Brockhaus AG DEU. Dist: Continental Bk. Co., Inc.

Kuntverlag, Deutscher, ed. Christiane Moebus: Chausseestrasse. 2008. (GER & ENG., Illus.). 112p. pap. 29.95 *(978-3-422-06702-8(7)*, Art Stock Bks. Ltd/Csi) Continental Sales, Inc.

Lammer, Frank (esher) & R.k.d.u., eds. We Come at Night: A Corporate Street Attack. 2008. (Illus.). 144p. *(978-3-89955-216-4(4))* Die Gestalten Verlag.

Landert, Markus, ed. Olaf Nicolai. Mirador: Mirador. 2011. (ENG., Illus.). 80p. pap. 45.00 *(978-3-86984-033-8(1))* Verlag fur Moderne Kunst DEU. Dist: D.A.P./Distributed Art Pubs.

Lange, Justus. Die Wilkes: Eine Künstlerfamilie der Moderne Aus Braunschweig. 2008. (GER., Illus.). 55p. *(978-3-937664-91-0(2))* Stadt Braunschweig, Stadtisches Museum.

Legat-Verlag Staff, ed. Icons. 2006. 368p. 59.95 *(978-3-932942-20-4(5))* Legat-Verlag GmbH & Company KG DEU. Dist: Independent Pubs. Group.

Leipzig, Zentrum. Where do we go from here? 2010. (ENG.). 192p. pap. 28.00 *(978-3-422-06934-3(8)*, Art Stock Bks. Ltd/Csi) Continental Sales, Inc.

Leitner, Bernhard. P. U. L. S. E. Raume der Zeit/Spaces in Time. 2008. (GER & ENG., Illus.). 208p. 60.00 *(978-3-7757-2047-2(2))* Hatje Cantz Verlag GmbH & Co KG DEU. Dist: D.A.P./Distributed Art Pubs.

Lemmel, Katerina, et al. Katerina's Windows: Donation & Devotion, Art & Music, As Heard & Seen Through the Writings of a Birgittine Nun. 2009. (ENG.). 608p. 110.00 *(978-0-271-03369-3(X))* Pennsylvania State Univ. Pr.

Lenz, Christian. Hans Purrmann: Aquarelle und Gouachen. Werkverzeichnis. 2009. (ENG., Illus.). 336p. 300.00 *(978-3-7757-2178-3(9))* Hatje Cantz Verlag GmbH & Co KG DEU. Dist: D.A.P./Distributed Art Pubs.

Lewandowsky, Via. Via Lewandowsky: Applause. 2009. (GER & ENG., Illus.). 104p. pap. 25.00 *(978-3-86560-568-9(0))* Verlag der Buchhandlung Walther Konig DEU. Dist: D.A.P./Distributed Art Pubs.

Lombardi, Elena, ed. L' Archivio Di Giovanni Poggi (1880-1961) Soprintendente Alle Gallerie Fiorentine. 2011. (Dagli Archivi delle Arti Ser.). (ITA., Illus.). 466p. (C). pap. 40.00 ***(978-88-596-0831-8(7))*** Polistampa ITA. Dist: Brown, David Bk. Co., The.

Loock, Ulrich, ed. Schütte, Thomas.Public/Political. 2012. (ENG., Illus.). 240p. pap. 59.95 ***(978-3-86560-414-9(5))*** Verlag der Buchhandlung Walther Konig DEU. Dist: D.A.P./Distributed Art Pubs.

Lorch, Catrin, et al, texts. Matti Braun: Kola. 2009. (ENG., Illus.). 242p. 44.00 *(978-3-86560-596-2(6))* Verlag der Buchhandlung Walther Konig DEU. Dist: D.A.P./Distributed Art Pubs.

Luckert, Steven & Bachrach, Susan. State of Deception: The Power of Nazi Propaganda. 2009. (ENG., Illus.). 288p. 45.00 *(978-0-89604-714-3(8)*, 47143) Norton, W. W. & Co., Inc.

Luders, Marc. Marc Lüders. 2010. (ENG., Illus.). 176p. 55.00 *(978-3-7757-2515-6(6))* Hatje Cantz Verlag GmbH & Co KG DEU. Dist: D.A.P./Distributed Art Pubs.

Lutgens, Annelie & Kirschner, Esther Barbara, eds. Leichtigkeit und Enthusiasmus. Ease & Eagerness: Junge Kunst und die Moderne. Modernism today. 2009. (ENG & GER., Illus.). 176p. pap. 45.00 *(978-3-7757-2433-3(8))* Hatje Cantz Verlag GmbH & Co KG DEU. Dist: D.A.P./Distributed Art Pubs.

Mack, Heinz. Mack. Die Sprache meiner Hand. 2011. (ENG., Illus.). 288p. 60.00 ***(978-3-7757-2978-9(X))*** Hatje Cantz Verlag GmbH & Co KG DEU. Dist: D.A.P./Distributed Art Pubs.

Mack, Heinz & text. Heinz Mack: Licht der ZERO-Zeit. 2010. (ENG., Illus.). 152p. 49.50 *(978-3-86678-334-8(5))* Kerber Verlag DEU. Dist: D.A.P./Distributed Art Pubs.

Mack, Ute, ed. Heinz Mack. Leben und Werk. Ein Buch vom Künstler über den Künstler 1931-2011. 2011. (GER & ENG., Illus.). 500p. 110.00 *(978-3-8321-9353-9(7))* DuMont DEU. Dist: D.A.P./Distributed Art Pubs.

Maier-Aichen, Hansjerg, ed. New Talents: State of the Arts. Stand der Dinge. 2009. (ENG & GER., Illus.). 176p. pap. 35.00 *(978-3-89986-110-5(8)*, Avedition Gmbh,Csi) Continental Sales, Inc.

Masterpieces of Kunsthistorisches. 128p. *(978-88-8029-550-1(0))* Casa Editrice Bonechi.

Masterpieces of Landeszeughaus. 64p. *(978-88-7009-754-2(4))* Casa Editrice Bonechi.

Matt, Gerald, ed. & text. Thomas Ruff. Oberfächen, Tiefen. 2009. (ENG & GER., Illus.). 288p. 60.00 *(978-3-941185-50-0(0))* Verlag fur Moderne Kunst DEU. Dist: D.A.P./Distributed Art Pubs.

Max, Peter. The Universe According to Peter Max: A Psychedelic Odyssey. 2012. (ENG.). 288p. 35.00 ***(978-0-06-212139-4(1)***, Collins Design) HarperCollins Pubs.

Maxwell, Susan. The Court Art of Friedrich Sustris: Patronage in Late Renaissance Bavaria. 2011. (Visual Culture in Early Modernity Ser.). (Illus.). 250p. 109.95 *(978-0-7546-6887-9(8))* Ashgate Publishing Co.

Mayer, Katharina, et al. Katharina Mayer, Paula Modersohn-Becker: Eine Begegnung. 2008. (GER., Illus.). 55p. *(978-3-9810296-2-8(3)*, Spotlight Poets) Bottcherstrae GmbH.

McEvilley, Thomas. Art, Love, Friendship: Marina Abramovic & Ulay, Together & Apart. 2010. (Illus.). 304p. 27.00 *(978-0-929701-93-6(3)*, Documentext) McPherson & Co.

McKinney, Rose Mary. Hans Friedrich Grohs A Memento Mori for Elisabeth Grohs Treskow. McKinney, Rose Mary, tr. 2011. (Illus.). 52p. 75.00 ***(978-0-9830254-0-5(1))*** Frauken Grohs Collinson-Grohs Collection Trust.

Meese, Jonathan. Jonathan Meese: Dash Snow Fanzine. 2011. (ENG., Illus.). 46p. pap. 18.00 *(978-3-931355-54-8(3))* Walter Konig Verlag DEU. Dist: D.A.P./Distributed Art Pubs.

—Totale Neutralität. Jonathan Meese: Diktatur der Kunst. 2009. (ENG., Illus.). 150p. 60.00 *(978-3-86560-506-1(0))* Verlag der Buchhandlung Walther Konig DEU. Dist: D.A.P./Distributed Art Pubs.

Mettig, Klaus, photos by. Don't Be Left Behind, 1 vol. 2011. (ENG & GER., Illus.). 310p. pap. 75.00 *(978-3-86521-595-6(5))* Steidl, Gerhard Druckerei und Verlag DEU. Dist: Innovative Logistics.

Metzger, Rainer. Berlin: The Twenties. Brandstetter, Christian, ed. 2007. (ENG., Illus.). 400p. 45.00 *(978-0-8109-9329-7(5))* Abrams.

Meyer, Anna. Internationale: 2001-2006, 1 vol. 2007. (GER & ENG., Illus.). 248p. pap. 35.00 *(978-3-939633-22-8(4))* Jovis Verlag GmbH DEU. Dist: D.A.P./Distributed Art Pubs.

Meyer-Hermann, Eva, ed. Kippenberger meets Picasso. 2011. (ENG., Illus.). 144p. pap. 44.95 ***(978-3-86560-967-0(8))*** Verlag der Buchhandlung Walther Konig DEU. Dist: D.A.P./Distributed Art Pubs.

Miedza, Joerg & Woellert, Jan Leonardo. Painting with Light: Light Art Performance Photography. 2011. (ENG., Illus.). 224p. pap. 39.95 *(978-1-933952-74-1(1))* Rocky Nook.

Miller, Laurence, ed. I Wanted to See the World. 2011. (ENG., Illus.). 96p. pap. 40.00 ***(978-3-86828-170-5(3))*** Kehrer Verlag Heidelberg, Klaus Kehrer DEU. Dist: Consortium Bk. Sales & Distribution.

Moeller, Magdalena M. Ernst Ludwig Kirchner in Berlin. 2008. (Illus.). 200p. (C). pap. 55.00 *(978-3-7774-4485-7(5))* Hirmer Verlag GmbH DEU. Dist: Brown, David Bk. Co., The.

—Sammlung Rolf Horn: Werke aus der Stiftung Rolf Horn. Moeller, Magdalena M., ed. 2009. (GER., Illus.). 316p. (C). 64.00 *(978-3-7774-2071-4(9))* Hirmer Verlag GmbH DEU. Dist: Brown, David Bk. Co., The.

Mohr, Daniel, illus. Daniel Mohr: Zuruck Zur Natur/Back to Nature, 1 vol. 2007. (ENG.). 88p. 38.00 *(978-3-86678-049-1(4))* Kerber Verlag DEU. Dist: D.A.P./Distributed Art Pubs.

Möller, Magdalena M. & Moller, Magdalena M., eds. Dokumente der Kunstlergruppe Brucke. 2007. (BRUCKE-ARCHIV Ser.). (GER., Illus.). 200p. (C). pap. 45.00 *(978-3-7774-3545-9(7))* Hirmer Verlag GmbH DEU. Dist: Brown, David Bk. Co., The.

Moore, Evelyn K. & Simpson, Patricia Anne, eds. The Enlightened Eye: Goethe & Visual Culture. 2007. (Amsterdamer Beiträge Zur Neueren Germanistik Ser.: 62). 322p. 85.00 *(978-90-420-2124-2(1))* Rodopi.

Morton, Mary, ed. Oudry's Painted Menagerie: Portraits of Exotic Animals in Eighteenth-Century France. 2007. 192p. (ENG.). 60.00 *(978-0-89236-879-2(9))*; (Illus.). pap. 40.00 *(978-0-89236-889-1(6))* Oxford Univ. Pr., Inc.

Moschel, Ulrike, ed. Ulrike Möschel: Als ich ein Junge war. 2011. (ENG., Illus.). 70p. 45.00 *(978-3-86678-435-2(X))* Kerber Verlag DEU. Dist: D.A.P./Distributed Art Pubs.

Mossinger, Ingrid & Drechsel, Kerstin, eds. Wolfgang Mattheuer: The Prints-the Hartmut Koch Donation. 2010. (ENG., Illus.). 256p. 78.00 ***(978-3-86832-034-3(2))*** Wienand GmbH, Druck- & Verlagshaus DEU. Dist: Independent Pubs. Group.

Muller, Frank-Heinrich, ed. & photos by. East/For the Record, 1 vol. 2009. (ENG., Illus.). 192p. 55.00 *(978-3-86521-929-9(2))* Steidl, Gerhard Druckerei und Verlag DEU. Dist: Innovative Logistics.

Muller, Karsten, text. Michael Buthe: Der Engel und sein Schatten / The Angel & his Shadow. 2010. (ENG., Illus.). 136p. 50.00 *(978-3-86678-242-6(X))* Kerber Verlag DEU. Dist: D.A.P./Distributed Art Pubs.

Muller, Kathrin, ed. Arabische Handschriften: Reihe B. Teil 10. Arabische Handschriften der Bayerischen Staatsbibliothek zu Munchen. Band 3. Cod. Arab. 2300-2552. 2010. (Verzeichnis der Orientalischen Handschriften in Deutschland Ser.). (GER., Illus.). 644p. (C). 135.00 *(978-3-515-09775-8(9))* Steiner, Franz Verlag Wiesbaden GmbH DEU. Dist: Brown, David Bk. Co., The.

Muller, Markus. Picasso: Linocuts. 2011. (Illus.). 191p. 49.95 ***(978-3-7774-3981-5(9))*** Hirmer Verlag GmbH DEU. Dist: Chicago Distribution Ctr.

Multiple. Irdische Paradiese. Earthly Paradises: Meisterwerke aus der Kasser Art Foundation. 2009. (ENG.). 450p. 48.00 *(978-3-422-06906-0(2)*, Art Stock Bks. Ltd/Csi) Continental Sales, Inc.

Munder, Heike, ed. Christoph Ruckhäberle: Figur. 2010. (ENG., Illus.). 158p. pap. 45.00 *(978-3-03764-055-5(3))* JRP Ringier Kunstverlag AG CHE. Dist: D.A.P./Distributed Art Pubs.

Mundt, Barbara. Der Pommersche Kunstschrank: des Augsburger Unternehmers Hainhofer für den gelehrten Herzog vom Pommern. 2009. (GER., Illus.). 447p. *(978-3-7774-8045-9(2))* Hirmer Verlag GmbH.

Nachtigaller, Roland, et al, texts. Martin Walde: A Second Home for Schrödinger's Cat. 2010. (ENG., Illus.). 232p. pap. 50.00 *(978-3-7757-2623-8(3))* Hatje Cantz Verlag GmbH & Co KG DEU. Dist: D.A.P./Distributed Art Pubs.

—PAOLO CHIASERA: Unter freiem Himmel. 2010. (ENG., Illus.). 72p. pap. 40.00 *(978-3-86678-301-0(9))* Kerber Verlag DEU. Dist: D.A.P./Distributed Art Pubs.

Nagler-Zanier, Cordula. Ringschmuck der Hallstattzeit Aus Bayern: (Arm- und Fussringe, Halsringe, Ohrringe, Fingerringe, Hohlwulstringe) 2006. (Prahistorische Bronzefunde (PBF) Ser.). (GER., Illus.). 226p. (C). 150.00 *(978-3-515-08593-6(5))* Steiner, Franz Verlag Wiesbaden GmbH DEU. Dist: Brown, David Bk. Co., The.

Nefzger, Jurgen. Nocturnes. 2009. (ENG., Illus.). 128p. 45.00 *(978-3-7757-2334-3(X))* Hatje Cantz Verlag GmbH & Co KG DEU. Dist: D.A.P./Distributed Art Pubs.

Nefzger, Jurgen, photos by. Jürgen Nefzger: Fluffy Clouds. 2010. (ENG., Illus.). 144p. 55.00 *(978-3-7757-2598-9(9))* Hatje Cantz Verlag GmbH & Co KG DEU. Dist: D.A.P./Distributed Art Pubs.

Nemes, Loredana, photos by. Loredana Nemes: Beyond. 2011. (ENG & GER., Illus.). 112p. 60.00 *(978-3-7757-2697-9(7))* Hatje Cantz Verlag GmbH & Co KG DEU. Dist: D.A.P./Distributed Art Pubs.

Nerdinger, Winfried. Fotografie für Architekten: Die Fotosammlung des Architekturmuseumsder TU München. 2011. (GER & ENG., Illus.). 216p. 65.00 ***(978-3-86560-989-2(9))*** Verlag der Buchhandlung Walther Konig DEU. Dist: D.A.P./Distributed Art Pubs.

Nicolai, Olaf. Olaf Nicolai: Korallengärten und ihre Magie. 2012. (ENG., Illus.). 144p. pap. 60.00 *(978-3-7757-2449-4(4))* Hatje Cantz Verlag GmbH & Co KG DEU. Dist: D.A.P./Distributed Art Pubs.

Nicolai, Olaf & text. Olaf Nicolai Arbeiten/Works 2003-2006, 1 vol. 2007. (ENG., Illus.). 56p. pap. 30.00 *(978-3-938821-23-7(X))* Verlag fur Moderne Kunst DEU. Dist: D.A.P./Distributed Art Pubs.

Niemeyer Chini, Valerie & Chini, Valerie Niemeyer. Stefano Bardini e Wilhelm Bode: Mercanti e connaisseur fra Ottocento e Novecento. 2009. (ITA., Illus.). 288p. (C). pap. 54.00 *(978-88-596-0668-0(3))* Polistampa ITA. Dist: Brown, David Bk. Co., The.

Nisbet, Peter. Birthday Presents: Acquisitions for the 100th Anniversary of the Busch-Reisinger Museum, Harvard University. 2006. (Paperback Ser.). (ENG., Illus.). 56p. pap. 15.00 *(978-1-891771-37-8(X)*, Harvard Art Museum (Acc)) Antique Collectors' Club GBR. Dist: National Bk. Network.

Nohbauer, Hans F. Munich: City of the Arts. 2007. (Illus.). 346p. 99.00 *(978-3-7774-6250-9(0))* Hirmer Verlag GmbH DEU. Dist: Perseus-PGW.

Notz, Adrian & Obrist, Hans Ulrich, eds. Merz World: Processing the Complicated Order. 2008. (ENG., Illus.). 124p. pap. 15.00 *(978-3-905701-37-1(5))* JRP Ringier Kunstverlag AG CHE. Dist: D.A.P./Distributed Art Pubs.

Obrist, Hans Ulrich, ed. Hans Ulrich Obrist & Dan Graham: Conversation Series: Volume 25. 2012. (ENG., Illus.). 134p. pap. 25.00 ***(978-3-86560-791-1(8))*** Verlag der Buchhandlung Walther Konig DEU. Dist: D.A.P./Distributed Art Pubs.

—Interview. 2010. (ENG., Illus.). 130p. pap. 49.95 *(978-3-86560-660-0(1))* Verlag der Buchhandlung Walther Konig DEU. Dist: D.A.P./Distributed Art Pubs.

—Pars Pro Toto II. 2009. (ENG., Illus.). 256p. pap. 90.00 *(978-3-86828-055-5(3))* Kehrer Verlag Heidelberg, Klaus Kehrer DEU. Dist: Consortium Bk. Sales & Distribution.

—Susan Hefuna: Pars Pro Toto. 2009. (ARA & ENG., Illus.). 256p. pap. 90.00 *(978-3-939583-76-9(6))* Kehrer Verlag Heidelberg, Klaus Kehrer DEU. Dist: Consortium Bk. Sales & Distribution.

Obrist, Hans Ulrich & Kittelmann, Udo, eds. Thomas Bayrle: 40 Years Chinese Rock N' Roll, 1 vol. 2007. (ENG., Illus.). 320p. pap. 70.00 *(978-3-86560-100-1(6))* Verlag der Buchhandlung Walther Konig DEU. Dist: D.A.P./Distributed Art Pubs.

Oehlen, Albert. Albert Oehlen. 2012. (ENG, FRE & GER., Illus.). 54p. 50.00 ***(978-3-935567-54-1(5))*** Holzwarth Pubns. DEU. Dist: D.A.P./Distributed Art Pubs.

Olafur Eliasson & Ursprung, Philip. Studio Eliasson Encyclopedia. Riemschneider, Burkhard, ed. 2008. (ENG., Illus.). 500p. 150.00 *(978-3-8228-4426-7(8))* TASCHEN DEU. Dist: Ingram Pub. Services.

op de Weegh, Ard & Hottendorff, Kay. The Fate of the Sleeping Beauties. 2010. (ENG., Illus.). 160p. 59.95 *(978-1-84584-070-9(4)*, 1845840704) Veloce Publishing Ltd. GBR. Dist: MBI Distribution Services/Quayside Distribution.

Osterholt, Manuel. Neo Utopia: the art & work of SUPERBLAST. 2008. (Illus.). pap. *(978-3-939566-11-3(X))* Publikat Verlags- und Handels KG.

Paeffgen, C. O. C.O. Paeffgen: Aus der Sammlung Großhaus ergänzt mit Arbeiten aus den Sammlungen Falckenberg und T.A.L. 2010. (ENG., Illus.). 96p. pap. 35.00 *(978-3-86678-340-9(X))* Kerber Verlag DEU. Dist: D.A.P./Distributed Art Pubs.

Paret, Peter. An Artist against the Third Reich: Ernst Barlach, 1933-1938. 2007. (ENG., Illus.). 248p. pap. 28.99 *(978-0-521-03570-5(8))* Cambridge Univ. Pr.

Parke-Taylor, Michael, ed. Angelika Hoerle: The Comet of Cologne Dada. 2010. (ENG., Illus.). 128p. pap. 39.00 *(978-3-86560-631-0(8))* Verlag der Buchhandlung Walther Konig DEU. Dist: D.A.P./Distributed Art Pubs.

Perell, Josep, ed. Sommerer & Mignonneau: Living Systems. 2011. 96p. pap. 70.00 *(978-84-92861-79-8(7))* Actar Birkhauser Distribution.

Pernice, Manfred. Manfred Pernice: Que-Sah. 2011. (ENG & GER., Illus.). 208p. pap. 70.00 *(978-3-940748-53-9(6))* Verlag fur Moderne Kunst DEU. Dist: D.A.P./Distributed Art Pubs.

Platen, Angelika, photos by. Angelika Platen. 2010. (ENG., Illus.). 240p. 75.00 *(978-3-7757-2653-5(5))* Hatje Cantz Verlag GmbH & Co KG DEU. Dist: D.A.P./Distributed Art Pubs.

Porell Dennis R. Allach Porcelain, 1936-1945 Vol. 1: Political Figures, Moriskens, Plaques, Presentation Plates,Candleholders, Specialty Pieces, Germanic Ceramics, Ceramics, 2 vols. 2010. (Illus.). 208p. 99.99 *(978-0-7643-3530-3(8))* Schiffer Publishing, Ltd.

—Allach Porcelain, 1936-1945 Vol. 2: Historical Military Figures, Peasants, Figurines, Animals,Vases, Dinnerware, Miscellaneous, 2 vols. 2010. (Illus.). 208p. 99.99 *(978-0-7643-3531-0(6))* Schiffer Publishing, Ltd.

Powers, John S. Temporary Art & Public Place: Comparing Berlin with Los Angeles. 2009. (Europäische Hochschulschriften. Reihe 28: Kunstgeschichte Ser.). (Illus.). 404p. pap. 99.95 *(978-3-631-56430-1(9))* Lang, Peter GmbH, Europaischer Verlag der Wissenschaften DEU. Dist: Lang, Peter.

Publikat. Power of Style: Berlin Stylewriting. 2007. pap. 29.95 *(978-3-939566-14-4(4))* Publikat Verlags- und Handels KG DEU. Dist: Gingko Pr., Inc.

Puhle, Matthias. Aufbruch in die Gotik, 2 vols. 2009. (GER., Illus.). 1124p. (C). 135.00 *(978-3-8053-4062-5(1))* Zabern, Philipp von Verlag, GmbH DEU. Dist: Brown, David Bk. Co., The.

Rehberger, Tobias. cOPy BrAIN copY TOB IAS R EHB ER GER. 2010. (ENG., Illus.). 336p. pap. 44.95 *(978-3-8321-9315-7(4))* DuMont DEU. Dist: D.A.P./Distributed Art Pubs.

—Flach. 2010. (GER., Illus.). 160p. *(978-3-942405-00-3(8))* Die Gestalten Verlag.

Rektor, Edmond. The Art of Adolf Hitler: Paintings, Drawings & Sketches. Rektor, Edmond, ed. 2008. pap. 29.95 *(978-0-9798547-3-6(3))* Harvard Pr.

Remm, Christiane. Erlebnis Farbe: Aquarelle aus dem Brucke Museum. 2007. (GER., Illus.). 176p. (C). pap. 45.00 *(978-3-7774-3575-6(9))* Hirmer Verlag GmbH DEU. Dist: Brown, David Bk. Co., The.

Renfert, Christof. Melancholie und Expressionismus. (GER.). 160p. pap. 40.95 *(978-3-631-56865-1(7))* Lang, Peter GmbH, Europaischer Verlag der Wissenschaften DEU. Dist: Lang, Peter Publishing, Inc.

Reuther, Manfred, ed. Emil Nolde: Die Südseereise 1913 - 1914. 2008. (GER & ENG., Illus.). 144p. *(978-3-8321-9083-5(X))* DuMont.

Richter, Gerhard. Gerhard Richter: Wald. 2009. (ENG., Illus.). 396p. 85.00 *(978-3-86560-503-0(6))* Verlag der Buchhandlung Walther Konig DEU. Dist: D.A.P./Distributed Art Pubs.

Richter, Gerhard. Gerhard Richter. Eis. 2011. (ENG., Illus.). 152p. 59.95 ***(978-3-86560-924-3(4))*** Verlag der Buchhandlung Walther Konig DEU. Dist: D.A.P./Distributed Art Pubs.

Richter, Gerhard, et al. Gerhard Richter: Early Work, 1951-1972. 2011. (ENG., Illus.). 176p. 50.00 *(978-1-60606-040-7(6)*, J. Paul Getty Museum) Getty Pubns.

Roeck, Bernd. Civic Culture & Everyday Life in Early Modern Germany. 2006. (Studies in Medieval & Reformation Traditions: History, Culture, Religion, Ideas: Vol. 115). (Illus.). 286p. *(978-90-04-15269-4(5))* BRILL.

Rogge, Claudia, photos by. Claudia Rogge: A Retrospective. 2010. (RUS, GER & ENG., Illus.). 128p. 60.00 *(978-3-7757-2574-3(1))* Hatje Cantz Verlag GmbH & Co KG DEU. Dist: D.A.P./Distributed Art Pubs.

Rosen, Barry, ed. Dieter Roth. 2010. (ENG., Illus.). 238p. 45.00 *(978-0-300-17079-5(3))* Yale Univ. Pr.

Roth, Lynette. Painting as a Weapon: Progressive Cologne 1920 - 1930. 2008. (ENG., Illus.). 160p. (C). 59.95 *(978-3-86560-398-2(X))* Verlag der Buchhandlung Walther Konig DEU. Dist: D.A.P./Distributed Art Pubs.

Roth, Martin & Sommerschuh, Jens-Uwe, texts. The Fairest of Them All. 2010. (ENG., Illus.). 240p. 60.00 *(978-3-7757-2457-9(5))* Hatje Cantz Verlag GmbH & Co KG DEU. Dist: D.A.P./Distributed Art Pubs.

Rothmann, Gerd. Gerd Rothmann: Werkverzeichnis 1967-2008. 2009. (ENG., Illus.). 404p. pap. 70.00 *(978-3-89790-306-7(7))* Arnoldsche Art Pubs. DEU. Dist: Antique Collectors' Club.

Rudolph, Monika. Naum Slutzky: Meister am Bauhaus Goldschmied und Designer. (GER., Illus.). 240p. 95.00 *(978-3-925369-06-3(6))* Arnoldsche Art Pubs. DEU. Dist: Antique Collectors' Club.

Ruetz, Michael, photos by. Michael Ruetz: Spring of Discontent, 1964-1974, 1 vol. 2009. (ENG., Illus.). 192p. 55.00 *(978-3-86521-866-7(0))* Steidl, Gerhard Druckerei und Verlag DEU. Dist: Innovative Logistics.

Rugoff, Ralph, ed. Johannes Kahrs. 2009. (ENG., Illus.). 152p. 60.00 *(978-3-7757-2401-2(X))* Hatje Cantz Verlag GmbH & Co KG DEU. Dist: D.A.P./Distributed Art Pubs.

Russell, Mark A. Beyond Tradition & Modernity: Aby Warburg & the Public Purposes of Art in Hamburg, 1896-1918. 2007. (Monographs in German History). (Illus.). 272p. 90.00 *(978-1-84545-369-5(7))* Berghahn Bks., Inc.

Russell, P. Craig. The Art of P. Craig Russell. Pruett, Joe, ed. aut. ed. 2010. (Illus.). 256p. 79.99 *(978-0-9795939-0-1(5))* Idea & Design Works, LLC.

Saehrendt, Christian. Kunst als Botschafter einer künstlichen Nation: Pallas Athene - 27. Studien zur Rolle der bildenden Kunst in der Auswärtigen Kulturpolitik der DDR. 2009. (Pallas Athene. Beitrage zur Universitats- und Wissenschaftsgeschichte Ser.). (GER., Illus.). 197p. (C). 52.00 *(978-3-515-09227-2(7))* Steiner, Franz Verlag Wiesbaden GmbH DEU. Dist: Brown, David Bk. Co., The.

Sagmeister, S. & Koehler, D. W. OUBEY MINDKISS. 2010. (ENG.). 240p. pap. 178.00 *(978-3-422-06797-4(3))* Deutscher Kunstverlag GmbH DEU. Dist: Independent Pubs. Group.

Sailstorfer, Michael. Michael Sailstorfer: 10000 Stones. 2008. (ENG., Illus.). 64p. pap. 36.00 *(978-3-86560-465-1(X))* Verlag der Buchhandlung Walther Konig DEU. Dist: D.A.P./Distributed Art Pubs.

Saletnik, Jeffrey & Schuldenfrei, Robin, eds. Bauhaus Construct: Fashioning Identity, Discourse & Modernism. 2009. (ENG., Illus.). 288p. (C). 165.00 *(978-0-415-77835-0(2))*; pap. 49.95 *(978-0-415-77836-7(0))* Routledge.

Sandkuhl, Kurt. Breitbandkommunikation Im Computergestützten Publizieren: Das Bilus-Projekt und Seine Ergebnisse. (Studien zur Wirtschaftsinformatik Ser.). (GER.). XVI, 239p. 210.00 ***(978-3-11-180749-2(5))*** De Gruyter, Walter Inc.

Saxton, Malcolm. Creme de la Crematorium. 2008. 60p. pap. 15.49 *(978-1-4389-0902-8(0))* AuthorHouse.

Schachner, Andreas. Bilder Eines Weltreichs: Kunst- und Kulturgeschichtliche Untersuchungen Zu Den Verzierungen Eines Tores Aus Balawat (Imgur-Enlil) Aus der Zeit Von Salmanassar III, Konig Von Assyrien. 2007. (Subartu Ser.). (Illus.). 354p. pap. 132.00 *(978-2-503-52437-5(0))* Brepols Pubs. BEL. Dist: Brown, David Bk. Co., The.

Schade, D. & Christl, Markus. Kacao77: The visual adventures of Kacao 77. 2008. (Illus.). 144p. pap. *(978-3-9809909-8-1(2))* Publikat Verlags- und Handels KG.

Schafhausen, Nicolaus & Gray, Zoe, eds. Cosima von Bonin: Source Book 9. 2011. (ENG., Illus.). 208p. pap. 15.00 *(978-90-73362-91-8(1))* Witte De With Centre for Contemporary Art NLD. Dist: D.A.P./Distributed Art Pubs.

Schaller, Matthias, photos by. Purple Desks, 1 vol. 2009. (ENG., Illus.). 72p. 49.90 *(978-3-86521-597-0(1))* Steidl, Gerhard Druckerei und Verlag DEU. Dist: Innovative Logistics.

Scheler, Max & Harder, Matthias, eds. The Essential Herbert List: Photographs 1930-1972. 2008. (Illus.). 327p. pap. *(978-3-8296-0349-2(5))* Schirmer/Mosel Verlag GmbH.

Schimpf, Simone, ed. & text. Konkret: Die Sammlung Heinz und Anette Teufel im Kunstmuseum Stuttgart / Concrete Art. The Heinz & Anette Teufel Collection in the Kunstmuseum Stuttgart. 2010. (ENG., Illus.). 308p. 60.00 *(978-3-7757-2419-7(2))* Hatje Cantz Verlag GmbH & Co KG DEU. Dist: D.A.P./Distributed Art Pubs.

Schink, Hans-Christian, photos by. Hans-Christian Schink. 2011. (ENG., Illus.). 180p. 75.00 ***(978-3-7757-2826-3(0))*** Hatje Cantz Verlag GmbH & Co KG DEU. Dist: D.A.P./Distributed Art Pubs.

Schink, Hans-Christian, photos by. Hans-Christian Schink: 1 h. 2011. (ENG., Illus.). 96p. 85.00 *(978-3-7757-2661-0(6))* Hatje Cantz Verlag GmbH & Co KG DEU. Dist: D.A.P./Distributed Art Pubs.

Schnetz, Salome, ed. Ai Weiwei: Fairytale: A Reader. 2012. (ENG., Illus.). 248p. pap. 34.95 ***(978-3-03764-210-8(6))*** JRP Ringier Kunstverlag AG CHE. Dist: D.A.P./Distributed Art Pubs.

Scholtz, Andrea. Models: Designculture in Germany. 2008. (GER & ENG.). 84p. 32.00 *(978-3-89986-106-8(X)*, Avedition Gmbh,Csi) Continental Sales, Inc.

Schreiber, Daniel, ed. & text. Thomas Florschuetz. Imperfekt. Werke 1997 - 2010. 2011. (GER & ENG., Illus.). 112p. 45.00 *(978-3-86560-855-0(8))* Verlag der Buchhandlung Walther Konig DEU. Dist: D.A.P./Distributed Art Pubs.

Schreier, Christian & Haldemann, Anita, eds. Rosemarie Trockel: Drawings, Collages, & Book Drafts. 2010. (ENG., Illus.). 164p. pap. 60.00 *(978-3-7757-2613-9(6))* Hatje Cantz Verlag GmbH & Co KG DEU. Dist: D.A.P./Distributed Art Pubs.

Schreier, Christoph. Karin Sander. (ENG & GER., Illus.). 64p. 19.95 *(978-3-89322-665-8(6))* Edition Cantz DEU. Dist: D.A.P./Distributed Art Pubs.

Schwenk, Bernhart & Gohlke, Gierret, texts. Albert Weis: Condition, 1 vol. 2008. (ENG., Illus.). 112p. (C). pap. 45.00 *(978-3-939738-65-7(4))* Verlag fur Moderne Kunst DEU. Dist: D.A.P./Distributed Art Pubs.

Seifermann, Ellen, et al, texts. André Butzer: Viele Tote im Heimatland: Fanta, Sprite, H-Milch, Micky und Donald! Gemälde/Paintings 1999-2008. 2010. (ENG., Illus.). 120p. 45.00 *(978-3-86678-297-6(7))* Kerber Verlag DEU. Dist: D.A.P./Distributed Art Pubs.

Seiffarth, Carsten. Singuhr 1996 - 2006: hoergalerie in parochial berlin. Seiffarth, Carsten, ed. 2011. (ENG., Illus.). 296p. 54.00 ***(978-3-939583-23-3(5))*** Kehrer Verlag Heidelberg, Klaus Kehrer DEU. Dist: Consortium Bk. Sales & Distribution.

Seippel, Ralf-P. Jürgen Schadeberg. 2008. (ENG., Illus.). 288p. 85.00 *(978-3-7757-2150-9(9))* Hatje Cantz Verlag GmbH & Co KG DEU. Dist: D.A.P./Distributed Art Pubs.

Seiwert, Wolf-Dieter. Jewellery from the Orient: Treasures from the Dr. Bir Collection. 2010. (ENG., Illus.). 320p. 85.00 *(978-3-89790-319-7(9))* Arnoldsche Art Pubs. DEU. Dist: Antique Collectors' Club.

Sendlinger, Marcus. Marcus Sendlinger: Lost Reality. 2011. (GER & ENG., Illus.). 48p. 34.95 ***(978-3-86678-450-5(3))*** Kerber Verlag DEU. Dist: D.A.P./Distributed Art Pubs.

Seyfarth, Ludwig, et al, texts. Thorsten Passfeld: It's Me Again. 2011. (ENG., Illus.). 128p. 39.95 *(978-3-86678-408-6(2))* Kerber Verlag DEU. Dist: D.A.P./Distributed Art Pubs.

Simon, Robert, ed. Ben Willikens: Counterspaces. (Illus.). 196p. 45.00 *(978-3-89322-954-3(X))* Edition Cantz DEU. Dist: D.A.P./Distributed Art Pubs.

Skrypzak, Joann M. Sporting Modernity. 2008. 336p. pap. *(978-3-8364-6533-5(7))* VDM Verlag Dr. Mueller e.K.

Slominski, Andreas. Andreas Slominski. 2010. (ENG., Illus.). 144p. 55.00 *(978-3-7757-2603-0(9))* Hatje Cantz Verlag GmbH & Co KG DEU. Dist: D.A.P./Distributed Art Pubs.

Smith, Jeffrey Chipps. The Art of the Goldsmith in Late Fifteenth-Century Germany: The Kimbell Virgin & Her Bishop. 2006. (Kimbell Masterpiece Ser.). (ENG., Illus.). 86p. pap. 16.95 *(978-0-300-11736-3(1))* Kimbell Art Museum.

—The Kimbell Virgin & Her Bishop: The Art of the Goldsmith in Late Fifteenth-Century Germany. 2006. (Kimbell Masterpiece Ser.). (Illus.). vii, 86p. *(978-0-912804-45-3(9))* Kimbell Art Museum.

Southcombe, George, ed. English Nonconformist Poetry, 1660-1700, 3 vols., Set. 2012. (ENG., Illus.). 1168p. 495.00 *(978-1-85196-965-4(9))* Pickering & Chatto Pubs., Ltd. GBR. Dist: Ashgate Publishing Co.

Spies, Werner. Max Ernst Dream & Revolution. Degel, Kirsten, ed. 2009. (ENG., Illus.). 256p. 60.00 *(978-3-7757-2235-3(1))* Hatje Cantz Verlag GmbH & Co KG DEU. Dist: D.A.P./Distributed Art Pubs.

Spinks, Jennifer. Monstrous Births & Visual Culture in Sixteenth-Century Germany, 1 vol. 2009. (Religious Cultures in the Early Modern World Ser.). (ENG., Illus.). 224p. 99.00 *(978-1-85196-630-1(7))* Pickering & Chatto Pubs., Ltd. GBR. Dist: Ashgate Publishing Co.

Starr, Figura. German Expressionism: The Graphic Impulse - Masterworks from the Museum of Modern Art. 2011. (ENG., Illus.). 288p. 60.00 *(978-0-87070-795-7(7))* Museum of Modern Art.

Stationen der Moderne. 175.00 *(978-3-88375-082-8(4))* Verlag der Buchhandlung Walther Konig DEU. Dist: D.A.P./Distributed Art Pubs.

Steinle, Christa, ed. Giulio Paolini: Da Oggi a Ieri. (ITA & GER., Illus.). 368p. 65.00 *(978-3-89322-357-2(6))* Edition Cantz DEU. Dist: D.A.P./Distributed Art Pubs.

Stemmrich, Gregor. Rita Mcbride: Public Works. 2010. (ENG.). 280p. pap. 55.00 *(978-3-8321-9156-6(9))* DuMont DEU. Dist: D.A.P./Distributed Art Pubs.

Stenschke, Jochen. Jochen Stenschke: Bilder im schwarzen Kasten. 2010. (ENG., Illus.). 96p. pap. 29.95 (978-3-86678-307-2(8)) Kerber Verlag DEU. Dist: D.A.P./Distributed Art Pubs.

Strasser, Josef. 50 Bauhaus Icons You Should Know. 2009. (Illus.). 176p. pap. 19.95 (978-3-7913-4196-5(0)) Prestel Publishing.

Stüttgen, Johannes, et al, texts. Joseph Beuys: Parallel Processes. 2010. (Illus.). 432p. 75.00 (978-3-8296-0482-6(3)) Schirmer/Mosel Verlag GmbH DEU. Dist: Prestel Publishing.

Style Needs No Color Staff, contrib. by. Schwarz auf Weiss II: Style Needs No Color. 2011. (ENG., Illus.). 128p. 29.95 (978-3-937946-06-1(3)) From Here To Fame GmbH DEU. Dist: SCB Distributors.

Taylor, Brandon. The Nazification of Art: Art, Design, Architecture, Music & Film in the Third Reich. (Illus.). 280p. pap. 24.95 (978-0-9506783-9-9(2)) Winchester Schl. of Art Pr. GBR. Dist: Paul & Co. Pubs. Consortium, Inc.

teNeues. AAD Berlin: Art Architecture Design. 2010. (Illus.). 168p. pap. 12.95 (978-3-8327-9433-0(6)) teNeues Publishing Co.

Tennigkeit, Alex. Usurper's Choice: Eine ausgewählte Sammlung von Kuriosen Gemälden, Zeichnungen und Opjekten 2006 - 2009. 2010. (ENG., Illus.). 104p. 49.95 (978-3-86678-179-5(2)) Kerber Verlag DEU. Dist: D.A.P./Distributed Art Pubs.

Thiel, Markus. Die Verwaltete Kunst: Rechtliche und Organisatorische Aspekte Öffentlicher Kulturverwaltung. (Europaische Hochschulschriften Ser.: Vol. 3583). (GER.). 325 S.p. 43.95 (978-3-631-50480-2(2)) Lang, Peter Publishing, Inc.

Turin, Ulrike. UlrikeTurin: Portrait und Selbstportrait. 2009. (GER., Illus.). 144p. (978-3-7774-9025-0(3)) Hirmer Verlag GmbH.

Uelsberg, Gabriele & Holthuis, Gabriele. Christoph Loos: Nann-Paradox. 2007. 148p. 49.95 (978-3-87909-891-0(3)) Wienand GmbH, Druck- & Verlagshaus DEU. Dist: Independent Pubs. Group.

Unverzart, Olaf, photos by. Olaf Unverzart: don't fade to grey. 2011. (GER & ENG., Illus.). 104p. 60.00 (978-3-86984-190-8(7)) Verlag fur Moderne Kunst DEU. Dist: D.A.P./Distributed Art Pubs.

Urbaschek, Stephan, ed. Fast Forward: Media Art - the Goetz Collection, 1 vol. 2006. (GER & ENG., Illus.). 532p. 60.00 (978-3-7757-1865-3(6)) Hatje Cantz Verlag GmbH & Co KG DEU. Dist: D.A.P./Distributed Art Pubs.

Van Buhren, Ralf. Die Werke der Barmherzigkeit in der Kunst des 12.-18. Jahrhunderts. Date not set. (Studien zur Kunstgeschichte Ser.: Bd. 115). (GER., Illus.). 424p. (978-3-487-10319-8(2)) Olms, Georg Verlag AG.

van Haaren, Bettina. Bettina van Haaren: Häutungen. Malerei und Zeichnung / Paintings & Drawings. 2010. (ENG., Illus.). 104p. 47.50 (978-3-86678-361-4(2)) Kerber Verlag DEU. Dist: D.A.P./Distributed Art Pubs.

Van Ravenswaay, Charles. The Arts & Architecture of German Settlements in Missouri: A Survey of a Vanishing Culture. 2nd ed. 2006. (ENG., Illus.). 576p. (C). 59.95 (978-0-8262-1700-4(1)) Univ. of Missouri Pr.

Vogt, Ernst. Das Leipziger Antikenmuseum und die griechische Literatur. (Lectiones Teubnerianae (LT) Ser.). (GER.). 58p. 210.00 (978-3-11-181303-5(7)) De Gruyter, Walter Inc.

Vogt, Margrit. Von Kunstworten und -werten: Die Entstehung der deutschen Kunstkritik in Periodika der Aufklärung. 2010. (Wolfenbütteler Studien zur Aufklärung Ser.). (GER., Illus.). VII, 364p. 112.00 (978-3-11-023318-6(5)) De Gruyter, Walter Inc.

Voigt, Jorinde. Jorinde Voigt: Nexus. 2011. (ENG., Illus.). 144p. pap. 55.00 (978-3-7757-2823-2(6)) Hatje Cantz Verlag GmbH & Co KG DEU. Dist: D.A.P./Distributed Art Pubs.

Voit, Robert, photos by. New Trees, 1 vol. 2011. (ENG., Illus.). 120p. 78.00 (978-3-86521-825-4(3)) Steidl, Gerhard Druckerei und Verlag DEU. Dist: Innovative Logistics.

Von Bismarck, Beatrice, ed. Games, Fights, Collaborations: Art & Culture Studies in the Nineties. (ENG & GER., Illus.). 244p. pap. 29.95 (978-3-89322-847-8(0)) Edition Cantz DEU. Dist: D.A.P./Distributed Art Pubs.

Von Brandenburg, Ulla & Nitsche, Frank. Sette Scene Di Nouva Pittura Germanica, 1 vol. 2007. (ENG, ITA & GER., Illus.). 88p. per. 34.95 (978-88-8158-608-0(8)) Charta ITA. Dist: D.A.P./Distributed Art Pubs.

Von Halasz, Joachim, ed. Hitler's Art 1937 - the Great German Art Exhibition 1937 in the House of German Art in Munich - Official Exhibition Catalogue / First Published As Gro. 2008. 200p. pap. (978-1-905742-09-7(6)) Foxley Books.

—Hitler's Art 1938 - the Great German Art Exhibition 1938 - in the House of German Art in Munich - Official Exhibition Catalogue / First Published As ' 2009. 192p. pap. (978-1-905742-22-6(3)) Foxley Books.

—Hitler's Art 1939 - the Great German Art Exhibition 1939 - in the House of German Art in Munich - Official Exhibition Catalogue / First Published As ' 2009. 212p. pap. (978-1-905742-23-3(1)) Foxley Books.

—Hitler's Day of German Art 1937 - First Published As 'Tag der Deutschen Kunst Mnnchen 1937' 2009. 52p. pap. (978-1-905742-20-2(7)) Foxley Books.

—Hitler's Day of German Art 1938 - the Programme of the Procession - First Published As 'Zweitausend Jahre Deutsche Kunst - Festzug Am Tag der Deutsche. 2009. 48p. pap. (978-1-905742-21-9(5)) Foxley Books.

—Hitler's Day of German Art 1939 / First Published As 'Tag der Deutschen Kunst 1939' 2008. 48p. pap. (978-1-905742-10-3(X)) Foxley Books.

—Hitler's Degenerate Art - the Exhibition Catalogue - First Published in 1937 As Entartete Kunst Austellungsnhrer' 2008. 48p. pap. (978-1-905742-08-0(8)) Foxley Books.

von Wittenau, Clementine Schack. Karl Schmoll von Eisenwerth (1879-1948) Paintings, Graphic Art, Glass Art. (GER., Illus.). 224p. 75.00 (978-3-925369-47-6(3)) Arnoldsche Art Pubs. DEU. Dist: Antique Collectors' Club.

Vorkoeper, Ute, ed. Anna Oppermann Ensembles 1968-1992, 1 vol. 2007. (ENG., Illus.). 288p. pap. 50.00 (978-3-7757-1995-7(4)) Hatje Cantz Verlag GmbH & Co KG DEU. Dist: D.A.P./Distributed Art Pubs.

Wachmann, Wiebke Maria. Spaces 98-03. 64p. (978-3-89955-063-4(3)) Die Gestalten Verlag.

Waldvogel, Florian, ed. Stefan Marx: I Guess I Shouldn't Be Telling You. 2011. (ENG., Illus.). 96p. 39.95 (978-3-03764-132-3(0)) JRP Ringier Kunstverlag AG CHE. Dist: D.A.P./Distributed Art Pubs.

Warhol, Andy. Cars: Andy Warhol, Sylvie Fleury, Robert Longo, Vincent Szarek. 2010. (ENG & GER., Illus.). 248p. 60.00 (978-3-7757-2582-8(2)) Hatje Cantz Verlag GmbH & Co KG DEU. Dist: D.A.P./Distributed Art Pubs.

Weber, Christianne. Schmuck der 20er und 30er Jahre in Deutschland. (GER., Illus.). 408p. 145.00 (978-3-925369-05-6(8)) Arnoldsche Art Pubs. DEU. Dist: Antique Collectors' Club.

Weikop, Christian. New Perspectives on Bruke Expressionism: Bridging History. 2011. (Illus.). 342p. 124.95 (978-1-4094-1203-8(2)) Ashgate Publishing Co.

Weiss, Jeffrey, text. The Helga & Walther Lauffs Collection Vol. 1, 1 vol. 2010. (ENG., Illus.). 416p. 175.00 (978-3-86521-850-6(4)) Steidl, Gerhard Druckerei und Verlag DEU. Dist: Innovative Logistics.

Westheider, Ortrud. Zwischen Himmel und Hölle: Kunst des Mittelalters von der Gotik bis Baldung Grien. Katalogbuch zur Ausstellung Hamburg 19.09.2009-10.01.2010 Bucerius Kunst Forum. Westheider, Ortrud & Philipp, Michael, eds. 2009. (GER., Illus.). 256p. (C). 64.00 (978-3-7774-2201-5(0)) Hirmer Verlag GmbH DEU. Dist: Brown, David Bk. Co., The.

Wiehager, Renate, ed. Art & Stars & Cars. 2011. (ENG., Illus.). 216p. pap. 50.00 (978-3-7757-3185-0(7)) Hatje Cantz Verlag GmbH & Co KG DEU. Dist: D.A.P./Distributed Art Pubs.

Willett, John. The Weimar Years: A Culture Cut Short. 2011. (ENG., Illus.). 160p. pap. 19.95 (978-0-500-27311-1(1), 527311) Thames & Hudson.

Williams, Gregory H. Permission to Laugh: Humor & Politics in Contemporary German Art. 2012. (ENG., Illus.). 248p. 49.00 (978-0-226-89895-7(4)) Univ. of Chicago Pr.

Wolbergs, Benjamin. Urban Illustration: Street Art City Guide Berlin. 2007. (Illus.). 359p. pap. 29.95 (978-1-58423-291-9(9)) Gingko Pr., Inc.

Wolf, Norbert. Dürer. 2010. (25 Ser.). (ENG.). 96p. 14.99 (978-3-8365-1348-7(X)) TASCHEN DEU. Dist: Ingram Pub. Services.

Wolf, Norbert & Lorenz, Ralph, eds. Brucke. 2008. (Basic Genre Ser.). (ENG., Illus.). 96p. pap. 9.99 (978-3-8228-5474-7(3)) TASCHEN DEU. Dist: Ingram Pub. Services.

Worringer, Christoph. Christoph Worringer. 2010. (ENG., Illus.). 170p. 45.00 (978-3-7757-2640-5(3)) Hatje Cantz Verlag GmbH & Co KG DEU. Dist: D.A.P./Distributed Art Pubs.

Wye, Deborah. Kirchner & the Berlin Street. 2008. (ENG., Illus.). 138p. 35.00 (978-0-87070-741-4(8)) Museum of Modern Art.

Wylie, Charles. Sigmar Polke: The Dream of Menelaus. 2011. (ENG., Illus.). 64p. pap. 19.95 (978-0-300-15900-4(5)) Dallas Museum of Art.

Young, Joan & Dillon, Brian. Julie Mehretu (New York) 2009. 45.00 (978-0-89207-406-8(X)) Guggenheim, Solomon R. Museum.

Zdenek. Thomas Helbig Homo Homini Lupus. 2008. (ENG., Illus.). 208p. 60.00 (978-3-7757-2164-6(9)) Hatje Cantz Verlag GmbH & Co KG DEU. Dist: D.A.P./Distributed Art Pubs.

Zern. Erik Niedling Formation. 2009. (ENG., Illus.). 96p. 45.00 (978-3-7757-2269-6(6)) Hatje Cantz Verlag GmbH & Co KG DEU. Dist: D.A.P./Distributed Art Pubs.

Zuffi, Stefano. Dürer: Masters of Art. 2012. (Illus.). 160p. pap. 12.95 (978-3-7913-4657-1(1)) Prestel Publishing.

Zybok, Oliver, text. Pietro Sanguineti. 2010. (ENG., Illus.). 136p. 45.00 (978-3-7757-2557-6(1)) Hatje Cantz Verlag GmbH & Co KG DEU. Dist: D.A.P./Distributed Art Pubs.

ART, GOTHIC

Alberino, Dawn. Cherries Journal. 2008. 200p. 38.38 (978-1-4357-5890-2(0)) Lulu Enterprises Inc.

American Art Association. Gothic & Renaissance Art: The Collection of the Late Thomas Fortune Ryan. 2011. 38p. 35.95 (978-1-258-02381-2(4)) Literary Licensing, LLC.

Becket-Griffith, Jasmine. Gothic Art Now. 2008. (ENG.). 192p. 29.95 (978-0-06-162699-9(6), Collins Design) HarperCollins Pubs.

Bednorz, Achim. Gothic: Architecture - Sculpture - Painting, 1 vol. Toman, Rolf, ed. 2011. (ENG.). 520p. 19.99 (978-3-8331-6007-3(1)) h.f.ullmann DEU. Dist: Innovative Logistics.

Brusen, Claus. Quadrant Fantasy. 2012. (ENG.). 96p. pap. 29.95 (978-87-992147-7-8(6)) Fantasmus-Art DNK. Dist: Independent Pubs. Group.

Charles, Victoria & Carl, Klaus H. Gothic Art. 2008. (Art of Century Ser.). (ENG., Illus.). 199p. 19.95 (978-1-84484-461-6(7)) Parkstone International GBR. Dist: Ingram Pub. Services.

Collas, I. Hans & Schandel, P., eds. Manuscrits de Louis de Bruges. 2010. (Manuscrits enlumines des anciens Pays-Bas Meridionaux Ser.). (FRE., Illus.). 347p. (C). 218.00 (978-2-7177-2396-0(X)) Brepols Pubs. BEL. Dist: ISD.

Cram101 Textbook Reviews. Outlines & Highlights for Gothic Art: Glorious Visions by Michael Camille, ISBN. 2011. 86p. pap. 27.95 (978-1-61812-401-2(3)) Cram101 Inc.

Delvoye, Wim. Knockin' on Heaven's Door. 2011. (FRE, DUT & ENG., Illus.). 240p. 70.00 (978-90-209-9248-9(1), Lannoo Pubs. (Acc)) Antique Collectors' Club GBR. Dist: National Bk. Network.

Folga-Januszewska, Dorota & Majewski, Lech. The Mystic Middle Ages. 2008. 160p. 50.00 (978-83-87730-59-8(9)) Bosz, Szymanik i wspolnicy POL. Dist: Independent Pubs. Group.

Fossi, Gloria. Romanesque & Gothic. 2008. (ENG., Illus.). 192p. pap. 14.95 (978-1-4027-5924-6(X)) Sterling Publishing Co., Inc.

Fryklund, C. Late-Gothic Flemish Wall Painting. 2011. (ENG., Illus.). 435p. (C). 160.00 (978-2-503-51237-2(2)) Brepols Pubs. BEL. Dist: ISD.

Iorio, Richard, 2nd. Colonial Gothic: The Grimoire. Carroll, Sean, ed. 2011. (Illus.). 120p. pap. 10.99 (978-0-9826598-5-4(7)) Rogue Games, Inc.

Jordan, Matt Dukes. Weirdo Noir. 2010. (ENG., Illus.). 192p. pap. 24.95 (978-0-8118-7110-5(5)) Chronicle Bks. LLC.

Kavka, Misha, et al, eds. Gothic NZ: The Darker Side of Kiwi Culture. 2006. (Illus.). 176p. (C). pap. 39.95 (978-1-877372-23-0(4)) Otago University Pr. NZL. Dist: International Specialized Bk. Services.

Lillich, Meredith Parsons. The Gothic Stained Glass of Reims Cathedral. 2011. (ENG.). 400p. 59.95 (978-0-271-03777-6(6)) Pennsylvania State Univ. Pr.

Martindale, Andrew. El Arte Gotico. (SPA., Illus.). 288p. 39.95 (978-84-233-2347-0(1), DE471) Ediciones Destino ESP. Dist: Continental Bk. Co., Inc.

Matheson, Susan B. & Churchill, Derek D. Modern Gothic: The Revival of Medieval Art. 2006. (ENG., Illus.). 96p. pap. 20.95 (978-0-89467-090-9(5)) Yale Univ. Art Gallery.

McDonald, Fiona. Gothic Knits. 2012. (ENG., Illus.). 80p. pap. 19.95 (978-1-84448-648-9(6)) Search Pr., Ltd. GBR. Dist: Independent Pubs. Group.

Mgle, Emile. The Gothic Image: Religious Art in France in the Thirteenth-Century. 2008. 456p. pap. 41.00 (978-1-59740-502-7(7)) ACLS Humanities E-Book.

Mohrmann, Karl & Eichwede, I. F. Gothic & Medieval Designs CD-ROM & Book. 2007. (Dover Electronic Clip Art Ser.). (Illus.). 48p. pap. 14.95 (978-0-486-99823-7(1)) Dover Pubns., Inc.

Opacic, Z. & Timmerman, A., eds. Architecture, Liturgy & Identity. 2011. (Studies in Gothic Art Ser.). (ENG., Illus.). 334p. (C). pap. 116.00 (978-2-503-53167-0(9)) Brepols Pubs. BEL. Dist: ISD.

—Image, Memory & Devotion. 2011. (Studies in Gothic Art Ser.). (ENG., Illus.). 287p. (C). pap. 116.00 (978-2-503-53168-7(7)) Brepols Pubs. BEL. Dist: ISD.

Pacht, O. Gothic Around 1400. 2006. (ENG.). (C). 174.00 (978-1-872501-14-7(1)) Miller, Harvey Pubs. GBR. Dist: Brown, David Bk. Co., The.

Puhle, Matthias. Aufbruch in die Gotik, 2 vols. 2009. (GER., Illus.). 1124p. (C). 135.00 (978-3-8053-4062-5(1)) Zabern, Philipp von Verlag, GmbH DEU. Dist: Brown, David Bk. Co., The.

Recht, Roland. Believing & Seeing: The Art of Gothic Cathedrals. Whittall, Mary, tr. from FRE. (ENG., Illus.). 392p. 2010. pap. 27.50 (978-0-226-70607-8(9)) 2008. 45.00 (978-0-226-70606-1(0)) Univ. of Chicago Pr.

Rudolph, Conrad, ed. A Companion to Medieval Art: Romanesque & Gothic in Northern Europe. 2010. (Blackwell Companions to Art History Ser.: 3). (ENG.). 704p. pap. 53.95 (978-1-4051-9878-3(8), Wiley-Blackwell) Wiley, John & Sons, Inc.

Sauerländer, Willibald. Gothic Art & Thought in the Later Medieval Period: Essays in Honor of Willibald Sauerländer. Hourihane, Colum, ed. 2011. (Index of Christian Art: Occasional Papers Ser.). (ENG.). 336p. pap. 35.00 (978-0-9768202-9-1(3)) Pennsylvania State Univ. Pr.

Schmidlin, Clemens & Gerner, Caroline Eva. Gothic, 1 vol. 2009. (ENG., Illus.). 288p. pap. 16.99 (978-3-8331-4936-8(1)) h.f.ullmann DEU. Dist: Innovative Logistics.

Smith, Harriet. Gothic Jewelry: 35 Unique Projects to Make, Give, & Wear. 2011. (ENG., Illus.). 128p. pap. 19.95 (978-1-907563-82-9(2)) CICO Bks. GBR. Dist: Ryland Peters & Small.

Toman, Rolf, ed. Gothic: Architecture, Sculpture, Painting. 2008. (Architecture Sculpture Painting Ser.). (Illus.). 520p. per. 24.95 (978-0-8416-0068-3(6)) American Map Corp.

Ullmann, H. F., ed. Art Pocket Gothic. 2009. (Art Pocket Ser.). 288p. 14.95 (978-0-8416-0349-3(9)) American Map Corp.

Weniger, Matthias, et al. Gothic. 2006. (Basic Art Ser.). (ENG., Illus.). 95p. pap. 9.99 (978-3-8228-5292-7(9)) TASCHEN DEU. Dist: Ingram Pub. Services.

ART, GRAPHIC

see Graphic Arts

ART, GRECO-ROMAN

Here are entered works on Roman art exhibiting strong Greek influence and produced almost exclusively by Greek artists, particularly in Italy until about 100 A.D.

The Art & History of Paestum. 80p. pap. (978-88-8029-077-3(0)) Casa Editrice Bonechi.

Tarbell, F. B. A History of Greek Art. 2008. 160p. 22.99 (978-0-554-37682-0(2)) 2008. 160p. 25.99 (978-0-554-28379-1(4)) 2007. (ENG.). 142p. pap. 18.99 (978-1-4346-5255-3(6)) 2007. (ENG.). 156p. pap. 21.99 (978-1-4346-5256-0(4)) BiblioBazaar.

—A History of Greek Art. 20.00 (978-0-8196-2014-9(9)) Biblo & Tannen Booksellers & Pubs., Inc.

Tarbell, Frank Bigelow. Illustrated Catalogue of Carbon Prints on the Rise & Progress of Greek & Roman Art. 2009. 108p. pap. 15.99 (978-1-103-49517-7(8)) BiblioBazaar.

Winckelmann. Schriften und Nachlass / Monumenti antichi inediti spiegati ed illustrati. Roma 1767. Borbein & Kunze, eds. 2011. (Schriften und Nachlass Ser.). (GER & ITA., Illus.). 622p. (C). 123.00 (978-3-8053-4193-6(8)) Zabern, Philipp von Verlag, GmbH DEU. Dist: Brown, David Bk. Co., The.

ART, GREEK

see also Art, Cretan; Art, Greco-Roman; Art, Mycenaean

Albersmeier, Sabine. The Art of Ancient Greece. 2008. (ENG., Illus.). 176p. 47.00 (978-0-85667-643-7(8)) Wilson, Philip Pubs., Ltd. GBR. Dist: Macmillan.

—The Art of Ancient Greece. 2007. (Illus.). 206p. pap. (978-0-911886-69-6(9)) Walters Art Museum, US.

—The Art of Ancient Greece: The Walters Art Museum. 2008. (ENG., Illus.). 176p. pap. 27.95 (978-0-85667-646-8(2)) Wilson, Philip Pubs., Ltd. GBR. Dist: Macmillan.

Albersmeier, Sabine & Anderson, Michael J. Heroes: Mortals & Myths in Ancient Greece. 2009. pap. (978-0-911886-73-3(7)) Walters Art Museum, US.

Anderson, H. T. Codex Sinaiticus: the H. T. Anderson New Testament. 2010. 600p. pap. 35.65 (978-0-557-27476-5(1)) Lulu Enterprises Inc.

Bartsch, Tatjana, et al, eds. Das Originale der Kopie: Kopien als Produkte und Medien der Transformation von Antike. 2010. (Transformationen der Antike Ser.).Tr. of Originality of Copies. (GER., Illus.). VIII, 349p. 112.00 (978-3-11-022544-0(1)) De Gruyter, Walter Inc.

Bonn, Landschaftsverband Rheinland / LVR-LandesMuseum, ed. Alter in der Antike: Die Blüte des Alters aber ist die Weisheit. 2009. (GER., Illus.). 192p. (C). 38.00 (978-3-8053-3979-7(8)) Zabern, Philipp von Verlag, GmbH DEU. Dist: Brown, David Bk. Co., The.

Bravo García, A., et al. The Legacy of Bernard de Montfaucon: Three Hundred Years of Studies on Greek Handwriting: Proceedings of the Seventh International Colloquium of Greek Palaeography (Madrid-Salamanca, 15-20 September 2008), 2 vols. 2010. (ITA, GRE, FRE, GER & SPA., Illus.). 938p. (C). 247.00 (978-2-503-53520-3(8)) Brepols Pubs. BEL. Dist: ISD.

Campbell, Gordon. The Grove Encyclopedia of Classical Art & Architecture, 2 vols. 2007. (ENG., Illus.). 1600p. 345.00 (978-0-19-530082-6(3)) Oxford Univ. Pr., Inc.

Carpenter, Rhys. Greek Art: A Study of the Formal Evolution of Style. 2011. 256p. 47.95 (978-1-258-10300-2(1)) Literary Licensing, LLC.

Charles Thomas, Newton. Essays on Art & Archaeology. 2010. (Cambridge Library Collection - Archaeology Ser.). (ENG., Illus.). 500p. pap. 37.99 (978-1-108-01741-1(X)) Cambridge Univ. Pr.

Clair, Jean. Picasso & Greece. 2006. (ENG., Illus.). 136p. 85.00 (978-88-422-1271-3(7)) Allemandi, Umberto & Co. GBR. Dist: Antique Collectors' Club.

Cohen, Ada. Art in the Era of Alexander the Great: Paradigms of Manhood & Their Cultural Traditions. 2010. (ENG., Illus.). 422p. (C). 95.00 (978-0-521-76904-4(3)) Cambridge Univ. Pr.

Coltman, Viccy. Making Sense of Greek Art. 2012. (Illus.). 272p. 95.00 (978-0-85989-830-0(X)) Univ. of Exeter Pr. GBR. Dist: Chicago Distribution Ctr.

Der Nessessian, Sirarpie. Two Slavonic Parallels of the Greek Tetraevangelia: Paris 74. 2010. 86.48 (978-1-61143-262-6(6)) Gorgias Pr., LLC.

Dierichs, Angelika. Erotik in der Kunst Griechenlands: Zaberns Bildbände zur Archäologie. Sonderbände der antiken Welt. 2008. (GER., Illus.). 151p. 45.00 (978-3-8053-3834-9(1)) Zabern, Philipp von Verlag, GmbH DEU. Dist: Brown, David Bk. Co., The.

Fairbanks, Arthur. Greek Gods & Heroes As Represented in. 2006. pap. 18.95 (978-1-4286-6110-3(7)) Kessinger Publishing, LLC.

Fowler, Harold & Wheeler, James. A Handbook of Greek Archeology. 25.00 (978-0-8196-2009-5(2)) Biblo & Tannen Booksellers & Pubs., Inc.

Gallazzi, Claudio. Intorno Al Papiro Di Artemidoro: Atti Del Convegno Internazionale Del 15 Novembre 2008 Presso la Scuola Normale Superiore Di Pisa. 2009. (ITA, GER & ENG.). (978-88-7916-422-1(8)) LED Edizioni Universitarie.

Gardner, Ernest A. Religion & Art in Ancient Greece. 2007. 68p. per. (978-1-4065-2758-2(0)) Dodo Pr.

Gardner, Ernest Arthur. Religion & Art in Ancient Greece. 2010. (ENG.). 140p. pap. 20.75 (978-1-176-94007-9(4)) BiblioBazaar.

—Religion & Art in Ancient Greece. 2010. (Illus.). 40p. pap. 14.14 (978-1-153-75484-2(3)) General Bks. LLC.

Gere, Cathy. Knossos & the Prophets of Modernism. 2011. (Illus.). 288p. pap. 18.00 (978-0-226-28954-0(0)) Univ. of Chicago Pr.

Gerstel, Sharon E. J. Beholding the Sacred Mysteries: Programs of the Byzantine Sanctuary. 2009. 226p. 34.00 (978-1-59740-724-3(0)); pap. 22.00 (978-1-59740-746-5(1)) ACLS Humanities E-Book.

Goette, Hans Rupprecht & Palagia, Olga, eds. Sailing to Classical Greece: Papers on Greek Art, Archaeology & Epigraphy Presented to Petros Themelis. 2011. (ENG, ITA, FRE & GER., Illus.). 120p. (C). pap. 50.00 (978-1-84217-422-7(3)) Oxbow Bks., Ltd. GBR. Dist: Brown, David Bk. Co., The.

Gröschel, Sepp-Gustav & Wrede, Henning, eds. Ernst Curtius' Vorlesung 'Griechische Kunstgeschichte' Nach der Mitschrift Wilhelm Gurlitts im Winter 1864/65. (Transformationen der Antike Ser.).Tr. of Ernst Curtius's Lecture the History of Greek Art. (GER.). VI, 491p. 2011. 168.00 (978-3-11-174531-2(7)) 2010. (Illus.). 112.00 (978-3-11-022878-6(5)) De Gruyter, Walter Inc.

Gunter, Ann. Greek Art & the Orient. 2009. (ENG., Illus.). 272p. 92.00 (978-0-521-83257-1(8)) Cambridge Univ. Pr.

Gunter, Ann C. Greek Art & the Orient. 2012. (ENG., Illus.). 272p. (C). pap. 32.99 (978-0-521-18299-7(9)) Cambridge Univ. Pr.

Harrison, Jane Ellen. Introductory Studies in Greek Art. 2010. (Cambridge Library Collection - Classics Ser.). (Illus.). 352p. pap. 29.99 (978-1-108-01208-9(6)) Cambridge Univ. Pr.

Hart, Mary Louise. The Art of Ancient Greek Theater. 2010. (Illus.). 176p. 50.00 (978-1-60606-037-7(6), J. Paul Getty Museum) Getty Pubns.

Hawes, Harriet. A Gift of Themistocles: The Ludovisi Throne & the Boston Relief. 2009. pap. 19.96 *(978-1-60724-450-9(0))* Gorgias Pr., LLC.
Iozzi, Mario. Greece. (Illus.). 192p. pap. 18.95 *(978-88-8029-435-1(0))* Casa Editrice Bonechi ITA. Dist: CPG Publishing, Inc.
J. Paul Getty Museum Staff, contrib. by. The Antiquities Collection. 2nd ed. 2010. *(978-0-89236-997-3(3),* J. Paul Getty Museum) Getty Pubns.
Jackson, Monica M., contrib. by. Hellenistic Gold Eros Jewellery Style, Technique Chronology. 2006. (BAR International Ser.: Vol. 1510). (ENG., Illus.). 240p. (C). pap. 142.50 *(978-1-84171-944-3(7))* British Archaeological Reports Ltd. GBR. Dist: Brown, David Bk. Co., The.
Jacobson, David. The Hellenistic Paintings of Marisa. 2007. (Palestine Exploration Fund Annuals Ser.). (ENG., Illus.). 260p. (C). 120.00 *(978-1-904350-98-9(4))* Maney Publishing GBR. Dist: Brown, David Bk. Co., The.
Jay Hambidge. Dynamic Symmetry: The Greek Vase. 2007. 192p. per. 12.95 *(978-1-60386-037-6(1),* Merchant Bks.) Rough Draft Printing.
Johnson, Robert Bowie. Noah in Ancient Greek Art. 2007. (ENG.). 112p. pap. 11.95 *(978-0-9705438-4-4(0))* Solving Light Bks.
Junker, Klaus. Interpreting the Images of Greek Myths: An Introduction. 2011. (ENG., Illus.). 240p. (C). 95.00 ***(978-0-521-89582-8(0))*** Cambridge Univ. Pr.
Kaltsas, Nikolaos, ed. Athens-Sparta. 2006. (ENG., Illus.). 319p. (C). pap. 30.00 *(978-0-9776598-1-4(X))* Onassis, Alexander S. Public Benefit Foundation (US).
Kentridge, William. William Kentridge: Lexicon. 2011. (ENG., Illus.). 160p. 40.00 ***(978-0-9797642-4-0(6))*** A.S.A.P.
Kistler, Erich. Funktionalisierte Keltenbilder: Die Indienstnahme der Kelten Zur Vermittlung Von Normen und Werten in der Hellenistischen Welt. 2010. (GER., Illus.). 432p. (C). 120.00 ***(978-3-938032-36-7(7))*** Antike, Verlag, e.K. DEU. Dist: ISD.
Koons, Jeff, ed. Skin Fruit: A View of a Collection. 2012. (ENG., Illus.). 92p. pap. 25.00 ***(978-1-935202-77-6(4))*** Deste Foundation GRC. Dist: D.A.P./Distributed Art Pubs.
Kounellis, Jannis. Kounellis. 2011. (ENG & ITA., Illus.). 132p. 40.00 *(978-88-366-1801-9(4))* Silvana ITA. Dist: D.A.P./Distributed Art Pubs.
Koutsomallis, Kyriakos. Ancient Greece & Masson: The Goulandris Foundation. 2007. (ENG., Illus.). 180p. 60.00 *(978-88-422-1497-7(3))* Allemandi, Umberto & Co. GBR. Dist: Antique Collectors' Club.
Kraus, Chris, et al, eds. Visualizing the Tragic: Drama, Myth, & Ritual in Greek Art & Literature; Essays in Honour of Froma Zeitlin. 2007. (ENG., Illus.). 480p. 175.00 *(978-0-19-927602-8(1))* Oxford Univ. Pr., Inc.
Künzl-Snodgrass, Annemarie & Snodgrass, Anthony, trs. from GER. Interpreting the Images of Greek Myths: An Introduction. 2011. (ENG., Illus.). 240p. (C). pap. 32.99 ***(978-0-521-72007-6(9))*** Cambridge Univ. Pr.
Kurtz, Donna & Sparkes, Brian, eds. The Eye of Greece: Studies in the Art of Athens. 2010. (ENG.). 264p. pap. 32.99 *(978-0-521-12840-7(4))* Cambridge Univ. Pr.
Langdon, Susan. Art & Identity in Dark Age Greece, 1100-700 BC. 2010. (ENG., Illus.). 408p. pap. 45.00 *(978-0-521-17192-2(X))* Cambridge Univ. Pr.
Lowenstam, Steven. As Witnessed by Images: The Trojan War Tradition in Greek & Etruscan Art. 2008. (ENG., Illus.). 248p. (gr. 17). 52.00 *(978-0-8018-8775-5(5))* Johns Hopkins Univ. Pr.
Mahaffy, John Pentland. Rambles & Studies in Greece. 2009. 248p. pap. 21.89 *(978-1-150-69660-2(5))* General Bks. LLC.
—Rambles & Studies in Greece. 2007. (ENG.). 500p. 53.95 *(978-0-548-34708-9(5));* per. 38.95 *(978-0-548-28623-5(9))* Kessinger Publishing, LLC.
Maltomini, Francesca. Tradizione Antologica Dell'epigramma Greco: Le Sillogi Minori Di Età Bizantina e Umanistica. 2008. (ITA., Illus.). 214p. *(978-88-8498-480-7(7))* Storia e Letteratura.
Matsela, Virginia, et al. He Hellenike Kasela. 2010. (GRE & GER., Illus.). 296p. (C). 90.00 ***(978-960-6878-12-1(0))*** Kapon, Ekdoseis GRC. Dist: ISD.
Mertens, Joan R. How to Read Greek Vases. 2011. (ENG., Illus.). 176p. pap. 25.00 *(978-0-300-15523-5(9))* Yale Univ. Pr.
Minns, Ellis Hovell. Scythians & Greeks: A Survey of Ancient History & Archaeology on the North Coast of the Euxine from the Danube to the Caucasus. 2011. (Cambridge Library Collection - Archaeology Ser.). (Illus.). 820p. pap. 53.00 *(978-1-108-02487-7(4))* Cambridge Univ. Pr.
Muth, Susanne. Gewalt im Bild: Das Phänomen der medialen Gewalt im Athen des 6. und 5. Jahrhunderts v. Chr. 2008. (Image & Context Ser.: Vol. 1). (GER., Illus.). XVI, 800p. 147.00 *(978-3-11-018420-4(6))* De Gruyter, Walter Inc.
Neer, Richard T. Greek Art & Archaeology: A New History, C. 2500-C. 150 BCE. 2011. (ENG., Illus.). 400p. (C). pap. 80.00 net. ***(978-0-500-28877-1(1),*** 528877) Thames & Hudson.
Palagia, Olga, ed. Art in Athens During the Peloponnesian War. 2009. (ENG., Illus.). 302p. (C). 90.00 *(978-0-521-84933-3(0))* Cambridge Univ. Pr.
Parke-Bernet Galleries. Egyptian, Greek & Roman Antiquities, Ancient Glass, Gothic & Renaissance Furniture & Works of Art. 2011. 158p. 41.95 ***(978-1-258-07381-7(1))*** Literary Licensing, LLC.
Pater, Walter. Greek Studies: A Series of Essays. Lt. ed. 2006. (ENG.). 176p. pap. 21.99 *(978-1-4264-1058-1(1))* BiblioBazaar.
—Greek Studies: A Series of Essays. 2006. pap. *(978-1-84702-407-7(6))* Echo Library.
Pedley, John Griffiths. Greek Art & Archaeology. 5th ed. 2011. (ENG., Illus.). 400p. (C). pap. 112.00 *(978-0-205-00133-0(5),* Prentice Hall) Prentice Hall PTR.
Perrone, Serena. Comoedia et Mimus. XXXI, 148p. 344.00 ***(978-3-11-185405-2(1))*** De Gruyter, Walter Inc.
Perrone, Serena. Comoedia Et Mimus, Vol. 4. 2009. (Illus.). XXXI, 148p. 210.00 *(978-3-11-021459-6(8))* De Gruyter, Walter Inc.
Phillips, Lisa, text. Skin Fruit. 2010. (ENG., Illus.). 208p. pap. 45.00 *(978-1-935202-19-6(7))* New Museum of Contemporary Art, The.
Picon, Carlos A., et al. Art of the Classical World in the Metropolitan Museum of Art: Greece - Cyprus - Etruria - Rome. 2007. (ENG., Illus.). 520p. 75.00 *(978-0-300-12031-8(1))* Yale Univ. Pr.
Platt, Verity. Facing the Gods: Epiphany & Representation in Graeco-Roman Art, Literature & Religion. 2011. (Greek Culture in the Roman World Ser.). (ENG., Illus.). 500p. 130.00 *(978-0-521-86171-7(3))* Cambridge Univ. Pr.
Posamentir, Richard. Chersonesan Studies 1: The Polychrome Grave Stelai from the Early Hellenistic Necropolis. 2010. (ENG., Illus.). 510p. 75.00 *(978-0-292-72312-2(1))* Univ. of Texas Pr.
Pottier, Edmond. Douris & the Painters of Greek Vases. Kahnweiler, Bettina, tr. (Illus.). 115p. reprint ed. 30.00 *(978-0-89241-431-4(6))* Caratzas, Aristide D. Pub.
—Douris & the Painters of Greek Vases. Kahnweiler, Bettina, tr. 2008. 160p. 36.95 *(978-1-4369-0556-5(7));* pap. 21.95 *(978-1-4368-2530-6(X))* Kessinger Publishing, LLC.
Rhodes. 128p. pap. *(978-88-8029-465-8(2))* Casa Editrice Bonechi.
Richardson, Bessie E. Old Age among the Ancient Greeks. (Illus.). reprint ed. 42.50 *(978-0-404-05289-8(4))* AMS Pr., Inc.
Rodgers, Nigel. The Art & Architecture of Ancient Greece: An Illustrated Account of Classical Greek Buildings, Sculptures & Paintings, Shown in 200 Glorious Photographs & Drawings. 2012. (ENG., Illus.). 128p. pap. 17.99 ***(978-1-84476-802-8(3))*** Anness Publishing GBR. Dist: National Bk. Network.
Rodgers, Nigel. Greek World: The Acient People & Places. 2010. (ENG., Illus.). 256p. 35.00 *(978-0-7548-1774-1(1))* Anness Publishing GBR. Dist: National Bk. Network.
Ruskin, John. The Queen of the Air. 2009. 224p. 23.99 *(978-1-103-33145-1(0))* 2009. 224p. pap. 17.99 *(978-1-103-33142-0(6))* 2008. 144p. 21.99 *(978-0-554-33640-4(5))* 2008. 144p. 24.99 *(978-0-554-24337-5(7))* BiblioBazaar.
—The Queen of the Air. 2007. (ENG.). 120p. per. *(978-1-4065-6374-0(9))* Dodo Pr.
—The Queen of the Air. 2008. pap. *(978-1-84830-060-6(3),* Wildhern Pr.) Echo Library.
—The Queen of the Air: Being a Study of the Greek Myths of Cloud & Storm. 2009. 192p. 22.99 *(978-1-103-66018-6(7))* 2009. 192p. pap. 16.99 *(978-1-103-66012-4(8))* 2009. 192p. 22.99 *(978-1-103-38568-3(2))* 2009. 192p. pap. 16.99 *(978-1-103-38565-2(8))* 2007. 128p. pap. 18.99 *(978-1-4264-6203-0(4))* 2006. (ENG.). 140p. pap. 19.99 *(978-1-4264-6258-0(1))* BiblioBazaar.
Scheps, Marc & Kounellis, Jannis. Jannis Kounellis: XXII Stations on an Odyssey 1969-2010. 2010. (Illus.). 360p. 120.00 *(978-3-7913-5012-7(9))* Prestel Verlag GmbH & Co KG. DEU. Dist: Prestel Publishing.
Schlegelmilch, Sabine. Bürger, Gott und Götterschützling: Kinderbilder der hellenistischen Kunst und Literatur. 2009. (Beiträge zur Altertumskunde Ser.).Tr. of Citizens, God & God's Chosen Ones. Portrayals of Children in Hellenistic Art & Literature. (GER., Illus.). VIII, 311p. 140.00 *(978-3-11-021765-0(1))* De Gruyter, Walter Inc.
Schultz, Peter & Von Den Hoff, Ralf, eds. Early Hellenistic Portraiture: Image, Style, Context. 2007. (ENG., Illus.). 312p. 99.99 *(978-0-521-86659-0(6))* Cambridge Univ. Pr.
Seemann, O. The Mythology of Greece & Rome with Special Reference to Its Use in Art 1896. Bianchi, G. H., ed. 2007. (ENG.). 310p. 45.95 *(978-0-548-05370-6(7))* Kessinger Publishing, LLC.
Seifert, Martina. Aphrodite: Herrin des Krieges, Göttin der Liebe. Seifert, Martina, ed. 2009. (GER., Illus.). 141p. (C). 45.00 *(978-3-8053-3942-1(9))* Zabern, Philipp von Verlag, GmbH DEU. Dist: Brown, David Bk. Co., The.
Shapiro, H. A. Worshiping Women: Ritual & Reality in Classical Athens. 2008. (ENG., Illus.). 367p. (C). pap. 35.00 *(978-0-9776598-4-5(4))* Onassis, Alexander S. Public Benefit Foundation (US).
Shepard, Katharine. The Fish-Tailed Monster in Greek & Etruscan Art. 2011. 156p. pap. 24.95 ***(978-1-61646-074-7(1))*** Coachwhip Pubns.
Smith, Amy Claire. Polis & Personification in Classical Athenian Art. 2011. (Illus.). xiv, 202p. ***(978-90-04-19417-5(7))*** BRILL.
Smith, Tyler Jo & Plantzos, Dimitris, eds. A Companion to Greek Art. 2012. (Blackwell Companions to the Ancient World Ser.: 90). (ENG.). 892p. 350.00 ***(978-1-4051-8604-9(6),*** Wiley-Blackwell) Wiley, John & Sons, Inc.
Snodgrass, Anthony M. Narration & Allusion in Archaic Greek Art. (ENG., Illus.). 23p. (C). pap. 7.00 *(978-0-904920-08-6(9))* Brown, David Bk. Co., The.
Spanos, Apostolos. Codex Lesbiacus Leimonos. 11th ed. 2010. (Byzantinisches Archiv Ser.). (ENG, MUS & GEC., Illus.). XXIX, 452p. 238.00 *(978-3-11-022129-9(2))* De Gruyter, Walter Inc.
Sparkes, Brian A. Greek Art. 2nd ed. 2011. (New Surveys in the Classics Ser.). (ENG., Illus.). 190p. pap. 27.99 ***(978-1-107-60150-5(9))*** Cambridge Univ. Pr.
Stansbury-O'Donnell, Mark D. Looking at Greek Art. 2010. (ENG., Illus.). (C). 300p. pap. 27.99 *(978-0-521-12557-4(X));* 268p. 90.00 *(978-0-521-11038-9(6))* Cambridge Univ. Pr.
Stewart, Andrew. Classical Greece & the Birth of Western Art. 2008. (ENG., Illus.). 376p. (C). 90.00 *(978-0-521-85321-7(4))* Cambridge Univ. Pr.
Stewart, Andrew & Stewart, Andrew F. Classical Greece & the Birth of Western Art. 2008. (ENG., Illus.). 376p. (C). pap. 28.99 *(978-0-521-61835-9(5))* Cambridge Univ. Pr.
Tanner, Jeremy. The Invention of Art History in Ancient Greece: Religion, Society & Artistic Rationalisation. 2009. (Cambridge Classical Studies). (ENG., Illus.). 347p. pap. 47.00 *(978-0-521-11422-6(5))* Cambridge Univ. Pr.
Tarbell, F. B. A History of Greek Art. 2007. (ENG.). 298p. 43.95 *(978-0-548-02508-6(8))* Kessinger Publishing, LLC.
Tarbell, Frank Bigelow. Illustrated Catalogue of Carbon Prints on the Rise & Progress of Greek & Roman Art. 2009. 108p. pap. 15.99 *(978-1-103-49517-7(8))* BiblioBazaar.
Thomsen, Arne. Die Wirkung der Götter: Bilder Mit Flügelfiguren auf Griechischen Vasen des 6. und 5. Jahrhunderts V. Chr. (Image & Context Ser.).Tr. of Impact of the Gods. (GER.). XII, 506p. 2012. (gr. 17). E-Book 210.00 ***(978-3-11-219164-4(1))*** 2011. (Illus.). 140.00 ***(978-3-11-023898-3(5))*** De Gruyter, Walter Inc.
Vogt, Ernst. Das Leipziger Antikenmuseum und die griechische Literatur. (Lectiones Teubnerianae (LT) Ser.). (GER.). 58p. 210.00 ***(978-3-11-181303-5(7))*** De Gruyter, Walter Inc.
Waldstein, Charles. The Earliest Hellenic Art & Civilization & the Argive Heraeum. 2009. pap. 20.08 *(978-1-60724-492-9(6))* Gorgias Pr., LLC.
Winckelmann. Schriften und Nachlass / Monumenti antichi inediti spiegati ed illustrati. Roma 1767. Borbein & Kunze, eds. 2011. (Schriften und Nachlass Ser.). (GER & ITA., Illus.). 622p. (C). 123.00 ***(978-3-8053-4193-6(8))*** Zabern, Philipp von Verlag, GmbH DEU. Dist: Brown, David Bk. Co., The.

ART, GUATEMALAN

Aoyama, Kazuo. Elite Craft Producers, Artists, & Warriors at Aguateca: Lithic Analysis. 2009. (ENG., Illus.). 224p. 60.00 *(978-0-87480-959-6(2))* Univ. of Utah Pr.
Greene, David B. The Imagining of Community in the Arts of Guatemala: Weaving, Folk Tales, Marimba Performance, Contemporary Painting. 2010. (Illus.). viii, 182p. *(978-0-7734-1311-5(1))* Mellen, Edwin Pr., The.

ART, HAITIAN

Bloom, Minerva. Every Shade the Garden: Bilingual Haiga. 2010. 100p. pap. 34.00 *(978-0-557-33128-4(5))* Lulu Enterprises Inc.
Polk, Patrick Arthur. Haitian Vodou Flags. 2010. (Folk Art & Artists Ser.). (ENG.). 72p. (C). pap. 30.00 *(978-1-61703-017-8(1))* Univ. Pr. of Mississippi.

ART, HINDU

see Hindu Art

ART, HISPANIC AMERICAN

see Hispanic American Art

ART, HITTITE

Ward, William. The Hittite Gods in Hittite Art. 2009. pap. 20.68 *(978-1-60724-489-9(6))* Gorgias Pr., LLC.

ART, HUNGARIAN

Ackermann, Rita, et al. Rita Ackermann. 2011. (ENG., Illus.). 224p. 65.00 *(978-0-8478-3664-2(9))* Rizzoli International Pubns., Inc.
Baki, Péter, et al. Hungarian Photography in the Twentieth Century: Brassaï, Capa, Kertész, Moholy-Nagy, Munkácsi. 2011. (ENG., Illus.). 248p. 65.00 *(978-1-905711-76-5(X))* Royal Academy of Arts GBR. Dist: Hachette Bk. Group.
Farbaky, Peter & Waldman, Louis A., eds. Italy & Hungary: Humanism & Art in the Early Renaissance. Acts of an International Conference, Florence, Villa I Tatti, June 6-8 2007. 2011. (Villa I Tatti Ser.). (Illus.). 772p. 85.00 *(978-0-674-06346-4(5))* Villa I Tatti.
Komiss, Peter. Attachment 1967-2008. 2010. (ENG.). 288p. 75.00 *(978-963-227-167-5(X))* Univ. of New Mexico Pr.
Krempel, Ulrich, text. Gia Edzgveradze: Welcome Foam - Farewell Human. 2010. (ENG., Illus.). 288p. pap. 60.00 *(978-3-7757-2396-1(X))* Hatje Cantz Verlag GmbH & Co KG DEU. Dist: D.A.P./Distributed Art Pubs.
Kürti, Emese. Bukarest-Budapest Híd: Kortárs Román és Magyar Muvészet: Hunya Gábor Gyujteménye. 2010. (HUN & ENG., Illus.). 216p. 24.95 ***(978-963-9731-89-9(7))*** Vince Kiado Kft HUN. Dist: Independent Pubs Group.
Legrady, Kata & Rosenberg, David, eds. Kata Legrady: Bombs & Candies. 2011. (ENG., Illus.). 80p. 75.00 *(978-88-572-0860-2(5))* Skira Editore ITA. Dist: Random Hse., Inc.
Moholy-Nagy, Laszlo, photos by. Laszlo Moholy-Nagy: the Art of Light. 2010. (ENG., Illus.). 256p. 55.00 *(978-84-92841-34-9(6))* La Fabrica ESP. Dist: D.A.P./Distributed Art Pubs.
Szivos, Erika. Social History of Fine Arts in Hungary, 1867-1918. 2011. (ENG.). 300p. (gr. 17). 60.00 *(978-0-88033-670-3(6))* Eastern European Monographs.
Westheider, Ortrud. Sturz in die Welt: Die Kunst des Manierismus in Europa. Mit Beiträgen von Szilvia Bodnár, Eszter Ágnes Czoma, Anna Ecsedy, Ildikó Ember, Miklós Gálos, Zsuzsa Gonda, Annamária Gosztola, Zoltán Kárpáti, Szilárd Papp, Manga Pattantyús, Michael Philipp, Judit Sebö, Miriam Szöcs, Júlia Tátrai, Vilmos Tátrai, Michael Thimann und Axel Vécsey. Phillip, Michael- & Westheider, Ortrus, eds. 2008. (GER., Illus.). 216p. (C). 55.00 *(978-3-7774-4455-0(3))* Hirmer Verlag GmbH DEU. Dist: Brown, Davic Bk. Co., The.

ART, ICELANDIC

Icepick: Icelandic Street Art. 2007. (Illus.). 220p. 29.95 *(978-1-58423-224-7(2))* Gingko Pr., Inc.
Paravicini, Flurina and Gianni, ed. Dieter Roth: Tears in Lucerne. 2011. (ENG., Illus.). 128p. pap. 29.00 *(978-3-907474-83-9(X))* Periferia, Edizioni, Poschiavo / Lucerna CHE. Dist: D.A.P./Distributed Art Pubs.

ART, IMMORAL

see Erotic Art

ART, INDIAN

see Indian Art

ART, INDIC

Adajania, Nancy, ed. Shilpa Gupta. 2010. (Illus.). 248p. 60.00 *(978-3-7913-5017-2(X))* Prestel Publishing.
Albanese, Marilia. Archaeology: Northern India. 2008. (White Star Guides). (ENG., Illus.). 168p. pap. 18.95 *(978-88-544-0041-2(6))* White Star ITA. Dist: Random Hse., Inc.
Andersen, Hans Christian. The Flight of the Mermaid. 2009. (ENG., Illus.). 32p. (gr. 2-4). 29.95 *(978-81-906756-0-4(5))* Tara Publishing IND. Dist: Perseus-PGW.
Arastu, Salma. The Lyrical Line: Embracing All & Flowing. Hinh, Angie, ed. 2008. (Illus.). 104p. 45.00 *(978-0-9719552-9-5(8),* Half Full Pr.) Source Bk. Pubns.
Bapat, Madhuri. New Improved-RangoLee-A Step by Step Learning Book. 2009. pap. 20.00 *(978-1-61658-260-9(X))* Independent Pub.
Bharadwaj, Monisha. India Style. (Illus.). 160p. pap. 32.95 *(978-1-85626-495-2(5))* Cathie, Kyle Ltd. GBR. Dist: Graphic Arts Ctr. Publishing Co.
Bisvasa, Bidhana. Solasilpa. 2008. (BEN., Illus.). 62p. *(978-81-89956-02-8(7))* Folk & Tribal Cultural Centre.
Blacker, J. F. Abc of Indian Art. 2006. pap. 33.95 *(978-1-4286-5868-4(8))* Kessinger Publishing, LLC.
Burgess, Jas. Buddhist Art in India. 2007. pap. ***(978-1-4067-5631-9(8))*** Read Bks.
Cameron, Dan, et al, texts. Subodh Gupta: Gandhi's Three Monkeys, 1 vol. 2010. (ENG.). 318p. 150.00 *(978-0-9800735-1-5(0))* Shainman, Jack Gallery.
Carvalho, Pedro Moura. Luxury for Export: Artistic Exchange between India & Portugal Around 1600. 2008. (Illus.). 77p. 25.00 *(978-1-934772-96-6(8))* Periscope Publishing.
Casey, Jane, et al. Divine Presence: Arts of India & the Himalayas. 2006. (Illus.). *(978-88-7439-022-9(X))* 5 Continents.
Chaudhary, Zahid R. Afterimage of Empire: Photography in Nineteenth-Century India. 2012. 256p. pap. 30.00 ***(978-0-8166-7749-8(2));*** (Illus.). 90.00 ***(978-0-8166-7748-1(4))*** Univ. of Minnesota Pr.
Chawla, Rupika. Raja Ravi Varma: Life & Times in Colonial India. 2010. 75.00 *(978-0-944142-41-7(9))* Grantha Corp.
Chawla, Rupika. Raja Ravi Varma: Painter of Colonial India. 2012. (ENG.). 360p. 75.00 ***(978-81-89995-08-9(1))*** Mapin Publishing Pvt. Ltd IND. Dist: National Bk. Network.
Chilakamarri, Romib Chary. India Nail Art. 2008. 50p. pap. 16.95 *(978-1-60474-491-0(X))* PublishAmerica, Inc.
Clarke, John. Jewellery of Tibet & the Himalayas. 2008. (ENG., Illus.). 128p. 45.00 *(978-1-85177-423-4(8))* V & A Pubns. GBR. Dist: Hachette Bk. Group.
Coomaraswamy, Ananda Kentish. Buddhist Primitives. 2006. pap. 15.95 *(978-1-4286-8032-6(2))* Kessinger Publishing, LLC.
—The Dance of Siva: Fourteen Indian Essay. 2007. (ENG.). 148p. per. 20.95 *(978-1-4304-4857-0(1))* Kessinger Publishing, LLC.
—Indian Music. 2006. pap. 15.95 *(978-1-4286-8031-9(4))* Kessinger Publishing, LLC.
—Introduction to Indian Art. 184p. 2008. 37.95 *(978-1-4366-7383-9(6))* 2007. (ENG.). per. 22.95 *(978-1-4325-7763-6(8))* Kessinger Publishing, LLC.
Cram101 Textbook Reviews. Outlines & Highlights for Indian Art by Dehejia, Isbn: 0714834963. 2011. 216p. pap. 30.95 ***(978-1-61812-857-7(4))*** Cram101 Inc.
Dallapiccola, A. L. Indian Art in Detail. 2007. (Art in Detail Ser.). (Illus.). 144p. 22.95 *(978-0-674-02691-9(8))* Harvard Univ. Pr.
—Indian Love Poetry. 2006. (ENG., Illus.). 100p. 17.95 *(978-1-56656-656-9(8))* Interlink Publishing Group, Inc.
Dalmia, Yashodhara. Contemporary Indian Art: Other Realities. 2006. (Illus.). 140p. 65.00 *(978-81-85026-55-6(6))* Marg Pubns. IND. Dist: National Bk. Network.
Dalmia, Yashodhara. Journeys: Four Generations of Indian Artists in Their Own Words two-volume Set, 2 vols. 2011. (ENG., Illus.). 628p. 225.00 ***(978-0-19-807319-2(4))*** Oxford Univ. Pr., Inc.
Dalmia, Yashodhara & Hashmi, Salima. Memory, Metaphor, Mutations: The Contemporary Art of India & Pakistan. 2007. (ENG., Illus.). 239p. 199.00 *(978-0-19-567347-0(6))* Oxford Univ. Pr., Inc.
Datta, Ella. Treasures of the National Gallery of Modern Art, New Delhi. 2012. (ENG., Illus.). 252p. 70.00 *(978-1-890206-67-3(9))* Mapin Publishing Pvt. Ltd IND. Dist: National Bk. Network.
De, Aditi, et al. Lines from an Artistic Life: The Drawings of Adimoolam. 2008. (Illus.). 164p. 70.00 *(978-0-85331-982-5(0),* Lund Humphries Pubs.) Ashgate Publishing, Ltd. GBR. Dist: Ashgate Publishing Co.
Dehejia, Vidya. Delight in Design: Indian Silver for the Raj. 2008. (ENG., Illus.). 200p. 65.00 *(978-0-944142-43-1(5))* Mapin Publishing Pvt. Ltd IND. Dist: National Bk. Network.
Essel, Karlheinz, frwd. Chalo! India: A New Era of Indian Art. 2009. (GER & ENG., Illus.). 304p. 45.00 *(978-3-7913-4304-4(1))* Prestel Publishing.
Falconer, John. Waterhouse Albums. 2010. (ENG.). 256p. 70.00 *(978-0-944142-84-4(2))* Mapin Publishing Pvt. Ltd IND. Dist: National Bk. Network.
Ghose, Madhuvanti. Masterpieces of Indian Art at the Art Institute of Chicago. 2010. (Illus.). 112p. 18.95 *(978-0-300-16779-5(2))* Art Institute of Chicago.
Ghosh, Mrinal. Sojourns of a Painter: Shyamal Dutta Ray & His Times. (Contemporary Indian Art Ser.). (Illus.). 108p. pap. 30.00 *(978-81-85822-86-0(7))* Mapin Publishing Pvt. Ltd IND. Dist: Antique Collectors' Club.

Gill, Gagan & Lal, Sham. Ram Kumar: A Journey Within. 2010. (ENG., Illus.). 239p. 55.00 (978-81-87737-08-7(5), Vadehra Art Gallery (Acc)) Antique Collectors' Club GBR. Dist: National Bk. Network.

Gobhai, Noshir, et al. Hampi: A Story in Stone. 2009. (Illus.). 196p. (978-81-903821-6-8(0), Library of Congress — New Delhi Overseas Office) Eminence Designs.

Gopalakrishnan, K. V. Tirukkalukkunram (Pakshitirtham) & Its Temples. 2006. (TAM & ENG., Illus.). 164p. pap. 26.95 (978-81-7017-392-2(2)) Abhinav Pubns. IND. Dist: Independent Pubs. Group.

Goswamy, B. N. & Smith, Caron. I see no Stranger: Early Sikh Art & Devotion. 2006. (ENG., Illus.). 216p. 65.00 (978-1-890206-04-8(0)) Mapin Publishing Pvt. Ltd IND. Dist: National Bk. Network.

Gowda, Sheela. Sheela Gowda, 1 vol. 2008. (ENG., Illus.). 160p. 55.00 (978-3-86521-469-0(X)) Steidl, Gerhard Druckerei und Verlag DEU. Dist: Innovative Logistics.

Granoff, Phyllis. Victorious Ones: Jain Images of Perfection. 2010. (ENG.). 304p. 75.00 (978-0-944142-82-0(6)) Mapin Publishing Pvt. Ltd IND. Dist: National Bk. Network.

Granoff, Phyllis, ed. Victorious Ones: Jain Images of Perfection. 2009. (Illus.). 308p. (978-81-89995-29-4(4)) Serindia Pubns., Inc.

Guha-Thakurta, Tapati. The Making of a New 'Indian' Art: Artists, Aesthetics & Nationalism in Bengal, C. 1850-1920. 2007. (Cambridge South Asian Studies). (ENG.). 384p. pap. 53.00 (978-0-521-05273-3(4)) Cambridge Univ. Pr.

Gupta, S.P. Elements of Indian Art: Including Temple Architecture, Iconography & Iconometry. 2nd ed. 2007. (SAN & ENG., Illus.). xiv, 146p. (978-81-246-0214-0(X)) D. K. Print World (P) Ltd.

Gupta, Sunil & Singh, Radhika. Click! Contemporary Photography in India. 2010. (ENG., Illus.). 216p. pap. 75.00 (978-81-87737-81-0(6), Vadehra Art Gallery (Acc)) Antique Collectors' Club GBR. Dist: National Bk. Network.

Haidar, Navina Najat & Sardar, Marika, eds. Sultans of the South: Arts of India's Deccan Courts, 1323-1687. 2011. (ENG., Illus.). 336p. pap. 50.00 (978-0-300-17587-5(6)) Yale Univ. Pr.

Havell, E.B. Hand Book of Indian Art. 2006. 280p. per. (978-1-4067-0254-5(4), Hesperides Pr.) Read Bks.

Heller, Amy. Early Himalayan Art. 2008. (ENG., Illus.). 160p. pap. 24.95 (978-1-85444-209-3(0)) Ashmolean Museum GBR. Dist: Antique Collectors' Club.

Howes, Jennifer. Illustrating India: The Early Colonial Investigations of Colin Mackenzie, 1784-1821. 2010. (ENG., Illus.). 312p. 145.00 (978-0-19-806441-1(1)) Oxford Univ. Pr., Inc.

Hutton, Deborah S. & Hutton, Deborah. Art of the Court of Bijapur. 2006. (Contemporary Indian Studies). (ENG., Illus.). 240p. 49.95 (978-0-253-34784-8(X), 025334784X) Indiana Univ. Pr.

Jaffer, Amin. Made for Maharajas: A Design Diary of Princely India. Singh, Martand, ed. 2006. (ENG., Illus.). 276p. 65.00 (978-0-86565-174-6(4)) Vendome Pr., The.

Jain, Jyotindra. Clemente: Made in India. 2011. (ENG., Illus.). 240p. pap. 45.00 **(978-88-8158-809-1(9))** Charta ITA. Dist: D.A.P./Distributed Art Pubs.

Jain, Kajri. Gods in the Bazaar: The Economies of Indian Calendar Art. 2007. (Objects/Histories Ser.). (ENG., Illus.). 448p. per. 29.95 (978-0-8223-3926-7(9)); 99.95 (978-0-8223-3906-9(4)) Duke Univ. Pr.

Jamkhedkar, A. P. Ajanta. 2009. (Monumental Legacy Ser.). (ENG., Illus.). 112p. 29.95 (978-0-19-569785-8(5)) Oxford Univ. Pr., Inc.

Jamme, Franck Andr#xE9;, ed. & text. Tantra Song: Tantric Painting from Rajasthan. 2011. (ENG., Illus.). 112p. 39.95 **(978-0-9799562-7-0(7))** Siglio Pr.

Janah, Sunil. Photographing India. 2012. (ENG., Illus.). 280p. 74.00 **(978-0-19-806580-7(9))** Oxford Univ. Pr., Inc.

Jhaveri, Amrit. 101: A Guide to 101 Modern & Contemporary Indian Artists. 2008. (Artists Ser.). (Illus.). 191p. pap. 29.95 (978-81-7508-423-0(5)) India Bk. Hse. Pvt., Ltd. IND. Dist: Antique Collectors' Club.

John, Simpson. The Begram Hoard: Indian Ivories from Afghanistan. 2011. (ENG., Illus.). 96p. (C). pap. 15.95 (978-0-7141-1178-0(3)) British Museum Pr. GBR. Dist: Brown, David Bk. Co., The.

Joshi, Tinoo. Timeless Traditions; Contemporary Forms: Arts & Crafts of Madhya Pradesh. 2010. (ENG., Illus.). 90p. 34.95 (978-81-8328-159-1(1)) Wisdom Tree IND. Dist: SCB Distributors.

Jumabhoy, Zehra. The Empire Strikes Back: Indian Art Today. 2010. (ENG., Illus.). 208p. 60.00 (978-0-8478-3468-6(9), Skira) Rizzoli International Pubns., Inc.

Kabir, Ananya Jahanara. Territory of Desire: Representing the Valley of Kashmir. 2009. (ENG., Illus.). 304p. 75.00 (978-0-8166-5356-0(9)); pap. 25.00 (978-0-8166-5357-7(7)) Univ. of Minnesota Pr.

Kadari, Sohana. Sohan Qadri. Mitter, Partha & Dewan, Deepali, eds. 2012. (ENG., Illus.). 144p. 75.00 (978-88-572-0647-9(5)) Skira Editore ITA. Dist: Random Hse., Inc.

Kapoor, Anish. Anish Kapoor: Turning the World Upside Down. 2011. (ENG., Illus.). 240p. 49.95 (978-3-86560-916-8(3)) Verlag der Buchhandlung Walther Konig DEU. Dist: D.A.P./Distributed Art Pubs.

Krishna, Kalyan, et al. In Adoration of Krishna: Pichhwais of Shrinathji, Tapi Collection. 2008. (ENG., Illus.). 225p. 100.00 (978-81-905935-0-2(1)) Roli Bks. Private, Ltd. IND. Dist: Ingram Pub. Services.

Kumar, R. Siva. Sensibility Objectified: The Sculptures of Sarbari Roy Choudhury. 2010. (ENG.). 136p. 40.00 (978-1-890206-03-1(2)) Mapin Publishing Pvt. Ltd IND. Dist: National Bk. Network.

Majumdar, et al. Paritosh Sen: In Retrospect Mansi. (Contemporary Indian Art Ser.). (Illus.). 164p. pap. 40.00 (978-81-85822-93-8(X)) Mapin Publishing Pvt. Ltd IND. Dist: Antique Collectors' Club.

Malani, Nalini, illus. Nalini Malani, 1 vol. 2007. (ENG.). 144p. 55.00 (978-88-8158-644-8(4)) Charta ITA. Dist: D.A.P./Distributed Art Pubs.

Markel, Stephen. India's Fabled City: The Art of Courtly Lucknow. 2010. (978-0-87587-206-3(9)) Los Angeles County Museum of Art.

Mason, Darielle. Kantha: The Embroidered Quilts of Bengal from the Jill & Sheldon Bonovitz Collection & the Stella Kramrisch Collection of the Philadelphia Museum of Art. 2010. (Illus.). xiii, 290p. (978-0-87633-218-4(1)); (978-0-87633-219-1(X)) Philadelphia Museum of Art.

—Kantha: The Embroidered Quilts of Bengal from the Jill & Sheldon Bonovitz Collection & the Stella Kramrisch Collection of the Philadelphia Museum of Art. 2010. (Illus.). 304p. 60.00 (978-0-300-15442-9(9)) Yale Univ. Pr.

Mathur, Saloni. India by Design: Colonial History & Cultural Display. 2007. (Illus.). 219p. per. 24.95 (978-0-520-25231-8(4)) Univ. of California Pr.

Mehta, Anupa. India 20: Conversations with Contemporary Artists. 2008. (ENG., Illus.). 216p. pap. 45.00 (978-0-944142-60-8(5)) Mapin Publishing Pvt. Ltd IND. Dist: National Bk. Network.

Michell, George I. The Majesty of Mughal Decoration: The Art & Architecture of Islamic India. 2007. (ENG., Illus.). 288p. 65.00 (978-0-500-51377-4(5)) Thames & Hudson.

Mitter, Partha. The Triumph of Modernism: India's Artists & the Avant-Garde, 1922-1947. 2007. (ENG., Illus.). 256p. pap. 45.00 (978-1-86189-318-5(3)) Reaktion Bks., Ltd. GBR. Dist: Chicago Distribution Ctr.

Neumayer, Erwin & Schelberger, Christine. Bharat Mata: Calendar Art & India's Freedom Struggle. 2008. (ENG., Illus.). 216p. 275.00 (978-0-19-568518-3(0)) Oxford Univ. Pr., Inc.

Neutres, Jerome. New Delhi, New Wave. Neutres, Jerome, ed. 2008. (ITA & ENG., Illus.). 288p. 70.00 (978-88-6208-023-1(9)) Damiani ITA. Dist: D.A.P./Distributed Art Pubs.

Nosu, Kosetsu. Life of Buddha in Frescoes: Mulagandhakuti Vihara, Sarnath. 2011. 54p. 36.95 **(978-1-258-02549-6(3))** Literary Licensing, LLC.

Obrist, Hans Ulrich, et al, eds. Indian Highway. 2011. (ENG., Illus.). 320p. pap. 59.95 **(978-3-86560-963-2(5))** Walther König, Köln/Koenig Bks.

Osian, creator. Osian's Forty Masterpieces: The Masterpieces & Museum-Quality Series. 2006. (ENG., Illus.). 240p. pap. 65.00 (978-1-890206-83-3(0)) Mapin Publishing Pvt. Ltd IND. Dist: National Bk. Network.

Owen, Lisa N. Carving Devotion in the Jain Caves at Ellora. 2012. **(978-90-04-20629-8(9))** BRILL.

Parker, Samuel K., et al. What Is a Trade? Donald Fels & Signboard Painters of South India. 2008. (Illus.). 80p. pap. (978-0-924335-26-6(2)) Tacoma Art Museum.

Pinney, Christopher. The Coming of Photography in India. 2008. (ENG., Illus.). 160p. 65.00 (978-0-7123-4972-7(3)) British Library, The GBR. Dist: Chicago Distribution Ctr.

Pinto, Jerry & Sippy, Sheena. Bollywood Posters. 2009. (ENG., Illus.). 216p. pap. 34.95 (978-0-500-28776-7(7), 528776) Thames & Hudson.

Prestel. Art of India Postcard Book. 4.95 (978-3-7913-2040-3(8)) Prestel Publishing.

Puri, Ina. Rooted Landscapes: The Art of Rini Dhumal. Puri, Ina, ed. 2011. (ENG.). 248p. 65.00 (978-81-89995-45-4(6)) Mapin Publishing Pvt. Ltd IND. Dist: National Bk. Network.

Ramaswamy, Sumathi, ed. Barefoot Across the Nation: M F Husain & the Idea of India. 2010. (Visual & Media Histories Ser.). (ENG., Illus.). 312p. (C). 150.00 (978-0-415-58594-1(5)) Routledge.

Rocca, Fedrico, ed. Contemporary Indian Fashion. 2009. (ENG., Illus.). 208p. pap. 60.00 (978-88-6208-100-9(6)) Damiani ITA. Dist: D.A.P./Distributed Art Pubs.

Saeed, Yousuf. Symbols of Plural Faith: The Muslim Popular Visual Culture of India. 2011. (ENG.). 228p. (C). 95.00 (978-0-415-67838-4(2), Routledge India) Taylor & Francis Group GBR. Dist: Taylor & Francis Group.

Schmitz, Barbara. From Lahore: Essays on Painting & Calligraphy. 2010. 160p. 65.00 (978-81-85026-97-8(1)) Marg Pubns. IND. Dist: National Bk. Network.

Schmitz, Barbara, ed. After the Great Mughals: Painting in Delhi & the Regional Courts in the 18th & 19th Centuries. 2006. (Illus.). 168p. 66.00 (978-81-85026-56-5(4)) Marg Pubns. IND. Dist: Antique Collectors' Club.

Seid, Betty. New Narratives: Contemporary Art from India. 2007. (ENG., Illus.). 144p. 50.00 (978-1-890206-08-6(3)) Mapin Publishing Pvt. Ltd IND. Dist: National Bk. Network.

Sheh, Pratima, text. Dictionary of Indian Art & Artists. 2007. (ENG., Illus.). 65.00 (978-1-890206-33-8(4)) Mapin Publishing Pvt. Ltd IND. Dist: National Bk. Network.

Silva, Nuno Vassallo E. Goa & the Great Mughal. Flores, Jorge, ed. 2011. (ENG., Illus.). 240p. pap. 40.00 (978-1-85759-693-9(5)) Scala, Editions FRA. Dist: National Bk. Network.

Singh, Dayanita, photos by. Dayanita Singh: House of Love. 2011. (ENG., Illus.). 185p. 45.00 (978-1-934435-27-4(9)) Radius Bks.

Sinha, Gayarti & Sternberger, Paul. India: Public Places, Private Spaces: Contemporary Photography & Video Art. Drolet, Brian, ed. 2008. (Illus.). 164p. pap. 30.00 (978-81-85026-82-4(3)) Marg Pubns. IND. Dist: National Bk. Network.

Sinha, Gayatri. Art & Visual Culture in India: 1857 - 2007. 2009. (Illus.). 300p. 85.00 (978-81-85026-92-3(0)) Marg Pubns. IND. Dist: National Bk. Network.

—The Art of Adimoolam. 2006. (ENG., Illus.). 104p. 45.00 (978-1-890206-82-6(2)) Mapin Publishing Pvt. Ltd IND. Dist: National Bk. Network.

—Voices of Change: 20 Indian Artists. 2011. (Illus.). 316p. 80.00 (978-93-80581-06-4(8)) Marg Foundation, The.

Smith, Vincent Arthur. Art of India. 2012. (Temporis Ser.). (ENG., Illus.). 256p. 39.95 (978-1-84484-806-5(X)) Parkstone International GBR. Dist: Ingram Pub. Services.

Subramanian, V. K. & Khokar, Mohan Aashis. Art Shrines of Ancient India. 2006. 328p. pap. 94.95 (978-81-7017-431-8(7)) Abhinav Pubns. IND. Dist: Independent Pubs. Group.

Tartakov, Gary Michael, ed. Dalit Art & Visual Imagery. 2012. (ENG., Illus.). 480p. 99.00 **(978-0-19-807936-1(2))** Oxford Univ. Pr., Inc.

Topsfield, Andrew. The Art of Play: Board & Card Games of India. 2007. 168p. 66.00 (978-81-502-6769-6(7)) Marg Pubns. IND. Dist: National Bk. Network.

Tuli, Neville. A Historic Epic: India in the Making 1757-1950: From Surrender to Revolt: Swaraj to Responsibility. (Masterpieces & Museum Quality Ser.). (Illus.). 288p. 75.00 (978-81-88204-11-3(0)) Mapin Publishing Pvt. Ltd IND. Dist: Antique Collectors' Club.

—A Historical Mela: the ABC of India: The Art, Book & Cinema. (Masterpieces & Museum Quality Ser.). (Illus.). 320p. 60.00 (978-81-88204-07-6(2)) Mapin Publishing Pvt. Ltd IND. Dist: Antique Collectors' Club.

—Indian Contemporary Art Vol. 4: Books, Paintings & Sculpture. 2006. (Masterpieces & Museum-Quality Ser.). (ENG., Illus.). 208p. pap. 65.00 (978-1-890206-76-5(8)) Mapin Publishing Pvt. Ltd IND. Dist: National Bk. Network.

—Osian's A Historical Epic: From Surrender to Revolt, Swaraj to Responsibility. 2006. (ENG., Illus.). 45.00 (978-1-890206-51-2(2)) Mapin Publishing Pvt. Ltd IND. Dist: National Bk. Network.

—Osian's A Historical Mela: The Art, Books & Cinema. 2006. (ENG., Illus.). pap. 60.00 (978-1-890206-49-9(0)) Mapin Publishing Pvt. Ltd IND. Dist: National Bk. Network.

—Osians Historical Series III. 2007. 65.00 (978-0-944142-52-3(4)) Antique Collectors' Club.

Tuli, Neville, text. India: A Historical Lila: Auctions of Indian Modern & Contemporary Paintings, Drawings & Graphic Art. 2006. (Paintings, Drawings & Graphic Art Ser.). (ENG., Illus.). 224p. pap. 50.00 (978-1-890206-39-0(3)) Mapin Publishing Pvt. Ltd IND. Dist: National Bk. Network.

—Osian's Indian Contemporary Art: Null: Paintings, Drawings & Sculpture. 2006. (ENG., Illus.). 208p. pap. 65.00 (978-1-890206-84-0(9)) Mapin Publishing Pvt. Ltd IND. Dist: National Bk. Network.

Tyabji, Laila. Threads & Voices. 2007. (ENG., Illus.). 148p. 66.00 (978-81-85026-79-4(3)) Marg Pubns. IND. Dist: National Bk. Network.

Vadehra Art Gallery Staff & Grosvenor Vadehra (Art Gallery: London, England) Staff, contrib. by. Indian Art, 3 vols. 2010. (ENG., Illus.). 101p. 19.95 (978-81-87737-27-8(1)); 146p. 19.95 (978-81-87737-19-3(0)); 129p. pap. 19.95 (978-81-87737-22-3(0)) Antique Collectors' Club GBR. (Vadehra Art Gallery (Acc)). Dist: National Bk. Network.

Van Dinter, Maarten Hesselt. Native Designs from India. 2007. (Illus.). 102p. pap. incl. cd-rom (978-90-810543-6-2(8)) Mundurucu Pubs.

Van Ham, Peter. Heavenly Himalayas: The Murals of Mangyu & Other Discoveries in Ladakh. 2011. (Illus.). 176p. 75.00 (978-3-7913-4543-7(5)) Prestel Publishing.

Verghese, Anila & Dallapiccola, Anna, eds. South India under Vijayanagara: Art & Archaeology. 2011. (ENG., Illus.). 392p. 45.00 (978-0-19-806861-7(1)) Oxford Univ. Pr., Inc.

Verma, Archana. Temple Imagery from Early Mediaeval Peninsular India. 2012. (Illus.). 312p. 119.95 **(978-1-4094-3029-2(4))** Ashgate Publishing Co.

Waldrep, Joel & Weller, Alan. Designs from India. 2007. (Dover Pictura Electronic Clip Art Ser.). (ENG., Illus.). 128p. pap. 39.95 (978-0-486-99886-2(X)) Dover Pubns., Inc.

Wolf, Gita & Shyam, Bhajju, eds. Signature: Patterns in Gond Art. 2010. (ENG., Illus.). 88p. 24.95 (978-93-80340-02-9(8)) Tara Publishing IND. Dist: Perseus-PGW.

ART, INDONESIAN

Achjadi, Judi. Glory of Batik: The Danar Hadi Collection. 2011. (ENG., Illus.). 336p. pap. 39.95 (978-602-98697-0-5(1)) Tuttle Publishing.

Ave, Joop, et al. Indonesian Arts & Crafts. 2009. (ENG., Illus.). 228p. 49.95 (978-979-8926-27-3(7)) Archipelago Pr IDN. Dist: Tuttle Publishing.

Batuan, Dewa Nyoman. Mandalas of Bali: A Hand-Held Tool for Meditation. 2nd ed. 2009. (ENG., Illus.). 160p. pap. 39.95 (978-1-932907-65-0(3)) Wiese, Michael Productions.

Bernet Kempers, A. J. Ancient Indonesian Art. 22.50 (978-0-674-03350-4(7)) Harvard Univ. Pr.

Bickerton, Derek, et al. Ashley Bickerton. 2011. (Illus.). 400p. 3750.00 (978-1-906967-39-0(3)) Other Criteria GBR. Dist: Abrams.

Brinkgreve, Francine. Sumatra: Crossroads Of. 2010. 204p. 38.00 (978-90-6718-356-7(3)) KITLV Pr. NLD. Dist: Univ. of Hawaii Pr.

Carpenter, Bruce. Ethnic Jewellery from Indonesia: Continuity & Evolution. 2012. (ENG., Illus.). 480p. 90.00 **(978-981-4260-68-8(1)**, Didier Millet,Csi) Continental Sales, Inc.

Carpenter, Bruce & Smith, David B. Javanese Antique Furniture & Folk Art. 2010. (ENG., Illus.). 256p. 65.00 (978-981-4217-76-7(X), Didier Millet,Csi) Continental Sales, Inc.

Ciclitira, Serenella. Indonesian Eye: Contemporary Indonesian Art. 2012. (ENG., Illus.). 376p. pap. 60.00 **(978-88-572-1075-9(8))** Skira Editore ITA. Dist: Random Hse., Inc.

Ciric, Biljana. Contemporaneity: Contemporary Art of Indonesia. 2011. (ENG & CHI., Illus.). 343p. pap. 29.95 (978-988-18907-7-1(2)) Timezone 8 Ltd. HKG. Dist: D.A.P./Distributed Art Pubs.

Cooper, Thomas L. Sacred Painting in Bali: Tradition in Transition. 2006. (ENG., Illus.). 192p. 45.00 (978-974-524-034-6(6)) Orchid Pr. THA. Dist: National Bk. Network.

Couteau, Ph.D., Jean. Bali Inspires: The Rudana Art Collection. 2011. (ENG., Illus.). 310p. 49.95 (978-602-95704-1-0(2)) Tuttle Publishing.

Elliott, Inger McCabe. Batik: Fabled Cloth of Java. 2010. (ENG., Illus.). 240p. pap. 29.95 (978-0-7946-0668-8(7)) Tuttle Publishing.

Hazra, Kanai Lal. Indonesia: Political History & Hindu, & Buddhist Cultural Influences, 2 vols. 2007. (Illus.). xxix, 1102p. (978-81-86921-39-5(7)); (978-81-86921-38-8(9)); (978-81-86921-37-1(0)) Decent Bks.

Keurs, Pieter ter. Colonial Collections Revisited. 2011. (CNWS Publications). (Illus.). viii, 269p. (978-90-5789-152-6(2), Leiden Univ. Pr.) Amsterdam Univ. Pr.

Knol, Meta, et al, eds. Beyond the Dutch: Indonesia, the Netherlands & the Arts from 1990 to Date. 2010. 200p. 39.00 (978-94-6022-059-3(2)) Royal Tropical Institute Pr. (KIT (Koninklijk Instituut voor de Tropen) NLD. Dist: Stylus Publishing, LLC.

Marella, Primo, ed. Indonesian Art. 2010. (ENG., Illus.). 96p. 45.00 (978-88-6208-131-3(6)) Damiani ITA. Dist: D.A.P./Distributed Art Pubs.

Miksic, John. Old Javanese Gold: The Hunter Thompson Collection at the Yale University Art Gallery. 2nd ed. 2011. (ENG., Illus.). 284p. 60.00 (978-0-300-16910-2(8)) Yale Univ. Art Gallery.

Miller, Harland & Stillman, Nick. Recent Wurg. 2009. (ENG., Illus.). 36p. 50.00 (978-1-906967-13-0(X)) Other Criteria GBR. Dist: Hachette Bk. Group.

—Recent Wurg: Ashley Bickerton. aut. ed. 2009. (ENG.). 36p. 80.00 (978-1-906967-14-7(8)) Other Criteria GBR. Dist: Hachette Bk. Group.

Niessen, Sandra. Legacy in Cloth: Batak. 2010. 568p. 69.00 (978-90-6718-351-2(2)) KITLV Pr. NLD. Dist: Univ. of Hawaii Pr.

Princess Mirah's Crafts Staff, contrib. by. Color Your World with Princess Mirah Batiks: With Princess Mirah Batiks. 2008. (ENG., Illus.). 64p. pap. 19.95 (978-1-57120-563-6(2)) C & T Publishing.

Rubin, Leon & Sedana, I. Nyoman. Performance in Bali. 2008. (Illus.). 176p. 39.95 (978-0-415-48299-8(2)) Routledge.

Schmidt, Andrea & van Duuren, David. Ancestors of the Lake: Art of Lake Sentani & Humboldt Bay, New Guinea. Webb, Virginia-Lee, ed. 2011. (ENG., Illus.). 136p. 50.00 (978-0-300-16610-1(9)) Yale Univ. Pr.

Strassler, Karen. Refracted Visions: Popular Photography & National Modernity in Java. 2010. (Objects/Histories Ser.). (ENG., Illus.). 400p. pap. 26.95 (978-0-8223-4611-1(7)); 94.95 (978-0-8223-4593-0(5)) Duke Univ. Pr.

Strohschein, Heather. Between Modern Dance & Intercultural Performance: The Multiple Truths of the Bird Belly Princess. 2008. 108p. pap. (978-3-8364-7808-3(0)) VDM Verlag Dr. Mueller e.K.

van der Zee, Pauline. Art as Contact with the Ancestors: Visual Arts of the Kamoro & Asmat of West Papua. 2009. (Bulletins of the Royal Tropical Institute Ser.). 112p. pap. 35.00 (978-90-6832-644-4(9)) Royal Tropical Institute Pr. (KIT (Koninklijk Instituut voor de Tropen) NLD. Dist: Stylus Publishing, LLC.

Van Der Zee, Pauline. Bisj-Poles: Sculptures from the Rain Forest. 2007. (Illus.). 119p. pap. 45.00 (978-90-6832-478-5(0)) Royal Tropical Institute Pr. (KIT (Koninklijk Instituut voor de Tropen) NLD. Dist: Stylus Publishing, LLC.

van Vuuren, Marianne. Ikat from Tanimbar. 2012. (ENG., Illus.). 180p. pap. 36.00 (978-974-524-097-1(4)) Orchid Pr. THA. Dist: National Bk. Network.

ART, IRANIAN

Álvarez-Mon, Javier & Garrison, Mark B. Elam & Persia. 2010. 79.50 (978-1-57506-166-5(X)) Eisenbrauns, Inc.

Ayazi, Souri. Luristan Bronze Disc-Headed Pins. 2008. 260p. 130.00 (978-3-932942-27-3(2)) Legat-Verlag GmbH & Company KG DEU. Dist: Independent Pubs. Group.

Beattie, May H. Carpets of Central Persia: With Special Reference to Rugs of Kirman: Exhibition Catalogue. 2007. (Illus.). 104p. reprint ed. pap. 27.00 (978-1-4223-6822-0(X)) DIANE Publishing Co.

Clark, Martin. Michael Stevenson. 2008. (ENG., Illus.). 64p. 19.00 (978-3-905829-48-8(7)) JRP Ringier Kunstverlag AG CHE. Dist: D.A.P./Distributed Art Pubs.

Demange, F. Glass, Gilding, & Grand Design: Art of Sasanian Iran (224-642) 2007. (Illus.). 47p. (978-0-87848-106-4(0)) Asia Society, Inc.

Dowlatshahi, Ali. Persian Designs & Motifs. 2007. (Dover Electronic Clip Art Ser.). (ENG., Illus.). 48p. pap. 14.95 (978-0-486-99875-6(4)) Dover Pubns., Inc.

Ettinghausen, Richard & Schroeder, Eric, eds. Iranian & Islamic Art. 2011. 216p. 44.95 **(978-1-258-02786-5(0))** Literary Licensing, LLC.

Flaskerud, Ingvild. Visualizing Belief & Piety in Iranian Shiism. 2010. (ENG., Illus.). 320p. 130.00 (978-1-4411-4907-7(4)) Continuum International Publishing Group, Ltd. GBR. Dist: National Bk. Network.

Hermitage Amsterdam, creator. Persia: Thirty Centuries of Art & Culture. 2007. (Illus.). 128p. 40.00 (978-0-85331-973-3(1), Lund Humphries Pubs.) Ashgate Publishing, Ltd. GBR. Dist: Ashgate Publishing Co.

Hillenbrand, Robert, et al, eds. Ferdowsi, the Mongols & the History of Iran: Art, Literature & Culture from Early Islam to Qajar. 2013. (ENG., Illus.). 416p. 105.00 **(978-1-78076-015-5(9))** I. B. Tauris & Co., Ltd. GBR. Dist: Macmillan.

Issa. Iranian Photography Now. 2009. (ENG., Illus.). 236p. 60.00 (978-3-7757-2257-5(2)) Hatje Cantz Verlag GmbH & Co KG DEU. Dist: D.A.P./Distributed Art Pubs.

Kadoi, Yuka. Islamic Chinoiserie: The Art of Mongol Iran. 2009. (Edinburgh Studies in Islamic Art Ser.). (ENG., Illus.). 320p. (gr. 17). 115.00 (978-0-7486-3582-5(3)) Edinburgh Univ. Pr. GBR. Dist: Columbia Univ. Pr.

Kennet, Derek & Luft, Paul, eds. Current Research in Sasanian Archaeology, Art & History. 2008. (Bar S Ser.). (ENG., Illus.). 171p. (C). pap. 83.00 (978-1-4073-0299-7(X)) British Archaeological Reports Ltd. GBR. Dist: Brown, David Bk. Co., The.

Korn, Lorenz, et al, eds. Die Grenzen der Welt: Arabica et Iranica ad honorem Heinz Gaube. 2008. (ENG & GER., Illus.). 324p. (C). 115.00 *(978-3-89500-675-3(0))* Reichert, Ludwig Dr. DEU. Dist: Brown, David Bk. Co., The.

Mark Batty Publishing Staff. Urban Iran. 2008. (ENG., Illus.). 176p. 27.95 *(978-0-9799666-1-3(2))* Batty, Mark Pub., LLC.

Melville, C. P. & Brend, Barbara. Epic of the Persian Kings: The Shahnameh of Ferdowsi. Brend, Barbara & Melville, Charles, eds. 2011. (ENG., Illus.). 288p. pap. 49.50 ***(978-1-84885-656-1(3))*** I. B. Tauris & Co., Ltd. GBR. Dist: Macmillan.

Minorsky, Vladimir. Geographical Factors in Persian Art. 2011. 83.96 *(978-1-61143-908-3(6))* Gorgias Pr., LLC.

Mottahedeh, Negar. Displaced Allegories: Post-Revolutionary Iranian Cinema. 2008. (ENG., Illus.). 216p. (C). 79.95 *(978-0-8223-4260-1(X))*; pap. 22.95 *(978-0-8223-4275-5(8))* Duke Univ. Pr.

Navab, Aphrodite. De-Orientalizing Iran: The Art of Sevruguin, Neshat, Navab & Ghazel. 2011. (Illus.). 232p. pap. ***(978-3-8454-0547-6(3))*** Lambert Academic Publishing.

Neshat, Shirin, et al. Shahram Karimi: In Between. Cameron, Dan, ed. 2011. (ENG & GER., Illus.). 96p. pap. 47.50 *(978-88-8158-797-1(1))* Charta ITA. Dist: D.A.P./Distributed Art Pubs.

Obrist, Hans Ulrich & Marta, Karen, eds. Monir Shahroudy Farmanfarmaian. 2011. (ENG., Illus.). 256p. 70.00 ***(978-88-6208-175-7(8))*** Damiani ITA. Dist: D.A.P./Distributed Art Pubs.

Parkstone Press Staff. Persian Miniatures. 2010. (Mega Square Ser.). (ENG., Illus.). 256p. 12.95 *(978-1-84484-782-2(9))* Parkstone International GBR. Dist: Ingram Pub. Services.

Satrapi, Marjane. Chicken with Plums. 2009. (ENG., Illus.). 96p. pap. 12.95 *(978-0-375-71475-7(8)*, Pantheon) Knopf Doubleday Publishing Group.

Shahbazi, Shirana, illus. Shirana Shahbazi: Meanwhile. 2008. (ENG.). 64p. 30.00 *(978-3-905829-05-1(3))* JRP Ringier Kunstverlag AG CHE. Dist: D.A.P./Distributed Art Pubs.

Stierlin, Henri. Persian Art & Architecture. 2012. (ENG., Illus.). 280p. 65.00 ***(978-0-500-51642-3(1)***, 551642) Thames & Hudson.

Stierlin, Henri. Splendors of the Persian Empire. 2006. (ENG., Illus.). 288p. 60.00 *(978-88-544-0146-4(3)*, White Star) Rizzoli International Pubns., Inc.

Tanavoli, Parviz. Undiscovered Minimalism: Gelims from Northern Iran. 2012. (ENG., Illus.). 256p. 155.00 ***(978-1-898113-76-8(9))*** King, Laurence Publishing GBR. Dist: Hachette Bk. Group.

ART, IRISH

see also Art, Celtic

Arrhenius, Sara. Hubbard/Birchler No Room to Answer. Hatley, Pam, ed. 2008. (ENG., Illus.). 192p. pap. 55.00 *(978-3-7757-2267-4(X))* Hatje Cantz Verlag GmbH & Co KG DEU. Dist: D.A.P./Distributed Art Pubs.

Bedient, Calvin. The Yeats Brothers & Modernism's Love of Motion. 2008. (ENG., Illus.). 424p. 48.00 *(978-0-268-02206-8(2))* Univ. of Notre Dame Pr.

Bewick, Pauline & Hayes, Alan. Pauline Bewick: Seven Ages. 2007. (Illus.). 312p. pap. *(978-1-903631-87-4(4))* Arlen Hse.

Bhreathnach-Lynch, Sighle. Ireland's Art, Ireland's History: Representing Ireland, 1845 to Present. 2007. (ENG., Illus.). 304p. per. 44.95 *(978-1-881871-51-4(7))* Fordham Univ. Pr.

Brown, Karen E. The Yeats Circle Word & Image in Ireland, 1880-1935. 2011. (Illus.). 208p. 104.95 *(978-0-7546-6644-8(1))* Ashgate Publishing Co.

Butler, Patricia. The Silent Companion: An Illustrated History of the Water Colour Society of Ireland. 2010. (ENG., Illus.). 344p. *(978-1-85149-644-0(0)*, Antique Collectors Club Dist) Antique Collectors' Club.

Clark, Adrian. British & Irish Art, 1945-1951: From War to Festival. 2010. (Illus.). 272p. 50.00 ***(978-0-9554063-4-8(X))*** Holberton, Paul Publishing GBR. Dist: Casemate Pubs. & Bk. Distributors, LLC.

Costigan, Lucy & Cullen, Michael. Strangest Genius: The Stained Glass of Harry Clare. 2010. (ENG., Illus.). 320p. 75.00 ***(978-1-84538-971-5(1))*** History Pr. Ltd., The GBR. Dist: Independent Pubs. Group.

Cullen, Fintan. Ireland on Show: Art Union & Nationhood. 2012. (Illus.). 124.95 ***(978-1-4094-3109-1(6))*** Ashgate Publishing Co.

Dunne, Aidan. Patrick Scott. 2008. (ENG.). 256p. 249.95 *(978-1-905483-53-2(8))* Liberties Pr. IRL. Dist: Dufour Editions, Inc.

Hartop, Christopher. British & Irish Silver in the Fogg Art Museum, Harvard University Art Museums. 2007. (Illus.). 263p. *(978-1-891771-46-0(9))* Harvard Univ. Art Museums.

—British & Irish Silver in the Fogg Art Museum, Harvard University Art Museums. 2007. (Harvard University Art Museums Ser.). (ENG., Illus.). 264p. 75.00 *(978-0-300-11770-7(1))* Yale Univ. Pr.

Healy, Ciara. A Multiple Belonging. 2010. 196p. pap. *(978-3-8383-7055-2(4))* Lambert Academic Publishing.

Helland, Janice. British & Irish Home Arts & Industries 1880-1914: Marketing Craft, Making Fashion. 2007. (Illus.). 219p. (C). pap. 32.50 *(978-0-7165-2891-3(6))* Irish Academic Pr. IRL. Dist: International Specialized Bk. Services.

—British & Irish Home Arts & Industries, 1880-1914: Marketing Craft, Making Fashion. 2007. (Illus.). 219p. (C). 75.00 *(978-0-7165-2890-6(8))* Irish Academic Pr. IRL. Dist: International Specialized Bk. Services.

Helwein, Mercedes, illus. Walk the Floor. 2010. (ENG.). 40p. 33.00 *(978-88-88493-65-7(4))* Drago Arts & Communication ITA. Dist: SCB Distributors.

Herrero, Marta. Irish Intellectuals & Aesthetics: The Making of a Modern Art Collection. 2007. (Illus.). 214p. 75.00 *(978-0-7165-3327-6(8))*; pap. 30.00 *(978-0-7165-3328-3(6))* Irish Academic Pr. IRL. Dist: International Specialized Bk. Services.

Hourihane, Colum, ed. Insular & Anglo-Saxon Art & Thought in the Early Medieval Period. 2011. (Illus.). 360p. pap. 35.00 ***(978-0-9837537-0-4(9))*** Index of Christian Art, Princeton Univ., The.

IMMA Staff & Kissane, Seán, eds. Vertical Thoughts: Morton Feldman & the Visual Arts. 2011. (ENG., Illus.). 318p. pap. 45.00 *(978-1-907020-08-7(X))* Irish Museum of Modern Art IRL. Dist: D.A.P./Distributed Art Pubs.

Irvine, Jak & text. The Square Root of Minus One Is Plus or Minus I: Assembled Works, 1993-2008. 2009. (ENG., Illus.). 160p. pap. 49.95 *(978-88-8158-702-5(5))* Charta ITA. Dist: D.A.P./Distributed Art Pubs.

Irwin, Tony. Bounded By. 2010. 64p. pap. *(978-3-8383-7027-9(9))* Lambert Academic Publishing.

Juncosa, Enrique, et al, texts. William Mckeown. 2009. (ENG., Illus.). 88p. pap. 37.95 *(978-88-8158-715-5(7))* Charta ITA. Dist: D.A.P./Distributed Art Pubs.

Juncosa, Enrique & Kennedy, Christina, eds. The Moderns: The Arts in Ireland from the 1900s to The 1970s. 2011. (ENG., Illus.). 596p. 100.00 *(978-1-907020-49-0(7))* Irish Museum of Modern Art IRL. Dist: D.A.P./Distributed Art Pubs.

Keown, Edwina & Taaffe, Carol. Irish Modernism: Origins, Contexts, Publics. 2009. (Reimagining Ireland Ser.). (Illus.). 256p. 55.95 *(978-3-03911-894-6(3))* Lang, Peter AG GBR. Dist: Lang, Peter.

Khosravi, Gholam. Seventh Vision I. 2007. 672p. 49.95 *(978-1-4251-3787-8(3))* Trafford Publishing.

—Seventh Vision II. 2007. 664p. 49.95 *(978-1-4251-3786-1(5))* Trafford Publishing.

Kissane, Sean & Juncosa, Enrique, eds. Alan Phelan: Fragile Absolutes. 2010. (ENG., Illus.). 268p. 75.00 *(978-88-8158-763-6(7))* Charta ITA. Dist: D.A.P./Distributed Art Pubs.

Le Brocquy, Louis. The Head Image: Notes on Painting & Awareness, 1 vol. 2007. (ENG., Illus.). 56p. pap. 19.95 *(978-88-8158-616-5(9))* Charta ITA. Dist: D.A.P./Distributed Art Pubs.

McGuinne, Dermot. Irish Type Design: A History of Printing Types in the Irish Character. 2nd rev. ed. 2010. (Illus.). 236p. 55.00 *(978-0-9543799-5-7(0))*; pap. 35.00 *(978-0-9543799-6-4(9))* National Print Museum IRL. Dist: Oak Knoll Pr.

Mianowski, Marie, ed. Irish Contemporary Landscapes in Literature & the Arts. 2012. (ENG., Illus.). 336p. 85.00 ***(978-0-230-31939-4(4))*** Palgrave Macmillan.

Moss, Rachel, et al, eds. Art & Devotion in Late Medieval Ireland. 2006. (Illus.). 234p. (C). 70.00 *(978-1-85182-987-3(3))* Four Courts Pr. IRL. Dist: International Specialized Bk. Services.

Ospina, Alison. West Cork Inspires. 2011. (ENG., Illus.). 176p. 50.00 *(978-0-85442-196-1(3))* Stobart Davies, Ltd. GBR. Dist: Brown, David Bk. Co., The.

Petullo, Anthony. Art Without Category: British & Irish Art from the Anthony Petullo Collection. 2009. (Illus.). 84p. *(978-1-60743-122-0(X))* Independent Pub.

Rault, Jasmine. Eileen Gray & the Design of Sapphic Modernity: Staying In. 2011. (Illus.). 196p. 104.95 *(978-0-7546-6961-6(0))* Ashgate Publishing Co.

Ryan, Vera. Movers & Shapers 2: Irish Visual Art 1940-2006. 2006. (ENG., Illus.). 392p. per. 36.95 *(978-1-905172-03-0(6))* Collins Pr., The IRL. Dist: Dufour Editions, Inc.

Sayres, Meghan Nuttall. Weaving Tapestry in Rural Ireland: Taipes Gael, Donegal. 2007. (ENG., Illus.). 212p. 42.95 *(978-0-9535353-3-0(9))* Attic Pr. IRL. Dist: Dufour Editions, Inc.

Scott, Yvonne & Moss, Rachel, eds. Crossing Boundaries: New Research in Irish Art History. 2012. (Illus.). 176p. 55.00 *(978-1-84682-020-5(0))* Four Courts Pr. IRL. Dist: International Specialized Bk. Services.

Stalley, Roger, ed. Limerick & South-West Ireland: Medieval Art & Architecture. 2011. (Baa conference transactions Ser.). (ENG., Illus.). 271p. (C). 130.00 *(978-1-907625-07-7(0))*; pap. 62.00 *(978-1-907625-08-4(9))* Maney Publishing GBR. Dist: Brown, David Bk. Co., The.

Starmore, Alice. Aran Knitting: New & Expanded Edition. 2010. (Dover Knitting, Crochet, Tatting, Lace Ser.). (ENG., Illus.). 224p. pap. 29.95 *(978-0-486-47842-5(4))* Dover Pubns., Inc.

ART, ISLAMIC

see Islamic Art

ART, ISRAELI

The Art & History of Haifa. 64p. *(978-88-8029-124-4(6))* Casa Editrice Bonechi.

The Art & History of Nazareth. 64p. *(978-88-8029-309-5(5))* Casa Editrice Bonechi.

The Art & History of Tel Aviv. 64p. pap. *(978-88-8029-172-5(6))* Casa Editrice Bonechi.

Bar, Noma. Negative Space. 2009. (ENG., Illus.). 128p. pap. 21.95 *(978-0-9817805-5-9(5))* Batty, Mark Pub., LLC.

Ben-Gal, Avner, et al. Avner Ben-Gal: Sudden Poverty. 2007. (Illus.). 76p. *(978-0-934324-42-7(5))* Aspen Art Museum.

Bianucci, Rita. Art & History of Jerusalem. (Illus.). 192p. *(978-88-8029-441-2(5))* Casa Editrice Bonechi.

Bram, Shahar. The Ambassadors of Death: The Sister Arts, Western Canon & the Silent Lines of a Hebrew Survivor. 2011. (ENG., Illus.). 207p. 69.95 *(978-1-84519-450-5(0))* Sussex Academic Pr. GBR. Dist: International Specialized Bk. Services.

Cats, Ruth, ed. As Is: Arte Israeliana Contemporanea. 2010. (ITA & ENG., Illus.). 240p. 52.00 *(978-88-492-1583-0(5))* Gangemi ITA. Dist: International Publishers Marketing.

Cohen, Mark. Ilan Averbuch: Public Projects. 2010. (ENG., Illus.). 96p. pap. 39.95 *(978-88-8158-774-2(2))* Charta ITA. Dist: D.A.P./Distributed Art Pubs.

Ezer, Oded. Oded Ezer: The Typographers Guide to the Galaxy. 2009. (Illus.). 192p. *(978-3-89955-242-3(3))* Die Gestalten Verlag.

Gandolfi, Peter. Passover Haggadah. 2008. 128p. pap. 19.95 *(978-965-229-418-0(7))* Gefen Publishing Hse., Ltd ISR. Dist: Gefen Bks.

Goodman, Susan Tumarkin, ed. Dateline: Israel: New Photography & Video Art. 2007. (ENG., Illus.). 120p. 35.00 *(978-0-300-11156-9(8))* Yale Univ. Pr.

Gwily, Ruth, ed. Cycle. 2008. 142p. *(978-84-612-1482-2(X))* Actar Birkhauser Distribution.

Horn, Gabriele. Sigalit Landau. 2008. (GER & ENG., Illus.). 290p. 45.00 *(978-3-7757-2104-2(5))* Hatje Cantz Verlag GmbH & Co KG DEU. Dist: D.A.P./Distributed Art Pubs.

Kaiser, Philipp. Avner Ben-Gal. 2008. (GER & ENG., Illus.). 152p. pap. 40.00 *(978-3-7757-2151-6(7))* Hatje Cantz Verlag GmbH & Co KG DEU. Dist: D.A.P./Distributed Art Pubs.

Kenaan-Kedar, Nurith. Ha-Madonah Shel Siah Ha-Tsabar: Masoret Ve-Hidush Ba-Tsiyur Ha-Notsri Ba-Arets Ba-Meot Ha-19 Veha-20: Kenesiyat Ha-Bikur Be-En-Kerem U-Khenesiyat Ba-Besorah Be-Natsrat. 2009. (HEB., Illus.). 158p. *(978-965-217-300-3(2))* Yad Izhak Ben-Zvi.

Lockmiller, Alice. Teacher's Guide for Thomas, Scribe of Israel. 2010. 52p. pap. 13.95 *(978-0-557-37111-2(2))* Lulu Enterprises Inc.

Masterpieces of the Israel Museum. 64p. *(978-88-7009-627-9(0))* Casa Editrice Bonechi.

Nes, Adi, et al. Access to Israel. 2008. (GER & ENG., Illus.). 116p. pap. 40.00 *(978-3-86560-463-7(3))* Verlag der Buchhandlung Walther Konig DEU. Dist: D.A.P./Distributed Art Pubs.

Omer, Mordechai. Adam Berg: Evidence. 2011. (ENG., Illus.). 48p. pap. 17.95 *(978-88-8158-800-8(5))* Charta ITA. Dist: D.A.P./Distributed Art Pubs.

Pfeffer, Susanne, ed. Absalon. 2011. (GER & ENG., Illus.). 352p. pap. 65.00 ***(978-3-86560-952-6(X))*** Verlag der Buchhandlung Walther Konig DEU. Dist: D.A.P./Distributed Art Pubs.

Schantz, Jim & Robison, Paula. Places of the Spirit: The Holy Land: Music & Images Inspired by Israel. 2008. (Illus.). 24p. audio compact disk *(978-1-879985-19-3(5))* Pucker Gallery.

Schwarz, Jessica & Ha'Tell, Aaron. A Celebration of Light: Treasured Hanukkah Menorahs of Early Israel. 2010. (ENG.). 162p. pap. 16.99 *(978-0-557-13711-4(X))* Lulu Enterprises Inc.

The Tender among Us: Project Series 32: Liat Yossifor. 2007. (Illus.). 24p. pap. 10.00 *(978-0-9786996-3-5(7))* Pomona College Museum of Art.

ART, ITALIAN

Ajmar, Marta & Dennis, Flora. At Home in Renaissance Italy. 2010. (ENG., Illus.). 416p. pap. 45.00 *(978-1-85177-489-0(0))* V & A Pubns. GBR. Dist: Hachette Bk. Group.

Alessandro, Rabottini, ed. Pietro Roccasalva. 2008. (ENG., Illus.). 64p. 35.00 *(978-3-905770-97-1(0))* JRP Ringier Kunstverlag AG CHE. Dist: D.A.P./Distributed Art Pubs.

Alexander-Skipnes & Alexander-Skipnes, Ingrid. Cultural Exchange Between the Low Countries & Italy (1400-1600) 2007. (Museums at the Crossroads Ser.). (ENG., Illus.). 292p. (C). pap. 116.00 *(978-2-503-51838-1(9))* Brepols Pubs. BEL. Dist: ISD.

Allen, Grant. Florence. 2009. 188p. pap. *(978-0-217-72319-0(5))*; 126p. pap. *(978-0-217-83528-2(7))* Books LLC.

Ames-Lewis, Francis, ed. Florence. 2011. (Artistic Centers of the Italian Renaissance Ser.). (ENG., Illus.). 438p. 175.00 *(978-0-521-85162-6(9))* Cambridge Univ. Pr.

Anne, Muller Von Der Haegen. Art & Architecture Tuscany. 2010. (Art & Architecture Pocket Ser.). 626p. pap. 16.99 *(978-0-8416-7153-9(2))* Langenscheidt Publishing Group.

Annichiarico, Silvana, ed. Serials & One-Offs: Triennale Design Museum. 2009. (ENG & ITA., Illus.). 304p. pap. 97.50 *(978-88-370-6920-9(0))* Electa ITA. Dist: Trans-Atlantic Pubns., Inc.

Aquino, Lucia. Leonardo da Vinci. 2009. (Skira MINI Artbooks Ser.). (ENG., Illus.). 96p. pap. 8.99 *(978-88-6130-737-7(X))* Skira Editore ITA. Dist: Random Hse., Inc.

Argentini, Guido, photos by. Guido Argentini: Shades of a Woman, 1 vol. 2012. (ENG, ITA, FRE, GER & SPA., Illus.). 200p. 60.00 ***(978-88-6208-199-3(5))*** Damiani ITA. Dist: D.A.P./Distributed Art Pubs.

The Art & History of Sorrento. (Illus.). 128p. *(978-88-7009-743-6(9))* Casa Editrice Bonechi.

Ash-Milby, Kathleen E., et al. Most Serene Republics: Edgar Heap of Birds. 2008. *(978-1-933565-12-5(8))* Smithsonian National Museum of the American Indian.

Baggs, Robert. Bitter Rivals make Great Art: Motivation for Patronage of the Sassetti Chapel. 2008. 112p. pap. *(978-3-639-10535-3(4))* VDM Verlag Dr. Mueller e.K.

Bailey, Gauvin A. Between Renaissance & Baroque: Jesuit Art in Rome, 1565-1610. 2009. (ENG., Illus.). 552p. pap. *(978-1-4426-1030-9(1))* Univ. of Toronto Pr.

Ballerini, Isabella Lapi, ed. Agnolo Gaddi e la Cappella della Cintola: La storia, l'arte, il Restauro. 2009. (ITA., Illus.). 168p. (C). pap. 48.00 *(978-88-596-0686-4(1))* Polistampa ITA. Dist: Brown, David Bk. Co., The.

Barbero, Luca Massimo. Carlo Cardazzo: Una Nuova Visione Dell'arte. Barbero, Luca Massimo, ed. 2009. (ITA., Illus.). 400p. 117.50 *(978-88-370-6534-8(5))* Electa ITA. Dist: Trans-Atlantic Pubns., Inc.

Barbero, Luca Massimo & Widenheim, Cecilia. Milan-Turin 1958-1968 No. 2. 2008. (ENG., Illus.). 112p. pap. 50.00 *(978-3-86521-639-7(0))* Steidl, Gerhard Druckerei und Verlag DEU. Dist: D.A.P./Distributed Art Pubs.

Barbolani di Montauto, Novella & Chappell, Miles L. Colorire Naturale e Vero: Figline, il Cigoli e I Suoi Amici. 2008. (citta degli Uffizi Ser.). (ITA., Illus.). 176p. (C). 50.00 *(978-88-596-0481-5(8))* Polistampa ITA. Dist: Brown, David Bk. Co., The.

Barcham, William, et al. Passion in Venice: Crivelli to Tintoretto & Veronese - The Man of Sorrows in Venetian Art. 2011. (ENG., Illus.). 176p. 45.00 *(978-1-904832-82-9(2))* Giles, D. Ltd. GBR. Dist: Antique Collectors' Club.

Barkan, Leonard. Michelangelo: A Life on Paper. 2010. (ENG., Illus.). 352p. 49.50 *(978-0-691-14766-6(3))* Princeton Univ. Pr.

Barovier, Marino, ed. Venetian Glass: From Modern to Contemporary. 2009. (ITA & ENG., Illus.). 400p. pap. 19.95 *(978-88-7179-208-8(4)*, Ore Cultura Srl (Acc)) Antique Collectors' Club GBR. Dist: National Bk. Network.

Bartz, Gabriele & Konig, Eberhard. Michelangelo: Buonarroti 1475-1564. 2008. (Masters of Italian Art Ser.). (Illus.). 138p. pap. 9.95 *(978-0-8416-0082-9(1))* American Map Corp.

Baskins, Cristelle. The Triumph of Marriage: Painted Cassoni of the Renaissance. 2008. (Illus.). 264p. 45.00 *(978-1-934772-86-7(0))* Periscope Publishing.

Baxandall, Michael. Words for Pictures: Seven Papers on Renaissance Art & Criticism. 2011. (ENG., Illus.). 208p. pap. 24.00 ***(978-0-300-17678-0(3))*** Yale Univ. Pr.

Bayer, Andrea. Art & Love in Renaissance Italy. 2008. (Illus.). xv, 376p. 65.00 *(978-1-58839-300-5(3))*; 45.00 *(978-1-58839-301-2(1))* Metropolitan Museum of Art, The.

Bayer, Andrea, ed. & contrib. by. Art & Love in Renaissance Italy. 2008. (ENG., Illus.). 392p. 65.00 *(978-0-300-12411-8(2))* Yale Univ. Pr.

Bazzini, Marco. The Young Artists Biennale of Monza 2011: 30 Artists, 5 Critics. 2012. (ENG., Illus.). 136p. pap. 28.00 ***(978-88-422-2017-6(5))*** Allemandi, Umberto & Co. GBR. Dist: National Bk. Network.

Beatrice, Luca. Miami Swing. 2010. (ENG & ITA., Illus.). 104p. (C). pap. 35.00 *(978-88-596-0718-2(3))* Polistampa ITA. Dist: Brown, David Bk. Co., The.

Beecroft, Vanessa. VB65 PAC Milano. 2010. (ENG & ITA., Illus.). 120p. pap. 45.00 *(978-88-370-7105-9(1)*, Mondadori Electa (Acc)) Antique Collectors' Club GBR. Dist: National Bk. Network.

Bellesi, Sandro, et al. Giovacchino Fortini: Scultura, Architettura, Decorazione e Committenza a Firenze Al Tempo Degli Ultimi Medici, 2 vols. 2008. (ITA., Illus.). 412p. (C). 230.00 *(978-88-596-0379-5(X))* Edizioni Polistampa ITA. Dist: Brown, David Bk. Co., The.

Belli, Gabriella & Panza di Biumo, Giuseppe, texts. Conceptual Art. 2011. (ITA & ENG., Illus.). 144p. pap. 50.00 *(978-88-366-1820-0(0))* Silvana ITA. Dist: D.A.P./Distributed Art Pubs.

Bellinato, Claudio. Giotto, the Scrovegni Chapel (boxed set W/CD) 2006. (ENG.). 90.00 incl. lp *(978-88-7200-248-3(6))* Vianello Libri ITA. Dist: National Bk. Network.

Benelli, Francesco. The Architecture in Giotto's Paintings. 2011. (ENG., Illus.). 312p. 99.00 ***(978-1-107-01632-3(0))*** Cambridge Univ. Pr.

Berruti, Valerio. Valerio Berruti: Isaac's Daughter. 2010. (ENG., Illus.). 136p. 35.00 *(978-88-6208-122-1(7))* Damiani ITA. Dist: D.A.P./Distributed Art Pubs.

Berti, Fausto. La Farmacia Storica Fiorentina: I "Fornimenti" in Maiolica Di Montelupo, Secc. XV- XVIII. 2010. (ITA., Illus.). 224p. (C). pap. 58.00 *(978-88-596-0797-7(3))* Polistampa ITA. Dist: Brown, David Bk. Co., The.

Bertola, Chiara, ed. The Spirit in Any Condition Does Not Burn. 2009. (ENG., Illus.). 168p. pap. 39.95 *(978-88-8158-722-3(X))* Charta ITA. Dist: D.A.P./Distributed Art Pubs.

Bertola, Chiara & Maraniello, Gianfranco, eds. On Mobility: Giovani Artisti Italiani, 1 vol. 2007. (ENG., Illus.). 120p. pap. 34.95 *(978-88-8158-631-8(2))* Charta ITA. Dist: D.A.P./Distributed Art Pubs.

Biancolini Fea, Daniela, et al. Il Tesoro Della Sindone: Mirabilia Del Sacro e Incisioni Sindoniche Di Umberto II Di Savoia. 2010. (ITA., Illus.). 124p. *(978-88-7889-242-2(4))* Piazza D.

Bietoletti, Silvestra, et al. Florence: Art & Architecture. 2008. (Art & Architecture Ser.). (Illus.). 528p. pap. 29.95 *(978-0-8416-0067-6(8))* American Map Corp.

Bill, Wheelock. The Wrong Idea: Maurizio Cattelan in the Economy of Attention. 2011. 120p. pap. ***(978-3-639-32334-4(3))*** VDM Verlag Dr. Mueller e.K.

Birnbaum, Daniel, text. What Good Is the Moon? 2010. (ENG., Illus.). 368p. 60.00 *(978-3-7757-2666-5(7))* Hatje Cantz Verlag GmbH & Co KG DEU. Dist: D.A.P./Distributed Art Pubs.

Bisceglia, Anna & Morolli, Gabriele. Chiesa e Convento Di San Bonaventura a Bosco Ai Frati: Guida Alla Visita Della Chiesa e Del Convento e Alla Scoperta Del Territorio. 2008. (Piccoli, grandi Musei Ser.). (ITA & ENG., Illus.). 288p. (C). 24.00 *(978-88-596-0390-0(0))* Polistampa ITA. Dist: Brown, David Bk. Co., The.

Bissell, R. Ward, et al. Masters of Italian Baroque Painting: The Detroit Institute of Arts. 2006. (Master Paintings from Dia Ser.). (ENG., Illus.). 176p. 65.00 *(978-1-904832-05-8(9))* Giles, D. Ltd. GBR. Dist: Antique Collectors' Club.

Blech, Benjamin & Doliner, Roy. The Sistine Secrets: Michelangelo's Forbidden Messages in the Heart of the Vatican. 2008. (ENG., Illus.). 336p. 26.95 *(978-0-06-146904-6(1)*, HarperOne) HarperCollins Pubs.

Blum, Dilys & Capucci, Roberto. Roberto Capucci: Art into Fashion. 2010. (Illus.). 202p. *(978-0-87633-229-0(7))* Philadelphia Museum of Art.

Bocchi, Francesca. The Beauties of the City of Florence: A Guidebook Of 1591. Frangenberg, Thomas & Williams, Robert, trs. from ITA. 2006. (Studies in Medieval & Early Renaissance Art History Ser.). (ENG., Illus.). 300p. (C).

116.00 (978-1-872501-44-4(3)) Brepols Pubs. BEL. Dist: Brown, David Bk. Co., The.

Boehm, Barbara Drake. Choirs of Angels: Painting in Italian Choir Books, 1300-1500. 2009. (ENG., Illus.). 64p. pap. 19.95 (978-0-300-14142-9(4)) Yale Univ. Pr.

Boer, Waldemar H. de. Francesco Albertini: Memorial of Many Statues & Paintings in the Famous City of Florence. Boer, De Waldemar H., ed. 2011. (Illus.). 240p. pap. 65.00 (978-88-7038-492-5(6)) Centro Di ITA. Dist: Antique Collectors' Club.

Boetti, Alighiero, et al. Order & Disorder: Alighiero Boetti by Afghan Women. 2012. (ENG., Illus.). 132p. pap. 25.00 (978-0-9778344-8-8(4)) Univ. of California, Los Angeles, Fowler Museum of Cultural History.

Bonami, Francesco. Spirit & Space: Sandretto Re Rebaudengo Collection. 2011. (ENG., Illus.). 200p. pap. 43.00 (978-84-92441-36-5(4)) T.F. Editores ESP. Dist: National Bk. Network.

Bonechi, Casa. Art & History of Capri: English Edition. pap. (978-88-7009-281-3(X)) Casa Editrice Bonechi.

—Art & History of Florence. rev. ed. (Illus.). 192p. pap. (978-88-7009-422-0(7)) Casa Editrice Bonechi.

—Art & History of Venice: English Edition. rev. ed. (Illus.). 174p. pap. (978-88-7009-302-5(6)) Casa Editrice Bonechi.

—Masterpieces of Pinacoteca. (Illus.). 96p. (978-88-7009-465-7(0)) Casa Editrice Bonechi.

—Pompeii. (Illus.). 128p. pap. (978-88-7009-454-1(5)) Casa Editrice Bonechi.

Bonfante-Warren, Alexandra. The Pitti Palace Collections. 2006. (Illus.). 320p. (978-0-88363-513-1(5)) Levin, Hugh Lauter Assocs.

Bonito Oliva, Achille. Gino De Dominicis: The Immortal. 2011. (ENG., Illus.). 388p. pap. 99.00 (978-88-370-7590-3(1)) Electa ITA. Dist: National Bk. Network.

Bonito Oliva, Achille. Marisa Albanese. 2011. (ENG., Illus.). 208p. pap. 45.00 (978-88-8158-804-6(8)) Charta ITA. Dist: D.A.P./Distributed Art Pubs.

Bonvicini, Monica, et al. Monica Bonvicini: Both Ends. 2011. (GER & ENG., Illus.). 168p. pap. 50.00 (978-3-86560-873-4(6)) Verlag der Buchhandlung Walther Konig DEU. Dist: D.A.P./Distributed Art Pubs.

Borghini, Raffaello & Ellis, Lloyd H., Jr. Il Riposo. 2008. (Lorenzo Da Ponte Italian Library). 384p. (978-0-8020-9743-9(X)) Univ. of Toronto Pr.

Bortolossi, Walter & Spieth, Darius. All That Happened Had to Happen. 2011. (Illus.). 104p. pap. 55.00 (978-0-8071-4236-3(0)) Louisiana State Univ. Pr.

Bosoni, Giampiero & Cogeval, Guy, eds. Il Modo Italiano: Italian Design & Avant-Garde in the 20th Century. 2006. (ENG., Illus.). 384p. 75.00 (978-88-7624-537-4(5)) Skira Editore ITA. Dist: Random Hse., Inc.

Bourdua, Louise. The Franciscans & Art Patronage in Late Medieval Italy. 2011. (ENG., Illus.). 256p. (C). pap. 36.99 (978-0-521-28128-7(8)) Cambridge Univ. Pr.

Bradshaw, Marilyn. Italian Renaissance Art. 2008. (ENG., Illus.). 368p. (C). pap. 45.80 (978-0-13-606128-1(1), Prentice Hall) Prentice Hall PTR.

Branko, Mitrovic, et al. Lucy + Jorge Orta: Food, Water, Life. 2011. (ENG., Illus.). 192p. 40.00 (978-1-56898-991-4(1)) Princeton Architectural Pr.

Braun, Emily, et al, texts. Chaos & Classicism: Art in France, Italy, & Germany, 1918-1936. 2011. (ENG., Illus.). 192p. pap. 40.00 (978-0-89207-405-1(1)) Guggenheim, Solomon R. Museum.

Brey, Ilaria Dagnini. The Venus Fixers: The Remarkable Story of the Allied Soldiers Who Saved Italy's Art During World War II. 2010. (ENG., Illus.). 336p. pap. 16.00 (978-0-312-42990-4(8)) Picador.

Brigitte, Hintzen Bohlen. Art & Architecture Rome. 2010. (Art & Architecture Pocket Ser.). 626p. pap. 16.99 (978-0-8416-7154-6(0)) Langenscheidt Publishing Group.

Brignolo, Armando & Giannella, Salvatore. The Nicolas: Restoration Tales in a Family History. 2011. (Illus.). 144p. 55.00 (978-88-422-1660-5(7)) Allemandi, Umberto & Co. GBR. Dist: Antique Collectors' Club.

Bruzelius, Caroline & Tronzo, William. Medieval Naples: An Architectural & Urban History, 400-1400. 2011. (ENG., Illus.). 160p. 30.00 (978-1-59910-202-3(1)) Italica Pr.

—Medieval Naples: An Architectural & Urban History, 400¿1400. 2011. (ENG., Illus.). 160p. pap. 20.00 (978-1-59910-203-0(X)) Italica Pr.

Buranelli, Francesco. Between God & Man: Angels in Italian Art. Dietrick, Robin C., ed. 2007. (ENG., Illus.). 192p. 34.95 (978-1-887422-15-4(3)) Univ. Pr. of Mississippi.

Burckhardt, Titus. Siena, City of the Virgin. 2008. (Sacred Art in Tradition Ser.). (ENG., Illus.). 144p. pap. 22.95 (978-1-933316-59-8(4)) World Wisdom, Inc.

Burke, Jill. Rethinking the High Renaissance: The Culture of the Visual Arts in Early Sixteenth-Century Rome. 2012. (Visual Culture in Early Modernity Ser.). (Illus.). 370p. 134.95 (978-1-4094-2558-8(4)) Ashgate Publishing Co.

Butler, Samuel. Ex Voto. 2008. 192p. 25.99 (978-0-554-30346-8(9)); 22.99 (978-0-554-39649-1(1)) BiblioBazaar.

—Ex Voto. 2009. 162p. pap. (978-0-217-47180-0(3)) Books LLC.

—Ex Voto. 2008. 152p. pap. (978-1-4065-9560-4(8)) Dodo Pr.

—Ex Voto: An Account of the Sacro Monte or New Jerusalem At. 2007. (ENG.). 170p. pap. 20.75 (978-1-4375-0024-0(2)); 190p. pap. 23.75 (978-1-4375-0025-7(0)) BiblioBazaar.

—Ex Voto an Account of the Sacro Monte or. 2006. pap. (978-1-4068-2207-6(8)) Echo Library.

Caffarelli, Maria Luisa & Carmi, Elio, eds. Cento Lumi per Casale Monferrato: Lampade di Chanukkah - Una Collezione tra Storia, Arte e Design. 2011.Tr. of Hundred Lights for Casale Monferrato - Hanukkah Lamps - A Collection of History, Art & Design. (ENG & ITA., Illus.). 176p. pap. 45.00 (978-88-572-0593-9(2)) Skira Editore ITA. Dist: Random Hse., Inc.

Cameron, Dan & Power, Kevin. Juliao Sarmento Vol. 1: 1990-1992. Cameron, Dan, ed. 2009. (ENG & SPA., Illus.). 64p. pap. 35.00 (978-84-343-1195-4(X)) Polígrafa, Ediciones, S. A. ESP. Dist: D.A.P./Distributed Art Pubs.

Campbell, Stephen J. & Cole, Michael W. Italian Renaissance Art. 2011. (ENG., Illus.). 696p. (C). pap. 90.00 net. (978-0-500-28943-3(3), 528943) Thames & Hudson.

Campeggi, Silvano & Righi, Giuliana. Verso Campaldino: Dal Pian Di Ripoli Alla Battaglia. 2010. (ITA & ENG., Illus.). 119p. (978-88-7970-471-7(0)) Edifir.

Caneva, Caterina. Museo D'arte Sacra Dell'Abbazia Di Vallombrosa: Guida Alla Visita Del Museo e Alla Scoperta Del Territorio. 2007. (Piccoli, grandi Musei Ser.). (Illus.). 257p. (C). 24.00 (978-88-596-0212-5(2)) Polistampa ITA. Dist: Brown, David Bk. Co., The.

—Tre Piccoli, Grandi Musei e Altre Testimonianze, Scritti 2002-2008. Paolini, Claudio, ed. 2009. (Interventi e Testimonianze Ser.). (ITA., Illus.). 144p. (C). pap. 28.00 (978-88-596-0692-5(6)) Polistampa ITA. Dist: Brown, David Bk. Co., The.

Cantini, Lorenzo & Michelli, Carla. La Raccolta D'arte Esso: 1949-1983. 2007. (ITA & ENG., Illus.). 299p. 75.00 (978-88-370-5687-2(7)) Electa ITA. Dist: Trans-Atlantic Pubns., Inc.

Capitel, Antón, et al. Images in Time: A Century of Photography in the Alhambra. 2011. (SPA & ENG., Illus.). 208p. pap. 47.00 (978-84-89162-27-3(1), T.F. Editores, S.L.C.) Antique Collectors' Club GBR. Dist: National Bk. Network.

Carli, Enzo. Estensione. 2008. (ITA & ENG., Illus.). 112p. pap. 40.00 (978-88-6302-003-8(5), Art Stock Bks. Ltd/Csi) Continental Sales, Inc.

Caskey, Jill. Art & Patronage in the Medieval Mediterranean: Merchant Culture in the Region of Amalfi. 2011. (ENG., Illus.). 344p. pap. 65.00 (978-0-521-28426-4(0)) Cambridge Univ. Pr.

Caterina Proto Pisani, Rosanna. La Valle Dei Tesori: Capolavori Allo Specchio. 2006. (Piccoli, grandi Musei Ser.). (ITA & ENG., Illus.). 185p. (C). 29.50 (978-88-596-0068-8(5)) Edizioni Polistampa ITA. Dist: Brown, David Bk. Co., The.

Cecchetto, Stefano & Vanni, Maurizio, eds. Jean Dubuffet: E L'Italia. 2011. (ITA & ENG., Illus.). 120p. pap. 35.00 (978-88-366-1971-9(1)) Silvana ITA. Dist: D.A.P./Distributed Art Pubs.

Celant, Germano. Arte Povera: Storia e Storie. Celant, Germano, ed. 2011. (ENG & ITA., Illus.). 560p. pap. 95.00 (978-88-370-7542-2(1)) Electa ITA. Dist: National Bk. Network.

—Paolo Canevari. Celant, Germano, ed. 2011. (ITA & ENG., Illus.). 312p. pap. 87.50 (978-88-370-7603-0(7), Mondadori Electa (Acc)) Antique Collectors' Club GBR. Dist: National Bk. Network.

—Tobias Rehberger: on Otto. Celant, Germano et al, eds. 2008. (ENG., Illus.). 120p. 160.00 (978-88-87029-39-0(3)) Fondazione Prada ITA. Dist: D.A.P./Distributed Art Pubs.

Cera, Deanna Farneti. Fashion Jewels Coppola e Toppo. 2010. (ENG., Illus.). 284p. (978-1-85149-611-2(4), Antique Collectors Club Dist) Antique Collectors' Club.

Champagne, John. Aesthetic Modernism & Masculinity in Fascist Italy. 2012. (Popular Culture & World Politics Ser.). (ENG., Illus.). 256p. (C). 130.00 (978-0-415-52862-7(3)) Routledge.

Chiodi, Stefano, ed. Space: From Maxxi's Collections of Art & Architecture. 2010. 320p. pap. 72.50 (978-88-370-7587-3(1)) Electa ITA. Dist: Trans-Atlantic Pubns., Inc.

Chivot, Dominique. Vatican. 2009. (ENG., Illus.). 224p. 65.00 (978-2-7594-0393-6(9)) Assouline FRA. Dist: Perseus Distribution.

Christiansen, Keith. Duccio & the Origins of Western Painting. 2008. (Illus.). 61p. 19.95 (978-1-58839-289-3(9)) Metropolitan Museum of Art, The.

Christiansen, Keith, et al. The Renaissance Portrait: From Donatello to Bellini. 2011. 65.00 (978-1-58839-425-5(5)); (Illus.). xii, 420p. pap. 45.00 (978-1-58839-426-2(3)) Metropolitan Museum of Art, The.

—The Renaissance Portrait: From Donatello to Bellini. Weppelmann, Stefan, ed. 2011. (ENG., Illus.). 432p. 65.00 (978-0-300-17591-2(4)) Yale Univ. Pr.

Christov-Bakargiev, Carolyn & Beccaria, Marcella, eds. Gianni Colombo. 2010. (ENG., Illus.). 312p. 80.00 (978-88-572-0314-0(X)) Skira Editore ITA. Dist: Random Hse., Inc.

Cibic, Aldo, ed. Verso Expo Milano 2015: [in English & Italian]. 2011. 144p. pap. 32.50 (978-88-370-8548-3(6)) Electa ITA. Dist: Trans-Atlantic Pubns., Inc.

Coen, Ester, ed. Futurismo 100: Illuminazioni. 2009. (ITA., Illus.). 450p. 142.50 (978-88-370-6777-9(1)) Electa ITA. Dist: Trans-Atlantic Pubns., Inc.

Coffin, David R. Magnificent Buildings, Splendid Gardens. Sellers, Vanessa Bezemer, ed. 2008. (ENG., Illus.). 320p. (C). pap. 42.00 (978-0-691-13677-6(7)) Princeton Univ. Pr.

Coffin, David R. & Sellers, Vanessa Bezemer. Magnificent Buildings, Splendid Gardens. 2008. (ENG., Illus.). 320p. (C). 85.00 (978-0-691-13664-6(5)) Princeton Univ. Pr.

Colantuono, Anthony. Titian, Colonna & the Renaissance Science of Procreation: Equicola's Seasons of Desire. 2010. (Visual Culture in Early Modernity Ser.). (Illus.). 342p. 119.95 (978-0-7546-6962-3(9)) Ashgate Publishing Co.

Coldwell, Paul. Morandi's Legacy: Influences on British Art. 2006. (ENG., Illus.). 80p. 42.00 (978-0-85667-620-8(9)) Wilson, Philip Pubs., Ltd. GBR. Dist: Macmillan.

Cole, Michael W., ed. Sixteenth-Century Italian Art. 2006. (Blackwell Anthologies in Art History Ser.: 2). (ENG., Illus.). 568p. 136.95 (978-1-4051-0840-9(1)); per. 57.95 (978-1-4051-0841-6(X)) Wiley, John & Sons, Inc. (Wiley-Blackwell).

Consolo, C. V., et al. Indiscrezioni: Giuseppe Tornatore Fotografie. Alinari Staff, ed. 2008. (ITA & ENG., Illus.). 208p. pap. 68.00 (978-88-95849-01-0(9), Art Stock Bks. Ltd/Csi) Continental Sales, Inc.

Coppola, Giuseppe & Coppola, Guiseppe. Le Luci e la Pietra: Lights & Stone: The Urban Object: Art, Architecture & Design [in English & Italian]. 2010. 300p. pap. 82.50 (978-88-370-7633-7(9)) Electa ITA. Dist: Trans-Atlantic Pubns., Inc.

Couturier, Sonia. Drawn to Art: French Artists & Art Lovers in 18th-Century Rome. 2012. (ENG., Illus.). 256p. pap. 45.00 (978-88-366-2054-8(X)) Silvana ITA. Dist: D.A.P./Distributed Art Pubs.

Cram101 Textbook Reviews. Outlines & Highlights for Art in Renaissance Italy by Paoletti & Radke, Isbn: 013091830x. 2011. 310p. pap. 32.95 (978-1-61812-926-0(0)) Cram101 Inc.

Cram101 Textbook Reviews. Outlines & Highlights for Italian Renaissance Art by Laurie Schneider Adams, Isbn: 9780813336916. 2010. 160p. pap. 29.95 (978-1-61654-064-7(8)) Cram101 Inc.

Crispolti, Enrico, ed. I Futuristi e le Quadriennali. 2009. (ITA., Illus.). 272p. pap. 55.00 (978-88-370-6778-6(X)) Electa ITA. Dist: Trans-Atlantic Pubns., Inc.

Crumpacker, Darrel & Master of the Die. Identifying Master of the Die: Re-examining Sixteenth Century Italian Printmaking. 2010. 48p. 20.00 (978-0-9667532-9-5(1)) Blue Moon - Lee Pr.

Culkin, Kate. Harriet Hosmer: A Cultural Biography. 2010. (Illus.). 248p. pap. 26.95 (978-1-55849-839-6(7)); lib. bdg. 80.00 (978-1-55849-838-9(9)) Univ. of Massachusetts Pr.

Dacos, Nicole. The Loggia of Raphael: A Vatican Art Treasure. 2008. (ENG., Illus.). 352p. 125.00 (978-0-7892-1004-3(5)) Abbeville Pr., Inc.

De Armas, Frederick A. & de Armas, Frederick A. Quixotic Frescoes: Cervantes & Italian Renaissance Art. 2006. (Illus.). 344p. (978-0-8020-9074-4(5)) Univ. of Toronto Pr.

De Berardinis, Valerio. Camere Oscure: The Best of Valerio de Berardinis' Photographic Productions. Mondadori Electa, ed. 2009. (ENG & ITA., Illus.). 212p. 115.00 (978-88-370-6838-7(7)) Electa ITA. Dist: Trans-Atlantic Pubns., Inc.

De Biasi, Mario & Ferrari, Raffaella. Mario De Biasi: Dal Fotogiornalismo Alla Fotografia Astratta. 2010. (Illus.). 111p. (978-88-317-0759-6(0)) Marsilio Editori spa.

De Concilis, Ettore. Ettore De Concilis: Opere 1982-2009. 2009. (ITA., Illus.). 155p. (978-88-7831-236-4(3), Spotlight Poets) Cigno Galileo Galilei.

De Luca, Joseph, ed. Joseph de Luca - Selected Works: Drawings, Paintings, Constructions. 2011. (Illus.). 172p. pap. 60.00 (978-0-578-08259-2(4)) De Luca, Joseph.

De Vries, Annette, ed. Cultural Mediators: Artists & Writers at the Crossroads of Tradition, Innovation & Reception in the Low Countries & Italy 1450-1650. 2008. (Groningen Studies in Cultural Change Ser.). (ENG.). 234p. (C). 66.00 (978-90-429-2043-9(2)) Peeters Pubs. & Booksellers BEL. Dist: Brown, David Bk. Co., The.

Degl'Innocenti, Cristina & Leboie, Maria Pilar. Arte Orafa a Firenze: La Cultura Di un Mestiere = Florentine Goldsmith: The Culture of a Craft. 2007. (ENG & ITA., Illus.). 112p. (C). pap. 23.00 (978-88-596-0215-6(7)) Edizioni Polistampa ITA. Dist: Brown, David Bk. Co., The.

Deimling, Barbara & Radke, Gary, eds. Italian, Art, Society, & Politics. 2008. 276p. pap. 24.95 (978-88-95250-02-1(8)) Syracuse Univ. Pr.

Deliyannis, Deborah Mauskopf. Ravenna in Late Antiquity. 2010. (ENG., Illus.). 464p. (C). 99.00 (978-0-521-83672-2(7)) Cambridge Univ. Pr.

Dempsey, Charles. The Early Renaissance & Vernacular Culture. 2012. (Bernard Berenson Lectures on the Italian Renaissance Delivered at Villa I Tatti Ser.). (ENG., Illus.). 398p. 39.95 (978-0-674-04952-9(7)) Harvard Univ. Pr.

Denker, Eric & Earenfight, Phillip. Reflections & Undercurrents: Ernest Roth & Printmaking in Venice, 1900-1940. 2012. (ENG.). 174p. pap. 24.95 (978-0-9826156-4-5(7)) Dickinson College, The Trout Gallery.

Detroit Institute Of Arts. Decorative Arts of the Italian Renaissance, 1400-1600. 2011. 182p. 42.95 (978-1-258-01796-5(2)) Literary Licensing, LLC.

Di Martino, Enzo, ed. Mimmo Paladino: Sculptures, 1980-2008. 2010. (ENG., Illus.). 488p. 260.00 (978-88-572-0419-2(7)) Skira Editore ITA. Dist: Random Hse., Inc.

Dixon, Susan M., ed. Italian Baroque Art. 2008. (Blackwell Anthologies in Art History Ser.). (ENG., Illus.). 416p. 120.95 (978-1-4051-3966-3(8), Wiley-Blackwell) Wiley, John & Sons, Inc.

—Italian Baroque Art. 2008. (Blackwell Anthologies in Art History Ser.: 3). (ENG., Illus.). 416p. pap. 54.95 (978-1-4051-3967-0(6), Wiley-Blackwell) Wiley, John & Sons, Inc.

Dorigato, Attila, et al. Venice: 3 Visions in Glass. 2009. (Illus.). 466p. 85.00 (978-3-89790-303-6(2)) Arnoldsche Art Pubs. Dist: Antique Collectors' Club.

Dorothy Circus Gallery Staff. City Slang: The Street Comes to the Gallery. 2008. (ENG.). 40p. pap. 38.00 (978-88-88493-40-4(9)) Drago Arts & Communication ITA. Dist: SCB Distributors.

Duby, Georges, et al. History of Venice in Painting: A New Vision. 2007. (ENG., Illus.). 496p. 235.00 (978-0-7892-0933-7(0)) Abbeville Pr., Inc.

Ebert-Schifferer, Sybille & Kieven, Elisabeth, eds. Romisches Jahrbuch der Bibliotheca Hertziana - Band 38. 2010. (Romisches Jahrbuch der Bibliotheca Hertziana Ser.). (GER., Illus.). 240p. (C). 195.00 (978-3-7774-2311-1(4)) Hirmer Verlag GmbH DEU. Dist: Brown, David Bk. Co., The.

Eccher, Danilo, ed. Paolo Chiasera: [in English & Italian]. 2008. 82p. pap. 56.50 (978-88-370-6248-4(6)) Electa ITA. Dist: Trans-Atlantic Pubns., Inc.

Eisen, Thomas. Lava Fabrizio Plessi. 2007. (GER & ENG., Illus.). 240p. 40.00 (978-3-939583-19-6(7)) Kehrer Verlag Heidelberg, Klaus Kehrer DEU. Dist: Consortium Bk. Sales & Distribution.

Emison, Patricia. The Italian Renaissance & Cultural Memory. 2011. (ENG., Illus.). 238p. 90.00 (978-1-107-00526-6(4)) Cambridge Univ. Pr.

Fabiani, Francesca, ed. MAXXI Architettura: Fotografia: Le Collezioni. 2010. (ITA., Illus.). 416p. pap. 72.50 (978-88-370-7579-8(0)) Electa ITA. Dist: Trans-Atlantic Pubns., Inc.

Faietti, Marzia, ed. Fausto Melotti Graphiko's. 2010. (ITA., Illus.). 248p. pap. 72.50 (978-88-370-7700-6(9)) Electa ITA. Dist: Trans-Atlantic Pubns., Inc.

Fantoli, Michèle. Siena: Playing with Art. 2006. (ENG.). 48p. 8.50 (978-88-7461-033-4(5)) Mandragora ITA. Dist: Antique Collectors' Club.

Fattori, Giovanni. I Luoghi Di Giovanni Fattori Nell'Accademia Di Belle Arti Di Firenze: Passato e Presente. 2008. (ITA., Illus.). 383p. (C). 56.00 (978-88-564-0035-9(9)) Edizioni Polistampa ITA. Dist: Brown, David Bk. Co., The.

Faure, Elie. The Italian Renaissance. 2011. 176p. 42.95 (978-1-258-04969-0(4)) Literary Licensing, LLC.

Feigenbaum, Gail, et al. Sacred Possessions: Collecting Italian Religious Art, 1500-1900. 2011. (Issues & Debates Ser.). (ENG., Illus.). 256p. pap. 30.00 (978-1-60606-042-1(2)) Getty Pubns.

Ferrari, Giulio. Italian Ironwork: Medieval, Renaissance, Baroque, Neo Classical. 2010. (Illus.). 112p. 29.99 (978-0-7643-3560-0(X)) Schiffer Publishing, Ltd.

Ferretti, Dante. Marche: People & Land. Ponciroli, Virginia, ed. 2007. (Illus.). 248p. 75.00 (978-88-370-5463-2(7)) Electa ITA. Dist: Trans-Atlantic Pubns., Inc.

Ficacci, Luigi. Piranesi: 25 Jahre TASCHEN, 2 vols. 2011. (25 Ser.). (ENG., Illus.). 800p. 59.99 (978-3-8365-3196-2(8)) TASCHEN DEU. Dist: Ingram Pub. Services.

Fintoni, Monica, et al, eds. Imaginary Creatures: The Library on Display. 2008. (ENG., Illus.), 80p. pap. 19.95 (978-88-7461-098-3(X)) Mandragora ITA. Dist: Antique Collectors' Club.

Finzi, Silvia, et al, eds. Architectures et architectes Italiens au Maghreb: Actes du colloque international tenu aux Archives Nationales de Tunisie (Tunis, 10-12 Decembre 2009) 2011. (ITA & FRE., Illus.). 256p. (C). pap. 35.00 (978-88-596-0726-7(4)) Polistampa ITA. Dist: Brown, David Bk. Co., The.

Fleck, Cathleen A. The Clement Bible at the Medieval Courts of Naples & Avignon: A Story of Papal Power Royal Prestige & Patronage. 2010. (Illus.). 370p. 124.95 (978-0-7546-6980-7(7)) Ashgate Publishing Co.

Frantz, Susanne K. & Kangas, Matthew. Viva Vetro! Glass Alive!: Venice & America. 2008. (ENG., Illus.). 202p. pap. 29.95 (978-0-88039-048-4(4)) Carnegie Museum of Art, The.

Freedman, Dennis, ed. Maurizio Cattelan: Toilet Paper. 2012. (ENG., Illus.). 220p. 65.00 (978-88-6208-210-5(X)) Damiani ITA. Dist: D.A.P./Distributed Art Pubs.

Freedman, Luba. The Revival of the Olympian Gods in Renaissance Art. 2010. (ENG., Illus.). 320p. (C). pap. 44.00 (978-0-521-18103-7(8)) Cambridge Univ. Pr.

Frongia, Antonello & Guerrieri, William, eds. Mose: A Preliminary Report. 2011. (ENG., Illus.). 72p. pap. 55.00 (978-3-86560-394-4(7)) Verlag der Buchhandlung Walther Konig DEU. Dist: D.A.P./Distributed Art Pubs.

Frugoni, Chiara & Armandi Barbolini, Marina. The Cathedral of Modena, 3 vols. 2009. (ITA & ENG., Illus.). 1340p. 1160.00 (978-88-7686-982-2(4)) Panini Franco Cosimo ITA. Dist: Antique Collectors' Club.

Furlotti, Barbara & Rebecchini, Guido. The Art of Mantua: Power & Patronage in the Renaissance. Jenkens, A. Lawrence, tr. from ITA. 2008. (Illus.). 280p. 84.95 (978-0-89236-840-2(3)) Oxford Univ. Pr., Inc.

Galimberti, Carlo A. & Galimberti, Carlo Adelio. Mogli, garzoni e Amanti: Amore ed erotismo nella vita e nelle opere degli artisti del Cinquecento. 2011. (Storie del Mondo Ser.). (ITA., Illus.). 200p. pap. 29.00 (978-88-564-0149-3(5)) Polistampa ITA. Dist: Brown, David Bk. Co., The.

Galleria degli Uffizi Staff, contrib. by. Medusa: Il Mito, L'antico e I Medici. 2008. (I mai Visti Ser.). (ITA., Illus.). 139p. (C). 29.50 (978-88-596-0513-3(X)) Edizioni Polistampa ITA. Dist: Brown, David Bk. Co., The.

Galli, Aldo. Pollaiuolo. 2008. (Gallery of the Arts Ser.). (ENG., Illus.). 92p. 14.95 (978-88-7439-130-1(7)) 5 Continents ITA. Dist: Hachette Bk. Group.

Gandini, Manuela. Gigi Rigamonti: Cross Stories. Gandini, Manuela, ed. 2009. (ENG., Illus.). 96p. pap. 29.95 (978-88-8158-736-0(X)) Charta ITA. Dist: D.A.P./Distributed Art Pubs.

Gardin, Gianni Berengo, photos by. Giorgio Morandi's Studio, 1 vol. 2009. (ENG.). 104p. 45.00 (978-88-8158-720-9(3)) Charta ITA. Dist: D.A.P./Distributed Art Pubs.

Gardner, Julian & Giotto. Giotto & His Publics: Three Paradigms of Patronage. 2011. (Bernard Berenson Lectures on the Italian Renaissance Delivered at Villa I Tatti Ser.). (Illus.). 256p. 35.00 (978-0-674-05080-8(0)) Harvard Univ. Pr.

Geck, Francis Joseph. Bibliography of Italian Early Renaissance Art. 2011. 44p. 35.95 (978-1-258-02103-0(X)) Literary Licensing, LLC.

Gilman, Claire, text. Mario Merz: Disegni. 2008. (ITA & ENG., Illus.). 380p. 100.00 (978-88-7757-217-2(5)) Hopefulmonster Editore ITA. Dist: D.A.P./Distributed Art Pubs.

Ginex, Giovanna, et al. Radical Light: Italy's Divisionist Painters, 1891-1910. Fraquelli, Simona, ed. 2008. (ENG., Illus.). 192p. 65.00 (978-1-85709-409-1(3)) Yale Univ. Pr.

Gingeras, Alison M. Sequence 1: Painting & Sculpture from the François Pinault Collection. 2008. (FRE, ITA & ENG., Illus.). 328p. 75.00 (978-88-6130-206-8(8)) Skira Editore ITA. Dist: Random Hse., Inc.

Giulio, Decio & Carugati, D. G. R. Marazzi: [in English & Italian]. 2007. 160p. 75.00 (978-88-370-5322-2(3)) Electa ITA. Dist: Trans-Atlantic Pubns., Inc.

Giusti Galardi, Giovanna. Vivere in Coppia Al Museo: Percorsi in Libertà Alla Galleria Degli Uffizi. 2010. (Illus.). 71p. (978-88-8347-560-3(7)) Sillabe.

Godfrey, Mark. Alighiero e Boetti. 2011. (ENG., Illus.). 288p. 60.00 (978-0-300-14875-6(5)) Yale Univ. Pr.

Gorbman, Claudia. Maestro: Recent Work by Lino Tagliapietra. 2012. (ENG., Illus.). 96p. 50.00 (978-0-295-99226-6(3)) Museum of Glass.

Gregori, Mina, et al. The First Medusa: Caravaggio. 2012. (Illus.). 160p. 75.00 (978-88-7439-582-8(5)) 5 Continents ITA. Dist: Abrams.

Gregory, Sharon. Vasari & the Renaissance Print. 2012. (Visual Culture in Early Modernity Ser.). (Illus.). 384p. 124.95 (978-1-4094-2926-5(1)) Ashgate Publishing Co.

Grieco, Roberto. Roman Micromosaic. 2010. 322p. 90.00 (978-88-492-1390-4(5)) Gangemi ITA. Dist: International Publishers Marketing.

Gromling, Alexandra. Buonarroti. 2008. (Art in Focus (Konemann) Ser.). (Illus.). 95p. pap. 5.95 (978-0-8416-0054-6(6)) American Map Corp.

Gronert, Stephen & Thielemann, Andreas, eds. Adam Elsheimer in Rom: Werk - Kontext - Wirkung. 2008. (Roemische studien der bibliotheca Hertziana Ser.). (GER & ENG., Illus.). 256p. (C). 134.00 (978-3-7774-4255-6(0)) Hirmer Verlag GmbH DEU. Dist: Brown, David Bk. Co., The.

Gucci, Jenny. Gucci Wars. 2008. (ENG., Illus.). 304p. 29.95 (978-1-84454-532-2(6)) Blake, John Publishing, Ltd. GBR. Dist: Independent Pubs. Group.

Guilloux, Fabien. Saint François D'Assise et L'ange Musicien: Thème et Variations Iconographiques Dans les Collections du Museo Francescano de Rome. 2010. (FRE., Illus.). 165p. (978-88-88001-73-9(5)) Ist. Storico dei Cappuccini.

Haggerty, Michael, tr. Bertozzi & Casoni: Le Bugie Dell'arte. 2008. (ENG., Illus.). 112p. 40.00 (978-88-6208-005-7(0)) Damiani ITA. Dist: D.A.P./Distributed Art Pubs.

Hairston, Julia L. & Stephens, Walter, eds. The Body in Early Modern Italy. 2010. (ENG., Illus.). 448p. (gr. 17). 70.00 (978-0-8018-9414-5(X)) Johns Hopkins Univ. Pr.

Hangar Design Group Staff. H - Hangar Design Group: As I Told You Before Ideas Not Airships. 2011. (ENG., Illus.). 512p. 65.00 (978-88-572-0628-8(9)) Skira Editore ITA. Dist: Random Hse., Inc.

Hartt, Frederick & Wilkins, David G. History of Italian Renaissance Art: Painting, Sculpture, Architecture. 7th ed. 2010. (ENG., Illus.). 736p. (C). pap. 136.20 (978-0-205-70581-8(2), Prentice Hall) Prentice Hall PTR.

Haskell, Naomi. Piero Della Francesca. 2nd ed. 2008. (Sculptors Ser.). (Illus.). 136p. pap. (978-1-85171-161-8(1)) Crescent Moon Publishing.

Heartney, Eleanor & Heiss, Alanna. Federico Diaz: Outside Itself. 2012. (ENG., Illus.). 116p. pap. 27.50 (978-88-8158-822-0(6)) Charta ITA. Dist: D.A.P./Distributed Art Pubs.

Hewison, Robert. Ruskin on Venice: The Paradise of Cities. 2010. (ENG., Illus.). 500p. 85.00 (978-0-300-12178-0(4)) Yale Univ. Pr.

Hewlett, Maurice. Earthwork Out of Tuscany. 2008. 148p. 24.99 (978-0-554-22878-5(5)); 21.99 (978-0-554-32181-3(5)) BiblioBazaar.

—Earthwork Out of Tuscany. 2009. 124p. pap. (978-1-4099-1213-2(2)) Dodo Pr.

—Earthwork out of Tuscany: Being Impressions & Translations of Maurice Hewlett. 2007. (ENG.). 134p. pap. 18.99 (978-1-4264-3265-1(8)); 146p. pap. 19.99 (978-1-4264-3320-7(4)) BiblioBazaar.

Hind, Arthur Mayger. Early Italian Engraving: A Critical Catalogue with Complete Reproduction of All the Prints Described, 7 vols. 2006. (Illus.). 1717p. 550.00 (978-1-57898-536-1(2)) Martino Publishing.

Hinz, Manfred. Die Zukunft der Katastrophe: Mythische und rationalistische Geschichtstheorie im italienischen Futurismus. (European University Institute - Series C Ser.). (GER.). VIII, 287p. 225.00 (978-3-11-187476-0(1)) De Gruyter, Walter Inc.

Hopkinson, Martin. Italian Prints 1875-1975. 2007. (Illus.). 208p. pap. 55.00 (978-0-85331-962-7(6), Lund Humphries Pubs.) Ashgate Publishing, Ltd. GBR. Dist: Ashgate Publishing Co.

Hornik, Heidi J. Michele Tosini & the Ghirlandaio Workshop in Cinquecento Florence. 2009. (ENG., Illus.). 211p. pap. 55.00 (978-1-84519-186-3(2)) Sussex Academic Pr. GBR. Dist: International Specialized Bk. Services.

Hudson, Mark. Titian: The Last Days. 2009. (ENG., Illus.). 320p. 27.00 (978-0-8027-1076-5(X)) Walker & Co.

Humfrey, Peter, ed. Venice & the Veneto. 2008. (Artistic Centers of the Italian Renaissance Ser.). (ENG., Illus.). 424p. 172.00 (978-0-521-80843-9(X)) Cambridge Univ. Pr.

Hutton, Edward. Florence & Northern Tuscany with Genoa. 2008. 460p. 33.99 (978-0-554-25956-7(7)) BiblioBazaar.

Imorde, Joseph & Pieper, Jan. Die Grand Tour in Moderne und Nachmoderne. 2008. (Reihe der Villa Vigoni Ser.).Tr. of Grand Tour in the Modern & Post-Modern Age. (GER., Illus.). VI, 281p. pap. (978-3-484-67020-4(7)) Verlag Max Niemeyer.

Imorde, Joseph & Pieper, Jan, eds. Die Grand Tour in Moderne und Nachmoderne. 2008. (Reihe der Villa Vigoni Ser.).Tr. of Grand Tour in the Modern & Post-Modern Age. (GER.). VI, 281p. 140.00 (978-3-11-916036-0(9)) De Gruyter, Walter Inc.

Istituto nazionale per la grafica (Italy) Staff & Italy, Ministero per i beni e le attività culturali Staff, contrib. by. Paolo Canevari: Decalogo. 2008. (ITA., Illus.). 71p. (978-88-370-6794-6(1)) Electa.

Jameson. The Diary of an Ennuyee. 2007. (ENG.). 340p. 46.95 (978-0-548-09214-9(1)) Kessinger Publishing, LLC.

Jameson, Anna Brownell. The Diary of an Ennuyée. 2007. (ENG.). 206p. pap. 20.99 (978-1-4264-5091-4(5)) BiblioBazaar.

—The Diary of an Ennuyee. 2008. 236p. 24.99 (978-0-554-33160-7(8)); 27.99 (978-0-554-23857-9(8)) BiblioBazaar.

—The Diary of an Ennuyee. 2007. 196p. per. (978-1-4065-2693-6(2)) Dodo Pr.

—The Diary of an Ennuyée. Lt. ed. 2007. (ENG.). 234p. pap. 22.99 (978-1-4264-5392-2(2)) BiblioBazaar.

Jewett, Sophie. Italian Sketches. 2007. (ENG.). 108p. 34.95 (978-0-548-04478-0(3)) Kessinger Publishing, LLC.

Jones, Pamela M. Altarpieces & Their Viewers in the Churches of Rome from Caravaggio to Guido Reni. 2008. (Visual Culture in Early Modernity Ser.). (Illus.). 390p. 134.95 (978-0-7546-6179-5(2)) Ashgate Publishing Co.

Kaminski, Marion. Art & Architecture Venice. 2010. (Art & Architecture Pocket Ser.). 578p. pap. 16.99 (978-0-8416-7161-4(3)) Langenscheidt Publishing Group.

—Venice. 2008. (Art & Architecture Ser.). (Illus.). 578p. 19.95 (978-0-8416-0053-9(8)) American Map Corp.

—Venice, 1 vol. 2010. (ENG., Illus.). 578p. pap. 9.99 (978-3-8331-5287-0(7)) h.f.ullmann DEU. Dist: Innovative Logistics.

Katz, Dana E. The Jew in the Art of the Italian Renaissance. 2008. (Jewish Culture & Contexts Ser.). (Illus.). 240p. (C). 59.95 (978-0-8122-4085-6(5)) Univ. of Pennsylvania Pr.

Kennedy, Ruth Wedgwood. The Italian Renaissance. 2011. 26p. 35.95 (978-1-258-01242-7(1)) Literary Licensing, LLC.

King, Ross. Michelangelo & the Pope's Ceiling. 2006. (Illus.). 373p. reprint ed. 28.00 (978-1-4223-5579-4(9)) DIANE Publishing Co.

Knowlton, John Howard Barnes & Hinman, Helen E. A Syllabus of Italian Renaissance Art. 2011. 162p. 41.95 (978-1-258-01298-4(7)) Literary Licensing, LLC.

Ladis, Andrew, et al. The Historical Eye: Essays on Italian Art in Honor of Andrew Ladis: Georgia Museum of Art, Athens, Georgia, September 7-9, 2006. 2008. (978-0-915977-69-7(9)) Univ. of Georgia, Georgia Museum of Art.

Lagerfeld, Karl. Byzantine Fragments, 1 vol. 2011. (ENG., Illus.). 52p. 110.00 (978-3-86930-246-1(1)) Steidl, Gerhard Druckerei und Verlag DEU. Dist: Innovative Logistics.

Lamboy, Stephen, et al. Giancarlo & Stefano Pedretti: Maestri Incisori = Master Engravers. 2010. (Illus.). 256p. (978-1-886768-97-0(8)) Blue Bk. Pubns., Inc.

Laurenza, Domenico. Art & Anatomy in Renaissance Italy: Images from a Scientific Revolution. 2012. (ENG., Illus.). 48p. pap. 14.95 (978-0-300-17957-6(X)) Yale Univ. Pr.

Lavin, Marilyn Aronberg. Artists' Art in the Renaissance. 2009. (ENG., Illus.). 230p. (C). 220.00 (978-1-904597-43-8(2)) Pindar Pr. GBR. Dist: Brown, David Bk. Co., The.

Lavin, Marilyn Aronberg, ed. Rome, Italy, Renaissance: Essays in Art History Honoring Irving Lavin on His Sixtieth Birthday. 2009. (ENG., Illus.). 304p. pap. 30.00 (978-1-59910-124-8(6)) Italica Pr.

Lawless, Cather. Life Virgin Tuscan Icon 1300-1528. 2006. (Routledge Studies in Medieval Religion & Culture Ser.). (ENG.). 125.00 (978-0-415-36101-9(X)) Routledge.

Leonardo. The Temple of the Soul: The Anatomy of Leonardo Da Vinci Between Mondinus & Berengarius: Twenty-Two Sheets of Manuscripts & Drawings in the Royal Library of Windsor & in Other Collections in Their Chronological Order. Pedretti, Carlo, ed. 2nd ed. 2008. (ENG., Illus.). 240p. (C). pap. 60.00 (978-88-95686-08-0(X)) Cartei, C.B. & Bianchi Edizioni ITA. Dist: Brown, David Bk. Co., The.

Levy, Allison, ed. Sex Acts in Early Modern Italy: Practice, Performance, Perversion, Punishment. 2010. (Visual Culture in Early Modernity Ser.). (Illus.). 302p. 124.95 (978-0-7546-6748-3(0)) Ashgate Publishing Co.

Lex & Sten, illus. Lex & Sten. 2010. (36 Chambers Ser.). (ENG.). 96p. pap. 29.00 (978-88-88493-62-6(X)) Drago Arts & Communication ITA. Dist: SCB Distributors.

Libby, Alexandra & Stanton, Thomas. Venice in the Age of Canaletto. 2009. (Illus.). 224p. 60.00 (978-3-7913-8000-1(1)) Prestel Publishing.

Libero, Chiara. The Treasures of Florence & Tuscany: Art, Architecture & Landscape. Manferto De Fabianis, Valeria, ed. 2010. (ENG., Illus.). 192p. 35.00 (978-88-544-0416-8(0)) White Star ITA. Dist: Sterling Publishing Co., Inc.

Lorenzi, Lorenzo. Devils in Art: Florence from the Middle Ages to the Renaissance. Roberts, Mark, tr. from ITA. 2006. (ENG., Illus.). 132p. 40.00 (978-88-7038-438-3(1)) Centro Di ITA. Dist: Antique Collectors' Club.

Lucas, E. V. A Wanderer in Florence. 2008. 340p. 29.99 (978-0-554-23418-2(1)) 2008. 340p. 28.99 (978-0-554-32721-1(X)) 2007. (ENG.). 300p. pap. 21.99 (978-1-4264-4372-5(2)) 2007. (ENG.). 336p. pap. 24.99 (978-1-4264-4410-4(9)) BiblioBazaar.

—A Wanderer in Florence. 2009. 278p. pap. (978-0-217-31399-5(X)) Books LLC.

—A Wanderer in Florence. 2007. (ENG.). 280p. per. (978-1-4065-6698-7(5)) Dodo Pr.

—A Wanderer in Venice. 2007. (ENG.). 312p. per. (978-1-4065-6746-5(9)) Dodo Pr.

—A Wanderer in Venice. 2010. (Illus.). 162p. pap. 24.95 (978-1-4432-0916-8(3)) General Bks. LLC.

Lucas, E. 1868-1938. A Wanderer in Venice. 2010. (ENG.). 472p. pap. 37.75 (978-1-172-41403-1(3)) BiblioBazaar.

Lucas, Edward Verrall. A Wanderer in Venice. 2011. 454p. pap. 36.75 (978-1-179-13872-5(4)) 2010. 456p. pap. 36.75 (978-1-145-78234-1(5)) 2010. 452p. pap. 36.75 (978-1-142-15898-9(5)) 2010. 492p. pap. 38.75 (978-1-143-21037-2(9)) 2008. 320p. 28.99 (978-0-554-35335-7(0)) 2008. 320p. 29.99 (978-0-554-26032-7(8)) 2007. 282p. pap. 21.99 (978-1-4346-0238-1(9)) 2007. (ENG.). 318p. pap. 24.99 (978-1-4346-0312-8(1)) BiblioBazaar.

—A Wanderer in Venice. 2009. 250p. pap. (978-0-217-91039-2(4)) Books LLC.

—A Wanderer in Venice. 2010. 450p. 41.56 (978-1-164-80118-4(X)) 2010. 450p. pap. 29.56 (978-1-164-55657-2(6)) 2008. 452p. 51.95 (978-1-4370-0231-7(5)) 2008. 452p. pap. 36.95 (978-1-4367-5769-0(X)) Kessinger Publishing, LLC.

Lucentini, Mauro, et al. Rome Guide: Step by Step through the Art, Culture & History of the Eternal City. 2011. (ENG., Illus.). 735p. pap. 25.00 (978-1-56656-836-4(6), Interlink Bks.) Interlink Publishing Group, Inc.

Luciano, Eleonora, et al. Antico. 2011. (Illus.). 224p. 55.00 (978-1-907372-27-8(X)) Holberton, Paul Publishing GBR. Dist: Casemate Pubs. & Bk. Distributors, LLC.

Luzzatto, Sylvia, ed. Buccellati: Timeless Art. 2009. (ENG., Illus.). 208p. 85.00 (978-88-7439-508-8(6)) 5 Continents ITA. Dist: Hachette Bk. Group.

Maffei, Giorgio. Sol Lewitt: Artist's Books. Maffei, Giorgio & De Donno, Emanuele, eds. 2010. (ENG., Illus.). 144p. pap. 40.00 (978-88-903459-2-0(6)) Corraini ITA. Dist: D.A.P./Distributed Art Pubs.

Malaguzzi, Sylvia. Food & Feasting in Art. Phillips, Brian, tr. from ITA. 2008. (Guide to Imagery Ser.). (Illus.). 384p. pap. 24.95 (978-0-89236-914-0(0)) Oxford Univ. Pr., Inc.

Manghetti, Gloria & Porto, Silvia, eds. Bruciamo le biblioteche... il libro futurista nelle collezioni pubbliche Fiorentine - Album, 1909-1994. 2009. (ITA., Illus.). 92p. (C). pap. 27.00 (978-88-596-0591-1(1)) Polistampa ITA. Dist: Brown, David Bk. Co., The.

Mannini, Lucia. Le stanze dei Tesori: Collezionisti e antiquari a Firenze tra Ottocento e Novecento. 2011. (Piccoli, grandi Musei Ser.). (ENG & ITA., Illus.). 312p. (C). 75.00 (978-88-596-0965-0(8)) Polistampa ITA. Dist: Brown, David Bk. Co., The.

Maraini, D. & Marainai, T. Our Sud: Photographs by Fosco Maraini. 2010. (ITA & ENG., Illus.). 256p. pap. (978-88-6302-037-3(X)) Alinari (IDEA).

Marr, Alexander. Between Raphael & Galileo: Mutio Oddi & the Mathematical Culture of Late Renaissance Italy. 2011. (ENG., Illus.). 384p. 45.00 (978-0-226-50628-9(2)) Univ. of Chicago Pr.

Martellini, Patrizia Angiolini, ed. The Basilica of San Vitale in Ravenna, 2 vols. 2008. (ITA & ENG., Illus.). 670p. 825.00 (978-88-7686-806-1(2)) Panini Franco Cosimo ITA. Dist: Antique Collectors' Club.

Martini, Rae. Rae Martini: 24 Carat Dirt. 2012. (ENG., Illus.). 208p. 40.00 (978-88-6208-207-5(X)) Damiani ITA. Dist: D.A.P./Distributed Art Pubs.

Marziani, Gianluca. Scala Mercalli: The Creative Earthquake of Italian Street Art. 2009. 208p. 59.00 (978-88-88493-42-8(5)) Drago Arts & Communication ITA. Dist: SCB Distributors.

Masi, Alessandro. L'occhio Del Critico: Storia Dell'arte in Italia Tra Otto e Novecento. 2009. (ITA.). 251p. (978-88-8427-163-1(0)) Vallecchi.

Matt, Leonard von. Renaissance Art in Rome: The Roma Series. Mariani, Valerio, ed. 2011. 64p. 36.95 (978-1-258-03917-2(6)) Literary Licensing, LLC.

Mattusch, Carol C. Pompeii & the Roman Villa: Art & Culture Around the Bay of Naples. 2008. (978-0-89468-353-4(5)) National Gallery of Art.

Mazza, Antonino & Zuffetti, Zaira. Il Miracolo Dell'Incoronata: Un Capolavoro Visto Da Vicino. 2010. (ITA., Illus.). 207p. (978-88-7827-191-3(8)) Bolis.

Mazzilli, Francesco. The Success of a Stylist: The struggle for existence in the South of Italy. 2008. 168p. per. 7.95 (978-1-4327-2033-9(3)) Outskirts Pr., Inc.

McGee, Barry, et al, texts. Dumbo: Acts of Vandalism & Stories of Love, 1 vol. 2007. (ENG., Illus.). 136p. 35.00 (978-88-89431-95-5(4)) Damiani ITA. Dist: D.A.P./Distributed Art Pubs.

McIntosh, Jane. Raphael's Stanza Della Segnatura: Audio Guide to the Stanza Della Segnatura in the Vatican & Its Remarkable Fresco Cycle. unabr. ed. 2007. (Jane's Smart Art Guides Ser.). audio compact disk 19.95 (978-0-9769052-4-0(8)) Context Audio Guides, LLC.

Melotti, Massimo, ed. Pistoletto - Works: Massimo Melotti Talks to Michelangelo Pistoletto. 2012. (ENG.). 88p. 20.00 (978-88-422-1963-7(0)) Allemandi, Umberto & Co. GBR. Dist: Antique Collectors' Club.

Mentasti, Rosa Barovier, ed. Exquisite Glass Ornaments: The Nineteenth-Century Glass Revival. 2011. (ENG., Illus.). 124p. 39.50 (978-88-317-0650-6(0)) Marsilio Editori spa ITA. Dist: Random Hse., Inc.

Michalsky, Tanja. Medien der Macht: Kunst Zur Zeit der Anjous In Italien. (GER & ITA., Illus.). 348p. (978-3-496-01231-3(5)) Reimer, Dietrich.

Micheli-Lamboy, Elena, et al. Firmo Fracassi: Maestro Incisore = Master Engraver. 2008. (Illus.). 236p. (978-1-886768-83-3(8)) Blue Bk. Pubns., Inc.

Miller, Peter Benson. Politics, Philosophy & the Arts in Venice 1600-1650. 2007. (Illus.). 192p. 30.00 (978-0-300-11924-4(0)) Yale Univ. Pr.

Miracco, Renato. Italian Artists in New York. 2010. (ITA & ENG., Illus.). 152p. pap. 49.95 (978-88-8158-747-6(5)) Charta ITA. Dist: D.A.P./Distributed Art Pubs.

Mirko: Archetype & Mythology, 1937-1968. 2010. 48p. pap. 26.95 (978-88-492-1240-2(2)) Gangemi ITA. Dist: International Publishers Marketing.

Mojon, Luc. Michelangelo: Die Entwürfe zu San Giovanni dei Fiorentini. 2009. (GRE & GER., Illus.). 139p. (978-3-03911-577-8(4)) Lang, Peter.

Mondadori Electa, ed. Museo del Novecento: The Collection. 2010. 373p. 75.00 (978-88-370-7992-5(3)) Electa ITA. Dist: Trans-Atlantic Pubns., Inc.

Morena, Francesco. Chinoiserie: Evolution of the Oriental Style in Italy from the 14th to the 19th Century. 2010. (ENG., Illus.). 320p. pap. 90.00 (978-88-7038-451-2(9)) Centro Di ITA. Dist: Antique Collectors' Club.

Mueller von der Haegen, Anne & Strasser, Ruth. Tuscany. 2008. (Art & Architecture Ser.). (Illus.). 626p. 19.95 (978-0-8416-0052-2(X)) American Map Corp.

Munari, Bruno & Bianchino, Gloria. Bruno Munari: Il Disegno, il Design. 2009. (ITA & ENG., Illus.). 248p. pap. 65.00 (978-88-7570-160-4(1)) Corraini ITA. Dist: D.A.P./Distributed Art Pubs.

Mutti, Roberto, et al. Giuseppe Ripa: Lightly: Milan's New Trade Fair. 2008. (ITA & ENG., Illus.). 96p. 55.00 (978-88-8158-674-5(6)) Charta ITA. Dist: D.A.P./Distributed Art Pubs.

Napoleone, Caterina, ed. Villa Madama. 2008. (ENG., Illus.). 176p. 85.00 (978-88-422-1525-7(2)) Allemandi, Umberto & Co. GBR. Dist: Antique Collectors' Club.

Nardinocchi, Elisabetta & Paolini, Claudio, eds. Paolo Staccioli: Opere / Sculptures 1991-2011. 2011. (ITA & ENG., Illus.). 80p. (C). pap. 42.00 (978-88-596-0903-2(8)) Polistampa ITA. Dist: Brown, David Bk. Co., The.

Neri, Grazia, ed. Icone. 7. 24 X 0. 26 Gallery: [in English & Italian]. 2008. 146p. pap. 65.00 (978-88-370-6332-0(6)) Electa ITA. Dist: Trans-Atlantic Pubns., Inc.

Nesfield-Cookson, Bernard. At the Dawn of a New Consciousness: Art, Philosophy & the Birth of the Modern World. 2010. (Illus.). 129p. pap. (978-1-906999-11-7(2)) Temple Lodge Publishing.

Nicolai, Vincenzo F., et al. The Christian Catacombs of Rome. 2009. (ENG.). 208p. pap. 39.95 (978-3-7954-2212-7(4), Art Stock Bks. Ltd/Csi) Continental Sales, Inc.

Niemeyer Chini, Valerie & Chini, Valerie Niemeyer. Stefano Bardini e Wilhelm Bode: Mercanti e connaisseur fra Ottocento e Novecento. 2009. (ITA., Illus.). 288p. (C). pap. 54.00 (978-88-596-0668-0(3)) Polistampa ITA. Dist: Brown, David Bk. Co., The.

Nittve, Lars, et al, texts. Time & Place, 3 vols. 2009. (ENG., Illus.). 430p. 100.00 (978-3-86521-641-0(2)) Steidl, Gerhard Druckerei und Verlag DEU. Dist: D.A.P./Distributed Art Pubs.

Onori, Lorenza Mochi, ed. Raffaello e Urbino: La sua formazione e I rapporti con la citta Natale. 2009. (ITA., Illus.). 320p. pap. 67.50 (978-88-370-6812-7(3)) Electa ITA. Dist: Trans-Atlantic Pubns., Inc.

Orta, Lucy & Orta, Jorge. Lucy & Jorge Orta: Clouds, Versailles. 2012. (ENG & FRE., Illus.). 224p. pap. 40.00 (978-88-6208-216-7(9)) Damiani ITA. Dist: D.A.P./Distributed Art Pubs.

Panza, Giuseppe. Giuseppe Panza: Memories of a Collector. 2008. (ENG., Illus.). 416p. pap. 37.50 (978-0-7892-0944-3(6)) Abbeville Pr., Inc.

Paoletti, John T. & Radke, Gary M. Art in Renaissance Italy. 4th rev. ed. 2011. (ENG., Illus.). 576p. (C). pap. 128.67 (978-0-205-01047-9(4), Prentice Hall) Prentice Hall PTR.

Paoluzzo, Marco. Ethiopia. 2007. (ENG., Illus.). 128p. (978-3-7165-1483-2(7), Benteli Verlags Ag Dist) Antique Collectors' Club.

Parkstone Press Staff. Leonardo Da Vinci. 2010. (Mega Square Ser.). (ENG., Illus.). 256p. 12.95 (978-1-84484-838-6(8)) Parkstone Pr. USA, Ltd.

—Michelangelo. 2010. (Mega Square Ser.). (ENG., Illus.). 256p. 12.95 (978-1-84484-839-3(6)) Parkstone Pr. USA, Ltd.

—Raphael. 2010. (Mega Square Ser.). (ENG., Illus.). 256p. 12.95 (978-1-84484-442-5(0)) Parkstone Pr. USA, Ltd.

Parmiggiani, Claudio. Incipit. 2008. (ENG., Illus.). 120p. 45.00 (978-88-422-1589-9(9)) Allemandi, Umberto & Co. GBR. Dist: Antique Collectors' Club.

Parmiggiani, Claudio & Clair, Jean. Claudio Parmiggiani: Apocalypsis Cum Figuris. 2008. (FRE, ITA & ENG., Illus.). 404p. 50.00 (978-88-422-1575-2(9)) Allemandi, Umberto & Co. GBR. Dist: Antique Collectors' Club.

Paul, Carole. The Borghese Collections & the Display of Art in the Age of the Grand Tour. 2008. (Illus.). 358p. 134.95 (978-0-7546-6134-4(2)) Ashgate Publishing Co.

Pelizzari, Luciano, et al. Menzel in Verona: Die Italienreisen des Grossen Deutschen Malers des 19. Jahrhunderts. 2008. (GER., Illus.). 417p. (978-3-86502-198-4(0)) Seemann Henschel GmbH & Company KG.

Pelizzari, Maria Antonella. Photography & Italy. 2010. (Reaktion Books - Exposures Ser.). (ENG., Illus.). 176p. pap. 29.95 (978-1-86189-769-5(3)) Reaktion Bks., Ltd. GBR. Dist: Chicago Distribution Ctr.

Peoschke, Joachim. Italian Mosaics: 300-1300. Stockman, Russell, tr. from GER. 2010. (ENG., Illus.). 432p. 150.00 (978-0-7892-1076-0(2)) Abbeville Pr., Inc.

Pero, Valentina. Che Fare? Arte Povera - The Historic Years. Malsch, Friedemann & Meyer-Stoll, Christine, eds. 2011. (ENG., Illus.). 384p. 50.00 (978-3-86828-167-5(3)) Kehrer Verlag Heidelberg, Klaus Kehrer DEU. Dist: Consortium Bk. Sales & Distribution.

Perrella, Cristiana, ed. Francesco Vezzoli: Greed. 2011. (ENG., Illus.). 96p. 39.95 (978-3-86560-949-6(X)) Verlag der Buchhandlung Walther Konig DEU. Dist: D.A.P./Distributed Art Pubs.

Petican, Laura. Arte Povera & the Baroque: Building an International Identity. 2011. 275p. pap. (978-3-0343-0477-1(3)) Lang, Peter.

Pezzano, Chiara & Morolli, Gabriele. La galleria d'Arte Moderna di Firenze: Il luogo, le Collezioni (1784-1914) 2009. (ITA., Illus.). 240p. (C). pap. 30.00 (978-88-596-0572-0(5)) Polistampa ITA. Dist: Brown, David Bk. Co., The.

Pfeiffer, Heinrich, et al. Andrea Pozzo a Mondovi. 2010. (Illus.). 253p. (978-88-16-60430-8(1)) Jaca Bk.

Pieri, Piero & Weber, Luigi. Atlante Dei Movimenti Culturali Dell'Emilia-Romagna Dall'Ottocento Al Contemporaneo. 2010. (ITA.). (978-88-491-3319-6(7)) CLUEB Editrice.

Pistoletto, Michelangelo. Facing Pistoletto. 2010. (ENG., Illus.). 240p. pap. 35.00 (978-3-03764-093-7(6)) JRP Ringier Kunstverlag AG CHE. Dist: D.A.P./Distributed Art Pubs.

—The Mirror of Judgement. 2012. (ENG., Illus.). 104p. pap. 34.95 (978-3-86335-054-3(5)) Walther König, Köln/Koenig Bks.

Pistoletto, Michelangelo. The Third Paradise. 2010. (ENG., Illus.). 96p. 24.95 (978-88-317-0649-0(7)) Marsilio Editori spa ITA. Dist: Random Hse., Inc.

Poeschke, Joachim. Mosaiken in Italien 300-1300. 2009. (GER., Illus.). 432p. (C). 220.00 (978-3-7774-2101-8(4)) Hirmer Verlag GmbH DEU. Dist: Brown, David Bk. Co., The.

Poggi, Christine. Inventing Futurism: The Art & Politics of Artificial Optimism. 2008. (ENG., Illus.). 392p. (C). 46.95 (978-0-691-13370-6(0)) Princeton Univ. Pr.

Ponti, Gio. Gio Ponti: Fascination for Ceramics. 2012. (ENG & ITA., Illus.). 160p. pap. 40.00 (978-88-366-2064-7(7)) Silvana ITA. Dist: D.A.P./Distributed Art Pubs.

Pool, Mary Jane & Howard, Linn. The Angel Tree: Celebrating Christmas at the Metropolitan Museum of Art. 2011. (ENG., Illus.). 128p. 24.95 (978-0-8109-9692-2(8)) Abrams.

Powell, Christine & Allen, Zoe. Italian Renaissance Frames at the V&A: A Technical Study. 2009. (ENG., Illus.). 224p. 79.95 (978-0-7506-8619-8(7)) Routledge.

Prada, Miuccia & Bertelli, Patrizio. Prada. 2010. (ENG., Illus.). 704p. 125.00 (978-88-87029-44-4(X)) Abrams.

Proto Pisani, Rosanna Caterina. La Gerusalemme Di San Vivaldo: Guida Alla Visita Del Museo e Alla Scoperta Del Territorio. 2006. (Piccoli, grandi Musei Ser.). (Illus.). 244p. (C). pap. 24.00 (978-88-596-0125-8(8)) Polistampa ITA. Dist: Brown, David Bk. Co., The.

—Museo D'arte Sacra Di Certaldo: Guida Alla Visita Del Museo e Alla Scoperta Del Territorio. 2006. (Piccoli, grandi Musei Ser.). (Illus.). 271p. (C). 24.00 (978-88-596-0078-7(2)) Polistampa ITA. Dist: Brown, David Bk. Co., The.

—Museo D'arte Sacra Di Montespertoli: Guida Alla Visita Del Museo e Alla Scoperta Del Territorio. 2006. (Piccoli, grandi Musei Ser.). (Illus.). 259p. (C). 24.00 (978-88-596-0069-5(3)) Polistampa ITA. Dist: Brown, David Bk. Co., The.

Quintavalle, Arturo Carlo. Medioevo: Le Officine: Atti Del Convegno Internazionale Di Studi, Parma, 22-27 Settembre 2009. 2010. (FRE, ITA & ENG., Illus.). 663p. (978-88-370-7847-8(1)) Electa.

Quiviger, Francois. Sensory World of Italian Renaissance Art. 2010. (ENG., Illus.). 206p. 27.00 (978-1-86189-657-5(3)) Reaktion Bks., Ltd. GBR. Dist: Chicago Distribution Ctr.

Rabbia, Luisa. Luisa Rabbia: Traveling under the Same Sky. 2010. (ENG., Illus.). 160p. 45.00 (978-88-7757-244-8(2)) Hopefulmonster Editore ITA. Dist: D.A.P./Distributed Art Pubs.

Ratti, Annie. Annie Ratti, 1 vol. 2007. (ENG., Illus.). 112p. pap. 34.95 (978-88-8158-630-1(4)) Charta ITA. Dist: D.A.P./Distributed Art Pubs.

Red Publishing Staff, creator. Xtreme Italian Brochures: Experimental Brochure & Folders. 2007. (Illus.). 199p. 59.95 (978-88-88492-08-7(9)) Red Book ITA. Dist: Gingko Pr., Inc.

Refice, Paola. Museo D'arte Sacra Della Collegiata Di San Lorenzo a Montevarchi: Guida Alla Visita Del Museo e Alla Scoperta Del Territorio. 2007. (Piccoli, grandi Musei Ser.). (ITA & ENG., Illus.). 203p. (C). 24.00 (978-88-596-0208-8(4)) Polistampa ITA. Dist: Brown, David Bk. Co., The.

Richmond, W. B. Assisi: Impressions of Half A Century. 2007. (ENG.). 292p. 43.95 (978-0-548-04714-9(6)) Kessinger Publishing, LLC.

Riegl, Alois, et al. The Origins of Baroque Art in Rome. Hopkins, Andrew & Witte, Arnold Alexander, eds. 2010. (Texts & Documents Ser.). (ENG., Illus.). 292p. pap. 50.00 (978-1-60606-041-4(4), Getty Research Institute) Getty Pubns.

Rock, J. B. & Diamond, illus. Roma Omnia Vincit. 2011. (ENG.). 40p. 33.00 (978-88-88493-64-0(6)) Drago Arts & Communication ITA. Dist: SCB Distributors.

Rogers Mariotti, Josephine & Mariotti, Josephine Rogers. Monna Lisa: La 'Gioconda' del Magnifico Giuliano. 2009. (I Grani Ser.). (ITA., Illus.). 96p. (C). 20.00 (978-88-596-0667-3(5)) Polistampa ITA. Dist: Brown, David Bk. Co., The.

Rogers, Tinagli. Women & the Visual Arts in Italy C. 1400-1650: Luxury & Leisure, Duty & Devotion - A Sourcebook. Rogers, Mary & Tinagli, Paola, eds. 2012. (ENG., Illus.). 288p. 100.00 (978-0-7190-8098-2(3)); pap. 34.95 (978-0-7190-8099-9(1)) Manchester Univ. Pr. GBR. Dist: Macmillan.

Romanelli, Giandomenico, ed. Venice: Art & Architecture. 2008. (Art & Architecture Ser.). (Illus.). 735p. pap. 29.95 (978-0-8416-0096-6(1)) American Map Corp.

Rotondo, Marina. Bulgari: Made in Italy. Scott, Jeremy, tr. from ITA. 2006. (Illus.). 220p. reprint ed. 18.00 (978-1-4223-5354-7(0)) DIANE Publishing Co.

Rowland, Ingrid D. From Heaven to Arcadia: The Sacred & the Profane in the Renaissance. 2008. (ENG.). 324p. pap. 17.95 (978-1-59017-295-7(7)) New York Review of Bks., Inc., The.

Rubin, Patricia Lee. Images & Identity in Fifteenth-Century Florence. 2007. (ENG., Illus.). 256p. 60.00 (978-0-300-12342-5(6)) Yale Univ. Pr.

Ruskin, John. Mornings in Florence. 2009. 72p. pap. (978-1-151-35833-2(9)) Books LLC.

—Mornings in Florence. 2007. (ENG.). 116p. per. (978-1-4065-6372-6(2)) Dodo Pr.

—Mornings in Florence. 2007. (ENG.). 88p. per. (978-1-4068-4087-2(4)) Echo Library.

—Mornings in Florence. 2009. 176p. pap. 7.95 (978-1-151-25399-6(5)) General Bks. LLC.

—Mornings in Florence. 2007. (ENG.). 192p. per. (978-1-4067-8848-8(1), Pomona Pr.) Read Bks.

—Mornings in Florence. 2009. (ENG.). 116p. pap. (978-1-4385-1462-8(X), Book Jungle) Standard Pubns., Inc.

—Mornings in Florence & the Two Paths. 2008. 292p. 25.99 (978-0-554-35770-6(4)) 2008. 292p. 28.99 (978-0-554-26467-7(6)) 2007. (ENG.). 258p. pap. 21.99 (978-1-4346-1177-2(9)) 2007. (ENG.). 290p. pap. 23.99 (978-1-4346-1248-9(1)) BiblioBazaar.

—St Marks Rest the History of Venice. 2006. pap. 27.95 (978-1-4286-3556-2(4)) Kessinger Publishing, LLC.

—Stones of Venice: Introductory Chapters & Local Indices for the Use of Travellers While Staying in Venice & Verona. 2006. 200p. pap. 19.99 (978-1-4264-3687-1(4)) 2007. (ENG.). 268p. pap. 23.99 (978-1-4264-3744-1(7)) BiblioBazaar.

Sacchi Lodispoto, Teresa & Spinazzé, Sabrina. Umberto Prencipe, 1879-1962: Realtà e Visione. 2009. (ITA., Illus.). 174p. (978-88-6060-218-3(1)) Palombi Fratelli.

Salaris, Claudia. Dizionario Del Futurismo: Idee, Provocazioni e Parole D'ordine Di una Grande Avanguardia. (ITA.). 182p. (978-88-359-4142-2(3)) Editori Riuniti.

Salerno, Giovan Battista, et al. Alighiero E Boetti. 2006. (ENG.). 62p. pap. 37.00 (978-88-422-1433-5(7)) Allemandi, Umberto & Co. GBR. Dist: Antique Collectors' Club.

Save Venice Inc., intro. Save Venice Inc: Four Decades of Restoration. 2010. (ENG.). pap. 65.00 (978-0-9623364-1-6(6)) Save Venice, Inc.

Scacchetti, Luca. Guglielmo Ulrich, 1904-1977. 2010. (ITA & ENG., Illus.). 512p. 95.00 (978-88-7179-612-3(8), Ore Cultura Srl (Acc)) Antique Collectors' Club GBR. Dist: National Bk. Network.

Scammacca, Nat, ed. A Meeting with Nicolo D'Alessandro & Nat Scammacca. (Sicilian Antigruppo Ser.: No. 1). (ENG & ITA., Illus.). 15.00 (978-0-89304-502-9(0)) Cross-Cultural Communications.

Schatz, Evelina, ed. Fausta Squatriti: Ecce Homo. 2010. (ENG., Illus.). 184p. pap. 39.95 (978-88-8158-769-8(6)) Charta ITA. Dist: D.A.P./Distributed Art Pubs.

Schieren, Mona & Sick, Andrea, eds. Look at Me: Celebrity Culture at the Venice Art Biennale. 2011. (ENG., Illus.). 232p. pap. 35.00 (978-3-86984-177-9(X)) Verlag fur Moderne Kunst DEU. Dist: D.A.P./Distributed Art Pubs.

Schiffer, Nancy N. Harry Bertoia Monoprints. 2011. (Illus.). 304p. 89.99 (978-0-7643-3850-2(1)) Schiffer Publishing, Ltd.

Schneider, Angela & Daemgen, Anke, eds. Jannis Kounellis: In der Neuen Nationalgalerie/in the Neue Nationalgalerie. 2008. (GER & ENG., Illus.). 240p. 60.00 (978-3-7757-2108-0(8)) Hatje Cantz Verlag GmbH & Co KG DEU. Dist: D.A.P./Distributed Art Pubs.

Schoen, Christian, ed. Ragnar Kjartansson: the End. 2009. (ENG., Illus.). 120p. 40.00 (978-3-7757-2333-6(1)) Hatje Cantz Verlag GmbH & Co KG DEU. Dist: D.A.P./Distributed Art Pubs.

Sconci, Maria Selene & Robinson, Christopher. Maiolica Medievale: Una Moderna Interpretazione. 2006. (ITA & ENG., Illus.). 63p. (C). 13.00 (978-88-596-0094-7(4)) Edizioni Polistampa ITA. Dist: Brown, David Bk. Co., The.

Seymour, Frederick H. A. Siena & Her Artists. 2009. 100p. pap. 14.14 (978-0-217-87505-9(X)) General Bks. LLC.

Sframeli, Maria & Nitti, Patrizia. Trésor des Médicis. 2010. (FRE., Illus.). 271p. (978-2-08-124505-1(1)) Editions Flammarion.

Simari, Maria Matilde, ed. Il Museo di Arte Sacra di San Donnino: Guida alla visita del museo e alla scoperta del Territorio. 2010. (Piccoli, grandi Musei Ser.). (ENG & ITA., Illus.). 264p. (C). pap. 25.00 (978-88-596-0836-3(8)) Polistampa ITA. Dist: Brown, David Bk. Co., The.

Simari, Maria Matilde & Bisceglia, Anna. Museo D'arte Sacra e Religiosità Popolare "Beato Angelico" a Vicchio: Guida Alla Visita Del Museo e Alla Scoperta Del Territorio. 2008. (Piccoli, grandi Musei Ser.). (Illus.). 404p. (C). 24.00 (978-88-596-0381-8(1)) Polistampa ITA. Dist: Brown, David Bk. Co., The.

Smith, Lorenza. Venice: Art & History. 2011. (Illus.). 192p. 45.00 (978-88-7743-349-7(3)) Arsenale Editrice SRL ITA. Dist: Antique Collectors' Club.

Sohm, Philip. The Artist Grows Old: The Aging of Art & Artists in Italy, 1500-1800. 2007. (ENG., Illus.). 224p. 50.00 (978-0-300-12123-0(7)) Yale Univ. Pr.

Spier, Jeffrey. Picturing the Bible: The Earliest Christian Art. 2009. (ENG., Illus.). 328p. pap. 50.00 (978-0-300-14934-0(4)) Yale Univ. Pr.

Stemp, Richard. The Secret Language of the Renaissance: Decoding the Hidden Symbolism of Italian Art. 2006. (978-1-84483-413-6(1)) Duncan Baird Pubs.

—The Secret Language of the Renaissance: Decoding the Hidden Symbolism of Italian Art. 2006. (ENG., Illus.). 224p. 35.00 (978-1-84483-322-1(4)) Duncan Baird Pubs. GBR. Dist: Sterling Publishing Co., Inc.

Sten & Lex, illus. Sten & Lex. 2010. (ENG.). 40p. pap. 33.00 (978-88-88493-60-2(3)) Drago Arts & Communication ITA. Dist: SCB Distributors.

Stoppini, Luca, ed. Fausto Melotti. 2009. (ITA., Illus.). 80p. pap. 57.50 (978-88-370-6662-8(7)) Electa ITA. Dist: Trans-Atlantic Pubns., Inc.

Storia dell'Arte Italiana, 1901-1940, 11. Vols. in 25 pts. Incl. Vol. 1. Dai primordi dell'arte cristiana al tempo di Giustiniano. Vol. 2. Dell'arte barbarica all romanica. Vol. 3. Aret Romanica. Vol. 4. Scultura del Trecento e le Sue Origini. Vol. 5. Pittura del Trecento e le Sue Origini. Vol. 6. Scultura del Quattrocento. Vol. 7 (in 4 pts.). Pittura del Quattrocento. Vol. 8 (in 2 pts.). Architetura del Quattrocento. Vol. 9 (in 7 pts.). Pittura del Cinquecento. Vol. 10 (in 3 pts.). Scultura del Cinquecento. Vol. 11 (in 3 pts.). Architetura del Cinquecento. 4150.00 (978-0-8115-3505-2(3)) Periodicals Service Co.

Strasser, Ruth & Mueller von der Haegen, Anne. Tuscany, 1 vol. 2010. (ENG., Illus.). 626p. pap. 9.99 (978-3-8331-5286-3(9)) h.f.ullmann DEU. Dist: Innovative Logistics.

Suida, William E. The Art of the Italian Renaissance: From the Samuel H. Kress Collection. 2011. 66p. 36.95 (978-1-258-04426-8(9)) Literary Licensing, LLC.

Symonds, John Addington. Renaissance in Italy: The Fine Arts - Volume III. 2007. 340p. pap. 23.99 (978-1-4264-4750-1(7)); 388p. pap. 26.99 (978-1-4264-4788-4(4)) BiblioBazaar.

—Renaissance in Italy V1. 2011. 992p. 81.95 (978-1-258-04001-7(8)) Literary Licensing, LLC.

—Renaissance in Italy V2. 2011. 1076p. 84.95 (978-1-258-04020-8(4)) Literary Licensing, LLC.

Symonds, John Addington. Renaissance in Italy Volume I. 2007. 430p. pap. 26.99 (978-1-4264-8590-9(5)) BiblioBazaar.

Syson, Luke, et al. Renaissance Siena: Art for a City. 2008. (ENG., Illus.). 372p. 65.00 (978-1-85709-392-6(5)) Yale Univ. Pr.

Tartuferi, Angelo, ed. Arte a Figline Valdarno: Dal Maestro della Maddalena a Masaccio. 2010. (citta degli Uffizi Ser.). (ITA., Illus.). 200p. (C). 60.00 (978-88-596-0832-5(5)) Polistampa ITA. Dist: Brown, David Bk. Co., The.

Tavella, Aldo, et al. Aldo Tavella (1909-2004) Il Respiro Di una Vita. 2009. (ITA., Illus.). 143p. (978-88-6052-280-1(3)) Editoriale Giorgio Mondadori.

Tedeschi, Mario & Leavitt, Thomas W. The New Renaissance in Italy: Twentieth Century Italian Art. 2011. 36p. 35.95 (978-1-258-04891-4(4)) Literary Licensing, LLC.

Testa, Judith Anne. An Art Lover's Guide to Florence. 2012. 306p. pap. 22.50 (978-0-87580-680-8(5)) Northern Illinois Univ. Pr.

Tichy, Miroslav, photos by. Miroslav Tich: Form of Truth. 2011. (ENG., Illus.). 248p. 85.00 (978-80-7437-039-7(9)) Kant CZE. Dist: D.A.P./Distributed Art Pubs.

Toman, Rolf. The Art of the Italian Renaissance: Architecture, Sculpture, Painting, Drawing, 1 vol. 2011. (ENG.). 464p. 19.99 (978-3-8331-6043-1(8)) h.f.ullmann DEU. Dist: Innovative Logistics.

Toman, Rolf, ed. The Art of the Italian Renaissance: Architecture, Sculpture, Painting, Drawing. 2008. (Architecture Sculpture Painting Ser.). (Illus.). 463p. per. 24.95 (978-0-8416-0071-3(6)) American Map Corp.

Triossi, Amanda, ed. Bulgari: 125 Years of Italian Magnificence Grand Palais. 2011. (ENG., Illus.). 388p. 80.00 (978-88-572-0830-5(3)) Skira Editore ITA. Dist: Random Hse., Inc.

Tv Boy. TV Boy: Start a Revolution Without Weapons. 2008. (ENG., Illus.). 96p. pap. 29.00 (978-88-88493-24-4(7)) Drago Arts & Communication ITA. Dist: SCB Distributors.

TvBoy, et al. Animal Collective. 2008. (ENG., Illus.). 96p. pap. 29.00 (978-88-88493-23-7(9)) Drago Arts & Communication ITA. Dist: SCB Distributors.

Unknown. Venetian Masks: And the Commedia dell'Arte. 2010. (Discovering Venice Ser.). (ENG., Illus.). 48p. pap. 9.95 (978-88-7743-341-1(8)) Arsenale Editrice SRL ITA. Dist: Antique Collectors' Club.

Valdes, Giuliano. The Art & History of Sicily. Hill, Rowena, tr. from ITA. (Illus.). 174p. pap. (978-88-7009-697-2(1)) Casa Editrice Bonechi.

—The Art & History of Umbria. (Illus.). 128p. pap. (978-88-7009-984-3(9)) Casa Editrice Bonechi.

—Pisa. (Illus.). 128p. pap. (978-88-8029-024-7(X)) Casa Editrice Bonechi.

Valeriani, Roberto. Antiques in Italian Interiors, Vol.II. 2010. (ENG., Illus.). 318p. 95.00 (978-1-905216-18-5(1)) Verba Volant, Ltd. GBR. Dist: Ingram Pub. Services.

Valeriani, Roberto & Valeriani, Robert. Antiques in Italian Interiors. 2006. (ENG., Illus.). 302p. 85.00 (978-0-9544288-5-3(4)) Verba Volant, Ltd. GBR. Dist: Ingram Pub. Services.

Vallora, Marco. Marco Fantini: Antlogia. 2011. (ITA & ENG., Illus.). 176p. pap. 39.95 (978-88-8158-802-2(1)) Charta ITA. Dist: D.A.P./Distributed Art Pubs.

Van der Sman, Gert Jan. Lorenzo & Giovanna: Life & Art in Renaissance Florence. 2011. (ENG., Illus.). 160p. pap. 25.00 (978-88-7461-128-7(5)) Mandragora ITA. Dist: Antique Collectors' Club.

Vaughan, Herbert M. Studies in the Italian Renaissance. 312p. 2010. pap. 24.76 (978-1-163-16189-0(6)) 2008. 45.95 (978-1-4366-8328-9(9)) 2007. (ENG.). per. 30.95 (978-1-4325-6243-4(6)) Kessinger Publishing, LLC.

Vecchio, Stefania. Inventari Seicenteschi Della Pinacoteca Ambrosiana. 2009. (ITA., Illus.). xxii, 222p. (978-88-7470-084-4(9)) Pagina.

Verdicchio, Pasquale. Looters, Photographers, & Thieves: Aspects of Italian Photographic Culture in the Nineteenth & Twentieth Centuries. 2011. (Fairleigh Dickinson University Press Series in Italian Studies). (ENG., Illus.). 194p. 65.00 (978-1-61147-018-5(8)) Fairleigh Dickinson Univ. Pr.

Verkerk, Dorothy. Early Medieval Bible Illumination & the Ashburnham Pentateuch. 2011. (ENG., Illus.). 272p. pap. 34.99 (978-1-107-40200-3(X)) Cambridge Univ. Pr.

Vezzoli, Francesco. Francesco Vezzoli: A True Hollywood Story. 2009. (ENG., Illus.). 118p. 45.00 (978-1-894212-12-0(6)) Power Plant, The CAN. Dist: D.A.P./Distributed Art Pubs.

Vignelli, Massimo, ed. & des. Tuscany: Vistas, Churches, Museums, Art, Villas & Gardens. 2010. (ENG., Illus.). 368p. 125.00 (978-0-8478-3138-8(8)) Rizzoli International Pubns., Inc.

Wackernagel, Martin & Luchs, Alison. The World of the Florentine Renaissance Artist: Projects & Patrons, Workshop & Art Market. 2011. (RSART: Renaissance Society of America Reprint Text Ser.). xxx, 447p. pap. (978-1-4426-1184-9(7)) Univ. of Toronto Pr.

Warr, Cordelia & Elliott, Janis, eds. Art & Architecture in Naples, 1266-1713. 2010. (Art History Special Issues Ser.: 4). (ENG., Illus.). 192p. pap. 34.95 (978-1-4051-9861-5(3), Wiley-Blackwell) Wiley, John & Sons, Inc.

Whitaker, Lucy & Clayton, Martin. Italian Paintings & Drawings: The Royal Collection. 2007. (ENG., Illus.). 192p. pap. 19.95 (978-1-85759-486-7(X)) Scala, Editions FRA. Dist: National Bk. Network.

White, Jonathan. Italian Cultural Lineages. 2007. (Toronto Italian Studies). (ITA, FRE & ENG., Illus.). 336p. pap. (978-0-8020-9458-2(9)) Univ. of Toronto Pr.

Wiederin, Alex, text. Dolce & Gabbana. 2008. (Illus.). 400p. 295.00 (978-88-370-5750-3(4)) Electa ITA. Dist: Trans-Atlantic Pubns., Inc.

Willard, Ashton Rollins. History of Modern Italian Art. 2009. 268p. pap. (978-0-217-22220-4(X)); 294p. pap. (978-0-217-22357-7(5)) Books LLC.

Williams, Robert. Art, Theory, & Culture in Sixteenth-Century Italy: From Techne to Metatechne. 2011. (ENG.). 256p. pap. 35.99 (978-0-521-18433-5(9)) Cambridge Univ. Pr.

Wilson, Kathryn J. Death in Florence. 2009. 80p. pap. (978-3-639-13131-4(2)) VDM Verlag Dr. Mueller e.K.

Wilson, Timothy. Italian Maiolica. 2nd rev. ed. 2006. (ENG., Illus.). 80p. reprint ed. pap. 15.95 (978-1-85444-176-8(0)) Ashmolean Museum GBR. Dist: Antique Collectors' Club.

—Maiolica: Italian Renaissance Ceramics in the Ashmolean Museum. 2nd rev. ed. 2006. (Ashmolean Handbooks). (ENG., Illus.). 80p. reprint ed. 22.95 (978-1-85444-177-5(9)) Ashmolean Museum GBR. Dist: Antique Collectors' Club.

Wirtz, Rolf. Art & Architecture Florence. 2010. (Art & Architecture Pocket Ser.). 56p. pap. 16.99 (978-0-8416-7151-5(6)) Langenscheidt Publishing Group.

Wirtz, Rolf C. Florence. 2008. (Art & Architecture Ser.). (Illus.). 560p. 19.95 (978-0-8416-0148-2(8)) American Map Corp.

—Florence, 1 vol. 2010. (ENG., Illus.). 560p. pap. 9.99 (978-3-8331-5282-5(6)) h.f.ullmann DEU. Dist: Innovative Logistics.

Wolf, Norbert. Titian. 2012. (Illus.). 144p. pap. 19.95 (978-3-7913-4697-7(0)) Prestel Publishing.

Wood, J. Copies & Adaptations from Renaissance & Later Artists: Italian Masters. Raphael & his School, 2 vols. 2010. (Corpus Rubenianum Ludwig Burchard Ser.). (ENG., Illus.). 717p. (C). 261.00 (978-1-905375-39-4(5)) Miller, Harvey Pubs. GBR. Dist: Brown, David Bk. Co., The.

Wood, Jeremy. Copies & Adaptations from Renaissance & Later Artists: Italian Masters. Artists Working in Central Italy & France, 2 vols. 2011. (Corpus Rubenianum Ludwig Burchard Ser.). (ENG., Illus.). 704p. (C). 261.00 (978-1-905375-41-7(7)) Miller, Harvey Pubs. GBR. Dist: Brown, David Bk. Co., The.

Wood, John. Copies & Adaptations from Renaissance & Later Artists: Italian Masters. Titian & North Italian Art, 2 vols. 2010. (Corpus Rubenianum Ludwig Burchard Ser.). (ENG., Illus.). 680p. (C). 261.00 (978-1-905375-40-0(9)) Miller, Harvey Pubs. GBR. Dist: Brown, David Bk. Co., The.

Zaccheddu, Maria Pia, ed. Il museo di Arte Sacra di San Martino a Gangalandi: Guida alla visita del museo e alla scoperta del Territorio. 2010. (Piccoli, grandi Musei Ser.). (ENG & ITA., Illus.). 240p. (C). pap. 25.00 (978-88-596-0835-6(X)) Polistampa ITA. Dist: Brown, David Bk. Co., The.

Zannier, Sabrina, ed. Olivo Barbieri: Viaggi in Italia 1982-2009. 2011. (ENG & ITA., Illus.). 136p. 35.00 (978-88-572-0731-5(5)) Skira Editore ITA. Dist: Random Hse., Inc.

Zanot, Francesco. Attraverso Milano. Photographing Milan: [in English & Italian]. 2008. 124p. pap. 57.50 (978-88-370-6265-1(6)) Electa ITA. Dist: Trans-Atlantic Pubns., Inc.

Zuffi, Stefano. Caravaggio: Masters of Art. 2012. (Illus.). 160p. pap. 12.95 (978-3-7913-4656-4(3)) Prestel Publishing.

Zuliani, Stefania, ed. Filberto Menna: La Linea Analitica Dell'Arte Contemporanea. 2010. (ITA., Illus.). 80p. pap. 43.50 (978-88-370-7570-5(7)) Electa ITA. Dist: Trans-Atlantic Pubns., Inc.

ART, JAMAICAN

Bender, Wolfgang. The Rastafarian Art of Jamaica. 2006. (Illus.). 176p. 35.00 (978-1-894622-77-6(4)) Warwick Publishing CAN. Dist: Perseus Distribution.

Martiniz-Ruiz, Barbaro. Art & Emancipation in Jamaica: Isaac Mendes Belisario & His Worlds. Barringer, Tim & Forrester, Gillian, eds. 2007. (Illus.). 612p. 75.00 (978-0-300-11661-8(6)) Yale Ctr. for British Art.

Thompson, Ralph, et al. Writers Who Paint Painters Who Write: 3 Jamaican Artists. 2008. (ENG.). 64p. pap. 19.95 (978-1-84523-064-7(7)) Peepal Tree Pr., Ltd. GBR. Dist: Independent Pubs. Group.

ART, JAPANESE

Actar, creator. Japan Graphics 2. 2006. (Illus.). 280p. pap. 34.95 (978-84-96540-14-9(6)) Kunst-Werke Berlin e.V. DEU. Dist: Actar Birkhauser Distribution.

Addiss, Stephen. The Art of Haiku: Its History Through Poems & Paintings by Japanese Masters. 2012. (ENG., Illus.). 352p. 24.95 (978-1-59030-886-8(7)) Shambhala Pubns., Inc.

Adolphson, Mikael, et al, eds. Heian Japan: Centers & Peripheries. 2007. (Illus.). 450p. 57.00 (978-0-8248-3013-7(X)) Univ. of Hawaii Pr.

Aida, Makoto. Monument for Nothing. 2007. 248p. pap. 59.95 (978-4-7661-1804-9(9)) Graphic-Sha JPN. Dist: Gingko Pr., Inc.

Alpha Planning Inc., Staff. Best POP Design. Planning, Alpha, ed. 2009. (ENG., Illus.). 256p. 70.00 (978-4-568-50348-7(5)) Azur Corp. JPN. Dist: Antique Collectors' Club.

Alpha Planning Inc., Staff, ed. Tokyo Ginza Graphics. 2009. (JPN & ENG., Illus.). 352p. 85.00 (978-4-568-50353-1(1)) Azur Corp. JPN. Dist: Antique Collectors' Club.

Amstutz, Walter, ed. Japanese Emblems & Designs. 2007. (Full-Color Electronic Design Ser.). (ENG., Illus.). 56p. pap. 14.95 (978-0-486-99825-1(8)) Dover Pubns., Inc.

Araki, Nobuyoshi, photos by. Nobuyoshi Araki: Self Life Death. abr. ed. 2011. (ENG., Illus.). 196p. 49.95 (978-0-7148-6116-6(2)) Phaidon Pr., Inc.

Asano, Shugo & Smith, Lawrence, intros. British Museum, Vol. 1. (Illus.). 268p. 300.00 (978-0-87011-855-5(2)) Kodansha America, Inc.

Audsley, George Ashdown. The Ornamental Arts of Japan: 60 Full-Color Plates. 2008. (Dover Fine Art, History of Art Ser.). (ENG., Illus.). 64p. pap. 12.95 (978-0-486-46549-4(7)) Dover Pubns., Inc.

Azur Corporation Editors. Display, Commercial Space & Sign Design, Vol. 34. 2007. (JPN & ENG., Illus.). 342p. 85.00 *(978-4-89737-570-0(3))* Azur Corp. JPN. Dist: Antique Collectors' Club.

—Pop. 2007. (ENG., Illus.). 212p. 70.00 *(978-4-948759-33-1(X))* Azur Corp. JPN. Dist: Antique Collectors' Club.

—Renewal Open Graphics: And Grand Opening Graphics. 2010. (ENG., Illus.). 270p. 85.00 *(978-4-568-50368-5(X))* Azur Corp. JPN. Dist: Antique Collectors' Club.

—49th Tokyo Art Directors' Club Annual. 2007. (ENG.). 436p. 85.00 *(978-4-568-53105-3(5))* Azur Corp. JPN. Dist: Antique Collectors' Club.

Azur Corporation Editors, creator. Graphic Design in Japan 2005. 2006. (ENG., Illus.). 464p. 89.95 *(978-4-89737-531-1(2))* Azur Corp. JPN. Dist: Antique Collectors' Club.

—Spa-De: Space & Design - International Review of Interior Design. 2006. (ENG., Illus.). 173p. 50.00 *(978-4-89737-515-1(0))* Azur Corp. JPN. Dist: Antique Collectors' Club.

Azur Corporation Editors & Iwamoto, Katsuya. Katsuya Iwamoto: Embody Design. 2007. (ENG., Illus.). 232p. 65.00 *(978-4-948759-84-8(8))* Azur Corp. JPN. Dist: Antique Collectors' Club.

Bairei, Kono. The Birds & Flowers of Kono Bairei: An Album of Japanese Woodblock Prints. 2011. (Dover Fine Art, History of Art Ser.). (ENG., Illus.). 160p. pap. 24.95 *(978-0-486-47050-4(4))* Dover Pubns., Inc.

Barcelona, Picasso, ed. Secret Images: Picasso & the Japanese Erotic Print. 2010. (ENG., Illus.). 168p. 50.00 *(978-0-500-09354-2(7)*, 509354) Thames & Hudson.

Berndt, Jacqueline & Kammerling-Meibauer, Bettina, eds. Manga's Cultural Crossroads. 2012. (Routledge Advances in Art & Visual Studies). (ENG., Illus.). 272p. (C). 125.00 ***(978-0-415-50450-8(3))*** Routledge.

Bogel, Cynthea. With a Single Glance: Buddhist Icons & Early Mikkyo Vision. 2010. (ENG., Illus.). 496p. 75.00 *(978-0-295-98920-4(3))* Univ. of Washington Pr.

Bordignon, Laura. The Golden Age of Japanese Okimono: The Dr. A. M. Kanter Collection. 2010. (JPN & ENG., Illus.). 304p. *(978-1-85149-609-9(2)*, Antique Collectors Club Dist) Antique Collectors' Club.

Bouquillard, Jocelyn. Hokusai's Mount Fuji: The Complete Views in Color. Getlein, Mark, tr. from FRE. 2007. (ENG., Illus.). 120p. 32.50 *(978-0-8109-9340-2(6))* Abrams.

Bouquillard, Jocelyn & Marquet, Christophe. Hokusai, First Manga Master. 2007. (ENG., Illus.). 80p. pap. 21.95 *(978-0-8109-9341-9(4))* Abrams.

Brandt, Kim. Kingdom of Beauty: Mingei & the Politics of Folk Art in Imperial Japan. 2007. (Asia-Pacific, Culture, Politics, & Society Ser.). (ENG., Illus.). 320p. 89.95 *(978-0-8223-3983-0(8))*; per. 24.95 *(978-0-8223-4000-3(3))* Duke Univ. Pr.

Brau, Lorie. Rakugo: Performing Comedy & Cultural Heritage in Contemporary Tokyo. 2008. (ENG., Illus.). 274p. 78.99 *(978-0-7391-2245-7(2))*; per. 36.99 *(978-0-7391-2246-4(0))* Lexington Bks.

Brinkley, Frank. Japan: Its History Arts & Literature. 2007. (ENG.). 464p. 52.95 *(978-0-548-11276-2(2))*; 540p. 57.95 *(978-0-548-11277-9(0))* Kessinger Publishing, LLC.

Briscoe, Susan. Japanese Quilt Blocks to Mix & Match. 2007. (Illus.). 128p. 26.95 *(978-1-56836-365-3(6))* Kodansha America, Inc.

—Japanese Taupe Quilts: 125 Blocks in Calm & Neutral Colors, 1 vol. 2010. (ENG., Illus.). 128p. 26.95 *(978-1-56836-378-3(8))* Kodansha America, Inc.

Brown, Kendall, ed. Dangerous Beauties & Dutiful Wives: Popular Portraits of Women in Japan, 1910-1925. 2011. (Dover Fine Art, History of Art Ser.). (ENG., Illus.). 128p. pap. 19.95 *(978-0-486-47639-1(1))* Dover Pubns., Inc.

Brown, Kendall H. Deco Japan: Shaping Art & Culture, 1920-1945. 2012. ***(978-0-88397-157-4(7))*** Art Services International.

Calza, Gian Carlo & Utamaro. Poem of the Pillow & Other Stories. 2010. (ENG., Illus.). 384p. 49.95 *(978-0-7148-4996-6(0))* Phaidon Pr., Inc.

Camerota, Remo. Drainspotting: Japanese Manhole Covers. 2010. (ENG.). 96p. 14.95 *(978-0-9820754-7-0(2))* Batty, Mark Pub., LLC.

—Graffiti Japan. 2011. (Illus.). 144p. pap. 21.95 *(978-1-935613-30-5(8))* Batty, Mark Pub., LLC.

Carpenter, J. Reading Surimono: The Interplay of Text & Image in Japanese Prints. 2008. 408p. *(978-90-04-16841-1(9))* BRILL.

Casarosa, Enrico, et al. Three Trees Make a Forest. 2006. (Illus.). 84p. 24.95 *(978-1-58423-226-1(9))* Gingko Pr., Inc.

Chiu, Melissa & Tezuka, Miwako. Yoshitomo Nara: Nobody's Fool. 2010. (ENG., Illus.). 272p. 60.00 *(978-0-8109-9414-0(3))* Abrams.

Chow, Brian G. & Sun, Seunghye. The Lure of Painted Poetry: Japanese & Korean Art. 2011. (Illus.). 120p. 50.00 *(978-1-55595-364-5(6))* Hudson Hills Pr. LLC.

Chu, Petra ten-Doesschate. The Orient Expressed: Japan's Influence on Western Art, 1854-1918. Weisberg, Gabriel P., ed. 2011. (ENG., Illus.). 192p. 34.95 *(978-1-887422-19-2(6))* Mississippi Museum of Art.

Clark, John. Japanese Exchanges in Art 1850s To 1930s: With Britain, Continental Europe, & the USA. 2007. (Illus.). 368p. per. 39.00 *(978-1-86487-303-0(5))* Univ. of Illinois Pr.

Clark, Timothy. Hokusai's Great Wave. 2011. (Objects in Focus Ser.). (ENG., Illus.). 64p. pap. 10.00 *(978-0-7141-2467-4(2))* British Museum Pr. GBR. Dist: Brown, David Bk. Co., The.

Cocoro Books Staff. Big Hair in Japan: Horrid Haircuts from the Land of the Rising Sun. 2008. (Illus.). 80p. pap. 15.00 *(978-1-932897-63-0(1)*, cocoro bks.) DH Publishing, Inc.

Collia-Suzuki, Gina. Utamaro Revealed. 2008. (Illus.). 208p. pap. 47.50 *(978-0-9559796-0-6(9))* Nezu Pr. GBR. Dist: Lulu Enterprises Inc.

Cram, Ralph Adams. Impressions of Japanese Architecture. 2010. (Tuttle Classics Ser.). (ENG., Illus.). 160p. pap. 14.95 *(978-4-8053-1107-3(X))* Tuttle Publishing.

Crilley, Mark. Mastering Manga with Mark Crilley: 30 drawing lessons from the creator of Akiko. 2012. (ENG., Illus.). 128p. pap. 22.99 ***(978-1-4403-0931-1(0)***, Impact) F&W Media, Inc.

Croissant, Doris & Mostow, Joshua S., eds. Performing "Nation" Gender Politics in Literature, Theater, & the Visual Arts of China & Japan, 1880-1940. 2008. (Sinica Leidensia Ser.). (Illus.). xxxii, 448p. *(978-90-04-17019-3(7))* BRILL.

De Goncourt, Edmond. Hokusai. 2009. (Temporis Ser.). (FRE & ENG., Illus.). 256p. 39.95 *(978-1-84484-652-8(0))* Parkstone International GBR. Dist: Ingram Pub. Services.

Dick, Stewart. Arts & Crafts of Old Japan. 2007. (ENG.). 228p. 41.95 *(978-0-548-09079-4(3))* Kessinger Publishing, LLC.

Dover. Hiroshige. 2010. (Dover Postcards Ser.). (ENG., Illus.). 24p. pap. 6.95 *(978-0-486-48078-7(X))* Dover Pubns., Inc.

Dover Publications Inc. Staff, creator. Japanese Stencil Designs: 168 Royalty-Free Designs. 2007. (Dover Electronic Clip Art Ser.). (ENG., Illus.). 48p. pap. 16.95 *(978-0-486-99813-8(4))* Dover Pubns., Inc.

Dover Publications Inc. Staff & Grafton, Carol Belanger. Japanese Vector Designs. Weller, Alan, ed. 2008. (Dover Pictura Electronic Clip Art Ser.). (ENG.). 128p. pap. 49.95 *(978-0-486-99023-1(0))* Dover Pubns., Inc.

Durston, Diane. Wabi Sabi: The Art of Everyday Life. 2006. (ENG., Illus.). 368p. pap. 8.95 *(978-1-58017-628-6(3)*, 1580176283) Storey Publishing, LLC.

Earle, Joe. Buriki: Japanese Tin Toys from the Golden Age of the American Automobile. 2009. (ENG., Illus.). 96p. pap. 19.95 *(978-0-300-15157-2(8))* Japan Society Gallery.

—New Bamboo: Contemporary Japanese Masters. 2008. (Illus.). 128p. 25.00 *(978-0-300-14141-2(6))* Japan Society Gallery.

Earle, Joe, et al. Arts of Japan: MFA Highlights. 2008. (ENG., Illus.). 320p. pap. 24.95 *(978-0-87846-714-3(9))* Museum of Fine Arts, Boston.

—Japanese Art & Design. Earle, Joe, ed. 2009. (ENG., Illus.). 236p. pap. 39.95 *(978-1-85177-562-0(5))* V & A Pubns. GBR. Dist: Hachette Bk. Group.

Eck, Stefan. Oeil. 2009. 42p. pap. 32.00 *(978-0-557-14577-5(5))* Lulu Enterprises Inc.

Ehrli, Vivane, ed. Shiraishi. (ENG & GER., Illus.). 184p. 29.95 *(978-3-89322-867-6(5))* Edition Cantz DEU. Dist: D.A.P./Distributed Art Pubs.

Elliott, David, et al, texts. The Group 1965: We Are Boys. 2012. (ENG, JPN & GER., Illus.). 188p. pap. 40.00 ***(978-88-366-2094-4(9))*** Silvana ITA. Dist: D.A.P./Distributed Art Pubs.

Elliott, David & Ozaki, Tetsuya. Bye Bye Kitty!!! Between Heaven & Hell in Contemporary Japanese Art. 2011. (ENG., Illus.). 136p. pap. 35.00 *(978-0-300-16690-3(7))* Yale Univ. Pr.

Endo, Kyoko. The Post Art Works of Kyoko Endo. 2006. (ENG., Illus.). 136p. 50.00 *(978-88-7200-177-6(3))* Vianello Libri ITA. Dist: Antique Collectors' Club.

Enlightenment, des. After the Reality, 1 vol. 2007. (ENG., Illus.). 52p. pap. 20.00 *(978-0-9753243-8-7(1))* Deitch, Jeffrey Inc.

Epprecht, Katharina, ed. Kannon: Divine Compassion: Early Buddhist Art from Japan. 2007. (Reitberg Museum, Zurich Ser.). (ENG., Illus.). 196p. 50.00 *(978-3-907077-30-6(X))* Holberton, Paul Publishing GBR. Dist: Univ. of Washington Pr.

Ernest Francisco Fenollosa Set: Published Writings in English, 3 vols. 2010. 2700p. 700.00 *(978-4-86166-112-9(9))* Routledge.

Exley. Izima Kaoru: Landscapes with a Corpse. 2008. (ENG., Illus.). 192p. 95.00 *(978-3-7757-2237-7(8))* Hatje Cantz Verlag GmbH & Co KG DEU. Dist: D.A.P./Distributed Art Pubs.

Fenollosa, Ernest F., ed. Epochs of Chinese & Japanese Art: An Outline History of East Asiatic Design, 2 vols. 2007. (Stone Bridge Classics Ser.). (ENG., Illus.). 676p. per. 18.95 *(978-1-933330-26-6(0))* Stone Bridge Pr.

Fischer, Felice. The Art of Japanese Craft: 1875 to the Present. 2008. *(978-0-87633-202-3(5))* Philadelphia Museum of Art.

Flores, Irene & McSpadden, Krisanne. Shojo Fashion Manga Art School, Year 2: Draw modern Looks. 2012. (ENG., Illus.). 144p. pap. 22.99 ***(978-1-4403-1080-5(7)***, Impact) F&W Media, Inc.

Forrer, Matthi. The Baur Collection: Japanese Prints, 2 vols. (Illus.). 680p. 175.00 *(978-2-88031-007-3(5))* Baur Foundation CHE. Dist: Art Media Resources, Inc.

—Hokusai. 2010. (Illus.). 288p. 120.00 *(978-3-7913-4438-6(2))* Prestel Publishing.

Fraleigh, Sondra Horton. Dancing into Darkness: Butoh, Zen, & Japan. 2010. (Illus.). 288p. pap. 24.95 *(978-0-8229-6115-4(6))* Univ. of Pittsburgh Pr.

Franciolli, Marco, et al, eds. Gutai. 2011. (ENG & ITA., Illus.). 264p. pap. 49.95 *(978-88-366-1815-6(4))* Silvana ITA. Dist: D.A.P./Distributed Art Pubs.

Grafton, Carol Belanger, ed. Traditional Japanese Vector Motifs. 2010. (Dover Electronic Clip Art Ser.). (ENG., Illus.). 48p. pap. 19.95 *(978-0-486-99056-9(7))* Dover Pubns., Inc.

Grafton, Carol Belanger & Dover Staff. Artistic Japan: 300 Traditional Spot Illustrations. Bing, Siegfried, ed. 2009. (Dover Pictorial Archive Ser.). (ENG., Illus.). 128p. pap. 19.95 *(978-0-486-46777-1(5))* Dover Pubns., Inc.

Graphic-Sha. A Complete Guide to Special Effects Makeup: Conceptual Artwork by Japanese Makeup Artists: Conceptual Artwork by Japanese Makeup Artists. 2008. 136p. pap. 22.99 *(978-4-7661-1833-9(2))* Graphic-Sha JPN. Dist: Diamond Bk. Distributors.

—Gothic & Lolita, Vol. 5. 2009. (Illus.). 128p. (YA). pap. 19.99 *(978-4-7661-2003-5(5))* Graphic-Sha JPN. Dist: Diamond Bk. Distributors.

Gray, Peter. The Practical Guide to Drawing Manga. 2012. (Great Drawing Step-by-Step Ser.). (ENG.). 48p. (YA). (gr. 5-8). lib. bdg. 27.95 ***(978-1-4488-7213-8(8)***, Rosen Central) Rosen Publishing Group, Inc., The.

Gunner, Janice. Shibori for Textile Artists, 1 vol. 2010. (ENG., Illus.). 128p. pap. 22.95 *(978-1-56836-380-6(X))* Kodansha America, Inc.

Guth, Christine. Art of Edo Japan: The Artist & the City, 1615-1868. 2010. (ENG., Illus.). 176p. pap. 20.00 *(978-0-300-16413-8(0))* Yale Univ. Pr.

Hagedorn, Michael. Post-Dated: The Schooling of an Irreverent Bonsai Monk. 2008. (Illus.). 172p. pap. 14.95 *(978-0-9801094-7-4(7))* Crataegus Bks.

Harrington, Lee "Bridgett". Shibari You Can Use: Japanese Rope Bondage & Erotic Macramé. 2007. 156p. pap. 21.99 *(978-0-615-14490-0(X))* Mystic Productions.

Harrison, John & Harrison, Edward. Idle Idol: The Japanese Mascot. 2010. (ENG., Illus.). 144p. 16.95 *(978-0-9841906-1-4(9))* Batty, Mark Pub., LLC.

Hart, Christopher. Basic Anatomy for the Manga Artist: Everything You Need to Start Drawing Authentic Manga Characters. 2011. (ENG., Illus.). 160p. pap. 21.99 *(978-0-8230-4770-3(9))* Watson-Guptill Pubns., Inc.

—Manga for the Beginner Chibis: Everything You Need to Start Drawing the Super-Cute Characters of Japanese Comics. 2010. (ENG., Illus.). 192p. pap. 21.99 *(978-0-8230-1488-0(6))* Watson-Guptill Pubns., Inc.

—Manga for the Beginner Shoujo: Everything You Need to Start Drawing the Most Popular Style of Japanese Comics. 2010. (ENG., Illus.). 192p. pap. 21.99 *(978-0-8230-3329-4(5))* Watson-Guptill Pubns., Inc.

Hartmann, Sadakichi. Japanese Art. 2008. 352p. 28.99 *(978-0-559-87595-3(9))*; pap. 31.75 *(978-0-559-87592-2(4))* BiblioBazaar.

—Japanese Art. 2009. 98p. pap. 14.14 *(978-1-151-65165-5(6))* General Bks. LLC.

—Japanese Art. 2008. 334p. 45.95 *(978-1-4372-4809-8(8))*; pap. 30.95 *(978-1-4371-2046-2(6))* Kessinger Publishing, LLC.

Hasegawa, Machiko. Wonderful World Of Sazae-San, 12 vols., Set. Young, Jules, tr. *(978-4-7700-2435-0(5))* Kodansha International JPN. Dist: Kodansha America, Inc.

Hata, Tomoaki, photos by. The Night Is Still Young. 2010. (ENG., Illus.). 104p. pap. 24.95 *(978-1-57687-552-0(0))* powerHouse Cultural Entertainment, Inc.

Hatakeyama, Naoya & Watanabe, Osamu, photos by. Naoshima. 2011. (ENG & JPN., Illus.). 232p. 60.00 *(978-3-7757-2703-7(5))* Hatje Cantz Verlag GmbH & Co KG DEU. Dist: D.A.P./Distributed Art Pubs.

Hayakawa, Monta. Shunga: Japanese Erotic Art. 2010. (ENG., Illus.). 400p. pap. 35.00 *(978-4-89444-802-5(5)*, PIE Bks.) Rizzoli International Pubns., Inc.

Hein, Laura & Jennison, Rebecca, eds. Imagination Without Borders: Feminist Artist Tomiyama Taeko & Social Responsibility. 2010. (Illus.). 164p. 60.00 *(978-1-929280-62-9(9))* Univ. of Michigan, Ctr. for Japanese Studies.

—Imagination Without Borders: Feminist Artist Tomiyama Taeko & Social Responsibility. 2010. (Illus.). 164p. pap. 24.00 *(978-1-929280-63-6(7))* Univ. of Michigan, Ctr. for Japanese Studies.

Hino, Matsuri. Vampire Knight Artbook: Matsuri Hino Illustrations. 2011. (Vampire Knight Ser.). (ENG., Illus.). 96p. 24.99 *(978-1-4215-4005-4(3))* Viz Media.

Histoire de l'art du Japon, par la Commission imperiale du Japon a l'Exposition universelle de Paris 1900. 2008. (ENG.). 500p. 525.00 *(978-4-901481-99-1(1))* Synapse, Edition JPN. Dist: Taylor & Francis Group.

Hunter, Jack. Dream Spectres: Extreme Ukiyo-E: Sex, Blood & the Supernatural. 2010. (Illus.). 128p. pap. *(978-1-84068-301-1(5))* Creation Bks. GBR. Dist: SCB Distributors.

Ikari Studio Staff. Monster Book of Manga - Boys. 2010. (ENG.). 384p. pap. 25.99 *(978-0-06-173298-0(2)*, Collins Design) HarperCollins Pubs.

Ikeda, Ryoji. Ryoji Ikeda: Dataphonics. 2010. (ENG., Illus.). 64p. pap. 40.00 *(978-2-914563-51-2(5))* Dis Voir Editions FRA. Dist: D.A.P./Distributed Art Pubs.

Imperia, Giovanna. Kumihimo Wire Jewelry: Essential Techniques & 20 Jewelry Projects for the Japanese Art of Braiding. 2011. (ENG., Illus.). 144p. pap. 21.99 *(978-0-8230-8551-4(1))* Watson-Guptill Pubns., Inc.

Impey, Oliver & Seaman, Joyce. Japanese Decorative Arts of the Meiji Period. 2006. (Ashmolean Handbooks). (ENG., Illus.). 96p. pap. 15.95 *(978-1-85444-198-0(1))* Ashmolean Museum GBR. Dist: Antique Collectors' Club.

Impey, Oliver R. & Seaman, Joyce. Japanese Decorative Arts of the Meiji Period: 1868-1912. 2006. (Ashmolean Handbooks). (ENG., Illus.). 96p. 22.95 *(978-1-85444-197-3(3))* Ashmolean Museum GBR. Dist: National Bk. Network.

Inro & Netsuke: Tokyo National Museum Collection. (Illus.). 250p. pap. 85.00 *(978-4-544-02401-2(3))* Nigensha Publishing Co., Ltd. JPN. Dist: Art Media Resources, Inc.

Ippolito, Jean M. The Search for New Media: Late 20th Century Art & Technology in Japan. 2011. ***(978-1-86335-949-8(4))***; pap. ***(978-1-86335-947-4(8))*** Common Ground Publishing Pty, Ltd.

Isager, Marianne. Japanese Inspired Knits. 2009. (Marianne Isager Collection). (ENG., Illus.). 144p. pap. 22.95 *(978-1-59668-114-9(4))* Interweave Pr., LLC.

Izu, Kenro. Kenro Izu, a Thirty Year Retrospective. 2010. (Illus.). 200p. *(978-1-59005-270-9(6))* Nazraeli Pr.

Jacobson, Christa. Warrior Expressions. 2010. 83p. pap. 14.99 *(978-0-557-47670-1(4))* Lulu Enterprises Inc.

JAGDA Yearbook Editorial Team Staff. Graphic Design in Japan 2008. 2009. (JPN & ENG., Illus.). 480p. 95.00 *(978-4-89737-615-8(7))* Azur Corp. JPN. Dist: Antique Collectors' Club.

Japan Graphic Designers Association Inc., ed. Graphic Design in Japan 2009. 2010. (ENG., Illus.). 480p. 100.00 *(978-4-89737-643-1(2))* Azur Corp. JPN. Dist: Antique Collectors' Club.

Japan Package Design Association Staff, ed. Japan Package Design Members' Work Today 2008. 2009. (JPN & ENG., Illus.). 420p. 85.00 *(978-4-89737-606-6(8))* Azur Corp. JPN. Dist: Antique Collectors' Club.

Japanese Acrobats: Flip Book. 2012. (ENG., Illus.). 160p. pap. 5.99 *(978-950-889-213-3(7))* La Marca ARG. Dist: D.A.P./Distributed Art Pubs.

Jirka-Schmitz, Patrizia. Netsuke Vol. 2: Four Centuries of Masterpieces. 2007. (ENG., Illus.). 416p. 135.00 *(978-3-925369-90-2(2))* Arnoldsche Art Pubs. DEU. Dist: Antique Collectors' Club.

Jouwenhoven. Japanese Prints. 2006. (Illus.). 144p. pap. *(978-90-74822-87-9(8))* BRILL.

Kamikaze Factory Studio. Shojo Manga: Pop & Romance. 2011. (ENG., Illus.). 352p. pap. 25.99 *(978-0-06-202351-3(9)*, Collins Design) HarperCollins Pubs.

Kamikaze Factory Studio Staff. Kodomo Manga - Super Cute! 2009. (ENG., Illus.). 384p. pap. 24.99 *(978-0-06-192755-3(4)*, Collins Design) HarperCollins Pubs.

Kanzaka, Sekka & Marks, Andreas. Kamisaka Sekka: Rinpa Traditionalist, Modern Designer. 2012. 192p. ***(978-0-7649-6175-5(6))*** Pomegranate Communications, Inc.

Katz, Janice. Beyond Golden Clouds: Japanese Screens from the Art Institute of Chicago & the Saint Louis Art Museum. 2009. (Illus.). 216p. pap. *(978-0-86559-232-2(2))* Art Institute of Chicago.

Katz, Janice, ed. Beyond Golden Clouds: Japanese Screens from the Art Institute of Chicago & the Saint Louis Art Museum. 2009. (ENG., Illus.). 216p. 55.00 *(978-0-300-11948-0(8))* Art Institute of Chicago.

Kelly, Daniel. Daniel Kelly: An American Artist in Japan, 1 vol. 2010. (ENG., Illus.). 128p. 45.00 *(978-4-7700-3133-4(5))* Kodansha America, Inc.

Kendall, Richard & Devonyar, Jill. Degas & the Art of Japan. 2007. (ENG., Illus.). 112p. per. 24.95 *(978-0-300-12633-4(6))* Yale Univ. Pr.

Kendall, Richard & DeVonyar, Jill, texts. Degas & the Art of Japan. 2007. (YA). per. 35.00 *(978-0-9654594-6-4(2))* Reading Public Museum.

Kent, Douglas. Complete Shibari: Land, Vol. 1. 2010. (Complete Shibari Ser.). (ENG.). 96p. pap. 30.00 *(978-0-9736688-1-0(4))* Mental Gears Pubng. CAN. Dist: SCB Distributors.

—Complete Shibari: Sky, Vol. 2. 2010. (Complete Shibari Ser.). (ENG.). 96p. pap. 30.00 *(978-0-9736688-2-7(2))* Mental Gears Pubng. CAN. Dist: SCB Distributors.

Kiefer, Anselm. Deja-Vu 14: The 'Provoke' Issue. pap. 25.00 *(978-4-309-90334-7(7))* Fiction, Inc. JPN. Dist: D.A.P./Distributed Art Pubs.

King, James. Beyond the Great Wave: The Japanese Landscape Print, 1727-1960. 2010. (Illus.). 244p. pap. *(978-3-0343-0317-0(3))* Lang, Peter.

King, James & Iwakiri, Yuriko. Japanese Warrior Prints 1646-1904. 2006. (Illus.). 280p. *(978-90-74822-84-8(3))* BRILL.

kitamura, takahiro. Underway Is the Only Way. 2008. (ENG.). pap. *(978-0-9798682-1-4(1))* State of Grace Inc.

Klauke, Jürgen & Poetter, Jochen. Jurgen Klauke. (GER & ENG., Illus.). 168p. 49.95 *(978-3-89322-395-4(9))* Edition Cantz DEU. Dist: D.A.P./Distributed Art Pubs.

Knutsen, Roald. Sun Tzu & the Art of Medieval Japanese Warfare. 2006. (Illus.). 190p. *(978-1-905246-00-7(5))* BRILL.

Kobayashi, Hirayama. Japanese Art: Osterreiches Museum fur Angewandte Kunst, Vienna - Naprestek Museum & National Gallery, Prague - Museum of Applied Arts, Budapest, Vol. 11. 208p. 550.00 *(978-4-06-253211-2(5))* Kodansha, Ltd. JPN. Dist: Kodansha America, Inc.

Konan, Tanigami. Japanese Woodblock Flower Prints. 2008. (Dover Fine Art, History of Art Ser.). (ENG., Illus.). 128p. pap. 16.95 *(978-0-486-46442-8(3))* Dover Pubns., Inc.

Koyama-Richard, Brigitte. One Thousand Years of Manga. 2008. (ENG., Illus.). 248p. 49.95 *(978-2-08-030029-4(6))* Flammarion et Cie FRA. Dist: Random Hse., Inc.

Kusama, Yayoi. Yayoi Kusama. Neri, Louise, ed. 2012. (ENG., Illus.). 272p. 75.00 ***(978-0-8478-3908-7(7))*** Rizzoli International Pubns., Inc.

Lambourne, Lionel. Japonisme: Cultural Crossings Between Japan & the West. rev. ed. 2007. (ENG., Illus.). 240p. pap. 49.95 *(978-0-7148-4797-9(6))* Phaidon Pr., Inc.

Li, Yishan. Faces & Hair: The Pocket Guide to Drawing All Manga Face & Hair Styles. 2010. (Mini Manga Ser.). (ENG., Illus.). 192p. pap. 7.95 *(978-1-84448-523-9(4))* Search Pr., Ltd. GBR. Dist: Independent Pubs. Group.

—Hands & Feet: The Pocket Guide to Drawing Hands & Feet from Every Angle. 2010. (Mini Manga Ser.). (ENG., Illus.). 192p. pap. 7.95 *(978-1-84448-522-2(6))* Search Pr., Ltd. GBR. Dist: Independent Pubs. Group.

—500 Manga Creatures. 2008. 528p. pap. 19.95 *(978-0-06-165050-5(1)*, Collins Design) HarperCollins Pubs.

—500 Manga Villains & Heroes. 2010. (ENG.). 528p. pap. 19.99 *(978-0-06-196880-8(3)*, Collins Design) HarperCollins Pubs.

Lillehoj, Elizabeth, ed. Acquisition: Art & Ownership in EDO-Period Japan. 2007. (ENG., Illus.). 208p. per. 50.00 *(978-1-891640-50-6(X))* Floating World Editions.

Lin, Selena. Manga School Vol. 1: Draw Your Own Manga. 2008. (Illus.). 128p. pap. 14.99 *(978-1-4278-1023-6(0))* TOKYOPOP, Inc.

Lippit, Yukio. Colorful Realm: Japanese Bird-and-Flower Paintings by Ito Jakuchu. 2012. (ENG., Illus.). 224p. 50.00 ***(978-0-226-48460-0(2))*** Univ. of Chicago Pr.

Lupas, Liana. On Eagles' Wings: The King James Turns 400. Lupas, Liana & Pongracz, Patricia C., eds. 2011. pap. 29.95 ***(978-0-9777839-8-4(7))*** Museum of Biblical Art.

Mabuchi, Aiko, ed. Mabuchi: William Anderson: the Pictorial Arts of Japan: Western sources on japanese art & japonism, Series 4. 2008. 2700p. 825.00 *(978-4-86166-028-3(9))* Synapse, Edition JPN. Dist: Taylor & Francis Group.

Machotka, Ewa. Visual Genesis of Japanese National Identity: Hokusai's Hyakunin Isshu. 2009. 256p. pap. 44.95 *(978-90-5201-482-1(5))* PIE - Peter Lang BEL. Dist: Lang, Peter.

Maggia, Filippo & Dall'Olio, Chiara, eds. Yasuzo Nojima. 2011. (ITA & ENG., Illus.). 144p. 45.00 *(978-88-572-0471-0(5))* Skira Editore ITA. Dist: Random Hse., Inc.

Mandelbaum, Jill "Horiyuki". Studying Horiyoshi III: A Westerner's Journey into Japanese Tattoo. 2008. (Illus.). 160p. pap. 29.99 *(978-0-7643-2968-5(5))* Schiffer Publishing, Ltd.

Masao, Yamamoto & Bois, Arpais du. Where We Met. 2012. (ENG, JPN & FRE., Illus.). 128p. 140.00 ***(978-90-209-5788-4(0))*** Lannoo Pubs./Racine.

McCormick, Melissa & Tokyo National Museum Staff. Elegant Perfection: Masterpieces of Courtly & Religious Art from the Tokyo National Museum. 2012. (ENG., Illus.). 128p. 45.00 *(978-0-300-17593-6(0))* Museum of Fine Arts, Houston.

Menegazzo, Rossella. 100 Japanese Posters, 2001-2010. 2011. (JPN, ITA & ENG., Illus.). 144p. pap. 65.00 *(978-88-370-7829-4(3))* Electa ITA. Dist: National Bk. Network.

Merewether, Charles & Hiro, Rika Iezumi, eds. Art, Anti-Art, Non-Art: Experimentations in the Public Sphere in Postwar Japan, 1950-1970. 2007. (ENG., Illus.). 158p. 45.00 *(978-0-89236-866-2(7))* Oxford Univ. Pr., Inc.

Mizuta, Tamae, ed. Mizuta: Foundations of Japanese Feminism: A Collection of Western Sources: Series 1: books translated into japanese during the meiji & taisho era in five Volumes. 2008. (ENG.). 2700p. 1035.00 *(978-4-86166-055-9(6))* Synapse, Edition JPN. Dist: Taylor & Francis Group.

Modegi, Masaaki. The Making of Japanese Kites: Tradition, Beauty & Creation, 1 vol. 2007. (ENG., Illus.). 112p. per. 16.95 *(978-4-88996-222-2(0))* Japan Pubns. Trading Co. JPN. Dist: Oxford Univ. Pr., Inc.

Moll, Frank-Thorsten & Görner, Veit, eds. Araki Meets Hokusai. 2008. (GER & ENG., Illus.). 288p. 70.00 *(978-3-939583-78-3(2))* Kehrer Verlag Heidelberg, Klaus Kehrer DEU. Dist: Consortium Bk. Sales & Distribution.

Morita, Toshiro, photos by. Noh: Classical Japanese Performing Art. 2010. (ENG., Illus.). 280p. pap. 34.50 *(978-4-89444-846-9(7)*, PIE Bks.) Rizzoli International Pubns., Inc.

Morrison, Jasper, et al, texts. Muji. 2010. (ENG., Illus.). 256p. 65.00 *(978-0-8478-3487-7(5))* Rizzoli International Pubns., Inc.

Moshino, Katsura. Raw Communication. 2006. 127p. 58.00 *(978-4-7949-6680-3(6))* Trucatriche.

Muller, Lars & Miki, Akiko, eds. Insular Insight: Where Art & Architecture Conspire with Nature. 2011. (ENG., Illus.). 480p. 70.00 ***(978-3-03778-255-2(2))*** Lars Muller Pubs. CHE. Dist: Prestel Publishing.

Munro, Majella. Understanding Shunga: A Guide to Japanese Erotic Art. 2009. 160p. 55.00 *(978-1-904989-54-7(3))* Erotic Print Society GBR. Dist: SCB Distributors.

Munroe, Alexandra. Lee Ufan: Marking Infinity. 2012. (ENG., Illus.). 200p. 65.00 ***(978-0-89207-418-1(3))*** Guggenheim, Solomon R. Museum.

Murakami, Takashi & Schimmel, Paul. Murakami. 2007. *(978-1-933751-06-1(1))* Museum of Contemporary Art, Los Angeles.

Murase, Miyeko. Through the Seasons: Japanese Art in Nature. 2008. *(978-0-931102-77-6(4))* Clark, Sterling & Francine Art Institute.

—Through the Seasons: Japanese Art in Nature. 2009. (ENG., Illus.). 84p. pap. 19.95 *(978-0-300-14188-7(2))* Yale Univ. Pr.

Nadel, Dan, ed. The Ganzfeld 5: Japanada!, 5. 2007. (Illus.). 186p. pap. 29.95 *(978-1-58423-251-3(X))* Gingko Pr., Inc.

Nakajo, Masayoshi, des. Hanatsubaki & Nakajo: Shiseido Hanatsubaki Magazine 1968-2008: Fashion, Art & Culture. 2009. (ENG., Illus.). 448p. pap. 55.00 *(978-4-89444-742-4(8)*, PIE Bks.) Rizzoli International Pubns., Inc.

Namie Wren. When the Atomic Ash Blows Away, the Wild Flowers Grow Stronger. 2009. 36p. pap. 17.00 *(978-1-4269-1878-0(X))* Trafford Publishing.

Nara, Hiroshi. Inexorable Modernity: Japan's Grappling with Modernity in the Arts. 2007. (ENG., Illus.). 284p. per. 34.99 *(978-0-7391-1842-9(0))* Lexington Bks.

Nara, Yoshitomo. Yoshitomo Nara: The Complete Works. 2011. (ENG.). 800p. 250.00 *(978-0-8118-7028-3(6))* Chronicle Bks. LLC.

Narahashi, Asako. Half Awake & Half Asleep in the Water: Photographs. 2007. (Illus.). 75p. *(978-1-59005-215-0(3))* Nazraeli Pr.

Nbc, 1st. Indian Influence on the Art of Japan. 2009. 220p. lib. bdg. *(978-81-7211-269-1(6))* Northern Bk. Ctr.

Negri, Paul, ed. Japanese Animal & Floral Crest Designs. 2007. (Dover Pictorial Archive Ser.). (ENG., Illus.). 64p. per. 8.95 *(978-0-486-45811-3(3))* Dover Pubns., Inc.

Ninagawa, Mika, photos by. Mika Ninagawa. 2010. (ENG., Illus.). 352p. 75.00 *(978-0-8478-3397-9(6))* Rizzoli International Pubns., Inc.

Oba, Yoshiyuki, ed. Heroes & Heroines. 2012. (ENG., Illus.). 208p. pap. 29.95 ***(978-4-7562-4169-6(7))*** Rizzoli International Pubns., Inc.

Oda, Eiichiro. One Piece Color Walk Art Book Vol. 2. 2012. (One Piece Ser.). (ENG.). 110p. pap. 19.99 ***(978-1-4215-4113-6(0))*** Viz Media.

Ogawa, Morihiro, ed. Art of the Samurai: Japanese Arms & Armor, 1156-1868. 2009. (Illus.). 356p. 65.00 *(978-0-300-14205-1(6))* Yale Univ. Pr.

Ogawa, Morihiro & Harada, Kazutoshi. Art of the Samurai: Japanese Arms & Armor, 1156-1868. 2009. 65.00 *(978-1-58839-345-6(3))* Metropolitan Museum of Art, The.

Oguchi, Masami, et al. Japanese Bamboo Baskets: Meiji, Modern, & Contemporary, 1 vol. Frew, Gavin, tr. from JPN. 2007. (ENG., Illus.). 160p. 45.00 *(978-4-7700-3062-7(2))* Kodansha America, Inc.

Ohki, Sadako & Watanabe, Takeshi. Tea Culture of Japan. 2009. (ENG., Illus.). 112p. pap. 19.95 *(978-0-300-14692-9(2))* Yale Univ. Art Gallery.

Okada, Koichiro, et al. Masters of Bamboo: Artistic Lineages in the Lloyd Cotsen Japanese Basket Collection. 2008. (ENG., Illus.). 144p. pap. 25.00 *(978-0-939117-40-6(1))* Asian Art Museum of San Francisco.

Okakura, Kakuzo. Ideals of the East: The Spirit of Japanese Art. 2007. (ENG.). 120p. per. 9.95 *(978-1-60206-073-9(8))* Cosimo, Inc.

—The Ideals of the East: With Special Reference to the Art of Japan. 2007. (Stone Bridge Classics Ser.). (ENG., Illus.). 152p. per. 10.95 *(978-1-933330-25-9(2))* Stone Bridge Pr.

Oltheten, Paulien. Pauline Oltheten: Walk on a Line. 2011. (ENG., Illus.). 240p. pap. 45.00 ***(978-90-5662-799-7(6))*** NAi Uitgevers / Publishers Stichting NLD. Dist: D.A.P./Distributed Art Pubs.

Onuma, Tomoyuki. Japanese Art Deco CD-ROM & Book. 2008. (Dover Electronic Clip Art Ser.). (ENG., Illus.). 64p. pap. 22.95 *(978-0-486-99030-9(3))* Dover Pubns., Inc.

Papp, Zilia. Anime & Its Roots in Early Japanese Monster Art, 1 vol. 2010. (ENG., Illus.). 240p. *(978-1-906876-18-0(5))* BRILL.

Pate, Alan Scott. Japanese Dolls: The Fascinating World of Ningyo. 2008. (ENG., Illus.). 272p. 49.95 *(978-4-8053-0922-3(9))* Tuttle Publishing.

Perry, Fred, et al. How to Draw Manga: Next Generation Pocket Manga Volume 1: Next Generation Pocket Manga Volume 1. 2009. (Illus.). 144p. pap. 12.95 *(978-0-9816647-8-1(4))* Antarctic Pr., Inc.

Phillips, Christopher & Fuku, Noriko, eds. Hiroh Kikai, 1 vol. 2008. (ENG., Illus.). 264p. 70.00 *(978-3-86521-601-4(3))* Steidl, Gerhard Druckerei und Verlag DEU. Dist: Innovative Logistics.

Pie Books Editorial Staff. Mythical Beasts of Japan: From Evil Creatures to Sacred Beings. Taki, Akiko, ed. 2010. (ENG & JPN., Illus.). 392p. pap. 35.00 *(978-4-89444-788-2(6)*, PIE Bks.) Rizzoli International Pubns., Inc.

Pie Books Staff. Illustration Book Pro 01: 150 of the Hottest Illustrators in Japan Today. Pict, ed. 2008. (JPN & ENG., Illus.). 320p. pap. 34.95 *(978-4-89444-587-1(5))* Rizzoli International Pubns., Inc.

—Pictogram & Icon Graphics 2. Miyazaki, Ami & Sekita, Rie, eds. 2009. (ENG., Illus.). 200p. 75.00 *(978-4-89444-585-7(9))* Rizzoli International Pubns., Inc.

—Summer Kimonos & the Colors of Japan: Kimono Collection of Katsumi Yumioka. Yumioka, Katsumi, ed. 2009. (JPN & ENG., Illus.). 232p. pap. 34.50 *(978-4-89444-531-4(X))* Rizzoli International Pubns., Inc.

—Wave, Cloud, Pine: Traditional Patterns in Japanese Design. Hamada, Nobuyoshi, ed. 2008. (ENG & JPN., Illus.). 400p. pap. 35.00 *(978-4-89444-533-8(6))* Rizzoli International Pubns., Inc.

Pie Books Staff & Shaughnessy, Adrian. Illustration Book Pro 2. 2009. (JPN & ENG., Illus.). 320p. pap. 34.95 *(978-4-89444-722-6(3)*, PIE Bks.) Rizzoli International Pubns., Inc.

Pier, Garrett Chatfield. Temple Treasures of Japan 1914. 2007. (ENG.). 410p. 49.95 *(978-0-548-05427-7(4))* Kessinger Publishing, LLC.

Poysden, Mark & Bratt, Marco. A History of Japanese Body Suit Tattooing. 2006. (Illus.). 224p. pap. *(978-90-74822-75-6(4))* BRILL.

Quintanilla, Sonya Rhie, et al. Dyeing Elegance: Asian Modernism & the Art of Kuboku & Hisako Takaku, 1 vol. 2012. (ENG., Illus.). 64p. 25.00 ***(978-0-615-56210-0(8))*** San Diego Museum of Art.

Reeve, John. Japanese Art in Detail. 2006. (Art in Detail Ser.). (Illus.). 144p. 22.95 *(978-0-674-02391-8(9))* Harvard Univ. Pr.

Relativision. 2007. pap. 45.00 *(978-4-7661-1677-9(1))* Graphic-Sha JPN. Dist: Gingko Pr., Inc.

Richie, Donald. A Tractate on Japanese Aesthetics. 2007. (ENG.). 80p. per. 9.95 *(978-1-933330-23-5(6))* Stone Bridge Pr.

Ridgely, Steven C. Japanese Counterculture: The Antiestablishment Art of Terayama Shuji. 2011. (ENG., Illus.). 264p. 67.50 *(978-0-8166-6752-9(7))*; pap. 22.50 *(978-0-8166-6753-6(5))* Univ. of Minnesota Pr.

Rimer, J. Thomas & McCallum, Toshiko M. Since Meiji: Perspectives on the Japanese Visual Arts, 1868-2000. 2011. 60.00 ***(978-0-8248-3441-8(0))***; pap. 28.00 ***(978-0-8248-3582-8(4))*** Univ. of Hawaii Pr.

Rousmaniere, Nicole, ed. Crafting Beauty in Modern Japan: Celebrating Fifty Years of the Japan Traditional Art Crafts Exhibition. 2007. (ENG., Illus.). 208p. pap. 45.00 *(978-0-295-98733-0(2))* Univ. of Washington Pr.

Russian Avant-Garde. 2010. (Illus.). 200p. *(978-1-84484-443-2(9))* Parkstone International.

Sadao, Tsuneko S. & Wada, Stephanie. Discovering the Arts of Japan: A Historical Overview. 2010. (ENG., Illus.). 284p. pap. 29.95 *(978-0-7892-1035-7(5))* Abbeville Pr., Inc.

Sakai, Tadayasu. Wakabayashi Isamu Inu ni Natta Chokokuka. 2008. (JPN., Illus.). 239p. *(978-4-622-07354-3(4))* Misuzu Shobo.

Sato, Doshin. Modern Japanese Art & the Meiji State: The Politics of Beauty. 2011. (ENG., Illus.). 376p. 75.00 *(978-1-60606-059-9(7))* Getty Pubns.

Schiermeier, Kris & Forrer, Matthi. Wonders of Imperial Japan: Meiji Art from the Khalili Collection. 2007. (ENG., Illus.). 128p. per. 30.00 *(978-90-400-8225-2(1))* Waanders B.V., Uitgeverij NLD. Dist: National Bk. Network.

Schneider, Fredric T. The Art of Japanese Cloisonne Enamel: History, Techniques & Artists, 1600 to the Present. 2010. (ENG., Illus.). 372p. 95.00 *(978-0-7864-4732-9(X))* McFarland & Co., Inc. Pubs.

Schodt, Frederik L. Dreamland Japan: Writings on Modern Manga, Gift Edition. 2011. (ENG., Illus.). 360p. 29.95 ***(978-1-933330-95-2(3))*** Stone Bridge Pr.

Schroder, Tim. Hiroshi Suzuki. 2010. (ENG., Illus.). 80p. pap. 24.95 *(978-1-85759-625-0(0))* Scala, Editions FRA. Dist: National Bk. Network.

Screech, Timon. Sex & the Floating World: Erotic Images in Japan, 1700-1820. 2nd ed. 2009. (ENG., Illus.). 304p. pap. 35.00 *(978-1-86189-432-8(5))* Reaktion Bks., Ltd. GBR. Dist: Chicago Distribution Ctr.

Seelig, Tim, et al. How to Draw Digital Manga & Anime. 2012. (ENG., Illus.). 96p. pap. 15.99 ***(978-1-78019-141-6(3))*** Anness Publishing GBR. Dist: National Bk. Network.

Seelig, Timothy & Li, Yishan. How to Draw Manga: A Step-by-Step Guide with over 750 Illustrations: Expert Techniques for Creating Your Own Manga Characters & Stories, with More Than 50 Exercises & Projects. 2012. (ENG., Illus.). 160p. pap. 19.99 ***(978-1-78019-014-3(X))*** Anness Publishing GBR. Dist: National Bk. Network.

Sega. Tony's Artworks from Shining World. 2011. (Illus.). 208p. (YA). pap. 39.99 *(978-1-926778-18-1(9))* URON Entertainment Corp. CAN. Dist: Diamond Bk. Distributors.

Self, James & Hirose, Nobuko. Japanese Art Signatures: A Handbook & Practical Guide. 2nd ed. 2006. (ENG., Illus.). 400p. reprint ed. pap. 50.00 *(978-1-891640-09-4(7))* Floating World Editions.

Shirahara, Yukiko. Japan Envisions the West: 16th-19th Century Japanese Art from Kobe City Museum. 2007. (ENG., Illus.). 216p. *(978-0-295-98740-8(5))* Seattle Art Museum.

Skinner, Tina. Geisha Fan Book. 2007. (Illus.). 128p. pap. 24.95 *(978-0-7643-2746-9(1))* Schiffer Publishing, Ltd.

Slade, Toby. Japanese Fashion: A Cultural History. 2009. (ENG.). 1p. 99.95 *(978-1-84788-253-0(6))*; pap. 29.95 *(978-1-84788-252-3(8))* Berg Pubs. GBR. Dist: Macmillan.

Starkman, Christine. Unrivalled Splendor: The Kimiko & John Powers Collection of Japanese Art. 2012. (ENG., Illus.). 272p. 65.00 ***(978-0-300-17962-0(6))*** Museum of Fine Arts, Houston.

Suess, Barbara B. Japanese Temari: A Colorful Spin on an Ancient Craft. 2007. (ENG., Illus.). 160p. per. 24.95 *(978-1-933308-12-8(5))* Breckling Pr.

Sun, Seunghye. The Lure of Painted Poetry: Japanese & Korean Art. 2011. (Illus.). 109p. ***(978-1-935294-04-7(0))*** Cleveland Museum of Art.

Tabata, Ayako. Tabaimo. 2007. (ENG.). 92p. 40.00 *(978-0-500-97670-8(8))* Thames & Hudson.

Tamura, Rieko, photos by. Taizo Kuroda, White Porcelain. 2008. (Illus.). 28p. pap. *(978-0-9626731-0-8(2))* Yoshii Gallery.

Tanabe, Rika, ed. Package Design in Japan. 2008. (Illus.). 280p. *(978-84-96774-15-5(5))* Index Bks., Spain.

Tanaka, Ryohei. Killer Cuts & Killing Shapes. 2007. (Illus.). 64p. per. 8.00 *(978-0-9789671-1-6(9))* Rowan Morrison.

Tanikawa, Koichi. 100 Posters of Tadanori Yokoo. Date not set. (Illus.). 112p. 30.00 *(978-0-9664202-3-4(3))* Square One Pubs.

Tanimoto, Ichiro, ed. Chrysanthemums & Autumn Leaves. 2008. (Shikosha Design Library). (Illus.). 120p. pap. 16.95 *(978-1-933330-75-4(9))* Stone Bridge Pr.

—Flowers of Four Seasons. 2008. (Shikosha Design Library). (Illus.). 120p. pap. 16.95 *(978-1-933330-76-1(7))* Stone Bridge Pr.

Teramoto, John Tadao & Tawara, Yusaku. Universe Is Flux: The Art of Tawara Yusaku, 1 vol. 2011. (ENG., Illus.). 144p. pap. 40.00 ***(978-0-295-99159-7(3))*** Univ. of Washington Pr.

The Tokyo Type Director's Club. Tokyo TDC Vol. 18: The Best in International Typography & Design. The Tokyo Type Director's Club, ed. 2008. (ENG., Illus.). 268p. 50.00 *(978-4-903233-30-7(8))* Azur Corp. JPN. Dist: Antique Collectors' Club.

Thomsen, Hans Bjarne. The Floating World: Ukiyo-e Prints from the Wallace B. Rogers Collection of the Lauren Rogers Museum of Art. Chancey, Jill R., ed. 2008. (ENG., Illus.). 29.95 *(978-0-935903-10-2(0))* Lauren Rogers Museum of Art.

Till, Barry. Shin Hanga: The New Print Movement in Japan. 2007. (Pomegranate Catalog Ser.). (Illus.). 112p. 24.95 *(978-0-7649-4039-2(2)*, A136) Pomegranate Communications, Inc.

Tillack, Peter. Living the Somehow Life -Tanaka Yasuo, Banana Yoshimoto & Postmodern Japan. 2007. 180p. per. *(978-3-8364-2750-0(8))* VDM Verlag Dr. Mueller e.K.

Treade, Melanie & Bichler, Lorenz. Hiroshige. 2010. (Go Ser.). (ENG.). 240p. 39.99 *(978-3-8365-2120-8(2))* TASCHEN DEU. Dist: Ingram Pub. Services.

Tsuda, Noritake. A History of Japanese Art: From Prehistory to the Taisho Period. 2009. (Tuttle Classics Ser.). (ENG., Illus.). 480p. pap. 24.95 *(978-4-8053-1031-1(6))* Tuttle Publishing.

Ueda, Ali & RicoRico Staff. Japanese Fantasy Manga. 2011. (ENG., Illus.). 224p. pap. 24.99 *(978-0-06-200470-3(0)*, Collins Design) HarperCollins Pubs.

Uhl, Robertta A. Japanese Washi Paper Crafts: Seventeen Delightful Projects to Make with Washi Paper. 2nd ed. 2007. (ENG., Illus.). 96p. pap. 16.95 *(978-0-8048-3813-9(5))* Tuttle Publishing.

Ullrich, Ferdinand & Schwalm, Hans-Jurgen, eds. Tatsuo Miyajima: Time Train. 2009. (GER & ENG., Illus.). 144p. 85.00 *(978-3-86678-180-1(6))* Kerber Verlag DEU. Dist: D.A.P./Distributed Art Pubs.

Vartanian, Ivan. Killer Kaiju Monsters: Strange Beasts of Japanese Film. 2010. (ENG., Illus.). 144p. 27.99 *(978-0-06-165579-1(1)*, Collins Design) HarperCollins Pubs.

Vartanian, Ivan & Wada, Kyoko. See/Saw: Connections Between Japanese Art Then & Now. 2011. (ENG., Illus.). 176p. pap. 27.50 *(978-0-8118-6957-7(1))* Chronicle Bks. LLC.

Vartanian, Ivan, et al. Japanese Goth. 2009. (ENG., Illus.). 240p. pap. 27.50 *(978-0-7893-1852-7(0))* Universe Publishing.

Veleanu, Mircea. Netsuke. 2008. (Illus.). 256p. bds. 79.95 *(978-0-7643-2847-3(6))* Schiffer Publishing, Ltd.

Vorano, Norman, et al. Inuit Prints, Japanese Inspiration: Early Printmaking in the Canadian Arctic. 2011. (ENG., Illus.). 100p. (C). pap. 29.95 *(978-0-660-19970-2(X))* Canadian Museum of Civilization/Musee Canadien des Civilisations CAN. Dist: Univ. of Washington Pr.

Wang, Ziyi. Zhong Ri Tao Ci Cha Qi Wen Hua Bi Jiao Yan Jiu: Comparative Study of Ceramic Tea Ware Culture in China & Japan. 2010. (CHI., Illus.). *(978-7-01-008507-4(2))* People's Publishing Hse., The.

Watase, Yuu. The Art of Fushigi Yugi: The Mysterious Play. 2006. (Fushigi Yugi Ser.). (ENG., Illus.). 96p. 19.99 *(978-1-4215-0715-6(3))* Viz Media.

Weisenfeld, Gennifer S. Imaging Disaster: Tokyo & the Visual Culture of Japan's Great Earthquake of 1923. 2012. (Asia: Local Studies / Global Themes Ser.). (ENG.). 400p. 60.00 ***(978-0-520-27195-1(5))*** Univ. of California Pr.

Weller, Alan. Geisha & Courtesans CD-ROM & Book. 2009. (Dover Electronic Clip Art Ser.). (ENG., Illus.). 48p. pap. 22.95 *(978-0-486-99011-8(7))* Dover Pubns., Inc.

—Kimonos & Obis CD-ROM & Book. 2009. (Dover Electronic Clip Art Ser.). (ENG., Illus.). 48p. pap. 22.95 *(978-0-486-99012-5(5))* Dover Pubns., Inc.

Weller, Alan, ed. Japanese Ghosts & Demons CD-ROM & Book. 2009. (Dover Electronic Clip Art Ser.). (ENG.). 48p. pap. 19.95 *(978-0-486-99052-1(4))* Dover Pubns., Inc.

Weller, Alan & Clip Art Staff. Hokusai Manga CD-ROM & Book. 2012. (Electronic Clip Art Ser.). (ENG., Illus.). 48p. pap. 19.95 ***(978-0-486-99178-8(4))*** Dover Pubns., Inc.

Western Sources of Japanese Art & Japonism V: Oeuvres choisies de critiques d'art, marchands d'art et collectionneurs sur le japonisme Set: Oeuvres Choisies de Critiques D'Art, Marchands D'Art et Collectionneurs sur le Japonisme, 2 vols. 2010. 2700p. 465.00 *(978-4-86166-057-3(2))* Routledge.

White, Garrett, et al, eds. Design: Isamu Noguchi & Isamu Kenmochi. 2007. (ENG., Illus.). 192p. 50.00 *(978-0-9794727-0-1(9))* Five Ties Publishing.

Wilkins, Amy. In & Out of Design. Stroud, Marion Boulton, ed. 2010. (ENG., Illus.). 184p. 30.00 *(978-0-9797642-3-3(8))* A.S.A.P.

Wong, Yoke-Sum. The Aesthetics of Cute in Contemporary Japanese Art. 2012. (Critical Studies in Gender, Sexuality, & Culture Ser.). (ENG., Illus.). 256p. 85.00 ***(978-0-230-10539-3(4))*** Palgrave Macmillan.

Wylie, Charles, et al, texts. On Kawara: 10 Tableaux & 16,952 Pages. 2008. (ENG., Illus.). 192p. 50.00 *(978-0-300-13734-7(6))* Dallas Museum of Art.

Yamaguchi, Yumi. Warriors of Art: A Guide to Contemporary Japanese Artists, 1 vol. Tanaka, Arthur, tr. from JPN. 2007. (ENG., Illus.). 176p. 34.95 *(978-4-7700-3031-3(2))* Kodansha America, Inc.

Yoshioka, Sachio, ed. Cherry Blossoms. 2007. (Shikosha Design Library). (ENG., Illus.). 120p. pap. 16.95 *(978-1-933330-57-0(0))* Stone Bridge Pr.

Yuki, Kaori. The Art of Angel Sanctuary 2: Lost Angel. Roman, Annette, ed. 2007. (Angel Sanctuary Ser.). (ENG.). 100p. 19.99 *(978-1-4215-1503-8(2))* Viz Media.

Zenko, Adachi. My Life in Japanese Art & Gardens: From Entrepreneur to Connoisseur. 2010. (ENG.). 256p. 29.95 *(978-1-933330-86-0(4))* Stone Bridge Pr.

Zhou, Joanna. Super-Cute Chibis to Draw & Paint: Giant-Sized Fun from a Micro-Sized World. 2011. (ENG.). 128p. pap. 21.99 *(978-0-7641-4677-0(7))* Barron's Educational Series, Inc.

ART, JEWISH

see Jewish Art

ART, KHMER

Bracken, Gregory Byrne. Angkor: Sketches of an Ancient City, 1 vol. 2010. (ENG.). 120p. pap. 24.50 *(978-981-261-875-7(9))* Marshall Cavendish Corp.

Jessup, Helen Ibbitson. Masterpieces of the National Museum of Cambodia/An Introduction to the Collection: Chefs D'uvre du Musée National du Cambodge: Introduction Aux Collections. 2006. (JPN, FRE, MUL & ENG., Illus.). 112p. pap. 25.00 *(978-99950-836-0-1(4))* Friends Of Khmer Culture.

Marchal, Sappho. Khmer Costumes & Ornaments: Of the Devatas of Angkor Wat. Hansen, Merrily P., tr. from FRE. 2006. (ENG., Illus.). 128p. pap. 16.95 *(978-974-524-057-5(5))* Orchid Pr. THA. Dist: National Bk. Network.

ART, KINETIC

see Kinetic Art

ART, KOREAN

Ahn, Sang-Soo & Yim, Young-Joo, contrib. by. Dokkaebi: Korean Motifs, 1 vol. 2006. (ENG., Illus.). 292p. 49.50 *(978-3-8030-0657-8(0))* Wasmuth, Ernst J. Verlag GmbH & Co. DEU. Dist: D.A.P./Distributed Art Pubs.

Bae, Yong Joon. A Journey in Search of Korea's Beauty. 2010. (Illus.). 428p. pap. 44.50 *(978-1-56591-307-3(8))* Hollym International Corp.

Bul, Lee. Lee Bul: On Every New Shadow. 2008. (ENG.). 128p. 40.00 *(978-0-500-97498-8(5))* Thames & Hudson.

Cho, Soon C. Color of Nature. 2008. *(978-2-7594-0315-8(7))* Assouline.

—Empty the Mind. 2008. (Illus.). 165p. *(978-2-7594-0314-1(9))* Assouline.

Ch'oe, Yol. Misul Kwa Sahoe: Ch'oe Yol Pip'yong Chonso, 1976-2008. 2009. (KOR., Illus.). 468p. *(978-89-7278-279-7(3))* Cheong-nyeonsa.

Chow, Brian G. & Sun, Seunghye. The Lure of Painted Poetry: Japanese & Korean Art. 2011. (Illus.). 120p. 50.00 *(978-1-55595-364-5(6))* Hudson Hills Pr. LLC.

Dziewior, Yilmaz, ed. Haegue Yang: Arrivals. 2011. (ENG., Illus.). 351p. 65.00 (978-3-86560-968-7(6)) Kunsthaus Bregenz AUT. Dist: D.A.P./Distributed Art Pubs.

Frank, Rudiger. Exploring North Korean Arts. 2012. (ENG., Illus.). 304p. pap. 65.00 (978-3-86984-214-1(8)) Verlag fur Moderne Kunst DEU. Dist: D.A.P./Distributed Art Pubs.

Frey Norris Gallery, prod. Inkie Whang: American Debut. 2008. 20p. pap. 10.00 (978-0-9795141-3-5(4)) Norris, Frey Gallery.

Hichi, et al. Toxic Volume 1. 2012. (Illus.). 192p. pap. 39.99 (978-1-926778-44-0(8)) URON Entertainment Corp. CAN. Dist: Diamond Bk. Distributors.

Ho, Kyun. Sibiji Ui Munhwasa. 2010. (KOR., Illus.). 176p. (978-89-7199-372-9(3)) Dolbegae Publishing Co.

Kang, Hee Jin, photos by. No Sleep. 2011. (ENG., Illus.). 96p. 50.00 (978-3-86828-194-1(0)) Kehrer Verlag Heidelberg, Klaus Kehrer DEU. Dist: Consortium Bk. Sales & Distribution.

Kim, Hee-Jin. Maedeup: The Art of Traditional Korean Knots. 2007. (Illus.). 160p. pap. (978-1-56591-233-5(0)) Hollym International Corp.

Kim, Miki Wick. Korean Contemporary Art. 2012. (Illus.). 192p. 60.00 (978-3-7913-5157-5(5)) Prestel Publishing.

Korean Spirit & Culture Promotion Project. Fifty Wonders of Korea, Vol. 1. 2007. (Korean Spirit & Culture Ser.: Vols. 4-5). (Illus.). pap. (978-0-9797263-1-6(X)) Korean Spirit & Culture Promotion Project.

Korean Spirit & Culture Promotion Project Staff & Diamond Sutra Recitation Group Staff, contrib. by. Fifty Wonders of Korea. 2007. (Korean Spirit & Culture Ser.: Vols. 4-5). (Illus.). (978-0-9797263-4-7(4)) Korean Spirit & Culture Promotion Project.

Ku, Pon-Jin. Misulca Ui Chojak Inkyokkwon. 2010. (KOR.). xv, 419p. (978-89-499-0737-6(2)) Kyung-in.

Kungnip Chungang Pangmulgwan (Korea) Staff & Museum of Fine Arts, Houston Staff, contrib. by. Treasures from the National Museum of Korea. 2007. (978-0-89090-159-5(7)); pap. (978-0-89090-161-8(9)) Museum of Fine Arts, Houston.

Lachman, Charles. The Ten Symbols of Longevity. 2006. (Collection in Context). (ENG., Illus.). 56p. per. 19.95 (978-0-295-98657-9(3)) Univ. of Washington Pr.

Lee, Soyoung. Art of the Korean Renaissance, 1400-1600. 2009. (ENG., Illus.). 140p. 40.00 (978-0-300-14891-6(7)) Yale Univ. Pr.

Lee, Soyoung, et al. Art of the Korean Renaissance, 1400-1600. 2009. (Illus.). xii, 128p. 40.00 (978-1-58839-310-4(0)) Metropolitan Museum of Art, The.

Marino, Joshua. Kwanjangnim Original: Haidong Gumdo. 2009. 144p. pap. 19.95 (978-1-4327-3553-1(5)) Outskirts Pr., Inc.

Morsiani, Paola & Kim, Beom. Kim Beom: Objects Being Taught They Are Nothing but Tools. 2010. (Illus.). 50p. pap. (978-1-935294-02-3(4)) Cleveland Museum of Art.

O, Se-Ch'ang. Kunmuk, 5 vols. 2009. (KOR., Illus.). (978-89-7986-797-8(2)); (978-89-7986-798-5(0)) Sungkyunkwan Univ.Pr. (Spotlight Poets).

Sala Rekalde (Bilbao, prod. Haegue Yang Asymmetric Equality. 2008. (Illus.). 215p. pap. 40.00 (978-0-9749831-9-6(5)) California Institute of the Arts.

Stahel. Kyungwoo Chun Thousands. 2008. (ENG., Illus.). 128p. 50.00 (978-3-7757-2167-7(3)) Hatje Cantz Verlag GmbH & Co KG DEU. Dist: D.A.P./Distributed Art Pubs.

Stallabrass, Julian, et al, texts. Haegue Yang: Wild Against Gravity. 2012. (ENG., Illus.). 190p. 45.00 (978-1-901352-52-8(8)) Museum of Modern Art, Oxford GBR. Dist: D.A.P./Distributed Art Pubs.

Starkman, Christine & Zelevansky, Lynn. Your Bright Future: 12 Contemporary Artists from Korea. 2009. (Illus.). 208p. 50.00 (978-0-300-14689-9(2)) Museum of Fine Arts, Houston.

Suh, Jae-Sik, photos by. Korean Patterns. 2007. (Illus.). 240p. lib. bdg. 68.00 (978-1-56591-239-7(X)) Hollym International Corp.

Sun, Seunghye. The Lure of Painted Poetry: Japanese & Korean Art. 2011. (Illus.). 109p. (978-1-935294-04-7(0)) Cleveland Museum of Art.

Tucker, Anne Wilkes, et al. Chaotic Harmony: Contemporary Korean Photography. 2009. (ENG., Illus.). 160p. pap. 35.00 (978-0-300-15753-6(3)) Museum of Fine Arts, Houston.

Unsoo, Kim & Iwatate, Marcia. Korea Style. 2006. (ENG., Illus.). 224p. 44.95 (978-0-8048-3750-7(3)) Tuttle Publishing.

Various. Apple Selection Volume 1: Summer. 2012. (Illus.). 200p. (YA). pap. 39.99 (978-1-926778-29-7(4)) URON Entertainment Corp. CAN. Dist: Diamond Bk. Distributors.

Various. Apple Selection Volume 2: Autumn: Autumn. 2012. (Illus.). 160p. (YA). pap. 39.99 (978-1-926778-36-5(7)) URON Entertainment Corp. CAN. Dist: Diamond Bk. Distributors.

Von Wedel, Amelie, et al, eds. Korean Eye: Contemporary Korean Art. 2010. (ENG., Illus.). 390p. pap. 60.00 (978-88-572-0467-3(7)) Skira Editore ITA. Dist: Random Hse., Inc.

Yu, Hong-Jun. Yu Hong-Jun Ui Han'guk Misulsa Kangui: Story of Korean Art. 2010. (KOR., Illus.). (978-89-90620-44-6(9)) Nulwa Co.

Yun, Pom-Mo. Kim Pok-Chin Yon'gu: Iiche Kangjom Ha Choso Yesul Kwa Munye Undong. 2010. (Illus.). 559p. (978-89-7801-275-1(2)) Dong-guk Univ. Pr.

ART, LATIN AMERICAN

Adams, Beverly, et al. Constructing a Poetic Universe: The Diane & Bruce Halle Collection of Latin American Art. 2007. (ENG., Illus.). 282p. 49.95 (978-1-85894-392-3(2)) Merrell Pubs. Ltd. GBR. Dist: Perseus Distribution.

Aranda-Alvarado, Rocio, et al, contrib. by. El Museo's Bienal: The (S) Files 2011. 2011. (Illus.). 194p. pap. 25.00 (978-1-882454-02-6(2)) El Museo del Barrio.

Biron, Rebecca. City/Art: The Urban Scene in Latin America. 2009. (ENG., Illus.). 288p. 84.95 (978-0-8223-4455-1(6)) Duke Univ. Pr.

Biron, Rebecca E. City/Art: The Urban Scene in Latin America. 2009. (ENG., Illus.). 288p. pap. 23.95 (978-0-8223-4470-4(X)) Duke Univ. Pr.

Brodsky, Marcelo & Pantoja, Julio, eds. Body Politics. 2010. (ENG & SPA., Illus.). 206p. pap. 39.95 (978-950-889-192-1(0)) La Marca ARG. Dist: D.A.P./Distributed Art Pubs.

Cammitzer, Luis, ed. It's not Neutral. 2008. 180p. pap. (978-84-612-5628-0(X)) Actar Birkhauser Distribution.

Camnitzer, Luis. Conceptualism in Latin American Art: Didactics of Liberation. 2007. (Joe R. & Teresa Lozano Long Series in Latin American & Latino Art & Culture). (ENG., Illus.). 364p. 75.00 (978-0-292-71639-1(7)); pap. 27.95 (978-0-292-71629-2(X)) Univ. of Texas Pr.

—On Art, Artists, Latin America, & Other Utopias. Weiss, Rachel, ed. 2009. (ENG.). 272p. 45.00 (978-0-292-71976-7(0)) Univ. of Texas Pr.

Cano Murillo, Kathy. The Crafty Chica Collection: Beautiful Ideas for Crafts, Home Decorations & Shrines from the Queen of Latina Style. 2006. (ENG., Illus.). 152p. pap. 24.99 (978-1-59253-305-3(1), 1592533051, Quarry Books) Quayside.

Cazali, Rosina & Terré, Laura, eds. Peso y Levedad: Fotografía Latinoamericana Entre el Humanismo y la Violencia. 2012. (ENG & SPA., Illus.). 256p. pap. 50.00 (978-84-15303-25-1(4)) La Fábrica/Arts Santa Mònica, Barcelona ESP. Dist: D.A.P./Distributed Art Pubs.

Child, Jack. Latin American History Through Its Art & Literature. 2nd ed. 2010. (ENG.). 284p. pap. 38.50 (978-0-7618-5282-7(4)) Univ. Pr. of America, Inc.

Cisneros Fontanals Art Foundation Staff, contrib. by. Positions in Context: 2007 CIFO Grants Program Exhibition. 2007. (SPA & ENG., Illus.). 48p. (978-0-9774079-7-2(7)) Cisneros Fontanals Art Foundation.

Craven, David. Art & Revolution in Latin America, 1910-1990. 2006. (ENG., Illus.). 240p. pap. 38.00 (978-0-300-12046-2(X)) Yale Univ. Pr.

Cullen, Deborah, ed. Arte No es Vida. 2008. (SPA & ENG., Illus.). 320p. (C). pap. 45.00 (978-1-882454-25-9(1)) El Museo del Barrio.

—Nexus New York: Latin/American Artists in the Modern Metropolis. 2009. (ENG., Illus.). 288p. pap. 45.00 (978-0-300-15896-0(3)) Yale Univ. Pr.

Davidson, Peter. The Universal Baroque. 2008. (ENG., Illus.). 224p. 89.00 (978-0-7190-7572-8(6)) Manchester Univ. Pr. GBR. Dist: Macmillan.

Davila-Villa, Ursula, ed. & intro. Recovering Beauty: The 1990s in Buenos Aires. 2011. (ENG., Illus.). 144p. pap. 25.00 (978-0-9815738-5-4(1)) Blanton Museum of Art, Univ. of Texas at Austin.

DiCesare, Catherine. Sweeping the Way: Divine Transformation in the Aztec Festival of Ochpaniztli. 2009. (Mesoamerican Worlds Ser.). (ENG., Illus.). 248p. 60.00 (978-0-87081-943-8(7)) Univ. Pr. of Colorado.

Donahue-Wallace, Kelly. Art & Architecture of Viceregal Latin America, 1521-1821. 2008. (Dialogos Ser.). (ENG., Illus.). 304p. (C). pap. 34.95 (978-0-8263-3459-6(8)) Univ. of New Mexico Pr.

d'Orgeval, Domitille, et al. Geometry Beyond Limits: Latin American Contemporary Art. 2010. (ENG & FRE., Illus.). 246p. 60.00 (978-88-7439-542-2(6)) 5 Continents ITA. Dist: Hachette Bk. Group.

Fabry, Alexis, text. Fotografía Latinoamericana 1895-2008. 2009. (ENG., Illus.). 206p. 65.00 (978-84-92480-29-6(7)) R.M. Editorial, S.A. de C.V. MEX. Dist: D.A.P./Distributed Art Pubs.

Freire, Cristina & Longoni, Ana. Conceitualismos Do Sul/Sur: Conceptualismos Del Sur. 2009. (POR & SPA., Illus.). 361p. (978-85-7419-957-3(5)) Annablume Editora Comunicacao Ltda.

Gallo, Lylia. Gerardo Aragon. 2007. (ENG., Illus.). 168p. 56.00 (978-958-8306-02-5(7)) Villegas Editores S.A. COL. Dist: Independent Pubs. Group.

Giunta, Andrea. Avant-Garde, Internationalism, & Politics: Argentine Art in the Sixties. Kahn, Peter, tr. from SPA. 2007. (Latin America Otherwise Ser.). (ENG., Illus.). 432p. per. 27.95 (978-0-8223-3893-2(9)); 99.95 (978-0-8223-3877-2(7)) Duke Univ. Pr.

Hanor, Stephanie, et al, contrib. by. Transactions: Contemporary Latin American & Latino Art, 1 vol. 2006. (SPA & ENG., Illus.). 176p. 49.95 (978-0-934418-65-2(9)) Museum of Contemporary Art, San Diego.

Harris, Jonathan. Identity Theft: The Cultural Colonization of Contemporary Art. Harris, Jonathan, ed. 2009. (ENG., Illus.). 272p. 85.00 (978-1-84631-103-1(9)) Liverpool Univ. Pr. GBR. Dist: Chicago Distribution Ctr.

Harris, Jonathan, ed. Identity Theft: The Cultural Colonisation & Contemporary Art. 2009. (Liverpool University Press - Tate Liverpool Critical Forum Ser.). (ENG., Illus.). 272p. pap. 39.95 (978-1-84631-102-4(0)) Liverpool Univ. Pr. GBR. Dist: Chicago Distribution Ctr.

IDB Cultural Center Staff, et al, contrib. by. 50 Años, 50 Obras: Obras Sobresalientes Del Arte de América Latina y el Caribe Del Siglo XX. 2009. (ENG & SPA., Illus.). 89p. (978-1-59782-088-2(1)) Inter-American Development Bank.

Jiménez, Ariel. Alfredo Boulton y Sus Contemporaneos: Diálogos Críticos en el Arte Venezolano, 1912-1974. 2009. (SPA., Illus.). 392p. pap. (978-0-87070-783-4(3)) Museum of Modern Art.

Jimenez, Ariel. A Constructive Vision. 2010. (ENG., Illus.). 344p. 65.00 (978-0-9823544-0-7(1)) Fundacion Cisneros.

Jones, Adam. Latin American Portraits. 2008. (Illus.). 197p. pap. 29.99 (978-0-9782526-3-2(2)) Key Publishing Hse., Inc., The CAN. Dist: AtlasBooks Distribution.

Jones, David M. The Art & Architecture of the Incas. 2012. (ENG., Illus.). 128p. pap. 16.99 (978-1-78019-138-6(3)) Anness Publishing GBR. Dist: National Bk. Network.

Katz, Vincent, et al. Retro/Active: The Work of Rafael Ferrer. Cullen, Deborah, ed. 2010.Tr. of Retro/activa: la obra de Rafael Ferrer. (ENG & SPA., Illus.). 160p. pap. 35.00 (978-1-882454-27-3(8)) El Museo del Barrio.

Katzew, Ilona, ed. Contested Visions in the Spanish Colonial World. 2011. (ENG., Illus.). 320p. 70.00 (978-0-300-17664-3(3)) Yale Univ. Pr.

Kuitca, Guillermo. Guillermo Kuitca, 1 vol. 2008. (ENG., Illus.). 88p. 68.00 (978-3-86521-848-3(2)) Steidl, Gerhard Druckerei und Verlag DEU. Dist: Innovative Logistics.

Lampert, Catherine, et al, texts. Flavio Garciandia: I Insulted Flavio Garciandia in Havana. 2009. (ENG., Illus.). 410p. pap. 55.00 (978-84-7506-843-5(X)) Turner, Ediciones S.A. ESP. Dist: D.A.P./Distributed Art Pubs.

Ledezma, Juan. The Sites of Latin American Abstraction/Los Sitios de la Abstraccion Lationoamericana. 2008. (ENG., Illus.). 248p. 75.00 (978-88-8158-664-6(9)) Charta ITA. Dist: D.A.P./Distributed Art Pubs.

Lopez, Marcos, photos by. Marcos Lopez: Debut & Farewell, 1978-2009. 2011. (ENG., Illus.). 232p. 65.00 (978-84-92480-93-7(9)) RM Verlag, S.L. ESP. Dist: D.A.P./Distributed Art Pubs.

Noé, Luis Felipe. Noescritos/ No-writings about that Thing Called Art: Sobre eso que se llama arte. 2007. (SPA.). 507p. pap. (978-987-1156-74-0(X)) Hidalgo, Adriana Editora S.A.

Perez-Barreiro, Gabriel. Contemporary Art in Latin America. Monem, Nadine & Kotsopoulos, Nikos, eds. 2010. (ENG., Illus.). 240p. 49.95 (978-1-906155-64-3(X)) Black Dog Publishing Ltd. GBR. Dist: Perseus Distribution.

Pérez-Barreiro, Gabriel. The Geometry of Hope: Latin American Abstract Art from the Patricia Phelps de Cisneros Collection. 2007. (ENG & SPA.). 45.00 (978-0-9771453-7-9(9)) Univ. of Texas at Austin, The.

Perez-Barreiro, Gabriel, ed. Francisco Matto: the Modern & the Mythic. 2009. (ENG., Illus.). 120p. pap. 29.95 (978-0-9815738-3-0(5)) Blanton Museum of Art, Univ. of Texas at Austin.

—The Geometry of Hope: Latin American Abstract Art from the Patricia Phelps de Cisneros Collection, 1 vol. 2007. (ENG & SPA., Illus.). 344p. pap. 29.95 (978-0-9771453-6-2(0)) Blanton Museum of Art, Univ. of Texas at Austin.

Phillips, Richard E. & McIntyre, Kellen Kee, eds. Woman & Art in Early Modern Latin America. 2006. (Atlantic World Ser.). (Illus.). 449p. (978-90-04-15392-9(6)) BRILL.

Ramirez, Mari Carmen & Pacheco, Marcelo. Modern & Contemporary Masterworks from MALBA. 2012. (ENG., Illus.). 156p. 35.00 (978-0-300-18100-5(0)) Museum of Fine Arts, Houston.

Ramirez, Mari Carmen, et al. Resisting Categories: Latin American And/Or Latino?, Vol. 1. 2012. (Critical Documents Ser.). (ENG., Illus.). 1200p. 60.00 (978-0-300-14697-4(3)) Museum of Fine Arts, Houston.

Rangel, Gabriela & Falconi, José Luis, eds. A Principality of Its Own: 40 Years of Visual Arts at the Americas Society. 2007. (David Rockefeller Center for Latin American Studies, Art Catalogs Ser.). (Illus.). 304p. pap. 27.95 (978-1-879128-31-6(4)) Americas Society.

Rishel, Joseph J. The Arts in Latin America, 1492-1820. 2006. (Philadelphia Museum of Art Ser.). (ENG., Illus.). 592p. 75.00 (978-0-300-12003-5(6)) Yale Univ. Pr.

Rishel, Joseph J. & Stratton, Suzanne L. The Arts in Latin America, 1492-1820. 2006. (Philadelphia Museum of Art Ser.). (Illus.). xxiii, 568p. (978-0-87633-251-1(3)); (978-0-87633-250-4(5)) Philadelphia Museum of Art.

Ruiz, Alma, text. Suprasensorial: Experiments in Light, Color, & Space. 2012. (SPA & ENG., Illus.). 148p. pap. 45.00 (978-1-933751-16-0(9)) Museum of Contemporary Art, Los Angeles.

Ruiz, Maximiliano, ed. Nuevo Mundo: Latin American Street Art. 2011. (Illus.). 256p. (978-3-89955-337-6(3)) Die Gestalten Verlag.

Sardinas, Zelda Comesanas. Great Masters of Cuban Art, 1900-1958/Grandes Maestros del Arte Cubano: Ramos Collection/Coleccion Ramos. 2009. (ENG & SPA., Illus.). 288p. 60.00 (978-0-615-24045-9(3)) Univ. Pr. of Florida.

Schwartz, Constance. ¡Latinas! Latin American Women in Art. 2010. (Illus.). pap. (978-0-9815644-6-3(1)) Nassau County Museum of Art.

Shipp, Steve. Latin American & Caribbean Artists of the Modern Era: A Biographical Dictionary of More Than 12,700 Persons, 2 vols. alt. ed. 2012. (ENG., Illus.). 916p. pap. 75.00 (978-0-7864-6626-9(X)) McFarland & Co., Inc. Pubs.

Smit, Jennifer & de Rooy, Felix. Curaçao Classics: Visual Arts from the 20th Century & Onwards. 2012. 160p. 49.50 (978-94-6022-158-3(0)) Royal Tropical Institute Pr. (KIT (Koninklijk Instituut voor de Tropen) NLD. Dist: Stylus Publishing, LLC.

Stone, Rebecca. Art of the Andes: From Chavín to Inca. 3rd rev. ed. 2012. (ENG., Illus.). 248p. pap. 21.95 (978-0-500-20415-3(2), 520415) Thames & Hudson.

Suarez, Mercedes. Letras y Arte de Nuestra America. 2006. (SPA & ENG., Illus.). 610p. pap. 24.95 (978-958-8160-61-0(8)) Villegas Editores S.A. COL. Dist: Independent Pubs. Group.

Suarez, Osbel, text. Cold America. 2011. 504p. 85.00 (978-84-7075-588-0(9)) Fundacion Juan March ESP. Dist: Actar Birkhauser Distribution.

Sullivan, Edward J. The Language of Objects in the Art of the Americas. 2007. (ENG., Illus.). 336p. 65.00 (978-0-300-11106-4(1)) Yale Univ. Pr.

TwoPoints.Net, ed. Latino-Grafico: Visual Culture from Latin America. 2010. (SPA & ENG., Illus.). 224p. (978-3-89955-311-6(X)) Die Gestalten Verlag.

Vicario, Gilbert. Cosmopolitan Routes: Houston Collects Latin American Art. 2011. (ENG., Illus.). 144p. 35.00 (978-0-300-16993-5(0)) Museum of Fine Arts, Houston.

Villafranca, Jordi. Typo Latino. 2012. (ENG., Illus.). 400p. 34.95 (978-84-92643-77-6(3)) Index Bks., Spain ESP. Dist: Innovative Logistics.

Wiedemann, Julius & Taborda, Felipe, eds. Latin American Graphics: Communicacion Visual - The Best Latin Designers from Yesterday & Today. 2008. (Illus.). 543p. pap. 39.99 (978-3-8228-4035-1(1)) TASCHEN DEU. Dist: Ingram Pub. Services.

Zamora, Lois Parkinson. The Inordinate Eye: New World Baroque & Latin American Fiction. 2006. (Illus.). 424p. 55.00 (978-0-226-97856-7(7)) Univ. of Chicago Pr.

Zamora, Lois Parkinson & Kaup, Monika, eds. Baroque New Worlds: Representation, Transculturation, Counterconquest. 2010. (ENG., Illus.). 688p. 99.95 (978-0-8223-4630-2(3)); pap. 29.95 (978-0-8223-4642-5(7)) Duke Univ. Pr.

zu Schlochtern, Thomas Meijer, ed. Paramaribo SPAN: Contemporary Art in Suriname. 2010. 200p. pap. 39.95 (978-94-6022-081-4(9)) Royal Tropical Institute Pr. (KIT (Koninklijk Instituut voor de Tropen) NLD. Dist: Stylus Publishing, LLC.

ART, MAORI

Reading, Nigel & Wyatt, Gary. Manawa: Pacific Heartbeat - A Celebration of Contemporary Maori & Pacific Northwest Coast Art, 1 vol. (ENG., Illus.). 144p. pap. 35.00 (978-1-55365-139-0(1)) D&M Pubs. Inc. CAN. Dist: Perseus-PGW.

Salmond, Amiria & Raymond, Rosanna, eds. Pasifika Styles: Artists Inside the Museum. 2008. (Illus.). 146p. (C). pap. 49.99 (978-1-877372-60-5(9)) Otago University Pr. NZL. Dist: International Specialized Bk. Services.

ART, MAYA

see Maya Art

ART, MEDIEVAL

see also Art, Byzantine; Art, Carolingian; Art, Gothic; Art, Romanesque; Cistercian Art; Illumination of Books and Manuscripts

Arnold, Hugh. Stained Glass of the Middle Ages in England & France. 2010. (Illus.). 92p. pap. 20.00 (978-1-154-92610-1(9)); 90p. pap. 20.00 (978-1-151-82189-8(6)) General Bks. LLC.

Arnold, Hugh & Saint, Lawrence B. Stained Glass of the Middle Ages in England & France. 2010. 496p. pap. 38.75 (978-1-177-75319-7(7)) BiblioBazaar.

Arnold, Hugh & Saint, Lawrence Bradford. Stained Glass of the Middle Ages in England & France. 2010. (ENG.). 492p. pap. 38.75 (978-1-171-81196-1(9)) BiblioBazaar.

As-Vijvers, Anne Margreet. The Making of the Margin: The Master of the David Scenes & Ghent-Bruges Manuscript Illumination. 2012. (Ars Nova Ser.). (ENG.). 250p. (C). 203.00 (978-2-503-51684-4(X)) Brepols Pubs. BEL. Dist: Brown, David Bk. Co., The.

Babelon, Jean. Histoire de l'Art Vol. 2: L'Europe Medievale. (FRE.). 1748p. (978-0-8288-7601-8(0)) French & European Pubns., Inc.

Bagnoli, Martina & Gerry, Kathryn B. The Medieval World: The Walters Art Museum. 2011. (ENG., Illus.). 208p. 45.00 (978-1-904832-96-6(2)) Giles, D. Ltd. GBR. Dist: Antique Collectors' Club.

Bagnoli, Martina & Gerry, Kathryn B. The Medieval World: The Walters Art Museum. 2011. (Illus.). 216p. pap. (978-0-911886-75-7(3)) Walters Art Museum, US.

Baragli, Sandra. European Art of the Fourteenth Century. Phillips, Brian D., tr. from ITA. 2007. (Art Through the Centuries Ser.). (Illus.). 384p. pap. 24.95 (978-0-89236-859-4(4)) Oxford Univ. Pr., Inc.

Barton, Paulette E. Mercy & the Misericord in Late Medieval England: Cathedral Theology & Architecture. 2009. (Illus.). 272p. 109.95 (978-0-7734-4841-4(1)) Mellen, Edwin Pr., The.

Batalov, A. L. & Smirnova, E. S. Drevnerusskoe Iskusstvo: Ideia I Obraz, Opyty Izucheniia Vizantiiskogo I Drevnerusskogo Iskusstva. 2009. (Illus.). 478p. (978-5-94431-303-4(X)) Severnyj palomnik.

Becker, Carl & Warncke, Carsten-Peter. Becker - Decorative Arts, 3 vols. 2011. (FRE, GER & ENG., Illus.). 412p. 150.00 (978-3-8365-0518-5(5)) TASCHEN DEU. Dist: Ingram Pub. Services.

Becksmann, Rü, et al. Die mittelalterlichen Glasmalereien in Freiburg im Breisgau: Corpus Vitrearum Medii Aevi Deutschland 2.2, 2 vols. 2010. (GER., Illus.). (978-3-87157-226-5(8)) Deutscher Verlag fur Kunstwissenschaft.

Benton, Janetta Rebold. Materials, Methods, & Masterpieces of Medieval Art, 1 vol. 2009. (Praeger Series on the Middle Ages Ser.). (Illus.). 303p. 150.00 (978-0-275-99418-1(X), C9418, Praeger Pubs.) Greenwood Publishing Group, Inc.

Boer, Waldemar H. de. Francesco Albertini: Memorial of Many Statues & Paintings in the Famous City of Florence. Boer, De Waldemar H., ed. 2011. (Illus.). 240p. pap. 65.00 (978-88-7038-492-5(6)) Centro Di ITA. Dist: Antique Collectors' Club.

Brenk, Beat. Medieval Image-Concepts & the Meaning of Visual Programs. 2013. (ENG., Illus.). 560p. (C). 300.00 (978-1-899828-73-9(7)) Pindar Pr. GBR. Dist: Brown, David Bk. Co., The.

Brown, Michelle P. The Lindisfarne Gospels & the Early Medieval World. 2010. (Illus.). 160p. 45.00 (978-0-7123-5801-9(3)) British Library, The GBR. Dist: Chicago Distribution Ctr.

Brush, Kathryn. The Shaping of Art History: Wilhelm Vöge, Adolph Goldschmidt, & the Study of Medieval Art. 2010. (ENG.). 280p. pap. 39.99 (978-0-521-14762-0(X)) Cambridge Univ. Pr.

Bruzelius, Caroline & Tronzo, William. Medieval Naples: An Architectural & Urban History, 400-1400. 2011. (ENG., Illus.). 160p. 30.00 (978-1-59910-202-3(1)) Italica Pr.

—Medieval Naples: An Architectural & Urban History, 400¿1400. 2011. (ENG., Illus.). 160p. pap. 20.00 *(978-1-59910-203-0(X))* Italica Pr.

Bucklow, Spike. The Alchemy of Paint: Art, Science & Secrets from the Middle Ages. 2009. (ENG., Illus.). 336p. pap. 17.95 *(978-0-7145-3172-4(3))* Boyars, Marion Pubs., Ltd. GBR. Dist: Consortium Bk. Sales & Distribution.

Buhl, Gudrun, et al, eds. Spatantike und byzantinische Elfenbeinbildwerke im Diskurs. 2008. (Spatantike-Fruhes Christentum-Byzanz Ser.). (GER, ENG & FRE., Illus.). 320p. (C). 199.00 *(978-3-89500-497-1(9))* Reichert, Ludwig Dr. DEU. Dist: Brown, David Bk. Co., The.

Cahill, Thomas. Mysteries of the Middle Ages: And the Beginning of the Modern World. 2008. (Hinges of History Ser.). (ENG., Illus.). 368p. pap. 22.00 *(978-0-385-49556-1(0),* Anchor) Knopf Doubleday Publishing Group.

Cannon, Jon & Williamson, Beth, eds. The Medieval Art, Architecture & History of Bristol Cathedral: An Enigma Explored. 2011. (Bristol Studies in Medieval Cultures Ser.: Volume 2). (Illus.). 376p. 95.00 *(978-1-84383-680-3(7),* Boydell Press) Boydell & Brewer, Ltd. GBR. Dist: Boydell & Brewer, Inc.

Caskey, Jill. Art & Patronage in the Medieval Mediterranean: Merchant Culture in the Region of Amalfi. 2011. (ENG., Illus.). 344p. pap. 65.00 *(978-0-521-28426-4(0))* Cambridge Univ. Pr.

Caskey, Jill, et al. Confronting the Borders of Medieval Art. 2011. XVI, 230p. pap. ***(978-90-04-20749-3(X))*** BRILL.

Cassady, Richard F. The Emperor & the Saint: Frederick II of Hohenstaufen, Francis of Assisi, & Journeys to Medieval Places. 2011. (ENG., Illus.). 472p. 35.00 *(978-0-87580-439-2(X))* Northern Illinois Univ. Pr.

Charles, Victoria & Carl, Klaus H. Medieval Art in Europe from 987 To 1489. 2012. (Must Ser.). (ENG.). 400p. 49.95 *(978-1-906981-03-7(5))* Parkstone Pr. USA, Ltd.

Clifford, Helen. A Treasured Inheritance: 600 Years of Oxford College Silver. 2006. (ENG., Illus.). 160p. 22.95 *(978-1-85444-195-9(7))* Ashmolean Museum GBR. Dist: National Bk. Network.

Cram101 Textbook Reviews. Outlines & Highlights for Medieval Art: Painting, Sculpture, Architecture, 4th-14th Century by Henry Luttikhuizen, Dorothy Verkerk, ISBN. 2010. 76p. pap. 27.95 *(978-1-61698-258-4(6))* Cram101 Inc.

Cunningham, C. c. Religious Art of the Middle Ages & Renaissance. 2011. 50p. 35.95 ***(978-1-258-03699-7(1))*** Literary Licensing, LLC.

Cutler, Anthony & Papaconstantinou, Arietta, eds. The Material & the Ideal: Essays in Medieval Art & Archaeology in Honour of Jean-Michel Spieser. 2007. (Medieval Mediterranean Ser.). (FRE, GER & ENG., Illus.). 240p. *(978-90-04-16286-0(0))* BRILL.

Cyrus, Cynthia J. Scribes for Women's Convents in Late Medieval Germany. 2009. (ENG.). 432p. *(978-0-8020-9369-1(8))* Univ. of Toronto Pr.

Davies, Glyn & Kennedy, Kirstin. Medieval & Renaissance Art: People & Possessions. 2009. (ENG., Illus.). 320p. 80.00 *(978-1-85177-579-8(X))* V & A Pubns. GBR. Dist: Hachette Bk. Group.

de Hamel, Christpher, intro. Book of Beasts: A Facsimile of MS Bodley 764. fac. ed. 2010. (LAT & ENG., Illus.). 316p. (C). 250.00 *(978-1-85124-317-4(8))* Bodleian Library GBR. Dist: Brown, David Bk. Co., The.

den Hollander, A. A. Virtuelle Vergangenheit: Die Textrekonstruktion einer verlorenen mittelniederlandischen Evangelienharmonie. Die Handschrift Utrecht Universitatsbibliothek 1009. 2007. (Bibliotheca Ephemeridum Theologicarum Lovaniensium Ser.). (GER.). 168p. (C). pap. 85.00 *(978-90-429-1989-1(2))* Peeters Pubs. & Booksellers BEL. Dist: Brown, David Bk. Co., The.

Der Nessessian, Sirarpie. Two Slavonic Parallels of the Greek Tetraevangelia: Paris 74. 2010. 86.48 *(978-1-61143-262-6(6))* Gorgias Pr., LLC.

Descatoire, Christine. Treasures of the Black Death. 2009. (ENG., Illus.). 112p. pap. 40.00 *(978-0-900785-95-5(0))* Holberton, Paul Publishing GBR. Dist: Casemate Pubs. & Bk. Distributors, LLC.

Deshman, Robert & Cohen, Adam S. Eye & Mind: Collected Essays in Anglo-Saxon & Early Medieval Art. 2009. *(978-1-58044-122-3(X)); (978-1-58044-121-6(1))* Medieval Institute Pubns.

Didron, M. Christian Iconography or the History of. 2006. pap. 40.95 *(978-1-4286-3862-4(8))* Kessinger Publishing, LLC.

Driver, Martha W. & Orr, Michael T. An Index of Images in English Manuscripts: From the Time of Chaucer to Henry VIII, C. 1380-C. 1509. 2007. (Index of Images in English Manuscripts from Chaucer to Henry Ser.). (Illus.). 176p. pap. 81.00 *(978-1-905375-22-6(0))* Miller, Harvey Pubs. GBR. Dist: Brown, David Bk. Co., The.

Dückers, Rob & Roelofs, Pieter. The Limbourg Brothers: Reflections on the Origins & the Legacy of Three Illuminators from Nijmegen. 2009. *(978-90-04-17512-9(1))* BRILL.

Eikelmann, Renate & Eikelmann. The Cleveland Musuem of Art: Meisterwerke von 300 Bis 1550. 2007. (GER., Illus.). 304p. (C). pap. 56.00 *(978-3-7774-3565-7(1))* Hirmer Verlag GmbH DEU. Dist: Brown, David Bk. Co., The.

Engel, Ute & Gajewski, Alexandrea. Mainz & the Middle Rhine Valley: Medieval Art, Architecture, & Archaeology. 2007. (British Archaeological Association Conference Transactions Ser.). (Illus.). 256p. (C). 94.00 *(978-1-904350-82-8(8));* 56.00 *(978-1-904350-83-5(6))* Northern Universities Pr. GBR. Dist: Brown, David Bk. Co., The.

Faure, Élie, et al. Medieval Art. 2010. (Illus.). 256p. *(978-1-84484-683-2(0))* Parkstone International.

Fogg, Sam. Art of the Middle Ages. 2008. (Illus.). 140p. pap. 40.00 *(978-0-9553393-1-8(6))* Holberton, Paul Publishing GBR. Dist: Univ. of Washington Pr.

Folda, Jaroslav. Crusader Art: The Art of the Crusaders in the Holy Land, 1099-1291. 2008. (Illus.). 176p. 100.00 *(978-0-85331-995-5(2),* Lund Humphries Pubs.) Ashgate Publishing, Ltd. GBR. Dist: Ashgate Publishing Co.

Frugoni, Chiara & Armandi Barbolini, Marina. The Cathedral of Modena, 3 vols. 2009. (ITA & ENG., Illus.). 1340p. 1160.00 *(978-88-7686-982-2(4))* Panini Franco Cosimo ITA. Dist: Antique Collectors' Club.

Gauvard, Claude. Le Moyen ge. 2010. (FRE., Illus.). 279p. *(978-2-7324-4135-1(X))* Editions de la Martiniere.

Gertsman, E. The Dance of Death in the Middle Ages: Image, Text, Performance. 2010. (Studies in the Visual Cultures of the Middle Ages Ser.). (ENG., Illus.). 356p. (C). 123.00 *(978-2-503-53063-5(X))* Brepols Pubs. BEL. Dist: ISD.

Gertsman, Elina. Visualizing Medieval Performance: Perspectives, Histories, Contexts. 2008. (Illus.). 366p. 144.95 *(978-0-7546-6436-9(8))* Ashgate Publishing Co.

Gertsman, Elina & Stevenson, Jill, eds. Thresholds of Medieval Visual Culture: Liminal Spaces. 2012. (Boydell Studies in Medieval Art & Architecture Ser.: Volume 4). (Illus.). 406p. 99.00 ***(978-1-84383-697-1(1),*** Boydell Press) Boydell & Brewer, Ltd. GBR. Dist: Boydell & Brewer, Inc.

Ghabin, Ahmad. Hisba, Arts & Crafts in Islam. 2009. (Arabisch-Islamische Welt in Tradition und Moderne Ser.). (ENG.). 287p. (C). pap. 72.00 *(978-3-447-05932-9(X))* Harrassowitz, Otto Verlag DEU. Dist: ISD.

Givens, Jean A., et al. Visualizing Medieval Medicine & Natural History 1200-1500. 2006. (AVISTA Studies in the History of Medieval Technology, Science & Art: 5 Ser.). (Illus.). 300p. 150.00 *(978-0-7546-5296-0(3))* Ashgate Publishing Co.

Goodyear, W. H. Roman & Medieval Art. 20.00 *(978-0-8196-2008-8(4))* Biblo & Tannen Booksellers & Pubs., Inc.

Gorgievski, Sandra. Face to Face with Angels: Images in Medieval Art & in Film. 2010. (ENG., Illus.). 232p. pap. 55.00 *(978-0-7864-4220-1(4))* McFarland & Co., Inc. Pubs.

Grassi, Francesca. La Ceramica, L'alimentazione, L'artigianato e le Vie di Commercio Tra VIII e XIV Secolo. 2010. (Bar S Ser.). (ITA & ENG., Illus.). 216p. (C). pap. 102.50 *(978-1-4073-0666-7(9))* British Archaeological Reports Ltd. GBR. Dist: Brown, David Bk. Co., The.

Groebner, Valentin. Defaced: The Visual Culture of Violence in the Late Middle Ages. Selwyn, Pamela, tr. from GER. 2009. (ENG., Illus.). 217p. (gr. 17). pap. 22.95 *(978-1-890951-38-2(2))* Zone Bks.

Hamburger, J., et al, eds. Frauen-Kloster-Kunst: Neue Forschungen zur Kulturgeschichte des Mittelalters. 2007. (Illus.). 500p. (C). 181.00 *(978-2-503-52357-6(9))* Brepols Pubs. BEL. Dist: Brown, David Bk. Co., The.

Hamburger, Jeffrey F. & Marti, Susan, eds. Crown & Veil: Female Monasticism from the Fifth to the Fifteenth Centuries. Hamburger, Dietlinde, tr. from GER. 2008. (ENG., Illus.). 344p. (gr. 17). 45.00 *(978-0-231-13980-9(2))* Columbia Univ. Pr.

Harris, Stephen, et al. Misconceptions about the Middle Ages. Grigsby, Bryon L., ed. 2007. (Routledge Studies in Medieval Religion & Culture Ser.). 320p. 141.00 *(978-0-415-77053-8(X))* Routledge.

Havsteen. Creations Volume 2 Medieval Rituals, the Arts, & the Concept of Creation. 2007. (Ritus et Artes Ser.). (ENG., Illus.). 269p. (C). 102.00 *(978-2-503-52295-1(5))* Brepols Pubs. BEL. Dist: ISD.

Hayes, Elizabeth R. The Evolution of Visual, Literary, & Performing Arts from Tribal Cultures Through the Middle Ages. 2009. (Illus.). xii, 226p. pap. *(978-0-7409-3153-6(9),* Ohio Univ. Ctr. for International Studies) Paper House Productions.

Hayman, Richard. The Green Man. 2010. (Shire Library). (ENG., Illus.). 56p. pap. 12.95 *(978-0-7478-0784-1(1))* Shire Pubns., Ltd. GBR. Dist: Random Hse., Inc.

Hebgin-Barnes, Penny. The Medieval Stained Glass of Cheshire. 2010. (ENG., Illus.). 642p. 210.00 *(978-0-19-726469-0(7))* Oxford Univ. Pr., Inc.

Heller, Ena Giurescu & Pongracz, Patricia C., eds. Perspectives on Medieval Art: Learning Through Looking. 2009. (Illus.). 224p. pap. 30.00 *(978-0-9777839-5-3(2))* Museum of Biblical Art.

Ho, Cynthia, et al, eds. Finding Saint Francis in Literature & Art. 2009. (New Middle Ages Ser.). (ENG.). 240p. 100.00 *(978-0-230-60286-1(X))* Palgrave Macmillan.

Hoffman, Eva R., ed. Late Antique & Medieval Art of the Mediterranean World. 2007. (Blackwell Anthologies in Art History Ser.). (ENG., Illus.). 448p. pap. 56.95 *(978-1-4051-2072-2(X));* 122.95 *(978-1-4051-2071-5(1))* Wiley, John & Sons, Inc. (Wiley-Blackwell).

Holcomb, Melanie. Pen & Parchment: Drawing in the Middle Ages. 2009. (Illus.). xii, 188p. 50.00 *(978-1-58839-318-0(6))* Metropolitan Museum of Art, The.

—Pen & Parchment: Drawing in the Middle Ages. 2009. (ENG., Illus.). 200p. 50.00 *(978-0-300-14894-7(1))* Yale Univ. Pr.

Hourihane, Colum. The Grove Encyclopedia of Medieval Art & Architecture. 2012. (ENG.). 4070p. 895.00 ***(978-0-19-539536-5(0))*** Oxford Univ. Pr., Inc.

Hourihane, Colum. Looking Beyond: Visions, Dreams & Insights in Medieval Art & Thought. 2010. (Index of Christian Art: Occasional Papers Ser.). (ENG., Illus.). 400p. pap. 35.00 *(978-0-9768202-8-4(5))* Index of Christian Art, Princeton Univ., The.

Hourihane, Colum, ed. Insular & Anglo-Saxon Art & Thought in the Early Medieval Period. 2011. (Illus.). 360p. pap. 35.00 ***(978-0-9837537-0-4(9))*** Index of Christian Art, Princeton Univ., The.

Hourihane, Colum, et al. Pontius Pilate, Anti-Semitism, & the Passion in Medieval Art. 2009. (ENG., Illus.). 496p. (C). 57.50 *(978-0-691-13956-2(3))* Princeton Univ. Pr.

Howard, Helen. Pigments of English Medieval Wall Painting. 2007. (ENG., Illus.). 314p. 130.00 *(978-1-873132-48-7(4))* Archetype Pubns. GBR. Dist: National Bk. Network.

Huizinga, J. The Waning of the Middle Ages. 2010. 338p. pap. 50.50 *(978-1-4457-0162-2(6))* Lulu Enterprises Inc.

Immerzeel, M. Identity Puzzles: Medieval Christian Art in Syria & Lebanon. 2009. (Orientalia Lovaniensia Analecta Ser.). (ENG.). 334p. (C). 116.00 *(978-90-429-2149-8(8))* Peeters Pubs. & Booksellers BEL. Dist: Brown, David Bk. Co., The.

Jackson, Deirdre. Marvellous to Behold: Miracles in Illuminated Manuscripts. 2007. (ENG., Illus.). 160p. 35.00 *(978-0-7123-4946-8(4))* British Library, The GBR. Dist: Chicago Distribution Ctr.

Keane, A. H. The Early Teutonic, Italian & French Masters. 2007. (ENG.). 574p. 58.95 *(978-0-548-04492-6(9))* Kessinger Publishing, LLC.

Kerssen, Ludger. Das Interesse am Mittelalter im Deutschen Nationaldenkmal. (Arbeiten zur Frahmittelalterforschung Ser.). (GER.). VIII, 202p. 210.00 ***(978-3-11-178910-1(1))*** De Gruyter, Walter Inc.

Klein, Holger A. Sacred Gifts & Worldly Treasures: Medieval Masterworks from the Cleveland Museum of Art. 2007. (Illus.). 319p. *(978-94-071-7916-8(8))* Cleveland Museum of Art.

Klemettila. Epitomes of Evil Representations of Executioners in Northern France & the Low Countri. 2006. (Studies in European Urban History (1100-1800) Ser.). (ENG.). 388p. (C). pap. 94.00 *(978-2-503-52278-4(5))* Brepols Pubs. BEL. Dist: ISD.

Kolve, V. A. Telling Images: Chaucer & the Imagery of Narrative II. (ENG., Illus.). 408p. 2010. pap. 24.95 *(978-0-8047-7658-5(X))* 2009. 65.00 *(978-0-8047-5583-2(3))* Stanford Univ. Pr.

LaCroix, Paul, et al. Medieval Life & People. Grafton, Carol Belanger, ed. 2007. (Dover Electronic Clip Art Ser.). (Illus.). 48p. pap. 14.95 *(978-0-486-99852-7(5))* Dover Pubns., Inc.

Lane, Evelyn Staudinger, et al, eds. The Four Modes of Seeing: Approaches to Medieval Imagery in Honor of Madeline Harrison Caviness. 2009. (Illus.). 610p. 139.95 *(978-0-7546-6010-1(9))* Ashgate Publishing Co.

Lavin, Marilyn Aronberg, ed. Rome, Italy, Renaissance: Essays in Art History Honoring Irving Lavin on His Sixtieth Birthday. 2009. (ENG., Illus.). 304p. pap. 30.00 *(978-1-59910-124-8(6))* Italica Pr.

Lawless, Cather. Life Virgin Tuscan Icon 1300-1528. 2006. (Routledge Studies in Medieval Religion & Culture Ser.). (ENG.). 125.00 *(978-0-415-36101-9(X))* Routledge.

Lee, Sonya S. Surviving Nirvana: Death of the Buddha in Chinese Visual Culture. 2010. (CHI., Illus.). 372p. ***(978-988-220-744-8(8))*** Hong Kong Univ. Pr.

—Surviving Nirvana: Death of the Buddha in Chinese Visual Culture. 2010. (ENG., Illus.). 372p. (gr. 17). 55.00 *(978-962-209-125-2(3))* Hong Kong Univ. Pr. HKG. Dist: Columbia Univ. Pr.

Lethaby, William R. Medieval Art. 20.00 *(978-0-8196-2015-6(7))* Biblo & Tannen Booksellers & Pubs., Inc.

—Medieval Art, 321-1350. *(978-0-8022-0960-3(2))* Philosophical Library, Inc.

Lewis, Michael J., et al, eds. New Research on the Bayeux Tapestry: The Proceedings of a Conference at the British Museum. 2011. (ENG., Illus.). 211p. (C). 90.00 *(978-1-84217-976-5(4))* Oxbow Bks., Ltd. GBR. Dist: Brown, David Bk. Co., The.

Lindquist, Sherry C. M. The Meanings of Nudity in Medieval Art. 2012. (Illus.). 450p. 139.95 ***(978-1-4094-2284-6(4))*** Ashgate Publishing Co.

Lloyd-Morgan, Ceridwen. Welsh Manuscripts & English Manuscripts in Wales. 2011. (Index of images in english Manuscripts). (ENG & WEL., Illus.). 128p. (C). pap. 94.00 ***(978-1-905375-81-3(6))*** Brepols Pubs. BEL. Dist: Brown, David Bk. Co., The.

Lorenzi, Lorenzo. Devils in Art: Florence from the Middle Ages to the Renaissance. Roberts, Mark, tr. from ITA. 2006. (ENG., Illus.). 132p. 40.00 *(978-88-7038-438-3(1))* Centro Di ITA. Dist: Antique Collectors' Club.

Lowden, John. Medieval Ivories & Works of Art in the Thomson Collection. 2008. (Illus.). 128p. pap. 50.00 ***(978-1-903470-80-0(3))*** Holberton, Paul Publishing GBR. Dist: Casemate Pubs. & Bk. Distributors, LLC.

Luxford, J. & Michael, M., eds. Nigel M. Morgan: Contexts of Medieval Art - Images, Objects & Ideas. 2010. (Tributes Ser.). (ENG., Illus.). 386p. (C). 218.00 *(978-1-905375-29-5(8))* Miller, Harvey Pubs. GBR. Dist: Brown, David Bk. Co., The.

Maguire, Henry & Nelson, Robert S., eds. San Marco, Byzantium, & the Myths of Venice. 2010. (Dumbarton Oaks Byzantine Symposia & Colloquia Ser.). (ENG., Illus.). 304p. 60.00 *(978-0-88402-360-9(5))* Dumbarton Oaks.

Marti, Susan. Splendour of the Burgundian Court: Charles the Bold (1433-1477) Borchert, Till-Holger & Keck, Gabriele, eds. 2009. (Illus.). 384p. 80.00 *(978-0-8014-4853-9(0))* Cornell Univ. Pr.

Martin, Therese. Reassessing the Roles of Women As 'makers' of Medieval Art & Architecture. 2012. ***(978-90-04-22828-3(4)); (978-90-04-22827-6(6)); (978-90-04-18555-5(0))*** BRILL.

Maxwell, Robert A., ed. Representing History, 900-1300: Art, Music, History. 2010. (ENG.). 296p. 79.95 *(978-0-271-03636-6(2))* Pennsylvania State Univ. Pr.

McNeill, John, ed. King's Lynn & the Fens: Medieval Art, Architecture & Archaeology. 2008. (British Archaeological Association (BAA) Conference Transaction Ser.). (ENG., Illus.). 256p. (C). 144.00 *(978-1-906540-15-9(2));* pap. 68.00 *(978-1-906540-16-6(0))* Maney Publishing GBR. Dist: Brown, David Bk. Co., The.

Michalsky, Tanja. Medien der Macht: Kunst Zur Zeit der Anjous In Italien. (GER & ITA., Illus.). 348p. *(978-3-496-01231-3(5))* Reimer, Dietrich.

Milliken, Roberta. Ambiguous Locks: An Iconology of Hair in Medieval Art & Literature. 2012. (ENG.). 300p. pap. 65.00 ***(978-0-7864-4870-8(9))*** McFarland & Co., Inc. Pubs.

Moffitt, John F. The Enthroned Corpse of Charlemagne: The Lord-in-Majesty Theme in Early Medieval Art & Life. 2006. (ENG., Illus.). 239p. per. 39.95 *(978-0-7864-2767-3(1))* McFarland & Co., Inc. Pubs.

Mohrmann, Karl & Eichwede, I. F. Gothic & Medieval Designs CD-ROM & Book. 2007. (Dover Electronic Clip Art Ser.). (Illus.). 48p. pap. 14.95 *(978-0-486-99823-7(1))* Dover Pubns., Inc.

Monckton, Linda & Morris, Richard. Coventry: Medieval Art, Architecture & Archaeology. 2011. (Baa conference transactions Ser.). (ENG., Illus.). 363p. (C). 130.00 *(978-1-906540-63-0(2))* Maney Publishing GBR. Dist: Brown, David Bk. Co., The.

Monckton, Linda & Morris, Richard K. Coventry: Medieval Art, Architecture & Archaeology. 2011. (Baa conference transactions Ser.). (ENG., Illus.). 363p. (C). pap. 62.00 *(978-1-906540-62-3(4))* Maney Publishing GBR. Dist: Brown, David Bk. Co., The.

Moss, Rachel, ed. Making & Meaning in Insular Art. 2007. (Illus.). 342p. (C). 85.00 *(978-1-85182-986-6(5))* Four Courts Pr. IRL. Dist: International Specialized Bk. Services.

Nash, Susie. No Equal in Any Land: Andre Beauneveu, Artist to the Courts of France & Flanders. 2008. (Illus.). 216p. pap. 60.00 *(978-1-903470-66-4(8))* Holberton, Paul Publishing GBR. Dist: Casemate Pubs. & Bk. Distributors, LLC.

Nie, Giselle de. Envisioning Experience in Late Antiquity & the Middle Ages: Dynamic Patterns in Texts & Images. Noble, Thomas F. X., ed. 2012. (Illus.). 180p. 104.95 ***(978-1-4094-3948-6(8))*** Ashgate Publishing Co.

Norris, Michael. Medieval Art: A Resource for Educators. 2006. (Metropolitan Museum of Art Ser.). (ENG., Illus.). 199p. 79.95 *(978-0-300-10196-6(1))* Yale Univ. Pr.

Nosch, Marie-Louise & Pedersen, Kathrine Vestergard. The Medieval Broadcloth: Changing Trends in Fashions, Manufacturing & Consumption. 2009. (Ancient textiles Ser.). (ENG., Illus.). 170p. (C). pap. 50.00 *(978-1-84217-381-7(2))* Oxbow Bks., Ltd. GBR. Dist: Brown, David Bk. Co., The.

Oakes, Cathy & Oakes, Catherine. Ora Pro Nobis: The Virgin As Intercessor in Medieval Art & Devotion. 2008. (Studies in Medieval & Early Renaissance Art History Ser.). (Illus.). 300p. (C). 174.00 *(978-1-905375-24-0(7))* Miller, Harvey Pubs. GBR. Dist: Brown, David Bk. Co., The.

Oliver, Judith H., et al. Singing with Angels: Liturgy, Music, & Art in the Gradual of Gisela Von Kerssenbrock. 2007. (ENG., Illus.). 384p. (C). 174.00 *(978-2-503-51680-6(7))* Brepols Pubs. BEL. Dist: ISD.

Osborne, John. Medieval Rome: A History in Art. 2013. (ENG., Illus.). 620p. (C). 300.00 *(978-1-904597-41-4(6))* Pindar Pr. GBR. Dist: Brown, David Bk. Co., The.

Panayotova, Dora. Bulgarian Mural Paintings of the 14th Century. Alexieva, Marguerite & Athanassova, Theodora, trs. (Illus.). 40.50 *(978-0-8057-5003-4(7))* Irvington Pubs.

Pancaroglu, Oya. Perpetual Glory: Medieval Islamic Ceramics from the Harvey B. Plotnick Collection. 2007. (ENG., Illus.). 160p. (C). 50.00 *(978-0-300-11943-5(7))* Art Institute of Chicago.

Pesch, Alexandra. Die Goldbrakteaten der Volkerwanderungszeit: Thema und Variation. 2007. (Erganzungsbande Zum Reallexikon der Germanischen Altertumsku Ser.). (GER., Illus.). 600p. 231.00 *(978-3-11-020110-9(0))* De Gruyter, Walter Inc.

Phillips, Sam. The Art Lovers' Guide - London: The Finest Art in London by Museum, Artist, or Period. 2011. (Illus.). 240p. pap. 19.95 *(978-0-8478-3628-4(2),* Skira) Rizzoli International Pubns., Inc.

Pongracz, Patricia, et al. Perspectives on Medieval Art: Learning Through Looking. Heller, Ena Giurescu, ed. 2009. (ENG., Illus.). 224p. 60.00 *(978-1-904832-69-0(5))* Giles, D. Ltd. GBR. Dist: Antique Collectors' Club.

Quintavalle, Arturo Carlo. Medioevo: Le Officine: Atti Del Convegno Internazionale Di Studi, Parma, 22-27 Settembre 2009. 2010. (FRE, ITA & ENG., Illus.). 663p. *(978-88-370-7847-8(1))* Electa.

Ravioire, F. & Dietrich, A., eds. La cuisine et la table dans la France de la fin du Moyen-Age: Contenus et contenants du XIV au XVIe siecle. Actes du colloque de Sens (2004) 2009. (Publications du Centre de Recherches Archéologiques et Historiques Médiévales Ser.). (FRE.). 455p. (C). pap. 62.00 *(978-2-902685-37-0(8))* Brepols Pubs. BEL. Dist: Brown, David Bk. Co., The.

Robinson, James. Masterpieces Medieval Art. 2008. (ENG., Illus.). 320p. 39.95 *(978-0-7141-2815-3(5))* British Museum Pr. GBR. Dist: Brown, David Bk. Co., The.

Rodríguez Barral, Paulino. Imagen Del Judío en la España Medieval, la el Conflicto Entre Cristianismo y Judaísmo en Las Artes Visuales Góticas. 2009. 290p. pap. *(978-84-475-3366-4(2))* Univ. de Barcelona Pubns.

Rooney, Dawn F. Ancient Sukhothai: Thailand's Cultural Heritage. 2008. (ENG., Illus.). 220p. pap. 30.00 *(978-974-9863-42-8(9))* River Bks. THA. Dist: Antique Collectors' Club.

Sconci, Maria Selene & Robinson, Christopher. Maiolica Medievale: Una Moderna Interpretazione. 2006. (ITA & ENG., Illus.). 63p. (C). 13.00 *(978-88-596-0094-7(4))* Edizioni Polistampa ITA. Dist: Brown, David Bk. Co., The.

Snelders, B. Identity in Christian-Muslim Interaction: Medieval Art of the Syrian Orthodox from the Mosul Area. 2010. (Orientalia Lovaniensia Analecta Ser.). (ENG.). 591p. (C). 124.00 *(978-90-429-2386-7(5))* Peeters Pubs. & Booksellers BEL. Dist: Brown, David Bk. Co., The.

Stalley, Roger, ed. Limerick & South-West Ireland: Medieval Art & Architecture. 2011. (Baa conference transactions Ser.). (ENG., Illus.). 271p. (C). 130.00

(978-1-907625-07-7(0)); pap. 62.00 (978-1-907625-08-4(9)) Maney Publishing GBR. Dist: Brown, David Bk. Co., The.
Stokstad, Marilyn & Cothren, Michael. Art History Portable, Book 2: Medieval Art. 4th ed. 2010. (ENG.). 240p. (C). pap. 80.00 (978-0-205-79092-0(5), Prentice Hall) Prentice Hall PTR.
Talbot, A. M. Dumbarton Oaks Papers, Vol. 62. Talbot, Alice-Mary, ed. 2010. (Dumbarton Oaks Papers). (Illus.). 400p. 125.00 (978-0-88402-355-5(9)) Dumbarton Oaks.
Talbot, Alice-Mary & Whitehouse, David, eds. Dumbarton Oaks Papers, Vol. 59. 2007. (Dumbarton Oaks Papers). (Illus.). 400p. 125.00 (978-0-88402-312-8(5)) Dumbarton Oaks.
Taylor, Henry Osborn. The Classical Heritage of the Middle Ages. 2009. 412p. pap. 31.45 (978-1-4446-3588-1(3)) Barclay Pr., Inc.
—The Classical Heritage of the Middle Ages. 2009. 310p. pap. (978-0-217-57719-9(9)); 314p. pap. (978-0-217-75450-7(3)) Books LLC.
—The Classical Heritage of the Middle Ages. 2009. 298p. pap. 20.21 (978-0-217-88841-7(0)) General Bks. LLC.
Terry-Fritsch, Allie, et al. Beholding Violence in Medieval & Early Modern Europe. 2012. (Illus.). 250p. (978-1-4094-4286-8(1)) Ashgate Publishing, Ltd.
Trachtenberg, Marvin. Dominion of the Eye: Urbanism, Art, & Power in Early Modern Florence. 2008. (ENG., Illus.). 380p. pap. 52.99 (978-0-521-72825-6(8)) Cambridge Univ. Pr.
Van Marle. Iconographie de l'Art Profane au Moyen Age et a la Renaissance et la Decoration des Demeures, 2 tomes, Set. (FRE.). 516.00 (978-0-8288-8022-0(0)) French & European Pubns., Inc.
Verlag, Hirmer & Hirmer Verlag. Meisterwerke mittelalterlicher Kunst au dem Nationalmuseum Warschau. 2006. (GER., Illus.). 192p. (C). pap. 42.00 (978-3-7774-3275-5(X)) Hirmer Verlag GmbH DEU. Dist: Brown, David Bk. Co., The.
Verma, Archana. Temple Imagery from Early Mediaeval Peninsular India. 2012. (Illus.). 312p. 119.95 (978-1-4094-3029-2(4)) Ashgate Publishing Co.
Walker, Alicia & Luyster, Amanda. Negotiating Secular & Sacred in Medieval Art: Christian, Islamic, & Buddhist. 2009. (Illus.). 242p. 119.95 (978-0-7546-6327-0(2)) Ashgate Publishing Co.
Webster, Leslie. Anglo-Saxon Art. 2011. 256p. pap. 29.95 (978-0-8014-7766-9(2)) Cornell Univ. Pr.
Westheider, Ortrud. Zwischen Himmel und Hölle: Kunst des Mittelalters von der Gotik bis Baldung Grien. Katalogbuch zur Ausstellung Hamburg 19.09.2009-10.01.2010 Bucerius Kunst Forum. Westheider, Ortrud & Philipp, Michael, eds. 2009. (GER., Illus.). 256p. (C). 64.00 (978-3-7774-2201-5(0)) Hirmer Verlag GmbH DEU. Dist: Brown, David Bk. Co., The.
Whitfield, Niamh. Design & Techniques in Early Medieval Celtic Metalwork. 2013. (ENG., Illus.). 580p. (C). 300.00 (978-1-904597-33-9(5)) Pindar Pr. GBR. Dist: Brown, David Bk. Co., The.
Williamson, Paul. Medieval & Renaissance Treasures from the V&A. Motture, Peta, ed. 2007. (ENG., Illus.). 96p. 27.50 (978-1-85177-526-2(9)) V & A Pubns. GBR. Dist: Hachette Bk. Group.
Zchomelidse, Nino & Freni, Giovanni. Meaning in Motion - Semantiocs of Movement in Medieval Art. 2011. (Publications of the Department of Art & Archaeology, Princeton University Ser.). (ENG., Illus.). 288p. (C). 49.95 (978-0-691-15193-9(8)) Princeton Univ. Pr.

ART, MESOPOTAMIAN

Bradford, Rosalind E. The Guyuan Sarcophagus. 2011. (Illus.). 404p. pap. (978-3-8433-8985-3(3)) Lambert Academic Publishing.
von Oppenheim, Baron Max. Tell Halaf: A New Culture in Oldest Mesopotamia. Wheeler, Gerald, tr. 2007. (Gorgias Classic Archaeological Reprints Ser.: 8). 89.00 (978-1-59333-633-2(0)) Gorgias Pr., LLC.

ART, MEXICAN

see also Aztec Art; Maya Art

Ades, Dawn & McClean, Alison. Revolution on Paper: Mexican Prints 1910-1960. 2009. (ENG., Illus.). 192p. pap. 39.95 (978-0-292-72248-4(6)) Univ. of Texas Pr.
Alderete, Jorge. Graficos Mexicanos. 2011. (ENG.). 256p. 44.95 (978-1-907621-02-4(4)) Korero Books LLP GBR. Dist: Independent Pubs. Group.
Amorales, Carlos. Carlos Amorales: Caca Grande. 2010. (ENG., Illus.). 66p. pap. 25.00 (978-84-92480-64-7(5)) RM Verlag, S.L. ESP. Dist: D.A.P./Distributed Art Pubs.
—Escultura Social: A New Generation of Art from Mexico City. Widholm, Julie Rodrigues, ed. 2007. (SPA & ENG., Illus.). 224p. pap. 39.95 (978-0-300-13427-8(4)) Yale Univ. Pr.
Arnold, Grant & Thom, Ian M. Shore, Forest & Beyond: Art from the Audain Collection. 1 vol. 2012. (ENG., Illus.). 144p. 55.00 (978-1-55365-929-7(5)) D&M Pubs. Inc. CAN. Dist: Perseus-PGW.
Asthon, Dore. Manuel Felguerez. 2010. (ENG., Illus.). 218p. 45.00 (978-84-92480-77-7(7)) RM Verlag, S.L. ESP. Dist: D.A.P./Distributed Art Pubs.
Azuela, Alicia & Palacios, Guillermo. La Mirada Mirada: Transculturalidad e Imaginarios Del México Revolucionario, 1910- 1945. 2009. (Estudios Históricos Ser.). (SPA., Illus.). 309p. pap. 44.99 (978-607-462-045-0(8)) El Colegio de México, A.C., Biblioteca Miguel Cosio Villegas MEX. Dist: Fondo de Cultura Economica USA.
Baum, Sandy & Skodnick, Roy. Mexican Arts Series: Hammered Copper. 2010. (Illus.). 160p. pap. 29.99 (978-0-7643-3502-0(2)) Schiffer Publishing, Ltd.
Berrin, Kathleen & Fields, Virginia M., eds. Olmec: Colossal Masterworks of Ancient Mexico. 2010. (Illus.). 272p. 65.00 (978-0-300-16676-7(1)) Yale Univ. Pr.
Blanco Cano, Rosana. Cuerpos Disidentes Del México Imaginado: Cultura, Género, Etnia y Nación Más Allá Del Proyecto Posrevolucionario. 2010. (SPA., Illus.). 225p. pap. 29.80 (978-84-8489-509-1(2)) Iberoamericana Vervuert Publishing Corp.
Bravo, Manuel Alvarez, photos by. Manuel Alvarez Bravo: Photopoetry. 2008. (ENG.). 320p. 75.00 (978-0-8118-6532-6(0)) Chronicle Bks. LLC.
Brenner, Anita. Avant-Garde Art & Artists in Mexico: Anita Brenner's Journals of the Roaring Twenties. Glusker, Susannah Joel, ed. 2010. (ENG., Illus.). 901p. 125.00 (978-0-292-72184-5(6)) Univ. of Texas Pr.
Carrillo Azpéitia, Rafael. El Arte Barroco en Mexico. (Panorama of Mexico Ser.). (SPA., Illus.). 162p. 10.95 (978-968-38-0062-6(9), PN629) Panorama Editorial MEX. Dist: Continental Bk. Co., Inc.
—Mural Painting Mexico. (Panorama of Mexico Ser.). (SPA., Illus.). 155p. 10.95 (978-968-38-0026-8(2), PN262E) Panorama Editorial MEX. Dist: Continental Bk. Co., Inc.
Casillas, Mercurio López. Images of Death in Mexican Prints. 2008. (ENG., Illus.). 256p. 65.00 (978-968-5208-89-5(1)) R.M. Editorial, S.A. de C.V. MEX. Dist: D.A.P./Distributed Art Pubs.
Charlot, Jean. Mexican Art & the Academy of San Carlos, 1785-1915. 2011. 176p. 42.95 (978-1-258-08509-4(7)) Literary Licensing, LLC.
Colonetti, Aldo. Raymundo Sesma: Campo Expandido. 2009. (ENG., Illus.). 288p. 77.95 (978-88-8158-734-6(3)) Charta ITA. Dist: D.A.P./Distributed Art Pubs.
Cruzvillegas, Abraham, et al, texts. Daniel Guzman & Steven Shearer: Double Album. 1 vol. 2008. (ENG., Illus.). 224p. 49.95 (978-0-915557-91-2(6)) New Museum of Contemporary Art, The.
Cuadriello, Jaime. The Glories of the Republic of Tlaxcala: Art & Life in Viceregal Mexico. Follett, Christopher J., tr. from SPA. 2011. (ENG., Illus.). 400p. 55.00 (978-0-292-72360-3(1)) Univ. of Texas Pr.
Curatorial 060, Laboratorio. Laboratorio Curatorial 060. 2008. 8.00 (978-0-9797964-3-2(1)) CUE Art Foundation.
Davalos, Karen Mary, text. The Mexican Museum of San Francisco Papers, 1971-2006. 2011. (ENG., Illus.). 266p. (C). pap. 19.95 (978-0-89551-122-5(3)) UCLA Chicano Studies Research Ctr. Pr.
de Haro, Fernando & Fuentes, Omar. Mexico: Handcrafted Art, Central Region. 2007. (ENG., Illus.). 224p. 45.00 (978-970-9726-81-7(1)) AM Editores MEX. Dist: Perseus-PGW.
De Oliveira, Nicolas & Pirotte, Philippe, eds. Stefan Bruggemann. 2008. (ENG., Illus.). 64p. 35.00 (978-3-905829-64-8(9)) JRP Ringier Kunstverlag AG CHE. Dist: D.A.P./Distributed Art Pubs.
Debroise, Olivier, ed. Informe. 2010. (ENG & SPA., Illus.). 246p. 40.00 (978-968-9056-35-5(2)) Turner, Ediciones S.A. ESP. Dist: D.A.P./Distributed Art Pubs.
Diaz de León, Francisco. Francisco Díaz de León. 2011. (ENG., Illus.). 160p. 45.00 (978-84-936123-6-8(7)) RM Verlag, S.L. ESP. Dist: D.A.P./Distributed Art Pubs.
Evans, Susan Toby. Ancient Mexican Art at Dumbarton Oaks. 2010. (Pre-Columbian Art at Dumbarton Oaks Ser.). (Illus.). 304p. 70.00 (978-0-88402-345-6(1)) Dumbarton Oaks.
Falconi, José Luis & Reyes, Pedro, eds. Ad Usum: To Be Used. 2007. (David Rockefeller Center for Latin American Studies, Art Catalogs Ser.). (Illus.). 98p. pap. 17.95 (978-0-674-02515-8(6)) Harvard Univ. Pr.
Fort, Ilene Susan, et al, contrib. by. In Wonderland: The Surrealist Adventures of Women Artists in Mexico & the United States. 2012. (ENG., Illus.). 256p. 60.00 (978-3-7913-5141-4(9)) Prestel Publishing.
Frenk, Mariana & García Bonilla, Roberto. Arte Entre DOS Continentes: Artículos y Ensayos. 2009. (SPA., Illus.). xvii, 275p. 20.40 (978-968-23-2585-4(4)) Siglo XXI Ediciones MEX. Dist: Sony Electronics.
Gallo, Rubén. Mexican Modernity: The Avant-Garde & the Technological Revolution. 2010. (ENG., Illus.). 280p. (gr. 17). pap. 17.95 (978-0-262-51496-5(6)) MIT Pr.
Gould, Kerin. Living Art: Designs & Crafts of the Otomí of San Pablito. 2009. 92p. 24.95 (978-0-7649-5099-5(1)) Pomegranate Communications, Inc.
Grafton, Carol Belanger, ed. Pre-Columbian Mexican Designs. 2008. (Dover Electronic Clip Art Ser.). (ENG., Illus.). 48p. pap. 22.95 (978-0-486-99865-7(7)) Dover Pubns., Inc.
Gruner, Silvia. Silvia Gruner: un Chant D'amour. 2009. (ENG., Illus.). 168p. pap. 35.00 (978-84-92480-44-9(0)) RM Verlag, S.L. ESP. Dist: D.A.P./Distributed Art Pubs.
He, Jianping, ed. Alejandro Magallanes. 2008. (New Generation of Design Ser.). (Illus.). 215p. pap. (978-981-245-508-6(6)) Page One Publishing.
Jimenez, Agustin, photos by. Agustin Jimenez: Memoirs of the Avant-Garde. 2008. (ENG., Illus.). 192p. 50.00 (978-968-9345-11-4(7)) R.M. Editorial, S.A. de C.V. MEX. Dist: D.A.P./Distributed Art Pubs.
Jones, Anny Brooksbank. Visual Culture in Spain & Mexico. 2011. (ENG., Illus.). 224p. pap. 25.95 (978-0-7190-5679-6(9)) Manchester Univ. Pr. GBR. Dist: Macmillan.
Koontz, Rex. Lightning Gods & Feathered Serpents: The Public Sculpture of el Tajín. 2009. (ENG., Illus.). 152p. 60.00 (978-0-292-71899-9(3)) Univ. of Texas Pr.
Lake, Rodrigo Rivero. Namban: Art in Viceregal Mexico, 1 vol. 2006. (ENG., Illus.). 327p. 75.00 (978-84-7506-693-6(3)) Turner, Ediciones S.A. ESP. Dist: D.A.P./Distributed Art Pubs.
Lakra, Dr. & López, Jerónimo. Dr. Lakra. 2010. (ENG., Illus.). 116p. 35.00 (978-84-92480-86-9(6)) RM Verlag, S.L. ESP. Dist: D.A.P./Distributed Art Pubs.
Lockmiller, Alice. Teacher's Guide for Zaltana, Princess of Ancient Mexico. 2010. 44p. pap. 13.95 (978-0-557-32469-9(6)) Lulu Enterprises Inc.
Lynch, Cheryl. Quilt Fiesta! Surprising Designs from Mexican Tiles. 2011. (Illus.). 96p. pap. 26.99 (978-1-60468-003-4(2)) Martingale & Co.
Maldonado Ortiz, Carlos. Rarámuri: Freedom at Twilight - Memories from the Tarahumara. 2010. 168p. pap. 52.49 (978-1-4490-3376-7(8)) AuthorHouse.
Margolles, Teresa, et al. ¿De Que Otra Cosa Podríamos Hablar? 2009. (SPA., Illus.). 158p. (978-84-92480-65-4(3)) RM Verlag, S.L.
McLaughlin, Judith. Sacred Feminine. 2009. 224p. 32.95 (978-1-890689-52-0(1), Rio Grande Bks.) LPD Pr.
Meschede, Friedrich, ed. Survival of the Idea/Supervivencia de la idea: Failure of the Object: Sketches & Projects/Fracaso del Objeto: Apuntes y Proyectos, 1991-2007. 2008. (SPA & ENG., Illus.). 128p. 35.00 (978-3-7757-2075-5(8)) Hatje Cantz Verlag GmbH & Co KG DEU. Dist: D.A.P./Distributed Art Pubs.
Moffitt, John F. Our Lady of Guadalupe: The Painting, the Legend & the Reality. 2006. (ENG., Illus.). 271p. per. 39.95 (978-0-7864-2667-6(5)) McFarland & Co., Inc. Pubs.
Monsiváis, Carlos. Imágenes de la Tradición Viva. 2007. (Tezontle Ser.). (SPA.). 671p. 129.00 (978-968-16-8041-1(3)) Fondo de Cultura Economica USA.
Morgan, Jessica. Tate Modern Artists: Gabriel Orozco. 2011. (ENG., Illus.). 128p. pap. 27.50 (978-1-85437-912-2(7)) Tate Publishing, Ltd. GBR. Dist: Hachette Bk. Group.
Murphy, Sean, ed. Gonzalo Lebrija. aut. ed. 2010. (ENG., Illus.). 104p. 130.00 (978-1-906967-03-1(2)) Other Criteria GBR. Dist: Abrams.
Murphy, Sean, ed. Gonzalo Lebrija (Spanish Edition) 2011. (SPA.). 104p. pap. 95.00 (978-1-906967-34-5(2)) Abrams.
Musacchio, Humberto. El Taller de Gráfica Popular. 2007. (Tezontle Ser.). (SPA.). 214p. 49.95 (978-968-16-7703-9(X)) Fondo de Cultura Economica USA.
Naples Museum of Art. 20th-Century Mexican Art: The Pollak Collection. 2007. (Illus.). 172p. 40.00 (978-0-9773018-7-4(7)); per. 30.00 (978-0-9773018-6-7(9)) Naples Museum of Art.
Orozco, Gabriel. Gabriel Orozco. Bois, Yve-Alain, ed. 2009. (October Files Ser.). (ENG., Illus.). 216p. (gr. 17). 38.00 (978-0-262-01318-5(5)) MIT Pr.
Orozco, Gabriel & Bois, Yve-Alain. Gabriel Orozco. Bois, Yve-Alain, ed. 2009. (October Files Ser.). (ENG., Illus.). 216p. (gr. 17). pap. 19.95 (978-0-262-51301-2(3)) MIT Pr.
Orozco, Jos#xE9; Clemente, et al. Diego Rivera, David Alfaro Siqueiros, José Clemente Orozco. 2011. (ENG., Illus.). 48p. pap. 9.95 (978-0-87070-820-6(1)) Museum of Modern Art.
Palazón Mayoral, María Rosa. La Estética en México, Siglo XX: Diálogos Entre Filósofos. 2006. (Filosofía Ser.). (SPA.). 452p. pap. 25.99 (978-968-16-8112-8(6)) Fondo de Cultura Económica.
Paoli, Cristina. Mexican Blackletter. 2006. (ENG., Illus.). 96p. 24.95 (978-0-9772827-8-4(3)) Batty, Mark Pub., LLC.
Parks, Walter P. The Miracle of Mata Ortiz: Juan Quezada & the Potters of Northern Chihuahua. 2011. (Illus.). 212p. 40.00 (978-1-933855-61-5(4)) Rio Nuevo Pubs.
Parr, Martin, et al, photos by. Visual Correspondences. 2010. (ENG & SPA., Illus.). 336p. pap. 39.95 (978-950-889-183-9(1)) La Marca ARG. Dist: D.A.P./Distributed Art Pubs.
Pina, Leslie. Mexican Jewelry & Metal Art. 2008. (Illus.). 89p. 89.99 (978-0-7643-3140-4(X)) Schiffer Publishing, Ltd.
Piña, Leslie. Mexican Silver Jewelry Details. 2008. (Illus.). 304p. bds. 89.99 (978-0-7643-3081-0(0)) Schiffer Publishing, Ltd.
Pohl, John. Sorcerers of the Fifth Heaven: Nahua Art & Ritual of Ancient Southern Mexico. 2007. (Illus.). 49p. pap. 21.95 net. (978-0-943012-45-2(7)) Princeton Univ. Art Museum.
Pohl, John M. D. Narrative Mixtec Ceramics of Ancient Mexico. 2007. (PLAS Cuadernos Ser.). pap. 19.95 (978-0-943012-46-9(5)) Princeton Univ. Art Museum.
Powell, Melissa, ed. Huichol Art & Culture: Balancing the World. 2010. (ENG.). 176p. pap. (978-0-89013-563-1(0)) Museum of New Mexico Pr.
Ramírez, Jerónimo López & Lakra, Dr. Dr. Lakra: Health & Efficiency. 2009. (ENG., Illus.). 88p. 45.00 (978-84-92480-32-6(7)) R.M. Editorial, S.A. de C.V. MEX. Dist: D.A.P./Distributed Art Pubs.
Rashkin, Elissa J. Stridentist Movement in Mexico: The Avant-Garde & Cultural Change in the 1920s. 2009. (ENG., Illus.). 278p. 78.99 (978-0-7391-3156-5(7)) Lexington Bks.
Rebora, Ballo. Carving the Mariachi. 2008. (ENG & SPA.). 64p. pap. 14.99 (978-0-7643-3147-3(7)) Schiffer Publishing, Ltd.
Rulfo, Juan, photos by & text. Juan Rulfo: 100 Photographs. 2011. (ENG., Illus.). 140p. 55.00 (978-84-92480-92-0(0)) RM Verlag, S.L. ESP. Dist: D.A.P./Distributed Art Pubs.
Schuessler, Michael K., ed. Mexico se escribe con J/Mexico is Written with J. 2011. 271p. pap. 23.95 (978-607-07-0578-6(5)) Editorial Planeta Mexicana MEX. Dist: Perseus Distribution.
Stallings, Tyler, et al. Gabriela León: Sunday Walk to the Zócalo of Oaxaca. Stallings, Tyler, ed. 2008.Tr. of Gabriela león: Paseo Dominical por el zócalo de Oaxaca. (ENG & SPA.). 40p. pap. (978-0-932173-21-8(7)) Sweeney Art Gallery.
Standish, Peter. A Companion to Mexican Studies. 2006. (Monografías A Ser.: Volume 230). (SPA., Illus.). 244p. 90.00 (978-1-85566-134-9(9), Tamesis Bks.) Boydell & Brewer, Ltd. GBR. Dist: Boydell & Brewer, Inc.
Stromberg, Gobi & Mallet Cárdenas, Ana Elena. Silver Seduction: The Art of Mexican Modernist Antonio Pineda. 2008. (Illus.). 188p. pap. (978-0-9778344-0-2(9)) Univ. of California, Los Angeles, Fowler Museum of Cultural History.
Tavera, Maria Cristina, intro. Mexican Pulp Art. 2007. (ENG., Illus.). 140p. pap. 16.00 (978-1-932595-22-2(8)) Feral Hse.
Tibol, Raquel & Rivera, Diego. Diego Rivera: Great Illustrator. 2008. (ENG., Illus.). 308p. 65.00 (978-968-9345-00-8(1)) R.M. Editorial, S.A. de C.V. MEX. Dist: D.A.P./Distributed Art Pubs.
Turner, Frederick, frwd. Dark Beauty: Photographs of New Mexico by Jack Parsons. 2011. (ENG., Illus.). 148p. 60.00 (978-1-55595-370-6(0)) Hudson Hills Pr. LLC.
Van Dinter, Maarten Hesselt. Native Designs from Ancient Mexico & Peru. 2007. (Illus.). 105p. pap. incl. cd-rom (978-90-810543-4-8(1)) Mundurucu Pubs.
Weller, Alan. The Mexican Prints of Posada & Manilla. 2012. (Dover Pictorial Archive Ser.). (ENG.). 128p. pap. 19.95 (978-0-486-49177-1(6)) Dover Pubns., Inc.
Zavala, Adriana. Becoming Modern, Becoming Tradition. 2010. (ENG., Illus.). 408p. pap. 44.95 (978-0-271-03524-6(2)) Pennsylvania State Univ. Pr.
Zavala, Adriana. Becoming Modern, Becoming Tradition: Women, Gender, & Representation in Mexican Art. 2010. (Illus.). 376p. 95.00 (978-0-271-03471-3(8)) Pennsylvania State Univ. Pr.
Zavala, Adriana, et al. Mexico Beyond Its Revolution. 2010.Tr. of Mexico mas alla de su Revolucion. (ENG & SPA., Illus.). 112p. pap. 10.00 (978-1-880593-08-0(4)) Tufts Univ. Gallery.
Zayas, Marius de. Marius de Zayas: Un Destierro Moderno. 2009. (Illus.). 289p. (SPA.). (978-607-7622-28-4(1)); (SPA., (978-968-9416-19-7(7)); (978-607-7605-21-8(2)) Aldus, Editorial, S.A.

ART, MICRONESIAN

Kaeppler, Adrienne L. The Pacific Arts of Polynesia & Micronesia. 2008. (Oxford History of Art Ser.). (ENG., Illus.). 256p. pap. 27.95 (978-0-19-284238-1(2)) Oxford Univ. Pr., Inc.
Rubinstein, Donald. Paul Jacoulet's Vision of Micronesia. 2007. 40p. pap. 30.00 (978-0-9800331-0-6(1)) Univ. of Guam, Micronesian Area Research Ctr.
Wavell, Barbara. Arts & Crafts of Micronesia: Trading with Tradition. 2010. (Illus.). 264p. pap. 29.95 (978-1-57306-309-8(6)) Bess Pr., Inc.

ART, MIDDLE EASTERN

Aruz, Joan, et al, eds. Beyond Babylon: Art, Trade, & Diplomacy in the Second Millennium B. C. 2008. (ENG., Illus.). 548p. 75.00 (978-0-300-14143-6(2)) Yale Univ. Pr.
Aruz, Joan, et al. Beyond Babylon: Art, Trade, & Diplomacy in the Second Millennium B.C. 2008. (Illus.). xxiii, 524p. 75.00 (978-1-58839-295-4(3)) Metropolitan Museum of Art, The.
Bahrani, Zainab & Shabout, Nada M. Modernism & Iraq. 2009. (Illus.). 99p. (978-1-884919-22-0(7)) Columbia Univ., The Miriam & Ira D. Wallach Art Gallery.
Benzel, Kim. Art of the Ancient Near East: A Resource for Educators. 2010. (Illus.). 134p. 79.95 (978-1-58839-358-6(5)) Metropolitan Museum of Art, The.
Benzel, Kim, et al. Art of the Ancient Near East: A Resource for Educators. 2010. (ENG., Illus.). 140p. 79.95 (978-0-300-16708-5(3)) Yale Univ. Pr.
Boullata, Kamal. Palestinian Art: From 1850 to the Present. 2009. (ENG., Illus.). 363p. pap. 34.95 (978-0-86356-648-6(0)) Saqi Bks. GBR. Dist: Consortium Bk. Sales & Distribution.
Canby, Sheila, intro. The Shahnama of Shah Tahmasp: The Persian Book of Kings. 2011. (ENG., Illus.). 288p. 200.00 (978-0-300-17586-8(8)) Yale Univ. Pr.
Castagno, John. African, Asian & Middle Eastern Artists: Signatures & Monograms From 1800. 2008. (ENG., Illus.). 150p. 125.00 (978-0-8108-6357-6(X)) Scarecrow Pr., Inc.
Curatola, Giovanni, ed. The Art & Architecture of Mesopotamia. 2007. (ENG., Illus.). 280p. 95.00 (978-0-7892-0921-4(7)) Abbeville Pr., Inc.
Curatola, Giovanni & Scarcia, Gianroberto. Art & Architecture of Persia. Shore, Marguerite, tr. from ITA. 2007. (ENG., Illus.). 263p. 95.00 (978-0-7892-0920-7(9)) Abbeville Pr., Inc.
Eichner, Ina & Tsamakda, Vasiliki, eds. Syrien und seine Nachbarn von der Spatantike bis in die islamische Zeit. 2009. (Spatantike-Fruhes Christentum-Byzanz Ser.). (GER., Illus.). 308p. (C). 168.00 (978-3-89500-674-6(2)) Reichert, Ludwig Dr. DEU. Dist: Brown, David Bk. Co., The.
Eigner, Saeb. Art of the Middle East: Modern & Contemporary Art of the Arab World & Iran. 2010. (ENG., Illus.). 352p. 69.95 (978-1-85894-500-2(3)) Merrell Pubs. Ltd. GBR. Dist: Perseus Distribution.
Erlich, Adi. The Art of Hellenistic Palestine. 2009. (Bar S Ser.). (ENG., Illus.). 139p. (C). pap. 85.00 (978-1-4073-0586-8(7)) British Archaeological Reports Ltd. GBR. Dist: Brown, David Bk. Co., The.
Fini, Claudia, et al, eds. Contemporary Photography from Africa & Middle East: Breaking News. 2011. (Illus.). 208p. 55.00 (978-88-572-0645-5(9)) Skira Editore ITA. Dist: Random Hse., Inc.
Jacir, Emily. Emily Jacir & Susan Buck-Morss. 2011. (ENG., Illus.). 48p. pap. 10.00 (978-3-7757-2853-9(8)) Hatje Cantz Verlag GmbH & Co KG DEU. Dist: D.A.P./Distributed Art Pubs.
Jacir, Emily & Wäspe, Roland. Emily Jacir. 2008. (GER & ENG., Illus.). 96p. 65.00 (978-3-939738-57-2(3)) Verlag fur Moderne Kunst DEU. Dist: D.A.P./Distributed Art Pubs.

A

Karahan, A. Byzantine Holy Images - Transcendence & Immanence. the Theological Background of the Iconography & Aesthetics of the Chora Church. 2010. (Orientalia Lovaniensia Analecta Ser.). (ENG.). 365p. (C). 109.00 *(978-90-429-2080-4(7))* Peeters Pubs. & Booksellers BEL. Dist: Brown, David Bk. Co., The.

Khouri, Rami & Casule, Francesca. Art & History of Jordan. Giorgi, Simonetta, ed. Pauli, Erika, tr. from ITA. (Illus.). 128p. *(978-88-8029-416-0(4))* Casa Editrice Bonechi.

Krohn, Zia & Lagerweij, Joyce. Concrete Messages: Street Art on the Israeli - Palestinian Separation Barrier. 2010. (ENG., Illus.). 128p. 29.95 *(978-91-85639-38-0(9))* Dokument forlag, Fotograf Malcolm Jacobsson SWE. Dist: SCB Distributors.

Monem, Nadine, ed. Contemporary Art in the Middle East: Artworld. 2009. (ENG., Illus.). 240p. 49.95 *(978-1-906155-56-8(9))* Black Dog Publishing Ltd. GBR. Dist: Perseus Distribution.

Muller, Walter, ed. Die Bedeutung der minoischen und mykenischen Glyptik. 2010. (Corpus der Minoischen und Mykenischen Siegel Ser.). (ENG & FRE., Illus.). 446p. (C). 195.00 *(978-3-8053-4260-5(8))* Zabern, Philipp von Verlag, GmbH DEU. Dist: Brown, David Bk. Co., The.

Nieuwkerk, Karin van. Muslim Rap, Halal Soaps, & Revolutionary Theater: Artistic Developments in the Muslim World. 2012. (Illus.). vi, 291p. E-Book ***(978-0-292-73552-1(9))*** Univ. of Texas Pr.

Obrist, Hans Ulrich. Films, 1987 - 2010: Serpentine Gallery. Marta, Karen et al, eds. 2011. (ART & ENG., Illus.). 200p. 69.95 *(978-3-86560-943-4(0))* Walther König, Köln/Koenig Bks.

Panini, Augusto. Middle Eastern & Venetian Glass Beads: Eighth to Twentieth Centuries. 2008. (ENG., Illus.). 312p. 100.00 *(978-88-6130-164-1(9))* Skira Editore ITA. Dist: Random Hse., Inc.

Paz, Sarit. Drums, Women, & Goddesses: Drumming & Gender in Iron Age II Israel. 2007. (Orbis Biblicus et Orientalis Ser.). (GER., Illus.). 143p. (C). 47.00 *(978-3-525-53031-3(5))* Vandenhoeck & Ruprecht GmbH & Co. KG DEU. Dist: ISD.

Rahimi, Walid. Ornamental Expressionismus: - eine Verortung von Soziale Energie. 2011. 98p. pap. 23.90 ***(978-3-8423-2956-0(3))*** Bks. on Demand.

Saatchi Gallery Staff, contrib. by. Unveiled: New Art from the Middle East. 2009. (ENG., Illus.). 208p. 35.00 *(978-1-86154-313-4(1))* Booth-Clibborn Editions GBR. Dist: Hachette Bk. Group.

Schmandt-Besserat, Denise. When Writing Met Art: From Symbol to Story. 2007. (ENG., Illus.). 144p. 45.00 *(978-0-292-71334-5(7))* Univ. of Texas Pr.

Shalem, Avinoam, photos by & text. Facing the Wall: The Palestinian-Israeli Barriers. 2011. (ENG., Illus.). 160p. pap. 49.95 ***(978-3-86560-948-9(1))*** Verlag der Buchhandlung Walther Konig DEU. Dist: D.A.P./Distributed Art Pubs.

Snelders, B. Identity in Christian-Muslim Interaction: Medieval Art of the Syrian Orthodox from the Mosul Area. 2010. (Orientalia Lovaniensia Analecta Ser.). (ENG.). 591p. (C). 124.00 *(978-90-429-2386-7(5))* Peeters Pubs. & Booksellers BEL. Dist: Brown, David Bk. Co., The.

Terrace, Edward Lee Bockman. The Art of the Ancient near East in Boston. 2011. 82p. 37.95 ***(978-1-258-09378-5(2))*** Literary Licensing, LLC.

Unwin, Sheila. Arab Chest. 2007. (ENG., Illus.). 144p. (C). 50.00 *(978-0-9544792-6-8(2))* Arabian Publishing, Ltd. GBR. Dist: Brown, David Bk. Co., The.

Weaver, Nigel, et al. Edward Bawden in the Middle East. 2008. (ENG., Illus.). 96p. *(978-1-85149-565-8(7)*, Antique Collectors Club Dist) Antique Collectors' Club.

Winter, Irene, et al. Ancient near Eastern Art in Context: Studies in Honor of Irene J. Winter by Her Students. 2007. (Culture & History of the Ancient near East Ser.). (Illus.). 536p. *(978-90-04-15702-6(6))* BRILL.

Wollesen, Jens. The Frescoes in the Royal Chapel at Pyrga on Cyprus: New Evidence & Datings. 2010. (Studies & Texts). (ENG., Illus.). 194p. 95.00 *(978-0-88844-169-0(X))* Pontifical Institute of Mediaeval Studies, Dept. of Pubns. CAN. Dist: Univ. of Toronto Pr.

ART, MINIMAL

see Minimal Art

ART, MODERN

see also Gothic Revival (Art); Neoclassicism (Art)

Afif, Liz. Psychescapes. 2010. 92p. pap. 34.99 *(978-0-557-46361-9(0))* Lulu Enterprises Inc.

Arntzen, Etta. Krannert Art Museum: Selected Works. 2009. (ENG., Illus.). 360p. 39.95 *(978-1-883015-41-1(3))* Krannert Art Museum.

Art Basel, ed. Art 41 Basel. 2010. (ENG., Illus.). 750p. pap. 70.00 *(978-3-7757-2607-8(1))* Hatje Cantz Verlag GmbH & Co KG DEU. Dist: D.A.P./Distributed Art Pubs.

Baechler, Donald. Donald Baechler: Early Drawings & Working Slides. 2012. (ENG., Illus.). 120p. 40.00 *(978-0-9820947-3-0(6))* PictureBox, Inc.

Baron, Denis, text. The Mutant Flesh. 2009. (ENG., Illus.). 96p. pap. 35.00 *(978-2-914563-42-0(6))* Dis Voir Editions FRA. Dist: D.A.P./Distributed Art Pubs.

Barrett, Terry. Making Art: Form & Meaning. 2010. (ENG., Illus.). 288p. (C). pap. 98.33 *(978-0-07-252178-8(3)*, 0072521783) McGraw-Hill Cos., The.

Barrett, Terry. Why Is That Art? Aesthetics & Criticism of Contemporary Art, 1 vol. 2nd ed. 2011. (ENG., Illus.). 288p. (C). pap. 34.95 ***(978-0-19-975880-7(8))*** Oxford Univ. Pr., Inc.

Batchelor, David, ed. Colour. 2008. (Documents of Contemporary Art Ser.). (ENG., Illus.). 240p. (gr. 17). pap. 24.95 *(978-0-262-52481-0(3))* MIT Pr.

Benford, Steve & Giannachi, Gabriella. Performing Mixed Reality. 2011. (ENG., Illus.). 312p. (gr. 17). 35.00 *(978-0-262-01576-9(5))* MIT Pr.

Birnie, Annabelle. Art in the Office. 2007. (ENG., Illus.). 240p. 45.00 *(978-90-400-8255-9(3))* Waanders B.V., Uitgeverij NLD. Dist: National Bk. Network.

Biro, Matthew. The Dada Cyborg: Visions of the New Human in Weimar Berlin. 2009. (ENG., Illus.). 400p. pap. 29.50 *(978-0-8166-3620-4(6))* Univ. of Minnesota Pr.

Blumin, Stuart M. The Encompassing City: Streetscapes in Early Modern Art & Culture. 2008. (ENG., Illus.). 256p. 89.00 *(978-0-7190-7663-3(3))* Manchester Univ. Pr. GBR. Dist: Macmillan.

Boym, Svetlana, text. Territories of Terror: Mythologies & Memories of the Gulag in Contemporary Russian-American Art. 2007. (ENG., Illus.). 64p. pap. 20.00 *(978-1-881450-25-2(2))* Boston Univ., Art Gallery.

Britt, David, ed. Modern Art: Impressionism to Post-Modernism. 2008. (ENG., Illus.). 416p. 29.95 *(978-0-500-23841-7(3)*, 523841) Thames & Hudson.

Broderick, Mick & Traverso, Antonio, eds. Interrogating Trauma: Collective Suffering in Global Arts & Media. 2010. (ENG., Illus.). 224p. (C). 125.00 *(978-0-415-58278-0(4))* Routledge.

Celant, Germano, ed. Mimmo Rotella: Selected Works. 2007. (ENG., Illus.). 592p. 154.00 *(978-88-8491-359-3(4))* Skira Editore ITA. Dist: Random Hse., Inc.

Celant, Germano & Maraniello, Gianfranco, eds. Vertigo: A Century of Multimedia Art from Futurism to the Web. 2008. (ENG., Illus.). 464p. 50.00 *(978-88-6130-562-5(8))* Skira Editore ITA. Dist: Random Hse., Inc.

Charuca. I Love Kawaii. 2011. (ENG., Illus.). 272p. 19.99 *(978-0-06-208282-4(5)*, Collins Design) HarperCollins Pubs.

Chilvers, Ian & Glaves-Smith, John. A Dictionary of Modern & Contemporary Art. 2nd ed. (ENG., Illus.). 784p. 2010. pap. 19.95 *(978-0-19-923966-5(5))* 2009. 65.00 *(978-0-19-923965-8(7))* Oxford Univ. Pr., Inc.

Chiu, Melissa. Chinese Contemporary Art 7 Things You Should Know. 2008. (Illus.). 112p. *(978-0-9785764-3-1(8))* Art Issue Editions, AW Asia.

Chuang, Joshua. First Doubt: Optical Confusion in Modern Photography. 2008. (ENG., Illus.). 220p. 50.00 *(978-0-300-14133-7(5))* Yale Univ. Art Gallery.

Clarke, David. Chinese Art & Its Encounter with the World. 2011. 272p. ***(978-988-8053-84-1(1))*** Hong Kong Univ. Pr.

Clemence, Paul & Davidow, Julie. Miami: Contemporary Artists. 2007. (Illus.). 288p. pap. 49.95 *(978-0-7643-2647-9(3))* Schiffer Publishing, Ltd.

Cork, Richard. The Healing Presence of Art: A History of Western Art in Hospitals. 2012. (ENG., Illus.). 496p. 90.00 ***(978-0-300-17036-8(X))*** Yale Univ. Pr.

Crowther, Paul. The Phenomenology of Modern Art: Exploding Deleuze, Illuminating Style. 2012. (ENG., Illus.). 296p. 140.00 ***(978-1-4411-3091-4(8))***; pap. 44.95 ***(978-1-4411-4258-0(4))*** Continuum International Publishing Group, Ltd. GBR. Dist: National Bk. Network.

Curtin, Gemma, et al, eds. Kenneth Grange: Making Britain Modern. 2011. (ENG., Illus.). 192p. pap. 29.95 *(978-1-907317-54-5(6))* Black Dog Publishing Ltd. GBR. Dist: Perseus Distribution.

Dariotis, Wei Ming. War Baby / Love Child: Mixed Race Asian American Art. Kina, Laura, ed. 2012. (ENG., Illus.). 304p. pap. 45.00 ***(978-0-295-99225-9(5))*** Univ. of Washington Pr.

Davisson, Darrell D. Art after the Bomb: Iconographies of Trauma in Late Modern Art. 2008. 304p. pap. 73.99 *(978-1-4389-0718-5(4))* AuthorHouse.

Decadence Now! Visions of Excess. 2011. (ENG., Illus.). 300p. 65.00 *(978-80-87164-60-0(1))* Nakladatelstvi Arbor vitae CZE. Dist: D.A.P./Distributed Art Pubs.

Dempsey, Amy. Destination Art. 2006. (Illus.). 272p. 60.00 *(978-0-520-25025-3(7))* Univ. of California Pr.

Dickey, Frances. The Modern Portrait Poem: From Dante Gabriel Rossetti to Ezra Pound. 2012. E-Book ***(978-0-8139-3269-9(6))***; (ENG., Illus.). 288p. (gr. 17). 45.00 ***(978-0-8139-3263-7(7))*** Univ. Pr. of Virginia.

Dole-Recio, Lecia. Lecia Dole-Recio, 1 vol. 2006. (ENG., Illus.). 48p. per. 24.95 *(978-0-914357-98-8(0))* Museum of Contemporary Art, Los Angeles.

Educacion y Accion Cultural Musac, ed. Working from Diversity: Learning Experiences through Art of the Present, Educacion y Accion Cultural MUSAC. 2010. 148p. pap. *(978-84-92861-34-7(7))* Actar Birkhauser Distribution.

Elms, Anthony. Blast Counterblast. Reinke, Steve, ed. 2012. (ENG., Illus.). 192p. pap. 24.00 ***(978-1-926627-17-5(2))*** WhiteWalls, Inc.

Febres, Carlos. Nindo Ryu Gendai Ninjutsu: Introduction to Theories & Applications in the Modern Art of Perseverance. Date not set. (Illus.). 90p. pap. 13.95 *(978-0-7392-0143-5(3)*, P03078) Morris Publishing.

Fletcher, Helmreich. Rise of Modern Art Market in London: The Rise of the Modern Art Market in London. Fletcher, Pamela & Helmreich, Anne, eds. 2012. (ENG., Illus.). 336p. 100.00 ***(978-0-7190-8460-7(1))*** Manchester Univ. Pr. GBR. Dist: Macmillan.

Fogel, Joshua. The Role of Japan in Modern Chinese Art. 2011. (ENG.). 384p. pap. 96.95 *(978-0-9845909-7-1(8))* Institute for International Studies, Univ. of California, Berkeley.

Frisch, Walter. German Modernism: Music & the Arts. 2007. (California Studies in 20th-Century Music). (Illus.). 322p. per. 29.95 *(978-0-520-25148-9(2))* Univ. of California Pr.

Fuentes, Carlos. Viendo Visiones. 2006. (Arte Universal Ser.). (SPA.). 511p. 104.99 *(978-968-16-7529-5(0))* Fondo de Cultura Economica USA.

Furlong, William. Speaking of Art: Four Decades of Art in Conversation. 2010. (ENG., Illus.). 272p. 39.95 *(978-0-7148-4506-7(X))* Phaidon Pr., Inc.

Gibbons, Joan. Contemporary Art & Memory: Images of Recollection & Remembrance. 2008. (ENG., Illus.). 344p. pap. 29.00 *(978-1-84511-619-4(4))* I. B. Tauris & Co., Ltd. GBR. Dist: Macmillan.

Gompertz, Will. What Are You Looking At? The Surprising, Shocking, & Sometimes Strange Story of One Hundred Years of Modern Art. 2012. (ENG., Illus.). 320p. (gr. 12). 27.95 ***(978-0-525-95267-1(5)***, Dutton Adult) Penguin Group (USA) Inc.

Gorlenko, Kateryna. Art Museums in Global Age. 2011. 80p. pap. ***(978-3-639-33217-9(2))*** VDM Verlag Dr. Mueller e.K.

Gottler, Christine. Last Things: Art & the Religious Imagination in the Age of Reform. 2010. (Proteus Ser.). (ENG., Illus.). 437p. (C). 218.00 *(978-2-503-52397-2(8))* Brepols Pubs. BEL. Dist: ISD.

Grau, Oliver, et al. Imagery in the 21st Century. 2011. (ENG., Illus.). 416p. (gr. 17). 40.00 *(978-0-262-01572-1(2))* MIT Pr.

Groys, Boris. Empty Zones: Andrei Monastyrski & 'Collective Actions' 2011. (ENG., Illus.). 128p. pap. 29.95 *(978-1-907317-34-7(1))* Black Dog Publishing Ltd. GBR. Dist: Perseus Distribution.

Guillon, Roland. Harmonie, Rythme et Sociétés: Genèse de L'art Contemporain. 2010. (FRE.). 199p. pap. *(978-2-296-13086-9(0))* Harmattan Pr.

Guston, P. Writing & Talking. 2010. (Documents of Twentieth-Century Art Ser.). (Illus.). 352p. 65.00 *(978-0-520-23509-0(6))* Univ. of California Pr.

Halsall, Francis, et al. Rediscovering Aesthetics: Transdisciplinary Voices from Art History, Philosophy, & Art Practice. Halsall, Francis et al, eds. 2008. (ENG.). 336p. 65.00 *(978-0-8047-5990-8(1))*; pap. 24.95 *(978-0-8047-5991-5(X))* Stanford Univ. Pr.

Harris, Jonathan. Identity Theft: The Cultural Colonization of Contemporary Art. Harris, Jonathan, ed. 2009. (ENG., Illus.). 272p. 85.00 *(978-1-84631-103-1(9))* Liverpool Univ. Pr. GBR. Dist: Chicago Distribution Ctr.

Harris, Jonathan, ed. Identity Theft: The Cultural Colonisation & Contemporary Art. 2009. (Liverpool University Press - Tate Liverpool Critical Forum Ser.). (ENG., Illus.). 272p. pap. 39.95 *(978-1-84631-102-4(0))* Liverpool Univ. Pr. GBR. Dist: Chicago Distribution Ctr.

Havranek, Vit, ed. Katerina Seda: for Every Dog a Different Master. 2008. (ENG., Illus.). 200p. pap. 39.00 *(978-3-905829-66-2(5))* JRP Ringier Kunstverlag AG CHE. Dist: D.A.P./Distributed Art Pubs.

Heinich, Nathalie. Guerre Culturelle et Art Contemporain: Une Comparaison Franco-Américaine. 2010. (FRE.). 170p. *(978-2-7056-7063-4(7))* Hermann.

Hellandsjo, Karin. The Erling Neby Collection. 2011. (ENG., Illus.). 240p. 80.00 *(978-88-572-0862-6(1))* Skira Editore ITA. Dist: Random Hse., Inc.

Hickl, Mario. Management of Modern Art. 2008. 148p. (GER.). 32.50 *(978-1-4092-0312-4(3))*; pap. 20.95 *(978-1-4092-0286-8(0))* Lulu Enterprises Inc.

Hirst, Damien. I Want to Spend the Rest of My Life Everywhere, with Everyone, One to One, Always, Forever, Now. aut. ed. 2008. (ENG.). 330p. 900.00 *(978-1-904212-30-0(1))* Booth-Clibborn Editions GBR. Dist: Hachette Bk. Group.

Holzwarth, Hans Werner, ed. 100 Contemporary Artists: 100 zeitgenössische Künstler von A - Z, 2 vols. 2009. (25 Ser.). (ENG, FRE & GER., Illus.). 704p. 59.99 *(978-3-8365-1490-3(7))* TASCHEN DEU. Dist: Ingram Pub. Services.

Jarzombek, Mark. The Psychologizing of Modernity: Art, Architecture & History. 2011. (ENG., Illus.). 340p. pap. 34.99 *(978-0-521-14763-7(8))* Cambridge Univ. Pr.

Jay, Bill. Occam's Razor. (Illus.). 144p. 17.95 *(978-3-923922-13-0(2))* Nazraeli Pr. DEU. Dist: D.A.P./Distributed Art Pubs.

Jirat-Wasiutynski, Vojtech, ed. Modern Art & the Idea of the Mediterranean. 2007. (ENG., Illus.). 480p. *(978-0-8020-9170-3(9))* Univ. of Toronto Pr.

Judy Collischan. Made in the U S A: Modern/Contemporary Art in America. 2010. 560p. pap. 44.95 *(978-1-4401-9854-0(3))* iUniverse, Inc.

Kahnweiler, Daniel-Henry. The Rise of Cubism. 2nd ed. 2008. (Documents of Modern Art Ser.). (Illus.). 48p. 25.00 *(978-0-8150-0100-3(2))* Wittenborn Art Bks.

Kames, Andrea & Thistlethwaite, Mark. Modern Art Museum of Fort Worth: 110 Masterworks. Auping, Michael, tr. & intro. by. 2006. (ENG., Illus.). 45.00 *(978-1-903942-14-7(4)*, Third Millenium Pub Ltd) Antique Collectors' Club GBR. Dist: National Bk. Network.

Kaplan, Peter, comment. Arthur Carter: Sculptures - Paintings - Drawings. 2009. (ENG., Illus.). 208p. 50.00 *(978-0-8109-0595-5(7))* Abrams.

Kastner, Jeffrey. Nature. 2012. (Whitechapel: Documents of Contemporary Art Ser.). (ENG.). 240p. (gr. 17). pap. 24.95 ***(978-0-262-51766-9(3))*** MIT Pr.

Kiasma - Steven Holl: Museum of Contemp. Art/Helsinki. (Illus.). 98p. 55.00 *(978-951-682-488-1(9))* Building Information Ltd. FIN. Dist: Gingko Pr., Inc.

Kirshenblatt-Gimblett, Barbara & Karp, Jonathan, eds. The Art of Being Jewish in Modern Times. 2007. (Jewish Culture & Contexts Ser.). (Illus.). 464p. (C). 59.95 *(978-0-8122-4002-3(2))* Univ. of Pennsylvania Pr.

Kitamura, Takahiro. Tattooing from Japan to the West. 2007. (Illus.). 160p. per. 29.95 *(978-0-7643-2123-8(4))* Schiffer Publishing, Ltd.

Kosky, Jeffrey L. Arts of Wonder: Enchanting Secularity - Walter de Maria, Diller + Scofidio, James Turrell, Andy Goldsworthy. 2012. (Religion & Postmodernism Ser.). (Illus.). 248p. 40.00 ***(978-0-226-45106-0(2))*** Univ. of Chicago Pr.

Lanchner, Carolyn & Miró, Joan. Joan Miró. 2008. (ENG., Illus.). 48p. pap. 9.95 *(978-0-87070-725-4(6))* Museum of Modern Art.

Leber, Christina. Kunstsammlungen in deutschen Wirtschaftsunternehmen im Zeitraum zwischen 1965 Und 2000: Eine Untersuchung der Sammlungsmodelle der HERTA GmbH, der Tetra Pak Rausing & Co. KG, der Deutsche Bank AG, der Adolf Würth GmbH & Co. KG sowie der DG BANK Deutsche Genossenschaftsbank AG. 2008. (Europäische Hochschulschriften. Reihe 28: Kunstgeschichte Ser.). (GER.). 408p. pap. 99.95 *(978-3-631-55431-9(1))* Lang, Peter GmbH, Europaischer Verlag der Wissenschaften DEU. Dist: Lang, Peter.

Leger, Marc James. Brave New Avant Garde: Essays on Contemporary Art & Politics. 2012. (ENG., Illus.). 208p. pap. 22.95 ***(978-1-78099-050-7(2))*** Hunt, John Publishing Ltd. GBR. Dist: National Bk. Network.

Lippy, Tod, ed. Esopus 16. 2011. (ENG., Illus.). 172p. pap. 14.00 *(978-0-9815745-5-4(6))* Esopus Foundation Ltd.

Lippy, Tod, ed. Esopus 17. 2011. (ENG., Illus.). 172p. pap. 14.00 ***(978-0-9815745-6-1(4))*** Esopus Foundation Ltd.

Lorente, J. Pedro. The Museums of Contemporary Art, 1800-2008: Concept & Historical Development. 2011. (Illus.). 330p. 124.95 *(978-1-4094-0586-3(9))* Ashgate Publishing Co.

Los, Sergio. Scarpa. Gossel, Peter, ed. 2009. (ENG.). 96p. pap. 9.99 *(978-3-8365-0728-8(5))* TASCHEN DEU. Dist: Ingram Pub. Services.

Lovisi, Gary. The Dames, Dolls & Delinquents: A Collector's Guide to Sexy Pulp Fiction Paperbacks. 2009. (ENG.). 224p. pap. 24.99 *(978-0-89689-968-1(3))* Krause Pubns.

Lucie-Smith, Edward. Lives of the Great Modern Artists. 2nd rev. ed. 2009. (ENG., Illus.). 368p. pap. 34.95 *(978-0-500-28191-8(2)*, 528191) Thames & Hudson.

Lutgens, Annelie & Kirschner, Esther Barbara, eds. Leichtigkeit und Enthusiasmus. Ease & Eagerness: Junge Kunst und die Moderne. Modernism today. 2009. (ENG & GER., Illus.). 176p. pap. 45.00 *(978-3-7757-2433-3(8))* Hatje Cantz Verlag GmbH & Co KG DEU. Dist: D.A.P./Distributed Art Pubs.

Lüth, Nanna & Wilcke, Jole. Pöpp68: Privat, öffentlich, Persönlich, Politisch: Partizipation Einwände Trotzdem: Texte, Gespräche und Beteiligung = Participation Objections Anyhow: Texts, Dialogues & Participation. 2009. (FRE, GER & ENG., Illus.). 294p. pap. *(978-3-938515-24-2(4))* Neue Gesellschaft.

Lynton, Norbert. William Scott. 2007. (ENG., Illus.). 504p. per. 60.00 *(978-0-500-97672-2(4))* Thames & Hudson.

McLean, Ian, ed. How Aborigines Invented the Idea of Contemporary Art: Writings on Aboriginal Contemporary Art. 2011. (ENG., Illus.). 360p. (C). pap. 49.95 *(978-0-909952-37-2(X))* Power Pubns. AUS. Dist: Univ. of Washington Pr.

Meador, Clifton K. Memory Lapse: An Artist's Book. (Illus.). 192p. 55.00 *(978-0-932526-83-0(7))* Nexus Pr.

Mitwasi, Faten Nastas. Sliman Mansour. 2008. (ENG.). 112p. pap. 29.95 *(978-3-86568-370-0(3)*, Art Stock Bks. Ltd/Csi) Continental Sales, Inc.

Mondrian, Piet. Plastic Art & Pure Plastic Art: Essays 1937-43. 2nd ed. 2008. (Documents of Modern Art Ser.). (Illus.). 35.00 *(978-0-8150-0101-0(0))* Wittenborn Art Bks.

Moreno Galván, José María & Moreno Galvan, Jose Maria. Autocritica del Arte. 2012. (SPA., Illus.). 224p. pap. 25.95 ***(978-84-95764-70-6(9))*** Ediciones Barataria ESP. Dist: Independent Pubs. Group.

Munder, Heike, ed. Migros Museum fur Gegenwartskunst. 2008. (ENG., Illus.). 416p. 115.00 *(978-3-905829-42-6(8))* JRP Ringier Kunstverlag AG CHE. Dist: D.A.P./Distributed Art Pubs.

Nassau County Museum of Art Staff, contrib. by. Long Island Collects: Cézanne, Degas, Renoir & Chagall Come to Long Island. 2009. (Illus.). 28p. *(978-0-9815644-3-2(7))* Nassau County Museum of Art.

Oxford University Press Staff, ed. Art History VSI Set: Consisting of Art History VSI, Modern Art VSI, Dada & Surrealism VSI, Renaissance Art VSI, & Contemporary Art VSI. 2006. pap. 35.00 *(978-0-19-532597-3(4))* Oxford Univ. Pr., Inc.

Pabedinskas, Tomas. Contemporary Lithuanian Photography. 2010. 172p. pap. *(978-3-8383-4312-9(3))* Lambert Academic Publishing.

Peiter, Sebastian & Werner, Goetz. Guerilla Art. 2009. (ENG., Illus.). 112p. 19.95 *(978-1-85669-593-0(X))* King, Laurence Publishing GBR. Dist: Hachette Bk. Group.

Peleggi, Maurizio, et al, eds. Eye of the Beholder: Reception, Audience, & Practice of Modern Asian Art. 2007. (University of Sydney East Asian Ser.: Vol. 15). (Illus.). 324p. per. *(978-1-876957-10-0(7))* Wild Peony Bk. Pubs. Pty., Ltd.

Porstmann, Gisbert & Schmidt, Johannes, eds. Welt und System / World & System: Zeitgenössische Kunst zwischen Analyse, Erkenntnissuche und Dilemma / Contemporary Art between Analysis, the Search for Meaning & Dilemma. 2011. (ENG., Illus.). 156p. 50.00 ***(978-3-86984-159-5(1))*** Verlag fur Moderne Kunst DEU. Dist: D.A.P./Distributed Art Pubs.

preez, marion. I feel like I'm changing from one day to Another. 2008. 110p. pap. 57.95 *(978-1-4092-0294-3(1))* Lulu Enterprises Inc.

Reichert, Marcus, frwd. Art Without Art: Selected Writing from the World of Blunt Edge. 2008. (Illus.). 137p. pap. 29.50 *(978-0-9546656-6-1(X))* Ziggurat Bks. GBR. Dist: Trans-Atlantic Pubns., Inc.

Reiter, Irmgard. 'Ways through Art' Kunsthaus Marktplatz Innsbruck-contemporary house of art. 2008. 64p. pap. *(978-3-639-09270-7(8))* VDM Verlag Dr. Mueller e.K.

Rofofsky Marcus, Sara. Binary Art. 2010. 33p. pap. 14.32 *(978-0-557-24547-5(8))* Lulu Enterprises Inc.

Roselione-Valadez, Juan, ed. Time Capsule: Age 13 to 21, the Contemporary Art Collection of Jason Rubell. 2011. (ENG., Illus.). 180p. pap. 39.95 ***(978-0-9821195-4-9(2))*** Rubell Family Collection.

Rosenfeld, Alla. Moscow Conceptualism in Context. 2011. (Illus.). 464p. 75.00 *(978-3-7913-4547-5(8))* Prestel Publishing.

Ruf, Beatrix, ed. Sean Landers. 2008. (ENG., Illus.). 160p. pap. 55.00 *(978-3-905829-87-7(8))* JRP Ringier Kunstverlag AG CHE. Dist: D.A.P./Distributed Art Pubs.

Saksi. Offpiste in the Land of Kustaa Saksi. 2008. 50.00 *(978-3-89955-229-4(6))* Die Gestalten Verlag DEU. Dist: Prestel Publishing.

San Juan, Rose Marie. Vertiginous Mirrors. 2011. (Rethinking Art's Histories Ser.). (ENG., Illus.). 240p. 95.00 *(978-0-7190-8481-2(4))* Manchester Univ. Pr. GBR. Dist: Macmillan.

Sans, Jerome & Xiaoyan, Guo, texts. Qui Zhijie: Breaking the Ice, a History. 2010. (ENG., Illus.). 288p. 50.00 *(978-988-18034-0-5(3))* Timezone 8 Ltd. HKG. Dist: D.A.P./Distributed Art Pubs.

Shiqiang, Gao. Gao Shiqiang: the Other There. 2010. (ENG., Illus.). 350p. 90.00 *(978-988-18034-7-4(0))* Timezone 8 Ltd. HKG. Dist: D.A.P./Distributed Art Pubs.

Silverman, Kaja. Flesh of My Flesh. 2009. (ENG., Illus.). 304p. 60.00 *(978-0-8047-6207-6(4))*; pap. 21.95 *(978-0-8047-6208-3(2))* Stanford Univ. Pr.

Slome, Manon, ed. & text. The Aesthetics of Terror. 2009. (ENG., Illus.). 104p. pap. 39.95 *(978-88-8158-727-8(0))* Charta ITA. Dist: D.A.P./Distributed Art Pubs.

Steinle, Christa, ed. Giulio Paolini: Da Oggi a Ieri. (ITA & GER., Illus.). 368p. 65.00 *(978-3-89322-357-2(6))* Edition Cantz DEU. Dist: D.A.P./Distributed Art Pubs.

Taxali, Gary, photos by. I love You, OK? 2011. 144p. 19.95 *(978-3-8327-9511-5(1))* teNeues Publishing Co.

Tellgren, Anna, ed. & text. The History Book, 1 vol. 2009. (ENG., Illus.). 500p. 75.00 *(978-3-86521-642-7(0))* Steidl, Gerhard Druckerei und Verlag DEU. Dist: Innovative Logistics.

Trulove, James Grayson. Arts & Crafts: Modern. 2008. 192p. 35.00 *(978-0-06-137471-5(7)*, Collins Design) HarperCollins Pubs.

Ullrich, Ferdinand & Schwalm, Hans-Jurgen, eds. Tatsuo Miyajima: Time Train. 2009. (GER & ENG., Illus.). 144p. 85.00 *(978-3-86678-180-1(6))* Kerber Verlag DEU. Dist: D.A.P./Distributed Art Pubs.

Voltaire. Candide: The Porfolio. 2011. (ENG & FRE., Illus.). 84p. 495.00 ***(978-1-936205-21-9(1))*** Austin, Stephen F. State Univ. Pr.

Von Berner, Darya, illus. Lupus Viator Atlanta. 220p. 50.00 *(978-0-932526-58-8(6))* Nexus Pr.

Wainwright, Leon. Timed Out: Art & the Transnational Caribbean. 2012. (Rethinking Art's Histories Ser.). (ENG., Illus.). 208p. pap. 30.95 ***(978-0-7190-8594-9(2))*** Manchester Univ. Pr. GBR. Dist: Macmillan.

—Timed Out: Art & the Transnational Caribbean. 2012. (Rethinking Art's Histories Ser.). (ENG., Illus.). 208p. 95.00 ***(978-0-7190-8484-3(9))*** Manchester Univ. Pr. GBR. Dist: Macmillan.

Weibel, Peter, et al. Light Art from Artificial Light: Light As a Medium in 20th & 21st Century Art, 1 vol. 2006. (ENG & GER., Illus.). 700p. pap. 105.00 *(978-3-7757-1774-8(9))* Hatje Cantz Verlag GmbH & Co KG DEU. Dist: D.A.P./Distributed Art Pubs.

Weidemann, Christiane. 50 Modern Artists You Should Know. 2010. (Illus.). 160p. pap. 19.95 *(978-3-7913-4470-6(6))* Prestel Publishing.

Whiteley, Jon. Poussin to Cezanne: French Drawings & Watercolours. 2006. (Ashmolean Handbooks: Vol. 19). (ENG., Illus.). 112p. pap. 15.95 *(978-1-85444-168-3(X)*, 168X) Ashmolean Museum GBR. Dist: Antique Collectors' Club.

Wilson, Simon & Lack, Jessica. Tate Guide to Modern Art Terms. 2009. (ENG., Illus.). 320p. pap. 16.95 *(978-1-85437-750-0(7))* Tate Publishing, Ltd. GBR. Dist: Hachette Bk. Group.

Wolfson, Rutger, ed. This Is the Flow: the Museum as a Space for Ideas. 2009. (ENG., Illus.). 260p. pap. 32.50 *(978-90-78088-24-0(9))* Valiz NLD. Dist: D.A.P./Distributed Art Pubs.

Yang, Xiying & Li, Honglei. Reconstituting History & Culture in New Media Art. 2010. 160p. pap. *(978-3-8383-8067-4(3))* Lambert Academic Publishing.

yaqoob, aazam. A-way art Book 2. 2010. 39p. pap. 21.99 *(978-0-557-51689-6(7))* Lulu Enterprises Inc.

Yekani, Elahe Haschemi. The Privilege of Crisis: Narratives of Masculinities in Colonial & Postcolonial Literature, Photography, & Film. 2011. (ENG.). 320p. pap. 49.00 *(978-3-593-39399-5(9))* Campus Verlag GmbH DEU. Dist: Chicago Distribution Ctr.

Yu, Miao. Imagining & Inventing Shanghai. 2008. 88p. pap. *(978-3-639-05519-1(5))* VDM Verlag Dr. Mueller e.K.

Zelevansky, Lynn. Carnegie Museum of Art: Director's Choice. 2010. (ENG., Illus.). 80p. pap. 14.95 *(978-1-85759-653-3(6))* Scala, Editions FRA. Dist: National Bk. Network.

Zuber, Ed. Scrambled & Colored Eggs. 2010. 128p. pap. 38.49 *(978-1-4389-5517-9(0))* AuthorHouse.

ART, MODERN—JAPANESE INFLUENCES

De More, Barry. From the Academies to the Rising Sun. 2009. 76p. pap. *(978-3-639-20659-3(2))* VDM Verlag Dr. Mueller e.K.

Johnson-Woods, Toni, ed. Manga: An Anthology of Global & Cultural Perspectives. 2010. (ENG., Illus.). 368p. 100.00 *(978-0-8264-2937-7(8))* Continuum International Publishing Group, Ltd. GBR. Dist: National Bk. Network.

Lambourne, Lionel. Japonisme: Cultural Crossings Between Japan & the West. rev. ed. 2007. (ENG., Illus.). 240p. pap. 49.95 *(978-0-7148-4797-9(6))* Phaidon Pr., Inc.

Moscatiello, Manuela. Le Japonisme de Giuseppe de Nittis: Un Peintre Italien en France à la Fin du XIXe Siècle. 2011. (FRE., Illus.). 441p. *(978-3-03911-796-3(3))* Lang, Peter Publishing, Inc.

Sigur, Hannah. Influence of Japanese Art on Design, 1 vol. 2008. (ENG., Illus.). 224p. 40.00 *(978-1-58685-749-3(5))* Gibbs Smith, Publisher.

Tsunetomo, Yamamoto. The Art of the Samurai: Yamamoto Tsunetomo's Hagakure. Steben, Barry D., tr. from JPN. 2008. (Art of Wisdom Ser.). (ENG., Illus.). 272p. 24.95 *(978-1-84483-720-5(3))* Duncan Baird Pubs. GBR. Dist: Sterling Publishing Co., Inc.

Western Sources of Japanese Art & Japonism V: Oeuvres choisies de critiques d'art, marchands d'art et collectionneurs sur le Japonisme Set: Oeuvres Choisies de Critiques D'Art, Marchands D'Art et Collectionneurs sur le Japonisme, 2 vols. 2010. 2700p. 465.00 *(978-4-86166-057-3(2))* Routledge.

ART, MODERN—17TH-18TH CENTURIES

Cram101 Textbook Reviews Staff. Outlines & Highlights for Seventeenth Century Art & Architecture by Ann Sutherland Harris, Isbn: 9780136033721. 2009. 64p. pap. 27.95 *(978-1-4288-9217-0(6))* Cram101 Inc.

Darish, Patricia & Binkley, David A. Kuba. 2010. (Visions of Africa Ser.). (ENG., Illus.). 144p. pap. 34.95 *(978-88-7439-404-3(7))* 5 Continents ITA. Dist: Hachette Bk. Group.

Dover & Weller, Alan. Insects. 2008. (Dover Pictura Electronic Clip Art Ser.). (ENG.). 128p. pap. 39.95 *(978-0-486-99752-0(9))* Dover Pubns., Inc.

Elderfield, John. Manet & the Execution of Maximilian, 1 vol. 2006. (ENG., Illus.). 200p. pap. 29.95 *(978-0-87070-423-9(0))* Museum of Modern Art.

Gott, Ted & Benson, Laurie. Painting & Sculpture Before 1800: In the International Collections of the National Gallery of Victoria. 2006. (Illus.). 134p. pap. 39.95 *(978-0-7241-0223-5(X))* National Gallery of Victoria AUS. Dist: Antique Collectors' Club.

Harris, Ann Sutherland. Seventeenth Century Art & Architecture. 2nd ed. 2007. (ENG., Illus.). 456p. (C). per. 135.00 *(978-0-13-603372-1(5)*, Prentice Hall) Prentice Hall PTR.

Hart, Clive & Stevenson, Kay Gilliland. Heaven & the Flesh: Imagery of Desire from the Renaissance to the Rococo. 2008. (ENG., Illus.). 256p. pap. 37.99 *(978-0-521-07094-2(5))* Cambridge Univ. Pr.

Kromm, Jane & Bakewell, Susan Benforado, eds. A History of Visual Culture: Western Civilization from the 18th to the 21st Century. 2010. (ENG., Illus.). 1p. 119.95 *(978-1-84520-493-8(X))*; 480p. pap. 39.95 *(978-1-84520-492-1(1))* Berg Pubs. GBR. Dist: Macmillan.

Landgraf, Edgar. Improvisation as Art: Conceptual Challenges, Historical Perspectives. 2011. (ENG.). 176p. 110.00 *(978-1-4411-4694-6(6))* Continuum International Publishing Group, Ltd. GBR. Dist: National Bk. Network.

Ploeg, Peter van der, et al, contrib. by. Princely Patrons: The Collection of Frederick Henry of Orange & Amalia of Solms in the Hague. (Illus.). 276p. *(978-90-400-9193-3(5))* Waanders B.V., Uitgeverij.

Redington, Ginny, et al. Georgian Jewellery, 1714-1830. 2007. (ENG., Illus.). 200p. *(978-1-85149-539-9(8)*, Antique Collectors Club Dist) Antique Collectors' Club.

Rutherford, Emma. Silhouette: The Art of the Shadow. 2009. (ENG., Illus.). 256p. 65.00 *(978-0-8478-3077-0(2))* Rizzoli International Pubns., Inc.

Simons, D. Brenton. Boston Beheld: Antique Town & Country Views. 2008. (ENG., Illus.). 164p. 35.00 *(978-1-58465-740-8(5))* Univ. Pr. of New England.

Tummers, Anna & Jonckheere, Koenraad, eds. Art Market & Connoisseurship: A Closer Look at Paintings by Rembrandt, Rubens & Their Contemporaries. 2009. (Amsterdam Studies in the Dutch Golden Age Ser.). (ENG., Illus.). 192p. pap. *(978-90-8964-032-1(0)*, Leiden Univ. Pr.) Amsterdam Univ. Pr.

Westermann, Mariet. Sound, Silence, & Modernity in Dutch Pictures of Manners: The Watson Gordon Lecture 2007. 2011. (ENG., Illus.). 32p. *(978-1-906270-25-4(2))* National Galleries of Scotland.

Zastrow, Oleg. Crosses & Crucifixes: Treasures from the 8th to 19th Centuries. 2009. (ENG & ITA., Illus.). 352p. 95.00 *(978-88-7439-523-1(X))* 5 Continents ITA. Dist: Hachette Bk. Group.

ART, MODERN—19TH CENTURY

see also Impressionism (Art); Neo-Impressionism (Art); Post-Impressionism (Art)

Abelovsky, Jan & Bajcurova, Katarina. Art in Changing Times: Painting & Sculpture in Slovakia 1890-1949. 2007. (Illus.). 384p. 100.00 *(978-80-7145-412-0(5))* Slovart, Vydavatel'stvo, spol. s.r.o. SVK. Dist: Independent Pubs. Group.

Ackerman, Gerald M. Orientalistes de l'Ecole Britannique. 2010. (Orientalists Ser.). (FRE., Illus.). 336p. 170.00 *(978-2-86770-049-1(3))* ACR Edition FRA. Dist: Antique Collectors' Club.

Albany Institute of History and Art Staff. Paul Cushman: The Work & World of an Early 19th Century Albany Potter. 2007. (Albany Institute of History & Art Ser.). (Illus.). 142p. pap. 34.95 *(978-0-939072-15-6(7)*, Suny Pr.) State Univ. of New York Pr.

Archuleta, Margaret, et al. Red River Crossings: Contemporary Native American Artists Respond to Peter Rindisbacher (1806-1834) Date not set. (Illus.). 60p. (Orig.). pap. 15.00 *(978-1-884692-04-8(4))* Swiss Institute.

Armstrong, Christopher. The Painted Valley: Artists along Alberta's Bow River, 1845-2000. 2007. (ENG., Illus.). 176p. per. 54.95 *(978-1-55238-207-3(9))* Univ. of Calgary Pr. CAN. Dist: Chicago Distribution Ctr.

Balducci, Temma, et al. Interior Portraiture & Masculine Identity in France, 1789-1914. 2010. (Illus.). 300p. 119.95 *(978-0-7546-6784-1(7))* Ashgate Publishing Co.

Balken, Debra Bricker. Dove - O'Keeffe: Circles of Influence. 2009. (Illus.). 168p. 45.00 *(978-0-300-13410-0(X))* Yale Univ. Pr.

Bardazzi, Francesca, et al. Cézanne in Florence: Two Collectors & the 1910 Exhibition of Impressionism. 2007. (Illus.). 272p. pap. *(978-88-370-4971-3(4))* Electa.

Barringer, T. J. Object Lessons. 2007. *(978-0-89467-967-4(8))* Yale Univ. Art Gallery.

Beaulieu, Jill, et al, eds. Refracting Vision: Essays on the Writings of Michael Fried. 2012. (ENG., Illus.). 407p. (C). per. 35.00 *(978-1-86487-024-4(9))* Power Pubns. AUS. Dist: Univ. of Washington Pr.

Busch, Jason T. & Futter, Catherine L. Inventing the Modern World: Decorative Arts at the World's Fairs, 1851-1939. 2012. (ENG., Illus.). 304p. 75.00 ***(978-0-8478-3809-7(9)***, Skira) Rizzoli International Pubns., Inc.

Champney, Benjamin. Sixty Years' Memories of Art & Artists. 2010. 224p. pap. 25.75 *(978-1-178-07509-0(5))* BiblioBazaar.

—Sixty Years' Memories of Art & Artists. 2010. 68p. pap. 20.00 *(978-1-151-81929-1(8))* General Bks. LLC.

Cheshire, Jim, et al. Tennyson Transformed: Alfred Lord Tennyson & Visual Culture. 2009. (Illus.). 160p. 80.00 *(978-1-84822-003-4(0)*, Lund Humphries Pubs.) Ashgate Publishing, Ltd. GBR. Dist: Ashgate Publishing Co.

Chu, Petra ten-Doesschate & Dixon, Laurinda S., eds. Twenty-First-Century Perspectives on Nineteenth-Century Art: Essays in Honor of Gabriel P. Weisberg. 2008. (Illus.). (C). *(978-0-87413-011-9(5))* Univ. of Delaware Pr.

Crepaldi, Gabriele. Modern Art: The Age of Avant-Gardes. 2007. (Illus.). 400p. 49.95 *(978-0-06-136312-2(X)*, Collins Design) HarperCollins Pubs.

Cumming, Elizabeth. Phoebe Anna Traquair: 1852-1936. 2006. (ENG., Illus.). 112p. pap. *(978-1-903278-65-9(1))* National Galleries of Scotland.

Dabakis, Melissa. Visualizing Labor in American Sculpture: Monuments, Manliness, & the Work Ethic, 1880-1935. 2011. (Cambridge Studies in American Visual Culture Ser.). (ENG.). 314p. pap. 60.00 *(978-0-521-28327-4(2))* Cambridge Univ. Pr.

Dempsey, Amy. Styles, Schools & Movements: The Essential Encyclopaedic Guide to Modern Art. 2nd rev. ed. 2011. (ENG., Illus.). 312p. pap. 31.95 *(978-0-500-28844-3(5)*, 528844) Thames & Hudson.

Di Bello, Patrizia & Koureas, Gabriel, eds. Art History & the Senses: 1830 to the Present. 2010. (Illus.). 224p. 124.95 *(978-0-7546-6863-3(0))* Ashgate Publishing Co.

Di Ozesanmuseum Bamberg, et al, eds. Tactile: High Touch Visuals. 2007. (Illus.). 207p. 69.00 *(978-3-89955-200-3(8))* Die Gestalten Verlag DEU. Dist: Prestel Publishing.

Dillow, Katie. Spanish Modernism in Nineteenth-France. 2011. 76p. pap. ***(978-3-8433-8466-7(5))*** Lambert Academic Publishing.

Dorontchenkov. Russian & Soviet Views of Modern Western Art. 2009. (Documents of Twentieth-Century Art Ser.). (Illus.). xv, 347p. 65.00 *(978-0-520-22103-1(6))* Univ. of California Pr.

Dorontchenkov, Ilia & Dorontchenkov, I. Russian & Soviet Views of Modern Western Art, 1890s to Mid-1930s. Dorontchenkov, Ilia & Gourianova, Nina, eds. Rougle, Charles, tr. 2009. (Documents of Twentieth-Century Art Ser.). (ENG., Illus.). 400p. pap. 29.95 *(978-0-520-25372-8(8))* Univ. of California Pr.

D'Souza, Aruna & McDonough, Tom, eds. The Invisible Flaneuse? Gender, Public Space & Visual Culture in Nineteenth Century Paris. 2010. (Critical Perspectives in Art History Ser.). (ENG., Illus.). 224p. pap. 26.95 *(978-0-7190-7942-9(X))* Manchester Univ. Pr. GBR. Dist: Macmillan.

Dunlap, Sarah & Buck, Stephanie. Fitz Henry Lane: Family & Friends. 2007. (Illus.). 185p. pap. 18.95 *(978-0-615-15729-0(7))* Church & Mason Publishing.

Duty, Michael & McGarry, Susan Hallsten. Texas Traditions: Contemporary Artists of the Lone Star State. 2010. (ENG., Illus.). 240p. 85.00 *(978-1-934491-24-9(1))* Fresco Fine Art Pubns., LLC.

Eisenman, Stephen F. Nineteenth Century Art: A Critical History. 4th ed. 2011. (ENG., Illus.). 504p. (C). pap. 85.00 net. *(978-0-500-28888-7(7)*, 528888) Thames & Hudson.

Facos, Michelle. An Introduction to Nineteenth Century Art. 2011. (ENG., Illus.). 464p. (C). 135.00 *(978-0-415-78070-4(5))*; pap. 69.95 *(978-0-415-78072-8(1))* Routledge.

—Symbolist Art in Context. 2009. (ENG., Illus.). 304p. pap. 31.95 *(978-0-520-25582-1(8))* Univ. of California Pr.

Facos, Michelle & Facos, M. Symbolist Art in Context. 2009. (ENG., Illus.). 304p. 70.00 *(978-0-520-25499-2(6))* Univ. of California Pr.

Fred L. Emerson Gallery Staff, contrib. by. The Best Kind of Life: Edward W. Root As Teacher, Collector, & Naturalist, Emerson Gallery, Hamilton College, September 27, 2007-January 6, 2008. 2007. (Illus.). 55p. *(978-1-880640-11-1(2))* Hamilton College, Emerson Gallery.

Gamboni, Dario. The Destruction of Art: Iconoclasm & Vandalism since the French Revolution. 2007. (Reaktion Books - Picturing History Ser.). (ENG., Illus.). 416p. per. 29.95 *(978-1-86189-316-1(7))* Reaktion Bks., Ltd. GBR. Dist: Chicago Distribution Ctr.

Games Design Workshop Staff. Blood & Iron. (Illus.). 224p. *(978-1-85585-000-2(1)*, Collins & Brown) Anova Bks.

Goetzmann, William H. & Goetzmann, William N. The West of the Imagination. 2nd rev. ed. 2009. (ENG., Illus.). 640p. 65.00 *(978-0-8061-3533-5(6))* Univ. of Oklahoma Pr.

Greene, Vivien, ed. Utopia Matters. 2010. 45.00 *(978-0-89207-400-6(0))* Guggenheim, Solomon R. Museum.

Gualdoni, Flaminio. Post-Impressionism. 2008. (Skira MINI Artbooks Ser.). (ENG., Illus.). 96p. pap. 8.99 *(978-88-6130-675-2(6))* Skira Editore ITA. Dist: Random Hse., Inc.

Guha-Thakurta, Tapati. The Making of a New 'Indian' Art: Artists, Aesthetics & Nationalism in Bengal, C. 1850-1920. 2007. (Cambridge South Asian Studies). (ENG.). 384p. pap. 53.00 *(978-0-521-05273-3(4))* Cambridge Univ. Pr.

Hagman. The Artist's Mind: A Psychoanalytic Perspective on Creativity, Modern Art & Modern Artists. 2010. (ENG.). 192p. (C). 90.00 *(978-0-415-46705-6(5))* Routledge.

Hagman, George. The Artist's Mind: A Psychoanalytic Perspective on Creativity, Modern Art & Modern Artists. 2010. (ENG.). 192p. (C). pap. 34.95 *(978-0-415-46706-3(3))* Routledge.

Harris, Roy. The Great Debate about Art. 2010. 130p. pap. 12.95 *(978-0-9842010-0-6(9))* Prickly Paradigm Pr., LLC.

Harrison, Charles. Since 1950: Art & Its Criticism. 2009. (ENG., Illus.). 272p. 45.00 *(978-0-300-15186-2(1))* Yale Univ. Pr.

International Miscellany of Literature Art & Science: Vol. 1 No. 3 Oct. 1 1850. Lt. ed. 2007. (ENG.). 456p. pap. 30.99 *(978-1-4264-8059-1(8))*; 406p. pap. 26.99 *(978-1-4264-8002-7(4))* BiblioBazaar.

Jackson, David. Wandereers & Critical Realism in Nineteenth-Century Russian Painting. 2011. (Critical Perspectives in Art History Ser.). (ENG., Illus.). 232p. pap. 32.95 *(978-0-7190-6435-7(X))* Manchester Univ. Pr. GBR. Dist: Macmillan.

—The Wanderers & Critical Realism in Nineteenth-Century Russian Art. 2006. (ENG., Illus.). 224p. 94.00 *(978-0-7190-6434-0(1))* Manchester Univ. Pr. GBR. Dist: Macmillan.

Joyner, Brooks. Legends of the West: The Foxley Collection. 2006. *(978-0-936364-34-6(3))* Joslyn Art Museum.

Kammen, Michael G. Visual Shock: A History of Art Controversies in American Culture. 2007. (Vintage Ser.). (ENG., Illus.). 480p. pap. 18.00 *(978-1-4000-3464-2(7)*, Vintage) Knopf Doubleday Publishing Group.

Katlan, Alexander. The Black & White Exhibitions of the Salmagundi Sketch Club 1878 to 1887: A Guide to Etchings, Engravings, Drawings, Sculpture, Ceramics, Oils, & Monotypes. 2007. (Illus.). 273p. *(978-0-9791290-0-1(1))* Katlan, Alexander Conservator, Inc.

Keith Haring Foundation Staff. Haring: Heart to Heart. 10.95 *(978-3-8238-4668-0(X))* teNeues Publishing Co.

Kennedy, Ian & Treuherz, Julian. The Railway: Art in the Age of Steam. 2008. (ENG., Illus.). 288p. 65.00 *(978-0-300-13878-8(4))* Yale Univ. Pr.

Koss, Juliet. Modernism after Wagner. 2010. (ENG., Illus.). 392p. 88.50 *(978-0-8166-5158-0(2))*; pap. 29.50 *(978-0-8166-5159-7(0))* Univ. of Minnesota Pr.

Kramer, Hilton. The Age of the Avant-Garde: 1956-1972. 2008. (ENG., Illus.). 588p. pap. 34.95 *(978-1-4128-0834-7(0))* Transaction Pubs.

Kromm, Jane & Bakewell, Susan Benforado, eds. A History of Visual Culture: Western Civilization from the 18th to the 21st Century. 2010. (ENG., Illus.). 1p. 119.95 *(978-1-84520-493-8(X))*; 480p. pap. 39.95 *(978-1-84520-492-1(1))* Berg Pubs. GBR. Dist: Macmillan.

Kronberg Frederiksen, Nanna, text. French Art at Ordrupgaard: Complete Catalogue of Paintings, Sculptures, Pastels, Drawings, & Prints. 2011. (ENG., Illus.). 544p. 120.00 *(978-3-7757-2671-9(3))* Hatje Cantz Verlag GmbH & Co KG DEU. Dist: D.A.P./Distributed Art Pubs.

Lahor, Jean. Art of Century: Art Nouveau. 2008. (Illus.). 199p. pap. 17.95 *(978-970-718-621-7(6)*, Numen) Advanced Marketing, S. de R. L. de C. V. MEX. Dist: Perseus-PGW.

Landgraf, Edgar. Improvisation as Art: Conceptual Challenges, Historical Perspectives. 2011. (ENG.). 176p. 110.00 *(978-1-4411-4694-6(6))* Continuum International Publishing Group, Ltd. GBR. Dist: National Bk. Network.

Leith, Caoimh'n Mac, text. Christopher Orr. 2009. (ENG., Illus.). 88p. 45.00 *(978-1-934171-08-0(5))* Thread Waxing Space.

Lindey, Christine. Keywords of Nineteenth-Century Art. 2007. (ENG.). 240p. 35.00 *(978-0-9532609-3-5(3))*; (Illus.). pap. 19.95 *(978-0-9532609-1-1(7))* Antique Collectors' Club GBR. (Sansom (Acc)). Dist: National Bk. Network.

Lombardi, Laura. From Realism to Art Nouveau. 2009. (ENG., Illus.). 192p. pap. 14.95 *(978-1-4027-5926-0(6))* Sterling Publishing Co., Inc.

MacAdam, Barbara J., ed. Embracing Elegance, 1885-1920: American Art from the Huber Family Collection. 2011. (Illus.). 116p. pap. 24.95 *(978-0-944722-41-1(5))* Hood Museum of Art.

Maloon, Terence, ed. Paths to Abstraction 1867-1917. 2011. (Illus.). 295p. 65.00 *(978-3-7913-5091-2(9))* Prestel Publishing.

Mathieu, Pierre-Louis. Gustave Moreau: The Assembler of Dreams. Penwarden, Charles, tr. from FRE. 2010. (Pocket Colour Ser.). (ENG., Illus.). 192p. pap. 27.50 *(978-2-86770-194-8(5))* ACR Edition FRA. Dist: Antique Collectors' Club.

McMenamin, Donna. Popular Arts of Mexico, 1850-1950. 2nd rev. ed. 2009. (ENG & SPA., Illus.). 240p. 59.99 *(978-0-7643-3284-5(8))* Schiffer Publishing, Ltd.

Meedendorp, Teio, ed. Drawings & Prints by Vincent van Gogh: In the Collection of the Kroller-Muller Museum. 2009. (Illus.). 192p. 99.95 *(978-90-78964-05-6(7)*, Leiden Univ. Pr.) Amsterdam Univ. Pr. NLD. Dist: Chicago Distribution Ctr.

Meyer, Jonathan. Great Exhibitions: London - New York - Paris - Philadelphia, 1851-1900. 2006. (ENG., Illus.). 400p. *(978-1-85149-527-6(4)*, Antique Collectors Club Dist) Antique Collectors' Club.

Mukherji, Subha, ed. Thinking on Thresholds: The Poetics of Transitive Spaces. 2011. (ENG., Illus.). 252p. 99.00 *(978-0-85728-665-9(X))* Anthem Pr. GBR. Dist: Books International, Inc.

Neff, Emily Ballew. The Modern West: American Landscapes, 1890-1950. 2006. (Illus.). (ENG.). 315p. 65.00 *(978-0-300-11448-5(6))*; xix, 315p. pap. *(978-0-89090-145-8(7))* Yale Univ. Pr.

Parshall, Peter, et al. The Darker Side of Light: Arts of Privacy, 1850-1900. 2009. (Illus.). 192p. 75.00 *(978-1-84822-021-8(9)*, Lund Humphries Pubs.) Ashgate Publishing, Ltd. GBR. Dist: Ashgate Publishing Co.

Payne, John. Framing the Nineteenth Century: Picture Frames, 1837-1935. Owen, Wendy, ed. 2007. (ENG., Illus.). 128p. 35.00 *(978-1-86470-199-9(4))* Images Publishing Group AUS. Dist: National Bk. Network.

Pool, Phoebe. El Impresionismo. (SPA., Illus.). 288p. 39.95 (978-84-233-1972-5(5), DE725) Ediciones Destino ESP. Dist: Continental Bk. Co., Inc.

Resnick, Mark. The American Image: U. S. Posters from the 19th to the 21st Century. 2nd ed. 2007. (Illus.). 112p. 29.99 (978-1-933360-28-7(3), RIT Cary Graphic Arts Pr.) Rochester Institute of Technology, Cary Graphic Arts Pr.

Rewald, Sabine. Rooms with a View: The Open Window in the 19th Century. 2011. (Illus.). 204p. pap. 30.00 (978-0-300-16977-5(9)) Yale Univ. Pr.

Rhodes, Kimberly. Ophelia & Victorian Visual Culture: Representing Body Politics in the Nineteenth Century. 2008. (Illus.). 224p. 124.95 (978-0-7546-5876-4(7)) Ashgate Publishing Co.

Richter Verlag Publishing, creator. Hans Arp: Die Natur der Dinge, 1 vol. 2008. (ENG., Illus.). 236p. 95.00 (978-3-937572-74-1(0)) Richter Verlag DEU. Dist: D.A.P./Distributed Art Pubs.

Roberts, David. The Total Work of Art in European Modernism. 2011. (Signale: Modern German Letters, Cultures, & Thought Ser.). 304p. pap. 37.50 (978-0-8014-5023-5(3)) Cornell Univ. Pr.

Rutherford, Emma. Silhouette: The Art of the Shadow. 2009. (ENG., Illus.). 256p. 65.00 (978-0-8478-3077-0(2)) Rizzoli International Pubns., Inc.

Scarisbrick, Diana. Scottish Jewellery: A Victorian Passion. 2009. (ENG., Illus.). 128p. 45.00 (978-88-7439-524-8(8)) 5 Continents ITA. Dist: Hachette Bk. Group.

Schapiro, Meyer. Modern Art: 19th & 20th Centuries - Selected Papers. 2011. (ENG., Illus.). 278p. pap. 27.95 (978-0-8076-1607-9(9), 761607) Braziller, George Inc.

Scheuerle, William H. George Baxter, the First Color Printing from Metal Plates & Wood Blocks: Portraying Victorian Values of England's Rising Middle Class. 2011. (Illus.). 180p. 129.95 (**978-0-7734-3920-7(X)**) Mellen, Edwin Pr., The.

Schmidt, Christoph. Vom Messias zum Prolet: Arbeiter in der Kunst. 2010. (GER., Illus.). 132p. (C). pap. 44.00 (978-3-515-09808-3(9)) Steiner, Franz Verlag Wiesbaden GmbH DEU. Dist: Brown, David Bk. Co., The.

Schulz, Max F. Paradise Preserved: Recreations in Eden in Eighteenth- & Nineteenth-Century England. 2009. 388p. pap. 42.00 (978-0-521-11892-7(1)) Cambridge Univ. Pr.

Serullaz, Arlette & Sérullaz, Arlette. Delacroix. 2008. (Drawing Gallery Ser.). (ENG., Illus.). 96p. pap. 15.95 (978-88-7439-105-9(6)) 5 Continents ITA. Dist: Hachette Bk. Group.

Simons, D. Brenton. Boston Beheld: Antique Town & Country Views. 2008. (ENG., Illus.). 164p. 35.00 (978-1-58465-740-8(5)) Univ. Pr. of New England.

Spain, Sharon. Asian American Art: A History, 1850-1970. Chang, Gordon H. et al, eds. 2008. (Asian America Ser.). (ENG.). 576p. pap. 39.95 (978-0-8047-5752-2(6)); (Illus.). 80.00 (978-0-8047-5751-5(8)) Stanford Univ. Pr. (Stanford General Bks.).

Spence, David. Cezanne. 2009. (Ticktock Essential Artists Ser.). (ENG.). 32p. (J). (gr. 4-7). pap. 6.95 (978-1-84696-970-6(0)) TickTock Bks. GBR. Dist: Independent Pubs. Group.

—Gauguin. 2009. (Ticktock Essential Artists Ser.). (ENG.). 32p. (J). (gr. 4-7). pap. 6.95 (978-1-84696-971-3(9)) TickTock Bks. GBR. Dist: Independent Pubs. Group.

Stauffer, Karl, et al. "Verfluchter Kerl!" Karl Stauffer-Bern, Maler, Radierer, Plastiker. 2007. (Illus.). 240p. 29.95 (978-3-03823-362-6(5)) Neue Zurcher Zeitung, NZZ, Buchverlag.

Strauber, Susan, et al. Women in Impressionism: From Mythical Feminine to Modern Woman. Sondergaard, Sidsel Maria, ed. 2007. (ENG., Illus.). 288p. 55.00 (978-88-7624-787-3(4)) Skira Editore ITA. Dist: Random Hse., Inc.

Sureda, Joan, photos by. Goya & Italy. 2008. (ENG., Illus.). 310p. pap. 69.00 (978-84-7506-808-4(1)) Turner, Ediciones S.A. ESP. Dist: D.A.P./Distributed Art Pubs.

Toman, Rolf. NEOCLASSICISM & ROMANTICISM, 1 vol. 2011. (ENG., Illus.). 520p. 19.99 (978-3-8331-3556-9(5)) h.f.ullmann DEU. Dist: Innovative Logistics.

Utley, Gertje R., et al. A Fine Regard: Essays in Honor of Kirk Varnedoe. 2008. (Illus.). 356p. 54.95 (978-0-7546-6217-4(9)) Ashgate Publishing Co.

Walther, Ingo F. T25 kr van Gogh. 2012. (25 Ser.). (ENG., Illus.). 96p. 14.99 (**978-3-8365-3154-2(2)**) TASCHEN DEU. Dist: Ingram Pub. Services.

Ward, Martha & Leonard, Anne. Looking & Listening in Nineteenth-Century France. 2008. (Illus.). 104p. 24.00 (978-0-935573-44-2(5)) Univ. of Chicago, David & Alfred Smart Museum.

Welchman, John, ed. Black Sphinx: on the Comedic in Modern Art. 2010. (ENG., Illus.). 280p. pap. 34.95 (978-3-905770-96-4(2)) JRP Ringier Kunstverlag AG CHE. Dist: D.A.P./Distributed Art Pubs.

Winter, William. Life & Art of Edwin Booth. 2009. (ENG.). 355p. 38.99 (978-1-117-32957-4(7)) 2009. (ENG.). 355p. pap. 31.75 (978-1-117-32958-1(5)) 2009. 360p. 26.99 (978-1-103-07927-8(1)) 2009. 360p. pap. 20.99 (978-1-103-07924-7(7)) 2008. 360p. 29.99 (978-0-559-66929-3(1)) 2008. 360p. pap. 31.75 (978-0-559-66926-2(7)) BiblioBazaar.

—Life & Art of Edwin Booth. 2007. (ENG.). 364p. per. (978-1-4067-3017-3(3)) Read Bks.

Wolf, Norbert. Symbolism. 2009. (ENG., Illus.). 96p. pap. 9.99 (978-3-8228-5482-2(4)) TASCHEN DEU. Dist: Ingram Pub. Services.

Yount, Sylvia. Private Passion, Public Promise: The James W. & Frances G. Mcglothlin Collection of American Art. 2010. (ENG., Illus.). 96p. (gr. 17). 30.00 (978-0-917046-95-7(1)) Univ. Pr. of Virginia.

Zastrow, Oleg. Crosses & Crucifixes: Treasures from the 8th to 19th Centuries. 2009. (ENG & ITA., Illus.). 352p. 95.00 (978-88-7439-523-1(X)) 5 Continents ITA. Dist: Hachette Bk. Group.

ART, MODERN—19TH CENTURY—JAPANESE INFLUENCES

see Art, Modern—Japanese Influences

ART, MODERN—20TH CENTURY

see also Art, Abstract; Art Deco; Artists' Books; Assemblage (Art); Body Art; Computer Art; Conceptual Art; Concrete Art; Constructivism (Art); Cubism; De Stijl (Art Movement); Earthworks (Art); Expressionism (Art); Fauvism; Found Objects (Art); Futurism (Art); Happening (Art); Installations (Art); Kinetic Art; Letter-Pictures; Minimal Art; Modernism (Art); Optical Art; Photo-Realism; Pop Art; Post-Impressionism (Art); Social Realism; Video Art

Aalto, Alvar. Friedrich Christian Flick Collection Im Hamburger Bahnhof, 1 vol. 2009. (ENG., Illus.). 585p. (gr. 13-18). 150.00 (978-3-8321-7496-5(6)) DuMont DEU. Dist: D.A.P./Distributed Art Pubs.

Abaza, Mona. Collecting Modern Egyptian Art: Sherwet Shafei & the Pioneer Painters of the Twentieth Century. 2011. (ENG.). 208p. 49.50 (978-977-416-394-4(X)) American Univ. in Cairo Pr. EGY. Dist: Oxford Univ. Pr., Inc.

Abelovsky, Jan & Bajcurova, Katarina. Art in Changing Times: Painting & Sculpture in Slovakia 1890-1949. 2007. (Illus.). 384p. 100.00 (978-80-7145-412-0(5)) Slovart, Vydavateľstvo, spol. s.r.o. SVK. Dist: Independent Pubs. Group.

Adamowicz, Eiza & Robertson, Eric, eds. Dada & Beyond: Volume 1: Dada Discourses. 2011. (Illus.). 260p. 74.00 (**978-90-420-3355-9(X)**) Rodopi.

Adang, Marc. Voor Sociaal-Democratie, Smaakopvoeding en Verheffend Genot: De Amsterdamse Vereniging Kunst Aan Het Volk, 1903-1928. 2008. (DUT., Illus.). 766p. 57.50 (**978-90-5260-314-8(6)**) Aksant Academic Pubs. NLD. Dist: Amsterdam Univ. Pr.

Ades, Dawn, et al, contrib. by. Surrealist Art: The Lindy & Edwin Bergman Collection at the Art Institute of Chicago. (Illus.). 256p. pap. (978-0-500-27995-3(0)) Thames & Hudson.

Agustin, Perez Rubio, ed. Discursive Variants. 2010. (ENG., Illus.). 320p. pap. (978-84-92861-27-9(4)) Actar Birkhauser Distribution.

Aida, Makoto. Monument for Nothing. 2007. 248p. pap. 59.95 (978-4-7661-1804-9(9)) Graphic-Sha JPN. Dist: Gingko Pr., Inc.

Allen, Gwen. Artists' Magazines: An Alternative Space for Art. 2011. (ENG., Illus.). 376p. (gr. 17). 37.95 (978-0-262-01519-6(6)) MIT Pr.

Aloi, Giovanni. Art & Animals. 2011. (Art and... Ser.). (ENG., Illus.). 192p. 75.00 (**978-1-84885-524-3(9)**); pap. 27.50 (**978-1-84885-525-0(7)**) I. B. Tauris & Co., Ltd. GBR. Dist: Macmillan.

Altshuler, Bruce. Collecting the New: Museums & Contemporary Art. 2007. (ENG., Illus.). 208p. (C). per. 21.95 (978-0-691-13373-7(5)) Princeton Univ. Pr.

Amey, Claude. Arts et Pouvoir: Séminaire Interarts de Paris, 2005-2006. 2007. (FRE.). 264p. (C). pap. 29.00 (**978-2-252-03642-6(7)**) Klincksieck, Editions FRA. Dist: ISD.

Anderson, Laurie. Night Life, 1 vol. 2009. (ENG., Illus.). 96p. 35.00 (978-3-86521-339-6(1)) Steidl, Gerhard Druckerei und Verlag DEU. Dist: Innovative Logistics.

Andersson, Mamma & Nordstrom, Jockum. Mamma Andersson & Jockum Nordstrom: Who Is Sleeping on My Pillow. 2010. (ENG., Illus.). 247p. 75.00 (978-1-935202-26-4(X)) Zwirner, David Inc.

Archbold, Rick. Natural Worlds. 2010. (ENG., Illus.). 192p. 40.00 (978-1-897330-47-0(2)) Madison Pr. Bks. CAN. Dist: Independent Pubs. Group.

Armstrong, Carol & de Zegher, Catherine, eds. Women Artists at the Millennium. 2011. (October Bks.). (ENG., Illus.). 472p. (gr. 17). pap. 24.95 (978-0-262-51594-8(6)) MIT Pr.

Armstrong, Christopher. The Painted Valley: Artists along Alberta's Bow River, 1845-2000. 2007. (ENG., Illus.). 176p. per. 54.95 (978-1-55238-207-3(9)) Univ. of Calgary Pr. CAN. Dist: Chicago Distribution Ctr.

Arnason, H. H. & Mansfield, Elizabeth. History of Modern Art. 6th ed. 2009. (ENG.). 848p. (C). 150.20 (978-0-205-67367-4(8), Prentice Hall) Prentice Hall PTR.

Arnason, H. H. & Mansfield, Elizabeth C. History of Modern Art. 6th ed. 2009. (ENG., Illus.). 848p. (C). pap. 132.00 (978-0-13-606206-6(7), Prentice Hall) Prentice Hall PTR.

Arnold, Grant & Henry, Karen, eds. Traffic: Conceptual Art in Canada 1965-1980, 1 vol. 2012. (ENG., Illus.). 176p. 59.00 (**978-1-895442-88-5(5)**) D&M Pubs. Inc. CAN. Dist: Perseus-PGW.

Art Guide 2009 Staff. Contemporary Europe Art Guide 2009. 2009. (ENG., Illus.). 368p. pap. 45.00 (978-3-7757-2336-7(6)) Hatje Cantz Verlag GmbH & Co KG DEU. Dist: D.A.P./Distributed Art Pubs.

Art of the Western World. (Dantes Subject Standardized Tests Ser.). 49.95 (978-0-8373-6561-9(9), DANTES-61, Passbooks) National Learning Corp.

Artzybasheff, Boris. As I See: The Fantastic World of Boris Artzybasheff. 2008. (ENG., Illus.). 96p. 19.95 (978-1-84576-767-9(5), Titan Bks.) Titan Bks. Ltd. GBR. Dist: Random Hse., Inc.

Avgikos, Jan. Marlene Dumas. 2nd rev. ed. 2009. (ENG., Illus.). 240p. 69.95 (978-0-7148-4584-5(1)) Phaidon Pr., Inc.

Avital, Tsion. Art versus Nonart: Art out of Mind. Harries, John G., tr. from HEB. 2010. (Contemporary Artists & their Critics Ser.). (ENG.). 461p. pap. 55.00 (978-0-521-15480-2(4)) Cambridge Univ. Pr.

Bajac, Quentin & Chéroux, Clément, eds. Collection Photographs, 1 vol. 2008. (ENG., Illus.). 468p. 85.00 (978-3-86521-480-5(0)) Steidl, Gerhard Druckerei und Verlag DEU. Dist: Innovative Logistics.

Baldessari, John, et al. Autumn 2009, No. 86. 2009. (ENG., Illus.). 300p. pap. 32.00 (978-3-907582-46-6(2)) Parkett Verlag AG CHE. Dist: D.A.P./Distributed Art Pubs.

Baron, F. Xavier & Clarke, Graham, eds. London in 20th Century Art. (Art in Context Ser.). 500p. (978-1-903206-10-2(3)) Helm Information, Ltd.

Barriault, Anne B. Selections from the Virginia Museum of Fine Arts. 2nd rev. ed. 2007. (ENG., Illus.). 376p. 45.00 (978-0-917046-82-7(X)) Virginia Museum of Fine Arts.

Barringer, T. J. Object Lessons. 2007. (978-0-89467-967-4(8)) Yale Univ. Art Gallery.

Barron, Stephanie. Envisioning Modernism: The Janice & Henri Lazarof Collection. 2012. (Illus.). 224p. 49.95 (**978-3-7913-5201-5(6)**) Prestel Publishing.

Barron, Stephanie. Magritte & Contemporary Art: The Treachery of Images, 1 vol. 2006. (ENG., Illus.). 256p. 60.00 (978-90-5544-621-6(1)) Ludion BEL. Dist: D.A.P./Distributed Art Pubs.

Basar, Shumon, et al, eds. Hans Ulrich Obrist Interviews, Vol. 2. 2010. (ENG., Illus.). 950p. pap. 75.00 (978-88-8158-731-5(9)) Charta ITA. Dist: D.A.P./Distributed Art Pubs.

Bascom, Mansfield. Wharton Esherick: The Journey of a Creative Mind. 2010. (ENG., Illus.). 276p. 80.00 (978-0-8109-9575-8(1)) Abrams.

Baudin-Renau, Katia, ed. Franz West. 2010. 350p. 72.50 (978-88-370-7466-1(2)) Electa ITA. Dist: Trans-Atlantic Pubns., Inc.

Baum, Kelly. Nobody's Property: Art, Land, Space, 2000-2010. 2010. (ENG., Illus.). 144p. 45.00 (978-0-300-14928-9(X)) Yale Univ. Pr.

Beaulieu, Jill, et al, eds. Refracting Vision: Essays on the Writings of Michael Fried. 2012. (ENG., Illus.). 407p. (C). per. 35.00 (978-1-86487-024-4(9)) Power Pubns. AUS. Dist: Univ. of Washington Pr.

Bedford, Emma, ed. Decade of Democracy: South African Art, 1994-2004. 2010. (Illus.). 150p. pap. 51.95 (978-1-919930-50-3(7)) Double Storey Bks. ZAF. Dist: International Publishers Marketing.

Belli, Gabriella, et al. The Artistic Culture between the Wars 1920-1945, 5 vols. Terraroli, Valerio, ed. 2007. (Art of the Twentieth Century (Skira) Ser.). (ENG., Illus.). 448p. 60.00 (978-88-7624-804-7(8)) Skira Editore ITA. Dist: Random Hse., Inc.

Bellini, Andrea, et al, eds. Collecting Contemporary Art. 2009. (ENG., Illus.). 128p. pap. 15.00 (978-3-03764-015-9(4)) JRP Ringier Kunstverlag AG CHE. Dist: D.A.P./Distributed Art Pubs.

Berger, Maurice, ed. The 1980s: A Virtual Discussion, 1 vol. 2006. (ENG., Illus.). 240p. pap. 14.95 (978-1-890761-09-7(5)) Univ. of Maryland Baltimore County, Fine Arts Gallery.

Berggruen, Olivier. The Writing of Art. 2012. (ENG.). 120p. pap. 16.00 (**978-1-906548-62-9(5)**) Pushkin Pr., Ltd. GBR. Dist: Consortium Bk. Sales & Distribution.

Berghaus, Günter. International Futurism, 1945-2009: A Bibliographic Reference Shelf. 2013. (ENG.). 1200p. (gr. 17-17). 419.00 (978-3-11-021580-9(2)) De Gruyter, Walter Inc.

Bernard, Christian. Claude Lévêque. 2010. (ENG., Illus.). 224p. 75.00 (978-2-08-030127-7(6)) Flammarion et Cie FRA. Dist: Random Hse., Inc.

Bertola, Chiara & Maraniello, Gianfranco, eds. On Mobility: Giovani Artisti Italiani, 1 vol. 2007. (ENG., Illus.). 120p. pap. 34.95 (978-88-8158-631-8(2)) Charta ITA. Dist: D.A.P./Distributed Art Pubs.

Beyeler, Ernst & Mory, Christophe. A Passion for Art. 2012. (ENG., Illus.). 204p. 39.00 (**978-3-85881-727-3(9)**) Scheidegger und Spiess AG, Verlag CHE. Dist: Antique Collectors' Club.

Biasi, Vittoria. Architetture Del Bianco: Viaggio Teorico-Creativo Attorno Alle Lingue Del Bianco. 2009. (ITA., Illus.). 238p. (978-88-492-1676-9(9)) Gangemi.

Bickerton, Derek, et al. Ashley Bickerton. 2011. (Illus.). 400p. 3750.00 (978-1-906967-39-0(3)) Other Criteria GBR. Dist: Abrams.

Bird, Michael. The St Ives Artists: A Cultural Biography 1939-64. 2008. (Illus.). 192p. pap. 40.00 (978-0-85331-956-6(1), Lund Humphries Pubs.) Ashgate Publishing, Ltd. GBR. Dist: Ashgate Publishing Co.

Bischof, Elizabeth, et al. Maine Moderns: Art in Seguinland, 1900-1940. 2011. (ENG., Illus.). 184p. 50.00 (978-0-300-16948-5(5)) Yale Univ. Pr.

Bishop, Janet, et al, intros. The Steins Collect: Matisse, Picasso, & the Parisian Avant-Garde. 2011. (Illus.). 492p. 75.00 (978-0-300-16941-6(8)) Yale Univ. Pr.

Der Blaue Reiter. (Poster Calendars Ser.). (Illus.). spiral bd. 29.99 (978-3-8327-1009-5(4)) teNeues Publishing Co.

Blom, Ina. On the Style Site. 2007. (Illus.). 264p. pap. 29.95 (978-1-933128-30-6(5)) Sternberg Pr.

Blomberg, Nancy J. [Re]inventing the Wheel: Advancing the Dialogue on Contemporary American Indian Art. 2008. pap. (978-0-914738-59-6(3)) Denver Art Museum.

Bonami, Francesco. Spirit & Space: Sandretto Re Rebaudengo Collection. 2011. (ENG., Illus.). 200p. pap. 43.00 (**978-84-92441-36-5(4)**) T.F. Editores ESP. Dist: National Bk. Network.

Bonham-Carter, Charlotte & Hodge, David. The Contemporary Art Book. 2011. (ENG., Illus.). 256p. 39.95 (978-1-84796-005-4(7), Goodman Pubs.) Carlton Bks., Ltd. GBR. Dist: Sterling Publishing Co., Inc.

Bordowitz, Gregg. General Idea: Imagevirus. 2010. (One Work Ser.). (ENG., Illus.). 121p. (gr. 17). pap. 16.00 (978-1-84638-065-5(0)) Afterall Publishing GBR. Dist: MIT Pr.

Bottoms, Greg. The Colorful Apocalypse: Journeys in Outsider Art. 2007. xv, 182p. pap. (978-0-226-06687-5(8)) Univ. of Chicago Pr.

Bourriaud, Nicolas. The Radicant. 2009. 192p. pap. 19.95 (978-1-933128-42-9(9), Lukas & Sternberg) Sternberg Pr.

Bowlt, John E. Moscow & St. Petersburg 1900-1920: Art, Life, & Culture of the Russian Silver Age. 2008. (978-0-86565-191-3(4)) Vendome Pr., The.

Bradford, Mark, et al. Parkett No. 89: Mark Bradford, Oscar Tuazon, Charline von Heyl, Haegue Yang. 2011. (ENG., Illus.). 300p. pap. 45.00 (**978-3-907582-49-7(7)**) Parkett Verlag AG CHE. Dist: D.A.P./Distributed Art Pubs.

Brainin-Donnenberg, Wilbrig & Loebenstein, Michael, eds. Gustav Deutsch. 2009. (Austrian Film Museum Bks.). (ENG & GER., Illus.). 240p. (gr. 17). pap. 27.50 (978-3-901644-30-6(X)) Synema Gesellschaft fur Film u. Medien AUT. Dist: Columbia Univ. Pr.

Brand, Heather, ed. Red Hot: Asian Art Today from the Chaney Family Collection. 2008. (ENG., Illus.). 208p. pap. 39.95 (978-0-300-13889-4(X)) Museum of Fine Arts, Houston.

Brodskaya, Nathalia. Symbolism. 2007. (Art of Century Ser.). (ENG., Illus.). 199p. pap. 19.95 (978-1-85995-677-9(7)) Parkstone International GBR. Dist: Ingram Pub. Services.

Broglio, Ron. Surface Encounters: Thinking with Animals & Art. 2011. (Posthumanities Ser.). (ENG., Illus.). 176p. 75.00 (**978-0-8166-7296-7(2)**); pap. 25.00 (**978-0-8166-7297-4(0)**) Univ. of Minnesota Pr.

Brown, Brice & Shortliffe, Mark, eds. The Sienese Shredder Issue 4. 2010. (ENG., Illus.). 254p. pap. 30.00 (978-0-9787108-3-5(5)) Sienese Shredder Editions.

Brown, Karen. Women's Contributions to Visual Culture, 1918-1939: Agency & Mediation. 2008. (Illus.). 200p. 124.95 (978-0-7546-6400-0(7)) Ashgate Publishing Co.

Bru, Sascha, et al, eds. Regarding the Popular: Modernism, the Avant-Garde & High & Low Culture. 2011. (European Avant-Garde & Modernism Studies). (Illus.). XII, 490p. (ENG.). 210.00 (**978-3-11-027470-7(1)**); (FRE, GER & ENG., 140.00 (**978-3-11-027456-1(6)**) De Gruyter, Walter Inc.

Brunet, Lynn. The Masonic Presence in Contemporary Art. 2008. 288p. pap. (978-3-639-10526-1(5)) VDM Verlag Dr. Mueller e.K.

Brutvan, Cheryl. Antonio López Garcia. 2008. (ENG., Illus.). 160p. pap. 24.95 (978-0-87846-733-4(5)) Museum of Fine Arts, Boston.

Buric, Anka. Problemi U Crnogorskoj Savremenoj Likovnoj Umjetnosti: Radovi Sa Okruglog Stola, Podgorica, 12. Jun 2008. Godine. 2009. (Illus.). 102p. (978-86-7215-217-3(4)) Crnogorska akademija nauka i umjetnosti.

Burstein, Jessica. Cold Modernism: Literature, Fashion, Art. 2012. (ENG.). 296p. pap. (**978-0-271-05376-9(3)**) Pennsylvania State Univ. Pr.

Butler, Cornelia & Schwartz, Alexandra, eds. Modern Women: Women Artists at the Museum of Modern Art. 2010. (ENG., Illus.). 512p. 65.00 (978-0-87070-771-1(X)) Museum of Modern Art.

Butovski, Viktor & Orlova, Maria. The Russian Ornament Sourcebook, 1 vol. 2011. (ENG., Illus.). 336p. 39.95 (978-1-908126-02-3(7)) Vivays Pubng. Ltd. GBR. Dist: Innovative Logistics.

Cabanas, Kaira, ed. Seven Sounds, Seven Circles. 2009. (ENG., Illus.). 168p. pap. 60.00 (978-3-86560-537-5(0)) Kunsthaus Bregenz AUT. Dist: D.A.P./Distributed Art Pubs.

Cage, John. John Cage Book of Days 2012. Kuhn, Laura, ed. 2011. (ENG., Illus.). 120p. pap. 25.00 (**978-1-935202-64-6(2)**) D.A.P./Distributed Art Pubs.

Cameron, Dan, et al. ArtWorks: The Progressive Collection, 1 vol. 2007. (ENG., Illus.). 292p. 55.00 (978-1-933045-72-6(8)) D.A.P./Distributed Art Pubs.

Cammitzer, Luis, ed. It's not Neutral. 2008. 180p. pap. (978-84-612-5628-0(X)) Actar Birkhauser Distribution.

Camnitzer, Luis. On Art, Artists, Latin America, & Other Utopias. Weiss, Rachel, ed. 2009. (ENG.). 272p. 45.00 (978-0-292-71976-7(0)) Univ. of Texas Pr.

Carels, Edwin, et al. All That Is Solid Melts into Air: Five Reflections on Materialistic Spirituality in Contemporary Art. 2009. (ENG., Illus.). 256p. pap. (978-90-209-8318-0(0), Lannoo Pubs. (Acc)) Antique Collectors' Club.

Castelli, Leo. Jasper Johns. 2008. (978-2-7594-0316-5(5)) Assouline.

Cattelan, Maurizio, ed. Maurizio Cattelan: All. 2011. (ENG., Illus.). 255p. 45.00 (**978-0-89207-416-7(7)**) Guggenheim, Solomon R. Museum.

Celant, Germano. The American Tornado: Art in Power, 1949-2008. 2008. (ENG., Illus.). 448p. pap. 55.00 (978-88-6130-068-2(5)) Skira Editore ITA. Dist: Random Hse., Inc.

Chametzky, Peter. Objects as History in Twentieth-Century German Art: Beckmann to Beuys. 2010. (ENG., Illus.). 304p. 49.95 (978-0-520-26042-9(2)) Univ. of California Pr.

Chen, Xhingyu. Chinese Artists: New Media, 1990-2010. 2011. (Illus.). 176p. 50.00 (978-0-7643-3675-1(4)) Schiffer Publishing, Ltd.

Chevalier, Haakon M., tr. Dali on Modern Art: The Cuckolds of Antiquated Modern Art. 2011. 156p. 41.95 (**978-1-258-00231-2(0)**) Literary Licensing, LLC.

Chiu, Melissa & Genocchio, Benjamin. Contemporary Art in Asia: A Critical Reader. 2011. (Illus.). ix, 430p. (978-0-262-01491-5(2)) MIT Pr.

Cho, Soon C. Empty the Mind. 2008. (Illus.). 165p. (978-2-7594-0314-1(9)) Assouline.

Ciclitira, Serenella. Indonesian Eye: Contemporary Indonesian Art. 2012. (ENG., Illus.). 376p. pap. 60.00 (**978-88-572-1075-9(8)**) Skira Editore ITA. Dist: Random Hse., Inc.

Clark, Sheila W., text. The Stettheimer Dollhouse. 2009. 64p. 19.95 (978-0-7649-4802-2(4)) Pomegranate Communications, Inc.

Clark, Steve, et al, eds. Blake 2. 0: William Blake in Twentieth-Century Art, Music & Culture. 2012. (ENG., Illus.). 328p. 85.00 (**978-0-230-28033-5(1)**) Palgrave Macmillan.

Clarke, David. Chinese Art & Its Encounter with the World: Negotiating Alterity in Art & Its Historical Interpretation. 2011. (ENG., Illus.). 272p. (gr. 17). 40.00 (978-988-8083-06-0(6)) Hong Kong Univ. Pr. HKG. Dist: Columbia Univ. Pr.

Clough, Rosa Trillo. Futurism: The Story of A Modern Art Movement. 2011. 326p. 50.95 ***978-1-258-06499-0(5))*** Literary Licensing, LLC.

Cohen, Jean-Louis & Moeller, Gerard Martin, Jr. Liquid Stone: New Architecture in Concrete. Cohen, Jean-Louis, ed. 2006. (ENG., Illus.). 248p. 65.00 *(978-1-56898-570-1(3))* Princeton Architectural Pr.

Connolly, Maeve. The Place of Artists' Cinema: Space, Site, & Screen. 2009. (ENG., Illus.). 240p. pap. 40.00 *(978-1-84150-246-5(4))* Intellect, Ltd. GBR. Dist: Chicago Distribution Ctr.

Cork, Richard & Sewell, Brian, contrib. by. History of the Saatchi Gallery. 2nd ed. 2011. (ENG., Illus.). 1008p. 125.00 *(978-1-86154-315-8(8))* Booth-Clibborn Editions GBR. Dist: Hachette Bk. Group.

Couture, Francine & Vanlaethem, France. Conservation de L'art Contemporain et de L'architecture Moderne: L'authenticité en Question. 2010. (FRE., Illus.). viii, 158p. *(978-2-89544-136-6(7))* Editions MultiMondes.

Coyle, Rebecca & Hayward, Philip. Apparition: Holographic Art in Australia. 2011. (ENG.). 144p. (C). pap. 26.95 *(978-0-909952-37-3(2))* Power Pubns. AUS. Dist: Univ. of Washington Pr.

Craddock, Sacha. Angus Fairhurst. 2009. (ENG., Illus.). 112p. 53.00 *(978-0-85667-659-8(4))* Wilson, Philip Pubs., Ltd. GBR. Dist: Macmillan.

Cramerotti, Alfredo. Aesthetic Journalism: How to Inform Without Informing. 2009. (ENG.). 112p. pap. 35.00 *(978-1-84150-268-7(5))* Intellect, Ltd. GBR. Dist: Chicago Distribution Ctr.

Cram101 Textbook Reviews Staff. Outlines & Highlights for History of Modern Art by H H Arnason, Isbn: 9780131840690. 2009. 188p. pap. 30.95 *(978-1-4288-9537-9(X))* Cram101 Inc.

Crepaldi, Gabriele. Modern Art: The Age of Avant-Gardes. 2007. (Illus.). 400p. 49.95 *(978-0-06-136312-2(X)*, Collins Design) HarperCollins Pubs.

Crowley, David, et al. The Power of Fantasy: Modern & Contemporary Art from Poland. 2011. (ENG., Illus.). 160p. 49.95 ***(978-3-7913-5145-2(1))*** Prestel Publishing.

Crumb, R. & Obrist, Hans Ulrich, texts. Crumb/Obrist, 1 vol. 2007. (ENG.). 47p. pap. 16.00 *(978-3-88375-948-7(1))* Verlag der Buchhandlung Walther Konig DEU. Dist: D.A.P./Distributed Art Pubs.

Cumming, Elizabeth. Phoebe Anna Traquair: 1852-1936. 2006. (ENG., Illus.). 112p. pap. *(978-1-903278-65-9(1))* National Galleries of Scotland.

Czernin, Franz Josef. Bildsatz: Texte Zu Bildender Kunst. 2008. (GER., Illus.). 367p. *(978-3-8321-9100-9(3))* DuMont.

Dabakis, Melissa. Visualizing Labor in American Sculpture: Monuments, Manliness, & the Work Ethic, 1880-1935. 2011. (Cambridge Studies in American Visual Culture Ser.). (ENG.). 314p. pap. 60.00 *(978-0-521-28327-4(2))* Cambridge Univ. Pr.

Dammann, April. Exhibitionist: Earl Stendhal, Art Dealer As Impressario. 2011. (Illus.). 192p. *(978-1-883318-86-4(6))* Angel City Pr.

Daniel, Malcolm. Stieglitz, Steichen, Strand: Masterworks from the Metropolitan Museum of Art. 2010. (Illus.). 180p. 35.00 *(978-0-300-16901-0(9))* Yale Univ. Pr.

Dantini, Michele. Modern & Contemporary Art. 2008. (ENG., Illus.). 192p. pap. 14.95 *(978-1-4027-5921-5(5))* Sterling Publishing Co., Inc.

Danto, Arthur C. Unnatural Wonders: Essays from the Gap Between Art & Life. 2007. (ENG., Illus.). 408p. (gr. 17). pap. 25.00 *(978-0-231-14115-4(7))* Columbia Univ. Pr.

Danzker, Jo-Anne Birnie & Bott, Gian Casper, eds. Seance: Albert Von Keller & the Occult. 2010. (ENG., Illus.). 104p. 30.00 *(978-0-295-99082-8(1))* Frye Art Museum.

David, Adrian. Homo Arte - Omnibus: 101 Confidences of an Art Collector. 2011. (FRE, DUT & ENG., Illus.). 320p. pap. *(978-90-209-9157-4(4)*, Lannoo Pubs. (Acc)) Antique Collectors' Club.

Davies, Hugh M. & Irwin, Robert, contrib. by. Robert Irwin: Primaries & Secondaries, 1 vol. 2008. (ENG., Illus.). 220p. 65.00 *(978-0-934418-67-6(5))* Museum of Contemporary Art, San Diego.

Davis, Randal B. Hybrid Visions: The Multimedia Works of Ken Butler. pap. 2.00 *(978-0-914435-14-3(0))* Marylhurst Univ. Art Dept.

Day, Gail. Dialectical Passions: Negation in Postwar Art Theory. 2010. (Columbia Themes in Philosophy, Social Criticism, & the Arts Ser.). (ENG., Illus.). 320p. (gr. 17). 50.00 *(978-0-231-14938-9(7))* Columbia Univ. Pr.

de Duve, Thierry. Sewn in the Sweatshops of Marx: Beuys, Warhol, Klein, Duchamp. Krauss, Rosalind E., tr. 2012. 120p. pap. 22.50 ***(978-0-226-92239-6(3))***; (Illus.). 60.00 ***(978-0-226-92237-9(5))*** Univ. of Chicago Pr.

De Lafayette, Maximillien. World Who's Who in Contemporary Art: Thematic & Biographical Encyclopedia of Living Artists & Styles. 2007. (Illus.). 400p. per. 69.95 *(978-0-9759750-9-7(3))* Elite Assocs. International-Times Square Pr.

Debroise, Olivier, ed. Informe. 2010. (ENG & SPA., Illus.). 246p. 40.00 *(978-968-9056-35-5(2))* Turner, Ediciones S.A. ESP. Dist: D.A.P./Distributed Art Pubs.

Dempsey, Amy. Destination Art. 2010. (ENG.). 272p. pap. 29.95 *(978-0-520-26789-3(3))* Univ. of California Pr.

—Styles, Schools & Movements: The Essential Encyclopaedic Guide to Modern Art. 2nd rev. ed. 2011. (ENG., Illus.). 312p. pap. 31.95 *(978-0-500-28844-3(5)*, 528844) Thames & Hudson.

Dezeuze, Anna, ed. The 'Do-It-Yourself' Artwork. 2012. (ENG., Illus.). 328p. pap. 34.95 ***(978-0-7190-8747-9(3))*** Manchester Univ. Pr. GBR. Dist: Macmillan.

Dezeuze, Anna, ed. The 'Do-it-Yourself' Artwork: Participation from Fluxus to New Media. 2010. (Rethinking Art's Histories Ser.). (ENG., Illus.). 336p. 90.00 *(978-0-7190-8144-6(0))* Manchester Univ. Pr. GBR. Dist: Macmillan.

Di Bello, Patrizia & Koureas, Gabriel, eds. Art History & the Senses: 1830 to the Present. 2010. (Illus.). 224p. 124.95 *(978-0-7546-6863-3(0))* Ashgate Publishing Co.

Di Ozesanmuseum Bamberg, et al, eds. Tactile: High Touch Visuals. 2007. (Illus.). 207p. 69.00 *(978-3-89955-200-3(8))* Die Gestalten Verlag DEU. Dist: Prestel Publishing.

Diacono, Mario, text. Iconography & Archetypes. 2011. (ENG., Illus.). 488p. pap. 45.00 *(978-88-366-1633-6(X))* Silvana ITA. Dist: D.A.P./Distributed Art Pubs.

Dillon, Brian. Ruins. 2011. (Whitechapel: Documents of Contemporary Art Ser.). (ENG.). 240p. (gr. 17). pap. 24.95 ***(978-0-262-51637-2(3))*** MIT Pr.

Domesle, Andrea. Leucht-Schrift-Kunst: Kosuth, Merz, Nannucci, Naumann, Holzer. (GER., Illus.). 368p. *(978-3-496-01186-6(6))* Reimer, Dietrich.

Dorontchenkov. Russian & Soviet Views of Modern Western Art. 2009. (Documents of Twentieth-Century Art Ser.). (Illus.). xv, 347p. 65.00 *(978-0-520-22103-1(6))* Univ. of California Pr.

Dorontchenkov, Ilia & Dorontchenkov, I. Russian & Soviet Views of Modern Western Art, 1890s to Mid-1930s. Dorontchenkov, Ilia & Gourianova, Nina, eds. Rougle, Charles, tr. 2009. (Documents of Twentieth-Century Art Ser.). (ENG., Illus.). 400p. pap. 29.95 *(978-0-520-25372-8(8))* Univ. of California Pr.

Doschka, Roland, ed. Marc Chagall: Origins & Paths. 2010. (Illus.). 232p. pap. 19.95 *(978-3-7913-4395-2(5))* Prestel Publishing.

Douglas, Stan, ed. Vancouver Anthology. 2nd rev. ed. 2009. (ENG.). 368p. 35.00 ***(978-0-88922-614-2(8))*** Talonbooks, Ltd. CAN. Dist: Consortium Bk. Sales & Distribution.

Dover. Dali: Postcards. 2011. (Dover Postcards Ser.). (ENG., Illus.). 24p. pap. 6.95 *(978-0-486-48082-4(8))* Dover Pubns., Inc.

Dreier, et al. Three Lectures on Modern Art. *(978-0-8022-0418-9(X))* Philosophical Library, Inc.

Dreishpoon, Douglas, ed. The Long Curve: 150 Years of Visionary Collecting at the Albright-Knox Art Gallery. 2011. (ENG., Illus.). 268p. 65.00 ***(978-88-572-1040-7(5))*** Skira Editore ITA. Dist: Random Hse., Inc.

Drucker, Johanna. Sweet Dreams: Contemporary Art & Complicity. 2006. (Illus.). 264p. per. 30.00 *(978-0-226-16505-9(1))* Univ. of Chicago Pr.

Durden, Mark. Variable Capital. 2008. (ENG., Illus.). 192p. 39.95 *(978-1-84631-126-0(8))* Liverpool Univ. Pr. GBR. Dist: Chicago Distribution Ctr.

Duty, Michael & McGarry, Susan Hallsten. Texas Traditions: Contemporary Artists of the Lone Star State. 2010. (ENG., Illus.). 240p. 85.00 *(978-1-934491-24-9(1))* Fresco Fine Art Pubns., LLC.

Ehmann, Arne, ed. Intuition/(Im)Precision. 2012. (ENG & GER., Illus.). 100p. pap. 67.00 ***(978-3-901935-49-7(5))*** Galerie Thaddaeus Ropac, Eigenverlag AUT. Dist: D.A.P./Distributed Art Pubs.

Elam, Kimberly. Geometry of Design: Studies in Proportion & Composition. 2nd rev. ed. 2011. (ENG., Illus.). 144p. pap. 24.95 *(978-1-61689-036-0(3))* Princeton Architectural Pr.

Elder, R. Bruce. Harmony & Dissent: Film & Avant-garde Art Movements in the Early Twentieth Century. 2010. (Film & Media Studies). (ENG., Illus.). 516p. pap. 34.95 *(978-1-55458-226-6(1))* Wilfrid Laurier Univ. Pr. CAN. Dist: Univ. of Toronto Pr.

—Harmony & Dissent: Film & Avant-Garde Art Movements in the Early Twentieth Century. 2008. (Film & Media Studies). (ENG.). 516p. 85.00 *(978-1-55458-028-6(5))* Wilfrid Laurier Univ. Pr. CAN. Dist: Univ. of Toronto Pr.

Ellis, Patricia, contrib. by. New Labour. (Illus.). 64p. pap. 32.00 *(978-0-9538587-2-9(3))* Saatchi Gallery GBR. Dist: D.A.P./Distributed Art Pubs.

Evans, David, ed. Appropriation. 2009. (Documents of Contemporary Art Ser.). (ENG.). 239p. (gr. 17). pap. 24.95 *(978-0-262-55070-3(9))* MIT Pr.

Eversole, Finley. Art & Spiritual Transformation: The Seven Stages of Death & Rebirth. 2009. (ENG., Illus.). 1p. pap. 24.95 *(978-1-59477-281-8(9))* Inner Traditions International, Ltd.

Fang, Chung-Yu. Contemporary Art in Taiwan After 1987. 2010. 86p. pap. *(978-3-8383-5759-1(0))* Lambert Academic Publishing.

Farr, Ian. Memory. 2012. pap. ***(978-0-262-51776-8(0))*** MIT Pr.

Farrell, Jennifer. Get There First, Decide Promptly: The Richard Brown Baker Collection of Postwar Art. 2012. (ENG., Illus.). 372p. 50.00 *(978-0-300-15302-6(3))* Yale Univ. Art Gallery.

Feinstein, Roni. Circa 1958: Breaking Ground in American Art. 2008. (Distributed for the Ackland Art Museum Ser.). (ENG., Illus.). 160p. pap. 34.00 *(978-0-8078-5949-0(4))* Univ. of North Carolina Pr.

Fenner, Cathy & Fenner, Arnie, eds. Spectrum 18: The Best in Contemporary Fantastic Art. 2011. (ENG.). 304p. 45.00 *(978-1-59929-059-1(6))*; (Illus.). pap. 35.00 *(978-1-59929-058-4(8))* Underwood Books.

—Spectrum 6: The Best in Contemporary Fantastic Art. 2010. (ENG.). 176p. pap. 27.95 *(978-1-59929-045-4(6))* Underwood Books.

Ferrari, Claudia Gian & Pontiggia, Elena, eds. A Loving Hunt: Italian Interbellum Art in the Iannaccone Collection. 2010. (ENG., Illus.). 256p. 90.00 *(978-88-572-0382-9(4))* Skira Editore ITA. Dist: Random Hse., Inc.

Ferus, Katharina & Rübel, Dietmar. "Die Tücke des Objekts" Vom Umgang MIT Dingen. 2009. (Illus.). 253p. *(978-3-496-02807-9(6))* Reimer, Dietrich.

Fineberg, Jonathan David. Art since 1940. 3rd ed. 2010. (ENG., Illus.). 560p. (C). pap. 112.33 *(978-0-13-193479-5(1)*, Prentice Hall) Prentice Hall PTR.

Fischli, Peter & Weiss, David, photos by. Plötzlich diese Übersicht. 4th ed. 2008. (POR, GER & ENG., Illus.). 180p. pap. 58.00 *(978-3-906135-41-0(1))* Verlag der Buchhandlung Walther Konig DEU. Dist: D.A.P./Distributed Art Pubs.

Fisher, Mark. Michael Wilkinson: 1979. 2012. (ENG.). 192p. pap. 29.95 *(978-1-907317-43-9(0))* Black Dog Publishing Ltd. GBR. Dist: Perseus Distribution.

Fitzgerald, Kenneth & VanderLans, Rudy. Volume: Writings on Graphic Design, Music, Art, & Culture. 2010. (ENG., Illus.). 256p. pap. 24.95 *(978-1-56898-964-8(4))* Princeton Architectural Pr.

Fogg, Marnie. Fashion Illustration, 1930 to 1970. 2011. (ENG., Illus.). 208p. 24.95 *(978-1-906388-81-2(4)*, Batsford, B. T. Ltd.) Anova Bks. GBR. Dist: Sterling Publishing Co., Inc.

Foster, Hal, et al. Art Since 1900: 1900 To 1944. 2nd ed. 2011. (ENG., Illus.). 392p. (C). pap. 50.00 net. ***(978-0-500-28952-5(2)***, 528952) Thames & Hudson.

—Art Since 1900: 1945 to the Present. 2nd ed. 2011. (ENG., Illus.). 504p. (C). pap. 60.00 net. ***(978-0-500-28953-2(0)***, 528953) Thames & Hudson.

—Art Since 1900: Modernism, Antimodernism, Postmodernism. 2nd ed. 2011. (ENG., Illus.). 896p. (C). pap. 90.00 net. ***(978-0-500-28951-8(4)***, 528951) Thames & Hudson.

—Art since 1900: Modernism Antimodernism Postmodernism. 2nd rev. ed. 2011. (ENG., Illus.). 816p. 100.00 ***(978-0-500-23889-9(8)***, 523889) Thames & Hudson.

Frank, Jane. Science Fiction & Fantasy Artists of the Twentieth Century: A Biographical Dictionary. 2009. (ENG.). 534p. 135.00 *(978-0-7864-3423-7(6))* McFarland & Co., Inc. Pubs.

Frascina, Francis. Modern Art Culture: A Reader. Frascina, Francis, ed. 2009. (Illus.). 400p. pap. 39.95 *(978-0-415-23152-7(3))*; (ENG., 488p. (C). 125.00 *(978-0-415-23151-0(5))* Routledge.

Fraser, Craig. Fashion & Imagination, 1 vol. Djonge Hond Staff, ed. 2010. (ENG., Illus.). 413p. pap. 80.00 *(978-90-8910-140-2(3))* Exhibitions International BEL. Dist: Innovative Logistics.

Frederick R. Weisman Art Foundation Collection. 2007. *(978-0-9740908-1-8(6))* Weisman, Frederick R. Philanthropic Foundation.

Frehner, Matthias & Friedli, Susanne, eds. James Lee Byars: Im Full of Byars. 2009. (ENG., Illus.). 264p. pap. 55.00 *(978-3-86678-155-9(5))* Kerber Verlag DEU. Dist: D.A.P./Distributed Art Pubs.

Frenk, Mariana & Garcia Bonilla, Roberto. Arte Entre DOS Continentes: Artículos y Ensayos. 2009. (SPA., Illus.). xvii, 275p. 20.40 *(978-968-23-2585-4(4))* Siglo XXI Ediciones MEX. Dist: Sony Electronics.

Freybourg, Anne Marie & Freybourg, Anne Marie. Die Inszenierung des Künstlers. 2008. (GER., Illus.). 111p. pap. *(978-3-86859-031-9(5))* Jovis Verlag GmbH.

Fried, Michael. Four Honest Outlaws: Sala, Ray, Marioni, Gordon. 2011. (ENG., Illus.). 224p. 45.00 *(978-0-300-17053-5(X))* Yale Univ. Pr.

Fuchs, Rudi. With a Probability of Being Seen: Dorothee & Konrad Fischer: Archives of an Attitude. 2010. 384p. 65.00 *(978-84-92505-43-2(5))* Museu d'Art Contemporani de Barcelona ESP. Dist: Actar Birkhauser Distribution.

Galenson, David W. Conceptual Revolutions in Twentieth-Century Art. 2009. (ENG.). 460p. 95.00 *(978-0-521-11232-1(X))*; pap. 26.99 *(978-0-521-12909-1(5))* Cambridge Univ. Pr. GBR. Dist: Cambridge Univ. Pr.

Gamboni, Dario. The Destruction of Art: Iconoclasm & Vandalism since the French Revolution. 2007. (Reaktion Books - Picturing History Ser.). (ENG., Illus.). 416p. per. 29.95 *(978-1-86189-316-1(7))* Reaktion Bks., Ltd. GBR. Dist: Chicago Distribution Ctr.

Gao, Minglu. Total Modernity & the Avant-Garde in Twentieth-Century Chinese Art. 2011. (ENG., Illus.). 424p. (gr. 17). 39.95 *(978-0-262-01494-6(7))* MIT Pr.

Gaunt, Pamela. Decorative Art in the Twentieth Century. 2010. 156p. pap. *(978-3-639-22348-4(9))* VDM Verlag Dr. Mueller e.K.

Geary, Caron. It's a Man's Man's Man's World. 2010. 76p. pap. *(978-3-639-22275-3(X))* VDM Verlag Dr. Mueller e.K.

Gennaro, I. de, et al. Artists & Intellectuals & the Requests of Power. 2009. (Studies on the Interaction of Art, Thought & Power). (Illus.). 224p. *(978-90-04-17213-5(0))* BRILL.

Gerard, Alain. Denis Felix: Au fil de L'Homme. 2012. (ENG & FRE., Illus.). 168p. 51.95 ***(978-2-7572-0497-9(1))*** Somogy Editions d'Art FRA. Dist: Independent Pubs. Group.

Getsy, David. From Diversion to Subversion: Games, Play, & Twentieth-Century Art. 2011. (Refiguring Modernism Ser.). (ENG.). 240p. pap. 74.95 *(978-0-271-03703-5(2))* Pennsylvania State Univ. Pr.

Geuna, Elena. Zhang Huan: Ashman. 2011. (ENG., Illus.). 160p. 55.00 *(978-88-7179-642-0(X)*, Ore Cultura Srl (Acc)) Antique Collectors' Club GBR. Dist: National Bk. Network.

Gielen, Denis. Atlas of Contemporary Art for Use by Everyone, 1 vol. Austrums, Laura, tr. 2008. (ENG., Illus.). 400p. 99.95 *(978-2-930368-21-4(7))* Exhibitions International N.V. BEL. Dist: D.A.P./Distributed Art Pubs.

Gillick, Liam. Liam Gillick: Factories in the Snow, 1 vol. 2006. (GER & ENG., Illus.). 160p. pap. 45.00 *(978-3-905701-64-7(2))* JRP Ringier Kunstverlag AG CHE. Dist: D.A.P./Distributed Art Pubs.

Goetzmann, William H. & Goetzmann, William N. The West of the Imagination. 2nd rev. ed. 2009. (ENG., Illus.). 640p. 65.00 *(978-0-8061-3533-5(6))* Univ. of Oklahoma Pr.

Goldstein, Ann, et al. This Is Not to Be Looked At: Highlights from the Permanent Collection of the Museum of Contemporary Art, Los Angeles. 2008. (ENG., Illus.). 384p. 59.95 *(978-1-933751-07-8(X))* Museum of Contemporary Art, Los Angeles.

Golomstock, Igor. Totalitarian Art: In the Soviet Union, the Third Reich, Fascist Italy, & the People's Republicof China. Chandler, Robert, tr. 2011. (ENG.). 464p. (gr. 12). 45.00 *(978-1-59020-317-0(8))* Overlook Pr., The.

González, Jennifer A. Subject to Display: Reframing Race in Contemporary Installation Art. 2011. (ENG., Illus.). 320p. (gr. 17). pap. 17.95 *(978-0-262-51602-0(0))* MIT Pr.

Gott, Ted & Benson, Laurie. 20th Century Painting & Sculpture: In the International Collections of the National Gallery of Victoria. 2006. (Illus.). 134p. pap. 39.95 *(978-0-7241-0231-0(0))* National Gallery of Victoria AUS. Dist: Antique Collectors' Club.

Gough, Paul. Terrible Beauty. 2013. (ENG., Illus.). 256p. pap. 65.00 *(978-1-906593-00-1(0))* Sansom & Co. Ltd. GBR. Dist: National Bk. Network.

Grammel, Soren & Kunstverein, Grazer, eds. Der Symolische Auftraggeber/the Symbolic Commissioner. 2011. (ENG & GER., Illus.). 224p. 34.00 ***(978-1-934105-35-1(X))*** Sternberg Pr.

Grant, Catherine. Girls! Girls! Girls! In Contemporary Art. Waxman, Lori, ed. 2011. (ENG., Illus.). 188p. pap. 40.00 *(978-1-84150-348-6(7))* Intellect, Ltd. GBR. Dist: Chicago Distribution Ctr.

Grant, Kim. Surrealism & the Visual Arts: Theory & Reception. 2012. (ENG., Illus.). 416p. pap. 39.99 ***(978-1-107-40334-5(0))*** Cambridge Univ. Pr.

Griffith, Terri, et al, eds. The Essential New Art Examiner. 2011. (ENG.). 350p. pap. 22.50 ***(978-0-87580-662-4(7))*** Northern Illinois Univ. Pr.

Groys, Boris. Art Power. 2008. (ENG.). 200p. (gr. 17). 25.95 *(978-0-262-07292-2(0))* MIT Pr.

—Boris Groys: Going Public. 2011. (E-Flux Journal Ser.). (ENG., Illus.). 168p. pap. 15.00 ***(978-1-934105-30-6(9))*** Sternberg Pr.

Groys, Boris. The Total Art of Stalinism: Avant-Garde, Aesthetic Dictatorship, & Beyond. Rougle, Charles, tr. from GER. 2011. (ENG.). 144p. pap. 19.95 *(978-1-84467-707-8(9)*, 844707) Verso Bks. GBR. Dist: Norton, W. W. & Co., Inc.

Guglielmino, Giorgio. How to Look at Contemporary Art: (... And Like It) 2008. (ENG., Illus.). 216p. pap. 44.00 *(978-88-422-1644-5(5))* Allemandi, Umberto & Co. GBR. Dist: Antique Collectors' Club.

Guha-Thakurta, Tapati. The Making of a New 'Indian' Art: Artists, Aesthetics & Nationalism in Bengal, C. 1850-1920. 2007. (Cambridge South Asian Studies). (ENG.). 384p. pap. 53.00 *(978-0-521-05273-3(4))* Cambridge Univ. Pr.

Hagman. The Artist's Mind: A Psychoanalytic Perspective on Creativity, Modern Art & Modern Artists. 2010. (ENG.). 192p. (C). 90.00 *(978-0-415-46705-6(5))* Routledge.

Hagman, George. The Artist's Mind: A Psychoanalytic Perspective on Creativity, Modern Art & Modern Artists. 2010. (ENG.). 192p. (C). pap. 34.95 *(978-0-415-46706-3(3))* Routledge.

Hardmeier, M. Radar: Texts on Contemporary Art; Essays & Interviews by Peter Stohler. Stürzl, W., ed. 2008. (ENG., Illus.). 128p. pap. 45.00 *(978-3-89790-278-7(8))* Arnoldsche Art Pubs. DEU. Dist: Antique Collectors' Club.

Harmon, Katharine & Clemans, Gayle. The Map as Art: Contemporary Artists Explore Cartography. 2010. (ENG., Illus.). 256p. pap. 29.95 *(978-1-56898-972-3(5))* Princeton Architectural Pr.

Harris, Jonathan. Dead History, Live Art? Spectacle, Subjectivity & Subversion in Visual Culture since the 1960s. 2008. (Liverpool University Press - Tate Liverpool Critical Forum Ser.). (ENG., Illus.). 256p. 90.00 *(978-0-85323-189-9(3))* Liverpool Univ. Pr. GBR. Dist: Chicago Distribution Ctr.

Harris, Jonathan, ed. Globalization & Contemporary Art. 2011. (ENG., Illus.). 552p. 115.95 *(978-1-4051-7951-5(1))*; pap. 49.95 *(978-1-4051-7950-8(3))* Wiley, John & Sons, Inc. (Wiley-Blackwell).

Harris, Roy. The Great Debate about Art. 2010. 130p. pap. 12.95 *(978-0-9842010-0-6(9))* Prickly Paradigm Pr., LLC.

Harrison, Charles. Since 1950: Art & Its Criticism. 2009. (ENG., Illus.). 272p. 45.00 *(978-0-300-15186-2(1))* Yale Univ. Pr.

Hatebur, Barbara. Sammlung Credit Suisse: Kunst im Geschäftsumfeld. Credit Suisse Art Staff & Rogger, André, eds. 2011. (ENG., Illus.). 464p. 110.00 *(978-3-85881-324-4(9))* Scheidegger und Spiess AG, Verlag CHE. Dist: Antique Collectors' Club.

Hathaway, Norman. Electrical Banana: Masters of Psychedelic Art. 2012. (ENG., Illus.). 208p. pap. 39.95 ***(978-88-6208-204-4(5))*** Damiani ITA. Dist: D.A.P./Distributed Art Pubs.

Hauptman, Jodi, et al, texts. Picasso to Warhol: Fourteen Modern Masters. 2011. (ENG., Illus.). 192p. 50.00 ***(978-0-87070-805-3(8))*** Museum of Modern Art.

Helander, Bruce. Learning to See: An Artist's View on Contemporary Artists from Artschwager to Zakanitch. 2008. (Illus.). 191p. 95.00 *(978-1-884886-88-1(4))* StarGroup International.

Heller, Reinhold, text. The Birth of Expressionism, 1905-1913. 2009. (ENG., Illus.). 232p. 55.00 *(978-3-7757-2351-0(X))* Hatje Cantz Verlag GmbH & Co KG DEU. Dist: D.A.P./Distributed Art Pubs.

Henselelt, Frank. Rafa Forteza. 2008. (GER & SPA., Illus.). 128p. 59.00 *(978-3-87909-918-4(9))* Wienand GmbH, Druck- & Verlagshaus DEU. Dist: Independent Pubs. Group.

Herd, Kerstin. Walt Disneys Bildwelten in der zeitgenössischen Kunst: und ihr Ursprung in der Malerei des 18. bis 20. Jahrhunderts. 2010. 112p. pap. *(978-3-639-26640-5(4))* VDM Verlag Dr. Mueller e.K.

Hess, Donald & Steiner, Myrtha, texts. Hess Art Collection. 2010. (ENG., Illus.). 372p. 60.00 *(978-3-7757-2139-4(8))* Hatje Cantz Verlag GmbH & Co KG DEU. Dist: D.A.P./Distributed Art Pubs.

Hicks, Alistar. Contemporary Art at Deutsche Bank. (Illus.). 167p. 39.95 *(978-3-89322-825-6(X))* Edition Cantz DEU. Dist: D.A.P./Distributed Art Pubs.

Hiles. A Survey of Contemporary Art since 1938. 2012. (ENG.). (C). pap. 83.95 ***(978-0-534-63927-3(5))*** Wadsworth.

Hine, Thomas. The Great Funk: Styles of the Shaggy, Sexy, Shameless 1970s. 2009. (ENG., Illus.). 256p. pap. 16.00 *(978-0-374-53167-6(6))* Farrar, Straus & Giroux.

Hirschland, Ellen B. & Ramage, Nancy. The Cone Sisters of Baltimore: Collecting at Full Tilt. 2008. (ENG., Illus.). 352p. 34.95 *(978-0-8101-2481-3(5))* Northwestern Univ. Pr.

Hirsh, Jennie & Wallace, Isabelle Loring. Contemporary Art & Classical Myth. 2011. (Illus.). 410p. 124.95 *(978-0-7546-6974-6(2))* Ashgate Publishing Co.

Hirst, Damien & Beard, Jason, eds. Requiem I & II: Text in English & Ukrainian. aut. ed. 2009. (ENG., Illus.). 326p. 675.00 *(978-1-906967-07-9(5))* Other Criteria GBR. Dist: Hachette Bk. Group.

Hollins, C. J. The Animal Within: Explaining the Bizarre & Ludicrous in Modern Art. 2010. (Illus.). 175p. 37.50 *(978-1-84624-504-6(4))* Book Guild, Ltd. GBR. Dist: Trans-Atlantic Pubns., Inc.

Holman, Martin. Richard Rome. 2011. (Illus.). 96p. 60.00 *(978-1-84822-081-2(2),* Lund Humphries Pubs.) Ashgate Publishing, Ltd. GBR. Dist: Ashgate Publishing Co.

Holzer, Jenny. Jenny Holzer, 1 vol. 2011. (ENG., Illus.). 200p. (Orig.). 145.00 *(978-3-86521-937-4(3))* Steidl, Gerhard Druckerei und Verlag DEU. Dist: Innovative Logistics.

Holzwarth, Hans Werner, ed. Christopher Wool: With an Original Artwork. 2008. (Illus.). 500p. 0.03 *(978-3-8365-0361-7(1))* TASCHEN DEU. Dist: Ingram Pub. Services.

Hubbard, Sue. Adventures in Art: Selected Writings, 1990-2010. 2010. (ENG., Illus.). 302p. pap. 37.50 *(978-1-906967-21-5(0))* Other Criteria GBR. Dist: Hachette Bk. Group.

Hugill, Andrew. 'Pataphysics: A Useless Guide. 2012. ***(978-0-262-01779-4(2))*** MIT Pr.

Hummelen, IJsbrand M. C. & Sillé, Dionne. Modern Art - Who Cares? An Interdisciplinary Research Project & an International Symposium on the Conservation of Modern & Contemporary Art. 2006. (ENG., Illus.). 450p. pap. 90.00 *(978-1-904982-02-9(6))* Archetype Pubns. GBR. Dist: National Bk. Network.

Hung, Wu, ed. Wu Hung on Contemporary Chinese Artists. 2009. (ENG., Illus.). 268p. 25.00 *(978-988-18034-3-6(8))* Timezone 8 Ltd. HKG. Dist: D.A.P./Distributed Art Pubs.

Hutchison, Alice L. Kenneth Anger. 2011. (ENG., Illus.). 224p. pap. 34.95 *(978-1-907317-51-4(1))* Black Dog Publishing Ltd. GBR. Dist: Perseus Distribution.

Indiana, Robert. Robert Indiana: Hard Edge. 2009. (ENG., Illus.). 68p. 60.00 *(978-0-9794164-4-6(2))* Kasmin, Paul Gallery.

Iversen, Margaret. Beyond Pleasure: Freud, Lacan, Barthes. 2007. (Refiguring Modernism Ser.). (ENG., Illus.). 272p. 40.00 *(978-0-271-02971-9(4))* Pennsylvania State Univ. Pr.

—Chance. 2010. (Documents of Contemporary Art Ser.). (ENG.). 238p. (gr. 17). pap. 24.95 *(978-0-262-51392-0(7))* MIT Pr.

James, N. P. Interviews - Artists: Recordings from Cv/Visual Arts Research Archive 1988-96. 4th ed. 2007. (Illus.). 144p. pap. *(978-1-905571-50-5(X))* Cv Pubns.

Jansen, Gregor & Thiel, Thomas, eds. Vertrautes Terrain: Aktuelle Kunst in & über Deutschland. 2009. (ENG.). 500p. pap. 45.00 *(978-3-86828-064-7(2))* Kehrer Verlag Heidelberg, Klaus Kehrer DEU. Dist: Consortium Bk. Sales & Distribution.

Jencks, Charles. Critical Modernism: Where Is Post-Modernism Going What Is Post-Modernism? 5th ed. 2007. (ENG., Illus.). 240p. pap. 55.00 *(978-0-470-03011-0(9));* 115.00 *(978-0-470-03010-3(0))* Wiley, John & Sons, Inc. (Academy Pr.).

Jhaveri, Amriti. 101: A Guide to 101 Modern & Contemporary Indian Artists. 2008. (Artists Ser.). (Illus.). 191p. pap. 29.95 *(978-81-7508-423-0(5))* India Bk. Hse. Pvt., Ltd. IND. Dist: Antique Collectors' Club.

Johnson, Ken. Are You Experienced? How Psychedelic Consciousness Transformed Modern Art. 2011. (Illus.). 240p. 49.95 *(978-3-7913-4498-0(6))* Prestel Publishing.

Johnson, Mark Dean, et al. Asian American Modern Art: Shifting Currents, 1900-1970. Cornell, Daniel & Johnson, Mark Dean, eds. 2008. (ENG., Illus.). 168p. 50.00 *(978-0-520-25864-8(9))* Univ. of California Pr.

Johnstone, Stephen. The Everyday. 2008. (Documents of Contemporary Art Ser.). (ENG.). 240p. (gr. 17). pap. 24.95 *(978-0-262-60074-3(9))* MIT Pr.

Johung, Jennifer. Replacing Home: From Primordial Hut to Digital Network in Contemporary Art. 2011. (ENG., Illus.). 232p. 75.00 ***(978-0-8166-7287-5(3));*** pap. 25.00 ***(978-0-8166-7288-2(1))*** Univ. of Minnesota Pr.

Jones, Caroline A., ed. Sensorium: Embodied Experience, Technology, & Contemporary Art. 2006. (ENG., Illus.). 268p. (gr. 17). 34.00 *(978-0-262-10117-2(3))* MIT Pr.

Jones, Stephen. Synthetics: Aspects of Art & Technology in Australia, 1956-1975. 2011. (Leonardo Bks.). (ENG., Illus.). 416p. (gr. 17). 40.00 *(978-0-262-01496-0(3))* MIT Pr.

Kargl, Georg. Georg Kargl, Fine Arts Since 1998: Box Since 2005, 1 vol. 2006. (ENG., Illus.). 328p. per. 35.00 *(978-3-86560-063-9(8))* Verlag der Buchhandlung Walther Konig DEU. Dist: D.A.P./Distributed Art Pubs.

Kastner, Jeffrey, ed. Land & Environmental Art. 2010. (ENG., Illus.). 204p. pap. 19.95 *(978-0-7148-5643-8(6))* Phaidon Pr., Inc.

Keiso, Fassih. The Body in Twilight. 2008. 224p. pap. *(978-3-639-05984-7(0))* VDM Verlag Dr. Mueller e.K.

Kelleher, Diane Elizabeth. How to Research, Write & Publish an Art History Book in American Art. 2011. 48p. pap. 10.95 ***(978-1-4634-6799-9(0))*** AuthorHouse.

Keller, Jan. Pieces from My Crazy Quilt. Roberts, Janetta & Holzworth, Amy, eds. Date not set. (Illus.). 128p. pap. 12.95 *(978-1-889579-00-9(9))* Black Sheep Bks. & Publishing.

Kelly, Caleb, ed. Sound. 2011. (Documents of Contemporary Art Ser.). (ENG., Illus.). 240p. (gr. 17). pap. 24.95 *(978-0-262-51568-9(7))* MIT Pr.

Kelly, Julia. Art, Ethnography & Life of Objects: Paris, C. 1925¿35. 2012. (Critical Perspectives in Art History Ser.). (ENG., Illus.). 188p. pap. 24.95 ***(978-0-7190-6941-3(6))*** Manchester Univ. Pr. GBR. Dist: Macmillan.

Kelly, Julia. Art, Ethnography & the Life of Objects: Paris, C. 1925-35. 2007. (Critical Perspectives in Art History Ser.). (ENG., Illus.). 192p. 94.00 *(978-0-7190-6940-6(8))* Manchester Univ. Pr. GBR. Dist: Macmillan.

Kienholz, Lyn. L. A. Rising: SoCal Artists Before 1980. Betinski, Elizabeta & Nelson, Corinne, eds. 2011. (Illus.). 516p. 75.00 net. *(978-0-917571-13-8(4))* California/International Arts Foundation.

King, Ross. Defiant Spirits: The Modernist Revolution of the Group of Seven, 1 vol. 2011. (ENG., Illus.). 504p. pap. 24.95 *(978-1-55365-882-5(5))* D&M Pubs. Inc. CAN. Dist: Perseus-PGW.

Klin, Richard. Something to Say: Thoughts on Art & Politics in America. 2011. (ENG., Illus.). 168p. pap. 14.95 ***(978-1-935248-19-4(7))*** Leapfrog Pr.

Knafo, Danielle. In Her Own Image: Women's Self-Representation in Twentieth-Century Art. 2009. 62.50 *(978-0-8386-4210-8(1))* Fairleigh Dickinson Univ. Pr.

Koch, Polly. The Old, Weird America, 1 vol. 2008. (ENG., Illus.). 160p. 34.99 *(978-1-933619-12-5(0))* Contemporary Arts Museum, Houston.

Koolhaas, Rem. London - A Portrait of a City: Serpentine Gallery 24-Hour Interview. Marathon. Koolhas, Rem & Obrist, Hans Ulrich, eds. 2012. (ENG.). 272p. pap. 29.95 *(978-88-572-0059-0(0))* Skira Editore ITA. Dist: Random Hse., Inc.

Koons, Jeff. Jeff Koons: Versailles. 2nd ed. 2009. (ENG., Illus.). 192p. 85.00 *(978-2-915173-41-3(9))* Barral, Xavier Editions FRA. Dist: D.A.P./Distributed Art Pubs.

Koss, Juliet. Modernism after Wagner. 2010. (ENG., Illus.). 392p. 88.50 *(978-0-8166-5158-0(2));* pap. 29.50 *(978-0-8166-5159-7(0))* Univ. of Minnesota Pr.

Kotsopoulos, Nikolaos, ed. Contemporary Art in Eastern Europe: Artworld. 2010. (Artworld Ser.). (ENG., Illus.). 240p. 49.95 *(978-1-906155-84-1(4))* Black Dog Publishing Ltd. GBR. Dist: Perseus Distribution.

Kovtun, Evgueny. Russian Avant-Garde. 2007. (Art of Century Ser.). (ENG., Illus.). 199p. pap. 19.95 *(978-1-85995-678-6(5))* Parkstone International GBR. Dist: Ingram Pub. Services.

Kramer, Hilton. The Age of the Avant-Garde: 1956-1972. 2008. (ENG., Illus.). 588p. pap. 34.95 *(978-1-4128-0834-7(0))* Transaction Pubs.

—The Triumph of Modernism: The Art World, 1987-2005. 2006. (ENG.). 352p. 27.50 *(978-1-56663-708-4(2))* Dee, Ivan R. Pub.

Kraus, Karola. 'Jeder Künstler ist ein Mensch!'. Positionen des Selbstportraits. 2011. (GER & ENG., Illus.). 256p. 59.95 *(978-3-86560-884-0(1))* Verlag der Buchhandlung Walther Konig DEU. Dist: D.A.P./Distributed Art Pubs.

Krauss, Rosalind E. Perpetual Inventory. 2010. (October Bks.). (ENG., Illus.). 320p. (gr. 17). 31.95 *(978-0-262-01380-2(0))* MIT Pr.

Kronberg Frederiksen, Nanna, text. French Art at Ordrupgaard: Complete Catalogue of Paintings, Sculptures, Pastels, Drawings, & Prints. 2011. (ENG., Illus.). 544p. 120.00 *(978-3-7757-2671-9(3))* Hatje Cantz Verlag GmbH & Co KG DEU. Dist: D.A.P./Distributed Art Pubs.

Kuh, Katharine. My Love Affair with Modern Art: Behind the Scenes with a Legendary Curator. Berman, Avis, ed. 2012. (ENG.). 336p. pap. 14.95 ***(978-1-61145-506-9(5),*** 611506, Arcade Publishing) Skyhorse Publishing Co., Inc.

Kula, Ömür. The Rupture in Visual Language. 2010. 236p. pap. *(978-3-639-25468-6(6))* VDM Verlag Dr. Mueller e.K.

Kürti, Emese. Bukarest-Budapest Híd: Kortárs Román és Magyar Muvészet: Hunya Gábor Gyujteménye. 2010. (HUN & ENG., Illus.). 216p. 24.95 ***(978-963-9731-89-9(7))*** Vince Kiado Kft HUN. Dist: Independent Pubs. Group.

Kuspit, Donald. Psychodrama: Modern Art as Group Therapy. 2010. 540p. pap. 19.95 *(978-0-9561038-9-5(8))* Ziggurat Bks. GBR. Dist: Trans-Atlantic Pubns., Inc.

LaBelle, Brandon, ed. Leif Elggren: Death Travels Backwards. 2011. (ENG., Illus.). 12p. 18.00 *(978-0-9827439-2-8(0))* Errant Bodies Pr.

Lahor, Jean. Art of Century: Art Nouveau. 2008. (Illus.). 199p. pap. 17.95 *(978-970-718-621-7(6),* Numen) Advanced Marketing, S. de R. L. de C. V. MEX. Dist: Perseus-PGW.

Lange, Sami Lynn, ed. Bob Nugent. Elizabetsky, Roberto, tr. 2007. (ENG.). 160p. pap. 35.00 *(978-0-9794809-1-1(4));* (Illus.). 55.00 *(978-0-9794809-0-4(6))* Abandoned Pr.

Leepa, Allen. The Challenge of Modern Art. 2009. 310p. 43.95 *(978-1-104-84662-6(4))* 2007. (ENG.). 308p. per. 28.95 *(978-0-548-38855-6(5))* Kessinger Publishing, LLC.

—The Challenge of Modern Art. 2007. pap. ***(978-1-4067-5759-0(4))*** Read Bks.

Lerheim, Karen & Ydstie, Ingebjorg, eds. Munch's Laboratory: The Path to the Aula. 2011. 350p. 49.00 ***(978-82-90128-73-4(8))*** Oslo kommunes kunstsamlinger NOR. Dist: International Specialized Bk. Services.

Letscher, Lance. Lance Letscher: Collage. collector's ed. 2010. (ENG., Illus.). 224p. 250.00 *(978-0-292-72395-5(4))* Univ. of Texas Pr.

Levi, Corrado. E' Andata Cosi: Cronaca e Critica Delle'Atre 1970-2008. 2009. (ITA., Illus.). 160p. pap. 54.50 *(978-88-370-6819-6(0))* Electa ITA. Dist: Trans-Atlantic Pubns., Inc.

Levinson, Drunell. Art at the Margins. 2009. 168p. pap. *(978-3-639-17386-4(4))* VDM Verlag Dr. Mueller e.K.

Lias, Stephen, ed. Contemporary Art Music in Texas. 2011. (ENG., Illus.). 60p. pap. 19.95 ***(978-1-936205-15-8(7))*** Austin, Stephen F. State Univ. Pr.

Liss, Andrea. Feminist Art & the Maternal. 2009. (Illus.). 192p. 75.00 *(978-0-8166-4622-7(6));* pap. 24.95 *(978-0-8166-4623-4(6))* Univ. of Minnesota Pr.

Logan, Melissa & Murray-Leslie, Alex. Don't Art, Fashion, Music: Chicks on Speed. 2010. (ENG., Illus.). 208p. pap. 35.00 *(978-1-86154-319-6(0))* Booth-Clibborn Editions GBR. Dist: Hachette Bk. Group.

Lombardi, Laura. From Realism to Art Nouveau. 2009. (ENG., Illus.). 192p. pap. 14.95 *(978-1-4027-5926-0(6))* Sterling Publishing Co., Inc.

Lucas, Sarah & Garbay, Olivier, photos by. The MUG. 2009. (ENG., Illus.). 640p. 125.00 *(978-1-904212-51-5(4))* Other Criteria GBR. Dist: Hachette Bk. Group.

MacDonald, Rory & Irwin, Kathleen, eds. Sighting, Citing, Siting: Crossfiring/Mama Wetotan: Theorising Practice. 2009. (University of Regina Publications (UR) Ser.). (ENG., Illus.). 208p. mass mkt. 40.00 *(978-0-88977-228-1(2))* Canadian Plains Research Ctr. CAN. Dist: Univ. of Toronto Pr.

Malagrida, Anna & TF Editores, C. A. Anna Malagrida. 2011. (Illus.). 200p. 58.00 *(978-84-92441-00-6(3),* T.F. Editores, S.L.C.) Antique Collectors' Club GBR. Dist: National Bk. Network.

Malik, Amna & Malik, A. Sarah Lucas: Au Naturel. 2009. (One Work Ser.). (ENG., Illus.). 112p. (gr. 17). pap. 16.00 *(978-1-84638-054-9(5))* Afterall Publishing GBR. Dist: MIT Pr.

Malpas, William. Land Art: A complete guide to landscape, environmental, earthworks, nature, scupture & installation Art. 2nd ed. 2008. (Illus.). 302p. 75.00 *(978-1-86171-232-5(4))* Crescent Moon Publishing GBR. Dist: NACSCORP, Inc.

—Land Art in Close-up. 2007. (Illus.). 288p. pap. 40.00 *(978-1-86171-052-9(6))* Crescent Moon Publishing GBR. Dist: Gardners Bks. Ltd.

Mannari, Enrica. Pink Attitude: The Contemporary Female Creativity. 2008. (Illus.). 218p. *(978-88-86416-72-6(5))* Happy Bks.

Markin, Tracy Kamenstein. The Markin Collection. 2007. (Illus.). 443p. *(978-0-9793194-0-2(4))* ToTo The Outsider Pub.

Marter, Joan, ed. Abstract Expressionism: The International Context. 2007. (Na Ser.). (ENG., Illus.). 320p. pap. 29.95 *(978-0-8135-3975-1(7))* Rutgers Univ. Pr.

Mauche, Jérôme & Raguénès, Loïc. Loïc Raguénès: Autant Que Faire Se Peut. 2009. (FRE., Illus.). 93p. *(978-2-84066-341-6(4))* les presses du reel.

Mavridorakis, Valerie, ed. Francis Baudevin: Hello Spiral. 2009. (ENG., Illus.). 72p. pap. 15.00 *(978-3-905829-69-3(X))* JRP Ringier Kunstverlag AG CHE. Dist: D.A.P./Distributed Art Pubs.

McCarthy, Laurette E. & Pach, Walter. Walter Pach (1883-1958) The Armory Show & the Untold Story of Modern Art in America. 2011. (ENG.). 272p. 59.95 *(978-0-271-03740-0(7))* Pennsylvania State Univ. Pr.

McEvilley, Thomas. The Triumph of Anti-Art: Conceptual & Performance Art in the Formation of Post-Modernism. 2012. (ENG., Illus.). 391p. pap. 23.00 *(978-0-929701-92-9(5),* Documentext) McPherson & Co.

—Yves the Provocateur: Yves Klein & Twentieth-Century Art. 2010. (Illus.). 272p. 27.00 *(978-0-929701-91-2(7))* McPherson & Co.

McGregor, Ken & Zimmer, Jenny. Tim Storrier. 2007. (Macmillan Mini-Art Ser.). (Illus.). 144p. (C). 35.00 *(978-1-921394-12-6(9))* Macmillan Art Publishing AUS. Dist: Brown, David Bk. Co., The.

McMenamin, Donna. Popular Arts of Mexico, 1850-1950. 2nd rev. ed. 2009. (ENG & SPA., Illus.). 240p. 59.99 *(978-0-7643-3284-5(8))* Schiffer Publishing, Ltd.

McPherson, Tara. Lost Constellations: The Art of Tara McPherson. 2011. (Illus.). 112p. 22.99 *(978-1-59582-222-2(4))* Dark Horse Comics.

Mercer, Kobena, ed. Discrepant Abstraction. 2006. (Annotating Art's Histories Ser.: Vol. 2). (ENG., Illus.). 224p. (gr. 17). pap. 27.00 *(978-0-262-63337-6(X))* MIT Pr.

Meskimmon. Contemporary Art & the Cosmopolitan Imagination: Politics, Ethics, Affect. 2010. (ENG., Illus.). 144p. (C). 37.95 *(978-0-415-46920-3(1));* 110.00 *(978-0-415-46919-7(8))* Routledge.

Meyer, Richard & Int'l Center of Photography. Naked Hollywood: Weegee in Los Angeles. 2011. (ENG., Illus.). 144p. 45.00 ***(978-0-8478-3762-5(9),*** Skira) Rizzoli International Pubns., Inc.

Mileaf, Janine. Please Touch: Dada & Surrealist Objects after the Readymade. 2010. (Interfaces: Studies in Visual Culture Ser.). (Illus.). 312p. (C). 85.00 *(978-1-58465-882-5(7));* pap. 39.95 *(978-1-58465-934-1(3))* Univ. Pr. of New England. (Dartmouth College Press).

Miller, Harland & Stillman, Nick. Recent Wurg. 2009. (ENG., Illus.). 36p. 50.00 *(978-1-906967-13-0(X))* Other Criteria GBR. Dist: Hachette Bk. Group.

—Recent Wurg: Ashley Bickerton. aut. ed. 2009. (ENG.). 36p. 80.00 *(978-1-906967-14-7(8))* Other Criteria GBR. Dist: Hachette Bk. Group.

Millett-Gallant, Ann. The Disabled Body in Contemporary Art. (ENG., Illus.). 2012. 188p. pap. 27.00 ***(978-0-230-34142-5(X))*** 2010. 192p. 79.00 *(978-0-230-10406-8(1))* Palgrave Macmillan.

Mitter, Partha. The Triumph of Modernism: India's Artists & the Avant-Garde, 1922-1947. 2007. (ENG., Illus.). 256p. pap. 45.00 *(978-1-86189-318-5(3))* Reaktion Bks., Ltd. GBR. Dist: Chicago Distribution Ctr.

Moineau, Jean-Claude. Retour du Futur: L'art à Contre-Courant. 2010. (FRE.). 367p. *(978-2-915453-59-1(4),* Spotlight Poets) Ere.

Mondadori Electa, ed. Museo del Novecento: The Collection. 2010. 373p. 75.00 *(978-88-370-7992-5(3))* Electa ITA. Dist: Trans-Atlantic Pubns., Inc.

Moriceau, Benoît-Marie, et al. Psycho: [conversation Avec Benoît-Marie Moriceau]. 2010. (FRE & ENG., Illus.). 66p. *(978-2-36008-025-0(3))* Archibooks.

Morley, Simon, ed. The Sublime. 2010. (Documents of Contemporary Art Ser.). (ENG.). 237p. (gr. 17). pap. 24.95 *(978-0-262-51391-3(9))* MIT Pr.

Morris, Catherine, ed. 9 Evenings Reconsidered: Art, Theatre, & Engineering 1966, 1 vol. 2006. (ENG., Illus.). 88p. per. 25.00 *(978-0-938437-69-7(0))* Massachusetts Institute of Technology, List Visual Arts Ctr.

Morris, Francis, ed. The Tate Modern Handbook. 2nd ed. 2006. (ENG., Illus.). 240p. pap. 35.00 *(978-1-85437-577-3(6))* Tate Publishing, Ltd. GBR. Dist: Hachette Bk. Group.

Muller, Franz. Martin Disler. 2007. (Illus.). 272p. 152.00 ***(978-3-85881-179-0(3))*** Scheidegger und Spiess AG, Verlag CHE. Dist: Antique Collectors' Club.

Muller, Lars & Miki, Akiko, eds. Insular Insight: Where Art & Architecture Conspire with Nature. 2011. (ENG., Illus.). 480p. 70.00 ***(978-3-03778-255-2(2))*** Lars Muller Pubs. CHE. Dist: Prestel Publishing.

Mumford, Eric, et al. Hans Hofmann: the Chimbote Project: The Synergistic Promise of Modern Art & Urban Architecture. 2007. (Illus.). 133p. *(978-84-89771-07-9(3))* Actar Birkhauser Distribution.

Mumford, Lewis. Mumford on Modern Art in The 1930s. Wojtowicz, Robert, ed. 2006. (Illus.). 265p. 45.00 *(978-0-520-24858-8(9))* Univ. of California Pr.

Mumford, Robert & Mumford, Lewis. Mumford on Modern Art in The 1930s. Wojtowicz, Robert, ed. 2008. (Illus.). 288p. pap. 22.95 *(978-0-520-25808-2(8))* Univ. of California Pr.

Munder, Heike. It's Time for Action (There's No Option) About Feminism. 2008. (GER & ENG., Illus.). 164p. 39.00 *(978-3-905770-53-7(9))* JRP Ringier Kunstverlag AG CHE. Dist: D.A.P./Distributed Art Pubs.

Museum of Fine Arts, Houston Staff, contrib. by. Core: Artists & Critics in Residence. 2008. (Illus.). 206p. *(978-0-89090-162-5(7))* Museum of Fine Arts, Houston.

Napp, Antonia & Röder, Kornelia, eds. Impuls Marcel Duchamp: Where do we go from here? 2011. (ENG & GER., Illus.). 208p. pap. 30.00 ***(978-3-7757-3182-9(2))*** Hatje Cantz Verlag GmbH & Co KG DEU. Dist: D.A.P./Distributed Art Pubs.

National Museum of the American Indian (U.S.) Staff, contrib. by. Essays on Native Modernism: Complexity & Contradiction in American Indian Art. 2006. (NMAI Editions Ser.). (Illus.). 112p. *(978-1-933565-02-6(0))* Smithsonian National Museum of the American Indian.

Nead, Lynda. The Haunted Gallery: Painting, Photography, Film C. 1900. 2008. (ENG., Illus.). 256p. 40.00 *(978-0-300-11291-7(2))* Yale Univ. Pr.

Neumark, Norie & Chandler, Annmarie, eds. At a Distance: Precursors to Art & Activism on the Internet. 2006. (Leonardo Bks.). (ENG., Illus.). 496p. (gr. 17). per. 19.95 *(978-0-262-53285-3(9))* MIT Pr.

Noble, Richard & Noble, R. Utopias. Noble, Richard, ed. 2009. (Documents of Contemporary Art Ser.). (ENG., Illus.). 240p. (gr. 17). pap. 24.95 *(978-0-262-64069-5(4))* MIT Pr.

Noever, Peter, ed. & text. 20/21: MAK Collection of Contemporary Art. 2010. (ENG., Illus.). 244p. pap. 40.00 *(978-3-941185-29-6(2))* Verlag fur Moderne Kunst DEU. Dist: D.A.P./Distributed Art Pubs.

Obrist, Hans Ulrich, ed. Hans Ulrich Obrist & Christian Boltanski: the Conversation Series. 2009. (ENG., Illus.). 234p. pap. 34.00 *(978-3-86560-513-9(3))* Verlag der Buchhandlung Walther Konig DEU. Dist: D.A.P./Distributed Art Pubs.

—Hans Ulrich Obrist & Rosemarie Trockel: the Conversation Series. 2012. (ENG., Illus.). 128p. pap. 22.00 *(978-3-86560-170-4(7))* Verlag der Buchhandlung Walther Konig DEU. Dist: D.A.P./Distributed Art Pubs.

O'Doherty, Brian. Christo & Jeanne-Claude: Remembering the Running Fence, Sonoma & Marin Counties, California, 1972-1976. 2010. (ENG., Illus.). 178p. 49.95 *(978-0-520-26646-9(3))* Univ. of California Pr.

Oehlen, Albert. Albert Oehlen: 1991-2008. 2009. (ENG & GER., Illus.). 88p. 50.00 *(978-3-935567-48-0(0))* Holzwarth Pubns. DEU. Dist: D.A.P./Distributed Art Pubs.

Olbricht, Thomas. Rockers Island Olbricht Collection: Museum Folkwang, 1 vol. 2008. (ENG., Illus.). 288p. 50.00 *(978-3-86521-471-3(1))* Steidl, Gerhard Druckerei und Verlag DEU. Dist: Innovative Logistics.

Oldknow, Tina & Russell, Cristine. Voices of Contemporary Glass: The Heineman Collection. 2009. (ENG., Illus.). 382p. 85.00 *(978-1-55595-314-0(X))* Hudson Hills Pr. LLC.

Oliva, Achille Bonito. Encyclopaedia of the World: Artist Dialogues, 1968-2008. 2010. (ENG., Illus.). 414p. 45.00 *(978-88-572-0463-5(4))* Skira Editore ITA. Dist: Random Hse., Inc.

Oliver, Valerie Cassel, ed. & text. Ben Patterson: in the State of Fluxus. 2012. (ENG., Illus.). 260p. pap. 34.95 *(978-1-933619-29-3(5))* Contemporary Arts Museum, Houston.

O'Neill, Paul, ed. & text. Neighbourhood Secrets. 2010. (ENG., Illus.). 384p. pap. 60.00 *(978-82-7547-349-1(7))* Pr., Forlaget NOR. Dist: D.A.P./Distributed Art Pubs.

O'Reilly, Sally. The Body in Contemporary Art. 2009. (World of Art Ser.). (ENG., Illus.). 224p. pap. 19.95 *(978-0-500-20400-9(4),* 520400) Thames & Hudson.

Orenduff, Lai-Kent Chew. The Transformation of Catholic Religious Art in the Twentieth Century: Father Marie-Alain Couturier & the Church at Assy, France. 2008. (Illus.). 212p. 109.95 *(978-0-7734-4985-5(X))* Mellen, Edwin Pr., The.

Orlan, illus. Orlan: The Narrative/le Recit. 2008. (FRE & ENG.). 336p. 75.00 *(978-88-8158-652-3(5))* Charta ITA. Dist: D.A.P./Distributed Art Pubs.

Osthoff, Simone. Performing the Archive: The transformation of the archive in Contemporary art from repository of documents to art Medium. Schirmacher, Wolfgang, ed. 2009. (Illus.). 208p. pap. 21.95 *(978-0-9825309-0-0(0))* Atropos Pr.

Ottmann, Klaus. Thought Through My Eyes: Writings on Art, 1977-2005. 2006. (Art & Knowledge Ser.: Vol. 2). (ENG., Illus.). 224p. per. 22.00 (978-0-88214-578-5(9)) Spring Pubns., Inc.

Paglia, Michael & Chandler, Mary Voetz. Colorado Abstract: Paintings & Sculpture. 2009. (ENG., Illus.). 319p. 85.00 (978-1-934491-12-6(8)) Fresco Fine Art Pubns., LLC.

Palencar, John Jude. Origins: The Art of John Jude Palencar. Fenner, Arnie & Fenner, Cathy, eds. 2007. (ENG., Illus.). 128p. 27.00 (978-1-59929-004-1(9)) Underwood Books.

Panza, Giuseppe. Giuseppe Panza: Memories of a Collector. 2008. (ENG., Illus.). 416p. pap. 37.50 (978-0-7892-0944-3(6)) Abbeville Pr., Inc.

Papadakis, Alexandra & Papadakis, Andreas, eds. Innovations: From Experimentation to Realisation. 2006. (ENG., Illus.). pap. 30.00 (978-1-901092-46-2(1)) Papadakis Dist A/C.

Paparoni, Demetrio, ed. Eretica: The Transcendent & the Profane in Contemporary Art. 2007. (ENG., Illus.). 264p. pap. 24.95 (978-88-6130-069-9(3)) Skira Editore ITA. Dist: Random Hse., Inc.

Parkett Publishers, creator. Autumn 2006: Trisha Donnelly, Carsten H'ller & Rudolf Stingel, 1 vol. 2006. (ENG., Illus.). 300p. pap. 32.00 (978-3-907582-37-4(3)) Parkett Verlag AG CHE. Dist: D.A.P./Distributed Art Pubs.

Parrella, Christiana. Kutlug Ataaman: Mesopotamian Dramaturgies. 2011. (ENG., Illus.). 112p. pap. 55.00 (978-88-370-7578-1(2)) Electa ITA. Dist: National Bk. Network.

Pasini, Roberto. Il Vuoto Nell'arte Contemporanea. 2010. (ITA., Illus.). 174p. (978-88-6464-051-8(7)) QuiEdit.

Passion Bild: Russische Kunst seit 1970. 2010. (Illus.). 280p. 171.00 **(978-3-85881-199-8(8))** Scheidegger und Spiess AG, Verlag CHE. Dist: Antique Collectors' Club.

Paunero, Daniel & Daniel, Paunero. S/T (Sin Titulo) La Exposición Como Taller. 2010. (SPA., Illus.). 67p. (978-84-441-0244-3(X)) Centro Atlantico de Arte Moderno.

Payne, John. Framing the Nineteenth Century: Picture Frames, 1837-1935. Owen, Wendy, ed. 2007. (ENG., Illus.). 128p. 35.00 (978-1-86470-199-9(4)) Images Publishing Group AUS. Dist: National Bk. Network.

Pedersen, B. Martin, Jr. Graphis Branding 5. 2009. (Illus.). 256p. 70.00 (978-1-932026-20-7(7)) Graphis, U.S., Inc.

Peffer, John. Art & the End of Apartheid. 2009. (ENG., Illus.). 352p. 90.00 (978-0-8166-5001-9(2)); pap. 29.95 (978-0-8166-5002-6(0)) Univ. of Minnesota Pr.

Pejic, Bojana, ed. Gender Check: A Reader. 2011. (ENG.). 380p. pap. 39.95 (978-3-86560-883-3(3)) Verlag der Buchhandlung Walther Konig DEU. Dist: D.A.P./Distributed Art Pubs.

Peng, Lu. A Pocket History of 20th-Century Chinese Art. 2011. (ENG., Illus.). 1124p. pap. 59.95 (978-88-8158-796-4(3)) Charta ITA. Dist: D.A.P./Distributed Art Pubs.

Peng, Lu. Pure Views: Remote from Streams & Mountains: New Painting from China. 2011. (ENG., Illus.). 208p. pap. 55.00 **(978-88-8158-821-3(8))** Charta ITA. Dist: D.A.P./Distributed Art Pubs.

Peppiatt, Michael. Interviews with Artists, 1966-2011. 2012. (ENG., Illus.). 434p. 40.00 **(978-0-300-17662-9(7))** Yale Univ. Pr.

Perez-Barreiro, Gabriel. Contemporary Art in Latin America. Monem, Nadine & Kotsopoulos, Nikos, eds. 2010. (ENG., Illus.). 240p. 49.95 (978-1-906155-64-3(X)) Black Dog Publishing Ltd. GBR. Dist: Perseus Distribution.

Perry, Mike. Wondering Around Wandering: Work-So-Far by Mike Perry. 2012. (ENG., Illus.). 248p. 39.95 **(978-0-8478-3803-3(0))** Rizzoli International Pubns., Inc.

Petrovich, Dushko & White, Roger, eds. Paper Monument. 2007. 100p. per. 10.00 (978-0-9797575-0-1(9)) Paper Monument.

Phelan, Peggy, ed. Live Art in La. 2012. (ENG., Illus.). 256p. 125.00 **(978-0-415-68422-4(6))**; pap. 39.95 **(978-0-415-68423-1(4))** Routledge.

Philipsen, Lotte. Globalizing the Art World: The Impact of New Internationalism in Contemporary. 2010. (ENG., Illus.). 214p. (C). pap. 45.00 (978-87-7934-507-9(3)) Aarhus Universitetsforlag DNK. Dist: ISD.

Phillips, John & Doniger, Wendy. John Ransom Phillips: A Contemporary Book of the Dead. 2009. (ENG., Illus.). 328p. 65.00 (978-1-55595-315-7(8)) Hudson Hills Pr. LLC.

Poli, Francesco. Post-Modern Art, 1945-2008. 2008. (ENG., Illus.). 400p. 60.00 (978-0-06-166577-6(0), Collins Design) HarperCollins Pubs.

Pollack, Barbara, text. The Wild, Wild East: an American Art Critic's Adventures in China. 2010. (ENG., Illus.). 208p. pap. 24.95 (978-988-18034-9-8(7)) Timezone 8 Ltd. HKG. Dist: D.A.P./Distributed Art Pubs.

Powers, John S. Temporary Art & Public Place: Comparing Berlin with Los Angeles. 2009. (Europäische Hochschulschriften. Reihe 28: Kunstgeschichte Ser.). (Illus.). 404p. pap. 99.95 (978-3-631-56430-1(9)) Lang, Peter GmbH, Europaischer Verlag der Wissenschaften DEU. Dist: Lang, Peter.

Pratt, Elspeth & Slade, Kathy. Elspeth Pratt. 2012. (ENG.). 144p. 39.95 **(978-0-921356-37-0(4))** Scott, Charles H. Gallery, Emily Carr College of Art & Design CAN. Dist: D.A.P./Distributed Art Pubs.

Pucci, Ralph & Goodman, Wendy. Wall. 2011. (ENG., Illus.). 128p. 30.00 (978-0-9823799-8-1(6)) Glitterati, Inc.

Rancière, Jacques. The Future of the Image. Elliott, Gregory, tr. from FRE. 2009. (ENG.). 160p. pap. 17.95 (978-1-84467-297-4(2), 844297) Verso Bks. GBR. Dist: Norton, W. W. & Co., Inc.

Ravenal, John B. Modern & Contemporary Art at the Virginia Museum of Fine Arts. 2007. (ENG., Illus.). 252p. 19.50 (978-0-917046-80-3(3)) Virginia Museum of Fine Arts.

Raw Vision #37. pap. 13.00 (978-1-56466-088-6(5)) Archer Fields, Inc.

Reckitt, Helena. Art & Feminism. 2006. (SPA.). 49.95 (978-0-7148-9836-0(8)) Phaidon Pr., Inc.

Reckitt, Helena, ed. Art & Feminism. 2012. (ENG., Illus.). 204p. pap. 19.95 **(978-0-7148-6391-7(2))** Phaidon Pr., Inc.

Renfert, Christof. Melancholie und Expressionismus. (GER.). 160p. pap. 40.95 (978-3-631-56865-1(7)) Lang, Peter GmbH, Europaischer Verlag der Wissenschaften DEU. Dist: Lang, Peter Publishing, Inc.

Rewald, Sabine & Dabrowski, Magdalena. The American Matisse: The Dealer, His Artists, His Collection. 2010. (ENG., Illus.). 208p. 60.00 (978-0-300-15510-5(7)) Yale Univ. Pr.

—The American Matisse: The Dealer, His Artists, His Collection: The Pierre & Maria-Gaetana Matisse Collection. 2010. (Illus.). ix, 195p. 60.00 (978-1-58839-352-4(6)) Metropolitan Museum of Art, The.

Rhodes, Zandra & Knight, Anne. Art of Zandra Rhodes. Date not set. 49.95 (978-1-85479-997-5(5)) O'Mara, Michael Bks., Ltd. GBR. Dist: Trans-Atlantic Pubns., Inc.

Ribalta, Jorge, text. Relational Objects: Macba Collection 2002-2007. 2010. (ENG.). 272p. pap. 39.95 (978-84-92505-12-8(5)) Museu d'Art Contemporani de Barcelona ESP. Dist: Actar Birkhauser Distribution.

Roberts, David. The Total Work of Art in European Modernism. 2011. (Signale: Modern German Letters, Cultures, & Thought Ser.). 304p. pap. 37.50 (978-0-8014-5023-5(3)) Cornell Univ. Pr.

Robertson, Jean & McDaniel, Craig. Themes of Contemporary Art: Visual Art After 1980. (ENG., Illus.). (C). 2nd ed. 2009. 352p. pap. 39.95 (978-0-19-536757-7(X)) 3rd ed. 2012. 416p. pap. 39.95 **(978-0-19-979707-3(2))** Oxford Univ. Pr., Inc.

Robinson, Julia, ed. New Realisms, 1957-1962: Object Strategies Between Readymade & Spectacle. 2010. (ENG., Illus.). 294p. (gr. 17). pap. 44.95 (978-0-262-51522-1(9)) MIT Pr.

Rondeau, James. Judith Neisser Collection: Minimal & Postminimal Innovation. 2011. (Contemporary Collecting Ser.). (ENG., Illus.). 160p. 35.00 (978-0-300-17024-5(6)) Art Institute of Chicago.

Roojen, Pepin Van. Psychedelic. 2012. (ENG., Illus.). 320p. pap. 44.99 incl. audio compact disk **(978-94-6009-009-7(5))** Pepin Pr. NLD. Dist: National Bk. Network.

Rosen, Barry, ed. Dieter Roth. 2010. (ENG., Illus.). 238p. 45.00 (978-0-300-17079-5(3)) Yale Univ. Pr.

Rosen, Kay. Kay Rosen: AKAK. 2010. (ENG., Illus.). 232p. 49.95 (978-0-9815449-5-3(9)) Regency Arts Pr.

Rosenberg, David. Art Game Book. 2010. (ENG.). 400p. 45.00 (978-2-7594-0483-4(8)) Assouline FRA. Dist: Perseus Distribution.

Ross, Christine. The Past Is the Present; It's the Future Too: The Temporal Turn in Contemporary Art. 2012. (ENG., Illus.). 336p. 160.00 **(978-1-4411-1604-8(4))** Continuum International Publishing Group, Ltd. GBR. Dist: National Bk. Network.

Rubin, Susan Goldman. Breaking the Rules: What Is Contemporary Art? 2010. (978-1-933751-15-3(0)) Museum of Contemporary Art, Los Angeles.

Ruf, Beatrix, ed. A Refusal to Accept Limits. 2010. (ENG & GER., Illus.). 168p. pap. 55.00 (978-3-03764-032-6(4)) JRP Ringier Kunstverlag AG CHE. Dist: D.A.P./Distributed Art Pubs.

Rush, Michael. The Rose Art Museum Collection. 2009. (ENG., Illus.). 288p. 60.00 (978-0-8109-5574-5(1)) Abrams.

Russell, Charles. Groundwaters: A Century of Art by Self-Taught & Outsider Artists. 2011. (ENG., Illus.). 256p. 65.00 **(978-3-7913-4490-4(0))** Prestel Publishing.

Saatchi Gallery Staff. The Revolution Continues: New Art from China. 2008. (ENG., Illus.). 272p. 29.95 (978-0-8478-3206-4(6)) Rizzoli International Pubns., Inc.

Saltzman, Lisa. Making Memory Matter: Strategies of Remembrance in Contemporary Art. 2006. (ENG., Illus.). 128p. 55.00 (978-0-226-73407-1(2)); per. 22.00 (978-0-226-73408-8(0)) Univ. of Chicago Pr.

Sandifer, Rosie. Rosie Sandifer: Language of Art. 2007. (ENG., Illus.). 184p. 75.00 (978-0-9679034-3-9(2)) Fresco Fine Art Pubns., LLC.

Schädler-Saub, Ursula & Weyer, Angela. Theory & Practice in the Conservation of Modern & Contemporary Art: Reflections on the Roots & the Perspectives. 2010. (ENG., Illus.). 210p. 90.00 (978-1-904982-54-8(9)) Archetype Pubns. GBR. Dist: National Bk. Network.

Schapiro, Meyer. Modern Art: 19th & 20th Centuries - Selected Papers. 2011. (ENG., Illus.). 278p. pap. 27.95 (978-0-8076-1607-9(9), 761607) Braziller, George Inc.

Schavemaker, Margriet & Rakier, Mischa. Right about Now: Art & Theory since the 1990s, 1 vol. 2008. (ENG., Illus.). 184p. pap. 29.95 (978-90-78088-17-2(6)) Valiz NLD. Dist: D.A.P./Distributed Art Pubs.

Scheel, Werner & Bering, Kunibert. Kunst und Asthetik. (GER., Illus.). 208p. (978-3-496-01168-2(8)) Reimer, Dietrich.

Schellmann, Jorg, ed. Forty Are Better Than One: Contemporary Art Production Munchen New York 1969-2009. 2010. (ENG., Illus.). 456p. 70.00 (978-3-7757-2236-0(X)) Hatje Cantz Verlag GmbH & Co KG DEU. Dist: D.A.P./Distributed Art Pubs.

Schinzel, Hiltrud. Touching Vision: Essays on Restoration Theory & the Perception of Art. 2008. (ENG., Illus.). 262p. pap. 28.95 (978-90-5487-352-5(3)) VUB Univ. Pr. BEL. Dist: Independent Pubs. Group.

Schmidt, Christoph. Vom Messias zum Prolet: Arbeiter in der Kunst. 2010. (GER., Illus.). 132p. (C). pap. 44.00 (978-3-515-09808-3(9)) Steiner, Franz Verlag Wiesbaden GmbH DEU. Dist: Brown, David Bk. Co., The.

Schulz-Hoffmann, Carla, ed. Niki de Saint Phalle: My Art, My Dreams. 2008. (Illus.). 176p. pap. 39.95 (978-3-7913-3984-9(2)) Prestel Publishing.

Schumacher, Rogier. Neo-avant-garde in Nederland: Museumjournaal als forum van een nieuw Kunstbegrip. 2010. (DUT., Illus.). 368p. pap. (978-90-8964-070-3(3)) Amsterdam Univ. Pr.

Sedley, Jeremy. New Art International. 178p. Vol. 9. pap. 9.95 (978-0-9713859-3-1(9)) Vol. IX. (Illus.). 24.00 (978-0-9713859-2-4(0)) Bk. Art Pr.

Sedley, Jeremy, compiled by. New Art International. 2008. (ENG.). 26.00 (978-0-9773540-6-1(7)) Bk. Art Pr.

Sedley, Jeremy, et al, eds. New Art International: A Compendium of Recent Works by Contemporary Artist, Volume XI. 11th ed. 2007. (New Art International Ser.). (ENG., Illus.). 152p. 26.00 (978-0-9773540-2-3(4)) Bk. Art Pr.

—New Art International, Volume 12: A Compendium of Recent Works by World Contemporary Artists. 2008. (New Art International Ser.). (Illus.). 179p. 26.00 (978-0-9773540-4-7(0)) A.R.T. Pr.

Selby, Art & Text. Monem, Nadine, ed. 2009. (ENG., Illus.). 288p. 45.00 (978-1-906155-65-0(8)) Black Dog Publishing Ltd. GBR. Dist: Perseus Distribution.

Sevsnen, Erkki. Towards a New Kind of System of Art: The Shift from the Modern to the Contemporary Sphereof Art from the Standpoint of System-Theoretical andSystemic Sociology. 2008. 160p. pap. (978-3-639-09893-8(5)) VDM Verlag Dr. Mueller e.K.

Shchurik, Natalia Leonidovna. Kuban I Velikie Pobedy Rossii: V Tvorchestve Khudozhnikov Krasnodarskogo Kraia. 2010. (RUS., Illus.). 157p. (978-5-91050-082-6(1)) Diapazon-V.

Shifrin, Susan. Re-Framing Representations of Women: Figuring, Fashioning, Portraiting, & Telling in the 'Picturing' Women Project. Shifrin, Susan, ed. 2008. (Illus.). 354p. 149.95 (978-0-7546-6077-4(X)) Ashgate Publishing Co.

Silver, Kenneth E. Paris Portraits: Artists, Friends, & Lovers. 2008. (ENG., Illus.). 144p. 50.00 (978-0-300-14543-4(8)) Yale Univ. Pr.

SLC Visual Art Review. Sarah Lawrence Visual Art Review. 2010. pap. 14.99 (978-0-578-05594-7(5)) SLCVAR.

Smith, Karen, ed. Nine Lives: the Birth of Avant-Garde Art in New China. 2008. (ENG., Illus.). 473p. pap. 50.00 (978-988-17143-3-6(8)) Timezone 8 Ltd. HKG. Dist: D.A.P./Distributed Art Pubs.

Smith, Patti. Trois. 2008. (ENG.). 96p. pap. 45.00 (978-0-500-97686-9(4)) Thames & Hudson.

Smith, Terry. Contemporary Art: World Currents. 2011. (ENG., Illus.). 304p. (C). pap. 68.00 **(978-0-205-78971-9(4))**, Prentice Hall) Prentice Hall PTR.

Smith, Terry. What Is Contemporary Art? 2009. (Illus.). 300p. 66.66 (978-0-226-76430-6(3)); (ENG., 344p. pap. 25.00 (978-0-226-76431-3(1)) Univ. of Chicago Pr.

Smith, Tracey. Creative Relationships. 2009. 77p. pap. 24.96 (978-1-4092-7946-4(4)) Lulu Enterprises Inc.

Spain, Sharon. Asian American Art: A History, 1850-1970. Chang, Gordon H. et al, eds. 2008. (Asian America Ser.). (ENG.). 576p. pap. 39.95 (978-0-8047-5752-2(6)); (Illus.). 80.00 (978-0-8047-5751-5(8)) Stanford Univ. Pr. (Stanford General Bks.).

Spalding, Frances. The Bloomsbury Group. 2006. (National Portrait Gallery Insights Ser.). (Illus.). 108p. 19.95 (978-1-85514-351-7(8)) National Portrait Gallery Pubns. GBR. Dist: Antique Collectors' Club.

Speer, George V. Things of the Spirit: Art & Healing in the American Body Politic, 1929-1941. 2012. 258p. (C). 83.95 **(978-1-4331-1568-4(9))** Lang, Peter Publishing, Inc.

Spieker, Sven. The Big Archive: Art from Bureaucracy. 2008. (ENG., Illus.). 240p. (gr. 17). 27.95 (978-0-262-19570-6(4)) MIT Pr.

Spira, Andrew. The Avant-Garde Icon: Russian Avant-Garde Art & the Icon Painting Tradition. 2008. (Illus.). 224p. 100.00 (978-0-85331-975-7(8), Lund Humphries Pubs.) Ashgate Publishing, Ltd. GBR. Dist: Ashgate Publishing Co.

Spurlock, J. David & Wilshire, Patrick. Art of the Dragon: The Definitive Collection of Contemporary Dragon Painting. 2012. (ENG.). 136p. 39.95 (978-1-934331-43-9(0)); 132p. pap. 24.95 (978-1-934331-44-6(9)) Vanguard Productions.

Stallabrass, Julian. High Art Lite: The Rise & Fall of young british Art. rev. exp. ed. 2006. (ENG., Illus.). 356p. pap. 24.95 (978-1-84467-085-7(6), 844085) Verso Bks. GBR. Dist: Norton, W. W. & Co., Inc.

Stange, Raimar, ed. The Evil. 2007. (GER & ENG., Illus.). 118p. (978-3-8321-9000-2(7)) DuMont.

Steinberg, Leo. Other Criteria: Confrontations with Twentieth-Century Art. 2007. (Illus.). 448p. per. 37.50 (978-0-226-77185-4(7)) Univ. of Chicago Pr.

Steiner, Wendy. The Real Real Thing: The Model in the Mirror of Art. 2010. (Illus.). 240p. 32.50 (978-0-226-77219-6(5)) Univ. of Chicago Pr.

Stiles, Kristine & Selz, Peter. Theories & Documents of Contemporary Art: A Sourcebook of Artists' Writings. 2nd rev. exp. ed. 2012. (ENG., Illus.). 1135p. 75.00 (978-0-520-25374-2(4)); pap. 34.95 (978-0-520-25718-4(9)) Univ. of California Pr.

Stockebrand, Marianne, ed. Chinati: The Vision of Donald Judd. 2010. (ENG., Illus.). 328p. 65.00 (978-0-300-16939-3(6)) Yale Univ. Pr.

Story of Modern Art The. 2008. (Story of Ser.). 120p. 9.95 (978-0-8416-0358-5(8)) American Map Corp.

Strasser, Josef. 50 Bauhaus Icons You Should Know. 2009. (Illus.). 176p. pap. 19.95 (978-3-7913-4196-5(0)) Prestel Publishing.

Striker, Susan. Meet the Masters. 2011. 112p. pap. 61.99 **(978-1-4535-2540-1(8))** Xlibris Corp.

Strombotne, James. 78. 2007. (Illus.). 85p. 120.00 (978-0-9799393-0-3(5)) 78, Inc.

Strosberg, Eliane. The Human Figure & Jewish Culture. (ENG., Illus.). 208p. 2011. pap. 29.95 (978-0-7892-1056-2(8)) 2010. 45.00 (978-0-7892-1054-8(1)) Abbeville Pr., Inc.

Suh, H. Anna. Van Gogh's Letters: The Mind of the Artist in Paintings, Drawings, & Words, 1875-1890. 2010. (ENG., Illus.). 320p. pap. 19.95 (978-1-57912-859-3(9), 1579128599) Black Dog & Leventhal Pubs., Inc.

Szulakowska, Urszula. Alchemy in Contemporary Art. 2011. (Illus.). 236p. 114.95 (978-0-7546-6736-0(7)) Ashgate Publishing Co.

Taylor, Brandon. Urban Walls: A Generation of Collage in Europe & America. 2008. (ENG., Illus.). 184p. 60.00 (978-1-55595-288-4(7)) Hudson Hills Pr. LLC.

Tedeschi, Ermanno & Coen, Vittoria. Campolungo: The Sensitive Horizon of Contemporary Art. 2010. 144p. 44.95 (978-88-492-1730-8(7)) Gangemi ITA. Dist: International Publishers Marketing.

Terraroli, Valerio, ed. Neo-Avant-Gardes, Postmodern & Global Art, 1969-1999, Vol. 4. 2009. (ENG., Illus.). 432p. 60.00 (978-88-6130-642-4(X)) Skira Editore ITA. Dist: Random Hse., Inc.

Thompson, Chris. Felt: Fluxus, Joseph Beuys, & the Dalai Lama. 2011. (Illus.). 320p. 82.50 (978-0-8166-5354-6(2)); pap., pap. 27.50 (978-0-8166-5355-3(0)) Univ. of Minnesota Pr.

Thompson, Don. The $12 Million Stuffed Shark: The Curious Economics of Contemporary Art. 2010. (ENG., Illus.). 272p. pap. 17.00 (978-0-230-62059-9(0)) Palgrave Macmillan.

Thompson, Mary Shine, ed. The Fire I' the Flint: Essays on the Creative Imagination. 2009. (Illus.). 200p. 65.00 (978-1-84682-073-1(1)) Four Courts Pr. IRL. Dist: International Specialized Bk. Services.

Tomasula, Steve. The And Now Awards: The Best Innovative Writing. Archambeau, Robert & Schneiderman, Davis, eds. 2009. (ENG., Illus.). 400p. pap. 19.95 (978-0-9823156-0-6(0)) Lake Forest College Pr.

Tomkins, Calvin. Lives of the Artists. 2010. (ENG.). 272p. pap. 15.00 (978-0-8050-9144-1(0), Holt Paperback) Holt, Henry & Co.

Tong, Darlene. Contemporary Art Periodicals by Artists: Documentation & Index for the Decade of the Seventies. (Contemporary Documents Ser.). (Illus.). 400p. pap. (978-0-931818-03-5(6)) Contemporary Arts Pr.

Touchon, Cecil. Natural Born Fluxus - Childhood Event Scores by Fluxus Artists. 2009. 279p. pap. 24.51 (978-0-578-00333-7(3)) Ontological Museum Pubns.

Trans: Arts, Culture, Media. No. 6. 245p. pap. 15.00 (978-1-888209-03-7(8))No. 7. 203p. pap. 15.00 (978-1-888209-08-2(9))No. 8. 323p. pap. 15.00 (978-1-888209-09-9(7))No. 9 & 10. 400p. pap. 15.00 (978-1-888209-12-9(7)) PASSIM, Inc.

Tuli, Neville. Indian Contemporary Art Vol. 4: Books, Paintings & Sculpture. 2006. (Masterpieces & Museum-Quality Ser.). (ENG., Illus.). 208p. pap. 65.00 (978-1-890206-76-5(8)) Mapin Publishing Pvt. Ltd IND. Dist: National Bk. Network.

—Osian's Forty Masterpieces. 2006. (ENG., Illus.). 128p. 45.00 (978-1-890206-59-8(8)) Mapin Publishing Pvt. Ltd IND. Dist: National Bk. Network.

Tuli, Neville, text. Osian's Indian Contemporary Art: Null: Paintings, Drawings & Sculpture. 2006. (ENG., Illus.). 208p. pap. 65.00 (978-1-890206-84-0(9)) Mapin Publishing Pvt. Ltd IND. Dist: National Bk. Network.

Tworkov, Jack. The Extreme of the Middle: Writings of Jack Tworkov. Schor, Mira, ed. 2009. (ENG., Illus.). 480p. pap. 45.00 (978-0-300-14102-3(5)) Yale Univ. Pr.

Underwood, Tim, et al, eds. Shameless Art: 20th Century Genre & the Artists That Defined It. 2010. (ENG., Illus.). 112p. 15.00 (978-1-59929-051-5(0)) Underwood Books.

Utley, Gertje R., et al. A Fine Regard: Essays in Honor of Kirk Varnedoe. 2008. (Illus.). 356p. 54.95 (978-0-7546-6217-4(9)) Ashgate Publishing Co.

Vajay, Sigismond de. Of Bridges & Borders. 2010. (SPA & ENG., Illus.). 408p. 60.00 (978-3-03764-081-4(2)) JRP Ringier Kunstverlag AG CHE. Dist: D.A.P./Distributed Art Pubs.

Valli, Marc, ed. Elephant, Issue 5: The Art & Visual Culture Magazine. 2011. (Elephant Ser.). (ENG., Illus.). 208p. pap. 19.99 (978-90-77174-38-8(9)) Frame Pubs. NLD. Dist: Consortium Bk. Sales & Distribution.

Vardi, David, ed. Supermix: The Union of Diverse Contemporary Art in Miami. 2008. (ENG & SPA., Illus.). 303p. lib. bdg. 20.00 (978-0-9778621-3-9(5)) Edge Zones, Inc.

Vargas, George. Contemporary Chican@ Art: Color & Culture for a New America. 2010. (ENG., Illus.). 303p. pap. 27.95 (978-0-292-72117-3(X)) Univ. of Texas Pr.

Various Authors. Rubell Family Collection: Paintings. 2012. (ENG., Illus.). 240p. pap. 48.00 **(978-84-15253-35-8(4))** T.F. Editores ESP. Dist: National Bk. Network.

Velthuis, Olav. Talking Prices: Symbolic Meanings of Prices on the Market for Contemporary Art. 2007. (Princeton Studies in Cultural Sociology). (ENG., Illus.). 288p. (C). per. 22.95 (978-0-691-13403-1(0)) Princeton Univ. Pr.

Vergine, Lea. When Trash Becomes Art: Trash Rubbish Mongo. 2007. (ENG., Illus.). 176p. pap. 19.95 (978-88-7624-728-6(9)) Skira Editore ITA. Dist: Random Hse., Inc.

Vetter, Ingrid. Moderne Keramik des 20. Jahrhunderts: Bestandskatalog der Sammlung Hinder/Reimers des Landes Rheinland-Pfalz. 2008. (ENG &

A

GER., Illus.). 304p. 110.00 *(978-3-89790-275-6(3))* Arnoldsche Art Pubs. DEU. Dist: Antique Collectors' Club.

Vickery, Jonathan & Costello, Diarmuid, eds. Art: Key Contemporary Thinkers. 2007. (ENG.). 256p. pap. 26.95 *(978-1-84520-320-7(8))* Berg Pubs. GBR. Dist: Macmillan.

—Art: Key Contemporary Thinkers. 2007. (ENG.). 1p. 99.95 *(978-1-84520-319-1(4))* Berg Pubs. GBR. Dist: Macmillan.

Vine, Richard. New China, New Art: (Revised & Expanded Edition) 2nd rev. ed. 2011. (ENG., Illus.). 256p. pap. 39.95 ***(978-3-7913-4550-5(8))*** Prestel Publishing.

Vine, Richard. New China New Art: Zhongguo Dang Dai Yi Shu. 2008. (Illus.). 256p. 60.00 *(978-3-7913-3942-9(7))* Prestel Publishing.

Volk, Tina. Transfer und Rezeption des italienischen Futurismus in Frankreich: Kulturtransferprozesse im Bereich der Bildenden Kunst. 2009. 160p. pap. *(978-3-639-22136-7(2))* VDM Verlag Dr. Mueller e.K.

Von Wedel, Amelie, et al, eds. Korean Eye: Contemporary Korean Art. 2010. (ENG., Illus.). 390p. pap. 60.00 *(978-88-572-0467-3(7))* Skira Editore ITA. Dist: Random Hse., Inc.

Wagner-Koch, Elisabeth. Kunstszenarien in Unternehmen. (GER., Illus.). 230p. *(978-3-496-01196-5(3))* Reimer, Dietrich.

Walter Foster Creative Team Staff & Mollica, Patti. Modern Acrylics: Innovative Tools, Mediums, & Techniques for Today's Artist. 2011. (Artist's Studio Ser.). (ENG., Illus.). 64p. pap. 9.95 ***(978-1-60058-220-2(6)***, 1600582206) Foster, Walter Publishing, Inc.

Wang, Tianhua. Qiang Xiu Jing Pin Tu Yang Ji = Qiang Embroidery. 2009. (Illus.). 207p. *(978-7-5410-3848-8(2))* Sichuan Fine Arts Publishing Hse.

Ward, Robin. Math Art Fun: Activities for Discovering Mathematical Magic in Modern Art. 2012. (ENG., Illus.). 159p. pap. 16.95 *(978-1-933979-89-2(5))* Bright Sky Pr.

Weinberger, Lois. Lois Weinberger: Notes from the Hortus. (ENG & GER., Illus.). 88p. pap. *(978-3-89322-329-9(0))* Edition Cantz DEU. Dist: D.A.P./Distributed Art Pubs.

Welchman, John, ed. Black Sphinx: on the Comedic in Modern Art. 2010. (ENG., Illus.). 280p. pap. 34.95 *(978-3-905770-96-4(2))* JRP Ringier Kunstverlag AG CHE. Dist: D.A.P./Distributed Art Pubs.

Weller, Alan. Fairies & Elves Vector Motifs. 2011. (Dover Electronic Clip Art Ser.). (ENG.). 48p. pap. 19.95 *(978-0-486-99174-0(1))* Dover Pubns., Inc.

Weschler, Lawrence. Everything That Rises: A Book of Convergences. 2007. (ENG., Illus.). 200p. pap. 22.00 *(978-1-932416-86-2(2))* McSweeney's Publishing.

—Seeing Is Forgetting the Name of the Thing One Sees: Expanded Edition. exp. ed. 2009. (ENG., Illus.). 336p. pap. 26.95 *(978-0-520-25609-5(3))* Univ. of California Pr.

—Seeing Is Forgetting the Name of the Thing One Sees: Over Thirty Years of Conversations with Robert Irwin. exp. ed. 2009. (Illus.). 352p. 50.00 *(978-0-520-25608-8(5))* Univ. of California Pr.

Whitehead-Lopez, Rudy. The Intimate Real - Enpowering the Quiet Art. 2008. 76p. pap. *(978-3-639-07876-3(4))* VDM Verlag Dr. Mueller e.K.

Whitelaw, Anne, et al, eds. The Visual Arts in Canada: The Twentieth Century. 2011. (ENG., Illus.). 496p. pap. 59.95 *(978-0-19-543459-0(5))* Oxford Univ. Pr., Inc.

Whiteley, Nigel. Art & Pluralism: Lawrence Alloway's Cultural Criticism. 2012. (ENG., Illus.). 384p. 120.00 ***(978-1-84631-645-6(6))*** Liverpool Univ. Pr. GBR. Dist: Chicago Distribution Ctr.

Wiehager, Renate, ed. Charlotte Posenenske. 2009. (ENG., Illus.). 216p. 85.00 *(978-3-7757-2363-3(3))* Hatje Cantz Verlag GmbH & Co KG DEU. Dist: D.A.P./Distributed Art Pubs.

—Discourses in Painting: Painting, Prints, & Object Art from the Daimler Art Collection, 1908-2010. 2011. (ENG., Illus.). 360p. pap. 75.00 *(978-3-7757-2730-3(2))* Hatje Cantz Verlag GmbH & Co KG DEU. Dist: D.A.P./Distributed Art Pubs.

Willett, John. The Weimar Years: A Culture Cut Short. 2011. (ENG., Illus.). 160p. pap. 19.95 *(978-0-500-27311-1(1)*, 527311) Thames & Hudson.

Williams, Emmett. A Flexible History of Fluxus Facts & Fictions. 2007. (ENG., Illus.). 152p. 45.00 *(978-0-500-97664-7(3))* Thames & Hudson.

Williams, Gilda, ed. The Gothic. 2007. (Documents of Contemporary Art Ser.). (ENG.). 239p. (gr. 17). per. 24.95 *(978-0-262-73186-7(X))* MIT Pr.

Williams, Gregory H. Permission to Laugh: Humor & Politics in Contemporary German Art. 2012. (ENG., Illus.). 248p. 49.00 ***(978-0-226-89895-7(4))*** Univ. of Chicago Pr.

Willis, Gary. Art As Mime. 2010. 232p. pap. *(978-3-8383-1920-9(6))* Lambert Academic Publishing.

Wilson, Sarah. Visual World of French Theory: Figurations. 2010. (Illus.). 240p. 65.00 *(978-0-300-16281-3(2))* Yale Univ. Pr.

Winters, Terry. Terry Winters: Knotted Graphs. 2009. (ENG., Illus.). 104p. 60.00 *(978-1-880146-50-7(9))* Marks, Matthew Gallery.

Wolf, Rachel Rubin. Strokes of Genius: The Best of Drawing. 2007. (Strokes of Genius Ser.). (ENG., Illus.). 144p. 32.99 *(978-1-58180-861-2(5)*, North Light Bks.) F&W Media, Inc.

—Strokes of Genius 2: Light & Shadow. 2009. (Strokes of Genius Ser.). (ENG., Illus.). 144p. 32.99 *(978-1-60061-158-2(3)*, North Light Bks.) F&W Media, Inc.

Wong, Yoke-Sum. The Aesthetics of Cute in Contemporary Japanese Art. 2012. (Critical Studies in Gender, Sexuality, & Culture Ser.). (ENG., Illus.). 256p. 85.00 ***(978-0-230-10539-3(4))*** Palgrave Macmillan.

Yersin, Veronique, ed. Forde 1994-2009. 2010. (ENG., Illus.). 522p. pap. 45.00 *(978-3-03764-082-1(0))* JRP Ringier Kunstverlag AG CHE. Dist: D.A.P./Distributed Art Pubs.

Yount, Sylvia. Private Passion, Public Promise: The James W. & Frances G. Mcglothlin Collection of American Art. 2010. (ENG., Illus.). 96p. (gr. 17). 30.00 *(978-0-917046-95-7(1))* Univ. Pr. of Virginia.

Yvars, J, ed. Vision & Sign: The Painting of Rafols-Casamada, 1 vol. 2006. (ENG., Illus.). 328p. 80.00 *(978-84-343-1085-8(6))* Poligrafa, Ediciones, S. A. ESP. Dist: D.A.P./Distributed Art Pubs.

Zepke, Stephen & O'Sullivan, Simon, eds. Deleuze & Contemporary Art. 2010. (Deleuze Connections Ser.). (ENG., Illus.). 280p. (gr. 17). 115.00 *(978-0-7486-3837-6(7))*; pap. 35.00 *(978-0-7486-3838-3(5))* Edinburgh Univ. Pr. GBR. Dist: Columbia Univ. Pr.

Zijlmans, Kitty, et al, texts. Take Place. 2010. (ENG., Illus.). 288p. pap. 28.95 *(978-90-78088-35-6(4))* Valiz NLD. Dist: D.A.P./Distributed Art Pubs.

ART, MODERN—20TH CENTURY—EXHIBITIONS

Ackley, Clifford, ed. Rhythms of Modern Life: British Prints 1914-1939. 2008. (ENG., Illus.). 224p. 60.00 *(978-0-87846-724-2(6))* Museum of Fine Arts, Boston.

Acquaviva, Frederic. Gil J. Wolman. I am immortal & Alive. 2010. 184p. pap. 39.95 *(978-84-92505-40-1(0))* Museu d'Art Contemporani de Barcelona ESP. Dist: Actar Birkhauser Distribution.

Adamowsky, Natascha, et al, texts. Unter Wasser / Über Wasser: Vom Aquarium - zum Videobild. 2010. (ENG., Illus.). 115p. 40.00 *(978-3-86678-274-7(8))* Kerber Verlag DEU. Dist: D.A.P./Distributed Art Pubs.

Adams, Henry. The Beauty of Damage: The World of Christopher Pekoc. 2008. (Illus.). pap. 19.95 *(978-0-9758843-9-3(5))* Green Panda Pr.

Ades, Dawn & McClean, Alison. Revolution on Paper: Mexican Prints 1910-1960. 2009. (ENG., Illus.). 192p. pap. 39.95 *(978-0-292-72248-4(6))* Univ. of Texas Pr.

Affron, Matthew, et al. Matisse, Picasso, & Modern Art in Paris: The T. Catesby Jones Collections at the Virginia Museum of Fine Arts & the University of Virginia Art Museum. 2009. (ENG., Illus.). 160p. pap. 39.95 *(978-0-917046-88-9(9))* Univ. Pr. of Virginia.

Agee, William C. & Faxon, Susan C. Coming of Age: American Art, 1850s to 1950s. 2006. (Illus.). 136p. pap. *(978-1-885444-33-2(8))* American Federation of Arts, The.

—Coming of Age: American Art, 1850s To 1950s. 2006. (ENG., Illus.). 136p. 55.00 *(978-0-300-11523-9(7))* Yale Univ. Pr.

Albiñana, Salvador. Mexico Illustrated 1920-1950. 2011. (SPA & ENG., Illus.). 288p. 65.00 *(978-84-92480-87-6(4))* RM Verlag, S.L. ESP. Dist: D.A.P./Distributed Art Pubs.

Albiñana, Salvador, ed. México Ilustrado: Libros, Revistas y Carteles, 1920-1950. 2010. (SPA., Illus.). 376p. *(978-607-7515-56-2(6))* R.M. Editorial, S.A. de C.V.

Alexander, Darsie, et al, texts. The Spectacular of Vernacular. 2011. (ENG., Illus.). 128p. pap. 19.99 *(978-0-935640-99-1(1))* Walker Art Ctr.

Allemand-Cosneau, Claude, et al. Henry Moore: From the Inside Out. 2009. (Illus.). 200p. pap. 19.95 *(978-3-7913-4176-7(6))* Prestel Publishing.

Allen, Mark, et al, eds. The Machine Project: A Field Guide to the Los Angeles County Museum of Art. 2010. (ENG., Illus.). 172p. pap. 25.00 *(978-0-9753140-4-3(1))* Machine Project Pr.

Allen, Stuart & Lane, Allison Hays. Stuart Allen: 2926'14" N 9828'55" W: Mapping Daylight. 2007. *(978-1-883502-16-4(0))* San Antonio Museum of Art.

Alys, Francis. Francis Alys: A Story of Deception. 2010. (ENG., Illus.). 192p. pap. 35.00 *(978-0-87070-790-2(6))* Museum of Modern Art.

Amory, Dita, ed. & contrib. by. Pierre Bonnard: The Late Still Lifes & Interiors. 2009. (ENG., Illus.). 208p. 50.00 *(978-0-300-14889-3(5))* Yale Univ. Pr.

Anfam, David & Pousette-Dart, Richard. Pousette-Dart: Predominantly White Paintings, 1 vol. 2010. (ENG.). 64p. pap. 24.95 *(978-0-943044-36-1(7))* Phillips Collection, The.

Ángel, Félix. Extended Boundary: Latin America & Caribbean Artists in Miami: Frontera Extendida, Artistas Latinoamericanos y Caribeños en Miami. 2008. (Illus.). 62p. *(978-1-59782-071-4(7))* Inter-American Development Bank.

Anne, Umland. Picasso Guitars, 1912-1914. 2011. (ENG., Illus.). 112p. 24.95 *(978-0-87070-794-0(9))* Museum of Modern Art.

Annicchiarico, Silvana. Il Design in Italia: 1945-2000: 100 Oggetti Della Collezione Permanente Del Design Italiano Della Triennale Di Milano. 2010. (ITA & ENG., Illus.). 214p. pap. 38.95 *(978-88-492-0183-3(4))* Gangemi ITA. Dist: International Publishers Marketing.

Antille, Emmanuelle, et al. Swiss Made: The Art of Falling Apart. 2006. (ENG & DUT., Illus.). 96p. pap. 35.00 *(978-90-400-9078-3(5))* Waanders B.V., Uitgeverij NLD. Dist: National Bk. Network.

Arnold, Grant & Thom, Ian M. Shore, Forest & Beyond: Art from the Audain Collection, 1 vol. 2012. (ENG., Illus.). 144p. 55.00 ***(978-1-55365-929-7(5))*** D&M Pubs. Inc. CAN. Dist: Perseus-PGW.

Arnold, Grant, et al. Ken Lum, 1 vol. 2011. (ENG., Illus.). 144p. 55.00 *(978-1-55365-498-8(6))* D&M Pubs. Inc. CAN. Dist: Perseus-PGW.

Arnold, Sara C., ed. The Life & Art of Alfred Hutty: Woodstock to Charleston. 2011. 224p. 49.95 ***(978-1-61117-041-2(9))***; pap. 24.95 ***(978-1-61117-042-9(7))*** Univ. of South Carolina Pr.

Arot, Dominique. La Grèce des Modernes: L'impression D'un Voyage, les Artistes, les écrivains et la Grèce 1933-1968: [exposition Réalisée Dans le Cadre de la Manifestation Feuille à Feuille, Estampe et Images Imprimées Dans les Collections des Musées du Nord-Pas-De-Calais, Organisée Par L'Association des Conservateurs des Musées du Nord-Pas-De-Calais D'octobre 2006 à Juin 2007, et Présentée du 20 Janvier Au 22 Avril, 2007. 2008. (FRE & ENG., Illus.). 192p. pap. 45.00 *(978-2-35340-013-3(2))* Gourcuff Gradenigo FRA. Dist: National Bk. Network.

Art Basel Miami Beach 2011. 2011. (ENG., Illus.). 650p. pap. 65.00 ***(978-3-7757-3139-3(3))*** Hatje Cantz Verlag GmbH & Co KG DEU. Dist: D.A.P./Distributed Art Pubs.

Art Works. 2011. (ENG., Illus.). 256p. pap. 55.00 ***(978-3-7757-2777-8(9))*** Hatje Cantz Verlag GmbH & Co KG DEU. Dist: D.A.P./Distributed Art Pubs.

Asten, Astrid von & Schick, Karin. Sophie Taeuber-Arp 1889 - 1943: Bewegung und Gleichgewicht / Movement & Balance. 2010. (GER & ENG., Illus.). 160p. 50.00 *(978-3-86678-320-1(5))* Kerber Verlag DEU. Dist: D.A.P./Distributed Art Pubs.

Asthon, Dore. Manuel Felguerez. 2010. (ENG., Illus.). 218p. 45.00 *(978-84-92480-77-7(7))* RM Verlag, S.L. ESP. Dist: D.A.P./Distributed Art Pubs.

Auerbach, Ruth, et al. 3 Perspectives: Eugenio Espinoza, Alvaro Oyarzún, José Alejandro Restrepo: Cisneros Fontanals Art Foundation 2007 Commissions Program Exhibition. 2007. (SPA & ENG., Illus.). 60p. ***(978-0-9774079-5-8(0))*** Cisneros Fontanals Art Foundation.

Aupetitallot, Yves & Prat, Thierry, eds. Kader Attia, 1 vol. 2007. (FRE & ENG., Illus.). 112p. 29.00 *(978-2-940271-81-8(X))* JRP Ringier Kunstverlag AG CHE. Dist: D.A.P./Distributed Art Pubs.

Auther, Elissa. West of Center: Art & the Counterculture Experiment in America, 1965-1977. Lerner, Adam, ed. 2011. (ENG., Illus.). 448p. pap. 39.95 ***(978-0-8166-7726-9(3))*** Univ. of Minnesota Pr.

Auther, Elissa & Lerner, Adam, eds. West of Center: Art & the Counterculture Experiment in America, 1965-1977. 2011. (ENG., Illus.). 448p. 120.00 ***(978-0-8166-7725-2(5))*** Univ. of Minnesota Pr.

Avery, Charles. Charles Avery: Onomatopoeia. 2011. (ITA, FRE, GER & ENG., Illus.). 80p. 39.95 *(978-3-86560-840-6(X))* Verlag der Buchhandlung Walther Konig DEU. Dist: D.A.P./Distributed Art Pubs.

Avery, Kevin J., et al. Alexis Rockman: A Fable for Tomorrow. 2011. (ENG., Illus.). 176p. 49.95 *(978-1-904832-86-7(5))* Giles, D. Ltd. GBR. Dist: National Bk. Network.

Baas, Jacquelynn, ed. Fluxus & the Essential Questions of Life. 2011. (ENG., Illus.). 144p. pap. 30.00 *(978-0-226-03359-4(7))* Univ. of Chicago Pr.

Bacon, Francis & Hirst, Damien, illus. Triptychs & a Thousand Years: Francis Bacon & Damien Hirst. 2008. (ENG.). 104p. 180.00 *(978-1-904212-49-2(2))* Other Criteria GBR. Dist: Abrams.

Bahrani, Zainab & Shabout, Nada M. Modernism & Iraq. 2009. (Illus.). 99p. *(978-1-884919-22-0(7))* Columbia Univ., The Miriam & Ira D. Wallach Art Gallery.

Bakker, Conrad. Conrad Bakker: Objects & Economies: Untitled Projects 1997-2007. 2009. (ENG., Illus.). 80p. pap. 8.95 *(978-1-879003-51-4(1))* Des Moines Art Ctr.

Baldessari, John. John Baldessari: A Print Retrospective from the Collections of Jordan D. Schnitzer & his Family Foundation. 2010. (ENG., Illus.). 160p. 59.95 *(978-1-935202-10-3(3))* D.A.P./Distributed Art Pubs.

—Miracle Chips, 1 vol. 2010. (ENG., Illus.). 80p. pap. 34.00 *(978-3-86521-677-9(3))* Steidl, Gerhard Druckerei und Verlag DEU. Dist: Innovative Logistics.

Balken, Debra Bricker. John Marin: Modernism at Midcentury. 2011. (Illus.). xi, 108p. pap. *(978-0-300-17635-3(X))*; (ENG., 120p. 40.00 *(978-0-300-14993-7(X))* Yale Univ. Pr.

Balsells, David, ed. & text. Praha, Paris, Barcelona. 2010. (ENG., Illus.). 250p. 70.00 *(978-84-92841-02-8(8))* Museu Nacional d'Art de Catalunya ESP. Dist: D.A.P./Distributed Art Pubs.

Bankowsky, Jack, et al, eds. Pop Life: Art in a Material World. 2010. (ENG., Illus.). 208p. pap. 60.00 *(978-1-85437-920-7(8))* Tate Publishing, Ltd. GBR. Dist: Hachette Bk. Group.

Barbaro, Luca M. & Pola, Francesca, eds. A Roma, la Nostra Era Avanguardia. 2010. (ENG & ITA.). 192p. pap. 62.50 *(978-88-370-7488-3(3))* Electa ITA. Dist: Trans-Atlantic Pubns., Inc.

Barbero, Luca Massimo. Carlo Cardazzo: Una Nuova Visione Dell'arte. Barbero, Luca Massimo, ed. 2009. (ITA., Illus.). 400p. 117.50 *(978-88-370-6534-8(5))* Electa ITA. Dist: Trans-Atlantic Pubns., Inc.

Barbero, Luca Massimo & Widenheim, Cecilia. Milan-Turin 1958-1968 No. 2. 2008. (ENG., Illus.). 112p. pap. 50.00 *(978-3-86521-639-7(0))* Steidl, Gerhard Druckerei und Verlag DEU. Dist: D.A.P./Distributed Art Pubs.

Bardazzi, Francesca, et al. Cézanne in Florence: Two Collectors & the 1910 Exhibition of Impressionism. 2007. (Illus.). 272p. pap. *(978-88-370-4971-3(4))* Electa.

Barilleaux, Rene Paul. Tom Slick: International Art Collector: An Exhibition. 2009. *(978-0-916677-53-4(2))* McNay, Marion Koogler Art Museum.

Barker, Scott Grant & Myers, Jane. Intimate Modernism: Fort Worth Circle Artists in The 1940s. 2008. (ENG., Illus.). 208p. 39.95 *(978-0-88360-103-7(6))* Amon Carter Museum.

Barron, Stephanie, et al. Art of Two Germanys - Cold War Cultures. 2009. (Illus.). 460p. *(978-0-8109-7647-4(1))* Abrams.

Barryte, Bernard, ed. Rodin & America. 2011. (ENG., Illus.). 384p. 75.00 ***(978-88-366-2000-5(0))*** Silvana ITA. Dist: D.A.P./Distributed Art Pubs.

Bartlett, Bo. Bo Bartlett: Paintings 1981-2010. 2011. (ENG., Illus.). 64p. pap. *(978-0-578-06122-1(8))* Inspiration Point Pr.

Baselitz, Georg. Georg Baselitz: Works from the 1960s And 1970s, 1 vol. 2007. (ENG., Illus.). 60.00 *(978-1-934171-00-4(X))* Thread Waxing Space.

Basquiat, Jean-Michel. Jean-Michel Basquiat. 2010. (ENG., Illus.). 224p. 65.00 *(978-3-7757-2593-4(8))* Hatje Cantz Verlag GmbH & Co KG DEU. Dist: D.A.P./Distributed Art Pubs.

Bastiaans, Christiaan & text. Christiaan Bastiaans: Club Mama Gemutlich. 2010. (ENG., Illus.). 192p. 55.00 *(978-3-86678-287-7(X))* Kerber Verlag DEU. Dist: D.A.P./Distributed Art Pubs.

Basualdo, Carlos & Battle, Erica F., eds. Bruce Nauman: Topological Gardens - Installation Views. 2010. (Illus.). 60p. pap. 12.00 *(978-0-300-16463-3(7))* Yale Univ. Pr.

Bauermeister, Mary, et al. Welten in der Schachtel / Worlds in a Box: Mary Bauermeister und die experimentelle Kunst der 1960er Jahre / Mary Bauermeister & the Experimental Art of the Sixties. 2011. (GER & ENG., Illus.). 176p. 55.00 *(978-3-86678-449-9(X))* Kerber Verlag DEU. Dist: D.A.P./Distributed Art Pubs.

Baum, Kelly. Transactions: An Exhibition. 2007. (Illus.). 47p. *(978-0-9771453-4-8(4))* Univ. of Texas at Austin, The.

Baume, Nicholas, ed. Super Vision. 2006. (ENG., Illus.). 176p. (gr. 17). 34.95 *(978-0-262-02609-3(0))* MIT Pr.

Baur, Andreas. Fabrice Gygi. 2009. (ENG., Illus.). 176p. pap. 55.00 *(978-3-905829-44-0(4))* JRP Ringier Kunstverlag AG CHE. Dist: D.A.P./Distributed Art Pubs.

Beard, Mark & Chronicle Books Staff. Bruce Sargeant & His Circle: Figure & Form. 2010. (ENG., Illus.). 128p. 45.00 *(978-0-8118-7227-0(0))* Chronicle Bks. LLC.

Bearden, Romare. Romare Bearden: Idea to Realization. 2011. (ENG., Illus.). 30p. pap. 20.00 ***(978-0-9826316-5-2(0))*** DC Moore Gallery.

Beckmann, Max. Seestucke: Von Max Beckmann bis Gerhard Richter. Richter, Gerhard et al, eds. 2007. (GER., Illus.). 215p. (C). 49.00 *(978-3-7774-3665-4(8))* Hirmer Verlag GmbH DEU. Dist: Brown, David Bk. Co., The.

Beechey, James & Stephens, Chris, eds. Picasso & Modern British Art. 2012. (ENG., Illus.). 240p. pap. 35.00 ***(978-1-85437-890-3(2))*** Tate Publishing, Ltd. GBR. Dist: Hachette Bk. Group.

Belasco, Daniel. Reinventing Ritual: Contemporary Art & Design for Jewish Life. 2009. (Illus.). 176p. 39.95 *(978-0-300-14682-0(5))* Yale Univ. Pr.

Berg, Stephan & Solakov, Nedko. Emotions. 2008. (GER & ENG., Illus.). 224p. 60.00 *(978-3-7757-2211-7(4))* Hatje Cantz Verlag GmbH & Co KG DEU. Dist: D.A.P./Distributed Art Pubs.

Bergdoll, Barry. Bauhaus 1919-1933: Workshops for Modernity. 2009. (ENG., Illus.). 328p. 75.00 *(978-0-87070-758-2(2))* Museum of Modern Art.

Berry, Ian, et al. Joseph Grigely: St. Cecilia. 2007. (Opener Ser.: Vol. 13). (Illus.). 127p. *(978-0-9765723-4-3(6))* Tang, Frances Young Teaching Museum & Art Gallery at Skidmore College, The.

Bertram, Eva, photos by. Eva Bertram: 2 Ein Kind - 2 One Child. 2010. (ENG., Illus.). 160p. 45.00 *(978-3-7757-2621-4(7))* Hatje Cantz Verlag GmbH & Co KG DEU. Dist: D.A.P./Distributed Art Pubs.

Bezzola, Tobia & Kurzmeyer, Roman, eds. Harald Szeemann: with by Through Because Towards Despite: Catalogue of All Exhibitions 1957-2005. 2007. (Edition Voldemeer Ser.). (MUL & ENG., Illus.). 759p. 129.00 *(978-3-211-83632-3(2)*, 3211836322) Springer Wien AUT. Dist: Springer.

Bickerton, Ashley & Oosterhof, Gosse. Horn of Plenty: 16 Artists from NYC. (GER & ENG., Illus.). 103p. 29.50 *(978-90-5006-026-4(9))* Stedelijk Museum NLD. Dist: D.A.P./Distributed Art Pubs.

Biesenbach, Klaus. Marina Abramovic: The Artist Is Present. 2010. (ENG., Illus.). 224p. 50.00 *(978-0-87070-747-6(7))* Museum of Modern Art.

Bing, Xu. Xu Bing, 1 vol. 2012. (ENG., Illus.). 280p. 85.00 ***(978-0-9568670-0-1(6))*** Albion Editions GBR. Dist: D.A.P./Distributed Art Pubs.

Birnbaum, Daniel. Making Worlds: 53rd International Art Exhibition - La Biennale Di Venezia. Birnbaum, Daniel, ed. 2009. (ENG., Illus.). 660p. pap. 90.00 *(978-88-317-9696-5(8))* Marsilio Editori spa ITA. Dist: Random Hse., Inc.

Bishop, Janet C., et al. The Steins Collect: Matisse, Picasso, & the Parisian Avant-Garde. 2011. pap. *(978-0-918471-87-1(7))* San Francisco Museum of Modern Art.

Blackwell, Kelsey, des. Living, Looking, Making: Giacometti, Fontana, Twombly, Serra. 2007. (Illus.). 116p. 80.00 *(978-1-932598-49-0(9))* Gagosian Gallery.

Bladen, Ronald, illus. Skulptur/Sculpture: Werke der Sammlung Marzona/Works from the Marzona Collection, 1 vol. 2008. (ENG.). 80p. 48.00 *(978-3-86560-214-5(2))* Verlag der Buchhandlung Walther Konig DEU. Dist: D.A.P./Distributed Art Pubs.

Blake, Peter. Venice Fantasies. Livingstone, Marco, ed. 2010. (ENG., Illus.). 96p. 47.95 *(978-1-904634-92-8(3))* Enitharmon Pr. GBR. Dist: Dufour Editions, Inc.

Blauvelt, Andrew. Worlds Away: New Suburban Landscapes. 2008. (ENG., Illus.). 336p. pap. 34.95 *(978-0-935640-90-8(8))* Walker Art Ctr.

Blazwick, Iwona & Yiakoumaki, Nayia, frwds. This Is Tomorrow. 2011. (ENG., Illus.). 132p. spiral bd. 24.95 *(978-0-85488-186-4(7))* Whitechapel Art Gallery GBR. Dist: D.A.P./Distributed Art Pubs.

Blum, Dilys & Capucci, Roberto. Roberto Capucci: Art into Fashion. 2010. (Illus.). 202p. *(978-0-87633-229-0(7))* Philadelphia Museum of Art.

Blyth, Jenny & Zeldin, Theodore. Gary Hill & Gerry Judah. 2007. 60p. pap. 29.95 *(978-2-7572-0132-9(8))* Somogy Editions d'Art FRA. Dist: Independent Pubs. Group.

Boellert, Arvid. Drei Farben, Weiss: Three Colours, White. 2007. (GER & ENG., Illus.). 125p. *(978-3-89930-199-1(4))* Schiler, Hans.

Bois. Leger Paris-Newyork. 2008. (ENG., Illus.). 208p. 75.00 *(978-3-7757-2161-5(4))* Hatje Cantz Verlag GmbH & Co KG DEU. Dist: D.A.P./Distributed Art Pubs.

Bollinger, Bill & Meyer-Stoll, Christiane. Bill Bollinger. 2012. (ENG., Illus.). 256p. 59.95 ***(978-3-86335-058-1(8))*** Verlag der Buchhandlung Walther Konig DEU. Dist: D.A.P./Distributed Art Pubs.

Bonami, Francesco, ed. & contrib. by. Jeff Koons. 2008. (ENG., Illus.). 136p. 45.00 *(978-0-300-14194-8(7))* Yale Univ. Pr.

Bonami, Francesco, text. Helmut Middendorf: over the under the Over. 2010. (ENG., Illus.). 160p. 45.00 *(978-3-86678-225-9(X))* Kerber Verlag DEU. Dist: D.A.P./Distributed Art Pubs.

Bonami, Francesco & Gingeras, Alison, eds. La Collezione Di Punta Della Dogana: The Catalogue of the Contemporary Art Center in Venice. 2009. (ITA & FRE., Illus.). 300p. 115.00 *(978-88-370-6994-0(4))* Electa ITA. Dist: Trans-Atlantic Pubns., Inc.

Bonetti, David & Dreishpoon, Douglas. The Panza Collection: An Experience of Color & Light. 2007. (Illus.). 119p. *(978-1-887457-08-8(9))* Buffalo Fine Arts/Albright-Knox Art Gallery.

Bonin, Cosima von, et al. Dressing the Message: Transformationen Von Kunst und Mode. 2008. (Illus.). 120p. *(978-3-89169-208-0(0))* Sprengel Museum.

Bonito Oliva, Achille. Gino De Dominicis: The Immortal. 2011. (ENG., Illus.). 388p. pap. 99.00 *(978-88-370-7590-3(1))* Electa ITA. Dist: National Bk. Network.

Bonvicini, Monica, et al. Monica Bonvicini: Both Ends. 2011. (GER & ENG., Illus.). 168p. pap. 50.00 *(978-3-86560-873-4(6))* Verlag der Buchhandlung Walther Konig DEU. Dist: D.A.P./Distributed Art Pubs.

Borchardt-Hume, Achim, text. Keeping It Real: From the Ready-Made to the Everyday. 2011. (ENG., Illus.). 132p. pap. 35.00 *(978-0-85488-181-9(6))* Whitechapel Art Gallery GBR. Dist: D.A.P./Distributed Art Pubs.

Borja-Villel, Manuel J. Drifts & Derivations: Experiences, Journeys & Morphologies. 2011. (ENG.). 301p. pap. 54.95 *(978-84-8026-425-9(X))* Museo Nacional Centro de Arte Reina Sofia ESP. Dist: Actar Birkhauser Distribution.

Bosch, Eulalia. Frequencies: Eugènia Balcells. 2009. *(978-84-92861-03-3(7))* Actar Birkhauser Distribution.

Bourgeois, Caroline. Elogio Del Dubbio: Eloge du Doute = in Praise of Doubt. 2012. (ITA & ENG., Illus.). 204p. 65.00 ***(978-88-370-8508-7(7))*** Electa ITA. Dist: National Bk. Network.

Bovier, Lionel, ed. Michael Cline. 2010. (ENG., Illus.). 64p. 35.00 *(978-3-03764-052-4(9))* JRP Ringier Kunstverlag AG CHE. Dist: D.A.P./Distributed Art Pubs.

—Troy Brauntuch. 2010. (ENG., Illus.). 144p. 80.00 *(978-3-905770-81-0(4))* JRP Ringier Kunstverlag AG CHE. Dist: D.A.P./Distributed Art Pubs.

Bracewell, Michael & Pies, Daniel. Be Nice Share Everything Have Fun. Kalmar, Stefan, ed. 2010. (GER & ENG., Illus.). 314p. pap. 65.00 *(978-3-86560-771-3(3))* Verlag der Buchhandlung Walther Konig DEU. Dist: D.A.P./Distributed Art Pubs.

Bradley, Joanne Tatham & Tom O'Sullivan: A Charming Meaning, a Solid Meaning, a Struggling Meaning. 2010. (GER & ENG., Illus.). 128p. pap., pap. 29.95 *(978-3-8321-9022-4(8))* DuMont DEU. Dist: D.A.P./Distributed Art Pubs.

Braun, Emily, et al, texts. Chaos & Classicism: Art in France, Italy, & Germany, 1918-1936. 2011. (ENG., Illus.). 192p. pap. 40.00 *(978-0-89207-405-1(1))* Guggenheim, Solomon R. Museum.

Breitwieser, Sabine, ed. Edward Krasinski: Les Mises en Scene, 1 vol. 2007. (ENG., Illus.). 350p. 63.00 *(978-3-86560-103-2(0))* Verlag der Buchhandlung Walther Konig DEU. Dist: D.A.P./Distributed Art Pubs.

Breitz, Candice. Candice Breitz: Same Same. 2010. (ENG., Illus.). 130p. pap. 47.00 *(978-1-894212-29-8(0))* Power Plant, The CAN. Dist: D.A.P./Distributed Art Pubs.

Brighton, Andrew. Francis Bacon. 2010. (ENG., Illus.). 80p. pap. 16.50 *(978-1-85437-307-6(2))* Tate Publishing, Ltd. GBR. Dist: Hachette Bk. Group.

Bronfen, Elisabeth, text. Julia Stoschek Collection, Number Two. 2009. (ENG., Illus.). 432p. 105.00 *(978-3-7757-2379-4(X))* Hatje Cantz Verlag GmbH & Co KG DEU. Dist: D.A.P./Distributed Art Pubs.

Brookman, Philip, et al. Essential Modernism. 2008. (ENG., Illus.). 192p. 19.95 *(978-0-88675-079-4(2))* Distribution General.

Brougher, Kerry, et al, texts. The Panza Collection. 2009. (ENG., Illus.). 96p. pap. 25.00 *(978-0-9789063-1-3(4))* Hirshhorn Museum & Sculpture Garden.

Brown, Betty Ann & White, John M., contrib. by. Lifelines: John M. White: A Retrospective Exhibition of Performance, Installation, Sculpture, Painting & Drawing. 2011. (ENG., Illus.). 56p. pap. 25.00 ***(978-0-9833385-0-5(7))*** Armory Ctr. for the Arts.

Brown, Iona Rozeal. Iona Rozeal Brown. 2010. (ENG., Illus.). 96p. 45.00 *(978-3-7757-2601-6(2))* Hatje Cantz Verlag GmbH & Co KG DEU. Dist: D.A.P./Distributed Art Pubs.

Brown, Kendall H. Deco Japan: Shaping Art & Culture, 1920-1945. 2012. ***(978-0-88397-157-4(7))*** Art Services International.

Brown, Neal & Emin, Tracey. Tracey Emin. 2006. (ENG., Illus.). 128p. pap. 27.50 *(978-1-85437-542-1(3))* Tate Publishing, Ltd. GBR. Dist: Hachette Bk. Group.

Bucarelli, Angelo. Il Drago e la Farfalla: Arte Contemporanea in Vietnam Ròng Và Bm. 2010. (ITA & ENG., Illus.). 144p. pap. 23.95 *(978-88-492-1015-6(9))* Gangemi ITA. Dist: International Publishers Marketing.

Buchhart, Dieter & Knack, Hartwig, eds. Otto Dix: Zwischen Paradies und Untergang. 2009. (Illus.). 128p. (C). 36.00 *(978-3-7774-2021-9(2))* Hirmer Verlag GmbH DEU. Dist: Brown, David Bk. Co., The.

Buck, Stephanie, et al. The Courtauld Cézannes. 2008. (ENG., Illus.). 160p. pap. 45.00 *(978-1-903470-84-8(6))* Holberton, Paul Publishing GBR. Dist: Casemate Pubs. & Bk. Distributors, LLC.

Buhr, Elke. Begegnung Bauhaus: Kurt Schmidt und Künstler der Avantgarde Von Kandinsky Bis Vasarely: Kunstsammlung Gera, 25. März Bis 28. Juni 2009. 2009. (Illus.). 159p. pap. *(978-3-910051-52-2(9))* Glaux Verlag Christine Jager KG.

Bullock, Margaret E., et al. A Turbulent Lens: The Photographic Art of Virna Haffer, 1 vol. 2011. (ENG., Illus.). 144p. pap. 19.95 ***(978-0-924335-32-7(7))*** Tacoma Art Museum.

Burke, Gregory, et al, texts. Scott Lyall: the Color Ball. 2010. (ENG., Illus.). 96p. 42.50 *(978-1-894212-27-4(4))* Power Plant, The CAN. Dist: D.A.P./Distributed Art Pubs.

Burton, Johanna. Pop Art: Contemporary Perspectives: Princeton University Art Museum. 2007. (Illus.). 159p. *(978-0-943012-44-5(9))* Princeton Univ. Art Museum.

Busch, Jason T. & Futter, Catherine L. Inventing the Modern World: Decorative Arts at the World's Fairs, 1851-1939. 2012. (ENG., Illus.). 304p. 75.00 ***(978-0-8478-3809-7(9)***, Skira) Rizzoli International Pubns., Inc.

Butler, Brian, ed. Speculation, 1 vol. 2007. (ENG., Illus.). 224p. pap. 25.00 *(978-3-905770-75-9(X))* JRP Ringier Kunstverlag AG CHE. Dist: D.A.P./Distributed Art Pubs.

Cage, John. Every Day Is a Good Day: the Visual Art of John Cage. 2010. (ENG., Illus.). 160p. pap. 30.00 *(978-1-85332-283-9(0))* Hayward Gallery Publishing GBR. Dist: D.A.P./Distributed Art Pubs.

Campbell, Jim. Jim Campbell. 2010. (ENG., Illus.). 168p. 55.00 *(978-3-7757-2542-2(3))* Hatje Cantz Verlag GmbH & Co KG DEU. Dist: D.A.P./Distributed Art Pubs.

Cantini, Lorenzo & Michelli, Carla. La Raccolta D'arte Esso: 1949-1983. 2007. (ITA & ENG., Illus.). 299p. 75.00 *(978-88-370-5687-2(7))* Electa ITA. Dist: Trans-Atlantic Pubns., Inc.

Carlano, Annie. Contemporary British Studio Ceramics. 2010. (ENG., Illus.). 224p. 60.00 *(978-0-300-16719-1(9))* Yale Univ. Pr.

Carlisle, Fionna. Energy: North Sea Portraits. 2007. (Illus.). 48p. pap. *(978-1-903278-92-5(9))* National Galleries of Scotland.

Carlson, Ann & Strom, Mary Ellen. Carlson/Strom: New Performance Video. 2009. (Illus.). 48p. *(978-0-945506-60-7(0))* DeCordova Museum & Sculpture Park.

Carrington, Leonora. Leonora Carrington: What She Might Be. 2008. (Illus.). 100p. pap. *(978-0-936227-29-0(X))* Dallas Museum of Art.

Carson, Juli, ed. MFA Thesis Exhibitions 2007. 2007. per. *(978-1-884355-08-0(0))* Univ. of California, Irvine, Univ. Art Gallery.

Cash, Sarah, et al. George Bellows. Brock, Charles, ed. 2012. (Illus.). 336p. 60.00 ***(978-3-7913-5187-2(7))*** Prestel Publishing.

Casper, Jens & Shryen, Annette, texts. Boros Collection. 2010. (ENG., Illus.). 198p. 75.00 *(978-3-7757-2478-4(8))* Hatje Cantz Verlag GmbH & Co KG DEU. Dist: D.A.P./Distributed Art Pubs.

Castle, James & Percy, Ann. James Castle: A Retrospective. 2008. *(978-0-87633-206-1(8))*; *(978-0-87633-207-8(6))* Philadelphia Museum of Art.

Cavadini, Nicoletta Ossanna. Bruno Monguzzi: Fifty Years of Paper, 1961-2011. 2011. (ENG., Illus.). 256p. pap. 55.00 ***(978-88-572-1105-3(3))*** Skira Editore ITA. Dist: Random Hse., Inc.

Cecchetto, Stefano & Vanni, Maurizio, eds. Jean Dubuffet: E L'Italia. 2011. (ITA & ENG., Illus.). 120p. pap. 35.00 ***(978-88-366-1971-9(1))*** Silvana ITA. Dist: D.A.P./Distributed Art Pubs.

Celant, Germano. Manzoni: A Retrospective. 2009. (ENG., Illus.). 376p. 95.00 *(978-88-572-0050-7(7))* Skira Editore ITA. Dist: Random Hse., Inc.

Central Washington University Staff, contrib. by. Crossroads & Connections: Central Washington University Art Alumni Exhibition. 2008. (Illus.). 128p. pap. 29.95 *(978-0-87422-300-2(8))* Washington State Univ. Pr.

Cerizza, Luca, ed. Maps & Legends. 2009. (ENG., Illus.). 280p. 27.00 *(978-3-905829-13-6(4))* JRP Ringier Kunstverlag AG CHE. Dist: D.A.P./Distributed Art Pubs.

Cerizza, Luca & Pecoil, Vincent, texts. Ils Sont Peintres. 2009. (ENG & FRE., Illus.). 128p. 22.00 *(978-3-905829-23-5(1))* JRP Ringier Kunstverlag AG CHE. Dist: D.A.P./Distributed Art Pubs.

Cézanne, Paul, et al. Cezanne & American Modernism. 2009. pap. *(978-0-9824716-0-9(2))* Montclair Art Museum.

Chadwick, Whitney, ed. Bent: Gender & Sexuality in Contemporary Scandinavian Art. 2006. (Illus.). 64p. per. 21.95 *(978-0-295-98613-5(1))* Univ. of Washington Pr.

Chagall, Marc & Tériade, E. Chagall et Tériade: L'empreinte D'un Peintre. 2008. (ENG., Illus.). 224p. pap. 60.00 *(978-2-35340-012-6(4))* Gourcuff Gradenigo FRA. Dist: National Bk. Network.

Chaille, Francois & Aliaga, Michel. Cartier: Innovation Through the 20th Century. 2008. (ENG., Illus.). 280p. 65.00 *(978-2-08-030041-6(5))* Flammarion et Cie FRA. Dist: Random Hse., Inc.

Chang, Alexandra, text. Envisioning Diaspora, Asian American Visual Arts Collectives. 2009. (ENG., Illus.). 266p. pap. 35.00 *(978-988-17522-3-9(X))* Timezone 8 Ltd. HKG. Dist: D.A.P./Distributed Art Pubs.

Chapin, Mary Weaver. Posters of Paris: Toulouse-Lautrec & his Contemporaries. 2012. (Illus.). 176p. 49.95 ***(978-3-7913-5204-6(0))*** Prestel Publishing.

Chapman, Jake & Chapman, Dinos. Flogging a Dead Horse: The Life & Works of Jake & Dinos Chapman. Fuel Staff, ed. 2011. (ENG., Illus.). 336p. 85.00 *(978-0-8478-3478-5(6))* Rizzoli International Pubns., Inc.

Chassey, Eric de & Stroun, Fabrice. Europunk. 2011. (ENG., Illus.). 320p. pap. 55.00 ***(978-88-88493-72-5(7))*** Drago Arts & Communication ITA. Dist: SCB Distributors.

Cherix, Christophe, et al, texts. Francis Baudevin: Miscellaneous Abstract. 2010. (ENG., Illus.). 160p. pap. 55.00 *(978-3-03764-067-8(7))* JRP Ringier Kunstverlag AG CHE. Dist: D.A.P./Distributed Art Pubs.

Cherix, Christophe & Tremblay, John. Plastic. 2008. (ENG., Illus.). 64p. pap. 15.00 *(978-3-905770-60-5(1))* JRP Ringier Kunstverlag AG CHE. Dist: D.A.P./Distributed Art Pubs.

Chicuri, Abelardo Mena, et al. Cuba Avant-Garde: Contemporary Cuban Art from the Farber Collection / Arte Contemporaneo Cubano de la Coleccion Farber. Delson, Susan, ed. Lizarraga, Felix, tr. 2007. (SPA & ENG., Illus.). 188p. pap. 29.95 *(978-0-9762552-5-3(1))* Univ. Pr. of Florida.

—Cuba Avant-Garde: Contemporary Cuban Art from the Farber Collection /Arte Contemporaneo Cubano de la Coleccion Farber. Delson, Susan, ed. Lizarraga, Felix, tr. 2007. (SPA & ENG., Illus.). 188p. 59.95 *(978-0-9762552-4-6(3))* Univ. Pr. of Florida.

Chiodi, Stefano, ed. Space: From Maxxi's Collections of Art & Architecture. 2010. 320p. pap. 72.50 *(978-88-370-7587-3(1))* Electa ITA. Dist: Trans-Atlantic Pubns., Inc.

Chiu, Melissa & Shengtian, Zheng. Art & China's Revolution. 2008. (Illus.). 280p. 65.00 *(978-0-300-14064-4(9))* Yale Univ. Pr.

Chiu, Melissa & Tezuka, Miwako. Yoshitomo Nara: Nobody's Fool. 2010. (ENG., Illus.). 272p. 60.00 *(978-0-8109-9414-0(3))* Abrams.

Chiu, Melissa & Zheng, Shengtian. Art & China's Revolution. 2008. pap. *(978-0-87848-108-8(7))* Yale Univ. Pr.

Chong, Doryun & Raymond, Yasmil, texts. Brave New Worlds, 1 vol. 2007. (ENG., Illus.). 272p. pap. 39.95 *(978-0-935640-89-2(4))* Walker Art Ctr.

Chu, Petra ten-Doesschate. The Orient Expressed: Japan's Influence on Western Art, 1854-1918. Weisberg, Gabriel P., ed. 2011. (ENG., Illus.). 192p. 34.95 *(978-1-887422-19-2(6))* Mississippi Museum of Art.

Clark, Vicky A. Popular Salon of the People: Associated Artists of Pittsburgh, 1910-2006. 2007. (Illus.). 164p. *(978-0-88039-050-7(6))* Carnegie Museum of Art, The.

Closky, Claude & Muracciole, Marie. 02, Claude Closky: Climb at Your Own Risk. 2007. (Illus.). 89p. *(978-88-370-5154-9(9))* Electa.

Coetzee, Mark & Lagos, Luisa. Memorials of Identity: New Media from the Rubell Family Collection. 2009. (ENG., Illus.). 175p. 30.00 *(978-0-9716341-8-3(1))* Rubell Family Collection.

Collier, Brian, et al. Say It Isn't So. Friese, Peter, ed. 2008. (GER & ENG., Illus.). 260p. 40.00 *(978-3-939583-30-1(8))* Kehrer Verlag Heidelberg, Klaus Kehrer DEU. Dist: Consortium Bk. Sales & Distribution.

Contreras Gómez, Carmen, text. Ryan Mcginness: Studio Franchise. 2010. (ENG.). 196p. 35.00 *(978-84-96917-63-7(0))* Caja de Madrid ESP. Dist: Actar Birkhauser Distribution.

Cooke, Lynne & Vila-Matas, Enrique, texts. Dominique Gonzalez-Foerster: Chronotopes & Dioramas. 2010. (ENG., Illus.). 128p. 25.00 *(978-0-944521-57-1(6))* Dia Ctr. for the Arts.

Cork, Richard. Michael Craig-Martin. 2007. (ENG., Illus.). 256p. 60.00 *(978-0-500-09332-0(6))* Thames & Hudson.

Cork, Richard & Martin, Elliott Zooey. End Game: British Contemporary Art from the Chaney Family Collection. 2008. (ENG., Illus.). 80p. pap. 14.95 *(978-0-300-14201-3(3))* Museum of Fine Arts, Houston.

Corral, Maria de & Lane, John R., eds. Fast Forward: Contemporary Collections for the Dallas Museum of Art. 2007. (ENG., Illus.). 328p. 65.00 *(978-0-300-12291-6(8))* Dallas Museum of Art.

Cossa, Egidio & Schlinkert, Guido. IbridAAfricA: Hybrid 3. 2010. 144p. pap. 29.95 *(978-88-492-0268-7(7))* Gangemi ITA. Dist: International Publishers Marketing.

Cotton, Michelle, text. Design Research Unit, 1942-72. 2012. (ENG., Illus.). 120p. pap. 35.00 ***(978-3-86335-040-6(5))*** Walther König, Köln/Koenig Bks.

Cowling, Elizabeth & Kendall, Richard. Picasso Looks at Degas. 2010. (Illus.). xiii, 354p. *(978-0-931102-85-1(5))*; *(978-0-931102-86-8(3))* Clark, Sterling & Francine Art Institute.

Coyle, Heather Campbell, ed. Howard Pyle: American Master Rediscovered. 2011. (Illus.). 192p. (C). pap. 45.00 *(978-0-9771644-3-1(8))* Univ. of Pennsylvania Pr.

Cozzolino, Robert. Art in Chicago: Resisting Regionalism, Transforming Modernism, 1 vol. 1000th ed. 2007. (ENG., Illus.). 80p. per. 19.95 *(978-0-943836-29-4(8))* Pennsylvania Academy of the Fine Arts.

Cragg, Tony & Loyrette, Henri. Tony Cragg: Figure out Figure In. 2011. (ENG., Illus.). 102p. 39.95 ***(978-2-916275-87-1(8))*** Verlag der Buchhandlung Walther Konig DEU. Dist: D.A.P./Distributed Art Pubs.

Crawley, Susan. Bill Traylor: Drawings from the Collections of the High Museum of Art & the Montgomery Museum of Fine Arts. 2012. (Illus.). 104p. 29.95 ***(978-3-7913-5199-5(0))*** Prestel Publishing.

Crawley, Susan Mitchell. The Treasure of Ulysses Davis: Sculpture from a Savannah Barbershop. 2008. (ENG., Illus.). 119p. 30.00 *(978-1-932543-27-8(9))* Univ. Pr. of Mississippi.

Cremin, Mary. Romuald Hazoume. 2011. (ENG., Illus.). 160p. pap. 40.00 *(978-1-907020-52-0(7))* Irish Museum of Modern Art IRL. Dist: D.A.P./Distributed Art Pubs.

Critchley, Simon, et al, texts. The Luminous Interval. 2011. (ENG., Illus.). 207p. 49.95 *(978-0-89207-412-9(4))* Guggenheim, Solomon R. Museum.

Crowley, David. Posters of the Cold War. 2008. (ENG., Illus.). 112p. pap. 29.95 *(978-1-85177-545-5(5))* V & A Pubns. GBR. Dist: Hachette Bk. Group.

Crowley, David & Pavitt, Jane. Cold War Modern: Design 1945-1970. Crowley, David & Pavitt, Jane, eds. 2008. (ENG., Illus.). 320p. 80.00 *(978-1-85177-543-9(9))* V & A Pubns. GBR. Dist: Hachette Bk. Group.

Cutler, Amy. Amy Cutler: Turtle Fur, 1 vol. 2011. (ENG., Illus.). 160p. 60.00 *(978-3-7757-2809-6(0))* Hatje Cantz Verlag GmbH & Co KG DEU. Dist: D.A.P./Distributed Art Pubs.

Dale, Chihuly & Davira, Taragin. Persians. Portland Press Staff, ed. 2010. (Illus.). 112p. 14.95 *(978-1-57684-175-4(8))* Portland Pr., Inc.

Daros-Latinamerica Collec Staff. Face to Face. 2008. (ENG., Illus.). 288p. 55.00 *(978-3-7757-2112-7(6))* Hatje Cantz Verlag GmbH & Co KG DEU. Dist: D.A.P./Distributed Art Pubs.

Davidson, Russ, ed. Latin American Posters: Public Aesthetics & Mass Politics. 2006. (ENG., Illus.). 188p. *(978-0-89013-487-0(1))*; pap. *(978-0-89013-492-4(8))* Museum of New Mexico Pr.

De Cruz, Gemma, frwd. Ant Noises at the Saatchi Gallery. (Illus.). 56p. pap. 20.00 *(978-0-9538587-0-5(7)*, A20007) Saatchi Gallery GBR. Dist: D.A.P./Distributed Art Pubs.

Dean, Tacita. Seven Books Grey, 7 vols. 2011. (ENG & GER., Illus.). 976p. pap. 98.00 ***(978-3-86930-299-7(2))*** Steidl, Gerhard Druckerei und Verlag DEU. Dist: Innovative Logistics.

Dean, Tacita, illus. & text. Tacita Dean: Film Works. 2008. (ENG.). 112p. per. 34.95 *(978-88-8158-663-9(0))* Charta ITA. Dist: D.A.P./Distributed Art Pubs.

Deena, Chalabi & Shabout, Nada M., eds. Interventions: A Dialogue Between the Modern & the Contemporary. 2011. (ENG & ARA., Illus.). 104p. 35.00 *(978-88-572-0817-6(6))* Skira Editore ITA. Dist: Random Hse., Inc.

Dehejia, Vidya. Delight in Design: Indian Silver for the Raj. 2008. (ENG., Illus.). 200p. 65.00 *(978-0-944142-43-1(5))* Mapin Publishing Pvt. Ltd IND. Dist: National Bk. Network.

Denker, Eric & Earenfight, Phillip. Reflections & Undercurrents: Ernest Roth & Printmaking in Venice, 1900-1940. 2012. (ENG.). 174p. pap. 24.95 ***(978-0-9826156-4-5(7))*** Dickinson College, The Trout Gallery.

Derieux, Florence, ed. Marine Hugonnier. 2010. (ENG., Illus.). 160p. pap. 55.00 *(978-3-03764-079-1(0))* JRP Ringier Kunstverlag AG CHE. Dist: D.A.P./Distributed Art Pubs.

Dervaux, Isabelle. Drawing Connections: Baselitz, Kelly, Penone, Rockburne, & the Old Masters. 2007. *(978-0-87598-147-5(X))* Pierpont Morgan Library.

Dervaux, Isabelle & Flavin, Dan. Dan Flavin: Drawing. 2012. ***(978-0-87598-162-8(3))*** Giles, D. Ltd.

Derycke, Luc, des. Philip Taaffe. 2007. (Illus.). 48p. 60.00 *(978-1-932598-47-6(2))* Gagosian Gallery.

Deutscher Designer Club (DDC), ed. Gute Gestaltung / Good Design 07. 2007. (GER & ENG., Illus.). 348p. 54.95 *(978-3-7643-8383-1(6)*, 3764383836) Springer.

Devonyar, Jill & Kendall, Richard. Degas & the Ballet: Picturing Movement. 2011. (ENG., Illus.). 288p. 65.00 *(978-1-905711-68-0(9))* Royal Academy of Arts GBR. Dist: Hachette Bk. Group.

Di Suvero, Mark. Mark Di Suvero: Sculpture & Drawings: January 28-March 12, 2011. 2011. (Illus.). 48p. ***(978-0-9794823-3-5(X))*** Tasende Gallery.

Dibenedetto, Steve. Steve Dibenedetto: Recent Paintings & Drawings, 1 vol. 2006. (ENG., Illus.). 46p. 40.00 *(978-0-9771714-9-1(3))* Nolan, David Gallery.

Dietrich. Above the Fold. 2009. (ENG.). 160p. 45.00 *(978-3-7757-2229-2(7))* Hatje Cantz Verlag GmbH & Co KG DEU. Dist: D.A.P./Distributed Art Pubs.

Dietz, Steve. Steina, 1970-2000. 2008. (ENG., Illus.). 128p. 25.00 *(978-0-9764492-7-0(7))* Site Santa Fe.

Dion, Mark. Mark Dion. 2008. (ENG., Illus.). 160p. 60.00 *(978-3-7757-2197-4(5))* Hatje Cantz Verlag GmbH & Co KG DEU. Dist: D.A.P./Distributed Art Pubs.

Dir#xE9;, Ci#xE9;ment, ed. Isabelle Cornaro. 2012. (ENG., Illus.). 64p. 35.00 ***(978-3-03764-208-5(4))*** JRP Ringier Kunstverlag AG CHE. Dist: D.A.P./Distributed Art Pubs.

Documenta. Archive in Motion: 50 Jahre/Years Documenta 1955-2005. (Illus.). 424p. pap. 25.00 *(978-3-86521-398-3(7))* Steidl, Gerhard Druckerei und Verlag DEU. Dist: D.A.P./Distributed Art Pubs.

Donovan, Molly, et al. Warhol: Headlines. 2011. (Illus.). ix, 214p. pap. ***(978-0-89468-373-2(X))*** National Gallery of Art.

d'Orgeval, Domitille, et al. Geometry Beyond Limits: Latin American Contemporary Art. 2010. (ENG & FRE., Illus.). 246p. 60.00 *(978-88-7439-542-2(6))* 5 Continents ITA. Dist: Hachette Bk. Group.

Döring, Jürgen. Lichtenstein Posters. 2009. (GER & ENG., Illus.). 152p. 39.95 *(978-3-7913-4192-7(8))* Prestel Publishing.

Doswald, Christoph, ed. Hanspeter Hofmann: Bonheur Automatique II. 2008. (ENG., Illus.). 180p. 28.00 *(978-3-905829-81-5(9))* JRP Ringier Kunstverlag AG CHE. Dist: D.A.P./Distributed Art Pubs.

Dressler, Iris & Christ, Hans, eds. Subversive Praktiken: Kunst unter Bedingungen politischer Repression 60er-80er / Südamerika / Europa. 2011. (ENG., Illus.). 584p. 60.00 *(978-3-7757-2755-6(8))* Hatje Cantz Verlag GmbH & Co KG DEU. Dist: D.A.P./Distributed Art Pubs.

Dube, Prince Mbusi & Dube, Prince, eds. Dumile Feni Retrospective: Johannesburg Art Gallery. 2007. (ENG., Illus.). 250p. 79.95 *(978-1-86814-442-6(9))* Witwatersrand Univ. Pr. Pubns. ZAF. Dist: Transaction Pubs.

Duchamp, Marcel, et al. Marcel Duchamp: Una Obra Que No Es una Obra "De Arte" 2008. (SPA., Illus.). 358p. *(978-987-21336-7-2(0))* Fundacion Proa.

Dumas, Marlene & Butler, Cornelia H. Marlene Dumas: Measuring Your Own Grave. 2008. (ENG., Illus.). 288p. (C). 55.00 *(978-1-933751-08-5(8))* Museum of Contemporary Art, Los Angeles.

Duncan, Michael, et al. Charles Garabedian: A Retrospective. 2011. *(978-0-89951-111-5(2))* Santa Barbara Museum of Art.

Durant, Sam & Ketchum-Heap of Birds, Shanna. Sam Durant: Scenes from the Pilgrim Story: Myths, Massacres, & Monuments. 2007. (Illus.). 76p. *(978-0-9771419-3-7(4))* Massachusetts College of Art.

Durner, Jurgen, ed. Jurgen Durner: Disappearance. 2010. (ENG., Illus.). 144p. 58.00 *(978-3-86678-349-2(3))* Kerber Verlag DEU. Dist: D.A.P./Distributed Art Pubs.

Dziewior. Michael Hakimi. 2009. (ENG., Illus.). 138p. pap. 40.00 *(978-3-7757-2268-1(8))* Hatje Cantz Verlag GmbH & Co KG DEU. Dist: D.A.P./Distributed Art Pubs.

Ebony, David. Emily Mason: The Fifth Element. 2007. (Illus.). 128p. 39.95 *(978-0-8076-1570-6(6))* Braziller, George Inc.
Eccles, Tom, frwd. At Home/Not at Home. 2010. (ENG., Illus.). 168p. 40.00 *(978-1-936192-07-6(1))* Ctr. for Curatorial Studies, The.
Ecker, Berthold & Hilger, Wolfgang, eds. Die fünfziger Jahre: Kunst und Kunstverständnis in Wien. 2009. (ENG & GER., Illus.). 432p. 49.95 *(978-3-7091-0051-6(8))* Springer Wien AUT. Dist: Actar Birkhauser Distribution.
Eckmann, Sabine & Koepnick, Lutz. Grid()Matrix. 2007. (MLKAM-Screen Arts & New Media Aesthetics Ser.). (ENG., Illus.). 80p. pap. 15.00 *(978-0-936316-20-8(9))* Washington Univ., Mildred Lane Kemper Art Museum.
Eckmann, Sabine & Malone, Meredith. Thaddeus Strode: Absolutes & Nothings. 2008. (Mildred Lane Kemper Art Museum-Contemporary Projects Ser.). (Illus.). 80p. 30.00 *(978-0-936316-24-6(1))* Washington Univ., Mildred Lane Kemper Art Museum.
Eckmann, Sabine, et al. Reality Bites: Making Avant-garde Art in Post-Wall Germany. 2007.Tr. of Reality Bites: Kunst nach dem Mauerfall. (GER.). per. 55.00 *(978-0-936316-21-5(7))* Washington Univ., Mildred Lane Kemper Art Museum.
Eisler, Eva, et al, texts. Cartier: The Power of Style. 2011. (ENG., Illus.). 320p. 49.95 *(978-2-08-020075-4(5))* Flammarion et Cie FRA. Dist: Random Hse., Inc.
Eklund, Douglas. The Pictures Generation, 1974-1984. 2009. 60.00 *(978-1-58839-314-2(3))*; 40.00 *(978-1-58839-315-9(1))* Metropolitan Museum of Art, The.
—The Pictures Generation, 1974-1984. 2009. (ENG., Illus.). 352p. 60.00 *(978-0-300-14892-3(5))* Yale Univ. Pr.
Eleey, Peter, et al, texts. Now You See It. 2009. (ENG., Illus.). 72p. 35.00 *(978-0-934324-47-2(6))* Aspen Art Museum.
Elliott, David & Ozaki, Tetsuya. Bye Bye Kitty!!! Between Heaven & Hell in Contemporary Japanese Art. 2011. (ENG., Illus.). 136p. pap. 35.00 *(978-0-300-16690-3(7))* Yale Univ. Pr.
Elliott, Patrick. Another World: Dalí, Magritte, Miró & the Surrealists. 2011. (ENG., Illus.). 224p. pap. *(978-1-906270-30-8(9))* National Galleries of Scotland.
Elsen, Thomas. Lava Fabrizio Plessi. 2007. (GER & ENG., Illus.). 240p. 40.00 *(978-3-939583-19-6(7))* Kehrer Verlag Heidelberg, Klaus Kehrer DEU. Dist: Consortium Bk. Sales & Distribution.
Emin, Tracey. Tracey Emin: Love Is What You Want. 2011. (ENG., Illus.). 260p. pap. 45.00 ***(978-1-85332-293-8(8))*** Hayward Gallery Publishing GBR. Dist: D.A.P./Distributed Art Pubs.
Emin, Tracey & Freedman, Carl. Tracey Emin: Works, 1963-2006. Luard, Honey, ed. 2006. (ENG., Illus.). 414p. 75.00 *(978-0-8478-2877-7(8))* Rizzoli International Pubns., Inc.
Enaday, Imelda Cajipe. Society of Philippine American Artist Book 2: Selected Works. 2009. *(978-1-61584-052-6(4))* Independent Pub.
Endaya, Imelda Cajipe-, ed. Society of Phillippine American Artists Book 2: Selected Wroks. 2009. pap. *(978-1-61623-680-9(9))* Independent Pub.
Engberg, Siri, ed. & text. Lifelike. 2012. (ENG., Illus.). 192p. pap. 40.00 ***(978-0-935640-68-7(1))*** Walker Art Ctr.
Engler, M. D. & Bee, A. Peter Roehr: Ausstellung von 28. November 2009 bis 7. März 2010. 2010. (ENG.). 184p. 60.00 *(978-3-86568-522-3(6))*, Art Stock Bks. Ltd/Csi) Continental Sales, Inc.
Ensor, James. Doctrinal Nourishment: Art & Anarchism in the Time of James Ensor. 2009. (ENG., Illus.). 88p. pap. 20.00 *(978-0-87587-199-8(2))* Los Angeles County Museum of Art.
Fajardo-Hill, Cecilia, ed. Fortunate Objects/Objetos Afortunados. 2008. (ENG., Illus.). 160p. per. 49.95 *(978-88-8158-662-2(2))* Charta ITA. Dist: D.A.P./Distributed Art Pubs.
Falckenberg, Harald & Weibel, Peter, eds. Paul Thek: Artist's Artist. 2009. (ENG., Illus.). 550p. (gr. 17). 75.00 *(978-0-262-01254-6(5))* MIT Pr.
Farias, Agnaldo, text. Delson Uchoa. 2010. (ENG., Illus.). 120p. 49.95 *(978-88-8158-746-9(7))* Charta ITA. Dist: D.A.P./Distributed Art Pubs.
Farouk Hosny: The Energy of Abstraction. 2008. (Illus.). 58p. pap. 19.95 *(978-0-9678056-5-8(1))* Nova Southeastern Univ., Museum of Art Fort Lauderdale.
Favre, Valerie. Valerie Favre: Visions. 2009. (ENG., Illus.). 208p. 45.00 *(978-3-7757-2443-2(5))* Hatje Cantz Verlag GmbH & Co KG DEU. Dist: D.A.P./Distributed Art Pubs.
Feireiss, Kristin, et al. And: Interdisciplinary Creative Arts from China. 2007. (GER & ENG., Illus.). 71p. *(978-3-937093-83-3(4))* Commerell, Hans-Jurgen, Aedes Pubs.
Felix, Zdenek, text. Remote Memories. 2010. (ENG & GER., Illus.). 72p. 29.00 *(978-3-86678-339-3(6))* Kerber Verlag DEU. Dist: D.A.P./Distributed Art Pubs.
Fer, Briony, et al, texts. James Castle: Show & Store. 2011. (ENG., Illus.). 224p. 55.00 ***(978-1-935202-70-7(7))*** D.A.P./Distributed Art Pubs.
Ferdandez Polanco, Aurora. Impure Vision: Works from the Permanent Collection 1. 2009. 176p. pap. 29.95 *(978-84-8026-287-3(7))* Museo Nacional Centro de Arte Reina Sofia ESP. Dist: Actar Birkhauser Distribution.
Ferguson, Russell. Larry Johnson. 2009. (Illus.). 120p. 45.00 *(978-3-7913-4391-4(2))* Prestel Publishing.
Ferguson, Russell & Alÿs, Francis. Francis Alÿs: Politics of Rehearsal. 2007. (SPA & ENG., Illus.). 142p. *(978-0-943739-32-8(2))* Yale Univ. Pr.
Fibicher, Bernhard, ed. L' Art Expose. (ENG, FRE & GER., Illus.). 320p. pap. *(978-3-89322-784-6(9))* Edition Cantz DEU. Dist: D.A.P./Distributed Art Pubs.
Filipovic, Elena, et al, eds. The Biennial Reader, 2 vols. 2010. (ENG., Illus.). 568p. pap. 55.00 *(978-3-7757-2610-8(1))* Hatje Cantz Verlag GmbH & Co KG DEU. Dist: D.A.P./Distributed Art Pubs.
Fineberg, Jonathan, intro. Ilya & Emilia Kabakov: The Center of Cosmic Energy, 1 vol. 2008. (ENG., Illus.). 92p. 25.00 *(978-1-880593-06-6(8))* Tufts Univ. Gallery.
Finessi, Beppe. Mangiarotti. Finessi, Beppe, ed. 2010. (ENG & ITA., Illus.). 120p. 49.95 *(978-88-7570-220-5(9))* Corraini ITA. Dist: D.A.P./Distributed Art Pubs.
Firmin, Sandra. Artpark: 1974-1984. 2011. *(978-0-9842518-1-0(2))* Princeton Architectural Pr.
Firmin, Sandra Q. & Joyce, Julie, eds. Mudman: The Odyssey of Kim Jones. 2007. (ENG., Illus.). 159p. (gr. 17). pap. 19.95 *(978-0-262-56224-9(3))* MIT Pr.
Fischli, Peter & Weiss, David, photos by. Plötzlich diese Übersicht. 4th ed. 2008. (POR, GER & ENG., Illus.). 180p. pap. 58.00 *(978-3-906135-41-0(1))* Verlag der Buchhandlung Walther Konig DEU. Dist: D.A.P./Distributed Art Pubs.
Fleckner, Uwe. The Invention of the 20th Century: Carl Einstein & the Avant-Gardes. 2009. 324p. pap. 65.00 *(978-84-8026-386-3(5))* Museo Nacional Centro de Arte Reina Sofia ESP. Dist: Actar Birkhauser Distribution.
Flinterman, Koos, ed. SuperStories. 2009. (ENG., Illus.). 240p. *(978-90-5856-304-0(9))*, Stichting Kunstboak (Acc)) Antique Collectors' Club.
Fort, Ilene Susan, et al, contrib. by. In Wonderland: The Surrealist Adventures of Women Artists in Mexico & the United States. 2012. (ENG., Illus.). 256p. 60.00 ***(978-3-7913-5141-4(9))*** Prestel Publishing.
Foster, Elena & Obrist, Hans Ulrich, eds. Ways Beyond Art: Ai Weiwei. 2009. (SPA & ENG., Illus.). 133p. *(978-0-9559613-2-8(7))* Ivory Pr.
Foster, Susan Leigh, et al. Move. Choreographing You: Art & Dance since the 1960s. Rosenthal, Stephanie, ed. 2011. (ENG., Illus.). 176p. (gr. 17). pap. 35.00 *(978-0-262-51629-7(2))* MIT Pr.
Fox, Ron. Cow Parade West Hartford: Around the World & Home Again. 2007. pap. 22.00 *(978-1-933197-42-5(0))* Orange Frazer Pr.
Fox, Sandi & Kiracofe, Roderick. Going West! Quilts & Community. 2007. (ENG., Illus.). 144p. 25.00 *(978-1-904832-45-4(8))* Giles, D. Ltd. GBR. Dist: Antique Collectors' Club.
Franco, James. James Franco: Dangerous Book Four Boys. Heiss, Alanna, ed. 2012. (ENG., Illus.). 208p. 50.00 ***(978-0-8478-3813-4(7)***, Skira) Rizzoli International Pubns., Inc.
Frank, Fiona & Coyle, Judith. Hannah Frank: Footsteps on the Sands of Time; A Hundredth Birthday Celebration Gallimaufry. 2008. (Illus.). 148p. pap. *(978-1-904999-73-7(5))* Kennedy & Boyd.
Frecon, Suzan. Suzan Frecon. 2010. (ENG., Illus.). 108p. 55.00 *(978-1-934435-29-8(5))* Radius Bks.
Fred L. Emerson Gallery Staff, contrib. by. The Best Kind of Life: Edward W. Root As Teacher, Collector, & Naturalist, Emerson Gallery, Hamilton College, September 27, 2007-January 6, 2008. 2007. (Illus.). 55p. *(978-1-880640-11-1(2))* Hamilton College, Emerson Gallery.
Freiman, Lisa D., et al. Gloria: Allora & Calzadilla. 2011. (ENG., Illus.). 160p. 45.00 ***(978-3-7913-5137-7(0))*** Prestel Publishing.
Frey Norris Gallery, prod. Wolfgang Paalen: Implicit Spaces. 2007. pap. 25.00 *(978-0-9795141-0-4(X))* Norris, Frey Gallery.
Friedel, Helmut & Hoberg, Annegret. Kandinsky Complete Prints. 2009. (GER & ENG., Illus.). 296p. 69.00 *(978-3-87909-964-1(2)*, Art Stock Bks. Ltd/Csi) Continental Sales, Inc.
Friedrich, Julia & K#xF6;nig, Kasper, eds. Wüste, Meer und Sterne: Desert, Sea & Stars. 2011. (GER & ENG., Illus.). 152p. 55.00 ***(978-3-86560-971-7(6))*** Verlag der Buchhandlung Walther Konig DEU. Dist: D.A.P./Distributed Art Pubs.
Frieling, Rudolf. The Art of Participation, 1950 to Now. 2008. (ENG., Illus.). 224p. 39.95 *(978-0-500-23858-5(8))* Thames & Hudson.
Frieze Art Fair Yearbook 2008-9. 2008. (ENG., Illus.). 544p. pap. 35.00 *(978-0-9553201-3-2(5))* Frieze GBR. Dist: D.A.P./Distributed Art Pubs.
Fryberger, Betsy G., et al. Picasso: Graphic Magician - Prints from the Norton Simon Museum. Date not set. 176p. *(978-0-937031-12-4(7))* Cantor, Iris & B. Gerald Ctr. for Visual Arts at Stanford Univ.
Fuchs, Rudi, contrib. by. With a Probability of Being Seen. Dorothee & Konrad Fischer: Archives of an Attitude. 2011. 384p. 65.00 *(978-84-92505-44-9(3))* Museu d'Art Contemporani de Barcelona ESP. Dist: Actar Birkhauser Distribution.
Fuentes, Carlos. Frida Kahlo: National Homage 1907-2007. 2008. (ENG., Illus.). 400p. 65.00 *(978-968-5208-88-8(3))* R.M. Editorial, S.A. de C.V. MEX. Dist: D.A.P./Distributed Art Pubs.
Fundacio Joan Miro, creator. Modernitat Americana: Obres de la Corcoran Gallery of Art: 1 Novembre 2008-25 Gener 2009. 2009. (ENG, FRE & SPA., Illus.). 172p. *(978-84-934730-8-2(1))* Fundacio Joan Miro.
Furness, Rosalind. Frieze Art Fair Yearbook, 1 vol. 2007. (ENG., Illus.). 480p. pap. 30.00 *(978-0-9553201-2-5(7))* Frieze GBR. Dist: D.A.P./Distributed Art Pubs.
Furness, Rosalind & Starling, Anna. Frieze Art Fair Yearbook 2009-10. 2009. (ENG., Illus.). 548p. pap. 35.00 *(978-0-9553201-4-9(3))* Frieze GBR. Dist: D.A.P./Distributed Art Pubs.
Gagosian Gallery Staff, compiled by. Glenn Brown. 2010. (ENG., Illus.). 148p. 100.00 *(978-0-8478-3488-4(3))* Rizzoli International Pubns., Inc.
Gagosian Gallery Staff, et al, contrib. by. Ferus. 2nd ed. 2009. (Illus.). 146p. 55.00 *(978-0-8478-3234-7(1))* Rizzoli International Pubns., Inc.
Gale, Matthew, ed. Dali & Film, 1 vol. 2007. (ENG., Illus.). 238p. 60.00 *(978-0-87070-730-8(2))* Museum of Modern Art.
Gass, Alison & Zimbardo, Tanya. Fifty Years of Bay Area Art: The SECA Awards. 2011. (Illus.). 168p. ***(978-0-918471-89-5(3))*** San Francisco Museum of Modern Art.
Gelburd, Gail. Ajiaco: Stirrings of the Cuban Soul. 2010. (ENG., Illus.). 112p. pap. 29.95 *(978-1-58465-847-4(9))* Univ. Pr. of New England.
Gellatly, Kelly. Gordon Bennett. 2008. (ENG., Illus.). 135p. pap. 29.95 *(978-0-7241-0290-7(6))* National Gallery of Victoria AUS. Dist: National Bk. Network.
George, Stephanie & Haider, Carlota F. Sowing Dreams, Cultivating Lives: Nikkei Farmers in Pre-World War II Orange County. 2009. pap. *(978-0-930046-27-9(7))* California State Univ. Fullerton, Ctr. for Oral & Public History.
Georgia Museum of Art Staff & Goldfarb, Stephen J., contrib. by. The South in Black & White: The Graphic Works of James E. Routh Jr. , 1939-1946. 2009. (ENG.). 34p. pap. 20.00 *(978-0-915977-71-0(0))* Univ. of Georgia, Georgia Museum of Art.
Gercken, Gü, et al. Ernst Ludwig Kirchner: Farbige Druckgraphik. 2008. (GER., Illus.). 200p. (C). pap. 55.00 *(978-3-7774-4345-4(X))* Hirmer Verlag GmbH DEU. Dist: Brown, David Bk. Co., The.
German, Andrew. John Stobart: The Grandeur of America's Age of Sail. 2009. 168p. 34.95 *(978-0-9635775-4-2(9))*; (ENG.). pap. 24.95 *(978-0-9635775-5-9(7))* Osmington Hse. Publishing.
Gingeras, Alison M. Sequence 1: Painting & Sculpture from the François Pinault Collection. 2008. (Illus.). 328p. (ENG, FRE & ITA.). 75.00 *(978-88-6130-216-7(5))*; (FRE, ITA & ENG., 75.00 *(978-88-6130-206-8(8))* Skira Editore ITA. Dist: Random Hse., Inc.
Giviskos, Christine & Martin Martin, Fernando. Picasso & the Circus: Fin-de-Siecle Paris & the Suite de Saltimbanques, 1 vol. Earenfight, Phillip J., ed. 2011. (ENG., Illus.). 72p. pap. 19.95 ***(978-0-9826156-2-1(0))*** Dickinson College, The Trout Gallery.
Goetz, Ingvild & Urbaschek, Stephan, eds. Peter Fischli, David Weiss. 2011. (ENG & GER., Illus.). 192p. 55.00 *(978-3-7757-2735-8(3))* Hatje Cantz Verlag GmbH & Co KG DEU. Dist: D.A.P./Distributed Art Pubs.
Gomez, Edward Madrid, text. Sam Glankoff: Print-Paintings. 2007. (Illus.). 23p. *(978-0-9777686-7-7(8))* Carberry, Valerie Gallery, Inc.
Görner, Veit & Moll, Frank-Thorsten, eds. Compeshitstem: The New Deal. 2010. (ENG.). 114p. 35.00 *(978-3-86828-087-6(1))* Kehrer Verlag Heidelberg, Klaus Kehrer DEU. Dist: Consortium Bk. Sales & Distribution.
Gorner, Veit & Schrader, Kristin, eds. Jake & Dinos Chapman: Memento Moronika. 2009. (ENG & GER., Illus.). 94p. pap. 35.00 *(978-3-86560-582-5(6))* Verlag der Buchhandlung Walther Konig DEU. Dist: D.A.P./Distributed Art Pubs.
Goude, Jean-Paul. Jean-Paul Goude. 2012. (ENG., Illus.). 432p. pap. 49.95 ***(978-0-500-51604-1(9***, 551604) Thames & Hudson.
Grassi, Francesca, ed. Rirkrit Tiravanija: A Retrospective: Tomorrow Is Another Fine Day, 1 vol. 2007. (ENG., Illus.). 218p. 75.00 *(978-3-905770-32-2(6))* JRP Ringier Kunstverlag AG CHE. Dist: D.A.P./Distributed Art Pubs.
Gray, Zoe & Szewczyk, Monika. Billy Apple(r). Schafhausen, Nicolaus, ed. 2010. (ENG., Illus.). 112p. pap. 15.00 *(978-90-73362-89-5(X))* Witte De With Centre for Contemporary Art NLD. Dist: D.A.P./Distributed Art Pubs.
Green, Renée. Renee Green: Endless Dreams & Time-Based Streams. 2011. (ENG., Illus.). 144p. pap. 35.00 *(978-0-9826789-0-9(8))* Yerba Buena Ctr. for the Arts.
Greene, Balcomb & Peters, Lisa N. Balcomb Greene, 1904-1990: A Retrospective: November 20, 2008-January 3, 2009. 2008. (Illus.). 24p. pap. *(978-0-945936-94-7(X))* Spanierman Gallery.
Greene, Vivien, ed. Utopia Matters. 2010. 45.00 *(978-0-89207-400-6(0))* Guggenheim, Solomon R. Museum.
Grenville, Bruce & Steedman, Scott, eds. Visions of British Columbia: A Landscape Manual, 1 vol. 2010. (ENG., Illus.). 256p. pap. 35.00 *(978-1-55365-500-8(1))* D&M Pubs. Inc. CAN. Dist: Perseus-PGW.
Gronert, Stefan & Berg, Stephan, eds. Der Westen leuchtet. 2011. (ENG & GER., Illus.). 416p. 65.00 *(978-3-86678-432-1(5))* Kerber Verlag DEU. Dist: D.A.P./Distributed Art Pubs.
Gronlund, Melissa, ed. Frieze Art Fair Yearbook, 1 vol. 2006. (ENG., Illus.). 480p. pap. 30.00 *(978-0-9527414-9-7(0))* Frieze GBR. Dist: D.A.P./Distributed Art Pubs.
Grunenberg, Christoph. Peter Blake. Sillars, Laurence, ed. 2007. (ENG., Illus.). 216p. pap. 49.95 *(978-1-85437-717-3(5))* Tate Publishing, Ltd. GBR. Dist: Hachette Bk. Group.
Gualdoni, Flaminio & Romano, Eileen. Surrealism. 2008. (Skira MINI Artbooks Ser.). (ENG., Illus.). 96p. pap. 8.99 *(978-88-6130-537-3(7))* Skira Editore ITA. Dist: Random Hse., Inc.
Guilbaut, Serge, contrib. by. Be-Bomb: The Transatlantic War of Images & All That Jazz. 1946-1956. 2008. (Illus.). 774p. pap. *(978-84-89771-47-5(2))* Museu d'Art Contemporani de Barcelona.
Gulen, Mai & Lerheim, Karen, eds. Emunch. No - Text & Image. 2011. 303p. 50.00 *(978-82-90128-71-0(1))* Oslo kommunes kunstsamlinger NOR. Dist: International Specialized Bk. Services.
Guo-Qiang, Cai. Cai Guo-Qiang: Fallen Blossoms. 2010. (ENG., Illus.). 208p. 55.00 *(978-0-9724556-5-7(5))* Fabric Workshop, Inc.
Gustafson, Donna, ed. Images from the World Between: The Circus in Twentieth-Century American Art. 2007. (ENG., Illus.). 184p. (gr. 17). pap. 19.95 *(978-0-262-57241-5(9))* MIT Pr.
Guyton, Wade. Wade Guyton: Zeichnungen FüR ein Kleines Zimmer. 2011. (ENG., Illus.). 130p. pap. 49.95 ***(978-3-86560-988-5(0))*** Verlag der Buchhandlung Walther Konig DEU. Dist: D.A.P./Distributed Art Pubs.
Gygax, Raphael & Munder, Heike, eds. Alex Bag. 2011. (ENG., Illus.). 230p. 55.00 ***(978-3-03764-220-7(3))*** JRP Ringier Kunstverlag AG CHE. Dist: D.A.P./Distributed Art Pubs.
Haass, Ulrich, ed. As We Like It: Jewellery & Tableware 1988-2008. 2008. (ENG., Illus.). 320p. 70.00 *(978-3-89790-291-6(5))* Arnoldsche Art Pubs. DEU. Dist: Antique Collectors' Club.
Hahn, Eckart. Grand Ouvert: Diese Publikation erschien anlässlich der Ausstellungen: Kammerspiele, Galerie Rothamel, Frankfurt a. M. 4.September - 17.Oktober 2009, Intimate Play, WAGNER+PARTNER, Berlin 6.November 2009 - 2.Januar 2010. 2010. (ENG., Illus.). 48p. 27.00 *(978-3-86678-343-0(4))* Kerber Verlag DEU. Dist: D.A.P./Distributed Art Pubs.
Hall, Sarah J. & McPherson, Craig. Steel: Pittsburgh Drawings by Craig Mcpherson. 2008. (Illus.). 48p. pap. 14.95 *(978-0-9703425-9-1(4))* Frick Art & Historical Ctr.,The.
Hamilton, Richard. Richard Hamilton: Modern Moral Matters, 1 vol. 2010. (ENG., Illus.). 96p. pap. 45.00 *(978-3-86560-751-5(9))* Verlag der Buchhandlung Walther Konig DEU. Dist: D.A.P./Distributed Art Pubs.
Hammond, Jane. Jane Hammond: Paper Work. Doezema, Marianne, ed. 2007. (ENG., Illus.). 152p. pap. 35.00 *(978-0-271-02981-8(1))* Pennsylvania State Univ. Pr.
Hanru, Hou, contrib. by. China Onward: The Estella Collection: Chinese Contemporary Art, 1996-2006, 1 vol. 2007. (ENG., Illus.). 468p. 85.00 *(978-87-91607-38-7(8))* Louisana DNK. Dist: D.A.P./Distributed Art Pubs.
Hanru, Hou & Scardi, Gabi, eds. Wherever We Go/Ovunque Andiamo: Arte, Identita, Culture in Transito/Art, Identity, Cultures in Transit. 2008. (ITA & ENG., Illus.). 300p. pap. 45.00 *(978-88-7439-390-9(3))* 5 Continents ITA. Dist: Hachette Bk. Group.
Hansen, Elisabeth Delin, et al, eds. Gil & Moti: Totally Devoted to You. 2011. (ENG., Illus.). 160p. 45.00 ***(978-3-7757-2847-8(3))*** Hatje Cantz Verlag GmbH & Co KG DEU. Dist: D.A.P./Distributed Art Pubs.
Hanzal, Carla M. Contemporary, Cool & Collected. 2007. *(978-0-9762300-3-8(8))* Mint Museum, The.
Harrison, Rachel. Rachel Harrison: Museum with Walls. 2010. (ENG., Illus.). 272p. 65.00 *(978-1-936192-03-8(9))*, Ctr. for Curatorial Studies) Bard College Pubns. Office.
Hart, Deborah. Imants Tillers: One World Many Visions. 2007. (ENG., Illus.). 136p. 60.00 *(978-0-642-54150-5(7))* National Gallery of Australia AUS. Dist: Univ. of Washington Pr.
Hartley, Keith. Andy Warhol: A Celebration of Life & Death. 2008. (ENG., Illus.). 112p. pap. *(978-1-903278-99-4(6))* National Galleries of Scotland.
Harvey, Doug. Heart & Torch: Rick Griffin's Transcendence. 2007. (Illus.). 155p. pap. 29.95 *(978-1-58423-279-7(X))* Gingko Pr., Inc.
—Heart & Torch: Rick Griffin's Transcendence. 2007. *(978-0-940872-32-5(3))* Laguna Beach Museum of Art.
Haskell, Barbara, et al. Lyonel Feininger: At the Edge of the World. 2011. (Illus.). ix, 277p. *(978-0-300-17730-5(5))* Whitney Museum of American Art.
Hassrick, Peter H., et al, contrib. by. A Century of Sanctuary: The Art of Zion National Park. 2008. (ENG.). 61p. *(978-0-915630-47-9(8))*; pap. *(978-0-915630-48-6(6))* Zion Natural History Assn.
Hauser, Jens, ed. Sk-Interfaces: Exploding Borders in Art, Science & Technology. 2008. (ENG., Illus.). 160p. 50.00 *(978-1-84631-149-9(7))* Liverpool Univ. Pr. GBR. Dist: Chicago Distribution Ctr.
HC Porter Fine Art Book: Backyards & Beyond: Mississippians & Their Stories. 2008. (Illus.). 200p. 45.00 *(978-0-9818499-0-4(3))* Backyards & Beyond.
Hegyi, Lorand, et al, contrib. by. From One Century to Another: The Collection of the Musee d'Art Moderne de Saint-Etienne Métropole. 2008. (ENG., Illus.). 272p. 65.00 *(978-88-6130-453-6(2))* Skira Editore ITA. Dist: Random Hse., Inc.
Hegyi, Lorand, ed. Essential Experiences. 2010. 168p. pap. 63.50 *(978-88-370-7390-9(9))* Electa ITA. Dist: Trans-Atlantic Pubns., Inc.
Held, Peter, ed. Eden Revisited: The Ceramic Art of Kurt Weiser. 2007. (ENG.). 96p. ***(978-0-9777624-5-3(9))*** Arizona State Univ. Art Museum.
Hentschel, Martin, ed. Andreas Gursky: Werke 80-08. 2011. (ENG., Illus.). 272p. 60.00 ***(978-3-7757-3022-8(2))*** Hatje Cantz Verlag GmbH & Co KG DEU. Dist: D.A.P./Distributed Art Pubs.
Herndon-Consagra, Francesca & Norton, Sydney. The Immediate Touch: German, Austrian + Swiss Drawings from Saint Louis Collections. Steiner, Mary Ann, ed. 2008. (Illus.). 192p. pap. 39.99 *(978-0-89178-090-8(4))* St. Louis Art Museum.
Herzog, Hans-Michael. Guillermo Kuitca, 1 vol. 2007. (SPA & ENG., Illus.). 236p. 55.00 *(978-3-7757-1923-0(7))* Hatje Cantz Verlag GmbH & Co KG DEU. Dist: D.A.P./Distributed Art Pubs.
Hesse, Eva. Datebooks, 1964/65: A Facsimile Edition, 3 vols., Set. 2007. (ENG., Illus.). 320p. 50.00 *(978-0-300-11109-5(6))* Yale Univ. Pr.
Hickey, Dave, text. Sunflowers. 2010. (ENG., Illus.). 88p. 50.00 *(978-3-86521-836-0(9))* Steidl, Gerhard Druckerei und Verlag DEU. Dist: D.A.P./Distributed Art Pubs.
Hickey, Dave, et al. James Hayward: Works 1975-2007. 2007. 45.00 *(978-0-9761509-3-0(X))* Modernism, Inc.
Higa, Karin. Living Flowers: Ikebana & Contemporary Art. 2009. (Illus.). 88p. *(978-1-881161-16-5(1))* Japanese American National Museum.
Higgie, Jennifer, text. Scenes. 2010. (ENG., Illus.). 64p. 39.95 *(978-3-03764-029-6(4))* JRP Ringier Kunstverlag AG CHE. Dist: D.A.P./Distributed Art Pubs.
Higgins, Steven. Still Moving: The Film & Media Collections of the Museum of Modern Art, 1 vol. 2006. (ENG., Illus.). 376p. (gr. 13-18). 65.00 *(978-0-87070-326-3(9))* Museum of Modern Art.
High Museum of Art Staff. John Portman: Art & Architecture. 2009. (ENG., Illus.). 160p. pap. 30.00 *(978-1-932543-30-8(9))* High Museum of Art.

Hirschhorn, Thomas & Bizzarri, Thomas, eds. Thomas Hirschhorn: Establishing a Critical Corpus. 2011. (ENG., Illus.). 365p. 44.95 ***(978-3-03764-185-9(1))*** JRP Ringier Kunstverlag AG CHE. Dist: D.A.P./Distributed Art Pubs.

Hirst, Damien. Cornucopia. 2010. (ENG.). 160p. 240.00 *(978-1-906967-32-1(6))*; (Illus.). 85.00 *(978-1-906967-31-4(8))* Other Criteria GBR. Dist: Abrams, Hachette Bk. Group.

—Corpus: Drawings 1981-2006. Wilner, Millicent, ed. 2008. (ENG., Illus.). 410p. 140.00 *(978-1-932598-42-1(1))* Other Criteria GBR. Dist: Hachette Bk. Group.

—Dark Trees. 2010. (ENG.). 80p. 210.00 *(978-1-906967-28-4(8))*; (Illus.). 70.00 *(978-1-906967-27-7(X))* Other Criteria GBR. Dist: Abrams, Hachette Bk. Group.

—In the Darkest Hour There May Be Light: Works from Damien Hirst's Murderme Collection. Beard, Jason, ed. 2008. (ENG., Illus.). 152p. 75.00 *(978-1-905190-12-6(3))* Other Criteria GBR. Dist: Hachette Bk. Group.

—No Love Lost. 2010. (ENG., Illus.). 64p. 40.00 *(978-1-906967-22-2(9))*; 200.00 *(978-1-906967-23-9(7))* Other Criteria GBR. Dist: Hachette Bk. Group.

—Nothing Matters. 2010. (ENG., Illus.). 120p. 80.00 *(978-1-906967-19-2(9))*; 72p. 240.00 *(978-1-906967-20-8(2))* Other Criteria GBR. Dist: Hachette Bk. Group.

Hirst, Damien. Poisons + Remedies. aut. ltd. ed. 2011. (ENG.). 88p. pap. 265.00 ***(978-1-906967-45-1(8))*** Abrams.

Hlavajova Maria, et al, eds. Open 16: the Art Biennial as a Global Phenomenon. 2009. (ENG., Illus.). 112p. pap. 30.00 *(978-90-5662-667-9(1))* NAi Uitgevers / Publishers Stichting NLD. Dist: D.A.P./Distributed Art Pubs.

Hochdorfer, Achim, text. Josh Smith: Hidden Darts Reader. 2009. (ENG & GER., Illus.). 220p. pap. 39.95 *(978-3-86560-495-8(1))* Verlag der Buchhandlung Walther Konig DEU. Dist: D.A.P./Distributed Art Pubs.

Hodermarsky, Elisabeth & Childs, Elizabeth C. John La Farge's Second Paradise: Voyages in the South Seas, 1890-1891. 2010. (Illus.). xvi, 224p. pap. *(978-0-89467-976-6(7))* Yale Univ. Art Gallery.

Hodermarsky, Elisabeth, et al. John la Farge's Second Paradise: Voyages in the South Seas, 1890-1891. 2010. (Illus.). 240p. 55.00 *(978-0-300-14135-1(1))* Yale Univ. Pr.

Hoet, Jan. Documenta IX: Main Catalog, 3 vols. 2nd ed. (GER., Illus.). 896p. *(978-3-89322-381-7(9))* Edition Cantz DEU. Dist: D.A.P./Distributed Art Pubs.

Holland, Allison. Joseph Beuys & Rudolph Steiner: Imaginat. 2008. (ENG.). 104p. pap. 19.95 *(978-0-7241-0291-4(4))* National Gallery of Victoria AUS. Dist: National Bk. Network.

Holler-Schuster, Gunther, ed. Alois Mosbacher: Outside Fiction. 2011. (ENG., Illus.). 240p. pap. 60.00 *(978-3-7757-2729-7(9))* Hatje Cantz Verlag GmbH & Co KG DEU. Dist: D.A.P./Distributed Art Pubs.

Holzach, Cornelie, ed. Art Déco Schmuck und Accessoires: Ein neuer Stil für eine neue Welt. 2008. (ENG., Illus.). 160p. 70.00 *(978-3-89790-290-9(7))* Arnoldsche Art Pubs. DEU. Dist: Antique Collectors' Club.

Holzer, Jenny. Jenny Holzer: Retro. 2011. (ENG., Illus.). 68p. 30.00 ***(978-1-61623-719-6(8))*** Independent Pub.

Hood Museum of Art. Men of Fire: Jose Clemente Orozco & Jackson Pollock. 2012. (ENG., Illus.). 120p. pap. 24.95 ***(978-0-944722-42-8(3))*** Hood Museum of Art.

Hultén, Pontus. Andy Warhol: Catalogue Published on the Occasion of the Andy Warhol Exhibition at Moderna Museet in Stockholm, February-March 1968. Warhol, Andy & Konig, Kasper, eds. 2010. (ENG., Illus.). 648p. pap. 50.00 *(978-3-86521-614-4(5))* Steidl, Gerhard Druckerei und Verlag DEU. Dist: D.A.P./Distributed Art Pubs.

Hunches, Geometrics, Organics: Paintings by Frederick Hammersley. 2007. (Illus.) 52p. pap. 20.00 *(978-0-9786996-4-2(5))* Pomona College Museum of Art.

Hung, Wu, ed. & text. Hung Liu: Great Granary. 2011. (ENG., Illus.). 220p. 50.00 *(978-988-18907-3-3(X))* Timezone 8 Ltd. HKG. Dist: D.A.P./Distributed Art Pubs.

Hushka, Rock. The Eloquent Silver Curve: The Jewelry of Flora Book. 2011. pap. ***(978-0-924335-34-1(3))*** Tacoma Art Museum.

Husslein-Arco, Agnes & Koja, Stephan, eds. Rodin & Vienna. 2011. (Illus.). 175p. 49.95 *(978-3-7774-3311-0(X))* Hirmer Verlag GmbH DEU. Dist: Chicago Distribution Ctr.

IDB Cultural Center Staff, et al, contrib. by. 50 Años, 50 Obras: Obras Sobresalientes Del Arte de América Latina y el Caribe Del Siglo XX. 2009. (ENG & SPA., Illus.). 89p. ***(978-1-59782-088-2(1))*** Inter-American Development Bank.

Iles, Chrissie. Paul Mccarthy: Central Symmetrical Rotation Movement: Three Installations, Two Films. 2008. (Illus.). 72p. 18.95 *(978-0-300-14138-2(6))* Yale Univ. Pr.

IMMA Staff & Kissane, Seán, eds. Vertical Thoughts: Morton Feldman & the Visual Arts. 2011. (ENG., Illus.). 318p. pap. 45.00 *(978-1-907020-08-7(X))* Irish Museum of Modern Art IRL. Dist: D.A.P./Distributed Art Pubs.

Inglot, Joanna. Warm: A Feminist Art Collective in Minnesota. 2007. (Illus.). 224p. pap. 34.95 *(978-0-8166-5038-5(1))* Univ. of Minnesota Pr.

Inselmann, Andrea. A Private Eye: Dada, Surrealism, & More from the Brandt Collection. 2006. (Illus.). 160p. pap. 25.00 *(978-0-9646042-3-0(X))* Cornell Univ., Herbert F. Johnson Museum of Art.

Inselmann, Andrea & Arning, Bill. Marc Swanson: Hurry on Sundown. 2009. (Illus.). 96p. pap. *(978-1-934260-09-8(6))* Cornell Univ., Herbert F. Johnson Museum of Art.

Ireson, Nancy & Robins, Anna Gruetzner. Toulouse Lautrec & Jane Avril: Beyond the Moulin Rouge. 2011. (Illus.). 160p. pap. 50.00 ***(978-1-907372-24-7(5))*** Holberton, Paul Publishing GBR. Dist: Casemate Pubs. & Bk. Distributors, LLC.

Issa, Rose, ed. Parastou Forouhar: Art, Life & Death in Iran. 2011. (ENG., Illus.). 128p. pap. 21.95 ***(978-0-86356-448-2(8))*** Saqi Bks. GBR. Dist: Consortium Bk. Sales & Distribution.

Jancar, Ivan & Kriska, Fedor. Dusan Kallay: Magical World. 2007. (Illus.). 360p. 140.00 *(978-80-7145-911-8(9))* Slovart, Vydavatel'stvo, spol. s.r.o. SVK. Dist: Independent Pubs. Group.

Jane, Xylor. Xylor Jane. 2010. (ENG., Illus.). 64p. pap. 20.00 *(978-0-9820947-8-5(7))* PictureBox, Inc.

Jankowski, Christian. Christian Jankowski: Everything Fell Together, 1 vol. 2006. (ENG., Illus.). 200p. pap. 45.00 *(978-1-879003-42-2(2))* Des Moines Art Ctr.

Jenkins, David Fraser. Paul Nash: The Elements. 2010. (ENG., Illus.). 168p. pap. 39.95 *(978-1-85759-519-9(6))* Scala, Editions FRA. Dist: National Bk. Network.

Johns, Jasper. Light Bulb. 2008. (ENG., Illus.). 96p. 45.00 *(978-0-934418-69-0(1))* Museum of Contemporary Art, San Diego.

Jones, Amelia, et al, texts. ASCO: Elite of the Obscure. 2011. (ENG., Illus.). 432p. 60.00 ***(978-3-7757-3003-7(6))*** Hatje Cantz Verlag GmbH & Co KG DEU. Dist: D.A.P./Distributed Art Pubs.

Jose de Rivera: Valerie Carberry Gallery, January 5 - March 3, 2007. 2007. 15.00 *(978-0-9777686-3-9(5))* Carberry, Valerie Gallery, Inc.

Joyce, Julie. Pasadena to Santa Barbara: A Selected History of Art in Southern California, 1951-1969. 2012. ***(978-0-89951-113-9(9))*** Santa Barbara Museum of Art.

Judd, Donald. Donald Judd, 1 vol. 2012. (ENG., Illus.). 128p. 65.00 ***(978-3-86930-390-1(5))*** Steidl, Gerhard Druckerei und Verlag DEU. Dist: Innovative Logistics.

Jungmann, Burglind. Life in Ceramics: Five Contemporary Korean Artists. 2010. (ENG., Illus.). 56p. pap. 20.00 *(978-0-9778344-3-3(3))* Univ. of California, Los Angeles, Fowler Museum of Cultural History.

Kamps, Toby. Art of Our Time: Selections from the Ulrich Museum of Art, Wichita State University. McDonnell, Patricia & Stamey, Emily, eds. 2010. (ENG., Illus.). 168p. 49.95 *(978-0-295-99024-8(4))*; pap. 29.95 *(978-0-295-99025-5(2))* Wichita State Univ., Ulrich Museum of Art.

Kaneda, Shirley & text. Shirley Kaneda: New Paintings. 2007. (Illus.). 30p. per. *(978-0-9795501-0-2(6))* Danese.

Kaplin, David L. California Design, 1930-1965: Living in a Modern Way. Kaplan, Wendy, ed. 2011. (ENG., Illus.). 360p. (gr. 17). 60.00 ***(978-0-262-01607-0(9))*** MIT Pr.

Kapoor, Anish. Anish Kapoor: Turning the World Upside Down. 2011. (ENG., Illus.). 240p. 49.95 *(978-3-86560-916-8(3))* Verlag der Buchhandlung Walther Konig DEU. Dist: D.A.P./Distributed Art Pubs.

—Anish Kapoor: Flashback. 2011. (ENG., Illus.). 96p. 35.00 *(978-1-85332-288-4(1))* Hayward Gallery Publishing GBR. Dist: D.A.P./Distributed Art Pubs.

Karmel, Pepe, ed. & text. New York Cool: Painting & Sculpture from the NYU Art Collection. 2009. (ENG., Illus.). 208p. pap. 40.00 *(978-0-615-18105-9(8))* Grey Art Gallery & Study Ctr., New York Univ.

Karnes, Andrea. Pretty Baby: February 23-May 27, 2007. 2007. *(978-0-929865-26-3(X))* Modern Art Museum of Fort Worth.

katlan, Alexander/w., Sr. The Salmagundi Club Painting Exhibition Records 1889 To 1939: A Guide to the Annual Exhibition of Oil Paintings & the Annual Exhibition & Auction Sale of Pictures. 2008. (Illus.). 480p. 65.00 *(978-0-9791290-1-8(X))* Katlan, Alexander Conservator, Inc.

Katz, Alex. Alex Katz: Prints. 2010. (ENG., Illus.). 240p. 60.00 *(978-3-7757-2585-9(7))* Hatje Cantz Verlag GmbH & Co KG DEU. Dist: D.A.P./Distributed Art Pubs.

Katz, Vincent, et al. Retro/Active: The Work of Rafael Ferrer. Cullen, Deborah, ed. 2010.Tr. of Retro/activa: la obra de Rafael Ferrer. (ENG & SPA., Illus.). 160p. pap. 35.00 *(978-1-882454-27-3(8))* El Museo del Barrio.

Kellner, Clive & Gonzalez, Sergio-Albio, eds. Thami Mnyele + Medu: Art Ensemble Retrospective. 2010. (ENG., Illus.). 264p. pap. 45.00 *(978-1-77009-688-2(4))* Jacana Media ZAF. Dist: Independent Pubs. Group.

Kennedy, Brian & Burke, Emily Shubert, eds. Modern & Contemporary Art at Dartmouth: Highlights from the Hood Museum of Art. 2009. (Illus.). 240p. pap. 40.00 *(978-1-58465-787-3(1))* Hood Museum of Art.

Kennedy, Brian P. & Burke, Emily. Modern & Contemporary Art at Dartmouth: Highlights from the Hood Museum of Art. 2009. (Illus.). x, 230p. *(978-1-58465-786-6(3))* Hood Museum of Art.

Kennedy, Ian & Treuherz, Julian. The Railway: Art in the Age of Steam. 2008. (ENG., Illus.). 288p. 65.00 *(978-0-300-13878-8(4))* Yale Univ. Pr.

Kentridge, William. William Kentridge: Carnets D'Egypte. 2010. (FRE., Illus.). 64p. *(978-2-35031-295-8(X))*; *(978-2-916275-84-0(3))* Dilecta, Editions.

Kentridge, William & text. Trace: Prints from the Museum of Modern Art. 2010. (ENG., Illus.). 112p. 29.95 *(978-0-87070-779-7(5))* Museum of Modern Art.

Kesser, Caroline. Jan Krugier: My Journey with Art - Interviews with Caroline Kesser. 2012. (ENG., Illus.). 150p. 49.00 *(978-3-85881-719-8(8))* Scheidegger und Spiess AG, Verlag CHE. Dist: Antique Collectors' Club.

Kessler, Jon, illus. Jon Kessler: The Palace at 4 A. M. 2008. (GER & ENG.). 144p. 55.00 *(978-88-8158-658-5(4))* Charta ITA. Dist: D.A.P./Distributed Art Pubs.

Kiecol, Hubert & Melcher, Ralph. Hubert Kiecol: Separee Public. 2010. (FRE, GER & ENG., Illus.). 116p. pap. 48.00 *(978-3-86560-612-9(1))* Verlag der Buchhandlung Walther Konig DEU. Dist: D.A.P./Distributed Art Pubs.

Kiefer, Anselm. Anselm Kiefer. 2012. (ENG., Illus.). 136p. 35.00 *(978-87-91607-83-7(3))* Louisana DNK. Dist: D.A.P./Distributed Art Pubs.

Kiefer, Anselm. Anselm Kiefer: Next Year in Jerusalem. 2012. (ENG., Illus.). 216p. 75.00 ***(978-3-7913-4583-3(4))*** Prestel Publishing.

Kiefer, Anselm & Bastian, Heiner. Anselm Kiefer Bücher: Mit einem Vorwort von Heiner Bastian und einem Text von Anselm Kiefer. 2008. (Illus.). 88p. *(978-3-8296-0402-4(5))* Schirmer/Mosel Verlag GmbH.

Kimes, Beverly Rae. Otis Chandler: The Pursuit of Uncommon Excellence. Wilkins, Amy, ed. 2007. *(978-0-9618705-1-5(6))* Art Ctr. College of Design.

Kimmerle, Constance. Elsie Driggs: The Quick & the Classical. 2008. (Illus.). 160p. (C). 39.95 *(978-0-8122-4104-4(5))* Univ. of Pennsylvania Pr.

King, Elliott H. Salvador Dalí: The Late Work. 2010. (Illus.). 176p. 45.00 *(978-1-932543-37-7(6))*; (ENG., pap. 30.00 *(978-1-932543-39-1(2))* High Museum of Art.

King, Sarah, ed. Lucky Number Seven. 2008. (ENG., Illus.). 396p. 50.00 *(978-0-9764492-8-7(5))* Site Santa Fe.

Kinsella, John, ed. Salt 9. 18.26 *(978-1-86368-200-8(7))* Fremantle Pr. AUS. Dist: Independent Pubs. Group.

Kirchner, Ernst Ludwig. Ernst Ludwig Kirchner: Art to Hear. 2010. (ENG., Illus.). 44p. 30.00 *(978-3-7757-2555-2(5))* Hatje Cantz Verlag GmbH & Co KG DEU. Dist: D.A.P./Distributed Art Pubs.

Kissane, Sean & Juncosa, Enrique, eds. Alan Phelan: Fragile Absolutes. 2010. (ENG., Illus.). 268p. 75.00 *(978-88-8158-763-6(7))* Charta ITA. Dist: D.A.P./Distributed Art Pubs.

KIT Publishers. Betsabee Romero: Cars & Traces. 2010. 160p. pap. 30.00 *(978-94-6022-123-1(8))* Royal Tropical Institute Pr. (KIT (Koninklijk Instituut voor de Tropen) NLD. Dist: Stylus Publishing, LLC.

Kittelmann, Udo, ed. Vadim Zakharov: Retrospective 1987-1995. (GER & RUS., Illus.). 180p. 29.95 *(978-3-89322-775-4(X))* Edition Cantz DEU. Dist: D.A.P./Distributed Art Pubs.

Kittelmann, Udo, et al, eds. Who Knows Tomorrow. Afrika. SMB. Hamburger Bahnhof. 2011. (GER & ENG., Illus.). 632p. 75.00 *(978-3-86560-789-8(6))* Verlag der Buchhandlung Walther Konig DEU. Dist: D.A.P./Distributed Art Pubs.

Klauke, Jürgen, photos by. Jürgen Klauke: Ästhetische Paranoia. 2010. (ENG., Illus.). 252p. 60.00 *(978-3-7757-2594-1(6))* Hatje Cantz Verlag GmbH & Co KG DEU. Dist: D.A.P./Distributed Art Pubs.

Klee, Paul. Klee & CoBrA: Child's Play. 2011. (ENG., Illus.). 224p. 50.00 ***(978-3-7757-2983-3(6))*** Hatje Cantz Verlag GmbH & Co KG DEU. Dist: D.A.P./Distributed Art Pubs.

Kleeblatt, Norman L. Action/Abstraction: Pollock, de Kooning, & American Art, 1940-1976. Kleeblatt, Norman L., ed. 2009. (ENG., Illus.). 344p. pap. 50.00 *(978-0-300-13920-4(9))* Yale Univ. Pr.

Klingsö, et al. Lovis Corinth: Seelenlandschaften. Walchenseebilder und Selbstbildnisse. 2009. (GER., Illus.). 119p. *(978-3-87909-979-5(0))* Wienand GmbH, Druck- & Verlagshaus.

Knol, Meta, et al, eds. Beyond the Dutch: Indonesia, the Netherlands & the Arts from 1990 to Date. 2010. 200p. 39.00 *(978-94-6022-059-3(2))* Royal Tropical Institute Pr. (KIT (Koninklijk Instituut voor de Tropen) NLD. Dist: Stylus Publishing, LLC.

Knoller, Paco, illus. Paco Knöller: Schnitte. Riskante Euphorien, 1 vol. 2008. (ENG.). 96p. 55.00 *(978-3-937572-80-2(5))* Richter Verlag DEU. Dist: D.A.P./Distributed Art Pubs.

Kolesnikov, Ivan, et al, contrib. by. New Angelarium. 2007. (ENG & RUS., Illus.). 352p. per. 145.00 *(978-0-9754829-7-1(1))* Kolodzei Art Foundation, Inc.

Koons, Jeff. Jeff Koons. 2010. (ENG & GER., Illus.). 36p. 40.00 *(978-3-935567-49-7(9))* Holzwarth Pubns. DEU. Dist: D.A.P./Distributed Art Pubs.

Koons, Jeff, ed. Skin Fruit: A View of a Collection. 2012. (ENG., Illus.). 92p. pap. 25.00 ***(978-1-935202-77-6(4))*** Deste Foundation GRC. Dist: D.A.P./Distributed Art Pubs.

Koralova, Ilina, ed. Formschon: Exhibition views by Tilo Schulz, 1 vol. 2007. (ENG., Illus.). 34p. pap. 20.00 *(978-3-939633-32-7(1))* Jovis Verlag GmbH DEU. Dist: D.A.P./Distributed Art Pubs.

Kort, Pamela, text. Ernst Ludwig Kirchner: Berlin Street Scene. 2008. (ENG., Illus.). 92p. 30.00 *(978-1-931794-15-2(4))* Neue Galerie New York.

Kosinski, Dorothy M. & Ottmann, Klaus. Per Kirkeby: Paintings & Sculpture. 2012. (ENG., Illus.). 144p. 50.00 ***(978-0-300-18122-7(1))*** Yale Univ. Pr.

Kostenevich, A. Matisse to Malevich: Poineers of Modern Art from the Hermitage, 1 vol. 2011. (ENG.). 288p. pap. 66.00 ***(978-90-78653-18-9(3))*** Exhibitions International BEL. Dist: Innovative Logistics.

Koudelka, Josef, photos by. Chaos. 2008. (ENG.). 79.95 *(978-0-7148-4594-4(9))* Phaidon Pr., Inc.

Kraus, Kitty. Kitty Kraus. 2010. (ENG., Illus.). 168p. pap. 40.00 *(978-3-86678-327-0(2))* Kerber Verlag DEU. Dist: D.A.P./Distributed Art Pubs.

Kruger, Barbara, et al. Barbara Kruger: Circus. 2011. (GER & ENG., Illus.). 64p. pap. 27.50 ***(978-3-86560-945-8(7))*** Verlag der Buchhandlung Walther Konig DEU. Dist: D.A.P./Distributed Art Pubs.

Kusama, Yayoi. Yayoi Kusama. Neri, Louise, ed. 2012. (ENG., Illus.). 272p. 75.00 ***(978-0-8478-3908-7(7))*** Rizzoli International Pubns., Inc.

Lachowicz, Andrzej, et al. Andrzej Lachowicz: Obserwacje I Notacje = Observations & Notations. 2008. (POL & ENG.). 154p. *(978-83-61156-03-1(8))* Centre for Contemporary Art Ujazdowski.

Laguna Art Museum. In the Land of Retinal Delights. 2008. (Illus.). 160p. *(978-1-58423-317-6(6))* Laguna Art Museum Store.

Lahuerta, Juan Jose. Dalí, Lorca y la Residencia de Estudiantes, 2 vols. 2010. (Illus.). (SPA.). *(978-84-92827-85-5(8))*; (ENG & SPA., *(978-84-92827-90-9(4))*; (ENG & SPA., *(978-84-92827-89-3(0))* Sociedad Estatal de Conmemoraciones Culturales.

Lamonaca, Marianne, et al. Liberty, Equality, & Fraternity. Lamonaca, Marianne, ed. 2011. (ENG.). pap. 50.00 ***(978-0-9677359-4-8(7))*** Wolfsonian-Florida International Univ., The.

Landert, Markus, ed. Olaf Nicolai. Mirador: Mirador. 2011. (ENG., Illus.). 80p. pap. 45.00 *(978-3-86984-033-8(1))* Verlag fur Moderne Kunst DEU. Dist: D.A.P./Distributed Art Pubs.

Lange, Christiane & Ohlsen, Nils, eds. Serge Poliakoff: Retrospektive. 2007. (GER., Illus.). 200p. (C). 52.50 *(978-3-7774-3505-3(8))* Hirmer Verlag GmbH DEU. Dist: Brown, David Bk. Co., The.

Lapthisophon, Stephen. Writing Art Cinema 1988-2010. 2011. 103p. pap. 12.00 *(978-1-4507-4210-8(6))* Green Lantern Pr.

Larner, Melissa & Fergusson, Ben, eds. Paul Chan: 7 Lights. 2008. (ENG., Illus.). 150p. 72.00 *(978-3-86560-247-3(9))* Verlag der Buchhandlung Walther Konig DEU. Dist: D.A.P./Distributed Art Pubs.

Le Restif, Claire, et al. Blaise Drummond. 2010. (GER & ENG., Illus.). 112p. 40.00 *(978-3-86678-377-5(9))* Kerber Verlag DEU. Dist: D.A.P./Distributed Art Pubs.

Leavitt, William, et al. William Leavitt: Theater Objects. 2011. (ENG., Illus.). 144p. pap. 40.00 *(978-1-933751-18-4(5))* Museum of Contemporary Art, Los Angeles.

Leca, Benedict, et al. Monet in Giverny: Landscapes of Reflection. 2012. (ENG., Illus.). 96p. pap. 15.95 ***(978-1-907804-03-8(X))*** Giles, D. Ltd. GBR. Dist: Antique Collectors' Club.

Leddy, Annette & Conwell, Donna. Farewell to Surrealism: The Dyn Circle in Mexico. 2012. ***(978-1-60606-118-3(6))*** Getty Pubns.

Leeds, Valerie Ann. Robert Henri in Santa Fe: His Work & Influence. 2011. (ENG., Illus.). 192p. pap. 25.00 ***(978-0-935037-83-8(7))*** Peters, Gerald Gallery.

Leismann, Burhad & Scherer, Ralf. Diagnosis (Art) Contemporary Art Reflecting Medicine. 2007. 220p. *(978-3-87909-902-3(2))* Wienand GmbH, Druck- & Verlagshaus.

Leon, Eli. Something Pertaining to God: The Patchwork Art of Rosie Lee Tompkins. 2007. (Illus.). 32p. 12.95 *(978-0-939384-33-4(7))* Shelburne Museum, Inc.

Lewison, Jeremy. Turner Monet Twombly: Later Paintings. 2012. (Illus.). 272p. 40.00 ***(978-1-84976-012-6(8))*** Tate Publishing, Ltd. GBR. Dist: Abrams.

Libin, Liu, et al, eds. Visible/Invisible, 1 vol. 2008. (ENG., Illus.). 240p. 80.00 *(978-988-99265-7-1(1))* Timezone 8 Ltd. HKG. Dist: D.A.P./Distributed Art Pubs.

Ligon, Glenn, et al, texts. 30 Americans. 2009. (ENG., Illus.). 232p. 60.00 *(978-0-9821195-1-8(8))* Rubell Family Collection.

Ligon, Glenn, et al. Glenn Ligon. 2009. (ENG & FRE., Illus.). 200p. 40.00 *(978-1-894212-06-9(1))* Power Plant, The CAN. Dist: D.A.P./Distributed Art Pubs.

Lippard, Lucy & Fox, William, texts. Land/Art: New Mexico. 2010. (ENG., Illus.). 196p. 45.00 *(978-1-934435-17-5(1))* Radius Bks.

Lippard, Lucy, et al. Ree Morton: At the Still Point of the Turning World. 2009. (Illus.). 118p. pap. 20.00 *(978-0-942324-48-8(X))* Drawing Ctr.

Lippincott, Louise & Avinoff, Andrey. Andrey Avinoff: In Pursuit of Beauty. 2011. (ENG., Illus.). 104p. pap. 24.95 *(978-0-88039-053-8(0))* Carnegie Museum of Art, The.

Liu, Shi-Yee & Hearn, Maxwell K. Straddling East & West: Lin Yutang, a Modern Literatus: The Lin Yutang Family Collection of Chinese Painting & Calligraphy. 2007. 24.95 *(978-1-58839-270-1(8))* Metropolitan Museum of Art, The.

Locke, Harvey. Yellowstone to Yukon: The Journey of Wildlife & Art. 2012. ***(978-1-56373-192-1(4))*** Fulcrum Publishing.

Loebl, Suzanne. America's Medicis: The Rockefellers & Their Astonishing Cultural Legacy. 2010. (ENG.). 448p. 34.99 *(978-0-06-123722-5(1))* HarperCollins Pubs.

Lomas, David. Narcissus Reflected. 2011. (ENG., Illus.). 176p. pap. 27.00 *(978-0-947912-99-4(1))* Reaktion Bks., Ltd. GBR. Dist: Chicago Distribution Ctr.

Lovell, Whitfield. Mercy, Patience & Destiny: the Women of Whitfield Lovell's Tableaux. 2010. (ENG., Illus.). 58p. pap. 20.00 *(978-0-615-22202-8(1))* Savannah College of Art & Design Exhibitions.

Lowry, Glenn D., text. Masterworks of Modern Art: From the Museum of Modern Art, New York, 1 vol. 2011. (ENG., Illus.). 302p. 60.00 *(978-88-8117-298-6(4))* Scala Grp. ITA. Dist: D.A.P./Distributed Art Pubs.

Lucas, Renata, et al. Renata Lucas. 2007. 25.00 *(978-0-9749831-7-2(9))* California Institute of the Arts.

Luduvico, Rosilene. Rosilene Luduvico: See it Coming. 2008. (ENG., Illus.). 136p. pap. 55.00 *(978-3-938821-64-0(7))* Verlag fur Moderne Kunst DEU. Dist: D.A.P./Distributed Art Pubs.

Lupas, Liana. On Eagles' Wings: The King James Turns 400. Lupas, Liana & Pongracz, Patricia C., eds. 2011. pap. 29.95 ***(978-0-9777839-8-4(7))*** Museum of Biblical Art.

Lynch, David, photos by. David Lynch: Dark Splendor. 2010. (ENG., Illus.). 352p. 85.00 *(978-3-7757-2644-3(6))* Hatje Cantz Verlag GmbH & Co KG DEU. Dist: D.A.P./Distributed Art Pubs.

MacAdam, Barbara J., ed. Embracing Elegance, 1885-1920: American Art from the Huber Family Collection. 2011. (Illus.). 116p. pap. 24.95 *(978-0-944722-41-1(5))* Hood Museum of Art.

Macel, Christine, ed. Promises of the Past. 2010. (ENG., Illus.). 256p. pap. 65.00 *(978-3-03764-099-9(5))* JRP Ringier Kunstverlag AG CHE. Dist: D.A.P./Distributed Art Pubs.

Mach, David & Wilding, Alison. Royal Academy Illustrated. 2006. (ENG., Illus.). 192p. per. 29.95 *(978-1-903973-76-9(7))* Royal Academy of Arts GBR. Dist: Hachette Bk. Group.

Mack, Heinz & text. Heinz Mack: Licht der ZERO-Zeit. 2010. (ENG., Illus.). 152p. 49.50 *(978-3-86678-334-8(5))* Kerber Verlag DEU. Dist: D.A.P./Distributed Art Pubs.

Macnair, Peter L., et al. The Legacy: Tradition & Innovation in Northwest Coast Indian Art, 1 vol. 2007. (Royal BC Museum Ser.). (ENG., Illus.). 196p. pap. 36.95 *(978-0-7726-5609-4(6))* UBC Pr. CAN. Dist: Univ. of Washington Pr.

Maeght, Isabelle, et al. The Maeght Family: A Passion for Modern Art. Edwards, Graham, tr. from FRE. 2007. (ENG., Illus.). 312p. 75.00 *(978-0-8109-3080-3(3))* Abrams.

Malone, Meredith. Tomas Saraceno: Cloud-Specific. Marjanovic, Igor, ed. 2012. (ENG., Illus.). 120p. pap. 30.00 ***(978-0-936316-35-2(7))*** Washington Univ., Mildred Lane Kemper Art Museum.

Maloon, Terence, ed. Paths to Abstraction 1867-1917. 2011. (Illus.). 295p. 65.00 *(978-3-7913-5091-2(9))* Prestel Publishing.

Manacorda, Francesco. Martian Museum of Terrestrial Art. 2008. (Illus.). 224p. 44.95 *(978-1-85894-459-3(7))* Merrell Pubs. Ltd. GBR. Dist: Perseus Distribution.

Manoguerra, Paul, et al, contrib. by. Amazing Grace: Self-Taught Artists from the Mullis Collection. 2007. (ENG.). 162p. 48.00 *(978-0-915977-63-5(X))* Univ. of Georgia, Georgia Museum of Art.

Margolles, Teresa, et al. ¿De Que Otra Cosa Podríamos Hablar? 2009. (SPA., Illus.). 158p. *(978-84-92480-65-4(3))* RM Verlag, S.L.

Mark Dagley - Shaped Canvas. 2008. (Illus.). 16p. pap. 15.00 *(978-0-9677326-9-5(7))* Abaton Bk. Co.

Mark, Lisa Gabrielle & Butler, Cornelia, eds. Wack! Art & the Feminist Revolution. 2007. (ENG., Illus.). 512p. (gr. 17). 62.95 *(978-0-914357-99-5(9))* MIT Pr.

Markonish, Denise, ed. Badlands: New Horizons in Landscape. 2008. (ENG., Illus.). 232p. (gr. 17). pap. 26.95 *(978-0-262-63366-6(3))* MIT Pr.

Marsh, Joanna & Rockman, Alexis. Alexis Rockman: A Fable for Tomorrow. 2010. (Illus.). 176p. *(978-0-9790678-8-4(X))* Smithsonian American Art Museum.

Martin, David F. The Art of Richard Bennett. 2010. (ENG., Illus.). 80p. pap. 24.95 *(978-0-939806-07-2(X))* Historical Society of Seattle & King County/Museum of History & Industry.

Massimo Barbero, Luca, text. Luigi Ontani: MarmArmonia, 1 vol. 2007. (ITA & ENG., Illus.). 104p. 34.95 *(978-88-8158-651-6(7))* Charta ITA. Dist: D.A.P./Distributed Art Pubs.

Matt, Gerald, ed. & text. Elevator to the Gallows. 2009. (ENG., Illus.). 172p. pap. 45.00 *(978-3-941185-35-7(7))* Verlag fur Moderne Kunst DEU. Dist: D.A.P./Distributed Art Pubs.

Matt, Gerald, et al, eds. Andro Wekua: Pink Wave Hunter, 3 Volumes. 2011. (ENG., Illus.). 388p. pap. 49.95 ***(978-3-86560-961-8(9))*** Verlag der Buchhandlung Walther Konig DEU. Dist: D.A.P./Distributed Art Pubs.

Matt, Gerald & Blickle, Ursula, eds. The Cabinet of Jan Svankmajer: The Pendulum, the Pit, & Other Peculiarities. 2012. (ENG & GER., Illus.). 240p. 55.00 ***(978-3-86984-256-1(3))*** Verlag fur Moderne Kunst DEU. Dist: D.A.P./Distributed Art Pubs.

Matt, Gerald & Hug, Cath#xE9;rine, eds. Weltraum: Kunst und ein Traum. 2011. (ENG & GER., Illus.). 320p. pap. 60.00 ***(978-3-86984-175-5(3))*** Verlag fur Moderne Kunst DEU. Dist: D.A.P./Distributed Art Pubs.

Matton, Sylvie. Charles Matton: Enclosures. 2011. (ENG., Illus.). 256p. 85.00 *(978-2-08-020087-7(9))* Flammarion et Cie FRA. Dist: Random Hse., Inc.

Maurer, Simon, ed. & text. Klaudia Schifferle: sumsum im Universum. 2011. (ENG., Illus.). 108p. 45.00 *(978-3-86984-155-7(9))* Verlag fur Moderne Kunst DEU. Dist: D.A.P./Distributed Art Pubs.

McCallum, Bradley & Tarry, Jacqueline, illus. Whitewash, 1 vol. 2007. (ENG.). 77p. 30.00 *(978-988-99264-1-0(5))* Timezone 8 Ltd. HKG. Dist: D.A.P./Distributed Art Pubs.

McCarthy, Dan. Dan Mccarthy, Drawings 2007. 2007. (J). 12.00 *(978-0-9800935-1-3(1))* Hassia Bks.

McDonnell, Patricia. Marsden Hartley: American Modern. 2007. (ENG., Illus.). 84p. per. 27.95 *(978-1-885116-12-3(8))* Weisman, Frederick R. Art Museum.

Mecklenburg, Virginia M. Modern Masters: American Abstraction at Midcentury. 2009. (ENG., Illus.). 272p. 65.00 *(978-1-904832-59-1(8))* Giles, D. Ltd. GBR. Dist: Antique Collectors' Club.

Medina, Cuauhtémoc. Teresa Margolles: What Else Could We Talk About? Medina, Cuauhtemoc, ed. 2010. (ENG., Illus.). 160p. 35.00 *(978-84-92480-66-1(1))* RM Verlag, S.L. ESP. Dist: D.A.P./Distributed Art Pubs.

Melcher, Ralph, et al. Alexander Archipenko: Retrospektive. 2008. (GER., Illus.). 240p. (C). 63.00 *(978-3-7774-4425-3(1))* Hirmer Verlag GmbH DEU. Dist: Brown, David Bk. Co., The.

Melotti, Massimo, ed. Pistoletto - Works: Massimo Melotti Talks to Michelangelo Pistoletto. 2012. (ENG.). 88p. 20.00 ***(978-88-422-1963-7(0))*** Allemandi, Umberto & Co. GBR. Dist: Antique Collectors' Club.

Mercurio, Gianni & Paparoni, Demetrio. Anish Kapoor: Dirty Corner. 2011. (ENG., Illus.). 408p. 75.00 ***(978-88-572-1061-2(8))*** Skira Editore ITA. Dist: Random Hse., Inc.

Mercurio, Gianni, et al. Tony Oursler: Open Obscura. 2011. (ITA & ENG., Illus.). 176p. 55.00 *(978-88-7179-663-5(2))* Antique Collectors' Club.

Merewether, Charles & Hiro, Rika Iezumi, eds. Art, Anti-Art, Non-Art: Experimentations in the Public Sphere in Postwar Japan, 1950-1970. 2007. (ENG., Illus.). 158p. 45.00 *(978-0-89236-866-2(7))* Oxford Univ. Pr., Inc.

Messager, Annette. Annette Messager, the Messengers: The Messengers. 2008. (Illus.). 608p. 85.00 *(978-3-7913-3922-1(2))* Prestel Publishing.

Messinger, Lisa Mintz & Dabrowski, Magdalena. Stieglitz & His Artists: Matisse to O'Keeffe: The Alfred Stieglitz Collection in the Metropolitan Museum of Art. 2011. 65.00 ***(978-1-58839-433-0(6))*** Metropolitan Museum of Art, The.

Meurs, Paul, et al, eds. Brazil Contemporary. 2009. (ENG., Illus.). 318p. pap. 45.00 *(978-90-5662-677-8(9))* NAi Uitgevers / Publishers Stichting NLD. Dist: D.A.P./Distributed Art Pubs.

Meyer, Christian, text. Vienna 1900. 2011. (ENG., Illus.). 272p. 75.00 *(978-3-7757-2685-6(3))* Hatje Cantz Verlag GmbH & Co KG DEU. Dist: D.A.P./Distributed Art Pubs.

Michael, Cora, et al. Stieglitz & His Artists: Matisse to O'Keeffe. Messinger, Lisa Mintz, ed. 2011. (ENG., Illus.). 360p. 65.00 *(978-0-300-17588-2(4))* Yale Univ. Pr.

Michael Hurson: Paintings, Drawings & Sculpture. 2008. (Illus.). 112p. 40.00 *(978-0-9760250-9-2(4),* Plain Paper Pr.) Plain White Pr., LLC.

Might. Works From 1965-1971, 1 vol. 2006. (ENG., Illus.). 20p. 35.00 *(978-1-891027-21-5(2))* Thread Waxing Space.

Miles, M. R. & Yabuuchi, S. The Vision & Art of Shinjo Ito. Alinari 24 Ore Staff, ed. 2008. (ENG., Illus.). 182p. 75.00 *(978-88-6302-002-1(7),* Art Stock Bks. Ltd/Csi) Continental Sales, Inc.

Miller, Dan, des. Richard Phillips. 2007. (Illus.). 61p. 80.00 *(978-1-932598-48-3(0))* Gagosian Gallery.

Miller, Dana, ed. Legacy: The Emily Fisher Landau Collection. 2011. (ENG., Illus.). 388p. 75.00 *(978-0-300-17108-2(0))* Yale Univ. Pr.

Miller, Laurence, ed. I Wanted to See the World. 2011. (ENG., Illus.). 96p. pap. 40.00 ***(978-3-86828-170-5(3))*** Kehrer Verlag Heidelberg, Klaus Kehrer DEU. Dist: Consortium Bk. Sales & Distribution.

Milosch, Jane & Frantz, Susanne K. From the Ground Up: Renwick Craft Invitational 2007. 2007. pap. *(978-0-9790678-1-5(2))* Smithsonian American Art Museum.

Miró, Joan & Beltramo Ceppi Zevi, Claudia. Joan Miró: I Miti Del Mediterraneo. 2010. (ITA., Illus.). 261p. *(978-88-09-75559-8(6))* Giunti Gruppo Editoriale.

Moeller, Magdalena M. Sammlung Rolf Horn: Werke aus der Stiftung Rolf Horn. Moeller, Magdalena M., ed. 2009. (GER., Illus.). 316p. (C). 64.00 *(978-3-7774-2071-4(9))* Hirmer Verlag GmbH DEU. Dist: Brown, David Bk. Co., The.

Mohr, Daniel, illus. Daniel Mohr: Zuruck Zur Natur/Back to Nature, 1 vol. 2007. (ENG.). 88p. 38.00 *(978-3-86678-049-1(4))* Kerber Verlag DEU. Dist: D.A.P./Distributed Art Pubs.

Moles, Kathleen & Arnaud, Jean-Pierre. John Franklin Koenig: Northwest Master, Home & Away. 2008. (Illus.). 74p. pap. 20.00 *(978-0-938506-13-3(7))* Whatcom Museum of History & Art.

Molesworth, Helen, ed. Catherine Opie: Empty & Full. 2011. (ENG., Illus.). 96p. 40.00 *(978-3-7757-3015-0(X))* Hatje Cantz Verlag GmbH & Co KG DEU. Dist: D.A.P./Distributed Art Pubs.

Molesworth, Helen, ed. & text. Josiah Mcelheny: Notes for a Sculpture & a Film, 1 vol. 2006. (ENG., Illus.). 40p. per. 11.95 *(978-1-881390-40-4(3))* Ohio State Univ., Wexner Ctr. for the Arts.

Mondrian, Piet. MondrianDe Stijl. 2011. (GER & ENG., Illus.). 304p. 60.00 ***(978-3-7757-3023-5(0))*** Hatje Cantz Verlag GmbH & Co KG DEU. Dist: D.A.P./Distributed Art Pubs.

Mondrian, Piet & Léal, Brigitte. Mondrian. 2010. (FRE., Illus.). 357p. *(978-2-84426-451-0(4))* Centre National d'Art et de Culture Georges Pompidou.

Monem, Nadine, ed. Contemporary Art in the Middle East: Artworld. 2009. (ENG., Illus.). 240p. 49.95 *(978-1-906155-56-8(9))* Black Dog Publishing Ltd. GBR. Dist: Perseus Distribution.

Monrad, Kasper. Hammershoi & Europe. 2012. (Illus.). 272p. 49.95 ***(978-3-7913-5174-2(5))*** Prestel Publishing.

Moore, Bridget, intro. Charles Burchfield 1920: the Architecture of Painting. 2009. (ENG., Illus.). 120p. 50.00 *(978-0-9815250-5-1(9))* DC Moore Gallery.

Moos, David, et al. Iain Baxterand & Works, 1958-2011. Moos, David, ed. 2012. (ENG., Illus.). 220p. pap. 45.00 ***(978-0-86492-646-3(4))*** Goose Lane Editions CAN. Dist: Univ. of Toronto Pr.

Morgan, Jessica. Carsten Holler: Test Site. 2007. (ENG., Illus.). 140p. pap. 14.95 *(978-1-85437-712-8(4))* Tate Publishing, Ltd. GBR. Dist: Hachette Bk. Group.

Morgan, Jessica, ed. TH 2058 - Dominique Gonzalez-Foerster. 2009. (ENG., Illus.). 224p. 29.95 *(978-1-85437-739-5(6))* Tate Publishing, Ltd. GBR. Dist: Hachette Bk. Group.

Morris, Catherine. The Six Years Project: Lucy R. Lippard & the Emergence of Conceptual Art. 2012. ***(978-0-262-01816-6(0))*** MIT Pr.

Morsiani, Paola & Kim, Beom. Kim Beom: Objects Being Taught They Are Nothing but Tools. 2010. (Illus.). 50p. pap. *(978-1-935294-02-3(4))* Cleveland Museum of Art.

Mucha, Stefan, pref. The Way Things Are. 2008. (ENG., Illus.). 216p. pap. 48.00 *(978-3-86560-485-9(4))* Verlag der Buchhandlung Walther Konig DEU. Dist: D.A.P./Distributed Art Pubs.

Muir, Gregor, ed. Henry Moore: Ideas for Sculpture. 2010. (ENG., Illus.). 164p. 85.00 *(978-3-03764-073-9(1))* JRP Ringier Kunstverlag AG CHE. Dist: D.A.P./Distributed Art Pubs.

Muller, Florence & Sigal, Patrick. Costume Jewelry for Haute Couture. 2007. (ENG., Illus.). 272p. 75.00 *(978-0-86565-182-1(5))* Vendome Pr., The.

Muller, Karsten, text. Michael Buthe: Der Engel und sein Schatten / The Angel & his Shadow. 2010. (ENG., Illus.). 136p. 50.00 *(978-3-86678-242-6(X))* Kerber Verlag DEU. Dist: D.A.P./Distributed Art Pubs.

Muller, Markus. Picasso: Linocuts. 2011. (Illus.). 191p. 49.95 ***(978-3-7774-3981-5(9))*** Hirmer Verlag GmbH DEU. Dist: Chicago Distribution Ctr.

Munch, Andreas, ed. Fabrice Gygi: A Manual. 2010. (ENG., Illus.). 224p. pap. 35.00 *(978-3-03764-057-9(X))* JRP Ringier Kunstverlag AG CHE. Dist: D.A.P./Distributed Art Pubs.

Munder, Heike, ed. Christoph Ruckhäberle: Figur. 2010. (ENG., Illus.). 158p. pap. 45.00 *(978-3-03764-055-5(3))* JRP Ringier Kunstverlag AG CHE. Dist: D.A.P./Distributed Art Pubs.

Munroe, Alexandra. Lee Ufan: Marking Infinity. 2012. (ENG., Illus.). 200p. 65.00 ***(978-0-89207-418-1(3))*** Guggenheim, Solomon R. Museum.

Munroe, Alexandra & Cai, Guoqiang. I Want to Believe. 2008. (Illus.). 315p. pap. *(978-0-89207-372-6(1))* Guggenheim, Solomon R. Museum.

Murakami, Takashi & Schimmel, Paul. Murakami. 2007. *(978-1-933751-06-1(1))* Museum of Contemporary Art, Los Angeles.

Murray, Mary E., et al. Auspicious Vision: Edward Wales Root & American Modernism. 2008. *(978-0-915895-34-2(X))* Munson-Williams-Proctor Institute.

MUSAC, creator. End: Marina Nunez. 2009. (Illus.). *(978-84-96540-30-9(8))* Charta.

Museum of Design, Zurich, Zurich, compiled by. Freitag - Out of the Bag, 1 vol. 2012. (ENG., Illus.). 256p. pap. 35.00 ***(978-3-03778-278-1(1))*** Lars Muller Pubs. CHE. Dist: Prestel Publishing.

Museum Tinguely (Basel, Switzerland) Staff, ed. Car Fetish: I Drive Therefore I Am. 2011. (ENG., Illus.). 300p. pap. 65.00 ***(978-3-86828-228-3(9))*** Kehrer Verlag Heidelberg, Klaus Kehrer DEU. Dist: Consortium Bk. Sales & Distribution.

Nakashima, Tom, et al. Tom Nakashima: Two Decades. 2007. (Illus.). 44p. pap. *(978-1-890021-20-7(2))* Morris Museum of Art.

Naples Museum of Art. 20th-Century Mexican Art: The Pollak Collection. 2007. (Illus.). 172p. 40.00 *(978-0-9773018-7-4(7))*; per. 30.00 *(978-0-9773018-6-7(9))* Naples Museum of Art.

Nardinocchi, Elisabetta & Paolini, Claudio, eds. Paolo Staccioli: Opere / Sculptures 1991-2011. 2011. (ITA & ENG., Illus.). 80p. (C). pap. 42.00 ***(978-88-596-0903-2(8))*** Polistampa ITA. Dist: Brown, David Bk. Co., The.

Nassau County Museum of Art Staff, contrib. by. Miro/DuBuffet/Basquiat. 2010. (Illus.). 24p. ***(978-0-9815644-7-0(X))*** Nassau County Museum of Art.

National Gallery of Ireland Staff, creator. Samuel Beckett: A Passion for Painting. 2007. (ENG., Illus.). 128p. pap. 50.00 *(978-1-904288-16-9(2))* Holberton, Paul Publishing GBR. Dist: Univ. of Washington Pr.

Nauman, Bruce & Battle, Erica F. Bruce Nauman: Topological Gardens: Installation Views. 2010. (Illus.). 59p. *(978-0-87633-220-7(3))* Philadelphia Museum of Art.

Neff, Emily Ballew. The Modern West: American Landscapes, 1890-1950. 2006. (Illus.). (ENG.). 315p. 65.00 *(978-0-300-11448-5(6))*; xix, 315p. pap. *(978-0-89090-145-8(7))* Yale Univ. Pr.

Neff, John H. & Silverman, Lanny. Karl Wirsum: Winsome Works(some) 2007. (Illus.). 68p. pap. 25.00 *(978-0-938903-40-6(3))* City of Chicago, Dept. of Cultural Affairs.

Nefzger, Jurgen, photos by. Jürgen Nefzger: Fluffy Clouds. 2010. (ENG., Illus.). 144p. 55.00 *(978-3-7757-2598-9(9))* Hatje Cantz Verlag GmbH & Co KG DEU. Dist: D.A.P./Distributed Art Pubs.

Nelson, Mike. Mike Nelson: A Psychic Vacuum. 2010. (ENG., Illus.). 196p. 39.95 *(978-1-928570-11-0(9))* Creative Time.

Neshat, Shirin, et al. Shahram Karimi: In Between. Cameron, Dan, ed. 2011. (ENG & GER., Illus.). 96p. pap. 47.50 *(978-88-8158-797-1(1))* Charta ITA. Dist: D.A.P./Distributed Art Pubs.

Neto, Ernesto, contrib. by. Ernesto Neto: from Sebastian to Olivia (BAD ISBN DNU) 2008. (ENG., Illus.). 120p. 69.00 *(978-3-935567-45-9(6))* Holzwarth Pubns. DEU. Dist: D.A.P./Distributed Art Pubs.

Neubauer, Susanne, ed. Anne-Mie van Kerckhoven: Nothing More Natural. 2009. (DUT, FRE, GER & ENG., Illus.). 272p. pap. 69.95 *(978-3-86560-528-3(1))* Verlag der Buchhandlung Walther Konig DEU. Dist: D.A.P./Distributed Art Pubs.

Newark Museum Staff, contrib. by. The Art of Glass from Gallé to Chihuly: Highlights from the Lowenbach Collection. 2007. (Illus.). 48p. pap. *(978-0-932828-39-2(6))* Newark Museum Assn., The.

Newman, Michael. Richard Prince - Untitled (Couple) 2006. (One Work Ser.). (ENG., Illus.). 176p. (gr. 17). pap. 16.00 *(978-1-84638-003-7(0))* Afterall Publishing GBR. Dist: MIT Pr.

Nisbet, Peter & Feininger, Lyonel. Lyonel Feininger: Drawings & Watercolors from the William S. Lieberman Bequest to the Busch-Reisinger Museum. 2011. *(978-1-891771-54-5(X))* Hatje Cantz Verlag GmbH & Co KG.

—Lyonel Feininger: Drawings & Watercolors from the William S. Lieberman Bequest to the Busch-Reisinger Museum. 2011. (ENG., Illus.). 144p. 45.00 *(978-3-7757-2787-7(6))* Hatje Cantz Verlag GmbH & Co KG DEU. Dist: D.A.P./Distributed Art Pubs.

Nittve, Lars, et al, texts. Time & Place, 3 vols. 2009. (ENG., Illus.). 430p. 100.00 *(978-3-86521-641-0(2))* Steidl, Gerhard Druckerei und Verlag DEU. Dist: D.A.P./Distributed Art Pubs.

Nolde, Emil, et al. Emil Nolde: Bewundert, gefürchtet und begehrt - Emil Nolde malt die Frauen / Admired, Feared, & Desired - Emil Nolde Paints Women. 2011. (GER & ENG., Illus.). 144p. 45.00 *(978-3-8321-9325-6(1))* DuMont DEU. Dist: D.A.P./Distributed Art Pubs.

Noriega, Chon A., et al, eds. L. A. Xicano. 2011. (ENG., Illus.). 240p. (C). 39.95 *(978-0-89551-145-4(2))* UCLA Chicano Studies Research Ctr. Pr.

Norr, David, ed. & text. Teresita Fernandez: Blind Landscape. 2010. (ENG., Illus.). 160p. pap. 55.00 *(978-3-03764-049-4(9))* JRP Ringier Kunstverlag AG CHE. Dist: D.A.P./Distributed Art Pubs.

Nye, Tim, ed. Tim Hawkinson, 1 vol. 2007. (ENG., Illus.). 96p. 55.00 *(978-1-934171-03-5(4))* Thread Waxing Space.

Obrist, Hans Ulrich. Films, 1987 - 2010: Serpentine Gallery. Marta, Karen et al, eds. 2011. (ART & ENG., Illus.). 200p. 69.95 *(978-3-86560-943-4(0))* Walther König, Köln/Koenig Bks.

Ocean, Humphrey, ed. Royal Academy Illustrated 2008. 2008. (ENG., Illus.). 200p. pap. 35.00 *(978-1-905711-12-3(3))* Royal Academy of Arts GBR. Dist: Hachette Bk. Group.

Ochoa Foster, Elena, ed. Drama Turquesa: Los Carpinteros. 2010. (SPA & ENG., Illus.). 166p. pap. 39.95 *(978-0-9564339-1-6(X))* Ivory Pr. ESP. Dist: Actar Birkhauser Distribution.

Oehlen, Albert. Albert Oehlen. 2012. (ENG, FRE & GER., Illus.). 54p. 50.00 ***(978-3-935567-54-1(5))*** Holzwarth Pubns. DEU. Dist: D.A.P./Distributed Art Pubs.

Ofili, Chris. Chris Ofili: The Blue Rider, 1 vol. 2006. (ENG & GER., Illus.). 114p. 65.00 *(978-3-931355-30-2(6))* Verlag der Buchhandlung Walther Konig DEU. Dist: D.A.P./Distributed Art Pubs.

Ogden Museum of Southern Art Staff. One World, Two Artists: John Alexander & Walter Anderson. Strachan, Sue, ed. 2011. (ENG., Illus.). 90p. 55.00 *(978-0-9833707-0-3(2),* Univ. Pr. of Mississippi/Ogden Museum of Southern Art) Univ. Pr. of Mississippi.

Ogg, Kirsty, ed. & text. Claire Barclay: Shadow Spans. 2012. (ENG., Illus.). 56p. pap. 19.95 ***(978-0-85488-191-8(3))*** Whitechapel Art Gallery GBR. Dist: D.A.P./Distributed Art Pubs.

O'Kane, Martin, ed. Bible, Art, Gallery. 2011. 220p. ***(978-1-906055-63-9(7))*** Sheffield Phoenix Pr.

O'Keeffe, Georgia, et al. Georgia O'Keeffe in New Mexico: Architecture, Katsinam, & the Land. 2012. pap. ***(978-0-89013-547-1(9))*** Museum of New Mexico Pr.

Oklahoma City Museum of Art, et al. Breaking the Mold: Selections from the Washington Gallery of Modern Art, 1961-1968. George, Hardy S. & Pavelka, Jeffrey J., eds. 2008. (Illus.). 144p. pap. 25.00 *(978-0-911919-05-9(8))* Oklahoma City Museum of Art.

Olea, Hector, et al. Building on a Construct: The Adolpho Leirner Collection of Brazilian Constructive Art at the Museum of Fine Arts, Houston. 2010. (ENG., Illus.). 408p. 70.00 *(978-0-300-14698-1(1))* Museum of Fine Arts, Houston.

Oliva, Achille Bonito, et al, texts. Braco Dimitrijevic. 2010. (ENG., Illus.). 248p. 75.00 *(978-88-8158-748-3(3))* Charta ITA. Dist: D.A.P./Distributed Art Pubs.

Oliver-Smith, Kerry, et al. Project Europa: Imagining the (Im)possible. 2010. (ENG., Illus.). 116p. pap. 29.95 *(978-0-9762552-9-1(4))* Univ. Pr. of Florida.

'ollein, Max & Schlicht, Esther, eds. Kunst fur Millionen: 100 Skulpturen der Mao-Zeit. 2009. (GER., Illus.). 200p. (C). pap. 64.00 *(978-3-7774-2231-2(2))* Hirmer Verlag GmbH DEU. Dist: Brown, David Bk. Co., The.

Orozco, Gabriel. Gabriel Orozco. 2009. (ENG., Illus.). 256p. 55.00 *(978-0-87070-762-9(0))* Museum of Modern Art.

—Gabriel Orozco: Catálogo de la Exposición el Palacio de Cristal. 2006. (Illus.). 162p. 60.00 *(978-84-8026-254-5(0))* Museo Nacional Centro de Arte Reina Sofia ESP. Dist: D.A.P./Distributed Art Pubs.

Orsillo, Artist Bob. The Sequence. 2007. 69p. pap. 27.50 *(978-0-615-17524-9(4))* North River Editions.

Orta, Lucy & Orta, Jorge. Lucy & Jorge Orta: Clouds, Versailles. 2012. (ENG & FRE., Illus.). 224p. pap. 40.00 ***(978-88-6208-216-7(9))*** Damiani ITA. Dist: D.A.P./Distributed Art Pubs.

Oursler, Tony. Tony Oursler: Lock 2, 4, 6. 2010. (ENG & GER., Illus.). 160p. 68.00 *(978-3-86560-719-5(5))* Kunsthaus Bregenz AUT. Dist: D.A.P./Distributed Art Pubs.

Paeffgen, C. O. C.O. Paeffgen: Aus der Sammlung Großhaus ergänzt mit Arbeiten aus den Sammlungen Falckenberg und T.A.L. 2010. (ENG., Illus.). 96p. pap. 35.00 *(978-3-86678-340-9(X))* Kerber Verlag DEU. Dist: D.A.P./Distributed Art Pubs.

Pakesch, Peter. China Welcomes You. 2008. (GER & ENG., Illus.). 175p. pap. 49.95 *(978-3-86560-271-8(1))* Verlag der Buchhandlung Walther Konig DEU. Dist: D.A.P./Distributed Art Pubs.

Pakesch, Peter, ed. Catch Me! Geschwindigkeit fassen: Catch Me! Grasping Speed. 2010. (ENG & GER., Illus.). 120p. pap. 34.50 *(978-3-86560-784-3(5))* Verlag der Buchhandlung Walther Konig DEU. Dist: D.A.P./Distributed Art Pubs.

Paolozzi, Eduardo. Eduardo Paolozzi: the Jet Age Compendium. 2010. (ENG., Illus.). 108p. pap. 19.95 *(978-0-9545025-8-4(2))* Four Corners Bks. GBR. Dist: D.A.P./Distributed Art Pubs.

Parcerisas, Pila, ed. Viennese Actionism. 2008. 440p. pap. *(978-84-96954-44-1(7))* Actar Birkhauser Distribution.

Pardo, Jorge. Jorge Pardo. 2011. (ENG., Illus.). 144p. 70.00 *(978-3-941263-03-1(X))* Richter Verlag DEU. Dist: D.A.P./Distributed Art Pubs.

Parke-Taylor, Michael, ed. Angelika Hoerle: The Comet of Cologne Dada. 2010. (ENG., Illus.). 128p. pap. 39.00 *(978-3-86560-631-0(8))* Verlag der Buchhandlung Walther Konig DEU. Dist: D.A.P./Distributed Art Pubs.

Payne, Oliver & Relph, Nick. Oliver Payne & Nick Relph, 1 vol. 2006. (ENG., Illus.). 196p. 38.00 *(978-3-905701-45-6(6))* JRP Ringier Kunstverlag AG CHE. Dist: D.A.P./Distributed Art Pubs.

Peabody, Rebecca, et al, eds. Pacific Standard Time: Los Angeles Art, 1945-1980. 2011. (ENG., Illus.). 352p. 59.95 *(978-1-60606-072-8(4),* Getty Research Institute) Getty Pubns.

Pearson, Fiona & Stevenson, Sara. Joan Eardley. 2008. (ENG., Illus.). 96p. pap. *(978-1-906270-04-9(X))* National Galleries of Scotland.

Penny, Evan. Evan Penny: Rendering Realities. 2011. (ITA, GER & ENG., Illus.). 160p. 45.00 ***(978-3-86560-990-8(2))*** Verlag der Buchhandlung Walther Konig DEU. Dist: D.A.P./Distributed Art Pubs.

Pepall, Rosalind. Tiffany Glass: A Passion for Color. 2010. (ENG., Illus.). 264p. 60.00 *(978-0-8478-3426-6(3))* Rizzoli International Pubns., Inc.

Pérez-Barreiro, Gabriel. The Geometry of Hope: Latin American Abstract Art from the Patricia Phelps de Cisneros Collection. 2007. (ENG & SPA.). 45.00 *(978-0-9771453-7-9(9))* Univ. of Texas at Austin, The.

Perez-Barreiro, Gabriel, ed. Francisco Matto: the Modern & the Mythic. 2009. (ENG., Illus.). 120p. pap. 29.95 *(978-0-9815738-3-0(5))* Blanton Museum of Art, Univ. of Texas at Austin.

—The Geometry of Hope: Latin American Abstract Art from the Patricia Phelps de Cisneros Collection, 1 vol. 2007. (ENG & SPA., Illus.). 344p. pap. 29.95 *(978-0-9771453-6-2(0))* Blanton Museum of Art, Univ. of Texas at Austin.

Perez-Barreiro, Gabriel, et al, eds. New York Graphic Workshop: 1964-1970. 2009. (ENG., Illus.). 128p. pap. 36.00 *(978-0-9815738-2-3(7))* Blanton Museum of Art, Univ. of Texas at Austin.

Perl, Jed. A Culture in the Making: New York & San Francisco in the 1950s And '60s. 2006. (Illus.). 124p. 30.00 *(978-1-933399-11-9(2))* Hackett-Freedman Gallery, Inc.

Perret, Roger & Kurzmeyer, Roman, eds. Dunkelschwestern. Annemarie von Matt - Sonja Sekula. 2008. (Illus.). 368p. 147.00 *(978-3-85881-213-1(7))* Scheidegger und Spiess AG, Verlag CHE. Dist: Antique Collectors' Club.

Peter Selz. Botero in La: Drawings Paintings Sculpture. 2010. (Illus.). 58p. 20.00 *(978-0-9794823-0-4(5))* Tasende Gallery.

Pettibon, Raymond. Here's Your Irony Back, 1 vol. 2011. (ENG., Illus.). 200p. 50.00 *(978-3-85521-741-7(9))* Steidl, Gerhard Druckerei und Verlag DEU. Dist: Innovative Logistics.

Pfeffer, Susanne, ed. Absalon. 2011. (GER & ENG., Illus.). 352p. pap. 65.00 ***(978-3-86560-952-6(X))*** Verlag der Buchhandlung Walther Konig DEU. Dist: D.A.P./Distributed Art Pubs.

Pfeifer, Mario, et al. Mario Pfeifer: Reconsidering the New Industrial Parks near Irvine, California by Lewis Baltz 1974. 2011. (ENG., Illus.). 93p. pap. 19.95 ***(978-1-934105-29-0(5))*** Sternberg Pr.

Phagan, Patricia. A Taste for the Modern: Gifts from Blanchette Hooker Rockefeller, Edna Bryner Schwab, & Virginia Herrick Deknatel. 2011. pap. ***(978-0-9820606-3-6(7))*** Loeb, Frances Lehman Art Ctr., Vassar Coll., The.

Phillippi, Michael & Westheider, Otrud. Modern Life. Edward Hopper & His Time. 2009. (ENG.). 240p. 59.95 *(978-3-7774-2001-1(8)*, Art Stock Bks. Ltd/Csi) Continental Sales, Inc.

Phillips, Glenn. California Video: Artists & Histories. 2008. pap. *(978-0-89236-923-2(X))* Getty Pubns.

Phillips, Glenn, et al. California Video: Artists & Histories. 2008. (Illus.). 320p. 39.95 *(978-0-89236-922-5(1))* Oxford Univ. Pr., Inc.

Phillips, Lisa, text. Skin Fruit. 2010. (ENG., Illus.). 208p. pap. 45.00 *(978-1-935202-19-6(7))* New Museum of Contemporary Art, The.

Picasso, Pablo. A Picasso Portfolio: Prints from the Museum of Modern Art. 2010. (ENG., Illus.). 200p. 40.00 *(978-0-87070-780-3(9))* Museum of Modern Art.

Picasso, Pablo, et al. Picasso in the Metropolitan Museum of Art. 2010. (Illus.). xi, 364p. 35.00 *(978-1-58839-371-5(2))*; 60.00 *(978-1-58839-370-8(4))* Metropolitan Museum of Art, The.

Pistoletto, Michelangelo. The Mirror of Judgement. 2012. (ENG., Illus.). 104p. pap. 34.95 ***(978-3-88335-054-3(5))*** Walther König, Köln/Koenig Bks.

Pivi, Paola. Paola Pivi: It Just Keeps Getting Better. 2008. (ENG., Illus.). 118p. 58.00 *(978-3-86560-292-3(4))* Verlag der Buchhandlung Walther Konig DEU. Dist: D.A.P./Distributed Art Pubs.

Platzer, Monika. Wiener Kinetismus: eine bewegte ModerneViennese Kineticism: Modernism in Motion: Eine Bewegte Moderne Viennese Kineticism: Modernism in Motion. Best, Gerald, ed. 2011. (ENG.). 256p. 69.95 *(978-3-211-99143-5(3))* Springer Wien AUT. Dist: Actar Birkhauser Distribution.

Pongracz, Patricia. Minding Traditions? Twentieth-Century Artists & the Judeo-Christian Legacy. 2006. 224p. pap. 40.00 *(978-1-904832-29-4(6))* Giles, D. Ltd. GBR. Dist: Antique Collectors' Club.

Prager, Heinz-Günter, et al. Tiefoben: Heinz-Günter Prager. 2008. (GER & ENG., Illus.). 176p. 55.00 *(978-3-87909-924-5(3))* Wienand GmbH, Druck- & Verlagshaus DEU. Dist: Independent Pubs. Group.

Price, Marshall. The Abstract Impulse: Fifty Years of Abstraction at the National Academy, 1956-2006. 2007. (ENG., Illus.). 88p. pap. 29.50 *(978-1-887149-17-4(1))* Hudson Hills Pr. LLC.

Price, Marshall N., et al. Martin Kline: Romantic Nature. 2012. (ENG., Illus.). 160p. 50.00 ***(978-1-55595-348-5(4))*** Hudson Hills Pr. LLC

Prina, Stephen. The Second Sentence of Everything I Read Is You. 2009. (ENG., Illus.). 176p. pap. 45.00 *(978-3-86560-512-2(5))* Verlag der Buchhandlung Walther Konig DEU. Dist: D.A.P./Distributed Art Pubs.

Prince, Richard. Richard Prince: 3rd Place. 2008. (ENG., Illus.). 82p. pap. 30.00 *(978-3-86560-492-7(7))* Verlag der Buchhandlung Walther Konig DEU. Dist: D.A.P./Distributed Art Pubs.

Proll, Astrid, et al. Goodbye to London: Radical Art & Politics in the Seventies. 2011. (GER & ENG., Illus.). 208p. 45.00 ***(978-3-7757-2739-6(6))*** Hatje Cantz Verlag GmbH & Co KG DEU. Dist: D.A.P./Distributed Art Pubs.

Proud, Hayden. Revisions+ Expanding the Narrative of South African Art - The Campbell Smith Collection. 2nd ed. 2008. (Illus.). 104p. pap. 43.00 *(978-1-874817-36-9(7))* Unisa Press / Uitgewers GBR. Dist: International Specialized Bk. Services.

Ptak, Elisabeth. Ranches Rolling. 2008. (Illus.). 148p. 50.00 *(978-0-915269-25-9(2))* Windgate Pr.

Qotbi, Mehdi. Qotbi: Mehdi Qotbi: écrits et Esprits. (FRE., Illus.). 181p. *(978-2-8123-0298-5(4))* Editions du Chene.

Quackenbush, Liz, et al, contrib. by. Esme Thompson: The Alchemy of Deisgn. 2011. (Illus.). 84p. pap. 19.95 *(978-0-944722-40-4(7))* Hood Museum of Art.

Quintanilla, Faustino. A Life for Art: The Jaime Andrade Collection. 2011. ***(978-1-936658-07-7(0))*** QCC Art Gallery.

Quintanilla, Sonya Rhie, et al. Dyeing Elegance: Asian Modernism & the Art of Kuboku & Hisako Takaku, 1 vol. 2012. (ENG., Illus.). 64p. 25.00 ***(978-0-615-56210-0(8))*** San Diego Museum of Art.

R, Tal. Tal R: Adieu Interessant. 2008. (ENG., Illus.). 144p. 180.00 *(978-3-86560-482-8(X))* Verlag der Buchhandlung Walther Konig DEU. Dist: D.A.P./Distributed Art Pubs.

Rabinow, Rebecca A., et al, eds. Cezanne to Picasso: Ambroise Vollard, Patron of the Avant-Garde. 2006. (Metropolitan Museum of Art Publications). (ENG., Illus.). 464p. 65.00 *(978-0-300-11779-0(5))* Yale Univ. Pr.

Rabinow, Rebecca A., et al. Cézanne to Picasso: Ambroise Vollard, Patron of the Avant-Garde. 2006. (Metropolitan Museum of Art Publications). (Illus.). 400p. 65.00 *(978-1-58839-195-7(7))* Metropolitan Museum of Art, The.

Rabinowitch, David. Birth of Romanticism Drawings, 1 vol. 2011. (ENG.). 82p. 55.00 *(978-0-935875-24-9(7))* Blum, Peter Edition.

Radical Structures. 2007. (Illus.). pap. 10.00 *(978-0-9677326-8-8(9))* Abaton Bk. Co.

Ramirez, Mari Carmen & Pacheco, Marcelo. Modern & Contemporary Masterworks from MALBA. 2012. (ENG., Illus.). 156p. 35.00 ***(978-0-300-18100-5(0))*** Museum of Fine Arts, Houston.

Ramírez, Mari Carmen, et al. Hélio Oiticica: The Body of Color. 2007. (Illus.). 416p. *(978-0-89090-150-2(3))*; pap. *(978-0-89090-144-1(9))* Museum of Fine Arts, Houston.

Ramos, Todd & Rushbury, Julia. Henry Rushbury - Prints: A Catalogue Raisonné. 2011. (ENG., Illus.). 107p. 45.00 *(978-1-905711-85-7(9))* Royal Academy of Arts GBR. Dist: Hachette Bk. Group.

Rapaport, Brooke Kamin, et al. Houdini: Art & Magic. 2010. (Illus.) 280p. 39.95 *(978-0-300-14684-4(1))* Yale Univ. Pr.

Rattemeyer, Christian, ed. Exhibiting the New Art: 'Op Losse Schroeven' & 'When Attitudes Become Form' 1969. 2011. (ENG., Illus.). 280p. pap. 27.50 *(978-3-86560-859-8(0))* Verlag der Buchhandlung Walther Konig DEU. Dist: D.A.P./Distributed Art Pubs.

Rauschenberg, Robert. Robert Rauschenberg & Jean Tinguely: Collaborations. 2010. (ENG & GER., Illus.). 244p. 65.00 *(978-3-86678-354-6(X))* Kerber Verlag DEU. Dist: D.A.P./Distributed Art Pubs.

Reid, Dennis, ed. Jack Chambers: Light, Spirit, Time, Place, & Life. 2011. (ENG., Illus.). 240p. pap. 45.00 ***(978-0-86492-645-6(6))*** Goose Lane Editions CAN. Dist: Univ. of Toronto Pr.

Reid, Sheila. Art Memories: The Life & Works of Sheila Reid. ltd. ed. 2010. (Illus.). 128p. *(978-0-9646268-4-3(5))* Rush Editions.

—A Place Between Thoughts: The Art of Sheila Reid. ltd. ed. 2010. 173p. pap. *(978-0-9646268-2-9(9))* Rush Editions.

Reifenscheid, Beate, ed. The Final Freedom: from the Pioneers of Land Art. 2011. (GER & ENG., Illus.). 192p. pap. 40.00 ***(978-88-366-2002-9(7))*** Silvana ITA. Dist: D.A.P./Distributed Art Pubs.

Reifenscheid, Beate & Morsbach, Christiane. Daniel Spoerri: Eaten by ... 2010. (GER & ENG., Illus.). 144p. 49.50 *(978-3-86678-342-3(6))* Kerber Verlag DEU. Dist: D.A.P./Distributed Art Pubs.

Reilly, Maura & Nochlin, Linda. Global Feminisms: New Directions in Contemporary Art. 2007. (Illus.). 304p. pap. *(978-0-87273-157-8(X))* Merrell Pubs. Ltd.

Renoir, Auguste. Renoir in the 20th Century. 2010. (ENG., Illus.). 480p. 85.00 *(978-3-7757-2539-2(3))* Hatje Cantz Verlag GmbH & Co KG DEU. Dist: D.A.P./Distributed Art Pubs.

Resnick, Mark. The American Image: U. S. Posters from the 19th to the 21st Century. 2nd ed. 2007. (Illus.). 112p. 29.99 *(978-1-933360-28-7(3)*, RIT Cary Graphic Arts Pr.) Rochester Institute of Technology, Cary Graphic Arts Pr.

Resnick, Mark & Remington, R. Roger. The American Image: U. S. Posters from the 19th to the 21st Century. 2nd ed. 2007. (Illus.). 112p. 50.00 *(978-1-933360-27-0(5)*, RIT Cary Graphic Arts Pr.) Rochester Institute of Technology, Cary Graphic Arts Pr.

Reyes, Pedro & Holtz, Hans, eds. The Air Is Blue. 2007. 208p. 30.00 *(978-1-933045-49-8(3))* D.A.P./Distributed Art Pubs.

Ribas, Joao. Matt Mullican: A Drawing Translates the Way of Thinking. 2008. (Illus.). pap. 18.00 *(978-0-942324-03-7(X))* Drawing Ctr.

Ribas, Joao & Vine, Richard. Sun Xun: Shock of Time. 2009. pap. 10.00 *(978-0-942324-45-7(5))* Drawing Ctr.

Richter, Daniel, illus. Die Palette 1995-2007. 2007. 248p. 60.00 *(978-3-8321-9001-9(5))* Merrell Pubs. Ltd. GBR. Dist: Perseus Distribution.

Richter, Gerhard. Atlas, 1 vol. Friedel, Helmut, ed. 2011. (ENG., Illus.). 864p. 60.00 *(978-1-933045-47-4(7))* D.A.P./Distributed Art Pubs.

Richter Verlag Publishing, creator. Hans Arp: Die Natur der Dinge, 1 vol. 2008. (ENG., Illus.). 236p. 95.00 *(978-3-937572-74-1(0))* Richter Verlag DEU. Dist: D.A.P./Distributed Art Pubs.

Riese, Hans-Peter. Sovak. 2007. (ENG.). 344p. 120.00 *(978-3-87909-921-4(9))* Wienand GmbH, Druck- & Verlagshaus DEU. Dist: Independent Pubs. Group.

Riley, Andrew. Let us Face the Future: British Art 1945-1968. 2011. (ENG & SPA.). 283p. 54.95 *(978-84-937610-8-0(7))* Fundacio Joan Miro ESP. Dist: Actar Birkhauser Distribution.

Rivolta, Francis, intro. Morphing Systems. (ENG & GER., Illus.). 218p. pap. 39.95 *(978-3-905509-30-4(X))* Frey, Patrick Edition im Verlag der Alltag CHE. Dist: D.A.P./Distributed Art Pubs.

Rizzoli. Charles Ledray. 2010. (ENG., Illus.). 160p. 45.00 *(978-0-8478-3527-0(8)*, Skira) Rizzoli International Pubns., Inc.

Roberts, Claire, ed. Other Histories: Guan Wei's Fable for a Contemporary World; Documentation of an Exhibition. 2009. (Illus.). 165p. pap. 45.00 *(978-1-876957-13-1(1))* Univ. of Hawaii Pr.

Roca, Marcel-Li Antunez. Metamembrana. 2009. (ENG, FRE & SPA., Illus.). 127p. pap. *(978-84-96954-87-8(0))* Actar Birkhauser Distribution.

Rolnik, Suely, et al, texts. Antonio Dias: Anywhere Is My Land. 2010. (ENG., Illus.). 188p. pap. 60.00 *(978-3-7757-2459-3(1))* Hatje Cantz Verlag GmbH & Co KG DEU. Dist: D.A.P./Distributed Art Pubs.

Ron, Linden. Ron Linden. 2007. pap. 8.00 *(978-0-9791843-9-0(8))* CUE Art Foundation.

Rondeau, James, et al. Jasper Johns: Gray. 2007. (Illus.). 320p. pap. *(978-0-86559-224-7(1))* Art Institute of Chicago.

Ronduda, Lukasz & Zeyfang, Florian, eds. 1,2,3... Avant-Gardes: Film/Art between Experiment & Archive. 2007. (ENG & GER., Illus.). 224p. pap. 29.95 *(978-1-933128-24-5(0))* Sternberg Pr.

Roselione-Valadez, Juan, ed. Beg Borrow & Steal: Rubell Family Collection. 2011. (ENG., Illus.). 272p. pap. 49.95 *(978-0-9821195-2-5(6))* Rubell Family Collection.

Rosen, Kay. Kay Rosen: AKAK. 2010. (ENG., Illus.). 232p. 49.95 *(978-0-9815449-5-3(9))* Regency Arts Pr.

Roth, Lynette. Painting as a Weapon: Progressive Cologne 1920 - 1930. 2008. (ENG., Illus.). 160p. (C). 59.95 *(978-3-86560-398-2(X))* Verlag der Buchhandlung Walther Konig DEU. Dist: D.A.P./Distributed Art Pubs.

Rothkopf, Scott. Jeff Koons: Hulk Elvis. 2010. (ENG., Illus.). 140p. 80.00 *(978-0-8478-3359-7(3))* Rizzoli International Pubns., Inc.

Rothschild, Deborah, ed. Making It New: The Art & Style of Sara & Gerald Murphy. 2007. (Illus.). 237p. 60.00 *(978-0-520-25238-7(1))*; pap. 36.95 *(978-0-520-25240-0(3))* Univ. of California Pr.

Royal Academy of Arts. Royal Academy Illustrated 2007. 2007. (ENG., Illus.). 192p. per. 22.95 *(978-1-905711-20-8(4))* Royal Academy of Arts GBR. Dist: Hachette Bk. Group.

Royal Academy of Arts (Great Britain) Staff, contrib. by. Royal Academy Illustrated 2011: A Selection from the 243rd Summer Exhibition. 2011. (ENG., Illus.). 192p. pap. 35.00 ***(978-1-905711-87-1(5))*** Royal Academy of Arts GBR. Dist: Hachette Bk. Group.

Royal Academy Of Arts Staff. Royal Academy 2010: A Selection from the 242nd Summer Exhibition. 2010. (ENG., Illus.). 192p. pap. 35.00 *(978-1-905711-56-7(5))* Royal Academy of Arts GBR. Dist: Hachette Bk. Group.

Rubin, David S. Psychedelic: Optical & Visionary Art since the 1960s. 2010. (ENG., Illus.). 138p. (gr. 17). 29.95 *(978-0-262-01404-5(1))* MIT Pr.

Rubio, Agustín, ed. Terence Koh: 1980-2008. 2009. (ENG., Illus.). 208p. 55.00 *(978-3-7757-2308-4(0))* Hatje Cantz Verlag GmbH & Co KG DEU. Dist: D.A.P./Distributed Art Pubs.

Ruf, Beatrix, ed. Blasted Allegories. 2008. (ENG., Illus.). 300p. 65.00 *(978-3-905829-40-2(1))* JRP Ringier Kunstverlag AG CHE. Dist: D.A.P./Distributed Art Pubs.

—Jennifer Allora & Guillermo Calzadilla. 2010. (ENG., Illus.). 156p. 55.00 *(978-3-03764-027-2(8))* JRP Ringier Kunstverlag AG CHE. Dist: D.A.P./Distributed Art Pubs.

Rugoff, Ralph & Sultan, Terrie. Jean-Luc Mylayne: English-French Edition. 2010. (ENG., Illus.). 120p. 45.00 *(978-88-7439-530-9(2))* 5 Continents ITA. Dist: Hachette Bk. Group.

Rumma, Lia. William Kentridge: Streets of the City. 2011. (ENG.). 144p. 75.00 *(978-88-370-7340-4(2)*, Mondadori Electa (Acc)) Antique Collectors' Club GBR. Dist: National Bk. Network.

Sala, Anri. Why the Lion Roars: Forecasts. 2011. (ENG., Illus.). 1536p. 180.00 *(978-3-86560-779-9(9))* Verlag der Buchhandlung Walther Konig DEU. Dist: D.A.P./Distributed Art Pubs.

Salmagundi Club Painting Exhibition Records 1940-1951 & Water Color Exhibition Records 1900-1951. 2009. (Illus.). 623p. 65.00 *(978-0-9791290-2-5(8))* Katlan, Alexander Conservator, Inc.

San Francisco Museum of Modern Art Staff, contrib. by. Calder to Warhol: Introducing the Fisher Collection. 2010. *(978-0-918471-85-7(0))* San Francisco Museum of Modern Art.

Sasnal, Wilhelm. Wilhelm Sasnal. Borchardt-Hume, Achim, ed. 2012. (ENG., Illus.). 106p. pap. 40.00 ***(978-0-85488-199-4(9))*** Whitechapel Art Gallery GBR. Dist: D.A.P./Distributed Art Pubs.

Sasse, Julie. Thanks for Being with Us: Contemporary Art from the Douglas Nielsen Collection. 2010. (ENG., Illus.). 52p. pap. 20.00 *(978-0-911611-39-7(8))* Tucson Museum of Art.

Sasse, Julie, et al. Trouble in Paradise: Examining Discord Between Nature & Society. 2009. (Illus.). 206p. *(978-0-911611-37-3(1))* Tucson Museum of Art.

Sasse, Julie R. An Eclectic Eye: Selections from the Dan leach Collection. 2007. (Illus.). 180p. pap. 30.00 *(978-0-911611-34-2(7))* Tucson Museum of Art.

Saxenhuber, Hedwig. Kunst + Politik / Art + Politics. 2008. (GER & ENG., Illus.). 251p. pap. 39.95 *(978-3-211-09460-0(1))* Springer Wien AUT. Dist: Actar Birkhauser Distribution.

Schabus, Hans. Hans Schabus: Deserted Conquest, 1 vol. Lefrak, Joanne & Zavitovski, Katia, eds. 2008. (ENG., Illus.). 100p. 20.00 *(978-0-9764492-6-3(9))* Site Santa Fe.

Schafhausen, Nicolaus, et al, eds. Edith Dekyndt: Source Book 8. 2011. (ENG., Illus.). 112p. pap. 15.00 *(978-90-73362-90-1(3))* Witte De With Centre for Contemporary Art NLD. Dist: D.A.P./Distributed Art Pubs.

Scheicher, Harald & Biller, Barbara. Macht des Bildes - Visionen des Göttliche: Kunst und Transzendent in Österreich im 20. Jahrhundert. Katalogbuch zur Ausstellung in Bleiburg, 26.04.2009-08.11.2009, Werner Berg Museum Bleiburg. 2009. (Illus.). 383p. *(978-3-7774-8055-8(X))* Hirmer Verlag GmbH.

Schimmel, Paul. Under the Big Black Sun: California Art, 1974-1981. 2011. (ENG., Illus.). 320p. 60.00 ***(978-3-7913-5139-1(7))*** Prestel Publishing.

Schimpf, Simone, ed. & text. Konkret: Die Sammlung Heinz und Anette Teufel im Kunstmuseum Stuttgart / Concrete Art. The Heinz & Anette Teufel Collection in the Kunstmuseum Stuttgart. 2010. (ENG., Illus.). 308p. 60.00 *(978-3-7757-2419-7(2))* Hatje Cantz Verlag GmbH & Co KG DEU. Dist: D.A.P./Distributed Art Pubs.

Schmuckli, Claudia, et al. Jon Pylypchuk. 2010. (ENG., Illus.). 96p. 39.95 *(978-0-941193-45-0(4))* Blaffer Art Museum.

Schneider, Eckhard, ed. Michael Craig-Martin: Signs of Life, 1 vol. 2006. (ENG., Illus.). 128p. 65.00 *(978-3-86560-085-1(9))* Kunsthaus Bregenz AUT. Dist: D.A.P./Distributed Art Pubs.

—Re-Object. 2007. 160p. 70.00 *(978-3-902289-06-3(6))* Kunsthaus Bregenz AUT. Dist: D.A.P./Distributed Art Pubs.

Schneider, Gregor, photos by. Gregor Schneider. End. 2010. (ENG & GER., Illus.). 216p. 55.00 *(978-3-86560-422-4(6))* Verlag der Buchhandlung Walther Konig DEU. Dist: D.A.P./Distributed Art Pubs.

Schönhuth, Friederik. Jason Dodge: I Woke Up, There Was a Note in My Pocket Explaining What Had Happened. 2010. (ENG., Illus.). 216p. pap. 45.00 *(978-3-7757-2618-4(7))* Hatje Cantz Verlag GmbH & Co KG DEU. Dist: D.A.P./Distributed Art Pubs.

Schoonmaker, Trevor, ed. Barkley L. Hendricks: Birth of the Cool. 2008. (ENG., Illus.). 140p. 39.95 *(978-0-938989-31-8(6))* Duke Univ. Pr.

Schor, Gabriele. Donna avanguardia femminista negli Anni '70: From the Sammlung Verbund Wien. 2010. (ITA & ENG., Illus.). 256p. 80.00 *(978-88-370-7414-2(X))* Electa ITA. Dist: National Bk. Network.

Schreiber, Daniel, ed. & text. Thomas Florschuetz. Imperfekt. Werke 1997 - 2010. 2011. (GER & ENG., Illus.). 112p. 45.00 *(978-3-86560-855-0(8))* Verlag der Buchhandlung Walther Konig DEU. Dist: D.A.P./Distributed Art Pubs.

Schröder, Klaus Albrecht. Monet to Picasso, the Batliner Collection. 2008. 420p. 70.00 *(978-3-86568-319-9(3))* Imhof, Michael Verlag GmbH & Co. KG DEU. Dist: Independent Pubs. Group.

Schulman, Daniel, ed. A Force for Change: African American Art & the Julius Rosenwald Fund. 2009. (ENG., Illus.). 176p. pap. 39.95 *(978-0-8101-2588-9(9))* Northwestern Univ. Pr.

Schumacher, Rainald, et al, eds. Mike Kelley: Goetz Collection. 2009. (ENG., Illus.). 272p. 50.00 *(978-3-939894-11-7(7))* Goetz, Ingvild, Kunstverlag, GmbH DEU. Dist: D.A.P./Distributed Art Pubs.

Schwabsky, Barry, text. Chloe Piene. 2008. (ENG., Illus.). 104p. 45.00 *(978-2-907550-33-5(5))* Carre d'Art FRA. Dist: D.A.P./Distributed Art Pubs.

Scott, Bill & Coyle, Heather Campbell. Painted Poetry: The Art of Mary Page Evans. 2012. (ENG., Illus.). 96p. 45.00 ***(978-1-55595-374-4(3))*** Hudson Hills Pr. LLC.

Seaton, Elizabeth G., ed. Paths to the Press: Printmaking & American Women Artists, 1910-1960. 2006. (Illus.). 261p. pap. 40.00 *(978-1-890751-13-5(8))* Kansas State Univ., Marianna Kistler Beach Museum of Art, The.

Secchi, C. & Pozzi, D. Milano Expo 1906. 2008. (ENG., Illus.). 160p. 68.00 *(978-88-6302-010-6(8)*, Art Stock Bks. Ltd/Csi) Continental Sales, Inc.

Secrest, Tom. Tom Secrest. 2007. pap. 8.00 *(978-0-9797964-2-5(3))* CUE Art Foundation.

Seda, Katerina. Katerina Seda: over & Over. 2010. (ENG., Illus.). 312p. 45.00 *(978-3-03764-111-8(8))* JRP Ringier Kunstverlag AG CHE. Dist: D.A.P./Distributed Art Pubs.

Seelig, Thomas, et al. Sergey Bratkov: Glory Days / Heldenzeiten. Eine ausgewählte Werkübersicht 1995-2007. Seelig, Thomas & De Baere, Bart, eds. 2008. (GER & ENG., Illus.). 208p. 70.00 *(978-3-85881-218-6(8))* Scheidegger und Spiess AG, Verlag CHE. Dist: Antique Collectors' Club.

Sekler, Eduard F., contrib. by. Yearning for Beauty: The Wiener Werkstatte & the Stoclet House, 1 vol. 2006. (ENG., Illus.). 452p. 95.00 *(978-3-7757-1778-6(1))* Hatje Cantz Verlag GmbH & Co KG DEU. Dist: D.A.P./Distributed Art Pubs.

Shapiro, Mark, ed. A Chosen Path: The Ceramic Art of Karen Karnes. 2010. (ENG., Illus.). 129p. 40.00 *(978-0-8078-3427-5(0))* Univ. of North Carolina Pr.

Sharf, Frederic. Art of Collecting: The Spaulding Brothers & Their Legacy, 1 vol. 2008. (ENG., Illus.). 144p. pap. 24.95 *(978-0-87846-723-5(8))* Museum of Fine Arts, Boston.

Sikander, Shahzia, illus. Shahzia Sikander, 1 vol. 2007. (ENG.). 160p. 70.00 *(978-88-8158-642-4(8))* Charta ITA. Dist: D.A.P./Distributed Art Pubs.

Sillevis, John. The Baroque World of Fernando Botero. 2007. (ENG., Illus.). 283p. 65.00 *(978-0-300-12359-3(0))* Yale Univ. Pr.

Sillevis, John & Botero, Fernando. The Baroque World of Fernando Botero. 2007. *(978-0-88397-148-2(8))*; (Illus.). 283p. *(978-0-88397-147-5(X))* Art Services International.

Simmonds, Charles, et al. Landscape Body Dwelling: Charles Simonds at Dumbarton Oaks. 2012. (ENG., Illus.). 116p. pap. 40.00 *(978-0-88402-371-5(0))* Dumbarton Oaks.

Simon, Amy, photos by. Amy Simon: A Different State of Mind. 2010. (ENG., Illus.). 80p. 45.00 *(978-3-7757-2622-1(5))* Hatje Cantz Verlag GmbH & Co KG DEU. Dist: D.A.P./Distributed Art Pubs.

Sinnreich, Ursula, ed. James Turrell: Geometrie des Lichts. 2009. (ENG & GER., Illus.). 128p. 55.00 *(978-3-7757-2369-5(2))* Hatje Cantz Verlag GmbH & Co KG DEU. Dist: D.A.P./Distributed Art Pubs.

Sisley, Logan. Richard Tuttle: Triumphs. 2012. (ENG., Illus.). 102p. pap. 45.00 ***(978-1-901702-37-8(5))*** Lane, Hugh Gallery IRL. Dist: D.A.P./Distributed Art Pubs.

Skira, et al, eds. Lights On: Norwegian Contemporary Art. 2009. (ENG., Illus.). 192p. pap. 45.00 *(978-88-6130-792-6(2))* Skira Editore ITA. Dist: Random Hse., Inc.

Slominski, Andreas. Andreas Slominski. 2010. (ENG., Illus.). 144p. 55.00 *(978-3-7757-2603-0(9))* Hatje Cantz Verlag GmbH & Co KG DEU. Dist: D.A.P./Distributed Art Pubs.

Smerling, Walter. Anthony Cragg: Dinge im Kopf / Things on the Mind. Skulpturen, Zeichnungen, Grafiken / Sculptures, Drawings, Graphic Art. Smerling, Walter, ed. 2011. (ENG & GER., Illus.). 136p. pap. 58.95 ***(978-3-86832-052-7(0))*** Wienand GmbH, Druck- & Verlagshaus DEU. Dist: Independent Pubs. Group.

Smith, Jessica Todd & Murphy, Kevin M. Pressed in Time: American Prints, 1905-1950. 2008. (Illus.). 88p. pap. 19.95 *(978-0-87328-234-5(5))* Huntington Library Pr.

Smith, Katharine & Schiller, Joyce. Illustrating Her World: Ellen B. T. Pyle. 2009. pap. *(978-0-9771644-0-0(3))* Delaware Art Museum, The.

South Carolina State Museum. Edmund Yaghjian: A Retrospective. 2011. (Distributed for the South Carolina State Museum Ser.). 88p. 19.95 ***(978-0-9836794-2-4(8))*** Univ. of South Carolina Pr.

Spanjaard, Helena & Welling, Wouter. The Dono Code: Installations, Sculptures, Paintings. 2009. 72p. pap. 29.95 *(978-94-6022-052-4(5))* Royal Tropical Institute Pr. (KIT (Koninklijk Instituut voor de Tropen) NLD. Dist: Stylus Publishing, LLC.

Spies, Werner. Max Ernst Dream & Revolution. Degel, Kirsten, ed. 2009. (ENG., Illus.). 256p. 60.00 *(978-3-7757-2235-3(1))* Hatje Cantz Verlag GmbH & Co KG DEU. Dist: D.A.P./Distributed Art Pubs.

Spoerri, Daniel. Daniel Spoerri: Weißt Du, Schwarzt Du? 2011. (GER & ENG., Illus.). 160p. 40.00 ***(978-3-86678-447-5(3))*** Kerber Verlag DEU. Dist: D.A.P./Distributed Art Pubs.

Srp, Karel, et al. New Formations: Czech Avant-Garde Art & Modern Glass from the Roy & Mary Cullen Collection. 2011. (ENG., Illus.). 320p. 75.00 *(978-0-300-16996-6(5))* Museum of Fine Arts, Houston.

Stallings, Tyler, ed. Absurd Recreation: Contemporary Art from China. 2008. 48p. pap. 20.00 net. *(978-0-932173-00-3(4))* Sweeney Art Gallery.

Starkman, Christine. Unrivalled Splendor: The Kimiko & John Powers Collection of Japanese Art. 2012. (ENG., Illus.). 272p. 65.00 ***(978-0-300-17962-0(6))*** Museum of Fine Arts, Houston.

Stationen der Moderne. 175.00 *(978-3-88375-082-8(4))* Verlag der Buchhandlung Walther Konig DEU. Dist: D.A.P./Distributed Art Pubs.

Stavitsky, Gail & Rothkopf, Katherine. Cezanne & American Modernism. 2009. (ENG., Illus.). 376p. 65.00 *(978-0-300-14715-5(5))* Yale Univ. Pr.

Stenschke, Jochen. Jochen Stenschke: Bilder im schwarzen Kasten. 2010. (ENG., Illus.). 96p. pap. 29.95 *(978-3-86678-307-2(8))* Kerber Verlag DEU. Dist: D.A.P./Distributed Art Pubs.

Stief, Angela, ed. Power up: Female Pop Art. 2011. (ENG., Illus.). 288p. pap. 45.00 *(978-3-8321-9356-0(1))* DuMont DEU. Dist: D.A.P./Distributed Art Pubs.

Stingel, Rudolf. Rudolf Stingel: MCA Chicago/Whitney New York. 2009. (ENG., Illus.). 128p. 55.00 *(978-3-7757-2339-8(0))* Hatje Cantz Verlag GmbH & Co KG DEU. Dist: D.A.P./Distributed Art Pubs.

Stohler, Peter & Rüttimann, Sylvia. Risk & Allure. 2007. (ENG & GER., Illus.). 160p. 15.00 *(978-3-89790-248-0(6))* Arnoldsche Art Pubs. DEU. Dist: Antique Collectors' Club.

Stooss, Toni, ed. Alberto Giacometti: the Origin of Space. 2011. (ENG., Illus.). 200p. 60.00 *(978-3-7757-2715-0(9))* Hatje Cantz Verlag GmbH & Co KG DEU. Dist: D.A.P./Distributed Art Pubs.

Strauss. Beat Zoderer. 2009. (GER & ENG., Illus.). 224p. 70.00 *(978-3-7757-2294-0(7))* Hatje Cantz Verlag GmbH & Co KG DEU. Dist: D.A.P./Distributed Art Pubs.

Strauss, Cindi, et al. Shifting Paradigms in Contemporary Ceramics: The Garth Clark & Mark Del Vecchio Collection. 2012. (ENG., Illus.). 576p. 100.00 ***(978-0-300-16997-3(3))*** Yale Univ. Pr.

Struycken, Peter, illus. P. Struycken. 2008. (ENG.). 272p. 75.00 *(978-90-5662-606-8(X))* NAi Uitgevers / Publishers Stichting NLD. Dist: D.A.P./Distributed Art Pubs.

Stuhlman, Jonathan & DuBois, Michelle. Seeing the World Within. Stuhlman, Jonathan, ed. 2012. (ENG & ITA.). 35.00 ***(978-0-9831942-4-8(6))*** Mint Museum, The.

Stutzer, Beat, et al. Corsin Fontana: Werke 1966 - 2009. Stutzer, Beat, ed. 2010. (Illus.). 288p. ***(978-3-85881-292-6(7))*** Antique Collectors' Club.

Stutzer, Beat, et al. The Unseen Giacometti: Unknown Photographs & Drawings. Stutzer, Beat, ed. 2011. (ENG., Illus.). 255p. 99.00 *(978-3-85881-726-6(0))* Scheidegger und Spiess AG, Verlag CHE. Dist: Antique Collectors' Club.

Suarez, Osbel, text. Cold America. 2011. 504p. 85.00 *(978-84-7075-588-0(9))* Fundacion Juan March ESP. Dist: Actar Birkhauser Distribution.

Subiros, Pep. Apartheid: The South African Mirror. 2007. (Illus.). 205p. pap. *(978-84-96954-03-8(X))* Actar Birkhauser Distribution.

Subiros, Pep, ed. Apartheid: El Espejo Sudafricano. 2007. (Illus.). 204p. per. *(978-84-96954-02-1(1))* Actar Birkhauser Distribution.

Symmes, Marilyn F. Pop Art & After: Prints+popular Culture. 2008. (Illus.). 131p. *(978-0-9769030-9-3(1))* Zimmerli, Jane Voorhees Art Museum.

Szymczyk, Adam, ed. Daniel Knorr: Led R. Nanirok. 2010. (ENG., Illus.). 304p. pap. 28.00 *(978-3-03764-078-4(2))* JRP Ringier Kunstverlag AG CHE. Dist: D.A.P./Distributed Art Pubs.

Szymczyk, Adam, text. Kilian Rüthemann: Double Rich. 2010. (ENG., Illus.). 4036p. 55.00 *(978-3-7757-2674-0(8))* Hatje Cantz Verlag GmbH & Co KG DEU. Dist: D.A.P./Distributed Art Pubs.

Szymczyk, Adam & Filipovic, Elena. When Things Cast No Shadow. 2008. (GER & ENG., Illus.). 592p. pap. 45.00 *(978-3-905829-58-7(4))* JRP Ringier Kunstverlag AG CHE. Dist: D.A.P./Distributed Art Pubs.

Taaffe, Philip, et al. Philip Taaffe: Anima Mundi. 2011. (ENG., Illus.). 126p. pap. 40.00 ***(978-1-907020-60-5(8))*** Irish Museum of Modern Art IRL. Dist: D.A.P./Distributed Art Pubs.

Tamayo, Museo. La Maquina y el Juglar Coleccion Renault. 2006. 69p. pap. 41.00 *(978-968-5979-11-5(1))* Trucatriche.

Tannenbaum, Judith. Wunderground: Providence, 1995 to the Present. 2006. (Illus.). 104p. per. 24.95 *(978-1-58423-262-9(5))* Gingko Pr., Inc.

Taragin, Davira S., et al. Bigger, Better, More: The Art of Viola Frey. 2009. (ENG., Illus.). 136p. 50.00 *(978-1-55595-305-8(0))* Hudson Hills Pr. LLC.

Taylor, Elena. Grace Crowley: Being Modern. 2007. (ENG., Illus.). 64p. pap. *(978-0-642-54192-5(2))* National Gallery of Australia.

Taylor, Michael & Chagall, Marc. Paris Through the Window: Marc Chagall & His Circle. 2010. *(978-0-87633-230-6(0))* Philadelphia Museum of Art.

Taylor, Michael & Chimes, Thomas. Thomas Chimes: Adventures in Pataphysics. 2007. (Illus.). xi, 255p. *(978-0-87633-253-5(X))*; *(978-0-87633-252-8(1))* Philadelphia Museum of Art.

Taylor, Michael R. Thomas Chimes: Adventures In 'Pataphysics. 2007. (ENG., Illus.). 267p. 50.00 *(978-0-300-12217-6(9))* Yale Univ. Pr.

Thomas, Elizabeth, ed. Matrix: Berkeley. 2009. (ENG., Illus.). 560p. pap. 35.00 *(978-0-9719397-8-3(0))* Univ. of California, Berkeley Art Museum & Pacific Film Archive.

Thompson, Carol. Radcliffe Bailey: Memory as Medicine. 2011. 160p. 45.00 *(978-1-932543-42-1(2))* High Museum of Art.

Tinterow, Gary, et al. Abstract Expressionism & Other Modern Works: The Muriel Kallis Steinberg Newman Collection in the Metropolitan Museum of Art. 2007. (Illus.). x, 214p. 29.95 *(978-1-58839-274-9(0))* Metropolitan Museum of Art, The.

Tobias, Gert. Gert und Uwe Tobias: Zeichnungen und Collagen. 2010. (GER & ENG., Illus.). 66p. pap. 27.50 *(978-3-86678-371-3(X))* Kerber Verlag DEU. Dist: D.A.P./Distributed Art Pubs.

Tregulova, Zelfira & Bowlt, John E., eds. A Festival of Wonders: Serghei Diaghilev & the Ballets Russes. 2009. (ENG., Illus.). 320p. 60.00 *(978-88-572-0090-3(6))* Skira Editore ITA. Dist: Random Hse., Inc.

Tricot, Xavier. James ensor the complete Prints, 1 vol. 2011. (ENG.). 304p. 140.00 ***(978-90-5779-119-2(6))*** Exhibitions International BEL. Dist: Innovative Logistics.

Tufnell, Ben, ed. Frank Stella: Connections. 2012. (ENG., Illus.). 96p. 55.00 ***(978-3-7757-3271-0(3))*** Hatje Cantz Verlag GmbH & Co KG DEU. Dist: D.A.P./Distributed Art Pubs.

Tunberg, Despina. International Contemporary Masters. Tunberg, Thomas & Tunberg, Despina, eds. 2008. (Illus.). 60p. pap. 24.95 *(978-0-9802079-0-3(8))* Omma Gallery Santa Barbara, LLC.

Tupitsyn, Margarita, ed. Rodchenko & Popova: Defining Constructivism. 2009. (ENG., Illus.). 192p. pap. 39.95 *(978-1-85437-796-8(5))* Tate Publishing, Ltd. GBR. Dist: Hachette Bk. Group.

Tupitsyn, Margarita & International Center of Photography Staff, contrib. by. Gustav Klutsis & Valentina Kulagina: Photography & Montage after Constructivism, 1 vol. 2008. (ENG., Illus.). 256p. 60.00 *(978-3-88243-974-8(2))* Steidl, Gerhard Druckerei und Verlag DEU. Dist: Innovative Logistics.

Turrell, James. James Turrell: The Wolfsburg Project. 2010. (ENG & GER., Illus.). 184p. 60.00 *(978-3-7757-2455-5(9))* Hatje Cantz Verlag GmbH & Co KG DEU. Dist: D.A.P./Distributed Art Pubs.

Tuymans, Luc. Against the Day, 1 vol. 2010. (ENG., Illus.). 96p. 55.00 *(978-3-86930-047-4(7))* Steidl, Gerhard Druckerei und Verlag DEU. Dist: Innovative Logistics.

Tuymans, Luc & Gas, Alison. Luc Tuymans: The Reality of the Lowest Rank - A Vision of Central Europe. 2011. (ENG., Illus.). 300p. 85.00 *(978-90-209-8997-7(9))* Lannoo Pubs./Racine.

TV Arts TV. 2011. (ENG., Illus.). 160p. pap. 35.00 *(978-84-92841-60-8(5))* La Fabrica ESP. Dist: D.A.P./Distributed Art Pubs.

Twombly, Cy. States of Mind. Catalog MUMOK, Vienna. 2009. (Illus.). 160p. *(978-3-8296-0445-1(9))* Schirmer/Mosel Verlag GmbH.

Udall, Sharyn R. & Weekly, Nancy. Sensory Crossovers: Synesthesia in American Art. Hall, Dawn, ed. 2010. (Illus.). 111p. pap. 37.00 *(978-0-9779910-5-1(9))* Albuquerque Museum of Art and History.

Untiefen: Raumwahrnehmung in Bildern. *(978-3-926154-27-9(6))* Kunstsammlung Nordrhein-Westfalen.

Vadehra Art Gallery Staff & Grosvenor Vadehra (Art Gallery: London, England) Staff, contrib. by. Indian Art, 3 vols. 2010. (ENG., Illus.). 146p. 19.95 *(978-81-87737-19-3(0))*; 101p. 19.95 *(978-81-87737-27-8(1))*; 129p. pap. 19.95 *(978-81-87737-22-3(0))* Antique Collectors' Club GBR. (Vadehra Art Gallery (Acc)). Dist: National Bk. Network.

Valldosera, Eulalia. The Navel of the World: Eulalia Valldosera. 2009. 176p. pap. 39.95 *(978-84-8026-382-5(2))* Museo Nacional Centro de Arte Reina Sofia ESP. Dist: Actar Birkhauser Distribution.

Vallora, Marco. Marco Fantini: Antilogia. 2011. (ITA & ENG., Illus.). 176p. pap. 39.95 *(978-88-8158-802-2(1))* Charta ITA. Dist: D.A.P./Distributed Art Pubs.

Van Assche, Annie. Fashioning Kimono: Dress & Modernity in Early Twentieth-Century Japan: The Montgomery Collection. 2008. *(978-0-88397-149-9(6))* Art Services International.

Van Severen, David. Office: Kersten Geers David Van Severen. 2010. (ENG., Illus.). 80p. pap. 45.00 *(978-3-7757-2572-9(5))* Hatje Cantz Verlag GmbH & Co KG DEU. Dist: D.A.P./Distributed Art Pubs.

Vann, Philip. Tessa Newcomb. 2013. (ENG., Illus.). 144p. 50.00 *(978-1-904537-94-6(4))* Sansom & Co. Ltd. GBR. Dist: National Bk. Network.

Vazquez, Victor, photos by. Victor Vazquez: 1989-2007, 1 vol. 2008. (ENG., Illus.). 300p. 85.00 *(978-0-9773932-4-4(0))* Museo de Arte de Ponce.

Veith, Barbara & Frelinghuysen, Alice Cooney. Aesthetic Ambitions: Edward Lycett & Brooklyn's Faience Manufacturing Company. 2011. (Illus.). 119p. ***(978-0-9765047-9-5(0))*** Univ. of Richmond Museums.

Venancio Filho, Paulo. Rio de Janeiro 1956-1964: Time & Place. 2008. (ENG., Illus.). 112p. pap. 40.00 *(978-3-86521-638-0(2))* Steidl, Gerhard Druckerei und Verlag DEU. Dist: Innovative Logistics.

Ventos, Ernesto. Smell Colour: Chemistry, Art & Pedagogy. 2011. 112p. pap. ***(978-84-92861-99-6(1))*** Actar Birkhauser Distribution.

Vergne, Philippe & Carmine, Giovanni, eds. Gedi Sibony. 2009. (ENG., Illus.). 64p. 35.00 *(978-3-905829-89-1(4))* JRP Ringier Kunstverlag AG CHE. Dist: D.A.P./Distributed Art Pubs.

Veryeri-Alaca, Ilgim. Ilgim Veryeri-Alaca: Recent Prints & Drawings. 2007. (Illus.). 14p. *(978-0-9765047-4-0(X))* Univ. of Richmond Museums.

Vettese, Angela. Lawrence Carroll. 2008. (ENG., Illus.). 160p. 75.00 *(978-88-8158-668-4(1))* Charta ITA. Dist: D.A.P./Distributed Art Pubs.

Vicario, Gilbert, et al, texts. Daniel Joseph Martinez. 2009. (ENG., Illus.). 248p. 60.00 *(978-3-7757-2305-3(6))* Hatje Cantz Verlag GmbH & Co KG DEU. Dist: D.A.P./Distributed Art Pubs.

Vivian, Helen, ed. When You Think About Art: The Ewing & George Paton Gallery, 1971-2008. 2008. (Illus.). 288p. (C). 80.00 *(978-1-921394-02-7(1))* Macmillan Art Publishing AUS. Dist: Brown, David Bk. Co., The.

Voigt, Wolfgang, et al, texts. Gottfried Böhm, 1 vol. 2007. (ENG., Illus.). 272p. 60.00 *(978-3-936314-19-9(5))* Jovis Verlag GmbH DEU. Dist: D.A.P./Distributed Art Pubs.

von Gustorf, Oliver Koerner, text. Banks Violette. 2009. (ENG., Illus.). 83p. pap. 60.00 *(978-3-901935-35-0(5))* Galerie Thaddaeus Ropac FRA. Dist: D.A.P./Distributed Art Pubs.

Vorano, Norman, et al. Inuit Prints, Japanese Inspiration: Early Printmaking in the Canadian Arctic. 2011. (ENG., Illus.). 100p. (C). pap. 29.95 *(978-0-660-19970-2(X))* Canadian Museum of Civilization/Musee Canadien des Civilisations CAN. Dist: Univ. of Washington Pr.

Voss, Roy, text. Daniel Sturgis: Don't Argue, 2007- exhibition catalog with an essay by Roy Voss. 2007. (Illus.). per. *(978-0-9774221-1-1(9))* Broan, Cynthia Gallery.

Vriesendorp, Madelon, et al. The World of Madelon Vriesendorp: Paintings, Postcards, Objects, Games. 2008. (Illus.). 277p. *(978-1-902902-63-0(7))* Actar Birkhauser Distribution.

Wainwright, Lisa. Things of Nature & the Nature of Things: John Wilde in the Mcclain Collection. 2007. (Chazen Museum of Art Catalogs Ser.). (Illus.). 46p. pap. 29.95 *(978-0-932900-98-2(4))* Univ. of Wisconsin-Madison, Chazen Museum of Art.

Wakefield, Neville, text. Banks Violette, 12 vols. 2009. (ENG., Illus.). 68p. 60.00 *(978-3-86560-457-6(9))* Verlag der Buchhandlung Walther Konig DEU. Dist: D.A.P./Distributed Art Pubs.

Walker, Andrew & Turk, Janeen. Joe Jones: Radical Painter of the American Scene. 2010. (Illus.). 224p. (ENG.). 60.00 *(978-0-89178-094-6(7))*; pap. 40.00 *(978-0-89178-093-9(9))* St. Louis Art Museum.

Wallace, Catherine. Catching the Light: The Art & Life of Henry Scott Tuke, 1858-1929. 2008. (ENG., Illus.). 160p. *(978-1-873830-20-8(3)*, Fine Art Society (Acc)) Antique Collectors' Club.

Waller, Richard. The Space of Freedom: Apartment Exhibitions in Leningrad, 1964-1986. Schlatter, N. Elizabeth & Maitre, Joan, eds. 2007. (RUS & ENG., Illus.). 108p. pap. *(978-0-9765047-3-3(1))* Univ. of Richmond Museums.

Wallinger, Mark & text. Mark Wallinger: the Russian Linesman. 2009. (ENG., Illus.). 144p. pap. 40.00 *(978-1-85332-272-3(5))* Hayward Gallery Publishing GBR. Dist: D.A.P./Distributed Art Pubs.

Walsh, Michael J. K., ed. London, Modernism, And 1914. 2010. (ENG., Illus.). 314p. 89.00 *(978-0-521-19580-5(2))* Cambridge Univ. Pr.

Ward, Gerald W. R., et al. Shy Boy, She Devil & Isis: The Art of Conceptual Craft. 2007. 183p. pap. 35.00 *(978-0-87846-720-4(3))* Museum of Fine Arts, Boston.

Warhol, Andy. Andy Warhol: the Early Sixties. 2010. (ENG., Illus.). 244p. 60.00 *(978-3-7757-2651-1(9))* Hatje Cantz Verlag GmbH & Co KG DEU. Dist: D.A.P./Distributed Art Pubs.

Warhol, Andy & Barilleaux, Rene Paul. Andy Warhol: Fame & Misfortune. 2012. (ENG., Illus.). 80p. 29.95 ***(978-0-916677-57-2(5))*** McNay, Marion Koogler Art Museum.

Warhol, Andy, et al. Warhol from the Sonnabend Collection. 2009. (ENG., Illus.). 180p. 85.00 *(978-0-8478-3277-4(5))* Rizzoli International Pubns., Inc.

Warren, Isensee. Warren Isensee. 2008. (Illus.). 34p. per. *(978-0-9795501-2-6(2))* Danese.

Warren, Lynne. Chicago Imagists. 2011. ***(978-0-913883-36-5(0))*** Madison Art Ctr., Inc.

Watkins, Nicholas. Behind the Mirror: Miro, Giacometti, Calder, Braque. 2008. (ENG., Illus.). 160p. 65.00 *(978-1-905711-38-3(7))* Royal Academy of Arts GBR. Dist: Hachette Bk. Group.

Weissman, Benjamin & Dalton, Trinie, contrib. by. Matt Greene Surrender!, 1 vol. 2007. (ENG., Illus.). 56p. 20.00 *(978-0-9753243-9-4(X))* Deitch, Jeffrey Inc.

Weissweiler, Lilli. Futuristen Auf Europa-Tournee: Zur Vorgeschichte, Konzeption und Rezeption der Ausstellungen Futuristischer Malerei (1911-1913) 2009. (Illus.). 287p. pap. *(978-3-8376-1205-9(8))* Transcript Verlag.

Wesley, John, illus. John Wesley: The Bumsteads, 1 vol. 2008. (ENG.). 56p. 40.00 *(978-0-615-15827-3(7))* Fredericks & Freiser.

West, Franz. Franz West: Early Work, 1 vol. 2006. (ENG., Illus.). 156p. 65.00 *(978-0-9708884-6-4(5))* Zwirner & Wirth.

White, Julia M. Mahjong: Art, Film, & Change in China. 2008. (ENG., Illus.). 100p. pap. 25.00 *(978-0-9719397-7-6(2))* Univ. of California, Berkeley Art Museum & Pacific Film Archive.

White, Mark Andrew & Hrdy, Olinka. Oklahoma Moderne: The Art & Design of Olinka Hrdy. 2007. (Illus.). 86p. *(978-0-9717187-4-6(1))* Jones Jr., Fred Museum of Art.

Whitford, Frank, text. Royal Academy Illustrated 2009: A Selection from the 241st Summer Exhibition. 2009. (ENG., Illus.). 200p. pap. 35.00 *(978-1-905711-43-7(3))* Royal Academy of Arts GBR. Dist: Hachette Bk. Group.

Whitney. Christian Marclay - Festival, 3 vols. 2010. (Illus.). 200p. pap. *(978-0-300-16900-3(0))* Yale Univ. Pr.

Wien, Architekturzentrum, ed. Lessons from Bernard Rudofsky: Life as a Voyage. 2007. (Illus.). 296p. 64.95 *(978-3-7643-8360-2(7)*, 3764383607) Springer.

Williams, Michael Hue & Dixon, Andrew Graham. James Turrell: A Life in Light. 2007. (Illus.). 160p. *(978-2-7572-0102-2(6))* Somogy Editions d'Art.

Wilmerding, John. Maine Sublime: Frederic Edwin Church's Landscapes of Mount Desert & Mount Katahdin. 2012. (Olana Collection Ser.). (ENG.). 80p. 24.95 ***(978-0-8014-5103-4(5))*** Cornell Univ. Pr.

Wilson, Andrew. Richard Long: Heaven & Earth. Wallis, Clarrie, ed. 2009. (ENG., Illus.). 240p. pap. 37.50 *(978-1-85437-841-5(4))* Tate Publishing, Ltd. GBR. Dist: Hachette Bk. Group.

Wilson, Kristina. The Modern Eye: Stieglitz, Moma & the Art of the Exhibition, 1925-1934. 2009. (ENG., Illus.). 256p. 50.00 *(978-0-300-14916-6(6))* Yale Univ. Pr.

Wisniewska, Karina. Karina Wisniewska. Bewegte Stille - Silent Dynamism. Von Burg, Dominique, ed. 2010. (ENG., Illus.). 176p. *(978-3-7165-1577-8(9)*, Benteli Verlags Ag Dist) Antique Collectors' Club.

Wolfe, Ann M., ed. Chris Drury: Mushrooms - Clouds. 2010. (Center for American Places-Center Books on American Places Ser.). (ENG., Illus.). 96p. 49.50 *(978-1-935195-02-3(6))*; pap. 29.95 *(978-1-935195-04-7(2))* Ctr. for American Places, Inc.

Wolfs, Rein, et al. Meschac Gaba: Museum of Contemporary African Art & More. 2010. (GER, SPA & ENG., Illus.). 160p. pap. 48.00 *(978-3-86560-750-8(0))* Verlag der Buchhandlung Walther Konig DEU. Dist: D.A.P./Distributed Art Pubs.

Wood, Brian & Pearce, Shelley. Brian Wood: 2009-2010 Dr. Roy E. Morgan Exhibition, January 18-March 14, 2010. 2009. (Illus.). 28p. *(978-0-942945-31-7(X))* Wilkes College, Sordoni Art Gallery.

Wood, Wilma. The Vanishing Landscape. 2007. pap. 27.95 *(978-1-55059-340-2(4))* Detselig Enterprises, Ltd. CAN. Dist: Temeron Bks., Inc.

Wool, Christopher, photos by. Christopher Wool. 2008. (ENG., Illus.). 40p. 50.00 *(978-3-935567-42-8(1))* Holzwarth Pubns. DEU. Dist: D.A.P./Distributed Art Pubs.

Worringer, Christoph. Christoph Worringer. 2010. (ENG., Illus.). 170p. 45.00 *(978-3-7757-2640-5(3))* Hatje Cantz Verlag GmbH & Co KG DEU. Dist: D.A.P./Distributed Art Pubs.

Yee, Lydia, ed. Laurie Anderson, Trisha Brown, Gordon Matta-Clark: Pioneers of the Downtown Scene, New York 1970s. 2011. (Illus.). 240p. 49.95 *(978-3-7913-5122-3(2))* Prestel Publishing.

York University (Toronto, Ont.), Art Gallery Staff, contrib. by. Matthew Brannon: To Say the Very Least. 2008. (ENG., Illus.). 184p. pap. 60.00 *(978-0-921972-50-1(4))* Art Gallery of York Univ. CAN. Dist: D.A.P./Distributed Art Pubs.

Young, Clara, et al. Alberto Morrocco 1917-1998. 2nd ed. 2009. (ENG., Illus.). 118p. *(978-1-873830-07-9(6)*, Fine Art Society (Acc)) Antique Collectors' Club.

Zavala, Adriana, et al. Mexico Beyond Its Revolution. 2010.Tr. of Mexico mas alla de su Revolucion. (ENG & SPA., Illus.). 112p. pap. 10.00 *(978-1-880593-08-0(4))* Tufts Univ. Gallery.

Zavistovski, Katia, ed. Stephen Bush: Gelderland, 1 vol. 2007. (ENG., Illus.). 96p. 20.00 *(978-0-9764492-5-6(0))* Site Santa Fe.

Zayas, Marius de. Marius de Zayas: Un Destierro Moderno. 2009. (Illus.). 289p. (SPA.). *(978-968-9416-19-7(7))*; *(978-607-7605-21-8(2))*; (SPA., *(978-607-7622-28-4(1))* Aldus, Editorial, S.A.

Zehnder, Amanda, ed. Modern Japanese Prints. 2009. (ENG., Illus.). 200p. pap. 34.95 *(978-0-88039-049-1(2))* Carnegie Museum of Art, The.

Zeller, Ursula & Buchsteiner, Thomas, eds. Andreas Feininger: Ein Fotografenleben1906-1999. 2011. (ENG., Illus.). 192p. 45.00 *(978-3-7757-2704-4(3))* Hatje Cantz Verlag GmbH & Co KG DEU. Dist: D.A.P./Distributed Art Pubs.

Zeller, Ursula & Moore, Elke aus dem. Barbara Klemm: Helldunkel - Fotografien aus Deutschland / Light & Dark - Photographs from Germany. 2010. (ENG., Illus.). 196p. 80.00 *(978-3-86984-031-4(5))* Verlag der Buchhandlung Walther Konig DEU. Dist: D.A.P./Distributed Art Pubs.

Zimmer, Nina, ed. Soutine & Modernism. 2008. (GER & ENG., Illus.). 224p. *(978-3-8321-9079-8(1))* DuMont.

Zolkoski, Edwin. Down by the Depot: Brush & Ink Art. Date not set. (Illus.). 128p. pap. 12.95 *(978-0-945092-41-4(5))* EZ Nature Bks.

2007 Portland Museum of Art Biennial. 2007. per. 13.95 (978-0-916857-44-8(1)) Portland Museum of Art.

ART, MODERN—20TH CENTURY—HISTORY

Araeen. Third Text. 2007. 49.95 (978-0-415-44118-6(8)) Taylor & Francis Group.

Araeen, Rasheed & Sardar, Ziauddin, eds. Third Text. 2007. (ENG.). 10p. 49.95 (978-0-415-44120-9(X), Taylor & Francis) Taylor & Francis Group GBR. Dist: Taylor & Francis Group.

Baetens, Jan & Van Gelder, Hilde, eds. Critical Realism in Contemporary Art: Around Allan Sekula's Photography. 2008. (Lieven Gavaert Ser.). (Illus.). 207p. (Orig.). pap. 29.95 (978-90-5867-563-7(7)) Leuven Univ. Pr. BEL. Dist: Cornell Univ. Pr.

Bartel, Maya. The 1960s Body Through Sculptural Movement & Static Dance - the Works of George Segal, Allan Kaprow, & Yvonne Rainer. 2008. (Illus.). 104p. pap. (978-3-639-05554-2(3)) VDM Verlag Dr. Mueller e.K.

Blundell, Sally, ed. Look This Way: New Zealand Writers on New Zealand Artists. 2007. (ENG., Illus.). 200p. pap. 39.95 (978-1-86940-371-3(1)) Auckland Univ. Pr. NZL. Dist: Independent Pubs. Group.

Bolt, Mikkel & Wamberg, Jacob, eds. Totalitarian Art & Modernity. 2010. (ENG., Illus.). 359p. (C). pap. 64.00 (978-87-7934-560-7(3)) Aarhus Universitetsforlag DNK. Dist: ISD.

Botey, Mariana, et al, texts. MEX/la: Mexican Modernisms in Los Angeles 1930-1985. 2011. (ENG & SPA., Illus.). 224p. 60.00 (978-3-7757-3133-1(4)) Hatje Cantz Verlag GmbH & Co KG DEU. Dist: D.A.P./Distributed Art Pubs.

Buchholz, Elke Linda & Zimmermann, Beate. Pablo Picasso: Life & Work. 2008. (Art in Focus (Konemann) Ser.). (Illus.). 95p. pap. 5.95 (978-0-8416-0055-3(4)) American Map Corp.

Burshell, Carlo & Scheiffele, Heinz. Ikora & Myra Glass by WMF: One-of-a-Kind & Mass-Produced Glass from the 1920s to the 1950s. 2007. (ENG & GER., Illus.). 60.00 (978-3-89790-189-6(7)) Arnoldsche Art Pubs. DEU. Dist: Antique Collectors' Club.

Chong, Doryun & Raymond, Yasmil, texts. Brave New Worlds, 1 vol. 2007. (ENG., Illus.). 272p. pap. 39.95 (978-0-935640-89-2(4)) Walker Art Ctr.

Cufer, Eda. Transnacionala: Highway Collisions Between East & West at the Crossroads of Art. pap. 27.00 (978-961-6211-62-8(5)) tudentska organizacija Univerze v Ljubljani, tudentska zalo'ba SVN. Dist: D.A.P./Distributed Art Pubs.

Curiger, Bice, ed. Parkett No.88 - 2011. 2011. (ENG., Illus.). 300p. pap. 45.00 (978-3-907582-48-0(9)) Parkett Verlag AG CHE. Dist: D.A.P./Distributed Art Pubs.

Danto, Arthur C. Andy Warhol. 2009. (Icons of America Ser.). (ENG., Illus.). 192p. 24.00 (978-0-300-13555-8(6)) Yale Univ. Pr.

de Duve, Thierry. Clement Greenberg Between the Lines: Including a Debate with Clement Greenberg. Holmes, Brian, tr. from FRE. 2010. (ENG.). 160p. pap. 17.00 (978-0-226-17516-4(2)) Univ. of Chicago Pr.

Despont, Thierry W. Studio. 2008. (ENG.). 350.00 (978-2-7594-0302-8(5)) Assouline FRA. Dist: Perseus Distribution.

Eimert, Dorothea. Art of the 20th Century, 2 vols. 2010. (Prestige Ser.). (GER, FRE & ENG., Illus.). 256p. 82.50 (978-1-84484-672-6(5)) Parkstone International GBR. Dist: Ingram Pub. Services.

—Early 20th Century Art, 2. 2010. (Illus.). 256p. (978-1-84484-687-0(3)) Parkstone International.

—Late 20th Century Art. 2. 2010. (Illus.). 256p. (978-1-84484-688-7(1)) Parkstone International.

Faure, Élie, et al. Art of the Modern Era. 2010. 256p. (978-1-84484-685-6(7)) Parkstone International.

—Twentieth Century Art. 2010. 256p. (978-1-84484-685-3(5)) Parkstone International.

Fitzgerald, Oscar P. Studio Furniture of the Renwick Gallery: Smithsonian American Art Museum. 2008. (ENG., Illus.). 223p. pap. 35.00 (978-1-56523-367-6(0)) Fox Chapel Publishing Co., Inc.

Gierstberg, Frits & Bool, Flip. Questioning History: Imagining the Past in Contemporary Art. 2009. (ENG., Illus.). 180p. pap. 32.00 (978-90-5662-659-4(0)) NAi Uitgevers / Publishers Stichting NLD. Dist: D.A.P./Distributed Art Pubs.

Gualdoni, Flaminio. Art: The Twentieth Century. 2009. (ENG., Illus.). 560p. pap. 29.95 (978-88-6130-801-5(5)) Skira Editore ITA. Dist: Random Hse., Inc.

Gy#xF6;rcy, P#xE9;ter. Péter György: Die beiden Kassels: gleiche Zeit, anderer Ort. 2011. (ENG., Illus.). 32p. pap. 10.00 (978-3-7757-2865-2(1)) Hatje Cantz Verlag GmbH & Co KG DEU. Dist: D.A.P./Distributed Art Pubs.

Hadar, Dori. Mingering Mike: The Amazing Career of an Imaginary Soul Superstar. 2007. (ENG., Illus.). 192p. pap. 24.95 (978-1-56898-569-5(X)) Princeton Architectural Pr.

Hammer, Martin. The Naked Portrait 1900 to 2007. 2007. (ENG., Illus.). 176p. pap. (978-1-903278-95-6(3)) National Galleries of Scotland.

Haynes, Deborah J. Bakhtin & the Visual Arts. 2008. (Cambridge Studies in New Art History & Criticism Ser.). (ENG., Illus.). 240p. pap. 36.99 (978-0-521-06604-4(2)) Cambridge Univ. Pr.

He, Jianping, ed. All Men Are Brothers. 2007. (Illus.). pap. (978-981-245-424-9(1)) Page One Publishing.

Hung, Wu, text. Making History: Wu Hung on Contemporary Art. 2009. (ENG., Illus.). 278p. 50.00 (978-988-99617-0-1(9)) Timezone 8 Ltd. HKG. Dist: D.A.P./Distributed Art Pubs.

Hutchinson, Elizabeth. The Indian Craze: Primitivism, Modernism, & Transculturation in American Art, 1890-1915. 2009. (Objects/Histories Ser.). (ENG., Illus.). 304p. 89.95 (978-0-8223-4390-5(8)); pap. 24.95 (978-0-8223-4408-7(4)) Duke Univ. Pr.

Kabakov, Ilia Iosifovich & Kabakov, Emilia. Zhizn Mukh. 2008. (RUS., Illus.). 167p. (978-3-86678-200-6(4)) Kerber Verlag.

Kahn, Robin. The Intelligent Woman's Guide to Art, 1 vol. 2006. (ENG., Illus.). 34p. 16.95 (978-1-933045-37-5(X)) D.A.P./Distributed Art Pubs.

Kammen, Michael G. Visual Shock: A History of Art Controversies in American Culture. 2007. (Vintage Ser.). (ENG., Illus.). 480p. pap. 18.00 (978-1-4000-3464-2(7), Vintage) Knopf Doubleday Publishing Group.

Kromm, Jane & Bakewell, Susan Benforado, eds. A History of Visual Culture: Western Civilization from the 18th to the 21st Century. 2010. (ENG., Illus.). 1p. 119.95 (978-1-84520-493-8(X)); 480p. pap. 39.95 (978-1-84520-492-1(1)) Berg Pubs. GBR. Dist: Macmillan.

Lanker, Brian & Newnham, Nicole. They Drew Fire: Combat Artists of World War II. (Illus.). 192p. 39.95. 54.90 incl. VHS Public Broadcasting Service (PBS).

Lavin, Irving. The Form of Meaning / the Meaning of Form: Studies in the History of Art from Late Antiquity to Jackson Pollock, Volume II. 2013. (ENG., Illus.). 650p. (C). 300.00 (978-1-904597-47-6(5)) Pindar Pr. GBR. Dist: Brown, David Bk. Co., The.

Lee, Pamela M. Art History since the Sixties. 2012. (Theories of Modernism & Postmodernism in the Visual Arts Ser.). (ENG., Illus.). 192p. (C). 125.00 (978-0-415-98879-7(9)) Routledge.

Legge, Elizabeth & Legge, E. Michael Snow: Wavelength. 2009. (One Work Ser.). (ENG., Illus.). 104p. (gr. 17). pap. 16.00 (978-1-84638-056-3(1)) Afterall Publishing GBR. Dist: MIT Pr.

Lista, Giovanni. Arte Povera. 2008. (Gallery of the Arts Ser.). (ENG., Illus.). 112p. 18.95 (978-88-7439-215-5(X)) 5 Continents ITA. Dist: Hachette Bk. Group.

McGarry, Susan Hallsten & Tobey, Rebecca. Partners in Art: Gene & Rebecca Tobey. 2007. (ENG., Illus.). 360p. 75.00 (978-1-934491-02-7(0)) Fresco Fine Art Pubns., LLC.

McLaren, Graham. Studio Glass, 1960-2000. 2008. (Shire Library). (ENG., Illus.). 48p. pap. 12.95 (978-0-7478-0527-4(X)) Shire Pubns., Ltd. GBR. Dist: Random Hse., Inc.

Menkes, Suzy & Tymauer, Matt. Valentino. Chitolina, Armando, ed. 2009. (ENG., Illus.). 576p. 69.99 (978-3-8365-0329-7(8)) TASCHEN DEU. Dist: Ingram Pub. Services.

Metzger, Rainer. Berlin: The Twenties. Brandstetter, Christian, ed. 2007. (ENG., Illus.). 400p. 45.00 (978-0-8109-9329-7(5)) Abrams.

Miller, Tyrus. Singular Examples: Artistic Politics & the Neo-Avant-Garde. 2009. (Avant-Garde & Modernism Studies). (ENG.). 270p. pap. 34.95 (978-0-8101-2512-4(9)); (Illus.). 69.95 (978-0-8101-2511-7(0)) Northwestern Univ. Pr.

Millet, Catherine. Contemporary Art in France. 2006. (ENG., Illus.). 384p. 60.00 (978-2-08-030524-4(7)) Flammarion et Cie FRA. Dist: Random Hse., Inc.

Molesworth, Helen. Solitaire: Lee Lozano, Sylvia Plimack Mangold, Joan Semmel. Molesworth, Helen, ed. 2008. (ENG., Illus.). 164p. pap. 24.95 (978-0-300-12529-0(1)) Yale Univ. Pr.

Molesworth, Helen. This Will Have Been: Art, Love, & Politics in the 1980s. 2012. (ENG., Illus.). 448p. pap. 50.00 (978-0-300-18110-4(8)) Yale Univ. Pr.

Motherwell, Robert. The Writings of Robert Motherwell. Ashton, Dore, ed. 2007. (Documents of Twentieth-Century Art Ser.). (Illus.). 387p. 70.00 (978-0-520-25047-5(8)); per. 34.95 (978-0-520-25048-2(6)) Univ. of California Pr.

Mukherji, Subha, ed. Thinking on Thresholds: The Poetics of Transitive Spaces. 2011. (ENG., Illus.). 252p. 99.00 (978-0-85728-665-9(X)) Anthem Pr. GBR. Dist: Books International, Inc.

Mulder, Arjen. From Image to Interaction. 2011. (ENG., Illus.). 240p. pap. 30.00 (978-90-5662-819-2(4)) NAi Uitgevers / Publishers Stichting NLD. Dist: D.A.P./Distributed Art Pubs.

Nickas, Robert. Theft Is Vision: Collected Writings & Interviews, 1 vol. 2007. (ENG., Illus.). 160p. (C). pap. 22.00 (978-3-905770-36-0(9)) JRP Ringier Kunstverlag AG CHE. Dist: D.A.P./Distributed Art Pubs.

Papini, Roberto. Arts in The 20's: Architecture & Decorative Arts in Europe. 2006. (ENG.). 480p. (978-0-9544288-3-9(8)) Verba Volant, Ltd.

Paraskos, Michael. Reading Read: New Views on Herbert Read. 2008. (Illus.). 237p. pap. 36.95 (978-1-904491-08-8(1)) Freedom Pr. GBR. Dist: AK Pr. Distribution.

Paravicini, Flurina and Gianni, ed. Dieter Roth: Tears in Lucerne. 2011. (ENG., Illus.). 128p. pap. 29.00 (978-3-907474-83-9(X)) Periferia, Edizioni, Poschiavo / Lucerna CHE. Dist: D.A.P./Distributed Art Pubs.

Peiry, Lucienne. Art Brut: The Origins of Outsider Art. 2nd rev. ed. 2006. (ENG., Illus.). 320p. pap. 24.95 (978-2-08-030543-5(3)) Flammarion et Cie FRA. Dist: Random Hse., Inc.

Ponce, Alexandra Garcia, et al, contrib. by. Chic by Accident. 2006. (Illus.). 220p. (gr. 13-18). 50.00 (978-84-7506-726-1(3)) D.A.P./Distributed Art Pubs.

Potts, Vanessa. Monet. (SPA.). 256p. (978-1-4054-1497-5(9)) Parragon, Inc.

Pound, Francis. The Invention of New Zealand: Art & National Identity, 1930-1970. 2010. (ENG., Illus.). 450p. 44.95 (978-1-86940-414-7(9)) Auckland Univ. Pr. NZL. Dist: Independent Pubs. Group.

Rabb, Theodore K. The Artist & the Warrior: Military History Through the Eyes of the Masters. 2011. (Illus.). 288p. 45.00 (978-0-300-12637-2(9)) Yale Univ. Pr.

Raunig, Gerald. Art & Revolution: Transversal Activism in the Long Twentieth Century. Derieg, Aileen, tr. from GER. 2007. (Semiotext(e) / Active Agents Ser.). (ENG.). 320p. (gr. 17). per. 18.95 (978-1-58435-046-0(6)) Semiotexte/Smart Art.

Rösch, Felix. Hans J Morgenthau & the Weimar Republic. 2008. 88p. per. (978-3-8364-7076-6(4)) VDM Verlag Dr. Mueller e.K.

Rothenstein, J. Moderns & Their World. (Illus.). 128p. (978-0-8022-1385-3(5)) Philosophical Library, Inc.

Sardar, Ziauddin & Rasheed, Araeen, eds. Third Text: Critical Perspectives on Contemporary Art & Culture. 2007. (Illus.). 112p. per. 49.95 (978-0-415-44117-9(X)) Taylor & Francis Group.

Soussloff, Catherine M. The Subject in Art: Portraiture & the Birth of the Modern. 2006. (ENG., Illus.). 192p. 79.95 (978-0-8223-3658-7(8)); per. 22.95 (978-0-8223-3670-9(7)) Duke Univ. Pr.

Spies, Werner. Werner Spies: the Eye & the Word: Collected Writings on Art & Literature, the Gagosian Edition, 10 vols. Gabriel, John et al, trs. from GER. 2011. (ENG., Illus.). 4500p. pap. 250.00 (978-0-8109-9835-3(1)) Abrams.

Stones, Alison. Studies in Arthurian Illustration. 2012. (ENG., Illus.). 560p. (C). 300.00 (978-1-904597-37-7(8)) Pindar Pr. GBR. Dist: Brown, David Bk. Co., The.

Storia dell'Arte Italiana, 1901-1940, 11. Vols. in 25 pts. Incl. Vol. 1. Dai primordi dell'arte cristiana al tempo di Giustiniano. Vol. 2. Dell'arte barbarica all romanica. Vol. 3. Aret Romanica. Vol. 4. Scultura del Trecento e le Sue Origini. Vol. 5. Pittura del Trecento e le Sue Origini. Vol. 6. Scultura del Quattrocento. Vol. 7 (in 4 pts.). Pittura del Quattrocento. Vol 8 (in 2 pts.). Architetura del Quattrocento. Vol. 9 (in 7 pts.). Pittura del Cinquecento. Vol. 10 (in 3 pts.). Scultura del Cinquecento. Vol. 11 (in 3 pts.). Architetura del Cinquecento. 4150.00 (978-0-8115-3505-2(3)) Periodicals Service Co.

Terraroli, Valerio, et al. The Birth of Contemporary Art, 1946-1968, 5 vols., Vol. 3. 2008. (ENG., Illus.). 448p. 60.00 (978-88-6130-194-8(0)) Skira Editore ITA. Dist: Random Hse., Inc.

Thompson, Donald N. The $12 Million Stuffed Shark: The Curious Economics of Contemporary Art. 2008. (ENG., Illus.). 272p. 26.00 (978-0-230-61022-4(6)) Palgrave Macmillan.

Tojner, Poul Erik & Holm, Michael, eds. I Know How You Must Feel... Essays on Modern Art. 2012. (ENG., Illus.). 192p. 60.00 (978-87-91607-21-9(3)) Louisana DNK. Dist: D.A.P./Distributed Art Pubs.

Varas, Valerie, ed. Monochromes: From Malevich to the Present. 2007. (Illus.). 240p. pap. 39.95 (978-0-520-24937-0(2)) Univ. of California Pr.

Vasa, Melanie. Gender & the Written Word in Recent Art. 2009. 52p. pap. (978-3-639-13503-9(2)) VDM Verlag Dr. Mueller e.K.

Weibel, Peter & Vasulka, Woody. Buffalo Heads: Media Study, Media Practice, Media Pioneers, 1973-1990. Vasulka, Steina & Weibel, Peter, eds. Vasulka, Woody, ed. 2008. (ENG., Illus.). 840p. (gr. 17). pap. 59.95 (978-0-262-72050-2(7)) MIT Pr.

Weiwei, Ai & Li, Pi, eds. In Production Mode, Contemporary Art in China. 2009. (ENG., Illus.). 276p. pap. 50.00 (978-988-17522-9-1(9)) Timezone 8 Ltd. HKG. Dist: D.A.P./Distributed Art Pubs.

ART, MODERN—20TH CENTURY—JAPANESE INFLUENCES

see Art, Modern—Japanese Influences

ART, MODERN—21ST CENTURY

see also Modernism (Art)

Adler, Phoebe, ed. Contemporary Art in the United Kingdom. 2012. (Artworld Ser.). (ENG., Illus.). 240p. pap. 29.95 (978-1-907317-68-2(6)) Black Dog Publishing Ltd. GBR. Dist: Perseus Distribution.

Agustin, Perez Rubio, ed. Discursive Variants. 2010. (ENG., Illus.). 320p. pap. (978-84-92861-27-9(4)) Actar Birkhauser Distribution.

Aida, Makoto. Monument for Nothing. 2007. 248p. pap. 59.95 (978-4-7661-1804-9(9)) Graphic-Sha JPN. Dist: Gingko Pr., Inc.

Alberro, Alexander & Stimson, Blake, eds. Institutional Critique: An Anthology of Artists′ Writings. 2011. (ENG., Illus.). 512p. (gr. 17). pap. 21.95 (978-0-262-51664-8(0)) MIT Pr.

Allen, Bale Creek. Empire. 2011. (Illus.). 72p. mass mkt. 10.00 (978-0-9817987-5-2(6)) Grand Central Pr.

Allès, Chantal. Crazy Art, 1 vol. 2011. (ENG., Illus.). 192p. pap. 24.95 (978-1-908126-08-5(6)) Vivays Pubng. Ltd. GBR. Dist: Innovative Logistics.

Aloi, Giovanni. Art & Animals. 2011. (Art and... Ser.). (ENG., Illus.). 192p. 75.00 (978-1-84885-524-3(9)); pap. 27.50 (978-1-84885-525-0(7)) I. B. Tauris & Co., Ltd. GBR. Dist: Macmillan.

Alston, David. Into Painting: The Work of Brendan Stuart Burns. 2007. (ENG., Illus.). 100p. pap. 17.95 (978-1-85411-446-4(8)) Seren Bks. GBR. Dist: Independent Pubs. Group.

Altshuler, Bruce. Collecting the New: Museums & Contemporary Art. 2007. (ENG., Illus.). 208p. (C). per. 21.95 (978-0-691-13373-7(5)) Princeton Univ. Pr.

Amilus Inc., compiled by. American Illustration 28. 2010. (ENG., Illus.). 416p. 75.00 (978-1-885212-31-2(7)) Amilus Inc.

Andersson, Mamma & Nordstrom, Jockum. Mamma Andersson & Jockum Nordstrom: Who Is Sleeping on My Pillow. 2010. (ENG., Illus.). 247p. 75.00 (978-1-935202-26-4(X)) Zwirner, David Inc.

Annichiarico, Silvana, ed. Serials & One-Offs: Triennale Design Museum. 2009. (ENG & ITA., Illus.). 304p. pap. 97.50 (978-88-370-6920-9(0)) Electa ITA. Dist: Trans-Atlantic Pubns., Inc.

Antonelli, Paola, et al, texts. AC/DC: Contemporary Art/Contemporary Design. 2009. (ENG., Illus.). 280p. pap. 45.00 (978-3-03764-012-8(X)) JRP Ringier Kunstverlag AG CHE. Dist: D.A.P./Distributed Art Pubs.

Atwell, Wendy Weil. The River Spectacular: Light, Sound, Color & Craft on the San Antonio River. 2010. (Illus.). 64p. pap. 38.95 (978-1-893271-56-2(0)) Maverick Publishing Co.

Avgikos, Jan. Marlene Dumas. 2nd rev. ed. 2009. (ENG., Illus.). 240p. 69.95 (978-0-7148-4584-5(1)) Phaidon Pr., Inc.

Bahtsetzis, Sotirios & Clau, Ingo, eds. Urban Art. 2010. (ENG & GER., Illus.). 192p. pap. 40.00 (978-3-7757-2503-3(2)) Hatje Cantz Verlag GmbH & Co KG DEU. Dist: D.A.P./Distributed Art Pubs.

Banca della Svizzera Italiana Staff, contrib. by. Free Zone - China. 2008. (ITA & ENG., Illus.). 174p. 22.00 (978-3-905829-61-7(4)) JRP Ringier Kunstverlag AG CHE. Dist: D.A.P./Distributed Art Pubs.

Barany, Les, ed. Carnivora. 2008. 176p. pap. 29.95 (978-0-9795132-1-3(9)) Scapegoat Publishing.

Barbour, Kim. Constructing Artistic Integrity. 2008. 100p. pap. (978-3-639-05307-4(9)) VDM Verlag Dr. Mueller e.K.

Baum, Kelly. Nobody's Property: Art, Land, Space, 2000-2010. 2010. (ENG., Illus.). 144p. 45.00 (978-0-300-14928-9(X)) Yale Univ. Pr.

Beard, Steve. Voodoo Science Park. Rushdy, Hatem, ed. 2011. (ENG., Illus.). 115p. pap. 14.95 (978-1-84694-527-4(5)) O Bks., John Hunt.

Becker, Katja M. & Podobinski, Stephanie. Young German Design, 2 vols. 2009. (ENG., Illus.). 624p. 119.95 (978-3-938666-56-2(0)) DOM Pubs. DEU. Dist: Innovative Logistics.

Bedford, Emma, ed. Decade of Democracy: South African Art, 1994-2004. 2010. (Illus.). 150p. pap. 51.95 (978-1-919930-50-3(7)) Double Storey Bks. ZAF. Dist: International Publishers Marketing.

Bellavita, Alessandra & Daftari, Fereshteh, eds. Ali Banisadr. Bouniort, Jeanne, tr. 2012. (ENG., Illus.). 52p. pap. 30.00 (978-2-910055-39-4(6)) Galerie Thaddeus Ropac, Eigenverlag AUT. Dist: D.A.P./Distributed Art Pubs.

Bellini, Andrea, et al, eds. Collecting Contemporary Art. 2009. (ENG., Illus.). 128p. pap. 15.00 (978-3-03764-015-9(4)) JRP Ringier Kunstverlag AG CHE. Dist: D.A.P./Distributed Art Pubs.

Berghaus, Günter. International Futurism, 1945-2009: A Bibliographic Reference Shelf. 2013. (ENG.). 1200p. (gr. 17-17). 419.00 (978-3-11-021580-9(2)) De Gruyter, Walter Inc.

Bertola, Chiara, ed. The Spirit in Any Condition Does Not Burn. 2009. (ENG., Illus.). 168p. pap. 39.95 (978-88-8158-722-3(X)) Charta ITA. Dist: D.A.P./Distributed Art Pubs.

Bertola, Chiara & Maraniello, Gianfranco, eds. On Mobility: Giovani Artisti Italiani, 1 vol. 2007. (ENG., Illus.). 120p. pap. 34.95 (978-88-8158-631-8(2)) Charta ITA. Dist: D.A.P./Distributed Art Pubs.

Biasi, Vittoria. Architetture Del Bianco: Viaggio Teorico-Creativo Attorno Alle Lingue Del Bianco. 2009. (ITA., Illus.). 238p. (978-88-492-1676-9(9)) Gangemi.

Bifo, Franco Berardi, et al, contrib. by. E-Flux Journal: Are You Working Too Much? Post-Fordism, Precarity, & the Labor of Art. 2011. (ENG., Illus.). 212p. pap. 15.00 (978-1-934105-31-3(7)) Sternberg Pr.

Birnbaum, Daniel, et al. Defining Contemporary Art: 25 Years in 200 Pivotal Artworks. 2011. (ENG., Illus.). 448p. 75.00 (978-0-7148-6209-5(6)) Phaidon Pr., Inc.

Bittanti, Matteo & Quaranta, Domenico. Gamescenes: Art in the Age of Videogames. 2009. (Illus.). 456p. (978-88-6010-010-8(0), Johan & Levi Editore (Acc)) Antique Collectors' Club.

Blocker, Jane. Seeing Witness: Visuality & the Ethics of Testimony. 2009. (ENG., Illus.). 192p. 75.00 (978-0-8166-5476-5(X)); pap. 25.00 (978-0-8166-5477-2(8)) Univ. of Minnesota Pr.

Blom, Ina. On the Style Site. 2007. (Illus.). 264p. pap. 29.95 (978-1-933128-30-6(5)) Sternberg Pr.

Blythe, Blonde. Big Eye Art: Resurrected & Transformed. 2008. (Illus.). 222p. pap. (978-1-85894-436-4(8)) Merrell Pubs. Ltd.

Bonham-Carter, Charlotte & Hodge, David. The Contemporary Art Book. 2011. (ENG., Illus.). 256p. 39.95 (978-1-84796-005-4(7), Goodman Pubs.) Carlton Bks., Ltd. GBR. Dist: Sterling Publishing Co., Inc.

Bonin, Cosima von, et al. Dressing the Message: Transformationen Von Kunst und Mode. 2008. (Illus.). 120p. (978-3-89169-208-0(0)) Sprengel Museum.

Bortman, Alan, intro. Dirtypilot.com Year 1 Rewind: The Art of Dirty Pilot. 2009. (Illus.). 80p. 19.95 (978-0-86719-712-9(9)) Last Gasp of San Francisco.

Boullata, Kamal, ed. Belonging & Globalisation: Critical Essays in Contemporary Art & Culture. 2008. (ENG., Illus.). 168p. per. 21.95 (978-0-86356-666-0(9)) Saqi Bks. GBR. Dist: Consortium Bk. Sales & Distribution.

Bouroullec, Ronan, et al. Ronan & Erwan Bouroullec: Lianes. 2011. (ENG., Illus.). 64p. 39.95 (978-3-03764-150-7(9)) JRP Ringier Kunstverlag AG CHE. Dist: D.A.P./Distributed Art Pubs.

Bourriaud, Nicolas. The Radicant. 2009. 192p. pap. 19.95 (978-1-933128-42-9(9), Lukas & Sternberg) Sternberg Pr.

Brand, Heather, ed. Red Hot: Asian Art Today from the Chaney Family Collection. 2008. (ENG., Illus.). 208p. pap. 39.95 (978-0-300-13889-4(X)) Museum of Fine Arts, Houston.

Briand, Mathieu. Mathieu Briand & Juan Gimenez: Ubiq, A Mental Odyssey, 1 vol. Riviere, Daniele, ed. 2008. (ENG., Illus.). 128p. pap. 39.50 (978-2-914563-36-9(1)) Dis Voir Editions FRA. Dist: D.A.P./Distributed Art Pubs.

Broglio, Ron. Surface Encounters: Thinking with Animals & Art. 2011. (Posthumanities Ser.). (ENG., Illus.). 176p. 75.00 (978-0-8166-7296-7(2)); pap. 25.00 (978-0-8166-7297-4(0)) Univ. of Minnesota Pr.

Broida, Edward R., contrib. by. Against the Grain: Contemporary Art from the Edward R. Broida Collection, 1 vol. 2006. (ENG., Illus.). 128p. 40.00 (978-0-87070-090-3(1)) Museum of Modern Art.

Brotherton, Gregory & Branwyn, Gareth. Device Vol. 1: Fantastic Contraption. 2008. (Illus.). 120p. pap. 19.99 (978-1-60010-326-1(X)) Idea & Design Works, LLC.

Brrothers. Baetulona: 100 Designs for History, 1 vol. 2011. (ENG, CAT & SPA., Illus.). 240p. (978-84-92810-23-9(8)) Promotora de prensa internacional S.A.

Bruter, Claude P., ed. Mathematics & Modern Art. 2012. (Springer Proceedings in Mathematics Ser.: 18). (ENG., Illus.). viii, 178p. 124.00 ***(978-3-642-24496-4(3)***, 3642244963) Springer.

Burda, Hubert. The Digital Wunderkammer: 10 Chapters on the Iconic Turn, 1 vol. 2011. (ENG., Illus.). 202p. 45.00 ***(978-3-7705-5193-4(1))*** Wilhelm/Fink#GmbH & Co. Verlags-KG DEU. Dist: D.A.P./Distributed Art Pubs.

Bürgi, Brigitt & Fischer, Peter. Lebenszeichen / Signs of Life: Kunstmuseum Luzern. 2011. (ENG., Illus.). 136p. 40.00 ***(978-3-86828-161-3(4))*** Kehrer Verlag Heidelberg, Klaus Kehrer DEU. Dist: Consortium Bk. Sales & Distribution.

Buszek, Maria Elena, ed. Extra/Ordinary: Craft & Contemporary Art. 2011. (ENG., Illus.). 320p. 89.95 *(978-0-8223-4739-2(3))*; pap. 24.95 *(978-0-8223-4762-0(8))* Duke Univ. Pr.

Butler, Cornelia & Schwartz, Alexandra, eds. Modern Women: Women Artists at the Museum of Modern Art. 2010. (ENG., Illus.). 512p. 65.00 *(978-0-87070-771-1(X))* Museum of Modern Art.

Carels, Edwin, et al. All That Is Solid Melts into Air: Five Reflections on Materialistic Spirituality in Contemporary Art. 2009. (ENG., Illus.). 256p. pap. *(978-90-209-8318-0(0)*, Lannoo Pubs. (Acc)) Antique Collectors' Club.

Cattelan, Maurizio, ed. Maurizio Cattelan: All. 2011. (ENG., Illus.). 255p. 45.00 ***(978-0-89207-416-7(7))*** Guggenheim, Solomon R. Museum.

Cattelan, Maurizio & Ferrari, Pierpaolo, eds. Toilet Paper: Issue 2. 2011. (ENG., Illus.). 40p. pap. 12.00 ***(978-1-935202-59-2(6))*** Deste Foundation GRC. Dist: D.A.P./Distributed Art Pubs.

—Toilet Paper: Issue 4. 2011. (ENG., Illus.). 40p. pap. 12.00 ***(978-1-935202-78-3(2))*** Deste Foundation GRC. Dist: D.A.P./Distributed Art Pubs.

Celaya, Enrique Martinez. Nomad: Miami Art Museum November 2, 2007 - January 13 2008. 2007. (ENG., Illus.). 128p. 35.00 *(978-0-9673608-9-8(7))* Whale & Star Pr.

Celii, Alana & Feinstein, Jon, eds. The Collector's Guide to Emerging Art Photography. 2009. (ENG., Illus.). 176p. pap. 49.95 *(978-0-9796425-0-0(7))* Humble Arts Foundation, Inc.

Chang, Patty, et al. The Hugo Boss Prize 2008. 2008. (ENG., Illus.). 112p. pap. 24.95 *(978-0-89207-373-3(X))* Guggenheim, Solomon R. Museum.

Chia, Althea. Bliss Express: Illustrating Happiness. 2006. (Illus.). 224p. *(978-0-9735867-1-8(0))* Guu Pr.

Ciclitira, Serenella. Indonesian Eye: Contemporary Indonesian Art. 2012. (ENG., Illus.). 376p. pap. 60.00 ***(978-88-572-1075-9(8))*** Skira Editore ITA. Dist: Random Hse., Inc.

Clarke, David. Chinese Art & Its Encounter with the World: Negotiating Alterity in Art & Its Historical Interpretation. 2011. (ENG., Illus.). 272p. (gr. 17). 40.00 *(978-988-8083-06-0(6))* Hong Kong Univ. Pr. HKG. Dist: Columbia Univ. Pr.

Connolly, Maeve. The Place of Artists' Cinema: Space, Site, & Screen. 2009. (ENG., Illus.). 240p. pap. 40.00 *(978-1-84150-246-5(4))* Intellect, Ltd. GBR. Dist: Chicago Distribution Ctr.

Cooper, Justin, intro. IdN Extra 03: Society 6. 2011. (ENG., Illus.). 148p. pap. 25.00 *(978-988-18470-4-1(4))* Systems Design, Ltd. HKG. Dist: D.A.P./Distributed Art Pubs.

Craddock, Sacha. Angus Fairhurst. 2009. (ENG., Illus.). 112p. 53.00 *(978-0-85667-659-8(4))* Wilson, Philip Pubs., Ltd. GBR. Dist: Macmillan.

Craig, Blanche. Collage: Assembling Contemporary Art. 2008. (ENG., Illus.). 238p. 65.00 *(978-1-906155-39-1(9))* Black Dog Publishing Ltd. GBR. Dist: Perseus Distribution.

Cramerotti, Alfredo. Aesthetic Journalism: How to Inform Without Informing. 2009. (ENG.). 112p. pap. 35.00 *(978-1-84150-268-7(5))* Intellect, Ltd. GBR. Dist: Chicago Distribution Ctr.

Crawford, Holly, ed. Artistic Bedfellows: Histories, Theories, & Conversations in Collaborative Art Practices. 2008. (ENG.). 330p. pap. 44.50 *(978-0-7618-4064-0(8))* Univ. Pr. of America, Inc.

Crowley, David, et al. The Power of Fantasy: Modern & Contemporary Art from Poland. 2011. (ENG., Illus.). 160p. 49.95 ***(978-3-7913-5145-2(1))*** Prestel Publishing.

Curiger, Bice, ed. Autumn 2008 No. 83: Robert Frank, Wade Guton & Christoper Wool. 2008. (ENG.). 300p. pap. 32.00 *(978-3-907582-43-5(8))* Parkett Verlag AG CHE. Dist: D.A.P./Distributed Art Pubs.

—Parkett No. 85: Maria Lassnig, Beatriz Milhazes, Jean-Luc Mylayne, Josh Smith. 2009. (ENG., Illus.). 300p. pap. 32.00 *(978-3-907582-45-9(4))* Parkett Verlag AG CHE. Dist: D.A.P./Distributed Art Pubs.

—Parkett 82 Summer 2008: Rachel Harrison, Pawel Althamer & Louise Bourgeois. 2008. (ENG., Illus.). 300p. pap. 32.00 *(978-3-907582-42-8(X))* Parkett Verlag AG CHE. Dist: D.A.P./Distributed Art Pubs.

—Winter 2009, No. 84. 2009. (ENG.). 300p. pap. 32.00 *(978-3-907582-44-2(6))* Parkett Verlag AG CHE. Dist: D.A.P./Distributed Art Pubs.

Czernin, Franz Josef. Bildsatz: Texte Zu Bildender Kunst. 2008. (GER., Illus.). 367p. *(978-3-8321-9100-9(3))* DuMont.

Daniels, Dieter, ed. Audiovisuology - See This Sound No. 1: An Interdisciplinary Survey of Audiovisual Culture. 2010. (ENG., Illus.). 452p. pap. 49.95 *(978-3-86560-686-0(5))* Verlag der Buchhandlung Walther Konig DEU. Dist: D.A.P./Distributed Art Pubs.

Daniels, Dieter, et al. See This Sound. 2011. (ENG., Illus.). 260p. pap. 49.95 ***(978-3-86560-687-7(3))*** Verlag der Buchhandlung Walther Konig DEU. Dist: D.A.P./Distributed Art Pubs.

David, Adrian. Homo Arte - Omnibus: 101 Confidences of an Art Collector. 2011. (FRE, DUT & ENG., Illus.). 320p. pap. *(978-90-209-9157-4(4)*, Lannoo Pubs. (Acc)) Antique Collectors' Club.

Dawood, Shezad. The Killing of Chief Crazy Horse - a Metaphorical Allegory in 3 Parts. 2011. 136p. pap. ***(978-3-8443-2051-0(2))*** Lambert Academic Publishing.

Day, Gail. Dialectical Passions: Negation in Postwar Art Theory. 2010. (Columbia Themes in Philosophy, Social Criticism, & the Arts Ser.). (ENG., Illus.). 320p. (gr. 17). 50.00 *(978-0-231-14938-9(7))* Columbia Univ. Pr.

De Lafayette, Maximillien. World Who's Who in Contemporary Art: Thematic & Biographical Encyclopedia of Living Artists & Styles. 2007. (Illus.). 400p. per. 69.95 *(978-0-9799750-9-7(3))* Elite Assocs. International-Times Square Pr.

Dempsey, Amy. Destination Art. 2010. (ENG.). 272p. pap. 29.95 *(978-0-520-26789-3(3))* Univ. of California Pr.

Desai, Dipti, et al. History As Art, Art As History: Contemporary Art & Social Studies Education. 2009. (ENG., Illus.). 288p. 150.00 *(978-0-415-99375-3(X))* Routledge.

Devon, Marjorie. Migrations: New Directions in Native American Art. 2006. (ENG., Illus.). 143p. pap. 29.95 *(978-0-8263-3769-6(4))* Univ. of New Mexico Pr.

Dezeuze, Anna, ed. The 'Do-It-Yourself' Artwork. 2012. (ENG., Illus.). 328p. pap. 34.95 ***(978-0-7190-8747-9(3))*** Manchester Univ. Pr. GBR. Dist: Macmillan.

Dezeuze, Anna, ed. The 'Do-it-Yourself' Artwork: Participation from Fluxus to New Media. 2010. (Rethinking Art's Histories Ser.). (ENG., Illus.). 336p. 90.00 *(978-0-7190-8144-6(0))* Manchester Univ. Pr. GBR. Dist: Macmillan.

Diederichsen, Diedrich. Judgment & Contemporary Art Criticism. O'Brian, Melanie & Khonsary, Jeff, eds. 2011. (ENG.). 176p. pap. 20.00 *(978-0-9738133-6-4(9))* Projectile Publishing Society CAN. Dist: D.A.P./Distributed Art Pubs.

Dillon, Brian. Ruins. 2011. (Whitechapel: Documents of Contemporary Art Ser.). (ENG.). 240p. (gr. 17). pap. 24.95 ***(978-0-262-51637-2(3))*** MIT Pr.

Doctor Roncero, Rafael, ed. The Musac Collection, Volume II. 2007. (Illus.). 623p. *(978-84-96954-20-5(X))* Charta.

Donovan, Art. The Art of Steampunk: Extraordinary Devices & Ingenious Contraptions from the Leading Artists of the Steampunk Movement. 2011. (ENG., Illus.). 128p. pap. 19.95 *(978-1-56523-573-1(8))* Fox Chapel Publishing Co., Inc.

Drucker, Johanna. Sweet Dreams: Contemporary Art & Complicity. 2006. (Illus.). 264p. per. 30.00 *(978-0-226-16505-9(1))* Univ. of Chicago Pr.

Duquenne, Olivier. Pinocchio & Co: Fairy Tales & Contemporary Art. 2012. (ENG., Illus.). 120p. 50.00 ***(978-90-5856-398-9(7))*** Stichting Kunstboek Bvba BEL. Dist: National Bk. Network.

Durden, Mark. Variable Capital. 2008. (ENG., Illus.). 192p. 39.95 *(978-1-84631-126-0(8))* Liverpool Univ. Pr. GBR. Dist: Chicago Distribution Ctr.

Eaton, Tristan. The 3D Art Book. 2011. (Illus.). 224p. pap. 35.00 *(978-3-7913-4549-9(4))* Prestel Publishing.

Edited by the Dipartimento Educazione del Castello di Rivoli Museo d Arte Contemporanea & the Istituto dei Sordi di Torino. Dictionary of Contemporary Art in Italian Sign Language: Silence Speaks about Art. 2011. (ITA & ENG., Illus.). 208p. pap. 37.00 *(978-88-422-1841-8(3))* Allemandi, Umberto & Co. GBR. Dist: Antique Collectors' Club.

Ehmann, Arne, ed. Intuition/(Im)Precision. 2012. (ENG & GER., Illus.). 100p. pap. 67.00 *(978-3-901935-49-7(5))* Galerie Thaddaeus Ropac, Eigenverlag AUT. Dist: D.A.P./Distributed Art Pubs.

Erik Abel, Klutch & Michael Fields, David Stein. Invision: A Collection of Visual Art in Portland + Beyond. 2008. 80p. pap. 22.00 *(978-0-9776051-7-0(5))* Another Sky Pr.

Estévez, Alberto T., ed. Genetic Architectures III / Arquitecturas Genéticas III. 2010. (ENG.). 208p. pap. 22.00 *(978-0-930829-68-1(9))* Lumen, Inc.

Eversole, Finley. Art & Spiritual Transformation: The Seven Stages of Death & Rebirth. 2009. (ENG., Illus.). 1p. pap. 24.95 *(978-1-59477-281-8(9))* Inner Traditions International, Ltd.

Fairs, Marcus. 21st Century Design: New Design Icons from Mass Market to Avant-Garde. 2009. (ENG., Illus.). 464p. 39.95 *(978-1-84732-280-7(8))* Carlton Bks., Ltd. GBR. Dist: Sterling Publishing Co., Inc.

Farr, Ian. Memory. 2012. pap. ***(978-0-262-51776-8(0))*** MIT Pr.

Fenner, Amie. Strange Days: Aliens, Adventurers, Devils, & Dames. Fenner, Cathy, ed. 2009. (ENG., Illus.). 32p. 17.95 *(978-1-59929-039-3(1))* Underwood Books.

Fenner, Arnie & Fenner, Cathy, eds. Spectrum 13: The Best in Contemporary Fantastic Art. 2006. (Spectrum: the Best in Contemporary Fantastic Art Ser.). (ENG., Illus.). 224p. 39.95 *(978-1-59929-002-7(2))* Underwood Books.

Fenz, Werner, et al, eds. Kunst im öffentlichen Raum Steiermark. Art in Public Space Styria: Projekte / Projects 2007-2008. 2010. 344p. pap. *(978-3-7091-0118-6(2))* Actar Birkhauser Distribution.

Ferus, Katharina & Rübel, Dietmar. "Die Tücke des Objekts" Vom Umgang MIT Dingen. 2009. (Illus.). 253p. *(978-3-496-02807-9(6))* Reimer, Dietrich.

Fitzgerald, Kenneth & VanderLans, Rudy. Volume: Writings on Graphic Design, Music, Art, & Culture. 2010. (ENG.). 256p. pap. 24.95 *(978-1-56898-964-8(4))* Princeton Architectural Pr.

Fok, Siu-Har Silvia. Zhongguo Xing Wei Yi Shu: Shen Ti Yu Chang Yu = Performance Art in China: Site & the Body. 2010. (CHI., Illus.). 159p. *(978-986-6565-81-6(5))* Artist Publishing Co.

Form & Function: Mathematics & beyond in Contemporary Art. 2006. 5.00 *(978-0-9723951-5-1(6))* Noyes Museum of Art.

Fraser, Craig. Fashion & Imagination, 1 vol. Djonge Hond Staff, ed. 2010. (ENG., Illus.). 413p. pap. 80.00 *(978-90-8910-140-2(3))* Exhibitions International BEL. Dist: Innovative Logistics.

Freybourg, Anne Maria & Freybourg, Anne Marie. Die Inszenierung des Künstlers. 2008. (GER., Illus.). 111p. pap. *(978-3-86859-031-9(5))* Jovis Verlag GmbH.

Fried, Michael. Four Honest Outlaws: Sala, Ray, Marioni, Gordon. 2011. (ENG., Illus.). 224p. 45.00 *(978-0-300-17053-5(X))* Yale Univ. Pr.

Furnas, Barnaby. Barnaby Furnas: Floods. 2010. (ENG., Illus.). 54p. 13.95 *(978-1-931867-16-0(X))* Museum of Contemporary Art, Denver.

Gauguin, Paul. Noa Noa. Griffin, Jonathan, tr. 2011. (ENG.). 96p. pap. 15.95 *(978-1-84368-061-1(0))* Pallas Athene GBR. Dist: Independent Pubs. Group.

Gavin, Francesca. 100 New Artists. 2011. (ENG., Illus.). 336p. pap. 39.95 *(978-1-85669-734-7(7))* King, Laurence Publishing GBR. Dist: Hachette Bk. Group.

Geary, Caron. It's a Man's Man's Man's World. 2010. 76p. pap. *(978-3-639-22275-3(X))* VDM Verlag Dr. Mueller e.K.

Gelitin, ed. Gelatin's ACB. 2008. (GER & ENG., Illus.). 326p. 115.00 *(978-3-86560-408-8(0))* Verlag der Buchhandlung Walther Konig DEU. Dist: D.A.P./Distributed Art Pubs.

Geuna, Elena. Zhang Huan: Ashman. 2011. (ENG., Illus.). 160p. 55.00 *(978-88-7179-642-0(X)*, Ore Cultura Srl (Acc)) Antique Collectors' Club GBR. Dist: National Bk. Network.

Ghosh, Mrinal. Sojourns of a Painter: Shyamal Dutta Ray & His Times. (Contemporary Indian Art Ser.). (Illus.). 108p. pap. 30.00 *(978-81-85822-86-0(7))* Mapin Publishing Pvt. Ltd IND. Dist: Antique Collectors' Club.

Giarla, Justin, ed. Looking In. 2007. 128p. 39.95 *(978-0-9766325-3-5(5))* 9mm Bks.

Gielen, Denis. Atlas of Contemporary Art for Use by Everyone, 1 vol. Austrums, Laura, tr. 2008. (ENG., Illus.). 400p. 99.95 *(978-2-930368-21-4(7))* Exhibitions International N.V. BEL. Dist: D.A.P./Distributed Art Pubs.

Gludowacz, Irene, et al, eds. Global Art. 2010. (ENG., Illus.). 312p. pap. 25.00 *(978-3-7757-2201-8(7))* Hatje Cantz Verlag GmbH & Co KG DEU. Dist: D.A.P./Distributed Art Pubs.

Goehler, Adrienne, ed. Zur Nachahmung empfohlen! Expeditionen in Ästhetik und Nachhaltigkeit, 2 vols. 2011. (ENG., Illus.). 416p. pap. 75.00 *(978-3-7757-2772-3(8))* Hatje Cantz Verlag GmbH & Co KG DEU. Dist: D.A.P./Distributed Art Pubs.

Goldstein, Ann, et al. This Is Not to Be Looked At: Highlights from the Permanent Collection of the Museum of Contemporary Art, Los Angeles. 2008. (ENG., Illus.). 384p. 59.95 *(978-1-933751-07-8(X))* Museum of Contemporary Art, Los Angeles.

Goldstein, Jesse & Chen, Mary, compiled by. Space 1026 Volume One: Pulling Teeth. 2000th ltd. ed. 2006. (Illus.). 128p. 25.00 *(978-0-9776523-0-3(0))* Tonearm/Lawrence Pubns.

González, Jennifer A. Subject to Display: Reframing Race in Contemporary Installation Art. 2011. (ENG., Illus.). 320p. (gr. 17). pap. 17.95 *(978-0-262-51602-0(0))* MIT Pr.

Grande, John K. Dialogues in Diversity: Art from Marginal to Mainstream. 2007. (ENG., Illus.). 192p. pap. *(978-88-901960-7-2(6))* Pari Publishing.

Grant, Catherine. Girls! Girls! Girls! In Contemporary Art. Waxman, Lori, ed. 2011. (ENG., Illus.). 188p. pap. 40.00 *(978-1-84150-348-6(7))* Intellect, Ltd. GBR. Dist: Chicago Distribution Ctr.

Griffith, Terri, et al, eds. The Essential New Art Examiner. 2011. (ENG.). 350p. pap. 22.50 ***(978-0-87580-662-4(7))*** Northern Illinois Univ. Pr.

Groom, Simon, et al, eds. The Real Thing: Contemporary Art from China. 2008. (ENG., Illus.). 208p. pap. 40.00 *(978-1-85437-713-5(2))* Tate Publishing, Ltd. GBR. Dist: Hachette Bk. Group.

Groys, Boris. Boris Groys: Going Public. 2011. (E-Flux Journal Ser.). (ENG., Illus.). 168p. pap. 15.00 ***(978-1-934105-30-6(9))*** Sternberg Pr.

Guertin, Carolyn. Digital Prohibition: Piracy & Authorship in New Media Art. 2012. (ENG., Illus.). 304p. 120.00 ***(978-1-4411-0610-0(3))***; pap. 34.95 ***(978-1-4411-3190-4(6))*** Continuum International Publishing Group, Ltd. GBR. Dist: National Bk. Network.

Guglielmino, Giorgio. How to Look at Contemporary Art: (... And Like It) 2008. (ENG., Illus.). 216p. pap. 44.00 *(978-88-422-1644-5(5))* Allemandi, Umberto & Co. GBR. Dist: Antique Collectors' Club.

Gun, Le, compiled by. Le Gun 1-3: Magazine of International Illustration. 2011. (ENG., Illus.). 400p. 120.00 *(978-0-9817805-0-4(4))* Batty, Mark Pub., LLC.

Guo-Qiang, Cai. Bunker: Museum of Contemporary Art, Kinmen Island, 1 vol. 2006. (ENG., Illus.). 168p. pap. 45.00 *(978-88-8158-598-4(7))* D.A.P./Distributed Art Pubs.

Hack, Jefferson. Another Art Book, 1 vol. 2011. (ENG., Illus.). 320p. pap. 85.00 *(978-3-86521-860-5(1))* Steidl, Gerhard Druckerei und Verlag DEU. Dist: Innovative Logistics.

Haime, Nohra, ed. Hugo Bastidas: Bridges, Paths & Portals, Where Do We Go from Here. 2007. (Illus.). 8p. pap. 15.00 *(978-0-9786750-8-0(8))* Haime, Nohra Gallery.

Hak, Belinda, ed. Jet: Junior Editorial Team. 2010. (ENG., Illus.). 160p. pap. 19.95 *(978-90-73362-87-1(3))* Witte De With Centre for Contemporary Art NLD. Dist: D.A.P./Distributed Art Pubs.

Hardmeier, M. Radar: Texts on Contemporary Art; Essays & Interviews by Peter Stohler. Stürzl, W., ed. 2008. (ENG., Illus.). 128p. pap. 45.00 *(978-3-89790-278-7(8))* Arnoldsche Art Pubs. DEU. Dist: Antique Collectors' Club.

Harmon, Katharine A. & Clemans, Gayle. The Map as Art: Contemporary Artists Explore Cartography. 2009. (ENG., Illus.). 256p. 45.00 *(978-1-56898-762-0(5))* Princeton Architectural Pr.

Harris, Jonathan. Dead History, Live Art? Spectacle, Subjectivity & Subversion in Visual Culture since the 1980s. 2008. (Liverpool University Press - Tate Liverpool Critical Forum Ser.). (ENG., Illus.). 256p. 90.00 *(978-0-85323-189-9(3))* Liverpool Univ. Pr. GBR. Dist: Chicago Distribution Ctr.

Harris, Jonathan, ed. Globalization & Contemporary Art. 2011. (ENG., Illus.). 552p. 115.95 *(978-1-4051-7951-5(1))*; pap. 49.95 *(978-1-4051-7950-8(3))* Wiley, John & Sons, Inc. (Wiley-Blackwell).

Harvey, Doug & Fernandez, Veronica. Sean Duffy. 2011. (Front Forty Press - Front Forty Profiles Ser.). (Illus.). 122p. pap. 25.00 *(978-0-615-40146-1(5))* Front Forty Pr.

Hatebur, Barbara. Sammlung Credit Suisse: Kunst im Geschäftsumfeld. Credit Suisse Art Staff & Rogger, André, eds. 2011. (ENG., Illus.). 464p. 110.00 *(978-3-85881-324-4(9))* Scheidegger und Spiess AG, Verlag CHE. Dist: Antique Collectors' Club.

Helander, Bruce. Learning to See: An Artist's View on Contemporary Artists from Artschwager to Zakanitch. 2008. (Illus.). 191p. 95.00 *(978-1-884886-88-1(4))* StarGroup International.

Heller, Steven & Talarico, Lita. Design School: Extraordinary Class Projects from International Design Schools. 2011. (ENG., Illus.). 224p. pap. 25.00 *(978-1-59253-759-4(6)*, 1592537596) Quayside.

Hemachandra, Ray & Rossi-Wilcox, Susan M. Blown Glass: Major Works by Leading Artists. 2010. (Masters Ser.). (ENG., Illus.). 330p. pap. 24.95 *(978-1-60059-474-8(3))* Lark Bks.

Hiles. A Survey of Contemporary Art since 1938. 2012. (ENG.). (C). pap. 83.95 ***(978-0-534-63927-3(5))*** Wadsworth.

Hirsh, Jennie & Wallace, Isabelle Loring. Contemporary Art & Classical Myth. 2011. (Illus.). 410p. 124.95 *(978-0-7546-6974-6(2))* Ashgate Publishing Co.

Hively, Charles, ed. Three by Three Illustration Annual No. 8. 2011. (Illus.). 428p. pap. 30.00 ***(978-0-9819405-7-1(9))*** 3x3 Magazine.

Hodgkin, Beatrice. Affordable Contemporary Art: A Guide to Buying & Collecting, 1 vol. 2011. (ENG., Illus.). 208p. pap. 35.00 *(978-1-908126-06-1(X))* Vivays Pubng. Ltd. GBR. Dist: Innovative Logistics.

Hoffman, Jens & Mercer, Kobena. Hew Locke: Stranger in Paradise. 2011. (ENG., Illus.). 144p. pap. 45.00 *(978-1-907317-38-5(4))* Black Dog Publishing Ltd. GBR. Dist: Perseus Distribution.

Hoffmann, Jens, et al. Capp Street Project: Mario Ybarra JR, 1 vol. 2008. (ENG., Illus.). 48p. per. 12.00 *(978-0-9725080-7-0(4))* CCA Wattis Institute for Contemporary Arts.

Hollins, C. J. The Animal Within: Explaining the Bizarre & Ludicrous in Modern Art. 2010. (Illus.). 175p. 37.50 *(978-1-84624-504-6(4))* Book Guild, Ltd. GBR. Dist: Trans-Atlantic Pubns., Inc.

Holzwarth, Hans Werner, ed. Art Now! 03: 25 Years. 2012. (25 Ser.). (ENG, FRE & GER., Illus.). 320p. 14.99 ***(978-3-8365-3618-9(8))*** TASCHEN DEU. Dist: Ingram Pub. Services.

Holzwarth, Hans Werner, ed. Christopher Wool. 2009. (FRE, GER & ENG., Illus.). 500p. 1500.00 *(978-3-8228-0851-1(2))* TASCHEN DEU. Dist: Ingram Pub. Services.

Horvitz, David. Everything That Can Happen in A Day. 2010. (ENG., Illus.). 128p. 27.95 *(978-1-935613-06-0(5))* Batty, Mark Pub., LLC.

Hubbard, Sue. Adventures in Art: Selected Writings, 1990-2010. 2010. (ENG., Illus.). 302p. pap. 37.50 *(978-1-906967-21-5(0))* Other Criteria GBR. Dist: Hachette Bk. Group.

Huber, Jorg Huber & Zhao, Chuan, eds. A New Thoughtfulness in Contemporary China: Critical Voices in Art & Aesthetics. 2011. 250p. pap. ***(978-988-8083-37-4(6))*** Hong Kong Univ. Pr.

Huldisch, Henriette & Momin, Shamim M. Whitney Biennial 2008. 2008. (ENG., Illus.). 288p. pap. 45.00 *(978-0-300-13689-0(7))* Yale Univ. Pr.

Humphrey, Joanne Fenton. Ameen. 2009. (Illus.). 121p. 49.95 *(978-0-615-29130-7(9))* Windjammer Adventure Publishing.

Hung, Shu & Magliaro, Joseph, eds. By Hand: The Use of Craft in Contemporary Art. 2010. (ENG., Illus.). 176p. pap. 24.95 *(978-1-56898-942-6(3))* Princeton Architectural Pr.

Hung, Wu, ed. Wu Hung on Contemporary Chinese Artists. 2009. (ENG., Illus.). 268p. 25.00 *(978-988-18034-3-6(8))* Timezone 8 Ltd. HKG. Dist: D.A.P./Distributed Art Pubs.

Indiana, Robert. Robert Indiana: Hard Edge. 2009. (ENG., Illus.). 68p. 60.00 *(978-0-9794164-4-6(2))* Kasmin, Paul Gallery.

Iversen, Margaret. Chance. 2010. (Documents of Contemporary Art Ser.). (ENG.). 238p. (gr. 17). pap. 24.95 *(978-0-262-51392-0(7))* MIT Pr.

Jansen, Gregor & Thiel, Thomas, eds. Vertrautes Terrain: Aktuelle Kunst in & über Deutschland. 2009. (ENG.). 500p. pap. 45.00 *(978-3-86828-064-7(2))* Kehrer Verlag Heidelberg, Klaus Kehrer DEU. Dist: Consortium Bk. Sales & Distribution.

Jodidio, Philip. Tadao Ando Venice: The Pinault Collection at the Palazzo Grassi & the Punta Della Dogana. 2010. (ENG., Illus.). 160p. 60.00 *(978-0-8478-3410-5(7))* Rizzoli International Pubns., Inc.

Johnstone, Stephen. The Everyday. 2008. (Documents of Contemporary Art Ser.). (ENG.). 240p. (gr. 17). pap. 24.95 *(978-0-262-60074-3(9))* MIT Pr.

Johung, Jennifer. Replacing Home: From Primordial Hut to Digital Network in Contemporary Art. 2011. (ENG., Illus.). 232p. 75.00 ***(978-0-8166-7287-5(3))***; pap. 25.00 ***(978-0-8166-7288-2(1))*** Univ. of Minnesota Pr.

Jones, Caroline A., ed. Sensorium: Embodied Experience, Technology, & Contemporary Art. 2006. (ENG., Illus.). 268p. (gr. 17). 34.00 *(978-0-262-10117-2(3))* MIT Pr.

Jones, Lisa, et al. EyeMinded: Living & Writing Contemporary Art. 2011. (ENG., Illus.). 528p. 99.95 (978-0-8223-4861-0(6)); pap. 27.95 (978-0-8223-4873-3(X)) Duke Univ. Pr.
Juxtapoz. Juxtapoz Illustration. 2008. (Illus.). 192p. 29.95 (978-1-58423-289-6(7)) Gingko Pr., Inc.
Kagan, Sacha. Art & Sustainability: Connecting Patterns for a Culture of Complexity. 2011. (ENG & GER., Illus.). 476p. pap. 54.95 **(978-3-8376-1803-7(X))** Transcript Verlag DEU. Dist: Transaction Pubs.
Kargl, Georg. Georg Kargl, Fine Arts Since 1998: Box Since 2005, 1 vol. 2006. (ENG., Illus.). 328p. per. 35.00 **(978-3-86560-063-9(8))** Verlag der Buchhandlung Walther Konig DEU. Dist: D.A.P./Distributed Art Pubs.
Kelly, Caleb, ed. Sound. 2011. (Documents of Contemporary Art Ser.). (ENG., Illus.). 240p. (gr. 17). pap. 24.95 **(978-0-262-51568-9(7))** MIT Pr.
Kelsey, John. John Kelsey: Rich Texts: Selected Writing for Art. 2011. (ENG., Illus.). 243p. pap. 19.95 **(978-1-934105-23-8(6))** Sternberg Pr.
Kendra Binney, Dan Ness & Tim Karpinski, Chris Haberman. Invision: A Collection of Visual Art in Portland, Oregon. Michael Fields, ed. 2007. 80p. per. 22.00 (978-0-9776051-4-9(0)) Another Sky Pr.
Klanten, R., et al, eds. Art & Agenda: Political Art & Activism. 2011. (Illus.). 288p. (978-3-89955-342-0(X)) Die Gestalten Verlag.
Klanten, R. & Hübner, M., eds. Tangible: High Touch Visuals. 2009. (Illus.). 208p. (978-3-89955-232-4(6)) Die Gestalten Verlag.
Klanten, R. & Schulze, F. Erratic: Visual Impact in Current Design. 2011. (ENG., Illus.). 192p. pap. 45.00 **(978-3-89955-370-3(5))** Die Gestalten Verlag DEU. Dist: Prestel Publishing.
Klanten, Robert, ed. Hair'em Scare'em. 2009. (Illus.). 224p. pap. 50.00 (978-3-89955-275-1(X)) Die Gestalten Verlag DEU. Dist: Prestel Publishing.
Klin, Richard. Something to Say: Thoughts on Art & Politics in America. 2011. (ENG., Illus.). 168p. pap. 14.95 **(978-1-935248-19-4(7))** Leapfrog Pr.
Kobler, Florian, ed. Studio Olafur Eliasson; Art Edition. 2008. 1000.00 (978-3-8365-0761-5(7)) TASCHEN DEU. Dist: Ingram Pub. Services.
Koch, Polly. The Old, Weird America, 1 vol. 2008. (ENG., Illus.). 160p. 34.99 (978-1-933619-12-5(0)) Contemporary Arts Museum, Houston.
Korero Books Staff & Korero Books. Art that Creeps: A Macabre Menagerie of Art. 2009. (ENG., Illus.). 208p. 35.00 (978-0-9558336-7-0(1)) Korero Books LLP GBR. Dist: Independent Pubs. Group.
Korero Books Staff & Strongman, Jay. Steampunk: The Art of Victorian Futurism. 2011. (ENG.). 176p. 35.00 (978-1-907621-03-1(2)) Korero Books LLP GBR. Dist: Independent Pubs. Group.
Kotsopoulos, Nikolaos, ed. Contemporary Art in Eastern Europe: Artworld. 2010. (Artworld Ser.). (ENG., Illus.). 240p. 49.95 (978-1-906155-84-1(4)) Black Dog Publishing Ltd. GBR. Dist: Perseus Distribution.
Kramer, Hilton. The Triumph of Modernism: The Art World, 1987-2005. 2006. (ENG.). 352p. 27.50 (978-1-56663-708-4(2)) Dee, Ivan R. Pub.
Kraus, Chris. Where Art Belongs. 2011. (Semiotext(e) / Intervention Ser.). (ENG.). 176p. (gr. 17). pap. 12.95 (978-1-58435-098-9(9)) Semiotexte/Smart Art.
Krauss, Rosalind E. Perpetual Inventory. 2010. (October Bks.). (ENG., Illus.). 320p. (gr. 17). 31.95 (978-0-262-01380-2(0)) MIT Pr.
Kriemann, Susanne. Reading Susanne Kriemann. Dickel, Hans & Puyplat, Lisa, eds. 2011. (ENG.). 215p. 24.95 **(978-1-934105-49-8(X))** Sternberg Pr.
Krols, Birgit. 3D Street Art, 1 vol. 2011. (ENG., Illus.). 192p. pap. 39.95 (978-90-79761-29-6(X)) Tectum B.V.B.A. BEL. Dist: Innovative Logistics.
Lazarides, Steve. Outsiders: Art by People. 2009. (ENG., Illus.). 264p. pap. 26.95 (978-1-84605-546-1(6)) Random Hse. GBR. Dist: Independent Pubs. Group.
Lee, Pamela M. Forgetting the Art World. 2012. **(978-0-262-01773-2(3))** MIT Pr.
Lepik, Andres, et al, texts. Sauerbruch Hutton Architects: Museum Brandhorst. 2009. (ENG., Illus.). 128p. 40.00 (978-3-7757-2355-8(2)) Hatje Cantz Verlag GmbH & Co KG DEU. Dist: D.A.P./Distributed Art Pubs.
Letscher, Lance. Lance Letscher: Collage. collector's ed. 2010. (ENG., Illus.). 224p. 250.00 (978-0-292-72395-5(4)) Univ. of Texas Pr.
Levey, Haran. Highbrow. Lowbrow. Nobrow. 2011. (Mocart Ser.). (Illus.). 255p. 29.95 **(978-1-58423-457-9(1))** Gingko Pr., Inc.
Lewisohn, Cedar. Abstract Graffiti. 2011. (ENG., Illus.). 176p. 29.95 (978-1-85894-526-2(7)) Merrell Pubs. Ltd. GBR. Dist: Perseus Distribution.
Lidinsky, Richard, ed. DADDY Number 6. 2008. (Illus.). pap. 15.00 (978-0-9778819-6-3(2)) Peres Projects, Los Angeles Berlin.
Lindemann, Adam. T25 Collecting Contemporary Art. 2010. (25 Ser.). (ENG., Illus.). 300p. 14.99 (978-3-8365-2308-0(6)) TASCHEN DEU. Dist: Ingram Pub. Services.
Lodermeyer, Peter, ed. Personal Structures: Time. Space. Existence. 2010. (MUL & ENG., Illus.). 448p. 59.95 (978-3-8321-9279-2(4)) DuMont DEU. Dist: D.A.P./Distributed Art Pubs.
Lowry, Glenn. Oil & Sugar: Contemporary Art & Islamic Culture Third Annual Eva Holtby Lecture on Contemporary Culture. 2009. (Eva Holtby Lecture on Contemporary Culture Ser.). (ENG.). 64p. 19.99 (978-0-88854-469-8(3)) Royal Ontario Museum CAN. Dist: Univ. of Toronto Pr.
Lucas, Sarah & Garbay, Olivier, photos by. The MUG. 2009. (ENG., Illus.). 640p. 125.00 (978-1-904212-51-5(4)) Other Criteria GBR. Dist: Hachette Bk. Group.
Mackey, Clarke. Random Acts of Culture: Reclaiming Art & Community in the 21st Century. 2010. 286p. pap. 26.95 (978-1-897071-64-9(7)) Between the Lines CAN. Dist: Univ. of Toronto Pr.
Magliaro, Joseph. By Hand: The Use of Craft in Contemporary Art. Hung, Shu & Magliaro, Joseph, eds. 2006. (ENG., Illus.). 176p. 34.95 (978-1-56898-610-4(6)) Princeton Architectural Pr.
Magnin, André & Magnin, Andre. African Art Now: Masterpieces from the Jean Pigozzi Collection. (Illus.). 224p. (978-1-85894-289-6(6)) Merrell Pubs. Ltd.
Malagrida, Anna & TF Editores, C. A. Anna Malagrida. 2011. (Illus.). 200p. 58.00 (978-84-92441-00-6(3), T.F. Editores, S.L.C.) Antique Collectors' Club GBR. Dist: National Bk. Network.
Mandušic, Danijela. Living in the Interface. 2009. 96p. pap. (978-3-639-15368-2(5)) VDM Verlag Dr. Mueller e.K.
Mannari, Enrica. Pink Attitude: The Contemporary Female Creativity. 2008. (Illus.). 218p. (978-88-86416-72-6(5)) Happy Bks.
Marcus, Caleb Cain, photos by. Caleb Cain Marcus: the Silent Aftermath of Space. 2010. (ENG., Illus.). 48p. 50.00 (978-88-6208-112-2(X)) Damiani ITA. Dist: D.A.P./Distributed Art Pubs.
McDaniel, Lynda. Contemporary Hawaii Woodworkers: The Wood, the Art, the Aloha. 2009. (Illus.). 224p. 44.95 (978-0-615-29944-0(X)) Contemporary Pubns
McFadden, David Revere, frwd. Otherworldly: Optical Delusions & Small Realities. 2011. (ENG., Illus.). 272p. 45.00 (978-0-9832983-1-1(9)) Channel Photographics.
McKenna, Martin. Fantasy Art Now. 2011. 192p. pap. 19.99 (978-0-06-200270-9(8), Collins Design) HarperCollins Pubs.
—Fantasy Art Now: The Very Best in Contemporary Fantasy Art & Illustration. 2007. (ENG.). 192p. 29.99 (978-0-06-137097-7(5), Collins Design) HarperCollins Pubs.
McLendon, Matthew. Beyond Bling: Voices of Hip Hop in Art. 2011. (ENG., Illus.). 128p. pap. 19.95 (978-1-85759-697-7(8)) Scala, Editions FRA. Dist: National Bk. Network.
Meier, Simon. Chinese Youth Identities in Cao Fei's Storage Box, Fresh & Cosplayers. 2011. 60p. pap. **(978-3-640-64098-0(5))** Hammer, Patrick, Tanja Hammer, Matthias Knoop, Julius Mittenzwei, Georg Steinbach u. Michael Teltscher. GRIN Verlag GbR.
Meskimmon. Contemporary Art & the Cosmopolitan Imagination: Politics, Ethics, Affect. 2010. (ENG., Illus.). 144p. (C). 37.95 (978-0-415-46920-3(1)); 110.00 (978-0-415-46919-7(8)) Routledge.
Mihm, Nina & Nelson, Mary Carroll, eds. Visual Journeys: Art of the 21st Century Society of Layerists in Multi-Media. 2010. (ENG., Illus.). 160p. 40.00 (978-1-934491-23-2(3)) Fresco Fine Art Pubns., LLC.
Millett-Gallant, Ann. The Disabled Body in Contemporary Art. (ENG., Illus.). 2012. 188p. pap. 27.00 **(978-0-230-34142-5(X))** 2010. 192p. 79.00 (978-0-230-10406-8(1)) Palgrave Macmillan.
Moisdon, Stephanie & Obrist, Hans Ulrich. 00s — L'histoire D'une Décennie Qui N'est Pas Encore Nommée. 2007. (Illus.). 304p. (978-2-84066-221-1(3)) JRP Ringier Kunstverlag AG.
Morley, Simon, ed. The Sublime. 2010. (Documents of Contemporary Art Ser.). (ENG.). 237p. (gr. 17). pap. 24.95 (978-0-262-51391-3(9)) MIT Pr.
Muller, Lars & Miki, Akiko, eds. Insular Insight: Where Art & Architecture Conspire with Nature. 2011. (ENG., Illus.). 480p. 70.00 **(978-3-03778-255-2(2))** Lars Muller Pubs. CHE. Dist: Prestel Publishing.
Munder, Heike. It's Time for Action (There's No Option) About Feminism. 2008. (GER & ENG., Illus.). 164p. 39.00 (978-3-905770-53-7(9)) JRP Ringier Kunstverlag AG CHE. Dist: D.A.P./Distributed Art Pubs.
Munder, Heike, et al, eds. It's Not a Garden Table. 2011. (ENG., Illus.). 272p. pap. 47.50 **(978-3-03764-211-5(4))** JRP Ringier Kunstverlag AG CHE. Dist: D.A.P./Distributed Art Pubs.
Museum of Fine Arts, Houston Staff, contrib. by. Core: Artists & Critics in Residence. 2008. (Illus.). 206p. (978-0-89090-162-5(7)) Museum of Fine Arts, Houston.
Native, et al. The Sessions. 2007. (ENG., Illus.). 96p. pap. 29.00 (978-88-88493-22-0(0)) Drago Arts & Communication ITA. Dist: SCB Distributors.
Nicolas, Harry. Harry's Art. 2007. (ENG.). 148p. 24.95 (978-0-595-91889-8(1)); 80p. per. 14.95 (978-0-595-44113-6(0)) iUniverse, Inc.
Niculescu, Alexandru, ed. Romanian Cultural Resolution: Zeitgenössische Kunst aus Rumänien. 2011. (ENG., Illus.). 232p. pap. 55.00 **(978-3-7757-2848-5(1))** Hatje Cantz Verlag GmbH & Co KG DEU. Dist: D.A.P./Distributed Art Pubs.
Noble, Richard & Noble, R. Utopias. Noble, Richard, ed. 2009. (Documents of Contemporary Art Ser.). (ENG., Illus.). 240p. (gr. 17). pap. 24.95 (978-0-262-64069-5(4)) MIT Pr.
Noever, Peter, ed. & text. 20/21: MAK Collection of Contemporary Art. 2010. (ENG., Illus.). 244p. pap. 40.00 (978-3-941185-29-6(2)) Verlag fur Moderne Kunst DEU. Dist: D.A.P./Distributed Art Pubs.
Obrist, Hans Ulrich & Moisdon, Stephanie, eds. Lyon Biennial: The History of a Decade That Has Not yet Been Named. 2008. (ENG., Illus.). 304p. 45.00 (978-3-905829-02-0(9)) JRP Ringier Kunstverlag AG CHE. Dist: D.A.P./Distributed Art Pubs.
Oehlen, Albert. Albert Oehlen: 1991-2008. 2009. (ENG & GER., Illus.). 88p. 50.00 (978-3-935567-48-0(0)) Holzwarth Pubns. DEU. Dist: D.A.P./Distributed Art Pubs.
Olbricht, Thomas. Rockers Island Olbricht Collection: Museum Folkwang, 1 vol. 2008. (ENG., Illus.). 288p. 50.00 (978-3-86521-471-3(1)) Steidl, Gerhard Druckerei und Verlag DEU. Dist: Innovative Logistics.
Oliva, Achille Bonito. Encyclopaedia of the World: Artist Dialogues, 1968-2008. 2010. (ENG., Illus.). 414p. 45.00 (978-88-572-0463-5(4)) Skira Editore ITA. Dist: Random Hse., Inc.
O'Reilly, Sally. The Body in Contemporary Art. 2009. (World of Art Ser.). (ENG., Illus.). 224p. pap. 19.95 (978-0-500-20400-9(4), 520400) Thames & Hudson.
Osthoff, Simone. Performing the Archive: The transformation of the archive in Contemporary art from repository of documents to art Medium. Schirmacher, Wolfgang, ed. 2009. (Illus.). 208p. pap. 21.95 (978-0-9825309-0-0(0)) Atropos Pr.
Owens, Annie & Attaboy, eds. Hi-Fructose Collected Edition Volume 2: Under-the-Counter Culture. 2010. (ENG., Illus.). 300p. 39.95 (978-0-86719-744-0(7)) Last Gasp of San Francisco.
Owens, Annie & Attaboy! Hi-Fructose Collected Edition Hardcover. 2009. (Illus.). 250p. 35.00 (978-0-86719-713-6(7)) Last Gasp of San Francisco.
Paglia, Michael & Chandler, Mary Voetz. Colorado Abstract: Paintings & Sculpture. 2009. (ENG., Illus.). 319p. 85.00 (978-1-934491-12-6(8)) Fresco Fine Art Pubns., LLC.
Pakesch, Peter, ed. Human Condition: Empathy & Emancipation in Precarious Times. 2011. (ENG & GER., Illus.). 268p. pap. 45.00 (978-3-86560-845-1(0)) Verlag der Buchhandlung Walther Konig DEU. Dist: D.A.P./Distributed Art Pubs.
Palencar, John Jude. Origins: The Art of John Jude Palencar. Fenner, Arnie & Fenner, Cathy, eds. 2007. (ENG., Illus.). 128p. 27.00 (978-1-59929-004-1(9)) Underwood Books.
Papadakis, Alexandra & Papadakis, Andreas, eds. Innovations: From Experimentation to Realisation. 2006. (ENG., Illus.). pap. 30.00 (978-1-901092-46-2(1)) Papadakis Dist A/C.
Paparoni, Demetrio, ed. Eretica: The Transcendent & the Profane in Contemporary Art. 2007. (ENG., Illus.). 264p. pap. 24.95 (978-88-6130-069-9(3)) Skira Editore ITA. Dist: Random Hse., Inc.
Passion Bild: Russische Kunst seit 1970. 2010. (Illus.). 280p. 171.00 **(978-3-85881-199-8(8))** Scheidegger und Spiess AG, Verlag CHE. Dist: Antique Collectors' Club.
Paterson, James. Jim's Grandiose Big Bible Picture Book. 2007. (ENG., Illus.). 96p. 35.00 (978-0-9782221-4-7(8)) ECW Pr. CAN. Dist: Independent Pubs. Group.
Patrick, Nguyen & Stuart, MacKenzie. Beyond the Street: With the 100 Most Important Players in Urban Art. 2010. (Illus.). 400p. 78.00 (978-3-89955-290-4(3)) Die Gestalten Verlag DEU. Dist: Prestel Publishing.
Paunero, Daniel & Daniel, Paunero. S/T (Sin Título) La Exposición Como Taller. 2010. (SPA., Illus.). 67p. (978-84-441-0244-3(X)) Centro Atlantico de Arte Moderno.
Pejic, Bojana, ed. Gender Check: A Reader. 2011. (ENG.). 380p. pap. 39.95 (978-3-86560-883-3(3)) Verlag der Buchhandlung Walther Konig DEU. Dist: D.A.P./Distributed Art Pubs.
Peppiatt, Michael. Interviews with Artists, 1966-2011. 2012. (ENG., Illus.). 434p. 40.00 **(978-0-300-17662-9(7))** Yale Univ. Pr.
Petrovich, Dushko & White, Roger, eds. Paper Monument. 2007. 100p. per. 10.00 (978-0-9797575-0-1(9)) Paper Monument.
Petry, Michael. The Art of Not Making: The New Artist/Artisan Relationship. 2012. (ENG., Illus.). 208p. pap. 34.95 **(978-0-500-29026-2(1)**, 529026) Thames & Hudson.
Phaidon Press Editors, ed. Creamier: Contemporary Art in Culture: 10 Curators, 100 Contemporary Artists, 10 Sources. 2010. (ENG., Illus.). 448p. 39.95 (978-0-7148-5663-4(5)) Phaidon Pr., Inc.
Philipsen, Lotte. Globalizing Art. Place, Identity & Transformation. Stavning Thomsen, Bodil Marie & Ørjasæter, Kristin, eds. 2011. (ENG., Illus.). 296p. (C). pap. 48.00 **(978-87-7934-572-0(7))** Aarhus Universitetsforlag DNK. Dist: ISD.
Poli, Francesco. Post-Modern Art, 1945-2008. 2008. (ENG., Illus.). 400p. 60.00 (978-0-06-166577-6(0), Collins Design) HarperCollins Pubs.
Pollack, Barbara, text. The Wild, Wild East: an American Art Critic's Adventures in China. 2010. (ENG., Illus.). 208p. pap. 24.95 (978-988-18034-9-8(7)) Timezone 8 Ltd. HKG. Dist: D.A.P./Distributed Art Pubs.
Qian, Zifen. The Art of Zifen Qian. 2007. (Illus.). 174p. 49.99 (978-1-59879-356-7(X)) Lifevest Publishing, Inc.
Ramadan, Khaled D., ed. Peripheral Insider: Perspectives on Contemporary Internationalism in Visual Culture. 2007. (Illus.). 240p. pap. 32.00 (978-87-7289-967-1(0)) Museum Tusculanum Pr. DNK. Dist: Chicago Distribution Ctr.
Rancière, Jacques. The Future of the Image. Elliott, Gregory, tr. from FRE. 2009. (ENG.). 160p. pap. 17.95 (978-1-84467-297-4(2), 844297) Verso Bks. GBR. Dist: Norton, W. W. & Co., Inc.
Rattemeyer, Christian, ed. The Judith Rothschild Foundation Contemporary Drawings Collection: Catalogue Raisonne. 2009. (ENG., Illus.). 296p. 60.00 (978-0-87070-751-3(5)) Museum of Modern Art.
Rattemeyer, Christian, ed. & text. Compass in Hand: Sections from the Judith Rothschild Foundation Contemporary Drawings Collection. 2009. (ENG., Illus.). 320p. 65.00 (978-0-87070-745-2(0)) Museum of Modern Art.
Ribalta, Jorge, text. Relational Objects: Macba Collection 2002-2007. 2010. (ENG.). 272p. pap. 39.95 (978-84-92505-12-8(5)) Museu d'Art Contemporani de Barcelona ESP. Dist: Actar Birkhauser Distribution.
Roberts, John. The Intangibilities of Form: Skill & Deskilling in Art after the Readymade. 2007. (ENG., Illus.). 256p. 95.00 (978-1-84467-163-2(1), 844163); per. 27.95 (978-1-84467-167-0(4), 844167) Verso Bks. GBR. Dist: Norton, W. W. & Co., Inc.
Roberts, Rebecca, ed. MOMA Highlights Since 1980, 1 vol. 2008. (ENG., Illus.). 280p. pap. 19.95 (978-0-87070-713-1(2)) Museum of Modern Art.
Robertson, Jean & McDaniel, Craig. Themes of Contemporary Art: Visual Art After 1980. (ENG., Illus.). (C). 2nd ed. 2009. 352p. pap. 39.95 (978-0-19-536757-7(X)) 3rd ed. 2012. 416p. pap. 39.95 **(978-0-19-979707-3(2))** Oxford Univ. Pr., Inc.
Rocca, Alessandro. Natural Architecture. 2007. (ENG., Illus.). 216p. pap. 39.95 (978-1-56898-721-7(8)) Princeton Architectural Pr.
Rochlitz, Rainer. Subversion & Subsidy: Contemporary Art & Aesthetics. Roberts, Dafydd, tr. from FRE. 2008. (SB-the French List Ser.). (ENG.). 240p. 99.95 (978-1-905422-70-8(9)); pap. 29.95 (978-1-905422-71-5(7)) Seagull Bks. GBR. Dist: Chicago Distribution Ctr.
Rondeau, James. Judith Neisser Collection: Minimal & Postminimal Innovation. 2011. (Contemporary Collecting Ser.). (ENG., Illus.). 160p. 35.00 (978-0-300-17024-5(6)) Art Institute of Chicago.
Rosen, Kay. Kay Rosen: AKAK. 2010. (ENG., Illus.). 232p. 49.95 (978-0-9815449-5-3(9)) Regency Arts Pr.
Ross, Christine. The Past Is the Present; It's the Future Too: The Temporal Turn in Contemporary Art. 2012. (ENG., Illus.). 336p. 160.00 **(978-1-4411-1604-8(4))** Continuum International Publishing Group, Ltd. GBR. Dist: National Bk. Network.
Rubin, Susan Goldman. Breaking the Rules: What Is Contemporary Art? 2010. (978-1-933751-15-3(0)) Museum of Contemporary Art, Los Angeles.
Rugg, Judith. Exploring Site-Specific Art: Issues of Space & Internationalism. 2010. (ENG., Illus.). 224p. pap. 28.00 (978-1-84885-064-4(6)) I. B. Tauris & Co., Ltd. GBR. Dist: Macmillan.
Rush, Michael. The Rose Art Museum Collection. 2009. (ENG., Illus.). 288p. 60.00 (978-0-8109-5574-5(1)) Abrams.
Russ, Nadia. Neopoprealism Starz: 21st Century ART, 2nd Volume, Erotica As A High Artistic Aspiration. 2010. 68p. pap. 31.99 (978-1-4500-4995-5(8)) Xlibris Corp.
Russell, Charles. Groundwaters: A Century of Art by Self-Taught & Outsider Artists. 2011. (ENG., Illus.). 256p. 65.00 **(978-3-7913-4490-4(0))** Prestel Publishing.
Sanders, Jay, et al, eds. Performa 2007. 2010. (ENG., Illus.). 340p. pap. 45.00 (978-3-03764-034-0(0)) JRP Ringier Kunstverlag AG CHE. Dist: D.A.P./Distributed Art Pubs.
Sauter, Joachim, et al. Art+com: Media Spaces & Installations. 2011. (ENG., Illus.). 256p. 60.00 **(978-3-89955-285-0(7))** Die Gestalten Verlag DEU. Dist: Prestel Publishing.
Schädler-Saub, Ursula & Weyer, Angela. Theory & Practice in the Conservation of Modern & Contemporary Art: Reflections on the Roots & the Perspectives. 2010. (ENG., Illus.). 210p. 90.00 (978-1-904982-54-8(9)) Archetype Pubns. GBR. Dist: National Bk. Network.
Schaschl, Sabine, ed. Omer Fast: in Memory. 2010. (ENG., Illus.). 176p. 45.00 (978-3-941544-14-4(9)) Green Box, The DEU. Dist: D.A.P./Distributed Art Pubs.
Schavemaker, Margriet, et al, eds. Now Is the Time. 2010. (ENG., Illus.). 192p. pap. 40.00 (978-90-5662-721-8(X)) NAi Uitgevers / Publishers Stichting NLD. Dist: D.A.P./Distributed Art Pubs.
Schavemaker, Margriet & Rakier, Mischa. Right about Now: Art & Theory since the 1990s, 1 vol. 2008. (ENG., Illus.). 184p. pap. 29.95 (978-90-78088-17-2(6)) Valiz NLD. Dist: D.A.P./Distributed Art Pubs.
Schellmann, Jorg, ed. Forty Are Better Than One: Contemporary Art Production Munchen New York 1969-2009. 2010. (ENG., Illus.). 456p. 70.00 (978-3-7757-2236-0(X)) Hatje Cantz Verlag GmbH & Co KG DEU. Dist: D.A.P./Distributed Art Pubs.
Schor, Mira. A Decade of Negative Thinking: Essays on Art, Politics, & Daily Life. 2010. (ENG., Illus.). 336p. 89.95 (978-0-8223-4584-8(6)); pap. 24.95 (978-0-8223-4602-9(8)) Duke Univ. Pr.
Schulte-Goltz, Colmar, ed. Wolfgang Neumann: Mittelbemindert (Reduced Means) 2009. (ENG., Illus.). 104p. 35.00 (978-3-86678-143-6(1)) Kerber Verlag DEU. Dist: D.A.P./Distributed Art Pubs.
Seijdel, Jorinde, et al, contrib. by. Open 10: (in)tolerance, on Freedom of Expression in Art & the Public Domain. 2006. (Illus.). 160p. pap. 30.00 (978-90-5662-492-7(X)) NAi Uitgevers / Publishers Stichting NLD. Dist: D.A.P./Distributed Art Pubs.
Sener, Seval. A Singular Art: A theoretical & artistic survey on Miniature. 2010. 96p. pap. (978-3-8383-7588-5(2)) Lambert Academic Publishing.
Sevsnen, Erkki. Towards a New Kind of System of Art: The Shift from the Modern to the Contemporary Sphereof Art from the Standpoint of System-Theoretical andSystemic Sociology. 2008. 160p. pap. (978-3-639-09893-8(5)) VDM Verlag Dr. Mueller e.K.
Shaoqiang, Wang, ed. Box. 2009. (Illus.). 371p. (978-981-245-696-0(1)) Page One Publishing.
Sheffield, Margaret. The Expressive Edge. 2010. (ENG., Illus.). 120p. pap. 37.95 (978-88-8158-737-7(8)) Charta ITA. Dist: D.A.P./Distributed Art Pubs.
Sherman Contemporary Art Foundation Ltd. Contemporary Art & Philanthropy No. 7: Exploring the Foundations. Smith, Terry, ed. 2007. (ENG.). 104p. pap. (978-0-86840-951-1(0), UNSW Press) NewSouth Publishing AUS. Dist: Independent Pubs. Group.
Shifrin, Susan. Re-Framing Representations of Women: Figuring, Fashioning, Portraiting, & Telling in the 'Picturing' Women Project. Shifrin, Susan, ed. 2008. (Illus.). 354p. 149.95 (978-0-7546-6077-4(X)) Ashgate Publishing Co.
Shiming, Gao. Liu Wei: 2006-2007. Boers, Waling, ed. 2009. (ENG., Illus.). 139p. 50.00 (978-988-17143-2-9(X)) Timezone 8 Ltd. HKG. Dist: D.A.P./Distributed Art Pubs.
Sholette, Gregory. Dark Matter: Art & Politics in the Age of Enterprise Culture. 2010. (Marxism & Culture Ser.). (ENG., Illus.). 304p. pap. 30.00 (978-0-7453-2752-5(4)); lib. bdg. 96.00 (978-0-7453-2753-2(2)) Pluto Pr. GBR. Dist: Macmillan.
Siedell, Daniel A. Martinez Celaya: Early Work. 2007. (ENG., Illus.). 392p. 69.00 (978-0-9673608-6-7(2)) Whale & Star Pr.

Silbergeld, Jerome & Ching, Dora C. Articulations - Undefining Chinese Contemporary Art. 2010. (Publications of the Department of Art & Archaeology, Princeton University Ser.). (ENG., Illus.). 320p. (C). pap. 29.95 *(978-0-691-14860-1(0))* Princeton Univ. Pr.
Sinha, Modhurima. Call of the Real: Contemporary Indian Artists from Bengal. (Contemporary Indian Art Ser.). (Illus.). 180p. 65.00 *(978-81-88204-28-1(5))* Mapin Publishing Pvt. Ltd IND. Dist: Antique Collectors' Club.
Sinnott, Kevin. Behind the Canvas. 2009. (ENG., Illus.). 160p. pap. 29.95 *(978-1-85411-445-7(X))* Seren Bks. GBR. Dist: Independent Pubs. Group.
Skov, Mara Holt & Holt, Steven Skov. Manufractured: The Conspicuous Transformation of Everyday Objects. 2008. (ENG., Illus.). 144p. 35.00 *(978-0-8118-6509-8(6))* Chronicle Bks. LLC.
Smith, Karen, ed. Nine Lives: the Birth of Avant-Garde Art in New China. 2008. (ENG., Illus.). 473p. pap. 50.00 *(978-988-17143-3-6(8))* Timezone 8 Ltd. HKG. Dist: D.A.P./Distributed Art Pubs.
Smith, Patti. Trois. 2008. (ENG.). 96p. pap. 45.00 *(978-0-500-97686-9(4))* Thames & Hudson.
Smith, Terry. Antinomies of Art & Culture: Modernity, Postmodernity, Contemporaneity. Smith, Terry et al, eds. Enwezor, Okwui et al, contrib. by. 2009. (ENG., Illus.). 456p. 99.95 *(978-0-8223-4186-4(7))*; pap. 27.95 *(978-0-8223-4203-8(0))* Duke Univ. Pr.
Smith, Terry. Contemporary Art: World Currents. 2011. (ENG., Illus.). 304p. (C). pap. 68.00 ***(978-0-205-78971-9(4)***, Prentice Hall) Prentice Hall PTR.
Solidor, André S. The Art of André S. Solidor. 2009. (FRE, ITA, GER, SPA & ENG., Illus.). 96p. 59.95 *(978-3-8327-9362-3(3))* teNeues Publishing Co.
—The Art of Andre S. Solidor A. K. A. Elliott Erwitt with Cohiba Cigar with Smoking Fish Photoprint. 2009. 96p. 3250.00 *(978-3-8327-9175-9(2))* teNeues Publishing Co.
—The Art of Andre S. Solidor A. K. A. Elliott Erwitt with Security Guards with Mannequin & Moose Photoprint. 2009. 96p. 3250.00 *(978-3-8327-9182-7(5))* teNeues Publishing Co.
Solomon R Guggenheim Foundation, creator. The Hugo Boss Prize, 1 vol. 2007. (ENG., Illus.). 108p. pap. 29.95 *(978-0-89207-361-0(6))* Guggenheim, Solomon R. Museum.
Stange, Raimar, ed. The Evil. 2007. (GER & ENG., Illus.). 118p. *(978-3-8321-9000-2(7))* DuMont.
Steiner, Wendy. The Real Real Thing: The Model in the Mirror of Art. 2010. (Illus.). 240p. 32.50 *(978-0-226-77219-6(5))* Univ. of Chicago Pr.
Stiles, Kristine & Selz, Peter. Theories & Documents of Contemporary Art: A Sourcebook of Artists' Writings. 2nd rev. exp. ed. 2012. (ENG., Illus.). 1135p. 75.00 *(978-0-520-25374-2(4))*; pap. 34.95 *(978-0-520-25718-4(9))* Univ. of California Pr.
Stockebrand, Marianne, ed. Chinati: The Vision of Donald Judd. 2010. (ENG., Illus.). 328p. 65.00 *(978-0-300-16939-3(6))* Yale Univ. Pr.
Studio on Fire. Studio on Fire: Iron Beasts Make Great Beauty. 2011. (ENG., Illus.). 144p. 30.00 ***(978-3-89955-381-9(0))*** Die Gestalten Verlag DEU. Dist: Prestel Publishing.
Sultan, Terrie, ed. Damaged Romanticism: A Mirror of Modern Emotion. 2008. (Illus.). pap. *(978-0-941193-39-9(X))* Blaffer Art Museum.
Sultan, Terrie, et al. Damaged Romanticism: A Mirror of Modern Emotion. 2008. (ENG., Illus.). 136p. pap. 44.95 *(978-1-904832-51-5(2))* Giles, D. Ltd. GBR. Dist: Antique Collectors' Club.
Systems Design Limited, creator. Two Faced: The Changing Face of Portraiture. 2007. (Illus.). 311p. pap. *(978-988-98992-5-7(6))* Systems Design, Ltd.
Sze, Sarah. Sarah Sze: Infinite Line. 2011. (ENG., Illus.). 144p. 55.00 ***(978-0-87848-113-2(3))*** Yale Univ. Pr. GBR. Dist: D.A.P./Distributed Art Pubs.
Tamas, Klara. Klara Tamas' Art. 2011. 36p. pap. 21.99 ***(978-1-4568-6440-8(8))*** Xlibris Corp.
Terraroli, Valerio, ed. 2000 & Beyond Vol. 5: Contemporary Tendencies. 2010. (ENG., Illus.). 432p. 60.00 *(978-88-572-0128-3(7))* Skira Editore ITA. Dist: Random Hse., Inc.
Thom, Ian M. Challenging Traditions: Contemporary First Nations Art of the Northwest Coast. 2009. (ENG.). 176p. 65.00 *(978-0-295-98919-8(X))* Univ. of Washington Pr.
Thompson, Don. The $12 Million Stuffed Shark: The Curious Economics of Contemporary Art. 2010. (ENG., Illus.). 272p. pap. 17.00 *(978-0-230-62059-9(0))* Palgrave Macmillan.
Thompson, Nato. Seeing Power: Art & Activism in the Age of Cultural Production. 2012. (ENG., Illus.). 176p. pap. 21.95 *(978-1-61219-044-0(8))* Melville Hse. Publishing.
Toilet Paper: Issue 3. 2011. (ENG., Illus.). 40p. pap. 12.00 ***(978-1-935202-60-8(X))*** Deste Foundation GRC. Dist: D.A.P./Distributed Art Pubs.
Toilet Paper: Tar Edition. 2011. (ENG., Illus.). 40p. pap. 12.00 ***(978-1-935202-74-5(X))*** Deste Foundation GRC. Dist: D.A.P./Distributed Art Pubs.
Tomasula, Steve. The And Now Awards: The Best Innovative Writing. Archambeau, Robert & Schneiderman, Davis, eds. 2009. (ENG., Illus.). 400p. pap. 19.95 *(978-0-9823156-0-6(0))* Lake Forest College Pr.
Trummer, Thomas, ed. Voice & Void. 2008. (ENG., Illus.). 183p. 35.00 *(978-1-888332-31-5(X))* Aldrich Museum of Contemporary Art, Inc., The.
Tuli, Neville. Indian Contemporary Art Vol. 4: Books, Paintings & Sculpture. 2006. (Masterpieces & Museum-Quality Ser.). (ENG., Illus.). 208p. pap. 65.00 *(978-1-890206-76-5(8))* Mapin Publishing Pvt. Ltd IND. Dist: National Bk. Network.
Tuli, Neville, text. Osian's Indian Contemporary Art: Null: Paintings, Drawings & Sculpture. 2006. (ENG., Illus.). 208p. pap. 65.00 *(978-1-890206-84-0(9))* Mapin Publishing Pvt. Ltd IND. Dist: National Bk. Network.
Ulysses; Departures, Journeys, & Returns: The Artwork of Andrew Schoultz. 3000th ed. 2007. (Illus.). 180p. 29.00 *(978-0-9788739-0-5(4))* Paper Museum Pr.
Vaillant, Alexis, et al. Options with Nostrils. 2011. (ENG., Illus.). pap. 18.00 ***(978-1-934105-16-0(3))*** Sternberg Pr.
Vajay, Sigismond de. Of Bridges & Borders. 2010. (SPA & ENG., Illus.). 408p. 60.00 *(978-3-03764-081-4(2))* JRP Ringier Kunstverlag AG CHE. Dist: D.A.P./Distributed Art Pubs.
Vardi, David, ed. Supermix: The Union of Diverse Contemporary Art in Miami. 2008. (ENG & SPA., Illus.). 303p. lib. bdg. 20.00 *(978-0-9778621-3-9(5))* Edge Zones, Inc.
Vargas, George. Contemporary Chican@ Art: Color & Culture for a New America. 2010. (ENG., Illus.). 303p. pap. 27.95 *(978-0-292-72117-3(X))* Univ. of Texas Pr.
Vickery, Jonathan & Costello, Diarmuid, eds. Art: Key Contemporary Thinkers. 2007. (ENG.). 256p. pap. 26.95 *(978-1-84520-320-7(8))* Berg Pubs. GBR. Dist: Macmillan.
—Art: Key Contemporary Thinkers. 2007. (ENG.). 1p. 99.95 *(978-1-84520-319-1(4))* Berg Pubs. GBR. Dist: Macmillan.
Vine, Richard. New China, New Art: (Revised & Expanded Edition) 2nd rev. ed. 2011. (ENG., Illus.). 256p. pap. 39.95 ***(978-3-7913-4550-5(8))*** Prestel Publishing.
Vine, Richard. New China New Art: Zhongguo Dang Dai Yi Shu. 2008. (Illus.). 256p. 60.00 *(978-3-7913-3942-9(7))* Prestel Publishing.
von Hantelmann, Dorothea. How to Do Things with Art. Marta, Karen, ed. 2010. (ENG., Illus.). 208p. pap. 29.95 *(978-3-03764-104-0(5))* JRP Ringier Kunstverlag AG CHE. Dist: D.A.P./Distributed Art Pubs.
Von Szombathy, Chris. Fire Away. 2008. (ENG., Illus.). 96p. pap. *(978-1-897299-49-4(4))* Drawn & Quarterly Pubns.
Von Wedel, Amelie, et al, eds. Korean Eye: Contemporary Korean Art. 2010. (ENG., Illus.). 390p. pap. 60.00 *(978-88-572-0467-3(7))* Skira Editore ITA. Dist: Random Hse., Inc.
Waanders Editors, creator. Urban Larsson: Paintings 1991-2006. 2008. (ENG., Illus.). 96p. 45.00 *(978-90-400-8381-5(9))* Waanders B.V., Uitgeverij NLD. Dist: National Bk. Network.
Wang, Tianhua. Qiang Xiu Jing Pin Tu Yang Ji = Qiang Embroidery. 2009. (Illus.). 207p. *(978-7-5410-3848-8(2))* Sichuan Fine Arts Publishing Hse.
Warren, Lynne, ed. Alexander Calder & Contemporary Art: Form - Balance - Joy. 2010. (ENG., Illus.). 176p. 45.00 *(978-0-500-51523-5(9)*, 551523) Thames & Hudson.
Weather, Head. Outside In: New Realms for Taiwan Art. 2008. per. *(978-0-9669997-1-6(1))* 66 Communication, Inc.
Weidemann, Christiane & Finger, Brad. 50 Contemporary Artists You Should Know. 2011. (Illus.). 160p. pap. 19.95 *(978-3-7913-4530-7(3))* Prestel Publishing.
Weinhart, Martina, ed. The Making of Art. 2009. (ENG & GER., Illus.). 240p. pap. 38.00 *(978-3-86560-586-3(9))* Verlag der Buchhandlung Walther Konig DEU. Dist: D.A.P./Distributed Art Pubs.
Whitehead-Lopez, Rudy. The Intimate Real - Enpowering the Quiet Art. 2008. 76p. pap. *(978-3-639-07876-3(4))* VDM Verlag Dr. Mueller e.K.
Wiedemann, Pascale, et al. Morbus infinitus & Subkutan, 2 vols. 2008. (GER & ENG., Illus.). 184p. 60.00 *(978-3-85881-206-3(4))* Scheidegger und Spiess AG, Verlag CHE. Dist: Antique Collectors' Club.
Williams, Gareth. Telling Tales: Fantasy & Fear in Contemporary Design. 2009. (ENG., Illus.). 128p. 39.95 *(978-1-85177-560-6(9))* V & A Pubns. GBR. Dist: Hachette Bk. Group.
Williams, Gilda, ed. The Gothic. 2007. (Documents of Contemporary Art Ser.). (ENG.). 239p. (gr. 17). per. 24.95 *(978-0-262-73186-7(X))* MIT Pr.
Willis, Gary. Art As Mime. 2010. 232p. pap. *(978-3-8383-1920-9(6))* Lambert Academic Publishing.
Wilson, Michael. Contemporary Art in North America: Artworld. Black Dog Publishing Staff, ed. 2011. (Artworld Ser.). (ENG., Illus.). 240p. 49.95 *(978-1-907317-23-1(6))* Black Dog Publishing Ltd. GBR. Dist: Perseus Distribution.
Wilson, Stephen. Art + Science Now: How Scientific Research & Technological Innovation Are Becoming Key to 21st-Century Aesthetics. 2010. (ENG., Illus.). 208p. 50.00 *(978-0-500-23868-4(5)*, 523868) Thames & Hudson.
Winkfield, Trevor, ed. The Sienese Shredder Issue 3, 1 vol. 2009. (ENG.). 274p. pap. 30.00 *(978-0-9787108-2-8(7))* Sienese Shredder Editions.
Wolf, Rachel Rubin. Strokes of Genius: The Best of Drawing. 2007. (Strokes of Genius Ser.). (ENG., Illus.). 144p. 32.99 *(978-1-58180-861-2(5)*, North Light Bks.) F&W Media, Inc.
—Strokes of Genius 2: Light & Shadow. 2009. (Strokes of Genius Ser.). (ENG., Illus.). 144p. 32.99 *(978-1-60061-158-2(3)*, North Light Bks.) F&W Media, Inc.
Wong, Yoke-Sum. The Aesthetics of Cute in Contemporary Japanese Art. 2012. (Critical Studies in Gender, Sexuality, & Culture Ser.). (ENG., Illus.). 256p. 85.00 ***(978-0-230-10539-3(4))*** Palgrave Macmillan.
Wrenn, Tony & Turberg, Edward, intros. Porchscapes, the Colors of Beaufort, NC: Three Centuries of History Woven Through Art & Words. 2009. (Illus.). 176p. *(978-0-9659506-5-7(4))* Eastern Offset Publishing Co.
Yersin, Veronique, ed. Forde 1994-2009. 2010. (ENG., Illus.). 522p. pap. 45.00 *(978-3-03764-082-1(0))* JRP Ringier Kunstverlag AG CHE. Dist: D.A.P./Distributed Art Pubs.
Zijlmans, Kitty, et al, texts. Take Place. 2010. (ENG., Illus.). 288p. pap. 28.95 *(978-90-78088-35-6(4))* Valiz NLD. Dist: D.A.P./Distributed Art Pubs.
Zolghadr, Tirdad, et al, eds. Internal Necessity: A Reader Tracing the Inner Logics of the Contemporary Art Field. 2011. (ENG., Illus.). 208p. pap. 24.95 ***(978-1-934105-05-4(8))*** Sternberg Pr.
Zuo, Jing. Work in Progress. 2011. (ENG., Illus.). 278p. pap. 30.00 *(978-988-18816-5-6(X))* Timezone 8 Ltd. HKG. Dist: D.A.P./Distributed Art Pubs.

ART, MODERN—21ST CENTURY—EXHIBITIONS

Aarons, Philip, et al, texts. The X Initiative Yearbook. 2011. (ENG., Illus.). 168p. pap. 25.00 *(978-88-96501-29-0(6))* Mousse Magazine and Pubng. ITA. Dist: D.A.P./Distributed Art Pubs.
Ackerman, Rita, et al. Between Zones: On the Representation of the Performative & the Notation of Movement. 2011. (GER & ENG., Illus.). 352p. 45.00 *(978-3-03764-125-5(8))* JRP Ringier Kunstverlag AG CHE. Dist: D.A.P./Distributed Art Pubs.
Adamowsky, Natascha, et al, texts. Unter Wasser / Über Wasser: Vom Aquarium - zum Videobild. 2010. (ENG., Illus.). 115p. 40.00 *(978-3-86678-274-7(8))* Kerber Verlag DEU. Dist: D.A.P./Distributed Art Pubs.
Adams, Henry. The Beauty of Damage: The World of Christopher Pekoc. 2008. (Illus.). pap. 19.95 *(978-0-9758843-9-3(5))* Green Panda Pr.
Adams, Marina. Marina Adams. 2008. pap. 0.00 *(978-0-9797964-9-4(0))* CUE Art Foundation.
Adamson, Glenn, et al, contrib. by. Hot House: Expanding the Field of Fiber at Cranbrook, 1970-2007. 2007. 96p. pap. *(978-0-9668577-6-4(3))* Cranbrook Art Museum.
Adolphs, Volker. Ferne Nähe: »Natur« in der Kunst der Gegenwart. 2010. (ENG.). 200p. 55.00 *(978-3-86832-004-6(0)*, Art Stock Bks. Ltd/Csi) Continental Sales, Inc.
Agee, William C., et al. American Vanguards: Graham, Davis, Gorky, de Kooning, & Their Circle, 1927-1942. 2011. (ENG., Illus.). 256p. 65.00 *(978-0-300-12167-4(9))* Yale Univ. Pr.
Alexander, Darsie, et al, texts. The Spectacular of Vernacular. 2011. (ENG., Illus.). 128p. pap. 19.99 *(978-0-935640-99-1(1))* Walker Art Ctr.
Allen, Mark, et al, eds. The Machine Project: A Field Guide to the Los Angeles County Museum of Art. 2010. (ENG., Illus.). 172p. pap. 25.00 *(978-0-9753140-4-3(1))* Machine Project Pr.
Allen, Stuart & Lane, Allison Hays. Stuart Allen: 2926'14" N 9828'55" W: Mapping Daylight. 2007. *(978-1-883502-16-4(0))* San Antonio Museum of Art.
Alonzo, Pedro. Viva La Revolución. 2011. *(978-1-58423-424-1(5))* Gingko Pr., Inc.
The American Society of Botanical Artists & the Horticultural Society of New York Present: The Ninth Annual International Juried Botanical Art Exhibition 2006. 2006. per. 20.00 *(978-0-9744153-4-5(0))* American Society of Botanical Artists.
Antonas, Aristide, et al, texts. FACE, Investigations of a Dog. 2011. (ENG., Illus.). 160p. pap. 15.00 ***(978-3-03764-171-2(1))*** JRP Ringier Kunstverlag AG CHE. Dist: D.A.P./Distributed Art Pubs.
Aronson, Lisa & Weber, John S. Environment & Object: Recent African Art. 2011. ***(978-3-7913-5209-1(1))*** Tang, Frances Young Teaching Museum & Art Gallery at Skidmore College, The.
Arot, Dominique. La Grèce des Modernes: L'impression D'un Voyage, les Artistes, les écrivains et la Grèce 1933-1968: [exposition Réalisée Dans le Cadre de la Manifestation Feuille à Feuille, Estampe et Images Imprimées Dans les Collections des Musées du Nord-Pas-De-Calais, Organisée Par L'Association des Conservateurs des Musées du Nord-Pas-De-Calais D'octobre 2006 à Juin 2007, et Présentée du 20 Janvier Au 22 Avril, 2007. 2008. (FRE & ENG., Illus.). 192p. pap. 45.00 *(978-2-35340-013-3(2))* Gourcuff Gradenigo FRA. Dist: National Bk. Network.
Art Basel Miami Beach 2011. 2011. (ENG., Illus.). 650p. pap. 65.00 ***(978-3-7757-3139-3(3))*** Hatje Cantz Verlag GmbH & Co KG DEU. Dist: D.A.P./Distributed Art Pubs.
The Art of Milford Zornes: From Private Collections. 2010. (Illus.). 96p. pap. 23.95 *(978-0-9842797-0-8(9))* Sasse, Gene.
Art Works. 2011. (ENG., Illus.). 256p. pap. 55.00 ***(978-3-7757-2777-8(9))*** Hatje Cantz Verlag GmbH & Co KG DEU. Dist: D.A.P./Distributed Art Pubs.
Asoma, Yayoi. Yayoi Asoma. 2008. pap. 0.00 *(978-0-9797964-8-7(2))* CUE Art Foundation.
Atkinson, Nora. The Book Borrowers. 2009. (Illus.). 49p. *(978-0-942342-19-2(4))* Bellevue Arts Museum.
Baade, Carrie Ann & Hightower, Nancy E. Cute & Creepy, 1 vol. 2011. (ENG., Illus.). 68p. pap. 19.95 ***(978-1-889282-24-4(3))*** Florida State Univ., Museum of Fine Arts.
Back to the Garden: Daily Life of Spiritual Vision. 2008. per. 20.00 *(978-0-9669997-2-3(X))* 66 Communication, Inc.
Badiola, Txomin. Ana Laura Alaez Using Your Guns. 2008. (ENG., Illus.). 160p. pap. 55.00 *(978-88-8158-675-2(4))* Charta ITA. Dist: D.A.P./Distributed Art Pubs.
Bahrani, Zainab & Shabout, Nada M. Modernism & Iraq. 2009. (Illus.). 99p. *(978-1-884919-22-0(7))* Columbia Univ., The Miriam & Ira D. Wallach Art Gallery.
Bailer, Juli Cho. Fresh! Contemporary Takes on Nature & Allegory. 2007. (Context 1 Ser.). (ENG., Illus.). 64p. pap. 24.95 *(978-0-9726649-2-9(0))* Museum of Glass.
—Mining Glass. 2007. *(978-0-9726649-3-6(9))* Museum of Glass.
Bailey, Radcliffe. Radcliffe Bailey: Memory As Medicine. 2011. (ENG., Illus.). 160p. 45.00 ***(978-3-7913-5154-4(0))*** Prestel Publishing.
Baker, Joe & McMaster, Gerald. Remix: New Modernities in a Post-Indian World. 2007. *(978-1-933565-10-1(1))* Smithsonian National Museum of the American Indian.
Bakker, Conrad. Conrad Bakker: Objects & Economies: Untitled Projects 1997-2007. 2009. (ENG., Illus.). 80p. pap. 8.95 *(978-1-879003-51-4(1))* Des Moines Art Ctr.
Baldessari, John. John Baldessari: A Print Retrospective from the Collections of Jordan D. Schnitzer & his Family Foundation. 2010. (ENG., Illus.). 160p. 59.95 *(978-1-935202-10-3(3))* D.A.P./Distributed Art Pubs.
Bancroft, Sarah C. 2010 California Biennial: Orange County Museum of Art. 2011. (Illus.). 208p. pap. 39.95 *(978-3-7913-5119-3(2))* Prestel Publishing.
Bankowsky, Jack & Gingeras, Alison M., eds. Where Are We Going? Selections from the Francois Pinault Collection. 2006. (ENG., Illus.). 272p. 65.00 *(978-88-7624-756-9(4))* Skira Editore ITA. Dist: Random Hse., Inc.
Bannier, Sigrid, et al, eds. The Climate Is Changing: International Touring Exhibition Featuring the Work of Artist Felt Makers from across the World. 2010. (ENG, GER & ITA., Illus.). 132p. (C). pap. 40.00 *(978-88-596-0786-1(8))* Polistampa ITA. Dist: Brown, David Bk. Co., The.
Barilleaux, Rene Paul. Tom Slick: International Art Collector: An Exhibition. 2009. *(978-0-916677-53-4(2))* McNay, Marion Koogler Art Museum.
Barney, Matthew, illus. Matthew Barney: Drawing Restraint Volume V: 1987-2007, 1 vol. 2008. (ENG.). 233p. pap. 65.00 *(978-3-86560-318-0(1))* Verlag der Buchhandlung Walther Konig DEU. Dist: D.A.P./Distributed Art Pubs.
Barragan, Paco, text. The Art Fair Age. 2008. (ENG., Illus.). 240p. pap. 44.95 *(978-88-8158-682-0(7))* Charta ITA. Dist: D.A.P./Distributed Art Pubs.
Bartelik, Marek, ed. Poza: On the Polishness of Polish Contemporary Art, 1 vol. 2008. (ENG., Illus.). 168p. pap. 35.00 *(978-0-9717859-3-9(7))* Real Art Ways.
Bartlett, Bo. Bo Bartlett: Paintings 1981-2010. 2011. (ENG., Illus.). 64p. pap. *(978-0-578-06122-1(8))* Inspiration Point Pr.
Basting, Anne Davis. Hiding Places: Memory in the Arts. 2011. ***(978-0-9710703-3-2(4))*** Kohler, John Michael Arts Ctr.
Basualdo, Carlos, et al. William Kentridge: Tapestries. 2008. (ENG., Illus.). 120p. 35.00 *(978-0-300-12686-0(7))* Yale Univ. Pr.
Bauer, Michael, et al. Rive gauche / Rive Droite. 2011. (ENG., Illus.). 160p. pap. 15.00 *(978-3-03764-154-5(1))* JRP Ringier Kunstverlag AG CHE. Dist: D.A.P./Distributed Art Pubs.
Baum, Kelly. Transactions: An Exhibition. 2007. (Illus.). 47p. *(978-0-9771453-4-8(4))* Univ. of Texas at Austin, The.
Baumann, Daniel & Bellini, Andrea, eds. John Mccracken. 2011. (ENG., Illus.). 262p. 65.00 *(978-88-572-0776-6(5))* Skira Editore ITA. Dist: Random Hse., Inc.
Baume, Nicholas, ed. Super Vision. 2006. (ENG., Illus.). 176p. (gr. 17). 34.95 *(978-0-262-02609-3(0))* MIT Pr.
Baume, Nicholas, intro. Double Take. 2010. (ENG., Illus.). 48p. pap. 9.95 *(978-0-9608488-6-7(X))* Public Art Fund.
Bazzini, Marco. The Young Artists Biennale of Monza 2011: 30 Artists, 5 Critics. 2012. (ENG., Illus.). 136p. pap. 28.00 ***(978-88-422-2017-6(5))*** Allemandi, Umberto & Co. GBR. Dist: National Bk. Network.
Bebout, Nicole & Hofstetter, Sonja. See You on the Flip Side! 2011. 88p. pap. 14.00 ***(978-0-9841309-3-1(4))*** AC Institute.
Belasco, Daniel. Reinventing Ritual: Contemporary Art & Design for Jewish Life. 2009. (Illus.). 176p. 39.95 *(978-0-300-14682-0(5))* Yale Univ. Pr.
Bell, Nicholas R., et al. History in the Making: Renwick Craft Invitational 2011. 2011. (ENG., Illus.). 104p. pap. 24.95 *(978-1-85759-703-5(6))* Scala, Editions FRA. Dist: National Bk. Network.
Berg, Stephan & Solakov, Nedko. Emotions. 2008. (GER & ENG., Illus.). 224p. 60.00 *(978-3-7757-2211-7(4))* Hatje Cantz Verlag GmbH & Co KG DEU. Dist: D.A.P./Distributed Art Pubs.
Berruti, Valerio. Valerio Berruti: Isaac's Daughter. 2010. (ENG., Illus.). 136p. 35.00 *(978-88-6208-122-1(7))* Damiani ITA. Dist: D.A.P./Distributed Art Pubs.
Berry, Ian, et al. Joseph Grigely: St. Cecilia. 2007. (Opener Ser.: Vol. 13). (Illus.). 127p. *(978-0-9765723-4-3(6))* Tang, Frances Young Teaching Museum & Art Gallery at Skidmore College, The.
Bertoldini, Marisa, ed. Esprit Spherique, 1 vol. 2007. (ENG & ITA., Illus.). 400p. 65.00 *(978-88-8158-619-6(3))* Charta ITA. Dist: D.A.P./Distributed Art Pubs.
Betro, M., ed. Ippolito Rosellini & the dawn of Egyptology. 2011. (ENG., Illus.). 229p. (C). 120.00 ***(978-1-906137-26-7(9))*** Golden Hse. Pubns. GBR. Dist: Brown, David Bk. Co., The.
Biesenbach, Klaus, et al, texts. Greater New York 2010, 1 vol. 2010. (ENG.). 250p. pap. 19.00 *(978-0-9841776-2-2(0))* P.S.1 Contemporary Art Ctr.
Bijl, Marc. Marc Bijl: in Case You Didn't Feel Like Showing Up. 2009. (ENG & SPA., Illus.). 160p. pap. 40.00 *(978-90-5662-682-2(5))* NAi Uitgevers / Publishers Stichting NLD. Dist: D.A.P./Distributed Art Pubs.
Birnbaum, Daniel. 50 Moons of Saturn: T2 - Second Torino Triennale 2008. Birnbaum, Daniel, ed. 2009. (ENG., Illus.). 480p. 55.00 *(978-88-6130-267-9(X))* Skira Editore ITA. Dist: Random Hse., Inc.
Birnhaum, Daniel. Making Worlds: 53rd International Art Exhibition - La Biennale Di Venezia. Birnbaum, Daniel, et al. 2009. (ENG., Illus.). 660p. pap. 90.00 *(978-88-317-9696-5(8))* Marsilio Editori spa ITA. Dist: Random Hse., Inc.
Bismuth, Pierre & Fischer, Alfred M. Yesterday will be better: Mit der Erinnerung in die Zukunft. 2011. (GER & ENG., Illus.). 228p. pap. 55.00 ***(978-3-86678-409-3(0))*** Kerber Verlag DEU. Dist: D.A.P./Distributed Art Pubs.
Blackwell, Kelsey, des. Living, Looking, Making: Giacometti, Fontana, Twombly, Serra. 2007. (Illus.). 116p. 80.00 *(978-1-932598-49-0(9))* Gagosian Gallery.

Bland, Bartholomew F. I WANT Candy: The Sweet Stuff in American Art. 2007. (Illus.). 50p. per. 9.99 *(978-0-943651-34-7(4))* Hudson River Museum.

Blaut, Julia, et al. Glorious Sky: Herbert Katzman's New York. 2010. (ENG., Illus.). 144p. 45.00 *(978-1-904832-83-6(0))* Giles, D. Ltd. GBR. Dist: Antique Collectors' Club.

Blauvelt, Andrew. Worlds Away: New Suburban Landscapes. 2008. (ENG., Illus.). 336p. pap. 34.95 *(978-0-935640-90-8(8))* Walker Art Ctr.

Blessing, Jennifer & Trotman, Nat, eds. Haunted: Contemporary Photography. 2010. (ENG., Illus.). 208p. 50.00 *(978-0-89207-399-6(5))* Guggenheim, Solomon R. Museum.

Blomberg, Katja, ed. Melhus, Bjorn. Live Action Hero. 2011. (ENG., Illus.). 103p. pap. 29.95 ***(978-3-86560-965-6(1))*** Verlag der Buchhandlung Walther Konig DEU. Dist: D.A.P./Distributed Art Pubs.

Bluhm, Andreas & Krischel, Roland, eds. Hotel California: Katalog zur Ausstellung, Wallraf-Richartz-Museum & Foundation Corboud, 7.09.2007-18.11.2007. 2007. (GER., Illus.). 95p. (C). 35.00 *(978-3-7774-3855-9(3))* Hirmer Verlag GmbH DEU. Dist: Brown, David Bk. Co., The.

Boettger, Suzaan & Solakov, Nedko. 99 Fears. 2008. (ENG., Illus.). 112p. 29.95 *(978-0-7148-4888-4(3))* Phaidon Pr., Inc.

Bolton King, Michelle, ed. Phantasmania. 2008. (ENG., Illus.). 96p. 29.95 *(978-1-891246-15-9(1))* Kemper Museum of Contemporary Art & Design.

Bonami, Francesco. Spirit & Space: Sandretto Re Rebaudengo Collection. 2011. (ENG., Illus.). 200p. pap. 43.00 ***(978-84-92441-36-5(4))*** T.F. Editores ESP. Dist: National Bk. Network.

Bonami, Francesco. 2010: Whitney Biennial. Carrion-Muryari, Gary, ed. 2010. (Illus.). 264p. pap. 45.00 *(978-0-300-16242-4(1))* Yale Univ. Pr.

Bonami, Francesco, ed. & contrib. by. Jeff Koons. 2008. (ENG., Illus.). 136p. 45.00 *(978-0-300-14194-8(7))* Yale Univ. Pr.

Bonami, Francesco, text. Helmut Middendorf: over the under the Over. 2010. (ENG., Illus.). 160p. 45.00 *(978-3-86678-225-9(X))* Kerber Verlag DEU. Dist: D.A.P./Distributed Art Pubs.

Bonami, Francesco & Canarutto, Sarah C. Gabriel Orozco. 2008. (Illus.). 108p. pap. 37.50 *(978-88-370-6072-5(6))* Electa ITA. Dist: Trans-Atlantic Pubns., Inc.

Bonami, Francesco & Gingeras, Alison, eds. La Collezione Di Punta Della Dogana: The Catalogue of the Contemporary Art Center in Venice. 2009. (ITA & FRE., Illus.). 300p. 115.00 *(978-88-370-6994-0(4))* Electa ITA. Dist: Trans-Atlantic Pubns., Inc.

Bonansinga, Kate. Full & Spare: Ceramics in the 21st Century. 2008. (Illus.). 64p. *(978-1-889282-20-6(0))* Florida State Univ., Museum of Fine Arts.

Bonetti, David & Draishpoon, Douglas. The Panza Collection: An Experience of Color & Light. 2007. (Illus.). 119p. *(978-1-887457-08-8(9))* Buffalo Fine Arts/Albright-Knox Art Gallery.

Bonito Oliva, Achille. Art in Process. 2011. (ENG., Illus.). 144p. pap. 45.00 *(978-88-7570-247-2(0))* Corraini ITA. Dist: D.A.P./Distributed Art Pubs.

Borchardt-Hume, Achim, text. Keeping It Real: From the Ready-Made to the Everyday. 2011. (ENG., Illus.). 132p. pap. 35.00 *(978-0-85488-181-9(6))* Whitechapel Art Gallery GBR. Dist: D.A.P./Distributed Art Pubs.

Boris, Staci. The New Authentics: Artists of the Post-Jewish Generation. 2008. (ENG., Illus.). 144p. per. 29.95 *(978-0-935982-65-7(5))* Spertus College of Judaica Pr., The.

Bourgeois, Caroline. Elogio Del Dubbio: Eloge du Doute = in Praise of Doubt. 2012. (ITA & ENG., Illus.). 204p. 65.00 ***(978-88-370-8508-7(7))*** Electa ITA. Dist: National Bk. Network.

Bourguignon, Jean-Pierre & Casse, Michael. Mathematics, A Beautiful Elsewhere. 2012. (ENG., Illus.). 224p. 55.00 ***(978-0-500-97030-0(0)***, 597030) Thames & Hudson.

Bovier, Lionel & Caratsch, Andrea, eds. Milan Kunc: Sculpture. 2010. (ENG., Illus.). 96p. 35.00 *(978-3-03764-062-3(6))* JRP Ringier Kunstverlag AG CHE. Dist: D.A.P./Distributed Art Pubs.

Bowles, Hamish. Balenciaga & Spain. 2011. pap. *(978-0-88401-132-3(1))* Fine Arts Museums of San Francisco.

Bracewell, Michael & Pies, Daniel. Be Nice Share Everything Have Fun. Kalmar, Stefan, ed. 2010. (GER & ENG., Illus.). 314p. pap. 65.00 *(978-3-86560-771-3(3))* Verlag der Buchhandlung Walther Konig DEU. Dist: D.A.P./Distributed Art Pubs.

Bradford, Mark. Mark Bradford: Merchant Posters. 2010. (ENG., Illus.). 160p. 50.00 *(978-0-9800242-2-7(6))* Miller, Gregory & Co.

Breitz, Candice. Candice Breitz: Same Same. 2010. (ENG., Illus.). 130p. pap. 47.00 *(978-1-894212-29-8(0))* Power Plant, The CAN. Dist: D.A.P./Distributed Art Pubs.

Brett, Guy, ed. & text. Cildo Meireles. 2009. (ENG., Illus.). 192p. 45.00 *(978-1-933045-91-7(4))* D.A.P./Distributed Art Pubs.

Bronfen, Elisabeth, text. Julia Stoschek Collection, Number Two. 2009. (ENG., Illus.). 432p. 105.00 *(978-3-7757-2379-4(X))* Hatje Cantz Verlag GmbH & Co KG DEU. Dist: D.A.P./Distributed Art Pubs.

Broodthaers, Marcel. Marcel Broodthaers heute. Von realer Gegenwart. 2011. (ENG., Illus.). 228p. pap. 45.00 *(978-3-86560-891-8(4))* Verlag der Buchhandlung Walther Konig DEU. Dist: D.A.P./Distributed Art Pubs.

Brüggebors, Nadine, text. Andy Denzler Paintings: The Human Nature Project. 2011. (ENG., Illus.). 128p. 55.00 *(978-3-7757-2803-4(1))* Hatje Cantz Verlag GmbH & Co KG DEU. Dist: D.A.P./Distributed Art Pubs.

Bryan-Wilson, Julia, et al, texts. Lisi Raskin: Mobile Observation, 1 vol. 2010. (ENG.). 208p. pap. 35.00 *(978-0-615-30525-7(3))* Raskin, Lisi Studio.

Bucarelli, Angelo. Il Drago e la Farfalla: Arte Contemporanea in Vietnam Ròng Và Bm. 2010. (ITA & ENG., Illus.). 144p. pap. 23.95 *(978-88-492-1015-6(9))* Gangemi ITA. Dist: International Publishers Marketing.

Buchan, Suzanne, et al. Animated Painting. 2007. (Illus.). 139p. pap. *(978-0-937108-40-6(5))* San Diego Museum of Art.

Burke, Gregory, et al, texts. Scott Lyall: the Color Ball. 2010. (ENG., Illus.). 96p. 42.50 *(978-1-894212-27-4(4))* Power Plant, The CAN. Dist: D.A.P./Distributed Art Pubs.

Burris, Jennifer, et al. Fore - Closed Between Crisis & PoS - Sibility. 2012. (ENG., Illus.). 152p. pap. 16.95 ***(978-0-300-17867-8(0))*** Yale Univ. Pr.

Butler, Brian, ed. Speculation, 1 vol. 2007. (ENG., Illus.). 224p. pap. 25.00 *(978-3-905770-75-9(X))* JRP Ringier Kunstverlag AG CHE. Dist: D.A.P./Distributed Art Pubs.

Cairns, Steven, ed. Frieze Art Fair New York 2012. 2012. (ENG., Illus.). 532p. pap. 39.95 ***(978-0-9553201-8-7(6))*** Frieze GBR. Dist: D.A.P./Distributed Art Pubs.

Cameron, Dan, ed. Prospect. 1 New Orleans. 2008. (ENG., Illus.). 408p. 50.00 *(978-0-9815622-9-2(9))* PictureBox, Inc.

Canty, Scott & Gabrielle. Wearable Expressions 2008: 6th Biennial International Exhibition Featuring the Ultimate in Wearable Art. 2008. (Illus.). 48p. pap. 10.00 *(978-0-9717365-6-6(1))* Palos Verdes Art Ctr.

Carlano, Annie. Contemporary British Studio Ceramics. 2010. (ENG., Illus.). 224p. 60.00 *(978-0-300-16719-1(9))* Yale Univ. Pr.

Carlson, Ann & Strom, Mary Ellen. Carlson/Strom: New Performance Video. 2009. (Illus.). 48p. *(978-0-945506-60-7(0))* DeCordova Museum & Sculpture Park.

Carson, Juli, ed. & text. Exile of the Imaginary: Politics Aesthetics Love, 1 vol. 2007. (ENG., Illus.). 184p. pap. 29.00 *(978-3-86560-211-4(8))* Verlag der Buchhandlung Walther Konig DEU. Dist: D.A.P./Distributed Art Pubs.

Casper, Jens & Shryen, Annette, texts. Boros Collection. 2010. (ENG., Illus.). 198p. 75.00 *(978-3-7757-2478-4(8))* Hatje Cantz Verlag GmbH & Co KG DEU. Dist: D.A.P./Distributed Art Pubs.

Casula Powerhouse, compiled by. Federico Mendoza: Folding Histories. 2007. (Illus.). *(978-1-876418-78-6(8))* Casula Powerhouse.

—Mil-Pra 15th Annual Exhibition. 2007. (Illus.). *(978-1-876418-82-3(6))* Casula Powerhouse.

Cats, Ruth, ed. As Is: Arte Israeliana Contemporanea. 2010. (ITA & ENG., Illus.). 240p. 52.00 *(978-88-492-1583-0(5))* Gangemi ITA. Dist: International Publishers Marketing.

Cattelan, Maurizio, et al, eds. Charley 05, 1 vol. 2007. (ENG., Illus.). 368p. pap. 29.95 *(978-1-933045-67-2(1))* Deste Foundation GRC. Dist: D.A.P./Distributed Art Pubs.

Central Washington University Staff, contrib. by. Crossroads & Connections: Central Washington University Art Alumni Exhibition. 2008. (Illus.). 128p. pap. 29.95 *(978-0-87422-300-2(8))* Washington State Univ. Pr.

Cerizza, Luca, ed. Maps & Legends. 2009. (ENG., Illus.). 280p. 27.00 *(978-3-905829-13-6(4))* JRP Ringier Kunstverlag AG CHE. Dist: D.A.P./Distributed Art Pubs.

Chang, Alexandra, text. Envisioning Diaspora, Asian American Visual Arts Collectives. 2009. (ENG., Illus.). 266p. pap. 35.00 *(978-988-17522-3-9(X))* Timezone 8 Ltd. HKG. Dist: D.A.P./Distributed Art Pubs.

Chanse, Samantha. Activist Imagination: Is an Exhibition & Series of Discussions Investigating, Exploring, & Imagining the Past, Present, & Future of Activism: Artists, Bob Hsiang, Donna Keiko Ozawa, Christine Wong Yap. 2008. (Illus.). 72p. *(978-0-9797707-2-2(6))* Kearny Street Workshop.

Chassey, Eric de & Stroun, Fabrice. Europunk. 2011. (ENG., Illus.). 320p. pap. 55.00 ***(978-88-88493-72-5(7))*** Drago Arts & Communication ITA. Dist: SCB Distributors.

Chhangur, Emelie, et al. FastwÜrms: Donky Ninja Witch: A Living Retrospective. 2011. (ENG., Illus.). 112p. *(978-0-921972-60-0(1))* Art Gallery of York Univ.

Chicuri, Abelardo Mena, et al. Cuba Avant-Garde: Contemporary Cuban Art from the Farber Collection / Arte Contemporaneo Cubano de la Coleccion Farber. Delson, Susan, ed. Lizarraga, Felix, tr. 2007. (SPA & ENG., Illus.). 188p. pap. 29.95 *(978-0-9762552-5-3(1))* Univ. Pr. of Florida.

—Cuba Avant-Garde: Contemporary Cuban Art from the Farber Collection /Arte Contemporaneo Cubano de la Coleccion Farber. Delson, Susan, ed. Lizarraga, Felix, tr. 2007. (SPA & ENG., Illus.). 188p. 59.95 *(978-0-9762552-4-6(3))* Univ. Pr. of Florida.

Chihuly, Dale & Belcovson, Joe. Chihuly at the Salk. 2010. (Illus.). ***(978-1-57684-186-0(3))*** Portland Pr., Inc.

Chikukwa, Raphael. Seeing Ourselves. 2012. (ENG., Illus.). 76p. pap. 24.95 ***(978-88-8158-823-7(4))*** Charta ITA. Dist: D.A.P./Distributed Art Pubs.

Chiodi, Stefano, ed. Space: From Maxxi's Collections of Art & Architecture. 2010. 320p. pap. 72.50 *(978-88-370-7587-3(1))* Electa ITA. Dist: Trans-Atlantic Pubns., Inc.

Chong, Doryun & Raymond, Yasmil, texts. Brave New Worlds, 1 vol. 2007. (ENG., Illus.). 272p. pap. 39.95 *(978-0-935640-89-2(4))* Walker Art Ctr.

Christov-Bakargiev, Carolyn. Carolyn Christov-Bakargiev: Brief an einen Freund. 2011. (ENG., Illus.). 48p. pap. 10.00 ***(978-3-7757-2852-2(X))*** Hatje Cantz Verlag GmbH & Co KG DEU. Dist: D.A.P./Distributed Art Pubs.

Cibic, Aldo, ed. Verso Expo Milano 2015: [in English & Italian]. 2011. 144p. pap. 32.50 ***(978-88-370-8548-3(6))*** Electa ITA. Dist: Trans-Atlantic Pubns., Inc.

Cichocki, Sebastian, et al, texts. Antje Majewski: My Very Gestures. 2009. (ENG & GER., Illus.). 112p. pap. 29.95 *(978-1-933128-56-6(9))* Sternberg Pr.

Ciric, Biljana. Rejected Collection: Rejected Proposals by Chinese Contemporary Artists. 2009. (ENG., Illus.). 240p. pap. 47.95 *(978-88-8158-709-4(2))* Charta ITA. Dist: D.A.P./Distributed Art Pubs.

Cisneros Fontanals Art Foundation Staff, contrib. by. Positions in Context: 2007 CIFO Grants Program Exhibition. 2007. (SPA & ENG., Illus.). 48p. *(978-0-9774079-7-2(7))* Cisneros Fontanals Art Foundation.

Clark-Langager, Sarah & Dietrich, William, eds. Critical Messages: Contemporary Northwest Artists on the Environment. 2010. (ENG., Illus.). 80p. pap. 24.95 *(978-1-878237-07-1(1))* Western Washington Univ., Western Gallery.

Clark, Vicky A. Popular Salon of the People: Associated Artists of Pittsburgh, 1910-2006. 2007. (Illus.). 164p. *(978-0-88039-050-7(6))* Carnegie Museum of Art, The.

Coffin, Peter, text. Peter Coffin: Plant Book. 2009. (Illus.). 296p. 60.00 *(978-0-615-16652-0(0))* Coffin, Peter.

Collier, Brian, et al. Say It Isn't So. Friese, Peter, ed. 2008. (GER & ENG., Illus.). 260p. 40.00 *(978-3-939583-30-1(8))* Kehrer Verlag Heidelberg, Klaus Kehrer DEU. Dist: Consortium Bk. Sales & Distribution.

Comyn, Christine. Marie-Antoinette: La Douceur de l'Ignorance. 2010. (ENG., Illus.). 96p. *(978-90-209-9084-3(5)*, Lannoo Pubs. (Acc)) Antique Collectors' Club.

Condo, George. Mental States. 2011. (ENG., Illus.). 168p. 50.00 *(978-1-85332-289-1(X))* Hayward Gallery Publishing GBR. Dist: D.A.P./Distributed Art Pubs.

Conforti, Michael, et al. The Clark Brothers Collect: Impressionist & Early Modern Paintings. 2006. (ENG., Illus.). 384p. 65.00 *(978-0-300-11619-9(5))* Yale Univ. Pr.

Coppola, Giuseppe & Coppola, Guiseppe. Le Luci e la Pietra: Lights & Stone: The Urban Object: Art, Architecture & Design [in English & Italian]. 2010. 300p. pap. 82.50 ***(978-88-370-7633-7(9))*** Electa ITA. Dist: Trans-Atlantic Pubns., Inc.

Cork, Richard & Martin, Elliott Zooey. End Game: British Contemporary Art from the Chaney Family Collection. 2008. (ENG., Illus.). 80p. pap. 14.95 *(978-0-300-14201-3(3))* Museum of Fine Arts, Houston.

Corral, Maria de & Lane, John R., eds. Fast Forward: Contemporary Collections for the Dallas Museum of Art. 2007. (ENG., Illus.). 328p. 65.00 *(978-0-300-12291-6(8))* Dallas Museum of Art.

Cossa, Egidio & Schlinkert, Guido. IbridAAfricA: Hybrid 3. 2010. 144p. pap. 29.95 *(978-88-492-0268-7(7))* Gangemi ITA. Dist: International Publishers Marketing.

Coulis, Michael, et al. Journeys Beyond the Neatline: Expanding the Boundaries of Cartography. 2010. (ENG., Illus.). 90p. pap. *(978-1-55195-258-1(0))* Univ. of Alberta Pr. CAN. Dist: Michigan State Univ. Pr.

Creed, Martin. Martin Creed: Works. 2010. (ENG., Illus.). 624p. 65.00 *(978-0-500-09353-5(9)*, 509353) Thames & Hudson.

Creischer, Alice, ed. Alice Creischer. 2008. 144p. pap. *(978-84-89771-56-7(1))* Actar Birkhauser Distribution.

Critchley, Simon, et al, texts. The Luminous Interval. 2011. (ENG., Illus.). 207p. 49.95 *(978-0-89207-412-9(4))* Guggenheim, Solomon R. Museum.

Crow, Nancy. Crossroads: Constructions, Markings, & Structures. 2008. (ENG., Illus.). 64p. per. 22.95 *(978-1-933308-19-7(2))* Breckling Pr.

Crowley, David. Posters of the Cold War. 2008. (ENG., Illus.). 112p. pap. 29.95 *(978-1-85177-545-3(5))* V & A Pubns. GBR. Dist: Hachette Bk. Group.

Cruzvillegas, Abraham, et al, texts. Daniel Guzman & Steven Shearer: Double Album, 1 vol. 2008. (ENG., Illus.). 224p. 49.95 *(978-0-915557-91-2(6))* New Museum of Contemporary Art, The.

Curiger, Bice, ed. Illuminations - 54th International Venice Biennale Art Exhibition: La Biennale Di Venezia. 2011. (Illus.). 604p. pap. 90.00 *(978-88-317-0820-3(1))* Marsilio Editori spa ITA. Dist: Random Hse., Inc.

Cytter, Keren, et al. Ars Viva 08/09: Mise en Scene. 2009. (ENG., Illus.). 176p. 40.00 *(978-3-7757-2323-7(4))* Hatje Cantz Verlag GmbH & Co KG DEU. Dist: D.A.P./Distributed Art Pubs.

Dailey, Meghan & Rosenthal, Norman. USA Today: New American Art from the Saatchi Gallery. 2007. (ENG., Illus.). 400p. 55.00 *(978-1-903973-96-7(1))* Royal Academy of Arts GBR. Dist: Hachette Bk. Group.

Daros-Latinamerica Collec Staff. Face to Face. 2008. (ENG., Illus.). 288p. 55.00 *(978-3-7757-2112-7(6))* Hatje Cantz Verlag GmbH & Co KG DEU. Dist: D.A.P./Distributed Art Pubs.

Davis, Tim, photos by. Tim Davis: the New Antiquity. 2010. (ENG., Illus.). 106p. 40.00 *(978-88-6208-116-0(2))* Damiani ITA. Dist: D.A.P./Distributed Art Pubs.

de la Fuente, Alejandro, ed. Queloides: Race & Racism in Cuban Contemporary Art. 2011. (ENG & SPA., Illus.). 164p. pap. 40.00 *(978-0-8229-6152-9(0))* Univ. of Pittsburgh Pr.

de Weck, Ziba Ardalan, ed. Eija-Liisa Ahtila: Where Is Where? 2011. (ENG., Illus.). 128p. 59.95 ***(978-3-86560-759-1(4))*** Verlag der Buchhandlung Walther Konig DEU. Dist: D.A.P./Distributed Art Pubs.

Dean, Tacita, illus. & text. Tacita Dean: Film Works. 2008. (ENG.). 112p. per. 34.95 *(978-88-8158-663-9(0))* Charta ITA. Dist: D.A.P./Distributed Art Pubs.

Deena, Chalabi & Shabout, Nada M., eds. Interventions: A Dialogue Between the Modern & the Contemporary. 2011. (ENG & ARA., Illus.). 104p. 35.00 *(978-88-572-0817-6(6))* Skira Editore ITA. Dist: Random Hse., Inc.

Degl'Innocenti, Cristina & Lebole, Maria Pilar. Arte Orafa a Firenze: La Cultura Di un Mestiere = Florentine Goldsmith: The Culture of a Craft. 2007. (ENG & ITA., Illus.). 112p. (C). pap. 23.00 *(978-88-596-0215-6(7))* Edizioni Polistampa ITA. Dist: Brown, David Bk. Co., The.

Delany, Max, frwd. Brook Andrew: Eye to Eye. 2007. (Illus.). 86p. *(978-0-9775782-3-8(2))* Monash Univ. Museum of Art.

Denicke, Lars, et al, eds. Prepare for Pictopia, 1 vol. 2010. (ENG.). 328p. 44.95 *(978-3-9810458-7-1(4))* Pictoplasma Publishing DEU. Dist: Innovative Logistics.

Dewulf, Bernard, ed. Raoul De Keyser: Replay Gemälde 1964-2008. 2010. (ENG., Illus.). 160p. 55.00 *(978-3-7757-2489-0(3))* Hatje Cantz Verlag GmbH & Co KG DEU. Dist: D.A.P./Distributed Art Pubs.

Di'an, Fan & Ga, Zhang, eds. Synthetic Times: Media Art China 2008. 2009. (ENG., Illus.). 358p. (gr. 17). pap. 44.95 *(978-0-262-51226-8(2))* MIT Pr.

Dion, Mark. Mark Dion. 2008. (ENG., Illus.). 160p. 60.00 *(978-3-7757-2197-4(5))* Hatje Cantz Verlag GmbH & Co KG DEU. Dist: D.A.P./Distributed Art Pubs.

Dion, Mark & Courtney, Julie. Travels of William Bartram Reconsidered. 2010. (Illus.). 111p. 35.00 *(978-0-615-25748-8(8))* Bartram, John Assn.

Domela, Paul, ed. Made Up! Liverpool Biennial International 08. 2008. (ENG., Illus.). 96p. pap. 34.95 *(978-1-84631-171-0(3))* Liverpool Univ. Pr. GBR. Dist: Chicago Distribution Ctr.

Dorigato, Attila, et al. Venice: 3 Visions in Glass. 2009. (Illus.). 466p. 85.00 *(978-3-89790-303-6(2))* Arnoldsche Art Pubs. DEU. Dist: Antique Collectors' Club.

Dorothy Circus Gallery Staff. City Slang: The Street Comes to the Gallery. 2008. (ENG.). 40p. pap. 38.00 *(978-88-88493-40-4(9))* Drago Arts & Communication ITA. Dist: SCB Distributors.

Douglas, aka Elbow Toe, By Brian Adam. Paper Cuts. 2011. (ENG.). 80p. 50.00 ***(978-88-88493-77-0(8))*** Drago Arts & Communication ITA. Dist: SCB Distributors.

Drathen, Doris von. Cosmic Maps. 2008. (ENG., Illus.). 128p. 69.95 *(978-88-8158-685-1(1))* Charta ITA. Dist: D.A.P./Distributed Art Pubs.

Dubin, Lois Sherr. Grand Procession: Contemporary Artistic Visions of American Indians the Diker Collection at the Denver Art Museum. 2011. (ENG., Illus.). 64p. 19.95 ***(978-0-914738-67-1(4))*** Denver Art Museum.

Duggan, Ginger Gregg & Fox, Judith Hoos. Under Control. 2010. (Illus.). 60p. pap. 25.00 *(978-1-883015-43-5(X))* Univ. of Washington Pr.

Durant, Sam & Ketchum-Heap of Birds, Shanna. Sam Durant: Scenes from the Pilgrim Story: Myths, Massacres, & Monuments. 2007. (Illus.). 76p. *(978-0-9771419-3-7(4))* Massachusetts College of Art.

Dzama, Marcel. Marcel Dzama: the Infidels, 1 vol. 2010. (ENG.). 152p. 79.95 *(978-3-941100-88-6(2))* DruckVerlag Kettler GmbH DEU. Dist: D.A.P./Distributed Art Pubs.

Dziewior. Michael Hakimi. 2009. (ENG., Illus.). 138p. pap. 40.00 *(978-3-7757-2268-1(8))* Hatje Cantz Verlag GmbH & Co KG DEU. Dist: D.A.P./Distributed Art Pubs.

Eamon, Christopher. Rearview Mirror: New Art from Central & Eastern Europe. 2012. (ENG., Illus.). 100p. 45.00 ***(978-0-88950-160-7(2))*** Art Gallery of Alberta CAN. Dist: D.A.P./Distributed Art Pubs.

Ebersberger, Eva, ed. Jorge Otero-Pailos: the Ethics of Dust. 2010. (ENG., Illus.). 104p. pap. 33.00 *(978-3-86560-655-6(5))* Verlag der Buchhandlung Walther Konig DEU. Dist: D.A.P./Distributed Art Pubs.

Eccher, Danilo, ed. Paolo Chiasera: [in English & Italian]. 2008. 82p. pap. 56.50 *(978-88-370-6248-4(6))* Electa ITA. Dist: Trans-Atlantic Pubns., Inc.

Eccles, Tom, frwd. At Home/Not at Home. 2010. (ENG., Illus.). 168p. 40.00 *(978-1-936192-07-6(1))* Ctr. for Curatorial Studies, The.

Eckmann, Sabine. Precarious Worlds: Contemporary Art from Germany. 2012. (ENG., Illus.). 72p. 30.00 ***(978-0-936316-34-5(9))*** Washington Univ., Mildred Lane Kemper Art Museum.

Eckmann, Sabine. Sharon Lockhart: Lunch Break. 2010. (Illus.). 160p. pap. 40.00 *(978-0-936316-29-1(2))* Washington Univ., Mildred Lane Kemper Art Museum.

Eckmann, Sabine & Koepnick, Lutz. Grid()Matrix. 2007. (MLKAM-Screen Arts & New Media Aesthetics Ser.). (ENG., Illus.). 80p. pap. 15.00 *(978-0-936316-20-8(9))* Washington Univ., Mildred Lane Kemper Art Museum.

Eckmann, Sabine, et al. Reality Bites: Making Avant-garde Art in Post-Wall Germany. 2007.Tr. of Reality Bites: Kunst nach dem Mauerfall. (GER.). per. 55.00 *(978-0-936316-21-5(7))* Washington Univ., Mildred Lane Kemper Art Museum.

Edelmann, Frederic. Positions. Edelmann, Freder, ed. 2008. 216p. *(978-84-96954-50-2(1))* Actar Birkhauser Distribution.

Eden, Xandra, et al. The Lining of Forgetting: Internal & External memory in Art. 2008. (Illus.). 135p. lib. bdg. 35.00 *(978-1-890949-11-2(6))* Univ. of North Carolina at Greensboro, Weatherspoon Art Museum.

Eiling, Alexandra, et al, texts. Lumière Noire. Neue Kunst aus Frankreich: New Art from France. 2011. (ENG., Illus.). 232p. pap. 55.00 ***(978-3-86560-996-0(1))*** Verlag der Buchhandlung Walther Konig DEU. Dist: D.A.P./Distributed Art Pubs.

Eisenhauer, Paul & Farrington, Lynne, eds. Wharton Esherick & the Birth of the American Modern. 2011. (Illus.). 160p. 29.99 *(978-0-7643-3788-8(2))* Schiffer Publishing, Ltd.

Elaine, James, et al, texts. Hammer Projects. 2009. (ENG., Illus.). 432p. 60.00 *(978-0-943739-35-9(7))* Hammer Museum.

Elderfield, John & Monrad, Kasper. Bob Dylan: The Brazil Series. 2010. (Illus.). 192p. 49.95 *(978-3-7913-5098-1(6))* Prestel Publishing.

Eleey, Peter, ed. Haluk Akakce: Sky Is the Limit, 1 vol. 2007. (ENG., Illus.). 56p. per. 29.95 *(978-1-928570-04-2(6))* Creative Time.

Eleey, Peter, et al, texts. Now You See It. 2009. (ENG., Illus.). 72p. 35.00 *(978-0-934324-47-2(6))* Aspen Art Museum.

Elliott, David, et al, texts. The Group 1965: We Are Boys. 2012. (ENG, JPN & GER., Illus.). 88p. pap. 40.00 ***(978-88-366-2094-4(9))*** Silvana ITA. Dist: D.A.P./Distributed Art Pubs.

Ellis, Elsi Vassdal & Rogers, Bertha, comments. Book Arts 2010, the Word & Image Gallery, Bright Hill Literary Center. 2010. 140p. pap. 16.00 *(978-1-892471-63-5(9))* Bright Hill Pr.

A

Ellis, Patricia, frwd. Newspeak. 2010. (ENG., Illus.). 368p. pap. 55.00 (978-1-86154-314-1(X)) Booth-Clibborn Editions GBR. Dist: Hachette Bk. Group.

Emmerling, Leonhard, text. Out of This World. 2011. (ENG., Illus.). 72p. 37.50 **(978-3-86678-469-7(4))** Kerber Verlag DEU. Dist: D.A.P./Distributed Art Pubs.

Engberg, Siri, ed. & text. Lifelike. 2012. (ENG., Illus.). 192p. pap. 40.00 **(978-0-935640-68-7(1))** Walker Art Ctr.

Essel, Karlheinz, frwd. Chalo! India: A New Era of Indian Art. 2009. (GER & ENG., Illus.). 304p. 45.00 (978-3-7913-4304-4(1)) Prestel Publishing.

Falkenberg, Merrill. All the More Real: Portrayals of Intimacy & Empathy. 2007. pap. (978-0-943526-51-5(5)) Parrish Art Museum, The.

Fang, Hu, et al, texts. The Work of Glenn Kaino: Communicating Rooks. 2009. (ENG., Illus.). 144p. 55.00 (978-3-7757-2304-6(8)) Hatje Cantz Verlag GmbH & Co KG DEU. Dist: D.A.P./Distributed Art Pubs.

Farouk Hosny: The Energy of Abstraction. 2008. (Illus.). 58p. pap. 19.95 (978-0-9678056-5-8(1)) Nova Southeastern Univ., Museum of Art Fort Lauderdale.

Favre, Valerie. Valerie Favre: Visions. 2009. (ENG., Illus.). 208p. 45.00 (978-3-7757-2443-2(5)) Hatje Cantz Verlag GmbH & Co KG DEU. Dist: D.A.P./Distributed Art Pubs.

Ferre, Albert, ed. Patent Constructions: New Architecture Made in Catalonia. 2007. (Illus.). 240p. pap. (978-84-96954-09-0(9)) Actar Birkhauser Distribution.

Fleming, Jennie A. Out of Place. 2007. (Illus.). 48p. (978-0-937123-45-4(5)) Univ. of Maryland, Art Gallery, The.

—Trajectories: Marking Time in Contemporary Art. 2008. (Illus.). 51p. (978-0-937123-46-1(3)) Univ. of Maryland, Art Gallery, The.

Flinterman, Koos, ed. SuperStories. 2009. (ENG., Illus.). 240p. (978-90-5856-304-0(9), Stichting Kunstboak (Acc)) Antique Collectors' Club.

Flynn, William. Armed Chair: From Observation to Metaphor. 2007. (Illus.). 96p. 35.00 (978-1-880515-60-0(1)) School of the Museum of Fine Arts.

Fogle, Douglas, ed. Life on Mars. 2008. (ENG., Illus.). 436p. 39.95 (978-0-88039-051-4(4)) Carnegie Museum of Art, The.

Foster, Elena & Obrist, Hans Ulrich, eds. Ways Beyond Art: Ai Weiwei. 2009. (SPA & ENG., Illus.). 133p. (978-0-9559613-2-8(7)) Ivory Pr.

Foster, Susan Leigh, et al. Move. Choreographing You: Art & Dance since the 1960s. Rosenthal, Stephanie, ed. 2011. (ENG., Illus.). 176p. (gr. 17). pap. 35.00 (978-0-262-51629-7(2)) MIT Pr.

Fotomuseum Winterthur, Switzerland Staff, ed. Forschen und Erfinden/Research & Invention: Die Recherche Mit Bildren in der Zeitgenossoschen Fotografie/Investigations with Images in Contemporary Photography. 2008. (Illus.). 132p. 35.00 (978-3-85881-198-1(X)) Scheidegger und Spiess AG, Verlag CHE. Dist: Antique Collectors' Club.

Frantz, Susanne K. Lino Tagliapietra in Retrospect: A Modern Renaissance in Italian Glass. 2008. (ENG., Illus.). 208p. 50.00 (978-0-295-98825-2(8)) Univ. of Washington Pr.

Frantz, Susanne K. & Kangas, Matthew. Viva Vetro! Glass Alive!: Venice & America. 2008. (ENG., Illus.). 202p. pap. 29.95 (978-0-88039-048-4(4)) Carnegie Museum of Art, The.

Fredericks, Stephen & Jetter, Frances, texts. The Art of Persuasion. 2007. (978-0-9728613-9-7(4)) New York Society of Etchers, Inc., The.

Frelin, Adam. Diviner. 250th ed. 2010. 25.00 (978-0-615-38714-7(4)) Bemis Ctr. for Contemporary Arts.

Frey Norris Gallery, prod. Inkie Whang: American Debut. 2008. 20p. pap. 10.00 (978-0-9795141-3-5(4)) Norris, Frey Gallery.

Fried, Michael & Rhomberg, Kathrin. 6. Berlin Biennale für zeitgenössische Kunst, 6th Berlin Biennial for Contemporary Art. Reader. 2011. (GER & ENG., Illus.). 240p. pap. 37.50 (978-3-8321-9338-6(3)) DuMont DEU. Dist: D.A.P./Distributed Art Pubs.

Frieling, Rudolf. The Art of Participation, 1950 to Now. 2008. (ENG., Illus.). 224p. 39.95 (978-0-500-23858-5(8)) Thames & Hudson.

Fuchs, Rainer, et al, texts. China: Facing Reality. 2008. (GER & ENG., Illus.). 206p. 80.00 (978-3-939738-87-9(5)) Verlag fur Moderne Kunst DEU. Dist: D.A.P./Distributed Art Pubs.

Funcke, Bettina & Ruf, Beatrix, eds. Guyton, Price, Smith, Walker, 1 vol. 2011. (ENG., Illus.). 192p. pap. 35.00 (978-3-905770-30-8(X)) JRP Ringier Kunstverlag AG CHE. Dist: D.A.P./Distributed Art Pubs.

Furness, Rosalind, ed. Frieze Art Fair Yearbook 2010-11. 2010. (ENG., Illus.). 544p. pap. 35.00 (978-0-9553201-6-3(X)) Frieze GBR. Dist: D.A.P./Distributed Art Pubs.

Furness, Rosalind & Starling, Anna. Frieze Art Fair Yearbook 2009-10. 2009. (ENG., Illus.). 548p. pap. 35.00 (978-0-9553201-4-9(3)) Frieze GBR. Dist: D.A.P./Distributed Art Pubs.

Gaewsky, Timothy. Timothy Gaewsky: Little Drop of Poison. 2010. 37p. pap. 19.99 (978-0-557-53568-2(9)) Lulu Enterprises Inc.

Gagosian Gallery Staff, compiled by. Glenn Brown. 2010. (ENG., Illus.). 148p. 100.00 (978-0-8478-3488-4(3)) Rizzoli International Pubns., Inc.

Galiotto, Angelo, ed. Perino & Vele: [in English & Italian]. 2008. 127p. 56.50 (978-88-370-6036-7(X)) Electa ITA. Dist: Trans-Atlantic Pubns., Inc.

Gallery, David Klein. Bo Bartlett. 2009. pap. (978-1-61623-737-0(6)) Independent Pub.

Gallery, Simpson Gallagher. T. D. Kelsey & Julie Oriet Unplugged & Unleashed. 2009. pap. (978-1-61623-068-5(1)) Independent Pub.

Garcia, Miki & Lovero, Elizabeth. Something New for Another Sunny Day: Call for Entries 2005-2006. Garcia, Miki, ed. 2006. pap. 10.00 (978-1-880658-26-0(7)) Santa Barbara Contemporary Arts Forum.

Garrels, Gary, contrib. by. Eden's Edge: Fifteen la Artists, 1 vol. 2007. (ENG., Illus.). 144p. 35.00 (978-0-943739-31-1(4)) Hammer Museum.

Gass, Alison & Zimbardo, Tanya. Fifty Years of Bay Area Art: The SECA Awards. 2011. (Illus.). 168p. **(978-0-918471-89-5(3))** San Francisco Museum of Modern Art.

Gelburd, Gail. Ajiaco: Stirrings of the Cuban Soul. 2010. (ENG., Illus.). 112p. pap. 29.95 (978-1-58465-847-4(9)) Univ. Pr. of New England.

Gevers, Ine, et al, texts. Difference on Display. 2010. (ENG., Illus.). 384p. pap. 45.00 (978-90-5662-715-7(5)) NAi Uitgevers / Publishers Stichting NLD. Dist: D.A.P./Distributed Art Pubs.

Ghosn, Saad, ed. Sos Art 2006. 2007. (Illus.). 57p. spiral bd. 20.00 (978-0-9758604-6-5(1)) Ghosn Publishing.

Gilman, Claire, text. Mario Merz: Disegni. 2008. (ITA & ENG., Illus.). 380p. 100.00 (978-88-7757-217-2(5)) Hopefulmonster Editore ITA. Dist: D.A.P./Distributed Art Pubs.

Gingeras, Alison M. Sequence 1: Painting & Sculpture from the François Pinault Collection. 2008. (Illus.). 328p. (ENG, FRE & ITA.). 75.00 (978-88-6130-216-7(5)); (FRE, ITA & ENG., 75.00 (978-88-6130-206-8(8)) Skira Editore ITA. Dist: Random Hse., Inc.

Godinat, Aloïs. Alois Godinat. Bovier, Lionel, ed. 2010. (ENG., Illus.). 64p. 35.00 (978-3-03764-044-9(8)) JRP Ringier Kunstverlag AG CHE. Dist: D.A.P./Distributed Art Pubs.

Goldberg, Phyllis. Phyllis Goldberg. 2007. pap. 8.00 (978-0-9791843-5-2(5)) CUE Art Foundation.

Gonzalez-Foerster, Dominique. Nocturama. Gonzalez-Foerst, ed. 2008. (Illus.). 300p. (978-84-96954-39-7(0)) Actar Birkhauser Distribution.

Gotwald, William H., Sr. African Masquerade & the Collector's Dilemma: Masks from the Collection of William H. Gotwald, Jr. , Emeritus Professor of Biology, Utica College, Utica, New York. 2011. (Illus.). 60p. pap. 29.95 **(978-0-578-09224-9(7))** Barrett, Edith Langley Fine Arts Gallery.

Graham, Rodney. Rodney Graham: Through the Forest, 1 vol. 2010. (ENG.). 168p. pap. 55.00 (978-3-7757-2577-4(6)) Hatje Cantz Verlag GmbH & Co KG DEU. Dist: D.A.P./Distributed Art Pubs.

Grassi, Francesca, ed. Rirkrit Tiravanija: A Retrospective: Tomorrow Is Another Fine Day, 1 vol. 2007. (ENG., Illus.). 218p. 75.00 (978-3-905770-32-2(6)) JRP Ringier Kunstverlag AG CHE. Dist: D.A.P./Distributed Art Pubs.

Grenville, Bruce & Steedman, Scott, eds. Visions of British Columbia: A Landscape Manual, 1 vol. 2010. (ENG., Illus.). 256p. pap. 35.00 (978-1-55365-500-8(1)) D&M Pubs. Inc. CAN. Dist: Perseus-PGW.

Grimonprez, Johan. Johan Grimonprez: It's a Poor Sort of Memory that Only Works Backwards. 2011. (ENG., Illus.). 352p. 45.00 **(978-3-7757-3130-0(X))** Hatje Cantz Verlag GmbH & Co KG DEU. Dist: D.A.P./Distributed Art Pubs.

Gronert, Stefan & Berg, Stephan, eds. Der Westen leuchtet. 2011. (ENG & GER., Illus.). 416p. 65.00 (978-3-86678-432-1(5)) Kerber Verlag DEU. Dist: D.A.P./Distributed Art Pubs.

Grosenick, Uta & Ochs, Alexander, eds. Yang Shaobin. 2010. (ENG, POR & GER., Illus.). 116p. 44.95 (978-3-8321-9265-5(4)) DuMont DEU. Dist: D.A.P./Distributed Art Pubs.

Grosse, Katharina. Katharina Grosse: Shadowbox. 2010. (GER & ENG., Illus.). 132p. pap. 46.00 (978-3-86560-611-2(3)) Verlag der Buchhandlung Walther Konig DEU. Dist: D.A.P./Distributed Art Pubs.

Gupta, Subodh, et al. Subodh Gupta: Common Man. 2011. (ENG., Illus.). 88p. 45.00 (978-3-03764-143-9(6)) JRP Ringier Kunstverlag AG CHE. Dist: D.A.P./Distributed Art Pubs.

Gygax, Raphael, ed. Deterioration, They Said. 2010. (ENG., Illus.). 92p. 35.00 (978-3-03764-076-0(6)) JRP Ringier Kunstverlag AG CHE. Dist: D.A.P./Distributed Art Pubs.

Hahn, Sylvia, et al. Paradies: Neue Blicke auf einen alten Traum. 2009. (GER., Illus.). 135p. (978-3-422-06898-8(8)) Deutscher Kunstverlag GmbH.

Hall, Sarah J. & McPherson, Craig. Steel: Pittsburgh Drawings by Craig Mcpherson. 2008. (Illus.). 48p. pap. 14.95 (978-0-9703425-9-1(4)) Frick Art & Historical Ctr.,The.

Hamilton, Richard & Todoli, Vicente, eds. Comida para Pensar, Pensar Sobre el Comer. 2009. (SPA., Illus.). 343p. (978-84-96954-71-7(4)) Actar Birkhauser Distribution.

Han, Heng-Gil & Ho, Christopher K. Jamaica Flux: Workspaces & Windows 2010: Art As Action, April 10, 2010-June 12, 2010. 2010. (978-0-9762853-7-3(1)) Jamaica Ctr. for Arts & Learning.

Han, Heng-Gil & Ortiz, Lori. 2011 Studio LLC. 2012. **(978-0-9762853-9-7(8))** Jamaica Ctr. for Arts & Learning.

Han, Heng-Gil, et al. Jamaica Flux: Workspaces & Windows 2007. 2008. (ENG., Illus.). 194p. 39.95 (978-0-9762853-6-6(3)) Jamaica Ctr. for Arts & Learning.

Hanru, Hou, contrib. by. China Onward: The Estella Collection: Chinese Contemporary Art, 1996-2006, 1 vol. 2007. (ENG., Illus.). 468p. 85.00 (978-87-91607-38-7(8)) Louisana DNK. Dist: D.A.P./Distributed Art Pubs.

Hansen, Elisabeth Delin, et al, eds. Gil & Moti: Totally Devoted to You. 2011. (ENG., Illus.). 160p. 45.00 **(978-3-7757-2847-8(3))** Hatje Cantz Verlag GmbH & Co KG DEU. Dist: D.A.P./Distributed Art Pubs.

Hanzal, Carla M. Contemporary, Cool & Collected. 2007. (978-0-9762300-3-8(8)) Mint Museum, The.

Hao, Lu, ed. See a World in Grain of Sand. 2010. (ENG., Illus.). 168p. 50.00 (978-7-5006-8730-6(3)) China Youth Publishing Hse. CHN. Dist: D.A.P./Distributed Art Pubs.

Hapgood, Susan. Slightly Unbalanced. 2008. (ENG., Illus.). 72p. per. 19.95 (978-0-916365-78-3(6)) Independent Curators International.

Harton, David B. & Harton, Barbara, eds. The Complete Plan for Iran: President George W. Bush ... As He Would Have Expressed It ... 2007. per. 14.95 (978-0-9798591-1-3(5), BSG Pr.) Beaver Street Gallery.

—The Complete Plan for Iraq: President George W. Bush ... as he would have expressed It ... 2007. per. 14.95 (978-0-9798591-0-6(7), BSG Pr.) Beaver Street Gallery.

Haruko Tanaka. 2007. 8.00 (978-0-9791843-0-7(4)) CUE Art Foundation.

Hauser, Jens, ed. Sk-Interfaces: Exploding Borders in Art, Science & Technology. 2008. (ENG., Illus.). 160p. 50.00 (978-1-84631-149-9(7)) Liverpool Univ. Pr. GBR. Dist: Chicago Distribution Ctr.

Healy, Brian. Brian Healy: Commonplaces. 2008. (ENG., Illus.). 110p. pap. 24.95 (978-0-9793801-7-4(0)) Oro Editions.

Heathfield, Adrian, et al. Out of Now: The Lifeworks of Tehching Hsieh. 2008. (ENG., Illus.). 384p. (gr. 17). 49.95 (978-0-262-01255-3(3)) MIT Pr.

Hegyi, Lorand, ed. Essential Experiences. 2010. 168p. pap. 63.50 (978-88-370-7390-9(9)) Electa ITA. Dist: Trans-Atlantic Pubns., Inc.

Hegyi, Lorand & Seung, Kim. Domicile: Prive/Public. 2006. 224p. pap. (978-2-85056-897-8(X)) Somogy Editions d'Art.

Heil, Axel & Schoppmann, Wolfgang, eds. Peter Zimmerman: Epoxiology, 1 vol. 2007. (FRE, GER & ENG., Illus.). 148p. 60.00 (978-3-86560-179-7(0)) Verlag der Buchhandlung Walther Konig DEU. Dist: D.A.P./Distributed Art Pubs.

Heinrich, Christoph, et al. Embrace!, 2 vols. 2009. (Illus.). (978-0-914738-61-9(5)) Denver Art Museum.

Hellandsjo, Karin. The Henie Onstad Art Centre: The Art of Tomorrow Today. 2009. (ENG., Illus.). 240p. 75.00 (978-88-6130-944-9(5)) Skira Editore ITA. Dist: Random Hse., Inc.

Hemsworth, Gerard. Hidden Agenda, 1 vol. 2010. (GER & ENG., Illus.). 84p. 45.00 (978-3-941185-89-0(6)) Verlag fur Moderne Kunst DEU. Dist: D.A.P./Distributed Art Pubs.

Hentschel, Martin, ed. John Baldessari: Brick Bldg, Lg Windows W/Xlent Views, Partially Furnished, Renowned Architect. 2010. (GER & ENG., Illus.). 136p. 45.00 (978-3-86678-306-5(X)) Kerber Verlag DEU. Dist: D.A.P./Distributed Art Pubs.

Hentschel, Martin & Stange, Raimar, eds. Allora & Calzadilla. 2010. (GER & ENG., Illus.). 128p. 50.00 (978-3-941185-62-3(4)) Verlag fur Moderne Kunst DEU. Dist: D.A.P./Distributed Art Pubs.

Hickey, Dave. The Outwin Boochever Portrait Competition 2006. 2006. (ENG., Illus.). 88p. pap. 19.95 (978-0-295-98655-5(7)) Univ. of Washington Pr.

Himmelsbach, Sabine & Eppeneder, Ralf, eds. Gateways: Kunst und vernetzte Kultur. 2011. (GER & ENG., Illus.). 240p. pap. 55.00 **(978-3-7757-2796-9(5))** Hatje Cantz Verlag GmbH & Co KG DEU. Dist: D.A.P./Distributed Art Pubs.

Hirst, Damien. The Elusive Truth! Beard, Jason, ed. 2008. (ENG.). 112p. 250.00 (978-1-932598-11-7(1)); 56p. pap. 30.00 (978-1-904212-14-0(X)); (Illus.). 112p. 2500.00 (978-1-904212-44-7(1)) Other Criteria GBR. Dist: Hachette Bk. Group.

Hirst, Damien, et al. Beyond Belief. Beard, Jason, ed. 2008. (ENG., Illus.). 194p. 140.00 (978-1-904212-21-8(2)) Other Criteria GBR. Dist: Hachette Bk. Group.

Hlavajova, Maria, et al, eds. Open 16: the Art Biennial as a Global Phenomenon. 2009. (ENG., Illus.). 112p. pap. 30.00 (978-90-5662-667-9(1)) NAi Uitgevers / Publishers Stichting NLD. Dist: D.A.P./Distributed Art Pubs.

Hoeller, Silvia. Lois & Franziska Weinberger: Feldarbeit / Field Work. Bertsch, Christoph, ed. 2008. (Illus.). 272p. 34.95 (978-3-7082-3225-6(9)) Skarabaeus AUT. Dist: SCB Distributors.

Hoff, Svein Olav. Jon Doblougs Samling. 2009. (NOR., Illus.). 232p. (978-82-91388-59-5(8)) Labyrinth Pr.

Hooper, Rachel, ed. & intro. 2008 School of Art Masters Thesis Exhibition. 2008. (Illus.). 20p. (C). pap. 5.00 net. (978-0-941193-41-2(1)) Blaffer Art Museum.

Hooper, Rachel & Coolquitt, Andy. Andy Coolquitt. 2012. (ENG.). 185p. 50.00 **(978-0-292-73894-2(3))** Univ. of Texas Pr.

Hopkins, Candice & Swanson, Kerry. Shapeshifters, Time Travellers, & Storytellers. 2009. (ENG., Illus.). 192p. 19.99 (978-0-88854-455-1(3)) Royal Ontario Museum CAN. Dist: Univ. of Toronto Pr.

Hough, Jessica & Ramirez-Montagut, Monica, eds. Revisiting the Glass House: Contemporary Art & Modern Architecture. 2008. (ENG., Illus.). 134p. pap. 39.95 (978-0-300-13587-9(4)) Yale Univ. Pr.

Hughes, Eleanor & Trumble, Angus. The Independent Eye: Contemporary British Art from the Collection of Samuel & Gabrielle Lurie. 2010. (Illus.). 144p. 65.00 (978-0-300-17139-6(0)) Yale Ctr. for British Art.

Hushka, Rock. The Eloquent Silver Curve: The Jewelry of Flora Book. 2011. pap. **(978-0-924335-34-1(3))** Tacoma Art Museum.

Iles, Chrissie. Paul Mccarthy: Central Symmetrical Rotation Movement: Three Installations, Two Films. 2008. (Illus.). 72p. 18.95 (978-0-300-14138-2(6)) Yale Univ. Pr.

Independent Curators International & Thompson, Nato. Experimental Geography: Radical Approaches to Landscape, Cartography, & Urbanism. 2009. (ENG., Illus.). 168p. pap. 29.95 (978-0-09-163658-6(2)) Melville Hse. Publishing.

Inselmann, Andrea. Dangerous Waters. 2007. 20.00 net. (978-1-934260-00-5(2)) Cornell Univ., Herbert F. Johnson Museum of Art.

Irace, Fulvio, ed. Triennale 2005-2008. 2009. (ENG & ITA., Illus.). 128p. 67.50 (978-88-370-6921-6(9)) Electa ITA. Dist: Trans-Atlantic Pubns., Inc.

Istituto nazionale per la grafica (Italy) Staff & Italy, Ministero per i beni e le attività culturali Staff, contrib. by. Paolo Canevari: Decalogo. 2008. (ITA., Illus.). 71p. (978-88-370-6794-6(1)) Electa.

Jaar, Alfredo, et al, contrib. by. Emergency. 2006. (Illus.). 261p. (gr. 13-18). 29.95 (978-84-95951-90-8(8)) D.A.P./Distributed Art Pubs.

Jacob, Mary Jane. Grain of Emptiness: Buddhist-Inspired Contemporary Art. 2010. (978-0-9772131-9-1(6)) Serindia Pubns., Inc.

Jacobson, Heidi Zuckerman, et al. Like Color in Pictures: February 16-April 15, 2007, Aspen Art Museum. 2007. (Illus.). 80p. (978-0-934324-39-7(5)) Aspen Art Museum.

Jamie, Cameron. Cameron Jamie, 1 vol. 2007. (ENG., Illus.). 176p. 34.95 (978-0-935640-87-8(8)) Walker Art Ctr.

Jancou, Marc. In Geneva No One Can Hear You Scream: A Project. 2008. (ENG., Illus.). 208p. 29.00 (978-3-905829-57-0(6)) JRP Ringier Kunstverlag AG CHE. Dist: D.A.P./Distributed Art Pubs.

Jankowski, Christian. Christian Jankowski: Briefing. 2009. (ENG., Illus.). 288p. 60.00 (978-3-7757-2317-6(X)) Hatje Cantz Verlag GmbH & Co KG DEU. Dist: D.A.P./Distributed Art Pubs.

—Christian Jankowski: Everything Fell Together, 1 vol. 2006. (ENG., Illus.). 200p. pap. 45.00 (978-1-879003-42-2(2)) Des Moines Art Ctr.

Jasmine Justice. 2007. 8.00 (978-0-9791843-4-5(7)) CUE Art Foundation.

Johanson, Chris. Chris Johanson: Totalities, 1 vol. 2010. (ENG.). 112p. 45.00 (978-0-9815771-6-6(4)) Deitch, Jeffrey Inc.

Jonathan Elderfield. 2007. 8.00 (978-0-9791843-3-8(9)) CUE Art Foundation.

Joo, Eungie. The Ungovernables: 2012 New Museum Triennial. 2012. (ENG., Illus.). 256p. 60.00 **(978-0-8478-3899-8(4)**, Skira) Rizzoli International Pubns., Inc.

Juncosa, Enrique, et al, texts. William Mckeown. 2009. (ENG., Illus.). 88p. pap. 37.95 (978-88-8158-715-5(7)) Charta ITA. Dist: D.A.P./Distributed Art Pubs.

Juncosa, Enrique & Thomas, Rachael. Elizabeth Peyton Reading & Writing. 2009. (ENG., Illus.). 128p. 49.95 (978-88-8158-738-4(6)) Charta ITA. Dist: D.A.P./Distributed Art Pubs.

Juncosa, Enrique, et al. Francis Alys: Le\Temps du Sommeil. 2010. (ENG., Illus.). 184p. 49.95 (978-88-8158-777-3(7)) Charta ITA. Dist: D.A.P./Distributed Art Pubs.

Jungmann, Burglind. Life in Ceramics: Five Contemporary Korean Artists. 2010. (ENG., Illus.). 56p. pap. 20.00 (978-0-9778344-3-3(3)) Univ. of California, Los Angeles, Fowler Museum of Cultural History.

Kachur, Lewis. Past Pop: Robert Rauschenberg & James rosenquist Graphics of The 1970s. 2009. pap. (978-1-61584-017-5(6)) Independent Pub.

Kaiser, Fritz. Degenerate Art Exhibition Guide 1937 - Bilingual Edition German/English. von Halasz, Joachim, ed. & tr. by. 2010. 78p. pap. (978-1-905742-30-1(4)) Foxley Books.

Kaiser, Philipp. Jack Goldstein X 10,000. 2012. (Illus.). 240p. pap. 49.95 **(978-3-7913-5193-3(1))** Prestel Publishing.

Kamps, Toby. Art of Our Time: Selections from the Ulrich Museum of Art, Wichita State University. McDonnell, Patricia & Stamey, Emily, eds. 2010. (ENG., Illus.). 168p. 49.95 (978-0-295-99024-8(4)); pap. 29.95 (978-0-295-99025-5(2)) Wichita State Univ., Ulrich Museum of Art.

Karen Azoulay. 2007. 8.00 (978-0-9791843-1-4(2)) CUE Art Foundation.

Kastner, Jeffrey, text. Jeff Gibson: Sarsaparilla to Sorcery, 1 vol. 2007. (ENG., Illus.). 72p. (C). 24.95 (978-0-9779789-1-5(5)) Binghamton Univ., Art Museum, State Univ. of New York.

Kataoka, Mami. Laughing in a Foreign Language. 2008. (ENG., Illus.). 152p. pap. 35.00 (978-1-85332-266-2(0)) Hayward Gallery Publishing GBR. Dist: D.A.P./Distributed Art Pubs.

Kataoka, Mami & Harding, Allison. Phantoms of Asia: Contemporary Awakens the Past. 2012. (ENG., Illus.). 256p. 35.00 **(978-0-939117-59-8(2))** Asian Art Museum of San Francisco.

Keiter, Ellen J., et al. Shattering Glass: New Perspectives: November 11, 2007-February 24, 2008, Katonah Museum of Art. 2007. (Illus.). 40p. pap. (978-0-915171-73-6(2)) Katonah Gallery.

Kelley, Jeff. Half-Life of a Dream: Contemporary Chinese Art from the Logan Collection. 2008. (Illus.). 144p. 40.00 (978-0-520-25779-5(0)) Univ. of California Pr.

Kelley, Mike. "Day Is Done" 2007. (ENG., Illus.). 500p. 125.00 (978-0-300-12425-5(2)) Yale Univ. Pr.

Kennedy, Brian & Burke, Emily Shubert, eds. Modern & Contemporary Art at Dartmouth: Highlights from the Hood Museum of Art. 2009. (Illus.). 240p. pap. 40.00 (978-1-58465-787-3(1)) Hood Museum of Art.

Kennedy, Brian P. & Burke, Emily. Modern & Contemporary Art at Dartmouth: Highlights from the Hood Museum of Art. 2009. (Illus.). x, 230p. (978-1-58465-786-6(3)) Hood Museum of Art.

Kennon, Brian. Untitled #1, 2006 (Mike Kelley, Silver Ball) 2006. 40p. per. 28.00 (978-0-9786830-2-3(1)) 2nd Cannons Pubns.

Kentridge, William & Basualdo, Carlos. William Kentridge: Tapestries. 2007. (978-0-87633-256-6(4)) Philadelphia Museum of Art.

Kerry, John, frwd. Warcuts. 2011. (ENG., Illus.). 100p. 35.00 **(978-1-936205-13-4(0))** Austin, Stephen F. State Univ. Pr.

Kessler, Jon, illus. Jon Kessler: The Palace at 4 A. M. 2008. (GER & ENG.). 144p. 55.00 (978-88-8158-658-5(4)) Charta ITA. Dist: D.A.P./Distributed Art Pubs.

Kiblitsky, Alexander. Sheila Isham. 2006. (ENG.). 224p. 50.00 (978-3-935298-99-5(4)) Kiblitsky, Joseph Palace Editions DEU. Dist: National Bk. Network.

King, Sarah, ed. The Dissolve. 2010. (ENG., Illus.). 240p. 50.00 (978-0-9764492-9-4(3)) Site Santa Fe.

—Lucky Number Seven. 2008. (ENG., Illus.). 396p. 50.00 (978-0-9764492-8-7(5)) Site Santa Fe.

Kirkpatrick, Gail, et al, eds. Josephine Meckseper. 2009. (ENG., Illus.). 114p. 35.00 (978-3-03764-047-0(2)) JRP Ringier Kunstverlag AG CHE. Dist: D.A.P./Distributed Art Pubs.

Kittelmann, Udo. Simon Dybbroe Moller: Black, white, gray, cyan, magenta, Yellow. 2010. (GER & ENG., Illus.). 64p. 30.00 *(978-3-86560-571-9(0))* Verlag der Buchhandlung Walther Konig DEU. Dist: D.A.P./Distributed Art Pubs.

Knol, Meta, et al, eds. Beyond the Dutch: Indonesia, the Netherlands & the Arts from 1990 to Date. 2010. 200p. 39.00 *(978-94-6022-059-3(2))* Royal Tropical Institute Pr. (KIT (Koninklijk Instituut voor de Tropen)) NLD. Dist: Stylus Publishing, LLC.

KnollTextiles: 60 Years. 2007. *(978-0-9793156-0-2(3))* Knoll.

Koekebakker, Olof, text. PrixdeRome. NL 2010. 2010. (ENG., Illus.). 120p. pap. 35.00 *(978-90-5662-753-9(8))* NAi Uitgevers / Publishers Stichting NLD. Dist: D.A.P./Distributed Art Pubs.

Kolesnikov, Ivan, et al, contrib. by. New Angelarium. 2007. (ENG & RUS., Illus.). 352p. per. 145.00 *(978-0-9754829-7-1(1))* Kolodzei Art Foundation, Inc.

Kook-Anderson, Grace, et al. Best Kept Secret: UCI & the Development of Contemporary Art in Southern California, 1964-1971. 2011. ***(978-0-940872-37-0(4))*** Laguna Art Museum Store

Koolhaas, Rem. The Gulf. 2007. (Illus.). 25p. per. 19.95 *(978-3-03778-088-6(6), 3037780886)* Lars Muller Pubs. CHE. Dist: Springer.

Koons, Jeff, ed. Skin Fruit: A View of a Collection. 2012. (ENG., Illus.). 92p. pap. 25.00 ***(978-1-935202-77-6(4))*** Deste Foundation GRC. Dist: D.A.P./Distributed Art Pubs.

Kosuth, Joseph. Language of Equilibrium. 2009. (ENG & ITA., Illus.). 102p. 82.50 *(978-88-370-7139-4(6))* Electa ITA. Dist: Trans-Atlantic Pubns., Inc.

Kramer, Jennifer. Kesu' The Art & Life of Doug Cranmer. 1 vol. 2012. (ENG., Illus.). 160p. pap. 34.95 ***(978-0-295-99144-3(5))*** Univ. of Washington Pr.

Krone, Larry. Larry Krone: Artist/Entertainer, 1 vol. 2006. (ENG., Illus.). 56p. lthr. 75.00 *(978-0-9777528-0-5(1))* Contemporary Art Museum St. Louis.

Kroner, Magdalena, et al, texts. Giacomo Santiago Rogado: First Second Patience. 2010. (ENG., Illus.). 132p. 45.00 *(978-3-86678-246-4(2))* Kerber Verlag DEU. Dist: D.A.P./Distributed Art Pubs.

Kung, Christian Kerez: Construction, Privacy, Politics, Conflicts & Obsessions. Kueng, Moritz, ed. 2009. (ENG., Illus.). 200p. pap. 45.00 *(978-3-7757-2280-3(7))* Hatje Cantz Verlag GmbH & Co KG DEU. Dist: D.A.P./Distributed Art Pubs.

Kuntverlag, Deutscher, ed. Christiane Moebus: Chausseestrasse. 2008. (GER & ENG., Illus.). 112p. pap. 29.95 *(978-3-422-06702-8(7)*, Art Stock Bks. Ltd/Csi) Continental Sales, Inc.

Kunz, Sabine, ed. Observing Beast, Time, Evolution: Art & Natural Science. 2009. (ENG., Illus.). 128p. pap. 28.50 *(978-3-86678-206-8(3))* Kerber Verlag DEU. Dist: D.A.P./Distributed Art Pubs.

Kurjakovic, Daniel, et al, texts. Conflicting Tales. 2010. (ENG., Illus.). 228p. 49.95 *(978-3-03764-070-8(7))* JRP Ringier Kunstverlag AG CHE. Dist: D.A.P./Distributed Art Pubs.

La Spina, Elena & Nancy, Jean-Luc, texts. Claudio Parmiggiani: L'Lsola del Silenzio. 2007. (ITA., Illus.). 104p. pap. 37.00 *(978-88-422-1409-0(4))* Allemandi, Umberto & Co. GBR. Dist: Antique Collectors' Club.

Laguna Art Museum. In the Land of Retinal Delights. 2008. (Illus.). 160p. *(978-1-58423-317-6(6))* Laguna Art Museum Store.

Lamonaca, Marianne, et al. Liberty, Equality, & Fraternity. Lamonaca, Marianne, ed. 2011. (ENG.). pap. 50.00 ***(978-0-9677359-4-8(7))*** Wolfsonian-Florida International Univ., The.

Lamp, Frederick John, et al, contrib. by. Accumulating Histories: African Art from the Charles B. Benenson Collection at the Yale University Art Gallery. 2012. (ENG., Illus.). 328p. 75.00 ***(978-0-300-16992-8(2))*** Yale Univ. Art Gallery.

Lange, Christiane. Realismus: Das Abenteuer der Wirklichkeit. Katalogbuch zur Ausstellung in Emden, Kunsthalle Emden, 23.01.-24.05.2010, München, Kunsthalle der Hypo-Kulturstiftung, 11.06.2010-05.09.2010. Lange, C. & Ohlsen, Nils, eds. 2010. (GER., Illus.). 300p. (C). 59.00 *(978-3-7774-2421-7(8))* Hirmer Verlag GmbH DEU. Dist: Brown, David Bk. Co., The.

Lark Books. Quilt National 2011. 2011. (Quilt National Ser.). (ENG., Illus.). 112p. 27.95 *(978-1-60059-799-2(8))* Lark Bks.

Lark Books Staff. Quilt National 2009: The Best of Contemporary Quilts - More Than 80 Inspiring Creations. 2009. (Quilt National Ser.). (ENG., Illus.). 112p. 24.95 *(978-1-60059-423-6(9))* Lark Bks.

Lee, Tim. Tim Lee: Capp Street Project. 2008. (ENG., Illus.). 88p. pap. 15.99 *(978-0-9802055-0-3(5))* CCA Wattis Institute for Contemporary Arts.

Leismann, Burhad & Scherer, Ralf. Diagnosis (Art) Contemporary Art Reflecting Medicine. 2007. 220p. *(978-3-87909-902-3(2))* Wienand GmbH, Druck- & Verlagshaus.

Lenore, Malen. Lenore Malen: The New Society for Universal Harmony. 2007. pap. 8.00 *(978-0-9791843-6-9(3))* CUE Art Foundation.

Leon, Eli. Something Pertaining to God: The Patchwork Art of Rosie Lee Tompkins. 2007. (Illus.). 32p. 12.95 *(978-0-939384-33-4(7))* Shelburne Museum, Inc.

Libin, Liu, et al, eds. Visible/Invisible, 1 vol. 2008. (ENG., Illus.). 240p. 80.00 *(978-988-99265-7-1(1))* Timezone 8 Ltd. HKG. Dist: D.A.P./Distributed Art Pubs.

Lindbergh, Peter, photos by. Anish Kapoor: Monumenta 2011. 2011. (ENG., Illus.). 96p. pap. 20.00 ***(978-2-7118-5817-0(0))*** Editions de la Reunion des Musees nationaux FRA. Dist: D.A.P./Distributed Art Pubs.

Littman, Brett & Cadava, Eduardo. Leon Golub: Live & Die Like a Lion? 2010. (Drawing Papers). (Illus.). pap. 20.00 *(978-0-942324-59-4(5))* Drawing Ctr.

Löckemann Karst & Eeley, Peter. Imagination Becomes Reality Pa. 2007. (GER & ENG., Illus.). 214p. 40.00 *(978-3-939894-02-5(8))* Goetz, Ingvild, Kunstverlag, GmbH DEU. Dist: D.A.P./Distributed Art Pubs.

Lockemann, Karsten, ed. Jan Davidoff, 2005-2009. 2010. (ENG., Illus.). 100p. 40.00 *(978-3-86678-281-5(0))* Kerber Verlag DEU. Dist: D.A.P./Distributed Art Pubs.

Lorenz, Ulrike. Tobias Rehberger 1997 -2009: Public. 2010. (ENG.). 104p. 44.00 *(978-3-86832-016-9(4)*, Art Stock Bks. Ltd/Csi) Continental Sales, Inc.

Lorz, Julienne, ed. Stop, Repair, Prepare. 2009. (GER & ENG., Illus.). 80p. 49.95 *(978-3-86560-474-3(9))* Verlag der Buchhandlung Walther Konig DEU. Dist: D.A.P./Distributed Art Pubs.

Lu, Shengzhong. Square Earth, Round Heaven. 2007. (CHI & ENG., Illus.). 128p. pap. 40.00 *(978-0-9787666-4-1(4))* Chambers Fine Art LLC.

Lyle, Val. The Truths: The brutal tenderness of Appalachia. 2009. pap. *(978-1-61584-0'9-9(2))* Independent Pub.

Lynch, David. David Lynch: Lithos. 2010. (ENG & FRE., Illus.). 192p. 60.00 *(978-3-7757-2673-3(X))* Hatje Cantz Verlag GmbH & Co KG DEU. Dist: D.A.P./Distributed Art Pubs.

Macel, Christine, ed. Philippe Parreno. 2009. (ENG., Illus.). 256p. 65.00 *(978-3-03764-033-3(2))* JRP Ringier Kunstverlag AG CHE. Dist: D.A.P./Distributed Art Pubs.

Maciejunes, Nannette V. Material Matters: Quiltmaking in the 21st Century. 2008. *(978-0-918881-63-2(3))* Columbus Museum of Art.

Manacorda, Francesco. Martian Museum of Terrestrial Art. 2008. (Illus.). 224p. 44.95 *(978-1-85894-459-3(7))* Merrell Pubs. Ltd. GBR. Dist: Perseus Distribution.

Mandragora. As Soon as Possible: Acceleration in Contemporary Society. 2011. (ENG & ITA., Illus.). 144p. 25.00 *(978-88-96532-11-9(6))* Mandragora ITA. Dist: Antique Collectors' Club.

Manetas, Miltos, ed. Neen, 1 vol. 2006. (ENG & ITA., Illus.). 168p. pap. 39.95 *(978-88-8158-601-1(0))* Charta ITA. Dist: D.A.P./Distributed Art Pubs.

Manifesta 8. 2010. (ENG., Illus.). 384p. pap. 50.00 *(978-88-366-1697-8(6))* Silvana ITA. Dist: D.A.P./Distributed Art Pubs.

Mann, Stephan, et al, texts. Talia Keinan: The mountain & the shivering fact. 2011. (ENG., Illus.). 80p. pap. 29.95 ***(978-3-86678-479-6(1))*** Kerber Verlag DEU. Dist: D.A.P./Distributed Art Pubs.

Marclay, Christian. Christian Marclay: Fourth of July, 1 vol. 2010. (ENG., Illus.). 128p. pap. 35.00 *(978-0-9753921-3-3(1))* Cooper, Paula Gallery.

Marcoci, Roxana & Eagleton, Terry, texts. Sanja Ivekovic? Sweet Violence. 2011. (ENG., Illus.). 192p. 50.00 ***(978-0-87070-811-4(2))*** Museum of Modern Art.

Marella, Primo, ed. Indonesian Art. 2010. (ENG., Illus.). 96p. 45.00 *(978-88-6208-131-3(6))* Damiani ITA. Dist: D.A.P./Distributed Art Pubs.

Mars, Chris. Tolerance. 2008. (Illus.). 176p. 40.00 *(978-0-86719-694-8(7))* Last Gasp of San Francisco.

Martinez, Daniel Joseph, contrib. by. Capitalism in Question (Because It Is) Ian Arenas, Matthew Brandt, James Melinat, Gabie Strong, Kara Tanaka, Grant Vetter. 2010. (ENG.). pap. *(978-0-615-31623-9(9))* Pitzer College Art Galleries.

Marziani, Gianluca & Mazzanti, Alexandra. Pop Surrealism: What a Wonderfool World. 2010. (ENG., Illus.). 96p. 34.95 *(978-88-88493-69-5(7))* Drago Arts & Communication ITA. Dist: SCB Distributors.

Massimo Barbero, Luca, text. Luigi Ontani: MarmArmonia, 1 vol. 2007. (ITA & ENG., Illus.). 104p. 34.95 *(978-88-8158-651-6(7))* Charta ITA. Dist: D.A.P./Distributed Art Pubs.

Matt, Gerald & Hug, Cath#xE9;rine, eds. Weltraum: Kunst und ein Traum. 2011. (ENG & GER., Illus.). 320p. pap. 60.00 ***(978-3-86984-175-5(3))*** Verlag fur Moderne Kunst DEU. Dist: D.A.P./Distributed Art Pubs.

McCallum, Bradley & Tarry, Jacqueline, illus. Whitewash, 1 vol. 2007. (ENG.). 77p. 30.00 *(978-988-99264-1-0(5))* Timezone 8 Ltd. HKG. Dist: D.A.P./Distributed Art Pubs.

McCarthy, Paul. Paul Mccarthy's Low Life Slow Life. 2010. (ENG., Illus.). 640p. pap. 75.00 *(978-3-7757-2573-6(3))* Hatje Cantz Verlag GmbH & Co KG DEU. Dist: D.A.P./Distributed Art Pubs.

McCarthy, Tom & Petersens, Magnus, texts. Eclipse: Art in a Dark Age, 1 vol. 2008. (ENG., Illus.). 160p. pap. 40.00 *(978-3-86521-643-4(9))* Steidl, Gerhard Druckerei und Verlag DEU. Dist: Innovative Logistics.

McDonnell, Patricia. Marsden Hartley: American Modern. 2007. (ENG., Illus.). 84p. per. 27.95 *(978-1-885116-12-3(8))* Weisman, Frederick R. Art Museum.

McGee, Mike & Frankel, David. Manuel Pardo: Universo Soñado in Technicolor. 2011.Tr. of Universal Dream in Technicolor. (Illus.). 277p. 45.00 ***(978-0-9817987-6-9(4))*** Grand Central Pr.

McVaugh, Robert. An Architect's Vision: Paul Rudolph & Colgate's Creative Arts Center. 2011. (Illus.). 48p. pap. 0.00 net. ***(978-0-9729352-6-5(6))*** Picker Art Gallery.

Mehretu, Julie, contrib. by. Huma Bhabha, 1 vol. 2011. (ENG.). 140p. 75.00 *(978-0-935875-25-6(5))* Blum, Peter Edition.

Mercurio, Gianni & Paparoni, Demetrio, eds. Timer: Contemporary Art after Nine Eleven. 2008. (ITA & ENG., Illus.). 320p. pap. 50.00 *(978-88-6130-190-0(8))* Skira Editore ITA. Dist: Random Hse., Inc.

Michael, Linda. 21st Century Modern: 2006 Adelaide Biennial of Australian Art. 2006. (Illus.). 88p. 24.95 *(978-0-7308-3038-2(1))* Art Gallery of South Australia AUS. Dist: Antique Collectors' Club.

Miguel Luciano. 2007. 8.00 *(978-0-9776417-8-9(3))* CUE Art Foundation.

Miller, Dana, ed. Legacy: The Emily Fisher Landau Collection. 2011. (ENG., Illus.). 388p. 75.00 *(978-0-300-17108-2(0))* Yale Univ. Pr.

Modern Institute Staff & Peterson, Mick. Tony Swain Paintings. 2010. (ENG., Illus.). 64p. pap. 22.95 *(978-3-8321-9040-8(6))* DuMont DEU. Dist: D.A.P./Distributed Art Pubs.

Mohr, Daniel, illus. Daniel Mohr: Zuruck Zur Natur/Back to Nature, 1 vol. 2007. (ENG.). 88p. 38.00 *(978-3-86678-049-1(4))* Kerber Verlag DEU. Dist: D.A.P./Distributed Art Pubs.

Monahan, Matthew. Matthew Monahan. 2012. (ENG., Illus.). 248p. 60.00 ***(978-3-7757-3164-5(4))*** Hatje Cantz Verlag GmbH & Co KG DEU. Dist: D.A.P./Distributed Art Pubs.

Monem, Nadine, ed. Contemporary Art in the Middle East: Artworld. 2009. (ENG., Illus.). 240p. 49.95 *(978-1-906155-56-8(9))* Black Dog Publishing Ltd. GBR. Dist: Perseus Distribution.

Mosaka, Tumelo. Infinite Island: Contemporary Caribbean Art. 2007. (ENG., Illus.). 224p. 58.00 *(978-0-85667-641-3(1))* Wilson, Philip Pubs., Ltd. GBR. Dist: Macmillan.

Mosaka, Tumelo, et al. Infinite Island: Contemporary Caribbean Art. 2007. pap. *(978-0-87273-158-5(8))* Brooklyn Museum, The.

Mosquera, Gerardo, et al. Tania Bruguera on the Political Imaginary. 2010. (ENG., Illus.). 144p. pap. 39.95 *(978-88-8158-764-3(5))* Charta ITA. Dist: D.A.P./Distributed Art Pubs.

Mosset, Olivier, et al, texts. Born To Be Wild. Homage to Steven Parrino. 2010. (ENG., Illus.). 96p. pap. 40.00 *(978-3-941185-55-5(1))* Verlag fur Moderne Kunst DEU. Dist: D.A.P./Distributed Art Pubs.

Mossinger, Ingrid & Ritter, Beate. Björn Nörgaard: Mythos und Morphologie. 2010. (ENG.). 128p. 58.00 *(978-3-86832-001-5(6)*, Art Stock Bks. Ltd/Csi) Continental Sales, Inc.

Mucha, Stefan, pref. The Way Things Are. 2008. (ENG., Illus.). 216p. pap. 48.00 *(978-3-86560-485-9(4))* Verlag der Buchhandlung Walther Konig DEU. Dist: D.A.P./Distributed Art Pubs.

Müller, Vanessa Joan, et al, eds. Ian Wallace: A Literary of Images. 2008. (Illus.). 220p. 49.95 *(978-1-933128-51-1(8))* Sternberg Pr.

Munder, Heike, ed. & text. Tatiana Trouvé. 2011. (ENG., Illus.). 228p. 75.00 *(978-3-86560-858-1(2))* Verlag der Buchhandlung Walther Konig DEU. Dist: D.A.P./Distributed Art Pubs.

Munder, Heike & Trummer, Thomas, eds. Displaced Fractures. 2011. (ENG & GER., Illus.). 112p. 45.00 ***(978-3-03764-177-4(0))*** JRP Ringier Kunstverlag AG CHE. Dist: D.A.P./Distributed Art Pubs.

Munroe, Alexandra & Cai, Guoqiang. I Want to Believe. 2008. (Illus.). 315p. pap. *(978-0-89207-372-6(1))* Guggenheim, Solomon R. Museum.

Muz, Julie Atlas, et al. Womanizer. 2007. (Illus.). 48p. per. 20.00 *(978-0-9778686-1-2(3))* Deitch, Jeffrey Inc.

Nakashima, Tom, et al. Tom Nakashima: Two Decades. 2007. (Illus.). 44p. pap. *(978-1-890021-20-7(2))* Morris Museum of Art.

Nashat, Shahryar. Shahryar Nashat: Downscaled & Overthrown. 2011. (Illus.). 157p. 32.00 ***(978-1-934105-26-9(0))*** Sternberg Pr.

Neff, John H. & Silverman, Lanny. Karl Wirsum: Winsome Works(some) 2007. (Illus.). 68p. pap. 25.00 *(978-0-938903-40-6(3))* City of Chicago, Dept. of Cultural Affairs.

Netzhammer. Yves Netzhammer. 2009. (GER & ENG., Illus.). 216p. 60.00 *(978-3-7757-2318-3(8))* Hatje Cantz Verlag GmbH & Co KG DEU. Dist: D.A.P./Distributed Art Pubs.

Noorthoorn, Victoria, ed. Beginning with a Bang! From Confrontation to Intimacy. 2008. (David Rockefeller Center for Latin American Studies, Art Cat Ser.). (Illus.). 108p. pap. 22.95 *(978-1-879128-34-7(9))* Americas Society.

Ochoa Foster, Elena, ed. Drama Turquesa: Los Carpinteros. 2010. (SPA & ENG., Illus.). 166p. pap. 39.95 *(978-0-9564339-1-6(X))* Ivory Pr. ESP. Dist: Actar Birkhauser Distribution.

Okenholt, Marianne Torp. Reality Check: Statens Museum for Kunst Copenhagen, 6 September 2008-4 January 2009. 2008. (Illus.). 144p. *(978-87-92023-21-6(5))* Statens Museum for Kunst.

of California, Phranc. Phranc: The Cardboard Cobbler. 2007. pap. 8.00 *(978-0-9797964-0-1(7))* CUE Art Foundation.

Oliver-Smith, Kerry, et al. Project Europa: Imagining the (Im)possible. 2010. (ENG., Illus.). 116p. pap. 29.95 *(978-0-9762552-9-1(4))* Univ. Pr. of Florida.

Oliver, Valerie Cassel, ed. & text. Hand + Made: the Performative Impulse in Art & Craft. 2010. (ENG., Illus.). 100p. pap. 19.95 *(978-1-933619-26-2(0))* Contemporary Arts Museum, Houston.

On&on. 2011. (ENG & SPA.). 110p. pap. 29.95 *(978-84-96917-75-0(4))* Caja de Madrid ESP. Dist: Actar Birkhauser Distribution.

Oppenheim, Dennis. Dennis Oppenheim. 2012. (ENG & FRE., Illus.). 136p. pap. 30.00 ***(978-88-366-2044-9(2))*** Silvana ITA. Dist: D.A.P./Distributed Art Pubs.

Pace, Stephen. Stephen Pace: Abstract Expressionist. 2011. (Illus.). 32p. ***(978-1-935617-11-2(7)***, Orbit Books) Spanierman Gallery.

Paiano, Rosalba & Barbero, Luca Massimo, texts. David Tremlett. 2009. (ENG., Illus.). 106p. pap. 35.00 *(978-88-6208-083-5(2))* Damiani ITA. Dist: D.A.P./Distributed Art Pubs.

Pakesch, Peter. China Welcomes You. 2008. (GER & ENG., Illus.). 175p. pap. 49.95 *(978-3-86560-271-8(1))* Verlag der Buchhandlung Walther Konig DEU. Dist: D.A.P./Distributed Art Pubs.

Pakesch, Peter, ed. Catch Me! Geschwindigkeit fassen: Catch Me! Grasping Speed. 2010. (ENG & GER., Illus.). 120p. pap. 34.50 *(978-3-86560-784-3(5))* Verlag der Buchhandlung Walther Konig DEU. Dist: D.A.P./Distributed Art Pubs.

Pakesch, Peter & Diederichsen, Diedrich, eds. Schere - Stein - Papier. / Rock - Paper - Scissors. Pop-Musik als Gegenstand Bildender Kunst / Pop Music as Subject of Visual Art. 2010. (ENG & GER., Illus.). 140p. pap. 48.00 *(978-3-86560-657-0(1))* Verlag der Buchhandlung Walther Konig DEU. Dist: D.A.P./Distributed Art Pubs.

Papcun, Martin. House, turned inside Out. 2012. (ENG., Illus.). 84p. 50.00 ***(978-0-9761920-2-2(0))*** CEC ArtsLink.

Parreno, Philippe & Obrist, Hans Ulrich, texts. Hans Ulrich Obrist & Philippe Parreno: the Conversation Series. 2008. (ENG., Illus.). 154p. pap. 22.00 *(978-3-86560-340-1(8))* Verlag der Buchhandlung Walther Konig DEU. Dist: D.A.P./Distributed Art Pubs.

Phillips, Christopher. Shanghai Kaleidoscope. 2008. (ENG., Illus.). 144p. 59.99 *(978-0-88854-460-5(X))*; pap. 34.99 *(978-0-88854-461-2(8))* Royal Ontario Museum CAN. Dist: Univ. of Toronto Pr.

Phillips, Lisa, text. Skin Fruit. 2010. (ENG., Illus.). 208p. pap. 45.00 *(978-1-935202-19-6(7))* New Museum of Contemporary Art, The.

Phillips, Sam. Frieze Art Fair Yearbook 2011 - 12. 2011. (ENG., Illus.). 530p. pap. 35.00 ***(978-0-9553201-7-0(8))*** Frieze GBR. Dist: D.A.P./Distributed Art Pubs.

Philosophy of Time Travel. 2007. per. *(978-0-942949-33-9(1))* Studio Museum in Harlem, The.

Picton, John, et al, eds. The Poetics of Cloth: African Textiles/Recent Art. 2009. (ENG., Illus.). 112p. pap. 25.00 *(978-0-615-22083-3(5))* Grey Art Gallery & Study Ctr., New York Univ.

Politi, Gea, et al, eds. Prague Biennale, No. 4. 2010. (ENG., Illus.). 364p. pap. 35.00 *(978-88-7816-149-8(7))* Politi, Giancarlo Editore ITA. Dist: D.A.P./Distributed Art Pubs.

Ponciroli, Virginia, ed. Biennale Puglia 2008: Young Artists from Europe & the Mediteranean [in English & Italian]. 2008. 272p. pap. 57.50 *(978-88-370-6382-5(2))* Electa ITA. Dist: Trans-Atlantic Pubns., Inc.

Porter, Jenelle & Mitchell, Harvey, texts. Joshua Mosley: Dread. 2009. (ENG., Illus.). 32p. 25.00 *(978-0-88454-116-5(9))* Univ. of Pennsylvania, Institute of Contemporary Art.

Porter, Venetia, et al. Ahmed Mater. 2010. (ENG & ARA., Illus.). 160p. 40.00 *(978-1-86154-318-9(2))* Booth-Clibborn Editions GBR. Dist: Hachette Bk. Group.

Preheim, Peggy. Peggy Preheim. 2008. (ENG., Illus.). 144p. 60.00 *(978-0-9800242-1-0(8))* Miller, Gregory & Co.

Price, Marshall. The Abstract Impulse: Fifty Years of Abstraction at the National Academy, 1956-2006. 2007. (ENG., Illus.). 88p. pap. 29.50 *(978-1-887149-17-4(1))* Hudson Hills Pr. LLC.

Ptak, Elisabeth. Ranches Rolling. 2008. (Illus.). 148p. 50.00 *(978-0-915269-25-9(2))* Windgate Pr.

Quintanilla, Faustino. A Life for Art: The Jaime Andrade Collection. 2011. ***(978-1-936658-07-7(0))*** QCC Art Gallery.

Rabottini, Alessandro, ed. Permanent Mimesis: An Exhibition about Simulation & Realism. 2010. 112p. 47.50 *(978-88-370-7793-8(9))* Electa ITA. Dist: Trans-Atlantic Pubns., Inc.

Ramirez, Mari Carmen & Pacheco, Marcelo. Modern & Contemporary Masterworks from MALBA. 2012. (ENG., Illus.). 156p. 35.00 ***(978-0-300-18100-5(0))*** Museum of Fine Arts, Houston.

Rapaport, Brooke Kamin, et al. Houdini: Art & Magic. 2010. (Illus.). 280p. 39.95 *(978-0-300-14684-4(1))* Yale Univ. Pr.

Rapp, James. Observations: Selected Sketches from the Commonplace Books of James Rapp 1956-2006. 100th ltd. ed. 2007. *(978-0-9777432-0-9(9))* Cattle Track Pr.

Reifenscheid, Beate, ed. China's Revision: Focus Beijing. 2009. (CHI, GER & ENG., Illus.). 144p. 39.95 *(978-3-7913-4274-0(6))* Prestel Publishing.

Reifenscheid, Beate, ed. The Final Freedom: from the Pioneers of Land Art. 2011. (GER & ENG., Illus.). 192p. pap. 40.00 ***(978-88-366-2002-9(7))*** Silvana ITA. Dist: D.A.P./Distributed Art Pubs.

Reilly, Maura & Nochlin, Linda. Global Feminisms: New Directions in Contemporary Art. 2007. (Illus.). 304p. pap. *(978-0-87273-157-8(X))* Merrell Pubs. Ltd.

Resnick, Mark. The American Image: U. S. Posters from the 19th to the 21st Century. 2nd ed. 2007. (Illus.). 112p. 29.99 *(978-1-933360-28-7(3)*, RIT Cary Graphic Arts Pr.) Rochester Institute of Technology, Cary Graphic Arts Pr.

Resnick, Mark & Remington, R. Roger. The American Image: U. S. Posters from the 19th to the 21st Century. 2nd ed. 2007. (Illus.). 112p. 50.00 *(978-1-933360-27-0(5)*, RIT Cary Graphic Arts Pr.) Rochester Institute of Technology, Cary Graphic Arts Pr.

Richter, Daniel, illus. Die Palette 1995-2007. 2007. 248p. 60.00 *(978-3-8321-9001-9(5))* Merrell Pubs. Ltd. GBR. Dist: Perseus Distribution.

Robert Seydel. 2007. 8.00 *(978-0-9791843-2-1(0))* CUE Art Foundation.

Rodriguez Fominaya, Álvaro. Weather Report: Cambio Climático y Artes Visuales. 2008. (ENG & SPA., Illus.). 352p. *(978-84-89152-86-1(1))* Actar Birkhauser Distribution.

Rogers, Bertha & Smith, Keith A. Book Arts 2008, Bright Hill Center. 2008. 80p. pap. 16.00 *(978-1-892471-56-7(6))* Bright Hill Pr.

Ron, Linden. Ron Linden. 2007. pap. 8.00 *(978-0-9791843-9-0(8))* CUE Art Foundation.

Roques, K. A. V. Contemporary Art from Egypt. 2008. (ENG.). 200p. 59.00 *(978-3-87909-938-2(3))* Wienand GmbH, Druck- & Verlagshaus DEU. Dist: Independent Pubs. Group.

Roselione-Valadez, Juan, ed. Beg Borrow & Steal: Rubell Family Collection. 2011. (ENG., Illus.). 272p. pap. 49.95 *(978-0-9821195-2-5(6))* Rubell Family Collection.

Rosen, Kay. Kay Rosen: AKAK. 2010. (ENG., Illus.). 232p. 49.95 *(978-0-9815449-5-3(9))* Regency Arts Pr.

Rosenthal, Norman. Julian Schnabel: Permanently Becoming & the Architecture of Seeing. 2012. (ENG., Illus.). 150p. 65.00 ***(978-88-572-1102-2(9))*** Skira Editore ITA. Dist: Random Hse., Inc.

Rubell Family Collection Staff, contrib. by. Red Eye: L.A. Artists from the Rubell Family Collection, December 6, 2006-May 31, 2007. 2008. (ENG., Illus.). 218p. 40.00 *(978-0-9789888-7-6(6))* Rubell Family Collection.

Rubin, David S. Psychedelic: Optical & Visionary Art since the 1960s. 2010. (ENG., Illus.). 138p. (gr. 17). 29.95 *(978-0-262-01404-5(1))* MIT Pr.

Ruckhaberle, Christoph. Die Flasche Bakbuk, 1 vol. 2006. (ENG & GER., Illus.). 128p. 55.00 *(978-3-938025-29-1(8))* Kerber Verlag DEU. Dist: D.A.P./Distributed Art Pubs.

Ruf, Beatrix, ed. Blasted Allegories. 2008. (ENG., Illus.). 300p. 65.00 *(978-3-905829-40-2(1))* JRP Ringier Kunstverlag AG CHE. Dist: D.A.P./Distributed Art Pubs.

Rugg, Judith & Sedgwick, Michèle, eds. Issues in Curating Contemporary Art & Performance. 2012. 184p. pap. 30.00 ***(978-1-84150-536-7(6))*** Intellect, Ltd. GBR. Dist: Chicago Distribution Ctr.

Rugoff, Ralph, ed. Amateurs. 2008. (ENG., Illus.). 112p. pap. 29.99 *(978-0-9802055-1-0(4))* CCA Wattis Institute for Contemporary Arts.

Ruiz, Alma, text. Suprasensorial: Experiments in Light, Color, & Space. 2012. (SPA & ENG., Illus.). 148p. pap. 45.00 *(978-1-933751-16-0(9))* Museum of Contemporary Art, Los Angeles.

Ruiz, Alma & Cixous, Hélène, texts. Moca Focus: Alexandra Grant, 1 vol. 2007. (ENG., Illus.). 72p. pap. 24.95 *(978-1-933751-01-6(0))* Museum of Contemporary Art, Los Angeles.

Russ, Nadia. Neopoprealism Starz: 21st Century Art Compendium of New Millennium Contemporary Art. 2009. 64p. pap. 31.99 *(978-1-4415-7085-7(3))* Xlibris Corp.

Russ, Sabine & Volk, Gregory. Surface Charge. 2006. (ENG., Illus.). 56p. per. 20.00 *(978-0-935519-26-0(9))* Anderson Gallery.

Salmond, Amiria & Raymond, Rosanna, eds. Pasifika Styles: Artists Inside the Museum. 2008. (Illus.). 146p. (C). pap. 49.99 *(978-1-877372-60-5(9))* Otago University Pr. NZL. Dist: International Specialized Bk. Services.

Samman, Nadim, ed. One of a Thousand Ways to Defeat Entropy: Hans Op de Beeck, Adrian Ghenie, Ryoichi Kurokawa, Alexander Ponomarev. 2011. (ENG., Illus.). 160p. 60.00 ***(978-3-7757-3189-8(X))*** Hatje Cantz Verlag GmbH & Co KG DEU. Dist: D.A.P./Distributed Art Pubs.

San Francisco Museum of Modern Art Staff, contrib. by. Calder to Warhol: Introducing the Fisher Collection. 2010. *(978-0-918471-85-7(0))* San Francisco Museum of Modern Art.

Sans, Jerome. Stray Alchemists: Matt Bryans, Amy Granat, Lim Tzay Chuen, Takeshi Murata, Robin Rhode, Sterling Ruby. Fowle, Kate, ed. 2009. (ENG., Illus.). 140p. pap. 23.00 *(978-988-17521-3-0(2))* Timezone 8 Ltd. HKG. Dist: D.A.P./Distributed Art Pubs.

Sans, Jerome, text. Breaking Forecast. 2011. (ENG., Illus.). 226p. pap. 35.00 *(978-988-18816-7-0(6))* Timezone 8 Ltd. HKG. Dist: D.A.P./Distributed Art Pubs.

Sarmento, Juli#xE3;o. Juli#xE3;o Sarmento: Close Distance. 2011. (ENG., Illus.). 128p. 35.00 ***(978-84-343-1278-4(6))*** Polígrafa, Ediciones, S. A. ESP. Dist: D.A.P./Distributed Art Pubs.

Sasse, Julie. Thanks for Being with Us: Contemporary Art from the Douglas Nielsen Collection. 2010. (ENG., Illus.). 52p. pap. 20.00 *(978-0-911611-39-7(8))* Tucson Museum of Art.

Sasse, Julie, et al. Trouble in Paradise: Examining Discord Between Nature & Society. 2009. (Illus.). 206p. *(978-0-911611-37-3(1))* Tucson Museum of Art.

Sasse, Julie R. An Eclectic Eye: Selections from the Dan leach Collection. 2007. (Illus.). 180p. pap. 30.00 *(978-0-911611-34-2(7))* Tucson Museum of Art.

Satellite of Love. 2007. 150.00 *(978-1-931867-03-0(8))* Museum of Contemporary Art, Denver.

Scala, Mark W., ed. Fairy Tales, Monsters, & the Genetic Imagination. 2012. (Frist Center for the Visual Arts Title Ser.). (ENG., Illus.). 160p. pap. 29.95 *(978-0-8265-1814-9(1))* Vanderbilt Univ. Pr.

Scardi, Gabi, et al, texts. Aware: Art Fashion Identity. 2011. (ENG., Illus.). 256p. pap. 40.00 *(978-88-6208-162-7(6))* Damiani ITA. Dist: D.A.P./Distributed Art Pubs.

Schaffner, Ingrid, et al, texts. Dirt on Delight: Impulses That Form Clay. 2009. (ENG., Illus.). 112p. pap. 35.00 *(978-0-88454-117-2(7))* Univ. of Pennsylvania, Institute of Contemporary Art.

Schmal, Peter & Wenjun, Zhi, eds. M8 in China: Contemporary Chinese Architects. Zeitgenössische chinesische Architekten. 2010. (ENG., Illus.). 160p. 39.95 *(978-3-86859-025-8(0))* Jovis Verlag GmbH DEU. Dist: D.A.P./Distributed Art Pubs.

Schmuckli, Claudia. 2008 Houston Area Exhibition. 2008. (Illus.). 44p. pap. *(978-0-941193-42-9(X))* Blaffer Art Museum.

Schmuckli, Claudia, frwd. Bitter, Black Thoughts. 2011. (ENG., Illus.). 104p. pap. 29.99 *(978-0-941193-48-1(9))* Blaffer Art Museum.

Schmuckli, Claudia, et al, texts. Gabriel Kuri: Nobody Needs to Know the Price of Your Saab. 2011. (ENG., Illus.). 130p. pap. 39.99 *(978-0-941193-49-8(7))* Blaffer Art Museum.

Schopf, Christine & Stocker, Gerfried, eds. Ars Electronica 2009: Human Nature. 2010. (ENG., Illus.). 431p. pap. 45.00 *(978-3-7757-2498-2(2))* Hatje Cantz Verlag GmbH & Co KG DEU. Dist: D.A.P./Distributed Art Pubs.

Schulman, Michael. Francesco Vezzoli: Right You Are (If You Think You Are) Castellani, Valentina & McDonald, Alison, eds. 2009. (ENG., Illus.). 128p. pap. 39.95 *(978-88-8158-666-0(5))* Charta ITA. Dist: D.A.P./Distributed Art Pubs.

Schwabsky, Barry, text. Chloe Piene. 2008. (ENG., Illus.). 104p. 45.00 *(978-2-907650-33-5(5))* Carre d'Art FRA. Dist: D.A.P./Distributed Art Pubs.

Schwenk, Bernhart & Gohlke, Gierret, texts. Albert Weis: Condition, 1 vol. 2008. (ENG., Illus.). 112p. (C). pap. 45.00 *(978-3-939738-65-7(4))* Verlag fur Moderne Kunst DEU. Dist: D.A.P./Distributed Art Pubs.

Sconce, Jeffrey. Mike Kelley: Exploded Fortress of Solitude. 2012. (ENG., Illus.). 200p. 100.00 ***(978-0-8478-3717-5(3))*** Rizzoli International Pubns., Inc.

Secrest, Tom. Tom Secrest. 2007. pap. 8.00 *(978-0-9797964-2-5(3))* CUE Art Foundation.

Seher Shah: Jihad Pop. 2008. (Illus.). 75p. pap. *(978-0-9815598-3-4(2))* Bose Pacia.

Seifermann, Ellen, ed. Her Home. 2009. (ENG., Illus.). 168p. 45.00 *(978-3-86678-186-3(5))* Kerber Verlag DEU. Dist: D.A.P./Distributed Art Pubs.

Seiffarth, Carsten. Singuhr 1996 - 2006: hoergalerie in parochial berlin. Seiffarth, Carsten, ed. 2011. (ENG., Illus.). 296p. 54.00 ***(978-3-939583-23-3(5))*** Kehrer Verlag Heidelberg, Klaus Kehrer DEU. Dist: Consortium Bk. Sales & Distribution.

Seligman, Rachel, et al. Infinite Images: Technologies of Printmaking & Beyond. Seligman, Rachel, ed. 2007. (Illus.). 32p. per. *(978-0-9763207-4-6(6))* Union College, Mandeville Gallery.

Serota, Nicholas & Godfrey, Mark, eds. Gerhard Richter: Panorama, 1 vol. 2011. (ENG.). 288p. 65.00 ***(978-1-935202-71-4(5))*** D.A.P./Distributed Art Pubs.

Seyfarth, Ludwig, et al, texts. Thorsten Passfeld: It's Me Again. 2011. (ENG., Illus.). 128p. 39.95 *(978-3-86678-408-6(2))* Kerber Verlag DEU. Dist: D.A.P./Distributed Art Pubs.

Shapiro, Mark, ed. A Chosen Path: The Ceramic Art of Karen Karnes. 2010. (ENG., Illus.). 129p. 40.00 *(978-0-8078-3427-5(0))* Univ. of North Carolina Pr.

Simon, Jane, et al, texts. Return to Function. 2009. (ENG., Illus.). 96p. pap. 24.95 *(978-0-913883-35-8(2))* Madison Art Ctr., Inc.

Sims, Lowery Stokes & King-Hammond, Leslie, eds. Global Africa Project. 2010. (Illus.). 224p. 45.00 *(978-3-7913-5084-4(6))* Prestel Publishing.

Sinnreich, Ursula, ed. James Turrell: Geometrie des Lichts. 2009. (ENG & GER., Illus.). 128p. 55.00 *(978-3-7757-2369-5(2))* Hatje Cantz Verlag GmbH & Co KG DEU. Dist: D.A.P./Distributed Art Pubs.

Skira, et al, eds. Lights On: Norwegian Contemporary Art. 2009. (ENG., Illus.). 192p. pap. 45.00 *(978-88-6130-792-6(2))* Skira Editore ITA. Dist: Random Hse., Inc.

Smerling, Walter. Doing It My Way: Perspectives on Belgian Art. 2008. (GER & ENG., Illus.). 104p. pap. 49.00 *(978-3-87909-954-2(5)*, Art Stock Bks. Ltd/Csi) Continental Sales, Inc.

Smith, Allison. Allison Smith: Needle Work. 2010. (Illus.). 64p. pap. 15.00 *(978-0-936316-30-7(6))* Washington Univ., Mildred Lane Kemper Art Museum.

Smith, Valerie, et al, texts. Generation 1. 5. 2009. (ENG., Illus.). 176p. 24.95 *(978-1-929641-13-0(3))* Queens Museum of Art.

Sofa Chicago 2008. 2008. per. 15.00 net. *(978-0-9789206-1-6(9))* Art Fair Co., Inc., The.

Sofa new York 2007. 2007. per. 20.00 *(978-0-9713714-8-4(2))* Art Fair Co., Inc., The.

Sofa new York 2008. 2008. per. 15.00 net. *(978-0-9789206-0-9(0))* Art Fair Co., Inc., The.

Solway, Carl, text. The Greatest Use of Life Is to Spend It for Something That Outlasts It: University of Kentucky Art Faculty Exhibition. var. ed. 2007. *(978-0-9779541-2-4(9))* Univ. of Kentucky Art Museum.

Spanjaard, Helena & Welling, Wouter. The Dono Code: Installations, Sculptures, Paintings. 2009. 72p. pap. 29.95 *(978-94-6022-052-4(5))* Royal Tropical Institute Pr. (KIT (Koninklijk Instituut voor de Tropen) NLD. Dist: Stylus Publishing, LLC.

Spoor, Nathan. Suggestivism. 2011. (ENG., Illus.). 237p. 34.95 ***(978-1-58423-447-0(4))*** Gingko Pr., Inc.

Stallabrass, Julian, et al, texts. Haegue Yang: Wild Against Gravity. 2012. (ENG., Illus.). 190p. 45.00 ***(978-1-901352-52-8(8))*** Museum of Modern Art, Oxford GBR. Dist: D.A.P./Distributed Art Pubs.

Starkman, Christine & Zelevansky, Lynn. Your Bright Future: 12 Contemporary Artists from Korea. 2009. (Illus.). 208p. 50.00 *(978-0-300-14689-9(2))* Museum of Fine Arts, Houston.

Starling, Simon. Simon Starling: the Nanjing Particles. 2009. (ENG., Illus.). 96p. pap. 32.00 *(978-0-9764276-7-4(2))* MASS MoCA Foundation, The.

Stegmann, Markus, ed. Ulrich Meister. 2010. (ENG., Illus.). 168p. 55.00 *(978-3-7757-2475-3(3))* Hatje Cantz Verlag GmbH & Co KG DEU. Dist: D.A.P./Distributed Art Pubs.

Stemmrich, Gregor. Rita Mcbride: Public Works. 2010. (ENG.). 280p. pap. 55.00 *(978-3-8321-9156-6(9))* DuMont DEU. Dist: D.A.P./Distributed Art Pubs.

Stohler, Peter & Rüttimann, Sylvia. Risk & Allure. 2007. (ENG & GER., Illus.). 160p. 15.00 *(978-3-89790-248-0(6))* Arnoldsche Art Pubs. DEU. Dist: Antique Collectors' Club.

Storr, Robert. Nalini Malani: Listening to the Shades. 2009. (ENG., Illus.). 160p. 55.00 *(978-88-8158-703-2(3))* Charta ITA. Dist: D.A.P./Distributed Art Pubs.

Subiros, Pep. Apartheid: The South African Mirror. 2007. (Illus.). 205p. pap. *(978-84-96954-03-8(X))* Actar Birkhauser Distribution.

Subiros, Pep, ed. Apartheid: El Espejo Sudafricano. 2007. (Illus.). 204p. per. *(978-84-96954-02-1(1))* Actar Birkhauser Distribution.

Subotnick, Ali, text. Nine Live: Visionary Artists from L. A. 2009. (ENG., Illus.). 200p. 30.00 *(978-0-943739-36-6(5))* Hammer Museum.

Suchan, Tom, et al, eds. Looking Both Ways: A Contemporary Art Exhibition Coinciding with the Centennial of the Xinhai Revolution. 2011. 72p. pap. 15.00 ***(978-0-912042-98-5(2))*** Eastern Michigan Univ. Pr.

Surls, James, ed. Finding Balance: Reconciling the Masculine/Feminine in Contemporary Art & Culture. 2006. (ENG., Illus.). 102p. 35.00 *(978-0-9787407-0-2(X))* Houston Ctr. for Contemporary Craft.

Szymczyk, Adam & Filipovic, Elena. When Things Cast No Shadow. 2008. (GER & ENG., Illus.). 592p. pap. 45.00 *(978-3-905829-58-7(4))* JRP Ringier Kunstverlag AG CHE. Dist: D.A.P./Distributed Art Pubs.

Tamayo, Museo. Felicidad Indecible. 2006. 83p. pap. 37.00 *(978-968-5979-09-2(X))* Trucatriche.

Tanguy, Sarah. Mapping: Memory & Motion in Contemporary Art. 2010. (Illus.). 52p. ***(978-0-915171-80-4(5))*** Katonah Gallery.

Tannenbaum, Judith. Wunderground: Providence, 1995 to the Present. 2006. (Illus.). 104p. per. 24.95 *(978-1-58423-262-9(5))* Gingko Pr., Inc.

Taragin, Davira S., et al. Bigger, Better, More: The Art of Viola Frey. 2009. (ENG., Illus.). 136p. 50.00 *(978-1-55595-305-8(0))* Hudson Hills Pr. LLC.

Tatay, Helena, ed. Anna Maria Maiolino. 2011. (ENG., Illus.). 256p. 45.00 *(978-3-86560-913-7(9))* Verlag der Buchhandlung Walther Konig DEU. Dist: D.A.P./Distributed Art Pubs.

Tayes, Debra Loomis, intro. Watercolor U. S. A. 2008. 2008. (Illus.). 24p. pap. 15.00 *(978-0-934306-61-4(3))* Springfield Art Museum.

Ten Curators Staff. Ice Cream, 10 Curators, 100 Contemporary Artists, 10 Source Artists. Phaidon Press Editors, ed. 2009. (ENG., Illus.). 448p. pap. 59.95 *(978-0-7148-4950-8(2))* Phaidon Pr., Inc.

Tennigkeit, Alex. Usurper's Choice: Eine ausgewählte Sammlung von Kuriosen Gemälden, Zeichnungen und Opjekten 2006 - 2009. 2010. (ENG., Illus.). 104p. 49.95 *(978-3-86678-179-5(2))* Kerber Verlag DEU. Dist: D.A.P./Distributed Art Pubs.

Teramoto, John Tadao & Tawara, Yusaku. Universe Is Flux: The Art of Tawara Yusaku, 1 vol. 2011. (ENG., Illus.). 144p. pap. 40.00 ***(978-0-295-99159-7(3))*** Univ. of Washington Pr.

Thater, Diana. — Drawing, Stretching & Fainting in Coils- An Exhibition [by] Leo Estevez ... Dawson Weber. 2008. (ENG., Illus.). 96p. pap. 25.00 *(978-1-60585-191-4(4))* Bayersiche Staatsoper/Pinakothek der Moderne.

Thun-Hohenstein, Christoph, pref. East by South West. 2012. (ENG & GER., Illus.). 179p. pap. 40.00 ***(978-3-86984-224-0(5))*** Verlag fur Moderne Kunst DEU. Dist: D.A.P./Distributed Art Pubs.

The Timeless Cowrie. 2007. 10.00 *(978-0-9725066-3-2(2))* Bead Museum of Washington DC, The.

Tobias, Gert & Tobias, Uwe. Gert & Uwe Tobias - Ausstellungskatalog Den Haag. 2011. (ENG & GER., Illus.). 88p. ***(978-3-940953-80-3(6))*** Snoeck Verlagsgesellschaft mbH.

Tracey Emin: You Left Me Breathing. 2008. (Illus.). *(978-1-932598-60-5(X))* Gagosian Gallery.

Tri Postal (Organization: Lille, France) Staff, contrib. by. La Route de la Soie: The Silk Road: Lille3000, Saatchi Gallery. 2010. (FRE & ENG., Illus.). 96p. *(978-2-84278-806-3(0))* Beaux Arts.

Tunberg, Despina. International Contemporary Masters. Tunberg, Thomas & Tunberg, Despina, eds. 2008. (Illus.). 60p. pap. 24.95 *(978-0-9802079-0-3(8))* Omma Gallery Santa Barbara, LLC.

Tung, Lisa & Zaug, Chloé. "Crafty" Elaine Bradford, Nick Cave, Rob Conger ... 2007. (Illus.). 75p. *(978-0-9771419-2-0(6))* Massachusetts College of Art.

Turgeon, Mark. Mark Turgeon. 2007. 8.00 *(978-0-9791843-7-6(1))* CUE Art Foundation.

Tuymans, Luc & Weiwei, Ai, eds. The State of Things - Brussels/Beijing. 2010. (ENG., Illus.). 256p. *(978-90-209-8683-9(X)*, Lannoo Pubs. (Acc)) Antique Collectors' Club.

TV Arts TV. 2011. (ENG., Illus.). 160p. pap. 35.00 *(978-84-92841-60-8(5))* La Fabrica ESP. Dist: D.A.P./Distributed Art Pubs.

Uchill, Rebecca, et al. On Procession: Art on Parade. Uchill, Rebecca, ed. 2009. (Illus.). 120p. pap. 24.95 *(978-0-936260-87-7(4))* Indianapolis Museum of Art.

Underground Pop. 2010. (Illus.). 50p. pap. 25.00 *(978-0-943526-47-8(7))* Parrish Art Museum, The.

Vadehra Art Gallery Staff & Grosvenor Vadehra (Art Gallery: London, England) Staff, contrib. by. Indian Art, 3 vols. 2010. (ENG., Illus.). 146p. 19.95 *(978-81-87737-19-3(0))*; 101p. 19.95 *(978-81-87737-27-8(1))*; 129p. pap. 19.95 *(978-81-87737-22-3(0))* Antique Collectors' Club GBR. (Vadehra Art Gallery (Acc)). Dist: National Bk. Network.

van der Ley, Sabrina, ed. Pedro Cabrita Reis: One after Another, A Few Silent Steps. 2010. (ENG., Illus.). 368p. 75.00 *(978-3-7757-2558-3(X))* Hatje Cantz Verlag GmbH & Co KG DEU. Dist: D.A.P./Distributed Art Pubs.

Vanderbeek, Stan, et al. Amazement Park: Stan, Sara, & Johannes VanDerBeek. 2011. ***(978-0-9821486-5-5(8))*** Tang, Frances Young Teaching Museum & Art Gallery at Skidmore College, The.

Vanderlinden, Barbara. Brussels Biennial. 2009. (ENG., Illus.). 336p. pap. 45.00 *(978-3-86560-555-9(9))* Verlag der Buchhandlung Walther Konig DEU. Dist: D.A.P./Distributed Art Pubs.

Varadinis, Mirjam. Shifting Identities: (Swiss) Art Now: This Publication Is Released on the Occasion of the Exhibition Shifting Identities - (Swiss) Art Now at Kunsthaus Zürich from June 6th to August 31st, 2008. Varadinis, Mirjam, ed. 2008. (ENG., Illus.). 240p. pap. 55.00 *(978-3-905829-70-9(3))* JRP Ringier Kunstverlag AG CHE. Dist: D.A.P./Distributed Art Pubs.

Vasquez de la Horra, Sandra. Sandra Vásquez de la Horra. 2010. (ENG., Illus.). 184p. 60.00 *(978-3-7757-2655-9(1))* Hatje Cantz Verlag GmbH & Co KG DEU. Dist: D.A.P./Distributed Art Pubs.

Vazquez, Victor, photos by. Victor Vazquez: 1989-2007, 1 vol. 2008. (ENG., Illus.). 300p. 85.00 *(978-0-9773932-4-4(0))* Museo de Arte de Ponce.

Ventos, Ernesto. Smell Colour: Chemistry, Art & Pedagogy. 2011. 112p. pap. ***(978-84-92861-99-6(1))*** Actar Birkhauser Distribution.

Vervoordt, Axel. Tra edge of Becoming, 1 vol. 2011. (ENG., Illus.). 296p. 110.00 ***(978-94-90693-17-6(0))*** Exhibitions International BEL. Dist: Innovative Logistics.

Vicario, Gilbert, et al, texts. Daniel Joseph Martinez. 2009. (ENG., Illus.). 248p. 60.00 *(978-3-7757-2305-3(6))* Hatje Cantz Verlag GmbH & Co KG DEU. Dist: D.A.P./Distributed Art Pubs.

Villareal, Leo. Leo Villareal. 2010. (ENG., Illus.). 192p. 55.00 *(978-3-7757-2656-6(X))* Hatje Cantz Verlag GmbH & Co KG DEU. Dist: D.A.P./Distributed Art Pubs.

Virilio, Paul, text. Native Land. 2010. (ENG., Illus.). 158p. pap. 15.00 *(978-2-7427-8904-7(9))* Actes Sud FRA. Dist: D.A.P./Distributed Art Pubs.

Vivian, Helen, ed. When You Think About Art: The Ewing & George Paton Gallery, 1971-2008. 2008. (Illus.). 288p. (C). 80.00 *(978-1-921394-02-7(1))* Macmillan Art Publishing AUS. Dist: Brown, David Bk. Co., The.

Volk, Gregory & Russ, Sabine, texts. Carnival Within. An Exhibition Made in America: Discover Us! 2010. (ENG., Illus.). 298p. pap. 42.00 *(978-3-941185-20-3(9))* Verlag fur Moderne Kunst DEU. Dist: D.A.P./Distributed Art Pubs.

Voorhies, James. Consumption Junction. 2007. per. 0.00 *(978-0-9797476-0-1(0))* Columbus College of Art & Design.

Voss, Roy, text. Daniel Sturgis: Don't Argue, 2007- exhibition catalog with an essay by Roy Voss. 2007. (Illus.). per. *(978-0-9774221-1-1(9))* Broan, Cynthia Gallery.

Wakefield, Neville, text. Banks Violette, 12 vols. 2009. (ENG., Illus.). 68p. 60.00 *(978-3-86560-457-6(9))* Verlag der Buchhandlung Walther Konig DEU. Dist: D.A.P./Distributed Art Pubs.

Wakefield, Neville, et al, texts. Frieze Projects & Frieze Talks 2006-2008. 2010. (ENG., Illus.). 308p. pap. 35.00 *(978-0-9553201-5-6(1))* Frieze GBR. Dist: D.A.P./Distributed Art Pubs.

Wallinger, Mark & text. Mark Wallinger: the Russian Linesman. 2009. (ENG., Illus.). 144p. pap. 40.00 *(978-1-85332-272-3(5))* Hayward Gallery Publishing GBR. Dist: D.A.P./Distributed Art Pubs.

Wang, Jianwei. Dilemma- Three Way Fork in the Road. 2007. (ENG & CHI., Illus.). 125p. pap. 40.00 *(978-0-9787666-5-8(2))* Chambers Fine Art LLC.

Warren, Isensee. Warren Isensee. 2008. (Illus.). 34p. per. *(978-0-9795501-2-6(2))* Danese.

Weiwei, Ai. Ai Weiwei Interlacing. 2011. (ENG., Illus.). 496p. pap. 58.00 ***(978-3-86930-337-6(9))*** Steidl, Gerhard Druckerei und Verlag DEU. Dist: Innovative Logistics.

Wekua, Andro. Andro Wekua. 2008. (ENG., Illus.). 72p. 30.00 *(978-3-905829-51-8(7))* JRP Ringier Kunstverlag AG CHE. Dist: D.A.P./Distributed Art Pubs.

—Andro Wekua: Workshop Report. 2010. (ENG., Illus.). 48p. 39.95 *(978-3-86560-648-8(2))* Verlag der Buchhandlung Walther Konig DEU. Dist: D.A.P./Distributed Art Pubs.

White, James J. & Bruno, Lugene B. 12th International Exhibition of Botanical Art & Illustration. 2007. (ENG., Illus.). 190p. pap. 25.00 *(978-0-913196-82-3(7))* Hunt Institute for Botanical Documentation.

White, Julia M. Mahjong: Art, Film, & Change in China. 2008. (ENG., Illus.). 100p. pap. 25.00 *(978-0-9719397-7-6(2))* Univ. of California, Berkeley Art Museum & Pacific Film Archive.

Wiehaer, Renate, ed. Maximin. 2008. 270p. pap. *(978-84-89935-81-5(5))* Actar Birkhauser Distribution.

Witt-Dorring, Christian, text. Josef Hoffmann: Interiors 1902-1913. 2009. (ENG., Illus.). 88p. 45.00 *(978-1-931794-20-6(0))* Neue Galerie New York.

Xiaochun, Miao. Miao Xiaochun: Macromania. 2011. (ENG., Illus.). 164p. 25.00 *(978-988-18907-0-2(5))* Timezone 8 Ltd. HKG. Dist: D.A.P./Distributed Art Pubs.

Yihan, Wang, ed. China International Gallery Exposition 2006, 1 vol. 2007. (ENG., Illus.). 429p. pap. 46.00 *(978-988-99015-6-1(0))* Timezone 8 Ltd. HKG. Dist: D.A.P./Distributed Art Pubs.

Young, Paul, ed. Remote Viewing. 2011. (ENG., Illus.). 96p. pap. 25.00 *(978-84-92841-48-6(6))* La Fabrica ESP. Dist: D.A.P./Distributed Art Pubs.

Yo.V.A.3 - Young Viennese Architects 3. 2010. 128p. pap. 39.95 *(978-3-7091-0334-0(7))* Springer Wien AUT. Dist: Actar Birkhauser Distribution.

Zhenqing, Gu, ed. Two Asias, Two Europes: An International Exhibition of Contemporary Art, 1 vol. 2008. (ENG., Illus.). 215p. pap. 48.00 *(978-988-99609-4-0(X))* Timezone 8 Ltd. HKG. Dist: D.A.P./Distributed Art Pubs.

Zhong Biao: American Debut. 2007. pap. 20.00 *(978-0-9795141-1-1(8))* Norris, Frey Gallery.

Ziegler, Tina. Hunt & Gather: Discovering New Art. 2010. (ENG., Illus.). 148p. 45.00 *(978-0-9819600-3-6(0))* Batty, Mark Pub., LLC.

Zimmer, Nina, ed. Soutine & Modernism. 2008. (GER & ENG., Illus.). 224p. *(978-3-8321-9079-8(1))* DuMont.

zu Schlochtern, Thomas Meijer, ed. Paramaribo SPAN: Contemporary Art in Suriname. 2010. 200p. pap. 39.95 *(978-94-6022-081-4(9))* Royal Tropical Institute Pr. (KIT (Koninklijk Instituut voor de Tropen) NLD. Dist: Stylus Publishing, LLC.

Zybok, Oliver, ed. The Mage's Pantry. 2008. (ENG., Illus.). 104p. 45.00 *(978-3-7757-2107-3(X))* Hatje Cantz Verlag GmbH & Co KG DEU. Dist: D.A.P./Distributed Art Pubs.

Zybok, Oliver, text. Pietro Sanguineti. 2010. (ENG., Illus.). 136p. 45.00 *(978-3-7757-2557-6(1))* Hatje Cantz Verlag GmbH & Co KG DEU. Dist: D.A.P./Distributed Art Pubs.

Zybok, Oliver & Emerling, Susan, texts. Pae White: Material Mutters. 2011. (ENG., Illus.). 80p. 45.00 ***(978-1-894212-32-8(0))*** Power Plant, The CAN. Dist: D.A.P./Distributed Art Pubs.

2007 Portland Museum of Art Biennial. 2007. per. 13.95 *(978-0-916857-44-8(1))* Portland Museum of Art.

ART, MODERN—21ST CENTURY—HISTORY

Aranda, Julieta, et al. E-flux Journal: What Is Contemporary Art? 2010. (Illus.). 216p. pap. 15.00 ***(978-1-934105-10-8(4))*** Sternberg Pr.

Buchholz, Elke Linda & Zimmermann, Beate. Pablo Picasso: Life & Work. 2008. (Art in Focus (Konemann) Ser.). (Illus.). 95p. pap. 5.95 *(978-0-8416-0055-3(4))* American Map Corp.

Cannon, Joanna, et al, eds. Trade in Artists' Materials. 2010. (ENG., Illus.). 512p. 180.00 *(978-1-904982-25-8(5))* Archetype Pubns. GBR. Dist: National Bk. Network.

Chong, Doryun & Raymond, Yasmil, texts. Brave New Worlds, 1 vol. 2007. (ENG., Illus.). 272p. pap. 39.95 *(978-0-935640-89-2(4))* Walker Art Ctr.

Congost, Carles, et al. All Hawaii Entrées - Lunar Reggae, 1 vol. 2007. (ENG., Illus.). 224p. 70.00 *(978-88-8158-579-3(0))* Charta ITA. Dist: D.A.P./Distributed Art Pubs.

Desai, Vishakha N., ed. Asian Art History in the Twenty-First Century. 2008. (Clark Studies in the Visual Arts). (ENG., Illus.). 272p. (C). pap. 24.95 *(978-0-300-12553-5(4))* Yale Univ. Pr.

Faure, Élie, et al. Art of the Modern Era. 2010. 256p. *(978-1-84484-685-6(7))* Parkstone International.

Foss, Paul, et al. The &-Files: Art & Text, 1981-2002. 2009. (ENG., Illus.). 116p. pap. 18.95 *(978-0-9799752-1-9(2))* Whale & Star Pr.

Frazier, Craig, illus. Three by Three Illustration Directory 2007: Curated by 3x3, the Magazine of Contemporary Illustration. 2007. 496p. per. 35.95 net. *(978-0-9755158-4-6(5))* 3x3 Magazine.

Gierstberg, Frits & Bool, Flip. Questioning History: Imagining the Past in Contemporary Art. 2009. (ENG., Illus.). 180p. pap. 32.00 *(978-90-5662-659-4(0))* NAi Uitgevers / Publishers Stichting NLD. Dist: D.A.P./Distributed Art Pubs.

Hammer, Martin. The Naked Portrait 1900 to 2007. 2007. (ENG., Illus.). 176p. pap. *(978-1-903278-95-6(3))* National Galleries of Scotland.

He, Jianping, ed. All Men Are Brothers. 2007. (Illus.). pap. *(978-981-245-424-9(1))* Page One Publishing.

Hernachandra, Ray & Lark Books Staff. 500 Art Quilts: An Inspiring Collection of Contemporary Work. 2010. (500 Ser.). (ENG., Illus.). 432p. pap. 24.95 *(978-1-60059-058-0(6))* Lark Bks.

Holler, Christian. Time Action Vision. 2010. (ENG., Illus.). 222p. pap. 29.95 *(978-3-03764-124-8(X))* JRP Ringier Kunstverlag AG CHE. Dist: D.A.P./Distributed Art Pubs.

Kromm, Jane & Bakewell, Susan Benforado, eds. A History of Visual Culture: Western Civilization from the 18th to the 21st Century. 2010. (ENG., Illus.). 1p. 119.95 *(978-1-84520-493-8(X))*; 480p. pap. 39.95 *(978-1-84520-492-1(1))* Berg Pubs. GBR. Dist: Macmillan.

Menkes, Suzy & Tymauer, Matt. Valentino. Chitolina, Armando, ed. 2009. (ENG., Illus.). 576p. 69.99 *(978-3-8365-0329-7(8))* TASCHEN DEU. Dist: Ingram Pub. Services.

Millet, Catherine. Contemporary Art in France. 2006. (ENG., Illus.). 384p. 60.00 *(978-2-08-030524-4(7))* Flammarion et Cie FRA. Dist: Random Hse., Inc.

Pezold, Friedrike, ed. Art for the 21st Century: Design of a Counterworld. (Illus.). 224p. pap. 39.95 *(978-3-89322-812-6(8))* Edition Centz DEU. Dist: D.A.P./Distributed Art Pubs.

Phillips, Sam. The Art Lovers' Guide - London: The Finest Art in London by Museum, Artist, or Period. 2011. (Illus.). 240p. pap. 19.95 *(978-0-8478-3628-4(2)*, Skira) Rizzoli International Pubns., Inc.

Polsky, Richard. I Sold Andy Warhol (Too Soon) 2011. 288p. pap. 15.95 *(978-1-59051-456-6(4))* Other Pr., LLC.

Richard Terrell. The Liberal Arts in the Twenty-First Century: Exploring the Future of a Tradition. 2009. 76p. pap. 10.95 *(978-1-4401-6680-8(3))* iUniverse, Inc.

Thompson, Donald N. The $12 Million Stuffed Shark: The Curious Economics of Contemporary Art. 2008. (ENG., Illus.). 272p. 26.00 *(978-0-230-61022-4(6))* Palgrave Macmillan.

Tojner, Poul Erik & Holm, Michael, eds. I Know How You Must Feel... Essays on Modern Art. 2012. (ENG., Illus.). 192p. 60.00 *(978-87-91607-21-9(3))* Louisiana DNK. Dist: D.A.P./Distributed Art Pubs.

Varas, Valerie, ed. Monochromes: From Malevich to the Present. 2007. (Illus.). 240p. pap. 39.95 *(978-0-520-24937-0(2))* Univ. of California Pr.

Vasa, Melanie. Gender & the Written Word in Recent Art. 2009. 52p. pap. *(978-3-639-13503-9(2))* VDM Verlag Dr. Mueller e.K.

ART, MODERNIST

see Modernism (Art)

ART, MOORISH

see Islamic Art

ART, MUNICIPAL

see also City Planning

Alminana, et al. Sitte, Hegemann & the Metropolis: Modern Civic Art & International Exchanges. Lejeune, Jean-François & Bohl, Charles, eds. 2009. (ENG., Illus.). 336p. 165.00 *(978-0-415-42406-6(2))* Routledge.

—Sitte, Hegemann & the Metropolis: Modern Civic Art & International Exchanges. 2007. (Illus.). 272p. 53.95 *(978-0-415-42407-3(0))* Taylor & Francis Group.

Basa, Lynn. The Artist's Guide to Public Art: How to Find & Win Commissions. 2008. (ENG., Illus.). 240p. pap. 19.95 *(978-1-58115-501-3(8))*, 115501, Allworth Pr.) Skyhorse Publishing Co., Inc.

Hegemann, Werner & Peets, Elbert. The American Vitruvius: an Architect's Handbook of Urban Design. 2010. (Dover Architecture Ser.). (ENG., Illus.). 320p. pap. 29.95 *(978-0-486-47315-4(5))* Dover Pubns., Inc.

Parkstone Press Staff. Urban Sculptures. 2012. (Our Earth Ser.). (ENG., Illus.). 192p. 24.95 *(978-1-84484-860-7(4))* Parkstone Pr. USA, Ltd.

ART, MUSLIM

see Islamic Art

ART, MYCENAEAN

Holland, Leicester. Mycenaean Plumes. 2009. pap. 19.96 *(978-1-60724-460-8(8))* Gorgias Pr., LLC.

Muller, Walter, ed. Die Bedeutung der minoischen und mykenischen Glyptik. 2010. (Corpus der Minoischen und Mykenischen Siegel Ser.). (ENG & FRE., Illus.). 446p. (C). 195.00 *(978-3-8053-4260-5(8))* Zabern, Philipp von Verlag, GmbH DEU. Dist: Brown, David Bk. Co., The.

Uhl, Jason. A Brief Introduction to Ancient Aegean Art: Cycladic, Minoan, & Mycenaean Art & Architecture. 2007. 76p. per. 16.95 *(978-1-4241-8204-6(2))* PublishAmerica, Inc.

ART, NEAR EASTERN

see Art, Middle Eastern

ART, NEPALI

Casey, Jane, et al. Divine Presence: Arts of India & the Himalayas. 2006. (Illus.). *(978-88-7439-022-9(X))* 5 Continents.

Jackson, David Paul. The Nepalese Legacy in Tibetan Painting. 2010. (Masterworks of Tibetan Painting Ser.). (ENG., Illus.). 288p. 75.00 *(978-0-9772131-8-4(8))* Rubin Museum of Art.

—The Nepalese Stylistic Legacy in Tibetan Painting: From Early Beri to Ngor. 2010. pap. *(978-0-9772131-7-7(X))* Serindia Pubns., Inc.

Shimkhada, Deepak, ed. Nepal: Nostalgia & Modernity. 2011. (ENG.). 128p. 68.00 ***(978-93-80581-08-8(4))*** Marg Pubns. IND. Dist: National Bk. Network.

Shrestha, Romio, creator. Celestial Gallery. 2009. (ENG.). 64p. 24.95 *(978-1-60109-051-5(X))* Mandala Publishing.

Shrestha, Romio & Baker, Ian. Buddhas of the Celestial Gallery. 2012. (ENG., Illus.). 64p. 75.00 *(978-1-60109-060-7(9))* Mandala Publishing.

Slusser, Mary & Jett, Paul. The Antiquity of Nepalese Wood Carving: A Reassessment. 2010. (ENG., Illus.). 325p. 75.00 *(978-0-295-99029-3(5))* Univ. of Washington Pr.

ART, NEW ZEALAND

Bollinger, Nick. 100 Essential New Zealand Albums. 2010. (100 Essential New Zealand Ser.). (ENG., Illus.). 208p. 28.95 *(978-0-9582750-3-3(3))* Awa Pr. NZL. Dist: Independent Pubs. Group.

Cross, David. One Day Sculpture. 2010. (ENG., Illus.). 276p. pap. 35.00 *(978-3-86678-333-1(7))* Kerber Verlag DEU. Dist: D.A.P./Distributed Art Pubs.

Gray, Zoe & Szewczyk, Monika. Billy Apple(r). Schafhausen, Nicolaus, ed. 2010. (ENG., Illus.). 112p. pap. 15.00 *(978-90-73362-89-5(X))* Witte De With Centre for Contemporary Art NLD. Dist: D.A.P./Distributed Art Pubs.

Henderson, Derek, photos by. Mercy Mercer. 2011. (ENG., Illus.). 152p. 80.00 *(978-0-9582831-4-4(1))* Lett, Michael Publishing NZL. Dist: D.A.P./Distributed Art Pubs.

McLean, Fred. New Zealand Art for Investment. 160p. pap. 19.95 *(978-0-908876-88-4(2))* Transpress NZL. Dist: Pacific Island Bks.

Neich, Roger, et al. The Maori Collections of the British Museum. 2011. (ENG., Illus.). 336p. (C). 150.00 *(978-0-7141-2594-7(6))* British Museum Pr. GBR. Dist: Brown, David Bk. Co., The.

Painter-Arps, Sharon. Cross Culture in Art in New Zealand. 2010. 112p. pap. *(978-3-8383-5963-2(1))* Lambert Academic Publishing.

Steer, Laurie. A Fatal Cycle. 2010. 64p. pap. *(978-3-639-22775-8(1))* VDM Verlag Dr. Mueller e.K.

Thomas, Nicholas, ed. Rauru: Tene Waitere, Maori Carving, Colonial History. 2009. (Illus.). 183p. 120.00 *(978-1-877372-61-2(7))* Otago University Pr. NZL. Dist: International Specialized Bk. Services.

Tobin, Paul. White Cloud Worlds. 2012. (ENG., Illus.). 128p. 29.99 ***(978-0-06-219785-6(1)***, Collins Design) HarperCollins Pubs.

ART, NIGERIAN

Berns, Marla C., et al, eds. Central Nigeria Unmasked: Arts of the Benue River Valley. 2011. (ENG., Illus.). 608p. 100.00 ***(978-0-9778344-6-4(8))*** Univ. of California, Los Angeles, Fowler Museum of Cultural History.

—Central Nigeria Unmasked: Arts of the Benue River Valley, 1 vol. 2011. (ENG., Illus.). 608p. pap. 75.00 ***(978-0-9778344-5-7(X))*** Univ. of California, Los Angeles, Fowler Museum of Cultural History.

Cole, Herbert M. Invention & Tradition: The Art of Southeastern Nigeria. 2012. (Illus.). 144p. 75.00 ***(978-3-7913-4600-7(8))*** Prestel Publishing.

Mulle, Christopher. Christopher Muller: Looking Pictures. 2011. (ENG., Illus.). 192p. 60.00 ***(978-3-86984-182-3(6))*** Verlag fur Moderne Kunst DEU. Dist: D.A.P./Distributed Art Pubs.

Offoedu-Okeke, Onyema. Artists of Nigeria. 2012. (Illus.). 720p. 95.00 *(978-88-7439-547-7(7))* 5 Continents ITA. Dist: Abrams.

Ola, Yomi. Satires of Power in Yoruba Visual Culture. 2012. pap. ***(978-1-61163-037-4(1))*** Carolina Academic Pr.

Onyile, Onyile Bassey. Ancestral Spirits Embodied in Ekpu Figurines of the Oron People: A Study in Nigerian Traditional Art. 2007. (Illus.). 264p. 109.95 *(978-0-7734-5334-0(2))* Mellen, Edwin Pr., The.

Plankensteiner, Barbara. Benin. 2010. (ENG., Illus.). 136p. pap. 34.95 *(978-88-7439-410-4(1))* 5 Continents ITA. Dist: Hachette Bk. Group.

Probst, Peter. Osogbo & the Art of Heritage: Monuments, Deities, & Money. 2011. (African Expressive Cultures Ser.). (ENG., Illus.). 224p. 70.00 *(978-0-253-35611-6(3)*, 0253356113); pap. 24.95 *(978-0-253-22295-4(8)*, 0253222958) Indiana Univ. Pr.

ART, NON-OBJECTIVE

see Art, Abstract

ART, NORWEGIAN

Aamundsen, Martin Berdahl & Horvei, Øivin, eds. Street Art Norway. deluxe ed. 2011. (NOR & ENG., Illus.). 224p. pap. 29.95 ***(978-82-997687-9-5(9))*** Kontur Publishing NOR. Dist: SCB Distributors.

Bergmann, Benjamin. Benjamin Bergmann. tief unten tag hell: Arbeiten 1999 - 2009. 2010. (ENG & GER., Illus.). 160p. 59.95 *(978-3-8321-9288-4(3))* DuMont DEU. Dist: D.A.P./Distributed Art Pubs.

Bomberg, Katja, ed. Melhus, Bjorn. Live Action Hero. 2011. (ENG., Illus.). 103p. pap. 29.95 ***(978-3-86560-965-6(1))*** Verlag der Buchhandlung Walther Konig DEU. Dist: D.A.P./Distributed Art Pubs.

Eeg-Tverbakk, Lars O Ramberg. 2009. (ENG.). 248p. 60.00 *(978-3-7757-2038-0(3))* Hatje Cantz Verlag GmbH & Co KG DEU. Dist: D.A.P./Distributed Art Pubs.

Elling, Lars. Lars Elling: Palimpsest. 2010. (ENG., Illus.). 200p. pap. 50.00 *(978-82-7547-386-6(1))* Pr., Forlaget NOR. Dist: D.A.P./Distributed Art Pubs.

Forum Gallery. Odd Nerdrum: Paintings, 1 vol. 2007. (ENG., Illus.). 32p. per. 30.00 *(978-0-9675826-8-9(7))* Forum Gallery.

Gilje, Karianne Bjellås, ed. Grete Prytz Kittelsen: The Art of Enamel Design. 2012. (ENG., Illus.). 296p. 55.00 ***(978-0-393-73331-0(9)***, 73331) Norton, W. W. & Co., Inc.

Gulen, Mai & Lerheim, Karen, eds. Emunch. No - Text & Image. 2011. 303p. 50.00 *(978-82-90128-71-0(1))* Oslo kommunes kunstsamlinger NOR. Dist: International Specialized Bk. Services.

Hjalmen, Øyvind, photos by. Elsewhere. 2011. (ENG., Illus.). 96p. 40.00 ***(978-3-86828-198-9(3))*** Kehrer Verlag Heidelberg, Klaus Kehrer DEU. Dist: Consortium Bk. Sales & Distribution.

Hoff, Svein Olav. Jon Doblougs Samling. 2009. (NOR., Illus.). 232p. *(978-82-91388-59-5(8))* Labyrinth Pr.

Kosel, Janine. Norwegian Handknits: Heirloom Designs from Vesterheim Museum. 2012. (ENG., Illus.). 144p. pap. 24.99 ***(978-0-7603-4255-8(5)***, 0760342555, Voyageur Pr) MBI Publishing Co. LLC.

Lerheim, Karen & Ydstie, Ingebjorg, eds. Munch's Laboratory: The Path to the Aula. 2011. 350p. 49.00 ***(978-82-90128-73-4(8))*** Oslo kommunes kunstsamlinger NOR. Dist: International Specialized Bk. Services.

Prelinger, Elizabeth, et al. Edvard Munch: Master Prints. 2010. (Illus.). 168p. *(978-3-7913-5059-2(5))* National Gallery of Art.

Skira. Bjarne Melgaard: Jealous. Arbu, Grete et al, eds. 2010. (ENG., Illus.). 96p. pap. 29.95 *(978-88-572-0465-9(0))* Skira Editore ITA. Dist: Random Hse., Inc.

Skira, et al, eds. Lights On: Norwegian Contemporary Art. 2009. (ENG., Illus.). 192p. pap. 45.00 *(978-88-6130-792-6(2))* Skira Editore ITA. Dist: Random Hse., Inc.

Templeton, Joan. Munch's Ibsen: A Painter's Visions of a Playwright. 2008. (ENG.). 256p. 35.00 *(978-0-295-98776-7(6))* Univ. of Washington Pr.

Veiteberg, Jorunn, et al. Konrad Mehus: Stories in Jewellery. 2012. (ENG & NOR., Illus.). 200p. 70.00 ***(978-3-89790-360-9(1))*** Arnoldsche Art Pubs. DEU. Dist: Antique Collectors' Club.

Weibel, Peter & Beitin, Andreas, eds. Elmgreen & Dragset - Celebrity: The One & the Many. 2011. (ENG., Illus.). 384p. 59.95 *(978-3-86560-908-3(2))* Verlag der Buchhandlung Walther Konig DEU. Dist: D.A.P./Distributed Art Pubs.

Wendt, Selene & Gurholt, Crispin, eds. Live Photo. 2010. (ENG & NOR., Illus.). 160p. 40.00 *(978-88-572-0264-8(X))* Skira Editore ITA. Dist: Random Hse., Inc.

ART, OCCIDENTAL

see Art

ART, OPTICAL

see Optical Art

ART, ORIENTAL

see Art, Asian

ART, PACIFIC ISLAND

Abels, Birgit, ed. Austronesian Soundscapes: Performing Arts in Oceania & Southeast Asia. 2011. (IIAS Publications Ser.). (ENG., Illus.). 336p. pap. *(978-90-8964-085-7(1))* Amsterdam Univ. Pr.

Balme, Christopher. Pacific Performances: Theatricality & Cross-Cultural Encounter in the South Seas. 2007. (Studies in International Performance Ser.). (ENG., Illus.). 264p. 105.00 *(978-1-4039-8598-9(7))* Palgrave Macmillan.

Butler, Brian, ed. Speculation, 1 vol. 2007. (ENG., Illus.). 224p. pap. 25.00 *(978-3-905770-75-9(X))* JRP Ringier Kunstverlag AG CHE. Dist: D.A.P./Distributed Art Pubs.

D'Alleva, Anne. Arts of the Pacific Islands. 2010. (ENG., Illus.). 176p. pap. 20.00 *(978-0-300-16412-1(2))* Yale Univ. Pr.

Ellis, George R. Oceanic Art: A Celebration of Form. 2009. pap. *(978-0-937108-46-8(4))* San Diego Museum of Art.

Kjellgren, Eric. Oceania: Art of the Pacific Islands in the Metropolitan Museum of Art. 2007. (ENG., Illus.). 368p. 45.00 ***(978-0-300-12030-1(3))*** Yale Univ. Pr.

—Oceania: Art of the Pacific Islands in the Metropolitan Museum of Art. 2007. 45.00 *(978-1-58839-237-4(6))*; 24.95 *(978-1-58839-238-1(4))* Metropolitan Museum of Art, The.

Newell, Jennifer. Pacific Art in Detail. 2011. (Art in Detail Ser.). (Illus.). 128p. 22.95 *(978-0-674-05578-0(0))* Harvard Univ. Pr.

Stepan, Peter. Picasso's Collection of African & Oceanic Art: Masters of Metamorphosis. 2006. (Illus.). 136p. 85.00 *(978-3-7913-3691-6(6))* Prestel Publishing.

Sweet, Barry. Split Seconds: Four Decades of News Photography from the Pacific Northwest & Beyond. 2012. (ENG., Illus.). 160p. (gr. 9). pap. 19.95 ***(978-0-615-54736-7(2))*** Raleigh Pr.

Takeuchi, Floyd. Pasefika: The Festival of Pacific Arts. 2011. (Illus.). 186p. pap. 40.00 *(978-0-615-44146-7(7))* Takeuchi, Floyd K.

Van Dinter, Maarten Hesselt. Tribal Tattoo Designs from the Pacific. 2007. (SPA & ENG., Illus.). 283p. pap. incl. cd-rom *(978-90-810543-9-3(2))* Mundurucu Pubs.

ART, PAPUAN

Craig, Barry, et al. Living Spirits with Fixed Abodes: The Masterpieces Exhibition: Papua New Guinea National Museum & Art Gallery. 2010. (Illus.). xxii, 286p. ***(978-1-86333-258-3(8))***; ***(978-0-8248-3151-6(9))*** Univ. of Hawaii Pr.

Friede, John, et al, eds. New Guinea Highlands: Art from the Jolika Collection. 2011. (Illus.). 672p. 120.00 *(978-3-7913-5055-4(2))* Prestel Publishing.

Gunn, Michael & Peltier, Philippe, eds. New Ireland: Art of the South Pacific. 2008. (ENG., Illus.). 304p. pap. 60.00 *(978-88-7439-369-5(5))* 5 Continents ITA. Dist: Hachette Bk. Group.

ART, PENNSYLVANIA DUTCH

Bridgewater, Alan. Painted Wood Projects in the Pennsylvania Folk Art Style. 2008. (ENG.). 143p. 28.00 *(978-1-4379-6407-3(9))* DIANE Publishing Co.

Dehan, Amy Miller. Outside the Ordinary: Contemporary Art in Glass, Wood, & Ceramics from the Wolf Collection. 2009. (ENG.). 176p. pap. 30.00 *(978-0-8214-1861-1(0))* Ohio Univ. Pr.

ART, PERSIAN

see Art, Iranian

ART, PERUVIAN

Bryce, Fernando. Americas. 2009. (ENG., Illus.). 128p. pap. 60.00 *(978-84-343-1200-5(X))* Poligrafa, Ediciones, S. A. ESP. Dist: D.A.P./Distributed Art Pubs.

Charing, Howard G. The Ayahuasca Visions of Pablo Amaringo. 2011. (ENG.). 1p. 40.00 *(978-1-59477-345-7(9))* Inner Traditions International, Ltd.

Dyer, Chris. Positive Creations: The Visionary Art of Chris Dyer. 2011. (Illus.). 256p. 39.99 ***(978-0-7643-3913-4(3)***, Schiffer Publishing Ltd) Schiffer Publishing, Ltd.

Paris Musees Les Musees de La Ville de Paris. Peru: Art from the Chavin to the Incas. Lemasson, Patrick, ed. 2006. (Collections du Petit Palais, Musee des Beaux-Arts de la VILL Ser.). (Illus.). 224p. 60.00 *(978-88-7624-692-0(4))* Skira Editore ITA. Dist: Random Hse., Inc.

Peabody Museum Publisher. Twenty-Five Centuries of Peruvian Art: 700 B. C. to 1800 A. D. 2011. 68p. 36.95 ***(978-1-258-09128-6(3))*** Literary Licensing, LLC.

Testino, Mario. Mario Testino: Todo o Nada. 2010. (Illus.). *(978-84-96233-98-0(7))* Fundacion Coleccion Thyssen-Bornemisza.

Vallejo, Boris & Bell, Julie. Boris Vallejo & Julie Bell: The Ultimate Illustrations. 2009. (ENG.). 144p. 19.99 *(978-0-06-173358-1(X)*, Collins Design) HarperCollins Pubs.

Van Dinter, Maarten Hesselt. Native Designs from Ancient Mexico & Peru. 2007. (Illus.). 105p. pap. incl. cd-rom *(978-90-810543-4-8(1))* Mundurucu Pubs.

ART, PHILIPPINE

Flores, et al. Imelda Cajipe Endaya Stitching Paint into Collage: E. 2009. pap. 35.00 *(978-1-61623-179-8(3))* Independent Pub.

Henkel, David, et al. Land of the Morning: The Philippines & its People. 2011. 176p. pap. 30.00 ***(978-971-0579-07-5(X))*** Artpostasia Inc. PHL. Dist: National Bk. Network.

See, Sarita Echavez. The Decolonized Eye: Filipino American Art & Performance. 2009. (ENG., Illus.). 232p. 75.00 *(978-0-8166-5318-8(6))* Univ. of Minnesota Pr.

ART, PICTISH

Cummins, W. A. Decoding the Pictish Symbols. 2010. (ENG., Illus.). 224p. pap. 32.95 *(978-0-7524-5239-5(8))* History Pr. Ltd., The GBR. Dist: Independent Pubs. Group.

Driscoll, Stephen T. & Geddes, Jane, eds. Pictish Progress: New Studies on Northern Britain in the Middle Ages. 2010. (Northern World Ser.). (Illus.). 416p. *(978-90-04-18759-7(6))* BRILL.

Goodman, Robin F. & Fahnestock, Andrea Henderson. The Day Our World Changed: Children's Art Of 9/11. 2006. (Illus.). 128p. reprint ed. 20.00 *(978-1-4223-5685-2(X))* DIANE Publishing Co.

Henderson, George & Henderson, Isabel. The Art of the Picts: Sculpture & Metalwork in Early Medieval Scotland. 2011. (ENG., Illus.). 256p. pap. 39.95 *(978-0-500-28963-1(8)*, 528963) Thames & Hudson.

ART, POLISH

Abakanowicz, Magdalena. Magdalena Abakanowicz: La Corte Del Rey Arturo: Palacio de Cristal, Parque Del Retiro, Madrid, 13 de Marzo-16 de Junio de 2008. 2009. (ENG & SPA., Illus.). 134p. pap. 35.00 *(978-84-8026-356-6(3))* Museo Nacional Centro de Arte Reina Sofia ESP. Dist: Actar Birkhauser Distribution.

Althamer, Pawel, et al, texts. Pawel Althamer. 2011. (ENG., Illus.). 160p. pap. 45.00 *(978-0-7148-6085-5(9))* Phaidon Pr., Inc.

Bartelik, Marek, ed. Poza: On the Polishness of Polish Contemporary Art, 1 vol. 2008. (ENG., Illus.). 168p. pap. 35.00 *(978-0-9717859-3-9(7))* Real Art Ways.

Blondiau, Geneviève, et al. Krakow - Cracow Rediscovering the Young Poland Movement: Secession in & around Cracow, 1 vol. 2011. (ENG & POL.). 141p.

pap. 30.00 *(978-83-914839-4-7(0))* Centre International Pour La Ville, L'Architecture Et Le Paysage BEL. Dist: Innovative Logistics.

Breitwieser, Sabine, ed. Edward Krasinski: Les Mises en Scene, 1 vol. 2007. (ENG., Illus.). 350p. 63.00 *(978-3-86560-103-2(0))* Verlag der Buchhandlung Walther Konig DEU. Dist: D.A.P./Distributed Art Pubs.

Budny, Michal. Michal Budny. 2010. (ENG., Illus.). 168p. 44.95 *(978-3-86678-319-5(1))* Kerber Verlag DEU. Dist: D.A.P./Distributed Art Pubs.

Crowley, David, et al. The Power of Fantasy: Modern & Contemporary Art from Poland. 2011. (ENG., Illus.). 160p. 49.95 ***(978-3-7913-5145-2(1))*** Prestel Publishing.

Deutsche, Rosalyn. Hiroshima after Iraq: Three Studies in Art & War. 2011. (Wellek Library Lectures). (ENG., Illus.). 104p. (gr. 17). pap. 18.00 ***(978-0-231-15279-2(5))*** Columbia Univ. Pr.

Elena, Filipovic. Alina Szapocznikow Sculpture Undone, 1955 - 1972. 2012. (ENG., Illus.). 216p. pap. 45.00 ***(978-0-87070-824-4(4))*** Museum of Modern Art.

Esche, Charles, et al, texts. Polish! 2011. (ENG., Illus.). 320p. 60.00 ***(978-3-7757-2845-4(7))*** Hatje Cantz Verlag GmbH & Co KG DEU. Dist: D.A.P./Distributed Art Pubs.

Grabowska-Konwent, Anna. Zoografika: Gnieznienskie Spotkania Z Plakatem: Spotkanie 8: Plakat, Grafika, Druki Ze Zbiorów Muzeum Narodowego W Poznaniu. 2009. (POL., Illus.). 189p. *(978-83-61391-16-6(9))* Muzeum Poczatkow Panstwa Polskiego w Gniezńie.

Grasslin, Karola & Cadere, André. André Cadere: Catalogue Raisonné. 2009. (FRE, GER & ENG., Illus.). 208p. pap. 45.00 *(978-3-86560-358-6(0))* Verlag der Buchhandlung Walther Konig DEU. Dist: D.A.P./Distributed Art Pubs.

Jakubowska, Agata, ed. Alina Szapocznikow: Awkward Objects. 2011. (ENG., Illus.). 288p. pap. 29.00 ***(978-83-924044-6-0(7))*** Muzeum Sztuki Nowoczesnej w Warszawie POL. Dist: Chicago Distribution Ctr.

Kendra Binney, Dan Ness & Tim Karpinski, Chris Haberman. Invision: A Collection of Visual Art in Portland, Oregon. Michael Fields, ed. 2007. 80p. per. 22.00 *(978-0-9776051-4-9(0))* Another Sky Pr.

Lebenstein, Jan. Jan Lebenstein: Warszawa — Paryz: Prace Z Lat 1956-1972: Zacheta Narodowa Galeria Sztuki, 25 Czerwca-28 Sierpnia 2010. Koczowski, Piotr & Szewczyk, Agnieszka, trs. 2010. (POL., Illus.). 199p. *(978-83-89945-48-8(7))* Zacheta, Panstwowa Galeria Sztuki.

Munder, Heike, ed. & text. Tadeusz Kantor, 1 vol. 2009. (ENG.). 156p. 55.00 *(978-3-03764-022-7(7))* JRP Ringier Kunstverlag AG CHE. Dist: D.A.P./Distributed Art Pubs.

Muthesius, Stefan. Polska - Art, Architecture, Design, 1966-1970. (ENG, FRE, GER & POL.). lib. bdg. 39.95 *(978-3-7845-7612-1(5))* Langewiesche DEU. Dist: Abaris Bks.

Neret, Gilles. De Lempicka. 2011. (25 Ser.). (ENG., Illus.). 96p. 14.99 ***(978-3-8365-3184-9(4))*** TASCHEN DEU. Dist: Ingram Pub. Services.

Piotrowska, Irena G. Art of Poland. *(978-0-8022-1980-0(2))* Philosophical Library, Inc.

Reno, Jesse. Truth Will Measure: The Art of Jesse Reno. 2007. 132p. per. 29.99 *(978-0-9776051-3-2(2))* Another Sky Pr.

Sasnal, Wilhelm. Wilhelm Sasnal. Borchardt-Hume, Achim, ed. 2012. (ENG., Illus.). 106p. pap. 40.00 ***(978-0-85488-199-4(9))*** Whitechapel Art Gallery GBR. Dist: D.A.P./Distributed Art Pubs.

ART, POLYNESIAN

Green, Kaye C. & Leach, Foss. Vastly Ingenious: The Archaeology of Pacific Material Culture. 2007. (Illus.). 319p. 59.95 *(978-1-877372-45-2(5))* Otago University Pr. NZL. Dist: International Specialized Bk. Services.

Greub, Suzanne, ed. Gauguin Polynesia. 2012. (Illus.). 400p. 59.95 ***(978-3-7774-4261-7(5))*** Hirmer Verlag GmbH DEU. Dist: Chicago Distribution Ctr.

Hamilton, Augustus. The Art Workmanship of the Maori Race in New Zealand. (Illus.). reprint ed. 84.00 *(978-0-404-14427-2(6))* AMS Pr., Inc.

Hooper, Steven. Pacific Encounters: Art & Divinity in Polynesia, 1760-1860. 2006. (Illus.). 288p. pap. 46.00 *(978-0-8248-3084-7(9))* Univ. of Hawaii Pr.

Kaeppler, Adrienne L. The Pacific Arts of Polynesia & Micronesia. 2008. (Oxford History of Art Ser.). (ENG., Illus.). 256p. pap. 27.95 *(978-0-19-284238-1(2))* Oxford Univ. Pr., Inc.

Kaeppler, Adrienne L. & Kaeppler, Adrienne Lois. Polynesia: The Mark & Carolyn Blackburn Collection of Polynesian Art. 2010. (Illus.). xxxv, 410p. ***(978-1-883528-38-6(0))*** Ai Pohaku Pr.

Kaeppler, Adrienne Lois. Polynesia: The Mark & Carolyn Blackburn Collection of Polynesian Art. 2010. (Illus.). xxxv, 410p. ***(978-1-883528-40-9(2))*** Ai Pohaku Pr.

King, David Shaw. Food for the Flames: Idols & Missionaries in Central Polynesia. 2011. (ENG., Illus.). 256p. (C). 80.00 *(978-1-907372-16-2(4))* Holberton, Paul Publishing GBR. Dist: Univ. of Washington Pr.

Roberts, Phillip. Waikiki Tiki. 2010. 264p. 22.95 *(978-1-57306-311-1(8))* Bess Pr., Inc.

Stewart, Frank, et al, eds. Varua Tupu: New Writing from French Polynesia. 2006. (Illus.). 196p. pap. 29.99 *(978-0-8248-3019-9(9))*, Latitude 20 Bks.) Univ. of Hawaii Pr.

Strongman, Jay. Tiki Mugs: Cult Artifacts of Polynesian Pop. 2008. (ENG., Illus.). 176p. 39.95 *(978-0-9553398-1-3(2))* Korero Books LLP GBR. Dist: Independent Pubs. Group.

Teitelbaum, James. Tiki Road Trip: A Guide to Tiki Culture in North America. 2nd ed. 2007. (ENG., Illus.). 312p. per. 16.95 *(978-1-59580-019-0(0))* Santa Monica Pr.

Vallance, Jeffrey, frwd. Tiki Art Two: The Second Coming of a New Art God. 2006. (Illus.). 112p. pap. 19.95 *(978-0-9766325-7-3(8))* 9mm Bks.

ART, POP

see Pop Art

ART, POPULAR

see Art Industries and Trade; Folk Art

ART, PORTUGUESE

Cameron, Dan & Power, Kevin. Juliao Sarmento Vol. 2: 2000-2001, 1 vol. 2008. (ENG, MUL & SPA., Illus.). 64p. 35.00 *(978-84-343-1153-4(4))* Poligrafa, Ediciones, S. A. ESP. Dist: D.A.P./Distributed Art Pubs.

Dix, Steffen & Pizarro, Jerónimo, eds. Portuguese Modernisms: Multiple Perspectives on Literature & the Visual Arts. 2011. (Legenda Main Ser.). (ENG., Illus.). 406p. (C). 89.50 *(978-1-906540-79-1(9))* European Humanities Research Ctr. GBR. Dist: Brown, David Bk. Co., The.

Farto, Alexandre. VHILS Selected Works, 300 vols. 2011. (ENG.). 160p. pap. 25.95 *(978-90-488-0705-5(0))* Lebowski NLD. Dist: SCB Distributors.

Ferreira, Carolin Overhoff. Dekalog 02: On Manoel de Oliveira. 2009. (Dekalog - Wallflower Ser.). (ENG., Illus.). 160p. (gr. 17). pap. 20.00 *(978-1-905674-80-0(5))* Wallflower Pr. GBR. Dist: Columbia Univ. Pr.

Lisbon. 128p. pap. *(978-88-8029-394-1(X))* Casa Editrice Bonechi.

Nogueira, Carlos. Desenhos Construções e Outros Acidentes: Drawings Constructions & Other Accidents. 2008. (Illus.). 111p. *(978-972-37-1392-3(6))* Assirio e Alvim.

Rosengarten, Ruth. Love & Authority in the Work: Narrating the Family Romance. 2011. (ENG., Illus.). 224p. 89.95 *(978-0-7190-8070-8(3))* Manchester Univ. Pr. GBR. Dist: Macmillan.

Sapega, Ellen W. & Sapega, Ellen. Consensus & Debate in Salazar's Portugal: Visual & Literary Negotiations of the National Text, 1933-1948. 2008. (ENG., Illus.). 184p. (C). 45.00 *(978-0-271-03410-2(6))* Pennsylvania State Univ. Pr.

Silence to Light: Contemporary Art in Portugal. 30.00 *(978-4-900398-20-7(9))* Watari-Um JPN. Dist: D.A.P./Distributed Art Pubs.

Silva, Nuno Vassallo E. Goa & the Great Mughal. Flores, Jorge, ed. 2011. (ENG., Illus.). 240p. pap. 40.00 *(978-1-85759-693-9(5))* Scala, Editions FRA. Dist: National Bk. Network.

Trusted, Marjorie. The Arts of Spain: Iberia & Latin America 1450-1700. 2007. (ENG.). 256p. 47.50 *(978-0-271-03337-2(1))* Pennsylvania State Univ. Pr.

van der Ley, Sabrina, ed. Pedro Cabrita Reis: One after Another, A Few Silent Steps. 2010. (ENG., Illus.). 368p. 75.00 *(978-3-7757-2558-3(X))* Hatje Cantz Verlag GmbH & Co KG DEU. Dist: D.A.P./Distributed Art Pubs.

Von Drathen, Doris. Rui Chafes. 2008. (ENG., Illus.). 152p. 59.95 *(978-88-8158-657-8(6))* Charta ITA. Dist: D.A.P./Distributed Art Pubs.

ART, PREHISTORIC

see also Art, Primitive; Rock Paintings

Anati, Emmanuel. World Rock Art: The Primordial Language. 3rd rev. ed. 2010. (ENG., Illus.). 181p. (C). pap. 39.95 *(978-1-905739-31-8(1))* Archaeopress GBR. Dist: Brown, David Bk. Co., The.

Anati, Emmanuel, ed. Prehistoric Art & Ideology. 2008. (Bar S Ser.). (Illus.). 123p. (C). 70.00 *(978-1-4073-0352-9(X))* British Archaeological Reports Ltd. GBR. Dist: Brown, David Bk. Co., The.

Bahn, Paul. An Enquiring Mind: Studies in Honor of Alexander Marshack. 2009. (American school of prehistoric research Monograph Ser.). (ENG., Illus.). 352p. (C). 35.00 *(978-1-84217-383-1(9))* Oxbow Bks., Ltd. GBR. Dist: Brown, David Bk. Co., The.

Bahn, Paul G. Prehistoric Rock Art: Polemics & Progress. 2010. (ENG., Illus.). 238p. (C). 90.00 *(978-0-521-19278-1(1))*; pap. 27.99 *(978-0-521-14087-4(0))* Cambridge Univ. Pr.

Barnett, Tertia & Sharpe, K., eds. Carving a Future for British Rock Art: New Directions for Research, Management & Presentation. 2010. (ENG., Illus.). 191p. (C). 130.00 *(978-1-84217-364-0(2))* Oxbow Bks., Ltd. GBR. Dist: Brown, David Bk. Co., The.

Bataille, Georges. The Cradle of Humanity: Prehistoric Art & Culture. Kendall, Stuart & Bataille, Georges, eds. & trs. by. from FRE. Kendall, Michelle, tr. from FRE. 2009. (ENG., Illus.). 210p. (gr. 17). pap. 22.95 *(978-1-890951-56-6(0))* Zone Bks.

Beckensall, Stan. Prehistoric Rock Art in Northumberland. (ENG., Illus.). 208p. pap. 35.00 *(978-0-7524-1945-9(5))* History Pr. Ltd.,The GBR. Dist: Trafalgar Square Publishing.

Bednarik, Robert G. & Hodgston, Derek, eds. Pleistocene Palaeoart of the World, 19. 2008. (Bar S Ser.). (ENG., Illus.). 75p. (C). pap. 62.50 *(978-1-4073-0291-1(4))* British Archaeological Reports Ltd. GBR. Dist: Brown, David Bk. Co., The.

Blundell, Geoffrey, et al, eds. Seeing & Knowing: Understanding Rock Art with & without Ethnography. 2011. (ENG., Illus.). 328p. pap. 36.95 *(978-1-61132-048-0(8))* Left Coast Pr., Inc.

Boado, Felipe Criado, et al, eds. Representations & Communications: Creating an Archaeological Matrix of Late Prehistoric Rock Art. 2010. (ENG., Illus.). 167p. (C). pap. 50.00 *(978-1-84217-397-8(9))* Oxbow Bks., Ltd. GBR. Dist: Brown, David Bk. Co., The.

Bouvry, Florence. Une Anthropologie des Manifestations Esthetiques Du Mesolithique Europeen De la Fin Du Tardiglaciaire et Durant le Postglaciaire. 2008. (Bar S Ser.). (FRE., Illus.). 643 p. (C). 175.00 *(978-1-4073-0255-3(8))* British Archaeological Reports Ltd. GBR. Dist: Brown, David Bk. Co., The.

Bradley, Richard. Image & Audience: Rethinking Prehistoric Art. 2009. (Illus.). 280p. 110.00 *(978-0-19-953385-5(7))* Oxford Univ. Pr., Inc.

Brooke, Beatrice D. & Magalhães, Roberto Carvalho de. Art & Culture of the Prehistoric World. 2010. (Ancient Art & Cultures Ser.). (ENG., Illus.). 40p. (YA). pap. 11.75 *(978-1-61532-879-6(3))* Rosen Publishing Group, Inc., The.

Brown, Paul & Brown, Barbara. Prehistoric Rock Art the Northern Dales. 2008. (ENG., Illus.). 320p. 46.95 *(978-0-7524-4246-4(5))* History Pr. Ltd.,The GBR. Dist: Independent Pubs. Group.

Budin, Stephanie Lynn. Images of Woman & Child from the Bronze Age: Reconsidering Fertility, Maternity, & Gender in the Ancient World. 2011. (ENG., Illus.). 390p. 95.00 *(978-0-521-19304-7(4))* Cambridge Univ. Pr.

Burkitt, M. C. Prehistory: A Study of Early Cultures in Europe & the Mediterranean Basin. 2012. (ENG.). 460p. pap. 53.00 ***(978-1-107-69684-6(4))*** Cambridge Univ. Pr.

Clottes, Jean. Cave Art. 2010. (ENG., Illus.). 336p. pap. 39.95 *(978-0-7148-5723-7(8))* Phaidon Pr., Inc.

Coimbra, Fernando & Dubal, Leo, eds. Symbolism in Rock Art, 25. 2008. (Bar S Ser.). (Illus.). 62p. (C). 55.00 *(978-1-4073-0281-2(7))* British Archaeological Reports Ltd. GBR. Dist: Brown, David Bk. Co., The.

Da Silva, Arturo Rey. Iconografia Náutica de la Península Ibérica en la Protohistoria. 2009. (Bar S Ser.). (SPA & ENG., Illus.). 108p. (C). pap. 72.50 *(978-1-4073-0514-1(X))* British Archaeological Reports Ltd. GBR. Dist: Brown, David Bk. Co., The.

Deacon, Janette, contrib. by. Some Views on Rock Paintings in the Cederberg. 2nd ed. (Illus.). *(978-1-875012-25-1(7))* National Monuments Council.

Deger-Jalkotzy, Sigrid & Schindel, Nikolaus, eds. Gold: Tagung anlasslich der Grundung des Zentrums Archaologie und Altertumswissenschaften an der Osterreichischen Akademie der Wissenschaften, 19. 20. April 2007. 2009. (Denkschriften der Phil. -Hist. Klasse Ser.). (GER., Illus.). 206p. (C). pap. 102.00 *(978-3-7001-6547-7(1))* Austrian Academy of Sciences Press AUT. Dist: Brown, David Bk. Co., The.

Desdemaines-Hugon, Christine. Stepping-Stones: A Journey through the Ice Age Caves of the Dordogne. 2010. (Illus.). 272p. 30.00 *(978-0-300-15266-1(3))* Yale Univ. Pr.

Dijkstra, Marjolein Efting. The Animal Substitute: An Ethnological Perspective on the Origin of Image-making & Art. 2011. (Illus.). 304p. 30.00 *(978-90-5972-422-8(4))* Eburon Academic Pubs. NLD. Dist: Chicago Distribution Ctr.

Dimitriadis, George, et al, eds. Rock Art & Museum. 2009. (FRE & ENG., Illus.). 86p. (C). pap. 70.00 *(978-1-4073-0531-8(X))* British Archaeological Reports Ltd. GBR. Dist: Brown, David Bk. Co., The.

Djindjian, François & Oosterbeek, Luiz, eds. Symbolic Spaces in Prehistoric Art. 2009. (FRE & ENG., Illus.). 118p. (C). pap. 77.50 *(978-1-4073-0533-2(6))* British Archaeological Reports Ltd. GBR. Dist: Brown, David Bk. Co., The.

Gamble, Clive. Origins & Revolutions: Human Identity in Earliest Prehistory. 2007. (ENG., Illus.). 364p. per. 32.99 *(978-0-521-67749-3(1))* Cambridge Univ. Pr.

Groenen, Marc, et al, eds. Session C74: Methods of Art History Tested against Prehistory; Session C81: Spirals & Circular Forms: the Most Commom Rock Art in the World? Session C85: European Cave Art; Session S02: Euro-Mediterranean Rock Art Studies; Session S07: Global State of the Art; Session WS37: Current State of North American Rock Art, Vol. 35. 2010. (Bar S Ser.). (POR, FRE & ENG., Illus.). 177p. (C). pap. 92.50 *(978-1-4073-0649-0(9))* British Archaeological Reports Ltd. GBR. Dist: Brown, David Bk. Co., The.

Heyd, Thomas & Clegg, John. Aesthetics & Rock Art III Symposium. 2008. (Bar S Ser.). (ENG., Illus.). 102p. (C). pap. 70.00 *(978-1-4073-0304-8(X))* British Archaeological Reports Ltd. GBR. Dist: Brown, David Bk. Co., The.

Kelker, Nancy L. & Bruhns, Karen O. Faking Ancient Mesoamerica. 2009. (ENG., Illus.). 256p. pap. 29.95 *(978-1-59874-149-0(7))*; lib. bdg. 89.00 *(978-1-59874-150-6(0))* Left Coast Pr., Inc.

Langdon, Susan. Art & Identity in Dark Age Greece, 1100-700 BC. 2010. (ENG., Illus.). 408p. pap. 45.00 *(978-0-521-17192-2(X))* Cambridge Univ. Pr.

Langdon, Susan & Langdon, Susan Helen. Art & Identity in Dark Age Greece, 1100-700 B.C.E. 2008. (ENG., Illus.). 406p. (C). 98.00 *(978-0-521-51321-0(9))* Cambridge Univ. Pr.

Legrand-Pineau, Alexandra, et al, eds. Ancient & Modern Bone Artefacts from America to Russia. 2010. (Bar S Ser.). (ENG., Illus.). 324p. (C). pap. 132.50 *(978-1-4073-0677-3(4))* British Archaeological Reports Ltd. GBR. Dist: Brown, David Bk. Co., The.

Lodoen, Trond & Mandt, Gro. The Rock Art of Norway. 2010. (ENG., Illus.). 344p. pap. 60.00 *(978-1-905119-28-8(3))* Windgather Pr. GBR. Dist: Brown, David Bk. Co., The.

Loendorf, Lawrence L. Thunder & Herds: Rock Art of the High Plains. 2008. (ENG., Illus.). 254p. 94.00 *(978-1-59874-152-0(7))*; pap. 32.95 *(978-1-59874-151-3(9))* Left Coast Pr., Inc.

Mazel, Aron, et al, eds. Art as Metaphor: The Prehistoric Rock-Art of Britain. 2007. (ENG., Illus.). 256p. (C). pap. 39.95 *(978-1-905739-16-5(8))* Archaeopress GBR. Dist: Brown, David Bk. Co., The.

National Park Service (U.S.), compiled by. Early Art of the Northern Far East: the Stone Age. 2009. (ENG., Illus.). 323p. pap. 46.00 *(978-0-16-082222-3(X))* National Park Service Div. of Pubns.

Poggiani Keller, Raffaella, et al, eds. Rock Art Data Base. 2009. (ENG., Illus.). 76p. (C). pap. 67.50 *(978-1-4073-0530-1(1))* British Archaeological Reports Ltd. GBR. Dist: Brown, David Bk. Co., The.

Seglie, Dario, et al, eds. Prehistoric Art: Signs, Symbols, Myth, Ideology. 2009. (Bar S Ser.). (FRE, SPA & ENG., Illus.). 156p. (C). pap. 125.00 *(978-1-4073-0605-6(7))* British Archaeological Reports Ltd. GBR. Dist: Brown, David Bk. Co., The.

Washburn, Dorothy K. Structure & Cognition in Art. 2011. (New Directions in Archaeology Ser.). (ENG.). 176p. pap. 26.99 *(978-0-521-18006-1(6))* Cambridge Univ. Pr.

ART, PRIMITIVE

Here are entered works discussing collectively the traditional art of the preliterate and nonindustrialized peoples of the world. Works on such art from a specific place or specific people are entered under the heading for the art of that place or people, e.g. Art, Polynesian; Aztec Art.

see also Art, Prehistoric; Folk Art; Idols and Images; Sculpture, Primitive

Boas, Franz. Primitive Art. 2010. (ENG., Illus.). 432p. pap. 19.95 *(978-0-486-47330-7(9))* Dover Pubns., Inc.

Burkitt, M. C. South Africa's Past in Stone & Paint. 2012. (ENG., Illus.). 216p. pap. 45.00 ***(978-1-107-64133-4(0))*** Cambridge Univ. Pr.

Castro, Iné, et al. Paradiese der Südsee: Mythos und Wirklichkeit. 2008. (GER., Illus.). 248p. (C). 53.00 *(978-3-8053-3915-5(1))* Zabern, Philipp von Verlag, GmbH DEU. Dist: Brown, David Bk. Co., The.

Colleyn, Jean-Paul, et al. Boli. 2010. (FRE & ENG., Illus.). 176p. 50.00 *(978-2-35340-075-1(2))* Gourcuff Gradenigo FRA. Dist: National Bk. Network.

deLaguna, Frederica. A Comparison of Eskimo & Palaeolithic Art. 2009. pap. 25.36 *(978-1-60724-466-0(7))* Gorgias Pr., LLC.

Harrison, Jane Ellen. Ancient Art & Ritual. 2009. 258p. 25.99 *(978-0-559-65723-8(4))* 2009. 258p. pap. 25.75 *(978-0-559-65720-7(X))* 2008. 152p. 24.99 *(978-0-554-26236-9(3))* 2008. 152p. 21.99 *(978-0-554-35539-9(6))* BiblioBazaar.

—Ancient Art & Ritual. 2007. (Illus.). 136p. per. *(978-1-4065-3280-7(0))* Dodo Pr.

Hayes, Elizabeth R. The Evolution of Visual, Literary, & Performing Arts from Tribal Cultures Through the Middle Ages. 2009. (Illus.). xii, 226p. pap. *(978-0-7409-3153-6(9)*, Ohio Univ. Ctr. for International Studies) Paper House Productions.

Janis, Sidney. They Taught Themselves: American Primitive Painters of the 20th Century. reprint ed. 72.50 *(978-0-404-20134-0(2))* AMS Pr., Inc.

Kohl, Karl-Heinz. Zwischen Kunst und Kontext: Zur Renaissance des Völkerkundemuseums. 2010. (Wissenschaftliche Gesellschaft an der Johann Wolfgang Goethe-Sitzungsberichte (WGF-S) Ser.). (GER., Illus.). 27p. (C). pap. 22.00 *(978-3-515-09818-2(6))* Steiner, Franz Verlag Wiesbaden GmbH DEU. Dist: Brown, David Bk. Co., The.

Le Fur, Yves, ed. Musée du Quai Branly: The Collection - Art from Africa, Asia, Oceania, & the Americas. 2009. (ENG., Illus.). 480p. 95.00 *(978-2-08-122579-4(4))* Flammarion et Cie FRA. Dist: Random Hse., Inc.

Meyer, Laure. Art & Craft in Africa. 2008. (Illus.). 256p. pap. 23.50 *(978-2-87939-337-7(X))* Terrail, Pierre Editions FRA. Dist: Wybel Marketing Group.

O'Neal, William B. Primitive into Painter: Life & Letters of John Toole. 2011. 154p. 41.95 ***(978-1-258-03574-7(X))*** Literary Licensing, LLC.

Sibeth, Achim, ed. Being Object, Being Art, 1 vol. 2010. (ENG.). 324p. 75.00 *(978-3-8030-3338-3(1))* Wasmuth, Ernst J. Verlag GmbH & Co. DEU. Dist: D.A.P./Distributed Art Pubs.

Siegel, Morris. The MacKenzie Collection: A Study of West African Carved Gambling Chips. Linton, Ralph & Herskovits, Melville J., eds. 2011. 88p. 38.95 ***(978-1-258-08773-9(1))*** Literary Licensing, LLC.

Washburn, Dorothy K. Structure & Cognition in Art. 2011. (New Directions in Archaeology Ser.). (ENG.). 176p. pap. 26.99 *(978-0-521-18006-1(6))* Cambridge Univ. Pr.

Waterfield, Hermione & King, J. C. H. Provenance: Twelve Collectors of Ethnographic Art in England 1760-1990. 2010. (Illus.). 176p. pap. 45.00 *(978-1-903470-96-1(X))* Univ. of Washington Pr.

—Provenance: Twelve Collectors of Ethnographic Art in England, 1760-1990. 2009. (Illus.). 175p. *(978-1-903470-97-8(8))* Holberton, Paul Publishing.

Weltfish, Gene. The Origins of Art. 2011. 300p. 48.95 ***(978-1-258-08236-9(5))*** Literary Licensing, LLC.

ART, PUBLIC

see Public Art

ART, PUERTO RICAN

Katz, Vincent, et al. Retro/Active: The Work of Rafael Ferrer. Cullen, Deborah, ed. 2010.Tr. of Retro/activa: la obra de Rafael Ferrer. (ENG & SPA., Illus.). 160p. pap. 35.00 *(978-1-882454-27-3(8))* El Museo del Barrio.

Vazquez, Victor, photos by. Victor Vazquez: 1989-2007, 1 vol. 2008. (ENG., Illus.). 300p. 85.00 *(978-0-9773932-4-4(0))* Museo de Arte de Ponce.

Vilaró, Viveca Venegas. To Love until It Hurts. 2009. 140p. pap. 12.99 *(978-1-4389-8918-1(0))* AuthorHouse.

Zimmerman, Marc. Defending Their Own in the Cold: The Cultural Turns of U. S. Puerto Ricans. 2011. (Latinos in Chicago & Midwest Ser.). (ENG., Illus.). 232p. 55.00 ***(978-0-252-03646-0(8))*** Univ. of Illinois Pr.

ART, RENAISSANCE

Ajmar, Marta & Dennis, Flora. At Home in Renaissance Italy. 2010. (ENG., Illus.). 416p. pap. 45.00 *(978-1-85177-489-0(0))* V & A Pubns. GBR. Dist: Hachette Bk. Group.

—At Home in Renaissance Italy: Art & Life in the Italian House, 1400-1600. 2006. (ENG., Illus.). 420p. 85.00 *(978-1-85177-488-3(2))* V & A Pubns. GBR. Dist: Hachette Bk. Group.

Alexander-Skipnes & Alexander-Skipnes, Ingrid. Cultural Exchange Between the Low Countries & Italy (1400-1600) 2007. (Museums at the Crossroads Ser.). (ENG., Illus.). 292p. (C). pap. 116.00 *(978-2-503-51838-1(9))* Brepols Pubs. BEL. Dist: ISD.

Ambers, J., et al. Italian Renaissance Drawings: Technical Examination & Analysis. 2010. (ENG., Illus.). 174p. pap. 70.00 *(978-1-904982-58-6(1))* Archetype Pubns. GBR. Dist: National Bk. Network.

American Art Association. Gothic & Renaissance Art: The Collection of the Late Thomas Fortune Ryan. 2011. 38p. 35.95 ***(978-1-258-02381-2(4))*** Literary Licensing, LLC.

Ames-Lewis, Francis, ed. Florence. 2011. (Artistic Centers of the Italian Renaissance Ser.). (ENG., Illus.). 438p. 175.00 *(978-0-521-85162-6(9))* Cambridge Univ. Pr.

Art Renaissance Club, compiled by. A Century of Art Renaissance Club. 2007. 77p. lib. bdg. *(978-0-9640163-4-7(6))* Melton Art Reference Library.

Aston, Margaret. The Renaissance Complete. 2009. (ENG., Illus.). 368p. pap. 34.95 *(978-0-500-28459-9(8)*, 528459) Thames & Hudson.

Babelon, Jean. Histoire de l'Art Vol. 3: Renaissance, Baroque, Romantisme. (FRE.). 1704p. *(978-0-8288-7602-5(9))* French & European Pubns., Inc.

Baggs, Robert. Bitter Rivals make Great Art: Motivation for Patronage of the Sassetti Chapel. 2008. 112p. pap. *(978-3-639-10535-3(4))* VDM Verlag Dr. Mueller e.K.

Barbolani di Montauto, Novella & Chappell, Miles L. Colorire Naturale e Vero: Figline, il Cigoli e I Suoi Amici. 2008. (citta degli Uffizi Ser.). (ITA., Illus.). 176p. (C). 50.00 *(978-88-596-0481-5(8))* Polistampa ITA. Dist: Brown, David Bk. Co., The.

Bartz, Gabriele & Konig, Eberhard. Michelangelo: Buonarroti 1475-1564. 2008. (Masters of Italian Art Ser.). (Illus.). 138p. pap. 9.95 *(978-0-8416-0082-9(1))* American Map Corp.

Baxandall, Michael. Words for Pictures: Seven Papers on Renaissance Art & Criticism. 2011. (ENG., Illus.). 208p. pap. 24.00 ***(978-0-300-17678-0(3))*** Yale Univ. Pr.

Bayer, Andrea. Art & Love in Renaissance Italy. 2008. (Illus.). xv, 376p. 45.00 *(978-1-58839-301-2(1))*; 65.00 *(978-1-58839-300-5(3))* Metropolitan Museum of Art, The.

Bayer, Andrea, ed. & contrib. by. Art & Love in Renaissance Italy. 2008. (ENG., Illus.). 392p. 65.00 *(978-0-300-12411-8(2))* Yale Univ. Pr.

Belting, Hans. Florence & Baghdad: Renaissance Art & Arab Science. Schneider, Deborah Lucas, tr. from GER. 2011. Orig. Title: Florenz und Bagdad: eine westöstliche Geschichte des Blicks. (ENG., Illus.). 312p. 39.95 *(978-0-674-05004-4(5)*, Belknap Pr.) Harvard Univ. Pr.

Berenson, Bernard. Italian Painters of the Renaissance. 2011. 536p. 62.95 ***(978-1-258-10320-0(6))*** Literary Licensing, LLC.

Berenson, Bernhard. The Central Italian Painters of the Renaissance. 2007. (ENG.). 212p. 39.95 *(978-0-548-09661-1(9))* Kessinger Publishing, LLC.

—The Florentine Painters of the Renaissance. 2009. 226p. 28.99 *(978-1-110-45457-0(0))* 2009. 166p. 26.99 *(978-1-110-45451-8(1))* 2009. 226p. pap. 24.75 *(978-1-110-45454-9(6))* 2009. 166p. pap. 20.75 *(978-1-110-45448-8(1))* 2008. 192p. 25.99 *(978-0-554-27275-7(X))* 2008. 192p. 22.99 *(978-0-554-36578-7(2))* BiblioBazaar.

—The Florentine Painters of the Renaissance. 2007. (ENG.). 156p. per. *(978-1-4065-5251-4(5))* Dodo Pr.

—The Florentine Painters of the Renaissance. 2007. (ENG.). 164p. 36.95 *(978-0-548-09662-8(7))* Kessinger Publishing, LLC.

—The Florentine Painters of the Renaissance: With an Index to Their Works. 2007. (ENG.). 172p. per. 19.99 *(978-1-4346-2862-6(0))*; 190p. per. 21.99 *(978-1-4346-2897-8(3))* BiblioBazaar.

Blanc, J. & Maes, G., eds. Echanges artistiques entre les anciens Pays-Bas et la France. 2010. (Museums at the Crossroads Ser.). (DUT, ENG & FRE., Illus.). 365p. (C). pap. 109.00 *(978-2-503-53095-6(8))* Brepols Pubs. BEL. Dist: Brown, David Bk. Co., The.

Bober, Phyllis & Rubinstein, Ruth. Renaissance Artists & Antique Sculpture: A Handbook of Sources. New, revised, & updated Edition. 2nd ed. 2010. (Studies in Medieval & Early Renaissance Art History Ser.). (ENG., Illus.). 581p. (C). 217.00 *(978-1-905375-60-8(3))* Miller, Harvey Pubs. GBR. Dist: Brown, David Bk. Co., The.

Bodart, Diane. Renaissance & Mannerism. 2008. (ENG., Illus.). 192p. pap. 14.95 *(978-1-4027-5922-2(3))* Sterling Publishing Co., Inc.

Boer, Waldemar H. de. Francesco Albertini: Memorial of Many Statues & Paintings in the Famous City of Florence. Boer, De Waldemar H., ed. 2011. (Illus.). 240p. pap. 65.00 ***(978-88-7038-492-5(6))*** Centro Di ITA. Dist: Antique Collectors' Club.

Bourdua, Louise & Dunlop, Anne, eds. Art & the Augustinian Order in Early Renaissance Italy. 2007. (Church, Faith & Culture in the Medieval West Ser.). (Illus.). 250p. 124.95 *(978-0-7546-5655-5(1))* Ashgate Publishing Co.

Boyd, Catherine E. The French Renaissance: Illustrative Set No. 3. 2011. 96p. 38.95 ***(978-1-258-04692-7(X))*** Literary Licensing, LLC.

Bradshaw, Marilyn. Italian Renaissance Art. 2008. (ENG., Illus.). 368p. (C). pap. 45.80 *(978-0-13-606128-1(1)*, Prentice Hall) Prentice Hall PTR.

Campbell, Gordon. The Grove Encyclopedia of Northern Renaissance Art, 3 vols. 2009. (Grove Art Ser.). (ENG., Illus.). 1300p. (C). 357.00 *(978-0-19-533467-8(1))*;Set. 2114p. 415.00 *(978-0-19-533466-1(3))* Oxford Univ. Pr., Inc.

Campbell, Stephen J. & Cole, Michael W. Italian Renaissance Art. 2011. (ENG., Illus.). 696p. (C). pap. 90.00 net. ***(978-0-500-28943-3(3)***, 528943) Thames & Hudson.

Carman, Charles H. Renaissance Theories of Vision. Shannon, John, ed. 2010. (Visual Culture in Early Modernity Ser.). (Illus.). 258p. 119.95 *(978-1-4094-0024-0(7))* Ashgate Publishing Co.

Cast, David. The Delight of Art: Giorgio Vasari & the Traditions of Humanist Discourse. 2009. (ENG.). 296p. 95.00 *(978-0-271-03442-3(4))* Pennsylvania State Univ. Pr.

Caterina Proto Pisani, Rosanna. La Valle Dei Tesori: Capolavori Allo Specchio. 2006. (Piccoli, grandi Musei Ser.). (ITA & ENG., Illus.). 185p. (C). 29.50 *(978-88-536-0068-8(5))* Edizioni Polistampa ITA. Dist: Brown, David Bk. Co., The.

Chapuis, Julien, ed. Invention: Northern Renaissance Studies in Honor of Molly Faries. 2008. (Me Fecit Ser.). (ENG., Illus.). 231p. (C). 116.00 *(978-2-503-52768-0(X))* Brepols Pubs. BEL. Dist: ISD.

Charles, Victoria. Art of Century: Renacimiento. 2008. (Illus.). 199p. pap. 17.95 *(978-970-718-622-4(4)*, Numen) Advanced Marketing, S. de R. L. de C. V. MEX. Dist: Perseus-PGW.

—Renaissance Art. 2007. (Art of Century Ser.). (ENG., Illus.). 199p. pap. 19.95 *(978-1-85995-676-2(9))* Parkstone International GBR. Dist: Ingram Pub. Services.

Chen, Althea. Renaissance Design. 2007. (Dover Pictura Electronic Clip Art Ser.). (ENG., Illus.). 128p. pap. 39.95 *(978-0-486-99889-3(4))* Dover Pubns., Inc.

Christadler, Maike. Kreativitaet & Geschlecht: Giorgio Vasaris "Vite" & Sofonisba Anguissolas Selbst-Bilder. (GER., Illus.). 284p. *(978-3-496-01221-4(8))* Reimer, Dietrich.

Cohen, Simona. Animals as Disguised Symbols in Renaissance Art. 2008. 352p. (C). *(978-90-04-17101-5(0))* BRILL.

Colantuono, Anthony. Titian, Colonna & the Renaissance Science of Procreation: Equicola's Seasons of Desire. 2010. (Visual Culture in Early Modernity Ser.). (Illus.). 342p. 119.95 *(978-0-7546-6962-3(9))* Ashgate Publishing Co.

Cole, Michael W., ed. Sixteenth-Century Italian Art. 2006. (Blackwell Anthologies in Art History Ser.: 2). (ENG., Illus.). 568p. 136.95 *(978-1-4051-0840-9(1))*; per. 57.95 *(978-1-4051-0841-6(X))* Wiley, John & Sons, Inc. (Wiley-Blackwell).

Collas, I. Hans & Schandel, P., eds. Manuscrits de Louis de Bruges. 2010. (Manuscrits enluminés des anciens Pays-Bas Meridionaux Ser.). (FRE., Illus.). 347p. (C). 218.00 *(978-2-7177-2396-0(X))* Brepols Pubs. BEL. Dist: ISD.

Cram101 Textbook Reviews. Outlines & Highlights for Art in Renaissance Italy by Paoletti & Radke, Isbn: 013091830x. 2011. 310p. pap. 32.95 ***(978-1-61812-926-0(0))*** Cram101 Inc.

Cram101 Textbook Reviews. Outlines & Highlights for Italian Renaissance Art by Laurie Schneider Adams, Isbn: 9780813336916. 2010. 160p. pap. 29.95 *(978-1-61654-064-7(8))* Cram101 Inc.

Cunningham, C. c. Religious Art of the Middle Ages & Renaissance. 2011. 50p. 35.95 ***(978-1-258-03699-7(1))*** Literary Licensing, LLC.

Cusk, Rachel. The Last Supper: A Summer in Italy. 2010. (ENG., Illus.). 256p. pap. 15.00 *(978-0-312-42965-2(7))* Picador.

Dacos, Nicole. The Loggia of Raphael: A Vatican Art Treasure. 2008. (ENG., Illus.). 352p. 125.00 *(978-0-7892-1004-3(5))* Abbeville Pr., Inc.

Daneo, Angelica. The Kress Collection at the Denver Art Museum. 2011. (ENG., Illus.). 168p. pap. 25.00 *(978-0-914738-69-5(0))* Denver Art Museum.

Davies, Glyn & Kennedy, Kirstin. Medieval & Renaissance Art: People & Possessions. 2009. (ENG., Illus.). 320p. 80.00 *(978-1-85177-579-8(X))* V & A Pubns. GBR. Dist: Hachette Bk. Group.

De Armas, Frederick A. & de Armas, Frederick A. Quixotic Frescoes: Cervantes & Italian Renaissance Art. 2006. (Illus.). 344p. *(978-0-8020-9074-4(5))* Univ. of Toronto Pr.

Dempsey, Charles. The Early Renaissance & Vernacular Culture. 2012. (Bernard Berenson Lectures on the Italian Renaissance Delivered at Villa I Tatti Ser.). (ENG., Illus.). 398p. 39.95 *(978-0-674-04952-9(7))* Harvard Univ. Pr.

Dover. Renaissance & Baroque Ceiling Masterpieces. 2008. (Dover Pictorial Archive Ser.). (ENG., Illus.). 80p. pap. 17.95 *(978-0-486-46529-6(2))* Dover Pubns., Inc.

Edgerton, Samuel Y. The Mirror, the Window, & the Telescope. 2009. (Illus.). 224p. 68.50 *(978-0-8014-4758-7(5))*; pap. 19.95 *(978-0-8014-7480-4(9))* Cornell Univ. Pr.

Edgertonsamuel, Y. The Renaissance Rediscovery of Linear Perspective. 2008. 232p. pap. 22.00 *(978-1-59740-508-9(6))* ACLS Humanities E-Book.

Elkins, James & Williams, Robert, eds. Renaissance Theory. 2008. (Art Seminar Ser.). (Illus.). (ENG.). 560p. (C). 125.00 *(978-0-415-96045-8(2))*; 550p. pap. 32.95 *(978-0-415-96046-5(0))* Routledge.

Elsig, Frederic. Painting in France in the 15th Century. 2008. (Gallery of the Arts Ser.: Vol. 1). (ENG., Illus.). 156p. 19.95 *(978-88-7439-120-2(X))* 5 Continents ITA. Dist: Hachette Bk. Group.

Emison, Patricia. The Italian Renaissance & Cultural Memory. 2011. (ENG., Illus.). 238p. 90.00 *(978-1-107-00526-6(4))* Cambridge Univ. Pr.

Farbaky, Peter & Waldman, Louis A., eds. Italy & Hungary: Humanism & Art in the Early Renaissance. Acts of an International Conference, Florence, Villa I Tatti, June 6-8 2007. 2011. (Villa I Tatti Ser.). (Illus.). 772p. 85.00 *(978-0-674-06346-4(5))* Villa I Tatti.

Farinella, Vincenzo. Rapheal. 2008. (Gallery of the Arts Ser.). (ENG., Illus.). 128p. 15.95 *(978-88-7439-121-9(8))* 5 Continents ITA. Dist: Hachette Bk. Group.

Farthing, Stephen. The Renaissance Art. 2010. (ENG., Illus.). 14p. 40.00 *(978-0-7893-2080-3(0))* Universe Publishing.

Faure, Elie. The Italian Renaissance. 2011. 176p. 42.95 ***(978-1-258-04969-0(4))*** Literary Licensing, LLC.

Faure, Élie, et al. Renaissance Art. 2010. (Illus.). 256p. *(978-1-84484-684-9(9))* Parkstone International.

Fisher, Celia. Flowers of the Renaissance. 2011. (ENG., Illus.). 160p. 39.95 *(978-1-60606-062-9(7)*, J. Paul Getty Museum) Getty Pubns.

Folin, Marco, ed. Courts & Courtly Arts in Renaissance Italy: Arts, Culture & Politics, 1395-1530. 2010. (ENG., Illus.). 444p. 95.00 *(978-1-85149-643-3(2))* Antique Collectors' Club.

Franklin, Michael W., et al, eds. Renaissance Art Reconsidered: An Anthology of Primary Sources. 2007. (ENG., Illus.). 472p. per. 41.95 *(978-1-4051-4641-8(9)*, Wiley-Blackwell) Wiley, John & Sons, Inc.

Freedman, Luba. The Revival of the Olympian Gods in Renaissance Art. 2010. (ENG., Illus.). 320p. (C). pap. 44.00 *(978-0-521-18103-7(8))* Cambridge Univ. Pr.

Furlotti, Barbara & Rebecchini, Guido. The Art of Mantua: Power & Patronage in the Renaissance. Jenkens, A. Lawrence, tr. from ITA. 2008. (Illus.). 280p. 84.95 *(978-0-89236-840-2(3))* Oxford Univ. Pr., Inc.

Galimberti, Carlo A. & Galimberti, Carlo Adelio. Mogli, garzoni e Amanti: Amore ed erotismo nella vita e nelle opere degli artisti del Cinquecento. 2011. (Storie del Mondo Ser.). (ITA., Illus.). 200p. pap. 29.00 ***(978-88-564-0149-3(5))*** Polistampa ITA. Dist: Brown, David Bk. Co., The.

Galli, Aldo. Pollaiuolo. 2008. (Gallery of the Arts Ser.). (ENG., Illus.). 92p. 14.95 *(978-88-7439-130-1(7))* 5 Continents ITA. Dist: Hachette Bk. Group.

Geck, Francis Joseph. Bibliography of Italian Early Renaissance Art. 2011. 44p. 35.95 ***(978-1-258-02103-0(X))*** Literary Licensing, LLC.

Gibson, Clare. The Hidden Life of Renaissance Art. 2007. (Illus.). 208p. *(978-1-887354-59-2(X))* Saraband (Scotland) Ltd.

Gibson, Walter S. Figures of Speech: Picturing Proverbs in Renaissance Netherlands. 2010. (ENG., Illus.). 256p. 49.95 *(978-0-520-25954-6(8))* Univ. of California Pr.

Gromling, Alexandra. Buonarroti. 2008. (Art in Focus (Konemann) Ser.). (Illus.). 95p. pap. 5.95 *(978-0-8416-0054-6(6))* American Map Corp.

Hairston, Julia L. & Stephens, Walter, eds. The Body in Early Modern Italy. 2010. (ENG., Illus.). 448p. (gr. 17). 70.00 *(978-0-8018-9414-5(X))* Johns Hopkins Univ. Pr.

Hartt, Frederick & Wilkins, David G. History of Italian Renaissance Art: Painting, Sculpture, Architecture. 7th ed. 2010. (ENG., Illus.). 736p. (C). pap. 136.20 *(978-0-205-70581-8(2)*, Prentice Hall) Prentice Hall PTR.

Hatfield, Rab, ed. Sandro Botticelli Herbert Horn. 2009. 160p. pap. 24.95 *(978-88-95250-04-5(4))* Syracuse Univ. Pr.

Hattori, Natsu. Performing Cures. 2009. pap. 100.00 *(978-0-415-20512-2(3))*; pap. 34.95 *(978-0-415-20513-9(1))* Routledge.

Hersey, George L. Falling in Love with Statues: Artificial Humans from Pygmalion to the Present. 2009. (ENG., Illus.). 200p. 40.00 *(978-0-226-32779-2(5))* Univ. of Chicago Pr.

Hickson, Sally Anne. Women Art & Architectural Patronage in Renaissance Mantua: Matrons Mystics & Monasteries. 2012. (Women & Gender in the Early Modern World Ser.). (Illus.). 204p. 104.95 ***(978-1-4094-2752-0(8))*** Ashgate Publishing Co.

Hirakawa, Kayo. The Pictorialization of Dürer's Drawings in Northern Europe in the Sixteenth & Seventh Centuries. 2009. (Illus.). 178p. pap. *(978-3-03911-725-3(4))* Lang, Peter.

Hornik, Heidi J. Michele Tosini & the Ghirlandaio Workshop in Cinquecento Florence. 2009. (ENG., Illus.). 211p. pap. 55.00 *(978-1-84519-186-3(2))* Sussex Academic Pr. GBR. Dist: International Specialized Bk. Services.

Humfrey, Peter, ed. Venice & the Veneto. 2008. (Artistic Centers of the Italian Renaissance Ser.). (ENG., Illus.). 424p. 172.00 *(978-0-521-80843-9(X))* Cambridge Univ. Pr.

Johnson, Christopher D. Memory, Metaphor, & Aby Warburg's Atlas of Images. 2012. (Signale: Modern German Letters, Cultures, & Thought Ser.). (ENG.). 288p. pap. 35.00 ***(978-0-8014-7742-3(5))*** Cornell Univ. Pr.

Jokisch, Christoph & Volz, Peter. Emblems of Eminence: German Renaissance Portrait Medals. 2008. (GER., Illus.). 224p. (C). 154.00 *(978-3-7774-4235-8(6))* Hirmer Verlag GmbH DEU. Dist: Brown, David Bk. Co., The.

Kaplan, Peter. comment. Arthur Carter: Sculptures - Paintings - Drawings. 2009. (ENG., Illus.). 208p. 50.00 *(978-0-8109-0595-5(7))* Abrams.

Katz, Dana E. The Jew in the Art of the Italian Renaissance. 2008. (Jewish Culture & Contexts Ser.). (Illus.). 240p. (C). 59.95 *(978-0-8122-4085-6(5))* Univ. of Pennsylvania Pr.

Keane, A. H. The Early Teutonic, Italian & French Masters. 2007. (ENG.). 574p. 58.95 *(978-0-548-04492-6(9))* Kessinger Publishing, LLC.

Kennedy, Ruth Wedgwood. The Italian Renaissance. 2011. 26p. 35.95 ***(978-1-258-01242-7(1))*** Literary Licensing, LLC.

Kent, Dale. Friendship, Love, & Trust in Renaissance Florence. 2009. (Bernard Berenson Lectures on the Italian Renaissance Delivered at Villa I Tatti Ser.). (Illus.). 288p. 33.00 *(978-0-674-03137-1(7))* Harvard Univ. Pr.

Kershner, Frederick Doyl. Spiritual Message of Great Art an Interp. 2006. pap. 24.95 *(978-1-4286-5940-7(4))* Kessinger Publishing, LLC.

King, Catherine E. Representing Renaissance Art, C. 1500-C. 1600. 2008. (ENG., Illus.). 384p. pap. 34.00 *(978-0-7190-7557-5(2))*; 94.00 *(978-0-7190-7556-8(4))* Manchester Univ. Pr. GBR. Dist: Macmillan.

King, Ross. Michelangelo & the Pope's Ceiling. 2006. (Illus.). 373p. reprint ed. 28.00 *(978-1-4223-5579-4(9))* DIANE Publishing Co.

Knowlton, John Howard Barnes & Hinman, Helen E. A Syllabus of Italian Renaissance Art. 2011. 162p. 41.95 ***(978-1-258-01298-4(7))*** Literary Licensing, LLC.

Konig, Eberhard, ed. Great Painters of Italian Renaissance. 2008. 1304p. 150.00 *(978-0-8416-0346-2(4))* American Map Corp.

Lavin, Marilyn Aronberg. Artists' Art in the Renaissance. 2009. (ENG., Illus.). 230p. (C). 220.00 *(978-1-904597-43-8(2))* Pindar Pr. GBR. Dist: Brown, David Bk. Co., The.

Lawless, Cather. Life Virgin Tuscan Icon 1300-1528. 2006. (Routledge Studies in Medieval Religion & Culture Ser.). (ENG.). 125.00 *(978-0-415-36101-9(X))* Routledge.

Lee, Soyoung. Art of the Korean Renaissance, 1400-1600. 2009. (ENG., Illus.). 140p. 40.00 *(978-0-300-14891-6(7))* Yale Univ. Pr.

Lee, Soyoung, et al. Art of the Korean Renaissance, 1400-1600. 2009. (Illus.). xii, 128p. 40.00 *(978-1-58839-310-4(0))* Metropolitan Museum of Art, The.

Levy, Allison. Re-Membering Masculinity in Early Modern Florence: Widowed Bodies, Mourning & Portraiture. 2006. (Women & Gender in the Early Modern World Ser.). (Illus.). 214p. 130.00 *(978-0-7546-5404-9(4))* Ashgate Publishing Co.

Lorenzi, Lorenzo. Devils in Art: Florence from the Middle Ages to the Renaissance. Roberts, Mark, tr. from ITA. 2006. (ENG., Illus.). 132p. 40.00 *(978-88-7038-438-3(1))* Centro Di ITA. Dist: Antique Collectors' Club.

Lubbock, Jules. Storytelling in Christian Art from Giotto to Donatello. 2006. (Illus.). 353p. 50.00 *(978-0-300-11727-1(2))* Yale Univ. Pr.

Luchs, A. The Mermaids of Venice: Fantastic Sea Creatures in Venetian Renaissance Art. 2010. (Studies in Medieval & Early Renaissance Art History Ser.). (ENG., Illus.). 273p. (C). 181.00 *(978-1-905375-45-5(X))* Miller, Harvey Pubs. GBR. Dist: Brown, David Bk. Co., The.

Mallet, J. V. G. Xanto: Pottery-Painter, Poet, Man of the Italian Renaissance. 2011. (Illus.). 216p. pap. 45.00 ***(978-0-900785-98-6(5))*** Holberton, Paul Publishing GBR. Dist: Casemate Pubs. & Bk. Distributors, LLC.

Mandel, Nathalie. Portraits of the Renaissance. 2007. (ENG., Illus.). 128p. 70.00 *(978-2-84323-890-1(0))* Assouline FRA. Dist: Perseus Distribution.

Masters, Christopher. Renaissance. 2008. (Illus.). 256p. 49.95 *(978-1-85894-448-7(1))* Merrell Pubs. Ltd. GBR. Dist: Perseus Distribution.

Matt, Leonard von. Renaissance Art in Rome: The Roma Series. Mariani, Valerio, ed. 2011. 64p. 36.95 ***(978-1-258-03917-2(6))*** Literary Licensing, LLC.

Maxwell, Susan. The Court Art of Friedrich Sustris: Patronage in Late Renaissance Bavaria. 2011. (Visual Culture in Early Modernity Ser.). (Illus.). 250p. 109.95 *(978-0-7546-6887-9(8))* Ashgate Publishing Co.

Meyer, Eric Christopher. Art in the Renaissance: Text Pairs. 2008. (Bridges/Navigators Ser.). (J). (gr. 6). 89.00 *(978-1-4108-8430-5(9))* Benchmark Education Co.

Motture, Peta & O'Malley, Michelle, eds. Re-Thinking Renaissance Objects: Design, Function & Meaning. 2012. (ENG., Illus.). 232p. pap. 34.95 *(978-1-4443-3775-4(0)*, Wiley-Blackwell) Wiley, John & Sons, Inc.

Müntz, Eugène. Leonardo Da Vinci. 2013. (Prestige Ser.). (ENG., Illus.). 496p. 54.00 *(978-1-84484-675-7(X))* Parkstone International GBR. Dist: Ingram Pub. Services.

Murray, Timothy. Baroque Interface. pap. *(978-0-8047-3466-0(6))* Stanford Univ. Pr.

Nagel, Alexander. The Controversy of Renaissance Art. 2011. (ENG., Illus.). 376p. 60.00 *(978-0-226-56772-3(9))* Univ. of Chicago Pr.

Nancy, Jean-Luc. Noli Me Tangere: On the Raising of the Body. Clift, Sarah et al, trs. from FRE. 3rd ed. 2008. (Perspectives in Continental Philosophy Ser.). (ENG., Illus.). 128p. 70.00 *(978-0-8232-2889-8(4))*; pap. 22.00 *(978-0-8232-2890-4(8))* Fordham Univ. Pr.

Nash, Susie. Northern Renaissance Art. 2009. (Oxford History of Art Ser.). (ENG., Illus.). 384p. pap. 29.95 *(978-0-19-284269-5(2))* Oxford Univ. Pr., Inc.

Neri, Janice. The Insect & the Image: Visualizing Nature in Early Modern Europe, 1500-1700. 2011. (ENG., Illus.). 280p. 82.50 ***(978-0-8166-6764-2(0))***; pap. 27.50 ***(978-0-8166-6765-9(9))*** Univ. of Minnesota Pr.

Nichols, Tom. Renaissance Art: A Beginner's Guide. 2010. (Beginners Guide (Oneworld) Ser.). (ENG., Illus.). 240p. pap. 14.95 *(978-1-85168-724-4(6))* Oneworld Pubns. GBR. Dist: National Bk. Network.

Nickerson, Angela K. A Journey into Michelangelo's Rome. 2008. (ArtPlace Ser.). (ENG., Illus.). 180p. pap. 21.95 *(978-0-9777429-1-2(1))* Roaring Forties Pr.

Noever, Peter, ed. GLOBAL:LAB: Kunst als Botschaft. Asien und Europa / Art as a Message Asia & Europe 1500-1700. 2009. (ENG., Illus.). 368p. pap. 75.00 *(978-3-7757-2474-6(5))* Hatje Cantz Verlag GmbH & Co KG DEU. Dist: D.A.P./Distributed Art Pubs.

Oakes, Cathy & Oakes, Catherine. Ora Pro Nobis: The Virgin As Intercessor in Medieval Art & Devotion. 2008. (Studies in Medieval & Early Renaissance Art History Ser.). (Illus.). 300p. (C). 174.00 *(978-1-905375-24-0(7))* Miller, Harvey Pubs. GBR. Dist: Brown, David Bk. Co., The.

O'Malley, Michelle & Welch, Evelyn, eds. Material Renaissance. 2010. (Studies in Design & Material Culture Ser.). (ENG., Illus.). 328p. pap. 30.95 *(978-0-7190-8125-5(4))* Manchester Univ. Pr. GBR. Dist: Macmillan.

Onori, Lorenza Mochi, ed. Raffaello e Urbino: La sua formazione e I rapporti con la citta Natale. 2009. (ITA., Illus.). 320p. pap. 67.50 *(978-88-370-6812-7(3))* Electa ITA. Dist: Trans-Atlantic Pubns., Inc.

Oxford University Press Staff, ed. Art History VSI Set: Consisting of Art History VSI, Modern Art VSI, Dada & Surrealism VSI, Renaissance Art VSI, & Contemporary Art VSI. 2006. pap. 35.00 *(978-0-19-532597-3(4))* Oxford Univ. Pr., Inc.

Paoletti, John T. & Radke, Gary M. Art in Renaissance Italy. 4th rev. ed. 2011. (ENG., Illus.). 576p. (C). pap. 128.67 *(978-0-205-01047-9(4)*, Prentice Hall) Prentice Hall PTR.

Parke-Bernet Galleries. Egyptian, Greek & Roman Antiquities, Ancient Glass, Gothic & Renaissance Furniture & Works of Art. 2011. 158p. 41.95 ***(978-1-258-07391-7(1))*** Literary Licensing, LLC.

Parkstone Press Staff. Michelangelo. 2010. (Mega Square Ser.). (ENG., Illus.). 256p. 12.95 *(978-1-84484-839-3(6))* Parkstone Pr. USA, Ltd.

—Raphael. 2010. (Mega Square Ser.). (ENG., Illus.). 256p. 12.95 *(978-1-84484-442-5(0))* Parkstone Pr. USA, Ltd.

Partridge, Loren & Partridge, L. Art of Renaissance Florence, 1400-1600. 2009. (ENG., Illus.). 256p. pap. 36.95 *(978-0-520-25774-0(X))* Univ. of California Pr.

Pater, Walter. The Renaissance. 2008. 176p. 25.99 *(978-0-554-26822-4(1))*; 22.99 *(978-0-554-36125-3(6))* BiblioBazaar.

—The Renaissance. 2009. 144p. pap. 7.50 *(978-1-60459-704-2(6))* Wilder Pubns., Ltd.

—The Renaissance: Studies in Art & Poetry. reprint ed. lib. bdg. 98.00 *(978-0-7426-2418-4(8))* Classic Bks.

—Renaissance Studies in Art & Poetry. 2006. pap. *(978-1-84702-421-3(1))* Echo Library.

Phillips-Court, Kristin. The Perfect Genre Drama & Painting in Renaissance Italy. 2011. (Illus.). 286p. 99.95 *(978-1-4094-0683-9(0))* Ashgate Publishing Co.

Pinson. The Fools' Journey. a Myth of Obsession in Northern Renaissance Art. 2009. (ENG., Illus.). 226p. (C). pap. 152.00 *(978-2-503-52612-6(8))* Brepols Pubs. BEL. Dist: ISD.

Powell, Katie Tierney. Capturing the Sublime: Italian Drawings of the Renaissance & Baroque. McCullagh, Suzanne Folds, ed. 2012. (ENG., Illus.). 312p. 65.00 ***(978-0-300-17970-5(7))*** Art Institute of Chicago.

Quiviger, Francois. Sensory World of Italian Renaissance Art. 2010. (ENG., Illus.). 206p. 27.00 *(978-1-86189-657-5(3))* Reaktion Bks., Ltd. GBR. Dist: Chicago Distribution Ctr.

Radke, Gary M. Leonardo da Vinci & the Art of Sculpture. 2009. (ENG., Illus.). 224p. 50.00 *(978-0-300-15473-3(9))* Yale Univ. Pr.

Renaissance Art. 2010. (Illus.). 200p. *(978-1-84484-522-4(2))* Parkstone International.

Richardson, Carol M., ed. Locating Renaissance Art. 2007. (Renaissance Art Reconsidered Ser.). (ENG., Illus.). 352p. pap. 35.00 *(978-0-300-12188-9(1))* Yale Univ. Pr.

Richardson, Carol M., et al, eds. Renaissance Art Reconsidered: An Anthology of Primary Sources. 2007. (ENG., Illus.). 472p. 126.95 *(978-1-4051-4640-1(0)*, Wiley-Blackwell) Wiley, John & Sons, Inc.

Rijser, David. Raphael's Poetics: Art & Poetry in High Renaissance Rome. 2012. (ENG., Illus.). 520p. pap. ***(978-90-8964-342-1(7))*** Amsterdam Univ. Pr.

Roberts, Ann. Dominican Women & Renaissance Art: The Convent of San Domenico of Pisa. 2008. (Women & Gender in the Early Modern World Ser.). (Illus.). 390p. 144.95 *(978-0-7546-5530-5(X))* Ashgate Publishing Co.

Rogers Mariotti, Josephine & Mariotti, Josephine Rogers. Monna Lisa: La 'Gioconda' del Magnifico Giuliano. 2009. (I Grani Ser.). (ITA., Illus.). 96p. (C). 20.00 *(978-88-596-0667-3(5))* Polistampa ITA. Dist: Brown, David Bk. Co., The.

Rowland, Ingrid D. From Heaven to Arcadia: The Sacred & the Profane in the Renaissance. 2008. (ENG.). 324p. pap. 17.95 *(978-1-59017-295-7(7))* New York Review of Bks., Inc., The.

Scallen, Catherine B. Art of the Northern Renaissance. 2007. per. 49.95 *(978-1-59803-333-5(6))* Teaching Co., LLC, The.

Schmitz-Von Ledebur, Katja. Habsburg Treasures: Renaissance Tapestries from the Kunsthistorisches Museum, Vienna. 2010. *(978-0-9767102-8-8(5))* International Arts & Artists.

Simpson, Lucie. The Greek Spirit in Renaissance Art. 2011. 234p. 46.95 ***(978-1-258-05288-1(1))*** Literary Licensing, LLC.

Stemp, Richard. The Secret Language of the Renaissance: Decoding the Hidden Symbolism of Italian Art. 2006. *(978-1-84483-413-6(1))* Duncan Baird Pubs.

—The Secret Language of the Renaissance: Decoding the Hidden Symbolism of Italian Art. 2006. (ENG., Illus.). 224p. 35.00 *(978-1-84483-322-1(4))* Duncan Baird Pubs. GBR. Dist: Sterling Publishing Co., Inc.

Suida, William E. The Art of the Italian Renaissance: From the Samuel H. Kress Collection. 2011. 66p. 36.95 ***(978-1-258-04426-8(9))*** Literary Licensing, LLC.

Symonds, John Addington. Renaissance in Italy: The Fine Arts - Volume III. 2007. 340p. pap. 23.99 *(978-1-4264-4750-1(7))*; 388p. pap. 26.99 *(978-1-4264-4788-4(4))* BiblioBazaar.

Symonds, John Addington. Renaissance in Italy V1. 2011. 992p. 81.95 ***(978-1-258-04001-7(8))*** Literary Licensing, LLC.

Sypher, Wylie. Four Stages of Renaissance Style. 2008. (Illus.). 34.50 *(978-0-8446-3043-4(8))* Smith, Peter Pub., Inc.

Syson, Luke, et al. Renaissance Siena: Art for a City. 2008. (ENG., Illus.). 372p. 65.00 *(978-1-85709-392-6(5))* Yale Univ. Pr.

Tanner, M. Jerusalem on the Hill: Rome & the Vision of St. Peter's in the Renaissance. 2010. (Studies in Medieval & Early Renaissance Art History Ser.). (ENG., Illus.). 288p. (C). 174.00 *(978-1-905375-49-3(2))* Miller, Harvey Pubs. GBR. Dist: Brown, David Bk. Co., The.

Tedeschi, Mario & Leavitt, Thomas W. The New Renaissance in Italy: Twentieth Century Italian Art. 2011. 36p. 35.95 ***(978-1-258-04891-4(4))*** Literary Licensing, LLC.

Terjanian, Pierre. Princely Armor in the Age of Durer: A Renaissance Masterpiece in the Philadelphia Museum of Art. 2012. (ENG., Illus.). 56p. pap. 18.00 *(978-0-300-17631-5(7))* Yale Univ. Pr.

Terry-Fritsch, Allie, et al. Beholding Violence in Medieval & Early Modern Europe. 2012. (Illus.). 250p. ***(978-1-4094-4286-8(1))*** Ashgate Publishing, Ltd.

Testa, Judith Anne. An Art Lover's Guide to Florence. 2012. 306p. pap. 22.50 ***(978-0-87580-680-8(5))*** Northern Illinois Univ. Pr.

Thompson, James Westfall, et al. The Civilization of the Renaissance. 2011. 156p. 41.95 ***(978-1-258-04389-6(0))*** Literary Licensing, LLC.

Toman, Rolf. The Art of the Italian Renaissance: Architecture, Sculpture, Painting, Drawing. 1 vol. 2011. (ENG.). 464p. 19.99 ***(978-3-8331-6043-1(8))*** h.f.ullmann DEU. Dist: Innovative Logistics.

Toman, Rolf, ed. The Art of the Italian Renaissance: Architecture, Sculpture, Painting, Drawing. 2008. (Architecture Sculpture Painting Ser.). (Illus.). 463p. per. 24.95 *(978-0-8416-0071-3(6))* American Map Corp.

Turner, Nicholas. Drawn to Italian Drawings: The Goldman Collection. 2009. (ENG., Illus.). 336p. 65.00 *(978-0-300-14104-7(1))* Art Institute of Chicago.

Van Cleave, Claire. Master Drawings of the Italian Renaissance. 2007. (Illus.). 192p. 35.00 *(978-0-674-02677-3(2))* Harvard Univ. Pr.

Van de Velde, C., ed. Classical Mythology in the Netherlands in the Age of Renaissance & Baroque - la mythologie classique aux temps de la Renaissance et du Baroque dans les Pays-Bas: Proceedings of the International Conference Antwerp, 19-21 May 2005 - Actes du Colloque international Anvers, 19-21 Mai 2005. 2009. (Travaux de la Renaissance et de L'Humanisme Ser.). (ENG & FRE., Illus.). 394p. (C). pap. 95.00 *(978-90-429-2052-1(1))* Peeters Pubs. & Booksellers BEL. Dist: Brown, David Bk. Co., The.

Van der Sman, Gert Jan. Lorenzo & Giovanna: Life & Art in Renaissance Florence. 2011. (ENG., Illus.). 160p. pap. 25.00 *(978-88-7461-128-7(5))* Mandragora ITA. Dist: Antique Collectors' Club.

Van Marle. Iconographie de l'Art Profane au Moyen Age et a la Renaissance et la Decoration des Demeures, 2 tomes, Set. (FRE.). 516.00 *(978-0-8288-8022-0(0))* French & European Pubns., Inc.

Varriano, John. Tastes & Temptations: Food & Art in Renaissance Italy. (California Studies in Food & Culture Ser.). (Illus.). 2011. 280p. pap. 19.95 *(978-0-520-26994-1(2))* 2009. (ENG., 275p. 45.00 *(978-0-520-25904-1(1))* Univ. of California Pr.

Vaughan, Herbert M. Studies in the Italian Renaissance. 312p. 2010. pap. 24.76 *(978-1-163-16189-0(6))* 2008. 45.95 *(978-1-4366-8328-9(9))* 2007. (ENG.). per. 30.95 *(978-1-4325-6243-4(6))* Kessinger Publishing, LLC.

Villata, Edoardo. Leonardo Da Vinci. 2008. (Gallery of the Arts Ser.). (ENG., Illus.). 120p. 15.95 *(978-88-7439-126-4(9))* 5 Continents ITA. Dist: Hachette Bk. Group.

Wackernagel, Martin & Luchs, Alison. The World of the Florentine Renaissance Artist: Projects & Patrons, Workshop & Art Market. 2011. (RSART: Renaissance Society of America Reprint Text Ser.). xxx, 447p. pap. ***(978-1-4426-1184-9(7))*** Univ. of Toronto Pr.

Wallace, William E. Michelangelo: The Complete Sculpture, Painting, Architecture. 2009. (ENG., Illus.). 268p. 45.00 *(978-0-7893-1887-9(3))* Universe Publishing.

Williams, Robert. Art, Theory, & Culture in Sixteenth-Century Italy: From Techne to Metatechne. 2011. (ENG.). 256p. pap. 35.99 *(978-0-521-18433-5(9))* Cambridge Univ. Pr.

Williamson, Paul. Medieval & Renaissance Treasures from the V&A. Motture, Peta, ed. 2007. (ENG., Illus.). 96p. 27.50 *(978-1-85177-526-2(9))* V & A Pubns. GBR. Dist: Hachette Bk. Group.

Wolf, Norbert. Albrecht Durer. 2010. (Illus.). 304p. 120.00 *(978-3-7913-4426-3(9))* Prestel Publishing.

Wolff, Martha. Kings, Queens, & Courtiers: Art in Early Renaissance France. 2011. (ENG., Illus.). 208p. 60.00 *(978-0-300-17025-2(4))* Art Institute of Chicago.

Wolfthal, Diane. In & Out of the Marital Bed: Seeing Sex in Renaissance Europe. 2010. (Illus.). 224p. 55.00 *(978-0-300-14154-2(8))* Yale Univ. Pr.

Wolk-Simon, Linda & Bambach, Carmen C. An Italian Journey: Drawings from the Tobey Collection, Correggio to Tiepolo. 2010. (Illus.). 268p. 50.00 *(978-0-300-15524-2(7))* Yale Univ. Pr.

Woods, Kim W., ed. Making Renaissance Art. 2007. (Renaissance Art Reconsidered Ser.). (ENG., Illus.). 352p. (C). pap. 35.00 *(978-0-300-12189-6(X))* Yale Univ. Pr.

Woods, Kim W., et al, eds. Viewing Renaissance Art. 2007. (Renaissance Art Reconsidered Ser.: Vol. 3). (ENG., Illus.). 352p. pap. 35.00 *(978-0-300-12343-2(4))* Yale Univ. Pr.

Wright, Rosemary Muir & Wright, Rosemary. Sacred Distance: Representing the Virgin Mary in Italian Alterpieces, 1300-1630. 2006. (ENG., Illus.). 176p. 84.00 *(978-0-7190-5545-4(8))* Manchester Univ. Pr. GBR. Dist: Macmillan.

Zeckhauser, Richard J. & Nelson, Jonathan K. Conspicuous Commissions in Renaissance Italy & Beyond. 2008. (ENG., Illus.). 256p. (C). 45.00 *(978-0-691-12541-1(4))* Princeton Univ. Pr.

Zirpolo, Lilian H. The A to Z of Renaissance Art. 93rd ed. 2009. (A to Z Guide Ser.: No. 93). (ENG.). 632p. pap. 34.45 *(978-0-8108-6880-9(6))* Scarecrow Pr., Inc.

—Historical Dictionary of Renaissance Art. 2007. (Historical Dictionaries of Literature & the Arts Ser.: No. 21). (ENG., Illus.). 632p. 133.00 *(978-0-8108-5800-8(2))* Scarecrow Pr., Inc.

Zorach, Rebecca, ed. The Virtual Tourist in Renaissance Rome: Printing & Collecting the Speculum Romanae Magnificentiae. 2008. (Illus.). 176p. pap. 25.00 *(978-0-943056-37-1(3))* Univ. of Chicago, Library, The.

Zuffi, Stefano. European Art of the Sixteenth Century. Shugaar, Antony, tr. from ITA. 2006. (Art through the Centuries Ser.). (Illus.). 384p. pap. 24.95 *(978-0-89236-846-4(2))* Oxford Univ. Pr., Inc.

ART, ROCOCO

Bailey, Gauvin Alexander. Baroque & Rococo. 2012. (ENG., Illus.). 448p. pap. 29.95 ***(978-0-7148-5742-8(4))*** Phaidon Pr., Inc.

Baur, Eva-Gesine & Walther, Ingo F. Rococo. 2007. (ENG., Illus.). 96p. pap. 9.99 *(978-3-8228-5306-1(2))* TASCHEN DEU. Dist: Ingram Pub. Services.

Bussagli, Marco & Reiche, Mattia. Baroque & Rococo. 2009. (ENG., Illus.). 192p. pap. 14.95 *(978-1-4027-5925-3(8))* Sterling Publishing Co., Inc.

Carl, Klaus H. & Charles, Victoria. Baroque Art. 2009. (Art of Century Ser.). (ENG., Illus.). 200p. 19.95 *(978-1-84484-621-4(0))* Parkstone International GBR. Dist: Ingram Pub. Services.

Charles, Victoria & Carl, Klaus H. Rococo. 2010. (Art of Century Ser.). (ENG., Illus.). 200p. 19.95 *(978-1-84484-740-2(3))* Parkstone International GBR. Dist: Ingram Pub. Services.

Cram101 Textbook Reviews. Outlines & Highlights for Baroque & Rococo: Art & Culture by Minor. 2011. 266p. pap. 31.95 ***(978-1-61812-932-1(5))*** Cram101 Inc.

Milam, Jennifer D. Historical Dictionary of Rococo Art. 2011. (Historical Dictionaries of Literature & the Arts Ser.). (ENG.). 334p. 80.00 *(978-0-8108-6183-1(6))* Scarecrow Pr., Inc.

Milam, Jennifer D., et al. Fragonard's Playful Paintings: Visual Games in Rococo Art. 2007. (Critical Perspectives in Art History Ser.). (ENG., Illus.). 208p. 94.00 *(978-0-7190-7516-2(5))* Manchester Univ. Pr. GBR. Dist: Macmillan.

Milam, Jennifer Dawn. Historical Dictionary of Rococo Art. 2011. E-Book *(978-0-8108-7952-2(2))* Scarecrow Pr., Inc.

Van der Stighelen, Katlijne & Watteeuw, Bert, eds. Pokerfaced: Flemish & Dutch Baroque Faces Unveiled. 2011. (Museum at the Crossroads Ser.). (DUT, ENG & GER., Illus.). 277p. (C). pap. 109.00 *(978-2-503-52564-8(4))* Brepols Pubs. BEL. Dist: ISD.

ART, ROMAN

see also Art, Greco-Roman

Andreae, Bernard. Kleopatra und die Caesaren: Katalogband zur Ausstellung im Bucerius Kunst Forum, Hamburg. 2006. (GER., Illus.). 264p. (C). pap. 42.00 *(978-3-7774-3245-8(9))* Hirmer Verlag GmbH DEU. Dist: Brown, David Bk. Co., The.

Barbaro, Luca M. & Pola, Francesca, eds. A Roma, la Nostra Era Avanguardia. 2010. (ENG & ITA.). 192p. pap. 62.50 *(978-88-370-7488-3(3))* Electa ITA. Dist: Trans-Atlantic Pubns., Inc.

Bartsch, Tatjana, et al, eds. Das Originale der Kopie: Kopien als Produkte und Medien der Transformation von Antike. 2010. (Transformationen der Antike Ser.).Tr. of Originality of Copies. (GER., Illus.). VIII, 349p. 112.00 *(978-3-11-022544-0(1))* De Gruyter, Walter Inc.

Beacham, Richard & Denard, Hugh. Performing Culture: Theatre & Theatricality in Roman Pictorial Arts. 2006. 256p. 45.00 *(978-0-300-11515-4(6))* Yale Univ. Pr.

Bergmann, Birgit. Der Kranz des Kaisers. 2010. (Image & Context Ser.).Tr. of Emperor8__s Wreath. (GER., Illus.). XX, 515p. 140.00 *(978-3-11-020258-8(1))* De Gruyter, Walter Inc.

Bonn, Landschaftsverband Rheinland / LVR-LandesMuseum, ed. Alter in der Antike: Die Blüte des Alters aber ist die Weisheit. 2009. (GER., Illus.). 192p. (C). 38.00 *(978-3-8053-3979-7(8))* Zabern, Philipp von Verlag, GmbH DEU. Dist: Brown, David Bk. Co., The.

Buhl, Gudrun, et al, eds. Spatantike und byzantinische Elfenbeinbildwerke im Diskurs. 2008. (Spatantike-Fruhes Christentum-Byzanz Ser.). (GER, ENG & FRE., Illus.). 320p. (C). 199.00 *(978-3-89500-497-1(9))* Reichert, Ludwig Dr. DEU. Dist: Brown, David Bk. Co., The.

Burke, Jill & Bury, Michael. Art & Identity in Early Modern Rome. 2008. (Illus.). 308p. 134.95 *(978-0-7546-5690-6(X))* Ashgate Publishing Co.

Bussagli, Marco, ed. Rome: Art & Architecture. 2008. (Art & Architecture Ser.). (Illus.). 679p. per. 29.95 *(978-0-8416-0091-1(0))* American Map Corp.

Campbell, Gordon. The Grove Encyclopedia of Classical Art & Architecture, 2 vols. 2007. (ENG., Illus.). 1600p. 345.00 *(978-0-19-530082-6(3))* Oxford Univ. Pr., Inc.

Charles, Victoria & Carl, Klaus H. Romanesque Art. 2008. (Art of Century Ser.). (ENG., Illus.). 199p. 19.95 *(978-1-84484-460-9(9))* Parkstone International GBR. Dist: Ingram Pub. Services.

Christian, Kathleen Wren. Empire Without End: Antiquities Collections in Renaissance Rome, C. 1350-1527. 2010. (Illus.). 288p. 70.00 *(978-0-300-15421-4(6))* Yale Univ. Pr.

D'Ambra, Eve & Metraux, Guy P. R., eds. The Art of Citizens, Soldiers, & Freedmen in the Roman World. 2006. (BAR International Ser.: Vol. 1526). (ENG., Illus.). 167p. (C). pap. 100.00 *(978-1-84171-963-4(3))* British Archaeological Reports Ltd. GBR. Dist: Brown, David Bk. Co., The.

A Day in Pompeii. 2007. per. *(978-1-933245-08-9(5))* Documentary Media LLC.

De Luca, Araldo, photos by. The Art of Pompeii. 2011. (ENG., Illus.). 176p. 60.00 *(978-88-544-0501-1(9))* White Star ITA. Dist: Sterling Publishing Co., Inc.

Deger-Jalkotzy, Sigrid & Schindel, Nikolaus, eds. Gold: Tagung anlasslich der Grundung des Zentrums Archaologie und Altertumswissenschaften an der Osterreichischen Akademie der Wissenschaften, 19. 20. April 2007. 2009. (Denkschriften der Phil. -Hist. Klasse Ser.). (GER., Illus.). 206p. (C). pap. 102.00 *(978-3-7001-6547-7(1))* Austrian Academy of Sciences Press AUT. Dist: Brown, David Bk. Co., The.

Dennison, Walter. A New Head of the So-Called Scipio Type: An Attempt at Its Identification. 2009. pap. 20.08 *(978-1-60724-510-0(8))* Gorgias Pr., LLC.

—Studies in East Christian & Roman Art. 2010. 124p. pap. 21.42 *(978-1-152-61902-9(0))* General Bks. LLC.

Dennison, Walter, et al. Studies in East Christian & Roman Art. 2010. 348p. pap. 32.75 *(978-1-177-69814-6(5))* BiblioBazaar.

Dillon, Sheila & Welch, Katherine E., eds. Representations of War in Ancient Rome. 2009. (ENG., Illus.). 380p. (C). pap. 40.99 *(978-0-521-13083-7(2))* Cambridge Univ. Pr.

Durando, Furio, ed. Italy: A Journey in Search of Great Art & Architecture. 2010. (ENG., Illus.). 368p. 45.00 *(978-88-544-0427-4(6))* White Star ITA. Dist: Random Hse., Inc.

Elsner, Jas. Roman Eyes: Visuality & Subjectivity in Art & Text. 2007. (ENG., Illus.). 376p. (C). 62.95 *(978-0-691-09677-3(5))* Princeton Univ. Pr.

Frothingham, Arthur. A Revised List of Roman Memorial & Triumphal Arches. 2009. pap. 20.08 *(978-1-60724-507-0(8))* Gorgias Pr., LLC.

Gabucci, Ada. Rome. Hyams, Jay, tr. from ITA. 2007. (Dictionaries of Civilization Ser.). (Illus.). 383p. pap. 25.95 *(978-0-520-25265-3(9))* Univ. of California Pr.

Garrison, Eliza. Ottonian Imperial Art & Portraiture: The Artistic Patronage of Otto III & Henry II. 2012. (Illus.). 228 & 8 lour pp. 104.95 ***(978-0-7546-6968-5(8))*** Ashgate Publishing Co.

Gazda, Elaine K., ed. Roman Art in the Private Sphere: New Perspectives on the Architecture & Decor of the Domus, Villa, & Insula. 2nd ed. 2010. (ENG., Illus.). 232p. pap. 52.50 *(978-0-472-03439-0(1))* Univ. of Michigan Pr.

Giroire, Cécile & Roger, Daniel. Roman Art from the Louvre. 2009. (ENG., Illus.). 280p. pap. 45.00 *(978-1-885444-35-6(4))* Hudson Hills Pr. LLC.

Gold, Barbara K., ed. Literary & Artistic Patronage in Ancient Rome. 2012. (ENG.). 208p. pap. 19.95 ***(978-0-292-74098-3(0))*** Univ. of Texas Pr.

González-Palacios, Alvar. Studi Romani: Antologia di Belli Arti. 2006. (ENG, SPA, FRE & ITA., Illus.). 180p. 65.00 *(978-88-422-1298-0(9))* Allemandi, Umberto & Co. GBR. Dist: Antique Collectors' Club.

Goodyear, W. H. Roman & Medieval Art. 20.00 *(978-0-8196-2008-8(4))* Biblo & Tannen Booksellers & Pubs., Inc.

Guaitoli, Maria Teresa. Rome. 2006. (Treasures Ancient Civilization Ser.). (ENG., Illus.). 208p. 35.00 *(978-88-544-0147-1(1)*, White Star) Rizzoli International Pubns., Inc.

Hardie, Philip. Paradox & the Marvellous in Augustan Literature & Culture. 2009. (ENG., Illus.). 408p. 145.00 *(978-0-19-923124-9(9))* Oxford Univ. Pr., Inc.

Hill, Julian & Rowsome, Peter. Roman London & the Walbrook Stream Crossing: Excavations at 1 Poultry & Vicinity, 2 vols. 2012. (MoLAS Monograph Ser.). (ENG., Illus.). 592p. (C). 116.00 ***(978-1-907586-04-0(0))*** Museum of London Archaeology Service GBR. Dist: Brown, David Bk. Co., The.

Hintzen-Bohlen, Brigitte. Rome: And the Vatican City. 2008. (Art & Architecture Ser.). (Illus.). 626p. 19.95 *(978-0-8416-0051-5(1))* American Map Corp.

Johns, Catherine. The Hoxne Late Roman Treasure: Gold Jewellery & Silver Plate. 2010. (ENG., Illus.). 288p. (C). 120.00 *(978-0-7141-1817-8(6))* British Museum Pr. GBR. Dist: Brown, David Bk. Co., The.

Kleiner, Diana E. E. Cleopatra & Rome. 2009. (Illus.). 352p. pap. 24.50 *(978-0-674-03236-1(5)*, Belknap Pr.) Harvard Univ. Pr.

Kleiner, Fred S. A History of Roman Art. 2010. (ENG.). 384p. (C). pap. 134.95 *(978-0-495-90987-3(4))* Wadsworth.

Lavin, Marilyn Aronberg, ed. Rome, Italy, Renaissance: Essays in Art History Honoring Irving Lavin on His Sixtieth Birthday. 2009. (ENG., Illus.). 304p. pap. 30.00 *(978-1-59910-124-8(6))* Italica Pr.

Leone, Stephanie C., ed. The Pamphilj & the Arts: Patronage & Consumption in Baroque Rome. 2011. (ENG & ITA., Illus.). 200p. pap. 45.00 *(978-1-892850-17-1(6))* McMullen Museum of Art, Boston College.

Lo Sardo, Eugenio. The She-Wolf & the Sphinx: Rome & Egypt from History to Myth. Lo Sardo, Eugenio, ed. 2008. (Illus.). 216p. 65.00 *(978-88-370-6223-1(0))* Electa ITA. Dist: Trans-Atlantic Pubns., Inc.

Mackreth, D. F. Brooches in Late Iron Age & Roman Britain, 2 vols., Vol. 2. 2011. (ENG., Illus.). 448p. (C). 140.00 *(978-1-84217-411-8(X))* Oxbow Bks., Ltd. GBR. Dist: Brown, David Bk. Co., The.

Marlowe, Elizabeth. Shaky Ground. 2012. (ENG.). 160p. pap. 24.95 ***(978-0-7156-4064-7(X))*** Duckworth Publishers GBR. Dist: International Publishers Marketing.

Mattusch, Carol C. Pompeii & the Roman Villa: Art & Culture Around the Bay of Naples. 2008. *(978-0-89468-353-4(5))* National Gallery of Art.

Mattusch, Carol C., ed. Pompeii & the Roman Villa: Art & Culture Around the Bay of Naples. 2008. (ENG., Illus.). 360p. 60.00 *(978-0-500-51436-8(4)*, 551436) Thames & Hudson.

McGowen, S. L. Sacred & Civic Stone Monuments of the Northwest Roman Provinces. 2010. (Bar S Ser.). (ENG., Illus.). 159p. (C). pap. 87.50 *(978-1-4073-0650-6(2))* British Archaeological Reports Ltd. GBR. Dist: Brown, David Bk. Co., The.

Minor, Vernon Hyde & Curran, Brian A., eds. Memoirs of the American Academy in Rome Vol. 55. 2011. (Memoirs of the American Academy in Rome Ser.). (ENG., Illus.). 338p. 70.00 ***(978-1-879549-19-7(0))*** American Academy in Rome.

Morelli, Angela. Roman Britain & Classical Deities. 2009. (ENG., Illus.). 75p. (C). pap. 67.50 *(978-1-4073-0427-4(5))* British Archaeological Reports Ltd. GBR. Dist: Brown, David Bk. Co., The.

Nasrallah, Laura Salah. Christian Responses to Roman Art & Architecture: The Second-Century Church amid the Spaces of Empire. (ENG., Illus.). (C). 2011. 352p. pap. 39.99 ***(978-1-107-64499-1(2))*** 2010. 350p. 99.00 *(978-0-521-76652-4(4))* Cambridge Univ. Pr.

Opper, Thorsten. Hadrian: Empire & Conflict. 2010. (Illus.). 224p. pap. 21.95 *(978-0-674-05742-5(2))* Harvard Univ. Pr.

Parke-Bernet Galleries. Egyptian, Greek & Roman Antiquities, Ancient Glass, Gothic & Renaissance Furniture & Works of Art. 2011. 158p. 41.95 ***(978-1-258-07381-7(1))*** Literary Licensing, LLC.

Petersen, Lauren Hackworth. The Freedman in Roman Art & Art History. 2011. (ENG., Illus.). 320p. pap. 50.00 ***(978-1-107-60359-2(5))*** Cambridge Univ. Pr.

Picon, Carlos A., et al. Art of the Classical World in the Metropolitan Museum of Art: Greece - Cyprus - Etruria - Rome. 2007. (ENG., Illus.). 520p. 75.00 *(978-0-300-12031-8(1))* Yale Univ. Pr.

Platt, Verity. Facing the Gods: Epiphany & Representation in Graeco-Roman Art, Literature & Religion. 2011. (Greek Culture in the Roman World Ser.). (ENG., Illus.). 500p. 130.00 *(978-0-521-86171-7(3))* Cambridge Univ. Pr.

Ramage, Nancy H. & Ramage, Andrew. Roman Art: Romulus to Constantine. 4th ed. 2006. pap., pap. *(978-0-13-240554-6(7))* Pearson Education Canada.
—Roman Art: Romulus to Constantine. 5th ed. 2008. (ENG., Illus.). 384p. (C). per. 113.40 *(978-0-13-600097-6(5))*, Prentice Hall) Prentice Hall PTR.
Reynolds, Paul. Hispania & the Roman Mediterranean AD 100-700: Ceramics & Trade. 2010. (Illus.). 224p. 130.00 *(978-0-7156-3862-0(9))* Duckworth Publishers GBR. Dist: International Publishers Marketing.
Roger, Daniel & Giroire, Cecile. Roman Art from the Louvre. 2007. (ENG., Illus.). 280p. 65.00 *(978-1-55595-283-9(6))* Hudson Hills Pr. LLC.
Rydberg, Viktor. Roman Days. Clark, Alfred Corning, tr. 2007. (ENG.). 376p. 48.95 *(978-0-548-04729-3(4))* Kessinger Publishing, LLC.
Schoppa, Helmut. L' Art Romain Dans les Gaules, en Germanie, et Dans les Iles Britanniques. (FRE., Illus.). 141p. lib. bdg. *(978-0-8288-3943-3(3))* French & European Pubns., Inc.
Seemann, O. The Mythology of Greece & Rome with Special Reference to Its Use in Art 1896. Bianchi, G. H., ed. 2007. (ENG.). 310p. 45.95 *(978-0-548-05370-6(7))* Kessinger Publishing, LLC.
Stewart, Peter. The Social History of Roman Art. 2008. (Key Themes in Ancient History Ser.). (ENG., Illus.). 216p. 109.00 *(978-0-521-81632-8(7))*; pap. 33.99 *(978-0-521-01659-9(2))* Cambridge Univ. Pr.
Suzawa, Yukako. The Genesis of Early Christian Art. 2009. (Bar S Ser.). (ENG., Illus.). 163p. (C). pap. 82.50 *(978-1-4073-0372-7(4))* British Archaeological Reports Ltd. GBR. Dist: Brown, David Bk. Co., The.
Taylor, Rabun. The Moral Mirror of Roman Art. 2008. (ENG., Illus.). 288p. 103.00 *(978-0-521-86612-5(X))* Cambridge Univ. Pr.
Thompson, Nancy L. Roman Art: A Resource for Educators. 2007. (ENG., Illus.). 216p. 79.95 *(978-0-300-12694-5(8))* Yale Univ. Pr.
Williams, Dyfri. The Warren Cup. 2006. (British Museum Objects in Focus Ser.). (Illus.). 64p. pap. 12.95 *(978-0-7141-2260-1(2))* British Museum Pr. GBR. Dist: Brown, David Bk. Co., The.
Wolf, Norbert, ed. Roman Art. 2007. (Basic Art Ser.). (ENG., Illus.). 95p. pap. 9.99 *(978-3-8228-5454-9(9))* TASCHEN DEU. Dist: Ingram Pub. Services.
Zanker, Paul. Roman Art. (Illus.). 2012. (ENG.). 224p. pap. 30.00 ***(978-1-60606-101-5(1))*** 2010. 216p. 60.00 *(978-1-60606-030-8(9))* Getty Pubns. (J. Paul Getty Museum).

ART, ROMANESQUE

Bednorz, Achim. Romanesque: Architecture - Sculpture - Painting, 1 vol. Toman, Rolf, ed. 2011. (ENG.). 480p. 19.99 ***(978-3-8331-6005-9(5))*** h.f.ullmann DEU. Dist: Innovative Logistics.
Fossi, Gloria. Romanesque & Gothic. 2008. (ENG., Illus.). 192p. pap. 14.95 *(978-1-4027-5924-6(X))* Sterling Publishing Co., Inc.
García Guinea, Miguel Angel, et al. Enciclopedia Del Románico en Aragón: Zaragoza, 2 vols. 2010. (Illus.). *(978-84-89483-67-5(1))*; (SPA., *(978-84-89483-68-2(X))*; (SPA., *(978-84-89483-69-9(8))* Fundacion Santa Maria La Real, Centro de Estudios del Romanico.
Hourihane, Colum, ed. Romanesque Art & Thought in the Twelfth Century. 2008. (Illus.). 368p. (ENG.). 35.00 *(978-0-9768202-7-7(7))*; 85.00 *(978-0-9768202-6-0(9))* Index of Christian Art, Princeton Univ., The.
Rudolph, Conrad, ed. A Companion to Medieval Art: Romanesque & Gothic in Northern Europe. 2010. (Blackwell Companions to Art History Ser.: 3). (ENG.). 704p. pap. 53.95 *(978-1-4051-9878-3(8))*, Wiley-Blackwell) Wiley, John & Sons, Inc.
Toman, Rolf. Romanesque, 1 vol. 2010. (ENG., Illus.). 480p. pap. 19.99 ***(978-3-8331-3600-9(6))*** h.f.ullmann DEU. Dist: Innovative Logistics.
Toman, Rolf, ed. Romanesque: Architecture, Sculpture, Painting. 2008. (Architecture Sculpture Painting Ser.). (Illus.). 480p. per. 24.95 *(978-0-8416-0090-4(2))* American Map Corp.
Williamson, Paul. Medieval Ivory Carvings: Early Christian to Romanesque. 2010. (ENG., Illus.). 32p. 150.00 *(978-1-85177-612-2(5))* V & A Pubns. GBR. Dist: Hachette Bk. Group.
Wolf, Norbert. Romanesque (Basic Genres) 2007. (Basic Art Ser.). (ENG., Illus.). 95p. pap. 9.99 *(978-3-8228-5446-4(8))* TASCHEN DEU. Dist: Ingram Pub. Services.

ART, ROMANIAN

Cantor, Mircea. Mircea Cantor: the Silence of the Lambs. 2008. (Illus.). 100p. pap. 29.95 *(978-3-86560-235-0(5))* Verlag der Buchhandlung Walther Konig DEU. Dist: D.A.P./Distributed Art Pubs.
Dziewanska, Marta. Ion Grigorescu: In the Body of the Victim. 2011. (ENG & POL., Illus.). 312p. pap. 29.00 ***(978-83-924044-1-5(6))*** Muzeum Sztuki Nowoczesnej w Warszawie POL. Dist: Chicago Distribution Ctr.
Kallestrup, Shona. Art & Design in Romania, 1866-1927: Local & International Aspects of the Search for National Expression, EEM #684. 2006. (ENG., Illus.). 320p. (gr. 17). 50.00 *(978-0-88033-582-9(3))* Eastern European Monographs.
Knorr, Daniel. Daniel Knorr: Carte de Artist. 2008. (Illus.). 200p. pap. 248.00 *(978-3-86560-239-8(8))* Verlag der Buchhandlung Walther Konig DEU. Dist: D.A.P./Distributed Art Pubs.
Kürti, Emese. Bukarest-Budapest Híd: Kortárs Román és Magyar Művészet: Hunya Gábor Gyujteménye. 2010. (HUN & ENG., Illus.). 216p. 24.95 ***(978-963-9731-89-9(7))*** Vince Kiado Kft HUN. Dist: Independent Pubs. Group.
Meret, Sasha. Lost & Found Appointments. 2012. ***(978-0-923389-03-1(2))*** Spuyten Duyvil.
Mihai, Aurelia, illus. Unter Freiem Himmel/in the Open Air. 2008. (ENG.). 96p. pap. 29.50 *(978-3-86678-056-9(7))* Kerber Verlag DEU. Dist: D.A.P./Distributed Art Pubs.
Niculescu, Alexandru, ed. Romanian Cultural Resolution: Zeitgenössische Kunst aus Rumänien. 2011. (ENG., Illus.). 232p. pap. 55.00 ***(978-3-7757-2848-5(1))*** Hatje Cantz Verlag GmbH & Co KG DEU. Dist: D.A.P./Distributed Art Pubs.
Obrist, Hans Ulrich, et al, eds. Victor Man. 2008. (ENG., Illus.). 64p. 35.00 *(978-3-905829-31-0(2))* JRP Ringier Kunstverlag AG CHE. Dist: D.A.P./Distributed Art Pubs.
Stiles, Kristine, ed. States of Mind: Dan & Lia Perjovschi. 2007. (ENG., Illus.). 236p. pap. 35.00 *(978-0-938989-30-1(8))* Duke Univ. Pr.
Szymczyk, Adam, ed. Daniel Knorr: Led R. Nanirok. 2010. (ENG., Illus.). 304p. pap. 28.00 *(978-3-03764-078-4(2))* JRP Ringier Kunstverlag AG CHE. Dist: D.A.P./Distributed Art Pubs.
Tamas, Klara & Hobbick, Cade. Klara Tamas: Tapestries, Paintings, Drawings, Posters. 2008. (Illus.). 31.99 *(978-1-4257-9634-1(6))* Xlibris Corp.
Tobias, Gert. Gert und Uwe Tobias: Zeichnungen und Collagen. 2010. (GER & ENG., Illus.). 66p. pap. 27.50 *(978-3-86678-371-3(X))* Kerber Verlag DEU. Dist: D.A.P./Distributed Art Pubs.
Varadinis, Miriam, ed. Mircea Cantor. 2011. (ENG & GER., Illus.). 224p. pap. 45.00 ***(978-3-86828-107-1(X))*** Kehrer Verlag Heidelberg, Klaus Kehrer DEU. Dist: Consortium Bk. Sales & Distribution.

ART, RUSSIAN

see also Suprematism in Art

Adlam, Carol & Simpson, Juliet, eds. Critical Exchange: Art Criticism of the Eighteenth & Nineteenth Centuries in Russia & Western Europe. 2009. (Cultural Interactions: Studies in the Relationship between the Arts Ser.). (ENG.). 420p. pap. 92.95 *(978-3-03911-556-3(1))* Lang, Peter GmbH, Europaischer Verlag der Wissenschaften DEU. Dist: Lang, Peter.
Alaniz, José. Komiks: Comic Art in Russia. 2010. (ENG., Illus.). 288p. 55.00 *(978-1-60473-366-2(7))* Univ. Pr. of Mississippi.
Alpatov, Mikhail. Russian Impact on Art. Wolf, Martin L., ed. Litvinov, Ivy, tr. 2011. 406p. 54.95 ***(978-1-258-07522-4(9))*** Literary Licensing, LLC.
Anisimova, Elena, et al. Art Nouveau During the Reign of the Last Tsars. 2008. (Illus.). 128p. 40.00 *(978-0-85331-987-0(1))*, Lund Humphries Pubs.) Ashgate Publishing, Ltd. GBR. Dist: Ashgate Publishing Co.
Becker, Katharina, ed. Flight, Distance, Disappearance: Moscow Conceptual Art. (ENG, RUS, GER & CZE., Illus.). 336p. pap. 29.95 *(978-3-89322-802-7(0))* Edition Cantz DEU. Dist: D.A.P./Distributed Art Pubs.
Billington, James H. The Face of Russia: Anguish, Aspiration, & Achievement in Russian Culture. 2008. (Illus.). 296p. pap. 32.00 *(978-1-55635-676-6(5))* Wipf & Stock Pubs.
Blakesley, Rosalind P. & Reid, Susan E., eds. Russian Art & the West: A Century of Dialogue in Painting, Architecture, & the Decorative Arts. 2006. (Illus.). 256p. 42.00 *(978-0-87580-360-9(1))* Northern Illinois Univ. Pr.
Boguslavskaelia, Irina eliAkovlevna. Russian Folk Toys in the Collection of the Russian Museum. 2006. (MUL & ENG., Illus.). 176p. 80.00 *(978-3-935298-29-2(3)*, Palace Editions) Mandala Publishing.
Bonafoux, Pascal & Bidaine, Philippe. Boris Zaborov. 2008. (ENG., Illus.). 160p. 80.00 *(978-88-6130-122-1(3))* Skira Editore ITA. Dist: Random Hse., Inc.
Borovsky, Alexander, et al, texts. Alexander Kosolapov: Sots Art. 2010. (ENG., Illus.). 184p. 55.00 *(978-3-86678-227-3(6))* Kerber Verlag DEU. Dist: D.A.P./Distributed Art Pubs.
Bowlt, John E. A Century of Russian Art: 1900-2000. 2013. (Cultural Revolutions: Russia in the Twentieth Century Ser.). (ENG., Illus.). 350p. 95.00 *(978-1-934843-77-2(6))* Academic Studies Pr.
—Moscow & St Petersburg 1900-1920: Art, Life, & Culture of the Russian Silver Age. 2008. (ENG., Illus.). 400p. 50.00 *(978-0-86565-184-5(1))* Vendome Pr., The.
Brezner, Evgeny & Tchmyreva, Irina. Contemporary Russian Photography: FotoFest 2012 Biennial. 2012. (ENG., Illus.). 320p. 45.00 ***(978-90-5330-768-7(0))*** Mets en Schilt Uitgevers NLD. Dist: Ingram Pub. Services.
Brumfield, William C. & Velimirovic, Milos M., eds. Christianity & the Arts in Russia. 2008. (ENG., Illus.). 268p. pap. 31.99 *(978-0-521-08923-4(9))* Cambridge Univ. Pr.
Bukin, Denis, et al. A Complete Guide to Nail Art & Decorative Manicure. 2009. 118p. pap. 40.90 *(978-1-4092-5603-8(0))* Lulu Enterprises Inc.
Coen, Ester, ed. Futurismo 100: Illuminazioni. 2009. (ITA., Illus.). 450p. 142.50 *(978-88-370-6777-9(1))* Electa ITA. Dist: Trans-Atlantic Pubns., Inc.
Cohen, Aaron J. Imagining the Unimaginable: World War, Modern Art, & the Politics of Public Culture in Russia, 1914-1917. 2008. (Studies in War, Society, & the Military). (ENG., Illus.). 246p. (C). 45.00 *(978-0-8032-1547-4(9))* Univ. of Nebraska Pr.
de Guitaut, Caroline. Royal Fabergé. 2011. (Illus.). 156p. 24.95 *(978-1-905686-37-7(4))* Royal Collection Enterprises Ltd. GBR. Dist: Chicago Distribution Ctr.
De Montclos, Brigitte. Moscow: Splendours of the Romanovs. 2009. (ENG., Illus.). 304p. 50.00 *(978-88-572-0256-3(9))* Skira Editore ITA. Dist: Random Hse., Inc.
Dorontchenkov. Russian & Soviet Views of Modern Western Art. 2009. (Documents of Twentieth-Century Art Ser.). (Illus.). xv, 347p. 65.00 *(978-0-520-22103-1(6))* Univ. of California Pr.
Dorontchenkov, Ilia & Dorontchenkov, I. Russian & Soviet Views of Modern Western Art, 1890s to Mid-1930s. Dorontchenkov, Ilia & Gourianova, Nina, eds. Rougle, Charles, tr. 2009. (Documents of Twentieth-Century Art Ser.). (ENG., Illus.). 400p. pap. 29.95 *(978-0-520-25372-8(9))* Univ. of California Pr.
Doschka, Roland, ed. Marc Chagall: Origins & Paths. 2010. (Illus.) 232p. pap. 19.95 *(978-3-7913-4395-2(5))* Prestel Publishing.
Ducamp, Emmanuel, ed. The Summer Palace of the Romanovs: Treasures from Tsarskoye Selo. 2012. (ENG., Illus.). 360p. 100.00 ***(978-0-500-51647-8(2)***, 551647) Thames & Hudson.
Eskenazi, Jason & Nistratov, Valeri. Title Nation. 2011. (RUS & ENG., Illus.). 216p. 35.00 *(978-90-5330-739-7(7))* Mets en Schilt Uitgevers NLD. Dist: Ingram Pub. Services.
Ferre, Rosa, ed. Red Cavalry: Creation & Power in Soviet Russia between 1917 And 1945. 2011. 500p. 69.95 *(978-84-96917-78-1(9))*, Caja de Madrid ESP. Dist: Actar Birkhauser Distribution.
Giloy-Hirtz, Petra, ed. Igor Sacharow-Ross: Reanimation. (ENG, GER & FRE., Illus.). 112p. *(978-3-89322-349-7(5))* Edition Cantz DEU. Dist: D.A.P./Distributed Art Pubs.
Greenfield, Douglas M. & Gatrall, Jefferson J. A. Alter Icons: The Russian Icon & Modernity. 2010. (ENG.). 264p. 74.95 *(978-0-271-03677-9(X))* Pennsylvania State Univ. Pr.
Gregory, Jarrett & Valdez, Sarah, eds. Ostalgia. 2011. (ENG., Illus.) 120p. pap. 35.00 ***(978-0-915557-96-7(7))*** New Museum of Contemporary Art, The.
Groys, Boris. Empty Zones: Andrei Monastyrski & 'Collective Actions' 2011. (ENG., Illus.). 128p. pap. 29.95 *(978-1-907317-34-7(1))* Black Dog Publishing Ltd. GBR. Dist: Perseus Distribution.
—History Becomes Form: Moscow Conceptualism. 2010. (ENG., Illus.). 208p. (gr. 17). 27.95 *(978-0-262-01423-6(8))* MIT Pr.
—The Total Art of Stalinism: Avant-Garde, Aesthetic Dictatorship, & Beyond. Rougle, Charles, tr. from GER. 2011. (ENG.). 144p. pap. 19.95 *(978-1-84467-707-8(9)*, 844707) Verso Bks. GBR. Dist: Norton, W. W. & Co., Inc.
Herman, Nicholas, et al, eds. Russian Art in Translation, 1 vol. 2007. (ENG., Illus.). 136p. per. 25.00 *(978-0-9792919-0-6(9))* Ante Pubns.
Hill, Gerard, et al. Faberge & the Russian Master Goldsmiths. 2008. (ENG., Illus.). 320p. 24.95 *(978-0-7893-9970-0(9))* Universe Publishing.
Hilton, Alison. Russian Folk Art. 2011. (Indiana-Michigan Series in Russian & East European Studies). (ENG., Illus.). 384p. pap. 24.95 *(978-0-253-22335-7(0)*, 0253223350) Indiana Univ. Pr.
Humphries, Lund, et al. Collectors in St Petersburg. 2007. (Illus.). 128p. 40.00 *(978-0-85331-960-3(X)*, Lund Humphries Pubs.) Ashgate Publishing, Ltd. GBR. Dist: Ashgate Publishing Co.
Ippolitov, Arkady, et al, texts. Boris Smelov: Retrospective. 2010. (ENG., Illus.). 448p. 165.00 *(978-3-86678-264-8(0))* Kerber Verlag DEU. Dist: D.A.P./Distributed Art Pubs.
Jackson, David. The Wanderers & Critical Realism in Nineteenth-Century Russian Art. 2006. (ENG., Illus.). 224p. 94.00 *(978-0-7190-6434-0(1))* Manchester Univ. Pr. GBR. Dist: Macmillan.
Jackson, Matthew Jesse. The Experimental Group: Ilya Kabakov, Moscow Conceptualism, Soviet Avant-Gardes. 2010. (Illus.). 336p. 55.00 *(978-0-226-38941-7(3))* Univ. of Chicago Pr.
Kabakov, Ilia Iosifovich & Kabakov, Emilia. Zhizn Mukh. 2008. (RUS., Illus.). 167p. *(978-3-86678-200-6(4))* Kerber Verlag.
Kabakov, Ilya. Ilya Kabakov: Total Installation. (GER., Illus.). 240p. pap. 49.95 *(978-3-89322-713-6(X))* D.A.P./Distributed Art Pubs.
Kabakov, Ilya & Kabakov, Emilia, illus. Under the Snow/Unter Dem Schnee. 2008. (ENG.). 100p. 42.00 *(978-3-86560-348-7(3))* Verlag der Buchhandlung Walther Konig DEU. Dist: D.A.P./Distributed Art Pubs.
Karpova, E. V. & Petrova, Yevgenia. Portraiture in Russia XX Century: From the Collection of the State Russian Museum in St. Petersburg. Petrova, Yevgenia, ed. 2006. (ENG., Illus.). 408p. 85.00 *(978-3-935298-11-7(0)*, Palace Editions) Mandala Publishing.
Keefe, John Webster. Fabergé: The Hodges Family Collection. O'Shello, Wanda, ed. 2009. (ENG., Illus.). 310p. 65.00 *(978-0-89494-108-5(9))* New Orleans Museum of Art.
Keller, Christoph, ed. Boris Groys & Andro Wekua: Wait to Wait. 2009. (ENG., Illus.). 160p. 28.00 *(978-3-03764-021-0(9))* JRP Ringier Kunstverlag AG CHE. Dist: D.A.P./Distributed Art Pubs.
Khromtchenko, Evelina. Russian Style. 2009. (ENG.). 219p. 60.00 *(978-2-7594-0395-0(5))* Assouline FRA. Dist: Perseus Distribution.
King, David. Red Star over Russia: A Visual History of the Soviet Union from the Revolution to the Death of Stalin. 2009. (ENG., Illus.). 352p. 50.00 *(978-0-8109-8279-6(X))* Abrams.
Kittelmann, Udo, ed. Vadim Zakharov: Retrospective 1987-1995. (GER & RUS., Illus.). 180p. 29.95 *(978-3-89322-775-4(X))* Edition Cantz DEU. Dist: D.A.P./Distributed Art Pubs.
Kivelson, Valerie A. & Neuberger, Joan, eds. Picturing Russia: Explorations in Visual Culture. 2010. (ENG., Illus.). 336p. pap. 32.00 *(978-0-300-16421-3(1))* Yale Univ. Pr.
Kogan, Simon. Simon Kogan: Sculptor. 2008. (Illus.). *(978-0-9798608-0-5(6))* Kan sasana Printer.
Kolesnikov, Ivan, et al, contrib. by. New Angelarium. 2007. (ENG & RUS., Illus.). 352p. per. 145.00 *(978-0-9754829-7-1(1))* Kolodzei Art Foundation, Inc.
Konemann Staff. St. Petersburg: Art & Architecture. Date not set. (Illus.). 250p. 29.95 *(978-3-8290-5035-7(6)*, 521828) Konemann.
Koretsky, Viktor. Koretsky: The Soviet Photo Poster, 1930-1984. Wolf, Erika, ed. 2012. (ENG., Illus.). 448p. 60.00 *(978-1-59558-542-4(7))* New Pr., The.
Kostenevich, Albert. From Russia: French & Russian Master Paintings 1870-1925 from Moscow & St. Petersburg. 2008. (ENG., Illus.). 312p. 90.00 *(978-1-905711-15-4(8))* Royal Academy of Arts GBR. Dist: Abrams.
Kovtun, Evgueny. Russian Avant-Garde. 2007. (Art of Century Ser.). (ENG., Illus.). 199p. pap. 19.95 *(978-1-85995-678-6(5))* Parkstone International GBR. Dist: Ingram Pub. Services.
Kuznetsov, Alexander. Pavel Tchelitchew: Metamorphoses. 2012. (ENG., Illus.). 320p. 95.00 ***(978-3-89790-368-5(7))*** Arnoldsche Art Pubs. DEU. Dist: Antique Collectors' Club.
LaFont, Maria. Soviet Posters: The Sergo Grigorian Collection. 2007. (Illus.). 285p. pap. 25.00 *(978-3-7913-3752-4(1))* Prestel Publishing.
Lund Humphries, creator. Silver Wonders from the East: Filigree of the Tsars. 2006. (Illus.). 128p. 40.00 *(978-0-85331-948-1(0)*, Lund Humphries Pubs.) Ashgate Publishing, Ltd. GBR. Dist: Ashgate Publishing Co.
Nakov, Andréi. Malevich: Painting the Absolute, 4 vols. 2010. (Illus.). 1656p. 600.00 *(978-1-84822-046-1(4)*, Lund Humphries Pubs.) Ashgate Publishing, Ltd. GBR. Dist: Ashgate Publishing Co.
Namdakov, Dashi & Marts, Liudmila Viktorovna. Dashi Namdakov: Skulptura, Grafika, Iuvelirnoe Iskusstvo = Dadhi Namdakov: Sculpture, Graphics & Jewellery. 2010. (RUS., Illus.). 159p. *(978-5-91340-011-6(9))* SkanRus, Izdatel'stvo, OOO.
Nazaryan, Alexander & Merenzon, Ilya. Russian Povera: Art That Makes Trash Monumental. 2011. 272p. 35.00 *(978-1-59020-460-3(3))* Overlook Pr., The.
Nelson, Bruce. Simply Baroque: 27 Well Known Masterpieces. 2008. (Simply Ser.). (ENG.). 80p. pap. 12.95 *(978-0-7390-5181-8(4))* Alfred Publishing Co., Inc.
Norris, Stephen M. A War of Images: Russian Popular Prints, Wartime Culture, & National Identity, 1812-1945. 2006. (Illus.). 291p. 40.00 *(978-0-87580-363-0(6))* Northern Illinois Univ. Pr.
Odom, Anne. Russian Silver in America: Surviving the Melting Pot. 2011. (ENG., Illus.). 232p. 69.95 *(978-1-904832-81-2(4))* Giles, D. Ltd. GBR. Dist: Antique Collectors' Club.
Palace Editions. Ludwig Museum in the Russian Museum: Museum Ludwig Im Russischen Museum. 2006. (ENG., Illus.). 65.00 *(978-3-930775-59-0(X)*, Palace Editions) Mandala Publishing.
Palace Editions, creator. St Petersburg in Black & White. 2006. (MUL & ENG., Illus.). 216p. 75.00 *(978-3-935298-51-3(X)*, Palace Editions) Mandala Publishing.
Passion Bild: Russische Kunst seit 1970. 2010. (Illus.). 280p. 171.00 ***(978-3-85881-199-8(8))*** Scheidegger und Spiess AG, Verlag CHE. Dist: Antique Collectors' Club.
Petric, Vlada. Constructivism in Film - A Cinematic Analysis: The Man with the Movie Camera. 2nd rev. ed. 2010. (ENG.). 356p. pap. 34.99 *(978-0-521-13788-1(8))* Cambridge Univ. Pr.
Petrova, E. A. & Petrova, Yevgenia, eds. Abstraction in Russia, 2 vols. 2006. (ENG., Illus.). pap. 160.00 *(978-3-935298-50-6(1)*, Palace Editions) Mandala Publishing.
—Russian Futurism. 2006. (ENG., Illus.). 240p. 75.00 *(978-3-930775-91-0(3)*, Palace Editions) Mandala Publishing.
Petrova, Yevgenia. Drawing & Watercolours in Russian Culture: The First Half of the Nineteenth Century. 2006. (ENG., Illus.). 288p. 110.00 *(978-3-938051-32-0(9)*, Palace Editions) Mandala Publishing.
Petrova, Yevgenia. Unofficial Meeting: From the Brykina Collection. 2011. (Illus.). 192p. ***(978-3-86384-038-9(0))*** Brykina, Nadja Gallery AG.
Petrova, Yevgenia, ed. The Golden Treasure Trove of the Russian Museum: The Century of the Russian Museum, 1898-1998. 2006. (ENG., Illus.). 215p. 65.00 *(978-3-930775-46-0(8)*, Palace Editions) Mandala Publishing.
—Play & Passion in Russian Fine Art. 2006. (ENG., Illus.). 360p. 75.00 *(978-3-930775-62-0(X)*, Palace Editions) Mandala Publishing.
Podnar, Gregor, ed. Vadim Fishkin: Orbit Edges. 2008. (ENG., Illus.). 152p. 37.00 *(978-3-905770-72-8(5))* JRP Ringier Kunstverlag AG CHE. Dist: D.A.P./Distributed Art Pubs.
Prince Michael of Greece & Prince Michael of Greece. Jewels of the Tsars: The Romanovs & Imperial Russia. 2006. (ENG., Illus.). 192p. 55.00 *(978-0-86565-171-5(X))* Vendome Pr., The.
Pritchard, Jane & Marsh, Geoffrey, eds. Diaghilev & the Golden Age of the Ballet Russes 1909-1929. 2010. (ENG., Illus.). 240p. 55.00 *(978-1-85177-613-9(3))* V & A Pubns. GBR. Dist: Hachette Bk. Group.
Reviakin, Sergei. The Russian Experiment Continues. 2010. 88p. pap. *(978-3-8383-7925-8(X))* Lambert Academic Publishing.
Roberts, Peter. George Costakis: A Russian Life in Art. (Illus.). 225p. *(978-0-88629-206-5(9))* McGill-Queen's Univ. Pr.
Rosenfeld, Alla. Moscow Conceptualism in Context. 2011. (Illus.). 464p. 75.00 *(978-3-7913-4547-5(8))* Prestel Publishing.
Rubissow, Helen. Art of Russia. *(978-0-8022-1405-8(3))* Philosophical Library, Inc.
Schonle, Andreas. The Ruler in the Garden: Politics & Landscape Design in Imperial Russia. 2007. (Illus.). 395p. pap. 90.95 *(978-3-03911-113-8(2))* Lang, Peter Publishing, Inc.
Schurch, Charlene. Mostly Mittens: Ethnic Knitting Designs from Russia. rev. ed. 2009. (ENG., Illus.). 112p. pap. *(978-1-56477-929-8(7))* Martingale & Co.
Shatskikh, Aleksandra. Vitebsk: The Life of Art. Tsan, Katherine Foshko, tr. from RUS. 2007. (ENG., Illus.). 408p. 55.00 *(978-0-300-10108-9(2))* Yale Univ. Pr.
Shchurik, Natalia Leonidovna. Kuban I Velikie Pobedy Rossii: V Tvorchestve Khudozhnikov Krasnodarskogo Kraia. 2010. (RUS., Illus.). 157p. *(978-5-91050-082-6(1))* Diapazon-V.
Solntsev, F. G. & Whittaker, Cynthia H. Visualizing Russia: Fedor Solntsev & Crafting a National Past. 2010. (Russian History & Culture Ser.). (Illus.). XXXII, 184p. *(978-90-04-18343-8(4))* BRILL.

Sorrell, Stephen & Murray, Damon, eds. Russian Criminal Tattoo Encyclopaedia, Set. ltd. ed. 2012. (ENG., Illus.). 1200p. 1995.00 *(978-0-9558620-3-8(5))* FUEL Publishing GBR. Dist: D.A.P./Distributed Art Pubs.

Spira, Andrew. The Avant-Garde Icon: Russian Avant-Garde Art & the Icon Painting Tradition. 2008. (Illus.). 224p. 100.00 *(978-0-85331-975-7(8)*, Lund Humphries Pubs.) Ashgate Publishing, Ltd. GBR. Dist: Ashgate Publishing Co.

Tarasov, Oleg. Framing Russian Art. 2011. (ENG., Illus.). 415p. 70.00 *(978-1-86189-762-6(6))* Reaktion Bks., Ltd. GBR. Dist: Chicago Distribution Ctr.

Traisman, Yuri, ed. Ode to Joy. 2009. (ENG., Illus.). 260p. bds. 150.00 *(978-0-615-24715-1(6))* Traisman, Yuri.

Tupitsyn, Margarita, ed. Rodchenko & Popova: Defining Constructivism. 2009. (ENG., Illus.). 192p. pap. 39.95 *(978-1-85437-796-8(5))* Tate Publishing, Ltd. GBR. Dist: Hachette Bk. Group.

Tupitsyn, Margarita & International Center of Photography Staff, contrib. by. Gustav Klutsis & Valentina Kulagina: Photography & Montage after Constructivism, 1 vol. 2008. (ENG., Illus.). 256p. 60.00 *(978-3-88243-974-8(2))* Steidl, Gerhard Druckerei und Verlag DEU. Dist: Innovative Logistics.

Tupitsyn, Victor. The Museological Unconscious. 2009. (ENG., Illus.). 352p. (gr. 17). 34.95 *(978-0-262-20173-5(9))* MIT Pr.

Tupitsyn, Victor. The Museological Unconscious: Communal (Post)Modernism in Russia. 2012. (ENG., Illus.). 352p. (gr. 17). pap. 17.95 ***(978-0-262-51751-5(5))*** MIT Pr.

Vasic, Smiljka. Imenice Suglasnickih Osnova U Marijinom Jevanelju. 2010. (Illus.). 96p. *(978-86-7746-208-6(2))* Filozofski Fakultet Pristina, Izdavacka Delatnost.

Volkov, Solomon. Magical Chorus: A History of Russian Culture from Tolstoy to Solzhenitsyn. 2009. (Vintage Ser.). (ENG., Illus.). 368p. pap. 18.95 *(978-1-4000-7786-1(9)*, Vintage) Knopf Doubleday Publishing Group.

Wagenblass, Katherine. Russian Enamel Style Designs. Eisenstadter, Dave, ed. 2008. (Illus.). 48p. pap. 7.95 *(978-0-88045-173-4(4)*, International Design Library) Stemmer Hse. Pubs.

Waller, Richard. The Space of Freedom: Apartment Exhibitions in Leningrad, 1964-1986. Schlatter, N. Elizabeth & Maitre, Joan, eds. 2007. (RUS & ENG., Illus.). 108p. pap. *(978-0-9765047-3-3(1))* Univ. of Richmond Museums.

Walton, Ann Thorson. The International Decorative Arts Exposition in St. Petersburg, 1908. 2009. (Illus.). xv, 213p. pap. *(978-0-9791218-4-5(1))* Modern Greek Studies.

Weiss, Evelyn, ed. Komar & Melamid: The Most Wanted - The Most Unwanted Painting. (ENG & GER., Illus.). 72p. pap. 29.95 *(978-3-89322-344-2(4))* Edition Cantz DEU. Dist: D.A.P./Distributed Art Pubs.

Yoo, Hee-Gwone & Regina, Kristen A., compiled by. Visual Resources from Russia & Eastern Europe in the New York Public Library: A Checklist. 2008. (Illus.). 140.00 *(978-0-88354-046-6(0))* Ross Publishing Incorporated.

Zegers, Peter. Windows on the War: Soviet TASS Posters at Home & Abroad, 1941-1945. 2011. (ENG., Illus.). 400p. 65.00 *(978-0-300-17023-8(8))* Art Institute of Chicago.

ART, SARACENIC

see Islamic Art

ART, SCANDINAVIAN

Chadwick, Whitney, ed. Bent: Gender & Sexuality in Contemporary Scandinavian Art. 2006. (Illus.). 64p. per. 21.95 *(978-0-295-98613-5(1))* Univ. of Washington Pr.

Gruenhaeuser, Amber. Sabe: Free Your Spirit. 2010. (ENG.). 128p. 19.95 *(978-3-937946-23-8(3))*; (Illus.). pap. 14.95 *(978-3-937946-22-1(5))* From Here To Fame GmbH DEU. Dist: SCB Distributors.

Rasmussen, Mikkel Bolt & Jakobsen, Jakob. Expect Anything, Fear Nothing: The Situationist Movement in Scandinavia & Elsewhere. 2011. (Illus.). 288p. pap. 25.00 ***(978-87-993651-2-8(X))*** Autonomedia.

Saksi. Offpiste in the Land of Kustaa Saksi. 2008. 50.00 *(978-3-89955-229-4(6))* Die Gestalten Verlag DEU. Dist: Prestel Publishing.

Weinstein, A. Northern Arts - the Breakthrough of Scandinavian Literature And. 2010. (ENG., Illus.). 544p. (C). pap. 27.95 *(978-0-691-14824-3(4))* Princeton Univ. Pr.

ART, SCOTTISH

Avery, Charles. Charles Avery: Onomatopoeia. 2011. (ITA, FRE, GER & ENG., Illus.). 80p. 39.95 *(978-3-86560-840-6(X))* Verlag der Buchhandlung Walther Konig DEU. Dist: D.A.P./Distributed Art Pubs.

Bath, Michael. Renaissance Decorative Painting in Scotland. 2006. (ENG., Illus.). 226p. pap. 49.95 *(978-1-901663-60-0(4)*, 3064) NMS Enterprises Ltd. - Publishing GBR. Dist: National Bk. Network.

Billcliffe, Roger. Glasgow Boys. rev. ed. 2009. (ENG., Illus.). 396p. 75.00 *(978-0-7112-2906-8(6))* Lincoln, Frances Ltd. GBR. Dist: Perseus-PGW.

Black, Karla. Karla Black: It's Proof That Counts. 2010. (ENG & GER., Illus.). 192p. 55.00 *(978-3-03764-084-5(7))* JRP Ringier Kunstverlag AG CHE. Dist: D.A.P./Distributed Art Pubs.

Black, Peter, ed. "My Highest Pleasures" William Hunter's Art Collection. 2011. (ENG., Illus.). 192p. 50.00 *(978-1-903470-31-2(5))* Holberton, Paul Publishing GBR. Dist: Casemate Pubs. & Bk. Distributors, LLC.

Boyce, Martin. Martin Boyce. 2009. (ENG., Illus.). 160p. pap. 55.00 *(978-3-905770-74-2(1))* JRP Ringier Kunstverlag AG CHE. Dist: D.A.P./Distributed Art Pubs.

Clifford, Timothy. Choice: Twenty-One Years of Collecting for Scotland. 2006. (ENG., Illus.). 256p. pap. *(978-1-903278-73-4(2))* National Galleries of Scotland.

Clifford, Timothy, et al. The Three Graces. 2006. (ENG., Illus.). 112p. pap. *(978-0-903598-59-0(0))* National Galleries of Scotland.

Creed, Martin. Martin Creed: Works. 2010. (ENG., Illus.). 624p. 65.00 *(978-0-500-09353-5(9)*, 509353) Thames & Hudson.

Cruickshank, Graeme. Scottish Pottery: A Brief History. 2nd ed. 2008. (Shire Library). (ENG., Illus.). 64p. per. 12.95 *(978-0-7478-0639-4(X))* Shire Pubns., Ltd. GBR. Dist: Random Hse., Inc.

Euler, Laura. The Glasgow Style: Artists in the Decorative Arts, Circa 1900. 2008. (Illus.). 272p. 69.99 *(978-0-7643-3044-5(6))* Schiffer Publishing, Ltd.

Feitelson, Ann. The Art of Fair Isle Knitting. abr. ed. 2008. 34.99 *(978-1-60514-979-0(9))* Findaway World, LLC.

—Art of Fair Isle Knitting: History, Technique, Color & Patterns. 2009. (ENG., Illus.). 184p. pap. 24.95 *(978-1-59668-138-5(1))* Interweave Pr., LLC.

Finlay, Alec, et al. Specimen Colony: Six Colonies for a European City. 2008. (ENG., Illus.). 192p. pap. 29.95 *(978-1-84631-133-8(0))* Liverpool Univ. Pr. GBR. Dist: Chicago Distribution Ctr.

Fowle, Frances. Impressionism & Scotland. 2008. (ENG., Illus.). 120p. pap. *(978-1-906270-07-0(4))* National Galleries of Scotland.

Glenn, Virginia. Romanesque & Gothic Metalwork & Ivory Carvings in the Museum of Scotland. 2006. (ENG., Illus.). pap. 39.95 *(978-1-901663-55-6(8))* NMS Enterprises Ltd. - Publishing GBR. Dist: National Bk. Network.

Gordon, Douglas. Superhumanatural. 2007. (ENG., Illus.). 144p. pap. *(978-1-903278-85-7(6))* National Galleries of Scotland.

Hewison, Robert. John Byrne: The Art & Life of John Byrne. ltd. ed. 2011. (Illus.). 144p. 900.00 ***(978-1-84822-080-5(4)***, Lund Humphries Pubs.) Ashgate Publishing, Ltd. GBR. Dist: Ashgate Publishing Co.

Holloway, James. The Face of Scotland: The Scottish National Portrait Gallery at Kirkcudbright. 2009. (ENG., Illus.). 48p. pap. *(978-1-906270-13-1(9))* National Galleries of Scotland.

Humfrey, Peter. Tiziano. 2008. (SPA.). 240p. 39.95 *(978-0-7148-9882-7(1))* Phaidon Pr., Inc.

Hunter, R. Civil Twilight & Other Social Works. Hunter, J., ed. 2007. (Illus.). 172p. per. *(978-0-9553927-1-9(3))* Nute Publishing, Ltd.

Kamm, Antony. Scottish Printed Books. 2008. (Illus.). 52p. pap. *(978-1-905207-21-3(2))* Silvermine International Bks., LLC.

Kelvingrove Art Gallery Staff. The Curators & Employees of Kelvingrove Art Gallery & Museum. 2009. (ENG., Illus.). 128p. pap. 20.00 *(978-0-85667-665-9(9))* Wilson, Philip Pubs., Ltd. GBR. Dist: Macmillan.

Knox, Patty. Fabulous Fair Isle Knitting. 2010. (ENG., Illus.). 128p. pap. 22.99 *(978-0-7153-3780-6(7))* David & Charles Pubs. GBR. Dist: F&W Media, Inc.

Leighton, John, ed. Masterpieces from the National Galleries of Scotland. 2012. (ENG., Illus.). 272p. pap. *(978-1-906270-01-8(5))* National Galleries of Scotland.

Lockmiller, Alice. Teacher's Guide for Kensie, Storyteller of Scotland. 2010. 52p. pap. 13.95 *(978-0-557-37386-4(7))* Lulu Enterprises Inc.

Maepas, William. Andy goldsworthy in America. 2010. (Illus.). 344p. 60.00 *(978-1-86171-250-9(2))* Crescent Moon Publishing GBR. Dist: NACSCORP, Inc.

Manley, Bill. Egyptian Treasures. 2010. (ENG., Illus.). 176p. 29.95 *(978-1-905267-17-0(7))* NMS Enterprises Ltd. - Publishing GBR. Dist: National Bk. Network.

Martini, Adrienne. Sweater Quest: My Year of Knitting Dangerously. l.t. ed. 2010. (ENG.). 285p. 31.99 *(978-1-4104-2816-5(8))* Thorndike Pr.

Mucklestone, Mary Jane. 200 Fair Isle Motifs: A Knitter's Directory. 2011. (ENG., Illus.). 208p. pap. 24.95 *(978-1-59668-437-9(2))* Interweave Pr., LLC.

National Galleries of Scotland Staff, contrib. by. Henry Raeburn & His Printmakers. 2007. (Illus.). 32p. pap. *(978-1-903278-90-1(2))* National Galleries of Scotland.

Pearson, Fiona & Stevenson, Sara. Joan Eardley. 2008. (ENG., Illus.). 96p. pap. *(978-1-906270-04-9(X))* National Galleries of Scotland.

Richardson, Craig. Scottish Art Since 1960: Historical Reflections & Critical Overview. 2011. (Illus.). 230p. 124.95 *(978-0-7546-6124-5(5))* Ashgate Publishing Co.

Ruf, Beatrix, ed. Scott Myles. 2008. (GER & ENG., Illus.). 96p. 30.00 *(978-3-905701-63-0(4))* JRP Ringier Kunstverlag AG CHE. Dist: D.A.P./Distributed Art Pubs.

Scarisbrick, Diana. Scottish Jewellery: A Victorian Passion. 2009. (ENG., Illus.). 128p. 45.00 *(978-88-7439-524-8(8))* 5 Continents ITA. Dist: Hachette Bk. Group.

Strang, Alice. F. C. B. Cadell. 2012. (ENG., Illus.). 96p. pap. ***(978-1-906270-40-7(6))*** National Galleries of Scotland.

Taylor, Kathleen. Fearless Fair Isle Knitting: 30 Gorgeous Original Sweaters, Socks, Mittens, & More. 2011. (ENG., Illus.). 176p. pap. 24.95 *(978-1-60085-327-2(7))* Taunton Pr., Inc.

The Curators and Employees of Kelvingrove Art Gallery and Museum. Kelvingrove Art Gallery & Museum: The Curators & employees of Kelvingrove Art Gallery & Museum. 2009. (ENG., Illus.). 128p. pap. 20.00 *(978-0-85667-667-3(5))* Wilson, Philip Pubs., Ltd. GBR. Dist: Macmillan.

Thomson, Duncan, ed. Benjamin West & the Death of a Stag: The Story Behind the Painting & its Conservation. 2009. (ENG., Illus.). 32p. pap. *(978-1-906270-12-4(0))* National Galleries of Scotland.

White, Colin. A Guide to the Printed Work of Jessie M. King. 2007. (Illus.). 238p. 90.00 *(978-1-58456-204-7(8))* Oak Knoll Pr.

ART, SCYTHIAN

Aruz, Joan, et al, eds. The Golden Deer of Eurasia: Perspectives on the Steppe Nomads of the Ancient World: the Metropolitan Museum of Art Symposia. 2007. (Metropolitan Museum of Art Ser.). (ENG., Illus.). 256p. pap. 25.00 *(978-0-300-12403-3(1))* Yale Univ. Pr.

Kemenczei, Tibor. Studien Zu Den Denkmälern Skythisch Geprägter Alföld Gruppe. 2009. (GER., Illus.). 410p. *(978-963-7061-63-9(0))* Magyar Nemzeti Muzeum.

Minns, Ellis Hovell. Scythians & Greeks: A Survey of Ancient History & Archaeology on the North Coast of the Euxine from the Danube to the Caucasus. 2011. (Cambridge Library Collection - Archaeology Ser.). (Illus.). 820p. pap. 53.00 *(978-1-108-02487-7(4))* Cambridge Univ. Pr.

Salmony, Alfred. Sino-Siberian Art in the Collection of C. T. Loo. 2006. (ENG., Illus.). 119p. 70.00 *(978-1-878529-36-7(6))* Orchid Pr. THA. Dist: National Bk. Network.

Vickers, Michael. Scythian & Thracian Antiquities in Oxford. 2006. (Ashmolean Handbooks). (ENG., Illus.). 80p. pap. 15.95 *(978-1-85444-180-5(9))* Ashmolean Museum GBR. Dist: Antique Collectors' Club.

ART, SERBIAN

Mihajlovic, Branislav. Branislav Mihajlovic: Slike: Biblioteka Grada Beograda, Galerija Atrijum, 16. Januar - 12. Februar 2009. 2009. (Illus.). 16 p. *(978-86-7191-168-9(3))* Biblioteka grada Beograda.

ART, SHAKER

see Shaker Art

ART, SIBERIAN

Gorbatcheva, Valentina & Federova, Marina. Art of Siberia. 2008. (Temporis Ser.). (ENG., Illus.). 287p. 39.95 *(978-1-84484-562-0(1))* Parkstone International GBR. Dist: Ingram Pub. Services.

ART, SOUTH AFRICAN

Adendorff, Adele. Nomadic Figurations of Identity. 2011. 164p. pap. ***(978-3-8454-1060-9(4))*** Lambert Academic Publishing.

Avgikos, Jan. Marlene Dumas. 2nd rev. ed. 2009. (ENG., Illus.). 240p. 69.95 *(978-0-7148-4584-5(1))* Phaidon Pr., Inc.

Bedford, Emma, ed. Decade of Democracy: South African Art, 1994-2004. 2010. (Illus.). 150p. pap. 51.95 *(978-1-919930-50-3(7))* Double Storey Bks. ZAF. Dist: International Publishers Marketing.

Bedford, Emma & Dumas, Marlene. Marlene Dumas: Intimate Relations. 2008. (Illus.). 140p. pap. 34.95 *(978-1-77009-381-2(8))* Jacana Media ZAF. Dist: Independent Pubs. Group.

Boutoux, Thomas & Rosenthal, Stephanie. Robin Rhode: Walk Off, 1 vol. 2007. (ENG., Illus.). 208p. 55.00 *(978-3-7757-2069-4(3))* Hatje Cantz Verlag GmbH & Co KG DEU. Dist: D.A.P./Distributed Art Pubs.

Breitz, Candice. Candice Breitz: Inner & Outer Space. 2009. (GER & ENG., Illus.). 120p. pap. 45.00 *(978-3-86560-546-7(X))* Verlag der Buchhandlung Walther Konig DEU. Dist: D.A.P./Distributed Art Pubs.

—Candice Breitz: Same Same. 2010. (ENG., Illus.). 130p. pap. 47.00 *(978-1-894212-29-8(0))* Power Plant, The CAN. Dist: D.A.P./Distributed Art Pubs.

—Exposicion Multiple/Multiple Exposure. 2007. (Illus.). 251p. *(978-84-96540-60-6(X))* Actar Birkhauser Distribution.

Compion, Shem. Insider's Guide: Top Wildlife Photography Spots in South Africa. 2011. (ENG., Illus.). 289p. pap. 30.95 *(978-1-77009-835-0(6))* Jacana Media ZAF. Dist: Independent Pubs. Group.

Croquet, Pierre, photos by. Pierre Crocquet de Rosemond: Pinky Promise. 2011. (ENG., Illus.). 280p. 60.00 ***(978-3-7757-3173-7(3))*** Hatje Cantz Verlag GmbH & Co KG DEU. Dist: D.A.P./Distributed Art Pubs.

Diserens, Corinne, ed. Chasseur Dombres: Santu Mofokeng. 2011. (ENG.). 240p. 50.00 ***(978-3-7913-4586-4(9))*** Prestel Publishing.

Dube, Hlengiwe. Zulu Beadwork: Talk with Beads. 2009. (Illus.). 112p. pap. 35.00 *(978-0-9816267-0-3(X))* Africa Direct.

Dube, Prince Mbusi. Dumile Feni: The Story of a Great Artist. 2011. 286p. 61.95 ***(978-0-9869833-0-6(6))*** STE Pubs. ZAF. Dist: Independent Pubs. Group.

Dubois, Hughes, photos by. Solomon Islands Art: The Conru Collection. 2008. (ENG., Illus.). 256p. 125.00 *(978-88-7439-493-7(4))* 5 Continents ITA. Dist: Hachette Bk. Group.

Dubow, Jessica. Settling the Self. 2009. (Illus.). 208p. pap. *(978-3-639-17075-7(X))* VDM Verlag Dr. Mueller e.K.

Faith47. Faith47. 2011. (On the Run Bks.). (ENG., Illus.). 128p. 19.95 *(978-3-937946-09-2(8))*; pap. 14.95 *(978-3-937946-08-5(X))* From Here To Fame GmbH DEU. Dist: SCB Distributors.

Fitzgerald, Diane. Zulu Inspired Beadwork: Weaving Techniques & Projects. 2007. (ENG., Illus.). 128p. pap. 24.95 *(978-1-59668-034-0(2))* Interweave Pr., LLC.

Garb, Tamar. Figures & Fictions: Contemporary South African Photography. 2011. (ENG., Illus.). 256p. 58.00 *(978-3-86930-266-9(6))* Steidl, Gerhard Druckerei und Verlag DEU. Dist: Innovative Logistics.

Hecker, Judith, text. Impressions from South Africa, 1965 to Now: Prints from the Museum of Modern Art. 2011. (ENG., Illus.). 96p. pap. 29.95 *(978-0-87070-756-8(6))* Museum of Modern Art.

Jamal, Ashraf, et al. Lien Botha. (TAXI Art Bks.: Bk. 5). (Illus.). 16p. (C). pap., tchr. ed., suppl. ed. *(978-0-9584496-2-5(7))* Krut, David Publishing.

Kentridge, William & text. Trace: Prints from the Museum of Modern Art. 2010. (ENG., Illus.). 112p. 29.95 *(978-0-87070-779-7(5))* Museum of Modern Art.

Klopper, Sandra. The Art of Southern Africa: The Terence Pethica Collection. 2008. (ENG., Illus.). 216p. 75.00 *(978-88-7439-405-0(5))* 5 Continents ITA. Dist: Hachette Bk. Group.

Lewis-Williams, J. David. San Rock Art. 2011. (Pocket History Guides). (Illus.). 160p. pap. 12.95 ***(978-1-4314-0100-0(5))*** Jacana Media ZAF. Dist: Independent Pubs. Group.

Mason, Andy. What's So Funny? Under the Skin of South African Cartooning. 2011. 256p. pap. 24.95 *(978-1-77013-071-5(3))* Double Storey Bks. ZAF. Dist: International Publishers Marketing.

Miles, Elza. Land & Lives: A Story of Early Black Artists. (Illus.). 190p. *(978-0-7981-3658-7(8))* Human & Rousseau.

Peffer, John. Art & the End of Apartheid. 2009. (ENG., Illus.). 352p. 90.00 *(978-0-8166-5001-9(2))*; pap. 29.95 *(978-0-8166-5002-6(0))* Univ. of Minnesota Pr.

Proud, Hayden. Revisions+ Expanding the Narrative of South African Art - The Campbell Smith Collection. 2nd ed. 2008. (Illus.). 104p. pap. 43.00 *(978-1-874817-36-9(7))* Unisa Press / Uitgewers GBR. Dist: International Specialized Bk. Services.

Proud, Hayden, ed. Scratches on the Face: Antiquity & Contemporaneity in South African Works of Art from Iziko Museums of Cape Town. 2008. 64p. pap. 35.00 *(978-1-874817-39-0(1))* Unisa Press / Uitgewers GBR. Dist: International Specialized Bk. Services.

Rhode, Robin. Robin Rhode: Who Saw Who. 2009. (ENG., Illus.). 120p. 40.00 *(978-1-85332-271-6(7))* Hayward Gallery Publishing GBR. Dist: D.A.P./Distributed Art Pubs.

Rowland, Jen & Stowe, Tori. Catalogue of Eastern Cape Craft. 2006. (Illus.). 96p. *(978-1-920033-02-6(5))* NISC (Pty) Ltd.

Rumma, Lia. William Kentridge: Streets of the City. 2011. (ENG.). 144p. 75.00 *(978-88-370-7340-4(2)*, Mondadori Electa (Acc)) Antique Collectors' Club GBR. Dist: National Bk. Network.

Seidman, Judy. Red on Black: The Story of the South African Poster Movement. 2008. (ENG.). 240p. pap. 39.00 *(978-1-919855-90-5(4))* STE Pubs. ZAF. Dist: Independent Pubs. Group.

Skotnes. Unconquerable Spirit: G Stow's Paintings of the San. 2008. (Illus.). 218p. *(978-1-77009-599-1(3))* Ohio Univ. Pr.

Skotnes, Pippa, ed. Rock Art Made in Translation: Framing Images of & from the Landscape. 2011. (ENG., Illus.). 104p. pap. 24.95 *(978-1-4314-0080-5(7))* Jacana Media ZAF. Dist: Independent Pubs. Group.

Subiros, Pep. Apartheid: The South African Mirror. 2007. (Illus.). 205p. pap. *(978-84-96954-03-8(X))* Actar Birkhauser Distribution.

Subiros, Pep, ed. Apartheid: El Espejo Sudafricano. 2007. (Illus.). 204p. per. *(978-84-96954-02-1(1))* Actar Birkhauser Distribution.

—Jane Alexander: Surveys (from the Cape of Good Hope) 2011. (ENG., Illus.). 192p. (C). 45.00 *(978-0-945802-57-0(9))* Museum for African Art.

Thurman, Chris. At Large: Reviewing the Arts in South Africa. 2011. pap. ***(978-1-86335-927-6(3))*** Common Ground Publishing Pty, Ltd.

Turner, Irina. Comprehending Gender Issues Through Photography. 2008. 92p. pap. *(978-3-8364-8819-8(1))* VDM Verlag Dr. Mueller e.K.

Van Grasdorff & Carman, Jillian. Uplifting the Colonial Philistine: Florence Phillips & the Making of the Johannesburg Art Gallery. 2007. (ENG., Illus.). 452p. (gr. 11). pap. 34.95 *(978-1-86814-436-5(4))* Witwatersrand Univ. Pr. Pubns. ZAF. Dist: Transaction Pubs.

Vladislavic, Ivan, et al, texts. Home Lands - Land Marks: Contemporary Art from South Africa. 2009. (ENG., Illus.). 168p. 50.00 *(978-1-905620-25-8(X))* Haunch of Venison GBR. Dist: D.A.P./Distributed Art Pubs.

Williamson, Sue. Resistance Art in South Africa 2005. 2010. (Illus.). 160p. pap. 47.95 *(978-1-919930-69-5(8))* Double Storey Bks. ZAF. Dist: International Publishers Marketing.

—South African Art Now. 2009. (Illus.). 320p. 65.00 *(978-0-06-134351-3(X)*, Collins Design) HarperCollins Pubs.

ART, SPANISH

Abrantes, Ricardo, et al. Arte Español para Extranjeros. Cámara, Alicia, ed. 4th ed. 2006. (SPA., Illus.). 256p. pap. 36.95 ***(978-84-89569-36-2(3))*** Nerea Editorial ESP. Dist: Independent Pubs. Group.

Ahtila, Eija-Liisa, et al, contrib. by. The Musac Collection, Vol. 1. 2006. (Illus.). 700p. (gr. 13-18). pap. 75.00 *(978-84-932325-5-9(6))* D.A.P./Distributed Art Pubs.

Alcala, Luisa Elena, et al. Sacred Spain: Art & Belief in the Spanish World. Kasl, Ronda, ed. 2010. (ENG., Illus.). 400p. 65.00 *(978-0-300-15471-9(2))* Yale Univ. Pr.

Asunción, Josep, et al. Arts Sòlides o Líquides? Les Arts Visuals Als Països Catalans, 1975-2008. 2008. (CAT.). 175p. *(978-84-96349-76-6(4))* Cep i la Nansa Edicions, El.

Badiola, Txomin. Ana Laura Alaez Using Your Guns. 2008. (ENG., Illus.). 160p. pap. 55.00 *(978-88-8158-675-2(4))* Charta ITA. Dist: D.A.P./Distributed Art Pubs.

Banks, William. James Turrell. 2009. (SPA & ENG., Illus.). 96p. pap. 29.95 *(978-88-8158-730-8(0))* Charta ITA. Dist: D.A.P./Distributed Art Pubs.

Barros Guerton, Javier. About Urban Spain-B&W. 2009. 144p. pap. 20.50 *(978-1-4092-8726-1(2))* Lulu Enterprises Inc.

Bassegoda i Hugas, Bonaventura. Col·leccionistes, Col·leccions I Museus: Episodis de la Història Del Patrimoni Artístic de Catalunya. 2007. (CAT., Illus.). 291p. *(978-84-475-3166-0(X))* Univ. de Barcelona Pubns.

Bernade, Anita. CD for Spanish Patterns & Designs. 2007. (Illus.). cd-rom 12.95 *(978-0-88045-166-6(1)*, International Design Library) Stemmer Hse. Pubs.

Berts, Jean-Michel, et al. Manolo Valdes. 2011. (ENG.). 100p. pap. 95.00 ***(978-1-61428-003-3(7))*** Assouline FRA. Dist: Perseus Distribution.

Bomgasser & Scheffler. Madrid & Prado. 2009. 432p. 59.99 *(978-0-8416-1647-9(7))* American Map Corp.

Bosch, Eualia. Frequencies: Eugènia Balcells. 2009. *(978-84-92861-03-3(7))* Actar Birkhauser Distribution.

Coleman, Catherine. Janus: Photography's Face: Works from the Permanent Collection 3. 2009. 222p. pap. 29.95 *(978-84-8026-347-4(4))* Museo Nacional Centro de Arte Reina Sofia ESP. Dist: Actar Birkhauser Distribution.

Cox, Neil. Picasso's 'Toys for Adults' Cubism As Surrealism. 2011. (ENG., Illus.). 48p. *(978-1-906270-26-1(0))* National Galleries of Scotland.

Dagen, Philippe. Picasso. 2009. (ENG., Illus.). 512p. 150.00 *(978-1-58093-257-6(6))* Monacelli Pr., Inc.

De Bunes Ibarra, Miguel Angel, et al. The Invention of Glory: Afonso V & the Pastrana Tapestries. 2012. (ENG., Illus.). 104p. 65.00 ***(978-1-55595-375-1(1))*** Hudson Hills Pr. LLC.

Douglas, Kris, ed. Inigo Manglano-Ovalle: Blinking Out of Existence, 1 vol. 2008. (ENG., Illus.). 65p. 29.95 *(978-0-9792364-0-2(1))* Rochester Art Ctr.

Englert, Klaus. New Museums in Spain. 2010. (GER & ENG., Illus.). 160p. 89.00 *(978-3-936681-17-6(1))* Edition Axel Menges GmbH DEU. Dist: National Bk. Network.

Esteban, Angel, ed. Madrid Habanece: Cuba y España en el Punto de Mira Transatlántico. 2011. pap. 29.80 ***(978-84-8489-576-3(9))*** Iberoamericana Vervuert Publishing Corp.

Fabry, Alexis, text. Fotografía Latinoamericana 1895-2008. 2009. (ENG., Illus.). 206p. 65.00 *(978-84-92480-29-6(7))* R.M. Editorial, S.A. de C.V. MEX. Dist: D.A.P./Distributed Art Pubs.

Ferdandez Polanco, Aurora. Impure Vision: Works from the Permanent Collection 1. 2009. 176p. pap. 29.95 *(978-84-8026-287-3(7))* Museo Nacional Centro de Arte Reina Sofia ESP. Dist: Actar Birkhauser Distribution.

García Guinea, Miguel Angel, et al. Enciclopedia Del Románico en Aragón: Zaragoza, 2 vols. 2010. (Illus.). (SPA.). *(978-84-89483-69-9(8))*; *(978-84-89483-67-5(1))*; (SPA., *(978-84-89483-68-2(X))* Fundacion Santa Maria La Real, Centro de Estudios del Romanico.

Gargallo, Pablo & Salazar, María José. Pablo Gargallo (1881-1934) Dibujos: Catálogo Razonado, 2 vols. 2010. (ENG & SPA., Illus.). 1155p. *(978-84-96655-68-3(7))*; *(978-84-96655-67-6(9))*; *(978-84-96655-66-9(0))* Fundación Marcelino Botín.

Giralt-Miracle, Daniel & Altaio, Vicenc. Visualkultur. Cat: Art/Design/Books. 2007. (Illus.). 339p. per. *(978-84-96540-93-4(6))* Actar Birkhauser Distribution.

Glendinning, Nigel & McCartney, Hilary, eds. Spanish Art in Britain & Ireland, 1750-1920: Studies in Reception in Memory of Enriqueta Harris Frankfort. 2011. (Monografías A Ser.: Volume 290). (Illus.). 344p. 90.00 *(978-1-85566-223-0(X)*, Tamesis Bks.) Boydell & Brewer, Ltd. GBR. Dist: Boydell & Brewer, Inc.

Gómez González, Concepción. Dau Al Set: Joan Brossa, Juan Eduardo Cirlot, Modest Cuixart, Jaon Ponç, Arnau Puig, Antoni Tàpies, Joan-Joseph Tharrats: Zaragoza, Ibercaja, Patio de la Infanta ... Del 6 de Octubre Al 13 de Diciembre de 2009. 2009. (SPA., Illus.). 139p. *(978-84-8324-283-4(4))* Caja de Ahorros y Monte de Piedad de Zaragoza, Aragon y Rioja.

Hayon, Jaime. Jaime Hayon Works. 2008. (Illus.). 317p. *(978-3-89955-207-2(5))* Die Gestalten Verlag.

He, Jianping, ed. Isidro Ferrer. 2008. (New Generation of Design Ser.). (Illus.). 215p. pap. *(978-981-245-510-9(8))* Page One Publishing.

Hellwig, Karin. Spanien und Deutschland: Kulturtransfer Im 19. Jahrhundert = España y Alemania: Intercambio Cultural en el Siglo XIX. 2007. (MUL, GER & SPA., Illus.). 313p. pap. 56.00 *(978-84-8489-337-0(5))* Iberoamericana Vervuert Publishing Corp.

Hintzen-Bohlen, Brigitte. Andalusia. 2008. (Art & Architecture Ser.). (Illus.). 536p. 19.95 *(978-0-8416-0146-8(1))* American Map Corp.

—Andalusia, 1 vol. 2010. (ENG., Illus.). 536p. pap. 9.99 *(978-3-8331-5280-1(X))* h.f.ullmann DEU. Dist: Innovative Logistics.

Hintzen, Bohlen Brigitte. Art & Architecture Andalusia. 2010. (Art & Architecture Pocket Ser.). 536p. pap. 16.99 *(978-0-8416-7150-8(8))* Langenscheidt Publishing Group.

Ibañez, Pere. EneME. 2010. 216p. pap. 71.95 *(978-0-557-68170-9(7))* Lulu Enterprises Inc.

—EneME (Spanish Edition) 2010. 216p. pap. 71.95 *(978-0-557-72743-8(X))* Lulu Enterprises Inc.

Jones, Anny Brooksbank. Visual Culture in Spain & Mexico. 2011. (ENG., Illus.). 224p. pap. 25.95 *(978-0-7190-5679-6(9))* Manchester Univ. Pr. GBR. Dist: Macmillan.

Katzew, Ilona, ed. Contested Visions in the Spanish Colonial World. 2011. (ENG., Illus.). 320p. 70.00 *(978-0-300-17664-3(3))* Yale Univ. Pr.

King, Elliot H., et al, contrib. by. Salvador Dalí: The Late Work. 2010. (Illus.). 176p. 39.95 *(978-0-300-16828-0(4))* Yale Univ. Pr.

Kroesen, J. E. A. Staging the Liturgy: The Medieval Altarpiece in the Iberian Peninsula. 2009. (Liturgia Condenda Ser.). (ENG.). 607p. (C). pap. 95.00 *(978-90-429-2116-0(1))* Peeters Pubs. & Booksellers BEL. Dist: Brown, David Bk. Co., The.

L#xF3;pez Garc#xED;a, Antonio & text. Antonio L#xF3;pez Garc#xED;a: Paintings & Sculpture. 2011. (ENG., Illus.). 288p. 75.00 ***(978-1-935202-65-3(0))*** D.A.P./Distributed Art Pubs.

Llanos, Fernando. Cursi Agridulce. 2008. (SPA.). 152p. pap. 21.00 *(978-968-6842-94-4(2))* Trilce Ediciones S.A. de C.V. MEX. Dist: Independent Pubs. Group.

Luxenberg, Alisa. The Galerie Espagnole & the Museo Nacional 1835-1853: Saving Spanish Art, or the Politics of Patrimony. 2008. (Illus.). 300p. 124.95 *(978-0-7546-6190-0(3))* Ashgate Publishing Co.

Mann, Vivian B., ed. & contrib. by. Uneasy Communion: Jews, Christians, & the Altarpieces of Medieval Spain. 2010. 49.95 *(978-0-9777839-6-0(0))* Museum of Biblical Art.

March, Guillem. Cover Girls HC. 2012. (Illus.). 80p. 16.99 ***(978-1-60706-491-6(X))*** Image Comics.

Martin, Luz. Texture: Valencia Street Art. 2009. (ENG & SPA., Illus.). 144p. 34.95 *(978-0-9820754-6-3(4))* Batty, Mark Pub., LLC.

Mateo, Jesus, photos by & text. Jesus Mateo: The Ninth Day of Creation. 2010. (ENG., Illus.). 240p. pap. 85.00 *(978-84-96466-05-0(1))* La Fabrica ESP. Dist: D.A.P./Distributed Art Pubs.

Medina, Cuauhtémoc, ed. Domino Canibal. 2011. (ENG., Illus.). 256p. pap. 40.00 *(978-84-343-1262-3(X))* Poligrafa, Ediciones, S. A. ESP. Dist: D.A.P./Distributed Art Pubs.

Miró, Joan & Beltramo Ceppi Zevi, Claudia. Joan Miró: I Miti Del Mediterraneo. 2010. (ITA., Illus.). 261p. *(978-88-09-75559-8(6))* Giunti Gruppo Editoriale.

Morcillo, Aleja, ed. In Pectore. 2008. 112p. *(978-84-612-4426-3(5))* Actar Birkhauser Distribution.

Muntadas, Antoni. Antoni Muntadas: On Translation, I Giardini, Venice Biennale 2005. 2006. (Illus.). 446p. (gr. 13-18). 38.00 *(978-84-7232-952-2(6))* D.A.P./Distributed Art Pubs.

Nunez, Jose Arturo Rodriguez. Four Decades of Books & Publications of Spanish Artists Ortiz, Diego, ed. 2008. 272p. pap. *(978-84-96933-15-6(6))* Actar Birkhauser Distribution.

Oliveira, Olivia. Marcas Y Trademarks2. 2006. 928p. 80.00 *(978-84-252-2073-9(4))* Trucatriche.

Padilla, Carmella & Pierce, Donna. Conexiones: Connections in Spanish Colonial Art. (Illus.). 176p. 50.00 *(978-0-9719103-0-0(8))* Spanish Colonial Arts Society, Inc.

Parr, Martin, et al, photos by. Visual Correspondences. 2010. (ENG & SPA., Illus.). 336p. pap. 39.95 *(978-950-889-183-9(1))* La Marca ARG. Dist: D.A.P./Distributed Art Pubs.

Paunero, Daniel & Daniel, Paunero. S/T (Sin Título) La Exposición Como Taller. 2010. (SPA., Illus.). 67p. *(978-84-441-0244-3(X))* Centro Atlantico de Arte Moderno.

Picasso, Pablo. A Picasso Portfolio: Prints from the Museum of Modern Art. 2010. (ENG., Illus.). 200p. 40.00 *(978-0-87070-780-3(9))* Museum of Modern Art.

Picasso, Pablo, illus. Picasso's Paintings, Watercolors, Drawings & Sculpture. a Comprehensive Illustrated Catalogue 1885-1973. the Rose Period. 1905-1906. Paris, Holland & Gósol. 2012. 368p. 150.00 ***(978-1-55660-328-0(2))*** Wofsy, Alan Fine Arts.

Picasso, Pablo, et al. Picasso in the Metropolitan Museum of Art. 2010. (Illus.). xi, 364p. 35.00 *(978-1-58839-371-5(2))*; 60.00 *(978-1-58839-370-8(4))* Metropolitan Museum of Art, The.

Pique, Ramon, ed. Silenci? 2009. 310p. *(978-84-96954-45-8(5))* Actar Birkhauser Distribution.

Ribalta, Jorge, text. Relational Objects: Macba Collection 2002-2007. 2010. (ENG.). 272p. pap. 39.95 *(978-84-92505-12-8(5))* Museu d'Art Contemporani de Barcelona ESP. Dist: Actar Birkhauser Distribution.

Robinson, Cynthia. Courting the Alhambra: Cross-Disciplinary Approaches to the Hall of Justice Ceilings. Pinet, Simone, ed. 2008. 293p. pap. *(978-90-04-17342-2(0))* BRILL.

Rosser-Owen, Mariam. Islamic Arts from Spain. 2010. (ENG., Illus.). 160p. 55.00 *(978-1-85177-598-9(6))* V & A Pubns. GBR. Dist: Hachette Bk. Group.

Ruff, Thomas, et al, contrib. by. Matador M. 2010. (ENG., Illus.). pap. 85.00 *(978-84-92841-09-7(5))* La Fabrica ESP. Dist: D.A.P./Distributed Art Pubs.

Sala, Mauis. Poster Design, 1 vol. 2010. (ENG., Illus.). 320p. pap. 34.95 *(978-84-92643-34-9(X))* Index Bks., Spain ESP. Dist: Innovative Logistics.

Schommer, Alberto, photos by. Alberto Schommer. 2010. (SPA & ENG., Illus.). 112p. pap. 20.00 *(978-84-95471-53-6(1))* La Fabrica ESP. Dist: D.A.P./Distributed Art Pubs.

Schoth, Sarah, ed. Art in Spain & the Hispanic World. 2010. (Illus.). 368p. pap. 60.00 *(978-1-907372-00-1(8))* Univ. of Washington Pr.

Schroth, Sarah & Baer, Ronni. El Greco to Velazquez: Art During the Reign of Philip III. 2008. 351p. pap. 40.00 *(978-0-87846-727-3(0))*; (ENG., Illus.). 352p. 65.00 *(978-0-87846-726-6(2))* Museum of Fine Arts, Boston.

Serrano Marqués, Mercedes & Piñar Samos, Javier. En Los Confines de un Mismo Mar: Los Palacios de la Alhambra y Topkapi en la Fotografía Del Viaje a Oriente/Ayni Denizin Uçlarinda: Dogu'ya Yolculugun Fotografinda el Hamra Ve Topkapi Saraylari. 2009. (Illus.). 220p. *(978-84-96933-33-0(4))*; *(978-84-92441-65-5(8))* Sociedad Estatal para la Accion Cultural Exterior, S.A.

Simal Lozano, Jesús Ángel. Láminas de Compostela. 2010. (ENG & SPA., Illus.). 102p. *(978-84-9887-286-6(3))* Universidad de Santiago de Compostela, Servicio de Publicaciones e Intercambio Cientifico.

Socias, Jordi, photos by. Jordi Socias: PHotoBolsillo. 2010. (ENG & SPA., Illus.). 112p. pap. 20.00 *(978-84-92841-04-2(4))* La Fabrica ESP. Dist: D.A.P./Distributed Art Pubs.

Spanish Photo and Video a Staff. Nuevas Historias: A New View of Spanish Photography & Video Art. 2009. (SPA & ENG., Illus.). 240p. 60.00 *(978-3-7757-2340-4(4))* Hatje Cantz Verlag GmbH & Co KG DEU. Dist: D.A.P./Distributed Art Pubs.

Strauss, Beat Zoderer. 2009. (GER & ENG., Illus.). 224p. 70.00 *(978-3-7757-2294-0(7))* Hatje Cantz Verlag GmbH & Co KG DEU. Dist: D.A.P./Distributed Art Pubs.

Sureda, Joan. The Golden Age of Spain: Painting, Sculpture, Architecture. 2008. (ENG., Illus.). 304p. 85.00 *(978-0-86565-198-2(1))* Vendome Pr., The.

Terre, Laura. Photo-Identities: Miguel Trillo. 2009. *(978-84-96540-74-3(X))* Actar Birkhauser Distribution.

Tinterow, Gary & Stein, Susan Alyson, eds. Picasso in the Metropolitan Museum of Art. 2010. (ENG., Illus.). 376p. 60.00 *(978-0-300-15525-9(5))* Yale Univ. Pr.

Trusted, Marjorie. The Arts of Spain: Iberia & Latin America 1450-1700. 2007. (ENG.). 256p. 47.50 *(978-0-271-03337-2(1))* Pennsylvania State Univ. Pr.

Universidad de Alcalá, Museo Luis González Robles Staff, contrib. by. 60 Artistas Del Museo Luis González Robles en Los 500 Años Del Primer Curso Académico de la Universidad de Alcalá: Una Mirada a la Colección. 2009. (SPA., Illus.). 97p. *(978-84-8138-838-1(6))* Universidad de Alcala de Henares. Servicio de Publicaciones.

Universitat de Barcelona, Centre de Recerca de Dones Staff, contrib. by. Col·lecció D'Art I Punt D'Investigació "La Relació", Duoda, Universitat de Barcelona: Documents 2000-2008. 2009. (CAT & SPA., Illus.). 114p. *(978-84-475-3414-2(6))* Univ. de Barcelona Pubns.

Valldosera, Eulalia. The Navel of the World: Eulalia Valldosera. 2009. 176p. pap. 39.95 *(978-84-8026-382-5(2))* Museo Nacional Centro de Arte Reina Sofia ESP. Dist: Actar Birkhauser Distribution.

Vitali, Christoph. Picasso, Miró, Dalí: Angry Young Men - The Birth of Modernity. Carmona, Eugenio, ed. 2011. (Illus.). 208p. 55.00 *(978-88-572-0978-4(4))* Skira Editore ITA. Dist: Random Hse., Inc.

Williams, Leonard. The Arts & Crafts of Older Spain. 2010. (ENG.). 436p. pap. 35.75 *(978-1-177-41606-1(9))*; 370p. pap. 32.75 *(978-1-149-28937-2(6))*; 434p. 41.99 *(978-1-140-15934-6(8))*; 434p. pap. 35.75 *(978-1-140-15935-3(6))*; 438p. pap. 35.75 *(978-1-144-63258-6(7))*; 366p. pap. 32.75 *(978-1-142-13465-5(2))*; 438p. pap. 35.75 *(978-1-141-96990-6(4))* BiblioBazaar.

—The Arts & Crafts of Older Spain. 2009. 110p. pap. *(978-1-151-73679-6(1))*; 188p. pap. *(978-0-217-88493-8(8))*; 106p. pap. *(978-0-217-37833-8(1))*; 172p. pap. *(978-0-217-37834-5(X))*; 120p. pap. *(978-0-217-28896-5(0))* Books LLC.

—The Arts & Crafts of Older Spain. 2010. 100p. pap. 20.00 *(978-1-153-29250-4(5))*; 120p. pap. 21.05 *(978-1-153-35811-8(5))* General Bks. LLC.

ART, SWEDISH

Akay & Baranowski, Peter. Urban Recreation: City Art by Akay & Peter. 2006. (ENG., Illus.). 192p. 29.95 *(978-91-973981-7-6(9))* Dokument forlag, Fotograf Malcolm Jacobsson SWE. Dist: SCB Distributors.

Andersen, Ivar & Borg, Kristian. Playground Sweden. 2007. (ENG.). 144p. (YA). 29.95 *(978-91-85639-07-6(9))* Dokument forlag, Fotograf Malcolm Jacobsson SWE. Dist: SCB Distributors.

Andersson, Mamma & Nordstrom, Jockum. Mamma Andersson & Jockum Nordstrom: Who Is Sleeping on My Pillow. 2010. (ENG., Illus.). 247p. 75.00 *(978-1-935202-26-4(X))* Zwirner, David Inc.

Bladh, Krister. The Guardian of the Spectacle. 2010. 76p. pap. 8.00 *(978-0-557-47522-3(8))* Lulu Enterprises Inc.

Cavalli-Björkman, Görel. Dutch & Flemish Paintings III: Flemish Paintings C. 1600 - C. 1800. 2010. (Illus.). 487p. 250.00 *(978-91-7100-822-0(5))* Moderna Museet SWE. Dist: Coronet Bks.

Djurberg, Nathalie. Nathalie Djurberg Denn Es Ist Schoen Zu. 2007. (Illus.). 99p. pap. *(978-3-939738-24-4(7))* Verlag fur Moderne Kunst.

—Nathalie Djurberg: Turn into Me. 2008. (ENG., Illus.). 247p. 120.00 *(978-88-87029-41-3(5))* Fondazione Prada ITA. Dist: D.A.P./Distributed Art Pubs.

Eksell, Olle. Olle Eksell: Swedish Graphic Designer. Pie Books Staff & Takahashi, Kaoru, eds. 2011. (ENG., Illus.). 240p. pap. 39.95 *(978-4-89444-547-5(6))* Rizzoli International Pubns., Inc.

Farson, Laura. New Twists on Twined Knitting: A Fresh Look at a Traditional Technique. 2009. (ENG., Illus.). 96p. pap. *(978-1-56477-870-3(3))* Martingale & Co.

Forlag, Arvinius, text. Swede Illustrations. 2009. (Illus.). 408p. *(978-981-245-338-9(5))* Page One Publishing.

LaBelle, Brandon, ed. Leif Elggren: Death Travels Backwards. 2011. (ENG., Illus.). 12p. 18.00 *(978-0-9827439-2-8(0))* Errant Bodies Pr.

Larsen, Lars Bang, ed. The Model: A Model for a Qualitative Society (1968) Palle Nielsen. 2010. 240p. pap. 35.00 *(978-84-92505-34-0(6))* Museu d'Art Contemporani de Barcelona ESP. Dist: Actar Birkhauser Distribution.

Leiderstam, Matts. Matts Leiderstam: Seen from Here. 2010. (ENG., Illus.). 144p. pap. 50.00 *(978-3-86984-029-1(3))* Verlag der Buchhandlung Walther Konig DEU. Dist: D.A.P./Distributed Art Pubs.

Lundberg, Helene S. Swedish Christmas Crafts. 2008. (ENG., Illus.). 96p. 14.95 *(978-1-60239-330-1(3))* Skyhorse Publishing Co., Inc.

Nilson, Greger Ulf. Swedish Red. Eneroth, Joakim, ed. & photos by by. 2011. (ENG., Illus.). 72p. 45.00 *(978-3-86521-613-7(7))* Steidl, Gerhard Druckerei und Verlag DEU. Dist: Innovative Logistics.

Nilsson, John Peter, ed. The Second Museum of Our Wishes, 1 vol. 2010. (ENG & SWE., Illus.). 140p. pap. 40.00 *(978-3-86930-145-7(7))* Steidl, Gerhard Druckerei und Verlag DEU. Dist: Innovative Logistics.

Ohman, Nina. Moderna Museet, Stockholm: A Celebration of 40 Years. 2006. (ENG., Illus.). 50.00 *(978-1-85759-178-1(X))* Scala, Editions FRA. Dist: National Bk. Network.

Tellgren, Anna, ed. Another Story: Photography from the Moderna Museet Collection, 1 vol. 2012. (ENG., Illus.). 340p. 65.00 ***(978-3-86930-384-0(0))*** Steidl, Gerhard Druckerei und Verlag DEU. Dist: Innovative Logistics.

Tunbjork, Lars & Ulf Nilson, Greger, eds. Year One, 1 vol. 2011. (ENG., Illus.). 240p. 45.00 *(978-3-86521-537-6(8))* Steidl, Gerhard Druckerei und Verlag DEU. Dist: Innovative Logistics.

Ulf Nilson, Greger & Petersen, Anders, eds. City Diary, 3 vols. 2011. (ENG., Illus.). 216p. 98.00 *(978-3-86521-536-9(X))* Steidl, Gerhard Druckerei und Verlag DEU. Dist: Innovative Logistics.

ART, SWISS

Andrés, Alberto de & Calame, Alexandre. Alpine Views: Alexandre Calame & the Swiss Landscape. 2006. (Illus.). 88p. *(978-0-931102-68-4(5))* Clark, Sterling & Francine Art Institute.

Antille, Emmanuelle, et al. Swiss Made: The Art of Falling Apart. 2006. (ENG & DUT., Illus.). 96p. pap. 35.00 *(978-90-400-9078-3(5))* Waanders B.V., Uitgeverij NLD. Dist: National Bk. Network.

Arenski, Jay, et al. Swiss Carvings: Art of the Black Forest. 2007. (ENG., Illus.). 184p. *(978-1-85149-493-4(6)*, Antique Collectors Club Dist) Antique Collectors' Club.

Armleder, John, illus. John Armleder: Pfcbdmrsrgbmnf Pcispsbmpfcbs, 5 vols. 2008. (ITA & ENG.). 88p. 15.00 *(978-3-905701-46-3(4))* JRP Ringier Kunstverlag AG CHE. Dist: D.A.P./Distributed Art Pubs.

Arns, Inke, et al. Mediale Kunst Zürich/Media Arts Zurich: 13 Positionen aus dem Studienbereich Neue Medien. 13 Positions from the New Media Program. 2008. (Illus.). 204p. 60.00 *(978-3-85881-210-0(2))* Scheidegger und Spiess AG, Verlag CHE. Dist: Antique Collectors' Club.

Asten, Astrid von & Schick, Karin. Sophie Taeuber-Arp 1889 - 1943: Bewegung und Gleichgewicht / Movement & Balance. 2010. (GER & ENG., Illus.). 160p. 50.00 *(978-3-86678-320-1(5))* Kerber Verlag DEU. Dist: D.A.P./Distributed Art Pubs.

Aubry, Bastien & Broquard, Dimitri. Bastien Aubrey & Dimitri Broquard: & Let There Be Light, 1 vol. 2007. (ENG., Illus.). 176p. pap. 22.00 *(978-3-905701-97-5(9))* JRP Ringier Kunstverlag AG CHE. Dist: D.A.P./Distributed Art Pubs.

Baur, Andreas. Fabrice Gygi. 2009. (ENG., Illus.). 176p. pap. 55.00 *(978-3-905829-44-0(4))* JRP Ringier Kunstverlag AG CHE. Dist: D.A.P./Distributed Art Pubs.

Benedetti, Lorenzo, et al. Max Bill: No Beginning, No End. Museum MARTa Herford Staff, ed. 2008. (Illus.). 200p. pap. 50.00 *(978-3-85881-214-8(5))* Scheidegger und Spiess AG, Verlag CHE. Dist: Chicago Distribution Ctr.

Berwick, John, tr. Masterpieces of the Kunsthaus Zurich. 2010. (ENG., Illus.). 44p. 30.00 *(978-3-7757-2545-3(8))* Hatje Cantz Verlag GmbH & Co KG DEU. Dist: D.A.P./Distributed Art Pubs.

Beyeler, Ernst & Mory, Christophe. A Passion for Art. 2012. (ENG., Illus.). 204p. 39.00 ***(978-3-85881-727-3(9))*** Scheidegger und Spiess AG, Verlag CHE. Dist: Antique Collectors' Club.

Bideau, Fabienne, et al, texts. Utopics: Systems & Landmarks. 2010. (ENG., Illus.). 162p. 45.00 *(978-3-03764-056-2(1))* JRP Ringier Kunstverlag AG CHE. Dist: D.A.P./Distributed Art Pubs.

Bisang, Bruno, photos by. Bruno Bisang: 30 Years of Polaroids. 2011. (ENG, GER, FRE, SPA & ITA., Illus.). 208p. 90.00 ***(978-3-8327-9530-6(8))*** teNeues Publishing Co.

Bloch, Peter Andre. Sils: Gerhard Richter. 2010. (GER, SPA & ENG., Illus.). 86p. 24.95 *(978-0-9559613-5-9(1))* Ivory Pr. ESP. Dist: Actar Birkhauser Distribution.

Bovier, Lionel, ed. ECAL: A Success Story in Art & Design. 2008. (ENG., Illus.). 390p. 49.00 *(978-3-905770-90-2(3))* JRP Ringier Kunstverlag AG CHE. Dist: D.A.P./Distributed Art Pubs.

—Philippe Decrauzat. Miller, Chris, tr. 2008. (ENG., Illus.). 64p. 30.00 *(978-3-905770-87-2(3))* JRP Ringier Kunstverlag AG CHE. Dist: D.A.P./Distributed Art Pubs.

Brändle, Christian, ed. François Berthoud Studio: Die Kunst der Modeillustration. 2011. (GER & ENG., Illus.). 240p. pap. 55.00 ***(978-3-7757-3014-3(1))*** Hatje Cantz Verlag GmbH & Co KG DEU. Dist: D.A.P./Distributed Art Pubs.

Braun, Ariane Kristina. Thomas Hirschhorns Bataille Monument: Ein ephemeres Denkmal auf der Documenta11. 2010. 124p. pap. *(978-3-639-27173-7(4))* VDM Verlag Dr. Mueller e.K.

Breuning, Olaf. Olaf Breuning: Queen Mary II. 2011. (ENG., Illus.). 152p. pap. 29.95 *(978-3-03764-160-6(6))* JRP Ringier Kunstverlag AG CHE. Dist: D.A.P./Distributed Art Pubs.

Brüggebors, Nadine, text. Andy Denzler Paintings: The Human Nature Project. 2011. (ENG., Illus.). 128p. 55.00 *(978-3-7757-2803-4(1))* Hatje Cantz Verlag GmbH & Co KG DEU. Dist: D.A.P./Distributed Art Pubs.

Buetti, Daniele, illus. Maybe You Can Be One of Us. 2008. (ENG.). 240p. 60.00 *(978-3-7757-2095-3(2))* Hatje Cantz Verlag GmbH & Co KG DEU. Dist: D.A.P./Distributed Art Pubs.

Bühler, Kathleen, et al. Switzerlart: A Collection of Swiss Art in Five Chapters. 2011. (ENG., Illus.). 380p. 29.95 ***(978-3-03764-164-4(9))*** JRP Ringier Kunstverlag AG CHE. Dist: D.A.P./Distributed Art Pubs.

Cavadini, Nicoletta Ossanna. Bruno Monguzzi: Fifty Years of Paper, 1961-2011. 2011. (ENG., Illus.). 256p. pap. 55.00 ***(978-88-572-1105-3(3))*** Skira Editore ITA. Dist: Random Hse., Inc.

Cherix, Christophe, et al, texts. Francis Baudevin: Miscellaneous Abstract. 2010. (ENG., Illus.). 160p. pap. 55.00 *(978-3-03764-067-8(7))* JRP Ringier Kunstverlag AG CHE. Dist: D.A.P./Distributed Art Pubs.

Comte, Michel, photos by. Michel Comte: Not Only Women. 2011. (ENG., Illus.). 72p. pap. 28.00 ***(978-88-366-1875-0(8))*** Silvana ITA. Dist: D.A.P./Distributed Art Pubs.

Cueff, Alain & Maurer, Simon. Marie jose Burki: These Days, 1 vol. 2007. (ENG., Illus.). 176p. 50.00 *(978-3-86521-479-9(7))* Steidl, Gerhard Druckerei und Verlag DEU. Dist: Innovative Logistics.

Drescher, Jürgen, et al. Jürgen Drescher: Arbeiten Bis Heute: Galerie Isabella Czarnowska, Berlin, Mai 36 Galerie Zürich. 2008. (GER & ENG., Illus.). 144p. 64.00 *(978-3-86560-330-2(0))* Verlag der Buchhandlung Walther Konig DEU. Dist: D.A.P./Distributed Art Pubs.

Effendi, Rena, photos by. Pipe Dreams: A Chronicle of Lives along the Pipeline. 2010. (ENG.). 176p. 55.00 *(978-90-5330-695-6(1))* Mets en Schilt Uitgevers NLD. Dist: Ingram Pub. Services.

Egli, Michael, et al. Meisterwerke und Kleinode: Sammlung der Peyerschen Tobias Stimmer-Stiftung, Museum zu Allerheiligen, Schaffhausen. Gesamtkatalog. The Swiss Institute for Art Research SIK-ISEA. Essays by Walter R. C. Abegglen, ed. 2010. (Illus.). 156p. ***(978-3-85881-135-6(1))*** Antique Collectors' Club.

Essays, Zürich, et al. Sophie Taeuber-Arp: Gestalterin, Architektin, Tänzerin. 2008. (Illus.). 72p. 49.00 *(978-3-85881-196-7(3))* Scheidegger und Spiess AG, Verlag CHE. Dist: Antique Collectors' Club.

Faure, Nicolas, photos by. Landscape A, 1 vol. 2008. (ENG., Illus.). 144p. 55.00 *(978-3-86521-212-2(3))* Steidl, Gerhard Druckerei und Verlag DEU. Dist: Innovative Logistics.

Favre, Valerie. Valerie Favre: Visions. 2009. (ENG., Illus.). 208p. 45.00 *(978-3-7757-2443-2(5))* Hatje Cantz Verlag GmbH & Co KG DEU. Dist: D.A.P./Distributed Art Pubs.

Federal Office for Culture, Bern, ed. Swiss Federal Design Awards 2011: Prix fédéraux de design 2011 / Eidgenössische Preise für Design. 2011. (ENG, FRE & GER.). 208p. pap. 39.95 ***(978-3-0346-0795-7(4))*** Birkhauser Verlag AG CHE. Dist: Actar Birkhauser Distribution.

Felzmann, Lukas & Pfrunder, Peter. Swarm. 2011. (ENG., Illus.). 112p. 70.00 ***(978-3-03778-241-5(2))*** Lars Muller Pubs. CHE. Dist: Prestel Publishing.

Frehner, Matthias, frwd. Yves Netzhammer: the Refuge for Drawbacks. 2011. (ENG., Illus.). 136p. 50.00 ***(978-3-86984-158-8(3))*** Verlag fur Moderne Kunst DEU. Dist: D.A.P./Distributed Art Pubs.

Gastaldon, Vidya. Vidya Gastaldon: Call It What You Like. 2009. (ENG., Illus.). 160p. pap. 45.00 *(978-3-905829-84-6(3))* JRP Ringier Kunstverlag AG CHE. Dist: D.A.P./Distributed Art Pubs.

Godinat, Aloïs. Aloïs Godinat. Bovier, Lionel, ed. 2010. (ENG., Illus.). 64p. 35.00 *(978-3-03764-044-9(8))* JRP Ringier Kunstverlag AG CHE. Dist: D.A.P./Distributed Art Pubs.

Goetz, Ingvild & Urbaschek, Stephan, eds. Peter Fischli, David Weiss. 2011. (ENG & GER., Illus.). 192p. 55.00 *(978-3-7757-2735-8(3))* Hatje Cantz Verlag GmbH & Co KG DEU. Dist: D.A.P./Distributed Art Pubs.

Haemmerli, Thomas & Kung, Max. Hannes Wettstein: Seeking Archetypes. 2011. (FRE, GER & ENG., Illus.). 300p. 85.00 ***(978-3-03778-265-1(X))*** Lars Muller Pubs. CHE. Dist: Prestel Publishing.

Halpern, Emanuel. Emanuel Halpern: Diselbrugger Apokalypse. 2011. (ENG., Illus.). 56p. 45.00 ***(978-3-905714-89-0(2))*** Nieves CHE. Dist: D.A.P./Distributed Art Pubs.

Hatebur, Barbara. Sammlung Credit Suisse: Kunst im Geschäftsumfeld. Credit Suisse Art Staff & Rogger, André, eds. 2011. (ENG., Illus.). 464p. 110.00 *(978-3-85881-324-4(9))* Scheidegger und Spiess AG, Verlag CHE. Dist: Antique Collectors' Club.

Herzog, Hans-Michael & Steffen, Katrin, eds. Painted: Beate Gunther, Richard Allen Morris, Guillermo Kuitca. 2009. (ENG., Illus.). 172p. pap. 60.00 *(978-3-7757-2328-2(5))* Hatje Cantz Verlag GmbH & Co KG DEU. Dist: D.A.P./Distributed Art Pubs.

Heuser, Mechthild. Tell im Visier: Plakate aus der Schweizerischen Nationalbibliothek. 2010. (GER., Illus.). 392p. pap. 81.00 ***(978-3-85881-202-5(1))*** Scheidegger und Spiess AG, Verlag CHE. Dist: Antique Collectors' Club.

Hirschhorn, Thomas & Bizzarri, Thomas, eds. Thomas Hirschhorn: Establishing a Critical Corpus. 2011. (ENG., Illus.). 365p. 44.95 ***(978-3-03764-185-9(1))*** JRP Ringier Kunstverlag AG CHE. Dist: D.A.P./Distributed Art Pubs.

Janser, Andres & Junod, Barbara, eds. Corporate Diversity: Swiss Graphic Design & Advertising by Geigy 1940 - 1970. 2009. (Illus.). 208p. pap. *(978-3-03778-160-9(2))* Lars Muller Pubs.

Julin, Richard & Praun, Tessa, eds. Pipilotti Rist Congratulations! 2007. (Illus.). 159p. 34.95 *(978-3-03778-108-1(4)*, 3037781084) Springer.

Keller, Walter & Tettamanti, Joël. Davos. 2010. (Illus.). 136p. 80.00 *(978-3-85881-298-8(6))* Scheidegger und Spiess AG, Verlag CHE. Dist: Antique Collectors' Club.

Kesser, Caroline. Jan Krugier: My Journey with Art - Interviews with Caroline Kesser. 2012. (ENG., Illus.). 150p. 49.00 *(978-3-85881-719-8(8))* Scheidegger und Spiess AG, Verlag CHE. Dist: Antique Collectors' Club.

Keusch, Beat & Voss, Jan, eds. Dieter Roth: Souvenirs. 2011. (GER & ENG., Illus.). 152p. 85.00 ***(978-3-7757-2818-8(X))*** Hatje Cantz Verlag GmbH & Co KG DEU. Dist: D.A.P./Distributed Art Pubs.

Kurjakovic, Daniel, ed. Album: On & Around Urs Fischer, Yves Netzhammer, Ugo Rondinone, & Christine Streuli, Participating at the 52nd Venice Biennale 2007, 1 vol. 2007. (ENG., Illus.). 320p. per. 25.00 *(978-3-905770-70-4(9))* JRP Ringier Kunstverlag AG CHE. Dist: D.A.P./Distributed Art Pubs.

Kurzmeyer, Roman. Viereck und Kosmos: Kunstler, Lebensreformer, Okkultisten, Spiritisten in Amden 1901-1912. Max Nopper, Josua Klein, Fidus, Otto Meyer-Amden. (Edition Voldemeer Ser.). (GER., Illus.). 258p. 44.95 *(978-3-211-83371-1(4)*, 3211833714) Springer.

Lange, Christiane & Diederen, Roger, eds. Das Ewige Auge: Von Rembrandt bis Picasso. Meisterwerke der Sammlung Jan Krugier und Marie-Anne Krugier-Poniatowski. 2007. (GER., Illus.). 511p. (C). 56.00 *(978-3-7774-3695-1(X))* Hirmer Verlag GmbH DEU. Dist: Brown, David Bk. Co., The.

Lange, Christiane & Frehner, Matthias. Giacometti, Hodler, Klee. Das Kunstmuseum Bern zu Gast: Katalog zur Ausstellung in München, Kunsthalle der Hypo-Kulturstiftung; 17.09.2010-09.01.2111. Frehner, Matthias & Lange, C., eds. 2010. (GER., Illus.). 236p. (C). 59.00 *(978-3-7774-2931-1(7))* Hirmer Verlag GmbH DEU. Dist: Brown, David Bk. Co., The.

Lohse, Richard. Richard Paul Lohse. Drucke Prints: Dokumentation + Werkverzeichnis, Documentation + Catalogue raisonnè. 2009. (ENG., Illus.). 472p. 120.00 *(978-3-7757-2309-1(9))* Hatje Cantz Verlag GmbH & Co KG DEU. Dist: D.A.P./Distributed Art Pubs.

Luthi, Urs. Urs Luthi: Art Is the Better Life. 2010. (ENG., Illus.). 1824p. lthr. 69.00 *(978-3-907474-51-8(1))* Periferia, Edizioni, Poschiavo / Lucerna CHE. Dist: D.A.P./Distributed Art Pubs.

Marty, Urs. Urs Marty. 2010. (ENG., Illus.). 276p. 65.00 *(978-3-86930-041-2(8))* Steidl, Gerhard Druckerei und Verlag DEU. Dist: D.A.P./Distributed Art Pubs.

Maurer, Simon, ed. & text. Klaudia Schifferle: sumsum im Universum. 2011. (ENG., Illus.). 108p. 45.00 *(978-3-86984-155-7(9))* Verlag fur Moderne Kunst DEU. Dist: D.A.P./Distributed Art Pubs.

Moos, Stanislaus von. Nicht Disneyland: Und Andere Aufsätze über Modernität und Nostalgie. 2010. (GER., Illus.). 240p. 78.00 ***(978-3-85881-162-2(9))*** Scheidegger und Spiess AG, Verlag CHE. Dist: Antique Collectors' Club.

Mora, Gilles, ed. & text. A Kind of Infatuation, 1 vol. 2009. (ENG., Illus.). 312p. 78.00 *(978-3-86521-830-8(X))* Steidl, Gerhard Druckerei und Verlag DEU. Dist: Innovative Logistics.

Mossinger, Ingrid, ed. Cesare Lucchini: What Remains. 2009. (ENG., Illus.). 120p. 45.00 *(978-3-86678-213-6(6))* Kerber Verlag DEU. Dist: D.A.P./Distributed Art Pubs.

Muller, Franz. Martin Disler. 2007. (Illus.). 272p. 152.00 ***(978-3-85881-179-0(3))*** Scheidegger und Spiess AG, Verlag CHE. Dist: Antique Collectors' Club.

Müller, Lars, ed. Helvetica Forever: Story of a Typeface. 2008. (Illus.). 128p. 39.95 *(978-3-03778-121-0(1)*, 3037781211) Springer.

Munch, Andreas, ed. Fabrice Gygi: A Manual. 2010. (ENG., Illus.). 224p. pap. 35.00 *(978-3-03764-057-9(X))* JRP Ringier Kunstverlag AG CHE. Dist: D.A.P./Distributed Art Pubs.

Munder, Heike, ed. Robert Kusmirowski. 2009. (ENG., Illus.). 68p. pap. 75.00 *(978-3-905770-52-0(0))* JRP Ringier Kunstverlag AG CHE. Dist: D.A.P./Distributed Art Pubs.

Museum für Gestaltung Zürich. Paradise Switzerland. 2010. 96p. pap. 35.00 *(978-3-03778-205-7(6))* Lars Muller Pubs. CHE. Dist: Prestel Publishing.

Nashat, Shahryar. Shahryar Nashat: Downscaled & Overthrown. 2011. (Illus.). 157p. 32.00 ***(978-1-934105-26-9(0))*** Sternberg Pr.

Netzhammer. Yves Netzhammer. 2009. (GER & ENG., Illus.). 216p. 60.00 *(978-3-7757-2318-3(8))* Hatje Cantz Verlag GmbH & Co KG DEU. Dist: D.A.P./Distributed Art Pubs.

Nguyen, Cat Tuong & Olonetzky, Nadine. Underdog Suite: Fotografien und Collagen 1996-2009. 2010. (Illus.). 312p. 95.00 *(978-3-85881-237-7(4))* Scheidegger und Spiess AG, Verlag CHE. Dist: Antique Collectors' Club.

Niederer, Caro. Waiting for Returns. 2010. (ENG., Illus.). 128p. 45.00 *(978-3-86521-628-1(5))* Steidl, Gerhard Druckerei und Verlag DEU. Dist: D.A.P./Distributed Art Pubs.

Obrist, Hans Ulrich, ed. Hans Ulrich Obrist & Cedric Price: the Conversation Series. 2010. (ENG., Illus.). 172p. pap. 35.00 *(978-3-86560-093-6(X))* Verlag der Buchhandlung Walther Konig DEU. Dist: D.A.P./Distributed Art Pubs.

Oppenheim, Meret. Meret Oppenheim: Brunnengeschichten. 2010. (ENG & GER., Illus.). 128p. 40.00 *(978-3-7757-2590-3(3))* Hatje Cantz Verlag GmbH & Co KG DEU. Dist: D.A.P./Distributed Art Pubs.

Peppiatt, Michael & Giacometti, Alberto. Nello Studio Di Giacometti/Michael Peppiatt. 2011. (ITA., Illus.). 219p. ***(978-88-370-8507-0(9))*** Electa.

Perret, Roger & Kurzmeyer, Roman, eds. Dunkelschwestern. Annemarie von Matt - Sonja Sekula. 2008. (Illus.). 368p. 147.00 *(978-3-85881-213-1(7))* Scheidegger und Spiess AG, Verlag CHE. Dist: Antique Collectors' Club.

Pong, Elodie. Elodie Pong: We Are Knights on the Trajectories of a Post-Everything Era. 2008. (ENG., Illus.). 64p. pap. 15.00 *(978-3-905701-36-4(7))* JRP Ringier Kunstverlag AG CHE. Dist: D.A.P./Distributed Art Pubs.

Reifenscheid, Beate & Morsbach, Christiane. Daniel Spoerri: Eaten by ... 2010. (GER & ENG., Illus.). 144p. 49.50 *(978-3-86678-342-3(6))* Kerber Verlag DEU. Dist: D.A.P./Distributed Art Pubs.

Reinhard-Felice, Mariantonia, ed. Oskar Reinhart Collection 'Am Römerholz' Winterthur: Complete Catalogue. 2006. (Illus.). 712p. (C). 120.00 *(978-1-903470-38-1(2))* Holberton, Paul Publishing GBR. Dist: Casemate Pubs. & Bk. Distributors, LLC.

Rivolta, Francis, intro. Morphing Systems. (ENG & GER., Illus.). 218p. pap. 39.95 *(978-3-905509-30-4(X))* Frey, Patrick Edition im Verlag der Alltag CHE. Dist: D.A.P./Distributed Art Pubs.

Rosenthal, Stephanie, ed. Pipilotti Rist. 2011. (ENG., Illus.). 200p. 40.00 ***(978-1-85332-295-2(4))*** Hayward Gallery Publishing GBR. Dist: D.A.P./Distributed Art Pubs.

Ruedin, Pascal. Beaux-arts et représentation Nationale: La participation des artites suisses aux expositions universelles de Paris (1855-1900) 2010. (atelier. Travaux d'Histoire de l'art et de Muséologie/das Atelier. Arbeiten zur Kunstgeschichte und Museumskunde/the Workshop. Art History & Museum Studies). (FRE.). 693p. pap. *(978-3-0343-0041-4(7))* Lang, Peter.

Schneider, Nadia, ed. Alberto Giacometti: Retrospective. 2010. (ENG., Illus.). 280p. 45.00 *(978-3-03764-060-9(X))* JRP Ringier Kunstverlag AG CHE. Dist: D.A.P./Distributed Art Pubs.

Spoerri, Daniel. Daniel Spoerri: Weißt Du, Schwarzt Du? 2011. (GER & ENG., Illus.). 160p. 40.00 ***(978-3-86678-447-5(3))*** Kerber Verlag DEU. Dist: D.A.P./Distributed Art Pubs.

Stadler, Hilar, ed. Die kolorierten Lichtbilder des Ballonpioniers Eduard Spelterini. 2010. (GER & ENG., Illus.). 152p. 55.00 *(978-3-85881-303-9(6))* Scheidegger und Spiess AG, Verlag CHE. Dist: Antique Collectors' Club.

Stauffer, Karl, et al. "Verfluchter Kerl!" Karl Stauffer-Bern, Maler, Radierer, Plastiker. 2007. (Illus.). 240p. *(978-3-03823-362-6(5))* Neue Zurcher Zeitung, NZZ, Buchverlag.

Stutzer, Beat, et al. Corsin Fontana: Werke 1966 - 2009. Stutzer, Beat, ed. 2010. (Illus.). 288p. ***(978-3-85881-292-6(7))*** Antique Collectors' Club.

Suter, H. Paul Klee & His Illness: Bowed but Not Broken by Suffering & AdversityTranslated from the German by G. Mckay; N. Mckay. 2010. (ENG., Illus.). 272p. *(978-3-8055-9381-6(3))* Karger, S. AG.

Swiss Institute for Art Research Staff, ed. Hodler: Catalogue Raisonné der Gemälde. Band 1 - Die Landschaften, 2 vols. 2nd ed. 2009. (GER., Illus.). 700p. 900.00 *(978-3-85881-244-5(7))* Scheidegger und Spiess AG, Verlag CHE. Dist: Antique Collectors' Club.

Turrell, James. James Turrell: Zug Zuoz. 2010. (ENG., Illus.). 176p. 60.00 *(978-3-7757-2602-3(0))* Hatje Cantz Verlag GmbH & Co KG DEU. Dist: D.A.P./Distributed Art Pubs.

Uhlig, Helmut. On the Path to Enlightenment: The Berti Aschmann Foundation of Tibetan Art at the Museum Rietberg Zürich. 2011. (ENG., Illus.). 226p. (C). 50.00 *(978-3-907070-60-4(7))* Holberton, Paul Publishing GBR. Dist: Univ. of Washington Pr.

Van Dijk, Maite, et al. Sculptuur Studies 2006. 2007. (ENG., Illus.). 160p. pap. 30.00 *(978-90-400-8258-0(8))* Waanders B.V., Uitgeverij NLD. Dist: National Bk. Network.

Varadinis, Mirjam. Shifting Identities: (Swiss) Art Now: This Publication Is Released on the Occasion of the Exhibition Shifting Identities - (Swiss) Art Now at Kunsthaus Zürich from June 6th to August 31st, 2008. Varadinis, Mirjam, ed. 2008. (ENG., Illus.). 240p. pap. 55.00 *(978-3-905829-70-9(3))* JRP Ringier Kunstverlag AG CHE. Dist: D.A.P./Distributed Art Pubs.

Von Moos, Stanislaus. Max Huber. 2011. (ENG., Illus.). 240p. pap. 45.00 *(978-0-7148-6110-4(3))* Phaidon Pr., Inc.

Walter, Bernadette, text. Verena Loewensberg: Prints. 2009. (ENG., Illus.). 112p. pap. 38.00 *(978-3-905714-51-7(5))* Nieves CHE. Dist: D.A.P./Distributed Art Pubs.

Wekua, Andro. Andro Wekua: Workshop Report. 2010. (ENG., Illus.). 48p. 39.95 *(978-3-86560-648-8(2))* Verlag der Buchhandlung Walther Konig DEU. Dist: D.A.P./Distributed Art Pubs.

Wertenschlag-Birkhauser, Eva. Windows on Eternity: The Paintings of Peter Birkhauser. 2008. 198p. 49.00 *(978-3-85630-715-8(X))* Daimon Verlag CHE. Dist: AtlasBooks Distribution.

Weski, Thomas, et al. Photography, Made in Zürich. Weski, Thomas, ed. 2007. (Illus.). 300p. 35.00 *(978-3-85881-187-5(4))* Scheidegger und Spiess AG, Verlag CHE. Dist: Antique Collectors' Club.

Wiedemann, Pascale, et al. Morbus infinitus & Subkutan, 2 vols. 2008. (GER & ENG., Illus.). 184p. 60.00 *(978-3-85881-206-3(4))* Scheidegger und Spiess AG, Verlag CHE. Dist: Antique Collectors' Club.

Wisniewska, Karina. Karina Wisniewska. Bewegte Stille - Silent Dynamism. Von Burg, Dominique, ed. 2010. (ENG., Illus.). 176p. *(978-3-7165-1577-8(9)*, Benteli Verlags Ag Dist) Antique Collectors' Club.

Yersin, Veronique, ed. Forde 1994-2009. 2010. (ENG., Illus.). 522p. pap. 45.00 *(978-3-03764-082-1(0))* JRP Ringier Kunstverlag AG CHE. Dist: D.A.P./Distributed Art Pubs.

ART, TANTRIC

see Tantric Art

ART, THAI

Assavavirulhakarn, Prapod, et al. Past Lives of the Bhudda: Wat Si Chum & the Art of Sukhothai. 2007. (Illus.). 350p. 60.00 *(978-974-9863-22-0(4))* River Bks. THA. Dist: Antique Collectors' Club.

Brown, Roxanna Maude. Ming Gap & Shipwreck Ceramics in Southeast Asia: Towards a Chronology of Thai Trade Ware. 2009. (ENG., Illus.). 206p. 50.00 *(978-974-9863-77-0(1))* River Bks. THA. Dist: Antique Collectors' Club.

Clark, John. Asian Modernities: Chinese & Thai Art Compared, 1980-1999. 2011. (ENG., Illus.). 288p. (C). pap. 59.95 *(978-0-909952-38-9(8))* Power Pubns. AUS. Dist: Univ. of Washington Pr.

Krairiksh, Piriya. Roots of Thai Art. 2012. (ENG., Illus.). 360p. 65.00 ***(978-616-7339-11-5(2))*** River Bks. THA. Dist: Antique Collectors' Club.

Le May, Reginald. A Concise History of Buddhist Art in Siam. 2011. 278p. 47.95 ***(978-1-258-06111-1(2))*** Literary Licensing, LLC.

McGill, Forrest & Chirapravati, M. L. Pattaratorn. Emerald Cities: Arts of Siam & Burma 1775-1950. 2009. (ENG., Illus.). 224p. 49.00 *(978-0-939117-50-5(9))* Asian Art Museum of San Francisco.

Skilling, Peter, et al. Past Lives of the Buddha: Wat Si Chum-Art, Architecture & Inscriptions. 2008. (ENG., Illus.). 296p. 75.00 *(978-974-9863-45-9(3))* River Bks. THA. Dist: Antique Collectors' Club.

Suksri, Naengnoi & Piammattawat, Paisarn. Grand Palace & Rattanakosin Island. 2012. (ENG., Illus.). 230p. pap. 30.00 *(978-974-9863-41-1(0))* River Bks. THA. Dist: Antique Collectors' Club.

Tiravanija, Rirkrit. Rirkrit Tiravanija's Soccer Half-Time Cookery Book: Kochbuch Für Die Halbzeit Pause, 1 vol. 2006. (GER & ENG., Illus.). 64p. pap. 35.00 *(978-3-938821-40-4(X))* Verlag fur Moderne Kunst DEU. Dist: D.A.P./Distributed Art Pubs.

ART, TIBETAN

Baker, Ian. Goddesses of the Celestial Gallery. 2011. (ENG., Illus.). 64p. 24.95 *(978-1-60887-022-6(7))* Palace Pr. International.

Buckley, Chris. Tibetan Furniture. 2006. (ENG., Illus.). 240p. 60.00 *(978-1-891640-20-9(8))* Floating World Editions.

Casey, Jane, et al. Divine Presence: Arts of India & the Himalayas. 2006. (Illus.). *(978-88-7439-022-9(X))* 5 Continents.

Elliot, Sanje. How to Write Tibetan Calligraphy: The Alphabet & Beyond. 2012. (ENG.). 96p. pap. 14.95 ***(978-0-86171-699-9(X))*** Wisdom Pubns.

Harris, Clare. The Museum on the Roof of the World: Art, Politics, & the Representation of Tibet. 2012. (Buddhism & Modernity Ser.). (Illus.). 336p. 45.00 ***(978-0-226-31747-2(1))*** Univ. of Chicago Pr.

Heller, Amy. Hidden Treasures of the Himalayas: Tibetan Manuscripts, Paintings & Sculptures of Dolpo. 2009. *(978-1-932476-44-6(X))* Serindia Pubns., Inc.

Jackson, David & Jackson, Janice A. Tibetan Thangka Painting: Methods & Materials. 2006. (ENG., Illus.). 208p. pap. 39.95 *(978-1-55939-257-0(6))* Snow Lion Pubns., Inc.

Jackson, David P. Mirror of the Budda: Early Portraits from Tibet, 1 vol. 2011. (ENG., Illus.). 240p. 75.00 *(978-0-9845190-2-6(5))* Rubin Museum of Art.

Jackson, David P. Mirror of the Buddha: Early Portraits from Tibet. 2011. (ENG., Illus.). pap. 75.00 ***(978-0-9845190-3-3(3))*** Rubin Museum of Art.

Klimburg-Salter, Deborah, et al, eds. Text, Image & Song in Transdisciplinary Dialogue. 2007. (Brill's Tibetan Studies Library: Vol. 10). (Illus.). 247p. incl. audio compact disk *(978-90-04-15549-7(X))* BRILL.

Landaw, Jonathan & Weber, Andy. Images of Enlightenment: Tibetan Art in Practice. 2006. (ENG., Illus.). 272p. pap. 24.95 *(978-1-55939-258-7(4))* Snow Lion Pubns., Inc.

Rhie, Marylin & Thurman, Robert. A Shrine for Tibet: The Alice S. Kandell Collection of Tibetan Sacred Art. 2010. (ENG.). 336p. (gr. 12). 60.00 *(978-1-59020-310-1(0))* Overlook Pr., The.

Rhie, Marylin M. & Thurman, Robert A. F. A Shrine for Tibet: The Alice S. Kandell Collection. 2009. *(978-0-9670115-7-8(4))* Overlook Pr., The.

Schrempf, Mona, ed. Proceedings of the Tenth Seminar of the IATS, 2003, Volume 10 Soundings in Tibetan Medicine: Anthropological & Historical Perspectives. 2007. 450p. *(978-90-04-15550-3(3))* BRILL.

Shrestha, Romio, creator. Celestial Gallery. 2009. (ENG.). 64p. 24.95 *(978-1-60109-051-5(X))* Mandala Publishing.

Shrestha, Romio & Baker, Ian. Buddhas of the Celestial Gallery. 2012. (ENG., Illus.). 64p. 75.00 *(978-1-60109-060-7(9))* Mandala Publishing.

Veleanu, Mircea. Tibetan Artifacts. 2009. (Illus.). 256p. bds. 59.99 *(978-0-7643-3360-6(7))* Schiffer Publishing, Ltd.

Verlag, Hirmer & Hirmer Verlag. Tibet: Kloester oeffnen ihre Schatzkammern. 2006. (GER., Illus.). 664p. (C). pap. 63.00 *(978-3-7774-3115-4(X))* Hirmer Verlag GmbH DEU. Dist: Brown, David Bk. Co., The.

Williamson, Laila & Young, Serinity, eds. Body & Spirit: Tibetan Medical Paintings. 2009. (ENG., Illus.). 264p. pap. 45.00 *(978-0-295-98869-6(X))* Univ. of Washington Pr.

ART, TURKISH

Ballian, Anna. Relics of the Past: Treasusres of the Greek Orthodox Church & the Population Exchange. 2011. (ENG & FRE., Illus.). 232p. pap. 42.50 *(978-88-7439-575-0(2))* 5 Continents ITA. Dist: Hachette Bk. Group.

Barlas, Seyda. Visions of Aesthetics & Culture in Yeni Adam. 2010. 184p. pap. *(978-3-639-26956-7(X))* VDM Verlag Dr. Mueller e.K.

Cameron, Dan, text. Taner Ceylan: 1997-2009. 2011. (ENG., Illus.). 184p. 50.00 ***(978-88-6208-173-3(1))*** Damiani ITA. Dist: D.A.P./Distributed Art Pubs.

Curatola, Giovanni, ed. Turkish Art & Architecture: From the Seljuks to the Ottomans. 2010. (ENG., Illus.). 280p. 95.00 *(978-0-7892-1082-1(7))* Abbeville Pr., Inc.

Diba, Layla S. Turkmen Jewelry: Silver Ornaments from the Marshall & Marilyn R. Wolf Collection. 2011. (ENG., Illus.). 264p. 60.00 *(978-0-300-12404-0(X))* Yale Univ. Pr.

Ermacora, Beate, ed. Simon Wachsmuth: Aporia/Europa. 2011. (ENG., Illus.). 104p. 37.50 ***(978-3-86678-448-2(1))*** Kerber Verlag DEU. Dist: D.A.P./Distributed Art Pubs.

Gans, Ulrich-Walter. Attalidische Herrscherbildnisse: Studien Zur Hellenistischen Porträtplastik Pergamons. 2006. (Philippika Ser.). (GER., Illus.). 184p. (C). pap. 72.00 *(978-3-447-05430-0(1))* Harrassowitz, Otto Verlag DEU. Dist: ISD.

Isn, Ekrem. Saltanatn Dervisleri Dervislerin Saltanat: Istanbul'da Mevlevîlik = the Dervishes of Sovereignty, the Sovereignty of Dervishes: The Mevlevî Order in Istanbul. 2007. (TUR & ENG., Illus.). 274p. *(978-975-9123-41-3(X))* Suna Ve Inan Kirac Vakfi.

Karamustafa, Gülsün. Gulsun Karamustafa: Etiquette. 2011. (ENG., Illus.). 84p. pap. 35.00 ***(978-3-86984-180-9(X))*** Verlag fur Moderne Kunst DEU. Dist: D.A.P./Distributed Art Pubs.

Kula, Ömür. The Rupture in Visual Language. 2010. 236p. pap. *(978-3-639-25468-6(6))* VDM Verlag Dr. Mueller e.K.

Nachtig#xE4;ller, Roland, pref. Spagat! Istanbul Design. 2011. (ENG., Illus.). 320p. 44.95 ***(978-3-86678-493-2(7))*** Kerber Verlag DEU. Dist: D.A.P./Distributed Art Pubs.

Zhan Yüksel, Serra. Satiyorum, Satiyorum, Sattim! 2011. 52p. pap. **(978-3-8433-8810-8(5))** Lambert Academic Publishing.

Parrella, Christiana. Kutlug Ataman: Mesopotamian Dramaturgies. 2011. (ENG., Illus.). 112p. pap. 55.00 *(978-88-370-7578-1(2))* Electa ITA. Dist: National Bk. Network.

Roberts, Mary. Intimate Outsiders: The Harem in Ottoman & Orientalist Art & Travel Literature. 2007. (Objects/Histories Ser.). (ENG., Illus.). 248p. per. 23.95 *(978-0-8223-3967-0(6))*; (C). 84.95 *(978-0-8223-3956-4(0))* Duke Univ. Pr.

Schilling, J#xFC;rgen & Scholz, Dieter, texts. Dennis Gun. 2011. (ENG., Illus.). 110p. 85.00 **(978-3-7757-2793-8(0))** Hatje Cantz Verlag GmbH & Co KG DEU. Dist: D.A.P./Distributed Art Pubs.

Schmitz, Britta, ed. Ays Erkmen: Weggefährten. 2009. (GER & ENG., Illus.). 224p. pap. 45.00 *(978-3-86560-516-0(8))* Verlag der Buchhandlung Walther Konig DEU. Dist: D.A.P./Distributed Art Pubs.

Serrano Marqués, Mercedes & Piñar Samos, Javier. En Los Confines de un Mismo Mar: Los Palacios de la Alhambra y Topkapi en la Fotografía Del Viaje a Oriente/Ayni Denizin Uçlarinda: Dogu'ya Yolculugun Fotografinda el Hamra Ve Topkapi Saraylari. 2009. (Illus.). 220p. *(978-84-92441-65-5(8))*; *(978-84-96933-33-0(4))* Sociedad Estatal para la Accion Cultural Exterior, S.A.

Signell, Karl. Makam: Modal Practice innTurkish Art Music. 2008. 215p. per. 20.00 *(978-0-9760455-1-9(6))* Usul Editions.

Soganci, Ismail Ozgur. An Interdisciplinary Study of Problematizing a Curricular Muteness. 2010. 352p. pap. *(978-3-8383-5682-2(5))* Lambert Academic Publishing.

Turkey. 176p. pap. *(978-88-8029-563-1(2))* Casa Editrice Bonechi.

Veryeri-Alaca, Ilgim. Ilgim Veryeri-Alaca: Recent Prints & Drawings. 2007. (Illus.). 14p. *(978-0-9765047-4-0(X))* Univ. of Richmond Museums.

Williams, Jennette. The Bathers. 2009. (Center for Documentary Studies/Honickman First Book Prize in Photography Ser.). (ENG., Illus.). 72p. 39.95 *(978-0-8223-4623-4(0))* Duke Univ. Pr.

ART, UKRAINIAN

Arendar, Hanna. Silver Tableware of the 17th-20th Centuries: Collection in the V.V. Tarnovsky Chernihiv Historical Museum, Ukraine. 2010. (ENG & UKR.). 176p. 49.00 *(978-966-7845-25-4(7),* Art Stock Bks. Ltd/Csi) Continental Sales, Inc.

Bobrovskyi, Tymur, et al. Materialy Kruhloho Stolu "Zasnuvannia Sofiiskoho Soboru V Kyievi: Problemy Novykh Datuvan" (7 Kvitnia 2010 R., M. Kyiv) 2010. (UKR., Illus.). 119p. *(978-966-02-5649-1(3))* National Academy of Sciences of Ukraine.

Foundation for International Arts and Education Staff, et al, contrib. by. The Glory of Ukraine: Sacred Images from the 11th to the 19th Centuries: For Exhibition at Museum of Biblical Art, New York, New York: Meridian International Center, Washington, DC: Joslyn Art Museum, Omaha, Nebraska. 2010. (Illus.). viii, 176p. *(978-0-9678451-7-3(3))* Foundation for International Arts & Education.

Hoptman, Laura, et al. Tomma Abts. 2008. (ENG., Illus.). 135p. 49.95 *(978-0-7148-4882-2(4))* Phaidon Pr., Inc.

Humesky, Assya. Mirtala Pylypenko: Skulptor I Poet. 2007. (UKR., Illus.). 135p. *(978-966-658-093-4(4))* Misioner.

Makaryk, Irena R. & Tkacz, Viriana. Modernism in Kyiv: Jubilant Experimentation. 2010. (Illus.). 680p. *(978-1-4426-4098-6(7))* Univ. of Toronto Pr.

Oliva, Achille Bonito, et al, texts. Oksana Mas. 2012. (ENG., Illus.). 136p. pap. 39.95 **(978-88-8158-826-8(9))** Charta ITA. Dist: D.A.P./Distributed Art Pubs.

Ruban, Valentyna & Demko, Alexander, frwds. Paintings from the Estate of Vasyl Hryhorovych Krychevsky. ltd. ed. 2007. (Illus.). 136p. 25.00 *(978-0-9771995-2-5(5))* Zorya Fine Art, LLC.

Seelig, Thomas, et al. Sergey Bratkov: Glory Days / Heldenzeiten. Eine ausgewählte Werkübersicht 1995-2007. Seelig, Thomas & De Baere, Bart, eds. 2008. (GER & ENG., Illus.). 208p. 70.00 *(978-3-85881-218-6(8))* Scheidegger und Spiess AG, Verlag CHE. Dist: Antique Collectors' Club.

St. Bushak, V. & Sakharuk, I. Cossack Mamai. 2010. (ENG & UKR.). 304p. 79.00 *(978-966-7845-40-7(0),* Art Stock Bks. Ltd/Csi) Continental Sales, Inc.

ART, WEARABLE

see Wearable Art

ART, YUGOSLAV

McEvilley, Thomas. Art, Love, Friendship: Marina Abramovic & Ulay, Together & Apart. 2010. (Illus.). 304p. 27.00 *(978-0-929701-93-6(3),* Documentext) McPherson & Co.

Oliva, Achille Bonito, et al, texts. Braco Dimitrijevic. 2010. (ENG., Illus.). 248p. 75.00 *(978-88-8158-748-3(3))* Charta ITA. Dist: D.A.P./Distributed Art Pubs.

Reuter, Laurel & Mojsilov, Zoran. Zoran Mojsilov. 2009. (Illus.). 91p. *(978-0-943107-20-2(2))* North Dakota Museum of Art.

Richards, Mary. Marina Abramovic. 2009. (Routledge Performance Practitioners Ser.). (ENG., Illus.). 168p. 30.95 *(978-0-415-43208-5(1))* Routledge.

Rosen, Margit, ed. A Little-Known Story about a Movement, a Magazine & the Computer′s Arrival in Art: New Tendencies & Bit International, 1961-1973. 2011. (ENG., Illus.). 576p. (gr. 17). pap. 49.95 *(978-0-262-51581-8(4))* MIT Pr.

ART, WELSH

Deacon, Richard. The Missing Part. 2010. (ENG., Illus.). 268p. 65.00 *(978-3-86560-793-5(4))* Verlag der Buchhandlung Walther Konig DEU. Dist: D.A.P./Distributed Art Pubs.

Jones, Ruth, et al. Holy Hiatus: Ritual & Community in Public Art. Jones, Ruth, ed. 2011. (ENG., Illus.). 148p. 25.95 *(978-1-905762-55-2(0))* Parthian Bks. GBR. Dist: Independent Pubs. Group.

Lord, Peter. The Meaning of Pictures: Images of Personal, Social & Political Identity. 2009. (ENG., Illus.). 256p. 55.00 *(978-0-7083-2221-5(2))* Univ. of Wales Pr. GBR. Dist: Chicago Distribution Ctr.

Musac, Leon. Cerith Wyn Evans. 2008. (SPA & ENG., Illus.). 176p. 70.00 *(978-3-7757-2131-8(2))* Hatje Cantz Verlag GmbH & Co KG DEU. Dist: D.A.P./Distributed Art Pubs.

Walters, Evan. Evan Walters: Moments of Vision. Plummer, Barry, ed. 2011. (ENG., Illus.). 200p. pap. 30.95 **(978-1-85411-542-3(1))** Seren Bks. GBR. Dist: Independent Pubs. Group.

ART AND ANTHROPOLOGY

Blundell, Geoffrey, et al, eds. Seeing & Knowing: Rock Art with & Without Ethnography. 2011. (ENG., Illus.). 384p. pap. 60.00 *(978-1-86814-513-3(1))* Witwatersrand Univ. Pr. Pubns. ZAF. Dist: Transaction Pubs.

Bujok, Elke & Mueller, Claudius, eds. Weiter als der Horizont: Kunst der Welt. 2008. (GER., Illus.). 288p. (C). pap. 49.00 *(978-3-7774-3895-5(2))* Hirmer Verlag GmbH DEU. Dist: Brown, David Bk. Co., The.

Donahoe, Brian & Habeck, Joachim Otto, eds. Reconstructing the House of Culture: Community, Self, & the Makings of Culture in Russia & Beyond. 2011. (ENG., Illus.). 348p. 95.00 *(978-0-85745-275-7(4))* Berghahn Bks., Inc.

Drosteri, Gerard, et al. Intruders: Reflections on Art & Entnological Mu: Reflections on art & the ethnological Museum. 2006. (ENG.). 192p. pap. 35.00 *(978-90-400-8968-8(X))* Waanders B.V., Uitgeverij NLD. Dist: National Bk. Network.

George, Jim & George, Kenneth M. Picturing Islam: Art & Ethics in a Muslim Lifeworld. 2010. (ENG., Illus.). 184p. 94.95 *(978-1-4051-2958-9(1),* Wiley-Blackwell) Wiley, John & Sons, Inc.

Grimshaw, Anna & Ravetz, Amanda. Observational Cinema: Anthropology, Film, & the Exploration of Social Life. 2009. (ENG., Illus.). 224p. 65.00 *(978-0-253-35424-2(2),* 0253354242); pap. 24.95 *(978-0-253-22158-2(7),* 0253221587) Indiana Univ. Pr.

Gunn, Wendy, ed. Fieldnotes & Sketchbooks: Challenging the Boundaries Between Descriptions & Processes of Describing. 2009. (Illus.). 242p. pap. 61.95 *(978-3-631-57492-8(4))* Lang, Peter GmbH, Europaischer Verlag der Wissenschaften DEU. Dist: Lang, Peter.

Ingold, Tim. Redrawing Anthropology: Materials Movements Lines. 2011. (Anthropological Studies of Creativity & Perception Ser.). (Illus.). 216p. 99.95 **(978-1-4094-1774-3(3))** Ashgate Publishing Co.

Kokoli, Alexandra, ed. Susan Hiller: the Provisional Texture of Reality. 2008. (ENG., Illus.). 160p. pap. 22.00 *(978-3-905829-56-3(8))* JRP Ringier Kunstverlag AG CHE. Dist: D.A.P./Distributed Art Pubs.

Lesure, Richard G. Interpreting Ancient Figurines: Context, Comparison, & Prehistoric Art. 2011. (ENG., Illus.). 276p. 95.00 *(978-0-521-19745-8(7))* Cambridge Univ. Pr.

Lord, Angela. Easter: Rudolf Steiner's Watercolor Painting. 2011. (ENG., Illus.). 80p. pap. 25.00 *(978-0-88010-723-5(5))* SteinerBooks, Inc.

Marcus, George. Ethnographica Moralia: Experiments in Interpretive Anthropology. Panourgia, Neni, ed. 2008. (ENG.). 224p. 70.00 *(978-0-8232-2886-7(X))*; 2nd ed. pap. 28.00 *(978-0-8232-2887-4(8))* Fordham Univ. Pr.

Morphy, Howard. Becoming Art: Exploring Cross-Cultural Categories. 2007. (ENG., Illus.). 1p. 104.95 *(978-1-84520-656-7(8))*; 288p. pap. 29.95 *(978-1-84520-657-4(6))* Berg Pubs. GBR. Dist: Macmillan.

Pellizzi, Francesco. Absconding, Vol. 55/56. 2010. (Res: Anthropology & Aesthetics Ser.). (Illus.). 360p. pap. 50.00 *(978-0-87365-854-6(X))* Peabody Museum of Archaeology & Ethnology, Harvard Univ., Pubns. Dept.

Pellizzi, Francesco, ed. Res 53/54 Spring/Autumn 2008: Anthropology & Aesthetics, Vol. 53. 2008. (Res: Anthropology & Aesthetics Ser.). (Illus.). 350p. pap. 50.00 *(978-0-87365-840-9(X))* Peabody Museum of Archaeology & Ethnology, Harvard Univ., Pubns. Dept.

—West by Nonwest, Vol. 42. 2006. (Illus.). 272p. pap. 30.00 *(978-0-87365-842-3(6))* Peabody Museum of Archaeology & Ethnology, Harvard Univ., Pubns. Dept.

Pellizzi, Francesco, et al. Res 57/58: Anthropology & Aesthetics, Spring/Autumn 2010. 2011. (Res: Anthropology & Aesthetics Ser.). (Illus.). 376p. pap. 50.00 *(978-0-87365-861-4(2))* Peabody Museum of Archaeology & Ethnology, Harvard Univ., Pubns. Dept.

Smart, Pamela G. Sacred Modern: Faith, Activism, & Aesthetics in the Menil Collection. 2011. (ENG., Illus.). 294p. pap. 25.00 **(978-0-292-73758-7(0))**; 45.00 *(978-0-292-72333-7(4))* Univ. of Texas Pr.

Svasek, Maruska. Anthropology, Art & Cultural Production, 1 vol. 2007. (Anthropology, Culture & Society Ser.). (ENG., Illus.). 280p. lib. bdg. 100.00 *(978-0-7453-1795-3(2))* Pluto Pr. GBR. Dist: Macmillan.

—Anthropology, Art & Cultural Production: Histories, Themes, Perspectives. 2007. (Anthropology, Culture & Society Ser.). (ENG., Illus.). 280p. 30.00 *(978-0-7453-1794-6(4))* Pluto Pr. GBR. Dist: Macmillan.

Wright, Christopher & Schneider, Arnd, eds. Between Art & Anthropology: Contemporary Ethnographic Practice. 2010. (Contemporary Ethnographic Practice Ser.). (ENG., Illus.). 1p. 99.95 *(978-1-84788-501-2(2))*; 224p. pap. 29.95 *(978-1-84788-500-5(4))* Berg Pubs. GBR. Dist: Macmillan.

ART AND HISTORY

see also History in Art

Barringer, Tim. Art & the British Empire. Quilley, Geoff et al, eds. 2007. (ENG., Illus.). 464p. 94.00 *(978-0-7190-7392-2(8))* Manchester Univ. Pr. GBR. Dist: Macmillan.

Caskey, Jill, et al. Confronting the Borders of Medieval Art. 2011. XVI, 230p. pap. **(978-90-04-20749-3(X))** BRILL.

Costello, Leo. J. M. W. Turner & the Subject of History. 2012. (Illus.). 280p. 119.95 **(978-0-7546-6922-7(X))** Ashgate Publishing Co.

Darom, David. The Great Collections: Modern Custom Knives. 2008. (ENG., Illus.). 288p. 24.99 *(978-0-7858-2360-5(3),* 0785823603) Book Sales, Inc.

Desai, Dipti, et al. History As Art, Art As History: Contemporary Art & Social Studies Education. 2009. (ENG., Illus.). 288p. 150.00 *(978-0-415-99375-3(X))* Routledge.

—History As Art As History: Contemporary Art & Social Studies Education. 2009. (ENG., Illus.). 288p. 48.95 *(978-0-415-99376-0(8))* Routledge.

Dziewior, Yilmaz, ed. That's the Way We Do It: Techniques & Aesthetics of Appropriation, from El Arakawa to Andy Warhol. 2011. (ENG., Illus.). 288p. 60.00 **(978-3-86560-986-1(4))** Kunsthaus Bregenz AUT. Dist: D.A.P./Distributed Art Pubs.

Fabius, Laurent. Le Cabinet des Douze: Regards Sur des Tableaux Qui Font la France. 2010. (Illus.). 214p. *(978-2-07-013039-9(8))*, Gallimard, Editions.

Forrest, Tara. The Politics of Imagination: Benjamin, Kracauer, Kluge. 2008. (ENG.). 198p. pap. 34.95 *(978-3-89942-681-6(9))* Transcript Verlag DEU. Dist: Transaction Pubs.

Garrison, Eliza. Ottonian Imperial Art & Portraiture: The Artistic Patronage of Otto III & Henry II. 2012. (Illus.). 228 & 8 lour pp. 104.95 **(978-0-7546-6968-5(8))** Ashgate Publishing Co.

Guernsey, Daniel R. The Artist & the State, 1777-1855: The Politics of Progress & Decline from James Barry to Gustave Courbet 1777-1855. 2007. (Illus.). 270p. 124.95 *(978-0-7546-5720-0(5))* Ashgate Publishing Co.

Hinz, Manfred. Die Zukunft der Katastrophe: Mythische und rationalistische Geschichtstheorie im italienischen Futurismus. (European University Institute - Series C Ser.). (GER.). VIII, 287p. 225.00 **(978-3-11-187476-0(1))** De Gruyter, Walter Inc.

Jonsson, Stefan. A Brief History of the Masses: Three Revolutions. 2008. (Columbia Themes in Philosophy, Social Criticism, & the Arts Ser.). (ENG., Illus.). 248p. (gr. 17). 32.50 *(978-0-231-14526-8(8))* Columbia Univ. Pr.

Kivelson, Valerie A. & Neuberger, Joan, eds. Picturing Russia: Explorations in Visual Culture. 2010. (ENG., Illus.). 336p. pap. 32.00 *(978-0-300-16421-3(1))* Yale Univ. Pr.

Nelson, Christopher & Nelson, Christopher T. Dancing with the Dead: Memory, Performance, & Everyday Life in Postwar Okinawa. 2008. (Asia-Pacific: Culture, Politics, & Society Ser.). (ENG., Illus.). 288p. 84.95 *(978-0-8223-4349-3(5))* Duke Univ. Pr.

Nelson, Christopher T. Dancing with the Dead: Memory, Performance, & Everyday Life in Postwar Okinawa. 2008. (Asia-Pacific: Culture, Politics, & Society Ser.). (ENG., Illus.). 288p. pap. 23.95 *(978-0-8223-4371-4(1))* Duke Univ. Pr.

Quilley, Barringer. Art & the British Empire. Barringer, Timothy et al, eds. 2009. (ENG., Illus.). 464p. pap. 50.00 *(978-0-7190-8193-4(9))* Manchester Univ. Pr. GBR. Dist: Macmillan.

Rome & the Vatican. (Illus.). 192p. pap., pap. 18.95 *(978-88-476-0178-9(9))* Casa Editrice Bonechi ITA. Dist: CPG Publishing, Inc.

Saltzman, Lisa. Making Memory Matter: Strategies of Remembrance in Contemporary Art. 2006. (ENG., Illus.). 128p. 55.00 *(978-0-226-73407-1(2))*; per. 22.00 *(978-0-226-73408-8(0))* Univ. of Chicago Pr.

Spieker, Sven. The Big Archive: Art from Bureaucracy. 2008. (ENG., Illus.). 240p. (gr. 17). 27.95 *(978-0-262-19570-6(4))* MIT Pr.

Williamson, Beth. The Madonna of Humility: Development, Dissemination & Reception, C.1340-1400. 2010. (Bristol Studies in Medieval Cultures Ser.: Volume 1). (Illus.). 212p. 90.00 *(978-1-84383-419-9(7),* D. S. Brewer) Boydell & Brewer, Ltd. GBR. Dist: Boydell & Brewer, Inc.

ART AND INDUSTRY

see also Art Patronage; Commercial Art

Carr, Adrian & Hancock, Philip, eds. Work & Organization: The Aesthetic Dimension. 2009. (Illus.). x, 202p. pap. 24.99 *(978-0-9817032-5-1(9))* Emergent Pubns.

Dohm, Katharina & Hoffmann, Justin, texts. Kunstmaschinen Maschinenkunst. 2008. (GER & ENG.). 184p. pap. 40.00 *(978-3-939583-40-0(5))* Kehrer Verlag Heidelberg, Klaus Kehrer DEU. Dist: Consortium Bk. Sales & Distribution.

Helland, Janice. British & Irish Home Arts & Industries 1880-1914: Marketing Craft, Making Fashion. 2007. (Illus.). 219p. (C). pap. 32.50 *(978-0-7165-2891-3(6))* Irish Academic Pr. IRL. Dist: International Specialized Bk. Services.

—British & Irish Home Arts & Industries, 1880-1914: Marketing Craft, Making Fashion. 2007. (Illus.). 219p. (C). 75.00 *(978-0-7165-2890-6(8))* Irish Academic Pr. IRL. Dist: International Specialized Bk. Services.

Marshall, Jennifer Jane. Machine Art 1934. 2012. (ENG., Illus.). 240p. 45.00 **(978-0-226-50715-6(7))** Univ. of Chicago Pr.

Mori, Giovanna, et al. Advertising & Art: International Graphics from the Affiche to Pop Art. Salsi, Claudio, ed. 2008. (ENG., Illus.). 224p. 69.00 *(978-88-6130-457-4(5))* Skira Editore ITA. Dist: Random Hse., Inc.

Riggs, Timothy. At the Heart of Progress: Coal, Iron, & Steam Since 1750. 2009. (Distributed for the Ackland Art Museum Ser.). (ENG., Illus.). 50p. pap. 15.95 *(978-0-8078-5980-3(X))* Univ. of North Carolina Pr.

Steiner, Barbara, ed. The Captured Museum. 2011. (ENG., Illus.). 256p. pap. 40.00 *(978-3-86859-059-3(5))* Jovis Verlag GmbH DEU. Dist: D.A.P./Distributed Art Pubs.

Tamayo, Museo. La Maquina y el Juglar Coleccion Renault. 2006. 69p. pap. 41.00 *(978-968-5979-11-5(1))* Trucatriche.

Wagner-Koch, Elisabeth. Kunstszenarien in Unternehmen. (GER., Illus.). 230p. *(978-3-496-01196-5(3))* Reimer, Dietrich.

ART AND INSANITY

see Art and Mental Illness

ART AND LAW

see Law and Art

ART AND LITERATURE

see also Ut Pictura Poesis (Aesthetics)

Adams, Hazard. William Blake on His Poetry & Painting: A Study of A Descriptive Catalogue, Other Prose Writings & Jerusalem. 2010. (ENG., Illus.). 196p. pap. 55.00 *(978-0-7864-4986-6(1))* McFarland & Co., Inc. Pubs.

Addiss, Stephen. The Art of Haiku: Its History Through Poems & Paintings by Japanese Masters. 2012. (ENG., Illus.). 352p. 24.95 **(978-1-59030-886-8(7))** Shambhala Pubns., Inc.

Altieri, Charles. Painterly Abstraction in Modernist American Poetry: The Contemporaneity of Modernism. 2009. (Cambridge Studies in American Literature & Culture Ser.). (ENG.). 540p. (C). pap. 57.00 *(978-0-521-10729-7(6))* Cambridge Univ. Pr.

Baer, Joachim T. Vladimir Ivanovic Dal' as a Belletrist. (ENG.). 204p. 210.00 **(978-3-11-180663-1(4))** De Gruyter, Mouton DEU. Dist: de Gruyter, Walter GmbH & Co. KG.

Baguley, David. Art & Literature of the Second Empire. 2012. (Durham Modern Languages Ser.). (ENG.). 200p. pap. 24.95 *(978-0-7190-8585-7(3))* Manchester Univ. Pr. GBR. Dist: Macmillan.

Bakos, Judit. Painting & Writing. 2009. (Illus.). 144p. pap. *(978-3-639-13500-8(8))* VDM Verlag Dr. Mueller e.K.

Bal, Mieke. Reading Rembrandt: Beyond the Word-Image Opposition. 2006. (Amsterdam Academic Archive Ser.). (Illus.). 498p. per. *(978-90-5356-858-3(1),* Leiden Univ. Pr.) Amsterdam Univ. Pr.

Bar Hebraeus, Gregory. The Barn of Mysteries. 2010. (SYR.). 149.96 *(978-1-61143-246-6(4))* Gorgias Pr., LLC.

Bass, Laura R. The Drama of the Portrait: Theater & Visual Culture in Early Modern Spain. 2008. (ENG., Illus.). 264p. 75.00 *(978-0-271-03304-4(5))* Pennsylvania State Univ. Pr.

Basso, Eric. Decompositions: Essays on Art & Literature, 1973-1989. 2007. (Illus.). 186p. per. 20.00 *(978-1-878580-58-0(2))* Leaping Dog Pr.

Baumeister, Martin, et al, eds. Die Kunst der Geschichte: Historiographie, Ästhetik, Erzählung. 2009. (GER., Illus.). 398p. (C). 68.00 *(978-3-525-36384-3(2))* Vandenhoeck & Ruprecht GmbH & Co. KG DEU. Dist: ISD.

Beaumont, Matthew. Adventures in Realism. 2007. (Concise Companions to Literature & Culture Ser.). (ENG., Illus.). 320p. 104.95 *(978-1-4051-3577-1(8),* Wiley-Blackwell) Wiley, John & Sons, Inc.

Berg, William J. Imagery & Ideology: Fiction & Painting in Nineteenth-Century France. 2008. (Illus.). 269p. 52.50 *(978-0-87413-995-2(3))* 2007. (ENG.). 52.50 *(978-1-61149-331-3(5))* Univ. of Delaware Pr.

Bills, Mark, et al. Dickens & the Artists. 2012. (ENG., Illus.). 200p. 55.00 **(978-0-300-17602-5(3))** Yale Univ. Pr.

Bowie, Malcolm, et al. "When Familiar Meanings Dissolve —" Essays in French Studies in Memory of Malcolm Bowie. 2011. (Romanticism & after in France/le Romantisme et après en France Ser.). (ENG., Illus.). 381p. pap. 79.95 **(978-3-0343-0108-4(1))** Lang, Peter AG GBR. Dist: Lang, Peter.

Bram, Shahar. The Ambassadors of Death: The Sister Arts, Western Canon & the Silent Lines of a Hebrew Survivor. 2011. (ENG., Illus.). 207p. 69.95 *(978-1-84519-450-5(0))* Sussex Academic Pr. GBR. Dist: International Specialized Bk. Services.

Broglio, Ron. Technologies of the Picturesque: British Art, Poetry, & Instruments, 1750-1830. 2008. (Illus.). (C). *(978-0-8387-5700-0(6))* Bucknell Univ. Pr.

Brogniez, Laurence, ed. Ecrit(ure)s de peintres Belges. 2008. (Comparatisme et Société / Comparatism & Society Ser.). (FRE., Illus.). 256p. pap. 48.95 *(978-90-5201-446-3(9))* PIE - Peter Lang BEL. Dist: Lang, Peter.

Brown, Karen E. The Yeats Circle Word & Image in Ireland, 1880-1935. 2011. (Illus.). 208p. 104.95 *(978-0-7546-6644-8(1))* Ashgate Publishing Co.

Campbell, C. Jean. The Commonwealth of Nature: Art & Poetic Community in the Age of Dante. 2008. (ENG., Illus.). 192p. 65.00 *(978-0-271-03261-0(8))* Pennsylvania State Univ. Pr.

Cappucci, Paul R. William Carlos Williams, Frank O'Hara, & the New York Art Scene. 2010. (Illus.). 167p. 48.50 *(978-0-8386-4218-4(7))*; (ENG.). 168p. 60.00 *(978-1-61147-422-0(1))* Fairleigh Dickinson Univ. Pr.

Casaliggi, Carmen & March-Russell, Paul, eds. The Legacies of Romanticism: Literature, Aesthetics, Landscape. 2012. (Routledge Studies in Romanticism Ser.). (ENG., Illus.). 304p. (C). 125.00 *(978-0-415-89008-3(X))* Routledge.

Cavanaugh, Cecelia. New Lenses for Lorca: Literature, Art, & Science in the Edad de Plata. 2011. (ENG., Illus.). 204p. (gr. 17). 65.00 **(978-1-61148-376-5(X))** Lexington Bks.

Chaney, Michael A. Fugitive Vision: Slave Image & Black Identity in Antebellum Narrative. 2009. (Blacks in the Diaspora Ser.). (ENG., Illus.). 272p. pap. 19.95 *(978-0-253-22108-7(0),* 0253221080) Indiana Univ. Pr.

Cheeke, Stephen. Writing for Art: The Aesthetics of Ekphrasis. (ENG., Illus.). 2011. 224p. pap. 24.95 *(978-0-7190-8324-2(9))* 2008. 240p. 89.00 *(978-0-7190-7650-3(1))* Manchester Univ. Pr. GBR. Dist: Macmillan.

Colantuono, Anthony. Titian, Colonna & the Renaissance Science of Procreation: Equicola's Seasons of Desire. 2010. (Visual Culture in Early Modernity Ser.). (Illus.). 342p. 119.95 *(978-0-7546-6962-3(9))* Ashgate Publishing Co.

Concilio, Carmen & Lane, Richard J., eds. Image Technologies in Canadian Literature: Narrative, Film, & Photography. 2009. (Études Canadiennes -

Canadian Studies). 164p. pap. 42.95 (978-90-5201-474-6(4)) PIE - Peter Lang BEL. Dist: Lang, Peter.

Cooke, Simon & Goldman, Paul. Reading Victorian Illustration: 1855-1875:Spoils of the Lumber Room. 2012. (Illus.). 225p. 99.95 (978-1-4094-1165-9(6)) Ashgate Publishing Co.

Cozma, Codrina. The Power of the Spoken Word - Literature in the American Broadcasting & Film Industry of The 1990s. 2008. 140p. pap. (978-3-639-01256-9(9)) VDM Verlag Dr. Mueller e.K.

Czernin, Franz Josef. Bildsatz: Texte Zu Bildender Kunst. 2008. (GER., Illus.). 367p. (978-3-8321-9100-9(3)) DuMont.

Dakota, Dane. Woman As Beauty. 2010. 132p. pap. 10.00 (978-1-935271-55-0(5)) Published by Westview, Inc.

Dalton, Trinie, ed. Mythtym. 2008. (ENG., Illus.). 160p. 30.00 (978-0-9815622-4-7(8)) PictureBox, Inc.

Delyfer, Catherine. Art & Womanhood in Fin-de-Siecle Writing: The Fiction of Lucas Malet, 1880-1931, 1 vol. 2011. (Gender & Genre Ser.). (ENG., Illus.). 224p. 99.00 (978-1-84893-105-3(0)) Pickering & Chatto Pubs., Ltd. GBR. Dist: Ashgate Publishing Co.

Elizabeth Clayton. Unto Relationship: A Short Primer of Twelve Essays. 2009. 64p. pap. 10.49 (978-1-4269-2028-8(8)) Trafford Publishing.

Elms, Anthony. Blast Counterblast. Reinke, Steve, ed. 2012. (ENG., Illus.). 192p. pap. 24.00 (978-1-926627-17-5(2)) WhiteWalls, Inc.

Enss, Chris. Frontier Teachers: Stories of Heroic Women of the Old West. 2008. (ENG., Illus.). 160p. pap. 14.95 (978-0-7627-4819-8(2), TwoDot) Globe Pequot Pr., The.

Fay, Elizabeth A. Fashioning Faces: The Portraitive Mode in British Romanticism. 2010. (Becoming Modern: New Nineteenth-Century Studies). (ENG., Illus.). 340p. lib. bdg. 55.00 (978-1-58465-778-1(2), University of New Hampshire Press) Univ. Pr. of New England.

Fernando, Devika & Aubert, Frederic. Visions. 2008. 68p. pap. 38.95 (978-1-4092-1742-8(6)) Lulu Enterprises Inc.

Fernie, Deanna. Hawthorne Sculpture & the Question of American Art. 2011. (Illus.). 294p. 99.95 (978-0-7546-5479-7(6)) Ashgate Publishing Co.

Findlay, James A. & Perricone, Lillian. WPA Museum Extension Project, 1935-1943: Government Created Visual Aids for Children from the Collections of the Bienes Museum of the Modern Book. 2009. (ENG., Illus.). 188p. per. 35.00 net. (978-0-9762267-1-0(5)) Bienes Museum of the Modern Bk., Broward County.

Fisher, Susan Greenberg. Picasso & the Allure of Language. 2009. (Yale University Art Gallery Ser.). (Illus.). 272p. pap. 40.00 (978-0-300-13546-6(7)) Yale Univ. Pr.

Fliedl, Konstanze, et al, eds. Handbuch der Kunstzitate. 2 Bände: Malerei, Skulptur, Fotografie in der Deutschsprachigen Literatur der Moderne, 2 vols. 2011. (GER., Illus.). XXII, 966p. 419.00 (978-3-11-020500-8(9)) De Gruyter, Walter Inc.

Florence, Penny. Mallarmé, Manet & Redon: Visual & Aural Signs & the Generation of Meaning. 2009. (Cambridge Studies in French Ser.). (ENG.). 188p. pap. 29.99 (978-0-521-11458-5(6)) Cambridge Univ. Pr.

Frankel, Nicholas. Masking the Text: Essays on Literature & Mediation in the 1890s. 2009. (Illus.). 279p. (978-1-904201-14-4(8)) Rivendale Pr.

Galvez, Marisa. Songbook: How Lyrics Became Poetry in Medieval Europe. 2012. (ENG., Illus.). 296p. 35.00 (978-0-226-28051-6(9)) Univ. of Chicago Pr.

Goddard, Linda. Aesthetic Rivalries: Word & Image in France, 1880-1926. 2012. (Cultural Interactions: Studies in the Relationship between the Arts Ser.). (ENG.). 323p. pap. 69.95 (978-3-03911-879-3(X)) Lang, Peter AG GBR. Dist: Lang, Peter.

Goodwin, James. Modern American Grotesque: Literature & Photography. 2009. (ENG.). 264p. 61.95 (978-0-8142-1108-3(9)); cd-rom 14.95 (978-0-8142-9205-1(4)) Ohio State Univ. Pr.

Gracia, Jorge J. E. Painting Borges: Philosophy Interpreting Art Interpreting Literature. 2012. (SUNY series in Latin American & Iberian Thought & Culture Ser.). (ENG.). 288p. 90.00 (978-1-4384-4177-1(0)); pap. 25.95 (978-1-4384-4178-8(9)) State Univ. of New York Pr.

Haggarty, Sarah & Mee, Jon. Blake & Conflict. Haggarty, Sarah & Mee, Jon, eds. 2009. (ENG., Illus.). 248p. 89.00 (978-0-230-57387-1(8)) Palgrave Macmillan.

Halter, Peter. The Revolution in the Visual Arts & the Poetry of William Carlos Williams. 2009. (Cambridge Studies in American Literature & Culture Ser.). (ENG., Illus.). 288p. pap. 41.00 (978-0-521-10266-7(9)) Cambridge Univ. Pr.

Haupt, Sabine & Stadler, Ulrich, eds. Das Unsichtbare Sehen: Bildzauber, optische Medien und Literatur. 2006. (Edition Voldemeer Ser.). (Illus.). 304p. pap. 39.95 (978-3-211-36647-9(4), 3211366474) Springer.

Hedeman, Anne D. Translating the Past: Laurent de Premierfait & Boccaccio's de Casibus. 2008. (Illus.). 240p. 60.00 (978-0-89236-935-5(3)) Oxford Univ. Pr., Inc.

Helsinger, Elizabeth K. Poetry & the Pre-Raphaelite Arts: Dante Gabriel Rossetti & William Morris. 2008. (ENG., Illus.). 352p. 50.00 (978-0-300-12273-2(X)) Yale Univ. Pr.

Hoerandner, Wolfram & Rhoby, Andreas. Die Kulturhistorische Bedeutung byzantinischer Epigramme: Akten des internationalen Workshops (Wien, 1. -2. Dezember 2006) 2008. (VERoFFENTLICHUNGEN ZUR BYZANZFORSCHUNG Ser.). (GER., Illus.). 124p. (C). pap. 63.00 (978-3-7001-6495-1(5)) Austrian Academy of Sciences Press AUT. Dist: Brown, David Bk. Co., The.

Hoffmann, Nora. Photographie, Malerei und Visuelle Wahrnehmung Bei Theodor Fontane. 2011. (Schriften der Theodor Fontane Gesellschaft Ser.). (GER.). VIII, 376p. 140.00 (978-3-11-025992-6(3)) De Gruyter, Walter Inc.

Hönnighausen, Lothar. The Symbolist Tradition in English Literature: A Study of Pre-Raphaelitism & Fin de Siécle. Hönnighausen, Gisela, tr. from GER. 2010. (European Studies in English Literature Ser.). (ENG., Illus.). 360p. pap. 29.99 (978-0-521-15896-1(6)) Cambridge Univ. Pr.

Honnighausen, Lothar. William Faulkner: The Art of Stylization in his Early Graphic & Literary Work. 2009. (Cambridge Studies in American Literature & Culture Ser.). (ENG.). 231p. pap. 33.99 (978-0-521-10728-0(8)) Cambridge Univ. Pr.

James, Elizabeth, ed. Art & Text in Byzantine Culture. 2010. (ENG.). 246p. (C). pap. 36.99 (978-0-521-16876-2(7)) Cambridge Univ. Pr.

Joe, Damen. Mapping the Self-Portrait - Navigating Identity & Autobiography in Visual Art. 2008. 88p. pap. (978-3-639-02096-0(0)) VDM Verlag Dr. Mueller e.K.

Johnson, W. McAllister. Versified Prints. 2012. (ENG., Illus.). 232p. (978-1-4426-4285-0(8)) Univ. of Toronto Pr.

Junod, Karen. Writing the Lives of Painters: Biography & Artistic Identity in Britain 1760-1810. 2011. (Oxford English Monographs). (ENG., Illus.). 264p. 110.00 (978-0-19-959700-0(6)) Oxford Univ. Pr., Inc.

Kolve, V. A. Telling Images: Chaucer & the Imagery of Narrative II. (ENG., Illus.). 408p. 2010. pap. 24.95 (978-0-8047-7658-5(X)) 2009. 65.00 (978-0-8047-5583-2(3)) Stanford Univ. Pr.

Kooistra, Lorraine Janzen. Poetry, Pictures, & Popular Publishing: The Illustrated Gift Book & Victorian Visual Culture, 1855-1875. 2011. (ENG., Illus.). 312p. 59.95 (978-0-8214-1964-9(1)) Ohio Univ. Pr.

Korzilius, Jean-Loup, ed. Art et Littérature: Le voyage entre texte et Image. 2006. (Faux Titre Ser.: 286). (FRE.). 314p. pap. 82.00 (978-90-420-2052-8(0)) Rodopi.

Langdon, Ida. Materials for a Study of Spenser's Theory of Fine Art. 2009. 196p. 22.99 (978-0-559-97928-6(2)); pap. 16.99 (978-0-559-97927-9(4)) BiblioBazaar.

—Materials for a Study of Spenser's Theory of Fine Art. 2009. 156p. pap. (978-0-217-01709-1(6)) Books LLC.

—Materials for a Study of Spenser's Theory of Fine Art. 2008. 188p. 37.95 (978-1-4365-5440-4(3)) 2007. 192p. per. 22.95 (978-0-548-75313-2(X)) Kessinger Publishing, LLC.

Larrabee, Stephen A. English Bards & Grecian Marbles: The Relationship Between Sculpture & Poetry Especially in the Romantic Period. reprint ed. 59.00 (978-0-403-08621-4(3)) Somerset Pubs., Inc.

Loizeaux, Elizabeth Bergmann. Twentieth-Century Poetry & the Visual Arts. (ENG., Illus.). 274p. 2011. pap. 35.99 (978-0-521-18020-7(1)) 2008. 93.00 (978-0-521-88795-3(X)) Cambridge Univ. Pr.

Lombardi, Enrico. Edoardo Albinati: Voci Nel Buio/Voices in the Dark: Enrico Lombardi: Immagini/Images, 1 vol. 2006. (ENG., Illus.). 104p. per. 29.95 (978-88-8158-582-3(0)) D.A.P./Distributed Art Pubs.

Losano, Antonia. The Woman Painter in Victorian Literature. 2008. (ENG., Illus.). 400p. 52.95 (978-0-8142-1081-9(3)); xiii, 300p. cd-rom 14.95 (978-0-8142-9160-3(0)) Ohio State Univ. Pr.

Louvel, Liliane & Petit, Laurence. Poetics of the Iconotext. Jacobs, Karen, ed. Petit, Laurence, tr. from FRE. 2011. 212p. 99.95 (978-1-4094-0031-8(X)) Ashgate Publishing Co.

Maritain, Jacques. Art & Poetry. (978-0-8022-1056-2(2)) Philosophical Library, Inc.

Markonish, Denise. Petah Coyne: Everything That Rises Must Converge. 2010. (ENG., Illus.). 128p. pap. 25.00 (978-0-300-16770-2(9)) Yale Univ. Pr.

Marshall, Gail, ed. The Cambridge Companion to the Fin de Siecle. 2007. (Cambridge Companions to Literature Ser.). (ENG., Illus.). 288p. 105.00 (978-0-521-85063-6(0)); 298p. per. 29.99 (978-0-521-61561-7(5)) Cambridge Univ. Pr.

Matthews, Susan. Blake, Sexuality & Bourgeois Politeness. 2011. (Cambridge Studies in Romanticism Ser.). (ENG., Illus.). 286p. 90.00 (978-0-521-51357-9(X)) Cambridge Univ. Pr.

Mattix, Micah. Frank O'Hara & the Poetics of Saying "I" 2011. (978-0-8386-4268-9(3)); (ENG.). 182p. 60.00 (978-1-61147-046-8(3)) Fairleigh Dickinson Univ. Pr.

Maurer, Louise & Hillman, Roger. Reading Images, Viewing Texts: Crossdisciplinary Perspectives. (ENG & FRE., Illus.). pap. 48.95 (978-3-03910-768-1(2)) Lang, Peter CHE. Dist: Lang, Peter Publishing, Inc.

Merril, Stuart. Pastels in Prose. 2009. 114p. pap. (978-1-151-18638-6(4)) Books LLC.

Merrill, Stuart, tr. Pastels in Prose. 2009. 288p. 43.95 (978-1-104-43997-2(2)); pap. 28.95 (978-1-104-36203-4(1)) Kessinger Publishing, LLC.

Moore, Robert Etheridge. Hogarth's Literary Relationships. 2009. (ENG.). 218p. pap. 50.00 (978-0-8166-5966-1(4)) Univ. of Minnesota Pr.

Morgan, Jo-Ann. Uncle Tom's Cabin as Visual Culture. 2007. (ENG., Illus.). 280p. (C). 39.95 (978-0-8262-1715-8(X)) Univ. of Missouri Pr.

Murphet, Julian. Multimedia Modernism: Literature & the Anglo-American Avant-garde. 2009. (ENG., Illus.). 230p. 93.00 (978-0-521-51345-6(6)) Cambridge Univ. Pr.

Nie, Giselle de. Envisioning Experience in Late Antiquity & the Middle Ages: Dynamic Patterns in Texts & Images. Noble, Thomas F. X., ed. 2012. (Illus.). 180p. 104.95 (978-1-4094-3948-6(8)) Ashgate Publishing Co.

Novak, Barbara. Voyages of the Self: Pairs, Parallels & Patterns in American Art & Literature. 2009. (ENG., Illus.). 232p. pap. 24.95 (978-0-19-538791-9(0)) Oxford Univ. Pr., Inc.

O'Neill, Liam & Ní Shúilleabháin, Brenda. Corca Dhuibhne. 2010. (ENG., Illus.). 224p. 159.95 (978-0-86322-408-9(3)) Brandon/Mount Eagle Pubns., Ltd. IRL. Dist: Dufour Editions, Inc.

Orestano, Francesca & Frigerio, Francesca. Strange Sisters: Literature & Aesthetics in the Nineteenth Century. 2009. (Cultural Interactions: Studies in the Relationship between the Arts Ser.). (Illus.). 324p. 55.95 (978-3-03911-840-3(4)) Lang, Peter AG GBR. Dist: Lang, Peter.

Orlando, Emily J. Edith Wharton & the Visual Arts. (Amer Lit Realism & Naturalism Ser.). (ENG.). 2008. 264p. pap. 29.95 (978-0-8173-5552-4(9)) 2007. (Illus.). 280p. 47.50 (978-0-8173-1537-5(3)) Univ. of Alabama Pr.

Pan, Daan. The Lyrical Resonance of Chinese Poets & Painters: The Tradition & Poetics of Tihuashi. 2011. (978-1-60497-741-7(8)) Cambria Pr.

Parkes, Adam. A Sense of Shock: The Impact of Impressionism on Modern British & Irish Writing, 1 vol. 2011. (ENG., Illus.). 304p. 65.00 (978-0-19-538381-2(8)) Oxford Univ. Pr., Inc.

Parron, Carmen. Arte y Literatura en la Cuestion Palpitante y Las Novelas Cortas De Emilia Pardo Bazan. 2008. (ENG & SPA., Illus.). 304p. 119.95 (978-0-7734-5232-9(X)) Mellen, Edwin Pr., The.

Pater, Walter. The Works of Walter Pater. 2011. (Cambridge Library Collection - Literary Studies). (ENG.). 234p. pap. 22.99 (978-1-108-03425-8(X)); 310p. pap. 24.99 (978-1-108-03429-6(2)); 292p. pap. 23.99 (978-1-108-03428-9(4)); 256p. pap. 23.99 (978-1-108-03424-1(1)); 264p. pap. 23.99 (978-1-108-03430-2(6)); 332p. pap. 28.99 (978-1-108-03426-5(8)); 272p. pap. 23.99 (978-1-108-03427-2(6)); (Illus.). 264p. pap. 23.99 (978-1-108-03423-4(3)) Cambridge Univ. Pr.

Pearson, Lisa, ed. It Is Almost That: A Collection of Image & Text Work by Women Artists & Writers. 2011. (ENG., Illus.). 296p. 45.00 (978-0-9799562-6-3(9)) Siglio Pr.

Perez, Rolando. Severo Sarduy & the Neo-Baroque Image of Thought in the Visual Arts. 2011. (Purdue Studies in Romance Literatures Ser.). 319p. pap. 45.00 (978-1-55753-604-4(X)) Purdue Univ. Pr.

Phillips-Court, Kristin. The Perfect Genre Drama & Painting in Renaissance Italy. 2011. (Illus.). 286p. 99.95 (978-1-4094-0683-9(0)) Ashgate Publishing Co.

Plesch, Veronique, et al, eds. Efficacité/Efficacy: How to Do Things with Words & Images? 2011. (FRE., Illus.). 322p. pap. 96.00 (978-90-420-3374-0(6)) Rodopi.

Polyak, Alina. Tradition & Modernity in Contemporary Jewish American Literature. 2010. 124p. pap. (978-3-639-26265-0(4)) VDM Verlag Dr. Mueller e.K.

Ragg, Edward. Wallace Stevens & the Aesthetics of Abstraction. 2010. (ENG.). 262p. 89.00 (978-0-521-19086-2(X)) Cambridge Univ. Pr.

Read, Peter. Picasso & Apollinaire: The Persistence of Memory. (Illus.). 2010. (ENG.). 336p. pap. 34.95 (978-0-520-26592-9(0)) 2008. 317p. 55.00 (978-0-520-24361-3(7)) Univ. of California Pr.

Ruskin, John. On Genius. 2011. (On Ser.). (ENG.). 120p. pap. 12.95 (978-1-84391-614-7(2)) Hesperus Pr. GBR. Dist: Independent Pubs. Group.

Salter, Elizabeth. English & International: Studies in the Literature, Art & Patronage of Medieval England. Pearsall, Derek & Zeeman, Nicolette, eds. 2010. (ENG.). 408p. pap. 42.00 (978-0-521-13161-2(8)) Cambridge Univ. Pr.

Scott, David H. T. Pictorialist Poetics: Poetry & the Visual Arts in Nineteenth-Century France. 2009. (Cambridge Studies in French Ser.). (ENG.). 224p. pap. 33.99 (978-0-521-11059-4(9)) Cambridge Univ. Pr.

Shapiro, Gavriel. The Sublime Artist's Studio: Nabokov & Painting. 2009. (ENG., Illus.). 320p. 45.00 (978-0-8101-2559-9(5)) Northwestern Univ. Pr.

Shepherd, Lynn. Clarissa's Painter: Portraiture, Illustration, & Representation in the Novels of Samuel Richardson. 2010. (Oxford English Monographs). (ENG., Illus.). 288p. 120.00 (978-0-19-956669-3(0)) Oxford Univ. Pr., Inc.

Silverberg, Mark. The New York School Poets & the Neo-Avant-Garde: Between Radical Art & Radical Chic. 2010. (Illus.). 296p. 104.95 (978-0-7546-6298-3(5)) Ashgate Publishing Co.

Smart, Tom. Immolation: Recent Figuration by Graham Metson. (Illus.). 48p. pap. 5.00 (978-0-920674-30-7(5)) Beaverbrook Art Gallery CAN. Dist: Goose Lane Editions.

Smith, Riggs Alden. The Primacy of Vision in Virgil's Aeneid. 2010. (ENG., Illus.). 271p. pap. 25.00 (978-0-292-72622-2(8)) Univ. of Texas Pr.

Squire, Michael. Image & Text in Graeco-Roman Antiquity. 2009. (ENG., Illus.). 560p. 124.00 (978-0-521-75601-3(4)) Cambridge Univ. Pr.

Stasková, Alice & Lützeler, Paul Michael, eds. Hermann Broch und die Künste. 2009.Tr. of Hermann Broch & the Arts. (GER.). VI, 263p. 126.00 (978-3-11-020955-6(1)) De Gruyter, Walter Inc.

Stout, Janis P. Picturing a Different West: Vision, Illustration, & the Tradition of Cather & Austin. 2007. (Grover E. Murray Studies in the American Southwest Ser.). (Illus.). 352p. 40.00 (978-0-89672-610-9(X)) Texas Tech Univ. Pr.

Thomas, Sophie. Romanticism & Visuality: Fragments, History, Spectacle. (Illus.). 246p. 2009. pap. 39.95 (978-0-415-87579-0(X)) 2007. (ENG., 125.00 (978-0-415-96118-9(1)) Routledge.

Tondro, Jason. Superheroes of the Round Table: Comics Connections to Medieval & Renaissance Literature. 2011. (ENG., Illus.). 248p. pap. 40.00 (978-0-7864-6068-7(7)) McFarland & Co., Inc. Pubs.

Tucker, Amy. The Illustration of the Master: Henry James & the Magazine Revolution. 2010. (ENG., Illus.). 280p. 60.00 (978-0-8047-6874-0(9)) Stanford Univ. Pr.

Varnum, Robin & Gibbons, Christina T., eds. The Language of Comics: Word & Image. 2007. (ENG., Illus.). 222p. pap. 25.00 (978-1-57806-414-4(7)) Univ. Pr. of Mississippi.

Waanders Editors. Sculptuur Studies 2009. 2010. (ENG., Illus.). 176p. pap. 50.00 (978-90-400-7689-3(8)) Waanders B.V., Uitgeverij NLD. Dist: National Bk. Network.

Wacior, Slawomir. Explaining Imagism: The Imagist Movement in Poetry & Art. 2007. 316p. (978-0-7734-5427-9(6)) Mellen, Edwin Pr., The.

Wagner, Peter, ed. Icons - Texts - Iconotexts: Essays on Ekphrasis & Intermediality. (European Cultures Ser.). (ENG.). VIII, 406p. 255.00 (978-3-11-179675-8(2)) De Gruyter, Walter Inc.

Wagstaff, Emma. Writing Art: French Literary Responses to the Work of Alberto Giacometti. 2011. (Cultural Interactions: Studies in the Relationship between the Arts Ser.). 197p. pap. 60.95 (978-3-03911-871-7(4)) Lang, Peter AG GBR. Dist: Lang, Peter.

Wakefield, David. French Romantics. 2007. (Illus.). 240p. 50.00 (978-1-904449-59-1(X)) Pop Art Bks. GBR. Dist: International Publishers Marketing.

Wall, Anthony. Words & Images: A French Rendezvous. Rocha, Carolina, ed. 2010. (ENG., Illus.). 276p. pap. 39.95 (978-1-55238-259-2(1)) Univ. of Calgary Pr. CAN. Dist: Chicago Distribution Ctr.

Wendorf, Richard, ed. Articulate Images: The Sister Arts from Hogarth to Tennyson. 2009. (ENG.). 288p. pap. 50.00 (978-0-8166-5890-9(0)) Univ. of Minnesota Pr.

Wilde, Oscar. The Critic As Artist. Moore, Andrew, ed. 2007. 124p. per. 13.85 (978-1-59569-082-1(4)) Mondial.

Willems, Gottfried. Anschaulichkeit: Zu Theorie und Geschichte der Wort-Bild-Beziehun- gen und des literarischen Darstellungsstils. (Studien zur deutschen Literatur Ser.). (GER.). VIII, 484p. 195.00 (978-3-11-183806-9(4)) De Gruyter, Walter Inc.

Womack, Peter. Dialogue. 2011. (New Critical Idiom Ser.). (ENG.). 176p. 95.00 (978-0-415-32921-7(3)); pap. 22.95 (978-0-415-32922-4(1)) Routledge.

Yeazell, Ruth Bernard. Art of the Everyday: Dutch Painting & the Realist Novel. (ENG., Illus.). 296p. (C). 2009. pap. 25.95 (978-0-691-14323-1(4)) 2007. 52.50 (978-0-691-12726-2(3)) Princeton Univ. Pr.

Yoo, Yae Jin. La Peinture ou les leçons esthétiques chez Marcel Proust. 2011. 160p. (C). 71.95 (978-1-4331-1700-8(2)) Lang, Peter Publishing, Inc.

Yousif, Keri. Balzac Grandville & the Rise of Book Illustration. 2012. (Illus.). 200p. 99.95 (978-1-4094-1808-5(1)) Ashgate Publishing Co.

Zanker, Graham. Modes of Viewing in Hellenistic Poetry & Art. 2007. (Wisconsin Studies in Classics Ser.). (ENG., Illus.). 248p. per. 26.95 (978-0-299-19454-3(X)) Univ. of Wisconsin Pr.

ART AND MEDICINE

see Medicine and Art

ART AND MENTAL ILLNESS

Baker, Bobby. Diary Drawings. 2010. (ENG., Illus.). 224p. pap. 22.95 (978-1-84668-374-9(2)) Profile Bks. Ltd. GBR. Dist: Consortium Bk. Sales & Distribution.

Chapadjiev, Sabrina, ed. Live Through This: On Creativity & Self-Destruction. 2008. (ENG., Illus.). 250p. pap. 17.95 (978-1-58322-827-2(6)) Seven Stories Pr.

Guzzo, Lou. When Did I Die? Richard Lachman, the Artist America Forgot. 2007. 176p. per. 15.95 (978-1-59800-878-4(1)) Outskirts Pr., Inc.

Hagstrm Sthl, Kristina. Incorporating Performance: Melancholia & Performativity in Post-Catastrophic Art. 2013. (Studies in International Performance Ser.). (ENG.). 256p. 85.00 (978-0-230-23461-1(5)) Palgrave Macmillan.

Kottler, Jeffrey A. Divine Madness: Ten Stories of Creative Struggle. 2006. (ENG., Illus.). 336p. pap. 15.95 (978-0-7879-9413-6(8), Jossey-Bass) Wiley, John & Sons, Inc.

Prinzhorn, Hans. The Art of Insanity: An Analysis of Ten Schizophrenic Artists. 2011. (Solar Books - Solar Research Archive Ser.). (Illus.). 160p. pap. 29.95 (978-0-9832480-0-2(1)) Solar Bks.

Richter, Hans-Gunther. Diesseits und Jenseits in der Kunst von Außenseitern und Spiritisten. 2009. (GER.). 194p. pap. 57.95 (978-3-631-59184-0(5)) Lang, Peter GmbH, Europaischer Verlag der Wissenschaften DEU. Dist: Lang, Peter.

Wacker, Anita. Therapists' Art & Traum. 2008. 208p. pap. (978-3-639-01778-6(1)) VDM Verlag Dr. Mueller e.K.

ART AND MORALS

see also Erotic Art; Music—Moral and Ethical Aspects; Nude in Art

Cashell, Kieran. Aftershock: The Ethics of Contemporary Transgressive Art. 2009. (ENG., Illus.). 272p. pap. 32.50 (978-1-84511-524-1(4)) I. B. Tauris & Co., Ltd. GBR. Dist: Macmillan.

Chamarette, Jenny & Higgins, Jennifer, eds. Guilt & Shame: Essays in French Literature, Thought & Visual Culture. 2009. (Modern French Identities Ser.). (FRE & ENG.). 223p. pap. 53.95 (978-3-03911-563-1(4)) Lang, Peter AG GBR. Dist: Lang, Peter.

Costello, Diarmuid & Willsdon, Dominic, eds. The Life & Death of Images. 2008. (Illus.). 256p. 76.95 (978-0-8014-4698-6(8)) Cornell Univ. Pr.

—The Life & Death of Images: Ethics & Aesthetics. 2008. (Illus.). 255p. pap. 24.95 (978-0-8014-7455-2(8)) Cornell Univ. Pr.

Dreisbach, Christopher. Collingwood on the Moral Principles of Art. 2008. (ENG.). 203p. 48.50 (978-1-57591-124-3(8)) Susquehanna Univ. Pr.

Freeman, Damien. Art's Emotions: Ethics, Expression & Aesthetic Experience. 2012. (ENG.). 240p. (C). (978-0-7735-4005-7(9)); pap. (978-0-7735-4006-4(7)) McGill-Queen's Univ. Pr.

Gaut, Berys. Art, Emotion & Ethics. 2007. (ENG., Illus.). 288p. 95.00 (978-0-19-926321-9(3)) Oxford Univ. Pr., Inc.

Hontanilla, Ana. El Gusto de la Razón: Debates de Arte y Moral en el Siglo XVIII Español. 2010. (SPA., Illus.). 366p. pap. 56.00 (978-84-8489-523-7(8)) Iberoamericana Vervuert Publishing Corp.

Iliescu, Sanda, ed. The Hand & the Soul: Aesthetics & Ethics in Architecture & Art. 2009. (ENG., Illus.). 320p. (C). (gr. 13-17). pap. 25.00 (978-0-8139-2772-5(2)) Univ. Pr. of Virginia.

Jones, W. Gareth & Tolstoy, Leo. Tolstoy: What Is Art? 2011. (Russian Texts). (ENG & RUS.). 284p. pap. 19.95 *(978-1-85399-381-7(6))* Bristol Classical Pr. GBR. Dist: International Publishers Marketing.

Murray, Julia K. Mirror of Morality: Chinese Narrative Illustration & Confucian Ideology. 2007. (Illus.). 194p. 60.00 *(978-0-8248-3001-4(6))* Univ. of Hawaii Pr.

Ranciere, Jacques. Aesthetics & Its Discontents. 2009. (ENG.). 176p. 64.95 *(978-0-7456-4630-5(1))*; pap. 19.95 *(978-0-7456-4631-2(X))* Polity Pr. GBR. Dist: Wiley, John & Sons, Inc.

Schellekens, Elisabeth & Schellekens. Aesthetics & Morality. 2008. (Continuum Aesthetics Ser.). (ENG.). 172p. 29.95 *(978-0-8264-9762-8(4))* Continuum International Publishing Group, Ltd. GBR. Dist: National Bk. Network.

Stroud, Scott R. John Dewey & the Artful Life: Pragmatism, Aesthetics, & Morality. 2011. (American & European Philosophy Ser.). (ENG.). 248p. 69.95 *(978-0-271-05007-2(1))* Pennsylvania State Univ. Pr.

Taylor, Rabun. The Moral Mirror of Roman Art. 2008. (ENG., Illus.). 288p. 103.00 *(978-0-521-86612-5(X))* Cambridge Univ. Pr.

ART AND MUSIC

see also Music in Art

Beatrice, Luca & Campo, Alberto, texts. Sound & Vision. 1 vol. 2007. (ENG., Illus.). 260p. pap. 35.00 *(978-88-89431-98-6(9))* Damiani ITA. Dist: D.A.P./Distributed Art Pubs.

Blom, Ina, text. Saadane Afif: Technical Specifications. 2009. (ENG., Illus.). 148p. 25.00 *(978-90-73362-84-0(9))* Witte De With Centre for Contemporary Art NLD. Dist: D.A.P./Distributed Art Pubs.

Caruso Jr., John. Creating Multicultural Communities Through Art & Music. 2008. 84p. pap. *(978-3-639-07836-7(5))* VDM Verlag Dr. Mueller e.K.

Chassey, Eric de & Stroun, Fabrice. Europunk. 2011. (ENG., Illus.). 320p. pap. 55.00 ***(978-88-88493-72-5(7))*** Drago Arts & Communication ITA. Dist: SCB Distributors.

Chu, Kalaiv. Music & Visual Art: Their Correspondences & Value in Education. 2009. 256p. pap. *(978-3-639-12383-8(2))* VDM Verlag Dr. Mueller e.K.

Clip Art. The Art of Music CD-ROM & Book. Grafton, Carol Belanger, ed. 2012. (Dover Electronic Clip Art Ser.). (ENG.). 48p. pap. 19.95 ***(978-0-486-48913-1(2))*** Dover Pubns., Inc.

Da, Yan. Across* 2010. 84p. pap. *(978-3-639-25198-2(9))* VDM Verlag Dr. Mueller e.K.

Daniels, Dieter, ed. Audiovisuology - See This Sound No. 1: An Interdisciplinary Survey of Audiovisual Culture. 2010. (ENG., Illus.). 452p. pap. 49.95 *(978-3-86560-686-0(5))* Verlag der Buchhandlung Walther Konig DEU. Dist: D.A.P./Distributed Art Pubs.

Daniels, Dieter, et al. See This Sound. 2011. (ENG., Illus.). 260p. pap. 49.95 ***(978-3-86560-687-7(3))*** Verlag der Buchhandlung Walther Konig DEU. Dist: D.A.P./Distributed Art Pubs.

Dayan, Peter. Art As Music Music As Poetry Poetry As Art: From Whistler to Stravinsky. 2011. (Illus.). 196p. 99.95 *(978-0-7546-6791-9(X))* Ashgate Publishing Co.

Dopp, Hans-Jurgen & Döpp, Hans-Jürgen. Music & Eros. 2008. (Temporis Ser.). (ENG., Illus.). 255p. 39.95 *(978-1-85995-679-3(3))* Parkstone International GBR. Dist: Ingram Pub. Services.

Gelder, Hilde van, et al. In the Name of Mozart. (Illus.). 31p. pap. 19.50 *(978-90-5867-569-9(6))* Leuven Univ. Pr. BEL. Dist: Cornell Univ. Pr.

Greiner, William. Discovering Art & Music: A Contemporary Approach. 2008. (ENG.). (C). pap. 65.60 *(978-0-558-11641-5(8))* Pearson Learning Solutions.

Greiner, William & McMullian, Neal. Awakening the Senses to Art & Music. 3rd ed. 2010. (ENG.). 230p. (C). pap. 88.80 *(978-0-558-73586-6(6))* Pearson Learning Solutions.

Hegarty, Antony & Johnsons, Antony. Antony & the Johnsons: Swanlights. 2010. (ENG., Illus.). 144p. 35.00 *(978-0-8109-9680-9(4)*, Abrams Image) Abrams.

Herrera, Pol S. Polinearism. 2011. 172p. pap. 81.99 ***(978-1-4568-1810-4(4))*** Xlibris Corp.

IMMA Staff & Kissane, Seán, eds. Vertical Thoughts: Morton Feldman & the Visual Arts. 2011. (ENG., Illus.). 318p. pap. 45.00 *(978-1-907020-08-7(X))* Irish Museum of Modern Art IRL. Dist: D.A.P./Distributed Art Pubs.

Kelley, Brian S. Mac Arnold & Plate Full O Blues. 2009. pap. *(978-1-61658-323-1(1))* Independent Pub.

Kim-Cohen, Seth. In the Blink of an Ear: Toward a Non-Cochlear Sonic Art. 2009. (ENG., Illus.). 296p. 80.00 *(978-0-8264-2970-4(X))*; pap. 22.95 *(978-0-8264-2971-1(8))* Continuum International Publishing Group, Ltd. GBR. Dist: National Bk. Network.

Kim, Yourree. An Analysis & Performance Guide to Benjamin Lees' Odyssey I & II. 2008. 128p. pap. *(978-3-8364-9398-7(5))* VDM Verlag Dr. Mueller e.K.

Kozlova, Yulia. Sources of Inspiration in Selected Piano Works by Sergei Slonimsky. 2009. 92p. pap. *(978-3-639-16262-2(5))* VDM Verlag Dr. Mueller e.K.

Lock, Graham & Murray, David. The Hearing Eye: Jazz & Blues Influences in African American Visual Art. Lock, Graham & Murray, David, eds. 2009. (ENG., Illus.). 288p. 99.00 *(978-0-19-534050-1(7))* Oxford Univ. Pr., Inc.

Lock, Graham & Murray, David, eds. The Hearing Eye: Jazz & Blues Influences in African American Visual Art. 2009. (ENG., Illus.). 288p. pap. 24.95 *(978-0-19-534051-8(5))* Oxford Univ. Pr., Inc.

Mavridorakis, Valerie, ed. Francis Baudevin: Hello Spira. 2009. (ENG., Illus.). 72p. pap. 15.00 *(978-3-905829-69-3(X))* JRP Ringier Kunstverlag AG CHE. Dist: D.A.P./Distributed Art Pubs.

Mazow, Leo G. & Benton, Thomas Hart. Thomas Hart Benton & the American Sound. 2012. (ENG.). 200p. ***(978-0-271-05083-6(7))*** Pennsylvania State Univ. Pr.

Molon, Dominic, et al. Sympathy for the Devil: Art & Rock & Roll Since 1967. 2007. (ENG., Illus.). 288p. 50.00 *(978-0-300-13426-1(6))* Yale Univ. Pr.

Morawinska, Agnieszka. Inwazja Dzwieku: Muzyka I Sztuki Wizualne = Invasion of Sound: Music & the Visual Arts. 2009. (POL & ENG., Illus.). 142p. *(978-83-60713-28-0(6))* Zacheta, Panstwowa Galeria Sztuki.

Mustaqim, Kama. Visual Musicality in Graphic Expression. 2011. 144p. pap. ***(978-3-8443-3037-3(2))*** Lambert Academic Publishing.

Naldi, Fabiola, et al, contrib. by. Sound & Vision. 2006. (Illus.). 256p. pap. 35.00 *(978-88-89431-55-9(5))* Damiani ITA. Dist: D.A.P./Distributed Art Pubs.

ömke, Vladimir. Moritz von Schwinds Sängerkriegsfresko auf der Wartburg: Die historischen Quellen und deren Auslegung inder Kunst des 19. Jahrhunderts. 2008. (Europäische Hochschulschriften. Reihe 28: Kunstgeschichte Ser.). (GER., Illus.). 472p. pap. 107.95 *(978-3-631-56511-7(9))* Lang, Peter GmbH, Europaischer Verlag der Wissenschaften DEU. Dist: Lang, Peter.

Owerko, Lyle. The Boombox Project: The Machines, the Music, & the Urban Underground. 2010. (ENG., Illus.). 160p. 24.95 *(978-0-8109-8275-8(7)*, Abrams Image) Abrams.

Pakesch, Peter & Diederichsen, Diedrich, eds. Schere - Stein - Papier. / Rock - Paper - Scissors. Pop-Musik als Gegenstand Bildender Kunst / Pop Music as Subject of Visual Art. 2010. (ENG & GER., Illus.). 140p. pap. 48.00 *(978-3-86560-657-0(1))* Verlag der Buchhandlung Walther Konig DEU. Dist: D.A.P./Distributed Art Pubs.

Price, Peter & Burba, Tyler. On Becoming-Music: Between Boredom & Ecstasy. Schirmacher, Wolfgang, ed. 2010. 148p. pap. 16.95 *(978-0-9827067-4-9(X))* Atropos Pr.

Radrizzani, Dominique. Kokoschka: Et la Musique/and Music. 2008. (ENG., Illus.). 128p. pap. 30.00 *(978-88-7439-414-2(4))* 5 Continents ITA. Dist: Hachette Bk. Group.

Richards, Annette. The Free Fantasia & the Musical Picturesque. 2006. (New Perspectives in Music History & Criticism Ser.). (ENG., Illus.). 272p. pap. 55.00 *(978-0-521-02753-3(5))* Cambridge Univ. Pr.

Sanders, Donald. Music at the Gonzaga Court in Mantua. 2012. (ENG.). 200p. 65.00 ***(978-0-7391-6726-7(X))*** Lexington Bks.

Sans, Jerome, ed. It's Not Only Rock & Roll Baby! 2008. 244p. pap. *(978-84-935844-6-7(0))* Actar Birkhauser Distribution.

Strand, Charlie, ed. Project Iceland - Music, Art, Fashion. 2008. (ENG., Illus.). 272p. pap. 49.50 *(978-1-86154-308-0(5))* Booth-Clibborn Editions GBR. Dist: Hachette Bk. Group.

Vergo, Peter. The Music of Painting: Music, Modernism & the Visual Arts. 2012. (ENG., Illus.). 368p. pap. 39.95 ***(978-0-7148-6386-3(6))*** Phaidon Pr., Inc.

Vergo, Peter. The Music of Painting: Music, Modernism, & the Visual Arts from the Romantics to John Cage. 2010. (ENG., Illus.). 368p. 69.95 *(978-0-7148-5762-6(9))* Phaidon Pr., Inc.

Ware, Robert, et al. To Form from Air: Music & the Art of Raymond Jonson. 2010. (ENG., Illus.). 96p. *(978-0-89013-571-6(1))* Museum of New Mexico Pr.

Wisniewska, Karina. Karina Wisniewska. Bewegte Stille - Silent Dynamism. Von Burg, Dominique, ed. 2010. (ENG., Illus.). 176p. *(978-3-7165-1577-8(9)*, Bentell Verlags Ag Dist) Antique Collectors' Club.

ART AND MYTHOLOGY

Alber, Dave. Myth & Medium. 2007. 72p. pap. 25.60 *(978-1-4116-6126-4(5))* Lulu Enterprises Inc.

Atac, Mehmet Ali. The Mythology of Kingship in Neo-Assyrian Art. 2010. (ENG., Illus.). 300p. (C). 99.00 *(978-0-521-51790-4(7))* Cambridge Univ. Pr.

Ausoni, Alberto. Music in Art. 2009. (Guide to Imagery Ser.). (Illus.). 384p. pap. 24.95 *(978-0-89236-965-2(5))* Oxford Univ. Pr., Inc.

Belan, Kyra. Art Myths & Rituals: Visual Language for the New Reality - Text. rev. ed. 2010. 136p. pap. 25.88 *(978-1-933005-69-0(6))* Kendall Hunt Publishing Co.

—Art Myths & Rituals: Visual Language for the New Reality - Workbook. rev. ed. 2010. 48p. pap. 25.88 *(978-1-933005-82-9(3))* Kendall Hunt Publishing Co.

Burns, Sarah. Painting the Dark Side: Art & the Gothic Imagination in Nineteenth-Century America. 2006. (Illus.). 303p. pap. 27.95 *(978-0-520-24987-5(9))* Univ. of California Pr.

Chemara, Martine, photos by. Sacred Walls of Kerala: Murals of Temples & Palaces. 2007. (ENG.). 208p. *(978-81-8386-049-9(4))* India Research Pr. IND. Dist: Independent Pubs. Group.

De Rynck, Patrick. How to Read Bible Stories & Myths in Art: Decoding the Old Masters from Giotto to Goya. 2009. (ENG., Illus.). 360p. pap. 37.50 *(978-0-8109-8400-4(8))* Abrams.

Dover & Weller, Alan. Greek & Roman Mythology. 2008. (Dover Pictura Electronic Clip Art Ser.). (ENG., Illus.). 128p. pap. 39.95 *(978-0-486-99028-6(1))* Dover Pubns., Inc.

Galleria degli Uffizi Staff, contrib. by. Medusa: Il Mito, L'antico e I Medici. 2008. (I mai Visti Ser.). (ITA., Illus.). 139p. (C). 29.50 *(978-88-596-0513-3(X))* Edizioni Polistampa ITA. Dist: Brown, David Bk. Co., The.

Gardner, Ernest Arthur. Religion & Art in Ancient Greece. 2010. (ENG.). 140p. pap. 20.75 *(978-1-176-94007-9(4))* BiblioBazaar.

—Religion & Art in Ancient Greece. 2010. (Illus.). 40p. pap. 14.14 *(978-1-153-75484-2(3))* General Bks. LLC.

Gerson, Denise M. Sacred Stories, Timeless Tales: Mythic Perspectives in World Art. 2011. (Illus.). 50p. pap. 19.95 ***(978-0-9788213-7-1(8))*** Lowe Art Museum.

Gooding, Francis & Gooding. Black Light: Myth & Meaning in Modern Painting. 2009. (Critical Quarterly Book Ser.). (ENG., Illus.). 128p. pap. 34.95 *(978-1-4051-9114-2(7)*, Wiley-Blackwell) Wiley, John & Sons, Inc.

Grigorian, Natasha. European Symbolism: In Search of Myth (1860-1910) 2008. (Romanticism & after in France/le Romantisme et après en France Ser.). (Illus.). 65.95 *(978-3-03911-531-0(6))* Lang, Peter GmbH, Europaischer Verlag der Wissenschaften DEU. Dist: Lang, Peter.

Held, Heinz-Georg, ed. Winckelmann und die Mythologie der Klassik: Narrative Tendenzen in der Ekphrase der Kunstperiode. 2009. (Reihe der Villa Vigoni Ser.).Tr. of Winckelmann & the Mythology of the Neoclassical Age. (GER & ITA.). VI, 264p. 140.00 ***(978-3-11-173136-0(7))*** De Gruyter, Walter Inc.

Held, Heinz Georg, ed. Winckelmann und die Mythologie der Klassik / Winckelmann e i miti del classico: Narrative Tendenzen in der Ekphrase der Kunstperiode / Decrizione d'arte e sviluppi narrativi. 2009. (Reihe der Villa Vigoni Ser.).Tr. of Winckelmann & the Mythology of the Neoclassical Age. (GER & ITA., Illus.). VI, 264p. pap. *(978-3-484-67022-8(3))* Verlag Max Niemeyer.

Henderson, Lucia. Producer of the Living, Eater of the Dead: Revealing Tlahtecuhtli, the Two-Faced Aztec Earth. 2007. (Bar S Ser.). (Illus.). iv, 71p. (C). pap. 62.50 *(978-1-4073-0083-2(0))* British Archaeological Reports Ltd. GBR. Dist: Brown, David Bk. Co., The.

Hirsh, Jennie & Wallace, Isabelle Loring. Contemporary Art & Classical Myth. 2011. (Illus.). 410p. 124.95 *(978-0-7546-6974-6(2))* Ashgate Publishing Co.

Huang, Minwen. The Matrix Trilogy as a Postmodern Myth. 2008. 92p. pap. *(978-3-639-03836-1(3))* VDM Verlag Dr. Mueller e.K.

Hunt, Patrick, ed. Myth & Art in Ekphrasis. 2010. (C). 0.00 *(978-1-60927-777-2(5))* Univ. Readers.

King, James & Iwakiri, Yuriko. Japanese Warrior Prints 1646-1904. 2006. (Illus.). 280p. *(978-90-74822-84-8(3))* BRILL.

Mansfield, Elizabeth. Too Beautiful to Picture: Zeuxis, Myth, & Mimesis. 2007. (Illus.). 240p. per. 25.00 *(978-0-8166-4749-1(6))* Univ. of Minnesota Pr.

Mansfield, Elizabeth C. Too Beautiful to Picture: Zeuxis, Myth, & Mimesis. 2007. (Illus.). 240p. 75.00 *(978-0-8166-4748-4(8))* Univ. of Minnesota Pr.

Morales, Helen. Classical Mythology: A Very Short Introduction. 2007. (Very Short Introductions Ser.). (ENG., Illus.). 166p. per. 11.95 *(978-0-19-280476-1(6))* Oxford Univ. Pr., Inc.

Morris, Ann, et al. Sculpture Woods: Studio Grounds of Ann Morris. 2008. (ENG., Illus.). 164p. *(978-0-295-98827-6(4))* Museum of Northwest Art.

Rao, Sirish & Mohanty, Raja, texts. The Circle of Fate. 2009. (ENG., Illus.). 24p. 30.00 *(978-81-86211-58-8(6))* Tara Publishing IND. Dist: Perseus-PGW.

Renan, Ernest & Belan, Kyra. Images of the Divine. 2012. (Prestige Ser.). (ENG.). 512p. 82.50 *(978-1-84484-887-4(6))* Parkstone Pr. USA, Ltd.

Singer, Irving. Cinematic Mythmaking: Philosophy in Film. 2008. (Irving Singer Library). (ENG.). 256p. (gr. 17). 24.95 *(978-0-262-19589-8(5))* MIT Pr.

Van de Velde, C., ed. Classical Mythology in the Netherlands in the Age of Renaissance & Baroque - la mythologie classique aux temps de la Renaissance et du Baroque dans les Pays-Bas: Proceedings of the International Conference Antwerp, 19-21 May 2005 - Actes du Colloque international Anvers, 19-21 Mai 2005. 2009. (Travaux de la Renaissance et de L'Humanisme Ser.). (ENG & FRE., Illus.). 394p. (C). pap. 95.00 *(978-90-429-2052-1(1))* Peeters Pubs. & Booksellers BEL. Dist: Brown, David Bk. Co., The.

Vézilier, Sandrine. Sensualité et Volupté: Le Corps Féminin Dans la Peinture Flamande des XVIe et XVIIe Siècles. 2010. (DUT & FRE., Illus.). 127p. *(978-88-366-1809-5(X))* Silvana.

Wastiau, Boris. Medusa: The African Sculpture of Enchantment. 2009. (ENG., Illus.). 256p. 65.00 *(978-88-7439-469-2(1))* 5 Continents ITA. Dist: Hachette Bk. Group.

Waters, Clara Erskine Clement. A Handbook of Legendary & Mythological Art. 2009. 212p. pap. *(978-0-217-15873-2(0))*; 310p. pap. *(978-0-217-67037-1(7))*; 216p. pap. *(978-1-4432-8367-0(3))*; 338p. pap. *(978-1-4432-8365-6(7))* Books LLC.

Wessing, Michael, et al, texts. Reloaded, 1 vol. 2007. (GER & ENG., Illus.). 128p. 49.50 *(978-3-86678-021-7(4))* Kerber Verlag DEU. Dist: D.A.P./Distributed Art Pubs.

Ziolkowski, Theodore. Minos & the Moderns: Cretan Myth in Twentieth-Century Literature & Art. 2008. (Classical Presences Ser.). (ENG., Illus.). 208p. 55.00 *(978-0-19-533691-7(7))* Oxford Univ. Pr., Inc.

ART AND NATURE

see Nature (Aesthetics)

ART AND PHOTOGRAPHY

Adams, James. Fist Full of Devils. 2010. 60p. pap. 24.00 *(978-0-557-54577-3(3))* Lulu Enterprises Inc.

Aguilera, Steven. A New Perspective #8213; Photography & Filmmaking Edition. 2008. 120p. pap. 24.95 *(978-0-573-00039-8(3))* Artistech Bks.

Aubenas, Sylvie, et al. The Lens of Impressionism: Photography & Painting along the Normandy Coast, 1850-1874. 2009. (ENG., Illus.). 208p. 50.00 *(978-1-55595-325-6(5))* Hudson Hills Pr. LLC.

Bann, Stephen, ed. Art & the Early Photographic Album. 2011. (Studies in the History of Art Ser.). (ENG., Illus.). 288p. 70.00 *(978-0-300-13590-9(4))* National Gallery of Art.

Bergstein, Mary. Mirrors of Memory: Freud, Photography, & the History of Art. 2010. (Cornell Studies in the History of Psychiatry). (Illus.). 296p. 29.95 *(978-0-8014-4819-5(0))* Cornell Univ. Pr.

Blessing, Jennifer & Trotman, Nat, eds. Haunted: Contemporary Photography. 2010. (ENG., Illus.). 208p. 50.00 *(978-0-89207-398-6(5))* Guggenheim, Solomon R. Museum.

Bochner, Jay. An American Lens: Scenes from Alfred Stieglitz's New York Secession. 2008. (ENG., Illus.). 389p. (gr. 17). pap. 19.95 *(978-0-262-52488-9(0))* MIT Pr.

The Book of Fey. 2008. 96p. (ENG.). *(978-0-9749603-3-3(0))*; *(978-0-9749603-4-0(9))*; *(978-0-9749603-5-7(7))* Olive Tree Publishing.

Campany, David. Art & Photography. 2006. (SPA.). 49.95 *(978-0-7148-9838-4(4))* Phaidon Pr., Inc.

Carey, Tom G. Sketches of a Good Life. 2009. 68p. pap. 41.99 *(978-1-4415-0585-9(7))* Xlibris Corp.

Chester, T. L. Idiosynkrasia. 2009. 32p. pap. 18.50 *(978-0-557-03871-8(5))* Lulu Enterprises Inc.

Costello, Diarmuid & Iversen, Margaret, eds. Photography after Conceptual Art. 2010. (Art History Special Issues Ser.: 6). (ENG., Illus.). 208p. pap. 34.95 *(978-1-4443-3360-2(7)*, Wiley-Blackwell) Wiley, John & Sons, Inc.

Danly, Susan. Georgia O'Keeffe & the Camera: The Art of Identity. 2008. (Illus.). xii, 122p. *(978-0-916857-48-6(4))*; (ENG., 136p. 45.00 *(978-0-300-12682-2(4))* Yale Univ. Pr.

Easton, Elizabeth, et al. Snapshot: Painters & Photography, Bonnard to Vuillard. 2011. (ENG., Illus.). 248p. 50.00 *(978-0-300-17236-2(2))* Yale Univ. Pr.

Easton, Elizabeth Wynne. Snapshot: Painter/Photographers from Bonnard to Vuillard. 2011. ***(978-90-79310-28-9(X))*** Yale Univ. Pr.

Elsen, Thomas. To Inhabit a Place. 2006. (ENG & GER., Illus.). 48p. 24.00 *(978-3-936636-75-8(3))* Kehrer Verlag Heidelberg, Klaus Kehrer DEU. Dist: Consortium Bk. Sales & Distribution.

Ezawa, Kota, photos by. The History of Photography Remix. 2006. (Illus.). 56p. 50.00 *(978-1-59005-178-8(5))* Nazraeli Pr.

Fantom No. 7: Summer 2011, 1 vol. 2011. (ENG., Illus.). 120p. pap. 20.00 *(978-88-96677-10-0(6))* Boiler Corp. ITA. Dist: D.A.P./Distributed Art Pubs.

Fraenkel, Jeffrey, intro. Edward Hopper & Company, 1 vol. 2009. (ENG., Illus.). 120p. 50.00 *(978-1-881337-26-3(X))* Fraenkel Gallery.

Garcia-Alix, Alberto, photos by. Alberto Garcia-Alix: from Where There Is No Return. 2010. (SPA & ENG., Illus.). 340p. 75.00 *(978-84-92841-43-1(5))* La Fabrica ESP. Dist: D.A.P./Distributed Art Pubs.

Halcour, Dorothee. Wie Wirkt Kunst? Zur Psychologie Ästhetischen Erlebens. (Europaische Hochschulschriften Ser.: Vol. 697). (GER., Illus.). xvi, 369p. 43.95 *(978-3-631-39801-2(8))* Lang, Peter Publishing, Inc.

Hills, Patricia & Hills, P. Painting Harlem Modern: The Art of Jacob Lawrence. 2010. (ENG., Illus.). 400p. 55.00 *(978-0-520-25241-7(1))* Univ. of California Pr.

Hodge, Susie. The Complete Guide to Painting Pictures from Photos. 2008. (ENG., Illus.). 128p. pap. 22.99 *(978-0-7153-2801-9(8))* David & Charles Pubs. GBR. Dist: F&W Media, Inc.

I Love Art. pap. 35.00 *(978-4-900398-13-9(6))* Watari-Um JPN. Dist: D.A.P./Distributed Art Pubs.

Kanazawa, Hitoshi, et al, eds. The Light with It's Harmony: Shinzo Fukuhara/Roso Fukuhara Photographs 1913-1941. 50.00 *(978-4-900398-17-7(9))* Watari-Um JPN. Dist: D.A.P./Distributed Art Pubs.

Lardinois, Brigitte, et al. Eve Arnold's People. 2009. (ENG., Illus.). 176p. 40.00 *(978-0-500-54371-9(2)*, 554371) Thames & Hudson.

Lattu, Brandon. Brandon Lattu: Office Gray Case, 1 vol. 2010. (ENG., Illus.). 88p. 55.00 *(978-3-86560-351-7(3))* Verlag der Buchhandlung Walther Konig DEU. Dist: D.A.P./Distributed Art Pubs.

Lazarus, Marvin. Perfect Timing: Artists in New York, 19581962. 2010. (ENG.). 144p. 39.95 *(978-0-9794727-7-0(8))* Five Ties Publishing.

Liu, Xiaodong. The Richness of Life: Personal Photographs of Contemporary Chinese Artist Liu Xiaodong, 1 vol. 2008. (ENG., Illus.). 590p. pap. 92.00 *(978-988-99609-8-8(2))* Timezone 8 Ltd. HKG. Dist: D.A.P./Distributed Art Pubs.

Lowe, Rebecca. Forgotten Things. 2010. 45p. pap. 19.99 *(978-0-557-38102-9(9))* Lulu Enterprises Inc.

Lynes, Barbara Buhler & Weinberg, Jonathan. Shared Intelligence: American Painting & the Photograph. 2011. (ENG., Illus.). 274p. 39.95 *(978-0-520-26906-4(3))* Univ. of California Pr.

McTighe, Monica E. Framed Spaces: Photography & Memory in Contemporary Installation Art. 2012. (Interfaces: Studies in Visual Culture Ser.). (ENG., Illus.). 248p. (C). 85.00 ***(978-1-61168-205-2(3))***; pap. 35.00 ***(978-1-61168-206-9(1))*** Univ. Pr. of New England. (Dartmouth College Press).

Muller, Ulrike. Bauhaus Women: Art, Handicraft, Design. 2009. (ENG., Illus.). 152p. 39.95 *(978-2-08-030120-8(9))* Flammarion et Cie FRA. Dist: Random Hse., Inc.

Mundy, Jennifer. Duchamp, Man Ray, Picabia. 2008. (Illus.). 256p. 55.00 *(978-1-85437-758-6(2))*; (ENG., pap. 55.00 *(978-1-85437-731-9(0))* Tate Publishing, Ltd. GBR. Dist: Abrams, Hachette Bk. Group.

Nordstrom, Alison. TruthBeauty: Pictorialism & the Photograph as Art, 1845-1945, 1 vol. 2011. (ENG., Illus.). 160p. 60.00 ***(978-1-55365-981-5(3))*** D&M Pubs. Inc. CAN. Dist: Perseus-PGW.

Rabinowitz, Cay Sophie, ed. Fantom No. 5. 2011. (ENG., Illus.). 120p. pap. 20.00 *(978-88-96677-07-0(6))* Boiler Corp. ITA. Dist: D.A.P./Distributed Art Pubs.

Rabinowitz, Cay Sophie & Barni, Selva, eds. Fantom No. 6: Spring 2011. 2011. (ENG., Illus.). 120p. pap. 20.00 *(978-88-96677-09-4(2))* Boiler Corp. ITA. Dist: D.A.P./Distributed Art Pubs.

Rabinowitz, Cay Sophie & Barni, Selva, eds. Fantom No. 9: Fall 2011: Photographic Quarterly. 2012. (ENG., Illus.). 128p. pap. 20.00 ***(978-88-96677-14-8(9))*** Boiler Corp. ITA. Dist: D.A.P./Distributed Art Pubs.

Randell, Roy. Spiritual Art. 2010. 125p. pap. 44.80 *(978-0-557-39643-6(3))* Lulu Enterprises Inc.
Waggoner, Diane, et al. The Pre-Raphaelite Lens: British Photography & Painting , 1848-1875. 2010. (Illus.). 240p. 65.00 *(978-1-84822-067-6(7),* Lund Humphries Pubs.) Ashgate Publishing, Ltd. GBR. Dist: Ashgate Publishing Co.
Woolman, Matt. Formats, Folds & Bindings. 2008. (ENG., Illus.). 144p. pap. 19.95 incl. cd-rom *(978-1-906245-07-8(X),* Angela Patchell Bks.,Csi) Continental Sales, Inc.

ART AND RELIGION

see also Art and Mythology; Christian Art and Symbolism; Gods in Art; Idols and Images

Adi Da Samraj. Perfect Abstraction: New Essays Written for Transcendental Realism: The Image-Art of Egoless Coincidence with Reality Itself: On the Occasion of Adi Da Samaraj's Exhibition at the Cenacolo Di Ognissanti, Florence, 2008. 2008. (Illus.). 47p. pap. *(978-1-57097-250-8(8))* Dawn Horse Pr.
Albanese, Marilia. Archaeology: Northern India. 2008. (White Star Guides). (ENG., Illus.). 168p. pap. 18.95 *(978-88-544-0041-2(6))* White Star ITA. Dist: Random Hse., Inc.
Andreopoulos, Andreas. Art As Theology: From the Postmodern to the Medieval. 2007. (Cross Cultural Theologies Ser.). (ENG.). 224p. (C). 99.95 *(978-1-84553-170-6(1));* per. 29.95 *(978-1-84553-171-3(X))* Equinox Publishing Ltd. GBR. Dist: ISD.
Aston, Nigel. Art & Religion in Eighteenth-Century Europe. 2009. (ENG., Illus.). 320p. 45.00 *(978-1-86189-377-2(9))* Reaktion Bks., Ltd. GBR. Dist: Chicago Distribution Ctr.
Ault, Julie. Come Alive! The Spirited Art of Sister Corita, 1 vol. 2007. (ENG., Illus.). 128p. pap. 29.95 *(978-0-9545025-2-2(3))* Four Corners Bks. GBR. Dist: D.A.P./Distributed Art Pubs.
Bakker, Boudewijn & Webb, Diane. The Religious Roots of Dutch Landscape Painting: From Van Eyck to Rembrandt. 2012. (Illus.). 352p. ***(978-1-4094-0486-6(2))*** Ashgate Publishing, Ltd.
Barker, Sebastian, et al. Rowan Williams' Theology of Art & Other Essays. 2009. 87p. ***(978-0-7734-4861-2(6))*** Mellen, Edwin Pr., The.
Barwell, Michael John. Patterns of Redemption. 2008. 264p. pap. *(978-3-639-07782-7(2))* VDM Verlag Dr. Mueller e.K.
Bergmann, Sigurd. In the Beginning Is the Icon: A Liberative Theology of Images, Visual Arts, & Culture. 2009. (ENG., Illus.). 208p. (C). 95.00 *(978-1-84553-172-0(8))* Equinox Publishing Ltd. GBR. Dist: ISD.
Berkwitz, Stephen C., et al. Buddhist Manuscript Cultures: Knowledge, Ritual & Art. Berkwitz, Stephen C. et al, eds. 2009. (Routledge Critical Studies in Buddhism Ser.). (ENG., Illus.). 222p. 170.00 *(978-0-415-77616-5(3))* Routledge.
Bernier, Ronald R., ed. Beyond Belief. 2010. (Illus.). 150p. pap. 19.00 *(978-1-60899-087-0(7),* Pickwick Pubns.) Wipf & Stock Pubs.
Bristow, Janet & Cole-Galo, Victoria A. The Prayer Shawl Companion: 38 Knitted Designs to Embrace, Inspire, & Celebrate Life. 2008. (ENG., Illus.). 172p. pap. 19.95 *(978-1-60085-003-5(0),* Taunton) Taunton Pr., Inc.
Brown, Kate. Sense of the Sacramental. (Illus.). 224p. 25.00 *(978-0-281-04849-6(5))* SPCK Publishing GBR. Dist: Pilgrim Pr., The/United Church Pr.
Brown, S. Talmond. The Shadow of Beauty: Art, Faith, & the Culture of Freedom. 2010. pap. 21.99 *(978-1-61566-961-5(2))* Tate Publishing & Enterprises, LLC.
Brumfield, William C. & Velimirovic, Milos M., eds. Christianity & the Arts in Russia. 2008. (ENG., Illus.). 268p. pap. 31.99 *(978-0-521-08923-4(9))* Cambridge Univ. Pr.
Burckhardt, Titus. Foundations of Oriental Art & Symbolism. 2009. (ENG., Illus.). 148p. pap. 22.95 *(978-1-933316-72-7(1))* World Wisdom, Inc.
Christoffersen, Svein Aage, et al, eds. Transfiguration 2009: Journal of Religion & the Arts. 2010. 200p. pap. 26.00 *(978-87-635-3093-4(7))* Museum Tusculanum Pr. DNK. Dist: Chicago Distribution Ctr.
Cocteau, Jean & Maritain, Jacques. Art & Faith: Letters Between Jacques Maritain & Jean Cocteau. Coleman, John, tr. 2011. 138p. 40.95 ***(978-1-258-06769-4(2))*** Literary Licensing, LLC.
Coffey, Kathy. The Art of Faith: 40 Steps Toward Living Artfully. 2007. (Illus.). 151p. per. 14.95 *(978-1-58595-603-6(1))* Twenty-Third Pubns./Bayard.
Cohen. Art with Heart - Assisting the Work of Wellness. 2009. 136p. pap. 40.99 *(978-1-4389-3416-7(5))* AuthorHouse.
Crown, Carol & Russell, Charles, eds. Sacred & Profane: Voice & Vision in Southern Self-Taught Art. 2007. (ENG., Illus.). 286p. 50.00 *(978-1-57806-916-3(5))* Univ. Pr. of Mississippi.
Culbertson, Philip Leroy. The Bible in/and Popular Culture: A Creative Encounter. Culbertson, Philip & Wainwright, Elaine M., eds. 2011. (ENG.). VIII, 210p. ***(978-90-04-18699-6(9))*** BRILL.
Dale, Marilyn. Energize Your Art Ministry. 2007. 32p. 16.95 *(978-1-4303-2975-6(0))* Lulu Enterprises Inc.
De Chateaubrian, Viscount. Genius of Christianity or the Spirit and. 2006. pap. 52.95 *(978-1-4286-3505-0(X))* Kessinger Publishing, LLC.
Drewal, Henry John & Drewal et al., Henry John. Mami Wata: Arts for Water Spirits in Africa & Its Diasporas. 2008. (ENG., Illus.). 228p. pap. *(978-0-9748729-9-5(7))* Univ. of California, Los Angeles, Fowler Museum of Cultural History.
du Toit, Herman & Dant, Doris R., eds. Pious Pictures: Personal Expression in Faith-Based Art. 2010. (Illus.). 320p. pap. 21.95 *(978-0-8425-2707-1(9),* Brigham Young Univ. Studies) Brigham Young Univ.
Dyas, Dee, ed. Images of Salvation: The Story of the Bible through Medieval Art (New & Improved Third Edition) 3rd ed. 2011. (ENG.). (C). cd-rom 24.95 *(978-0-9550673-3-4(2))* Christianity and Culture Project GBR. Dist: Brown, David Bk. Co., The.
Elixir Refused. ltd. ed. 2007. per. *(978-0-9794878-0-4(3))* Big Heaven.
Flaskerud, Ingvild. Visualizing Belief & Piety in Iranian Shiism. 2010. (ENG., Illus.). 320p. 130.00 *(978-1-4411-4907-7(4))* Continuum International Publishing Group, Ltd. GBR. Dist: National Bk. Network.
Fujimura, Makoto. Refractions: A Journey of Faith, Art, & Culture. 2009. (Exploring the Great Ideas Ser.). (ENG.). 176p. pap. 24.99 *(978-1-60006-301-5(2))* NavPress Publishing Group.
Garcia, James R. The Authentication of Rembrandt's Titus F 1655. 2010. 180p. pap. 16.99 *(978-1-60957-508-3(3))* Xulon Pr., Inc.
Gardner, Ernest A. Religion & Art in Ancient Greece. 2007. 68p. per. *(978-1-4065-2758-2(0))* Dodo Pr.
Gardner, Ernest Arthur. Religion & Art in Ancient Greece. 2010. (ENG.). 140p. pap. 20.75 *(978-1-176-94007-9(4))* BiblioBazaar.
—Religion & Art in Ancient Greece. 2010. (Illus.). 40p. pap. 14.14 *(978-1-153-75484-2(3))* General Bks. LLC.
George, Jim & George, Kenneth M. Picturing Islam: Art & Ethics in a Muslim Lifeworld. 2010. (ENG., Illus.). 184p. 94.95 *(978-1-4051-2958-9(1),* Wiley-Blackwell) Wiley, John & Sons, Inc.
Gifford, Julie. Buddhist Practice & Visual Culture. 2011. (Routledge Critical Studies in Buddhism Ser.). (ENG., Illus.). 248p. (C). 138.00 *(978-0-415-78098-8(5))* Routledge.
Givens, Terryl C. People of Paradox: A History of Mormon Culture. 2007. (ENG., Illus.). 432p. 29.99 *(978-0-19-516711-5(2))* Oxford Univ. Pr., Inc.
Givens, Terryl L. People of Paradox: A History of Mormon Culture. 2012. (ENG., Illus.). 464p. pap. 24.95 ***(978-0-19-991598-9(9))*** Oxford Univ. Pr., Inc.
Goldburg, Peta. Religious Education & the Creative Arts. 2010. 272p. pap. *(978-3-639-27363-2(X))* VDM Verlag Dr. Mueller e.K.
Graham, Gordon. The Re-enchantment of the World: Art versus Religion. 2010. (ENG.). 224p. pap. 29.95 *(978-0-19-958137-5(1))* Oxford Univ. Pr., Inc.
—The Re-Enchantment of the World: Art Versus Religion. 2007. (ENG.). 176p. 75.00 *(978-0-19-926596-1(8))* Oxford Univ. Pr., Inc.
Grewe, Cordula A. Painting the Sacred in the Age of Romanticism: Ainting Religion in the Age of Romaniticism. 2009. (Histories of Vision Ser.). (Illus.). 436p. 124.95 *(978-0-7546-0645-1(7))* Ashgate Publishing Co.
Grundy, Gordy. Fortuna Now. 2007. 80p. pap. 74.85 *(978-1-4303-2126-2(1))* Lulu Enterprises Inc.
Haynes, Deborah J. Book of This Place: The Land, Art, & Spirituality. 2009. 212p. pap. 23.00 *(978-1-60608-703-9(7),* Pickwick Pubns.) Wipf & Stock Pubs.
Hofmann, Friedhelm. 'Kometenstreifen des Himmels' Über das Geistliche in der Kunst. 2nd ed. 2009. (GER., Illus.). 107p. *(978-3-429-03070-4(6))* Echter Wuerzburg.
Hughes, Amanda M. & Wood, Carolyn H. A Place for Meaning: Art, Faith, & Museum Culture. 2010. (Distributed for the Ackland Art Museum Ser.). (ENG., Illus.). 245p. pap. 30.00 *(978-0-9743656-3-3(7))* Univ. of North Carolina Pr.
Joby, Christopher Richard & Joby, C. R. Calvinism in the Arts: A Re-Assessment. 2007. (Studies in Philosophical Theology Ser.). (ENG., Illus.). 240p. (C). pap. 63.00 *(978-90-429-1923-5(X))* Peeters Pubs. & Booksellers BEL. Dist: Brown, David Bk. Co., The.
Kahan, Leonard, et al, eds. Surfaces: Color, Substances, & Ritual Applications on African Sculpture. 2009. (African Expressive Cultures Ser.). (ENG., Illus.). 536p. 75.00 *(978-0-253-35251-4(7),* 0253352517) Indiana Univ. Pr.
Klausen, Jytte. The Cartoons That Shook the World. 2009. (Illus.). 240p. 35.00 *(978-0-300-12472-9(4))* Yale Univ. Pr.
Korn, Irene. Judaism in Art. 2006. 128p. 17.95 *(978-1-59764-223-1(1))* New Line Bks.
Küster, Volker. Visual Arts & Religion. Alma, Hans & Barnard, Marcel, eds. 2011. (ENG.). 208p. pap. 44.95 *(978-3-8258-0708-5(8))* Lit Verlag DEU. Dist: Transaction Pubs.
Lee, Sonya S. Surviving Nirvana: Death of the Buddha in Chinese Visual Culture. 2010. (CHI., Illus.). 372p. ***(978-988-220-744-8(8))*** Hong Kong Univ. Pr.
—Surviving Nirvana: Death of the Buddha in Chinese Visual Culture. 2010. (ENG., Illus.). 372p. (gr. 17). 55.00 *(978-962-209-125-2(3))* Hong Kong Univ. Pr. HKG. Dist: Columbia Univ. Pr.
Leidy, Denise Patry. The Art of Buddhism: An Introduction to Its History & Meaning. 2009. (ENG., Illus.). 352p. pap. 29.95 *(978-1-59030-670-3(8))* Shambhala Pubns., Inc.
Loza, Steven, ed. Religion as Art: Guadalupe, Orishas, & Sufi. 2009. (ENG.). 367p. pap. 40.00 *(978-0-8263-4570-7(0))* Univ. of New Mexico Pr.
MacBeth, Sybil. Praying in Color: Drawing a New Path to God. 2007. (Active Prayer Ser.). (ENG., Illus.). 110p. (gr. 7). per. 16.95 *(978-1-55725-512-9(1))* Paraclete Pr., Inc.
Maleuvre, Didier. The Religion of Reality: Inquiry into the Self, Art, & Transcendence. 2006. 318p. 79.95 *(978-0-8132-1454-2(8))* Catholic Univ. of America Pr.
Maritain, Jacques. Art & Faith. *(978-0-8022-1055-5(4))* Philosophical Library, Inc.
Martin, Jean-Hubert. Arte Religione Politica: Art, Religion, Politics. 2008. (ENG., Illus.). 104p. 19.95 *(978-88-7439-236-0(2))* 5 Continents ITA. Dist: Hachette Bk. Group.
Merry, Eleanor. Art Inspired by Rudolf Steiner. (Illus.). 94p. pap. 55.00 *(978-0-85440-536-7(4),* 1457) Steiner, Rudolf Pr. GBR. Dist: Steiner, Rudolf Pr.
Meyer, Birgit, et al. Material Religion Volume 5 Issue 3: The Journal of Objects, Art & Belief. 2010. (Material Religion Ser.). (Illus.). 128p. pap. 59.95 *(978-1-84788-519-7(5))* Berg Pubs. GBR. Dist: Macmillan.
Miles, Margaret R. Carnal Knowing: Female Nakedness & Religious Meaning in the Christian West. 2006. (Illus.). 270p. pap. 27.00 *(978-1-59752-901-3(X),* Wipf and Stock) Wipf & Stock Pubs.
Morgan, David. The Embodied Eye: Religious Visual Culture & the Social Life of Feeling. 2012. (ENG., Illus.). 288p. 70.00 ***(978-0-520-27222-4(6));*** pap. 29.95 ***(978-0-520-27223-1(4))*** Univ. of California Pr.
Nasrallah, Laura, et al, eds. From Roman to Early Christian Thessalonike: Studies in Religion & Archaeology. 2011. (Harvard Theological Studies: 64). (ENG., Illus.). 350p. pap. 40.00 *(978-0-674-05322-9(2))* Harvard Univ. Pr.
Padhi, Braja Kishor. Religious Art & Architecture of North-East India. 2009. (Illus.). xix, 284p. *(978-81-7320-091-5(2),* Library of Congress — New Delhi Overseas Office) Agam Kala Prakashan.
Paleotti, Gabriele & McCuaig, William. Discourse on Sacred & Profane Images. 2012. pap. ***(978-1-60606-116-9(X))*** Getty Pubns.
Paul, Benjamin. Nuns & Reform Art in Early Modern Venice: The Architecture of Santi Cosma E Damiano & Its Decoration from Tintoretto to Tiepolo. 2012. (Illus.). 344p. 124.95 ***(978-1-4094-1186-4(9))*** Ashgate Publishing Co.
Pezzoli-Olgiati, Daria & Rowland, Christopher. Approaches to the Visual in Religion. 2011. (Research in Contemporary Religion Ser.). (ENG., Illus.). 268p. (C). 95.00 *(978-3-525-60442-7(4))* Vandenhoeck & Ruprecht GmbH & Co. KG DEU. Dist: ISD.
Polistena, Joyce Carol, et al. The Religious Paintings of Eugène Delacroix (1798-1863) The Initiator of the Style of Modern Religious Art. 2008. 368p. 119.95 *(978-0-7734-4973-2(6))* Mellen, Edwin Pr., The.
Pongracz, Patricia. Minding Traditions? Twentieth-Century Artists & the Judeo-Christian Legacy. 2006. 224p. pap. 40.00 *(978-1-904832-29-4(6))* Giles, D. Ltd. GBR. Dist: Antique Collectors' Club.
Pope Pius Xii & Pizzardo, Joseph. The Function of Art, Addresses of Pope Pius Xii: On Sacred Art, Instruction of the Supreme Sacred Congregation of the Holy Office. 2011. 12p. pap. 35.95 ***(978-1-258-04844-0(2))*** Literary Licensing, LLC.
Preziosi, Donald. Art Religion & Amnesia. 2012. (ENG.). 224p. (C). pap. 39.95 ***(978-0-415-77861-9(1))*** Routledge.
Quash, Ben. Theology & the Drama of History. 2008. (Cambridge Studies in Christian Doctrine Ser.). (ENG.). 252p. pap. 36.00 *(978-0-521-09082-7(2))* Cambridge Univ. Pr.
Read, Herbert. Art & Society. 216p. 2008. 39.95 *(978-1-4367-0772-5(2))* 2007. (ENG.). per. 24.95 *(978-1-4325-6833-7(7))* Kessinger Publishing, LLC.
Richardson, Keith. Doorways to Heaven: A Spiritual Journey Guided by Angels, Miracles & the Art of Andy Lakey. 2010. 256p. pap. 16.95 *(978-1-4327-6080-9(7))* Outskirts Pr., Inc.
Richter, Gottfried. Art & Human Consciousness. 272p. pap. 35.00 *(978-0-88010-478-4(3))* SteinerBooks, Inc.
Roncace, Mark & Gray, Patrick. Teaching the Bible Through Popular Culture & the Arts. 2008. 393p. *(978-90-04-15116-1(8))* BRILL.
—Teaching the Bible Through Popular Culture & the Arts. 2007. (Resources for Biblical Study Ser.). 37.95 *(978-1-58983-244-2(2))* Society of Biblical Literature.
Rosewell, Roger. Stained Glass. 2012. (Shire Library). (ENG., Illus.). 96p. pap. 12.95 ***(978-0-7478-1147-3(4))*** Shire Pubns., Ltd. GBR. Dist: Random Hse., Inc.
Ross, Leslie D. Art & Architecture of the World's Religions, 2 vols. 2009. (Illus.). 395p. 225.00 *(978-0-313-34286-8(5),* GR4286) Greenwood Publishing Group, Inc.
Rossi, Corinna. The Treasures of the Monastery of Saint Catherine. 2010. (ENG., Illus.). 208p. 40.00 *(978-88-544-0142-6(0))* White Star ITA. Dist: Sterling Publishing Co., Inc.
Roveda, Vittorio. Buddhist Painting in Cambodia. 2009. (ENG., Illus.). 200p. *(978-974-9863-52-7(6),* River Bks. Pr. Dist A C) Antique Collectors' Club.
Ruggier, Joe & John Paul. Pope Caesar's Wake- Letters to Pope Woytyla. 3rd ed. 2012. ***(978-1-897303-17-7(3))*** Multicultural Bks.
Sansi & Sansi-Roca, Roger. Fetishes & Monuments: Afro-Brazilian Art & Culture in the Twentieth Century. 2007. (Remapping Cultural History Ser.: Vol. 6). (Illus.). 224p. 90.00 *(978-1-84545-363-3(8))* Berghahn Bks., Inc.
Schaeffer, Francis A. Art & the Bible. 2006. (IVP Classics Ser.). (ENG.). 95p. (Orig.). per. 8.00 *(978-0-8308-3401-3(X),* IVP Bks.) InterVarsity Pr.
Schmidt, Maurice. The Tabernacle of Exodus as a Work of Art: An Aesthetic of Monotheism. 2010. (Illus.). xiv, 338p. *(978-0-7734-3782-1(7))* Mellen, Edwin Pr., The.
Schwain, Kristin. Signs of Grace: Religion & American Art in the Gilded Age. 2007. (Illus.). 172p. 29.95 *(978-0-8014-4577-4(9))* Cornell Univ. Pr.
Sharma, Charan. Brushing the Spirit: The Magical Art of Charan Sharma. 2006. (ENG., Illus.). 160p. 45.00 *(978-1-932771-90-9(5))* Mandala Publishing.
Shashibala & Shashibala. Divine Art. 2007. (ENG., Illus.). 143p. 19.95 *(978-81-7436-321-3(1))* Roli Bks. Private, Ltd. IND. Dist: Ingram Pub. Services.
Siedell, Daniel A. God in the Gallery: A Christian Embrace of Modern Art. 2008. (Cultural Exegesis Ser.). (Illus.). 192p. (C). pap. 25.00 *(978-0-8010-3184-7(2))* Baker Academic.
Skinner, Susan. Symbols of the Soul: Sacred Beasts. 2012. (ENG.). 84p. pap. 14.95 ***(978-1-84694-670-7(0))*** Hunt, John Publishing Ltd. GBR. Dist: National Bk. Network.
Smart, Pamela G. Sacred Modern: Faith, Activism, & Aesthetics in the Menil Collection. 2011. (ENG., Illus.). 294p. pap. 25.00 ***(978-0-292-73758-7(0));*** 45.00 *(978-0-292-72333-7(4))* Univ. of Texas Pr.
Smith, Brendan Powell. The Brick Bible: A New Spin on the Old Testament. 2011. (ENG., Illus.). 272p. pap. 19.95 *(978-1-61608-421-9(9),* 608421) Skyhorse Publishing Co., Inc.
Southcombe, George, ed. English Nonconformist Poetry, 1660-1700, 3 vols., Set. 2012. (ENG., Illus.). 1168p. 495.00 *(978-1-85196-965-4(9))* Pickering & Chatto Pubs., Ltd. GBR. Dist: Ashgate Publishing Co.
Spence, Bob. In the Beginning: The Art of Bob Spence. 2010. 48p. 29.95 *(978-0-692-00367-1(3))* Adonai Art Designs, LLC.
Spinks, Jennifer. Monstrous Births & Visual Culture in Sixteenth-Century Germany, 1 vol. 2009. (Religious Cultures in the Early Modern World Ser.). (ENG., Illus.). 224p. 99.00 *(978-1-85196-630-1(7))* Pickering & Chatto Pubs., Ltd. GBR. Dist: Ashgate Publishing Co.
Steiner, Rudolf. Rosicrucianism Renewed: The Unity of Art, Science, & Religion: the Theosophical Congress of Whitsun 1907. Allen, Joan deRis, ed. Post, Marsha, tr. from GER. 2007. (Collected Works of Rudolf Steiner: No. 284). (Illus.). 325p. per. 40.00 *(978-0-88010-611-5(5))* SteinerBooks, Inc.
Stephenson, Jody. Faltering Towards Perfection: Art, Faith, & Everything in Between. 2007. (Illus.). 192p. 24.95 *(978-0-9798998-0-5(X))* Planet Eureka Springs Pr.
Taylor, W. David O., ed. For the Beauty of the Church: Casting a Vision for the Arts, 1 vol. 2010. (ENG.). 208p. pap. 15.99 *(978-0-8010-7191-7(7))* Baker Bks.
Tepper, Steven J. Not Here, Not Now, Not That! Protest over Art & Culture in America. 2011. (ENG., Illus.). 384p. 90.00 *(978-0-226-79286-6(2));* pap. 30.00 *(978-0-226-79287-3(0))* Univ. of Chicago Pr.
Thistlethwaite, David. The Art of God & the Religions of Art. 2008. (Illus.). 198p. pap. 23.00 *(978-1-55635-721-3(4))* Wipf & Stock Pubs.
Thomsen, Arne. Die Wirkung der Götter: Bilder Mit Flügelfiguren auf Griechischen Vasen des 6. und 5. Jahrhunderts V. Chr. (Image & Context Ser.).Tr. of Impact of the Gods. (GER.). XII, 506p. 2012. (gr. 17). E-Book 210.00 ***(978-3-11-219164-4(1))*** 2011. (Illus.). 140.00 ***(978-3-11-023898-3(5))*** De Gruyter, Walter Inc.
Tisci, Riccardo, ed. Visionaire No. 60: Religion: Edited by Riccardo Tisci in Collaboration with Givenchy. 2011. (ENG., Illus.). 228p. 425.00 ***(978-1-888645-86-6(5))*** Visionaire Publishing.
Trungpa, Chogyam & Trungpa, Chögyam. True Perception: The Path of Dharma Art. Lief, Judith L., ed. 2nd rev. ed. 2008. (ENG., Illus.). 224p. pap. 18.95 *(978-1-59030-588-1(4))* Shambhala Pubns., Inc.
Verleysen, Catherine. Maurice Denis et la Belgique, 1890-1930. 2011. (KADOC Artes Ser.). (Illus.). 176p. 80.00 *(978-90-5867-808-9(3))* Leuven Univ. Pr. BEL. Dist: Cornell Univ. Pr.
Wainwright, Elaine Mary & Culbertson, Philip Leroy. The Bible In/And Popular Culture: Creative Encounter. 2010. vii, 210p. *(978-1-58983-493-4(3));* *(978-1-58983-494-1(1))* Society of Biblical Literature.
Weah, Lisa M. Creative Worship in a Contemporary Milieu. 2010. 110p. pap. 13.95 *(978-1-4327-5903-2(5))* Outskirts Pr., Inc.
Wehlander, Keri. Creating Change: The Arts as Catalyst for Spiritual Transformation. 2008. (ENG., Illus.). 160p. pap. 29.95 *(978-1-55145-568-6(4),* Copperhouse) Wood Lake Publishing, Inc. CAN. Dist: Westminster John Knox Pr.
Weisberg, Ruth, illus. Ruth Weisberg Unfurled. 2007. (ENG.). 96p. per. 19.95 *(978-0-9704295-7-5(6))* Skirball Cultural Ctr.
Williams, James A. Signs of God Religious Stained Glass Patterns: 35 Designs - 22 Pieces or Less! 2010. 41p. pap. 13.95 *(978-1-4327-6466-1(7))* Outskirts Pr., Inc.
Zock, T. H., ed. At the Crossroads of Art & Religion: Imagination, Commitment, Transcendence. 2008. (Groningen Studies in Cultural Change Ser.). (ENG.). 206p. (C). 70.00 *(978-90-429-2173-3(0))* Peeters Pubs. & Booksellers BEL. Dist: Brown, David Bk. Co., The.

ART AND SCIENCE

see also Medicine and Art; Scientific Illustration

Addison, Laura. The Art & Artifice of Science. 2007. pap. 24.95 *(978-0-9675106-9-9(4))* New Mexico Museum of Art.
Aerts, Diederik, et al, eds. Science & Art: The Red Book of 'Einstein Meets Magritte' 2010. (Einstein Meets Magritte: an Interdisciplinary Reflection on Science, Nature, Art, Human Action & Society Ser.). (Illus.). 288p. pap. 229.00 *(978-90-481-5241-4(0),* 9048152410) Springer.
Alexenberg, Mel. The Future of Art in a Postdigital Age: From Hellenistic to Hebraic Consciousness. 2nd ed. 2011. (ENG.). 270p. 60.00 *(978-1-84150-377-6(0))* Intellect, Ltd. GBR. Dist: Chicago Distribution Ctr.
Altaio, Vicenc. Think Art - Act Science: Artists in Labs. 2011. 96p. pap. *(978-84-92861-70-5(3))* Actar Birkhauser Distribution.
—Think Art - Act Science (Spanish Ed.) Artists in Labs. 2011. (SPA.). 96p. pap. *(978-84-92861-69-9(X))* Actar Birkhauser Distribution.
Anker, Suzanne & Talasek, J. D., eds. Visual Culture & Bioscience. 2009. (ENG., Illus.). 256p. pap. 19.95 *(978-1-890761-12-7(5))* Univ. of Maryland Baltimore County, Fine Arts Gallery.
Anker, Verena. Digital Dance. 2008. (Illus.). 68p. pap. *(978-3-639-00364-2(0))* VDM Verlag Dr. Mueller e.K.
Barrow, John. The Artful Universe Expanded. 2nd ed. 2011. (ENG., Illus.). 336p. pap. 19.95 *(978-0-19-960133-2(X))* Oxford Univ. Pr., Inc.

Bender, John B. & Marrinan, Michael. The Culture of Diagram. 2010. (ENG., Illus.). 296p. 60.00 *(978-0-8047-4504-8(8))*; pap. 2*.95 *(978-0-8047-4505-5(6))* Stanford Univ. Pr.

Benjamin, Patricia J. Pearson's Massage Therapy: Blending Art with Science. 2010. (ENG.). 800p. (C). pap. 79.47 *(978-0-13-229668-7(3)*, Prentice Hall) Prentice Hall PTR.

Bhadury, Poushali. Science, Literature, & Aesthetics. Dev, Amiya, ed. 2009. (Illus.). 851p. 175.00 *(978-81-87586-39-5(7))* Centre for Studies in Civilizations IND. Dist: Coronet Bks.

Blackwell, Stephen H. The Quill & the Scalpel: Nabokov's Art & the Worlds of Science. 2009. (ENG.). 320p. 69.95 *(978-0-8142-1099-4(6))*; cd-rom 14.95 *(978-0-8142-9197-9(X))* Ohio State Univ. Pr.

Blühm, Andreas. The Moon: "Houston, Tranquility Base Here. the Eagle Has Landed" 2009. pap. *(978-0-89090-170-0(8))* Museum of Fine Arts, Houston.

Breidbach, Olaf. Visions of Nature: The Art & Science of Ernst Haeckel. 2006. (Illus.). 320p. 100.00 *(978-3-7913-3664-0(9))* Prestel Publishing.

Brown, James Robert, et al, eds. Thought Experiments in Science, Philosophy, & the Arts. 2012. (Routledge Studies in the Philosophy of Science Ser.). (ENG., Illus.). 272p. (C). 125.00 *(978-0-415-88544-7(2))* Routledge.

Buckland, David. UNFOLD (Edition Angewandte) 2010. (Edition Angewandte Ser.). 120p. 49.95 *(978-3-7091-0220-6(0))* Springer Wien AUT. Dist: Springer.

Burguete, Maria. Arts: A Science Matter. 2011. 400p. 78.00 *(978-981-4324-93-9(0))* World Scientific Publishing Co., Inc.

Burke, Gregory, text. Universal Code: Art & Cosmology in the Information Age. 2010. (ENG., Illus.). 136p. 58.00 *(978-1-894212-28-1(2))* Power Plant, The CAN. Dist: D.A.P./Distributed Art Pubs.

Castel, Boris & Sismondo, Sergio. The Art of Science. 2nd ed. 2008. (ENG.). 200p. pap. *(978-1-4426-0098-0(5))* Univ. of Toronto Pr.

Castillo Deball, Mariana & Kopelman, Irene, eds. A for Alibi. 2007. (Illus.). 239p. pap. 29.95 *(978-1-933128-33-7(X))* Sternberg Pr.

Castro, Sixto J. & Marcos, Alfredo. The Paths of Creation: Creativity in Science & Art. 2011. (Natur, Wissenschaft und die Künste/Nature, Science & the Arts/Nature, Science et les Arts Ser.). (ENG.). 277p. pap. ***(978-3-0343-0511-2(7))*** Lang, Peter.

Clark, Constance Areson. God- Or Gorilla: Images of Evolution in the Jazz Age. 2008. (Medicine, Science, & Religion in Historical Context Ser.). (ENG., Illus.). 312p. (gr. 17). 36.00 *(978-0-8018-8825-0(5))* Johns Hopkins Univ. Pr.

Collier, Brian, et al. Say It Isn't So. Friese, Peter, ed. 2008. (GER & ENG., Illus.). 260p. 40.00 *(978-3-939583-30-1(8))* Kehrer Verlag Heidelberg, Klaus Kehrer DEU. Dist: Consortium Bk. Sales & Distribution.

Comfort, Alex. Darwin & the Naked Lady: Discursive Essays on Biology & Art. 2008. (Illus.). VIII, 176p. 140.00 *(978-0-415-47440-5(X))* Routledge.

Cottrell, Philip, et al. Leonardo Da Vinci: The Codex Leicester. 2007. (ENG., Illus.). 112p. pap. 29.95 *(978-1-85759-502-4(5))* Scala, Editions FRA. Dist: National Bk. Network.

Creagh, Dudley, ed. Physical Techniques in the Study of Art, Archaeology & Cultural Heritage, Vol. 2. 2007. (Physical Techniques in the Study of Art, Archaeology & Cultural Heritage Ser.: 2). (ENG., Illus.). 282p. 106.00 *(978-0-444-52856-8(3)*, Elsevier Science) Elsevier Science & Technology Bks.

Cuir, Raphael. The Development of the Study of Anatomy from the Renaissance to Cartesianism: Da Carpi, Vesalius, Estienne, Bidloo. 2009. (Illus.). 278p. 109.95 *(978-0-7734-4657-1(5))* Mellen, Edwin Pr., The.

da Costa, Beatriz & Philip, Kavita, eds. Tactical Biopolitics: Art, Activism, & Technoscience. (Leonardo Bks.). (ENG., Illus.). 536p. (gr. 17). 2010. pap. 20.00 *(978-0-262-51491-0(5))* 2008. 42.00 *(978-0-262-04249-9(5))* MIT Pr.

Dackerman, Susan, et al. Prints & the Pursuit of Knowledge in Early Modern Europe. 2011. (ENG., Illus.). 442p. pap. 60.00 *(978-0-300-17107-5(2))* Yale Univ. Pr.

Daniels, et al. Artists As Inventors, Inventors As Artists. 2008. (ENG., Illus.). 240p. pap. 45.00 *(978-3-7757-2153-0(3))* Hatje Cantz Verlag GmbH & Co KG DEU. Dist: D.A.P./Distributed Art Pubs.

Daston, Lorraine, ed. Things That Talk: Object Lessons from Art & Science. 2007. (ENG., Illus.). 447p. (gr. 17). per. 21.95 *(978-1-890951-44-3(7))* Zone Bks.

Debus, Allen A. & Debus, Diane E. Paleoimagery: The Evolution of Dinosaurs in Art. alt. ed. 2011. (ENG., Illus.). 293p. pap. 45.00 *(978-0-7864-6420-3(8))* McFarland & Co., Inc. Pubs.

Deifel, Valerie, et al, eds. An Envelope for Arts, Sciences, Politics & Us: Mixing Realities & Mediating Myths & Methods. 2012. (Edition Angewandte Ser.). (ENG., Illus.). 244p. pap. 39.95 ***(978-3-7091-0989-2(2)***, 3709109892) Springer Wien AUT. Dist: Springer.

Donald, Diana, et al, eds. Endless Forms: Charles Darwin, Natural Science, & the Visual Arts. 2009. (ENG., Illus.). 346p. 75.00 *(978-0-300-14826-8(7))* Yale Univ. Pr.

Douglas, Janet G., et al, told to. Scientific Research in the Field of Asian Art: Proceedings of the First Forbes Symposium at the Feer Gallery of Art. 2007. (ENG., Illus.). 208p. 120.00 *(978-1-873132-38-8(7))* Archetype Pubns. GBR. Dist: National Bk. Network.

Edwards, David. Artscience: Creativity in the Post-Google Generation. 2010. 208p. pap. 17.00 *(978-0-674-03464-8(3))* Harvard Univ. Pr.

—The Lab: Creativity & Culture. 2010. (ENG., Illus.). 224p. 22.95 *(978-0-674-05719-7(8))* Harvard Univ. Pr.

Elkins, James. The Drunken Conversation Between Science & Painting. *(978-0-8047-3781-4(9))*; pap. *(978-0-8047-3782-1(7))* Stanford Univ. Pr.

—Six Stories from the End of Representation: Images in Painting, Photography, Astronomy, Microscopy, Particle Physics, & Quantum Mechanics, 1980-2000. 2008. (Writing Science Ser.). (ENG.). 320p. 65.00 *(978-0-8047-4147-7(6))*; (Illus.). per. 29.95 *(978-0-8047-4148-4(4))* Stanford Univ. Pr.

Fogel, Krista M. The Experience of Doing Science with an Artistic Spirit. 2009. 124p. pap. *(978-3-639-15800-7(8))* VDM Verlag Dr. Mueller e.K.

Fryer, Paul. Radiations. Beard, Jason, ed. 2008. (Illus.). 96p. (ENG.). 70.00 *(978-1-904212-19-5(0))*; 120.00 *(978-1-904212-38-6(7))* Other Criteria GBR. Dist: Hachette Bk. Group, Abrams.

Fulda, Daniel. Wissenschaft aus Kunst: Die Entstehung der modernen deutschen Geschichtsschreibung 1760-1860. (European Cultures Ser.). (GER.). IX, 547p. 255.00 ***(978-3-11-175828-2(1))*** De Gruyter, Walter Inc.

Fusillo, Lawrence J. Fusillo Knowledge Infrastructure: Knowledge Classification System. 2011. pap. 39.95 ***(978-0-7414-6647-1(3))*** Infinity Publishing.

Gere, Charlie & Gardiner, Hazel, eds. Art Practice in a Digital Culture. 2010. (Digital Research in the Arts & Humanities Ser.). (Illus.). 226p. 99.95 *(978-0-7546-7523-2(4))* Ashgate Publishing Co.

Gonzales, Laurence. Surviving Survival: The Art & Science of Resilience. 2012. (ENG.). 304p. 26.95 ***(978-0-393-08318-7(7)***, 8318) Norton, W. W. & Co., Inc.

Gorman, Michael John, ed. A Mysterious Masterpiece: The World of the Linder Gallery. 2010. (ENG., Illus.). 135p. pap. 17.50 *(978-88-96532-02-7(7))* Mandragora ITA. Dist: Antique Collectors' Club.

Grau, Oliver. MediaArtHistories. 2010. (Leonardo Bks.). (ENG., Illus.). 488p. (gr. 17). pap. 23.00 *(978-0-262-51498-9(2))* MIT Pr.

Gross, Charles G. A Hole in the Head: More Tales in the History of Neuroscience. 2012. (ENG., Illus.). 368p. (gr. 17). pap. 18.00 ***(978-0-262-51733-1(7))*** MIT Pr.

Gross, Charles G. & Gross, C. A Hole in the Head: More Tales in the History of Neuroscience. 2009. (ENG., Illus.). 368p. (gr. 17). 35.00 *(978-0-262-01338-3(X))* MIT Pr.

Hallager, Erik. Science & Art: Present Activities of the Danish Institute at Athens. 2006. (ENG., Illus.). 64p. (C). pap. 13.00 *(978-87-7934-117-3(9))* Aarhus Universitetsforlag DNK. Dist: ISD.

Hauser, Jens, ed. Sk-Interfaces: Exploding Borders in Art, Science & Technology. 2008. (ENG., Illus.). 160p. 50.00 *(978-1-84631-149-9(7))* Liverpool Univ. Pr. GBR. Dist: Chicago Distribution Ctr.

Jackson, Lesley. From Atoms to Patterns: Crystal Structure Designs from the 1951 Festival of Britain: The Story of the Festival Pattern Group. 2010. (ENG., Illus.). 124p. pap. 40.00 *(978-0-9553741-1-1(1))* Dennis, Richard Pubns. GBR. Dist: National Bk. Network.

Kemp, Martin. Leonardo Da Vinci: Experience, Experiment, & Design. 2006. (ENG., Illus.). 224p. 60.00 *(978-0-691-12905-1(3))* Princeton Univ. Pr.

—Seen/Unseen: Art, Science, & Intuition from Leonardo to the Hubble Telescope. 2006. (ENG., Illus.). 368p. 60.00 *(978-0-19-929572-2(7))* Oxford Univ. Pr., Inc.

Kremers, David. White Paper, Black Space: Science Images That Don't Leave the Audience in the Dark. 2007. (Illus.). 150p. 59.00 *(978-0-87969-671-9(0))* Cold Spring Harbor Laboratory Pr.

Kusukawa, Sachiko. Picturing the Book of Nature: Image, Text, & Argument in Sixteenth-Century Human Anatomy & Medical Botany. 2012. (ENG., Illus.). 304p. 45.00 *(978-0-226-46529-6(2))* Univ. of Chicago Pr.

Leavy, Patricia. Method Meets Art: Arts-Based Research Practice. 2008. (ENG., Illus.). 286p. 60.00 *(978-1-59385-843-8(4))*; pap. 40.00 *(978-1-59385-259-7(2))* Guilford Pubns., Inc.

Lee, Laura & Lombaerde, Piet, eds. Comparative Methodologies: The World into Culture - Liber Amicorum Richard Focque. 2010. (ENG., Illus.). 368p. pap. 57.00 *(978-90-5487-630-4(1))* VUB Univ. Pr. BEL. Dist: Independent Pubs. Group.

Leibowitz, J. R. Hidden Harmony: The Connected Worlds of Physics & Art. 2008. (ENG., Illus.). 160p. 28.00 *(978-0-8018-8866-3(2))* Johns Hopkins Univ. Pr.

Lischka, Christoph & Sick, Andrea, eds. Machines as Agency: Artistic Perspectives. 2008. (ENG., Illus.). 248p. (gr. 11). pap. 34.95 *(978-3-89942-646-5(0))* Transcript Verlag DEU. Dist: Transaction Pubs.

Lising, Ian T. Across the House the Art & Science of World Universities Championship Debating. 2011. (ENG.). 154p. pap. 52.88 *(978-0-7575-7410-8(6))* Kendall Hunt Publishing Co.

Marr, Alexander. Between Raphael & Galileo: Mutio Oddi & the Mathematical Culture of Late Renaissance Italy. 2011. (ENG., Illus.). 384p. 45.00 *(978-0-226-50628-9(2))* Univ. of Chicago Pr.

Marshall, Alan. Wild Design: Ecofriendly Innovations Inspired by Nature. 2009. (ENG., Illus.). 168p. pap. 18.95 *(978-1-55643-790-8(0))* North Atlantic Bks.

MARTIN, Stanley. General (bLACK_bOX) Theory of re-CONSTRUCTION: (YES!) 2007. 542p. pap. 62.50 *(978-1-84753-690-7(5))* Lulu Enterprises Inc.

Meyers, Amy R. W. & O'Malley, Therese, eds. The Art of Natural History: Illustrated Treatises & Botanical Paintings, 1400-1850. 2008. (Studies in the History of Art Ser.). (ENG., Illus.). 280p. 65.00 *(978-0-300-12158-2(X))* National Gallery of Art.

Mignonneau, Laurent. Christa Sommerer & Laurent Mignonneau: Interactive Art Research. Stocker, Gerfried & Sommerer, Christa, eds. 2009. (ENG., Illus.). 232p. 59.95 *(978-3-211-99015-5(1)*, 3211990151) Springer.

Munira, Nasreen. Information Needs & Seeking Behavior of Media Practitioners: A Case of Media Practitioners Working in Radio, Tv & News Paper Houses of Karachi. 2011. 268p. pap. ***(978-3-639-32576-8(1))*** VDM Verlag Dr. Mueller e.K.

Najafi, Sina, ed. Cabinet 43: Forensics. 2011. (ENG., Illus.). 112p. pap. 12.00 ***(978-1-932698-42-8(6))*** Cabinet.

Obrist, Hans Ulrich. Formulas for Now. 2008. (ENG., Illus.). 160p. 24.95 *(978-0-500-23850-9(2))* Thames & Hudson.

O'Malley, Therese & Meyers, Amy R. W., eds. The Art of Natural History: Illustrated Treatises & Botanical Paintings, 1400-1850. 2010. (Studies in the History of Art Ser.). (ENG., Illus.). 280p. 45.00 *(978-0-300-16024-6(0))* National Gallery of Art.

Popper, Frank. From Technological to Virtual Art. 2006. (Leonardo Bks.). (ENG., Illus.). 504p. (gr. 17). 50.00 *(978-0-262-16230-2(X))* MIT Pr.

Post, Jeffrey. Modern Technology. 2008. 128p. pap. *(978-3-639-08679-9(1))* VDM Verlag Dr. Mueller e.K.

Reeves, Daniel M. G. S. A Treatise on the Science of Music. 2011. (Cambridge Library Collection - Music Ser.). (ENG.). 246p. pap. 22.99 ***(978-1-108-03880-5(8))*** Cambridge Univ. Pr.

Reichle, Ingeborg. Art in the Age of Technoscience: Genetic Engineering, Robotics, & Artificial Life in Contemporary Art. 2009. (Illus.). 452p. pap. *(978-3-211-78160-9(9)*, 3211781609) Actar Birkhauser Distribution.

Rothenberg, David. The Survival of the Beautiful: Art, Science, & Evolution. 2011. (ENG., Illus.). 320p. 30.00 *(978-1-60819-216-8(4))* Bloomsbury Publishing.

Rousseau, Jean-Jacques. Discours sur les Sciences et les Arts: Avec: Discours sur l'Origine et l'Inegalite. (Folio Ser.: No. 1874). (FRE.). pap. 12.95 *(978-2-07-037874-6(8))* Schoenhof's Foreign Bks., Inc.

Sala, Nicoletta, ed. Chaos & Complexity in Arts & Architecture. 2006. 178p. (C). 39.00 *(978-1-60021-232-1(8))* Nova Science Pubs., Inc.

Schafhausen, Nicolaus, ed. Edith Dekyndt: I Remember Earth, 1 vol. 2010. (ENG.). 288p. 74.00 *(978-2-9600513-5-3(1))* Exhibitions International BEL. Dist: Innovative Logistics.

Schmalzried, Hermann. Zeichen, Bilder, Modelle: ästhetische Betrachtungen in Kunst und Naturwissenschaft. 2008. (GER., Illus.). 51p. pap. *(978-3-7776-1639-1(7))* Hirzel, S. Verlag GmbH & Co.

Schopf, Christine & Stocker, Gerfried, eds. Ars Electronica 2010: Repair - sind wir noch zu retten. 2011. (ENG & GER., Illus.). 468p. pap. 45.00 *(978-3-7757-2723-5(X))* Hatje Cantz Verlag GmbH & Co KG DEU. Dist: D.A.P./Distributed Art Pubs.

Schramm, Helmar, et al. Instruments in Art & Science: On the Architectonics of Cultural Boundaries in the 17th Century. 2008. (ENG., Illus.). XXVII, 575p. 189.00 *(978-3-11-020240-3(9))* De Gruyter, Walter Inc.

Science Museum Staff, ed. FutureWorld: Where Science Fiction Becomes Science. 2008. (ENG., Illus.). 128p. 23.50 *(978-0-7522-2672-9(X)*, Macmillan) Pan Macmillan GBR. Dist: Trans-Atlantic Pubns., Inc.

Scott, Jill. ARTISTS-in-LABS: Networking in the Margins. 2010. (Illus.). 212p. pap. 49.95 *(978-3-7091-0320-3(7))* Springer Wien AUT. Dist: Springer.

Smarandache, Florentin. Neogeometrism. 2007. (Illus.). 132p. *(978-1-59973-023-3(5))* Multimedia Larga.

Smith, Pamela H. The Body of the Artisan: Art & Experience in the Scientific Revolution. 2006. (Illus.). 408p. pap. 40.00 *(978-0-226-76423-8(0))* Univ. of Chicago Pr.

Syme, Alison & Sargent, John Singer. A Touch of Blossom: John Singer Sargent & the Queer Flora of Fin-de-Siècle Art. 2010. (ENG.). 328p. 74.95 *(978-0-271-03622-9(2))* Pennsylvania State Univ. Pr.

Thompson, Ronald S. Attacking the Standardized Exam: The Art of Mastering Multiple Choice Standardized Tests. 2011. 112p. 24.99 ***(978-1-4634-2206-6(7))***; pap. 15.99 ***(978-1-4634-2207-3(5))*** AuthorHouse.

Uman, Martin A. The Art & Science of Lightning Protection. 2008. (ENG., Illus.). 254p. 114.00 *(978-0-521-87811-1(X))* Cambridge Univ. Pr.

Vanderbeeken, Robrecht, et al, eds. Drunk on Capitalism: An Interdisciplinary Reflection on Market Economy, Art & Science. 2011. (Einstein Meets Magritte: an Interdisciplinary Reflection on Science, Nature, Art, Human Action & Society Ser.). (ENG., Illus.). xxiii, 180p. 139.00 ***(978-94-007-2081-7(5)***, 9400720815) Springer.

Vickers-Rich, Patricia, et al. The Artist & the Scientists: Bringing Prehistory to Life, 1 vol. 2010. (ENG., Illus.). 320p. pap. 48.00 *(978-0-521-16299-9(8))* Cambridge Univ. Pr.

Waldvogel, Christian, et al. Christian Waldvogel: Earth Extremes. 2010. (GER & ENG., Illus.). 495p. 110.00 *(978-3-85881-305-3(2))* Scheidegger und Spiess AG, Verlag CHE. Dist: Antique Collectors' Club.

Wheye, Darryl & Kennedy, Donald. Humans, Nature, & Birds: Science Art from Cave Walls to Computer Screens. (ENG., Illus.). 240p. 2009. pap. 22.00 *(978-0-300-15862-5(9))* 2008. 37.50 *(978-0-300-12388-3(4))* Yale Univ. Pr.

Wilder, Kelley. Photography & Science. 2009. (Reaktion Books - Exposures Ser.). (ENG., Illus.). 144p. pap. 29.95 *(978-1-86189-399-4(X))* Reaktion Bks., Ltd. GBR. Dist: Chicago Distribution Ctr.

Williams, Kim, ed. Crossroads: History of Science, History of Art: Essays by David Speiser, vol. II. 2011. (ENG., Illus.). xii, 154p. 89.95 *(978-3-0348-0138-6(6)*, 3034801386) Birkhauser Verlag AG CHE. Dist: Springer.

Wilson, Stephen. Art + Science Now: How Scientific Research & Technological Innovation Are Becoming Key to 21st-Century Aesthetics. 2010. (ENG., Illus.). 208p. 50.00 *(978-0-500-23868-4(5)*, 523868) Thames & Hudson.

Winter, John, ed. Scientific Research on the Pictorial Arts of Asia: Proceedings of the Second Forbes Symposium at the Freer Gallery of Art. 2007. (ENG., Illus.). 166p. 120.00 *(978-1-873132-74-6(3))* Archetype Pubns. GBR. Dist: National Bk. Network.

Wolfson, Rutger, ed. This Is the Flow: the Museum as a Space for Ideas. 2009. (ENG., Illus.). 260p. pap. 32.50 *(978-90-78088-24-0(9))* Valiz NLD. Dist: D.A.P./Distributed Art Pubs.

Xenakis, Iannis. Arts/Sciences: Alloys. Kanach, Sharon, tr. 2010. 143p. pap. 48.00 *(978-1-57647-189-0(6))* Pendragon Pr.

Zielinski, Siegfried & Fürlus, Eckhard, eds. Variantology 4: On Deep Time Relations of Arts, Sciences & Technologies in the Arabic-Islamic World & Beyond. 2011. (ENG., Illus.). 518p. pap. 75.00 *(978-3-86560-732-4(2))* Verlag der Buchhandlung Walther Konig DEU. Dist: D.A.P./Distributed Art Pubs.

ART AND SOCIETY

see also Art and Religion; Art and State; Art Industries and Trade; Folk Art; Street Art

Adams, Ann Jensen. Public Faces & Private Identities in Seventeenth Century Holland: Portraiture & the Production of Community. 2009. (ENG., Illus.). 412p. 103.00 *(978-0-521-44455-2(1))* Cambridge Univ. Pr.

Adamson, Glenn, et al, eds. Global Design History. 2011. (ENG., Illus.). 240p. (C). 120.00 *(978-0-415-57285-9(1))*; pap. 39.95 *(978-0-415-57287-3(8))* Routledge.

Ades, Dawn & McClean, Alison. Revolution on Paper: Mexican Prints 1910-1960. 2009. (ENG., Illus.). 192p. pap. 39.95 *(978-0-292-72248-4(6))* Univ. of Texas Pr.

Alberro, Alexander & Stimson, Blake, eds. Institutional Critique: An Anthology of Artists′ Writings. 2011. (ENG., Illus.). 512p. (gr. 17). pap. 21.95 ***(978-0-262-51664-8(0))*** MIT Pr.

Allen, Felicity. Education. 2011. (Whitechapel: Documents of Contemporary Art Ser.). (ENG.). 240p. (gr. 17). pap. 24.95 *(978-0-262-51636-5(5))* MIT Pr.

Amariglio, Jack. Sublime Economy: On the intersection of art & Economics. 2010. pap. 42.95 *(978-0-415-78121-3(3))* Routledge.

Ames, Kenneth L. American Christmas Cards, 1900-1960. 2011. (ENG., Illus.). 320p. pap. 40.00 *(978-0-300-17687-2(2))* Yale Univ. Pr.

Amorales, Carlos. Escultura Social: A New Generation of Art from Mexico City. Widholm, Julie Rodrigues, ed. 2007. (SPA & ENG., Illus.). 224p. pap. 39.95 *(978-0-300-13427-8(4))* Yale Univ. Pr.

Andersen, Ivar & Borg, Kristian. Playground Sweden. 2007. (ENG.). 144p. (YA). 29.95 *(978-91-85639-07-6(9))* Dokument forlag, Fotograf Malcolm Jacobsson SWE. Dist: SCB Distributors.

Antliff, Allan. Anarchy & Art: From the Paris Commune to the Fall of the Berlin Wall. 2007. (ENG., Illus.). 224p. pap. 23.95 *(978-1-55152-218-0(7))* Arsenal Pulp Pr. CAN. Dist: Consortium Bk. Sales & Distribution.

Apel, Dora. War Culture & the Contest of Images. 2012. (New Directions in International Studies). 272p. 72.00 ***(978-0-8135-5395-5(4))***; pap. 29.95 ***(978-0-8135-5394-8(6))*** Rutgers Univ. Pr.

Areford, David. The View & the Printed Image in Late Medieval Europe. 2010. (Visual Culture in Early Modernity Ser.). (Illus.). 346p. 124.95 *(978-0-7546-6762-9(6))* Ashgate Publishing Co.

Ater, Renée & Fuller, Meta Warrick. Remaking Race & History: The Sculpture of Meta Warrick Fuller. 2011. (ENG., Illus.). 208p. 49.95 *(978-0-520-26212-6(3))* Univ. of California Pr.

Atkinson, Dennis. Art, Equality & Learning: Pedagogies Against the State. 2011. 194p. ***(978-94-6091-453-9(5))***; pap. ***(978-94-6091-452-2(7))*** Sense Pubs.

Auther, Elissa. West of Center: Art & the Counterculture Experiment in America, 1965-1977. Lerner, Adam, ed. 2011. (ENG., Illus.). 448p. pap. 39.95 ***(978-0-8166-7726-9(3))*** Univ. of Minnesota Pr.

Auther, Elissa & Lerner, Adam, eds. West of Center: Art & the Counterculture Experiment in America, 1965-1977. 2011. (ENG., Illus.). 448p. 120.00 ***(978-0-8166-7725-2(5))*** Univ. of Minnesota Pr.

Bal, Mieke, et al. Digital & Other Virtualities: Renegotiating the Image. Pollock, Griselda, ed. 2010. (New Encounters: Arts, Cultures, Concepts Ser.). (ENG., Illus.). 320p. pap. 30.00 *(978-1-84511-568-5(6))* I. B. Tauris & Co., Ltd. GBR. Dist: Macmillan.

Baladran, Zbynek & Havranek, Vit, eds. Atlas of Transformation. 2011. (ENG., Illus.). 724p. pap. 45.00 *(978-3-03764-147-7(9))* JRP Ringier Kunstverlag AG CHE. Dist: D.A.P./Distributed Art Pubs.

Banca della Svizzera italiana Staff, contrib. by. Free Zone - China. 2008. (ITA & ENG., Illus.). 174p. 22.00 *(978-3-905829-61-7(4))* JRP Ringier Kunstverlag AG CHE. Dist: D.A.P./Distributed Art Pubs.

Bankowsky, Jack, et al, eds. Pop Life: Art in a Material World. 2010. (ENG., Illus.). 208p. pap. 60.00 *(978-1-85437-920-7(8))* Tate Publishing, Ltd. GBR. Dist: Hachette Bk. Group.

Barker, Elizabeth E. & Wright, Joseph. Joseph Wright of Derby in Liverpool. Kidson, Alex & Barker, Elizabeth, eds. 2008. (ENG., Illus.). 224p. (C). 75.00 *(978-0-300-11745-5(0))* Yale Ctr. for British Art.

Barrett, Estelle. Kristeva Reframed: A Guide for the Arts Student. 2011. (Contemporary Thinkers Reframed Ser.). (ENG., Illus.). 160p. pap. 25.00 *(978-1-84511-660-6(7))* I. B. Tauris & Co., Ltd. GBR. Dist: Macmillan.

Barringer, Tim. Art & the British Empire. Quilley, Geoff et al, eds. 2007. (ENG., Illus.). 464p. 94.00 *(978-0-7190-7392-2(8))* Manchester Univ. Pr. GBR. Dist: Macmillan.

Bartsch, Tatjana, et al, eds. Das Originale der Kopie: Kopien als Produkte und Medien der Transformation von Antike. 2010. (Transformationen der Antike Ser.).Tr. of Originality of Copies. (GER., Illus.). VIII, 349p. 112.00 *(978-3-11-022544-0(1))* De Gruyter, Walter Inc.

Becker, Howard S. Art Worlds. 25th ed. 2008. (Illus.). 408p. pap. 26.95 *(978-0-520-25636-1(0))* Univ. of California Pr.

Becker, Howard Saul. Telling about Society. 2007. (Chicago Guides to Writing, Editing, & Publishing Ser.). (ENG., Illus.). 304p. 40.00 *(978-0-226-04125-4(5))*; per. 15.00 *(978-0-226-04126-1(3))* Univ. of Chicago Pr.

Becker, Konrad & Fleming, Jim, eds. Critical Strategies in Art & Media: Perspectives on New Cultural Practices. 2010. (ENG.). 182p. pap. 12.95 *(978-1-57027-214-1(X))* Autonomedia.

Beckmann, Max. Of Truths Impossible to Put in Words: Max Beckmann Contextualized. Long, Rose-Carol Washton & Makela, Maria Martha, eds. 2009. (Illus.). 436p. pap. 68.95 (978-3-03910-704-9(6)) Lang, Peter AG GBR. Dist: Lang, Peter.

Bedard, Jean-Francois. Decorative Games: Ornament, Rhetoric, & Noble Culture in the Work of Gilles-Marie Oppenord, 1672-1742. 2011. (Studies in Seventeenth- & Eighteenth- Century Art & Culture Ser.). (ENG & FRE., Illus.). 288p. 75.00 (978-1-61149-008-4(1)) Univ. of Delaware Pr.

Bédard, Jean-François & Oppenord, Gilles-Marie. Decorative Games: Ornament, Rhetoric, & Noble Culture in the Work of Gilles-Marie Oppenord (1672-1742) 2010. (978-0-87413-097-3(2)) Univ. of Delaware Pr.

Bedford, Christopher & Walker, Hamza. Mark Bradford. 2010. (Illus.). 256p. 65.00 (978-0-300-16358-2(4)) Yale Univ. Pr.

Beller, Jonathan. Acquiring Eyes: Philippine Visuality, Nationalist Struggle, & the World-Media System. 2008. 336p. (C). pap. 87.00 (978-971-550-495-9(7)) Univ. of Hawaii Pr.

Bellion, Wendy. Citizen Spectator: Art, Illusion, & Visual Perception in Early National America. 2011. (Published for the Omohundro Institute of Early American History & Culture, Williamsburg, Virginia Ser.). (ENG., Illus.). 388p. 45.00 (978-0-8078-3388-9(6)) Univ. of North Carolina Pr.

Belting, Hans & Buddensieg, Andrea, eds. The Global Art World. 2009. (ENG., Illus.). 408p. pap. 45.00 (978-3-7757-2407-4(9)) Hatje Cantz Verlag GmbH & Co KG DEU. Dist: D.A.P./Distributed Art Pubs.

Benfey, Christopher. Red Brick, Black Mountain, White Clay: Reflections on Art, Family, & Survival. 2012. (ENG.). 288p. (gr. 12). 25.95 (978-1-59420-326-8(1), Penguin Pr. HC, The) Penguin Group (USA) Inc.

Benjamin, Walter. The Work of Art in the Age of Its Technological Reproducibility, & Other Writings on Media. Jennings, Michael W. et al, eds. Jephcott, Edmund & Livingstone, Rodney, trs. from GER. 2008. (Illus.). 448p. pap. 18.95 (978-0-674-02445-8(1), Belknap Pr.) Harvard Univ. Pr.

Bentkowska-Kafel, Anna, et al. Digital Visual Culture: Theory & Practice. Bentkowska-Kafel, Anna et al, eds. 2009. (Intellect Books - Computers & the History of Art Ser.). (ENG., Illus.). 112p. pap. 40.00 (978-1-84150-248-9(0)) Intellect, Ltd. GBR. Dist: Chicago Distribution Ctr.

Bently, Tamara Heimarck. The Figurative Works of Chen Hongshou, 1599-1652: Authentic Voices/Expanding Markets. 2012. (Visual Culture in Early Modernity Ser.). (Illus.). 320p. 124.95 (978-0-7546-6672-1(7)) Ashgate Publishing Co.

Bernier, Ronald R., ed. Beyond Belief. 2010. (Illus.). 150p. pap. 19.00 (978-1-60899-087-0(7), Pickwick Pubns.) Wipf & Stock Pubs.

Bessire, Mark H. C. & Bessire, Mark. Stairway to Heaven: From Chinese Streets to Monuments & Skyscrapers. 2009. (ENG & CHI., Illus.). 148p. pap. 29.95 (978-1-58465-728-6(6)) Univ. Pr. of New England.

Bills, Mark, et al. Dickens & the Artists. 2012. (ENG., Illus.). 200p. 55.00 (978-0-300-17602-5(3)) Yale Univ. Pr.

Bingham, Shawn Chandler, et al. The Art of Social Critique: Painting Mirrors of Social Life. 2012. (ENG.). 594p. (gr. 17). 105.00 (978-0-7391-4923-2(7)) Lexington Bks.

Bishop, Claire. Artificial Hells: Participatory Art & the Politics of Spectatorship. 2012. (ENG., Illus.). 368p. pap. 26.95 (978-1-84467-690-3(0), 844690) Verso Bks. GBR. Dist: Norton, W. W. & Co., Inc.

Blanco Cano, Rosana. Cuerpos Disidentes Del México Imaginado: Cultura, Género, Etnia y Nación Más Allá Del Proyecto Posrevolucionario. 2010. (SPA., Illus.). 225p. pap. 29.80 (978-84-8489-509-1(2)) Iberoamericana Vervuert Publishing Corp.

Blom, Ina. On the Style Site. 2007. (Illus.). 264p. pap. 29.95 (978-1-933128-30-6(5)) Sternberg Pr.

Boime, Albert. Art in an Age of Civil Struggle, 1848-1871. 2008. (Social History of Modern Art Ser.). (Illus.). 784p. 65.00 (978-0-226-06328-7(3)) Univ. of Chicago Pr.

—Revelation of Modernism: Responses to Cultural Crises in Fin-de-Siècle Painting. 2008. (ENG., Illus.). 304p. (C). 54.95 (978-0-8262-1780-6(X)) Univ. of Missouri Pr.

Bolton King, Michelle, ed. Phantasmania. 2008. (ENG., Illus.). 96p. 29.95 (978-1-891246-15-9(1)) Kemper Museum of Contemporary Art & Design.

Bosch, Lindsay J. & Mancoff, Debra. Icons of Beauty: Art, Culture, & the Image of Women, 2 vols. 2009. (Greenwood Icons Ser.). (Illus.). 746p. 175.00 (978-0-313-33821-2(3), GR3821) Greenwood Publishing Group, Inc.

Boullata, Kamal. Palestinian Art: From 1850 to the Present. 2009. (ENG., Illus.). 363p. pap. 34.95 (978-0-86356-648-6(0)) Saqi Bks. GBR. Dist: Consortium Bk. Sales & Distribution.

Braddock, Alan C. Thomas Eakins & the Cultures of Modernity. 2009. (ENG., Illus.). 304p. 55.00 (978-0-520-25520-3(8)) Univ. of California Pr.

Brauer, Fae & Callen, Anthea. Art, Sex & Eugenics: Corpus Delecti. Brauer, Fae & Callen, Anthea, eds. 2008. (Illus.). 316p. 134.95 (978-0-7546-5827-6(9)) Ashgate Publishing Co.

Briefel, Aviva. The Deceivers: Art Forgery & Identity in the Nineteeth Century. 2006. (Illus.). 243p. 45.95 (978-0-8014-4460-9(8)) Cornell Univ. Pr.

Brockman, John. Culture: Leading Scientists Explore Societies, Art, Power, & Technology. 2011. (ENG.). 288p. pap. 14.99 (978-0-06-202313-1(6), HarperPerennial) HarperCollins Pubs.

Bronfen, Elisabeth. Crossmappings: Essays on Visual Culture. 2010. (Illus.). 256p. 49.00 (978-3-85881-715-0(5)) Scheidegger und Spiess AG, Verlag CHE. Dist: Chicago Distribution Ctr.

Brown, Kathryn. Women Readers in French Painting 1870-1890: A Space for the Imagination. 2012. (Illus.). 272p. 124.95 (978-1-4094-0875-8(2)) Ashgate Publishing Co.

Bruce, Katie & Hollows, Victoria. Towards an Engaged Gallery: Contemporary art & human Rights. 2007. (Illus.). 96p. per. (978-0-902752-88-7(X)) Glasgow Museums.

Bruno, Giuliana. Public Intimacy: Architecture & the Visual Arts. 2007. (Writing Architecture Ser.). (ENG., Illus.). 256p. (gr. 17). pap. 24.95 (978-0-262-52465-0(1)) MIT Pr.

Buick, Kirsten. Child of the Fire: Mary Edmonia Lewis & the Problem of Art History's Black & Indian Subject. 2010. (ENG., Illus.). 344p. 94.95 (978-0-8223-4247-2(2)); pap. 25.95 (978-0-8223-4266-3(9)) Duke Univ. Pr.

Burgin, Victor. Parallel Texts: Interviews & Interventions about Art. 2011. (ENG., Illus.). 248p. pap. 35.00 (978-1-86189-813-5(4)) Reaktion Bks., Ltd. GBR. Dist: Chicago Distribution Ctr.

Burke, Jill & Bury, Michael. Art & Identity in Early Modern Rome. 2008. (Illus.). 308p. 134.95 (978-0-7546-5690-6(X)) Ashgate Publishing Co.

Butler, Patricia. The Silent Companion: An Illustrated History of the Water Colour Society of Ireland. 2010. (ENG., Illus.). 344p. (978-1-85149-644-0(0), Antique Collectors Club Dist) Antique Collectors' Club.

Büttner, Nils. Herr P.P. Rubens: Von der Kunst, Berühmt Zu Werden. 2006. (Rekonstruktion der Künste Ser.). (GER., Illus.). 278p. (C). pap. 93.00 (978-3-525-47906-3(9)) Vandenhoeck & Ruprecht GmbH & Co. KG DEU. Dist: ISD.

Cahill, James. Pictures for Use & Pleasure: Vernacular Painting in High Qing China. 2010. (Illus.). 280p. 49.95 (978-0-520-25857-0(6)) Univ. of California Pr.

Cameron, Dan, et al, texts. Nick Cave: Meet Me at the Center of the Earth. 2010. (ENG., Illus.). 240p. 49.95 (978-0-615-24593-5(5)) Yerba Buena Ctr. for the Arts.

Candida Smith, Richard. The Modern Moves West: California Artists & Democratic Culture in the Twentieth Century. 2009. (Arts & Intellectual Life in Modern America Ser.). (Illus.). 264p. (C). 39.95 (978-0-8122-4188-4(6)) Univ. of Pennsylvania Pr.

Cannatella, Howard. Creating a Better Place to Live: The Argument for Craft Education. 2011. 184p. pap. (978-1-86335-971-9(0)) Common Ground Publishing Pty, Ltd.

Caplow, Deborah. Leopoldo Méndez: Revolutionary Art & the Mexican Print. 2007. (Joe R. & Teresa Lozano Long Series in Latin American & Latino Art & Culture). (ENG., Illus.). 327p. 55.00 (978-0-292-71250-8(2)) Univ. of Texas Pr.

Carlisle, Janice. Picturing Reform in Victorian Britain. 2012. (Cambridge Studies in Nineteenth-Century Literature & Culture Ser.: 79). (ENG., Illus.). 320p. 99.00 (978-0-521-86836-5(X)) Cambridge Univ. Pr.

Carrick, Jill. Nouveau Réalisme, 1960s France, & the Neo-Avant-Garde: Topographies of Chance & Return. 2010. (Illus.). 184p. 104.95 (978-0-7546-6141-2(5)) Ashgate Publishing Co.

Cashell, Kieran. Aftershock: The Ethics of Contemporary Transgressive Art. 2009. (ENG., Illus.). 272p. pap. 32.50 (978-1-84511-524-1(4)) I. B. Tauris & Co., Ltd. GBR. Dist: Macmillan.

Cast, David. The Delight of Art: Giorgio Vasari & the Traditions of Humanist Discourse. 2009. (ENG.). 296p. 95.00 (978-0-271-03442-3(4)) Pennsylvania State Univ. Pr.

Cazalet, Daphne. Water over Skin. 2011. 160p. pap. (978-3-8383-8259-3(5)) Lambert Academic Publishing.

Chadwick, Whitney. Mujer Arte y Sociedad. 2nd ed. (SPA., Illus.). 448p. 39.95 (978-84-233-2247-3(5), DE475) Ediciones Destino ESP. Dist: Continental Bk. Co., Inc.

Chadwick, Whitney. Women, Art, & Society. 5th rev. ed. 2012. (World of Art Ser.). (ENG., Illus.). 536p. (Orig.). pap. 24.95 (978-0-500-20405-4(5), 520405) Thames & Hudson.

Chamberlayne, Prue. Art, Creativity & Imagination in Social Work Practice. Smith, Martin, ed. 2009. (ENG.). 172p. (C). 140.00 (978-0-415-46508-3(7)) Routledge.

Chanse, Samantha. Activist Imagination: Is an Exhibition & Series of Discussions Investigating, Exploring, & Imagining the Past, Present, & Future of Activism: Artists, Bob Hsiang, Donna Keiko Ozawa, Christine Wong Yap. 2008. (Illus.). 72p. (978-0-9797707-2-2(6)) Kearny Street Workshop.

Charney, Noah, ed. Art & Crime: Exploring the Dark Side of the Art World, 1 vol. 2009. (Illus.). 261p. 49.95 (978-0-313-36635-2(7), C36635, Praeger Pubs.) Greenwood Publishing Group, Inc.

Cherry, Brigid. Spectacle & Display. Cherry, Deborah & Cullen, Fintan, eds. 2008. (Art History Special Issues Ser.). (ENG., Illus.). 200p. pap. 29.95 (978-1-4051-7524-1(9), Wiley-Blackwell) Wiley, John & Sons, Inc.

Chung, Sheng Kuan. Social Reconstructionism in Art Education. 2008. 200p. pap. (978-3-639-05192-6(0)) VDM Verlag Dr. Mueller e.K.

Cleveland, William. Art & Upheaval: Artists on the World's Frontlines. 2008. (ENG.). 332p. pap. 20.01 (978-0-9766054-6-1(5)) New Village Pr.

Codell, Julie F., ed. Transculturation in British Art, 1770-1930. 2012. (British Art: Global Contexts Ser.). (Illus.). 312 + 4 lourp. 119.95 (978-1-4094-0977-9(5)) Ashgate Publishing Co.

Cohen, Aaron J. Imagining the Unimaginable: World War, Modern Art, & the Politics of Public Culture in Russia, 1914-1917. 2008. (Studies in War, Society, & the Military). (ENG., Illus.). 246p. (C). 45.00 (978-0-8032-1547-4(9)) Univ. of Nebraska Pr.

Connah, Roger. The Rest Is Silence Zahoor Ul Akhlaq: Art & Society in Pakistan. 2012. (ENG., Illus.). 350p. 99.00 (978-0-19-547472-5(4)) Oxford Univ. Pr., Inc.

Connor, James A. The Last Judgment: Michelangelo & the Death of the Renaissance. 2010. (ENG., Illus.). 256p. pap. 16.00 (978-0-230-62389-7(1)) Palgrave Macmillan.

Cooks, Bridget R. Exhibiting Blackness: African Americans & the American Art Museum. 2011. (Illus.). 240p. pap. 29.95 (978-1-55849-875-4(3)) Univ. of Massachusetts Pr.

Cooper, Tarnya. Citizen Portrait: Portrait Painting & the Urban Elites of Tudor & Jacobean England & Wales. 2012. (ENG.). 264p. 85.00 (978-0-300-16279-0(0)) Yale Univ. Pr.

Cordova, Ruben Charles. Con Safo: The Chicano Art Group & the Politics of South Texas. 2011. (ENG., Illus.). 110p. (C). pap. 14.95 (978-0-89551-121-8(5)) UCLA Chicano Studies Research Ctr. Pr.

Coudert, Thierry. Café Society: [mondains, Mécènes et Artistes, 1920-1960]. 2010. (FRE., Illus.). 320p. (978-2-08-011479-2(4)) Flammarion et Cie.

—Café Society: Socialites, Patrons, & Artists, 1920-1960. 2010. (ENG., Illus.). 320p. 75.00 (978-2-08-030157-4(8)) Flammarion et Cie FRA. Dist: Random Hse., Inc.

Coutts, Glen & Jokela, Timo, eds. Art, Community & Environment: Educational Perspectives. (Intellect Books - Readings in Art & Design Education Ser.). (ENG., Illus.). 2010. 328p. pap. 35.00 (978-1-84150-257-1(X)) 2008. 304p. 50.00 (978-1-84150-189-5(1)) Intellect, Ltd. GBR. Dist: Chicago Distribution Ctr.

Cram101 Textbook Reviews. Outlines & Highlights for Framing Americ: A Social History of American Art by Frances K. Pohl, ISBN. 2011. 384p. pap. 34.95 (978-1-61812-561-3(3)) Cram101 Inc.

Cram101 Textbook Reviews & Cram101 Textbook Reviews. Outlines & Highlights for Art in an Age of Civil Struggle, 1848-1871 by Albert Boime, Isbn: 9780226063287. 2011. 268p. pap. 31.95 (978-1-61461-825-6(9)) Cram101 Inc.

—Outlines & Highlights for Practices of Looking: An Introduction to Visual Culture by Marita Sturken & Lisa Cartwright, ISBN. 2011. 418p. pap. 35.95 (978-1-4288-8223-2(5)) Cram101 Inc.

Crowell, Aron & Worl, Rosita, eds. Living Our Cultures, Sharing Our Heritage: The First Peoples of Alaska. 2010. (ENG., Illus.). 312p. 50.00 (978-1-58834-270-6(0)) Smithsonian Institution Pr.

Crowley, John E. Imperial Landscapes: Britain's Global Visual Culture, 1745-1820. 2011. (Paul Mellon Centre for Studies in Britis Ser.). (ENG., Illus.). 320p. 85.00 (978-0-300-17050-4(5)) Yale Univ. Pr.

Cuadriello, Jaime. The Glories of the Republic of Tlaxcala: Art & Life in Viceregal Mexico. Follett, Christopher J., tr. from SPA. 2011. (ENG., Illus.). 400p. 55.00 (978-0-292-72360-3(1)) Univ. of Texas Pr.

Culkin, Kate. Harriet Hosmer: A Cultural Biography. 2010. (Illus.). 248p. pap. 26.95 (978-1-55849-839-6(7)); lib. bdg. 80.00 (978-1-55849-838-9(9)) Univ. of Massachusetts Pr.

Cullen, Fintan. Ireland on Show: Art Union & Nationhood. 2012. (Illus.). 124.95 (978-1-4094-3109-1(6)) Ashgate Publishing Co.

Curtis, Neal, ed. The Pictorial Turn. 2011. (ENG.). 256p. (C). pap. 45.95 (978-0-415-50874-2(6)) Routledge.

Cusack, Tricia. Art & Identity at the Water's Edge. 2012. (Illus.). 232p. 124.95 (978-1-4094-2121-4(X)) Ashgate Publishing Co.

Dadi, Iftikhar. Modernism & the Art of Muslim South Asia. 2010. (Islamic Civilization & Muslim Networks Ser.). (ENG., Illus.). 360p. 39.95 (978-0-8078-3358-2(4)) Univ. of North Carolina Pr.

Daldal, Asli. Art, Politics & Society. 2010. 107.60 (978-1-61719-112-1(4)) Gorgias Pr., LLC.

D'Ambra, Eve & Metraux, Guy P. R., eds. The Art of Citizens, Soldiers, & Freedmen in the Roman World. 2006. (BAR International Ser.: Vol. 1526). (ENG., Illus.). 167p. (C). pap. 100.00 (978-1-84171-963-4(3)) British Archaeological Reports Ltd. GBR. Dist: Brown, David Bk. Co., The.

Damiani, Luca. Dance with Me: Art, Design & Social Beliefs. 2010. (Illus.). 80p. pap. (978-1-85756-700-7(5)) Janus Publishing Co.

Danto, Arthur C. Andy Warhol. (Icons of America Ser.). (ENG., Illus.). 192p. 2010. pap. 16.00 (978-0-300-16908-9(6)) 2009. 24.00 (978-0-300-13555-8(6)) Yale Univ. Pr.

Davis, Jessica Hoffmann & Hoffmann Davis, Jessica. Why Our Schools Need the Arts. 2007. (ENG., Illus.). 160p. pap. 22.95 (978-0-8077-4834-3(X)) Teachers College Pr., Teachers College, Columbia Univ.

Davis, W. A General Theory of Visual Culture. 2011. (ENG., Illus.). 432p. (C). 55.00 (978-0-691-14765-9(5)) Princeton Univ. Pr.

De Bruyne, Paul & Gielen, Pascal, eds. Community Art: The Politics of Trespassing. 2011. (ENG., Illus.). 373p. pap. 28.95 (978-90-78088-50-9(8)) Valiz NLD. Dist: D.A.P./Distributed Art Pubs.

De Gruchy, John W. Christianity, Art & Transformation: Theological Aesthetics in the Struggle for Justice. 2008. (ENG., Illus.). 288p. pap. 41.00 (978-0-521-08950-0(6)) Cambridge Univ. Pr.

De Maria, Blake. Becoming Venetian: Immigrants & the Arts in Early Modern Venice. 2010. (ENG., Illus.). 256p. 65.00 (978-0-300-14881-7(X)) Yale Univ. Pr.

Deoldere, Luc. Tlc - The Low Countries 17: Arts & Society in Flanders & the Netherlands. 2011. (ENG., Illus.). 320p. pap. 65.00 (978-90-79705-00-9(4)) Lannoo Pubs./Racine.

—TLC - The Low Countries 18: Arts & Society in Flanders & the Netherlands. 2011. (ENG., Illus.). 316p. pap. 65.00 (978-90-79705-05-4(5)) Lannoo Pubs./Racine.

Dimbleby, David. Seven Ages of Britain. 2010. (ENG., Illus.). 256p. 42.95 (978-0-340-99408-5(8)) Murray, John GBR. Dist: Independent Pubs. Group.

Dixon, Annette & Chapin, Mary Weaver. The Dancer: Degas, Forain, Toulouse-Lautrec. 2008. (ENG., Illus.). 256p. 39.95 (978-1-883124-27-4(1)) Portland Art Museum.

Donahoe, Brian & Habeck, Joachim Otto, eds. Reconstructing the House of Culture: Community, Self, & the Makings of Culture in Russia & Beyond. 2011. (ENG., Illus.). 348p. 95.00 (978-0-85745-275-7(4)) Berghahn Bks., Inc.

Donahue, David M. & Stuart, Jennifer, eds. Artful Teaching: Integrating the Arts for Understanding Across the Curriculum. 2010. (ENG., Illus.). 192p. pap. 24.95 (978-0-8077-5080-3(8)); 57.00 (978-0-8077-5081-0(6)) Teachers College Pr., Teachers College, Columbia Univ.

Donald, Diana, et al, eds. Endless Forms: Charles Darwin, Natural Science, & the Visual Arts. 2009. (ENG., Illus.). 346p. 75.00 (978-0-300-14826-8(7)) Yale Univ. Pr.

Doris, Sara. Pop Art & the Contest over American Culture. 2006. (ENG., Illus.). 316p. 106.99 (978-0-521-83658-6(1)) Cambridge Univ. Pr.

Dorsch, Michael. French Sculpture Following the Franco-Prussian War, 1870-1880: Realist Allegories & the Commemoration of Defeat. 2010. (Illus.). 220p. 109.95 (978-1-4094-0352-4(1)) Ashgate Publishing Co.

Drucker, Johanna. Sweet Dreams: Contemporary Art & Complicity. 2006. (Illus.). 264p. per. 30.00 (978-0-226-16505-9(1)) Univ. of Chicago Pr.

Drucker, Johanna & McVarish, Emily. Graphic Design History. 2nd rev. ed. 2012. (ENG.). 416p. (C). pap. 85.33 (978-0-205-21946-9(2)) Prentice Hall PTR.

Drucker, Johanna & McVarish, Emily. Graphic Design History: A Critical Guide. 2008. (ENG., Illus.). 416p. (C). pap. 89.80 (978-0-13-241075-5(3), Prentice Hall) Prentice Hall PTR.

Dubin, Nina L. & Robert, Hubert. Futures & Ruins: Eighteenth-Century Paris & the Art of Hubert Robert. 2010. (ENG., Illus.). 208p. 50.00 (978-1-60606-023-0(6)) Getty Pubns.

Durden, Mark. Variable Capital. 2008. (ENG., Illus.). 192p. 39.95 (978-1-84631-126-0(8)) Liverpool Univ. Pr. GBR. Dist: Chicago Distribution Ctr.

Durrant, Sam & Lord, Catherine M., eds. Essays in Migratory Aesthetics: Cultural Practices Between Migration & Art-making. 2007. 236p. per. 65.00 (978-90-420-2236-2(1)) Rodopi.

Eckmann, Teresa. Neo-Mexicanism: Mexican Figurative Painting & Patronage in the 1980s. 2011. (ENG., Illus.). 320p. (C). 45.00 (978-0-8263-4742-8(8)) Univ. of New Mexico Pr.

Edelstein, Teri, et al. Art for All: British Posters for Transport. 2010. (Illus.). 280p. 50.00 (978-0-300-15297-5(3)) Yale Univ. Pr.

Elliott, David & Ozaki, Tetsuya. Bye Bye Kitty!!! Between Heaven & Hell in Contemporary Japanese Art. 2011. (ENG., Illus.). 136p. pap. 35.00 (978-0-300-16690-3(7)) Yale Univ. Pr.

Esche, Charles & Lewis, Mark. Art & Social Change: A Critical Reader. Bradley, Will, ed. 2008. (ENG., Illus.). 480p. pap. 39.95 (978-1-85437-626-8(8)) Tate Publishing, Ltd. GBR. Dist: Hachette Bk. Group.

Eshun, Kodwo. Dan Graham: Rock My Religion. 2012. (Afterall Ser.). (ENG., Illus.). 112p. (gr. 17). 35.00 (978-1-84638-085-3(5)); pap. 16.00 (978-1-84638-086-0(3)) MIT Pr.

Facos, Michelle. An Introduction to Nineteenth Century Art. 2011. (ENG., Illus.). 464p. (C). 135.00 (978-0-415-78070-4(5)); pap. 69.95 (978-0-415-78072-8(1)) Routledge.

—Symbolist Art in Context. 2009. (ENG., Illus.). 304p. pap. 31.95 (978-0-520-25582-1(8)) Univ. of California Pr.

Facos, Michelle & Facos, M. Symbolist Art in Context. 2009. (ENG., Illus.). 304p. 70.00 (978-0-520-25499-2(6)) Univ. of California Pr.

Ferrell, Robyn. Sacred Exchanges: Images in Global Context. 2012. (Columbia Themes in Philosophy, Social Criticism, & the Arts Ser.). (ENG., Illus.). 192p. (gr. 17). 50.00 (978-0-231-14880-1(1)) Columbia Univ. Pr.

Finlay, Robert. The Pilgrim Art: Cultures of Porcelain in World History. 2010. (California World History Library). (ENG., Illus.). 441p. 36.95 (978-0-520-24468-9(0)) Univ. of California Pr.

Fitzpatrick, Tracy. Art & the Subway: New York Underground. 2009. (ENG., Illus.). 304p. 29.95 (978-0-8135-4452-6(1)) Rutgers Univ. Pr.

Fordham, Douglas. British Art & the Seven Years' War: Allegiance & Autonomy. 2010. (Illus.). 352p. (C). 65.00 (978-0-8122-4243-0(2)) Univ. of Pennsylvania Pr.

Frattarolo, Eleonora & Cremonini, Leonardo. La Necessità Dell'arte Oggi: Rappresentare o Presentare?: Atti Del Convegno. 2010. (ITA.). 95p. (978-88-8016-988-8(2)) De Luca Editori d'Arte.

Freeman, Kirrily. Bronzes to Bullets: Vichy & the Destruction of French Public Statuary, 1941-1944. 2008. (ENG., Illus.). 264p. 65.00 (978-0-8047-5889-5(1)) Stanford Univ. Pr.

Freeman, Mark Philip. Finding the Muse: A Sociopsychological Inquiry into the Conditions of Artistic Creativity. 2007. (ENG.). 344p. pap. 69.00 (978-0-521-04479-0(0)) Cambridge Univ. Pr.

Freybourg, Anne Maria & Freybourg, Anne Marie. Die Inszenierung des Künstlers. 2008. (GER., Illus.). 111p. pap. (978-3-86859-031-9(5)) Jovis Verlag GmbH.

Frye, Susan. Pens & Needles: Women's Textualities in Early Modern England. 2010. (Material Texts). (Illus.). 344p. (C). 65.00 (978-0-8122-4238-6(6)) Univ. of Pennsylvania Pr.

Galenson, David W. Conceptual Revolutions in Twentieth-Century Art. 2009. (ENG.). 460p. 95.00 (978-0-521-11232-1(X)); pap. 26.99 (978-0-521-12909-1(5)) Cambridge Univ. Pr. GBR. Dist: Cambridge Univ. Pr.

Ganz, James A. Impressionist Paris: City of Light. 2010. pap. (978-0-88401-134-7(8)); (Illus.). 156p. (978-3-7913-5081-3(1)) Fine Arts Museums of San Francisco.

Gao, Minglu. Total Modernity & the Avant-Garde in Twentieth-Century Chinese Art. 2011. (ENG., Illus.). 424p. (gr. 17). 39.95 (978-0-262-01494-6(7)) MIT Pr.

Garoian, Charles R. & Gaudelius, Yvonne M. Spectacle Pedagogy: Art, Politics, & Visual Culture. 2008. (Illus.). 164p. (C). 59.50 *(978-0-7914-7385-6(6))*; 163p. pap. 24.95 *(978-0-7914-7386-3(4))* State Univ. of New York Pr.

Gaughan, Martin Ignatius. German Art 1907-1937: Modernism & Modernisation. (Illus.). 351p. pap. 89.95 *(978-3-03910-900-5(6))* Lang, Peter CHE. Dist: Lang, Peter Publishing, Inc.

Gibson, Michael R. From ower 2 Empowerment: Critical Literacy in Visual Culture. 2009. pap. 16.36 *(978-1-61584-094-6(X))* Independent Pub.

Gilbert, Helen & Lo, Jacqueline. Performance & Cosmopolitics: Cross-Cultural Transactions in Australasia. 2009. (Studies in International Performance Ser.). (ENG., Illus.). 256p. pap. 32.00 *(978-0-230-23402-4(X))* Palgrave Macmillan.

Gludowacz, Irene, et al, eds. Global Art. 2010. (ENG., Illus.). 312p. pap. 25.00 *(978-3-7757-2201-8(7))* Hatje Cantz Verlag GmbH & Co KG DEU. Dist: D.A.P./Distributed Art Pubs.

Goggin, Maureen Daly & Tobin, Beth Fowkes. Women & the Material Culture of Needlework & Textiles, 1750-1950. 2009. (Illus.). 312p. 124.95 *(978-0-7546-6538-0(0))* Ashgate Publishing Co.

Grams, Diane. Producing Local Color: Art Networks in Ethnic Chicago. 2010. (ENG., Illus.). 328p. 40.00 *(978-0-226-30517-2(1))* Univ. of Chicago Pr.

Grande, John K. Dialogues in Diversity: Art from Marginal to Mainstream. 2007. (ENG., Illus.). 192p. pap. *(978-88-901960-7-2(6))* Pari Publishing.

Graw, Isabelle. Der große Preis: Kunst zwischen Markt und Celebrity. 2008. (GER., Illus.). 255p. pap. *(978-3-8321-9007-1(4))* DuMont.

Greene, David / B. 0. The Imagining of Community in European Art & Architecture, 1140-1617: Envisioning Transcendence of, Authority in, & Foundations for Community. 2010. (Illus.). viii, 203p *(978-0-7734-3713-5(4))* Mellen, Edwin Pr., The.

Greene, Vivien, ed. Utopia Matters. 2010. 45.00 *(978-0-89207-400-6(0))* Guggenheim, Solomon R. Museum.

Greenfeld, Liah. Different Worlds: A Sociological Study of Taste, Choice & Success in Art. 2006. (American Sociological Association Rose Monographs). (ENG.). 216p. pap. 46.00 *(978-0-521-03013-7(7))* Cambridge Univ. Pr.

Greenfield, Douglas M. & Gatrall, Jefferson J. A. Alter Icons: The Russian Icon & Modernity. 2010. (ENG.). 264p. 74.95 *(978-0-271-03677-9(X))* Pennsylvania State Univ. Pr.

Groys, Boris. Boris Groys: Going Public. 2011. (E-Flux Journal Ser.). (ENG., Illus.). 168p. pap. 15.00 ***(978-1-934105-30-6(9))*** Sternberg Pr.

Guégan, Stéphane & Thomine, Alice. Birth of Impressionism: Masterpieces from the Musée D'Orsay. 2010. (Illus.). 255p. *(978-3-7913-6297-7(6))*; *(978-3-7913-6296-0(8))* Fine Arts Museums of San Francisco.

Guegan, Stephane & Thomine-Berrada, Alice, eds. Birth of Impressionism: Masterpieces from the Musee D'Orsay. 2010. (Illus.). 256p. 50.00 *(978-3-7913-5045-5(5))* Prestel Publishing.

Guilbaut, Serge, contrib. by. Be-Bomb: The Transatlantic War of Images & All That Jazz. 1946-1956. 2008. (Illus.). 774p. pap. *(978-84-89771-47-5(2))* Museu d'Art Contemporani de Barcelona.

Guillon, Roland. Harmonie, Rythme et Sociétés: Genèse de L'art Contemporain. 2010. (FRE.). 199p. pap. *(978-2-296-13086-9(0))* Harmattan Pr.

György, Péter & Peter, Gyorgy. Spirit of the Place: From Mauthausen to Moma. 2009. (ENG., Illus.). 286p. 45.00 *(978-963-9776-33-3(5))* Central European Univ. Pr.

Haskins, Katherine. The Art-Journal & Fine Art Publishing in Victorian England, 1850-1880. 2012. (Illus.). 232p. 119.95 ***(978-1-4094-1810-8(3))*** Ashgate Publishing Co.

Hatherley, Owen. Militant Modernism. 2009. (ENG., Illus.). 160p. pap. 19.95 *(978-1-84694-176-4(8))* O Bks.,John Hunt.

Haynes, Deborah J. Book of This Place: The Land, Art, & Spirituality. 2009. 212p. pap. 23.00 *(978-1-60608-703-9(7),* Pickwick Pubns.) Wipf & Stock Pubs.

Hebel, Udo J. & Wagner, Christoph, eds. Pictorial Cultures & Political Iconographies: Approaches, Perspectives, Case Studies from Europe & America. 2011. (ENG., Illus.). 445p. 210.00 ***(978-3-11-219088-3(2))***; 140.00 ***(978-3-11-023785-6(7))*** De Gruyter, Walter Inc.

Heller, Steven. Pop: How Graphic Design Shapes Popular Culture. 2010. (ENG., Illus.). 288p. pap. 24.95 *(978-1-58115-715-4(0),* 115715, Allworth Pr.) Skyhorse Publishing Co., Inc.

Heller, Steven & Chwast, Seymour. Illustration: A Visual History. 2008. (ENG., Illus.). 272p. 42.00 *(978-0-8109-7284-1(0))* Abrams.

Herz, Rebecca Shulman. Looking at Art in the Classroom: Art Investigations From the Guggenheim Museum. 2010. (ENG., Illus.). 160p. pap. 23.95 *(978-0-8077-5047-6(6))* Teachers College Pr., Teachers College, Columbia Univ.

Heywood, Ian & Sandywell, Barry. The Handbook of Visual Culture. 2012. (ENG., Illus.). 608p. 140.00 ***(978-1-84788-573-9(X))*** Berg Pubs. GBR. Dist: Macmillan.

Hinderliter, Beth, et al, eds. Communities of Sense: Rethinking Aesthetics & Politics. 2009. (ENG., Illus.). 384p. 94.95 *(978-0-8223-4497-1(1))*; pap. 26.95 *(978-0-8223-4513-8(7))* Duke Univ. Pr.

Hoen, H. W. & Kemperinck, M., eds. Vision in Text & Image: The Cultural Turn in the Study of Arts. 2008. (Groningen Studies in Cultural Change Ser.). (ENG., Illus.). 197p. (C). 70.00 *(978-90-429-2042-2(4))* Peeters Pubs. & Booksellers BEL. Dist: Brown, David Bk. Co., The.

Hopkins, David, ed. Neo-avant-garde. 2006. (Avant Garde Critical Studies: 20). (Illus.). 464p. *(978-90-420-2125-9(X))* Rodopi.

Humphrey, Walter Beach. Walter Beach Humphrey's "Hovey Murals" at Dartmouth College: A Cultural History. Kennedy, Brian P., ed. 2011. (Illus.). 164p. pap. 39.95 *(978-1-61168-029-4(8))* Hood Museum of Art & Univ. Pr. of New England.

Hunter, R. Civil Twilight & Other Social Works. Hunter, J , ed. 2007. (Illus.). 172p. per. *(978-0-9553927-1-9(3))* Nute Publishing, Ltd.

Hutton, Deborah S. & Hutton, Deborah. Art of the Court of Bijapur. 2006. (Contemporary Indian Studies). (ENG., Illus.). 240p. 49.95 *(978-0-253-34784-6(X),* 025334784X) Indiana Univ. Pr.

Hyde, Lewis. The Gift: Creativity & the Artist in the Modern World. 25th ed. 2007. (Vintage Ser.). (ENG., Illus.). 464p. pap. 16.00 *(978-0-307-27950-7(2),* Vintage) Knopf Doubleday Publishing Group.

Indych-Lopez, Anna. Muralism without Walls: Rivera, Orozco, & Siqueiros in the United States, 1927-1940. 2009. (Pitt Illuminations Ser.). (ENG., Illus.). 352p. (C). 45.00 *(978-0-8229-4384-6(0))* Univ. of Pittsburgh Pr.

Inglis, David & Herrero, Marta, eds. Art & Aesthetics, 4 vols. 2009. (Critical Concepts in the Social Sciences Ser.). (ENG., Illus.). 1430p. (C). 1430.00 *(978-0-415-45011-9(X))* Routledge.

Isaacs, John. In Advance of the Institution. 2008. (ENG., Illus.). 188p. 140.00 *(978-1-904212-16-4(6))* Other Criteria GBR. Dist: Hachette Bk. Group.

—In Advance of the Institution. Beard, Jason, ed. 2008. (ENG.). 188p. 190.00 *(978-1-904212-29-4(8))* Other Criteria GBR. Dist: Hachette Bk. Group.

Isager, Jacob. Pliny on Art & Society: The Elder Pliny's Chapters on the History of Art. 2010. 256p. pap. 39.95 *(978-0-415-58901-7(0))* Routledge.

Ivey, Bill. Arts, Inc: How Greed & Neglect Have Destroyed Our Cultural Rights. 2010. (ENG., Illus.). 368p. pap. 17.95 *(978-0-520-26792-3(3))* Univ. of California Pr.

Ivey, Bill J. Arts, Inc: How Greed & Neglect Have Destroyed Our Cultural Rights. 2008. (Illus.). 342p. 40.00 *(978-0-520-24112-1(6))* Univ. of California Pr.

Jacob, Preminda. Celluloid Deities: The Visual Culture of Cinema & Politics in South India. 2008. (ENG., Illus.). 318p. 83.99 *(978-0-7391-1060-7(8))* Lexington Bks.

Jahn, Marisa, ed. Byproduct: On the Excess of Embedded Art Practices. 2011. (ENG., Illus.). 192p. pap. 29.95 *(978-0-920397-51-0(4))* Y Y Z Artists Outlet CAN. Dist: D.A.P./Distributed Art Pubs.

Jelinek, Robert, ed. OFFSHORE CENSUS: The Citizens of the State of Sabotage. 2011. (GER., Illus.). 410p. 59.95 *(978-3-7091-0533-7(1),* 3709105331) Springer Wien AUT. Dist: Springer.

Johnson, Julie M. The Memory Factory: The Forgotten Women Artists of Vienna 1900. 2012. (Central European Studies). (ENG., Illus.). 368p. pap. 35.00 ***(978-1-55753-613-6(9))*** Purdue Univ. Pr.

Johnstone, Stephen. The Everyday. 2008. (Documents of Contemporary Art Ser.). (ENG.). 240p. (gr. 17). pap. 24.95 *(978-0-262-60074-3(9))* MIT Pr.

Jones, Malcolm. The Print in Early Modern England: An Historical Oversight. 2010. (ENG., Illus.). 352p. 95.00 *(978-0-300-13697-5(8))* Yale Univ. Pr.

Jones, Pamela M. Altarpieces & Their Viewers in the Churches of Rome from Caravaggio to Guido Reni. 2008. (Visual Culture in Early Modernity Ser.). (Illus.). 390p. 134.95 *(978-0-7546-6179-5(2))* Ashgate Publishing Co.

Jones, Ruth, et al. Holy Hiatus: Ritual & Community in Public Art. Jones, Ruth, ed. 2011. (ENG., Illus.). 148p. 25.95 *(978-1-905762-55-2(0))* Parthian Bks. GBR. Dist: Independent Pubs. Group.

Jordan, Mel & Miles, Malcolm, eds. Art & Theory after Socialism. 2008. (Illus.). 144p. pap. 40.00 *(978-1-84150-211-3(1))* Intellect, Ltd. GBR. Dist: Chicago Distribution Ctr.

Joselit, David. States of Form - the Object in Networks. 2012. (POINT: Essays on Architecture Ser.). (ENG.). 152p. (C). 19.95 ***(978-0-691-15044-4(3))*** Princeton Univ. Pr.

Kabir, Ananya Jahanara. Territory of Desire: Representing the Valley of Kashmir. 2009. (ENG., Illus.). 304p. 75.00 *(978-0-8166-5356-0(9))*; pap. 25.00 *(978-0-8166-5357-7(7))* Univ. of Minnesota Pr.

Kagan, Sacha. Art & Sustainability: Connecting Patterns for a Culture of Complexity. 2011. (ENG & GER., Illus.). 476p. pap. 54.95 ***(978-3-8376-1803-7(X))*** Transcript Verlag DEU. Dist: Transaction Pubs.

Kahan, Leonard, et al, eds. Surfaces: Color, Substances, & Ritual Applications on African Sculpture. 2009. (African Expressive Cultures Ser.). (ENG., Illus.). 536p. 75.00 *(978-0-253-35251-4(7),* 0253352517) Indiana Univ. Pr.

Kalmal, Padma Audrey. Scattered Goddesses: Travels with the Yoginis. 2011. ***(978-0-924304-67-5(7))*** Assn. for Asian Studies, Inc.

Kalantzis, Mary & Cope, Bill, eds. The International Journal of the Arts in Society: Volume 4, Number 5. 2010. 546p. 0.00 *(978-1-86335-743-2(2))* Common Ground Publishing Pty, Ltd.

—The International Journal of the Arts in Society: Volume 4, Number 6. 2010. 368p. 0.00 *(978-1-86335-763-0(7))* Common Ground Publishing Pty, Ltd.

Kamehiro, Stacy L. The Arts of Kingship: Hawaiian Art & National Culture of the Kalakaua ERA. 2009. (Illus.). xii, 266p. (C). 60.00 *(978-0-8248-3263-6(9))*; pap. 24.00 *(978-0-8248-3358-9(9))* Univ. of Hawaii Pr.

Kammen, Michael. Meadows of Memory: Images of Time & Tradition in American Art & Culture. 2012. (ENG., Illus.). 220p. pap. 25.00 ***(978-0-292-74232-1(0))*** Univ. of Texas Pr.

Kammen, Michael G. Visual Shock: A History of Art Controversies in American Culture. 2007. (Vintage Ser.). (ENG., Illus.). 480p. pap. 18.00 *(978-1-4000-3464-2(7),* Vintage) Knopf Doubleday Publishing Group.

Karkov, Catherine E. The Art of Anglo-Saxon England. 2011. (Boydell Studies in Medieval Art & Architecture Ser.: Volume 1). (Illus.). 348p. 80.00 *(978-1-84383-628-5(9),* Boydell Press) Boydell & Brewer, Ltd. GBR. Dist: Boydell & Brewer, Inc.

Katzew, Ilona, ed. Contested Visions in the Spanish Colonial World. 2011. (ENG., Illus.). 320p. 70.00 *(978-0-300-17664-3(3))* Yale Univ. Pr.

Kelley, Jeff. Half-Life of a Dream: Contemporary Chinese Art from the Logan Collection. 2008. (Illus.). 144p. 40.00 *(978-0-520-25779-5(0))* Univ. of California Pr.

Kermode, Mark, et al. Censoring the Moving Image. 2008. (Manifestos for the 21st Century Ser.). (ENG., Illus.). 128p. 20.00 *(978-1-905422-55-5(5))* Seagull Bks. GBR. Dist: Chicago Distribution Ctr.

Kiaer, Christina. Imagine No Possessions: The Socialist Objects of Russian Constructivism. 2008. (ENG., Illus.). 344p. (gr. 17). pap. 28.95 *(978-0-262-61221-0(6))* MIT Pr.

Kiely, Robert. Blessed & Beautiful: Picturing the Saints. 2010. (Illus.). 288p. 40.00 *(978-0-300-16277-6(4))* Yale Univ. Pr.

King, James. Beyond the Great Wave: The Japanese Landscape Print, 1727-1960. 2010. (Illus.). 244p. pap. *(978-3-0343-0317-0(3))* Lang, Peter.

King, Ross. The Judgment of Paris: The Revolutionary Decade That Gave the World Impressionism. 2006. (ENG., Illus.). 464p. pap. 17.00 *(978-0-8027-1516-6(8))* Walker & Co.

Kocur, Zoya, ed. Global Visual Cultures: An Anthology. 2011. (ENG., Illus.). 424p. 104.95 *(978-1-4051-6921-9(4))*; pap. 39.95 *(978-1-4051-6920-2(6))* Wiley, John & Sons, Inc. (Wiley-Blackwell).

Kokoli, Alexandra, ed. Susan Hiller: the Provisional Texture of Reality. 2008. (ENG., Illus.). 160p. pap. 22.00 *(978-3-905829-56-3(8))* JRP Ringier Kunstverlag AG CHE. Dist: D.A.P./Distributed Art Pubs.

Komaroff, Linda. The Gift Tradition in Islamic Art. 2012. (ENG., Illus.). 160p. pap. 45.00 ***(978-0-300-18435-8(2))*** Yale Univ. Pr.

Koretsky, Viktor. Vision & Communism: Viktor Koretsky & Dissident Public Visual Culture. Jackson, Matthew Jesse et al, eds. 2011. (ENG., Illus.). 176p. pap. 24.95 *(978-1-59558-625-4(3))* New Pr., The.

Korn, Irene. Great Masterpieces of the World. 2nd rev. ed. 2009. 128p. 17.95 *(978-1-59764-122-7(7))* New Line Bks.

Labno, Jeannie. Commemorating the Polish Renaissance Child: Funeral Monuments & Their European Context. 2011. (Illus.). 472p. 134.95 *(978-0-7546-6825-1(8))* Ashgate Publishing Co.

Lacy, Suzanne. Leaving Art: Writings on Performance, Politics, & Publics, 1974-2007. 2010. (ENG., Illus.). 424p. 99.95 *(978-0-8223-4552-7(8))*; pap. 27.95 *(978-0-8223-4569-5(2))* Duke Univ. Pr.

LaGamma, Alisa. Heroic Africans: Legendary Leaders, Iconic Sculptures. 2011. 60.00 ***(978-1-58839-432-3(8))*** Metropolitan Museum of Art, The.

Langdon, Susan. Art & Identity in Dark Age Greece, 1100-700 BC. 2010. (ENG., Illus.). 408p. pap. 45.00 *(978-0-521-17192-2(X))* Cambridge Univ. Pr.

Langdon, Susan & Langdon, Susan Helen. Art & Identity in Dark Age Greece, 1100-700 B.C.E. 2008. (ENG., Illus.). 406p. (C). 98.00 *(978-0-521-51321-0(9))* Cambridge Univ. Pr.

Lause, Mark A. The Antebellum Crisis & America's First Bohemians. 2011. 45.00 *(978-1-60635-033-1(1))* Kent State Univ. Pr.

Leach, Eleanor Winsor. The Social Life of Painting in Ancient Rome & on the Bay of Naples. 2011. (ENG., Illus.). 370p. (C). pap. 50.00 ***(978-1-107-69046-2(3))*** Cambridge Univ. Pr.

Leader, Anne. The Badia of Florence: Art & Observance in a Renaissance Monastery. 2011. (ENG., Illus.). 340p. 65.00 *(978-0-253-35567-6(2),* 0253355672) Indiana Univ. Pr.

Leavy, Patricia. Method Meets Art: Arts-Based Research Practice. 2008. (ENG., Illus.). 286p. 60.00 *(978-1-59385-843-8(4))*; pap. 40.00 *(978-1-59385-259-7(2))* Guilford Pubns., Inc.

Leca, Benedict, ed. Thomas Gainsborough & the Modern Woman. 2010. (Illus.). 196p. pap. *(978-0-931537-37-0(1))* Cincinnati Art Museum.

Lee, De-Nin D. The Night Banquet: A Chinese Scroll Through Time. 2010. (ENG., Illus.). 172p. (C). 40.00 *(978-0-295-99072-9(4))* Univ. of Washington Pr.

Lehmbeck, Leah Rosenblatt. Proof: The Rise of Printmaking in Southern California. Lehmbeck, Leah, ed. 2011. (Illus.). 256p. ***(978-1-60606-093-3(7))*** Getty Pubns.

Leibsohn, Dana & Peterson, Jeanette Favrot, eds. Seeing Across Cultures in the Early Modern World. 2012. (Transculturalisms, 1400ndash;1700 Ser.). (Illus.). 270p. 119.95 ***(978-1-4094-1189-5(3))*** Ashgate Publishing Co.

Leja, Michael. Looking Askance: Skepticism & American Art from Eakins to Duchamp. 2007. (Illus.). 300p. pap. 37.95 *(978-0-520-24996-7(8))* Univ. of California Pr.

Lent, John A. Cartooning in Africa. 2008. (Illus.). 304p. (C). *(978-1-57273-553-8(8))*; pap. *(978-1-57273-554-5(6))* Hampton Pr., Inc.

Lesure, Richard G. Interpreting Ancient Figurines: Context, Comparison, & Prehistoric Art. 2011. (ENG., Illus.). 276p. 95.00 *(978-0-521-19745-8(7))* Cambridge Univ. Pr.

Leuthold, Steven. Cross-Cultural Issues in Art: Frames for Understanding. 2011. (ENG., Illus.). 336p. (C). 136.00 *(978-0-415-57799-1(3))*; pap. 57.95 *(978-0-415-57800-4(0))* Routledge.

Levine, Caroline. Provoking Democracy: Why We Need the Arts. 2007. (Blackwell Manifestos Ser.: 12). (ENG., Illus.). 256p. pap. 39.95 *(978-1-4051-5927-2(8))*; 104.95 *(978-1-4051-5926-5(X))* Wiley, John & Sons, Inc. (Wiley-Blackwell).

Levy, Ellen. Criminal Ingenuity: Moore, Cornell, Ashbery, & the Struggle Between the Arts. 1 vol. 2011. (Modernist Literature & Culture Ser.). (ENG., Illus.). 304p. 49.95 *(978-0-19-974635-4(4))* Oxford Univ. Pr., Inc.

Llorens, Tomàs, et al. Portraits of the Belle Époque. 2012. (ENG., Illus.). 272p. 85.00 ***(978-1-55595-349-2(2))*** Hudson Hills Pr. LLC.

Long, Rose-Carol Washton, et al, eds. Jewish Dimensions in Modern Visual Culture: Antisemitism, Assimilation, Affirmation. 2009. (ENG., Illus.). 356p. lib. bdg. 55.00 *(978-1-58465-795-8(2),* Brandeis University Press) Univ. Pr. of New England.

Lovejoy, Margot, et al. Context Providers: Conditions of Meaning in Media Arts. 2011. (Illus.). 350p. pap. 35.00 *(978-1-84150-308-0(8))* Intellect, Ltd. GBR. Dist: Chicago Distribution Ctr.

Lovell, Margaretta M. Art in a Season of Revolution: Painters, Artisans, & Patrons in Early America. 2007. (Early American Studies). (Illus.). 360p. (C). per. 29.95 *(978-0-8122-1991-3(0))* Univ. of Pennsylvania Pr.

Lowenstam, Steven. As Witnessed by Images: The Trojan War Tradition in Greek & Etruscan Art. 2008. (ENG., Illus.). 248p. (gr. 17). 52.00 *(978-0-8018-8775-8(5))* Johns Hopkins Univ. Pr.

Luk#xE1;cs, Gy#xF6;rgy. György Lukács: Notizen zu Georg Simmels Vorlesungen, 1906/07, und zur »Kunstsoziologie«, ca. 1909. 2011. (ENG., Illus.). 48p. pap. 10.00 ***(978-3-7757-2854-6(6))*** Hatje Cantz Verlag GmbH & Co KG DEU. Dist: D.A.P./Distributed Art Pubs.

Machotka, Ewa. Visual Genesis of Japanese National Identity: Hokusai's Hyakunin Isshu. 2009. 256p. pap. 44.95 *(978-90-5201-482-1(5))* PIE - Peter Lang BEL. Dist: Lang, Peter.

Mackey, Clarke. Random Acts of Culture: Reclaiming Art & Community in the 21st Century. 2010. 286p. pap. 26.95 *(978-1-897071-64-9(7))* Between the Lines CAN. Dist: Univ. of Toronto Pr.

Mann, Vivian, et al. Uneasy Communion: Jews, Christians, & the Altarpieces of Medieval Spain. 2010. (ENG., Illus.). 176p. 60.00 *(978-1-904832-70-6(9))* Giles, D. Ltd. GBR. Dist: Antique Collectors' Club.

Mann, Vivian B., ed. & contrib. by. Uneasy Communion: Jews, Christians, & the Altarpieces of Medieval Spain. 2010. 49.95 *(978-0-9777839-6-0(0))* Museum of Biblical Art.

Marcus, Greil. Lipstick Traces: A Secret History of the Twentieth Century. 20th annot. ed. 2009. (Illus.). 496p. pap. 26.50 *(978-0-674-03480-8(5),* Belknap Pr.) Harvard Univ. Pr.

Markel, Stephen. India's Fabled City: The Art of Courtly Lucknow. 2010. *(978-0-87587-206-3(9))* Los Angeles County Museum of Art.

Marks, Andreas & Quintanilla, Sonya Rhie, eds. Dreams & Diversions: Essays on Japanese Woodblock Prints. 2010. (ENG., Illus.). 216p. 50.00 *(978-0-937108-47-5(2))* San Diego Museum of Art.

Marshall, Nancy Rose. City of Gold & Mud: Painting Victorian London. 2012. (Paul Mellon Centre for Studies in British Art Ser.). (ENG., Illus.). 320p. 75.00 ***(978-0-300-17446-5(2))*** Yale Univ. Pr.

Martin, Therese. Reassessing the Roles of Women As 'makers' of Medieval Art & Architecture. 2012. ***(978-90-04-18555-5(0))***; ***(978-90-04-22828-3(4))***; ***(978-90-04-22827-6(6))*** BRILL.

Masten, April F. Art Work: Women Artists & Democracy in Mid-Nineteenth-Century New York. 2008. (Arts & Intellectual Life in Modern America Ser.). (Illus.). 312p. (C). 59.95 *(978-0-8122-4071-9(5))* Univ. of Pennsylvania Pr.

McCarthy, Laurette E. & Pach, Walter. Walter Pach (1883-1958) The Armory Show & the Untold Story of Modern Art in America. 2011. (ENG.). 272p. 59.95 *(978-0-271-03740-0(7))* Pennsylvania State Univ. Pr.

McIver, Katherine. Wives Widows Mistresses & Nuns in Early Modern Italy: Making the Invisible Visible Through Art & Patronage. 2012. (Women & Gender in the Early Modern World Ser.). (Illus.). 286p. 119.95 ***(978-0-7546-6953-1(X))*** Ashgate Publishing Co.

McKay, Marylin J. Picturing the Land: Narrating Territories in Canadian Landscape Art, 1500-1950. 2011. (McGill-Queen's/Beaverbrook Canadian Foundation Studies in Art History Ser.). (ENG., Illus.). 384p. (C). pap. *(978-0-7735-3817-7(8))* McGill-Queen's Univ. Pr.

Medina, Cuauhtémoc. Teresa Margolles: What Else Could We Talk About? Medina, Cuauhtemoc, ed. 2010. (ENG., Illus.). 160p. 35.00 *(978-84-92480-66-1(1))* RM Verlag, S.L. ESP. Dist: D.A.P./Distributed Art Pubs.

Merali, Shaheen. New York States of Mind: Art in the City. Merali, Shaheen, ed. 2007. (ENG., Illus.). 320p. 29.95 *(978-0-86356-681-3(2))* Saqi Bks. GBR. Dist: Consortium Bk. Sales & Distribution.

Michel, Régis. Ideal Beauty: A Western Phantasy. Pleasance, Simon & Woods, Fronza, trs. 2009. (Illus.). 292p. pap. 60.00 *(978-0-89236-768-9(7))* Oxford Univ. Pr., Inc.

Miles, Malcolm. Herbert Marcuse: An Aesthetics of Liberation. 1 vol. 2012. (Modern European Thinkers Ser.). (ENG., Illus.). 208p. 37.00 ***(978-0-7453-3038-9(X))***; lib. bdg. 105.00 ***(978-0-7453-3039-6(8))*** Pluto Pr. GBR. Dist: Macmillan.

Millett-Gallant, Ann. The Disabled Body in Contemporary Art. (ENG., Illus.). 2012. 188p. pap. 27.00 ***(978-0-230-34142-5(X))*** 2010. 192p. 79.00 *(978-0-230-10406-8(1))* Palgrave Macmillan.

Mitchell, Alexandre. Greek Vase-Painting & the Origins of Visual Humour. 2009. (ENG., Illus.). 398p. 98.00 *(978-0-521-51370-8(7))* Cambridge Univ. Pr.

Moore, Mandy & Prain, Leanne. Yarn Bombing: The Art of Crochet & Knit Graffiti. 2009. (ENG., Illus.). 232p. pap. 19.95 *(978-1-55152-255-5(1))* Arsenal Pulp Pr. CAN. Dist: Consortium Bk. Sales & Distribution.

Morgan, Jo-Ann. Uncle Tom's Cabin as Visual Culture. 2007. (ENG., Illus.). 280p. (C). 39.95 *(978-0-8262-1715-8(X))* Univ. of Missouri Pr.

Muth, Marcia. A World Set Apart: Memory Paintings. 2006. (ENG., Illus.). 92p. per. 28.95 *(978-0-86534-526-3(0))* Sunstone Pr.

Myers, Fred R. Empire of Things: Regimes of Value & Material Culture. (Advanced Seminar Ser.). (Illus.). 368p. 34.95 *(978-1-930618-05-3(0))* School for Advanced Research Pr./SAR Pr.

Neumark, Norie & Chandler, Annmarie, eds. At a Distance: Precursors to Art & Activism on the Internet. 2006. (Leonardo Bks.). (ENG., Illus.). 496p. (gr. 17). per. 19.95 *(978-0-262-53285-3(9))* MIT Pr.

Noble, Richard & Noble, R. Utopias. Noble, Richard, ed. 2009. (Documents of Contemporary Art Ser.). (ENG., Illus.). 240p. (gr. 17). pap. 24.95 (978-0-262-64069-5(4)) MIT Pr.

Noriega, Chon A., et al, eds. L. A. Xicano. 2011. (ENG., Illus.). 240p. (C). 39.95 (978-0-89551-145-4(2)) UCLA Chicano Studies Research Ctr. Pr.

O'Connor, Eimear, ed. Sean Keating in Context: Responses to Culture & Politics in Post-Civil War Ireland. 2010. (ENG.). 194p. pap. 49.95 (978-1-904505-41-9(4)) Carysfort Pr. IRL. Dist: Dufour Editions, Inc.

O'Hear, Anthony. The Landscape of Humanity: Art, Culture & Society. 2008. (St. Andrews Studies in Philosophy & Public Affairs Ser.). (ENG.). 242p. 80.00 (978-1-84540-145-0(X)) Imprint Academic GBR. Dist: Ingram Pub. Services.

Orr, Penelope & Dorn, Charles M. Art Education in a Climate of Reform: The Need for Measurable Goals in Art Instruction. 2008. (ENG., Illus.). 136p. 70.00 (978-1-57886-788-2(6)); pap. 32.95 (978-1-57886-789-9(4)) Rowman & Littlefield Education.

Orrell, Paula. Jorge+Lucy Orta Pattern Book: An Introduction to Collaborative Practices. Orta, Lucy, ed. 2007. (ENG., Illus.). 157p. pap. 29.95 (978-1-904772-75-0(7)) Black Dog Publishing Ltd. GBR. Dist: Perseus Distribution.

Ose, Meredith. Art History. 2010. (Daily Warm-Ups Ser.). 223p. pap. 18.99 incl. cd-rom (978-0-8251-6589-4(X)) Walch Education.

Ostrowitz, Judith. Interventions: Native American Art for Far-Flung Territories. 2008. (ENG., Illus.). 240p. 45.00 (978-0-295-98851-1(7)) Univ. of Washington Pr.

Padiyar, Satish. Chains: David, Canova, & the Fall of the Public Hero in Postrevolutionary France. 2007. (ENG., Illus.). 224p. 60.00 (978-0-271-02963-4(3)) Pennsylvania State Univ. Pr.

Paglia, Camille. Glittering Images: A Journey Through Art from Egypt to Star Wars. 2012. (ENG., Illus.). 224p. 30.00 **(978-0-375-42460-1(1)**, Pantheon) Knopf Doubleday Publishing Group.

Pakesch, Peter, ed. Human Condition: Empathy & Emancipation in Precarious Times. 2011. (ENG & GER., Illus.). 268p. pap. 45.00 (978-3-86560-845-1(0)) Verlag der Buchhandlung Walther Konig DEU. Dist: D.A.P./Distributed Art Pubs.

Pan, Lynn. Shanghai Style: Art & Design Between the Wars. 2008. (ENG.). 312p. pap. 24.95 (978-1-59265-078-1(3)) Long River Pr.

Paret, Peter & Thieme, Helga. Myth & Modernity: Barlach's Drawings on the Nibelungen. 2012. (ENG.). 116p. 45.00 **(978-0-85745-346-4(7))** Berghahn Bks., Inc.

Park, J. P. Art by the Book: Painting Manuals & the Leisure Life in Late Ming China, 1 vol. 2012. (ENG., Illus.). 336p. (C). 50.00 **(978-0-295-99176-4(3))** Univ. of Washington Pr.

Parshall, Peter, ed. The Woodcut in Fifteenth-Century Europe. 2009. (Studies in the History of Art Ser.). (ENG., Illus.). 352p. 70.00 (978-0-300-12163-6(6)) National Gallery of Art.

Parshall, Peter, et al. The Darker Side of Light: Arts of Privacy, 1850-1900. 2009. (978-0-89468-354-1(3)) National Gallery of Art.

Peffer, John. Art & the End of Apartheid. 2009. (ENG., Illus.). 352p. 90.00 (978-0-8166-5001-9(2)); pap. 29.95 (978-0-8166-5002-6(0)) Univ. of Minnesota Pr.

Pezzoli-Olgiati, Daria & Rowland, Christopher. Approaches to the Visual in Religion. 2011. (Research in Contemporary Religion Ser.). (ENG., Illus.). 268p. (C). 95.00 (978-3-525-60442-7(4)) Vandenhoeck & Ruprecht GmbH & Co. KG DEU. Dist: ISD.

Pistoletto, Michelangelo. The Third Paradise. 2010. (ENG., Illus.). 96p. 24.95 (978-88-317-0649-0(7)) Marsilio Editori spa ITA. Dist: Random Hse., Inc.

Pistoletto, Michelangelo, et al. Michelangelo Pistoletto: From One to Many, 1956-1974. 2010. (978-0-87633-224-5(6)); (978-0-87633-223-8(8)) Philadelphia Museum of Art.

Pohl, Frances K. Framing America: A Social History of American Art. 3rd ed. 2012. (ENG., Illus.). 616p. (C). pap. 70.00 net. **(978-0-500-28983-9(2)**, 528983) Thames & Hudson.

Pohlsander, Hans A. German Monuments in the Americas: Bonds Across the Atlantic. 2010. (ENG., Illus.). 251p. pap. 68.95 (978-3-0343-0138-1(3)) Lang, Peter AG GBR. Dist: Lang, Peter.

Pointon, Marcia. Brilliant Effects: A Cultural History of Gem Stones & Jewellery. 2010. (Illus.). 368p. 85.00 (978-0-300-14278-5(1)) Yale Univ. Pr.

Porterfield, Todd, ed. The Efflorescence of Caricature, 1715-1838. 2010. (Illus.). 240p. 99.95 (978-0-7546-6591-5(7)) Ashgate Publishing Co.

Powers, John S. Temporary Art & Public Place: Comparing Berlin with Los Angeles. 2009. (Europäische Hochschulschriften. Reihe 28: Kunstgeschichte Ser.). (Illus.). 404p. pap. 99.95 (978-3-631-56430-1(9)) Lang, Peter GmbH, Europaischer Verlag der Wissenschaften DEU. Dist: Lang, Peter.

Preziosi, Donald & Farago, Claire. Art Is Not What You Think It Is. 2012. (Blackwell Manifestos Ser.: 60). (ENG., Illus.). 192p. pap. 26.95 **(978-1-4051-9239-2(9))**; 79.95 **(978-1-4051-9240-8(2))** Wiley, John & Sons, Inc. (Wiley-Blackwell).

Probst, Peter. Osogbo & the Art of Heritage: Monuments, Deities, & Money. 2011. (African Expressive Cultures Ser.). (ENG., Illus.). 224p. 70.00 (978-0-253-35611-6(3), 0253356113); pap. 24.95 (978-0-253-22295-4(8), 0253222958) Indiana Univ. Pr.

Proulx, Donald A. A Sourcebook of Nasca Ceramic Iconography: Reading a Culture through Its Art. 2009. (ENG., Illus.). 274p. pap. 39.95 (978-1-58729-829-5(5)) Univ. of Iowa Pr.

Purves, Ted & Thacher, Sara. Revelry & Risk: Approaches to Social Practice, or Something Like That. 2007. 48p. pap. 18.40 (978-1-4303-2128-6(8)) Lulu Enterprises Inc.

Quilley, Barringer. Art & the British Empire. Barringer, Timothy et al, eds. 2009. (ENG., Illus.). 464p. pap. 50.00 (978-0-7190-8193-4(9)) Manchester Univ. Pr. GBR. Dist: Macmillan.

Raguin, Virginia Chieffo. Art, Piety & Destruction in the Christian West, 1500-1700. 2010. (Visual Culture in Early Modernity Ser.). (Illus.). 238p. 109.95 (978-0-7546-6946-3(7)) Ashgate Publishing Co.

Ran, Faye. A History of Installation Art & the Development of New Art Forms: Technology & the Hermeneutics of Time & Space in Modern & Postmodern Art from Cubism to Installation. 2009. (Illus.). 266p. (C). 75.95 (978-1-4331-0519-7(5)) Lang, Peter Publishing, Inc.

Rashkin, Elissa. Stridentist Movement in Mexico: The Avant-Garde & Cultural Change in the 1920s. 2011. (ENG.). 288p. pap. 32.95 (978-0-7391-3157-2(5)) Lexington Bks.

Rashkin, Elissa J. Stridentist Movement in Mexico: The Avant-Garde & Cultural Change in the 1920s. 2009. (ENG., Illus.). 278p. 78.99 (978-0-7391-3156-5(7)) Lexington Bks.

Read, Herbert. Art & Society. 216p. 2008. 39.95 (978-1-4367-0772-5(2)) 2007. (ENG.). per. 24.95 (978-1-4325-6833-7(7)) Kessinger Publishing, LLC.

Reichert, Marcus, frwd. Art Without Art: Selected Writing from the World of Blunt Edge. 2008. (Illus.). 137p. pap. 29.50 (978-0-9546656-6-1(X)) Ziggurat Bks. GBR. Dist: Trans-Atlantic Pubns., Inc.

Reilly, Maura, et al. Richard Bell: Uz vs. Them. 2011. (Illus.). 80p. pap. (978-1-885444-40-0(0)) American Federation of Arts, The.

—Richard Bell: Uz vs. Them. 2011. (ENG., Illus.). 80p. 35.00 (978-1-904832-95-9(4)) Giles, D. Ltd. GBR. Dist: Antique Collectors' Club.

Rennie, Paul. Modern British Posters: Art, Design & Communication. 2010. (ENG., Illus.). 192p. 49.95 (978-1-906155-97-1(6)) Black Dog Publishing Ltd. GBR. Dist: Perseus Distribution.

Rich, Adrienne. A Human Eye: Essays on Art in Society, 1996-2008. 2009. (ENG.). 208p. 24.95 (978-0-393-07006-4(9), 7006) Norton, W. W. & Co., Inc.

—A Human Eye: Essays on Art in Society, 1997-2008. 2010. (ENG.). 180p. pap. 15.95 (978-0-393-33830-0(4), 33830) Norton, W. W. & Co., Inc.

Richards, Melanie. A Call to Arts: How Artistic Living Can Redeem Us. 2010. 98p. pap. 13.98 (978-0-557-27291-4(2)) Lulu Enterprises Inc.

Richardson, Carol. The Possessions of a Cardinal: Art, Piety, & Politics, 1450-1700. 2010. (ENG., Illus.). 456p. 85.00 (978-0-271-03468-3(8)) Pennsylvania State Univ. Pr.

Richardson, Craig. Scottish Art Since 1960: Historical Reflections & Critical Overview. 2011. (Illus.). 230p. 124.95 (978-0-7546-6124-5(5)) Ashgate Publishing Co.

Ritchin, Fred. After Photography. (ENG., Illus.). 2010. 199p. pap. 19.95 (978-0-393-33773-0(1), 33773) 2008. 200p. 29.95 (978-0-393-05024-0(6), 5024) Norton, W. W. & Co., Inc.

Roberts, David. The Total Work of Art in European Modernism. 2011. (Signale: Modern German Letters, Cultures, & Thought Ser.). 304p. pap. 37.50 (978-0-8014-5023-5(3)) Cornell Univ. Pr.

Rolling, James H. Cinderella Story: A Scholarly Sketchbook about Race, Identity, Barack Obama, the Human Spirit, & Other Stuff That Matters. 2010. (Crossroads in Qualitative Inquiry Ser.). (ENG., Illus.). 228p. 75.00 (978-0-7591-1176-9(6)) AltaMira Pr.

Roper, Lyndal. The Witch in the Western Imagination. 2012. E-Book **(978-0-8139-3300-9(5))**; (ENG., Illus.). 248p. (gr. 17). 39.50 **(978-0-8139-3297-2(1))** Univ. Pr. of Virginia.

Rose, Karel & Kincheloe, Joe L. Art, Culture, & Education: Artful Teaching in a Fractured Landscape. (Counterpoints Ser.). xiii, 162p. pap. 31.95 (978-0-8204-5745-1(0)) Lang, Peter Publishing, Inc.

Rubin, Patricia Lee. Images & Identity in Fifteenth-Century Florence. 2007. (ENG., Illus.). 256p. 60.00 (978-0-300-12342-5(6)) Yale Univ. Pr.

Ruffini, Marco. Art Without an Author: Vasari's Lives & Michelangelo's Death. 2011. (Modern Language Initiative Ser.). (ENG., Illus.). 208p. 80.00 (978-0-8232-3455-4(X)); pap. 26.00 (978-0-8232-3456-1(8)) Fordham Univ. Pr.

Ruggles, D. Fairchild, ed. Islamic Art & Visual Culture: An Anthology of Sources. 2011. (ENG.). 200p. pap. 31.95 (978-1-4051-5402-4(0), Wiley-Blackwell) Wiley, John & Sons, Inc.

Ruskin, John. The Complete Works of John Ruskin, 39 vols., Set. Incl. Bible of Amiens, Valle Crucis, the Art of Enland, the Pleasurers of England. reprint ed. lib. bdg. 98.00 (978-1-58201-373-2(X)); Bibliography, Catalogue of Ruskin's Drawings, Addena et Corrigenda. reprint ed. lib. bdg. 98.00 (978-1-58201-378-7(0)); Bibliotheca Pastorum, the Economist of Xenophon, Rock Honeycomb. reprint ed. lib. bdg. 98.00 (978-1-58201-371-8(3)); Cestus of Aglaia, the Queen of the Air. reprint ed. lib. bdg. 98.00 (978-1-58201-359-6(4)); Deucalion & Other Studies in Rocks & Stones. reprint ed. lib. bdg. 98.00 (978-1-58201-366-4(7)); Early Prose Writings, 1834-1843. 550p. reprint ed. lib. bdg. 98.00 (978-1-58201-341-1(1)); General Index. reprint ed. lib. bdg. 98.00 (978-1-58201-379-4(9)); Giotto, His Works in Padua, The Cavalli Monuments, Guide to the Academy, St. Mark's Rest. reprint ed. lib. bdg. 98.00 (978-1-58201-364-0(0)); Guild & Museum of St. George. reprint ed. lib. bdg. 98.00 (978-1-58201-370-1(5)); Harbours of England. 646p. reprint ed. lib. bdg. 98.00 (978-1-58201-353-4(5)); Joy Forever. 487p. reprint ed. lib. bdg. 98.00 (978-1-58201-356-5(X)); Lectures on Architecture & Painting. 603p. reprint ed. lib. bdg. 98.00 (978-1-58201-352-7(7)); Lectures on Art, Artra Pentelici. reprint ed. lib. bdg. 98.00 (978-1-58201-360-2(8)); Love's Meinie & Proserpina. reprint ed. lib. bdg. 98.00 (978-1-58201-365-7(9)); Notes on Prout & Hunt & Other Art Criticisms. 499p. reprint ed. lib. bdg. 98.00 (978-1-58201-354-1(3)); Poems. 541p. reprint ed. lib. bdg. 98.00 (978-1-58201-342-8(X)); Praeterita & Dilecta. reprint ed. lib. bdg. 98.00 (978-1-58201-375-6(6)); Ruskin Art Collection at Oxford. reprint ed. lib. bdg. 98.00 (978-1-58201-361-9(6)); Seven Lamps of Architecture. lib. bdg. 98.00 (978-1-58201-348-0(9)); Stones of Venice. lib. bdg. 98.00 (978-1-58201-349-7(7)); Storm-Cloud of the Nineteenth Century; On the Old Road; Arrows of the Chace; Ruskiniana. reprint ed. lib. bdg. 98.00 (978-1-58201-374-9(8)); Studies of Peasant Life, the Story of Ida, Roadside, Songs of Tuscany. reprint ed. lib. bdg. 98.00 (978-1-58201-372-5(1)); Unto This Last Munera Pulveris Time & Tide. 565p. reprint ed. lib. bdg. 98.00 (978-1-58201-357-2(8)); Val d'Arno, the Schools of Florence, Mornings in Florence, the Shepherd's Tower. reprint ed. lib. bdg. 98.00 (978-1-58201-363-3(2)); Pt. 1. Fors Clavigera Letters, 1-36. reprint ed. lib. bdg. 98.00 (978-1-58201-367-1(5)); Pt. 1. Letters of John Ruskin, 1827-1869. reprint ed. lib. bdg. 98.00 (978-1-58201-376-3(4)); Pt. 1. Modern Painters. 607p. reprint ed. lib. bdg. 98.00 (978-1-58201-343-5(8)); Pt. 2. Fors Clavigera Letters, 37-72. reprint ed. lib. bdg. 98.00 (978-1-58201-368-8(3)); Pt. 2. Letters of John Ruskin, 1870-1889. reprint ed. lib. bdg. 98.00 (978-1-58201-377-0(2)); Pt. 2. Modern Painters. 399p. reprint ed. lib. bdg. 98.00 (978-1-58201-344-2(6)); Pt. 2. Stones of Venice. 470p. reprint ed. lib. bdg. 98.00 (978-1-58201-350-3(0)); Pt. 3. Fors Clavigera Letters, 73-96. reprint ed. lib. bdg. 98.00 (978-1-58201-369-5(1)); Pt. 3. Modern Painters. 439p. reprint ed. lib. bdg. 98.00 (978-1-58201-345-9(4)); Pt. 3. Stones of Venice. 436p. reprint ed. lib. bdg. 98.00 (978-1-58201-351-0(9)); Pt. 4. Modern Painters. 407p. reprint ed. lib. bdg. 98.00 (978-1-58201-346-6(2)); Pt. 5. Modern Painters. 495p. reprint ed. lib. bdg. 98.00 (978-1-58201-347-3(0)); 1999. Set lib. bdg. 3822.00 o.p. (978-1-58201-340-4(3)) Classic Bks.

Saad, Rhonda & Schlegel, Amy Ingrid. Empire & Its Discontents. Koles, Jeanne Vee, ed. 2009. (ENG., Illus.). 72p. pap. 20.00 (978-1-880593-07-3(6)) Tufts Univ. Gallery.

Sansi, Roger. Fetishes & Monuments: Afro-Brazilian Art & Culture in the 20th Century. 2009. (Illus.). 224p. 24.50 (978-1-84545-711-2(0)) Berghahn Bks., Inc.

Saul, Nigel. English Church Monuments in the Middle Ages: History & Representation. (ENG., Illus.). 2011. 432p. pap. 45.00 (978-0-19-960613-9(7)) 2009. 400p. 150.00 (978-0-19-921598-0(7)) Oxford Univ. Pr., Inc.

Scheuerle, William H. George Baxter, the First Color Printing from Metal Plates & Wood Blocks: Portraying Victorian Values of England's Rising Middle Class. 2011. (Illus.). 180p. 129.95 **(978-0-7734-3920-7(X))** Mellen, Edwin Pr., The.

Schopf, Christine & Stocker, Gerfried, eds. Ars Electronica 2009: Human Nature. 2010. (ENG., Illus.). 431p. pap. 45.00 (978-3-7757-2498-2(2)) Hatje Cantz Verlag GmbH & Co KG DEU. Dist: D.A.P./Distributed Art Pubs.

Schrank, Sarah. Art & the City: Civic Imagination & Cultural Authority in Los Angeles. (Illus.). 224p. (C). 2011. pap. 24.95 (978-0-8122-2153-4(2)) 2008. 55.00 (978-0-8122-4117-4(7)) Univ. of Pennsylvania Pr.

Schwartz, Alexandra. Los Angeles. 2010. (ENG., Illus.). 336p. (gr. 17). 29.95 (978-0-262-01364-2(9)) MIT Pr.

Schwartz, Judith S. Confrontational Ceramics. 2008. (Illus.). 256p. 55.00 (978-0-8122-4139-6(8)) Univ. of Pennsylvania Pr.

See, Sarita Echavez. The Decolonized Eye: Filipino American Art & Performance. 2009. (ENG., Illus.). 232p. 75.00 (978-0-8166-5318-8(6)) Univ. of Minnesota Pr.

Seijdel, Jorinde, et al, contrib. by. Open 10: (in)tolerance, on Freedom of Expression in Art & the Public Domain. 2006. (Illus.). 160p. pap. 30.00 (978-90-5662-492-7(X)) NAi Uitgevers / Publishers Stichting NLD. Dist: D.A.P./Distributed Art Pubs.

Seijdel, Jorinde & Heerkens, Noud, eds. Pixels & Place: Video Art in Public Spaces. 2010. (ENG., Illus.). 160p. 40.00 (978-90-5662-738-6(4)) NAi Uitgevers / Publishers Stichting NLD. Dist: D.A.P./Distributed Art Pubs.

Seijdel, Jorinde & Melis, Liesbeth, eds. Open 14: Art as a Public Issue. 2008. (ENG., Illus.). 160p. pap. 30.00 (978-90-5662-435-4(0)) NAi Uitgevers / Publishers Stichting NLD. Dist: D.A.P./Distributed Art Pubs.

—Open 18: 2030 War Zone Amsterdam. 2010. (ENG., Illus.). 160p. pap. 30.00 (978-90-5662-710-2(4)) NAi Uitgevers / Publishers Stichting NLD. Dist: D.A.P./Distributed Art Pubs.

Shannon, Joshua. The Disappearance of Objects: New York Art & the Rise of the Postmodern City. 2009. (ENG., Illus.). 232p. 60.00 (978-0-300-13706-4(0)) Yale Univ. Pr.

Shaw, George Bernard. The Sanity of Art. reprint ed. lib. bdg. 98.00 (978-0-7426-3225-7(3)) Classic Bks.

—The Sanity of Art. 2009. 58p. pap. 14.14 (978-0-217-97406-6(6)) General Bks. LLC.

Sheriff, Mary D. & Watteau, Antoine. Antoine Watteau: Perspectives on the Artist & the Culture of His Time. 2006. (University of Delaware Press Studies in 17th- & 18th- Century Art & Culture). (Illus.). 201p. 62.50 (978-0-87413-934-1(1)) Univ. of Delaware Pr.

Shteir, Ann B. & Lightman, Bernard, eds. Figuring It Out: Science, Gender, & Visual Culture. 2006. (Interfaces: Studies in Visual Culture Ser.). (ENG., Illus.). 416p. per. 29.95 (978-1-58465-603-6(4)) Univ. Pr. of New England.

Siegel, Katy. Since '45: America & the Making of Contemporary Art. 2011. (ENG., Illus.). 224p. 29.00 (978-1-86189-773-2(1)) Reaktion Bks., Ltd. GBR. Dist: Chicago Distribution Ctr.

Simpson, Pamela H. Corn Palaces & Butter Queens: A History of Crop Art & Dairy Sculpture. 2012. (Illus.). 264p. 90.00 **(978-0-8166-7619-4(4))**; pap. 29.95 **(978-0-8166-7620-0(8))** Univ. of Minnesota Pr.

Sinha, Gayatri. Art & Visual Culture in India: 1857 - 2007. 2009. (Illus.). 300p. 85.00 (978-81-85026-92-3(0)) Marg Pubns. IND. Dist: National Bk. Network.

Sisson, Elaine & King, Linda, eds. Ireland, Design & Visual Culture: Negotiating Modernity 1922-1992. 2011. (Illus.). 320p. 49.00 (978-1-85918-472-1(3)) Cork Univ. Pr. IRL. Dist: Stylus Publishing, LLC.

Sladen, Mark & Yedgar, Ariella. Panic Attack! Art in the Punk Years. 2007. (ENG., Illus.). 224p. 44.95 (978-1-85894-403-6(1)) Merrell Pubs. Ltd. GBR. Dist: Perseus Distribution.

Sloan, Johanne, ed. Urban Ciphers: Montreal, Toronto, & the Problem of Comparison. 2007. (Culture of Cities Ser.). (ENG.). 312p. (C). (978-0-7735-3181-9(5)) McGill-Queen's Univ. Pr.

Smith, David R. Parody & Festivity in Early Modern Art: Essays on Comedy As Social Vision. 2012. (Illus.). 230p. 119.95 **(978-1-4094-3030-8(8))** Ashgate Publishing Co.

Smith, Paul Julian & Smith, Paul. Spanish Visual Culture: Cinema, Television, Internet. 2007. (ENG., Illus.). 192p. 84.00 (978-0-7190-7517-9(3)); pap. 26.00 (978-0-7190-7536-0(X)) Manchester Univ. Pr. GBR. Dist: Macmillan.

Smith, Terry. Antinomies of Art & Culture: Modernity, Postmodernity, Contemporaneity. Smith, Terry et al, eds. Enwezor, Okwui et al, contrib. by. 2009. (ENG., Illus.). 456p. 99.95 (978-0-8223-4186-4(7)); pap. 27.95 (978-0-8223-4203-8(0)) Duke Univ. Pr.

Solkin, David H. Painting Out of the Ordinary: Modernity & the Art of Everday Life in Early Nineteenth-Century England. 2008. (Paul Mellon Centre for Studies in British Art). (ENG., Illus.). 288p. 75.00 (978-0-300-14061-3(4)) Yale Univ. Pr.

Soudavar, Abolala. Decoding Old Masters: Patrons, Princes & Enigmatic Paintings of the 15th Century. 2007. (ENG., Illus.). 192p. 73.00 (978-1-84511-658-3(5)) I. B. Tauris & Co., Ltd. GBR. Dist: Macmillan.

Speer, George V. Things of the Spirit: Art & Healing in the American Body Politic, 1929-1941. 2012. 258p. (C). 83.95 **(978-1-4331-1568-4(9))** Lang, Peter Publishing, Inc.

Squire, Michael. The Art of the Body: Antiquity & Its Legacy, 1 vol. 2011. (Ancients & Moderns Ser.). (Illus.). 224p. (ENG.). 99.00 (978-0-19-538080-4(0)); pap. 24.95 (978-0-19-538081-1(9)) Oxford Univ. Pr., Inc.

Stewart, Peter. The Social History of Roman Art. 2008. (Key Themes in Ancient History Ser.). (ENG., Illus.). 216p. 109.00 (978-0-521-81632-8(7)); pap. 33.99 (978-0-521-01659-9(2)) Cambridge Univ. Pr.

Strobel, Heidi A. The Artistic Matronage of Queen Charlotte (1744-1818) How a Queen Promoted Both Art & Female Artists in English Society. 2011. (Illus.). 412p. 159.95 **(978-0-7734-1579-9(3))** Mellen, Edwin Pr., The.

Sturken, Marita & Cartwright, Lisa. Practices of Looking: An Introduction to Visual Culture. 2nd rev. ed. 2009. (ENG., Illus.). 416p. (C). pap. 79.95 (978-0-19-531440-3(9)) Oxford Univ. Pr., Inc.

Synder, Janet E. Early Gothic Column-Figure Sculpture in France: Appearance Materials & Significance. 2011. (Illus.). 306p. 119.95 (978-1-4094-0065-3(4)) Ashgate Publishing Co.

Tanner, Jeremy. The Invention of Art History in Ancient Greece: Religion, Society & Artistic Rationalisation. 2009. (Cambridge Classical Studies). (ENG., Illus.). 347p. pap. 47.00 (978-0-521-11422-6(5)) Cambridge Univ. Pr.

Tartakov, Gary Michael, ed. Dalit Art & Visual Imagery. 2012. (ENG., Illus.). 480p. 99.00 **(978-0-19-807936-1(2))** Oxford Univ. Pr., Inc.

Tatum, Stephen. In the Remington Moment. 2010. (ENG., Illus.). 280p. 55.00 (978-0-8032-2528-2(8)) Univ. of Nebraska Pr.

Thofner, Margit. Common Art: Urban Ceremonials in Antwerp & Brussels. 2007. (ENG., Illus.). 288p. 90.00 (978-90-400-8295-5(2)) Waanders B.V., Uitgeverij NLD. Dist: National Bk. Network.

Thomas, Greg M. Impressionist Children: Childhood, Family, & Modern Identity in French Art. 2011. (ENG., Illus.). 240p. 65.00 (978-0-300-11285-6(8)) Yale Univ. Pr.

Thompson, Nato, ed. A Guide to Democracy in America. 2008. (ENG., Illus.). 224p. pap. 15.00 (978-1-928570-08-0(9)) Creative Time.

Thompson, Nato, ed. Living as Form: Socially Engaged Art From, 1991-2011. 2012. (ENG., Illus.). 280p. (gr. 17). 39.95 **(978-0-262-01734-3(2))** MIT Pr.

Thyssen-Bornemisza Art Contemporary. Kuba: Journey Against the Current. 2006. (Illus.). 182p. pap. (978-3-211-36513-7(3), 3211365133) Actar Birkhauser Distribution.

Till, Barry, text. Japan Awakens: Woodblock Prints of the Meiji Period (1868-1912) 2008. 128p. 29.95 (978-0-7649-4635-6(8)) Pomegranate Communications, Inc.

Tillman, Gregory. Hoopla in Harlem! The Renaissance of African American Art & Culture. 2009. (ENG.). 84p. pap. 17.99 (978-0-7618-4570-6(4)) Univ. Pr. of America, Inc.

Timmermans, Bert. Patronen Van Patronage in Het Zeventiende-Eeuwse Antwerpen: Een Elite Als Actor Binnen Een Kunstwereld. 2008. (Studies Stadsgeschiedenis Ser.). (DUT., Illus.). 427p. 50.50 **(978-90-5260-247-9(6))** Aksant Academic Pubs. NLD. Dist: Amsterdam Univ. Pr.

Toynton, Evelyn. Jackson Pollock. 2012. (Icons of America Ser.). (ENG., Illus.). 160p. 26.00 (978-0-300-16325-4(8)) Yale Univ. Pr.

Trask, Jeffrey. Things American: Art Museums & Civic Culture in the Progressive Era. 2011. (Arts & Intellectual Life in Modern America Ser.). (Illus.). 312p. (C). 39.95 **(978-0-8122-4362-8(5))** Univ. of Pennsylvania Pr.

Tsuji, Midori, ed. Aesthetic Movement in Victorian Life. 2008. (ENG.). 1665.00 (978-4-86166-019-1(X)) Synapse, Edition JPN. Dist: Taylor & Francis Group.

Turvey, Malcolm. The Filming of Modern Life: European Avant-Garde Film of the 1920s. 2011. (October Bks.). (ENG., Illus.). 232p. (gr. 17). 29.95 (978-0-262-01518-9(8)) MIT Pr.

Uchill, Rebecca, et al. On Procession: Art on Parade. Uchill, Rebecca, ed. 2009. (Illus.). 120p. pap. 24.95 *(978-0-936260-87-7(4))* Indianapolis Museum of Art.

Unger, Daniel M. Guercino's Piantings & His Patrons' Politics in Early Modern Italy. 2010. (Visual Culture in Early Modernity Ser.). (Illus.). 212p. 124.95 *(978-0-7546-6909-8(2))* Ashgate Publishing Co.

Valli, Marc, ed. Elephant, Issue 5: The Art & Visual Culture Magazine. 2011. (Elephant Ser.). (ENG., Illus.). 208p. pap. 19.99 *(978-90-77174-38-8(9))* Frame Pubs. NLD. Dist: Consortium Bk. Sales & Distribution.

Van der Stighelen, K., ed. The Nude & the Norm in the Early Modern Low Countries. 2011. (Museums at the Crossroads Ser.). (ENG., Illus.). 220p. (C). pap. 94.00 *(978-2-503-53569-2(0))* Brepols Pubs. BEL. Dist: ISD.

Van Dyke, Nella, contrib. by. Art & Context: The '50s And '60s. 2006. (Illus.). 78p. *(978-0-9755662-2-0(9))* Museum of Art, Washington State Univ.

van Maanen, Hans. How to Study Art Worlds: On the Societal Functioning of Aesthetic Values. 2010. 256p. pap. *(978-90-8964-152-6(1))* Amsterdam Univ. Pr.

Vanderbeeken, Robrecht, et al, eds. Drunk on Capitalism: An Interdisciplinary Reflection on Market Economy, Art & Science. 2011. (Einstein Meets Magritte: an Interdisciplinary Reflection on Science, Nature, Art, Human Action & Society Ser.). (ENG., Illus.). xxii, 180p. 139.00 ***(978-94-007-2081-7(5)***, 9400720815) Springer.

Verwoert, Jan. Tell Me What You Want, What You Really, Really Want. Ohlraun, Vanessa, ed. 2011. (ENG., Illus.). 312p. 22.00 ***(978-1-934105-14-6(7))*** Sternberg Pr.

Volpe, Pasquale & Minnetti, Tommaso, contrib. by. Good 50x70: The Social Communication Project. 2010. (ENG., Illus.). 288p. pap. 25.00 *(978-90-6369-218-6(8))* Bis B.V., Uitgeverij(BIS Publishers) NLD. Dist: Consortium Bk. Sales & Distribution.

von Hantelmann, Dorothea. How to Do Things with Art. Marta, Karen, ed. 2010. (ENG., Illus.). 208p. pap. 29.95 *(978-3-03764-104-0(5))* JRP Ringier Kunstverlag AG CHE. Dist: D.A.P./Distributed Art Pubs.

Wahrman, Dror. Mr. Collier's Letter Racks: A Tale of Art & Illusion at the Threshold of the Modern Information Age. 2012. (ENG., Illus.). 288p. 34.95 ***(978-0-19-973886-1(6))*** Oxford Univ. Pr., Inc.

Walker, Alicia. The Emperor & the World: Exotic Elements in the Imagining of Middle Byzantine Imperial Power. 2012. (ENG., Illus.). 400p. 95.00 *(978-1-107-00477-1(2))* Cambridge Univ. Pr.

Walker, Andrew & Turk, Janeen. Joe Jones: Radical Painter of the American Scene. 2010. (Illus.). 224p. (ENG.). 60.00 *(978-0-89178-094-6(7))*; pap. 40.00 *(978-0-89178-093-9(9))* St. Louis Art Museum.

Walwin, Jeni, ed. Searching for Art's New Publics. 2010. (Illus.). 224p. pap. 35.00 *(978-1-84150-311-0(8))* Intellect, Ltd. GBR. Dist: Chicago Distribution Ctr.

Wamberg, Jacob. Landscape as World Picture: Tracing Cultural Evolution in Images. 2007. (ENG., Illus.). 2p. (C). 79.95 *(978-87-7934-232-3(9))* Aarhus Universitetsforlag DNK. Dist: Brown, David Bk. Co., The.

Watt, James C. Y. The World of Khubilai Khan: Chinese Art in the Yuan Dynasty. 2010. (Illus.). xviii, 342p. 65.00 ***(978-1-58839-402-6(6))*** Metropolitan Museum of Art, The.

Weibel, Peter, et al, eds. Global Studies: Mapping Contemporary Art & Culture. 2012. (ENG., Illus.). 456p. pap. 60.00 ***(978-3-7757-3202-4(0))*** Hatje Cantz Verlag GmbH & Co KG DEU. Dist: D.A.P./Distributed Art Pubs.

Weiermair, Peter. Image of the Body. 55.00 *(978-3-905514-08-7(7))* Edition Stemmle CHE. Dist: D.A.P./Distributed Art Pubs.

Weikop, Christian. New Perspectives on Bruke Expressionism: Bridging History. 2011. (Illus.). 342p. 124.95 *(978-1-4094-1203-8(2))* Ashgate Publishing Co.

Weisenfeld, Gennifer S. Imaging Disaster: Tokyo & the Visual Culture of Japan's Great Earthquake of 1923. 2012. (Asia: Local Studies / Global Themes Ser.). (ENG.). 400p. 60.00 ***(978-0-520-27195-1(5))*** Univ. of California Pr.

Weiss, Rachel. To & from Utopia in the New Cuban Art. 2011. (ENG., Illus.). 368p. pap. 34.95 *(978-0-8166-6515-0(X))* Univ. of Minnesota Pr.

Westwood, Martin. Martin Westwood. Beard, Jason, ed. aut. ed. 2008. (ENG.). 88p. pap. 95.00 *(978-1-904212-09-6(3))* Other Criteria GBR. Dist: Hachette Bk. Group.

White, Anthony. Lucio Fontana: Between Utopia & Kitsch. 2011. (October Bks.). (ENG., Illus.). 344p. (gr. 17). 29.95 *(978-0-262-01592-9(7))* MIT Pr.

Whiteley, Gillian. Junk: Art & the Politics of Trash. (ENG., Illus.). 192p. 2011. pap. 26.00 *(978-1-84885-413-0(7))* 2010. 85.00 *(978-1-84885-412-3(9))* I. B. Tauris & Co., Ltd. GBR. Dist: Macmillan.

Williams, John A. Weimar Culture Revisited. 2011. (Studies in European Culture & History Ser.). (ENG., Illus.). 262p. 89.00 *(978-0-230-10942-1(X))* Palgrave Macmillan.

Williams, Robert. Art, Theory, & Culture in Sixteenth-Century Italy: From Techne to Metatechne. 2011. (ENG.). 256p. pap. 35.99 *(978-0-521-18433-5(9))* Cambridge Univ. Pr.

Winegar, Jessica. Creative Reckonings: The Politics of Art & Culture in Contemporary Egypt. 2006. (Stanford Studies in Middle Eastern & Islamic Societies & Cultures). (ENG., Illus.). 416p. 70.00 *(978-0-8047-5476-7(4))*; per. 26.95 *(978-0-8047-5477-4(2))* Stanford Univ. Pr.

Wolbergs, Benjamin. Urban Illustration: Street Art City Guide Berlin. 2007. (Illus.). 359p. pap. 29.95 *(978-1-58423-291-9(9))* Gingko Pr., Inc.

Wolf, Norbert & Schneider, Norbert. Still Life. 25th ed. 2009. (ENG., Illus.). 216p. 14.99 *(978-3-8365-1018-9(9))* TASCHEN DEU. Dist: Ingram Pub. Services.

Woodson-Boulton, Amy. Transformative Beauty: Art Museums in Industrial Britain. 2012. (ENG., Illus.). 288p. 55.00 ***(978-0-8047-7804-6(3))*** Stanford Univ. Pr.

Wright, Kristina Dziedzic. Art, Culture, & Tourism on an Indian Ocean Island: An Ethnographic Study of Jua Kali Lamu. 2009. (Illus.). 252p. 109.95 *(978-0-7734-3874-3(2))* Mellen, Edwin Pr., The.

Wright, Terence. Visual Impact: Culture & the Meaning of Images. 2009. (ENG., Illus.). 192p. 109.95 *(978-1-85973-468-1(5))*; 1p. pap. 39.95 *(978-1-85973-473-5(1))* Berg Pubs. GBR. Dist: Macmillan.

Wroth, William & Gavin, Robin Farwell, eds. Converging Streams: Art of the Hispanic & Native American Southwest from Precontquest Times to the Twentieth Century. 2010. (ENG.). 256p. *(978-0-89013-568-6(1))*; pap. *(978-0-89013-570-9(3))* Museum of New Mexico Pr.

Yazykova, Irina. Hidden & Triumphant: the Underground Struggle to Save Russian Iconography. Greneir, Paul, tr. from RUS. 2010. (ENG.). 196p. (gr. 11). 26.99 *(978-1-55725-564-8(4))* Paraclete Pr., Inc.

Yonan, Michael E. & Cavanagh, Alden. The Cultural Aesthetics of Eighteenth-Century Procelain. 2010. (Illus.). 244p. 109.95 *(978-0-7546-6386-7(8))* Ashgate Publishing Co.

Zarobell, John. Empire of Landscape: Space & Ideology in French Colonial Algeria. 2009. (ENG., Illus.). 240p. 95.00 *(978-0-271-03443-0(2))* Pennsylvania State Univ. Pr.

Zavala, Adriana. Becoming Modern, Becoming Tradition. 2010. (ENG., Illus.). 408p. pap. 44.95 ***(978-0-271-03524-6(2))*** Pennsylvania State Univ. Pr.

Zavala, Adriana. Becoming Modern, Becoming Tradition: Women, Gender, & Representation in Mexican Art. 2010. (Illus.). 376p. 95.00 *(978-0-271-03471-3(8))* Pennsylvania State Univ. Pr.

Zavala, Adriana, et al. Mexico Beyond Its Revolution. 2010.Tr. of Mexico mas alla de su Revolucion. (ENG & SPA., Illus.). 112p. pap. 10.00 *(978-1-880593-08-0(4))* Tufts Univ. Gallery.

Ziskin, Rochelle. Sheltering Art: Collecting & Social Identity in Early Eighteenth-Century Paris. 2012. (ENG.). 360p. ***(978-0-271-03785-1(7))*** Pennsylvania State Univ. Pr.

Zylinska, Joanna. Cyborg Experiments: The Extensions of the Body in the Media Age. 2007. (Technologies). (Illus.). 256p. *(978-0-8264-9640-9(7))* Continuum International Publishing Group, Ltd.

ART AND STATE

Here are entered works on government policy toward the arts. Works on support of the arts by individuals and corporations are entered under Art Patronage.

see also Art and War

Bendixen, Peter. Managing Art: An Introduction into Principles & Conceptions. 2011. (ENG., Illus.). 256p. pap. 34.95 *(978-3-643-50063-2(7))* Lit Verlag DEU. Dist: Transaction Pubs.

Blake, Casey Nelson, ed. The Arts of Democracy: Art, Public Culture, & the State. 2007. (Arts & Intellectual Life in Modern America Ser.). (Illus.). 384p. (C). 49.95 *(978-0-8122-4029-0(4))* Univ. of Pennsylvania Pr.

—The Arts of Democracy: Art, Public Culture, & the State. 2009. (Arts & Intellectual Life in Modern America Ser.). (Illus.). 384p. (C). pap. 26.50 *(978-0-8122-2001-8(3))* Univ. of Pennsylvania Pr.

Botting, Eileen & Sapega, Ellen. Consensus & Debate in Salazar's Portugal: Visual & Literary Negotiations of the National Text, 1933-1948. Locke, Jill, ed. 2008. (ENG., Illus.). 184p. (C). pap. 35.00 *(978-0-271-03411-9(4))* Pennsylvania State Univ. Pr.

Calirman, Claudia. Brazilian Art under Dictatorship: Antonio Manuel, Artur Barrio, & Cildo Meireles. 2012. (ENG., Illus.). 264p. 89.95 ***(978-0-8223-5139-9(0))***; pap. 24.95 ***(978-0-8223-5153-5(6))*** Duke Univ. Pr.

Codell, Julie F. The Political Economy of Art: Making the Nation of Culture. 2008. (Illus.). 232p. (C). 75.00 *(978-0-8386-4168-2(7))* Fairleigh Dickinson Univ. Pr.

Cowen, Tyler. Good & Plenty: The Creative Successes of American Arts Funding. 2010. (ENG.). 208p. (C). pap. 21.95 *(978-0-691-14626-3(8))* Princeton Univ. Pr.

De Grazia, Alfred. 40 Stases & Theses: Problems & Solutions of the World Order. 2007. (Illus.). 84p. 69.00 *(978-1-60377-000-2(3))* Metron Pubns.

The Economic & Employment Impact of the Arts & Music Industry: Hearing Before the Committee on Education & Labor, U.S. House of Representatives, One Hundred Eleventh Congress, First Session, Hearing Held in Washington, DC, March 26, 2009. 2009. (Illus.). iii, 70p. *(978-0-16-083562-9(3)*, 552-070-39280-7) United States Government Printing Office.

Finch, L. Boyd. Legacies of Camelot: Stewart & Lee Udall, American Culture, & the Arts. 2008. (ENG., Illus.). 208p. 24.95 *(978-0-8061-3879-4(3))* Univ. of Oklahoma Pr.

Folin, Marco, ed. Courts & Courtly Arts in Renaissance Italy: Arts, Culture & Politics, 1395-1530. 2010. (ENG., Illus.). 444p. 95.00 *(978-1-85149-643-3(2))* Antique Collectors' Club.

Forrest, Tara. The Politics of Imagination: Benjamin, Kracauer, Kluge. 2008. (ENG.). 198p. pap. 34.95 *(978-3-89942-681-6(9))* Transcript Verlag DEU. Dist: Transaction Pubs.

Gale, Peggy, et al. Art at Work/L'Art Au Travail: rt Bank of the Canada Council of the Arts/le Banque d'Oeuvres d'Art du Conseil des Arts du Canada. Henry, Victoria, ed. 2007. (ENG & FRE., Illus.). 144p. pap. 45.00 *(978-0-86492-429-2(1))* Goose Lane Editions CAN. Dist: Univ. of Toronto Pr.

Grieve, Victoria. The Federal Art Project & the Creation of Middlebrow Culture. 2009. (ENG., Illus.). 240p. 47.00 *(978-0-252-03421-3(X))* Univ. of Illinois Pr.

Groys, Boris. Art Power. 2008. (ENG.). 200p. (gr. 17). 25.95 *(978-0-262-07292-2(0))* MIT Pr.

Hite, Katherine. Politics & the Art of Commemoration. 2011. (Interventions Ser.). (ENG., Illus.). 160p. (C). 130.00 *(978-0-415-78071-1(3))* Routledge.

Hortiguera, Hugo & Rocha, Carolina, eds. Argentinean Cultural Production During the Neoliberal Years (1989-2001) 2007. 248p. *(978-0-7734-5348-7(2))* Mellen, Edwin Pr., The.

Ivey, Bill. Arts, Inc: How Greed & Neglect Have Destroyed Our Cultural Rights. 2010. (ENG., Illus.). 368p. pap. 17.95 *(978-0-520-26792-3(3))* Univ. of California Pr.

Ivey, Bill J. Arts, Inc: How Greed & Neglect Have Destroyed Our Cultural Rights. 2008. (Illus.). 342p. 40.00 *(978-0-520-24112-1(6))* Univ. of California Pr.

Jachec, Nancy. Politics & Painting at the Venice Biennale, 1948-1964: Italy & the Idea of Europe. 2008. (Critical Perspectives in Art History Ser.). (ENG., Illus.). 224p. 84.00 *(978-0-7190-6896-6(7))* Manchester Univ. Pr. GBR. Dist: Macmillan.

Jennings, Sarah. Art & Politics: The History of the National Arts Centre. 2009. (ENG., Illus.). 426p. 50.00 *(978-1-55002-886-7(3)*, Dundurn Pr.) Dundurn CAN. Dist: Ingram Pub. Services.

Johnson, Patricia. Ovid before Exile: Art & Punishment in the Metamorphoses. 2010. (Wisconsin Studies in Classics Ser.). (ENG.). 200p. pap. 29.95 *(978-0-299-22404-2(X))* Univ. of Wisconsin Pr.

Johnson, Patricia J. Ovid Before Exile: Art & Punishment in the Metamorphoses. 2007. (Wisconsin Studies in Classics). (ENG.). 184p. 50.00 *(978-0-299-22400-4(7))* Univ. of Wisconsin Pr.

Kaneff, Deema & Kapferer, Judith. The State & the Arts: Articulating Power & Subversion. 2008. (Illus.). 240p. 27.95 *(978-1-84545-578-1(9))* Berghahn Bks., Inc.

Kelleher, Joe. Theatre & Politics. 2009. (Theatre And Ser.). (ENG.). 80p. pap. 9.00 *(978-0-230-20523-9(2))* Palgrave Macmillan.

Kidd, Dustin. Legislating Creativity: The Intersections of Art & Politics. 2009. (Illus.). xvi, 174p. 95.00 *(978-0-203-85979-7(0))* Routledge.

Lang, Jack. Les Batailles du Grand Louvre. 2010. (FRE., Illus.). 260p. pap. *(978-2-7118-5789-0(1))* Editions de la Reunion des Musees nationaux.

Levine, Caroline. Provoking Democracy: Why We Need the Arts. 2007. (Blackwell Manifestos Ser.: 12). (ENG., Illus.). 256p. pap. 39.95 *(978-1-4051-5927-2(8))*; 104.95 *(978-1-4051-5926-5(X))* Wiley, John & Sons, Inc. (Wiley-Blackwell).

Linn, Julius, Jr., et al, eds. Digging Out of the Great Depression: Federal Programs at Work in & Around Birmingham. 2010. (Illus.). 148p. pap. 24.95 *(978-0-943994-35-2(7))* Birmingham Historical Society.

Michalski, Sergiusz. Public Monuments: Art in Political Bondage 1870-1997. 2006. 236p. reprint ed. pap. 25.00 *(978-1-4223-5342-4(7))* DIANE Publishing Co.

Mitchell, John. Out of the Dark Ages. 2008. (Illus.). 192p. pap. 27.00 *(978-0-7156-3685-5(5))* Duckworth Publishers GBR. Dist: International Publishers Marketing.

Mute, prod. Mute Volume II 5 Spring/Summer 2007: It's not easy being green - the climate change Issue. 2007. 124p. per. *(978-0-9554796-4-9(9))* Mute Publishing, Ltd.

Norris, Stephen M. A War of Images: Russian Popular Prints, Wartime Culture, & National Identity, 1812-1945. 2006. (Illus.). 291p. 40.00 *(978-0-87580-363-0(6))* Northern Illinois Univ. Pr.

Ondaatje, Elizabeth H. & Lowell, Julia. The Arts & State Governments: At Arms Length on Arm in Arm? 2006. (Illus.). 100p. per. 20.00 *(978-0-8330-3867-8(2)*, MG359) RAND Corp., The.

Pieprzak, Katarzyna. Imagined Museums: Art & Modernity in Postcolonial Morocco. 2010. (Illus.). 280p. 75.00 *(978-0-8166-6518-1(4))*; (ENG., pap. 25.00 *(978-0-8166-6519-8(2))* Univ. of Minnesota Pr.

Piotrowski, Piotr, tr. Art & Democracy in Post-Communist Europe. 2012. (Illus.). 272p. pap. 32.00 ***(978-1-86189-895-1(9))*** Reaktion Bks., Ltd. GBR. Dist: Chicago Distribution Ctr.

Robertson, Clive. Policy Matters: Administrations of Art & Culture. 2006. (ENG., Illus.). 288p. per. 19.95 *(978-0-920397-36-7(0))* Y Y Z Artists Outlet CAN. Dist: LitDistCo.

Sabatier, Gérard. Le Prince et les Arts: Stratégies Figuratives de la Monarchie Française, de la Renaissance Aux Lumières. 2010. (FRE., Illus.). 459p. *(978-2-87673-542-2(3))* Champ Vallon.

Samuel P. Ham Museum of Art Staff, contrib. by. Continuity & Change: Three Generations of Ethiopian Artists. 2007. (Illus.). 124p. *(978-0-9762552-3-9(5))* Ham Museum of Art.

Sato, Doshin. Modern Japanese Art & the Meiji State: The Politics of Beauty. 2011. (ENG., Illus.). 376p. 75.00 *(978-1-60606-059-9(7))* Getty Pubns.

Schwartz, D. T. Art, Education, & the Democratic Commitment: A Defense of State Support for the Arts. 2010. (Philosophical Studies in Contemporary Culture Ser.). (Illus.). 192p. pap. 129.00 *(978-90-481-5450-0(2)*, 9048154502) Springer.

Slauter, Eric. The State as a Work of Art: The Cultural Origins of the Constitution. 2009. (ENG., Illus.). 392p. 40.00 *(978-0-226-76195-4(9))* Univ. of Chicago Pr.

Smith, David A. Money for Art: The Tangled Web of Art & Politics in American Democracy. 2008. (ENG.). 320p. 27.50 *(978-1-56663-768-8(6))* Dee, Ivan R. Pub.

Sotiropoulos, Karen. Staging Race: Black Performers in Turn of the Century America. 2008. (Illus.). 304p. per. 22.50 *(978-0-674-02760-2(4))* Harvard Univ. Pr.

Steinhoff, Judith & Smith, Timothy B. Art as Politics in Late Medieval & Renaissance Siena. 2012. (Illus.). 250p. ***(978-1-4094-0066-0(2))*** Ashgate Publishing Co.

Taylor, Brandon. The Nazification of Art: Art, Design, Architecture, Music & Film in the Third Reich. (Illus.). 280p. pap. 24.95 *(978-0-9506783-9-9(2))* Winchester Schl. of Art Pr. GBR. Dist: Paul & Co. Pubs. Consortium, Inc.

Thompson, Nato, ed. A Guide to Democracy in America. 2008. (ENG., Illus.). 224p. pap. 15.00 *(978-1-928570-08-0(9))* Creative Time.

Tupitsyn, Victor. The Museological Unconscious. 2009. (ENG., Illus.). 352p. (gr. 17). 34.95 *(978-0-262-20173-5(9))* MIT Pr.

Tupitsyn, Victor. The Museological Unconscious: Communal (Post)Modernism in Russia. 2012. (ENG., Illus.). 352p. (gr. 17). pap. 17.95 ***(978-0-262-51751-5(5))*** MIT Pr.

Uzzi, Jeannine Diddle. Children in the Visual Arts of Imperial Rome. 2011. (ENG.). 268p. pap. 35.99 ***(978-1-107-40337-6(5))*** Cambridge Univ. Pr.

van Elzen, Sus, text. Dragon & Rose Garden. 2010. (ENG., Illus.). 208p. pap. 19.95 *(978-90-814503-0-0(1))* Timezone 8 Ltd. HKG. Dist: D.A.P./Distributed Art Pubs.

Weiwei, Ai, et al. Art & Cultural Policy in China: A Conversation between Ai Weiwei, Uli Sigg & Yung Ho Chang, moderated by Peter Pakesch. 2009. (GER & ENG., Illus.). 132p. pap. 39.95 *(978-3-211-89240-4(0))* Springer Wien AUT. Dist: Actar Birkhauser Distribution.

Wilmer, Stephen, ed. National Theatres in a Changing Europe. 2008. (Studies in International Performance Ser.). (ENG.). 240p. 89.00 *(978-0-230-52109-4(6))* Palgrave Macmillan.

ART AND STATE—FRANCE

Adamson, Natalie. Painting Politics & the Struggle for the Ecole de Paris 1944-1964. 2009. (Illus.). 330p. 134.95 *(978-0-7546-5928-0(3))* Ashgate Publishing Co.

Baguley, David. Art & Literature of the Second Empire. 2012. (Durham Modern Languages Ser.). (ENG.). 200p. pap. 24.95 *(978-0-7190-8585-7(3))* Manchester Univ. Pr. GBR. Dist: Macmillan.

Freeman, Kirrily. Bronzes to Bullets: Vichy & the Destruction of French Public Statuary, 1941-1944. 2008. (ENG., Illus.). 264p. 65.00 *(978-0-8047-5889-5(1))* Stanford Univ. Pr.

Karlsgodt, Elizabeth Campbell. Defending National Treasures: French Art & Heritage under Vichy. 2011. (ENG., Illus.). 404p. 60.00 *(978-0-8047-7018-7(2))* Stanford Univ. Pr.

Kearns, James & Vaisse, Pierre. "Ce Salon à Quoi Tout Se Ramène" Le Salon de Peinture et de Sculpture, 1791-1890. 2009. (French Studies of the Eighteenth & Nineteenth Centuries Ser.). (FRE., Illus.). 164p. 48.95 *(978-3-03910-931-9(6))* Lang, Peter AG GBR. Dist: Lang, Peter.

Orgogozo, Chantal & Lintz, Yannick. Vases, Bronzes, Marbres et Autres Antiques: Dépôts du Musée du Louvre en 1875: étude Historique et Catalogue. 2008. (FRE & ENG., Illus.). 304p. 125.00 *(978-2-35340-027-0(2))* Gourcuff Gradenigo FRA. Dist: National Bk. Network.

ART AND STATE—GERMANY

Baker, Barrie. Theatre Censorship in Honecker's Germany: From Volker Braun to Samuel Beckett. 2007. (German Linguistic & Cultural Studies Ser.: Vol. 23). (Illus.). 208p. pap. 55.95 *(978-3-03911-086-5(1))* Lang, Peter Publishing, Inc.

Braun, Matthias. Kulturinsel und Machtinstrument: Die Akademie der Künste, die Partei und die Staatssicherheit. 2007. (Analysen und Dokumente. Wissenschaftliche Reihe der Bundesbeauftragten fur die Unterlagen des Staatssicherheitsdienstes der ehemaligen Deutschen Demokratischen Republik (BStU) Ser.). (GER., Illus.). 480p. (C). 44.00 *(978-3-525-35049-2(X))* Vandenhoeck & Ruprecht GmbH & Co. KG DEU. Dist: ISD.

Kaiser, Fritz. Degenerate Art Exhibition Guide 1937 - Bilingual Edition German/English. von Halasz, Joachim, ed. & tr. by. 2010. 78p. pap. *(978-1-905742-30-1(4))* Foxley Books.

Kelly, Elaine & Wlodarski, Amy, eds. Art Outside the Lines: New Perspectives on GDR Art Culture. 2011. (Illus.). 298p. pap. 8400.00 *(978-90-420-3341-2(X))* Rodopi.

Peters, Olaf. Neue Sachlichkeit & Nationalsozialismus: Affirmation & Kritik. (GER., Illus.). 351p. *(978-3-496-01182-8(3))* Reimer, Dietrich.

Saehrendt, Christian. Kunst als Botschafter einer künstlichen Nation: Pallas Athene - 27. Studien zur Rolle der bildenden Kunst in der Auswärtigen Kulturpolitik der DDR. 2009. (Pallas Athene. Beitrage zur Universitats- und Wissenschaftsgeschichte Ser.). (GER., Illus.). 197p. (C). 52.00 *(978-3-515-09227-2(7))* Steiner, Franz Verlag Wiesbaden GmbH DEU. Dist: Brown, David Bk. Co., The.

Spotts, Frederic. Hitler & the Power of Aesthetics. 2009. (ENG.). 464p. (gr. 12). pap. 19.95 *(978-1-59020-178-7(7))* Overlook Pr., The.

ART AND STATE—GREAT BRITAIN

Carson, Andrea, frwd. Flash Forward 2008: Emerging Photographers from Canada, the United Kingdom & the United States. 2008. (ENG.). 192p. 30.00 *(978-0-9739739-6-9(X))* Magenta Publishing for the Arts CAN. Dist: Consortium Bk. Sales & Distribution.

Hoock, Holger. Empires of the Imagination: Politics, War, & the Arts in the British World, 1750-1850. 2010. (ENG., Illus.). 512p. 45.95 *(978-1-86197-859-2(6))* Profile Bks. Ltd. GBR. Dist: Consortium Bk. Sales & Distribution.

Smith, Melanie Kay. Cultural Planning for Urban Regeneration. 2010. 208p. pap. *(978-3-8383-9203-5(5))* Lambert Academic Publishing.

Vinney & Selwood. Culture & Media in the UK. 2008. 224p. pap. 45.95 *(978-0-415-35524-7(9))*; (Illus.). 130.00 *(978-0-415-35523-0(0))* Routledge.

Woodson-Boulton, Amy. Transformative Beauty: Art Museums in Industrial Britain. 2012. (ENG., Illus.). 288p. 55.00 ***(978-0-8047-7804-6(3))*** Stanford Univ. Pr.

ART AND THEATER

see Actors—Portraits; Theater in Art; Theaters—Stage Setting and Scenery

ART AND WAR

see also Art Treasures in War

Apel, Dora. War Culture & the Contest of Images. 2012. (New Directions in International Studies). 272p. 72.00 ***(978-0-8135-5395-5(4))***; pap. 29.95 ***(978-0-8135-5394-8(6))*** Rutgers Univ. Pr.

A

Balfour, Michael, et al. Performance in Place of War. 2009. (Enactments Ser.). (ENG., Illus.). 392p. 29.00 *(978-1-906497-14-9(1))* Seagull Bks. GBR. Dist: Chicago Distribution Ctr.
Bisio, Tom. Strategy & Change: An Examination of Military Strategy, the I-Ching & Ba Gua Zhang. 2010. 329p. pap. 29.95 *(978-1-4327-5055-8(0))* Outskirts Pr., Inc.
Brandon, Laura. Art & War. 2007. (Art and... Ser.). (ENG., Illus.). 168p. 94.00 *(978-1-84511-236-3(9))*; pap. 27.00 *(978-1-84511-237-0(7))* I. B. Tauris & Co., Ltd. GBR. Dist: Macmillan.
Brandon, Laura & Ogden, Glenn. A Brush with War: Military Art from Korea to Afghanistan. 2009. (ENG., Illus.). 72p. pap. 19.95 *(978-0-660-19854-5(1))* Canadian Museum of Civilization/Musee Canadien des Civilisations CAN. Dist: Univ. of Washington Pr.
Calica, Lovella. Warrior Writers: Re-Making Sense: A Collection of Artwork. 2008. (Illus.). 208p. pap. *(978-0-9801665-0-7(0))* Iraq Veterans Against the War.
Danchev, Alex. On Art & War & Terror. (ENG., Illus.). 256p. (gr. 17). 2011. pap. 32.00 *(978-0-7486-4259-5(5))* 2009. 75.00 *(978-0-7486-3915-1(2))* Edinburgh Univ. Pr. GBR. Dist: Columbia Univ. Pr.
Deutsche, Rosalyn. Hiroshima after Iraq: Three Studies in Art & War. (Wellek Library Lectures). (ENG., Illus.). 104p. (gr. 17). 2011. pap. 18.00 ***(978-0-231-15279-2(5))*** 2010. 22.50 *(978-0-231-15278-5(7))* Columbia Univ. Pr.
Fordham, Douglas. British Art & the Seven Years' War: Allegiance & Autonomy. 2010. (Illus.). 352p. (C). 65.00 *(978-0-8122-4243-0(2))* Univ. of Pennsylvania Pr.
Norris, Stephen M. A War of Images: Russian Popular Prints, Wartime Culture, & National Identity, 1812-1945. 2006. (Illus.). 291p. 40.00 *(978-0-87580-363-0(6))* Northern Illinois Univ. Pr.
Pavitt, Jane. Fear & Fashion in the Cold War. 2008. (ENG., Illus.). 128p. pap. 37.50 *(978-1-85177-544-6(7))* V & A Pubns. GBR. Dist: Hachette Bk. Group.
Saunders, Nicholas J. Trench Art. 2nd rev. ed. 2012. (Illus.). 160p. pap. 24.95 ***(978-1-84884-637-1(1))*** Pen & Sword Bks. Ltd. GBR. Dist: Casemate Pubs. & Bk. Distributors, LLC.
Seijdel, Jorinde & Melis, Liesbeth, eds. Open 18: 2030 War Zone Amsterdam. 2010. (ENG., Illus.). 160p. pap. 30.00 *(978-90-5662-710-2(4))* NAi Uitgevers / Publishers Stichting NLD. Dist: D.A.P./Distributed Art Pubs.
Thompson, James A., Jr. & Hughes, Jenny. Performance in Place of War. Balfour, Michael, ed. 2009. (Enactments Ser.). (ENG., Illus.). 282p. pap. 29.95 *(978-1-906497-13-2(3))* Seagull Bks. GBR. Dist: Chicago Distribution Ctr.

ART APPRECIATION

see also Art—Study and Teaching; Art Criticism

Abrahams, Philippa. Beneath the Surface: A Thousand Years of Artists at Work. 2008. (ENG., Illus.). 192p. 45.00 *(978-0-7112-2756-9(X))* Lincoln, Frances Ltd. GBR. Dist: Perseus-PGW.
Acton. Learning to Look at Paintings. 2nd rev. ed. 2008. (ENG., Illus.). 336p. 136.00 *(978-0-415-43517-8(X))*; 34.95 *(978-0-415-43518-5(8))* Routledge.
Aldrich, Megan & Hutt, Julia. Understanding Art Objects: Thinking Through the Eye. Godfrey, Tony, ed. 2009. (Illus.). 176p. 50.00 *(978-1-84822-016-4(2),* Lund Humphries Pubs.) Ashgate Publishing, Ltd. GBR. Dist: Ashgate Publishing Co.
Ambers, J., et al. Italian Renaissance Drawings: Technical Examination & Analysis. 2010. (ENG., Illus.). 174p. pap. 70.00 *(978-1-904982-58-6(1))* Archetype Pubns. GBR. Dist: National Bk. Network.
Anderson, Kim & Carson, Jenny. Art 101: Understanding Visual Artforms in Our World Workbook. rev. ed. 2010. (ENG.). 38p. spiral bd. 28.50 *(978-0-7575-7460-3(2))* Kendall Hunt Publishing Co.
Anderson, Kimberly & Carson, Jenny. Art 101: Understanding Visual Artforms in Our World. 2010. (Illus.). xi, 309p. *(978-0-7575-7459-7(9))* Kendall Hunt Publishing Co.
Artinger, Kai. Paula Modersohn-Becker: Der andere Blick. 2009. (GER., Illus.). 160p. pap. *(978-3-7861-2596-9(1))* Gebruder Mann Verlag.
Bailey, David, photos by. David Bailey, NY JS DB 62, 1 vol. 2008. (ENG., Illus.). 66p. 50.00 *(978-3-86521-414-0(2))* Steidl, Gerhard Druckerei und Verlag DEU. Dist: Innovative Logistics.
Barbe-Gall, Francoise. How to Look at a Painting. 2011. (ENG., Illus.). 312p. pap. 24.95 *(978-0-7112-3212-9(1))* Lincoln, Frances Ltd. GBR. Dist: Perseus-PGW.
Barbe-Gall, Françoise. How to Talk to Children about Modern Art. 2012. (ENG., Illus.). 176p. pap. 19.95 ***(978-0-7112-3289-1(X))*** Lincoln, Frances Ltd. GBR. Dist: Perseus-PGW.
BarCharts, Inc. Art Appreciation. 2011. (ENG.). 6p. 5.95 *(978-1-4232-1633-9(4))* Barcharts, Inc.
Barryte, Bernard, ed. Rodin & America. 2011. (ENG., Illus.). 384p. 75.00 ***(978-88-366-2000-5(0))*** Silvana ITA. Dist: D.A.P./Distributed Art Pubs.
The Beauty of Art. 30.00 *(978-0-930061-62-3(4))* Interspace Bks.
Beckett, Wendy. Sister Wendy's Bible Treasury: Stories & Wisdom Through the Eyes of Great Painters. 2012. ***(978-1-57075-972-7(3))*** Orbis Bks.
Bedia, José. Jose Bedia: A Monograph, 1 vol. Power, Kevin, ed. 2007. (SPA & ENG., Illus.). 256p. (gr. 13-18). 75.00 *(978-84-7506-615-8(1))* Turner, Ediciones S.A. ESP. Dist: D.A.P./Distributed Art Pubs.
Belting, Hans & Buddensieg, Andrea, eds. The Global Art World. 2009. (ENG., Illus.). 408p. pap. 45.00 *(978-3-7757-2407-4(9))* Hatje Cantz Verlag GmbH & Co KG DEU. Dist: D.A.P./Distributed Art Pubs.
Bishop, Philip E. A Beginner's Guide to the Humanities. 3rd ed. 2009. (ENG.). 176p. (C). pap. 38.00 *(978-0-205-66514-3(4),* Prentice Hall) Prentice Hall PTR.
Brogger, Andreas & Kholeif, Omar, eds. Vision, Memory & Media. 2011. (Liverpool University Press - Foundation for Art Creative Technology Ser.). (ENG., Illus.). 96p. pap. 19.95 *(978-1-84631-637-1(5))* Liverpool Univ. Pr. GBR. Dist: Chicago Distribution Ctr.
Brommer, Frank, ed. Discover Art History. 3rd ed. (Illus.). tchr. ed. *(978-0-87192-313-4(0))*; 68p. tchr. ed. 234.95 *(978-0-87192-312-7(2))* Davis Pubns., Inc.
Brommer, Gerald F. Discover Art History: Overhead Transparencies. 74.95 *(978-0-87192-310-3(6))* Davis Pubns., Inc.
Brooks, Julian. Master Drawings: Close-Up. 2010. (Illus.). 136p. pap. 24.95 *(978-1-60606-019-3(8))* Oxford Univ. Pr., Inc.
Burns-Clair, Pam, et al. Walt Disney's First Lady of Imagineering, Harriet Burns. 2010. *(978-1-57864-600-5(6))* Donning Co. Pubs.
Cameron, Dan & Power, Kevin. Juliao Sarmento Vol. 2: 2000-2001, 1 vol. 2008. (ENG, MUL & SPA., Illus.). 64p. 35.00 *(978-84-343-1153-4(4))* Poligrafa, Ediciones, S. A. ESP. Dist: D.A.P./Distributed Art Pubs.
Carman, Charles H. Renaissance Theories of Vision. Shannon, John, ed. 2010. (Visual Culture in Early Modernity Ser.). (Illus.). 258p. 119.95 *(978-1-4094-0024-0(7))* Ashgate Publishing Co.
Cast, David. The Delight of Art: Giorgio Vasari & the Traditions of Humanist Discourse. 2009. (ENG.). 296p. 95.00 *(978-0-271-03442-3(4))* Pennsylvania State Univ. Pr.
Clark, Steve. Reception of Blake in the Orient. Suzuki, Masashi, ed. 2009. (Continuum Reception Studies). (ENG.). 360p. 65.00 *(978-0-8264-3805-8(9))* Continuum International Publishing Group, Ltd. GBR. Dist: National Bk. Network.
Clarke, David, ed. Tippett Studies. 2006. (Cambridge Composer Studies). (ENG.). 252p. pap. 50.00 *(978-0-521-02683-3(0))* Cambridge Univ. Pr.
Constantinos, Taliotis. Under the Fridge's Light: The Jouissance of Misinterpretation & the Pleasure of Misconstruction. 2011. 64p. pap. ***(978-3-639-31917-0(6))*** VDM Verlag Dr. Mueller e.K.
Costache, Irina D. The Art of Understanding Art: A Behind the Scenes Story. 2012. (ENG., Illus.). 280p. 89.95 ***(978-0-470-65832-1(0),*** Wiley-Blackwell) Wiley, John & Sons, Inc.
Couturier, Sonia. Drawn to Art: French Artists & Art Lovers in 18th-Century Rome. 2012. (ENG., Illus.). 256p. pap. 45.00 ***(978-88-366-2054-8(X))*** Silvana ITA. Dist: D.A.P./Distributed Art Pubs.
Cram101 Textbook Reviews. Outlines & Highlights for Living with Art by Getlein, Isbn: 0072317264 0072870478. 2011. 408p. pap. 35.95 ***(978-1-61812-994-9(5))*** Cram101 Inc.
Cram101 Textbook Reviews. Outlines & Highlights for Power of Art by Richard L Lewis, Isbn: 9780534641030. 2010. 388p. pap. 34.95 *(978-1-61698-094-8(X))* Cram101 Inc.
Cram101 Textbook Reviews & Cram101 Textbook Reviews. Outlines & Highlights for Humanities Through the Arts by F David Martin. 2011. 400p. pap. 35.95 ***(978-1-61830-675-3(8))*** Cram101 Inc.
—Outlines & Highlights for Humanities Through the Arts by Martin, Isbn: 9780073138633 0073138630. 2011. 248p. pap. 31.95 ***(978-1-61490-863-0(X))*** Cram101 Inc.
—Outlines & Highlights for Living with Art by Mark Getlein, Isbn: 9780073379203 0073379204. 2011. 546p. pap. 38.95 ***(978-1-61490-076-4(0))*** Cram101 Inc.
—Outlines & Highlights for Power of Art by Richard L Lewis, Isbn: 9780495501916 0495501913. 2011. 450p. pap. 36.95 ***(978-1-61490-681-0(5))*** Cram101 Inc.
Day, Lewis Foreman. Every-Day Art. 2009. 150p. pap. *(978-0-217-47511-2(6))* Books LLC.
—Every-Day Art. 2008. 300p. pap. *(978-1-906600-07-5(4))* Mills, Jeremy Publishing.
Deitch, Jeffrey & Gruen, Julia. Keith Haring. Geiss, Suzanne, ed. 2008. (ENG., Illus.). 522p. 60.00 *(978-0-8478-3139-5(6))* Rizzoli International Pubns., Inc.
Fang, et al, eds. Ouyang Chun: Luminescent, 1 vol. 2008. (ENG., Illus.). 350p. 52.00 *(978-988-99265-1-9(2))* Timezone 8 Ltd. HKG. Dist: D.A.P./Distributed Art Pubs.
Fang Fang, et al, eds. Gao Yu: Specimen, 1 vol. Ambrozy, Lee, tr. 2008. (ENG., Illus.). 156p. 42.00 *(978-988-99617-4-9(1))* Timezone 8 Ltd. HKG. Dist: D.A.P./Distributed Art Pubs.
Farthing, Stephen. 1001 Paintings You Must See Before You Die: Revised & Updated. 2011. (ENG., Illus.). 960p. 36.95 *(978-0-7893-2231-9(5))* Universe Publishing.
Farthing, Stephen, ed. 1001 Paintings You Must See Before You Die. 2007. (ENG., Illus.). 960p. 36.95 *(978-0-7893-1524-3(6))* Universe Publishing.
Fichner-Rathus, Lois. Thomson Advantage Books: Understanding Art: A Concise History. 2007. (ENG., Illus.). 320p. (C). per. 85.95 *(978-0-495-10492-6(2))* Wadsworth.
Findlay, Michael. The Value of Art: Money, Power, Beauty. 2012. (Illus.). 208p. 29.95 ***(978-3-7913-4638-0(5))*** Prestel Publishing.
Fuentes, Carlos. Frida Kahlo: National Homage 1907-2007. 2008. (ENG., Illus.). 400p. 65.00 *(978-968-5208-88-8(3))* R.M. Editorial, S.A. de C.V. MEX. Dist: D.A.P./Distributed Art Pubs.
Gandolfi, Peter. Passover Haggadah. 2008. 128p. pap. 19.95 *(978-965-229-418-0(7))* Gefen Publishing Hse., Ltd ISR. Dist: Gefen Bks.
Gaut, Berys, ed. Thinking about Art: Classic & Contemporary Philosophical Readings. 2009. 560p. 34.00 *(978-0-415-40576-8(9))*; 122.00 *(978-0-415-40575-1(0))* Routledge.
Getlein, Mark. Living with Art. 9th ed. 2009. (ENG., Illus.). 592p. (C). pap. 153.67 *(978-0-07-337920-3(4),* 0073379204) McGraw-Hill Cos., The.
Gilbert, Rita. Living with Art. 2nd rev. ed. cd-rom *(978-0-07-250009-7(3))* McGraw-Hill Cos., The.
Gilbert, Rita & Getlein, Mark. Living with Art. 7th ed. pap. *(978-0-07-285934-8(2))* McGraw-Hill Cos., The.
Hagen, Rose-Marie. What Great Paintings Say, 2 vols. 2007. (ENG., Illus.). 720p. 29.99 *(978-3-8228-4790-9(9))* TASCHEN DEU. Dist: Ingram Pub. Services.
Hagen, Rose-Marie, et al. 100 Masterpieces in Detail, 3 vols. 2010. (Go Ser.). (ENG., Illus.). 720p. 59.99 *(978-3-8365-1549-8(0))* TASCHEN DEU. Dist: Ingram Pub. Services.
Hampl, Patricia. Blue Arabesque: A Search for the Sublime. (ENG.). 224p. 2007. pap. 13.00 *(978-0-15-603311-4(9),* Mariner Bks.) 2006. 22.00 *(978-0-15-101506-1(6))* Houghton Mifflin Harcourt Trade & Reference Pubs.
Harris, Clare. The Museum on the Roof of the World: Art, Politics, & the Representation of Tibet. 2012. (Buddhism & Modernity Ser.). (Illus.). 336p. 45.00 ***(978-0-226-31747-2(1))*** Univ. of Chicago Pr.
He, Jianping, ed. Alejandro Magallanes. 2008. (New Generation of Design Ser.). (Illus.). 215p. pap. *(978-981-245-508-6(6))* Page One Publishing.
Heinich, Nathalie. Guerre Culturelle et Art Contemporain: Une Comparaison Franco-Américaine. 2010. (FRE.). 170p. *(978-2-7056-7063-4(7))* Hermann.
Herrera, Jochy. Seducir los Sentidos. 2010. 246p. pap. 15.00 *(978-0-557-32456-9(4))* Lulu Enterprises Inc.
Hollins, C. J. The Animal Within: Explaining the Bizarre & Ludicrous in Modern Art. 2010. (Illus.). 175p. 37.50 *(978-1-84624-504-6(4))* Book Guild, Ltd. GBR. Dist: Trans-Atlantic Pubns., Inc.
Homes, A. M. & Fischl, Eric. Eric Fischl: Beach Paintings. 2009. (ENG., Illus.). 224p. 65.00 *(978-0-8478-3183-8(3))* Rizzoli International Pubns., Inc.
Howard, Michael. Van Gogh: His Life & Works in 500 Images. 2010. (ENG., Illus.). 256p. 35.00 *(978-0-7548-1954-7(X))* Anness Publishing GBR. Dist: National Bk. Network.
Hustvedt, Siri. Mysteries of the Rectangle: Essays on Painting. 2006. (ENG., Illus.). 204p. pap. 24.95 *(978-1-56898-618-0(1))* Princeton Architectural Pr.
Hutter, Michael & Throsby, David, eds. Beyond Price: Value in Culture, Economics, & the Arts. (Murphy Institute Studies in Political Economy Ser.). (ENG., Illus.). 334p. 2011. pap. 45.00 ***(978-0-521-18300-0(6))*** 2007. 96.00 *(978-0-521-86223-3(X))* Cambridge Univ. Pr.
Jackins, Harvey. The Good & the Great in Art.Tr. of De Goeden en de Groten in de Kunst. pap. 2.00 *(978-0-913937-94-5(0))* Rational Island Pubs.
Kettenmann, Andrea. Kahlo: Leid und Leidenschaft. 25th ed. 2009. (ENG., Illus.). 96p. 14.99 *(978-3-8365-1264-0(5))* TASCHEN DEU. Dist: Ingram Pub. Services.
Konemann Staff. Tapies, Vol. 5. Date not set. (Tapies Ser.: Vol. 5). (Illus.). 504p. 99.95 *(978-3-8290-4647-3(2),* 880061) Konemann.
Kraler-Bergmann, Doris. Sylvia Plathæs Lyrical Responses to Works of Art. 2008. 96p. pap. *(978-3-639-03464-6(3))* VDM Verlag Dr. Mueller e.K.
Kundera, Milan. Encounter. Asher, Linda, tr. from FRE. 2010. 192p. 23.99 *(978-0-06-189441-1(9))* HarperCollins Pubs.
Lermer, Andrea & Shalem, Avinoam, eds. After One Hundred Years: The 1910 Exhibition Meisterwerke muhammedanischer Kunst Reconsidered. 2010. (Islamic History & Civilization Ser.). (GER & ENG., Illus.). 440p. *(978-90-04-19001-6(5))* BRILL.
Lewis, Richard L. & Lewis, Susan Ingalls. The Power of Art. 2nd ed. 2008. (ENG.). 528p. (C). pap. 113.95 *(978-0-534-64103-0(2))* Wadsworth.
Liang, Jiang. Zhongguo Mei Shu Jian Cang Shi Gao: Aoutline [sic] History of the Chinese Art Appreciation & Collection. 2009. (CHI., Illus.). 339p. *(978-7-5010-2904-4(0))* Cultural Relics Publishing Hse.
The Lucie Awards 5: International Photography Awards. 2006. (Illus.). 104p. 35.00 *(978-0-9778533-0-4(6))* IPA Bks.
Maguire, Gregory. Making Mischief: A Maurice Sendak Appreciation. 2009. (ENG., Illus.). 208p. 27.50 *(978-0-06-168916-1(5),* Morrow, William & Co.) HarperCollins Pubs.
Martin, F. David & Jacobus, Lee A. Humanities through the Arts. 8th ed. 2010. (ENG., Illus.). 496p. (C). pap. 133.33 *(978-0-07-337663-9(9),* 0073376639) McGraw-Hill Cos., The.
—Telecourse Guide for Humanities through the Arts. 8th ed. 2010. (ENG.). 384p. (C). pap. 65.67 *(978-0-07-733326-3(8),* 0077333268) McGraw-Hill Cos., The.
Merrill, Linda, et al. Picturing America: Teachers Resource Book. 2008. *(978-0-615-20793-3(6))* National Endowment for the Humanities.
Mezger, Claudine & Grossmann, Elisabeth. Ueli Berger - Alles in Allem: Arbeiten auf Papier, 1967 2007. Frehner, Matthias, ed. 2008. (Illus.). 112p. pap. 60.00 *(978-3-85881-191-2(2))* Scheidegger und Spiess AG, Verlag CHE. Dist: Antique Collectors' Club.
Moineau, Jean-Claude. Retour du Futur: L'art à Contre-Courant. 2010. (FRE.). 367p. *(978-2-915453-59-1(4),* Spotlight Poets) Ere.
Nelson, Robert S. Later Byzantine Painting: Art Agency & Appreciation. 2007. (Variorum Collected Studies). (Illus.). 430p. 190.00 *(978-0-86078-997-0(7))* Ashgate Publishing Co.
Noyes, Carleton. The Gate of Appreciation: Studies in the Relation of Art to Life. 2008. 144p. pap. *(978-1-4099-5785-0(3))* Dodo Pr.
—The Gate of Appreciation: Studies in the Relation of Art to Life. 2007. (ENG.). 290p. 43.95 *(978-0-548-01774-6(3))* Kessinger Publishing, LLC.
Nuridsany, Michel. 100 Masterpieces of Painting: From Lascaux to Basquiat, from Florence to Shanghai. (ENG., Illus.). 208p. 2009. 17.98 *(978-2-08-030124-6(1))* 2006. 34.95 *(978-2-08-030529-9(8))* Flammarion et Cie FRA. Dist: Random Hse., Inc.
Paley, Morton D. Samuel Taylor Coleridge & the Fine Arts. 2008. (ENG., Illus.). 288p. 99.00 *(978-0-19-923305-2(5))* Oxford Univ. Pr., Inc.
Parshall, Peter, et al. The Darker Side of Light: Arts of Privacy, 1850-1900. 2009. (Illus.). 192p. 75.00 *(978-1-84822-021-8(9),* Lund Humphries Pubs.) Ashgate Publishing, Ltd. GBR. Dist: Ashgate Publishing Co.
Paton, Justin. How to Look at a Painting. 2nd ed. 2009. (ENG., Illus.). 136p. 24.95 *(978-0-9582916-0-6(8))* Awa Pr. NZL. Dist: Independent Pubs. Group.
Pearson Education Staff. For Art Appreciation. 2012. (ENG.). (C). 33.33 ***(978-0-205-13484-7(X),*** Prentice Hall) Prentice Hall PTR.
Pergam, Elizabeth A. The Manchester Art Treasures Exhibition of 1857: Entrepreneurs, Connoisseurs & the Public. 2011. (Illus.). 396p. 124.95 *(978-1-4094-1830-6(8))* Ashgate Publishing Co.
Pooke, Grant & Whitham, Graham. Art History. 2nd ed. 2009. (Teach Yourself: Reference Ser.). (ENG.). 224p. pap. 14.95 *(978-0-07-162586-9(0),* 0071625860) McGraw-Hill Cos., The.
—Understand Art History. 2011. (Teach Yourself Ser.). (ENG., Illus.). 224p. pap. 19.95 *(978-1-4441-0497-4(7),* Hodder & Stoughton) Hodder General Publishing Div. GBR. Dist: Independent Pubs. Group.
—Understand Contemporary Art. 2011. (Teach Yourself: General Reference Ser.). (ENG.). 224p. pap. 15.00 *(978-0-07-163691-9(9),* 0071636919) McGraw-Hill Cos., The.
Rancière, Jacques. The Emancipated Spectator. 2011. (ENG., Illus.). 134p. pap. 16.95 *(978-1-84467-761-0(3),* 844761) Verso Bks. GBR. Dist: Norton, W. W. & Co., Inc.
Ren, Liu, illus. Liu Ren's Photographs, 1 vol. 2008. (ENG.). 48p. pap. 18.00 *(978-988-99609-1-9(5))* Timezone 8 Ltd. HKG. Dist: D.A.P./Distributed Art Pubs.
Schloesser, Stephen. Mystic Masque: Semblance & Reality in Georges Rouault, 1871-1958. 2008. (Illus.). 300p. pap. 80.00 *(978-1-892850-14-0(1))* McMullen Museum of Art, Boston College.
Schoen, Max. Enjoyment of the Arts. *(978-0-8022-1504-8(1))* Philosophical Library, Inc.
Schulte, Jessica. Can You Find It Inside? Search & Discover for Young Art Lovers. 2009. (ENG.). 27p. (J). 13.00 *(978-1-4379-6650-3(0))* DIANE Publishing Co.
Screech, Timon. Obtaining Images: Art, Production & Display in Edo Japan. 2012. 50.00 ***(978-0-8248-3613-9(8))*** Univ. of Hawaii Pr.
Siesling & Siesling, Jan. About Art: Appreciation in 33 Lessons. rev. ed. 2011. (ENG.). 104p. pap. 60.30 *(978-0-7575-7997-4(3))* Kendall Hunt Publishing Co.
Smith, Michael & Pittel, Christine. Houses. 2008. (ENG., Illus.). 208p. 50.00 *(978-0-8478-3070-1(5))* Rizzoli International Pubns., Inc.
Soudavar, Abolala. Decoding Old Masters: Patrons, Princes & Enigmatic Paintings of the 15th Century. 2007. (ENG., Illus.). 192p. 73.00 *(978-1-84511-658-3(5))* I. B. Tauris & Co., Ltd. GBR. Dist: Macmillan.
Stewart, Marilyn G. & Katter, Eldon. Explorations in Art - A Community Connection SE. 2nd ed. 2008. (ENG., Illus.). 334p. stu. ed. 61.95 *(978-0-87192-882-5(5))* Davis Pubns., Inc.
—Explorations in Art - A Community Connection TE. 2nd ed. 2008. (ENG., Illus.). 334p. pap., tchr. ed. 85.95 *(978-0-87192-896-2(5))* Davis Pubns., Inc.
—Explorations in Art - A Global Pursuit SE. 2nd ed. 2008. (Explorations in Art Ser.). (ENG., Illus.). 344p. stu. ed. 61.95 *(978-0-87192-881-8(7))* Davis Pubns., Inc.
—Explorations in Art - A Global Pursuit TE. 2nd ed. 2008. (Explorations in Art Ser.). (ENG., Illus.). 344p. pap., tchr. ed. 85.95 *(978-0-87192-895-5(7))* Davis Pubns., Inc.
Taddeo, Julie Anne. Catherine Cookson Country: On the Borders of Legitimacy Fiction & History. 2012. (Illus.). 240p. 99.95 ***(978-1-4094-0580-1(X))*** Ashgate Publishing Co.
Tarasov, Oleg. Framing Russian Art. 2011. (ENG., Illus.). 415p. 70.00 *(978-1-86189-762-6(6))* Reaktion Bks., Ltd. GBR. Dist: Chicago Distribution Ctr.
TASCHEN, Angelika, ed. Masterpieces in Detail - 2012. 2011. (ENG.). 13.99 *(978-3-8365-2943-3(2))* TASCHEN DEU. Dist: Ingram Pub. Services.
The University of Arizona Museum of Art. The Aesthetic Code: Unraveling the Secrets of Art. The University of Arizona Museum of Art, ed. 2010. (Illus.). 40p. (C). pap. 14.95 *(978-0-9814840-3-7(4))* Univ. of Arizona Museum of Art.
Thompson, Jon. How to Read a Modern Painting: Understanding & Enjoying the Modern Masters. 2006. (ENG., Illus.). 400p. 37.50 *(978-0-8109-4944-7(X))* Abrams.
Tolstoy, Leo. What Is Art? 2009. 280p. 30.99 *(978-1-110-63321-0(1))*; pap. 26.75 *(978-1-110-63320-3(3))* BiblioBazaar.
—What Is Art? 2009. 218p. pap. 19.99 *(978-1-4589-9350-2(7))* General Bks. LLC.
Tsong-Zung, Chang & Power, Kevin. Emily Cheng: Chasing Clouds: A Decade of Studies, 1 vol. 2008. (ENG., Illus.). 384p. 75.00 *(978-988-99617-6-3(8))* Timezone 8 Ltd. HKG. Dist: D.A.P./Distributed Art Pubs.
Watson, Dudley C. Art of Eugene & Elizabeth Kormendi Wit. 2006. pap. 16.95 *(978-1-4286-5686-4(3))* Kessinger Publishing, LLC.
Weinshenker, Anne Betty. A God or a Bench: Sculpture As a Problematic Art During the Ancien Régime. 2008. (Illus.). 379p. pap. 99.95 *(978-3-03910-543-4(4))* Lang, Peter AG GBR. Dist: Lang, Peter.
Woods, Kim W., et al, eds. Viewing Renaissance Art. 2007. (Renaissance Art Reconsidered Ser.: Vol. 3). (ENG., Illus.). 352p. pap. 35.00 *(978-0-300-12343-2(4))* Yale Univ. Pr.
Zakaras, Laura & Lowell, Julia F. Cultivating Demand for the Arts: Arts Learning, Arts Engagement, & State Arts Policy. 2008. 172p. pap. 30.50 *(978-0-8330-4184-5(3),* mg-640) RAND Corp., The.

Zelanski, Paul & Fisher, Mary Pat. The Art of Seeing. 8th ed. 2010. (ENG., Illus.). 560p. (C). pap. 152.67 *(978-0-205-74834-1(1),* Prentice Hall) Prentice Hall PTR.

ART AS A PROFESSION
see Art—Vocational Guidance

ART AS AN INVESTMENT
Bryce, Alan D. Art Smart: The Intelligent Guide to Investing in the Canadian Art Market. 2007. (ENG., Illus.). 176p. pap. 24.99 *(978-1-55002-676-4(3),* Dundurn Pr.) Dundurn CAN. Dist: Ingram Pub. Services.
Goodwin, James. The International Art Markets: The Essential Guide for Collectors & Investors. Goodwin, James, ed. 2008. (ENG., Illus.). 448p. 99.00 *(978-0-7494-4835-6(0))* Kogan Page, Ltd. GBR. Dist: Ingram Pub. Services.
—International Art Markets: The Essential Guide for Collectors & Investors. 2010. (ENG., Illus.). 448p. pap. 45.95 *(978-0-7494-5592-7(6))* Kogan Page, Ltd. GBR. Dist: Ingram Pub. Services.
Horowitz, N. Art of the Deal: Contemporary Art in a Global Financial Market. 2011. (ENG., Illus.). 384p. (C). 39.50 *(978-0-691-14832-8(5))* Princeton Univ. Pr.
McAndrew, Clare. The Art Economy: An Investor's Guide to the Art Market. 2012. (ENG.). 280p. pap. 39.95 *(978-1-905785-60-5(7))* Liffey Pr., The IRL. Dist: Dufour Editions, Inc.
McAndrew, Clare, ed. Fine Art & High Finance: Expert Advice on the Economics of Ownership. 2010. (Bloomberg Ser.: 36). (ENG., Illus.). 336p. 39.95 *(978-1-57660-333-8(4),* Bloomberg Pr.) Wiley, John & Sons, Inc.
McLean, Fred. New Zealand Art for Investment. 160p. pap. 19.95 *(978-0-908876-88-4(2))* Transpress NZL. Dist: Pacific Island Bks.
M'Closkey, Kathy. Swept under the Rug: A Hidden History of Navajo Weaving. 2008. (University of Arizona Southwest Centre Ser.). (ENG., Illus.). 336p. (C). pap. 27.95 *(978-0-8263-2832-8(6))* Univ. of New Mexico Pr.
Nazvanov, Greg. The australian aboriginal art investment Handbook. 2010. 374p. pap. 40.47 *(978-1-4457-7607-1(3))* Lulu Enterprises Inc.
—Noble's Secrets of Art Funds & Art Investing. 2010. 63p. pap. 9.99 *(978-1-4457-2079-1(5))* Lulu Enterprises Inc.
Patterson, Jan. Smart Book: The Smart Mart to the Arts. 3rd ed. Date not set. pap. 24.95 *(978-0-9643197-2-1(1))* Patterson Marketing.
Yu, Jianhua & Yu, Jin. Dan Qing Yi Hen Mi Zu Zhen. 2009. (Illus.). 328p. *(978-7-80730-913-0(X))* Xuelin Publishing Hse.

ART AUCTIONS
Art Auction Records International 1994: Companies-Products-Services, 7 vols. (Illus.). 2200p. 295.00 *(978-0-7605-0630-1(2))* Rector Pr., Ltd.
Balai Lelang Larasati Staff, contrib. by. Larasati: Pictures of Indonesia Fine Art Auction, Jakarta, 11 February 2007. 2007. (Illus.). 191p. *(978-979-3774-09-1(6))* Balai Lelang Larasati.
DeFurio, Steve, photos by. The World of Andy Anderson. 2007. (Illus.). 68p. 34.99 *(978-0-9799984-0-9(9))* High Noon Western Americana.
Gruhn, Elke. Christian Jankowski: Strip the Auctioneer at Christie's. 2011. (GER & ENG., Illus.). 96p. pap. 35.00 *(978-3-86560-796-6(9))* Verlag der Buchhandlung Walther Konig DEU. Dist: D.A.P./Distributed Art Pubs.
Jonckheere, Koenraad. The Auction of King William's Paintings (1713) 2008. (C). *(978-90-272-4962-3(8));* pap. *(978-90-272-4963-0(6))* Benjamins, John Publishing Co.
Larasati Muse Investments Pte. Ltd Staff, contrib. by. Larasati: Pictures of Asia Fine Art Auction, Singapore, 30 April 2007. 2007. (Illus.). 216p. *(978-979-3774-10-7(X))* Balai Lelang Larasati.
Levine, Rebecca. Art Sales Index 2010, 2 vols. 40th ed. 2010. 2724p. pap. 225.00 *(978-1-933295-40-4(6))* LTB Gordonsart, Inc.
Thornton, Sarah. Seven Days in the Art World. 2009. (ENG., Illus.). 256p. pap. 15.95 *(978-0-393-33712-9(X),* 33712) Norton, W. W. & Co., Inc.
Tuli, Neville. Osians Historical Series III. 2007. 65.00 *(978-0-944142-52-3(4))* Antique Collectors' Club.
Turner, Adriana & Warren, Jeremy, eds. Auctions, Agents & Dealers: The Mechanisms of the Art Market 1660-1830. 2008. (Studies in the history of Collections). (ENG., Illus.). 173p. (C). pap. 50.00 *(978-1-903767-10-8(5))* Archaeopress GBR. Dist: Brown, David Bk. Co., The.
Vermeylen, Filip, et al, eds. Art Auctions & Dealers: The Dissemination of Netherlandish Painting During the Ancien Regime. 2009. (Studies in European Urban History (1100-1800) Ser.). (ENG.). 174p. (C). pap. 94.00 *(978-2-503-51620-2(3))* Brepols Pubs. BEL. Dist: ISD.

ART CENTERS
see also Community Centers
also names of individual art centers
Alliance for the Arts Staff. The Hudson Valley. Swett, Benjamin, ed. 2009. (ENG., Illus.). 288p. instr.'s gde. ed. 29.95 *(978-1-59372-035-3(1),* 372035) Quantuck Lane Pr. & The Mill Road Collaborative, The.
The ANKAAA Art Book: The Art of the Northern, Kimberley & Arnhem Land Art Centres. 2008. pap. *(978-1-86465-065-5(6))* IAD Pr.
Blone, Cecilia. Cultural Centres: Architecture 1990-2011. 2010. (ENG., Illus.). 280p. 75.00 *(978-88-6413-002-6(0),* Ore Cultura Srl (Acc)) Antique Collectors' Club GBR. Dist: National Bk. Network.
Bomford et al, David. Seeing the Getty Center Set: Collections, Building, & Gardens, 3 vols. 2009. (ENG., Illus.). 192p. pap. 24.95 *(978-0-89236-975-1(2))* Oxford Univ. Pr., Inc.
Donahoe, Brian & Habeck, Joachim Otto, eds. Reconstructing the House of Culture: Community, Self, & the Makings of Culture in Russia & Beyond. 2011. (ENG., Illus.). 348p. 95.00 *(978-0-85745-275-7(4))* Berghahn Bks., Inc.
Hackman, William & Greenberg, Mark, eds. Inside the Getty. 2008. (Illus.). 152p. pap. 14.95 *(978-0-89236-911-9(6))* Oxford Univ. Pr., Inc.
Hatakeyama, Naoya & Watanabe, Osamu, photos by. Naoshima. 2011. (ENG & JPN., Illus.). 232p. 60.00 *(978-3-7757-2703-7(5))* Hatje Cantz Verlag GmbH & Co KG DEU. Dist: D.A.P./Distributed Art Pubs.
Incerti, Guido, et al. Diller + Scofidio (+ Renfro) The Ciliary Function - Works & Projects 1979-2007. 2007. (ENG., Illus.). 224p. 39.99 *(978-88-6130-067-5(7))* Skira Editore ITA. Dist: Random Hse., Inc.
Jennings, Sarah. Art & Politics: The History of the National Arts Centre. 2009. (ENG., Illus.). 426p. 50.00 *(978-1-55002-886-7(3),* Dundurn Pr.) Dundurn CAN. Dist: Ingram Pub. Services.
Merrick, Jay. Firstsite: Art Spaces. 2012. (ENG., Illus.). 64p. pap. 7.95 *(978-1-85759-755-4(9))* Scala, Editions FRA. Dist: National Bk. Network.
O'Doherty, Brian. Studio & Cube: On the Relationship Between Where Art Is Made & Where Art Is Displayed. 2008. (ENG.). 80p. 24.95 *(978-1-883584-44-3(2))* Princeton Architectural Pr.
Schultz, Sarah & Peters, Sarah, eds. Open Field: Conversations on the Commons. 2012. (ENG., Illus.). 144p. pap. 9.99 ***(978-1-935963-00-4(7))*** Walker Art Ctr.
Sellen, Betty-Carol. Art Centers: American Studios & Galleries for Artists with Developmental or Mental Disabilities. 2008. (ENG., Illus.). 212p. pap. 49.95 *(978-0-7864-4140-2(2))* McFarland & Co., Inc. Pubs.

ART COLLECTIONS
see Art Museums

ART COLLECTIONS, PRIVATE
see Art—Private Collections

ART COLLECTORS
see Art—Collectors and Collecting; Art Objects—Collectors and Collecting

ART CRITICISM
see also Art Appreciation; Feminist Art Criticism
Abadie, Daniel. Lalanne(S) 2008. (ENG., Illus.). 352p. 125.00 *(978-2-08-030071-3(7))* Flammarion et Cie FRA. Dist: Random Hse., Inc.
Abadie, Daniel & Segui, Antonio. Antonio Seguí. 2010. (FRE., Illus.). 319p. *(978-2-7541-0505-7(0))* Hazan, Fernand, Editeur.
Abbas, Hamra. Hamra Abbas: Object Lessons. 2010. (ENG., Illus.). 72p. 32.00 *(978-0-9551779-9-6(5))* Cardamom, Green GBR. Dist: D.A.P./Distributed Art Pubs.
Abdul, Lisa & Caragliano, Renata. Lisa Abdul. 2009. (ITA & ENG., Illus.). 172p. 45.00 *(978-88-7757-223-3(X))* Hopefulmonster Editore ITA. Dist: D.A.P./Distributed Art Pubs.
Adams, Laurie Schneider. Art: A Beginner's Guide. 2012. (ENG., Illus.). 240p. pap. 14.95 ***(978-1-85168-853-1(6))*** Oneworld Pubns. GBR. Dist: National Bk. Network.
Adelson, Warren & Sargent, John Singer. Sargent's Women. 2007. (ENG., Illus.). 152p. pap. 35.00 *(978-0-9741621-0-2(8))* Adelson Galleries, Inc.
Adlam, Carol & Simpson, Juliet, eds. Critical Exchange: Art Criticism of the Eighteenth & Nineteenth Centuries in Russia & Western Europe. 2009. (Cultural Interactions: Studies in the Relationship between the Arts Ser.). (ENG.). 420p. pap. 92.95 *(978-3-03911-556-3(1))* Lang, Peter GmbH, Europaischer Verlag der Wissenschaften DEU. Dist: Lang, Peter.
Adler, Kathleen. A Time & a Place: Near Sydenham Hill by Camille Pissarro. 2011. (Kimbell Masterpiece Ser.). (ENG., Illus.). 86p. pap. 16.95 *(978-0-300-17577-6(9))* Kimbell Art Museum.
Alberti, Donald & Hentschel, Martin. Alan Uglow. 2010. (GER & ENG., Illus.). 144p. 55.00 *(978-3-86678-385-0(X))* Kerber Verlag DEU. Dist: D.A.P./Distributed Art Pubs.
Albright, Ann Cooper. Modern Gestures: Abraham Walkowitz Draws Isadora Duncan Dancing. 2010. (ENG., Illus.). 100p. 29.95 *(978-0-8195-7077-2(X))* Wesleyan Univ. Pr.
Allan, Scott Christopher & Morton, Mary G. Reconsidering Gérôme. 2010. (ENG., Illus.). 168p. pap. 27.50 *(978-1-60606-038-4(4),* J. Paul Getty Museum) Getty Pubns.
Allemand-Cosneau, Claude, et al. Henry Moore: From the Inside Out. 2009. (Illus.). 200p. pap. 19.95 *(978-3-7913-4176-7(6))* Prestel Publishing.
Allmer, Patricia. Rene Magritte: Beyond Painting. 2010. (ENG., Illus.). 256p. 89.95 *(978-0-7190-7928-3(4))* Manchester Univ. Pr. GBR. Dist: Macmillan.
Allthorpe-Guyton, Marjorie, et al. Ian McKeever: Paintings. 2009. (Illus.). 208p. 80.00 *(978-1-84822-037-9(5),* Lund Humphries Pubs.) Ashgate Publishing, Ltd. GBR. Dist: Ashgate Publishing Co.
Alston, David. Into Painting: The Work of Brendan Stuart Burns. 2007. (ENG., Illus.). 100p. pap. 17.95 *(978-1-85411-446-4(8))* Seren Bks. GBR. Dist: Independent Pubs. Group.
Amado, Antonio. Voiture Minimum: Le Corbusier & the Automobile. 2011. (ENG., Illus.). 368p. (gr. 17). 49.95 *(978-0-262-01536-3(6))* MIT Pr.
Ambers, J., et al. Italian Renaissance Drawings: Technical Examination & Analysis. 2010. (ENG., Illus.). 174p. pap. 70.00 *(978-1-904982-58-6(1))* Archetype Pubns. GBR. Dist: National Bk. Network.
Amsellem, Patrick. Jesper Just: Romantic Delusions. 2008. *(978-0-87273-160-8(X))* Brooklyn Museum, The.
Anderberg, Birgitte & Knudsen, Vibeke. Henri de Toulouse-Lautrec: The Human Comedy. 2011. (ENG., Illus.). 176p. 49.95 ***(978-3-7913-5144-5(3))*** Prestel Publishing.
Antin, David. Radical Coherency: Selected Essays on Art & Literature 1966 to 2005. 2011. (ENG.). 384p. 75.00 *(978-0-226-02096-9(7));* pap. 25.00 *(978-0-226-02097-6(5))* Univ. of Chicago Pr.
Aquino, Lucia. Leonardo da Vinci. 2009. (Skira MINI Artbooks Ser.). (ENG., Illus.). 96p. pap. 8.99 *(978-88-6130-737-7(X))* Skira Editore ITA. Dist: Random Hse., Inc.
Araki, Nobuyoshi, photos by. Nobuyoshi Araki: Self Life Death. abr. ed. 2011. (ENG., Illus.). 196p. 49.95 *(978-0-7148-6116-6(2))* Phaidon Pr., Inc.
Arcq, Tere & et al. Cinco llaves del mundo secreto de Remedios Varo. 2008. (SPA.). 216p. *(978-970-683-335-8(8))* Artes de Mexico y del Mundo, S.A. de C.V.
Arnold, Matthias. Toulouse-Lautrec. 2012. (25 Ser.). (ENG., Illus.). 96p. 14.99 ***(978-3-8365-3162-7(3))*** TASCHEN DEU. Dist: Ingram Pub. Services.
Arya, Rina. Francis Bacon: Critical & Theoretical Perspectives. 2012. (Illus.). 224p. pap. 49.50 *(978-1-84519-383-6(0))* Sussex Academic Pr. GBR. Dist: International Specialized Bk. Services.
Arya, Rina. Francis Bacon: Painting in a Godless World. 2012. (Illus.). 176p. 80.00 ***(978-1-84822-044-7(8),*** Lund Humphries Pubs.) Ashgate Publishing, Ltd. GBR. Dist: Ashgate Publishing Co.
Ater, Renée & Fuller, Meta Warrick. Remaking Race & History: The Sculpture of Meta Warrick Fuller. 2011. (ENG., Illus.). 208p. 49.95 *(978-0-520-26212-6(3))* Univ. of California Pr.
Auricchio, Laura. Adélaïde Labille-Guiard: Artist in the Age of Revolution. 2009. (ENG., Illus.). 144p. 29.95 *(978-0-89236-954-6(X))* Oxford Univ. Pr., Inc.
Aurisch, Helga Kessler & Czymmek, Götz. German Impressionist Landscape Painting: Liebermann - Corinth - Slevogt. 2010. (Illus.). 256p. 70.00 ***(978-3-89790-321-0(0))*** Arnoldsche Art Pubs. DEU. Dist: Antique Collectors' Club.
Azimi, Roxana, ed. Une Image de Faisal Samra. 2012. (ENG., Illus.). 208p. pap. 55.00 ***(978-88-572-1097-1(9))*** Skira Editore ITA. Dist: Random Hse., Inc.
Baal-Teshuva, Jacob. Rothko. 25th ed. 2009. (ENG., Illus.). 96p. 14.99 *(978-3-8365-1283-1(1))* TASCHEN DEU. Dist: Ingram Pub. Services.
Bacon, Francis. Francis Bacon - A Terrible Beauty, 1 vol. 2009. (ENG., Illus.). 208p. pap. 34.95 *(978-3-86930-027-6(2))* Steidl, Gerhard Druckerei und Verlag DEU. Dist: Innovative Logistics.
Bade, Patrick, et al. 30 Centuries of Sculpture. 2012. (30 Millennia of Art Ser.). (ENG., Illus.). 544p. 29.95 *(978-1-84484-817-1(5))* Parkstone International GBR. Dist: Ingram Pub. Services.
Bader, Graham, ed. Roy Lichtenstein. 2009. (October Files Ser.). (ENG., Illus.). 216p. (gr. 17). pap. 17.95 *(978-0-262-51231-2(9))* MIT Pr.
Bader, R. Roy Lichtenstein. Bader, Graham, ed. 2009. (October Files Ser.). (ENG., Illus.). 216p. (gr. 17). 35.00 *(978-0-262-01258-4(8))* MIT Pr.
Baetens, Jan & Van Gelder, Hilde, eds. Critical Realism in Contemporary Art: Around Allan Sekula's Photography. 2008. (Lieven Gevaert Ser.). (Illus.). 207p. (Orig.). pap. 29.95 *(978-90-5867-563-7(7))* Leuven Univ. Pr. BEL. Dist: Cornell Univ. Pr.
Bailey, Colin B. Renoir: Impressionism & Full-Length Painting. 2012. (ENG., Illus.). 288p. 65.00 ***(978-0-300-18108-1(6))*** Yale Univ. Pr.
Baker, Christopher, et al. Paul Sandby. 2009. (ENG., Illus.). 248p. 55.00 *(978-1-905711-48-2(4))* Royal Academy of Arts GBR. Dist: Hachette Bk. Group.
Baker, Nicholas & Betts, Margaret/M. John Prentiss Benson: American Marine Artist. 2009. (Illus.). 136p. 65.00 *(978-0-9821761-0-8(4))* Baker Marine Pubns.
Bal, Mieke. The Artemisia Files: Artemisia Gentileschi for Feminists & Other Thinking People. 2006. (Illus.). 245p. pap. 20.00 *(978-0-226-03582-6(4))* Univ. of Chicago Pr.
—Of What One Cannot Speak: Doris Salcedo's Political Art. 2011. (ENG., Illus.). 296p. 45.00 *(978-0-226-03578-9(6))* Univ. of Chicago Pr.
Balken, Debra Bricker. John Marin: Modernism at Midcentury. 2011. (Illus.). xi, 108p. pap. *(978-0-300-17635-3(X))* Yale Univ. Pr.
Ball, David M. & Kuhlman, Martha B., eds. The Comics of Chris Ware. 2010. (ENG., Illus.). 288p. 55.00 *(978-1-60473-442-3(6))* Univ. Pr. of Mississippi.
—The Comics of Chris Ware: Drawing Is a Way of Thinking. 2010. (ENG., Illus.). 288p. pap. 28.00 *(978-1-60473-443-0(4))* Univ. Pr. of Mississippi.
Banerji, Debashish. The Alternate Nation of Abanindranath Tagore. 2010. (Illus.). 228p. (C). 39.95 *(978-81-321-0239-7(8),* B02397C) SAGE Pubns., Inc.
Banks, Eric. Christopher Wool. Holzwarth, Hans Werner, ed. 2012. (ENG, FRE & GER., Illus.). 432p. 69.99 ***(978-3-3365-3562-5(9))*** TASCHEN DEU. Dist: Ingram Pub. Services.
Bannon, Anthony & Wells, Benedict. Roger Eberhard. Wilted Country. Keller, Walter, ed. 2010. (GER & ENG., Illus.). 80p. 55.00 *(978-3-85881-306-0(0))* Scheidegger und Spiess AG, Verlag CHE. Dist: Antique Collectors' Club.
Bareau, Juliet Wilson, et al. Division & Revision: Manet's Reichshoffen Revealed. 2008. (Illus.). 96p. pap. 40.00 ***(978-1-903470-77-0(3))*** Holberton, Paul Publishing GBR. Dist: Casemate Pubs. & Bk. Distributors, LLC.
Barikin, Amelia. Parallel Presents: The Art of Pierre Huyghe. 2012. ***(978-0-262-01780-0(6))*** MIT Pr.
Barkan, Leonard. Michelangelo: A Life on Paper. 2010. (ENG., Illus.). 352p. 49.50 *(978-0-691-14766-6(3))* Princeton Univ. Pr.
Barnes, Bernadine. Michelangelo in Print: Reproductions as Response in the Sixteenth-Century. 2010. (Illus.). 244p. 109.95 *(978-0-7546-6378-2(7))* Ashgate Publishing Co.
Barnet, Sylvan. A Short Guide to Writing about Art. 10th ed. 2010. (ENG., Illus.). 384p. (C). pap. 52.20 *(978-0-205-70825-3(0),* Prentice Hall) Prentice Hall PTR.
Barrett & Barrett, Terry. Criticizing Art: Understanding the Contemporary. 3rd ed. 2011. (ENG., Illus.). 256p. (C). pap. 55.33 *(978-0-07-337919-7(0),* 0073379190) McGraw-Hill Cos., The.
Barrett, Terry. Making Art: Form & Meaning. 2010. (ENG., Illus.). 288p. (C). pap. 98.33 *(978-0-07-252178-8(3),* 0072521783) McGraw-Hill Cos., The.
Bartlett, W. H. C. Elements of Analytical Mechanics, by W H C Bartlett. 2006. 516p. per. 29.99 *(978-1-4255-5779-9(1))* MPublishing.
Bastian, M. S. & L, Isabelle. Bastokalypse. 2010. (Illus.). 128p. pap. 59.00 *(978-3-85881-296-4(X))* Scheidegger und Spiess AG, Verlag CHE. Dist: Antique Collectors' Club.
Bateman, Robert. Bateman: New Works, 1 vol. 2010. (ENG., Illus.). 176p. 50.00 *(978-1-55365-579-4(6),* Greystone Bks.) D&M Pubs. Inc. CAN. Dist: Perseus-PGW.
Battistini, Matilde. Astrology, Magic, & Alchemy in Art. Frongia, Rosanna M. Giammanco, tr. from ITA. 2007. (Guide to Imagery Ser.). (Illus.). 384p. per. 24.95 *(978-0-89236-907-2(8))* Oxford Univ. Pr., Inc.
Baudelaire, Charles. The Mirror of Art, Critical Studies. Mayne, Jonathan, ed. (Illus.). reprint ed. 32.50 *(978-0-404-16303-7(3))* AMS Pr., Inc.
Bauer, Claudia. Frida Kahlo. 2007. (Illus.). 128p. pap. 14.95 *(978-3-7913-3780-7(7))* Prestel Publishing.
Baxandall, Michael. Words for Pictures: Seven Papers on Renaissance Art & Criticism. 2011. (ENG., Illus.). 208p. pap. 24.00 ***(978-0-300-17678-0(3))*** Yale Univ. Pr.
Beaulieu, Jill, et al, eds. Refracting Vision: Essays on the Writings of Michael Fried. 2012. (ENG., Illus.). 407p. (C). per. 35.00 *(978-1-86487-024-4(9))* Power Pubns. AUS. Dist: Univ. of Washington Pr.
Beaumont, Mary Rose. Albert Irvin: The Complete Prints. ltd. ed. 2010. (Illus.). 136p. 600.00 *(978-1-84822-055-3(3),* Lund Humphries Pubs.) Ashgate Publishing, Ltd. GBR. Dist: Ashgate Publishing Co.
Beaumont, Mary Rose & Irvin, Albert. Albert Irvin: The Complete Prints. 2010. (Illus.). 136p. 70.00 *(978-1-84822-054-6(5),* Lund Humphries Pubs.) Ashgate Publishing, Ltd. GBR. Dist: Ashgate Publishing Co.
Beckmann, Max. Of Truths Impossible to Put in Words: Max Beckmann Contextualized. Long, Rose-Carol Washton & Makela, Maria Martha, eds. 2009. (Illus.). 436p. pap. 68.95 *(978-3-03910-704-9(6))* Lang, Peter AG GBR. Dist: Lang, Peter.
Becks-Malorny, Ulrike. Cezanne. 2011. (25 Ser.). (ENG., Illus.). 96p. 14.99 ***(978-3-8365-3110-8(0))*** TASCHEN DEU. Dist: Ingram Pub. Services.
Bédard, Jean-François & Oppenord, Gilles-Marie. Decorative Games: Ornament, Rhetoric, & Noble Culture in the Work of Gilles-Marie Oppenord (1672-1742) 2010. *(978-0-87413-097-3(2))* Univ. of Delaware Pr.
Beddington, Charles. Venice: Canaletto & His Rivals. 2010. (ENG., Illus.). 192p. 50.00 *(978-1-85709-418-3(2))* Yale Univ. Pr.
Beekman, Klaus & Vries, Jan De, eds. Avant-Garde & Criticism. 2007. (Avant Garde Critical Studies: 21). (ENG., Illus.). 368p. 95.00 *(978-90-420-2152-5(7))* Rodopi.
Beletsky, Misha. The Book Jackets of Ismar David: A Calligraphic Legacy. 2011. (Illus.). 48p. pap. 19.95 *(978-1-933360-51-5(8),* RIT Cary Graphic Arts Pr.) Rochester Institute of Technology Cary Graphic Arts Pr.
Belting, Hans, text. Looking through Duchamp's Door: Art & Perspective in the Work of Duchamp, Sugimoto, Jeff Wall. 2010. (ENG., Illus.). 192p. pap. 49.95 *(978-3-86560-605-1(9))* Verlag der Buchhandlung Walther Konig DEU. Dist: D.A.P./Distributed Art Pubs.
Benedetti, Lorenzo, et al. Max Bill: No Beginning, No End. Museum MARTa Herford Staff, ed. 2008. (Illus.). 200p. pap. 50.00 *(978-3-85881-214-8(5))* Scheidegger und Spiess AG, Verlag CHE. Dist: Chicago Distribution Ctr.
Benjamin, Walter. Archive: Images, Texts, Signs. Marx, Ursula et al, eds. Leslie, Esther, tr. from GER. 2007. (ENG., Illus.). 311p. 27.95 *(978-1-84467-196-0(8),* 844196) Verso Bks. GBR. Dist: Norton, W. W. & Co., Inc.
Benke, Britta. T25 O'Keeffe. 2011. (25 Ser.). (ENG., Illus.). 96p. 14.99 ***(978-3-8365-3188-7(7))*** TASCHEN DEU. Dist: Ingram Pub. Services.
Berggruen, Olivier. The Writing of Art. 2012. (ENG.). 120p. pap. 16.00 ***(978-1-906548-62-9(5))*** Pushkin Pr., Ltd. GBR. Dist: Consortium Bk. Sales & Distribution.
Berkum, Ans van. Willem Van Genk: Builds His Universe. 2011. (ENG & DUT., Illus.). 144p. pap. *(978-90-209-9270-0(8),* Lannoo Pubs. (Acc)) Antique Collectors' Club.
Berman, Avis, et al. Adam Van Doren. 2006. (ENG., Illus.). 144p. 50.00 *(978-1-55595-272-3(0))* Hudson Hills Pr. LLC.
Bernier, Rosamond. Some of My Lives: A Scrapbook Memoir, 1 vol. 2011. (ENG., Illus.). 304p. 30.00 *(978-0-374-26661-5(1))* Farrar, Straus & Giroux.
Bessa, Antonio Sergio. Oyvind Fahlström: The Art of Writing. 2008. (Avant-Garde & Modernism Studies). (ENG., Illus.). 192p. pap. 29.95 *(978-0-8101-2298-7(7))* Northwestern Univ. Pr.
Bettelheim, Judith & Berlo, Janet Catherine. Transcultural Pilgrim: Three Decades of Work by José Bedia, 1 vol. 2011. (ENG., Illus.). 216p. pap. 35.00 ***(978-0-9778344-7-1(6))*** Univ. of California, Los Angeles, Fowler Museum of Cultural History.
Betzer, Sarah E. & Ingres, Jean-Auguste-Dominique. Ingres & the Studio: Women, Painting, History. 2012. (ENG.). 296p. *(978-0-271-04875-8(1))* Pennsylvania State Univ. Pr.
Bickerton, Derek, et al. Ashley Bickerton. 2011. (Illus.). 400p. 375.00 *(978-1-906967-38-3(5))* Other Criteria GBR. Dist: Abrams.
Biggs, Iain. Art As Research: Creative practice & academic Authority. 2009. 152p. pap. *(978-3-639-15691-1(9))* VDM Verlag Dr. Mueller e.K.
Bill, Wheelock. The Wrong Idea: Maurizio Cattelan in the Economy of Attention. 2011. 120p. pap. ***(978-3-639-32334-4(3))*** VDM Verlag Dr. Mueller e.K.
Bills, Mark, et al. G. F. Watts: Victorian Visionary - Highlights from the Watts Gallery Collection. 2009. (ENG., Illus.). 310p. 75.00 *(978-0-300-14257-0(9))* Yale Univ. Pr.

Bird, Jon. Leon Golub: Echoes of the Real. 2nd rev. ed. 2011. (ENG., Illus.). 272p. 75.00 (978-1-86189-783-1(9)); pap. 39.00 (978-1-86189-765-7(0)) Reaktion Bks., Ltd. GBR. Dist: Chicago Distribution Ctr.

Bird, Michael. Sandra Blow. 2011. (Illus.). 172p. pap. 50.00 (978-1-84822-089-8(8), Lund Humphries Pubs.) Ashgate Publishing, Ltd. GBR. Dist: Ashgate Publishing Co.

Bird, Michael & Wynter, Bryan. Bryan Wynter. 2010. (Illus.). 216p. 70.00 (978-1-84822-009-6(X), Lund Humphries Pubs.) Ashgate Publishing, Ltd. GBR. Dist: Ashgate Publishing Co.

Bischoff Ulrich. Munch. 2011. (ENG., Illus.). 96p. 14.99 (978-3-8365-2718-7(9)) TASCHEN DEU. Dist: Ingram Pub. Services.

Black, Jonathan. The Face of Courage: Eric Kennington, Portraiture & the Second World War. 2011. (ENG., Illus.). 160p. pap. 35.00 (978-0-85667-705-2(1)) Wilson, Philip Pubs., Ltd. GBR. Dist: Macmillan.

Blackwood, Jonathan. The Sculpture of John Skeaping. 2011. (British Sculptors & Sculpture Ser.). (Illus.). 152p. 90.00 (978-0-85331-931-3(6), Lund Humphries Pubs.) Ashgate Publishing, Ltd. GBR. Dist: Ashgate Publishing Co.

Blair, Dike. Again: Selected Interviews & Essays. 2007. (Illus.). 144p. per. 15.00 (978-0-945323-14-3(X)) WhiteWalls, Inc.

Blanes, Juan Manuel & Assunção, Octavio C. The Art of Juan Manuel Blanes. 2009. (ENG., Illus.). 200p. pap. 25.00 (978-1-879128-08-8(X)) Americas Society.

Blanz, Hubert. Slideshow. 2009. (GER., Illus.). 176p. 39.95 (978-3-211-85781-6(8)) Springer Wien AUT. Dist: Actar Birkhauser Distribution.

Bleckner, Ross, et al. John Newsom: Allegories of Naturalism. 2011. (ENG., Illus.). 136p. 55.00 (978-88-8158-801-5(3)) Charta ITA. Dist: D.A.P./Distributed Art Pubs.

Blinderman, Barry, ed. & text. Jim Lutes. 2010. (ENG., Illus.). 72p. pap. 25.00 (978-0-945558-39-2(2)) Univ. Galleries of Illinois State Univ.

Blocklehurst, John, et al. Balthus: Works, Interviews. 2008. (ENG., Illus.). 160p. 45.00 (978-84-343-1165-7(8)) Poligrafa, Ediciones, S. A. ESP. Dist: D.A.P./Distributed Art Pubs.

Blom, Ina. On the Style Site. 2007. (Illus.). 264p. pap. 29.95 (978-1-933128-30-6(5)) Sternberg Pr.

Blundell Jones, Peter. Gunnar Asplund. 2012. (ENG., Illus.). 240p. pap. 39.95 (978-0-7148-6315-3(7)) Phaidon Pr., Inc.

Bock-Weiss, Catherine & Matisse, Henri. Henri Matisse: Modernist Against the Grain. 2009. (ENG., Illus.). 232p. 65.00 (978-0-271-03512-3(9)) Pennsylvania State Univ. Pr.

Boenders, Frans. Lieve Dejonghe: The More You Look, the Larger the World Becomes. 2012. (ENG, CHI, FRE & DUT., Illus.). 128p. 65.00 (978-90-209-5766-2(X)) Lannoo Pubs./Racine.

Boetti, Alighiero, et al. Order & Disorder: Alighiero Boetti by Afghan Women. 2012. (ENG., Illus.). 132p. pap. 25.00 (978-0-9778344-8-8(4)) Univ. of California, Los Angeles, Fowler Museum of Cultural History.

Boggi, Favio, et al. The Life & Career of Lippo Di Dalmasio, a Bolognese Painter of the Late Fourteenth Century: With Illustrations & a Catalogue of His Works. 2010. (Illus.). ix, 194p. 109.95 (978-0-7734-3684-8(7)) Mellen, Edwin Pr., The.

Bogh, Mikkel, et al, eds. Images of Culture: Art History as Cultural History. 2012. (Illus.). 250p. pap. 43.00 (978-87-635-0478-2(2)) Museum Tusculanum Pr. DNK. Dist: Chicago Distribution Ctr.

Bois, Yve-Alain, et al, contrib. by. Malevich & the American Legacy. 2011. (ENG., Illus.). 224p. 100.00 (978-3-7913-4582-6(6)) Prestel Publishing.

Bolton, Andrew & Koda, Harold. Alexander McQueen: Savage Beauty. 2011. (Illus.). 240p. 50.00 (978-0-300-16978-2(7)) Yale Univ. Pr.

Bonami, Francesco. Stefano Arienti. 2007. (Illus.). 108p. pap. 37.50 (978-88-370-4980-5(3)) Electa ITA. Dist: Trans-Atlantic Pubns., Inc.

Bonaventura, Paul. The Art & Craft of Richard Woods. 2012. (Illus.). 250p. 80.00 (978-1-84822-108-6(8), Lund Humphries Pubs.) Ashgate Publishing, Ltd. GBR. Dist: Ashgate Publishing Co.

Bonevardi, Gustavo & Bennett, John, eds. Bonevardi: Chasing Shadows, Constructing Art. 2007. (ENG., Illus.). 448p. 60.00 (978-0-292-71436-6(X)) Univ. of Texas Pr.

Bonnier, Bernadette & Carpiaux, Vronique. Museum Félicien Rops. 2010. (ENG., Illus.). 96p. pap., instr.'s gde. ed. (978-90-5856-334-7(0), Stichting Kunstboek (Acc)) Antique Collectors' Club.

Booth, Stanley. An Appreciation of the Artist & a Selection of His Paintings. 2nd ed. 2011. (ENG., Illus.). 68p. 27.50 (978-0-85667-695-6(0)) Wilson, Philip Pubs., Ltd. GBR. Dist: Macmillan.

Borchardt-Hume, Achim. Rothko. 2009. (ENG., Illus.). 256p. 60.00 (978-1-85437-788-3(4)) Tate Publishing, Ltd. GBR. Dist: Hachette Bk. Group.

Bosch Ballbona, Joan. Agustí Pujol: La culminació de l'escultura renaixentista a Catalunya. 2009. 388p. pap. (978-84-475-3330-5(1)) Univ. de Barcelona Pubns.

Bowron, Edgar Peters, et al. Pompeo Batoni: Prince of Painters in Eighteenth-Century Rome. 2007. 240p. pap. (978-0-89090-158-8(9)) Yale Univ. Pr.

Bracewell, Michael & Wood, Catherine. Alessandro Raho. 2011. (Illus.). 144p. 70.00 (978-1-84822-093-5(6), Lund Humphries Pubs.) Ashgate Publishing, Ltd. GBR. Dist: Ashgate Publishing Co.

Bragdon, Claude Fayette, et al. Claude Bragdon & the Beautiful Necessity: Eleven Essays. 2010. (978-1-933360-43-0(7)) Rochester Institute of Technology, Cary Graphic Arts Pr.

Bram, Shahar. The Ambassadors of Death: The Sister Arts, Western Canon & the Silent Lines of a Hebrew Survivor. 2011. (ENG., Illus.). 207p. 69.95 (978-1-84519-450-5(0)) Sussex Academic Pr. GBR. Dist: International Specialized Bk. Services.

Branko, Mitrovic, et al. Lucy + Jorge Orta: Food, Water, Life. 2011. (ENG., Illus.). 192p. 40.00 (978-1-56898-991-4(1)) Princeton Architectural Pr.

Brennan, Marcia. Flowering Light: Kabbalistic Mysticism & the Art of Elliot R. Wolfson. 2008. (978-0-89263-009-7(4)); (978-0-89263-008-0(6)) Rice Univ. Pr.

Brettell, Richard R. James Magee: The Hill. 2010. (Illus.). 200p. 40.00 (978-3-7913-5079-0(X)) Prestel Publishing.

Brettell, Richard R. & Fonsmark, Anne-Birgitte. Gauguin & Impressionism. 2007. (Illus.). 366p. pap. 45.00 (978-0-300-13434-6(7)) Yale Univ. Pr.

Briginshaw, Valerie A. & Burt, Ramsay. Writing Dancing Together. 2009. (ENG., Illus.). 248p. 95.00 (978-0-230-53564-0(X)) Palgrave Macmillan.

Brodsky, Joyce. Experiences of Passage: The Paintings of Yun Gee & Li-lan. 2008. (ENG., Illus.). 248p. 40.00 (978-0-295-98775-0(8)) Univ. of Washington Pr.

Bronfen, Elisabeth. Crossmappings: Essays on Visual Culture. 2010. (Illus.). 256p. 49.00 (978-3-85881-715-0(5)) Scheidegger und Spiess AG, Verlag CHE. Dist: Chicago Distribution Ctr.

Brush, Daniel. 30 Years Work Bk. 1: "Animals", 3 vols. 2008. (ENG., Illus.). 320p. 85.00 (978-3-86521-476-8(2)) Steidl, Gerhard Druckerei und Verlag DEU. Dist: Innovative Logistics.

Brush, Kathryn. The Shaping of Art History: Wilhelm Vöge, Adolph Goldschmidt, & the Study of Medieval Art. 2010. (ENG.). 280p. pap. 39.99 (978-0-521-14762-0(X)) Cambridge Univ. Pr.

Bryant, Julius. Anthony Caro: Figurative & Narrative Sculpture. 2009. (Illus.). 128p. 60.00 (978-1-84822-032-4(4), Lund Humphries Pubs.) Ashgate Publishing, Ltd. GBR. Dist: Ashgate Publishing Co.

Buchloh, Benjamin H. D., ed. & afterword by. Gerhard Richter. 2009. (October Files Ser.). (ENG., Illus.). 200p. (gr. 17). pap. 18.95 (978-0-262-51312-8(9)) MIT Pr.

Buchloh, Benjamin H. D., et al. Blinky Palermo: Retrospective 1964-77. 2010. (Illus.). 192p. 50.00 (978-0-300-15366-8(X)) Yale Univ. Pr.

Buck, Paul & Petit, Catherine, trs. Narrativity: How Visual Arts, Cinema & Literature Are Telling the World Today, 1 vol. 2007. (ENG., Illus.). 128p. pap. 35.00 (978-2-914563-30-7(2)) Dis Voir Editions FRA. Dist: D.A.P./Distributed Art Pubs.

Buhling-Schultz, Christiane, ed. Cornelia Schleime: 'Wer aus mir trinkt, wird ein Reh' / 'Whoever drinks from me will turn into a deer' 2011. (ENG & GER., Illus.). 88p. 49.95 (978-3-86678-416-1(3)) Kerber Verlag DEU. Dist: D.A.P./Distributed Art Pubs.

Burgard, Timothy Anglin. Matter & Spirit: Stephen de Staebler. 2012. (ENG., Illus.). 224p. 65.00 (978-0-520-27230-9(7)) Univ. of California Pr.

—Matter & Spirit - Stephen de Staebler. 2012. (ENG., Illus.). 224p. pap. 34.95 (978-0-520-27231-6(5)) Univ. of California Pr.

Burnage, Sarah, et al. William Etty: Art & Controversy. 2011. (ENG., Illus.). 256p. 55.00 (978-0-85667-701-4(9)) Wilson, Philip Pubs., Ltd. GBR. Dist: Macmillan.

Burnett, Katharine P. Dimensions of Originality: Essays on Seventeenth-century Chinese Art Criticism. 2011. (ENG., Illus.). 450p. (gr. 17). 60.00 (978-962-996-456-6(2)) Chinese Univ. of Hong Kong, The HKG. Dist: Columbia Univ. Pr.

Buster, Kendall & Crawford, Paula. The Critique Handbook: The Student's Sourcebook & Survival Guide. 2nd ed. 2009. (ENG.). 160p. (C). pap. 26.80 (978-0-205-70811-6(0), Prentice Hall) Prentice Hall PTR.

Butler, Samuel. Essays on Life; Art & Science. 2008. 196p. 22.99 (978-0-554-38259-3(8)) 2008. 196p. 25.99 (978-0-554-28956-4(3)) 2007. 174p. pap. 19.99 (978-1-4346-6618-5(2)) BiblioBazaar.

—Essays on Life, Art & Science. 2008. 164p. pap. (978-1-4065-9558-1(6)) Dodo Pr.

—Essays on Life, Art & Science. 2010. (Illus.). 110p. pap. 20.12 (978-1-153-60491-8(4)) General Bks. LLC.

—Essays on Life, Art & Science. 2010. 144p. 28.76 (978-1-169-26153-2(1)); pap. 16.76 (978-1-162-66166-7(6)); 35.95 (978-1-161-43031-8(8)) Kessinger Publishing, LLC.

—Essays on Life, Art, & Science. 2011. 358p. pap. 32.75 (978-1-246-40020-5(0)) BiblioBazaar.

—Essays on Life, Art, & Science. 2009. (Illus.). 124p. pap. (978-1-150-34376-6(1)) Books LLC.

—Essays on Life; Art & Science. l.t. ed. 2007. (ENG.). 192p. pap. 21.99 (978-1-4346-6619-2(0)) BiblioBazaar.

—Essays on Life Art & Science Large Pri. 2006. pap. (978-1-4068-2208-3(6)) Echo Library.

Butler, Samuel & Streatfeild, R. A. Essays on Life, Art, & Science. 2009. 354p. 31.99 (978-1-113-70936-3(7)); 354p. 29.99 (978-1-113-70934-9(0)); 354p. pap. 31.75 (978-1-113-70929-5(4)); (ENG.). 353p. pap. 25.99 (978-1-113-70926-4(X), BiblioLife); (ENG.). 353p. pap. 26.99 (978-1-113-70928-8(6), BiblioLife); 354p. pap. 32.75 (978-1-113-70932-5(4)) BiblioBazaar.

Butler, Samuel & Streatfeild, Richard Alexander. Essays on Life, Art, & Science. 2010. 356p. pap. 32.75 (978-1-143-66822-7(7)); 364p. pap. 32.75 (978-1-142-02697-4(3)) BiblioBazaar.

Caiger-Smith, Martin. Antony Gormley. 2010. (ENG., Illus.). 128p. pap. 27.50 (978-1-85437-797-5(3)) Tate Publishing, Ltd. GBR. Dist: Hachette Bk. Group.

Calasso, Roberto. La la Folie Baudelaire, 1 vol. McEwen, Alastair, tr. from ITA. 2012. (ENG., Illus.). 352p. 35.00 (978-0-374-18334-9(1)) Farrar, Straus & Giroux.

Calasso, Roberto. Tiepolo Pink. McEwen, Alastair, tr. 2011. (ENG., Illus.). 320p. pap. 29.95 (978-0-375-71208-1(9), Knopf) Knopf Doubleday Publishing Group.

Calo, Mary Ann. Distinction & Denial: Race, Nation, & the Critical Construction of the African American Artist, 1920-40. 2007. (ENG.). 280p. 84.50 (978-0-472-11468-9(9)); per. 37.50 (978-0-472-03230-3(5)) Univ. of Michigan Pr.

Campany, David. Jeff Wall: Picture for Women. 2011. (Afterall Ser.). (ENG., Illus.). 118p. (gr. 17). pap. 16.00 (978-1-84638-071-6(5)) Afterall Publishing GBR. Dist: MIT Pr.

Campbell, Peter. At... Writing, Mainly about Art, from the London Review of Books. 2010. (ENG.). 400p. pap. 35.00 (978-0-907259-43-5(X)) Hyphen Pr. GBR. Dist: Hachette Bk. Group.

Campin, Robert & van der Weyden, Rogier. The Master of Flemalle & Rogier van der Weyden: Art to Hear Series. 2009. (ENG., Illus.). 48p. 30.00 (978-3-7757-2365-7(X)) Hatje Cantz Verlag GmbH & Co KG DEU. Dist: D.A.P./Distributed Art Pubs.

Cannon, Patrick F. & Sullivan, Louis H. Louis Sullivan: Creating a New American Architecture. 2011. (Illus.). 192p. 39.95 (978-0-7649-5771-0(6)) Pomegranate Communications, Inc.

Capati, Massimiliano. Leonardo da Vinci: A Life Through Paintings. 2009. (ENG., Illus.). 160p. pap. 18.99 (978-88-7461-111-9(0)) Mandragora ITA. Dist: Antique Collectors' Club.

Caplow, Deborah. Leopoldo Méndez: Revolutionary Art & the Mexican Print. 2007. (Joe R. & Teresa Lozano Long Series in Latin American & Latino Art & Culture). (ENG., Illus.). 327p. 55.00 (978-0-292-71250-8(2)) Univ. of Texas Pr.

Carl, Klaus H., et al. 30 Centuries of Erotic Art. 2012. (30 Millennia of Art Ser.). (ENG., Illus.). 544p. 29.95 (978-1-84484-832-4(9)) Parkstone International GBR. Dist: Ingram Pub. Services.

—30 Centuries of Painting. 2012. (30 Millennia of Art Ser.). (ENG., Illus.). 544p. 29.95 (978-1-84484-815-7(9)) Parkstone International GBR. Dist: Ingram Pub. Services.

Carolyn, Lanchner. Fernand Léger. 2010. (ENG., Illus.). 48p. pap. 9.95 (978-0-87070-786-5(8)) Museum of Modern Art.

Carroll, Noël. Art in Three Dimensions. 2010. 536p. 74.00 (978-0-19-955931-2(7)) Oxford Univ. Pr., Inc.

Carroll, Noel. Art in Three Dimensions. 2012. (ENG.). 548p. pap. 45.00 (978-0-19-965592-2(8)) Oxford Univ. Pr., Inc.

Carroll, Noel. On Criticism. 2008. (Thinking in Action Ser.). (ENG.). 224p. 125.00 (978-0-415-39620-2(4)); pap. 21.95 (978-0-415-39621-9(2)) Routledge.

Carson, David & Blackwell, Lewis. The End of Print: The Grafik Design of David Carson. 2nd rev. ed. 2012. (ENG., Illus.). 192p. 45.00 (978-1-85669-888-7(2)) King, Laurence Publishing GBR. Dist: Hachette Bk. Group.

Causey, Andrew & Moore, Henry. The Drawings of Henry Moore. 2010. (Illus.). 160p. 50.00 (978-1-84822-029-4(4), Lund Humphries Pubs.) Ashgate Publishing, Ltd. GBR. Dist: Ashgate Publishing Co.

Celender, Donald. Donald - Celender: 28 Years of Writings, Questions & Answers. Date not set. 500p. pap. 29.95 (978-0-923183-25-7(6)) A.R.T. Pr.

Cernuschi, Claude. Barnett Newman & Heideggerian Philosophy. 2012. (ENG., Illus.). 348p. (gr. 17). 80.00 (978-1-61147-519-7(8)) Fairleigh Dickinson Univ. Pr.

Chare, Nicholas. After Frances Bacon: Synaesthesia & Sex in Paint. 2012. (Illus.). 192p. 114.95 (978-1-4094-1170-3(2)) Ashgate Publishing Co.

Charney, Noah. Stealing the Mystic Lamb: The True Story of the World's Most Coveted Masterpiece. 2010. (ENG., Illus.). 336p. 27.95 (978-1-58648-800-0(7)) PublicAffairs.

Chase, Linda. John Salt: The Complete Works, 1969-2007. 2007. (ENG., Illus.). 192p. 63.00 (978-0-85667-634-5(9)) Wilson, Philip Pubs., Ltd. GBR. Dist: Macmillan.

Chawla, Rupika. Raja Ravi Varma: Life & Times in Colonial India. 2010. 75.00 (978-0-944142-41-7(9)) Grantha Corp.

Cheetham, Mark A. Artwriting Nation & Cosmopolitanism in Britain: The Englishness of English Art Theory since the Eighteenth Century. 2012. (British Art: Global Contexts Ser.). (Illus.). 200p. 104.95 (978-1-4094-2073-6(6)) Ashgate Publishing Co.

Chen Zengshou — A Man of the Past Age — and His Poems in Praise of Flowers. 2007. pap. 10.00 (978-1-59343-057-3(4), Cozy Publishing Hse.) Cozy Graphics Corp.

Cheney, Liana De. Giorgio Vasari's Prefaces: Art & Theory; with a foreword by Wolfram Prinz. 2012. (LAT, ITA & ENG., Illus.). lxxiii, 333p. (C). 47.95 (978-1-4331-0799-3(6)) Lang, Peter Publishing, Inc.

Chesterton, G. K. G. F. Watts. reprint ed. lib. bdg. 98.00 (978-0-7426-3007-9(2)) Classic Bks.

Chiappini, Rudy, ed. Bacon. 2008. (ENG., Illus.). 176p. 90.00 (978-88-6130-293-8(9)) Skira Editore ITA. Dist: Random Hse., Inc.

Chihuly, Dale & Taragin, Davira. Baskets. Portland Press Staff, ed. 2009. (Illus.). 112p. 14.95 (978-1-57684-172-3(3)) Portland Pr., Inc.

—Chandeliers & Towers. Portland Press Staff, ed. 2009. (Illus.). 112p. 14.95 (978-1-57684-174-7(X)) Portland Pr., Inc.

—Putti. Portland Press Staff, ed. 2009. (Illus.). 112p. 14.95 (978-1-57684-173-0(1)) Portland Pr., Inc.

Ch'oe, Yol. Misul Kwa Sahoe: Ch'oe Yol Pip'yong Chonso, 1976-2008. 2009. (KOR., Illus.). 468p. (978-89-7278-279-7(3)) Cheong-nyeonsa.

Christiansen, Keith. Duccio & the Origins of Western Painting. (Illus.). 2009. (ENG.). 62p. pap. 19.95 (978-0-300-14544-1(6)) 2008. 61p. 19.95 (978-1-58839-289-3(9)) Metropolitan Museum of Art, The.

Christiansen, Keith & Mantegna, Andrea. The Genius of Andrea Mantegna. 2010. (Illus.). 63p. 14.95 (978-1-58839-356-2(9)) Metropolitan Museum of Art, The.

Christov-Bakargiev, Carolyn & Beccaria, Marcella, eds. Gianni Colombo. 2010. (ENG., Illus.). 312p. 80.00 (978-88-572-0314-0(X)) Skira Editore ITA. Dist: Random Hse., Inc.

Clarke, David. Chinese Art & Its Encounter with the World. 2011. 272p. (978-988-8053-84-1(1)) Hong Kong Univ. Pr.

Clarke, David, ed. Tippett Studies. 2006. (Cambridge Composer Studies). (ENG.). 252p. pap. 50.00 (978-0-521-02683-3(0)) Cambridge Univ. Pr.

Clarke, Jay A. y. Becoming Edvard Munch: Influence, Anxiety, & Myth. 2009. (Illus.). 231p. pap. (978-0-86559-228-5(4)) Art Institute of Chicago.

Clinton, Clare. Donald Hamilton Fraser: A Retrospective - Metamorphosis Not Metaphor. 2009. (Illus.). 152p. 70.00 (978-1-84822-042-3(1), Lund Humphries Pubs.) Ashgate Publishing, Ltd. GBR. Dist: Ashgate Publishing Co.

Clippel, Karolien de. Joos Van Craesbeeck (1605/06-Ca.1660) Een Brabants Genreschilder, 2 vols. 2006. (DUT., Illus.). 608p. (C). 196.00 (978-2-503-52380-4(3)) Brepols Pubs. BEL. Dist: ISD.

Cocker, Mark, et al. Kurt Jackson: A New Genre of Landscape Painting. 2012. (Illus.). 144p. pap. 40.00 (978-1-84822-102-4(9), Lund Humphries Pubs.) Ashgate Publishing, Ltd. GBR. Dist: Ashgate Publishing Co.

Colace-Scarabino, Gabrielle. Pourquoi Roue de Bicyclette Est une Uvre D'art. 2010. (FRE., Illus.). 214p. (978-2-84301-293-8(7)) Aleas, Editeur.

Cole, Michael W. Ambitious Form: Giambologna, Ammanati, & Danti in Florence. 2010. (ENG., Illus.). 372p. (C). 49.50 (978-0-691-14744-4(2)) Princeton Univ. Pr.

Coliva, Anna & Aikema, Bernard. Lucas Cranach: The Other Renaissance. 2011. (ENG., Illus.). 224p. pap. 60.00 (978-88-7179-647-5(0)) Antique Collectors' Club.

Consuegra, Hugo. Hugo Consuegra. Herryman, Lisset Martínez & Valdés, Gustavo, eds. 2007. (Coleccion Arte Ser.). (Illus.). 197p. pap. 50.00 (978-1-59388-086-6(3)) Ediciones Universal.

Cooper, Suzanne Fagence. Effie: The Passionate Lives of Effie Gray, John Ruskin & John Everett Millais. (ENG.). 288p. 2012. pap. 15.99 (978-1-250-01625-6(8), St. Martin's Griffin) 2011. (Illus.). 26.99 (978-0-312-58173-2(4)) St. Martin's Pr.

Cooperman, Emily T. & Sherk, Lea Carson. William Birch: Picturing the American Scene. 2010. (Illus.). 352p. (C). 75.00 (978-0-8122-4248-5(3)) Univ. of Pennsylvania Pr.

Cordero, Raul. Raul Cordero. 2011. (SPA & ENG., Illus.). 220p. pap. 30.00 (978-84-7506-842-8(1)) Turner, Ediciones S.A. ESP. Dist: D.A.P./Distributed Art Pubs.

Corgnati, Martina, text. Eugenio Carmi, 1 vol. 2007. (ITA & ENG., Illus.). 176p. 60.00 (978-88-8158-623-3(1)) Charta ITA. Dist: D.A.P./Distributed Art Pubs.

Cornell, Joseph. Joseph Cornell's Dreams, 1 vol. 2007. (ENG., Illus.). 160p. (gr. 13-18). per. 15.95 (978-1-878972-41-5(3)) Exact Change.

Corris, Michael. Ad Reinhardt. 2008. (ENG., Illus.). 256p. 39.95 (978-1-86189-356-7(6)) Reaktion Bks., Ltd. GBR. Dist: Chicago Distribution Ctr.

Cortez, Constance. Carmen Lomas Garza. 2010. (Ver Ser.). (ENG., Illus.). 108p. 60.00 (978-0-89551-124-9(X)); pap. 24.95 (978-0-89551-125-6(8)) Univ. of Minnesota Pr.

Costello, Leo. J. M. W. Turner & the Subject of History. 2012. (Illus.). 280p. 119.95 (978-0-7546-6922-7(X)) Ashgate Publishing Co.

Cox, Kenyon. The Classic Point of View. 2009. 74p. pap. (978-1-151-54766-8(2)) Books LLC.

Cox, Neil. The Picasso Book. 2010. (ENG., Illus.). 224p. pap. 29.95 (978-1-85437-843-9(0)) Tate Publishing, Ltd. GBR. Dist: Hachette Bk. Group.

—Picasso's 'Toys for Adults' Cubism As Surrealism. 2011. (ENG., Illus.). 48p. (978-1-906270-26-1(0)) National Galleries of Scotland.

Coxon, Ann. Louise Bourgeois. 2010. (ENG., Illus.). 540p. pap. 27.50 (978-1-85437-882-8(1)) Tate Publishing, Ltd. GBR. Dist: Hachette Bk. Group.

Craig, James. Frank Vining Smith: Maritime Painting in the 20th Century. 2010. (ENG., Illus.). 172p. 65.00 (978-1-55595-329-4(8)) Hudson Hills Pr. LLC.

Craven, David & Winkenweder, Brian, eds. Dialectical Conversions: Donald Kuspit's Art Criticism. 2011. (Liverpool University Press - Value-Art-Politics Ser.). (ENG., Illus.). 276p. 95.00 (978-1-84631-479-7(8)) Liverpool Univ. Pr. GBR. Dist: Chicago Distribution Ctr.

Crone, Rainer F., et al. Louise Bourgeois: The Secret of the Cells. 2011. (ENG., Illus.). 192p. pap. 19.95 (978-3-7913-4562-8(1)) Prestel Publishing.

Crowe, Victoria. Victoria Crowe: Painted Insights. 2nd ed. 2009. (ENG., Illus.). 144p. 55.00 (978-1-85149-589-4(4)) Antique Collectors' Club.

Crumpacker, Darrel & Master of the Die. Identifying Master of the Die: Re-examining Sixteenth Century Italian Printmaking. 2010. 48p. 20.00 (978-0-9667532-9-5(1)) Blue Moon - Lee Pr.

Cruzvillegas, Abraham & Kim, Clara. Abraham Cruzvillegas: Autoconstrucción: The Book. 2009. (978-0-9825390-1-9(0)) California Institute of the Arts.

Ctte 23. 4. 2011. pap. 40.00 (978-0-415-55327-8(X)) Routledge.

Cufer, Eda. Transnacionala: Highway Collisions Between East & West at the Crossroads of Art. pap. 27.00 (978-961-6211-62-8(5)) tudentska organizacija Univerze v Ljubljani, tudentska zalo'ba SVN. Dist: D.A.P./Distributed Art Pubs.

Curators Staff. Artists on Art: Yale University Art Gallery. 2006. (Yale University Art Gallery Ser.). (ENG.). 71p. pap. 15.00 (978-0-89467-087-9(5)) Yale Univ. Art Gallery.

Curcic, Slobodan & Hadjitryphonos, Evangelia. Architecture as Icon: Perception & Representation of Architecture in Byzantine Art. 2010. (ENG., Illus.). 376p. pap. 60.00 *(978-0-300-12211-4(X))* Yale Univ. Pr.

Curiger, Bice, ed. Parkett No. 85: Maria Lassnig, Beatriz Milhazes, Jean-Luc Mylayne, Josh Smith. 2009. (ENG., Illus.). 300p. pap. 32.00 *(978-3-907582-45-9(4))* Parkett Verlag AG CHE. Dist: D.A.P./Distributed Art Pubs.

—Parkett No.88 - 2011. 2011. (ENG., Illus.). 300p. pap. 45.00 *(978-3-907582-48-0(9))* Parkett Verlag AG CHE. Dist: D.A.P./Distributed Art Pubs.

Curtis, Neal, ed. The Pictorial Turn. (ENG.). 256p. (C). 2011. pap. 45.95 ***(978-0-415-50874-2(6))*** 2010. (Illus.). 125.00 *(978-0-415-54982-0(5))* Routledge.

Czernin, Franz Josef. Bildsatz: Texte Zu Bildender Kunst. 2008. (GER., Illus.). 367p. *(978-3-8321-9100-9(3))* DuMont.

Czymmek, Götz & Geil, Bernhard. German Impressionist Landscape Painting: Liebermann-Corinth-Slevogt. Aurisch, Helga, ed. 2010. (Illus.). 256p. 65.00 *(978-0-300-16614-9(1))* Museum of Fine Arts, Houston.

Dagen, Philippe. Picasso. 2009. (ENG., Illus.). 512p. 150.00 *(978-1-58093-257-8(6))* Monacelli Pr., Inc.

D'Alessandro, Stephanie & Elderfield, John. Matisse: Radical Invention, 1913-1917. 2010. (Illus.). 368p. pap. *(978-0-86559-237-7(3))* Art Institute of Chicago.

—Matisse: Radical Invention, 1913-1917. 2011. (ENG., Illus.). 368p. pap. 50.00 *(978-0-300-17724-4(0))* Yale Univ. Pr.

D'Alleva, Anne. Methods & Theories of Art History. 2009. (ENG., Illus.). 192p. pap. 18.95 *(978-1-85669-417-9(8))* King, Laurence Publishing GBR. Dist: Hachette Bk. Group.

Dalli Regoli, Gigetta. Verrocchio, Lorenzo di Credi, Francesco di Simone Ferrucci. 2008. (Drawing Gallery Ser.). (ENG., Illus.). 92p. pap. 14.95 *(978-88-7439-068-7(8))* 5 Continents ITA. Dist: Hachette Bk. Group.

Damiani, Giovanna & Vervat, Muriel. Con la matita e col pennello. Giovanni Fattori: Indagini e restauri dei dipinti della Galleria d'Arte Moderna di Palazzo Pitti. 2009. (ITA., Illus.). 384p. (C). 56.00 *(978-88-564-0080-9(4))* Polistampa ITA. Dist: Brown, David Bk. Co., The.

Dannowski, Hans Werner. Wie schad', dass ich kein Pfaffe bin: Wilhelm Busch und die Religion. 2008. (Illus.). 128p. *(978-3-7859-0980-5(2))* Lutherisches Verlagshaus GmbH.

Danto, Arthur C. Andy Warhol. 2010. (Icons of America Ser.). (ENG., Illus.). 192p. pap. 16.00 *(978-0-300-16908-9(6))* Yale Univ. Pr.

Davidson, Peter. The Universal Baroque. 2008. (ENG., Illus.). 224p. 89.00 *(978-0-7190-7572-8(6))* Manchester Univ. Pr. GBR. Dist: Macmillan.

Davidts, Wouter, et al, texts. The Fall of the Studio. 2009. (ENG., Illus.). 249p. pap. 27.50 *(978-90-78088-29-5(X))* Valiz NLD. Dist: D.A.P./Distributed Art Pubs.

Davies, Glen C. Stranger in Paradise: The Works of Reverend Howard Finster. 2010. (Illus.). 152p. 40.00 *(978-1-883015-44-2(8))* Univ. of Washington Pr.

Davin, Solange & Jackson, Rhona, eds. Television & Criticism. 2008. 128p. pap. 40.00 *(978-1-84150-147-5(6))* Intellect, Ltd. GBR. Dist: Chicago Distribution Ctr.

Davis, Ann, ed. Cover & Uncover: Eric Cameron. 2011. (ENG., Illus.). 132p. pap. 59.95 ***(978-1-55238-534-0(5))*** Univ. of Calgary Pr. CAN. Dist: Chicago Distribution Ctr.

Davis, Julia. Giovanni Bellini. 2nd ed. 2008. (Illus.). 124p. pap. ***(978-1-86171-164-9(6))*** Crescent Moon Publishing.

Davis, Keith F. & Aspinwall, Jane L. Timothy H. O'Sullivan: The King Survey Photographs. 2011. (ENG., Illus.). 252p. 60.00 ***(978-0-300-17984-2(7))*** Yale Univ. Pr.

Davison, Betsy & Davison, Elizabeth. The Furniture of John Shearer, 1790-1820: 'A True North Britain' in the Southern Backcountry. 2011. (ENG.). 240p. 99.00 *(978-0-7591-1954-3(6))* AltaMira Pr.

De, Aditi, et al. Lines from an Artistic Life: The Drawings of Adimoolam. 2008. (Illus.). 164p. 70.00 *(978-0-85331-982-5(0)*, Lund Humphries Pubs.) Ashgate Publishing, Ltd. GBR. Dist: Ashgate Publishing Co.

de Brugerolle, Marie, text. Guy de Cointet. 2011. (ENG., Illus.). 160p. 45.00 ***(978-3-03764-069-2(3))*** JRP Ringier Kunstverlag AG CHE. Dist: D.A.P./Distributed Art Pubs.

De Dominizio Durini, Lucrezia. Beuys Voice. 2011. (Illus.). 960p. 125.00 ***(978-88-370-8567-4(2))*** Electa ITA. Dist: National Bk. Network.

de Duve, Thierry. Clement Greenberg Between the Lines: Including a Debate with Clement Greenberg. Holmes, Brian, tr. from FRE. 2010. (ENG.). 160p. pap. 17.00 *(978-0-226-17516-4(2))* Univ. of Chicago Pr.

de Menil, Dominique. The Rothko Chapel: Writings on Art & the Threshold of the Divine. 2010. (ENG., Illus.). 124p. pap. 20.00 *(978-0-300-16777-1(6))* Yale Univ. Pr.

De Oliveira, Nicolas, et al. Hans Op de Beeck: On Vanishing, 1 vol. 2008. (ENG., Illus.). 368p. 115.00 *(978-90-6153-711-3(8))* Exhibitions International N.V. BEL. Dist: D.A.P./Distributed Art Pubs.

Debailleux, Henri-Francois, et al. Philippe Pasqua: Paradise. 2010. (ENG., Illus.). 160p. 65.00 *(978-88-572-0466-6(9))* Skira Editore ITA. Dist: Random Hse., Inc.

Degas, Edgar. Degas & the Nude. 2011. (ENG., Illus.). 241p. 65.00 ***(978-0-87846-773-0(4))*** Museum of Fine Arts, Boston.

Dejardin, Ian A. C. Painting Canada: Tom Thomson & the Group of Seven. 2011. (ENG., Illus.). 208p. 65.00 ***(978-0-85667-708-3(6))*** Wilson, Philip Pubs., Ltd. GBR. Dist: Macmillan.

Delson, Susan. Ai Weiwei: Circle of Animals. 2011. (ENG., Illus.). 186p. 49.95 ***(978-3-7913-4636-6(9))*** Prestel Publishing.

Denenberg, Thomas Andrew. Winslow Homer & the Poetics of Place. 2010. (Illus.). 71p. *(978-0-916857-53-0(0))* Portland Museum of Art.

Dennis, Kelly. Art/Porn: A History of Seeing & Touching. 2009. (ENG., Illus.). 1p. 109.95 *(978-1-84788-057-4(6))*; pap. 29.95 *(978-1-84788-067-3(3))* Berg Pubs. GBR. Dist: Macmillan.

Derieux, Florence, ed. Dexter Dalwood. 2010. (ENG., Illus.). 160p. pap. 55.00 *(978-3-03764-126-2(6))* JRP Ringier Kunstverlag AG CHE. Dist: D.A.P./Distributed Art Pubs.

Des Cars, Laurence, et al. Jean-Leon Gerome. 2010. (ENG., Illus.). 374p. pap. 75.00 *(978-88-572-0702-5(1))* Skira Editore ITA. Dist: Random Hse., Inc.

Desai, Vishakha N. Asian Art History in the Twenty-First Century. 2007. (Clark Studies in the Visual Arts). (Illus.). xiii, 253p. *(978-0-931102-73-8(1))* Clark, Sterling & Francine Art Institute.

Desai, Vishakha N., ed. Asian Art History in the Twenty-First Century. 2008. (Clark Studies in the Visual Arts). (ENG., Illus.). 272p. (C). pap. 24.95 *(978-0-300-12553-5(4))* Yale Univ. Pr.

Deshmukh, Marion F., et al, eds. Max Liebermann & International Modernism: An Artist's Career from Empire to Third Reich. 2011. (SGH Ser.). (Illus.). 332p. 39.95 *(978-1-84545-662-7(9))* Berghahn Bks., Inc.

Desmond, Kathleen K. Ideas about Art. 2011. (ENG., Illus.). 280p. pap. 34.95 *(978-1-4051-7882-2(5)*, Wiley-Blackwell) Wiley, John & Sons, Inc.

—Ideas about Art. 2011. (ENG., Illus.). 280p. 89.95 *(978-1-4051-7883-9(3)*, Wiley-Blackwell) Wiley, John & Sons, Inc.

Deutsche Guggenheim Berlin Staff, contrib. by. Matthew Barney & Joseph Beuys: All in the Present Must Be Transformed, 1 vol. 2007. (ENG., Illus.). 180p. 45.00 *(978-0-89207-355-9(1))* Guggenheim, Solomon R. Museum.

Deutsche, Rosalyn. Hiroshima after Iraq: Three Studies in Art & War. 2010. (Wellek Library Lectures). (ENG., Illus.). 104p. (gr. 17). 22.50 *(978-0-231-15278-5(7))* Columbia Univ. Pr.

Di Piero, W. S. When Can I See You Again: New Art Writings. 2010. 300p. pap. 17.50 *(978-0-9824100-6-6(9))* Pressed Wafer Pr.

Diacono, Mario, text. Iconography & Archetypes. 2011. (ENG., Illus.). 488p. pap. 45.00 *(978-88-366-1633-6(X))* Silvana ITA. Dist: D.A.P./Distributed Art Pubs.

DiazCasas, Rafael, et al. Hard Light: The Work of Emilio Sanchez. 2011. (ENG., Illus.). 192p. 45.00 ***(978-3-7913-5131-5(1))*** Prestel Publishing.

Dickerson, C. D., III. Raw Painting: The Butcher's Shop by Annibale Carracci. 2010. (Kimbell Masterpiece Ser.). (ENG., Illus.). 100p. pap. 16.95 *(978-0-300-16640-8(0))* Kimbell Art Museum.

Diederichsen, Diedrich. Judgment & Contemporary Art Criticism. O'Brian, Melanie & Khonsary, Jeff, eds. 2011. (ENG.). 176p. pap. 20.00 *(978-0-9738133-6-4(9))* Projectile Publishing Society CAN. Dist: D.A.P./Distributed Art Pubs.

Disselkamp, Martin. Die Stadt der Gelehrten: Studien zu Johann Joachim Winckelmanns Briefen aus Rom. (Studien zur deutschen Literatur Ser.). (GER.). VII, 423p. 180.00 ***(978-3-11-182129-0(3))*** De Gruyter, Walter Inc.

Dolan, Therese. Perspectives on Manet. 2012. (Illus.). 244p. 119.95 ***(978-1-4094-2074-3(4))*** Ashgate Publishing Co.

Dolkart, Judith F., et al. James Tissot: The Life of Christ. 2009. (ENG., Illus.). 304p. 59.95 *(978-1-85894-496-8(1))* Merrell Pubs. Ltd. GBR. Dist: Perseus Distribution.

Donohue, A. A. Greek Sculpture & the Problem of Description. 2011. (ENG., Illus.). 278p. (C). pap. 36.99 *(978-1-107-40050-4(3))* Cambridge Univ. Pr.

Dorfles, Gillo. Salvador Presta: A Retrospective of the Works of Salvador Presta. 2007. (ENG, ITA, FRE & SPA.). 64p. 35.00 *(978-0-9758739-0-8(3))* Madi Museum.

Dorontchenkov. Russian & Soviet Views of Modern Western Art. 2009. (Documents of Twentieth-Century Art Ser.). (Illus.). xv, 347p. 65.00 *(978-0-520-22103-1(6))* Univ. of California Pr.

Dorontchenkov, Ilia & Dorontchenkov, I. Russian & Soviet Views of Modern Western Art, 1890s to Mid-1930s. Dorontchenkov, Ilia & Gourianova, Nina, eds. Rougle, Charles, tr. 2009. (Documents of Twentieth-Century Art Ser.). (ENG., Illus.). 400p. pap. 29.95 *(978-0-520-25372-8(8))* Univ. of California Pr.

Douglas, Robert L. Resistance, Insurgence, & Identity: The Art of Mari Evans, Nelson Stevens, & the Black Arts Movement. 2008. *(978-1-59221-564-5(5))* Africa World Pr.

Drew, Ned, et al. Purity of Aim: The Book Jackets of Alvin Lustig. 2010. (Illus.). 88p. 21.95 *(978-1-933360-48-5(8)*, RIT Cary Graphic Arts Pr.) Rochester Institute of Technology, Cary Graphic Arts Pr.

Drucker, Johanna. Sweet Dreams: Contemporary Art & Complicity. 2006. (Illus.). 264p. per. 30.00 *(978-0-226-16505-9(1))* Univ. of Chicago Pr.

Du Pont, Diana C. & Tamayo, Rufino. Tamayo: A Modern Icon Reinterpreted. 2007. (Illus.). 461p. pap. *(978-84-7506-772-8(7))* Santa Barbara Museum of Art.

Dubin, Nina L. & Robert, Hubert. Futures & Ruins: Eighteenth-Century Paris & the Art of Hubert Robert. 2010. (ENG., Illus.). 208p. 50.00 *(978-1-60606-023-0(6))* Getty Pubns.

Duchamp, Marcel, et al. Étant Donnés: Manual of Instructions. 2009. (FRE & ENG., Illus.). ***(978-0-87633-212-2(2))*** Philadelphia Museum of Art.

Duchting, Hajo. T25 kr Kandinsky. 2012. (25 Ser.). (ENG., Illus.). 96p. 14.99 ***(978-3-8365-3146-7(1))*** TASCHEN DEU. Dist: Ingram Pub. Services.

Duchting, Hajo & Dchting, Hajo. Cézanne. 25th ed. 2009. (ENG., Illus.). 224p. 14.99 *(978-3-8365-1012-7(X))* TASCHEN DEU. Dist: Ingram Pub. Services.

Duffy, Michael H. & Wissman, Fronia E. The Influence of Charles-Francois Daubigny (1817-1378) on French Plein Air Landscape Painting: Rustic Portrayals of Everyday Life in the Work of a Forerunner to Impressionism. 2011. (Illus.). iv, 242p. 129.95 *(978-0-7734-4648-9(6))* Mellen, Edwin Pr., The.

Dufour-Kowalska, Gabrielle. Emil Nolde: L'expressionisme Devant Dieu. 2007. (FRE., Illus.). 216p. (C). pap. 35.00 ***(978-2-252-03623-5(0))*** Klincksieck, Editions FRA. Dist: ISD.

Dunne, Tom & Pressly, William L. James Barry 1741-1806: History Painter. 2010. (Illus.). 300p. 119.95 *(978-0-7546-6634-9(4))* Ashgate Publishing Co.

Dupin, Jacques. Miró. 2012. (ENG., Illus.). 480p. 44.95 ***(978-2-08-020101-0(8))*** Flammarion et Cie FRA. Dist: Random Hse., Inc.

Durden, Mark. Dorothea Lange. 2012. (ENG., Illus.). 128p. 12.95 ***(978-0-7148-6357-3(2))*** Phaidon Pr., Inc.

Dürer, Albrecht. The Essential Dürer. Silver, Larry & Smith, Jeffrey Chipps, eds. 2010. (Illus.). 312p. (C). 65.00 *(978-0-8122-4187-7(8))* Univ. of Pennsylvania Pr.

Dzeiwior, Yilmaz, ed. Cosima von Bonin. The Fatigue Empire. Das Internationale Wollsekretariat 1989 - 2010: The Fatigue Empire. 2011. (ENG., Illus.). 320p. 65.00 *(978-3-86560-817-8(5))* Kunsthaus Bregenz AUT. Dist: D.A.P./Distributed Art Pubs.

Dziewanska, Marta. Ion Grigorescu: In the Body of the Victim. 2011. (ENG & POL., Illus.). 312p. pap. 29.00 ***(978-83-924044-1-5(6))*** Muzeum Sztuki Nowoczesnej w Warszawie POL. Dist: Chicago Distribution Ctr.

Dzine. The Beautiful Struggle: The Art of Dzine. 2011. (Illus.). 224p. *(978-3-89955-329-1(2))* Die Gestalten Verlag.

Ebony, David. Emily Mason: The Fifth Element. 2nd ed. 2009. (Illus.). 128p. 39.95 *(978-0-9777571-5-2(3))* Findlay, David Jr., Inc.

Echinger-Maurach, Claudia. Michelangelos Grabmal für Papst Julius II. 2009. (GER., Illus.). 210p. (C). 154.00 *(978-3-7774-4355-3(7))* Hirmer Verlag GmbH DEU. Dist: Brown, David Bk. Co., The.

Eckhardt, Joseph P. So Bravely & So Well: The Life & Art of William T. Trego. 2011. (Illus.). 208p. pap. 39.95 *(978-1-879636-24-8(7))* Univ. of Pennsylvania Pr.

Edwards, Jason & Taylor, Stephanie L., eds. Joseph Cornell: Opening the Box. 2007. (Illus.). 350p. (C). pap. 73.95 *(978-0-8204-9343-5(0))* Lang, Peter Publishing, Inc.

Eeg-Tverbakk, Lars O Ramberg. 2009. (ENG.). 248p. 60.00 *(978-3-7757-2038-0(3))* Hatje Cantz Verlag GmbH & Co KG DEU. Dist: D.A.P./Distributed Art Pubs.

Egerton, Judy. George Stubbs, Painter: Catalogue Raisonne. 2007. (Illus.). 655p. 200.00 *(978-0-300-12509-2(7))* Yale Univ. Pr.

Eisenman, Stephen. Paul Gauguin. 2011. (ENG., Illus.). 96p. 25.00 *(978-84-343-1249-4(2))* Poligrafa, Ediciones, S. A. ESP. Dist: D.A.P./Distributed Art Pubs.

Elam, Caroline. Roger Fry's Journey from Primitives to the Post-Impressionists. 2011. (ENG., Illus.). 48p. *(978-1-906270-11-7(2))* National Galleries of Scotland.

Eldredge, Charles C. John Steuart Curry's Hoover & the Flood: Painting Modern History. 2007. (ENG., Illus.). 112p. 34.95 *(978-0-8078-3087-1(9))* Univ. of North Carolina Pr.

Eldredge, Charles C., et al. The Legend of Rex Slinkard. 2011. *(978-0-937031-35-3(6))* Univ. of California Pr.

Elger, Dietmar. Gerhard Richter: A Life in Painting. Solaro, Elizabeth M., tr. from GER. 2nd ed. 2010. (ENG., Illus.). 408p. 45.00 *(978-0-226-20323-2(9))* Univ. of Chicago Pr.

Eliasoph, Philip, et al. Colleen Browning: The Enchantment of Realism. 2012. (ENG., Illus.). 180p. 60.00 *(978-1-55595-366-9(2))* Hudson Hills Pr. LLC.

Eliens, Titus M. Pablo Picasso: Keramiek/Ceramics. 2007. (DUT & ENG., Illus.). 96p. 30.00 *(978-90-400-8315-0(C))* Waanders B.V., Uitgeverij NLD. Dist: National Bk. Network.

Elkins, et al. The State of Art Criticism. 2007. (Art Seminar Ser.). (ENG., Illus.). 416p. pap. 35.95 *(978-0-415-97787-6(8))* Routledge.

Elkins, James. Chinese Landscape Painting As Western Art History. 2010. (ENG., Illus.). 208p. (gr. 17). 45.00 *(978-962-209-000-2(1))* Hong Kong Univ. Pr. HKG. Dist: Columbia Univ. Pr.

—Chinese Landscape Painting As Western Art History. 2010. 208p. *(978-9971-69-523-1(5))* Hong Kong Univ. Pr.

Elkins, James & Newman, Michael. The State of Art Criticism. Elkins, James & Newman, Michael, eds. 2006. (Art Seminar Ser.). (Illus.). 410p. 125.00 *(978-0-415-97786-9(X))* Routledge.

Eller, Wolfgang L. Giorgione: Catalogue Raisonne. 2007. (Illus.). 216p. 89.00 *(978-3-86568-126-3(3))* Wybel Marketing Group.

Elliott, Patrick. Tony Cragg: Sculptures & Drawings. 2012. (ENG., Illus.). 120p. 45.00 ***(978-0-300-17898-2(0))*** Yale Univ. Pr.

Elwood, Marie B. The Egyptian Album of John Elliott Woolford: Original Watercolours by John Elliott Woolford & with Maps by the Ninth Earl of Dalhousie. 2009. (Illus.). 202p. 149.95 *(978-0-7734-3880-4(7))* Mellen, Edwin Pr., The.

Emmerling Leonhard. Basquiat. 2011. (ENG., Illus.). 96p. 14.99 *(978-3-8365-2714-9(6))* TASCHEN DEU. Dist: Ingram Pub. Services.

Enke, Dieter. Andries Dirk Copier: Ideas in glass. Unica & more. 2010. (ENG., Illus.). 200p. 70.00 incl. cd-rom *(978-3-89790-299-2(0))* Arnoldsche Art Pubs. DEU. Dist: Antique Collectors' Club.

Erben, Walter & Düchting, Hajo. Miro t25 Edition. 2008. (ENG., Illus.). 240p. 14.99 *(978-3-8228-3750-4(4))* TASCHEN DEU. Dist: Ingram Pub. Services.

Esanu, Octavian. Jfl: What Does Why Mean?, 1 vol. 2nd ed. 2007. (ENG.). 200p. per. 10.00 *(978-0-9746908-4-1(8))* J&L Bks., Inc.

Esner, Rachel & Schavemaker, Margriet, eds. Vincent Everywhere: Van Gogh's (Inter)National Identities. 2011. (Illus.). 184p. pap. *(978-90-8964-198-4(X))* Amsterdam Univ. Pr.

Essers, Volkmar. Matisse. 2012. (25 Ser.). (ENG., Illus.). 96p. 14.99 ***(978-3-8365-3126-9(7))*** TASCHEN DEU. Dist: Ingram Pub. Services.

Evans, Dorinda. Gilbert Stuart & the Impact of Manic Depression. 2012. (Illus.). 256p. ***(978-1-4094-4164-9(4))*** Ashgate Publishing, Ltd.

Evans, Mark. John Constable: Oil Sketches from the Victoria & Albert Museum. 2011. (ENG., Illus.). 160p. 34.95 *(978-1-85177-626-9(5))* V & A Pubns. GBR. Dist: Hachette Bk. Group.

Fabius, Laurent. Le Cabinet des Douze: Regards Sur des Tableaux Qui Font la France. 2010. (Illus.). 214p. *(978-2-07-013039-9(8))* Gallimard, Editions.

Faitakis, Stelios. Hell on Earth: Stelios Faitakis. 2011. (ENG., Illus.). 160p. 60.00 ***(978-3-89955-384-0(5))*** Die Gestalten Verlag DEU. Dist: Prestel Publishing.

Farago, Claire. Re-Reading Leonardo: The Treatise on Painting Across Europe, 1550-1900. 2009. (Illus.). 652p. 139.95 *(978-0-7546-6532-8(1))* Ashgate Publishing Co.

Farago, Claire J., ed. Leonardo Da Vinci & the Ethics of Style. 2008. (ENG., Illus.). 288p. 89.00 *(978-0-7190-7814-9(8))* Manchester Univ. Pr. GBR. Dist: Macmillan.

Farr, William E. Julius Seyler & the Blackfeet: An Impressionist at Glacier National Park. 2009. (Charles M. Russell Center on Art & Photography of the American West Ser.). (ENG.). 256p. (C). 45.00 *(978-0-8061-4014-8(3))* Univ. of Oklahoma Pr.

Fassl, Johanna. Sacred Eloquence: Giambattista Tiepolo & the Rhetoric of the Altarpiece. 2010. (Illus.). 383p. pap. 88.95 *(978-3-0343-0035-3(2))* Lang, Peter Publishing, Inc.

Faure, Élie, et al. Twentieth Century Art. 2010. 256p. *(978-1-84484-686-3(5))* Parkstone International.

Feld, Ross. Guston in Time: Remembering Philip Guston. 2011. (ENG., Illus.). 172p. pap. 15.95 *(978-1-58243-792-8(3)*, Counterpoint) Counterpoint LLC.

Ferre, Rosa, ed. Red Cavalry: Creation & Power in Soviet Russia between 1917 And 1945. 2011. 500p. 69.95 *(978-84-96917-78-1(9))* Caja de Madrid ESP. Dist: Actar Birkhauser Distribution.

Ficacci, Luigi. Bacon. 25th ed. 2010. (25 Ser.). (ENG., Illus.). 96p. 14.99 *(978-3-8365-2544-2(5))* TASCHEN DEU. Dist: Ingram Pub. Services.

Ficacci, Luigi. Piranesi: 25 Jahre TASCHEN, 2 vols. 2011. (25 Ser.). (ENG., Illus.). 800p. 59.99 ***(978-3-8365-3196-2(8))*** TASCHEN DEU. Dist: Ingram Pub. Services.

Finch, Christopher. Chuck Close: Work. 2010. (Illus.). 352p. 85.00 *(978-3-7913-4466-9(8))* Prestel Publishing.

Finn, Maria. Images Between the Word & the Film. 2011. 144p. pap. ***(978-3-8443-8741-4(2))*** Lambert Academic Publishing.

Fiorenza, Giancarlo. Dosso Dossi: Paintings of Myth, Magic, & the Antique. 2008. (ENG., Illus.). 256p. (C). 70.00 *(978-0-271-03204-7(9))* Pennsylvania State Univ. Pr.

Fischer, Matthias, et al. Fritz Zbinden: Ein Malerleben 1896-1968. Fischer, Matthias, ed. 2010. (Illus.). 320p. 136.00 ***(978-3-85881-289-6(7))*** Scheidegger und Spiess AG, Verag CHE. Dist: Antique Collectors' Club.

Fiz, Alberto, ed. Antoni Tàpies: Materia e Tempo. 2010. (ITA & ENG., Illus.). 240p. 87.50 *(978-88-370-7175-2(2))* Electa ITA. Dist: Trans-Atlantic Pubns., Inc.

Flett, George. George Flett: Ledger Art. 2008. (ENG., Illus.). vii, 81p. 69.00 *(978-0-923910-25-9(5))* New Media Ventures, Inc.

Florensky, Pavel. Beyond Vision: Essays on the Perception of Art. 2006. 256p. pap. 45.00 *(978-1-86189-307-9(6))* Reaktion Bks., Ltd. GBR. Dist: Chicago Distribution Ctr.

Flores d'Arcais, Francesca. Giotto. 2012. (ENG., Illus.). 391p. 135.00 ***(978-0-7892-1114-9(9))*** Abbeville Pr., Inc.

Folgarait, Leonard. So Far from Heaven: David Alfaro Siqueiros' the March of Humanity & Mexican Revolutionary Politics. 2009. (Cambridge Iberian & Latin American Studies). (ENG., Illus.). 192p. pap. 28.99 *(978-0-521-12334-1(8))* Cambridge Univ. Pr.

Folie, Sabine, ed. Un Coup de des: Writing Turned Image, an Alphabet of Pensive Language. 2009. (GER & ENG., Illus.). 250p. pap. 59.95 *(978-3-86560-543-6(5))* Verlag der Buchhandlung Walther Konig DEU. Dist: D.A.P./Distributed Art Pubs.

Forrer, Matthi. Hokusai: Mountains & Water, Flowers & Birds. 2011. (ENG., Illus.). 96p. pap. 14.95 ***(978-3-7913-4614-4(8))*** Prestel Publishing.

Forrester, Gillian, ed. Rebecca Salter: Into the Light of Things. 2011. (ENG., Illus.). 282p. 60.00 *(978-0-300-17042-9(4))* Yale Univ. Pr.

Fort, Ilene Susan & Eakins, Thomas. Manly Pursuits: Writings on the Sporting Images of Thomas Eakins. 2011. ***(978-0-87587-211-7(5))*** Los Angeles County Museum of Art.

Foster, Hal. 'The Hardest Kind of Archetype' - Reflections on Roy Lichetenstein: The Watson Gordon Lecture 2010. 2011. (ENG., Illus.). 48p. ***(978-1-906270-38-4(4))*** National Galleries of Scotland.

Foster, Kathleen A. & Tucker, Mark S. An Eakins Masterpiece Restored: Seeing the Gross Clinic Anew. 2012. ***(978-0-87633-235-1(1))*** Philadelphia Museum of Art.

Foster, Kathleen A. & Tucker, Mark S., eds. An Eakins Masterpiece Restored: Seeing the Gross Clinic Anew. 2012. (ENG., Illus.). 184p. pap. 27.50 ***(978-0-300-17979-8(0))*** Yale Univ. Pr.

Foster, Norman & text. Norman Foster Set: Drawings, 1958-2008, 2 vols. 2011. (ENG., Illus.). 232p. 150.00 *(978-0-9564339-2-3(8))* Ivory Pr. ESP. Dist: D.A.P./Distributed Art Pubs.

Foucault, Michel. Manet & the Object of Painting. 2010. (ENG., Illus.). 80p. 21.95 (978-1-85437-845-3(7)) Tate Publishing, Ltd. GBR. Dist: Hachette Bk. Group.

Francis, Jacqueline. Making Race: Modernism & Racial Art in America. 2011. (ENG., Illus.). 256p. pap. 40.00 (978-0-295-99145-0(3)) Univ. of Washington Pr.

Frank, Marie. Denman Ross & American Design Theory. 2011. (Illus.). 344p. (C). 85.00 (978-1-58465-969-3(6)); (ENG., pap. 39.95 (978-1-61168-025-6(5)) Univ. Pr. of New England.

Frank, Susan Behrends. David Smith Invents. 2011. (ENG., Illus.). 112p. 30.00 (978-0-300-16965-2(5)) Yale Univ. Pr.

Frey, Raman & Norris, Wendi, intros. Underground Together: The Art & Life of Harvey Dinnerstein. 2008. (ENG.). 208p. 50.00 (978-0-8118-8965-0(3)) Chronicle Bks. LLC.

Fried, Michael. Four Honest Outlaws: Sala, Ray, Marioni, Gordon. 2011. (ENG., Illus.). 224p. 45.00 (978-0-300-17053-5(X)) Yale Univ. Pr.

—The Moment of Caravaggio. 2010. (A. W. Mellon Lectures in the Fine Arts Ser.). (ENG., Illus.). 328p. 49.50 (978-0-691-14701-7(9)) Princeton Univ. Pr.

Friedman, Daniel & Church, Jennifer, eds. El Laberinto de Frida Kahlo: Cartas ilustradas, dibujos y Notas intimas. Stark-Ortega, Polly, tr. 2008.Tr. of Labyrinth of Frida Kahlo: Death, Pain, & Ambivalence. Illustrated Letters, Drawings & Intimate Notes. (SPA., Illus.). 176p. pap. 24.95 (978-0-615-23125-9(X)) CIAM Pr.

Friedman, Julia. Beyond Symbolism & Surrealism: Alexei Remizov's Synthetic Art. 2011. (ENG., Illus.). 286p. 69.95 (978-0-8101-2617-6(6)) Northwestern Univ. Pr.

Frimark, Arlene, text. Images of Prayer: An Art Siddur for Shabbat Morning. 2008. (Illus.). 114p. 71.99 (978-1-4363-0487-0(3)) Xlibris Corp.

Fürlus, Eckhard, ed. Variantology 3. 2008. (ENG., Illus.). 478p. pap. 98.00 (978-3-86560-366-1(1)) Verlag der Buchhandlung Walther Konig DEU. Dist: D.A.P./Distributed Art Pubs.

Galassi, Susan Grace & McCully, Marilyn. Picasso's Drawings, 1890-1921: Reinventing Tradition. 2011. (ENG., Illus.). 224p. 60.00 (978-0-300-17073-3(4)) Yale Univ. Pr.

Gale, Matthew & Daniel, Marko. Miró: The Ladder of Escape. 2011. (Illus.). 240p. (978-1-85437-944-3(5)) D.A.P./Distributed Art Pubs.

Gallo, Lylia. Gerardo Aragon. 2007. (ENG., Illus.). 168p. 56.00 (978-958-8306-02-5(7)) Villegas Editores S.A. COL. Dist: Independent Pubs. Group.

Gambone, Robert L. Life on the Press: The Popular Art & Illustrations of George Benjamin Luks. 2009. (ENG., Illus.). 240p. 50.00 (978-1-60473-222-1(9)) Univ. Pr. of Mississippi.

Garcia, Erin C. & Man Ray. Man Ray in Paris. 2011. (ENG., Illus.). 128p. 24.95 (978-1-60606-060-5(0), J. Paul Getty Museum) Getty Pubns.

Gardner, Julian & Giotto. Giotto & His Publics: Three Paradigms of Patronage. 2011. (Bernard Berenson Lectures on the Italian Renaissance Delivered at Villa I Tatti Ser.). (Illus.). 256p. 35.00 (978-0-674-05080-8(0)) Harvard Univ. Pr.

Garramuño, Florencia. Modernidades Primitivas: Tango, Samba y Nación. 2007. (Tierra Firme Ser.). (SPA., Illus.). 269p. pap. 13.95 (978-950-557-701-9(X)) Fondo de Cultura Economica USA.

Garrard, Laura. Brice Marden. 3rd ed. 2011. (Painter's Ser.). (Illus.). 200p. pap. 24.00 (978-1-86171-318-6(5)) Crescent Moon Publishing GBR. Dist: NACSCORP, Inc.

Gaspar de Alba, Alicia & López, Alma, eds. Our Lady of Controversy: Alma López's Irreverent Apparition. 2011. (ENG., Illus.). 348p. 55.00 (978-0-292-71992-7(2)); pap. 27.95 (978-0-292-72642-0(2)) Univ. of Texas Pr.

Gayford, Martin. Man with a Blue Scarf: On Sitting for a Portrait by Lucian Freud. 2010. (ENG., Illus.). 256p. 40.00 (978-0-500-23875-2(8), 523875) Thames & Hudson.

Gentry, Alistair. Career Suicide. 2010. 276p. pap. 25.50 (978-1-4461-5292-8(8)) Lulu Enterprises Inc.

Getsy, David J. Rodin: Sex & the Making of Modern Sculpture. 2011. (ENG., Illus.). 240p. 45.00 (978-0-300-16725-2(3)) Yale Univ. Pr.

Geuna, Elena. Zhang Huan: Ashman. 2011. (ENG., Illus.). 160p. 55.00 (978-88-7179-642-0(X), Ore Cultura Srl (Acc)) Antique Collectors' Club GBR. Dist: National Bk. Network.

Ghosh, Mrinal. Sojourns of a Painter: Shyamal Dutta Ray & His Times. (Contemporary Indian Art Ser.). (Illus.). 108p. pap. 30.00 (978-81-85822-86-0(7)) Mapin Publishing Pvt. Ltd IND. Dist: Antique Collectors' Club.

Gibbons, Joan. Contemporary Art & Memory: Images of Recollection & Remembrance. 2008. (ENG., Illus.). 344p. pap. 29.00 (978-1-84511-619-4(4)) I. B. Tauris & Co., Ltd. GBR. Dist: Macmillan.

Gibson, Michael. Redon. 2011. (ENG., Illus.). 96p. pap. 9.99 (978-3-8365-3003-3(1)) TASCHEN DEU. Dist: Ingram Pub. Services.

Gierstberg, Frits & Bool, Flip. Questioning History: Imagining the Past in Contemporary Art. 2009. (ENG., Illus.), 180p. pap. 32.00 (978-90-5662-659-4(0)) NAi Uitgevers / Publishers Stichting NLD. Dist: D.A.P./Distributed Art Pubs.

Gil, Santiago Alcolea & Alcolea i Gil, Santiago. Zurbaran. 2008. (ENG., Illus.). 128p. 34.00 (978-84-343-1172-5(0)) Poligrafa, Ediciones, S. A. ESP. Dist: D.A.P./Distributed Art Pubs.

Gill, Bob. Bob Gill, So Far. 2011. (ENG., Illus.). 304p. 50.00 (978-1-85669-819-1(X)) King, Laurence Publishing GBR. Dist: Hachette Bk. Group.

Gillgren, Peter. Siting Federico Barocci & the Renaissance Aesthetic. 2011. (Visual Culture in Early Modernity Ser.). (Illus.). 342p. 124.95 (978-0-7546-6868-8(1)) Ashgate Publishing Co.

Ginsberg, Mimi & Pensler, Alan. Abraham Manievich. 2012. (ENG., Illus.). 192p. 60.00 (978-1-55595-345-4(X)) Hudson Hills Pr. LLC.

Gledhill, John. Matthew Smith: Catalogue Raisonné of the Oil Paintings. 2009. (Illus.). 312p. 260.00 (978-0-85331-998-6(7), Lund Humphries Pubs.) Ashgate Publishing, Ltd. GBR. Dist: Ashgate Publishing Co.

Glibota, Vladimir & Rozhin, Alezander I. Alexander Rukavishnikov. 2009. (ENG., Illus.). 240p. 70.00 (978-88-6130-987-6(9)) Skira Editore ITA. Dist: Random Hse., Inc.

Glissant, Edouard. Poetic Intention. Stephens, Nathalie, tr. from FRE. 2010. (ENG.). 248p. pap. 16.95 (978-0-9822645-3-9(4)) Nightboat Bks.

Glover, Kaiama L. Haiti Unbound: A Spiralist Challenge to the Postcolonial Canon. 2011. (Liverpool University Press - Contemporary French & Francophone Cultures Ser.). (ENG.). 262p. 95.00 (978-1-84631-499-5(2)) Liverpool Univ. Pr. GBR. Dist: Chicago Distribution Ctr.

Glynn, Eugene. Desperate Necessity: Writings on Art & Creativity in Psychoanalytic Theory. 2008. (Illus.). 104p. 20.00 (978-1-934772-88-1(7)) Periscope Publishing.

Gohr. On Per Kirkeby. 2009. (ENG., Illus.). 128p. 40.00 (978-3-7757-2321-3(8)) Hatje Cantz Verlag GmbH & Co KG DEU. Dist: D.A.P./Distributed Art Pubs.

Goldie, Peter & Schellekens, Elizabeth. Who's Afraid of Conceptual Art? 2009. (Illus.). 160p. (ENG.). (C). pap. 27.95 (978-0-415-42282-6(5)); 100.00 (978-0-415-42281-9(7)) Routledge.

Gordon, Rivca & Gordon, Hayim. Hobbema & Heidegger: On Truth & Beauty. 2008. 150p. (C). 60.95 (978-0-8204-8168-5(8)) Lang, Peter Publishing, Inc.

Gorschluter, Peter, ed. The Fifth Floor: Ideas Taking Space. 2009. (ENG., Illus.). 192p. pap. 59.95 (978-1-84631-204-5(3)) Liverpool Univ. Pr. GBR. Dist: Chicago Distribution Ctr.

Gracia, Jorge J. E. Images of Thought: Philosophical Interpretations of Carlos Estevez's Art. 2009. (SUNY series in Latin American & Iberian Thought & Culture Ser.). (Illus.). 224p. 74.50 (978-0-7914-9379-3(2)) State Univ. of New York Pr.

Gracia, Jorge J. E., et al. Images of Thought: Philosophical Interpretations of Carlos Estevez's Art. 2009. (SUNY Series in Latin American & Iberian Thought & Culture). (Illus.). 224p. pap. 29.95 (978-0-7914-9380-9(6)) State Univ. of New York Pr.

Graf, Arturo. Art of the Devil. 2009. (Temporis Ser.). (ENG., Illus.). 256p. 39.95 (978-1-84484-646-7(6)) Parkstone International GBR. Dist: Ingram Pub. Services.

Graham, Dan. Dan Graham. Kitnick, Alex, ed. 2011. (October Files Ser.). (ENG., Illus.). 232p. (gr. 17). 35.00 (978-0-262-01528-8(5)); pap. 19.95 (978-0-262-51577-1(6)) MIT Pr.

Grant, Catherine, et al, eds. Creative Writing & Art History. 2012. (Art History Special Issues Ser.: 8). (ENG., Illus.). 208p. pap. 39.95 (978-1-4443-5039-5(0), Wiley-Blackwell) Wiley, John & Sons, Inc.

Grant, Kim. Surrealism & the Visual Arts: Theory & Reception. 2012. (ENG., Illus.). 416p. pap. 39.99 (978-1-107-40334-5(0)) Cambridge Univ. Pr.

Grant, Simon, ed. In My View: Personal Reflections on Art by Today's Leading Artists. 2012. (ENG., Illus.). 208p. 40.00 (978-0-500-23896-7(0), 523896) Thames & Hudson.

Greenaway, Peter, text. The Wedding at Cana. 2010. (ENG., Illus.). 92p. pap. 47.50 (978-88-8158-757-5(2)) Charta ITA. Dist: D.A.P./Distributed Art Pubs.

Greene, David B. How to Respond to Strangeness in Art: Four Studies in the Unfamiliar. 2006. (Illus.). 204p. (978-0-7734-5779-9(8)) Mellen, Edwin Pr., The.

Gregori, Mina, et al. The First Medusa: Caravaggio. 2012. (Illus.). 160p. 75.00 (978-88-7439-582-8(5)) 5 Continents ITA. Dist: Abrams.

Gregory, Noel. Turner: In Acrylics. 2011. (Ready to Paint the Masters Ser.). (ENG., Illus.). 88p. pap. 19.95 (978-1-84448-579-6(X)) Search Pr., Ltd. GBR. Dist: Independent Pubs. Group.

Gregory, Sharon. Vasari & the Renaissance Print. 2012. (Visual Culture in Early Modernity Ser.). (Illus.). 384p. 124.95 (978-1-4094-2926-5(1)) Ashgate Publishing Co.

Grenfell, Michael & Hardy, Cheryl. Art Rules: Pierre Bourdieu & the Visual Arts. rev. ed. 2007. (ENG., Illus.). 256p. 109.95 (978-1-84520-233-0(3)); 1p. pap. 29.95 (978-1-84520-234-7(1)) Berg Pubs. GBR. Dist: Macmillan.

Grishin, Sasha. Bruno Leti: Portrait of a Printmaker. 2012. (ENG.). 192p. (C). 89.95 (978-1-921394-71-3(4)) Macmillan Art Publishing AUS. Dist: Brown, David Bk. Co., The.

Grosenick, Uta & Ochs, Alexander, eds. Yin Xiuzhen: Universes in My Universe. 2011. (ENG & GER.). 200p. (978-3-942405-23-2(7)) Die Gestalten Verlag.

Gross, Alex. Discrepancies. 2010. (978-1-58423-426-5(1)) Gingko Pr., Inc.

Gross, Frederick. Diane Arbus's 1960s: Auguries of Experience. 2012. 248p. 75.00 (978-0-8166-7011-6(0)); pap. 24.95 (978-0-8166-7012-3(9)) Univ. of Minnesota Pr.

Gruen, John. Callas Kissed Me... Lenny Too! A Critic's Memoir. 2008. (ENG., Illus.). 376p. 29.95 (978-1-57687-424-0(9)) powerHouse Cultural Entertainment, Inc.

Gruner, Silvia. Silvia Gruner: un Chant D'amour. 2009. (ENG., Illus.). 168p. pap. 35.00 (978-84-92480-44-9(0)) RM Verlag, S.L. ESP. Dist: D.A.P./Distributed Art Pubs.

Guercio, Gabriele & Guercio, G. Art as Existence: The Artist's Monograph & Its Project. 2009. (ENG., Illus.). 392p. (gr. 17). pap. 27.95 (978-0-262-51320-3(X)) MIT Pr.

Guins, Raiford & Candlin, Fiona, eds. The Object Reader. 2009. (In Sight: Visual Culture Ser.). (ENG., Illus.). 576p. pap. 42.95 (978-0-415-45230-4(9)) Routledge.

Guston, P. Writing & Talking. 2010. (Documents of Twentieth-Century Art Ser.). (Illus.). 352p. 65.00 (978-0-520-23509-0(6)) Univ. of California Pr.

Gute, Charles & Prandoni, Alessandro. Magic Line, 1 vol. De Martin, Maria Pia et al, trs. 2007. (ITA, GER & ENG., Illus.). 112p. pap. 39.95 (978-88-8158-632-5(0)) Charta ITA. Dist: D.A.P./Distributed Art Pubs.

Haböck, Almut. Paul Kirnig (1891-1955) 2009. (GER.). 96p. pap. 35.95 (978-3-631-58456-9(3)) Lang, Peter GmbH, Europaischer Verlag der Wissenschaften DEU. Dist: Lang, Peter.

Haemmerli, Thomas & Kung, Max. Hannes Wettstein: Seeking Archetypes. 2011. (FRE, GER & ENG., Illus.). 300p. 85.00 (978-3-03778-265-1(X)) Lars Muller Pubs. CHE. Dist: Prestel Publishing.

Haidu, Rachel. The Absence of Work: Marcel Broodthaers, 1964-1976. 2010. (October Bks.). (ENG., Illus.). 400p. (gr. 17). 36.95 (978-0-262-01450-2(5)) MIT Pr.

Haladyn, Julian Jason. Marcel Duchamp: Étant Donnés. 2010. (One Work Ser.). (ENG., Illus.). 112p. (gr. 17). pap. 16.00 (978-1-84638-059-4(6)) Afterall Publishing GBR. Dist: MIT Pr.

Hall, Jane E. The Art & Embroidery of Jane Hall: Reflections of Nature. 2010. (ENG., Illus.). 128p. pap. 30.00 (978-1-84448-484-3(X)) Search Pr., Ltd. GBR. Dist: Independent Pubs. Group.

Harambourg, Lydia. Helman. 2011. (ENG., Illus.). 64p. 19.95 (978-2-7022-0944-8(0)) Cercle d'Art, Editions FRA. Dist: National Bk. Network.

Harris, Alexandra. Romantic Moderns: English Writers, Artists & the Imagination from Virginia Woolf to John Piper. 2010. (ENG., Illus.). 320p. 40.00 (978-0-500-25171-3(1), 525171) Thames & Hudson.

Harris, Jonathan, ed. Inside the Death Drive: Excess & Apocalypse in the World of the Chapman Brothers. 2010. (Liverpool University Press - Tate Liverpool Critical Forum Ser.). (ENG., Illus.). 240p. pap. 49.95 (978-1-84631-192-5(6)) Liverpool Univ. Pr. GBR. Dist: Chicago Distribution Ctr.

—Value Art Politics: Criticism, Meaning & Interpretation after Postmodernism. 2007. (Liverpool University Press - Value-Art-Politics Ser.). (ENG., Illus.). 320p. 90.00 (978-1-84631-041-6(5)); pap. 40.00 (978-1-84631-042-3(3)) Liverpool Univ. Pr. GBR. Dist: Chicago Distribution Ctr.

Harris, Roy. The Great Debate about Art. 2010. 130p. pap. 12.95 (978-0-9842010-0-6(9)) Prickly Paradigm Pr., LLC.

Harrison, Martin, ed. New Studies: Centenary Essays, 1 vol. 2010. (ENG., Illus.). 272p. 58.00 (978-3-86521-946-6(2)) Steidl, Gerhard Druckerei und Verlag DEU. Dist: Innovative Logistics.

Harrison, Michael. Alan Reynolds. 2011. (Illus.). 192p. 80.00 (978-1-84822-068-3(5), Lund Humphries Pubs.) Ashgate Publishing, Ltd. GBR. Dist: Ashgate Publishing Co.

Harvey, Doug. Heart & Torch: Rick Griffin's Transcendence. 2007. (Illus.). 155p. pap. 29.95 (978-1-58423-279-7(X)) Gingko Pr., Inc.

—Heart & Torch: Rick Griffin's Transcendence. 2007. (978-0-940872-32-5(3)) Laguna Beach Museum of Art.

Haskell, Barbara, ed. Lyonel Feininger: At the Edge of the World. 2011. (ENG., Illus.). 288p. 65.00 (978-0-300-16846-4(2)) Yale Univ. Pr.

Haskell, Naomi. Piero Della Francesca. 2nd ed. 2008. (Sculptors Ser.). (Illus.). 136p. pap. (978-1-86171-161-8(1)) Crescent Moon Publishing.

Hassrick, Peter H., et al. In Contemporary Rhythm: The Art of Ernest L. Blumenschein. 2008. (Charles M. Russell Center Ser. on Art & Photography of the American West Ser.: Vol. 2). (ENG., Illus.). 416p. (C). pap. 34.95 (978-0-8061-3948-7(X)) Univ. of Oklahoma Pr.

Hatch, Kevin & Conner, Bruce. Looking for Bruce Conner. 2012. (October Bks.). (ENG., Illus.). 352p. (gr. 17). 29.95 (978-0-262-01681-0(8)) MIT Pr.

He, Jianping, ed. Gerwin Schmidt. 2008. (New Generation of Design Ser.). (Illus.). 215p. pap. (978-981-245-507-9(8)) Page One Publishing.

—Isidro Ferrer. 2008. (New Generation of Design Ser.). (Illus.). 215p. pap. (978-981-245-510-9(8)) Page One Publishing.

—Jianping He. 2008. (New Generation of Design Ser.). (Illus.). 215p. pap. (978-981-245-509-3(4)) Page One Publishing.

—Laboratoires Cccp = Dr. Leche + Melle Rose. 2008. (New Generation of Design Ser.). (Illus.). 215p. pap. (978-981-245-511-6(6)) Page One Publishing.

—The Master of Design: Niklaus Troxler. 2007. (Master of Design Ser.). (Illus.). 311p. pap. 39.95 (978-981-245-426-3(8)) Page One Publishing SGP. Dist: Gingko Pr., Inc.

—The Master of Design: Pierre Bernard. 2007. (Master of Design Ser.). (Illus.). 309p. pap. 39.95 (978-981-245-427-0(6)) Page One Publishing SGP. Dist: Gingko Pr., Inc.

—The Master of Design: Werner Jeker. 2007. (Master of Design Ser.). (Illus.). 309p. pap. 39.95 (978-981-245-428-7(4)) Page One Publishing SGP. Dist: Gingko Pr., Inc.

Heilingsetzer, Semirah, ed. Thage: Malerei zwischen Konvention und Avantgarde. 2009. (GER.). 159p. 47.95 (978-3-631-58203-9(X)) Lang, Peter GmbH, Europaischer Verlag der Wissenschaften DEU. Dist: Lang, Peter.

Hein, Laura & Jennison, Rebecca, eds. Imagination Without Borders: Feminist Artist Tomiyama Taeko & Social Responsibility. 2010. (Illus.). 164p. 60.00 (978-1-929280-62-9(9)) Univ. of Michigan, Ctr. for Japanese Studies.

—Imagination Without Borders: Feminist Artist Tomiyama Taeko & Social Responsibility. 2010. (Illus.). 164p. pap. 24.00 (978-1-929280-63-6(7)) Univ. of Michigan, Ctr. for Japanese Studies.

Heinrich, Christoph. Monet. 2011. (25 Ser.). (ENG., Illus.). 96p. 14.99 (978-3-8365-3134-4(8)) TASCHEN DEU. Dist: Ingram Pub. Services.

Heiss, Alanna, et al. Judith Murray: From Vibrato to Legato. 2006. (ENG., Illus.). 132p. 50.00 (978-1-890206-07-9(5)) Mapin Publishing Pvt. Ltd IND. Dist: National Bk. Network.

Held, Heinz-Georg, ed. Winckelmann und die Mythologie der Klassik: Narrative Tendenzen in der Ekphrase der Kunstperiode. 2009. (Reihe der Villa Vigoni Ser.).Tr. of Winckelmann & the Mythology of the Neoclassical Age. (GER & ITA.). VI, 264p. 140.00 (978-3-11-173136-0(7)) De Gruyter, Walter Inc.

Held, Heinz Georg, ed. Winckelmann und die Mythologie der Klassik / Winckelmann e i miti del classico: Narrative Tendenzen in der Ekphrase der Kunstperiode / Decrizione d'arte e sviluppi narrativi. 2009. (Reihe der Villa Vigoni Ser.).Tr. of Winckelmann & the Mythology of the Neoclassical Age. (GER & ITA., Illus.). VI, 264p. pap. (978-3-484-67022-8(3)) Verlag Max Niemeyer.

Henderikse, Jan. Jan Henderikse: Acheiropoieta Bilder, nicht von Menschenhand gemacht 1957-2010. 2010. (ENG., Illus.). 216p. 75.00 (978-3-7757-2597-2(0)) Hatje Cantz Verlag GmbH & Co KG DEU. Dist: D.A.P./Distributed Art Pubs.

Henry, Tom & Signorelli, Luca. The Life & Art of Luca Signorelli. 2012. (ENG., Illus.). 472p. 85.00 (978-0-300-17926-2(X)) Yale Univ. Pr.

Hentschel, Martin, ed. Sherrie Levine: Pairs & Posses. 2011. (ENG., Illus.). 96p. 45.00 (978-3-7757-2775-4(2)) Hatje Cantz Verlag GmbH & Co KG DEU. Dist: D.A.P./Distributed Art Pubs.

Herbert, Elizabeth & Snow, John. Art of John Snow. 2010. (Illus.). 220p. pap. 49.95 (978-1-55238-516-6(7)) Univ. of Calgary Pr. CAN. Dist: Michigan State Univ. Pr.

Hertel, Christiane & Günther, Ignaz. Pygmalion in Bavaria: The Sculptor Ignaz Günther & Eighteenth-Century Aesthetic Art Theory. 2011. (ENG.). 344p. 99.95 (978-0-271-03737-0(7)) Pennsylvania State Univ. Pr.

Herz, Ruth. The Art of Justice: The Judge's Perspective. 2012. (ENG., Illus.). 118p. 54.95 (978-1-84946-127-6(9)) Hart Publishing Ltd. GBR. Dist: International Specialized Bk. Services.

Hesign, ed. The Master of Design. 2007. (Illus.). 336p. pap. 39.95 (978-981-245-429-4(2)) Page One Publishing SGP. Dist: Gingko Pr., Inc.

Heß, Gilbert, et al, eds. Raffael als Paradigma: Rezeption, Imagination und Kult im 19. Jahrhundert. 2011.Tr. of Raphael as Paradigm. (GER., Illus.). XXIX, 426p. 168.00 (978-3-11-025562-1(6)) De Gruyter, Walter Inc.

Hill, John. Ken Loach: The Politics of Film & Television. 2011. (ENG., Illus.). 288p. 90.00 (978-1-84457-202-1(1)); 256p. pap. 28.00 (978-1-84457-203-8(X)) BFI Publishing GBR. Dist: Macmillan.

Hiller, Susan & Gallagher, Ann. Susan Hiller. 2011. (ENG., Illus.). 192p. pap. 39.95 (978-1-85437-888-0(0)) Tate Publishing, Ltd. GBR. Dist: Hachette Bk. Group.

Hillier, Mary. Chloe Preston & the Peek-a-Boos. 2006. (ENG., Illus.). 84p. pap. 40.00 (978-0-903685-66-5(3), Richard Dennis Pubns. Di) Antique Collectors' Club GBR. Dist: National Bk. Network.

Hinrichs, Bruce H. Film & Art. 2007. (ENG.). per. 24.00 (978-0-9790129-1-4(0)) Ellipse Publishing Co.

Hinrichs, Ernst & Zernack, Klaus, eds. Daniel Chodowiecki (1726-1801) Kupferstecher, Illustrator, Kaufmann. (Wolfenbatteler Studien zur Aufklärung Ser.).Tr. of Daniel Chodowiecki (1726-1801). Engraver, genre painter, Merchant. (GER.). X, 265p. 165.00 (978-3-11-179461-7(X)) De Gruyter, Walter Inc.

Hinton, Jack, et al. Encountering Genius: Houdon's Portraits of Benjamin Franklin. 2011. (978-0-87633-225-2(4)) Philadelphia Museum of Art.

—Encountering Genius: Houdon's Portraits of Benjamin Franklin. 2011. (Illus.). 92p. pap. 25.00 (978-0-300-14164-1(5)) Yale Univ. Pr.

Hirakawa, Kayo. The Pictorialization of Dürer's Drawings in Northern Europe in the Sixteenth & Seventh Centuries. 2009. (Illus.). 178p. pap. (978-3-03911-725-3(4)) Lang, Peter.

Hirsch, Andreas & Hundertwasser, Friedensreich. Hundertwasser: Die Kunst des grünen Weges. The Art of the Green Path. 2011. (ENG., Illus.). 224p. 35.00 (978-3-7913-5156-8(7)) Prestel Publishing.

Hobbs, Robert. André Ethier: André Ethier's Knowing Naiveté. 2007. (Illus.). 48p. pap. 25.00 (978-0-9779002-1-3(5)) Derek Eller Gallery, Inc.

Hobbs, Robert & Hobbs;, Robert. Milton Avery. 2007. (ENG., Illus.). 264p. 85.00 (978-0-933920-95-8(4)) Hudson Hills Pr. LLC.

Hodge, Susie. Renoir: His Life & Works in 500 Images. 2012. (ENG., Illus.). 256p. 35.00 (978-0-7548-2347-6(4)) Anness Publishing GBR. Dist: National Bk. Network.

Hoeniger, Cathleen Sara & Raphael. The Afterlife of Raphael's Paintings. 2010. (ENG., Illus.). 456p. 95.00 (978-0-521-19694-9(9)) Cambridge Univ. Pr.

Hoffmann, Leni. leni hoffmann: RGB: Künstierbuch. 2010. (GER & ENG., Illus.). 144p. pap. 59.95 (978-3-8321-9290-7(5)) DuMont DEU. Dist: D.A.P./Distributed Art Pubs.

Hollein, Max. Julian Schnabel. Moos, David & Schnabel, Julian, eds. 2009. (ENG., Illus.). 432p. 90.00 (978-88-6130-317-1(X)) Skira Editore ITA. Dist: Random Hse., Inc.

Hollmann, Eckhard. The Blue Rider. 2011. (Illus.). 192p. pap. 19.95 (978-3-7913-4528-4(1)) Prestel Publishing.

Holman, Martin. Richard Rome. 2011. (Illus.). 96p. 60.00 (978-1-84822-081-2(2), Lund Humphries Pubs.) Ashgate Publishing, Ltd. GBR. Dist: Ashgate Publishing Co.

Holman, Valerie & Ferran, Denise. The Sculpture of F. E. Mcwilliam. 2012. (British Sculptors & Sculpture Ser.). (Illus.). 192p. 90.00 (978-1-84822-049-2(9), Lund Humphries Pubs.) Ashgate Publishing, Ltd. GBR. Dist: Ashgate Publishing Co.

Holzwarth, Hans Werner, ed. Christopher Wool. 2009. (FRE, GER & ENG., Illus.). 500p. 1500.00 (978-3-8228-0851-1(2)) TASCHEN DEU. Dist: Ingram Pub. Services.

—Jeff Koons. 2009. (ENG., Illus.). 591p. 69.99 (978-3-8365-0328-0(X)) TASCHEN DEU. Dist: Ingram Pub. Services.

Homburg, Cornelia, ed. Vincent Van Gogh: Timeless Country - Modern City. 2011. (ENG., Illus.). 280p. 75.00 (978-88-572-0825-1(7)) Skira Editore ITA. Dist: Random Hse., Inc.

Hoptman, Laura, ed. Brion Gysin. 2010. (ENG., Illus.). 192p. 39.95 (978-1-85894-521-7(6)) Merrell Pubs. Ltd. GBR. Dist: Perseus Distribution.

Hozee, Robert, ed. Raoul De Keyser: The Things I see. 2011. (ENG & DUT., Illus.). 96p. pap. 42.00 (978-94-6117-010-1(6)) Exhibitions International BEL. Dist: Innovative Logistics.

Hub, Bertold & Polalli, Angeliki, eds. Reconstructing Francesco Di Giorgio Architect. 2011. 212p. pap. 56.95 (978-3-631-57584-0(X)) Lang, Peter GmbH, Europaischer Verlag der Wissenschaften DEU. Dist: Lang, Peter.

Hudson, Hugh. Jan Van Eyck. 2008. 328p. pap. (978-3-639-07126-9(3)) VDM Verlag Dr. Mueller e.K.

Hudson, Suzanne Perling. Robert Ryman: Used Paint. 2009. (October Bks.). (ENG., Illus.). 336p. (gr. 17). 41.95 (978-0-262-01280-5(4)) MIT Pr.

Hull, Roger. Harry Widman: Image, Myth, & Modernism. 2009. (ENG., Illus.). 110p. pap. 24.95 (978-1-930957-60-2(2)) Ford, Hallie Museum of Art.

Humesky, Assya. Mirtala Pylypenko: Skulptor I Poet. 2007. (UKR., Illus.). 135p. (978-966-658-093-4(4)) Misioner.

Hung, Wu, text. Making History: Wu Hung on Contemporary Art. 2009. (ENG., Illus.). 278p. 50.00 (978-988-99617-0-1(9)) Timezone 8 Ltd. HKG. Dist: D.A.P./Distributed Art Pubs.

Huppauf, Bernd. The Dynamics & Performance of Imagination: Images Between the Visible & the Invisible. 2009. (Routledge Research in Cultural & Media Studies). (ENG., Illus.). 386p. (C). 136.00 (978-0-415-99093-6(9)) Routledge.

Husslein-Arco, Agnes & Kallir, Jane. Egon Schiele: Self-Portraits & Portraits. 2011. (Illus.). 300p. 60.00 (978-3-7913-5109-4(5)) Prestel Publishing.

Illetschko, Georgia. Michelangelo. 2010. (Illus.). 160p. pap. 19.95 (978-3-7913-4472-0(2)) Prestel Publishing.

Indych-Lopez, Anna. Muralism without Walls: Rivera, Orozco, & Siqueiros in the United States, 1927-1940. 2009. (Pitt Illuminations Ser.). (ENG., Illus.). 352p. (C). 45.00 (978-0-8229-4384-6(0)) Univ. of Pittsburgh Pr.

Inglis, Erik. Jean Fouquet & the Invention of France: Art & Nation after the Hundred Years War. 2011. (Illus.). 320p. 75.00 (978-0-300-13443-8(6)) Yale Univ. Pr.

Irish, Sharon & Lacy, Suzanne. Suzanne Lacy. 2010. (ENG., Illus.). 288p. pap. 25.00 (978-0-8166-6096-4(4)) Univ. of Minnesota Pr.

—Suzanne Lacy: Spaces Between. 2010. (Illus.). 288p. 75.00 (978-0-8166-6095-7(6)) Univ. of Minnesota Pr.

Israel, Mei-Ling. The World as Light: An Introduction to the Art of Adi Da Samraj. 2007. (Illus.). 127p. per. (978-1-57097-230-0(3)) Dawn Horse Pr.

Iversen, Margaret, et al. Still Standing: Antony Gormley at the Hermitage. 2011. (ENG., Illus.). 128p. 40.00 (978-1-906257-09-5(4)) Fontanka GBR. Dist: National Bk. Network.

Ivey, Paul Eli, et al. Barbara Rogers: The Imperative of Beauty. 2012. (ENG., Illus.). 224p. 60.00 (978-1-55595-347-8(6)) Hudson Hills Pr. LLC.

Jacobs, Steven. Raoul De Keyser: Retour, 1964-2006, 1 vol. 2008. (DUT & ENG., Illus.). 256p. 90.00 (978-90-5544-709-1(9)) Ludion BEL. Dist: D.A.P./Distributed Art Pubs.

Jaffe, David. Rubens's Massacre of the Innocents in the Thomson Collection. 2009. (Illus.). 128p. pap. 50.00 (978-1-903470-81-7(1)) Holberton, Paul Publishing GBR. Dist: Casemate Pubs. & Bk. Distributors, LLC.

Jahn, Andrea. Louise Bourgeois - Subversionen des Koerpers: Die Kunst der 40er bis 70er Jahre. (GER., Illus.). 270p. (978-3-496-01185-9(8)) Reimer, Dietrich.

Jahn, Marisa, ed. Byproduct: On the Excess of Embedded Art Practices. 2011. (ENG., Illus.). 192p. pap. 29.95 (978-0-920397-51-0(4)) Y Y Z Artists Outlet CAN. Dist: D.A.P./Distributed Art Pubs.

Jakubowska, Agata, ed. Alina Szapocznikow: Awkward Objects. 2011. (ENG., Illus.). 288p. pap. 29.00 (978-83-924044-6-0(7)) Muzeum Sztuki Nowoczesnej w Warszawie POL. Dist: Chicago Distribution Ctr.

Jenkins, David Fraser. Paul Nash: The Elements. 2010. (ENG., Illus.). 168p. pap. 39.95 (978-1-85759-619-9(6)) Scala, Editions FRA. Dist: National Bk. Network.

Jennings, Patricia & Ausherman, Maria. Georgia O'Keeffe's Hawai'i. 2012. (ENG.). 124p. 35.00 (978-1-935646-10-5(9)) Koa Bks., Inc.

Jeppesen, Travis. Disorientations: Art on the Margins of the Contemporary. 2008. 388p. pap. (978-0-9552829-8-0(5)) Social Disease.

John Young: Silhouettes & Polychromes. pap. (978-1-86395-399-3(X)) Bookman Pr.

Johnson, Christopher D. Memory, Metaphor, & Aby Warburg's Atlas of Images. 2012. (Signale: Modern German Letters, Cultures, & Thought Ser.). (ENG.). 288p. pap. 35.00 (978-0-8014-7742-3(5)) Cornell Univ. Pr.

Johnson, Maureen & Johnson, Douglas. Art Models 4: Life Nude Photos for the Visual Arts. 2009. (Art Models Ser.). (ENG., Illus.). 128p. 36.95 (978-0-9816249-3-6(6)) Live Model Bks.

Jones, Anny Brooksbank. Visual Culture in Spain & Mexico. 2011. (ENG., Illus.). 224p. pap. 25.95 (978-0-7190-5679-6(9)) Manchester Univ. Pr. GBR. Dist: Macmillan.

Jones, Caroline A. Eyesight Alone: Clement Greenberg's Modernism & the Bureaucratization of the Senses. (Illus.). 544p. 2008. pap. 35.00 (978-0-226-40953-5(8)) 2006. 47.50 (978-0-226-40951-1(1)) Univ. of Chicago Pr.

Jones, W. Gareth & Tolstoy, Leo. Tolstoy: What Is Art? 2011. (Russian Texts). (ENG & RUS.). 284p. pap. 19.95 (978-1-85399-381-7(6)) Bristol Classical Pr. GBR. Dist: International Publishers Marketing.

Journal Editorial Collecive, Sr. Journal of Aesthetics & Protest #5. 2007. (Illus.). 122p. pap. 11.00 (978-0-9791377-1-6(3)) Journal of Aesthetics and Protest Pr./Herbst.

Judovitz, Dalia & Duchamp, Marcel. Drawing on Art: Duchamp & Company. 2010. (Illus.). 288p. 75.00 (978-0-8166-6529-7(X)); (ENG., pap. 24.95 (978-0-8166-6530-3(3)) Univ. of Minnesota Pr.

Jungmann, Burglind, et al, eds. Shifting Paradigms in East Asian Visual Culture: A Festschrift in Honour of Lothar Ledderose. 2012. (ENG.). 400p. 89.00 (978-3-496-01440-9(7)) Reimer, Dietrich DEU. Dist: Independent Pubs. Group.

Kadish, Mortimer R. & Hewlett, Barry S. Reason & Controversy in the Arts. 2010. (ENG.). 293p. pap. 29.95 (978-1-4128-1123-1(6)) Transaction Pubs.

Kapoor, Anish. Anish Kapoor: Memory. 2009. (Illus.). 127p. (978-0-89207-395-5(0)) Guggenheim, Solomon R. Museum.

—Memory. 2008. (ENG., Illus.). 120p. 45.00 (978-0-89207-378-8(0)) Guggenheim, Solomon R. Museum.

Karam, Savo. Ameen Fares Rihani. 2011. 308p. pap. (978-3-8443-1513-4(6)) Lambert Academic Publishing.

Karcher, Eva & Walther, Ingo F. Dix. 2010. (25 Ser.). (ENG.). 224p. 14.99 (978-3-8365-2485-8(6)) TASCHEN DEU. Dist: Ingram Pub. Services.

Karlstrom, Paul J. & Karlstrom, Ann. Peter Selz: Sketches of a Life in Art. 2012. (ENG., Illus.). 321p. 34.95 (978-0-520-26935-4(7)) Univ. of California Pr.

Katzeff, Miriam, ed. Real Life Magazine: Selected Writings & Projects, 1979-1994, 1 vol. 2007. (ENG., Illus.). 288p. per. 30.00 (978-0-9788697-0-0(2)) Primary Information.

Kelley, Mike. On the Beyond: A Conversation between Mike Kelley, Jim Shaw & John C. Welchman. 2011. (Kunst und Architektur im Gespräch Art & Architecture in Discussion(closed) Ser.). (Illus.). 128p. pap. 39.95 (978-3-7091-0260-2(X), 370910260X) Springer Wien AUT. Dist: Springer.

Kellman, Tila L. Figuring Redemption: Resighting My Self in the Art of Michael Snow. 2010. (ENG.). 222p. (C). pap. 39.95 (978-1-55458-249-5(0)) Wilfrid Laurier Univ. Pr. CAN. Dist: Univ. of Toronto Pr.

Kemp, Martin. Leonardo. rev. ed. 2011. (ENG., Illus.). 320p. pap. 17.95 (978-0-19-958335-5(8)) Oxford Univ. Pr., Inc.

—Leonardo Da Vinci: The Marvellous Works of Nature & Man. 2007. (ENG., Illus.). 416p. pap. 29.95 (978-0-19-920778-7(X)) Oxford Univ. Pr., Inc.

Kendall, Richard & Devonyar, Jill. Degas & the Art of Japan. 2007. (ENG., Illus.). 112p. per. 24.95 (978-0-300-12633-4(6)) Yale Univ. Pr.

Kermode, Frank. Forms of Attention: Botticelli & Hamlet. 2011. (ENG.). 112p. pap. 16.00 (978-0-226-43175-8(4)) Univ. of Chicago Pr.

Kessler, Stephen. The Tolstoy of the Zulus. 2011. 368p. pap. 20.00 (978-0-9795285-8-3(5)) El Leon Literary Arts.

Kettler, Wilfried. Der Berner Totentanz des Niklaus Manuel: Philologische, epigraphische sowie historische Überlegungen zu einem Sprach- und Kunstdenkmal der frühen Neuzeit. 2009. (GER., Illus.). 272p. (978-3-03911-817-5(X)) Lang, Peter.

Killiam, Marie-Therese. The End of Art: A Comparative Analysis of French Postmodern Art Theorists. 2011. x, 89p. pap. (978-1-86335-894-1(3)) Common Ground Publishing Pty, Ltd.

Kim, Sojin. Chicano Graffiti & Murals: The Neighborhood Art of Peter Quezada. 2010. (Folk Art & Artists Ser.). (ENG.). 72p. (C). pap. 30.00 (978-1-61703-066-6(X)) Univ. Pr. of Mississippi.

King, Averil. Paula Modersohn-Becker. 2009. (ENG., Illus.). 144p. (978-1-85149-586-3(X), Antique Collectors Club Dist) Antique Collectors' Club.

King, Elliott H., et al, contrib. by. Salvador Dali: The Late Work. 2010. (Illus.). 176p. 39.95 (978-0-300-16828-0(4)) Yale Univ. Pr.

King-Hammond, Leslie & Lee-Smith, Hughie. Hughie Lee-Smith. 2010. (David C. Driskell Ser. of African American Art Ser.: Vol. 8). (Illus.). 124p. 35.00 (978-0-7649-5351-4(6)) Pomegranate Communications, Inc.

King, Ross. Leonardo & the Last Supper. 2012. (ENG., Illus.). 352p. 28.00 (978-0-8027-1705-4(5)) Walker & Co.

Kinley, Catherine. Peter Kinley. 2010. (Illus.). 128p. 70.00 (978-1-84822-005-8(7), Lund Humphries Pubs.) Ashgate Publishing, Ltd. GBR. Dist: Ashgate Publishing Co.

Kirby-Welch, David & Lee, John Morton. Thomas Bush Hardy, 1842-1897: A Master Painter of Marine & Coastal Watercolours. 2009. (ENG., Illus.). 224p. (978-1-85149-597-9(5), Antique Collectors Club Dist) Antique Collectors' Club.

Kirchner, Ernst Ludwig. Ernst Ludwig Kirchner: Art to Hear. 2010. (ENG., Illus.). 44p. 30.00 (978-3-7757-2555-2(5)) Hatje Cantz Verlag GmbH & Co KG DEU. Dist: D.A.P./Distributed Art Pubs.

Kirtley, Susan E. & Barry, Lynda. Lynda Barry: Girlhood Through the Looking Glass. 2012. (Great Comics Artists Ser.). (ENG., Illus.). 208p. 65.00 (978-1-61703-234-9(4)); pap. 25.00 (978-1-61703-235-6(2)) Univ. Pr. of Mississippi.

Kitchen, Denis & Buhle, Paul. The Art of Harvey Kurtzman: The Mad Genius of Comics. 2009. (ENG., Illus.). 256p. 45.00 (978-0-8109-7296-4(4)) Abrams.

Kleeblatt, Norman L. Action/Abstraction: Pollock, de Kooning, & American Art, 1940-1976. Kleeblatt, Norman L., ed. 2009. (ENG., Illus.). 344p. pap. 50.00 (978-0-300-13920-4(9)) Yale Univ. Pr.

Klein, Yves. Yves Klein: With the Void, Full Powers. 2010. (ENG., Illus.). 352p. 65.00 (978-0-935640-94-6(0)) Walker Art Ctr.

—Yves Klein: Expressing the Immaterial. 2011. (ENG., Illus.). 208p. 31.00 (978-2-916275-74-1(6)) Dilecta, Editions FRA. Dist: D.A.P./Distributed Art Pubs.

Klein, Yves, et al. Yves Klein: With the Void, Full Powers. 2010. (Illus.). 352p. (978-3-7757-2649-8(7)) Walker Art Ctr.

Kleinbub, Christian K. Vision & the Visionary in Raphael. 2011. (ENG.). 240p. 90.00 (978-0-271-03704-2(0)) Pennsylvania State Univ. Pr.

Klimt. (SPA.). 256p. (978-1-4054-1494-4(4)) Parragon, Inc.

Knowles, Kim. A Cinematic Artist: The Films of Man Ray. 2009. (Cultural Interactions: Studies in the Relationship between the Arts Ser.). (Illus.). 342p. 61.95 (978-3-03911-884-7(6)) Lang, Peter AG GBR. Dist: Lang, Peter.

Knox, Giles. The Late Paintings of Velázquez: Theorizing Painterly Performance. 2009. (Visual Culture in Early Modernity Ser.). (Illus.). 208p. 119.95 (978-0-7546-6677-6(8)) Ashgate Publishing Co.

Kochhar-Lindgren, Gray. Philosophy, Art, & the Specters of Jacques Derrida. 2011. 238p. (978-1-60497-788-2(4)) Cambria Pr.

Krauss, Rosalind E. Perpetual Inventory. 2010. (October Bks.). (ENG., Illus.). 320p. (gr. 17). 31.95 (978-0-262-01380-2(0)) MIT Pr.

Krempel, Ulrich, text. Gia Edzgveradze: Welcome Foam - Farewell Human. 2010. (ENG., Illus.). 288p. pap. 60.00 (978-3-7757-2396-1(X)) Hatje Cantz Verlag GmbH & Co KG DEU. Dist: D.A.P./Distributed Art Pubs.

Kroiz, Lauren. Creative Composites: Modernism, Race, & the Stieglitz Circle. 2012. (Phillips Book Prize Ser.). (ENG.). 271p. 49.95 (978-0-520-27249-1(8)) Univ. of California Pr.

Krystof, Doris. Amedeo Modigliani. 25th ed. 2009. (ENG., Illus.). 96p. 14.99 (978-3-8365-1271-8(8)) TASCHEN DEU. Dist: Ingram Pub. Services.

Kuhl, Isabel. Egon Schiele. 2010. (Illus.). 128p. pap. 14.95 (978-3-7913-4491-1(9)) Prestel Publishing.

Kuhn, Heinrich, photos by. Heinrich Kuhn: Perfect Photography. 2010. (ENG., Illus.). 280p. 75.00 (978-3-7757-2569-9(5)) Hatje Cantz Verlag GmbH & Co KG DEU. Dist: D.A.P./Distributed Art Pubs.

Kürtös, Karl. Henri Michaux et le Visuel: Ekphrasis, Mimésis, Énergie. 2009. (FRE.). 237p. pap. (978-3-03911-685-0(1)) Lang, Peter.

Kuznetsov, Alexander. Pavel Tchelitchew: Metamorphoses. 2012. (ENG., Illus.). 320p. 95.00 (978-3-89790-368-5(7)) Arnoldsche Art Pubs. DEU. Dist: Antique Collectors' Club.

Lack, H. Walter & Dressendorfer, Werner. The Most Beautiful Flowers. 2009. (ENG.). 300p. 69.99 (978-3-8365-0515-4(0)) TASCHEN DEU. Dist: Ingram Pub. Services.

Lajer-Burcharth, Ewa. Chardin Material. Birnbaum, Daniel & Graw, Isabelle, eds. 2011. (ENG., Illus.). 69p. pap. 19.95 (978-1-934105-47-4(3)) Sternberg Pr.

Lamb-Faffelberger, Margarete. Staging Export: Valie zu Ehren. 2010. (Austrian Culture Ser.). (GER.). 240p. (C). 75.95 (978-1-4331-1061-0(X)) Lang, Peter Publishing, Inc.

Lambirth, Adrew & Wardell, Gareth. Barbara Rae (Limited Edition) 2008. (Illus.). 192p. 600.00 (978-0-85331-991-7(X), Lund Humphries Pubs.) Ashgate Publishing, Ltd. GBR. Dist: Ashgate Publishing Co.

Lambirth, Andrew. John Armstrong: The Complete Paintings. 2010. (ENG., Illus.). 240p. 70.00 (978-0-85667-668-0(3)) Wilson, Philip Pubs., Ltd. GBR. Dist: Macmillan.

—John Hoyland Ra. 2010. (ENG., Illus.). 160p. 65.00 (978-1-906509-07-1(7)) Unicorn Pr., London GBR. Dist: National Bk. Network.

—Margaret Mellis. 2010. (Illus.). 200p. 80.00 (978-1-84822-048-5(0), Lund Humphries Pubs.) Ashgate Publishing, Ltd. GBR. Dist: Ashgate Publishing Co.

—Rose Hilton: Something to Keep the Balance. 2009. 176p. (Illus.). 80.00 (978-1-84822-008-9(1)); 400.00 (978-1-84822-025-6(1)) Ashgate Publishing, Ltd. GBR. (Lund Humphries Pubs.). Dist: Ashgate Publishing Co.

Lambirth, Andrew & Wardell, Gareth. Barbara Rae. 2008. (Illus.). 192p. 80.00 (978-0-85331-990-0(1), Lund Humphries Pubs.) Ashgate Publishing, Ltd. GBR. Dist: Ashgate Publishing Co.

Lampert, Catherine, et al, texts. Flavio Garciandia: I Insulted Flavio Garciandia in Havana. 2009. (ENG., Illus.). 410p. pap. 55.00 (978-84-7506-843-5(X)) Turner, Ediciones S.A. ESP. Dist: D.A.P./Distributed Art Pubs.

Lampert, Catherine & Kendall, Richard. Euan Uglow: The Complete Paintings. 2007. (ENG., Illus.). 352p. 125.00 (978-0-300-12349-4(3)) Yale Univ. Pr.

Lang, Karen. Chaos & Cosmos: On the Image in Aesthetics & Art History. 2006. (Illus.). 320p. 68.95 (978-0-8014-4166-0(8)); 295p. per. 26.95 (978-0-8014-8855-9(9)) Cornell Univ. Pr.

Lauterbach, Iris. Antoine Watteau 1684-1721. 2008. (Basic Art Ser.). (ENG., Illus.). 96p. pap. 9.99 (978-3-8228-5318-4(6)) TASCHEN DEU. Dist: Ingram Pub. Services.

Lavin, Irving. Genius of the Baroque, 3 vols. 2007. (ENG., Illus.). 651p. (C). 300.00 (978-1-899828-39-5(7)) Pindar Pr. GBR. Dist: Brown, David Bk. Co., The.

Lawrence, James & Richardson, John. Robert Rauschenberg. 2011. (Illus.). 256p. 75.00 (978-3-7913-4557-4(5)) Prestel Publishing.

Leabhart, Thomas. The Decroux Sourcebook. Chamberlain, Franc, ed. 2009. (ENG., Illus.). 210p. pap. 34.95 (978-0-415-47800-7(6)) Routledge.

Leca, Benedict, ed. Thomas Gainsborough & the Modern Woman. 2010. (Illus.). 196p. pap. (978-0-931537-37-0(1)) Cincinnati Art Museum.

Leonardo. Leonardo & Painting. Taglialagamba, Sara, ed. 2010. (Leonardo Collection). (ENG., Illus.). 152p. (C). pap. 24.95 (978-88-95686-24-0(1)) Cartei, C.B. & Bianchi Edizioni ITA. Dist: Brown, David Bk. Co., The.

Leppanen-Guerra, Analisa. Children's Stories & 'Child-Time' in the Works of Joseph Cornell & the Trans-Atlantic Avant-Garde. 2011. (Ashgate Studies in Surrealism Ser.). (Illus.). 286p. 99.95 (978-1-4094-0156-8(1)) Ashgate Publishing Co.

Levy, Aaron & Dimitrijevic, Braco. Tractatus Post-Historicus (1976) Braco Dimitrijevic. 2009. pap. (978-0-9815409-5-5(3)) Slought Foundation.

Levy, Ellen. Criminal Ingenuity: Moore, Cornell, Ashbery, & the Struggle Between the Arts, 1 vol. 2011. (Modernist Literature & Culture Ser.). (ENG., Illus.). 304p. 49.95 (978-0-19-974635-4(4)) Oxford Univ. Pr., Inc.

Levy, Evonne, et al, eds. Bernini's Biographies: Critical Essays. 2007. (ENG., Illus.). 376p. 65.00 (978-0-271-02901-6(3)) Pennsylvania State Univ. Pr.

Liedtke, Walter A. The Milkmaid by Johannes Vermeer. 2009. 9.95 (978-1-58839-344-9(5)) Metropolitan Museum of Art, The.

Lin, Mu. Fu Baoshi Ping Zhuan: The Comments of Fu Baoshi. 2009. (CHI., Illus.). (978-7-80725-988-6(4)) Shanghai Calligraphy and Painting Publishing Hse.

Lin, Xiaoping. Children of Marx & Coca-Cola: Chinese Avant-Garde Art & Independent Cinema. 2009. (Illus.). 312p. (C). 47.00 (978-0-8248-3336-7(8)) Univ. of Hawaii Pr.

Ling, Averil & King, Averil. Isaak Levitan: Lyrical Landscape. 2011. (ENG., Illus.). 160p. 75.00 (978-1-85149-645-7(9)) Antique Collectors' Club.

Lingo, Estelle. Francois Duquesnoy & the Greek Ideal. 2007. (Illus.). 240p. 75.00 (978-0-300-12483-5(X)) Yale Univ. Pr.

Lippy, Tod, ed. Esopus 16. 2011. (ENG., Illus.). 172p. pap. 14.00 (978-0-9815745-5-4(6)) Esopus Foundation Ltd.

Lippy, Tod, ed. Esopus 17. 2011. (ENG., Illus.). 172p. pap. 14.00 (978-0-9815745-6-1(4)) Esopus Foundation Ltd.

Lister, Kenneth R., text. Paul Kane, the Artist: Wilderness to Studio. 2010. (ENG.). 416p. 75.00 (978-0-88854-480-3(4)) Royal Ontario Museum CAN. Dist: Univ. of Toronto Pr.

Little, Carl. The Art of Dahlov Ipcar. 2010. 128p. 50.00 (978-0-89272-809-1(4)) Down East Bks.

Little, Carl & Hopper, Edward. Edward Hopper's New England. 2nd rev. ed. 2011. (Illus.). 88p. 29.95 (978-0-7649-5648-9(8)) Pomegranate Communications, Inc.

Livingstone, Marco. Peter Blake: One Man Show. (Illus.). 240p. 2011. pap. 50.00 (978-1-84822-015-7(4)) 2009. 1000.00 (978-1-84822-039-3(1)) Ashgate Publishing, Ltd. GBR. (Lund Humphries Pubs.). Dist: Ashgate Publishing Co.

Lobel, Michael, et al. James Rosenquist: Pop Art, Politics, & History in the 1960s. 2009. (ENG., Illus.). 240p. 55.00 (978-0-520-25303-2(5)) Univ. of California Pr.

Long, Phil. Elizabeth Blackadder. 2012. (ENG., Illus.). 112p. 45.00 (978-0-300-17900-2(6)) Yale Univ. Pr.

Luchinat, Cristina Acidini. Michelangelo: Sculptor. 2010. (ENG., Illus.). 320p. pap. 39.95 (978-88-7179-640-6(3), Ore Cultura Srl (Acc)) Antique Collectors' Club GBR. Dist: National Bk. Network.

Lyon, Christopher. Nancy Spero: The Work. 2010. (Illus.). 312p. 85.00 (978-3-7913-4416-4(1)) Prestel Publishing.

Lyotard, Jean-Francois. Les Transformateurs Duchamp/Duchamp's TRANS/formers. Parret, Herman, ed. 2011. (Jean-François Lyotard: Writings on Contemporary Art & Artists Ser.). 256p. 49.50 (978-90-5867-790-7(7)) Leuven Univ. Pr. BEL. Dist: Cornell Univ. Pr.

Mabuchi, Aiko, ed. Mabuchi: William Anderson: the Pictorial Arts of Japan: Western sources on japanese art & japonism, Series 4. 2008. 2700p. 825.00 (978-4-86166-028-3(9)) Synapse, Edition JPN. Dist: Taylor & Francis Group.

MacDonald, Heather, text. Stormy Skies, Calm Waters: Vernet's Lansdowne Landscapes. 2011. (Illus.). 48p. pap. 19.95 (978-0-936227-00-9(1)) Dallas Museum of Art.

Mack, Heinz & text. Heinz Mack: Licht der ZERO-Zeit. 2010. (ENG., Illus.). 152p. 49.50 (978-3-86678-334-8(5)) Kerber Verlag DEU. Dist: D.A.P./Distributed Art Pubs.

MacKay, E. Anne. Tradition & Originality: A Study of Exekias. 2011. (Bar S Ser.). (ENG., Illus.). 2092p. (C). pap. 187.50 (978-1-4073-0568-4(9)) British Archaeological Reports Ltd. GBR. Dist: Brown, David Bk. Co., The.

MacLean, Hope. The Shaman's Mirror: Visionary Art of the Huichol. 2011. (ENG., Illus.). 292p. 50.00 (978-0-292-72376-9(X)) Univ. of Texas Pr.

Mactaggart, Allister. The Film Paintings of David Lynch: Challenging Film Theory. 2010. (Illus.). 203p. pap. 25.00 (978-1-84150-332-5(0)) Intellect, Ltd. GBR. Dist: Chicago Distribution Ctr.

Maepas, William. Andy goldsworthy in America. 2010. (Illus.). 344p. 60.00 (978-1-86171-250-9(2)) Crescent Moon Publishing GBR. Dist: NACSCORP, Inc.

Main, Marisa Jones. The Language of Art. 2008. 92p. pap. (978-3-8364-2721-0(4)) VDM Verlag Dr. Mueller e.K.

Majumdar, et al. Paritosh Sen: In Retrospect Mansi. (Contemporary Indian Art Ser.). (Illus.). 164p. pap. 40.00 (978-81-85822-93-8(X)) Mapin Publishing Pvt. Ltd IND. Dist: Antique Collectors' Club.

Makart, Hans, et al. Hans Makart: Painter of the Senses. 2011. (ENG., Illus.). 256p. 49.95 (978-3-7913-5151-3(5)) Prestel Publishing.

Malpas, William. Andy Goldsworthy in America. 2nd ed. 2010. (Sculptors Ser.). (Illus.). 336p. pap. 40.00 (978-1-86171-304-9(5)) Crescent Moon Publishing GBR. Dist: NACSCORP, Inc.

—Andy goldsworthy in Close-up. 4th ed. 2010. (Sculptors Ser.). (Illus.). 292p. pap. 40.00 (978-1-86171-293-6(6)) Crescent Moon Publishing GBR. Dist: NACSCORP, Inc.

Mangini, Shirley. Maruja Mallo & the Spanish Avant-Garde. 2010. (Ashgate Studies in Surrealism Ser.). (Illus.). 272p. 119.95 *(978-0-7546-6932-6(7))* Ashgate Publishing Co.

Marini, Francesca & Marini, F. Modigliani. 2009. (ENG., Illus.). 96p. pap. 8.99 *(978-88-572-0045-3(0))* Skira Editore ITA. Dist: Random Hse., Inc.

Marling, Karal Ann & Heimann, Jim. The Very Stuff of the American Dream. 2010. (25 Ser.). (ENG., Illus.). 96p. 14.99 *(978-3-8365-2352-3(3))* TASCHEN DEU. Dist: Ingram Pub. Services.

Masi, Alessandro. L'occhio Del Critico: Storia Dell'arte in Italia Tra Otto e Novecento. 2009. (ITA.). 251p. *(978-88-8427-163-1(0))* Vallecchi.

Masselos, Jim, ed. The Great Empires of Asia. 2010. (ENG.). 240p. 34.95 *(978-0-520-26859-3(8))* Univ. of California Pr.

Massing, Jean-Michel. Studies in Imagery. 2007. (FRE & ENG., Illus.). 446p. (C). 300.00 *(978-1-899828-98-2(2))* Pindar Pr. GBR. Dist: Brown, David Bk. Co., The.

Mathieu, Marianne. Berthe Morisot. 2012. (ENG., Illus.). 264p. pap. 50.00 ***(978-0-300-18201-9(5))*** Yale Univ. Pr.

Mathieu, Pierre-Louis. Gustave Moreau: The Assembler of Dreams. Penwarden, Charles, tr. from FRE. 2010. (Pocket Colour Ser.). (ENG., Illus.). 192p. pap. 27.50 *(978-2-86770-194-8(5))* ACR Edition FRA. Dist: Antique Collectors' Club.

Matt, Gerald, text. Assume Astrid Vivid Focus: Open Call. 2007. (GER & ENG., Illus.). 100p. pap. 12.00 *(978-3-938821-88-6(4))* Verlag fur Moderne Kunst DEU. Dist: D.A.P./Distributed Art Pubs.

Max, Gabriel Cornelius von. Gabriel Von Max, 1 vol. Danzker, Jo-Anne Birnie, ed. 2011. (ENG., Illus.). 128p. 30.00 ***(978-0-295-99146-7(1))*** Univ. of Washington Pr.

Maxwell, Susan. The Court Art of Friedrich Sustris: Patronage in Late Renaissance Bavaria. 2011. (Visual Culture in Early Modernity Ser.). (Illus.). 250p. 109.95 *(978-0-7546-6887-9(8))* Ashgate Publishing Co.

Mazow, Leo G. & Benton, Thomas Hart. Thomas Hart Benton & the American Sound. 2012. (ENG.). 200p. ***(978-0-271-05083-6(7))*** Pennsylvania State Univ. Pr.

Mazzotta, Antonio. Titian - A Fresh Look at Nature. 2012. (ENG., Illus.). 88p. pap. 20.00 ***(978-1-85709-544-9(8))*** Yale Univ. Pr.

McCarthy, Laurette E. & Pach, Walter. Walter Pach (1883-1958) The Armory Show & the Untold Story of Modern Art in America. 2011. (ENG.). 272p. 59.95 *(978-0-271-03740-0(7))* Pennsylvania State Univ. Pr.

McConkey, Kenneth. John Lavery. 2nd ed. 2010. (ENG., Illus.). 248p. 75.00 *(978-1-873830-21-5(1),* Fine Art Society (Acc)) Antique Collectors' Club GBR. Dist: National Bk. Network.

McCorquodale, Duncan, ed. Krzysztof Wodiczko. 2011. (ENG., Illus.). 352p. 59.95 *(978-1-907317-13-2(9))* Black Dog Publishing Ltd. GBR. Dist: Perseus Distribution.

McEvilley, Thomas. Art, Love, Friendship: Marina Abramovic & Ulay, Together & Apart. 2010. (Illus.). 304p. 27.00 *(978-0-929701-93-6(3),* Documentext) McPherson & Co.

—Yves the Provocateur: Yves Klein & Twentieth-Century Art. 2010. (Illus.). 272p. 27.00 *(978-0-929701-91-2(7))* McPherson & Co.

McEwen, John. Paula Rego: Behind the Scenes. 2008. (ENG., Illus.). 216p. 79.95 *(978-0-7148-4806-8(9))* Phaidon Pr., Inc.

McGarry, Susan Hallsten. Bruce Aiken's Grand Canyon: An Intimate Affair. 2007. (ENG., Illus.). 160p. 55.00 *(978-0-938216-93-3(7))* Grand Canyon Assn.

McGarry, Susan Hallsten & Palmore, Thomas. Earthlings: The Paintings of Tom Palmore. 2008. (ENG., Illus.). 120p. (C). 45.00 *(978-0-934397-05-3(9))* Quaid Publishing.

McKeown, William. The Role of Venetian Renaissance Painting in John Ruskin's Utopian Theories: A Sociopolitical History of Art. 2011. (ENG., Illus.). xvii, 298p. 129.95 *(978-0-7734-1508-9(4))* Mellen, Edwin Pr., The.

McMakin, Roy. Roy McMakin: When Is a Chair Not a Chair? 2010. (ENG., Illus.). 208p. 65.00 *(978-0-8478-3357-3(7),* Skira) Rizzoli International Pubns., Inc.

McWilliam, Neil, ed. A Bibliography of Salon Criticism in Paris from the Ancien Régime to the Restoration, 1699-1827, Vol. 1. 2008. (Cambridge Studies in the History of Art Ser.). (ENG.). 284p. pap. 38.99 *(978-0-521-06914-4(9))* Cambridge Univ. Pr.

—A Bibliography of Salon Criticism in Paris from the July Monarchy to the Second Republic, 1831-1851, Vol. 2. 2009. (Cambridge Studies in the History of Art Ser.). (ENG.). 324p. pap. 42.00 *(978-0-521-10270-4(7))* Cambridge Univ. Pr.

Medved, Andrej, et al. Rojstvo Modernizma: Prelomnica V Slikarstvu 1976-1980: Tomo Podgornik & Emerik Bernard. 2009. (SLV., Illus.). 139p. *(978-961-6394-15-4(0))* Hyperion Pr.

Mehring, Christine. Blinky Palermo: Abstraction of an Era. 2009. (ENG., Illus.). 320p. 60.00 *(978-0-300-12238-1(1))* Yale Univ. Pr.

Merriam, Susan. Seventeenth-Century Flemish Garland Paintings: Still Life & the Devotional Image. 2012. (Visual Culture in Early Modernity Ser.). (Illus.). 200p. 104.95 ***(978-1-4094-0305-0(X))*** Ashgate Publishing Co.

Merrifield, Andy. John Berger. 2012. (Reaktion Books - Critical Lives Ser.). (Illus.). 224p. pap. 16.95 ***(978-1-86189-904-0(1))*** Reaktion Bks., Ltd. GBR. Dist: Chicago Distribution Ctr.

Mesch, Claudia & Michely, Viola, eds. Joseph Beuys: The Reader. 2007. (ENG., Illus.). 352p. (gr. 17). pap. 26.95 *(978-0-262-63351-2(5))* MIT Pr.

Meyer, Scott. With Fire: Richard Hirsch: A Life Between Chance & Design. 2012. ***(978-1-933360-54-6(2))*** Rochester Institute of Technology, Cary Graphic Arts Pr.

Michely, Viola Maria. Glueck in der Kunst? Das Werk von James Lee Byars. (GER., Illus.). 288p. *(978-3-496-01209-2(9))* Reimer, Dietrich.

Millar, Jeremy & Hoare, Philip. Tania Kovats. 2011. (Illus.). 144p. 70.00 *(978-1-84822-078-2(2),* Lund Humphries Pubs.) Ashgate Publishing, Ltd. GBR. Dist: Ashgate Publishing Co.

Miller, David Lee & Levine, Nina, eds. A Touch More Rare: Harry Berger, Jr., & the Arts of Interpretation. 2009. (ENG., Illus.). 336p. 65.00 *(978-0-8232-3030-3(9))* Fordham Univ. Pr.

Miller, John. John Miller: the Ruin of Exchange. Alberro, Alexander, ed. & text by. 2012. (ENG., Illus.). 256p. pap. 24.95 ***(978-3-03764-194-1(0))*** JRP Ringier Kunstverlag AG CHE. Dist: D.A.P./Distributed Art Pubs.

Millet, Catherine & Sealous, Tricia. Dalí & Me. 2008. (Illus.). 240p. 60.00 *(978-3-85881-711-2(2))* Scheidegger und Spiess AG, Verlag CHE. Dist: Antique Collectors' Club.

Milner, John. Rodchenko: Design. 2009. (ENG., Illus.). 96p. *(978-1-85149-591-7(6),* Antique Collectors Club Dist) Antique Collectors' Club.

Mink, Janis. T25 kr Miro. 2012. (25 Ser.). (ENG., Illus.). 96p. 14.99 ***(978-3-8365-3130-6(5))*** TASCHEN DEU. Dist: Ingram Pub. Services.

Mirzoeff, Nicholas. The Right to Look: A Counterhistory of Visuality. 2011. (ENG., Illus.). 408p. pap. 26.95 *(978-0-8223-4918-1(3))* Duke Univ. Pr.

Mishori, Efrat. Mika Rottenberg. 2011. (ENG., Illus.). 204p. 45.00 *(978-0-9826813-0-5(5))* Miller, Gregory & Co.

Mojon, Luc. Michelangelo: Die Entwürfe zu San Giovanni dei Fiorentini. 2009. (GRE & GER., Illus.). 139p. *(978-3-03911-577-8(4))* Lang, Peter.

Molderings, Herbert. Duchamp & the Aesthetics of Chance: Art as Experiment. Brogden, John V., tr. from GER. 2010. (Columbia Themes in Philosophy, Social Criticism, & the Arts Ser.). (ENG., Illus.). 240p. (gr. 17). 27.50 *(978-0-231-14762-0(7))* Columbia Univ. Pr.

Molesworth, Helen. Solitaire: Lee Lozano, Sylvia Plimack Mangold, Joan Semmel. Molesworth, Helen, ed. 2008. (ENG., Illus.). 164p. pap. 24.95 *(978-0-300-12529-0(1))* Yale Univ. Pr.

Mondadori Electa. Leonor Fini. 2012. (ITA & ENG., Illus.). 304p. 80.00 *(978-88-370-7744-0(0))* Electa ITA. Dist: National Bk. Network.

Moore-Mccann, Brenda. Brian O'Doherty - Patrick Ireland: Between Categories. 2009. (Illus.). 208p. 80.00 *(978-1-84822-014-0(6),* Lund Humphries Pubs.) Ashgate Publishing, Ltd. GBR. Dist: Ashgate Publishing Co.

Moorhouse, Paul. Anthony Caro: Presence. 2010. (Illus.). 152p. 60.00 *(978-1-84822-053-9(7),* Lund Humphries Pubs.) Ashgate Publishing, Ltd. GBR. Dist: Ashgate Publishing Co.

Morgan, Jessica. Tate Modern Artists: Gabriel Orozco. 2011. (ENG., Illus.). 128p. pap. 27.50 *(978-1-85437-912-2(7))* Tate Publishing, Ltd. GBR. Dist: Hachette Bk. Group.

Morgan, Robert, ed. Gary Hill. 2009. (Art + Performance Ser.). (ENG.). 352p. pap. 20.95 *(978-1-55554-083-8(X))* PAJ Pubns.

Morgan, Robert C., ed. Bruce Nauman. 2011. (Art + Performance Ser.). (ENG., Illus.). 396p. pap. 22.95 ***(978-1-55554-155-2(0))*** PAJ Pubns.

Morgan, Stuart. Inclinations: Further Writings & Interviews, 1 vol. 2007. (ENG., Illus.). 448p. pap. 27.00 *(978-0-9527414-8-0(2))* Frieze GBR. Dist: D.A.P./Distributed Art Pubs.

Mori, Gioia. Tamara de Lempicka: The Queen of the Modern. 2011. (ENG., Illus.). 390p. 80.00 *(978-88-572-0931-9(8))* Skira Editore ITA. Dist: Random Hse., Inc.

Morris, Stuart. Vincent Van Gogh: Visionary Landscapes. 2nd ed. 2008. (Painters Ser.). (Illus.). 132p. pap. *(978-1-86171-185-4(9))* Crescent Moon Publishing.

Moscatiello, Manuela. Le Japonisme de Giuseppe de Nittis: Un Peintre Italien en France à la Fin du XIXe Siècle. 2011. (FRE., Illus.). 441p. *(978-3-03911-796-3(3))* Lang, Peter Publishing, Inc.

Moseneder, Karl. Streit Um Bilder. (GER., Illus.). xxxvii, 235p. *(978-3-496-01169-9(6))* Reimer, Dietrich.

Moss, Karen. Illumination: The Paintings of Georgia O'Keeffe, Agnes Pelton, Agnes Martin, & Florence Miller Pierce. Moss, Karen, ed. 2009. (Illus.). 192p. 49.95 *(978-1-85894-481-4(3))* Merrell Pubs. Ltd. GBR. Dist: Perseus Distribution.

Muir, Gregor, ed. Henry Moore: Ideas for Sculpture. 2010. (ENG., Illus.). 164p. 85.00 *(978-3-03764-073-9(1))* JRP Ringier Kunstverlag AG CHE. Dist: D.A.P./Distributed Art Pubs.

Multiple. Talents 14, Young Photography/Art Criticism. 2009. (ENG.). 80p. pap. 28.00 *(978-3-422-06848-3(1))* Deutscher Kunstverlag GmbH DEU. Dist: Independent Pubs. Group.

Mumford, Lewis. Mumford on Modern Art in The 1930s. Wojtowicz, Robert, ed. 2006. (Illus.). 265p. 45.00 *(978-0-520-24858-8(9))* Univ. of California Pr.

Mumford, Robert & Mumford, Lewis. Mumford on Modern Art in The 1930s. Wojtowicz, Robert, ed. 2008. (Illus.). 288p. pap. 22.95 *(978-0-520-25808-2(8))* Univ. of California Pr.

Munder, Heike, ed. & text. Tadeusz Kantor, 1 vol. 2009. (ENG.). 156p. 55.00 *(978-3-03764-022-7(7))* JRP Ringier Kunstverlag AG CHE. Dist: D.A.P./Distributed Art Pubs.

Munro, Thomas. The Journal of Aesthetics & Art Criticism, V20, No 2, Winter 1961. Munro, Thomas et al, eds. 2011. 112p. 39.95 ***(978-1-258-05481-6(7))*** Literary Licensing, LLC.

Munro, Thomas, ed. The Journal of Aesthetics & Art Criticism, V12, No 1, September 1953. 2011. 146p. 40.95 ***(978-1-258-08092-1(3))*** Literary Licensing, LLC.

—The Journal of Aesthetics & Art Criticism, V15, No 3, March 1957. 2011. 124p. 40.95 ***(978-1-258-01048-5(8))*** Literary Licensing, LLC.

Murawska-Muthesius, Katarzyna & Zarzecka, Natalia, eds. Kantor Was Here: Tadeusz Kantor in Great Britain. 2011. (ENG., Illus.). 192p. pap. 29.95 *(978-1-907317-32-3(5))* Black Dog Publishing Ltd. GBR. Dist: Perseus Distribution.

Murphy, J. J. The Black Hole of the Camera: The Films of Andy Warhol. 2012. (ENG.). 336p. 70.00 ***(978-0-520-27187-6(4))***; pap. 29.95 ***(978-0-520-27188-3(2))*** Univ. of California Pr.

Murphy, Sinead. The Art Kettle. 2012. (ENG.). 86p. pap. 14.95 ***(978-1-84694-984-5(X))*** Hunt, John Publishing Ltd. GBR. Dist: National Bk. Network.

Museum für Gestaltung Zürich, ed. Otto Baumberger. 2008. (Poster Collection). (GER & ENG., Illus.). 96p. pap. 35.00 *(978-3-03778-129-6(7),* 3037781297) Springer.

Myrone, Martin, ed. John Martin. 2011. (ENG., Illus.). 240p. pap. 34.95 *(978-1-85437-889-7(9))* Tate Publishing, Ltd. GBR. Dist: Hachette Bk. Group.

Nahas, Dominique. The Worlds of Hunt Slonem. 2011. (ENG., Illus.). 288p. 90.00 *(978-0-86565-265-1(1))* Vendome Pr., The.

Nair, Parvati. A Different Light: The Photography of Sebastião Salgado. 2012. (ENG., Illus.). 376p. 99.95 ***(978-0-8223-5031-6(9))***; pap. 29.95 ***(978-0-8223-5048-4(3))*** Duke Univ. Pr.

Najafi, Sina, ed. Cabinet 34: Testing. 2009. (ENG., Illus.). 112p. pap. 12.00 *(978-1-932698-32-9(9))* Cabinet.

—Cabinet 35: Dust. 2009. (ENG., Illus.). 112p. pap. 12.00 *(978-1-932698-33-6(7))* Cabinet.

—Cabinet 37: Bubbles. 2010. (ENG., Illus.). 112p. pap. 12.00 *(978-1-932698-35-0(3))* Cabinet.

Najafi, Sina, et al, eds. The Underground. 2008. (ENG., Illus.). 112p. pap. 12.00 *(978-1-932698-28-2(0))* Cabinet.

Nakov, Andréi. Malevich: Painting the Absolute, 4 vols. 2010. (Illus.). 1656p. 600.00 *(978-1-84822-046-1(4),* Lund Humphries Pubs.) Ashgate Publishing, Ltd. GBR. Dist: Ashgate Publishing Co.

Nasby, Judith, et al. Will Gorlitz: Nowhere If Not Here. 2009. (ENG., Illus.). 120p. pap. 38.95 *(978-1-55458-049-1(8))* Wilfrid Laurier Univ. Pr. CAN. Dist: Univ. of Toronto Pr.

Nash, Susie. "No Equal in Any Land" André Beauneveu: Artist to the Courts of France & Flanders. 2007. (Illus.). 192p. *(978-1-903470-70-1(6))*; *(978-1-903470-71-8(4))* Holberton, Paul Publishing. (Spotlight Poets).

Naumann, Francis, ed. & text. Marcel Duchamp: The Art of Chess. 2009. (ENG., Illus.). 148p. 45.00 *(978-0-9800556-2-7(8))* Naumann, Francis M. Fine Art, LLC.

Nerdrum, Odd. Odd Nerdrum: Kitsch, More than Art, 1 vol. 2011. (ENG.). 376p. 75.00 ***(978-82-516-3638-4(8))*** Schibsted NOR. Dist: D.A.P./Distributed Art Pubs.

Neret, Gilles. Dali. 2011. (25 Ser.). (ENG., Illus.). 96p. 14.99 ***(978-3-8365-3118-4(6))*** TASCHEN DEU. Dist: Ingram Pub. Services.

—De Lempicka. 2011. (25 Ser.). (ENG., Illus.). 96p. 14.99 ***(978-3-8365-3184-9(4))*** TASCHEN DEU. Dist: Ingram Pub. Services.

—Klimt. 2011. (25 Ser.). (ENG., Illus.). 96p. 14.99 ***(978-3-8365-3142-9(9))*** TASCHEN DEU. Dist: Ingram Pub. Services.

Néret, Gilles & Caravaggio, Michelangelo Merisi da. Caravaggio. 2010. (25 Ser.). (ENG., Illus.). 96p. 14.99 *(978-3-8365-2381-3(7))* TASCHEN DEU. Dist: Ingram Pub. Services.

Nickas, Robert. Theft Is Vision: Collected Writings & Interviews, 1 vol. 2007. (ENG., Illus.). 160p. (C). pap. 22.00 *(978-3-905770-36-0(9))* JRP Ringier Kunstverlag AG CHE. Dist: D.A.P./Distributed Art Pubs.

Nieto, Margarita & Stern, Louis. Alfredo Ramos Martinez & Modernismo. Chambers, Marie, ed. 2009. (ENG & SPA., Illus.). 252p. 175.00 *(978-0-615-31520-1(8))* Martinez, Alfredo Ramos Research Project.

Nixon, Bruce, et al. Manuel Neri: The Figure in Relief. 2007. (ENG., Illus.). 198p. 65.00 *(978-1-883124-25-0(5))* Hudson Hills Pr. LLC.

Noakes, Aubrey. Spencelayh. 2006. (Chaucer Art Ser.). (Illus.). 192p. 55.00 *(978-1-904449-49-2(2))* Chaucer Pr. GBR. Dist: International Publishers Marketing.

Noble, Bonnie. Lucas Cranach the Elder: Art & Devotion of the German Reformation. 2009. (ENG.). 256p. 62.99 *(978-0-7618-4337-5(X))*; pap. 36.99 *(978-0-7618-4338-2(8))* Univ. Pr. of America, Inc.

Noël, Bernard & Ruhaut, Christian. Christian Ruhaut. 2010. (FRE., Illus.). 86p. *(978-2-7022-0945-5(9))* Cercle d'Art, Editions.

Noever, Peter, ed. GLOBAL:LAB: Kunst als Botschaft. Asien und Europa / Art as a Message Asia & Europe 1500-1700. 2009. (ENG., Illus.). 368p. pap. 75.00 *(978-3-7757-2474-6(5))* Hatje Cantz Verlag GmbH & Co KG DEU. Dist: D.A.P./Distributed Art Pubs.

—Thomas Feichtner - Edge to Edge: Experimentelles Design / Experimentelle Gestaltung. 2010. (ENG & GER., Illus.). 200p. pap. 59.95 *(978-3-0346-0342-3(8))* Birkhauser Verlag AG CHE. Dist: Actar Birkhauser Distribution.

Nolde, Emil, et al. Emil Nolde: Bewundert, gefürchtet und begehrt - Emil Nolde malt die Frauen / Admired, Feared, & Desired - Emil Nolde Paints Women. 2011. (GER & ENG., Illus.). 144p. 45.00 *(978-3-8321-9325-6(1))* DuMont DEU. Dist: D.A.P./Distributed Art Pubs.

Noyes, Carleton. The Gate of Appreciation: Studies in the Relation of Art to Life. 2008. 144p. pap. *(978-1-4099-5785-0(3))* Dodo Pr.

—The Gate of Appreciation: Studies in the Relation of Art to Life. 2007. (ENG.). 290p. 43.95 *(978-0-548-01774-6(3))* Kessinger Publishing, LLC.

N'Ret, Gilles & Arnold, Matthias. Toulouse-Lautrec. Walther, Ingo F., ed. 25th ed. 2009. (ENG., Illus.). 200p. 14.99 *(978-3-8365-1005-9(7))* TASCHEN DEU. Dist: Ingram Pub. Services.

N'Ret, Gilles, et al. Henri Matisse: Cut-Outs - Drawing with Scissors, 2 vols. 2009. (ENG., Illus.). 486p. 200.00 *(978-3-8228-3052-9(6))* TASCHEN DEU. Dist: Ingram Pub. Services.

Nuechterlein, Jeanne. Translating Nature into Art: Holbein, the Reformation, & Renaissance Rhetoric. 2011. (ENG.). 264p. 84.95 *(978-0-271-03692-2(3))* Pennsylvania State Univ. Pr.

Ogg, Kirsty, ed. & text. Claire Barclay: Shadow Spans. 2012. (ENG., Illus.). 56p. pap. 19.95 ***(978-0-85488-191-8(3))*** Whitechapel Art Gallery GBR. Dist: D.A.P./Distributed Art Pubs.

O'Gorman, James F. Henry Austin: In Every Variety of Architectural Style. 2009. (ENG., Illus.). 252p. 35.00 *(978-0-8195-6896-0(1))* Wesleyan Univ. Pr.

Olaf, Hajek. Flowerhead: The Illustrations of Olaf Hajek. 2010. (Illus.). 144p. 60.00 *(978-3-89955-281-2(4))* Die Gestalten Verlag DEU. Dist: Prestel Publishing.

Oldenburg, Claes & Rottner, Nadja. Claes Oldenburg. 2012. (October Files Ser.). (ENG., Illus.). 224p. (gr. 17). 35.00 ***(978-0-262-01710-7(5))***; pap. 18.95 ***(978-0-262-51693-8(4))*** MIT Pr.

Oleksijczuk, Denise Blake. The First Panoramas: Visions of British Imperialism. 2011. (Illus.). 264p. 90.00 *(978-0-8166-4860-3(3))*; pap. 29.95 *(978-0-8166-4861-0(1))* Univ. of Minnesota Pr.

Omer, Mordechai. Adam Berg: Evidence. 2011. (ENG., Illus.). 48p. pap. 17.95 *(978-88-8158-800-8(5))* Charta ITA. Dist: D.A.P./Distributed Art Pubs.

O'Neill, Morna. Walter Crane: The Arts & Crafts, Painting, & Politics. 2011. (Paul Mellon Centre for Studies in Britis Ser.). (Illus.). 320p. 75.00 *(978-0-300-16768-9(7))* Yale Univ. Pr.

Onians, John. Compression vs. Expression: Containing & Explaining the World's Art. 2006. (Clark Studies in the Visual Arts). (ENG., Illus.). 268p. per. 24.95 *(978-0-300-09790-0(5))* Yale Univ. Pr.

Orcutt, Kimberly. John Rogers: American Stories. 2010. (ENG., Illus.). 224p. 50.00 *(978-0-85667-689-5(6))* Wilson, Philip Pubs., Ltd. GBR. Dist: Macmillan.

Orlan. Fabulous Harlequin: Orlan & the Patchwork Self. Veneciano, Jorge Daniel & Garelick, Rhonda K., eds. 2010. (Life in Performance Ser.). (ENG., Illus.). 176p. pap. 44.95 *(978-0-8032-3475-8(9))* Univ. of Nebraska Pr.

Ormiston, Rosalind. Leonardo Da Vinci: His Life & Works in 500 Images. 2011. (ENG., Illus.). 256p. 35.00 *(978-0-7548-2326-1(1))* Anness Publishing GBR. Dist: National Bk. Network.

—Michelangelo: His Life & Works in 500 Images. 2011. (ENG., Illus.). 256p. 35.00 *(978-0-7548-2077-2(7))* Anness Publishing GBR. Dist: National Bk. Network.

Ormiston, Rosalind. Rembrandt: His Life & Works in 500 Images - An Illustrated Exploration of the Artist, His Life & Context, with a Gallery of 300 of His Finest Works. 2012. (ENG., Illus.). 256p. 35.00 ***(978-0-7548-2378-0(4))*** Anness Publishing GBR. Dist: National Bk. Network.

Orozco, Gabriel. Gabriel Orozco. Bois, Yve-Alain, ed. 2009. (October Files Ser.). (ENG., Illus.). 216p. (gr. 17). 38.00 *(978-0-262-01318-5(5))* MIT Pr.

Orozco, Gabriel & Bois, Yve-Alain. Gabriel Orozco. Bois, Yve-Alain, ed. 2009. (October Files Ser.). (ENG., Illus.). 216p. (gr. 17). pap. 19.95 *(978-0-262-51301-2(3))* MIT Pr.

Oswalt, Philipp, ed. The Bauhaus Debate 1919-2009, 1 vol. 2010. (ENG., Illus.). 304p. pap. 30.00 *(978-3-7757-2488-3(5))* Hatje Cantz Verlag GmbH & Co KG DEU. Dist: D.A.P./Distributed Art Pubs.

Zhan Yüksel, Serra. Satiyorum, Satiyorum, Sattim! 2011. 52p. pap. ***(978-3-8433-8810-8(5))*** Lambert Academic Publishing.

Paik, Nam June. Nam June Paik. Lee, Sook-Kyung & Rennert, Susanne, eds. 2011. (ENG., Illus.). 208p. 45.00 *(978-1-85437-924-5(0))* Tate Publishing, Ltd. GBR. Dist: Hachette Bk. Group.

Palau, Marta & Barrios, Jose Luis. Marta Palau: Naualli, 1 vol. 2007. (SPA & ENG., Illus.). 260p. 65.00 *(978-968-9056-02-7(6))* Turner, Ediciones S.A. ESP. Dist: D.A.P./Distributed Art Pubs.

Palermo, et al. Blinky Palermo: To the People of New York. 2009. (ENG., Illus.). 208p. 60.00 *(978-3-937572-52-9(X))* Richter Verlag DEU. Dist: D.A.P./Distributed Art Pubs.

Panyard, Christine M. & Michelangelo Buonarroti. A Biblical Tour Through the Sistine Chapel: Celebrating 500 Years under the Ceiling of Michelangelo. 2011. (Illus.). 96p. *(978-0-8091-0593-9(4))* Paulist Pr.

Papanikolas, Theresa. Anarchism & the Advent of Paris Dada: Art & Criticism, 1914-1924. 2010. (Illus.). 206p. 99.95 *(978-0-7546-6626-4(3))* Ashgate Publishing Co.

Paquet, Marcel. T25 kr Magritte. 2012. (25 Ser.). (ENG., Illus.). 96p. 14.99 ***(978-3-8365-3122-1(4))*** TASCHEN DEU. Dist: Ingram Pub. Services.

Paraskos, Michael. Reading Read: New Views on Herbert Read. 2008. (Illus.). 237p. pap. 36.95 *(978-1-904491-08-8(1))* Freedom Pr. GBR. Dist: AK Pr. Distribution.

Paraskos, Michael & Holland, Jools. Clive Head. 2010. (Illus.). 200p. 80.00 *(978-1-84822-062-1(6),* Lund Humphries Pubs.) Ashgate Publishing, Ltd. GBR. Dist: Ashgate Publishing Co.

Parker, Deborah. Bronzino: Renaissance Painter as Poet. 2010. (ENG., Illus.). 246p. pap. 31.99 *(978-0-521-17853-2(3))* Cambridge Univ. Pr.

Parkstone Press Staff. Cézanne. 2010. (Mega Square Ser.). (ENG., Illus.). 256p. 12.95 *(978-1-84484-933-8(3))* Parkstone Pr. USA, Ltd.

—Gauguin. 2010. (Mega Square Ser.). (ENG., Illus.). 256p. 12.95 *(978-1-84484-957-4(0))* Parkstone Pr. USA, Ltd.

—Leonardo Da Vinci. 2010. (Mega Square Ser.). (ENG., Illus.). 256p. 12.95 *(978-1-84484-838-6(8))* Parkstone Pr. USA, Ltd.

—Michelangelo. 2010. (Mega Square Ser.). (ENG., Illus.). 256p. 12.95 *(978-1-84484-839-3(6))* Parkstone Pr. USA, Ltd.

—Monet. 2010. (Mega Square Ser.). (ENG., Illus.). 256p. 12.95 *(978-1-84484-956-7(2))* Parkstone Pr. USA, Ltd.

—Raphael. 2010. (Mega Square Ser.). (ENG., Illus.). 256p. 12.95 (978-1-84484-442-5(0)) Parkstone Pr. USA, Ltd.

—Van Gogh. 2010. (Mega Square Ser.). (ENG., Illus.). 256p. 12.95 (978-1-84484-953-6(8)) Parkstone Pr. USA, Ltd.

Parliament, Ian C. & Cadafalch, Antonio. Day of the Dead: Celebrating the Dia de Los Muertos in pop art, graphics & Installations. Alderete, ed. 2011. (ENG., Illus.). 176p. 35.00 (978-1-907621-01-7(6)) Korero Books LLP GBR. Dist: Independent Pubs. Group.

Parsons, Christopher & Ward, Martha. A Bibliography of Salon Criticism in Second Empire Paris. 2010. (Cambridge Studies in the History of Art Ser.). (ENG.). 304p. pap. 24.99 (978-0-521-15494-9(4)) Cambridge Univ. Pr.

Partsch Susanna. T25 Klee. 2011. (ENG., Illus.). 96p. 14.99 (978-3-8365-2722-4(7)) TASCHEN DEU. Dist: Ingram Pub. Services.

Pas, Johan. Fred Bervoets: Printwork, 1990-2010. 2011. (ENG., Illus.). 288p. 75.00 (978-90-209-9731-6(9)) Lannoo Pubs./Racine.

Pater, Walter. The Works of Walter Pater. 2011. (Cambridge Library Collection - Literary Studies). (ENG.). 234p. pap. 22.99 **(978-1-108-03425-8(X))**; 310p. pap. 24.99 **(978-1-108-03429-6(2))**; 292p. pap. 23.99 **(978-1-108-03428-9(4))**; 332p. pap. 28.99 **(978-1-108-03426-5(8))**; 272p. pap. 23.99 **(978-1-108-03427-2(6))**; 264p. pap. 23.99 **(978-1-108-03430-2(6))**; 256p. pap. 23.99 **(978-1-108-03424-1(1))**; (Illus.). 264p. pap. 23.99 **(978-1-108-03423-4(3))** Cambridge Univ. Pr.

Paton, Justin. How to Look at a Painting. 2nd ed. 2009. (ENG., Illus.). 136p. 24.95 (978-0-9582916-0-6(8)) Awa Pr. NZL. Dist: Independent Pubs. Group.

Patrizi, M. L. & Witting, Felix. Caravaggio. 2012. (Mega Square Ser.). (ENG., Illus.). 256p. 12.95 **(978-1-906981-43-3(4))** Parkstone Pr. USA, Ltd.

Payne, Christiana & Brett, Charles. John Brett: Pre-Raphaelite Landscape Painter. 2010. (Paul Mellon Centre for Studies in Britis Ser.). (Illus.). 304p. 90.00 (978-0-300-16575-3(7)) Yale Univ. Pr.

Peake and Eldred & Winnington. Mervyn Peake: The Man & His Art. 2008. (ENG., Illus.). 240p. pap. 29.95 (978-0-7206-1321-6(3)) Owen, Peter Ltd. GBR. Dist: Independent Pubs. Group.

Pearson, James. Constantin Brancusi: Sculpting the Essence of Things. 3rd ed. 2010. (Sculptors Ser.). (Illus.). 180p. (978-1-86171-268-4(5)); pap. (978-1-86171-284-4(7)) Crescent Moon Publishing.

—Frank Stella: American Abstract Artist. 4th ed. 2011. (Painters Ser.). (Illus.). 132p. (ENG.). 45.00 **(978-1-86171-317-9(7))**; pap. 16.00 **(978-1-86171-316-2(9))** Crescent Moon Publishing GBR. Dist: Gardners Bks. Ltd.

—Leonardo Da Vinci. 2nd ed. 2008. (Painters Ser.). (Illus.). 186p. pap. (978-1-86171-163-2(8)) Crescent Moon Publishing.

Pearson, James. Mark Rothko: The Art of Transcendence. 4th ed. 2011. (Painters Ser.). (Illus.). 132p. 45.00 **(978-1-86171-315-5(0))**; pap. 16.00 **(978-1-86171-314-8(2))** Crescent Moon Publishing GBR. Dist: Gardners Bks. Ltd.

Pelkonen, Eeva-Liisa. Kevin Roche: Architecture as Environment. 2011. (ENG., Illus.). 280p. 65.00 (978-0-300-15223-4(X)) Yale Univ. Pr.

Peltomäki, Kirsi & Asher, Michael. Situation Aesthetics: The Work of Michael Asher. 2010. (ENG., Illus.). 240p. (gr. 17). 27.95 (978-0-262-01368-0(1)) MIT Pr.

Peng Ma. Peng Ma: Abstract Ink Painting. Chao, Lien, ed. 2011. (ENG & CHI., Illus.). 100p. pap. 48.00 (978-1-894770-57-6(9)) TSAR Pubns. CAN. Dist: Univ. of Toronto Pr.

Penser L'art: Séminaire Interarts de Paris. 2009. (FRE.). 320p. (C). pap. 44.00 **(978-2-252-03739-3(3))** Klincksieck, Editions FRA. Dist: ISD.

Peppiatt, Michael. Francis Bacon in the 1950s. 2009. (ENG., Illus.). 224p. pap. 33.00 (978-0-300-15121-3(7)) Yale Univ. Pr.

Perez, Rolando. Severo Sarduy & the Neo-Baroque Image of Thought in the Visual Arts. 2011. (Purdue Studies in Romance Literatures Ser.). 319p. pap. 45.00 (978-1-55753-604-4(X)) Purdue Univ. Pr.

Perkinson, Stephen. The Likeness of the King: A Prehistory of Portraiture in Late Medieval France. 2009. (ENG., Illus.). 352p. 55.00 (978-0-226-65879-7(1)) Univ. of Chicago Pr.

Perry, Alan R. The Don Camillo Stories of Giovannino Guareschi: A Humorist Portrays the Sacred. 2008. (Toronto Italian Studies). (ENG., Illus.). 224p. (978-0-8020-9756-9(1)) Univ. of Toronto Pr.

Pesenti, Allegra, et al. Zarina: Paper Like Skin. 2012. (ENG., Illus.). 128p. 39.95 **(978-3-7913-5166-7(4))** Prestel Publishing.

Phaidon Press Editors & Bluttal, Steven. Andy Warhol "Giant" Size. l.t. ed. 2009. (ENG., Illus.). 624p. 49.95 (978-0-7148-4980-5(4)) Phaidon Pr., Inc.

Pheysey, Dawn C. The Master's Hand: The Art of Carl Heinrich Bloch. 2010. 168p. 32.99 (978-1-60641-926-7(9)) Deseret Bk. Co.

Picasso Lessons: The Sixth Woman of les Demoiselles D'Avignon. rev. ed. 2008. (ENG., Illus.). 16p. 11.00 (978-0-9744922-1-6(3)) Architect Painter Pr., The.

Pinna, Baignio, ed. Art & Perception. Towards a Visual Science of Art, Part 2. 2008. 428p. (C). (978-90-04-16630-1(0)) BRILL.

Plax, Julie Anne. Watteau & the Cultural Politics of Eighteenth-Century France. 2011. (ENG., Illus.). 274p. pap. 50.00 (978-0-521-20084-4(9)) Cambridge Univ. Pr.

Plesch, Veronique. The Wisdom of the Imagination: The Livres d'Artiste of Lucie Lambert. Martineau, Sheila, ed. 2012. (ENG., Illus.). 64p. 24.95 (978-1-897476-27-7(2)) Simply Read Bks. CAN. Dist: Perseus-PGW.

Polistena, Joyce Carol, et al. The Religious Paintings of Eugène Delacroix (1798-1863) The Initiator of the Style of Modern Religious Art. 2008. 368p. 119.95 (978-0-7734-4973-2(6)) Mellen, Edwin Pr., The.

Pollock, Griselda, ed. Conceptual Odysseys: Passages to Cultural Analysis. 2008. (New Encounters Ser.). (ENG., Illus.). 288p. 89.00 (978-1-84511-522-7(8)); 320p. pap. 31.00 (978-1-84511-523-4(6)) I. B. Tauris & Co., Ltd. GBR. Dist: Macmillan.

Pong, Elodie. Elodie Pong: We Are Knights on the Trajectories of a Post-Everything Era. 2008. (ENG., Illus.). 64p. pap. 15.00 (978-3-905701-36-4(7)) JRP Ringier Kunstverlag AG CHE. Dist: D.A.P./Distributed Art Pubs.

Pops, Martin. The Life & Art of Albert Pinkham Ryder (1847-1917) The Achievement of an American Artist. 2011. (Illus.). 616p. 199.95 (978-0-7734-1564-5(5)) Mellen, Edwin Pr., The.

Porcu, Costantino & Porcu, Constantino. Dalì. 2009. (ENG., Illus.). 96p. pap. 8.99 (978-88-572-0044-6(2)) Skira Editore ITA. Dist: Random Hse., Inc.

Porter, Fairfield. Art in Its Own Terms: Selected Criticism. 2007. (Illus.). 288p. (C). pap. 14.95 (978-1-55921-325-7(6)) Moyer Bell.

Postle, Martin. Johan Zoffany RA: Society Observed. 2011. (ENG., Illus.). 320p. 75.00 (978-0-300-17604-9(X)) Yale Univ. Pr.

Powers, Alan. Eric Ravilious: Imagined Realities. 2012. (ENG., Illus.). 144p. pap. 30.00 **(978-1-78130-001-5(1))** Wilson, Philip Pubs., Ltd. GBR. Dist: Macmillan.

Prat, Louis-Antoine & Rosenberg, Pierre. Antoine Watteau: The Drawings. 2011. (ENG., Illus.). 192p. 55.00 (978-1-905711-70-3(0)) Royal Academy of Arts GBR. Dist: Hachette Bk. Group.

Presenti, Allegra. Rachel Whiteread Drawings. 2010. (Illus.). 224p. 49.95 (978-3-7913-5038-7(2)) Prestel Publishing.

Pride, Jennifer. The Poetics of Black. 2009. 148p. pap. (978-3-639-13271-7(8)) VDM Verlag Dr. Mueller e.K.

Printz, Othon. Paul Gauguin, le Peintre-écrivain: Un Essai Illustré Par Quelques Réflexions Autour des Uvres Conservées Au Musée D'art Moderne et Contemporain de Strasbourg. 2010. (FRE., Illus.). 120p. (978-2-84960-223-2(X)) Bentzinger, Jerome Do Editeur.

Prosperitti, Leopoldine. Landscape & Philosophy in the Art of Jan Brueghel the Elder (1568-1625) 2009. (Illus.). 294p. 124.95 (978-0-7546-6090-3(7)) Ashgate Publishing Co.

Purcell, Kerry William. Alexey Brodovitch. 2011. (ENG.). 272p. pap. 39.95 **(978-0-7148-6317-7(3))** Phaidon Pr., Inc.

Quinnell, Susan. Alison Wilding: The Embrace of Sculpture. 2nd ed. 2008. (Sculptors Ser.). (Illus.). 156p. pap. (978-1-86171-169-4(7)) Crescent Moon Publishing.

Rabinowitch, David. Birth of Romanticism Drawings, 1 vol. 2011. (ENG.). 82p. 55.00 (978-0-935875-24-9(7)) Blum, Peter Edition.

Radke, Gary. Leonardo da Vinci & the Art of Sculpture. 2009. (Illus.). 224p. 50.00 (978-1-932543-31-5(7)); (ENG., pap. 35.00 (978-1-932543-32-2(5)) High Museum of Art.

Rainer M & Walther I. T25 kr Chagall. 2012. (25 Ser.). (ENG., Illus.). 96p. 14.99 **(978-3-8365-3114-6(3))** TASCHEN DEU. Dist: Ingram Pub. Services.

Ramirez, Mari Carmen & Olea, Hector. Carlos Cruz-Diez: Color in Space & Time. 2011. (ENG., Illus.). 512p. 75.00 (978-0-300-16994-2(9)) Museum of Fine Arts, Houston.

Ramos, Mel, et al. Mel Ramos: 100+ Zeichnungen. 2011. (GER & ENG., Illus.). 128p. 39.95 **(978-3-86678-444-4(9))** Kerber Verlag DEU. Dist: D.A.P./Distributed Art Pubs.

Raskin, David. Donald Judd. 2010. (Illus.). 220p. 55.00 (978-0-300-16276-9(6)) Yale Univ. Pr.

Rauschenberg, Robert. Robert Rauschenberg. 2010. (ENG., Illus.). 48p. pap. 9.95 (978-0-87070-767-4(1)) Museum of Modern Art.

Rautert, Timm, photos by. Josef Sudek, Prag 1967, 1 vol. 2008. (ENG., Illus.). 98p. 45.00 (978-3-86521-712-7(5)) Steidl, Gerhard Druckerei und Verlag DEU. Dist: Innovative Logistics.

Reason, Akela & Eakins, Thomas. Thomas Eakins & the Uses of History. 2010. 232p. (C). 55.00 (978-0-8122-4198-3(3)) Univ. of Pennsylvania Pr.

Reid, Mary. Anthony Caro: Drawing in Space. 2009. (Illus.). 152p. 60.00 (978-1-84822-030-0(8), Lund Humphries Pubs.) Ashgate Publishing, Ltd. GBR. Dist: Ashgate Publishing Co.

Reid, Mary, et al. Anthony Caro Set: Drawing in Space - Interior & Exterior - Figurative & Narrative Sculpture - Presence, 5 vols. 2010. (Illus.). 736p. 240.00 (978-1-84822-057-7(X), Lund Humphries Pubs.) Ashgate Publishing, Ltd. GBR. Dist: Ashgate Publishing Co.

Reid, Sheila. Art Memories: The Life & Works of Sheila Reid. ltd. ed. 2010. (Illus.). 126p. (978-0-9646268-4-3(5)) Rush Editions.

—A Place Between Thoughts: The Art of Sheila Reid. ltd. ed. 2010. 173p. pap. (978-0-9646268-2-9(9)) Rush Editions.

Reinke, Steve. The Shimmering Beast. 2011. 120p. pap. 19.95 **(978-0-945323-21-1(2))** WhiteWalls, Inc.

Rembrandt Harmenszoon van Rijn. Rembrandt & the Face of Jesus. 2011. (Illus.). xv, 255p. (978-0-87633-227-6(0)); (978-0-87633-228-3(9)) Philadelphia Museum of Art.

Rembrandt Harmenszoon van Rijn & Tucker, Mark S. Rembrandt & the Face of Jesus. DeWitt, Lloyd, ed. 2011. (ENG., Illus.). 256p. 65.00 (978-0-300-16957-7(4)) Yale Univ. Pr.

Rendell, Jane. Site-Writing: The Architecture of Art Criticism. 2011. (ENG., Illus.). 288p. pap. 28.00 (978-1-84511-999-7(1)) I. B. Tauris & Co., Ltd. GBR. Dist: Macmillan.

Rey, Jean Dominique. Giotto: Frescoes in the Upper Church, Assisi. 2011. 62p. 36.95 **(978-1-258-03722-2(X))** Literary Licensing, LLC.

Richard Bampi: Modern Ceramicist / Catalogue of Works. 2006. 409p. 135.00 **(978-3-925369-14-8(7))** Arnoldsche Art Pubs. DEU. Dist: Antique Collectors' Club.

Riché, David. Art of Faery. 2012. (ENG., Illus.). 112p. pap. 19.95 **(978-1-84340-306-7(4)**, Collins & Brown) Anova Bks. GBR. Dist: Sterling Publishing Co., Inc.

Richter, Gerhard, et al. Gerhard Richter: Early Work, 1951-1972. 2011. (ENG., Illus.). 176p. 50.00 (978-1-60606-040-7(6), J. Paul Getty Museum) Getty Pubns.

Richter, Gerhard, et al. Gerhard Richter: Red-Yellow-Blue. 2011. (ENG., Illus.). 128p. pap. 19.95 **(978-3-7913-4609-0(1))** Prestel Publishing.

Ridgely, Steven C. Japanese Counterculture: The Antiestablishment Art of Terayama Shuji. 2011. (ENG., Illus.). 264p. 67.50 (978-0-8166-6752-9(7)); pap. 22.50 (978-0-8166-6753-6(5)) Univ. of Minnesota Pr.

Rieber, Kristin, ed. Erik Bulatov: O. 2009. (ENG., Illus.). 72p. 38.00 (978-3-86678-234-1(9)) Kerber Verlag DEU. Dist: D.A.P./Distributed Art Pubs.

Rijser, David. Raphael's Poetics: Art & Poetry in High Renaissance Rome. 2012. (ENG., Illus.). 520p. pap. **(978-90-8964-342-1(7))** Amsterdam Univ. Pr.

Rivière, Jacques. The Ideal Reader: Proust, Freud, & the Reconstruction of European Culture. 2009. (ENG.). 282p. pap. 29.95 (978-1-4128-1033-3(7)) Transaction Pubs.

Rizzoli. Charles Ledray. 2010. (ENG., Illus.). 160p. 45.00 (978-0-8478-3527-0(8), Skira) Rizzoli International Pubns., Inc.

Roberts, John. The Intangibilities of Form: Skill & Deskilling in Art after the Readymade. 2007. (ENG., Illus.). 256p. 95.00 (978-1-84467-163-2(1), 844163); per. 27.95 (978-1-84467-167-0(4), 844167) Verso Bks. GBR. Dist: Norton, W. W. & Co., Inc.

Robins, Anna Gruetzner. A Fragile Modernism: Whistler & His Impressionist Followers. 2008. (ENG., Illus.). 256p. 60.00 (978-0-300-13545-9(9)) Yale Univ. Pr.

Robinson, Alistair & Lambton, Lucinda. David Harrison. 2010. (ENG., Illus.). 128p. 50.00 (978-0-85667-671-0(3)) Wilson, Philip Pubs., Ltd. GBR. Dist: Macmillan.

Robinson, Greg, et al, eds. Miné Okubo: Following Her Own Road. 2008. (ENG., Illus.). 224p. pap. 26.95 (978-0-295-98774-3(X)) Univ. of Washington Pr.

Robinson, Jeremy Mark. Andrei Tarkovsky: Pocket Guide. 2010. (Illus.). 276p. pap. (978-1-86171-300-1(2)) Crescent Moon Publishing.

—The Art of Kurt Jackson: Painting-Sea-Sky-Light-Land-Cornwall. 2009. (Painters Ser.). (Illus.). 168p. pap. (978-1-86171-078-9(X)) Crescent Moon Publishing.

Robinson, Michael. Turner: His life & works in 500 Images. 2010. (ENG., Illus.). 256p. 35.00 (978-0-7548-2084-0(X)) Anness Publishing GBR. Dist: National Bk. Network.

Rochlitz, Rainer. Subversion & Subsidy: Contemporary Art & Aesthetics. Roberts, Dafydd, tr. from FRE. 2008. (SB-the French List Ser.). (ENG.). 240p. 99.95 (978-1-905422-70-8(9)); pap. 29.95 (978-1-905422-71-5(7)) Seagull Bks. GBR. Dist: Chicago Distribution Ctr.

Rodari, Florian. Kosta Alex. 2011. (ENG., Illus.). 180p. 65.00 (978-0-300-17665-0(1)) Yale Univ. Pr.

Rodenbeck, Judith F. Radical Prototypes: Allan Kaprow & the Invention of Happenings. 2011. (ENG., Illus.). 312p. (gr. 17). 34.95 (978-0-262-01620-9(6)) MIT Pr.

Roelstraete, Dieter. Richard Long: A Line Made by Walking. 2010. (One Work Ser.). (ENG., Illus.). 112p. (gr. 17). pap. 16.00 (978-1-84638-058-7(8)) Afterall Publishing GBR. Dist: MIT Pr.

Romo, Terezita. Malaquias Montoya. 2011. (Ver Ser.). (Illus.). 200p. 60.00 (978-0-89551-106-5(1)); pap. 24.95 (978-0-89551-107-2(X)) UCLA Chicano Studies Research Ctr. Pr.

Ronda, Bruce A. Reading the Old Man: John Brown in American Culture. 2008. (ENG., Illus.). 218p. 39.95 (978-1-57233-620-9(X)) Univ. of Tennessee Pr.

Rorimer, Anne, et al. Ger Van Elk: Monograph. 2009. (DUT & ENG., Illus.). 304p. pap. (978-90-78964-28-5(6), Thieme Art (Acc)) Antique Collectors' Club.

Ros, Xon de. Primitivismo y Modernismo: El Legado de Maria Blanchard. 2007. (Hispanic Studies Ser.: Vol. 5). (SPA., Illus.). 250p. pap. 63.95 (978-3-03910-937-1(5)) Lang, Peter Publishing, Inc.

Rosand, David. Edward Koren: The Capricious Line. 2010. (ENG., Illus.). 106p. pap. 30.00 (978-1-884919-26-8(X)) Columbia Univ., The Miriam & Ira D. Wallach Art Gallery.

Rosanne, Van Cruyningen. Oscar Wilde & the Influence of John Ruskin & Walter Pater: An Inquiry into the Image of John Ruskin As the Good Angel & Walter Pater As the Bad Angel on Wilde's Shoulders. 2011. 72p. pap. **(978-3-639-32887-5(6))** VDM Verlag Dr. Mueller e.K.

Rosen, Aaron. Imagining Jewish Art: Encounters with the Masters in Chagall, Guston, & Kitaj. 2012. (Legenda Studies in Comparative Literature Ser.: 16). (ENG., Illus.). 140p. (C). 89.50 (978-1-906540-54-8(3)) European Humanities Research Ctr. GBR. Dist: Brown, David Bk. Co., The.

Rosen, Barry, ed. Dieter Roth. 2010. (ENG., Illus.). 238p. 45.00 (978-0-300-17079-5(3)) Yale Univ. Pr.

Rosengarten, Ruth. Love & Authority in the Work: Narrating the Family Romance. 2011. (ENG., Illus.). 224p. 89.95 (978-0-7190-8070-8(3)) Manchester Univ. Pr. GBR. Dist: Macmillan.

Rosenthal, T. G. Paula Rego: The Complete Graphic Work. 2nd rev. exp. ed. 2012. (ENG., Illus.). 392p. 125.00 **(978-0-500-09368-9(7)**, 509368) Thames & Hudson.

Rothfuss, Joan, ed. Eiko & Koma: Time Is Not Even, Space Is Not Empty. 2011. (ENG., Illus.). 288p. pap. 35.00 (978-0-935640-97-7(5)) Walker Art Ctr.

Rubinstein, Raphael. Critical Mess: Art Critics on the State of Their Practice. 2006. 125p. per. 24.95 (978-1-889097-67-1(5)) Hard Pr. Editions.

Ruf, Beatrix, ed. Scott Myles. 2008. (GER & ENG., Illus.). 96p. 30.00 (978-3-905701-63-0(4)) JRP Ringier Kunstverlag AG CHE. Dist: D.A.P./Distributed Art Pubs.

Rupe, Shade. Dark Stars Rising: Conversations from the Outer Realms. 2011. (ENG., Illus.). 560p. pap. 27.95 (978-1-900486-69-9(5)) Headpress GBR. Dist: SCB Distributors.

Ruskin, John. The Harbours of England. Thomas J. Wise, ed. 2007. (ENG., Illus.). 72p. per. (978-1-4065-6365-8(X)) Dodo Pr.

—Lectures on Architecture & Painting Delivered at Edinburgh in November 1853. 2009. 296p. 24.99 (978-1-103-26494-0(X)); pap. 18.99 (978-1-103-26491-9(5)) BiblioBazaar.

—Lectures on Art. 2009. 216p. 23.99 (978-1-103-68125-9(7)) 2009. 216p. pap. 17.99 (978-1-103-68124-2(9)) 2008. 202p. 25.99 (978-0-554-74583-1(5)) 2008. 144p. 24.99 (978-0-554-25865-2(X)) 2008. 144p. 21.99 (978-0-554-35168-1(4)) 2008. 149p. 28.99 (978-0-554-74574-9(7)) 2008. 202p. pap. 27.75 (978-0-554-74580-0(1)) 2008. 149p. pap. 28.75 (978-0-554-74576-3(3)) BiblioBazaar.

—Lectures on Art. 2007. (ENG.). 120p. per. (978-1-4065-6369-6(2)) Dodo Pr.

Ruskin, John & O'Gorman, Francis. Praeterita. 2012. (Oxford World's Classics Ser.). (ENG.). 512p. pap. 16.95 **(978-0-19-280241-5(0))** Oxford Univ. Pr., Inc.

russell, david. David Russell Self-portrait of the Painter. 2010. 183p. pap. 21.95 (978-1-4452-4950-6(2)) Lulu Enterprises Inc.

Russell, Vivian. Monet's Water Lilies. 2011. (ENG., Illus.). 96p. pap. 14.95 (978-0-7112-3231-0(8)) Lincoln, Frances Ltd. GBR. Dist: Perseus-PGW.

Safer, Samantha Erin. Textile Revolution: Medals, Wiggles & Pop, 1961-1971. 2010. (ENG., Illus.). 264p. pap. (978-1-85149-648-8(3), Antique Collectors Club Dist) Antique Collectors' Club.

Sagner, Karin. Gustave Caillebotte: Neue Perspektiven des Impressionismus. 2009. (GER., Illus.). 200p. (C). 110.00 (978-3-7774-2161-2(8)) Hirmer Verlag GmbH DEU. Dist: Brown, David Bk. Co., The.

Salas, Charles G., ed. The Life & the Work: Art & Biography. 2007. (Illus.). 200p. 45.00 (978-0-89236-823-5(3)) Oxford Univ. Pr., Inc.

Saltz, Jerry. Seeing Out Louder: Art Criticism, 2003-2009. 2009. (ENG.). 420p. 40.00 (978-1-55595-318-8(2)) Hudson Hills Pr. LLC.

Sanders, Michael. Cezanne: In Acrylics. 2011. (Ready to Paint the Masters Ser.). (ENG., Illus.). 88p. pap. 19.95 (978-1-84448-575-8(7)) Search Pr., Ltd. GBR. Dist: Independent Pubs. Group.

Sargent, John Singer. John Singer Sargent's Triumph of Religion at the Boston Public Library: Creation & Restoration. Khandekar, Narayan et al, eds. 2010. (ENG., Illus.). 296p. 65.00 (978-0-300-12290-9(X)) Yale Univ. Pr.

Sargent, John Singer, et al. John Singer Sargent's Triumph of Religion at the Boston Public Library: Creation & Restoration. 2010. (Illus.). 295p. (978-1-891771-51-4(5)) Harvard Univ. Art Museums.

Sauer, Christel. Robert Ryman at Inverleith House, Royal Botanic Garden, Edinburgh: Raussmüller Collection, 1 vol. 2007. (ENG., Illus.). 126p. pap. 35.00 (978-3-905777-01-7(0)) Verlag der Buchhandlung Walther Konig DEU. Dist: D.A.P./Distributed Art Pubs.

Sauvage, Claude. Laurent Coderre: Artiste Peintre, L'uvre D'une Vie. 2010. (FRE., Illus.). 156p. (978-2-923715-38-4(1)) Broquet, Inc.

Sawin, Martica. Alan Gussow: A Painter's Nature. 2009. (ENG., Illus.). 268p. 70.00 (978-1-55595-308-9(5)) Hudson Hills Pr. LLC.

Sayre, Henry M. Writing about Art. 6th ed. 2008. (ENG., Illus.). 160p. (C). pap. 40.20 (978-0-205-64578-7(X), Prentice Hall) Prentice Hall PTR.

Scacchetti, Luca. Guglielmo Ulrich, 1904-1977. 2010. (ITA & ENG., Illus.). 512p. 95.00 (978-88-7179-612-3(8), Ore Cultura Srl (Acc)) Antique Collectors' Club GBR. Dist: National Bk. Network.

Schatz, Evelina, ed. Fausta Squatriti: Ecce Homo. 2010. (ENG., Illus.). 184p. pap. 39.95 (978-88-8158-769-8(6)) Charta ITA. Dist: D.A.P./Distributed Art Pubs.

Schavemaker, Margriet & Rakier, Mischa. Right about Now: Art & Theory since the 1990s, 1 vol. 2008. (ENG., Illus.). 184p. pap. 29.95 (978-90-78088-17-2(6)) Valiz NLD. Dist: D.A.P./Distributed Art Pubs.

Scheijen, Sjeng. Diaghilev: A Life, 1 vol. 2012. (ENG., Illus.). 560p. pap. 27.95 **(978-0-19-989178-8(8))** Oxford Univ. Pr., Inc.

Scheppe, Wolfgang, ed. Done. Book. 2011. (ENG., Illus.). 368p. 45.00 (978-3-7757-2773-0(6)) Hatje Cantz Verlag GmbH & Co KG DEU. Dist: D.A.P./Distributed Art Pubs.

Scheuerle, William H. George Baxter, the First Color Printing from Metal Plates & Wood Blocks: Portraying Victorian Values of England's Rising Middle Class. 2011. (Illus.). 180p. 129.95 **(978-0-7734-3920-7(X))** Mellen, Edwin Pr., The.

Schianchi, Lucia Fornari. Correggio. 2007. (Illus.). 112p. (978-88-7439-213-1(3)) 5 Continents.

Schiebler, Ralf. Salvador Dalí: The Reality of Dreams. 2011. (ENG., Illus.). 128p. pap. 14.95 **(978-3-7913-4612-0(1))** Prestel Publishing.

Schmidt-Burkhardt, Astrit, ed. Maciunas' Learning Machines: From Art History to a Chronology of Fluxus. 2nd ed. 2011. Orig. Title: Maciunas' Learning Machines. (ENG., Illus.). 216p. pap. 59.95 (978-3-7091-0479-8(3), 3709104793) Springer Wien AUT. Dist: Springer.

Schmied, Wieland. Edward Hopper: Portraits of America. 2011. (ENG., Illus.). 128p. pap. 14.95 **(978-3-7913-4613-7(X))** Prestel Publishing.

Schneider, Nadia, ed. Alberto Giacometti: Retrospective. 2010. (ENG., Illus.). 280p. 45.00 (978-3-03764-060-9(X)) JRP Ringier Kunstverlag AG CHE. Dist: D.A.P./Distributed Art Pubs.

Schnier, Jacques. Art Symbolism & the Unconscious: The Journal of Aesthetics & Art Criticism, V12, No. 1, September 1953. Munro, Thomas, ed. 2011. 12p. pap. 35.95 **(978-1-258-08126-3(1))** Literary Licensing, LLC.

A

Schoen, Christian, ed. Ragnar Kjartansson: the End. 2009. (ENG., Illus.). 120p. 40.00 (978-3-7757-2333-6(1)) Hatje Cantz Verlag GmbH & Co KG DEU. Dist: D.A.P./Distributed Art Pubs.

Schueller, Herbert M., et al, eds. Criticism V4, No 1, Winter 1962: A Quarterly for Literature & the Arts. 2011. 100p. 39.95 (978-1-258-01135-2(2)) Literary Licensing, LLC.

Schwabsky, Barry. Dana Schutz. 2010. (Illus.). 144p. 45.00 (978-0-8478-3329-0(1)) Rizzoli International Pubns., Inc.

Schwenk, Bernhard & Vinken, Barbara. Wow! Jewels of Norman Weber. Maurer, Ellen, ed. 2010. (GER & ENG., Illus.). 144p. 50.00 (978-3-89790-331-9(8)) Arnoldsche Art Pubs. DEU. Dist: Antique Collectors' Club.

Schwitters, Kurt & Schwitters, Ernst. Kurt Schwitters: Three Stories. Reichardt, Jasia, ed. 2011. (ENG., Illus.). 32p. 15.95 (978-1-85437-909-2(7)) Tate Publishing, Ltd. GBR. Dist: Hachette Bk. Group.

Scott, Gail R. E. Ambrose Webster: Chasing the Sun. 2009. (ENG., Illus.). 224p. 50.00 (978-1-55595-303-4(4)) Hudson Hills Pr. LLC.

Seaman, Natasha T. The Religious Paintings of Hendrick Ter Brugghen: Reinventing Christian Painting after the Reformation in Utrecht. 2012. (Visual Culture in Early Modernity Ser.). (Illus.). 200p. 104.95 (978-1-4094-3495-5(8)) Ashgate Publishing Co.

Sega. Tony's Artworks from Shining World. 2011. (Illus.). 208p. (YA). pap. 39.99 (978-1-926778-18-1(9)) URON Entertainment Corp. CAN. Dist: Diamond Bk. Distributors.

Seippel, Ralf-P. Jürgen Schadeberg. 2008. (ENG., Illus.). 288p. 85.00 (978-3-7757-2150-9(9)) Hatje Cantz Verlag GmbH & Co KG DEU. Dist: D.A.P./Distributed Art Pubs.

Selz, Peter, et al. Fletcher Benton: The Kinetic Years. 2009. (ENG., Illus.). 252p. 60.00 (978-1-55595-295-2(X)) Hudson Hills Pr. LLC.

Sendlinger, Marcus. Marcus Sendlinger: Lost Reality. 2011. (GER & ENG., Illus.). 48p. 34.95 (978-3-86678-450-5(3)) Kerber Verlag DEU. Dist: D.A.P./Distributed Art Pubs.

Sewell, Brian. Nothing Wasted. 2010. (ENG., Illus.). 272p. 50.00 (978-0-85667-683-3(7)) Wilson, Philip Pubs., Ltd. GBR. Dist: Macmillan.

Shanes, Eric. Dalí. 2nd ed. 2011. (Temporis Ser.). (ENG, FRE & GER., Illus.). 256p. 39.95 (978-1-84484-818-8(3)) Parkstone International GBR. Dist: Ingram Pub. Services.

Shapiro, Gavriel. The Sublime Artist's Studio: Nabokov & Painting. 2009. (ENG., Illus.). 320p. 45.00 (978-0-8101-2559-9(5)) Northwestern Univ. Pr.

Sharp, Charles. The Sovereignty of Art: Two Discourses Delivered in the Liverpool. 2007. pap. 18.95 (978-1-4304-9294-8(5)) Kessinger Publishing, LLC.

Shaw, George Bernard. The Sanity of Art. reprint ed. lib. bdg. 98.00 (978-0-7426-3225-7(3)) Classic Bks.

—The Sanity of Art. 2009. 58p. pap. 14.14 (978-0-217-97406-6(6)) General Bks. LLC.

Shaw-Miller, Simon & Smiles, Sam, eds. Samuel Palmer Revisited. 2010. (Illus.). 184p. 114.95 (978-0-7546-6747-6(2)) Ashgate Publishing Co.

Shawhan, Dorothy Sample & Norris, Carolyn. Spirit of the Delta: The Art of Carolyn Norris. 2011. (ENG., Illus.). 128p. 35.00 (978-1-60473-992-3(4)) Univ. Pr. of Mississippi.

Sheikh, Mohammed & Shiv Kumar, R. Benodebehari Mukherjee: A Centenary Retrospective Exhibition. 2010. (ENG., Illus.). 365p. 100.00 (978-81-87737-24-7(7), Vadehra Art Gallery (Acc)) Antique Collectors' Club GBR. Dist: National Bk. Network.

Shepherd, Simon & Donger, Simon, eds. Orlan: A Hybrid Body of Artworks. 2010. (ENG., Illus.). 240p. 115.00 (978-0-415-56233-1(3)); pap. 40.95 (978-0-415-56234-8(1)) Taylor & Francis Group GBR. (Routledge). Dist: Taylor & Francis Group.

Sheridan, Michael. Room 606: The Sas House & the Work of Arne Jacobsen. 2011. (ENG., Illus.). 272p. pap. 45.00 (978-0-7148-6108-1(1)) Phaidon Pr., Inc.

Shiff, Richard. Doubt. 2007. (Theories of Modernism & Postmodernism in the Visual Arts Ser.). (ENG., Illus.). 216p. 125.00 (978-0-415-97308-3(2)); per. 29.95 (978-0-415-97309-0(0)) Routledge.

Short, Christopher. The Art Theory of Wassily Kandinsky, 1909-1928: The Quest for Synthesis. 2009. (Illus.). xiv, 241p. 61.95 (978-3-03911-399-6(2)) Lang, Peter AG GBR. Dist: Lang, Peter.

Siedell, Daniel A. An Excavation of Tenth Street: Essays on the History of Abstract Expressionism. 2011. (ENG.). 225p. pap. 18.95 (978-0-9799752-5-7(5)) Whale & Star Pr.

Silver, Larry. Pieter Bruegel. 2011. (ENG., Illus.). 424p. 150.00 (978-0-7892-1104-0(1)) Abbeville Pr., Inc.

Silver, Larry & Smith, Jeffrey Chipps, eds. The Essential Durer. 2011. (Illus.). 312p. (C). pap. 29.95 (978-0-8122-2178-7(8)) Univ. of Pennsylvania Pr.

Silverman, Peter & Whitney, Catherine. Leonardo's Lost Princess: One Man's Quest to Authenticate an Unknown Portrait by Leonardo Da Vinci. 2012. (ENG., Illus.). 272p. 25.95 (978-0-470-93640-5(1), Wiley) Wiley, John & Sons, Inc.

Simic, Charles. Dime-Store Alchemy: The Art of Joseph Cornell. 2011. (ENG., Illus.). 88p. pap. 14.00 (978-1-59017-486-9(0), NYRB Classics) New York Review of Bks., Inc., The.

Singerman, Howard. Art History, after Sherrie Levine. 2011. (ENG., Illus.). 304p. 65.00 (978-0-520-26721-3(4)); pap. 24.95 (978-0-520-26722-0(2)) Univ. of California Pr.

Sirmans, Franklin & White, Michelle. Vija Celmins: Television & Disaster, 1964-1966. 2011. (ENG., Illus.). 64p. 21.95 (978-0-300-16612-5(5)) Yale Univ. Pr.

Sitte, Camillo, et al. Schriften Zu Kunstkritik und Kunstgewerbe. 2008. (GER., Illus.). 642p. (978-3-205-77581-2(3)) Bohlau Verlag Gmbh & Cie.

Slive, Seymour. Jacob Van Ruisdael: Windmills & Water Mills. 2011. (ENG., Illus.). 128p. 22.95 (978-1-60606-055-1(4), J. Paul Getty Museum) Getty Pubns.

Smart, Tom. Tom Forrestall: Paintings, Drawings, Writings. 2008. (ENG., Illus.). 152p. 49.95 (978-1-55470-005-9(1)) Key Porter Bks. CAN. Dist: Perseus-PGW.

Smith, Karen, et al, texts. Ai Weiwei. 2009. (ENG., Illus.). 160p. pap. 45.00 (978-0-7148-4889-1(1)) Phaidon Pr., Inc.

Smith, Paul & Wilde, Carolyn, eds. A Companion to Art Theory. 2007. (Blackwell Companions in Cultural Studies: 21). (ENG., Illus.). 552p. 209.95 (978-0-631-20762-7(7), Wiley-Blackwell) Wiley, John & Sons, Inc.

Smith, Richard G. Lee Bontecou: A Retrospective. Smith, Elizabeth A. T., ed. & contrib. by by. Storr, Robert, contrib. by. 2008. (ENG., Illus.). 240p. pap. 50.00 (978-0-300-13746-0(X)) Yale Univ. Pr.

Smithgall, Elsa, ed. Kandinsky & the Harmony of Silence: Painting with White Border. 2011. (ENG., Illus.). 136p. 45.00 (978-0-300-17078-8(5)) Yale Univ. Pr.

Smulders, Caroline & Perlein, Gilbert. Robert Longo. 2010. (ENG., Illus.). 176p. 55.00 (978-0-8478-3435-8(2)) Rizzoli International Pubns., Inc.

Sobel, Mechal. Painting a Hidden Life: The Art of Bill Traylor. 2009. (Illus.). 256p. 34.95 (978-0-8071-3401-6(5)) Louisiana State Univ. Pr.

Sohm, Philip. The Artist Grows Old: The Aging of Art & Artists in Italy, 1500-1800. 2007. (ENG., Illus.). 224p. 50.00 (978-0-300-12123-0(7)) Yale Univ. Pr.

Solntsev, F. G. & Whittaker, Cynthia H. Visualizing Russia: Fedor Solntsev & Crafting a National Past. 2010. (Russian History & Culture Ser.). (Illus.). XXXII, 184p. (978-90-04-18343-8(4)) BRILL.

Soulier-Détis, Elisabeth. Guess at the Rest: Cracking the Hogarth Code. 2010. (ENG., Illus.). 233p. pap. 58.00 (978-0-7188-9215-9(1)) Lutherworth Pr., The GBR. Dist: Brown, David Bk. Co., The.

Spalding, Frances. Prunella Clough: Seeing the World Sideways. 2012. (Illus.). 240p. 70.00 (978-1-84822-011-9(1), Lund Humphries Pubs.) Ashgate Publishing, Ltd. GBR. Dist: Ashgate Publishing Co.

Spieler, Reinhard. T25 Beckmann. 2011. (25 Ser.). (ENG., Illus.). 200p. 19.99 (978-3-8365-3253-2(0)) TASCHEN DEU. Dist: Ingram Pub. Services.

Spies, Werner. Werner Spies: the Eye & the Word: Collected Writings on Art & Literature, the Gagosian Edition, 10 vols. Gabriel, John et al, trs. from GER. 2011. (ENG., Illus.). 4500p. pap. 250.00 (978-0-8109-9835-3(1)) Abrams.

Spilsbury, Maria & Yeldham, Charlotte. Maria Spilsbury (1766-1820) Artist & Evangelical. 2010. (Illus.). 230p. 124.95 (978-0-7546-6991-3(2)) Ashgate Publishing Co.

Spring, Justin. Wolf Kahn. rev. ed. 2011. (ENG., Illus.). 196p. 55.00 (978-0-8109-9790-5(8)) Abrams.

Stanley, Michael. Thomas Houseago: What Went Down. 2011. (Illus.). 240p. 70.00 (978-1-901352-50-4(1), Lund Humphries Pubs.) Ashgate Publishing, Ltd. GBR. Dist: Ashgate Publishing Co.

Stebbing, Peter. The Goetheanum Cupola Motifs of Rudolf Steiner: Paintings by Gerard Wagner. 2011. (Illus.). 248p. (978-0-88010-737-2(5)) SteinerBooks, Inc.

Steeves, Andrew. Colville Tributes. 2011. (ENG.). 96p. pap. (978-1-55447-091-4(8)) Gaspereau Pr.

Steiner, Reinhard. Schiele. 2011. (25 Ser.). (ENG., Illus.). 96p. 14.99 (978-3-8365-3138-2(0)) TASCHEN DEU. Dist: Ingram Pub. Services.

Steiner, Wendy. Boaz Vaadia. 2012. 284p. 60.00 (978-1-55595-376-8(X)) Hudson Hills Pr. LLC.

Stella, Frank. Frank Stella: Irregular Polygons, 1965-66. Kennedy, Brian P., ed. 2010. (Illus.). 150p. 45.00 (978-0-944722-39-8(3)) Univ. Pr. of New England.

Stoppa, Jacopo. The Timeline Book of Rembrandt. 2008. (Timeline Book Of... Ser.). (ENG., Illus.). 36p. (978-1-85149-547-4(9), Antique Collectors Club Dist) Antique Collectors' Club.

—The Timeline Book of Turner. 2008. (Timeline Book Of... Ser.). (ENG., Illus.). 36p. (978-1-85149-552-8(5), Antique Collectors Club Dist) Antique Collectors' Club.

Strand, Mark. Hopper. 2011. (ENG., Illus.). 96p. 27.50 (978-0-307-70124-4(7), Knopf) Knopf Doubleday Publishing Group.

Strauss, David Levi. From Head to Hand: Art & the Manual. 2010. (ENG., Illus.). 176p. 24.95 (978-0-19-539122-0(5)) Oxford Univ. Pr., Inc.

Strong, Lisa Maria. Sentimental Journey: The Art of Alfred Jacob Miller. 2008. (ENG.). 238p. (C). 45.00 (978-0-88360-105-1(2)) Amon Carter Museum of American Art.

Stüttgen, Johannes, et al, texts. Joseph Beuys: Parallel Processes. 2010. (Illus.). 432p. 75.00 (978-3-8296-0482-6(3)) Schirmer/Mosel Verlag GmbH DEU. Dist: Prestel Publishing.

Sullivan, Edward J. Fragile Demon: Juan Soriano in Mexico, 1935 to 1950. 2008. (ENG., Illus.). 60p. pap. 19.95 (978-0-300-13688-3(9)) Yale Univ. Pr.

Sullivan, Margaret A. Bruegel & the Creative Process, 1559-1563. 2010. (Illus.). 268p. 124.95 (978-0-7546-6979-1(3)) Ashgate Publishing Co.

Sullivan, Michael & Gu, Hongzhong. The Night Entertainments of Han Xizai: A Scroll by Gu Hongzhong. 2008. (Illus.). 82p. 50.00 (978-0-520-25209-7(8)) Univ. of California Pr.

Susan, Weil. Susan Weil: Moving Pictures. 2011. (ENG., Illus.). 192p. 75.00 (978-88-572-0646-2(7)) Skira Editore ITA. Dist: Random Hse., Inc.

Sussman, Elisabeth & Wilson, Jane. Jane Wilson: Horizons. 2009. (Illus.). 192p. (978-1-85894-488-3(0)) Merrell Pubs. Ltd.

Suter, Rudolf. Hans Arp: Weltbild und Kunstauffassung im Spatwerk. (GER., Illus.). 594p. pap. 94.95 (978-3-03911-428-3(X)) Lang, Peter Publishing, Inc.

Swoon. Swoon. 2010. (ENG., Illus.). 192p. 35.00 (978-0-8109-8485-1(7)) Abrams.

Syme, Alison & Sargent, John Singer. A Touch of Blossom: John Singer Sargent & the Queer Flora of Fin-de-Siècle Art. 2010. (ENG.). 328p. 74.95 (978-0-271-03622-9(2)) Pennsylvania State Univ. Pr.

Tagliaferro, T. & Aikema, B. Le Botteghe di Tiziano. 2010. (ENG.). 600p. 135.00 (978-88-6302-017-5(5), Art Stock Bks. Ltd/Csi) Continental Sales, Inc.

Tait, Simon. Philip Sutton: Life & Work. 2008. (ENG., Illus.). 160p. 55.00 (978-1-905711-32-1(8)) Royal Academy of Arts GBR. Dist: Hachette Bk. Group.

Tatham, David. Winslow Homer in London. 2010. (Illus.). 168p. 24.95 (978-0-8156-0953-7(1)) Syracuse Univ. Pr.

Tatum, Stephen. In the Remington Moment. 2010. (ENG., Illus.). 280p. 55.00 (978-0-8032-2528-2(8)) Univ. of Nebraska Pr.

Taylor, John Russell, et al. Kurt Jackson: A New Genre of Landscape Painting. 2010. (Illus.). 144p. 70.00 (978-1-84822-041-6(3), Lund Humphries Pubs.) Ashgate Publishing, Ltd. GBR. Dist: Ashgate Publishing Co.

Taylor, Mark C. Refiguring the Spiritual: Beuys, Barney, Turrell, Goldsworthy. 2012. (Religion, Culture, & Public Life Ser.). (ENG., Illus.). 244p. (gr. 17). 27.50 (978-0-231-15766-7(5)) Columbia Univ. Pr.

Taylor, Michael R. Marcel Duchamp: Étant Donnés. 2009. (978-0-87633-210-8(6)); (978-0-87633-211-5(4)) Philadelphia Museum of Art.

Tazartes, Maurizia & Tazartes, Maurizia. Piero di Cosimo: Ingegno astratto e Difforme. 2010. (artisti raccontati nel loro Tempo Ser.). (ITA., Illus.). 160p. (C). pap. 36.00 (978-88-564-0096-0(0)) Polistampa ITA. Dist: Brown, David Bk. Co., The.

Tedeschi, Ermanno & Coen, Vittoria. Campolungo: The Sensitive Horizon of Contemporary Art. 2010. 144p. 44.95 (978-88-492-1730-8(7)) Gangemi ITA. Dist: International Publishers Marketing.

Templeton, Joan. Munch's Ibsen: A Painter's Visions of a Playwright. 2008. (ENG.). 256p. 35.00 (978-0-295-98776-7(6)) Univ. of Washington Pr.

Teukolsky, Rachel. Literate Eye: Victorian Art Writing & Modernist Aesthetics. 2009. (ENG., Illus.). 336p. 35.00 (978-0-19-538137-5(8)) Oxford Univ. Pr., Inc.

Theriault, Kim S. Rethinking Arshile Gorky. 2009. (ENG., Illus.). 264p. 90.00 (978-0-271-03647-2(8)); pap. 45.00 (978-0-271-03646-5(X)) Pennsylvania State Univ. Pr.

Thomas, Paul. Reconfiguring Space. 2009. 168p. pap. (978-3-639-14088-0(5)) VDM Verlag Dr. Mueller e.K.

Thomas, Stanton, et al. Carl Gutherz: Poetic Vision & Academic Ideals. Masler, Marilyn & Pacini, Marina, eds. 2009. (ENG., Illus.). 200p. pap. 39.95 (978-0-915525-11-9(9)) Memphis Brooks Museum of Art, Inc.

Thompson, Jon. The Collected Writings of Jon Thompson. Akerman, Jeremy & Daly, Eileen, eds. 2011. (ENG., Illus.). 536p. pap. (978-1-905464-37-1(1)) Ridinghouse.

Thomson, Richard. Vincent Van Gogh: The Starry Night. 2008. (ENG., Illus.). 48p. pap. 9.95 (978-0-87070-748-3(5)) Museum of Modern Art.

Thornton, Sarah. Seven Days in the Art World. (ENG., Illus.). 2009. 256p. pap. 15.95 (978-0-393-33712-9(X), 33712) 2008. 304p. 24.95 (978-0-393-06722-4(X), 6722) Norton, W. W. & Co., Inc.

Thorpe, Nigel, ed. James McNeill Whistler (1834-1903) Whistler on Art. (Illus.). 192p. pap. (978-1-85754-094-9(8)) Carcanet Pr., Ltd. GBR. Dist: Paul & Co. Pubs. Consortium, Inc.

Tolstoy, Leo. What Is Art? 2009. 280p. 30.99 (978-1-110-63321-0(1)); pap. 26.75 (978-1-110-63320-3(3)) BiblioBazaar.

—What Is Art? 2009. 218p. pap. 19.99 (978-1-4589-9350-2(7)) General Bks. LLC.

Tompkins Rivas, Pilar, et al, contrib. by. Bas Jan Ader. 2010. (ENG., Illus.). 69p. pap. 7.95 (978-0-9829956-0-0(1)) Pitzer College Art Galleries.

Tosches, Nick & Gravleu, Thierry Alonso. Never Trust a Loving God. 2009. (ENG.). 124p. 45.00 (978-2-7572-0264-7(2)) Somogy Editions d'Art FRA. Dist: Independent Pubs. Group.

Toynton, Evelyn. Jackson Pollock. 2012. (Icons of America Ser.). (ENG., Illus.). 160p. 26.00 (978-0-300-16325-4(8)) Yale Univ. Pr.

Treuherz, Julian. Ford Madox Brown: Pre-Raphaelite Pioneer. 2011. (ENG., Illus.). 336p. 55.00 (978-0-85667-700-7(0)) Wilson, Philip Pubs., Ltd. GBR. Dist: Macmillan.

Trippi, Peter, ed. J. W. Waterhouse: The Modern Pre-Raphaelite. 2009. (ENG., Illus.). 242p. 75.00 (978-1-905711-36-9(0)) Royal Academy of Arts GBR. Dist: Hachette Bk. Group.

Tromp, Henk. A Real Van Gogh: How the Art World Struggles with Truth. 2010. (Illus.). 351p. pap. (978-90-8964-176-2(9)) Amsterdam Univ. Pr.

Tsao, Hsingyuan & Ames, Roger T., eds. Xu Bing & Contemporary Chinese Art: Cultural & Philosophical Reflections. 2011. (SUNY series in Chinese Philosophy & Culture Ser.). (Illus.). 240p. 75.00 (978-1-4384-3791-0(9)); pap. 24.95 (978-1-4384-3790-3(0)) State Univ. of New York Pr.

Tucker, Thomas Deane. Derridada: Duchamp as Readymade Deconstruction. 2010. (ENG.). 110p. pap. 24.50 (978-0-7391-1623-4(1)) Lexington Bks.

Turner, Silvie. Julian Trevelyan Catalogue Raisonne of Prints: Revised Reprint. rev. ed. 2011. (Illus.). 184p. 170.00 (978-1-84822-077-5(4), Lund Humphries Pubs.) Ashgate Publishing, Ltd. GBR. Dist: Ashgate Publishing Co.

Turrell, James. James Turrell: Zug Zuoz. 2010. (ENG., Illus.). 176p. 60.00 (978-3-7757-2602-3(0)) Hatje Cantz Verlag GmbH & Co KG DEU. Dist: D.A.P./Distributed Art Pubs.

Twombly, Cy. Cy Twombly: Cycles & Seasons. 2008. (ENG., Illus.). 256p. 55.00 (978-1-933045-88-7(4)) D.A.P./Distributed Art Pubs.

Udo, Kittelmann & Silke, Krohn, eds. Hans Bellmer / Louise Bourgeois: Double Sexus. 2010. 160p. 60.00 (978-3-89955-403-8(5)) Die Gestalten Verlag DEU. Dist: Prestel Publishing.

Ueberwasser, Walter, intro. Giotto: Frescoes. 2011. 44p. pap. 35.95 (978-1-258-02774-2(7)) Literary Licensing, LLC.

Umberto Allemandi and Company Staff. Noguchi: Between East & West. 2011. (ENG., Illus.). 176p. 49.00 (978-88-422-1876-0(6)) Allemandi, Umberto & Co. GBR. Dist: Antique Collectors' Club.

Umland, Annette, ed. Joan Miró: Painting & Anti-Painting, 1927-1937. 2008. (ENG., Illus.). 242p. 50.00 (978-0-87070-734-6(5)) Museum of Modern Art.

Unger, Daniel M. Guercino's Piantings & His Patrons' Politics in Early Modern Italy. 2010. (Visual Culture in Early Modernity Ser.). (Illus.). 212p. 124.95 (978-0-7546-6909-8(2)) Ashgate Publishing Co.

Van De Vall, Renee & Vall, Renée van de. At the Edges of Vision: A Phenomenological Aesthetics of Contemporary Spectatorship. 2008. (Histories of Vision Ser.). (Illus.). 190p. 114.95 (978-0-7546-4073-8(6)) Ashgate Publishing Co.

Van De Wettering. Rembrandt. 2009. (Illus.). 356p. pap. (978-90-8964-033-8(9)) Amsterdam Univ. Pr.

van Dyke, James A. Franz Radziwill & the Contradictions of German Art History, 1919-45. 2010. (Social History, Popular Culture, & Politics in Germany Ser.). (ENG., Illus.). 340p. (C). 80.00 (978-0-472-11628-7(2)) Univ. of Michigan Pr.

van Gogh, Vincent. Vincent Van Gogh - De Brieven: De Volledige, Geïllustreerde en Geannoteerde Uitgave. Luijten, Hans et al, eds. 2nd ed. 2010.Tr. of Vincent Van Gogh - The Letters. (DUT., Illus.). 2240p. (978-90-8964-102-1(5)) Amsterdam Univ. Pr.

van Haaren, Bettina. Bettina van Haaren: Häutungen. Malerei und Zeichnung / Paintings & Drawings. 2010. (ENG., Illus.). 104p. 47.50 (978-3-86678-361-4(2)) Kerber Verlag DEU. Dist: D.A.P./Distributed Art Pubs.

Vann, Philip. Cyril Power Linocuts: A Complete Catalogue. 2008. (Illus.). 112p. pap. 50.00 (978-1-84822-018-8(9), Lund Humphries Pubs.) Ashgate Publishing, Ltd. GBR. Dist: Ashgate Publishing Co.

—Tessa Newcomb. 2013. (ENG., Illus.). 144p. 50.00 (978-1-904537-94-6(4)) Sansom & Co. Ltd. GBR. Dist: National Bk. Network.

Veen, Wouter van der & Gogh, Vincent van. Van Gogh: A Literary Mind: Literature in the Correspondence of Vincent Van Gogh. 2010. (ENG., Illus.), 264p. 85.00 (978-90-400-8562-8(5)) Waanders B.V., Uitgeverij NLD. Dist: National Bk. Network.

Veiteberg, Jorunn, et al. Sigurd Bronger: Laboratorium Mechanum. 2011. (NOR, GER & ENG., Illus.). 184p. 85.00 (978-3-89790-345-6(8)) Arnoldsche Art Pubs. DEU. Dist: Antique Collectors' Club.

Verleysen, Catherine. Maurice Denis et la Belgique, 1890-1930. 2011. (KADOC Artes Ser.). (Illus.). 176p. 80.00 (978-90-5867-808-9(3)) Leuven Univ. Pr. BEL. Dist: Cornell Univ. Pr.

Verwoert, Jan. Tell Me What You Want, What You Really, Really Want. Ohlraun, Vanessa, ed. 2011. (ENG., Illus.). 312p. 22.00 (978-1-934105-14-6(7)) Sternberg Pr.

Victoria, Charles & Klaus, Carl H. 1000 Portraits of Genius. 2011. (Book Ser.). (Illus.). 544p. 24.95 (978-1-84484-803-4(5)) Parkstone International GBR. Dist: Ingram Pub. Services.

Vidler, Anthony. James Fraser Stirling: Notes from the Archive. 2010. (Illus.). 300p. 70.00 (978-0-300-16723-8(7)) Yale Univ. Pr.

Viliani, Andrea, ed. Stefano Cagol: Public Opinion. 2011. (ITA & ENG., Illus.). 232p. pap. 55.00 (978-88-8158-820-6(X)) Charta ITA. Dist: D.A.P./Distributed Art Pubs.

Vivas, Eliseo. D H Lawrence: The Failure & the Triumph of Art. 2011. 320p. 50.95 (978-1-258-02735-3(6)) Literary Licensing, LLC.

Viveros-Faune, Christian & Schwabsky, Barry, texts. Yishai Jusidman: Paintworks. 2009. (ENG., Illus.). 240p. 45.00 (978-84-7506-847-3(2)) Turner, Ediciones S.A. ESP. Dist: D.A.P./Distributed Art Pubs.

Vodret, Rossella, ed. & text. Caravaggio: The Complete Works, 1 vol. 2010. (ENG.). 216p. 60.00 (978-88-366-1662-6(3)) Silvana ITA. Dist: D.A.P./Distributed Art Pubs.

Vogt, Margrit. Von Kunstworten und -werten: Die Entstehung der deutschen Kunstkritik in Periodika der Aufklärung. 2010. (Wolfenbütteler Studien zur Aufklärung Ser.). (GER., Illus.). VII, 364p. 112.00 (978-3-11-023318-6(5)) De Gruyter, Walter Inc.

Volk, Alicia. In Pursuit of Universalism: Yorozu Tetsugoro & Japanese Modern Art. 2010. (Phillips Book Prize Ser.). (ENG., Illus.). 352p. 49.95 (978-0-520-25952-2(1)) Univ. of California Pr.

Von Moos, Stanislaus. Max Huber. 2011. (ENG., Illus.). 240p. pap. 45.00 (978-0-7148-6110-4(3)) Phaidon Pr., Inc.

Waanders Editors. Jan Van Goyen: Portraitist of the Hague. 2010. (ENG., Illus.). 104p. 24.95 (978-90-400-8670-0(2)) Waanders B.V., Uitgeverij NLD. Dist: National Bk. Network.

—Rogier van der Weyden 1400-1464: Master of Passions. 2010. (ENG., Illus.). 576p. 130.00 (978-90-8526-105-6(8)) Waanders B.V., Uitgeverij NLD. Dist: National Bk. Network.

—Visions: Gauguin & His Time - Van Gogh Studies 3. 2010. (ENG., Illus.). 208p. 85.00 (978-90-400-7659-6(6)) Waanders B.V., Uitgeverij NLD. Dist: National Bk. Network.

Wagnermaier, Silvia, ed. Variantology 1: On Deep Time Relations of Arts, Sciences & Technologies, 1 vol. 2007. (ENG., Illus.). 384p. per. 45.00 (978-3-88375-914-2(7)) Verlag der Buchhandlung Walther Konig DEU. Dist: D.A.P./Distributed Art Pubs.

Wahrman, Dror. Mr. Collier's Letter Racks: A Tale of Art & Illusion at the Threshold of the Modern Information Age. 2012. (ENG., Illus.). 288p. 34.95 (978-0-19-973886-1(6)) Oxford Univ. Pr., Inc.

Walker, Stephen. Gordon Matta-Clark: Art, Architecture & the Attack on Modernism. 2009. (ENG., Illus.). 224p. pap. 31.00 *(978-1-84511-966-9(5))* I. B. Tauris & Co., Ltd. GBR. Dist: Macmillan.

Walther, Ingo F. T25 kr van Gogh. 2012. (25 Ser.). (ENG., Illus.). 96p. 14.99 ***(978-3-8365-3154-2(2))*** TASCHEN DEU. Dist: Ingram Pub. Services.

Ware, Robert, et al. To Form from Air: Music & the Art of Raymond Jonson. 2010. (ENG., Illus.). 96p. *(978-0-89013-571-6(1))* Museum of New Mexico Pr.

Warhol, Andy. Warhol after Munch. 2010. (ENG., Illus.). 128p. 35.00 *(978-87-91607-79-0(5))* Louisana DNK. Dist: D.A.P./Distributed Art Pubs.

Warkel, Harriet G. Paper to Paint: Edward Hopper's Hotel Lobby. 2008. (ENG., Illus.). 60p. pap. 14.95 *(978-0-936260-84-6(X))* Indianapolis Museum of Art.

Warrell, Ian. Turner Inspired: In the Light of Claude. 2012. (ENG., Illus.). 144p. 45.00 ***(978-1-85709-537-1(5))*** Yale Univ. Pr.

Warrell, Ian & Moorby, Nicola, eds. How to Paint Like Turner. 2010. (ENG., Illus.). 144p. pap. 24.95 *(978-1-85437-883-5(X))* Tate Publishing, Ltd. GBR. Dist: Hachette Bk. Group.

Warren, Lynne. Jim Nutt: Coming into Character. 2011. (ENG., Illus.). 136p. 35.00 *(978-0-300-17236-6(9))* Yale Univ. Pr.

Watson, Gray. Art & Sex. 2008. (Art and... Ser.). (ENG., Illus.). 168p. 79.00 *(978-1-84511-664-4(X))*; pap. 28.00 *(978-1-84511-665-1(8))* I. B. Tauris & Co., Ltd. GBR. Dist: Macmillan.

Watson, Stephen. Crescent Moon over the Rational: Philosophical Interpretations of Paul Klee. 2009. (ENG., Illus.). 256p. 50.00 *(978-0-8047-6125-3(6))* Stanford Univ. Pr.

Watt, James C. Y., ed. The World of Khubilai Khan: Chinese Art in the Yuan Dynasty. 2010. (ENG., Illus.). 360p. 65.00 *(978-0-300-16656-9(7))* Yale Univ. Pr.

Webb, Brian & Artmonsky, Ruth. FHK Henrion. 2011. (ENG., Illus.). 96p. 19.95 *(978-1-85149-632-7(7))* Antique Collectors' Club.

Webb, Brian & Skipwith, Peyton. David Gentleman: Design. 2009. (ENG., Illus.). 96p. *(978-1-85149-595-5(9)*, Antique Collectors Club Dist) Antique Collectors' Club.

Wedde, Ian & Culbert, Bill. Bill Culbert: Making Light Work. 2010. (ENG., Illus.). 280p. 49.95 *(978-1-86940-439-0(4))* Auckland Univ. Pr. NZL. Dist: Independent Pubs. Group.

Weibel, Peter & Buddensieg, Andrea, eds. Contemporary Art & the Museum: A Global Perspective, 1 vol. 2007. (ENG., Illus.). 256p. per. 40.00 *(978-3-7757-1933-9(4))* Hatje Cantz Verlag GmbH & Co KG DEU. Dist: D.A.P./Distributed Art Pubs.

Wells, Walter. Silent Theater: The Art of Edward Hopper. 2012. (ENG., Illus.). 372p. pap. 39.95 ***(978-0-7148-6309-2(2))*** Phaidon Pr., Inc.

Wendt, Selene & Gurholt, Crispin, eds. Live Photo. 2010. (ENG & NOR., Illus.). 160p. 40.00 *(978-88-572-0264-8(X))* Skira Editore ITA. Dist: Random Hse., Inc.

Wesseling, Janneke, ed. See It Again, Say It Again: The Artist as Researcher. 2011. (ENG., Illus.). 305p. pap. 28.95 ***(978-90-78088-53-0(2))*** Valiz NLD. Dist: D.A.P./Distributed Art Pubs.

Westley, Hannah. Sheila Girling. 2008. (Illus.). 200p. 80.00 *(978-0-85331-974-0(X)*, Lund Humphries Pubs.) Ashgate Publishing, Ltd. GBR. Dist: Ashgate Publishing Co.

White, Anthony. Lucio Fontana: Between Utopia & Kitsch. 2011. (October Bks.). (ENG., Illus.). 344p. (gr. 17). 29.95 *(978-0-262-01592-9(7))* MIT Pr.

Whitehead. Interpreting Art in the Museum, Gallery & Beyond. 2012. (ENG., Illus.). 216p. (C). 115.00 *(978-0-415-41920-8(4))*; pap. 38.95 *(978-0-415-41922-2(0))* Routledge.

Wieseman, Marjorie E., et al. Vermeer's Women: Secrets & Silence. 2011. (ENG., Illus.). 224p. 35.00 *(978-0-300-17899-9(9))* Yale Univ. Pr.

Wilcox, Timothy. Constable & Salisbury: The Soul of Landscape. 2011. (ENG., Illus.). 196p. pap. 39.95 *(978-1-85759-678-6(1))* Scala, Editions FRA. Dist: National Bk. Network.

Wildenstein, Daniel. Monet or the Triumph of Impressionism. 2010. (25 Ser.). (ENG., Illus.). 480p. 29.99 *(978-3-8365-2321-9(3))* TASCHEN DEU. Dist: Ingram Pub. Services.

Wilkin, Karen. Anthony Caro: Interior & Exterior. 2009. (Illus.). 152p. 60.00 *(978-1-84822-031-7(6)*, Lund Humphries Pubs.) Ashgate Publishing, Ltd. GBR. Dist: Ashgate Publishing Co.

Wilkin, Karen & Yau, John. The Interior, Exterior & Scenic: The Paintings of Cynthia Polsky, 1963-1974. 2007. (ENG., Illus.). 132p. 73.00 *(978-0-85667-628-4(4))* Wilson, Philip Pubs., Ltd. GBR. Dist: Macmillan.

Williams, Charlotte & Williams, Evelyn A., eds. Denis Williams: New & Collected Essays.: A Life in Works. 2010. (ENG., Illus.). 262p. 75.00 *(978-90-420-2791-6(6))* Rodopi.

Williams, Robert. Art, Theory, & Culture in Sixteenth-Century Italy: From Techne to Metatechne. 2011. (ENG.). 256p. pap. 35.99 *(978-0-521-18433-5(9))* Cambridge Univ. Pr.

Wilmers, Gertrude de G. & Sloan, Julie L. Frederic Crowninshield: A Renaissance Man in Gilded Age. 2010. (Illus.). 448p. 39.95 *(978-1-55849-864-8(8))* Univ. of Massachusetts Pr.

Wilson, Andrew. Richard Hamilton - Swingeing London 67. 2011. (Afterall Ser.). (ENG., Illus.). 120p. (gr. 17). pap. 16.00 ***(978-1-84638-077-8(4))*** Afterall Publishing GBR. Dist: MIT Pr.

Withers, Rachel, et al. Roman Signer. 2010. (ENG., Illus.). 192p. pap., pap. 59.95 *(978-3-8321-7720-1(5))* DuMont DEU. Dist: D.A.P./Distributed Art Pubs.

Witkovsky, Matthew S., ed. Dawoud Bey: Harlem U. S. A. 2012. (ENG., Illus.). 88p. 25.00 ***(978-0-300-18126-5(4))*** Art Institute of Chicago.

Wolf, Norbert. Albrecht Durer. 2010. (Illus.). 304p. 120.00 *(978-3-7913-4426-3(9))* Prestel Publishing.

—Dürer. 2010. (25 Ser.). (ENG.). 96p. 14.99 *(978-3-8365-1348-7(X))* TASCHEN DEU. Dist: Ingram Pub. Services.

Wolfe, Gregory. Sacred Passion: The Art of William Schickel, Second Edition. 2nd ed. 2010. (ENG., Illus.). 240p. 75.00 *(978-0-268-04417-6(1))* Univ. of Notre Dame Pr.

Woodall, Joanna. Anthonis Mor: Art & Authority. 2008. (Studies in Netherlandish Art & Cultural History Ser.). (ENG., Illus.). 512p. 175.00 *(978-90-400-8421-8(1))* Waanders B.V., Uitgeverij NLD. Dist: National Bk. Network.

Wurm, Erwin. Erwin Wurm. 2010. (ENG., Illus.). 336p. 75.00 *(978-3-8321-9259-4(X))* DuMont DEU. Dist: D.A.P./Distributed Art Pubs.

Wyss, Beat. Hegel's Art History & the Critique of Modernity: The 'Sorrow of Perfect' in the Aesthetics of German Idealism & Modern Art Criticism. 2008. (Res Monographs in Anthropology & Aesthetics). (ENG., Illus.). 308p. pap. 63.00 *(978-0-521-06680-8(8))* Cambridge Univ. Pr.

Yarnall, James L. John la Farge A Biographical & Critical Study. 2012. (Illus.). 384p. 99.95 ***(978-1-4094-1172-7(9))*** Ashgate Publishing Co.

Yun, Pom-Mo. Kim Pok-Chin Yon'gu: Ilche Kangjom Ha Choso Yesul Kwa Munye Undong. 2010. (Illus.). 559p. *(978-89-7801-275-1(2))* Dong-guk Univ. Pr.

Zabel, Barbara Beth & Calder, Alexander. Calder's Portraits: A New Language. 2011. (ENG.). 176p. 65.00 *(978-0-9788460-9-1(5))* Smithsonian Institution Scholarly Pr.

Zelevansky, Lynn & Sussman, Elisabeth, eds. Paul Thek: Diver, A Retrospective. 2010. (ENG., Illus.). 304p. 65.00 *(978-0-300-16595-1(1))* Yale Univ. Pr.

Zielinski, Siegfried & Furlus, Eckhard, eds. Variantology V: Neapolitan Affairs. 2011. (ENG., Illus.). 608p. pap. 75.00 ***(978-3-86560-887-1(6))*** Verlag der Buchhandlung Walther Konig DEU. Dist: D.A.P./Distributed Art Pubs.

Zinn, Howard, et al. Eleanor Rubin Dreams of Despair. 2011. (ENG., Illus.). 64p. pap. 24.95 *(978-88-8158-788-9(2))* Charta ITA. Dist: D.A.P./Distributed Art Pubs.

Zoellner, Frank. Botticelli. 2009. (Illus.). 320p. 65.00 *(978-3-7913-4358-7(0))* Prestel Publishing.

Zollner, Frank. Leonardo. 2010. (25 Ser.). (ENG., Illus.). 96p. 14.99 *(978-3-8365-1355-5(2))* TASCHEN DEU. Dist: Ingram Pub. Services.

Zollner, Frank & Nathan, Johannes. T25 Leonardo Da Vinci, 2 vols. 2011. (25 Ser.). (ENG., Illus.). 700p. pap. 29.99 ***(978-3-8365-2975-4(0))*** TASCHEN DEU. Dist: Ingram Pub. Services.

Zöllner, Frank, et al. Michelangelo. 2010. (Go Ser.). (ENG., Illus.). 388p. 39.99 *(978-3-8365-2117-8(2))* TASCHEN DEU. Dist: Ingram Pub. Services.

Zuffi, Stefano. How to Read Italian Renaissance Painting. 2010. (ENG., Illus.). 400p. pap. 35.00 *(978-0-8109-8940-5(9))* Abrams.

ART DEALERS

Balk, Dennis. Colin de Land: American Fine Arts. 2008. (ENG., Illus.). 256p. 45.00 *(978-1-57687-425-7(7))* powerHouse Cultural Entertainment, Inc.

Beyeler, Ernst & Mory, Christophe. A Passion for Art. 2012. (ENG., Illus.). 204p. 39.00 ***(978-3-85881-727-3(9))*** Scheidegger und Spiess AG, Verlag CHE. Dist: Antique Collectors' Club.

Boll, Dirk, text. Art for Sale, 1 vol. 2011. (ENG.). 192p. pap. 25.00 *(978-3-7757-2815-7(5))* Hatje Cantz Verlag GmbH & Co KG DEU. Dist: D.A.P./Distributed Art Pubs.

Brown, Shana Julia. Pastimes: From Art & Antiquarianism to Modern Chinese Historiography. 2011. 232p. 48.00 ***(978-0-8248-3498-2(4))*** Univ. of Hawaii Pr.

Cassidy, Brendan. Gavin Hamilton (1723-1798) Artist, Antiquarian & Art Dealer in Eighteenth-Century Rome. with an Edition of his Letters, 2 vols. 2011. (Collectors & Dealers Ser.). (ENG., Illus.). 750p. (C). 196.00 *(978-1-905375-59-2(X))* Brepols Pubs. BEL. Dist: Brown, David Bk. Co., The.

Clarke, William M. Palace of the Hidden Treasures: Saving the Romanov Jewels. 2009. (Illus.). 192p. pap. 24.95 *(978-1-905267-25-5(8))* NMS Enterprises Ltd. - Publishing GBR. Dist: Antique Collectors' Club.

Clayton, Timothy. Colnaghi: The History. 2010. (ENG., Illus.). 68p. pap. 40.00 *(978-1-907372-07-0(5))* Holberton, Paul Publishing GBR. Dist: Univ. of Washington Pr.

Cohen-Solal, Annie. Leo & His Circle: The Life of Leo Castelli. 2010. (ENG., Illus.). 576p. 35.00 *(978-1-4000-4427-6(8)*, Knopf) Knopf Doubleday Publishing Group.

Dammann, April. Exhibitionist: Earl Stendhal, Art Dealer As Impressario. 2011. (Illus.). 192p. *(978-1-883318-86-4(6))* Angel City Pr.

Duveen, James Henry. Secrets of an Art Dealer. 2007. 312p. per. *(978-1-4067-6914-2(2))* Read Bks.

Egloff, Brian. Bones of the Ancestors: The Ambum Stone: from the New Guinea Highlands to the Antiquities Market to Australia. 2008. (ENG., Illus.) 240p. 80.00 *(978-0-7591-1159-2(6))* AltaMira Pr.

Fowle, Frances. Van Gogh's Twin: The Scottish Art Dealer Alexander Reid. 2011. (ENG., Illus.) 180p. *(978-1-906270-29-2(5))* National Galleries of Scotland.

Groothof, Frank. Vincent & Theo: Brothers in Art. 2006. (ENG., Illus.). 48p. 19.95 *(978-90-400-9354-8(7))* Waanders B.V., Uitgeverij NLD. Dist: National Bk. Network.

Hall, Ron. What Difference Do It Make? Stories of Hope & Healing. lt. ed. 2010. (ENG.). 253p. 30.99 *(978-1-4104-2778-6(1))* Thorndike Pr.

Hall, Ron & Moore, Denver. Same Kind of Different As Me: A Modern-Day Slave, an International Art Dealer, & the Unlikely Woman Who Bound Them Together. lt. ed. 2010. (ENG.). 448p. pap. 17.99 *(978-1-59415-318-1(3))* Cengage Gale.

—Same Kind of Different As Me: A Modern-Day Slave, an International Art Dealer, & the Unlikely Woman Who Bound Them Together. 0 vols. 2008. 256p. pap. 15.99 *(978-0-8499-1910-7(X))* Nelson, Thomas Inc.

—Same Kind of Different As Me: A Modern-Day Slave, an International Art Dealer, & the Unlikely Woman Who Bound Them Together. lt. ed. 2010. (ENG.). 440p. 30.95 *(978-1-4104-2456-3(1))* Thorndike Pr.

Heiberg, S., et al, eds. Pieter Isaacsz (1569-1625) Court Painter, Art Trader & Spy. 2007. (ENG., Illus.). 320p. (C). 102.00 *(978-2-503-52466-5(4))* Brepols Pubs. BEL. Dist: ISD.

Herstatt, Claudia, text. Women Gallerists: In the 20th & 21st Centuries. 2009. (ENG., Illus.). 208p. 45.00 *(978-3-7757-1975-9(X))* Hatje Cantz Verlag GmbH & Co KG DEU. Dist: D.A.P./Distributed Art Pubs.

International Directory of Arts 2012, 3 vols. 36th ed. 2011. (ENG., Illus.). XXIV, 2954p. ***(978-3-11-023488-6(2))*** Saur, K. G. Verlag GmbH & Co.

Johnson, Peter. Heart in Art: A Life in Paintings. 2011. (ENG., Illus.). 176p. 38.95 *(978-1-903071-31-1(3))* Bene Factum Publishing, Ltd. GBR. Dist: Independent Pubs. Group.

Lammertse, Friso & Van Der Veen, Jaap. Uylenburgh & Son: Art & Commerce from Rembrandt to de Lairesse, 1625-1675. 2007. (ENG., Illus.). 192p. 65.00 *(978-90-400-8164-4(6))* Waanders B.V., Uitgeverij NLD. Dist: National Bk. Network.

Mannini, Lucia. Le stanze dei Tesori: Collezionisti e antiquari a Firenze tra Ottocento e Novecento. 2011. (Piccoli, grandi Musei Ser.). (ENG & ITA., Illus.). 312p. (C). 75.00 ***(978-88-596-0965-0(8))*** Polistampa ITA. Dist: Brown, David Bk. Co., The.

Mileti, Nick James. The Unscrupulous: Scams, Cons, Fakes, & Frauds that Poison the Fine Arts. 2009. 314p. pap. 20.00 *(978-1-59954-003-0(7))* Bordighera Incorporated.

Morioka, Michiyo. An American Artist in Tokyo: Frances Blakemore, 1906-1997. 2008. (Illus.). 199p. 35.00 *(978-0-295-98773-6(1))* Univ. of Washington Pr.

Page, John R. & Bayer, Thomas M. The Development of the Art Market in England: Money as Muse, 1730-1900, 1 vol. 2011. (Financial History Ser.). (ENG., Illus.). 288p. 99.00 *(978-1-84893-043-8(7))* Pickering & Chatto Pubs., Ltd. GBR. Dist: Ashgate Publishing Co.

Pollock, Lindsay. The Girl with the Gallery: Edith Gregor Halpert & the Making of the Modern Art Market. 2007. (ENG., Illus.). 504p. per. 24.00 *(978-1-58648-512-2(1))* PublicAffairs.

Polsky, Richard. The Art Prophets: The Artists, Dealers, & Tastemakers Who Shook the Art World. 2011. (ENG., Illus.). 272p. 24.95 *(978-1-59051-406-1(8))* Other Pr., LLC.

Ridley, Jo Ann. Zoë Dusanne: An Art Dealer Who Made a Difference. 2011. (ENG.). 176p. pap. 15.95 *(978-1-56474-505-7(8)*, Fithian Pr) Daniel & Daniel, Pubs., Inc.

Silvestrini, Chiara. Mariano Rocchi Antiquario: Il Commercio D'arte Sull'asse Perugia-Roma Tra Otto e Novecento. 2008. (ITA., Illus.). 301p. *(978-88-89298-67-1(7))* Effe.

Strauss, Michel. Pictures, Passions & Eye: A Life at Sotheby's. 2011. (ENG.). 308p. 45.00 *(978-1-905559-21-3(6))* Halban Pubs. GBR. Dist: Independent Pubs. Group.

Turner, Adriana & Warren, Jeremy, eds. Auctions, Agents & Dealers: The Mechanisms of the Art Market 1660-1830. 2008. (Studies in the history of Collections). (ENG., Illus.). 173p. (C). pap. 50.00 *(978-1-903767-10-8(5))* Archaeopress GBR. Dist: Brown, David Bk. Co., The.

Velthuis, Olav. Talking Prices: Symbolic Meanings of Prices on the Market for Contemporary Art. 2007. (Princeton Studies in Cultural Sociology). (ENG., Illus.). 288p. (C). per. 22.95 *(978-0-691-13403-1(0))* Princeton Univ. Pr.

Vermeylen, Filip, et al, eds. Art Auctions & Dealers: The Dissemination of Netherlandish Painting During the Ancien Regime. 2009. (Studies in European Urban History (1100-1800) Ser.). (ENG.). 174p. (C). pap. 94.00 *(978-2-503-51620-2(3))* Brepols Pubs. BEL. Dist: ISD.

ART DECO

Alonso, Alejandro G. Havana Deco. 2007. 39.95 *(978-0-7937-3232-6(8))* Norton, W. W. & Co., Inc.

Alonso, Alejandro G., et al. Havana Deco. 2007. (ENG., Illus.). 192p. 39.95 *(978-0-393-73232-0(0)*, 73232) Norton, W. W. & Co., Inc.

Benedictus, Edouard. 177 Art Deco Designs. 2006. (Dover Electronic Clip Art Ser.). (ENG., Illus.). 48p. pap. 19.95 *(978-0-486-99766-7(9))* Dover Pubns., Inc.

Brown, Kendall H. Deco Japan: Shaping Art & Culture, 1920-1945. 2012. ***(978-0-88397-157-4(7))*** Art Services International.

Camard, Florence. Ruhlmann. 2011. (ENG., Illus.). 512p. 150.00 *(978-0-8478-5799-9(9))* Rizzoli International Pubns., Inc.

Casey, Andrew. Art Deco Ceramics in Britain. 2007. (ENG., Illus.). 280p. *(978-1-85149-544-3(4)*, Antique Collectors Club Dist) Antique Collectors' Club.

—Clarice Cliff. 2010. (ENG., Illus.). 144p. instr.'s gde. ed. *(978-1-85149-599-3(1)*, Antique Collectors Club Dist) Antique Collectors' Club.

Charayron, A. & Durand, Léon. Art Nouveau Stencil Designs in Color. 2009. (ENG., Illus.). 64p. pap. 16.95 *(978-0-486-47216-4(7))* Dover Pubns., Inc.

Charles, Victoria & Klaus, Carl H. Art Deco. 2011. (Art of Century Ser.). (ENG., Illus.). 200p. 19.95 *(978-1-84484-846-1(9))* Parkstone Pr. USA, Ltd.

Crowe, Michael F. & Bowen, Robert W. San Francisco Art Deco. 2007. (Images of America Ser.). (ENG., Illus.). 128p. per. 21.99 *(978-0-7385-4734-3(4))* Arcadia Publishing.

Dover. Egyptian Motifs in the Art Deco Style. 2011. (Dover Pictorial Archive Ser.). (ENG., Illus.). 80p. pap. 16.95 ***(978-0-486-48446-4(7))*** Dover Pubns., Inc.

Dover Publications Inc. Staff, creator. Dazzling Art Deco Designs. 2007. (Dover Electronic Clip Art Ser.). (ENG., Illus.). 48p. pap. 19.95 *(978-0-486-99848-0(7))* Dover Pubns., Inc.

Dover Publications Inc. Staff, ed. Art Deco Design. 2007. (Dover Pictura Electronic Clip Art Ser.). (ENG., Illus.). 128p. pap. 39.95 *(978-0-486-99807-7(X))* Dover Pubns., Inc.

Down, Barrie. Art Deco & British Car Design: The Airline Cars of the 1930s. 2010. (ENG., Illus.). 144p. reprint ed. 44.95 *(978-1-84584-252-9(9)*, 1845842529) Veloce Publishing Ltd. GBR. Dist: MBI Distribution Services/Quayside Distribution.

Duncan, Alastair. El Art Deco. (SPA., Illus.). 215p. 39.95 *(978-84-233-2436-1(2)*, DE362) Ediciones Destino ESP. Dist: Continental Bk. Co., Inc.

—Art Deco Complete: The Definitive Guide to the Decorative Arts of the 1920s & 1930s. 2009. (ENG., Illus.). 544p. 125.00 *(978-0-8109-8046-4(0))* Abrams.

—High Style: Masterworks from the Bernard & Sylvia Ostry Collection in the Royal Ontario Museum. 2006. (ENG., Illus.). 148p. *(978-0-88854-446-9(4))* Royal Ontario Museum.

Farmer, Will. Clarice Cliff. 2010. (Shire Library). (ENG., Illus.). 64p. pap. 12.95 *(978-0-7478-0774-2(4))* Shire Pubns., Ltd. GBR. Dist: Random Hse., Inc.

Gladky, Serge. Jazz Age Art Deco. 2007. (Dover Electronic Clip Art Ser.). (ENG., Illus.). 48p. pap. 22.95 *(978-0-486-99883-1(5))* Dover Pubns., Inc.

Grafton, Carol Belanger, ed. East Meets West Art Deco Motifs CD-ROM & Book. 2010. (Dover Electronic Clip Art Ser.). (ENG., Illus.). 48p. pap. 19.95 *(978-0-486-99114-6(8))* Dover Pubns., Inc.

Green, Nancy E. Joie de Vivre: Art Nouveau & Art Deco Ceramics from the Shatzman Collection. 2009. (Illus.). 71p. *(978-1-934260-10-4(X))* Cornell Univ., Herbert F. Johnson Museum of Art.

Holzach, Cornelie, ed. Art Déco Schmuck und Accessoires: Ein neuer Stil für eine neue Welt. 2008. (ENG., Illus.). 160p. 70.00 *(978-3-89790-290-9(7))* Arnoldsche Art Pubs. DEU. Dist: Antique Collectors' Club.

Johnson, Donald-Brian & Pina, Leslie. Deco Decor: Porcelain, Glass, & Metal Accessories for the Home. 2009. (Illus.). 240p. bds. 69.99 *(978-0-7643-3178-7(7))* Schiffer Publishing, Ltd.

Knight, Lynn. Clarice Cliff. 2007. (ENG., Illus.). 1p. pap. 16.95 *(978-0-7475-7960-1(1))* Bloomsbury Publishing Plc GBR. Dist: Independent Pubs. Group.

Lesher, Leigh. Warman's Vintage Jewelry: Identification & Price Guide. 2008. (ENG., Illus.). 256p. pap. 24.99 *(978-0-89689-639-0(0))* Krause Pubns.

Lindemann, Wilhelm & Lindemann, W., eds. Bengel Art Déco-Schmuck: Der Schmuck und das Industrie-Denkmal in Idar-Oberstein. 2007. (ENG., Illus.). 200p. 85.00 *(978-3-89790-271-8(0))* Arnoldsche Art Pubs. DEU. Dist: Antique Collectors' Club.

MacDonald, Donald & Nadel, Ira. Golden Gate Bridge: History & Design of an Icon. 2008. (ENG., Illus.). 128p. 16.95 *(978-0-8118-6337-7(9))* Chronicle Bks. LLC.

Malcles, Laurent. Art Deco Wood Designs CD-ROM & Book. 2006. (Dover Electronic Clip Art Ser.). (ENG., Illus.). 48p. pap. 14.95 *(978-0-486-99783-4(9))* Dover Pubns., Inc.

Martorelli, Barbara & Martorelli, Barbara (ed). George Barbier: The Birth of Art Deco. Martorelli, Barbara, ed. 2009. (ENG., Illus.). 176p. 50.00 *(978-88-317-9464-0(7))* Marsilio Editori spa ITA. Dist: Random Hse., Inc.

Miller, Judith. Art Deco. 2007. 76p. (C). 40.00 *(978-0-13-208129-0(6))* Prentice Hall Higher Education.

Mori, Gioia. Tamara de Lempicka: The Queen of the Modern. 2011. (ENG., Illus.). 390p. 80.00 *(978-88-572-0931-9(6))* Skira Editore ITA. Dist: Random Hse., Inc.

Noble, Marty. Art Deco Designs Stained Glass Coloring Book. 2006. (Dover Design Stained Glass Coloring Book Ser.). (ENG., Illus.). 32p. (gr. -1-3). 6.99 *(978-0-486-44814-5(2))* Dover Pubns., Inc.

Pandora. Wolfers Dynasty. 2008. (Illus.). 488p. 80.00 *(978-90-5325-278-9(9))* Petraco-Pandora N. V. BEL. Dist: Antique Collectors' Club.

Parsons, Jim & Bush, David. Houston Deco: Modernistic Architecture of the Texas Coast. 2008. (ENG., Illus.). 128p. 24.95 *(978-1-933979-06-9(2))* Bright Sky Pr.

Pepin Press. Art Deco - revised Edition. rev. exp. ed. 2009. (MUL & ENG., Illus.). 168p. pap. 24.99 incl. cd-rom *(978-90-5768-141-7(2))* Pepin Pr. NLD. Dist: National Bk. Network.

Posseme, Evelyne. Art Deco Jewelry: Modernist Masterworks & Their Makers. 2009. (ENG., Illus.). 256p. 60.00 *(978-0-500-51477-1(1)*, 551477) Thames & Hudson.

Raskin, E. H. Art Deco Design Fantasies. 2009. (Dover Pictorial Archive Ser.). (ENG.). 64p. pap. 14.95 *(978-0-486-47402-1(X))* Dover Pubns., Inc.

Samuels, Charlotte. Art Deco Textiles. 2011. (ENG., Illus.). 144p. pap. 29.95 *(978-1-85177-391-6(6))* V & A Pubns. GBR. Dist: Hachette Bk. Group.

Séguy, E. A. Seguy's Art Deco Designs CD-ROM & Book. 2006. (Dover Electronic Clip Art Ser.). (ENG., Illus.). 48p. pap. 19.95 *(978-0-486-99780-3(4))* Dover Pubns., Inc.

Slater, Greg. Clarice Cliff for Collectors. 2009. (ENG., Illus.). 256p. pap. 39.95 *(978-0-500-28819-1(4)*, 528819) Thames & Hudson.

Subes, Raymond. French Art Deco Ironwork Designs. 2007. (Dover Jewelry & Metalwork Ser.). (ENG., Illus.). 48p. per. 9.95 *(978-0-486-45459-7(2))* Dover Pubns., Inc.

Weber, Edith. Art Nouveau & Deco Fashion Postcards. 2009. (Illus.). 112p. bds. 29.99 *(978-0-7643-3270-8(8))* Schiffer Publishing, Ltd.

Weller, Alan & Dover Staff. Art Deco Vector Designs. 2012. (Dover Pictura Electronic Clip Art Ser.). (ENG., Illus.). 128p. pap. 49.95 ***(978-0-486-99076-7(1))*** Dover Pubns., Inc.

Wood, Ghislaine. Art Deco 1910-1939. Waite, Dianne, ed. 2008. (ENG., Illus.). 320p. pap. 49.95 *(978-0-7241-0296-9(5))* National Gallery of Victoria AUS. Dist: National Bk. Network.

Yancey, Diane. Art Deco. 2011. (Eye on Art Ser.). 128p. lib. bdg. 33.45 *(978-1-4205-0340-1(5),* Lucent Bks.) Cengage Gale.

Yorke, Trevor. Art Deco House Styles. 2011. (ENG., Illus.). 80p. (C). pap. 14.95 *(978-1-84674-247-7(1))* Countryside Bks. GBR. Dist: Brown, David Bk. Co., The.

ART DECO (ARCHITECTURE)

Anspach, Isabelle, contrib. by. Museum & Gardens van Buuren. 2012. (ENG., Illus.). 128p. 34.00 *(978-90-6153-771-7(1))* Mercatorfonds N. V. BEL. Dist: D.A.P./Distributed Art Pubs.

Berenholtz, Richard, photos by. New York Deco. (ENG., Illus.). 2009. 160p. 19.95 *(978-1-59962-078-7(2))* 2008. 184p. 125.00 *(978-1-59962-053-4(7))* Welcome Enterprises, Inc. (Welcome Bks.).

Bly, John & Knowles, Eric. English Furniture. 2010. (Shire Collections). (ENG., Illus.). 136p. pap. 19.95 *(978-0-7478-0786-5(8))* Shire Pubns., Ltd. GBR. Dist: Random Hse., Inc.

Brooke, Steven. Miami Beach Deco. 2011. (ENG., Illus.). 224p. 17.95 *(978-0-7893-2241-8(2))* Universe Publishing.

Bush, David & Parsons, Jim. Hill Country Deco: Modernistic Architecture of Central Texas. 2010. (ENG., Illus.). 224p. 35.00 *(978-0-87565-413-3(4))* Texas Christian Univ. Pr.

Heinrich, Christoph, et al. Embrace!, 2 vols. 2009. (Illus.). *(978-0-914738-61-9(5))* Denver Art Museum.

Koskoff, Sharon. Art Deco of the Palm Beaches. 2007. (Images of America Ser.). (ENG., Illus.). 128p. per. 19.99 *(978-0-7385-4415-1(9))* Arcadia Publishing.

Kurten, Stefan, illus. Inside Out, 1 vol. 2006. (ENG.). 64p. 20.00 *(978-1-891273-06-3(X))* Artspace Bks.

Lemmen, Hans. Art Deco Tiles. 2012. (Shire Library). (ENG., Illus.). 64p. pap. 12.95 ***(978-0-7478-1199-2(7))*** Shire Pubns., Ltd. GBR. Dist: Random Hse., Inc.

Loeb, Marcia. Dover Digital Design Source #7: Art Deco Designs, Motifs & Alphabets. 2010. (Dover Electronic Clip Art Ser.). (ENG., Illus.). 128p. pap. 19.95 *(978-0-486-99072-9(9))* Dover Pubns., Inc.

Montinola, Lourdes, ed. Art Deco in the Philippines. 2011. (Illus.). 140p. 40.00 ***(978-971-0579-06-8(1))*** Artpostasia Inc. PHL. Dist: National Bk. Network.

Montinola, Lourdes, ed. Art Deo in the Philippines. 2011. (ENG., Illus.). 160p. pap. 35.00 *(978-971-0579-05-1(3))* Artpostasia Inc. PHL. Dist: National Bk. Network.

Poletti, Therese & Paiva, Tom. Art Deco San Francisco: The Architecture of Timothy Pflueger. 2008. (ENG., Illus.). 256p. 55.00 *(978-1-56898-756-9(0))* Princeton Architectural Pr.

Ramani, Navin. Bombay Art Deco Architecture: A Visual Journey: 1930-1953. Cerwinske, Laura, ed. 2007. (ENG., Illus.). 295p. 34.95 *(978-81-7436-447-0(1))* Roli Bks. Private, Ltd. IND. Dist: Ingram Pub. Services.

Russell, Susan. South Beach Postcards. 2007. (Illus.). 20p. pap. 8.95 *(978-0-7643-2630-1(9))* Schiffer Publishing, Ltd.

Schwartzman, Arnold. London Art Deco. 2011. (ENG., Illus.). 160p. pap. 14.95 *(978-0-9564448-7-5(3))* Palazzo Editions, Ltd. GBR. Dist: Independent Pubs. Group.

Stroud, Marion Boulton & Wilkins, Amy. Robert Venturi, Denise Scott Brown, & Steven Izenour at Acadia Summer Arts Program. Stroud, Marion Boulton, ed. 2010. (ENG., Illus.). 124p. 30.00 *(978-0-9797642-2-6(X))* A.S.A.P.

Tottis, James W. The Guardian Building: Cathedral of Finance. 2008. (Illus.). 160p. 50.00 *(978-0-8143-3385-3(0))* Wayne State Univ. Pr.

Ullmann, H. F., ed. Art Pocket Art Nouveau. 2009. (Art Pocket Ser.). 288p. 14.95 *(978-0-8416-0348-6(0))* American Map Corp.

Végh, Christina. Jorge Pardo. 2008. (ENG., Illus.). 160p. pap. 45.00 *(978-0-7148-4658-3(9))* Phaidon Pr. Ltd. GBR. Dist: Hachette Bk. Group.

Whitley, David S. Introduction to Rock Art Research, Second Edition. 2nd ed. 2011. (ENG., Illus.). 256p. (C). 89.00 *(978-1-59874-610-5(3))* Left Coast Pr., Inc.

ART EDUCATION

see Art—Study and Teaching

ART FORGERIES

see Forgery of Works of Art

ART GALLERIES

see Art Museums

ART GALLERIES, COMMERCIAL

Clayton, Timothy. Colnaghi: The History. 2010. (ENG., Illus.). 68p. pap. 40.00 *(978-1-907372-07-0(5))* Holberton, Paul Publishing GBR. Dist: Univ. of Washington Pr.

Crawford, Tad & Mellon, Susan. The Artist-Gallery Partnership: A Practical Guide to Consigning Art. 3rd ed. 2008. (ENG., Illus.). 216p. pap. 19.95 *(978-1-58115-645-4(6),* 115645, Allworth Pr.) Skyhorse Publishing Co., Inc.

Gagosian Gallery Staff, et al, contrib. by. Ferus. 2nd ed. 2009. (Illus.). 146p. 55.00 *(978-0-8478-3234-7(1))* Rizzoli International Pubns., Inc.

Giancarlo Politi Editore, compiled by. Art Diary International 2009-2010. 2009. (Illus.). 624p. pap. 35.00 *(978-88-18-16148-9(2))* Politi, Giancarlo Editore ITA. Dist: D.A.P./Distributed Art Pubs.

Giancarlo Politi Editore, ed. Art Diary International 2007-2008: The World Art Directory, 1 vol. 2007. (ENG., Illus.). 570p. pap. 30.00 *(978-88-7816-143-6(8))* Politi, Giancarlo Editore ITA. Dist: D.A.P./Distributed Art Pubs.

Lürzer, Walter. Art Diary International 2009 2010. 2009. (ENG., Illus.). 624p. pap. 35.00 *(978-88-7816-148-1(9))* Politi, Giancarlo Editore ITA. Dist: D.A.P./Distributed Art Pubs.

Momement, Caroline, ed. & compiled by. Craft Galleries Guide: 2009/10. 10th ed. 2009. (ENG., Illus.). 356p. pap. 28.95 *(978-0-9550026-7-0(2))* BCF Bks. GBR. Dist: Macmillan.

Politi, Giancarlo. Art Diary International 2006-2007: Flash Art Diary, 1 vol. 2006. (ENG., Illus.). 570p. pap. 25.00 *(978-88-7816-137-5(3))* Politi, Giancarlo Editore ITA. Dist: D.A.P./Distributed Art Pubs.

Ruston, Annabelle & Sims, Mike. Starting up a Gallery. 2011. (ENG.). 240p. pap. 22.95 *(978-0-7136-8475-9(5))* A & C Black GBR. Dist: Macmillan.

Winkleman, Edward. How to Start & Run a Commercial Art Gallery. 2009. (ENG.). 256p. pap. 24.95 *(978-1-58115-664-5(2),* 115664, Allworth Pr.) Skyhorse Publishing Co., Inc.

ART HISTORIANS

Baxandall, Michael. Episodes: A Memory Book. 2010. (ENG., Illus.). 144p. 24.95 *(978-0-7112-3115-3(X))* Lincoln, Frances Ltd. GBR. Dist: Perseus-PGW.

Bradford, Rosalind E. The Guyuan Sarcophagus. 2011. (Illus.). 404p. pap. ***(978-3-8433-8985-3(3))*** Lambert Academic Publishing.

Degl'Innocenti, Martina, et al. Mary. 2009. (ENG., Illus.). 732p. 19.95 *(978-0-8109-8285-7(4))* Abrams.

Dilly, Heinrich. Altmeister moderner Kunstgeschichte: Kunstgeschichte zur Einführung. (GER.). *(978-3-496-01203-0(X))* Reimer, Dietrich.

Esterman, Daniel, et al. Meyer Schapiro Abroad: Letters to Lillian & Travel Notebooks. 2009. (Illus.). 208p. 39.95 *(978-0-89236-893-8(4))* Oxford Univ. Pr., Inc.

Frank, Mitchell & Adler, Daniel. German Art History & Scientific Thought: Beyond Formalism. 2012. (Illus.). 194p. 114.95 ***(978-1-4094-4023-9(0))*** Ashgate Publishing Co.

Games, Stephen. Pevsner: The Early Life - Germany & Art. 2010. (ENG., Illus.). 256p. 39.95 *(978-1-4411-4386-0(6))* Continuum International Publishing Group, Ltd. GBR. Dist: National Bk. Network.

—Pevsner: The Early Life: Germany & Art. 2011. (ENG., Illus.). 256p. pap. 16.95 *(978-1-4411-9093-2(7))* Continuum International Publishing Group, Ltd. GBR. Dist: National Bk. Network.

Grabski, Joanna & Magee, Carol. African Art, Interviews, Narratives: Bodies of Knowledge at Work. 2012. (African Expressive Cultures Ser.). (ENG.). 216p. pap. 28.00 ***(978-0-253-00691-2(0),*** 0253006910); (Illus.). 80.00 ***(978-0-253-00687-5(2),*** 0253006872) Indiana Univ. Pr.

Hamerton, Eugénie. Philip Gilbert Hamerton: An Autobiography, 1834-1858, & a Memoir by His Wife, 1858-1894. 2006. 564p. pap. 30.99 *(978-1-4264-3052-7(3))* BiblioBazaar.

—Philip Gilbert Hamerton: An Autobiography, 1834-1858, & a Memoir by His Wife, 1858-1895. l.t. ed. 2007. (ENG.). 630p. pap. 33.99 *(978-1-4264-3117-3(1))* BiblioBazaar.

Hamerton, Philip Gilbert. Philip Gilbert Hamerton. 2009. 442p. pap. *(978-1-4588-4111-7(1));* 422p. pap. *(978-0-217-52788-0(4))* Books LLC.

—Philip Gilbert Hamerton. 2007. 532p. per. *(978-1-4065-1955-6(3))* Dodo Pr.

Harries, Susie & Harries, Meirion. Nikolaus Pevsner: The Life. 2011. (ENG., Illus.). 866p. 49.95 ***(978-0-7011-6839-1(0))*** Random Hse. GBR. Dist: Independent Pubs. Group.

Karlstrom, Paul J. & Karlstrom, Ann. Peter Selz: Sketches of a Life in Art. 2012. (ENG., Illus.). 321p. 34.95 *(978-0-520-26935-4(7))* Univ. of California Pr.

Lohse, Richard. Richard Paul Lohse. Drucke Prints: Dokumentation + Werkverzeichnis, Documentation + Catalogue raisonnè. 2009. (ENG., Illus.). 472p. 120.00 *(978-3-7757-2309-1(9))* Hatje Cantz Verlag GmbH & Co KG DEU. Dist: D.A.P./Distributed Art Pubs.

McGee, Julie L. Artist & Scholar. 2006. (Illus.). 216p. 45.00 *(978-0-7649-3747-7(2),* A127) Pomegranate Communications, Inc.

Noever, Peter, et al, eds. Alois Riegl Revisited: Beiträge zu Werk und Rezeption - Contributions to the Opus & its Reception. 2010. (VERoFFENTLICHUNGEN der KOMMISSION FuR KUNSTGESCHICHTE Ser.). 148p. (C). pap. 73.00 *(978-3-7001-6498-2(X))* Austrian Academy of Sciences Press AUT. Dist: Brown, David Bk. Co., The.

Panofsky, Erwin & Wuttke, Dieter. Korrespondenz 1910 Bis 1968: Eine Kommentierte Auswahl in Fu¿nf Ba¿nden. 2008. (GER & ENG., Illus.). 1388p. (C). 270.00 ***(978-3-447-05784-4(X))*** Harrassowitz, Otto Verlag DEU. Dist: ISD.

Russell, Mark A. Beyond Tradition & Modernity: Aby Warburg & the Public Purposes of Art in Hamburg, 1896-1918. 2007. (Monographs in German History). (Illus.). 272p. 90.00 *(978-1-84545-369-5(7))* Berghahn Bks., Inc.

Sandler, Irving. A Sweeper-Up after Artists: A Memoir. 2009. (ENG.). 382p. pap. 18.95 *(978-0-500-28767-5(8))* Thames & Hudson.

Schoth, Sarah, ed. Art in Spain & the Hispanic World. 2010. (Illus.). 368p. pap. 60.00 *(978-1-907372-00-1(8))* Univ. of Washington Pr.

Shone, Richard & Stonard, John-Paul. The Books That Shaped Art History: From Gombrich & Greenberg to Alpers & Krauss. 2012. (ENG., Illus.). 208p. 34.95 ***(978-0-500-23895-0(2),*** 523895) Thames & Hudson.

Strauss, Michel. Pictures, Passions & Eye: A Life at Sotheby's. 2011. (ENG.). 308p. 45.00 *(978-1-905559-21-3(6))* Halban Pubs. GBR. Dist: Independent Pubs. Group.

ART IN ADVERTISING

see Commercial Art

ART IN LITERATURE

Bearden, Elizabeth R. The Emblematics of the Self: Ekphrasis & Identity in Renaissance Imitations of Greek Romance. 2011. (Illus.). 272p. ***(978-1-4426-4346-8(3))*** Univ. of Toronto Pr.

Berg, William J. Imagery & Ideology: Fiction & Painting in Nineteenth-Century France. 2008. (Illus.). 269p. 52.50 *(978-0-87413-995-2(3))* 2007. (ENG.). 52.50 *(978-1-61149-331-3(5))* Univ. of Delaware Pr.

Blatt, Ari J. Pictures into Words: Images in Contemporary French Fiction. 2012. (Stages Ser.). (ENG., Illus.). 264p. 50.00 ***(978-0-8032-3805-3(3))*** Univ. of Nebraska Pr.

Buckner, Leroy. Generational Genocide Devastation of a Nation. 2011. 44p. pap. 23.95 *(978-1-4567-4614-8(6))* AuthorHouse.

Cappucci, Paul R. William Carlos Williams, Frank O'Hara, & the New York Art Scene. 2010. (Illus.). 167p. 48.50 *(978-0-8386-4218-4(7));* (ENG.). 168p. 60.00 *(978-1-61147-422-0(1))* Fairleigh Dickinson Univ. Pr.

De Armas, Frederick A. Quixotic Frescoes: Cervantes & Italian Renaissance Art. 2009. (ENG., Illus.). 344p. pap. *(978-1-4426-1031-6(X))* Univ. of Toronto Pr.

Delyfer, Catherine. Art & Womanhood in Fin-de-Siecle Writing: The Fiction of Lucas Malet, 1880-1931, 1 vol. 2011. (Gender & Genre Ser.). (ENG., Illus.). 224p. 99.00 *(978-1-84893-105-3(0))* Pickering & Chatto Pubs., Ltd. GBR. Dist: Ashgate Publishing Co.

Denham, Robert D. Poets on Paintings: A Bibliography. 2010. (ENG., Illus.). 341p. pap. 95.00 *(978-0-7864-4725-1(7))* McFarland & Co., Inc. Pubs.

Doll, Eileen J. El Papel Del Artista en la Dramaturgia de Jerónimo López Mozo: Juegos Temporales e Intermediales. 2008. (SPA.). 205p. pap. 29.80 *(978-84-8489-427-8(4))* Iberoamericana Vervuert Publishing Corp.

Edwards, Natalie, et al, eds. Textual & Visual Selves: Photography, Film, & Comic Art in French Autobiography. 2011. (ENG., Illus.). 288p. pap. 25.00 *(978-0-8032-3631-8(X))* Univ. of Nebraska Pr.

Francescato, Simone. Collecting & Appreciating: Henry James & the Transformation of Aesthetics in the Age of Consumption. 2010. 217p. pap. 51.95 *(978-3-0343-0163-3(4))* Lang, Peter AG GBR. Dist: Lang, Peter.

Gibson, William. Art & Money in the Writings of Tobias Smollett. 2006. (Bucknell Studies in Eighteenth-Century Literature & Culture). (Illus.). (C). *(978-0-8387-5637-9(9))* Bucknell Univ. Pr.

Hepburn, Allan. Enchanted Objects: Visual Art in Contemporary Fiction. 2010. (Illus.). 288p. *(978-1-4426-4100-6(2))* Univ. of Toronto Pr.

Hunt, John Dixon, et al. Art, Word & Image: 2,000 Years of Visual/Textual Interaction. 2011. (Illus.). 416p. pap. 39.00 *(978-1-86189-745-9(6))* Reaktion Bks., Ltd. GBR. Dist: Chicago Distribution Ctr.

Hunt, Patrick, ed. Myth & Art in Ekphrasis. 2010. (C). 0.00 *(978-1-60927-777-2(5))* Univ. Readers.

Kelly, Catriona & Lovell, Stephen, eds. Russian Literature, Modernism & the Visual Arts. 2008. (Cambridge Studies in Russian Literature Ser.). (ENG., Illus.). 336p. pap. 48.00 *(978-0-521-08790-2(2))* Cambridge Univ. Pr.

Kolb, Alexandra. Performing Femininity: Dance & Literature in German Modernism. 2009. (Illus.). 330p. pap. 61.95 *(978-3-03911-351-4(8))* Lang, Peter AG GBR. Dist: Lang, Peter.

Lin, Tzu Yu Allison. Narrative & Visual Arts in Virginia Woolf's London Writings: The Aesthetics of Words & Arts. 2011. 340p. pap. ***(978-3-639-28082-1(2))*** VDM Verlag Dr. Mueller e.K.

Mardaus, Frank. Fotografische Zeichen: Uwe Johnsons Bildprogramm in Den "Jahrestagen" 2008. (Johnson-Studien Ser.). (GER., Illus.). 196p. (C). 48.00 *(978-3-525-20948-6(7))* Vandenhoeck & Ruprecht GmbH & Co. KG DEU. Dist: ISD.

Mayers, Kathryn. Visions of Empire in Colonial Spanish American Ekphrastic Writing. 2011. (ENG.). 186p. 65.00 ***(978-1-61148-392-5(1))*** Lexington Bks.

McKeown, William. The Role of Venetian Renaissance Painting in John Ruskin's Utopian Theories: A Sociopolitical History of Art. 2011. (ENG., Illus.). xvii, 298p. 129.95 *(978-0-7734-1508-9(4))* Mellen, Edwin Pr., The.

Morgan, Stuart. Inclinations: Further Writings & Interviews, 1 vol. 2007. (ENG., Illus.). 448p. pap. 27.00 *(978-0-9527414-8-0(2))* Frieze GBR. Dist: D.A.P./Distributed Art Pubs.

Mukai, Kumiko. Hawthorne's Visual Artists & the Pursuit of a Transatlantic Aesthetics. 2008. (Illus.). 246p. pap. 76.95 *(978-3-03911-368-2(2))* Lang, Peter AG GBR. Dist: Lang, Peter.

Oliveira, Luiz Sérgio de & D'Angelo, Martha. Walter Benjamin: Arte e Experiência. 2010. (POR.). 327p. *(978-85-228-0526-6(1)); (978-85-85936-79-2(7))* Universidade Federal Fluminense. Editora.

Rees, Emma L. E. Can't: Uncovering the postmodern Vagina. 2012. (Transformations Ser.). (ENG.). 224p. (C). 130.00 ***(978-0-415-68932-8(5))*** Routledge.

Samarasinghe, Semini Pabodha. An Imaginative Guide: On How One Could Live in an Ecological Paradise. 2011. 252p. pap. 81.51 *(978-1-4567-7270-3(8))* AuthorHouse.

Samuels, Peggy. Deep Skin: Elizabeth Bishop & Visual Art. 2010. (Illus.). 256p. 39.95 *(978-0-8014-4826-3(3))* Cornell Univ. Pr.

Schakel, Peter J. Imagination & the Arts in C. S. Lewis: Journeying to Narnia & Other Worlds. 2011. (ENG., Illus.). 232p. (C). (gr. 13). pap. 30.00 *(978-0-8262-1937-4(3))* Univ. of Missouri Pr.

Scott, David H. T. Pictorialist Poetics: Poetry & the Visual Arts in Nineteenth-Century France. 2009. (Cambridge Studies in French Ser.). (ENG.). 224p. pap. 33.99 *(978-0-521-11059-4(9))* Cambridge Univ. Pr.

Siraganian, Lisa. Modernism's Other Work: The Art Object's Political Life, 1 vol. 2012. (ENG., Illus.). 304p. 65.00 ***(978-0-19-979655-7(6))*** Oxford Univ. Pr., Inc.

Stašková, Alice & Lützeler, Paul Michael, eds. Hermann Broch und die Künste. 2009.Tr. of Hermann Broch & the Arts. (GER.). VI, 263p. 126.00 *(978-3-11-020955-6(1))* De Gruyter, Walter Inc.

Stewart, Jack. Color, Space, & Creativity: Art & Ontology in Five British Writers. 2008. (Illus.). 320p. (C). 63.50 *(978-0-8386-4165-1(2))* Fairleigh Dickinson Univ. Pr.

Sullivan, Karen. Rousseau's Aesthetics of Feeling: Time, Place, & the Arts in Julie Ou la Nouvelle Héloïse. 2007. (Illus.). 186p. 99.95 *(978-0-7734-5317-3(2))* Mellen, Edwin Pr., The.

Sykes-Davies, Hugh. Wordsworth & the Worth of Words. 2010. (ENG.). 340p. pap. 42.00 *(978-0-521-12914-5(1))* Cambridge Univ. Pr.

Thaggert, Miriam. Images of Black Modernism: Verbal & Visual Strategies of the Harlem Renaissance. 2010. (Illus.). 256p. (ENG.). pap. 28.95 *(978-1-55849-831-0(1));* lib. bdg. 80.00 *(978-1-55849-830-3(3))* Univ. of Massachusetts Pr.

Wagstaff, Emma. Writing Art: French Literary Responses to the Work of Alberto Giacometti. 2011. (Cultural Interactions: Studies in the Relationship between the Arts Ser.). 197p. pap. 60.95 *(978-3-03911-871-7(4))* Lang, Peter AG GBR. Dist: Lang, Peter.

Wilson, Harold S. Meanings of Nature in Renaissance Literature: The Journal of the History of Ideas, V2, No. 4, October 1941. 2011. 22p. 35.95 ***(978-1-258-03624-9(X))*** Literary Licensing, LLC.

ART IN MOTION

see Kinetic Art

ART IN MOTION PICTURES

Here are entered works dealing with motion pictures on art subjects, both instructional and documentary.

Baumann, Shyon. Hollywood Highbrow: From Entertainment to Art. 2007. (Princeton Studies in Cultural Sociology). (ENG., Illus.). 242p. (C). 42.00 *(978-0-691-12527-5(9))* Princeton Univ. Pr.

Clemente, Chiara & text. Our City Dreams. 2010. (ENG., Illus.). 120p. pap. 39.95 *(978-88-8158-749-0(1))* Charta ITA. Dist: D.A.P./Distributed Art Pubs.

Columpar, Corinn. Unsettling Sights: The Fourth World on Film. 2010. (ENG., Illus.). 248p. pap. 35.00 *(978-0-8093-2962-5(X))* Southern Illinois Univ. Pr.

Dean, Tacita. Darmstädter Werkblock, 1 vol. deluxe ed. 2009. (ENG., Illus.). 100p. pap. 100.00 *(978-3-86521-703-5(6))* Steidl, Gerhard Druckerei und Verlag DEU. Dist: Innovative Logistics.

Haas, Philip & Warner, Malcolm. Butchers, Dragons, Gods & Skeletons: Film Installations by Philip Haas. 2009. (Illus.). ix, 94p. *(978-0-912804-50-7(5))* Kimbell Art Museum.

Harper, Graeme & Rayner, Jonathan, eds. Cinema & Landscape. 2010. (Illus.). 315p. pap. 25.00 *(978-1-84150-309-7(6))* Intellect, Ltd. GBR. Dist: Chicago Distribution Ctr.

Jacobs, Steven. Framing Pictures: Film & the Visual Arts. 2011. (Edinburgh Studies in Film Ser.). (ENG., Illus.). 208p. (gr. 17). 95.00 ***(978-0-7486-4017-1(7))*** Edinburgh Univ. Pr. GBR. Dist: Columbia Univ. Pr.

King, Elliott H. & King, Elliott. Dali, Surrealism & Cinema. 2007. (ENG., Illus.). 192p. 16.95 *(978-1-904048-90-9(0))* Oldcastle Bks., Ltd. GBR. Dist: Independent Pubs. Group.

King, Sarah, ed. The Dissolve. 2010. (ENG., Illus.). 240p. 50.00 *(978-0-9764492-9-4(3))* Site Santa Fe.

Orr, John. Romantics & Modernists in British Cinema. 2012. (Edinburgh Studies in Film Ser.). (ENG., Illus.). 208p. (gr. 17). pap. 35.00 ***(978-0-7486-4937-2(9))*** Edinburgh Univ. Pr. GBR. Dist: Columbia Univ. Pr.

Orr, John & Letwin, Daniel. Romantics & Modernists in British Cinema. 2010. (Edinburgh Studies in Film Ser.). (ENG., Illus.). 208p. (gr. 17). 105.00 *(978-0-7486-4014-0(2))* Edinburgh Univ. Pr. GBR. Dist: Columbia Univ. Pr.

Ragnar. The Art of Big City. 2011. (ENG., Illus.). 180p. 40.00 ***(978-1-61404-001-9(X))*** Baby Tattoo Bks.

Solana, Gemma & Boneu, Antonio. Uncredited: Graphic Design & Opening Titles in Movies. 2008. (Illus.). 320p. *(978-84-96309-52-4(5))* Index Bks., Spain.

Walker, John Albert. Art & artists on Screen. 2010. 302p. reprint ed. pap. *(978-0-9545702-5-5(1))* Institute of Artology.

ART IN UNIVERSITIES AND COLLEGES

Daichendt, G. James. Artist Scholar: Reflections on Writing & Research. 2011. (ENG., Illus.). 161p. pap. 25.00 *(978-1-84150-487-2(4))* Intellect, Ltd. GBR. Dist: Chicago Distribution Ctr.

ART INDUSTRIES AND TRADE

see also Antiques; Art, Decorative; Arts and Crafts Movement; Carving (Decorative Arts); Folk Art; Jewelry; Marquetry

also particular industries, trades, etc., e.g. Glass Painting and Staining; Leatherwork; Mosaics

Becker, Konrad & Fleming, Jim, eds. Critical Strategies in Art & Media: Perspectives on New Cultural Practices. 2010. (ENG.). 182p. pap. 12.95 *(978-1-57027-214-1(X))* Autonomedia.

Chapin, Kari. The Handmade Marketplace: How to Sell Your Crafts Locally, Globally, & On-Line. 2010. (ENG., Illus.). 224p. pap. 14.95 *(978-1-60342-477-6(6),* 1603424776) Storey Publishing, LLC.

Entrepreneur Press Staff & McDougall, J. S. Start Your Own Arts & Crafts Business: Retail, Carts & Kiosks, Craft Shows, Street Fairs. 2nd ed. 2007. (ENG., Illus.). 156p. per. 17.95 *(978-1-59918-100-4(2),* 1599181002) Entrepreneur Pr. dba Entrepreneur Media, Inc.

Mundelius, Marco. The Reliance of Berlin 's Creative Industries on Milieus: An Organisational & Spatial Analysis. 2008. (Illus.). 156p. pap. *(978-3-8364-8235-6(5))* VDM Verlag Dr. Mueller e.K.

ART INSTITUTE OF CHICAGO

Art Institute of Chicago, creator. Old Masters at the Art Institute of Chicago. 2006. (Museum Studies). (ENG., Illus.). 96p. pap. 16.95 *(978-0-300-11951-0(8))* Art Institute of Chicago.

Art Institute of Chicago Staff. Miniature Rooms: The Thorne Rooms at the Art Institute of Chicago. 2nd ed. 2009. (ENG., Illus.). 184p. 45.00 *(978-0-300-14159-7(9))* Art Institute of Chicago.

Art Institute of Chicago Staff, contrib. by. The Essential Guide. 3rd ed. 2009. (Illus.). 336p. pap. *(978-0-86559-229-2(2))* Art Institute of Chicago.

Barter, Judith A. & Downs, Jennifer M. American Modernism at the Art Institute of Chicago: From World War I to 1955. 2009. (ENG., Illus.). 368p. 75.00 *(978-0-300-11738-7(8))* Art Institute of Chicago.

Barter, Judith A. & Obniski, Monica. For Kith & Kin: The Folk Art Collection at the Art Institute of Chicago. 2012. (ENG., Illus.). 112p. 30.00 ***(978-0-300-17972-9(3))*** Art Institute of Chicago.

Cozzolino, Robert. Art in Chicago: Resisting Regionalism, Transforming Modernism, 1 vol. 1000th ed. 2007. (ENG., Illus.). 80p. per. 19.95 *(978-0-943836-29-4(8))* Pennsylvania Academy of the Fine Arts.

Cuno, James, selected by. Master Paintings in the Art Institute of Chicago. 3rd ed. 2009. (ENG., Illus.). 168p. 39.95 *(978-0-300-15103-9(9))* Art Institute of Chicago.

Cuno, James, et al. The Modern Wing: Renzo Piano & the Art Institute of Chicago. 2009. (ENG., Illus.). 168p. 60.00 *(978-0-300-14112-2(2))* Art Institute of Chicago.

Cuno, James B., et al. The Modern Wing: Renzo Piano & the Art Institute of Chicago. 2009. (Illus.). 167p. pap. *(978-0-86559-231-5(4))* Art Institute of Chicago.

Dorin, Lisa B. Film, Video, & New Media at the Art Institute of Chicago: With the Donna & Howard Stone Gift. 2009. (Museum Studies). (ENG., Illus.). 112p. pap. 16.95 *(978-0-300-14690-5(6))* Art Institute of Chicago.

Ghose, Madhuvanti. Masterpieces of Indian Art at the Art Institute of Chicago. 2010. (Illus.). 112p. 18.95 *(978-0-300-16779-5(2))* Art Institute of Chicago.

Groom, Gloria & Druick, Douglas W. The Age of French Impressionism: Masterpieces from the Art Institute of Chicago. 2010. (Illus.). 200p. 50.00 *(978-0-300-16780-1(6))* Art Institute of Chicago.

Groom, Gloria Lynn & Druick, Douglas W. The Age of French Impressionism: Masterpieces from the Art Institute of Chicago. 2010. (Illus.). 200p. pap. ***(978-0-86559-240-7(3))*** Art Institute of Chicago.

Hogan, Erin. The Art Institute of Chicago: From 1879 to the Modern Wing: Art Spaces. 2009. (ENG., Illus.). 64p. pap. 7.95 *(978-1-85759-580-2(7))* Scala, Editions FRA. Dist: National Bk. Network.

Kuh, Katharine. My Love Affair with Modern Art: Behind the Scenes with a Legendary Curator. Berman, Avis, ed. 2012. (ENG.). 336p. pap. 14.95 ***(978-1-61145-506-9(5)***, 611506, Arcade Publishing) Skyhorse Publishing Co., Inc.

Legge, Elizabeth & Legge, E. Michael Snow: Wavelength. 2009. (One Work Ser.). (ENG., Illus.). 104p. (gr. 17). pap. 16.00 *(978-1-84638-056-3(1))* Afterall Publishing GBR. Dist: MIT Pr.

Mann, Richard G., et al. Northern European & Spanish Paintings Before 1600 in the Art Institute of Chicago: A Catalogue of the Collection. Wolff, Martha, ed. 2008. (ENG., Illus.). 476p. 100.00 *(978-0-300-11944-2(5))* Art Institute of Chicago.

Moholy-Nagy, Hattula & Heyne, Renate, eds. Laszlo Moholy-Nagy: the Photograms. 2010. (ENG., Illus.). 312p. 120.00 *(978-3-7757-2341-1(2))* Hatje Cantz Verlag GmbH & Co KG DEU. Dist: D.A.P./Distributed Art Pubs.

Raz-Russo, Michal. The Three Graces: Snapshots of Twentieth-Century Women. 2011. (ENG., Illus.). 160p. 26.50 *(978-0-300-17734-3(8))* Yale Univ. Pr.

Tedeschi, Martha & Dahm, Kristi. John Marin's Watercolors: A Medium for Modernism. 2011. (ENG., Illus.). 192p. 50.00 *(978-0-300-16637-8(0))* Art Institute of Chicago.

ART INSTITUTE OF CHICAGO—GOODMAN THEATRE

see Goodman Theatre (Chicago, Ill.)

ART LIBRARIES

see also Architectural Libraries

Benedetti, Joan M. & Abid, Ann B. Art Museum Libraries & Librarianship. Benedetti, Joan M., ed. 2007. (ENG., Illus.). 336p. pap. 60.00 *(978-0-8108-5921-0(1))* Scarecrow Pr., Inc.

—Art Museum Libraries & Librarianship. Benedetti, Joan M., ed. 2007. (ENG., Illus.). 336p. 82.50 *(978-0-8108-5918-0(1))* Scarecrow Pr., Inc.

Glassman, Paul & Gluibizzi, Amanda. The Handbook of Art & Design Librarianship. 2010. xvii, 330p. pap. 115.00 ***(978-1-85604-702-9(4))*** Neal-Schuman Pubs., Inc.

Weller, Alan. Vector Pattern Library. 2011. (Dover Clip Art Design Tools Ser.). (ENG., Illus.). 208p. pap. 29.95 *(978-0-486-99107-8(5))* Dover Pubns., Inc.

ART METAL-WORK

see also Bronzes; Cloisonne; Copperwork; Decorative Cast-Ironwork; Goldwork; Ironwork; Jewelry; Medals; Metal Sculpture; Pewter; Plaques, Plaquettes; Silverwork

Anderson, Sean. Flames of Devotion: Oil Lamps from South & Southeast Asia & the Himalayas. 2006. (ENG., Illus.). 112p. pap. *(978-0-9748729-3-3(8))* Univ. of California, Los Angeles, Fowler Museum of Cultural History.

Anheuser, Kilian & Werner, Christine. Medieval Reliquary Shrines & Precious Metalwork: Proceedings of a Conference at the Musée D'art et D'histoire, Geneva, 12-15 September 2001/Châsses-Reliquaires et Orfèvrerie Médiévales: Actes du Colloque Au Musée D'art et D'histoire, Genève, 12-15 Septembre 2001. 2007. (ENG, FRE & GER., Illus.). 144p. 95.00 *(978-1-904982-18-0(2))* Archetype Pubns. GBR. Dist: National Bk. Network.

Ayazi, Souri. Luristan Bronze Disc-Headed Pins. 2008. 260p. 130.00 *(978-3-932942-27-3(2))* Legat-Verlag GmbH & Company KG DEU. Dist: Independent Pubs. Group.

Bierens, Cornel, et al. Private Passion: Artists' Jewelry of the 20th Century. Joris, Yvönne, ed. 2010. (ENG., Illus.). 176p. 70.00 *(978-3-89790-320-3(2))* Arnoldsche Art Pubs. DEU. Dist: National Bk. Network.

Bonduel, Charlotte. Walk with Me. 2009. (ENG., Illus.). 152p. 65.00 *(978-90-209-8111-7(0))* Lannoo Pubs./Racine.

Boston Architectural Club. The Metalworker's Art: A Pictorial Celebration. 2011. (Dover Jewelry & Metalwork Ser.). (ENG.). 112p. pap. 14.95 *(978-0-486-47313-0(9))* Dover Pubns., Inc.

Darom, David. The Great Collections: Modern Custom Knives. 2008. (ENG., Illus.). 288p. 24.99 *(978-0-7858-2360-5(3)*, 0785823603) Book Sales, Inc.

de Menil, Dominique, et al. Jim Love: From Now On. Quaintance, Don & Webb, Paula, eds. 2006. (ENG., Illus.). 208p. 50.00 *(978-0-85667-609-3(8))* Wilson, Philip Pubs., Ltd. GBR. Dist: Macmillan.

Descatoire, Christine. Treasures of the Black Death. 2009. (ENG., Illus.). 112p. pap. 40.00 *(978-0-900785-95-5(0))* Holberton, Paul Publishing GBR. Dist: Casemate Pubs. & Bk. Distributors, LLC.

East, Pam. Enameling on Metal Clay: Innovative Jewelry Projects. 2007. (ENG., Illus.). 96p. per. 19.95 *(978-0-87116-245-8(8))* Kalmbach Publishing Co., Bks. Div.

Ferrari, Giulio. Italian Ironwork: Medieval, Renaissance, Baroque, Neo Classical. 2010. (Illus.). 112p. 29.99 *(978-0-7643-3560-0(X))* Schiffer Publishing, Ltd.

Gareth, Williams. Treasures from Sutton Hoo. 2011. (ENG., Illus.). 48p. (C). pap. 9.95 *(978-0-7141-2825-2(2))* British Museum Pr. GBR. Dist: Brown, David Bk. Co., The.

Goodison, Nicholas. Matthew Boulton: Ormolu. 2006. (ENG., Illus.). 432p. 140.00 *(978-0-903432-70-2(6))* Christie, Manson & Woods, Ltd. GBR. Dist: Antique Collectors' Club.

Grancsay, Stephen V., frwd. Master French Gunsmiths' Designs of the Mid-Seventeenth Century. 2011. 48p. 35.95 ***(978-1-258-03180-0(9))*** Literary Licensing, LLC.

Grenier, Fleur. Pewter: Designs & Techniques, 1 vol. 2010. (ENG., Illus.). 160p. 37.95 *(978-1-84797-158-6(X))* Crowood Pr., Ltd. GBR. Dist: Independent Pubs. Group.

Griffiths Sandy. Pewter Craft. 2010. (ENG., Illus.). 144p. pap. 19.95 *(978-1-55407-603-1(X))* Firefly Bks., Ltd.

Guadalupi, Gianni. Treasures in Gold: Masterpieces of Jewelry from Antiquity to Modern Times. 2008. (ENG., Illus.). 336p. 39.95 *(978-88-544-0320-8(2))* White Star ITA. Dist: Random Hse., Inc.

Hamerton, Ian, ed. W. A. S. Benson: Arts & Crafts Luminary & Pioneer of Modern Design. 2007. (ENG., Illus.). 352p. *(978-1-85149-476-7(6)*, Antique Collectors Club Dist) Antique Collectors' Club.

Hettmansperger, Mary. Heat, Color, Set & Fire: Surface Effects for Metal Jewelry. 2012. (ENG., Illus.). 128p. 27.95 ***(978-1-4547-0016-6(5))*** Lark Bks.

Hettmansperger, Mary. Wrap, Stitch, Fold & Rivet: Making Designer Metal Jewelry. 2008. (Lark Jewelry Book Ser.). (ENG., Illus.). 128p. 24.95 *(978-1-60059-125-9(6))* Lark Bks.

Hinton, David A. & Hinton, David Alban. The Alfred Jewel: And Other Late Anglo-Saxon Decorated Metalwork. 2008. (Ashmolean Handbooks). (ENG., Illus.). 112p. pap. 15.95 *(978-1-85444-230-7(9))* Ashmolean Museum GBR. Dist: Antique Collectors' Club.

Joplin, Norman & Waterworth, John T. Britains New Toy Soldiers, 1973 to the Present: Traditional Gloss-Painted Metal Models. 2008. (Illus.). 272p. bds. 99.99 *(978-0-7643-3062-9(4))* Schiffer Publishing, Ltd.

Lee, Richard. The Production, Use & Disposal of Romano-British Pewter Tableware. 2009. (Bar Ser.). (Illus.). 257p. (C). 102.50 *(978-1-4073-0388-8(0))* British Archaeological Reports Ltd. GBR. Dist: Brown, David Bk. Co., The.

Lenk, Torsten. The Flintlock: Its Origin, Development, & Use. Urquart, G A, tr. from SWE. 2007. (ENG., Illus.). 200p. per. 19.95 *(978-1-60239-012-6(6)*, 239012) Skyhorse Publishing Co., Inc.

Levy, Thomas E., et al. Masters of Fire: Hereditary Bronze Casters of South India. 2008. (ENG., Illus.). 144p. (C). 60.00 *(978-3-937203-37-9(0))* Deutsches Bergbau-Museum DEU. Dist: Brown, David Bk. Co., The.

Loney, Jan. Metal Jewelry Made Easy: A Crafter's Guide to Fabricating Necklaces, Earrings, Bracelets & More. 2009. (ENG., Illus.). 128p. 22.95 *(978-1-60059-473-1(5))* Lark Bks.

Mandel Lisa Slovis. Pewter Studio: Contemporary Projects & Techniques. 2010. (ENG., Illus.). 128p. 24.95 *(978-1-60059-191-4(4))* Lark Bks.

Mann, Lindsey. Coloured Aluminium Jewellery. 2010. (ENG., Illus.). 128p. pap. 24.95 *(978-1-4081-0629-7(9))* A & C Black GBR. Dist: Macmillan.

McConnell, Kevin. Roycroft Art Metal. 4th exp. rev. ed. 2008. (Illus.). 152p. pap. 16.99 *(978-0-7643-2990-6(1))* Schiffer Publishing, Ltd.

Megaw, Ruth & Megaw, Vincent. Early Celtic Art in Britain & Ireland. 2nd ed. 2008. (Shire Archaeology Book Ser.). (ENG., Illus.). 80p. per. 13.95 *(978-0-7478-0613-4(6))* Shire Pubns., Ltd. GBR. Dist: Random Hse., Inc.

Neva, Elena. Jewelry of Central Asia. 2008. (Illus.). 144p. pap. *(978-1-934881-11-8(2)*, M-Graphics) M-Graphics Publishing.

O'Brien Timothy A. & Walsh, Margo Grant. Collecting by Design: Silver & Metalwork of the Twentieth Century from the Margo Grant Walsh Collection. 2008. (ENG., Illus.). 152p. pap. 25.00 *(978-0-300-13892-4(X))* Yale Univ. Pr.

Parr, Ann. The Art of Stitching on Metal. 2009. (ENG., Illus.). 128p. 40.00 *(978-1-84448-225-2(1))* Search Pr., Ltd. GBR. Dist: Independent Pubs. Group.

Peterson, Linda. Metalwork Jewelery. 2011. (ENG., Illus.). 128p. pap. 19.95 *(978-1-907563-33-1(4))* CICO Bks. GBR. Dist: Ryland Peters & Small.

Pina, Leslie. Mexican Jewelry & Metal Art. 2008. (Illus.). 89p. 89.99 *(978-0-7643-3140-4(X))* Schiffer Publishing, Ltd.

Saunders, Nicholas J. Trench Art. 2nd rev. ed. 2012. (Illus.). 160p. pap. 24.95 ***(978-1-84884-637-1(1))*** Pen & Sword Bks. Ltd. GBR. Dist: Casemate Pubs. & Bk. Distributors, LLC.

Signs of Life 2007. 2007. 12.00 *(978-0-9618302-3-6(9))* 3rd ed. 12.95 *(978-0-9785501-0-3(2))* Lorene Pubns.

Signs of Life 2008. 2008. 12.00 *(978-0-9618302-4-3(7))* Lorene Pubns.

Snyder, Jeffrey B. Art Jewelry Today 2. 2008. (Illus.). 256p. bds. 50.00 *(978-0-7643-3065-0(9))* Schiffer Publishing, Ltd.

St. Jean, Kim. Mixed Metal Mania: Solder, rivet, hammer, & wire exceptional Jewelry. 2011. (ENG., Illus.). 112p. pap. 21.95 *(978-0-87116-416-2(7))* Kalmbach Publishing Co., Bks. Div.

Stiles, Clare. Anodized Brilliant Colors & Bold Designs for Aluminum Jewelry. 2010. (ENG., Illus.). 128p. pap. 19.95 *(978-1-60059-520-2(0))* Lark Bks.

Sundseth, Dag. Gianfranco Pedersoli: Master Engraver. Fjestad, S. P. & Micheli-Lamboy, Elena, eds. 2007. (Illus.). 212p. 65.00 *(978-1-886768-71-0(4))* Blue Bk. Pubns., Inc.

Wurttembergishe, Metallwarenfa. Art Nouveau Domestic Metalwork: From Wurttembergische Metallwaren 1906. 2nd ed. 2008. (ENG., Illus.). 389p. 99.50 *(978-1-85149-510-8(X))* Antique Collectors' Club.

Xanthopoulou, M. Les lampes en bronze a l'epoque Paleochretienne. 2010. (Bibliotheque de l'antiquite Tardive Ser.). (FRE., Illus.). 352p. (C). pap. 102.00 *(978-2-503-53369-8(8))* Brepols Pubs. BEL. Dist: Brown, David Bk. Co., The.

Yamamoto, Yoshiko. Quiet Ripples. 2009. 230p. 90.00 *(978-0-692-00507-1(2))* Yamamoto, Yoshiko.

222 Jahre Zeichenakademie Hanau: Zwischen Kunst und Handwerk. (GER., Illus.). 248p. 75.00 *(978-3-925369-36-0(8))* Arnoldsche Art Pubs. DEU. Dist: Antique Collectors' Club.

ART METAL-WORK—TECHNIQUE

Ghiberti, Lorenzo, et al. The Gates of Paradise: Lorenzo Ghiberti's Renaissance Masterpiece. 2007. (Illus.). 182p. pap. *(978-1-932543-16-2(3))* High Museum of Art.

Radke, Gary & contrib. by. The Gates of Paradise: Lorenzo Ghiberti's Renaissance Masterpiece. 2007. (Illus.). 182p. 45.00 *(978-1-932543-15-5(5))* High Museum of Art.

Radke, Gary M., ed. The Gates of Paradise: Lorenzo Ghiberti's Renaissance Masterpiece. 2007. (ENG., Illus.). 184p. 45.00 *(978-0-300-12615-0(8))* Yale Univ. Pr.

ART METAL-WORK—PRIVATE COLLECTIONS

Falkenhausen, Lothar von. The Lloyd Cotsen Study Collection of Chinese Bronze Mirrors Vol. 1 & Vol. 2: Catalogue - Studies, 2 vols. Cahill, Susan, ed. 2011. (Monumenta Archaeologica Ser.). (ENG., Illus.). 264p. (C). 450.00 ***(978-0-9745168-8-2(0))*** Cotsen Institute of Archaeology at UCLA.

Hartop, Christopher. A Noble Feast: English Silver from the Jerome & Rita Gans Collection at the Virginia Museum of Fine Arts. 2007. (ENG., Illus.). 96p. pap. 25.00 *(978-0-917046-83-4(8))* Univ. Pr. of Virginia.

Mohamed, Bashir. The Arts of the Muslim Knight: The Furusiyya Art Foundation Collection. 2008. (ENG., Illus.). 416p. 100.00 *(978-88-7624-877-1(3))* Skira Editore ITA. Dist: Random Hse., Inc.

Riddick, Mark. Rotten Renderings. 2008. 112p. pap. 38.00 *(978-0-615-22340-7(0))* www.riddickart.com.

Schroder, Timothy. Renaissance Silver in the Schroder Collection. 2007. (Schroder Collection). (ENG., Illus.). 176p. pap. 50.00 *(978-0-900785-96-2(9))* Holberton, Paul Publishing GBR. Dist: Casemate Pubs. & Bk. Distributors, LLC.

ART METAL WORKERS

see also Tinsmiths

Waters, Deborah Dependahl, et al. The Jewelry & Metalwork of Marie Zimmermann. 2012. (ENG., Illus.). 400p. 65.00 ***(978-0-300-18114-2(0))*** Yale Univ. Pr.

ART MUSEUMS

see also Art Galleries, Commercial

also names of individual museums or galleries, e.g. Metropolitan Museum of Art (New York, N.Y.)

Adler, Kathleen. A Time & a Place: Near Sydenham Hill by Camille Pissarro. 2011. (Kimbell Masterpiece Ser.). (ENG., Illus.). 86p. pap. 16.95 *(978-0-300-17577-6(9))* Kimbell Art Museum.

Adriani, Gotz. Die Künstler der Kaiser. 2009. (GER., Illus.). 336p. *(978-3-8321-9200-6(X))* DuMont.

Affron, Matthew, et al. Matisse, Picasso, & Modern Art in Paris: The T. Catesby Jones Collections at the Virginia Museum of Fine Arts & the University of Virginia Art Museum. 2009. (ENG., Illus.). 160p. pap. 39.95 *(978-0-917046-88-9(9))* Univ. Pr. of Virginia.

Aitken, Jim. Oil Paintings in Public Ownership in Warwickshire. 2010. (ENG., Illus.). 302p. 85.00 *(978-1-904931-54-6(5))* Public Catalogue Foundation, The GBR. Dist: National Bk. Network.

Allen, Brian, et al. Oklahoma City Museum of Art: Paintings & Sculpture from the Collection. George, Hardy & Pavelka, Jeffrey J., eds. 2007. pap. 40.00 *(978-0-911919-06-6(6))* Oklahoma City Museum of Art.

Allen, Nancy. Art Museum Images in Scholarly Publishing. 2009. pap. *(978-0-89263-021-9(3))* Rice Univ. Pr.

Altshuler, Bruce. Collecting the New: Museums & Contemporary Art. 2007. (ENG., Illus.). 208p. (C). per. 21.95 *(978-0-691-13373-7(5))* Princeton Univ. Pr.

Altshuler, Bruce & Sharmacharja, Shamita. A Manual for the 21st Century Art Institution. 2010. (ENG., Illus.). 184p. pap. 42.00 *(978-3-86560-618-1(0))* Verlag der Buchhandlung Walther Konig DEU. Dist: D.A.P./Distributed Art Pubs.

Andera, Margaret & Stone, Lisa. Accidental Genius: Art from the Anthony Petullo Collection. 2012. ***(978-0-944110-97-3(5))*** Milwaukee Art Museum.

Anderson, Susan M. Collecting California: Selections from Laguna Art Museum. 2009. *(978-0-940872-36-3(6))* Laguna Art Museum Store.

Annichiarico, Silvana, ed. Serials & One-Offs: Triennale Design Museum. 2009. (ENG & ITA., Illus.). 304p. pap. 97.50 *(978-88-370-6920-9(0))* Electa ITA. Dist: Trans-Atlantic Pubns., Inc.

Anthem Press Staff, compiled by. Anthem Guide to the Art Galleries & Museums of Europe. 2009. (ENG., Illus.). 618p. pap. 24.95 *(978-1-84331-273-4(5))* Anthem Pr. GBR. Dist: Books International, Inc.

Appleyard, Charlotte & Salzmann, James. Corporate Art Collections: A Handbook to Corporate Buying. 2012. (Illus.). 240p. 60.00 ***(978-1-84822-071-3(5)***, Lund Humphries Pubs.) Ashgate Publishing, Ltd. GBR. Dist: Ashgate Publishing Co.

Art & Language, creator. Art & Language: Homes for Homes II, 1 vol. 2006. (ENG., Illus.). 260p. 35.00 *(978-3-905701-56-2(1))* JRP Ringier Kunstverlag AG CHE. Dist: D.A.P./Distributed Art Pubs.

Asano, Shugo & Smith, Lawrence, intros. British Museum, Vol. 1. (Illus.). 268p. 300.00 *(978-0-87011-855-5(2))* Kodansha America, Inc.

Axsom, Richard H. 100 Years, 100 Works of Art: Introduction to the Collection of the Grand Rapids Art Museum. 2010. *(978-0-615-39126-7(5))* Yale Univ. Pr.

Baan, Iwan, photos by. MAXXI: Zaha Hadid Architects. 2010. (ENG., Illus.). 164p. 55.00 *(978-0-8478-5800-2(6)*, Skira) Rizzoli International Pubns., Inc.

Backe-Dahmen, Annika. Die Rückkehr der Götter: Berlins verborgener Olymp. 2009. (ENG.). 424p. 69.00 *(978-3-7954-2113-7(6))*, Art Stock Bks. Ltd/Csi) Continental Sales, Inc.

Badiola, Txomin. Ana Laura Alaez Using Your Guns. 2008. (ENG., Illus.). 160p. pap. 55.00 *(978-88-8158-675-2(4))* Charta ITA. Dist: D.A.P./Distributed Art Pubs.

Baensch, Tanja. "Un Petit Berlin"? Die Neugründung der Strassburger Gemaldesammlung Durch Wilhelm Bode Im Zeitgenössischen Kontext: Ein Beitrag Zur Museumspolitik Im Deutschen Kaiserreich. 2007. (GER., Illus.). 678p. (C). 117.00 *(978-3-89971-380-0(X))* Vandenhoeck & Ruprecht GmbH & Co. KG DEU. Dist: ISD.

Ballon, Hilary. The Guggenheim: Frank Lloyd Wright & the Making of the Modern Museum. 2009. (ENG., Illus.). 228p. 65.00 *(978-0-89207-385-6(3))* Guggenheim, Solomon R. Museum.

Banovich, John & Cabela, David. Beast. 2009. 0264p. 69.95 *(978-0-9819761-0-5(7))* Banovich Art, Inc.

—Beast Signature Edition. 2009. 0264p. 175.00 *(978-0-9819761-1-2(5))* Banovich Art, Inc.

Barragan, Paco, text. The Art Fair Age. 2008. (ENG., Illus.). 240p. pap. 44.95 *(978-88-8158-682-0(7))* Charta ITA. Dist: D.A.P./Distributed Art Pubs.

Bartlett, Jennifer. Jennifer Bartlett, Writings. 2014. (ENG.). 300p. pap. 25.00 *(978-0-88214-570-9(3))* Spring Pubns., Inc.

Bassegoda I Hugas, Bonaventura. Col·leccionistes, Col·leccions I Museus: Episodis de la Història Del Patrimoni Artístic de Catalunya. 2007. (CAT., Illus.). 291p. *(978-84-475-3166-0(X))* Univ. de Barcelona Pubns.

Beall-Fofana, Barbara. Understanding the Art Museum. 2006. (ENG., Illus.). 128p. (C). pap. 28.00 *(978-0-13-195070-2(3)*, Prentice Hall) Prentice Hall PTR.

Becker, Cynthia & Loughran, Kristyne contrib. by. Desert Jewels: North African Jewelry & Photography from the Xavier Guerrand-Hermes Collection. 2009. (Illus.). 95p. pap. 19.95 *(978-0-945802-52-5(8))* Museum for African Art.

Bellini, Andrea, ed. Everything You Always Wanted to Know about Gallerists but Were Afraid to Ask. 2011. (ENG., Illus.). 334p. pap. 24.95 *(978-3-03764-087-6(1))* JRP Ringier Kunstverlag AG CHE. Dist: D.A.P./Distributed Art Pubs.

Belting, Hans & Buddensieg, Andrea, eds. The Global Art World. 2009. (ENG., Illus.). 408p. pap. 45.00 *(978-3-7757-2407-4(9))* Hatje Cantz Verlag GmbH & Co KG DEU. Dist: D.A.P./Distributed Art Pubs.

Benedetti, Joan M. & Abid, Ann B. Art Museum Libraries & Librarianship. Benedetti, Joan M., ed. 2007. (ENG., Illus.). 336p. pap. 60.00 *(978-0-8108-5921-0(1))* Scarecrow Pr., Inc.

—Art Museum Libraries & Librarianship. Benedetti, Joan M., ed. 2007. (ENG., Illus.). 336p. 82.50 *(978-0-8108-5918-0(1))* Scarecrow Pr., Inc.

Bernasek, Lisa. Artistry of the Everyday: Beauty & Craftsmanship in Berber Art. 2008. (Peabody Museum Collections Ser.). (Illus.). 128p. pap. 21.95 *(978-0-87365-405-0(6))* Peabody Museum of Archaeology & Ethnology, Harvard Univ., Pubns. Dept.

Berzock, Kathleen Bickford & Clarke, Christa, eds. Representing Africa in American Art Museums: A Century of Collecting & Display. 2010. (Mclellan Book Ser.). (ENG., Illus.). 320p. pap. 40.00 *(978-0-295-98961-7(0))* Univ. of Washington Pr.

Beumer, Marjolein. Capturing Museum Knowledge: A Twenty Year Evolution in Digitally Recording the Tropenmuseum Collection. 2009. (Bulletins of the Royal Tropical Institute Ser.). 112p. pap. 35.00 *(978-90-6832-749-6(6))* Royal

Tropical Institute Pr. (KIT (Koninklijk Instituut voor de Tropen) NLD. Dist: Stylus Publishing, LLC.

Bewer, Francesca G. A Laboratory for Art: Harvard's Fogg Museum & the Emergence of Conservation in America, 1900-1950. 2010. (Illus.). 365p. *(978-1-891771-53-8(1))* Harvard Univ. Art Museums.

—A Laboratory for Art: Harvard's Fogg Museum & the Emergence of Conservation in America, 1900-1950. 2010. (ENG., Illus.). 368p. pap. 40.00 *(978-0-300-15469-6(0))* Yale Univ. Pr.

Biesenbach, Klaus, et al, texts. Greater New York 2010, 1 vol. 2010. (ENG.). 250p. pap. 19.00 *(978-0-9841776-2-2(0))* P.S.1 Contemporary Art Ctr.

Bishop, Janet C., et al. San Francisco Museum of Modern Art: 75 Years of Looking Forward. 2009. *(978-0-918471-83-3(4))* San Francisco Museum of Modern Art.

Bladen, Ronald, illus. Skulptur/Sculpture: Werke der Sammlung Marzona/Works from the Marzona Collection, 1 vol. 2008. (ENG.). 80p. 48.00 *(978-3-86560-214-5(2))* Verlag der Buchhandlung Walther Konig DEU. Dist: D.A.P./Distributed Art Pubs.

Bloemheuvel, Marente & van Kooten, Toos, eds. Kroller-Muller Museum: the History of A Sculpture Garden, 1 vol. 2009. (ENG., Illus.). 368p. 62.50 *(978-90-5662-585-6(3))* NAi Uitgevers / Publishers Stichting NLD. Dist: D.A.P./Distributed Art Pubs.

Bogard, Roma. For the Love of Art: A Collection of Artistic Inspiration. 2009. 124p. pap. 37.49 *(978-1-4389-7378-4(0))* AuthorHouse.

Bonetti, David & Dreishpoon, Douglas. The Panza Collection: An Experience of Color & Light. 2007. (Illus.). 119p. *(978-1-887457-08-8(9))* Buffalo Fine Arts/Albright-Knox Art Gallery.

Bonfante-Warren, Alexandra. The Pitti Palace Collections. 2006. (Illus.). 320p. *(978-0-88363-513-1(5))* Levin, Hugh Lauter Assocs.

Borys, Stephen D., ed. The John & Mable Ringling Museum of Art: A guide to the Collections. 2008. (Illus.). per. *(978-0-916758-52-3(4))* Ringling, John & Mable Museum of Art Foundation, The.

Bourke, Marie. The Story of Irish Museums 1790 - 2000: Culture, Identity & Education. 2011. (Illus.). 600p. 59.00 *(978-1-85918-475-2(8))* Cork Univ. Pr. IRL. Dist: Stylus Publishing, LLC.

Bowman, Russell & Connors, Thomas. Friends of Art: Celebrating 50 Years. 2007. (Illus.). 79p. *(978-0-944110-90-4(8))* Milwaukee Art Museum.

Brandle, Christian & Formanek, Verena, eds. Every Thing Design. 2009. (ENG., Illus.). 800p. 45.00 *(978-3-7757-2331-2(5))* Hatje Cantz Verlag GmbH & Co KG DEU. Dist: D.A.P./Distributed Art Pubs.

Braun, Reinhard, contrib. by. A Picture Book: The Photography Collection of the Museum Folkwang, 1 vol. 2007. (ENG., Illus.). 288p. 55.00 *(978-3-86521-607-6(2))* Steidl, Gerhard Druckerei und Verlag DEU. Dist: Innovative Logistics.

Breazeale, William. A Pioneering Collection: Master Drawings from the Crocker Art Museum. 2010. (ENG., Illus.). 172p. pap. 45.00 *(978-1-884038-17-4(4))* Holberton, Paul Publishing GBR. Dist: Univ. of Washington Pr.

Brennan, Marcia. Curating Consciousness: Mysticism & the Modern Museum. 2010. (ENG., Illus.). 304p. (gr. 17). 29.95 *(978-0-262-01378-9(9))* MIT Pr.

Brilliant, Virginia. Triumph & Taste: Peter Paul Rubens at the Ringling Museum of Art. 2012. (ENG., Illus.). 128p. pap. 19.95 *(978-1-85759-712-7(5))* Scala, Editions FRA. Dist: National Bk. Network.

Brockhurst, Gerald Leslie & Ray, Romita. The Eternal Masquerade: Prints & Paintings by Gerald Leslie Brockhurst (1890-1978): From the Jacob Burns Foundation. 2006. (Illus.). 131p. *(978-0-915977-59-8(1))* Univ. of Georgia, Georgia Museum of Art.

Brotherton, Barbara, ed. S'abadeb, the Gifts: Pacific Coast Salish Art & Artists. 2008. (Illus.). 240p. pap. 40.00 *(978-0-295-98863-4(0))* Univ. of Washington Pr.

Brown, Hugh, ed. Eclectic. Everyday. Elegant: The Massillon Museum Celebrates 75 Years. 2008. (Illus.). 132p. pap. 30.00 *(978-0-9755555-8-3(8))* Massillon Museum.

Buchhart, Dieter & Erritzoe, Marie Louise, eds. Red Faction. 2008. (GER & ENG.). 160p. 40.00 *(978-3-939583-80-6(4))* Kehrer Verlag Heidelberg, Klaus Kehrer DEU. Dist: Consortium Bk. Sales & Distribution.

Buci, Luis, et al, illus. Mermaids 4: A Gallery Girls Collection. 2007. (Gallery Girls Collection). 64p. per. 9.95 *(978-0-86562-154-1(3))* S.Q. Productions, Inc.

Burnham, Rika & Kai-Kee, Elliott. Teaching in the Art Museum: Interpretation As Experience. 2011. (ENG., Illus.). 192p. pap. 30.00 *(978-1-60606-058-2(9)*, J. Paul Getty Museum) Getty Pubns.

Burtynsky, Edward & Fulford, Robert. Frank Gehry in Toronto: Transforming the Art Gallery of Ontario. 2008. (Illus.). 96p. 50.00 *(978-1-85894-467-8(8))* Merrell Pubs. Ltd. GBR. Dist: Perseus Distribution.

Busch, Jason, ed. & text. Carnegie Museum of Art: Decorative Arts & Design. 2010. (ENG., Illus.). 224p. pap. 19.95 *(978-0-88039-052-1(2))* Carnegie Museum of Art, The.

Buvelot, Quentin. Made in Holland: Highlights from the Collection of Eijk & Rose-Marie de Mol Van Otterloo. 2011. 152p. pap. 50.00 *(978-90-400-7744-9(4))* Waanders B.V., Uitgeverij NLD. Dist: National Bk. Network.

Canby, Sheila, et al, eds. Masterpieces from the Department of Islamic Art in the Metropolitan Museum of Art. 2011. (ENG., Illus.). 448p. 65.00 *(978-0-300-17585-1(X))* Yale Univ. Pr.

Candlin, Fiona. Art, Museums & Touch. 2010. (Rethinking Art's Histories Ser.). (ENG., Illus.). 240p. 90.00 *(978-0-7190-7933-7(0))* Manchester Univ. Pr. GBR. Dist: Macmillan.

Caneva, Caterina. Tre Piccoli, Grandi Musei e Altre Testimonianze, Scritti 2002-2008. Paolini, Claudio, ed. 2009. (Interventi e Testimonianze Ser.). (ITA., Illus.). 144p. (C). pap. 28.00 *(978-88-596-0692-5(6))* Polistampa ITA. Dist: Brown, David Bk. Co., The.

Carpenter, J. Reading Surimono: The Interplay of Text & Image in Japanese Prints. 2008. 408p. *(978-90-04-16841-1(9))* BRILL.

Carr, Annemarie Weyl. Imprinting the Divine: Byzantine & Russian Icons from the Menil Collection. 2011. (ENG., Illus.). 168p. 50.00 *(978-0-300-16968-3(X))* Yale Univ. Pr.

Caruso, Laura & Fulton, Andrea Kalivas, texts. Denver Art Museum. 2006. (ENG., Illus.). 64p. pap. 7.95 *(978-1-85759-431-7(2))* Scala, Editions FRA. Dist: National Bk. Network.

Chang, Alexandra, text. Envisioning Diaspora, Asian American Visual Arts Collectives. 2009. (ENG., Illus.). 266p. pap. 35.00 *(978-988-17522-3-9(X))* Timezone 8 Ltd. HKG. Dist: D.A.P./Distributed Art Pubs.

Cherry, Brigid. Spectacle & Display. Cherry, Deborah & Cullen, Fintan, eds. 2008. (Art History Special Issues Ser.). (ENG., Illus.). 200p. pap. 29.95 *(978-1-4051-7524-1(9)*, Wiley-Blackwell) Wiley, John & Sons, Inc.

Chiego, William J. Jane & Arthur Stieren Center for Exhibitions: McNay Art Museum. 2012. (ENG., Illus.). 64p. pap. 12.95 *(978-1-85759-668-7(4))* Scala, Editions FRA. Dist: National Bk. Network.

Chong, Alan & Murai, Noriko. Journeys East: Isabella Stewart Gardner & Asia. 2009. (Illus.). 420p. pap. 75.00 *(978-1-934772-75-1(5))* Periscope Publishing.

Chowdhry, Pritika. Visceral Mappings: Transdiasporic Art Practices. 2007. (Illus.). 50p. pap. 24.95 *(978-0-9797340-0-7(2))* Chowdhry, Pritika.

Clemmer, David. Serenading the Light: Painters of the Desert Southwest. 2nd rev. ed. 2007. (ENG., Illus.). 162p. 55.00 *(978-0-9719150-7-7(5))*; per. 39.00 *(978-0-9719150-8-4(3))* Schenck Southwest Publishing, LLC.

Clifford, Helen. A Treasured Inheritance: 600 Years of Oxford College Silver. 2006. (ENG., Illus.). 160p. 22.95 *(978-1-85444-195-9(7))* Ashmolean Museum GBR. Dist: National Bk. Network.

Cloudman, Ruth H. The Speed Art Museum: Highlights from the Collection. 2007. (ENG., Illus.). 240p. pap. 16.95 *(978-1-85894-409-8(0))* Merrell Pubs. Ltd. GBR. Dist: Perseus Distribution.

Coleman, Robert Randolf & Bohn, Babette. The Art of Disegno: Italian Prints & Drawings from the Georgia Museum of Art. 2007. *(978-0-915977-62-8(1))* Univ. of Georgia, Georgia Museum of Art.

Comfort, George Fisk. Art Museums in America. 2011. 18p. pap. 11.99 ***(978-1-4181-8951-8(0))*** MPublishing.

Conrads, Margaret. American Paintings Vol. 12: Collections of the Nelson-Atkins Museum of Art, 2 vols. 2007. (ENG.). 768p. 125.00 *(978-0-942614-37-4(2))* Nelson-Atkins Museum of Art, The.

Cooks, Bridget R. Exhibiting Blackness: African Americans & the American Art Museum. 2011. (Illus.). 240p. pap. 29.95 *(978-1-55849-875-4(3))* Univ. of Massachusetts Pr.

Cranston, J., ed. Venetian Painting Matters, 1450-1750. 2012. (Museums at the Crossroads Ser.). (ENG.). 200p. (C). pap. 94.00 *(978-2-503-53526-5(7))* Brepols Pubs. BEL. Dist: ISD.

Crookham, Alan. An Illustrated History. 2010. (ENG., Illus.). 128p. pap. 25.00 *(978-1-85709-463-3(8))* Yale Univ. Pr.

Curators at the National Gallery of Ireland Staff. National Gallery of Ireland. Davis, Christine, ed. Carroll, Barry, tr. 2008. (ENG., Illus.). 300p. pap. 24.95 *(978-1-85759-510-9(6))* Scala, Editions FRA. Dist: National Bk. Network.

Curators Gallery Staff. Whitworth Art Gallery: Art Spaces. 2011. (ENG., Illus.). 64p. pap. 7.95 *(978-1-85759-585-7(8))* Scala, Editions FRA. Dist: National Bk. Network.

Curators Staff. Artists on Art: Yale University Art Gallery. 2006. (Yale University Art Gallery Ser.). (ENG.). 71p. pap. 15.00 *(978-0-89467-087-9(5))* Yale Univ. Art Gallery.

Daneo, Angelica. The Kress Collection at the Denver Art Museum. 2011. (ENG., Illus.). 168p. pap. 25.00 *(978-0-914738-69-5(0))* Denver Art Museum.

Daros-Latinamerica Collec Staff. Face to Face. 2008. (ENG., Illus.). 288p. 55.00 *(978-3-7757-2112-7(6))* Hatje Cantz Verlag GmbH & Co KG DEU. Dist: D.A.P./Distributed Art Pubs.

Datta, Ella. Treasures of the National Gallery of Modern Art, New Delhi. 2012. (ENG., Illus.). 252p. 70.00 *(978-1-890206-67-3(9))* Mapin Publishing Pvt. Ltd IND. Dist: National Bk. Network.

Davila-Villa, Ursula, ed. & intro. Recovering Beauty: The 1990s in Buenos Aires. 2011. (ENG., Illus.). 144p. pap. 25.00 *(978-0-9815738-5-4(1))* Blanton Museum of Art, Univ. of Texas at Austin.

de Haro, Fernando & Fuentes, Omar, compiled by. Houses: Distinction with Style. 2008. (Houses Ser.). (ENG., Illus.). 192p. 39.95 *(978-970-9726-92-3(7))* AM Editores MEX. Dist: Perseus-PGW.

De Nicolay-Mazery, Christiane. The Yves Saint Laurent-Pierre Berge Collection: The Sale of the Century. 2009. (ENG., Illus.). 320p. 95.00 *(978-2-08-030130-7(6))* Flammarion et Cie FRA. Dist: Random Hse., Inc.

De Vries, Robbie. Snowprints: A Grandmother's Glimpses of New Life & Old Art. (Lifeprints Ser.: Vol. I). (Illus.). (Orig.). pap. *(978-0-9627886-0-4(0))* de Vries, Robbie Ray Parsons.

Dehan, Amy Miller. Outside the Ordinary: Contemporary Art in Glass, Wood, & Ceramics from the Wolf Collection. 2009. (ENG.). 176p. pap. 30.00 *(978-0-8214-1861-1(0))* Ohio Univ. Pr.

Denegri, Dobrila. Ernesto Neto 4: Macro / Hall. Denegri, Dobrila, ed. 2008. 80p. pap. 37.50 *(978-88-370-6250-7(8))* Electa ITA. Dist: Trans-Atlantic Pubns., Inc.

Denver Art Museum Staff, contrib. by. Denver Art Museum: Highlights from the Collection. 2006. (ENG., Illus.). 64p. pap. 8.95 *(978-1-85759-432-4(0))* Scala, Editions FRA. Dist: National Bk. Network.

Deputy Director of Curatorial Affairs Staff & Departmental Curators of the Museum Staff. Cincinnati Art Museum: Collection Highlights. 2009. (ENG., Illus.). 392p. 49.95 *(978-1-904832-53-9(9))* Giles, D. Ltd. GBR. Dist: Antique Collectors' Club.

Derksen, Tessa & Shen, Chen. Iconic 15: The ROM's Must-See Treasures. 2010. (ENG & FRE.). 80p. pap. 5.00 *(978-0-88854-467-4(7))* Royal Ontario Museum CAN. Dist: Univ. of Toronto Pr.

Detterer, Gabriele, ed. & text. Artist-Run Spaces: Non Profit Collective Oraganizations in the 1960s And 1970s. 2012. (ENG., Illus.). 280p. pap. 29.95 ***(978-3-03764-191-0(6))*** JRP Ringier Kunstverlag AG CHE. Dist: D.A.P./Distributed Art Pubs.

Dewdney, Andrew, et al, eds. Post Critical Museology. 2012. (ENG.). 336p. (C). 125.00 *(978-0-415-60600-4(4))*; pap. 44.95 *(978-0-415-60601-1(2))* Routledge.

Dickson, Rachel, et al. Whitechapel at War: Isaac Rosenberg & His Circle. 2009. (Illus.). 144p. 70.00 *(978-0-900157-09-7(7)*, Lund Humphries Pubs.) Ashgate Publishing, Ltd. GBR. Dist: Ashgate Publishing Co.

Diehr, Ursula & Steinemann, Holger. Art 42 Basel. 2011. (ENG., Illus.). 746p. pap. 70.00 *(978-3-7757-2785-3(X))* Hatje Cantz Verlag GmbH & Co KG DEU. Dist: D.A.P./Distributed Art Pubs.

Dietrich, Nikola, text. Little Theatre of Gestures. 2010. (ENG., Illus.). 164p. pap. 40.00 *(978-3-7757-2436-4(2))* Hatje Cantz Verlag GmbH & Co KG DEU. Dist: D.A.P./Distributed Art Pubs.

Dillon, Brian, et al, texts. Walking in My Mind. 2009. (ENG., Illus.). 160p. pap. 40.00 *(978-1-85332-277-8(6))* Hayward Gallery Publishing GBR. Dist: D.A.P./Distributed Art Pubs.

Dimitriadis, George, et al, eds. Rock Art & Museum. 2009. (FRE & ENG., Illus.). 86p. (C). pap. 70.00 *(978-1-4073-0531-8(X))* British Archaeological Reports Ltd. GBR. Dist: Brown, David Bk. Co., The.

Directory of Museums, Galleries & Buildings of Historic Interest in the United Kingdom. 4th rev. ed. 2009. (ENG.). 692p. 350.00 *(978-1-85743-489-7(7))* Routledge.

Dolkart, Judith F., et al. James Tissot: The Life of Christ. 2009. (ENG., Illus.). 304p. 59.95 *(978-1-85894-496-8(1))* Merrell Pubs. Ltd. GBR. Dist: Perseus Distribution.

Dorment, Richard, et al. Art, Power, Diplomacy: The Untold Story of the Government Art Collection. 2011. (ENG., Illus.). 192p. pap. 35.00 *(978-1-85759-691-5(9))* Scala, Editions FRA. Dist: National Bk. Network.

Drechsler, Wolfgang & Leutgeb, Doris, texts. Joseph Beuys, 1 vol. 2007. (ENG., Illus.). 184p. pap. 30.00 *(978-3-938821-72-5(8))* Verlag fur Moderne Kunst DEU. Dist: D.A.P./Distributed Art Pubs.

Dreishpoon, Douglas, ed. The Long Curve: 150 Years of Visionary Collecting at the Albright-Knox Art Gallery. 2011. (ENG., Illus.). 268p. 65.00 ***(978-88-572-1040-7(5))*** Skira Editore ITA. Dist: Random Hse., Inc.

Duffus, Robert L. American Renaissance. reprint ed. 34.50 *(978-0-404-02214-3(6))* AMS Pr., Inc.

Dulce, Román, et al. American Selections from the Samuel P. Harn Museum of Art. 2009. (ENG., Illus.). 160p. pap. 29.95 *(978-0-9762552-8-4(6))* Univ. Pr. of Florida.

Dunn-Morton, Julie. 160 Years of Art at the St. Louis Mercantile Library: A Handbook to the Collections: an Anniversary Publication, 1846-2006. 2008. (ENG., Illus.). 196p. (gr. 9). 39.95 *(978-0-9639804-9-6(1))* Univ. of Missouri Pr.

Durrschmidt, Jackwyn. The Finest Small Museum in the Country: A History of the Lyman Allyn Art Museum. 2007. 380p. (ENG.). 35.95 *(978-0-595-68339-0(8))*; per. 25.95 *(978-0-595-43038-3(4))* iUniverse, Inc.

Dziekian, Vince. Virtuality & the Art of Exhibition: Curatorial Design for the Multimedial Museum. 2012. (Illus.). 207p. pap. 40.00 *(978-1-84150-476-6(9))* Intellect, Ltd. GBR. Dist: Chicago Distribution Ctr.

Eckmann, Sabine & Malone, Meredith. Thaddeus Strode: Absolutes & Nothings. 2008. (Mildred Lane Kemper Art Museum-Contemporary Projects Ser.). (Illus.). 80p. 30.00 *(978-0-936316-24-6(1))* Washington Univ., Mildred Lane Kemper Art Museum.

Eliasson, Olafur & Thorsen, Kjetil. Serpentine Gallery Pavilion 2007. 2007. (Illus.). 125p. 34.95 *(978-3-03778-116-6(5)*, 3037781165) Springer.

Elliott, Clare, et al. The Menil Collection. 2008. (ENG., Illus.). 64p. pap. 7.95 *(978-1-85759-483-6(5))* Scala, Editions FRA. Dist: National Bk. Network.

Elliott, Patrick. Another World: Dalí, Magritte, Miró & the Surrealists. 2011. (ENG., Illus.). 224p. pap. *(978-1-906270-30-8(9))* National Galleries of Scotland.

Ellis. Oil Paintings in Public Ownership in Somerset. 2011. (ENG., Illus.). 300p. 85.00 *(978-1-904931-52-2(9))* Public Catalogue Foundation, The GBR. Dist: National Bk. Network.

Ellis, Andy. Oil Paintings in Public Ownership in Nottinghamshire. 2009. (ENG., Illus.). 300p. 85.00 *(978-1-904931-74-4(X))* Public Catalogue Foundation, The GBR. Dist: National Bk. Network.

—Oil Paintings in Public Ownership in the City of London. 2010. (ENG., Illus.). 282p. 85.00 *(978-1-904931-76-8(6))* Public Catalogue Foundation, The GBR. Dist: National Bk. Network.

Ellis, Marianne. Embroideries & Samplers from Islamic Egypt. 2006. (ENG., Illus.). 96p. 39.95 *(978-1-85444-154-6(X)*, 154X) Ashmolean Museum GBR. Dist: Antique Collectors' Club.

Ellis, Steve. Oil Paintings in Public Ownership Staffordshire. 2008. (ENG.). 381p. 85.00 *(978-1-904931-34-8(0))* Public Catalogue Foundation, The GBR. Dist: National Bk. Network.

Ellison, Harlan, intro. A Lovecraft Retrospective. 2008. (ENG.). 400p. 395.00 *(978-1-933618-34-0(5)*, Millipede Pr.) Cocytus Pr.

Elms, Anthony, et al, eds. Haha: Everyday Matters. 2007. (Illus.). 192p. pap. 25.00 *(978-0-945323-13-6(1))* WhiteWalls, Inc.

Fagaly, William A., ed. Ancestors of Congo Square: African Art in the New Orleans Museum of Art. 2011. (Illus.). 376p. 75.00 *(978-1-85759-698-4(6))* Scala, Editions FRA. Dist: National Bk. Network.

Fairclough, Oliver, et al. Turner to Cézanne: Masterpieces from the Davies Collection, National Museum Wales. 2009. (ENG., Illus.). 176p. 60.00 *(978-1-55595-299-0(2))* Hudson Hills Pr. LLC.

Falconer, Morgan. The Art Lovers' Guide - New York: The Finest Art in New York by Museum, Artist, or Period. 2011. (Illus.). 240p. pap. 19.95 *(978-0-8478-3627-7(4)*, Skira) Rizzoli International Pubns., Inc.

Fantoli, Michèle. Siena: Playing with Art. 2006. (ENG.). 48p. 8.50 *(978-88-7461-033-4(5))* Mandragora ITA. Dist: Antique Collectors' Club.

Felch, Jason & Frammolino, Ralph. Chasing Aphrodite: The Hunt for Looted Antiquities at the World's Richest Museum. 2011. (ENG., Illus.). 384p. 28.00 *(978-0-15-101501-6(5))* Houghton Mifflin Harcourt Trade & Reference Pubs.

Fietzek, Gerti, ed. Maria Eichhorn: the Artist's Contract. 2009. (ENG., Illus.). 336p. pap. 49.95 *(978-3-86560-421-7(8))* Verlag der Buchhandlung Walther Konig DEU. Dist: D.A.P./Distributed Art Pubs.

Fink, Lois Marie. A History of the Smithsonian American Art Museum: The Intersection of Art, Science, & Bureaucracy. 2007. (Illus.). 220p. 34.95 net. *(978-1-55849-616-3(5))* Univ. of Massachusetts Pr.

Fohl, Thomas & Siebenbrodt, Michael. Bauhaus-Museum Weimar. 3rd ed. 2007. (Museumsstuck Ser.). (ENG., Illus.). 152p. pap. 19.95 *(978-3-422-06596-3(2))* Deutscher Kunstverlag GmbH DEU. Dist: Independent Pubs. Group.

Folie, Sabine, ed. Un Coup de des: Writing Turned Image, an Alphabet of Pensive Language. 2009. (GER & ENG., Illus.). 250p. pap. 59.95 *(978-3-86560-543-6(5))* Verlag der Buchhandlung Walther Konig DEU. Dist: D.A.P./Distributed Art Pubs.

Foster, Norman & Powell, Kenneth. Sainsbury Centre for Visual Arts. 2010. (Illus.). 96p. 96.00 *(978-3-7913-4492-8(7))* Prestel Publishing.

Franchi, Elisabetta & Greco, Carla. Milan, City of Museums: Museums of the City. 2006. (ENG., Illus.). 88p. pap. 15.95 *(978-88-422-1251-5(2))* Allemandi, Umberto & Co. GBR. Dist: National Bk. Network.

Fredericq, Suzanne. Catalogue of the Inaugural Art Exhibit Eugene J. Martin: Spice of Life. 2009. 38p. 19.70 *(978-0-9825704-0-1(6))* Estate of Eugene James Martin.

Frederiksen, Jens & Harden, Trine, photos by. The Most Beautiful Museum in the World. 2012. (ENG., Illus.). 144p. 40.00 *(978-3-7757-2342-8(0))* Hatje Cantz Verlag GmbH & Co KG DEU. Dist: D.A.P./Distributed Art Pubs.

Fritsch, Juliette, ed. Museum Gallery Interpretation & Material Culture. 2011. (Routledge Research in Museum Studies). (ENG., Illus.). 276p. (C). 125.00 *(978-0-415-88575-1(2))* Routledge.

Gaddis, Eugene R. & Brandwein, Ann, eds. Magic Facade: the Austin House. 2007. (ENG., Illus.). 132p. pap. 34.00 *(978-0-918333-23-0(7))* Wadsworth Atheneum.

Gaehtgens, Thomas W. & Marchesano, Louis. Display & Art History: The Düsseldorf Gallery & Its Catalogue. 2011. (ENG., Illus.). 104p. pap. 20.00 *(978-1-60606-092-6(9))* Getty Pubns.

Gaiter, Colette, et al. Space Is the Place: Laurie Anderson ... Jane & Louise Wilson, 1 vol. 2007. (ENG., Illus.). 80p. pap. 23.00 *(978-0-916365-74-5(3))* Independent Curators International.

Gardiner Gates, Mimi & Ishikawa, Chiyo, texts. Seattle Art Museum Downtown. 2007. 72p. pap. 9.95 *(978-0-932216-59-5(5))* Seattle Art Museum.

Gardner Gates, Mimi, frwd. Olympic Sculpture Park. 2007. 72p. pap. 9.95 *(978-0-932216-57-1(9))* Seattle Art Museum.

Geddes Poole, Andrea. Stewards of the Nation's Art: Contested Cultural Authority, 1890-1939. 2010. (ENG.). 368p. *(978-0-8020-9960-0(2))* Univ. of Toronto Pr.

Gerlinger, Anne, ed. Valentino Aroma: 45 Years of Style at the Museum of Ara Pacis July 6th October 28th 2007. 2007. (ENG., Illus.). 119p. pap. 59.99 *(978-3-8365-0187-3(2))* TASCHEN DEU. Dist: Ingram Pub. Services.

Gerson, Denise M. Sacred Stories, Timeless Tales: Mythic Perspectives in World Art. 2011. (Illus.). 50p. pap. 19.95 ***(978-0-9788213-7-1(8))*** Lowe Art Museum.

Giancarlo Politi Editore, ed. Art Diary International 2007-2008: The World Art Directory, 1 vol. 2007. (ENG., Illus.). 570p. pap. 30.00 *(978-88-7816-143-6(8))* Politi, Giancarlo Editore ITA. Dist: D.A.P./Distributed Art Pubs.

Gingeras, Alison M. Sequence 1: Painting & Sculpture from the François Pinault Collection. 2008. (ENG, FRE & ITA., Illus.). 328p. 75.00 *(978-88-6130-216-7(5))* Skira Editore ITA. Dist: Random Hse., Inc.

Glimcher, Mildred, ed. Adventures in Art: 40 Years at Pace. (Illus.). 660p. 85.00 *(978-88-86482-79-0(5))* Leonardo International ITA. Dist: D.A.P./Distributed Art Pubs.

Glymph, Minnie. Sarah P. Duke Gardens: A Wonderful Wander. 2006. (Illus.). 142p. 44.00 *(978-0-9709847-5-3(8))* Duke Univ., Univ. Stores.

Gorlenko, Kateryna. Art Museums in Global Age. 2011. 80p. pap. ***(978-3-639-33217-9(2))*** VDM Verlag Dr. Mueller e.K.

Graff, Terry, ed. Masterworks from the Beaverbrook Art Gallery. 2012. (ENG., Illus.). 256p. 65.00 ***(978-0-86492-642-5(1))*** Goose Lane Editions CAN. Dist: Univ. of Toronto Pr.

Grayson, Kathy, ed. Panic Room: Selections from the Dakis Joannou Works on Paper Collection, 1 vol. 2007. (ENG., Illus.). 160p. pap. 30.00 *(978-0-9778686-3-6(X))* Deitch, Jeffrey Inc.

Green, Alexandra. Eclectic Collecting: Art from Burma in the Denison Museum. 2008. (C). 62.00 *(978-0-8248-3311-4(2))* Univ. of Hawaii Pr.

Grima, Joseph & Wong, Karen, eds. Shift: Sanaa & the New Museum. 2008. (Illus.). 136p. pap. 39.95 (978-3-03778-140-1(8), 3037781408) Springer.

Grosenick, Uta, ed. International Art Galleries: Post-War to Post-Millennium, 1 vol. 2009. (ENG., Illus.). 540p. (gr. 13-18). 95.00 (978-3-8321-7658-7(6)) DuMont DEU. Dist: D.A.P./Distributed Art Pubs.

Grundberg, Andy. Modern Photographs: the Machine, the Body & the City: Selections from the Charles Cowles Collection, 1 vol. 2007. (ENG., Illus.). 124p. per. 34.95 (978-0-9705005-4-0(8)) Miami Art Museum of Dade County Assn.

Gunzelman, Todd. Allan Linder 20th century & Beyond. 2010. 180p. pap. 68.50 (978-0-557-07998-8(5)) Lulu Enterprises Inc.

GWWO, Inc./Architects Staff & Mount Vernon Ladies' Association of the Union Staff, contrib. by. Integrity, Civility, Ingenuity: The Making of the Ford Orientation Center & the Donald W. Reynolds Museum & Education Center at Mount Vernon: A Reflection of George Washington. 2007. (978-0-9789779-3-1(9)) Creo Pr.

Haas, Philip & Warner, Malcolm. Butchers, Dragons, Gods & Skeletons: Film Installations by Philip Haas. 2009. (Illus.). ix, 94p. (978-0-912804-50-7(5)) Kimbell Art Museum.

Hackman, William. Los Angeles County Museum of Art. 2008. (ENG., Illus.). 64p. pap. 7.95 (978-1-85759-481-2(9)) Scala, Editions FRA. Dist: National Bk. Network.

Harris, Clare. The Museum on the Roof of the World: Art, Politics, & the Representation of Tibet. 2012. (Buddhism & Modernity Ser.). (Illus.). 336p. 45.00 **(978-0-226-31747-2(1))** Univ. of Chicago Pr.

Hatakeyama, Naoya & Watanabe, Osamu, photos by. Naoshima. 2011. (ENG & JPN., Illus.). 232p. 60.00 (978-3-7757-2703-7(5)) Hatje Cantz Verlag GmbH & Co KG DEU. Dist: D.A.P./Distributed Art Pubs.

Heartney, Eleanor & Serwer, Jacquelyn. Capital Collection: Masterworks from the Corcoran Gallery of Art. 2006. (ENG., Illus.). 288p. 39.95 (978-1-903942-15-4(2), Third Millenium Pub Ltd) Antique Collectors' Club GBR. Dist: National Bk. Network.

Heartney, Eleanor, et al. John Buck: Iconography. 2008. (Illus.). 144p. (978-0-910524-37-7(8)) Eastern Washington State Historical Society.

Hein, Hilde S. Public Art: Thinking Museums Differently. 2006. (ENG., Illus.). 198p. 87.50 (978-0-7591-0958-2(3)); per. 32.95 (978-0-7591-0959-9(1)) AltaMira Pr.

Heinrich, Christoph, et al. Embrace!, 2 vols. 2009. (Illus.). (978-0-914738-61-9(5)) Denver Art Museum.

Henare, Amiria. Museums, Anthropology & Imperial Exchange. 2008. (ENG., Illus.). 344p. pap. 46.00 (978-0-521-10074-8(7)) Cambridge Univ. Pr.

Heo, Soonran. The Potential of the Internet in Arts Management: Online & Offline Integrated Arts Management. 2008. 296p. pap. (978-3-639-09446-6(8)) VDM Verlag Dr. Mueller e.K.

Herrero, Marta. Irish Intellectuals & Aesthetics: The Making of a Modern Art Collection. 2007. (Illus.). 214p. pap. 30.00 (978-0-7165-3328-3(6)) Irish Academic Pr. IRL. Dist: International Specialized Bk. Services.

Herstatt, Claudia, text. Women Gallerists: In the 20th & 21st Centuries. 2009. (ENG., Illus.). 208p. 45.00 (978-3-7757-1975-9(X)) Hatje Cantz Verlag GmbH & Co KG DEU. Dist: D.A.P./Distributed Art Pubs.

Higonnet, Anne. A Musem of One's Own: Private Collecting, Public Gift. 2010. (Illus.). 260p. 49.95 (978-1-934772-92-8(5)) Periscope Publishing.

Hill, Rachel, et al, trs. Berlin Contemporary: Gallery Guide Berlin. 2008. (ENG., Illus.). 208p. pap. 24.95 (978-3-939633-77-8(1)) Jovis Verlag GmbH DEU. Dist: D.A.P./Distributed Art Pubs.

Hindman, Sandra. Toward an Art History of Medieval Rings: A Private Collection. 2007. (Illus.). 260p. pap. 40.00 (978-1-903470-64-0(1)) Holberton, Paul Publishing GBR. Dist: Casemate Pubs. & Bk. Distributors, LLC.

Hockley, Allen, et al. Public Spectacles, Personal Pleasures: Four Centuries of Japanese Prints from a Cincinnati Collection. 2006. (Illus.). 119p. (978-0-931537-29-5(0)) Cincinnati Art Museum.

Holladay, Wilhelmina Cole. A Museum of Their Own: The National Museum of Women in the Arts, 1987-2007. 2008. (ENG., Illus.). 240p. 50.00 (978-0-7892-1003-6(7)) Abbeville Pr., Inc.

Holohan, Patrick. Color My Vacation. 2007. 5.99 net. (978-1-60402-335-0(X)) Independent Pub.

Hoolboom, Michael. Projecting Questions: Mike Hoolboom's "Invisible Man" Between the Art Gallery & the Movie Theatre. 2009. (ENG.). 144p. pap. 20.00 (978-0-921972-52-5(0)) Art Gallery of York Univ. CAN. Dist: D.A.P./Distributed Art Pubs.

Horowitz, Deborah E., ed. The Hirshhorn Museum & Sculpture Garden. 2007. (ENG., Illus.). 64p. pap. 4.95 (978-1-904832-24-9(5)) Giles, D. Ltd. GBR. Dist: Antique Collectors' Club.

Horrall, Andrew. Bringing Art to Life: A Biography of Alan Jarvis. 2009. (McGill-Queen's/Beaverbrook Canadian Foundation Studies in Art History Ser.). (ENG., Illus.). 457p. (C). (978-0-7735-3574-9(5)) McGill-Queen's Univ. Pr.

Hostetler, Lisa. Street Seen: The Psychological Gesture in American Photography, 1940-1959. 2010. (978-3-7913-6284-7(4)) Milwaukee Art Museum.

Hu, Philip K. Later Chinese Bronzes: The Saint Louis Art Museum & Robert E. Kresko Collections. 2008. (Illus.). 208p. 59.95 (978-0-89178-091-5(2)) St. Louis Art Museum.

—Later Chinese Bronzes: The Saint Louis Art Museum & Robert E. Kresko Collections. Steiner, Mary Ann, ed. 2008. (ENG & CHI., Illus.). 208p. pap. 39.95 (978-0-89178-092-2(0)) St. Louis Art Museum.

Hughes, Amanda M. & Wood, Carolyn H. A Place for Meaning: Art, Faith, & Museum Culture. 2010. (Distributed for the Ackland Art Museum Ser.). (ENG., Illus.). 245p. pap. 30.00 (978-0-9743656-3-3(7)) Univ. of North Carolina Pr.

Hylton, Jane & Johnson, Vivien. Dreamings of the Desert: Aboriginal Dot Paintings of the Western Desert. 2007. (Illus.). 140p. 45.00 (978-0-7308-3073-3(X)) Art Gallery of South Australia AUS. Dist: Antique Collectors' Club.

Images Australia Pty Ltd Staff, contrib. by. Museum & Art Spaces: A Pictorial Review of Museum & Art Spaces. 2006. (ENG., Illus.). 208p. 55.00 (978-1-86470-067-1(X)) Images Publishing Group AUS. Dist: National Bk. Network.

International Directory of Arts 2012, 3 vols. 36th ed. 2011. (ENG., Illus.). XXIV, 2954p. **(978-3-11-023488-6(2))** Saur, K. G. Verlag GmbH & Co.

Jaffe, David. Rubens's Massacre of the Innocents in the Thomson Collection. 2009. (Illus.). 128p. pap. 50.00 **(978-1-903470-81-7(1))** Holberton, Paul Publishing GBR. Dist: Casemate Pubs. & Bk. Distributors, LLC.

Jones, Mike. Set for a King: 200 Years of Gardening at the Royal Pavilion. 2006. (ENG., Illus.). 192p. (978-0-948723-62-9(9), Royal Pavilion Libraries & Mus) Antique Collectors' Club.

Kahn, Louis I., et al. Light Is the Theme: Louis I. Kahn & the Kimbell Art Museum. 2012. (ENG., Illus.). 80p. pap. 15.00 **(978-0-300-17940-8(5))** Kimbell Art Museum.

Kames, Andrea & Thistlethwaite, Mark. Modern Art Museum of Fort Worth: 110 Masterworks. Auping, Michael, tr. & intro. by. 2006. (ENG., Illus.). 45.00 (978-1-903942-14-7(4), Third Millenium Pub Ltd) Antique Collectors' Club GBR. Dist: National Bk. Network.

Kanjo, Kathryn. Lasting Impressions. 2008. 40p. pap. 12.00 (978-0-942006-74-2(7)) Univ. of California, Santa Barbara, Art Museum.

Kargl, Georg. Georg Kargl, Fine Arts Since 1998: Box Since 2005, 1 vol. 2006. (ENG., Illus.). 328p. per. 35.00 (978-3-86560-063-9(8)) Verlag der Buchhandlung Walther Konig DEU. Dist: D.A.P./Distributed Art Pubs.

Karlsgodt, Elizabeth Campbell. Defending National Treasures: French Art & Heritage under Vichy. 2011. (ENG., Illus.). 404p. 60.00 (978-0-8047-7018-7(2)) Stanford Univ. Pr.

Karlstrom, Paul J. & Karlstrom, Ann. Peter Selz: Sketches of a Life in Art. 2012. (ENG., Illus.). 321p. 34.95 (978-0-520-26935-4(7)) Univ. of California Pr.

Katz, Janice. Beyond Golden Clouds: Japanese Screens from the Art Institute of Chicago & the Saint Louis Art Museum. 2009. (Illus.). 216p. pap. (978-0-86559-232-2(2)) Art Institute of Chicago.

Katz, Janice, ed. Beyond Golden Clouds: Japanese Screens from the Art Institute of Chicago & the Saint Louis Art Museum. 2009. (ENG., Illus.). 216p. 55.00 (978-0-300-11948-0(8)) Art Institute of Chicago.

Keel, Erich, et al. The Kreeger Museum. 2006. (Illus.). 200p. pap. 35.00 (978-0-9760905-3-3(8)) Bergamot Bks.

Keller, Corey & Roberts, Sarah Rehm. San Francisco Museum of Modern Art: 75 Years of Looking Forward. Bishop, Janet C., ed. 2010. (ENG., Illus.). 448p. pap. 55.00 (978-0-918471-84-0(2)) San Francisco Museum of Modern Art.

Keys, Melissa & text. The Weight of History. 2007. (Illus.). 4p. (978-0-9775782-4-5(0)) Monash Univ. Museum of Art.

King, Elspeth. A History of Stirling in 100 Objects. 2011. (ENG., Illus.). 144p. pap. 23.95 **(978-0-7524-5932-5(5))** History Pr. Ltd., The GBR. Dist: Independent Pubs. Group.

Kisluk-Grosheide, Danielle O. & Munger, Jeffrey. The Wrightsman Galleries for French Decorative Arts, the Metropolitan Museum of Art. 2010. (Illus.). 272p. 40.00 (978-0-300-15520-4(4)) Yale Univ. Pr.

Klonk, Charlotte. Spaces of Experience: Art Gallery Interiors from 1800 to 2000. 2009. (ENG., Illus.). 244p. 75.00 (978-0-300-15196-1(9)) Yale Univ. Pr.

Knapp, Gottfried. Ernst von Ihne / Heinz Tesar, Bode-Museum, Berlin. 2008. (Opus Ser.). (ENG & GER., Illus.). 72p. 52.00 (978-3-932565-63-2(0)) Edition Axel Menges GmbH DEU. Dist: National Bk. Network.

Koda, Harold, ed. 100 Shoes: The Costume Institute / the Metropolitan Museum of Art. 2011. (ENG., Illus.). 232p. pap. 24.95 (978-0-300-17240-9(0)) Yale Univ. Pr.

Kopplin, Monika. European Lacquer. 2010. (ENG.). 320p. 79.00 (978-3-7774-8930-8(1), Art Stock Bks. Ltd/Csi) Continental Sales, Inc.

Kramer, Trudy C., intro. The First Parrish Art Museum Design Biennial: Weathervanes. (Illus.). 40p. (Orig.). pap. 10.00 (978-0-943526-42-3(6)) Parrish Art Museum, The.

Kravchyna, Victoria & Hastings, S. K. Museums Websites & Their Visitors - Information Needs. 2008. 160p. pap. (978-3-639-11571-0(6)) VDM Verlag Dr. Mueller e.K.

Krempel, Ulrich, text. Gia Edzgveradze: Welcome Foam - Farewell Human. 2010. (ENG., Illus.). 288p. pap. 60.00 (978-3-7757-2396-1(X)) Hatje Cantz Verlag GmbH & Co KG DEU. Dist: D.A.P./Distributed Art Pubs.

LAB MAG 01 B/W Lulu Version. 2006. per. (978-0-9790077-1-2(2)) Lab Bks.

Laichas, William D., ed. New Mexico Millennium Collection: A Twenty-First Century Celebration of Fine Art in New Mexico. 2007. (ENG., Illus.). 160p. 45.00 (978-0-9679034-0-8(8)) New Mexico Millennium Collection, LLC.

Lanmon, Dwight P. The Golden Age of English Glass: 1650-1775. 2011. (ENG., Illus.). 376p. 95.00 (978-1-85149-656-3(4)) Antique Collectors' Club.

Lebédel-Carbonnel, Hélène. Catalogue des Peintures du Musée du Château de Blois. 2010. (FRE & ENG., Illus.). 208p. 40.00 (978-2-35340-048-5(5)) Gourcuff Gradenigo FRA. Dist: National Bk. Network.

Leclercq, Nicole & Van Goethem, Jan, eds. Du document à l'utilisateur/from Document to User: Rôles et responsabilités des centres spécialisés dans les artes du spectacle/the Roles & Responsabilities of Specialised Centres for Performing Arts. 2008. (FRE & ENG.). 275p. pap. 41.95 (978-90-5201-434-0(5)) PIE - Peter Lang BEL. Dist: Lang, Peter.

Leeman, Fred, et al. Odilon Redon & Emile Bernard: Masterpieces from the Andries Bonger Collection. 2009. (ENG., Illus.). 156p. 55.00 (978-90-400-8589-5(7)) Waanders B.V., Uitgeverij NLD. Dist: National Bk. Network.

Lepik, Andres, et al, texts. Sauerbruch Hutton Architects: Museum Brandhorst. 2009. (ENG., Illus.). 128p. 40.00 (978-3-7757-2355-8(2)) Hatje Cantz Verlag GmbH & Co KG DEU. Dist: D.A.P./Distributed Art Pubs.

Lessing, Erich, photos by. The Louvre: All the Paintings. 2011. (ENG., Illus.). 784p. 75.00 (978-1-57912-886-9(6), 1579128866) Black Dog & Leventhal Pubs., Inc.

Levitta-Kohn, Risa. Dead Sea Scrolls: Words that Changed the World. 2009. (ENG., Illus.). 64p. pap. 6.00 (978-0-88854-470-4(7)) Royal Ontario Museum CAN. Dist: Univ. of Toronto Pr.

Lochnan, Katherine A., ed. Drawing Attention: Selected Works on Paper from the Renaissance to Modernism, Art Gallery of Ontario. 2008. (Illus.). 272p. 125.00 (978-1-85894-444-9(9)) Merrell Pubs. Ltd. GBR. Dist: Perseus Distribution.

Longwell, Alicia G., intro. American Landscapes: Treasures from the Parrish Art Museum. 2010. (Illus.). 104p. (978-0-943526-53-9(1)) Parrish Art Museum, The.

—First Impressions: Nineteenth-Century American Master Prints. 2010. (Illus.). 96p. (978-0-943526-55-3(8)) Parrish Art Museum, The.

Longwell, Alicia Grant. American Landscapes: Treasures from the Parrish Art Museum. 2010. (ENG., Illus.). 104p. 39.95 (978-1-904832-74-4(1)) Giles, D. Ltd. GBR. Dist: Antique Collectors' Club.

—First Impressions: Nineteenth-Century American Master Prints. 2010. (ENG., Illus.). 96p. 39.95 (978-1-904832-75-1(X)) Giles, D. Ltd. GBR. Dist: Antique Collectors' Club.

Lorente, J. Pedro. The Museums of Contemporary Art, 1800-2008: Concept & Historical Development. 2011. (Illus.). 330p. 124.95 (978-1-4094-0586-3(9)) Ashgate Publishing Co.

Lowry, Glenn D., et al, contrib. by. Whose Muse? Art Museums & the Public Trust. 2006. (ENG., Illus.). 208p. (C). pap. 22.95 (978-0-691-12781-1(6)) Princeton Univ. Pr.

Lürzer, Walter. Art Diary International 2009 2010. 2009. (ENG., Illus.). 624p. pap. 35.00 (978-88-7816-148-1(9)) Politi, Giancarlo Editore ITA. Dist: D.A.P./Distributed Art Pubs.

MacAdam, Barbara J. Coastline to Skyline: The Philip H. Greene Gift of California Watercolors, 1930-1960. 2009. (Illus.). 72p. pap. 19.95 (978-0-944722-36-7(9)) Hood Museum of Art.

MacDonald, Deanna & Smith, Geoffrey. 100 Best Paintings in New York. 2008. (100 Best Painting Ser.). (ENG., Illus.). 256p. pap. 22.00 (978-1-56656-696-4(7), Interlink Bks.) Interlink Publishing Group, Inc.

Manasseh, Cyrus. The Problematic of Video Art in Museum, 1968-1990. 2009. 114.99 (978-1-60497-650-2(0)) Cambria Pr.

Marshall, Traute M. Art Museums PLUS: Cultural Excursions in New England. 2009. (ENG., Illus.). 400p. pap. 24.95 (978-1-58465-621-0(2)) Univ. Pr. of New England.

Marti, Virgil. Set Pieces: Curated by Virgil Marti from the Collection of the Philadelphia Museum of Art. 2011. (ENG., Illus.). 64p. pap. 20.00 (978-0-88454-119-5(3)) Univ. of Pennsylvania, Institute of Contemporary Art.

Martin, Gary. The Journal of the Museum Year. 2008. 716p. pap. 34.14 (978-1-4357-5806-4(3)) Lulu Enterprises Inc.

Marx, Harald. Picture-Gallery Old Masters. 2006. 72p. 24.95 (978-3-363-00581-3(4)) Dornier Gmbh DEU. Dist: Perseus-PGW.

Marzio, Frances. The Glassell Collections of the Museum of Fine Arts, Houston: Masterworks of Pre-Columbian, Indonesian, & African Gold. 2012. (ENG., Illus.). 404p. 60.00 (978-0-300-17595-0(7)) Museum of Fine Arts, Houston.

Matheson. Corpus Vasorum Antiquorum. United States of America / Corpus Vasorum Antiquorum. 2011. (Corpus Vasorum Antiquorum. United States of America Ser.). (ENG.). 98p. (C). 143.00 **(978-3-8053-4348-0(5))** Zabern, Philipp von Verlag, GmbH DEU. Dist: Brown, David Bk. Co., The.

Mathieu, Marc-Antoine. The Museum Vaults: Excerpts from the Journal of an Expert. 2008. (ENG., Illus.). 64p. pap. 14.95 (978-1-56163-514-6(6)) NBM Publishing Co.

Mazaroff, Stanley. Henry Walters & Bernard Berenson: Collector & Connoisseur. 2010. (ENG., Illus.). 248p. (gr. 17). 40.00 (978-0-8018-9512-8(X)) Johns Hopkins Univ. Pr.

McClellan, Andrew. The Art Museum from Boullée to Bilbao. 2007. (Illus.). 351p. pap. 34.95 (978-0-520-25126-7(1)) Univ. of California Pr.

McClusky, Pamela. Ancestral Modern: Australian Aboriginal Art. 2012. (ENG., Illus.). 176p. 50.00 **(978-0-300-18003-9(9))** Yale Univ. Pr.

McComas, Jennifer A. Masterworks from the Indiana University Art Museum. Calinescu, Adriana et al, eds. 2008. (ENG., Illus.). 384p. pap. 39.95 (978-0-253-21956-5(6), 0253219566) Indiana Univ. Pr.

McKee, Daniel. Colored in the Year's New Light: Japanese Surimono from the Becker Collection. 2008. (Illus.). 320p. pap. (978-1-934260-04-3(5)) Cornell Univ., Herbert F. Johnson Museum of Art.

McMaster, Gerald. Inuit Modern: Masterworks from the Samuel & Esther Sarick Collection, 1 vol. 2011. (ENG., Illus.). 288p. pap. 50.00 (978-1-55365-778-1(0), Douglas & McIntyre) D&M Pubs. Inc. CAN. Dist: Perseus-PGW.

Medda, Ambra. Destination: Limited-Edition Design: 60 Must-See Locations. Museums & Galleries Around the World. 2008. 224p. pap. 75.00 (978-88-370-6097-8(1)) Electa ITA. Dist: Trans-Atlantic Pubns., Inc.

Menges, Jeff A. & Menges, Jeff A., eds. Visions of Camelot: Great Illustrations of King Arthur & His Court. 2009. (Dover Fine Art, History of Art Ser.). (ENG., Illus.). 128p. pap. 14.95 (978-0-486-46816-7(X)) Dover Pubns., Inc.

Menz, Christopher. Morris & Co. 2007. (Illus.). 188p. 55.00 (978-0-7308-3029-0(2)) Art Gallery of South Australia AUS. Dist: Antique Collectors' Club.

Menzies, Jackie, et al. Asian Collections: The Art Gallery of New South Wales. (Illus.). 352p. pap. 39.95 (978-0-7347-6351-8(4)) Art Media Resources, Inc.

Merrick, Jay. Firstsite: Art Spaces. 2012. (ENG., Illus.). 64p. pap. 7.95 **(978-1-85759-755-4(9))** Scala, Editions FRA. Dist: National Bk. Network.

Messinger, Lisa Mintz, et al, eds. Abstract Expressionism & Other Modern Works: The Muriel Kallis Steinberg Newman Collection in the Metropolitan Museum of Art. 2007. (ENG., Illus.). 224p. 50.00 (978-0-300-12252-7(7)) Yale Univ. Pr.

Metrick-Chen, Lenore. Collecting Objects/Excluding People: Chinese Subjects & American Visual Culture, 1830-1900. 2012. (ENG.). 320p. 85.00 **(978-1-4384-4325-6(0))** State Univ. of New York Pr.

Metropolitan Museum of Art & Metropolitan Museum of Art. Monet: Includes 24 Framable Images. 2010. (Art Portfolios Ser.). (ENG.). 52p. pap. 19.99 (978-0-7641-4558-2(4)) Barron's Educational Series, Inc.

—Van Gogh: Includes 24 Framable Images. 2010. (Art Portfolios Ser.). (ENG.). 52p. pap. 19.99 (978-0-7641-4559-9(2)) Barron's Educational Series, Inc.

Mézin, Louis. La Villa Masséna: Du Premier Empire à la Belle Époque. 2010. (FRE., Illus.). 183p. (978-2-7572-0387-3(8)) Somogy Editions d'Art.

Michaux, Lisa Dickinson, et al. Expanding the Boundaries: Selected Drawings from the Yvonne & Gabriel P. Weisberg Collection. 2008. (Illus.). 96p. pap. (978-0-9800484-0-7(0)) Minneapolis Institute of Arts.

Miksic, John N. Icons of Art: The Collections of the National Museum of Indonesia. 2nd ed. 2007. (ENG., Illus.). 308p. 49.95 (978-979-8926-25-9(0)) Archipelago Pr IDN. Dist: Tuttle Publishing.

Miller, R. A. Lord Love You: Works by R. A. Miller from the Mullis Collection. 2009. (ENG., Illus.). 32p. 25.00 (978-0-915977-70-3(2)) Univ. of Georgia, Georgia Museum of Art.

Mintz, Robert. Japanese Cloisonné Enamels: The Stephen W. Fisher Collection. 2009. pap. (978-0-911886-71-9(0)) Walters Art Museum, US.

Mitchell, Kerry. Selected Works. 2009. 100p. pap. 44.95 (978-0-557-08398-5(2)) Lulu Enterprises Inc.

Montgomery Museum of Fine Arts Staff, contrib. by. Adventures in Collecting Art: American Paintings from the Collections of Charles & Babette Wampold & the Montgomery Museum of Fine Arts. 2006. (978-0-89280-050-6(X)) Montgomery Museum of Fine Arts.

Morris, Edward & Curators, Senior. The Walker Art Gallery. 2007. (ENG., Illus.). 96p. pap. 24.95 (978-1-85759-037-1(6)) Scala, Editions FRA. Dist: National Bk. Network.

Muller, Lars & Miki, Akiko, eds. Insular Insight: Where Art & Architecture Conspire with Nature. 2011. (ENG., Illus.). 480p. 70.00 **(978-3-03778-255-2(2))** Lars Muller Pubs. CHE. Dist: Prestel Publishing.

Multiple. Irdische Paradiese. Earthly Paradises: Meisterwerke aus der Kasser Art Foundation. 2009. (ENG.). 450p. 48.00 (978-3-422-06906-0(2), Art Stock Bks. Ltd/Csi) Continental Sales, Inc.

MURPHY, David Richard. Gold. 2008. 33p. 36.97 (978-1-4357-6054-7(9)) Lulu Enterprises Inc.

Murray, Mary E., et al. Auspicious Vision: Edward Wales Root & American Modernism. 2008. (978-0-915895-34-2(X)) Munson-Williams-Proctor Institute.

Museum of Fine Arts, Houston Staff, contrib. by. Looking at Art: An Art History Survey at the Museum of Fine Arts, Houston. 2009. pap. (978-0-89090-169-4(4)) Museum of Fine Arts, Houston.

Museyon Guides, ed. Art + NYC: A Complete Guide to New York City Art & Artists. 2011. (Art+ Ser.). (ENG., Illus.). 304p. pap. 19.95 (978-0-9822320-8-8(X)) Museyon Inc.

Nagy, Clinton, ed. Splendid Heritage-Deluxe Cloth Edition. 2009. (Illus.). 207p. 135.00 (978-0-87480-961-9(4)) Univ. of Utah Pr.

National Register Publishing, creator. American Art Directory. 63rd ed. 2008. (American Art Directory Ser.). 1035p. 371.25 (978-0-87217-755-0(6)) National Register Publishing.

Neidhardt, Hans Joachim. Picture-Gallery, New Masters. 2006. 64p. 24.95 (978-3-363-00621-6(7)) Dornier GmbH DEU. Dist: Perseus-PGW.

Nemmers, Laura K., et al, eds. Samuel P. Harn Museum of Art: Twenty Years - The Collection Catalogue. 2010. (ENG., Illus.). 288p. 50.00 (978-0-8130-3513-0(9)) Univ. Pr. of Florida.

Neri, Grazia, et al. Icone. 7. 24 X 0. 26 Gallery: [in English & Italian]. 2008. 146p. pap. 65.00 (978-88-370-6332-0(6)) Electa ITA. Dist: Trans-Atlantic Pubns., Inc.

Nesbitt, John. Catalogue of Byzantine Seals at Dumbarton Oaks & in the Fogg Museum of Art Vol.6: Emperors, Patriarchs of Constantinople, Addenda, 6. 2009. (Dumbarton Oaks Collection Ser.). (Illus.). 224p. 45.00 (978-0-88402-338-8(9)) Dumbarton Oaks.

Nevada Museum of Art, compiled by. Like Love Lust: Michael Sarich. 2007. (Illus.). 156p. 50.00 (978-0-9764800-4-4(2)) Nevada Museum of Art.

Newlands, Jennifer. Rubens' Vision for the Luxembourg Palace. 2009. 112p. pap. (978-3-639-15727-7(3)) VDM Verlag Dr. Mueller e.K.

Nicolaysen Art Museum, creator. Richard Renaldi: Western Lives. 2007. (Illus.). 32p. (YA). per. 15.00 (978-0-9798485-0-6(4)) Nicolaysen Art Museum.

Nisbet, Peter & Feininger, Lyonel. Lyonel Feininger: Drawings & Watercolors from the William S. Lieberman Bequest to the Busch-Reisinger Museum. 2011. (978-1-891771-54-5(X)) Hatje Cantz Verlag GmbH & Co KG.

—Lyonel Feininger: Drawings & Watercolors from the William S. Lieberman Bequest to the Busch-Reisinger Museum. 2011. (ENG., Illus.). 144p. 45.00

(978-3-7757-2787-7(6)) Hatje Cantz Verlag GmbH & Co KG DEU. Dist: D.A.P./Distributed Art Pubs.

Nohra Haime Gallery, ed. Artist Plates. 2007. (Illus.). 117p. pap. 15.00 *(978-0-9800881-1-3(9))* Haime, Nohra Gallery.

North Carolina Museum of Art Staff, contrib. by. North Carolina Museum of Art: Handbook of the Collections. 2010. pap. *(978-0-88259-992-2(5))* North Carolina Museum of Art.

Novacek, Gabrielle V. Ancient Israel: Highlights from the Collection of the Oriental Institute of the University of Chicago. 2011. (Oriental Institute Museum Publications). (ENG., Illus.). 130p. (C). pap. 41.95 *(978-1-885923-65-3(1))* Oriental Institute of the Univ. of Chicago, The.

O'Banks, Mark, concept. Nybelwyck Hall at the Hudson River Museum. 2006. (Illus.). 25p. 9.99 *(978-0-943651-33-0(6))* Hudson River Museum.

O'Doherty, Brian. Studio & Cube: On the Relationship Between Where Art Is Made & Where Art Is Displayed. 2008. (ENG.). 80p. 24.95 *(978-1-883584-44-3(2))* Princeton Architectural Pr.

Ohman, Nina. Moderna Museet, Stockholm: A Celebration of 40 Years. 2006. (ENG., Illus.). 50.00 *(978-1-85759-178-1(X))* Scala, Editions FRA. Dist: National Bk. Network.

Oino, Espen & Farameh, Patrice. Luxury Toys Top of the World. 2008. (ENG.). 59.95 *(978-3-8327-9254-1(6))* teNeues Publishing Co.

Olbricht, Thomas. Rockers Island Olbricht Collection: Museum Folkwang, 1 vol. 2008. (ENG., Illus.). 288p. 50.00 *(978-3-86521-471-3(1))* Steidl, Gerhard Druckerei und Verlag DEU. Dist: Innovative Logistics.

Os, Gerard van. Cowlection. 2007. 320p. *(978-90-808666-3-8(6))* Stockmans NV.

Palace Museum, Beijing Staff. Bamboo, Wood, Ivory, & Rhinoceros Horn Carvings: The Complete Collection of the Treasures of the Palace Museum, Beijing 44. (CHI., Illus.). 304p. 95.00 *(978-962-07-5347-3(X))* Commercial Pr., The CHN. Dist: Art Media Resources, Inc.

Pallasmaa, Juhani & Reenberg, Holger, texts. HEART: Herning Museum of Contemporary Art. 2010. (ENG., Illus.). 96p. 45.00 *(978-3-7757-2493-7(1))* Hatje Cantz Verlag GmbH & Co KG DEU. Dist: D.A.P./Distributed Art Pubs.

Pasadena Museum of California Art & Los Angeles Toy Doll & Amusements Museum, creators. Beyond Ultraman: Seven Artists Explore the Vinyl Frontier. 2008. (Illus.). 64p. pap. 25.00 *(978-0-9793307-2-8(6))* Baby Tattoo Bks.

Paul, Carole. The Borghese Collections & the Display of Art in the Age of the Grand Tour. 2008. (Illus.). 358p. 134.95 *(978-0-7546-6134-4(2))* Ashgate Publishing Co.

Pegazzano, Donatella. Committenza e Collezionismo Nel Cinquecento: La Famiglia Corsi a Firenze Tra Musica e Scultura. 2010. (ITA., Illus.). 76p. *(978-88-7970-451-9(6))* Edifir.

Phifer, Thomas. North Carolina Museum of Art: Thomas Phifer & Partners. 2011. (ENG., Illus.). 140p. 35.00 ***(978-1-935935-09-4(7))*** Oro Editions.

Piano, Renzo. Renzo Piano Museums. 2007. (ENG., Illus.). 214p. (gr. 13). 60.00 *(978-1-58093-189-2(8))* Monacelli Pr., Inc.

Pieprzak, Katarzyna. Imagined Museums: Art & Modernity in Postcolonial Morocco. 2010. (Illus.). 280p. 75.00 *(978-0-8166-6518-1(4))*; (ENG., pap. 25.00 *(978-0-8166-6519-8(2))* Univ. of Minnesota Pr.

Pierce, Donna. Companion to Spanish Colonial Art at the Denver Art Museum. 2012. (ENG., Illus.). 106p. pap. 19.95 ***(978-0-914738-78-7(X))*** Denver Art Museum.

Politi, Giancarlo. Art Diary International 2006-2007: Flash Art Diary, 1 vol. 2006. (ENG., Illus.). 570p. pap. 25.00 *(978-88-7816-137-5(3))* Politi, Giancarlo Editore ITA. Dist: D.A.P./Distributed Art Pubs.

Pollock, Grisel. Encounters in a Virtual Feminist Museum: Time, Space, & the Archive. 2007. (ENG., Illus.). 280p. (C). per. 44.95 *(978-0-415-41374-9(5))* Routledge.

Pollock, Griselda. Encounters in a Virtual Feminist Museum: Time, Space & the Archive. 2007. (ENG., Illus.). 280p. (C). 135.00 *(978-0-415-41373-2(7))* Routledge.

Potes, Ray. Hamburger Eyes: Inside Burgerworld. 2007. (ENG., Illus.). 192p. 35.00 *(978-1-57687-407-3(9)*, Miss Rosen Editions) powerHouse Cultural Entertainment, Inc.

Powell, Amy Knight. Depositions: Scenes from the Late Medieval Church & the Modern Museum. 2012. (ENG., Illus.). 384p. (gr. 17). 34.95 ***(978-1-935408-20-8(8))*** Zone Bks.

Prestel. Osterreichische Nationalbibliothek,Vienna. pap. 14.95 *(978-3-7913-3148-5(5))* Prestel Publishing.

Princeton University, Art Museum Staff. Princeton University Art Museum: Handbook of the Collections. 2008. (Illus.). xx, 364p. pap. 19.95 net. *(978-0-943012-47-6(3))* Princeton Univ. Art Museum.

Prodger, Phillip. Darwin's Camera: Art & Photography in the Theory of Evolution. 2009. (ENG., Illus.). 256p. 39.95 *(978-0-19-515031-5(7))* Oxford Univ. Pr., Inc.

Pub Cat Fdn Staff. Oil Paintings in Public Ownership in Hampshire. 2007. (ENG., Illus.). 360p. 85.00 *(978-1-904931-16-4(2))* Public Catalogue Foundation, The GBR. Dist: National Bk. Network.

—Oil Paintings in Public Ownership in North Yorkshire. 2007. (SPA & ENG., Illus.). 429p. 85.00 *(978-1-904931-22-5(7))* Public Catalogue Foundation, The GBR. Dist: National Bk. Network.

—Oil Paintings in Public Ownership in Surrey. 2007. (Oil Paintings in Public Ownership Ser.). (SPA & ENG., Illus.). 278p. 85.00 *(978-1-904931-24-9(3))* Public Catalogue Foundation, The GBR. Dist: National Bk. Network.

Pub Cat Fdn Staff & Roe, Sonia. Oil Paintings in Public Ownership in Hampshire: Southampton & the Isle of Wight. 2007. (ENG., Illus.). 305p. 85.00 *(978-1-904931-18-8(9))* Public Catalogue Foundation, The GBR. Dist: National Bk. Network.

—Oil Paintings in Public Ownership in Norfolk. 2007. (SPA & ENG., Illus.). 356p. 85.00 *(978-1-904931-20-1(0))* Public Catalogue Foundation, The GBR. Dist: National Bk. Network.

Pub Cat Fdn Staff, et al. Oil Paintings in Public Ownership in West Yorkshire. 2008. (ENG., Illus.). 400p. 85.00 *(978-1-904931-26-3(X))* Public Catalogue Foundation, The GBR. Dist: National Bk. Network.

Pubcatfon & Roe, Sonia. Oil Paintings in Public Ownership in East Sussex. 2006. (Oil Paintings in Public Ownership Ser.). (SPA & ENG., Illus.). 420p. 85.00 *(978-1-904931-08-9(1))* Public Catalogue Foundation, The GBR. Dist: National Bk. Network.

Public Catalogue Foundation & Roe, Sonia. Oil Paintings in Public Ownership in Essex. 2007. (SPA & ENG., Illus.). 332p. 85.00 *(978-1-904931-14-0(6))* Public Catalogue Foundation, The GBR. Dist: National Bk. Network.

Public Catalogue Foundation Staff. Northumberland, Tess Valley & Tyne & Wear. 2010. (ENG., Illus.). 282p. 85.00 *(978-1-904931-37-9(5))* Public Catalogue Foundation, The GBR. Dist: National Bk. Network.

—Oil Paintings in Public Ownership in Gloucestershire & Wiltshire. 2012. (ENG.). 396p. 85.00 *(978-1-904931-56-0(1))* Public Catalogue Foundation, The GBR. Dist: National Bk. Network.

Radford, Rod. Island to Empire: 300 Years of British Art 1550-1850. 2007. (Illus.). 336p. 60.00 *(978-0-7308-3014-6(4))* Art Gallery of South Australia AUS. Dist: Antique Collectors' Club.

Ramoran, Edwin T. Paper Remix: Dieu Donne Workspace Program: 1995-2000. Lin, Chen, ed. (Illus.). 14p. pap. 5.00 *(978-0-9704072-6-9(2))* Dieu Donne.

Rebay, Hilla. Museum of Non-Objective Painting. Vail, Karole, ed. 2009. (ENG., Illus.). 352p. 45.00 *(978-0-89207-393-1(4))* Guggenheim, Solomon R. Museum.

Reinking, Rik, ed. Fresh Air Smells Funny. 2008. (GER & ENG., Illus.). 128p. pap. 28.00 *(978-3-939583-94-3(4))* Kehrer Verlag Heidelberg, Klaus Kehrer DEU. Dist: Consortium Bk. Sales & Distribution.

Riley, C. M. Art at Lincoln Center: The Public Art & List Print & Poster Collections. 2008. (Illus.). 240p. 75.00 *(978-0-470-16913-1(3)*, Wiley) Wiley, John & Sons, Inc.

Riley, Terrence. Work in Progress: Herzog & de Meuron's Miami Art Museum. 2008. (Illus.). 63p. pap. *(978-0-9705505-5-2(3))* MAM Pubs.

Roberts, Perri Lee. Corpus of Early Italian Paintings in North American Public Collections. 2008. *(978-0-915977-64-2(8))* Univ. of Georgia, Georgia Museum of Art.

Robertson, Cheryl. The Domestic Scene (1897-1927) George M. Niedecken, Interior Architect. 2nd ed. 2008. (ENG., Illus.). 124p. pap. 32.00 *(978-0-944110-91-1(6))* Milwaukee Art Museum.

Robinson, Anne, et al. Every Way Possible: 125 Years of the Indianapolis Museum of Art. 2008. (Illus.). 303p. *(978-0-936260-85-3(8))* Indianapolis Museum of Art.

Roche, Catherine. Fleeting Beauty: Japanese Woodblock Prints. 2010. *(978-0-932216-66-3(8))* Seattle Art Museum.

Rocheleau, Caroline M. Ancient Egyptian Art: Systematic Catalogue of the Collection, North Carolina Museum of Art, Raleigh. 2012. ***(978-0-88259-996-0(8))*** North Carolina Museum of Art.

Roe. Oil Paintings in Public Ownership in Birmingham. 2008. (ENG., Illus.). 280p. 85.00 *(978-1-904931-38-6(3))* Public Catalogue Foundation, The GBR. Dist: National Bk. Network.

—Oil Paintings in Public Ownership in Staffordshire. 2009. (ENG., Illus.). 381p. 85.00 *(978-1-904931-32-4(4))* Public Catalogue Foundation, The GBR. Dist: National Bk. Network.

Roe & Roe, Sonia. Oil Paintings in Public Ownership in Cornwall & the Isles of Scilly. 2007. (ENG., Illus.). 250p. 85.00 *(978-1-904931-30-0(8))* Public Catalogue Foundation, The GBR. Dist: National Bk. Network.

Roe, Sonia. Oil Paintings in Public Ownership in Co Durham. 2009. (ENG., Illus.). 300p. 85.00 *(978-1-904931-48-5(0))* Public Catalogue Foundation, The GBR. Dist: National Bk. Network.

—Oil Paintings in Public Ownership in Kent. 2006. (SPA & ENG., Illus.). 276p. 85.00 *(978-1-904931-02-7(2))* Public Catalogue Foundation, The GBR. Dist: National Bk. Network.

—Oil Paintings in Public Ownership in Suffolk. Roe, Sonia, ed. 2007. (Oil Paintings in Public Ownership Ser.). (SPA & ENG., Illus.). 260p. 85.00 *(978-1-904931-10-2(3))* Public Catalogue Foundation, The GBR. Dist: National Bk. Network.

—Oil Paintings in Public Ownership in the City of London. 2012. (ENG., Illus.). 372p. 85.00 *(978-1-904931-77-5(4))* Public Catalogue Foundation, The GBR. Dist: National Bk. Network.

—Oil Paintings in Public Ownership in West Sussex. 2006. (Oil Paintings in Public Ownership Ser.). (SPA & ENG., Illus.). 204p. 85.00 *(978-1-904931-04-1(9))* Public Catalogue Foundation, The GBR. Dist: National Bk. Network.

—Oil Paintings in Public Ownership in West Yorkshire: Leeds. 2006. (SPA & ENG., Illus.). 300p. 85.00 *(978-1-904931-00-3(6))* Public Catalogue Foundation, The GBR. Dist: National Bk. Network.

Roe, Sonia & Glowacki, Robert. Oil Paintings in Public Ownership in Tyne & Wear Museums. 2009. (ENG., Illus.). 300p. 85.00 *(978-1-904931-44-7(8))* Public Catalogue Foundation, The GBR. Dist: National Bk. Network.

Román, Dulce María & Oliver-Smith, Kerry. Paradigms & the Unexpected: Modern & Contemporary Art from the Shey Collection. 2007. *(978-0-9762552-6-0(X))*; pap. *(978-0-9762552-7-7(8))* Harn Museum of Art.

Romanelli, Giandomenico, ed. Dogana da Mar: La Storia. 2010. (Venice: the Pinault Collection). (ITA & FRE., Illus.). 330p. pap. 150.00 *(978-88-370-6993-3(6)*, Mondadori Electa (Acc)) Antique Collectors' Club GBR. Dist: National Bk. Network.

Royal BC Museum Staff, et al. Exhibit Companion, 1 vol. 2007. (Royal Bc Museum Ser.). (ENG., Illus.). 60p. pap. 9.45 *(978-0-7726-5602-5(9))* Royal British Columbia Museum CAN. Dist: Heritage Group Distribution.

Ruprecht, Louis A. Winckelmann & the Vatican's First Profane Museum. 2011. (ENG., Illus.). 352p. 85.00 *(978-0-230-11069-4(X))* Palgrave Macmillan.

Rykwert, Joseph, et al, contrib. by. Neues Museum Berlin: By David Chipperfield Architects in Collaboration with Julian Harrap. 2010. (ENG., Illus.). 288p. pap. 65.00 *(978-3-86560-704-1(7))* Verlag der Buchhandlung Walther Konig DEU. Dist: D.A.P./Distributed Art Pubs.

Sabine Albersmeier & Albersmeier, Sabine. Bedazzled 5,000 Years of Jewelry: The Walters Art Museum. 2006. (ENG., Illus.). 64p. pap. 12.95 *(978-1-904832-16-4(4))* Giles, D. Ltd. GBR. Dist: Antique Collectors' Club.

Sanders, Terrence, ed. The Saratoga Collection. 2011. (ENG., Illus.). 104p. pap. 40.00 ***(978-1-60801-061-5(9))*** Univ Of New Orleans Pr.

Saunders, David. British Museum Technical Research Bulletin, Volume 4. 2011. (ENG., Illus.). 156p. pap. 40.00 *(978-1-904982-55-5(7))* Archetype Pubns. GBR. Dist: National Bk. Network.

Scala. The Holburne Museum. 2011. (ENG., Illus.). 88p. pap. 19.95 *(978-1-85759-665-6(X))* Scala, Editions FRA. Dist: National Bk. Network.

Scala Publishers Staff. The Hepworth Wakefield: Art Spaces. 2012. (ENG., Illus.). 64p. pap. 7.95 *(978-1-85759-679-3(X))* Scala, Editions FRA. Dist: National Bk. Network.

—McNay Art Museum: An Introduction. 2010. (Illus.). 64p. pap. 9.95 *(978-1-85759-664-9(1))* Scala, Editions FRA. Dist: National Bk. Network.

—Seattle Art Museum: Bridging Cultures. 2007. (ENG., Illus.). 80p. pap. 7.95 *(978-1-85759-480-5(0))* Scala, Editions FRA. Dist: National Bk. Network.

Schafhausen, Nicolaus, et al, texts. 20 Years of Witte de With. 2012. (ENG., Illus.). 304p. 39.95 *(978-90-73362-93-2(8))* Witte De With Centre for Contemporary Art NLD. Dist: D.A.P./Distributed Art Pubs.

Schultz, Sarah & Peters, Sarah, eds. Open Field: Conversations on the Commons. 2012. (ENG., Illus.). 144p. pap. 9.99 ***(978-1-935963-00-4(7))*** Walker Art Ctr.

Schulz, Regine. Khepereru-Scarabs: Scarabs, Scaraboids, & Plaques from Egypt & the Ancient near East in the Walters Art Museum, Baltimore. 2007. (ENG.). 186p. (C). pap. 52.00 *(978-1-892840-04-2(9))* Halgo Inc.

Schulze, Franz. Building a Masterpiece: Milwaukee Art Museum. 2009. (ENG., Illus.). 240p. pap. 40.00 *(978-1-55595-202-0(X))* Hudson Hills Pr. LLC.

Seckel, Al. Masters of Deception: Escher, Dali & the Artists of Optical Illusion. 2007. (ENG., Illus.). 320p. pap. 17.95 *(978-1-4027-5101-1(X))* Sterling Publishing Co., Inc.

Seifert, Christian Tico. Dürer's Fame. 2012. (ENG., Illus.). 48p. ***(978-1-906270-41-4(4))*** National Galleries of Scotland.

Seligman, Rachel, ed. & compiled by. ReView: Five Union Alumni. 2007. (Illus.). 12p. per. 3.00 net. *(978-0-9763207-5-3(4))* Union College, Mandeville Gallery.

Shallcross, Gilian, text. The MFA: A Guide to the Collections of the Museum of Fine Arts, Boston. 2009. (ENG., Illus.). 400p. pap. 24.95 *(978-0-87846-730-3(0))* Museum of Fine Arts, Boston.

Sherman, Daniel J. Museums & Difference. Sherman, Daniel J., ed. 2007. (21st Century Studies Ser.). (ENG., Illus.). 400p. pap. 30.00 *(978-0-253-21935-0(3)*, 0253219353) Indiana Univ. Pr.

Sherman, Daniel J., ed. Museums & Difference. 2007. (21st Century Studies Ser.). (ENG., Illus.). 400p. 75.00 *(978-0-253-34946-0(X)*, 025334946X) Indiana Univ. Pr.

Shields, Conal. Kenneth Thomson the Collector. 2009. (Illus.). 128p. pap. 50.00 ***(978-1-903470-79-4(X))*** Holberton, Paul Publishing GBR. Dist: Casemate Pubs. & Bk. Distributors, LLC.

Shire, Billy. La Luz de Jesus 25: The Little Gallery That Could. 2011. (ENG., Illus.). 320p. 40.00 ***(978-0-86719-764-8(1))*** Last Gasp of San Francisco.

Skull Project - Limited Edition Hardcover. 2007. (ENG., Illus.). 150.00 *(978-0-9795197-0-3(5))* TossAmey Pr.

Smith, Mariann W. Albright-Knox Art Gallery: Highlights from the Collection. 2012. (ENG., Illus.). 64p. pap. 17.95 *(978-1-85759-661-8(7))* Scala, Editions FRA. Dist: National Bk. Network.

Smith, Tracey. Creative Relationships. 2009. 77p. pap. 24.96 *(978-1-4092-7946-4(4))* Lulu Enterprises Inc.

Some Arts & Crafts. 327p. reprint ed. 98.00 *(978-0-7222-1605-7(X))* Library Reprints, Inc.

Sondergaard, Morten & Jacobsen, Mogens, eds. RE_ACTION - The Digital Archive Experience: Renegotiating the Competences of the Archive & the Museum in the 21st Century. 2009. (Illus.). 239p. pap. 52.95 *(978-87-7307-952-2(9))* Aalborg Universitetsforlag DNK. Dist: International Specialized Bk. Services.

Spies, Von Werner. Das Picasso Museum. 20.00 *(978-3-929078-36-7(8))* Kehayoff Verlag DEU. Dist: D.A.P./Distributed Art Pubs.

Staatliche Museum Kassel Staff. Old Masters Gallery, Kassel. 2006. (ENG., Illus.). 136p. pap. 29.95 *(978-1-85759-329-7(4))* Scala, Editions FRA. Dist: National Bk. Network.

Stadel Museum. 2009. (ENG.). 164p. pap., instr.'s gde. ed. 19.80 *(978-3-86568-420-2(3)*, Art Stock Bks. Ltd/Csi) Continental Sales, Inc.

Stebbins, Theodore E., et al. American Paintings at Harvard. 2008. (Illus.). *(978-1-891771-49-1(3))* Yale Univ. Pr.

Stephens, Simon. Ship Models in the Thomson Collection. 2009. (Illus.). 128p. pap. 50.00 ***(978-1-903470-82-4(X))*** Holberton, Paul Publishing GBR. Dist: Casemate Pubs. & Bk. Distributors, LLC.

Stone, Lisa. Accidental Genius: Art from the Anthony Petullo Collection. 2012. (Illus.). 240p. 60.00 ***(978-3-7913-5200-8(8))*** Prestel Publishing.

Stourton, James & Sebag-Montefiore, Charles. The British As Art Collectors: From the Tudors to the Present. 2012. (ENG., Illus.). 400p. 100.00 ***(978-1-85759-749-3(4))*** Scala, Editions FRA. Dist: National Bk. Network.

Stringer, John, et al. Closet Circus: The Lloyd & Elizabeth Horn Collection of Contemporary Western Australian Art. 2008. 224p. pap. 49.95 *(978-1-921361-27-2(1))* Fremantle Pr. AUS. Dist: Independent Pubs. Group.

Stubbs, Judith Ann & McComas, Jennifer A. Masterworks from the Indiana University Art Museum. Calinescu, Adriana et al, eds. 2008. (ENG., Illus.). 384p. 64.95 *(978-0-253-35069-5(7)*, 0253350697) Indiana Univ. Pr.

Suarez, Nicole M. Neville. Curatorial Practices at the Rijksmuseum. 2010. 192p. pap. *(978-3-8383-0077-1(7))* Lambert Academic Publishing.

Sundberg, Rick, intro. The Frye Art Museum: Olson Sundberg Kundig Allen Architects. 2007. per. *(978-1-933245-03-4(4))* Documentary Media LLC.

Swanson, Vern G., et al. Springville Museum of Art: History & Collection. 2011. 416p. 49.99 ***(978-1-55995-381-8(0))*** Cedar Fort, Inc./CFI Distribution.

—Springville Museum of Art Guidebook. 2011. ***(978-1-59955-381-8(3)***, Bonneville Bks.) Cedar Fort, Inc./CFI Distribution.

Sylvester, Christine. Art/Museums: International Relations Where We Least Expect It. (Media & Power Ser.). (Illus.). 240p. 2009. pap. 36.95 *(978-1-59451-465-4(8))* 2008. 125.00 *(978-1-59451-464-7(X))* Paradigm Pubs.

teNeues. AAD Berlin: Art Architecture Design. 2010. (Illus.). 168p. pap. 12.95 *(978-3-8327-9433-0(6))* teNeues Publishing Co.

—AAD New York: Art Architecture Design. 2010. (Illus.). 168p. pap. 12.95 *(978-3-8327-9435-4(2))* teNeues Publishing Co.

Thau, Carsten & Bjerkhof, Sven. Cronhammar: På Danske Kunstmuseer. 2007. (DAN., Illus.). 136p. *(978-87-92023-12-4(6))* Statens Museum for Kunst.

The Curators and Employees of Kelvingrove Art Gallery and Museum. Kelvingrove Art Gallery & Museum: The Curators & employees of Kelvingrove Art Gallery & Museum. 2009. (ENG., Illus.). 128p. pap. 20.00 *(978-0-85667-667-3(5))* Wilson, Philip Pubs., Ltd. GBR. Dist: Macmillan.

Thea, Carolee. On Curating: Interviews with Ten International Curators, 1 vol. Micchelli, Thomas, ed. 2010. (ENG., Illus.). 144p. pap. 29.95 *(978-1-935202-00-4(6))* D.A.P./Distributed Art Pubs.

Thomsen, Hans Bjarne. The Floating World: Ukiyo-e Prints from the Wallace B. Rogers Collection of the Lauren Rogers Museum of Art. Chancey, Jill R., ed. 2008. (ENG., Illus.). 29.95 *(978-0-935903-10-2(0))* Lauren Rogers Museum of Art.

Tietz, Jurgen & Schneider, Katja. Nieto Sobejano: Das Neue Kunstmuseum in Halle. 2008. (GER., Illus.). 80p. *(978-3-7774-5075-9(8))* Hirmer Verlag GmbH.

Till, Barry, text. Japan Awakens: Woodblock Prints of the Meiji Period (1868-1912) 2008. 128p. 29.95 *(978-0-7649-4635-6(8))* Pomegranate Communications, Inc.

The Timeless Cowrie. 2007. 10.00 *(978-0-9725066-3-2(2))* Bead Museum of Washington DC, The.

Tojner, Poul Erik, ed. Louisiana ABC: 100 Works from the Collection, 1 vol. 2012. (ENG., Illus.). 204p. 35.00 *(978-87-91607-35-6(3))* Louisana DNK. Dist: D.A.P./Distributed Art Pubs.

Trask, Jeffrey. Things American: Art Museums & Civic Culture in the Progressive Era. 2011. (Arts & Intellectual Life in Modern America Ser.). (Illus.). 312p. (C). 39.95 ***(978-0-8122-4362-8(5))*** Univ. of Pennsylvania Pr.

Umberto Allemandi and Company Staff. Dalí in the Third Dimension: The Stratton Foundation Collection. 2011. (Illus.). 338p. 120.00 *(978-88-422-1665-0(8))* Allemandi, Umberto & Co. GBR. Dist: Antique Collectors' Club.

—Discover the Dalí Theatre-Museum in Figures. 2011. (ENG., Illus.). 16p. pap. 12.50 *(978-88-422-1727-5(1))* Allemandi, Umberto & Co. GBR. Dist: Antique Collectors' Club.

Vallotton, Chantal Lafontant. Entre le Musee et le Marche: Heinrich Angst. (FRE.). 384p. pap. 48.95 *(978-3-03911-453-5(0))* Lang, Peter Publishing, Inc.

van Brakel, Koos & Legêne, Susan, eds. Collecting on Cultural Crossroads: Collection Policies & Approaches (2008-2011) at the Tropenmuseum. 2008. (Bulletins of the Royal Tropical Institute Ser.). 106p. (C). pap. 35.00 *(978-90-6832-647-5(3))* Royal Tropical Institute Pr. (KIT (Koninklijk Instituut voor de Tropen) NLD. Dist: Stylus Publishing, LLC.

van Dijk, Janneke & Legêne, Susan. The Netherlands East Indies at the Tropenmuseum. 2011. (Collections at the Tropenmuseum Ser.). 200p. 45.00 *(978-90-6832-751-9(8))* Royal Tropical Institute Pr. (KIT (Koninklijk Instituut voor de Tropen) NLD. Dist: Stylus Publishing, LLC.

Van Grasdorff & Carman, Jillian. Uplifting the Colonial Philistine: Florence Phillips & the Making of the Johannesburg Art Gallery. 2007. (ENG., Illus.). 452p. (gr. 11). pap. 34.95 *(978-1-86814-436-5(4))* Witwatersrand Univ. Pr. Pubns. ZAF. Dist: Transaction Pubs.

Van Tomme, Niels, ed. Where Do We Migrate To? 2011. (ENG., Illus.). 44p. 19.95 ***(978-1-890761-14-1(1))*** Univ. of Maryland Baltimore County, Fine Arts Gallery.

Venet, Diane, ed. From Picasso to Jeff Koons - The Artist As Jeweler. 2011. (ENG., Illus.). 240p. 70.00 ***(978-88-572-1156-5(8))*** Skira Editore ITA. Dist: Random Hse., Inc.

Villeneuve, Pat. From Periphery to Center: Art Museum Education in the 21st Century. 2007. (Illus.). 255p. pap. *(978-1-890160-38-8(5))* National Art Education Assn.

Von Rauch, Friederike, photos by. Neues Museum. 2009. (ENG., Illus.). 96p. 45.00 (978-3-7757-2376-3(5)) Hatje Cantz Verlag GmbH & Co KG DEU. Dist: D.A.P./Distributed Art Pubs.
Walker, Hamza, et al, texts. Restless Empathy. 2010. (ENG., Illus.). 192p. pap. 40.00 (978-0-934324-49-6(2)) Aspen Art Museum.
Wattenmaker, Richard J. American Paintings & Works on Paper in the Barnes Foundation. 2010. (Illus.). 404p. 75.00 (978-0-300-15877-9(7)) Yale Univ. Pr.
Webster, Polly. Antique Collectors Guide to New England: Antique Shops, Auction Houses, Museums & Historic Homes. 2011. 182p. 42.95 **(978-1-258-06763-2(3))** Literary Licensing, LLC.
Weddington USMC(Retired), Anthony. Making Marines: From the sketchbook of Colonel A. F. Weddington, USMC(Retired) 2007. (Illus.). 242p. 75.00 (978-0-9798065-2-0(6)) Weddington Art Gallery.
Weibel, Peter & Buddensieg, Andrea, eds. Contemporary Art & the Museum: A Global Perspective, 1 vol. 2007. (ENG., Illus.). 256p. per. 40.00 (978-3-7757-1933-9(4)) Hatje Cantz Verlag GmbH & Co KG DEU. Dist: D.A.P./Distributed Art Pubs.
Weisman, Hannah. Something for Everyone. 2010. 92p. pap. (978-3-8383-7426-0(6)) Lambert Academic Publishing.
Welsh, Caroline M., et al. The Adirondack World of A. F. Tait. 2011. (Illus.). 102p. pap. 24.95 **(978-0-910020-53-4(1))** Adirondack Museum, The.
Wenjun, Zhang. The Henan Museum. 2010. (ENG., Illus.). 192p. pap. 35.00 (978-1-85759-633-5(1)) Scala, Editions FRA. Dist: National Bk. Network.
Werner, Paul. Musée et Cie: Globalisation de la Culture. Werner, Paul, tr. from ENG. 2007. (FRE., Illus.). 68p. pap. 10.00 (978-0-9796414-0-4(3)) Orange Pr., The.
White, Julia M. Manjong: Art, Film, & Change in China. 2008. (ENG., Illus.). 100p. pap. 25.00 (978-0-9719397-7-6(2)) Univ. of California, Berkeley Art Museum & Pacific Film Archive.
White, Michelle, et al, ecs. Richard Serra Drawing: A Retrospective. 2011. (Illus.). 232p. 50.00 (978-0-300-16937-9(X)) Yale Univ. Pr.
Whitehead, Christopher. Museums & the Construction of Disciplines: Art & Archaeology in Nineteenth-Century Britain. 2009. (Duckworth Archaeology Ser.). (Illus.). 144p. pap. 24.95 (978-0-7156-3508-7(5)) Duckworth Publishers GBR. Dist: International Publishers Marketing.
Wiggers, Namita Gupta. 75 Gifts for 75 Years. 2011. (Illus.). 64p. pap. **(978-0-9728981-6-4(6))** Museum of Contemporary Craft.
Wilson, Kristina. The Modern Eye: Stieglitz, Moma & the Art of the Exhibition, 1925-1934. 2009. (ENG., Illus.). 256p. 50.00 (978-0-300-14916-6(6)) Yale Univ. Pr.
Winningham, Geoff. The Pozos Art Project: 2009. 2009. pap. 30.00 (978-1-61623-866-7(6)) Independent Pub.
Woodson-Boulton, Amy. Transformative Beauty: Art Museums in Industrial Britain. 2012. (ENG., Illus.). 288p. 55.00 **(978-0-8047-7804-6(3))** Stanford Univ. Pr.
Woollett, Anne T. Rembrandt in Southern California. 2009. (Illus.). 64p. 9.95 (978-0-89236-993-5(0)) Oxford Univ. Pr., Inc.
Wright, Barnaby, et al. Cézanne's Card Players. 2010. (ENG., Illus.). 160p. pap. 40.00 (978-1-907372-08-7(3)) Holberton, Paul Publishing GBR. Dist: Univ. of Washington Pr.
Wright, Christopher. British & Irish Paintings in Public Collections. 2006. (ENG., Illus.). 850p. 125.00 (978-0-300-11730-1(2)) Yale Univ. Pr.
Wylie, Diana. Enchantment: Pictures from the Tangier American Legation Museum. 2010. pap. (978-1-4507-2532-3(5)) Independent Pub.
Young, Karen, ed. 89 Seconds at Alcazar, 1 vol. 2007. (ENG., Illus.). 138p. pap. 45.00 (978-0-9785933-0-8(8)) Rufus Corp., The.
Young-Sánchez, Margaret. Nature & Spirit: Ancient Costa Rican Treasures in the Mayer Collection at the Denver Art Museum. 2011. (ENG.). 192p. (C). 49.95 (978-0-914738-68-8(2)) Denver Art Museum.
Zenko, Adachi. My Life in Japanese Art & Gardens: From Entrepreneur to Connoisseur. 2010. (ENG.). 256p. 29.95 (978-1-933330-86-0(4)) Stone Bridge Pr.
Zheng, Xinmiao. Tian Fu Yong Cang: Liang an Gu Gong Bo Wu Yuan Wen Wu Cang Pin Gai Shu. 2008. (CHI.). (978-7-80047-538-2(7)) Forbidden City Publishing Hse.
Zyman, Daniela & Ebersberger, Eva, eds. The Collection Book: Thyssen-Bornemisza Art Contemporary. 2009. (ENG., Illus.). 480p. 89.95 (978-3-86560-540-5(0)) Verlag der Buchhandlung Walther Konig DEU. Dist: D.A.P./Distributed Art Pubs.

ART NOUVEAU

see also Art Deco

Art Nouveau. 2010. (Illus.). 200p. (978-1-84484-520-0(6)) Parkstone International.
Asenbaum, Paul, et al. Glanzstucke: Emilie Flöge und der Schmuck der Wiener Werkstätte. 2009. (GER & ENG., Illus.). 152p. 70.00 (978-3-89790-298-5(2)) Arnoldsche Art Pubs. DEU. Dist: Antique Collectors' Club.
Aubert, Nathalie & Fraiture, Pierre-Philippe. From Art Nouveau to Surrealism: Belgian Modernity in the Making. 2007. (Legenda Main Ser.). (Illus.). 207p. 79.50 (978-1-904350-64-4(X)) European Humanities Research Ctr. GBR. Dist: Brown, David Bk. Co., The.
Balchin, Judy. Handmade Art Nouveau Cards. 2007. (Simple & Stunning Ser.). (ENG., Illus.). 48p. pap. 13.95 (978-1-84448-209-2(X)) Search Pr., Ltd. GBR. Dist: Independent Pubs. Group.
Balchin, Judy, et al. The Complete Book of Art Nouveau Designs. 2008. (ENG., Illus.). 96p. pap. 19.95 (978-1-84448-300-6(2)) Search Pr., Ltd. GBR. Dist: Independent Pubs. Group.
Beauclair, Rene. Full-Color Art Nouveau Patterns & Designs. 2007. (Dover Electronic Clip Art Ser.). (ENG., Illus.). 64p. pap. 19.95 (978-0-486-99850-3(9)) Dover Pubns., Inc.
Bedoyere, Camilla de la. Louis Comfort Tiffany Masterworks. 2011. 200p. 19.99 **(978-0-85775-268-0(5)**, 0857752685) Star Fire GBR. Dist: Book Sales, Inc.
Blondiau, Geneviève, et al. Krakow - Cracow Rediscovering the Young Poland Movement: Secession in & around Cracow, 1 vol. 2011. (ENG & POL.). 141p. pap. 30.00 (978-83-914839-4-7(0)) Centre International Pour La Ville, L'Architecture Et Le Paysage BEL. Dist: Innovative Logistics.
Buchholz, Kai. Art Nouveau & Theatre Art: In the Rhythm of Life. 2007. (ENG., Illus.). 192p. 85.00 (978-3-89790-270-1(2)) Arnoldsche Art Pubs. DEU. Dist: Antique Collectors' Club.
Campana, D. M. 571 Art Nouveau Designs. 2007. (Dover Electronic Clip Art Ser.). (ENG., Illus.). 48p. pap. 14.95 (978-0-486-99849-7(5)) Dover Pubns., Inc.
Carl, Klaus H. & Charles, Victoria. Viennese Secession. 2011. (Art of Century Ser.). (ENG., Illus.). 200p. 19.95 (978-1-84484-845-4(0)) Parkstone Pr. USA, Ltd.
Comfort, Kelly. European Aestheticism & Spanish American Modernismo: Artist Protagonists & the Philosophy of Art for Art's Sake. 2011. (ENG., Illus.). 200p. 80.00 (978-0-230-27809-7(4)) Palgrave Macmillan.
Desaint, A. Art Nouveau Stencil Designs. 2007. (Dover Pictorial Archive Ser.). (ENG., Illus.). 48p. per. 6.95 (978-0-486-45426-9(6)) Dover Pubns., Inc.
Dover. 990 Art Nouveau Monograms. 2007. (Dover Pictorial Archive Ser.). (ENG., Illus.). 64p. per. 7.95 (978-0-486-45423-8(1)) Dover Pubns., Inc.
Dover Publications Inc. Staff, creator. Viennese Art Nouveau Stained Glass Designs. 2007. (Dover Electronic Clip Art Ser.). (ENG., Illus.). 48p. pap. 22.95 (978-0-486-99881-7(9)) Dover Pubns., Inc.
Dover Publications Inc. Staff, et al. Art Nouveau Vector Designs. 2009. (Dover Pictura Electronic Clip Art Ser.). (ENG., Illus.). 128p. pap. 49.95 (978-0-486-99006-4(0)) Dover Pubns., Inc.
Durant, Judith & Campbell, Jean. Beadwork Inspired by Art: Art Nouveau Jewelry & Accessories. 2008. (Beading Works of Art Ser.). (ENG., Illus.). 96p. pap. 19.99 (978-1-58923-388-1(3), 1589233883, Creative Publishing International) Quayside.
Elffers, Joost, ed. Art Nouveau. 2008. (Gift Paper Ser.). 20p. pap. 9.95 (978-0-8416-0299-1(9)) American Map Corp.
Fahr-Becker, Gabriele. Art Nouveau. 2008. (Architecture Sculpture Painting Ser.). (Illus.). 425p. pap. 24.95 (978-0-8416-0057-7(0)) American Map Corp.
—Art Nouveau. 2007. (ENG., Illus.). 428p. pap. 19.99 (978-3-8331-3545-3(X)) h.f.ullmann DEU. Dist: Innovative Logistics.
Fahr-Becker, Gabriele, ed. Art Nouveau: Architecture - Sculpture - Painting, 1 vol. 2011. (ENG.). 428p. 19.99 **(978-3-8331-6003-5(9))** h.f.ullmann DEU. Dist: Innovative Logistics.
Falk, Fritz. Jugendstil-Schmuck aus Pforzheim // Art Nouveau Jewellery from Pforzheim. 2009. (ENG., Illus.). 288p. 85.00 (978-3-89790-280-0(X)) Arnoldsche Art Pubs. DEU. Dist: Antique Collectors' Club.
Gletrich, Gerhard & Wagner, Eckard. Kayserzinn: Engelbert Kayser. Jugendstilzinn aus Köln. 2011. (GER & ENG., Illus.). 288p. 85.00 **(978-3-89790-357-9(1))** Arnoldsche Art Pubs. DEU. Dist: Antique Collectors' Club.
Grafton, Carol Belanger, ed. Art Nouveau Decorative Borders & Frames CD-ROM & Book. 2008. (Dover Electronic Clip Art Ser.). (ENG., Illus.). 48p. pap. 16.95 (978-0-486-99860-2(6)) Dover Pubns., Inc.
Hilaire, Michel & Gaillemin, Jean Louis. Alphonse Mucha. Husslein-Arco, Agnes, ed. 2009. (Illus.). 356p. 65.00 (978-3-7913-4356-3(4)) Prestel Verlag GmbH & Co KG DEU. Dist: Prestel Publishing.
Hoffman, Julius, ed. Der Moderne Stil: Jugendstil 1899 bis 1905. 2006. (ENG & GER., Illus.). 448p. 135.00 (978-3-89790-229-9(X)) Arnoldsche Art Pubs. DEU. Dist: Antique Collectors' Club.
Hoffmann, Julius, ed. 356 Art Nouveau Floral Designs. 2007. (Dover Electronic Clip Art Ser.). (ENG., Illus.). 48p. pap. 22.95 (978-0-486-99858-9(4)) Dover Pubns., Inc.
Isaacs, Mollie. The Whalehead Club:: A Legacy Preserved. 2006. (Illus.). 140p. (978-1-57864-379-0(1)) Donning Co. Pubs.
Kutko, Lydia Barry. Art Style Guide. 2010. 42p. pap. 12.95 (978-0-557-73364-4(2)) Lulu Enterprises Inc.
Lahor, Jean. Art Nouveau. 2007. (Art of Century Ser.). (ENG., Illus.). 199p. pap. 19.95 (978-1-85995-673-1(4)) Parkstone International GBR. Dist: Ingram Pub. Services.
—Art of Century: Art Nouveau. 2008. (Illus.). 199p. pap. 17.95 (978-970-718-621-7(6), Numen) Advanced Marketing, S. de R. L. de C. V. MEX. Dist: Perseus-PGW.
Lange, C. Alfons Mucha. Gaillemin, J. -L. et al, eds. (GER., Illus.). 356p. (C). 65.00 (978-3-7774-7035-1(X)) Hirmer Verlag GmbH DEU. Dist: Brown, David Bk. Co., The.
Macaulay, James. Charles Rennie Mackintosh - A Biography. 2010. (ENG., Illus.). 256p. 65.00 (978-0-393-05175-9(7), 5175) Norton, W. W. & Co., Inc.
MacDonald, S. B. Absinthe Antiques: A Collection from la Belle Epoque. 2011. 46.95 **(978-0-7414-6375-3(X))** Infinity Publishing.
Macklowe Gallery. Dynamic Beauty: Sculpture of Art Nouveau Paris. 2011. (ENG., Illus.). 272p. 95.00 **(978-0-615-52534-1(2))** Macklowe Gallery.
Markowitz, Yvonne & Karlin, Elyse Zorn, texts. Imperishable Beauty. 2008. (ENG., Illus.). 176p. 45.00 (978-0-87846-734-1(3)) Museum of Fine Arts, Boston.
Markowitz, Yvonne J. & Karlin, Elyse Zorn. Imperishable Beauty: Art Nouveau Jewelry. 2008. (Illus.). 167p. pap. (978-0-87846-735-8(1)) Museum of Fine Arts, Boston.
Martin, Stephen A. Archibald Knox. 2008. (ENG., Illus.). 304p. 115.00 (978-1-902889-02-3(9)) Artmedia Pr. GBR. Dist: National Bk. Network.
Nassau County Museum of Art Staff, contrib. by. Tiffany. 2008. (Illus.). 48p. pap. (978-0-9815644-2-5(9)) Nassau County Museum of Art.
Passos Leite, Maria Fernanda. René Lalique at the Calouste Gulbenkian Museum. 2009. (ENG., Illus.). 136p. 40.00 (978-88-572-0042-2(6)) Skira Editore ITA. Dist: Random Hse., Inc.
Pepin Press. Art Nouveau Tiles. 2009. (Tile Design Ser.). (MUL & ENG.). 200p. 24.99 incl. cd-rom (978-90-5768-126-4(9)) Pepin Pr. NLD. Dist: National Bk. Network.
Pudor, Heinrich & Makus, Horst. Dokumente zum Jugendstil: Modernes Kunstgewerbe 1902-1908. 2012. (ENG., Illus.). 256p. 120.00 **(978-3-89790-355-5(5))** Arnoldsche Art Pubs. DEU. Dist: Antique Collectors' Club.
Raymond, Jehan. Art Nouveau Vectorized Craftwork Designs. 2012. (Electronic Clip Art Ser.). (ENG.). 64p. pap. 19.95 **(978-0-486-48464-8(5))** Dover Pubns., Inc.
Sembach, Klaus-Jurgen. Art Nouveau: Utopia: Reconciling the Irreconcilable. 25th ed. 2007. (ENG., Illus.). 240p. 14.99 (978-3-8228-3006-2(2)) TASCHEN DEU. Dist: Ingram Pub. Services.
Solo, Dan X., ed. Authentic Art Nouveau Designs CD-ROM & Book. 2008. (Dover Electronic Clip Art Ser.). (ENG., Illus.). 48p. pap. 16.95 (978-0-486-99754-4(5)) Dover Pubns., Inc.
Stegenga, Wil. Geometric Motifs. 2007. (Dover Electronic Clip Art Ser.). (ENG., Illus.). 56p. pap. 14.95 (978-0-486-99833-6(9)) Dover Pubns., Inc.
Stephan, Regina, ed. Joseph Maria Olbrich. 2010. (ENG., Illus.). 64p. 30.00 (978-3-7757-2551-4(2)) Hatje Cantz Verlag GmbH & Co KG DEU. Dist: D.A.P./Distributed Art Pubs.
Ullmann, H. F., ed. Art Pocket Art Nouveau. 2009. (Art Pocket Ser.). 288p. 14.95 (978-0-8416-0348-6(0)) American Map Corp.
Weber, Edith. Art Nouveau & Deco Fashion Postcards. 2009. (Illus.). 112p. bds. 29.99 (978-0-7643-3270-8(8)) Schiffer Publishing, Ltd.
Weller, Alan. Art Nouveau Vector Motifs. 2010. (Dover Electronic Clip Art Ser.). (ENG., Illus.). 48p. pap. 19.95 (978-0-486-99115-3(6)) Dover Pubns., Inc.
—Floral Vector Motifs. 2010. (Dover Electronic Clip Art Ser.). (ENG., Illus.). 48p. pap. 19.95 (978-0-486-99108-5(3)) Dover Pubns., Inc.
Wolf, Norbert. Art Nouveau. 2011. (ENG., Illus.). 304p. 75.00 **(978-3-7913-4542-0(7))** Prestel Publishing.
Zamperini, Alessandra. Ornament & the Grotesque: Fantastical Decoration from Antiquity to Art Nouveau. 2008. (ENG., Illus.). 320p. 95.00 (978-0-500-23856-1(1)) Thames & Hudson.

ART OBJECTS

Here are entered works on decorative art objects. Works on old decorative or utilitarian objects having aesthetic, historic and financial value are entered under Antiques.

see also Antiques; Miniature Objects

also classes of art objects and names of particular objects, e.g. Bronzes, Glassware, Jewelry, Metal-work, Plate, Pottery

Adams, Noel & Entwistle, Chris, eds. 'Intelligible Beauty' Recent Research on Byzantine Jewellery. 2010. (British Museum Research Publication). (ENG., Illus.). 245p. (C). pap. 90.00 (978-0-86159-178-7(X)) British Museum Pr. GBR. Dist: Brown, David Bk. Co., The.
Aldrich, Megan & Hutt, Julia. Understanding Art Objects: Thinking Through the Eye. Godfrey, Tony, ed. 2009. (Illus.). 176p. 50.00 (978-1-84822-016-4(2), Lund Humphries Pubs.) Ashgate Publishing, Ltd. GBR. Dist: Ashgate Publishing Co.
Bongioanni, Alessandro. Treasures of Tutankhamun & the Egyptian Museum of Cairo. 2008. 632p. 19.99 (978-88-540-0850-2(8)) White Star ITA. Dist: Book Sales, Inc.
Brandherm, Dirk & Trachsel, Martin, eds. A New Dawn for the Dark Age? Shifting Paradigms In Mediterranean Iron Age Chronology / L'ge Obscur Se Fait-Il Jour De Nouveau? Les Paradigmes Changeants De La Chronologie De L'Age Du Fer en Mediterranee. 2008. (Bar S Ser.). (Illus.). 176p. (C). 85.00 (978-1-4073-0351-2(1)) British Archaeological Reports Ltd. GBR. Dist: Brown, David Bk. Co., The.
Bremer-David, Charissa. Paris: Life & Luxury in the Eighteenth Century. 2011. (ENG., Illus.). 164p. 45.00 (978-1-60606-052-0(X), J. Paul Getty Museum) Getty Pubns.
Brock, J. K. Fortetsa: Early Greek Tombs near Knossos. 2011. (ENG., Illus.). 456p. pap. 34.99 (978-1-107-60145-1(2)) Cambridge Univ. Pr.
Brulotte, Ronda L. Between Art & Artifact: Archaeological Replicas & Cultural Production in Oaxaca, Mexico. 2012. (ENG., Illus.). 212p. 55.00 **(978-0-292-73779-2(3))** Univ. of Texas Pr.
Bucquoye, Moniek, et al, texts. Design Art, 1 vol. ltd. ed. 2011. (ENG., Illus.). 240p. 85.00 (978-90-5856-300-2(6)) Stichting Kunstboek Bvba BEL. Dist: Antique Collectors' Club.
Conn, Steven. Do Museums Still Need Objects? (Arts & Intellectual Life in Modern America Ser.). 272p. (C). 2010. pap. 24.95 (978-0-8122-2155-8(9)) 2009. (Illus.). 55.00 (978-0-8122-4190-7(8)) Univ. of Pennsylvania Pr.
Cormack, Robin & Vassilaki, Maria. Byzantium, 330-1453. 2008. (ENG., Illus.). 496p. 115.00 (978-1-905711-26-0(3)) Royal Academy of Arts GBR. Dist: Hachette Bk. Group.
Curtis, John. Oxus Treasure. 2012. (Objects in Focus Ser.). (ENG., Illus.). 64p. (C). pap. 10.00 (978-0-7141-5079-6(7)) British Museum Pr. GBR. Dist: Brown, David Bk. Co., The.
Dalton, O. M. Fitzwilliam Museum McClean Bequest: Catalogue of the Mediaeval Ivories, Enamels, Jewellery, Gems & Miscellaneous Objects Bequeathed to the Museum. 2009. (Cambridge Library Collection - Cambridge Ser.). (ENG., Illus.). 200p. pap. 19.99 (978-1-108-00441-1(5)) Cambridge Univ. Pr.
D'Ambra, Eve & Metraux, Guy P. R., eds. The Art of Citizens, Soldiers, & Freedmen in the Roman World. 2006. (BAR International Ser.: Vol. 1526). (ENG., Illus.). 167p. (C). pap. 100.00 (978-1-84171-963-4(3)) British Archaeological Reports Ltd. GBR. Dist: Brown, David Bk. Co., The.
de Guitaut, Caroline. Fabergé's Animals: A Royal Farm in Miniature. 2010. (Illus.). 119p. 24.95 (978-1-905686-12-4(9)) Royal Collection Enterprises Ltd. GBR. Dist: Chicago Distribution Ctr.
—Royal Fabergé. 2011. (Illus.). 156p. 24.95 (978-1-905686-37-7(4)) Royal Collection Enterprises Ltd. GBR. Dist: Chicago Distribution Ctr.
De Muga, Patricia, ed. Alvar Aalto: Objects & Furniture Design by Architects, 1 vol. 2007. (ENG., Illus.). 128p. 30.00 (978-84-343-1143-5(7)) Poligrafa, Ediciones, S. A. ESP. Dist: D.A.P./Distributed Art Pubs.
Desroches, Jean-Paul, et al. Fils du Ciel. 2009. (FRE., Illus.). 231p. (978-90-6153-886-8(6)); (978-90-6153-887-5(4)) Mercatorfonds N. V.
Eaton, Allen H. Beauty for the Sighted & the Blind. 2011. 268p. 47.95 **(978-1-258-00201-5(9))** Literary Licensing, LLC.
Garcia Hintze, Laura & De Muga, Patricia, eds. Charles & Ray Eames: Objects & Furniture Design by Architects, 1 vol. 2007. (ENG., Illus.). 128p. 30.00 (978-84-343-1145-9(3)) Poligrafa, Ediciones, S. A. ESP. Dist: D.A.P./Distributed Art Pubs.
Gauthier, Pauline. Alluring Presence. 2012. (ENG., Illus.). 176p. 59.95 **(978-1-897476-60-4(4))** Simply Read Bks. CAN. Dist: Perseus-PGW.
Glenn, Virginia. Romanesque & Gothic Metalwork & Ivory Carvings in the Museum of Scotland. 2006. (ENG., Illus.). pap. 39.95 (978-1-901663-55-6(8)) NMS Enterprises Ltd. - Publishing GBR. Dist: National Bk. Network.
Grzywacz, Cecily M. Monitoring for Gaseous Pollutants in Museum Environments. 2006. (Scientific Tools for Conservation Ser.). (Illus.). 160p. pap. 65.00 (978-0-89236-851-8(9)) Oxford Univ. Pr., Inc.
Han, Xin. Zi Jin Cheng Jian Zheng, 2 vols. 2009. (CHI., Illus.). 434p. (978-7-80168-490-5(7)) Study Publishing Hse.
Hemachandra, Ray & Belasco, Daniel. 500 Judaica: Innovative Contemporary Ritual Art. 2010. (500 Ser.). (ENG., Illus.). 420p. pap. 24.95 (978-1-60059-462-5(X)) Lark Bks.
Hill, Gerard, et al. Faberge & the Russian Master Goldsmiths. 2008. (ENG., Illus.). 320p. 24.95 (978-0-7893-9970-0(9)) Universe Publishing.
Keefe, John Webster. Fabergé: The Hodges Family Collection. O'Shello, Wanda, ed. 2009. (ENG., Illus.). 310p. 65.00 (978-0-89494-108-5(9)) New Orleans Museum of Art.
Knight, Michael, ed. Collector's Choice, Collector's Voice. 2011. (ENG., Illus.). 64p. pap. 12.95 (978-0-939117-49-9(5)) Asian Art Museum of San Francisco.
Komaroff, Linda, ed. Gifts of the Sultan: The Arts of Giving at the Islamic Courts. 2011. (ENG., Illus.). 336p. 65.00 (978-0-300-17110-5(2)) Yale Univ. Pr.
Lamp, Frederick John, et al, contrib. by. Accumulating Histories: African Art from the Charles B. Benenson Collection at the Yale University Art Gallery. 2012. (ENG., Illus.). 328p. 75.00 **(978-0-300-16992-8(2))** Yale Univ. Art Gallery.
Lin, James C. S. The Immortal Stone: Chinese Jades from the Neolithic Period to the Twentieth Century. 2009. (Illus.). 160p. 60.00 (978-1-85759-581-9(5)) Scala Pubs., Ltd. GBR. Dist: Antique Collectors' Club.
Mason, Charles. Spinach Green & Mutton-fat White: Chinese Jades of the Qing Dynasty (1644-1911) 2006. per. 24.95 (978-0-9762552-1-5(9)) Harn Museum of Art.
Meijer, W. Arnold & Dijk, Jacobus van. Objects for Eternity: Egyptian Antiquities from the W. Arnold Meijer Collection. 2006. (Illus.). 280p. 45.00 (978-3-8053-3651-2(9)) Zabern, Philipp von Verlag, GmbH DEU. Dist: Brown, David Bk. Co., The.
Morrison, Hedda Hammer & Gilpin, Laura, illus. Substance & Symbol in Chinese Toggles: Chinese Belt Toggles from the C. F. Bieber Collection. 2006. (ENG.). 256p. pap. 40.00 (978-1-891640-30-8(5)) Floating World Editions.
Motture, Peta & O'Malley, Michelle, eds. Re-Thinking Renaissance Objects: Design, Function & Meaning. 2012. (ENG., Illus.). 232p. pap. 34.95 (978-1-4443-3775-4(0), Wiley-Blackwell) Wiley, John & Sons, Inc.
Mrazek, Jan, ed. What's the Use of Art? Asian Visual & Material Culture in Context. 2007. (Illus.). 313p. 60.00 (978-0-8248-3063-2(6)) Univ. of Hawaii Pr.
Nys, Karin, ed. Journal of Prehistoric Religion, Vol. XIX-XX. 2006. (Illus.). 54p. pap. 29.50 (978-91-7081-224-8(1)) Astroms, Paul Forlag SWE. Dist: Coronet Bks.
Ogawa, Morihiro, ed. Art of the Samurai: Japanese Arms & Armor, 1156-1868. 2009. (Illus.). 356p. 65.00 (978-0-300-14205-1(6)) Yale Univ. Pr.
Pearce, Nicholas & Steuber, Jason, eds. Original Intentions: Essays on Production, Reproduction, & Interpretation in the Arts of China. 2012. (ENG., Illus.). 320p. 60.00 **(978-0-8130-3372-5(X))** Univ. Pr. of Florida.
Petzinger, Renate, ed. Ilya Kabakov: Werkverzeichnis der Gemälde 1957 - 2007. 2 Bände, 2 vols. 2009. (ENG., Illus.). 816p. 195.00 (978-3-86678-173-3(3)) Kerber Verlag DEU. Dist: D.A.P./Distributed Art Pubs.
Pfeifer Swezey, Marilyn, ed. The Tsar & the President: Alexander II & Abraham Lincoln, Liberator & Emancipator. 2009. (Illus.). 112p. pap. 24.95 (978-0-9787201-1-7(3)) Univ. of Wisconsin Pr.
Read, Charles Hercules & Dalton, O. M. Antiquities from the City of Benin & from Other Parts of West Africa in the British Museum. 2008. (Illus.). 95.00 (978-1-57898-701-6(6)) Martino Publishing.
Sachs, Tom, et al, contrib. by. Tom Sachs: Space Program. 2009. (ENG., Illus.). 280p. pap. 65.00 (978-0-8478-3226-2(0)) Rizzoli International Pubns., Inc.

Sayer, Chloë. Fiesta: Days of the Dead & Other Mexican Festivals. 2009. (ENG., Illus.). 128p. 29.95 *(978-0-292-72209-5(5))* Univ. of Texas Pr.

Shawah, Henry. Henry Shawah: Goldsmith & Sculptor. 2009. (ENG., Illus.). 132p. 65.00 *(978-1-55595-321-8(2))* Hudson Hills Pr. LLC.

Smeets, Job & Tynagel, Nynke. Studio Job: The Book of Job. 2010. (ENG., Illus.). 348p. 150.00 *(978-0-8478-3063-3(2))* Rizzoli International Pubns., Inc.

Strudwick, Nigel. Masterpieces of Ancient Egypt. 2006. (ENG., Illus.). 352p. 35.00 *(978-0-292-71662-9(1))* Univ. of Texas Pr.

Verlag, Hirmer & Hirmer Verlag. Tibet: Kloester oeffnen ihre Schatzkammern. 2006. (GER., Illus.). 664p. (C). pap. 63.00 *(978-3-7774-3115-4(X))* Hirmer Verlag GmbH DEU. Dist: Brown, David Bk. Co., The.

Von Habsburg, Geza. Faberge Revealed: At the Virginia Museum of Fine Arts. 2011. (ENG., Illus.). 436p. 65.00 *(978-0-8478-3738-0(6),* Skira) Rizzoli International Pubns., Inc.

Weber, Joanna. Call & Response. 2006. (ENG., Illus.). 123p. pap. 24.95 *(978-0-89467-093-0(X))* Yale Univ. Art Gallery.

Williams, Gareth. Telling Tales: Fantasy & Fear in Contemporary Design. 2009. (ENG., Illus.). 128p. 39.95 *(978-1-85177-560-6(9))* V & A Pubns. GBR. Dist: Hachette Bk. Group.

Youngman, Robert P., et al. The Youngman Collection: Chinese Jades from Neolithic to Qing. 2008. *(978-1-58886-098-9(1))* Art Media Resources, Inc.

Yu, Ming. Chinese Jade. 3rd ed. 2011. (Introductions to Chinese Culture Ser.). (ENG., Illus.). 152p. pap. 19.99 ***(978-0-521-18684-1(6))*** Cambridge Univ. Pr.

ART OBJECTS—COLLECTORS AND COLLECTING

Bartholomew, Terese, et al. Later Chinese Jades: Ming Dynasty to Early Twentieth Century. 2007. (ENG.). 368p. 95.00 *(978-0-939117-41-3(X))* Asian Art Museum of San Francisco.

Beevers, David, ed. Chinese Whispers: Chinoiserie in Britain 1650-1930. 2009. (ENG., Illus.). 144p. pap. *(978-0-948723-71-1(8),* Royal Pavilion Libraries & Mus) Antique Collectors' Club.

Fang, Gu, ed. The Complete Collection of Jades Unearthed in China. 2006. 3600p. *(978-7-03-016009-6(6))* BRILL.

Geary, Christraud M. & Xatart, Stephanie. Material Journey: Collecting African & Oceanic Art, 1945-2000, 1 vol. 2007. (ENG., Illus.). 250p. pap. 35.00 *(978-0-87846-715-0(7))* Museum of Fine Arts, Boston.

Getty, J. Paul. The Joys of Collecting. 2011. (ENG., Illus.). 80p. pap. 9.95 ***(978-1-60606-087-2(2),*** J. Paul Getty Museum) Getty Pubns.

Hiesinger, Kathryn B. Collecting Modern: Design at the Philadelphia Museum of Art since 1876. 2011. (ENG., Illus.). 304p. 65.00 *(978-0-300-12219-0(5))* Yale Univ. Pr.

Hu, Kemin. Modern Chinese Scholars' Rocks: A Guide for Collectors. 2006. (ENG., Illus.). 128p. per. 29.95 *(978-1-891640-34-6(8))* Floating World Editions.

M'Closkey, Kathy. Swept under the Rug: A Hidden History of Navajo Weaving. 2008. (University of Arizona Southwest Centre Ser.). (ENG., Illus.). 336p. (C). pap. 27.95 *(978-0-8263-2832-8(6))* Univ. of New Mexico Pr.

Mendelsohn, Michael. Life Is Short Art Is Long: Maximizing Estate Planning Strategies for Collectors of Art, Antiques & Collectibles. 2007. pap. 24.95 *(978-1-59969-109-1(4))* Wealth Management Pr.

Miller, Judith. 20th Century Design: The Definitive Illustrated Sourcebook. gif. ed. 2012. (ENG., Illus.). 304p. 19.99 ***(978-1-84533-723-0(9),*** Mitchell Beazley) Octopus Publishing Group GBR. Dist: Hachette Bk. Group.

Mulvany, Kevin & Rogers, Susie. Magnificent Miniatures: Inspiration & Technique for Grand Houses on a Small Scale. 2009. (ENG., Illus.). 144p. 29.95 *(978-0-7134-9059-6(4),* Batsford, B. T. Ltd.) Anova Bks. GBR. Dist: Sterling Publishing Co., Inc.

Panza, Giuseppe. Giuseppe Panza: Memories of a Collector. Haggerty, Michael, tr. from ITA. 2007. (ENG., Illus.). 411p. 50.00 *(978-0-7892-0943-6(8))* Abbeville Pr., Inc.

Rosenzweig, Daphne Lange & McCullough, Hollis Koons. Ladies, Landscapes & Loyal Retainers: Japanese Art from a Private Collection. (Illus.). 72p. pap. 19.95 *(978-0-933075-03-0(0))* Telfair Museum of Art.

Rothstein, Arden & Rothstein, Anya. Mexican Folk Art: From Oaxacan Artist Families. 2007. (Illus.). 192p. pap. 39.95 *(978-0-7643-2673-8(2))* Schiffer Publishing, Ltd.

Rujivacharakul, Vimalin. Collecting China: The World, China, & a Short History of Collecting. (Illus.). 2011. (ENG.). 240p. 65.00 *(978-1-61149-006-0(5))* 2010. 210p. *(978-0-87413-096-6(4))* Univ. of Delaware Pr.

Ruscha, Paul, photos by. Paul Ruscha's Full Moon, 1 vol. 2008. (ENG., Illus.). 184p. pap. 20.00 *(978-3-86521-231-3(X))* Steidl, Gerhard Druckerei und Verlag DEU. Dist: Innovative Logistics.

Rutledge, Steven. Ancient Rome as a Museum: Power, Identity, & the Culture of Collecting. 2012. (Oxford Studies in Ancient Culture & Representation Ser.). (Illus.). 424p. 135.00 ***(978-0-19-957323-3(9))*** Oxford Univ. Pr., Inc.

Skinner, Tina. Geisha Fan Book. 2007. (Illus.). 128p. pap. 24.95 *(978-0-7643-2746-9(1))* Schiffer Publishing, Ltd.

Snyder, Jeffrey B. Asian Ivory. 2007. (Illus.). 288p. pap. 79.95 *(978-0-7643-2728-5(3))* Schiffer Publishing, Ltd.

Wendorf, Richard. The Literature of Collecting & Other Essays. 2008. 49.95 *(978-1-58456-230-6(7))* Oak Knoll Pr.

ART OBJECTS—CONSERVATION AND RESTORATION

Bassett, Jean, et al. The Craftsman Revealed: Adrien de Vries, Sculptor in Bronze. 2008. (Illus.). 352p. 60.00 *(978-0-89236-919-5(1))* Oxford Univ. Pr., Inc.

Bayer, Andrea, et al, contrib. by. Metropolitan Museum Studies in Art, Science, & Technology 2010, Vol. 1. 2010. (Illus.). 164p. pap. 50.00 *(978-0-300-15160-2(8))* Yale Univ. Pr.

Becker, Konrad & Fleming, Jim, eds. Critical Strategies in Art & Media: Perspectives on New Cultural Practices. 2010. (ENG.). 182p. pap. 12.95 *(978-1-57027-214-1(X))* Autonomedia.

Castillejo, Marta, et al, eds. Lasers in the Conservation of Artworks: Proceedings of the International Conference Lacona VII, Madrid, Spain, 17 - 21 September 2007. 2008. (ENG., Illus.). 512p. 205.95 *(978-0-415-47596-9(1),* CRC Press) Taylor & Francis Group GBR. Dist: Taylor & Francis Group.

Dickmann, Klaus, et al, eds. Lasers in the Conservation of Artworks: LACONA V Proceedings, Osnabrack, Germany, Sept. 15-18 2003. 2010. (Springer Proceedings in Physics Ser.). (Illus.). xxi, 528p. pap. 319.00 *(978-3-642-06191-2(5),* 3642061915) Springer.

Jain, Kamal K. & Oakley, Victoria L. Essentials in the Care & Conservation of Historical Ceramic Objects. 2007. (ENG., Illus.). 116p. pap. 50.00 *(978-1-873132-73-9(5))* Archetype Pubns. GBR. Dist: National Bk. Network.

Jones, M. Conservation Science: Heritage Materials. May, Eric, ed. 2006. (Rsc Paperbacks Ser.). (ENG., Illus.). 390p. (C). 56.00 *(978-0-85404-659-1(3),* 0854046593) Royal Society of Chemistry, The GBR. Dist: Ingram Pub. Services.

Nimmrichter, Johann, et al, eds. Lasers in the Conservation of Artworks: LACONA VI Proceedings, Vienna, Austria, Sept. 21 — 25 2005. (Springer Proceedings in Physics Ser.). (Illus.). xxvi, 650p. 2010. pap. 359.00 *(978-3-642-09129-2(6),* 3642091296) 2007. 359.00 *(978-3-540-72129-1(0))* Springer.

Oakley, Victoria L. Essentials in the Care & Conservation of Historical Ceramic Objects. 2008. (ENG.). 117p. pap. 35.00 *(978-1-4379-6459-2(1))* DIANE Publishing Co.

Odegaard, Nancy, et al. Material Characterization Tests for Objects of Art. 2nd ed. 2007. (ENG., Illus.). 230p. 85.00 *(978-1-904982-09-8(3))* Archetype Pubns. GBR. Dist: National Bk. Network.

Pezzati, Luca & Salimbeni, Renzo. O3a: Optics for Arts, Architecture, & Archaeology III. 2011. (Proceedings of SPIE Ser.). 248p. pap. 80.00 ***(978-0-8194-8680-6(9))*** SPIE.

Poulsson, Tina Grette. Retouching of Art on Paper. 2008. (ENG., Illus.). 112p. pap. 50.00 *(978-1-904982-13-5(1))* Archetype Pubns. GBR. Dist: National Bk. Network.

Radvan, Roxana, ed. Lasers in the Conservation of Artworks Viii. 2010. (ENG., Illus.). 240p. 159.99 *(978-0-415-58073-1(0),* CRC Press) Taylor & Francis Group GBR. Dist: Taylor & Francis Group.

Salimbeni, Renzo & Pezzati, Luca. O3A: Optics for Arts, Architecture, & Archaeology II: 17-18 June 2009, Munich, Germany. 2009. (Proceedings of SPIE Ser.). (Illus.). 318p. pap. 80.00 ***(978-0-8194-7674-6(9))*** SPIE.

Salimbeni, Renzo, et al. O3A: Optics for Arts, Architecture, & Archaeology: 20-22 June 2007, Munich, Germany. 2007. (Proceedings of SPIE Ser.). (Illus.). 390p. pap. 105.00 *(978-0-8194-6760-7(X))* SPIE.

Sawicki, Malgorzata. Non-Traditional Gilding Techniques in Gilded Objects Conservation. 2010. (Illus.). 280p. pap. *(978-3-639-27139-3(4))* VDM Verlag Dr. Mueller e.K.

ART OBJECTS—PRICES

Husfloen, Kyle & Dolnick, Penny. Antique Trader Perfume Bottles Price Guide. 2009. (ENG.). 288p. pap. 19.99 *(978-0-89689-671-0(4))* Krause Pubns.

Miller, Robert L. The No. 1 Price Guide to M. I. Hummel Figurines, Plates, More... 10th ed. 2006. (No. 1 Price Guide to M. I. Hummel Figurines, Plates, More... Ser.). (Illus.). 606p. per. 29.95 *(978-1-932485-35-6(X))* Reverie Publishing Co.

Nind, Sarah. Painting As Metaphor. Schirmacher, Wolfgang, ed. 2010. 184p. pap. 21.95 *(978-0-9827067-0-1(7))* Atropos Pr.

ART OBJECTS—PRIVATE COLLECTIONS

Amme, Jochen. Historische Bestecke 2: Supplement zu Amme 2002. 2007. (ENG., Illus.). 192p. 75.00 *(978-3-89790-261-9(3))* Arnoldsche Art Pubs. DEU. Dist: Antique Collectors' Club.

Guitaut, Caroline de. Faberge in the Royal Collection. 2010. (Illus.). 272p. 65.00 *(978-1-902163-66-6(4))* Royal Collection Enterprises Ltd. GBR. Dist: Chicago Distribution Ctr.

Jokisch, Christoph & Volz, Peter. Emblems of Eminence: German Renaissance Portrait Medals. 2008. (GER., Illus.). 224p. (C). 154.00 *(978-3-7774-4235-8(6))* Hirmer Verlag GmbH DEU. Dist: Brown, David Bk. Co., The.

ART OBJECTS, FORGERY OF

see Forgery of Works of Art

ART PATRONAGE

Here are entered works on support of the arts by individuals and corporations. Works on government policy toward the arts are entered under Art and State.

see also Art and State; Art Patrons; Authors and Patrons

Andersen, Wayne. Marcel Duchamp: The Failed Messiah. 2010. 402p. 45.00 *(978-0-9725573-4-4(2))* Fabriart Editions, Ltd.

Bers, Rachel, ed. The Andy Warhol Foundation for the Visual Arts 20-Year Report: 1987-2007. 2007. (Illus.). 276p. pap. *(978-0-9765263-1-5(X))* Andy Warhol Foundation for the Visual Arts, The.

Brennan, Marcia, et al. A Modern Patronage: De Menil Gifts to American & European Museums. 2007. (ENG., Illus.). 120p. 40.00 *(978-0-300-12379-1(5))* Yale Univ. Pr.

Carder, James N., ed. A Home of the Humanities: The Collecting & Patronage of Mildred & Robert Woods Bliss. 2011. (Dumbarton Oaks Collection Ser.). (ENG., Illus.). 200p. 65.00 *(978-0-88402-365-4(6))* Dumbarton Oaks.

Caskey, Jill. Art & Patronage in the Medieval Mediterranean: Merchant Culture in the Region of Amalfi. 2011. (ENG., Illus.). 344p. pap. 65.00 *(978-0-521-28426-4(0))* Cambridge Univ. Pr.

Chandler, et al. Exile & Patronage: Cross-Cultural Negotiations Beyond the Third Reich. Chandler, Andrew et al, eds. 2007. (GER & ENG., Illus.). 216p. (gr. 11). pap. 47.95 *(978-3-8258-0014-7(8))* Lit Verlag DEU. Dist: Transaction Pubs.

Cherbo, Joni Maya, et al, eds. Understanding the Arts & Creative Sector in the United States. 2008. (Rutgers Series on the Public Life of the Arts). (ENG., Illus.). 224p. 68.00 *(978-0-8135-4307-9(X))*; pap. 26.95 *(978-0-8135-4308-6(8))* Rutgers Univ. Pr.

Coudert, Thierry. Café Society: [mondains, Mécènes et Artistes, 1920-1960]. 2010. (FRE., Illus.). 320p. *(978-2-08-011479-2(4))* Flammarion et Cie.

—Café Society: Socialites, Patrons, & Artists, 1920-1960. 2010. (ENG., Illus.). 320p. 75.00 *(978-2-08-030157-4(8))* Flammarion et Cie FRA. Dist: Random Hse., Inc.

Drogin, David & Christian, Kathleen Wren. Patronage & Italian Renaissance Sculpture. 2010. (Illus.). 286p. 109.95 *(978-0-7546-6842-8(8))* Ashgate Publishing Co.

Fenlon, Iain. Music & Patronage in Sixteenth-Century Mantua: Volume 1. 2008. (Cambridge Studies in Music Ser.). (ENG., Illus.). 248p. pap. 34.99 *(978-0-521-08833-6(X))* Cambridge Univ. Pr.

Furlotti, Barbara & Rebecchini, Guido. The Art of Mantua: Power & Patronage in the Renaissance. Jenkens, A. Lawrence, tr. from ITA. 2008. (Illus.). 280p. 84.95 *(978-0-89236-840-2(3))* Oxford Univ. Pr., Inc.

Gardner, Julian & Giotto. Giotto & His Publics: Three Paradigms of Patronage. 2011. (Bernard Berenson Lectures on the Italian Renaissance Delivered at Villa I Tatti Ser.). (Illus.). 256p. 35.00 *(978-0-674-05080-8(0))* Harvard Univ. Pr.

Glass, Dorothy F. The Sculpture of Reform in North Italy, Ca. 1095-1130: History & Patronage of Romanesque Façades. 2010. (Illus.). 296p. 124.95 *(978-1-4094-0002-8(6))* Ashgate Publishing Co.

Gold, Barbara K., ed. Literary & Artistic Patronage in Ancient Rome. 2012. (ENG.). 208p. pap. 19.95 ***(978-0-292-74098-3(0))*** Univ. of Texas Pr.

Hooper-Hamersley, Ro. The Hunt after Jeanne-Antoinette de Pompadour: Patronage, Politics, Art, & the French Enlightenment. 2011. (ENG., Illus.). 414p. 85.00 *(978-0-7391-4963-8(6))* Lexington Bks.

Kenney, Ellen V. Power & Patronage in Medieval Syria: The Architecture & Urban Works of Tankiz Al-Nasiri. 2009. *(978-0-9708199-4-9(3))* Univ. of Chicago, Middle East Documentation Ctr.

Lee, Hui-Shu. Empresses, Art, & Agency in Song Dynasty China. 2010. (ENG., Illus.). 336p. 65.00 *(978-0-295-98963-1(7))* Univ. of Washington Pr.

Leone, Stephanie C., ed. The Pamphilj & the Arts: Patronage & Consumption in Baroque Rome. 2011. (ENG & ITA., Illus.). 200p. pap. 45.00 *(978-1-892850-17-1(6))* McMullen Museum of Art, Boston College.

Lillehoj, Elizabeth, ed. Acquisition: Art & Ownership in EDO-Period Japan. 2007. (ENG., Illus.). 208p. per. 50.00 *(978-1-891640-50-6(X))* Floating World Editions.

Lovell, Margaretta M. Art in a Season of Revolution: Painters, Artisans, & Patrons in Early America. 2007. (Early American Studies). (Illus.). 360p. (C). per. 29.95 *(978-0-8122-1991-3(0))* Univ. of Pennsylvania Pr.

Martin, Therese. Queen as King: Politics & Architectural Propaganda in Twelfth-Century Spain. 2006. (Medieval & Early Modern Iberian World Ser.: Vol. 30). (Illus.). 292p. *(978-90-04-15297-7(0))* BRILL.

Maxwell, Susan. The Court Art of Friedrich Sustris: Patronage in Late Renaissance Bavaria. 2011. (Visual Culture in Early Modernity Ser.). (Illus.). 250p. 109.95 *(978-0-7546-6887-9(8))* Ashgate Publishing Co.

McCarthy, Kevin F., et al. Arts & Culture in the Metropolis: Strategies for Sustainability. 2007. (Illus.). 156p. per. 25.00 *(978-0-8330-3890-6(7),* MG-477) RAND Corp., The.

Mciver, Katherine. Wives Widows Mistresses & Nuns in Early Modern Italy: Making the Invisible Visible Through Art & Patronage. 2012. (Women & Gender in the Early Modern World Ser.). (Illus.). 286p. 119.95 ***(978-0-7546-6953-1(X))*** Ashgate Publishing Co.

McNair, Amy. Donors of Longmen: Faith, Politics, & Patronage in Medieval Chinese Buddhist Sculpture. 2007. (Illus.). 230p. 58.00 *(978-0-8248-2994-0(8))* Univ. of Hawaii Pr.

O'Malley, Michelle & Welch, Evelyn, eds. Material Renaissance. 2010. (Studies in Design & Material Culture Ser.). (ENG., Illus.). 328p. pap. 30.95 *(978-0-7190-8125-5(4))* Manchester Univ. Pr. GBR. Dist: Macmillan.

Pasternak, Anne. Creative Time. Peltason, Ruth, ed. 2008. (ENG., Illus.). 288p. pap. 35.00 *(978-1-56898-804-7(4))* Princeton Architectural Pr.

—Creative Time: 33 Years of Public Art in New York. Peltason, Ruth A. & Peltason, Ruth, eds. 2007. (ENG., Illus.). 288p. pap. 50.00 *(978-1-56898-696-8(3))* Princeton Architectural Pr.

Redford, Bruce. Dilettanti: The Antic & the Antique in Eighteenth-Century England. 2008. (ENG., Illus.). 236p. 50.00 *(978-0-89236-924-9(8))* Oxford Univ. Pr., Inc.

Richards, John. Petrarch's Influence on the Iconography of the Carrara Palace in Padua: The Conflict Between Ancestral & Antique Themes in the Fourteenth Century. (Illus.). 186p. 99.95 *(978-0-7734-5236-7(2))* Mellen, Edwin Pr., The.

Richardson, Carol. The Possessions of a Cardinal: Art, Piety, & Politics, 1450-1700. 2010. (ENG., Illus.). 456p. 85.00 *(978-0-271-03468-3(8))* Pennsylvania State Univ. Pr.

Richardson, Carol M., ed. Locating Renaissance Art. 2007. (Renaissance Art Reconsidered Ser.). (ENG., Illus.). 352p. pap. 35.00 *(978-0-300-12188-9(1))* Yale Univ. Pr.

Roberts, Jane. George III & Queen Charlotte: Patronage, Collecting & Court Taste. 2006. (Illus.). 65.00 *(978-1-902163-73-4(7))* Royal Collection Enterprises Ltd. GBR. Dist: Antique Collectors' Club.

Rosser-Owen, Mariam. Islamic Arts from Spain. 2010. (ENG., Illus.). 160p. 55.00 *(978-1-85177-598-9(6))* V & A Pubns. GBR. Dist: Hachette Bk. Group.

Salter, Elizabeth. English & International: Studies in the Literature, Art & Patronage of Medieval England. Pearsall, Derek & Zeeman, Nicolette, eds. 2010. (ENG.). 408p. pap. 42.00 *(978-0-521-13161-2(8))* Cambridge Univ. Pr.

Schuman. Economic Pressures & the Future. 2007. (ENG.). 112p. pap. 10.95 *(978-1-4165-7754-6(8),* Free Pr.) Free Pr.

Sherman Contemporary Art Foundation Ltd. Contemporary Art & Philanthropy No. 7: Exploring the Foundations. Smith, Terry, ed. 2007. (ENG.). 104p. pap. *(978-0-86840-951-1(0),* UNSW Press) NewSouth Publishing AUS. Dist: Independent Pubs. Group.

Silver, Larry. Marketing Maximilian: The Visual Ideology of a Holy Roman Emperor. 2008. (ENG., Illus.). 352p. (C). 59.95 *(978-0-691-13019-4(1))* Princeton Univ. Pr.

Sisi, Carlo, ed. Monumenti del Giardino Puccini: Un luogo del Romanticismo in Toscana. 2010. (ITA., Illus.). 400p. (C). 90.00 *(978-88-596-0857-8(0))* Polistampa ITA. Dist: Brown, David Bk. Co., The.

Timmermans, Bert. Patronen Van Patronage in Het Zeventiende-Eeuwse Antwerpen: Een Elite Als Actor Binnen Een Kunstwereld. 2008. (Studies Stadsgeschiedenis Ser.). (DUT., Illus.). 427p. 50.50 ***(978-90-5260-247-9(6))*** Aksant Academic Pubs. NLD. Dist: Amsterdam Univ. Pr.

Tittler, Robert. Portraits, Painters, & Publics in Provincial England, 1540-1640. 2012. (ENG., Illus.). 216p. 110.00 ***(978-0-19-958560-1(1))*** Oxford Univ. Pr., Inc.

Villani, John. Art Towns California: A Guide to Galleries, Museums, Festivals, Lodging & Dining. 2008. (ENG.). 272p. pap. 18.95 *(978-0-88150-696-9(6),* 150696) Countryman Pr.

Villani, John, et al. The 100 Best Art Towns in America: A Guide to Galleries, Museums, Festivals, Lodging & Dining. 5th ed. 2010. (ENG., Illus.). 504p. pap. 19.95 *(978-0-88150-867-3(5),* 150867) Countryman Pr.

Wackernagel, Martin & Luchs, Alison. The World of the Florentine Renaissance Artist: Projects & Patrons, Workshop & Art Market. 2011. (RSART: Renaissance Society of America Reprint Text Ser.). xxx, 447p. pap. ***(978-1-4426-1184-9(7))*** Univ. of Toronto Pr.

Wagner-Koch, Elisabeth. Kunstszenarien in Unternehmen. (GER., Illus.). 230p. *(978-3-496-01196-5(3))* Reimer, Dietrich.

Walker, Jo Ann. Emrys in Full Flower. 2008. lib. bdg. *(978-0-9773516-2-6(9))* Emrys Pr. of the Emrys Foundation, The.

ART PATRONS

Abell, Mora. Doctor Thomas Monro: Physician, Patron & Painter. 2009. 216p. pap. 20.00 *(978-1-4120-9973-8(0))* Trafford Publishing.

Baxter, Denise & Martin, Meredith S. Architectural Space in Eighteenth-Century Europe: Constructing Indentities an Interiors. 2010. (Illus.). 284p. 119.95 *(978-0-7546-6650-9(6))* Ashgate Publishing Co.

Ben-Arie, Daniella, et al. Thomas Hope: Regency Designer. Hewat-Jaboor, Philip, ed. 2008. (ENG., Illus.). 520p. 100.00 *(978-0-300-12416-3(3))* Yale Univ. Pr.

Berners, Lord. Dresden. 2008. (ENG.). 96p. pap. 9.95 *(978-1-933527-15-4(3),* Turtle Point) Turtle Point Pr.

Bernhard, Virginia. Ima Hogg: The Governor's Daughter. 2011. (Fred Rider Cotton Popular History Ser.). (Illus.). 144p. pap. 15.95 *(978-0-87611-245-8(9))* Texas State Historical Assn.

Bishop, Janet, et al, intros. The Steins Collect: Matisse, Picasso, & the Parisian Avant-Garde. 2011. (Illus.). 492p. 75.00 *(978-0-300-16941-6(8))* Yale Univ. Pr.

Blyth, Alastair. Managing the Brief for Better Design. 2nd ed. 2009. (Illus.). 220p. pap. 62.95 *(978-0-415-46031-6(X))*; 160.00 *(978-0-415-46030-9(1))* Taylor & Francis Group.

Bonyhady, Tim. Good Living Street: Portrait of a Patron Family, Vienna 1900. 2011. (ENG., Illus.). 400p. 35.00 *(978-0-307-37880-4(2),* Pantheon) Knopf Doubleday Publishing Group.

Halsey, William & Blackman, Lynne. William Halsey: Mastery of the Modern. 2006. *(978-0-9785365-1-0(7))* Charleston Renaissance Gallery, The.

Hannah, Rosemary. The Grand Designer: Third Marquess of Bute. 2012. (ENG., Illus.). 352p. 40.00 ***(978-1-78027-027-2(5))*** Birlinn, Ltd. GBR. Dist: Independent Pubs. Group.

Kirchner, Ernst Ludwig, et al. Das Ungewohnte Neue: Briefwechsel Ernst Ludwig Kirchner und George Reinhart. 2010. (GER., Illus.). 167p. pap. 45.00 ***(978-3-85881-140-0(8))*** Scheidegger und Spiess AG, Verlag CHE. Dist: Antique Collectors' Club.

Lawson-Johnston, Peter. Growing up Guggenheim: A Personal History of a Family Enterprise. 2006. (Illus.). 163p. per. 22.00 *(978-1-933859-19-4(9))* ISI Bks.

Lee, Hui-Shu. Empresses, Art, & Agency in Song Dynasty China. 2010. (ENG., Illus.). 336p. 65.00 *(978-0-295-98963-1(7))* Univ. of Washington Pr.

Mounger, William D. Amidst the Fray: My Life in Politics, Culture, & Mississippi. 2006. (Illus.). 480p. 26.95 *(978-1-893062-97-9(X))* Quail Ridge Pr., Inc.

Siva, Jessica Pooi Sun. Habitus Shock. 2009. 504p. pap. *(978-3-639-19314-5(8))* VDM Verlag Dr. Mueller e.K.

Stark, Gregor & Rayne, E. Catherine. El Delirio: The Santa Fe World of Elizabeth White. (Southwest Ser.). (Illus.). 144p. pap. 19.95 *(978-0-933452-52-7(7))* School for Advanced Research Pr./SAR Pr.

Styhre, Alexander. Managing Knowledge in the Construction Industry. 2009. (Spon Research Ser.). (ENG., Illus.). 216p. (C). 135.00 *(978-0-415-46344-7(0))* Routledge.

Timmermans, Bert. Patronen Van Patronage in Het Zeventiende-Eeuwse Antwerpen: Een Elite Als Actor Binnen Een Kunstwereld. 2008. (Studies Stadsgeschiedenis Ser.). (DUT., Illus.). 427p. 50.50 ***(978-90-5260-247-9(6))*** Aksant Academic Pubs. NLD. Dist: Amsterdam Univ. Pr.

Unger, Irwin. The Guggenheims: A Family History. 2005. (ENG.). 550p. pap. 17.00 *(978-1-4379-6780-7(9))* DIANE Publishing Co.

Unger, Irwin & Unger, Debi. The Guggenheims: A Family History. 2006. (Illus.). 550p. reprint ed. 30.00 *(978-1-4223-5383-7(4))* DIANE Publishing Co.

ART PHOTOGRAPHY

see Photography of Art

ART POTTERY

Cass, Claire. The Masters Box Set: Masterpieces of French Art Pottery, 1885-1910 & Clement Massier: Master of Iridescence, 2. 2007. (Illus.). 204p. 75.00 *(978-0-9788371-4-3(2))* Jason Jacques Gallery Pr. The.

Green, Nancy E. Reawakenings: Modern & Contemporary Ceramics from the Shatzman Collection. 2010. (ENG., Illus.). 68p. pap. *(978-1-934260-15-9(0))* Cornell Univ., Herbert F. Johnson Museum of Art.

Hemachandra, Ray. Lark Studio Series: Art Tiles. 2010. (ENG., Illus.). 204p. 12.95 *(978-1-60059-581-0(9))* Lark Bks.

Hemachandra, Ray & Galloway, Julia. 500 Vases: Contemporary Explorations of a Timeless Form. 2010. (500 Ser.). (ENG., Illus.). 420p. pap. 24.95 *(978-1-60059-246-1(5))* Lark Bks.

Kline, Jerry & Nickel, Mike. Pillin Pottery. 2011. (Illus.). 256p. 59.99 ***(978-0-7643-3922-6(2))*** Schiffer Publishing, Ltd.

Lark Crafts. The Best of 500 Ceramics: Celebrating a Decade in Clay. 2012. (500 Ser.). (ENG., Illus.). 420p. 30.00 ***(978-1-4547-0141-5(2))*** Lark Bks.

Nickl, Peter & Jeffries, Susan. Gilbert Portanier: Oeuvre 2000-2009. 2009. (ENG., Illus.). 200p. 85.00 *(978-3-89790-289-3(3))* Arnoldsche Art Pubs. DEU. Dist: Antique Collectors' Club.

Parks, Walter P. The Miracle of Mata Ortiz: Juan Quezada & the Potters of Northern Chihuahua. 2011. (Illus.). 212p. 40.00 ***(978-1-933855-61-5(4))*** Rio Nuevo Pubs.

Piepenburg, Robert. The Spirit of Ceramic Design: Cultivating Creativity with Clay. 2008. (Illus.). 253p. pap. 34.95 *(978-0-9628481-7-9(4))* Pebble Pr., Inc.

Punyet Miró, Joan, et al. Joan Miró, Josep Llorens Artigas: Ceramics: Catalogue Raisonné, 1941-1981. 2010. (ENG., Illus.). 398p. 335.00 *(978-2-86882-079-2(4))* Lelong, Galerie FRA. Dist: D.A.P./Distributed Art Pubs.

Schwartz, Judith S. Confrontational Ceramics. 2008. (Illus.). 256p. 55.00 *(978-0-8122-4139-6(8))* Univ. of Pennsylvania Pr.

Siemssen, Peter. Ceramics: A Lifelong Passion - Collection Peter Siemssen Foundation. 2008. (ENG., Illus.). 312p. 75.00 *(978-3-89790-256-5(7))* Arnoldsche Art Pubs. DEU. Dist: Antique Collectors' Club.

Snyder, Jeffrey B., ed. Ceramics Today. 2010. 50.00 *(978-0-7643-3465-8(4))* Schiffer Publishing, Ltd.

Studio Ceramics: Advanced Techniques. 2010. (Ceramic Arts Handbook Ser.). (Illus.). 144p. pap. 29.95 *(978-1-57498-308-1(3)*, CA90) American Ceramic Society, The.

Turner, Anderson, ed. Extruder, Mold & Tile: Forming Techniques. 2008. (Ceramics Monthly Handbooks Ser.). (Illus.). 144p. pap. 29.95 *(978-1-57498-291-6(5)*, CA 58) American Ceramic Society, The.

ART POTTERY, AMERICAN

Choi, Justine & Barletta, Destiny, eds. A Force of Nature: The Ceramic Art of Randy Johnston. 2011. (Illus.). 104p. 50.00 ***(978-1-879985-23-0(3))*** Pucker Gallery.

Gadsden, Nonie. Art & Reform: Sara Galner, the Saturday Evening Girls, & the Paul Revere Pottery, 1 vol. 2007. (ENG., Illus.). 104p. pap. 24.95 *(978-0-87846-716-7(5))* Museum of Fine Arts, Boston.

Gerratana, Terry. Santa Barbara Ceramic Design: Art Pottery from America's Riviera. 2011. (Illus.). 256p. 39.99 ***(978-0-7643-3888-5(9))*** Schiffer Publishing, Ltd.

Henzke, Lucile. Art Pottery of America. 4th rev. ed. 2008. (Illus.). 368p. bds. 45.00 *(978-0-7643-2879-4(4))* Schiffer Publishing, Ltd.

Humphrey, Joanne Fenton. Ameen. 2009. (Illus.). 121p. 49.95 *(978-0-615-29130-7(9))* Windjammer Adventure Publishing.

L-W Books. Rozane Ware: The Roseville Pottery Company. 2012. (Illus.). 44p. pap. 7.99 ***(978-0-7643-3858-8(7)***, Schiffer Publishing Ltd) Schiffer Publishing, Ltd.

Owen, Nancy Elizabeth. Rookwood Pottery at the Philadelphia Museum of Art: The Gerald & Virginia Gordon Collection. 2006. (ENG., Illus.). 136p. *(978-0-87633-167-5(3)*, Acc Us Distribution Bk. Title) Antique Collectors' Club.

Rago, Denise. Warmans Roseville Pottery. 2nd ed. 2007. (ENG.). 268p. pap. 24.99 *(978-0-89689-510-2(6))* Krause Pubns.

Shapiro, Mark, ed. A Chosen Path: The Ceramic Art of Karen Karnes. 2010. (ENG., Illus.). 129p. 40.00 *(978-0-8078-3427-5(0))* Univ. of North Carolina Pr.

Strauss, Cindi, et al. Shifting Paradigms in Contemporary Ceramics: The Garth Clark & Mark Del Vecchio Collection. 2012. (ENG., Illus.). 576p. 100.00 ***(978-0-300-16997-3(3))*** Yale Univ. Pr.

Thomas, John Wesley & Lynn, Sandra. Thanksgiving: An Illustrated History. 2011. (Illus.). 160p. pap. 29.99 ***(978-0-7643-3829-8(3)***, Schiffer Publishing Ltd) Schiffer Publishing, Ltd.

Veith, Barbara & Frelinghuysen, Alice Cooney. Aesthetic Ambitions: Edward Lycett & Brooklyn's Faience Manufacturing Company. 2011. (Illus.). 119p. ***(978-0-9765047-9-5(0))*** Univ. of Richmond Museums.

Vigna, Lena. Provocative Clay. 2007. *(978-0-9710703-4-9(2))* Kohler, John Michael Arts Ctr.

ART POTTERY, BRITISH

Cariano, Annie. Contemporary British Studio Ceramics. 2010. (ENG., Illus.). 224p. 60.00 *(978-0-300-16719-1(9))* Yale Univ. Pr.

Casey, Andrew. Clarice Cliff. 2010. (ENG., Illus.). 144p. instr.'s gde. ed. *(978-1-85149-599-3(1)*, Antique Collectors Club Dist) Antique Collectors' Club.

Cooper, Emmanuel. David Leach: A Biography by Emmanuel Cooper. 2006. (ENG., Illus.). pap. 45.00 *(978-0-903685-88-7(4)*, Richard Dennis Pubns. Di) Antique Collectors' Club GBR. Dist: National Bk. Network.

de Waal, Edmund. The Hare with Amber Eyes (Illustrated Edition) A Family's Century of Art & Loss. 2012. (ENG., Illus.). 368p. 26.00 ***(978-0-374-16828-5(3))*** Farrar, Straus & Giroux.

Whiting, David. Modern British Potters & Their Studios. 2012. (ENG., Illus.). 160p. 45.00 ***(978-0-7136-8732-3(0))*** A & C Black GBR. Dist: Macmillan.

ART ROBBERIES

see Art Thefts

ART SCHOOLS

see also Art—Study and Teaching

Armleder, John & Marks, Lisa. Piero Golia: Desert Interviews or How to Jump off the Roof & Not Hit the Ground. 2011. (ENG., Illus.). 100p. pap. 28.00 *(978-3-03764-106-4(1))* JRP Ringier Kunstverlag AG CHE. Dist: D.A.P./Distributed Art Pubs.

Avery, Charles. A School of Dolphins. 2009. (ENG., Illus.). 240p. 35.00 *(978-0-500-23861-5(8)*, 523861) Thames & Hudson.

Buckley, Brad & Conomos, John, eds. Rethinking the Contemporary Art School: The Artist, the PhD, & the Academy. 2010. (ENG.). 237p. pap. 25.00 *(978-0-919616-49-3(6))* Press of the Nova Scotia College of Art & Design CAN. Dist: D.A.P./Distributed Art Pubs.

Debono, Sandro & Scicluna, Bernadine. The Busuttil Family: A Legacy of Three Generations. 2010. (Illus.). 136p. pap. 52.00 *(978-99932-7-305-9(8))* Midsea Bks. Ltd. MLT. Dist: Brown, David Bk. Co., The.

Dietz, Donald, photos by. Celebrating West Side Story: North Carolina School of the Arts A 50th Anniversary Production. 2007. (Illus.). 144p. 50.00 *(978-0-9617507-0-1(7))*; (ENG., pap. 30.00 *(978-0-9617507-1-8(5))* North Carolina Schl. of the Arts Foundation, Inc.

Freedman, Tanya. Start & Run an Art Teaching Business. 2007. (Start & Run ... Ser.). (ENG., Illus.). 208p. pap. 18.95 *(978-1-55180-734-8(3))* Self-Counsel Pr., Inc. CAN. Dist: Midpoint Trade Bks., Inc.

Freeman, Helen. So You Want to Go to Drama School? 2011. (ENG.). 150p. pap. 20.95 ***(978-1-84842-016-8(1))*** Hern, Nick Bks., Ltd. GBR. Dist: Consortium Bk. Sales & Distribution.

Gifun, Frederick V. UMass Dartmouth, 1960-2006: Trials & Triumph. 2007. (Illus.). 416p. 49.00 *(978-0-9796830-0-8(9))* Univ. of Massachusetts Dartmouth.

Gore, Elaine Clift. Talent Knows No Color: The History of an Arts Magnet High School. 2007. (Research in Curriculum & Instruction Ser.). (ENG.). 196p. (C). *(978-1-59311-762-7(0))*; per. *(978-1-59311-761-0(2))* Information Age Publishing, Inc.

Hussey, Deborah. Monumental: The Reimagined World of Kevin O'Callaghan. 2010. (ENG., Illus.). 240p. 40.00 *(978-0-8109-8953-5(0))* Abrams.

Kiaer, Christina. Imagine No Possessions: The Socialist Objects of Russian Constructivism. 2008. (ENG., Illus.). 344p. (gr. 17). pap. 28.95 *(978-0-262-61221-0(6))* MIT Pr.

Loomis, John A. Revolution of Forms: Cuba's Forgotten Art Schools. rev. ed. 2011. (ENG., Illus.). 190p. pap. 29.95 *(978-1-56898-988-4(1))* Princeton Architectural Pr.

Mueller, Laura J. Competition & Collaboration: Japanese Prints of the Utagawa School. 2007. (Illus.). 231p. *(978-90-04-15539-8(2))* BRILL.

National Register Publishing, creator. American Art Directory. 63rd ed. 2008. (American Art Directory Ser.). 1035p. 371.25 *(978-0-87217-755-0(6))* National Register Publishing.

Nickless, Lea, text. Turning Twenty: Celebrating Two Decades of New World School of the Arts. 2007. per. 8.00 *(978-0-9795655-0-2(2))* New World School of the Arts.

Oswalt, Philipp, ed. The Bauhaus Debate 1919-2009, 1 vol. 2010. (ENG., Illus.). 304p. pap. 30.00 *(978-3-7757-2488-3(5))* Hatje Cantz Verlag GmbH & Co KG DEU. Dist: D.A.P./Distributed Art Pubs.

Peterson's Guides Staff. College Guide for Visual Arts Majors 2008: Real-World Admission Guide for All Fine Arts, Design, & Media Majors. Seghers, Linda, ed. 2007. (ENG., Illus.). 416p. pap. 24.00 *(978-0-7689-2423-7(5))* Peterson's.

Poletkina, Olga. School of Art for Juniors. 2011. 76p. pap. ***(978-3-8443-9902-8(X))*** Lambert Academic Publishing.

Sillevis, John & Tabak, Anne. The Hague School Book. 2006. Orig. Title: Le Livre de l'ecole de la Haye. (ENG., Illus.). 416p. 19.95 *(978-90-400-9037-0(8))* Waanders B.V., Uitgeverij NLD. Dist: National Bk. Network.

White, Kit. 101 Things to Learn in Art School. 2011. (ENG., Illus.). 224p. (gr. 17). 14.95 *(978-0-262-01621-6(4))* MIT Pr.

ART THEFTS

Alford, Kenneth D. Allied Looting in World War II: Thefts of Art, Manuscripts, Stamps & Jewelry in Europe. 2011. (ENG., Illus.). 288p. pap. 39.95 *(978-0-7864-6053-3(9))* McFarland & Co., Inc. Pubs.

Amore, Anthony M. & Mashberg, Tom. Stealing Rembrandts: The Untold Stories of Notorious Art Heists. 2011. (ENG., Illus.). 272p. 25.00 *(978-0-230-10853-0(9))* Palgrave Macmillan.

Amore, Anthony M. M. & Mashberg, Tom. Stealing Rembrandts: The Untold Stories of Notorious Art Heists. 2012. (ENG., Illus.). 272p. pap. 16.00 ***(978-0-230-33990-3(5))*** Palgrave Macmillan.

Anton, Michael. Illegaler Kulturgaterverkehr. 2010.Tr. of Illegal Trafficking of Cultural Goods & the International Art Trade. (GER.). XXXVI, 1301p. 419.00 ***(978-3-11-174020-1(X))*** De Gruyter, Walter Inc.

—Illegaler Kulturgüterverkehr. 2010.Tr. of Illegal Trafficking of Cultural Goods & the International Art Trade. (GER., Illus.). XXXVI, 1301p. 280.00 *(978-3-89949-722-9(8))* De Gruyter, Walter Inc.

—Internationales Kulturgüterprivat- und Zivilverfahrensrecht. 2010.Tr. of International Cultural Goods Private & Civil Procedural Law. (GER.). 800p. 280.00 *(978-3-89949-726-7(0))* De Gruyter Rechtswissenschaften Verlags GmbH DEU. Dist: de Gruyter, Walter GmbH & Co. KG.

—Rechtshandbuch Kulturgüterschutz und Kunstrestitutionsrecht. 2010. (GER., Illus.). XL, 1268p. 280.00 *(978-3-89949-724-3(4))* De Gruyter, Walter Inc.

Bazley, Thomas D. Crimes of the Art World, 1 vol. 2010. 230p. 44.95 *(978-0-313-36047-3(2)*, C36047, Praeger Pubs.) Greenwood Publishing Group, Inc.

Boser, Ulrich. The Gardner Heist: The True Story of the World's Largest Unsolved Art Theft. 2010. (ENG.). 272p. pap. 14.99 *(978-0-06-145184-3(3)*, Harper Paperbacks) HarperCollins Pubs.

—The Gardner Heist: The True Story of the World's Largest Unsolved Art Theft. 2009. (ENG., Illus.). 272p. 25.99 *(978-0-06-145183-6(5))* Smithsonian Institution Pr.

—The Gardner Heist: The True Story of the World's Largest Unsolved Art Theft. l.t. ed. 2009. 420p. 30.95 *(978-1-4104-1567-7(8))* Thorndike Pr.

Bundy, Barbara. Archaeological Looting & VanDalism in the Pacific Northwest. 2008. 304p. pap. *(978-3-639-06463-6(1))* VDM Verlag Dr. Mueller e.K.

Charney, Noah. Stealing the Mystic Lamb: The True Story of the World's Most Coveted Masterpiece. 2010. (ENG., Illus.). 336p. 27.95 *(978-1-58648-800-0(7))* PublicAffairs.

Coignard, Jerome. Une Femme Disparait: Le Vol de la Joconde Au Louvre en 1911. 2010. (FRE., Illus.). 358p. *(978-2-84742-156-9(4))* Passage, Uitgeverij.

Connor, Myles J. & Siler, Jenny. The Art of the Heist: Confessions of a Master Art Thief, Rock-and-Roller, & Prodigal Son. 2009. 304p. 26.99 *(978-0-06-167228-6(9))* HarperCollins Pubs.

—The Art of the Heist: Confessions of a Master Thief. 2010. (ENG.). 304p. pap. 14.99 *(978-0-06-167229-3(7)*, Harper Paperbacks) HarperCollins Pubs.

Edsel, Robert M. The Monuments Men: Allied Heroes, Nazi Thieves, & the Greatest Treasure Hunt in History. (ENG., Illus.). 2010. 512p. pap. 16.99 *(978-1-59995-150-8(9))* 2009. 496p. 26.99 *(978-1-59995-149-2(5))* Center St.

—Rescuing Da Vinci: Hitler & the Nazis Stole Europe's Great Art America & Her Allies Recovered It. 2006. (Illus.). 302p. 39.95 *(978-0-9774349-0-9(7))* Laurel Publishing, LLC.

Emberling, Geoff & Hanson, Katharyn, eds. Catastrophe! The Looting & Destruction of Iraq's Past. 2008. (Oriental Institute Museum Publications). (ENG., Illus.). 88p. (C). pap. 29.95 *(978-1-885923-56-1(2))* Oriental Institute of the Univ. of Chicago, The.

Felch, Jason & Frammolino, Ralph. Chasing Aphrodite: The Hunt for Looted Antiquities at the World's Richest Museum. 2011. (ENG., Illus.). 384p. 28.00 *(978-0-15-101501-6(5))* Houghton Mifflin Harcourt Trade & Reference Pubs.

Henry, Marilyn. Twice Stolen. 2008. *(978-0-8419-1452-0(4))* Holmes & Meier Pubs., Inc.

Hoobler, Dorothy & Hoobler, Thomas. The Crimes of Paris: A True Story of Murder, Theft, & Detection. 2009. (ENG., Illus.). 384p. 24.99 *(978-0-316-01790-9(6))* Little Brown & Co.

—The Crimes of Paris: A True Story of Murder, Theft, & Detection. 2010. (ENG., Illus.). 400p. pap. 19.95 *(978-0-8032-3432-1(5)*, Bison Bks.) Univ. of Nebraska Pr.

Houpt, Simon. Museum of the Missing: The High Stakes of Art Crime. 2009. (ENG.). 192p. pap. 24.95 *(978-1-897330-44-9(8))* Madison Pr. Bks. CAN. Dist: Independent Pubs. Group.

Jungblut, Marie-Paul. Looted! Current Questions Regarding the Cultural Looting by the National Socialists in Europe. 2008. (ENG.). 164p. pap. 38.00 *(978-3-422-06814-8(7)*, Art Stock Bks. Ltd/Csi) Continental Sales, Inc.

Kneiman, Joshua. Hot Art: Chasing Thieves & Detectives Through the Secret World of Stolen Art. 2012. (ENG.). 360p. pap. 16.95 ***(978-1-935639-38-1(2))*** Tin Hse. Bks., LLC.

Kurtz, Michael J. America & the Return of Nazi Contraband: The Recovery of Europe's Cultural Treasures. 2009. (ENG.). 288p. pap. 32.99 *(978-0-521-13340-1(8))* Cambridge Univ. Pr.

Manacorda, Stefano & Chappell, Duncan, eds. Crime in the Art & Antiquities World: Illegal Trafficking in Cultural Property. 2011. (ENG.). xii, 453p. 169.00 *(978-1-4419-7945-2(X)*, 144197945X) Springer.

McShane, Thomas. Stolen Masterpiece Tracker. 2006. (ENG., Illus.). 360p. 24.95 *(978-1-56980-314-1(5))* Barricade Bks., Inc.

Miles, Margaret Melanie. Art as Plunder: The Ancient Origins of Debate about Cultural Property. (ENG.). (C). 2009. 440p. pap. 34.99 *(978-0-521-17290-5(X))* 2008. (Illus.). 444p. 99.00 *(978-0-521-87280-5(4))* Cambridge Univ. Pr.

Muller, Melissa & Tatzkow, Monika. Lost Lives, Lost Art: Jewish Collectors, Nazi Art Theft, & the Quest for Justice. 2010. (ENG., Illus.). 248p. 40.00 *(978-0-86565-263-7(5))* Vendome Pr., The.

Nairne, Sandy. Art Theft & the Case of the Stolen Turners. 2011. (Illus.). 280p. 29.00 *(978-1-86189-851-7(7))* Reaktion Bks., Ltd. GBR. Dist: Chicago Distribution Ctr.

Noi, Chang. Jungle Book: Thailand's Politics, Moral Panic, & Plunder, 1996-2008. 2009. (ENG.). 255p. pap. 18.95 ***(978-974-9511-63-3(8))*** Silkworm Bks. THA. Dist: Univ. of Washington Pr.

Papadopoulos, Jeannette, ed. International Meeting on Illicit Traffic of Cultural Property. 2011. (Illus.). 224p. pap. 40.00 *(978-88-492-2037-7(5))* Gangemi ITA. Dist: International Publishers Marketing.

Renfrew, Colin. Loot, Legitimacy & Ownership: The Ethical Crisis in Archaeology. 2009. (Duckworth Debates in Archaeology). (Illus.). 160p. pap. 24.95 *(978-0-7156-3034-1(2))* Duckworth Publishers GBR. Dist: International Publishers Marketing.

Rudolph, Sabine. Restitution von Kunstwerken aus jüdischem Besitz: Dingliche Herausgabeansprüche nach deutschem Recht. 2007. (Schriften Zum Kulturgüterschutz / Cultural Property Studies). (GER.). XIX, 328p. 133.00 *(978-3-89949-436-5(9))* De Gruyter, Walter Inc.

Sandholtz, Wayne. Prohibiting Plunder: How Norms Change, 1 vol. 2007. (ENG., Illus.). 352p. 74.00 *(978-0-19-533723-5(9))* Oxford Univ. Pr., Inc.

Scotti, R. A. Vanished Smile: The Mysterious Theft of Mona Lisa. l.t. ed. 2009. (ENG.). 352p. pap. 23.95 *(978-0-7393-2836-1(0))* Random Hse. Large Print.

—Vanished Smile: The Mysterious Theft of the Mona Lisa. 2010. (Vintage Ser.). (Illus.). 256p. pap. 15.00 *(978-0-307-27838-8(7)*, Vintage) Knopf Doubleday Publishing Group.

Spurny, Till. Die Plünderung Von Kulturgütern in Peking 1900-1901. 2008. (GER.). 113p. *(978-3-86573-360-3(3)*, Spotlight Poets) Gaudig, Olaf, u. Klaus-Peter Veit, wvb Wissenschaftlicher Verlag Berlin.

Tuccille, Jerome. Gallery of Fools: The True Story of a Celebrated Manhattan Art Theft. 2008. 188p. per. 14.95 *(978-1-60008-032-6(4)*, Rooftop Publishing) AuthorHouse.

Ulph, Janet. The Illicit Trade in Art & Antiquities: International Recovery & Criminal & Civil Liability. 2012. 368p. 150.00 ***(978-1-84113-964-7(5))*** Hart Publishing Ltd. GBR. Dist: International Specialized Bk. Services.

Watson, Peter & Todeschini, Cecilia. The Medici Conspiracy: The Illicit Journey of Looted Antiquities, from Italy's Tomb Raiders to the World's Greatest Museums. annot. ed. 2007. (ENG., Illus.). 448p. per. 16.95 *(978-1-58648-438-5(9))* PublicAffairs.

Waxman, Sharon. Loot: The Battle over the Stolen Treasures of the Ancient World. (ENG., Illus.). 432p. 2009. pap. 18.00 *(978-0-8050-9088-8(6))* 2008. 30.00 *(978-0-8050-8653-9(6))* Holt, Henry & Co. (Times Bks.).

Webb, Jonathan. Stolen: The Gallery of Missing Masterpieces. 2009. (ENG., Illus.). 256p. 40.00 *(978-1-897330-35-7(9))* Madison Pr. Bks. CAN. Dist: Independent Pubs. Group.

Wittman, Robert K. & Shiffman, John. Priceless: How I Went Undercover to Rescue the World's Stolen Treasures. 2011. (ENG., Illus.). 336p. pap. 15.00 *(978-0-307-46148-3(3))* Broadway Bks.

ART THERAPY

Arnett, Margaret Carpenter. The Art of the Inner Journey: Symbol as Healing Agent. 2011. 196p. 29.99 ***(978-1-4568-8863-3(3))***; pap. 19.99 ***(978-1-4568-8862-6(5))*** Xlibris Corp.

Arrington, Doris Banowsky. Art, angst, & Trauma: Right Brain Interventions with Developmental Issues. 2007. (Illus.). 278p. *(978-0-398-07733-4(9))* Thomas, Charles C. Pub., Ltd.

—Art, angst, & Trauma: Right Brain Interventions with Development Issues. 2007. (Illus.). 278p. *(978-0-398-07732-7(0))* Thomas, Charles C. Pub., Ltd.

Bennett, Cat. The Confident Creative: Drawing to Free the Hand & Mind. 2010. (Illus.). 128p. pap. 14.95 *(978-1-84409-185-0(6))* Findhorn Pr. GBR. Dist: Independent Pubs. Group.

Brooke, Stephanie L. The Use of the Creative Therapies with Chemical Dependency Issues. 2009. 292p. 61.95 *(978-0-398-07861-4(0))*; pap. 41.95 *(978-0-398-07862-1(9))* Thomas, Charles C. Pub., Ltd.

—The Use of the Creative Therapies with Survivors of Domestic Violence. 2008. (Illus.). 370p. 85.95 *(978-0-398-07818-8(1))*; pap. 65.95 *(978-0-398-07819-5(X))* Thomas, Charles C. Pub., Ltd.

Brooke, Stephanie L., ed. The Use of the Creative Therapies with Autism Spectrum Disorders. 2009. 396p. 83.95 *(978-0-398-07891-1(2))*; pap. 59.95 *(978-0-398-07892-8(0))* Thomas, Charles C. Pub., Ltd.

—The Use of the Creative Therapies with Sexual abuse Survivors. 2007. (Illus.). 342p. 74.95 *(978-0-398-07701-3(0))* Thomas, Charles C. Pub., Ltd.

Brown Treadon, Carolyne. Art Therapy As an Agent for Change. 2008. 256p. per. *(978-3-8364-3491-1(1))* VDM Verlag Dr. Mueller e.K.

Buchalter, Susan I. Art Therapy & Creative Coping Techniques for Older Adults. 2011. (ENG., Illus.). 328p. pap. *(978-1-84905-830-8(X))* Kingsley, Jessica Ltd.

Bull, Stephanie & O'Farrell, Kevin, eds. Art Therapy for People with Learning Disabilities. 2012. (ENG., Illus.). 200p. (C). 128.00 ***(978-0-415-58323-7(3))***; pap. 31.95 ***(978-0-415-58324-4(1))*** Routledge.

Burt, Helene, ed. Art Therapy & Postmodernism: Creative Healing Through a Prism. 2011. (ENG., Illus.). 400p. pap. ***(978-1-84905-253-5(0))*** Kingsley, Jessica Ltd.

Camilleri, Vanessa A. Healing the Inner City Child: Creative Art Therapies with At-Risk Youth. 2007. (ENG., Illus.). 32p. per. *(978-1-84310-824-5(0))* Kingsley, Jessica Ltd.

Campanaro, Judith. Art for the Soul: The Healing Power of Creativity. 2006. (Illus.). 136p. per. 19.95 *(978-0-9749610-6-4(X)*, Creative Minds Pr.) Beagle Bay Bks.

A

Campbell, Jean, et al. Creative Art in Groupwork. 204p. spiral bd. *(978-0-86388-409-2(1),* 002-1544) Speechmark Publishing Ltd.
Carpendale, Monica. Essence & Praxis in the Art Therapy Studio. 2009. 256p. pap. 25.00 *(978-1-4269-1591-8(8))* Trafford Publishing.
Carpendale, Monica. A Traveler's Guide to Art Therapy Supervision. 2011. 196p. pap. 14.77 ***(978-1-4269-8991-9(1))*** Trafford Publishing.
Case, Caroline. Art Therapy with Children: From Infancy to Adolescence. Dalley, Tessa, ed. 2007. (ENG., Illus.). 288p. (C). 39.95 *(978-0-415-38630-2(6))* Routledge.
Case, Caroline & Dalley, Tessa. Art Therapy with Children: From Infancy to Adolescence. 2007. (ENG., Illus.). 288p. (C). 120.00 *(978-0-415-38629-6(2))* Routledge.
—Handbook Art Therapy. 2nd rev. ed. 2006. (ENG., Illus.). 328p. 110.00 *(978-1-58391-791-6(8));* per. 39.95 *(978-1-58391-792-3(6))* Routledge.
Challenger, Mary. The Long Road: Coping with Depression Through Art. 2009. (Illus.). 70p. 21.95 *(978-1-84624-364-6(5))* Book Guild, Ltd. GBR. Dist: Trans-Atlantic Pubns., Inc.
Chwast, Debra. An Unexpected Life: Speaking Through Art. 2011. (ENG., Illus.). 224p. 27.95 *(978-1-4027-7403-4(6))* Sterling Publishing Co., Inc.
Clacherty, Glynis. The Suitcase Stories: Refugee Children Reclaim Their Identities. 2008. (Illus.). 184p. pap. 29.95 *(978-1-919930-99-2(X))* Double Storey Bks. ZAF. Dist: International Publishers Marketing.
Cockey, E. J. Drawn from Memory: A personal story of healing through Art. 2008. 168p. pap. 13.95 *(978-1-934925-16-4(0),* Strategic Bk. Publishing) AEG Literary Publishing Services, Inc.
Cockey, Elizabeth Jane. Drawn from Memory: A Personal Story of Healing Through Art. 2007. (ENG.). 168p. per. 13.95 *(978-0-9790275-1-2(9))* Ovation Bks.
Combrinck, Celeste. The Psychological Implications of Creative Activities. 2010. 112p. pap. *(978-3-639-26532-3(7))* VDM Verlag Dr. Mueller e.K.
Creative Center Staff. Still Life: Documenting Cancer Survivorship. 2007. (ENG., Illus.). 80p. per. 29.95 *(978-1-884167-65-2(9))* Umbrage Editions.
Culbreth, John R. & Brown, Lori. State of the Art in Clinical Supervision. 2009. (ENG., Illus.). 253p. 49.95 *(978-0-415-99130-8(7))* Routledge.
Darley, Suzanne & Heath, Wende. The Expressive Arts: A Resource for Professionals. 2007. (ENG., Illus.). 224p. pap., act. bk. ed. *(978-1-84310-861-0(5))* Kingsley, Jessica Ltd.
David, Irene R. & Buckley, Mary, eds. Weaving New Visions: Art Therapy in Collaboration with Allied Professions. 178p. (Orig.). pap. 20.00 *(978-1-882147-50-2(2))* American Art Therapy Assn.
Dolce, Sylvia. Art Therapy in Psychosomatic Medicine. 2010. 76p. pap. *(978-3-8383-5083-7(9))* Lambert Academic Publishing.
Duffey, Thelma. Creative Interventions in Grief & Loss Therapy: When the Music Stops, a Dream Dies. 2007. (ENG.). 348p. pap. 52.95 *(978-0-7890-3554-7(5));* (Illus.). 125.00 *(978-0-7890-3553-0(7))* Routledge.
Ficko, Alenka. Art Therapy in Retirement Home. 2010. 156p. pap. *(978-3-639-22284-5(9))* VDM Verlag Dr. Mueller e.K.
Fowler, Susan. Sensory Stimulation: Sensory-Focused Activities for People with Physical & Multiple Disabilities. 2006. (ENG., Illus.). 176p. per. *(978-1-84310-455-1(5))* Kingsley, Jessica Ltd.
Frank, Rita. Art of the Heart: How to Understand & Help People with Alzheimer's & Related Disorders, Book I. 2008. pap. 11.00 *(978-0-8059-8950-2(1))* Dorrance Publishing Co., Inc.
Ganß, Michael & Sinapius, Peter, eds. Ich seh dich so gern Sprechen: Sprache im Bezugsfeld von Praxis und Dokumentation künstlerischer Therapien. 2008. (Wissenschaftliche Grundlagen der Kunsttherapie Ser.). 290p. pap. 74.95 *(978-3-631-56624-4(7))* Lang, Peter GmbH, Europaischer Verlag der Wissenschaften DEU. Dist: Lang, Peter.
Gilroy, Andrea. Art Therapy, Research & Evidence-Based Practice. 2006. (Illus.). 192p. (C). 119.00 *(978-0-7619-4113-2(4),* B41134C); per. 50.00 *(978-0-7619-4114-9(2),* B41134P) SAGE Pubns., Ltd. GBR. Dist: SAGE Pubns., Inc.
—Art Therapy Research in Practice. 2011. (Illus.). 322p. pap. 70.95 *(978-3-03911-994-3(X))* Lang, Peter AG GBR. Dist: Lang, Peter.
Gilroy, Andrea, et al, eds. Assessment in Art Therapy. 2012. (ENG., Illus.). 240p. (C). 100.00 ***(978-0-415-56794-7(7));*** pap. 34.95 ***(978-0-415-56796-1(3))*** Routledge.
Grace, Cathy & Shores, Elizabeth F. After the Crisis: Using Storybooks to Help Children Cope. 2010. (ENG.). 64p. pap. 9.95 *(978-0-87659-129-1(2))* Gryphon Hse., Inc.
Grey, Alex. Art Psalms. 2008. (ENG., Illus.). 204p. 24.95 *(978-1-55643-756-4(0))* North Atlantic Bks.
Gunter, Michael. Winnicott's Squiggle Technique Practi. 2007. 223p. pap. 38.95 *(978-1-85575-419-5(3))* Karnac Bks. GBR. Dist: Stylus Publishing, LLC.
Hartley, Nigel & Payne, Malcolm, eds. The Creative Arts in Palliative Care. 2008. (ENG., Illus.). 208p. pap. *(978-1-84310-591-6(8))* Kingsley, Jessica Ltd.
Hass-Cohen, et al. Art Therapy & Clinical Neuroscience. 2008. (ENG., Illus.). 336p. pap. ***(978-1-84310-868-9(2))*** Kingsley, Jessica Ltd.
Hayes, Jill. The Creative Arts in Dementia Care: Practical Person-Centred Approaches & Ideas. 2010. (ENG.). 176p. pap. *(978-1-84905-056-2(2))* Kingsley, Jessica Ltd.
Heer, I. M. The Pathless Path. 2009. 64p. pap. 31.99 *(978-1-4415-0487-6(7))* Xlibris Corp.
Hinz, Lisa. Expressive Therapies Continuum: A Framework for Using Art in Therapy. 2009. (ENG., Illus.). 309p. pap. 43.95 *(978-0-415-99585-6(X))* Routledge.
Hinz, Lisa D. Drawing from Within: Using Art to Treat Eating Disorders. 2006. (ENG., Illus.). 16p. per. *(978-1-84310-822-1(4))* Kingsley, Jessica Ltd.
—Expressive Therapies Continuum: A Framework for Using Art in Therapy. 2009. (ENG., Illus.). 309p. 135.00 *(978-0-415-96347-3(8))* Routledge.
Horovitz, Ellen G. Visually Speaking: Art Therapy & the Deaf. 2007. 250p. *(978-0-398-07715-0(0));* pap. *(978-0-398-07716-7(9))* Thomas, Charles C. Pub., Ltd.
Horovitz, Ellen G. & Eksten, Sarah/L, eds. The Art Therapists' Primer: A Clinical Guide to Writing Assessments, Diagnosis, & Treatment. 2009. 332p. 85.95 *(978-0-398-07840-9(8));* pap. 55.95 *(978-0-398-07841-6(6))* Thomas, Charles C. Pub., Ltd.
Hunter, Margaret R. Reflections of Body Image in Art Therapy: Exploring Self through Metaphor & Multi-Media. 2012. (ENG., Illus.). 176p. pap. ***(978-1-84905-892-6(X))*** Kingsley, Jessica Ltd.
Joe S. Outside the Lines. (Illus.). 69p. stu. ed. 10.95 *(978-1-880998-03-8(3))* State of the Art Publishing, Inc.
Johnson, Paul & St Thomas, Bruce. Empowering Children Through Art & Expression: Culturally Sensitive Ways of Healing Trauma & Grief. 2007. (ENG., Illus.). 224p. per. *(978-1-84310-789-7(9))* Kingsley, Jessica Ltd.
Joiner, Lindsay. Creativity Unleashed: Therapeutic Activities & Character Education Ideas for Working with Children & Teens. 2011. (Illus.). 256p. pap. ***(978-1-84905-865-0(2))*** Kingsley, Jessica Ltd.
Junge, Maxine B. Mourning, Memory & Life Itself: Essays by an Art Therapist. 2008. (Illus.). 292p. 61.95 *(978-0-398-07827-0(0));* pap. 41.95 *(978-0-398-07828-7(9))* Thomas, Charles C. Pub., Ltd.
Junge, Maxine Borowsky. The Modern History of Art Therapy in the United States. 2010. 370p. *(978-0-398-07940-6(4));* pap. *(978-0-398-07941-3(2))* Thomas, Charles C. Pub., Ltd.
Junge, Maxine Borowsky & Wadeson, Harriet, eds. Architects of art Therapy: Memoirs & Life Stories. 2006. (Illus.). 430p. 78.95 *(978-0-398-07685-6(5));* pap. 56.95 *(978-0-398-07686-3(3))* Thomas, Charles C. Pub., Ltd.
Kapitan, Lynn. An Introduction to Art Therapy Research. 2010. (ENG., Illus.). 328p. (C). 42.95 *(978-0-415-87147-1(6))* Routledge.
Kaplan, Frances F., ed. Art Therapy & Social Action. 2006. (ENG., Illus.). 272p. per. *(978-1-84310-798-9(8))* Kingsley, Jessica Ltd.
Karkou, Vicky, ed. Art Therapies in Schools: Research & Practice. (ENG., Illus.). 256p. pap. 39.95 *(978-1-84310-633-3(7))* Kingsley, Jessica Ltd. GBR. Dist: Books International, Inc.
Kerr, Christine, et al. Family Art Therapy: Foundations of Theory & Practice. 2007. (Family Therapy & Counseling Ser.). (ENG., Illus.). 264p. 44.95 *(978-0-415-95464-8(9))* Routledge.
Killick, John & Craig, Claire. Creativity & Communication in Persons with Dementia: A Practical Guide. 2011. (ENG., Illus.). 224p. pap. ***(978-1-84905-113-2(5))*** Kingsley, Jessica Ltd.
Kuri, Erin L. Helping to Make Them See. 2008. 80p. pap. *(978-3-639-03411-0(2))* VDM Verlag Dr. Mueller e.K.
Lafo, Rachel R., et al. Body & Soul: Contemporary Art & Healing. Date not set. 80p. (Orig.). pap. *(978-0-945506-15-7(5))* DeCordova Museum & Sculpture Park.
Levick, Myra F. Levick Emotional & Cognitive Art Therapy Assessment: A Normative Study. 2009. 204p. pap. 30.00 *(978-1-4389-4377-0(6))* AuthorHouse.
Lewis, Richard & Lewis, Susan I. The Power of Art. 2nd rev. ed. 2008. (ENG., Illus.). 528p. (Orig.). (C). per. 113.95 *(978-0-495-50191-6(3))* Wadsworth.
Liebmann, Marian, ed. Art Therapy & Anger. 2008. (ENG., Illus.). 256p. (C). pap. *(978-1-84310-425-4(3))* Kingsley, Jessica Ltd.
Luginbuehl-Oelhafen, Ruth/R. Art Therapy with Chronic Physically Ill Adolescents: Exploring the Effectiveness of Medical Art Therapy as a Complementary Treatment. 2009. 220p. pap. 37.95 *(978-0-398-07857-7(2))* Thomas, Charles C. Pub., Ltd.
Madori, Linda Levine. Therapeutic Thematic Arts Programming for Older Adults. 2007. (Illus.). 186p. 52.00 *(978-1-932529-03-6(9));* per. 38.00 *(978-1-932529-02-9(0))* Health Professions Pr.
Malchiodi, Cathy A. The Art Therapy. 2nd rev. ed. 2006. (Sourcebooks Ser.). (ENG., Illus.). 288p. per. 19.95 *(978-0-07-146827-5(7),* 0071468277) McGraw-Hill Cos., The.
Malchiodi, Cathy A., ed. Art Therapy. (Journal of the American Art Therapy Association Ser.: Vol. 10, No. 4). (Illus.). (C). pap. 18.00 *(978-1-882147-45-8(6))* American Art Therapy Assn.
—Creative Interventions with Traumatized Children. 2008. (ENG., Illus.). 332p. 40.00 *(978-1-59385-615-1(6))* Guilford Pubns., Inc.
Martin, Nicole. Art as an Early Intervention Tool for Children with Autism. 2009. (ENG., Illus.). 160p. pap. *(978-1-84905-807-0(5))* Kingsley, Jessica Ltd.
Martynova, Tamara & Xu, Mingtang. Zhong Yuan Qigong: First stage of Ascent. 2009. 484p. pap. 29.95 *(978-0-595-46628-3(1))* iUniverse, Inc.
McNiff, Shaun. Integrating the Arts in Therapy: History, Theory, & Practice. 2009. 280p. 59.95 *(978-0-398-07868-3(8));* pap. 39.95 *(978-0-398-07869-0(6))* Thomas, Charles C. Pub., Ltd.
Moon, Bruce L. Art-Based Group Therapy: Theory & Practice. 2010. (Illus.). 180p. pap. *(978-0-398-07961-1(7));* xxi, 157p. E-Book *(978-0-398-08315-1(0))* Thomas, Charles C. Pub., Ltd.
—Existential Art Therapy: The Canvas Mirror. 3rd ed. 2009. 284p. 64.95 *(978-0-398-07844-7(0));* pap. 44.95 *(978-0-398-07845-4(9))* Thomas, Charles C. Pub., Ltd.
—Introduction to Art Therapy: Faith in the Product. 2nd ed. 2008. (Illus.). 226p. *(978-0-398-07796-9(7));* pap. *(978-0-398-07797-6(5))* Thomas, Charles C. Pub., Ltd.
—The Role of Metaphor in Art Therapy: Theory, Method, & Experience. 2007. 154p. *(978-0-398-07752-5(5));* pap. *(978-0-398-07753-2(3))* Thomas, Charles C. Pub., Ltd.
Moon, Catherine Hyland, ed. Materials & Media in Art Therapy: Critical Understandings of Diverse Artistic Vocabularies. 2010. (ENG., Illus.). 335p. 52.95 *(978-0-415-99313-5(X))* Routledge.
Murphy, Nora & McDonald, John. The Message of a Master: A Classic Tale of Wealth, Wisdom, & the Secret of Success. 2009. (ENG.). 208p. pap. 14.00 *(978-1-57731-657-2(6))* New World Library.
Paret, Peter & Thieme, Helga. Myth & Modernity: Barlach's Drawings on the Nibelungen. 2012. (ENG.). 198p. 34.95 ***(978-0-85745-349-5(1))*** Berghahn Bks., Inc.
Pearman, Heather. Art Therapy for Children of All Ages. 2007. 104p. per. 33.95 *(978-1-4327-0672-2(1))* Outskirts Pr., Inc.
Rappaport, Laury. Focusing-Oriented Art Therapy: Accessing the Body's Wisdom & Creative Intelligence. 2008. (ENG., Illus.). 240p. pap. *(978-1-84310-760-6(0))* Kingsley, Jessica Ltd.
Rubin, Judith. The Art of Art Therapy: What Every Art Therapist Needs to Know. 2nd rev. ed. 2011. (ENG., Illus.). 304p. 49.95 *(978-0-415-96094-6(0))* Routledge.
—Art Therapy: Sources & Resources. 2nd rev. ed. 2009. (ENG., Illus.). 356p. 55.95 *(978-0-415-96093-9(2))* Routledge.
Samuels, Michael & Lane, Mary Rockwood. Creative Healing: How to Heal Yourself by Tapping Your Hidden Creativity. 2011. 304p. pap. 33.00 *(978-1-61097-045-7(4),* Resource Pubns.) Wipf & Stock Pubs.
Schaverien. Supervision in Art Psychotherapy: A Theoretical & Practical Handbook. 2007. (Supervision in the Arts Therapies Ser.). (ENG., Illus.). 256p. (C). 37.50 *(978-0-415-40961-2(6))* Routledge.
Schaverien, Joy & Case, Caroline, eds. Supervision of Art Psychotherapy: A Theoretical & Practical Handbook. 2007. (Supervision in the Arts Therapies Ser.). (ENG., Illus.). 256p. (C). 110.00 *(978-0-415-40960-5(8))* Routledge.
Schellenberg, Susan & Barnes, Rosemary. Committed to the Sane Asylum: Narratives on Mental Wellness & Healing. 2008. (GER & ENG., Illus.). 320p. pap. 32.95 *(978-1-55458-034-7(X))* Wilfrid Laurier Univ. Pr. CAN. Dist: Univ. of Toronto Pr.
Shalmon, Maya. Self-Mutilation: Pathology & Performance. 2008. 80p. pap. *(978-3-639-02980-2(1))* VDM Verlag Dr. Mueller e.K.
Snow, Stephen & D'Amico, Miranda, eds. Assessment in the Creative Arts Therapies: Designing & Adapting Assessment Tools for Adults with Developmental Disabilities. 2009. 338p. 65.95 *(978-0-398-07887-4(4));* pap. 45.95 *(978-0-398-07888-1(2))* Thomas, Charles C. Pub., Ltd.
Spring, Dee, ed. Art in Treatment: Transatlantic Dialogue. 2006. (Illus.). 268p. 55.95 *(978-0-398-07689-4(8));* pap. 37.95 *(978-0-398-07690-0(1))* Thomas, Charles C. Pub., Ltd.
Stepney, Stella A. Art Therapy with Students at Risk: Fostering Resilience & Growth Through Self-Expression. 2nd ed. 2009. 222p. pap. 38.95 *(978-0-398-07898-0(X))* Thomas, Charles C. Pub., Ltd.
—Art Therapy with Students at Risk: Fostering Resilience & Growth Through SelfpExpression. 2nd ed. 2009. 222p. 56.95 *(978-0-398-07897-3(1))* Thomas, Charles C. Pub., Ltd.
Thomashoff, Hans-Otto & Sukhanova, Ekaterina. The Person in Art: Conceptual & Pictorial Frames on Art & Mental Health. 2008. 98.00 *(978-1-60456-922-3(0))* Nova Science Pubs., Inc.
Thompson, Jason. Dying, Bereavement, & Healing Arts. Bolton, Gillie, ed. 2007. (ENG., Illus.). 216p. *(978-1-84310-516-9(0))* Kingsley, Jessica Ltd.
Tubbs, Carol & Drake, Margaret. Crafts & Creative Media in Therapy. 4th ed. 2012. 300p. (C). pap. 53.95 ***(978-1-55642-976-7(2))*** SLACK, Inc.
Tubbs, Janet. Creative Therapy for Children with Autism, Add, & Asperger's: Using Artistic Creativity to Reach, Teach, & Touch Our Children. 2008. (ENG.). 224p. pap. 18.95 *(978-0-7570-0300-4(1))* Square One Pubs.
Underwood, Pamela & Pamela, Underwood. Bodywriting Retreats for Women: How Does the Practice of Expressive Arts Therapy Help to Establish & Maintain a Safe Container for the Messy Chaos of the Creative Process? 2011. 196p. pap. ***(978-3-639-32090-9(5))*** VDM Verlag Dr. Mueller e.K.
Volkman, Marian K. Children & Traumatic Incident Reduction: Creative & Cognitive Approaches. 2007. (TIR Applications Ser.: No. 2). (ENG., Illus.). 220p. per. *(978-1-932690-30-9(1))* Loving Healing Pr., Inc.
Wacker, Anita. Therapists' Art & Traum. 2008. 208p. pap. *(978-3-639-01778-6(1))* VDM Verlag Dr. Mueller e.K.
Wadeson, Harriet. Art Psychotherapy. 2nd ed. 2010. (ENG., Illus.). 592p. 55.00 *(978-0-470-41700-3(5),* Wiley) Wiley, John & Sons, Inc.
Warren, Bernie, ed. Using the Creative Arts in Therapy & Healthcare: A Practical Introduction. 3rd rev. ed. 2008. (ENG., Illus.). 288p. 37.50 *(978-0-415-40404-4(5))* Routledge.
—Using the Creative Arts in Therapy & Healthcare: A Practical Introduction. 3rd rev. ed. 2008. (ENG., Illus.). 288p. 110.00 *(978-0-415-40403-7(7))* Routledge.
Warren, Frank. A Lifetime of Secrets: A Postsecret Book. 2007. (ENG., Illus.). 288p. 28.99 *(978-0-06-123860-4(0),* Morrow, William & Co.) HarperCollins Pubs.
—My Secret. 2006. (ENG., Illus.). 125p. 21.99 *(978-0-06-119668-3(1),* Morrow, William & Co.) HarperCollins Pubs.
—PostSecret: Confessions on Life, Death, & God. 2009. (ENG.). 288p. 22.99 *(978-0-06-185933-5(8),* Morrow, William & Co.) HarperCollins Pubs.
—The Secret Lives of Men & Women: A PostSecret Book. 2007. (ENG., Illus.). 125p. 21.99 *(978-0-06-119875-5(7),* Morrow, William & Co.) HarperCollins Pubs.
Williams, Lesley Duggins & Atkins, Sally S. Sourcebook in Expressive Arts Therapy. 2007. (Illus.). 134p. per. 24.95 *(978-1-933251-37-0(9))* Parkway Pubs., Inc.
Winkel, Michelle & Junge, Maxine Borowsky. Graphic Facilitation & Art Therapy: Imagery & Metaphor in Organizational Development. 2012. (Illus.). 178p. pap. 35.95 ***(978-0-398-08738-8(5))*** Thomas, Charles C. Pub., Ltd.
Wood, Chris. Critical Dict Art Therapy. 2010. (ENG., Illus.). 336p. (C). 99.00 *(978-0-415-22318-8(0));* pap. 39.95 *(978-0-415-22319-5(9))* Routledge.

ART TO WEAR

see Wearable Art

ART TREASURES, PROTECTION OF

see Cultural Property—Protection

ART TREASURES IN WAR

see also World War, 1939-1945—Art and the War

Alford, Kenneth D. Allied Looting in World War II: Thefts of Art, Manuscripts, Stamps & Jewelry in Europe. 2011. (ENG., Illus.). 288p. pap. 39.95 *(978-0-7864-6053-3(9))* McFarland & Co., Inc. Pubs.
Barenboim, Petr & Zakharov, Aleksandr, trs. Pakt Rerikha V XXI Veke: K Semidesiatipiatiletiiu Podpisaniia. 2010. (RUS., Illus.). 159p. *(978-5-98856-113-2(6))* Letnij Sad, izdatel'sko-torgovyj dom.
Bosman, Suzanne. The National Gallery in Wartime. 2008. (ENG., Illus.). 128p. pap. 24.95 *(978-1-85709-424-4(7))* Yale Univ. Pr.
Brey, Ilaria Dagnini. The Venus Fixers: The Remarkable Story of the Allied Soldiers Who Saved Italy's Art During World War II. 2010. (ENG., Illus.). 336p. pap. 16.00 *(978-0-312-42990-4(8))* Picador.
Dolnick, Edward. The Forger's Spell: A True Story of Vermeer, Nazis, & the Greatest Art Hoax of the Twentieth Century. 2009. (P. S. Ser.). (ENG.). 384p. pap. 15.99 *(978-0-06-082542-3(1),* HarperPerennial) HarperCollins Pubs.
Edsel, Robert M. The Monuments Men: Allied Heroes, Nazi Thieves, & the Greatest Treasure Hunt in History. 2009. (ENG., Illus.). 496p. 26.99 *(978-1-59995-149-2(5))* Center St.
—Rescuing Da Vinci: Hitler & the Nazis Stole Europe's Great Art America & Her Allies Recovered It. 2006. (Illus.). 302p. 39.95 *(978-0-9774349-0-9(7))* Laurel Publishing, LLC.
Karlsgodt, Elizabeth Campbell. Defending National Treasures: French Art & Heritage under Vichy. 2011. (ENG., Illus.). 404p. 60.00 *(978-0-8047-7018-7(2))* Stanford Univ. Pr.
Kirkpatrick, Sidney. Hitler's Holy Relics: A True Story of Nazi Plunder & the Race to Recover the Crown Jewels of the Holy Roman Empire. 2011. (ENG., Illus.). 336p. pap. 15.00 *(978-1-4165-9063-7(3))* Simon & Schuster.
Miles, Margaret Melanie. Art as Plunder: The Ancient Origins of Debate about Cultural Property. (ENG.). (C). 2009. 440p. pap. 34.99 *(978-0-521-17290-5(X))* 2008. (Illus.). 444p. 99.00 *(978-0-521-87280-5(4))* Cambridge Univ. Pr.
Sanchez-Jauregui Alpanes, Maria Dolores & Wilcox, Scott, eds. The English Prize: The Capture of the Westmorland, an Episode of the Grand Tour. 2012. (ENG., Illus.). 400p. 75.00 ***(978-0-300-17605-6(8))*** Yale Univ. Pr.
Spurny, Till. Die Plünderung Von Kulturgütern in Peking 1900-1901. 2008. (GER.). 113p. *(978-3-86573-360-3(3),* Spotlight Poets) Gaudig, Olaf, u. Klaus-Peter Veit, wvb Wissenschaftlicher Verlag Berlin.
Weiss, Wolfgang. Vorsicht, Marmor - nicht stürzen! Die wahre Geschichte über die Rettung der Kunstschätze in den Salinen von Altaussee 1945. 2009. (Illus.). 80p. pap. *(978-3-902475-77-0(3))* Stocker, Leopold Verlag.

ART TYPING

Leisure Arts Staff. Creating Keepsakes: You've Got Flair! — Creative Scrapbook Techniques & More. 2008. (ENG., Illus.). 288p. pap. 18.95 *(978-1-60140-527-2(8))* Leisure Arts, Inc.
Oar, Ross. Carving Wooden Santas, Elves & Gnomes: 28 Patterns for Hand-Carved Christmas Ornaments & Figures. 2008. (Woodcarving Illustrated Bks.). (ENG., Illus.). 95p. pap. 16.95 *(978-1-56523-383-6(2))* Fox Chapel Publishing Co., Inc.
Western, David. Fine Art of Carving Lovespoons: Understanding, Designing, & Carving Romantic Heirlooms. 2008. (ENG., Illus.). 200p. pap. 24.95 *(978-1-56523-374-4(3))* Fox Chapel Publishing Co., Inc.

ARTAGNAN, CHARLES DE BAATZ DE CASTELMORE, STYLING HIMSELF COMTE DE, 1611-1673

Nevill, Ralph. Memoirs of Monsieur Dartagnan. 2008. 356p. *(978-1-4437-2417-3(3),* Hesperides Pr.) Read Bks.

ARTAUD, ANTONIN, 1896-1948

Barber, Stephen. Antonin Artaud: Terminal Curses: The Notebooks, 1945-48. 2008. (Solar lit Directives 1 Ser.). (ENG., Illus.). 152p. pap. 15.95 *(978-0-9799847-6-1(9))* Solar Bks.
—The Last Words of Antonin Artaud. 2008. (Illus.). 160p. 55.00 *(978-1-86189-384-0(1))* Reaktion Bks., Ltd. GBR. Dist: Chicago Distribution Ctr.
Bradu, Fabienne. Artaud, Todavía. 2009. (Vida y Pensamiento de México Ser.). (SPA.). 196p. pap. 14.95 *(978-968-16-8458-7(3))* Fondo de Cultura Economica USA.
De Vos, Laurens. Cruelty & Desire in the Modern Theater: Antonin Artaud, Sarah Kane, & Samuel Beckett. 2011. (ENG.). 256p. 75.00 *(978-1-61147-044-4(7))* 2010. *(978-0-8386-4263-4(2))* Fairleigh Dickinson Univ. Pr.

Jannarone, Kimberly. Artaud & His Doubles. 2010. (Theater: Theory/Text/Performance Ser.). (ENG.). 272p. 55.00 *(978-0-472-11736-9(X))* Univ. of Michigan Pr.
Jones, Andy. Artaud & Strasberg A Quest for Reality. 2008. 96p. pap. 14.95 *(978-1-4092-2968-1(8))* Lulu Enterprises Inc.
Tribbett, Mitchell. Necessary Cruelty. 2008. 64p. pap. *(978-3-639-02868-3(6))* VDM Verlag Dr. Mueller e.K.

ARTEMISIA TRIDENTATA
see Sagebrush

ARTERIAL GRAFTS
Fogarty, Thomas J. & White, Rodney A. Peripheral Endovascular Interventions. 3rd ed. 2010. (Illus.). xix, 512p. E-Book *(978-1-4419-1387-6(4))* Springer.
He, Guo-Wei, ed. Arterial Grafting for Coronary Artery Bypass Surgery. 2nd ed. 2010. (Illus.). xix, 356p. pap. 339.00 *(978-3-642-06761-7(1)*, 3642067611) Springer.
Henry, Mitchell L. Vascular Access for Hemodialysis-X. 2007. *(978-1-56625-950-7(9))* Precept Pr.

ARTERIES
see also Aorta; Blood—Circulation; Blood-Vessels; Carotid Artery; Coronary Arteries; Veins
Antel, J., et al, eds. Pulmonary Arterial Hypertension - Focusing on a Future: Enhancing & Extending Life, Volume 10 Solvay Pharmaceuticals Conferences. 2010. 167.00 *(978-1-60750-601-0(7))* IOS Pr., Inc.
Caralis, Dennis G. & Bakris, George L., eds. Lower Extremity Arterial Disease. 2010. (Clinical Hypertension & Vascular Diseases Ser.). (Illus.). 320p. pap. 119.00 *(978-1-61737-639-9(6)*, 1617376396) Humana Pr.
Galen & Garofalo, Ivan. L'anatomie des Nerfs: L'anatomie des Veines et des Artères. 2008. (FRE & GEC.). 224p. (C). pap. 68.00 ***(978-2-251-00544-7(7))*** Societe d'edition Les Belles lettres FRA. Dist: ISD.
Halpern, William, et al. The Resistance Arteries: Integration of the Regulatory Pathways. 2010. (Experimental Biology & Medicine Ser.). 384p. pap. 179.00 *(978-1-61737-008-3(8)*, 1617370088) Humana Pr.
Nichols, Wilmer W., et al. McDonald's Blood Flow in Arteries: Theoretical, Experimental & Clinical Principles. 6th rev. ed. 2011. (ENG., Illus.). 768p. 198.50 *(978-0-340-98501-4(1))* Hodder Arnold Pubs.
Norgaard, Martin A. Bronchial Artery Revascularization in Lung Transplantation. 2009. 76p. pap. *(978-3-639-13387-5(0))* VDM Verlag Dr. Mueller e.K.
Saito, Shigeru. Chronic Total Occlusions. Saito, Shigeru & Waksman, Ron, eds. 2009. (ENG., Illus.). 256p. 146.95 *(978-1-4051-5703-2(8)*, Wiley-Blackwell) Wiley, John & Sons, Inc.
Wittram, Conrad. Atlas of Pulmonary Vascular Imaging: A Multimodality Approach. 2010. (ENG., Illus.). 176p. 99.99 *(978-1-60406-312-7(2))* Thieme Medical Pubs., Inc.

ARTERIES—DISEASES
see also Arteries—Radiography
Alonso, Alvaro, et al. Dx/Rx - Peripheral Artery Disease. 2010. 204p. pap. 42.95 *(978-0-7637-5538-6(9))* Jones & Bartlett Learning, LLC.
Barst, Robyn, ed. Pulmonary Arterial Hypertension: Diagnosis & Evidence-Based Treatment. 2008. (ENG., Illus.). 270p. 118.00 *(978-0-470-05972-2(9)*, Wiley) Wiley, John & Sons, Inc.
Cho, Byung-Kyu & Tominaga, Teiji. Moyamoya Disease Update. 2010. (ENG., Illus.). 350p. 219.00 *(978-4-431-99702-3(4)*, 4431997024) Springer.
Coffman, Jay D. & Eberhardt, Robert T., eds. Peripheral Arterial Disease. 2010. (Contemporary Cardiology Ser.). (Illus.). 368p. pap. 164.00 *(978-1-61737-326-8(5)*, 1617373265) Humana Pr.
Dangas, George D. & Moses, Jeffrey W., eds. Handbook of Chronic Total Occlusions. 2007. (ENG., Illus.). 250p. 189.95 *(978-1-84184-624-8(4)*, Informa Healthcare) Taylor & Francis Group GBR. Dist: Taylor & Francis Group.
Dieter, Robert S., et al. Peripheral Arterial Disease. 2009. (ENG., Illus.). 1104p. 147.00 *(978-0-07-148179-3(6)*, 0071481796) McGraw-Hill Professional Publishing.
Li, John K. J. The Arterial Circulation: Physical Principles & Clinical Applications. 2010. (Illus.). 288p. pap. 159.00 *(978-1-61737-106-6(8)*, 1617371068) Humana Pr.
Mohler, Emile R. & Hirsch, Alan T. Peripheral Arterial Disease. 2009. (ENG.). 108p. pap. 22.95 *(978-0-7637-5866-0(3))* Jones & Bartlett Learning, LLC.
O'Rourke, Michael F., et al, eds. Arterial Vasodilation. (ENG., Illus.). 256p. *(978-0-340-55398-5(7)*, Hodder Arnold) Hodder Education.
RovenskÃ1/2, Jozef, et al, eds. Polymyalgia Rheumatica & Giant Cell Arteritis. 2010. (ENG., Illus.). xii, 92p. 59.95 *(978-3-211-99358-3(4)*, 3211993584) Springer.
Rupp, James. Giant Cell Arteritis - an Elusive Odyssey. 2008. 168p. pap. 14.95 *(978-1-4357-1338-3(9))* Lulu Enterprises Inc.
Tamburino, Corrado. Left Main Coronary Artery Disease: A Practical Guide for the Interventional Cardiologist. 2009. (Illus.). xvi, 128p. pap. 79.95 *(978-88-470-1429-9(8))* Springer.
Yeghiazarians, Yerem & Owens, Christopher D., eds. Handbook of Endovascular Peripheral Interventions. 2011. (ENG., Illus.). xix, 449p. pap. 49.95 ***(978-1-4614-0838-3(5)***, 1461408385) Springer.

ARTERIES—RADIOGRAPHY
Cato, Ruth & Towne, Jonathan B. Techniques of Peripheral Arterial Sonography. Date not set. *(978-0-941022-31-6(5))* Davies Publishing, Inc.

ARTERIES—SURGERY
Baumgartner, R. W. Handbook on Cerebral Artery Dissection, Vol. 20. (Frontiers of Neurology & Neuroscience Ser.: Vol. 20). (Illus.). *(978-3-8055-7986-5(1))* Karger, S. AG.
Bruneau, Mickaël & George, Bernard, eds. Pathology & surgery around the vertebral Artery. 2010. (ENG.). xvi, 674p. 399.00 *(978-2-287-89786-3(0)*, 2287897860) Springer.
Gan, Huili. Pulmonary Embolism & Pulmonary Thromboendarterectomy. 2011. (Cardiology Research & Clinical Developments Ser.). (Illus.). xviii, 342p. 145.00 *(978-1-61122-289-0(3))* Nova Science Pubs., Inc.
Green, Richard M. Complex Aortic Surgery. 2006. 300p. 199.95 *(978-0-8247-4055-9(6)*, Informa Healthcare) Taylor & Francis Group.
Kpodonu, Jacques. Manual of Thoracic Endoaortic Surgery. 2010. (Illus.). x, 350p. pap. 69.95 *(978-1-84996-295-7(2)*, 1849962952) Springer.
Kpodonu, Jacques, et al. Endovascular & Hybrid Management of the Thoracic Aorta: A Case-Based Approach. 2008. (ENG., Illus.). 320p. 199.95 *(978-1-4051-7535-7(4)*, Wiley-Blackwell) Wiley, John & Sons, Inc.
Saw, Jacqueline & Casserly, Ivan P. Carotid Artery Stenting: The Basics: How to Set up & Maintain a Cath Lab. 2009. (Contemporary Cardiology Ser.). (ENG., Illus.). x, 264p. 219.00 *(978-1-60327-313-8(1))* Humana Pr.
Schaller, Bernhard, ed. Imaging of Carotid Artery Stenosis. 2006. (Illus.). 272p. 259.00 *(978-3-211-32332-8(5)*, 3211323325) Springer.
Takebayashi, Shigeo, et al. Transcatheter Coil Embolization of Visceral Arterial Aneurysms. 2009. (Cardiology Research & Clinical Developments Ser.). (Illus.). 93p. pap. 43.00 *(978-1-60741-439-1(2))* Nova Science Pubs., Inc.
Yeghiazarians, Yerem & Owens, Christopher D., eds. Handbook of Endovascular Peripheral Interventions. 2011. (ENG., Illus.). xix, 449p. pap. 49.95 ***(978-1-4614-0838-3(5)***, 1461408385) Springer.

ARTERIOGRAPHY
see Arteries—Radiography

ARTERIOSCLEROSIS
see also Atherosclerosis
De Guzmán, Alberto López, et al. Pathogenesis Mechanism & Cardiovascular Risk Factors for Arteriosclerosis in Rheumatoid Arthritis: The Importance & Implications of Early Diagnosis. 2011. (Immunology & Immune System Disorders Ser.). pap. 43.00 *(978-1-61122-782-6(8)*, Nova Novinka) Nova Science Pubs., Inc.
Hoffman, Gary S., et al, eds. Inflammatory Diseases of Blood Vessels. 2nd ed. 2012. 600p. 239.95 ***(978-1-4443-3822-5(6)***, Wiley-Blackwell) Wiley, John & Sons, Inc.
Kaur, Sukhinder C., ed. Biochemistry of Atherosclerosis. 2006. (Advances in Biochemistry in Health Disease Ser.: Vol. 1). (ENG., Illus.). xvi, 572p. 209.00 *(978-0-387-31252-1(8)*, 0387312528) Springer.
Nicholls, Stephen J. & Lundman, Pia. Practical Approach to Diagnosis & Management of Lipid Disorders. rev. ed. 2009. 150p. pap. 44.95 *(978-0-7637-5584-3(2))* Jones & Bartlett Learning, LLC.
Safar, Michel & Frohlich, Edward D. Atherosclerosis, Large Arteries, & Cardiovascular Risk. (Advances in Cardiology Ser.: Vol. 44). (Illus.). viii, 359p. *(978-3-8055-8176-9(9))* Karger, S. AG.
Sharp, Danae. Androgens Induce Gender- 2009. 240p. pap. *(978-3-639-15542-6(4))* VDM Verlag Dr. Mueller e.K.
World Health Organization Staff, contrib. by. Prevention of Cardiovascular Disease: Guidelines for Assessment & Management of Cardiovascular Risk. 2007. (Nonserial Publication). (ENG., Illus.). 92p. pap. 36.00 *(978-92-4-154717-8(0))* World Health Organization.

ARTERIOVENOUS FISTULA
see Fistula, Arteriovenous

ARTHRITIS
see also Gout; Rheumatoid Arthritis
Abbouc, Joseph A. & Abboud, Soo Kim. No More Joint Pain. 2010. (Yale University Press Health & Wellness Ser.). (ENG., Illus.). 288p. pap. 18.00 *(978-0-300-16452-7(1))* Yale Univ. Pr.
Adams, Julie & Katolik, Lee. Elbow Arthritis, an Issue of Hand Clinics. 2011. (Clinics: Orthopedics Ser.: 27-2). (ENG., Illus.). 120p. 110.00 *(978-1-4557-0456-9(3)*, Saunders) Elsevier - Health Sciences Div.
Aqeel, Javeed. Diclofenac Sodium & Equine Arthritis: The Role of Diclofenac Sodium in Equine Arthritis Management. 2011. 104p. pap. ***(978-3-639-22862-5(6))*** VDM Verlag Dr. Mueller e.K.
Arden, Elizabeth, et al. Osteoarthritis. 6th ed. 2008. (Facts Ser.). (ENG., Illus.). 184p. pap. 27.50 *(978-0-19-921138-8(8))* Oxford Univ. Pr., Inc.
Argen, Ralph. Arthritis Treatment: Its Exciting Past & Open-ended Future. Murray, Lawrence A., ed. 2007. 149p. pap. 17.50 *(978-0-9766599-7-6(2))* Sts. Jude imPress.
Arthritis Foundation's Joint American & Canadian Conference on Co Management Models of Care for Early Diagnosis of Inflammatory Arthritis Meeting Report. 2007. *(978-0-912423-54-8(4))* Arthritis Foundation.
Arthritis Today Magazine Editors. The Essential Guide to Arthritis Medications: Prescription & over-the-Counter Treatments for Your Joint Pain from A to Z. Klippel, John H., ed. 2006. 347p. per. 9.95 *(978-0-912423-48-7(X))* Arthritis Foundation.
Bagchi, Debasis, et al, eds. Arthritis. 2011. (ENG., Illus.). 607p. 139.95 *(978-1-4398-1686-8(7)*, CRC Press) Taylor & Francis Group GBR. Dist: Taylor & Francis Group.
Bales, Peter. Osteoarthritis: Preventing & Healing Without Drugs. 2008. (ENG., Illus.). 250p. pap. 18.98 *(978-1-59102-615-0(6))* Prometheus Bks., Pubs.
Barling, Emanuel & Brooks, Ashley F. Arthritis, Inflammation, Gout, Crohn?ÇÖs, IBD & IBS: How to Eliminate Pain & Extend Your Life. 2010. 350p. pap. 34.95 *(978-1-4327-4985-9(4))* Outskirts Pr., Inc.
Barlow, Julie. Living with Arthritis. 2009. (ENG., Illus.). 320p. 134.95 *(978-1-4051-0809-6(6)*, Wiley-Blackwell) Wiley, John & Sons, Inc.
Barlow, Julie & Barlow. Living with Arthritis. 2009. (ENG., Illus.). 320p. pap. 64.95 *(978-1-4051-0810-2(X)*, Wiley-Blackwell) Wiley, John & Sons, Inc.
Berriedale-Johnson, Michelle. Arthritis Cooking for Health: Over 50 Delicious Recipes Designed to Relieve the Symptoms of Arthritis. 2009. (ENG., Illus.). 96p. pap. 14.99 *(978-1-84476-633-8(0))* Anness Publishing GBR. Dist: National Bk. Network.
Blau, Richard H. & Tremblay, E. A. Too Young to Feel Old: The Arthritis Doctor's 28-Day Formula for Pain-Free Living. 2007. (ENG., Illus.). 288p. per. 15.95 *(978-0-7382-1115-2(X))* Da Capo Pr., Inc.
Bonnin, Michel. Osteoarthrisis of the Knee. 2008. (ENG.). xiii, 642p. pap. 149.00 *(978-2-287-74174-6(7)*, 2287741747) Springer.
Brandt, Kenneth D. Diagnosis & Nonsurgical Management of Osteoarthritis. 5th ed. 2010. (ENG.). 367p. pap. 24.95 *(978-1-932610-42-0(1))* Professional Communications, Inc.
Brewer, Sarah. Overcoming Arthritis: The Complete Complementary Health Program. 2009. (Natural Health Guru Ser.). (ENG., Illus.). 180p. pap. 14.95 *(978-1-84483-728-1(9))* Duncan Baird Pubs. GBR. Dist: Sterling Publishing Co., Inc.
Bronner, Felix & Farach-Carson, Mary C. Bone & Osteoarthritis. 2007. (Topics in Bone Biology Ser.). (Illus.). 215p. 399.00 *(978-1-84628-513-4(5))* Springer.
Bronner, Felix & Farach-Carson, Mary C., eds. Bone & Osteoarthritis. 2010. (Topics in Bone Biology Ser.). (Illus.). xiv, 218p. pap. 399.00 *(978-1-84996-617-7(6)*, 1849966176) Springer.
Brower, Anne C. & Flemming, Donald J. Arthritis in Black & White. 3rd ed. 2012. (ENG., Illus.). 416p. 129.00 *(978-1-4160-5595-2(9)*, Saunders) Elsevier - Health Sciences Div.
Brown, Thomas E., et al. Arthritis & Arthroplasty: the Hip: Expert Consult - Online, Print & DVD. 2009. (Arthritis & Arthroplasty Ser.). (ENG., Illus.). 448p. 250.00 *(978-1-4160-4973-9(8)*, Saunders) Elsevier - Health Sciences Div.
—Arthritis & Arthroplasty: the Knee: Expert Consult - Online, Print & DVD. 2009. (Arthritis & Arthroplasty Ser.). (ENG., Illus.). 352p. 250.00 *(978-1-4160-4974-6(6)*, Saunders) Elsevier - Health Sciences Div.
Bruno, Michael A., et al. Arthritis in Color: Advanced Imaging of Arthritis. 2009. (ENG., Illus.). 236p. 113.00 *(978-1-4160-4722-3(0)*, Saunders) Elsevier - Health Sciences Div.
Burge, Michael. The Real Cure for Arthritis. 2009. 77p. pap. 15.00 *(978-0-557-20267-6(1))* Lulu Enterprises Inc.
Caicedo, Carlos Florido. Artritis: Y Otras Enfermedades Reumaticas. 2008. (Manuales de la Salud Ser.). (SPA., Illus.). 161p. 16.95 *(978-958-709-195-1(X))* Circulo de Lectores S.A. COL. Dist: Random Hse., Inc.
Callaghan, Alison & Rayman, Margaret. Nutrition & Arthritis. 2006. (ENG., Illus.). 280p. pap. 104.99 *(978-1-4051-2418-8(0)*, Wiley-Blackwell) Wiley, John & Sons, Inc.
Cassidy, James T., et al. Pediatric Rheumatology. 6th ed. 2010. (ENG., Illus.). 800p. (C). 218.00 *(978-1-4160-6581-4(4)*, Saunders) Elsevier - Health Sciences Div.
Catanzariti, Alan, et al. Update on Ankle Arthritis, an Issue of Clinics in Podiatric Medicine & Surgery. 2009. (Clinics: Orthopedics Ser.: 26-2). (ENG., Illus.). 240p. 99.00 *(978-1-4377-0531-7(6)*, Saunders) Elsevier - Health Sciences Div.
Chhabra, A. Bobby & Isaacs, Jonathan E. The Hand, Wrist & Elbow. 2009. (Arthritis & Arthroplasty Ser.). (ENG., Illus.). 416p. 250.00 *(978-1-4160-4971-5(1)*, Saunders) Elsevier - Health Sciences Div.
Coetzee, Christian & Hurwitz, Shepard R. The Foot & Ankle. 2009. (Arthritis & Arthroplasty Ser.). (ENG., Illus.). 360p. 250.00 *(978-1-4160-4972-2(X)*, Saunders) Elsevier - Health Sciences Div.
Cooper, Grant. The Arthritis Handbook: Improve Your Health & Manage the Pain of Osteoarthritis. 2008. (Diamedica Guide to Optimum Wellness a Diamedica Guide to Opt Ser.). (ENG., Illus.). 224p. per. 14.95 *(978-0-9793564-1-4(5))* DiaMed, LLC.
Cope, Andrew P., ed. Arthritis Research: Methods & Protocols, 2 vols. 2007. (Methods in Molecular Medicine Ser.). (Illus.). XX, 446p. 159.00 *(978-1-58829-344-2(0)*, 1588293440) Humana Pr.
—Arthritis Research: Volume 1: Methods & Protocols. 2010. (Methods in Molecular Medicine Ser.). (Illus.). xx, 446p. pap. 159.00 *(978-1-61737-507-1(1)*, 1617375071) Humana Pr.
—Arthritis Research: Volume 2: Methods & Protocols. 2010. (Methods in Molecular Medicine Ser.). (Illus.). xxii, 432p. pap. 189.00 *(978-1-61737-845-4(3)*, 1617378453) Humana Pr.
Cram101 Textbook Reviews & Cram101 Textbook Reviews. Outlines & Highlights for Harrison's Rheumatology by Anthony Fauci. 2011. 96p. pap. 27.95 ***(978-1-61830-629-6(4))*** Cram101 Inc.
Czernichow, P. & Dannecker, G., eds. Juvenile Idiopathic Arthritis: Clinical Picture, Mechanisms of Disease & Effects of Growth Hormone Treatment:Experts Conference, Chantilly, May 2008. 2009. (Illus.). 70p. pap. *(978-3-8055-9292-5(2))* Karger, S. AG.
De Ceuninck, édéric, et al, eds. Cartilage & Osteoarthritis. 2010. (Methods in Molecular Medicine Ser.). (Illus.). 360p. pap. 159.00 *(978-1-61737-606-1(X)*, 161737606X) Humana Pr.
Dieppe, Paul, ed. Osteoarthritis: An Overview. 2009. (Orthopaedics Ser.). (ENG.). 1p. cd-rom 99.00 *(978-981-4284-04-2(1))* Focus Medica Pte Ltd. SGP. Dist: Independent Pubs. Group.
Dines, David, et al. Arthritis & Arthroplasty: the Shoulder: Expert Consult - Online, Print & DVD. 2009. (Arthritis & Arthroplasty Ser.). (ENG., Illus.). 336p. 250.00 *(978-1-4160-4975-3(4)*, Saunders) Elsevier - Health Sciences Div.
Dziedzic, Krysia & Hammond, Alison, eds. Rheumatology: Evidence-Based Practice for Physiotherapists & Occupational Therapists. 2010. (ENG., Illus.). 376p. (C). pap. 57.95 *(978-0-443-06934-5(4)*, Churchill Livingstone) Elsevier - Health Sciences Div.
Elkins, Rita. Glucosamine & Chondroitin: Powerful Help for Aching Joints. 2nd ed. 2007. (Woodland Health Ser.). 26p. pap. 4.95 *(978-1-58054-439-9(8))* Woodland Publishing, Inc.
Espinoza, Luis. Infections & Rheumatic Diseases, an Issue of Rheumatic Disease Clinics. 2009. (Clinics: Internal Medicine Ser.: 35-1). (ENG.). 99.00 *(978-1-4377-1271-1(1)*, Saunders) Elsevier - Health Sciences Div.
Fassbender, Hans G. Pathology & Pathobiology of Rheumatic Diseases. Davies, E. & Whittacker, M., trs. 2nd ed. 2010. (Illus.). xxv, 503p. pap. 209.00 *(978-3-642-08313-6(7)*, 3642083137) Springer.
Fauci, Anthony & Langford, Carol M. Harrison's Rheumatology, Second Edition. 2nd ed. 2010. (ENG., Illus.). 368p. pap. 82.00 *(978-0-07-174143-9(7)*, 0071741437) McGraw-Hill Professional Publishing.
Felson, David T. & Schaible, Hans-Georg. Pain in Osteoarthritis. 2009. (ENG., Illus.). 308p. 165.95 *(978-0-470-40388-4(8)*, Wiley-Blackwell) Wiley, John & Sons, Inc.
Fife, Bruce. The New Arthritis Cure: Eliminate Arthritis & Fibromyalgia Pain Permanently. 2009. (Illus.). 189p. pap. 15.95 *(978-0-941599-82-5(5))* Piccadilly Bks., Ltd.
Firestein, Gary S., et al. Textbook of Rheumatology, 2 vols., Set. 8th ed. 2008. (ENG., Illus.). 2064p. 415.00 *(978-1-4160-3285-4(1)*, Saunders) Elsevier - Health Sciences Div.
Fishman, Loren M. & Saltonstall, Ellen. Yoga for Arthritis: The Complete Guide. 2008. (ENG., Illus.). 336p. per. 19.95 *(978-0-393-33058-8(3)*, 33058) Norton, W. W. & Co., Inc.
Foltz-Gray, Dorothy. Alternative Treatments for Arthritis: An A to Z Guide. 2nd ed. 2007. 274p. per. 9.95 *(978-0-912423-53-1(6))* Arthritis Foundation.
Fox, Steven M. & Millis, Darryl. Multimodal Management of Canine Osteoarthritis. 2010. (ENG., Illus.). 96p. pap. 69.95 *(978-1-84076-129-0(6))* Manson Publishing, Ltd. GBR. Dist: Thieme Medical Pubs., Inc.
Gibbs, Lisa. When the Whole 'Bloke' Thing Starts to Crumble - Men's Access to Chronic Illness Self Management Programs. 2008. 224p. pap. *(978-3-639-05072-1(X))* VDM Verlag Dr. Mueller e.K.
Gladman, Dafna, et al. Psoriatic Arthritis. 2009. (ENG., Illus.). 160p. pap. 24.95 *(978-0-19-923122-5(2))* Oxford Univ. Pr., Inc.
Glickel, Steven Z. & Bernstein, Richard A., eds. Arthritis of the Hand & Upper Extremity: A Master Skills Publication. 2011. (Illus.). 300.00 *(978-1-935121-10-7(3))* American Society for Surgery of the Hand.
Göretzlehner, Gunther, et al. Arthritis & Arthroplasty: the Spine: Expert Consult - Online, Print & DVD. Shaffrey, Christopher & Shen, Francis H., eds. 2009. (Arthritis & Arthroplasty Ser.). (ENG., Illus.). 442p. 250.00 *(978-1-4160-5643-0(2)*, Saunders) Elsevier - Health Sciences Div.
Green, Wendy. 50 Things You Can Do to Manage Arth. 2011. (Personal Health Guides). (ENG.). 128p. pap. 10.95 ***(978-1-84953-054-5(8))*** Summerdale Pubs. GBR. Dist: Independent Pubs. Group.
Guermazi, Ali. Imaging of Osteoarthritis, an Issue of Radiologic Clinics of North America. 2009. (Clinics: Radiology Ser.: 47-4). (ENG.). 99.00 *(978-1-4377-1403-6(X)*, Saunders) Elsevier - Health Sciences Div.
—State of the Art Imaging of Osteoarthritis, an Issue of Rheumatic Disease Clinics. 2009. (Clinics: Internal Medicine Ser.: 35-3). (ENG.). 99.00 *(978-1-4377-1750-1(0)*, Saunders) Elsevier - Health Sciences Div.
Hansen, Mark Victor, et al. Arthritis. 2006. (Chicken Soup for the Soul Ser.). (ENG.). 144p. mass mkt. 4.99 *(978-0-7573-0524-5(5))* Health Communications, Inc.
Hills, Margaret. Curing Arthritis: More Ways to a Drug-Free Life. 2009. (ENG.). 182p. pap. 29.95 *(978-1-4128-1253-5(4))* Transaction Pubs.
Hip Reconstruction & Replacement: The Rothman Institute Approach. 2011. 99.00 *(978-981-4307-76-5(9))* World Scientific Publishing Co., Inc.
Hohler, Sharon E. Arthritis: A Patient's Guide. 2008. (McFarland Health Topics Ser.). (ENG., Illus.). 264p. pap. 35.00 *(978-0-7864-3450-3(3))* McFarland & Co., Inc. Pubs.
Holford, Patrick, et al. Say No to Arthritis: The Proven Drug-Free Guide to Preventing & Relieving Arthritis. 2010. (ENG., Illus.). 384p. pap. 18.95 *(978-0-7499-2013-5(0))* Piatkus Bks. GBR. Dist: Independent Pubs. Group.
Hostynek, Jurij J. & Maibach, Howard I., eds. Copper & the Skin. 2006. (Dermatology: Clinical & Basic Science Ser.). (ENG., Illus.). 328p. 250.00 *(978-0-8493-9532-1(1))* Taylor & Francis Group.
Hozack, William J., et al. Surgical Treatment of Hip Arthritis: Reconstruction, Replacement, & Revision. rev. ed. 2009. (ENG., Illus.). 544p. 268.00 *(978-1-4160-5898-4(2)*, Saunders) Elsevier - Health Sciences Div.
Hunder, Gene G. Atlas of Rheumatology. 4th ed. 2009. *(978-1-57340-357-3(1))* Current Medicine Group LLC.
Hunter, David. Osteoarthritis, an Issue of Medical Clinics. 2008. (Clinics: Internal Medicine Ser.: 93-1). (ENG., Illus.). 240p. 73.00 *(978-1-4377-0499-0(9)*, Saunders) Elsevier - Health Sciences Div.
Hunter, David J. Osteoarthritis, an Issue of Clinics in Geriatric Medicine. 2010. (Clinics: Internal Medicine Ser.: 26-3). (ENG.). 105.00 *(978-1-4377-2453-0(1)*, Saunders) Elsevier - Health Sciences Div.
Kelton, Alan. The Fit Arthritic: Fighting Knee & Hip Arthritis with Exercise. 2008. 72p. pap. 10.95 *(978-1-59858-620-6(3))* Dog Ear Publishing, LLC.

Khan, Owais, et al. Management of Arthritis. 2011. 160p. pap. ***(978-3-8433-9049-1(5))*** Lambert Academic Publishing.

Kraag, Gunnar, et al. Living Well with Arthritis: A Sourcebook for Understanding & Managing Your Arthritis. 2007. (ENG., Illus.). 352p. (gr. 12-18). 24.00 *(978-0-14-305558-7(5)*, Penguin Global) Penguin Group (USA) Inc.

Lausevic, Kathryn. The Long Search: Managing Rheumatoid Arthritis without the Use of Drugs A Personal Story. 2010. 308p. pap. 19.99 *(978-1-4520-0221-7(5))* AuthorHouse.

Leong, Amye L., et al. Arthritis. 2009. (Complete Idiot's Guide Ser.). (ENG.). 352p. (gr. 12-18). pap. 18.95 *(978-1-59257-837-5(3)*, Alpha Bks.) Penguin Group (USA) Inc.

Lytle, Larry. Universal Healer: Book I Osteoarthritis. 2008. 120p. pap. 17.99 *(978-1-4343-8672-4(4))* AuthorHouse.

Majumdar, Sharmila. Advances in Mri of the Knee for Osteoarthritis. 2010. 300p. 96.00 *(978-981-4271-70-7(5))* World Scientific Publishing Co., Inc.

Martin, Colin R. & Preedy, Victor R., eds. Scientific Basis of Healthcare. 2012. (ENG., Illus.). 150p. 69.95 ***(978-1-57808-730-3(9))*** BIOS Scientific Publishers Ltd. GBR. Dist: Taylor & Francis Group.

Mease, Med, Philip J & Helliwell, DM, Philip S, eds. Atlas of Psoriatic Arthritis. 2007. (Illus.). 118p. 199.00 *(978-1-84628-896-8(7))* Springer.

Mease, Philip, ed. Psoriatic Arthritis: Physician's Reference. 2009. (Orthopaedics Ser.). (ENG.). 1p. cd-rom 99.00 *(978-981-4206-72-3(5))* Focus Medica Pte Ltd. SGP. Dist: Independent Pubs. Group.

Mease, Philip J. & Helliwell, Philip S., eds. Atlas of Psoriatic Arthritis. 2010. (Illus.). x, 108p. pap. 49.95 *(978-0-85729-174-5(2)*, 0857291742) Springer.

Michael P. Angelillo. All about Arthritis- Find Updated Causes, Symptoms, Diagnostic Tests, New Alternative Treatments, Cures & Breakthroughs. 2009. 80p. pap. 10.95 *(978-1-4401-7460-5(1))* iUniverse, Inc.

Milford, Francine. Tuning Forks & Arthritis. 2008. 60p. pap. 12.99 *(978-1-4357-2886-8(6))* Lulu Enterprises Inc.

Miller, Marc L. J & B Clinical Card: Osteoarthritis. 2009. 12.95 *(978-0-7637-7587-2(8))* Jones & Bartlett Learning, LLC.

—J & B Clinical Card: Psoriatic Arthritis. 2009. 12.95 *(978-0-7637-7588-9(6))* Jones & Bartlett Learning, LLC.

Mitchell, Deborah. The Complete Guide to Healing Arthritis. 2011. (ENG.). 256p. mass mkt. 7.99 *(978-0-312-53416-5(7)*, St. Martin's Paperbacks) St. Martin's Pr.

Moskowitz, Roland W., et al, eds. Osteoarthritis: Diagnosis & Medical/Surgical Management. 4th rev. ed. 2006. (ENG., Illus.). 528p. 163.95 *(978-0-7817-6707-1(5))* Lippincott Williams & Wilkins.

Orme, Eve. My Fight Against OsteoArthritis. 2006. 108p. per. *(978-1-4067-9649-0(2)*, Hesperides Pr.) Read Bks.

Pack, Dr Louis & Pack, Louis. The Arthritis Revolution. 2011. 216p. pap. 23.95 ***(978-1-4583-8974-9(X))*** Lulu Enterprises Inc.

Panush, Richard S., ed. Year Book of Rheumatology, Arthritis & Musculoskeletal Disease, 2005. Date not set. (Illus.). 385p. *(978-0-323-01523-3(9))* Harcourt Health Sciences Group.

Pelt, Marc N., ed. Arthritis: Types, Treatment & Prevention. 2012. (Immunology & Immune System Disorders Ser.). 207p. 95.00 ***(978-1-61470-719-6(7))*** Nova Science Pubs., Inc.

Pisetsky, David & ACR. The ACR at 75: A Diamond Jubilee. 2009. (ENG., Illus.). 218p. 52.95 *(978-0-470-52377-3(8)*, Wiley-Blackwell) Wiley, John & Sons, Inc.

Prupas, Malin. Arthritis Made Simple! 2007. (ENG., Illus.). 224p. per. 24.95 *(978-1-58736-619-2(3))* Wheatmark.

Reid, David M., ed. Clinical Trials in Rheumatoid Arthritis & Osteoarthritis. 2008. (Clinical Trials Ser.). (Illus.). 256p. 119.00 *(978-1-85233-874-9(1))* Springer.

Ritchlin, Christopher & Fitzgerald, Oliver. Psoriatic & Reactive Arthritis: A Companion to Rheumatology. 2007. (Companion to Rheumatology Ser.). (ENG., Illus.). 256p. 147.00 *(978-0-323-03622-1(8)*, Mosby) Elsevier - Health Sciences Div.

Rounds, Sharon I. S. & Cope, Andrew P., eds. Arthritis Research: Methods & Protocols, 2 vols., Vol. 2. 2007. (Methods in Molecular Medicine Ser.). (Illus.). XXII, 432p. 189.00 *(978-1-58829-918-5(X)*, 158829918X) Humana Pr.

Rubin, Jordan S. The Great Physician's RX for Arthritis, 0 vols. 2007. (Great Physican's RX Ser.). 128p. 9.99 *(978-0-7852-1917-0(X))* Nelson, Thomas Inc.

Sabatini, Massimo, et al, eds. Cartilage & Osteoarthritis. 2010. (Methods in Molecular Medicine Ser.). (Illus.). 376p. pap. 154.00 *(978-1-61737-450-0(4)*, 1617374504) Humana Pr.

Saffar, P. Arthritis of the Bases of the Thumb. Date not set. (Illus.). 225p. (C). 175.00 *(978-0-387-59586-3(4))* Springer.

Satish R, Sathe & MRUDULA S., Kulkarni. Finite Element Analysis of Human Artificial Hip Joint Prosthesis. 2011. 176p. pap. ***(978-3-8383-0201-0(X))*** Lambert Academic Publishing.

Scott, Anna. Triumph over Arthritis: A Comprehensive & up-to-date Guide to the Help Available. (Illus.). 208p. pap. *(978-0-86806-373-7(8)*, Hale & Iremonger) GHR Pr., The.

Scott, David L., et al. Inflammatory Arthritis in Clinical Practice. 2007. (Illus.). 116p. pap. 69.95 *(978-1-84628-932-3(7))* Springer.

Seyfert, Warren H. Confronting & Overcoming Arthritis. 2007. 116p. per. 12.95 *(978-0-595-47850-7(6))* iUniverse, Inc.

Sharma, Leena & Berenbaum, Francis. Osteoarthritis: A Companion to Rheumatology. 2007. (Companion to Rheumatology Ser.). (ENG., Illus.). 296p. 99.95 *(978-0-323-03929-1(4)*, Mosby) Elsevier - Health Sciences Div.

Snaith, Michael. Your Guide to Arthritis. 2007. (Illus.). 160p. pap. 19.95 *(978-0-340-92601-7(5))* Hodder Arnold Pubs.

Sofue, Muroto & Endo, Naoto, eds. Treatment of Osteoarthritic Change in the Hip: Joint Preservation or Joint Replacement? 2007. (Illus.). 254p. 89.95 *(978-4-431-38198-3(8)*, 4431381988) Springer.

Stein, Michael & Taylor, Guy. The Encyclopedia of Arthritis. 2nd rev. ed. 2010. (Library of Health & Living Ser.). 432p. (C). (gr. 9). 75.00 *(978-0-8160-7767-0(3))* Facts On File, Inc.

Stokes, Barbara & Helewa, Antoine. Arthritis: How to Stay Active & Relieve Your Pain. 2007. (ENG., Illus.). 384p. per. 18.95 *(978-1-933503-03-5(3))* Bull Publishing Co.

Sutton, Amy, ed. Arthritis Sourcebook. 3rd rev. ed. 2010. (Health Reference Ser.). lib. bdg. 93.00 *(978-0-7808-1077-8(5))* Omnigraphics, Inc.

Swaim, Loring Tiffany. Arthritis, Medicine & the Spiritual Laws: The Power Beyond Science. 2011. 156p. 41.95 ***(978-1-258-06400-6(6))*** Literary Licensing, LLC.

Terkeltaub, Robert & Edwards, N. Lawrence. Gout: Diagnosis & Management of Gouty Arthritis & Hyperuricemia. 2011. 272p. pap. 24.95 ***(978-1-932610-70-3(7))*** Professional Communications, Inc.

Tétau, M. & Tourmente, C. Osteoarthritis, Rheumatism, Arthritis, 1 vol. 2010. (ENG.). 191p. 19.99 *(978-2-35934-065-5(4))* Alpen Editions FRA. Dist: Innovative Logistics.

Theodosakis, Jason. The Arthritis Cur. rev. ed. Date not set. mass mkt. 6.99 *(978-0-312-98870-8(2)*, St. Martin's Paperbacks) St. Martin's Pr.

Tsokos, George C., ed. Principles of Molecular Rheumatology. 2010. (Current Molecular Medicine Ser.). (Illus.). 542p. pap. 209.00 *(978-1-61737-182-0(3)*, 1617371823) Humana Pr.

Waddell, James P. Operative Techniques: Hip Arthritis Surgery: Book, Website & DVD. 2008. (Operative Techniques Ser.). (ENG., Illus.). 368p. 250.00 *(978-1-4160-3850-4(7)*, Saunders) Elsevier - Health Sciences Div.

Wadhwa, Vinod. Your Family Doctor Arthritis: Rheumatoid Arthritis, Osteo-Arthritis, Gout, Osteoporosis. 2007. (Illus.). 91p. per. 6.95 *(978-81-8328-032-7(3))* Wisdom Tree IND. Dist: SCB Distributors.

Weinberg, Jeffrey M., ed. Treatment of Psoriasis. 2008. (Milestones in Drug Therapy Ser.). (Illus.). 183p. 169.00 *(978-3-7643-7722-9(4))* Birkhauser Boston.

Weisman, Michael H., et al. Targeted Treatment of the Rheumatic Diseases. 2009. (ENG., Illus.). 496p. 195.00 *(978-1-4160-9993-2(X)*, Saunders) Elsevier - Health Sciences Div.

Weissman, Barbara N. W. Imaging of Arthritis & Metabolic Bone Disease: Expert Consult - Online & Print. 2009. (ENG., Illus.). 772p. 195.00 *(978-0-323-04177-5(9)*, Mosby) Elsevier - Health Sciences Div.

Wootton-Gorges, Sandra L. Pediatric Musculoskeletal Imaging: Magnetic Resonance Imaging Clinics. 2009. (Clinics: Radiology Ser.: 17-3). (ENG.). 575p. 99.00 *(978-1-4377-1238-4(X)*, Saunders) Elsevier - Health Sciences Div.

Zaffagnini, Stefano, et al, eds. Patellofemoral Pain, Instability, & Arthritis: Clinical Presentation, Imaging, & Treatment. 2010. (ENG., Illus.). xii, 344p. 219.00 *(978-3-642-05423-5(4)*, 3642054234) Springer.

Zur Nieden, Nicole I. Embryonic Stem Cell Therapy for Osteo-Degenerative Diseases: Methods & Protocols. 2011. (Illus.). xii, 336p. E-Book ***(978-1-60761-962-8(8))*** Humana Pr.

ARTHRITIS—PATIENTS

Gilbert, Patricia, tr. Osteoarthritis. (Illus.). 85p. *(978-0-85969-887-0(4)*, Sheldon Press) SPCK Publishing.

Harris, Stephanie & Hyatt, Gwen. Exercise & Arthritis. 2007. spiral bd. 89.00 *(978-0-9790787-2-9(5))* Desert Southwest Fitness, Inc.

McQuaig, Joey. How Strong Is Your Titanium: The Real Life Misadventures of a Knee & Hip Replacement Survivor. 2010. 144p. (ENG.). 24.95 *(978-1-4520-3703-5(5))*; pap. 15.95 *(978-1-4520-3702-8(7))* AuthorHouse.

Rosenstein, Ann A. Water Exercises for Osteoarthritis: The Effective Way to Reduce Pain & Stiffness, While Increasing Endurance & Strength. 2007. (Illus.). 291p. per. 18.00 *(978-1-882883-62-2(4))* Idyll Arbor, Inc.

Schwarz, Shelley Peterman & Demos Medical Publishing Staff. Arthritis: 300 Tips for Making Life Easier. 2008. (ENG.). 200p. pap. 16.95 *(978-1-932603-67-5(0))* Demos Medical Publishing, LLC.

Seyfert, Warren H. Confronting & Overcoming Arthritis. 2007. 116p. per. 12.95 *(978-0-595-47850-7(6))* iUniverse, Inc.

ARTHRITIS—PATIENTS—BIOGRAPHY

Coupar, Angela. The Daily Trials of Living with Fibromyalgia & Arthritic Pain. 2007. 144p. per. *(978-1-897312-42-1(3))* Adibbed Ltd.

Genovese, Julie B. Nothing Short of Joy. 2010. (ENG.). 249p. pap. 15.95 *(978-1-933016-59-7(0))* Behler Pubns., LLC.

Tripodi, Tony. My Cane & I: A Memoir of a Disability. 2009. 108p. 22.95 *(978-1-4401-2880-6(4))*; pap. 12.95 *(978-1-4401-2878-3(2))* iUniverse, Inc.

ARTHRITIS DEFORMAS

see Rheumatoid Arthritis

ARTHRODESIS

Hintermann, Beat. Current & New Techniques for Primary & Revision Arthrodesis, an Issue of Foot & Ankle Clinics. 2011. (Clinics: Orthopedics Ser.: 16-1). (ENG., Illus.). 232p. 106.00 *(978-1-4557-0447-4(4)*, Saunders) Elsevier - Health Sciences Div.

Muscarella, Vincent J. & Boc, Steven F. Arthrodesis of the Foot & Ankle, an Issue of Clinics in Podiatric Medicine & Surgery. 2012. (Clinics: Orthopedics Ser.: 29-1). (ENG., Illus.). xvi, 154p. 115.00 ***(978-1-4557-3921-9(9)***, Saunders) Elsevier - Health Sciences Div.

Victionary, creator. SimplyMaterial. 2007. (Simply (Victionary) Ser.). (Illus.). 271p. *(978-988-98228-7-3(3))* Victionary.

ARTHROPATHY

see Joints—Diseases

ARTHROPLASTY

Amstutz, Harlan C. Hip Resurfacing: Principles, Indications, Technique & Results Book & DVD. 2008. (ENG., Illus.). 272p. 272.00 *(978-1-4160-4724-7(7)*, Saunders) Elsevier - Health Sciences Div.

An, Kai-Nan & Sperling, John W., eds. Joint Replacement Arthroplasty: Basic Science, Elbow, & Shoulder. 4th rev. ed. 2010. (ENG.). 368p. 245.99 *(978-1-60831-467-6(7))* Lippincott Williams & Wilkins.

Anderson, Julie, et al. Surgeons, Manufacturers & Patients: A Transatlantic History of Total Hip Replacement. 2007. (Science, Technology & Medicine in Modern History Ser.). (ENG., Illus.). 256p. 95.00 *(978-0-230-55314-9(1))* Palgrave Macmillan.

Anderson, Martin. Tahoe Fracture Clinic's Guide to Joint Replacement. 2007. 213p. pap. 21.95 *(978-1-4303-1673-2(X))* Lulu Enterprises Inc.

Aoi, T. & Toshida, A. Hip Replacement: Approaches, Complications & Effectiveness. 2009. 129.00 *(978-1-60692-326-9(9))* Nova Science Pubs., Inc.

Benazzo, Francesco, et al, eds. Bioceramics & Alternative Bearings in Joint Arthroplasty: 11th BIOLOX Symposium. Proceedings. 2007. (Ceramics in Orthopaedics Ser.). (Illus.). xvii, 321p. pap. 89.95 *(978-3-7985-1634-2(0)*, 3798516340) Steinkopff, Dietrich DEU. Dist: Springer.

Berend, Keith R. & Cushner, Fred. Partial Knee Arthroplasty: Techniques & Optimal Outcomes. 2011. (ENG., Illus.). 288p. 239.00 *(978-1-4377-1756-3(X)*, Saunders) Elsevier - Health Sciences Div.

Bigliani, Louis U. & Flatow, Evan L., eds. Shoulder Arthroplasty. 2010. (ENG., Illus.). xii, 220p. pap. 219.00 *(978-1-4419-1973-1(2)*, 1441919732) Springer.

Brown, Thomas E., et al. Arthritis & Arthroplasty: the Hip: Expert Consult - Online, Print & DVD. 2009. (Arthritis & Arthroplasty Ser.). (ENG., Illus.). 448p. 250.00 *(978-1-4160-4973-9(8)*, Saunders) Elsevier - Health Sciences Div.

—Arthritis & Arthroplasty: the Knee: Expert Consult - Online, Print & DVD. 2009. (Arthritis & Arthroplasty Ser.). (ENG., Illus.). 352p. 250.00 *(978-1-4160-4974-6(6)*, Saunders) Elsevier - Health Sciences Div.

Buechel, Frederick F. & Pappas, Michael J. Principles of Human Joint Replacement: Design & Clinical Application. 2011. (ENG., Illus.). xii, 324p. 179.00 ***(978-3-642-23010-3(5)***, 3642230105) Springer.

Cammisa, Frank P., Jr. Dynamic Reconstruction of the Spine. Kim, Daniel H. & Fessler, Richard G., eds. 2006. (ENG., Illus.). 424p. 199.99 *(978-1-58890-484-3(9))* Thieme Medical Pubs., Inc.

Chang, Jun-Dong & Billau, Karl, eds. Bioceramics & Alternative Bearings in Joint Arthroplasty: 12th Biolox Symposium Seoul, Republic of Korea September 7-8, 2007 Proceedings. 2007. (Ceramics in Orthopaedics Ser.). (Illus.). 343p. per. 119.00 *(978-3-7985-1782-0(7))* Steinkopff, Dietrich DEU. Dist: Springer.

Chhabra, A. Bobby & Isaacs, Jonathan E. The Hand, Wrist & Elbow. 2009. (Arthritis & Arthroplasty Ser.). (ENG., Illus.). 416p. 250.00 *(978-1-4160-4971-5(1)*, Saunders) Elsevier - Health Sciences Div.

Cobb, Justin P., ed. Bioceramics & Alternative Bearings in Joint Arthroplasty: 13th BIOLOX Symposium Edingburgh, United KingdomSeptember 4 - 5, 2009, Proceedings. 2010. (Ceramics in Orthopaedics Ser.). (Illus.). 300p. 89.95 *(978-3-7985-1921-3(8)*, 3798519218) Steinkopff, Dietrich DEU. Dist: Springer.

Coetzee, Christian & Hurwitz, Shepard R. The Foot & Ankle. 2009. (Arthritis & Arthroplasty Ser.). (ENG., Illus.). 360p. 250.00 *(978-1-4160-4972-2(X)*, Saunders) Elsevier - Health Sciences Div.

Cofield, Robert H. Revision & Complex Shoulder Arthroplasty. Sperling, John W., ed. 2008. (ENG., Illus.). 352p. 249.99 *(978-0-7817-7747-6(X))* Lippincott Williams & Wilkins.

Cole, Brian & Gomoll, Andreas. Biologic Joint Reconstruction: Alternatives to Joint Arthroplasty. 2009. (ENG., Illus.). 376p. 162.95 *(978-1-55642-850-0(2))* SLACK, Inc.

Dines, David, et al. Arthritis & Arthroplasty: the Shoulder: Expert Consult - Online, Print & DVD. 2009. (Arthritis & Arthroplasty Ser.). (ENG., Illus.). 336p. 250.00 *(978-1-4160-4975-3(4)*, Saunders) Elsevier - Health Sciences Div.

Fealy, Stephen, et al, eds. Shoulder Arthroplasty: Complex Issues in the Primary & Revision Setting. 2008. (ENG., Illus.). 192p. 139.99 *(978-1-58890-505-5(5))* Thieme Medical Pubs., Inc.

Garino, Jonathan P. & Beredjiklian, Pedro K. Adult Reconstruction & Arthroplasty. 2007. (Core Knowledge in Orthopaedics Ser.). (ENG., Illus.). 368p. 130.00 *(978-0-323-03370-1(9)*, Mosby) Elsevier - Health Sciences Div.

Gartsman, Gary M. & Edwards, T. Bradley. Shoulder Arthroplasty. 2008. (ENG., Illus.). 544p. 218.00 *(978-1-4160-3857-3(4)*, Saunders) Elsevier - Health Sciences Div.

Göretzlehner, Gunther, et al. Arthritis & Arthroplasty: the Spine: Expert Consult - Online, Print & DVD. Shaffrey, Christopher & Shen, Francis H., eds. 2009. (Arthritis & Arthroplasty Ser.). (ENG., Illus.). 442p. 250.00 *(978-1-4160-5643-0(2)*, Saunders) Elsevier - Health Sciences Div.

Jacofsky, David J. & Hedley, Anthony K. Fundamentals of Revision Hip Arthroplasty: Diagnosis, Evaluation, & Treatment. 2012. (ENG.). 250p. 129.95 *(978-1-55642-952-1(5))* SLACK, Inc.

—Fundamentals of Revision Knee Arthroplasty: Diagnosis, Evaluation, & Treatment. 2012. (ENG.). 275p. pap. 129.95 *(978-1-55642-974-3(6))* SLACK, Inc.

Kaplanek, Beth A., et al. Pilates for Hip & Knee Syndromes & Arthroplasties. 2011. (Illus.). 384p. pap. 44.00 *(978-0-7360-9224-1(2))* Human Kinetics Pubs.

Mehta, Ajit Kumar. A Practical Operative Guide for Total Knee & Hip Replacement. 2009. (ENG., Illus.). 232p. 145.00 *(978-0-07-163437-3(1)*, 0071634371) McGraw-Hill Professional Publishing.

Mohamed Ezz El Din El Mikkawy, Dalia, et al. Rehabilitation after Total Knee Arthroplasty. 2011. 208p. pap. ***(978-3-8443-8642-4(4))*** Lambert Academic Publishing.

Ostermeier, Sven. Quadriceps Force after Non- Hinged & Hinged Tk. 2009. 52p. pap. *(978-3-639-16832-7(1))* VDM Verlag Dr. Mueller e.K.

Pagnano, Mark W., et al, eds. Joint Replacement Arthroplasty Vol. 2: Basic Science, Hip, Knee, & Ankle. 4th rev. ed. 2011. (ENG., Illus.). 800p. 249.00 *(978-1-60831-470-6(7))* Lippincott Williams & Wilkins.

Parvizi, Javad & Klatt, Brian. Essentials in Total Knee Arthroplasty. 2011. (ENG., Illus.). 240p. 139.95 *(978-1-55642-851-7(0))* SLACK, Inc.

Parvizi, Javad, et al. Essentials in Total Hip Arthroplasty. 2013. (ENG., Illus.). 240p. 139.95 *(978-1-55642-870-8(7))* SLACK, Inc.

Pfeil, Joachim & Siebert, Werner E. Minimally Invasive Surgery in Total Hip Arthroplasty. 2010. (ENG., Illus.). xiii, 98p. 139.00 *(978-3-642-00896-2(8)*, 3642008968) Springer.

Revell, P. A., ed. Joint Replacement Technology. 2008. (Illus.). 600p. 309.95 *(978-1-4200-7962-3(X))* CRC Pr. LLC.

Reynolds, L. Early Development of Total Hip Replacement. 2007. (Illus.). xxix, 167p. pap. *(978-0-85484-111-0(3))* Wellcome Institute for the History of Medicine.

Riemer, Jerry. Hip, Hip, Hooray! The True Story of a Bi-lateral Total Hip Replacement Patient. 2007. 122p. pap. 19.95 *(978-1-60441-235-2(6))* PublishAmerica, Inc.

Scott, W. Norman. Insall y Scott Cirugia de la Rodilla, 2 vols., Set. 4th ed. 2007. (SPA.). 483.00 *(978-84-8174-952-6(4)*, Elsevier Espana) Elsevier - Health Sciences Div.

Scuderi, Giles R. & Tria, Alfred J., eds. Minimally Invasive Surgery in Orthopedics. 2008. (Illus.). 1000p. 399.00 *(978-0-387-76607-2(3))* Springer.

Waddell, James P. Operative Techniques: Hip Arthritis Surgery: Book, Website & DVD. 2008. (Operative Techniques Ser.). (ENG., Illus.). 368p. 250.00 *(978-1-4160-3850-4(7)*, Saunders) Elsevier - Health Sciences Div.

Walenkamp, G. H. I M. Local Antibiotics in Arthroplasty. 2007. 170p. pap. 99.95 *(978-1-58890-607-6(8))* Thieme Medical Pubs., Inc.

Whiteside, Leo A. Ligament Balancing in Total Knee Arthroplasty. 2007. (Illus.). x, 115p. 89.95 *(978-3-540-20749-8(X)*, 354020749X) Springer.

Yue, James J., et al. Motion Preservation Surgery of the Spine: Advanced Techniques & Controversies. 2008. (ENG., Illus.). 816p. 319.00 *(978-1-4160-3994-5(5)*, Saunders) Elsevier - Health Sciences Div.

ARTHROPODA

see also Arachnida; Crustacea; Insects

Backyard Bugs. pap. 13.15 *(978-0-8136-4251-2(5))* Modern Curriculum Pr.

Backyard Bugs. (C). 271.20 *(978-1-4048-1522-3(8))* Picture Window Bks.

Basset, Yves, et al, eds. Arthropods of Tropical Forests: Spatio-Temporal Dynamics & Resource Use in the Canopy. 2008. (ENG., Illus.). 492p. pap. 90.00 *(978-0-521-08784-1(8))* Cambridge Univ. Pr.

Berenbaum, May R. The Earwig's Tail: A Modern Bestiary of Multi-Legged Legends. 2009. (Illus.). 216p. 23.95 *(978-0-674-03540-9(2))* Harvard Univ. Pr.

Byrd, Jason H. & Castner, James L., eds. Forensic Entomology: The Utility of Arthropods in Legal Investigations. 2nd rev. ed. 2009. (ENG., Illus.). 705p. 159.95 *(978-0-8493-9215-3(2)*, CRC Press) Taylor & Francis Group GBR. Dist: Taylor & Francis Group.

Fortey, Richard. Horseshoe Crabs & Velvet Worms: The Story of the Animals & Plants That Time Has Left Behind. 2012. (ENG.). 320p. pap. 16.95 ***(978-0-307-27553-0(1)***, Vintage); (Illus.). 352p. 28.95 ***(978-0-307-26361-2(4)***, Knopf) Knopf Doubleday Publishing Group.

Gill, Stanton, et al. Pests & Diseases of Herbaceous Perennials: The Biological Approach. 2nd ed. 2006. (ENG., Illus.). 440p. 64.95 *(978-1-883052-50-8(5))* Ball Publishing.

Golovatch, Sergei I. & Mesibov, Robert, eds. Advances in the Systematics of Diplopoda II. 2009. (ZooKeys Ser.). 110p. pap. 62.50 *(978-954-642-489-1(7))* Pensoft Pubs. BGR. Dist: Coronet Bks.

Hajek, Ann E., et al, eds. Use of Microbes for Control & Eradication of Invasive Arthropods. 2010. (Progress in Biological Control Ser.). xvi, 366p. pap. 189.00 *(978-90-481-7910-7(6)*, 9048179106) Springer.

Hajek, Ann E., et al. Use of Microbes for Control & Eradication of Invasive Arthropods. 2008. (Progress in Biological Control Ser.). (Illus.). xvi, 366p. 189.00 *(978-1-4020-8559-8(1))* Springer.

Hawksworth, David L. & Bull, Alan T., eds. Arthropod Diversity & Conservation. (Topics in Biodiversity & Conservation Ser.). 2010. viii, 528p. pap. 219.00 *(978-90-481-7309-9(4)*, 9048173094) 2006. (Illus.). 524p. 219.00 *(978-1-4020-5203-3(0)*, 1402052030) Springer.

Hunter, Wayne. Genome Mapping & Genomics in Arthropods. 2007. (Genome Mapping & Genomics in Animals Ser.). (Illus.). 170p. 179.00 *(978-3-540-73832-9(0)*, 3540738320) Springer.

Hunter, Wayne & Kole, Chittaranjan. Genome Mapping & Genomics in Arthropods. 2010. (Genome Mapping & Genomics in Animals Ser.). (Illus.). xviii, 122p. pap. 179.00 *(978-3-642-09305-0(1)*, 3642093051) Springer.

Ishaaya, Isaac, et al. Biorational Control of Arthropod Pests: Application & Resistance Management. Ishaaya, Isaac et al, eds. 2009. (ENG., Illus.). xi, 408p. 199.00 *(978-90-481-2315-5(1)*, 9048123151) Springer.

Krassilov & Rasnitsyn. Plant-Arthropod Interactions in the Early Angiosperm History: Evidence from the Cretaceous of Israel. 2008. 222p. (C). (978-90-04-17071-1(5)) BRILL.

Marlos, Daniel. The Curious World of Bugs: The Bugman's Guide to the Mysterious & Remarkable Lives of Things That Crawl. 2010. (ENG., Illus.). 224p. (gr. 12). 17.95 (978-0-399-53613-7(2), Perigee Trade) Penguin Group (USA) Inc.

Merkle, Tobias. Orientation & Search Strategies of Desert Arthropods. 2008. 200p. pap. (978-3-639-03107-2(5)) VDM Verlag Dr. Mueller e.K.

Muniappan, Rangaswamy, et al. Arthropod Pests of Horticultural Crops in Tropical Asia. 2012. (Illus.). 208p. 145.00 (978-1-84593-951-9(4)) CABI GBR. Dist: Stylus Publishing, LLC.

Punzo, Fred. Desert Arthropods: Life History Variations: Life History Variations. 2010. (Adaptations of Desert Organisms Ser.). (Illus.). xiii, 248p. pap. 239.00 (978-3-642-08532-1(6), 3642085326) Springer.

Ravensberg, Willem. A Roadmap to the Successful Development & Commercialization of Microbial Pest Control Products for Control of Arthropods. 2011. (Progress in Biological Control Ser.). (ENG., Illus.). xxv, 383p. 179.00 (978-94-007-0436-7(4), 9400704364) Springer.

Richards, A. Glenn. The Integument of Arthropods: The Chemical Components & Their Properties, the Anatomy & Development, & the Permeability. 2009. (ENG.). 428p. pap. 60.00 (978-0-8166-5857-2(9)) Univ. of Minnesota Pr.

Roques, Alain, ed. Alien Terrestrial Arthropods of Europe. 2010. (BioRisks Ser.). 555p. pap. 175.00 (978-954-642-554-6(0)); 504p. pap. 162.50 (978-954-642-555-3(9)) Pensoft Pubs. BGR. Dist: Coronet Bks.

Strausfeld, Nicholas James. Arthropod Brains: Evolution, Functional Elegance, & Historical Significance. 2012. (ENG., Illus.). 848p. 65.00 (978-0-674-04633-7(1), Belknap Pr.) Harvard Univ. Pr.

Takken, Willem & Knols, Bart G. J., eds. Emerging pests & vector-borne diseases in Europe, Vol. 1. 2007. (ECVD Ser.). (Illus.). 500p. 147.00 (978-90-8686-053-1(2)) Wageningen Academic Publishers NLD. Dist: Enfield Publishing & Distribution Co., Inc.

—Olfaction in vector-host interactions. 2010. (Illus.). 360p. 146.00 (978-90-8686-091-3(5)) Wageningen Academic Publishers NLD. Dist: Enfield Publishing & Distribution Co., Inc.

Whalon, Mark Edward & Hollingworth, Robert M. Global Pesticide Resistance in Arthropods. Mota-Sanchez, D., ed. 2008. (Illus.). 208p. 145.00 (978-1-84593-353-1(2)) CABI GBR. Dist: Stylus Publishing, LLC.

Zchori-Fein, Elinat & Bourtzis, Kostas. Manipulative Tenants: Bacteria Associated with Arthropods. 2011. (Frontiers in Microbiology Ser.). (ENG., Illus.). 306p. 129.95 (978-1-4398-2749-9(4), CRC Press) Taylor & Francis Group GBR. Dist: Taylor & Francis Group.

ARTHROPODA—PARASITES

Goddard, Jerome. Physician's Guide to Arthropods of Medical Importance. 5th rev. ed. 2007. (ENG., Illus.). 480p. 159.95 (978-0-8493-8539-1(3), CRC Press) Taylor & Francis Group GBR. Dist: Taylor & Francis Group.

ARTHROSCOPE

see Arthroscopy

ARTHROSCOPY

Abrams, Jeffrey. Management of the Unstable Shoulder: Arthroscopic & Open Repair. 2011. (ENG., Illus.). 336p. 149.95 (978-1-55642-925-5(8)) SLACK, Inc.

Abrams, Jeffrey S. & Bell, Robert H., eds. Rotator Cuff Surgery: A Practical Approach to Management. 2007. (Illus.). 416p. 206.00 (978-0-387-39340-7(4), 0387393404) Springer.

Alexander, Susan, et al, eds. Practical Shoulder Arthroscopy. 2011. 400p. pap. 129.00 (978-1-903378-60-1(5)) TFM Publishing Ltd. GBR. Dist: JAMCO Distribution.

Andrews, James & David, Tal. Arthroscopic Techniques of the Shoulder: A Visual Guide. 2009. (Visual Arthroscopy Ser.). (ENG.). 192p. pap. 99.95 (978-1-55642-838-8(3)) SLACK, Inc.

Burkhart, Steven, et al. The Cowboy's Companion: A Trail Guide for the Arthroscopic Shoulder Surgeon. 2012. (ENG., Illus.). 496p. 275.00 (978-1-60913-797-7(3)) Lippincott Williams & Wilkins.

Cram101 Textbook Reviews & Cram101 Textbook Reviews. Outlines & Highlights for Reconstructive Knee Surgery by Douglas W Jackson, Isbn: 9780781765633 0781765633. 2011. 154p. pap. 28.95 (978-1-61490-008-5(6)) Cram101 Inc.

Della Valle, Craig, ed. Complications in Orthopaedics Revision Total Hip Arthroplasty. 2008. (Complications in Orthopaedics Ser.). per. 55.00 (978-0-89203-500-7(5)) American Academy of Orthopaedic Surgeons.

Duralde, Xavier, ed. Complications in Orthopaedics Shoulder Arthroscopy. 2008. per. 55.00 (978-0-89203-499-4(8)) American Academy of Orthopaedic Surgeons.

Elani, Kriton & Arvidsson, Henri. Arthroscopy: Types, Procedures & Risks. 2012. (Surgery - Procedures, Complications, & Results Ser.). 145p. pap. 65.00 (978-1-61470-955-8(6)) Nova Science Pubs., Inc.

Frankle, Mark A. Rotator Cuff Deficiency of the Shoulder. 2008. 149.95 (978-3-13-141581-3(9)) Thieme Medical Pubs., Inc.

Frankle, Mark A., ed. Rotator Cuff Deficiency of the Shoulder. 2008. (ENG.). 200p. 169.99 (978-1-58890-506-2(3)) Thieme Medical Pubs., Inc.

Gartsman, Gary M. Shoulder Arthroscopy. 2nd ed. 2008. (ENG., Illus.). 392p. 262.00 (978-1-4160-4649-3(6), Saunders) Elsevier - Health Sciences Div.

Gill, Thomas. Arthroscopic Techniques of the Knee: A Visual Guide. 2009. (Visual Arthroscopy Ser.). (ENG.). 256p. pap. 99.95 (978-1-55642-858-6(8)) SLACK, Inc.

Kelly, Bryan T. & Philippon, Marc J. Arthroscopic Techniques of the Hip: A Visual Guide. 2009. (Visual Arthroscopy Ser.). (ENG., Illus.). 192p. pap. 99.95 (978-1-55642-886-9(3)) SLACK, Inc.

Master Skills: Wrist & Elbow Arthroscopy & Reconstruction. 2006. per. 125.00 (978-0-9740018-2-1(1)) American Society for Surgery of the Hand.

McKeon, Brian, et al, eds. Knee Arthroscopy. 2011. (ENG., Illus.). 206p. pap. 99.00 (978-1-4614-1055-3(X), 146141055X) Springer.

McKeon, Brian P., et al. Knee Arthroscopy. McKeon, Brian P. et al, eds. 2009. (ENG., Illus.). xiv, 206p. 199.00 (978-0-387-89503-1(5)) Springer.

Miller, Mark D. Operative Techniques in Sports Medicine Surgery. 2010. (ENG., Illus.). 576p. 189.99 (978-1-4511-0261-1(5)) Lippincott Williams & Wilkins.

Miller, Mark D., et al. Primer of Arthroscopy: Text with DVD. 2010. (ENG., Illus.). 208p. 130.00 (978-1-4377-0155-5(8), Saunders) Elsevier - Health Sciences Div.

Piñal, Francisco del, ed. Arthroscopic Management of Distal Radius Fractures. 2010. (ENG., Illus.). xiv, 264p. 189.00 (978-3-642-05353-5(X), 364205353X) Springer.

Rubin, Lawrence G. Foot & Ankle Arthroscopy: Clinics in Podiatric Medicine & Surgery. 2011. (Clinics: Orthopedics Ser.: 28-3). (ENG., Illus.). 183p. 110.00 (978-1-4557-1050-8(4), Saunders) Elsevier - Health Sciences Div.

Schneider, Diana M. & Lichtenberg, Maggie. The Shoulder Surgery Companion: Preparation & Guidance for Surgery & Rehabilitation. 2011. (ENG.). 160p. pap. 14.95 (978-0-9823219-1-1(0)) DiaMed, LLC.

Sgaglione, Nicholas A. & Hunter, Robert E. The Knee. 2010. (AANA Advanced Arthroscopy Ser.). (ENG., Illus.). 296p. 250.00 (978-1-4377-0664-2(9), Saunders) Elsevier - Health Sciences Div.

Slutsky, David J. New Advances in Wrist & Small Joint Arthroscopy, an Issue of Hand Clinics. 2011. (Clinics: Orthopedics Ser.: 27-3). (ENG., Illus.). xii, 238p. 110.00 (978-1-4557-1100-0(4), Saunders) Elsevier - Health Sciences Div.

Slutsky, David J. & Nagle, Daniel J. Techniques in Wrist & Hand Arthroscopy. 2007. (ENG., Illus.). 280p. 272.00 (978-0-443-06697-9(3), Churchill Livingstone) Elsevier - Health Sciences Div.

ARTHROSIS DEFORMANS

see Rheumatoid Arthritis

ARTHUR, CHESTER ALAN, 1830-1886

Coffin, Charles Carleton. The Life of James A. Garfield. 379p. reprint ed. 98.00 (978-0-7222-8647-0(3)) Library Reprints, Inc.

Dehler, Gregory J., ed. Chester Alan Arthur: the Life of a Gilded Age Politician & President. 2010. (First Men, America's Presidents Series - Peterson, Barbara Bennett (Oregon State University), Series Editor Ser.). pap. 29.00 (978-1-60876-913-1(5)) Nova Science Pubs., Inc.

ARTHUR, KING

Ashe, Geoffrey. King Arthur's Avalon: The Story of Glastonbury. 50th ed. 2008. (ENG., Illus.). 288p. pap. 23.95 (978-0-7509-4881-4(7)) History Pr. Ltd.,The GBR. Dist: Independent Pubs. Group.

Ashley, Mike. A Brief History of King Arthur. 2010. (ENG.). 320p. pap. 13.95 (978-0-7624-3897-6(5)) Running Pr. Bk. Pubs.

Bulfinch, Thomas. The Age of Arthur & His Knights of the Round Table. 2008. 262p. pap. 16.95 (978-1-4357-3145-5(X)) Lulu Enterprises Inc.

Burgess, Glyn S. & Pratt, Karen, eds. Arthur of the French: The Arthurian Legend in Medieval French & Occitan Literature. (ENG.). 2009. 668p. pap. 35.00 (978-0-7083-2196-6(8)) 2006. 637p. 99.95 (978-0-7083-1964-2(5)) Univ. of Wales Pr. GBR. Dist: Chicago Distribution Ctr.

Busby, Keith & Dalrymple, Roger, eds. Arthurian Literature XXIII. 2006. (Arthurian Literature Ser.: Volume 23). (Illus.). 188p. 80.00 (978-1-84384-097-8(9), D. S. Brewer) Boydell & Brewer, Ltd. GBR. Dist: Boydell & Brewer, Inc.

Caitlin & Matthew. The Arthurian Tarot Deck. 2007. (ENG., Illus.). 80p. 14.95 (978-1-85906-210-4(5)) Connections Bk. Publishing, Ltd. GBR. Dist: Red Wheel/Weiser.

Chaucer, Geoffrey. Sir Gawain & the Green Knight. Borroff, Marie, ed. & tr. by. from ENM. Howes, Laura, ed. 2009. (Norton Critical Editions Ser.). (ENG.). 237p. (C). pap. 14.00 net. (978-0-393-93025-2(4), 93025) Norton, W. W. & Co. Inc.

Collier, Neil. King Arthur's Last Command. 2009. 56p. pap. 29.50 (978-0-9558487-0-4(9)) Collier, Neil GBR. Dist: Lulu Enterprises Inc.

Cox, Simon & Oxbrow, Mark. An A to Z of King Arthur & the Holy Grail. 2008. (Simon Cox's A to Z Ser.). (ENG., Illus.). 240p. 23.95 (978-1-84596-075-9(0)) Mainstream Publishing Co., Ltd. GBR. Dist: Independent Pubs. Group.

Dixon-Kennedy, Mike. A Companion to Arthurian & Celtic Myths & Legend. 2006. (ENG., Illus.). 448p. pap. 22.95 (978-0-7509-3311-7(9)) History Pr. Ltd.,The GBR. Dist: Independent Pubs. Group.

Dunning, Robert W. Arthur: The King in the West. 2010. (ENG., Illus.). 160p. pap. 19.99 (978-1-84868-242-9(5)) Amberley Publishing GBR. Dist: Casemate Pubs. & Bk. Distributors, LLC.

Ellis, Ralph. King Jesus: From Egypt (Kam) to Camelot. 2008. (ENG.). 592p. pap. 29.00 (978-1-931882-86-6(X)) Adventures Unlimited Pr.

Frost, James. The Quest for King Arthur. 2010. 164p. pap. 15.72 (978-1-4269-0352-6(9)) Trafford Publishing.

Fulton, Helen, ed. A Companion to Arthurian Literature. (Blackwell Companions to Literature & Culture Ser.: 149). (ENG., Illus.). 2012. 592p. pap. 44.95 (978-0-470-67237-2(4)) 2009. 588p. 219.95 (978-1-4051-5789-6(5)) Wiley, John & Sons, Inc. (Wiley-Blackwell).

Gidlow, Christopher. Reign of Arthur: From History to Legend. 2007. (ENG., Illus.). 288p. pap. 24.95 (978-0-7509-3419-0(0)) History Pr. Ltd.,The GBR. Dist: Independent Pubs. Group.

—Revealing King Arthur: Swords, Stones & Digging for Camelot. 2010. (ENG., Illus.). 256p. 29.95 (978-0-7524-5507-5(9)) History Pr. Ltd.,The GBR. Dist: Independent Pubs. Group.

Hughes, Thomas, et al. Misfortunes of Arthur. (Tudor Facsimile Texts, Old English Plays Ser.: No. 56). reprint ed. 59.50 (978-0-404-53356-4(6)) AMS Pr., Inc.

Hutton, Ronald. Witches, Druids & King Arthur. 2006. (ENG., Illus.). 384p. per. 29.95 (978-1-85285-555-0(X), Hambledon Continuum) Continuum International Publishing Group, Ltd. GBR. Dist: National Bk. Network.

Larrington, Carolyne. King Arthur's Enchantresses: Morgan & Her Sisters in Arthurian Tradition. 2006. (ENG., Illus.). 272p. 40.00 (978-1-84511-113-7(3)) I. B. Tauris & Co., Ltd. GBR. Dist: Macmillan.

Laycock, Stuart. Warlords: The Struggle for Power in Post-Roman Britain. 2009. (ENG., Illus.). 192p. pap. 36.95 (978-0-7524-4796-4(3)) History Pr. Ltd.,The GBR. Dist: Independent Pubs. Group.

Liptak, Gyorgy. Four Arthurs. 2008. 56p. pap. (978-3-639-00936-1(3)) VDM Verlag Dr. Mueller e.K.

Lupack, Alan. The Oxford Guide to Arthurian Literature & Legend. 2007. (Oxford Paperback Reference Ser.). (ENG., Illus.). 512p. per. 17.95 (978-0-19-921509-6(X)) Oxford Univ. Pr., Inc.

Matthews, John. King Arthur: Dark Age Warrior & Mythic Hero. 2008. (Prime Time History Ser.). (Illus.). 127p. (YA). (gr. 9-12). lib. bdg. 39.95 (978-1-4042-1364-7(3)) Rosen Publishing Group, Inc., The.

Matthews, John & Matthews, Caitlin. King Arthur's Raid on the Underworld: The Oldest Grail Quest. 2008. (ENG., Illus.). 145p. 40.00 (978-0-906362-72-3(5)) Gothic Image Pubns. GBR. Dist: SCB Distributors.

Melrose, Robin. The Druids & King Arthur: A New View of Early Britain. 2010. (ENG., Illus.). 220p. pap. 35.00 (978-0-7864-5890-5(9)) McFarland & Co., Inc. Pubs.

Oestreicher, Paul. Camelot, Inc: Leadership & Management Insights from King Arthur & the Round Table. 1 vol. 2011. (Illus.). 152p. 34.95 (978-0-313-38695-4(1), A3140C); xx, 152p. E-Book (978-0-313-38696-1(X)) Greenwood Publishing Group, Inc. (Praeger Pubs.).

Ortenberg, Veronica & Ortenberg. In Search of the Holy Grail: The Quest for the Middle Ages. 2007. (ENG., Illus.). 320p. 27.95 (978-1-85285-532-1(0), Hambledon Continuum) Continuum International Publishing Group, Ltd. GBR. Dist: National Bk. Network.

Preston, Harriet. Troubadours & Trouveres New & Old. 2007. (ENG.). 290p. 43.95 (978-0-548-05144-3(5)) Kessinger Publishing, LLC.

Pyle, Howard. The Story of King Arthur & His Knights. lib. bdg. 25.95 (978-0-8488-2107-4(6)) Amereon LTD.

—The Story of King Arthur & His Knights. 2010. 344p. pap. 32.75 (978-1-146-48684-2(7)) 2010. 334p. pap. 31.75 (978-1-142-48163-6(8)) 2009. 334p. (gr. 5-9). 25.99 (978-1-110-01082-0(6)) 2009. 334p. (gr. 5-9). pap. 19.99 (978-1-110-01079-0(6)) BiblioBazaar.

—The Story of King Arthur & His Knights. 2009. 220p. pap. (978-1-150-63160-3(0)) Books LLC.

—The Story of the Grail & the Passing of Arthur. Date not set. 276p. 23.95 (978-0-8488-2660-4(4)) Amereon LTD.

—The Story of the Grail & the Passing of Arthur. 2009. 206p. (gr. 4-7). pap. (978-1-4589-3859-6(X)) Books LLC.

—The Story of the Grail & the Passing of Arthur. 2008. 276p. 42.95 (978-1-4373-9236-4(9)); (gr. 4-7). pap. 27.95 (978-1-4373-0436-7(2)) Kessinger Publishing, LLC.

Rackham, Arthur. Arthurian Legends. 2011. (ENG., Illus.). 224p. 22.95 (978-1-907892-08-0(7)) National Trust, Aylesbury GBR. Dist: Independent Pubs. Group.

Ranawake, Silvia, et al, eds. The Arthur of the Germans: The Arthurian Legend in Medieval German Literature & Life. 2012. (University of Wales Press - Arthurian Literature in the Middle Ages Ser.). (ENG.). 337p. pap. 65.00 (978-0-7083-2448-6(7)) Univ. of Wales Pr. GBR. Dist: Chicago Distribution Ctr.

Reiser, Oliver Leslie. This Holyest Erthe, the Glastonbury Zodiac & King Arthur's Camelot. 2007. pap. (978-1-59731-201-1(0)) Perennis, Sophia.

Reno, Frank D. Arthurian Figures of History & Legend: A Biographical Dictionary. 2010. (ENG., Illus.). 272p. pap. 39.95 (978-0-7864-4420-5(7)) McFarland & Co., Inc. Pubs.

—Historic Figures of the Arthurian Era: Authenticating the Enemies & Allies of Britain's Post-Roman King. alt. ed. 2009. (ENG., Illus.). 358p. pap. 35.00 (978-0-7864-4509-7(2)) McFarland & Co., Inc. Pubs.

San Souci, Robert D. Young Guinevere. 2011. (J). lib. bdg. (978-0-385-41624-5(5)) Knopf Doubleday Publishing Group.

Snyder, Christopher. The World of King Arthur. 2011. (ENG., Illus.). 192p. pap. 24.95 (978-0-500-28904-4(2), 528904) Thames & Hudson.

Soós-Vass, Nóra. Visions of King Arthur in Different Literary Works. 2008. 76p. pap. (978-3-639-00397-0(7)) VDM Verlag Dr. Mueller e.K.

Stirling, Simon Andrew. The King Arthur Conspiracy: How a Scottish Prince Became a Mythical Hero. 2012. (ENG., Illus.). 320p. 36.95 (978-0-7524-7685-8(8)) History Pr. Ltd.,The GBR. Dist: Independent Pubs. Group.

Tunison, Joseph Salathiel. The Graal Problem from Walter Map to Ric. 2006. pap. 20.95 (978-1-4286-6405-0(X)) Kessinger Publishing, LLC.

Wood, Michael. In Search of Myths & Heroes: Exploring Four Epic Legends of the World. 2007. (Illus.). 272p. per. 21.95 (978-0-520-25170-0(9)) Univ. of California Pr.

ARTHUR, KING—DRAMA

Schiller, F. Wallenstein. 2010. (ENG.). 164p. pap. 20.95 (978-1-84842-051-9(X)) Hern, Nick Bks., Ltd. GBR. Dist: Consortium Bk. Sales & Distribution.

ARTHURIAN ROMANCES

see also Galahad (Legendary Character); Gawain (Legendary Character); Lancelot (Legendary Character); Perceval (Legendary Character)

Anderson, Graham. The Earliest Arthurian Texts: Greek & Latin Sources of the Medieval Texts (Texts, Translations, & Commentary) 2007. 404p. 129.95 (978-0-7734-5376-0(8)) Mellen, Edwin Pr., The.

—King Arthur in Antiquity. 2009. 224p. pap. 39.95 (978-0-415-55500-5(0)) Routledge.

Archibald, Elizabeth & Johnson, David F., eds. Arthurian Literature XXV. 2008. (Arthurian Literature Ser.: Volume 25). (Illus.). 192p. 80.00 (978-1-84384-171-5(1), D. S. Brewer) Boydell & Brewer, Ltd. GBR. Dist: Boydell & Brewer, Inc.

—Arthurian Literature XXVI. 2009. (Arthurian Literature Ser.: Volume 26). 228p. 90.00 (978-1-84384-211-8(4), D. S. Brewer) Boydell & Brewer, Ltd. GBR. Dist: Boydell & Brewer, Inc.

—Arthurian Literature XXVII. 2010. (Arthurian Literature Ser.: Volume 27). 212p. 80.00 (978-1-84384-258-3(0), D. S. Brewer) Boydell & Brewer, Ltd. GBR. Dist: Boydell & Brewer, Inc.

Armitage, Simon. Sir Gawain & the Green Knight: A New Verse Translation. 2008. (ENG.). 208p. pap. 14.95 (978-0-393-33415-9(5), 33415) Norton, W. W. & Co., Inc.

Ashe, Geoffrey. King Arthur's Avalon: The Story of Glastonbury. 50th ed. 2008. (ENG., Illus.). 288p. pap. 23.95 (978-0-7509-4881-4(7)) History Pr. Ltd.,The GBR. Dist: Independent Pubs. Group.

Barron, W. R. J., ed. The Arthur of the English: The Arthurian Legend in Medieval English Life & Literature. 2012. (University of Wales Press - Arthurian Literature in the Middle Ages Ser.). (ENG.). 442p. pap. 65.00 (978-0-7083-2449-3(5)) Univ. of Wales Pr. GBR. Dist: Chicago Distribution Ctr.

Beardsley, Aubrey, illus. Le Morte D'Arthur. 2011. (ENG.). 592p. 29.99 (978-1-904633-97-6(8), 1904633978, Collector's Library) CRW Publishing, Ltd. GBR. Dist: Book Sales, Inc.

Bedier, Joseph. The Romance of Tristan & Iseult. Belloc, Hilaire, tr. 2007. (ENG.). 84p. per. (978-1-4065-3718-5(7)) Dodo Pr.

Bergeron, Guillaume. Les combats chevaleresques dans l'oeuvre de Chrétien de Troyes. 2008. 256p. pap. 64.95 (978-3-03911-012-4(8)) Lang, Peter AG GBR. Dist: Lang, Peter.

Besamusca, Bart, et al, eds. The European Dimensions of Arthurian Literature. 2007. (Arthurian Literature Ser.: Volume 24). (Illus.). 216p. 80.00 (978-1-84384-116-6(9), D. S. Brewer) Boydell & Brewer, Ltd. GBR. Dist: Boydell & Brewer, Inc.

Billings, Anna Hunt. A Guide to the Middle English Metrical Romances, Dealing with English & Germanic Legends, & with the Cycles of Charlemagne & of Arthur. 2008. 264p. 42.95 (978-1-4369-4426-7(0)); pap. 27.95 (978-1-4367-3052-5(X)) Kessinger Publishing, LLC.

Borroff, Marie. The Gawain Poet: Complete Works: Patience, Cleanness, Pearl, Saint Erkenwald, Sir Gawain & the Green Knight. 2011. (ENG., Illus.). 301p. (C). pap. 13.65 net. (978-0-393-91235-7(3), 91235) Norton, W. W. & Co., Inc.

Bowers, John M. An Introduction to TheGawainPoet. 2012. (New Perspectives on Medieval Literature: Authors & Traditions Ser.). (ENG.). 192p. 69.95 (978-0-8130-4015-8(9)) Univ. Pr. of Florida.

Brandsma, Frank. The Interlace Structure of the Third Part of the Prose Lancelot. 2010. (Arthurian Studies: Volume 76). 308p. 99.00 (978-1-84384-257-6(2), D. S. Brewer) Boydell & Brewer, Ltd. GBR. Dist: Boydell & Brewer, Inc.

Bruckner, Matilda Tomaryn. Chrétien Continued: A Study of the Conte du Graal & Its Verse Continuations. 2009. (ENG., Illus.). 296p. 125.00 (978-0-19-955721-9(7)) Oxford Univ. Pr., Inc.

Burgess, Glyn S. & Pratt, Karen, eds. Arthur of the French: The Arthurian Legend in Medieval French & Occitan Literature. (ENG.). 2009. 668p. pap. 35.00 (978-0-7083-2196-6(8)) 2006. 637p. 99.95 (978-0-7083-1964-2(5)) Univ. of Wales Pr. GBR. Dist: Chicago Distribution Ctr.

Busby, Keith & Dalrymple, Roger, eds. Arthurian Literature XXIII. 2006. (Arthurian Literature Ser.: Volume 23). (Illus.). 188p. 80.00 (978-1-84384-097-8(9), D. S. Brewer) Boydell & Brewer, Ltd. GBR. Dist: Boydell & Brewer, Inc.

Chaucer, Geoffrey & Trahern, Joseph B. The Wife of Bath's Prologue & Tale. Allen, Mark & Fisher, John H., eds. 2012. (Variorum Chaucer Ser.). (ENG., Illus.). 776p. 90.00 (978-0-8061-4224-1(3)) Univ. of Oklahoma Pr.

Cherewatuk, Karen & Whetter, K. S., eds. The Arthurian Way of Death: The English Tradition. 2009. (Arthurian Studies: Volume 74). (Illus.). 278p. 90.00 (978-1-84384-208-8(4), D. S. Brewer) Boydell & Brewer, Ltd. GBR. Dist: Boydell & Brewer, Inc.

Chrétien, et al. The Continuations of the Old French Perceval of Chretien de Troyes. 2007. (978-0-87169-301-3(1)) American Philosophical Society.

Cichon, Michael. Violence & Vengeance in Middle Welsh & Middle English Narrative: Owein & Ywain & Gawain. 2009. 264p. 109.95 (978-0-7734-4658-8(3)) Mellen, Edwin Pr., The.

Cooper, Helen, ed. Sir Gawain & the Green Knight. Harrison, Keith, tr. from ENM. 2008. (Oxford World's Classics Ser.). (ENG.). 160p. pap. 10.95 (978-0-19-954016-7(0)) Oxford Univ. Pr., Inc.

Cox, George W. & Jones, Eustace Hinton. Popular Romances of the Middle Ages. 2007. (ENG.). 524p. 55.95 *(978-0-548-09203-3(6))* Kessinger Publishing, LLC.

Däumer, Matthias, et al, eds. Artushof und Artusliteratur. 2010. (Schriften der Internationalen Artusgesellschaft Ser.).Tr. of Court of King Arthur & Arthurian Literature. (GER.). XI, 392p. 140.00 *(978-3-11-022135-0(7))* De Gruyter, Walter Inc.

de Troyes, Chrétien. Arthurian Romances. Comfort, William, tr. 2008. 260p. pap. 9.99 *(978-1-4209-3172-3(5))* Digireads.com.

—Arthurian Romances. 2008. 400p. 39.95 *(978-1-4344-7060-7(1))*; pap. 24.95 *(978-1-4344-7059-1(8))* Wildside Pr., LLC.

—Cligés. 2008. 116p. 24.99 *(978-0-554-27887-2(1))* 2008. 116p. 21.99 *(978-0-554-37190-0(1))* 2007. 104p. pap. 18.99 *(978-1-4346-4239-4(9))* 2007. 114p. pap. 19.99 *(978-1-4346-4240-0(2))* BiblioBazaar.

—Cligés. 2007. 76p. per. *(978-1-4068-4564-8(7))* Echo Library.

—Four Arthurian Romances: Erec et Enide , Cliges , Yvain , & Lancelot. 2009. 300p. pap. *(978-1-4068-9293-2(9))* 2007. 296p. per. *(978-1-4068-4565-5(5))* Echo Library.

—Lancelot. pap. 21.95 incl. audio compact disk *(978-88-7754-785-9(5))* Cideb ITA. Dist: Distribooks, Inc.

—Romans de la Table Ronde: Erec et Enide, Cliges, Lancelot, Yvain (MO) (Folio Ser.: No. 696). (FRE.). pap. 14.95 *(978-2-07-036696-5(0))* Schoenhof's Foreign Bks., Inc.

Dietl, Cora & Lauer, Claudia, eds. Studies in the Role of Cities in Arthurian Literature & in the Value of Arthurian Literature for a Civic Identity: When Arthuriana Meet Civic Spheres. 2009. (ITA, GER & ENG.). vi, 167p. 99.95 *(978-0-7734-3892-7(0))* Mellen, Edwin Pr., The.

Dixon-Kennedy, Mike. A Companion to Arthurian & Celtic Myths & Legend. 2006. (ENG., Illus.). 448p. pap. 22.95 *(978-0-7509-3311-7(9))* History Pr. Ltd.,The GBR. Dist: Independent Pubs. Group.

Dunning, Robert W. Arthur: The King in the West. 2010. (ENG., Illus.). 160p. pap. 19.99 *(978-1-84868-242-9(5))* Amberley Publishing GBR. Dist: Casemate Pubs. & Bk. Distributors, LLC.

Echard, Sian. The Arthur of Medieval Latin Literature. 2011. (University of Wales Press - Arthurian Literature in the Middle Ages Ser.). 199p. 70.00 *(978-0-7083-2201-7(8))* Univ. of Wales Pr. GBR. Dist: Chicago Distribution Ctr.

Eikelmann, Manfred & Tomasek, Tomas. Artusromane nach 1230, Gralromane, Tristanromane 2. 2009. (GER.). XVII, 695p. 293.00 *(978-3-11-017254-6(2))* De Gruyter, Walter Inc.

Elliott, Anna. Twilight of Avalon: A Novel of Trystan & Isolde. 2009. (ENG.). 448p. pap. 16.00 *(978-1-4165-8989-1(9)*, Touchstone) Touchstone.

Faral, Edmond, ed. La Legende Arthurienne, 3 vols., Set. (FRE.). reprint ed. 185.25 *(978-0-404-56515-2(8))* AMS Pr., Inc.

Farina, William. Chretien de Troyes & the Dawn of Arthurian Romance. 2010. (ENG., Illus.). 255p. pap. 35.00 *(978-0-7864-4866-1(0))* McFarland & Co., Inc. Pubs.

Finke, Laurie A. & Shichtman, Martin B. King Arthur & the Myth of History. 2009. (ENG., Illus.). 288p. pap. 29.95 *(978-0-8130-3415-7(9))* Univ. Pr. of Florida.

Fulton, Helen, ed. A Companion to Arthurian Literature. (Blackwell Companions to Literature & Culture Ser.: 149). (ENG., Illus.). 2012. 592p. pap. 44.95 ***(978-0-470-67237-2(4))*** 2009. 588p. 219.95 *(978-1-4051-5789-6(5))* Wiley, John & Sons, Inc. (Wiley-Blackwell).

Gardner, John E., ed. & tr. from ENM. Sir Gawain & the Green Knight: In a Modern English Version with a Critical Introduction. 2011. 224p. pap. 12.00 *(978-0-226-28328-9(3))* Univ. of Chicago Pr.

Greco, Gina L., et al. Dame Philology's Charrette: Approaching Medieval Textuality Through Chrétien's Lancelot: Essays in Memory of Karl D. Uitti. 2012. ***(978-0-86698-456-0(9))*** Arizona State Univ., Arizona Ctr. for Medieval & Renaissance Studies.

Harty, Kevin J., ed. Cinema Arthuriana: Twenty Essays, rev. Ed. alt. ed. 2010. (ENG., Illus.). 317p. pap. 49.95 *(978-0-7864-4683-4(8))* McFarland & Co., Inc. Pubs.

The High History of the Holy Graal. 2007. 418p. pap. 26.99 *(978-1-4346-5023-8(5))*; 468p. pap. 30.99 *(978-1-4346-5024-5(3))* BiblioBazaar.

Higham, N. J. King Arthur: Myth-Making & History. 2008. (Illus.). X, 310p. 33.95 *(978-0-415-48398-8(0))* Routledge.

Hill, Ordelle G. Looking Westward: Poetry, Landscape, & Politics in Sir Gawain & the Green Knight. 2009. (Illus.). 208p. 51.50 *(978-0-87413-049-2(2))* Univ. of Delaware Pr.

Hinton, Thomas. The Conte du Graal Cycle: Chrétien de Troyes' Perceval, the Continuations, & French Arthurian Romance. 2012. (Gallica Ser.: Volume 23). (Illus.). 290p. 99.00 ***(978-1-84384-285-9(8)***, D. S. Brewer) Boydell & Brewer, Ltd. GBR. Dist: Boydell & Brewer, Inc.

Jaffray, Robert. King Arthur & the Holy Grail. 2011. 260p. 47.95 ***(978-1-258-08970-2(X))*** Literary Licensing, LLC.

Kalinke, Marianne E., ed. The Arthur of the North: The Arthurian Legend in the Norse & Rus'realms. 2011. (University of Wales Press - Arthurian Literature in the Middle Ages Ser.). (ENG.). 223p. 85.00 *(978-0-7083-2353-3(7))* Univ. of Wales Pr. GBR. Dist: Chicago Distribution Ctr.

Koprivová, Monika. Women at the Round Table. 2010. 100p. pap. *(978-3-8383-6584-8(4))* Lambert Academic Publishing.

Lacey, Norris J., ed. Lancelot-Grail, Vol. 5. 2010. (Routledge Revivals: Lancelot-Grail Ser.). (ENG.). 450p. 110.00 *(978-0-415-87726-8(1)*, Routledge) Taylor & Francis Group GBR. Dist: Taylor & Francis Group.

—Lancelot-Grail Vol. 2: The Old French Arthurian Vulgate & Post-Vulgate in Translation. 2010. (ENG.). 342p. 110.00 *(978-0-415-87723-7(7)*, Routledge) Taylor & Francis Group GBR. Dist: Taylor & Francis Group.

—Lancelot-Grail Vol. 4: The Old French Arthurian Vulgate & Post-Vulgate in Translation. 2010. (Routledge Revivals: Lancelot-Grail Ser.). (ENG.). 290p. 110.00 *(978-0-415-87725-1(3))* Routledge.

Lacy, Norris, ed. Lancelot-Grail Set: The Old French Arthurian Vulgate & Post-Vulgate in Translation, 10 vols. 2010. pap. 340.00 *(978-0-85991-770-4(3)*, D. S. Brewer) Boydell & Brewer, Ltd. GBR. Dist: Boydell & Brewer, Inc.

—Lancelot-Grail 10: Chapter Summaries for the Vulgate & Post-Vulgate Cycles & Index of Proper Names, 10 vols. 2011. 312p. pap. 45.00 *(978-1-84384-252-1(1)*, D. S. Brewer) Boydell & Brewer, Ltd. GBR. Dist: Boydell & Brewer, Inc.

Lacy, Norris J. Lancelot-Grail: 5 Volumes (Routledge Revivals), 5 vols. 2010. (Routledge Revivals: Lancelot-Grail Ser.). 1888p. 500.00 *(978-0-415-87727-5(X))* Routledge.

—Lancelot-Grail Vol. 1: The Old French Arthurian Vulgate & Post-Vulgate in Translation. 2010. (ENG.). 458p. 110.00 *(978-0-415-87722-0(9))*; 348p. 110.00 *(978-0-415-87724-4(5))* Taylor & Francis Group GBR. (Routledge). Dist: Taylor & Francis Group.

Lacy, Norris J., ed. The History of the Holy Grail: The Old French Arthurian Vulgate & Post-Vulgate in Translation, 10 vols. Chase, Carol J., tr. from FRO. 2010. 348p. pap. 45.00 *(978-1-84384-224-8(6)*, D. S. Brewer) Boydell & Brewer, Ltd. GBR. Dist: Boydell & Brewer, Inc.

—Lancelot-Grail: The Post Vulgate Cycle - The Merlin Continuation - The Old French Arthurian Vulgate & Post-Vulgate in Translation, 10 vols. Asher, Martha, tr. from FRO. 2010. 458p. pap. 45.00 *(978-1-84384-238-5(6)*, D. S. Brewer) Boydell & Brewer, Ltd. GBR. Dist: Boydell & Brewer, Inc.

—Lancelot-Grail No. 5, Pt. V & VI: The Old French Arthurian Vulgate & Post-Vulgate in Translation, 10 vols. Carroll, Carleton W. & Kibler, William W., trs. from FRO. 2010. 448p. pap. 45.00 *(978-1-84384-236-1(X)*, D. S. Brewer) Boydell & Brewer, Ltd. GBR. Dist: Boydell & Brewer, Inc.

—Lancelot-Grail No. 5, Pt. V & VI: The Old French Arthurian Vulgate & Post-Vulgate in Translation, 10 vols. Pickens, Rupert T., tr. from FRO. 2010. 508p. pap. 45.00 *(978-1-84384-234-7(3)*, D. S. Brewer) Boydell & Brewer, Ltd. GBR. Dist: Boydell & Brewer, Inc.

—Lancelot-Grail No. 5, Pt. V & VI: The Old French Arthurian Vulgate & Post-Vulgate in Translation, 10 vols. Burns, E. Jane, tr. from FRO. 2010. 186p. pap. 45.00 *(978-1-84384-237-8(8)*, D. S. Brewer) Boydell & Brewer, Ltd. GBR. Dist: Boydell & Brewer, Inc.

—Lancelot-Grail Pts. 1 & 2: The Old French Arthurian Vulgate & Post-Vulgate in Translation, 10 vols. Carroll, Carleton W. & Rosenberg, Samuel N., trs. from FRO. 2010. 474p. pap. 45.00 *(978-1-84384-226-2(2)*, D. S. Brewer) Boydell & Brewer, Ltd. GBR. Dist: Boydell & Brewer, Inc.

—Lancelot-Grail Pts. 3 & 4: The Old French Arthurian Vulgate & Post-Vulgate in Translation - 4. Lancelot, 10 vols. Krueger, Roberta L. & Rosenberg, Samuel N., trs. from FRO. 2010. 410p. pap. 45.00 *(978-1-84384-235-4(1)*, D. S. Brewer) Boydell & Brewer, Ltd. GBR. Dist: Boydell & Brewer, Inc.

—Lancelot-Grail Vol. 9: The Post-Vulgate Cycle. the Quest for the Holy Grail & the Death of Arthur - The Old French Arthurian Vulgate & Post-Vulgate in Translation, 10 vols. Asher, Martha, tr. from FRO. 2010. 314p. pap. 45.00 *(978-1-84384-233-0(5)*, D. S. Brewer) Boydell & Brewer, Ltd. GBR. Dist: Boydell & Brewer, Inc.

Lacy, Norris J., ed. & tr. from FRO. The Death of Arthur: The Old French Arthurian Vulgate & Post-Vulgate in Translation, 10 vols. 2010. 150p. pap. 45.00 *(978-1-84384-230-9(0)*, D. S. Brewer) Boydell & Brewer, Ltd. GBR. Dist: Boydell & Brewer, Inc.

Lacy, Norris J. & Grimbert, Joan Tasker, eds. A Companion to Chrétien de Troyes. 2008. (Arthurian Studies: Volume 63). 260p. pap. 34.95 *(978-1-84384-161-6(4)*, D. S. Brewer) Boydell & Brewer, Ltd. GBR. Dist: Boydell & Brewer, Inc.

Lambdin, Laura Cooner & Lambdin, Robert Thomas, eds. Arthurian Writers: A Biographical Encyclopedia, 1 vol. 2007. 424p. 95.00 *(978-0-313-34682-8(8)*, GR4682) Greenwood Publishing Group, Inc.

Larrington, Carolyne. King Arthur's Enchantresses: Morgan & Her Sisters in Arthurian Tradition. 2006. (ENG., Illus.). 272p. 40.00 *(978-1-84511-113-7(3))* I. B. Tauris & Co., Ltd. GBR. Dist: Macmillan.

Lupack, Alan. The Oxford Guide to Arthurian Literature & Legend. 2007. (Oxford Paperback Reference Ser.). (ENG., Illus.). 512p. per. 17.95 *(978-0-19-921509-6(X))* Oxford Univ. Pr., Inc.

Maddox, Donald. The Arthurian Romances of Chrétien de Troyes: Once & Future Fictions. 2008. (Cambridge Studies in Medieval Literature Ser.). (ENG.). 196p. pap. 42.00 *(978-0-521-07057-7(0))* Cambridge Univ. Pr.

Malory, Thomas. Le Morte D'Arthur. 2009. 532p. pap. 14.99 *(978-1-4209-3281-2(0))* Digireads.com.

—Le Morte D'Arthur: King Arthur & the Legends of the Round Table. 2010. (ENG.). 576p. (gr. 12-18). 7.95 *(978-0-451-53149-0(3)*, Signet Classics) Penguin Group (USA) Inc.

—Le Morte D'Arthur: The Winchester Manuscript. Cooper, Helen, ed. 2008. (Oxford World's Classics Ser.). (ENG.). 624p. pap. 16.95 *(978-0-19-953734-1(8))* Oxford Univ. Pr., Inc.

—Le MORTE DARTHUR: the Book of King Arthur & of his Noble Knights of the Round Table [volume 1 Of 4]. 2009. 216p. pap. 16.50 *(978-1-4357-4940-5(5))* Lulu Enterprises Inc.

—Le MORTE DARTHUR: the Book of King Arthur & of his Noble Knights of the Round Table [volume 2 Of 4]. 2009. 224p. pap. 16.50 *(978-1-4357-4939-9(1))* Lulu Enterprises Inc.

—Le MORTE DARTHUR: the Book of King Arthur & of his Noble Knights of the Round Table [volume 3 Of 4]. 2009. 252p. pap. 16.50 *(978-1-4357-4938-2(3))* Lulu Enterprises Inc.

—Sir Thomas Malory's Morte Darthur: A New Modern English Translation Based on the Winchester Manuscript. Armstrong, Dorsey, ed. 2009. 698p. pap. 40.00 *(978-1-60235-103-5(1))* Parlor Pr.

Malory, Thomas & Anderson, Rasmus B., eds. The Arthurian Tales: the Greatest of Romances. 2007. pap. 33.95 *(978-1-4304-5014-6(2))* Kessinger Publishing, LLC.

Malory, Thomas & Caxton, William. Le Morte D'Arthur: The Book of King Arthur & of His Noble Knights of the Round Table. 2008. *(978-1-934941-40-9(9))* Red & Black Pubs.

Matthews, John. Arthurian Tradition. 2011. 140p. pap. 21.95 *(978-1-904658-42-9(3))* Aeon Bks. Ltd. GBR. Dist: Stylus Publishing, LLC.

—King Arthur: Dark Age Warrior & Mythic Hero. 2008. (Prime Time History Ser.). (Illus.). 127p. (YA). (gr. 9-12). lib. bdg. 39.95 *(978-1-4042-1364-7(3))* Rosen Publishing Group, Inc., The.

McHardy, Stuart. On the Trail of the Holy Grail. 2006. (On the Trail Of Ser.). (ENG., Illus.). 139p. per. 14.95 *(978-1-905222-53-7(X))* Luath Pr. Ltd. GBR. Dist: Ingram Pub. Services.

Moorman, Charles & Moorman, Ruth. An Arthurian Dictionary. 2011. pap. 30.00 *(978-1-61703-030-7(9))* Univ. Pr. of Mississippi.

Müller, Nicole. Feirefiz - das Schriftstück Gottes. 2008. (Bayreuther Beiträge zur Literaturwissenschaft Ser.). (GER.). 336p. pap. 81.95 *(978-3-631-58164-3(5))* Lang, Peter GmbH, Europaischer Verlag der Wissenschaften DEU. Dist: Lang, Peter.

Oestreicher, Paul. Camelot, Inc: Leadership & Management Insights from King Arthur & the Round Table, 1 vol. 2011. (Illus.). 152p. 34.95 *(978-0-313-38695-4(1)*, A3140C); xx, 152p. E-Book *(978-0-313-38696-1(X))* Greenwood Publishing Group, Inc. (Praeger Pubs.).

Olton, Bert. Arthurian Legends on Film & Television. alt. ed. 2008. (ENG., Illus.). 351p. pap. 35.00 *(978-0-7864-4076-4(7))* McFarland & Co., Inc. Pubs.

Otero Villena, Almudena. Zeitauffassung und Figurenidentität Im "Daniel Von Dem Blühenden Tal" und "Gauriel Von Muntabel" 2007. (Aventiuren Ser.). (GER.). 254p. (C). 53.00 ***(978-3-89971-405-0(9)***, V&R unipress) Vandenhoeck & Ruprecht GmbH & Co. KG DEU. Dist: ISD.

Parshall, Linda B. The Art of Narration in Wolfram's Parzival & Albrecht's Jüngerer Titurel. 2011. (Anglica Germanica Series 2 Ser.). (ENG.). 296p. pap. 36.99 *(978-0-521-16920-2(8))* Cambridge Univ. Pr.

Pochoda, Elizabeth T. Arthurian Propaganda: Le Morte d'Arthur as an Historical Ideal of Life. 2011. (ENG.). 208p. pap. 40.00 ***(978-0-8078-9752-2(3))*** Univ. of North Carolina Pr.

Pyle, Howard. The Story of King Arthur & His Knights. 25.95 *(978-0-89190-662-9(2))*; lib. bdg. 25.95 *(978-0-8488-2107-4(6))* Amereon LTD.

—The Story of the Grail & the Passing of Arthur. Date not set. 276p. 23.95 *(978-0-8488-2660-4(4))* Amereon LTD.

—The Story of the Grail & the Passing of Arthur. 2009. 206p. (gr. 4-7). pap. *(978-1-4589-3859-6(X))* Books LLC.

—The Story of the Grail & the Passing of Arthur. 2008. 276p. 42.95 *(978-1-4373-9236-4(9))*; (gr. 4-7). pap. 27.95 *(978-1-4373-0436-7(2))* Kessinger Publishing, LLC.

Rackham, Arthur. Arthurian Legends. 2011. (ENG., Illus.). 224p. 22.95 *(978-1-907892-08-0(7))* National Trust, Aylesbury GBR. Dist: Independent Pubs. Group.

Raffel, Burton, tr. & pref. Sir Gawain & the Green Knight. 2009. (ENG.). 160p. (Orig.). (gr. 12-18). 6.95 *(978-0-451-53119-3(1)*, Signet Classics) Penguin Group (USA) Inc.

Ranawake, Silvia, et al, eds. The Arthur of the Germans: The Arthurian Legend in Medieval German Literature & Life. 2012. (University of Wales Press - Arthurian Literature in the Middle Ages Ser.). (ENG.). 337p. pap. 65.00 ***(978-0-7083-2448-6(7))*** Univ. of Wales Pr. GBR. Dist: Chicago Distribution Ctr.

Reiser, Oliver Leslie. This Holyest Erthe, the Glastonbury Zodiac & King Arthur's Camelot. 2007. pap. *(978-1-59731-201-1(0))* Perennis, Sophia.

Reno, Frank D. Arthurian Figures of History & Legend: A Biographical Dictionary. 2010. (ENG., Illus.). 272p. pap. 39.95 *(978-0-7864-4420-5(7))* McFarland & Co., Inc. Pubs.

Schmitz, Bernhard A. & Schmitz, Bernhard Anton. Gauvain, Gawein, Walewein: Die Emanzipation des ewig Verspäteten. 2008. (Hermaea Ser.). (GER., Illus.). IX, 342p. pap. *(978-3-484-15117-8(X))* Verlag Max Niemeyer.

Sherman, Joseph, ed. Writers in Yiddish, 333. 2007. (Dictionary of Literary Biography Ser.). (ENG., Illus.). 480p. 315.00 *(978-0-7876-8151-7(2))* Cengage Gale.

Simpson, Roger. Radio Camelot: Arthurian Legends on the BBC, 1922-2005. 2007. (Arthurian Studies: Volume 70). (Illus.). 222p. 90.00 *(978-1-84384-140-1(1)*, D. S. Brewer) Boydell & Brewer, Ltd. GBR. Dist: Boydell & Brewer, Inc.

Snyder, Christopher. The World of King Arthur. 2011. (ENG., Illus.). 192p. pap. 24.95 *(978-0-500-28904-4(2)*, 28904) Thames & Hudson.

Soloveanu, Catalina. Madness in Yvain Re-Reconsidered. 2008. 60p. pap. *(978-3-639-05128-5(9))* VDM Verlag Dr. Mueller e.K.

Stein, Walter Johannes. The Death of Merlin: Arthurian Myth & Alchemy, 1 vol. 2008. (ENG.). 240p. pap. *(978-0-86315-641-0(X))* Floris Bks.

Strong, Gordon. Merlin: Master of Magick. 2010. (ENG.). 216p. pap. 15.95 *(978-0-7387-1847-7(5))* Llewellyn Pubns.

Tether, Leah. The Continuations of Chrétien's Perceval: Content & Construction, Extension & Ending. 2012. (Arthurian Studies: Volume 79). 256p. 95.00 ***(978-1-84384-316-0(1)***, D. S. Brewer) Boydell & Brewer, Ltd. GBR. Dist: Boydell & Brewer, Inc.

Thornton, Robert. Morte Arthure or the Death of Arthur. Brock, Edmund, ed. 2007. (ENG.). 232p. 41.95 *(978-0-548-13252-4(6))* Kessinger Publishing, LLC.

—Morte Arthure or the Death of Arthur. 2006. pap. 26.95 *(978-1-4286-4314-7(1))* Kessinger Publishing, LLC.

Tichelaar, Tyler. King Arthur's Children: A Study in Fiction & Tradition. 2011. *(978-1-61599-067-2(4))*; pap. *(978-1-61599-066-5(6))* Loving Healing Pr., Inc. (Modern History Pr.).

Tindall, Robert. The Battle of the Soul in Sir Gawain & the Green Knight. 2009. 76p. pap. *(978-3-639-16275-2(7))* VDM Verlag Dr. Mueller e.K.

Topsfield, L. T. Chrètien de Troyes: A Study of the Arthurian Romances. 2010. (ENG.). 376p. pap. 31.99 *(978-0-521-15529-8(0))* Cambridge Univ. Pr.

Verbeek, John, et al, eds. Walewein. 2008. (Tekst in Context Ser.). (DUT.). 120p. pap. *(978-90-5356-637-4(6))* Amsterdam Univ. Pr.

Von Aue, Hartmann. German Romance Vol. 3: Iwein or the Knight with the Lion. Edwards, Cyril, ed. & tr. by. from GEH. 2007. (Arthurian Archives Ser.: Volume 16). (GEH & ENG., Illus.). 450p. 99.00 *(978-1-84384-084-8(7))* Camden Hse.

von Eschenbachth cent, Wolfram. Parzival & Titurel. Edwards, Cyril, tr. from GER. 2009. (Oxford World's Classics Ser.). (ENG., Illus.). 464p. pap. 14.95 *(978-0-19-953920-8(0))* Oxford Univ. Pr., Inc.

Von Stoffeln, Konrad. German Romance: Gauriel Von Muntabel. Christoph, Siegfried Richard, ed. & tr. by. from GEH. 2007. (Arthurian Archives Ser.: Volume 15). (GEH & ENG.). 368p. 90.00 *(978-1-84384-077-0(4))* Camden Hse.

von Zatzikhoven, Ulrich. German Romance - Lanzelet. Meyer, Kathleen J., ed. & tr. by. from GEH. 2011. (Arthurian Archives Ser.: Volume 17). (GEH & ENG.). 530p. 99.00 *(978-1-84384-266-8(1)*, D. S. Brewer) Boydell & Brewer, Ltd. GBR. Dist: Boydell & Brewer, Inc.

—Lanzelet 1: Band 1: Text und Übersetzung. Band 2: Forschungsbericht und Kommentar, 2 vols. Kragl, Florian, ed. 2006. (GER & GEH.). XIX, 1389p. 461.00 *(978-3-11-018936-0(4))* De Gruyter, Walter Inc.

Waite, Arthur Edward. The Holy Grail: History, Legend & Symbolism. 2006. (Dover Books on the Occult). (ENG., Illus.). 640p. per. 29.95 *(978-0-486-45279-1(4))* Dover Pubns., Inc.

—The Holy Grail Legend & the Enchantments of Britain, the Times. 2006. pap. 9.95 *(978-1-4304-3401-6(5))* Kessinger Publishing, LLC.

Weston, Jessie L., tr. from GER. Tristan & Iseult, 2 vols., Set. reprint ed. 45.00 *(978-0-404-10038-4(4))* AMS Pr., Inc.

Weston, Jessie Laidlay. Sir Gawain & the Green Knight. 2009. 58p. pap. *(978-0-217-55493-0(8))* Books LLC.

Willingham. The Mort Artu: Edition the 13th Century Text from Yale 229, with Critical Essays, Notes and. 2008. (Illustrated Lancelot Prose Ser.). (ENG & FRO., Illus.). 322p. (C). pap. 124.00 *(978-2-503-51676-9(9))* Brepols Pubs. BEL. Dist: ISD.

Wolfzettel, Friedrich, ed. Körperkonzepte Im Arthurischen Roman. 2007. (Schriften der Internationalen Artusgesellschaft Ser.). (GER., Illus.). XIII, 476p. pap. *(978-3-484-10806-6(1))* Verlag Max Niemeyer.

ARTHURIAN ROMANCES—ADAPTATIONS

Álvarez-Faedo, María José. Avalon Revisited: Re-Workings of the Arthurian Myth. 270p. pap. 55.95 *(978-3-03911-231-9(7))* Lang, Peter Publishing, Inc.

B dier, M. Romance of Tristan & Iseult. 2006. 116p. 22.95 *(978-1-59818-383-2(4))* Aegypan.

Bashkirtseff, Marie. The Romance of Tristan & Iseult. Nicolosi, Vincent, ed. Belloc, Hilaire & Kernberger, Katherine, trs. 2011. (ENG.). 228p. 30.00 *(978-0-9844677-5-4(0))* Fonthill Pr., LLC.

Bedier, J. The Romance of Tristan & Iseult. Belloc, Hilaire, tr. 2010. 190p. 30.36 ***(978-1-169-28097-7(8))***; pap. 18.36 ***(978-1-162-62096-1(X))*** Kessinger Publishing, LLC.

Bedier, J. & Bedier, J. The Romance of Tristan & Iseult. Belloc, Hilaire, tr. 2010. 190p. 37.95 *(978-1-161-40410-4(4))* Kessinger Publishing, LLC.

Bédier, Joseph. The Romance of Tristan & Iseult. 2010. 200p. pap. 23.75 *(978-1-177-18640-7(3))* BiblioBazaar.

—The Romance of Tristan & Iseult. 2010. (Illus.). 48p. pap. 20.00 *(978-1-77045-170-4(6))* General Bks. LLC.

Bedier, M. Joseph. The Romance of Tristan & Iseult. 2010. 76p. pap. 5.85 ***(978-1-61720-096-0(4))*** Wilder Pubns., Ltd.

Boyle, Louis J. T. H. White's Reinterpretation of Malory's le Morte Darthur: An Analysis of Shifting Meaning & Unstable Language. 2009. 200p. 99.95 *(978-0-7734-4814-8(4))* Mellen, Edwin Pr., The.

Bulfinch, Thomas. The Age of Arthur & His Knights of the Round Table. 2008. 262p. pap. 16.95 *(978-1-4357-3145-5(X))* Lulu Enterprises Inc.

Clement, Nemours H. The Influence of the Arthurian Romances on the Five Books of Rabelais. 2011. 116p. 39.95 ***(978-1-258-05448-9(5))*** Literary Licensing, LLC.

Green, Thomas. Arthuriana: Early Arthurian Tradition & the Origins of the Legend. 2009. 290p. pap. 27.50 *(978-1-4452-2110-6(1))* Lulu Enterprises Inc.

Gurteen, S. Humphreys. Arthurian Epic A Comparative Study of Th. 2006. pap. 37.95 *(978-1-4286-5560-7(3))* Kessinger Publishing, LLC.

Hollick, Helen. The Kingmaking. 2009. (ENG.). 592p. pap. 16.99 *(978-1-4022-1888-0(5)*, Sourcebooks Landmark) Sourcebooks, Inc.

James, Cary. King & Raven. Date not set. *(978-0-312-85889-6(2),* Tor Bks.) Doherty, Tom Assocs., LLC.
Knowles, James. The Legends of King Arthur & His Knights. 2008. 284p. 25.99 *(978-0-554-33683-1(9))* 2008. 284p. 28.99 *(978-0-554-24380-1(6))* 2007. (ENG.). 248p. pap. 20.99 *(978-1-4264-6397-6(9))* 2007. 282p. pap. 23.99 *(978-1-4264-6471-3(1))* BiblioBazaar.
—The Legends of King Arthur & His Knights. 2007. (Illus.). 296p. per. *(978-1-4065-2932-5(X))* Dodo Pr.
—The Legends of King Arthur & His Knights. 2007. (ENG., Illus.). 280p. per. *(978-1-4068-2537-4(9))* Echo Library.
Malory, Thomas. The Death of King Arthur: The Immortal Legend. 2011. (ENG.). 336p. (gr. 12). 26.95 *(978-0-670-02307-3(8),* Viking Adult) Penguin Group (USA) Inc.
Morris, Gerald & Renier, Aaron. The Adventures of Sir Lancelot the Great. 2009. (Knights' Tales Ser.). (ENG., Illus.). 96p. (J). (gr. 3-7). pap. 4.99 *(978-0-547-23756-5(1),* Sandpiper) Houghton Mifflin Harcourt Trade & Reference Pubs.
Pyle, Howard. The Story of the Champions of the Round. 2006. pap. *(978-1-4068-3430-7(0))* Echo Library.
—The Story of the Champions of the Round Table. 25.95 *(978-0-89190-661-2(4))* Amereon LTD.
—The Story of the Champions of the Round Table. 2010. 356p. pap. 32.75 *(978-1-142-59179-3(4))* 2008. 416p. 30.99 *(978-0-554-32714-3(7))* 2008. 416p. 32.99 *(978-0-554-23411-3(4))* 2007. 372p. pap. 25.99 *(978-1-4264-4364-0(1))* 2007. (ENG.). 414p. pap. 28.99 *(978-1-4264-4402-9(8))* BiblioBazaar.
—The Story of the Champions of the Round Table. 2008. (Illus.). 412p. per. *(978-1-4065-6457-0(5))* Dodo Pr.
—The Story of the Champions of the Round Table. 2009. 228p. pap. 29.22 *(978-1-150-40978-3(9))* General Bks. LLC.
—The Story of the Champions of the Round Table (Illustrated by Howard Pyle) 2008. (Illus.). 352p. pap. 19.95 *(978-1-4344-6238-1(2))* Wildside Pr., LLC.
—The Story of the Champions of the Round Table [Illustrated by Howard Pyle]. 2008. 352p. 35.00 *(978-1-4344-6239-8(0))* Wildside Pr., LLC.
San Souci, Robert D. Young Guinevere. 2011. (J). lib. bdg. *(978-0-385-41624-5(5))* Knopf Doubleday Publishing Group.
Sutcliff, Rosemary. Sword at Sunset. 2008. (Rediscovered Classics Ser.). (ENG., Illus.). 512p. pap. 14.95 *(978-1-55652-759-3(4))* Chicago Review Pr., Inc.
Tennyson, Alfred Lord. Enid. 2007. (Illus.). 132p. (YA). pap. 14.95 *(978-1-60355-067-3(4))* Juniper Grove.
Wolf, Joan. The Road to Avalon. 2007. (Rediscovered Classics Ser.). (ENG.). 368p. pap. 14.95 *(978-1-55652-658-9(X))* Chicago Review Pr., Inc.

ARTICLES OF WAR
see Military Law

ARTICULATIO TEMPOROMANDIBULIS
see Temporomandibular Joint

ARTICULATION (EDUCATION)
Ecclestone, Kath. Change & Becoming Through the Lifecourse: Transitions & Learning in Education & Life. 2009. (ENG., Illus.). 240p. 140.00 *(978-0-415-48173-1(2))* Routledge.
Gilbert, Daymon W. & Swiney, Kathy A. Sound Strategies for Sound Production: A Multisensory Approach for Improving Intelligibility: Clinician's Manual. 2007. (Illus.). xviii, 123p. 48.00 *(978-1-4164-0123-0(7))* PRO-ED, Inc.
Hoffman, Nancy, et al, eds. Minding the Gap: Why Integrating High School with College Makes Sense & How to Do It. 2007. 330p. (ENG.). lib. bdg. 59.95 *(978-1-891792-46-5(6));* per. 29.95 *(978-1-891792-45-8(8))* Harvard Education Publishing Group (HEPG). (Harvard Education Pr.).
Mayers, Jr. Ph. D. Chalmers & Mayers, Jr. Segregation, Integration, & Resegregation in a Deep-Southern Town. 2010. 124p. pap. *(978-3-8383-5553-1(0))* Lambert Academic Publishing.
Mumy, Ana Paula. Articulation Strategies That Work: Effective Therapy Tools for Student Success. 2008. (ENG.). 48p. spiral bd. 89.00 net. *(978-0-9799245-4-5(5))* Northern Speech Services.
Simmons, Roberta G. & Blyth, Dale. Moving into Adolescence: The Impact of Pubertal Change & School Context. 2008. (ENG., Illus.). 457p. pap. 49.95 *(978-0-202-36294-6(9))* Aldine Transaction.

ARTICULATION DISORDERS
Bauman-Waengler, Jacqueline. Articulatory & Phonological Impairments: A Clinical Focus. 4th ed. 2011. (ENG.). 480p. (C). 135.40 *(978-0-13-256356-7(8))* Allyn & Bacon, Inc.
Bernthal, John E., et al. Articulation & Phonological Disorders. 6th ed. 2008. (ENG.). 480p. (C). 135.40 *(978-0-205-56926-7(9))* Allyn & Bacon, Inc.
Brooks, Adriana Pena & Hegde, M. N. Sound Stimuli: Volume 6 for Assessment & Treatment Protocols for Articulation & Phonological Disorders, 8 vols., Vol. 6. 2007. (Illus.). spiral bd. 14.95 *(978-1-59756-133-4(9))* Plural Publishing, Inc.
Cram101 Textbook Reviews. Outlines & Highlights for Articulation & Phonological Disorders by John E Bernthal, Nicholas W Bankson, Peter Flipsen, Isbn: 9780205569267 0205569. 2011. 268p. pap. 31.95 ***(978-1-61490-445-8(6))*** Cram101 Inc.
Cram101 Textbook Reviews & Cram101 Textbook Reviews. Outlines & Highlights for Clinical Management of Articulatory & Phonologic Disorders by Mary E Gordon-Brannan, Isbn: 9780781729512. 2011. 236p. pap. 31.95 ***(978-1-61461-231-5(5))*** Cram101 Inc.
Gilbert, Daymon W. & Swiney, Kathy A. Sound Strategies for Sound Production: A Multisensory Approach for Improving Intelligibility: Clinician's Manual. 2007. (Illus.). xviii, 123p. 48.00 *(978-1-4164-0123-0(7))* PRO-ED, Inc.
Hall, Penelope K., et al. Developmental Apraxia of Speech: Theory & Clinical Practice. 2nd ed. 2006. (Illus.). xv, 378p. 55.00 *(978-1-4164-0191-9(1))* PRO-ED, Inc.
Hegde, M. N. & Pena-Brooks, Adriana. Sound Stimuli: Volume 8 for Treatment Protocols for Articulation & Phonological Disorders, 8 vols., Vol. 8. 2007. (Illus.). spiral bd. 14.95 *(978-1-59756-135-8(5))* Plural Publishing, Inc.
Lowit, Anja & Kent, Raymond D., eds. Assessment of Motor Speech Disorders. 2010. 346p. pap. 79.95 *(978-1-59756-367-3(6))* Plural Publishing, Inc.
McNeil, Malcolm Ray. Clinical Management of Sensorimotor Speech Disorders. 2nd ed. 2008. (ENG., Illus.). 448p. 84.99 *(978-1-58890-514-7(4))* Thieme Medical Pubs., Inc.
Pena-Brooks, Adriana & Hedge, M. N. Assessment & Treatment of Articulation & Phonological Disorders in Children, Complete Kit. 2nd ed. 2007. 624p. 102.00 *(978-1-4164-0229-9(2))* PRO-ED, Inc.
Peña-Brooks, Adriana & Hegde, M. N. Articulation & Phonological Disorders: Assessment & Treatment Resource Manual. 2007. xiv, 319p. 60.00 *(978-1-4164-0231-2(4))* PRO-ED, Inc.
—Assessment & Treatment of Articulation & Phonological Disorders in Children. 2nd ed. 2006. (Illus.). xix, 624p. 75.00 *(978-1-4164-0230-5(6))* PRO-ED, Inc.
Pena-Brooks, Adriana & Hegde, M. N. Sound Stimuli: Volume 1 for Treatment Protocols for Articulation & Phonological Disorders, 8 vols., Vol. 1. 2007. (Illus.). spiral bd. 14.95 *(978-1-59756-128-0(2))* Plural Publishing, Inc.
—Sound Stimuli: Volume 3 for Treatment Protocols for Articulation & Phonological Disorders, 8 vols., Vol. 3. 2007. (Illus.). spiral bd. 14.95 *(978-1-59756-130-3(4))* Plural Publishing, Inc.
—Sound Stimuli: Volume 5 for Assessment & Treatment Protocols for Articulation & Phonological Disorders, 8 vols., Vol. 5. 2007. (Illus.). spiral bd. 14.95 *(978-1-59756-132-7(0))* Plural Publishing, Inc.
—Sound Stimuli: Volume 7 for Assessment & Treatment Protocols for Articulation & Phonological Disorders, 8 vols., Vol. 7. 2007. (Illus.). (gr. -1-3). spiral bd. 14.95 *(978-1-59756-134-1(7))* Plural Publishing, Inc.
—Sound Stimuli For /t/ /d/ /k/ /g/ /f/ /v/ /s/ /z/ /sh/ /ch/: Volume 4 for Assessment & Treatment Protocols for Articulation & Phonological Disorders. 2007. (Illus.). spiral bd. 59.95 *(978-1-59756-131-0(2))* Plural Publishing, Inc.
Robertson, Sandra & Thomson, Fay. Working with Dysarthrics: A Practical Guide to Therapy for Dysarthria. (Illus.). 100p. spiral bd. *(978-0-86388-365-1(6),* 002-0100) Speechmark Publishing Ltd.
Robertson, Sandra, et al. Dysarthria Sourcebook: Exercises to Photocopy. 140p. spiral bd. *(978-0-86388-428-3(8),* 002-0355) Speechmark Publishing Ltd.
Ruscello, Dennis M. Treating Articulation & Phonological Disorders in Children. 2007. (ENG., Illus.). 288p. (C). per. 68.95 *(978-0-323-03387-9(3),* Mosby) Elsevier - Health Sciences Div.
Rvachew, Susan & Brosseau-Lapre, Francoise. Developmental Phonological Disorders: Foundations of Clinical Practice. 2012. (Illus.). 574p. (C). pap. 89.95 *(978-1-59756-377-2(3))* Plural Publishing, Inc.
Sicola, Laura. No, they won't just sound like each Other: NNS-NNS Negotiated Interaction & Attention to Phonological Form on Targeted L2 Pronunciation Tasks. 2008. (Duisburger Arbeiten zur Sprach- und Kulturwissenschaft. Duisburg Papers on Research in Language & Culture Ser.). 130p. pap. 39.95 *(978-3-631-58476-7(8))* Lang, Peter GmbH, Europaischer Verlag der Wissenschaften DEU. Dist: Lang, Peter.

ARTICULATIONS
see Joints

ARTIFICIAL ANUS
see Colostomy

ARTIFICIAL BLOOD
see Blood Substitutes

ARTIFICIAL BLOOD CIRCULATION
see Blood—Circulation, Artificial

ARTIFICIAL CARDIAC PACING
see Cardiac Pacing

ARTIFICIAL CONSCIOUSNESS
see Conscious Automata

ARTIFICIAL DELAY LINES
see Delay Lines

ARTIFICIAL DIAMONDS
see Diamonds, Artificial

ARTIFICIAL FEEDING
British Pharmaceutical Nutrition Group, et al. Handbook of Drug Administration Via Enteral Feeding Tubes. 2006. (Illus.). 416p. 75.00 *(978-0-85369-648-3(9))* Pharmaceutical Pr. GBR. Dist: Smith Fulfillment Services.
Heiser, Angela. Rat Jugular Vein & Carotid Artery Catheterization for Acute Survival Studies: A Practical Guide. 2007. (Illus.). 115p. spiral bd. 114.00 *(978-0-387-49414-2(6))* Springer.
Kaur, Meera. Medical Foods from Natural Sources. 2008. (ENG., Illus.). xxvii, 212p. 129.00 *(978-0-387-79377-1(1),* 0387793771) Springer.
Koletzko, B., et al. Paediatric Parenteral Nutrition: A Practical Reference Guide. 2008. (Illus.). 66p. pap. *(978-3-8055-8606-1(X))* Karger, S. AG.
Krapfl, Lee Ann. Specialists Speak Series: Ostomies & Feeding Tube Management. rev. ed. 2008. (ENG.). 68p. (C). spiral bd. 39.95 *(978-1-58254-043-6(8))* Kendall Hunt Publishing Co.
Peter Austin Michael Stroud Staff. Prescribing Adult Intravenous Nutrition. 2007. (Illus.). 300p. pap. 59.99 *(978-0-85369-658-2(6))* Pharmaceutical Pr. GBR. Dist: Smith Fulfillment Services.
Skipper, Annalynn. Dietitian's Handbook of Enteral & Parenteral Nutrition. 3rd rev. ed. 2011. 364p. (C). 98.95 *(978-0-7637-4290-4(2))* Jones & Bartlett Learning, LLC.
Tollefsen, Christopher, ed. Artificial Nutrition & Hydration: The New Catholic Debate. (Philosophy & Medicine / Catholic Studies in Bioethics Ser.). 2010. xii, 230p. pap. 179.00 *(978-90-481-7567-3(4),* 9048175674) 2007. 229p. 179.00 *(978-1-4020-6206-3(0),* 1402062060) Springer.

ARTIFICIAL FIBERS
see Textile Fibers, Synthetic

ARTIFICIAL FLIES
see Flies, Artificial

ARTIFICIAL FLOWERS
Bellows, Nora. Noni Flowers: 40 Exquisite Knitted Flowers. 2012. (ENG., Illus.). 176p. pap. 24.99 ***(978-0-307-58671-1(5),*** Potter Craft) Crown Publishing Group.
Beveridge, Ardith. Faux Florals in Glass: 30-Plus Unique Arrangements in Clear Vases & Other Glassware. 2008. (ENG., Illus.). 144p. pap. 19.99 *(978-1-58923-423-9(5),* 1589234235, Creative Publishing International) Quayside.
Cockburn, Susan Tierney. Paper Bouquet: Using Paper Punches to Create Beautiful Flowers. 2008. (ENG., Illus.). 128p. pap. 14.95 *(978-1-60059-059-7(4))* Lark Bks.
Epstein, Nicky. Nicky Epstein's Knitted Flowers. 2010. (ENG., Illus.). 136p. pap. 19.95 *(978-1-933027-94-4(0))* Sixth&Spring Bks.
Hamilton, Anne & White, Kathleen. Making Silk Flowers. (Illus.). 144p. pap. 7.95 *(978-1-85391-153-8(4))* J.B. Fairfax Pr.
Hickey, Julie. Flower Power Papercrafts. 2008. (ENG., Illus.). 128p. pap. 19.99 *(978-0-7153-2867-5(0))* David & Charles Pubs. GBR. Dist: F&W Media, Inc.
Jueh-yu, Tai-yin. Paper Flowers. (Illus.). 120p. pap. *(978-957-629-241-5(7))* Hilit Publishing Co., Ltd.
Larsen, Cony. Crochet Bouquet: Quick-and-Easy Patterns for Adorable Flowers, Headbands & Hats. 2011. (Design Originals Ser.). (ENG., Illus.). 44p. pap. 12.99 ***(978-1-57421-346-1(6))*** Design Originals.
Swift, Jennifer. Creative Bloom: Projects & Inspiration with Fabric & Wire. 2010. (ENG., Illus.). 128p. pap. 24.99 *(978-1-4403-0316-6(9),* North Light Bks.) F&W Media, Inc.
Thompson, Suzann. Crochet Garden: Bunches of Flowers, Leaves, & Other Delights. 2012. (ENG., Illus.). 132p. pap. 16.95 ***(978-1-60059-927-9(3))*** Lark Bks.

ARTIFICIAL FUELS
see Synthetic Fuels

ARTIFICIAL HEART
see Heart, Artificial

ARTIFICIAL IMPLANTS
see Implants, Artificial

ARTIFICIAL INSEMINATION
see also Artificial Insemination, Human
Abdul Razzaque, Waquar Ahmed. Superovulatory Response with Injection of Fsh-P in Crossbred Cows. 2011. 76p. pap. ***(978-3-8443-0344-5(8),*** Lambert Academic Publishing.
Bansal, Amrit Kaur. Measurement & Prevention of Oxidative Stress in Bull Spermatozoa. 2010. 132p. pap. *(978-3-8383-3459-2(0))* Lambert Academic Publishing.
Dawn. What My Mother Never Told Me, 1 vol. 2009. 61p. pap. 12.95 *(978-1-61546-143-1(4))* PublishAmerica, Inc.
Farooq, Dr. Umer & Farooq, Umer. Factors Affecting a I in Cattle & Buffalo of Pakistan. 2010. 64p. pap. *(978-3-8383-8654-6(X))* Lambert Academic Publishing.
Patton, Phillip E. & Battaglia, David E., eds. Office Andrology. 2010. (Contemporary Endocrinology Ser.). (Illus.). 320p. pap. 159.00 *(978-1-61737-491-3(1),* 1617374911) Humana Pr.
Rütz, Eva Maria K. Heterologe Insemination - Die rechtliche Stellung des Samenspenders: Lösungsansätze zur rechtlichen Handhabung. 2009. (GER.). xxii, 249p. pap. *(978-3-540-75709-2(0))* Springer Singapore Pte. Ltd.
Samper, Juan C. Equine Breeding Management & Artificial Insemination. 2nd ed. 2008. (ENG., Illus.). 336p. 119.00 *(978-1-4160-5234-0(8),* Saunders) Elsevier - Health Sciences Div.
Schatten, Heide & Constantinescu, Gheorghe M. Comparative Reproductive Biology. 2007. (ENG., Illus.). 432p. 157.99 *(978-0-8138-1554-1(1),* Wiley-Blackwell) Wiley, John & Sons, Inc.
Swelum, Ayman. Some Trials for Improving Cryopreservation of Buffalo-Bull Semen. 2011. 156p. pap. ***(978-3-8383-3991-7(6))*** Lambert Academic Publishing.

ARTIFICIAL INSEMINATION, HUMAN
Abouighar, Mohamed & Rizk, Botros, eds. Ovarian Stimulation. 2010. (ENG., Illus.). 288p. 99.00 *(978-0-521-19735-9(X))* Cambridge Univ. Pr.
Almeling, Rene. Sex Cells: The Medical Market for Eggs & Sperm. 2011. (ENG., Illus.). 240p. 60.00 *(978-0-520-27095-4(9));* pap. 24.95 *(978-0-520-27096-1(7))* Univ. of California Pr.
Birk, Dewinder. Human Fertilisation & Embryology: The New Law. Birk, Dewinder, ed. 2009. (New Law Ser.). (ENG.). 448p. pap. *(978-1-84661-138-4(5))* Jordan Publishing, Ltd.
Committee on Assessing the Medical Risks of Human Oocyte Donation for Stem Cell Research & National Research Council. Assessing the Medical Risks of Human Oocyte Donation for Stem Cell Research: Workshop Report. Giudice, Linda et al, eds. 2007. (ENG.). 112p. pap. 29.75 *(978-0-309-10355-8(X))* National Academies Pr.
Dickey, Richard P., et al, eds. Manual of Intrauterine Insemination & Ovulation Induction. 2009. (ENG., Illus.). 200p. pap. 66.00 *(978-0-521-73562-9(9))* Cambridge Univ. Pr.
Edwards, Jeanette. European Kinship in the Age of Biotechnology. 2009. 232p. 90.00 *(978-1-84545-573-6(8))* Berghahn Bks., Inc.
John, Henrike. Die genetische Veränderung des Erbgutes menschlicher Embryonen: Chancen und Grenzen im deutschen und amerikanischen Recht. 2009. (Recht & Medizin Ser.). (GER.). 344p. pap. 81.95 *(978-3-631-58495-8(4))* Lang, Peter GmbH, Europaischer Verlag der Wissenschaften DEU. Dist: Lang, Peter.
Jones, Caroline. Why Donor Insemination Requires Developments in Family Law: The Need for New Definitions of Parenthood. 2007. 316p. *(978-0-7734-5257-2(5))* Mellen, Edwin Pr., The.
Kennedy, Jayne. Using a sperm donor - a patient's Guide. 2010. 36p. pap. 21.50 *(978-1-4452-7223-8(7))* Lulu Enterprises Inc.
Kindregan, Charles P. & McBrien, Maureen. Assisted Reproductive Technology: A Lawyer's Guide to the Emerging Law & Science. 2nd ed. 2012. (ENG.). 447p. pap. 89.95 ***(978-1-61632-093-5(1))*** American Bar Assn.
Mamo, Laura. Queering Reproduction: Achieving Pregnancy in the Age of Technoscience. 2007. (ENG., Illus.). 320p. (C). 89.95 *(978-0-8223-4057-7(7));* per. 24.95 *(978-0-8223-4078-2(X))* Duke Univ. Pr.
Morrissette, Mikki, ed. Voices of Donor Conception: Behind Closed Doors: Moving Beyond Secrecy & Shame. 2006. per. *(978-0-9772042-1-2(9))* Be-Mondo Publishing.
Plotz, David. The Genius Factory: The Curious History of the Nobel Prize Sperm Bank. 2006. (ENG., Illus.). 288p. per. 14.95 *(978-0-8129-7052-4(7),* Random Hse. Trade Paperbacks) Random House Publishing Group.
Vogt, Britta. Methoden der künstlicher Befruchtung. Dreierregel versus Single Embryo Transfer: Konflikt zwischen Rechtslage und Fortschritt der Reproduktionsmedizin in Deutschland im Vergleich mit sieben europäischen Ländern. 2008. (Recht & Medizin Ser.). 220p. pap. 56.95 *(978-3-631-57668-7(4))* Lang, Peter GmbH, Europaischer Verlag der Wissenschaften DEU. Dist: Lang, Peter.

ARTIFICIAL INTELLIGENCE
see also Adaptive Control Systems; Automatic Theorem Proving; Computer Vision; Error-Correcting Codes (Information Theory); GPS (Computer Program); Heuristic Programming; Knowledge Representation (Information Theory); Machine Translating; Natural Language Processing (Computer Science); Neural Networks (Computer Science); Perceptrons; Question-Answering Systems
A. Elbaset, Adel & H. El-Tamaly, H. Interconnecting Issues of Pv/Wind Hybrid System with Electric Utility. 2011. 264p. pap. ***(978-3-8443-0868-6(7))*** Lambert Academic Publishing.
A Halim, Shamimi & Ahmad, Rashidi. Snake Identification System. 2010. 120p. pap. *(978-3-8383-5224-4(6))* Lambert Academic Publishing.
Aarno, Daniel. Recognizing Intentions: Improving Human-Machine Collaboration by Recognizing Intentions. 2008. 116p. pap. *(978-3-639-09381-0(X))* VDM Verlag Dr. Mueller e.K.
Abbass, Hussein A. & Wiles, Janet, eds. Progress in Artificial Life: Third Australian Conference, ACAL 2007 Gold Coast, Australia, December 4-6, 2007 Proceedings. 2007. (Lecture Notes in Artificial Intelligence Ser.). (Illus.). 402p. pap. 89.95 *(978-3-540-76930-9(7))* Springer.
Abraham, Ajith, et al, eds. Innovations in Intelligent Systems. 2010. (Studies in Fuzziness & Soft Computing Ser.). xxvi, 468p. pap. 299.00 *(978-3-642-05784-7(5),* 3642057845) Springer.
—International Symposium on Distributed Computing & Artificial Intelligence. 2011. (Advances in Intelligent & Soft Computing Ser.). (Illus.). xvi, 448p. pap. 259.00 *(978-3-642-19933-2(X),* 364219933X) Springer.
—Stigmergic Optimization. 2006. (Studies in Computational Intelligence Ser.). (Illus.). xviii, 299p. 169.00 *(978-3-540-34689-0(9),* 3540346899) Springer.
—Swarm Intelligence in Data Mining. (Illus.). 2010. (Studies in Computational Intelligence Ser.). xviii, 267p. pap. 169.00 *(978-3-642-07117-1(1),* 3642071171) 2006. (Studies in Computational Intelligence: Vol. 34). XVIII, 267p. 169.00 *(978-3-540-34955-6(3),* 3540349553) Springer.
Abstraction, Reformulation, & Approximation: 7th International Symposium, SARA 2007 Whistler, Canada, July 1 18-21, 2007 Proceedings. 2007. (Lecture Notes in Computer Science Ser.). (Illus.). 418p. per. 79.95 *(978-3-540-73579-3(8))* Springer.
Abu-Khalaf, Murad, et al. Nonlinear H2/H-Infinity Constrained Feedback Control: A Practical Design Approach Using Neural Networks. 2006. (Advances in Industrial Control Ser.). (Illus.). xx, 203p. 159.00 *(978-1-84628-349-9(3),* 1846283493) Springer.
Achterberg, Tobias & Beck, J. Christopher, eds. Integration of AI & OR Techniques in Constraint Programming for Combinatorial Optimization Problems: 8th International Conference, CPAIOR 2011, Berlin, Germany, May 23-27, 2011. Proceedings. 2011. (Lecture Notes in Computer Science / Theoretical Computer Science & General Issues Ser.). (Illus.). x, 253p. pap. 72.00 *(978-3-642-21310-6(3),* 3642213103) Springer.
ACTA Press Staff, compiled by. IASTED International Conference on Internet & Multimedia Systems & Applications. 2007. 216p. pap. 157.00 *(978-1-60423-345-2(1))* Curran Assocs., Inc.

Adamatzky, Andrew & Komosinski, Maciej, eds. Artificial Life Models in Hardware. 2009. (ENG., Illus.). xviii, 270p. 99.00 *(978-1-84882-529-1(3)*, 1848825293) Springer.

Adeniran, Ahmed, et al. Artificial Intelligence Techniques in Reservoir Characterization. 2010. 156p. pap. *(978-3-639-24426-7(5))* VDM Verlag Dr. Mueller e.K.

Advances in artificial general intelligence. 2007. 137.00 *(978-1-58603-758-1(7))* IOS Pr., Inc.

Advances in Artificial Intelligence - Iberamia 2008. 2008. (Lecture Notes in Computer Science / Lecture Notes in Artificial Intelligence Ser.). spiral bd. 99.00 *(978-3-540-88308-1(8))* Springer.

Advances in Artificial Intelligence: 20th Conference of the Canadian Society for Computational Studies of Intelligence, Canadian AI 2007, Montreal, Canada, May 28-30, 2007 Proceedings. 2007. (Lecture Notes in Artificial Intelligence Ser.). (Illus.). 552p. per. 109.00 *(978-3-540-72664-7(0))* Springer.

Advances in Neural Networks - ISNN 2007: 4th International Symposium on Neutral Networks, ISNN 2007 Nanjing, China, June 3-7, 2007: Proceedings, Part I. 2007. (Lecture Notes in Computer Science Ser.). 1365p. pap. 189.00 *(978-3-540-72382-0(X))* Springer.

Agent & Multi-Agent Systems: Technologies & Applications: First KES International Symposium, KES-AMSTA 2007 Wroclaw, Poland, May 31-June 1, 2007 Proceedings. 2007. (Lecture Notes in Computer Science Ser.). (Illus.). 1046p. pap. 159.00 *(978-3-540-72829-0(5))* Springer.

Aghajan, Hamid, et al, eds. Human-Centric Interfaces for Ambient Intelligence. 2009. (ENG., Illus.). xxvii, 514p. 134.00 *(978-0-12-374708-2(2)*, Academic Pr.) Elsevier Science & Technology Bks.

Agotnes, T., ed. Stairs 2010: Proceedings of the Fifth Starting AI Researchers' Symposium - Frontiers in Artificial Intelligence & Applications. 2011. 380p. 189.00 ***(978-1-60750-675-1(0))*** IOS Pr., Inc.

Aguilera, Marcos K., et al, eds. Distributed Computing & Networking: 12th International Conference, ICDCN 2011, Bangalore, India, January 2-5, 2011, Proceedings. 2010. (Lecture Notes in Computer Science / Theoretical Computer Science & General Issues Ser.). xvii, 420p. pap. 95.00 *(978-3-642-17678-4(X)*, 364217678X) Springer.

Aha, David W., ed. Lazy Learning. 2010. 432p. pap. 145.00 *(978-90-481-4860-8(X)*, 904814860X) Springer.

Ahmad, Khurshid, ed. Affective Computing & Sentiment Analysis: Emotion, Metaphor & Terminology. 2011. (Text, Speech & Language Technology Ser.). (ENG., Illus.). xiv, 148p. 139.00 *(978-94-007-1756-5(3)*, 9400717563) Springer.

Ahmad, Khurshid, et al, eds. Words & Intelligence I: Selected Papers by Yorick Wilks. (Text, Speech & Language Technology Ser.). xii, 280p. 2010. pap. 169.00 *(978-90-481-7330-3(2)*, 9048173302) 2007. 169.00 *(978-1-4020-5284-2(7)*, 1402052847) Springer.

—Words & Intelligence II: Essays in Honor of Yorick Wilks. 2010. (Text, Speech & Language Technology Ser.). xiv, 279p. pap. 159.00 *(978-90-481-7451-5(1)*, 9048174511) Springer.

AI*Ia 2007: Artificial Intelligence & Human-Oriented Computing: 10th Congress of the Italian Association for Artificial Intelligence, Rome, Italy, September 10-13, 2007, Proceedings. 2007. (Lecture Notes in Computer Science Ser.). (Illus.). 859p. pap. 139.00 *(978-3-540-74781-9(8))* Springer.

Akman, Varol, et al, eds. Intelligent CAD Systems II: Implementational Issues. 2007. (Focus on Computer Graphics Ser.). (Illus.). x, 324p. 109.00 *(978-3-540-50914-1(3))* Springer.

Al. Computational Intelligence in Decision. . 2008. (Illus.). xxvi, 1173p. 252.00 *(978-981-279-946-3(X))* World Scientific Publishing Co., Inc.

AI 2008. 2008. (Lecture Notes in Computer Science / Lecture Notes in Artificial Intelligence Ser.). spiral bd. 109.00 *(978-3-540-89377-6(6)*, 3540893776) Springer.

Albornoz, Alvaro de & Reyes, Carlos A. MICAI 2006: Advances in Artificial Intelligence: 5th Mexican International Conference on Artificial Intelligence, Apizaco, Mexico, November 13-17, 2006: Proceedings. 2006. (Lecture Notes in Computer Science Ser.). (Illus.). XXVIII, 1232p. pap. 179.00 *(978-3-540-49026-5(4)*, 3540490264) Springer.

Alesso, H. Peter & Smith, Craig F. Thinking on the Web: Berners-Lee, Gödel & Turing. 2008. (ENG., Illus.). 292p. pap. 35.95 *(978-0-471-76866-1(9)*, Wiley-Interscience) Wiley, John & Sons, Inc.

Ali, Moonis & Dapoigny, Richard. Advances in Applied Artificial Intelligence: 19th International Conference on Industrial, Engineering & Other Applications of Applied Intelligent Systems, IEA/AIE 2006, Annecy, France, June 27-30, 2006, Proceedings. 2006. (Lecture Notes in Computer Science Ser.). (Illus.). XXIII, 1353p. pap. 149.00 *(978-3-540-35453-6(0)*, 3540354530) Springer.

Aliseda, Atocha. Abductive Reasoning: Logical Investigations into Discovery & Explanation. 2010. (Synthese Library). xvi, 225p. pap. 189.00 *(978-90-481-6993-1(3)*, 9048169933) Springer.

Alkhalifa, Eshaa M. & Gaid, Khulood. Cognitively Informed Intelligent Interfaces: Systems Design & Development. 2012. ***(978-1-4666-1630-1(X))***; ***(978-1-4666-1628-8(8))*** IGI Global.

Allenby, Braden R. & Sarewitz, Daniel R. The Techno-Human Condition. 2011. (ENG., Illus.). 240p. (gr. 17). 24.95 *(978-0-262-01569-1(2))* MIT Pr.

Almeida e Costa, Francesco. Advances in Artificial Life: 9th European Conference, ECAL 2007, Lisbon, Portugal, September 10-14, 2007, Proceedings. 2007. (Lecture Notes in Computer Science / Lecture Notes in Artificial Intelligence Ser.). (Illus.). xviii, 1215p. pap. 179.00 *(978-3-540-74912-7(8))* Springer.

Alonso, Eduardo & Mondragn, Esther, eds. Computational Neuroscience for Advancing Artificial Intelligence: Models, Methods & Applications. 2010. (Illus.). 350p. 245.00 *(978-1-60960-021-1(5)*, Medical Information Science Reference) IGI Global.

Alsinet, T & Puyol-Gruart, J., eds. Artificial Intelligence Research & Development: Proceedings of the 11th International Conference of the Catalan Association for Artificial Intelligence - Volume 184 Frontiers in Artificial Intelligence & Applications. 2008. (Illus.). 324p. 179.00 *(978-1-58603-925-7(3))* IOS Pr., Inc.

Alvarez, Jose R. & Mira, Jose, eds. Bio-Inspired Modeling of Cognitive Tasks: Second International Work-Conference on the Interplay Between Natural & Artificial Computation, IWINAC 2007. 2007. (Lecture Notes in Computer Science Ser.). (Illus.). 626p. pap. 119.00 *(978-3-540-73052-1(4))* Springer.

An, Aijun. Foundations of Intelligent Systems: 17th International Symposium, ISMIS 2008, Toronto, Canada, May 20-23, 2008. 2008. (Lecture Notes in Computer Science / Lecture Notes in Artificial Intelligence Ser.). (Illus.). spiral bd. 119.00 *(978-3-540-68122-9(1)*, 3540681221) Springer.

Anastassiou, George A. Intelligent Systems: Approximation by Artificial Neural Networks: Approximation by Artificial Neural Networks. 2011. (Intelligent Systems Reference Library). viii, 108p. 129.00 *(978-3-642-21430-1(4)*, 3642214304) Springer.

Anderson, Michael & Anderson, Susan Leigh, eds. Machine Ethics. 2011. (ENG., Illus.). 546p. (C). 99.00 *(978-0-521-11235-2(4))* Cambridge Univ. Pr.

Andrews, Paul S., et al. Artificial Immune Systems: 8th International Conference, ICARIS 2009, York, UK, August 9-12, 2009, Proceedings. 2009. (Lecture Notes in Computer Science / Theoretical Computer Science & General Issues Ser.). (ENG.). xi, 343p. pap. 79.95 *(978-3-642-03245-5(1)*, 3642032451) Springer.

Andrews, Simon, et al, eds. Conceptual Structures for Discovering Knowledge: 19th International Conference on Conceptual Structures, ICCS 2011, Derby, UK, July 25-29, 2011, Proceedings. 2011. (Lecture Notes in Computer Science / Lecture Notes in Artificial Intelligence Ser.). (Illus.). xiv, 424p. pap. 95.00 ***(978-3-642-22687-8(6)***, 3642226876) Springer.

Angulo, Cecilio & Godo, L. Artificial intelligence research & Development. 2007. 163.00 *(978-1-58603-798-7(6))* IOS Pr., Inc.

Anifowose, Fatai. Hybrid Ai Models for the Characterization of Oil & Gas Reservoirs. 2009. 148p. pap. *(978-3-639-14312-6(4))* VDM Verlag Dr. Mueller e.K.

Annicchiarico, Roberta, et al, eds. Agent Technology & E-Health. 2008. (Whitestein Series in Software Agent Technologies & Autonom Ser.). (Illus.). 148p. pap. 59.95 *(978-3-7643-8546-0(4))* Springer.

Antoniou, Grigoris, et al. Advances in Artificial Intelligence: 4th Helenic Conference on AI, SETN 2006, Heraklion, Crete, Greece, May 18-20, 2006, Proceedings. 2006. (Lecture Notes in Computer Science Ser.). (Illus.). XVII, 611p. pap. 109.00 *(978-3-540-34117-8(X)*, 354034117X) Springer.

Antoniou, Grigoris, et al, eds. The Semantic Web: Research & Applications: 8th Extended Semantic Web Conference, ESWC 2011, Heraklion, Crete, Greece, May 29 - June 2, 2011. Proceedings, Part II, 2 vols. 2011. (Lecture Notes in Computer Science / Information Systems & Applications, incl. Internet/Web, & HCI Ser.). (Illus.). xxiv, 520p. pap. 107.00 *(978-3-642-21063-1(5)*, 3642210635) Springer.

Antunes, Luis, et al. Multi-Agent-Based Simulation VIII: International Workshop, MABS 2007, Honolulu, HI, USA, May 15, 2007, Revised & Invited Papers. 2008. (Lecture Notes in Computer Science / Lecture Notes in Artificial Intelligence Ser.). ix, 141p. pap. 59.95 *(978-3-540-70915-2(0))* Springer.

Antunes, Luis & Pinto, H. Sofia, eds. Progress in Artificial Intelligence: 15th Portuguese Conference on Artificial Intelligence, EPIA 2011, Lisbon, Portugal, October 10-13, 2011, Proceedings. 2011. (Lecture Notes in Computer Science / Lecture Notes in Artificial Intelligence Ser.). (ENG., Illus.). xxv, 706p. pap. 131.00 ***(978-3-642-24768-2(7)***, 3642247687) Springer.

Ao, Sio-Iong, et al, eds. Intelligent Automation & Computer Engineering. 2009. (Lecture Notes in Electrical Engineering Ser.). (Illus.). x, 501p. 199.00 *(978-90-481-3516-5(8)*, 9048135168) Springer.

—Intelligent Automation & Systems Engineering. 2011. (Lecture Notes in Electrical Engineering Ser.). (ENG., Illus.). x, 430p. 179.00 ***(978-1-4614-0372-2(3)***, 1461403723) Springer.

—Intelligent Control & Innovative Computing. 2012. (Lecture Notes in Electrical Engineering Ser.). (ENG., Illus.). ix, 436p. 179.00 ***(978-1-4614-1694-4(9)***, 1461416949) Springer.

Archibald, Margaret, et al. Infinity in Logic & Computation: International Conference, ILC 2007, Cape Town, South Africa, November 3-5, 2007, Revised Selected Papers. 2009. (Lecture Notes in Computer Science / Lecture Notes in Artificial Intelligence Ser.). (ENG., Illus.). xiii, 139p. pap. 69.95 *(978-3-642-03091-8(2)*, 3642030912) Springer.

Aroyo, Lora, et al, eds. The Semantic Web — ISWC 2011: 10th International Semantic Web Conference, Bonn, Germany, October 23-27, 2011, Proceedings, Part I, 2 vols. 2011. (Lecture Notes in Computer Science / Information Systems & Applications, incl. Internet/Web, & HCI Ser.). (ENG., Illus.). xxiv, 813p. pap. 143.00 ***(978-3-642-25072-9(6)***, 3642250726) Springer.

—The Semantic Web — ISWC 2011: 10th International Semantic Web Conference, Bonn, Germany, October 23-27, 2011, Proceedings, Part II, 2 vols. 2011. (Lecture Notes in Computer Science / Information Systems & Applications, incl. Internet/Web, & HCI Ser.). (ENG., Illus.). xxiv, 395p. pap. 95.00 ***(978-3-642-25092-7(0)***, 3642250920) Springer.

Artificial Brains: An Evolved Neural Net Module Approach. 2011. 95.00 *(978-981-4304-27-6(1))* World Scientific Publishing Co., Inc.

Artificial Intelligence in Theory & Practice III: Third IFIP TC 12 International Conference on Artificial Intelligence, IFIP AI 2010, Held as Part of WCC 2010, Brisbane, Australia, September 20-23, 2010, Proceedings. 2010. (IFIP Advances in Information & Communication Technology Ser.). xv, 251p. 119.00 *(978-3-642-15285-6(6)*, 3642152856) Springer.

Artificial Neural Networks - ICANN 2006: 16th International Conference Athens, Greece, September 10-14, 2006 Proceedings, Part I, 2 vols. 2006. (Lecture Notes in Computer Science Ser.). (Illus.). 1008p. pap. 159.00 *(978-3-540-38625-4(4)*, 3540386254) Springer.

Artificial Neural Networks - ICANN 2006: 16th International Conference Athens, Greece, September 10-14, 2006 Proceedings, Part II, 2 vols. 2006. (Lecture Notes in Computer Science Ser.). (Illus.). 1028p. pap. 159.00 *(978-3-540-38871-5(0)*, 3540388710) Springer.

Artikis, Alexander, et al. Engineering Societies in the Agents World IX: 9th International Workshop, ESAW 2008, Saint-Etienne, France, September 24-26, 2008, Revised Selected Papers. 2009. (Lecture Notes in Computer Science / Lecture Notes in Artificial Intelligence Ser.). x, 281p. pap. 69.95 *(978-3-642-02561-7(7)*, 3642025617) Springer.

Asada, Minoru. From Animals to Animats 10: 10th International Conference on Simulation of Adaptive Behavior, SAB 2008, Osaka, Japan, July 7-12 2008, Proceedings. 2008. (Lecture Notes in Computer Science / Lecture Notes in Artificial Intelligence Ser.). (Illus.). xiii, 530p. pap. 99.00 *(978-3-540-69133-4(2)*, 3540691332) Springer.

Asama, Hajime, et al, eds. Distributed Autonomous Robotic System 8. 2009. (ENG., Illus.). xii, 588p. 259.00 *(978-3-642-00643-2(4)*, 3642006434) Springer.

Association for Computing Machinery (ACM) Staff, compiled by. International Workshop on the Role of Abstraction in Software Engineering (ROA'06) 2007. 28p. pap. 50.00 *(978-1-60423-111-3(4))* Curran Assocs., Inc.

—3rd International Conference on Knowledge Capture (K-CAP'05) 2007. 224p. pap. 93.00 *(978-1-60423-086-4(X))* Curran Assocs., Inc.

—9th International Conference on Artificial Intelligence & Law (ICAIL 2003) 2007. 291p. pap. 93.00 *(978-1-60423-122-9(X))* Curran Assocs., Inc.

—10th International Conference on Artificial Intelligence & Law (ICAIL 2005) 2007. 257p. pap. 93.00 *(978-1-60423-087-1(8))* Curran Assocs., Inc.

—11th International Conference on Artificial Intelligence & Law (ICAIL 2007) 2007. 269p. pap. 93.00 *(978-1-60423-399-5(0))* Curran Assocs., Inc.

Athar, Atifa & Ahmed, Khalil. Emotion Dynamics for Artificially Intelligent Agents. 2010. 84p. pap. *(978-3-639-25799-1(5))* VDM Verlag Dr. Mueller e.K.

Aubin, Jean-Pierre. Neural Networks & Qualitative Physics: A Viability Approach. 2011. (ENG.). 302p. pap. 60.00 *(978-1-107-40284-3(0))* Cambridge Univ. Pr.

Augusto, J. C. & Aghajan, H., eds. Workshop Proceedings of the 7th International Conference on Intelligent Environments. 2011. 844p. pap. 160.00 ***(978-1-60750-794-9(3))*** IOS Pr., Inc.

Augusto, Juan Carlos & Shapiro, Daniel. Advances in ambient Intelligence. 2007. 130.00 *(978-1-58603-800-7(1))* IOS Pr., Inc.

Ausiello, Giorgio, et al, eds. Fifth Ifip International Conference on Theoretical Computer Science - Tcs 2008: Ifip 20th World Computer Congress, Tc 1, Foundations of Computer Scien. 2008. (IFIP International Federation for Information Processing Ser.). XII, 553p. 219.00 *(978-0-387-09679-7(5)*, 0387096795) Springer.

Autexier, Serge, et al. Intelligent Computer Mathematics: 10th International Conference, AISC 2010, 17th Symposium, Calculemus 2010, & 9th International Conference, MKM 2010, Paris, France, July 5-10, 2010. Proceedings. 2010. (Lecture Notes in Computer Science / Lecture Notes in Artificial Intelligence Ser.). xv, 471p. pap. 99.00 *(978-3-642-14127-0(7)*, 3642141277) Springer.

Avison, David, et al, eds. The Past & Future of Information Systems: 1976 -2006 & Beyond: 1976 -2006 & Beyond. 2006. (International Federation for Information Processing (Series): Vol. 214). (Illus.). xviii, 254p. 169.00 *(978-0-387-34631-1(7)*, 0387346317) Springer.

Aßmann, Uwe, et al, eds. Reasoning Web. Semantic Technologies for Software Engineering: 6th International Summer School 2010, Dresden, Germany, August 30 - September 3, 2010. Tutorial Lectures. 2010. (Lecture Notes in Computer Science / Information Systems & Applications, incl. Internet/Web, & HCI Ser.). ix, 183p. pap. 72.00 *(978-3-642-15542-0(1)*, 3642155421) Springer.

Bacardit, Jaume, et al, eds. Learning Classifier Systems: 10th International Workshop, IWLCS 2006, Seattle, MA, USA, July 8, 2006, & 11th International Workshop, IWLCS 2007, London, UK, July 8, 2007 Revised Selected Papers. 2008. (Lecture Notes in Artifial Intelligence Ser.). (Illus.). 305p. pap. 79.95 *(978-3-540-88137-7(9))* Springer.

Bacchus, Fahiem, et al, eds. Proceedings of the Twenty-First International Conference on Automated Planning & Scheduling (ICAPS-11) 2011. (Illus.). 360p. pap. 50.00 ***(978-1-57735-503-8(2))*** AAAI Pr.

Bach, Joscha. Principles of Synthetic Intelligence PSI: An Architecture of Motivated Cognition. 2009. (Oxford Series on Cognitive Models & Architectures Ser.). (ENG., Illus.). 400p. 75.00 *(978-0-19-537067-6(8))* Oxford Univ. Pr., Inc.

Bach, Joscha & Edelkamp, Stefan, eds. KI 2011: Advances in Artificial Intelligence: 34th Annual German Conference on AI, Berlin, Germany, October 4-7,2011, Proceedings. 2011. (Lecture Notes in Computer Science / Lecture Notes in Artificial Intelligence Ser.). (ENG., Illus.). xiv, 370p. pap. 83.00 ***(978-3-642-24454-4(8)***, 3642244548) Springer.

Badica, Costin & Paprzycki, Marcin, eds. Advances in Intelligent & Distributed Computing: Proceedings of the 1st International Symposium on Intelligent & Distributed Computing Idc'2007, Craiova, Romania, October 2007. 2007. (Studies in Computational Intelligence Ser.). (Illus.). 309p. 159.00 *(978-3-540-74929-5(2))* Springer.

Baig, Mariam. Case-Based Reasoning. 2009. 136p. pap. *(978-3-639-15522-8(X))* VDM Verlag Dr. Mueller e.K.

Baker, Stephen. Final Jeopardy: Man vs. Machine & the Quest to Know Everything. 2011. (ENG.). 288p. 24.00 *(978-0-547-48316-0(3))* Houghton Mifflin Harcourt Trade & Reference Pubs.

Baker, Stephen. Final Jeopardy: The Story of Watson, the Computer That Will Transform Our World. 2012. (ENG.). 288p. pap. 14.95 ***(978-0-547-74719-4(5)***, Mariner Bks.) Houghton Mifflin Harcourt Trade & Reference Pubs.

Balcázar, José L., et al, eds. Machine Learning & Knowledge Discovery in Databases: European Conference, ECML PKDD 2010, Barcelona, Spain, September 20-24, 2010. Proceedings, Part I. 2010. (Lecture Notes in Computer Science / Lecture Notes in Artificial Intelligence Ser.). xxx, 620p. pap. 119.00 *(978-3-642-15879-7(X)*, 364215879X) Springer.

Baltes, Jacky, et al. RoboCup 2009: Robot Soccer World Cup XIII: Robot Soccer World Cup XIII. 2010. (Lecture Notes in Computer Science / Lecture Notes in Artificial Intelligence Ser.). 460p. pap. 99.00 *(978-3-642-11875-3(5)*, 3642118755) Springer.

Bandyopadhyay, Samir Kumar, et al, eds. Information Security & Assurance: 4th International Conference, ISA 2010, Miyazaki, Japan, June 23-25, 2010, Proceedings. 2010. (Communications in Computer & Information Science Ser.). 350p. pap. 99.00 *(978-3-642-13364-0(9)*, 3642133649) Springer.

Baofu, Peter. The Future of Post-Human Computing: A Preface to a New Theory of Hardware, Software, & the Mind. 2011. 532p. ***(978-1-907343-46-9(6))*** Cambridge International Science Publishing, Ltd.

Baral, Chitta. Knowledge Representation, Reasoning & Declarative Problem Solving. 2010. (ENG.). 548p. pap. 65.00 *(978-0-521-14775-0(1))* Cambridge Univ. Pr.

Barbakh, Wesam Ashour, et al. Non-Standard Parameter Adaptation for Exploratory Data Analysis. 2009. (Studies in Computational Intelligence Ser.). (Illus.). xii, 228p. 159.00 *(978-3-642-04004-7(7)*, 3642040047) Springer.

Bargiela, Andrzej & Pedrycz, Witold, eds. Human-Centric Information Processing Through Granular Modelling. 2009. (Studies in Computational Intelligence Ser.). (Illus.). viii, 404p. 199.00 *(978-3-540-92915-4(0))* Springer.

Baroni, P., et al, eds. Computational Models of Argument: Proceedings of COMMA 2010 - Volume 216 Frontiers in Artificial Intelligence & Applications. 2010. 210.00 *(978-1-60750-618-8(1))* IOS Pr., Inc.

Batyrshin, Ildar & Sidorov, Grigori, eds. Advances in Artificial Intelligence: 10th Mexican International Conference on Artificial Intelligence, MICAI 2011, Puebla, Mexico, November 26 - December 4, 2011, Proceedings, Part I. 2011. (Lecture Notes in Computer Science / Lecture Notes in Artificial Intelligence Ser.). (ENG., Illus.). xxv, 598p. pap. 119.00 ***(978-3-642-25323-2(7)***, 3642253237) Springer.

—Advances in Soft Computing: 10th Mexican International Conference on Artificial Intelligence, MICAI 2011, Puebla, Mexico, November 26 - December 4, 2011, Proceedings, Part II. 2011. (Lecture Notes in Computer Science / Lecture Notes in Artificial Intelligence Ser.). (ENG., Illus.). xxv, 540p. pap. 107.00 ***(978-3-642-25329-4(6)***, 3642253296) Springer.

Bechhofer, Sean. The Semantic Web: Research & Applications: 5th European Semantic Web Conference, ESWC 2008, Tenerife, Canary Islands, Spain, June 1-5, 2008. 2008. (Lecture Notes in Computer Science / Information Systems & Applications, incl. Internet/Web, & HCI Ser.). (Illus.). 916p. spiral bd. 149.00 *(978-3-540-68233-2(3)*, 3540682333) Springer.

Beck, J. Christopher & Smith, Barbara. Integration of AI & or Techniques in Constraint Programming for Combinatorial Optimization Problems: Third International Conference, CPAIOR 2006, Cork, Ireland, May 31 - June 2, 2006, Proceedings. 2006. (Lecture Notes in Computer Science Ser.: Vol. 3990). (Illus.). X, 301p. pap. 79.95 *(978-3-540-34306-6(7)*, 3540343067) Springer.

Becker-Asano, C., ed. Wasabi: Affect Simulation for Agents with Believable Interactivity - Volume 319 Dissertations in Artificial Intelligence. 2008. 232p. pap. 75.00 *(978-1-58603-911-0(3))* IOS Pr., Inc.

Bekele, Elias Getahun. Integrated Modeling System for Multi-Objective Watershed Management. 2008. 180p. pap. *(978-3-639-08097-1(1))* VDM Verlag Dr. Mueller e.K.

Bellazzi, Riccardo, et al, eds. Artificial Intelligence in Medicine: 11th Conference on Artificial Intelligence in Medicine in Europe, Aime 2007, Amsterdam, the Netherlands, July 7-11, 2007, Proceedings. 2007. (Lecture Notes in Artificial Intelligence Ser.). (Illus.). 509p. per. 89.95 *(978-3-540-73598-4(4))* Springer.

Bello Pena, David. Implementación de métodos de búsqueda Inteligencia Artificial. 2008. 85p. pap. 20.95 *(978-1-4092-2033-6(8))* Lulu Enterprises Inc.

Belpaeme, Tony, et al. Symbol Grounding. 2009. *(978-90-272-2251-0(7))* Benjamins, John Publishing Co.

Ben-Ari, Guy & Adams, Gordon. Transforming European Militaries: Coalition Operations & the Technology Gap. 2006. (Contemporary Security Studies). (Illus.). 176p. 160.00 *(978-0-415-39264-8(0))* Routledge.

Ben Yahia, Sadok, et al. Concept Lattices & Their Applications: Fourth International Conference, CLA 2006, Tunis, Tunisia, October 30 - November 1, 2006: Selected Papers. 2008. (Lecture Notes in Computer Science / Lecture Notes in Artificial Intelligence Ser.). (Illus.). xii, 281p. pap. 69.95 *(978-3-540-78920-8(0))* Springer.

Benferhat, Salem & Grant, John, eds. Scalable Uncertainty Management: 5th International Conference, SUM 2011, Dayton, OH, USA, October 10-13, 2011, Proceedings. 2011. (Lecture Notes in Computer Science / Lecture

Notes in Artificial Intelligence Ser.). (ENG., Illus.). xii, 562p. pap. 107.00 (978-3-642-23962-5(5), 3642239625) Springer.

Benyoucef, Lyes & Grabot, Bernard, eds. Artificial Intelligence Techniques for Networked Manufacturing Enterprises Management. 2010. (Springer Series in Advanced Manufacturing Ser.). (ENG., Illus.). xxvi, 510p. 239.00 (978-1-84996-118-9(2), 1849961182) Springer.

Benz, Anton, et al. Language, Games, & Evolution. 2011. (Lecture Notes in Computer Science / Lecture Notes in Artificial Intelligence Ser.). vii, 189p. pap. 72.00 (978-3-642-18005-7(1), 3642180051) Springer.

Bergler, S. Advances in Artificial Intelligence: 21st Conference of the Canadian Society for Computational Studies of Intelligence, Canadian AI 2008, Windsor, Canada, May 28-30, 2008: Proceedings. 2008. (Lecture Notes in Computer Science / Lecture Notes in Artificial Intelligence Ser.). (Illus.). xi, 382p. pap. 79.95 (978-3-540-68821-1(8)) Springer.

Berlatsky, Noah. Artificial Intelligence. 2011. (Opposing Viewpoints Ser.). (ENG.). 240p. (J). (gr. 10-12). pap. 28.90 (978-0-7377-5710-1(8), Greenhaven Pr., Inc.) Cengage Gale.

Berlatsky, Noah, ed. Artificial Intelligence. 2011. (Opposing Viewpoints Ser.). (ENG.). 240p. (J). (gr. 10-12). 41.70 (978-0-7377-5709-5(4), Greenhaven Pr., Inc.) Cengage Gale.

Bernstein, Randal B. & Curtis, Wesley N. Artificial Intelligence: New Research. 2008. (Illus.). x, 463p. 129.00 (978-1-60456-282-8(X)) Nova Science Pubs., Inc.

Bersini, Hugues & Carneiro, Jorge. Artificial Immune Systems: 5th International Conference, ICARIS 2006, Oeiras, Portugal, September 4-6, 2006, Proceedings. 2006. (Lecture Notes in Computer Science Ser.: Vol. 4163). (Illus.). 460p. pap. 99.00 (978-3-540-37749-8(2), 3540377492) Springer.

Berthold, M. & Hand, D. Intelligent Data Analysis: An Introduction. 2nd rev. ed. 2007. (Illus.). xi, 514p. 95.00 (978-3-540-43060-5(1), 3540430601) Springer.

Berthold, Michael R. & Hand, David J., eds. Intelligent Data Analysis: An Introduction. 2nd ed. 2010. (Illus.). xi, 514p. pap. 95.00 (978-3-642-07707-4(2), 3642077072) Springer.

Berthold, Michael R., et al. Foundations of Intelligent Data Analysis: Making Practical Sense of Real Data. 2010. (Texts in Computer Science Ser.). (ENG., Illus.). xii, 397p. 89.95 (978-1-84882-259-7(6), 1848822596) Springer.

Berto, Francesco, et al. The Mathematics of the Models of Reference. 2010. 186p. pap. (978-1-84890-011-0(2)) College Pubns.

Besnard, Philippe & Hunter, Anthony. Elements of Argumentation. 2008. (ENG., Illus.). 312p. (gr. 17). 38.00 (978-0-262-02643-7(0)) MIT Pr.

Besnard, Philippe, et al. Computational Models of Argument: Proceedings of COMMA 2008. 2008. (Illus.). ix, 429p. 210.00 (978-1-58603-859-5(1)) IOS Pr., Inc.

Bessis, Nik & Xhafa, Fatos, eds. Next Generation Data Technologies for Collective Computational Intelligence. 2011. (Studies in Computational Intelligence Ser.). (Illus.). xviii, 638p. 229.00 (978-3-642-20343-5(4), 3642203434) Springer.

Bi, Xiaojun. Xin Xi Zhi Neng Chu Li Ji Shu: Bi Xiaojun Bian Zhu. 2010. (CHI., Illus.). x, 353p. (978-7-121-10198-4(X)) Electronics Industry Publishing Hse.

Biere, A. & Heule, M., eds. Handbook of Satisfiability: Volume 185 Frontiers in Artificial Intelligence & Applications. 2009. (Illus.). 980p. 195.00 (978-1-58603-929-5(6)) IOS Pr., Inc.

Biswas, Gautam, et al, eds. Artificial Intelligence in Education: 15th International Conference, AIED 2011, Auckland, New Zealand, June 28 - July 2, 2011, Proceedings. 2011. (Lecture Notes in Computer Science / Lecture Notes in Artificial Intelligence Ser.). (Illus.). xxvi, 638p. pap. 119.00 (978-3-642-21868-2(7), 3642218687) Springer.

Bjorner, Nikolaj & Voronkov, Andrei, eds. Logic for Programming, Artificial Intelligence, & Reasoning: 18th International Conference, LPAR-18, Merida, Venezuela, March 11-15, 2012, Proceedings. 2012. (Lecture Notes in Computer Science / Theoretical Computer Science & General Issues Ser.: 7180). (ENG., Illus.). xi, 446p. pap. 95.00 (978-3-642-28716-9(6), 3642287166) Springer.

Blum, Christian & Merkle, Daniel, eds. Swarm Intelligence: Introduction & Applications. 2010. (Natural Computing Ser.). (Illus.). x, 286p. pap. 99.00 (978-3-642-09343-2(4), 3642093434) Springer.

Boddy, Mark, et al, eds. Proceedings of the Seventeenth International Conference on Automated Planning & Scheduling (ICAPS 2007) 2007. (Illus.). 378p. per. 70.00 (978-1-57735-344-7(7)) AAAI Pr.

Bonnici, Heidi. Automated Joke Explanation Generation. 2008. 80p. pap. (978-3-8364-6894-7(8)) VDM Verlag Dr. Mueller e.K.

Borges, Mario Neto & Almeida, Nival Nunes de, eds. Intelligent Educational Machines: Methodologies & Experiences. 2010. (Studies in Computational Intelligence Ser.). (Illus.). xviii, 185p. pap. 159.00 (978-3-642-07953-5(9), 3642079539) Springer.

Borrajo, Daniel, et al. Current Topics in Artificial Intelligence: 12th Conference of the Spanish Association for Artificial Intelligence, CAEPIA 2007, Salamanca, Spain, November 12-16, 2007, Selected Papers. 2007. (Lecture Notes in Artificial Intelligence Ser.). (Illus.). 280p. per. 69.95 (978-3-540-75270-7(6)) Springer.

Bossomaier, Terry R. J. & Green, David G., eds. Complex Systems. 2007. (ENG., Illus.). 420p. (C). pap. 83.00 (978-0-521-04371-7(9)) Cambridge Univ. Pr.

Bouça, Duarte. Agent-Based Computing. Gafagnão, Amaro, ed. 2010. (Computer Science, Technology & Applications Ser.). (Illus.). 343p. 129.00 (978-1-60876-684-0(5)) Nova Science Pubs., Inc.

Bouchachia, Abdelhamid. 2009 International Conference on Adaptive & Intelligent Systems; ICAIS 2009; Proceedings: 24-26 September 2009, Klagenfurt, Austria. 2009. (Illus.). xviii, 201p. pap. (978-0-7695-3827-3(4)) IEEE Computer Society Pr.

Boukis, Christos, et al, eds. Artificial Intelligence & Innovations 2007: from Theory to Applications: Proceedings of the 4th IFIP International Conference on Artificial Intelligence Applications & Innovations (AIAI 2007) 2007. (International Federation for Information Processing Ser.). (Illus.). 408p. 159.00 (978-0-387-74160-4(7)) Springer.

—Artificial Intelligence & Innovations 2007: from Theory to Applications: Proceedings of the 4th IFIP International Conference on Artificial Intelligence Applications & Innovations (AIAI2007) 2010. (IFIP Advances in Information & Communication Technology Ser.). (Illus.). xiv, 408p. pap. 159.00 (978-1-4419-4490-0(7), 1441944907) Springer.

Bourgine, Paul & Nadal, Jean-Pierre, eds. Cognitive Economics: An Interdisciplinary Approach. 2010. (Illus.). xiv, 479p. pap. 209.00 (978-3-642-07336-6(0), 3642073360) Springer.

Bouvry, Pascal, et al, eds. Security & Intelligent Information Systems: International Joint Confererence, SIIS 2011, Warsaw, Poland, June 13-14, 2011, Revised Selected Papers. 2012. (Lecture Notes in Computer Science / Information Systems & Applications, Incl. Internet/Web, & HCI Ser.). (ENG., Illus.). xvii, 401p. pap. 95.00 (978-3-642-25260-0(5), 3642252605) Springer.

Brambilla, Andrea. Artificial Intelligence in Space Systems. 2010. 116p. pap. (978-3-8383-6888-7(6)) Lambert Academic Publishing.

Bramer, M. A. Artificial Intelligence in Theory & Practice: IFIP 19th World Computer Congress, TC 12: IFIP AI 2006 Stream, August 21-24, 2006, Santiago, Chile. 2010. (IFIP Advances in Information & Communication Technology Ser.). (Illus.). xvi, 502p. pap. 209.00 (978-1-4419-4188-6(6), 1441941886) Springer.

—Artificial Intelligence in Theory & Practice II: IFIP 20th World Computer Congress, TC 12: IFIP AI 2008 Stream, September 7-10, 2008, Milano, Italy. 2010. (IFIP Advances in Information & Communication Technology Ser.). x, 470p. pap. 199.00 (978-1-4419-3518-2(5), 1441935185) Springer.

Bramer, M. A., et al. Research & Development in Intelligent Systems XXIV: Proceedings of AI-2007, the Twenty-seventh SGAI International Conference on Innovative Techniques & Applications of Artificial Intelligence. 2007. (ENG., Illus.). xvi, 398p. per. 159.00 (978-1-84800-093-3(6), 1848000936) Springer.

Bramer, Max. Artificial Intelligence: an International Perspective: An International Perspective. 2009. (Lecture Notes in Computer Science / Lecture Notes in Artificial Intelligence Ser.). (ENG.). vii, 260p. pap. 99.00 (978-3-642-03225-7(7), 3642032257) Springer.

Bramer, Max, ed. Artificial Intelligence in Theory & Practice: IFIP 19th World Computer Congress, TC-12 IFIP AI 2006 Stream, August 21-24, 2006, Santiago, Chile. 2006. (IFIP International Federation for Information Processing Ser.). (Illus.). xvi, 502p. 209.00 (978-0-387-34654-0(6), 0387346546) Springer.

Bramer, Max, et al, eds. Research & Development in Intelligent Systems XXV: Proceedings of AI-2008, the Twenty-eighth SGAI International Conference on Innovative Techniques & Applications of Artificial Intelligence. 2009. (Illus.). xiv, 374p. pap. 219.00 (978-1-84882-170-5(0)) Springer.

—Research & Development in Intelligent Systems XXVI: Incorporating Applications & Innovations in Intelligent Systems XVII. 2009. (ENG., Illus.). xv, 504p. pap. 199.00 (978-1-84882-982-4(5), 1848829825) Springer.

—Research & Development in Intelligent Systems XXVII: Incorporating Applications & Innovations in Intelligent Systems XVIII Proceedings of AI-2010, the Thirtieth SGAI International Conference on Innovative Techniques & Applications of Artificial Intelligence. 2010. (ENG., Illus.). xv, 494p. pap. 199.00 (978-0-85729-129-5(7), 0857291297) Springer.

Bramer, Max, et al, eds. Research & Development in Intelligent Systems XXVIII: Incorporating Applications & Innovations in Intelligent Systems XIX. 2011. (ENG., Illus.). xiv, 390p. pap. 189.00 (978-1-4471-2317-0(4), 1447123174) Springer.

Bramer, Max & Tuson, Andrew, eds. Research & Development in Intelligent Systems XXIII: Proceedings of AI-2006, the Twenty-Sixth SGAI International Conference on Innovative Techniques & Applications of Artificial Intelligence. 2006. (Illus.). 419p. per. 149.00 (978-1-84628-662-9(X)) Springer.

Braubach, Lars, et al. Multiagent System Technologies: 7th German Conference, MATES 2009 Hamburg, Germany, September 9-11, 2009 Proceedings. 2009. (Lecture Notes in Computer Science / Lecture Notes in Artificial Intelligence Ser.). xiii, 290p. pap. 83.00 (978-3-642-04142-6(6), 3642041426) Springer.

Brazier, F. M. T., et al, eds. Intelligent Distributed Computing V: Proceedings of the 5th International Symposium on Intelligent Distributed Computing - IDC 2011, Delft, the Netherlands - October 2011. 2011. (Studies in Computational Intelligence Ser.). (ENG., Illus.). xvi, 316p. 179.00 (978-3-642-24012-6(7), 3642240127) Springer.

Bredenfeld, Ansgar, et al. RoboCup 2005: Robot Soccer World Cup IX: Robot Soccer World Cup IX. 2006. (Lecture Notes in Computer Science Ser.). (Illus.). XVII, 727p. pap. 149.00 (978-3-540-35437-6(9), 3540354379) Springer.

Brewka, Gerhard, et al, eds. Nonmonotonic Reasoning Essays Celebrating its 30th Anniversary. 2011. 374p. pap. (978-1-84890-042-4(2)) College Pubns.

Briggle, Adam, et al. Current Issues in Computing & Philosophy. 2008. (Illus.). viii, 205p. 145.00 (978-1-58603-876-2(1)) IOS Pr., Inc.

Brighton, Henry & Selina, Howard. Introducing Artificial Intelligence: A Graphic Guide. 2012. (Introducing Ser.). (ENG., Illus.). 176p. pap. 9.95 (978-1-84831-214-2(8)) Totem Bks. GBR. Dist: Consortium Bk. Sales & Distribution.

Bruijn, Jos De, et al. Modeling Semantic Web Services: The Web Service Modeling Language. 2010. (ENG., Illus.). xiv, 192p. pap. 69.95 (978-3-642-08785-1(X), 364208785X) Springer.

Bruun, Charlotte, ed. Advances in Artificial Economics: The Economy as a Complex Dynamic System. 2006. (Lecture Notes in Economics & Mathematical Systems Ser.). (Illus.). 294p. per. 149.00 (978-3-540-37247-9(4), 3540372474) Springer.

Bruza, Peter, et al. Quantum Interaction: Third International Symposium, QI 2009, Saarbrücken, Germany, March 25-27, 2009, Proceedings. 2009. (Lecture Notes in Computer Science / Lecture Notes in Artificial Intelligence Ser.). ix, 315p. pap. 79.95 (978-3-642-00833-7(X)) Springer.

Buckley, Donagh, et al, eds. Artificial Intelligence for Data Center Management & Cloud Computing: Papers from the AAAI Workshop (WS-11-08) 2011. (Illus.). 44p. spiral bd. 25.00 (978-1-57735-524-3(5)) AAAI Pr.

Bui, Lam Thu & Alam, Sameer, eds. Multi-Objective Optimization in Computational Intelligence: Theory & Practice. 2008. (Premier Reference Source Ser.). (Illus.). 300+p. 180.00 (978-1-59904-498-9(6)) IGI Global.

Bull, Larry, et al, eds. Learning Classifier Systems in Data Mining. 2010. (Studies in Computational Intelligence Ser.). (Illus.). x, 230p. pap. 179.00 (978-3-642-09775-1(8), 3642097758) Springer.

Buller, Mark, et al, eds. Computational Physiology: Papers from the AAAI Spring Symposium (SS-11-04) 2011. (Illus.). 62p. spiral bd. 25.00 (978-1-57735-496-3(6)) AAAI Pr.

Burger, John Robert, et al. Human Memory Modeled with Standard Analog & Digital Circuits: Inspiration for Man-Made Computers. 2009. (ENG., Illus.). 366p. 161.00 (978-0-470-42435-3(4), Wiley) Wiley, John & Sons, Inc.

Burke, Edmund K. & Rudova, Hana, eds. Practice & Theory of Automated Timetabling VI: 6th International Conference, PATAT 2006 Brno, Czech Republic, August 30-September 1, 2006 Revised Selected Papers. 2008. (Lecture Notes in Computer Science Ser.). (Illus.). 412p. pap. 89.95 (978-3-540-77344-3(4)) Springer.

Burkhard, Hans-Dieter, et al. Multi-Agent Systems & Applications V: 5th International Central & Eastern European Conference on Multi-Agent Systems, CEEMAS 2007, Leipzig, Germany, September 25-27, 2007, Proceedings. 2007. (Lecture Notes in Computer Science / Lecture Notes in Artificial Intelligence Ser.). xii, 350p. pap. 79.95 (978-3-540-75253-0(6)) Springer.

Buse, David P. & Wu, Q. H. IP Network-based Multi-agent Systems for Industrial Automation: Information Management, Condition Monitoring & Control of Power Systems. 2010. (Power Systems Ser.). (Illus.). xviii, 187p. pap. 159.00 (978-1-84996-635-1(4), 1849966354) Springer.

Buse, David P. & Wu, Qing-Hua. IP Network-Based Multi-Agent Systems for Industrial Automation: Information Management, Condition Monitoring & Control of Power Systems. 2006. (Power Systems Ser.). (Illus.). xviii, 187p. 159.00 (978-1-84628-646-9(8), 1846286468) Springer.

Butterfield, Andrew, ed. Unifying Theories of Programming: Second International Symposium, UTP 2008, Dublin, Ireland, September 8-10, 2008, Revised Selected Papers. 2010. (Lecture Notes in Computer Science / Theoretical Computer Science & General Issues Ser.). (Illus.). ix, 279p. pap. 72.00 (978-3-642-14520-9(5), 3642145205) Springer.

Butz, Andreas, et al. Smart Graphics: 10th International Symposium, SG 2009, Salamanca, Spain, May 28-30, 2009, Proceedings. 2009. (Lecture Notes in Computer Science / Image Processing, Computer Vision, Pattern Recognition, & Graphics Ser.). (Illus.). xi, 300p. pap. 79.95 (978-3-642-02114-5(X), 364202114X) Springer.

—Smart Graphics: 8th International Symposium, SG 2007, Kyoto, Japan, June 25-27, 2007, Proceedings. 2007. (Lecture Notes in Computer Science / Image Processing, Computer Vision, Pattern Recognition, & Graphics Ser.). ix, 237p. pap. 69.95 (978-3-540-73213-6(6)) Springer.

Butz, Cory & Lingras, Pawan, eds. Advances in Artificial Intelligence: 24th Canadian Conference on Artificial Intelligence, Canadian AI 2011, St. John's, Canada, May 25-27, 2011, Proceedings. 2011. (Lecture Notes in Computer Science / Lecture Notes in Artificial Intelligence Ser.). (Illus.). xiv, 434p. pap. 95.00 (978-3-642-21042-6(2), 3642210422) Springer.

Caballé, Santi, et al, eds. Intelligent Networking, Collaborative Systems & Applications. 2010. (Studies in Computational Intelligence Ser.). 310p. 179.00 (978-3-642-16792-8(6), 3642167926) Springer.

Cabestany, Joan, et al. Bio-Inspired Systems: Computational & Ambient Intelligence: 10th International Work-Conference on Artificial Neural Networks, IWANN 2009, Salamanca, Spain, June 10-12, 2009. Proceedings, Part I. 2009. (Lecture Notes in Computer Science / Theoretical Computer Science & General Issues Ser.). (ENG.). li, 1356p. pap. 189.00 (978-3-642-02477-1(7), 3642024777) Springer.

Cabestany, Joan, et al, eds. Advances in Computational Intelligence: 11th International Work-Conference on Artificial Neural Networks, IWANN 2011, Torremolinos-Málaga, Spain, June 8-10, 2011, Proceedings, Part II. 2011. (Lecture Notes in Computer Science / Theoretical Computer Science & General Issues Ser.). xxxvii, 690p. pap. 131.00 (978-3-642-21497-4(5), 3642214975) Springer.

Cacciabue, P. Carlo, et al, eds. Human Modelling in Assisted Transportation: Models, Tools & Risk Methods. 2011. (ENG., Illus.). ix, 390p. 149.00 (978-88-470-1820-4(X), 884701820X) Springer.

Caferra, R. Logic for Computer Science & Artificial Intelligence. 2011. (Iste Ser.: 569). (ENG., Illus.). 544p. 195.00 (978-1-84821-301-2(8), Wiley-ISTE) Wiley, John & Sons, Inc.

Cai, Yang, ed. Computing with Instinct: Rediscovering Artificial Intelligence. 2011. (Lecture Notes in Computer Science / Lecture Notes in Artificial Intelligence Ser.). (Illus.). xiii, 163p. pap. 72.00 (978-3-642-19756-7(6), 3642197566) Springer.

Cai, Zhihua, et al. Advances in Computation & Intelligence: 4th International Symposium on Intelligence Computation & Applications, ISICA 2009, Huangshi, China, October 23-25 2009. 2009. (Lecture Notes in Computer Science / Theoretical Computer Science & General Issues Ser.). xiv, 554p. pap. 109.00 (978-3-642-04842-5(0), 3642048420) Springer.

Calero, Pedro Antonio Gómez-Martín & Gómez-Martín, Marco Antonio, eds. Artificial Intelligence for Computer Games. 2011. (ENG., Illus.). xii, 200p. 129.00 (978-1-4419-8187-5(X), 144198187X) Springer.

Calero, Pedro Antonio Gonzalez, ed. Artificial Intelligence for Computer Games. 2011. (Illus.). x, 290p. 129.00 (978-1-4419-7256-9(0), 1441972560) Springer.

Calmet, Jaques, et al, eds. Artificial Intelligence & Symbolic Computation: 8th International Conference, AISC 2006 Beijing, China, September 2006 Proceedings. 2007. (Lecture Notes in Computer Science Ser.). (Illus.). 268p. per. 79.95 (978-3-540-39728-1(0), 3540397280) Springer.

Camarinha-Matos, Luis M., ed. Technological Innovation for Sustainability: Second IFIP WG 5. 5/SOCOLNET Doctoral Conference on Computing, Electrical & Industrial Systems, DoCEIS 2011, Costa de Caparica, Portugal, February 22-24, 2011, Proceedings. 2011. (IFIP Advances in Information & Communication Technology Ser.). (Illus.). xvii, 615p. 189.00 (978-3-642-19169-5(X), 364219169X) Springer.

Cao, Bing-Yuan, et al, eds. Fuzzy Information & Engineering 2010: Vol 1 (Advances in Intelligent & Soft Computing) 2010. (Advances in Intelligent & Soft Computing Ser.). 1200p. pap. 440.00 (978-3-642-14879-8(4), 3642148794) Springer.

Carter, Matt. Minds & Computers: An Introduction to the Philosophy of Artificial Intelligence. 2007. (ENG., Illus.). 240p. (gr. 17). 120.00 (978-0-7486-2098-2(2)); pap. 36.00 (978-0-7486-2099-9(0)) Edinburgh Univ. Pr. GBR. Dist: Columbia Univ. Pr.

Casacuberta, David. Handbook of Research on Synthetic Emotions & Sociable Robotics: New Applications in Affective Computing & Artificial Intelligence. Valverdú, Jordi, ed. 2009. 598p. 265.00 (978-1-60566-354-8(9)) IGI Global.

Casasent, David P., et al. Intelligent Robots & Computer Vision XXI: Algorithms, Techniques, & Active Vision. (Proceedings of SPIE Ser.). 344p. pap. 90.00 (978-0-8194-5155-2(X)) SPIE.

Casasent, David Paul, et al. Intelligent Robots & Computer Vision XXIV: Algorithms, Techniques, & Active Vision: 3-4 October, 2006, Boston, Massachusetts, USA. 2006. (Proceedings of SPIE Ser.). (Illus.). 356p. pap. 80.00 (978-0-8194-6482-8(1)) SPIE.

—Intelligent Robots & Computer Vision XXV: Algorithms, Techniques, & Active Vision: 9-11 September, 2007, Boston, Massachusetts, USA. 2007. (Proceedings of SPIE Ser.). (Illus.). 378p. pap. 90.00 (978-0-8194-6924-3(6)) SPIE.

—Intelligent Robots & Computer Vision XXVI: Algorithms & Techniques: 19-20 January 2009, San Jose, California, USA. 2009. (Proceedings of SPIE Ser.). (Illus.). 296p. pap. 80.00 (978-0-8194-7502-2(5)) SPIE.

Casellas, Núria. Legal Ontology Engineering: Methodologies, Modelling Trends, & the Ontology of Professional Judicial Knowledge. 2011. (Law, Governance & Technology Ser.). (Illus.). xxi, 297p. 139.00 (978-94-007-1496-0(3), 9400714963) Springer.

Casillas, Jorge & Marínez López, Francisco José, eds. Marketing Intelligent Systems Using Soft Computing: Managerial & Research Applications. 2010. (Studies in Fuzziness & Soft Computing Ser.). 356p. 199.00 (978-3-642-15605-2(3), 3642156053) Springer.

Castillo, Oscar, et al, eds. Current Trends in Intelligent Systems & Computer Engineering. 2008. (Lecture Notes Electrical Engineering Ser.). (Illus.). 750p. 219.00 (978-0-387-74934-1(9)) Springer.

Castillo, Oscar & Xu, Li, eds. Trends in Intelligent Systems & Computer Engineering. 2010. (Lecture Notes in Electrical Engineering Ser.). xx, 670p. pap. 219.00 (978-1-4419-4520-4(2), 1441945202) Springer.

Catrillon, Laura Viana. Memoria Natural y Artificial. (Ciencia para Todos Ser.). (SPA.). pap. 6.99 (978-968-16-3481-0(0)) Fondo de Cultura Economica USA.

Cavallucci, Denis, et al, eds. Building Innovation Pipelines through Computer-Aided Innovation: 4th IFIP WG 5. 4 Working Conference, CAI 2011, Strasbourg, France, June 30 - July 1, 2011, Proceedings. 2011. (IFIP Advances in Information & Communication Technology Ser.). (Illus.). x, 193p. 109.00 (978-3-642-22181-1(5), 3642221815) Springer.

Cercone, Nick J., ed. Rough Sets & Knowledge Technology: Second International Conference, RSKT 2007 Toronto, Canada, May 14-16, 2007 Proceedings. 2007. (Lecture Notes in Computer Science Ser.). (Illus.). 576p. per. 109.00 (978-3-540-72457-5(5)) Springer.

Chahl, Javaan Singh, et al, eds. Innovations in Intelligent Machines - 1. (Studies in Computational Intelligence Ser.). (Illus.). xiv, 270p. 2010. pap. 189.00 (978-3-642-09177-3(6), 3642091776) 2007. 189.00 (978-3-540-72695-1(0)) Springer.

Chalkiadakis, Georgios, et al. Computational Aspects of Cooperative Game Theory. 2011. (Synthesis Lectures on Artificial Intelligence & Machine Learning Ser.). pap. 35.00 (978-1-60845-652-9(8)) Morgan & Claypool Pubs.

Chan, Tak-Wai. DIGITEL 2007: The First IEEE International Workshop on Digital Game & Intelligent Toy Enhanced Learning: Proceedings: 26-28 March, 2007, Jhongli, Taiwan. 2007. (Illus.). xiii, 228p. (978-0-7695-2801-4(5)) IEEE Computer Society Pr.

Chan, Yupo, et al, eds. Data Engineering: Mining, Information & Intelligence. 2009. (International Series in Operations Research & Management Science

Ser.). (ENG., Illus.). xvii, 447p. 209.00 *(978-1-4419-0175-0(2),* 1441901752) Springer.

Chang, Maiga, et al. Learning by Playing:. Game-based Education System Designing & Development: 4th International Conference on E-learning, Edutainment 2009, Banff, Canada, August 9-11, 2009, Proceedings. 2009. (Lecture Notes in Computer Science / Information Systems & Applications, incl. Internet/Web, & HCI Ser.). (ENG., Illus.). xvii, 579p. pap. 109.00 *(978-3-642-03363-6(6),* 3642033636) Springer.

Charles, Darryl, et al. Biologically Inspired Artificial Intelligence for Computer Games. 2007. (Illus.). 278p. 99.95 *(978-1-59140-646-4(3))* IGI Global.

Chaudhury, Santanu, et al. Pattern Recognition & Machine Intelligence: Third International Conference, PReMI 2009 New Delhi, India, December 16-20, 2009 Proceedings. 2009. (Lecture Notes in Computer Science / Image Processing, Computer Vision, Pattern Recognition, & Graphics Ser.). xxi, 631p. pap. 119.00 *(978-3-642-11163-1(7),* 3642111637) Springer.

Chen, Chang Wen, et al, eds. Intelligent Multimedia Communication: Techniques & Applications: Techniques & Applications. 2010. (Studies in Computational Intelligence Ser.). (Illus.). 300p. 129.00 *(978-3-642-11685-8(X),* 364211685X) Springer.

Chen, Lei Zhi, et al. Modelling & Optimization of Biotechnological Processes: Artificial Intelligence Approaches. 2010. (Studies in Computational Intelligence Ser.). (Illus.). viii, 123p. pap. 189.00 *(978-3-642-06792-1(1),* 3642067921) Springer.

Chen, Ran, ed. Intelligent Computing & Information Science: International Conference, ICICIS 2011, Chongqing, China, January 8-9, 2011. Proceedings, Part I. 2010. (Communications in Computer & Information Science Ser.). (ENG.). xxiv, 770p. pap. 143.00 *(978-3-642-18128-3(7),* 3642181287) Springer.

—Intelligent Computing & Information Science: International Conference, ICICIS 2011, Chongqing, China, January 8-9, 2011. Proceedings, Part II. 2010. (Communications in Computer & Information Science Ser.). xxiv, 722p. pap. 143.00 *(978-3-642-18133-7(3),* 3642181333) Springer.

Chen, Shan-Ben. Intelligentized Methodology for Arc Welding Dynamical Process. 2008. (Lecture Notes in Electrical Engineering Ser.). (Illus.). 351p. 159.00 *(978-3-540-85641-2(2),* 3540856412) Springer.

Chen, Zhe, et al. Correlative Learning: A Basis for Brain & Adaptive Systems. 2007. (Adaptive & Learning Systems for Signal Processing, Communications & Control Ser.: 49). (ENG., Illus.). 480p. 156.00 *(978-0-470-04488-9(8),* Wiley-Interscience) Wiley, John & Sons, Inc.

Cheng, Betty H. C., et al. Software Engineering for Self-Adaptive Sstems. 2009. (Lecture Notes in Computer Science / Theoretical Computer Science & General Issues Ser.). x, 261p. pap. 69.95 *(978-3-642-02160-2(3),* 3642021603) Springer.

Cheng, Maggie. Nano-Net: Third International Conference, NanoNet 2008, Boston, MS, USA, September 14-16, 2008. Revised Selected Papers. 2009. (Lecture Notes of the Institute for Computer Sciences, Social-Informatics & Telecommunications Engineering Ser.). (ENG., Illus.). xii, 131p. pap. 69.95 *(978-3-642-02426-9(2),* 3642024262) Springer.

Cherifi, Hocine, et al, eds. Digital Information & Communication Technology & Its Applications: International Conference, DICTAP 2011, Dijon, France, June 21-23, 2011. Proceedings, Part I, 2 vols. 2011. (Communications in Computer & Information Science Ser.). (Illus.). xii, 805p. pap. 155.00 ***(978-3-642-21983-2(7),*** 3642219837) Springer.

—Digital Information & Communication Technology & Its Applications: International Conference, DICTAP 2011, Dijon, France, June 21-23, 2011. Proceedings, Part II, 2 vols. 2011. (Communications in Computer & Information Science Ser.). (ENG., Illus.). 792p. pap. 143.00 ***(978-3-642-22026-5(6),*** 3642220266) Springer.

Chien, Been-Chian, et al. Next-Generation Applied Intelligence: 22nd International Conference on Industrial Engineering & Other Applications of Applied Intelligent Systems, IEA/AIE 2009, Tainan, Taiwan, June 24-27, 2009. Proceedings. 2009. (Lecture Notes in Computer Science / Lecture Notes in Artificial Intelligence Ser.). (ENG.). xx, 839p. pap. 149.00 *(978-3-642-02567-9(6),* 3642025676) Springer.

Chien, Been-Chian & Hong, Tzung-Pei, eds. Opportunities & Challenges for Next-Generation Applied Intelligence. 2009. (Studies in Computational Intelligence Ser.). (ENG., Illus.). xii, 344p. 169.00 *(978-3-540-92813-3(8))* Springer.

Chiong, Raymond, et al, eds. Variants of Evolutionary Algorithms for Real-World Applications. 2011. (ENG., Illus.). xiv, 466p. 179.00 ***(978-3-642-23423-1(2),*** 3642234232) Springer.

Chong, Seng Kwong, et al. Runtime Support Framework for Agile Manufacturing MacHinery. 2010. 220p. pap. *(978-3-639-12385-2(9))* VDM Verlag Dr. Mueller e.K.

Chountas, Panagiotis, et al, eds. Intelligent Techniques & Tools for Novel System Architectures. 2010. (Studies in Computational Intelligence Ser.). (Illus.). x, 548p. pap. 269.00 *(978-3-642-09636-5(0),* 3642096360) Springer.

Christian, Brian. The Most Human Human: What Talking with Computers Teaches Us about What It Means to Be Alive. 2011. (ENG.). 320p. 27.95 *(978-0-385-53306-5(3),* Doubleday) Knopf Doubleday Publishing Group.

Cipolla, Roberto & Giblin, Peter. Visual Motion of Curves & Surfaces. 2009. (ENG., Illus.). 196p. pap. 46.00 *(978-0-521-11818-7(2))* Cambridge Univ. Pr.

Clarke, Edmund M. & Voronkov, Andrei, eds. Logic for Programming, Artificial Intelligence, & Reasoning: 16th International Conference, LPAR-16, Dakar, Senegal, April 25 — May 1, 2010, Revised Selected Papers. 2011. (Lecture Notes in Computer Science / Lecture Notes in Artificial Intelligence Ser.). (ENG.). x, 517p. pap. 107.00 *(978-3-642-17510-7(4),* 3642175104) Springer.

Coelho, H. & Studer, R., eds. Ecai 2010: 19th European Conference on Artificial Intelligence - Volume 215 Frontiers in Artificial Intelligence & Applications. 2010. pap. 340.00 *(978-1-60750-605-8(X))* IOS Pr., Inc.

Combi, Carlo, et al. Artificial Intelligence in Medicine: 12th Conference on Artificial Intelligence in Medicine, AIME 2009, Verona, Italy, July 18-22, 2009, Proceedings. 2009. (Lecture Notes in Computer Science / Lecture Notes in Artificial Intelligence Ser.). (ENG.). xix, 439p. pap. 99.00 *(978-3-642-02975-2(2),* 3642029752) Springer.

Computational Intelligence & Multimedia Applications; Proceedings: 2007: Tamil Nadu, India, Vol. 4. 2007. 530p. pap. 576.00 *(978-0-7695-3050-5(8))* IEEE Computer Society Pr.

Conn, Karla. Supervised Reinforcement Learning - Application to an Embodied Mobile Robot. 2007. 112p. per. *(978-3-8364-2806-4(7))* VDM Verlag Dr. Mueller e.K.

Corchado, Emilio, et al. Hybrid Artificial Intelligence Systems: 4th International Conference, HAIS 2009, Salamanca, Spain, June 10-12, 2009, Proceedings. 2009. (Lecture Notes in Computer Science / Lecture Notes in Artificial Intelligence Ser.). (ENG.). xxii, 715p. pap. 129.00 *(978-3-642-02318-7(5),* 3642023185) Springer.

Corchado, Emilio, et al, eds. Hybrid Artificial Intelligent Systems: 6th International Conference, HAIS 2011, Wroclaw, Poland, May 23-25, 2011, Proceedings, Part I, 2 vols. 2011. (Lecture Notes in Computer Science / Lecture Notes in Artificial Intelligence Ser.). (Illus.). xxx, 472p. pap. 107.00 *(978-3-642-21218-5(2),* 3642212182) Springer.

—Hybrid Artificial Intelligent Systems: 6th International Conference, HAIS 2011, Wroclaw, Poland, May 23-25, 2011, Proceedings, Part II, 2 vols. 2011. (Lecture Notes in Computer Science / Lecture Notes in Artificial Intelligence Ser.). (Illus.). xxix, 490p. pap. 107.00 *(978-3-642-21221-5(2),* 3642212212) Springer.

—Innovations in Hybrid Intelligent Systems. 2007. (Advances in Soft Computing Ser.). (Illus.). 497p. 239.00 *(978-3-540-74971-4(3))* Springer.

Corchado, Juan M., et al, eds. Soft Computing Models in Industrial & Environmental Applications, 5th International Workshop (SOCO 2010) 2010. (Advances in Intelligent & Soft Computing Ser.). 260p. pap. 219.00 *(978-3-642-13160-8(3),* 3642131603) Springer.

—Trends in Practical Applications of Agents & Multiagent Systems: 9th International Conference on Practical Applications of Agents & Multiagent Systems. 2011. (Advances in Intelligent & Soft Computing Ser.). (Illus.). xiv, 186p. pap. 199.00 *(978-3-642-19930-1(5),* 3642199305) Springer.

Cordeschi, R. The Discovery of the Artificial: Behavior, Mind & Machines Before & Beyond Cybernetics. 2010. (Studies in Cognitive Systems Ser.). 336p. pap. 189.00 *(978-90-481-6015-0(4),* 9048160154) Springer.

Cornell Way, E. Knowledge Representation & Metaphor. 2010. (Studies in Cognitive Systems Ser.). 296p. pap. 269.00 *(978-90-481-4079-4(X),* 904814079X) Springer.

Cortes, Ulises. Agent Technology Applied to Environmental Issues. 2008. (Whitestein Series in Software Agent Technologies & Autonomic Computing Ser.). 250p. spiral bd. 59.95 *(978-3-7643-8897-3(8))* Birkhauser Boston.

Cox, Michael T. & Raja, Anita, eds. Metareasoning: Thinking about Thinking. 2011. (ENG., Illus.). 352p. (gr. 17). 45.00 *(978-0-262-01480-9(7))* MIT Pr.

Coyle, Lorcan & Freyne, Jill, eds. Artificial Intelligence & Cognitive Science: 20th Irish Conference, AICS 2009, Dublin, Ireland, August 19-21, 2009, Revised Selected Papers. 2010. (Lecture Notes in Computer Science / Lecture Notes in Artificial Intelligence Ser.). xi, 293p. pap. 83.00 *(978-3-642-17079-9(X),* 364217079X) Springer.

Cram101 Textbook Reviews. Outlines & Highlights for Fundamentals of the New Artificial Intelligence by Toshinori Munakata, Isbn: 9781846288388 184628838x. 2011. 80p. pap. 27.95 ***(978-1-61490-180-8(5))*** Cram101 Inc.

—Outlines & Highlights for Human Memory Modeled with Standard Analog & Digital Circuits: Inspiration for Man-made Computers by John Burger, ISBN. 2011. 112p. pap. 28.95 ***(978-1-61744-969-7(5))*** Cram101 Inc.

—Outlines & Highlights for Rigid Body Dynamics Algorithms by Roy Featherstone. 2011. 128p. pap. 28.95 ***(978-1-61905-618-3(6))*** Cram101 Inc.

—Outlines & Highlights for Situated Cognition: On Human Knowledge & Computer Representations by William J. Clancey. 2011. 58p. pap. 26.95 ***(978-1-4672-6729-8(5))*** Cram101 Inc.

Cram101 Textbook Reviews & Cram101 Textbook Reviews. Outlines & Highlights for Artificial Intelligence by Stuart Russell, Isbn: 9780136042594 0136042597. 2011. 690p. pap. 42.95 ***(978-1-61490-130-3(9))*** Cram101 Inc.

—Outlines & Highlights for Computational Intelligence & Pattern Analysis in Biology Informatics by Ujjwal Maulik, Isbn: 9780470581599. 2011. 60p. pap. 26.95 ***(978-1-61461-178-3(5))*** Cram101 Inc.

—Outlines & Highlights for MacHine Learning in Bioinformatics by Yanqing Zhang, Isbn: 9780470116623. 2011. 134p. pap. 28.95 ***(978-1-61461-171-4(8))*** Cram101 Inc.

Cram101 Textbook Reviews Staff. Outlines & Highlights for Artificial Intelligence: A Modern Approach by Russell & Norvig, ISBN. 2009. 380p. pap. 17.95 *(978-1-4288-6657-7(4))* Cram101 Inc.

Creignou, Nadia, et al. Complexity of Constraints: An Overview of Current Research Themes. 2008. (Lecture Notes in Computer Science / Theoretical Computer Science & General Issues Ser.). vii, 321p. pap. 69.95 *(978-3-540-92799-0(9))* Springer.

Crocker, Matthew W. & Siekmann, Jörg, eds. Resource-Adaptive Cognitive Processes. 2010. (Cognitive Technologies Ser.). (ENG., Illus.). x, 390p. 159.00 *(978-3-540-89407-0(1),* 3540894071) Springer.

Croitoru, Madalina, et al, eds. Conceptual Structures: from Information to Intelligence: 18th International Conference on Conceptual Structures, ICCS 2010, Kuching, Sarawak, Malaysia, July 26-30, 2010, Proceedings. 2010. (Lecture Notes in Computer Science / Lecture Notes in Artificial Intelligence Ser.). xii, 207p. pap. 72.00 *(978-3-642-14196-6(X),* 364214196X) Springer.

Czernicki, Bart. Next-Generation Business Intelligence Software with Silverlight 3. 2009. (ENG., Illus.). 576p. pap. 64.99 *(978-1-4302-2487-7(8))* Apress L. P.

da Rocha Costa, Antonio Carlos, et al, eds. Advances in Artificial Intelligence — SBIA 2010: 20th Brazilian Symposium on Artificial Intelligence, SÃ£o Bernardo do Campo, Brazil, October 23-28, 2010, Proceedings. 2010. (Lecture Notes in Computer Science / Lecture Notes in Artificial Intelligence Ser.). xv, 313p. pap. 83.00 *(978-3-642-16137-7(5),* 3642161375) Springer.

Dartnall, T., ed. Artificial Intelligence & Creativity: An Interdisciplinary Approach. 2010. (Studies in Cognitive Systems Ser.). 456p. pap. 329.00 *(978-90-481-4457-0(4),* 9048144574) Springer.

Das, Swagatam & Suganthan, P. N. Swarm & Evolutionary Computing: Algorithms, Analyses, & Applications. 2012. (IEEE Press Series on Computational Intelligence Ser.). (ENG., Illus.). 600p. 110.00 ***(978-0-470-88134-7(8),*** Wiley-IEEE Pr.) Wiley, John & Sons, Inc.

Dastani, Mehdi, et al, eds. Languages, Methodologies, & Development Tools for Multi-Agent Systems: Third International Workshop, LADS 2010, Lyon, France, August 30 — September 1, 2010, Revised Selected Papers. 2011. (Lecture Notes in Computer Science / Lecture Notes in Artificial Intelligence Ser.). (ENG., Illus.). ix, 153p. pap. 72.00 ***(978-3-642-22722-6(8),*** 3642227228) Springer.

D'Avila Garcez, Artur S., et al. Neural-Symbolic Cognitive Reasoning. 2008. (Cognitive Technologies Ser.). (Illus.). 265p. 89.95 *(978-3-540-73245-7(4),* 3540732454) Springer.

Davim, J. Paulo, ed. Artificial Intelligence in Manufacturing Research. 2010. (Materials & Manufacturing Technology (J. Paulo Davim, Univ. of Aveiro - Series Editor) Ser.). 192p. 89.00 *(978-1-60876-214-9(9))* Nova Science Pubs., Inc.

Davis, Ernest, et al, eds. Logical Formalizations of Commonsense Reasoning: Papers from the AAAI Spring Symposium (SS-11-06) 2011. (Illus.). 193p. spiral bd. 35.00 ***(978-1-57735-498-7(2))*** AAAI Pr.

Dawson, Michael Robert William, et al. From Bricks to Brains: The Embodied Cognitive Science of LEGO Robots. 2010. (AU Press Ser.). (ENG., Illus.). 448p. (C). pap. 48.95 *(978-1-897425-78-7(3))* UBC Pr. CAN. Dist: Univ. of Washington Pr.

de Castro, Leandro N., ed. Artificial Immune Systems: 6th International Conference, ICARIS 2007, Santos, Brazil, August 26-29, 2007, Proceedings. 2007. (Lecture Notes in Computer Science Ser.). (Illus.). 438p. per. 99.00 *(978-3-540-73921-0(1))* Springer.

de Macedo Mourelle, Luiza, ed. Int'l Conference on Intelligent Systems Design & Applications: 7th: 2007: Rio de Janeiro, Brazil. 2007. 964p. pap. 304.00 *(978-0-7695-2976-9(3))* IEEE Computational Intelligence Society.

De, Rajat K. & Pal, Sankar K., eds. Pattern Recognition & Machine Intelligence: Second International Conference, PReMI 2007, Kolkata, India, December 18-22, 2007, Proceedings. 2007. (Lecture Notes in Computer Science Ser.). (Illus.). 677p. pap. 119.00 *(978-3-540-77045-9(3))* Springer.

De Ruyter, Boris, et al, eds. Ambient Intelligence: First International Joint Conference, AmI 2010, Málaga, Spain, November 10-12, 2010, Proceedings. 2010. (Lecture Notes in Computer Science / Information Systems & Applications, incl. Internet/Web, & HCI Ser.). (Illus.). xvii, 354p. pap. 83.00 *(978-3-642-16916-8(3),* 3642169163) Springer.

Deb, Kalyanmoy, et al, eds. Simulated Evolution & Learning: 8th International Conference, SEAL 2010, Kanpur, India, December 1-4, 2010, Proceedings. 2010. (Lecture Notes in Computer Science / Theoretical Computer Science & General Issues Ser.). xvii, 719p. pap. 131.00 *(978-3-642-17297-7(0),* 3642172970) Springer.

Debenham, John, ed. Applications in AI Symposium. 2006. (IFIP International Federation for Information Processing Ser.). (Illus.). xii, 352p. 155.00 *(978-0-387-34655-7(4),* 0387346554) Springer.

—Professional Practice in Artificial Intelligence: IFIP 19th World Computer Congress, TC-12: Professional Practice Stream, August 21-24, 2006, Santiago, Chile. 2010. (IFIP Advances in Information & Communication Technology Ser.). (Illus.). xii, 352p. pap. 155.00 *(978-1-4419-4189-3(4),* 1441941894) Springer.

Dechter, Rina, et al, eds. Heuristics, Probability & Causality a Tribute to Judea Pearl. 2010. (Illus.). 580p. *(978-1-904987-66-6(4))*; pap. *(978-1-904987-65-9(6))* College Pubns.

Dechter, Rina & Richardson, Thomas, eds. Proceedings of the Twenty-Second Conference on Uncertainty in Artificial Intelligence: Uai 2006. 2006. pap. 60.00 *(978-0-9749039-2-7(2))* Assn. for Uncertainty in Artificial Intelligence (AUAI).

Demazeau, Yves, et al, eds. Advances in Practical Applications of Agents & Multiagent Systems: 8th International Conference on Practical Applications of Agents & Multiagent Systems. 2010. (Advances in Intelligent & Soft Computing Ser.). 300p. pap. 219.00 *(978-3-642-12383-2(X),* 364212383X) Springer.

—7th International Conference on Practical Applications of Agents & Multi-Agent Systems (PAAMS'09) 2009. (Advances in Intelligent & Soft Computing Ser.). (Illus.). xvi, 592p. pap. 439.00 *(978-3-642-00486-5(5))* Springer.

Dempster, Arthur P., et al, eds. Classic Works on the Dempster-Shafer Theory of Belief Functions. 2008. (Studies in Fuzziness & Soft Computing Ser.). 626p. 309.00 *(978-3-540-25381-5(5),* 3540253815) Springer.

Demri, Stéphane P. & Jensen, Christian S. 15th International Symposium on Temporal Representation & Reasoning: TIME 2008 Proceedings: 16-18 June, 2008, Montreal, Quebec, Canada. 2008. (Illus.). x, 173p. *(978-0-7695-3181-6(4))* IEEE Computer Society Pr.

Deng, Hepu, et al. Artificial Intelligence & Computational Intelligence: International Conference, AICI 2009, Shanghai, China, November 7-8, 2009, Proceedings. 2009. (Lecture Notes in Computer Science / Lecture Notes in Artificial Intelligence Ser.). xx, 737p. pap. 139.00 *(978-3-642-05252-1(5),* 3642052525) Springer.

Deng, Hepu, et al, eds. Artificial Intelligence & Computational Intelligence Pt. 1: Second International Conference, AICIS 2011, Taiyuan, China, September 24-25, 2011, Proceedings, 3 vols. 2011. (Lecture Notes in Computer Science / Lecture Notes in Artificial Intelligence Ser.). (ENG., Illus.). xxxiii, 686p. pap. 131.00 ***(978-3-642-23880-2(7),*** 3642238807) Springer.

—Artificial Intelligence & Computational Intelligence Pt. II: Second International Conference, AICI 2011, Taiyuan, China, September 24-25, 2011, Proceedings, 3 vols. 2011. (Lecture Notes in Computer Science / Lecture Notes in Artificial Intelligence Ser.). (ENG., Illus.). xviii, 718p. pap. 131.00 ***(978-3-642-23886-4(6),*** 3642238866) Springer.

—Artificial Intelligence & Computational Intelligence Pt. 3: Second International Conference, AICI 2011, Taiyuan, China, September 24-25, 2011, Proceedings, 3 vols. 2011. (Lecture Notes in Computer Science / Lecture Notes in Artificial Intelligence Ser.). (ENG., Illus.). xvii, 678p. pap. 119.00 ***(978-3-642-23895-6(5),*** 3642238955) Springer.

—Emerging Research in Artificial Intelligence & Computational Intelligence: International Conference, AICI 2011, Taiyuan, China, September 23-25, 2011. Proceedings. 2011. (Communications in Computer & Information Science Ser.). (ENG.). 628p. pap. 131.00 ***(978-3-642-24281-6(2),*** 3642242812) Springer.

Deng, Linzhong. Artificial Intelligence Techniques for Bridge Reliability Assessment. 2009. 188p. pap. *(978-3-639-14388-1(4))* VDM Verlag Dr. Mueller e.K.

Denzler, Joachim, et al. Pattern Recognition: 31st DAGM Symposium, Jena, Germany, September 9-11, 2009, Proceedings. 2009. (Lecture Notes in Computer Science / Image Processing, Computer Vision, Pattern Recognition, & Graphics Ser.). xv, 564p. pap. 109.00 *(978-3-642-03797-9(6),* 3642037976) Springer.

DePauli-Schimanovich, Werner. Kultur, Politik, Musik, Revolutionäres, Historisches, Literarisches. 2007. (GER & ENG., Illus.). viii, 632p. *(978-3-902514-89-9(2),* Spotlight Poets) Novum Verlag GmbH.

Dershowitz, Nachum & Voronkov, A. Logic for Programming, Artificial Intelligence, & Reasoning: 14th International Conference, LPAR 2007, Yerevan, Armenia, October 15-19, 2007: Proceedings. 2007. (Lecture Notes in Computer Science / Lecture Notes in Artificial Intelligence Ser.). (Illus.). xiii, 562p. 109.00 *(978-3-540-75558-6(6))* Springer.

Deshpande, Amol & Hunter, Anthony, eds. Scalable Uncertainty Management: 4th International Conference, SUM 2010, Toulouse, France, September 27-29, 2010, Proceedings. 2010. (Lecture Notes in Computer Science / Lecture Notes in Artificial Intelligence Ser.). xi, 389p. pap. 83.00 *(978-3-642-15950-3(8),* 3642159508) Springer.

Deutsch, Tobias. Human Bionically Inspired Autonomous Agents: The Framework Implementation ARSi11 of the Psychoanalytical Entity Id Applied to Embodied Agents. 2011. 212p. pap. ***(978-3-8381-2709-5(9))*** Südwestdeutscher Verlag für Hochschulschriften AG & Co. KG.

Di Gesù, Vito, et al. Fuzzy Logic & Applications: 8th International Workshop, WILF 2009 Palermo, Italy, June 9-12, 2009 Proceedings. 2009. (Lecture Notes in Computer Science / Lecture Notes in Artificial Intelligence Ser.). xiv, 378p. pap. 79.95 *(978-3-642-02281-4(2),* 3642022812) Springer.

Dicheva, Darina & Dochev, Danail, eds. Artificial Intelligence: Methodology, Systems, & Applications: 14th International Conference, AIMSA 2010, Varna, Bulgaria, September 8-10, 2010. Proceedings. 2010. (Lecture Notes in Computer Science / Lecture Notes in Artificial Intelligence Ser.). xiv, 286p. pap. 83.00 *(978-3-642-15430-0(1),* 3642154301) Springer.

Dickmann, Lutz, et al, eds. Smart Graphics: 11th International Symposium on Smart Graphics, Bremen, Germany, July 18-20, 2011. Proceedings. 2011. (Lecture Notes in Computer Science / Image Processing, Computer Vision, Pattern Recognition, & Graphics Ser.). (Illus.). xi, 203p. pap. 72.00 ***(978-3-642-22570-3(5),*** 3642225705) Springer.

Dietrich, Dietmar. Simulating the Mind: A Technical Neuropsychoanalytical Approach. Dietrich, Dietmar et al, eds. 2008. (ENG., Illus.). xvii, 436p. 179.00 *(978-3-211-09450-1(4),* 3211094504) Springer.

Dietrich, Dietmar, et al, eds. Simulating the Mind: A Technical Neuropsychoanalytical Approach. 2010. (ENG., Illus.). xvii, 436p. pap. 179.00 *(978-3-211-99869-4(1),* 3211998691) Springer.

Dignum, Frank, et al. Agents for Games & Simulations: Trends in Techniques, Conception & Design. 2009. (Lecture Notes in Computer Science / Lecture Notes in Artificial Intelligence Ser.). (Illus.). x, 273p. pap. 72.00 *(978-3-642-11197-6(1),* 3642111971) Springer.

Dignum, Frank, ed. Agents for Games & Simulations II: Trends in Techniques, Concepts & Design. 2011. (Lecture Notes in Computer Science / Lecture Notes in Artificial Intelligence Ser.). x, 207p. pap. 72.00 *(978-3-642-18180-1(5),* 3642181805) Springer.

Dillmann, Radiger, et al, eds. KI 2010: Advances in Artificial Intelligence: 33rd Annual German Conference on AI, Karlsruhe, Germany, September 21-24, 2010, Proceedings. 2010. (Lecture Notes in Computer Science / Lecture

Notes in Artificial Intelligence Ser.). xvi, 446p. pap. 95.00 *(978-3-642-16110-0(3),* 3642161103) Springer.

Dimitrova, Vania. Artificial Intelligence in Education: Building Learning Systems That Care: from Knowledge Representation to Affective Modelling. 2009. (Illus.). 827p. 247.00 *(978-1-60750-028-5(0))* IOS Pr., Inc.

Ding, Yongsheng. Zi Ran Ji Suan Yu Wang Luo Zhi Neng. 2008. (CHI., Illus.). *(978-7-313-04988-9(9))* Shanghai Jiaotong Univ. Pr.

Discovery Science. 2008. (Lecture Notes in Computer Science / Lecture Notes in Artificial Intelligence Ser.). spiral bd. 79.95 *(978-3-540-88410-1(6))* Springer.

Dodd, Will. Robotic Recall - Designing Cognitive Robotic Systems Using Working Memory. 2007. 176p. per. *(978-3-8364-2945-0(4))* VDM Verlag Dr. Mueller e.K.

Domingos, Pedro & Lowd, Daniel. Markov Logic: An Interface Layer for Artificial Intelligence. 2009. (Synthesis Lectures on Artificial Intelligence & Machine Learning Ser.). 155p. pap. 40.00 *(978-1-59829-692-1(2))* Morgan & Claypool Pubs.

Dong, Tiansi. Recognizing Variable Environments: The Theory of Cognitive Prism. 2011. (Studies in Computational Intelligence Ser.). (ENG., Illus.). xx, 124p. 129.00 ***(978-3-642-24057-7(7)***, 3642240577) Springer.

Dooling, Richard. Rapture for the Geeks: When AI Outsmarts IQ. 2009. (ENG.). 272p. pap. 14.00 *(978-0-307-40526-5(5),* Three Rivers Pr.) Crown Publishing Group.

Dorigo, Marco, et al, eds. Swarm Intelligence: 7th International Conference, ANTS 2010, Brussels, Belgium,September 8-10, 2010 Proceedings. 2010. (Lecture Notes in Computer Science / Theoretical Computer Science & General Issues Ser.). xviii, 582p. pap. 119.00 *(978-3-642-15460-7(3),* 3642154603) Springer.

Dror, Itiel E. Cognitive Technologies & the Pragmatics of Cognition. 2007. (Illus.). xi, 184p. *(978-90-272-2242-8(8))* Benjamins, John Publishing Co.

Druzovec, T. Welzer & Jaakkola, H., eds. Information Modelling & Knowledge Bases XXI: Volume 206 Frontiers in Artificial Intelligence & Applications. 2010. 456p. 199.00 *(978-1-60750-089-6(2))* IOS Pr., Inc.

Dufty, David F. How to Build an Android: The True Story of Philip K. Dick's Robotic Resurrection. 2012. (ENG., Illus.). 288p. 26.00 ***(978-0-8050-9551-7(9))*** Holt, Henry & Co.

Duindam, Vincent, et al, eds. Modeling & Control of Complex Physical Systems: The Port-Hamiltonian Approach. 2009. (ENG., Illus.). xxvi, 430p. 129.00 *(978-3-642-03195-3(1),* 3642031951) Springer.

Duzí, Marie. Information Modelling & Knowledge Bases XVIII. 2007. (Illus.). x, 321p. 131.00 *(978-1-58603-710-9(2))* IOS Pr., Inc.

Dyson, George B. Darwin among the Machines: The Evolution of Global Intelligence. 2nd ed. 2012. (ENG.). 304p. (gr. 9). pap. 16.99 ***(978-0-465-03162-7(5))*** Basic Bks.

Ekbia, Hamid R. Artificial Dreams: The Quest for Non-Biological Intelligence. 2008. (ENG., Illus.). 416p. 86.99 *(978-0-521-87867-8(5));* pap. 26.99 *(978-0-521-70339-0(5))* Cambridge Univ. Pr.

Eklund, Peter W. Conceptual Structures. 2008. (Lecture Notes in Computer Science / Lecture Notes in Artificial Intelligence Ser.). spiral bd. 79.95 *(978-3-540-70595-6(3))* Springer.

Elci, Atilla, et al, eds. Semantic Agent Systems: Foundations & Applications. 2011. (Studies in Computational Intelligence Ser.). (Illus.). xvi, 316p. 179.00 *(978-3-642-18307-2(7),* 3642183077) Springer.

Ellis, Richard & Petridis, Miltos. Applications & Innovations in Intelligent Systems XV: Proceedings of AI-2007, the Twenty-Seventh SGAI International Conference on Innovative Techniques & Applications of Artificial Intelligence. 2007. (ENG., Illus.). xii, 352p. per. 159.00 *(978-1-84800-085-6(5),* 1848000855) Springer.

Ellis, Richard & Petridis, Miltos, eds. Applications & Innovations in Intelligent Systems XVI: Proceedings of AI-2008, the Twenty-eighth SGAI International Conference on Innovative Techniques & Applications of Artificial Intelligence. 2008. (ENG., Illus.). xii, 260p. pap. 179.00 *(978-1-84882-214-6(6))* Springer.

Elmahalawy, Ahmed. Multi Agent Systems for Artificial Life Domain. 2010. 172p. pap. *(978-3-8383-4590-1(8))* Lambert Academic Publishing.

Engdahl, Sylvia. Artificial Intelligence. 2007. (Contemporary Issues Companion Ser.). (ENG.). 171p. (gr. 10-12). 27.50 *(978-0-7377-3891-9(X));* (Illus.). pap. 39.70 *(978-0-7377-3890-2(1))* Cengage Gale. (Greenhaven Pr., Inc.).

Engle, Eric. Computers, Games, & Art. 2010. 124p. pap. *(978-3-8383-5738-6(8))* Lambert Academic Publishing.

Epstein, Robert, et al, eds. Parsing the Turing Test: Philosophical & Methodological Issues in the Quest for the Thinking Computer. 2008. (ENG., Illus.). xxiv, 520p. pap. 79.95 *(978-1-4020-9624-2(0),* 1402096240) Springer.

Epstein, Robert, et al. Parsing the Turing Test: Philosophical & Methodological Issues in the Quest for the Thinking Computer. Epstein, Robert et al, eds. 2008. (ENG., Illus.). xxiv, 520p. 209.00 *(978-1-4020-6708-2(9),* 1402067089) Springer.

Ertel, Wolfgang. Introduction to Artificial Intelligence. Black, Nathanael T., tr. from GER. 2011. (Undergraduate Topics in Computer Science Ser.). Orig. Title: Grundkurs Kanstliche Intelligenz: eine praxisorientierte Einfahrung. (ENG., Illus.). xi, 316p. pap. 39.95 *(978-0-85729-298-6(6),* 0857292986) Springer.

Esik, Zoltán, et al, eds. Recent Advances in Formal Languages & Applications. 2006. (Studies in Computational Intelligence: Vol. 25). (Illus.). viii, 373p. (C). 239.00 *(978-3-540-33460-6(2),* 3540334602) Springer.

Esposito, Anna, et al. Multimodal Signals: Cognitive & Algorithmic Issues: International School Vietri sul Mare, Italy, April 21-26, 2008 Revised Selected & Invited Papers. 2009. (Lecture Notes in Computer Science / Lecture Notes in Artificial Intelligence Ser.). (Illus.). xiii, 348p. pap. 79.95 *(978-3-642-00524-4(1))* Springer.

Essaaidi, Mohammad, et al, eds. Intelligent Distributed Computing IV: Proceedings of the 4th International Symposium on Intelligent Distributed Computing - IDC 2010, Tangier, Morocco, September 2010. 2010. (Studies in Computational Intelligence Ser.). 309p. 199.00 *(978-3-642-15210-8(4),* 3642152104) Springer.

EUROCON 2007 - the International Conference on Computer as a Tool. 2007. pap. 384.00 *(978-1-4244-0812-2(1),* 07EX1617) IEEE.

Euzenat, Jerome & Domingue, John. Artificial Intelligence: Methodology, Systems, & Applications: 12th International Conference, AIMSA 2006 Varna, Bulgaria, September 12-15, 2006 Proceedings. 2007. (Lecture Notes in Computer Science Ser.). (Illus.) 289p. per. 79.95 *(978-3-540-40930-4(0),* 3540409300) Springer.

Falcone, Rino, et al. Trust in Agent Societies: 11th International Workshop, TRUST 2008, Estoril, Portugal, May 12 -13, 2008. Revised Selected & Invited Papers. 2008. (Lecture Notes in Computer Science / Lecture Notes in Artificial Intelligence Ser.). viii, 349p. pap. 79.95 *(978-3-540-92802-7(2))* Springer.

Falmagne, Jean-Claude & Doignon, Jean-Paul. Learning Spaces: Interdisciplinary Applied Mathematics. 2010. (ENG., Illus.). xv, 417p. 129.00 *(978-3-642-01038-5(5),* 3642010385) Springer.

Fang, Jiancheng & Wang, Zhongyu. Seventh International Symposium on Instrumentation & Control Technology: Sensors & Instruments, Computer Simulation, & Artificial Intelligence: 10-13 October, 2008, Beijing, China. 2008. (Proceedings of SPIE Ser.). (Illus.). 642p. pap. 130.00 *(978-0-8194-7361-5(8))* SPIE.

Farzindar, Atefeh & Keselj, Vlado, eds. Advances in Artificial Intelligence: 23rd Canadian Conference on Artificial Intelligence, Canadian AI 2010, Ottawa, Canada, May 31 - June 2, 2010, Proceedings. 2010. (Lecture Notes in Computer Science / Lecture Notes in Artificial Intelligence Ser.). xvi, 426p. pap. 99.00 *(978-3-642-13058-8(5),* 3642130585) Springer.

Fei, Minrui, et al, eds. Life System Modeling & Intelligent Computing: International Conference on Life System Modeling & Simulation, LSMS 2010, & International Conference on Intelligent Computing for Sustainable Energy & Environment, ICSEE 2010, Wuxi, China, September 17-20, 2010, Proceedings, Part I. 2010. (Lecture Notes in Computer Science / Theoretical Computer Science & General Issues Ser.). xxii, 518p. pap. 107.00 *(978-3-642-15620-5(7),* 3642156207) Springer.

—Life System Modeling & Intelligent Computing: International Conference on Life System Modeling & Simulation, LSMS 2010, & International Conference on Intelligent Computing for Sustainable Energy & Environment, ICSEE 2010, Wuxi, China, September 17-20, 2010, Proceedings, Part II. 2010. (Lecture Notes in Computer Science / Theoretical Computer Science & General Issues Ser.). xxi, 518p. pap. 107.00 *(978-3-642-15596-3(0),* 3642155960) Springer.

Fermüller, Christian G. & Voronkov, Andrei, eds. Logic for Programming, Artificial Intelligence, & Reasoning: 17th International Conference, LPAR-17, Yogyakarta, Indonesia, October 10-15, 2010, Proceedings. 2010. (Lecture Notes in Computer Science / Theoretical Computer Science & General Issues Ser.). xi, 656p. pap. 119.00 *(978-3-642-16241-1(X),* 364216241X) Springer.

Fernandez-Blanco, Enrique & Dorado, Julian. Generating Shapes & Processing Information with an Artificial Cell. 2010. 80p. pap. *(978-3-8383-5928-1(3))* Lambert Academic Publishing.

Fernández, José M., et al, eds. Foundations on Natural & Artificial Computation: 4th International Work-conference on the Interplay Between Natural & Artificial Computation, IWINAC 2011, la Palma, Canary Islands, Spain, May 30 - June 3, 2011. Proceedings, Part I. 2011. (Lecture Notes in Computer Science / Theoretical Computer Science & General Issues Ser.). (Illus.). xxv, 566p. pap. 107.00 *(978-3-642-21343-4(X),* 364221343X) Springer.

—New Challenges on Bioinspired Applications: 4th International Work-conference on the Interplay Between Natural & Artificial Computation, IWINAC 2011, la Palma, Canary Islands, Spain, May 30 - June 3, 2011. Proceedings, Part II. 2011. (Lecture Notes in Computer Science / Theoretical Computer Science & General Issues Ser.). (Illus.). xxv, 486p. pap. 107.00 *(978-3-642-21325-0(1),* 3642213251) Springer.

Ferraz, Christiano. Sample Design for Survey's Quality Evaluation. 2008. 92p. pap. *(978-3-639-07463-5(7))* VDM Verlag Dr. Mueller e.K.

Ferré, Sébastien & Rudolph, Sebastian. Formal Concept Analysis: 7th International Conference, ICFCA 2009 Darmstadt, Germany, May 21-24, 2009 Proceedings. 2009. (Lecture Notes in Computer Science / Lecture Notes in Artificial Intelligence Ser.). xii, 341p. pap. 79.95 *(978-3-642-01814-5(9),* 3642018149) Springer.

Fette, Bruce A., ed. Cognitive Radio Technology. 2nd ed. 2009. (ENG., Illus.). 848p. 103.00 *(978-0-12-374535-4(7),* Academic Pr.) Elsevier Science & Technology Bks.

Filgueiras, M., et al, eds. Natural Language Processing: EAIA '90, 2nd Advanced School in Artificial Intelligence Guarda, Portugal, October 8-12, 1990. Proceedings. 2007. (Lecture Notes in Computer Science Ser.). 268p. per. 69.95 *(978-3-540-53678-9(7))* Springer.

Filho, J. I. Da Silva, ed. Uncertainty Treatment Using Paraconsistent Logic. 2010. 174.00 *(978-1-60750-557-0(6))* IOS Pr., Inc.

Filipe, Joaquim, et al. Agents & Artificial Intelligence: International Conference, ICAART 2009, Porto, Portugal, January 19-21, 2009. Revised Selected Papers. 2010. (Communications in Computer & Information Science Ser.). 296p. pap. 89.95 *(978-3-642-11818-0(6),* 3642118186) Springer.

Filipe, Joaquim, et al, eds. Agents & Artificial Intelligence: Second International Conference, ICAART 2009, Valencia, Spain, January 22-24, 2009. Revised Selected Papers. 2011. (Communications in Computer & Information Science Ser.). (Illus.). xi, 251p. pap. 84.00 *(978-3-642-19889-2(9),* 3642198899) Springer.

Fink, Eugene. Changes of Problem Representation: Theory & Experiments. 2010. (Studies in Fuzziness & Soft Computing Ser.). (ENG., Illus.). xiv, 355p. pap. 139.00 *(978-3-7908-2518-3(2),* 3790825182) Physica-Verlag DEU. Dist: Springer.

Fischer, Klaus. Multiagent System Technologies: 4th German Conference, MATES 2006, Erfurt, Germany, September 19-20, 2006: Proceedings. Fischer, Klaus et al, eds. 2006. (Lecture Notes in Computer Science Ser.). (Illus.). 183p. pap. 69.95 *(978-3-540-45376-5(8),* 3540453768) Springer.

Fisher, Douglas & Maher, Mary Lou, eds. Artificial Intelligence & Sustainable Design: Papers from the AAAI Spring Symposium (SS-11-02) 2011. (Illus.). 122p. spiral bd. 30.00 ***(978-1-57735-494-9(X))*** AAAI Pr.

Fisher, Micheal & Van Der Hoek, Wiebe, eds. Logics in Artificial Intelligence: 10th European Conference, JELIA 2006 Liverpool, UK, September 13-15, 2006 Proceedings. 2007. (Lecture Notes in Computer Science Ser.). (Illus.). 516p. per. 109.00 *(978-3-540-39625-3(X),* 354039625X) Springer.

Floreano, Dario & Mattiussi, Claudio. Bio-Inspired Artificial Intelligence: Theories, Methods, & Technologies. 2008. (Intelligent Robotics & Autonomous Agents Ser.). (ENG., Illus.). 688p. 56.00 *(978-0-262-06271-8(2))* MIT Pr.

Fodor, János, et al, eds. Recent Advances in Intelligent Engineering Systems. 2011. (Studies in Computational Intelligence Ser.). (ENG., Illus.). xx, 440p. 179.00 ***(978-3-642-23228-2(0)***, 3642232280) Springer.

Fodor, János & Kacprzyk, Janusz, eds. Aspects of Soft Computing, Intelligent Robotics & Control. 2009. (Studies in Computational Intelligence Ser.). (ENG., Illus.). xii, 270p. 179.00 *(978-3-642-03632-3(5),* 3642036325) Springer.

Fogel, Gary B., et al, eds. Computational Intelligence in Bioinformatics. 2007. (IEEE Press Series on Computational Intelligence Ser.: 7). (ENG., Illus.). 355p. 99.95 *(978-0-470-10526-9(7),* Wiley-IEEE Pr.) Wiley, John & Sons, Inc.

Forbes-Pitt, Kate. The Assumption of Agency Theory. 2011. (ENG., Illus.). 184p. 140.00 *(978-0-415-78211-1(2))* Routledge.

Foundations of Intelligent Systems. 2007. (Lecture Notes in Computer Science Ser.). (Illus.). 767p. per. 139.00 *(978-3-540-45764-0(X),* 354045764X) Springer.

Fourli-Kartsouni, Florendia. Intelligent Workflow: Support for Context Sensitive Business Process Modeling. 2008. 108p. pap. *(978-3-8364-8054-3(9))* VDM Verlag Dr. Mueller e.K.

Francois, Damien. High-Dimensional Data Analysis. 2008. 176p. pap. *(978-3-8364-9309-3(8))* VDM Verlag Dr. Mueller e.K.

Frank, Juraj. Enhancing Tagging Systems. 2010. 56p. pap. *(978-3-8383-7035-4(X))* Lambert Academic Publishing.

Freksa, Christian, ed. KI 2006: Advances in Artificial Intelligence: 29th Annual German Conference on AI, KI 2006, Bremen, Germany, June 14-17, 2006, Proceedings. 2007. (Lecture Notes in Computer Science Ser.). (Illus.). 456p. per. 84.95 *(978-3-540-69911-8(2),* 3540699112) Springer.

Fremond, Michel & Maceri, Franco, eds. Mechanics, Models & Methods in Civil Engineering. 2011. (Lecture Notes in Applied & Computational Mechanics Ser.). (ENG., Illus.). xviii, 502p. 229.00 ***(978-3-642-24637-1(0)***, 3642246370) Springer.

Fujita, H., ed. New Trends in Software Methodologies, Tools & Techniques: Proceedings of the 9th SoMeT_10 - Volume 217 Frontiers in Artificial Intelligence & Applications. 2010. 210.00 *(978-1-60750-628-7(9))* IOS Pr., Inc.

Fujita, H. & Zualkeman, I., eds. New Trends in Software Methodologies, Tools & Techniques: Proceedings of the seventh SoMeT_08 - Volume 182 Frontiers in Artificial Intelligence & Applications. 2008. (Illus.). 450p. 179.00 *(978-1-58603-916-5(4))* IOS Pr., Inc.

Fujita, Hamido & Pisanelli, Domenico M. New trends in software methodologies, tools & Techniques. 2007. 195.00 *(978-1-58603-794-9(3))* IOS Pr., Inc.

Fukuda, Shuichi, ed. Emotional Engineering: Service Development. 2010. (Illus.). xviii, 395p. 179.00 *(978-1-84996-422-7(X),* 184996422X) Springer.

Furbach, Ulrich & Shankar, Natarajan. Automated Reasoning: Third International Joint Conference, IJCAR 2006, Seattle, WA, USA, August 17-20, 2006: Proceedings. 2007. (Lecture Notes in Computer Science Ser.). (Illus.). XV, 680p. pap. 119.00 *(978-3-540-37187-8(7),* 3540371877) Springer.

Furht, Borko, ed. Handbook of Augmented Reality. 2011. (ENG., Illus.). xxii, 746p. 199.00 *(978-1-4614-0063-9(5),* 1461400635) Springer.

—Handbook of Social Network Technologies & Applications. 2010. (ENG., Illus.). xviii, 716p. 199.00 *(978-1-4419-7141-8(6),* 1441971416) Springer.

Gabbay, D. Logic for Artificial Intelligence & Information Technology. 2007. 584p. per. *(978-1-904987-39-0(7))* College Pubns.

Gabrys, Bogdan, et al, eds. Do Smart Adaptive Systems Exist? Best Practice for Selection & Combination of Intelligent Methods. 2010. (Studies in Fuzziness & Soft Computing Ser.). (Illus.). x, 370p. pap. 239.00 *(978-3-642-06320-6(9),* 3642063209) Springer.

Gabrys, Bogdan, et al. Knowledge-Based Intelligent Information & Engineering Systems: 10th International Conference, KES 2006, Bournemouth, UK, October 9-11 2006, Proceedings, Part I, 3 vols. 2007. (Lecture Notes in Computer Science Ser.). (Illus.). 1297p. pap. 149.00 *(978-3-540-46535-5(9),* 3540465359) Springer.

—Knowledge-Based Intelligent Information & Engineering Systems: 10th International Conference, KES 2006, Bournemouth, UK, October 9-11 2006, Proceedings, Part II, 3 vols. 2007. (Lecture Notes in Computer Science Ser.). (Illus.). 1335p. pap. 159.00 *(978-3-540-46537-9(5),* 3540465375) Springer.

—Knowledge-Based Intelligent Information & Engineering Systems: 10th International Conference, KES 2006, Bournemouth, UK, October 9-11, 2006 Proceedings, Part III, 3 vols. 2007. (Lecture Notes in Computer Science Ser.). (Illus.). 1301p. pap. 179.00 *(978-3-540-46542-3(1),* 3540465421) Springer.

Gaïti, Dominique, ed. Autonomic Networks. 2008. (Iste Ser.: 282). (ENG., Illus.). 320p. 184.00 *(978-1-84821-002-8(7),* Wiley-ISTE) Wiley, John & Sons, Inc.

Gao, Yanqing, et al. Flexible Manipulators: Modeling, Analysis & Optimum Design. 2012. (ENG., Illus.). 260p. 125.00 ***(978-0-12-397036-7(9)***, Academic Pr.) Elsevier Science & Technology Bks.

Gao, Yong & Japkowicz, Nathalie. Advances in Artificial Intelligence: 22nd Canadian Conference on Artificial Intelligence, Canadian AI 2009 Kelowna, Canada, May 25-27, 2009 Proceedings. 2009. (Lecture Notes in Computer Science / Lecture Notes in Artificial Intelligence Ser.). xiv, 296p. pap. 79.95 *(978-3-642-01817-6(3))* Springer.

García-Pedrajas, Nicolás, et al, eds. Trends in Applied Intelligent Systems: 23rd International Conference on Industrial Engineering & Other Applications of Applied Intelligent Systems, IEA/AIE 2010, Cordoba, Spain, June 1-4, 2010, Proceedings, Part I. 2010. (Lecture Notes in Computer Science / Lecture Notes in Artificial Intelligence Ser.). xxxv, 770p. pap. 149.00 *(978-3-642-13021-2(6),* 3642130216) Springer.

—Trends in Applied Intelligent Systems: 23rd International Conference on Industrial Engineering & Other Applications of Applied Intelligent Systems, IEA/AIE 2010, Cordoba, Spain, June 1-4, 2010, Proceedings, Part II. 2010. (Lecture Notes in Computer Science / Lecture Notes in Artificial Intelligence Ser.). xix, 680p. pap. 129.00 *(978-3-642-13024-3(0),* 3642130240) Springer.

—Trends in Applied Intelligent Systems: 23rd International Conference on Industrial Engineering & Other Applications of Applied Intelligent Systems, IEA/AIE 2010, Cordoba, Spain, June 1-4, 2010, Proceedings, Part III. 2010. (Lecture Notes in Computer Science / Lecture Notes in Artificial Intelligence Ser.). xix, 674p. pap. 129.00 *(978-3-642-13032-8(1),* 3642130321) Springer.

Gargouri, Faiez & Jaziri, Wassim, eds. Ontology Theory, Management & Design: Advanced Tools & Models. 2010. (Illus.). 402p. 180.00 *(978-1-61520-859-3(3),* Information Science Reference) IGI Global.

Gelbukh, Alexander. Micai 2007 - Advances in Artificial Intelligence. 2007. (Lecture Notes in Computer Science / Lecture Notes in Artificial Intelligence Ser.). spiral bd. 179.00 *(978-3-540-76630-8(8))* Springer.

Gelbukh, Alexander & Morales, Angel Fernando Kuri. Proceedings, Sixth Mexican International Conference on Artificial Intelligence: MICAI 2007: November 4-10, 2007 Aguascalientes, Mexico. 2008. (Illus.). xv, 430p. *(978-0-7695-3124-3(5))* IEEE Computer Society Pr.

Gelbukh, Alexander & Morales, Eduardo F. Proceedings of the Special Session of the Seventh Mexican International Conference on Artificial Intelligence: MICAI 2008: October 27-31, 2008 Atizapán de Zaragoza, Mexico. 2008. (Illus.). xvii, 429p. *(978-0-7695-3441-1(4))* IEEE Computer Society Pr.

Georgilakis, Pavlos S. Spotlight on Modern Transformer Design. 2009. (Power Systems Ser.). (ENG., Illus.). xx, 427p. 239.00 *(978-1-84882-666-3(4),* 1848826664) Springer.

Gero, John S., ed. Artificial Intelligence in Design '02. 2010. (Illus.). 652p. pap. 299.00 *(978-90-481-6059-4(6),* 9048160596) Springer.

Gershenson, Carlos. Artificial Societies of Intelligent Agents. 2010. (Illus.). 120p. pap. *(978-3-8383-5773-7(6))* Lambert Academic Publishing.

Giunchiglia, Enrico & Walsh, Toby, eds. Sat 2005: Satisfiability Research in the Year 2005. 2006. (Illus.). vi, 294p. 139.00 *(978-1-4020-4552-3(2),* 1402045522) Springer.

Glitho, Roch, et al, eds. Intelligence in Communication Systems: IFIP International Conference on Intelligence in Communication Systems, INTELLCOMM 2005, Montreal, Canada, October 17-19 2005. 2010. (IFIP Advances in Information & Communication Technology Ser.). (Illus.). xiii, 312p. pap. 149.00 *(978-1-4419-3971-5(7),* 1441939717) Springer.

Godo, Lluis & Pugliese, Andrea. Scalable Uncertainty Management: Third International Conference, SUM 2009, Washington, DC, September 28-30, 2009, Proceedings. 2009. (Lecture Notes in Computer Science / Lecture Notes in Artificial Intelligence Ser.). x, 309p. pap. 83.00 *(978-3-642-04387-1(9),* 3642043879) Springer.

Goel, Ashok K., et al, eds. Diagrammatic Representation & Inference: 6th International Conference, Diagrams 2010, Portland, or, USA, August 9-11, 2010, Proceedings. 2010. (Lecture Notes in Computer Science / Lecture Notes in Artificial Intelligence Ser.). xiii, 356p. pap. 83.00 *(978-3-642-14599-5(X),* 364214599X) Springer.

Goertzel, Ben & Pennachin, Cassio, eds. Artificial General Intelligence. (Cognitive Technologies Ser.). 2010. xvi, 509p. pap. 119.00 *(978-3-642-06267-4(9),* 3642062679) 2006. (Illus.). 508p. 119.00 *(978-3-540-23733-4(X),* 354023733X) Springer.

Gökçay, Didem & Yildirim, Gülsen, eds. Affective Computing & Interaction: Psychological, Cognitive & Neuroscientific Perspectives. 2010. (Illus.). 350p. 180.00 *(978-1-61692-892-6(1),* Information Science Reference) IGI Global.

Gonzalez, Fabio A. & Romero, Eduardo, eds. Biomedical Image Analysis & Machine Learning Technologies: Applications & Techniques. 2009. 421p. 245.00 *(978-1-60566-956-4(3))* IGI Global.

Gordon, Brent M., ed. Artificial Intelligence: Approaches, Tools & Applications. 2011. (Scientific Revolutions Computer Science, Technology & Applications Ser.). (Illus.). 177p. 95.00 *(978-1-61324-019-9(8))* Nova Science Pubs., Inc.

Gordon, T.F. The Pleadings Game: An Artificial Intelligence Model of Procedural Justice. 2010. 264p. pap. 132.00 *(978-90-481-4591-1(0),* 9048145910) Springer.

A

Gottfried, Bjorn & Aghajan, Hamid, eds. Behaviour Monitoring & Interpretation - BMI: Well-Being - Volume 9 Ambient Intelligence & Smart Environments. 2011. 200p. 138.00 ***(978-1-60750-730-7(7))*** IOS Pr., Inc.

Gottfried, B. & Aghajan, H., eds. Behaviour Monitoring & Interpretation - Bmi: Smart Environments. 2009. (Ambient Intelligence & Smart Environments Ser.). (Illus.). 368p. 145.00 *(978-1-60750-048-3(5))* IOS Pr., Inc.

Governatori, G., ed. Legal Knowledge & Information Systems - Jurix 2009: The Twenty-Second Annual Conference. 2009. (Frontiers in Artificial Intelligence & Applications Ser.). 208p. 160.00 *(978-1-60750-082-7(5))* IOS Pr., Inc.

Grana, Manuel, ed. Computational & Ambient Intelligence: 9th International Work-Conference on Artificial Neural Networks, IWANN 2007, San Sebastian, Spain, June 20-22, 2007, Proceedings. 2007. (Lecture Notes in Computer Science Ser.). (Illus.). 1167p. per. 169.00 *(978-3-540-73006-4(0))* Springer.

Grant, Guy. Look Inside Your Mind. 2007. 112p. per. 17.95 *(978-1-4303-1358-8(7))* Lulu Enterprises Inc.

Grasso, Floriana, et al, eds. Computational Models of Natural Argument: Papers from the AAAI Workshop (WS-11-10) 2011. (Illus.). 36p. spiral bd. 25.00 ***(978-1-57735-526-7(1))*** AAAI Pr.

Grunenberg, Johannes. IASON Semantic Content Management System. 2008. 116p. pap. *(978-3-8364-9627-8(5))* VDM Verlag Dr. Mueller e.K.

Guenthner, Wolfgang. Enhancing Cognitive Assistance Systems with Inertial Measurement Units. 2010. (Studies in Computational Intelligence Ser.). (Illus.). x, 144p. pap. 159.00 *(978-3-642-09572-6(0)*, 3642095720) Springer.

Guesgen, Hans W. & Murray, R. Charles, eds. Proceedings of the Twenty-Third International Florida Artificial Intelligence Research Society Conference (FLAIRS-10) 2009. 600p. pap. 125.00 ***(978-1-57735-447-5(8))*** AAAI Pr.

Gunkel, David J. The Machine Question: Critical Perspectives on AI, Robots, & Ethics. 2012. ***(978-0-262-01743-5(1))*** MIT Pr.

Günthner, Wolfgang. Enhancing Cognitive Assistance Systems with Inertial Measurement Units. 2008. (Studies in Computational Intelligence Ser.). (Illus.). x, 144p. 159.00 *(978-3-540-76996-5(X)*, 354076996X) Springer.

Gupta, Jatinder N. D., et al, eds. Intelligent Decision-making Support Systems: Foundations, Applications & Challenges. 2010. (Decision Engineering Ser.). (Illus.). xxiv, 503p. pap. 219.00 *(978-1-84996-562-0(5)*, 1849965625) Springer.

Gutkind, Lee & Gutkind. Almost Human: Making Robots Think. 2009. (ENG., Illus.). 304p. pap. 15.95 *(978-0-393-33684-9(0)*, 33684) Norton, W. W. & Co., Inc.

Guttmann, Christian, et al, eds. Collaborative Agents - Research & Development: International Workshops, CARE@AI09 2009 / CARE@IAT10 2010Melbourne, Australia, December 1, 2009Toronto, Canada, August 31, 2010Revised Selected Papers. 2011. (Lecture Notes in Computer Science / Lecture Notes in Artificial Intelligence Ser.). (Illus.). viii, 187p. pap. 72.00 ***(978-3-642-22426-3(1)***, 3642224261) Springer.

Guyon, Isabelle, et al, eds. Feature Extraction: Foundations & Applications. 2006. (Studies in Fuzziness & Soft Computing Ser.: Vol. 207). (Illus.). XXIV, 778p. 349.00 *(978-3-540-35487-1(5)*, 3540354875) Springer.

Gvishiani, Alexej & Dubois, Jacques O. Artificial Intelligence & Dynamic Systems for Geophysical Applications. 2010. (ENG., Illus.). xv, 347p. pap. 269.00 *(978-3-642-07757-9(9)*, 3642077579) Springer.

Haddawy, P. Representing Plans Under Uncertainty: A Logic of Time, Chance, & Action. 2007. (Lecture Notes in Computer Science Ser.). 148p. per. 59.95 *(978-3-540-57697-6(5))* Springer.

Hadzic, Maja, et al. Ontology-Based Multi-Agent Systems. 2009. (Studies in Computational Intelligence Ser.). (Illus.). xiv, 274p. 239.00 *(978-3-642-01903-6(X)*, 364201903X) Springer.

Hakansson, Anne, et al. Agent & Multi-Agent Systems: Technologies & Applications: Third KES International Symposium, KES-AMSTA 2009, Uppsala, Sweden, June 3-5, 2009, Proceedings. 2009. (Lecture Notes in Computer Science / Lecture Notes in Artificial Intelligence Ser.). (ENG., Illus.). xx, 865p. pap. 149.00 *(978-3-642-01664-6(2)*, 3642016642) Springer.

Halavati, Ramin. Symbiogenetic Evolutionary Algorithms. 2010. 128p. pap. *(978-3-639-25444-0(9))* VDM Verlag Dr. Mueller e.K.

Hall, J. Storrs. Beyond AI: Creating the Conscience of the Machine. 2007. (ENG., Illus.). 1p. 28.98 *(978-1-59102-511-5(7))* Prometheus Bks., Pubs.

Haller, Susan, et al, eds. Computational Models of Mixed-Initiative Interaction. 2010. 404p. pap. 163.00 *(978-90-481-5171-4(6)*, 9048151716) Springer.

Halpin, Harry. Social Semantics: The Search for Meaning on the Web. 2012. (Semantic Web & Beyond Ser.: 13). (ENG., Illus.). ix, 225p. 109.00 ***(978-1-4614-1884-9(4)***, 1461418844) Springer.

Hanazawa, Akitoshi, et al, eds. Brain-Inspired Information Technology. 2010. (Studies in Computational Intelligence Ser.). (Illus.). x, 182p. 159.00 *(978-3-642-04024-5(1)*, 3642040241) Springer.

Hand, D. J. Artificial Intelligence & Psychiatry. 2009. (Scientific Basis of Psychiatry Ser.). (ENG.). 280p. pap. 42.00 *(978-0-521-11613-8(9))* Cambridge Univ. Pr.

Harlan, Jan, et al. A. I. Artificial Intelligence: From Stanley Kubrick to Steven Spielberg - The Vision Behind the Film. Harlan, Jan & Struthers, Jane, eds. 2009. (ENG., Illus.). 160p. 60.00 *(978-0-500-51489-4(5)*, 551489) Thames & Hudson.

Hart, Emma, et al, eds. Artificial Immune Systems: 9th International Conference, ICARIS 2010, Edinburgh, UK, July 26-29, 2010, Proceedings. 2010. (Lecture Notes in Computer Science / Theoretical Computer Science & General Issues Ser.). xi, 329p. pap. 83.00 *(978-3-642-14546-9(9)*, 3642145469) Springer.

Hasida, Koiti, ed. New Frontiers in Artificial Intelligence: JSAI 2003 & JSAI 2004 Conferences & Workshops, Niigata, Japan, June 23-27, 2003, Kanazawa, Japan, May 31-June 4, 2004, Revised Selected Papers. 2007. (Lecture Notes in Computer Science Ser.). (Illus.). 548p. pap. 109.00 *(978-3-540-71008-0(6)*, 3540710086) Springer.

Hassanien, Aboul Ella, et al, eds. Computational Intelligence in Multimedia Processing: Recent Advances: Recent Advances. 2010. (Studies in Computational Intelligence Ser.). (Illus.). xvi, 536p. pap. 239.00 *(978-3-642-09552-8(6)*, 3642095526) Springer.

—Computational Social Network Analysis: Trends, Tools & Research Advances. 2009. (Computer Communications & Networks Ser.). (ENG., Illus.). xii, 485p. 169.00 *(978-1-84882-228-3(6)*, 1848822286) Springer.

Hassanien, Aboul Ella, et al. Computational Intelligence in Multimedia Processing: Recent Advances. 2008. (Studies in Computational Intelligence Ser.). (Illus.). 401p. 239.00 *(978-3-540-76826-5(2))* Springer.

Hattori, Hiromitsu, et al. New Frontiers in Artificial Intelligence: JSAI 2008 Conference & Workshops, Asahikawa, Japan, June 11-13, 2008, Revised Selected Papers. 2009. (Lecture Notes in Computer Science / Lecture Notes in Artificial Intelligence Ser.). ix, 331p. pap. 79.95 *(978-3-642-00608-1(6))* Springer.

Hatzilygeroudis, Ioannis, et al, eds. Combinations of Intelligent Methods & Applications: Proceedings of the 2nd International Workshop, CIMA 2010, France, October 2010. 2012. (Smart Innovation, Systems & Technologies Ser.). (ENG., Illus.). x, 170p. 129.00 *(978-3-642-19617-1(9)*, 3642196179) Springer.

Haun, Matthias. Handbuch Robotik: Programmieren und Einsatz intelligenter Roboter. 2007. (VDI-Buch Ser.). (Illus.). XVIII, 550p. 279.00 *(978-3-540-25508-6(7)*, 3540255087) Springer.

Haupt, S. E., et al. Artificial Intelligence Methods in the Environmental Sciences. 2008. (Illus.). 1050p. 159.00 *(978-1-4020-9117-9(6))*; pap. 89.95 *(978-1-4020-9118-6(4))* Springer.

Hölldobler, Steffen, ed. Intellectics & Computational Logic: Papers in Honor of Wolfgang Bibel. 2010. (Applied Logic Ser.). 408p. pap. 239.00 *(978-90-481-5438-8(3)*, 9048154383) Springer.

He, Haibo. Self-Adaptive Systems for Machine Intelligence. 2011. (ENG., Illus.). 248p. 84.95 *(978-0-470-34396-8(6)*, Wiley-Interscience) Wiley, John & Sons, Inc.

Heimbrrger, A. & Kiyoki, Y., eds. Information Modelling & Knowledge Bases XXII - Frontiers in Artificial Intelligence & Applications. 2011. 460p. 210.00 ***(978-1-60750-689-8(0))*** IOS Pr., Inc.

Henderson & Harry. Artificial Intelligence. 2007. (Milestones in Discovery & Invention Ser.). 208p. (YA). (gr. 7-12). 35.00 *(978-0-8160-5749-8(4))* Facts On File, Inc.

Hepp, Martin, et al, eds. Ontology Management: Semantic Web, Semantic Web Services, & Business Applications. 2007. (Semantic Web & Beyond: Computing for Human Experience Ser.). (Illus.). 293p. 129.00 *(978-0-387-69899-1(X))* Springer.

Herik, Jaap van den. Advances in Computer Games: 11th International Conference, ACG 2005, Taipei, Taiwan, September 6-9, 2005: Revised Papers. Donkers, H. H. L. M. et al, eds. 2007. (Lecture Notes in Computer Science Ser.: Vol. 4250). (Illus.). XIV, 273p. pap. 69.95 *(978-3-540-48887-3(1)*, 3540488871) Springer.

Hernández Aguirre, Arturo, et al. MICAI 2009: Advances in Artificial Intelligence: 8th Mexican International Conference on Artificial Intelligence, Guanajuato, México, November 9-13, 2009 Proceedings. 2009. (Lecture Notes in Computer Science / Lecture Notes in Artificial Intelligence Ser.). xvii, 742p. pap. 139.00 *(978-3-642-05257-6(6)*, 3642052576) Springer.

Hernández Aguirre, Arturo, et al. Proceedings of Special Session: Ninth Mexican International Conference on Artificial Intelligence: MICAI 2010: Advances in Artificial Intelligence & Applications: 8-13 November 2010, Pachuca, Mexico. 2010. (Illus.). xiv, 178p. ***(978-0-7695-4284-3(0))*** IEEE Computer Society Pr.

Herrero, Álvaro & Corchado, Emilio, eds. Mobile Hybrid Intrusion Detection: The MOVICAB-IDS System. 2011. (Studies in Computational Intelligence Ser.). (Illus.). x, 146p. 129.00 *(978-3-642-18298-3(4)*, 3642182984) Springer.

Hertzberg, J., et al. KI 2007: Advances in Artificial Intelligence: 30th Annual German Conference on AI, KI 2007 Osnabruck, Germany, September 10-13, 2007, Proceedings. 2007. (Lecture Notes in Computer Science Ser.). (Illus.). 516p. pap. 99.00 *(978-3-540-74564-8(5))* Springer.

Herzog, O. & Rollinger, C.R., eds. Text Understanding in LILOG: Integrating Computational Linguistics & Artificial Intelligence. Final Report on the IBM Germany LILOG-Project. 2007. (Lecture Notes in Computer Science Ser.). 756p. per. 89.95 *(978-3-540-54594-1(8))* Springer.

Hinkelmann, Knut & Thönssen, Barbara, eds. AI for Business Agility: Papers from the AAAI Spring Symposium (SS-11-03) 2011. (Illus.). 80p. spiral bd. 30.00 ***(978-1-57735-495-6(8))*** AAAI Pr.

Hitchcock, David & Verheij, Bart, eds. Arguing on the Toulmin Model: New Essays in Argument Analysis & Evaluation. 2007. (Argumentation Library: Vol. 10). (ENG., Illus.). viii, 439p. 249.00 *(978-1-4020-4937-8(4)*, 1402049374) Springer.

Ho, Tu Bao & Zhou, Zhi-Hua. PRICAI 2008: Trends in Artificial Intelligence: 10th Pacific Rim International Conference on Artificial Intelligence, Hanoi, Vietnam, December 15-19, 2008, Proceedings. 2008. (Lecture Notes in Computer Science / Lecture Notes in Artificial Intelligence Ser.). xxiv, 1130p. pap. 159.00 *(978-3-540-89196-3(X))* Springer.

Hoefflinger, Bernd. High-Dynamic-Range (HDR) Vision: Microelectronics, Image Processing, Computer Graphics. 2010. (Springer Series in Advanced Microelectronics Ser.). (Illus.). xvi, 241p. pap. 239.00 *(978-3-642-07940-5(7)*, 3642079407) Springer.

Hofstadter, Douglas R. Godel, Escher, Bach: Un Eterno y Gracil Bucle. 2007. (Fabula (Tusquets Editores) Ser.). (Illus.). 882p. pap. *(978-84-8383-024-6(8))* Tusquets Editores.

Hofstedt, Petra. Multiparadigm Constraint Programming Languages. 2011. (Cognitive Technologies Ser.). (Illus.). xi, 180p. 99.00 *(978-3-642-17329-5(2)*, 3642173292) Springer.

Holmes, Dawn E. & Jain, Lakhmi C., eds. Innovations in Machine Learning: Theory & Applications. 2010. (Studies in Fuzziness & Soft Computing Ser.). (Illus.). xvi, 274p. pap. 149.00 *(978-3-642-06788-4(3)*, 3642067883) Springer.

Holst, Anders, et al. Tenth Scandinavian Conference on Artificial Intelligence: SCAI 2008. 2008. (Illus.). x, 217p. 140.00 *(978-1-58603-867-0(2))* IOS Pr., Inc.

Honkela, Timo, et al, eds. Artificial Neural Networks & Machine Learning - ICANN 2011: 21st International Conference on Artificial Neural Networks, Espoo, Finland, June 14-17, 2011, Proceedings, Part I, 2 vols. 2011. (Lecture Notes in Computer Science / Theoretical Computer Science & General Issues Ser.). (Illus.). xxi, 390p. pap. 95.00 ***(978-3-642-21734-0(6)***, 3642217346) Springer.

—Artificial Neural Networks & Machine Learning - ICANN 2011: 21st International Conference on Artificial Neural Networks, Espoo, Finland, June 14-17, 2011, Proceedings, Part II. 2011. (Lecture Notes in Computer Science / Theoretical Computer Science & General Issues Ser.). xxii, 474p. pap. 95.00 ***(978-3-642-21737-1(0)***, 3642217370) Springer.

Hou, Zengguang, ed. Advances in Neural Networks - ISNN 2007: 4th International Symposium on Neural Networks, ISNN 2007 Nanjing, China, June 3-7, 2007 Proceedings, Part III. 2007. (Lecture Notes in Computer Science Ser.). (Illus.). 1215p. pap. 179.00 *(978-3-540-72394-3(3))* Springer.

—Advances in Neural Networks - ISNN 2007: 4th International Symposium on Neutral Networks, ISNN 2007, Nanjing, China, June 3-7, 2007, Proceedings, Part II. 2007. (Lecture Notes in Computer Science Ser.). (Illus.). 1321p. pap. 189.00 *(978-3-540-72392-9(7))* Springer.

Howard, Daniel, et al, eds. Advances in Hybrid Information Technology: First International Conference, ICHIT 2006, Jeju Island, Korea, November 9-11, 2006, Revised Selected Papers. 2008. (Lecture Notes in Artificial Intelligence Ser.). (Illus.). 671p. pap. 119.00 *(978-3-540-77367-2(3))* Springer.

Hsu, Ching-Hsien, et al, eds. Ubiquitous Intelligence & Computing: 8th International Conference, UIC 2011, Banff, Canada, September 2-4, 2011, Proceedings. 2011. (Lecture Notes in Computer Science / Information Systems & Applications, incl. Internet/Web, & HCI Ser.). (Illus.). xv, 592p. pap. 119.00 ***(978-3-642-23640-2(5)***, 3642236405) Springer.

Hübner, Jomi Fred, et al. Coordination, Organizations, Institutions & Norms in Agent Systems IV: COIN 2008 International Workshops COIN@AAMAS 2008, Estoril, Portugal, May 12, 2008 COIN@AAAI 2008, Chicago, USA, July 14, 2008, Revised Selected Papers. 2009. (Lecture Notes in Computer Science / Lecture Notes in Artificial Intelligence Ser.). (ENG.). xii, 267p. pap. 69.95 *(978-3-642-00442-1(3))* Springer.

Hulth, Anette. Automatic Keyword Extraction. 2008. (Illus.). 104p. pap. *(978-3-639-03855-2(X))* VDM Verlag Dr. Mueller e.K.

Husbands, Philip, et al, eds. The Mechanical Mind in History. 2008. (ENG., Illus.). 472p. (gr. 17). 43.00 *(978-0-262-08377-5(9))* MIT Pr.

Hussein, Sherif. The Design of an Intelligent Active Orthosis for Lower Limbs. 2010. 192p. pap. *(978-3-639-24398-7(6))* VDM Verlag Dr. Mueller e.K.

Hutter, Marcus. Universal Artificial Intelligence: Sequential Decisions Based on Algorithmic Probability. 2010. (Texts in Theoretical Computer Science. an EATCS Ser.). xx, 280p. pap. 109.00 *(978-3-642-06052-6(8)*, 3642060528) Springer.

Hybrid Artificial Intelligence Systems. 2008. (Lecture Notes in Computer Science / Lecture Notes in Artificial Intelligence Ser.). spiral bd. 139.00 *(978-3-540-87655-7(3)*, 3540876553) Springer.

Hyvärinen, Aapo, et al. Natural Image Statistics: A probablistic approach to early computational Vision. 2009. (Computational Imaging & Vision Ser.). (ENG., Illus.). xx, 448p. 129.00 *(978-1-84882-490-4(4)*, 1848824904) Springer.

Iantovics, Barna Laszlo, et al, eds. Bics 2008: Proceedings of the 1st International Conference on Bio-Inspired Computational Methods Used for Difficult Problems Solving: Development of Intelligent & Complex Systems. 2009. (AIP Conference Proceedings Ser.). (ENG.). 244p. pap. 179.00 *(978-0-7354-0654-4(5)*, 0735406545) American Institute of Physics.

Ichalkaranje, Nikhil, et al, eds. Intelligent Paradigms for Assistive & Preventive Healthcare. 2012. (Studies in Computational Intelligence Ser.). (ENG., Illus.). xiii, 234p. pap. 139.00 *(978-3-642-06862-1(6)*, 3642068626) Springer.

IEEE Staff. Eighth ACIS International Conference on Software Engineering, Artificial Intelligence, Networking, & Parallel/Distributed Computing (SNPD 2007) 30 July - 01 August 2007 / Qingdao, China. 2007. (Illus.). 3024p. pap. 644.00 *(978-0-7695-2909-7(7))* IEEE Computer Society Pr.

—International Conference on Tools with Artificial Intelligence: 19th: 2007: Patras, Greece, 2 vols. 2007. 1118p. pap. 344.00 *(978-0-7695-3015-4(X))* IEEE Computer Society Pr.

—2007 IEEE International Conference on Information Reuse & Integration. 2007. pap. 286.00 *(978-1-4244-1499-4(7))* IEEE.

—2007 International Workshop on Robotic & Sensors Environments: Rose. 2007. pap. 180.00 *(978-1-4244-1526-7(8))* IEEE.

—2008 7th IEEE International Conference on Cognitive Informatics. 2008. pap. 228.00 *(978-1-4244-2538-9(7))* IEEE.

—2008 IEEE International Conference on Emerging Technologies & Factory Automation. 2008. pap. 384.00 *(978-1-4244-1505-2(5))* IEEE.

—2008 International Symposium on Information Technology. 2008. pap. 260.00 *(978-1-4244-2327-9(9))* IEEE.

—2009 8th IEEE International Conference on Cognitive Informatics. 2009. pap. 280.00 *(978-1-4244-4642-1(2))* IEEE.

—2009 IEEE Workshop on Robotic Intelligence in Informationally Structured Space. 2009. pap. 192.00 *(978-1-4244-2753-6(3))* IEEE.

IEEE Staff, ed. 2007 IEEE Symposium on Artificial Life. 2007. pap. 274.00 *(978-1-4244-0701-9(X)*, 07EX1567) IEEE.

—2007 IEEE Symposium on Computational Intelligence in Bioinformatics & Computational Biology. 2007. pap. 274.00 *(978-1-4244-0710-1(9)*, 07EX1576) IEEE.

Iida, Fumiya, et al, eds. 50 Years of Artificial Intelligence: Essays Dedicated to the 50th Anniversary of Artificial Intelligence. 2008. (Lecture Notes in Artificial Intelligence Ser.). (Illus.). 398p. pap. 89.95 *(978-3-540-77295-8(2))* Springer.

Ijcai & Ijcai Staff. 11th IJCAI Videotape Program 1989. pap. 66.50 *(978-1-55860-097-3(3)*, Morgan Kaufmann) Elsevier Science & Technology Bks.

—12th IJCAI 1991. pap. 66.50 *(978-1-55860-183-3(X)*, Morgan Kaufmann) Elsevier Science & Technology Bks.

—13th IJCAI Videotape Program 1993. pap. 66.50 *(978-1-55860-309-7(3)*, Morgan Kaufmann) Elsevier Science & Technology Bks.

IJCAI Staff. IJCAI: Proceedings of the International Joint Conferences on Articial Intelligence:, 14 vols. pap. 855.00 *(978-1-55860-364-6(6)*, Morgan Kaufmann) Elsevier Science & Technology Bks.

Iliadis, Lazaros, et al, eds. Artificial Intelligence Applications & Innovations: Proceedings of the 5th IFIP Conference on Artificial Intelligence Applications & Innovations (AIAI'2009), April 23-25, 2009, Thessaloniki, Greece. (IFIP Advances in Information & Communication Technology Ser.). (ENG., Illus.). viii, 535p. 2010. pap. 269.00 ***(978-1-4419-5497-8(X)***, 144195497X) 2009. 269.00 *(978-1-4419-0220-7(1)*, 1441902201) Springer.

Iliadis, Lazaros S., et al, eds. Artificial Intelligence Applications & Innovations: 12th International Conference, EANN 2011 & 7th IFIP WG 12. 5 International Conference, AIAI 2011, Corfu, Greece, September 15-18, 2011, Proceedings, Part II. 2011. (IFIP Advances in Information & Communication Technology Ser.). (ENG., Illus.). xxiii, 494p. 177.00 ***(978-3-642-23959-5(5)***, 3642239595) Springer.

Indulska, Jadwiga. Ubiquitous Intelligence & Computing: 4th International Conference, UIC 2007 Hong Kong, China, July 11-13, 2007 Proceedings. 2007. (Lecture Notes in Computer Science Ser.). (Illus.). 1257p. per. 149.00 *(978-3-540-73548-9(8))* Springer.

Integration of AI & or Techniques in Constraint Programming for Combinatorial Optimization Problems: 4th International Conference, CPAIOR 2007 Brussels, Belgium, May 23-26, 2007 Proceedings. 2007. (Lecture Notes in Computer Science Ser.). (Illus.). 390p. pap. 89.95 *(978-3-540-72396-7(X))* Springer.

Intelligent Agents: Artificial. 24.95 *(978-1-56529-343-4(6))* Que.

Intelligent Computer Mathematics. 2008. (Lecture Notes in Computer Science / Lecture Notes in Artificial Intelligence Ser.). spiral bd. 109.00 *(978-3-540-85109-7(7))* Springer.

Intelligent Robotics & Applications. 2008. (Lecture Notes in Computer Science / Lecture Notes in Artificial Intelligence Ser.). spiral bd. 179.00 *(978-3-540-88516-0(1)*, 3540885161); spiral bd. 189.00 *(978-3-540-88512-2(9)*, 3540885129) Springer.

International Association for Computer & Information Science Staff & IEEE Computer Society Staff, contrib. by. Ninth ACIS International Conference on Software Engineering, Artificial Intelligence, Networking, & Parallel/Distributed Computing: In Conjunction with Second International Worshop on Advanced Internet Technology & Aplications: Proceedings: August 6-8, 2008, Phuket, Thailand. 2008. (Illus.). xxix, 992p. *(978-0-7695-3263-9(2))* IEEE Computer Society Pr.

International Joint Conference on Artificial Intelligence Staff. 14th IJCAI Videotape Program 1995. pap. 66.50 *(978-1-55860-388-2(3)*, Morgan Kaufmann) Elsevier Science & Technology Bks.

Iocchi, Luca, et al. RoboCup 2008: Robot Soccer World Cup XII: Robot Soccer World Cup XII. 2009. (Lecture Notes in Computer Science / Lecture Notes in Artificial Intelligence Ser.). xv, 662p. pap. 119.00 *(978-3-642-02920-2(5)*, 3642029205) Springer.

Iserlis, Yuri. Artificial Intelligence Around Us. 2009. 273p. pap. 24.95 *(978-1-58909-668-4(1))* Bookstand Publishing.

Ishida, Toru, ed. The Language Grid: Service-Oriented Collective Intelligence for Language Resource Interoperability. 2011. (Cognitive Technologies Ser.). (ENG., Illus.). ix, 306p. 69.95 *(978-3-642-21177-5(1)*, 3642211771) Springer.

Islam, Rafiqul. Focus on Information, Intelligence, & Knowledge. 2011. *(978-1-61209-979-8(3))* Nova Science Pubs., Inc.

Ito, Takayuki, et al, eds. Advances in Agent-Based Complex Automated Negotiations. 2009. (Studies in Computational Intelligence Ser.). (ENG., Illus.). viii, 216p. 179.00 *(978-3-642-03189-2(7)*, 3642031897) Springer.

Iurgel, Ido A., et al. Interactive Storytelling: Second Joint International Conference on Interactive Digital Storytelling, ICIDS 2009, GuimarÃ£es, Portugal, December 9-11, 2009, Proceedings. 2009. (Lecture Notes in Computer Science / Information Systems & Applications, incl. Internet/Web, & HCI Ser.). (Illus.). xv, 360p. pap. 83.00 *(978-3-642-10642-2(0)*, 3642106420) Springer.

Jain, Lakhmi, ed. Knowledge-Based Intelligent Information & Engineering Systems: KES 2007 - WIRN 2007 Part I: 11th International Conference, KES 2007 XVII Italian Workshop on Neural Networks Vietri sul Mare, Italy, September 12-14, 2007 Proceedings, 3 vols. 2007. (Lecture Notes in Computer Science Ser.). (Illus.). 882p. pap. 149.00 *(978-3-540-74817-5(2))* Springer.

—Knowledge-Based Intelligent Information & Engineering Systems: KES 2007 - WIRN 2007 Part III: 11th International Conference, KES 2007 XVII Italian Workshop on Neural Networks Vietri sul Mare, Italy, September 12-14, 2007 Proceedings, 3 vols 2007. (Lecture Notes in Computer Science Ser.). (Illus.) 1126p. pap. 169.00 *(978-3-540-74828-1(8))* Springer.

—Knowledge-Based Intelligent Information & Engineering Systems: KES 2007-WIRN 2007: 11th International Conference, KES 2007 XVII Italian Workshop on Neural Networks Vietri sul Mare, Italy, September 12-14, 2007 Proceedings, Part II, 3 vols. 2007. (Lecture Notes in Computer Science Ser.). (Illus.). 1380p. pap. 189.00 *(978-3-540-74826-7(1))* Springer.

Jain, Lakhmi C., ed. Innovative Teaching & Learning: Knowledge-Based Paradigms. 2010. (Studies in Fuzziness & Soft Computing Ser.). (ENG., Illus.). xii, 352p. pap. 159.00 *(978-3-7908-2465-0(8)*, 3790824658) Physica-Verlag DEU. Dist: Springer.

Jain, Lakhmi C., et al, eds. Innovations in Defence Support Systems -2: Socio-Technical Systems. 2011. (Studies in Computational Intelligence Ser.). (Illus.). xiv, 290p. 179.00 *(978-3-642-17763-7(8)*, 3642177638) Springer.

—Intelligent Agents & Their Applications. 2010. (Studies in Fuzziness & Soft Computing Ser.). (ENG., Illus.). xx, 338p. pap. 159.00 *(978-3-7908-2510-7(7)*, 3790825107) Physica-Verlag DEU. Dist: Springer.

Jain, Lakhmi C. & Lim, Chee Peng, eds. Handbook on Decision Making: Vol 1: Techniques & Applications. 2010. (Intelligent Systems Reference Library). 540p. 269.00 *(978-3-642-13638-2(9)*, 3642136389) Springer.

Jalili, Mahdi. Synchronization in Dynamical Networks. 2009. 200p. pap. *(978-3-639-16249-3(3))* VDM Verlag Dr. Mueller e.K.

Janesick, Valerie J. Stretching Exercises for Qualitative Researchers. 3rd ed. 2010. (Illus.). 320p. (C). pap. 58.00 ***(978-1-4129-8045-6(3)***, B80456P) SAGE Pubns., Inc.

Janhunen, Tomi & Niemelä, Ilkka, eds. Logics in Artificial Intelligence: 12th European Conference, JELIA 2010, Helsinki, Finland, September 13-15, 2010, Proceedings. 2010. (Lecture Notes in Computer Science / Lecture Notes in Artificial Intelligence Ser.). xiv, 374p. pap. 83.00 *(978-3-642-15674-8(6)*, 3642156746) Springer.

Jantke, K. P. Analogical & Inductive Inference: International Workshop All'86 Wendisch-Rietz, GDR, October 6-10, 1986, Proceedings. 2007. (Lecture Notes in Computer Science Ser.). 240p. per. 34.95 *(978-3-540-18081-4(8))* Springer.

Jian, Kuodi. A Graph Planning Procedure within an Agent Architecture: Fast Planning & Distributed Agent Architecture. 2008. 184p. pap. *(978-3-639-09233-2(3))* VDM Verlag Dr. Mueller e.K.

Jiang, Liangzhong, ed. Proceedings of the 2011 International Conference on Informatics, Cybernetics, & Computer Engineering (ICCE2011) November 19-20, 2011, Melbourne, Australia: Volume 1: Intelligent Control & Network Communication. 2011. (Advances in Intelligent & Soft Computing Ser.). (Illus.). xvi, 720p. pap. 349.00 ***(978-3-642-25184-9(6)***, 3642251846) Springer.

Jin, Yaochu, ed. Multi-Objective Machine Learning. 2010. (Studies in Computational Intelligence Ser.). (Illus.). xiii, 660p. pap. 219.00 *(978-3-642-06796-9(4)*, 3642067964) Springer.

Johnston, Benjamin & Williams, Mary-Anne, eds. Artificial Intelligence & Smarter Living: Papers from the AAAI Workshop (WS-11-07): the Conquest of Complexity. 2011. (Illus.). 60p. spiral bd. 25.00 ***(978-1-57735-523-6(7))*** AAAI Pr.

Johnston, John. The Allure of Machinic Life: Cybernetics, Artificial Life, & the New AI. 2010. (ENG., Illus.). 480p. (gr. 17). pap. 20.00 *(978-0-262-51502-3(4))* MIT Pr.

Jones, M. Tim. Artificial Intelligence: A Systems Approach. 2007. (Illus.). 498p. 69.95 incl. cd-rom *(978-0-9778582-3-1(5))* Infinity Science Pr., LLC.

—Artificial Intelligence: A Systems Approach. 2008. (ENG.). 498p. 114.95 *(978-0-7637-7337-3(9)*, Jones & Bartlett Learning, LLC.

Juba, Brendan. Universal Semantic Communication. 2011. (ENG., Illus.). xix, 397p. 129.00 ***(978-3-642-23296-1(5)***, 3642232965) Springer.

Kaci, Souhila. Working with Preferences: Less Is More. 2011. (Cognitive Technologies Ser.). (ENG., Illus.). xvi, 202p. 99.00 *(978-3-642-17279-3(2)*, 3642172792) Springer.

Kacprzyk, Janusz, et al, eds. Dependable Computer Systems. 2011. (Advances in Intelligent & Soft Computing Ser.). (Illus.). xiv, 314p. pap. 259.00 *(978-3-642-21392-2(8)*, 3642213928) Springer.

—Intelligent Text Categorization & Clustering. 2010. (Studies in Computational Intelligence Ser.). (Illus.). xiv, 120p. pap. 159.00 *(978-3-642-09929-8(7)*, 3642099297) Springer.

Kalogirou, Soteris. Artificial Intelligence in Energy & Renewable Energy Systems. 2006. (Illus.). 471p. 79.00 *(978-1-60021-261-1(1))* Nova Science Pubs., Inc.

Kampis, György, et al, eds. Advances in Artificial Life: 10th European Conference, ECAL 2009, Budapest, Hungary, September 13-16, 2009, Revised Selected Papers. 2011. (Lecture Notes in Computer Science / Lecture Notes in Artificial Intelligence Ser.). xxii, 481p. pap. 99.00 *(978-3-642-21313-7(8)*, 3642213138) Springer.

Kampis, György, et al, eds. Advances in Artificial Life: 10th European Conference, ECAL 2009, Budapest, Hungary, September 13-16, 2009, Revised Selected Papers, Part I. 2011. (Lecture Notes in Computer Science / Lecture Notes in Artificial Intelligence Ser.). xxi, 501p. pap. 99.00 *(978-3-642-21282-6(4)*, 3642212824) Springer.

Kandel, Abraham, et al, eds. Data Mining & Computational Intelligence. 2010. (Studies in Fuzziness & Soft Computing Ser.). (ENG., Illus.). xii, 372p. pap. 159.00 *(978-3-7908-2484-1(4)*, 3790824844) Physica-Verlag DEU. Dist: Springer.

Kang, Byeong-Ho. AI 2006: Advances in Artificial Intelligence: 19th Australian Joint Conference on Artificial Intelligence, Hobart, Australia, December 4-8, 2006: Proceedings. 2007. (Lecture Notes in Computer Science Ser.). (Illus.). XXVII, 1303p. pap. 189.00 *(978-3-540-49787-5(0)*, 3540497870) Springer.

Kang, Lishan, et al. Advances in Computation & Intelligence: Second International Symposium, ISICA 2007 Wuhan, China, September 21-23, 2007 Proceedings. 2007. (Lecture Notes in Computer Science Ser.). (Illus.). 663p. pap. 119.00 *(978-3-540-74580-8(7))* Springer.

Karagiannis, D., ed. Information Systems & Artificial Intelligence: Integration Aspects: First Workshop, Ulm, FRG, March 19-21, 1990. Proceedings. 2007. (Lecture Notes in Computer Science Ser.). 308p. per. 39.95 *(978-3-540-53557-7(8))* Springer.

Kasabov, Nikola. Evolving Connectionist Systems: The Knowledge Engineering Approach. 2nd rev. ed. 2007. (ENG., Illus.). xxii, 451p. per. 189.00 *(978-1-84628-345-1(0)*, 1846283450) Springer.

Kasabov, Nikola, ed. Future Directions for Intelligent Systems & Information Sciences: The Future of Speech & Image Technologies, Brain Computers, WWW, & Bioinformatics. 2010. (Studies in Fuzziness & Soft Computing Ser.). (ENG., Illus.). viii, 424p. pap. 169.00 *(978-3-7908-2470-4(4)*, 3790824704) Physica-Verlag DEU. Dist: Springer.

Kaschek, Roland & Delcambre, Lois M. L. The Evolution of Conceptual Modeling: From a historical perspective towards the future of conceptual Modeling. 2011. (Lecture Notes in Computer Science / Information Systems & Applications, incl. Internet/Web, & HCI Ser.). (ENG.). xii, 360p. pap. 83.00 *(978-3-642-17504-6(X)*, 364217504X) Springer.

König, Andreas, et al, eds. Knowledge-Based & Intelligent Information & Engineering Systems, Part III: 15th International Conference, KES 2011, Kaiserslautern, Germany, September 12-14, 2011, Proceedings, Part III, 4 vols. 2011. (Lecture Notes in Computer Science / Lecture Notes in Artificial Intelligence Ser.). (ENG., Illus.). xxii, 653p. pap. 119.00 ***(978-3-642-23853-6(X)***, 364223853X) Springer.

—Knowledge-Based & Intelligent Information & Engineering Systems, Part IV: 15th International Conference, KES 2011, Kaiserslautern, Germany, September 12-14, 2011, Proceedings, Part IV, 4 vols. 2011. (Lecture Notes in Computer Science / Lecture Notes in Artificial Intelligence Ser.). (ENG., Illus.). xxi, 471p. pap. 95.00 ***(978-3-642-23865-9(3)***, 3642238653) Springer.

Kelemen, Árpád, et al, eds. Computational Intelligence in Bioinformatics. 2010. (Studies in Computational Intelligence Ser.). (Illus.). xvi, 326p. pap. 239.00 *(978-3-642-09550-4(X)*, 364209550X) Springer.

Kelemen, Árpád, et al. Computational Intelligence in Bioinformatics. 2007. (Studies in Computational Intelligence Ser.). (Illus.). 331p. 239.00 *(978-3-540-76802-9(5))* Springer.

Keyson, David, et al, eds. Ambient Intelligence: Second International Joint Conference, AmI 2011, Amsterdam, the Netherlands, November 16-18, 2011, Proceedings. 2011. (Lecture Notes in Computer Science / Information Systems & Applications, incl. Internet/Web, & HCI Ser.). (Illus.). xi, 355p. pap. 95.00 ***(978-3-642-25166-5(8)***, 3642251668) Springer.

Khosla, Rajiv & Bianchi-Berthou. Context-aware Emotion-based Multi-agent Systems. 2008. (Decision Engineering Ser.). (Illus.). 400p. 109.00 *(978-1-84628-370-3(1)*, 1846283701) Springer.

Kim, Kwang J. & Tadokoro, Satoshi, eds. Electroactive Polymers for Robotic Applications: Artificial Muscles & Sensors. 2010. (ENG., Illus.). x, 281p. pap. 169.00 *(978-1-84996-590-3(0)*, 1849965900) Springer.

Kimmel, Shawn. Motion Planning Strategies for Impass. 2009. 108p. pap. *(978-3-639-13318-9(8))* VDM Verlag Dr. Mueller e.K.

Kirby, Neil. Introduction to Game AI. 2010. (ENG., Illus.). 400p. pap. 39.99 *(978-1-59863-998-8(6))* Course Technology.

Kirn, Stefan, et al, eds. Multiagent Engineering: Theory & Applications in Enterprises. 2010. (International Handbooks on Information Systems Ser.). (Illus.). xiii, 626p. pap. 269.00 *(978-3-642-06848-5(0)*, 3642068480) Springer.

Kiyoki, Y. & Tokuda, T., eds. Information Modelling & Knowledge Bases XX - Volume 190 Frontiers in Artificial Intelligence & Applications. 2009. (Illus.). 450p. 199.00 *(978-1-58603-957-8(1))* IOS Pr., Inc.

Klement, E.P. & Slany, W., eds. Fuzzy Logic in Artificial Intelligence: 8th Austrian Artificial Intelligence Conference, FLAI'93, Linz, Austria, June 28-30, 1993. Proceedings. 2007. (Lecture Notes in Computer Science Ser.). 216p. per. 39.95 *(978-3-540-56920-6(0))* Springer.

Klügl, Franziska & Ossowski, Sascha, eds. Multiagent System Technologies: 8th German Conference, MATES 2011, Leipzig, Germany, October 6-7, 2011 Proceedings. 2011. (Lecture Notes in Computer Science / Lecture Notes in Artificial Intelligence Ser.). (ENG., Illus.). x, 197p. pap. 72.00 ***(978-3-642-24602-9(8)***, 3642246028) Springer.

Kluska, Jacek. Analytical Methods in Fuzzy Modeling & Control. 2009. (Studies in Fuzziness & Soft Computing Ser.). (Illus.). xxvi, 251p. 159.00 *(978-3-540-89926-6(X))* Springer.

Kocatürk, Tuba. Distributed Intelligence in Design. Medjdoub, Benachir, ed. 2011. (ENG., Illus.). 280p. 152.99 *(978-1-4443-3338-1(0)*, Wiley-Blackwell) Wiley, John & Sons, Inc.

Koenig, Andreas, et al, eds. Knowledge-Based & Intelligent Information & Engineering Systems, Part I: 15th International Conference, KES 2011, Kaiserslautern, Germany, September 12-14, 2011, Proceedings, Part I, 4 vols. 2011. (Lecture Notes in Computer Science / Lecture Notes in Artificial Intelligence Ser.). (ENG., Illus.). xxii, 615p. pap. 119.00 ***(978-3-642-23850-5(5)***, 3642238505) Springer.

—Knowledge-Based & Intelligent Information & Engineering Systems, Part II: 15th International Conference, KES 2011, Kaiserslautern, Germany, September 12-14, 2011, Proceedings, Part II, 4 vols. 2011. (Lecture Notes in Computer Science / Lecture Notes in Artificial Intelligence Ser.). (ENG., Illus.). xxiii, 703p. pap. 131.00 ***(978-3-642-23862-8(9)***, 3642238629) Springer.

Kofod-Petersen, A. & Heintz, F., eds. Eleventh Scandinavian Conference on Artificial Intelligence: SCAI 2011 - Frontiers in Artificial Intelligence & Applications. 2011. 212p. 160.00 ***(978-1-60750-753-6(6))*** IOS Pr., Inc.

Kolossa, Dorothea & Häb-Umbach, Reinhold, eds. Robust Speech Recognition of Uncertain or Missing Data: Theory & Applications. 2011. (ENG., Illus.). xiv, 380p. 129.00 *(978-3-642-21316-8(2)*, 3642213162) Springer.

Kolp, Manuel. Agent-Oriented Information Systems. 2008. (Lecture Notes in Computer Science / Lecture Notes in Artificial Intelligence Ser.). pap. 69.95 *(978-3-540-77989-6(2)*, 3540779892) Springer.

Kolp, Manuel, et al. Agent-Oriented Information Systems III: 7th International Bi-Conference Workshop, AOIS 2005, Utrecht, Netherlands, July 26, 2005 & Klagenfurt, Austria, October 27, 2005: Revised Selected Papers. 2007. (Lecture Notes in Computer Science Ser.: Vol. 3529). (Illus.). X, 231p. pap. 79.95 *(978-3-540-48291-8(1)*, 3540482911) Springer.

Komorowski, J. Methodologies for Intelligent Systems: 7th International Symposium, ISMIS'93, Trondheim, Norway, June 15-18, 1993. Proceedings. 2007. (Lecture Notes in Computer Science Ser.). 676p. per. 109.00 *(978-3-540-56804-9(2))* Springer.

Komosinski, Maciej & Adamatzky, Andrew, eds. Artificial Life Models in Software. 2nd ed. 2009. (ENG., Illus.). xxii, 442p. 139.00 *(978-1-84882-284-9(7)*, 1848822847) Springer.

Konar, Amit & Jain, Lakhmi C. Cognitive Engineering: A Distributed Approach to Machine Intelligence. 2010. (Advanced Information & Knowledge Processing Ser.). (Illus.). xviii, 353p. pap. 159.00 *(978-1-84996-984-0(1)*, 1849969841) Springer.

Kononkenko, Igor & Kukar, Matjaz. Machine Learning & Data Mining: Introduction to Principles & Algorithms. 2007. (ENG.). 480p. pap. 95.00 *(978-1-904275-21-3(4)*, Horwood Publishing, Ltd.) Woodhead Publishing Ltd. GBR. Dist: Ingram Pub. Services.

Konstantopoulos, Stasinos, et al, eds. Advances in Artificial Intelligence: Theories, Models, & Applications: 6th Hellenic Conference on AI, SETN 2010, Athens, Greece, May 4-7, 2010. Proceedings. 2010. (Lecture Notes in Computer Science / Lecture Notes in Artificial Intelligence Ser.). xv, 430p. pap. 99.00 *(978-3-642-12841-7(6)*, 3642128416) Springer.

Kopacek, Peter & Han, Man-Wook. Mobile, Intelligent Robots. 2008. 250p. pap. 69.95 *(978-3-211-36248-8(7)*, 3211362487) Springer.

Kopec, Danny & Lucci, Stephen. Artificial Intelligence in the 21st Century. 2012. 850p. 99.95 *(978-1-936420-23-0(6))* Mercury Learning & Information.

Korb, Kevin B., et al. Artificial Life: Borrowing from Biology: 4th Australian Conference, ACAL 2009, Melbourne, Australia, December 1-4, 2009, Proceedings. 2009. (Lecture Notes in Computer Science / Lecture Notes in Artificial Intelligence Ser.). xi, 283p. pap. 72.00 *(978-3-642-10426-8(6)*, 3642104266) Springer.

Korb, Kevin B. & Nicholson, Ann E. Bayesian Artificial Intelligence. 2nd rev. ed. 2010. (Chapman & Hall/CRC Computer Science & Data Analysis Ser.). (ENG., Illus.). 491p. 94.95 *(978-1-4398-1591-5(7)*, CRC Press) Taylor & Francis Group GBR. Dist: Taylor & Francis Group.

Kostiadis, Kostas. Learning to Co-operate in Multi-Agent Systems: Experiments with the RoboCup Simulator. 2008. 156p. pap. *(978-3-639-10259-8(2))* VDM Verlag Dr. Mueller e.K.

Koutsojannis, Constantinos. Tools & Applications with Artificial Intelligence. 2009. (Studies in Computational Intelligence Ser.). (ENG., Illus.). x, 214p. 149.00 *(978-3-540-88068-4(2))* Springer.

Kowalczyk, Ryszard. Transactions on Computational Collective Intelligence I. 2010. (Lecture Notes in Computer Science / Transactions on Computational Collective Intelligence Ser.). vii, 207p. pap. 72.00 *(978-3-642-15033-3(0)*, 3642150330) Springer.

Krueasuk, Wichit. Optimal Placement of Distributed Generation. 2010. 72p. pap. *(978-3-639-24698-8(5))* VDM Verlag Dr. Mueller e.K.

Krüger, Antonio, ed. Smart Graphics: 6th International Symposium, SG 2006, Vancouver, Canada, July 23-25, 2006, Proceedings. 2006. (Lecture Notes in Computer Science Ser.: Vol. 4073). (Illus.). 262p. pap. 59.95 *(978-3-540-36293-7(2)*, 3540362932) Springer.

Kryszkiewics, Marzena, et al, eds. Foundations of Intelligent Systems: 19th International Symposium, ISMIS 2011, Warsaw, Poland, June 28-30, 2011, Proceedings. 2011. (Lecture Notes in Computer Science / Lecture Notes in Artificial Intelligence Ser.). (ENG., Illus.). xix, 746p. pap. 131.00 ***(978-3-642-21915-3(2)***, 3642219152) Springer.

Kumar, Deepak, ed. Current Trends in SNePS - Semantic Network Processing System: First Annual SNePS Workshop, Buffalo, NY, November 13, 1989, Proceedings. 2007. (Lecture Notes in Computer Science Ser.). 176p. per. 59.95 *(978-3-540-52626-1(9))* Springer.

Kundu, Malay K., et al, eds. Perception & Machine Intelligence: First Indo-Japanese Conference, PerMIn 2012, Kolkata, India, January 12-13, 2011, Proceedings. 2012. (Lecture Notes in Computer Science / Image Processing, Computer Vision, Pattern Recognition, & Graphics Ser.). (ENG., Illus.). xvii, 380p. pap. 83.00 ***(978-3-642-27386-5(6)***, 3642273866) Springer.

Kuri-Morales, Angel & Simari, Guillermo R., eds. Advances in Artificial Intelligence - IBERAMIA 2010: 12th Ibero-American Conference on AI, Bahía Blanca, Argentina, November 1-5, 2010, Proceedings. 2010. (Lecture Notes in Computer Science / Lecture Notes in Artificial Intelligence Ser.). xx, 604p. pap. 119.00 *(978-3-642-16951-9(1)*, 3642169511) Springer.

Kurzweil, Ray. How to Create a Mind: The Secret of Human Thought Revealed. 2012. (ENG., Illus.). 384p. 27.95 ***(978-0-670-02529-9(1)***, Viking Adult) Penguin Group (USA) Inc.

Kuznetsov, Sergei O. & Schmidt, Stefan, eds. Formal Concept Analysis: 5th International Conference, ICFCA 2007, Clermont-Ferrand, France, February 12-16, 2007, Proceedings. 2007. (Lecture Notes in Computer Science Ser.). (Illus.). 327p. per. 79.95 *(978-3-540-70828-5(6)*, 3540708286) Springer.

Kwuida, Leonard & Sertkaya, Baris, eds. Formal Concept Analysis: 8th International Conference, ICFCA 2010, Agadir, Moroddo, March 15-18, 2010, Procedings. 2010. (Lecture Notes in Computer Science Ser.). xii, 340p. pap. 83.00 *(978-3-642-11927-9(1)*, 3642119271) Springer.

Lab-Volt Staff. Artificial Intelligence: Tech-Design ESeries. 2010. 31p. 4.00 *(978-1-60533-228-4(3))*; 117p. 12.00 *(978-1-60533-229-1(1))*; 58p. ring bd. 7.00 *(978-1-60533-230-7(5))* Lab-Volt Systems, Inc.

Ladner, Roy & Petry, Frederick E., eds. Net-Centric Approaches to Intelligence & National Security. 2010. (ENG., Illus.). x, 178p. pap. 115.00 *(978-1-4419-3716-2(1)*, 1441937161) Springer.

Lai, David. Let Portfolio Choose It's Own Funds: Revolution Of Finance — Artificial Intelligence In Finance. 2008. 72p. pap. *(978-3-639-10857-6(4))* VDM Verlag Dr. Mueller e.K.

Laird, John. The Soar Cognitive Architecture. 2012. (ENG., Illus.). 400p. (gr. 17). 40.00 ***(978-0-262-12296-2(0))*** MIT Pr.

Lakemeyer, Gerhard, et al, eds. RoboCup 2006: Robot Soccer World Cup X. 2007. (Lecture Notes in Artificial Intelligence Ser.). (ENG., Illus.). xiii, 566p. pap. 119.00 *(978-3-540-74023-0(6)*, 3540740236) Springer.

Lambert-Torres, G. & Abe, J. M., eds. Advances in Technological Applications of Logical & Intelligent Systems: Selected Papers from the Sixth Congress on Logic Applied to Technology - Volume 186 Frontiers in Artificial Intelligence & Applications. 2008. (Illus.). 296p. 167.00 *(978-1-58603-936-3(9))* IOS Pr., Inc.

Lamontagne, Luc & Marchand, Mario. Advances in Artificial Intelligence: 19th Conference of the Canadian Society for Computational Studies of Intelligence, Canadian AI 2006, Quebec City, Quebec, Canada, June 7-9, Proceedings. 2006. (Lecture Notes in Computer Science Ser.). (Illus.). XIII, 564p. pap. 109.00 *(978-3-540-34628-9(7)*, 3540346287) Springer.

Law, Edith & von Ahn, Luis. Human Computation: An Integrated Approach to Learning from the Crowd. 2011. (Synthesis Lectures on Artificial Intelligence & Machine Learning Ser.). 121p. pap. 35.00 *(978-1-60845-516-4(5))* Morgan & Claypool Pubs.

Lazere, Cathy & Shasha, Dennis. Natural Computing: DNA, Quantum Bits, & the Future of Smart Machines. 2010. (ENG., Illus.). 288p. pap. 16.95 *(978-0-393-33583-2(2)*, 33683) Norton, W. W. & Co., Inc.

Leavitt, David. The Man Who Knew Too Much: Alan Turing & the Invention of the Computer. 2006. (Great Discoveries Ser.). (ENG.). 336p. per. 14.95 *(978-0-393-32909-4(7)*, 32909) Atlas & Co.

Lecky-Thompson, Guy W. & Lecky-Thompson, Guy W. AI & Artificial Life in Video Games. 2008. (ENG., Illus.). 352p. 39.99 *(978-1-58450-558-7(3))* Charles River Media.

Lee, Changhoon, et al, eds. Secure & Trust Computing, Data Management, & Applications: STA 2011 Workshops: IWCS 2011 & STAVE 2011, Loutraki, Greece, June 28-30, 2011. Proceedings. 2011. (Communications in Computer & Information Science Ser.). (ENG., Illus.). xix, 205p. pap. 84.00 ***(978-3-642-22364-8(8)***, 3642223648) Springer.

Lee, Jaewook. Multiagent-Based Intelligent Environments: Collaborative Design as a Framework. 2008. 116p. pap. *(978-3-639-08321-7(0))* VDM Verlag Dr. Mueller e.K.

Lee, R. Shu Tak & Liu, J. Nga Kwok, eds. Invariant Object Recognition Based on Elastic Graph Matching: Theory & Applications. (Frontiers in Artificial Intelligence & Applications Ser.: Vol. 86). 250p. 97.00 *(978-1-58603-296-8(8))* IOS Pr., Inc.

Lee, Raymond S. T. Fuzzy-Neuro Approach to Agent Applications: From the AI Perspective to Modern Ontology. 2010. (Springer Series on Agent Technology Ser.). (Illus.). xviii, 376p. pap. 99.00 *(978-3-642-05949-0(X)*, 364205949X) Springer.

Lee, Roger. Software Engineering, Artificial Intelligence, Networking & Parallel/Distributed Computing. 2008. (Studies in Computational Intelligence Ser.). (Illus.). xiii, 257p. 179.00 *(978-3-540-70559-8(7)*, 3540705597) Springer.

—Software Engineering, Artificial Intelligence, Networking & Parallel/Distributed Computing 2010. Lee, Roger, ed. 2010. (Studies in Computational Intelligence Ser.). (Illus.). 250p. 159.00 *(978-3-642-13264-3(2)*, 3642132642) Springer.

Lee, Roger, ed. Software Engineering, Artificial Intelligence, Networking & Parallel/Distributed Computing. 2010. (Studies in Computational Intelligence Ser.). (Illus.). xiv, 260p. pap. 179.00 *(978-3-642-08949-7(6)*, 3642089496) Springer.

Lee, Roger, ed. Software Engineering, Artificial Intelligence, Networking & Parallel/Distributed Computing 2011. 2011. (Studies in Computational Intelligence Ser.). (Illus.). xii, 188p. 129.00 ***(978-3-642-22287-0(0)***, 3642222870) Springer.

Lee, Roger & Ishii, Naohiro, eds. Software Engineering, Artificial Intelligence, Networking & Parallel/Distributed Computing. (Studies in Computational Intelligence Ser.). (Illus.). xvi, 288p. 2010. (ENG.). pap. 159.00 ***(978-3-642-10173-1(9)***, 3642101739) 2009. 159.00 *(978-3-642-01202-0(7))* Springer.

Lee, Seungyeol. Glazed Panel Construction with Human-Robot Cooperation. 2011. (SpringerBriefs in Computer Science Ser.). (ENG., Illus.). x, 70p. pap. 39.95 ***(978-1-4614-1417-9(2)***, 1461414172) Springer.

Lee, Yeunsook, et al, eds. Aging Friendly Technology for Health & Independence: 8th International Conference on Smart Homes & Health Telematics, ICOST 2010, Seoul, Korea, June 22-24, 2010, Proceedings. 2010. (Lecture Notes in Computer Science / Information Systems & Applications, incl. Internet/Web, & HCI Ser.). xiv, 272p. pap. 72.00 *(978-3-642-13777-8(6)*, 3642137776) Springer.

Leung, Ho-fung, et al, eds. Service Intelligence & Service Science: Evolutionary Technologies & Challenges. 2010. (Illus.). 350p. 180.00 *(978-1-61520-819-7(4))* IGI Global.

Li. Invariant Algebras & Geometric Reasoning. 2008. (Illus.). (C). 150.00 *(978-981-270-808-3(1))* World Scientific Publishing Co., Inc.

Li, Deyi & Du, Yi. Artificial Intelligence with Uncertainty. 2007. (ENG., Illus.). 376p. 99.95 *(978-1-58488-998-4(5)*, Chapman & Hall/CRC) CRC Pr. LLC.

Li, Jiuyong, ed. AI 2010: Advances in Artificial Intelligence: 23rd Australasian Joint Conference, Adelaide, Australia, December 7-10, 2010. Proceedings. 2010. (Lecture Notes in Computer Science / Lecture Notes in Artificial Intelligence Ser.). xvii, 528p. pap. 107.00 *(978-3-642-17431-5(0)*, 3642174310) Springer.

Li, Kang, et al, eds. Life System Modeling & Intelligent Computing: International Conference on Life System Modeling & Simulation, LSMS 2010, & International Conference on Intelligent Computing for Sustainable Energy & Environment, ICSEE 2010, Wuxi, China, September 17-20, 2010, Proceedings, Part II. 2010. (Communications in Computer & Information Science Ser.). xviii, 255p. pap. 84.00 *(978-3-642-15858-2(7)*, 3642158587) Springer.

Li, Xiaodong, et al. Simulated Evolution & Learning: 7th International Conference, SEAL 2008, Melbourne, Australia, December 7-10, 2008, Proceedings. 2008. (Lecture Notes in Computer Science / Theoretical Computer Science & General Issues Ser.). xvi, 658p. pap. 119.00 *(978-3-540-89693-7(7))* Springer.

Liao, Hongen, et al, eds. Medical Imaging & Augmented Reality: 5th International Workshop, MIAR 2010, Beijing, China, September 19-20, 2010, Proceedings. 2010. (Lecture Notes in Computer Science / Image Processing, Computer Vision, Pattern Recognition, & Graphics Ser.). xvii, 573p. pap. 107.00 *(978-3-642-15698-4(3)*, 3642156983) Springer.

Ligozat, Gérard. Qualitative Spatial & Temporal Reasoning. 2011. (Iste Ser.: 524). (ENG., Illus.). 544p. 195.00 *(978-1-84821-252-7(6)*, Wiley-ISTE) Wiley, John & Sons, Inc.

Lin, Tsau Young, ed. International Conference on Intelligent Agent Technology: 2007: Silicon Valley, CA. 2007. 541p. pap. 272.00 *(978-0-7695-3027-7(3))* IEEE Computer Society Pr.

Lio, Pietro, et al, eds. Artificial Immune Systems: 10th International Conference, ICARIS 2011, Cambridge, UK, July 18-21, 2011. Proceedings. 2011. (Lecture Notes in Computer Science / Theoretical Computer Science & General Issues Ser.). (ENG., Illus.). xvi, 468p. pap. 95.00 ***(978-3-642-22370-9(2)***, 3642223702) Springer.

Liu, Dikai, et al, eds. Design & Control of Intelligent Robotic Systems. 2009. (Studies in Computational Intelligence Ser.). (Illus.). xxiv, 480p. 269.00 *(978-3-540-89932-7(4))* Springer.

Liu, Fang. Implement Artificial Intelligent Optimization Techniques with Matlab. 2011. 256p. pap. ***(978-3-8433-9310-2(9))*** Lambert Academic Publishing.

Liu, Honghai. Robot Intelligence: An Advanced Knowledge Processing Approach. Liu, Honghai et al, eds. 2010. (Advanced Information & Knowledge Processing Ser.). (Illus.). xiv, 301p. 149.00 *(978-1-84996-328-2(2)*, 1849963282) Springer.

Liu, Honghai, et al, eds. Intelligent Robotics & Applications: Third International Conference, ICIRA 2010, Shanghai, China, November 10-12, 2010. Proceedings, Part II, 2 vols. 2010. (Lecture Notes in Computer Science / Lecture Notes in Artificial Intelligence Ser.). (Illus.). xxiii, 771p. pap. 131.00 *(978-3-642-16586-3(9)*, 3642165869) Springer.

Liu, Jiming, et al, eds. Web Intelligence Meets Brain Informatics: First WICI International Workshop, WImBI 2006, Beijing, China, December 15-16, 2006, Revised Selected & Invited Papers. 2007. (Lecture Notes in Computer Science Ser.). (Illus.). 516p. pap. 89.95 *(978-3-540-77027-5(5))* Springer.

Liu, Jingnan, et al, eds. Advances in Computation & Intelligence: 5th International Symposium, ISICA 2010, Wuhan, China, October 22-24, 2010, Proceedings. 2010. (Lecture Notes in Computer Science / Theoretical Computer Science & General Issues Ser.). xv, 536p. pap. 107.00 *(978-3-642-16492-7(7)*, 3642164927) Springer.

Liu, Weiru. Propositional, Probabilistic & Evidential Reasoning: Integrating Numerical & Symbolic Approaches. 2010. (Studies in Fuzziness & Soft Computing Ser.). (ENG., Illus.). xiv, 274p. pap. 139.00 *(978-3-7908-2493-3(3)*, 3790824933) Physica-Verlag DEU. Dist: Springer.

Liu, Weiru, ed. Symbolic & Quantitative Approaches to Reasoning with Uncertainty: 11th European Conference, ECSQARU 2011, Belfast, UK, June 29-July 1, 2011, Proceedings. 2011. (Lecture Notes in Computer Science / Lecture Notes in Artificial Intelligence Ser.). (Illus.). xiv, 762p. pap. 131.00 ***(978-3-642-22151-4(3)***, 3642221513) Springer.

Logics in Artificial Intelligence. 2008. (Lecture Notes in Computer Science / Lecture Notes in Artificial Intelligence Ser.). spiral bd. 89.95 *(978-3-540-87802-5(5)*, 3540878025) Springer.

López, José Manual Molina, et al, eds. User-Centric Technologies & Applications: Proceedings of the CONTEXTS 2011 Workshop. 2011. (Advances in Intelligent & Soft Computing Ser.). (Illus.). x, 122p. pap. 199.00 *(978-3-642-19907-3(0)*, 3642199070) Springer.

Loukeris, Nikos. Bankruptcy Prediction, Portfolio Selection & Artificial Intelligence. 2010. 100p. pap. *(978-3-8433-5403-5(0))* Lambert Academic Publishing.

Loula, Angelo, et al. Artificial Cognition Systems. 2006. (Illus.). 403p. 94.95 *(978-1-59904-111-7(1))* IGI Global.

Lozano, Jose A., et al, eds. Advances in Artificial Intelligence: 14th Conference of the Spanish Association for Artificial Intelligence, CAEPIA 2011, la Laguna, Spain, November 7-11, 2011. Proceedings. 2011. (Lecture Notes in Computer Science / Lecture Notes in Artificial Intelligence Ser.). (ENG., Illus.). xv, 506p. pap. 107.00 ***(978-3-642-25273-0(7)***, 3642252737) Springer.

Lu, Jie, et al, eds. E-Service Intelligence: Methodologies, Technologies & Applications. 2006. (Studies in Computational Intelligence: Vol. 37). (Illus.). 711p. pap. 239.00 *(978-3-540-37015-4(3)*, 3540370153) Springer.

Lucas, Peter, et al, eds. Advances in Probabilistic Graphical Models. 2010. (Studies in Fuzziness & Soft Computing Ser.). (Illus.). x, 396p. pap. 189.00 *(978-3-642-08854-4(6)*, 3642088546) Springer.

Lucas, Peter & José A., Gámez, eds. Advances in Probabilistic Graphical Models. 2007. (Studies in Fuzziness & Soft Computing Ser.). (Illus.). X, 396p. 189.00 *(978-3-540-68994-2(X)*, 354068994X) Springer.

Luckin, Rosemary, et al. Artificial intelligence in Education. 2007. 169.00 *(978-1-58603-764-2(1))* IOS Pr., Inc.

Luger, George F. Artificial Intelligence: Structures & Strategies for Complex Problem Solving. 6th ed. 2008. (ENG., Illus.). 784p. (C). 141.00 *(978-0-321-54589-3(3))* Addison Wesley.

Lukose, Dickson & Shi, Zhongzhi. Autonomous Agents & Multi-Agent Systems: 8th Pacific Rim International Workshop on Multi-Agents, PRIMA 2005, Kuala Lumpur, Malaysia, September 26-28, 2005, Revised Selected Papers. 2009. (Lecture Notes in Computer Science / Lecture Notes in Artificial Intelligence Ser.). (ENG.). xiii, 412p. pap. 89.95 *(978-3-642-03337-7(7)*, 3642033377) Springer.

Luque, Gabriel & Alba, Enrique. Parallel Genetic Algorithms: Theory & Real World Applications. 2011. (Studies in Computational Intelligence Ser.). (Illus.). xii, 172p. 129.00 ***(978-3-642-22083-8(5)***, 3642220835) Springer.

Lutz, Carsten & Raskin, Jean-Francois. 16th International Symposium on Temporal Representation & Reasoning: Proceedings: Bressanone-Brixen, Italy 23-25 July 2009. 2009. (Illus.). x, 173p. pap. ***(978-0-7695-3727-6(8))*** IEEE Computer Society Pr.

Ma, Zongmin. Intelligent Databases: Technologies & Applications. 2006. (Illus.). 320p. 94.95 *(978-1-59904-120-9(0))* IGI Global.

Ma, Zongmin, ed. Artificial Intelligence for Maximizing Content Based Image Retrieval. 2009. 450p. 195.00 *(978-1-60566-174-2(0))* IGI Global.

Maccormick, John. Nine Algorithms That Changed the Future: The Ingenious Ideas That Drive Today's Computers. 2011. (ENG., Illus.). 248p. 27.95 ***(978-0-691-14714-7(0))*** Princeton Univ. Pr.

Macedo Mourelle, Luiza de. Mobile Robots: The Evolutionary Approach. Nedjah, Nadia & Coelho, Leandro dos Santos, eds. 2007. (Studies in Computational Intelligence Ser.). (Illus.). xxii, 224p. 149.00 *(978-3-540-49719-6(6)*, 3540497196) Springer.

Maghsoudi, Shahin. Epistemic Logic Planning - Case-Based Planning Adaptation, Using Epistemic Logic Revision for Robot's Decision Making. 2008. 120p. pap. *(978-3-639-05063-9(0))* VDM Verlag Dr. Mueller e.K.

Maglogiannis, Ilias & Karpouzis, Kostas, eds. Artificial Intelligence Applications & Innovations: 3rd IFIP Conference on Artificial Intelligence Applications & Innovations (AIAI), 2006, June 7-9, 2006, Athens, Greece. 2010. (IFIP Advances in Information & Communication Technology Ser.). (Illus.). xviii, 744p. pap. 229.00 *(978-1-4419-4168-8(1)*, 1441941681) Springer.

Maglogiannis, Ilias G. Emerging artificial intelligence applications in computer Engineering. 2007. 163.00 *(978-1-58603-780-2(3))* IOS Pr., Inc.

Magnenat-Thalmann, Nadia. New Advances in Virtual Humans. 2008. (Studies in Computational Intelligence Ser.). 239.00 *(978-3-540-79867-5(6))* Springer.

Magnenat-Thalmann, Nadia, et al, eds. New Advances in Virtual Humans: Artificial Intelligence Environment. 2010. (Studies in Computational Intelligence Ser.). (ENG., Illus.). viii, 180p. pap. 239.00 *(978-3-642-09862-8(2)*, 3642098622) Springer.

Mago, V. K. & Bhatia, Nitin. Cross-Disciplinary Applications of Artificial Intelligence & Pattern Recognition: Advancing Technologies. 2011. ***(978-1-61350-429-1(2))***; ***(978-1-61350-431-4(4))***; E-Book ***(978-1-61350-430-7(6))*** IGI Global.

Mahdavi, Iraj, et al, eds. Electronic Supply Network Coordination in Intelligent & Dynamic Environments: Modeling & Implementation. 2010. 350p. 180.00 *(978-1-60566-808-6(7)*, Business Science Reference) IGI Global.

Maheswaran, Rajiv, et al, eds. Help Me Help You: Papers from the AAAI Spring Symposium (SS-11-05) 2011. (Illus.). 80p. spiral bd. 30.00 ***(978-1-57735-497-0(4))*** AAAI Pr.

Mamei, Marco & Zambonelli, Franco. Field-Based Coordination for Pervasive Multiagent Systems. 2010. (Springer Series on Agent Technology Ser.). (Illus.). xii, 242p. pap. 119.00 *(978-3-642-06623-8(2)*, 3642066232) Springer.

Mandal, Deba P., et al, eds. Pattern Recognition & Machine Intelligence: 4th International Conference, PReMI 2011, Moscow, Russia, June 27 - July 1, 2011, Proceedings. 2011. (Lecture Notes in Computer Science / Image Processing, Computer Vision, Pattern Recognition, & Graphics Ser.). (Illus.). xvi, 467p. pap. 95.00 ***(978-3-642-21785-2(0)***, 3642217850) Springer.

Maniezzo, Vittorio, et al. Learning & Intelligent Optimization: Second International Conference, LION 2007 II, Trento, Italy, December 8-12, 2007. Selected Papers. 2008. (Lecture Notes in Computer Science / Theoretical Computer Science & General Issues Ser.). xii, 243p. pap. 69.95 *(978-3-540-92694-8(1))* Springer.

Manoonpong, Poramate. Neural Preprocessing & Control of Reactive Walking Machines: Towards Versatile Artificial Perception-Action Systems. (Cognitive Technologies Ser.). (Illus.). 2010. xvi, 188p. pap. 99.00 *(978-3-642-08835-3(X)*, 364208835X) 2007. 185p. 99.00 *(978-3-540-68802-0(1))* Springer.

Marchiori, Elena. Evolutionary Computation, Machine Learning & Data Mining in Bioinformatics. 2008. (Lecture Notes in Computer Science / Theoretical Computer Science & General Issues Ser.). pap. 69.95 *(978-3-540-78756-3(9)*, 3540787569) Springer.

Marchiori, Elena & Rajapakse, Jagath C., eds. Evolutionary Computation, Machine Learning & Data Mining in Bioinformatics: 5th European Conference, EvoBIO 2007, Valencia, Spain, April 11-13, 2007: Proceedings. 2007. (Lecture Notes in Computer Science Ser.: Vol. 4447). (Illus.). 302p. 79.95 *(978-3-540-71782-9(X)*, 354071782X) Springer.

Marciniak, Malgorzata & Mykowiecka, Agnieszka. Aspects of Natural Language Processing: Essays Dedicated to Leonard Bolc on the Occasion of His 75th Birthday. 2009. (Lecture Notes in Computer Science / Information Systems & Applications, incl. Internet/Web, & HCI Ser.). xii, 449p. pap. 99.00 *(978-3-642-04734-3(3)*, 3642047343) Springer.

Marik, V., et al, eds. Advanced Topics in Artificial Intelligence: International Summer School, Prague, Czechoslovakia, July 6-17, 1992. Proceedings. 2007. (Lecture Notes in Computer Science Ser.). 500p. per. 79.95 *(978-3-540-55681-7(8))* Springer.

Marin, Roque, et al, eds. Current Topics in Artificial Intelligence: 11th Conference of the Spanish Association for Artificial Intelligence, CAEPIA 2005, Santiago de Compostela, Spain, November 16-18, 2005, Revised Selected Papers. 2006. (Lecture Notes in Computer Science Ser.). (Illus.). 482p. pap. 99.00 *(978-3-540-45914-9(6)*, 3540459146) Springer.

Marques de Sa, Joaquim P. & Mandic, Danilo P., eds. Artificial Neural Networks - ICANN 2007 Part I: 17th International Conference Porto, Portugal, September 9-13, 2007 Proceedings. 2007. (Lecture Notes in Computer Science Ser.). (Illus.). 978p. per. 149.00 *(978-3-540-74689-8(7))* Springer.

Martial, Frank Von. Coordinating Plans of Autonomous Agents. 2007. (Lecture Notes in Computer Science Ser.). 268p. per. 49.95 *(978-3-540-55615-2(X))* Springer.

Martinez Del Rincón, Jesús. Feature-Based Human Tracking. 2009. 292p. pap. *(978-3-639-16577-7(2))* VDM Verlag Dr. Mueller e.K.

Martinsky, Ondrej. Intelligent Trading Systems: Applying Artificial Intelligence to Financial Markets. 2010. (Illus.). 212p. pap. 110.00 *(978-1-906659-53-0(2))* Harriman Hse. Publishing GBR. Dist: Ingram Pub. Services.

Masuch, Michael, ed. Organization, Management, & Expert Systems: Models of Automated Reasoning. (De Gruyter Studies in Organization Ser.). (ENG.). X, 250p. 196.00 ***(978-3-11-178316-1(2))*** De Gruyter, Walter Inc.

Mayorga, Rene V. & Perlovsky, Leonid, eds. Toward Artificial Sapience: Principles & Methods for Wise Systems. 2010. (ENG., Illus.). xviii, 239p. pap. 99.00 *(978-1-84996-698-6(2)*, 1849966982) Springer.

Mayorga, Rene V. & Perlovsky, Leonid I., eds. Toward Artificial Sapience: Principles & Methods for Wise Systems. 2007. (ENG., Illus.). xviii, 239p. 99.00 *(978-1-84628-998-9(X)*, 184628998X) Springer.

McAllester, David & Myllymäki, Petri, eds. Proceedings of the Twenty-Fourth Conference on Uncertainty in Artificial Intelligence: UAI 2008 July 9-12, 2008 Helsinki, Finland. 2008. pap. 40.00 *(978-0-9749039-4-1(9))* Assn. for Uncertainty in Artificial Intelligence (AUAI).

McBurney, Peter, et al, eds. Argumentation in Multi-Agent Systems: 7th International Workshop, ArgMAS 2010, Toronto, Canada, May 10, 2010, Revised Selected & Invited Papers. 2011. (Lecture Notes in Computer Science / Lecture Notes in Artificial Intelligence Ser.). (ENG., Illus.). x, 327p. pap. 83.00 ***(978-3-642-21939-9(X)***, 364221939X) Springer.

McCabe, Alan. Sign on the Dotted Line. 2010. 200p. pap. *(978-3-8383-5198-8(3))* Lambert Academic Publishing.

McClean, S. I. Intelligent Patient Management. 2009. (Illus.). xiii, 334p. E-Book *(978-3-642-00179-6(3))* Springer.

McFarland, David. Guilty Robots, Happy Dogs: The Question of Alien Minds. (ENG.). 256p. 2009. pap. 15.95 *(978-0-19-921930-8(3))* 2008. (Illus.). 39.95 *(978-0-19-921929-2(X))* Oxford Univ. Pr., Inc.

McFarland, David, et al, eds. The Complex Mind: An Interdisciplinary Approach. 2012. (ENG., Illus.). 312p. 85.00 ***(978-0-230-24757-4(1))*** Palgrave Macmillan.

McGinty, Lorraine & Wilson, David C. Case-Based Reasoning Research & Development: 8th International Conference on Case-Based Reasoning, ICCBR 2009 Seattle, WA, USA, July 20-23, 2009 Proceedings. 2009. (Lecture Notes in Computer Science / Lecture Notes in Artificial Intelligence Ser.). (ENG.). xiii, 526p. pap. 109.00 *(978-3-642-02997-4(3)*, 3642029973) Springer.

Meghanathan, Natarajan, et al, eds. Advanced Computing: First International Conference on Computer Science & Information Technology, CCSIT 2011, Bangalore, India, January 2-4, 2011. Proceedings, Part III. 2010. (Communications in Computer & Information Science Ser.). xxvi, 483p. pap. 119.00 *(978-3-642-17880-1(4)*, 3642178804) Springer.

Mehrotra, Kishan G., et al, eds. Developing Concepts in Applied Intelligence. 2011. (Studies in Computational Intelligence Ser.). (Illus.). x, 130p. 129.00 *(978-3-642-21331-1(6)*, 3642213316) Springer.

—Modern Approaches in Applied Intelligence: 24th International Conference on Industrial Engineering & Other Applications of Applied Intelligent Systems, IEA/AIE 2011, Syracuse, NY, USA, June 28 - July 1, 2011, Proceedings, Part I, 2 vols. 2011. (Lecture Notes in Computer Science / Lecture Notes in Artificial Intelligence Ser.). (Illus.). xx, 361p. pap. 83.00 ***(978-3-642-21821-7(0)***, 3642218210) Springer.

—Modern Approaches in Applied Intelligence: 24th International Conference on Industrial Engineering & Other Applications of Applied Intelligent Systems, IEA/AIE 2011, Syracuse, NY, USA, June 28 - July 1, 2011, Proceedings, Part II. 2011. (Lecture Notes in Computer Science / Lecture Notes in Artificial Intelligence Ser.). xx, 581p. pap. 119.00 ***(978-3-642-21826-2(1)***, 3642218261) Springer.

Mele, Francesco. Advances in Brain, Vision, & Artificial Intelligence. 2007. (Lecture Notes in Computer Science / Image Processing, Computer Vision, Pattern Recognition, & Graphics Ser.). spiral bd. 109.00 *(978-3-540-75554-8(3)*, 3540755543) Springer.

Meli, Urs. Adaptive Building Intelligence: A Second Approach to Adaptive Discovery of Functional Structure Using Swarm Intelligence. 2008. 52p. pap. *(978-3-639-09699-6(1))* VDM Verlag Dr. Mueller e.K.

Mellodge, Patricia. Model Abstraction in Dynamical Systems: Application to Mobile Robot Control. 2008. (Lecture Notes in Control & Information Sciences Ser.). (ENG., Illus.). xiv, 118p. pap. 129.00 *(978-3-540-70792-9(1)*, 3540707921) Springer.

Mellouli, Khaled. Symbolic & Quantitative Approaches to Reasoning with Uncertainty: 9th European Conference, ECSQARU 2007, Hammamet, Tunisia, October 31 - November 2, 2007, Proceedings. 2007. (Lecture Notes in Computer Science / Lecture Notes in Artificial Intelligence Ser.). xv, 914p. pap. 149.00 *(978-3-540-75255-4(2)*, 3540752552) Springer.

Merrick, Kathryn & Maher, Mary Lou. Motivated Reinforcement Learning: Adaptive Characters for Multiuser Games. 2009. (ENG., Illus.). xiv, 206p. 99.00 *(978-3-540-89186-4(2)*, 3540891862) Springer.

Mertsching, Bärbel, et al. KI 2009: Advances in Artificial Intelligence: 32nd Annual German Conference on AI, Paderborn, Germany, September 15-18, 2009, Proceedings. 2009. (Lecture Notes in Computer Science / Lecture Notes in Artificial Intelligence Ser.). xx, 737p. pap. 139.00 *(978-3-642-04616-2(9)*, 3642046169) Springer.

Merz, Hermann, et al. Building Automation: Communication systems with EIB/KNX, LON & BACnet. Backer, James et al, trs. from GER. 2012. (Signals & Communication Technology Ser.). (ENG., Illus.). x, 282p. pap. 109.00 ***(978-3-642-10025-3(2)***, 3642100252) Springer.

Meseguer, Pedro, et al, eds. Current Topics in Artificial Intelligence: 13th Conference of the Spanish Association for Artificial Intelligence, CAEPIA 2009, Seville, Spain, November 9-13, 2009, Selected Papers. 2010. (Lecture Notes in Computer Science / Lecture Notes in Artificial Intelligence Ser.). xii, 302p. pap. 83.00 *(978-3-642-14263-5(X)*, 364214263X) Springer.

Meyer, John-Jules Ch & Treur, Jan, eds. Handbook of Defeasible Reasoning & Uncertainty Management Systems: Volume 6: Dynamics & Management of Reasoning Processes. 2010. (Handbook of Defeasible Reasoning & Uncertainty Management Systems Ser.). 396p. pap. 279.00 *(978-90-481-5903-1(2)*, 9048159032) Springer.

—Handbook of Defeasible Reasoning & Uncertainty Management Systems: Volume 7: Agent-Based Defeasible Control in Dynamic Environments. 2010. (Handbook of Defeasible Reasoning & Uncertainty Management Systems Ser.). 480p. pap. 349.00 *(978-90-481-6109-6(6)*, 9048161096) Springer.

Meza, Isaura. Maquinas Vivientes. (Ciencia para Todos Ser.). (SPA.). pap. 6.99 *(978-968-16-4988-3(5))* Fondo de Cultura Economica USA.

Mezaine, Farid & Vadera, Sunil, eds. Artificial Intelligence Applications for Improved Software Engineering Development: New Prospects. 2009. (Advances in Intelligent Information Technologies (AIIT) Book Ser.). 370p. 180.00 *(978-1-60566-758-4(7))* IGI Global.

Miaoulis, Georgios & Plemenos, Dimitri, eds. Intelligent Scene Modelling Information Systems. 2009. (Studies in Computational Intelligence Ser.). (Illus.). xii, 216p. 159.00 *(978-3-540-92901-7(0))* Springer.

Micai 2008: Advances in Artificial Intelligence. 2008. (Lecture Notes in Computer Science / Lecture Notes in Artificial Intelligence Ser.). spiral bd. 159.00 *(978-3-540-88635-8(4)*, 3540886354) Springer.

Miccoli, Anthony. Posthuman Suffering & the Technological Embrace. 2010. (ENG.). 158p. 62.99 *(978-0-7391-2633-2(4))* Lexington Bks.

Millington, Ian & Funge, John. Artificial Intelligence for Games. 2nd ed. 2009. (ENG., Illus.). 896p. 77.95 *(978-0-12-374731-0(7)*, Morgan Kaufmann) Elsevier Science & Technology Bks.

Minker, Wolfgang, et al, eds. Advanced Intelligent Environments. 2009. (ENG., Illus.). xxii, 290p. 129.00 *(978-0-387-76484-9(4))* Springer.

Mira, José, et al. Methods & Models in Artificial & Natural Computation: A Homage to Professor Mira's Scientific Legacy: Third International Work-Conference on the Interplay Between Natural & Artificial Computation, IWINAC 2009, Santiago de Compostela, Spain, June 22-26, 2009, Proceedings, Part I. 2009. (Lecture Notes in Computer Science / Theoretical Computer Science & General Issues Ser.). (ENG.). xxi, 530p. pap. 109.00 *(978-3-642-02263-0(4)*, 3642022634) Springer.

Mira, Jose & Alvarez, Jose R., eds. Nature Inspired Problem-Solving Methods in Knowledge Engineering: Second International Work-Conference on the Interplay Between Natural & Artificial Computation, IWINAC 2007 la Manga del Mar Menor, Spain, June 18-21, 2007 Proceedings, Part II. 2007. (Lecture Notes in Computer Science Ser.). (Illus.). 650p. pap. 119.00 *(978-3-540-73054-5(0))* Springer.

Mitchell, John M. Communications Pioneer. Janson, Bobbi, ed. 2008. 212p. pap. 24.95 *(978-1-889131-79-5(2))* Janson Media Group.

Mitton, Simon & Dowd, Michael. Damage Detection of Bridge Decks Using Artificial Neural Networks. 2011. 64p. pap. ***(978-3-8383-8883-0(6))*** Lambert Academic Publishing.

Mo, Hongwei, ed. Handbook of Research on Artificial Immune Systems & Natural Computing: Applying Complex Adaptive Technologies. 2009. (Illus.). 634p. 325.00 *(978-1-60566-310-4(7))* IGI Global.

Moallem, Azin & Simone A. Ludwig, /. Using Swarm Intelligence for Distributed Job Scheduling on the Grid. 2010. 104p. pap. *(978-3-8383-0241-6(9))* Lambert Academic Publishing.

Model Checking & Artificial Intelligence: 4th Workshop, MoChArt IV Riva del Garda, Italy, August 29, 2006 Revised Selected & Invited Papers. 2007. (Lecture Notes in Computer Science Ser.). (Illus.). 184p. pap. 79.95 *(978-3-540-74127-5(5))* Springer.

Modeling Decisions for Artificial Intelligence. 2008. (Lecture Notes in Computer Science / Lecture Notes in Artificial Intelligence Ser.). spiral bd. 69.95 (*978-3-540-88268-8(5)*, 3540882685) Springer.

Montaner, Miquel. Collaborative Recommender Agents. 2011. 240p. pap. ***(978-3-8383-5426-2(5))*** Lambert Academic Publishing.

Montoya-Torres, Jairo R. Hybrid Algorithms for Service, Computing & Manufacturing Systems: Routing & Scheduling Solutions. 2011. ***(978-1-61350-088-0(2))*** IGI Global.

Montoya-Torres, Jairo R., et al, eds. Hybrid Algorithms for Service, Computing & Manufacturing Systems: Routing & Scheduling Solutions. 2011. 384p. 180.00 (*978-1-61350-086-6(6)*, Information Science Reference) IGI Global.

Morshed Computer Socitey Press Staff, ed. Software Engeering, Artificial Intelligence,Networking & Parellel/Distributed Computing, Proceedings. 2011. 235p. pap. 198.00 ***(978-0-7695-4475-5(4))*** IEEE Computer Society Pr.

Mourlas, Constantinos & Germanakos, Panagiotis. Intelligent User Interfaces: Adaptation & Personalization Systems & Technologies. 2008. (Illus.). 452p. 195.00 *(978-1-60566-032-5(9))* IGI Global.

Mukhopadhyay, Subhas Chandra & Sen Gupta, Gourab, eds. Smart Sensors & Sensing Technology. 2010. (Lecture Notes in Electrical Engineering Ser.). (Illus.). xxii, 412p. pap. 179.00 (*978-3-642-09852-9(5)*, 3642098525) Springer.

Multiagent System Technologies. 2008. (Lecture Notes in Computer Science / Lecture Notes in Artificial Intelligence Ser.). spiral bd. 69.95 (*978-3-540-87804-9(1)*, 3540878041) Springer.

Munakata, Toshinori. Fundamentals of the New Artificial Intelligence: Neural, Evolutionary, Fuzzy & More. 2nd ed. 2008. (Texts in Computer Science Ser.). (Illus.). 255p. 89.95 (*978-1-84628-838-8(X)*, 184628838X) Springer.

Murgante, Beniamino. Geocomputation & Urban Planning. Murgante, Beniamino et al, eds. 2009. (Studies in Computational Intelligence Ser.). (Illus.). vi, 282p. 159.00 *(978-3-540-89929-7(4))* Springer.

Murray, R. Charles & McCarthy, Philip M., eds. Proceedings of the Twenty-Fourth International Florida Artificial Intelligence Research Society Conference CD-ROM (FLAIRS-11) 2011. 692p. cd-rom 39.00 ***(978-1-57735-502-1(4))*** AAAI Pr.

—Proceedings of the Twenty-Fourth International Florida Artificial Intelligence Research Society Conference (FLAIRS-11) 2011. (Illus.). 692p. pap. 125.00 ***(978-1-57735-501-4(6))*** AAAI Pr.

Mutlu, Bilge, et al, eds. Social Robotics: Third International Conference on Social Robotics, ICSR 2011, Amsterdam, the Netherlands, November 24-25, 2011. Proceedings. 2011. (Lecture Notes in Computer Science / Programming & Software Engineering Ser.). (ENG., Illus.). xv, 237p. pap. 72.00 (***978-3-642-25503-8(5)***, 3642255035) Springer.

Nag, Barin, ed. Intelligent Systems in Operations: Methods, Models & Applications in the Supply Chain. 2010. 350p. 180.00 *(978-1-61520-605-6(1))* IGI Global.

Nakakoji, Kumiyo, et al, eds. New Frontiers in Artificial Intelligence: JSAI-isAI 2009 Workshops, LENLS, JURISIN, KCSD, LLLL, Tokyo, Japan, November 19-20, 2010, Revised Selected Papers. 2010. (Lecture Notes in Computer Science / Lecture Notes in Artificial Intelligence Ser.). xii, 374p. pap. 83.00 (*978-3-642-14887-3(5)*, 3642148875) Springer.

Nakamatsu, Kazumi, et al, eds. New Advances in Intelligent Decision Technologies: Results of the First KES International Symposium IDT'09. 2009. (Studies in Computational Intelligence Ser.). (ENG., Illus.). xvi, 656p. 269.00 (*978-3-642-00908-2(5)*, 3642009085) Springer.

Nakatsu, Robbie T. Diagrammatic Reasoning in AI. 2009. (ENG., Illus.). 330p. 122.00 (*978-0-470-33187-3(9)*, Wiley) Wiley, John & Sons, Inc.

Namatame, Akira, et al, eds. Emergent Intelligence of Networked Agents. 2010. (Studies in Computational Intelligence Ser.). (Illus.). xii, 258p. pap. 159.00 (*978-3-642-09014-1(1)*, 3642090141) Springer.

Narukawa, Yasuo & Torra, Vicenc. Modeling Decisions: Information Fusion & Aggregation Operators. 2007. (Cognitive Technologies Ser.). (Illus.). 284p. 99.00 (*978-3-540-68789-4(0)*, 3540687890) Springer.

Natarajan, Sriraam. Intelligent Assistants - a Decision-Theoretic Model. 2009. 176p. pap. *(978-3-639-14580-9(1))* VDM Verlag Dr. Mueller e.K.

Nath, Rajakishore. Philosophy of Artificial Intelligence: A Critique of the Mechanistic Theory of Mind. 2009. 190p. pap. *(978-1-59942-905-2(5))* Universal Pubs.

Nayak, Richi, et al, eds. Evolution of the Web in Artificial Intelligence Environments. 2010. (Studies in Computational Intelligence Ser.). (Illus.). viii, 280p. pap. 179.00 (*978-3-642-09802-4(9)*, 3642098029) Springer.

Nayak, Richi & Ichalkaranje, N., eds. Evolution of the Web in Artificial Intelligence Environments. 2008. (Studies in Computational Intelligence Ser.). (ENG., Illus.). viii, 280p. 179.00 (*978-3-540-79139-3(6)*, 3540791396) Springer.

Neapolitan, Richard E. Fundamentals of Artificial Intelliegence. 2012. (ENG., Illus.). 513p. 89.95 (***978-1-4398-4469-4(0)***, Chapman & Hall/CRC) CRC Pr. LLC.

Nebel, Bernard J. Reasoning & Revision in Hybrid Representation Systems. 2007. (Lecture Notes in Computer Science Ser.). 288p. per. 39.95 *(978-3-540-52443-4(6))* Springer.

Nedjah, Nadia, et al, eds. Computational Intelligence in Information Assurance & Security. 2007. (Studies in Computational Intelligence Ser.). (Illus.). xx, 256p. 139.00 (*978-3-540-71077-6(9)*, 3540710779) Springer.

—Intelligent Educational Machines: Methodologies & Experiences. 2007. (Studies in Computational Intelligence Ser.). (Illus.). xviii, 185p. 159.00 (*978-3-540-44920-1(5)*, 3540449205) Springer.

Nedjah, Nadia & Macedo Mourelle, Luiza de, eds. Swarm Intelligent Systems. 2006. (Studies in Computational Intelligence: Vol. 26). (Illus.). xx, 186p. (C). 169.00 (*978-3-540-33868-0(3)*, 3540338683) Springer.

Negnevitsky, Michael. Artificial Intelligence: A Guide to Intelligent Systems. 3rd rev. ed. 2011. (ENG., Illus.). 504p. pap. 99.50 ***(978-1-4082-2574-5(3))*** Pearson Education, Ltd. GBR. Dist: Trans-Atlantic Pubns., Inc.

Nehaniv, Chrystopher & Dautenhahn, Kerstin. Artificial Life Fundamentals: The Simulation & Synthesis of Living Systems. 2008. 400p. 59.95 (*978-3-540-00119-5(0)*, 3540001190) Springer.

Neves, Jose, et al, eds. Progress in Artificial Intelligence: 13th Portuguese Conference on Artificial Intelligence, EPIA 2007, Workshops: GAIW, AIASTS, ALEA, AMITA, BAOSW, BI, CMBSB, IROBOT, MASTA, STCS, & TEMA, Guimaraes, Portugal, December 3-7, 2007, Proceedings. 2007. (Lecture Notes in Artificial Intelligence Ser.). (Illus.). 704p. pap. 129.00 *(978-3-540-77000-8(3))* Springer.

Nguyen, Ngoc Thanh. Agent & Multi-Agent Systems - Technologies & Applications. 2008. (Lecture Notes in Computer Science / Lecture Notes in Artificial Intelligence Ser.). pap. 149.00 (*978-3-540-78581-1(7)*, 3540785817) Springer.

—Intelligent Agents in the Evolution of Web & Applications. 2009. (Studies in Computational Intelligence Ser.). (Illus.). viii, 332p. 199.00 *(978-3-540-88070-7(4))* Springer.

Nguyen, Ngoc Thanh, ed. Transactions of Computational Collective Intelligence IV. 2011. (Lecture Notes in Computer Science / Lecture Notes in Artificial Intelligence Ser.). (ENG., Illus.). ix, 211p. pap. 98.00 (***978-3-642-21883-5(0)***, 3642218830) Springer.

—Transactions on Computational Collective Intelligence III. 2011. (Lecture Notes in Computer Science / Transactions on Computational Collective Intelligence Ser.). (ENG., Illus.). ix, 215p. pap. 98.00 (*978-3-642-19967-7(4)*, 3642199674) Springer.

Nguyen, Ngoc Thanh, ed. Transactions on Computational Collective Intelligence V. 2011. (Lecture Notes in Computer Science / Transactions on Computational Collective Intelligence Ser.). (ENG., Illus.). x, 213p. pap. 95.00 (***978-3-642-24015-7(1)***, 3642240151) Springer.

Nguyen, Ngoc Thanh, et al, eds. New Challenges for Intelligent Information & Database Systems. 2011. (Studies in Computational Intelligence Ser.). (Illus.). x, 366p. 179.00 (*978-3-642-19952-3(6)*, 3642199526) Springer.

—New Challenges in Computational Collective Intelligence. 2009. (Studies in Computational Intelligence Ser.). (Illus.). x, 350p. 239.00 (*978-3-642-03957-7(X)*, 364203957X) Springer.

—New Frontiers in Applied Artificial Intelligence: 21st International Conference on Industrial, Engineering & Other Applications of Applied Intelligent Systems, IEA/AIE 2008 Wroclaw, Poland, June 18-20, 2008, Proceedings. 2008. (Lecture Notes in Computer Science Ser.). (Illus.). 879p. pap. 139.00 *(978-3-540-69045-0(X))* Springer.

Nicholson, Ann & Li, Xiaodong. AI 2009: Advances in Artificial Intelligence: 22nd Australasian Joint Conference, Melbourne, Australia, December 1-4, 2009, Proceedings. 2009. (Lecture Notes in Computer Science / Lecture Notes in Artificial Intelligence Ser.). xvi, 688p. pap. 139.00 (*978-3-642-10438-1(X)*, 364210438X) Springer.

Nijholt, Anton, et al, eds. Artifical Intelligence for Human Computing: ICMI 2006 & IJCAI 2007 International Workshops, Banff, Canada, November 3, 2006 & Hyderabad India, January 6, 2007, Revised Selected & Invited Papers. 2007. (Lecture Notes in Artificial Intelligence Ser.). (Illus.). 358p. per. 79.95 *(978-3-540-72346-2(3))* Springer.

Nilsson, Nils J. The Quest for Artificial Intelligence. 2009. (ENG., Illus.). 578p. 124.00 *(978-0-521-11639-8(2))* Cambridge Univ. Pr.

—The Quest for Artificial Intelligence: A History of Ideas & Achievement. 2009. (ENG., Illus.). 578p. pap. 39.99 *(978-0-521-12293-1(7))* Cambridge Univ. Pr.

Nolfi, Stefano, et al, eds. From Animals to Animats 9: 9th International Conference on Simulation of Adaptive Behavior, SAB 2006Rome, Italy, September 25-29, 2006Proceedings. 2006. (Lecture Notes in Computer Science Ser.). (Illus.). XV, 869p. pap. 139.00 (*978-3-540-38608-7(4)*, 3540386084) Springer.

Nolfi, Stefano & Mirolli, Marco, eds. Evolution of Communication & Language in Embodied Agents. 2009. (ENG., Illus.). xi, 313p. 129.00 (*978-3-642-01249-5(3)*, 3642012493) Springer.

Obdrzalek, David & Gottscheber, Achim, eds. Research & Education in Robotics - EUROBOT 2011: International Conference, Prague, Czech Republic, June 15-17, 2011. Proceedings. 2011. (Communications in Computer & Information Science Ser.). (Illus.). x, 350p. pap. 95.00 (***978-3-642-21974-0(8)***, 3642219748) Springer.

Obrst, L. & Janssen, T., eds. Ontologies & Semantic Technologies for Intelligence: Volume 213 Frontiers in Artificial Intelligence & Applications. 2010. 160.00 *(978-1-60750-580-8(0))* IOS Pr., Inc.

Ochoa Ortiz Zezzatti, Carlos Alberto. Logistics Management & Optimization Through Hybrid Artificial Intelligence Systems. 2012. ***(978-1-4666-0299-1(6))*** IGI Global.

Ogiela, Lidia & Ogiela, Marek R. Advances in Cognitive Information Systems. 2012. (Cognitive Systems Monographs: 17). (ENG., Illus.). viii, 124p. 109.00 (***978-3-642-25245-7(1)***, 3642252451) Springer.

Ohsawa, Yukio & Tsumoto, Shusaku, eds. Chance Discoveries in Real World Decision Making: Data-based Interaction of Human intelligence & Artificial Intelligence. 2006. (Studies in Computational Intelligence: Vol. 30). (Illus.). xiv, 404p. 239.00 (*978-3-540-34352-3(0)*, 3540343520) Springer.

Okuno, Hiroshi G. & Ali, Moonis. New Trends in Applied Artificial Intelligence: 20th International Conference on Industrial & Engineering Applications of Artificial Intelligence & Expert Systems, IEA/AIE 2007, Kyoto, Japan, June 26-29, 2007, Proceedings. 2007. (Lecture Notes in Computer Science / Lecture Notes in Artificial Intelligence Ser.). xxi, 1194p. pap. 169.00 *(978-3-540-73322-5(1))* Springer.

Olatunji, Sunday Olusanya. Carbonate Lithofacies & Permeability Estimation Using Fuzzy Logic. 2010. 184p. pap. *(978-3-639-25728-1(6))* VDM Verlag Dr. Mueller e.K.

Omatu, Sigeru, et al. Distributed Computing, Artificial Intelligence, Bioinformatics, Soft Computing & Ambient Assisted Living: 10th International Work-Conference on Artificial Neural Networks, IWANN 2009 Workshops, Salamanca, Spain, June 10-12, 2009. Proceedings, Part II. 2009. (Lecture Notes in Computer Science / Theoretical Computer Science & General Issues Ser.). (ENG.). lii, 1304p. pap. 189.00 (*978-3-642-02480-1(7)*, 3642024807) Springer.

Onken, Reiner & Schulte, Axel. System-Ergonomic Design of Cognitive Automation: Dual-Mode Cognitive Design of Vehicle Guidance & Control Work Systems. 2010. (Studies in Fuzziness & Soft Computing Ser.). (ENG., Illus.). xii, 384p. 199.00 (*978-3-642-03134-2(X)*, 364203134X) Springer.

Onoda, Takashi, et al, eds. New Frontiers in Artificial Intelligence: JSAI-isAI 2010 Workshops, LENLS, JURISIN, AMBN, ISS, Tokyo,Japan, November 18-19, 2010, Revised Selected Papers. 2012. (Lecture Notes in Computer Science / Lecture Notes in Artificial Intelligence Ser.). (ENG., Illus.). x, 342p. pap. 83.00 (***978-3-642-25654-7(6)***, 3642256546) Springer.

Orsucci, Franco F. & Sala, Nicoletta, eds. Reflexing Interfaces: The Complex Coevolution of Information Technology Ecosystems. 2008. (Premier Reference Source Ser.). (Illus.). 300+p. (C). 180.00 *(978-1-59904-627-3(X))* IGI Global.

Ortiz-Arroyo, Daniel, et al. Intelligence & Security Informatics: European Conference, EuroISI 2008, Esbjerg, Denmark, December 3-5, 2008. Proceedings. 2008. (Lecture Notes in Computer Science / Information Systems & Applications, incl. Internet/Web, & HCI Ser.). xi, 277p. pap. 69.95 *(978-3-540-89899-3(9))* Springer.

Ortiz Bas, Ángel, et al, eds. Balanced Automation Systems for Future Manufacturing Networks: 9th IFIP WG 5. 5 International Conference, BASYS 2010, Valencia, Spain, July 21-23, 2010, Proceedings. 2010. (IFIP Advances in Information & Communication Technology Ser.). xiv, 310p. 129.00 (*978-3-642-14340-3(7)*, 3642143407) Springer.

Ortiz Zezzati, Carlos Alberto Ochoa & Chira, Carmelia, eds. Logistics Management & Optimization through Hybrid Artificial Intelligence Systems. 2012. 422p. 195.00 (***978-1-4666-0297-7(X)***, Information Science Reference) IGI Global.

O'Shea, James, et al, eds. Agent & Multi-Agent Systems: Technologies & Applications: 5th KES International Conference, KES-AMSTA 2011, Manchester, UK, June 29 — July 1, 2011, Proceedings. 2011. (Lecture Notes in Computer Science / Lecture Notes in Artificial Intelligence Ser.). (ENG., Illus.). xvii, 704p. pap. 131.00 (***978-3-642-21999-3(3)***, 3642219993) Springer.

Padget, Julian, et al, eds. Coordination, Organizations, Institutions, & Norms in Agent Systems V: COIN 2009 International Workshops: COIN@AAMAS 2009 Budapest, Hungary, May 2009, COIN@IJCAI 2009, Pasadena, USA, July 2009, COIN@MALLOW 2009,Turin, Italy, September 2009, Revised Selected Papers. 2010. (Lecture Notes in Computer Science / Lecture Notes in Artificial Intelligence Ser.). xviii, 335p. pap. 83.00 (*978-3-642-14961-0(8)*, 3642149618) Springer.

Paiva, Ana, et al. Affective Computing & Intelligent Interaction: Second International Conference, ACII 2007, Lisbon, Portugal, September 12-14, 2007, Proceedings. 2007. (Lecture Notes in Computer Science / Image Processing, Computer Vision, Pattern Recognition, & Graphics Ser.). xviii, 781p. pap. 139.00 (*978-3-540-74888-5(1)*, 3540748881) Springer.

Pan, Jeng-Shyang, et al. Proceedings: Eighth International Conference on Intelligent Systems Design & Applications: ISDA 2008, 26-28 November 2008, Kaohsiung, Taiwan, 3 vols. 2008. (Illus.). *(978-0-7695-3382-7(5))* IEEE Computer Society Pr.

Pan, Yi, et al, eds. Biologically Inspired Cooperative Computing. 2006. (International Federation for Information Processing (Series): Vol. 216). (Illus.). x, 210p. 139.00 (*978-0-387-34632-8(5)*, 0387346325) Springer.

Pan, Zhigeng. Advances in Artificial Reality & Tele-Existence: 16th International Conference on Artificial Reality & Telexistence, ICAT 2006, Hangzhou, China, November 29 - December 1, 2006: Proceedings. 2006. (Lecture Notes in Computer Science Ser.: Vol. 4282). (Illus.). XXIII, 1347p. pap. 189.00 (*978-3-540-49776-9(5)*, 3540497765) Springer.

Panigrahi, Bijaya Ketan, et al, eds. Swarm, Evolutionary, & Memetic Computing: First International Conference on Swarm, Evolutionary, & Memetic Computing, SEMCCO 2010, Chennai, India, December 16-18, 2010, Proceedings. 2010. (Lecture Notes in Computer Science / Theoretical Computer Science & General Issues Ser.). xviii, 755p. pap. 131.00 (*978-3-642-17562-6(7)*, 3642175627) Springer.

Papadopoulos, Harris, et al, eds. Artificial Intelligence Applications & Innovations: 6th IFIP WG 12. 5 International Conference, AIAI 2010, Larnaca, Cyprus, October 6-7, 2010, Proceedings. 2010. (IFIP Advances in Information & Communication Technology Ser.). xvi, 404p. 149.00 (*978-3-642-16238-1(X)*, 364216238X) Springer.

Papasratorn, Borworn, et al. Advances in Information Technology: Third International Conference, IAIT 2009, Bangkok, Thailand, December 1-5, 2009, Proceedings. 2009. (Communications in Computer & Information Science Ser.). x, 211p. pap. 84.00 (*978-3-642-10391-9(X)*, 364210391X) Springer.

Papasratorn, Borworn, et al, eds. Advances in Information Technology: 4th International Conference, IAIT 2010, Bangkok, Thailand, November 4-5, 2010, Proceedings. 2010. (Communications in Computer & Information Science Ser.). viii, 215p. pap. 84.00 (*978-3-642-16698-3(9)*, 3642166989) Springer.

Paranjape, Raman. Multi-Agent Systems for Healthcare Simulation & Modeling: Applications for System Improvement. Paranjape, Raman & Sadanand, Asha, eds. 2009. 304p. 245.00 (*978-1-60566-772-0(2)*, Medical Information Science Reference) IGI Global.

Paris, Cecile L., et al, eds. Natural Language Generation in Artificial Intelligence & Computational Linguistics. 2010. (Springer International Series in Engineering & Computer Science Ser.). 432p. pap. 299.00 (*978-1-4419-5125-0(3)*, 1441951253) Springer.

Parker, Lynne E., et al, eds. Multi-Robot Systems. from Swarms to Intelligent Automata, Volume III: Proceedings from the 2005 International Workshop on Multi-Robot Systems. 2010. (ENG.). x, 302p. pap. 209.00 (*978-90-481-6849-1(X)*, 904816849X) Springer.

Parr, Ronald & Van der Gaag, Linda, eds. Proceedings of the Twenty-Third Conference on Uncertainty in Artificial Intelligence: UAI 2007 July 19-22, 2007 Vancouver, BC Canada. 2007. pap. 60.00 *(978-0-9749039-3-4(0))* Assn. for Uncertainty in Artificial Intelligence (AUAI).

Pastra, Katerina & Aloimonos, Yiannis, eds. Language-Action Tools for Cognitive Artificial Agents: Papers from the AAAI Workshop (WS-11-14) 2011. (Illus.). 62p. spiral bd. 25.00 ***(978-1-57735-530-4(X))*** AAAI Pr.

Patnaik, Srikanta. Robot Cognition & Navigation: An Experiment with Mobile Robots. 2010. (Cognitive Technologies Ser.). (Illus.). xvi, 292p. pap. 89.95 (*978-3-642-06247-6(4)*, 3642062474) Springer.

Patnaik, Srikatana & Patnaik, Srikanta. Robot Cognition & Navigation: An Experiment with Mobile Robots. 2007. (Cognitive Technologies Ser.). (Illus.). 288p. 89.95 (*978-3-540-23446-3(2)*, 3540234462) Springer.

Patten, Terry. Systemic Text Generation as Problem Solving. 2007. (Studies in Natural Language Processing Ser.). (ENG.). 228p. per. 56.00 *(978-0-521-03926-0(6))* Cambridge Univ. Pr.

Pawlewski, Pawel, et al, eds. Trends in Practical Applications of Agents & Multiagent Systems: 8th International Conference on Practical Applications of Agents & Multiagent Systems. 2010. (Advances in Intelligent & Soft Computing Ser.). 700p. pap. 349.00 (*978-3-642-12432-7(1)*, 3642124321) Springer.

Pazienza, Maria Teresa & Stellato, Armando. Semi-Automatic Ontology Development: Processes & Resources. 2012. ***(978-1-4666-0188-8(4))***; ***(978-1-4666-0190-1(6))*** IGI Global.

Pearce, D. Nonclassical Logics & Information Processing: International Workshop, Berlin, Germany, November 9-10, 1990. Proceedings. 2007. (Lecture Notes in Computer Science Ser.). 188p. per. 39.95 *(978-3-540-55745-6(8))* Springer.

Pearce, Q. L. Artificial Intelligence. 2011. (Technology 360 Ser.). 128p. (YA). (gr. 7-12). lib. bdg. 33.45 *(978-1-4205-0384-5(7))* Cengage Gale.

Pejas, Jerzy & Piegat, Andrzej, eds. Enhanced Methods in Computer Security, Biometric & Artificial Intelligence Systems. 2010. (ENG., Illus.). xii, 396p. pap. 185.00 (*978-1-4419-5438-1(4)*, 1441954384) Springer.

Pejas, Jerzy & Saeed, Khalid, eds. Advances in Information Processing & Protection. 2010. (ENG.). xiv, 460p. pap. 169.00 (*978-1-4419-4457-3(5)*, 1441944575) Springer.

Peled, Doron A. & Wooldridge, Michael. Model Checking & Artificial Intelligence: 5th International Workshop, MoChArt 2008, Patras, Greece, July 21, 2008, Revised Selected & Invited Papers. 2009. (Lecture Notes in Computer Science / Lecture Notes in Artificial Intelligence Ser.). vii, 189p. pap. 69.95 *(978-3-642-00430-8(X))* Springer.

Peleg, Mor, et al, eds. Artificial Intelligence in Medicine: 13th Conference on Artificial Intelligence in Medicine, AIME 2011, Bled, Slovenia, July 2-6, 2011, Proceedings. 2011. (Lecture Notes in Computer Science / Lecture Notes in Artificial Intelligence Ser.). (ENG., Illus.). xvii, 355p. pap. 83.00 (***978-3-642-22217-7(X)***, 364222217X) Springer.

Pelikan, Martin, et al, eds. Scalable Optimization via Probabilistic Modeling: From Algorithms to Applications. 2006. (Studies in Computational Intelligence Ser.). (Illus.). xx, 350p. 189.00 (*978-3-540-34953-2(7)*, 3540349537) Springer.

Pepperell, Robert & Pepperell, Julian. The Posthuman Condition: Consciousness Beyond the Brain. 2009. (Illus.). 224p. pap. 40.00 *(978-1-84150-290-8(1))* Intellect, Ltd. GBR. Dist: Chicago Distribution Ctr.

Pereira, Francisco Câmara. Creativity & Artificial Intelligence: A Conceptual Blending Approach. 2007. (Applications of Cognitive Linguistics [ACL] Ser.). (ENG., Illus.). IX, 253p. 154.00 *(978-3-11-018609-3(8))* De Gruyter, Mouton DEU. Dist: de Gruyter, Walter GmbH & Co. KG.

Perlovsky, Leonid I. & Kozma, Robert, eds. Neurodynamics of Cognition & Consciousness. 2007. (Understanding Complex Systems Ser.). (ENG., Illus.). xii, 366p. 139.00 (*978-3-540-73266-2(7)*, 3540732667) Springer.

Perron, Laurent. Integration of AI & OR Techniques in Constraint Programming for Combinatorial Optimization Problems: 5th International Conference, CPAIOR 2008, Paris, France, May 20-23, 2008. 2008. (Lecture Notes in Computer Science / Theoretical Computer Science & General Issues Ser.). (Illus.). 406p. spiral bd. 89.95 (*978-3-540-68154-0(X)*, 354068154X) Springer.

Peters, J. F. Transactions on Rough Sets. 2008. (Lecture Notes in Computer Science / Transactions on Rough Sets Ser.). xii, 499p. pap. 59.95 *(978-3-540-71198-8(8))* Springer.

Peters, James F., et al. Transactions on Rough Sets VII: Commemorating the Life & Work of Zdzislaw Pawlak, Part II. 2007. (Lecture Notes in Computer Science / Transactions on Rough Sets Ser.). (ENG.). x, 381p. pap. 99.00 *(978-3-540-71662-4(9),* 3540716629) Springer.

Peters, James F. & Skowron, Andrzej. Transactions on Rough Sets VIII. 2008. (Lecture Notes in Computer Science / Transactions on Rough Sets Ser.). x, 521p. pap. 139.00 *(978-3-540-85063-2(5))* Springer.

—Transactions on Rough Sets X. 2009. (Lecture Notes in Computer Science / Transactions on Rough Sets Ser.). (ENG.). ix, 275p. pap. 99.00 *(978-3-642-03280-6(X),* 364203280X) Springer.

—Transactions on Rough Sets XIII. 2011. (Lecture Notes in Computer Science / Transactions on Rough Sets Ser.). (Illus.). viii, 277p. pap. 98.00 *(978-3-642-18301-0(8),* 3642183018) Springer.

Petta, Paolo, et al. Multiagent System Technologies: 5th German Conference, MATES 2007, Leipzig, Germany, September 24-26, 2007, Proceedings. 2007. (Lecture Notes in Computer Science / Lecture Notes in Artificial Intelligence Ser.). x, 207p. pap. 69.95 *(978-3-540-74948-6(9))* Springer.

Pfeifer, Rolf & Bongard, Josh. How the Body Shapes the Way We Think: A New View of Intelligence. 2006. (ENG., Illus.). 418p. (gr. 17). 46.00 *(978-0-262-16239-5(3))* MIT Pr.

Phillips-Wren, Gloria, et al, eds. Advances in Intelligent Decision Technologies: Research of the Second KES International Symposium IDT 2010. 2010. (Smart Innovation, Systems & Technologies Ser.). 730p. 279.00 *(978-3-642-14615-2(5),* 3642146155) Springer.

—Intelligent Decision Making: an AI-Based Approach: An AI-Based Approach. 2010. (Studies in Computational Intelligence Ser.). (Illus.). xiv, 410p. pap. 199.00 *(978-3-642-09553-5(4),* 3642095534) Springer.

Phillips-Wren, Gloria E., et al. Intelligent Decision Making: An AI-Based Approach. 2008. (Studies in Computational Intelligence Ser.). (Illus.). 401p. 199.00 *(978-3-540-76828-9(9))* Springer.

Pirrone, Roberto & Sorbello, Filippo, eds. AI*IA 2011: Artificial Intelligence Around Man & Beyond: XIIth International Conference of the Italian Association for Artificial Intelligence, Palermo, Italy, September 15-17, 2011. Proceedings. 2011. (Lecture Notes in Computer Science / Lecture Notes in Artificial Intelligence Ser.). (ENG., Illus.). xv, 464p. pap. 95.00 ***(978-3-642-23953-3(6),*** 3642239536) Springer.

Pitrat, Jacques. Artificial Beings: The Conscience of a Conscious Machine. 2009. (Iste Ser.: 381). (ENG., Illus.). 256p. 105.00 *(978-1-84821-101-8(5),* Wiley-ISTE) Wiley, John & Sons, Inc.

Pizzuti, Clara, et al. Evolutionary Computation, Machine Learning & Data Mining in Bioinformatics: 7th European Conference, EvoBIO 2009 Tübingen, Germany, April 15-17, 2009 Proceedings. 2009. (Lecture Notes in Computer Science / Theoretical Computer Science & General Issues Ser.). xii, 203p. pap. 69.95 *(978-3-642-01183-2(7))* Springer.

Pizzuti, Clara, et al, eds. Evolutionary Computation, Machine Learning & Data Mining in Bioinformatics: 8th European Conference, EvoBIO 2010, Istanbul, Turkey, April 7-9, 2010, Proceedings. 2010. (Lecture Notes in Computer Science / Theoretical Computer Science & General Issues Ser.). (Illus.). xii, 249p. pap. 72.00 *(978-3-642-12210-1(8),* 3642122108) Springer.

—Evolutionary Computation, Machine Learning & Data Mining in Bioinformatics: 9th European Conference, EvoBIO 2011, Torino, Italy, April 27-29, 2011, Proceedings. 2011. (Lecture Notes in Computer Science / Theoretical Computer Science & General Issues Ser.). (Illus.). xii, 188p. pap. 72.00 *(978-3-642-20388-6(4),* 3642203884) Springer.

Plemenos, Dimitri & Miaoulis, Georgios, eds. Artificial Intelligence Techniques for Computer Graphics. 2010. (Studies in Computational Intelligence Ser.). (Illus.). viii, 216p. pap. 159.00 *(978-3-642-09884-0(3),* 3642098843) Springer.

Plimmer, B., ed. 6th International Conference New Zealand Chapter of the ACM's Special Interest Group on Computer-Human Interaction (SIGCHI-NZ) (CHINZ 2005) Making CHI Natural. 2007. (ACM International Conference Proceedings Ser.). 100p. pap. 62.00 *(978-1-60423-183-0(1))* Curran Assocs., Inc.

—7th International Conference NZ Chapter of the ACM's Special Interest Group on Human-Computer Interaction (SIGCHI-NZ) (CHINZ 2006) Design Centered HCI. 2007. (ACM International Conference Proceedings Ser.). 139p. pap. 75.00 *(978-1-60423-182-3(3))* Curran Assocs., Inc.

Polani, D., et al, eds. Fifth German Workshop on Artificial Life: Abstracting & Synthesizing the Principle of Living Systems. (INFIX). 274p. pap. 55.00 *(978-1-58603-242-5(9))* IOS Pr., Inc.

Poli, Riccardo, et al, eds. Particle Swarms: The Second Decade. 2008. 236p. pap. 35.00 *(978-977-454-037-0(9))* Hindawi Publishing Corp.

Polkowski, Lech. Approximate Reasoning by Parts: An Introduction to Rough Mereology. 2011. (Intelligent Systems Reference Library). (ENG., Illus.). xiv, 346p. 179.00 ***(978-3-642-22278-8(1),*** 3642222781) Springer.

Ponce de Leon F. de Carvalho, Andre, et al, eds. Distributed Computing & Artificial Intelligence: 7th International Symposium. 2010. (Advances in Intelligent & Soft Computing Ser.). 690p. pap. 389.00 *(978-3-642-14882-8(4),* 3642148824) Springer.

Ponzetto, S. P., ed. Knowledge Acquisition from a Collaboratively Generated Encyclopedia - Volume 327 Dissertations in Artificial Intelligence. 2010. 236p. pap. 73.00 *(978-1-60750-097-1(3))* IOS Pr., Inc.

Poole, David L. & Mackworth, Alan K. Artificial Intelligence: Foundations of Computational Agents. 2010. (ENG., Illus.). 688p. (C). 93.00 *(978-0-521-51900-7(4))* Cambridge Univ. Pr.

Pordel, Mostafa & Yekeh, Farahnaz. Model-Based Approach for Concurrent Development in Mde. 2010. 60p. pap. *(978-3-8383-8881-6(X))* Lambert Academic Publishing.

Porto Pazos, Ana B. Advancing Artificial Intelligence Through Biological Process Applications. Sierra, Alejandro Pazos & Buceta, Washington Buno, eds. 2008. (Illus.). 460p. 225.00 *(978-1-59904-996-0(1))* IGI Global.

Potyrailo, Radislav A., et al, eds. Combinatorial & Artificial Intelligence Methods in Materials Science II 804: 2003 MRS Fall Meeting Symposium Proceedings, Vol. 804. 2009. (Materials Research Society Symposium Proceedings Ser.: 804). (Illus.). 360p. 35.00 *(978-1-55899-742-4(3),* 804-C) Materials Research Society.

Pouzols, Federico Montesino, et al. Mining & Control of Network Traffic by Computational Intelligence. 2011. (Studies in Computational Intelligence Ser.). (Illus.). xvi, 312p. 179.00 *(978-3-642-18083-5(3),* 3642180833) Springer.

Prade, Henri & Subrahmanian, V. S. Scalable Uncertainty Management: First International Conference, SUM 2007, Washington, DC, USA, October 10-12, 2007, Proceedings. 2007. (Lecture Notes in Computer Science / Lecture Notes in Artificial Intelligence Ser.). 305p. pap. 69.95 *(978-3-540-75407-7(5))* Springer.

Prasad, Bhanu. Proceedings of the 3rd Indian International Conference on Artificial Intelligence. 2007. cd-rom *(978-0-9727412-2-4(4))* IICAI.

Pratihar, Dilip Kumar & Jain, Lakhmi C., eds. Intelligent Autonomous Systems: Foundations & Applications. 2010. (Studies in Computational Intelligence Ser.). 240p. 159.00 *(978-3-642-11675-9(2),* 3642116752) Springer.

Prince, Jerry L., et al. Information Processing in Medical Imaging: 21st International Conference, IPMI 2009, Williamsburg, VA, USA, July 5-10, 2009, Proceedings. 2009. (Lecture Notes in Computer Science / Image Processing, Computer Vision, Pattern Recognition, & Graphics Ser.). xviii, 727p. pap. 129.00 *(978-3-642-02497-9(1),* 3642024971) Springer.

Puddefoot. God & the Mind Machine. 128p. 14.95 *(978-0-281-04973-8(4))* International Publishers Marketing.

Puerta, Angel & Lau, Tessa. IUI 2007: 2007 International Conference on Intelligent User Interfaces: Hawaii, USA, January 28-31, 2007. 2007. (Illus.). xiii, 374p. *(978-1-59593-481-9(2))* Assn. for Computing Machinery.

Queiroz, Joao, ed. Semiotics & Intelligent Systems Development. 2006. (Illus.). 370p. 94.95 *(978-1-59904-063-9(8))* IGI Global.

Rabuñal, Juan Ramón, et al. Encyclopedia of Artificial Intelligence, 3 vols., Set. Dopico, Juan, ed. 2008. (Illus.). 1777p. (C). 965.00 *(978-1-59904-849-9(3))* IGI Global.

Rahwan, Iyad & Simari, Guillermo R. Argumentation in Artificial Intelligence. Rahwan, Iyad et al, eds. 2009. (ENG., Illus.). x, 494p. 148.00 *(978-0-387-98196-3(9),* 0387981969) Springer.

Ram, Ashwin & Wiratunga, Nirmalie, eds. Case-Based Reasoning Research & Development: 19th International Conference on Case-Based Reasoning, ICCBR 2011, London, UK, September 12-15, 2011, Proceedings. 2011. (Lecture Notes in Computer Science / Lecture Notes in Artificial Intelligence Ser.). (ENG., Illus.). xi, 498p. pap. 107.00 ***(978-3-642-23290-9(6),*** 3642232906) Springer.

Ramachandran, Muthu, ed. Knowledge Engineering for Software Development Life Cycles: Support Technologies & Applications. 2011. (Illus.). 350p. 180.00 *(978-1-60960-509-4(8),* Information Science Reference) IGI Global.

Ramacher, Ulrich & Malsburg, Christoph von der, eds. On the Construction of Artificial Brains. 2010. (ENG., Illus.). 370p. 169.00 *(978-3-642-00188-8(2),* 3642001882) Springer.

Ramsey, A. M., ed. Artificial Intelligence: Methodology, Systems, Applications. (Frontiers in Artificial Intelligence & Applications Ser.: Vol. 35). 400p. 105.00 *(978-90-5199-270-0(X))* IOS Pr., Inc.

Rao, R. Bharat, et al, eds. Knowledge-Driven Medicine: A Machine Learning Approach. 2012. (Chapman & Hall/CRC Data Mining & Knowledge Discovery Ser.). (ENG., Illus.). 300p. 89.95 *(978-1-4398-3887-7(9),* CRC Press) Taylor & Francis Group GBR. Dist: Taylor & Francis Group.

Ras, Zbigniew W. & Ribarsky, William, eds. Advances in Information & Intelligent Systems. 2009. (Studies in Computational Intelligence Ser.). (Illus.). xii, 352p. 199.00 *(978-3-642-04140-2(X),* 364204140X) Springer.

Ras, Zbigniew W. & Tsay, Li-Shiang, eds. Advances in Intelligent Information Systems. 2010. (Studies in Computational Intelligence Ser.). (ENG., Illus.). x, 374p. 199.00 *(978-3-642-05182-1(0),* 3642051820) Springer.

Rath, Durga Sankar & Prasad, Ard. Expert System for Automatic Cataloguing: A Heuristic Based Approach. 2011. 376p. pap. ***(978-3-639-34246-8(1))*** VDM Verlag Dr. Mueller e.K.

Ratsch, Ulrich, et al. Intelligence & Artificial Intelligence: An Interdisciplinary Debate. 2010. (Illus.). vii, 216p. pap. 86.95 *(978-3-642-08358-7(7),* 3642083587) Springer.

Rauch, Jan, et al. Foundations of Intelligent Systems: 18th International Symposium, ISMIS 2009, Prague, Czech Republic, September 14-17, 2009, Proceedings. 2009. (Lecture Notes in Computer Science / Lecture Notes in Artificial Intelligence Ser.). (Illus.). xvi, 624p. pap. 129.00 *(978-3-642-04124-2(8),* 3642041248) Springer.

Raynor, William. Artificial Intelligence. 2nd rev. ed. 2009. 300p. pap. 40.00 *(978-0-85297-657-9(7))* Financial World Publishing GBR. Dist: Stylus Publishing, LLC.

Rewski, Przemysaw, et al. Intelligent Open Learning Systems: Concepts, Models & Algorithms. 2011. (Intelligent Systems Reference Library). (ENG., Illus.). xviii, 258p. 129.00 ***(978-3-642-22666-3(3),*** 3642226663) Springer.

Reed, C. & Norman, T. J., eds. Argumentation Machines: New Frontiers in Argument & Computation. 2010. (Argumentation Library). 262p. pap. 219.00 *(978-90-481-6517-9(2),* 9048165172) Springer.

Reed, Jeffrey H. Designing Software & Cognitive Radios. 2nd ed. 2013. (Wiley Series in Telecommunications & Signal Processing Ser.). (ENG.). 600p. 125.00 *(978-0-470-28793-4(4),* Wiley-Interscience) Wiley, John & Sons, Inc.

Reich, Lance. Searching & Analyzing Intellectual Property on the Internet. 2010. 88p. pap. *(978-3-8383-3413-4(2))* Lambert Academic Publishing.

Reid, Bruce & Hancox, Peter J. Keyguide: Artificial Intelligence. 320p. *(978-0-7201-2007-3(1),* Burns & Oates) Continuum International Publishing Group, Ltd.

Reinfrank, M. Non-Monotonic Reasoning: 2nd International Workshop, Grassau, FRG, June 13-15, 1988. Proceedings. 2007. (Lecture Notes in Computer Science Ser.). 256p. per. 39.95 *(978-3-540-50701-7(9))* Springer.

Riano, David. Knowledge Management for Health Care Procedures. 2008. (Lecture Notes in Computer Science / Lecture Notes in Artificial Intelligence Ser.). pap. 59.95 *(978-3-540-78623-8(6),* 3540786236) Springer.

—Knowledge Management for Health Care Procedures: ECAI 2008 Workshop K4HelP 2008, Patras, Greece, July 21-22, 2008, Revised Selected Papers. 2009. (Lecture Notes in Computer Science / Lecture Notes in Artificial Intelligence Ser.). (ENG.). x, 167p. pap. 69.95 *(978-3-642-03261-5(3),* 3642032613) Springer.

Riano, David, et al. Knowledge Representation for Health-Care. Data, Processes & Guidelines: AIME 2009 Workshop KR4HC 2009, Verona, Italy, July 19, 2009, Revised Selected Papers. 2010. (Lecture Notes in Computer Science / Lecture Notes in Artificial Intelligence Ser.). 195p. pap. 72.00 *(978-3-642-11807-4(0),* 3642118070) Springer.

Riaño, David, et al, eds. Knowledge Representation for Health-Care: AIME 2011 Workshop KR4HC 2011, Bled, Slovenia, July 2-6, 2011. Revised Selected Papers. 2012. (Lecture Notes in Computer Science / Lecture Notes in Artificial Intelligence Ser.). (ENG., Illus.). x, 171p. pap. 72.00 ***(978-3-642-27696-5(2),*** 3642276962) Springer.

Riano, David, et al, eds. Knowledge Representation for Health-Care: ECAI 2010 Workshop KR4HC 2010, Lisbon, Portugal, August 17, 2010, Revised Selected Papers. 2011. (Lecture Notes in Computer Science / Lecture Notes in Artificial Intelligence Ser.). x, 153p. pap. 72.00 *(978-3-642-18049-1(3),* 3642180493) Springer.

Richards, Debbie & Kang, Byeong-Ho. Knowledge Management & Acquisition for Smart Systems & Services: 11th International Workshop, PKAW 2010, Daegue, Korea, August 30 - 31, 2010, Proceedings. 2010. (Lecture Notes in Computer Science / Lecture Notes in Artificial Intelligence Ser.). x, 313p. pap. 83.00 *(978-3-642-15036-4(5),* 3642150365) Springer.

Riesen, Kaspar & Bunke, Horst. Graph Classification & Clustering Based on Vector Space Embedding. 2010. (Illus.). 330p. 99.00 *(978-981-4304-71-9(9))* World Scientific Publishing Co., Inc.

Rintanen, jussi, et al, eds. Proceedings of the Eighteenth International Conference on Automated Planning & Scheduling. 2008. (Illus.). 438p. pap. 75.00 *(978-1-57735-386-7(2))* AAAI Pr.

—Proceedings of the Eighteenth International Conference on Automated Planning & Scheduling CD-ROM (ICAPS 2008) 2008. (Illus.). 438p. 39.00 *(978-1-57735-387-4(0))* AAAI Pr.

Riskin, Jessica, ed. Genesis Redux: Essays in the History & Philosophy of Artificial Life. 2007. (Illus.). 336p. 70.00 *(978-0-226-72080-7(2));* per. 30.00 *(978-0-226-72081-4(0))* Univ. of Chicago Pr.

Rodriguez, Emilio S. Corchado, et al, eds. Hybrid Artificial Intelligent Systems, Part II: 5th International Conference, HAIS 2010, San Sebastian, Spain, June 23-25, 2010, Proceedings. 2010. (Lecture Notes in Computer Science / Lecture Notes in Artificial Intelligence Ser.). 570p. pap. 109.00 *(978-3-642-13802-7(0),* 3642138020) Springer.

Roe, Ryan. Material Universe. 2008. 192p. pap. 9.95 *(978-1-59858-607-7(6))* Dog Ear Publishing, LLC.

Romay, Manuel Grana, et al, eds. Hybrid Artificial Intelligent Systems, Part I: 5th International Conference, HAIS 2010, San Sebastian, Spain, June 23-25, 2010. Proceedings. 2010. (Lecture Notes in Computer Science / Lecture Notes in Artificial Intelligence Ser.). pap. 129.00 *(978-3-642-13768-6(7),* 3642137687) Springer.

Ron, Dana. Property Testing: A Learning Theory Perspective, Vol. 1. 2008. (ENG.). 112p. pap. 80.00 *(978-1-60198-182-0(1))* Now Pubs.

Rondeau, Thomas W. & Bostian, Charles W. Artificial Intelligence in Wireless Communications. 2009. (Illus.). 270p. 99.00 *(978-1-60783-234-8(8))* Artech Hse., Inc.

RöNing, Juha, et al. Intelligent Robots & Computer Vision XXVIII: Algorithms & Techniques. 2011. (Proceedings of SPIE Ser.). 344p. pap. 80.00 ***(978-0-8194-8415-4(6))*** SPIE.

Rossi, et al. A Short Introducion to Preferences: Between Ai & Social Choice. 2011. (Synthesis Lectures on Artificial Intelligence & Machine Learning Ser.). 100p. pap. 35.00 ***(978-1-60845-586-7(6))*** Morgan & Claypool Pubs.

Rossi, Francesca & Tsoukis, Alexis. Algorithmic Decision Theory: First International Conference, ADT 2009, Venice, Italy, October 2009, Proceedings. 2009. (Lecture Notes in Computer Science / Lecture Notes in Artificial Intelligence Ser.). xii, 460p. pap. 99.00 *(978-3-642-04427-4(1),* 3642044271) Springer.

Roventa, Eugene & Spircu, Tiberiu. Management of Knowledge Imperfection in Building Intelligent Systems. (Studies in Fuzziness & Soft Computing Ser.). (Illus.). xiv, 254p. 2010. pap. 159.00 *(978-3-642-09613-6(1),* 3642096131) 2008. 159.00 *(978-3-540-77462-4(9))* Springer.

Ruan. Applied Artificial Intelligence. 2006. (Illus.). xx, 997p. 299.00 *(978-981-256-690-4(2))* World Scientific Publishing Co., Inc.

Ruan, Da, et al, eds. Intelligent Decision & Policy Making Support Systems. (Studies in Computational Intelligence Ser.). (Illus.). 2010. viii, 318p. pap. 239.00 *(978-3-642-09699-0(9),* 3642096999) 2008. VIII, 318p. 239.00 *(978-3-540-78306-0(7),* 3540783067) Springer.

Ruan, Da & Fantoni, Paolo F., eds. Power Plant Surveillance & Diagnostics: Applied Research with Artificial Intelligence. 2010. (Power Systems Ser.). (Illus.). xiii, 379p. pap. 229.00 *(978-3-642-07754-8(4),* 3642077544) Springer.

Rubtsov, Konstantin & ROMERIO, Giovanni. Hyperoperations for Science & Technology. 2011. 196p. pap. ***(978-3-8443-1516-5(0))*** Lambert Academic Publishing.

Rudas, Imre J., et al, eds. Towards Intelligent Engineering & Information Technology. 2009. (Studies in Computational Intelligence Ser.). (Illus.). xiv, 736p. 309.00 *(978-3-642-03736-8(4),* 3642037364) Springer.

Ruiz-del-Solar, Javier, et al, eds. RoboCup 2010: Robot Soccer World Cup XIV: Robot Soccer World Cup XIV. 2011. (Lecture Notes in Computer Science / Lecture Notes in Artificial Intelligence Ser.). (Illus.). xi, 432p. pap. 95.00 *(978-3-642-20216-2(0),* 3642202160) Springer.

Russell, Stuart, et al. Artificial Intelligence: A Modern Approach. 3rd ed. 2009. (ENG., Illus.). 1152p. (C). 151.00 *(978-0-13-604259-4(7),* Prentice Hall) Prentice Hall PTR.

Russell, Stuart J. & Wefald, Eric H. Do the Right Thing. 2009. (Artificial Intelligence Ser.). (ENG., Illus.). 224p. (gr. 17). pap. 20.00 *(978-0-262-51382-1(X))* MIT Pr.

Rutkowski, Leszek, et al. Artificial Intelligence & Soft Computing — ICAISC 2006: 8th International Conference, Zakopane, Poland, June 25-29, 2006, Proceedings. 2006. (Lecture Notes in Computer Science Ser.). (Illus.). XXI, 1235p. pap. 149.00 *(978-3-540-35748-3(3),* 3540357483) Springer.

Rutkowski, Leszek. Computational Intelligence: Methods & Techniques. (ENG., Illus.). xiv, 514p. 2010. pap. 109.00 *(978-3-642-09515-3(1),* 3642095151) 2008. 109.00 *(978-3-540-76287-4(6),* 3540762876) Springer.

Rutkowski, Leszek, et al, eds. Artificial Intelligence & Soft Computing, Part I: 10th International Conference, ICAISC 2010, Zakopane, Poland, June13-17, 2010, Part I, 2 vols. 2010. (Lecture Notes in Computer Science / Lecture Notes in Artificial Intelligence Ser.). (Illus.). 129.00 *(978-3-642-13207-0(3),* 3642132073) Springer.

—Artificial Intelligence & Soft Computing, Part II: 10th International Conference, ICAISC 2010, Zakopane, Poland, June 13-17, 2010, Part II Proceedings, 2 vols. 2010. (Lecture Notes in Computer Science / Lecture Notes in Artificial Intelligence Ser.). (Illus.). 711p. 139.00 *(978-3-642-13231-5(6),* 3642132316) Springer.

Saarinen, Jani & Rilla, Nina, eds. Changes in Innovation: Towards an Improved Understanding of Economic Renewal. 2009. (ENG., Illus.). 288p. 105.00 *(978-0-230-57744-2(X))* Palgrave Macmillan.

Saeed, Khalid, et al, eds. Biometrics, Computer Security Systems & Artificial Intelligence Applications. (ENG., Illus.). xii, 348p. 2010. pap. 175.00 *(978-1-4419-4212-8(2),* 1441942122) 2006. 175.00 *(978-0-387-36232-8(0),* 0387362320) Springer.

Sahin, Erol, et al, eds. Swarm Robotics: Second SAB 2006 International Workshop, Rome, Italy, September 30-October 1, 2006 Revised Selected Papers. 2008. (Lecture Notes in Computer Science Ser.). xii, 221p. pap. 69.95 *(978-3-540-71540-5(1))* Springer.

Sakai, Hiroshi, et al, eds. Transactions on Rough Sets XIV. 2011. (Lecture Notes in Computer Science / Transactions on Rough Sets Ser.). (Illus.). vii, 235p. pap. 98.00 ***(978-3-642-21562-9(9),*** 3642215629) Springer.

Salah, Albert Ali, et al, eds. Human Behavior Understanding: First International Workshop, HBU 2010, Istanbul, Turkey, August 22, 2010, Proceedings. 2010. (Lecture Notes in Computer Science / Image Processing, Computer Vision, Pattern Recognition, & Graphics Ser.). iv, 173p. pap. 72.00 *(978-3-642-14714-2(3),* 3642147143) Springer.

Salah, Albert Ali & Lepri, Bruno, eds. Human Behavior Understanding: Second International Workshop, HBU 2011, Amsterdam, the Netherlands, November 16, 2011, Proceedings. 2011. (Lecture Notes in Computer Science / Image Processing, Computer Vision, Pattern Recognition, & Graphics Ser.). (Illus.). x, 159p. pap. 72.00 ***(978-3-642-25445-1(4),*** 3642254454) Springer.

Sandri, S. & Sanchez-Marre, M., eds. Artificial Intelligence Research & Development: Proceedings of the 12th International Conference of the Catalan Association for Artificial Intelligence. 2009. (Frontiers in Artificial Intelligence & Applications Ser.). (Illus.). 456p. 189.00 *(978-1-60750-061-2(2))* IOS Pr., Inc.

Sarjoughian, Hessam S. & Cellier, Francois E., eds. Discrete Event Modeling & Simulation Technologies: A Tapestry of Systems & AI-Based Theories & Methodologies. 2010. (ENG., Illus.). xxvi, 397p. pap. 89.95 *(978-1-4419-2868-9(5),* 1441928685) Springer.

Sarma, Kandarpa Kumar, et al. Speech Corpus of Assamese Numerals. 2011. 296p. pap. ***(978-3-8443-8213-6(5))*** Lambert Academic Publishing.

Saunders, Brandon. Observational Intelligence. 2008. 192p. pap. *(978-3-8364-3632-8(9))* VDM Verlag Dr. Mueller e.K.

Savac, F. Acar. Artificial Intelligence & Neural Networks: 14th Turkish Symposium, TAINN 2005, Izmir, Turkey, June 16-17, 2005, Revised Selected Papers. 2006. (Lecture Notes in Computer Science / Lecture Notes in Artificial Intelligence Ser.). (Illus.). 226p. pap. 29.95 *(978-3-540-36713-0(6),* 3540367136) Springer.

Sawai, Hidefumi, ed. Biological Functions for Information & Communication Technologies: Theory & Inspiration. 2011. (Studies in Computational

Intelligence Ser.). Orig. Title: Life & ICT - Inspiring Life-like functions into ICT. (Illus.). xi, 280p. 129.00 *(978-3-642-15101-9(9)*, 3642151019) Springer.
Scalable Uncertainty Management. 2008. (Lecture Notes in Computer Science / Lecture Notes in Artificial Intelligence Ser.). spiral bd. 89.95 *(978-3-540-87992-3(7)*, 3540879927) Springer.
Scerri, Paul, et al, eds. Coordination of Large-Scale Multiagent Systems. 2010 (ENG., Illus.). viii, 352p. pap. 124.00 *(978-1-4419-3872-5(9)*, 1441938729) Springer.
Schalkoff, Robert J. Intelligent Systems: Principles, Paradigms & Pragmatics. rev. ed. 2009. (Illus.). 762p. 159.95 *(978-0-7637-8017-3(0))* Jones & Bartlett Learning, LLC.
Scherer, Klaus R., et al. A Blueprint for Affective Computing: A sourcebook & Manual. 2010. (ENG., Illus.). 412p. 110.00 *(978-0-19-956670-9(4))* Oxford Univ. Pr., Inc.
Schiller, M., ed. Granularity Analysis for Tutoring Mathematical Proofs: Dissertations in Artificial Intelligence. 2011. 272p. pap. 72.00 ***(978-1-60750-719-2(6))*** IOS Pr., Inc.
Schlapbach, A. Writer Identification & Verification. 2008. pap. 70.00 *(978-1-58603-825-0(7))* IOS Pr., Inc.
Schmidhuber, Jurgen, et al, eds. Artificial General Intelligence: 4th Internationa Conference, AGI 2011, Mountain View, CA, USA, August 3-6, 2011, Proceedings. 2011. (Lecture Notes in Computer Science / Lecture Notes in Artificial Intelligence Ser.). (ENG., Illus.). xiii, 416p. pap. 95.00 ***(978-3-642-22886-5(0)***, 3642228860) Springer.
Schmitt, Manfred, et al, eds. Computational Intelligence Processing in Medical Diagnosis. 2010. (Studies in Fuzziness & Soft Computing Ser.). (ENG., Illus.). xx, 496p. pap. 199.00 *(978-3-7908-2509-1(3)*, 3790825093) Physica-Verlag DEU Dist: Springer.
Schneider, M. & Kroner, A., eds. Workshops Proceedings of the 5th International Conference on Intelligent Environments. 2009. (Ambient Intelligence & Smart Environments Ser.). 354p. pap. 131.00 *(978-1-60750-056-8(6))* IOS Pr., Inc.
Schuster, Alfons. Robust Intelligent Systems. 2008. (ENG., Illus.). xii, 299p. 139.00 *(978-1-84800-260-9(2)*, 1848002602) Springer.
Schuster, Alfons, ed. Intelligent Computing Everywhere. 2007. (ENG., Illus.). x, 259p. 119.00 *(978-1-84628-942-2(4)*, 1846289424) Springer.
—Robust Intelligent Systems. 2010. (ENG., Illus.). xii, 299p. pap. 139.00 *(978-1-84996-765-5(2)*, 1849967652) Springer.
Schwab, Brian. AI Game Engine Programming. 2nd ed. 2008. (ENG., Illus.). 736p. pap. 54.99 *(978-1-58450-572-3(9))* Charles River Media.
Schwenker, Friedhelm & El Gayar, Neamat, eds. Artificial Neural Networks in Pattern Recognition: 4th IAPR TC3 Workshop, ANNPR 2010, Cairo, Egypt, April 11-13, 2010, Proceedings. 2010. (Lecture Notes in Computer Science / Lecture Notes in Artificial Intelligence Ser.). xii, 280p. pap. 72.00 *(978-3-642-12158-6(6)*, 3642121586) Springer.
Schwenker, Friedhelm & Marinai, Simone. Artificial Neural Networks in Pattern Recognition: Second IAPR Workshop, ANNPR 2006, Ulm, Germany, August 31-September 2, 2006, Proceedings. 2006. (Lecture Notes in Computer Science Ser.). (Illus.). 297p. pap. 74.95 *(978-3-540-37951-5(7)*, 354037951 7) Springer.
Scott, Randall. A Guide to Artificial Intelligence with Visual Prolog. 2010. (Illus.). 190p. pap. 25.95 *(978-1-4327-4936-1(6))* Outskirts Pr., Inc.
Seabra Lopes, Luis, et al. Progress in Artificial Intelligence: 14th Portuguese Conference on Artificial Intelligence, EPIA 2009, Aveiro, Portugal, October 12-15, 2009, Proceedings. 2009. (Lecture Notes in Computer Science / Lecture Notes in Artificial Intelligence Ser.). (Illus.). xxi, 686p. pap. 139.00 *(978-3-642-04685-8(1)*, 3642046851) Springer.
Seaman, Bill & Rossler, Otto E. Neosentience: The Benevolence Engine. 2011. (Illus.). 287p. pap. 40.00 *(978-1-84150-404-9(1))* Intellect, Ltd. GBR. Dist: Chicago Distribution Ctr.
Segaran, Toby. Programming Collective Intelligence: Building Smart Web 2. 0 Applications. 2007. (ENG., Illus.). 362p. per. 39.99 *(978-0-596-52932-1(5))* O'Reilly Media, Inc.
Segovia, Javier, et al, eds. E-Commerce & Intelligent Methods. 2010. (Studies in Fuzziness & Soft Computing Ser.). (ENG., Illus.). xx, 534p. pap. 179.00 *(978-3-7908-2514-5(X)*, 379082514X) Physica-Verlag DEU. Dist: Springer.
Seifert, I., ed. Spatial Planning Assistance: A Cooperative Approach - Volume 321 Dissertations in Artificial Intelligence. 2008. 246p. pap. 73.00 *(978-1-58603-953-0(9))* IOS Pr., Inc.
Selman, Bart & Kautz, Henry. Satisfiability Testing. 2012. (Synthesis Lectures on Artificial Intelligence & Machine Learning Ser.). 100p. pap. 40.00 *(978-1-59829-198-8(X))* Morgan & Claypool Pubs.
Selouani, Sid-Ahmed. Speech Processing & Soft Computing. 2011. (SpringerBriefs in Speech Technology Ser.). (ENG., Illus.). ix, 104p. pap. 49.95 *(978-1-4419-9684-8(2)*, 1441996842) Springer.
Sencar, Husrev T., et al, eds. Intelligent Multimedia Analysis for Security Applications. 2010. (Studies in Computational Intelligence Ser.). 350p. 199.00 *(978-3-642-11754-1(6)*, 3642117546) Springer.
Sendhoff, Bernhard, et al. Creating Brain-Like Intelligence: From Basic Principles to Complex Intelligent Systems. 2009. (Lecture Notes in Computer Science / Lecture Notes in Artificial Intelligence Ser.). (ENG., Illus.). viii, 351p. pap. 79.95 *(978-3-642-00615-9(9))* Springer.
Serra, Roberto & Cucchiara, Rita. AI*IA 2009: Advances in Artificial Intelligence: XIth International Conference of the Italian Association for Artificial Intelligence, Reggio Emilia, Italy, December 9-12, 2009, Proceedings. 2009 (Lecture Notes in Computer Science / Lecture Notes in Artificial Intelligence Ser.). xiv, 503p. pap. 109.00 *(978-3-642-10290-5(5)*, 3642102905) Springer.
Settles, Burr. Active Learning. 2011. (Synthesis Lectures on Artificial Intelligence & Machine Learning Ser.). 100p. pap. 35.00 ***(978-1-60845-725-0(7))*** Morgan & Claypool Pubs
Shaheen, Husam. Voltage Control Based on Fuzzy Adaptive Particle Swarm Optimization. 2011. 80p. pap. ***(978-3-8443-2181-4(0))*** Lambert Academic Publishing.
Shakarian, Paulo & Subrahmanian, Venkatramanan. Geospatial Abduction: Principles & Practice. 2011. (ENG., Illus.). xvi, 168p. 99.00 ***(978-1-4614-1793-4(7)***, 1461417937) Springer.
Shariff, Riyaz, et al. Real-Time Artificial Intelligence Control & Optimization of a Full Scale WTP. 2007. 184p. pap. 59.00 *(978-1-58321-512-8(3))* Water Research Foundation.
Shi, Yuhui, et al, eds. Handbook of Swarm Intelligence: Concepts, Principles & Applications. 2011. (Adaptation, Learning, & Optimization Ser.). (Illus.). xii, 544p. 229.00 *(978-3-642-17389-9(6)*, 3642173896) Springer.
Shi, Zhongzhi. Advanced Artificial Intelligence, Vol. 1. 2011. (Illus.). 660p. 148.00 *(978-981-4291-34-7(X))* World Scientific Publishing Co., Inc.
Shin, Yung C. & Xu Chengying. Intelligent Systems: Modeling, Optimization, & Control. 2008. (Automation & Control Engineering Ser.). (ENG., Illus.). 456p. 139.95 *(978-1-4200-5176-6(8)*, CRC Press) Taylor & Francis Group GBR. Dist: Taylor & Francis Group.
Sichman, Jaime Simao, et al. Advances in Artificial Intelligence - IBERAMIA-SBIA 2006: 2nd International Joint Conference, 10th Ibero-American Conference on AI, 18th Brazilian AI Symposium, Riberao Preto, Brazil, October 23-27 2006. 2006. (Lecture Notes in Computer Science Ser.). (Illus.). XXIII, 635p. pap. 149.00 *(978-3-540-45462-5(4)*, 3540454624) Springer.
Sidorov, Grigori, et al, eds. MICAI 2010: Advances in Artificial Intelligence: 9th Mexican International Conference on Artificial Intelligence, Pachuca, Mexico, November 8-13, 2010, Proceedings, Part I. 2010. (Lecture Notes in Computer Science / Lecture Notes in Artificial Intelligence Ser.). xxiii, 479p. pap. 107.00 *(978-3-642-16760-7(8)*, 3642167608) Springer.
Siegler, Simon & Wasser, Nathan, eds. Verification, Induction, Termination Analysis: Festschrift for Christoph Walther on the Occasion of His 60th Birthday. 2010. (Lecture Notes in Computer Science / Lecture Notes in Artificial Intelligence Ser.). xi, 145p. pap. 72.00 *(978-3-642-17171-0(0)*, 3642171710) Springer.
Sigaud, Olivier & Buffet, Olivier, eds. Markov Decision Processes & Artifical Intelligence. 2010. (Iste Ser.: 447). (ENG., Illus.). 480p. 158.00 *(978-1-84821-167-4(8)*, Wiley-ISTE) Wiley, John & Sons, Inc.
Simari, Gerardo I. & Parsons, Simon D. Markov Decision Processes & the Belief-Desire-Intention Model: Bridging the Gap for Autonomous Agents. 2011. (SpringerBriefs in Computer Science Ser.). (ENG., Illus.). viii, 63p. pap. 39.95 ***(978-1-4614-1471-1(7)***, 1461414717) Springer.
Singh, M. P. Multiagent Systems: A Theoretical Framework for Intentions, Know-How, & Communications. 2007. (Lecture Notes in Computer Science Ser.). 200p. per. 39.95 *(978-3-540-58026-3(3))* Springer.
Siqueira, Adriano A. G., et al. Robust Control of Robots: Fault Tolerant Approaches. 2011. (ENG., Illus.). xvi, 228p. 129.00 ***(978-0-85729-897-3(6)***, 0857298976) Springer.
Slezak, Dominik, et al. U- & E-Service, Science & Technology: International Conference, UNESST 2009, Held as Part of the Future Generation Information Technology Conference, FGIT 2009, Jeju Island, Korea, December 10-12, 2009, Proceedings. 2009. (Communications in Computer & Information Science Ser.). xii, 177p. pap. 89.95 *(978-3-642-10579-1(3)*, 3642105793) Springer.
Slowinski, Roman, et al, eds. Transactions on Rough Sets XII. 2010. (Lecture Notes in Computer Science / Transactions on Rough Sets Ser.). (Illus.). x, 339p. pap. 113.00 *(978-3-642-14466-0(7)*, 3642144667) Springer.
Smolinski, Tomasz G. Applications of Computational Intelligence in Biology. 2008. (Studies in Computational Intelligence Ser.). 239.00 *(978-3-540-78533-0(7))* Springer.
—Computational Intelligence in Biomedicine & Bioinformatics. 2008. (Studies in Computational Intelligence Ser.). (Illus.). xxiv, 432p. 199.00 *(978-3-540-70776-9(X))* Springer.
Smolinski, Tomasz G., et al, eds. Applications of Computational Intelligence in Biology: Current Trends & Open Problems. 2010. (Studies in Computational Intelligence Ser.). (Illus.). xxvi, 428p. pap. 239.00 *(978-3-642-09730-0(8)*, 3642097308) Springer.
—Computational Intelligence in Biomedicine & Bioinformatics: Current Trends & Applications. 2010. (Studies in Computational Intelligence Ser.). (Illus.). xxiv, 432p. pap. 199.00 *(978-3-642-08969-5(0)*, 3642089690) Springer.
Snasel, Vaclav, et al, eds. Digital Information Processing & Communications: International Conference, ICDIPC 2011, Ostrava, Czech Republic, July 7-9, 2011. Proceedings, 2 vols. 2011. (Communications in Computer & Information Science Ser.). (ENG., Illus.). xix, 573p. pap. 119.00 ***(978-3-642-22388-4(5)***, 3642223885) Springer.
Sohaib, Ahmed, et al. Signtium. 2011. 88p. pap. ***(978-3-8433-8655-5(2))*** Lambert Academic Publishing.
Solanas, Agusti. Advances in Artificial Intelligence for Privacy Protection & Security, Vol. 1. 2009. (Illus.). 404p. 99.00 *(978-981-279-032-3(2))* World Scientific Publishing Co., Inc.
Sombattheera, Chattrakul, et al, eds. Multi-disciplinary Trends in Artificial Intelligence: 5th International Workshop, MIWAI 2011, Hyderabad, India, December 7-9, 2011. Proceedings. 2011. (Lecture Notes in Computer Science / Lecture Notes in Artificial Intelligence Ser.). (ENG., Illus.). 444p. pap. 95.00 ***(978-3-642-25724-7(0)***, 3642257240) Springer.
Sordo, Margarita, et al, eds. Advanced Computational Intelligence Paradigms in Healthcare - 3. 2010. (Studies in Computational Intelligence Ser.). (Illus.). x, 258p. pap. 159.00 *(978-3-642-09644-0(1)*, 3642096441) Springer.
Sossai, Claudio & Chemello, Gaetano. Symbolic & Quantitative Approaches to Reasoning with Uncertainty: 10th European Conference, ECSQARU 2009, Verona, Italy, July 1-3, 2009, Proceedings. 2009. (Lecture Notes in Computer Science / Lecture Notes in Artificial Intelligence Ser.). xvii, 936p. pap. 149.00 *(978-3-642-02905-9(1)*, 3642029051) Springer.
Spaniol, Marc, et al. Advances in Web Based Learning - ICWL 2009: 8th International Conference, Aachen, Germany, August 19-21, 2009, Proceedings. 2009. (Lecture Notes in Computer Science / Information Systems & Applications, incl. Internet/Web, & HCI Ser.). (ENG.). xv, 478p. pap. 99.00 *(978-3-642-03425-1(X)*, 364203425X) Springer.
Spierling, Ulrike & Szilas, Nicolas. Interactive Storytelling: First Joint International Conference on Interactive Digital Storytelling, ICIDS 2008 Erfurt, Germany, November 26-29, 2008, Proceedings. 2008. (Lecture Notes in Computer Science / Information Systems & Applications, incl. Internet/Web, & HCI Ser.). (Illus.). xii, 334p. pap. 79.95 *(978-3-540-89424-7(1))* Springer.
Srinivasan, Ashwin. Donald Michie: Machine Intelligence, Biology & More. 2009. (ENG., Illus.). 352p. 45.00 *(978-0-19-957304-2(2))* Oxford Univ. Pr., Inc.
Stankovic, Radomir S. & Astola, Jaakko. From Boolean Logic to Switching Circuits & Automata: Towards Modern Information Technology. 2010. (Studies in Computational Intelligence Ser.). (Illus.). 150p. 129.00 *(978-3-642-11681-0(7)*, 3642116817) Springer.
Stepaniuk, J. Rough - Granular Computing in Knowledge Discovery & Data Mining. (Studies in Computational Intelligence Ser.). 2010. xiv, 158p. pap. 159.00 *(978-3-642-08972-5(0)*, 3642089720) 2008. (Illus.). xiii, 158p. 159.00 *(978-3-540-70800-1(6)*, 3540708006) Springer.
Stirling, Wynn C. Satisficing Games & Decision Making: With Applications to Engineering & Computer Science. 2007. (ENG.). 268p. pap. 62.00 *(978-0-521-03891-1(X))* Cambridge Univ. Pr.
Stock, Oliviero & Schaerf, Marco. Reasoning, Action & Interaction in AI Theories & Systems: Essays Dedicated to Luigia Carlucci Aiello. 2006. (Lecture Notes in Computer Science Ser.). (Illus.). 342p. pap. 89.95 *(978-3-540-37901-0(0)*, 3540379010) Springer.
Stock, Oliviero & Zancanaro, Massimo, eds. PEACH - Intelligent Interfaces for Museum Visits. 2007. (Cognitive Technologies Ser.). (Illus.). 316p. 149.00 *(978-3-540-68754-2(8)*, 3540687548) Springer.
Stoica, Adrian. Proceedings, LAB-RS 2008: 2008 ECSIS Symposium on Learning & Adaptive Behaviors for Robotic Systems: Proceedings, 6-8 August 2008, Edinburgh, Scotland, United Kingdom. 2008. (Illus.). xi, 115p. *(978-0-7695-3272-1(1))* IEEE Computer Society Pr.
Studeny, Milan. Probabilistic Conditional Independence Structures. 2010. (Information Science & Statistics Ser.). (Illus.). xiv, 285p. pap. 139.00 *(978-1-84996-948-2(5)*, 1849969485) Springer.
Stützle, Thomas. Learning & Intelligent Optimization: Designing, Implementing & Analyzing Effective Heuristics: Third International Conference, LION 2009 III, Trento, Italy, January 14-18, 2009. Selected Papers. 2009. (Lecture Notes in Computer Science / Theoretical Computer Science & General Issues Ser.). xii, 273p. pap. 72.00 *(978-3-642-11168-6(8)*, 3642111688) Springer.
Su, Yunlin & Yan, Song Y. Principles of Compilers: A New Approach to Compilers Including the Algebraic Method. 2011. (ENG., Illus.). 500p. 169.00 *(978-3-642-20834-8(7)*, 3642208347) Springer.
Sucar, L. Enrique, et al, eds. Decision Theory Models for Applications in Artificial Intelligence: Concepts & Solutions. 2010. 350p. 180.00 *(978-1-60960-165-2(3)*, Information Science Reference) IGI Global.
Suchanek, Fabian. Automated Reasoning & Common Sense. 2008. 72p. pap. *(978-3-639-00393-2(4))* VDM Verlag Dr. Mueller e.K.
Sudjono, Erick. Artificial Intelligence in Construction Management. 2008. 148p. pap. *(978-3-639-08247-0(8))* VDM Verlag Dr. Mueller e.K.
Sudweeks, Fay. Virtual Collaborative Groups. 2008. 400p. pap. *(978-3-639-03423-3(6))* VDM Verlag Dr. Mueller e.K.
Sugumaran, Vijay. Itelligent Information Technologies: Concepts, Methodologies, Tools & Applications, 4 vols. 2007. 2610p. 1550.00 *(978-1-59904-941-0(4))* IGI Global.
Sugumaran, Vijayan. Application of Agents & Intelligent Information Technologies. 2006. (Illus.). 392p. 99.95 *(978-1-59904-265-7(7))* IGI Global.
Sugumaran, Vijayan. Insights into Advancements in Intelligent Information Technologies: Discoveries. 2012. ***(978-1-4666-0160-4(4))***; ***(978-1-4666-0158-1(2))*** IGI Global.
Sugumaran, Vijayan, ed. Distributed Artificial Intelligence: Agent Technology & Collaborative Applications. 2008. (Advances in Intelligent Information Technologies Book Ser.). (Illus.). 450p. (C). 195.00 *(978-1-60566-144-5(9))* IGI Global.
—Intelligent, Adaptive & Reasoning Technologies: New Developments & Applications. 2011. 350p. 180.00 *(978-1-60960-595-7(0)*, Information Science Reference) IGI Global.
Sun, Dong & Ge, Shuzi Sam. Synchronization & Control of Multiagent Systems. 2010. (Automation & Control Engineering Ser.). (ENG., Illus.). 200p. 119.95 *(978-1-4398-2047-6(3)*, CRC Press) Taylor & Francis Group GBR. Dist: Taylor & Francis Group.
Supporting learning flow through integrative Technologies. 2007. pap. 208.00 *(978-1-58603-797-0(8))* IOS Pr., Inc.
Sutherland, Benjamin. Modern Warfare, Intelligence & Deterrence: The Technology That Are Transforming Them. 2012. (Economist Ser.). (ENG.). 320p. 24.95 ***(978-1-118-18537-7(4)***, Wiley) Wiley, John & Sons, Inc.
Swarm Intelligent Systems. 2010. (Studies in Computational Intelligence Ser.). (Illus.). xx, 186p. pap. 169.00 *(978-3-642-07041-9(8)*, 3642070418) Springer.
Syropoulos, Apostolos. Hypercomputation: Computing Beyond the Church-Turing Barrier. (ENG., Illus.). x, 260p. 2010. pap. 79.95 *(978-1-4419-4040-7(5)*, 1441940405) 2008. 79.95 *(978-0-387-30886-9(5)*, 0387308865) Springer.
Székely, Gábor & Hahn, Horst, eds. Information Processing in Medical Imaging: 22nd International Conference, IPMI 2011, Kloster Irsee, Germany, July 3-8, 2011, Proceedings. 2011. (Lecture Notes in Computer Science / Image Processing, Computer Vision, Pattern Recognition, & Graphics Ser.). (ENG., Illus.). xxi, 787p. pap. 131.00 ***(978-3-642-22091-3(6)***, 3642220916) Springer.
Tachwali, Yahia. Sensor Fusion Based Plastic Bottles Classification System. 2009. 168p. pap. *(978-3-639-14924-1(6))* VDM Verlag Dr. Mueller e.K.
Tan, Honghua & Luo, Qi. PIAGENG 2009: 11-12 July 2009 Zhangjiajie, China. 2009. (Proceedings of SPIE Ser.). (Illus.). 690p. pap. 130.00 *(978-0-8194-7801-6(6))* SPIE.
Tan, Yap-Peng, et al, eds. Intelligent Multimedia Processing with Soft Computing. 2010. (Studies in Fuzziness & Soft Computing Ser.). viii, 473p. pap. 239.00 *(978-3-642-06198-1(2)*, 3642061982) Springer.
Tavares, JoA£o Manuel R. S. & Jorge, R. M. Natal, eds. Computational Vision & Medical Image Processing: VipIMAGE 2009. 2009. (ENG.). 464p. 219.95 *(978-0-415-57041-1(7)*, CRC Press) Taylor & Francis Group GBR. Dist: Taylor & Francis Group.
Tavares, JoA£o Manuel R. S. & Natal Jorge, R. M., eds. Computational Vision & Medical Image Processing: VipIMAGE 2011. 2011. (ENG.). 460p. (C) 199.00 ***(978-0-415-68395-1(5)***, CRC Press) Taylor & Francis Group GBR. Dist: Taylor & Francis Group.
Taylor, Brian J., ed. Methods & Procedures for the Verification & Validation of Artificial Neural Networks. 2010. (ENG., Illus.). xi, 277p. pap. 155.00 *(978-1-4419-3935-7(0)*, 1441939350) Springer.
Taylor, Matthew & Tuyls, Karl. Adaptive Learning Agents: Second Workshop, ALA 2009, Held as Part of the AAMAS 2009 Conference in Budapest, Hungary, May 12, 2009. Revised Selected Papers. 2010. (Lecture Notes in Computer Science / Lecture Notes in Artificial Intelligence Ser.). 154p. pap. 72.00 *(978-3-642-11813-5(5)*, 3642118135) Springer.
Taylor, Robyn, et al, eds. Smart Graphics: 10th International Symposium on Smart Graphics, Banff, Canada, June 24-26 Proceedings. 2010. (Lecture Notes in Computer Science / Image Processing, Computer Vision, Pattern Recognition, & Graphics Ser.). 294p. pap. 72.00 *(978-3-642-13543-9(9)*, 3642135439) Springer.
Technologies for E-Learning & Digital Entertainment. 2008. (Lecture Notes in Computer Science / Information Systems & Applications, incl. Internet/Web, & HCI Ser.). spiral bd. 139.00 *(978-3-540-69734-3(9))* Springer.
Teodorescu, Horio-Nicolai, et al, eds. Intelligent Systems & Technologies: Methods & Applications. 2009. (Studies in Computational Intelligence Ser.). (Illus.). viii, 297p. 159.00 *(978-3-642-01884-8(X)*, 364201884X) Springer.
Terras, Melissa. Image to Interpretation: An Intelligent System to Aid Historians in Reading the Vindolanda Texts. 2006. (Oxford Studies in Ancient Documents Ser.). (ENG., Illus.). 264p. 110.00 *(978-0-19-920455-7(1))* Oxford Univ. Pr., Inc.
Thaung, Khine Soe, ed. Logistics, Informatics & Services Sciences. 2011. (Advances in Intelligent & Soft Computing Ser.). (ENG.) 800p. pap. 409.00 ***(978-3-642-25771-1(2)***, 3642257712) Springer.
Thielscher, Michael. Action Programming Languages. 2008. (Synthesis Lectures on Artificial Intelligence & Machine Learning Ser.). 91p. pap. 35.00 *(978-1-59829-544-3(6))* Morgan & Claypool Pubs.
Thornton, John, ed. AI 2007: Advances in Artificial Intelligence. 2007. (Lecture Notes in Computer Science Ser.). (Illus.). 841p. pap. 139.00 *(978-3-540-76926-2(9))* Springer.
Tiwari, U. S., et al, eds. Proceedings of the Second International Conference on Intelligent Human Computer Interaction (IHCI 2010) 2012. (ENG., Illus.). 384p. 269.00 ***(978-81-8489-540-7(2)***, 8184895402) Springer (India) Private Ltd. IND. Dist: Springer.
Topping, B. H., ed. Optimization & Artificial Intelligence in Civil & Structural Engineering: Volume I: Optimization in Civil & Structural Engineering Volume II: Artificial Intelligence in Civil & Structural Engineering. 2010. (NATO Science Series E: (closed) Ser.). (ENG.). 356p. pap. 319.00 *(978-90-481-4202-6(4)*, 9048142024); (Illus.). 672p. pap. 559.00 *(978-90-481-4201-9(6)*, 9048142016) Springer.
Topping, B. H. V., ed. Civil Engineering Computations: Tools & Techniques. 2008. (ENG., Illus.). 476p. 200.00 *(978-1-874672-32-6(6))* Saxe-Coburg Pubns. GBR. Dist: Independent Pubs. Group.
Torra, Vicenç, et al. Modeling Decisions for Artificial Intelligence: 6th International Conference, MDAI 2009, Awaji Island, Japan, November 30-December 2, 2009, Proceedings. 2009. (Lecture Notes in Computer Science / Lecture Notes in Artificial Intelligence Ser.). xi, 373p. pap. 83.00 *(978-3-642-04819-7(6)*, 3642048196) Springer.
Torra, Vicenç, et al, eds. Modeling Decisions for Artificial Intelligence: 7th International Conference, MDAI 2010, Perpignan, France, October 27-29, 2010, Proceedings. 2010. (Lecture Notes in Computer Science / Lecture Notes in Artificial Intelligence Ser.). xi, 299p. pap. 83.00 *(978-3-642-16291-6(6)*, 3642162916) Springer.
Torra, Vicenç, et al. Modeling Decisions for Artificial Intelligence: 4th International Conference, MDAI 2007, Kitakyushu, Japan, August 16-18, 2007, Proceedings. 2007. (Lecture Notes in Computer Science / Lecture Notes in Artificial Intelligence Ser.). xii, 502p. pap. 99.00 *(978-3-540-73728-5(6))*, Springer.

A

Torra, Vincenc, et al, eds. Modeling Decision for Artificial Intelligence: 8th International Conference, MDAI 2011, Changsha, Hunan, China, July 28-30, 2011, Proceedings. 2011. (Lecture Notes in Computer Science / Lecture Notes in Artificial Intelligence Ser.). (Illus.). xiv, 259p. pap. 72.00 ***(978-3-642-22588-8(8)***, 3642225888) Springer.

Trajkovski, Goran. An Imitation-Based Approach to Modeling Homogenous Agents Societies. 2006. (Computational Intelligence & Its Applications Ser.). (Illus.). 312p. 94.95 *(978-1-59140-839-0(3))* IGI Global.

Trajkovski, Goran & Collins, Samuel Gerald. Handbook of Research on Agent-Based Societies: Social & Cultural Interactions. 2009. (Illus.). 436p. 265.00 *(978-1-60566-236-7(4))* IGI Global.

Tsai, Tsung-Hsien. Short-Term Railway Passenger Demand Forecasting. 2009. 156p. pap. *(978-3-639-16149-6(1))* VDM Verlag Dr. Mueller e.K.

Tsourtos, George. Speed of Human Information Processing in Psychiatric Disorders. 2008. 208p. pap. *(978-3-639-06238-0(8))* VDM Verlag Dr. Mueller e.K.

Tuson, Andrew, ed. Applications & Innovations in Intelligent Systems XIV: Proceedings of AI-2006, the Twenty-Sixth SGAI International Conference on Innovative Techniques & Applications of Artificial Intelligence. 2006. (Illus.). 243p. per. 149.00 *(978-1-84628-665-0(4))* Springer.

Tyugu, E. Algorithms & architectures of artificial intelligence. 2007. 117.00 *(978-1-58603-770-3(6))* IOS Pr., Inc.

Ulinwa, V. C. I. Machine Intelligence Quotient: A Multiple Perspective Analysis of Intelligent Artificial Systems Including Educational Technology. 2008. 252p. pap. *(978-3-639-09692-7(4))* VDM Verlag Dr. Mueller e.K.

Ullrich, Carsten, et al, eds. Cognitive Systems: Joint Chinese-German Workshop, Shanghai, China, March 7-11, 2005 Revised Selected Papers. 2007. (Lecture Notes in Computer Science / Lecture Notes in Artificial Intelligence Ser.). (Illus.). 160p. per. 69.95 *(978-3-540-70933-6(9))*, 3540709339) Springer.

Umiltà, Carlo, et al. The Allure of Machinic Life: Cybernetics, Artificial Life, & the New AI. 2008. (ENG., Illus.). 480p. (gr. 17). 42.00 *(978-0-262-10126-4(2))* MIT Pr.

Unnikrishnan, Srija, et al, eds. Advances in Computing, Communication & Control: International Conference, ICAC3 2011, Mumbai, India, January 28-29, 2011. Proceedings. 2011. (Communications in Computer & Information Science Ser.). (Illus.). xviii, 538p. pap. 119.00 *(978-3-642-18439-0(1)*, 3642184391) Springer.

Urlings, T., ed. Heuristics & Metaheuristics for heavily constrained hybrid Flowshop Problems: Dissertations in Artificial Intelligence. 2011. 348p. pap. 73.00 ***(978-1-60750-678-2(5))*** IOS Pr., Inc.

Vadakkepat, Prahlad, et al, eds. Trends in Intelligent Robotics: 15th Robot World Cup & Congress, FIRA 2010, Bangalore, India, September15-19, 2010, Proceedings. 2010. (Communications in Computer & Information Science Ser.). xiii, 370p. pap. 95.00 *(978-3-642-15809-4(9)*, 3642158099) Springer.

Vaidya, S., et al, eds. Advanced Computational Intelligence Paradigms in Healthcare - 2. 2010. (Studies in Computational Intelligence Ser.). (Illus.). x, 150p. pap. 149.00 *(978-3-642-09143-8(1)*, 3642091431) Springer.

Vaidya, S. & Yoshida, H., eds. Advanced Computational Intelligence Paradigms in Healthcare-2. 2007. (Studies in Computational Intelligence Ser.). (Illus.). 150p. 149.00 *(978-3-540-72374-5(9))* Springer.

Vallverdú, Jordi, ed. Thinking Machines & the Philosophy of Computer Science: Concepts & Principles. 2010. (Illus.). 350p. 180.00 *(978-1-61692-014-2(9))* IGI Global.

Valtchev, Petko & Jäschke, Robert, eds. Formal Concept Analysis: 9th International Conference, ICFCA 2011, Nicosia, Cyprus, May 2-6, 2011, Proceedings. 2011. (Lecture Notes in Computer Science / Lecture Notes in Artificial Intelligence Ser.). xii, 266p. pap. 72.00 *(978-3-642-20513-2(5)*, 3642205135) Springer.

Vámos, Tibor. Knowledge & Computing: Computer Epistemology & Constructive Skepticism. 2010. 270p. 45.00 *(978-963-9776-64-7(5))* Central European Univ. Pr.

van den Herik, H. Jaap & Spronck, Pieter, eds. Advances in Computer Games: 12th International Conference, ACG 2009, Pamplona, Spain, May 11-13, 2009, Revised Papers. 2010. (Lecture Notes in Computer Science / Theoretical Computer Science & General Issues Ser.). (Illus.). xiv, 233p. pap. 72.00 *(978-3-642-12992-6(7)*, 3642129927) Springer.

van der Meyden, Ron & Smaus, Jan, eds. Model Checking & Artificial Intelligence: 6th International Workshop, MoChArt 2010, Atlanta, GA, USA, July 11, 2010, Revised Selected & Invited Papers. 2011. (Lecture Notes in Computer Science / Lecture Notes in Artificial Intelligence Ser.). (Illus.). xi, 131p. pap. 72.00 *(978-3-642-20673-3(5)*, 3642206735) Springer.

Van Dyke Parunak, H., ed. Environments for Multi-Agent Systems III: Third International Workshop, E4MAS 2006, Hakodate, Japan, May 8, 2006 Selected Revised & Invited Papers. 2007. (Lecture Notes in Computer Science Ser.). (Illus.). 271p. pap. 69.95 *(978-3-540-71102-5(3)*, 3540711023) Springer.

van Hoeve, Willem-Jan, et al. Integration of AI & or Techniques in Constraint Programming for Combinatorial Optimization Problems: 6th International Conference, CPAIOR 2009 Pittsburgh, PA, USA, May 27-31, 2009 Proceedings. 2009. (Lecture Notes in Computer Science / Theoretical Computer Science & General Issues Ser.). xi, 332p. pap. 79.95 *(978-3-642-01928-9(5))* Springer.

van Leeuwen, Jos P. & Timmermans, Harry J. P., eds. Recent Advances in Design & Decision Support Systems in Architecture & Urban Planning. 2010. (ENG.). xv, 358p. pap. 229.00 *(978-90-481-6653-4(5)*, 9048166535) Springer.

Vanhoof, Koen. Intelligent Decision Making Systems Vol. 2: Proceedings of the 4th International Iske Conference on Intelligent Systems & Knowledge. 2009. 724p. 280.00 *(978-981-4295-05-5(1))* World Scientific Publishing Co., Inc.

Vanneschi, Leonardo, et al. Genetic Programming: 12th European Conference, EuroGP 2009 Tübingen, Germany, April, 15-17, 2009 Proceedings. 2009. (Lecture Notes in Computer Science / Theoretical Computer Science & General Issues Ser.). xiii, 363p. pap. 79.95 *(978-3-642-01180-1(2))* Springer.

Vanstone, Bruce & Hahn, Tobias. Designing Stock Market Trading Systems: With & Without Soft Computing. 2010. (Illus.). 350p. pap. 100.00 *(978-1-906659-58-5(3))* Harriman Hse. Publishing GBR. Dist: Ingram Pub. Services.

Vasilakos, Athanasios V., et al. Autonomic Computing & Communications Systems: Third International ICST Conference, Autonomics 2009, Limassol, Cyprus, September 9-11, 2009, Revised Selected Papers. 2010. (Lecture Notes of the Institute for Computer Sciences, Social-Informatics & Telecommunications Engineering Ser.). xi, 269p. pap. 72.00 *(978-3-642-11481-6(4)*, 3642114814) Springer.

Velásquez, Juan D., et al. Knowledge-Based Intelligent Information & Engineering Systems: 13th International Conference, KES 2009, Santiago, Chile, September 28-30, 2009, Proceedings, Part I, 2 vols. 2009. (Lecture Notes in Computer Science / Lecture Notes in Artificial Intelligence Ser.). (Illus.). xxx, 381p. pap. 95.00 *(978-3-642-04594-3(4)*, 3642045944) Springer.

—Knowledge-Based Intelligent Information & Engineering Systems: 13th International Conference, KES 2009, Santiago, Chile, September 28-30, 2009, Proceedings, Part II, 2 vols. 2009. (Lecture Notes in Computer Science / Lecture Notes in Artificial Intelligence Ser.). (Illus.). xxix, 873p. pap. 159.00 *(978-3-642-04591-2(X)*, 364204591X) Springer.

Velik, Rosemarie. A Bionic Model for Human-Like MacHine Perception. 2008. 208p. pap. *(978-3-8381-0050-0(6))* VDM Verlag Dr. Mueller e.K.

Veloso, Manuela M. Proceedings of the Twentieth International Joint Conference on Artificial Intelligence (IJCAI-07) Hyderabad, India, 6-12 January 2007, 2 vols. 2007. (ENG., Illus.). 2954p. *(978-1-57735-298-3(X))* AAAI Pr.

Venugopal, K. R. & Patnaik, L. M., eds. Computer Networks & Intelligent Computing: 5th International Conference on Information Processing, ICIP 2011, Bangalore, India, August 5-7, 2011. Proceedings. 2011. (Communications in Computer & Information Science Ser.). (ENG.). xviii, 685p. pap. 143.00 ***(978-3-642-22785-1(6)***, 3642227856) Springer.

Verbeek, Fons J., ed. Human-Robot Personal Relationships: Third International Conference, HRPR 2010, Leiden, the Netherlands, June 23-24, 2010, Revised Selected Papers. 2011. (Lecture Notes of the Institute for Computer Sciences, Social-Informatics & Telecommunications Engineering Ser.). (Illus.). x, 139p. pap. 72.00 *(978-3-642-19384-2(6)*, 3642193846) Springer.

Verhaegh, W., et al, eds. Algorithms in Ambient Intelligence. 2010. (Philips Research Book Ser.). 354p. pap. 259.00 *(978-90-481-6490-5(7)*, 9048164907) Springer.

Vermaas, P. E. & Dignum, V., eds. Formal Ontologies Meet Industry: Proceedings of the 5th International Workshop (FOMI 2011) 2011. 136p. 145.00 ***(978-1-60750-784-0(6))*** IOS Pr., Inc.

Verulava, Otar & Khurodze, Ramaz. Theory of Rank Links: Modeling of Recognition Processes. 2010. (Mathematics Research Developments Ser.). pap. 43.00 *(978-1-61728-610-0(9)*, Nova Novinka) Nova Science Pubs., Inc.

Villmann, Thomas, et al. Similarity-Based Clustering: Recent Developments & Biomedical Applications. 2009. (Lecture Notes in Computer Science / Lecture Notes in Artificial Intelligence Ser.). (ENG., Illus.). xi, 203p. pap. 69.95 *(978-3-642-01804-6(1)*, 3642018041) Springer.

Virvou, Maria. Intelligent Interactive Systems in Knowledge-Based Environments. 2008. (Studies in Computational Intelligence Ser.). (ENG., Illus.). xii, 200p. 179.00 *(978-3-540-77470-9(X)*, 354077470X) Springer.

Virvou, Maria & Jain, Lakhmi C., eds. Intelligent Interactive Systems in Knowledge-Based Environments. 2010. (Studies in Computational Intelligence Ser.). (Illus.). xii, 200p. pap. 179.00 *(978-3-642-09617-4(4)*, 3642096174) Springer.

Vlassis, Nikos. A Concise Introduction to Multiagent Systems & Distributed Artificial Intelligence. 2007. (Synthesis Lectures on Artificial Intelligence & Machine Learning Ser.). (Illus.). 71p. per. 40.00 *(978-1-59829-526-9(8))* Morgan & Claypool Pubs.

Von Mammen, Sebastian. Evolving Artificial Constructive Swarms - Experimental Models & Methodologies. 2008. 92p. pap. *(978-3-8364-9903-3(7))* VDM Verlag Dr. Mueller e.K.

Voronkov, Andrei, ed. Logic for Programming, Artificial Intelligence, & Reasoning: 13th International Conference, Lpar 2006, Phnom Penh, Cambodia, November 13-17, 2006, Proceedings. 2007. (Lecture Notes in Computer Science Ser.). (Illus.). 588p. pap. 119.00 *(978-3-540-48281-9(4)*, 3540482814) Springer.

Vrakas, Dimitris & Vlahavas, Ioannis Pl. Artificial Intelligence for Advanced Problem Solving Techniques. 2008. (Illus.). 388p. 180.00 *(978-1-59904-705-8(5))* IGI Global.

Wachsmuth, Ipke. Modeling Communication with Robots & Virtual Humans. 2008. (Lecture Notes in Computer Science / Lecture Notes in Artificial Intelligence Ser.). (Illus.). x, 335p. spiral bd. 69.95 *(978-3-540-79036-5(5)*, 3540790365) Springer.

Wagelaar, Dennis. Platform Ontologies for the Model-Driven Architecture. 2009. (ENG., Illus.). 211p. pap. 48.00 *(978-90-5487-482-9(1))* VUB Univ. Pr. BEL. Dist: Independent Pubs. Group.

Walton, Douglas. Argumentation Methods for Artificial Intelligence in Law. 2010. (ENG., Illus.). xviii, 270p. pap. 179.00 *(978-3-642-06432-6(9)*, 3642064329) Springer.

—Character Evidence: An Abductive Theory. (Argumentation Library). xv, 239p. 2010. pap. 159.00 *(978-90-481-7235-1(7)*, 9048172357) 2006. (Illus.). (C). 159.00 *(978-1-4020-4942-2(0)*, 1402049420) Springer.

Walton, Douglas N. Witness Testimony Evidence: Argumentation, Artificial Intelligence, & Law. 2007. (ENG.). 384p. 88.99 *(978-0-521-88143-2(9))*; pap. 31.99 *(978-0-521-70770-1(6))* Cambridge Univ. Pr.

Wang, Dianhui & Reynolds, Mark, eds. AI 2011: Advances in Artificial Intelligence: 24th Australasian Joint Conference, Perth, Australia, December 5-8, 2011, Proceedings. 2011. (Lecture Notes in Computer Science / Lecture Notes in Artificial Intelligence Ser.). (ENG., Illus.). xiii, 823p. pap. 131.00 ***(978-3-642-25831-2(X)***, 364225831X) Springer.

Wang, Fei-Yue & Mao, Wenji. New Advances in Intelligence & Security Informatics. 2012. (ENG., Illus.). 116p. 125.00 ***(978-0-12-397200-2(0)***, Academic Pr.) Elsevier Science & Technology Bks.

Wang, Fu Lee, et al, eds. Artificial Intelligence & Computational Intelligence: International Conference, AICI 2010, Sanya, China, October 23-24, 2010, Proceedings, Part I. 2010. (Lecture Notes in Computer Science / Lecture Notes in Artificial Intelligence Ser.). xxi, 498p. pap. 107.00 *(978-3-642-16529-0(X)*, 364216529X) Springer.

—Artificial Intelligence & Computational Intelligence: International Conference, AICI 2010, Sanya, China, October 23-24, 2010, Proceedings, Part II. 2010. (Lecture Notes in Computer Science / Lecture Notes in Artificial Intelligence Ser.). xxii, 386p. pap. 95.00 *(978-3-642-16526-9(5)*, 3642165265) Springer.

Wang, Guoyin. Rough Sets & Knowledge Technology: Third International Conference, RSKT 2008, Chengdu, China, May 17-19, 2008. 2008. (Lecture Notes in Computer Science / Lecture Notes in Artificial Intelligence Ser.). (Illus.). 783p. spiral bd. 139.00 *(978-3-540-79720-3(3)*, 3540797203) Springer.

Wang, Hsiao-Fan, ed. Intelligent Data Analysis: Developing New Methodologies Through Pattern Discovery & Recovery. 2008. (Illus.). 366p. 180.00 *(978-1-59904-982-3(1))* IGI Global.

Wang, Huaiqing & Zhou, Zude. Manufacturing Intelligence for Industrial Engineering: Methods for System Self-Organization, Learning, & Adaptation. 2010. (Illus.). 387p. *(978-1-60566-864-2(8)*, Engineering Science Reference) IGI Global.

Wang, Patrick S. P., ed. Pattern Recognition, Machine Intelligence & Biometrics. 2011. (ENG., Illus.). 800p. 219.00 ***(978-3-642-22406-5(7)***, 3642224067) Springer.

Wang, Pei. Rigid Flexibility: The Logic of Intelligence. (Applied Logic Ser.). 2010. (Illus.). xvii, 412p. pap. 289.00 *(978-90-481-7264-1(0)*, 9048172640) 2006. xviii, 414p. (C). 289.00 *(978-1-4020-5044-2(5)*, 1402050445) Springer.

Wang, Q., et al, eds. Combinatorial Methods & Informatics in Materials Science. 2009. (Symposium Proceedings Ser.). (Illus.). xi, 356p. 104.00 *(978-1-55899-848-3(9))* Materials Research Society.

Wang, Tzai-Der, et al. Simulated Evolution & Learning: 6th International Conference, SEAL 2006, Hefei, China, October 15-18, 2006, Proceedings. 2006. (Lecture Notes in Computer Science Ser.). (Illus.). XXI, 940p. pap. 149.00 *(978-3-540-47331-2(9)*, 3540473319) Springer.

Wang, Yinglin & Li, Tianrui, eds. Foundations of Intelligent Systems: Proceedings of the Sixth International Conference on Intelligent Systems & Knowledge Engineering, Shanghai, China, Dec 2011 (ISKE 2011) 2011. (Advances in Intelligent & Soft Computing Ser.). (ENG., Illus.). xxx, 754p. pap. 399.00 ***(978-3-642-25663-9(5)***, 3642256635) Springer.

—Knowledge Engineering & Management: Proceedings of the Sixth International Conference on Intelligent Systems & Knowledge Engineering, Shanghai, China, Dec 2011 (ISKE 2011) 2011. (Advances in Intelligent & Soft Computing Ser.). (ENG., Illus.). xxx, 714p. pap. 349.00 ***(978-3-642-25660-8(0)***, 3642256600) Springer.

Wang, Yingxu, ed. Discoveries & Breakthroughs in Cognitive Informatics & Natural Intelligence. 2009. 375p. 180.00 *(978-1-60566-902-1(4)*, Information Science Reference) IGI Global.

—Novel Approaches in Cognitive Informatics & Natural Intelligence. 2008. (Advances in Cognitive Informatics & Natural Intelligence Book Ser.). (Illus.). 396p. 195.00 *(978-1-60566-170-4(8))* IGI Global.

Wang, Yuping, ed. Computational Intelligence & Security; Proceedings: International Conference on Computational Intelligence & Security (2007: Heilongjiang, China) 2007. 1081p. pap. 424.00 *(978-0-7695-3072-7(9))* IEEE Computer Society Pr.

—Computational Intelligence & Security; Proceedings: International Conference on Computational Intelligence & Security Workshops (2007: Heilongjiang, China) 2007. 958p. pap. 368.00 *(978-0-7695-3073-4(7))* IEEE Computer Society Pr.

Warwick, Kevin. Artificial Intelligence: The Basics. 2011. (Basics Ser.). (ENG., Illus.). 192p. (C). 90.00 *(978-0-415-56482-3(4))*; pap. 19.95 *(978-0-415-56483-0(2))* Routledge.

Washio, Takashi, et al. New Frontiers in Artificial Intelligence: Joint JSAI 2005 Workshop Post-Proceedings. 2006. (Lecture Notes in Computer Science Ser.). (Illus.). XIII, 484p. pap. 99.00 *(978-3-540-35470-3(0)*, 3540354700) Springer.

Washio, Takashi, et al, eds. New Frontiers in Artificial Intelligence: JSAI 2006 Conference & Workshops Tokyo, Japan, June 5-9, 2006 Revised Selected Papers. 2007. (Lecture Notes in Computer Science Ser.). (Illus.). 400p. per. 89.95 *(978-3-540-69901-9(5)*, 3540699015) Springer.

Watada, Junzo, et al, eds. Intelligent Decision Technologies: Proceedings of the 3rd International Conference on Intelligent Decision Technologies (IDT'2011) 2011. (Smart Innovation, Systems & Technologies Ser.). (ENG., Illus.). xiv, 930p. 279.00 ***(978-3-642-22193-4(9)***, 3642221939) Springer.

Watanabe, Toyohide & Jain, Lakhmi C., eds. Innovations in Intelligent Machines - 2: Intelligent Paradigms & Applications. 2011. (Studies in Computational Intelligence Ser.). (ENG., Illus.). xvi, 284p. 179.00 ***(978-3-642-23189-6(6)***, 3642231896) Springer.

Web Intelligence & Intelligent Agent Technology, Proceedings. 2008. 538p. pap. 256.00 *(978-0-7695-3028-4(1))* IEEE Computer Society Pr.

Weber, Rosina O. & Richter, Michael M. Case-Based Reasoning Research & Development: 7th International Conference on Case-Based Reasoning, ICCBR 2007 Belfast, Northern Ireland, UK, August 13-16, 2007 Proceedings. 2007. (Lecture Notes in Artificial Intelligence Ser.). (Illus.). 534p. per. 99.00 *(978-3-540-74138-1(0))* Springer.

Weichselberger, K. & Pohlmann, S. A Methodology for Uncertainty in Knowledge-Based Systems. 2007. (Lecture Notes in Computer Science Ser.). 320p. per. 29.95 *(978-3-540-52336-9(7))* Springer.

Weinshall, Daphna, et al, eds. Detection & Identification of Rare Audio-visual Cues. 2011. (Studies in Computational Intelligence Ser.). (ENG., Illus.). viii, 192p. 129.00 ***(978-3-642-24033-1(X)***, 364224033X) Springer.

Wellman, Michael. Trading Agents. 2011. (Synthesis Lectures on Artificial Intelligence & Machine Learning Ser.). 107p. pap. 40.00 *(978-1-59829-605-1(1))* Morgan & Claypool Pubs.

Wen, Peng, et al. Rough Sets & Knowledge Technology: 4th International Conference, RSKT 2009, Gold Coast, Australia, July 14-16, 2009, Proceedings. 2009. (Lecture Notes in Computer Science / Lecture Notes in Artificial Intelligence Ser.). xviii, 709p. pap. 129.00 *(978-3-642-02961-5(2)*, 3642029612) Springer.

Weyns, Danny & Uhrmacher, Adelinde. Multi-Agent Systems: Simulation & Applications. Uhrmacher, Adelinde M. & Weyns, Danny, eds. 2009. (Computational Analysis, Synthesis, & Design of Dynamic Systems Ser.). (ENG., Illus.). 566p. 144.95 *(978-1-4200-7023-1(1)*, CRC Press) Taylor & Francis Group GBR. Dist: Taylor & Francis Group.

Whitby, Blay. Artificial Intelligence. 2009. lib. bdg. 33.25 *(978-1-4358-5165-8(X))* Rosen Publishing Group, Inc., The.

—Artificial Intelligence: A Beginner's Guide. 2008. (Beginners Guide (Oneworld) Ser.). (ENG.). 160p. pap. 14.95 *(978-1-85168-607-0(X))* Oneworld Pubns. GBR. Dist: National Bk. Network.

Wide, Peter. Artificial Human Sensors. 2012. (ENG., Illus.). 220p. 149.95 *(978-981-4241-58-8(X))* Pan Stanford Publishing SGP. Dist: Taylor & Francis Group.

Wilks, Yorick. Close Engagements with Artificial Companions: Key Social, Psychological, Ethical & Design Issues. 2010. (Illus.). xxii, 315p. *(978-90-272-4994-4(6))* Benjamins, John Publishing Co.

Wilson, David C. & Sutcliffe, Geoffrey C. J., eds. Proceedings of the Twentieth International Florida Artificial Intelligence Research Society Conference (FLAIRS-07) 2007. (Illus.). 706p. per. 125.00 *(978-1-57735-319-5(6))* AAAI Pr.

Wilson, Elizabeth A. Affect & Artificial Intelligence. 2010. (In Vivo Ser.). (ENG., Illus.). 200p. (C). 60.00 *(978-0-295-99051-4(1))*; pap. 25.00 *(978-0-295-99047-7(3))* Univ. of Washington Pr.

Witbrock/Lefkowitz/Goolsbey. Researchcyc. 2007. (Synthesis Lectures on Artificial Intelligence & Machine Learning Ser.). 40.00 *(978-1-59829-200-8(5))* Morgan & Claypool Pubs.

Wolff, Karl Erich, et al, eds. Knowledge Processing & Data Analysis: First International Conference, KONT 2007, Novosibirsk, Russia, September 14-16, 2007,and First International Conference, KPP 2007, Darmstadt, Germany, September 28-30, 2007. Revised Selected Papers. 2011. (Lecture Notes in Computer Science / Lecture Notes in Artificial Intelligence Ser.). (ENG., Illus.). xiv, 321p. pap. 83.00 ***(978-3-642-22139-2(4)***, 3642221394) Springer.

Wrobel, Stefan. Concept Formation & Knowledge Revision. 2010. (ENG.). 256p. pap. 199.00 *(978-1-4419-5146-5(6)*, 1441951466) Springer.

Wu, Qingxiang. Computing Network Model for Intelligent Systems. 2010. 292p. pap. *(978-3-639-22560-0(0))* VDM Verlag Dr. Mueller e.K.

Wu, Yanwen, ed. Computing & Intelligent Systems: International Conference, ICCIC 2011, held in Wuhan, China, September 17-18, 2011. Proceedings, Part III. 2011. (Communications in Computer & Information Science Ser.). (ENG.). xii, 537p. pap. 119.00 ***(978-3-642-24009-6(7)***, 3642240097) Springer.

—Computing & Intelligent Systems: International Conference, ICCIC 2011, held in Wuhan, China, September 17-18, 2011. Proceedings, Part IV. 2011. (Communications in Computer & Information Science Ser.). (ENG.). xii, 537p. pap. 119.00 ***(978-3-642-24090-4(9)***, 3642240909) Springer.

Wu, Yanwen, ed. Software Engineering & Knowledge Engineering: Theory & Practice: Proceedings of 2009 International Conference on Knowledge Engineering & Software Engineering (KESE 2009) 2010. (Advances in Intelligent & Soft Computing Ser.). 800p. pap. 399.00 *(978-3-642-03717-7(8)*, 3642037178) Springer.

Wulfinghoff, M., ed. On Modeling the Spatiotemporal Processing Characteristics of the Retina: What is the Retina For? (Dissertations in Artificial Intelligence Ser.: Vol. 254). 352p. pap. 43.00 *(978-1-58603-241-8(0))* IOS Pr., Inc.

Xhafa, Fatos, et al, eds. Complex Intelligent Systems & Their Applications. 2010. (Springer Optimization & Its Applications Ser.). (ENG., Illus.). xiii, 271p. 149.00 *(978-1-4419-1635-8(0)*, 1441916350) Springer.

Xie, Ming, et al. Intelligent Robotics & Applications: Second International Conference, ICIRA 2009, Singapore, December 16-18, 2009, Proceedings. 2009. (Lecture Notes in Computer Science / Lecture Notes in Artificial

Intelligence Ser.). xxi, 1296p. pap. 219.00 *(978-3-642-10816-7(4),* 3642108164) Springer.

Xu, Weiliang & Bronlund, John E. Mastication Robots: Biological Inspiration to Implementation. 2010. (Studies in Computational Intelligence Ser.). 400p. 159.00 *(978-3-540-93902-3(4),* 3540939024) Springer.

Yang, Jianhua, et al. Information Systems: Modeling, Development, & Integration: Third International United Information Systems Conference, UNISCON 2009, Sydney, Australia, April 21-24, 2009, Proceedings. 2009. (Lecture Notes in Business Information Processing Ser.). (ENG., Illus.). xv, 564p. pap. 109.00 *(978-3-642-01111-5(X))* Springer.

Yang, Quiang & Webb, Geoff, eds. PRICAI 2006: Trends in Artificial Intelligence: 9th Pacific Rim International Conference on Artifical Intelligence Guilin, China, August 7-11, 2006Proceedings. 2006. (Lecture Notes in Computer Science Ser.) (Illus.). XXVIII, 1263p. pap. 179.00 *(978-3-540-36667-6(9),* 3540366679) Springer.

Yanushkevich, Svetlana N., ed. Artificial Intelligence in Logic Design. 2010. (Springer International Series in Engineering & Computer Science Ser.). (Illus.). xvii, 308p. pap. 229.00 *(978-90-481-6583-4(0),* 9048165830) Springer.

Yao, JingTao, et al., eds. Rough Set & Knowledge Technology: 6th International Conference, RSKT 2011, Banff, Canada, October 9-12, 2011, Proceedings. 2011. (Lecture Notes in Computer Science / Lecture Notes in Artificial Intelligence Ser.). (ENG., Illus.). xviii, 771p. pap. 131.00 ***(978-3-642-24424-7(6),*** 3642244246) Springer.

Yoe, Ricardo Zavela. Modelling & Control of Dynamical Systems: Numerical Implementation in a Behavioral Framework: Numerical Implementation in a Behavioral Framework. 2010. (Studies in Computational Intelligence Ser.). (Illus.). xiv, 154p. pap. 179.00 *(978-3-642-09752-2(9),* 3642097529) Springer.

Yoshida, Hiroyuki, et al, eds. Advanced Computational Intelligence Paradigms in Healthcare - 1. 2010. (Studies in Computational Intelligence Ser.). (Illus.). xxi, 290p. pap. 239.00 *(978-3-642-08001-2(4),* 3642080014) Springer.

Young, Tsau. Web Intelligence; Proceedings: IEEE/WIC/ACM Int'l Conference on Web Intelligence (2007: Silicon,Valley) 2007. 841p. pap. 288.00 *(978-0-7695-3026-0(5))* IEEE Computer Society Pr.

Yu, Jian, et al, eds. Rough Set & Knowledge Technology: 5th International Conference, RSKT 2010, Beijing, China, October 15-17, 2010, Proceedings. 2010. (Lecture Notes in Computer Science / Lecture Notes in Artificial Intelligence Ser.). (Illus.). xvii, 781p. pap. 131.00 *(978-3-642-16247-3(9),* 3642162479) Springer.

Yu, Shi, et al. Kernel-based Data Fusion for Machine Learning: Methods & Applications in Bioinformatics & Text Mining. 2011. (Studies in Computational Intelligence Ser.). (Illus.). xiv, 214p. 129.00 *(978-3-642-19405-4(2),* 3642194052) Springer.

Yu, Tina, et al, eds. Evolutionary Computation in Practice. 2010. (Studies in Computational Intelligence Ser.). (Illus.). xvi, 322p. pap. 199.00 *(978-3-642-09492-7(9),* 3642094929) Springer.

Yuan, Jun, et al. Constraint-Based Verification. 2010. (ENG., Illus.). xii, 253p. pap. 159.00 *(978-1-4419-3852-7(4),* 1441938524) Springer.

Zadeh, Lotfi A. & Kacprzyk, Janusz, eds. Computing with Words in Information/Intelligent Systems 2: Applications. 2010. (Studies in Fuzziness & Soft Computing Ser.). (ENG., Illus.). x, 609p. pap. 259.00 *(978-3-7908-2461-2(5),* 3790824615) Physica-Verlag DEU. Dist: Springer.

Zafar, Zain, et al. Autopilot System for an Unmanned Aerial Vehicle. 2011. 208p. pap. ***(978-3-8443-1560-8(8))*** Lambert Academic Publishing.

Zambak, Aziz Fevzi. Wittgenstein in the Chinese Room. 2010. 92p. pap. *(978-3-639-24582-0(2))* VDM Verlag Dr. Mueller e.K.

Zengin, Salih. Systemc Implementation of a Risc-Based Processor Architecture. 2009. 200p. pap. *(978-3-639-13035-5(9))* VDM Verlag Dr. Mueller e.K.

Zha, Xuan F. Artificial Intelligence & Integrated Intelligent Information Systems: Emerging Technologies & Applications. 2006. (Illus.). (C). 454p. 94.95 *(978-1-59904-249-7(5));* xxi, 454p. pap. 94.95 *(978-1-59904-250-3(9))* IGI Global.

Zhang, Byoung-Tak & Orgun, Mehmet A., eds. PRICAI 2010: Trends in Artificial Intelligence: 11th Pacific Rim International Conference on Artificial Intelligence, Daegu, Korea, August 30-September 2, 2010. Proceedings. 2010. (Lecture Notes in Computer Science / Lecture Notes in Artificial Intelligence Ser.). (Illus.). xviii, 715p. pap. 131.00 *(978-3-642-15245-0(7),* 3642152457) Springer.

Zhang, Du, et al. 2007 6th IEEE International Conference on Cognitive Informatics. 2007. pap. 224.00 *(978-1-4244-1327-0(3),* EX1833) IEEE.

Zhang, Jingqiao & Sanderson, Arthur C. Adaptive Differential Evolution: A Robust Approach to Multimodal Problem Optimization. 2009. (Evolutionary Learning & Optimization Ser.). (ENG., Illus.). xiv, 166p. 179.00 *(978-3-642-01526-7(3),* 3642015263) Springer.

Zhang, Wohua & Cai, Yuanqiang. Continuum Damage Mechanics & Numerical Applications. 2009. (Advanced Topics in Science & Technology in China Ser.). (Illus.). 1000p. 339.00 *(978-3-642-04707-7(6),* 3642047076) Springer.

Zhang Yan Staff. Cognitive Radio Networks: Architectures Protocols & Standards. Chen, Hsiao-Hwa, ed. 2010. (Wireless Networks & Mobile Communications Ser.). (ENG., Illus.). 484p. 99.95 *(978-1-4200-7775-9(9),* CRC Press) Taylor & Francis Group GBR. Dist: Taylor & Francis Group.

Zharkova, Valentina & Jain, L. C. Artificial Intelligence in Recognition & Classification of Astrophysical & Medical Images. 2007. (Studies in Computational Intelligence: Vol. 46). (Illus.). xvi, 374p. 219.00 *(978-3-540-47511-8(7))* Springer.

Zharkova, Valentina & Jain, Lakhmi C., eds. Artificial Intelligence in Recognition & Classification of Astrophysical & Medical Images. 2010. (Studies in Computational Intelligence Ser.). (Illus.). xvi, 374p. pap. 219.00 *(978-3-642-08000-5(6),* 3642080006) Springer.

Zhong, N. & Liu, J., eds. Advances in Intelligent IT: Handbook of Intelligent IT. (Frontiers in Artificial Intelligence & Applications Ser.: Vol. 90). 400p. 84.00 *(978-1-58603-300-2(X))* IOS Pr., Inc.

Zhong, Ning, et al, eds. Web Intelligence. 2010. (ENG., Illus.). xxiv, 440p. pap. 129.00 *(978-3-642-07936-8(9),* 3642079369) Springer.

Zhou, Changle. Zhong Yi Bian Zheng de Ji Qi Tui Yan. 2009. (CHI., Illus.). vii, 229p. pap. *(978-7-03-023321-9(2))* Science Pr.

Zhou, Shang-Ming & Wang, Wenwu, eds. WRI Global Congress on Intelligent Systems Proceedings. 2009. 2397p. pap. 460.00 *(978-0-7695-3571-5(2))* IEEE Computer Society Pr.

Zhou, Zude, et al. Digital Manufacturing Science. 2011. (Springer Series in Advanced Manufacturing Ser.). (ENG & DUT., Illus.). xiii, 366p. 179.00 *(978-0-85729-563-7(2),* 0857295632) Springer.

Zhuge. Knowledge Grid. 2nd ed. 2011. 96.00 *(978-981-4291-77-4(3))* World Scientific Publishing Co., Inc.

Zielesny, Achim. From Curve Fitting to Machine Learning: An Illustrative Guide to Scientific Data Analysis & Computational Intelligence. 2011. (Intelligent Systems Reference Library). (ENG., Illus.). xvi, 468p. 179.00 *(978-3-642-21279-6(4),* 3642212794) Springer.

Zomaya, Albert Y., ed. Handbook of Nature-Inspired & Innovative Computing: Integrating Classical Models with Emerging Technologies. 2010. (ENG., Illus.). xvi, 736p. pap. 159.00 *(978-1-4419-4268-5(8),* 1441942688) Springer.

14th International Symposium on Temporal Representation & Reasoning (TIME 2007) Alicante, Spain - 28-30 June 2007. 2007. pap. 193.00 *(978-0-7695-2836-6(5))* IEEE Computer Society Pr.

20th IEEE International Symposium on Computer-Based Medical Systems (CBMS 2007) Maribor, Slovenia 20-22 June 2007. 2007. pap. 280.00 *(978-0-7695-2905-9(4))* IEEE Computer Society Pr.

2007 IEEE 6th International Conference on Development & Learning. 2007. pap. 206.00 *(978-1-4244-1115-3(7),* 07EX1740) IEEE.

2007 IEEE Congress on Evolutionary Computation. 2007. pap. 784.00 *(978-1-4244-1339-3(7),* 07TH8963) IEEE.

2007 IEEE International Conference on Emerging Technologies & Factory Automation. 2007. pap. 430.00 *(978-1-4244-0825-2(3),* 07TH8932) IEEE.

2007 IEEE International Conference on Networking, Sensing & Control. 2007. pap. 340.00 *(978-1-4244-1075-0(4),* 07EX1723) IEEE.

2007 IEEE/RSJ International Conference on Intelligent Robots & Systems. 2007. pap. 1024.00 *(978-1-4244-0911-2(X),* 07CH37863) IEEE.

2007 International Conference on Intelligent & Advanced Systems. 2007. pap. 430.00 *(978-1-4244-1355-3(9),* 07EX1852) IEEE.

2007 International Conference on Intelligent Engineering Systems. 2007. pap. 224.00 *(978-1-4244-1147-4(5),* 07EX1751) IEEE.

ARTIFICIAL ISLANDS

see Offshore Structures

ARTIFICIAL KIDNEY

Cram101 Textbook Reviews & Cram101 Textbook Reviews. Outlines & Highlights for Review of Hemodialysis for Nurses & Dialysis Personnel by Judith Z Kallenbach, Isbn: 9780323028714. 2011. 100p. pap. 27.95 ***(978-1-61461-374-9(5))*** Cram101 Inc.

Kallenbach, Judith Z. Review of Hemodialysis for Nurses & Dialysis Personnel. 8th ed. 2011. (ENG., Illus.). 432p. pap. 59.95 *(978-0-323-07702-6(1),* Mosby) Elsevier - Health Sciences Div.

ARTIFICIAL LAKES

see Reservoirs

ARTIFICIAL LIGHT GARDENING

Kovach, Chris. The Hydroponic Bible. 2008. 348p. pap. 17.55 *(978-1-4357-3667-2(2))* Lulu Enterprises Inc.

ARTIFICIAL LIMBS

Hasegawa, Guy R. Mending Broken Soldiers: The Union & Confederate Programs to Supply Artificial Limbs. 2012. E-Book ***(978-0-8093-3131-4(4));*** (Illus.). 160p. 24.95 ***(978-0-8093-3130-7(6))*** Southern Illinois Univ. Pr.

ARTIFICIAL MODIFICATION OF CLOUDS

see Rain-Making

ARTIFICIAL NEURAL NETWORKS

see Neural Networks (Computer Science)

ARTIFICIAL ORGANS

see also Artificial Kidney; Heart, Artificial; Prosthesis

Dössel, Olaf & Becks, Thomas, eds. World Congress on Medical Physics & Biomedical Engineering, September 7-12, 2009 Munich, Germany: Biomaterials, Cellular & Tussue Engineering, Artificial Organs, Vol. 25/X 2009. (IFMBE Proceedings Ser.). (Illus.). xiv, 314p. pap. 299.00 *(978-3-642-03899-0(9),* 3642038999) Springer.

Hakim, Nadey S. Artificial Organs. Hakim, Nadey S., ed. 2009. (New Techniques in Surgery Ser.). (Illus.). x, 190p. 279.00 *(978-1-84882-281-8(2))* Springer.

Lysaght, Michael J. & Webster, Thomas. Biomaterials for Artificial Organs. 2011. (Woodhead Publishing Series in Biomaterials Ser.). (ENG., Illus.). 328p. 230.00 *(978-1-84569-653-5(0))* Woodhead Publishing Ltd. GBR. Dist: Ingram Pub. Services.

McMinn, Derek J. W., ed. Hip Resurfacing. 2008. (Illus.). 450p. 209.00 *(978-1-84800-087-2(1),* 1848000871) Springer.

Miller, Gerald E. Artifical Organs. 2006. (Synthesis Lectures on Biomedical Engineering Ser.). (Illus.). 72p. per. 35.00 *(978-1-59829-048-6(7))* Morgan & Claypool Pubs.

The Potential of an Artificial Pancreas: Improving Care for People with Diabetes: Hearing Before the Committee on Homeland Security & Governmental Affairs, United States Senate, One Hundred Ninth Congress, Second Session, September 27, 2006. 2007. (Illus.). iii, 61p. *(978-0-16-079414-8(5),* 552-070-36410-2) United States Government Printing Office.

Sharma, C. P., ed. Biointegration of Medical Implant Materials. 2010. (ENG., Illus.). 384p. 229.95 *(978-1-4398-3064-2(9),* CRC Press) Taylor & Francis Group GBR. Dist: Taylor & Francis Group.

—Biointegration of Medical Implant Materials: Science & Design. 2010. (Illus.). 424p. 245.00 *(978-1-84569-509-5(7))* Woodhead Publishing Ltd. GBR. Dist: Taylor & Francis Group.

Sharma, Kal. Transport Phenomena in Biomedical Engineering: Artifical organ Design & Development, & Tissue Engineering. 2010. (ENG., Illus.). 512p. 150.00 *(978-0-07-166397-7(5),* 0071663975) McGraw-Hill Professional Publishing.

ARTIFICIAL PACEMAKER (HEART)

see Pacemaker, Artificial (Heart)

ARTIFICIAL PERSONS

see Juristic Persons

ARTIFICIAL RESINS

see Gums and Resins, Synthetic

ARTIFICIAL RESPIRATION

see also Asphyxia; Respirators

American Academy of Orthopaedic Surgeons (AAOS) & Margolis, Gregg. Paramedic: Airway Management. 2011. 332p. pap. 79.95 ***(978-1-4496-4259-4(4))*** Jones & Bartlett Learning, LLC.

Branson, Richard D., et al. Mechanical Ventilation. 2nd ed. 2008. (ENG., Illus.). 528p. (C). per. 84.95 *(978-1-4160-3141-3(3),* Saunders) Elsevier - Health Sciences Div.

Brown, Melissa K., et al. Rapid Interpretation of Ventilator Waveforms. 2nd rev. ed. 2006. (ENG., Illus.). 160p. (C). per. 51.00 *(978-0-13-174922-1(6),* Prentice Hall) Prentice Hall PTR.

Cairo, J. M. Pilbeam's Mechanical Ventilation: Physiological & Clinical Applications. 5th ed. 2011. (ENG., Illus.). 608p. (C). pap. 83.95 ***(978-0-323-07207-6(0),*** Mosby) Elsevier - Health Sciences Div.

Esquinas, Antonio Matias, ed. Humidification in the Intensive Care Unit: The Essentials. 2012. (ENG., Illus.). x, 288p. 139.00 *(978-3-642-02973-6(6),* 3642029736) Springer.

Esquinas, Antonio Matias, ed. Noninvasive Mechanical Ventilation: Theory, Equipment, & Clinical Applications. 2010. (ENG., Illus.). xiv, 402p. 179.00 *(978-3-642-11364-2(8),* 3642113648) Springer.

Goldsmith, Jay P. & Karotkin, Edward. Assisted Ventilation of the Neonate. 5th ed. 2010. (ENG., Illus.). 656p. 99.95 *(978-1-4160-5624-9(6),* Saunders) Elsevier - Health Sciences Div.

Goldstein, Roger S. & Ambrosino, Nicoline, eds. Ventilatory Support for Chronic Respiratory Failure. 2008. (Lung Biology in Health & Disease Ser.: Vol. 225). (Illus.). 595p. 250.00 *(978-0-8493-8498-1(2),* Informa Healthcare) Taylor & Francis Group GBR. Dist: Taylor & Francis Group.

Hasan, Ashfaq. Understanding Mechanical Ventilation: A Practical Handbook. 2nd ed. 2010. (ENG., Illus.). xxi, 543p. pap. 69.95 *(978-1-84882-868-1(3),* 1848828683) Springer.

Kamat, Shaila. Practical Applications of Mechanical Ventilation. 2010. (ENG.). 592p. pap. 88.00 *(978-0-07-171810-3(9),* 0071718109) McGraw-Hill Professional Publishing.

Kinnear, William. Non-Invasive Ventilation Made Simple. 2008. (ENG., Illus.). 128p. pap. 60.00 *(978-1-904761-41-9(0))* Nottingham Univ. Pr. GBR. Dist: Independent Pubs. Group.

Klaas, Michael, et al, eds. Fundamental Medical & Engineering Investigations on Protective Artificial Respiration: A Collection of Papers from the DFG funded Research Program PAR. 2011. (Notes on Numerical Fluid Mechanics & Multidisciplinary Design Ser.). (Illus.). x, 186p. 219.00 *(978-3-642-20325-1(6),* 3642203256) Springer.

Mackenzie, Iain, ed. Core Topics in Mechanical Ventilation. 2008. (ENG., Illus.). 440p. 97.00 *(978-0-521-86781-8(9))* Cambridge Univ. Pr.

Orebaugh, Steven L. & Bigeleisen, Paul E. Atlas of Airway Management: Techniques & Tools. 2nd rev. ed. 2011. (ENG., Illus.). 432p. 124.95 *(978-1-4511-0339-7(5))* Lippincott Williams & Wilkins.

Papadakos, Peter J. & Lachmann, Burkhard. Mechanical Ventilation: Clinical Applications & Pathophysiology. 2007. (ENG., Illus.). 688p. 177.00 *(978-0-7216-0186-1(3),* Saunders) Elsevier - Health Sciences Div.

Pierce, Lynelle N. B. Management of the Mechanically Ventilated Patient. 2nd rev. ed. 2006. (ENG., Illus.). 544p. per. 60.95 *(978-0-7216-0397-1(1),* Saunders) Elsevier - Health Sciences Div.

Pilbeam, et al. Workbook for Pilbeam's Mechanical Ventilation: Physiological & Clinical Applications. 5th ed. 2012. (ENG., Illus.). 240p. (C). pap. 32.95 ***(978-0-323-07208-3(9),*** Mosby) Elsevier - Health Sciences Div.

Rello, Jordi, ed. Nosocomial Pneumonia: Strategies for Management. 2008. (ENG., Illus.). 312p. 174.00 *(978-0-470-05955-5(9),* Wiley-Interscience) Wiley, John & Sons, Inc.

Rimensberger, Peter C., ed. Pediatric & Neonatal Mechanical Ventilation: From Basics to Clinical Practice. 2013. (ENG., Illus.). 1000p. 409.00 *(978-3-642-01218-1(3),* 3642012183) Springer.

Simonds, Anika K., ed. Non-Invasive Respiratory Support. 3rd rev. ed. 2007. (ENG., Illus.). 368p. pap., instr.'s hndbk. ed. 65.00 *(978-0-340-92560-7(4))* Hodder Arnold Pubs.

Truwit, J. D., et al, eds. A Practical Guide to Mechanical Ventilation. 2011. (ENG., Illus.). 366p. pap. 127.00 *(978-0-470-05807-7(2),* Wiley) Wiley, John & Sons, Inc.

ARTIFICIAL SAMPLING

see Monte Carlo Method

ARTIFICIAL SATELLITES

see also Astronautics in Meteorology; Direct Broadcast Satellite Television; Meteorological Satellites; Project Vanguard; Space Stations

American Institute of Aeronautics and Astronautics Staff, contrib. by. Standard Electrical Power Systems for Unmanned Spacecraft. 2006. *(978-1-56347-913-7(3))* American Institute of Aeronautics & Astronautics.

Angelo, Joseph A. & Angelo, Joseph A., Jr. Satellites. 2006. (Frontiers in Space Ser.). (Illus.). 336p. (C). (gr. 9). 45.00 *(978-0-8160-5772-6(9))* Facts On File, Inc.

Antunes, Sandy. DIY Satellite Platforms: Building a Space-Ready General Base Picosatellite for Any Mission. 2012. (ENG.). 86p. pap. 7.99 ***(978-1-4493-1060-8(5))*** O'Reilly Media, Inc.

Ardanuy, Philip E. & Puschell, Jeffery John. Remote Sensing System Engineering: 11-13 August 2008, San Diego, California, USA. 2008. (Proceedings of SPIE Ser.). (Illus.). 246p. pap. 70.00 *(978-0-8194-7307-3(3))* SPIE.

Azzam, May. The Development of Communication Satellites in the Arab World. 2010. 124p. pap. *(978-3-8383-6256-4(X))* Lambert Academic Publishing.

Brzezinski, Matthew. Red Moon Rising: Sputnik & the Hidden Rivalries That Ignited the Space Age. 2008. (ENG., Illus.). 336p. pap. 17.00 *(978-0-8050-8858-8(X),* Holt Paperback) Holt, Henry & Co.

—Red Moon Rising: Sputnik & the Hidden Rivalries That Ignited the Space Age. l.t. ed. 2007. (Thorndike Nonfiction Ser.). (Illus.). 629p. 29.95 *(978-1-4104-0279-0(7))* Thorndike Pr.

Butler, James, et al. Earth Observing Systems XVI. 2011. (Proceedings of SPIE Ser.). 685p. pap. 130.00 ***(978-0-8194-8763-6(5))*** SPIE.

Butler, James J. & Xiong, Jack. Earth Observing Systems XI: 14-16 August, 2006, San Diego, California USA. 2006. (Proceedings of SPIE Ser.). (Illus.). 506p. pap. 120.00 *(978-0-8194-6375-3(2))* SPIE.

Butler, James J., et al. Earth Observing Systems XIV: 3-5 August 2009, San Diego, California, United States. 2009. (Proceedings of SPIE Ser.). (Illus.). 380p. pap. 90.00 *(978-0-8194-7742-2(7))* SPIE.

Chirila, Abel. Military Satellites: Issues, Goals & Challenges. 2009. (Defense, Security & Strategy Ser.). (Illus.). 117p. 79.00 *(978-1-60741-238-0(1))* Nova Science Pubs., Inc.

Cliff, Roger, et al. Ready for Takeoff: China's Advancing Aerospace Industry, 1 vol. 2011. (ENG.). 162p. (C). pap. 24.00 *(978-0-8330-5180-6(6))* RAND Corp., The.

Committee on Archiving and Accessing & National Research Council. An Environmental Data Management at NOAA: Archiving, Stewardship, & Access. 2007. (ENG.). 130p. pap. 32.75 *(978-0-309-11209-3(5))* National Academies Pr.

Committee on Scientific Accomplishments of Earth Observations from Space & National Research Council. Earth Observations from Space: The First 50 Years of Scientific Achievements. 2007. (ENG.). 144p. pap. 34.75 *(978-0-309-11095-2(5))* National Academies Pr.

Continued Oversight of the National Oceanic & Atmospheric Administration's Geostationary Weather Satellite System: Hearing Before the Subcommittee on Energy & Environment, Committee on Science & Technology, House of Representatives, One Hundred Eleventh Congress, First Session, April 23, 2009. 2009. (Illus.). iv, 57p. *(978-0-16-084556-7(4),* 552-070-40078-8) United States Government Printing Office.

Cox, Joseph L. & Motaghedi, Pejmun. Sensors & Systems for Space Applications III: 14-15 April 2009, Orlando, Florida, United States. 2009. (Proceedings of SPIE Ser.). (Illus.). 278p. pap. 80.00 *(978-0-8194-7596-1(3))* SPIE.

Cranford, Bruce, Jr., compiled by. Spacecraft & Satellite Dictionary: Unadbridged. 2007. spiral bd. 39.95 *(978-0-9711657-2-4(6))* Cranford, Bruce.

Cranmer, Steven R., et al. SOHO-23: Understanding a Peculiar Solar Minimum: Proceedings of a Workshop Held at Asticou Inn, Northeast Harbor, Maine, USA, 21-25 September 2009. 2010. (Illus.). xviii, 336p. *(978-1-58381-737-7(9)); (978-1-58381-736-0(0))* Astronomical Society of the Pacific, The.

D'Antonio, Michael. A Ball, a Dog, & a Monkey: 1957 — the Space Race Begins. 2008. (ENG., Illus.). 320p. pap. 19.99 *(978-0-7432-9432-4(7))* Simon & Schuster.

Di, Liping & Ramapriyan, H. K. Standard-Based Data & Information Systems for Earth Observation. 2009. (Lecture Notes in Geoinformation & Cartography Ser.). (ENG., Illus.). 400p. 199.00 *(978-3-540-88263-3(4),* Springer.

Dickson, Paul. Sputnik: The Shock of the Century. 2011. (ENG., Illus.). 320p. pap. 16.00 *(978-0-8027-7951-9(4))* Walker & Co.

Export Controls on Satellite Technology: Hearing Before the Subcommittee on Terrorism, Nonproliferation, & Trade of the Committee on Foreign Affairs, House of Representatives, One Hundred Eleventh Congress, First Session, April 2, 2009. 2009. iii, 78p. *(978-0-16-083647-3(6),* 552-070-39358-7) United States Government Printing Office.

Flournoy, Don M. Solar Power Satellites. 2011. (SpringerBriefs in Space Development Ser.). (ENG., Illus.). xi, 107p. pap. 49.95 ***(978-1-4614-1999-0(9),*** 1461419999) Springer.

Gom, Michael. Super Structures in Space. 2008. (Illus.). 192p. 39.95 (978-1-85894-417-3(1)) Merrell Pubs. Ltd. GBR. Dist: Perseus Distribution.

Hagiwara, Y. Approaching Micro-Arcsecond Resolution with VSOP-2: Astrophysics & Technology: Proceedings of a Workshop Held at Institute of Space & Astronautical Science, Japan Aerospace Exploration Agency, Sagamihara, Kanagawa, Japan, 03-07 December 2007. 2009. (Illus.). xix, 495p. (978-1-58381-680-6(1)); (978-1-58381-679-0(8)) Astronomical Society of the Pacific, The.

Howard, Richard T. & Motaghedi, Pejmun. Sensors & Systems for Space Applications II: 17-18 April, 2008, Orlando, Florida, USA. 2008. (Proceedings of SPIE Ser.). (Illus.). 246p. pap. 80.00 (978-0-8194-7149-9(6)) SPIE.

Institute of Electrical and Electronics Engineers Staff, contrib. by. 2007 3rd International Conference on Recent Advances in Space Technologies. 2007. pap. 340.00 (978-1-4244-1056-9(8), 07EX1710) IEEE.

Jasani, Bhupendra. International Safeguards & Satellite Imagery: Key Features of the Nuclear Fuel Cycle & Computer-Based Analysis. 2009. (ENG.). viii, 176p. 159.00 (978-3-540-79131-7(0), 3540791310) Springer.

Kokhanovsky, Alexander A. Aerosol Optics: Light Absorption & Scattering by Particles in the Atmosphere. 2010. (Springer Praxis Books / Environmental Sciences Ser.). viii, 148p. pap. 179.00 (978-3-642-06268-1(7), 3642062687) Springer.

Levin, Eugene. Dynamic Analysis of Space Tether Missions. 2007. (Advances in the Astronautical Sciences Ser.: Vol. 126). 462p. pap. 110.00 (978-0-87703-538-1(5)) Univelt, Inc.

Maini, Mr, Anil Kumar & Agrawal, Varsha. Satellite Technology: Principles & Applications. 2nd ed. 2010. (ENG., Illus.). 694p. 135.00 (978-0-470-66024-9(4), Wiley) Wiley, John & Sons, Inc.

Manyangadze, Tawanda. Application of Geostationary Satellites in Forest Fire Detection. 2011. 100p. pap. (978-3-8454-0096-9(X)) Lambert Academic Publishing.

Maui Economic Development Board Staff, compiled by. Advanced Maui Optical & Space Surveillance Technologies Conference (AMOS 2005) 2007. 883p. pap. 118.00 (978-1-60423-995-9(6)) Curran Assocs., Inc.

—Advanced Maui Optical & Space Surveillance Technologies Conference (AMOS 2006) 2007. 1008p. pap. 118.00 (978-1-60423-996-6(4)) Curran Assocs., Inc.

Meynart, Roland, et al. Sensors, Systems, & Next-Generation Satellites X: 11-13 September, 2006, Stockholm, Sweden. 2006. (Proceedings of SPIE Ser.). (Illus.). 488p. pap. 120.00 (978-0-8194-6456-9(2)) SPIE.

—Sensors, Systems, & Next-Generation Satellites XIII: 31 August-3 September 2009, Berlin, Germany. 2009. (Proceedings of SPIE Ser.). (Illus.). 622p. pap. 130.00 (978-0-8194-7779-8(6)) SPIE.

Naslin, Mathieu. Design of an Attitude Determination Subsystem for Nanosatellites. 2010. 112p. pap. (978-3-8383-1312-2(7)) Lambert Academic Publishing.

Norris, Pat. Spies in the Sky: Surveillance Satellites in War & Peace. 2007. (Springer Praxis Books / Space Exploration Ser.). (Illus.). 220p. per. 34.95 (978-0-387-71672-5(6), 0387716726, Springer-Praxis) Springer.

—Watching Earth from Space: How Surveillance Helps & Harms Us. 2010. (Springer Praxis Books / Space Exploration Ser.). (Illus.). xx, 284p. pap. 39.95 (978-1-4419-6937-8(3), 1441969373, Springer-Praxis) Springer.

P Thakker and W Shiroma, et al. Emergence of Pico- & Nanosatellites for Atmospheric Research & Technology Testing. 2010. (Illus.). xvi, 391p. (978-1-60086-768-2(5)) American Institute of Aeronautics & Astronautics.

Panel on Options to Ensure the Climate Record from the NPOESS and GOES-R Spacecraft & National Research Council. Options to Ensure the Climate Record from the NPOESS & GOES-R Spacecraft: A Workshop Report. 2007. (ENG.). 84p. pap. 18.00 (978-0-309-11276-5(1)) National Academies Pr.

Perryman, Michael. The Making of History's Greatest Star Map. 2010. (Astronomers' Universe Ser.). (Illus.). x, 275p. 29.95 (978-3-642-11601-8(9), 3642116019) Springer.

Pham, Khanh, et al. Sensors & Systems for Space Applications IV. 2011. (Proceedings of SPIE Ser.). 302p. pap. 80.00 (978-0-8194-8618-9(3)) SPIE.

Pizarro-Chong, Ary Druva. Dynamics of Multi-Tethered Satellite Formations. 2008. 156p. pap. (978-3-639-02691-7(8)) VDM Verlag Dr. Mueller e.K.

Remote Sensing Data: Applications & Benefits: Hearing Before the Subcommittee on Space & Aeronautics, Committee on Science & Technology, House of Representatives, One Hundred Tenth Congress, Second Session, April 7, 2008. 2008. (Illus.). iv, 98p. (978-0-16-082513-2(X), 552-070-38548-1) United States Government Printing Office.

Rino, Charles. The Theory of Scintillation with Applications in Remote Sensing. 2011. (ENG., Illus.). 230p. 105.00 (978-0-470-64477-5(X), Wiley-IEEE Pr.) Wiley, John & Sons, Inc.

Sachdev, D. K. Success Stories in Satellite Systems. 2009. 69.95 (978-1-56347-966-3(4)) American Institute of Aeronautics & Astronautics.

Sandau, Rainer, et al, eds. Small Satellite Missions for Earth Observation: New Developments & Trends. 2010. (ENG., Illus.). xx, 455p. 249.00 (978-3-642-03500-5(0), 3642035000) Springer.

—Small Satellites for Earth Observation: Selected Contributions. 2010. (ENG., Illus.). xxi, 406p. pap. 229.00 (978-90-481-7772-1(3), 9048177723) Springer.

Sandau, Rainer, et al. Small Satellites for Earth Observation: Selected Contributions. 2008. (ENG., Illus.). xxi, 406p. 229.00 (978-1-4020-6942-0(1), 1402069421) Springer.

Shibata, K., et al. New Solar Physics with Solar-B Mission: Proceedings of the Sixth Solar-B Science Meeting Held at the Kyoto International Community House, Kyoto, Japan, 8-11 November 2005. 2007. (Astronomical Society of the Pacific Conference Ser.: Vol. 369). (Illus.). xxi, 596p. 77.00 (978-1-58381-237-2(7)) Astronomical Society of the Pacific, The.

Smaller Satellites Operations near Geostationary Orbit. 2009. pap. 79.00 (978-1-60741-181-9(4)) Nova Science Pubs., Inc.

Sobhani-Tehrani, Ehsan & Khorasani, K. Fault Diagnosis of Nonlinear Systems Using a Hybrid Approach. 2009. (Illus.). xix, 265p. (978-0-387-92907-1(X)) Springer.

Space Systems Acquisition & the Industrial Base: Hearing Before the Strategic Forces Subcommittee of the Committee on Armed Services, House of Representatives, One Hundred Eleventh Congress, First Session, Hearing Held, April 30, 2009. 2010. (Illus.). iii, 73p. (978-0-16-085924-3(7), 552-070-41120-8) United States Government Printing Office.

Sternfeld, Ari, et al. Soviet Writings on Earth Satellites & Space Travel. 2011. 252p. 46.95 (978-1-258-08615-2(8)) Literary Licensing, LLC.

Strojnik, Marija. Infrared Spaceborne Remote Sensing XIV: 15-17 August, 2006, San Diego, California, USA. 2006. (Proceedings of SPIE Ser.). (Illus.). 356p. pap. 80.00 (978-0-8194-6376-0(0)) SPIE.

Strojnik, Marija & Paez, Gonzalo. Infrared Remote Sensing & Instrumentation XIX. 2011. (Proceedings of SPIE Ser.). 382p. pap. 90.00 (978-0-8194-8764-3(3)) SPIE.

Strojnik-Scholl, Marija. Infrared Spaceborne Remote Sensing & Instrumentation XV. 2007. (Proceedings of SPIE Ser.). 490p. pap. 120.00 (978-0-8194-6826-0(6)) SPIE.

Tappero, Fabrizio. Remote Synchronization Method for the Quasi-Zenith Satellite System. 2009. 268p. pap. (978-3-639-16004-8(5)) VDM Verlag Dr. Mueller e.K.

Van Leeuwen, Floor. Hipparcos, the New Reduction of the Raw Data. 2007. (Astrophysics & Space Science Library). (Illus.). 449p. 209.00 (978-1-4020-6341-1(5)) Springer.

van Leeuwen, Floor. Hipparcos, the New Reduction of the Raw Data. 2010. (Astrophysics & Space Science Library). xxxii, 449p. pap. 209.00 (978-90-481-7612-0(3), 9048176123) Springer.

Van Pelt, Michel. Space Invaders: How Robotic Spacecraft Explore the Solar System. 2006. (Illus.). 312p. 27.50 (978-0-387-33232-1(4), 0387332324) Springer.

Violante-Carvalho, Nelson. The Use of Ers Sar for Measurement of the Directional Wave Spectrum. 2010. 144p. pap. (978-3-8383-3425-7(6)) Lambert Academic Publishing.

Walter, Todd & El-Arini, M. Bakry, eds. Selected Papers on Satellite Based Augmentation Systems (SBASs) Date not set. (Global Positioning System Ser.: Vol. 6). (Illus.). pap. 50.00 (978-0-936406-06-0(2)) Institute of Navigation, The.

Wang, Zuoyue. In Sputnik's Shadow: The President's Science Advisory Committee & Cold War America. 2008. pap. (978-0-8135-4332-1(0)) Rutgers Univ. Pr.

ARTIFICIAL SATELLITES—ATTITUDE CONTROL SYSTEMS

Hawes, Dena L. Why Art Matters. 2009. 100p. pap. (978-3-639-13909-9(7)) VDM Verlag Dr. Mueller e.K.

ARTIFICIAL SATELLITES—LAUNCHING ROCKETS (AERONAUTICS)

see also Launch Vehicles (Astronautics)

Kayser, V. Launching Space Objects: Issues of Liability & Future Prospects: Issues of Liability & Future Prospects. 2010. (Space Regulations Library). 390p. pap. 289.00 (978-90-481-5840-9(0), 9048158400) Springer.

ARTIFICIAL SATELLITES—LAW AND LEGISLATION

see Space Law

ARTIFICIAL SATELLITES—MOON

see also Project Apollo (U.S.)

Byrne, Charles J. The Far Side of the Moon: A Photographic Guide. 2007. (Illus.). 215p. 39.95 incl. cd-rom (978-0-387-73205-3(5)) Springer.

Vondrak, R. R., et al, eds. Lunar Reconnaissance Orbiter Mission. 2010. (ENG.). iv, 304p. 169.00 (978-1-4419-6390-1(1), 1441963901) Springer.

ARTIFICIAL SATELLITES—ORBITS

Doornbos, Eelco. Thermospheric Density & Wind Determination from Satellite Dynamics. 2012. (Springer Theses Ser.). (ENG., Illus.). xv, 182p. 129.00 (978-3-642-25128-3(5), 3642251285) Springer.

Milani, Andrea & Gronchi, Giovanni. Theory of Orbit Determination. 2009. (ENG., Illus.). 392p. 75.00 (978-0-521-87389-5(4)) Cambridge Univ. Pr.

Simpson, John A., ed. Preservation of near-Earth Space for Future Generations. 2007. (ENG., Illus.). 264p. pap. 56.00 (978-0-521-03675-7(5)) Cambridge Univ. Pr.

Soop, E. M. Handbook of Geostationary Orbits. 2010. (Space Technology Library). 316p. pap. 319.00 (978-90-481-4453-2(1), 9048144531) Springer.

Vondrak, R. R., et al, eds. Lunar Reconnaissance Orbiter Mission. 2010. (ENG.). iv, 304p. 169.00 (978-1-4419-6390-1(1), 1441963901) Springer.

Zhang, Yuxiang. Ren Zao Wei Xing Ce Gui Fang Fa: Satellite Orbit Determination. 2007. (CHI., Illus.). xiii, 329p. (978-7-118-04934-3(4)) National Defence Industry Pr.

ARTIFICIAL SATELLITES—SCIENTIFIC APPLICATIONS

see Scientific Satellites

ARTIFICIAL SATELLITES—TRACKING

Carpenter, Leah. Tracking the Land. 2011. 380p. pap. (978-3-8443-1044-3(4)) Lambert Academic Publishing.

Forzati, Marco. A Genetic Algorithm for Satellite Antennas. 2008. 120p. pap. (978-3-639-08424-5(1)) VDM Verlag Dr. Mueller e.K.

Mallick, Mahendra, et al. Integrated Tracking, Classification, & Sensor Management: Theory & Applications. 2012. (ENG., Illus.). 768p. 145.00 (978-0-470-63905-4(9), Wiley-IEEE Pr.) Wiley, John & Sons, Inc.

Mansoor, Umair B. Quasi-Newton Least Mean Fourth Adaptive Algorithm. 2010. 104p. pap. (978-3-639-26296-4(4)) VDM Verlag Dr. Mueller e.K.

Meixner, Gerrit & Dörfler, Richard. Usability Analysis for a Satellite PerformanceMonitoring System: User-Centered Interface Development according to DIN EN ISO 13407 & DIN EN ISO 9241-110. 2008. 428p. pap. (978-3-639-02901-7(1)) VDM Verlag Dr. Mueller e.K.

Ng Heng San, Alvin. Unmanned Surveillance Ground Vehicle. 2010. 128p. pap. (978-3-8383-8460-3(1)) Lambert Academic Publishing.

ARTIFICIAL SATELLITES IN NAVIGATION

see also Global Positioning System

Bhatta, M. Global Navigation Satellite Systems: Insights into GPS, GLONASS, Galileo, Compas & Others. 2011. (ENG.). 438p. 139.95 (978-0-415-66560-5(4), CRC Press) Taylor & Francis Group GBR. Dist: Taylor & Francis Group.

Brown, Blaine, ed. Navstar Gps System Surveying for Civil Engineering, Topography & Construction. 2007. 344p. pap. 64.95 (978-1-934939-17-8(X)) Wexford College Pr.

Dragos, Zaharia. Galileo: The European Global Navigation Satellite System. 2012. (Iste Ser.: 366). (ENG.). 320p. 125.00 (978-1-84821-086-8(8), Wiley-ISTE) Wiley, John & Sons, Inc.

Ene, Alexandru. Utilization of Modernized Gnss for Aircraft-Based Navigation Integrity. 2009. 254p. pap. (978-3-639-18247-7(2)) VDM Verlag Dr. Mueller e.K.

Farrell, James L. GNSS Aided Navigation & Tracking. 2007. 288p. per. 26.95 (978-1-56167-979-9(8)) American Literary Pr.

Gebre-Egiabher, Demoz. Gnss Applications & Methods. Gleason, Scott, ed. 2009. (Illus.). 532p. 149.00 (978-1-59693-329-3(1)) Artech Hse., Inc.

GPS: Can We Avoid a Gap in Service?: Hearing Before the Subcommittee on National Security & Foreign Affairs of the Committee on Oversight & Government Reform, House of Representatives, One Hundred Eleventh Congress, First Session, May 7, 2009. 2010. (Illus.). iii, 128p. (978-0-16-086249-6(3), 552-070-41340-5) United States Government Printing Office.

Groves, Paul D. Principles of GNSS, Inertial, & Multisensor Integrated Navigation Systems. 2008. (GNSS Technology & Applications Ser.). (Illus.). 518p. 129.00 (978-1-58053-255-6(1)) Artech Hse., Inc.

Hofmann-Wellenhof, Bernhard, et al. GNSS: Global Navigation Satellite Systems: GPS, GLONASS, Galileo, & More. 2008. (Illus.). 516p. pap. 99.00 (978-3-211-73012-6(5)) Springer.

Holmes, Jack Kenneth. Spread Spectrum Systems for GNSS & Wireless Communications. 2007. (GNSS Technology & Applications Ser.). (Illus.). 855p. 169.00 (978-1-59693-083-4(7)) Artech Hse., Inc.

Howard, Richard T. & Richards, Robert D. Sensors & Systems for Space Applications: 9-11 April, 2007, Orlando, Florida, USA. 2007. (Proceedings of SPIE Ser.). (Illus.). 388p. pap. 105.00 (978-0-8194-6677-8(8)) SPIE.

Institute of Navigation Staff, compiled by. 19th International Technical Meeting of the Satellite Division of the Institute of Navigation (ION GNSS 2006) 2007. 3162p. pap. 325.00 (978-1-60423-503-6(9)) Curran Assocs., Inc.

Jacobson, Len. GNSS Markets & Applications. 2007. (GNSS Technology & Applications Ser.). (Illus.). 216p. 85.00 (978-1-59693-042-1(X)) Artech Hse., Inc.

Lees, Graham & Williamson, William. Handbook for Marine Radio Communication. 5th rev. ed. 2009. 344p. pap. 252.00 (978-1-84311-797-1(5)) Informa Professional GBR. Dist: International Specialized Bk. Services.

Li, Deren & Xia, Linyuan. Geoinformatics 2006: 28-29 October, 2006, Wuhan, China. 2006. (Proceedings of SPIE Ser.). (Illus.). 584p. pap. 105.00 (978-0-8194-6527-6(5)) SPIE.

Lighthouse Press, prod. Global Maritime Distress & Safety System (96 Days) 2007. pap. 14.95 (978-1-57785-643-6(0)) ProStar Pubns., Inc.

Logsdon, Tom. Understanding the Navstar: Gps, gis, Ivhs. 2nd ed. 2010. (ENG.). 350p. pap. 129.00 (978-1-4419-4741-3(8), 1441947418) Springer.

Nurmi, Jari, et al, eds. GALILEO Positioning Technology. 2012. (Signals & Communication Technology Ser.). (ENG.). 300p. 139.00 (978-94-007-1829-6(2), 9400718292) Springer.

Pany, Thomas. Navigation Signal Processing for GNSS Software Receivers. 2010. (Illus.). 330p. 149.00 (978-1-60807-027-5(1)) Artech Hse., Inc.

Re, Enrico & Ruggieri, Marina, eds. Satellite Communications & Navigation Systems. 2010. (Signals & Communication Technology Ser.). xvi, 768p. pap. 149.00 (978-1-4419-4292-0(0), 1441942920) Springer.

Sollbö, et al. Navigation related Communication with Galileo: Communction of Navigation Related Data. 2008. 132p. pap. (978-3-639-10530-8(3)) VDM Verlag Dr. Mueller e.K.

ARTIFICIAL SATELLITES IN TELECOMMUNICATION

see also Direct Broadcast Satellite Television; Radiotelephone; Television

American Institute of Aeronautics and Astronautics Staff, contrib. by. Adaptations & Conversions of CCSDS Space Link Extension Return All Frames Transfer Service. 2007. (978-1-56347-924-3(9)) American Institute of Aeronautics & Astronautics.

American Institute of Aeronautics and Astronautics Staff & American National Standards Institute Staff, contrib. by. Draft American National Standard Adaptations & Conversions of CCSDS Space Link Extension Forward Communications Link Transmission Unit Transfer Service. 2007. (978-1-56347-922-9(2)) American Institute of Aeronautics & Astronautics.

Aviv, David G. Laser Space Communications. 2006. (Artech House Space Technology & Applications Ser.). (Illus.). 194p. 99.00 (978-1-59693-028-5(4)) Artech Hse., Inc.

Braun, Teresa T. Satellite Payload in Digital Communications Systems: Design, Technology, & Analysis. 2012. (ENG & CHI.). 416p. 95.00 (978-0-470-54084-8(2), Wiley-IEEE Pr.) Wiley, John & Sons, Inc.

Competition & the Future of Digital Music: Hearing Before Antitrust Task Force of the Committee on the Judiciary, House of Representatives, One Hundred Tenth Congress, First Session, February 28, 2007. 2007. iii, 122p. (978-0-16-078627-3(4), 552-070-35871-4) United States Government Printing Office.

Corazza, Giovanni E., ed. Digital Satellite Communications. (Information Technology: Transmission, Processing & Storage Ser.). 2010. l, 533p. pap. 159.00 (978-1-4419-3816-9(8), 1441938168) 2006. (Illus.). 535p. 159.00 (978-0-387-25634-4(2), 0387256342) Springer.

Dragos, Zaharia. Galileo: The European Global Navigation Satellite System. 2012. (Iste Ser.: 366). (ENG.). 320p. 125.00 (978-1-84821-086-8(8), Wiley-ISTE) Wiley, John & Sons, Inc.

Dybdal, Robert. Communication Satellite Antennas: System Architecture, Technology, & Evaluation. 2009. (ENG., Illus.). 340p. 99.95 (978-0-07-160918-0(0), 0071609180) McGraw-Hill Professional Publishing.

Elbert, Bruce R. Introduction to Satellite Communication. 3rd ed. 2008. (Artech House Telecommunications Library). (Illus.). 315p. 109.00 (978-1-59693-210-4(4)) Artech Hse., Inc.

Eyes on You: Background & Issues Surrounding Surveillance from the Sky. 2009. (Intelligence & Counterintelligence Studies). 79.00 (978-1-60741-237-3(3)) Nova Science Pubs., Inc.

Fan, Linghang, et al, eds. IP Networking over Next-Generation Satellite Systems: International Workshop, Budapest, July 2007. 2007. (ENG., Illus.). xviii, 376p. 183.00 (978-0-387-75427-7(X), 038775427X) Springer.

Ford, Steve. The ARRL Satellite Handbook. 2008. (Illus.). pap. 24.95 (978-0-87259-985-7(X)) American Radio Relay League, Inc.

Gayraud, Thierry, et al, eds. Broadband Satellite Communication Systems & the Challenges of Mobility: IFIP TC6 Workshops on Broadband Satellite Communication Systems & Challenges of Mobility, World Computer Congress August 22-27, 2004, Toulouse, France. 2010. (IFIP Advances in Information & Communication Technology Ser.). xviii, 247p. pap. 175.00 (978-1-4419-3676-9(9), 1441936769) Springer.

Giambene, Giovanni, ed. Resource Management in Satellite Networks: Optimization & Cross-Layer Design. 2007. (ENG., Illus.). xxviii, 338p. 124.00 (978-0-387-36897-9(3), 0387368973) Springer.

—Resource Management in Satellite Networks: Optimization & Cross-Layer Design. 2010. (ENG., Illus.). xxviii, 338p. pap. 124.00 (978-1-4419-4235-7(1), 1441942351) Springer.

Giambene, Giovanni & Sacchi, Claudio, eds. Personal Satellite Services: Third International ICST Conference, PSATS 2011, Malaga, Spain, Februrary 17-18, 2911, Revised Selected Papers. 2011. (Lecture Notes of the Institute for Computer Sciences, Social-Informatics & Telecommunications Engineering Ser.). (ENG.). xiv, 412p. pap. 95.00 (978-3-642-23824-6(6), 3642238246) Springer.

Globecom 2007 - 2007 IEEE Global Telecommunications Conference. 2007. pap. 1052.00 (978-1-4244-1042-2(8), 07CH37886) IEEE.

Goodman, John M. Space Weather & Telecommunications. 2010. (Springer International Series in Engineering & Computer Science Ser.). (Illus.). xix, 388p. pap. 229.00 (978-1-4419-3651-6(3), 1441936513) Springer.

Goraya, Muhammad Aitsam-Ul-Haq, et al. Hardware Implementation of Digital Satellite Receiver. 2010. 148p. pap. (978-3-639-26210-0(7)) VDM Verlag Dr. Mueller e.K.

Grace, David & Mohorcic, Mihael. Broadband Communications Via High Altitude Platforms. 2010. (ENG., Illus.). 398p. 135.00 (978-0-470-69445-9(9), Wiley) Wiley, John & Sons, Inc.

Heinemann, Arnim, et al, eds. The Middle East in the Media: Conflicts, Censorship & Public Opinion. 2010. (ENG.). 300p. 50.00 (978-0-86356-658-5(8)) Saqi Bks. GBR. Dist: Consortium Bk. Sales & Distribution.

Heymann, Roger W., et al. Satellite Data Compression, Communications, & Archiving II: 13-14 August, 2006, San Diego, California, USA. 2006. (Proceedings of SPIE Ser.). (Illus.). 234p. pap. 70.00 (978-0-8194-6379-1(5)) SPIE.

—Satellite Data Compression, Communications, & Archiving III: 29-30 August 2007, San Diego, California, USA. 2007. (Proceedings of SPIE Ser.). (Illus.). 208p. pap. 70.00 (978-0-8194-6831-4(2)) SPIE.

Heymann, Roger W., et al. Satellite Data Compression, Communications, & Processing IV: 10-11 August 2008, San Diego, California, USA. 2008. (Proceedings of SPIE Ser.). (Illus.). 230p. pap. 70.00 (978-0-8194-7304-2(9)) SPIE.

Higgins, Jonathan. Satellite Newsgathering. 2nd ed. 2007. (ENG., Illus.). 480p. per. 74.95 (978-0-240-51973-9(6), Focal Pr.) Elsevier Science & Technology Bks.

Huang, Bormin. Satellite Data Compression, Communications, & Processing VI: 3-5 August 2010, San Diego, California, United States. 2010. (Proceedings of SPIE Ser.). (Illus.). 338p. pap. 90.00 (978-0-8194-8306-5(0)) SPIE.

Huang, Bormin, ed. Satellite Data Compression. 2011. (ENG., Illus.). ix, 309p. 129.00 (978-1-4614-1182-6(3), 1461411823) Springer.

Huang, Bormin, et al. Satellite Data Compression, Communication, & Processing V: 4-5 August 2009, San Diego, California, United States. 2009. (Proceedings of SPIE Ser.). (Illus.). 296p. pap. 90.00 (978-0-8194-7745-3(1)) SPIE.
Huang, Bormin, et al. Satellite Data Compression, Communications, & Processing VII. 2011. (Proceedings of SPIE Ser.). 252p. pap. 80.00 (978-0-8194-8767-4(8)) SPIE.
IEEE Staff. 2007 Milcom. 2007. pap. 696.00 (978-1-4244-1512-0(8)) IEEE.
Ilcev, Stojce Dimov. Global Mobile Satellite Communications: For Maritime, Land & Aeronautical Applications. 2011. (ENG.). xxiv, 494p. pap. 259.00 (978-1-4419-5436-7(8), 1441954368) Springer.
Imbriale, William A., et al. Space Antenna Handbook. 2012. (ENG.). 776p. 200.00 (978-1-119-99319-3(9), Wiley) Wiley, John & Sons, Inc.
Ippolito, Louis J. Satellite Communications Systems Engineering: Atmospheric Effects, Satellite Link Design & System Performance. 2008. (Wireless Communications & Mobile Computing Ser.). (ENG., Illus.). 394p. 130.00 (978-0-470-72527-6(3), Wiley) Wiley, John & Sons, Inc.
Jo, Kenneth Y. Satellite Communications Network Design & Analysis. 2011. (Illus.). 482p. 149.00 (978-1-60807-194-4(4)) Artech Hse., Inc.
Ketelaar, V. B. H. (Gini). Satellite Radar Interferometry: Subsidence Monitoring Techniques. 2009. (Remote Sensing & Digital Image Processing Ser.). (ENG., Illus.). x, 270p. 139.00 (978-1-4020-9427-9(2)) Springer.
Laskar, Joy & Lee, Chang-Ho. Compact Ku-Band Transmitter Design for Satellite Communication Applications: From System Analysis to Hardware Implementation. 2010. (ENG.). 184p. pap. 155.00 (978-1-4419-4956-1(9), 1441949569) Springer.
Lilensten, Jean, ed. Space Weather: Research Towards Applications in Europe. 2010. (Astrophysics & Space Science Library). xii, 332p. pap. 219.00 (978-90-481-7371-6(X), 904817371X) Springer.
Maral, Gerard & Bousquet, Michel. Satellite Communications Systems: Systems, Techniques & Technologies. 5th ed. 2010. (ENG., Illus.). 742p. 130.00 (978-0-470-71458-4(1), Wiley) Wiley, John & Sons, Inc.
Maral, Gerard & Restrepo, Joaquin. Broadband Satellite Communications & the Information Society: The Space Bridge for Digital Divide. 2007. (Illus.). 352p. 130.00 (978-0-470-01927-6(1)) Wiley, John & Sons, Inc.
Martin, Donald H., et al. Communication Satellites. 5th ed. 2006. (Illus.). 783p. (978-1-884989-19-3(5)) Aerospace Pr.
Mehrotra, Asha. VSAT Systems. 2008. 400p. 149.00 (978-1-59693-178-7(7)) Artech Hse., Inc.
Minoli, Daniel. Satellite Systems Engineering in an IPv6 Environment. 2009. (ENG., Illus.). 360p. 107.95 (978-1-4200-7868-8(2)) Auerbach Pubs., Inc.
Olla, Phillip, ed. Commerce in Space: Infrastructures, Technologies & Applications. 2007. (Premier Reference Source Ser.). (Illus.). 400p. 180.00 (978-1-59904-624-2(5)) IGI Global.
Parks, Lisa & Schwoch, James, eds. Down to Earth: Satellite Technologies, Industries, & Cultures. 2012. (New Directions in International Studies). (ENG.). 320p. 70.00 (978-0-8135-5273-6(7)); (C). pap. 29.95 (978-0-8135-5274-3(5)) Rutgers Univ. Pr.
Pelton, Joseph N. Satellite Communications. 2011. (SpringerBriefs in Space Development Ser.). (ENG., Illus.). vii, 126p. pap. 49.95 (978-1-4614-1993-8(X), 146141993X) Springer.
Re, Enrico & Ruggieri, Marina, eds. Satellite Communications & Navigation Systems. 2010. (Signals & Communication Technology Ser.). xvi, 768p. pap. 149.00 (978-1-4419-4292-0(0), 1441942920) Springer.
Reauthorization of the Satellite Home Viewer Extension & Reauthorization ACT of 2004: Hearing Before the Subcommittee on Communications, Technology, & the Internet of the Committee on Commerce, Science, & Transportation, United States Senate, One Hundred Eleventh Congress, First Session, October 7, 2009. 2010. iii, 65p. (978-0-16-086166-6(7), 552-070-41266-2) United States Government Printing Office.
Richharia, Madhavendra & Westbrook, Leslie David. Satellite Systems for Personal Applications: Concepts & Technology. 2010. (Wireless Communications & Mobile Computing Ser.). (ENG., Illus.). 476p. 115.00 (978-0-470-71428-7(X), Wiley) Wiley, John & Sons, Inc.
Roebuck, Kevin. Ka Band Satellite Communications: High-impact Technology - What You Need to Know. 2011. 170p. pap. (978-1-74304-415-5(1), Tebbo) Emereo Pty Ltd.
Rycroft, Michael J. & Crosby, Norma, eds. Smaller Satellites: Bigger Business? Concepts, Applications & Markets for Micro/Nanosatellites in a New Information World. 2010. (Space Studies). 516p. pap. 232.00 (978-90-481-5906-2(7), 9048159067) Springer.
Satellite Broadcast Research Compendium. Date not set. (978-1-884914-01-0(2)) American Music Therapy Asssoc.
Sergienko, Alexander, et al. Quantum Communication & Quantum Networking: First International Conference, QuantumComm 2009, Naples, Italy, October 26-30, 2009, Revised Selected Papers. 2010. (Lecture Notes of the Institute for Computer Sciences, Social-Informatics & Telecommunications Engineering Ser.). xii, 312p. pap. 83.00 (978-3-642-11730-5(9), 3642117309) Springer.
Sheriff, Ray E., et al, eds. Satellite Communications. 2007. 152p. per. 23.00 (978-977-454-012-7(3)) Hindawi Publishing Corp.
Sithamparanathan, Kandeepan, et al. Personal Satellite Services: Second International ICST Conference, PSATS 2010, Rome, Italy, February 4-5, 2010. Revised Selected Papers. 2010. (Lecture Notes of the Institute for Computer Sciences, Social-Informatics & Telecommunications Engineering Ser.). xiv, 452p. pap. 99.00 (978-3-642-13617-7(6), 3642136176) Springer.
Sithamparanathan, Kandeepan & Marchese, Mario. Personal Satellite Services: International Conference, PSATS 2009, Rome, Italy, March 18-19, 2009, Revised Selected Papers. 2009. (Lecture Notes of the Institute for Computer Sciences, Social-Informatics & Telecommunications Engineering Ser.). xii, 153p. pap. 72.00 (978-3-642-04259-1(7), 3642042597) Springer.
United States, Congress House Committee on Science Staff, contrib. by. The Future of NPOESS: Results of the Nunn-McCurdy Review of NOAA's Weather Satellite Program: Hearing Before the Committee on Science, House of Representatives, One Hundred Ninth Congress, Second Session, June 8, 2006. 2007. iv, 86p. (978-0-16-078309-8(7), 552-070-35631-2) United States Government Printing Office.
Zhao, Shanghong, et al. Wei Xing Guang Wang Luo Ji Shu. 2010. (CHI., Illus.). x, 268p. (978-7-03-027002-3(9)) Science Pr.
2007 6th Conference on Telecommunication Techno-Economics. 2007. pap. 180.00 (978-1-4244-1232-7(3), 07EX1789) IEEE.
2007 International Workshop on Satellite & Space Communication. 2007. pap. 212.00 (978-1-4244-0938-9(1), 07EX1664) IEEE.

ARTIFICIAL SWEETENERS
see Nonnutritive Sweeteners

ARTIFICIAL TEETH
see Dentures

ARTIFICIAL THINKING
see Artificial Intelligence

ARTIFICIAL WEATHER CONTROL
see Weather Control

ARTIGAS, JOSE GERVASIO, 1764-1850

Street, John. Artigas & the Emancipation of Uruguay. 2008. (ENG.). 432p. pap. 58.00 (978-0-521-08693-6(0)) Cambridge Univ. Pr.

ARTILLERY
see also Antitank Guns; Ordnance

Baxter, Ian. German Guns of the Third Reich: Rare Photographs from Wartime Archives. 2007. (Images of War Ser.). (Illus.). 128p. per. 24.95 (978-1-84415-567-5(6)) Pen & Sword Bks. Ltd. GBR. Dist: Casemate Pubs. & Bk. Distributors, LLC.
Bull, Stephen. 'the Furie of the Ordnance' Artillery in the English Civil Wars. 2008. (Armour & Weapons Ser.: Volume 2). (Illus.). 288p. 90.00 (978-1-84383-403-8(0), Boydell Press) Boydell & Brewer, Ltd. GBR. Dist: Boydell & Brewer, Inc.
Coco, Gregory A. A Concise Guide to the Artillery at Gettysburg. 2nd rev. ed. 2008. (ENG., Illus.). 104p. per. 9.95 (978-0-9777125-5-7(9)) Colecraft Industries.
Foss, Christopher F. & Strickland, Richard, eds. Janes Armour Artillery Upgrades 2006/07. 19th rev. ed. 2006. (Jane's Armour & Artillery Ser.). (Illus.). 893p. (978-0-7106-2748-3(3)) Jane's Information Group.
Gore-Brown, Lt S. Prussian Artillery in the Campaign of 18. 2008. (Illus.). 40p. pap. 16.95 (978-1-906033-05-7(6)) Helion & Co., Ltd. GBR. Dist: Casemate Pubs. & Bk. Distributors, LLC.
Gottfried, Bradley M. The Artillery of Gettysburg. 2008. (ENG., Illus.). 332p. 24.95 (978-1-58182-623-4(0)) Turner Publishing Co.
Haskew, Michael. Postwar Artillery 1945-Present. 2011. (Essential Weapons Identification Guide Ser.). (Illus.). 192p. 34.95 (978-1-907446-60-3(5)) Amber Bks. GBR. Dist: Casemate Pubs. & Bk. Distributors, LLC.
Jane's Armour & Artillery: The World's Authority on Battlefield Armour & Artillery. 560.00 (978-0-7106-2309-6(7)) Jane's Information Group, Inc.
Jane's Armour & Artillery Upgrades: Upgrade Your Subsystems Information. 510.00 (978-0-7106-2310-2(0)) Jane's Information Group, Inc.
Jobson, Philip. Royal Artillery Glossary of Terms & Abbreviations (Historical & Modern) Historical & Modern. 2009. (ENG., Illus.). 320p. 46.95 (978-1-86227-476-1(2)) History Pr. Ltd., The GBR. Dist: Independent Pubs. Group.
Kinard, Jeff. Artillery: An Illustrated History of Its Impact. 2007. (Weapons & Warfare Ser.). (Illus.). 536p. 85.00 (978-1-85109-556-8(X)) ABC-CLIO, LLC.
Manucy, Albert. Artillery Through the Ages: A History of the Development & Use of Cannons, Mortars, Rockets & Projectiles from Earliest Times to the Nineteenth Cent. 2011. 124p. (978-0-85706-673-2(0)); pap. (978-0-85706-674-9(9)) Leonaur Ltd.
McGrath, John J. Fire for Effect: Field Artillery & Close Air Support in the US Army. 2010. (Illus.). viii, 185p. (978-0-9841901-5-7(5)) United States Government Printing Office.
McKenney, Janice E. Organizational History of Field Artillery, 1775-2003 (Hardcover) 2008. (Army Lineage Ser.). (ENG., Illus.). 412p. 44.00 (978-0-16-077114-9(5), Dept. of the Army) United States Government Printing Office.
—Organizational History of Field Artillery, 1775-2003 (Paperbound) 2007. (Army Lineage Ser.). (ENG., Illus.). 412p. pap. 42.00 (978-0-16-077115-6(3), Dept. of the Army) United States Government Printing Office.
Mehl, Hans. Naval Guns: 500 years of Ship & Coastal Artillery. (Illus.). 216p. 65.00 (978-1-59114-557-8(0)) Naval Institute Pr.
Molina, Lucas & Jose Ma, Manrique Garcia. Flak Artillery of the Legion Condor: Flak Abteilung (Mot.) F/88 in the Spanish Civil War, 1936-1939. 2009. (Illus.). 160p. bds. 35.00 (978-0-7643-3231-9(7)) Schiffer Publishing, Ltd.
Norris, John. Artillery: A History. 2012. (ENG., Illus.). 240p. pap. 24.95 (978-0-7524-6189-2(3)) History Pr. Ltd., The GBR. Dist: Independent Pubs. Group.
Parker, John H. The Gatlings at Santiago: The History of the Gatling Gun Detachment, U. S. Fifth Army Corps, During the Spanish-American War, Cuba 1898. 2010. 212p. (978-1-84677-912-1(X)); pap. (978-1-84677-911-4(1)) Leonaur Ltd.
Stickland, Richard & Foss, Christopher F., eds. Jane's Armour & Artillery Upgrades: 2007-2008. 20th rev. ed. 2007. (Jane's Armour & Artillery Upgrades Ser.). (Illus.). 702p. (978-0-7106-2795-7(5)) Jane's Information Group.
Summerfield, Stephen, et al. Napoleonic Artillery. 2008. (ENG., Illus.). 304p. 49.95 (978-1-86126-923-2(4), 1861269234) Crowood Pr., Ltd. GBR. Dist: MBI Distribution Services/Quayside Distribution.
Tidball, John C. The Artillery Service in the War of the Rebellion, 1861-65. Kaplan, Lawrence M., ed. 2011. (ENG., Illus.). 400p. 30.00 (978-1-59416-149-0(6)) Westholme Publishing.
Wilkins, Alan. Roman Artillery. 2008. (Shire Archaeology Ser.). (ENG., Illus.). 80p. pap. 13.95 (978-0-7478-0575-5(X)) Shire Pubns., Ltd. GBR. Dist: Random Hse., Inc.

ARTILLERY—MUSEUMS
see Military Museums

ARTILLERY, RAILWAY
see Railway Artillery

ARTIODACTYLA, FOSSIL

Foss, Scott E. The Evolution of Artiodactyls. Foss, Scott E. & Prothero, Donald R., eds. 2007. (ENG., Illus.). 384p. (gr. 17). 125.00 (978-0-8018-8735-2(6)) Johns Hopkins Univ. Pr.

ARTISANS
see also Apprentices; Cottage Industries; Guilds; Informal Sector (Economics)
also particular classes of artisans, e.g. Barbers; Cabinetmakers

Allen, Lindy & Lakic, Mira. Women's Work: Aboriginal Women's Artefacts in the Museum of Victoria. 2007. (ENG., Illus.). 72p. pap. 19.95 (978-0-7306-8711-5(2)) Museum Victoria Publishing AUS. Dist: National Bk. Network.
Aoyama, Kazuo. Elite Craft Producers, Artists, & Warriors at Aguateca: Lithic Analysis. 2009. (ENG., Illus.). 224p. 60.00 (978-0-87480-959-6(2)) Univ. of Utah Pr.
Barbieri-Low, Anthony J. Artisans in Early Imperial China. 2007. (ENG., Illus.). 400p. 60.00 (978-0-295-98713-2(8)) Univ. of Washington Pr.
Beam, Lisa Sonora. The Creative Entrepreneur: A DIY Visual Guidebook for Making Business Ideas Real. 2008. (ENG., Illus.). 128p. pap. 19.99 (978-1-59253-459-3(7), 1592534597) Quayside.
Bell, Clark. Medico-Legal Studies. 2010. 282p. pap. 28.75 (978-1-149-01128-7(9)) BiblioBazaar.
Benavente, Carmen. Embroiderers of Ninhue: Stitching Chilean Rural Life. 2010. (Illus.). 240p. 45.00 (978-0-89672-648-2(7)) Texas Tech Univ. Pr.
Bieber, Susanneh. Off-Site: Four site-specific art projects: Amy Balkin, Jeff Knwolton & Naomi Spellman, Ed Osborn, Claudia Tennyson. 2006. 5.00 net. (978-0-9790112-1-4(3)) Fresno Metropolitan Museum.
Bijkerk, Pia Jane. Amsterdam: Made by Hand. 2010. (ENG., Illus.). 176p. pap. 19.95 (978-1-892145-84-0(7)) Little Bookroom.
—Paris: Made by Hand - 50 Shops Where Decorators & Stylists Source the Chic & Unique. 2009. (ENG., Illus.). 256p. pap. 18.95 (978-1-892145-70-3(7)) Little Bookroom.
Bunney, Tessa, photos by. Home Work: Domestic labour in the suburbs & villages in & around Hanoi, Vietnam. 2011. (ENG., Illus.). 112p. 35.00 (978-1-904587-90-3(9)) Lewis, Dewi Publishing GBR. Dist: Consortium Bk. Sales & Distribution.
Cavallo, Sandra. Artisans of the Body in Early Modern Italy: Identities, Families & Masculinities. (Gender in History Ser.). (ENG., Illus.). 2010. 296p. pap. 30.95 (978-0-7190-8151-4(3)) 2008. 320p. 89.00 (978-0-7190-7662-6(5)) Manchester Univ. Pr. GBR. Dist: Macmillan.
Cook, Scott & Binford, Leigh. Obliging Need: Rural Petty Industry in Mexican Capitalism. 2012. (ENG.). 338p. pap. 30.00 (978-0-292-74068-6(9), Univ. of Texas Pr.
Cunaccia, Cesare M. & AA., V. V. . The Whispered Directory of Craftsmanship Vol. II: A Contemporary Guide to the Italian Handmaking Ability. 2012. (ENG., Illus.). 200p. 60.00 (978-88-370-8832-3(9)) Electa ITA. Dist: National Bk. Network.
Doh, Jenny. Creative Pilgrimage: An Exploration of Artful Gatherings & Discovery of Innovative Art Techniques. 2012. (ENG., Illus.). 152p. pap. 24.99 (978-1-59253-753-2(7), 1592537537) Quayside.
Faroqhi, Suraiya. Artisans of Empire: Crafts & Craftspeople under the Ottomans. (ENG., Illus.). 2011. 304p. pap. 32.00 (978-1-84885-960-9(0)) 2009. 272p. 94.00 (978-1-84511-588-3(0)) I. B. Tauris & Co., Ltd. GBR. Dist: Macmillan.
Filippi Gabardi, Vittoria & Gabardi, Vittoria Filippi. The Whispered Directory of Craftsmanship: A Contemporary Guide to the Italian Handmaking Ability. 2011. (ENG., Illus.). 200p. 69.95 (978-88-370-8424-0(2)) Electa ITA. Dist: National Bk. Network.
Fischer, Felice. The Art of Japanese Craft: 1875 to the Present. 2008. (978-0-87633-202-3(5)) Philadelphia Museum of Art.
—The Art of Japanese Craft: 1875 to the Present. 2008. (ENG., Illus.). 60p. (C). pap. 19.95 (978-0-300-14212-9(9)) Yale Univ. Pr.
Floor, Willem M. Guilds, Merchants & Ulama in Nineteenth-Century Iran. 2009. 280p. pap. (978-1-933823-31-7(3)) Mage Pubs., Inc.
Frayling, Christopher. On Cinema. 2011. (Oberon Masters Ser.). (ENG.). 160p. 20.95 (978-1-84943-072-2(1)) Oberon Bks., Ltd. GBR. Dist: Consortium Bk. Sales & Distribution.
Goggin, Maureen Daly & Tobin, Beth Fowkes. Women & the Material Culture of Needlework & Textiles, 1750-1950. 2009. (Illus.). 312p. 124.95 (978-0-7546-6538-0(0)) Ashgate Publishing Co.
Goody, Esther N., ed. From Craft to Industry: The Ethnography of Proto-Industrial Cloth Production. 2009. (Cambridge Papers in Social Anthropology Ser.). (ENG.). 232p. pap. 34.99 (978-0-521-10498-2(X)) Cambridge Univ. Pr.
Gould, Kerin. Living Art: Designs & Crafts of the Otomí of San Pablito. 2009. 92p. 24.95 (978-0-7649-5099-5(1)) Pomegranate Communications, Inc.
Gurland, A. R. L. Fate of Small Business in Nazi Germany. 2006. pap. 21.95 (978-1-4286-6205-6(7)) Kessinger Publishing, LLC.
Hadassah-Brandeis Institute, prod. Jewish Women Artisans around the World: Contemporary Craft, Traditional Techniques. 2008. ring bd. (978-0-9770871-3-6(1)) Hadassah-Brandeis Institute, The.
Hale, Julie, et al. Beadweaving: Major Works by Leading Artists. Hemachandra, Ray, ed. 2008. (Masters Ser.). (ENG., Illus.). 300p. pap. 24.95 (978-1-60059-039-9(X)) Lark Bks.
Hanna, Nelly. Artisan Entrepreneurs in Cairo & Early-Modern Capitalism (1600-1800) 2011. 280p. (978-0-8156-3279-5(7)) Syracuse Univ. Pr.
Hanshew, Annie. Border to Border: Historic Quilts & Quiltmakers of Montana. 2010. (ENG., Illus.). 240p. pap. 24.95 (978-0-9759196-2-0(8)) Montana Historical Society Pr.
HEMINGSON, Vince. Alphabets & Scripts Tattoo Design Directory: The Essential Reference for Body Art. 2010. (ENG., Illus.). 192p. spiral bd. 14.99 (978-0-7858-2578-4(9), 0785825789, Chartwell) Book Sales, Inc.
Howell, Vickie. Craft Corps: Celebrating the Creative Community One Story at a Time. 2010. (ENG., Illus.). 288p. pap. 17.95 (978-1-60059-468-7(9)) Lark Bks.
Karper, Diane. A Walk in My Shoes: Our Lives of Hope: An Oral History of the Artists of the "Made in Honduras Craft Co-Op," Trujillo, Honduras. 2010. pap. (978-0-9711469-35-6(4)) Hood, Alan C. & Co., Inc.
Leutz, Pamela Train. The Thread That Binds: Interviews with Private Practice Bookbinders. 2010. 55.00 (978-1-58456-276-4(5)); pap. 34.95 (978-1-58456-274-0(9)) Oak Knoll Pr.
Littrell, Mary & Dickson, Marsha. Artisans in the Global Marketplace: The Fair Trade Facts. 2010. (Illus.). 230p. pap. 24.95 (978-1-56549-321-6(4)) Stylus Publishing, LLC.
McCann, Michael & Babin, Angela. Health Hazards Manual for Artists. 6th ed. 2008. (ENG., Illus.). 176p. pap. 14.95 (978-1-59921-318-7(4), Lyons Pr.) Globe Pequot Pr., The.
Misser, Kristian. Inside the Tattoo Circus: A Journey through the Modern World of Tattoos. 2008. (Illus.). 208p. pap. 39.99 (978-0-7643-3145-9(0)) Schiffer Publishing, Ltd.
Owens, Bill & Dikty, Alan, eds. The Art of Distilling Whiskey & Other Spirits: An Enthusiast's Guide to the Artisan Distilling of Potent Potables. 2009. (ENG., Illus.). 176p. pap. 24.99 (978-1-59253-569-9(0), 1592535690) Quayside.
Pauwels, Wim. Handmade: A Passion for Craftsmanship. 2010. (ENG., Illus.). 204p. (978-90-8944-057-9(4), Beta-Plus (Acc)) Antique Collectors' Club.
Peake, Harold J. & Fleure, Herbert J. Hunters & Artists, Vol. 2. (978-0-404-18252-6(6)) AMS Pr., Inc.
Pearl-McPhee, Stephanie. Free-Range Knitter: The Yarn Harlot Writes Again. 2010. (ENG.). 256p. pap. 12.99 (978-0-7407-6946-7(4)) Andrews McMeel Publishing.
Rothstein, Arden & Rothstein, Anya. Mexican Folk Art: From Oaxacan Artist Families. 2007. (Illus.). 192p. pap. 39.95 (978-0-7643-2573-8(2)) Schiffer Publishing, Ltd.
Scherm, Michael. Kleine und mittelständische Betriebe in unternehmerischen Netzwerken: Die Reidemeister auf der Vollme im vor- und frühindustriellen Metallgewerbe der Grafschaft Mark. 2009. (Beiträge zur Wirtschafts- und Sozialgeschichte (BWSG) Ser.). (GER., Illus.). 691p. (C). pap. 124.00 (978-3-515-09432-0(6)) Steiner, Franz Verlag Wiesbaden GmbH DEU. Dist: Brown, David Bk. Co., The.
Shimada, Izumi, ed. Craft Production in Complex Societies: Multicraft & Producer Perspectives. 2007. (Foundations of Archaeological Inquiry Ser.). (ENG., Illus.). 336p. 35.00 (978-0-87480-921-3(5)); per. 35.00 (978-0-87480-902-2(9)) Univ. of Utah Pr.
Sickert, Walter. A Free House! or, the Artist as Craftsman. Sitwell, Osbert, ed. reprint ed. 37.50 (978-0-404-18387-5(5)) AMS Pr., Inc.
Sonenscher, Michael. Work & Wages: Natural Law, Politics & the Eighteenth-Century French Trades. 2012. (ENG.). 440p. pap. 40.00 (978-1-107-40414-4(2)) Cambridge Univ. Pr.
Tanner, Andrew. Batch: Craft, Design & Product. 2011. (ENG., Illus.). 144p. 45.00 (978-1-4081-1008-9(3)) A & C Black GBR. Dist: Macmillan.
Teitelbaum, Vanesa E. Entre el Control y la Movilización: Honor, Trabajo y Solidaridades Artesanales en la Ciudad de México a Mediados Del Siglo XIX. 2008. (Estudios Históricos Ser.). (SPA.). 313p. pap. 39.00 (978-968-12-1373-2(4)) El Colegio de México, A.C., Biblioteca Miguel Cosio Villegas MEX. Dist: Fondo de Cultura Economica USA.
Wilhoit, Jennifer J. Common Ground Between Crafts Collectives & Conservation: Protecting Natural Resources Through Artisan Production. 2008. 128p. pap. (978-3-639-09858-7(7)) VDM Verlag Dr. Mueller e.K.
Wood, James A. The Society of Equality: Popular Republicanism & Democracy in Santiago de Chile, 1818-1851. 2011. (ENG., Illus.). 344p. (C). pap. 29.95 (978-0-8263-4941-5(2)) Univ. of New Mexico Pr.
Wright, Kristina Dziedzic. Art, Culture, & Tourism on an Indian Ocean Island: An Ethnographic Study of Jua Kali Lamu. 2009. (Illus.). 252p. 109.95 (978-0-7734-3874-3(2)) Mellen, Edwin Pr., The.

ARTISANS—GREAT BRITAIN

Bramwell, Valerie & Peck, Robert McCracken. All in the Bones: A Biography of Benjamin Waterhouse Hawkins. 2008. *(978-0-910006-65-1(2))* Academy of Natural Sciences Philadelphia.

Clarke, Lorraine & Richardson, Ruth. Lorraine Clarke: Nosce Te Ipsum. 2007. (ENG., Illus.). 24p. pap. 11.95 *(978-1-905313-42-6(X))* Univ. of Hertfordshire Pr. GBR. Dist: Independent Pubs. Group.

Frank, Christopher. Master & Servant Law: Chartists, Trade Unions, Radical Lawyers & the Magistracy in England, 1840-1865. 2010. 294p. 119.95 *(978-0-7546-6830-5(4))* Ashgate Publishing Co.

Megson, Barbara, ed. The Pinners' & Wiresellers' Book 1462-1511. 2009. (London Record Society Ser.: Volume 44). 114p. 45.00 *(978-0-900952-44-9(X))* London Record Society GBR. Dist: Boydell & Brewer, Inc.

Momement, Caroline, ed. & compiled by. Craft Galleries Guide: 2009/10. 10th ed. 2009. (ENG., Illus.). 356p. pap. 28.95 *(978-0-9550026-7-0(2))* BCF Bks. GBR. Dist: Macmillan.

Prothero, Iorwerth. Radical Artisans in England & France, 1830-1870. 2006. 444p. pap. 79.00 *(978-0-521-02812-7(4))* Cambridge Univ. Pr.

Suri, Piyush. Handmade in Britain: Appreciating Contemporary Artisans, 1 vol. 2012. (ENG., Illus.). 224p. pap. 29.95 ***(978-1-908126-38-2(8))*** Vivays Pubng. Ltd. GBR. Dist: Innovative Logistics.

ARTISANS—INDIA

Haynes, Douglas E. Small Town Capitalism in Western India: Artisans, Merchants & the Making of the Informal Economy, 1870-1960. 2012. (Cambridge Studies in Indian History & Society Ser.). (ENG., Illus.). 376p. 99.00 ***(978-0-521-19333-7(8))*** Cambridge Univ. Pr.

Littrell, Mary Ann & Dickson, Marsha Ann. Artisans & Fair Trade: Crafting Development. 2010. (Illus.). 288p. *(978-1-56549-322-3(2)*, Kumarian Pr) Stylus Publishing, LLC.

ARTISANS—PERU

Frank, Gabriela Lena. Suenos de Chambi: Snapshots for an Andean Album: For Violin & Piano. 2007. (ENG.). 34p. pap. 24.95 *(978-0-634-09034-9(8)*, 0634090348, G Schirmer, Inc.) Leonard, Hal Corp.

Garcia-Bryce, Inigo. Crafting the Republic: Lima's Artisans & Nation Building in Peru, 1821-1879. 2009. (ENG., Illus.). 239p. pap. 35.00 *(978-0-8263-3393-3(1))* Univ. of New Mexico Pr.

Waring, Rob. Peruvian Weavers (US) 2008. (ENG.). 24p. (C). pap. 10.95 *(978-1-4240-4410-8(3))* Cengage Heinle.

ARTISANS—UNITED STATES

Baillargeon, Morgan. North American Aboriginal Hide Tanning: The Act of Transformation & Revival. 2011. (ENG., Illus.). 156p. (C). pap. 29.95 *(978-0-660-19969-6(6))* Canadian Museum of Civilization/Musee Canadien des Civilisations CAN. Dist: Univ. of Washington Pr.

Benfey, Christopher. Red Brick, Black Mountain, White Clay: Reflections on Art, Family, & Survival. 2012. (ENG.). 288p. (gr. 12). 25.95 ***(978-1-59420-326-8(1)***, Penguin Pr. HC, The) Penguin Group (USA) Inc.

Bingham, Ted. The Celebrated Reels of Edward Vom Hofe. 2007. (Illus.). 160p. per. 45.00 *(978-0-615-16882-1(5))* Fishing Stuff.

Brewer, James H. The Confederate Negro: Virginia's Craftsmen & Military Laborers, 1861-1865. 2007. (ENG., Illus.). 238p. pap. 29.95 *(978-0-8173-5486-2(7))* Univ. of Alabama Pr.

Carlin, Bob. Regal Musical Instruments: 1895-1955. 2010. (Illus.). 250p. pap. 45.00 *(978-1-61774-042-8(X)*, 161774042X) Centerstream Publishing.

Dobney, Jayson. Guitar Heroes: Legendary Craftsmen from Italy to New York. 2011. (ENG., Illus.). 48p. pap. 14.95 *(978-0-300-16980-5(9))* Yale Univ. Pr.

Dyer, Walter A. Early American Craftsmen. 2008. (Illus.). 228p. pap. *(978-1-4099-3941-2(3))* Dodo Pr.

—Early American Craftsmen. 2007. (ENG.). 408p. 49.95 *(978-0-548-09124-1(2))* Kessinger Publishing, LLC.

—Early American Craftsmen. 2007. (ENG.). 408p. per. *(978-1-4067-6394-2(2))* Read Bks.

Gilbert, Samuel. Where Did God Come From, 1 vol. 2010. 82p. pap. 19.95 *(978-1-4512-9114-8(0))* PublishAmerica, Inc.

Halper, Vicki & Douglas, Diane, eds. Choosing Craft: The Artist's Viewpoint. 2009. (ENG., Illus.). 328p. 36.95 *(978-0-8078-3119-9(0))* Univ. of North Carolina Pr.

Heying, Charles. Brews to Bikes. 2010. (OpenBook Ser.). (ENG., Illus.). 304p. pap. 24.95 *(978-1-932010-32-9(7))* Ooligan Pr.

Jaffee, David. A New Nation of Goods: The Material Culture of Early America. 2010. (Early American Studies). (Illus.). 424p. (C). 45.00 *(978-0-8122-4257-7(2))* Univ. of Pennsylvania Pr.

Kaiser, Linda Pembroke. Pulling Strings: The Legacy of Melville A. Clark. 2010. 186p. 29.95 *(978-0-8156-0950-6(7))* Syracuse Univ. Pr.

Kennedy Fine Art & California Artists. Best of California Arists & Artisans, Vol. 1. 2007. per. *(978-0-9796358-1-6(0))* Kennedy Publishing.

Kristofferson, R. & Kristofferson, Robert B. Craft Capitalism: Craftworkers & Early Industrialization in Hamilton Ontario. 2007. (Canadian Social History Ser.). (ENG.). 288p. *(978-0-8020-9127-7(X))* Univ. of Toronto Pr.

Kristofferson, Robert B. Craft Capitalism: Craftworkers & Early Industrialization in Hamilton, Ontario, 1840-1872. 2007. (Canadian Social History Ser.). (ENG., Illus.). 288p. pap. *(978-0-8020-9408-7(2))* Univ. of Toronto Pr.

Lamoreux, Liz. Inner Excavation: Exploring Your Self Through Photography, Poetry & Mixed Media. 2010. (ENG., Illus.). 144p. pap. 24.99 *(978-1-4403-0309-6(6)*, North Light Bks.) F&W Media, Inc.

Levine, Faythe & Heimerl, Cortney. Handmade Nation: The Rise of DIY, Art, Craft, & Design. 2008. (ENG., Illus.). 176p. pap. 24.95 *(978-1-56898-787-3(0))* Princeton Architectural Pr.

Miller, Maria R. The Needle's Eye: Women & Work in the Age of Revolution. 2006. (Illus.). 302p. 80.00 *(978-1-55849-544-9(4))*; per. 24.95 *(978-1-55849-545-6(2))* Univ. of Massachusetts Pr.

Pensa, Rudy. Archtop Guitars: The Journey from Cremona to New York. 2011. (ENG.). 432p. 220.00 *(978-1-932026-70-2(3))* Graphis, U.S., Inc.

Petersen, Christine. The Glassblower. 2011. (Colonial People 2 Ser.). 48p. (gr. 3). 29.93 *(978-1-60870-413-2(0))* Marshall Cavendish GBR. Dist: Marshall Cavendish Corp.

Sann, Nathalie & Sann, Ted. Made in New York: Handcrafted Works by Master Artisans. 2012. (ENG., Illus.). 224p. 29.95 ***(978-0-8478-3801-1(3))*** Rizzoli International Pubns., Inc.

Seagrave, Ronald Roy. The Early Artisans & Mechanics of Petersburg Virginia, 1607-1860: The Building of a Multi-Cultural Maritime Community. 2009. 552p. pap. 49.95 *(978-1-4327-5058-9(5))* Outskirts Pr., Inc.

Stim, Richard. The Craft Artist's Legal Guide: Protect Your Work, Save on Taxes, Maximize Profits, 2 vols. 2010. (ENG.). 400p. pap. 39.99 *(978-1-4133-1212-6(8))* NOLO.

Tarule, Robert. The Artisan of Ipswich: Craftsmanship & Community in Colonial New England. 2007. (ENG., Illus.). 176p. (gr. 17). per. 27.00 *(978-0-8018-8752-9(6))* Johns Hopkins Univ. Pr.

Waldvogel, Merikay, et al, eds. The Quilters Hall of Fame: 42 Masters Who Have Shaped Our Art. 2011. (ENG., Illus.). 208p. 35.00 *(978-0-7603-3635-9(0)*, 0760336350, Voyageur Pr) MBI Publishing Co. LLC.

Wright-Correll, Arlene. Who's Who in Kentucky Arts & Crafts 2007 Edition. 2008. 53p. pap. 29.50 *(978-0-615-18494-4(4))* Trade Resources Unlimited.

ARTISTIC ANATOMY

see Anatomy, Artistic

ARTISTIC PHOTOGRAPHY

see Photography, Artistic

ARTISTS

see also Actors; Actresses; Architects; Authors; Cartoonists; Child Artists; Engravers; Entertainers; Illustrators; Jewish Artists; Musicians; Painters; Potters; Printmakers; Sculptors

also names of artists

ART for the World, ed. Stories on Human Rights by Filmmakers, Artists & Writers. 2008. (Illus.). 205p. pap. 42.50 *(978-88-370-6510-2(8))* Electa ITA. Dist: Trans-Atlantic Pubns., Inc.

Auping, Michael. 30 Years: Interviews & Outtakes. 2007. (Illus.). 286p. *(978-0-929865-27-0(8))* Modern Art Museum of Fort Worth.

Bal, Mieke, et al. World Rush 4 Artists. 2006. 190p. 19.95 *(978-0-7241-0227-3(2))* National Gallery of Victoria AUS. Dist: Antique Collectors' Club.

Bancroft, Shelly, et al, eds. Diaries of a Young Artist. 2009. (ENG., Illus.). 80p. pap. 15.00 *(978-0-9773680-1-3(7))* Darte Publishing LLC.

Barolsky, Paul. A Brief History of the Artist from God to Picasso. 2010. (ENG.). 152p. 49.95 *(978-0-271-03675-5(3))* Pennsylvania State Univ. Pr.

Bateman, Robert & Derry, Ramsay. The Art of Robert Bateman. anniv. ed. 2006. (Illus.). 180p. 45.00 *(978-0-7649-3765-1(0)*, A131) Pomegranate Communications, Inc.

Bead Review 3. 2008. 126p. pap. 21.00 *(978-0-9770831-5-2(2))* Pearson, Brad.

Benun, Ilise. The Creative Professional's Guide to Money: How to Think about It, How to Talk about it, How to Manage It. 2011. (ENG.). 240p. pap. 22.99 *(978-1-4403-0243-5(X)*, HOW Bks.) F&W Media, Inc.

Berry, Rick, et al. Sparrow Boxed Set 2. 2011. (Illus.). 288p. 75.00 ***(978-1-61377-087-0(1))*** Idea & Design Works, LLC.

Bickerton, Derek, et al. Ashley Bickerton. 2011. (Illus.). 400p. 375.00 *(978-1-906967-38-3(5))* Other Criteria GBR. Dist: Abrams.

Bliss, Karen. Hedley: Fan Lowdown. 2008. (Fan Lowdown Ser.). (ENG., Illus.). 64p. pap. 21.95 *(978-1-894917-75-9(8)*, Napoleon & Co.) Dundurn CAN. Dist: Ingram Pub. Services.

Bouqueret, Christian. Surrealist Photography. 2008. (Photofile Ser.). (ENG., Illus.). 144p. pap. 15.95 *(978-0-500-41092-9(5)*, 541092) Thames & Hudson.

Branagan, Alison. Pocket Business Guide for Artists & Designers: 100 Things You Need to Know. 2011. (ENG., Illus.). 160p. pap. 15.95 *(978-1-4081-2992-0(2))* A & C Black GBR. Dist: Macmillan.

Bruhn, Thomas P. The Art of Al Frueh. (Illus.). 16p. 2.00 *(978-0-918386-35-9(7))* William Benton Museum of Art.

Brusen, Claus. Imaginaire II: Magic Realism. 2012. (FRE & ENG., Illus.). 176p. 49.95 *(978-87-992147-4-7(1))* Fantasmus-Art DNK. Dist: Independent Pubs. Group.

Bucher, Stefan G., et al. Graphic Eye: Photographs by Graphic Designers from Around the Globe. 2009. (ENG.). 240p. pap. 35.00 *(978-0-8118-6903-4(2))* Chronicle Bks. LLC.

Bullen, Daniel. The Love Lives of the Artists: Five Stories of Creative Intimacy. 2011. (ENG., Illus.). 336p. 28.00 *(978-1-58243-775-0(0)*, Counterpoint) Counterpoint LLC.

Campana, D. M. Amateur Artist Encyclopedia. (Illus.). 13.95 *(978-0-939608-17-1(0))* Campana Art Co.

—The Artist & the Decorator. (Illus.). 14.95 *(978-0-939608-16-4(2))* Campana Art Co.

Cárcova, Ernesto de la. Cuadros de Viaje: Artistas Argentinos en Europa y Estados Unidos, 1880-1910. 2008. (Tierra Firme Ser.). (SPA., Illus.). 383p. pap. 30.99 *(978-950-557-779-8(6))* Fondo de Cultura Económica.

Carlsson, Benke & Louie, Hop. Street Art Cookbook: A Guide to Techniques & Materials. 2010. (Illus.). 140p. 29.95 *(978-91-85639-30-4(3))* Dokument forlag, Fotograf Malcolm Jacobsson SWE. Dist: SCB Distributors.

chanfro, laurence. Chanfro 1959/2009. 2010. 145p. pap. 68.95 *(978-1-4452-3340-6(1))* Lulu Enterprises Inc.

Cheliotis, Leonidas K., ed. The Arts of Imprisonment: Control, Resistance & Empowerment. 2012. (Advances in Criminology Ser.). (Illus.). 320p. 134.95 ***(978-0-7546-7586-0(6))*** Ashgate Publishing Co.

Christensen, Loren W. Warriors: Expanded & Updated Edition: More on Living with Courage, Discipline, & Honor. 2009. 452p. pap. 35.00 *(978-1-58160-696-6(6))* Paladin Pr.

Christensen, Warren. The National Resource Guide for the Placement of Artists: An Annotated Guide to Organizations & Publications Essential to Artists. Slean, Cheryl, ed. 249p. (Orig.). pap. 45.00 *(978-0-945941-04-0(8))* National Network for Artist Placement, The.

Ciuffi, Valentina & Angelotti, Martina. Pop Art. 2010. (ENG., Illus.). 304p. 14.95 *(978-88-544-0462-5(4))* White Star ITA. Dist: Random Hse., Inc.

Clement, Hutton. Artist of the Nineteenth Century. reprint ed. lib. bdg. 75.00 *(978-0-7812-0122-3(5))* Reprint Services Co.

Cleveland, William. Art & Upheaval: Artists on the World's Frontlines. 2008. (ENG.). 332p. pap. 20.01 *(978-0-9766054-6-1(5))* New Village Pr.

Cortissoz, Royal. Personalities in Art. 2007. 492p. per. *(978-1-4067-4438-5(7))* Read Bks.

Cox, Kenyon. Old Masters & New. 2009. 326p. 32.99 *(978-1-110-77359-6(5))*; pap. 29.75 *(978-1-110-77357-2(9))* BiblioBazaar.

Croft, Brenda L. Michael Riley Sights Unseen. 2007. (ENG., Illus.). 176p. 60.00 *(978-0-642-54162-8(0))* National Gallery of Australia AUS. Dist: Univ. of Washington Pr.

Danticat, Edwidge. Create Dangerously: The Immigrant Artist at Work. 2011. (Vintage Contemporaries Ser.). (ENG.). 208p. pap. 14.95 *(978-0-307-94643-0(6)*, Vintage) Knopf Doubleday Publishing Group.

—Create Dangerously: The Immigrant Artist at Work. 2010. (Toni Morrison Lecture Ser.). (ENG.). 208p. 19.95 *(978-0-691-14018-6(9))* Princeton Univ. Pr.

Danysz, Magda & Dana, Mary-Noelle. From Style Writing to Art: A Street Art Anthology. 2010. (Illus.). 400p. pap. 50.00 *(978-88-88493-52-7(2))*; (ENG., pap. 40.00 *(978-88-88493-66-4(2))* Drago Arts & Communication ITA. Dist: SCB Distributors.

Delbanco, Nicholas. Lastingness: The Art of Old Age. (ENG., Illus.). 272p. 2012. pap. 14.99 *(978-0-446-19965-0(6))* 2011. 24.99 *(978-0-446-19964-3(8))* Grand Central Publishing.

Denega, Danielle M. & Denega, Danielle. Have You Seen This Face? The Work of Forensic Artists. 2007. (24/7: Science Behind the Scenes Ser.). (ENG., Illus.). 64p. (YA). (gr. 9-12). 29.00 *(978-0-531-11823-8(1)*, Watts, Franklin) Scholastic Library Publishing.

Dziewior, Yilmaz & Huan, Zhang. Zhang Huan. 2009. (ENG., Illus.). 160p. pap. 45.00 *(978-0-7148-4924-9(3))* Phaidon Pr., Inc.

Esche, Charles & Lewis, Mark. Art & Social Change: A Critical Reader. Bradley, Will, ed. 2008. (ENG., Illus.). 480p. pap. 39.95 *(978-1-85437-626-8(8))* Tate Publishing, Ltd. GBR. Dist: Hachette Bk. Group.

Fisher, Charles J. & Highland Park Heritage Trust. Garvanza. 2010. (Images of America Ser.). (Illus.). 128p. pap. 21.99 *(978-0-7385-8120-0(8))* Arcadia Publishing.

Fliedl, Konstanze, et al, eds. Handbuch der Kunstzitate. 2 Bände: Malerei, Skulptur, Fotografie in der Deutschsprachigen Literatur der Moderne, 2 vols. 2011. (GER., Illus.). XXII, 966p. 419.00 ***(978-3-11-020500-8(9))*** De Gruyter, Walter Inc.

Foulon, Anne-Cecile. De l'Art pour Tous: Les Editions F. Bruckmann et leurs Revues d'Art dans Munich Ville d'Art vers 1900. (Munchener Studien zur Literarischen Kultur in Deutschland: Vol. 36). (FRE., Illus.). 448p. 57.95 *(978-3-631-50157-3(9))* Lang, Peter Publishing, Inc.

Francesca, Gavin & Gavin, Francesca. Creative Space: Urban Homes of Artists & Innovators. 2011. (ENG., Illus.). 208p. pap. 19.95 *(978-1-85669-758-3(4))* King, Laurence Publishing GBR. Dist: Hachette Bk. Group.

Franz Gertsch: Large-Scale Woodcuts. pap. *(978-3-7165-0537-3(4))* Benteli Verlag.

Freeman-Zachery, Rice. Destination Creativity: The Life-Altering Journey of the Art Retreat. 2011. (ENG.). 144p. pap. 24.99 *(978-1-4403-0869-7(1)*, North Light Bks.) F&W Media, Inc.

Freybourg, Anne Maria & Freybourg, Anne Marie. Die Inszenierung des Künstlers. 2008. (GER., Illus.). 111p. pap. *(978-3-86859-031-9(5))* Jovis Verlag GmbH.

Gavin, Francesca. 100 New Artists. 2011. (ENG., Illus.). 336p. pap. 39.95 *(978-1-85669-734-7(7))* King, Laurence Publishing GBR. Dist: Hachette Bk. Group.

Gentry, Alistair. Career Suicide. 2010. 276p. pap. 25.50 *(978-1-4461-5292-8(8))* Lulu Enterprises Inc.

Gibson, Lois. Forensic Art Essentials: A Manual for Law Enforcement Artists. 2007. (ENG., Illus.). 432p. per. 108.00 *(978-0-12-370898-4(2)*, Academic Pr.) Elsevier Science & Technology Bks.

Giuffre, Katherine. Collective Creativity: Art & Society in the South Pacific. 2009. (Anthropology & Cultural History in Asia & the Indo-Pacific Ser.). (Illus.). 182p. 99.95 *(978-0-7546-7664-5(1))* Ashgate Publishing Co.

Grande, John K. Dialogues in Diversity: Art from Marginal to Mainstream. 2007. (ENG., Illus.). 192p. pap. *(978-88-901960-7-2(6))* Pari Publishing.

Guiying, Xu & Soberoy, David. Designers League. 2009. (Illus.). 415p. *(978-981-245-548-2(5))* Page One Publishing.

Hadden, Peggy. The Quotable Artist. 2007. (ENG.). 224p. pap. 16.95 *(978-1-58115-494-8(1)*, 115494, Allworth Pr.) Skyhorse Publishing Co., Inc.

Hale, Edward Everett. Lights of Two Centuries. 2007. (ENG.). 610p. 59.95 *(978-0-548-16803-5(2))*; 612p. per. 44.95 *(978-1-4304-6523-2(9))* Kessinger Publishing, LLC.

Hamerton, Philip Gilbert. Portfolio Papers. 2009. (ENG.). 399p. 38.99 *(978-1-117-69665-2(0))*; 400p. pap. 33.75 *(978-1-117-69666-9(9))* BiblioBazaar.

—Portfolio Papers. 2009. 172p. pap. *(978-1-150-58469-5(6))* Books LLC.

He, Jianping. All Men Are Brothers: Graphic Designers, 1 vol. 2008. (DUT & ENG., Illus.). 660p. pap. 60.00 *(978-90-76886-70-1(9))* Tectum B.V.B.A. BEL. Dist: Innovative Logistics.

Heine, Achim, ed. Oliver Mark. 2010. (ENG., Illus.). 192p. 60.00 *(978-3-7757-2484-5(2))* Hatje Cantz Verlag GmbH & Co KG DEU. Dist: D.A.P./Distributed Art Pubs.

Held, Peter, ed. Eden Revisited: The Ceramic Art of Kurt Weiser. 2007. (ENG.). 96p. ***(978-0-9777624-5-3(9))*** Arizona State Univ. Art Museum.

Hemingson, Vince. Tattoo Design Directory: The Essential Reference for Body Art. 2009. (ENG., Illus.). 192p. spiral bd. 14.99 *(978-0-7858-2489-3(8)*, 0785824898, Chartwell) Book Sales, Inc.

Hemming, Henry. Misadventure in the Middle East: Travels As Tramp, Artist & Spy. 2007. (ENG., Illus.). 304p. per. 19.95 *(978-1-85788-395-4(0))* Ebsco Publishing.

Henderson, Bruce B. & Ostrander, Noam, eds. Understanding Disability Studies & Performance Studies. 2010. (ENG., Illus.). 272p. (C). 125.00 *(978-0-415-56553-0(7)*, Routledge) Taylor & Francis Group GBR. Dist: Taylor & Francis Group.

Hensky, Clyde. Luminous Shadows. 2007. 0.01 net. *(978-1-60402-214-8(0))* Independent Pub.

Hernert, Read. Diccionario del Arte y los Artistas. (SPA., Illus.). 412p. 39.95 *(978-84-233-2377-7(3)*, DE773) Ediciones Destino ESP. Dist: Continental Bk. Co., Inc.

Higa, Tori. Today's Top Stationery Artists. 2008. (Illus.). 112p. pap. 24.95 *(978-0-7643-2832-9(8))* Schiffer Publishing, Ltd.

—Today's Top Stationery Artists 2. 2011. (Illus.). 144p. pap. *(978-0-7643-3737-6(8)*, Schiffer Publishing Ltd) Schiffer Publishing, Ltd.

Holmes, Caroline. Impressionists in Their Gardens. 2012. (ENG., Illus.). 192p. 55.00 *(978-1-85149-653-2(X))* Antique Collectors' Club.

Honing, Henkjan. The Illiterate Listener: On Music Cognition, Musicality & Methodology. 2011. (ENG.). pap. ***(978-90-5629-689-6(2)***, Vossiupers UvA) Amsterdam Univ. Pr.

Horne, Olive Browne & Scobey, Katherine Lois. Stories of Great Artists. 2007. (ENG.). 160p. 36.95 *(978-0-548-09098-5(X))* Kessinger Publishing, LLC.

Huneker, James. Promenades of an Impressionist. 2009. 402p. pap. 34.75 *(978-1-116-00917-0(X))* 2008. 288p. 28.99 *(978-0-554-24594-2(9))* 2008. 288p. 25.99 *(978-0-554-33897-2(1))* 2006. (ENG.). 254p. pap. 21.99 *(978-1-4264-6905-3(5))* 2007. 284p. pap. 23.99 *(978-1-4264-6987-9(X))* BiblioBazaar.

—Promenades of an Impressionist. 2008. (ENG.). 264p. per. *(978-1-4065-6902-5(X))* Dodo Pr.

—Promenades of an Impressionist. 2007. (ENG.). 184p. per. *(978-1-4068-1371-5(0))* Echo Library.

—Promenades of an Impressionist. 2008. 408p. 49.95 *(978-1-4372-6448-7(4))*; 404p. pap. 34.95 *(978-1-4371-3787-3(3))* Kessinger Publishing, LLC.

Illman, Ruth. Art & Belief: Artists Engaged in Interreligious Dialogue. 2012. (Cross Cultural Theologies Ser.). (ENG.). 224p. (C). pap. 24.95 ***(978-1-84553-967-2(2))*** Equinox Publishing Ltd. GBR. Dist: Brown, David Bk. Co., The.

—Arts & Beleif: Artists Engaged in Interreligious Dialogue. 2012. (Cross Cultural Theologies Ser.). (ENG.). 224p. (C). 99.95 ***(978-1-84553-966-5(4))*** Equinox Publishing Ltd. GBR. Dist: ISD.

Impresionistas. (SPA.). 256p. *(978-1-4054-1495-1(2))* Parragon, Inc.

James, Harvey. Watching Them Be: The Movie Star Experience. Date not set. *(978-0-571-21197-5(6))* Faber & Faber, Inc.

James, N. P. Interviews - Artists: Recordings from Cv/Visual Arts Research Archive 1988-96. 4th ed. 2007. (Illus.). 144p. pap. *(978-1-905571-50-5(X))* Cv Pubns.

Joo, Eungie. The Ungovernables: 2012 New Museum Triennial. 2012. (ENG., Illus.). 256p. 60.00 ***(978-0-8478-3899-8(4)***, Skira) Rizzoli International Pubns., Inc.

Kokoli, Alexandra, ed. Susan Hiller: the Provisional Texture of Reality. 2008. (ENG., Illus.). 160p. pap. 22.00 *(978-3-905829-56-3(8))* JRP Ringier Kunstverlag AG CHE. Dist: D.A.P./Distributed Art Pubs.

La Londe, Richard Parker. Richard La Londe & Friends: Fused Glass, Vitreous Enamels & Other Techniques: Book II. 2009. (Illus.). 240p. *(978-0-9779126-1-2(2))* Ozone Pr.

Lemaire, Gerard-Georges. Artists' Houses. 2011. (ENG., Illus.). 192p. 29.95 *(978-0-86565-276-7(7))* Vendome Pr., The.

Luh, Peter. Der Allegorische Reichsadler von Conrad Celtis und Hans Burgkmair: Ein Werbeblatt fur das Collegium Poetarum et Mathematicorum in Wien. (Europaische Hochschulschriften Ser.: Vol. 390). (GER., Illus.). 118 S.p. 19.95 *(978-3-631-38530-2(7))* Lang, Peter Publishing, Inc.

Luz, Manuel. Imagine That: Discovering Your Unique Role as a Christian Artist. 2009. (ENG.). 184p. pap. 14.99 *(978-0-8024-2450-1(3))* Moody Pubs.

McCarthy, Mary. Florenz. Bethke, Ursula, tr. (KiWi Ser.: 375).Tr. of Stones of Florence. (GER.). 207p. pap. *(978-3-462-02429-6(9))* Kiepenheuer & Witsch GmbH & Company KG DEU. Dist: International Bk. Import Service, Inc.

McCartney, Mary. Mary McCartney: From Where I Stand. 2010. (ENG., Illus.). 192p. 35.00 (978-0-8109-9654-0(5)) Abrams.

McCaughan, Edward J. Art & Social Movements: Cultural Politics in Mexico & Aztlán. 2012. (ENG., Illus.). 240p. pap. 23.95 (978-0-8223-5182-5(X)) Duke Univ. Pr.

—Artists & Social Movements: Cultural Politics in Mexico & Aztlán. 2012. (ENG., Illus.). 240p. 84.95 (978-0-8223-5168-9(4)) Duke Univ. Pr.

Merrett, Andy. PicWords. 2010. 47p. pap. 16.95 (978-1-4457-4669-4(0)) Lulu Enterprises Inc.

Morgan, Les. The Significance of Diaspora Politics in the Visual Arts: Art, Protest & Belonging. 2008. 144p. pap. (978-3-639-08964-8(2)) VDM Verlag Dr. Mueller e.K.

Morgan, Michael H. Lost History: The Enduring Legacy of Muslim Scientists, Thinkers, & Artists. 2008. (ENG., Illus.). 320p. pap. 15.95 (978-1-4262-0280-3(6), National Geographic) National Geographic Society.

Mullin, Jill. Drawing Autism. 2012. (ENG., Illus.). 160p. pap. 27.95 (978-1-935613-48-0(0)) Batty, Mark Pub., LLC.

Musée de design et d'arts appliqués contemporains Staff, contrib. by. L'art du Verre Contemporain: Contemporary Glass Art = Zeitgenössische Glaskunst, 1 vol. 2007. (ENG., Illus.). 405p. 80.00 (978-2-88453-127-6(0)) La Bibliotheque des Arts FRA. Dist: D.A.P./Distributed Art Pubs.

Nagle, Jeanne. Tattoo Artists. 2009. (Tattooing Ser.). 64p. (gr. 5-6). 58.50 (978-1-60853-262-9(3)) Rosen Publishing Group, Inc., The.

Nagle, Jeanne M. Tattoo Artists. 2008. (Tattooing Ser.). (Illus.). 62p. (YA). (gr. 9-12). lib. bdg. 29.25 (978-1-4042-1790-4(8)) Rosen Publishing Group, Inc., The.

Nagler, Richard, photos by. Word on the Street. 2010. (978-1-59714-141-3(0)); pap. (978-1-59714-140-6(2)) Heyday.

Nowell, Iris. Painters Eleven: The Wild Ones of Canadian Art, 1 vol. 2011. (ENG., Illus.). 384p. 85.00 (978-1-55365-590-9(7)) D&M Pubs. Inc. CAN. Dist: Perseus-PGW.

O'Donnell, Timothy. Sketchbook: Conceptual Drawings from the World's Most Influential Designers. 2009. (ENG., Illus.). 192p. 40.00 (978-1-59253-521-7(6), 1592535216) Quayside.

Offf. Aim High, Keep Moving! 2011. (ENG., Illus.). 356p. 45.00 (978-84-92643-61-5(7)) Index Bks., Spain ESP. Dist: Innovative Logistics.

Olson, Kimber, ed. & compiled by. Land by Hand: Fiber Artists Explore Place. 2011. (Illus.). 36p. pap. 14.95 net. (978-0-9838693-0-6(8)) Textile Ctr.

Ottmann, Klaus. Thought Through My Eyes: Writings on Art, 1977-2005. 2006. (Art & Knowledge Ser.: Vol. 2). (ENG., Illus.). 224p. per. 22.00 (978-0-88214-578-5(9)) Spring Pubns., Inc.

Parry, Ben, ed. Cultural Hijack: Rethinking Intervention. 2012. (ENG., Illus.). 288p. pap. 45.00 (978-1-84631-751-4(7)) Liverpool Univ. Pr. GBR. Dist: Chicago Distribution Ctr.

Piras, Sebastian. A Pocketful of Contemporary Artists: Photographic Portraits. 2008. (ENG., Illus.). 256p. 25.00 (978-1-86470-293-4(1)) Images Publishing Group AUS. Dist: National Bk. Network.

Platen, Angelika, photos by. Angelika Platen. 2010. (ENG., Illus.). 240p. 75.00 (978-3-7757-2653-5(5)) Hatje Cantz Verlag GmbH & Co KG DEU. Dist: D.A.P./Distributed Art Pubs.

Rees, Darrel. How to Be an Illustrator. 2008. (ENG., Illus.). 160p. pap. 24.95 (978-1-85669-530-5(1)) King, Laurence Publishing GBR. Dist: Hachette Bk. Group.

Reich, Wilhelm. Fruehe Schriften: 1920-1925. (GER.). 438p. pap. (978-3-462-02590-3(2)) Kiepenheuer & Witsch GmbH & Company KG DEU. Dist: International Bk. Import Service, Inc.

Restany, Pierre & Hundertwasser, Friedensreich. Hundertwasser. 2008. (Temporis Collection). (ENG, FRE & GER., Illus.). 255p. 39.95 (978-1-85995-644-1(0)) Parkstone International GBR. Dist: Ingram Pub. Services.

Riemschneider, Burkhard. Kippenberger. Taschen, Angelika, ed. 2007. (ENG, FRE & GER., Illus.). 240p. pap. 19.99 (978-3-8228-2686-7(3)) TASCHEN DEU. Dist: Ingram Pub. Services.

Root, Tom & Kardon, Andrew. Artists on Comic Art, 2 vols., Vol. 2. 2007. (Artists on Comic Art Ser.). (Illus.). 256p. pap. (978-1-84576-054-0(9)) Titan Bks. Ltd.

Rosler, Martha. Martha Rossler: Rights of Passage. 15.95 (978-90-6917-002-2(7)) Derycke, L. BEL. Dist: D.A.P./Distributed Art Pubs.

Ruscha, Paul, photos by. Paul Ruscha's Full Moon, 1 vol. 2008. (ENG., Illus.). 184p. pap. 20.00 (978-3-86521-231-3(X)) Steidl, Gerhard Druckerei und Verlag DEU. Dist: Innovative Logistics.

Salie, Olaf. Rising: Young Artists to keep an Eye on! 2011. (ENG.). 384p. 90.00 (978-3-942597-03-6(9)) DAAB Media Gmbh DEU. Dist: Innovative Logistics.

Schmied, Erika, ed. Erika Schmied: in Profile, Portraits of Artists. 2010. (ENG & GER., Illus.). 144p. 55.00 (978-3-86678-374-4(4)) Kerber Verlag DEU. Dist: D.A.P./Distributed Art Pubs.

Shaw, Luci. Breath for the Bones, 0 vols. 2009. 224p. pap. 13.99 (978-0-8499-2964-9(4)) Nelson, Thomas Inc.

Smith, Anna Deavere. Letters to a Young Artist. 2011. 14.02 (978-0-7848-3399-5(0), Everbind) Marco Bk. Co.

Spooner, Shearjashub. Anecdotes of Painters, Engravers, Sculptors & Architects, & Curiosities of Art, Volume III. 2007. (ENG.). 214p. pap. 20.99 (978-1-4264-5185-0(7)); 238p. pap. 22.99 (978-1-4264-5486-8(4)) BiblioBazaar.

Springgay, Stephanie, et al, eds. Being with A/R/Tography. 2009. 318p. (978-90-8790-263-6(8)) Sense Pubs.

Steffen, Albert. The Crisis in the Life of the Artist. Mackaye, Arvia, tr. 2007. (ENG.). 48p. per. 15.95 (978-1-4325-9797-9(3)) Kessinger Publishing, LLC.

Stephenson, Jody. Faltering Towards Perfection: Art, Faith, & Everything in Between. 2007. (Illus.). 192p. 24.95 (978-0-9798998-0-5(X)) Planet Eureka Springs Pr.

Taverne, Nathalie & Lambert, Anna. Creatives' Homes. 2011. (ENG., Illus.). 96p. 25.00 (978-90-8989-283-6(4)) Lannoo Pubs./Racine.

Victionary, creator. Illustration Play: Craving for the Extraordinary. 2007. (Illus.). 223p. pap. 39.95 (978-988-98229-3-4(8)) Victionary HKG. Dist: Gingko Pr., Inc.

Von Dewitz, Bodo, ed. La Bohème: Artists in the 19th & 20th century photography, 1 vol. 2010. (GER & ENG., Illus.). 280p. 75.00 (978-3-86930-139-6(2)) Steidl, Gerhard Druckerei und Verlag DEU. Dist: Innovative Logistics.

White, Kit. 101 Things to Learn in Art School. 2011. (ENG., Illus.). 224p. (gr. 17). 14.95 (978-0-262-01621-6(4)) MIT Pr.

Winslow, Michael, et al. 101 Annoying Noises, Vol. 1. Date not set. (Illus.). (Orig.). mass mkt. (978-0-9651973-1-1(X)) Vocal Vision, Inc.

Wittkower, Rudolf & Wittkower, Margot. Born under Saturn: The Character & Conduct of Artists: A Documented History from Antiquity to the French Revolution. 2006. (New York Review Books Classics). (ENG., Illus.). 360p. pap. 18.95 (978-1-59017-213-1(2), NYRB Classics) New York Review of Bks., Inc., The.

Wyatt, Gary. Seekers & Travellers: Contemporary Art of the Pacific Northwest Coast. 2012. (ENG., Illus.). 160p. pap. 29.95 (978-0-295-99237-2(9)) Univ. of Washington Pr.

Yener, Setenay. The Svetlana in Me - How I Embraced My Turkish Identity in Order to Play a Russian/Estonian for an American Audience. 2008. 56p. pap. (978-3-639-11134-7(6)) VDM Verlag Dr. Mueller e.K.

ARTISTS—BIBLIOGRAPHY

Authors & Artists for Young Adults, Vol. 82. 2010. (Authors & Artists for Young Adults Ser.). (ENG.). 168.00 (978-0-7876-7801-2(5)) Cengage Gale.

Ferguson, Dana. Authors & Artists for Young Adults. 2008. (Authors & Artists for Young Adults Ser.: No. 78). (ENG.). 217p. 168.00 (978-0-7876-7797-8(3)) Cengage Gale.

La Blanc, Michael & Greve, Jennifer, eds. Authors & Artists for Young Adults, Vol. 73. 2007. (Authors & Artists fro Young Adults Ser.). (ENG., Illus.). 224p. 168.00 (978-0-7876-7792-3(2)) Cengage Gale.

Russell, Robert James, et al, eds. Authors & Artists for Young Adults, Volume 76. 2008. (Authors & Artists for Young Adults Ser.: Vol. 76). (ENG., Illus.). 224p. (J). 168.00 (978-0-7876-7795-4(7)) Cengage Gale.

Sams, Amanda. Authors & Artists for Young Adults. 2008. (Authors & Artists for Young Adults Ser.: Vol. 77). (ENG.). 224p. 168.00 (978-0-7876-7796-1(5)) Cengage Gale.

Thomson Gale, creator. Authors & Artists for Young Adults. (Authors & Artists for Young Adults Ser.). (ENG., Illus.). 224p. Vol. 71. 2006. 168.00 (978-0-7876-7790-9(6)) Vol. 75. 2007. 168.00 (978-0-7876-7794-7(9)) Cengage Gale.

—Authors & Artists for Young Adults: Volume 70, Vol. 70. 2006. (Authors & Artists for Young Adults Ser.). (ENG., Illus.). 250p. 168.00 (978-0-7876-7789-3(2)) Cengage Gale.

—Authors & Artists for Young Adults, Volume 72, Vol. 72. 2006. (Authors & Artists for Young Adults Ser.). (ENG., Illus.). 250p. 168.00 (978-0-7876-7791-6(4)) Cengage Gale.

—Authors & Artists for Young Adults Volume 74, Vol. 74. 2007. (Authors & Artists fro Young Adults Ser.). (ENG., Illus.). 240p. 168.00 (978-0-7876-7793-0(0)) Cengage Gale.

Topjon, Ann J. Carl Larsson: An Annotated Bibliography. 2008. (Illus.) 454p. 135.00 (978-1-58456-210-8(2)) Oak Knoll Pr.

ARTISTS—BIOGRAPHY

Abakanowicz, Magdalena. Fate & Art. 2008. (Confessions Ser.). (ENG., Illus.). 240p. pap. 70.00 (978-88-6130-035-4(9)) Skira Editore ITA. Dist: Random Hse., Inc.

Abdunnur, Sharif. My Brother's Bicycle. 2010. 64p. pap. 15.99 (978-1-4500-9196-1(2)) Xlibris Corp.

Abeyta, Rob, Jr. Compliments Of. 2007. (Illus.). 96p. 19.95 (978-0-9790862-0-5(5)) Upper Playground Pubng.

Ackerman, Gerald M. Orientalistes de l'Ecole Britannique. 2010. (Orientalists Ser.). (FRE., Illus.). 336p. 170.00 (978-2-86770-049-1(3)) ACR Edition FRA. Dist: Antique Collectors' Club.

Ackermann, Rita, et al. Rita Ackermann. 2011. (ENG., Illus.). 224p. 65.00 (978-0-8478-3664-2(9)) Rizzoli International Pubns., Inc.

Agabian, Nancy. Me As Her Again: [true Stories of an Armenian Daughter]. 2008. (ENG.). 216p. pap. 12.95 (978-1-879960-79-4(6)) Aunt Lute Bks.

Aguer, Montse. The Treasures of Dali. 2009. (Illus.). 88p. (978-1-84796-003-0(0)) Andre Deutsch.

Albers, Patricia. Joan Mitchell: Lady Painter. 2011. (ENG., Illus.). 544p. 40.00 (978-0-375-41437-4(1), Knopf) Knopf Doubleday Publishing Group.

Albus, Volker. Werner Aisslinger. Fast Forward: Einleitung von Volker Albus. 2010. (GER & ENG., Illus.). 180p. 54.00 (978-3-89986-139-6(6), Avedition Gmbh,Csl) Continental Sales, Inc.

Aldridge, Alan. The Man with Kaleidoscope Eyes: The Art of Alan Aldridge. 2009. (ENG., Illus.). 240p. 37.50 (978-0-8109-0596-2(5)) Abrams.

Alioth, Max. Susanna Biedermann: Learning to Look. 2011. (ARA, FRE, GER & ENG., Illus.). 448p. 98.00 (978-2-86770-198-6(8)) ACR Edition FRA. Dist: Antique Collectors' Club.

Allgemeines Künstler-Lexikon. 2011. (GER.). LII, 540p. 348.00 (978-3-11-023177-9(8)) De Gruyter, Walter Inc.

Ambrose, Tom. Heroes & Exiles Gay Icons Through the Ages. 2010. (ENG., Illus.). 224p. pap. 15.95 (978-1-84773-468-6(5)) New Holland Pubs., Ltd. GBR. Dist: National Bk. Network.

Amiet, Cuno, et al. Ferdinand Hodler: Biografische Erinnerungen. 2010. (GER., Illus.). 192p. 67.00 (978-3-85881-156-1(4)) Scheidegger und Spiess AG, Verlag CHE. Dist: Antique Collectors' Club.

Ammann, Helmut. Werktagebücher Eines Bildhauers und Malers. 2007. (Illus.). (978-3-937200-40-8(1)); (GER., (978-3-937200-57-6(6)); (978-3-937200-39-2(8)) Gerig, Hans, Musikverlage.

Amos, Robert. Artists in Their Studios: Where Art Is Born, 1 vol. 2007. (ENG., Illus.). 160p. (978-1-894898-58-4(3)) TouchWood Editions.

Anastasi, William & Levy, Aaron. The Cage Dialogues: A Memoir. 2011. pap. (978-1-936994-01-4(1)) Slought Foundation.

Andersen, Wayne. Marcel Duchamp: The Failed Messiah. 2011. (ENG.). 402p. pap. 19.50 (978-0-9725573-3-7(4)) Fabriart Editions, Ltd.

Anderson, Laurie. Laurie Anderson: Nothing in My Pockets. 2009. (ENG., Illus.). 62p. pap. 45.00 (978-2-914563-43-7(4)) Dis Voir Editions FRA. Dist: D.A.P./Distributed Art Pubs.

Anderson, Londa & Siefert, Joanna. The Illustrated Artwork of Londa M. Anderson: A person living with schizoaffective disorder in the 21st century - with Art, Comes Hope. 2009. 52p. pap. 34.60 (978-0-557-15859-1(1)) Lulu Enterprises Inc.

Anderson, Randy. On Making Off: Misadventures off-off Broadway. 2011. (ENG.). 306p. pap. 14.99 (978-1-4610-4168-9(6)) CreateSpace.

Andrae, Thomas. Creators of the Superheroes. 2011. (Illus.). 224p. pap. 39.99 (978-1-932563-53-5(9)) Hermes Pr.

Appleby, Dee. From Land & Sea: Nova Scotia's Contemporary Landscape Artists. 2010. (ENG., Illus.). 156p. 35.00 (978-1-55109-729-9(X)) Down East Bks.

Apter, Seth. The Pulse of Mixed Media: Secrets & Passions of 100 Artists Revealed. 2012. (ENG., Illus.). 144p. pap. 24.99 (978-1-4403-1070-6(X), North Light Bks.) F&W Media, Inc.

Arakelyan, Mikayel. Mesrop of Xizan: An Armenian Master of the Seventeenth Century. 2011. (ENG.). 128p. (C). pap. 40.00 (978-0-9553393-3-2(2)) Holberton, Paul Publishing GBR. Dist: Univ. of Washington Pr.

Archbold, Rick. An Artist in Nature. 2010. (ENG., Illus.). 175p. 40.00 (978-1-897330-46-3(4)) Madison Pr. Bks. CAN. Dist: Independent Pubs. Group.

Argyropoulou, Nadja & Aukeman, Anastasia. Lydia Venieri: Theogony. 2011. (ENG., Illus.). 152p. pap. 37.50 (978-88-8158-792-6(0)) Charta ITA. Dist: D.A.P./Distributed Art Pubs.

Armleder, John & Marks, Lisa. Piero Golia: Desert Interviews or How to Jump off the Roof & Not Hit the Ground. 2011. (ENG., Illus.). 100p. pap. 28.00 (978-3-03764-106-4(1)) JRP Ringier Kunstverlag AG CHE. Dist: D.A.P./Distributed Art Pubs.

Arobateau, Red Jordan. My Continuing Journey into Spritual, Artistic & Revolutionary Thoughts. 2009. 283p. pap. 19.99 (978-0-578-00682-6(0)) Red Jordan Pr.

The Artists of the World - Bio-bibliographical Index A-Z. 2nd ed. 2009. (ENG & GER.). XXXIX, 857p. (978-3-598-24567-1(X)); XXXIX, 864p. (978-3-598-24566-4(1)) Saur, K. G. Verlag GmbH & Co.

Arulpragasm, Maya. M. I. A. 2010. (ENG.). 96p. 10.00 (978-0-06-199528-6(2), Harper Paperbacks) HarperCollins Pubs.

Ashery, Oreet & Sansour, Larissa. The Novel of Nonel & Vovel. 2009. (ENG., Illus.). 188p. pap. 39.95 (978-88-8158-733-9(5)) Charta ITA. Dist: D.A.P./Distributed Art Pubs.

Aspley, Keith. Historical Dictionary of Surrealism. 2010. E-Book 125.00 (978-0-8108-7499-2(7)); (ENG.). 574p. 125.00 (978-0-8108-5847-3(9)) Scarecrow Pr., Inc.

Atalay, Bulent, et al. Leonardo's Universe: The Renaissance World of Leonardo Da Vinci. 2009. (ENG., Illus.). 288p. 35.00 (978-1-4262-0285-8(7), National Geographic) National Geographic Society.

Auad, Manuel, ed. Franklin Booth: American Illustrator. 2006. (Illus.). 128p. 24.95 (978-0-9669381-4-2(3)) Auad Publishing.

Audubon, John James. John James Audubon's Journal Of 1826: The Voyage to the Birds of America. Patterson, Daniel, ed. & intro. by. 2011. (ENG., Illus.). 536p. 50.00 (978-0-8032-2531-2(8)) Univ. of Nebraska Pr.

Auping, Michael, et al. Road Tested, 1 vol. 2011. (ENG., Illus.). 128p. 40.00 (978-3-7757-2810-2(4)) Hatje Cantz Verlag GmbH & Co KG DEU. Dist: D.A.P./Distributed Art Pubs.

Authors & Artists for Young Adults, Vol. 82. 2010. (Authors & Artists for Young Adults Ser.). (ENG.). 168.00 (978-0-7876-7801-2(5)) Cengage Gale.

Authors & Artists for Young Adults: A Biographical Guide to Novelists, Poets, Playwrights Screenwriters, Lyricists, Illustrators, Cartoonists, Animators, & Other Creative Artists. 2011. 168.00 (978-0-7876-9478-4(9)) Cengage Gale.

Baca, Judith & Ramos, Henry. Painting the River of Angels: The Autobiography of Judith F. Baca. 2008. pap. 16.95 (978-1-55885-488-8(6)) Arte Publico Pr.

Baglione, Giovanni, et al. Lives of Adam Elsheimer. 2007. (Lives of the Artists Ser.). (ENG., Illus.). 96p. pap. 15.95 (978-1-84368-013-0(0)) Pallas Athene GBR. Dist: Independent Pubs. Group.

Baile de Laperriere, Charles & Murray, Lynda. Who's Who in Art: 34th Edition. 34th ed. 2010. 837p. 190.00 (978-0-904722-44-4(9)) Hilmarton Manor Pr. GBR. Dist: Cengage Gale.

Bailey, Anthony. Velázquez & the Surrender of Breda: The Making of a Masterpiece. 2011. (ENG., Illus.). 288p. 32.00 (978-0-8050-8835-9(0), Holt, Henry & Co.

Bair, Deirdre. Saul Steinberg: A Biography. 2012. (ENG., Illus.). 752p. 40.00 (978-0-385-52448-3(X), Talese, Nan A.) Knopf Doubleday Publishing Group.

Baker, Bill. George Perez on His Work & Career. 2007. (Talking with Graphic Novelists Ser.). 105p. (YA). (gr. 9-12). lib. bdg. 30.50 (978-1-4042-1133-4(1)) Rosen Publishing Group, Inc., The.

Baker, William Spohn. The Engraved Portraits of Washington: Notices of the Originals & Brief Biographical Sketches of the Painters. 212p. reprint ed. 98.00 (978-0-7222-8969-3(3)) Library Reprints, Inc.

Baldinucci, Filippo, et al. Lives of Rembrandt: Sandrart, Baldinucci & Houbraken. 2008. (Lives of the Artists Ser.). (ENG.). 96p. pap. 13.95 (978-1-84368-016-1(5)) Pallas Athene GBR. Dist: Independent Pubs. Group.

Barrington, Emilie. G. F. Watts: Reminiscences. 2010. (Cambridge Library Collection - Women's Writing Ser.). (Illus.). 310p. pap. 24.99 (978-1-108-02220-0(0)) Cambridge Univ. Pr.

Bartoletti, Laurence. Creation en France: Arts decoratifs 1945-1965: Repertoire Alphabetique. 2010. (ENG.). 388p. pap. 95.00 (978-2-35340-019-5(1)) Gourcuff Gradenigo FRA. Dist: National Bk. Network.

Bartz, Gabriele & Konig, Eberhard. Michelangelo: Buonarroti 1475-1564. 2008. (Masters of Italian Art Ser.). (Illus.). 138p. pap. 9.95 (978-0-3416-0082-9(1)) American Map Corp.

Basar, Shumon, et al, eds. Hans Ulrich Obrist Interviews, Vol. 2. 2010. (ENG., Illus.). 950p. pap. 75.00 (978-88-8158-731-5(9)) Charta ITA. Dist: D.A.P./Distributed Art Pubs.

Baskin, Gere, ed. Robert Wilbert: Ennobling the Ordinary. 2011. 50.00 (978-0-615-45383-5(X)) Wayne State Univ. Pr.

Basualdo, Carlos, et al. Michelangelo Pistoletto: From One to Many, 1956-1974. 2010. (ENG., Illus.). 416p. 65.00 (978-0-300-16616-3(8)) Yale Univ. Pr.

Baume, Nicholas, ed. Sol Lewitt: Structures, 1965-2006. 2012. (ENG., Illus.). 192p. 50.00 (978-0-300-17861-6(1)) Yale Univ. Pr.

Bazzell, Paul. Famous Again: The Life & Times of Sorrells Pickard. 2009. 150p. pap. 19.95 (978-1-60563-738-9(6)) PublishAmerica, Inc.

Beaton, Roderick, et al. El Greco - The Cretan Years. 2009. (Publications of the Centre for Hellenic Studies, King's College London Ser.). (Illus.). 180p. 99.95 (978-0-7546-6897-8(5)) Ashgate Publishing Co.

Beauchamp, Monte, ed. The Life & Times of R. Crumb: Comments from Contemporaries. 2007. (Illus.). 182p. reprint ed. pap. 18.00 (978-1-4223-6268-6(X)) DIANE Publishing Co.

Becker, Katja M. & Podobinski, Stephanie. Graphic Design: Next Generation. 2009. (Illus.). 624p. (978-981-245-652-6(X)) Page One Publishing.

Becker, Stephen, ed. Theodore Wores in the Southwest. 2007. (California Historical Society Ser.). (Illus.). 98p. per. 24.95 (978-1-59714-047-8(3)) Heyday.

Bellesi, Sandro. Catalogo dei pittori fiorentini del '600 E '700: Trecento artisti. Biografie e Opere, 3 vols. 2009. (ITA., Illus.). 1088p. (C). 628.00 (978-88-596-0625-3(X)) Polistampa ITA. Dist: Brown, David Bk. Co., The.

Benavidez, Max. Gronk. 2007. (Ver — Revisioning Art History Ser.: Vol. 1). (Illus.). 200p. pap. 24.95 (978-0-89551-101-0(0)) UCLA Chicano Studies Research Ctr. Pr.

—Gronk. 2007. (Ver Ser.). (Illus.). 200p. 60.00 (978-0-89551-105-8(3)) Univ. of Minnesota Pr.

Benezit, Emmanuel. Benezit Dictionary of British Graphic Artists & Illustrators, 2 vols. 2012. (ENG., Illus.). 1344p. 295.00 (978-0-19-992305-2(1)) Oxford Univ. Pr., Inc.

Benezit, Emmanuel. Benezit Dictionnaire des Peintres, Sculpteurs, Dessinateurs, et Graveurs, 14 vols. 2010. (ENG., Illus.). 13440p. 2995.00 (978-0-19-977379-4(3)) Oxford Univ. Pr., Inc.

Benfey, Christopher. Red Brick, Black Mountain, White Clay: Reflections on Art, Family, & Survival. 2012. (ENG.). 288p. (gr. 12). 25.95 (978-1-59420-326-8(1), Penguin Pr. HC, The) Penguin Group (USA) Inc.

Bentley, G. E. William Blake's Conversations: A Compilation, Concordance, & Rhetorical Analysis. 2008. (Illus.). xlix, 297p. (978-0-7734-4848-3(9)) Mellen, Edwin Pr., The.

Berardi, Marianne & Adams, Henry. Discovering Margot Peet: The Artist & the Art World of Kansas City. 2008. (978-1-889274-32-4(1)) Posterity Pr.

berning, stan. About Art. 2009. 132p. pap. 15.00 (978-0-578-00623-9(5)) Berning, Stan.

Bertola, Chiara, ed. & text. Mona Hatoum: Interior Landscape. 2009. (ENG & ITA., Illus.). 168p. pap. 39.95 (978-88-8158-735-3(1)) Charta ITA. Dist: D.A.P./Distributed Art Pubs.

Beutin, Heidi & Beutin, Wolfgang, eds. Ernst Barlach (1870-1938) Sein Leben, sein Schaffen, seine Verfolgung in der NS-Diktatur. 2009. (Bremer Beiträge zur Literatur- und Ideengeschichte Ser.). (GER.). 298p. pap. 64.95 (978-3-631-58817-8(8)) Lang, Peter GmbH, Europaischer Verlag der Wissenschaften DEU. Dist: Lang, Peter.

Bewick, Thomas. A Memoir of Thomas Bewick. 2008. 372p. 48.95 (978-1-4369-8464-5(5)); pap. 33.95 (978-1-4367-4014-2(2)) Kessinger Publishing, LLC.

Biedenharn Jones, Ann. Ann Biedenharn Jones: Life & Art. 2010. (Illus.). 128p. 29.95 (978-0-615-38967-7(8)) Blue Lake Pr. LLC.

Bikker, Jonathan, et al. Dutch Paintings of the Seventeenth Century in the Rijksmuseum Amsterdam Vol. 1: Artists Born Between 1570 & 1600, 2 vols. 2008. (ENG., Illus.). 584p. 500.00 (978-90-8689-027-9(X)) Yale Univ. Pr.

Bilal, Wafaa. Shoot an Iraqi: Art, Life & Resistance under the Gun. 2008. (ENG., Illus.). 240p. pap. 16.95 (978-0-87286-491-7(X)) City Lights Bks.

Binyon, Helen. Eric Ravilious: Memoir of an Artist. 2007. (ENG., Illus.). 144p. pap. 60.00 (978-0-7188-2920-9(4)) Lutherworth Pr., The GBR. Dist: Brown, David Bk. Co., The.

A Biographical Guide to Novelists, Poets, Playwrights Screenwriters, Lyricists, Illustrators, Cartoonists, Animators, & Other Creative Artists, 79. 2009. (Authors & Artists for Young Adults Ser.). (ENG.). 224p. 168.00 (978-0-7876-7798-5(1)) Cengage Gale.

Biographiq. Andy Warhol - a Life of Pop Art. 2008. 76p. pap. 9.99 (978-1-59986-058-9(9), Biographiq) Filiquarian Publishing, LLC.

Bird, Michael. The St Ives Artists: A Cultural Biography 1939-64. 2008. (Illus.). 192p. pap. 40.00 (978-0-85331-956-6(1), Lund Humphries Pubs.) Ashgate Publishing, Ltd. GBR. Dist: Ashgate Publishing Co.

Birdsall, Byron & Garvey, Mike. People of the Saltchuk: Paintings by Byron Birdsall. 2009. (978-1-933245-17-1(4)) Documentary Media LLC.

Biró, Mihály, et al. Mihály Biró: Pathos in Red. 2011. (GER & ENG., Illus.). 144p. pap. 30.00 (978-3-86984-157-1(5)) Verlag fur Moderne Kunst DEU. Dist: D.A.P./Distributed Art Pubs.

Bishop, Anne Warner, Jr. Silver, the Life & Art of Sylvia Beckman Warner. 2007. 100.00 (978-0-9796438-1-1(3)) Bishop, Anne.

Bishop, Elizabeth. Exchanging Hats: Paintings, 1 vol. Benton, William, ed. 2011. (ENG., Illus.). 136p. pap. 35.00 (978-0-374-53343-4(1)) Farrar, Straus & Giroux.

Blackmon, Virginiae. Extreme Grandma on the Loose. 2008. 114p. pap. 10.95 (978-0-7414-4424-0(0)) Infinity Publishing.

Blanz, Hubert. Slideshow. 2009. (GER., Illus.). 176p. 39.95 (978-3-211-85781-6(8)) Springer Wien AUT. Dist: Actar Birkhauser Distribution.

Block, Herbert. Herblock: The Life & Work of the Great Political Cartoonist. Katz, Harry, ed. 2009. (ENG., Illus.). 304p. 35.00 (978-0-393-06772-9(6), 6772) Norton, W. W. & Co., Inc.

Bocquet, José-Louis, et al. The Adventures of Herge. 2011. (ENG., Illus.). 64p. 19.95 (978-1-77046-059-1(4)) Drawn & Quarterly Pubns. CAN. Dist: Macmillan.

Bohm-Duchen, Monica. Art & Life of Josef Herman. 2009. (Illus.). 200p. 80.00 (978-0-85331-945-0(6), Lund Humphries Pubs.) Ashgate Publishing, Ltd. GBR. Dist: Ashgate Publishing Co.

Boltanski, Christian & text. The Possible Life of Christian Boltanski. 2009. (ENG., Illus.). 242p. 35.00 (978-0-87846-746-4(7)) Museum of Fine Arts, Boston.

Bonin, Wibke von. Wanda Richter-Forgach: Paintings & Drawings. 2007. 72p. (978-2-87909-845-6(9)) Wienand GmbH, Druck- & Verlagshaus.

Boreham, F. W. Lover of Life: F. W. Boreham's Tribute to His Mentor (Revised & Expanded) rev. ed. 2007. 44p. pap. 9.00 (978-0-9790334-0-7(3)) Broadbanks, John Publishing.

Borg, Jessica & Sciberras, Keith. Francesco Zahra 1710-1773: His Life & Art in Mid-18th Century Malta y Keith Sciberras, with contributions by Jessica Borg & photography by Joe P. Borg. 2010. (ENG., Illus.). 272p. (C). 115.00 (978-99932-7-319-6(8)) Midsea Bks. Ltd. MLT. Dist: Brown, David Bk. Co., The.

Borsboom, Jos. Michael Jackson: The Icon. 2011. 402p. 38.50 (978-1-4476-1399-2(6)) Lulu Enterprises Inc.

Bos, Ben. AGI: Graphic Design Since 1950. Bos, Elly, ed. 2007. (ENG., Illus.). 800p. 65.00 (978-0-500-51342-2(2), 551342) Thames & Hudson.

Botha, Ted. The Girl with the Crooked Nose. 2012. (ENG., Illus.). 384p. (gr. 12). pap. 15.00 (978-0-425-24683-2(3), Berkley Trade) Penguin Group (USA) Inc.

Bott, Karsten. Karsten Bott: One of Each. 2007. (ENG., Illus.). 288p. 49.95 (978-3-86560-307-4(6)) Verlag der Buchhandlung Walther Konig DEU. Dist: D.A.P./Distributed Art Pubs.

Bourgeois, Caroline. Elogio Del Dubbio: Eloge du Doute = in Praise of Doubt. 2012. (ITA & ENG., Illus.). 204p. 65.00 (978-88-370-8508-7(7)) Electa ITA. Dist: National Bk. Network.

Boyden, Frank. Coexistence with Fire: Wood-Fired Ceramics by Frank Boyden, 1985-2006. 2008. (Illus.). 245p. (978-0-9816728-2-3(5)) American Museum of Ceramic Art.

Bradshaw, Richard Lee. Thomas Bradshaw: A Georgian Politician in the Time of the American Revolution. 2011. 162p. 29.99 (978-1-4653-4478-6(0)); pap. 19.99 (978-1-4653-4477-9(2)) Xlibris Corp.

Bradstreet, Tim. Archetype: The Art of Timothy Bradstreet. 2009. 256p. 49.99 (978-1-935002-00-0(7)); 79.99 (978-1-935002-01-7(5)) Desperado Publishing.

Bramwell, Valerie & Peck, Robert McCracken. All in the Bones: A Biography of Benjamin Waterhouse Hawkins. 2008. (978-0-910006-65-1(2)) Academy of Natural Sciences Philadelphia.

Branin, Larissa. Great Artists of the World. 2nd rev. ed. 2009. 128p. 17.95 (978-1-59764-121-0(9)) New Line Bks.

Briney, S. Self Portrait. 2010. 192p. pap. 15.99 (978-1-4490-6161-6(3)) AuthorHouse.

Brink, Andrew. Desire & Avoidance in Art: Psychobiographical Studies with Attachment Theory of Pablo Picasso, Hans Bellmer, Balthus, & Joseph Cornell. 2007. (Illus.). 222p. (C). 68.95 (978-0-8204-9721-1(5)) Lang, Peter Publishing, Inc.

Brinkmann, Bodo, text. Konrad Witz. 2011. (ENG., Illus.). 320p. 85.00 (978-3-7757-2761-7(2)) Hatje Cantz Verlag GmbH & Co KG DEU. Dist: D.A.P./Distributed Art Pubs.

Bristow, Roger. The Last Bohemians: The Two Roberts - Colquhoun & MacBryde. 2013. (ENG.). 460p. pap. 65.00 (978-1-906593-16-2(7)) Sansom & Co. Ltd. GBR. Dist: National Bk. Network.

Brommer, Bea. Johannes Ten Klooster (1873-1940) A Man with Two Lives. 2007. (Illus.). 96p. 49.95 (978-90-6832-486-0(1)) Royal Tropical Institute Pr. (KIT (Koninklijk Instituut voor de Tropen) NLD. Dist: Stylus Publishing, LLC.

Brooker, Peter. Bohemia in London: The Social Scene of Early Modernism. 2007. (ENG., Illus.). 224p. pap. 31.00 (978-0-230-54692-9(7)) Palgrave Macmillan.

Brougham, John. A Basket of Chips by John Brougham. 2006. 412p. per. 26.99 (978-1-4255-4467-6(3)) MPublishing.

Brown, James. James Brown: The Passion. pap. 145.00 (978-91-87952-04-3(1)) Propexus AB SWE. Dist: D.A.P./Distributed Art Pubs.

Brown, Jeffrey. Little Things: A Memoir in Slices. 2008. (ENG., Illus.). 352p. pap. 14.00 (978-1-4165-4946-8(3), Touchstone) Touchstone.

Brun, Carl, compiled by. Schweizerisches Künstler-lexikon, 4 vols., 2006. (GER.). 2698p. 395.00 (978-1-57898-593-7(5)) Martino Publishing.

Bruno, Lugene. 13th International Exhibition of Botanical Art & Illustration. 2010. (ENG., Illus.). 197p. pap. 25.00 (978-0-913196-84-7(3)) Hunt Institute for Botanical Documentation.

Bruskin, Grisha. Past Imperfect: 318 Episodes from the Life of a Russian Artist. 2008. (Judaic Traditions in Literature, Music, & Art Ser.). (Illus.). 34.95 (978-0-8156-0901-8(9)) Syracuse Univ. Pr.

Brutvan, Cheryl. Antonio López Garcia. 2008. (ENG., Illus.). 160p. pap. 24.95 (978-0-87846-733-4(5)) Museum of Fine Arts, Boston.

Bryant, Robert L. The Thin Black Line: Perspectives on Vince Colletta, Comics' Most Controversial Inker. 2010. (Illus.). 112p. pap. 14.95 (978-1-60549-028-1(8)) TwoMorrows Publishing.

Bubb, Roy. Visions from a White Mountain Palette: The Life & Times of Charles A. Hunt, Madison's White Mountain Painter. 2008. (Illus.). 112p. 40.00 (978-1-931807-73-9(6)) Randall, Peter E. Pub.

Buck, Ken. Bill Mason: Wilderness Artist: From Heart to Hand, 1 vol. 2010. (ENG., Illus.). 224p. (978-1-894765-60-2(5)) Rocky Mountain Bks.

Buckman, David. Artists in Britain since 1945, 2 vols. 2007. (ENG., Illus.). 1856p. 330.00 (978-0-9532609-5-9(X), Sansom (Acc)) Antique Collectors' Club GBR. Dist: National Bk. Network.

Bullen, Barrie & Bullen, J. B. Rossetti: Painter & Poet. 2011. (ENG., Illus.). 272p. 50.00 (978-0-7112-3225-9(3)) Lincoln, Frances Ltd. GBR. Dist: Perseus-PGW.

Burt, Eugene C. Dictionary of Erotic Artists: Painters, Sculptors, Printmakers, Graphic Designers, & Illustrators. 2010. (ENG.). 350p. pap. 55.00 (978-0-7864-4874-6(1)) McFarland & Co., Inc. Pubs.

Burton, Johanna, et al. Sherrie Levine: Mayhem. 2012. (ENG., Illus.). 216p. 60.00 (978-0-300-17596-7(5)) Yale Univ. Pr.

Büttner, Nils. Herr P.P. Rubens: Von der Kunst, Berühmt Zu Werden. 2006. (Rekonstruktion der Künste Ser.). (GER., Illus.). 278p. (C). pap. 93.00 (978-3-525-47906-3(9)) Vandenhoeck & Ruprecht GmbH & Co. KG DEU. Dist: ISD.

Cage, John. John Cage Book of Days 2012. Kuhn, Laura, ed. 2011. (ENG., Illus.). 120p. pap. 25.00 (978-1-935202-64-6(2)) D.A.P./Distributed Art Pubs.

Cahan, Susan, ed. & intro. I Remember Heaven: Jim Hodges & Andy Warhol, 1 vol. 2007. (ENG., Illus.). 112p. 35.00 (978-0-9777528-2-9(8)) Contemporary Art Museum St. Louis.

Cameron, Dan, text. Taner Ceylan: 1997-2009. 2011. (ENG., Illus.). 184p. 50.00 (978-88-6208-173-3(1)) Damiani ITA. Dist: D.A.P./Distributed Art Pubs.

Cárdenas, Juan, et al. Juan Cárdenas. 2010. (SPA., Illus.). 228p. 65.00 (978-958-8306-08-7(6)) Villegas Editores S.A. COL. Dist: Independent Pubs. Group.

Carlsson, Benke & Louie, Hop. Street Art Cookbook: A Guide to Techniques & Materials. 2011. (ENG., Illus.). 140p. mass mkt. 19.95 (978-91-85639-46-5(X)) Dokument forlag, Fotograf Malcolm Jacobsson SWE. Dist: SCB Distributors.

Carr, Cynthia. Fire in the Belly: The Life & Times of David Wojnarowicz. 2012. (ENG., Illus.). 624p. 35.00 (978-1-59691-533-6(1), 226195) Bloomsbury Publishing.

Carr, Emily. This & That: The Lost Stories of Emily Carr, 1 vol. 2007. (ENG., Illus.). 232p. per. (978-1-894898-61-4(3)) TouchWood Editions.

Carsello, Lance. Hamptons 21. 2010. 52p. pap. 11.99 (978-1-4520-1122-6(2)) AuthorHouse.

Celaya, Enrique Martínez. Enrique Martinez Celaya, 1990-2010: Collected Writings & Interviews. 2010. (ENG., Illus.). 272p. pap. 19.95 (978-0-8032-3474-1(0)) Univ. of Nebraska Pr.

Cellini, Benvenuto. The Life of Benvenuto Cellini. 2010. 580p. pap. 43.75 (978-1-142-59624-8(9)) 2009. 264p. pap. 24.99 (978-1-103-89767-4(5)) 2009. 264p. pap. 18.99 (978-1-103-89761-2(6)) BiblioBazaar.

—The Life of Benvenuto Cellini. 2009. 208p. pap. (978-1-151-10398-7(5)); 86p. pap. (978-0-217-94250-8(4)); 84p. pap. (978-0-217-94249-2(0)); 272p. pap. (978-0-217-94247-8(4)); 478p. pap. (978-0-217-33289-7(7)); 220p. pap. (978-0-217-33288-0(9)) Books LLC.

—The Life of Benvenuto Cellini. 2009. 478p. pap. 27.36 (978-1-4589-8199-8(1)) General Bks. LLC.

Cellini, Benvenuto & Maconell, Anne. The Life of Benvenuto Cellini. 2010. 272p. pap. 27.75 (978-1-141-18321-0(8)) BiblioBazaar.

Chagall, Marc. My Life: Marc Chagall. 2011. (Peter Owen Modern Classic Ser.). (ENG.). 200p. pap. 15.95 (978-0-7206-1356-8(6)) Owen, Peter Ltd. GBR. Dist: Independent Pubs. Group.

Chana, Leonard F., et al. The Sweet Smell of Home: The Life & Art of Leonard F. Chana. 2009. (ENG., Illus.). 176p. 40.00 (978-0-8165-2818-9(7)); pap. 21.95 (978-0-8165-2819-6(5)) Univ. of Arizona Pr.

Chillida, Eduardo. Eduardo Chillida: Writings. 2011. (ENG., Illus.). 160p. 40.00 (978-3-941263-07-9(2)) Richter Verlag DEU. Dist: D.A.P./Distributed Art Pubs.

Christensen, Ken. Up North with Uncle Bob. 2009. 248p. pap. 22.97 (978-0-557-09457-8(7)) Lulu Enterprises Inc.

Christman, Jill. Darkroom: A Family Exposure. 2011. (Association of Writers & Writing Programs Award for Creative Nonfiction Ser.). (ENG., Illus.). 264p. pap. 19.95 (978-0-8203-4174-3(6)) Univ. of Georgia Pr.

Clarke, Gill. Evelyn Dunbar: War & Country. 2007. (ENG., Illus.). 224p. per. 49.95 (978-1-904537-56-4(1), Sansom (Acc)) Antique Collectors' Club GBR. Dist: National Bk. Network.

Clarkson, Millie. Edna Hibel: An Artist's Story of Love & Compassion, 1 vol. 2006. (ENG., Illus.). 176p. 60.00 (978-1-58980-427-2(9)) Pelican Publishing Co., Inc.

Clearwater, Bonnie. The Rothko Book. 2007. (ENG., Illus.). 224p. pap. 29.95 (978-1-85437-573-5(3)) Tate Publishing, Ltd. GBR. Dist: Hachette Bk. Group.

Cloarec, Françoise. Storr: Architecte de L'ailleurs. 2010. (FRE., Illus.). 170p. (978-2-7529-0485-0(1)) Phebus, Editions.

Close, Lesley Mary. Hooked Rug Storytelling: The Art of Heather Ritchie. 2011. (Illus.). 192p. (978-0-7643-3695-9(9), Schiffer Publishing Ltd) Schiffer Publishing, Ltd.

Coleman, Loring W. Loring W. Coleman: Living & Painting in a Changing New England, an Autobiography. Fortmiller, Hugh, ed. 2011. (ENG., Illus.). 240p. 65.00 (978-1-55595-341-6(7)) Hudson Hills Pr. LLC.

Collins, Ian. John Craxton. 2011. (Illus.). 186p. 70.00 (978-1-84822-069-0(3), Lund Humphries Pubs.) Ashgate Publishing, Ltd. GBR. Dist: Ashgate Publishing Co.

—John McLean: A Life in Paint. 2009. (Illus.). 176p. 80.00 (978-1-84822-012-6(X), Lund Humphries Pubs.) Ashgate Publishing, Ltd. GBR. Dist: Ashgate Publishing Co.

—John Mclean: A life in paint:limited Edition. 2010. (Illus.). 176p. 600.00 (978-1-84822-013-3(8), Lund Humphries Pubs.) Ashgate Publishing, Ltd. GBR. Dist: Ashgate Publishing Co.

Collins, Thom & Fitzpatrick, Tracy, eds. American People, Black Light: Faith Ringgold's Paintings of The 1960s. 2011. (ENG., Illus.). 136p. pap. 30.00 (978-0-9795629-3-8(7)) Neuberger Museum of Art.

Colonetti, Aldo. Raymundo Sesma: Campo Expandido. 2009. (ENG., Illus.). 288p. 77.95 (978-88-8158-734-6(3)) Charta ITA. Dist: D.A.P./Distributed Art Pubs.

Connah, Roger. The Rest Is Silence Zahoor Ul Akhlaq: Art & Society in Pakistan. 2012. (ENG., Illus.). 350p. 99.00 (978-0-19-547472-5(4)) Oxford Univ. Pr., Inc.

Conover, Mary. Alchemy of Light. 2010. (ENG., Illus.). 368p. 59.00 (978-0-9799752-4-0(7)) Whale & Star Pr.

Constable, Freda & Simon, Sue. The England of Eric Ravilious. 3rd rev. ed. 2006. (Illus.). 104p. pap. 40.00 (978-0-85331-880-4(8), Lund Humphries Pubs.) Ashgate Publishing, Ltd. GBR. Dist: Ashgate Publishing Co.

Convis, Charles. Frontier Artists & Photographers. 2007. pap. 8.95 (978-1-892156-23-5(7)) Pioneer Pr.

Cook, Edward Tyas. The Life of John Ruskin, 1819-1860. 2010. (Cambridge Library Collection - Literary Studies). (ENG., Illus.). 580p. pap. 43.00 (978-1-108-00971-3(9)) Cambridge Univ. Pr.

Cooperman, Emily T. & Sherk, Lea Carson. William Birch: Picturing the American Scene. 2010. (Illus.). 352p. (C). 75.00 (978-0-8122-4248-5(3)) Univ. of Pennsylvania Pr.

Copley, William. William N. Copley: Cply X-Rated. 2011. (ENG., Illus.). 140p. 65.00 (978-0-9829433-1-8(8)) Paul Kasmin Gallery.

Cortez, Constance. Carmen Lomas Garza. 2010. (Ver Ser.). (ENG., Illus.). 108p. 60.00 (978-0-89551-124-9(X)); pap. 24.95 (978-0-89551-125-6(8)) Univ. of Minnesota Pr.

Cost, Patricia A. The Bentons: How an American Father & Son Changed the Printing Industry. 2011. (ENG., Illus.). 396p. pap. 24.95 (978-1-933360-42-3(9), RIT Pr.) Rochester Institute of Technology, Cary Graphic Arts Pr.

Couch, N. C. Christopher. Jerry Robinson: Ambassador of Comics. 2010. (ENG., Illus.). 128p. 35.00 (978-0-8109-7764-8(8)) Abrams.

Cowling, E., et al. Picasso: Challenging the Past. 2011. (Illus.). 176p. pap. 25.00 (978-1-85709-451-0(4)) Yale Univ. Pr.

Cromartie, James H. Nantucket Portrait: Fun & Games with the Super Rich... the Birth of Hard-Edge Realism. 2008. (Illus.). 176p. pap. 49.99 (978-0-7643-3112-1(4)) Schiffer Publishing, Ltd.

Curran, Jean A. In My Dreams I Ride Wild Horses: Biographical Sketches, Art, & Poetry of Appalachian Artist Billy Roper. 2011. 112p. pap. 39.95 (978-1-4567-2145-9(3)) AuthorHouse.

Curtis, Herb, et al. Bruno Bobak: The Full Palette. Riordon, Bernard, ed. 2006. (ENG., Illus.). 208p. 55.00 (978-0-86492-481-0(X)) Goose Lane Editions CAN. Dist: Univ. of Toronto Pr.

DAAB Media Staff, ed. Graphic Design Inspirations, 1 vol. 2010. (ENG.). 700p. 119.95 (978-3-86654-075-0(2)) DAAB Media Gmbh DEU. Dist: Innovative Logistics.

Daan Van Golden. pap. 35.00 (978-90-5006-058-5(7)) Stedelijk Museum NLD. Dist: D.A.P./Distributed Art Pubs.

Dabbs, Julia K. Life Stories of Women Artists 1550-1800. 2009. (Illus.). 504p. 124.95 (978-0-7546-5431-5(1)) Ashgate Publishing Co.

Dagen, Philippe, ed. Lamento. 2008. 272p. (978-2-919923-50-2(1)) Actar Birkhauser Distribution.

DAIM. DAIM: daring to push the boundaries. 2006. (Illus.). 108p. pap. 24.95 (978-3-00-014155-3(3)) Gingko Pr., Inc.

Dalli Regoli, Gigetta. Verrocchio, Lorenzo di Credi, Francesco di Simone Ferrucci. 2008. (Drawing Gallery Ser.). (ENG., Illus.). 92p. pap. 14.95 (978-88-7439-068-7(8)) 5 Continents ITA. Dist: Hachette Bk. Group.

Dalmia, Yashodhara. Journeys: Four Generations of Indian Artists in Their Own Words two-volume Set, 2 vols. 2011. (ENG., Illus.). 628p. 225.00 (978-0-19-807319-2(4)) Oxford Univ. Pr., Inc.

Dalton, David & Rosenquist, James. Painting below Zero: Notes on a Life in Art. 2009. (ENG., Illus.). 384p. 50.00 (978-0-307-26342-1(8), Knopf) Knopf Doubleday Publishing Group.

David Joseph Herrle. 158p. 4.99 (978-0-9706843-0-1(4)) Herrle, David Joseph.

Davies, Hugh M. & Irwin, Robert, contrib. by. Robert Irwin: Primaries & Secondaries, 1 vol. 2008. (ENG., Illus.). 220p. 65.00 (978-0-934418-67-6(5)) Museum of Contemporary Art, San Diego.

Davis, Richard F. Seized Again. 2011. 378p. 29.99 (978-1-4628-9256-3(6)); pap. 19.99 (978-1-4628-9255-6(8)) Xlibris Corp.

De Holanda, Francisco. Dialogues with Michelangelo. Holroyd, Charles, tr. 2007. (Illus.). 127p. pap. (978-1-84368-015-4(7)) Wilson, John Booksales.

De Kwiatkowski, Lulu. Lulu: Popular Edition. 2010. 192p. 49.95 (978-1-934429-45-7(7)) AMMO Bks., LLC.

De Lafayette, Maximillien. Bona Fide Divas & Femmes Fatales: The 700 Official Divas of the World in Cinema, Theater, Music, Opera, Jazz, Entertainment & Performing Arts. 2007. (Illus.). 400p. per. 69.95 (978-0-9799750-8-0(5)) Elite Assocs. International-Times Square Pr.

—World Who's Who in Contemporary Art: Thematic & Biographical Encyclopedia of Living Artists & Styles. 2007. (Illus.). 400p. per. 69.95 (978-0-9799750-9-7(3)) Elite Assocs. International-Times Square Pr.

De Lamartine, Alphonse. Raphael: Or, Pages of the Book of Life at Twenty. 2007. 152p. per. (978-1-4065-2575-5(8)) Dodo Pr.

de Werd, Guido, et al, texts. With a Probability of Being Seen. 2010. (ENG & GER., Illus.). 320p. 95.00 (978-3-941263-13-0(7)) Richter Verlag DEU. Dist: D.A.P./Distributed Art Pubs.

Dearden, James S. John Ruskin: An Illustrated Life of John Ruskin, 1819-1900. 2nd ed. 2008. (Shire Library). (ENG., Illus.). 64p. pap. 12.95 (978-0-7478-0599-1(7)) Shire Pubns., Ltd. GBR. Dist: Random Hse., Inc.

Debono, Sandro & Scicluna, Bernadine. The Busuttil Family: A Legacy of Three Generations. 2010. (Illus.). 136p. pap. 52.00 (978-99932-7-305-9(8)) Midsea Bks. Ltd. MLT. Dist: Brown, David Bk. Co., The.

DeLatte, Carolyn E. Lucy Audubon, a Biography. 2009. (Southern Biography Ser.). (Illus.). xxiii, 248p. pap. (978-0-8071-3381-1(7)) Louisiana State Univ. Pr.

Deneulin, Luc & Swinnen, Johan. Raoul Servais: The Wizard of Ostend: Commitment, Challenge, Recognition. 2009. (ENG, DUT & FRE., Illus.). 320p. pap. 54.00 (978-90-5487-480-5(5)) VUB Univ. Pr. BEL. Dist: Independent Pubs. Group.

DePastino, Todd. Bill Mauldin: A Life up Front. 2009. (ENG., Illus.). 384p. pap. 16.95 (978-0-393-33488-3(0), 33488) Norton, W. W. & Co., Inc.

di Stefano, Eva. Gustav Klimt: Art Nouveau Visionary. 2008. (ENG., Illus.). 240p. pap. 21.95 (978-1-4027-5920-8(7)) Sterling Publishing Co., Inc.

Dixon, David. Watts My Line? The Life & Work of Editorial Artist, Lawrie Watts. 2007. (ENG., Illus.). 216p. pap. 46.95 (978-0-9544357-7-6(X)) Redline Bks. GBR. Dist: MBI Distribution Services/Quayside Distribution.

Doerr, Nathan & Musgrave, Judy. The Life & Art of Bernard P. Thomas: Paint, Passion & Preservation. 2007. (Illus.). 104p. 24.95 (978-0-9792871-0-7(3)) Sherian County Historical Society Pr.

Donaldson, Don. Are You an Artist Mister. 2010. (Illus.). 290p. pap. (978-0-7552-1257-6(6)) Authors OnLine, Ltd.

Doonan, Simon. Nasty: My Family & Other Glamorous Varmints. 2007. (ENG., Illus.). 304p. pap. 20.95 (978-1-4165-8634-0(2)) Simon & Schuster.

Doubleday Publisher. Ernest Thompson Seton: A Biographical Sketch. 2011. 50p. 36.95 (978-1-258-02176-4(5)) Literary Licensing, LLC.

Doughty, Mike. The Book of Drugs: A Memoir. 2012. (ENG.). 256p. pap. 16.00 (978-0-306-81877-6(9)) Da Capo Pr., Inc.

Douglas, aka Elbow Toe, By Brian Adam. Paper Cuts. 2011. (ENG.). 80p. 50.00 (978-88-88493-77-0(8)) Drago Arts & Communication ITA. Dist: SCB Distributors.

Dowdy, Joanne Kilgour. Artful Stories: The Teacher, the Student, & the Muse. 2012. E-Book (978-1-4539-0524-1(3)); (C). pap. 34.95 (978-1-4331-1408-3(9)); xxiii, 149p. (C). pap. 139.95 (978-1-4331-1407-6(0)) Lang, Peter Publishing, Inc.

Drathen, Doris von. Manuela Filiaci. 2009. (ENG., Illus.). 144p. pap. 39.95 (978-88-8158-740-7(8)) Charta ITA. Dist: D.A.P./Distributed Art Pubs.

Droz, Dwight. The Art of the Midnight Poet. 2007. 152p. pap. 24.95 (978-0-9706357-9-2(6)) Scandia Patch Pr.

Drury, Nevill. Homage to Pan: The Life, Art & Sex-Magic of Rosaleen Norton. 2010. (Illus.). 255p. pap. (978-1-902197-26-5(7)) Oneiros Bks.

Drury, Nevill. The Magic of Pan. 2011. 444p. pap. (978-3-8443-2323-8(6)) Lambert Academic Publishing.

Dube, Prince Mbusi. Dumile Feni: The Story of a Great Artist. 2011. 286p. 61.95 (978-0-9869833-0-6(6)) STE Pubs. ZAF. Dist: Independent Pubs. Group.

Dunlap, Sarah & Buck, Stephanie. Fitz Henry Lane: Family & Friends. 2007. (Illus.). 185p. pap. 18.95 (978-0-615-15729-0(7)) Church & Mason Publishing.

Dunlop, Paul H. The Dictionary of Glass Paperweights: An Illustrated Primer. 2009. (Illus.). xv, 382p. (978-0-9619547-5-8(2)) Papier Pr.

Duty, Michael & McGarry, Susan Hallsten. Texas Traditions: Contemporary Artists of the Lone Star State. 2010. (ENG., Illus.). 240p. 85.00 (978-1-934491-24-9(1)) Fresco Fine Art Pubns., LLC.

Dwyer, Dennis E. God, Country & Tattoos. 2011. 268p. pap. 16.99 (978-1-61215-798-6(X)) Xulon Pr., Inc.

Eccher, Danilo. Marc Quinn: Myth. 2009. (ENG & ITA., Illus.). 120p. 49.95 *(978-88-8158-725-4(4))* Charta ITA. Dist: D.A.P./Distributed Art Pubs.
Eckhardt, Joseph P. So Bravely & So Well: The Life & Art of William T. Trego. 2011. (Illus.). 208p. pap. 39.95 *(978-1-879636-24-8(7))* Univ. of Pennsylvania Pr.
Eckmann, Teresa & Nakashima, Thomas V., texts. No Bounds: Luis Cruz Azaceta. 2007. per. 15.00 *(978-0-9669064-1-7(1))* Herbert, Gertrude Institute of Art.
Eden, Jenni. Face2faith: A Spiritual Journey Through Paint. 2010. 108p. pap. 33.49 *(978-1-4520-3910-7(0))* AuthorHouse.
Edmier, Keith. Keith Edmier 1991-2007. 2008. (ENG., Illus.). 176p. 125.00 *(978-1-86154-303-5(4))* Booth-Clibborn Editions GBR. Dist: Hachette Bk. Group.
Edwards, Gwynne. Lorca, Bunuel, Dali: Forbidden Pleasures & Connected Lives. 2009. (ENG., Illus.). 256p. 45.00 *(978-1-84885-007-1(7))* I. B. Tauris & Co., Ltd. GBR. Dist: Macmillan.
Egger, Heinz. Heinz Egger, 1 vol. 2007. (ENG., Illus.). 144p. 40.00 *(978-3-937572-60-4(0))* Richter Verlag DEU. Dist: D.A.P./Distributed Art Pubs.
Eichler, Dominic, et al. Wilhelm Sasnal. 2011. (ENG., Illus.). 160p. pap. 45.00 ***(978-0-7148-6079-4(4))*** Phaidon Pr., Inc.
Eksell, Olle. Olle Eksell: Swedish Graphic Designer. Pie Books Staff & Takahashi, Kaoru, eds. 2011. (ENG., Illus.). 240p. pap. 39.95 *(978-4-89444-547-5(6))* Rizzoli International Pubns., Inc.
Eliasoph, Philip. Robert Vickrey: The Magic of Realism. 2009. (ENG., Illus.). 240p. 75.00 *(978-1-55595-292-1(5))* Hudson Hills Pr. LLC.
Ellis, Edwin J. The Real Blake: A Portrait Biography. 2007. (ENG.). 480p. 53.95 *(978-0-548-09660-4(0))* Kessinger Publishing, LLC.
Ellis, Ella. Dune Child. 2011. 150p. pap. 20.00 ***(978-0-9795285-9-0(3))*** El Leon Literary Arts.
Elphick, Jonathan. Birds: The Art of Ornithology. 2008. (ENG., Illus.). 336p. 19.95 *(978-0-8478-3134-0(5))* Rizzoli International Pubns., Inc.
Emin, Tracey. One Thousand Drawings. 2009. (ENG., Illus.). 2016p. 75.00 *(978-0-8478-3202-6(3))* Rizzoli International Pubns., Inc.
—Tracey Emin: My Life in a Column. 2011. (ENG., Illus.). 368p. 35.00 *(978-0-8478-3807-1(3))* Rizzoli International Pubns., Inc.
Encounters: Richard Painter. 2006. (Illus.). 12p. pap. 8.00 *(978-1-885820-22-8(4))* Huntsville Museum of Art.
Ernst, Max. Max Ernst. 2006. 400p. 400.00 *(978-0-9712051-8-5(3))* Cocytus Pr.
Essays, Zürich, et al. Sophie Taeuber-Arp: Gestalterin, Architektin, Tänzerin. 2008. (Illus.). 72p. 49.00 *(978-3-85881-196-7(3))* Scheidegger und Spiess AG, Verlag CHE. Dist: Antique Collectors' Club.
Estermann, Lorenz. Lorenz Estermann: Public Hyperbindings. 2010. (ENG., Illus.). 104p. 55.00 *(978-3-7757-2609-2(8))* Hatje Cantz Verlag GmbH & Co KG DEU. Dist: D.A.P./Distributed Art Pubs.
Estrup, Carole. Barefoot Girl Out of Ohio. 2007. 408p. per. 25.95 *(978-0-595-43694-1(3))* iUniverse, Inc.
Evans, Al. Chee Chee: A Study of Aboriginal Suicide. 2010. (McGill-Queen's Native & Northern Ser.). (Illus.). 208p. (C). pap. *(978-0-7735-3759-0(7))* McGill-Queen's Univ. Pr.
Evans, Barbara A. Val Laigo's Passion. 2007. 234p. pap. 24.95 *(978-1-4241-7634-2(4))* PublishAmerica, Inc.
Evans, R. Tripp. Grant Wood: A Life. 2010. (ENG., Illus.). 432p. 37.50 *(978-0-307-26629-3(X),* Knopf) Knopf Doubleday Publishing Group.
Fagan, Dorothy. Dinner with the Muse the Yellow Door Cottage. 2008. 76p. pap. 12.95 *(978-1-4357-1860-9(7))* Lulu Enterprises Inc.
Farr, Michael. The Adventures of Herge: Creator of Tintin. 2008. (Illus.). 128p. 29.95 *(978-0-86719-679-5(3))* Last Gasp of San Francisco.
Farrachi, Armand. Michel-Ange Face Aux Murs. 2010. (FRE.). 118p. *(978-2-07-012980-5(2))* Gallimard, Editions.
Farrar, J. Maurice. Mary Anderson. 2007. 68p. per. *(978-1-4065-1688-3(0))* Dodo Pr.
Farrell, David. Micheal Farrell: The Life & Work of an Irish Artist. 2007. (ENG., Illus.). 214p. 47.95 *(978-1-904148-89-0(1))* Liffey Pr., The IRL. Dist: Dufour Editions, Inc.
Farthing, Stephen, ed. 501 Great Artists: A Comprehensive Guide to the Giants of the Art World. 2008. (ENG., Illus.). 640p. 29.99 *(978-0-7641-6133-9(4))* Barron's Educational Series, Inc.
Feast or Famine: Growing up Bohemian in Provincetown. 2008. (Illus.). 144p. 50.00 *(978-0-9818755-0-7(5))* Kelly, Julia.
Feaver, William. James Boswell: Unofficial War Artist. 2008. (Illus.). 136p. pap. *(978-0-9547959-2-4(X))* Muswell Press, The.
Feiffer, Jules. Backing into Forward: A Memoir. 2012. (ENG.). 456p. pap. 19.00 ***(978-0-226-24035-0(5))*** Univ. of Chicago Pr.
Feinstein, Patricia Stark. Sam Feinstein. 2008. (ENG., Illus.). 216p. 100.00 *(978-0-9790597-8-0(X))* Fields Publishing.
Felbinger, Udo. Henri de Toulouse-Lautrec: Life & Work. 2008. (Art in Focus (Konemann) Ser.). (Illus.). 95p. pap. 5.95 *(978-0-8416-0056-0(2))* American Map Corp.
Ferguson, Dana. Authors & Artists for Young Adults. 2008. (Authors & Artists for Young Adults Ser.: No. 78). (ENG.). 217p. 168.00 *(978-0-7876-7797-8(3))* Cengage Gale.
Fernandez Miro, Emi. Joan Miro 1956-1983: Sentiment, Emocio, Gest. 2007. (Illus.). 225p. pap. *(978-84-934730-2-0(2))* Actar Birkhauser Distribution.
Filonov, Pavel Nikolaevich & Pravoverova, L. L. Pavel Filonov: Realnost I Mify. 2008. (RUS.). 670p. *(978-5-7784-0353-6(4))* Agraf, LTD, OOO.
Finch, Christopher. Chuck Close: Life. 2010. (Illus.). 352p. 34.95 *(978-3-7913-3677-0(0))* Prestel Publishing.
Fingeroth, Danny. Disguised as Clark Kent: Jews, Comics, & the Creation of the Superhero. 2008. (ENG., Illus.). 216p. pap. 22.95 *(978-0-8264-3014-4(7))* Continuum International Publishing Group, Ltd. GBR. Dist: National Bk. Network.
Firouzeh. Portrait of A Life. 2011. (ENG.). 88p. pap. 17.50 ***(978-0-7618-5475-3(4))*** Hamilton Bks.
Fitzgerald, Paul. Will Eisner & PS Magazine. 2008. (Illus.). 320p. pap. 29.99 *(978-1-932563-01-6(6))* Hermes Pr.
Fleckner, Uwe. Jean-Auguste-Dominique Ingres: 1780-1867. 2008. (Masters Ser.). (Illus.). 140p. pap. 9.95 *(978-0-8416-0080-5(5))* American Map Corp.
Flemig, Kurt. Karikaturisten-Lexikon. (GER.). XIV, 325p. ***(978-3-11-186496-9(0))*** Saur, K. G. Verlag GmbH & Co.
Fleming, Geoffrey K. & Bramson, Ruth Ann. Charles Henry Miller, N. A. Painter of Long Island. 2012. (ENG., Illus.). 200p. 40.00 *(978-1-55595-343-0(3))* Hudson Hills Pr. LLC.
Fleming, Geoffrey K., et al. A Shared Aesthetic: Artists of Long Island's North Fork. 2008. (ENG., Illus.). 250p. 50.00 *(978-1-55595-300-3(X))* Hudson Hills Pr. LLC.
Forcellino, Antonio. Michelangelo: A Tormented Life. 2009. (ENG., Illus.). 300p. 25.00 *(978-0-7456-4005-1(2))* Polity Pr. GBR. Dist: Wiley, John & Sons, Inc.
Forrest, Tara & Scheer, Anna Teresa, eds. Christoph Schlingensief: Art without Borders. 2010. (Illus.). 176p. pap. 35.00 *(978-1-84150-319-6(3))* Intellect, Ltd. GBR. Dist: Chicago Distribution Ctr.
Foster, Alicia. Gwen John in London & Paris. 2007. (ENG., Illus.). 240p. 50.00 *(978-0-300-11854-4(6))* Yale Univ. Pr.
Foster, Barbara Spencer. Fremont Ellis. 2010. 124p. pap. 35.00 *(978-0-86534-632-1(1))* Sunstone Pr.
Francesca, Piero Della. Piero Della Francesca. (Colección Art Book) (SPA., Illus.). 144p. *(978-84-8156-220-0(3))* Sociedad Editorial Electa Espana ESP. Dist: Lectorum Pubns., Inc.
Frank, Fiona & Coyle, Judith. Hannah Frank: Footsteps on the Sands of Time; A Hundredth Birthday Celebration Gallimaufry (School Edition) 2008. (Illus.). 172p. pap. *(978-1-904999-74-4(3))* Kennedy & Boyd.
Frankel, Noralee. Stripping Gypsy: The Life of Gypsy Rose Lee, 1 vol. 2010. (ENG., Illus.). 320p. pap. 17.95 *(978-0-19-975433-5(0))* Oxford Univ. Pr., Inc.
Freeman, Ian. Cage Fighter: The True Story of Ian "the Machine" Freeman. 2009. (ENG., Illus.). 288p. pap. 13.95 *(978-1-84454-620-6(9))* Blake, John Publishing, Ltd. GBR. Dist: Independent Pubs. Group.
Fretz, Eric. Jean-Michel Basquiat: A Biography, 1 vol. 2010. (Greenwood Biographies Ser.). (Illus.). 199p. 35.00 *(978-0-313-38056-3(2),* A2215C) Greenwood Publishing Group, Inc.
Friedl, Peter. Peter Friedl: Work 1964-2006. 2007. (Illus.). 365p. pap. *(978-84-89771-25-3(1))* Actar Birkhauser Distribution.
Friends, text. A Woman's Journey: The Life & Work of Artis Lane. 2007. (Illus.). 96p. pap. 29.99 *(978-0-9789818-1-5(2))* Friends, the Foundation of the CAAM.
Fu, Shen. Chapters from a Floating Life. Black, Shirley, tr. 2007. 112p. per. 11.95 *(978-1-59654-382-9(5))* Disruptive Publishing.
Fuechtner, Veronika. Berlin Psychoanalytic: Psychoanalysis & Culture in Weimar Republic Germany & Beyond. 2011. (Weimar & Now: German Cultural Criticism Ser.). (ENG., Illus.). 248p. 49.95 ***(978-0-520-25837-2(1))*** Univ. of California Pr.
Furlong, William. Speaking of Art: Four Decades of Art in Conversation. 2010. (ENG., Illus.). 272p. 39.95 *(978-0-7148-4506-7(X))* Phaidon Pr., Inc.
Fusening, T. & Taatgen, Alice. Hans von Aachen, 1552-1615. 2010. (ENG.). 300p. 48.00 *(978-3-422-06972-5(0))* Deutscher Kunstverlag GmbH DEU. Dist: Independent Pubs. Group.
Galbally, Ann. A Remarkable Friendship: Vincent Van Gogh & John Peter Russell. 2008. (ENG.). 288p. 41.00 *(978-0-522-85376-6(5))* Melbourne Univ. Publishing AUS. Dist: Independent Pubs. Group.
Gale, ed. A Biographical Guide to Novelists, Poets, Playwrights Screenwriters, Lyricists, Illustrators, Cartoonists, Animators, & Other Creative Artists. (Authors & Artists for Young Adults Ser.). 2012. (ENG.). 264p. lib. bdg. 168.00 *(978-0-7876-9480-7(0))* 2011. 212p. lib. bdg. 168.00 *(978-0-7876-9479-1(7))* Cengage Gale.
Galliani, Omar. Omar Galliani: Santi: 1995-2007, 1 vol. 2007. (ENG., Illus.). 144p. 39.00 *(978-88-89431-90-0(3))* Damiani ITA. Dist: D.A.P./Distributed Art Pubs.
Galloway, Terry. Mean Little Deaf Queer: A Memoir. 2010. (ENG.). 248p. pap. 16.00 *(978-0-8070-7331-5(8))* Beacon Pr.
García, María Amalia. Tomás Maldonado in Conversation with María Amalia García. 2011. (ENG & SPA., Illus.). 136p. 25.00 *(978-0-9823544-3-8(6))* Fundacion Cisneros.
Garzonio, Stefano & Pavan, Stefania. I Russi e il Teatro Comunale: Firenze 1932 - 1954. 2009. (Anthropology of Contemporary Culture Ser.). (ITA., Illus.). 140p. pap. *(978-88-8398-057-2(3))* European Pr. Academic Publishing.
Gauthier, Michel, et al. Olivier Mosset: Works, 1966-2003. 2008. (ENG & GER., Illus.). 144p. 39.95 *(978-88-7439-056-4(4))* 5 Continents ITA. Dist: Hachette Bk. Group.
Gayford, Martin. A Bigger Message: Conversations with David Hockney. 2011. (ENG., Illus.). 248p. 34.95 *(978-0-500-23887-5(1),* 523887) Thames & Hudson.
George, Jim & George, Kenneth M. Picturing Islam: Art & Ethics in a Muslim Lifeworld. 2010. (ENG., Illus.). 184p. 94.95 *(978-1-4051-2958-9(1),* Wiley-Blackwell) Wiley, John & Sons, Inc.
Georgia O'Keeffe Museum Staff. Natural Affinities. 2008. (ENG., Illus.). 176p. 40.00 *(978-0-316-11832-3(X))* Little Brown & Co.
Geronimus, Dennis. Piero Di Cosimo: Visions Beautiful & Strange. 2007. (ENG., Illus.). 366p. 80.00 *(978-0-300-10911-5(3))* Yale Univ. Pr.
Getty. Diary of J. J. Grandville. 2010. 57.50 *(978-0-8386-4200-9(4))* Fairleigh Dickinson Univ. Pr.
Ghez, Didier. Walt's People - 2011. 328p. pap. 19.99 ***(978-1-4568-5150-7(0))*** Xlibris Corp.
Giannetto, David F. The Decoy Artist: America's Last Hunter-Carver, 1 vol. 2010. (ENG., Illus.). 208p. 39.95 *(978-1-58980-768-6(5))* Pelican Publishing Co., Inc.
Gianni, Gary, intro. Joseph Clement Coll: A Legacy in Line. 2007. (Illus.). 208p. pap. 24.95 *(978-0-9723758-3-2(X))* Flesk Pubns.
Gill, Eric. Eric Gill: Autobiography. 344p. 2008. 46.95 *(978-1-4367-0169-3(4))* 2007. (ENG.). per. 31.95 *(978-1-4304-3780-7(1))* Kessinger Publishing, LLC.
Gilmore, Robert. Alaska, Where the long trail Led: Chronicles of a Transplanted Okie. 2007. per. 17.95 *(978-1-59433-062-9(X),* Publishing Consultants) Publication Consultants.
Giuliana. Florence, Love, Art, Artists, Fragments of My Life. 2008. 154p. pap. 14.95 *(978-1-934246-34-4(4))* Peppertree Pr., The.
Glassie, Henry. Prince Twins Seven-Seven: His Art, His Life in Nigeria, His Exile in America. 2010. (African Expressive Cultures Ser.). (ENG., Illus.). 488p. 39.95 *(978-0-253-35439-6(0),* 0253354390) Indiana Univ. Pr.
The gold Chaser: The Life & Legacy of Master Craftsman Edmund Kavanagh. collector's ed. 2006. 39.95 *(978-0-9778545-2-3(3))* Borrego Publishing.
González, José Gamaliel. Bringing Aztlan to Chicago: My Life, My Work & My Art. Zimmerman, Marc, ed. 2010. (Latinos in Chicago & Midwest Ser.). (ENG.). 216p. pap. 30.00 *(978-0-252-07735-7(0))* Univ. of Illinois Pr.
—Bringing Aztlan to Mexican Chicago: My Life, My Work & My Art. Zimmerman, Marc, ed. 2010. (Latinos in Chicago & Midwest Ser.). (ENG., Illus.). 216p. 65.00 *(978-0-252-03538-8(0))* Univ. of Illinois Pr.
Gonzalez-Torres, Felix, et al. Felix Gonzalez-Torres. Ault, Julie, ed. 2008. (ENG., Illus.). 400p. 85.00 *(978-3-86521-196-5(8))* Steidl, Gerhard Druckerei und Verlag DEU. Dist: Innovative Logistics.
Goodman, Wendy & Vanderbilt, Gloria. The World of Gloria Vanderbilt. 2010. (ENG., Illus.). 224p. 40.00 *(978-0-8109-9592-5(1))* Abrams.
Graffito Books Staff. Street Artists: The Complete Guide. 2009. (ENG., Illus.). 156p. pap. 19.95 *(978-0-9560284-1-9(1),* Graffito Bks.) Korero Books LLP GBR. Dist: Independent Pubs. Group.
Graham-Dixon, Andrew. Caravaggio: A Life Sacred & Profane. 2011. (ENG., Illus.). 514p. 39.95 *(978-0-393-08149-7(4),* 8149) Norton, W. W. & Co., Inc.
Grayson, Richard. More Summer in Brooklyn. 2010. 234p. pap. 14.99 *(978-0-557-55573-4(6))* Lulu Enterprises Inc.
Greenberger Rafferty, Sara, et al, contrib. by. North Drive Press: Ndp#3. 2006. (Illus.). 35.00 *(978-1-933045-41-2(8))* North Drive Pr.
Greene, C. & Koehler, J. Woven Color: The Tapestry Art of James Koehler. 2010. pap. 98.95 *(978-1-4507-1443-3(9))* Independent Pub.
Gregory, Danny. An Illustrated Life: Drawing Inspiration from the Private Sketchbooks of Artists, Illustrators & Designers. 2008. (ENG., Illus.). 272p. pap. 19.99 *(978-1-60061-086-8(2),* HOW Bks.) F&W Media, Inc.
Gregory, Schaaf. Hopi Katsina: 1,600 Artist Biographies, 20 vols., Vol. 7. 2008. (American Indian Art Ser.). (ENG., Illus.). 342p. 65.00 *(978-0-9776552-1-1(6))* Ctr. for Indigenous Arts & Cultures (CIAC Pr.).
Greig, Geordie. Breakfast with Lucian, 1 vol. 2012. (ENG., Illus.). 288p. 28.00 ***(978-0-374-11648-4(2))*** Farrar, Straus & Giroux.
Greiser, Katrin. Ute Wrede: Poppy & Recollection. (ENG & GER.). 15.00 *(978-3-89322-364-0(9))* Edition Cantz DEU. Dist: D.A.P./Distributed Art Pubs.
Grey House Publishing Staff & Bass, Jennifer Durham. World Cultural Leaders of the Twentieth & Twenty-First Centuries, 2 vols., Set. 2nd ed. 2007. 800p. 175.00 *(978-1-59237-118-1(3))* Grey Hse. Publishing.
Grimm, Hermann F. Life of Michelangelo V1. Bunnett, Fanny Elizabeth, tr. 2007. (ENG.). 620p. 60.95 *(978-0-548-10998-4(2))* Kessinger Publishing, LLC.
—Life of Michelangelo V2. Bunnett, Fanny Elizabeth, tr. 2007. (ENG.). 588p. 58.95 *(978-0-548-10999-1(0))* Kessinger Publishing, LLC.
Grolle, Joist. Bericht von einem Schwierigen Leben: Walter Solmitz (1905-1962) (GER & ENG., Illus.). vi, 191p. *(978-3-496-02538-2(7))* Reimer, Dietrich.
Gromling, Alexandra. Buonarroti. 2008. (Art in Focus (Konemann) Ser.). (Illus.). 95p. pap. 5.95 *(978-0-8416-0054-6(6))* American Map Corp.
Gruitrooy, Gerhard. Renoir: A Master of Impressionism. 2nd rev. ed. 2009. (Great Masters Ser.). (Illus.). 144p. 19.95 *(978-1-59764-096-1(4))* New Line Bks.
Guercio, Gabriele & Guercio, G. Art as Existence: The Artist's Monograph & Its Project. 2009. (ENG., Illus.). 392p. (gr. 17). pap. 27.95 *(978-0-262-51320-3(X))* MIT Pr.
Gute, Charles, et al, eds. Brad Kahlhamer, 1 vol. Ligniti, Emily, tr. 2007. (ENG., Illus.). 184p. pap. 55.00 *(978-88-8158-629-5(0))* Charta ITA. Dist: D.A.P./Distributed Art Pubs.
Guzzo, Lou. When Did I Die? Richard Lachman, the Artist America Forgot. 2007. 176p. per. 15.95 *(978-1-59800-878-4(1))* Outskirts Pr., Inc.
Hagerty, Donald J. The Art of Maynard Dixon, 1 vol. 2010. (ENG.). 256p. 75.00 *(978-1-4236-0380-1(X))* Gibbs Smith, Publisher.
Hall, Marshall, ed. Artists of Cumbria: An Illustrated Dictionary of Cumberland, Westmorland, North Lancashire & North West Yorkshire Painters, Sculptors, Draughtsmen & Engravers Born 1615-1900. 2006. (Illus.). 112p. pap. 17.50 *(978-0-903858-01-4(0))* Antique Collectors' Club.
Hall, Michael D. Emerson Burkhart: An Ohio Painter's Song of Himself. 2010. (ENG., Illus.). 192p. 65.00 *(978-1-85759-595-6(5))* Scala, Editions FRA. Dist: National Bk. Network.
Hallmark, Kara Kelley. Encyclopedia of Asian American Artists, 1 vol. 2007. (Artists of the American Mosaic Ser.). (Illus.). 312p. 85.00 *(978-0-313-33451-1(X),* GR3451, Greenwood Pr.) Greenwood Publishing Group, Inc.
Hallum & Louveau. Choc des Cultures. 8.95 *(978-0-8219-1460-1(X),* 40334) EMC/Paradigm Publishing.
Hamilton, Ed. Legends of the Chelsea Hotel: Living with the Artists & Outlaws in New York's Rebel Mecca. 2007. (ENG., Illus.). 368p. per. 16.95 *(978-1-56858-379-2(6))* Da Capo Pr., Inc.
Hamilton, James. Arthur Rackham: A Life with Illustration. 2011. (ENG., Illus.). 200p. 35.00 *(978-1-86205-894-1(6))* Chrysalis Children's Bks. GBR. Dist: Independent Pubs. Group.
Hamilton, Vijali. World Wheel: One Woman's Quest for Peace. 2007. (Illus.). xii, 237p. *(978-0-9789055-1-4(2))* World Wheel Pr.
Hansen, Joan Maria. Lewis Foreman Day,1845-1910: Unity in Design & Industry. 2007. (ENG., Illus.). 300p. *(978-1-85149-534-4(7),* Antique Collectors's Club Dist) Antique Collectors' Club.
Hanson, Dian, ed. Bob's World: The Life & Boys of AMG's Bob Mizer. 2009. (ENG.). 288p. 59.99 *(978-3-8365-1230-5(0))* TASCHEN DEU. Dist: Ingram Pub. Services.
Harris, Godfrey. The Legacy of Leonardo Da Vinci. 2007. *(978-0-935047-63-9(8))* Americas Group, The.
Hartwagner - Hédouin. 2011. (GER.). LII, 540p. 348.00 ***(978-3-11-023175-5(1))*** De Gruyter, Walter Inc.
Harvey, Doug & Fernandez, Veronica. Sean Duffy. 2011. (Front Forty Press - Front Forty Profiles Ser.). (Illus.). 122p. pap. 25.00 *(978-0-615-40146-1(5))* Front Forty Pr.
Haspiel, Dean & Irving, Christopher. Graphic NYC Presents: Dean Haspiel: The Early Years. 2010. (Illus.). 192p. pap. 19.99 *(978-1-60010-825-9(3))*, Idea & Design Works, LLC.
Hauptman, William. Hodler: Gallery of the Arts. 2008. (Gallery of the Arts Ser.). (ENG., Illus.). 112p. 18.95 *(978-88-7439-362-6(8))* 5 Continents ITA. Dist: Hachette Bk. Group.
Hausler, Christa & Hausler, Wolfgang, eds. Judy Ledgerwood. 2010. (ENG., Illus.). 160p. 60.00 *(978-3-7757-2421-0(4))* Hatje Cantz Verlag GmbH & Co KG DEU. Dist: D.A.P./Distributed Art Pubs.
Häussler, Harriet. Aus Künstlersicht. 13 Fragen - 51 Interviews. 2010. (GER & ENG., Illus.). 244p. 37.50 *(978-3-86678-363-8(9))* Kerber Verlag DEU. Dist: D.A.P./Distributed Art Pubs.
Havens, Charnell & Badertscher, Vera Marie. Quincy Tahoma: The Life & Legacy of a Navajo Artist. 2011. (Illus.). 256p. *(978-0-7643-3708-6(4))* Schiffer Publishing, Ltd.
Hawksworth, Peggy. Christmas with the Postcard Artists 1898-1940. 2008. pap. 113.89 *(978-1-4251-1750-4(3))* Trafford Publishing.
Haydon, Benjamin Robert. The Autobiography & Memoirs of Benjamin Robert Haydon, V1-2, 1786-1846. Taylor, Tom, ed. 2011. 962p. 80.95 ***(978-1-258-09560-4(2))*** Literary Licensing, LLC.
Hayes, Drew. Deathreats: The Life & Times of a Comic Book Rock Star. 2009. (Illus.). 384p. pap. 14.95 *(978-1-57989-092-6(X))* Sirius Entertainment, Inc.
Head, Percy Rendell. Van Dyck. 2008. 160p. 22.99 *(978-0-559-89135-9(0))*; pap. 16.99 *(978-0-559-89134-2(2))* BiblioBazaar.
—Van Dyck. 2007. (ENG.). 154p. 36.95 *(978-0-548-02469-0(3))* Kessinger Publishing, LLC.
Healy, Patrick, et al. Jacobus Kloppenburg: The Archive for the Future. 2007. (Illus.). 413p. 120.00 *(978-3-87909-877-4(8))* Wienand GmbH, Druck- & Verlagshaus DEU. Dist: Independent Pubs. Group.
Hedgpeth, Don. Follow the Sun: Robert Lougheed. 2010. (ENG.). 360p. (C). 65.00 *(978-0-578-03970-1(2))* Univ. of Oklahoma Pr.
Hedquist - Hennicke. 2011. (GER.). LII, 538p. 348.00 ***(978-3-11-023176-2(X))*** De Gruyter, Walter Inc.
Heilmann, Mary. Mary Heilmann: The All Night Movie. (GER & ENG., Illus.). 147p. pap. 40.00 *(978-3-907496-00-8(0))* Offizin Zurich Verlag, OZV CHE. Dist: D.A.P./Distributed Art Pubs.
Henderson, Wyntoun Xavier. Common Threads of Freedom Compounding. 2007. 340p. pap. 23.95 *(978-1-59299-254-6(4))* Inkwater Pr.
Herrera, Hayden & Zamudio-Taylor, Victor, texts. Frida Kahlo, 1 vol. 2007. (ENG., Illus.). 304p. 49.95 *(978-0-935640-88-5(6))* Walker Art Ctr.
Herrmann, Luke. J. M. W. Turner. 2007. (Very Interesting People Ser.). 96p. per. 11.95 *(978-0-19-921755-7(6))* Oxford Univ. Pr., Inc.
Heslewood, Juliet. Mother: Portraits by 40 Great Artists. 2009. (ENG., Illus.). 96p. 19.95 *(978-0-7112-2965-5(1))* Lincoln, Frances Ltd. GBR. Dist: Perseus-PGW.
Hesse, Jochen. Der populäre Künstler: Das Beispiel Bernhard Luginbühl. 2008. (Europäische Hochschulschriften. Reihe 28: Kunstgeschichte Ser.). 246p. pap. *(978-3-03910-979-1(0))* Lang, Peter.
Heuer, Elizabeth. Eugene Savage: The Seminole Paintings. 2011. (ENG., Illus.). 64p. pap. 12.95 *(978-1-904832-99-7(7))* Giles, D. Ltd. GBR. Dist: Antique Collectors' Club.
Heunert - Höllwarth. 2011. (GER.). LII, 540p. 348.00 ***(978-3-11-023178-6(6))*** De Gruyter, Walter Inc.
Hewison, Robert. John Byrne: Art & Life. 2011. (Illus.). 144p. 70.00 *(978-1-84822-047-8(2),* Lund Humphries Pubs.) Ashgate Publishing, Ltd. GBR. Dist: Ashgate Publishing Co.
Higgins, Ross. Peter Flinsch: The Body in Question. 2008. (ENG., Illus.). 192p. pap. 27.95 *(978-1-55152-237-1(3))* Arsenal Pulp Pr. CAN. Dist: Consortium Bk. Sales & Distribution.

Hijikata, Hisakatsu, et al. Hijikata Hisakatsu Nikki. 2010. (JPN., Illus.). *(978-4-901906-74-6(7))* National Museum of Ethnology.

Hill, Marjorie & Spencer, Thel. The Journey Recalled: A Memoir of Marjorie Frances Hill. Wilks, Densel Dean, ed. (Illus.). 39.95 *(978-0-9713141-0-8(1))* Thelton Hall Publishing.

Hirst, Damien & Brown, Gordon. The Complete Spot Paintings, 1986-2011. 2012. (Illus.). 1024p. 280.00 ***(978-1-906967-48-2(2))*** Other Criteria GBR. Dist: Abrams.

Historical Society of Cheshire County, creator. Steps to Great Art: Barry Faulkner & the Art of the Muralist. 2007. (Illus.). 28p. 12.50 *(978-0-9724478-7-4(3))* Historical Society of Cheshire Cty.

Hoban, Phoebe. Alice Neel: The Art of Not Sitting Pretty. 2010. (ENG., Illus.). 512p. 35.00 *(978-0-312-60748-7(2))* St. Martin's Pr.

Hodge, Susie. Cezanne: His life & works in 500 Images: An illustrated exploration of the artist, his life & context, with a gallery of 300 of his finest Paintings. 2011. (ENG., Illus.). 256p. 35.00 *(978-0-7548-2313-1(X))* Anness Publishing GBR. Dist: National Bk. Network.

—Monet: His Life & Works in 500 Images. 2010. (ENG., Illus.). 256p. 35.00 *(978-0-7548-1953-0(1))* Anness Publishing GBR. Dist: National Bk. Network.

Hodges, William R. Carl Wimar: A Biography. 37p. reprint ed. lib. bdg. 88.00 *(978-0-7222-0737-6(9))* Library Reprints, Inc.

Hodgson, Michael. Patricia Roc the Goddess of the Odeons. 2010. 244p. 24.99 *(978-1-4520-4588-7(7))*; pap. 18.49 *(978-1-4520-4587-0(9))* AuthorHouse.

Hoet, Jan. Documenta IX: Main Catalog, 3 vols. 2nd ed. (GER., Illus.). 896p. *(978-3-89322-381-7(9))* Edition Cantz DEU. Dist: D.A.P./Distributed Art Pubs.

Hohenstatt, Peter. Leonardo da Vinci: 1452-1519. 2008. (Masters Ser.). (Illus.). 140p. pap. 9.95 *(978-0-8416-0081-2(3))* American Map Corp.

Holl, Jim. Jim Holl the Landscape Painter. 2009. (ENG., Illus.). 128p. pap. 37.95 *(978-88-8158-729-2(7))* Charta ITA. Dist: D.A.P./Distributed Art Pubs.

Holmes, Rand & Rosenkranz, Patrick. The Artist Himself. 2010. (ENG., Illus.). 328p. pap. 39.99 *(978-1-60699-170-1(1)*, 699170) Fantagraphics Bks.

Holzwarth, Hans Werner, ed. Jeff Koons. 2009. (ENG., Illus.). 591p. 69.99 *(978-3-8365-0328-0(X))* TASCHEN DEU. Dist: Ingram Pub. Services.

Hooven III, Valentine F. Tom of Finland - Life & Work of a Gay Hero. 2011. (Illus.). 256p. 52.99 ***(978-3-86787-166-2(3))*** Bruno Gmunder Verlag GmbH DEU. Dist: Bookazine Co., Inc.

Hoptman, Laura, et al. Tomma Abts. 2008. (ENG., Illus.). 135p. 49.95 *(978-0-7148-4882-2(4))* Phaidon Pr., Inc.

Horsley, Sebastian. Dandy in the Underworld: An Unauthorized Autobiography. 2008. (P. S. Ser.). (ENG.). 368p. pap. 13.99 *(978-0-06-146125-5(3)*, HarperPerennial) HarperCollins Pubs.

Horvath/Tortuga Pines Publishing. Irene's Night: N/a. Horvath/Tortuga Pines Publishing, ed. 2008. 600p. pap. *(978-0-9793415-2-6(3))* Tortuga Pines Publishing.

Hostyn, Norbert. James Ensor: Leven en Werk/Vie et Oeuvre/Life & Work/Leben und Werke. 2007. (ENG., Illus.). 135p. pap. *(978-90-74377-30-0(0)*, Stichting Kunstboak (Acc)) Antique Collectors' Club.

Hostyn, Norbet. Léon Spilliaert: Life & Work. 2007. (ENG., Illus.). 128p. pap. 35.00 *(978-90-5856-199-2(2))* Stichting Kunstboek Bvba BEL. Dist: National Bk. Network.

Howard, Michael. Van Gogh: His Life & Works in 500 Images. 2010. (ENG., Illus.). 256p. 35.00 *(978-0-7548-1954-7(X))* Anness Publishing GBR. Dist: National Bk. Network.

Howell, Andy. Art, Skateboarding & Life. 2007. (Illus.). pap. 29.95 *(978-1-58423-261-2(7))* Gingko Pr., Inc.

Hubbard, Elbert. Little Journeys to the Homes of the Great: Volume 06 Little Journeys to the Homes of Eminent Artists. 2006. 196p. pap. 19.99 *(978-1-4264-4913-0(5))* 2007. (ENG.). 220p. pap. 22.99 *(978-1-4264-5214-7(4))* BiblioBazaar.

Hudson, Mark. Titian: The Last Days. 2009. (ENG., Illus.). 320p. 27.00 *(978-0-8027-1076-5(X))* Walker & Co.

Hug, Catherine, ed. The Street as Studio: From Basquiat to Banksy. 2010. (ENG., Illus.). 200p. pap. 55.00 *(978-3-86984-016-1(1))* Verlag der Buchhandlung Walther Konig DEU. Dist: D.A.P./Distributed Art Pubs.

Hull, Roger. Henk Pander: Memory & Modern Life. 2011. (ENG., Illus.). 136p. (C). pap. 29.95 *(978-1-930957-63-3(7))* Ford, Hallie Museum of Art.

Hunt, Patrick. Caravaggio. (Life & Times Ser.). (Illus.). 192p. 15.95 *(978-1-904341-74-1(8))* Haus Publishing GBR. Dist: Consortium Bk. Sales & Distribution.

Husslein-Arco, Agnes, ed. Lovis Corinth: A Feast of Painting. 2010. (Illus.). 144p. 29.95 *(978-3-7913-4378-5(5))* Prestel Publishing.

Huxley, Geralyn & Wrbican, Matt. Andy Warhol Treasures. 2009. (Illus.). 128p. *(978-1-84796-004-7(9))* Carlton Bks., Ltd.

Iles, Chrissie, et al. A Decade in Conversation: A Ten-Year Celebration of the Bucksbaum Award, 2000-2010 - With Interviews with Paul Pfeiffer, Irit Batsry, Raymond Pettibon, Mark Bradford, & Omer Fast. 2010. (Illus.). 88p. 19.95 *(978-0-300-16755-9(5))* Yale Univ. Pr.

Illetschko, Georgia. Michelangelo. 2010. (Illus.). 160p. pap. 19.95 *(978-3-7913-4472-0(2))* Prestel Publishing.

Indiana Artists' Club Staff. Biographical Directory of Indiana Artists. 38p. reprint ed. lib. bdg. 88.00 *(978-0-7222-0590-7(2))* Library Reprints, Inc.

Israels, Josef. Rembrandt. Hare, T. Leman, ed. 2007. (Illus.). 48p. per. *(978-1-4065-3411-5(0))* Dodo Pr.

Jackson, Kevin. The Worlds of John Ruskin. 2010. (ENG.). 160p. pap. 24.95 *(978-1-84368-044-4(0))* Pallas Athene GBR. Dist: Independent Pubs. Group.

Jacob, Mary Jane & Baas, Jacquelynn, eds. Chicago Makes Modern: How Creative Minds Changed Society. 2012. (ENG., Illus.). 304p. pap. 35.00 ***(978-0-226-38956-1(1))*** Univ. of Chicago Pr.

James, Clive. Cultural Amnesia: Necessary Memories from History & the Arts. 2008. (ENG.). 912p. pap. 17.95 *(978-0-393-33354-1(X)*, 33354) Norton, W. W. & Co., Inc.

James, Russell. The Pocket Guide to Victorian Artists & Their Models. 2011. (Illus.). 240p. pap. 19.95 *(978-1-84468-095-5(9))* Pen & Sword Bks. Ltd. GBR. Dist: Casemate Pubs. & Bk. Distributors, LLC.

Jazzar, Bernard N. & Nelson, Harold B. Painting with Fire: Masters of Enameling in America, 1930-1980. 2006. 75.00 *(978-0-9712772-8-1(1))*; (Illus.). 288p. pap. 55.00 *(978-0-9712772-5-0(7))* Long Beach Museum of Art.

Jean, James. Rebus. 2011. (ENG., Illus.). 240p. 45.00 *(978-0-8118-7125-9(8))* Chronicle Bks. LLC.

Jerrold, Blanchard. Life of George Cruikshank in Two Epochs. 2006. pap. 38.95 *(978-1-4286-3549-4(1))* Kessinger Publishing, LLC.

Jiménez, Ariel. Carlos Cruz-Diez in Conversation with Ariel Jimenez, 1 vol. 2010. (ENG & SPA., Illus.). 248p. 25.00 *(978-0-9823544-2-1(8))* Fundacion Cisneros.

Jiménez, Ariel & Soto, Jesus Rafael. Jesús Soto in Conversation with Ariel Jiménez: Jesús Soto en Conversacion con Ariel Jiménez. 2012. (SPA & ENG., Illus.). 198p. 25.00 ***(978-0-9823544-6-9(0))*** Fundacion Cisneros.

Joe Novak. Something to Do with Wings: A Memoir. 2010. 360p. 33.95 *(978-1-4401-9777-2(6))* iUniverse, Inc.

Johns, Barbara. Paul Horiuchi: East & West. 2008. (Samuel & Althea Stroum Bks.). (ENG., Illus.). 128p. pap. 29.95 *(978-0-295-98795-8(2))* Univ. of Washington Pr.

Johnson, Dominic, ed. Franko B: Blinded by Love, 1 vol. 2007. (ENG., Illus.). 256p. 75.00 *(978-88-89431-79-5(2))* Damiani ITA. Dist: D.A.P./Distributed Art Pubs.

Johnson, Jeff. Tattoo Machine: Tall Tales, True Stories, & My Life in Ink. 2010. (ENG., Illus.). 272p. pap. 15.00 *(978-0-385-53072-9(2))* Spiegel & Grau.

Johnson, Pamela, ed. Peter Seitz, Desiging a Life. deluxe ed. 2007. pap. 35.00 *(978-0-9800893-0-1(1))* Minneapolis College of Art & Design.

Jones, Geoff. A Life Drawing. 2008. 152p. pap. *(978-1-904408-36-9(2))* Bank House Bks.

Jordan, Andre. Heaven Knows I'm Miserable Now. 2009. (ENG.). 256p. pap. 13.99 *(978-0-06-154730-0(1)*, HarperPerennial) HarperCollins Pubs.

Judge, Michael. Captured Horizons: An Artist's Journey. 2009. 292p. 35.00 *(978-0-9792012-6-4(8))* New Chapter Pub.

Julianelli, Jane. The Naked Shoe: The Artistry of Mabel Julianelli. 2010. (ENG., Illus.). 240p. *(978-1-85149-639-6(4)*, Antique Collectors Club Dist) Antique Collectors' Club.

Junge, Maxine B. Mourning, Memory & Life Itself: Essays by an Art Therapist. 2008. (Illus.). 292p. 61.95 *(978-0-398-07827-0(0))* Thomas, Charles C. Pub., Ltd.

Junillon, I. Edvard Munch face a Henrik Ibsen: Impressions d'un Lecteur. 2009. (FRE.). 490p. (C). pap. 61.00 *(978-90-429-2252-5(4))* Peeters Pubs. & Booksellers BEL. Dist: Brown, David Bk. Co., The.

K&apos, et al. Biography of Ku K'Ai-Chih. Shih-Hsiang, Chen, tr. 2011. 36p. 35.95 ***(978-1-258-07359-6(5))*** Literary Licensing, LLC.

Kahr, Joan. Edgar Brandt: Art Deco Ironwork. 2010. (Illus.). 240p. 79.99 *(978-0-7643-3666-9(5))* Schiffer Publishing, Ltd.

Kambalu, Samson. The Jive Talker: An Artist's Genesis. 2008. (ENG.). 336p. 24.00 *(978-1-4165-5931-3(0)*, Free Pr.) Free Pr.

Kaminski, Marion. Titian: Tiziano Vecellio: 1488/1490-1576. 2008. (Masters of Italian Art Ser.). (Illus.). 140p. pap. 9.95 *(978-0-8416-0084-3(8))* American Map Corp.

Karper, Diane. A Walk in My Shoes: Our Lives of Hope: An Oral History of the Artists of the "Made in Honduras Craft Co-Op," Trujillo, Honduras. 2010. pap. *(978-0-911469-35-6(4))* Hood, Alan C. & Co., Inc.

Katheryn Webb. Apprentice to Master. 2010. 312p. pap. 18.95 *(978-1-4269-2506-1(9))* Trafford Publishing.

Katz, Robert & Dars, Celestine. The Impressionists: A Comprehensive Visual Reference to One of the Best-Loved Periods of Art History, with over 450 Images. 2012. (ENG., Illus.). 352p. 30.00 ***(978-0-7548-2402-2(0))*** Anness Publishing GBR. Dist: National Bk. Network.

Kaufmann, Thomas DaCosta. Arcimboldo: Visual Jokes, Natural History, & Still-Life Painting. 2010. (ENG., Illus.). 336p. 65.00 *(978-0-226-42686-0(6))* Univ. of Chicago Pr.

Keane, A. H. The Early Teutonic, Italian & French Masters. 2007. (ENG.). 574p. 58.95 *(978-0-548-04492-6(9))* Kessinger Publishing, LLC.

Kellein, Thomas. The Dream of Fluxus: George Maciunas: an Artist's Biography. 2007. (ENG., Illus.). 160p. 45.00 *(978-0-500-97665-4(1))* Thames & Hudson.

Keller, Steve. Lost in Amyloidosis. 2008. 173p. pap. 65.95 *(978-0-615-19244-4(0))* Keller, Steve.

Kelly, James Edward & Styple, William B. Tell Me of Lincoln: Memories of Abraham Lincoln, the Civil War, & Life in Old New York. 2009. (Illus.). 326p. *(978-1-883926-23-6(8))* Belle Grove Publishing Co.

Kelly, Jerry. The Art of the Book in the Twentieth Century: A Study of Eleven Influential Book Designers from 1900 To 2000. 2011. (ENG., Illus.). 200p. 39.95 *(978-1-933360-46-1(1)*, RIT Cary Graphic Arts Pr.) Rochester Institute of Technology, Cary Graphic Arts Pr.

Kenny, Simon B. Bruce Lee. 2009. (Pocket Essential Ser.). (ENG.). 160p. pap. 10.95 *(978-1-84243-287-7(7))* Pocket Essentials GBR. Dist: Independent Pubs. Group.

Kent Gallery, ed. Llyn Foulkes. 2007. pap. 14.95 *(978-1-878607-66-9(9))* Kent Gallery.

Kernan, Nathan, text. Milton Resnick: A Question of Seeing: Paintings 1959-1963. 2008. (Illus.). 64p. 50.00 *(978-0-9797397-7-4(2))* Cheim & Read.

Ketchie, Cotton. A Country Boy's Education. 2007. 345p. pap. 17.95 *(978-0-7414-4338-0(4))* Infinity Publishing.

—Memories of a Country Boy. 2006. (ENG.). 280p. per. 17.95 *(978-0-7414-3588-0(8))* Infinity Publishing.

Keuthen, Monika. Paula Modersohn-Becker. (GER.). *(978-3-612-26605-7(5))* Econ-Verlag GmbH DEU. Dist: International Bk. Import Service, Inc.

Kiefer, Anselm & Arasse, Daniel. Rencontres Pour Mémoire. 2010. (FRE., Illus.). 101p. *(978-2-84105-254-7(0))* Editions du Regard, Les.

Kimmel, Bruce. There's Me!, There's Woody, & There's You: My Life in the Slow Lane. 2010. 416p. 28.49 *(978-1-4520-1117-2(6))*; pap. 17.99 *(978-1-4520-1116-5(8))* AuthorHouse.

King, Charles S. & Spivey, Richard L. The Life & Art of Tony Da. 2011. (Illus.). 160p. 40.00 ***(978-1-933855-60-8(6))*** Rio Nuevo Pubs.

King, Richard, ed. Art in Turmoil: The Chinese Cultural Revolution, 1966-76. 2010. (ENG., Illus.). 318p. pap. 35.95 *(978-0-7748-1543-7(4))* UBC Pr. CAN. Dist: Univ. of Washington Pr.

King, Sarah, ed. The Dissolve. 2010. (ENG., Illus.). 240p. 50.00 *(978-0-9764492-9-4(3))* Site Santa Fe.

Kintsurashvili, Ketevan & Ignatova, Ketevan. Koka Ignatov: The Life & Times of a Renowned Georgian Artist. 2012. (Focus on Civilizations & Cultures - Painting & Sculpture Ser.). 317p. pap. 43.00 *(978-1-61761-793-5(8))* Nova Science Pubs., Inc.

Kipniss, Robert. Robert Kipniss: A Working Artist's Life. 2011. (Illus.). 304p. 29.95 *(978-1-61168-004-1(2))* Univ. Pr. of New England.

Kippenberger, Susanne. Kippenberger: The Artist & His Families. Searls, Damion, tr. 2012. (ENG., Illus.). 564p. 34.95 *(978-0-9829642-1-7(8))* J&L Bks., Inc.

Kirk, Joanna. Joanna Kirk. 2010. (ENG., Illus.). 32p. 35.00 *(978-1-906957-08-7(8))* Murderme GBR. Dist: Hachette Bk. Group.

Kissane, Sean. Hughie O'Donohue: Recent Paintings & Selected Works. Kissane, Sean & Butler, Maeve, eds. 2009. 108p. pap. 42.50 *(978-1-907020-00-1(4))* Irish Museum of Modern Art IRL. Dist: Trans-Atlantic Pubns., Inc.

Kite, Stephen. Adrian Stokes: An Architectonic Eye. 2009. (Legenda Main Ser.). (ENG., Illus.). 249p. (C). 89.50 *(978-1-905981-89-2(9))* European Humanities Research Ctr. GBR. Dist: Brown, David Bk. Co., The.

Kittelmann, Udo. Michel Majerus. 2008. (GER & ENG., Illus.). 120p. pap. 49.00 *(978-3-905770-85-8(7))* JRP Ringier Kunstverlag AG CHE. Dist: D.A.P./Distributed Art Pubs.

Klein, Stefan. Leonardo's Legacy: How Da Vinci Reimagined the World. Frisch, Shelley, tr. 2011. (ENG., Illus.). 304p. pap. 16.00 *(978-0-306-82008-3(0))* Da Capo Pr., Inc.

Kloek, Wouter. Jan Steen, 1632-1679. 2006. (Rijksmuseum Dossiers Ser.). (ENG., Illus.). 96p. pap. 24.95 *(978-90-400-8992-3(2))* Waanders B.V., Uitgeverij NLD. Dist: National Bk. Network.

Koestenbaum, Robert, et al, texts. Lari Pittman. 2011. (Illus.). 276p. 75.00 *(978-0-8478-3576-8(6)*, Skira) Rizzoli International Pubns., Inc.

Koester, Thomas. 50 Artists You Should Know. 2006. (Illus.). 171p. pap. 19.95 *(978-3-7913-3716-6(5))* Prestel Publishing.

Konig, Eberhard, ed. Great Painters of Italian Renaissance. 2008. 1304p. 150.00 *(978-0-8416-0346-2(4))* American Map Corp.

Koolhaas, Rem. London - A Portrait of a City: Serpentine Gallery 24-Hour Interview. Marathon. Koolhaas, Rem & Obrist, Hans Ulrich, eds. 2012. (ENG.). 272p. pap. 29.95 *(978-88-572-0059-0(0))* Skira Editore ITA. Dist: Random Hse., Inc.

Kosice, Gyula. Kosice: Autobiografia. 2010. (SPA., Illus.). 270p. *(978-950-533-021-8(9))* Asunto Impreso, Ediciones.

Kress, W. John & Sherwood, Shirley. The Art of Plant Evolution. 2010. (ENG., Illus.). 320p. 53.00 *(978-1-84246-421-2(3))* Kew Publishing GBR. Dist: Chicago Distribution Ctr.

Kunzle, David. Father of the Comic Strip: Rodolphe Töpffer. 2007. (ENG., Illus.). 207p. 55.00 *(978-1-57806-947-7(5))*; per. 25.00 *(978-1-57806-948-4(3))* Univ. Pr. of Mississippi.

Kuo, Andrew. Andrew Kuo: What Me Worry. 2011. (ENG., Illus.). 208p. 49.95 *(978-88-6208-153-5(7))* Damiani ITA. Dist: D.A.P./Distributed Art Pubs.

Kusama, Yayoi. Infinity Net: The Autobiography of Yayoi Kusama. McCarthy, Ralph, tr. from JPN. 2012. (Illus.). 256p. 35.00 *(978-0-226-46498-5(9))* Univ. of Chicago Pr.

Kuspit, Donald. Bernar Venet: Art & Mathematics: in Search of the Sublime. 2006. (Illus.). 65.00 *(978-2-914922-03-6(5))* Hard Pr. Editions.

Kuzmanovic, Natasha. Yard: The Life & Magnificent Jewelry of Raymond C. Yard. 2008. (ENG., Illus.). 204p. 65.00 *(978-0-86565-185-2(X))* Vendome Pr., The.

L#xF3;pez Garc#xED;a, Antonio & text. Antonio L#xF3;pez Garc#xED;a: Paintings & Sculpture. 2011. (ENG., Illus.). 288p. 75.00 ***(978-1-935202-65-3(0))*** D.A.P./Distributed Art Pubs.

La Blanc, Michael & Greve, Jennifer, eds. Authors & Artists for Young Adults, Vol. 73. 2007. (Authors & Artists fro Young Adults Ser.). (ENG., Illus.). 224p. 168.00 *(978-0-7876-7792-3(2))* Cengage Gale.

La May, William T. & McCaffrey, Joseph P., eds. The Journals of Grace Hartigan, 1951-1955. 2009. (Illus.). 232p. pap. 29.95 *(978-0-8156-0916-2(7))* Syracuse Univ. Pr.

Lambirth, Andrew. Roger Hilton: The Figured Language of Thought. 2007. (ENG., Illus.). 288p. 65.00 *(978-0-500-09334-4(2))* Thames & Hudson.

Landau, Ellen G. Jackson Pollock. 2010. (ENG., Illus.). 286p. 50.00 *(978-0-8109-8496-7(2))* Abrams.

Landers, Sean. Sean Landers: [sic]. 2010. (ENG., Illus.). 454p. pap. 25.00 *(978-0-9820747-8-7(6))* Horowitz, Glenn Bookseller, Inc.

Lange, Sami Lynn, ed. Bob Nugent. Elizabetsky, Roberto, tr. 2007. (ENG.). 160p. pap. 35.00 *(978-0-9794809-1-1(4))*; (Illus.). 55.00 *(978-0-9794809-0-4(6))* Abandoned Pr.

Lanpher, Dorse A. Flyin' Chunks & Other Things to Duck: Memoirs of a Life Spent Doodling for Dollars. 2010. 216p. 27.95 *(978-1-4502-6100-5(0))*; pap. 17.95 *(978-1-4502-6099-2(3))* iUniverse, Inc.

Larass, Petra, et al. 50 Women Artists You Should Know. 2008. (Illus.). 173p. pap. 19.95 *(978-3-7913-3956-6(7))* Prestel Publishing.

Larsen, Wayne. A. Y. Jackson: The Life of a Landscape Painter. 2009. (ENG., Illus.). 266p. 60.00 *(978-1-55488-392-9(X)*, Dundum Pr.) Dundurn CAN. Dist: Ingram Pub. Services.

—James Wilson Morrice: Painter of Light & Shadow. 2008. (Quest Biography Ser.). (ENG., Illus.). 176p. (gr. 8). pap. 17.95 *(978-1-55002-818-8(9))* Dundurn CAN. Dist: Ingram Pub. Services.

Lauren, Ralph. Ralph Lauren Deluxe. 2007. (ENG., Illus.). 512p. 400.00 *(978-0-8478-3106-7(X))* Rizzoli International Pubns., Inc.

Lazzari, Margaret. The Practical Handbook for the Emerging Artist, Enhanced Edition. 2nd ed. 2010. (ENG.). 352p. (C). pap. 87.95 *(978-0-495-91026-8(0))* Wadsworth.

Le Sidaner, Henri, et al. Henri Le Sidaner. A Magical Impressionist. 2009. (GER & ENG., Illus.). 192p. 34.95 *(978-3-422-02213-3(9)*, Art Stock Bks. Ltd/Csl) Continental Sales, Inc.

Lea, Tom. The Two Thousand Yard Stare: Tom Lea's World War II. Greeley, Brendan M., Jr., ed. 2008. (Military History Ser.: No. 119). (ENG., Illus.). 256p. 40.00 *(978-1-60344-008-0(9))* Texas A&M Univ. Pr.

Lear, H. L. Sidney. A Christian Painter of the Nineteenth Century, Being the Life of Hippolyte Flandrin, by the Author of A Dominican Artist. 2006. 252p. per. 23.99 *(978-1-4255-2195-0(9))* MPublishing.

Lebrun, Louise-Elisabeth Vigee. Memoirs of Madame Vigee Lebrun. Strachey, Lionel, tr. 2007. 244p. (ENG.). 41.95 *(978-0-548-16816-5(4))*; per. 26.95 *(978-1-4304-6538-6(7))* Kessinger Publishing, LLC.

Leclerc, Franck. L'école de Nice: Paroles D'artistes. 2010. (Illus.). 429p. *(978-2-916954-57-8(0)*, Spotlight Poets) Verlhac Editions.

Ledbetter, Gordon T. Privilege & Poverty: The Life & Times of Irish Painter & Naturalist Alexander Williams, 1846-1930. 2011. (ENG., Illus.). 366p. 69.95 *(978-1-84889-034-3(6))* Collins Pr., The IRL. Dist: Dufour Editions, Inc.

Lee, Jim & Baker, Bill. Icons: The DC Comics & Wildstorm Art of Jim Lee. 2010. (Illus.). 296p. 39.95 *(978-1-84576-519-4(2)*, Titan Bks.) Titan Bks. Ltd. GBR. Dist: Random Hse., Inc.

Leffel, David A. Self-Portraits: A Visual Journey of Insight. 2009. (Illus.). 159p. *(978-0-9747074-6-4(5))* Bright Light Publishing, LLC.

Leiderstam, Matts. Matts Leiderstam: Seen from Here. 2010. (ENG., Illus.). 144p. pap. 50.00 *(978-3-86984-029-1(3))* Verlag der Buchhandlung Walther Konig DEU. Dist: D.A.P./Distributed Art Pubs.

Leimer, Jac. Jac Leimer in Conversation with Adele Nelson. 2011. (ENG & SPA., Illus.). 220p. 25.00 *(978-0-9823544-4-5(4))* Fundacion Cisneros.

Leung, L. P. Portraits of Pride II - Chinese-American Legacies - First 160 Years in America. 2011. (Illus.). 288p. 40.00 *(978-0-930377-01-4(X))* Chinese Historical Society of Southern California, Inc.

Levin, Bob. Most Outrageous: The Trials & Trespasses of Dwaine Tinsley & Chester the Molester. 2008. (ENG., Illus.). 200p. pap. 19.99 *(978-1-56097-919-7(4)*, 56919) Fantagraphics Bks.

Levin, Gail. Lee Krasner: A Biography. (ENG., 2012. Illus.). 400p. pap. 16.99 *(978-0-06-184527-7(2)*, William Morrow Paperbacks) 2011. 400p. 30.00 *(978-0-06-184525-3(6)*, Morrow, William & Co.) 2011. 884p. pap. 30.00 *(978-0-06-201779-6(9)*, HarperLuxe) HarperCollins Pubs.

Levinson, Drunell. Art at the Margins. 2009. 168p. pap. *(978-3-639-17386-4(4))* VDM Verlag Dr. Mueller e.K.

Levy, Evonne, et al, eds. Bernini's Biographies: Critical Essays. 2007. (ENG., Illus.). 376p. 65.00 *(978-0-271-02901-6(3))* Pennsylvania State Univ. Pr.

—Bernini's Biographies: Critical Essays. 2007. (ENG., Illus.). 376p. pap. 35.00 *(978-0-271-02902-3(1))* Pennsylvania State Univ. Pr.

Lew, Douglas. Great Composers in Watercolor. 2010. 172p. pap. 47.68 *(978-1-4269-3437-7(8))* Trafford Publishing.

Licciardi, Phyllis. Keep Smiling at Trouble... the Life of Artist Francesco Licciardi. rev. ed. 2010. (ENG.). 264p. pap. 29.99 *(978-0-7575-7738-3(5))* Kendall Hunt Publishing Co.

Lind, Jane. Perfect Red: The Life of Paraskeva Clark. 2009. (ENG.). 400p. 37.00 *(978-1-897151-44-0(6))* Cormorant Bks. Inc. CAN. Dist: Univ. of Toronto Pr.

Ling, Jian. Ling Jian: Moon in Glass. 2011. (ENG., Illus.). 104p. pap. 30.00 ***(978-988-19912-5-6(0))*** Timezone 8 Ltd. HKG. Dist: D.A.P./Distributed Art Pubs.

Lippard, Lucy. Michelle Stuart: Sculptural Objects. 2011. (ENG., Illus.). 184p. pap. 45.00 ***(978-88-8158-803-9(X))*** Charta ITA. Dist: D.A.P./Distributed Art Pubs.

Little, Carl. The Art of Dahlov Ipcar. 2010. 128p. 50.00 *(978-0-89272-809-1(4))* Down East Bks.

Littleton, Harvey & Byrd, Joan Falconer. Harvey K. Littleton: A Life in Glass: Founder of America's Studio Glass Movement. 2012. (ENG., Illus.). 208p. 45.00 ***(978-0-8478-3818-9(8)****, Skira)* Rizzoli International Pubns., Inc.

Lockemann, Karsten, ed. Michael Gerngroß: Spuren / Traces. 2011. (ENG., Illus.). 112p. 39.95 *(978-3-86678-423-9(6))* Kerber Verlag DEU. Dist: D.A.P./Distributed Art Pubs.

Lodermeyer, Peter, ed. Personal Structures: Time. Space. Existence. 2010. (MUL & ENG., Illus.). 448p. 59.95 *(978-3-8321-9279-2(4))* DuMont DEU. Dist: D.A.P./Distributed Art Pubs.

Londraville, Janis & Londraville, Richard. Corbino: From Rubens to Ringling. 2011. (Excelsior Editions Ser.). (Illus.). 304p. 29.95 (978-1-4384-3571-8(1)) State Univ. of New York Pr.

Lothar Strauch, 1907-1991. (GER.). (978-3-496-01043-2(6)) Reimer, Dietrich.

Low, Will H. A Painter's Progress. 2007. (ENG.). 356p. per. (978-1-4067-4343-2(7)) Read Bks.

Loxley, Simon. Printer's Devil: The Life & Work of Frederic Warde. 2012. (ENG., Illus.). 179p. 45.00 (978-1-56792-367-4(4)) Godine, David R. Pub.

Lozano, Lee. Lee Lozano. 2010. (ENG., Illus.). 272p. pap. 60.00 (978-3-7757-2567-5(9)) Hatje Cantz Verlag GmbH & Co KG DEU. Dist: D.A.P./Distributed Art Pubs.

Lucas, Charlie & Windham, Ben. Tin Man. 2nd ed. 2009. (ENG., Illus.). 192p. 49.95 (978-0-8173-1681-5(7)) Univ. of Alabama Pr.

Lucas, Renata & Christov-Bakargiev, Carolyn. Renata Lucas: Postpone the End. 2009. (FRE & ENG., Illus.). 115p. (978-88-366-1576-6(7)) Silvana.

Lucie-Smith, Edward. Lives of the Great Modern Artists. 2nd rev. ed. 2009. (ENG., Illus.). 368p. pap. 34.95 (978-0-500-28191-8(2), 528191) Thames & Hudson.

Lunch, Lydia. Will Work for Drugs. 2009. (ENG.). 160p. pap. 15.95 (978-1-933354-73-6(9)) Akashic Bks.

Lunday, Elizabeth. Secret Lives of Great Artists: What Your Teachers Never Told You about Master Painter & Sculptors. 2008. (Secret Lives Ser.). (ENG., Illus.). 288p. pap. 16.95 (978-1-59474-257-6(X)) Quirk Bks.

Lyell, Douglas. The Boogie Man. 2010. 212p. pap. (978-1-84748-746-9(7)) Athena Pr.

Lynch, Brendan. Prodigals & Geniuses: The Writers & Artists of Dublin's Baggotonia. 2012. (ENG., Illus.). 325p. pap. 31.95 (978-1-905785-96-4(8)) Liffey Pr., The IRL. Dist: Dufour Editions, Inc.

Macnair, Peter L., et al. The Legacy: Tradition & Innovation in Northwest Coast Indian Art, 1 vol. 2007. (Royal BC Museum Ser.). (ENG., Illus.). 196p. pap. 36.95 (978-0-7726-5609-4(6)) UBC Pr. CAN. Dist: Univ. of Washington Pr.

Magee, David. The Education of Mr. Mayfield: An Unusual Story of Social Change at Ole Miss. 2009. (Illus.). 256p. 21.95 (978-0-89587-366-8(4)) Blair, John F. Pub.

Manger, Barbara. Mary Nohl: Inside & Outside. 2009. (ENG., Illus.). 134p. pap. 29.95 (978-0-615-25118-9(8)) Univ. of Wisconsin Pr.

Maniscalco, Robert. Point of Art. 2007. 164p. per. 24.95 (978-1-4241-8649-5(8)) PublishAmerica, Inc.

Mansfield, Elizabeth C. The Perfect Foil: FranCois-Andre Vincent & the Revolution in French Painting. 2011. (ENG., Illus.). 320p. 105.00 **(978-0-8166-7580-7(5))**; pap. 35.00 **(978-0-8166-7581-4(3))** Univ. of Minnesota Pr.

Manson, David. Willy Tirr (1915 - 1991) Figure in a Landscape. 2010. (Illus.). 116p. pap. 35.49 (978-1-4520-0506-5(0)) AuthorHouse.

Marah, Bertie Stroup. Born with a Rusty Spoon: An Artist's Memoir. 2010. 192p. pap. 22.95 (978-1-935514-66-4(0)) Plain View Pr.

Mareyna-Fallo, Rafael. The Book-the Game. 2009. 56p. pap. 23.99 (978-1-4389-8275-5(5)) AuthorHouse.

Mari, Bartomeu. Lothar Baumgarten. Mari, Bartomeu, ed. 2008. 180p. pap. (978-84-89771-52-9(9)) Actar Birkhauser Distribution.

Marion, Joyce. Grab the Holy Spirit & Run On. 2010. 434p. 34.99 (978-1-61579-739-4(4)) Xulon Pr., Inc.

Mariscal, Javier. Drawing Life. 79.95 (978-0-7148-5752-7(1)) Phaidon Pr., Inc.

Marnham, Patrick. Sonar Con los Ojos Abiertos: Una Vida de Diego Rivera.Tr. of Dreaming with His Eyes Open. (SPA.). 29.95 (978-84-01-01266-2(X), PJ11250) Plaza & Janes Editories, S.A. ESP. Dist: Lectorum Pubns., Inc.

Marquis Who's Who, creator. Who's Who in American Art. 30th ed. 2009. (Who's Who in American Art Ser.). 1665p. 371.25 (978-0-8379-6309-9(5)) Marquis Who's Who, LLC.

Marquis Who's Who Staff. Who's Who in American Art 2008. 28th ed. 2007. 1512p. 297.00 (978-0-8379-6307-5(9)) Marquis Who's Who, LLC.

Marsden-Atlass, Lynn, ed. Thirteen Miles from Paradise: John Moore. 2009. (Illus.). 48p. pap. 29.95 (978-0-8122-2072-8(2)) Univ. of Pennsylvania Pr.

Marshall, Richard. Kenny Scharf. 2009. (ENG., Illus.). 272p. 85.00 (978-0-8478-3150-0(7)) Rizzoli International Pubns., Inc.

Martin, Fred. Lessons from the Masters. 2009. (ENG.). 36p. pap. 20.00 (978-0-557-09456-1(9)) Lulu Enterprises Inc.

Martindale, Andrew. Mantegna. 2008. (Chaucer Library of Art Ser.). (Illus.). 192p. 55.00 (978-1-904449-44-7(1)) Chaucer Pr. GBR. Dist: International Publishers Marketing.

Masefield, John. Jim Davis. 2008. 144p. 24.99 (978-0-554-22435-0(6)) 2008. 144p. 21.99 (978-0-554-31738-0(9)) 2007. (ENG.). 136p. pap. 18.99 (978-1-4264-2336-9(5)) BiblioBazaar.

—Jim Davis. 2008. 140p. pap. (978-1-4099-4175-0(2)) Dodo Pr.

—Jim Davis. 2008. 132p. pap. 10.95 (978-1-60597-451-4(X), Book Jungle) Standard Pubns., Inc.

Mason, Roger B. Franz Johnston. Date not set. 19.95 (978-1-55082-179-6(2)) Quarry Pr. CAN. Dist: LPC/InBook.

Mathews, Nancy Mowll & Cantor, Jay E. Mary Cassatt: Friends & Family. 2008. pap. (978-0-939384-34-1(5)) Shelburne Museum, Inc.

Matt, Gerald. Gerald Matt. 2008. (ENG., Illus.). 360p. (C). pap. 45.00 (978-3-86560-365-4(3)) Verlag der Buchhandlung Walther Konig DEU. Dist: D.A.P./Distributed Art Pubs.

Matthys, Daniël. Danny Matthy's: Monograph. (DUT., Illus.). 321p. (978-90-72191-08-3(0)) Imschoot.

Max, Peter. The Universe According to Peter Max: A Psychedelic Odyssey. 2012. (ENG.). 288p. 35.00 **(978-0-06-212139-4(1)**, Collins Design) HarperCollins Pubs.

May, Jill P., et al. Howard Pyle: Imagining an American School of Art. 2011. (ENG., Illus.). 296p. 45.00 (978-0-252-03626-2(3)) Univ. of Illinois Pr.

Mayer, Marc & Fishman, Ted C., contrib. by. Edward Burtynsky - China, 1 vol. 2008. (ENG., Illus.). 180p. 85.00 (978-3-86521-130-9(5)) Steidl, Gerhard Druckerei und Verlag DEU. Dist: Innovative Logistics.

McAuliffe, Chris. Jon Cattapan: Possible Histories. 2008. (ENG., Illus.). 240p. 41.00 (978-0-522-85498-5(2)) Melbourne Univ. Publishing AUS. Dist: Independent Pubs. Group.

McBride, Rita. Rita Mcbride. 2010. (ENG & GER., Illus.). 144p. 60.00 (978-3-941263-14-7(5)) Richter Verlag DEU. Dist: D.A.P./Distributed Art Pubs.

McCarthy, Laurette E. & Pach, Walter. Walter Pach (1883-1958) The Armory Show & the Untold Story of Modern Art in America. 2011. (ENG.). 272p. 59.95 (978-0-271-03740-0(7)) Pennsylvania State Univ. Pr.

McGarry, Susan Hallsten. John Nieto: Forces of Color & Spirit. 2010. (ENG., Illus.). 180p. 125.00 (978-1-934491-15-7(2)) Fresco Fine Art Pubns., LLC.

McGee, Julie L. Artist & Scholar. 2006. (Illus.). 216p. 45.00 (978-0-7649-3747-7(2), A127) Pomegranate Communications, Inc.

McGregor, Ken. Fred Cress: Whispers: Drawings 1958 - 2007. Oslen, ed. rev. ed. 2007. (Illus.). 256p. (C). 100.00 (978-1-876832-64-3(9)) Macmillan Art Publishing AUS. Dist: Brown, David Bk. Co., The.

McGregor, Ken & Zimmer, Jenny. Tim Storrier. 2007. (Macmillan Mini-Art Ser.). (Illus.). 144p. (C). 35.00 (978-1-921394-12-6(9)) Macmillan Art Publishing AUS. Dist: Brown, David Bk. Co., The.

Mehling, Robert. Mea Saurus: An Artist's Confessions. 2008. pap. 18.00 (978-0-8059-7949-7(2)) Dorrance Publishing Co., Inc.

Mejia Arango, Juan Luis. Hugo Zapata. 2010. (SPA.). 240p. 75.00 (978-958-8306-49-0(3)) Villegas Editores S.A. COL. Dist: Independent Pubs. Group.

Melotti, Massimo, ed. Pistoletto - Works: Massimo Melotti Talks to Michelangelo Pistoletto. 2012. (ENG.). 88p. 20.00 **(978-88-422-1963-7(0))** Allemandi, Umberto & Co. GBR. Dist: Antique Collectors' Club.

Messerscbmidt, Don. Against the Current: The Life of Lain Singh Bangdel: Writer, Painter & Art Historian of Nepal. 2006. (ENG., Illus.). 258p. 27.95 (978-974-524-052-0(4)) Orchid Pr. THA. Dist: National Bk. Network.

Metzger, Gustav & Obrist, Hans Ulrich. Gustav Metzger. 2009. (ENG., Illus.). 168p. pap. 25.00 (978-3-86560-498-9(6)) Verlag der Buchhandlung Walther Konig DEU. Dist: D.A.P./Distributed Art Pubs.

Michaelis, David. Schulz & Peanuts: A Biography. 2007. (ENG., Illus.). 672p. 34.95 (978-0-06-621393-4(2)) HarperCollins Pubs.

Milam, Jennifer D. Historical Dictionary of Rococo Art. 2011. (Historical Dictionaries of Literature & the Arts Ser.). (ENG.). 334p. 80.00 (978-0-8108-6183-1(6)) Scarecrow Pr., Inc.

Milam, Jennifer Dawn. Historical Dictionary of Rococo Art. 2011. E-Book (978-0-8108-7952-2(2)) Scarecrow Pr., Inc.

Miles, Lisa A. This Fantastic Struggle: The Life & Art of Esther Phillips. 2009. (Illus.). 461p. pap. 18.00 (978-0-9798236-1-9(7)) Miles, Lisa.

Miller, Eileen. The Girl Who Spoke with Pictures: Autism Through Art. 2008. (ENG., Illus.). 208p. (978-1-84310-889-4(5)) Kingsley, Jessica Ltd.

Miller, Francine Koslow. Metaphysical Dreamweaver: The Art of Enrico V. Pinardi. Barletta, Destiny, ed. 2011. (Illus.). lib. bdg. 50.00 (978-1-879985-22-3(5)) Pucker Gallery.

Millidge, Judith. Charles Marion Russell. 2009. (ENG.). 192p. 24.99 (978-0-7858-2535-7(5), 0785825355, Chartwell) Book Sales, Inc.

Milner, Richard. Charles R. Knight: The Artist Who Saw Through Time. 2012. (ENG., Illus.). 180p. 40.00 (978-0-8109-8479-0(2)) Abrams.

Minnery, David. Enrique Martinez Celaya. 2007. 284p. 69.95 (978-3-87909-765-4(8)) Wienand GmbH, Druck- & Verlagshaus DEU. Dist: Independent Pubs. Group.

Misheck, Barb. A Wing & a Prayer: An Artist's Journey with Muscular Dystrophy. 2007. 192p. per. 24.95 (978-1-4241-6337-3(4)) PublishAmerica, Inc.

Moffatt, Frederick C. The Life, Art, & Times of Joseph Delaney, 1904-1991. 2009. (ENG.). 44.95 (978-1-57233-676-6(5)) Univ. of Tennessee Pr.

Molesworth, Helen, ed. Catherine Opie: Empty & Full. 2011. (ENG., Illus.). 96p. 40.00 (978-3-7757-3015-0(X)) Hatje Cantz Verlag GmbH & Co KG DEU. Dist: D.A.P./Distributed Art Pubs.

Molesworth, Helen & Horrigan, Bill, texts. Dust, 1 vol. 2007. (ENG., Illus.). 64p. per. 19.95 (978-1-881390-44-2(6)) Ohio State Univ., Wexner Ctr. for the Arts.

Molesworth, Mollie. A Ladakhi Diary - with Watercolours of a Himalayan Trek In 1929. 2010. (Illus.). 104p. pap. (978-1-906393-24-3(9)) Trotamundas Pr., Ltd.

Monfeli, Stefano Pane. Stefano Pane Monfeli: the Life & Art of Pane. 2011. (ENG., Illus.). 208p. 39.90 **(978-88-6208-183-2(9))** Damiani ITA. Dist: D.A.P./Distributed Art Pubs.

Moon, Michael. Darger's Resources. 2012. (ENG., Illus.). 184p. 79.95 **(978-0-8223-5142-9(0))**; pap. 22.95 **(978-0-8223-5156-6(0))** Duke Univ. Pr.

Moore, Honor & Moore, H. The White Blackbird: A Life of the Painter Margarett Sargent by Her Granddaughter. 2009. (ENG., Illus.). 416p. pap. 17.95 (978-0-393-33611-5(5), 33611) Norton, W. W. & Co., Inc.

Morfogen, Zachary. YA Gotta Have Art! 2006. (ENG., Illus.). 100p. 15.00 (978-1-932646-24-5(8)) Ruder-Finn Pr.

Morgan, Anne Lee. Oxford Dictionary of American Art & Artists. 2008. (Oxford Paperback Reference Ser.). (ENG.). 560p. pap. 17.95 (978-0-19-537321-9(9)) Oxford Univ. Pr., Inc.

Morgan, James. Chasing Matisse: A Year in France Living My Dream. 2009. (ENG.). 288p. pap. 19.95 (978-1-4391-6724-3(9), Free Pr.) Free Pr.

Morgan, Jessica & Wood, Catherine. The World as a Stage. 2008. (ENG., Illus.). 64p. pap. 25.00 (978-1-85437-760-9(4)) Tate Publishing, Ltd. GBR. Dist: Hachette Bk. Group.

Morgan, Jessica, et al. John Baldessari: Pure Beauty. 2009. (Illus.). 329p. (978-0-87587-202-5(6)) Prestel Verlag GmbH & Co KG.

Morioka, Michiyo. An American Artist in Tokyo: Frances Blakemore, 1906-1997. 2008. (Illus.). 199p. 35.00 (978-0-295-98773-6(1)) Univ. of Washington Pr.

Morse, Samuel F. B. Samuel F. B. Morse His Letters & Journals Volume II. 2007. (ENG.). 394p. pap. 25.99 (978-1-4346-2191-7(X)); 440p. pap. 28.99 (978-1-4346-2251-8(7)) BiblioBazaar.

Moskaliuk, Vivien. Tomograph: Künstlerinnen im Gespräch. Interviews with Artists. Stürzl, Winfried, ed. 2009. (ENG., Illus.). 128p. pap. 50.00 (978-3-89790-309-8(1)) Arnoldsche Art Pubs. DEU. Dist: Antique Collectors' Club.

Mossinger, Ingrid, ed. Fortunate to Be an Artist. 2009. (ENG., Illus.). 256p. 55.00 (978-3-86678-174-0(1)) Kerber Verlag DEU. Dist: D.A.P./Distributed Art Pubs.

Muini Kirmanshahi, Nushin. Barguzidah-Yi Maqalahha: Az Sal-I 2003 Ta 2009. 2010. (PER., Illus.). 281p. (978-1-59584-253-4(5)) Ketab Corp.

Mulcahy, Susan, et al. Drawing Fashion: The Art of Kenneth Paul Block. 2008. (ENG., Illus.). 216p. 95.00 (978-0-9777875-4-8(0)) Pointed Leaf Pr.

Muller, Melissa & Piechocki, Reinhard. A Garden of Eden in Hell: The Life of Alice Herz-Sommer. 2007. (ENG., Illus.). 456p. 36.95 (978-0-230-52802-4(3)) Macmillan Pubs., Ltd. GBR. Dist: Independent Pubs. Group.

Muller, Melissa, et al. A Garden of Eden in Hell: The Life of Alice Herz-Sommer. 2008. (ENG., Illus.). 368p. 17.95 (978-0-330-45159-8(6)) Macmillan Pubs., Ltd. GBR. Dist: Independent Pubs. Group.

Mundy, Jennifer. Duchamp, Man Ray, Picabia. 2008. (ENG., Illus.). 256p. pap. 55.00 (978-1-85437-731-9(0)) Tate Publishing, Ltd. GBR. Dist: Hachette Bk. Group.

Muniz, Vik & text. Vik Muniz: Verso. 2009. (ENG., Illus.). 76p. pap. 34.95 (978-88-8158-723-0(8)) Charta ITA. Dist: D.A.P./Distributed Art Pubs.

Murphy, David Royce. Scenery, Curiosities, & Stupendous Rocks: William Quesenbury's Overland Sketches1850-1851. 2011. (ENG., Illus.). 304p. 45.00 (978-0-8061-4219-7(7)) Univ. of Oklahoma Pr.

Museyon Guides, ed. Art + NYC: A Complete Guide to New York City Art & Artists. 2011. (Art+ Ser.). (ENG., Illus.). 304p. pap. 19.95 (978-0-9822320-8-8(X)) Museyon Inc.

Music Sales Staff. Legendary Acoustic Guitar Songs. 2011. (ENG.). 256p. 49.99 (978-1-84938-463-6(0), 1849384630) Music Sales Corp.

Muti, Riccardo. Riccardo Muti: An Autobiography - First the Music, Then the Words. 2011. (ENG., Illus.). 244p. 29.95 (978-0-8478-3724-3(6)) Rizzoli International Pubns., Inc.

Nadel, Dan. Where Demented Wented: The Art & Comics of Rory Hayes. Pouncey, Glenn & Bray, Glenn, eds. 2008. (Illus.). 144p. pap. 22.99 (978-1-56097-923-4(2)) Fantagraphics Bks.

Naifeh, Steven & Smith, Gregory White. Van Gogh: The Life. 2012. (ENG.). 976p. pap. 25.00 **(978-0-375-75897-3(6)**, Random Hse. Trade Paperbacks) Random House Publishing Group.

—Van Gogh: The Life. 2011. (ENG., Illus.). 976p. 40.00 (978-0-375-50748-9(5)) Random Hse., Inc.

Nasgaard, Roald. Abstract Painting in Canada, 1 vol. 2007. (ENG., Illus.). 432p. pap. 50.00 (978-1-55365-394-3(7)) D&M Pubs. Inc. CAN. Dist: Perseus-PGW.

Neel, Alice, et al. Alice Neel: Painted Truths. 2010. (Illus.). 296p. 65.00 (978-0-300-16332-2(0)) Yale Univ. Pr.

Nemerov, Alexander. To Make a World: George Ault & 1940s America. 2011. (ENG., Illus.). 152p. 45.00 (978-0-300-17239-3(7)) Yale Univ. Pr.

Neygauz, Lina. Variatsii Prekrasnogo. rev. ed. 2008.Tr. of Variations of the Beautiful. (RUS., Illus.). 247p. 79.95 (978-0-9785403-1-9(X)) DAN.

Noble, Paul. Paul Noble. (GER & ENG., Illus.). 196p. pap. 40.00 (978-2-940271-67-2(4)) JRP Ringier Kunstverlag AG CHE. Dist: D.A.P./Distributed Art Pubs.

Nolen-Weathington, Eric. Jeff Smith. 2011. 120p. pap. 15.95 (978-1-60549-024-3(5)) TwoMorrows Publishing.

—Modern Masters Volume 2: George Perez. 2007. (Modern Masters Ser.: Vol. 2). 128p. pap. 14.95 (978-1-893905-25-2(X)) TwoMorrows Publishing.

North, Colleen. Florida Artist: Wm. North - His Life & Art. 2011. (Illus.). 100p. pap. 19.99 (978-1-935751-03-8(4)) Scribbulations LLC.

North, Marianne. Abundant Beauty: The Adventurous Travels of Marianne North, Botanical Artist, 1 vol. 2011. (ENG.). 224p. pap. 16.95 (978-1-55365-541-1(9), Greystone Bks.) D&M Pubs. Inc. CAN. Dist: Perseus-PGW.

Nyamndi, G. The Life & Times of Richard Onyango. 2008. 68p. pap. (978-9966-7008-5-8(4)) Kwani Trust KEN. Dist: Michigan State Univ. Pr.

Obrist, Hans Ulrich & Gonzalez-Foerster, Dominique, texts. Hans Ulrich Obrist & Dominique Gonzalez-Foerster: the Conversation Series. 2008. (ENG., Illus.). 190p. pap. 22.00 (978-3-86560-334-0(3)) Verlag der Buchhandlung Walther Konig DEU. Dist: D.A.P./Distributed Art Pubs.

Obrist, Hans Ulrich & Kittelmann, Udo, eds. Thomas Bayrle: 40 Years Chinese Rock N' Roll, 1 vol. 2007. (ENG., Illus.). 320p. pap. 70.00 (978-3-86560-100-1(6)) Verlag der Buchhandlung Walther Konig DEU. Dist: D.A.P./Distributed Art Pubs.

Obukhova, Alexandra, ed. Nihil Inhumanum A Me Alienum Puto, 1 vol. 2007. (ENG., Illus.). 368p. per. 65.00 (978-3-86678-045-3(1)) Kerber Verlag DEU. Dist: D.A.P./Distributed Art Pubs.

O'Byrne, Robert. Dictionary of Living Irish Artists. 2010. (ENG., Illus.). 400p. 97.50 (978-0-9563011-0-9(X), Plurabelle Publishing (Acc)) Antique Collectors' Club GBR. Dist: National Bk. Network.

Ochoa Foster, Elena, ed. Drama Turquesa: Los Carpinteros. 2010. (SPA & ENG., Illus.). 166p. pap. 39.95 (978-0-9564339-1-6(X)) Ivory Pr. ESP. Dist: Actar Birkhauser Distribution.

O'Keeffe, Paul. A Genius for Failure: The Life of Benjamin Robert Haydon. 2009. (ENG., Illus.). 568p. 44.95 (978-0-224-06247-3(6)) Random Hse. GBR. Dist: Independent Pubs. Group.

Oldham, Todd. Charley Harper: An Illustrated Life. 2009. (ENG, ITA, FRE, GER & SPA., Illus.). 420p. 49.95 (978-1-934429-37-2(6)) AMMO Bks., LLC.

—Wayne White: Maybe Now I'll Get the Respect I So Richly Deserve Popular Edition. 2010. (ENG.). 432p. lib. bdg. 29.95 (978-1-934429-67-9(8)) AMMO Bks., LLC.

Oliva, Achille Bonito. Encyclopaedia of the World: Artist Dialogues, 1968-2008. 2010. (ENG., Illus.). 414p. 45.00 (978-88-572-0463-5(4)) Skira Editore ITA. Dist: Random Hse., Inc.

Oliver, Valerie Cassel, et al. Donald Moffett: The Extravagant Vein. 2011. (ENG., Illus.). 224p. 65.00 (978-0-8478-3727-4(0), Skira) Rizzoli International Pubns., Inc.

O'Neill, Helen. Florence Broadhurst: Her Secret & Extraordinary Lives. 2007. (ENG., Illus.). 248p. 24.95 (978-0-8118-5937-0(1)) Chronicle Bks. LLC.

Ormiston, Rosalind. Leonardo Da Vinci: His Life & Works in 500 Images. 2011. (ENG., Illus.). 256p. 35.00 (978-0-7548-2326-1(1)) Anness Publishing GBR. Dist: National Bk. Network.

Ortiz, Luis. Infinity x Two: The Life & Art of Ed & Carol Emshwiller. 2007. (ENG., Illus.). 176p. 39.95 (978-1-933065-08-3(7)) Nonstop Pr.

O'Shaughnessy, Ann, ed. Art as a Way of Life: Artists on the Joys & Challenges of Living the Creative Life. 2006. (Illus.). 96p. per. 12.95 (978-1-933937-12-0(2)) Heron Dance.

Ottenberg, Simon. Olayinka: A Woman's View: The Life of an African Modern Artist. 2011. **(978-1-59221-832-5(6))**; (Illus.). 352p. pap. **(978-1-59221-833-2(4))** Africa World Pr.

Ottmann, Klaus, text. Joan Snyder: ... & seeking the Sublime. 2008. pap. 20.00 (978-0-9713548-5-2(5)) Nielsen Gallery.

Oweis, Fayeq S. Encyclopedia of Arab American Artists, 1 vol. 2007. (Artists of the American Mosaic Ser.). (Illus.). 336p. 85.00 (978-0-313-33730-7(6), GR3730, Greenwood Pr.) Greenwood Publishing Group, Inc.

Painter, Karen & Crow, Thomas, eds. Late Thoughts: Reflections on Artists & Composers at Work. 2006. (Issues & Debates Ser.: Vol. 14). (Illus.). 264p. pap. 40.00 (978-0-89236-813-6(6)) Oxford Univ. Pr., Inc.

Papastergiadis, Nikos, et al. Yang Shaobin: X-Blind Spot. 2009. (ENG., Illus.). 128p. 55.00 (978-88-8158-742-1(4)) Charta ITA. Dist: D.A.P./Distributed Art Pubs.

Pardue, Diana F. & PARDUE, Diana. Shared Images: The Innovative Jewelry of Yazzie Johnson & Gail Bird. 2007. (ENG., Illus.). 146p. 45.00 (978-0-89013-496-2(0)) Museum of New Mexico Pr.

Parille, Ken & Cates, Isaac, eds. Daniel Clowes: Conversations. 2010. (Conversations with Comics Artists Ser.). (ENG., Illus.). 240p. 50.00 (978-1-60473-440-9(X)); pap. 22.00 (978-1-60473-441-6(8)) Univ. Pr. of Mississippi.

Park, Yeon Hwan. Tae Kwon Do: My Life & Philosophy. 2009. 176p. pap. 16.95 (978-0-8160-7797-7(5), Checkmark Bks.) Facts On File, Inc.

Parker, Barbara Neville & Wheeler, Anne Bolling. John Singleton Copley: American Portraits in Oil, Pastel & Miniature, with Biographical Sketches. 2011. 428p. 56.95 **(978-1-258-10366-8(4))** Literary Licensing, LLC.

Parker, Terry. Softly Awakes My Heart. 2010. 200p. pap. 14.49 (978-1-4490-6797-7(2)) AuthorHouse.

Pat Musick. No New Thing under the Sun: One Artist's Chosen Journey. 2009. (Illus.). 144p. pap. 39.44 (978-1-4251-9213-6(0)) Trafford Publishing.

Paterson, Doris J. Confessions of A War Brde. 2011. 240p. pap. 16.95 **(978-1-4269-8958-2(X))** Trafford Publishing.

Patrizi, Eugene. Everybody's Uncle. 2010. 124p. pap. 17.95 (978-1-60844-343-7(4)) Dog Ear Publishing, LLC.

Patterson, Dan. Gil Cohen: Aviation Artist. 2009. (ENG., Illus.). 144p. 49.95 (978-1-55046-512-9(0)) Boston Mills Pr. CAN. Dist: Firefly Bks., Ltd.

Paul Gauguin. 128p. 9.99 (978-84-343-0638-7(7)) Poligrafa, Ediciones, S. A. ESP. Dist: Advanced Global Distribution Services.

Pauwels, Wim. Lionel Jadot: An Autobiography. 2010. (ENG., Illus.). 256p. (978-90-8944-058-7(5), Beta-Plus (Acc)) Antique Collectors' Club.

Payne, Matthew & Payne, James. Regarding Thomas Rowlandson, 1757-1827: His Life, art & Acquaintance. 2011. (ENG., Illus.). 352p. (C). 65.00 (978-0-9554063-5-5(8)) Holberton, Paul Publishing GBR. Dist: Univ. of Washington Pr.

Pearson, Joshua T. Alphabhetto. 2011. 56p. pap. 25.95 **(978-1-4634-0772-8(6))** AuthorHouse.

Peili, Zhang. Zhang Peili: Chinese Contemporary Art Awards 2010. 2012. (ENG., Illus.). 160p. 40.00 **(978-988-19912-7-0(7))** Timezone 8 Ltd. HKG. Dist: D.A.P./Distributed Art Pubs.

Peixotto, Ernest D. Ernest Clifford Peixotto: American Artist: A Biography, 1 vol. 2010. 460p. pap. 29.95 (978-1-61582-747-3(1)) PublishAmerica, Inc.

Peppiatt, Michael. Francis Bacon: Anatomy of an Enigma. 2009. (ENG., Illus.). 464p. pap. 16.95 (978-1-60239-762-0(7), 239762) Skyhorse Publishing Co., Inc.

Peppiatt, Michael. Interviews with Artists, 1966-2011. 2012. (ENG., Illus.). 434p. 40.00 **(978-0-300-17662-9(7))** Yale Univ. Pr.

Perret, Roger & Kurzmeyer, Roman, eds. Dunkelschwestern. Annemarie von Matt - Sonja Sekula. 2008. (Illus.). 368p. 147.00 (978-3-85881-213-1(7)) Scheidegger und Spiess AG, Verlag CHE. Dist: Antique Collectors' Club.

Perry, Robert. Uprising: Woody Crumbo's Indian Art. 2009. (ENG.). 256p. (C). 36.00 *(978-0-9797858-5-6(5))* Chickasaw Pr., The.

Pery, Jenny. Daphne Todd. 2008. (Illus.). 176p. 70.00 ***(978-1-905883-27-1(7))*** Messum, David Fine Paintings, Ltd. GBR. Dist: Antique Collectors' Club.

Peterman, Robert Leonard. Gillie: A Retrospective Biography of Robert Mcgill Mackall, Artist, 1889 - 1982. 2011. 354p. pap. 29.95 ***(978-1-4626-2094-4(9))*** PublishAmerica, Inc.

Peterson, Larry. Philip R. Goodwin. 2007. 388p. 95.00 *(978-0-87842-540-2(3))* Mountain Pr. Publishing Co., Inc.

Peterson, Larry Len & Russell, Charles M. Charles M. Russell: Printed Rarities from Private Collections. 2008. (Illus.). x, 213p. 70.00 *(978-0-87842-550-1(0))*; pap. 45.00 *(978-0-87842-551-8(9))* Mountain Pr. Publishing Co., Inc.

Pettibon, Raymond. Raymond Pettibon. Rugoff, Ralph, ed. 2012. (ENG., Illus.). 384p. 135.00 *(978-0-8478-3500-3(6))* Rizzoli International Pubns., Inc.

Pettus, Peter. Peter Pettus/Continental Drift. 2007. (Illus.). 304p. 85.00 *(978-0-615-13320-1(7))* Sharon Pr.

Pisano, Ronald G. William Merritt Chase Vol. 4: Still Lifes, Interiors, Figures, Copies of Old Masters, & Drawings, 4 vols. 2010. (Illus.). 240p. 65.00 *(978-0-300-11019-7(7))* Yale Univ. Pr.

Plain, Nancy & Russell, Charles M. Sagebrush & Paintbrush: The Story of Charlie Russell, the Cowboy Artist. 2006. *(978-1-59336-715-2(5))* Mondo Publishing.

Poets & Artists. (Illus.). 1.25 *(978-0-88396-539-9(9)*, Blue Mountain Pr.) Blue Mountain Arts Inc.

Pombo, Jorge, ed. Jorge R Pombo. 2008. 228p. *(978-84-96954-29-8(3))* Actar Birkhauser Distribution.

Pontegnie, Anne, ed. Mike Kelley: Educational Complex Onwards 1995-2008. 2010. (ENG., Illus.). 344p. 70.00 *(978-3-905829-80-8(0))* JRP Ringier Kunstverlag AG CHE. Dist: D.A.P./Distributed Art Pubs.

Pool-Goodrich, Nona. 90 Years... Still Counting. 2008. 56p. (YA). pap. 14.99 *(978-0-9655792-9-2(8))* Don Paul Publishing, LLC.

Porter, Gail. Laid Bare: My Story of Love, Fame & Survival. 2008. (ENG., Illus.). 320p. pap. 15.95 *(978-0-09-192041-8(8))* Ebury Publishing GBR. Dist: Independent Pubs. Group.

Postcard Books Staff. Edgar Degas. 4.95 *(978-3-7913-1884-4(5))* Prestel Publishing.

Price, Con & Britzman, H. E. Trails I Rode. 2011. 270p. 47.95 ***(978-1-258-10451-1(2))*** Literary Licensing, LLC.

Prideaux, Sue. Edvard Munch: Behind the Scream. 2007. (ENG., Illus.). 391p. pap. 30.00 *(978-0-300-12401-9(5))* Yale Univ. Pr.

Printz, Neil, et al. Catalogue Raisonn? Vol. 3: Paintings & Sculptures, 1970-1974. 2010. (ENG., Illus.). 544p. 495.00 *(978-0-7148-5698-8(3))* Phaidon Pr., Inc.

Prose, Francine. Caravaggio: Painter of Miracles. 2010. (ENG., Illus.). 160p. pap. 13.99 *(978-0-06-176890-3(1)*, HarperPerennial) HarperCollins Pubs.

Putterman, Florence. Entwined Metaphors. 2009. *(978-1-933153-11-7(3)*, Northern Liberties Pr.) Old City Publishing, Inc.

Pybus, C D. @ Mass Fear. 2008. 144p. per. *(978-1-84401-944-1(6))* Athena Pr.

Quillman, Catherine. 100 Artists of the Brandywine Valley. 2011. (Illus.). 240p. 45.00 *(978-0-7643-3674-4(6))* Schiffer Publishing, Ltd.

Quinlan, Mark. Architects & Sculptors of Remembrance. 2007. 180p. per. *(978-0-7552-0398-7(4))* Authors OnLine, Ltd.

Quinze, Arne. Arne Quinze: Modern Contemporary. 2011. (ENG., Illus.). 300p. 70.00 *(978-3-7757-2693-1(4))* Hatje Cantz Verlag GmbH & Co KG DEU. Dist: D.A.P./Distributed Art Pubs.

Radrizzani, Dominique. Kokoschka: Et la Musique/and Music. 2008. (ENG., Illus.). 128p. pap. 30.00 *(978-88-7439-414-2(4))* 5 Continents ITA. Dist: Hachette Bk. Group.

Ragionieri, Pina. Michelangelo: The Man & the Myth. 2008. (Illus.). 120p. (C). 55.00 *(978-0-8122-4148-8(7))*; pap. 29.95 *(978-0-8122-2054-4(4))* Univ. of Pennsylvania Pr.

Rand, Harry. Hundertwasser. 25th ed. 2007. (ENG., Illus.). 197p. 14.99 *(978-3-8228-3416-9(5))* TASCHEN DEU. Dist: Ingram Pub. Services.

Rankovic, Merima, et al. Expecting the Impossible. 2009. (ENG., Illus.). 280p. 65.00 *(978-0-85667-663-5(2))* Wilson, Philip Pubs., Ltd. GBR. Dist: Macmillan.

Rapoport, Sonya, et al. Pairing of Polarities: The Life & Art of Sonya Rapoport. 2012. pap. ***(978-1-59714-187-1(9))*** Heyday.

Rasilla, Carmen Garcia de la. Salvador Dali's Literary Self-Portrait: Approaches to a Surrealist Autobiography. 2009. (Illus.). 196p. 48.50 *(978-0-8387-5723-9(5))* Bucknell Univ. Pr.

Rau, Hartmut. Ton Schulten. 2006. (ENG.). 192p. 50.00 *(978-90-400-8957-2(4))* Waanders B.V., Uitgeverij NLD. Dist: National Bk. Network.

Ravenal, John B., et al. Xu Bing: Tobacco Project, Duke/Shanghai/Virginia, 1999-2011. Tomii, Reiko, ed. 2011. (ENG., Illus.). 144p. (C). (gr. 13-17). pap. 35.00 *(978-0-917046-96-4(X))* Univ. Pr. of Virginia.

Raye, Robynne & Strassburger, Michael. Inside the World of Board Graphics: Skate, Surf, Snow. 2011. (ENG., Illus.). 224p. pap. 35.00 *(978-1-59253-718-1(9)*, 1592537189); 50.00 ***(978-1-59253-800-3(2)***, 1592538002) Quayside.

Read, Dennis M. R. H. Cromek Engraver Editor & Entrepreneur. 2011. (Illus.). 194p. 99.95 *(978-0-7546-6399-7(X))* Ashgate Publishing Co.

Reich, Howard. The Van Cliburn Story, 0 vols. 2008. 460p. pap. 23.99 *(978-1-59555-228-0(6))* Nelson, Thomas Inc.

Reigosa, Carlos G. & González Reigosa, Carlos. Laxeiro per Si Mesmo. 2008. (GLG., Illus.). 140p. *(978-84-9782-940-3(9))* Xerais de Galicia, Edicions, S.A.

Reily, Nancy Hopkins. Georgia O'Keeffe, a Private Friendship Pt. II: Walking the Abiquiu & Ghost Ranch Land. 2009. 548p. 60.00 *(978-0-86534-452-5(3))* Sunstone Pr.

Remington, R. Roger & Fripp, Robert S. P. Design & Science: The Life & Work of Will Burtin. 2007. (Illus.). 160p. 80.00 *(978-0-85331-968-9(5)*, Lund Humphries Pubs.) Ashgate Publishing, Ltd. GBR. Dist: Ashgate Publishing Co.

Renes, Fernando, ed. Omnivorous Romance. 2008. 208p. *(978-84-96954-30-4(7))* Actar Birkhauser Distribution.

Renzi, Jen & Neumann, Vera. Vera. 2010. 40.00 *(978-0-8109-8904-7(2))* Abrams.

Restany, Pierre & Hundertwasser, Friedensreich. Hundertwasser. 2011. (Temporis Ser.). (ENG, FRE & GER., Illus.). 256p. 39.95 *(978-1-84484-840-9(X))* Parkstone Pr. USA, Ltd.

Rhode, Michael G., ed. Harvey Pekar: Conversations. 2008. (ENG., Illus.). 240p. pap. 22.00 *(978-1-60473-086-9(2))* Univ. Pr. of Mississippi.

Richardson, John. A Life of Picasso: The Cubist Rebel, 1907-1916. 2007. (Borzoi Bks.). (ENG., Illus.). 512p. pap. 32.50 *(978-0-375-71150-3(3)*, Knopf) Knopf Doubleday Publishing Group.

—A Life of Picasso: The Prodigy, 1881-1906. 2007. (Borzoi Bks.). (ENG., Illus.). 560p. pap. 30.00 *(978-0-375-71149-7(X)*, Knopf) Knopf Doubleday Publishing Group.

—A Life of Picasso: The Triumphant Years, 1917-1932. (Illus.). 608p. 2010. pap. 30.00 *(978-0-375-71151-0(1))* 2007. (ENG., 40.00 *(978-0-307-26665-1(6))* Knopf Doubleday Publishing Group. (Knopf).

Risso, Zach. Something Fierce: the Sketchbook Issue. 2009. 68p. pap. 34.95 *(978-0-557-04409-2(X))* Lulu Enterprises Inc.

Ristaino, Marcia R. China's Intrepid Muse. 2009. (ENG.). 176p. pap. 40.00 *(978-1-891640-57-5(7))* Floating World Editions.

Robert Karman. A Day's Ride from de Bullion: A Memoir. 2009. 412p. 36.90 *(978-1-4269-1239-9(0))*; pap. 26.90 *(978-1-4269-1238-2(2))* Trafford Publishing.

Robillard, David. David Robilliard: Life Isn't Good, It's Excellent. *(978-0-9509693-4-3(6))* Gilbert & George.

Robinson, Greg, et al, eds. Miné Okubo: Following Her Own Road. 2008. (ENG., Illus.). 224p. pap. 26.95 *(978-0-295-98774-3(X))* Univ. of Washington Pr.

Robinson, Michael. The Pre-Raphaelites: A study of the artists, their lives & context, with 500 images, & a gallery showing 300 of their most iconic Paintings. 2012. (ENG., Illus.). 256p. 35.00 ***(978-0-7548-2379-7(2))*** Anness Publishing GBR. Dist: National Bk. Network.

Robison, Margaret. The Long Journey Home: A Memoir. 2011. 400p. 26.00 *(978-1-4000-6869-2(X))* Spiegel & Grau.

Rodriguez, Narciso & Berne, Betsy. Narciso Rodriguez. 2008. (ENG., Illus.). 272p. 45.00 *(978-0-8478-3141-8(8))* Rizzoli International Pubns., Inc.

Roe, Sue. The Private Lives of the Impressionists. 368p. 2007. (ENG.). pap. 17.99 *(978-0-06-054559-8(3)*, HarperPerennial) 2006. (Illus.). 29.95 *(978-0-06-054558-1(5))* HarperCollins Pubs.

Rogaishio, Edward R. Midnight to Infinity: The Humor & History of a Mischievous Artist. 2009. *(978-1-58982-504-8(7))* American Bk. Publishing Group.

Rogak, Lisa. Boy Named Shel: The Life & Times of Shel Silverstein. 2nd ed. 2009. (ENG., Illus.). 256p. pap. 16.99 *(978-0-312-53931-3(2)*, St. Martin's Griffin) St. Martin's Pr.

Romain, Lothar & Mueller, Catherina. Martin Engelmann. 2007. 127p. 49.95 *(978-3-87909-678-7(3))* Wienand GmbH, Druck- & Verlagshaus DEU. Dist: Independent Pubs. Group.

Rondinone, Ugo. Ugo Rondinone: The Night of Lead. 2010. (ENG & SPA., Illus.). 384p. 90.00 *(978-3-03764-145-3(2))* JRP Ringier Kunstverlag AG CHE. Dist: D.A.P./Distributed Art Pubs.

Ross, Carolyn. Tony Hart: A Portrait of My Dad. 2010. (ENG., Illus.). 256p. 29.95 *(978-1-84358-184-0(1))* Blake, John Publishing, Ltd. GBR. Dist: Independent Pubs. Group.

Ross, Robert Baldwin. Aubrey Beardsley. 2009. (Illus.). 62p. pap. *(978-0-217-33404-4(0))* Books LLC.

Ross, Robert Baldwin & Vallance, Aymer. Aubrey Beardsley. 2008. 144p. 35.95 *(978-1-4368-9941-3(9))*; pap. 20.95 *(978-1-4367-8332-3(1))* Kessinger Publishing, LLC.

Rossi, Papik. Mr. Rossi: Pictures & Farts. 2007. (ENG., Illus.). 96p. pap. 29.00 *(978-88-88493-11-4(5))* Drago Arts & Communication ITA. Dist: SCB Distributors.

Roy, Ashok, ed. Artist's Pigments: A Handbook of Their History & Characteristics. (USA Publication). (Illus.). 234p. 29.95 *(978-0-89468-232-2(6))* National Gallery of Art.

Rudolph, William Keyse. Vaudechamp in New Orleans. 2007. (Illus.). 115p. *(978-7-80917-860-4(1))* Univ. Pr. of Florida.

Rusho, W. L., ed. The Mystery of Everett Ruess, 1 vol. 2010. (ENG.). 272p. pap. 16.99 *(978-1-4236-1711-2(8))* Gibbs Smith, Publisher.

Rusnak, Jarrett. Pondering Serendipity. 2009. 207p. pap. 79.97 *(978-0-557-23466-0(2))* Lulu Enterprises Inc.

russell, david. David Russell Self-portrait of the Painter. 2010. 183p. pap. 21.95 *(978-1-4452-4950-6(2))* Lulu Enterprises Inc.

Russell, Robert James, et al, eds. Authors & Artists for Young Adults, Volume 76. 2008. (Authors & Artists for Young Adults Ser.: Vol. 76). (ENG., Illus.). 224p. (J). 168.00 *(978-0-7876-7795-4(7))* Cengage Gale.

Sacco, Kevin. The Plane Story. 2011. (Illus.). 128p. (YA). pap. 19.99 *(978-1-60010-867-9(9))* Idea & Design Works, LLC.

Sagmeister, Stefan. Things I Have Learned in My Life So Far, 15 vols. 2008. (ENG., Illus.). 248p. 45.00 *(978-0-8109-9529-1(8))* Abrams.

Sal Buscema: Comic's Fast & Furious Artist. 2010. 192p. (YA). pap. 46.95 *(978-1-60549-022-9(9))* TwoMorrows Publishing.

Salcedo, Doris. Doris Salcedo - Plegiara Muda. 2011. (POR, SWE & ENG., Illus.). 196p. 49.95 ***(978-3-7913-5173-5(7))*** Prestel Publishing.

Sams, Amanda. Authors & Artists for Young Adults. 2008. (Authors & Artists for Young Adults Ser.: Vol. 77). (ENG.). 224p. 168.00 *(978-0-7876-7796-1(5))* Cengage Gale.

Samuels, Roy. Sailing Through Plate Glass Doors. 2010. 427p. pap. 33.95 *(978-1-4092-5185-9(3))* Lulu Enterprises Inc.

Sasse, Julie. Thanks for Being with Us: Contemporary Art from the Douglas Nielsen Collection. 2010. (ENG., Illus.). 52p. pap. 20.00 *(978-0-911611-39-7(8))* Tucson Museum of Art.

SASSpeedis. Horse Trails Have No Ends. 2011. 160p. 25.00 ***(978-1-4567-6823-2(9))***; pap. 11.70 ***(978-1-4567-6824-9(7))*** AuthorHouse.

Savage, Jeff. Tito Ortiz. 2012. (Xtreme Athletes Ser.). (Illus.). 111p. (YA). (gr. 7-12). 28.95 ***(978-1-59935-184-1(6))*** Reynolds, Morgan Inc.

Savignon, Jeromine. Jean-Louis Scherrer. 2007. (ENG., Illus.). 79p. 25.00 *(978-2-7594-0143-7(X))* Assouline FRA. Dist: Perseus Distribution.

Scheele, Friedrich, et al. Ludolf Backhuysen: Emden 1630 - Amsterdam 1708. 2008. (GER., Illus.). 180p. *(978-3-422-06875-9(9))* Deutscher Kunstverlag GmbH.

Schellenberg, Susan & Barnes, Rosemary. Committed to the Sane Asylum: Narratives on Mental Wellness & Healing. 2008. (GER & ENG., Illus.). 320p. pap. 32.95 *(978-1-55458-034-7(X))* Wilfrid Laurier Univ. Pr. CAN. Dist: Univ. of Toronto Pr.

Schelly, Bill. Man of Rock: A Biography of Joe Kubert. 2008. (ENG., Illus.). 320p. pap. 19.99 *(978-1-56097-928-9(3)*, 56928) Fantagraphics Bks.

Scherman, Tony & Dalton, David. Pop: The Genius of Andy Warhol. 528p. 2010. (ENG.). pap. 17.99 *(978-0-06-093663-1(0))* 2009. (Illus.). 40.00 *(978-0-06-621243-2(X))* HarperCollins Pubs.

Schimmel, Paul & Mark, Lisa Gabrielle, eds. Murakami. 2007. (ENG., Illus.). 376p. 65.00 *(978-0-8478-3003-9(9))* Rizzoli International Pubns., Inc.

Schoeser, Mary. Rozanne Hawksley. 2009. (Illus.). 200p. 80.00 *(978-1-84822-026-3(X)*, Lund Humphries Pubs.) Ashgate Publishing, Ltd. GBR. Dist: Ashgate Publishing Co.

Schoone-Jongen, Terence G. Shakespeare's Companies: William Shakespeare's Early Career & the Acting Companies ,1577-1594. 2008. (Studies in Performance & Early Modern Drama Ser.). 264p. 114.95 *(978-0-7546-6434-5(1))* Ashgate Publishing Co.

Schor, Gabriele, ed. Birgit Jurgenssen. 2010. (ENG., Illus.). 296p. 60.00 *(978-3-7757-2461-6(3))* Hatje Cantz Verlag GmbH & Co KG DEU. Dist: D.A.P./Distributed Art Pubs.

Schrag, Ariel. Awkward & Definition: The High School Comic Chronicles of Ariel Schrag. 2008. (ENG., Illus.). 144p. pap. 16.95 *(978-1-4165-5231-4(6)*, Touchstone) Touchstone.

Schuchard, Marsha Keith. William Blake's Sexual Path to Spiritual Vision. 2nd ed. 2008. (Illus.). 398p. pap. 19.95 *(978-1-59477-211-5(8))* Inner Traditions International, Ltd.

Schultz, Edward G. A Canvas Full of Miracles: An Easel full of Love. 2009. 39.95 *(978-1-61623-388-4(5))* Independent Pub.

Schwartz, Gary. Meet Rembrandt: Life & Work of the Master Painter. 2011. (Illus.). 112p. pap. 19.95 *(978-0-300-16764-1(4))* Yale Univ. Pr.

Scully, Sean. Sean Scully: Bodies of Lights. 2007. (Illus.). pap. *(978-84-89935-76-1(9))* Fundacion Juan March.

Scully, Sean, photos by. Sean Scully. 2010. (ENG., Illus.). 56p. 27.95 *(978-88-8158-741-4(6))* Charta ITA. Dist: D.A.P./Distributed Art Pubs.

Seales, Lennox & Dorsinville, Jean M. Curtain Call: The life & times of Franklyn Vincent Ellison Seales. 2011. 188p. 24.59 *(978-1-4520-9554-7(X))*; pap. 14.03 *(978-1-4520-9553-0(1))* AuthorHouse.

Secrest, Meryle. Modigliani: A Life. 2011. (ENG., Illus.). 416p. 35.00 *(978-0-307-26368-1(1)*, Knopf) Knopf Doubleday Publishing Group.

Seid, Susan. Vera: The Art & Life of an Icon. 2010. (ENG., Illus.). 208p. 35.00 *(978-0-8109-9604-5(9))* Abrams.

Serota, Nicholas & Godfrey, Mark, eds. Gerhard Richter: Panorama, 1 vol. 2011. (ENG.). 288p. 65.00 ***(978-1-935202-71-4(5))*** D.A.P./Distributed Art Pubs.

Shabla, Roy Anthony. (peace) Words. 2010. 52p. pap. 14.99 *(978-0-557-44083-2(1))* Lulu Enterprises Inc.

Shankar, Lalitha. Relentless Brush Strokes: A Memoir. 2008. 288p. pap. 15.49 *(978-1-4343-5803-5(8))* AuthorHouse.

Shawhan, Dorothy Sample & Norris, Carolyn. Spirit of the Delta: The Art of Carolyn Norris. 2011. (ENG., Illus.). 128p. 35.00 *(978-1-60473-992-3(4))* Univ. Pr. of Mississippi.

Shelbourn, Colin. Drawing Cartoons, 1 vol. 2010. (ENG., Illus.). 160p. 34.95 *(978-1-84797-172-2(5))* Crowood Pr., Ltd. GBR. Dist: Independent Pubs. Group.

Sheldon, George F. Hugh Williamson: Physician, Patriot & Founding Father. 2009. (ENG., Illus.). 340p. pap. 39.00 *(978-1-59102-770-6(5)*, Humanity Bks.) Prometheus Bks., Pubs.

Shen, Jiawei. Lan Wang. 2010. 350p. 85.00 *(978-1-876957-14-8(X))* Wild Peony Bk. Pubs. Pty., Ltd. AUS. Dist: Univ. of Hawaii Pr.

Shiff, Richard & Lampert, Catherine. Peter Doig. 2011. (ENG., Illus.). 400p. 150.00 *(978-0-8478-3473-0(5))* Rizzoli International Pubns., Inc.

Shiner, Eric C. & Tomii, Reiko. Making a Home: Japanese Contemporary Artists in New York. 2007. (ENG., Illus.). 224p. 65.00 *(978-0-300-12634-1(4))* Japan Society Gallery.

Shipp, Steve. Latin American & Caribbean Artists of the Modern Era: A Biographical Dictionary of More Than 12,700 Persons, 2 vols. alt. ed. 2012. (ENG., Illus.). 916p. pap. 75.00 *(978-0-7864-6626-9(X))* McFarland & Co., Inc. Pubs.

Simmons, Edward. From Seven to Seventy. 2008. 392p. *(978-1-4437-2232-2(4))* 2006. 388p. per. *(978-1-4067-1336-7(8))* Read Bks. (Hesperides Pr.).

Simon, Joe. Joe Simon: My Life in Comics - The Illustrated Autobiography. 2011. (ENG., Illus.). 256p. 24.95 *(978-1-84576-930-7(9)*, Titan Bks.) Titan Bks. Ltd. GBR. Dist: Random Hse., Inc.

Sims, Lowery Stokes, frwd. Llewellyn Xavier: His Life & Work. 2007. (ENG., Illus.). 224p. *(978-1-4050-8649-3(1))* Macmillan Caribbean.

Sinnott, Kevin. Behind the Canvas. 2009. (ENG., Illus.). 160p. pap. 29.95 *(978-1-85411-445-7(X))* Seren Bks. GBR. Dist: Independent Pubs. Group.

Sischy, Ingrid. Koons, Jeff: With an Original Artwork. Holzwarth, Hans Werner, ed. 2008. 606p. 9000.00 *(978-3-8365-0070-8(1))* TASCHEN DEU. Dist: Ingram Pub. Services.

Skinner, Alice Blackmer. Stay by Me, Roses: The Life of American Artist Alice Archer Sewall James (1870-1955) 2011. (Illus.). 288p. pap. *(978-0-87785-338-1(X))* Swedenborg Foundation, Inc.

Skrabec, Quentin R. Edward Drummond Libbey: A Biography of the American Glassmaker. 2011. (ENG., Illus.). 242p. pap. 45.00 *(978-0-7864-6335-0(X))* McFarland & Co., Inc. Pubs.

Slobodkina Foundation. Esphyr Slobodkina: Rediscovering a Pioneer of American Abstraction. 2008. pap. *(978-0-9793620-0-2(8))* Slobodkina Foundation, The.

Small, David. Stitches: A Memoir. 2010. (ENG., Illus.). 329p. pap. 16.95 *(978-0-393-33896-6(7)*, 33896) Norton, W. W. & Co., Inc.

Smart, Tom. Tom Forrestall: Paintings, Drawings, Writings. 2008. (ENG., Illus.). 152p. 49.95 *(978-1-55470-005-9(1))* Key Porter Bks. CAN. Dist: Perseus-PGW.

Smee, Sebastian, intro. Lucian Freud on Paper. 2009. (ENG., Illus.). 264p. 40.00 *(978-0-8478-3233-0(3))* Rizzoli International Pubns., Inc.

Smith, Kathy. Tocame la Nariz - Monstruos Multicolor. (Tocame la Nariz Ser.). (SPA.). 8p. 2.00 net. *(978-1-4054-2505-6(9))* Parragon, Inc.

Smith, Keri. Wreck This Journal. 2007. (ENG., Illus.). 192p. (gr. 12-18). 13.95 *(978-0-399-53346-4(X)*, Perigee Trade) Penguin Group (USA) Inc.

Smith, Zak. We Did Porn: Memoir & Drawings. 2009. (ENG., Illus.). 488p. 49.95 *(978-0-9820539-2-8(4))* Tin Hse. Bks., LLC.

Society of Illustrators Staff. Illustrators 50. 50th ed. 2009. (Illus.). 608p. pap. 45.00 *(978-0-06-158278-3(6)*, Collins Design) HarperCollins Pubs.

Spalding, Frances. The Bloomsbury Group. 2006. (National Portrait Gallery Insights Ser.). (Illus.). 108p. 19.95 *(978-1-85514-351-7(8))* National Portrait Gallery Pubns. GBR. Dist: Antique Collectors' Club.

—John Piper, Myfanwy Piper: Lives in Art. 2011. (ENG., Illus.). 624p. pap. 29.95 *(978-0-19-956762-1(X))* Oxford Univ. Pr., Inc.

Spector, Nancy, ed. & text. Felix Gonzalez-Torres, 1 vol. 2007. (ENG., Illus.). 228p. 45.00 *(978-0-89207-362-7(4))* Guggenheim, Solomon R. Museum.

Spence, David. Degas. 2009. (Ticktock Essential Artists Ser.). (ENG.). 32p. (J). (gr. 4-7). pap. 6.95 *(978-1-84696-975-1(1))* TickTock Bks. GBR. Dist: Independent Pubs. Group.

Spencer, Flora Macdonald. Evan Macdonald: A Painter's Life. Nasby, Judith, ed. 2008. (ENG., Illus.). 144p. pap. 29.95 *(978-1-55458-048-4(X))* Wilfrid Laurier Univ. Pr. CAN. Dist: Univ. of Toronto Pr.

Spike, John T. Young Michelangelo: The Path to the Sistine - A Biography. 2010. (ENG., Illus.). 272p. 27.95 *(978-0-86565-266-8(X))* Vendome Pr., The.

Spilsbury, Maria & Yeldham, Charlotte. Maria Spilsbury (1766-1820) Artist & Evangelical. 2010. (Illus.). 230p. 124.95 *(978-0-7546-6991-3(2))* Ashgate Publishing Co.

Spring, Justin. Wolf Kahn. rev. ed. 2011. (ENG., Illus.). 196p. 55.00 *(978-0-8109-9790-5(8))* Abrams.

Squires, William Tolliver. Art, Experience & Faith. 2010. (Illus.). 108p. pap. 11.95 *(978-1-4327-4419-9(4))* Outskirts Pr., Inc.

Steadman, Ralph. The Joke's Over: Bruised Memories: Gonzo, Hunter S. Thompson, & Me. 2007. (ENG., Illus.). 416p. pap. 15.00 *(978-0-15-603250-6(3)*, Mariner Bks.) Houghton Mifflin Harcourt Trade & Reference Pubs.

Stetz, Margaret D. Facing the Late Victorians: Portraits of Writers & Artists from the Mark Samuels Lasner Collection. 2007. (Illus.). 158p. pap. 49.00 *(978-0-87413-992-1(9))* Univ. of Delaware Pr.

Stice, Mike. Wolfgang Bloch: The Colors of Coincidence. 2008. (ENG., Illus.). 176p. 40.00 *(978-0-8118-6101-4(5))* Chronicle Bks. LLC.

Stiles, Kristine. Marina Abramovic. 2008. (ENG., Illus.). 160p. 45.00 *(978-0-7148-4802-0(6))* Phaidon Pr., Inc.

Stolzl, Gunta & text. Gunta Stolzl: Bauhaus Master. 2009. (ENG., Illus.). 144p. 39.95 *(978-0-87070-773-5(6))* Museum of Modern Art.

Storr, Robert, et al. Gary Panter. 2008. (ENG., Illus.). 700p. 95.00 *(978-0-9794153-1-9(4))* PictureBox, Inc.

Strauss, Dorothea, ed. Erik Steinbrecher: Minimalist Kitsch, 1 vol. 2007. (ENG., Illus.). 128p. 35.00 *(978-3-905701-77-7(4))* JRP Ringier Kunstverlag AG CHE. Dist: D.A.P./Distributed Art Pubs.

Sugarman, Tracy. Drawing Conclusions: An Artist Discovers His America. 2008. (Illus.). 179p. 29.95 *(978-0-8156-0871-4(3))* Syracuse Univ. Pr.

Sukrow, Oliver. Lea Grundig: Sozialistische Künstlerin und Präsidentin des Verbandes Bildender Künstler in der DDR (1964-1970) 2011. (DDR- Studien / East German Studies). (GER.). 275p. pap. 58.95 ***(978-3-0343-0297-5(5))*** Lang, Peter AG GBR. Dist: Lang, Peter.

Suter, H. Paul Klee & His Illness: Bowed but Not Broken by Suffering & AdversityTranslated from the German by G. Mckay; N. Mckay. 2010. (ENG., Illus.). 272p. *(978-3-8055-9381-6(3))* Karger, S. AG.

sykes, christopher simon. David Hockney: The Biography. 2012. (ENG., Illus.). 384p. 35.00 (978-0-385-53144-3(3), Talese, Nan A.) Knopf Doubleday Publishing Group.

Sylvia Beckman Warner, Her Life & Art. 2007. 50.00 net. (978-0-9796438-0-4(5)) Bishop, Anne.

Tames, Richard. William Morris: An Illustrated Life of William Morris, 1834-1896. 2nd ed. 2008. (Shire Library). (ENG., Illus.). 64p. pap. 12.95 (978-0-7478-0435-2(4)) Shire Pubns., Ltd. GBR. Dist: Random Hse., Inc.

Tàpies, Antoni. Antoni Tàpies Vol. II: Complete Writings, Collected Essays. Sobrer, Josep Miquel, tr. from CAT. 2nd ed. 2011. (ENG., Illus.). 600p. 39.95 (978-0-253-35503-4(6), 0253355036) Indiana Univ. Pr.

—A Personal Memoir Vol. 1: Fragments for an Autobiography. Sobrer, Josep Miquel, tr. from CAT. 2009. (ENG., Illus.). 430p. 39.95 (978-0-253-35489-1(7), 0253354897) Indiana Univ. Pr.

Telfair Museum of Art Staff. Picturing Savannah: The Art of Christopher A. D. Murphy. 2008. (ENG., Illus.). 120p. pap. 29.95 (978-0-933075-07-8(3)) Telfair Museum of Art.

Teraoka, Masami. Masami Teraoka: 1974-Present. 2008. (Illus.). 12p. (978-0-9743541-5-6(5)) Clark, Catherine Gallery.

Thames and Hudson Staff, et al. 60: Innovators Shaping Our Creative Future. 2009. (ENG., Illus.). 408p. 75.00 (978-0-500-51492-4(5), 551492) Thames & Hudson.

The Pace Gallery, prod. Robert Mangold: Ring Paintings. 2011. (Illus.). 30p. pap. 30.00 (978-1-935410-18-8(0)) Pace Gallery, The.

Theisen, Olive Jensen. A Life on Paper: The Drawings & Lithographs of John Thomas Biggers. 2006. (ENG., Illus.). 160p. 29.95 (978-1-57441-220-8(5)) Univ. of North Texas Pr.

Thirlwell, Angela. Into the Frame: The Four Loves of Ford Madox Brown. 2010. (ENG., Illus.). 328p. 39.95 (978-0-7011-7902-1(3), Chatto & Windus) Random Hse. GBR. Dist: Independent Pubs. Group.

Thom, Ian M. Challenging Traditions: Contemporary First Nations Art of the Northwest Coast. 2009. (ENG.). 176p. 65.00 (978-0-295-98919-8(X)) Univ. of Washington Pr.

Thomas, Maggie. Dishing the Dirt - 30 Years Behind the Scenes in Television Makeup. 2009. (Illus.). 106p. pap. (978-0-7552-0453-3(0)) Authors OnLine, Ltd.

Thompson, Kay. Eloise. (Eloise Ser.). pap. 19.95 (978-2-07-053845-4(1)) Gallimard, Editions FRA. Dist: Distribooks, Inc.

Thomson Gale, creator. Authors & Artists for Young Adults. (Authors & Artists for Young Adults Ser.). (ENG., Illus.). 224p. Vol. 71. 2006. 168.00 (978-0-7876-7790-9(6)) Vol. 75. 2007. 168.00 (978-0-7876-7794-7(9)) Cengage Gale.

—Authors & Artists for Young Adults: Volume 70, Vol. 70. 2006. (Authors & Artists for Young Adults Ser.). (ENG., Illus.). 250p. 168.00 (978-0-7876-7789-3(2)) Cengage Gale.

—Authors & Artists for Young Adults, Volume 72, Vol. 72. 2006. (Authors & Artists for Young Adults Ser.). (ENG., Illus.). 250p. 168.00 (978-0-7876-7791-6(4)) Cengage Gale.

—Authors & Artists for Young Adults Volume 74, Vol. 74. 2007. (Authors & Artists fro Young Adults Ser.). (ENG., Illus.). 240p. 168.00 (978-0-7876-7793-0(0)) Cengage Gale.

Thomson Gale Staff. Biographisches Handbuch der Rabbiner 1871-1943, 2 vols., Pt. 2. 2009. (GER.). XXIV, 745p. (978-3-598-24874-0(1)) Saur, K. G. Verlag GmbH & Co.

Thunfors, Jacquelyn. Journalist Without Words: 19 Years Painting International Conversations. 2007. (Illus.). 116p. per. (978-1-4243-2937-3(X)) Riverside Publishing Co.

Tibol, Raquel. Frida Kahlo en su Luz Mas Intima. 2008. (SPA.). 260p. pap. 19.00 (978-1-4379-5831-7(1)) DIANE Publishing Co.

Tilson, Joe & Di Martino, Enzo. Tilson: The Printed Works, 1963-2009. 2010. (ITA & ENG., Illus.). 216p. pap. 55.00 (978-1-905711-82-6(4)) Royal Academy of Arts GBR. Dist: Hachette Bk. Group.

Todd, Kim. Chrysalis: Maria Sibylla Merian & the Secrets of Metamorphosis. 2007. (ENG., Illus.). 352p. pap. 15.00 (978-0-15-603299-5(6), Mariner Bks.) Houghton Mifflin Harcourt Trade & Reference Pubs.

Togden, Doc. An Odd Boy: Volume One [paperback]. 2011. 342p. pap. (978-1-898185-20-8(4)) Aro Bks. worldwide.

Tokyo Bunkazai Kenkyujo, Kikaku Johobu Staff, contrib. by. Kuroda Seiki "Kohan" Kuroda Seiki, Lakeside. 2008. (Illus.). 92p. (978-4-8055-0571-7(0)) Chuo Koron Bijutsu Shuppan.

Tomkins, Calvin. Lives of the Artists. 2010. (ENG.). 272p. pap. 15.00 (978-0-8050-9144-1(0), Holt Paperback) Holt, Henry & Co.

Ton Schulten. 9.99 (978-3-8327-0764-4(6)); (ENG, FRE & GER.). 7.99 (978-3-8327-1259-4(3)); (ENG, FRE & GER.). 12.99 (978-3-8327-1092-7(2)); (Illus.). 3.99 (978-3-8327-1500-7(2)); (ENG, FRE & GER., Illus.). spiral bd. 14.99 (978-3-8327-1266-2(6)); (Illus.). spiral bd. 8.99 (978-3-8327-1321-8(2)); (Illus.). spiral bd. 65.00 (978-3-8327-0988-4(6)); (Illus.). spiral bd. 39.99 (978-3-8327-0990-7(8)); (Illus.). spiral bd. 39.99 (978-3-8327-0941-9(X)) teNeues Publishing Co.

Treadwell, Penelope. Johan Zoffany: Artist & Adventurer. 2009. (Illus.). 400p. pap. 50.00 (978-1-907372-04-9(0)) Holberton, Paul Publishing GBR. Dist: Casemate Pubs. & Bk. Distributors, LLC.

Trela, Christopher, ed. The Autobiography & Sex Life of Andy Warhol. 2010. (ENG., Illus.). 256p. 45.00 (978-0-9706126-1-8(3)) Trela.

Trese, Daniel, photos by. Walking Backwards. 2007. 64p. per. 16.00 (978-0-9747238-0-8(0)) Adolescent Bks.

Tretiack, Phillippe. Warhol's America. 2008. pap. (978-2-7594-0312-7(2)) Assouline.

Trovaioli, August P. & Toledano, Roulhac B. William Aiken Walker: Southern Genre Painter, 1 vol. 2007. (ENG., Illus.). 224p. 50.00 (978-1-58980-509-5(7)) Pelican Publishing Co., Inc.

Trumbull, John. Autobiography, Reminiscences & Letters of John Trumbull, from 1756 To 1841. 2010. 522p. pap. 39.75 (978-1-149-04703-3(8)); 512p. pap. 39.75 (978-1-148-14001-8(8)); 524p. pap. 39.75 (978-1-145-42423-4(6)); 512p. pap. 39.75 (978-1-142-98819-7(8)); 512p. pap. 39.75 (978-1-143-11069-6(2)) BiblioBazaar.

—Autobiography, Reminiscences & Letters of John Trumbull, from 1756 To 1841. 2009. 280p. pap. 35.91 (978-1-150-06093-9(X)) General Bks. LLC.

Trusky, Tom. James Castle: His Life & Art. 2nd ed. 2008. (Illus.). viii, 213p. (978-0-932129-46-8(3)); (978-0-932129-47-5(1)) Hemingway Western Studies Ctr. (Idaho Ctr. for the Bk.).

Tuthill, Louisa C. Success in Life: the Artist. 2006. 39.95 (978-1-4255-7435-2(1)) MPublishing.

Unger, Pat. Bill's Story: A Portrait of W. A. Sutton. 2009. (ENG., Illus.). 252p. pap. 29.95 (978-1-877257-70-4(2)) Canterbury Univ. Pr. NZL. Dist: Independent Pubs. Group.

Unverfehrt, Gerd & Dürer, Albrecht. Da Sah Ich Viel Köstliche Dinge: Albrecht Dürers Reise in Die Niederlande. 2007. (GER., Illus.). 261p. (C). pap. 51.00 (978-3-525-47010-7(X)) Vandenhoeck & Ruprecht GmbH & Co. KG DEU. Dist: ISD.

Ursprung, Philip. Studio Olafur Eliasson Jumbo. Eliasson, Olafur, ed. 2012. (ENG., Illus.). 528p. 39.99 (978-3-8365-2727-9(8)) TASCHEN DEU. Dist: Ingram Pub. Services.

Van der Veen, Wouter. Van Gogh in Auvers: His Last Days. 2010. (ENG., Illus.). 304p. 75.00 (978-1-58093-301-8(7)) Monacelli Pr., Inc.

van Dyke, James A. Franz Radziwill & the Contradictions of German Art History, 1919-45. 2010. (Social History, Popular Culture, & Politics in Germany Ser.). (ENG., Illus.). 340p. (C). 80.00 (978-0-472-11628-7(2)) Univ. of Michigan Pr.

Van Hamersveld, John. My Art, My Life. Clucas, David Lynn, ed. 2010. (ENG., Illus.). 176p. 100.00 (978-1-58731-523-7(8)); pap. 23.00 (978-1-58731-524-4(6)) St. Augustine's Pr., Inc.

Van Lieshout, Atelier, illus. Atelier Van Lieshout, 1 vol. 2007. (ENG.). 272p. pap. 55.00 (978-90-5662-482-8(2)) NAi Uitgevers / Publishers Stichting NLD. Dist: D.A.P./Distributed Art Pubs.

Vanderbilt, Gloria. It Seemed Important at the Time: A Romance Memoir. 2009. (ENG., Illus.). 176p. pap. 12.99 (978-1-4391-8982-5(X)) Simon & Schuster.

Varney, Carleton. Houses in My Heart: An International Decorator's Colorful Journey. 2008. (ENG., Illus.). 224p. 95.00 (978-0-9777875-5-5(9)) Shannongrove Pr.

Vasari, Giorgio. The Lives of the Artists. Bondanella, Julia Conway & Bondanella, Peter, trs. from ITA. 2008. (Oxford World's Classics Ser.). (ENG.). 624p. pap. 12.95 (978-0-19-953719-8(4)) Oxford Univ. Pr., Inc.

Vassilopoulos, Peter. John M. Horton: Mariner Artist, 1 vol. 2007. (ENG., Illus.). 176p. (978-1-894974-34-9(4)) Heritage Hse.

Vettese, Angela & Camartin, Iso. Rebecca Horn: Fata Morgana. 2010. (ENG., Illus.). 144p. 59.95 (978-88-8158-753-7(X)) Charta ITA. Dist: D.A.P./Distributed Art Pubs.

Vettriano, Jack. Jack Vettriano: A Life. 2nd ed. 2012. (ENG., Illus.). 208p. 45.00 (978-1-86205-944-3(6)) Chrysalis Children's Bks. GBR. Dist: Independent Pubs. Group.

Vettriano, Jack. Jack Vettriano: Studio Life. 2008. (ENG., Illus.). 160p. 35.00 (978-1-86205-743-2(5), Pavilion Bks., Ltd.) Anova Bks. GBR. Dist: Independent Pubs. Group.

Victore, James & Bierut, Michael. Victore or, Who Died & Made You Boss? 2010. (ENG., Illus.). 208p. 40.00 (978-0-8109-9591-8(3)) Abrams.

Vincent. 2009. (ENG., Illus.). 32p. (J). 18.95 (978-0-615-27618-2(0)) PRD Pr.

Vine, Richard, et al. Oh Chi Gyun: Defining Landscapes. 2008. (ENG., Illus.). 186p. 50.00 (978-1-55595-297-6(6)) Hudson Hills Pr. LLC.

Volkov, Solomon. Romanov Riches: Russian Writers & Artists under the Tsars. 2011. (ENG., Illus.). 304p. 30.00 (978-0-307-27063-4(7), Knopf) Knopf Doubleday Publishing Group.

Von D, Kat. High Voltage Tattoo. 2009. (ENG., Illus.). 144p. 29.99 (978-0-06-168438-8(4), Collins Design) HarperCollins Pubs.

von Spreter, Sophie, ed. Magne Furuholmen: in Transit. 2012. (ENG., Illus.). 304p. 80.00 (978-82-7547-413-9(2)) Pr., Forlaget NOR. Dist: D.A.P./Distributed Art Pubs.

VV Staff. El Bosco. (Colección Art Book). (SPA., Illus.). 144p. (978-84-8156-181-4(9)) Sociedad Editorial Electa Espana ESP. Dist: Lectorum Pubns., Inc.

—Van Gogh. (Colección Art Book). (SPA., Illus.). 144p. (978-84-8156-198-2(3)) Sociedad Editorial Electa Espana ESP. Dist: Lectorum Pubns., Inc.

Wainwright, J. A. Blazing Figures: A Life of Robert Markle. 2010. (Illus.). 304p. (C). 45.00 (978-1-55458-182-5(6)) Wilfrid Laurier Univ. Pr. CAN. Dist: Univ. of Toronto Pr.

Wakefield, Neville, et al, texts. Frieze Projects & Frieze Talks 2006-2008. 2010. (ENG., Illus.). 308p. pap. 35.00 (978-0-9553201-5-6(1)) Frieze GBR. Dist: D.A.P./Distributed Art Pubs.

Waldman, Anne, text. Pat Steir. 2007. (Illus.). 46p. per. 30.00 (978-0-9797397-3-6(X)) Cheim & Read.

Walker, Butch & Diehl, Matt. Drinking with Strangers: Music Lessons from a Teenage Bullet Belt. 2011. (ENG.). 304p. 25.99 (978-0-06-178731-7(0), Morrow, William & Co.) HarperCollins Pubs.

Wall, Jeff, photos by. Jeff Wall, 1 vol. 2007. (ENG., Illus.). 168p. 50.00 (978-0-87070-707-0(8)) Museum of Modern Art.

Wallace, Catherine. Catching the Light: The Art & Life of Henry Scott Tuke, 1858-1929. 2008. (ENG., Illus.). 160p. (978-1-873830-20-8(3), Fine Art Society (Acc)) Antique Collectors' Club.

Wallace, David. Exiles in Hollywood. 2006. (ENG., Illus.). 246p. per. 22.95 (978-0-87910-329-3(9), 0879103299, Limelight Editions) Leonard, Hal Corp.

Wallace, Kevin. River of Destiny: The Life & Work of Binh Pho. 2006. pap. 35.00 (978-0-9712772-6-7(5)) Long Beach Museum of Art.

Wallace, Kevin & Martin, Terry. New Masters of Woodturning: Expanding the Boundaries of Wood Art. 2008. (ENG.). 197p. 69.95 (978-1-56523-375-1(1)); (Illus.). pap. 29.95 (978-1-56523-334-8(4)) Fox Chapel Publishing Co., Inc.

Wallace, Paul A. W. Lloyd Mifflin: Poet & Painter of the Susquehanna. 2007. 27p. (C). pap. 15.00 (978-1-4223-1504-0(5)) DIANE Publishing Co.

Wallace, William. Michelangelo: The Artist, the Man & His Times. 2009. (ENG., Illus.). 428p. (C). 34.00 (978-0-521-11199-7(4)) Cambridge Univ. Pr.

Wallace, William E. Michelangelo: The Artist, the Man & his Times. 2011. (ENG., Illus.). 420p. (C). pap. 19.99 (978-1-107-67369-4(0)) Cambridge Univ. Pr.

—The Treasures of Michelangelo. 2010. (ENG., Illus.). 64p. 50.00 (978-0-233-00253-8(7)) Andre Deutsch GBR. Dist: Sterling Publishing Co., Inc.

Walpole, Josephine. Leonard Russell Squirrell RWS RE: Artist of East Anglia, 1893-1979. 2011. (ENG., Illus.). 128p. 49.50 (978-1-85149-666-2(1)) Antique Collectors' Club.

Walsh, Michael J. K. Hanging a Rebel: The Life of C. R. W. Nevinson. 2008. (ENG., Illus.). 368p. pap. 53.00 (978-0-7188-3090-8(3)) Lutterworth Pr., The GBR. Dist: Brown, David Bk. Co., The.

Walter, Bernadette, text. Verena Loewensberg: Prints. 2009. (ENG., Illus.). 112p. pap. 38.00 (978-3-905714-51-7(5)) Nieves CHE. Dist: D.A.P./Distributed Art Pubs.

Walters, Julie. That's Another Story: The Autobiograph. 2009. (ENG., Illus.). 368p. 14.95 (978-0-7538-2608-9(9), Phoenix) Orion Publishing Group, Ltd. GBR. Dist: Independent Pubs. Group.

Ward, David C. Charles Willson Peale: Art & Selfhood in the Early Republic. 2007. (Illus.). 236p. 30.00 (978-1-4223-6629-5(4)) DIANE Publishing Co.

Waters, John. Role Models, 1 vol. 2011. (ENG., Illus.). 320p. pap. 15.00 (978-0-374-53286-4(9)) Farrar, Straus & Giroux.

Watson, Daryl. Gifts to the Prairie: The Work of Pioneer Nurserymen & the Art of the Prestele Family. 2008. (Illus.). 32p. 15.00 (978-0-943788-34-0(X)) McLean County Historical Society.

Watson, J.N.P. Millais: Three Generations in Nature, Art & Sport. (Illus.). 176p. 45.00 (978-0-948253-28-7(2)) Sportsman's Pr., The GBR. Dist: Trafalgar Square Publishing.

Wearstler, Kelly. Hue (Limited Edition) Crist, Steve, ed. 2010. 85.00 (978-1-934429-52-5(X)) AMMO Bks., LLC.

Webb, Peter. Death, Desire & the Doll: The Life & Art of Hans Bellmer. 2008. (Solar Art Directives Ser.). (Illus.). 208p. per. 29.95 (978-0-9714578-5-7(7)) Solar Bks.

Weber, Nicholas Fox. The Bauhaus Group: Six Masters of Modernism. 2009. (ENG., Illus.). 544p. 40.00 (978-0-307-26836-5(5), Knopf) Knopf Doubleday Publishing Group.

—The Bauhaus Group: Six Masters of Modernism. 2011. (ENG., Illus.). 544p. pap. 27.50 (978-0-300-16984-3(1)) Yale Univ. Pr.

Weidemann, Christiane. Leonardo da Vinci. 2010. (Illus.). 128p. pap. 14.95 (978-3-7913-4336-5(X)) Prestel Publishing.

—Niki de Saint Phalle. 2010. (Illus.). 128p. pap. 14.95 (978-3-7913-4334-1(3)) Prestel Publishing.

—Salvador Dali. 2007. (Living Art Ser.). (Illus.). 128p. pap. 14.95 (978-3-7913-3813-2(7)) Prestel Publishing.

—50 Modern Artists You Should Know. 2010. (Illus.). 160p. pap. 19.95 (978-3-7913-4470-6(6)) Prestel Publishing.

Weidemann, Christiane & Finger, Brad. 50 Contemporary Artists You Should Know. 2011. (Illus.). 160p. pap. 19.95 (978-3-7913-4530-7(3)) Prestel Publishing.

Weir, John F. B. 1841. John Trumbull; a Brief Sketch of His Life, to Which Is Added a Catalogue of His Works. 2010. 144p. pap. 21.75 (978-1-176-29446-2(6)) BiblioBazaar.

Weir, John Ferguson. John Trumbull, a Brief Sketch of His Life: To Which Is Added A Catalogue of His Works (1901) 132p. 2010. 28.76 (978-1-169-70941-6(9)) 2010. 35.95 (978-1-161-89183-6(8)) 2009. pap. 20.95 (978-1-104-13593-5(0)) Kessinger Publishing, LLC.

—John Trumbull; a Brief Sketch of His Life, to Which Is Added a Catalogue of His Works, Prepared for the Committee on the Bi-Centennial. 2010. (Illus.). 42p. pap. 14.14 (978-1-154-46200-5(5)) General Bks. LLC.

Weisman, Mary-Lou. Al Jaffee's Mad Life: A Biography. 2010. (ENG., Illus.). 240p. 27.99 (978-0-06-186448-3(X)) HarperCollins Pubs.

Weiss, Andrea. In the Shadow of the Magic Mountain: The Erika & Klaus Mann Story. 2008. (Illus.). 310p. 27.50 (978-0-226-88672-5(7)) Univ. of Chicago Pr.

Weitman, Wendy. Kiki Smith: Prints, Books & Things, 1 vol. 2009. (ENG., Illus.). 150p. (gr. 13-18). 45.00 (978-0-87070-583-0(0)) Museum of Modern Art.

Welland, Sasha Su-Ling. A Thousand Miles of Dreams: The Journeys of Two Chinese Sisters. 2007. (Asian Voices Ser.). (ENG., Illus.). 392p. per. 19.95 (978-0-7425-5314-9(0)) Rowman & Littlefield Publishers, Inc.

Weller, Dennis P., intro. & text. Rembrandt: Paintings in America. 2011. (Illus.). 224p. pap. 50.00 (978-0-8478-3687-1(8), Skira) Rizzoli International Pubns., Inc.

Wertz, Julia. Drinking at the Movies. 2010. (ENG., Illus.). 192p. pap. 15.00 (978-0-307-59183-8(2), Three Rivers Pr.) Crown Publishing Group.

Weschler, Lawrence. Seeing Is Forgetting the Name of the Thing One Sees: Expanded Edition. exp. ed. 2009. (ENG., Illus.). 336p. pap. 26.95 (978-0-520-25609-5(3)) Univ. of California Pr.

—Seeing Is Forgetting the Name of the Thing One Sees: Over Thirty Years of Conversations with Robert Irwin. exp. ed. 2009. (Illus.). 352p. 50.00 (978-0-520-25608-8(5)) Univ. of California Pr.

Weschler, Lawrence & Hockney, David. True to Life: Twenty-Five Years of Conversations with David Hockney. 2009. (Illus.). 272p. pap. 26.95 (978-0-520-25879-2(7)) Univ. of California Pr.

White, Edmund. Arts & Letters. 2006. (ENG.). 376p. per. 15.95 (978-1-57344-248-0(8)) Cleis Pr.

Whiticar, George Curtis. Whiticar Waterway Tales: A Personal Narrative. 2007. (Illus.). 100p. pap. 18.95 (978-0-615-17770-0(0)) Darvill, Laura Kay.

Whitmer, Kathleen. The Glory in a Story: A Joyful Journey Through Memories. 2008. (Illus.). 198p. pap. 23.95 (978-0-9661079-5-1(0)) Peach Pubns., Inc.

Whittaker, Richard. The Conversations: Interviews with Sixteen Contemporary Artists. 2007. (Working Bks.). (ENG., Illus.). 240p. per. 18.95 (978-0-9673608-8-1(9)) Whale & Star Pr.

Wickersham, Sheldon. Randall Made Knives: A Timeline - the Quick Reference Guide. 3rd ed. 2007. 20.00 (978-0-9740474-3-0(0)) Blue Star Knives.

Williams, Emlyn. Emlyn Williams: The Complete Autobiography. 2006. (Illus.) 600p. pap. 14.95 (978-1-86057-023-0(2)) Welsh Academic Pr. GBR. Dist: International Specialized Bk. Services.

Williams, Jamal "Rise". I Have a Mic & a Dream. 2009. 120p. pap. 12.95 (978-1-4401-1825-8(6)) iUniverse, Inc.

Wilmers, Gertrude de G. & Sloan, Julie L. Frederic Crowninshield: A Renaissance Man in Gilded Age. 2010. (Illus.). 448p. 39.95 (978-1-55849-864-8(8)) Univ. of Massachusetts Pr.

Wilson, Franklin. Life Story of Franklin Wilson As Told by. 2006. pap. 20.95 (978-1-4286-6100-4(X)) Kessinger Publishing, LLC.

Wilson, Jonathan. Marc Chagall. 2007. (Jewish Encounters Ser.). (ENG., Illus.). 224p. 19.95 (978-0-8052-4201-0(5), Schocken) Knopf Doubleday Publishing Group.

Wilson-Powell, MaLin. Sarah Bienvenu: Taking Time: Thirty Years of Painting New Mexico. 2010. (ENG., Illus.). 64p. pap. 35.00 (978-1-934491-18-8(7)) Fresco Fine Art Pubns., LLC.

Wilson, Tom. Zig-Zagging: Loving Madly, Losing Badly - How Ziggy Saved My Life. 2009. (ENG., Illus.). 212p. 17.95 (978-0-7573-0793-5(0)) Health Communications, Inc.

Wilton, Andrew. Turner in His Time. rev. ed. 2007. (Illus.). 240p. 60.00 (978-0-500-23830-1(8)) Thames & Hudson.

Wingate, Ashmore Kyle Paterson. Life & Writings of John Ruskin. 2009. 154p. pap. (978-0-217-50392-1(6)) Books LLC.

Winnington, G. Peter, ed. Mervyn Peake: The Man & His Art. 2007. (Illus.). 216p. (978-0-7206-1284-4(5)) Owen, Peter Ltd.

Wissman, Pamela, et al, eds. Sketchbook Confidential 2: Enter the secret works of 41 master Artists. 2012. (ENG., Illus.). 176p. pap. 24.99 (978-1-4403-1695-1(3), North Light Bks.) F&W Media, Inc.

Wohl, Hellmut & Montanari, Tommaso, eds. Giovan Pietro Bellori: The Lives of the Modern Painters, Sculptors & Architects. 2009. (ENG., Illus.). 516p. (C). pap. 35.99 (978-0-521-13954-0(6)) Cambridge Univ. Pr.

Wood, Margaret. Remembering Miss O'Keefe. 2012. (ENG., Illus.). 64p. 19.95 (978-0-89013-546-4(0)) Museum of New Mexico Pr.

Woodward, Doris J. Harper Joy, Spokane's Man of Many Faces: Let the Show Begin. 2007. (Illus.). 128p. 14.95 (978-0-9740881-7-4(X)) Tornado Creek Pubns.

Wottreng, Stephan, et al. Eduard Spelterini - Fotografien des Ballonpioniers. Photographs of a Pioneer Balloonist. Stadler, Hilar & Kramer, Thomas, eds. 2007. (ENG., Illus.). 160p. 99.00 (978-3-85881-188-2(2)) Scheidegger und Spiess AG, Verlag CHE. Dist: Antique Collectors' Club.

Wright, Chely. Like Me: Confessions of a Heartland Country Singer. 2010. (ENG., Illus.). 304p. 25.95 (978-0-307-37886-6(1), Pantheon) Knopf Doubleday Publishing Group.

Wright, Doug. The Collected Doug Wright Vol. 1: Canada's Master Cartoonist. Mackay, Seth & Mackay, Brad, eds. 2009. (ENG., Illus.). 240p. 39.95 (978-1-897299-52-4(4)) Drawn & Quarterly Pubns. CAN. Dist: Macmillan.

Wulfekammer, Verna M. Ella Victoria Dobbs: A Portrait Biography. 2011. 262p. 47.95 (978-1-258-07546-0(6)) Literary Licensing, LLC.

Wullschlager, Jackie. Chagall: A Biography. 2008. (ENG., Illus.). 608p. 40.00 (978-0-375-41455-8(X), Knopf) Knopf Doubleday Publishing Group.

Wylie, Diana. Art & Revolution: The Life & Death of Thami Mnyele, South African Artist. 2008. (Reconsiderations in Southern African History Ser.). (ENG., Illus.). 264p. (C). (gr. 13-17). pap. 25.00 (978-0-8139-2764-0(1)) Univ. Pr. of Virginia.

Wyman, Anne Cabot. Kipling's Cat: A Memoir of My Father. 2009. (ENG., Illus.). 224p. 24.95 (978-0-9625780-4-5(5)) Protean Publishing Co.

Yacowar, Maurice. The Great Bratby: A Portrait of John Bratby RA. 2008. (Art + Design Ser.). (Illus.). 282p. 60.00 (978-1-904750-43-7(5)) Libri Publishing Ltd GBR. Dist: Independent Pubs. Group.

Yarnall, James L. John la Farge A Biographical & Critical Study. 2012. (Illus.). 384p. 99.95 (978-1-4094-1172-7(9)) Ashgate Publishing Co.

Yashima, Taro. The New Sun. 2008. (Illus.). (C). 23.00 (978-0-8248-3185-1(3)) Univ. of Hawaii Pr.

Yeager, Bunny. Striptease Artists of The 1950s. 2008. (Illus.). 160p. pap. 24.95 *(978-0-7643-2800-8(X))* Schiffer Publishing, Ltd.

Yong, Johnny. A Balanced Life. 2011. 144p. 24.95 ***(978-1-936343-99-7(1))***; pap. 14.95 ***(978-1-936343-98-0(3))*** Peppertree Pr., The.

Yorke, Malcolm. Edward Bawden & His Circle: The Inward Laugh. 2007. (ENG., Illus.). 264p. *(978-1-85149-542-9(8)*, Antique Collectors Club Dist) Antique Collectors' Club.

Young, Clara, et al. Alberto Morrocco 1917-1998. 2nd ed. 2009. (ENG., Illus.). 118p. *(978-1-873830-07-9(6)*, Fine Art Society (Acc)) Antique Collectors' Club.

Zara, Christopher. Tortured Artists: From Picasso & Monroe to Warhol & Winehouse, the Twisted Secrets of the World's Most Creative Minds. 2012. (ENG., Illus.). 272p. pap. 15.95 ***(978-1-4405-3003-6(3))*** Adams Media Corp.

Zheng, Da. Chiang Yee: The Silent Traveller from the East — A Cultural Biography. 2010. (ENG., Illus.). 358p. (C). 49.95 *(978-0-8135-4693-3(1))* Rutgers Univ. Pr.

Zhu, Zhu, et al, eds. Thirty Years of Adventures: Art & Artists From 1979. 2011. (ENG., Illus.). 792p. 75.00 ***(978-988-19912-4-9(2))*** Timezone 8 Ltd. HKG. Dist: D.A.P./Distributed Art Pubs.

Zimmer, Daniel & Hornung, David. Reynold Brown: A Life in Pictures. 2009. (Illus.). 224p. 39.95 *(978-0-9820041-2-8(5))* Illustrated Pr., Inc., The.

Zirpolo, Lilian H. The A to Z of Renaissance Art. 93rd ed. 2009. (A to Z Guide Ser.: No. 93). (ENG.). 632p. pap. 34.45 *(978-0-8108-6880-9(6))* Scarecrow Pr., Inc.

—Historical Dictionary of Renaissance Art. 2007. (Historical Dictionaries of Literature & the Arts Ser.: No. 21). (ENG., Illus.). 632p. 133.00 *(978-0-8108-5800-8(2))* Scarecrow Pr., Inc.

Zuffi, Stefano. Durero. (Colección Art Book). (SPA., Illus.). 144p. *(978-84-8156-179-1(7))* Sociedad Editorial Electa Espana ESP. Dist: Lectorum Pubns., Inc.

—Tiziano. (Colección Art Book). (SPA., Illus.). 144p. *(978-84-8156-178-4(9))* Sociedad Editorial Electa Espana ESP. Dist: Lectorum Pubns., Inc.

ARTISTS—CORRESPONDENCE

Bakker, Nienke, et al, eds. Vincent Van Gogh - The Letters, 6 vols. annot. ed. 2009. (ENG., Illus.). 2500p. 650.00 *(978-0-500-23865-3(0)*, 523865) Thames & Hudson.

Bakkom, Matthew, ed. New York City Museum of Complaint: Municipal Collection 1751-1969, 1 vol. 2009. (ENG., Illus.). 304p. 59.90 *(978-3-86521-745-5(1))* Steidl, Gerhard Druckerei und Verlag DEU. Dist: Innovative Logistics.

Buck, Stephanie, et al. The Courtauld Cézannes. 2008. (ENG., Illus.). 160p. pap. 45.00 *(978-1-903470-84-8(6))* Holberton, Paul Publishing GBR. Dist: Casemate Pubs. & Bk. Distributors, LLC.

Carr, Emily. Pause, 1 vol. 2007. (ENG., Illus.). 160p. pap. 12.95 *(978-1-55365-229-8(0))* D&M Pubs. Inc. CAN. Dist: Perseus-PGW.

Greenough, Sarah, ed. My Faraway One Vol. 1: Selected Letters of Georgia O'Keeffe & Alfred Stieglitz, 1915-1933. 2011. (Illus.). 832p. 39.95 *(978-0-300-16630-9(3))* Yale Univ. Pr.

Grimberg, Salomón, et al. I Will Never Forget You: Frida Kahlo to Nickolas Muray. 2006. (ENG., Illus.). 180p. pap. 24.95 *(978-0-8118-5692-8(5))* Chronicle Bks. LLC.

Gubler, Ernst & Werder, Kurt. Ernst Gubler - Max Gubler: Briefwechsel, 2 vols. 2010. (GER., Illus.). 888p. 170.00 ***(978-3-85881-176-9(9))*** Scheidegger und Spiess AG, Verlag CHE. Dist: Antique Collectors' Club.

Howe, Nancy J. Dear Owie. 2008. (ENG.). 623p. 28.95 *(978-0-533-15824-9(9))* Vantage Pr., Inc.

Kent, Rockwell. It's Me O Lord: The Autobiography of Rockwell Kent. 2011. 684p. 69.95 ***(978-1-258-08867-5(3))*** Literary Licensing, LLC.

Kirchner, Ernst Ludwig, et al. Das Ungewohnte Neue: Briefwechsel Ernst Ludwig Kirchner und George Reinhart. 2010. (GER., Illus.). 176p. pap. 45.00 ***(978-3-85881-140-0(8))*** Scheidegger und Spiess AG, Verlag CHE. Dist: Antique Collectors' Club.

Kirwin, Liza & Lord, Joan. With Love: Artists' Letters & Illustrated Notes. 2008. (Illus.). 128p. 19.95 *(978-0-06-144150-9(3)*, Collins Design) HarperCollins Pubs.

Leopold, Elisabeth, et al. Egon Schiele: Letters & Poems 1910-1912 from the Leopold Collection. 2008. (Illus.). 144p. 49.95 *(978-3-7913-3999-3(0))* Prestel Publishing.

Millidge, Judith. Charles Marion Russell. 2009. (ENG.). 192p. 24.99 *(978-0-7858-2535-7(5)*, 0785825355, Chartwell) Book Sales, Inc.

Morra, Linda M., ed. Corresponding Influence: Selected Letters of Emily Carr & Ira Dilworth. 2008. (ENG., Illus.). 350p. pap. *(978-0-8020-9575-6(5))* Univ. of Toronto Pr.

Obrist, Hans Ulrich, ed. Maria Lassnig: The Pen Is the Sister of the Brush, 1943-1997, 1 vol. 2010. (ENG., Illus.). 192p. 44.00 *(978-3-86521-739-4(7))* Steidl, Gerhard Druckerei und Verlag DEU. Dist: Innovative Logistics.

Parker, Deborah & Michelangelo Buonarroti. Michelangelo & the Art of Letter Writing. 2010. (ENG., Illus.). 168p. 80.00 *(978-0-521-76140-6(9))* Cambridge Univ. Pr.

Raimbach, Abraham. Memoirs & Recollections of the Late Abraham Raimbach, Esq. , Engraver: Including a Memoir of Sir David Wilkie. Raimbach, Michael Thomson Scott, ed. 2011. (Cambridge Library Collection - Printing & Publishing History Ser.). (Illus.). 216p. pap. 22.99 *(978-1-108-02716-8(4))* Cambridge Univ. Pr.

Rand, Ellen. Dear Females. 2009. pap. 80.00 *(978-1-61584-171-4(7))* Independent Pub.

Robertson, W. Graham. Letters to Frances White Emerson from W Graham Robertson. 2011. 64p. 36.95 ***(978-1-258-09079-1(1))*** Literary Licensing, LLC.

Roskill, Mark, ed. Letters of Vincent van Gogh. 2008. (ENG.). 352p. pap. 16.00 *(978-1-4165-8086-7(7)*, Touchstone) Touchstone.

Rouart, Denis & Morisot, Berthe. Berthe Morisot. Hubbard, Betty W., tr. from FRE. 2007. (Illus.). 246p. pap. 10.95 *(978-0-918825-62-9(8))* Moyer Bell.

Russell, Charles M. & Dippie, Brian W. The 100 Best Illustrated Letters of Charles M. Russell. 2008. *(978-0-88360-106-8(0))* Amon Carter Museum.

Schneemann, Carolee & Stiles, Kristine, eds. Correspondence Course: An Epistolary History of Carolee Schneemann & Her Circle. 2010. (ENG., Illus.). 576p. 99.95 *(978-0-8223-4500-8(5))*; pap. 29.95 *(978-0-8223-4511-4(0))* Duke Univ. Pr.

Simon, Barney. A Singing in Every Moment & Inch of Me: The Letters of Barney Simon to Lionel Abel. 2008. (ENG.). 176p. 23.95 *(978-1-58322-832-6(2))* Seven Stories Pr.

Starr, Sean. The Artist's Tao: 44 Principles for an Artist's Life. 2008. (Illus.). 100p. pap. 9.99 *(978-0-9799194-1-1(X))* Subculture Bks.

Stein, Gertrude & Picasso, Pablo. Correspondence: Pablo Picasso & Gertrude Stein. Madeline, Laurence, ed. Fox, Lorna Scott, tr. from FRE. 2008. (SB-the French List Ser.). (ENG., Illus.). 390p. 29.95 *(978-1-905422-91-3(1))* Seagull Bks. GBR. Dist: Chicago Distribution Ctr.

Tatham, Frederick. The Letters of William Blake. Russell, Archibald G., ed. (ENG.). 364p. 2007. 46.95 *(978-0-548-13915-8(6))* 2006. per. 31.95 *(978-1-4286-5092-3(X))* Kessinger Publishing, LLC.

Taylor, Anna Heyward, et al, eds. Selected Letters of Anna Heyward Taylor: South Carolina Artist & World Traveler. 2010. (Women's Diaries & Letters of the South Ser.). 39.95 *(978-1-57003-945-4(3))* Univ. of South Carolina Pr.

Thomas, Brad, ed. Ewan Gibbs: America. 2011. (ENG., Illus.). 100p. 50.00 *(978-1-890573-10-2(8))* Van Every Smith Galleries at Davidson College.

Trumbull, John. Autobiography, Reminiscences & Letters of John Trumbull, from 1756 To 1841. 2010. 522p. pap. 39.75 *(978-1-149-04703-3(8))*; 512p. pap. 39.75 *(978-1-148-14001-8(8))*; 524p. pap. 39.75 *(978-1-145-42423-4(6))*; 512p. pap. 39.75 *(978-1-142-98819-7(8))*; 512p. pap. 39.75 *(978-1-143-11069-6(2))* BiblioBazaar.

—Autobiography, Reminiscences & Letters of John Trumbull, from 1756 To 1841. 2009. 280p. pap. 35.91 *(978-1-150-06093-9(X))* General Bks. LLC.

van Gogh, Vincent. Vincent Van Gogh - De Brieven: De Volledige, Geïllustreerde en Geannoteerde Uitgave. Luijten, Hans et al, eds. 2nd ed. 2010.Tr. of Vincent Van Gogh - The Letters. (DUT., Illus.). 2240p. *(978-90-8964-102-1(5))* Amsterdam Univ. Pr.

Varlin, et al. Wenn ich dichten Könnte: Briefe und Schriften. 2010. (GER., Illus.). 352p. 89.00 ***(978-3-85881-101-1(7))*** Scheidegger und Spiess AG, Verlag CHE. Dist: Antique Collectors' Club.

Veen, Wouter van der & Gogh, Vincent van. Van Gogh: A Literary Mind: Literature in the Correspondence of Vincent Van Gogh. 2010. (ENG., Illus.). 264p. 85.00 *(978-90-400-8562-8(5))* Waanders B.V., Uitgeverij NLD. Dist: National Bk. Network.

Weber, Nicolas Fox. Josef Albers & Wassily Kandinsky: Friends in Exile - A Decade of Correspondence. 2010. (ENG., Illus.). 160p. pap. 29.95 *(978-1-55595-327-0(1))* Hudson Hills Pr. LLC.

Wünsche, Isabel, ed. Galka E. Scheyer & the Blue Four: Correspondence 1924-1945. 2006. (ENG., Illus.). 416p. 55.00 *(978-3-7165-1438-2(1))* Benteli Verlag CHE. Dist: Antique Collectors' Club.

Wyeth, Betsy James, ed. The Wyeths the Letters of N. C. Wyeth, 1901-1945. 2008. (Illus.). 904p. pap. *(978-0-9795872-3-8(9))* Brandywine River Museum.

ARTISTS—DICTIONARIES

Allgemeines Künstler-Lexikon. 2011. (GER.). LII, 540p. 348.00 ***(978-3-11-023177-9(8))*** De Gruyter, Walter Inc.

The Artists of the World - Bio-bibliographical Index A-Z. 2nd ed. 2009. (ENG & GER.). XXXIX, 864p. *(978-3-598-24566-4(1))*; XXXIX, 857p. *(978-3-598-24567-1(X))* Saur, K. G. Verlag GmbH & Co.

Aspley, Keith. Historical Dictionary of Surrealism. 2010. E-Book 125.00 *(978-0-8108-7499-2(7))*; (ENG.). 574p. 125.00 *(978-0-8108-5847-3(9))* Scarecrow Pr., Inc.

Baile de Laperriere, Charles & Murray, Lynda. Who's Who in Art: 34th Edition. 34th ed. 2010. 837p. 190.00 *(978-0-904722-44-4(9))* Hilmarton Manor Pr. GBR. Dist: Cengage Gale.

Bartoletti, Laurence. Creation en France: Arts decoratifs 1945-1965: Repertoire Alphabetique. 2010. (ENG.). 388p. pap. 95.00 *(978-2-35340-019-5(1))* Gourcuff Gradenigo FRA. Dist: National Bk. Network.

Benezit, Emmanuel. Benezit Dictionary of British Graphic Artists & Illustrators, 2 vols. 2012. (ENG., Illus.). 1344p. 295.00 ***(978-0-19-992305-2(1))*** Oxford Univ. Pr., Inc.

Bonham-Carter, Charlotte & Hodge, David. The Contemporary Art Book. 2011. (ENG., Illus.). 256p. 39.95 *(978-1-84796-005-4(7)*, Goodman Pubs.) Carlton Bks., Ltd. GBR. Dist: Sterling Publishing Co., Inc.

Brun, Carl, compiled by. Schweizerisches Künstler-lexikon, 4 vols., 2006. (GER.). 2698p. 395.00 *(978-1-57898-593-7(5))* Martino Publishing.

Buckman, David. Artists in Britain since 1945, 2 vols. 2007. (ENG., Illus.). 1856p. 330.00 *(978-0-9532609-5-9(X)*, Sansom (Acc)) Antique Collectors' Club GBR. Dist: National Bk. Network.

Burt, Eugene C. Dictionary of Erotic Artists: Painters, Sculptors, Printmakers, Graphic Designers, & Illustrators. 2010. (ENG.). 350p. pap. 55.00 *(978-0-7864-4874-6(1))* McFarland & Co., Inc. Pubs.

Chilvers, Ian. The Oxford Dictionary of Art & Artists. 4th ed. 2009. (Oxford Paperback Reference Ser.). (ENG., Illus.). 736p. pap. 18.99 *(978-0-19-953294-0(X))* Oxford Univ. Pr., Inc.

Encyclopaedia Britannica, Inc., compiled by. Britannica Encyclopaedia of Art & Britannica Biographical Encyclopaedia of Artists, 9 vols. 2007. *(978-1-59339-537-7(X))* Encyclopaedia Britannica, Inc.

Flemig, Kurt. Karikaturisten-Lexikon. (GER.). XIV, 325p. ***(978-3-11-186496-9(0))*** Saur, K. G. Verlag GmbH & Co.

Frank, Jane. Science Fiction & Fantasy Artists of the Twentieth Century: A Biographical Dictionary. 2009. (ENG.). 534p. 135.00 *(978-0-7864-3423-7(6))* McFarland & Co., Inc. Pubs.

Gray, Sara, ed. Dictionary of British Women Artists. 2009. (ENG., Illus.). 296p. pap. 64.00 *(978-0-7188-3084-7(9))* Lutherworth Pr., The GBR. Dist: Brown, David Bk. Co., The.

Hernert, Read. Diccionario del Arte y los Artistas. (SPA., Illus.). 412p. 39.95 *(978-84-233-2377-7(3)*, DE773) Ediciones Destino ESP. Dist: Continental Bk. Co., Inc.

Heunert - Höllwarth. 2011. (GER.). LII, 540p. 348.00 ***(978-3-11-023178-6(6))*** De Gruyter, Walter Inc.

Karel, David. Dictionnaire des Artistes de Langue Francaise en Amerique du Nord: Peintres, Sculpteurs, Dessinateurs, Graveurs, Photographes et Orfevres. (FRE., Illus.). lxxx, 964p. *(978-2-7637-7235-6(8))* Bow Historical Bks.

Kienholz, Lyn. L. A. Rising: SoCal Artists Before 1980. Betinski, Elizabeta & Nelson, Corinne, eds. 2011. (Illus.). 516p. 75.00 net. *(978-0-917571-13-8(4))* California/International Arts Foundation.

Milam, Jennifer D. Historical Dictionary of Rococo Art. 2011. (Historical Dictionaries of Literature & the Arts Ser.). (ENG.). 334p. 80.00 *(978-0-8108-6183-1(6))* Scarecrow Pr., Inc.

Milam, Jennifer Dawn. Historical Dictionary of Rococo Art. 2011. E-Book *(978-0-8108-7952-2(2))* Scarecrow Pr., Inc.

Morgan, Anne Lee. Oxford Dictionary of American Art & Artists. 2008. (Oxford Paperback Reference Ser.). (ENG.). 560p. pap. 17.95 *(978-0-19-537321-9(9))* Oxford Univ. Pr., Inc.

O'Byrne, Robert. Dictionary of Living Irish Artists. 2010. (ENG., Illus.). 400p. 97.50 *(978-0-9563011-0-9(X)*, Plurabelle Publishing (Acc)) Antique Collectors' Club GBR. Dist: National Bk. Network.

Phaidon Press Editors. The Art Book. 2006. (SPA.). pap. 24.95 *(978-0-7148-9854-4(6))* Phaidon Pr., Inc.

Zirpolo, Lilian H. Historical Dictionary of Renaissance Art. 2007. (Historical Dictionaries of Literature & the Arts Ser.: No. 21). (ENG., Illus.). 632p. 133.00 *(978-0-8108-5800-8(2))* Scarecrow Pr., Inc.

ARTISTS—DIRECTORIES

Baile De Laperriere, Charles & Murray, Lynda, eds. Who's Who in Art: Biographies of Leading Men & Women in the World of Art in Britain Today: Artists, Sculptors, Designers, Architects, Critics, Writers, Lecturers, Curators & Photographers. 33rd rev. ed. 2008. (Who's Who in Art Ser.). (Illus.). 1128p. *(978-0-904722-42-0(2))* Hilmarton Manor Pr.

Bennett, Margo E. & Lumbert, David E. A.S.C. Tattoo Directory 2008. 2008. 240p. pap. 20.00 *(978-1-887080-21-7(X))* Active Publishing, Inc.

Berger, Guy & Schiffer, Nancy N. Pueblo & Navajo Contemporary Pottery: And Directory of Artists. 2nd rev. exp. ed. 2007. (Schiffer Book for Collectors Ser.). (Illus.). 160p. per. 29.95 *(978-0-7643-1896-2(9))* Schiffer Publishing, Ltd.

Derks, Scott, ed. Working Americans, 1880-2011 Vol. 12: Artists & Musicians. 2011. 500p. 150.00 *(978-1-59237-762-6(9))* Grey Hse. Publishing.

Europa Publications Staff, contrib. by. International Who's Who in Classical Music 2008. 24th rev. ed. 2008. 960p. 430.00 *(978-1-85743-455-2(2))* Taylor & Francis Group GBR. Dist: Taylor & Francis Group.

Filippi Gabardi, Vittoria & Gabardi, Vittoria Filippi. The Whispered Directory of Craftsmanship: A Contemporary Guide to the Italian Handmaking Ability. 2011. (ENG., Illus.). 200p. 69.95 ***(978-88-370-8424-0(2))*** Electa ITA. Dist: National Bk. Network.

Frieze Art Fair Yearbook 2008-9. 2008. (ENG., Illus.). 544p. pap. 35.00 *(978-0-9553201-3-2(5))* Frieze GBR. Dist: D.A.P./Distributed Art Pubs.

Furness, Rosalind, ed. Frieze Art Fair Yearbook 2010-11. 2010. (ENG., Illus.). 544p. pap. 35.00 *(978-0-9553201-6-3(X))* Frieze GBR. Dist: D.A.P./Distributed Art Pubs.

Giancarlo Politi Editore, compiled by. Art Diary International 2009-2010. 2009. (Illus.). 624p. pap. 35.00 *(978-88-18-16148-9(2))* Politi, Giancarlo Editore ITA. Dist: D.A.P./Distributed Art Pubs.

Giancarlo Politi Editore, ed. Art Diary International 2007-2008: The World Art Directory, 1 vol. 2007. (ENG., Illus.). 570p. pap. 30.00 *(978-88-7816-143-6(8))* Politi, Giancarlo Editore ITA. Dist: D.A.P./Distributed Art Pubs.

Huynh, Uy Huu. Nghe Thuat Tao Hinh Viet Nam Hien Dai. ltd. ed. 2007. (VIE.). 60.00 *(978-0-9755673-2-6(2))* Vietnamese American Arts & Letters Association.

Kennedy Fine Art & California Artists. Best of California Artists & Artisans, Vol. 1. 2007. per. *(978-0-9796358-1-6(0))* Kennedy Publishing.

Massimiliano, Gioni, et al. The Younger Than Jesus Artist Directory. 2009. (ENG., Illus.). 480p. pap. 49.95 *(978-0-7148-4981-2(2))* Phaidon Pr., Inc.

Melton Art Reference Library. Directory of Oklahoma Artists. 2007. 50.00 *(978-0-9640163-3-0(8))* Melton Art Reference Library.

Politi, Giancarlo. Art Diary International 2006-2007: Flash Art Diary, 1 vol. 2006. (ENG., Illus.). 570p. pap. 25.00 *(978-88-7816-137-5(3))* Politi, Giancarlo Editore ITA. Dist: D.A.P./Distributed Art Pubs.

Die Visuelle Geschichte der Kunst. (GER.). *(978-3-8067-4503-0(X))* Gerstenberg DEU. Dist: International Bk. Import Service, Inc.

Williams, Jan & Smith, John E. Inked: Clever, Odd & Outrageous Tattoos. 2008. 19.95 *(978-3-8327-9280-0(5))* teNeues Publishing Co.

31. Ausgabe (Deutsche Benutzeroberfläche) / the Artists of the World. International Database of Artists. CD-ROM. 31st ed. 2009. (GER.). cd-rom *(978-3-598-40974-5(5))* Saur, K. G. Verlag GmbH & Co.

31st Edition (English User Interface) / the Artists of the World. International Database of Artists. CD-ROM. 31st ed. 2009. (GER.). cd-rom *(978-3-598-40976-9(1))* Saur, K. G. Verlag GmbH & Co.

ARTISTS—HEALTH AND HYGIENE

Berlin, Richard M., ed. Poets on Prozac: Mental Illness, Treatment, & the Creative Process. 2008. (ENG.). 200p. 24.00 *(978-0-8018-8839-7(5))* Johns Hopkins Univ. Pr.

Bogousslavsky, J., et al, eds. Neurological Disorders in Famous Artists - Part 3. 2010. (Frontiers of Neurology & Neuroscience Ser.). (Illus.). 242p. *(978-3-8055-9330-4(9))* Karger, S. AG.

Bogousslavsky, Julien, et al. Neurological disorders in famous artists Part 2. 2007. (Frontiers of Neurology & Neuroscience Ser.). (Illus.). *(978-3-8055-8265-0(X))* Karger, S. AG.

Cazden MFA MS-CCC, Joanna. How to take care of your Voice: The Lifestyle Guide for Singers & Talkers. 2007. 116p. pap. 14.95 *(978-1-60145-256-6(X))* Booklocker.com, Inc.

Dawson, William J. Fit as a Fiddle: The Musician's Guide to Playing Healthy. 2007. (ENG., Illus.). 174p. 55.00 *(978-1-57886-683-0(9))*; per. 21.95 *(978-1-57886-684-7(7))* Rowman & Littlefield Education.

Embouchure Rehabilitation: A Comprehensive Method for Overcoming Embouchure Overuse Syndrome in Brass Players. 2007. spiral bd. 25.00 *(978-0-9741007-2-2(2)*, Oscar's Hse. Pr.) Embouchures.com, Inc.

McCann, Michael & Babin, Angela. Health Hazards Manual for Artists. 6th ed. 2008. (ENG., Illus.). 176p. pap. 14.95 *(978-1-59921-318-7(4)*, Lyons Pr.) Globe Pequot Pr., The.

Olson, Mia & Hal Leonard Corporation Staff. Musician's Yoga: A Guide to Practice, Performance & Inspiration, 1 vol. 2009. (ENG., Illus.). 144p. pap. 14.99 *(978-0-87639-095-5(5)*, 0876390955, Berklee Pr.) Leonard, Hal Corp.

Soklaridis, Sophie. Integrative Health Care for Artists in a Hospital Setting. 2009. 288p. pap. *(978-3-639-15683-6(8))* VDM Verlag Dr. Mueller e.K.

ARTISTS—JUVENILE LITERATURE

Spence, David. Monet. 2010. (Great Artists & Their World Ser.). 48p. 32.80 *(978-1-84898-313-7(1))* Black Rabbit Bks.

ARTISTS—LEGAL STATUS, LAWS, ETC.

Amada, Richard. An Artist's Guide to the Law: Law & Legal Concepts Every Artist, Performer, Writer, or Other Creative Person Ought to Know. 2010. (ENG.). 210p. pap. 19.95 *(978-1-58510-356-0(X))* Focus Publishing/R. Pullins Co., Inc.

Crawford, Tad. Legal Guide for the Visual Artist. 5th ed. 2010. (ENG., Illus.). 304p. pap. 29.95 *(978-1-58115-742-0(8)*, 115742, Allworth Pr.) Skyhorse Publishing Co., Inc.

Duboff. Art Law. 2010. pap., stu. ed. 145.00 *(978-0-7355-9658-0(1)*, Aspen Pubs.) Wolters Kluwer Law & Business.

DuBoff, Leonard D., et al. Art Law: Cases & Materials. 2010. (Illus.). xxxi, 675p. *(978-0-7355-9659-7(X)*, Aspen Pubs.) Wolters Kluwer Law & Business.

Ganchan, Leigh N., et al. Immigration Options for Artists & Entertainers. 2007. (Illus.). x, 161p. *(978-1-57370-206-5(4)*, 918 F Street NW, Washington, DC 20004) American Immigration Lawyers Assn.

Gerstenblith, Patty. Art, Cultural Heritage, & the Law: Cases & Materials. 2nd ed. 2008. 1142p. 110.00 *(978-1-59460-543-7(2))* Carolina Academic Pr.

Graphic Artists Guild Staff, ed. Graphic Artist's Guild Handbook of Pricing & Ethical Guidelines. 13th ed. 2010. (ENG., Illus.). 352p. pap. 39.99 *(978-0-932102-15-7(8))* Graphic Artists Guild.

Ku, Pon-Jin. Misulga Ui Chojak Inkyokkwon. 2010. (KOR.). xv, 419p. *(978-89-499-0737-6(2))* Kyung-in.

Merryman, John Henry. Law, Ethics & the Visual Arts 5th Edition. 5th ed. 2007. (Illus.). xxix, 1324p. *(978-90-411-2518-7(3))* Kluwer Law International.

—Law, Ethics & the Visual Arts 5th Edition. 5th ed. 2007. (Illus.). xxix, 1324p. pap. *(978-90-411-2517-0(5))* Kluwer Law International.

Rhodes, Anne-Marie. Art Law & Transactions. 2011. (Illus.). 472p. 75.00 *(978-1-59460-773-8(7))* Carolina Academic Pr.

Schrage, Eltjo, et al, eds. Art & Law. 2008. (ENG.). 440p. 194.00 *(978-1-84113-819-0(3))* Hart Publishing Ltd. GBR. Dist: International Specialized Bk. Services.

ARTISTS—PSYCHOLOGY

Acocella, Joan. Twenty-Eight Artists & Two Saints. 2008. (Vintage Ser.). (ENG., Illus.). 560p. pap. 18.95 *(978-0-307-27576-9(0)*, Vintage) Knopf Doubleday Publishing Group.

Alpers, Svetlana. The Vexations of Art: Velazquez & Others. 2007. (ENG., Illus.). 298p. pap. 30.00 *(978-0-300-12613-6(1))* Yale Univ. Pr.

Binyon, Cicely Margaret Powell. The Mind of the Artist: Thoughts & Sayings of Painters & Sculptors on Their Art. 2007. 132p. pap. 18.99 *(978-1-4346-4023-9(X))*; (ENG.). 146p. pap. 19.99 *(978-1-4346-4070-3(1))* BiblioBazaar.

Brink, Andrew. Desire & Avoidance in Art: Psychobiographical Studies with Attachment Theory of Pablo Picasso, Hans Bellmer, Balthus, & Joseph Cornell. 2007. (Illus.). 222p. (C). 68.95 *(978-0-8204-9721-1(5))* Lang, Peter Publishing, Inc.

Cozzolino, Robert, text. Narcissus in the Studio: Artist Portraits & Self-Portraits. 2011. (ENG., Illus.). 128p. pap. 30.00 *(978-0-943836-36-2(0))* Pennsylvania Academy of the Fine Arts.

Cram101 Textbook Reviews & Cram101 Textbook Reviews. Outlines & Highlights for Humanities Through the Arts by Martin, Isbn: 9780073138633 0073138630. 2011. 248p. pap. 31.95 (978-1-61490-863-0(X)) Cram101 Inc.
Doh, Jenny. Art Saves: Stories, Inspiration & Prompts Sharing the Power of Art. 2011. (ENG., Illus.). 144p. pap. 24.99 (978-1-4403-0906-9(X), North Light Bks.) F&W Media, Inc.
Hagman. The Artist's Mind: A Psychoanalytic Perspective on Creativity, Modern Art & Modern Artists. 2010. (ENG.). 192p. (C). 90.00 (978-0-415-46705-6(5)) Routledge.
Hagman, George. The Artist's Mind: A Psychoanalytic Perspective on Creativity, Modern Art & Modern Artists. 2010. (ENG.). 192p. (C). pap. 34.95 (978-0-415-46706-3(3)) Routledge.
Haus, Andreas, et al. Material IM Prozess: Strategien Aesthetischer Produktivitaet. (GER & ENG., Illus.). 301p. (978-3-496-01227-6(7)) Reimer, Dietrich.
Henry, Michel. Seeing the Invisible: On Kandinsky. Davidson, Scott, tr. from FRE. 2009. (ENG.). 160p. 24.95 (978-1-84706-447-9(7)); 100.00 (978-1-84706-446-2(9)) Continuum International Publishing Group, Ltd. GBR. Dist: National Bk. Network.
Jacob, M. J. Learning Mind: Experience into Art. Baas, Jacquelynn & Jacob, Mary Jane, eds. 2010. (ENG., Illus.). 288p. 49.95 (978-0-520-26076-4(7)) Univ. of California Pr.
Lamoreux, Liz. Inner Excavation: Exploring Your Self Through Photography, Poetry & Mixed Media. 2010. (ENG., Illus.). 144p. pap. 24.99 (978-1-4403-0309-8(6), North Light Bks.) F&W Media, Inc.
MacLagan, David. Outsider Art: From the Margins to the Marketplace. 2010. (ENG., Illus.). 176p. 35.00 (978-1-86189-521-9(6)) Reaktion Bks., Ltd. GBR. Dist: Chicago Distribution Ctr.
Maisel, Eric. Creativity for Life: Practical Advice on the Artist's Personality, & Career from America's Foremost Creativity Coach. 2007. (ENG.). 400p. per. 19.95 (978-1-57731-558-2(8)) New World Library.
—Mastering Creative Anxiety: 24 Lessons for Writers, Painters, Musicians, & Actors from America's Foremost Creativity Coach. 2011. (ENG.). 272p. pap. 14.95 (978-1-57731-932-0(X)) New World Library.
—The Van Gogh Blues: The Creative Person's Path Through Depression. 2007. (ENG.). 272p. per. 14.95 (978-1-57731-604-6(5)) New World Library.
Maziarz, Mary Beth. Kick-Ass Creativity: An Energy Makeover for Artists, Explorers, & Creative Professionals. 2010. (ENG., Illus.). 256p. pap. 16.95 (978-1-57174-621-4(8)) Hampton Roads Publishing Co., Inc.
Nutt, Amy E. Shadows Bright as Glass: The Remarkable Story of One Man's Journey from Brain Trauma to Artistic Triumph. 2011. (ENG., Illus.). 288p. 26.00 (978-1-4391-4310-0(2), Free Pr.) Free Pr.
Nutt, Amy Ellis. Shadows Bright As Glass: An Accidental Artist & the Search for the Soul. 2011. pap. (978-1-4391-4311-7(0), Free Pr.) Free Pr.
Onians, John. Neuroarthistory: From Aristotle & Pliny to Baxandall & Zeki. 2008. (ENG., Illus.). 192p. 40.00 (978-0-300-12677-8(8)) Yale Univ. Pr.
Peixoto. Paisagens Urbanas. (POR., Illus.). 347p. (978-85-85578-92-3(0)) Servico Nacional de Aprendizagem Comercial, Senac.
Pierre, Summer. The Artist in the Office: How to Creatively Survive & Thrive Seven Days a Week. 2010. (ENG., Illus.). 128p. (gr. 12-18). 13.95 (978-0-399-53564-2(0), Perigee Trade) Penguin Group (USA) Inc.
Pitt, Kathy. Sourcing the Self: Debating the Relations between Language & Consciousness. 2008. (Contemporary Studies in Descriptive Linguistics Ser.). (Illus.). 220p. pap. 61.95 (978-3-03911-398-9(4)) Lang, Peter AG GBR. Dist: Lang, Peter.
Prinzhorn, Hans. The Art of Insanity: An Analysis of Ten Schizophrenic Artists. 2011. (Solar Books - Solar Research Archive Ser.). (Illus.). 160p. pap. 29.95 (978-0-9832480-0-2(1)) Solar Bks.
Ritter, Dominik & Schulz, Joerg. Finishing Touches. 2010. 92p. pap. (978-3-639-17857-9(2)) VDM Verlag Dr. Mueller e.K.
Rookmaaker, Hans R. Art Needs No Justification. 2010. 64p. pap. (978-1-57383-441-4(6)) Regent College Publishing.
Said, Edward W. On Late Style: Music & Literature Against the Grain. 2007. (Vintage Ser.). (ENG.). 208p. pap. 14.95 (978-0-375-72633-0(0), Vintage) Knopf Doubleday Publishing Group.
Shahn, Ben. The Biography of a Painting. 2011. 38p. 35.95 (978-1-258-08540-7(2)) Literary Licensing, LLC.
Wittkower, Rudolf & Wittkower, Margot. Born under Saturn: The Character & Conduct of Artists: A Documented History from Antiquity to the French Revolution. 2006. (New York Review Books Classics). (ENG., Illus.). 360p. pap. 18.95 (978-1-59017-213-1(2), NYRB Classics) New York Review of Bks., Inc., The.

ARTISTS—AFRICA

Adeleke, Kazeem. In a New Light: Conversations with Nine Nigerian Artists & Curators. 2011. 208p. pap. 24.95 (978-1-4560-8402-8(X)) PublishAmerica, Inc.
Adendorff, Adele. Nomadic Figurations of Identity. 2011. 164p. pap. (978-3-8454-1060-9(4)) Lambert Academic Publishing.
Agbo, Maduabuchi. The Linguistic Behaviour of Nigerian Hip Hop & Rap Artistes. 2010. 104p. pap. (978-3-8383-7476-5(2)) Lambert Academic Publishing.
Bester, Rory. Claudette Schreuders. 2011. (Illus.). 240p. 49.95 (978-3-7913-5110-0(9)) Prestel Publishing.
Dewi Lewis Publishin Staff & Sealy, Mark. Hotel Afrique. 2008. (ENG., Illus.). 48p. (978-1-904587-52-1(5)) Lewis, Dewi Media, Ltd.
Glassie, Henry. Prince Twins Seven-Seven: His Art, His Life in Nigeria, His Exile in America. 2010. (African Expressive Cultures Ser.). (ENG., Illus.). 488p. 39.95 (978-0-253-35439-6(0), 0253354390) Indiana Univ. Pr.
Goldwater, Robert. How to Appreciate Art: Abstraction in Art. 2011. 22p. 35.95 (978-1-258-08026-6(5)) Literary Licensing, LLC.
Hazoume, Romuald. Romuald Hazoumé: My Paradise - Made in Porto-Novo. 2010. (ENG., Illus.). 144p. 40.00 (978-3-7757-2645-0(4)) Hatje Cantz Verlag GmbH & Co KG DEU. Dist: D.A.P./Distributed Art Pubs.
Holm, Michael, ed. Candice Breitz. 2008. (ENG., Illus.). 48p. 30.00 (978-87-91607-22-6(1)) Louisana DNK. Dist: D.A.P./Distributed Art Pubs.
Lepecki, Andre & Boutoux, Thomas, texts. Robin Rhode: Walk Off. 2007. (Illus.). 183p. 55.00 (978-3-7757-2005-2(7)) Hatje Cantz Verlag GmbH & Co KG DEU. Dist: D.A.P./Distributed Art Pubs.
Malangatana. Malangatana. 2010. (POR., Illus.). 130p. (978-972-778-110-2(1)) Universidade de Evora.
Manley, Rachel. Horses in Her Hair: A Granddaughter's Story. 2009. (ENG., Illus.). 344p. pap. 19.95 (978-1-55470-206-0(2)) Key Porter Bks. CAN. Dist: Perseus-PGW.
Ogbechie, Sylvester Okwunodu. Ben Enwonwu: The Making of an African Modernist. 2008. (Rochester Studies in African History & the Diaspora Ser.: Volume 37). (Illus.). 333p. 75.00 (978-1-58046-235-8(9)) Univ. of Rochester Pr.
Ottenberg, Simon. Olayinka: A Woman's View: The Life of an African Modern Artist. 2011. (978-1-59221-832-5(6)); (Illus.). 352p. pap. (978-1-59221-833-2(4)) Africa World Pr.
Poliza, Michael, photos by. South Africa. 2010. (ENG., Illus.). 280p. 95.00 (978-3-8327-9390-6(9)) teNeues Publishing Co.
Rhode, Robin. Robin Rhode: Who Saw Who. 2009. (ENG., Illus.). 120p. 40.00 (978-1-85332-271-6(7)) Hayward Gallery Publishing GBR. Dist: D.A.P./Distributed Art Pubs.
Wylie, Diana. Art & Revolution: The Life & Death of Thami Mnyele, South African Artist. 2008. (Reconsiderations in Southern African History Ser.). (ENG., Illus.). 264p. (C). (gr. 13-17). pap. 25.00 (978-0-8139-2764-0(1)) Univ. Pr. of Virginia.

ARTISTS—ALASKA

Fejes, Claire. Cold Starry Night: An Artist's Memoir. 2nd rev. ed. 2007. (ENG., Illus.). 320p. (gr. 9). per. 17.95 (978-0-9790470-6-0(4)) Epicenter Pr., Inc.
Jones, Suzi, ed. Eskimo Drawings 2008. (Illus.). 208p. per. 24.95 (978-1-885267-05-4(3)) Anchorage Museum of History & Art.
Smith, Jamie & Helfferich, Deirdre, eds. Cartoon North: Sequential Art in Alaska. 2007. (Illus.). 56p. 12.00 (978-0-9749221-3-3(7)) Ester Republic Pr.

ARTISTS—ASIA

Abbas, Hamra. Hamra Abbas: Object Lessons. 2010. (ENG., Illus.). 72p. 32.00 (978-0-9551779-9-6(5)) Cardamom, Green GBR. Dist: D.A.P./Distributed Art Pubs.
Abidi, Bani. Bani Abidi: Videos, Photographs & Drawings. 2010. (ENG., Illus.). 92p. 32.00 (978-0-9551779-5-8(2)) Cardamom, Green GBR. Dist: D.A.P./Distributed Art Pubs.
Albrecht, Sally K., et al. The Drum: A Mini-Musical Based on a Tale of Generosity for Unison & 2-Part Voices. 2009. (ENG.). 52p. pap. 64.99 (978-0-7390-5842-8(8)) Alfred Publishing Co., Inc.
Bilal, Wafaa. Shoot an Iraqi: Art, Life & Resistance under the Gun. 2008. (ENG., Illus.). 240p. pap. 16.95 (978-0-87286-491-7(X)) City Lights Bks.
Clark, Steve. Reception of Blake in the Orient. Suzuki, Masashi, ed. 2009. (Continuum Reception Studies). (ENG.). 360p. 65.00 (978-0-8264-3805-8(9)) Continuum International Publishing Group, Ltd. GBR. Dist: National Bk. Network.
Connah, Roger. The Rest Is Silence Zahoor Ul Akhlaq: Art & Society in Pakistan. 2012. (ENG., Illus.). 350p. 99.00 (978-0-19-547472-5(4)) Oxford Univ. Pr., Inc.
Elkins, James, ed. Re-Enchantment. 2008. (Art Seminar Ser.). (ENG., Illus.). 336p. (C). 125.00 (978-0-415-96051-9(7)) Routledge.
—Transcendence. 2008. (Art Seminar Ser.). (ENG., Illus.). 336p. (C). pap. 35.95 (978-0-415-96052-6(5)) Routledge.
Falva, Rosa Maria, ed. Safiuddin Ahmed: Great Masters of Bangladesh. 2012. (ENG., Illus.). 288p. 95.00 (978-88-572-1076-6(6)) Skira Editore ITA. Dist: Random Hse., Inc.
—Shahidul Alam: My Journey as a Witness. 2011. (ENG., Illus.). 224p. 50.00 (978-88-572-0966-1(0)) Skira Editore ITA. Dist: Random Hse., Inc.
Falva, Rosa Maria, ed. Zainul Abedin: Great Masters of Bangladesh. 2012. (ENG., Illus.). 288p. 95.00 (978-88-572-1077-3(4)) Skira Editore ITA. Dist: Random Hse., Inc.
Falvo, Rosa Maria, ed. Kazi Ghiyasuddin: Contemporary Masters of Bangladesh. 2012. (ENG., Illus.). 288p. 95.00 (978-88-572-1063-6(4)) Skira Editore ITA. Dist: Random Hse., Inc.
Flores, et al. Imelda Cajipe Endaya Stitching Paint into Collage: E. 2009. pap. 35.00 (978-1-61623-179-8(3)) Independent Pub.
Huynh, Uy Huu. Nghe Thuat Tao Hinh Viet Nam Hien Dai. ltd. ed. 2007. (VIE.). 60.00 (978-0-9755673-2-6(2)) Vietnamese American Arts & Letters Association.
Issa, Rose, ed. Parastou Forouhar: Art, Life & Death in Iran. 2011. (ENG., Illus.). 128p. pap. 21.95 (978-0-86356-448-2(8)) Saqi Bks. GBR. Dist: Consortium Bk. Sales & Distribution.
Karamustafa, Gülsün. Gulsun Karamustafa: Etiquette. 2011. (ENG., Illus.). 84p. pap. 35.00 (978-3-86984-180-9(X)) Verlag fur Moderne Kunst DEU. Dist: D.A.P./Distributed Art Pubs.
Kiang, Lindsey, ed. Huynh Phuong Dong: Visions of War & Peace/Goc Nhin Chien Tranh Va Hoa Binh. Phuong, Nguyen Thi Minh, tr. 2007. (Illus.). 175p. 40.00 net. (978-1-880418-74-1(6)) Univ. of Massachusetts Pr.
Olsen, Dale A. Popular Music of Vietnam. 2010. (Illus.). 304p. pap. 39.95 (978-0-415-88397-9(0)) Routledge.
Sabapathy, T. K. Nyoman Masriadi: Reconfiguring the Body. 2011. 268p. 130.00 (978-981-08-7416-2(2)) Artpostasia Inc. PHL. Dist: National Bk. Network.
Sans, Jerome. Stray Alchemists: Matt Bryans, Amy Granat, Lim Tzay Chuen, Takeshi Murata, Robin Rhode, Sterling Ruby. Fowle, Kate, ed. 2009. (ENG., Illus.). 140p. pap. 23.00 (978-988-17521-3-0(2)) Timezone 8 Ltd. HKG. Dist: D.A.P./Distributed Art Pubs.
Sikander, Shahzia, illus. Shahzia Sikander, 1 vol. 2007. (ENG.). 160p. 70.00 (978-88-8158-642-4(8)) Charta ITA. Dist: D.A.P./Distributed Art Pubs.
Studio Rarekwai Staff, et al. Graffiti Asia. 2010. (ENG., Illus.). 128p. 24.95 (978-1-85669-649-4(9)) King, Laurence Publishing GBR. Dist: Hachette Bk. Group.
Tan, Fiona. Fiona Tan, Vox Populi: Switzerland. 2011. (ENG, FRE, GER & ITA., Illus.). 125p. pap. (978-1-906012-28-1(8)) Book Works.
Toufic, Jalal. Jalal Toufic: Poes »Das Ovale Porträt«, mit den Augen eines Engels gelesen und umgeschrieben. 2011. (ENG., Illus.). 24p. pap. 10.00 (978-3-7757-2860-7(0)) Hatje Cantz Verlag GmbH & Co KG DEU. Dist: D.A.P./Distributed Art Pubs.
Yoshihara, Mari. Musicians from a Different Shore: Asians & Asian Americans in Classical Music. 2008. (ENG., Illus.). 288p. pap. 24.95 (978-1-59213-333-8(9)) Temple Univ. Pr.

ARTISTS—AUSTRALIA

Asmodelle, Estelle. Transience. 2010. 78p. pap. 29.95 (978-1-4461-5046-7(1)) Lulu Enterprises Inc.
Bridgstock, Ruth. The Protean Careers of Artists. 2011. 440p. pap. (978-3-8443-2254-5(X)) Lambert Academic Publishing.
Castagno, John. Australian, British & Irish Artists: Signatures & Monograms from 1800. 2009. (ENG.). 524p. 225.00 (978-0-8108-6384-2(7)) Scarecrow Pr., Inc.
Casula Powerhouse, compiled by. Federico Mendoza: Folding Histories. 2007. (Illus.). (978-1-876418-78-6(8)) Casula Powerhouse.
Croft, Brenda L. Culture Warriors: National Indigenous Art Triennial '07. Clark, Deborah & Jenkins, Susan, eds. 2008. (Illus.). 218p. pap. (978-0-642-54133-8(7)) National Gallery of Australia.
Drury, Nevill. The Magic of Pan. 2011. 444p. pap. (978-3-8443-2323-8(6)) Lambert Academic Publishing.
Dutkiewicz, Michal, illus. Girls! from Line to Color: The Inks & the Pencils Behind the Fantasy Paintings of Michal Dutkiewicz. 2007. 48p. pap. 14.95 (978-0-86562-151-0(9)) S.Q. Productions, Inc.
Featherstone, Don. Creative Spirits: An Insight into the Life & Work of Some Extraordinary Australians. (Illus.). 148p. pap. (978-0-86806-610-3(9), Hale & Iremonger) GHR Pr., The.
Gray, Anne. George W. Lambert Retrospective: Heroes & Icons. 2008. (Illus.). 212p. (978-0-642-54127-7(2)); pap. (978-0-642-54121-5(3)) National Gallery of Australia.
Grishin, Sasha. Bruno Leti: Portrait of a Printmaker. 2012. (ENG.). 192p. (C). 89.95 (978-1-921394-71-3(4)) Macmillan Art Publishing AUS. Dist: Brown, David Bk. Co., The.
Holler-Schuster, Gunther, ed. Alois Mosbacher: Outside Fiction. 2011. (ENG., Illus.). 240p. pap. 60.00 (978-3-7757-2729-7(9)) Hatje Cantz Verlag GmbH & Co KG DEU. Dist: D.A.P./Distributed Art Pubs.
Kay, Hanna. Notes from the Shed: A Journal. rev. ed. 2007. (Illus.). 208p. (C). pap. 40.00 (978-1-876832-58-2(4)) Macmillan Art Publishing AUS. Dist: Brown, David Bk. Co., The.
König, Kasper, et al. Remembering Forward: Australian Aboriginal Painting since 1960. 2011. (ENG., Illus.). 188p. (C). 50.00 (978-1-907372-14-8(8)) Holberton, Paul Publishing GBR. Dist: Univ. of Washington Pr.
McAuliffe, Chris. Jon Cattapan: Possible Histories. 2008. (ENG., Illus.). 240p. 41.00 (978-0-522-85498-5(2)) Melbourne Univ. Publishing AUS. Dist: Independent Pubs. Group.
McGregor, Ken. Artists of the Western Desert: Portraits, 2006-11. 2011. (ENG., Illus.). 200p. (C). pap. 79.95 (978-1-921394-64-5(1)) Macmillan Art Publishing AUS. Dist: Brown, David Bk. Co., The.
McGregor, Ken. Fred Cress: Whispers: Drawings 1958 - 2007. Oslen, ed. rev. ed. 2007. (Illus.). 256p. (C). 100.00 (978-1-876832-64-3(9)) Macmillan Art Publishing AUS. Dist: Brown, David Bk. Co., The.
McGregor, Ken & Zimmer, Jenny. Tim Storrier. 2007. (Macmillan Mini-Art Ser.). (Illus.). 144p. (C). 35.00 (978-1-921394-12-6(9)) Macmillan Art Publishing AUS. Dist: Brown, David Bk. Co., The.
Pybus, C D. @ Mass Fear. 2008. 144p. per. (978-1-84401-944-1(6)) Athena Pr.
Scott, Denise. All That Happened at Number 26. (ENG., 256p. 2009. Illus.). pap. 15.95 (978-1-74066-867-5(7)) 2008. pap. 23.95 (978-1-74066-680-0(1)) Hardie Grant Bks. AUS. Dist: Independent Pubs. Group.
Smith, Tracey. Creative Relationships. 2009. 77p. pap. 24.96 (978-1-4092-7946-4(4)) Lulu Enterprises Inc.
Speers, Vee, photos by. The Birthday Party. 2009. (ENG., Illus.). 96p. 50.00 (978-1-904587-64-4(X)) Lewis, Dewi Publishing GBR. Dist: Consortium Bk. Sales & Distribution.
St Leon, Mark Valentine. Circus Dreams: Australian Themes. 2008. 432p. pap. (978-3-639-00839-5(1)) VDM Verlag Dr. Mueller e.K.
Vickers-Rich, Patricia, et al. The Artist & the Scientists: Bringing Prehistory to Life, 1 vol. 2010. (ENG., Illus.). 320p. pap. 48.00 (978-0-521-16299-9(8)) Cambridge Univ. Pr.

ARTISTS—BELGIUM

Brogniez, Laurence, ed. Ecrit(ure)s de peintres Belges. 2008. (Comparatisme et Société / Comparatism & Society Ser.). (FRE., Illus.). 256p. pap. 48.95 (978-90-5201-446-3(9)) PIE - Peter Lang BEL. Dist: Lang, Peter.
Büttner, Nils. Herr P.P. Rubens: Von der Kunst, Berühmt Zu Werden. 2006. (Rekonstruktion der Künste Ser.). (GER., Illus.). 278p. (C). pap. 93.00 (978-3-525-47906-3(9)) Vandenhoeck & Ruprecht GmbH & Co. KG DEU. Dist: ISD.
Cock, Jan de. Denkmal III, 5 vols. 2008. (Illus.). 650p. (978-90-808424-3-4(5)) Atelier Jan de Cock.
Colrier, Lise. Xavier Lust, 1 vol. 2007. (ENG., Illus.). 160p. 85.00 (978-90-5856-211-1(5)) Stichting Kunstboek Bvba BEL. Dist: Antique Collectors' Club.
Deneulin, Luc & Swinnen, Johan. Raoul Servais: The Wizard of Ostend: Commitment, Challenge, Recognition. 2009. (ENG, DUT & FRE., Illus.). 320p. pap. 54.00 (978-90-5487-480-5(5)) VUB Univ. Pr. BEL. Dist: Independent Pubs. Group.
Fabre, Jan. Jan Fabre: from the Cellar to the Attic-from the Feet to the Brain. 2009. (ENG., Illus.). 160p. 86.00 (978-3-86560-535-1(4)) Kunsthaus Bregenz AUT. Dist: D.A.P./Distributed Art Pubs.
Ferguson, Russell. Francis Alÿs: Politics of Rehearsal, 1 vol. 2009. (ENG & SPA., Illus.). 144p. pap. 45.00 (978-3-86521-474-4(6)) Steidl, Gerhard Druckerei und Verlag DEU. Dist: Innovative Logistics.
Holler, Carsten. Carsten Holler. 2011. (ENG., Illus.). 288p. 75.00 (978-3-7757-2395-4(1)) Hatje Cantz Verlag GmbH & Co KG DEU. Dist: D.A.P./Distributed Art Pubs.
Hostyn, Norbert. James Ensor: Leven en Werk/Vie et Oeuvre/Life & Work/Leben und Werke. 2007. (ENG., Illus.). 135p. pap. (978-90-74377-30-0(0), Stichting Kunstboak (Acc)) Antique Collectors' Club.
Hostyn, Norbet. Léon Spilliaert: Life & Work. 2007. (ENG., Illus.). 128p. pap. 35.00 (978-90-5856-199-2(2)) Stichting Kunstboek Bvba BEL. Dist: National Bk. Network.
Marcel Broodthaers. 85.00 (978-2-903004-00-2(5)) Galerie Isy Brachot FRA. Dist: D.A.P./Distributed Art Pubs.
Quinze. The Sequence Presents Arne Quinze's Colossal Wooden Sculpture Project in All of Its. 2009. (DUT & ENG., Illus.). 113p. pap. 35.00 (978-3-89955-243-0(1)) Die Gestalten Verlag DEU. Dist: Prestel Publishing.
Quinze, Arne. Arne Quinze: Modern Contemporary. 2011. (ENG., Illus.). 300p. 70.00 (978-3-7757-2693-1(4)) Hatje Cantz Verlag GmbH & Co KG DEU. Dist: D.A.P./Distributed Art Pubs.
Saegeman, Elie. Octave Landuyt: Ricorso. 2007. (ENG., Illus.). 304p. 60.00 (978-90-5856-239-5(5), Stichting Kunstboak (Acc)) Antique Collectors' Club GBR. Dist: National Bk. Network.
Stoeltie, Barbara & Stoeltie, René. Paper Illusions: The Art of Isabelle de Borchgrave. 2008. (ENG., Illus.). 208p. 80.00 (978-0-8109-7133-2(X)) Abrams.
Tuymans, Luc. Ende. 2009. (ENG., Illus.). 120p. 75.00 (978-3-89770-303-2(3)) Salon-Verlag DEU. Dist: D.A.P./Distributed Art Pubs.

ARTISTS—CANADA

Adamson, Jeremy. Canadian Paintings in the Thomson Collection. 2008. (Illus.). 144p. pap. 50.00 (978-1-903470-83-1(8)) Holberton, Paul Publishing GBR. Dist: Casemate Pubs. & Bk. Distributors, LLC.
Ahlers, Sonja. The Selves. 2010. (ENG., Illus.). 96p. pap. 19.95 (978-1-77046-010-2(1)) Drawn & Quarterly Pubns. CAN. Dist: Macmillan.
Ainslie, Patricia & LaViolette, Mary-Beth. Alberta Art & Artists: An Overview, 1 vol. 2007. (ENG., Illus.). 160p. 39.95 (978-1-894856-61-4(9)) Fitzhenry & Whiteside, Ltd. CAN. Dist: Ingram Pub. Services.
Amos, Robert. Artists in Their Studios: Where Art Is Born, 1 vol. 2007. (ENG., Illus.). 160p. (978-1-894898-58-4(3)) TouchWood Editions.
Appleby, Dee. From Land & Sea: Nova Scotia's Contemporary Landscape Artists. 2010. (ENG., Illus.). 156p. 35.00 (978-1-55109-729-9(X)) Down East Bks.
Askevold, David & Diviney, David. David Askevold: Il était une Fois Dans L'est. 2011. (FRE.). 160p. 50.00 (978-0-86492-666-1(9)) Goose Lane Editions CAN. Dist: Univ. of Toronto Pr.
Bantjes, Marian. I Wonder. 2010. (ENG., Illus.). 208p. 40.00 (978-1-58093-296-7(7)) Monacelli Pr., Inc.
Biyan, Sacha Dean, photos by. Spiritus Mundi. 2007. (Illus.). 40p. pap. 30.00 (978-0-9798631-0-3(4)) Great Circle Bks.
Braziel, Jana Evans. Artists, Performers, & Black Masculinity in the Haitian Diaspora. 2008. (Blacks in the Diaspora Ser.). (ENG., Illus.). 312p. 65.00 (978-0-253-35139-5(1), 0253351391); pap. 24.95 (978-0-253-21978-7(7), 0253219787) Indiana Univ. Pr.
Bright, Susan. Flash Forward 2007: Emerging photographers from Canada, the United Kingdom & the United States. 2007. (ENG.). 192p. 25.00 (978-0-9739739-2-1(7)) Magenta Publishing for the Arts CAN. Dist: Consortium Bk. Sales & Distribution.
Butcher, Alan D. Unlikely Paradise: The Life of Frances Gage. 2009. (ENG., Illus.). 264p. 35.00 (978-1-55488-423-0(3)) Dundurn CAN. Dist: Univ. of Toronto Pr.
Carr, Emily. This & That: The Lost Stories of Emily Carr, 1 vol. 2007. (ENG., Illus.). 232p. per. (978-1-894898-61-4(3)) TouchWood Editions.
Clifford-Ward, Lynn. Visions of Canadian Artists: Figure & Landscape. 60p. 29.95 (978-0-920674-17-8(8)) Beaverbrook Art Gallery CAN. Dist: Goose Lane Editions.

Curtis, Herb, et al. Bruno Bobak: The Full Palette. Riordon, Bernard, ed. 2006. (ENG., Illus.). 208p. 55.00 (978-0-86492-481-0(X)) Goose Lane Editions CAN. Dist: Univ. of Toronto Pr.
Czajkowski, Chris. A Mountain Year: Nature Diary of a Wilderness Dweller. unabr. ed. 2009. (ENG., Illus.). 184p. 19.95 (978-1-55017-441-0(X)) Harbour Publishing Co., Ltd. CAN. Dist: Ingram Pub. Services.
Dafoe, Frances. Figure Skating & the Arts: Eight Centuries of Sport & Inspiration. 2011. (Illus.). 192p. 45.00 (978-0-7643-3803-8(X), Schiffer Publishing Ltd) Schiffer Publishing, Ltd.
Davis, Ann, ed. Cover & Uncover: Eric Cameron. 2011. (ENG., Illus.). 132p. pap. 59.95 (978-1-55238-534-0(5)) Univ. of Calgary Pr. CAN. Dist: Chicago Distribution Ctr.
De Boer, Solange, ed. & contrib. by. Brian Jungen, 1 vol. 2007. (ENG., Illus.). 128p. 15.00 (978-90-73362-69-7(5)) Witte De With Centre for Contemporary Art NLD. Dist: D.A.P./Distributed Art Pubs.
Diviney, David. David Askevold: Once upon a Time in the East. 2011. (ENG.). 160p. 50.00 (978-0-86492-659-3(6)) Goose Lane Editions CAN. Dist: Univ. of Toronto Pr.
Doubleday Publisher. Ernest Thompson Seton: A Biographical Sketch. 2011. 50p. 36.95 (978-1-258-02176-4(5)) Literary Licensing, LLC.
Dyer, Chris. Positive Creations: The Visionary Art of Chris Dyer. 2011. (Illus.). 256p. 39.99 (978-0-7643-3913-4(3), Schiffer Publishing Ltd) Schiffer Publishing, Ltd.
Eagle Creek Press & Nca&t. Making College Pay: Strategies for Choosing Wisely, Doing Well & Maximizing Your Return. 2011. (ENG.). 224p. pap. 18.00 (978-0-9759366-9-6(7)) Eagle Creek Pr.
Evans, Al. Chee Chee: A Study of Aboriginal Suicide. 2010. (McGill-Queen's Native & Northern Ser.). (Illus.). 208p. (C). pap. (978-0-7735-3759-0(7)) McGill-Queen's Univ. Pr.
Evans, Carol. The Shores We Call Home: The Art of Carol Evans. unabr. ed. 2010. (ENG., Illus.). 96p. pap. (978-1-55017-465-6(7)) Harbour Publishing Co., Ltd.
Fillmore, Sarah. Jacques Hurtubise: Catalogue Raisonné. 2011. (FRE & ENG., Illus.). 256p. 60.00 (978-0-86492-662-3(6)) Goose Lane Editions CAN. Dist: Univ. of Toronto Pr.
Fisher, Jennifer, ed. Technologies of Intuition. 2007. (ENG., Illus.). 288p. pap. 26.95 (978-0-920397-43-5(3)) Y Y Z Artists Outlet CAN. Dist: LitDistCo.
Forsberg, Tor. North of Iskut: Grizzlies, Bannock & Adventure. unabr. ed. 2010. (ENG., Illus.). 224p. pap. 24.95 (978-1-894759-42-7(7)) Caitlin Pr., Inc. CAN. Dist: Partners Pubs. Group, Inc.
Gasztonyi, Gabor, photos by. A Room in the City. 2010. (ENG., Illus.). 200p. 40.00 (978-1-897535-28-8(7)) Anvil Pr. CAN. Dist: Univ. of Toronto Pr.
Gérin, Annie. Public Art in Canada: Critical Perspectives. MacLean, James S., ed. 2009. (ENG., Illus.). 336p. (978-0-8020-9847-4(9)); pap. (978-0-8020-9568-8(2)) Univ. of Toronto Pr.
Grace, Sherrill. Making Theatre: A Life of Sharon Pollock. Pollock, Sharon, ed. 2008. (ENG.). 480p. pap. 39.95 (978-0-88922-586-2(9)) Talonbooks, Ltd. CAN. Dist: Consortium Bk. Sales & Distribution.
Graham, Rodney. Rodney Graham: Friedrich Christian Flick Collection, 1 vol. 2009. (ENG., Illus.). 176p. (gr. 13-18). 59.95 (978-3-8321-7497-2(4)) DuMont DEU. Dist: D.A.P./Distributed Art Pubs.
Hedgpeth, Don. Follow the Sun: Robert Lougheed. 2010. (ENG.). 360p. (C). 65.00 (978-0-578-03970-1(2)) Univ. of Oklahoma Pr.
Herzog, Fred, photos by. Fred Herzog: Photographs, 1 vol. 2011. (ENG., Illus.). 192p. 45.00 (978-3-7757-2811-9(2)) Hatje Cantz Verlag GmbH & Co KG DEU. Dist: D.A.P./Distributed Art Pubs.
Heti, Sheila, text. Otherworld Uprising. 2008. (ENG., Illus.). 96p. 25.00 (978-1-894994-28-6(0)) Conundrum Pr. CAN. Dist: D.A.P./Distributed Art Pubs.
Jackson, Marion E., et al, eds. Inuit Women Artists: Voices from Cape Dorset, 1 vol. 2006. (ENG., Illus.). 256p. pap. 35.00 (978-1-55054-470-1(5)) D&M Pubs. Inc. CAN. Dist: Perseus-PGW.
Jodidio, Philip. Taizo Kuroda. 2009. (Illus.). 144p. 65.00 (978-3-7913-5003-5(X)) Prestel Publishing.
Kellman, Tila L. Figuring Redemption: Resighting My Self in the Art of Michael Snow. 2010. (ENG.). 222p. (C). pap. 39.95 (978-1-55458-249-5(0)) Wilfrid Laurier Univ. Pr. CAN. Dist: Univ. of Toronto Pr.
Kilbourn, Rosemary. Out of the Wood. 2011. (ENG., Illus.). 208p. pap. 27.95 (978-0-88984-346-2(5)) Porcupine's Quill, Inc. CAN. Dist: Univ. of Toronto Pr.
King, Ross. Defiant Spirits: The Modernist Revolution of the Group of Seven, 1 vol. 2011. (ENG., Illus.). 504p. pap. 24.95 (978-1-55365-882-5(5)) D&M Pubs. Inc. CAN. Dist: Perseus-PGW.
Ledwell, Frank. Dip & Veer: Reflections on the Art of Alex Colville. 64p. pap. 12.95 (978-0-9698606-2-4(5)) Acorn Pr., The CAN. Dist: Goose Lane Editions.
Legge, Elizabeth & Legge, E. Michael Snow: Wavelength. 2009. (One Work Ser.). (ENG., Illus.). 104p. (gr. 17). pap. 16.00 (978-1-84638-056-3(1)) Afterall Publishing GBR. Dist: MIT Pr.
Li, Xiaoping. Voices Rising: Asian Canadian Cultural Activism. 2007. (ENG., Illus.). 320p. pap. (978-0-7748-1222-1(2)) Univ. of British Columbia Pr.
Lind, Jane, ed. Joyce Wieland: Writings & Drawings, 1952-1971. 2009. (ENG., Illus.). 224p. pap. 27.95 (978-0-88984-321-9(X)) Porcupine's Quill, Inc. CAN. Dist: Univ. of Toronto Pr.
Lockhart, Amy. Dirty Dishes. 2010. (ENG., Illus.). 96p. pap. 14.95 (978-1-77046-004-1(7)) Drawn & Quarterly Pubns. CAN. Dist: Macmillan.
Macnair, Peter L., et al. The Legacy: Tradition & Innovation in Northwest Coast Indian Art, 1 vol. 2007. (Royal BC Museum Ser.). (ENG., Illus.). 196p. pap. 36.95 (978-0-7726-5609-4(6)) UBC Pr. CAN. Dist: Univ. of Washington Pr.
Moos, David, et al. Iain Baxterand & Works, 1958-2011. Moos, David, ed. 2012. (ENG., Illus.). 220p. pap. 45.00 (978-0-86492-646-3(4)) Goose Lane Editions CAN. Dist: Univ. of Toronto Pr.
Morris, Brian. Ernest Thompson Seton, Founder of the Woodcraft Movement 1860-1946: Apostle of Indian Wisdom & Pioneer Ecologist. 2006. 360p. 119.95 (978-0-7734-5474-3(8)) Mellen, Edwin Pr., The.
Nasgaard, Roald. Abstract Painting in Canada, 1 vol. 2007. (ENG., Illus.). 432p. pap. 50.00 (978-1-55365-394-3(7)) D&M Pubs. Inc. CAN. Dist: Perseus-PGW.
Newfeld, Frank. Drawing on Type. 2008. (ENG., Illus.). 336p. pap. 27.95 (978-0-88984-304-2(X)) Porcupine's Quill, Inc. CAN. Dist: Univ. of Toronto Pr.
Newlands, Anne. Canadian Paintings, Prints & Drawings. 2007. (ENG., Illus.). 368p. 69.95 (978-1-55407-290-3(5)) Firefly Bks., Ltd.
Newman, Michael. Jeff Wall: Works & Collected Writings, 1 vol. 2007. (ENG., Illus.). 304p. 75.00 (978-84-343-1131-2(3)) Poligrafa, Ediciones, S. A. ESP. Dist: D.A.P./Distributed Art Pubs.
O'Brian, Melanie. Vancouver Art & Economies. O'Brian, Melanie, ed. 2007. (ENG., Illus.). 300p. pap. 24.95 (978-1-55152-214-2(4)) Arsenal Pulp Pr. CAN. Dist: Consortium Bk. Sales & Distribution.
O'Driscoll, Treasa. Celtic Woman: A Memoir of Life's Poetic Journey. 2008. (ENG., Illus.). 353p. pap. 24.95 (978-0-9781600-2-9(9)) Dundurn CAN. Dist: Ingram Pub. Services.
Parsons, P. J. Another 'Pointe' of View: The Life & Times of a Ballet Mom. 2009. (ENG.). 216p. pap. 18.95 (978-0-9784179-8-7(4)) DreamCatcher Publishing CAN. Dist: Univ. of Toronto Pr.
Penny, Evan. Evan Penny: Rendering Realities. 2011. (ITA, GER & ENG., Illus.). 160p. 45.00 (978-3-86560-990-8(2)) Verlag der Buchhandlung Walther Konig DEU. Dist: D.A.P./Distributed Art Pubs.
Pratt, Elspeth & Slade, Kathy. Elspeth Pratt. 2012. (ENG.). 144p. 39.95 (978-0-921356-37-0(4)) Scott, Charles H. Gallery, Emily Carr College of Art & Design CAN. Dist: D.A.P./Distributed Art Pubs.
Randell, Roy. Spiritual Art. 2010. 125p. pap. 44.80 (978-0-557-39643-6(3)) Lulu Enterprises Inc.
Reid, Dennis, ed. Jack Chambers: Light, Spirit, Time, Place, & Life. 2011. (ENG., Illus.). 240p. pap. 45.00 (978-0-86492-645-6(6)) Goose Lane Editions CAN. Dist: Univ. of Toronto Pr.
Rimmer, Jim. Pie Tree Press: Memories from the Composing Room Floor. 2008. (ENG., Illus.). 128p. (978-1-55447-062-4(5)) Gaspereau Pr.
Robert Karman. A Day's Ride from de Bullion: A Memoir. 2009. 412p. 36.90 (978-1-4269-1239-9(0)); pap. 26.90 (978-1-4269-1238-2(2)) Trafford Publishing.
Robertson, Clive. Policy Matters: Administrations of Art & Culture. 2006. (ENG., Illus.). 288p. per. 19.95 (978-0-920397-36-7(0)) Y Y Z Artists Outlet CAN. Dist: LitDistCo.
Rogatnick, Abraham J., et al. B.C. Binning. (Illus.). 192p. 50.00 (978-1-55365-171-0(5)) D&M Pubs. Inc. CAN. Dist: Perseus-PGW.
Schellenberg, Susan & Barnes, Rosemary. Committed to the Sane Asylum: Narratives on Mental Wellness & Healing. 2008. (GER & ENG., Illus.). 320p. pap. 32.95 (978-1-55458-034-7(X)) Wilfrid Laurier Univ. Pr. CAN. Dist: Univ. of Toronto Pr.
Shapton, Leanne. Toronto, 1 vol. 2007. (ENG., Illus.). 112p. pap. 30.00 (978-0-9701656-8-8(4)) J&L Bks., Inc.
Silcox, David P. The Group of Seven & Tom Thomson. 2011. (ENG., Illus.). 444p. pap. 35.00 (978-1-55407-885-1(7)) Firefly Bks., Ltd.
Singer, Leah & Ranaldo, Lee. Lee Ranaldo & Leah Singer: Water Days. 2010. (ENG., Illus.). 64p. pap. 40.00 (978-2-914563-52-9(3)) Dis Voir Editions FRA. Dist: D.A.P./Distributed Art Pubs.
Smart, Tom. Tom Forrestall: Paintings, Drawings, Writings. 2008. (ENG., Illus.). 152p. 49.95 (978-1-55470-005-9(1)) Key Porter Bks. CAN. Dist: Perseus-PGW.
Tiessen, Hildi Froese & Tiessen, Paul Gerard. Woldemar Neufeld's Canada: A Mennonite Artist in the Canadian Landscape 1928-1994. Neufeld, Laurence & McKillen, Monika, eds. 2009. (ENG.). 152p. (C). 65.00 (978-1-55458-190-0(7)) Wilfrid Laurier Univ. Pr. CAN. Dist: Univ. of Toronto Pr.
Vallee, Julien. Rock, Paper, Scissors: The Work of Julien Vallee. 2011. (ENG., Illus.). 160p. 55.00 (978-3-89955-365-9(9)) Die Gestalten Verlag DEU. Dist: Prestel Publishing.
Virtue, John. Fred Taylor: Brother in the Shadows. 2008. (ENG., Illus.). 320p. (C). (978-0-7735-3359-2(1)) McGill-Queen's Univ. Pr.
Wall, Jeff, photos by. Jeff Wall. 2008. (ENG., Illus.). 48p. 85.00 (978-84-936123-9-9(1)) RM Verlag, S.L. ESP. Dist: D.A.P./Distributed Art Pubs.
Wallace, Ian. Ian Wallace: Die erste documenta 1955. 2011. (ENG., Illus.). 40p. pap. 10.00 (978-3-7757-2851-5(1)) Hatje Cantz Verlag GmbH & Co KG DEU. Dist: D.A.P./Distributed Art Pubs.
Williams, Barbara. A Gentlewoman in Upper Canada: The Journals, Letters, & Art of Anne Langton. 2008. (ENG., Illus.). 384p. (978-0-8020-3549-3(3)) Univ. of Toronto Pr.
Wright, Doug. The Collected Doug Wright Vol. 1: Canada's Master Cartoonist. Mackay, Seth & Mackay, Brad, eds. 2009. (ENG., Illus.). 240p. 39.95 (978-1-897299-52-4(4)) Drawn & Quarterly Pubns. CAN. Dist: Macmillan.

ARTISTS—CHINA

Bently, Tamara Heimarck. The Figurative Works of Chen Hongshou, 1599-1652: Authentic Voices/Expanding Markets. 2012. (Visual Culture in Early Modernity Ser.). (Illus.). 320p. 124.95 (978-0-7546-6672-1(7)) Ashgate Publishing Co.
Chen Zengshou — A Man of the Past Age — and His Poems in Praise of Flowers. 2007. pap. 10.00 (978-1-59343-057-3(4), Cozy Publishing Hse.) Cozy Graphics Corp.
Ciric, Biljana. Rejected Collection: Rejected Proposals by Chinese Contemporary Artists. 2009. (ENG., Illus.). 240p. pap. 47.95 (978-88-8158-709-4(2)) Charta ITA. Dist: D.A.P./Distributed Art Pubs.
Dong, Song. Song Dong: Dad & Mom, Don't Worry about Us, We Are All Well. 2011. (ENG., Illus.). 144p. 35.00 (978-0-9826789-2-3(4)) Yerba Buena Ctr. for the Arts.
Du, Huang. Wang Luyan. 2012. (ENG., Illus.). 232p. 60.00 (978-88-572-1128-2(2)) Skira Editore ITA. Dist: Random Hse., Inc.
Fu, Shen. Chapters from a Floating Life. Black, Shirley, tr. 2007. 112p. per. 11.95 (978-1-59654-382-9(5)) Disruptive Publishing.
Grosenick, Uta & Ochs, Alexander, eds. Yin Xiuzhen: Universes in My Universe. 2011. (ENG & GER., Illus.). 200p. (978-3-942405-23-2(7)) Die Gestalten Verlag.
Guo, Ruyu. The Artist Guo Ruyu in Chinese Fine Brushwork. 2007. (Illus.). 243p. 39.00 (978-0-9743293-6-9(3)) International Arts Publishing.
Holding, Julie. Hau Pei Jen: Bold Horizons in Ink & Color. 2010. 96p. pap. 32.50 (978-1-4490-9679-3(4)) AuthorHouse.
Hung, Wu, ed. Wu Hung on Contemporary Chinese Artists. 2009. (ENG., Illus.). 268p. 25.00 (978-988-18034-3-6(8)) Timezone 8 Ltd. HKG. Dist: D.A.P./Distributed Art Pubs.
King, Richard, ed. Art in Turmoil: The Chinese Cultural Revolution, 1966-76. 2010. (ENG., Illus.). 318p. pap. 35.95 (978-0-7748-1543-7(4)) UBC Pr. CAN. Dist: Univ. of Washington Pr.
Lei, Hong, illus. Hong Lei: Chinese Artists of Today: The Red Should Languish & Green Must Grow, 1 vol. 2008. (ENG.). 213p. 90.00 (978-7-5410-2991-2(2)) Timezone 8 Ltd. HKG. Dist: D.A.P./Distributed Art Pubs.
Mayer, Marc & Fishman, Ted C., contrib. by. Edward Burtynsky - China, 1 vol. 2008. (ENG., Illus.). 180p. 85.00 (978-3-86521-130-9(5)) Steidl, Gerhard Druckerei und Verlag DEU. Dist: Innovative Logistics.
Morin, France & Farmer, John, eds. The Quiet in the Land: Luang Prabang, Laos. 2010. (ENG., Illus.). 240p. 45.00 (978-0-9841667-0-1(X)) Quiet in the Land Inc., The.
Noe, Christoph, et al. Young Chinese Artists: The Next Generation. 2nd ed. 2010. (Illus.). 296p. pap. 29.95 (978-3-7913-5060-8(9)) Prestel Publishing.
Otie, Philippe. A Chinese Life. 2012. (Illus.). 720p. pap. 27.50 (978-1-906838-55-3(0), SelfMadeHero) Metro Media Ltd. GBR. Dist: Abrams.
Papastergiadis, Nikos, et al. Yang Shaobin: X-Blind Spot. 2009. (ENG., Illus.). 128p. 55.00 (978-88-8158-742-1(4)) Charta ITA. Dist: D.A.P./Distributed Art Pubs.
Pollack, Barbara, text. The Wild, Wild East: an American Art Critic's Adventures in China. 2010. (ENG., Illus.). 208p. pap. 24.95 (978-988-18034-9-8(7)) Timezone 8 Ltd. HKG. Dist: D.A.P./Distributed Art Pubs.
Ravenal, John B., et al. Xu Bing: Tobacco Project, Duke/Shanghai/Virginia, 1999-2011. Tomii, Reiko, ed. 2011. (ENG., Illus.). 144p. (C). (gr. 13-17). pap. 35.00 (978-0-917046-96-4(X)) Univ. Pr. of Virginia.
Ristaino, Marcia R. China's Intrepid Muse. 2009. (ENG.). 176p. pap. 40.00 (978-1-891640-57-5(7)) Floating World Editions.
Sans, Jerome, text. China Talks. 2009. (ENG., Illus.). 208p. pap. 29.95 (978-988-18033-0-6(6)) Timezone 8 Ltd. HKG. Dist: D.A.P./Distributed Art Pubs.
Scharf, Kenny, et al, texts. Tseng Kwong Chi: Self Portraits 1979-1989. 2009. (ENG., Illus.). 128p. 80.00 (978-0-9794164-5-3(0)) Kasmin, Paul Gallery.
Schmal, Peter & Wenjun, Zhi, eds. M8 in China: Contemporary Chinese Architects. Zeitgenössische chinesische Architekten. 2010. (ENG., Illus.). 160p. 39.95 (978-3-86859-025-8(0)) Jovis Verlag GmbH DEU. Dist: D.A.P./Distributed Art Pubs.
Silbergeld, Jerome, et al. Outside In: Chinese x American x Contemporary Art. 2009. (ENG., Illus.). 304p. 60.00 (978-0-300-12208-4(X)) Yale Univ. Pr.
Smith, Karen, et al, texts. Ai Weiwei. 2009. (ENG., Illus.). 160p. pap. 45.00 (978-0-7148-4889-1(1)) Phaidon Pr., Inc.
Tinari, Philip. Artists in China. 2011. (Illus.). 448p. 50.00 (978-1-905216-38-3(6)) Verbavolantedizioni ITA. Dist: Ingram Pub. Services.
Van Gulik, Robert H., tr. Mi Fu on Ink-Stones. 2006. (CHI & ENG., Illus.). 84p. 35.00 (978-974-524-083-4(4)) Orchid Pr. THA. Dist: National Bk. Network.
Welland, Sasha Su-Ling. A Thousand Miles of Dreams: The Journeys of Two Chinese Sisters. (Asian Voices Ser.). (ENG., Illus.). 392p. 2007. per. 19.95 (978-0-7425-5314-9(0)) 2006. 26.95 (978-0-7425-5313-2(2)) Rowman & Littlefield Publishers, Inc.
Yu, Peng & Yuan, Sun. Sun Yuan & Peng Yu: Can't Have it All. 2010. (ENG., Illus.). 250p. pap. 50.00 (978-988-18033-8-2(1)) Timezone 8 Ltd. HKG. Dist: D.A.P./Distributed Art Pubs.
Zuo, Jing. Work in Progress. 2011. (ENG., Illus.). 278p. pap. 30.00 (978-988-18816-5-6(X)) Timezone 8 Ltd. HKG. Dist: D.A.P./Distributed Art Pubs.

ARTISTS—CZECHOSLOVAKIA

Farova, Anna & Heller, Martin. Iren Stehlí, 1 vol. 2007. (ENG., Illus.). 176p. pap. 25.00 (978-80-7215-284-1(X)) TORST CZE. Dist: D.A.P./Distributed Art Pubs.
Heiss, Alanna, et al, texts. Federico Díaz & E Area: Resonance, 1 vol. 2009. (ENG., Illus.). 500p. 95.00 (978-88-8158-721-6(1)) Charta ITA. Dist: D.A.P./Distributed Art Pubs.
Moucha, Josef. Frantisek Drtikol, 1 vol. 2007. (CZE & ENG., Illus.). 178p. pap. 25.00 (978-80-7215-301-5(3)) TORST CZE. Dist: D.A.P./Distributed Art Pubs.
Scheufler, Pavel. Josef Binko, 1 vol. 2007. (CZE & ENG., Illus.). 148p. pap. 25.00 (978-80-7215-281-0(5)) TORST CZE. Dist: D.A.P./Distributed Art Pubs.
Sudek, Josef, photos by. Josef Sudek: the Advertising Photographs. 2009. (ENG., Illus.). 100p. 60.00 (978-80-7215-342-8(0)) TORST CZE. Dist: D.A.P./Distributed Art Pubs.

ARTISTS—EUROPE

Abramovic, Marina. Hans Ulrich Obrist & Marina Abramovic: the Conversation Series. 2010. (ENG., Illus.). 192p. pap. 35.00 (978-3-86560-475-0(7)) Verlag der Buchhandlung Walther Konig DEU. Dist: D.A.P./Distributed Art Pubs.
Alphen, E. van & Donnadieu, Marc. Marian Breedveld: Monograph. 2010. (ENG., Illus.). 128p. (978-90-78964-36-0(7), Thieme Art (Acc)) Antique Collectors' Club.
Althamer, Pawel, et al, texts. Pawel Althamer. 2011. (ENG., Illus.). 160p. pap. 45.00 (978-0-7148-6085-5(9)) Phaidon Pr., Inc.
Ant, Exupery. Maly Ksiaze. pap. 8.95 (978-83-7319-061-0(9)) Muza S.A. POL. Dist: Distribooks, Inc.
Bang, Larsen La, ed. Nomeda & Gediminas/Devices for Action. 2008. 188p. pap. (978-84-89771-65-9(0)) Actar Birkhauser Distribution.
Behr, Shulamith, et al. Forced Journeys: Artists in Exile in Britain C. 1933-45. 2009. (Illus.). 112p. 70.00 (978-0-900157-13-4(5), Lund Humphries Pubs.) Ashgate Publishing, Ltd. GBR. Dist: Ashgate Publishing Co.
Benzer, Christa, et al, eds. Continuing Dialogues: A Tribute to Igor Zabel. 2009. (ENG., Illus.). 218p. pap. 28.00 (978-3-905829-91-4(6)) JRP Ringier Kunstverlag AG CHE. Dist: D.A.P./Distributed Art Pubs.
Blanz, Hubert. Slideshow. 2009. (GER., Illus.). 176p. 39.95 (978-3-211-85781-6(8)) Springer Wien AUT. Dist: Actar Birkhauser Distribution.
Boettger, Suzaan & Solakov, Nedko. 99 Fears. 2008. (ENG., Illus.). 112p. 29.95 (978-0-7148-4888-4(3)) Phaidon Pr., Inc.
Borchardt-Hume, Achim, ed. Per Kirkeby. 2009. (ENG., Illus.). 176p. pap. 26.95 (978-1-85437-821-7(X)) Tate Publishing, Ltd. GBR. Dist: Hachette Bk. Group.
Braun, Ariane Kristina. Thomas Hirschhorns Bataille Monument: Ein ephemeres Denkmal auf der Documenta11. 2010. 124p. pap. (978-3-639-27173-7(4)) VDM Verlag Dr. Mueller e.K.
Brooks, Lynn Matluck, ed. Women's Work: Making Dance in Europe Before 1800. 2007. (Studies in Dance History Ser.). (ENG., Illus.). 288p. per. 27.95 (978-0-299-22534-6(8)) Univ. of Wisconsin Pr.
Castagno, John. European Artists II: Signatures & Monograms from 1800: A Comprehensive Directory. 2007. (ENG., Illus.). 416p. 250.00 (978-0-8108-5896-1(7)) Scarecrow Pr., Inc.
—European Artists III: Signatures & Monograms From 1800. 2008. (ENG.). 308p. 200.00 (978-0-8108-6208-1(5)) Scarecrow Pr., Inc.
Clark, John. Japanese Exchanges in Art 1850s To 1930s: With Britain, Continental Europe, & the USA. 2007. (Illus.). 368p. per. 39.00 (978-1-86487-303-0(5)) Univ. of Illinois Pr.
Cooke, Lynne & Vettese, Angela. Maja Bajevic. 2008. (ENG., Illus.). 144p. pap. 49.95 (978-88-8158-670-7(3)) Charta ITA. Dist: D.A.P./Distributed Art Pubs.
Debono, Sandro & Sciciuna, Bernadine. The Busuttil Family: A Legacy of Three Generations. 2010. (Illus.). 136p. pap. 52.00 (978-99932-7-305-9(8)) Midsea Bks. Ltd. MLT. Dist: Brown, David Bk. Co., The.
Dietrich, Nikola & Fabricius, Jacob, eds. Henrik Olesen, 1 vol. 2011. (ENG.). 224p. 60.00 (978-3-7757-2842-3(2)) Hatje Cantz Verlag GmbH & Co KG DEU. Dist: D.A.P./Distributed Art Pubs.
Dimitrijevic, Braco. Braco Dimitrijevic, 1 vol. 2006. (ENG., Illus.). 400p. 85.00 (978-88-8158-590-8(1)) Charta ITA. Dist: D.A.P./Distributed Art Pubs.
Duyves, Mattias & Put, Roos van. Ton of Holland: Contemporary Embroidery. 2013. (ENG., Illus.). 240p. 75.00 (978-90-78964-47-6(2)) Thieme Art NLD. Dist: National Bk. Network.
Eliasson, Olafur & text. Olafur Eliasson: Printed Matter. 2010. (ENG & ITA., Illus.). 142p. pap. 49.95 (978-3-86560-700-3(4)) Verlag der Buchhandlung Walther Konig DEU. Dist: D.A.P./Distributed Art Pubs.
Erika Giovanna Klien: Wien New York 1900-1957. (GER.). (978-3-7757-9069-7(1)) Hatje Cantz Verlag GmbH & Co KG DEU. Dist: D.A.P./Distributed Art Pubs.
Felderer, Brigitte, et al, texts. Christian Ruschitzka: Leitmotive. 2011. (ENG., Illus.). 192p. 55.00 (978-3-7757-3183-6(0)) Hatje Cantz Verlag GmbH & Co KG DEU. Dist: D.A.P./Distributed Art Pubs.
Fitch, Noel Riley. The Grand Literary Cafes of Europe. 2007. (ENG., Illus.). 160p. 39.95 (978-1-84537-114-2(3)) New Holland Pubs., Ltd. GBR. Dist: National Bk. Network.
Friedl, Peter. Peter Friedl: Work 1964-2006. 2007. (Illus.). 365p. pap. (978-84-89771-25-3(1)) Actar Birkhauser Distribution.
From Here to Fame Publishing Staff & Gruenhaeuser, Amber. Monsters of Art. ltd. ed. 2011. (On the Run Bks.). (ENG., Illus.). 224p. 24.95 (978-3-937946-69-6(1)) From Here To Fame GmbH DEU. Dist: SCB Distributors.
Gauditz, Frank, photos by. Casa Mare. 2010. (ENG., Illus.). 176p. 55.00 (978-3-7757-2492-0(3)) Hatje Cantz Verlag GmbH & Co KG DEU. Dist: D.A.P./Distributed Art Pubs.
Gohr. On Per Kirkeby. 2009. (ENG., Illus.). 128p. 40.00 (978-3-7757-2321-3(8)) Hatje Cantz Verlag GmbH & Co KG DEU. Dist: D.A.P./Distributed Art Pubs.
Hewison, Robert. John Byrne: Art & Life. 2011. (Illus.). 144p. 70.00 (978-1-84822-047-8(2), Lund Humphries Pubs.) Ashgate Publishing, Ltd. GBR. Dist: Ashgate Publishing Co.

Heydenreich, Gunnar. Lucas Cranach the Elder: Painting Materials, Techniques & Workshop Practice. 2007. (Illus.). 464p. pap. *(978-90-5356-745-6(3)*, Leiden Univ. Pr.) Amsterdam Univ. Pr.

Holert, Tom, et al, texts. Danica Dakic. 2010. (ENG., Illus.). 152p. pap. 49.95 *(978-3-86560-679-2(2))* Verlag der Buchhandlung Walther Konig DEU. Dist: D.A.P./Distributed Art Pubs.

Hooven III, Valentine F. Tom of Finland - Life & Work of a Gay Hero. 2011. (Illus.). 256p. 52.99 ***(978-3-86787-166-2(3))*** Bruno Gmunder Verlag GmbH DEU. Dist: Bookazine Co., Inc.

Horn, Roni & text. Vatnasafn - Library of Water. 2009. (ENG., Illus.). 176p. 45.00 *(978-3-86521-942-8(X))* Steidl, Gerhard Druckerei und Verlag DEU. Dist: D.A.P./Distributed Art Pubs.

Keane, A. H. The Early Teutonic, Italian & French Masters. 2007. (ENG.). 574p. 58.95 *(978-0-548-04492-6(9))* Kessinger Publishing, LLC.

Kosinski, Dorothy M. & Ottmann, Klaus. Per Kirkeby: Paintings & Sculpture. 2012. (ENG., Illus.). 144p. 50.00 ***(978-0-300-18122-7(1))*** Yale Univ. Pr.

Kramer, F. & Hollein, M. Johann Wilhelm Schirmer: Vom Rheinland in die Welt. Band 2 / Autobiographische Schriften. 2010. 260p. *(978-3-86568-544-5(7))* Imhof, Michael Verlag GmbH & Co. KG.

Kurenniemi, Erkki. Erkki Kurenniemi. 2011. (ENG., Illus.). 48p. pap. 10.00 ***(978-3-7757-2856-0(2))*** Hatje Cantz Verlag GmbH & Co KG DEU. Dist: D.A.P./Distributed Art Pubs.

Leopold, Elisabeth, et al. Egon Schiele: Letters & Poems 1910-1912 from the Leopold Collection. 2008. (Illus.). 144p. 49.95 *(978-3-7913-3999-3(0))* Prestel Publishing.

Long, Rose-Carol Washton, et al, eds. Jewish Dimensions in Modern Visual Culture: Antisemitism, Assimilation, Affirmation. 2009. (ENG., Illus.). 356p. lib. bdg. 55.00 *(978-1-58465-795-8(2)*, Brandeis University Press) Univ. Pr. of New England.

Macaulay, James. Charles Rennie Mackintosh - A Biography. 2010. (ENG., Illus.). 256p. 65.00 *(978-0-393-05175-9(7)*, 5175) Norton, W. W. & Co., Inc.

Mannari, Enrica. Pink Attitude: The Contemporary Female Creativity. 2008. (Illus.). 218p. *(978-88-86416-72-6(5))* Happy Bks.

Marcel Marien. pap. 35.00 *(978-2-903004-08-8(0))* Galerie Isy Brachot FRA. Dist: D.A.P./Distributed Art Pubs.

Meschede, Friedrich & Husch, Anette, texts. Ars Viva 10/11: Labor, Laboratory. 2011. (ENG., Illus.). 176p. pap. 45.00 *(978-3-7757-2778-5(7))* Hatje Cantz Verlag GmbH & Co KG DEU. Dist: D.A.P./Distributed Art Pubs.

Mestrovic, Maria. Ivan Mestrovic: The Making of a Master. 2008. (Illus.). 317p. 33.50 ***(978-1-905299-62-1(1)***, Stacey International) Stacey Publishing GBR. Dist: Midpoint Trade Bks., Inc.

Noever, Peter, ed. Hans Kupelwieser: Trans-Formation. (ENG & GER., Illus.). 80p. pap. 29.95 *(978-3-89322-687-0(7))* Edition Cantz DEU. Dist: D.A.P./Distributed Art Pubs.

—Otto Muhl 7. (ENG & GER., Illus.). 160p. 39.95 *(978-3-89322-927-7(2))* Edition Cantz DEU. Dist: D.A.P./Distributed Art Pubs.

Oetker, Brigitte & Oetker, Arend, eds. The Collection of Brigitte & Arend Oetker. 2009. (ENG., Illus.). 176p. 59.95 *(978-3-86560-525-2(7))* Verlag der Buchhandlung Walther Konig DEU. Dist: D.A.P./Distributed Art Pubs.

Otten, Josef. Tone Fink: Fabric.Art. (ENG & GER., Illus.). 80p. 39.95 *(978-3-89322-404-3(1))* Edition Cantz DEU. Dist: D.A.P./Distributed Art Pubs.

Pabijanek, Katarzyna. Representation of the Body in Polish Art after 1989: Towards a history of Polish art after 1989. 2008. 88p. pap. *(978-3-639-10610-7(5))* VDM Verlag Dr. Mueller e.K.

Paci, Adrian. Adrian Paci, 1 vol. 2006. (ENG., Illus.). 144p. pap. 39.95 *(978-88-8158-592-2(8))* Charta ITA. Dist: D.A.P./Distributed Art Pubs.

Peeters, Natasja. Invisible Hands? the Role & Status of the Painter's Journeyman in the Low Countries C. 1450 - C. 1650. Peeters, N., ed. 2007. (Groningen Studies in Cultural Change Ser.). (ENG., Illus.). 173p. (C). pap. 66.00 *(978-90-429-1937-2(X))* Peeters Pubs. & Booksellers BEL. Dist: Brown, David Bk. Co., The.

Persons, Timothy & Hiller, Katrin, texts. The Helsinki School. 2009. (ENG., Illus.). 192p. 60.00 *(978-3-7757-2404-3(4))* Hatje Cantz Verlag GmbH & Co KG DEU. Dist: D.A.P./Distributed Art Pubs.

Ponciroli, Virginia, ed. Biennale Puglia 2008: Young Artists from Europe & the Mediteranean [in English & Italian]. 2008. 272p. pap. 57.50 *(978-88-370-6382-5(2))* Electa ITA. Dist: Trans-Atlantic Pubns., Inc.

R, Tal. Tal R: Adieu Interessant. 2008. (ENG., Illus.). 144p. 180.00 *(978-3-86560-482-8(X))* Verlag der Buchhandlung Walther Konig DEU. Dist: D.A.P./Distributed Art Pubs.

Ramson, Sidsel. Sidsel Ramson: A Photographic Odyssey. 2011. (ENG., Illus.). 360p. 80.00 *(978-2-7022-0937-0(8))* Cercle d'Art, Editions FRA. Dist: National Bk. Network.

Restany, Pierre & Hundertwasser, Friedensreich. Hundertwasser. 2011. (Temporis Ser.). (ENG, FRE & GER., Illus.). 256p. 39.95 *(978-1-84484-840-9(X))* Parkstone Pr. USA, Ltd.

Richards, Mary. Marina Abramovic. 2009. (Routledge Performance Practitioners Ser.). (ENG., Illus.). 168p. 30.95 *(978-0-415-43208-5(1))* Routledge.

Rist, Pipilotti. Pipilotti Rist: the Tender Room. 2011. (ENG., Illus.). 72p. 24.95 ***(978-1-881390-49-7(7))*** Ohio State Univ., Wexner Ctr. for the Arts.

Ritter, Arno. Cornelius Kolig. *(978-3-7757-0454-0(X))* Hatje Cantz Verlag GmbH & Co KG DEU. Dist: D.A.P./Distributed Art Pubs.

Robinson, Julia, ed. New Realisms, 1957-1962: Object Strategies Between Readymade & Spectacle. 2010. (ENG., Illus.). 294p. (gr. 17). pap. 44.95 *(978-0-262-51522-1(9))* MIT Pr.

Rodriguez, Maria Ines. Modernidad Tropical. 2010. 160p. pap. *(978-84-92861-30-9(4))* Actar Birkhauser Distribution.

Ruban, Valentyna & Demko, Alexander, frwds. Paintings from the Estate of Vasyl Hryhorovych Krychevsky. ltd. ed. 2007. (Illus.). 136p. 25.00 *(978-0-9771995-2-5(5))* Zorya Fine Art, LLC.

Schmitz-von Ledebur, K. Die Planeten und ihre Kinder: Eine flaemische Tapisserienserie des 16. Jahrhunderts aus der Sammlung Herzog Albrechts V. 2009. (Studies in Western Tapestry Ser.). (GER.). 175p. (C). 138.00 *(978-2-503-52354-5(4))* Brepols Pubs. BEL. Dist: Brown, David Bk. Co., The.

Schneider, Eckhard, ed. & intro. Gottfried Bechtold: Reine und Gemischte Zustande, 1 vol. 2007. (ENG., Illus.). 160p. pap. 62.00 *(978-3-902525-45-1(2))* Kunsthaus Bregenz AUT. Dist: D.A.P./Distributed Art Pubs.

Schor, Gabriele, ed. Birgit Jurgenssen. 2010. (ENG., Illus.). 296p. 60.00 *(978-3-7757-2461-6(3))* Hatje Cantz Verlag GmbH & Co KG DEU. Dist: D.A.P./Distributed Art Pubs.

Sciberras, Keith. Baroque Painting in Malta. 2009. (ENG., Illus.). 450p. (C). 148.00 *(978-99932-7-249-6(3))* Midsea Bks. Ltd. MLT. Dist: Brown, David Bk. Co., The.

Seppanen, Jouni. Flower Stories: Jouni Seppänen. 2007. (ENG., Illus.). 144p. 120.00 *(978-90-5856-191-6(7)*, Stichting Kunstboak (Acc)) Antique Collectors' Club GBR. Dist: National Bk. Network.

Signer, Roman. Roman Signer: Vernissage: Invitations for Exhibitions 1973-2008. =Waspe, Roland & Mettler, Max, eds. 2008. (Illus.). 240p. 85.00 *(978-3-85881-224-7(2))* Scheidegger und Spiess AG, Verlag CHE. Dist: Antique Collectors' Club.

Sluijter, Eric Jan. Rembrandt & the Female Nude. 2007. (Amsterdam Studies in the Dutch Golden Age Ser.). (ENG., Illus.). 448p. pap. *(978-90-5356-837-8(9)*, Leiden Univ. Pr.) Amsterdam Univ. Pr.

Sosnowska, Monika & text. Monika Sosnowska: Photographs & Sketches, 1 vol. 2008. (ENG., Illus.). 112p. pap. 38.00 *(978-3-86521-723-3(0))* Steidl, Gerhard Druckerei und Verlag DEU. Dist: Innovative Logistics.

Starbird, Soren Solkaer. Closer. 2011. *(978-1-58423-402-9(4))* Gingko Pr., Inc.

Tojner, Poul Erik & Wilmes, Ulrich, eds. Per Kirkeby: Louisiana 2008. 2009. (ENG., Illus.). 192p. 40.00 *(978-87-91607-57-8(4))* Louisana DNK. Dist: D.A.P./Distributed Art Pubs.

Tomasso Brothers Fine Art Staff. Scultura III. 2010. (ENG., Illus.). 80p. (C). 50.00 *(978-1-907372-15-5(6))* Holberton, Paul Publishing GBR. Dist: Univ. of Washington Pr.

Topfer, Klaus & Wagner, Hilke, texts. Tue Greenfort: Linear Deflection. 2009. (ENG., Illus.). 192p. pap. 35.00 *(978-3-86560-526-9(5))* Verlag der Buchhandlung Walther Konig DEU. Dist: D.A.P./Distributed Art Pubs.

Ursprung, Philip. Studio Olafur Eliasson Jumbo. Eliasson, Olafur, ed. 2012. (ENG., Illus.). 528p. 39.99 ***(978-3-8365-2727-9(8))*** TASCHEN DEU. Dist: Ingram Pub. Services.

Von Furstenberg, Adelina, ed. Marina Abramovic: Balkan Epic. 2006. (ENG., Illus.). 112p. pap. 34.95 *(978-88-7624-678-4(9))* Random Hse., Inc.

von Huene, Stephan. Stephan von Huene: The Song of the Line/Die Zeichnungen 1950-1999. 2010. (ENG., Illus.). 144p. 45.00 *(978-3-7757-2642-9(X))* Hatje Cantz Verlag GmbH & Co KG DEU. Dist: D.A.P./Distributed Art Pubs.

Warrell, Ian & Kelly, Franklin, eds. J. M. W. Turner. 2007. (ENG., Illus.). 272p. 60.00 *(978-1-85437-690-9(X))* Tate Publishing, Ltd. GBR. Dist: Hachette Bk. Group.

Wendelski, Marc, photos by. Marc Wendelski: Nage Libre. 2009. (ENG., Illus.). 120p. 45.00 *(978-2-87340-222-8(9))* Yellow now BEL. Dist: D.A.P./Distributed Art Pubs.

West, Franz, et al. Franz West: In & Out. (GER., Illus.). 240p. *(978-3-7757-9068-0(3))* Hatje Cantz Verlag GmbH & Co KG DEU. Dist: D.A.P./Distributed Art Pubs.

Westcott, James. When Marina Abramovic Dies: A Biography. 2010. (ENG., Illus.). 344p. (gr. 17). 28.95 *(978-0-262-23262-3(6))* MIT Pr.

Wohl, Hellmut & Montanari, Tommaso, eds. Giovan Pietro Bellori: The Lives of the Modern Painters, Sculptors & Architects. 2009. (ENG., Illus.). 516p. (C). pap. 35.99 *(978-0-521-13954-0(6))* Cambridge Univ. Pr.

Zeb.Roc.Ski Staff. Zebster. 2012. (On the Run Bks.). (ENG., Illus.). 144p. 19.95 ***(978-3-937946-34-4(9))***; pap. 14.95 ***(978-3-937946-33-7(0))*** From Here To Fame GmbH DEU. Dist: SCB Distributors.

ARTISTS—FRANCE

Andersen, Wayne. Marcel Duchamp: The Failed Messiah. 2011. (ENG.). 402p. pap. 19.50 ***(978-0-9725573-3-7(4))*** Fabriart Editions, Ltd.

Avram, Paul. Non-Exhibited Works of the Masters - French School of Painting - 2008. 72p. pap. *(978-973-88662-2-5(7))* Inforom.

Bailey, Colin B. Renoir: Impressionism & Full-Length Painting. 2012. (ENG., Illus.). 288p. 65.00 ***(978-0-300-18108-1(6))*** Yale Univ. Pr.

Bajac, Quentin & Chéroux, Clément, eds. Collection Photographs, 1 vol. 2008. (ENG., Illus.). 468p. 85.00 *(978-3-86521-480-5(0))* Steidl, Gerhard Druckerei und Verlag DEU. Dist: Innovative Logistics.

Banier, François-Marie. Follow Me Vol. 8. 2011. (ENG & FRE., Illus.). 60p. 58.00 *(978-3-86930-161-7(9))* Steidl, Gerhard Druckerei und Verlag DEU. Dist: Innovative Logistics.

—François-Marie Banier Vol. 9: A2 Doigts, 1 vol. 2011. (ENG & FRE., Illus.). 32p. 58.00 *(978-3-86930-162-4(7))* Steidl, Gerhard Druckerei und Verlag DEU. Dist: Innovative Logistics.

—Francoismarie Banier? Optimism, 1 vol. 2011. (ENG., Illus.). 196p. 45.00 *(978-3-86930-163-1(5))* Steidl, Gerhard Druckerei und Verlag DEU. Dist: Innovative Logistics.

—Pense à Moi Vol. 11. 2011. (ENG & FRE., Illus.). 48p. pap. 58.00 *(978-3-86930-164-8(3))* Steidl, Gerhard Druckerei und Verlag DEU. Dist: Innovative Logistics.

—Poaime, 1 vol., Vol. 7. 2011. (ENG & FRE., Illus.). 80p. 125.00 *(978-3-86930-160-0(0))* Steidl, Gerhard Druckerei und Verlag DEU. Dist: Innovative Logistics.

Banier, Francoismarie. François-Marie Banier - Etoiles, 1 vol., Vol. 6. 2011. (ENG & FRE., Illus.). 92p. 125.00 *(978-3-86930-159-4(7))* Steidl, Gerhard Druckerei und Verlag DEU. Dist: Innovative Logistics.

Bartoletti, Laurence. Creation en France: Arts decoratifs 1945-1965: Repertoire Alphabetique. 2010. (ENG.). 388p. pap. 95.00 *(978-2-35340-019-5(1))* Gourcuff Gradenigo FRA. Dist: National Bk. Network.

Baudot, Francois. Poiret. 2007. (ENG., Illus.). 79p. 25.00 *(978-2-7594-0100-0(6))* Assouline FRA. Dist: Perseus Distribution.

Baur, Ruedi. Ruedi Baur Intigral. 2008. (GER, ENG & FRE., Illus.). 480p. 69.95 *(978-3-03778-134-0(3)*, 3037781343) Springer.

Belin, Valerie & Remy, Patrick. Valérie Belin, 1 vol. 2007. (ENG., Illus.). 260p. 65.00 *(978-3-86521-465-2(7))* Steidl, Gerhard Druckerei und Verlag DEU. Dist: D.A.P./Distributed Art Pubs.

Blom, Ina, text. Saadane Afif: Technical Specifications. 2009. (ENG., Illus.). 148p. 25.00 *(978-90-73362-84-0(9))* Witte De With Centre for Contemporary Art NLD. Dist: D.A.P./Distributed Art Pubs.

Boltanski, Christian & text. The Possible Life of Christian Boltanski. 2009. (ENG., Illus.). 242p. 35.00 *(978-0-87846-746-4(7))* Museum of Fine Arts, Boston.

Bonami, Francesco & Martini, Vittorio. Huang Yong Ping. 2008. (Illus.). 108p. pap. 37.50 *(978-88-370-6075-6(0))* Electa ITA. Dist: Trans-Atlantic Pubns., Inc.

Bott, Daniele. Thierry Mugler: Galaxy Glamour. 2010. (ENG., Illus.). 208p. 50.00 *(978-0-500-51520-4(4)*, 551520) Thames & Hudson.

Bramly, Serge. Chambre Close: A Fiction. 2007. (Illus.). 151p. 49.95 *(978-3-8296-0316-4(9))* Schirmer/Mosel Verlag GmbH DEU. Dist: Prestel Publishing.

Buck, Stephanie, et al. The Courtauld Cézannes. 2008. (ENG., Illus.). 160p. pap. 45.00 *(978-1-903470-84-8(6))* Holberton, Paul Publishing GBR. Dist: Casemate Pubs. & Bk. Distributors, LLC.

Buren, Daniel, photos by. Daniel Buren: Prospettive, 5 vols. 2008. (ITA & ENG., Illus.). 72p. 15.00 *(978-3-905701-49-4(9))* JRP Ringier Kunstverlag AG CHE. Dist: D.A.P./Distributed Art Pubs.

Bustamante, Jean-Marc. Jean-Marc Bustamante: A World at a Time. (Illus.). 64p. *(978-3-89322-670-2(2))* Edition Cantz DEU. Dist: D.A.P./Distributed Art Pubs.

Butler, Ruth. Hidden in the Shadow of the Master: The Model-Wives of Cezanne, Monet, & Rodin. 2010. (ENG., Illus.). 376p. pap. 22.00 *(978-0-300-16450-3(5))* Yale Univ. Pr.

Camus, Renaud. Demeures de L'esprit. 2008. (FRE., Illus.). *(978-2-213-65441-6(7))*; *(978-2-213-64300-7(8))* Fayard, Artheme, Librairie.

—Demeures de L'esprit: France I Sud-Ouest. 2008. (FRE., Illus.). *(978-2-213-63584-2(6))* Fayard, Artheme, Librairie.

Carrick, Jill. Nouveau Réalisme, 1960s France, & the Neo-Avant-Garde: Topographies of Chance & Return. 2010. (Illus.). 184p. 104.95 *(978-0-7546-6141-2(5))* Ashgate Publishing Co.

Chernow, Burt. Christo & Jeanne-Claude. Date not set. pap. *(978-0-312-30251-1(7)*, St. Martin's Griffin) St. Martin's Pr.

Chéroux, Clément. Discoveries: Henri Cartier-Bresson. 2008. (ENG., Illus.). 144p. pap. 14.95 *(978-0-8109-9826-1(2))* Abrams.

Cloarec, Françoise. Storr: Architecte de L'ailleurs. 2010. (FRE., Illus.). 170p. *(978-2-7529-0485-0(1))* Phebus, Editions.

Cooper Ed Mae. Starck. 2010. (25 Ser.). (GER, FRE & ENG., Illus.). 352p. 14.99 *(978-3-8365-2108-6(3))* TASCHEN DEU. Dist: Ingram Pub. Services.

Courbet, Gustave. Courbet: A Dream of Modern Art. 2011. (ENG., Illus.). 304p. 60.00 *(978-3-7757-2629-0(2))* Hatje Cantz Verlag GmbH & Co KG DEU. Dist: D.A.P./Distributed Art Pubs.

Cowling, E., et al. Picasso: Challenging the Past. 2011. (Illus.). 176p. pap. 25.00 *(978-1-85709-451-0(4))* Yale Univ. Pr.

Dagen, Philippe, ed. Lamento. 2008. 272p. *(978-2-919923-50-2(1))* Actar Birkhauser Distribution.

Delsaux, Cedric, photos by. Murakami Versailles. 2011. (ENG., Illus.). 256p. 85.00 *(978-2-915173-72-7(9))* Barral, Xavier Editions FRA. Dist: D.A.P./Distributed Art Pubs.

Deneuve, Catherine. The Private Diaries of Catherine Deneuve: My Life Behind the Camera with Luis Bunuel, Francois Truffaut, Roman Polanski, & Lars Von Trier. 2008. (ENG.). 240p. pap. 14.95 *(978-1-60598-019-5(6)*, 605019) Pegasus Bks.

Depardon, Raymond, photos by. Manhattan Out, 1 vol. 2009. (ENG., Illus.). 120p. 49.50 *(978-3-86521-704-2(4))* Steidl, Gerhard Druckerei und Verlag DEU. Dist: Innovative Logistics.

Diepois, Aline & Gizolme, Thomas, photos by. Dust Book, 1 vol. 2009. (ENG., Illus.). 104p. 49.00 *(978-3-86521-818-6(0))* Steidl, Gerhard Druckerei und Verlag DEU. Dist: Innovative Logistics.

Doisneau, Robert. Doisneau: Portraits of the Artists. 2008. (ENG., Illus.). 192p. 65.00 *(978-2-08-030064-5(4))* Flammarion et Cie FRA. Dist: Random Hse., Inc.

Doriéac, Laurence Bertrand, et al. Art of the Defeat: France, 1940-1944. Todd, Jane Marie, tr. from FRE. 2009. (ENG., Illus.). 416p. 45.00 *(978-0-89236-891-4(8))* Oxford Univ. Pr., Inc.

Doucet, Jacques. Jacques Doucet: Le CoBrA Français. 2010. (FRE, DUT & ENG., Illus.). 191p. *(978-2-35733-111-2(9))* Archibooks.

Doy, Gen. Claude Cahun: A Sensual Politics of Photography. 2008. (ENG., Illus.). 232p. pap. 29.00 *(978-1-84511-551-7(1))* I. B. Tauris & Co., Ltd. GBR. Dist: Macmillan.

Erwitt, Elliott, photos by. Personal Best. 2010. (Illus.). 448p. pap. 55.00 *(978-3-8327-9383-8(6))* teNeues Publishing Co.

Feibinger, Udo. Henri de Toulouse-Lautrec: Life & Work. 2008. (Art in Focus (Konemann) Ser.). (Illus.). 95p. pap. 5.95 *(978-0-8416-0056-0(2))* American Map Corp.

Folberg, Neil & Arison, Lin. Travels with Van Gogh & the Impressionists: Discovering the Connections. 2007. (ENG., Illus.). 284p. 45.00 *(978-0-7892-0932-0(2))* Abbeville Pr., Inc.

Goude, Jean-Paul. Jean-Paul Goude. 2012. (ENG., Illus.). 432p. pap. 49.95 ***(978-0-500-51604-1(9)***, 551604) Thames & Hudson.

He, Jianping, ed. The Master of Design: Pierre Bernard. 2007. (Master of Design Ser.). (Illus.). 309p. pap. 39.95 *(978-981-245-427-0(6))* Page One Publishing SGP. Dist: Gingko Pr., Inc.

Hoffmann, Felix, et al. Jerry Berndt: Insight, 1 vol. Hoffmann, Felix, ed. Schluter, Maik, ed. & text by. 2009. (GER & ENG., Illus.). 248p. 50.00 *(978-3-86521-725-7(7))* Steidl, Gerhard Druckerei und Verlag DEU. Dist: Innovative Logistics.

Hussein-Arco, Agnes, ed. Lovis Corinth: A Feast of Painting. 2010. (Illus.). 144p. 29.95 *(978-3-7913-4378-5(5))* Prestel Publishing.

Impressions: And claude monet: giverny & the north of france: americans in France, 1860-1930. 2007. per. 25.00 *(978-0-9773018-5-0(0))* Naples Museum of Art.

Kasmin, Paul, ed. Claude & Francois-Xavier Lalanne: Art. Work. Life. 2012. (ENG., Illus.). 240p. 60.00 ***(978-0-8478-3761-8(0)***, Skira) Rizzoli International Pubns., Inc.

Katz, Robert & Dars, Celestine. The Impressionists: A Comprehensive Visual Reference to One of the Best-Loved Periods of Art History, with over 450 Images. 2012. (ENG., Illus.). 352p. 30.00 ***(978-0-7548-2402-2(0))*** Anness Publishing GBR. Dist: National Bk. Network.

Leabhart, Thomas. The Decroux Sourcebook. Chamberlain, Franc, ed. 2009. (ENG., Illus.). 210p. pap. 34.95 *(978-0-415-47800-7(6))* Routledge.

Leclerc, Franck. L'école de Nice: Paroles D'artistes. 2010. (Illus.). 429p. *(978-2-916954-57-8(0)*, Spotlight Poets) Verlhac Editions.

Levy, Aaron & Dimitrijevic, Braco. Tractatus Post-Historicus (1976) Braco Dimitrijevic. 2009. pap. *(978-0-9815409-5-5(3))* Slought Foundation.

Lissoni, Piero. Piero Lissoni. 2011. (ENG., Illus.). 224p. 75.00 *(978-3-7757-2462-3(1))* Hatje Cantz Verlag GmbH & Co KG DEU. Dist: D.A.P./Distributed Art Pubs.

Machotka, Pavel. On Site with P. Cezanne in Provence. 2008. 144p. *(978-2-7537-0043-7(5))* Editions Crès.

Malaskauskas, Raimundas. Loris Greaud. 2008. (ENG., Illus.). 80p. pap. 15.00 *(978-3-905829-50-1(9))* JRP Ringier Kunstverlag AG CHE. Dist: D.A.P./Distributed Art Pubs.

Mansfield, Elizabeth C. The Perfect Foil: FranCois-Andre Vincent & the Revolution in French Painting. 2011. (ENG., Illus.). 320p. 105.00 ***(978-0-8166-7580-7(5))***; pap. 35.00 ***(978-0-8166-7581-4(3))*** Univ. of Minnesota Pr.

Martorelli, Barbara. George Barbier: The Birth of Art Deco. 2009. (ENG.). 176p. 50.00 *(978-88-317-9646-0(1))* Marsilio Editori spa ITA. Dist: Random Hse., Inc.

Mathews, Nancy Mowll & Cantor, Jay E. Mary Cassatt: Friends & Family. 2008. pap. *(978-0-939384-34-1(5))* Shelburne Museum, Inc.

Matton, Sylvie. Charles Matton: Enclosures. 2011. (ENG., Illus.). 256p. 85.00 *(978-2-08-020087-7(9))* Flammarion et Cie FRA. Dist: Random Hse., Inc.

McCullough, David. The Greater Journey: Americans in Paris. (ENG., Illus.). 576p. 2012. pap. 20.00 ***(978-1-4165-7177-3(9))*** 2011. 37.50 *(978-1-4165-7176-6(0))* Simon & Schuster.

—The Greater Journey: Americans in Paris. l.t. ed. 2011. (Illus.). 861p. 35.99 *(978-1-4104-3820-1(1))* Thorndike Pr.

McPhee, Laura. A Journey into Matisse's South of France. 2006. (ArtPlace Ser.). (ENG., Illus.). 180p. pap. 21.95 *(978-0-9766706-9-8(0))* Roaring Forties Pr.

Meunier, Sébastien. Visual Pollution, 1 vol. 2010. (ENG., Illus.). 192p. 78.00 *(978-3-86521-093-7(7))* Steidl, Gerhard Druckerei und Verlag DEU. Dist: Innovative Logistics.

Miller, Catherine, et al, texts. Tatiana Trouve. 2008. (ENG., Illus.). 244p. 85.00 *(978-3-86560-352-4(1))* Verlag der Buchhandlung Walther Konig DEU. Dist: D.A.P./Distributed Art Pubs.

Morgan, James. Chasing Matisse: A Year in France Living My Dream. 2009. (ENG.). 288p. pap. 19.95 *(978-1-4391-6724-3(9)*, Free Pr.) Free Pr.

Morgan, Jessica, ed. TH 2058 - Dominique Gonzalez-Foerster. 2009. (ENG., Illus.). 224p. 29.95 *(978-1-85437-739-5(6))* Tate Publishing, Ltd. GBR. Dist: Hachette Bk. Group.

Napp, Antonia & Röder, Kornelia, eds. Impuls Marcel Duchamp: Where do we go from here? 2011. (ENG & GER., Illus.). 208p. pap. 30.00 ***(978-3-7757-3182-9(2))*** Hatje Cantz Verlag GmbH & Co KG DEU. Dist: D.A.P./Distributed Art Pubs.

Neginsky, Rosina. Sergei Chepik: Between East & West. 2009. pap. *(978-1-61623-618-2(3))* Independent Pub.

Olivar, Jacques, photos by. Forever Young. 2012. (ENG, GER, FRE, SPA & ITA., Illus.). 128p. 85.00 ***(978-3-8327-9603-7(7))*** teNeues Publishing Co.

Poirier, Anne & Poirier, Patrick, illus. Anne e Patrick Poirier, 1 vol. 2007. (ITA & ENG.). 102p. pap. 30.00 *(978-88-89431-99-3(7))* Damiani ITA. Dist: D.A.P./Distributed Art Pubs.

A

Preaud, Maxime & Lazin, Lauren. Erik Desmazieres Imaginary Places. 2008. (ENG., Illus.). 128p. 39.95 *(978-88-7439-411-1(X))* 5 Continents ITA. Dist: Hachette Bk. Group.

Prodger, Phillip & Roscoe, Lynda. Man Ray Lee Miller: Partners in Surrealism. 2011. (ENG., Illus.). 160p. pap. 39.95 *(978-1-85894-557-6(7))* Merrell Pubs. Ltd. GBR. Dist: Perseus Distribution.

Richardson, John. A Life of Picasso: The Cubist Rebel, 1907-1916. 2007. (Borzoi Bks.). (ENG., Illus.). 512p. pap. 32.50 *(978-0-375-71150-3(3)*, Knopf) Knopf Doubleday Publishing Group.

—A Life of Picasso: The Prodigy, 1881-1906. 2007. (Borzoi Bks.). (ENG., Illus.). 560p. pap. 30.00 *(978-0-375-71149-7(X)*, Knopf) Knopf Doubleday Publishing Group.

—A Life of Picasso: The Triumphant Years, 1917-1932. 2010. (Illus.). 608p. pap. 30.00 *(978-0-375-71151-0(1)*, Knopf) Knopf Doubleday Publishing Group.

Richter Verlag Publishing, creator. Hans Arp: Die Natur der Dinge, 1 vol. 2008. (ENG., Illus.). 236p. 95.00 *(978-3-937572-74-1(0))* Richter Verlag DEU. Dist: D.A.P./Distributed Art Pubs.

Ristelhueber, Sophie. Sophie Ristelhueber: Fait. 2009. (ENG., Illus.). 96p. 39.95 *(978-1-935004-04-2(2))* Errata Editions.

Savides, Nick. Nick Savides: New York/Paris. 2009. (Illus.). 28p. pap. 10.00 *(978-0-9747030-6-0(0))* Nabi Pr.

Savignon, Jeromine. Jean-Louis Scherrer. 2007. (ENG., Illus.). 79p. 25.00 *(978-2-7594-0143-7(X))* Assouline FRA. Dist: Perseus Distribution.

Sbriglio, Jacques. Le Corbusier & Lucien Herve: A Dialogue Between Architect & Photographer. 2011. (ENG.). 296p. 74.95 *(978-1-60606-088-9(0)*, J. Paul Getty Museum) Getty Pubns.

Schmitt, Anne-Florence. Karl Lagerfeld: Trait par Trait, 1 vol. 2011. (ENG., Illus.). 144p. pap. 25.00 *(978-3-86521-552-9(1))* Steidl, Gerhard Druckerei und Verlag DEU. Dist: Innovative Logistics.

Siriex, Francoise & Siriex, Françoise. The House of Leleu: Classic French Style for a Modern World, 1920-1973. 2008. (ENG., Illus.). 480p. 160.00 *(978-1-55595-286-0(0))* Hudson Hills Pr. LLC.

Sirrulaz, Arlette. Gerard, Girodet, Gros: David's Studio. 2008. (Drawing Gallery Ser.). (ENG., Illus.). 92p. pap. 19.95 *(978-88-7439-253-7(2))* 5 Continents ITA. Dist: Hachette Bk. Group.

Sparth, illus. Structura: The Art of Sparth. 2008. (ENG.). 127p. pap. 24.95 *(978-1-933492-25-4(2))* Design Studio Pr.

Sparth & Sparth. Structura: The Art of Sparth. 2008. (ENG., Illus.). 127p. 34.95 *(978-1-933492-26-1(0))* Design Studio Pr.

Spence, David. Cezanne. 2009. (Ticktock Essential Artists Ser.). (ENG.). 32p. (J). (gr. 4-7). pap. 6.95 *(978-1-84696-970-6(0))* TickTock Bks. GBR. Dist: Independent Pubs. Group.

—Degas. 2009. (Ticktock Essential Artists Ser.). (ENG.). 32p. (J). (gr. 4-7). pap. 6.95 *(978-1-84696-975-1(1))* TickTock Bks. GBR. Dist: Independent Pubs. Group.

—Gauguin. 2009. (Ticktock Essential Artists Ser.). (ENG.). 32p. (J). (gr. 4-7). pap. 6.95 *(978-1-84696-971-3(9))* TickTock Bks. GBR. Dist: Independent Pubs. Group.

Szekely, Martin. Martin Szekely. 2010. (ENG & FRE., Illus.). 252p. 90.00 *(978-3-03764-098-2(7))* JRP Ringier Kunstverlag AG CHE. Dist: D.A.P./Distributed Art Pubs.

Taylor, Michael & Chagall, Marc. Paris Through the Window: Marc Chagall & His Circle. 2010. *(978-0-87633-230-6(0))* Philadelphia Museum of Art.

Todd, Pamela. The Impressionists at Leisure. 2007. (ENG., Illus.). 176p. 40.00 *(978-0-500-23839-4(1))* Thames & Hudson.

Weidemann, Christiane. Niki de Saint Phalle. 2010. (Illus.). 128p. pap. 14.95 *(978-3-7913-4334-1(3))* Prestel Publishing.

Wettlaufer, Alexandra. Portraits of the Artist as a Young Woman: Painting & the Novel in France & Britain, 1800-1860. 2011. cd-rom 14.95 *(978-0-8142-9244-0(5))* Ohio State Univ. Pr.

—Portraits of the Artist as a Young Woman: Painting & the Novel in France & Britain, 1800-1860. 2011. 368p. 59.95 *(978-0-8142-1145-8(3))* Ohio State Univ. Pr.

Whiteley, Jon & Sonnabend, Martin. Claude Lorrain (C. 1604 - 1682) An Exhibition of Prints, Drawings & Paintings. 2011. (ENG., Illus.). 200p. pap. 45.00 *(978-1-85444-260-4(0))* Ashmolean Museum GBR. Dist: National Bk. Network.

Wolff, Laetitia. Massin. 2007. (ENG., Illus.). 216p. 75.00 *(978-0-7148-4811-2(5))* Phaidon Pr., Inc.

YGREC. Kung Fu Panda et la puissance du Croire. 2009. 56p. pap. 16.50 *(978-1-4092-7602-9(3))* Lulu Enterprises Inc.

ARTISTS—GERMANY

Adriani, Gotz. Minimal Art. (GER., Illus.). 110p. *(978-3-7757-9075-8(6))* Hatje Cantz Verlag GmbH & Co KG DEU. Dist: D.A.P./Distributed Art Pubs.

Albus, Volker. Werner Aisslinger. Fast Forward: Einleitung von Volker Albus. 2010. (GER & ENG., Illus.). 180p. 54.00 *(978-3-89986-139-6(6)*, Avedition Gmbh,Csi) Continental Sales, Inc.

Alioth, Max. Susanna Biedermann: Learning to Look. 2011. (ARA, FRE, GER & ENG., Illus.). 448p. 98.00 *(978-2-86770-198-6(8))* ACR Edition FRA. Dist: Antique Collectors' Club.

Allen, Jennifer, et al, texts. Nina Fischer & Maroan el Sani: Blind Spots. 2008. (ENG., Illus.). 200p. pap. 25.00 *(978-3-905829-18-1(5))* JRP Ringier Kunstverlag AG CHE. Dist: D.A.P./Distributed Art Pubs.

Ammann, Helmut. Werktagebücher Eines Bildhauers und Malers. 2007. (Illus.). *(978-3-937200-39-2(8))*; (GER., *(978-3-937200-57-6(6))*; *(978-3-937200-40-8(1))* Gerig, Hans, Musikverlage.

Anklam, Axel. Axel Anklam: Die Bereitschaft Zu Glauben = the Readiness to Believe. 2009. (GER & ENG., Illus.). 76p. 35.00 *(978-3-86678-152-8(0))* Kerber Verlag DEU. Dist: D.A.P./Distributed Art Pubs.

Artinger, Kai. Paula Modersohn-Becker: Der andere Blick. 2009. (GER., Illus.). 160p. pap. *(978-3-7861-2596-9(1))* Gebruder Mann Verlag.

Assouline, ed. Provoking Magic: Lighting of Ingo Maurer. 2007. (ENG., Illus.). 160p. pap. *(978-0-910503-94-5(X))* Assouline FRA. Dist: Perseus Distribution.

Backhaus, Jessica, photos by. What Still Remains. 2009. (ENG., Illus.). 96p. 68.00 *(978-3-86828-019-7(7))* Kehrer Verlag Heidelberg, Klaus Kehrer DEU. Dist: Consortium Bk. Sales & Distribution.

Barzel, Amnon. Hans Hartung. 2007. (FRE & ENG., Illus.). 296p. *(978-88-7439-395-4(4))* 5 Continents.

Baselitz, Georg. Georg Baselitz: Works from the 1960s And 1970s, 1 vol. 2007. (ENG., Illus.). 60.00 *(978-1-934171-00-4(X))* Thread Waxing Space.

Bast, Gerald. Josip Kaiser: Segmente / Segments. 2009. (GER & ENG., Illus.). 224p. pap. 49.95 *(978-3-211-85751-9(6))* Springer Wien AUT. Dist: Actar Birkhauser Distribution.

Baumhauer, Till Ansgar, ed. Till Ansgar Baumhauer: Stranger Sampling. 2010. (ENG., Illus.). 120p. 45.00 *(978-3-86678-271-6(3))* Kerber Verlag DEU. Dist: D.A.P./Distributed Art Pubs.

Becker, Katja M. & Podobinski, Stephanie. Graphic Design: Next Generation. 2009. (Illus.). 624p. *(978-981-245-652-6(X))* Page One Publishing.

Benjamin, Walter. Archive: Images, Texts, Signs. Marx, Ursula et al, eds. Leslie, Esther, tr. from GER. 2007. (ENG., Illus.). 311p. 27.95 *(978-1-84467-196-0(8)*, 844196) Verso Bks. GBR. Dist: Norton, W. W. & Co., Inc.

Beutin, Heidi & Beutin, Wolfgang, eds. Ernst Barlach (1870-1938) Sein Leben, sein Schaffen, seine Verfolgung in der NS-Diktatur. 2009. (Bremer Beiträge zur Literatur- und Ideengeschichte Ser.). (GER.). 298p. pap. 64.95 *(978-3-631-58817-8(8))* Lang, Peter GmbH, Europaischer Verlag der Wissenschaften DEU. Dist: Lang, Peter.

Beuys, Joseph. Joseph Beuys: The Border to Eurasia. (Illus.). 35.00 *(978-4-900398-15-3(2))* Watari-Um JPN. Dist: D.A.P./Distributed Art Pubs.

Bitterli, Konrad. Karin Sander. (ENG & GER.). 80p. 29.95 *(978-3-89322-891-1(8))* Edition Cantz DEU. Dist: D.A.P./Distributed Art Pubs.

Blume, Anna, et al. Anna & Bernhard Blume. SX-70. Polaroids / Polaroid-Collages 1975-2000. 2011. (GER, FRE & ENG., Illus.). 160p. 60.00 *(978-3-86560-821-5(3))* Verlag der Buchhandlung Walther Konig DEU. Dist: D.A.P./Distributed Art Pubs.

Bohl, Henning. Henning Bohl: Kunstverein Braunschweig E.V. Kunstverein Für Die Rheinlande und Westfalen Düsseldorf, 1 vol. 2006. (GER & ENG., Illus.). 56p. pap. 20.00 *(978-3-86560-012-7(3))* Verlag der Buchhandlung Walther Konig DEU. Dist: D.A.P./Distributed Art Pubs.

Bohnenstengel, Christian. Max Reger's Telemann Variations, Op 134. 2008. 136p. pap. *(978-3-639-07835-0(7))* VDM Verlag Dr. Mueller e.K.

Bott, Karsten. Karsten Bott: One of Each. 2007. (ENG., Illus.). 288p. 49.95 *(978-3-86560-307-4(6))* Verlag der Buchhandlung Walther Konig DEU. Dist: D.A.P./Distributed Art Pubs.

Bredekamp, Horst. Stephan von Huene: Dancing on Tables. (Illus.). 72p. pap. *(978-3-89322-299-5(5))* Edition Cantz DEU. Dist: D.A.P./Distributed Art Pubs.

Brinkmann, Bodo, text. Konrad Witz. 2011. (ENG., Illus.). 320p. 85.00 *(978-3-7757-2761-7(2))* Hatje Cantz Verlag GmbH & Co KG DEU. Dist: D.A.P./Distributed Art Pubs.

Brohm, Joachim, photos by. Ohio, 1 vol. 2010. (GER & ENG., Illus.). 120p. 59.95 *(978-3-86521-698-4(6))* Steidl, Gerhard Druckerei und Verlag DEU. Dist: Innovative Logistics.

Bryson, Norman & Spies, Werner, texts. Andreas Gursky. 2010. (ENG., Illus.). 110p. 120.00 *(978-0-8478-3643-7(6))* Rizzoli International Pubns., Inc.

Buchhart, Dieter & Knack, Hartwig, eds. Otto Dix: Zwischen Paradies und Untergang. 2009. (Illus.). 128p. (C). 36.00 *(978-3-7774-2021-9(2))* Hirmer Verlag GmbH DEU. Dist: Brown, David Bk. Co., The.

Buscher, Wolfgang, et al. Neo Rauch. Holzwarth, Hans Weiner, ed. 2010. (GER, FRE & ENG., Illus.). 476p. 1500.00 *(978-3-8228-0872-6(5))* TASCHEN DEU. Dist: Ingram Pub. Services.

Bussmann, Klaus, ed. Hans Haacke. (ENG & GER., Illus.). 140p. pap. 29.95 *(978-3-89322-572-9(2))* Edition Cantz DEU. Dist: D.A.P./Distributed Art Pubs.

Cabanas, Kaira, ed. Seven Sounds, Seven Circles. 2009. (ENG., Illus.). 168p. pap. 60.00 *(978-3-86560-537-5(0))* Kunsthaus Bregenz AUT. Dist: D.A.P./Distributed Art Pubs.

Campens, Angelique, et al, intros. Based in Berlin. 2011. (ENG., Illus.). 200p. pap. 22.95 ***(978-3-86335-045-1(6))*** Verlag der Buchhandlung Walther Konig DEU. Dist: D.A.P./Distributed Art Pubs.

Creischer, Alice, ed. Alice Creischer. 2008. 144p. pap. *(978-84-89771-56-7(1))* Actar Birkhauser Distribution.

Ctink, illus. A/React. 2007. (ENG.). 96p. pap. 29.00 *(978-88-88493-18-3(2))* Drago Arts & Communication ITA. Dist: SCB Distributors.

de Werd, Guido, et al, texts. With a Probability of Being Seen. 2010. (ENG & GER., Illus.). 320p. 95.00 *(978-3-941263-13-0(7))* Richter Verlag DEU. Dist: D.A.P./Distributed Art Pubs.

Demand, Thomas & Obrist, Hans Ulrich, texts. Thomas Demand, 1 vol. 2007. (GER & ENG., Illus.). 174p. per. 25.00 *(978-3-86560-204-6(5))* Verlag der Buchhandlung Walther Konig DEU. Dist: D.A.P./Distributed Art Pubs.

Deshmukh, Marion F., et al, eds. Max Liebermann & International Modernism: An Artist's Career from Empire to Third Reich. 2011. (SGH Ser.). (Illus.). 332p. 39.95 *(978-1-84545-662-7(9))* Berghahn Bks., Inc.

Dichter, Claudia, ed. Horst Ademeit: Secret Universe. 2011. (ENG., Illus.). 112p. pap. 44.95 ***(978-3-86560-997-7(X))*** Verlag der Buchhandlung Walther Konig DEU. Dist: D.A.P./Distributed Art Pubs.

Doms, Annette, ed. S'nim Oh: Wishes. 2009. (ENG., Illus.). 118p. 48.00 *(978-3-86678-134-4(2))* Kerber Verlag DEU. Dist: D.A.P./Distributed Art Pubs.

Drathen, Doris von. Cosmic Maps. 2008. (ENG., Illus.). 128p. 69.95 *(978-88-8158-685-1(1))* Charta ITA. Dist: D.A.P./Distributed Art Pubs.

Dylla, Sabine. Karin Sander. (Illus.). 48p. 196.95 *(978-3-89322-619-1(2))* Edition Cantz DEU. Dist: D.A.P./Distributed Art Pubs.

Eckel, Michael, ed. Martin Liebscher Imprint. 2010. (ENG., Illus.). 80p. 450.00 *(978-3-7757-2251-3(3))* Hatje Cantz Verlag GmbH & Co KG DEU. Dist: D.A.P./Distributed Art Pubs.

Ehling, Thekla. Thekla Ehling: Sommerherz. 2009. (GER & ENG., Illus.). 72p. 78.00 *(978-3-86828-035-7(9))* Kehrer Verlag Heidelberg, Klaus Kehrer DEU. Dist: Consortium Bk. Sales & Distribution.

Elger, Dietmar. Hanne Darboven: Evolution Leibniz. (GER & ENG., Illus.). 240p. 39.95 *(978-3-89322-845-4(4))* Edition Cantz DEU. Dist: D.A.P./Distributed Art Pubs.

Ernst, Max. Max Ernst. 2006. 400p. 400.00 *(978-0-9712051-8-5(3))* Cocytus Pr.

Essl, Karlheinz, et al. Neo Rauch & Rosa Loy: Hinter den Gärten: Behind the Gardens. 2011. (ENG., Illus.). 160p. 49.95 ***(978-3-7913-5142-1(7))*** Prestel Publishing.

Evans, Cerith Wyn. Parkett No. 87: Cerith Wyn Evans, Katarina Fritsch, Annette Kelm, Kelly Walker. 2010. (ENG., Illus.). 300p. pap. 32.00 *(978-3-907582-47-3(0))* Parkett Verlag AG CHE. Dist: D.A.P./Distributed Art Pubs.

Feldmann, Hans-Peter, photos by. Foto: Hans-Peter Feldmann, 1 vol. 2007. (ENG., Illus.). 48p. pap. 25.00 *(978-80-902816-3-9(X))* Verlag der Buchhandlung Walther Konig DEU. Dist: D.A.P./Distributed Art Pubs.

Fischer, Volker, et al, contrib. by. Gunter Rambow Plakate. 2007. (GER & ENG., Illus.). 176p. 79.00 *(978-3-936681-19-2(8))* Edition Axel Menges GmbH DEU. Dist: National Bk. Network.

Flügge, Matthias. Mark Lammert: Paintings 1997-2010. 2011. (ENG., Illus.). 156p. 45.00 ***(978-3-941263-26-0(9))*** Richter Verlag DEU. Dist: D.A.P./Distributed Art Pubs.

Foos, Peter & van den Valentyn, Heike, texts. Stefan Loffelhardt. 2008. (ENG., Illus.). 88p. 54.00 *(978-3-86560-433-0(1))* Verlag der Buchhandlung Walther Konig DEU. Dist: D.A.P./Distributed Art Pubs.

Förg, Günther. Günther Förg: Watercolours: Aquarelle: Kunstverein Wilhelmshöhe Ettlingen. 2007. (Illus.). 142p. *(978-3-936859-52-2(3))* Snoeck-Ducaju en Zoon, N.V.

Forrest, Tara & Scheer, Anna Teresa, eds. Christoph Schlingensief: Art without Borders. 2010. (Illus.). 176p. pap. 35.00 *(978-1-84150-319-6(3))* Intellect, Ltd. GBR. Dist: Chicago Distribution Ctr.

Friedrich, Julia & Konig, Kaspar, frwds. Tomas Schmit: Are Humans Capable of Thought?, 1 vol. 2007. (ENG., Illus.). 72p. pap. 16.00 *(978-3-86560-264-0(9))* Verlag der Buchhandlung Walther Konig DEU. Dist: D.A.P./Distributed Art Pubs.

Friese, Peter, ed. Jochen Gerz: The Bremen Questionnaire Sine Somno Nihil, 1990-1995. (ENG & GER., Illus.). 144p. 29.95 *(978-3-89322-788-4(1))* Edition Cantz DEU. Dist: D.A.P./Distributed Art Pubs.

Frischkorn, Holger, et al. Atelier Goldstein Künstler. Schirrmacher, Gabi & Salzer, Christian, eds. 2008. (ENG & GER., Illus.). 240p. pap. 55.00 *(978-3-936314-89-2(6))* Jovis Verlag GmbH DEU. Dist: D.A.P./Distributed Art Pubs.

Fuhrmeister, C. American Artists in Munich: Artistic Migration & Cultural Exchange Processes. 2010. (ENG.). 272p. pap. 59.00 *(978-3-422-06833-9(3)*, Art Stock Bks. Ltd/Csi) Continental Sales, Inc.

Gaillard, Cyprien, et al. Cyprien Gaillard: Geographical Analogies. 2011. (ENG., Illus.). 224p. 90.00 *(978-3-03764-148-4(7))* JRP Ringier Kunstverlag AG CHE. Dist: D.A.P./Distributed Art Pubs.

Gefeller, Andreas. Andreas Gefeller: Photographs. 2010. (ENG & GER., Illus.). 130p. 60.00 *(978-3-7757-2446-3(X))* Hatje Cantz Verlag GmbH & Co KG DEU. Dist: D.A.P./Distributed Art Pubs.

Genzken, Isa. Oil: German Pavilion, Venice 2007. Schafhausen, Nicolaus, ed. 2010. (ITA & ENG., Illus.). 212p. 59.95 *(978-3-8321-7797-3(3))* DuMont DEU. Dist: D.A.P./Distributed Art Pubs.

Gioni, Massimiliano & Carrion-Murayari, Gary, eds. Gustav Metzger: Historic Photographs. 2011. (ENG., Illus.). 71p. pap. 14.95 ***(978-0-915557-94-3(0))*** New Museum of Contemporary Art, The.

Goetz, Ingvild & Löckemann, Karsten, eds. Mens Agitat Molem. 2010. (ENG., Illus.). 152p. 45.00 *(978-3-939894-12-4(5))* Goetz, Ingvild, Kunstverlag, GmbH DEU. Dist: D.A.P./Distributed Art Pubs.

Graham. Aura Rosenberg: Who am I?, What am I?, Where am I? 2009. (ENG., Illus.). 200p. 60.00 *(978-3-7757-2255-1(6))* Hatje Cantz Verlag GmbH & Co KG DEU. Dist: D.A.P./Distributed Art Pubs.

Hahn, Siegfried. Sigfried Hahn, My Life as Artist & Teacher. 2008. 141p. pap. 19.95 *(978-0-9801270-4-1(1))* Seven Locks Pr.

Harder. Thorsten Brinkmann. 2008. (ENG., Illus.). 168p. 55.00 *(978-3-7757-2205-6(X))* Hatje Cantz Verlag GmbH & Co KG DEU. Dist: D.A.P./Distributed Art Pubs.

Hatoum, Mona. Mona Hatoum: Unhomely. 2009. (ENG., Illus.). 104p. 50.00 *(978-3-935567-46-6(4))* Holzwarth Pubns. DEU. Dist: D.A.P./Distributed Art Pubs.

Heidemann, Christine, text. Susanne Pomrehn: Kollektive Formationen: Installative Raumkörper und Fotoschnitte 2004-2008. 2010. (ENG., Illus.). 112p. pap. 30.00 *(978-3-86678-324-9(8))* Kerber Verlag DEU. Dist: D.A.P./Distributed Art Pubs.

Heise, Bernd, ed. Sibylle Bergemann: Die Polaroids. 2011. (ENG., Illus.). 200p. 45.00 ***(978-3-7757-2843-0(0))*** Hatje Cantz Verlag GmbH & Co KG DEU. Dist: D.A.P./Distributed Art Pubs.

Heiss, Alanna, et al, texts. Federico Diaz & E Area: Resonance, 1 vol. 2009. (ENG., Illus.). 500p. 95.00 *(978-88-8158-721-6(1))* Charta ITA. Dist: D.A.P./Distributed Art Pubs.

Hempel, Lothar, illus. Alphabet City, 1 vol. 2007. (ENG.). 160p. pap. 45.00 *(978-3-905770-47-6(4))* JRP Ringier Kunstverlag AG CHE. Dist: D.A.P./Distributed Art Pubs.

Hentschel, Martin, ed. Andreas Gursky: Werke 80-08. 2011. (ENG., Illus.). 272p. 60.00 ***(978-3-7757-3022-8(2))*** Hatje Cantz Verlag GmbH & Co KG DEU. Dist: D.A.P./Distributed Art Pubs.

Hentschel, Martin, ed. Herbert Hamak. (ENG & GER., Illus.). 182p. 39.95 *(978-3-89322-850-8(0))* Edition Cantz DEU. Dist: D.A.P./Distributed Art Pubs.

Herold, Georg. Georg Herold. Sunny Side Up. 2011. (ENG., Illus.). 68p. 35.00 ***(978-3-931355-69-2(1))*** Verlag der Buchhandlung Walther Konig DEU. Dist: D.A.P./Distributed Art Pubs.

Higgins, Ross. Peter Flinsch: The Body in Question. 2008. (ENG., Illus.). 192p. pap. 27.95 *(978-1-55152-237-1(3))* Arsenal Pulp Pr. CAN. Dist: Consortium Bk. Sales & Distribution.

Hillenbrand, Rainer, ed. Halbzahm in einer Lumpenwelt: Briefe von und an Franz Freiherrn Gaudy. 345p. 43.95 *(978-3-631-39466-3(7))* Lang, Peter Publishing, Inc.

Hoffmann, Leni. leni hoffmann: RGB: Künstlerbuch. 2010. (GER & ENG., Illus.). 144p. pap. 59.95 *(978-3-8321-9290-7(5))* DuMont DEU. Dist: D.A.P./Distributed Art Pubs.

Holleczek, Andreas. Jean-Etienne Liotard: Erkenntnisvermogen und Kunstlerischer Anspruch. (Europaische Hochschulschriften Ser.). (GER., Illus.). 260p. 35.95 *(978-3-631-38919-5(1))* Lang, Peter Publishing, Inc.

Huber, Thomas. Thomas Huber: Sad Facets (Sketch Book) 2009. (ENG., Illus.). 128p. 65.00 *(978-3-86678-145-0(8))* Kerber Verlag DEU. Dist: D.A.P./Distributed Art Pubs.

Illenberger, Sarah. Sarah Illenberger. 2011. (ENG., Illus.). 128p. 30.00 ***(978-3-89955-385-7(3))*** Die Gestalten Verlag DEU. Dist: Prestel Publishing.

Der (Im) Perfekte Mensch: Vom Recht auf Unvollkommenheit. (GER.). *(978-3-7757-0997-2(5))* Hatje Cantz Verlag GmbH & Co KG DEU. Dist: D.A.P./Distributed Art Pubs.

Institut Fur Moderne Kunst Numberg, ed. Britta Lumer: Where Happiness Lives. 2008. (ENG., Illus.). 96p. 50.00 *(978-3-939738-92-3(1))* Verlag fur Moderne Kunst DEU. Dist: D.A.P./Distributed Art Pubs.

Jensen, Sergej, et al. Sergej Jensen, 1 vol. 2011. (ENG & GER., Illus.). 300p. pap. 60.00 *(978-3-942405-06-5(7))* Die Gestalten Verlag DEU. Dist: Prestel Publishing.

Jentsch, Ralph. George Grosz: Berlin-New York. 2008. (ENG., Illus.). 288p. 80.00 *(978-88-6130-294-5(7))* Skira Editore ITA. Dist: Random Hse., Inc.

Jonathan Monk: the Complete Ilford Works. 2008. (Illus.). 440p. 150.00 *(978-3-905829-63-1(0))* JRP Ringier Kunstverlag AG CHE. Dist: D.A.P./Distributed Art Pubs.

Joseph Beuys, Marcel Broodthaers, Robert Rauschenberg, Andy Warhol. pap. 15.00 *(978-2-903004-03-3(X))* Galerie Isy Brachot FRA. Dist: D.A.P./Distributed Art Pubs.

K#xF6;hler, Thomas, pref. Susanne Kriemann. 2011. (ENG., Illus.). 96p. 45.00 ***(978-3-86678-466-6(X))*** Kerber Verlag DEU. Dist: D.A.P./Distributed Art Pubs.

Karstie, Markus & Freudenberger, Christian, contrib. by. Schatten und Wesen: 9 Ausstellungen im Kunstverein Schwerte. 2011. (ENG., Illus.). 120p. pap. 49.95 ***(978-3-86678-486-4(4))*** Kerber Verlag DEU. Dist: D.A.P./Distributed Art Pubs.

Kater, Michael H. Never Sang for Hitler: The Life & Times of Lotte Lehmann, 1888-1976. 2008. (ENG., Illus.). 416p. 38.00 *(978-0-521-87392-5(4))* Cambridge Univ. Pr.

Katz, Benjamin, photos by. Markus Lupertz: Daphne, 1 vol. 2007. (ENG., Illus.). 80p. 40.00 *(978-3-938025-75-8(1))* Kerber Verlag DEU. Dist: D.A.P./Distributed Art Pubs.

Kiefer, Anselm. Anselm Kiefer: Maria Walks amid the Thorn. 2009. (GER & ENG., Illus.). 135p. 85.00 *(978-3-901935-36-7(3))* Galerie Thaddaeus Ropac FRA. Dist: D.A.P./Distributed Art Pubs.

Kiefer, Anselm & Arasse, Daniel. Rencontres Pour Mémoire. 2010. (FRE., Illus.). 101p. *(978-2-84105-254-7(0))* Editions du Regard, Les.

Kippenberger, Martin. Martin Kippenberger, 1 vol. Friedrich Christian Flick Collection, ed. 2006. (ENG., Illus.). 184p. 50.00 *(978-3-8321-7579-5(2))* DuMont DEU. Dist: D.A.P./Distributed Art Pubs.

Kippenberger, Susanne. Kippenberger: The Artist & His Families. Searls, Damion, tr. 2012. (ENG., Illus.). 564p. 34.95 *(978-0-9829642-1-7(8))* J&L Bks., Inc.

Kirchner, Ernst Ludwig, et al. Das Ungewohnte Neue: Briefwechsel Ernst Ludwig Kirchner und George Reinhart. 2010. (GER., Illus.). 176p. pap. 45.00 ***(978-3-85881-140-0(8))*** Scheidegger und Spiess AG, Verlag CHE. Dist: Antique Collectors' Club.

Knaus, Bernhard & Honnef, Klaus. Ralf Peters: Fotografie. 2010. (GER & ENG., Illus.). 212p. 60.00 *(978-3-7757-2608-5(X))* Hatje Cantz Verlag GmbH & Co KG DEU. Dist: D.A.P./Distributed Art Pubs.

Koerner, J. L. Caspar David Friedrich & the Subject of Landscape. 2nd ed. 2009. (ENG., Illus.). 364p. pap. 27.00 *(978-1-86189-439-7(2))* Reaktion Bks., Ltd. GBR. Dist: Chicago Distribution Ctr.

Kolding, Jakob, et al. Jakob Kolding: Shifting Realities. 2011. (ENG., Illus.). 96p. pap. 29.95 ***(978-3-03764-168-2(1))*** JRP Ringier Kunstverlag AG CHE. Dist: D.A.P./Distributed Art Pubs.

Koster, Heinz. Heinz Köster. 'Stern Spezial Fotografie 59' Berlinale 1954-1967 . 2010. (ENG., Illus.). 96p. 45.00 *(978-3-570-19899-5(5))* teNeues Publishing Co.

Krempel, Ulrich, ed. Jochen Gerz: Artist's Dream - Goethe in Buchenwald. (ENG & GER.). 64p. pap. *(978-3-7757-9004-8(7))* Hatje Cantz Verlag GmbH & Co KG DEU. Dist: D.A.P./Distributed Art Pubs.

—Mischa Kuball. (ENG & GER., Illus.). 40p. pap. incl. audio compact disk *(978-3-89322-255-1(3))* Edition Cantz DEU. Dist: D.A.P./Distributed Art Pubs.

Kreuzer, Stefanie, ed. Albrecht Schäfer: Ein Tag. 2011. (ENG., Illus.). 160p. 55.00 *(978-3-86678-392-8(2))* Kerber Verlag DEU. Dist: D.A.P./Distributed Art Pubs.

Kuhn, Nicola, text. Eva Teppe. 2011. (ENG., Illus.). 64p. pap. 22.95 ***(978-3-86678-518-2(6))*** Kerber Verlag DEU. Dist: D.A.P./Distributed Art Pubs.

Kuhn, Sebastian, ed. Sebastian Kuhn. 2009. (ENG., Illus.). 152p. 65.00 *(978-3-86678-136-8(9))* Kerber Verlag DEU. Dist: D.A.P./Distributed Art Pubs.

Lagerfeld, Karl. Work in Progress, 1 vol. 2011. (ENG., Illus.). 192p. pap. 25.00 *(978-3-86930-261-4(5))* Steidl, Gerhard Druckerei und Verlag DEU. Dist: Innovative Logistics.

Lammer, Frank (esher) & R.k.d.u., eds. We Come at Night: A Corporate Street Attack. 2008. (Illus.). 144p. *(978-3-89955-216-4(4))* Die Gestalten Verlag.

Landert, Markus, ed. Olaf Nicolai. Mirador: Mirador. 2011. (ENG., Illus.). 80p. pap. 45.00 *(978-3-86984-033-8(1))* Verlag fur Moderne Kunst DEU. Dist: D.A.P./Distributed Art Pubs.

Lange, Justus. Die Wilkes: Eine Künstlerfamilie der Moderne Aus Braunschweig. 2008. (GER., Illus.). 55p. *(978-3-937664-91-0(2))* Stadt Braunschweig, Stadtisches Museum.

Lehmann, Ulrike, ed. Michael Laube: In Between. 2010. (ENG., Illus.). 180p. 60.00 *(978-3-7757-2514-9(8))* Hatje Cantz Verlag GmbH & Co KG DEU. Dist: D.A.P./Distributed Art Pubs.

Lenz, Christian. Hans Purrmann: Aquarelle und Gouachen. Werkverzeichnis. 2009. (ENG., Illus.). 336p. 300.00 *(978-3-7757-2178-3(9))* Hatje Cantz Verlag GmbH & Co KG DEU. Dist: D.A.P./Distributed Art Pubs.

Lindbergh, Peter. Photographs & Films 1980-2010: Katalog C/O Berlin. 2010. (FRE, GER & ENG., Illus.). 216p. *(978-3-8296-0506-9(4))* Schirmer/Mosel Verlag GmbH.

Lockemann, Karsten, ed. Jan Davidoff, 2005-2009. 2010. (ENG., Illus.). 100p. 40.00 *(978-3-86678-281-5(0))* Kerber Verlag DEU. Dist: D.A.P./Distributed Art Pubs.

Lombardo, Mario. The Tender Spot: The Graphic Design of Mario Lombardo. 2010. (Illus.). 256p. *(978-3-89955-319-2(5))* Die Gestalten Verlag.

Long, Declan, et al. Ulla Von Brandenburg: Whose Beginning Is Not, nor End Cannot Be. 2009. (ENG., Illus.). 100p. 49.95 *(978-88-8158-693-6(2))* Charta ITA. Dist: D.A.P./Distributed Art Pubs.

Loock, Ulrich, ed. Schütte, Thomas.Public/Political. 2012. (ENG., Illus.). 240p. pap. 59.95 ***(978-3-86560-414-9(5))*** Verlag der Buchhandlung Walther Konig DEU. Dist: D.A.P./Distributed Art Pubs.

Lorenz, Detlef. Reklamekunst um 1900 - Kuenstlerlexikon fuer Sammelbilder. (GER., Illus.). 237p. *(978-3-496-01220-7(X))* Reimer, Dietrich.

Lützen, André, photos by. André Lützen: Before Elvis there was nothing. 2009. (ENG., Illus.). 112p. 55.00 *(978-3-86828-006-7(5))* Kehrer Verlag Heidelberg, Klaus Kehrer DEU. Dist: Consortium Bk. Sales & Distribution.

Luzern, Kuntsmuseum, ed. Remy Markowitsch. (ENG & GER., Illus.). 124p. pap. 29.95 *(978-3-89322-832-4(2))* Edition Cantz DEU. Dist: D.A.P./Distributed Art Pubs.

Mulle, Christopher. Christopher Muller: Looking Pictures. 2011. (ENG., Illus.). 192p. 60.00 ***(978-3-86984-182-3(6))*** Verlag fur Moderne Kunst DEU. Dist: D.A.P./Distributed Art Pubs.

Mack, Heinz. Mack. Die Sprache meiner Hand. 2011. (ENG., Illus.). 288p. 60.00 ***(978-3-7757-2978-9(X))*** Hatje Cantz Verlag GmbH & Co KG DEU. Dist: D.A.P./Distributed Art Pubs.

Mack, Ute, ed. Heinz Mack. Leben und Werk. Ein Buch vom Künstler über den Künstler 1931-2011. 2011. (GER & ENG., Illus.). 500p. 110.00 *(978-3-8321-9353-9(7))* DuMont DEU. Dist: D.A.P./Distributed Art Pubs.

Mandesmuseum. Toni Schneiders Photography. 2008. (ENG., Illus.). 208p. 60.00 *(978-3-7757-2182-0(7))* Hatje Cantz Verlag GmbH & Co KG DEU. Dist: D.A.P./Distributed Art Pubs.

Manson, David. Willy Tirr (1915 - 1991) Figure in a Landscape. 2010. (Illus.). 116p. pap. 35.49 *(978-1-4520-0506-5(0))* AuthorHouse.

Marcel Broodthaers. 85.00 *(978-2-903004-00-2(5))* Galerie Isy Brachot FRA. Dist: D.A.P./Distributed Art Pubs.

Mari, Bartomeu. Lothar Baumgarten. Mari, Bartomeu, ed. 2008. 180p. pap. *(978-84-89771-52-9(9))* Actar Birkhauser Distribution.

Maspero, Francois. Out of the Shadows: A Life of Gerda Taro. Strachan, Geoffrey, tr. from FRE. 2010. (ENG., Illus.). 144p. 19.95 *(978-0-285-63825-9(4))* Souvenir Pr. Ltd. GBR. Dist: Independent Pubs. Group.

Mayer, Katharina, et al. Katharina Mayer, Paula Modersohn-Becker: Eine Begegnung. 2008. (GER., Illus.). 55p. *(978-3-9810296-2-8(3)*, Spotlight Poets) Bottcherstrae GmbH.

Meese, Jonathan. Jonathan Meese: Dark Snow Fanzine. 2011. (ENG., Illus.). 46p. pap. 18.00 *(978-3-931355-54-8(3))* Walter Konig Verlag DEU. Dist: D.A.P./Distributed Art Pubs.

Mettig, Klaus, photos by. Don't Be Left Behind, 1 vol. 2011. (ENG & GER., Illus.). 310p. pap. 75.00 *(978-3-86521-595-6(5))* Steidl, Gerhard Druckerei und Verlag DEU. Dist: Innovative Logistics.

Metzger, Gustav & Obrist, Hans Ulrich. Gustav Metzger. 2009. (ENG., Illus.). 168p. pap. 25.00 *(978-3-86560-498-9(6))* Verlag der Buchhandlung Walther Konig DEU. Dist: D.A.P./Distributed Art Pubs.

Meyer, Anna. Internationale: 2001-2006, 1 vol. 2007. (GER & ENG., Illus.). 248p. pap. 35.00 *(978-3-939633-22-8(4))* Jovis Verlag GmbH DEU. Dist: D.A.P./Distributed Art Pubs.

Meyer-Hermann, Eva, ed. Kippenberger meets Picasso. 2011. (ENG., Illus.). 144p. pap. 44.95 ***(978-3-86560-967-0(8))*** Verlag der Buchhandlung Walther Konig DEU. Dist: D.A.P./Distributed Art Pubs.

Moki. How to Disappear. 2011. *(978-1-58423-417-3(2))* Gingko Pr., Inc.

Morgan, Jessica. Carsten Holler: Test Site. 2007. (ENG., Illus.). 140p. pap. 14.95 *(978-1-85437-712-8(4))* Tate Publishing, Ltd. GBR. Dist: Hachette Bk. Group.

Muller, Frank-Heinrich, ed. & photos by. East/For the Record, 1 vol. 2009. (ENG., Illus.). 192p. 55.00 *(978-3-86521-929-9(2))* Steidl, Gerhard Druckerei und Verlag DEU. Dist: Innovative Logistics.

Muller, Renate. Renate Muller: Toys & Design. 2011. (ENG., Illus.). 80p. 45.00 *(978-0-9704608-3-7(X))* R, LLC.

Nachtigaller, Roland, ed. Sonja Alhauser: Immerzu. 2008. (Illus.). 104p. pap. 34.00 *(978-3-86560-256-5(8))* Verlag der Buchhandlung Walther Konig DEU. Dist: D.A.P./Distributed Art Pubs.

Obrist, Hans Ulrich, ed. Hans Ulrich Obrist & Dan Graham: Conversation Series: Volume 25. 2012. (ENG., Illus.). 134p. pap. 25.00 ***(978-3-86560-791-1(8))*** Verlag der Buchhandlung Walther Konig DEU. Dist: D.A.P./Distributed Art Pubs.

Obrist, Hans Ulrich, ed. Pars Pro Toto II. 2009. (ENG., Illus.). 256p. pap. 90.00 *(978-3-86828-055-5(3))* Kehrer Verlag Heidelberg, Klaus Kehrer DEU. Dist: Consortium Bk. Sales & Distribution.

Obrist, Hans Ulrich & Kittelmann, Udo, eds. Thomas Bayrle: 40 Years Chinese Rock N' Roll, 1 vol. 2007. (ENG., Illus.). 320p. pap. 70.00 *(978-3-86560-100-1(6))* Verlag der Buchhandlung Walther Konig DEU. Dist: D.A.P./Distributed Art Pubs.

Ohlsen, Nils & Kuster, Ulf, texts. Uwe Kowski: Paintings & Watercolors 2000-2008. 2009. (ENG., Illus.). 188p. 50.00 *(978-3-935567-47-3(2))* Holzwarth Pubns. DEU. Dist: D.A.P./Distributed Art Pubs.

Pfanner, Meinhard, ed. & frwd. Helga Natz: Sculptures 1985-2005, 1 vol. 2007. (GER & ENG., Illus.). 144p. 48.00 *(978-3-938025-91-8(3))* Kerber Verlag DEU. Dist: D.A.P./Distributed Art Pubs.

Presenhuber, Eva, ed. Dieter Roth: Zeichnungen - Drawings. 2008. (ENG., Illus.). 336p. lthr. 80.00 *(978-3-905829-17-4(7))* JRP Ringier Kunstverlag AG CHE. Dist: D.A.P./Distributed Art Pubs.

Prinz, Bernhard. Bernhard Prinz, 1 vol. 2010. (ENG., Illus.). 200p. 65.00 *(978-3-86521-487-4(8))* Steidl, Gerhard Druckerei und Verlag DEU. Dist: Innovative Logistics.

Publishing, From Here To Fame. Color Me Graffiti 2. 2011. (ENG., Illus.). 48p. pap. 8.95 ***(978-3-937946-30-6(6))*** From Here To Fame GmbH DEU. Dist: SCB Distributors.

Puhringer, Alexander, ed. Leiko Ikemura. (ENG & GER., Illus.). 112p. pap. 39.95 *(978-3-89322-803-4(9))* Edition Cantz DEU. Dist: D.A.P./Distributed Art Pubs.

Rau, Hartmut. Ton Schulten. 2006. (ENG.). 192p. 50.00 *(978-90-400-8957-2(4))* Waanders B.V., Uitgeverij NLD. Dist: National Bk. Network.

Rauch, Neo. Neo Rauch. 2007. 248p. 50.00 *(978-3-8321-7732-4(9))* DuMont DEU. Dist: D.A.P./Distributed Art Pubs.

Rehberger, Tobias. Flach. 2010. (GER., Illus.). 160p. *(978-3-942405-00-3(8))* Die Gestalten Verlag.

Reinartz, Karin, ed. Dirk Reinartz: New York 1974, 1 vol. 2008. (ENG., Illus.). 144p. 55.00 *(978-3-86521-526-0(2))* Steidl, Gerhard Druckerei und Verlag DEU. Dist: Innovative Logistics.

Richter, Gerhard. Atlas, 1 vol. Friedel, Helmut, ed. 2011. (ENG., Illus.). 864p. 60.00 *(978-1-933045-47-4(7))* D.A.P./Distributed Art Pubs.

Richter, Gerhard. Gerhard Richter. Els. 2011. (ENG., Illus.). 152p. 59.95 ***(978-3-86560-924-3(4))*** Verlag der Buchhandlung Walther Konig DEU. Dist: D.A.P./Distributed Art Pubs.

Rosefeldt, Julian. Julian Rosefeldt: Living in Oblivion, 2 vols. 2011. (GER & ENG., Illus.). 104p. pap. 43.50 *(978-3-86678-414-7(7))* Kerber Verlag DEU. Dist: D.A.P./Distributed Art Pubs.

Roth, Dieter. Dieter Roth: The Rings of Dieter Roth. 2010. 144p. pap. 22.00 *(978-3-907474-33-4(3))* Periferia, Edizioni, Poschiavo / Lucerna CHE. Dist: D.A.P./Distributed Art Pubs.

—Dieter Roth: the Rings of Dieter Roth. 2010. (ENG., Illus.). 144p. pap. 22.00 *(978-3-907474-76-5(3))* Periferia, Edizioni, Poschiavo / Lucerna CHE. Dist: D.A.P./Distributed Art Pubs.

Roth, Dieter & text. Dieter Roth, Inserate: Advertisements 1971-1972. 2010. (ENG., Illus.). 280p. pap. 19.00 *(978-3-907474-77-8(5))* Periferia, Edizioni, Poschiavo / Lucerna CHE. Dist: D.A.P./Distributed Art Pubs.

Ruetz, Michael, photos by. Michael Ruetz: Spring of Discontent, 1964-1974, 1 vol. 2009. (ENG., Illus.). 192p. 55.00 *(978-3-86521-866-7(0))* Steidl, Gerhard Druckerei und Verlag DEU. Dist: Innovative Logistics.

Ruetz, Michael, photos by & text. Michael Ruetz: Eye on Infinity, 1 vol. 2008. (ENG.). 252p. pap. 70.00 *(978-3-86521-766-0(4))* Steidl, Gerhard Druckerei und Verlag DEU. Dist: Innovative Logistics.

Russell, P. Craig. The Art of P. Craig Russell. Pruett, Joe, ed. aut. ed. 2010. (Illus.). 256p. 79.99 *(978-0-9795939-0-1(5))* Idea & Design Works, LLC.

Sailstorfer, Michael. Michael Sailstorfer: 10000 Stones. 2008. (ENG., Illus.). 64p. pap. 36.00 *(978-3-86560-465-1(X))* Verlag der Buchhandlung Walther Konig DEU. Dist: D.A.P./Distributed Art Pubs.

Schaller, Matthias, photos by. Purple Desks, 1 vol. 2009. (ENG., Illus.). 72p. 49.90 *(978-3-86521-597-0(1))* Steidl, Gerhard Druckerei und Verlag DEU. Dist: Innovative Logistics.

Schink, Hans-Christian, photos by. Hans-Christian Schink. 2011. (ENG., Illus.). 180p. 75.00 ***(978-3-7757-2826-3(0))*** Hatje Cantz Verlag GmbH & Co KG DEU. Dist: D.A.P./Distributed Art Pubs.

Schink, Hans-Christian, photos by. Hans-Christian Schink: 1 h. 2011. (ENG., Illus.). 96p. 85.00 *(978-3-7757-2661-0(6))* Hatje Cantz Verlag GmbH & Co KG DEU. Dist: D.A.P./Distributed Art Pubs.

Schluter, Maik, ed. Tobias Zielony. 2010. (ENG., Illus.). 216p. pap. 60.00 *(978-3-7757-2284-1(X))* Hatje Cantz Verlag GmbH & Co KG DEU. Dist: D.A.P./Distributed Art Pubs.

Schmalen, Norbert, ed. Zeitungsphotos: Feldmann, 1 vol. 2007. (ENG., Illus.). 48p. pap. 22.00 *(978-3-86560-177-3(4))* Verlag der Buchhandlung Walther Konig DEU. Dist: D.A.P./Distributed Art Pubs.

Schmidt, Eva, ed. Piotr Nathan: Cuttings 1981-1993. (ENG & GER., Illus.). 96p. pap. 29.95 *(978-3-89322-654-2(0))* Edition Cantz DEU. Dist: D.A.P./Distributed Art Pubs.

Schneider, Helge. Guten Tach, Auf Widersehn: Autobiographie, Pt. 1. (GER., Illus.). 279p. pap. *(978-3-462-02196-7(6))* Kiepenheuer & Witsch GmbH & Company KG DEU. Dist: International Bk. Import Service, Inc.

Schnetz, Salome, ed. Ai Weiwei: Fairytale: A Reader. 2012. (ENG., Illus.). 248p. pap. 34.95 ***(978-3-03764-210-8(6))*** JRP Ringier Kunstverlag AG CHE. Dist: D.A.P./Distributed Art Pubs.

Schreier, Christian & Haldemann, Anita, eds. Rosemarie Trockel: Drawings, Collages, & Book Drafts. 2010. (ENG., Illus.). 164p. pap. 60.00 *(978-3-7757-2613-9(6))* Hatje Cantz Verlag GmbH & Co KG DEU. Dist: D.A.P./Distributed Art Pubs.

Schreier, Christoph. Karin Sander. (ENG & GER., Illus.). 64p. 19.95 *(978-3-89322-665-8(6))* Edition Cantz DEU. Dist: D.A.P./Distributed Art Pubs.

Schueller, Amos. Soshana: Leben und Werk. 2010. 320p. 79.95 *(978-3-7091-0274-9(X))* Springer Wien AUT. Dist: Actar Birkhauser Distribution.

Schütte, Thomas. Thomas Schütte: Friedrich Christian Flick Collection, 1 vol. 2009. (ENG., Illus.). 240p. (gr. 13-18). 59.95 *(978-3-8321-7501-6(6))* DuMont DEU. Dist: D.A.P./Distributed Art Pubs.

Seyfarth, Ludwig, text. Margret Wibmer: ambiguity - bodies, objects & spaces. 2011. (ENG., Illus.). 96p. 44.95 ***(978-3-86678-464-2(3))*** Kerber Verlag DEU. Dist: D.A.P./Distributed Art Pubs.

Seyfarth, Ludwig, et al, texts. Timm Ulrichs: Betreten der Ausstellung verboten. Werke von 1960-2010. 2011. (ENG., Illus.). 160p. 60.00 *(978-3-7757-2794-5(9))* Hatje Cantz Verlag GmbH & Co KG DEU. Dist: D.A.P./Distributed Art Pubs.

Shimizu, Minoru. Wolfgang Tillmans, 3 vols. 2011. (ENG, FRE & GER., Illus.). 556p. 39.99 ***(978-3-8365-3105-4(4))*** TASCHEN DEU. Dist: Ingram Pub. Services.

Stolzl, Gunta & text. Gunta Stolzl: Bauhaus Master. 2009. (ENG., Illus.). 144p. 39.95 *(978-0-87070-773-5(6))* Museum of Modern Art.

Strauss, Dorothea, ed. Erik Steinbrecher: Minimalist Kitsch, 1 vol. 2007. (ENG., Illus.). 128p. 35.00 *(978-3-905701-77-7(4))* JRP Ringier Kunstverlag AG CHE. Dist: D.A.P./Distributed Art Pubs.

Sukrow, Oliver. Lea Grundig: Sozialistische Künstlerin und Präsidentin des Verbandes Bildender Künstler in der DDR (1964-1970) 2011. (DDR- Studien / East German Studies). (GER.). 275p. pap. 58.95 ***(978-3-0343-0297-5(5))*** Lang, Peter AG GBR. Dist: Lang, Peter.

TF Editores. Gotthard Schuh. 2011. (ENG., Illus.). 240p. 64.00 ***(978-84-15253-02-0(8))*** T.F. Editores ESP. Dist: National Bk. Network.

Todd, Kim. Chrysalis: Maria Sibylla Merian & the Secrets of Metamorphosis. 2007. (ENG., Illus.). 352p. pap. 15.00 *(978-0-15-603299-5(6)*, Mariner Bks.) Houghton Mifflin Harcourt Trade & Reference Pubs.

Ton Schulten. (ENG, FRE & GER.). 12.99 *(978-3-8327-1092-7(2))*; 9.99 *(978-3-8327-0764-4(6))*; (ENG, FRE & GER.). 7.99 *(978-3-8327-1259-4(3))*; (Illus.). 3.99 *(978-3-8327-1500-7(2))*; (ENG, FRE & GER., Illus.). spiral bd. 14.99 *(978-3-8327-1266-2(6))*; (Illus.). spiral bd. 65.00 *(978-3-8327-0988-4(6))*; (Illus.). spiral bd. 39.99 *(978-3-8327-0990-7(8))*; (Illus.). spiral bd. 39.99 *(978-3-8327-0941-9(X))*; (Illus.). spiral bd. 8.99 *(978-3-8327-1321-8(2))* teNeues Publishing Co.

Ullrich, Wolfgang & Meyer, Kathrin, texts. Sibylle Springer: Gleam. 2011. (ENG., Illus.). 128p. 49.95 ***(978-3-86678-475-8(9))*** Kerber Verlag DEU. Dist: D.A.P./Distributed Art Pubs.

Unverfehrt, Gerd & Dürer, Albrecht. Da Sah Ich Viel Köstliche Dinge: Albrecht Dürers Reise in Die Niederlande. 2007. (GER., Illus.). 261p. (C). pap. 51.00 *(978-3-525-47010-7(X))* Vandenhoeck & Ruprecht GmbH & Co. KG DEU. Dist: ISD.

Valerie Carberry Gallery. Paul Kelpe: Paintings & Works on Paper, 1925-1935. 2007. (Illus.). 32p. per. 15.00 *(978-0-9777686-5-3(1))* Carberry, Valerie Gallery, Inc.

Vettese, Angela & Camartin, Iso. Rebecca Horn: Fata Morgana. 2010. (ENG., Illus.). 144p. 59.95 *(978-88-8158-753-7(X))* Charta ITA. Dist: D.A.P./Distributed Art Pubs.

Voigt, Jorinde. Jorinde Voigt: Nexus. 2011. (ENG., Illus.). 144p. pap. 55.00 ***(978-3-7757-2823-2(6))*** Hatje Cantz Verlag GmbH & Co KG DEU. Dist: D.A.P./Distributed Art Pubs.

Volt, Robert, photos by. New Trees, 1 vol. 2011. (ENG., Illus.). 120p. 78.00 *(978-3-86521-825-4(3))* Steidl, Gerhard Druckerei und Verlag DEU. Dist: Innovative Logistics.

Waldvogel, Florian, ed. Stefan Marx: I Guess I Shouldn't Be Telling You. 2011. (ENG., Illus.). 96p. 39.95 ***(978-3-03764-132-3(0))*** JRP Ringier Kunstverlag AG CHE. Dist: D.A.P./Distributed Art Pubs.

Webb, Peter. Death, Desire & the Doll: The Life & Art of Hans Bellmer. 2008. (Solar Art Directives Ser.). (Illus.). 208p. per. 29.95 *(978-0-9714578-6-7(7))* Solar Bks.

Weber, Nicholas Fox. The Bauhaus Group: Six Masters of Modernism. 2009. (ENG., Illus.). 544p. 40.00 *(978-0-307-26836-5(5)*, Knopf) Knopf Doubleday Publishing Group.

—The Bauhaus Group: Six Masters of Modernism. 2011. (ENG., Illus.). 544p. pap. 27.50 *(978-0-300-16984-3(1))* Yale Univ. Pr.

Weber, Nicolas Fox. Josef Albers & Wassily Kandinsky: Friends in Exile - A Decade of Correspondence. 2010. (ENG., Illus.). 160p. pap. 29.95 *(978-1-55595-327-0(1))* Hudson Hills Pr. LLC.

Weiss, Andrea. In the Shadow of the Magic Mountain: The Erika & Klaus Mann Story. 2008. (Illus.). 310p. 27.50 *(978-0-226-88672-5(7))* Univ. of Chicago Pr.

Wendt, Karin. Gunter Fruhtrunk Monographie und Werkverzeichnis: Moglichkeiten und Grenzen des Konkreten Bildes. (Schriften zur Bildenden Kunst Ser.: Bd. 10). (GER., Illus.). 380p. 52.95 *(978-3-631-37907-3(2))* Lang, Peter Publishing, Inc.

Wettengl, Kurt & Strauss, Dorothea, eds. Anna & Bernhard Blume: de-konstruktiv: Bilder aus dem wirklichen Leben, 1 vol. 2007. (ENG., Illus.). 136p. 45.00 *(978-3-86678-029-3(X))* Kerber Verlag DEU. Dist: D.A.P./Distributed Art Pubs.

Wrede, Thomas, photos by. Thomas Wrede: Manhattan / Picture Worlds. 2010. (ENG., Illus.). 120p. 65.00 *(978-3-86678-244-0(6))* Kerber Verlag DEU. Dist: D.A.P./Distributed Art Pubs.

Zdenek. Thomas Helbig Homo Homini Lupus. 2008. (ENG., Illus.). 208p. 60.00 *(978-3-7757-2164-6(9))* Hatje Cantz Verlag GmbH & Co KG DEU. Dist: D.A.P./Distributed Art Pubs.

Zeitgenossische, Galerie, ed. Weather Everything. (GER, ENG & FRE., Illus.). 96p. pap. 29.95 *(978-3-89322-400-5(9))* Edition Cantz DEU. Dist: D.A.P./Distributed Art Pubs.

Ziervogel, Ralf. Ralf Ziervogel: Every Adidas Got Its Story. 2009. (ENG., Illus.). 432p. 40.00 *(978-3-86560-499-6(4))* Verlag der Buchhandlung Walther Konig DEU. Dist: D.A.P./Distributed Art Pubs.

Zilioli, Ellen Maurer, et al. Helfried Kodré: Vedere L'Invisibile. 2006. (GER & ENG., Illus.). 96p. 45.00 *(978-3-89790-239-8(7))* Arnoldsche Art Pubs. DEU. Dist: Antique Collectors' Club.

ARTISTS—GREAT BRITAIN

Aldridge, Alan. The Man with Kaleidoscope Eyes: The Art of Alan Aldridge. 2009. (ENG., Illus.). 240p. 37.50 *(978-0-8109-0596-2(5))* Abrams.

Arnatt, Keith. I'm a Real Photographer: Keith Arnatt Photographs 1974-2002. 2009. (ENG., Illus.). 152p. 45.00 *(978-1-905712-05-2(7))* Boot, Chris GBR. Dist: D.A.P./Distributed Art Pubs.

Ashery, Oreet & Sansour, Larissa. The Novel of Nonel & Vovel. 2009. (ENG., Illus.). 188p. pap. 39.95 *(978-88-8158-733-9(5))* Charta ITA. Dist: D.A.P./Distributed Art Pubs.

Association of Contemporary Jewellers Staff. Jewellers the Directory. 2007. (ENG., Illus.). 184p. 24.95 *(978-0-7136-8409-4(7))* A & C Black GBR. Dist: Macmillan.

Baile de Laperriere, Charles & Murray, Lynda. Who's Who in Art: 34th Edition. 34th ed. 2010. 837p. 190.00 *(978-0-904722-44-4(9))* Hilmarton Manor Pr. GBR. Dist: Cengage Gale.

Baile De Laperriere, Charles & Murray, Lynda, eds. Who's Who in Art: Biographies of Leading Men & Women in the World of Art in Britain Today: Artists, Sculptors, Designers, Architects, Critics, Writers, Lecturers, Curators & Photographers. 33rd rev. ed. 2008. (Who's Who in Art Ser.). (Illus.). 1128p. *(978-0-904722-42-0(2))* Hilmarton Manor Pr.

Bailey, David, photos by. Is That So Kid: David Bailey, Anjelica Huston, 1 vol. 2008. (ENG., Illus.). 84p. 65.00 *(978-3-86521-632-8(3))* Steidl, Gerhard Druckerei und Verlag DEU. Dist: Innovative Logistics.

—Stern Spezial Portfolio 50 . David Bailey. 2008. (Illus.). 96p. pap. 22.95 *(978-3-570-19736-3(0))* teNeues Publishing Co.

Baldon, Diana, et al, texts. 2nd Athens Biennale 2009: Heaven. 2010. (ENG., Illus.). 360p. pap. 35.00 *(978-960-98893-1-5(X))* Athens Biennial GRC. Dist: D.A.P./Distributed Art Pubs.

Banksy. Wall & Piece. 2007. (ENG., Illus.). 192p. pap. 22.95 *(978-1-84413-787-9(2)*, Century) Random Hse. GBR. Dist: Independent Pubs. Group.

Bardwell, Leland. A Restless Life. 2009. (ENG., Illus.). 288p. pap. 32.95 *(978-1-905483-52-5(X))* Liberties Pr. IRL. Dist: Dufour Editions, Inc.

Barritt, Michael K. Eyes of the Admiralty: J. T. Serres - An Artist in the Channel Fleet, 1799-1800. 2008. (ENG., Illus.). 144p. 39.95 *(978-0-948065-79-8(6))* National Maritime Museum GBR. Dist: Independent Pubs. Group.

Beer, John. William Blake: A Literary Life. 2007. (Literary Lives Ser.). (ENG., Illus.). 264p. pap. 39.00 *(978-0-230-54682-0(X))* Palgrave Macmillan.

Behr, Shulamith, et al. Forced Journeys: Artists in Exile in Britain C. 1933-45. 2009. (Illus.). 112p. 70.00 *(978-0-900157-13-4(5)*, Lund Humphries Pubs.) Ashgate Publishing, Ltd. GBR. Dist: Ashgate Publishing Co.

Ben-Arie, Daniella, et al. Thomas Hope: Regency Designer. Hewat-Jaboor, Philip, ed. 2008. (ENG., Illus.). 520p. 100.00 *(978-0-300-12416-3(3))* Yale Univ. Pr.

Bendahán, Marcelo. Carnivals of the World. 2010. 200p. 50.00 *(978-90-809396-8-4(4))* Maestro Bks. NLD. Dist: International Publishers Marketing.

Benezit, Emmanuel. Benezit Dictionary of British Graphic Artists & Illustrators, 2 vols. 2012. (ENG., Illus.). 1344p. 295.00 ***(978-0-19-992305-2(1))*** Oxford Univ. Pr., Inc.

Bennet, Anita Feldman, et al. Hoglands: The Home of Henry & Irina Moore. 2007. (Illus.). 224p. 80.00 *(978-0-85331-961-0(8)*, Lund Humphries Pubs.) Ashgate Publishing, Ltd. GBR. Dist: Ashgate Publishing Co.

Bentley, G. E. William Blake's Conversations: A Compilation, Concordance, & Rhetorical Analysis. 2008. (Illus.). xix, 297p. *(978-0-7734-4848-3(9))* Mellen, Edwin Pr., The.

Bewick, Thomas. A Memoir of Thomas Bewick. 2008. 372p. 48.95 *(978-1-4369-8464-5(5))*; pap. 33.95 *(978-1-4367-4014-2(2))* Kessinger Publishing, LLC.

Bird, Michael. The St Ives Artists: A Cultural Biography 1939-64. 2008. (Illus.). 192p. pap. 40.00 *(978-0-85331-956-6(1)*, Lund Humphries Pubs.) Ashgate Publishing, Ltd. GBR. Dist: Ashgate Publishing Co.

Blake, Peter, illus. An Alphabet, 1 vol. 2008. (ENG.). 64p. 35.00 *(978-0-9552154-5-2(5))* Stolper, Paul GBR. Dist: D.A.P./Distributed Art Pubs.

Booth-Clibborn, Charles, et al. Contemporary Art in Print: The Publications of Charles Booth-Clibborn & His Imprint the Paragon Press 2001-2006. 2007. (ENG., Illus.). 336p. 85.00 *(978-1-86154-305-9(0))* Booth-Clibborn Editions GBR. Dist: Hachette Bk. Group.

Bradbury, Sue. Joanna, George, & Henry: A Pre-Raphaelite Tale of Art, Love & Friendship. 2012. (Illus.). 376p. 50.00 ***(978-1-84383-617-9(3)***, Boydell Press) Boydell & Brewer, Ltd. GBR. Dist: Boydell & Brewer, Inc.

Bramwell, Valerie & Peck, Robert McCracken. All in the Bones: A Biography of Benjamin Waterhouse Hawkins. 2008. *(978-0-910006-65-1(2))* Academy of Natural Sciences Philadelphia.

Branaghan, Sim & Chibnall, Stephen. British Film Posters: An Illustrated History. 2007. (ENG., Illus.). 288p. 127.50 *(978-1-84457-148-2(3))*; pap. 42.50 *(978-1-84457-221-2(8))* BFI Publishing GBR. Dist: Macmillan.

Bright, Susan. Flash Forward 2007: Emerging photographers from Canada, the United Kingdom & the United States. 2007. (ENG.). 192p. 25.00 *(978-0-9739739-2-1(7))* Magenta Publishing for the Arts CAN. Dist: Consortium Bk. Sales & Distribution.

Brown, Roy 'Chubby'. Common as Muck! My Autobiography. 2007. (ENG., Illus.). 384p. pap. 15.95 *(978-0-7515-3931-8(7))* Little, Brown Bk. Group Ltd. GBR. Dist: Independent Pubs. Group.

Buckman, David. Artists in Britain since 1945, 2 vols. 2007. (ENG., Illus.). 1856p. 330.00 *(978-0-9532609-5-9(X)*, Sansom (Acc)) Antique Collectors' Club GBR. Dist: National Bk. Network.

Bullen, Barrie & Bullen, J. B. Rossetti: Painter & Poet. 2011. (ENG., Illus.). 272p. 50.00 *(978-0-7112-3225-9(3))* Lincoln, Frances Ltd. GBR. Dist: Perseus-PGW.

Butters, Wes & Davies, Russell. Kenneth Williams Unseen: The Private Notes, Scripts & Photographs. 2008. (ENG., Illus.). 256p. 18.99 *(978-0-00-728085-8(8))* HarperCollins Pubs.

Camp, Jeffery & Kirk, Joanna. Almanac. 2010. (ENG., Illus.). 256p. 50.00 *(978-1-905711-64-2(6))* Royal Academy of Arts GBR. Dist: Hachette Bk. Group.

Carey-Thomas, Lizzie & Stout, Katharine. The Turner Prize & British Art. 2008. (ENG., Illus.). 112p. pap. 27.50 *(978-1-85437-742-5(6))* Tate Publishing, Ltd. GBR. Dist: Hachette Bk. Group.

Castagno, John. Australian, British & Irish Artists: Signatures & Monograms from 1800. 2009. (ENG.). 524p. 225.00 *(978-0-8108-6384-2(7))* Scarecrow Pr., Inc.

Causey, Andrew. Peter Lanyon: Modernism & the Land. 2006. (Reaktion Books - Essays in Art & Culture Ser.). (ENG., Illus.). 224p. pap. 24.95 *(978-1-86189-275-1(6))* Reaktion Bks., Ltd. GBR. Dist: Chicago Distribution Ctr.

Cavalli, Roberto. Roberto Cavalli. 2011. (ENG., Illus.). 192p. 85.00 *(978-0-8478-3609-3(6))* Rizzoli International Pubns., Inc.

Chalayan, Hussein. Hussein Chalayan. Violette, Robert, ed. 2011. (ENG., Illus.). 276p. 85.00 *(978-0-8478-3386-3(0))* Rizzoli International Pubns., Inc.

Clark, Adrian. British & Irish Art, 1945-1951: From War to Festival. 2010. (Illus.). 272p. 50.00 ***(978-0-9554063-4-8(X))*** Holberton, Paul Publishing GBR. Dist: Casemate Pubs. & Bk. Distributors, LLC.

Clarke, Brian. Brian Clarke: Work: Work, 1 vol. 2009. (ENG., Illus.). 1006p. 249.90 *(978-3-86521-633-5(1))* Steidl, Gerhard Druckerei und Verlag DEU. Dist: Innovative Logistics.

Clayton, Ellen C. English Female Artists, 2 Vols. reprint ed. 250.00 *(978-0-7222-1714-6(5))* Library Reprints, Inc.

Close, Lesley Mary. Hooked Rug Storytelling: The Art of Heather Ritchie. 2011. (Illus.). 192p. *(978-0-7643-3695-9(9)*, Schiffer Publishing Ltd) Schiffer Publishing, Ltd.

Collishaw, Mat. Mat Collishaw. Beard, Jason, ed. 2008. (ENG., Illus.). 176p. pap. 70.00 *(978-1-904212-15-7(8))* Other Criteria GBR. Dist: Hachette Bk. Group.

Constable, Freda & Simon, Sue. The England of Eric Ravilious. 3rd rev. ed. 2006. (Illus.). 104p. pap. 40.00 *(978-0-85331-880-4(8)*, Lund Humphries Pubs.) Ashgate Publishing, Ltd. GBR. Dist: Ashgate Publishing Co.

Cook, Edward Tyas. The Life of John Ruskin, 1860-1900, 2. 2010. (Cambridge Library Collection - Literary Studies). (ENG., Illus.). 640p. pap. 43.00 *(978-1-108-00972-0(7))* Cambridge Univ. Pr.

Cooper, Jeremy. Growing Up: The Young British Artists At 50. 2012. 176p. 39.95 ***(978-3-7913-4702-8(0))*** Prestel Publishing.

Cork, Richard & Wardell, Gareth. Barbara Rae Sketchbooks. 2011. (ENG., Illus.). 144p. 30.00 *(978-1-907533-10-5(9))* Royal Academy of Arts GBR. Dist: Hachette Bk. Group.

Cornish, Joe. A Photographer at Work. 2011. (ENG., Illus.). 144p. pap. 27.95 *(978-1-902538-60-0(9))* Aurum Pr., Ltd. GBR. Dist: Independent Pubs. Group.

Cory, Charlotte, photos by. The Visitors. 2008. (ENG., Illus.). 96p. 29.95 *(978-1-904587-50-7(X))* Lewis, Dewi Publishing GBR. Dist: Consortium Bk. Sales & Distribution.

Craddock, Sacha. Angus Fairhurst. 2009. (ENG., Illus.). 112p. 53.00 *(978-0-85667-659-8(4))* Wilson, Philip Pubs., Ltd. GBR. Dist: Macmillan.

Cragg, Tony. Tony Cragg. 55.00 *(978-90-70149-30-7(3))* Abbemuseum, Stedelijk van NLD. Dist: D.A.P./Distributed Art Pubs.

Craig-Martin, Michael & Thomas, Rachael, contrib. by. Rachael Thomas Interviews Michael Craig-Martin, 1 vol. 2007. (ENG., Illus.). 64p. pap. 24.95 *(978-88-8158-586-1(3))* Charta ITA. Dist: D.A.P./Distributed Art Pubs.

Cumberland, Richard. Memoirs of Richard Cumberland, Written by Himself Containing an Account of His Life & Writings, Interspersed with Anecdotes & Characters with Il. 2006. 416p. per. 26.99 *(978-1-4255-4463-8(0))* MPublishing.

Curd, Mary Bryan H. Flemish & Dutch Artists in Early Modern England: Collaboration & Competition, 1460-1680. 2010. (Visual Culture in Early Modernity Ser.). (Illus.). 256p. 119.95 *(978-0-7546-6712-4(X))* Ashgate Publishing Co.

Dadd, Richard. Richard Dadd: the Artist & the Asylum. 2011. (ENG., Illus.). 208p. 50.00 ***(978-1-935202-68-4(5))*** D.A.P./Distributed Art Pubs.

De La Sizeranne, Robert. The Pre-Raphaelites. 2008. (Art of Century Ser.). (ENG., Illus.). 199p. 19.95 *(978-1-84484-459-3(5))* Parkstone International GBR. Dist: Ingram Pub. Services.

de Zegher, Catherine, ed. Craigie Horsfield: Confluence & Consequence. 2011. (ENG., Illus.). 248p. 50.00 *(978-90-5544-832-6(X))* Lundion, Uitgeverij NLD. Dist: D.A.P./Distributed Art Pubs.

Dean, Roger & Dean, Martyn. Magnetic Storm. 2009. (ENG.). 160p. 29.99 *(978-0-06-171710-9(X)*, Collins Design) HarperCollins Pubs.

Dean, Roger, et al. Views. 2009. (ENG.). 160p. 29.95 *(978-0-06-171709-3(6)*, Collins Design) HarperCollins Pubs.

Doonan, Simon. Nasty: My Family & Other Glamorous Varmints. 2007. (ENG., Illus.). 304p. pap. 20.95 *(978-1-4165-8634-0(2))* Simon & Schuster.

Doron, Itai, photos by. Yassin: Circus Boy. 2009. (ENG., Illus.). 72p. pap. 70.00 *(978-1-904212-48-5(4))* Other Criteria GBR. Dist: Hachette Bk. Group.

Drummond, Maldwin. After You, Mr. Lear: In the Wake of Edward Lear in Italy. 2007. (ENG.). 240p. pap. 24.95 *(978-1-57409-255-4(3))* Sheridan Hse., Inc.

Eccher, Danilo. Marc Quinn: Myth. 2009. (ENG & ITA., Illus.). 120p. 49.95 *(978-88-8158-725-4(4))* Charta ITA. Dist: D.A.P./Distributed Art Pubs.

Ellis, Edwin J. The Real Blake: A Portrait Biography. 2007. (ENG.). 480p. 53.95 *(978-0-548-09660-4(0))* Kessinger Publishing, LLC.

Elphick, Jonathan. John Gould - Family of Toucans. 2011. (ENG.). 118p. pap. 99.99 ***(978-3-8365-0524-6(X))*** TASCHEN DEU. Dist: Ingram Pub. Services.

Emin, Tracey. Strangeland. 2006. (ENG.). 224p. pap. 14.95 ***(978-0-340-76946-1(7)***, Hodder & Stoughton) Hodder General Publishing Div. GBR. Dist: Independent Pubs. Group.

Emin, Tracey. Tracey Emin: My Life in a Column. 2011. (ENG., Illus.). 368p. 35.00 *(978-0-8478-5807-1(3))* Rizzoli International Pubns., Inc.

Evans, Cerith Wyn. Parkett No. 87: Cerith Wyn Evans, Katarina Fritsch, Annette Kelm, Kelly Walker. 2010. (ENG., Illus.). 300p. pap. 32.00 *(978-3-907582-47-3(0))* Parkett Verlag AG CHE. Dist: D.A.P./Distributed Art Pubs.

Fact, E.W., ed. Nick Crowe & Ian Rawlinson: At 25 Meters. 2008. (ENG., Illus.). 62p. pap. 25.00 *(978-1-84631-147-5(0))* Liverpool Univ. Pr. GBR. Dist: Chicago Distribution Ctr.

Farmer, Will. Clarice Cliff. 2010. (Shire Library). (ENG., Illus.). 64p. pap. 12.95 *(978-0-7478-0774-2(4))* Shire Pubns., Ltd. GBR. Dist: Random Hse., Inc.

Feaver, William. James Boswell: Unofficial War Artist. 2008. (Illus.). 136p. pap. *(978-0-9547959-2-4(X))* Muswell Press, The.

Ferguson, Russell, ed. Paul Graham: Photographs, 1981-2006, 1 vol. 2009. (ENG., Illus.). 376p. 78.00 *(978-3-86521-858-2(X))* Steidl, Gerhard Druckerei und Verlag DEU. Dist: Innovative Logistics.

Fornieles, Eloise. Eloise Fornieles. Beard, Jason, ed. 2009. (ENG., Illus.). 32p. pap. 35.00 *(978-1-904212-63-8(8))* Other Criteria GBR. Dist: Hachette Bk. Group.

Foss, Brian. War Paint: Art, War, State & Identity in Britain, 1939-1945. 2007. (Paul Mellon Centre for Studies in British Art). (ENG., Illus.). 264p. 75.00 *(978-0-300-10890-3(7))* Yale Univ. Pr.

Foss, Chris. Hardware: The Definitive SF Works of Chris Foss. 2011. (ENG., Illus.). 240p. reprint ed. 34.95 *(978-1-84856-698-9(0)*, Titan Bks.) Titan Bks. Ltd. GBR. Dist: Random Hse., Inc.

Frank, Fiona & Coyle, Judith. Hannah Frank: Footsteps on the Sands of Time; A Hundredth Birthday Celebration Gallimaufry. 2008. (Illus.). 148p. pap. *(978-1-904999-73-7(5))* Kennedy & Boyd.

Freeman, Ian. Cage Fighter: The True Story of Ian "the Machine" Freeman. 2009. (ENG., Illus.). 288p. pap. 13.95 *(978-1-84454-620-6(9))* Blake, John Publishing, Ltd. GBR. Dist: Independent Pubs. Group.

Frehner, Matthias, et al, texts. Edward Burne-Jones: the Earthly Paradise. 2010. (ENG., Illus.). 232p. 60.00 *(978-3-7757-2517-0(2))* Hatje Cantz Verlag GmbH & Co KG DEU. Dist: D.A.P./Distributed Art Pubs.

Fryer, Paul. Radiations. Beard, Jason, ed. 2008. (Illus.). 96p. (ENG.). 70.00 *(978-1-904212-19-5(0))*; 120.00 *(978-1-904212-38-6(7))* Other Criteria GBR. Dist: Hachette Bk. Group, Abrams.

Games, Naomi & Webb, Brian. Abram Games: Design. 2012. (ENG., Illus.). 96p. 19.95 ***(978-1-85149-677-8(7))*** Antique Collectors' Club.

Gayford, Martin. A Bigger Message: Conversations with David Hockney. 2011. (ENG., Illus.). 248p. 34.95 *(978-0-500-23887-5(1)*, 523887) Thames & Hudson.

Gere, Charlotte. Artistic Circles: Design & Decoration in the Aesthetic Movement. 2010. (ENG., Illus.). 240p. 60.00 *(978-1-85177-602-3(8))* V & A Pubns. GBR. Dist: Hachette Bk. Group.

Gill, Stephen, photos by. Stephen Gill: B Sides. 2010. (ENG., Illus.). 72p. 65.00 *(978-0-9556577-4-0(1))* Nobody GBR. Dist: D.A.P./Distributed Art Pubs.

Gillick, Liam, photos by. Liam Gillick: Woven/Intersected/Revised, 5 vols. 2008. (ITA & ENG., Illus.). 72p. 15.00 *(978-3-905701-47-0(2))* JRP Ringier Kunstverlag AG CHE. Dist: D.A.P./Distributed Art Pubs.

Gomer, Veit & Schrader, Kristin, eds. Jake & Dinos Chapman: Memento Moronika. 2009. (ENG & GER., Illus.). 94p. pap. 35.00 *(978-3-86560-582-5(6))* Verlag der Buchhandlung Walther Konig DEU. Dist: D.A.P./Distributed Art Pubs.

Grantham, Unity. Beginning Early, Starting Late (an Autobiography) 2008. 204p. per. 20.95 *(978-1-84799-393-9(1))* Lulu Enterprises Inc.

Gray, Colin. In Sickness & Health, 1 vol. 2011. (ENG., Illus.). 96p. 39.00 *(978-3-86521-940-4(3))* Steidl, Gerhard Druckerei und Verlag DEU. Dist: Innovative Logistics.

Gygax, Raphael & Munder, Heike, eds. Giotto's Play/Giottos Schauspiel. 2008. (ENG., Illus.). 296p. per. 65.00 *(978-3-905770-82-7(2))* JRP Ringier Kunstverlag AG CHE. Dist: D.A.P./Distributed Art Pubs.

Hall, Marshall, ed. Artists of Cumbria: An Illustrated Dictionary of Cumberland, Westmorland, North Lancashire & North West Yorkshire Painters, Sculptors, Draughtsmen & Engravers Born 1615-1900. 2006. (Illus.). 112p. pap. 17.50 *(978-0-903858-01-4(0))* Antique Collectors' Club.

Haller, Robert. Flesh Into Light: The Films of Amy Greenfield. 2010. (Illus.). 294p. pap. 35.00 *(978-1-84150-325-7(8))* Intellect, Ltd. GBR. Dist: Chicago Distribution Ctr.

Hamilton, James. Arthur Rackham: A Life with Illustration. 2011. (ENG., Illus.). 200p. 35.00 *(978-1-86205-894-1(6))* Chrysalis Children's Bks. GBR. Dist: Independent Pubs. Group.

Hamilton, Richard & Craig-Martin, Michael. Richard Hamilton. Foster, Hal, ed. 2010. (October Files Ser.). (ENG., Illus.). 176p. (gr. 17). 35.00 *(978-0-262-01381-9(9))*; pap. 18.95 *(978-0-262-51372-2(2))* MIT Pr.

Hanson, Dian, ed. Tom Poulton: The Secret Art of an English Gentleman. 2006. (ENG., Illus.). 223p. 39.99 *(978-3-8228-3062-8(3))* TASCHEN DEU. Dist: Ingram Pub. Services.

Harris, Alexandra. Romantic Moderns: English Writers, Artists & the Imagination from Virginia Woolf to John Piper. 2010. (ENG., Illus.). 320p. 40.00 *(978-0-500-25171-3(1)*, 525171) Thames & Hudson.

Harrison, Michael. Alan Reynolds. 2011. (Illus.). 192p. 80.00 *(978-1-84822-068-3(5)*, Lund Humphries Pubs.) Ashgate Publishing, Ltd. GBR. Dist: Ashgate Publishing Co.

Harvey, Marcus & Beard, Jason. Marcus Harvey. 2009. (Illus.). 208p. 140.00 *(978-1-904212-62-1(X))* Other Criteria GBR. Dist: Abrams.

Hawksley, Lucinda. 50 British Artists You Should Know. 2011. (Illus.). 160p. pap. 19.95 *(978-3-7913-4538-3(9))* Prestel Publishing.

Haydon, Benjamin Robert. The Autobiography & Memoirs of Benjamin Robert Haydon, V1-2, 1786-1846. Taylor, Tom, ed. 2011. 962p. 80.95 ***(978-1-258-09560-4(2))*** Literary Licensing, LLC.

Herbert, Martin. Mark Wallinger. 2011. (ENG., Illus.). 256p. 65.00 *(978-0-500-09356-6(3)*, 509356) Thames & Hudson.

Hirst, Damien. The Complete Vitrines. 2012. (Illus.). 180p. 150.00 *(978-1-906967-43-7(1))* Other Criteria GBR. Dist: Abrams.

—Corpus: Drawings 1981-2006. Beard, Jason, ed. aut. ed. 2008. (ENG., Illus.). 410p. 450.00 *(978-1-904212-28-7(X))* Other Criteria GBR. Dist: Hachette Bk. Group.

—The Death of God. Beard, Jason, ed. 2008. (ENG., Illus.). 170p. pap. 65.00 *(978-1-904212-13-3(1))*; 168p. pap. 200.00 *(978-1-904212-27-0(1))* Other Criteria GBR. Dist: Hachette Bk. Group.

—Forgotten Promises. 2012. (Illus.). 174p. pap. 200.00 ***(978-1-935263-33-3(1))*** Other Criteria GBR. Dist: Abrams.

—I Want to Spend the Rest of My Life Everywhere, with Everyone, One to One, Always, Forever, Now. aut. ed. 2008. (ENG.). 330p. 900.00 *(978-1-904212-30-0(1))* Booth-Clibborn Editions GBR. Dist: Hachette Bk. Group.

—In the Darkest Hour There May Be Light: Works from Damien Hirst's Murderme Collection. Beard, Jason, ed. 2008. (ENG., Illus.). 152p. 75.00 *(978-1-905190-12-6(3))* Other Criteria GBR. Dist: Hachette Bk. Group.

—New Religion. Beard, Jason, ed. 2008. (ENG., Illus.). 96p. 45.00 *(978-0-9552154-3-8(9))* Other Criteria GBR. Dist: Hachette Bk. Group.

—Poisons + Remedies. 2011. (ENG., Illus.). 88p. pap. 100.00 ***(978-1-935263-19-7(6))*** Abrams.

Hirst, Damien. 8 Minutes, 1 vol. 2009. (ENG., Illus.). 264p. 68.00 *(978-3-86521-864-3(4))* Steidl, Gerhard Druckerei und Verlag DEU. Dist: Innovative Logistics.

Hirst, Damien & Beard, Jason, eds. Requiem I & II: Text in English & Ukrainian. aut. ed. 2009. (ENG., Illus.). 326p. 675.00 *(978-1-906967-07-9(5))* Other Criteria GBR. Dist: Hachette Bk. Group.

Hirst, Damien & Brown, Gordon. The Complete Spot Paintings, 1986-2011. 2012. (Illus.). 1024p. 280.00 ***(978-1-906967-48-2(2))*** Other Criteria GBR. Dist: Abrams.

Hirst, Damien, et al. Beyond Belief. Beard, Jason, ed. 2008. (ENG., Illus.). 194p. 140.00 *(978-1-904212-21-8(2))* Other Criteria GBR. Dist: Hachette Bk. Group.

Howard, Leslie. Double Bind. 2011. 52p. pap. 14.03 ***(978-1-4567-8565-9(6))*** AuthorHouse.

Huijts, Stijn, intro. Stanley Donwood: Red Maze. 2011. (ENG., Illus.). 160p. 59.95 *(978-94-90624-03-3(9))* Schunck NLD. Dist: D.A.P./Distributed Art Pubs.

Hume, Gary. Gary Hume: Yardwork. 2010. (ENG., Illus.). 60p. 35.00 *(978-1-880146-53-8(3))* Marks, Matthew Gallery.

Hunt, William. William Hunt: Tempting Fate by Swimming Alone, 1 vol. 2009. (ENG., Illus.). 1p. 30.00 *(978-90-73362-83-3(0))* Witte De With Centre for Contemporary Art NLD. Dist: D.A.P./Distributed Art Pubs.

Isaacs, John. In Advance of the Institution. 2008. (ENG., Illus.). 188p. 140.00 *(978-1-904212-16-4(6))* Other Criteria GBR. Dist: Hachette Bk. Group.

—In Advance of the Institution. Beard, Jason, ed. 2008. (ENG.). 188p. 190.00 *(978-1-904212-29-4(8))* Other Criteria GBR. Dist: Hachette Bk. Group.

Jackson, Kevin. The Worlds of John Ruskin. 2010. (ENG.). 160p. pap. 24.95 *(978-1-84368-044-4(0))* Pallas Athene GBR. Dist: Independent Pubs. Group.

James, N. P. Interviews - Artists: Recordings from Cv/Visual Arts Research Archive 1988-96. 4th ed. 2007. (Illus.). 144p. pap. *(978-1-905571-50-5(X))* Cv Pubns.

Johnson, Alfred Edwin. Frank Reynolds, R I. 2007. (Illus.). 56p. per. *(978-1-4065-3478-8(1))* Dodo Pr.

Jones, Allen. Allen Jones: Showtime. 2010. (ENG., Illus.). 92p. 40.00 *(978-3-86678-352-2(3))* Kerber Verlag DEU. Dist: D.A.P./Distributed Art Pubs.

Jones, Geoff. A Life Drawing. 2008. 152p. pap. *(978-1-904408-36-9(2))* Bank House Bks.

Jordan, Andre. Heaven Knows I'm Miserable Now. 2009. (ENG.). 256p. pap. 13.99 *(978-0-06-154730-0(1)*, HarperPerennial) HarperCollins Pubs.

Kennedy, S. B. & Henry, Paul. Paul Henry: Paintings, Drawings, Illustrations. 2007. (ENG., Illus.). 416p. 125.00 *(978-0-300-11712-7(4))* Yale Univ. Pr.

Kinley, Catherine. Peter Kinley. 2010. (Illus.). 128p. 70.00 *(978-1-84822-005-8(7)*, Lund Humphries Pubs.) Ashgate Publishing, Ltd. GBR. Dist: Ashgate Publishing Co.

Klein, Jacky. Grayson Perry. 2009. (ENG., Illus.). 400p. 65.00 *(978-0-500-09350-4(4)*, 509350) Thames & Hudson.

Kress, W. John & Sherwood, Shirley. The Art of Plant Evolution. 2010. (Illus.). 320p. pap. 41.00 *(978-1-84246-417-5(5))* Kew Publishing GBR. Dist: Chicago Distribution Ctr.

Lambirth, Andrew. Barbara Rae: Prints. 2010. (ENG., Illus.). 160p. 60.00 *(978-1-905711-58-1(1))* Royal Academy of Arts GBR. Dist: Hachette Bk. Group.

—Nigel Hall: Sculpture & Works on Paper. 2008. (ENG., Illus.). 160p. 65.00 *(978-1-905711-30-7(1))* Royal Academy of Arts GBR. Dist: Hachette Bk. Group.

—Roger Hilton: The Figured Language of Thought. 2007. (ENG., Illus.). 288p. 65.00 *(978-0-500-09334-4(2))* Thames & Hudson.

Levinson, Orde & Jenkins, David Fraser. The Prints of John Piper: Quality & Experiment - A Catalogue Raisonné, 1923-91. Levinson, Orde, ed. 3rd rev. exp. ed. 2010. (Illus.). 232p. 250.00 *(978-1-84822-063-8(4)*, Lund Humphries Pubs.) Ashgate Publishing, Ltd. GBR. Dist: Ashgate Publishing Co.

Litchfield, R. B. Tom Wedgwood the First Photographer an A. 2006. pap. 30.95 *(978-1-4286-5615-4(4))* Kessinger Publishing, LLC.

Livingstone, Marco. Peter Blake: One-Man Show. 2009. (Illus.). 240p. 80.00 *(978-0-85331-980-1(4)*, Lund Humphries Pubs.) Ashgate Publishing, Ltd. GBR. Dist: Ashgate Publishing Co.

Livingstone, Marco & Burn, Gordon. Richard Woods. 2006. (Illus.). 192p. 90.00 *(978-0-9538525-5-0(5)*, Lund Humphries Pubs.) Ashgate Publishing, Ltd. GBR. Dist: Ashgate Publishing Co.

Long, Richard & Tufnell, Ben. Selected Statements And: R Long. 2009. (ENG., Illus.). 128p. pap. 35.00 *(978-1-905620-15-9(2))* Haunch of Venison GBR. Dist: D.A.P./Distributed Art Pubs.

Lousada, Sandra, photos by. Public Faces Private Places: Portraits of Artists, 1956-2008. 2009. (ENG., Illus.). 152p. 40.00 *(978-0-7112-3049-1(8))* Lincoln, Frances Ltd. GBR. Dist: Perseus-PGW.

Lutz, Deborah. Pleasure Bound: Victorian Sex Rebels & the New Eroticism. 2011. (ENG., Illus.). 331p. 27.95 *(978-0-393-06832-0(3)*, 6832) Norton, W. W. & Co., Inc.

Lyell, Douglas. The Boogie Man. 2010. 212p. pap. *(978-1-84748-746-9(7))* Athena Pr.

Mabberley, David. Arthur Harry Church: The Anatomy of Flowers. (Illus.). 128p. *(978-1-85894-116-5(4))* Merrell Pubs. Ltd.

MacCarthy, Fiona. The Last Pre-Raphaelite: Edward Burne-Jones & the Victorian Imagination. 2012. (Illus.). 656p. 35.00 ***(978-0-674-06579-6(4))*** Harvard Univ. Pr.

Malik, Amna & Malik, A. Sarah Lucas: Au Naturel. 2009. (One Work Ser.). (ENG., Illus.). 112p. (gr. 17). pap. 16.00 *(978-1-84638-054-9(5))* Afterall Publishing GBR. Dist: MIT Pr.

McCarthy, Paul, illus. Paul Mccarthy: Between Beauty & the Beast: Sculptures, Drawings & Photographs, 1 vol. 2007. (ENG.). 56p. 45.00 *(978-1-891027-23-9(9))* Four Corners Bks. GBR. Dist: D.A.P./Distributed Art Pubs.

McKean, Dave. Postcard from Vienna. 2006. (Illus.). 48p. lib. bdg. 15.00 *(978-0-9642069-7-7(8))* Spiegel, Allen Fine Arts.

McKernan, Alan & Whitfield, Matthew. Unfamiliar Journeys Continued. 2009. (ENG., Illus.). 96p. 44.95 *(978-1-84631-169-7(1))* Liverpool Univ. Pr. GBR. Dist: Chicago Distribution Ctr.

McLaren, Graham. Studio Glass, 1960-2000. 2008. (Shire Library). (ENG., Illus.). 48p. pap. 12.95 *(978-0-7478-0527-4(X))* Shire Pubns., Ltd. GBR. Dist: Random Hse., Inc.

Miglietti, Francesca Alfano. Franko B: I Still Love. 2011. (ITA & ENG., Illus.). 168p. 55.00 *(978-88-7179-656-7(X)*, Ore Cultura Srl (Acc)) Antique Collectors' Club GBR. Dist: National Bk. Network.

Miles, Barry. London Calling: A Countercultural History of London since 1945. 2011. (ENG., Illus.). 468p. pap. 15.95 ***(978-1-84354-614-6(0))*** Atlantic Bks., Ltd. GBR. Dist: Independent Pubs. Group.

—London Calling: A Countercultural History of London since 1945. Grove, Emma & Joyner, Louisa, eds. 2010. (ENG., Illus.). 468p. 35.00 ***(978-1-84354-613-9(2))*** Atlantic Bks., Ltd. GBR. Dist: Independent Pubs. Group.

Millar, Jeremy & Hoare, Philip. Tania Kovats. 2011. (Illus.). 144p. 70.00 *(978-1-84822-076-2(2)*, Lund Humphries Pubs.) Ashgate Publishing, Ltd. GBR. Dist: Ashgate Publishing Co.

Monk, Jonathan, et al, texts. David Shrigley - Brain Activity. 2012. (ENG., Illus.). 186p. 40.00 ***(978-1-85332-297-6(0))*** Hayward Gallery Publishing GBR. Dist: D.A.P./Distributed Art Pubs.

Mossinger, Ingrid, ed. Fortunate to Be an Artist. 2009. (ENG., Illus.). 256p. 55.00 *(978-3-86678-174-0(1))* Kerber Verlag DEU. Dist: D.A.P./Distributed Art Pubs.

Muir, Robin. Norman Parkinson: Portraits in Fashion. 2011. (ENG., Illus.). 192p. pap. 23.95 *(978-0-9564448-6-8(5))* Palazzo Editions, Ltd. GBR. Dist: Independent Pubs. Group.

Noble, Paul. Paul Noble. (GER & ENG., Illus.). 196p. pap. 40.00 *(978-2-940271-67-2(4))* JRP Ringier Kunstverlag AG CHE. Dist: D.A.P./Distributed Art Pubs.

Noble, Tim & Webster, Sue. Polymorphous Perverse. 2008. (ENG., Illus.). 56p. 75.00 *(978-1-904212-24-9(7))* Other Criteria GBR. Dist: Hachette Bk. Group.

—Polymorphous Perverse. Beard, Jason, ed. aut. ed. 2008. (ENG., Illus.). 56p. 130.00 *(978-1-904212-39-3(5))* Other Criteria GBR. Dist: Hachette Bk. Group.

Nolen-Weathington, Eric & Wilson, Nathan. Modern Masters Volume 26: Frazer Irving: Frazer Irving. 2011. 120p. pap. 15.95 *(978-1-60549-039-7(3))* TwoMorrows Publishing.

North, Marianne. Abundant Beauty: The Adventurous Travels of Marianne North, Botanical Artist, 1 vol. 2011. (ENG.). 224p. pap. 16.95 *(978-1-55365-541-1(9)*, Greystone Bks.) D&M Pubs. Inc. CAN. Dist: Perseus-PGW.

Ofili, Chris. Chris Ofili. 2009. (ENG., Illus.). 272p. 85.00 *(978-0-8478-3215-6(5))* Rizzoli International Pubns., Inc.

Oldfield Ford, Laura. Savage Messiah. 2011. (ENG., Illus.). 464p. pap. 29.95 *(978-1-84467-747-4(8)*, 844747) Verso Bks. GBR. Dist: Norton, W. W. & Co., Inc.

O'Reilly, Sally, ed. Brian Griffiths: Crummy Love. 2011. (ENG., Illus.). 208p. 55.00 ***(978-3-86560-957-1(0))*** Verlag der Buchhandlung Walther Konig DEU. Dist: D.A.P./Distributed Art Pubs.

Parker, Terry. Softly Awakes My Heart. 2010. 200p. pap. 14.49 *(978-1-4490-6797-7(2))* AuthorHouse.

Payne, Matthew & Payne, James. Regarding Thomas Rowlandson, 1757-1827: His Life, art & Acquaintance. 2011. (ENG., Illus.). 352p. (C). 65.00 *(978-0-9554063-5-5(8))* Holberton, Paul Publishing GBR. Dist: Univ. of Washington Pr.

Penrose, Antony. The Home of the Surrealists: Lee Miller, Roland Penrose & Their Circle at Farley Farm. 2008. (ENG., Illus.). 144p. pap. 29.95 *(978-0-7112-2832-0(9))* Lincoln, Frances Ltd. GBR. Dist: Perseus-PGW.

Peyton-Jones, Julia. Derek Jarman. 2008. (ENG., Illus.). 96p. pap. 52.00 *(978-3-86560-397-5(1))* Verlag der Buchhandlung Walther Konig DEU. Dist: D.A.P./Distributed Art Pubs.

Phagan, Patricia, et al. Thomas Rowlandson: Pleasures & Pursuits in Georgian England. 2011. (ENG., Illus.). 184p. 59.95 *(978-1-904832-78-2(4))* Giles, D. Ltd. GBR. Dist: Antique Collectors' Club.

—Thomas Rowlandson: Pleasures & Pursuits in Georgian England. 2011. (Illus.). 184p. *(978-0-9620606-1-2(0))* Loeb, Frances Lehman Art Ctr., Vassar Coll., The.

Porter, Gail. Laid Bare: My Story of Love, Fame & Survival. 2008. (ENG., Illus.). 320p. pap. 15.95 *(978-0-09-192041-8(8))* Ebury Publishing GBR. Dist: Independent Pubs. Group.

Prettejohn, Elizabeth, ed. The Cambridge Companion to the Pre-Raphaelites. 2012. (ENG., Illus.). 336p. (C). 95.00 ***(978-0-521-89515-6(4))***; pap. 29.99 ***(978-0-521-71931-5(3))*** Cambridge Univ. Pr.

Quinlan, Mark. Architects & Sculptors of Remembrance. 2007. 180p. per. *(978-0-7552-0398-7(4))* Authors OnLine, Ltd.

Ramos, Todd & Rushbury, Julia. Henry Rushbury - Prints: A Catalogue Raisonné. 2011. (ENG., Illus.). 107p. 45.00 *(978-1-905711-85-7(9))* Royal Academy of Arts GBR. Dist: Hachette Bk. Group.

Read, Dennis M. R. H. Cromek Engraver Editor & Entrepreneur. 2011. (Illus.). 194p. 99.95 *(978-0-7546-6399-7(X))* Ashgate Publishing Co.

Rebellato, Dan & Eatough, Graham, eds. The Suspect Culture Club. 2012. (ENG.). 260p. pap. 60.95 ***(978-1-84943-087-6(X))*** Oberon Bks., Ltd. GBR. Dist: Consortium Bk. Sales & Distribution.

Rickett, Sophy, photos by. Sophy Rickett, 1 vol. 2008. (ENG., Illus.). 112p. 35.00 *(978-3-86521-098-3(0))* Steidl, Gerhard Druckerei und Verlag DEU. Dist: Innovative Logistics.

Robinson, Michael. The Pre-Raphaelites: A study of the artists, their lives & context, with 500 images, & a gallery showing 300 of their most iconic Paintings. 2012. (ENG., Illus.). 256p. 35.00 ***(978-0-7548-2379-7(2))*** Anness Publishing GBR. Dist: National Bk. Network.

Ross, Carolyn. Tony Hart: A Portrait of My Dad. 2010. (ENG., Illus.). 256p. 29.95 *(978-1-84358-184-0(1))* Blake, John Publishing, Ltd. GBR. Dist: Independent Pubs. Group.

Ross, Robert Baldwin. Aubrey Beardsley. 2009. (Illus.). 62p. pap. *(978-0-217-33404-4(0))* Books LLC.

Ross, Robert Baldwin & Vallance, Aymer. Aubrey Beardsley. 2008. 144p. 35.95 *(978-1-4368-9941-3(9))*; pap. 20.95 *(978-1-4367-8332-3(1))* Kessinger Publishing, LLC.

Royal Botanic Gardens, Kew. Official Guide to the Marianne North Gallery. 2010. (Illus.). 208p. 22.00 *(978-1-84246-424-3(8))* Kew Publishing GBR. Dist: Chicago Distribution Ctr.

Saint, Andrew. Richard Norman Shaw. rev. ed. 2010. (ENG., Illus.). 488p. 65.00 *(978-0-300-15526-6(3))* Yale Univ. Pr.

Sans, Jerome. Stray Alchemists: Matt Bryans, Amy Granat, Lim Tzay Chuen, Takeshi Murata, Robin Rhode, Sterling Ruby. Fowle, Kate, ed. 2009. (ENG., Illus.). 140p. pap. 23.00 *(978-988-17521-3-0(2))* Timezone 8 Ltd. HKG. Dist: D.A.P./Distributed Art Pubs.

Schlenker, Ines. Marie-Louise Von Motesiczky: Catalogue Raisonné of the Paintings. 2009. (ENG., Illus.). 560p. 150.00 *(978-1-55595-322-5(0))* Hudson Hills Pr. LLC.

Schoeser, Mary. Rozanne Hawksley. 2009. (Illus.). 200p. 80.00 *(978-1-84822-026-3(X)*, Lund Humphries Pubs.) Ashgate Publishing, Ltd. GBR. Dist: Ashgate Publishing Co.

Schoone-Jongen, Terence G. Shakespeare's Companies: William Shakespeare's Early Career & the Acting Companies ,1577-1594. 2008. (Studies in Performance & Early Modern Drama Ser.). 264p. 114.95 *(978-0-7546-6434-5(1))* Ashgate Publishing Co.

Schuchard, Marsha Keith. William Blake's Sexual Path to Spiritual Vision. 2nd ed. 2008. (Illus.). 398p. pap. 19.95 *(978-1-59477-211-5(8))* Inner Traditions International, Ltd.

Schuppli, Madeleine & De Vries, Janneke, eds. Mark Wallinger. 2008. (ENG., Illus.). 160p. pap. 55.00 *(978-3-905829-78-5(9))* JRP Ringier Kunstverlag AG CHE. Dist: D.A.P./Distributed Art Pubs.

Scott, Richard. Artists at Walberswick: East Anglian Interludes, 1880-2000. 2012. (ENG., Illus.). 184p. pap. 40.00 *(978-1-904537-96-0(0))* Art Dictionaries Ltd. GBR. Dist: National Bk. Network.

Sever, Nancy & Haynes, Peter, comments. Phillip Hughes: Mountains of the Mind. 2008. (Illus.). 36p. pap. *(978-0-9804606-0-5(3))* Australian National University - Drill Hall Gallery.

Simpson, Jane & Groos, Ulrike. Fresh, Fresher. Beard, Jason, ed. 2008. (ENG.). 104p. pap. 90.00 *(978-1-904212-36-2(0))* Other Criteria GBR. Dist: Hachette Bk. Group.

—Jane Simpson: Fresh Fresher. Beard, Jason, ed. 2008. (ENG., Illus.). 104p. 45.00 *(978-1-904212-01-0(8))* Other Criteria GBR. Dist: Hachette Bk. Group.

Sinclair, Nicholas & Evans, Rian. Kyffin Williams. 2007. (ENG., Illus.). 136p. 55.00 *(978-1-905711-00-0(X))* Royal Academy of Arts GBR. Dist: Hachette Bk. Group.

Skipwith, Peyton & Webb, Brian. Edward Bawden's London. 2011. (ENG., Illus.). 160p. 40.00 *(978-1-85177-655-9(9))* V & A Pubns. GBR. Dist: Hachette Bk. Group.

Slinkachu. Big Bad City, 300 vols. 2011. (ENG.). 160p. pap. 25.95 *(978-90-488-0190-9(7))* Lebowski NLD. Dist: SCB Distributors.

Slinkachu, photos by. Little People in the City: The Street Art of Slinkachu. 2009. (ENG., Illus.). 128p. 14.95 *(978-0-7522-2664-4(9))* Macmillan Pubs., Ltd. GBR. Dist: Independent Pubs. Group.

Smith, Bob. I Should be in Charge: Bob & Roberta Smith. 2011. (ENG., Illus.). 240p. 49.95 *(978-1-907317-26-2(0))* Black Dog Publishing Ltd. GBR. Dist: Perseus Distribution.

Smith, Michael. Drawings: Simple, Obscure & Obtuse, 1 vol. 2007. (ENG., Illus.). 144p. per. 35.00 *(978-0-9749037-7-4(9))* Regency Arts Pr.

Sorensen, Lita. Bryan Talbot. 2009. (Library of Graphic Novelists Ser.). 112p. (gr. 7-12). 63.90 *(978-1-60853-653-5(X))* Rosen Publishing Group, Inc., The.

Spalding, Frances. The Bloomsbury Group. 2006. (National Portrait Gallery Insights Ser.). (Illus.). 108p. 19.95 *(978-1-85514-351-7(8))* National Portrait Gallery Pubns. GBR. Dist: Antique Collectors' Club.

—John Piper, Myfanwy Piper: Lives in Art. 2011. (ENG., Illus.). 624p. pap. 29.95 *(978-0-19-956762-1(X))* Oxford Univ. Pr., Inc.

Spencer, Stephanie. Francis Bedford, Landscape Photography & Nineteenth-Century British Culture: The Artist As Entrepreneur. 2011. (Illus.). 212p. 104.95 *(978-1-4094-0853-6(1))* Ashgate Publishing Co.

Staikos, Susie Stanton, et al. David Breuer - Weil Radical Visionary. 2011. (ENG., Illus.). 400p. 100.00 *(978-88-572-0863-3(X))* Skira Editore ITA. Dist: Random Hse., Inc.

Stanley, Michael. Thomas Houseago: What Went Down. 2011. (Illus.). 240p. 70.00 *(978-1-901352-50-4(1)*, Lund Humphries Pubs.) Ashgate Publishing, Ltd. GBR. Dist: Ashgate Publishing Co.

Starkey, Hannah. Hannah Starkey: One, 1 vol. Jobey, Liz & Kullmann, Isabella, eds. 2008. (ENG., Illus.). 112p. 60.00 *(978-3-86521-373-0(1))* Steidl, Gerhard Druckerei und Verlag DEU. Dist: Innovative Logistics.

Stemp, Sinty. Jean Muir: Beyond Fashion. 2009. (ENG., Illus.). 176p. *(978-1-85149-621-1(1)*, Antique Collectors Club Dist) Antique Collectors' Club.

Stetz, Margaret D. Facing the Late Victorians: Portraits of Writers & Artists from the Mark Samuels Lasner Collection. 2007. (Illus.). 158p. pap. 49.00 *(978-0-87413-992-1(9))* Univ. of Delaware Pr.

sykes, christopher simon. David Hockney: The Biography. 2012. (ENG., Illus.). 384p. 35.00 ***(978-0-385-53144-3(3)***, Talese, Nan A.) Knopf Doubleday Publishing Group.

Tatham, Frederick. The Letters of William Blake. Russell, Archibald G., ed. (ENG.). 364p. 2007. 46.95 *(978-0-548-13915-8(6))* 2006. per. 31.95 *(978-1-4286-5092-3(X))* Kessinger Publishing, LLC.

Taylor-Wood, Sam, photos by. Birth of a Clown, 1 vol. 2011. (ENG., Illus.). 112p. 95.00 *(978-3-86521-853-7(9))* Steidl, Gerhard Druckerei und Verlag DEU. Dist: Innovative Logistics.

Terry, Chris. Tattooed by the Family Business. 2011. (ENG., Illus.). 208p. 39.95 *(978-1-86205-883-5(0))* Chrysalis Children's Bks. GBR. Dist: Independent Pubs. Group.

Thirlwell, Angela. Into the Frame: The Four Loves of Ford Madox Brown. 2010. (ENG., Illus.). 328p. 39.95 *(978-0-7011-7902-1(3)*, Chatto & Windus) Random Hse. GBR. Dist: Independent Pubs. Group.

Thomas, Brad, ed. Ewan Gibbs: America. 2011. (ENG., Illus.). 100p. 50.00 *(978-1-890573-10-2(8))* Van Every Smith Galleries at Davidson College.

Thomas, Maggie. Dishing the Dirt - 30 Years Behind the Scenes in Television Makeup. 2009. (Illus.). 106p. pap. *(978-0-7552-0453-3(0))* Authors OnLine, Ltd.

Tracy, Nicholas. Britannia's Palette: The Arts of Naval Victory. 2007. (ENG., Illus.). 496p. (C). *(978-0-7735-3113-0(0))* McGill-Queen's Univ. Pr.

Turner, Silvie. Julian Trevelyan Catalogue Raisonne of Prints: Revised Reprint. rev. ed. 2010. (Illus.). 184p. 170.00 *(978-1-84822-077-5(4)*, Lund Humphries Pubs.) Ashgate Publishing, Ltd. GBR. Dist: Ashgate Publishing Co.

Valli, Marc & Brereton, Richard, eds. RGB: Reviewing Graphics in Britain. 2010. (Illus.). 288p. pap. *(978-84-96954-78-6(1))* Actar Birkhauser Distribution.

Vann, Philip. Cyril Power Linocuts: A Complete Catalogue. 2008. (Illus.). 112p. pap. 50.00 *(978-1-84822-018-8(9)*, Lund Humphries Pubs.) Ashgate Publishing, Ltd. GBR. Dist: Ashgate Publishing Co.

Verzotti, Giorgio & D'Argenzio, Mirta, eds. Douglas Gordon: Pretty Much Every Word Written, Spoken, Heard, Overheard from 1989... Voyage in Italy. 2007. (ENG., Illus.). 128p. pap. 36.95 *(978-88-6130-005-7(7))* Skira Editore ITA. Dist: Random Hse., Inc.

Von Zwehl, Bettina, photos by. Bettina Von Zwehl, 1 vol. 2008. (ENG., Illus.). 112p. 35.00 *(978-3-86521-288-7(3))* Steidl, Gerhard Druckerei und Verlag DEU. Dist: Innovative Logistics.

Walpole, Josephine. Leonard Russell Squirrell RWS RE: Artist of East Anglia, 1893-1979. 2011. (ENG., Illus.). 128p. 49.50 ***(978-1-85149-666-2(1))*** Antique Collectors' Club.

Walpole, Josephine. Suffolk Artists of the Eighteenth & Nineteenth Century. 2009. (ENG., Illus.). 160p. *(978-1-85149-579-5(7)*, Antique Collectors Club Dist) Antique Collectors' Club.

Webb, Brian & Artmonsky, Ruth. FHK Henrion. 2011. (ENG., Illus.). 96p. 19.95 *(978-1-85149-632-7(7))* Antique Collectors' Club.

Webb, Brian & Skipwith, Peyton. Harold Curwen & Oliver Simon: Curwen Press. 2009. (ENG., Illus.). 96p. *(978-1-85149-571-9(1)*, Antique Collectors Club Dist) Antique Collectors' Club.

—Peter Blake. 2010. (ENG., Illus.). 96p. *(978-1-85149-618-1(1)*, Antique Collectors Club Dist) Antique Collectors' Club.

Weschler, Lawrence. True to Life: Twenty-Five Years of Conversations with David Hockney. 2009. (ENG., Illus.). 304p. 50.00 *(978-0-520-24375-0(7))* Univ. of California Pr.

Westwood, Martin. Martin Westwood. Beard, Jason, ed. aut. ed. 2008. (ENG.). 88p. pap. 95.00 *(978-1-904212-09-6(3))* Other Criteria GBR. Dist: Hachette Bk. Group.

Wettlaufer, Alexandra. Portraits of the Artist as a Young Woman: Painting & the Novel in France & Britain, 1800-1860. 2011. cd-rom 14.95 *(978-0-8142-9244-0(5))* Ohio State Univ. Pr.

—Portraits of the Artist as a Young Woman: Painting & the Novel in France & Britain, 1800-1860. 2011. 368p. 59.95 *(978-0-8142-1145-8(3))* Ohio State Univ. Pr.

Wiggins, Colin, et al. Leon Kossoff: Drawing from Painting. 2007. (ENG., Illus.). 112p. pap. 25.00 *(978-1-85709-353-7(4))* Yale Univ. Pr.

Williams, Val & Bright, Susan. How We Are: Photographing Britain - From the 1840s to the Present. 2007. (ENG., Illus.). 244p. pap. 39.95 *(978-1-85437-714-2(0))* Tate Publishing, Ltd. GBR. Dist: Hachette Bk. Group.

Wilson, Franklin. Life Story of Franklin Wilson As Told by. 2006. pap. 20.95 *(978-1-4286-6100-4(X))* Kessinger Publishing, LLC.

Wilson, Timothy, et al. Edward Ardizzone. (Illus.). 16p. pap. 6.95 *(978-1-85444-144-7(2))* Ashmolean Museum GBR. Dist: Weatherhill, Inc.

Wilton, Andrew. Turner in His Time. rev. ed. 2007. (Illus.). 240p. 60.00 *(978-0-500-23830-1(8))* Thames & Hudson.

Wingate, Ashmore Kyle Paterson. Life & Writings of John Ruskin. 2009. 154p. pap. *(978-0-217-50392-1(6))* Books LLC.

Wootton, David & Nickerson, Fiona. The Definitive Thelwell. 2010. (ENG., Illus.). 104p. pap. *(978-1-905738-14-4(5))* Beeties, Chris Ltd.

Yorke, Malcolm. Edward Bawden & His Circle: The Inward Laugh. 2007. (ENG., Illus.). 264p. *(978-1-85149-542-9(8)*, Antique Collectors Club Dist) Antique Collectors' Club.

Zybok, Oliver, ed. Lothar Götz, Works - 2011. 2011. (ENG., Illus.). 231p. 60.00 ***(978-3-7757-3002-0(8))*** Hatje Cantz Verlag GmbH & Co KG DEU. Dist: D.A.P./Distributed Art Pubs.

ARTISTS—GREECE

Abranowicz, William, photos by. Hellas. 2011. (ENG., Illus.). 160p. 50.00 *(978-1-55595-333-1(6))* Hudson Hills Pr. LLC.

Argyropoulou, Nadja & Aukeman, Anastasia. Lydia Venieri: Theogony. 2011. (ENG., Illus.). 152p. pap. 37.50 *(978-88-8158-792-6(0))* Charta ITA. Dist: D.A.P./Distributed Art Pubs.

Baldon, Diana, et al, texts. 2nd Athens Biennale 2009: Heaven. 2010. (ENG., Illus.). 360p. pap. 35.00 *(978-960-98893-1-5(X))* Athens Biennial GRC. Dist: D.A.P./Distributed Art Pubs.

Chamberlain, Brenda. A Rope of Vines: Journal from a Greek Island. Smith, Dai, ed. 2009. (Library of Wales Ser.). (ENG., Illus.). 148p. pap. 12.95 *(978-1-905762-86-6(0))* Parthian Bks. GBR. Dist: Independent Pubs. Group.

Vassilaki, Maria & Vasilake, Maria. The Painter Angelos & Icon-Painting in Venetian Crete. 2009. (Variorum Collected Studies). (Illus.). 382p. 180.00 *(978-0-7546-5945-7(3))* Ashgate Publishing Co.

ARTISTS—HUNGARY

Legrady, Kata & Rosenberg, David, eds. Kata Legrady: Bombs & Candies. 2011. (ENG., Illus.). 80p. 75.00 *(978-88-572-0860-2(5))* Skira Editore ITA. Dist: Random Hse., Inc.

ARTISTS—INDIA

Adajania, Nancy, ed. Shilpa Gupta. 2010. (Illus.). 248p. 60.00 *(978-3-7913-5017-2(X))* Prestel Publishing.

Ahuja, Naman. Devi Prasad: The Making of a Modern Indian Artist. 2011. (ENG.). (C). 150.00 *(978-0-415-60229-7(7)*, Routledge India) Taylor & Francis Group GBR. Dist: Taylor & Francis Group.

Beach, Milo, et al, eds. Masters of Indian Painting, 1100-1900, 2 vols. 2011. (ENG., Illus.). 2p. (C). 200.00 ***(978-3-907077-50-4(4))*** Holberton, Paul Publishing GBR. Dist: Univ. of Washington Pr.

Dalmia, Yashodhara. Journeys: Four Generations of Indian Artists in Their Own Words two-volume Set, 2 vols. 2011. (ENG., Illus.). 628p. 225.00 ***(978-0-19-807319-2(4))*** Oxford Univ. Pr., Inc.

Dayanita Singh. Go Away Closer, 1 vol. 2009. (ENG., Illus.). 32p. pap. 15.00 *(978-3-86521-386-0(3))* Steidl, Gerhard Druckerei und Verlag DEU. Dist: Innovative Logistics.

De, Aditi, et al. Lines from an Artistic Life: The Drawings of Adimoolam. 2008. (Illus.). 164p. 70.00 *(978-0-85331-982-5(0)*, Lund Humphries Pubs.) Ashgate Publishing, Ltd. GBR. Dist: Ashgate Publishing Co.

Doron, Itai, photos by. Chokras' Mahal. 2011. (ENG., Illus.). 128p. 75.00 *(978-1-904212-47-8(6))* Other Criteria GBR. Dist: Hachette Bk. Group.

Gayatri Sinha. The Embrace of Love: Krishen Khanna. 2006. (Contemporary Indian Artists Ser.). (ENG., Illus.). 120p. 45.00 *(978-1-890206-90-1(3))* Mapin Publishing Pvt. Ltd IND. Dist: National Bk. Network.

Gowda, Sheela. Sheela Gowda, 1 vol. 2008. (ENG., Illus.). 160p. 55.00 *(978-3-86521-469-0(X))* Steidl, Gerhard Druckerei und Verlag DEU. Dist: Innovative Logistics.

Hoskote, Ranjit. Dancer on the Horse: Reflections on the Art of Iranna Gr. 2007. (Contemporary Indian Artists Ser.). (Illus.). 128p. 70.00 *(978-0-85331-965-8(0)*, Lund Humphries Pubs.) Ashgate Publishing, Ltd. GBR. Dist: Ashgate Publishing Co.

Huyler, Stephen P. Daughters of India: Art & Identity. 2008. (ENG., Illus.). 263p. 65.00 *(978-0-7892-1002-9(9))* Abbeville Pr., Inc.

Hyman, Timothy. Bhupen Khakhar. (Contemporary Indian Art Ser.). (Illus.). 127p. pap. 35.00 *(978-81-85822-55-6(7))* Mapin Publishing Pvt. Ltd IND. Dist: Antique Collectors' Club.

Jhaveri, Amrit. 101: A Guide to 101 Modern & Contemporary Indian Artists. 2008. (Artists Ser.). (Illus.). 191p. pap. 29.95 *(978-81-7508-423-0(5))* India Bk. Hse. Pvt., Ltd. IND. Dist: Antique Collectors' Club.

Kadari, Sohana. Sohan Qadri. Mitter, Partha & Dewan, Deepali, eds. 2012. (ENG., Illus.). 144p. 75.00 *(978-88-572-0647-9(5))* Skira Editore ITA. Dist: Random Hse., Inc.

Kwint, Marius & Sandler, Irving. Natvar Bhavsar: Poetics of Color. 2009. (ENG., Illus.). 192p. 80.00 *(978-88-6130-795-7(7))* Skira Editore ITA. Dist: Random Hse., Inc.

Malani, Nalini, illus. Nalini Malani, 1 vol. 2007. (ENG.). 144p. 55.00 *(978-88-8158-644-8(4))* Charta ITA. Dist: D.A.P./Distributed Art Pubs.

Mehta, Anupa. India 20: Conversations with Contemporary Artists. 2008. (ENG., Illus.). 216p. pap. 45.00 *(978-0-944142-60-8(5))* Mapin Publishing Pvt. Ltd IND. Dist: National Bk. Network.

Sarabhai, Rajshree. Zen of Seeing. 2007. (ENG., Illus.). 80p. 35.00 *(978-1-890206-81-9(4))* Mapin Publishing Pvt. Ltd IND. Dist: National Bk Network.

Sengupta, Ratnottama. Krishna's Cosmos: The Creativity of an Artist, Sculptor & Teacher. 2006. (ENG., Illus.). 132p. 45.00 *(978-1-890206-54-3(7))* Mapin Publishing Pvt. Ltd IND. Dist: National Bk. Network.

Sheh, Pratima, text. Dictionary of Indian Art & Artists. 2007. (ENG., Illus.). 65.00 *(978-1-890206-33-8(4))* Mapin Publishing Pvt. Ltd IND. Dist: National Bk. Network.

Sheikh, Mohammed & Shiv Kumar, R. Benodebehari Mukherjee: A Centenary Retrospective Exhibition. 2010. (ENG., Illus.). 365p. 100.00 *(978-81-87737-24-7(7)*, Vadehra Art Gallery (Acc)) Antique Collectors' Club GBR. Dist: National Bk. Network.

Singh, Dayanita, photos by. Dayanita Singh: House of Love. 2011. (ENG., Illus.). 185p. 45.00 *(978-1-934435-27-4(9))* Radius Bks.

A

Sinha, Gayatri. Voices of Change: 20 Indian Artists. 2011. (Illus.). 316p. 80.00 *(978-93-80581-06-4(8))* Marg Foundation, The.

Sinha, Modhurima. Call of the Real: Contemporary Indian Artists from Bengal. (Contemporary Indian Art Ser.). (Illus.). 180p. 65.00 *(978-81-88204-28-1(5))* Mapin Publishing Pvt. Ltd IND. Dist: Antique Collectors' Club.

Storr, Robert. Nalini Malani: Listening to the Shades. 2009. (ENG., Illus.). 160p. 55.00 *(978-88-8158-703-2(3))* Charta ITA. Dist: D.A.P./Distributed Art Pubs.

Upadhyay, Hema. Universe Revolves On. 2010. (Illus.). 104p. pap. 24.95 *(978-81-907226-3-6(8),* Vadehra Art Gallery (Acc)) Antique Collectors' Club GBR. Dist: National Bk. Network.

Venumadav. Mimicry & World Renowned. 2006. 132p. per. *(978-1-4067-2032-7(1),* Hesperides Pr.) Read Bks.

ARTISTS—IRELAND

Brougham, John. A Basket of Chips by John Brougham. 2006. 412p. per. 26.99 *(978-1-4255-4467-6(3))* MPublishing.

Clark, Adrian. British & Irish Art, 1945-1951: From War to Festival. 2010. (Illus.). 272p. 50.00 ***(978-0-9554063-4-8(X))*** Holberton, Paul Publishing GBR. Dist: Casemate Pubs. & Bk. Distributors, LLC.

Clarke, Harry, illus. Nightmares in Decay: The Edgar Allan Poe Illustrations of Harry Clarke. 2010. 88p. pap. 19.95 *(978-1-902197-30-2(5))* Oneiros Bks. GBR. Dist: SCB Distributors.

Cookson, Linda. Tea 'N Turps. 2009. 90p. pap. 26.95 *(978-1-60860-848-5(4),* Eloquent Bks.) AEG Literary Publishing Services, Inc.

Cork, Richard. Michael Craig-Martin. 2007. (ENG., Illus.). 256p. 60.00 *(978-0-500-09332-0(6))* Thames & Hudson.

Costigan, Lucy & Cullen, Michael. Strangest Genius: The Stained Glass of Harry Clare. 2010. (ENG., Illus.). 320p. 75.00 ***(978-1-84588-971-5(1))*** History Pr. Ltd.,The GBR. Dist: Independent Pubs. Group.

Dunne, Aidan. Patrick Scott. 2008. (ENG.). 256p. 249.95 *(978-1-905483-53-2(8))* Liberties Pr. IRL. Dist: Dufour Editions, Inc.

Evans, Paul. Uncle Hugo: The Story of the Wee Man from Strabane. 2009. (ENG., Illus.). 182p. pap. 26.95 *(978-0-85640-820-5(4))* Blackstaff Pr., Ltd. GBR. Dist: Dufour Editions, Inc.

Farrell, David. Micheal Farrell: The Life & Work of an Irish Artist. 2007. (ENG., Illus.). 214p. 47.95 *(978-1-904148-89-0(1))* Liffey Pr., The IRL. Dist: Dufour Editions, Inc.

Gerrard, John, photos by. John Gerrard. 2011. (ENG., Illus.). 176p. 55.00 ***(978-84-938340-3-6(3))*** Ivory Pr. ESP. Dist: D.A.P./Distributed Art Pubs.

Irwin, Tony. Bounded By. 2010. 64p. pap. *(978-3-8383-7027-9(9))* Lambert Academic Publishing.

Juncosa, Enrique, et al. Francis Alys: Le\Temps du Sommeil. 2010. (ENG., Illus.). 184p. 49.95 *(978-88-8158-777-3(7))* Charta ITA. Dist: D.A.P./Distributed Art Pubs.

LaFuente, Pablo, ed. Gerard Byrne: Images or Shadows. 2011. (ENG., Illus.). 224p. pap. 45.00 ***(978-1-907020-61-2(6))*** Irish Museum of Modern Art IRL. Dist: D.A.P./Distributed Art Pubs.

Lynch, Brendan. Parsons Bookshop: At the Heart of Bohemian Dublin, 1949-1989. 2007. (ENG., Illus.). 264p. per. 27.95 *(978-1-905785-11-7(9))* Liffey Pr., The IRL. Dist: Dufour Editions, Inc.

—Prodigals & Geniuses: The Writers & Artists of Dublin's Baggotonia. 2012. (ENG., Illus.). 325p. pap. 31.95 *(978-1-905785-96-4(8))* Liffey Pr., The IRL. Dist: Dufour Editions, Inc.

O'Byrne, Robert. Dictionary of Living Irish Artists. 2010. (ENG., Illus.). 400p. 97.50 *(978-0-9563011-0-9(X),* Plurabelle Publishing (Acc)) Antique Collectors' Club GBR. Dist: National Bk. Network.

O'Connor, Eimear, ed. Irish Women Artists, 1800-2009: Familiar but Unknown. 2010. (Illus.). 240p. 70.00 *(978-1-84682-250-6(5))* Four Courts Pr. IRL. Dist: International Specialized Bk. Services.

Ryan, Vera. Movers & Shapers 2: Irish Visual Art 1940-2006. 2006. (ENG., Illus.). 392p. per. 36.95 *(978-1-905172-03-0(6))* Collins Pr., The IRL. Dist: Dufour Editions, Inc.

ARTISTS—ISRAEL

Abdunnur, Sharif. My Brother's Bicycle. 2010. 64p. pap. 15.99 *(978-1-4500-9196-1(2))* Xlibris Corp.

Doron, Itai. End of Real. Beard, Jason, ed. 2008. (ENG.). 162p. 90.00 *(978-1-904212-32-4(8))* Other Criteria GBR. Dist: Hachette Bk. Group.

Doron, Itai. End of Real. Beard, Jason, ed. 2008. (ENG., Illus.). 162p. 65.00 *(978-1-904212-07-2(7))* Other Criteria GBR. Dist: Hachette Bk. Group.

Eccher, Danilo, ed. Nahum Tevet: [in English & Italian]. 2008. 80p. pap. 56.50 *(978-88-370-6144-9(7))* Electa ITA. Dist: Trans-Atlantic Pubns., Inc.

Grether, Reinhold. Manfred Stumpf. (GER & ENG., Illus.). 118p. *(978-3-89322-856-0(X))* Edition Cantz DEU. Dist: D.A.P./Distributed Art Pubs.

Joyce, Julie, et al. Ori Gersht: Lost in Time. 2011. pap. ***(978-0-89951-112-2(0))*** Santa Barbara Museum of Art.

Mishori, Efrat. Mika Rottenberg. 2011. (ENG., Illus.). 204p. 45.00 *(978-0-9826813-0-5(5))* Miller, Gregory & Co.

Rosenblum, Adi & Muntean, Markus. Muntean / Rosenblum. 2009. (ENG, MUL & GER., Illus.). 84p. 49.00 *(978-3-86678-167-2(9))* Kerber Verlag DEU. Dist: D.A.P./Distributed Art Pubs.

Sapir, Shaul. From Jerusalem with Love: Art, Photos & Souvenirs, 1799-1948. 2010. (ENG., Illus.). 224p. pap. 60.00 *(978-90-400-8638-0(9))* Waanders B.V., Uitgeverij NLD. Dist: National Bk. Network.

Steffensen. Tal R Etchings Masters & Method. 2008. (ENG., Illus.). 276p. 195.00 *(978-3-7757-2163-9(0))* Hatje Cantz Verlag GmbH & Co KG DEU. Dist: D.A.P./Distributed Art Pubs.

ARTISTS—ITALY

Artioli, Luca. Beyond the Dark: Medicine & Art. 2009. (ENG & ITA., Illus.). 112p. 87.50 *(978-88-370-6897-4(2))* Electa ITA. Dist: Trans-Atlantic Pubns., Inc.

Atalay, Bulent & Wamsley, Keith. Leonardo's Universe: The Renaissance World of Leonardo Da Vinci. 2008. (Illus.). 287p. *(978-1-4262-0286-5(5))* National Geographic Society.

Atalay, Bulent, et al. Leonardo's Universe: The Renaissance World of Leonardo Da Vinci. 2009. (ENG., Illus.). 288p. 35.00 *(978-1-4262-0285-8(7),* National Geographic) National Geographic Society.

Avery, Charles. Bertos: The Triumph of Motion. 2008. (ENG., Illus.). 400p. 100.00 *(978-88-422-1556-1(2))* Allemandi, Umberto & Co. GBR. Dist: Antique Collectors' Club.

Barnes, Bernadine. Michelangelo in Print: Reproductions as Response in the Sixteenth-Century. 2010. (Illus.). 244p. 109.95 *(978-0-7546-6378-2(7))* Ashgate Publishing Co.

Bellini, Andrea, ed. & text. Paolo Mussat Sartor. 2009. (ENG., Illus.). 296p. pap. 45.00 *(978-3-03764-004-3(9))* JRP Ringier Kunstverlag AG CHE. Dist: D.A.P./Distributed Art Pubs.

Bertola, Chiara & Maraniello, Gianfranco, eds. On Mobility: Giovani Artisti Italiani, 1 vol. 2007. (ENG., Illus.). 120p. pap. 34.95 *(978-88-8158-631-8(2))* Charta ITA. Dist: D.A.P./Distributed Art Pubs.

Biow, Douglas. In Your Face: Professional Improprieties & the Art of Being Conspicuous in Sixteenth-Century Italy. 2009. (ENG., Illus.). 272p. 70.00 *(978-0-8047-6215-1(5));* pap. 24.95 *(978-0-8047-6216-8(3))* Stanford Univ. Pr.

Bonito Oliva, Achille. Gino De Dominicis: The Immortal. 2011. (ENG., Illus.). 388p. pap. 99.00 *(978-88-370-7590-3(1))* Electa ITA. Dist: National Bk. Network.

Bonito Oliva, Achille. Marisa Albanese. 2011. (ENG., Illus.). 208p. pap. 45.00 ***(978-88-8158-804-6(8))*** Charta ITA. Dist: D.A.P./Distributed Art Pubs.

Bradley, John W. The Life & Works of Giorgio Giulio Clovio Miniaturist with Notices of His Contemporaries & of the Art of Book Decoration in the Sixteenth Century. 2007. (ENG.). 466p. 52.95 *(978-0-548-03483-5(4))* Kessinger Publishing, LLC.

Campigotto, Luca, photos by. Luca Campigotto: My Wild Places. 2011. (ENG., Illus.). 144p. 85.00 *(978-3-7757-2719-8(1))* Hatje Cantz Verlag GmbH & Co KG DEU. Dist: D.A.P./Distributed Art Pubs.

Casadio, Mariuccia. Fornasetti: The Complete Universe. Fornasetti, Barnaba, ed. 2010. (ENG., Illus.). 688p. 250.00 *(978-0-8478-3534-8(0))* Rizzoli International Pubns., Inc.

Cassidy, Brendan. Gavin Hamilton (1723-1798) Artist, Antiquarian & Art Dealer in Eighteenth-Century Rome. with an Edition of his Letters, 2 vols. 2011. (Collectors & Dealers Ser.). (ENG., Illus.). 750p. (C). 196.00 *(978-1-905375-59-2(X))* Brepols Pubs. BEL. Dist: Brown, David Bk. Co., The.

Celant, Germano. Paolo Canevari. Celant, Germano, ed. 2011. (ITA & ENG., Illus.). 312p. pap. 87.50 *(978-88-370-7603-0(7),* Mondadori Electa (Acc)) Antique Collectors' Club GBR. Dist: National Bk. Network.

Celant, Germano, ed. Francesco Vezzoli, 1 vol. 2006. (ENG., Illus.). 342p. lthr. 85.00 *(978-88-87029-32-1(6))* Fondazione Prada ITA. Dist: D.A.P./Distributed Art Pubs.

Cellini, Benvenuto. The Autobiography of Benvenuto Cellini. 2010. (ENG.). 504p. 28.00 *(978-0-307-59274-3(X),* Everyman's Library) Knopf Doubleday Publishing Group.

Cerizza, Luca. Alighiero e Boetti: Mappa. 2008. (One Work Ser.). (ENG., Illus.). 109p. (gr. 17). 35.00 *(978-1-84638-028-0(6))* Afterall Publishing GBR. Dist: MIT Pr.

—Alighiero e Boetti - Mappa. 2008. (One Work Ser.). (ENG., Illus.). 109p. (gr. 17). pap. 16.00 *(978-1-84638-027-3(8))* Afterall Publishing GBR. Dist: MIT Pr.

Ciampi, Mario. Tuscany Artists at Home. 2011. (ENG., Illus.). 326p. 39.95 ***(978-1-905216-35-2(1))*** Verba Volant, Ltd. GBR. Dist: Ingram Pub. Services.

Clapton, Nicholas. Moreschi: The Angel of Rome. 2008. (ENG., Illus.). 224p. 30.00 *(978-1-905791-42-2(9))* Haus Publishing GBR. Dist: Consortium Bk. Sales & Distribution.

Cole, Kevin, et al, eds. Pompeii: Art, Industry & Infrastructure. 2011. (ENG., Illus.). 200p. (C). pap. 70.00 *(978-1-84217-984-0(5))* Oxbow Bks., Ltd. GBR. Dist: Brown, David Bk. Co., The.

Condivi Ascanio. The Life of Michelangelo. 2007. (Illus.). 175p. pap. *(978-1-84368-012-3(2))* Wilson, John Booksales.

Corgnati, Martina, text. Eugenio Carmi, 1 vol. 2007. (ITA & ENG., Illus.). 176p. 60.00 *(978-88-8158-623-3(1))* Charta ITA. Dist: D.A.P./Distributed Art Pubs.

Curti, Denis, et al, texts. Maurizio Montagna: Billboards. 2009. (ENG., Illus.). 140p. pap. 55.00 *(978-88-6208-026-2(3))* Damiani ITA. Dist: D.A.P./Distributed Art Pubs.

da Vinci, Leonardo. Leonardo's Notebooks. Suh, H. Anna, ed. 2009. (ENG., Illus.). 336p. pap. 24.95 *(978-1-57912-817-3(3),* 1579128173) Black Dog & Leventhal Pubs., Inc.

D'Amico, Fabrizio & Sanfilippo, Antonio. Sanfilippo: Works on Paper. 2009. (Illus.). 143p. *(978-88-8016-919-2(X))* De Luca Editori d'Arte.

De Concilis, Ettore. Ettore De Concilis: Opere 1982-2009. 2009. (ITA., Illus.). 155p. *(978-88-7831-236-4(3),* Spotlight Poets) Cigno Galileo Galilei.

De Luca, Joseph, ed. Joseph de Luca - Selected Works: Drawings, Paintings, Constructions. 2011. (Illus.). 172p. pap. 60.00 ***(978-0-578-08259-2(4))*** De Luca, Joseph.

Dorfles, Gillo. Salvador Presta: A Retrospective of the Works of Salvador Presta. 2007. (ENG, ITA, FRE & SPA.). 64p. 35.00 *(978-0-9758739-0-8(3))* Madi Museum.

Farrachi, Armand. Michel-Ange Face Aux Murs. 2010. (FRE.). 118p. *(978-2-07-012980-5(2))* Gallimard, Editions.

Feinberg, Larry J. The Young Leonardo: Art & Life in Fifteenth-Century Florence. 2011. (ENG., Illus.). 216p. 95.00 ***(978-1-107-00239-5(7))*** Cambridge Univ. Pr.

Filippi Gabardi, Vittoria & Gabardi, Vittoria Filippi. The Whispered Directory of Craftsmanship: A Contemporary Guide to the Italian Handmaking Ability. 2011. (ENG., Illus.). 200p. 69.95 ***(978-88-370-8424-0(2))*** Electa ITA. Dist: National Bk. Network.

Forcellino, Antonio. Michelangelo: A Tormented Life. 2009. (ENG., Illus.). 300p. 25.00 *(978-0-7456-4005-1(2))* Polity Pr. GBR. Dist: Wiley, John & Sons, Inc.

Forcellino, Antonio. Michelangelo: A Turbulent Life. 2011. (ENG., Illus.). 300p. pap. 19.95 ***(978-0-7456-4006-8(0))*** Polity Pr. GBR. Dist: Wiley, John & Sons, Inc.

Frantz, Susanne K. Lino Tagliapietra in Retrospect: A Modern Renaissance in Italian Glass. 2008. (ENG., Illus.). 208p. 50.00 *(978-0-295-98825-2(8))* Univ. of Washington Pr.

Frongia, Antonello & Guerrieri, William, eds. Mose: A Preliminary Report. 2011. (ENG., Illus.). 72p. pap. 55.00 *(978-3-86560-394-4(7))* Verlag der Buchhandlung Walther Konig DEU. Dist: D.A.P./Distributed Art Pubs.

Frothingham, A. L. Notes on Roman Artists of the Middle Ages. 2009. pap. 21.52 *(978-1-60724-493-6(4))* Gorgias Pr., LLC.

Galimberti, Carlo A. & Galimberti, Carlo Adelio. Mogli, garzoni e Amanti: Amore ed erotismo nella vita e nelle opere degli artisti del Cinquecento. 2011. (Storie del Mondo Ser.). (ITA., Illus.). 200p. pap. 29.00 ***(978-88-564-0149-3(5))*** Polistampa ITA. Dist: Brown, David Bk. Co., The.

Galliani, Omar. Omar Galliani: Santi: 1995-2007, 1 vol. 2007. (ENG., Illus.). 144p. 39.00 *(978-88-89431-90-0(3))* Damiani ITA. Dist: D.A.P./Distributed Art Pubs.

Gamba, Claudio. Michelangelo. 2009. (Skira MINI Artbooks Ser.). (ENG., Illus.). 96p. pap. 8.99 *(978-88-6130-739-1(6))* Skira Editore ITA. Dist: Random Hse., Inc.

Gandini, Manuela. Gigi Rigamonti: Cross Stories. Gandini, Manuela, ed. 2009. (ENG., Illus.). 96p. pap. 29.95 *(978-88-8158-736-0(X))* Charta ITA. Dist: D.A.P./Distributed Art Pubs.

Gianfranco, Maraniello & Viliani, Andrea, eds. Giovanni Anselmo, 1 vol. 2007. (ENG., Illus.). 256p. pap. 65.00 *(978-88-7757-210-3(8))* Hopefulmonster Editore ITA. Dist: D.A.P./Distributed Art Pubs.

Gorbman, Claudia. Maestro: Recent Work by Lino Tagliapietra. 2012. (ENG., Illus.). 96p. 50.00 ***(978-0-295-99226-6(3))*** Museum of Glass.

Grimm, Hermann F. Life of Michelangelo V1. Bunnett, Fanny Elizabeth, tr. 2007. (ENG.). 620p. 60.95 *(978-0-548-10998-4(2))* Kessinger Publishing, LLC.

—Life of Michelangelo V2. Bunnett, Fanny Elizabeth, tr. 2007. (ENG.). 588p. 58.95 *(978-0-548-10999-1(0))* Kessinger Publishing, LLC.

Harris, Godfrey. The Legacy of Leonardo Da Vinci. 2007. *(978-0-935047-63-9(8))* Americas Group, The.

Hess, Barbara. Lucio Fontana: 1899-1968. 2006. (Basic Art Ser.). (ENG., Illus.). 96p. pap. 9.99 *(978-3-8228-4918-7(9))* TASCHEN DEU. Dist: Ingram Pub. Services.

Hinz, Manfred. Die Zukunft der Katastrophe: Mythische und rationalistische Geschichtstheorie im italienischen Futurismus. (European University Institute - Series C Ser.). (GER.). VIII, 287p. 225.00 ***(978-3-11-187476-0(1))*** De Gruyter, Walter Inc.

Horley & Spurlock. Alex Horley Sketchbook, 1 vol. 2009. (ENG.). 128p. 34.95 *(978-1-934331-28-6(7));* pap. 24.95 *(978-1-934331-27-9(9))* Vanguard Productions.

Illetschko, Georgia. Michelangelo. 2010. (Illus.). 160p. pap. 19.95 *(978-3-7913-4472-0(2))* Prestel Publishing.

Janssens, S. & Sellink, Manfred. Stradanus (1523-1605), Court Artist of the Medici. 2012. (ENG., Illus.). 304p. (C). pap. 60.00 *(978-2-503-52996-7(8))* Brepols Pubs. BEL. Dist: ISD.

Jodice, Mimmo, photos by. Citta Visibili/Visible Cities, 1 vol. 2007. (ITA & ENG., Illus.). 144p. 60.00 *(978-88-8158-628-8(2))* Charta ITA. Dist: D.A.P./Distributed Art Pubs.

Kelly, Jerry, et al. The Work of the Stamperia Valdonega: 1948-2008. 2009. (Illus.). 96p. 35.00 *(978-1-60583-021-6(6))* Grolier Club of New York, The.

King, Catherine E. Representing Renaissance Art, C. 1500-C. 1600. 2008. (ENG., Illus.). 384p. pap. 34.00 *(978-0-7190-7557-5(2))* Manchester Univ. Pr. GBR. Dist: Macmillan.

Klein, Stefan. Leonardo's Legacy: How Da Vinci Reimagined the World. Frisch, Shelley, tr. 2011. (ENG., Illus.). 304p. pap. 16.00 *(978-0-306-82008-3(0))* Da Capo Pr., Inc.

Ladis, Andrew. Victims & Villains in Vasari's Lives. 2008. (ENG., Illus.). 188p. 39.95 *(978-0-8078-3132-8(8))* Univ. of North Carolina Pr.

Lavin, Marilyn Aronberg. Artists' Art in the Renaissance. 2009. (ENG., Illus.). 230p. (C). 220.00 *(978-1-904597-43-8(2))* Pindar Pr. GBR. Dist: Brown, David Bk. Co., The.

Levy, Evonne, et al, eds. Bernini's Biographies: Critical Essays. 2007. (ENG., Illus.). 376p. 65.00 *(978-0-271-02901-6(3))* Pennsylvania State Univ. Pr.

—Bernini's Biographies: Critical Essays. 2007. (ENG., Illus.). 376p. pap. 35.00 *(978-0-271-02902-3(1))* Pennsylvania State Univ. Pr.

Maccari, Mino & Vallora, Marco. I Maccari Di Maccari. 2009. (ITA., Illus.). 238p. *(978-88-202-1930-7(1))* Mazzotta.

Maffei, Giorgio. Books by Ettore Sottsass. Maffei, Giorgio & Tonini, Bruno, eds. 2011. (ENG., Illus.). 296p. pap. 45.00 ***(978-88-7570-276-2(4))*** Corraini ITA. Dist: D.A.P./Distributed Art Pubs.

Maggio, Filippo & Hauser, Sigrid, texts. Walter Niedermayr Appearances. 2011. (ENG & ITA., Illus.). 108p. 55.00 *(978-88-572-0975-3(X))* Skira Editore ITA. Dist: Random Hse., Inc.

Mascetti, Daniela & Triossi, Amanda. Bvlgari. 2nd ed. 2007. (ENG., Illus.). 319p. 75.00 *(978-0-7892-0945-0(4))* Abbeville Pr., Inc.

Massimo Barbero, Luca, text. Luigi Ontani: MarmArmonia, 1 vol. 2007. (ITA & ENG., Illus.). 104p. 34.95 *(978-88-8158-651-6(7))* Charta ITA. Dist: D.A.P./Distributed Art Pubs.

Mendini, Alessandro. Alessandro Mendini: Wunderkammer Design. 2012. (ENG & GER., Illus.). 204p. 40.00 ***(978-3-86984-255-4(5))*** Verlag fur Moderne Kunst DEU. Dist: D.A.P./Distributed Art Pubs.

Miracco, Renato. Giuseppe Ripa: Liminal. 2011. (ITA & ENG., Illus.). 112p. 49.95 ***(978-88-8158-813-8(7))*** Charta ITA. Dist: D.A.P./Distributed Art Pubs.

Mulas, Ugo, photos by. Fausto Melotti with Photos by Ugo Mulas. 2009. (ENG., Illus.). 80p. pap. 27.95 *(978-88-8158-716-2(5))* Charta ITA. Dist: D.A.P./Distributed Art Pubs.

Muti, Riccardo. Riccardo Muti: An Autobiography - First the Music, Then the Words. 2011. (ENG., Illus.). 244p. 29.95 *(978-0-8478-3724-3(6))* Rizzoli International Pubns., Inc.

Ormiston, Rosalind. Leonardo Da Vinci: His Life & Works in 500 Images. 2011. (ENG., Illus.). 256p. 35.00 *(978-0-7548-2326-1(1))* Anness Publishing GBR. Dist: National Bk. Network.

—Michelangelo: His Life & Works in 500 Images. 2011. (ENG., Illus.). 256p. 35.00 *(978-0-7548-2077-2(7))* Anness Publishing GBR. Dist: National Bk. Network.

Panza, Giuseppe. Giuseppe Panza: Memories of a Collector. 2008. (ENG., Illus.). 416p. pap. 37.50 *(978-0-7892-0944-3(6))* Abbeville Pr., Inc.

Paolini, Giulio. Giulio Paolini. 2009. (ENG.). 96p. pap. 35.00 *(978-88-6208-045-3(X))* Damiani ITA. Dist: D.A.P./Distributed Art Pubs.

Paoluzzo, Marco. Ethiopia. 2007. (ENG., Illus.). 128p. *(978-3-7165-1483-2(7),* Benteli Verlags Ag Dist) Antique Collectors' Club.

Parker, Deborah & Michelangelo Buonarroti. Michelangelo & the Art of Letter Writing. 2010. (ENG., Illus.). 168p. 80.00 *(978-0-521-76140-6(9))* Cambridge Univ. Pr.

Pelligrin, Paolo, photos by. Stern Portfolio 57. Paolo Pellegrin. 2010. 96p. 45.00 *(978-3-570-19847-6(2))* teNeues Publishing Co.

Perrella, Cristiana, ed. Francesco Vezzoli: Greed. 2011. (ENG., Illus.). 96p. 39.95 ***(978-3-86560-949-6(X))*** Verlag der Buchhandlung Walther Konig DEU. Dist: D.A.P./Distributed Art Pubs.

Perry, Alan R. The Don Camillo Stories of Giovannino Guareschi: A Humorist Portrays the Sacred. 2008. (Toronto Italian Studies). (ENG., Illus.). 224p. *(978-0-8020-9756-9(1))* Univ. of Toronto Pr.

Pestriniero, Renato, text. Faces (boxed set W/CD) Volti Truccati Del Carnevale Veneziano. 2006. (ENG.). 180p. 90.00 *(978-88-7200-214-8(1))* Vianello Libri ITA. Dist: National Bk. Network.

Pfeiffer, Heinrich, et al. Andrea Pozzo a Mondovi. 2010. (Illus.). 253p. *(978-88-16-60430-8(1))* Jaca Bk.

Pinto, Roberto, ed. Stefano Cagol: Harajuku Influences, 1 vol. 2007. (JPN, ITA & ENG., Illus.). 128p. pap. 34.95 *(978-88-8158-618-9(5))* Charta ITA. Dist: D.A.P./Distributed Art Pubs.

Pivi, Paola. Paola Pivi: It Just Keeps Getting Better. 2008. (ENG., Illus.). 118p. 58.00 *(978-3-86560-392-4(4))* Verlag der Buchhandlung Walther Konig DEU. Dist: D.A.P./Distributed Art Pubs.

Ragionieri, Pina. Michelangelo: The Man & the Myth. 2008. (Illus.). 120p. (C). 55.00 *(978-0-8122-4148-8(7));* pap. 29.95 *(978-0-8122-2054-4(4))* Univ. of Pennsylvania Pr.

Romano, Dennis. The Likeness of Venice: A Life of Doge Francesco Foscari. 2007. (ENG., Illus.). 368p. 37.00 *(978-0-300-11202-3(5))* Yale Univ. Pr.

Rossi, Papik. Mr. Rossi: Pictures & Farts. 2007. (ENG., Illus.). 96p. pap. 29.00 *(978-88-88493-11-4(5))* Drago Arts & Communication ITA. Dist: SCB Distributors.

Ruskin, John. Mornings in Florence & the Two Paths. 2008. 292p. 25.99 *(978-0-554-35770-6(4))* 2008. 292p. 28.99 *(978-0-554-26467-7(6))* 2007. (ENG.). 258p. pap. 21.99 *(978-1-4346-1177-2(9))* 2007. (ENG.). 290p. pap. 23.99 *(978-1-4346-1248-9(1))* BiblioBazaar.

Salerno, Giovan Battista, et al. Alighiero E Boetti. 2006. (ENG.). 62p. pap. 37.00 *(978-88-422-1433-5(7))* Allemandi, Umberto & Co. GBR. Dist: Antique Collectors' Club.

Schieren, Mona & Sick, Andrea, eds. Look at Me: Celebrity Culture at the Venice Art Biennale. 2011. (ENG., Illus.). 232p. pap. 35.00 ***(978-3-86984-177-9(X))*** Verlag fur Moderne Kunst DEU. Dist: D.A.P./Distributed Art Pubs.

Sgaravatti, Mariella. Tuscany Artists Homes. 2006. (ENG.). 240p. *(978-0-9544288-4-6(6))* Verba Volant, Ltd.

Sohm, Philip. The Artist Grows Old: The Aging of Art & Artists in Italy, 1500-1800. 2007. (ENG., Illus.). 224p. 50.00 *(978-0-300-12123-0(7))* Yale Univ. Pr.

Spike, John T. Young Michelangelo: The Path to the Sistine - A Biography. 2010. (ENG., Illus.). 272p. 27.95 *(978-0-86565-266-8(X))* Vendome Pr., The.

Stingel, Rudolf. Rudolf Stingel: MCA Chicago/Whitney New York. 2009. (ENG., Illus.). 128p. 55.00 *(978-3-7757-2339-8(0))* Hatje Cantz Verlag GmbH & Co KG DEU. Dist: D.A.P./Distributed Art Pubs.

Symonds, John Addington. The Life of Michelangelo Buonarroti. 2008. 536p. 32.99 *(978-0-554-32936-9(0))* 2008. 536p. 35.99 *(978-0-554-23633-9(8))* 2006. 472p. pap. 28.99 *(978-1-4264-4822-5(8))* 2006. 532p. pap. 31.99 *(978-1-4264-4865-2(1))* BiblioBazaar.

—The Life of Michelangelo Buonarroti. 2008. pap. *(978-1-4065-7415-9(5))* Dodo Pr.

—The Life of Michelangelo Buonarroti. 2008. (ENG.). 452p. pap. 27.45 *(978-1-60597-675-4(X),* Book Jungle) Standard Pubns., Inc.

Tavella, Aldo, et al. Aldo Tavella (1909-2004) Il Respiro Di una Vita. 2009. (ITA., Illus.). 143p. *(978-88-6052-280-1(3))* Editoriale Giorgio Mondadori.

Vahland, Kia. Sebastiano Del Piombo: A Venetian in Rome. 2008. (ENG., Illus.). 96p. 30.00 (978-3-7757-2145-5(2)) Hatje Cantz Verlag GmbH & Co KG DEU. Dist: D.A.P./Distributed Art Pubs.

Vasari Giorgio. The Life of Michelangelo. 2007. (Illus.). 237p. pap. (978-1-84368-011-6(4)) Wilson, John Booksales.

Verzotti, Giorgio & Frangi, Giovanni. Pasadena. 2009. (ENG., Illus.). 80p. 39.95 (978-88-8158-699-8(1)) Charta ITA. Dist: D.A.P./Distributed Art Pubs.

Viliani, Andrea, ed. Stefano Cagol: Public Opinion. 2011. (ITA & ENG., Illus.). 232p. pap. 55.00 **(978-88-8158-820-6(X))** Charta ITA. Dist: D.A.P./Distributed Art Pubs.

Vitali, Massimo. Landscape with Figures, 1 vol. 2nd rev. ed. 2011. (ENG., Illus.). 200p. 98.00 (978-3-86930-197-6(X)) Steidl, Gerhard Druckerei und Verlag DEU. Dist: Innovative Logistics.

Wackernagel, Martin & Luchs, Alison. The World of the Florentine Renaissance Artist: Projects & Patrons, Workshop & Art Market. 2011. (RSART: Renaissance Society of America Reprint Text Ser.). xxx, 447p. pap. **(978-1-4426-1184-9(7))** Univ. of Toronto Pr.

Wallace, William. Michelangelo: The Artist, the Man & His Times. 2009. (ENG., Illus.). 428p. (C). 34.00 (978-0-521-11199-7(4)) Cambridge Univ. Pr.

Wallace, William E. Genius of Michelangelo. 2007. per. 49.95 (978-1-59803-337-3(9)) Teaching Co., LLC, The.

—Michelangelo: The Artist, the Man & his Times. 2011. (ENG., Illus.). 420p. (C). pap. 19.99 (978-1-107-67369-4(0)) Cambridge Univ. Pr.

—The Treasures of Michelangelo. 2010. (ENG., Illus.). 64p. 50.00 (978-0-233-00253-8(7)) Andre Deutsch GBR. Dist: Sterling Publishing Co., Inc.

Weidemann, Christiane. Leonardo da Vinci. 2010. (Illus.). 128p. pap. 14.95 (978-3-7913-4336-5(X)) Prestel Publishing.

Whitaker, Lucy & Clayton, Martin. Italian Paintings & Drawings: The Royal Collection. 2007. (ENG., Illus.). 192p. pap. 19.95 (978-1-85759-486-7(X)) Scala, Editions FRA. Dist: National Bk. Network.

Wiehager, Renata, ed. Zero Italy Azimut/Azimuth 1959/60 in Milan: And Today. (ITA & GER., Illus.). 216p. pap. 45.00 (978-3-89322-808-9(X)) Edition Cantz DEU. Dist: D.A.P./Distributed Art Pubs.

Willard, Ashton Rollins. History of Modern Italian Art. 2009. 294p. pap. (978-0-217-22357-7(5)); 268p. pap. (978-0-217-22220-4(X)) Books LLC.

Zilioli, Ellen Maurer, et al. Bruno Martinazzi: Jewellery & Myth. 2007. (ENG., Illus.). 112p. 45.00 (978-3-89790-260-2(5)) Arnoldsche Art Pubs. DEU. Dist: Antique Collectors' Club.

Zuliani, Stefania, ed. Filberto Menna: La Linea Analitica Dell'Arte Contemporanea. 2010. (ITA., Illus.). 80p. pap. 43.50 (978-88-370-7570-5(7)) Electa ITA. Dist: Trans-Atlantic Pubns., Inc.

ARTISTS—JAPAN

Clark, John. Japanese Exchanges in Art 1850s To 1930s: With Britain, Continental Europe, & the USA. 2007. (Illus.). 368p. per. 39.00 (978-1-86487-303-0(5)) Univ. of Illinois Pr.

Cooper, Martha. Tokyo Tattoo 1970. 2012. (ENG., Illus.). 72p. 39.95 **(978-91-85639-27-4(3))** Dokument forlag, Fotograf Malcolm Jacobsson SWE. Dist: SCB Distributors.

Deja-Vu 11: Inose Kou. pap. 25.00 (978-4-309-90331-6(2)) Fiction, Inc. JPN. Dist: D.A.P./Distributed Art Pubs.

Deja-Vu 12: Yasui Nakaji. pap. 25.00 (978-4-309-90332-3(0)) Fiction, Inc. JPN. Dist: D.A.P./Distributed Art Pubs.

Deja-Vu 8: Gocho Shigeo. pap. 25.00 (978-4-309-90328-6(2)) Fiction, Inc. JPN. Dist: D.A.P./Distributed Art Pubs.

Earle, Joe. New Bamboo: Contemporary Japanese Masters. 2008. (Illus.). 128p. 25.00 (978-0-300-14141-2(6)) Japan Society Gallery.

Ehrli, Vivane, ed. Shiraishi. (ENG & GER., Illus.). 184p. 29.95 (978-3-89322-867-6(5)) Edition Cantz DEU. Dist: D.A.P./Distributed Art Pubs.

English, Bonnie. Japanese Fashion Designers: The Work & Influence of Issey Miyake, Rei Kawakubo & Yohji Yamamoto. 2011. (ENG., Illus.). 192p. 99.95 (978-1-84788-311-7(7)); pap. 29.95 (978-1-84788-310-0(9)) Berg Pubs. GBR. Dist: Macmillan.

Fujita, Natsumi. The Next Generation: Japanese Women Designers, Photographers, & Illustrators. Takahashi, Kaoru, ed. 2011. (ENG., Illus.). 208p. pap. 39.95 (978-4-7562-4039-2(9)) Rizzoli International Pubns., Inc.

Hagedorn, Michael. Post-Dated: The Schooling of an Irreverent Bonsai Monk. 2008. (Illus.). 172p. pap. 14.95 (978-0-9801094-7-4(7)) Crataegus Bks.

Hesign, ed. The Master of Design. 2007. (Illus.). 336p. pap. 39.95 (978-981-245-429-4(2)) Page One Publishing SGP. Dist: Gingko Pr., Inc.

Hijikata, Hisakatsu, et al. Hijikata Hisakatsu Nikki. 2010. (JPN., Illus.). (978-4-901906-74-6(7)) National Museum of Ethnology.

Jefferies, Susan. Yasuhisa Kohyama: The Art of Ceramics. 2012. (ENG., Illus.). 104p. 50.00 **(978-3-89790-362-3(8))** Arnoldsche Art Pubs. DEU. Dist: Antique Collectors' Club.

Kagil, Yasuaki. Deep Blue: Diving to Inner Space. 2010. (ENG., Illus.). 256p. 39.95 (978-1-84796-002-3(2), Goodman Pubs.) Carlton Bks., Ltd. GBR. Dist: Sterling Publishing Co., Inc.

Kawauchi, Rinko, photos by. Rinko Kawauchi: Illuminance. 2011. (ENG., Illus.). 352p. 60.00 (978-1-59711-144-7(9)) Aperture Foundation, Inc.

Klauke, Jürgen & Poetter, Jochen. Jurgen Klauke. (GER & ENG., Illus.). 168p. 49.95 (978-3-89322-395-4(9)) Edition Cantz DEU. Dist: D.A.P./Distributed Art Pubs.

Kubo, Tite. Bleach Masked - Official Character, Bk. 2. 2012. (Bleach MASKED: Official Character Book 2 Ser.). (ENG.). 200p. pap. 14.99 **(978-1-4215-4230-0(7))** Viz Media.

Kusama, Yayoi. Infinity Net: The Autobiography of Yayoi Kusama. McCarthy, Ralph, tr. from JPN. 2012. (Illus.). 256p. 35.00 (978-0-226-46498-5(9)) Univ. of Chicago Pr.

Lecercle, Jean-Jacques & Kral, Françoise. Architecture & Philosophy: New Perspectives on the Work of Arakawa & Madeline Gins. 2010. (Illus.). 233p. pap. 64.00 (978-90-420-3189-0(1)) Rodopi.

McCausland, Shane & McKelway, Matthew P. Chinese Romance from a Japanese Brush: Kano Sansetsu's (1590-1651) Chogonka Scrolls in the Chester Beatty Library. 2009. (ENG., Illus.). 192p. pap. 55.00 (978-1-85759-597-0(1)) Scala, Editions FRA. Dist: National Bk. Network.

Moriyama, Daido. Tadanori Yokoo. 2006. (ENG., Illus.). 176p. 45.00 (978-0-500-97662-3(7)) Thames & Hudson.

Moriyama, Daido, photos by. Moriyama Zoo No. 1. 2009. (ENG., Illus.). 16p. 400.00 (978-4-434-11923-1(0)) Seiun-sha JPN. Dist: D.A.P./Distributed Art Pubs.

Nimura, J. M. Ken. Zero: JM Ken Niimura Illustrations TP: JM Ken Niimura Illustrations TP. 2011. (Illus.). 96p. pap. 12.99 (978-1-60706-371-1(9)) Image Comics.

Nobuyoshi, Araki. Obscenities. pap. 15.00 (978-4-309-90126-8(3)) Fiction, Inc. JPN. Dist: D.A.P./Distributed Art Pubs.

Obrist, Hans Ulrich, ed. Hans Ulrich Obrist & Kazuyo Sejima: Conversation Series: Volume 26. 2012. (ENG., Illus.). 110p. pap. 25.00 **(978-3-86560-927-4(9))** Verlag der Buchhandlung Walther Konig DEU. Dist: D.A.P./Distributed Art Pubs.

Rothfuss, Joan, ed. Eiko & Koma: Time Is Not Even, Space Is Not Empty. 2011. (ENG., Illus.). 288p. pap. 35.00 (978-0-935640-97-7(5)) Walker Art Ctr.

Schimmel, Paul & Mark, Lisa Gabrielle, eds. Murakami. 2007. (ENG., Illus.). 376p. 65.00 (978-0-8478-3003-9(9)) Rizzoli International Pubns., Inc.

Shiner, Eric C. & Tomii, Reiko. Making a Home: Japanese Contemporary Artists in New York. 2007. (ENG., Illus.). 224p. 65.00 (978-0-300-12634-1(4)) Japan Society Gallery.

Skira & Ando, Tadao. Museums. Molinari, Luca, ed. 2009. (ENG., Illus.). 240p. 75.00 (978-88-6130-680-6(2)) Skira Editore ITA. Dist: Random Hse., Inc.

Sturzenegger Foundation Schaffhausen Staff & Ikemura, Leiko. Leiko Ikemura: Tag, Nacht und Halbmond. Day, Night, Half Moon. Von Roda, Hortensia, ed. 2009. (GER & ENG., Illus.). 368p. 95.00 (978-3-85881-231-5(5)) Scheidegger und Spiess AG, Verlag CHE. Dist: Antique Collectors' Club.

Teraoka, Masami. Masami Teraoka: 1974-Present. 2008. (Illus.). 12p. (978-0-9743541-5-6(5)) Clark, Catherine Gallery.

Yamaguchi, Yumi. Warriors of Art: A Guide to Contemporary Japanese Artists, 1 vol. Tanaka, Arthur, tr. from JPN. 2007. (ENG., Illus.). 176p. 34.95 (978-4-7700-3031-3(2)) Kodansha America, Inc.

Yashima, Taro. The New Sun. 2008. (Illus.). (C). 23.00 (978-0-8248-3185-1(3)) Univ. of Hawaii Pr.

Yoshizawa, Katsuhiro. The Religious Art of Zen Master Hakuin. 2009. (ENG., Illus.). 256p. 26.00 (978-1-58243-454-4(9), Counterpoint Pr.) Basic Bks. GBR. Dist: Perseus-PGW.

ARTISTS—KENYA

Mutu, Wangechi. Wangechi Mutu: In Whose Image. 2009. (ENG., Illus.). 72p. pap. 25.00 (978-3-941185-06-7(3)) Verlag fur Moderne Kunst DEU. Dist: D.A.P./Distributed Art Pubs.

Nyamndi, G. The Life & Times of Richard Onyango. 2008. 68p. pap. (978-9966-7008-5-8(4)) Kwani Trust KEN. Dist: Michigan State Univ. Pr.

Rosa, Annelise Della. The Art of Recycling in Kenya. 2009. (ITA & ENG., Illus.). 136p. pap. 39.95 (978-88-8158-697-4(5)) Charta ITA. Dist: D.A.P./Distributed Art Pubs.

ARTISTS—KOREA

Bul, Lee. Lee Bul: On Every New Shadow. 2008. (ENG.). 128p. 40.00 (978-0-500-97498-8(5)) Thames & Hudson.

Byun, Bae, Bien-U Sacred Wood. 2009. (ENG., Illus.). 120p. 85.00 (978-3-7757-2283-4(1)) Hatje Cantz Verlag GmbH & Co KG DEU. Dist: D.A.P./Distributed Art Pubs.

Stallabrass, Julian, et al, texts. Haegue Yang: Wild Against Gravity. 2012. (ENG., Illus.). 190p. 45.00 **(978-1-901352-52-8(8))** Museum of Modern Art, Oxford GBR. Dist: D.A.P./Distributed Art Pubs.

ARTISTS—LATIN AMERICA

Atria, Magdalena. Poetics of the Handmade, 1 vol. 2007. (ENG., Illus.). 112p. pap., pap. 35.00 (978-1-933751-00-9(2)) Museum of Contemporary Art, Los Angeles.

Cammitzer, Luis, ed. It's not Neutral. 2008. 180p. pap. (978-84-612-5628-0(X)) Actar Birkhauser Distribution.

Camnitzer, Luis. Conceptualism in Latin American Art: Didactics of Liberation. 2007. (Joe R. & Teresa Lozano Long Series in Latin American & Latino Art & Culture). (ENG., Illus.). 364p. pap. 27.95 (978-0-292-71629-2(X)) Univ. of Texas Pr.

Cheroux, Clement, ed. Man Ray: Hollywood Paris Hollywood 1921-1976. 2011. (Illus.). 316p. (978-3-8296-0540-3(4)) Schirmer/Mosel Verlag GmbH.

Cisneros Fontanals Art Foundation Staff, contrib. by. Positions in Context: 2007 CIFO Grants Program Exhibition. 2007. (SPA & ENG., Illus.). 48p. (978-0-9774079-7-2(7)) Cisneros Fontanals Art Foundation.

Figueiredo, Luciano, et al. Helio Oiticica: The Body of Color. Ramirez, Mari Carmen, ed. 2007. (ENG.). 416p. pap. 45.00 (978-1-85437-743-2(4)) Tate Publishing, Ltd. GBR. Dist: Hachette Bk. Group.

Gonzalez-Torres, Felix, et al. Felix Gonzalez-Torres. Ault, Julie, ed. 2008. (ENG., Illus.). 400p. 85.00 (978-3-86521-196-5(8)) Steidl, Gerhard Druckerei und Verlag DEU. Dist: Innovative Logistics.

Henkes, Robert. Latin American Women Artists of the United States: The Works of 33 Twentieth-Century Women. rev. alt. ed. 2008. (ENG.). 259p. pap. 45.00 (978-0-7864-4056-6(2)) McFarland & Co., Inc. Pubs.

Iturbide, Graciela, photos by. Graciela Iturbide: No Hay Nadie, There Is No-One. 2011. (ENG., Illus.). 72p. 55.00 **(978-84-15303-17-6(3))** La Fabrica ESP. Dist: D.A.P./Distributed Art Pubs.

Mejia Arango, Juan Luis. Hugo Zapata. 2010. (SPA.). 240p. 75.00 (978-958-8306-49-0(3)) Villegas Editores S.A. COL. Dist: Independent Pubs. Group.

Perez-Oramas, Luis, ed. & text. Tangled Alphabets. 2009. (ENG., Illus.). 200p. 55.00 (978-0-87070-750-6(7)) Museum of Modern Art.

Pierce, Donna. Companion to Spanish Colonial Art at the Denver Art Museum. 2012. (ENG., Illus.). 106p. pap. 19.95 **(978-0-914738-78-7(X))** Denver Art Museum.

Shipp, Steve. Latin American & Caribbean Artists of the Modern Era: A Biographical Dictionary of More Than 12,700 Persons, 2 vols. alt. ed. 2012. (ENG., Illus.). 916p. pap. 75.00 (978-0-7864-6626-9(X)) McFarland & Co., Inc. Pubs.

Spector, Nancy, ed. & text. Felix Gonzalez-Torres, 1 vol. 2007. (ENG., Illus.). 228p. 45.00 (978-0-89207-362-7(4)) Guggenheim, Solomon R. Museum.

Youngblood, Wayne & Bonds, Ray. Mathew B. Brady: America's First Great Photographer. 2008. (ENG., Illus.). 256p. 29.99 (978-0-7858-2322-3(0), 0785823220, Chartwell) Book Sales, Inc.

ARTISTS—MEXICO

Beard, Jason. Gonzalo Lebrija. Murphy, Sean, ed. 2010. (ENG., Illus.). 104p. 95.00 (978-1-904212-66-9(2)) Other Criteria GBR. Dist: Hachette Bk. Group.

Bonami, Francesco & Canarutto, Sarah C. Gabriel Orozco. 2008. (Illus.). 108p. pap. 37.50 (978-88-370-6072-5(6)) Electa ITA. Dist: Trans-Atantic Pubns., Inc.

Bravo, Manuel Alvarez, photos by. Manuel Alvarez Bravo: Photopoetry. 2008. (ENG.). 320p. 75.00 (978-0-8118-6532-6(0)) Chronicle Bks. LLC.

Colonetti, Aldo. Raymundo Sesma: Campo Expandido. 2009. (ENG., Illus.). 288p. 77.95 (978-88-8158-734-6(3)) Charta ITA. Dist: D.A.P./Distributed Art Pubs.

Feher, Tony. Tony Feher. 2012. (ENG., Illus.). 264p. 60.00 **(978-0-9826813-3-6(X))** Miller, Gregory & Co.

Frecon, Suzan. Suzan Frecon. 2010. (ENG., Illus.). 108p. 55.00 (978-1-934435-29-8(5)) Radius Bks.

Goetz, Ingvild, et al, eds. Francis Alys. 2008. (GER & ENG., Illus.). 170p. pap. 40.00 (978-3-939894-10-0(9)) Goetz, Ingvild, Kunstverlag, GmbH DEU. Dist: D.A.P./Distributed Art Pubs.

Gonzalez, Mike, tr. from SPA. Autoconstrucción - Abraham Cruzvillegas. 2008. (SPA & ENG., Illus.). 96p. (978-1-873331-33-0(9)) Centre for Contemporary Arts, Glasgow GBR. Dist: Cornerhouse Pubns.

Herrera, Hayden & Zamudio-Taylor, Victor, texts. Frida Kahlo, 1 vol. 2007. (ENG., Illus.). 304p. 49.95 (978-0-935640-88-5(6)) Walker Art Ctr.

Mack, John, photos by. Revealing Mexico. 2010. (ENG., Illus.). 296p. 75.00 (978-1-57687-559-9(8), powerHouse Bks.) powerHouse Cultural Entertainment, Inc.

Murphy, Sean, ed. Gonzalo Lebrija (Spanish Edition) 2011. (SPA.). 104p. pap. 95.00 **(978-1-906967-34-5(2))** Abrams.

Orozco, Gabriel. Gabriel Orozco. 2009. (ENG., Illus.). 256p. 55.00 (978-0-87070-762-9(0)) Museum of Modern Art.

Ortega, Luis Felipe. Ocupación: Luis Felipe Ortega, 1 vol. 2007. (ENG & SPA., Illus.). 48p. 19.00 (978-968-9056-05-8(0)) Turner, Ediciones S.A. ESP. Dist: D.A.P./Distributed Art Pubs.

Palau, Marta & Barrios, Jose Luis. Marta Palau: Naualli, 1 vol. 2007. (SPA & ENG., Illus.). 260p. 65.00 (978-968-9056-02-7(6)) Turner, Ediciones S.A. ESP. Dist: D.A.P./Distributed Art Pubs.

Pasztory, Esther. Jean-Frederic Waldeck: Artist of Exotic Mexico. 2011. (ENG., Illus.). 240p. 55.00 (978-0-8263-4703-9(7)) Univ. of New Mexico Pr.

Rulfo, Juan, photos by & text. Juan Rulfo: 100 Photographs. 2011. (ENG., Illus.). 140p. 55.00 (978-84-92480-92-0(0)) RM Verlag, S.L. ESP. Dist: D.A.P./Distributed Art Pubs.

Schabus, Hans. Hans Schabus: Deserted Conquest, 1 vol. Lefrak, Joanne & Zavitovski, Katia, eds. 2008. (ENG., Illus.). 100p. 20.00 (978-0-9764492-6-3(9)) Site Santa Fe.

Schmuckli, Claudia, et al, texts. Gabriel Kuri: Nobody Needs to Know the Price of Your Saab. 2011. (ENG., Illus.). 130p. pap. 39.99 (978-0-941193-49-8(7)) Blaffer Art Museum.

Schuessler, Michael K., ed. Mexico se escribe con J/Mexico is Written with J. 2011. 271p. pap. 23.95 **(978-607-07-0578-6(5))** Editorial Planeta Mexicana MEX. Dist: Perseus Distribution.

Stewart, Virginia. Forty-Five Contemporary Mexican Artists: A Twentieth Century Renaissance. Farmer, Edward M., ed. 2011. 188p. 42.95 **(978-1-258-07537-8(7))** Literary Licensing, LLC.

ARTISTS—NETHERLANDS

Berkum, Ans van. Willem Van Genk: Builds His Universe. 2011. (ENG & DUT., Illus.). 144p. pap. (978-90-209-9270-0(8), Lannoo Pubs. (Acc)) Antique Collectors' Club.

Boonstra, Janrense. In Atmospheric Light: Pictorialism in Dutch Photography 1890-1925. 2010. (DUT & ENG., Illus.). 156p. 39.50 (978-90-400-7686-2(3)) Waanders B.V., Uitgeverij NLD. Dist: National Bk. Network.

Brommer, Bea. Johannes Ten Kloster (1873-1940) A Man with Two Lives. 2007. (Illus.). 96p. 49.95 (978-90-6832-486-0(1)) Royal Tropical Institute Pr. (KIT (Koninklijk Instituut voor de Tropen) NLD. Dist: Stylus Publishing, LLC.

de Jong, Erik A. Engraving with Light. 2010. (ENG., Illus.). 96p. pap. 25.00 (978-90-400-7704-3(5)) Waanders B.V., Uitgeverij NLD. Dist: National Bk. Network.

Duits, Rembrandt. Gold Brocade & Renaissance Painting: A Study in Material Culture. 2008. (Illus.). iv, 494p. (C). 300.00 (978-1-904597-42-1(4)) Pindar Pr. GBR. Dist: Brown, David Bk. Co., The.

Fuchs, Rudi, et al. Jasper Krabbe: 100 Selfportraits. 2008. (ENG., Illus.). 232p. 50.00 (978-90-400-8259-7(6)) Waanders B.V., Uitgeverij NLD. Dist: National Bk. Network.

Gastaldon, Vidya. Vidya Gastaldon, 1 vol. 2006. (ENG., Illus.). 64p. 29.00 (978-3-905701-69-2(3)) JRP Ringier Kunstverlag AG CHE. Dist: D.A.P./Distributed Art Pubs.

Geertgen & Reinhard-Felice, Mariantonia. Venite, Adoremus: Geertgen Tot Sint Jans & the Adoration of the Kings. 2007. (Illus.). 96p. pap. 39.00 (978-3-7774-4025-5(6)) Hirmer Verlag GmbH DEU. Dist: Chicago Distribution Ctr.

Goosen, Moosje, text. PrixdeRome.nl 2009. 2009. (ENG., Illus.). 136p. pap. 35.00 (978-90-5662-681-5(7)) NAi Uitgevers / Publishers Stichting NLD. Dist: D.A.P./Distributed Art Pubs.

Herndon-Consagra, Francesca & Crenshaw, Paul. Rembrandt: Master Etchings from St. Louis Collections. Steiner, Mary A., ed. 2006. (Illus.). 172p. pap. 29.95 (978-0-89178-089-2(0)) St. Louis Art Museum.

Jansen, Jan, et al. Jan Jansen. 2007. (ENG., Illus.). 200p. 50.00 (978-90-5897-725-0(0)) Lannoo Pubs./Racine.

Kaagman, Hugo. Stencil King. 2011. (ENG.). 160p. pap. 25.95 (978-90-488-0275-3(X)) Lebowski NLD. Dist: SCB Distributors.

King, Catherine E. Representing Renaissance Art, C. 1500-C. 1600. 2008. (ENG., Illus.). 384p. pap. 34.00 (978-0-7190-7557-5(2)) Manchester Univ. Pr. GBR. Dist: Macmillan.

Kriemann, Susanne. One Day. Schafhausen, Nicolaus & Szewczyk, Monika, eds. 2011. (ENG., Illus.). 144p. 30.00 (978-90-73362-95-6(4)) Witte De With Centre for Contemporary Art NLD. Dist: D.A.P./Distributed Art Pubs.

Maas, Barbara & Kester, Peter van. Herman Hermsen: Jewellery, Light & More. 2006. (ENG., Illus.). 144p. 60.00 (978-3-89790-252-7(4)) Arnoldsche Art Pubs. DEU. Dist: Antique Collectors' Club.

Maës, Gaëtane. Invention, Interprétation, Reproduction: Gravures des Anciens Pays-Bas (1550-1700), Musée de la Chartreuse, Douai, 4 Novembre 2006-4 Février 2007. 2008. (FRE & ENG., Illus.). 192p. pap. 45.00 (978-2-35340-009-6(4)) Gourcuff Gradenigo FRA. Dist: National Bk. Network.

Martens, Karel, et al. Printed Matter - Drukwerk. 3rd ed. 2011. (DUT & ENG., Illus.). 256p. pap. 60.00 (978-0-907259-41-1(3)) Hyphen Pr. GBR. Dist: Hachette Bk. Group.

Moss, Matthew, illus. Les Aventures de Rembrandt. 2007.Tr. of Adventures of Rembrandt. (FRE.). 120p. pap. (978-0-943884-04-2(7)) Conservation Pr.

Nielsen, Marjatta & Rathje, Annette, eds. Johannes Wiedewelt: A Danish Artist in Search of the Past, Shaping the Future. 2010. (Acta Hyperborea Ser.). (Illus.). 373p. pap. 65.00 (978-87-635-0787-5(0)) Museum Tusculanum Pr. DNK. Dist: Chicago Distribution Ctr.

Pijbes, Wim, et al. Tom Claassen. 2009. (ENG & DUT., Illus.). 112p. 40.00 (978-90-5662-645-7(0)) NAi Uitgevers / Publishers Stichting NLD. Dist: D.A.P./Distributed Art Pubs.

Pisano, Falke & text. Figures of Speech: Falke Pisano. 2010. (ENG., Illus.) 144p. pap. 39.95 (978-3-03764-110-1(X)) JRP Ringier Kunstverlag AG CHE. Dist: D.A.P./Distributed Art Pubs.

Poortvliet, Rien. Dutch Treat, the Artist Life. 21.95 (978-0-8488-1450-2(9)) Amereon LTD.

Priem, Ruud. Vermeer, Rembrandt & the Golden Age of Dutch Art: Masterpieces of the Rijksmuseum, 1 vol. 2009. (ENG., Illus.). 240p. pap. 39.95 (978-1-55365-471-1(4)) D&M Pubs. Inc. CAN. Dist: Perseus-PGW.

Reinhart-Felice, M. Venite Adoremus, the Adoretion of the Kings. 2008. (Illus.). 96p. pap. (978-3-7774-3815-3(4)) Hirmer Verlag GmbH.

Rob Birza: Cold Fusion. pap. 25.00 (978-90-5006-056-1(0)) Stedelijk Museum NLD. Dist: D.A.P./Distributed Art Pubs.

Rolnik, Suely, et al, texts. Manon de Boer. 2008. (ENG., Illus.). 244p. pap. 39.00 (978-90-73362-80-2(6)) Witte De With Centre for Contemporary Art NLD. Dist: D.A.P./Distributed Art Pubs.

Rossi, Daniel. Everyone We Know. 2010. 48p. pap. 22.00 (978-0-557-35248-7(7)) Lulu Enterprises Inc.

Telfair Museum Staff. Dutch Utopia: American Artists in Holland, 1880-1914. Stott, Annette, ed. 2009. (ENG.). 240p. 59.95 (978-0-933075-11-5(1)) Telfair Museum of Art.

Van Dijk, Maite, et al. Sculptuur Studies 2006. 2007. (ENG., Illus.). 160p. pap. 30.00 (978-90-400-8258-0(8)) Waanders B.V., Uitgeverij NLD. Dist: National Bk. Network.

Van Lieshout, Atelier, illus. Atelier Van Lieshout, 1 vol. 2007. (ENG.). 272p. pap. 55.00 (978-90-5662-482-8(2)) NAi Uitgevers / Publishers Stichting NLD. Dist: D.A.P./Distributed Art Pubs.

ARTISTS—NEW ZEALAND

Baker, Kriselle & Rankin, Elizabeth, eds. Fiona Pardington: The Pressure of Sunlight Falling. 2011. (MAO & ENG., Illus.). 160p. 120.00 **(978-1-877578-09-0(6))** Otago University Pr. NZL. Dist: International Specialized Bk. Services.

Blundell, Sally, ed. Look This Way: New Zealand Writers on New Zealand Artists. 2007. (ENG., Illus.). 200p. pap. 39.95 *(978-1-86940-371-3(1))* Auckland Univ. Pr. NZL. Dist: Independent Pubs. Group.

McLean, Fred. New Zealand Art for Investment. 160p. pap. 19.95 *(978-0-908876-88-4(2))* Transpress NZL. Dist: Pacific Island Bks.

Pound, Francis. The Invention of New Zealand: Art & National Identity, 1930-1970. 2010. (ENG., Illus.). 450p. pap. 44.95 *(978-1-86940-414-7(9))* Auckland Univ. Pr. NZL. Dist: Independent Pubs. Group.

Radner, Hilary, et al. Jane Campion: Cinema, Nation, Identity. 2009. (Illus.). 400p. pap. 34.95 *(978-0-8143-3432-4(6))* Wayne State Univ. Pr.

Serra, Richard & Reinartz, Dirk. Te Tuhirangi Contour, 1 vol. 2008. (ENG., Illus.). 76p. 35.00 *(978-3-86521-014-2(7))* Steidl, Gerhard Druckerei und Verlag DEU. Dist: Innovative Logistics.

Thomas, Nicholas, ed. Rauru: Tene Waitere, Maori Carving, Colonial History. 2009. (Illus.). 183p. 120.00 *(978-1-877372-61-2(7))* Otago University Pr. NZL. Dist: International Specialized Bk. Services.

ARTISTS—NORWAY

Blomberg, Katja, ed. Melhus, Bjorn. Live Action Hero. 2011. (ENG., Illus.). 103p. pap. 29.95 ***(978-3-86560-965-6(1))*** Verlag der Buchhandlung Walther Konig DEU. Dist: D.A.P./Distributed Art Pubs.

Camus, Renaud. Demeures de L'esprit: Danemark, Norvège. 2010. (FRE., Illus.). 453p. *(978-2-213-64389-2(X))* Fayard, Artheme, Librairie.

Estep, Jan. Searching for Ludwig Wittgenstein, Lake Eidsvatnet, Skjolden, Sogn, Norway. 2007. (Illus.). 10.00 *(978-0-9801764-1-4(7))* Estep, Jan.

Forum Gallery. Odd Nerdrum: Paintings, 1 vol. 2007. (ENG., Illus.). 32p. per. 30.00 *(978-0-9675826-8-9(7))* Forum Gallery.

Friedman, Ken, et al. Marianne Heske: A Doll's House. Johannesen, Ina & Wendt, Selene, eds. 2011. (ENG., Illus.). 120p. pap. 40.00 *(978-88-7624-746-0(7))* Skira Editore ITA. Dist: Random Hse., Inc.

Fronth, Per. Per Fronth. 2010. (ENG., Illus.). 304p. 80.00 *(978-82-7547-364-4(0))* Pr., Forlaget NOR. Dist: D.A.P./Distributed Art Pubs.

Hellandsjo, Karin. The Erling Neby Collection. 2011. (ENG., Illus.). 240p. 80.00 *(978-88-572-0862-6(1))* Skira Editore ITA. Dist: Random Hse., Inc.

Hoyland, Elin. The Brothers. 2011. (ENG., Illus.). 96p. 48.00 ***(978-1-907893-08-7(3))*** Lewis, Dewi Publishing GBR. Dist: Consortium Bk. Sales & Distribution.

Keller, Christoph, ed. Not Made Visible. 2008. (ENG., Illus.). 192p. per. 37.00 *(978-3-905770-92-6(X))* JRP Ringier Kunstverlag AG CHE. Dist: D.A.P./Distributed Art Pubs.

ARTISTS—PORTUGAL

Blaufuks, Daniel, photos by. Terezín: Terezin, 1 vol. 2010. (ENG., Illus.). 192p. 65.00 *(978-3-86521-699-1(4))* Steidl, Gerhard Druckerei und Verlag DEU. Dist: Innovative Logistics.

Nogueira, Carlos. Desenhos Construções e Outros Acidentes: Drawings Constructions & Other Accidents. 2008. (Illus.). 111p. *(978-972-37-1392-3(6))* Assirio e Alvim.

Nozolino, Paulo. Bone Lonely, 1 vol. 2011. (ENG., Illus.). 72p. 50.00 *(978-3-86521-861-2(X))* Steidl, Gerhard Druckerei und Verlag DEU. Dist: Innovative Logistics.

Rice, Shelley & Saramago, José, texts. Candida Höfer: Em Portugal/in Portugal. 2007. (POR & ENG., Illus.). 125p. 65.00 *(978-3-8296-0279-2(0))* Schirmer/Mosel Verlag GmbH DEU. Dist: Prestel Publishing.

ARTISTS—ROMANIA

Asavei, Maria-Alina. Rewriting the Canon of Visual Arts in Communist Romania: A Case Study. 2008. 100p. pap. *(978-3-639-10238-3(X))* VDM Verlag Dr. Mueller e.K.

Hentzsch, Sabine, ed. Perjovschi: Postmodern, 1 vol. 2007. (ENG., Illus.). 96p. pap. 34.00 *(978-3-86560-240-4(1))* Verlag der Buchhandlung Walther Konig DEU. Dist: D.A.P./Distributed Art Pubs.

Nye, Tim. Serge Spitzer Round Corner, 1 vol. 2007. (ENG., Illus.). 33p. pap. 35.00 *(978-1-891027-22-2(0))* Four Corners Bks. GBR. Dist: D.A.P./Distributed Art Pubs.

Perjovschi, Dan. Mad Cow, Bird Flu, Global Village. 2007. (ENG., Illus.). 120p. 17.95 *(978-1-84467-166-3(6)*, 844166) Verso Bks. GBR. Dist: Norton, W. W. & Co., Inc.

ARTISTS—RUSSIA (FEDERATION)

Alexejev, N. Ilya Kabakov: Noma - The Group of Moscow Conceptualists. (RUS & GER., Illus.). 192p. pap. 29.95 *(978-3-89322-615-3(X))* Edition Cantz DEU. Dist: D.A.P./Distributed Art Pubs.

Baryshnikov, Mikhail, photos by. Merce My Way, 1 vol. 2009. (ENG., Illus.). 128p. 45.00 *(978-0-9821726-0-5(5))* Baryshnikov Productions, Inc.

Bruskin, Grisha. Past Imperfect: 318 Episodes from the Life of a Russian Artist. 2008. (Judaic Traditions in Literature, Music, & Art Ser.). (Illus.). 34.95 *(978-0-8156-0901-8(9))* Syracuse Univ. Pr.

Chagall, Marc. My Life: Marc Chagall. 2011. (Peter Owen Modern Classic Ser.). (ENG.). 200p. pap. 15.95 *(978-0-7206-1356-8(6))* Owen, Peter Ltd. GBR. Dist: Independent Pubs. Group.

Filonov, Pavel Nikolaevich & Pravoverova, L. L. Pavel Filonov: Realnost I Mify. 2008. (RUS.). 670p. *(978-5-7784-0353-6(4))* Agraf, LTD, OOO.

Glibota, Vladimir & Rozhin, Alezander I. Alexander Rukavishnikov. 2009. (ENG., Illus.). 240p. 70.00 *(978-88-6130-987-6(9))* Skira Editore ITA. Dist: Random Hse., Inc.

Groys, Boris. Empty Zones: Andrei Monastyrski & 'Collective Actions' 2011. (ENG., Illus.). 128p. pap. 29.95 *(978-1-907317-34-7(1))* Black Dog Publishing Ltd. GBR. Dist: Perseus Distribution.

Keller, Christoph, ed. Boris Groys & Andro Wekua: Wait to Wait. 2009. (ENG., Illus.). 160p. 28.00 *(978-3-03764-021-0(9))* JRP Ringier Kunstverlag AG CHE. Dist: D.A.P./Distributed Art Pubs.

Kittelmann, Udo, ed. Vadim Zakharov: Retrospective 1987-1995. (GER & RUS., Illus.). 180p. 29.95 *(978-3-89322-775-4(X))* Edition Cantz DEU. Dist: D.A.P./Distributed Art Pubs.

Kolesnikov, Ivan, et al, contrib. by. New Angelarium. 2007. (ENG & RUS., Illus.). 352p. per. 145.00 *(978-0-9754829-7-1(1))* Kolodzei Art Foundation, Inc.

Kostenevich, A. Matisse to Malevich: Poineers of Modern Art from the Hermitage, 1 vol. 2011. (ENG.). 288p. pap. 66.00 ***(978-90-78653-18-9(3))*** Exhibitions International BEL. Dist: Innovative Logistics.

Ling, Averil & King, Averil. Isaak Levitan: Lyrical Landscape. 2011. (ENG., Illus.). 160p. 75.00 *(978-1-85149-645-7(9))* Antique Collectors' Club.

Mikhailov, Boris. Yesterday's Sandwich. 2009. (ENG.). 124p. 65.00 *(978-0-7148-4856-3(5))* Phaidon Pr., Inc.

Nazaryan, Alexander & Merenzon, Ilya. Russian Povera: Art That Makes Trash Monumental. 2011. 272p. 35.00 *(978-1-59020-460-3(3))* Overlook Pr., The.

Neygauz, Lina. Variatsii Prekrasnogo. rev. ed. 2008.Tr. of Variations of the Beautiful. (RUS., Illus.). 247p. 79.95 *(978-0-9785403-1-9(X))* DAN.

Obukhova, Alexandra, ed. Nihil Inhumanum A Me Alienum Puto, 1 vol. 2007. (ENG., Illus.). 368p. per. 65.00 *(978-3-86678-045-3(1))* Kerber Verlag DEU. Dist: D.A.P./Distributed Art Pubs.

Parton, Anthony. Goncharova: The Art & Design of Natalia Goncharova. 2010. (ENG., Illus.). 520p. *(978-1-85149-605-1(X)*, Antique Collectors Club Dist) Antique Collectors' Club.

PETIT, Lenard. The Michael Chekhov Handbook: For the Actor. 2009. (ENG., Illus.). 192p. 37.95 *(978-0-415-49672-8(1))* Routledge.

Petrova, E. A. & Petrova, Yevgenia, eds. Russian Futurism. 2006. (ENG., Illus.). 240p. 75.00 *(978-3-930775-91-0(3)*, Palace Editions) Mandala Publishing.

Petzinger, Renate, ed. Ilya Kabakov: Werkverzeichnis der Gemälde 1957 - 2007. 2 Bände, 2 vols. 2009. (ENG., Illus.). 816p. 195.00 *(978-3-86678-173-3(3))* Kerber Verlag DEU. Dist: D.A.P./Distributed Art Pubs.

Rostropovich, Mstislav. Msistlav Rostropovitch. 2007. 176p. 65.00 *(978-3-86521-402-7(9))* Steidl, Gerhard Druckerei und Verlag DEU. Dist: D.A.P./Distributed Art Pubs.

Sternine, Grigori & Kirillina, Elena. Ilya Repin. 2011. (Best Of Ser.). (ENG., Illus.). 200p. 19.95 *(978-1-84484-916-1(3))* Parkstone Pr. USA, Ltd.

Wageman, Patty, ed. Russian Legends: Folk Tales & Fairy Tales. 2008. (ENG., Illus.). 240p. pap. 49.95 *(978-90-5662-608-2(6))* NAi Uitgevers / Publishers Stichting NLD. Dist: D.A.P./Distributed Art Pubs.

Weber, Nicolas Fox. Josef Albers & Wassily Kandinsky: Friends in Exile - A Decade of Correspondence. 2010. (ENG., Illus.). 160p. pap. 29.95 *(978-1-55595-327-0(1))* Hudson Hills Pr. LLC.

Wilson, Jonathan. Marc Chagall. 2007. (Jewish Encounters Ser.). (ENG., Illus.). 224p. 19.95 *(978-0-8052-4201-0(5)*, Schocken) Knopf Doubleday Publishing Group.

ARTISTS—SOVIET UNION

Bacher, Lutz. Lutz Bacher: Do You Love Me. 2012. (ENG., Illus.). 440p. pap. 30.00 ***(978-0-9788697-9-3(6))*** Primary Information.

Chinn, Lenore & Asian Pacific Islander Cultural Center Staff. Cultural Confluences: The art of Lenore Chinn. 2010. (Illus.). pap. 21.95 ***(978-1-4507-5127-8(X))*** Independent Pub.

Kelley, Mike. Mike Kelley: Arenas. 2011. (ENG., Illus.). 44p. 30.00 *(978-1-61623-718-9(X))* Skarstedt Gallery.

Pronenko, L. I. Russian Calligraphy: One Teacher, 222 Students. 2007. *(978-1-934227-04-6(8))*; pap. *(978-1-934227-05-3(6))* Operina LLC.

ARTISTS—SPAIN

Abdessemed, Adel, et al. Testigos/Witnesses, 1 vol. 2006. (ENG & SPA., Illus.). 80p. pap. 34.95 *(978-88-8158-607-3(X))* Charta ITA. Dist: D.A.P./Distributed Art Pubs.

Aguer, Montse. The Treasures of Dali. 2009. (Illus.). 88p. *(978-1-84796-003-0(0))* Andre Deutsch.

Berts, Jean-Michel, et al. Manolo Valdes. 2011. (ENG.). 100p. pap. 95.00 ***(978-1-61428-003-3(7))*** Assouline FRA. Dist: Perseus Distribution.

Blahnik, Manolo. Manolo's New Shoes. 2010. (ENG., Illus.). 200p. pap. 50.00 *(978-1-58093-282-0(7))* Monacelli Pr., Inc.

Bosch, Eulalia. Frequencies: Eugènia Balcells. 2009. *(978-84-92861-03-3(7))* Actar Birkhauser Distribution.

Brennan, Jonathan, tr. Miquel Barcelo: the African Work. 2009. (ENG., Illus.). 264p. pap. 50.00 *(978-84-7506-831-2(6))* Turner, Ediciones S.A. ESP. Dist: D.A.P./Distributed Art Pubs.

Brutvan, Cheryl. Antonio López García. 2008. (ENG., Illus.). 160p. pap. 24.95 *(978-0-87846-734-5(5))* Museum of Fine Arts, Boston.

Castro Prieto, Juan Manuel & Mondéjar, Publio López. Juan Manuel Castro Prieto. 2010. (SPA & ENG., Illus.). 120p. pap. 20.00 *(978-84-96466-60-9(4))* La Fabrica ESP. Dist: D.A.P./Distributed Art Pubs.

Chillida, Eduardo. Eduardo Chillida: Writings. 2011. (ENG., Illus.). 160p. 40.00 *(978-3-941263-07-9(2))* Richter Verlag DEU. Dist: D.A.P./Distributed Art Pubs.

Conesa, Chema. Cristóbal Hara: El Instante Decisivo. 2010. (ENG & SPA., Illus.). 108p. pap. 20.00 *(978-84-95471-00-0(0))* La Fabrica ESP. Dist: D.A.P./Distributed Art Pubs.

Dillow, Katie. Spanish Modernism in Nineteenth-France. 2011. 76p. pap. ***(978-3-8433-8466-7(5))*** Lambert Academic Publishing.

Discoveries 2010. 2011. (ENG., Illus.). 206p. pap. 35.00 *(978-84-92841-54-7(0))* La Fabrica ESP. Dist: D.A.P./Distributed Art Pubs.

Edwards, Gwynne. Lorca, Bunuel, Dali: Forbidden Pleasures & Connected Lives. 2009. (ENG., Illus.). 256p. 45.00 *(978-1-84885-007-1(7))* I. B. Tauris & Co., Ltd. GBR. Dist: Macmillan.

Fernandez Miro, Emil. Joan Miro 1956-1983: Sentiment, Emocio, Gest. 2007. (Illus.). 225p. pap. *(978-84-934730-2-0(2))* Actar Birkhauser Distribution.

Fiz, Alberto, ed. Antoni Tàpies: Materia e Tempo. 2010. (ITA & ENG., Illus.). 240p. 87.50 *(978-88-370-7175-2(2))* Electa ITA. Dist: Trans-Atlantic Pubns., Inc.

Gargallo, Pablo & Salazar, María José. Pablo Gargallo (1881-1934) Dibujos: Catálogo Razonado, 2 vols. 2010. (ENG & SPA., Illus.). 1155p. *(978-84-96655-67-6(9))*; *(978-84-96655-68-3(7))*; *(978-84-96655-66-9(0))* Fundación Marcelino Botín.

Gil, Emilio. Book of the Year: 360 Days Dedicated to Graphic, Packaging & Product Design. 2009. (ENG., Illus.). 344p. 58.00 *(978-0-9817805-6-6(3))* Batty, Mark Pub., LLC.

—Book of the Year: 360 Days Dedicated to Graphic, Packaging & Product Design, 1 vol. Design and Design.com Editors, ed. 2009. (ENG.). 768p. 49.95 *(978-84-96309-80-7(0))* Index Bks., Spain ESP. Dist: Innovative Logistics.

Hansen, Joan Maria. Lewis Foreman Day,1845-1910: Unity in Design & Industry. 2007. (ENG., Illus.). 300p. *(978-1-85149-534-4(7)*, Antique Collectors Club Dist) Antique Collectors' Club.

Henseleit, Frank. Rafa Forteza. 2008. (GER & SPA., Illus.). 128p. 59.00 *(978-3-87909-918-4(9))* Wienand GmbH, Druck- & Verlagshaus DEU. Dist: Independent Pubs. Group.

Hughes, Robert. Goya. 2006. (ENG., Illus.). 448p. pap. 29.95 *(978-0-375-71128-2(7)*, Knopf) Knopf Doubleday Publishing Group.

Mari, Bartomeu. Asier Mendizabal. Mari, Bartomeu, ed. 2008. 180p. *(978-84-89771-51-2(0))* Actar Birkhauser Distribution.

Mari, Bartomeu, ed. Da Capo. 2008. 236p. *(978-84-89771-63-5(4))* Actar Birkhauser Distribution.

Mariscal, Javier. Drawing Life. 79.95 *(978-0-7148-5752-7(1))* Phaidon Pr., Inc.

Martin Llopis Paloma, ed. Alejandra Icaza: Marshmallows. 2011. (ENG., Illus.). 144p. 40.00 *(978-84-7506-912-8(6))* Turner, Ediciones S.A. ESP. Dist: D.A.P./Distributed Art Pubs.

Muntadas, Antoni. Antoni Muntadas: On Translation, I Giardini, Venice Biennale 2005. 2006. (Illus.). 446p. (gr. 13-18). 38.00 *(978-84-7232-952-2(6))* D.A.P./Distributed Art Pubs.

Nagel, Isolde, ed. José Salinas: Disembodiment. 2010. (ENG., Illus.). 144p. pap. 28.00 *(978-3-939633-97-6(6))* Jovis Verlag GmbH DEU. Dist: D.A.P./Distributed Art Pubs.

Nunez, Jose Arturo Rodriguez. Four Decades of Books & Publications of Spanish Artists. Ortiz, Diego, ed. 2008. 272p. pap. *(978-84-96933-15-6(6))* Actar Birkhauser Distribution.

Palermo, Charles. Fixed Ecstasy: Joan Miro in The 1920s. 2008. (Refiguring Modernism Ser.). (ENG., Illus.). 304p. pap. 50.00 *(978-0-271-02972-6(2))* Pennsylvania State Univ. Pr.

Pombo, Jorge, ed. Jorge R Pombo. 2008. 228p. *(978-84-96954-29-8(3))* Actar Birkhauser Distribution.

Rasilla, Carmen Garcia de la. Salvador Dali's Literary Self-Portrait: Approaches to a Surrealist Autobiography. 2009. (Illus.). 196p. 48.50 *(978-0-8387-5723-9(5))* Bucknell Univ. Pr.

Socias, Jordi, photos by. Jordi Socias: PHotoBolsillo. 2010. (ENG & SPA., Illus.). 112p. pap. 20.00 *(978-84-92841-04-2(4))* La Fabrica ESP. Dist: D.A.P./Distributed Art Pubs.

Stirling Maxwell, William. Annals of the Artists of Spain. 2010. 550p. pap. 41.75 *(978-1-147-19750-1(4))*; 556p. pap. 42.75 *(978-1-148-13274-7(0))*; 476p. pap. 37.75 *(978-1-144-52486-7(5))*; 576p. pap. 43.75 *(978-1-145-67463-9(1))*; 554p. pap. 41.75 *(978-1-142-35348-3(6))* BiblioBazaar.

—Annals of the Artists of Spain, Vol. 2. 2009. 508p. 53.95 *(978-1-104-03466-5(2))*; pap. 38.95 *(978-1-104-02513-7(2))* Kessinger Publishing, LLC.

—Essays Towards a Catalogue of Prints Engraved from the Works of Diego Rodriguez de Silva y Velazquez & Bartolomé Estéban Murillo. 2010. 162p. pap. 21.75 *(978-1-141-41277-8(2))* BiblioBazaar.

—Essays Towards a Catalogue of Prints Engraved from the Works of Diego Rodriguez de Silva y Velazquez & Bartolomé Estéban Murillo. 2009. 94p. pap. 14.14 *(978-1-151-34823-4(6))* General Bks. LLC.

Subirachs, José María, et al. Subirachs: Analogías, Dualidades, Oposiciones: La Lonja, Zaragoza, 14 Septiembre-31 Octubre 2010. 2010. (SPA., Illus.). 143p. *(978-88-6403-059-3(X))* Carlo Cambi Editore.

Tàpies, Antoni. Antoni Tàpies Vol. II: Complete Writings, Collected Essays. Sobrer, Josep Miquel, tr. from CAT. 2nd ed. 2011. (ENG., Illus.). 600p. 39.95 *(978-0-253-35503-4(6)*, 0253355036) Indiana Univ. Pr.

Van Veggel, Rob. The Potters & Pottery of Miravet: Production, Marketing & Consumption of Pottery in Catalonia. 2009. (Anthropology Matters Ser.: 3). (Illus.). 259p. 109.50 ***(978-0-9556400-2-5(4))*** Kingston, Sean Publishing GBR. Dist: Lightning Source, Inc.

Weidemann, Christiane. Salvador Dali. 2007. (Living Art Ser.). (Illus.). 128p. pap. 14.95 *(978-3-7913-3813-2(7))* Prestel Publishing.

ARTISTS—SWEDEN

Almqvist, Björn. Writers United: The Story of an European Graffiti Crew. 4th rev. ed. 2009. (Illus.). 128p. pap. 24.95 *(978-91-85639-17-5(6))* Dokument forlag, Fotograf Malcolm Jacobsson SWE. Dist: SCB Distributors.

Bessa, Antonio Sergio. Öyvind Fahlström: The Art of Writing. 2008. (Avant-Garde & Modernism Studies). (ENG., Illus.). 192p. pap. 29.95 *(978-0-8101-2298-7(7))* Northwestern Univ. Pr.

du Toit, Herman. The Modernist-Utopian Art of Karl Momen, B. 1934: A Persian-Russian-American Life. 2006. (Illus.). 196p. 99.95 *(978-0-7734-5503-0(5))* Mellen, Edwin Pr., The.

Fischli, Peter & Weiss, David, photos by. Plötzlich diese Übersicht. 4th ed. 2008. (POR, GER & ENG., Illus.). 180p. pap. 58.00 *(978-3-906135-41-0(1))* Verlag der Buchhandlung Walther Konig DEU. Dist: D.A.P./Distributed Art Pubs.

Mossinger, Ingrid, ed. & frwd. Nina Sten-Knudsen: Monumental Painting, 1 vol. 2007. (ENG., Illus.). 120p. 55.00 *(978-3-938025-94-9(8))* Kerber Verlag DEU. Dist: D.A.P./Distributed Art Pubs.

Nilson, Greger Ulf & Tunbjork, Lars, eds. Christer Stromholm: In Memory of Himself, 1 vol. 2008. (ENG., Illus.). 144p. 45.00 *(978-3-86521-298-6(0))* Steidl, Gerhard Druckerei und Verlag DEU. Dist: Innovative Logistics.

Nygren, Henrik & Smoliansky, Gunnar, eds. Gunnar Smoliansky: One Picture at a Time, 1 vol. 2009. (ENG., Illus.). 256p. 82.00 *(978-3-86521-615-1(3))* Steidl, Gerhard Druckerei und Verlag DEU. Dist: Innovative Logistics.

Osborn, Sarah Byng. Letters of Sarah Byng Osborn, 1721-1773. Bailey, Margery, ed. 2011. 170p. 42.95 ***(978-1-258-02952-4(9))*** Literary Licensing, LLC.

Tellgren, Anna, ed. & text. The History Book, 1 vol. 2009. (ENG., Illus.). 500p. 75.00 *(978-3-86521-642-7(0))* Steidl, Gerhard Druckerei und Verlag DEU. Dist: Innovative Logistics.

Tunbjork, Lars & Ulf Nilson, Greger, eds. Year One, 1 vol. 2011. (ENG., Illus.). 240p. 45.00 *(978-3-86521-537-6(8))* Steidl, Gerhard Druckerei und Verlag DEU. Dist: Innovative Logistics.

Ulf Nilson, Greger & Petersen, Anders, eds. City Diary, 3 vols. 2011. (ENG., Illus.). 216p. 98.00 *(978-3-86521-536-9(X))* Steidl, Gerhard Druckerei und Verlag DEU. Dist: Innovative Logistics.

ARTISTS—SWITZERLAND

Amiet, Cuno, et al. Ferdinand Hodler: Biografische Erinnerungen. 2010. (GER., Illus.). 192p. 67.00 ***(978-3-85881-156-1(4))*** Scheidegger und Spiess AG, Verlag CHE. Dist: Antique Collectors' Club.

Antille, Emmanuelle, photos by. Emmanuelle Antille: Tornadoes of My Heart, 1 vol. 2007. (ENG., Illus.). 112p. 29.00 *(978-3-905770-16-2(4))* JRP Ringier Kunstverlag AG CHE. Dist: D.A.P./Distributed Art Pubs.

Armleder, John, illus. John Armleder: Pfcbcdrrsrgbmpf Pclspsbmpfcbs, 5 vols. 2008. (ITA & ENG.). 88p. 15.00 *(978-3-905701-46-3(4))* JRP Ringier Kunstverlag AG CHE. Dist: D.A.P./Distributed Art Pubs.

Bastian, M. S. & L, Isabelle. Bastokalypse. 2010. (Illus.). 128p. pap. 59.00 *(978-3-85881-296-4(X))* Scheidegger und Spiess AG, Verlag CHE. Dist: Antique Collectors' Club.

Baur, Ruedi. Ruedi Baur Intigral. 2008. (GER, ENG & FRE., Illus.). 480p. 69.95 *(978-3-03778-134-0(3)*, 3037781343) Springer.

Becker, Christoph & Schädler, Linda. Félix Vallotton: Idyll on the Edge. Becker, Christoph, ed. 2007. (Illus.). 208p. 95.00 *(978-3-85881-707-5(4))* Scheidegger und Spiess AG, Verlag CHE. Dist: Antique Collectors' Club.

Bitterli, Koni. Alexander Hahn: Werke / Works 1976 - 2006. Vögele, Christoph, ed. 2007. (GER & ENG., Illus.). 216p. 36.00 *(978-3-939583-20-2(0))* Kehrer Verlag Heidelberg, Klaus Kehrer DEU. Dist: Consortium Bk. Sales & Distribution.

Boehm, Gottfried, et al. Windows for the Zurich Grossmunster. 2010. (ENG., Illus.). 208p. 65.00 *(978-3-907582-27-5(6))* Parkett Verlag AG CHE. Dist: D.A.P./Distributed Art Pubs.

Bovier, Lionel, ed. Philippe Decrauzat. Miller, Chris, tr. 2008. (ENG., Illus.). 64p. 30.00 *(978-3-905770-87-2(3))* JRP Ringier Kunstverlag AG CHE. Dist: D.A.P./Distributed Art Pubs.

Brändle, Christian, ed. François Berthoud Studio: Die Kunst der Modeillustration. 2011. (GER & ENG., Illus.). 240p. pap. 55.00 ***(978-3-7757-3014-3(1))*** Hatje Cantz Verlag GmbH & Co KG DEU. Dist: D.A.P./Distributed Art Pubs.

Brüggebors, Nadine, text. Andy Denzler Paintings: The Human Nature Project. 2011. (ENG., Illus.). 128p. 55.00 *(978-3-7757-2803-4(1))* Hatje Cantz Verlag GmbH & Co KG DEU. Dist: D.A.P./Distributed Art Pubs.

Brun, Carl, compiled by. Schweizerisches Künstler-lexikon, 4 vols., 2006. (GER.). 2698p. 395.00 *(978-1-57898-593-7(5))* Martino Publishing.

Carron, Valentin. Valentin Carron: Learning from Martigny. 2010. (ENG., Illus.). 128p. pap. 45.00 *(978-3-03764-095-1(2))* JRP Ringier Kunstverlag AG CHE. Dist: D.A.P./Distributed Art Pubs.

Carron, Valentin, et al. Valentin Carron, 1 vol. 2006. (ENG., Illus.). 64p. 29.00 *(978-3-905701-53-1(7))* JRP Ringier Kunstverlag AG CHE. Dist: D.A.P./Distributed Art Pubs.

Comunale Casa Rusca, Locarno Pinacoteca, et al. Wilfrid Moser: Milestones - Oeuvre, 1934-1997. Museum of Fine Arts Bern Staff, ed. 2009. (Illus.). 300p. 110.00 *(978-3-85881-716-7(3))* Scheidegger und Spiess AG, Verlag CHE. Dist: Antique Collectors' Club.

Crumb, R. & Obrist, Hans Ulrich, texts. Crumb/Obrist, 1 vol. 2007. (ENG.). 47p. pap. 16.00 *(978-3-88375-948-7(1))* Verlag der Buchhandlung Walther Konig DEU. Dist: D.A.P./Distributed Art Pubs.

Curiger, Bice & Jent, Louis. Friedrich Kuhn, 1926-1972: The Painter As Outlaw. Curiger, Bice, ed. 2009. (GER & ENG., Illus.). 192p. 75.00 *(978-3-85881-245-2(5))* Scheidegger und Spiess AG, Verlag CHE. Dist: Antique Collectors' Club.

Doswald, Christoph, ed. Hanspeter Hofmann: Bonheur Automatique. 2008. (ENG., Illus.). 160p. per. 49.00 *(978-3-905770-67-4(9))* JRP Ringier Kunstverlag AG CHE. Dist: D.A.P./Distributed Art Pubs.

Ehrli, Vivane, ed. Rita Ernst: Monograph. (ENG, ITA & GER., Illus.). 164p. 45.00 *(978-3-89322-890-4(X))* Edition Cantz DEU. Dist: D.A.P./Distributed Art Pubs.

Engler, Martin. John M. Armleder: Too Much Is Not Enough. Berg, Stefan, ed. 2007. (GER & ENG., Illus.). 120p. 36.00 *(978-3-939583-02-8(2))* Kehrer

Verlag Heidelberg, Klaus Kehrer DEU. Dist: Consortium Bk. Sales & Distribution.

Essays, Zürich, et al. Sophie Taeuber-Arp: Gestalterin, Architektin, Tänzerin. 2008. (Illus.). 72p. 49.00 *(978-3-85881-196-7(3))* Scheidegger und Spiess AG, Verlag CHE. Dist: Antique Collectors' Club.

Frank, Robert. Me & My Brother, 1 vol. 2008. (ENG., Illus.). 56p. pap. 50.00 *(978-3-86521-363-1(4))* Steidl, Gerhard Druckerei und Verlag DEU. Dist: Innovative Logistics.

Frehner, Matthias, frwd. Yves Netzhammer: the Refuge for Drawbacks. 2011. (ENG., Illus.). 136p. 50.00 ***(978-3-86984-158-8(3))*** Verlag fur Moderne Kunst DEU. Dist: D.A.P./Distributed Art Pubs.

Giacometti, Alberto & Rütimann, Donat. Le Reve, le Sphinx et la Mort de T. Der Traum, Die Sphinx und der Tod Von T. - Faksimileausgabe des Manuskriptes 2010. (FRE & GER., Illus.). 128p. pap. 78.00 ***(978-3-85881-170-7(X))*** Scheidegger und Spiess AG, Verlag CHE. Dist: Antique Collectors' Club.

Giezendanner, Ingo. GRR30: Urban Recordings. 2006. (Illus.). 345p. pap. 30.00 *(978-3-00-018496-3(1))* D.A.P./Distributed Art Pubs.

Giger, H. R. & Stutzer, Beat. HR Giger- das Schaffen vor Alien, 1961-1976. 2010. (GER., Illus.). 168p. 95.00 ***(978-3-85881-195-0(5))*** Scheidegger und Spiess AG, Verlag CHE. Dist: Antique Collectors' Club.

Gubler, Ernst & Werder, Kurt. Ernst Gubler - Max Gubler: Briefwechsel, 2 vols. 2010. (GER., Illus.). 888p. 170.00 ***(978-3-85881-176-9(9))*** Scheidegger und Spiess AG, Verlag CHE. Dist: Antique Collectors' Club.

Hauptman, William. Hodler: Gallery of the Arts. 2008. (Gallery of the Arts Ser.). (ENG., Illus.). 112p. 18.95 *(978-88-7439-362-6(8))* 5 Continents ITA. Dist: Hachette Bk. Group.

He, Jianping, ed. The Master of Design: Niklaus Troxler. 2007. (Master of Design Ser.). (Illus.). 311p. pap. 39.95 *(978-981-245-426-3(8))* Page One Publishing SGP. Dist: Gingko Pr., Inc.

—The Master of Design: Werner Jeker. 2007. (Master of Design Ser.). (Illus.). 309p. pap. 39.95 *(978-981-245-428-7(4))* Page One Publishing SGP. Dist: Gingko Pr., Inc.

Hesse, Jochen. Der populäre Künstler: Das Beispiel Bernhard Luginbühl. 2006. (Europäische Hochschulschriften. Reihe 28: Kunstgeschichte Ser.). 246p. pap. *(978-3-03910-979-1(0))* Lang, Peter.

Kamber, André & Kamber, Andre. Leonardo Bezzola: Photographs, 1948-2007. 2008. (Illus.). 200p. 95.00 *(978-3-85881-209-4(9))* Scheidegger und Spiess AG, Verlag CHE. Dist: Antique Collectors' Club.

Keller, Christoph, et al, eds. Zilla Leutenegger: Zilla & the 7th Room. 2009. (GER & ENG., Illus.). 128p. 59.00 *(978-3-905829-72-3(X))* JRP Ringier Kunstverlag AG CHE. Dist: D.A.P./Distributed Art Pubs.

Keusch, Beat & Voss, Jan, eds. Dieter Roth: Souvenirs. 2011. (GER & ENG., Illus.). 152p. 85.00 ***(978-3-7757-2818-8(X))*** Hatje Cantz Verlag GmbH & Co KG DEU. Dist: D.A.P./Distributed Art Pubs.

Kirchner, Ernst Ludwig, et al. Das Ungewohnte Neue: Briefwechsel Ernst Ludwig Kirchner und George Reinhart. 2010. (GER., Illus.). 176p. pap. 45.00 ***(978-3-85881-140-0(8))*** Scheidegger und Spiess AG, Verlag CHE. Dist: Antique Collectors' Club.

Kurjakovic, Daniel, ed. Album: On & Around Urs Fischer, Yves Netzhammer, Ugo Rondinone, & Christine Streuli, Participating at the 52nd Venice Biennale 2007, 1 vol. 2007. (ENG., Illus.). 320p. per. 25.00 *(978-3-905770-70-4(9))* JRP Ringier Kunstverlag AG CHE. Dist: D.A.P./Distributed Art Pubs.

Lohse, Richard. Richard Paul Lohse. Drucke Prints: Dokumentation + Werkverzeichnis, Documentation + Catalogue raisonné. 2009. (ENG., Illus.). 472p. 120.00 *(978-3-7757-2309-1(9))* Hatje Cantz Verlag GmbH & Co KG DEU. Dist: D.A.P./Distributed Art Pubs.

Lüthi, Urs & Barbero, Luca Massimo. Urs Lüthi: Just Another Story about Leaving. Forin, Elena, ed. 2010. (ITA & ENG., Illus.). 208p. 90.00 *(978-88-370-7464-7(6))* Electa ITA. Dist: Trans-Atlantic Pubns., Inc.

Magnaguagno, Guido & Omlin, Sibylle. Klaus Born - Malerei. 2008. (Illus.). 124p. 50.00 *(978-3-85881-226-1(9))* Scheidegger und Spiess AG, Verlag CHE. Dist: Antique Collectors' Club.

Mora, Gilles, ed. & text. A Kind of Infatuation, 1 vol. 2009. (ENG., Illus.). 312p. 78.00 *(978-3-86521-830-8(X))* Steidl, Gerhard Druckerei und Verlag DEU. Dist: Innovative Logistics.

Moser, Claudio, photos by. Claudio Moser: Nowhere Near Far Enough. 2011. (ENG., Illus.). 106p. 60.00 *(978-3-7757-2737-2(X))* Hatje Cantz Verlag GmbH & Co KG DEU. Dist: D.A.P./Distributed Art Pubs.

Mossinger, Ingrid, ed. Cesare Lucchini: What Remains. 2009. (ENG., Illus.). 120p. 45.00 *(978-3-86678-213-6(6))* Kerber Verlag DEU. Dist: D.A.P./Distributed Art Pubs.

Museum für Gestaltung Zürich, ed. Otto Baumberger. 2008. (Poster Collection). (GER & ENG., Illus.). 96p. pap. 35.00 *(978-3-03778-129-6(7),* 3037781297) Springer.

Obrist, Hans Ulrich, ed. Hans Ulrich Obrist & Jeff Koons: the Conversation Series. 2012. (ENG., Illus.). 158p. pap. 29.95 *(978-3-86560-635-8(0))* Verlag der Buchhandlung Walther Konig DEU. Dist: D.A.P./Distributed Art Pubs.

—Hans Ulrich Obrist & Yoko Ono: the Conversation Series. 2010. (ENG., Illus.). 96p. pap. 27.00 *(978-3-86560-652-5(0))* Verlag der Buchhandlung Walther Konig DEU. Dist: D.A.P./Distributed Art Pubs.

Olaf Breuning: Ugly. *(978-3-7757-1104-3(X))* Hatje Cantz Verlag GmbH & Co KG DEU. Dist: D.A.P./Distributed Art Pubs.

Perret, Roger & Kurzmeyer, Roman, eds. Dunkelschwestern. Annemarie von Matt - Sonja Sekula. 2008. (Illus.). 368p. 147.00 *(978-3-85881-213-1(7))* Scheidegger und Spiess AG, Verlag CHE. Dist: Antique Collectors' Club.

Petcher, Carole M., tr. BLACK INK: illustrations of ata 'TOAST' bozaci. 2007. (Illus.). 240p. 39.95 *(978-1-58423-294-0(3))* Gingko Pr., Inc.

Pong, Elodie. Elodie Pong: We Are Knights on the Trajectories of a Post-Everything Era. 2008. (ENG., Illus.). 64p. pap. 15.00 *(978-3-905701-36-4(7))* JRP Ringier Kunstverlag AG CHE. Dist: D.A.P./Distributed Art Pubs.

Ruf, Beatrix, ed. Peter Fischli & David Weiss: Sonne, Mond und Sterne. 2008. (ENG., Illus.). 800p. pap. 69.00 *(978-3-905829-41-9(X))* JRP Ringier Kunstverlag AG CHE. Dist: D.A.P./Distributed Art Pubs.

Signer, Roman. Roman Signer: Projektionen, 1975-2008, 1 vol. 2009. (ENG., Illus.). 176p. 85.00 *(978-3-86521-747-9(8))* Steidl, Gerhard Druckerei und Verlag DEU. Dist: Innovative Logistics.

Stutzer, Beat, et al. Ernst Ludwig Kirchner & Friends: Expressionism from the Swiss Mountains. Stutzer, Beat et al, eds. 2007. (Illus.). 320p. 110.00 *(978-3-85881-706-8(6))* Scheidegger und Spiess AG, Verlag CHE. Dist: Antique Collectors' Club.

—The Unseen Giacometti: Unknown Photographs & Drawings. Stutzer, Beat, ed. 2011. (ENG., Illus.). 255p. 99.00 ***(978-3-85881-726-6(0))*** Scheidegger und Spiess AG, Verlag CHE. Dist: Antique Collectors' Club.

Superfundi. 2008. pap. 19.00 *(978-3-905770-69-8(5))* JRP Ringier Kunstverlag AG CHE. Dist: D.A.P./Distributed Art Pubs.

Suter, H. Paul Klee & His Illness: Bowed but Not Broken by Suffering & Adversity Translated from the German by G. Mckay; N. Mckay. 2010. (ENG., Illus.). 272p. *(978-3-8055-9381-6(3))* Karger, S. AG.

Szymczyk, Adam, text. Kilian Rüthemann: Double Rich. 2010. (ENG., Illus.). 4036p. 55.00 *(978-3-7757-2674-0(8))* Hatje Cantz Verlag GmbH & Co KG DEU. Dist: D.A.P./Distributed Art Pubs.

Teagle, Rachel. Pipilotti Rist: Wishing for Synchronicity. Morsiani, Paola, ed. 2007. (Illus.). 160p. 50.00 *(978-3-7757-2006-9(5))* Hatje Cantz Verlag GmbH & Co KG DEU. Dist: D.A.P./Distributed Art Pubs.

Varlin, et al. Wenn ich dichten Könnte: Briefe und Schriften. 2010. (GER., Illus.). 352p. 89.00 ***(978-3-85881-101-1(7))*** Scheidegger und Spiess AG, Verlag CHE. Dist: Antique Collectors' Club.

Walter, Bernadette, text. Verena Loewensberg: Prints. 2009. (ENG., Illus.). 112p. pap. 38.00 *(978-3-905714-51-7(5))* Nieves CHE. Dist: D.A.P./Distributed Art Pubs.

Wiedemann, Pascale, et al. Morbus infinitus & Subkutan, 2 vols. 2008. (GER & ENG., Illus.). 184p. 60.00 *(978-3-85881-206-3(4))* Scheidegger und Spiess AG, Verlag CHE. Dist: Antique Collectors' Club.

Withers, Rachel, et al. Roman Signer. 2010. (ENG., Illus.). 192p. pap., pap. 59.95 *(978-3-8321-7720-1(5))* DuMont DEU. Dist: D.A.P./Distributed Art Pubs.

Zurich & Isernhagen, Hartwig. Karl Bodmer - Maler der amerikanischen Urvölker: A Swiss Artist in America. North America Native Museum Editors et al, eds. 2009. (GER & ENG., Illus.). 208p. 75.00 *(978-3-85881-236-0(6))* Scheidegger und Spiess AG, Verlag CHE. Dist: Antique Collectors' Club.

ARTISTS—UNITED STATES

Abell, Sam. The Life of a Photograph. 2008. (ENG., Illus.). 208p. 40.00 *(978-1-4262-0329-9(2),* National Geographic) National Geographic Society.

Ackerman, Nick, et al, illus. Artists of Invention: A Century of CCA, 1 vol. 2008. (ENG.). 166p. pap. 39.99 *(978-978-097-535-7(7))* California College of the Arts.

Adnan, Etel. Etel Adnan: Der Preis der Liebe, den wir nicht zahlen wollen. 2011. (ENG., Illus.). 32p. pap. 10.00 ***(978-3-7757-2855-3(4))*** Hatje Cantz Verlag GmbH & Co KG DEU. Dist: D.A.P./Distributed Art Pubs.

Agabian, Nancy. Me As Her Again: [true Stories of an Armenian Daughter]. 2008. (ENG.). 216p. pap. 12.95 *(978-1-879960-79-4(6))* Aunt Lute Bks.

Alexander, William. Is William Martinez Not Our Brother? Twenty Years of the Prison Creative Arts Project. 2010. (New Public Scholarship Ser.). (ENG., Illus.). 328p. pap. 37.50 *(978-0-472-05109-0(1));* 95.00 *(978-0-472-07109-8(2))* Univ. of Michigan Pr.

Ali, Laylah, illus. Laylah Ali: Typology, 1 vol. 2007. (ENG.). 48p. per. 20.00 *(978-0-943836-30-0(1))* Pennsylvania Academy of the Fine Arts.

Allen, Siemon, et al. Julie Mehretu: City Sitings, 1 vol. 2009. (ENG.). 88p. 40.00 *(978-0-89558-161-7(2))* Detroit Institute of Arts.

Alles, Virginia. Eye of the Beholder. 2008. (Illus.). 76p. pap. 13.95 *(978-0-9766083-7-0(5))* White Feather Press, LLC.

Aloi, Joseph Ari. Tatt Book: Visionaries of Tattoo. 2011. (ENG., Illus.). 288p. pap. 29.95 *(978-0-7893-2270-8(6))* Universe Publishing.

Alves, Wagner. Drawings Sketchbook. 2010. (Illus.). ix, 700p. E-Book ***(978-1-4500-4761-6(0))*** Xlibris Corp.

Amada, Richard. An Artist's Guide to the Law: Law & Legal Concepts Every Artist, Performer, Writer, or Other Creative Person Ought to Know. 2010. (ENG.). 210p. pap. 19.95 *(978-1-58510-356-0(X))* Focus Publishing/R. Pullins Co., Inc.

Amos Lee. 2008. (ENG.). 88p. pap. 19.95 *(978-1-60378-027-8(0),* 1603780270) Cherry Lane Music Co.

Anastas, Ayreen & Gabri, Rene, contrib. by. Paul Ryan: Zwei ist keine Zahl. Ein Gespräch mit Ayreen Anastas & Rene Gabri. 2011. (ENG., Illus.). 48p. pap. 10.00 ***(978-3-7757-2864-5(3))*** Hatje Cantz Verlag GmbH & Co KG DEU. Dist: D.A.P./Distributed Art Pubs.

Anastasi, William & Levy, Aaron. The Cage Dialogues: A Memoir. 2011. pap. ***(978-1-936994-01-4(1))*** Slought Foundation.

Anderson, Brooke, et al. Martín Ramírez. 2007. (Illus.). 191p. 45.00 *(978-0-9778028-1-4(7))* Marquand Bks., Inc.

Anderson, Brooke Davis. Martin Ramirez: The Last Works. 2008. 160p. 39.95 *(978-0-7649-4695-0(1))* Pomegranate Communications, Inc.

Anderson, Dustin Keith. Up Close & Personal: Observations on Color Texture & Life. 2010. 48p. 19.95 *(978-1-4490-6664-2(X))* AuthorHouse.

Anderson, Laurie. Night Life, 1 vol. 2009. (ENG., Illus.). 96p. 35.00 *(978-3-86521-339-6(1))* Steidl, Gerhard Druckerei und Verlag DEU. Dist: Innovative Logistics.

Anderson, Randy. On Making Off: Misadventures off-off Broadway. 2011. (ENG.). 306p. pap. 14.99 *(978-1-4610-4168-9(6))* CreateSpace.

Andrae, Thomas. Creators of the Superheroes. 2009. 224p. pap. 39.99 *(978-1-932563-26-9(1))* Hermes Pr.

Apak. The Little Otsu Living Things Series Volume 5: Mushroom Folk: A guide to the secret world of fungi & their Friends. 2011. (Illus.). 16p. 6.95 ***(978-1-934378-26-7(7))*** Little Otsu.

Arbitman, Kahren Jones & Gallo, Susan M. Picturing Florida: From the First Coast to the Space Coast. 2008. (ENG., Illus.). 223p. 75.00 *(978-1-934491-09-6(8))* Fresco Fine Art Pubns., LLC.

Archer, Michael. Jeff Koons - One Ball Total Equilibrium Tank. 2011. (Afterall Ser.). (ENG., Illus.). 120p. (gr. 17). 35.00 ***(978-1-84638-078-5(2))***; pap. 16.00 ***(978-1-84638-079-2(0))*** Afterall Publishing GBR. Dist: MIT Pr.

Arrhenius, Sara, et al. Tomás Saraceno: 14 Billions. 2012. (SWE & ENG., Illus.). 192p. 75.00 *(978-88-572-0857-2(5))* Skira Editore ITA. Dist: Random Hse., Inc.

Art of Enduring Value: The Sculpture of Barry Woods Johnston. (Illus.). 28p. 10.00 *(978-0-9620343-2-9(0))* Candel Publishing, LLC.

Ashbery, John, prologue by. Jess: To & from the Printed Page, 1 vol. 2007. (ENG., Illus.). 112p. pap. 29.95 *(978-0-916365-75-2(1))* Independent Curators International.

Attoe, Dan. Dan Attoe: I Made Most of This Shit Up. 2010. (ENG., Illus.). 216p. pap. 75.00 *(978-0-9817658-6-0(6))* Peres Projects, Los Angeles Berlin.

Auad, Manuel, ed. Franklin Booth: American Illustrator. 2006. (Illus.). 128p. 24.95 *(978-0-9669381-4-2(3))* Auad Publishing.

Audubon, John James. John James Audubon's Journal Of 1826: The Voyage to the Birds of America. Patterson, Daniel, ed. & intro. by. 2011. (ENG., Illus.). 536p. 50.00 *(978-0-8032-2531-2(8))* Univ. of Nebraska Pr.

Aupetitallot, Yves, ed. Kelley Walker. 2008. (ENG., Illus.). 160p. pap. 49.00 *(978-3-905770-68-1(7))* JRP Ringier Kunstverlag AG CHE. Dist: D.A.P./Distributed Art Pubs.

Auping, Michael, et al. Road Tested, 1 vol. 2011. (ENG., Illus.). 128p. 40.00 *(978-3-7757-2810-2(4))* Hatje Cantz Verlag GmbH & Co KG DEU. Dist: D.A.P./Distributed Art Pubs.

Baca, Judith & Ramos, Henry. Painting the River of Angels: The Autobiography of Judith F. Baca. 2008. pap. 16.95 *(978-1-55885-488-8(6))* Arte Publico Pr.

Bair, Deirdre. Saul Steinberg: A Biography. 2012. (ENG., Illus.). 752p. 40.00 ***(978-0-385-52448-3(X),*** Talese, Nan A.) Knopf Doubleday Publishing Group.

Baker, Bill. Michael Avon Oeming on His Work & Career. 2009. (Talking with Graphic Novelists Ser.). 164p. (gr. 9-9). 61.20 *(978-1-60853-260-5(7))* Rosen Publishing Group, Inc., The.

Baldessari, John. John Baldessari: Noses & Ears, etc. (Part Three) 2007. (Illus.). 51p. 40.00 *(978-1-880641-06-4(2))* Margo Leavin Gallery.

—Prima Facie Marilyn's Dress, 1 vol. 2007. (ENG., Illus.). 44p. 35.00 *(978-3-86560-088-2(3))* Verlag der Buchhandlung Walther Konig DEU. Dist: D.A.P./Distributed Art Pubs.

Balio, Tino T. United Artists, Volume 1, 1919-1950: The Company Built by the Stars. 2009. (ENG., Illus.). 360p. pap. 26.95 *(978-0-299-23004-3(X))* Univ. of Wisconsin Pr.

Balken, Debra Bricker. Dove - O'Keeffe: Circles of Influence. 2009. (Illus.). 168p. 45.00 *(978-0-300-13410-0(X))* Yale Univ. Pr.

Ball, David M. & Kuhlman, Martha B., eds. The Comics of Chris Ware: Drawing Is a Way of Thinking. 2010. (ENG., Illus.). 288p. pap. 28.00 *(978-1-60473-443-0(4))* Univ. Pr. of Mississippi.

Baltz, Lewis. Lewis Baltz: The Prototype Works. 2010. (ENG., Illus.). 112p. 50.00 *(978-3-86521-763-9(X))* Steidl, Gerhard Druckerei und Verlag DEU. Dist: D.A.P./Distributed Art Pubs.

—Lewis Baltz: The Tract Houses. 2010. (ENG., Illus.). 64p. 50.00 *(978-3-86521-762-2(1))* Steidl, Gerhard Druckerei und Verlag DEU. Dist: D.A.P./Distributed Art Pubs.

Bama, James. James Bama Sketchbook: A Seventy Year Journey, Traveling from the Far East to the Old West. 2010. 144p. pap. 24.95 *(978-1-933865-24-9(5))* Flesk Pubns.

Barry, Robert, photos by. Robert Barry: Real ... ... Personal, 5 vols. 2008. (ITA & ENG., Illus.). 56p. 15.00 *(978-3-905701-48-7(0))* JRP Ringier Kunstverlag AG CHE. Dist: D.A.P./Distributed Art Pubs.

Bartlett, Jennifer. Jennifer Bartlett, Writings. 2014. (ENG.). 300p. pap. 25.00 *(978-0-88214-570-9(3))* Spring Pubns., Inc.

Bartos, Adam, photos by. Adam Bartos: Yard Sale Photographs. 2009. (ENG., Illus.). 130p. 49.95 *(978-88-6208-078-1(6))* Damiani ITA. Dist: D.A.P./Distributed Art Pubs.

Baseman, Gary. Dying of Thirst. 2008. (Illus.). 48p. 24.95 *(978-0-86719-692-4(0))* Last Gasp of San Francisco.

Baseman, Gary & Williams, Robert. My Hunger for Venison. 2007. (Illus.). 240p. 29.95 *(978-0-9778949-3-2(2))* Baby Tattoo Bks.

Basile, Kenneth. The Sculpture of Grainger Mckoy. 2011. pap. ***(978-1-932543-43-8(0))*** High Museum of Art.

Baskind, Samantha. Encyclopedia of Jewish American Artists, 1 vol. 2006. (Artists of the American Mosaic Ser.). (Illus.). 352p. 85.00 *(978-0-313-33637-9(7),* GR3637, Greenwood Pr.) Greenwood Publishing Group, Inc.

Basualdo, C. Bruce Nauman: Topological Gardens. Basualdo, Carlos, ed. & contrib. by. by. Taylor, Michael R. et al, contrib. by. 2009. (ENG & ITA., Illus.). 240p. 40.00 *(978-0-300-14981-4(6))* Yale Univ. Pr.

Basualdo, Carlos & Battle, Erica F., eds. Bruce Nauman: Topological Gardens - Installation Views. 2010. (Illus.). 60p. pap. 12.00 *(978-0-300-16463-3(7))* Yale Univ. Pr.

Bauer, Anna. Anna Bauer: Backstage. Baron, Fabien, ed. 2012. (ENG., Illus.). 304p. 125.00 ***(978-3-943287-00-4(9))*** Angelika Bks.

Bazzell, Paul. Famous Again: The Life & Times of Sorrells Pickard. 2009. 150p. pap. 19.95 *(978-1-60563-738-9(6))* PublishAmerica, Inc.

Bean, Alan. Alan Bean: Painting Apollo - First Artist on Another World. 2009. (ENG.). 224p. 39.99 *(978-1-58834-264-5(6))* Smithsonian Institution Pr.

Becker, Stephen, ed. Theodore Wores in the Southwest. 2007. (California Historical Society Ser.). (Illus.). 98p. per. 24.95 *(978-1-59714-047-8(3))* Heyday.

Bell, Marc. Marc Bell's Hot Potatoe: Fine Arhwerks: 2001-2008. 2009. (ENG., Illus.). 272p. 39.95 *(978-1-897299-89-0(3))* Drawn & Quarterly Pubns. CAN. Dist: Macmillan.

Benjamin, Robert, photos by. Robert Benjamin: Notes from a Quiet Life. 2012. (ENG., Illus.). 72p. 45.00 ***(978-1-934435-37-3(6))*** Radius Bks.

Bernstein, Lee. America Is the Prison: Arts & Politics in Prison in The 1970s. 2010. (ENG., Illus.). 240p. 35.00 *(978-0-8078-3387-2(8))* Univ. of North Carolina Pr.

—America Is the Prison: Arts & Politics in Prison in the 1970s. 2010. (Illus.). xi, 244p. pap. *(978-0-8078-7117-1(6))* Univ. of North Carolina Pr.

Bertels, Alice S. John Steuart Curry: the Road Home. 2006. (Illus.). 32p. 23.95 *(978-1-58597-388-0(2))* Leathers Publishing.

Bingaman-Burt, Kate & Princeton Architectural Press Staff. Obsessive Consumption: What Did You Buy Today? 2010. (ENG., Illus.). 206p. pap. 19.95 *(978-1-56898-890-0(7))* Princeton Architectural Pr.

Biographiq. Andy Warhol - a Life of Pop Art. 2008. 76p. pap. 9.99 *(978-1-59986-058-9(9),* Biographiq) Filiquarian Publishing, LLC.

Biondi, Elisabeth, afterword by. Sylvia Plachy: Goings on about Town: Photographs for the New Yorker, 1 vol. 2007. (ENG., Illus.). 104p. 29.95 *(978-1-59711-051-8(5))* Aperture Foundation, Inc.

Bishop, Anne Warner, Jr. Silver, the Life & Art of Sylvia Beckman Warner. 2007. 100.00 *(978-0-9796438-1-1(3))* Bishop, Anne.

Black, Patti Carr. American Masters of the Mississippi Gulf Coast: George Ohr, Dusti Bonge, Walter Anderson, Richmond Barthe. 2008. (ENG., Illus.). 99p. 35.00 *(978-1-60473-205-4(9))* Univ. Pr. of Mississippi.

Block, Gay, photos by. Gay Block: about Love. 2011. (ENG., Illus.). 312p. 65.00 *(978-1-934435-32-8(5))* Radius Bks.

Block, Herbert. Herblock: The Life & Work of the Great Political Cartoonist. Katz, Harry, ed. 2009. (ENG., Illus.). 304p. 35.00 *(978-0-393-06772-9(6),* 6772) Norton, W. W. & Co., Inc.

Blondeau, Marc & Davet, Philippe, eds. Louise Lawler: The Tremaine Pictures 1984-2007. 2008. (ENG., Illus.). 108p. per. 25.00 *(978-3-905829-03-7(7))* JRP Ringier Kunstverlag AG CHE. Dist: D.A.P./Distributed Art Pubs.

Bluebird in my Window. 2007. (ITA & ENG.). 35.00 *(978-0-9762983-2-8(5))* El Leon Literary Arts.

Bob Dylan: The Gig Book. 2011. (ENG.). 304p. pap. 19.99 *(978-1-61780-315-4(4),* 1617803154) Music Sales Corp.

Bochner, Mel. Solar System & Rest Rooms: Writings & Interviews, 1965-2007. 2008. (Writing Art Ser.). (ENG., Illus.). 240p. (gr. 17). 39.95 *(978-0-262-02631-4(7))* MIT Pr.

Bojorquez, Chaz. The Art & Life of Chaz Bojorquez. 2010. (ENG., Illus.). 190p. 50.00 *(978-88-6208-121-4(9))* Damiani ITA. Dist: D.A.P./Distributed Art Pubs.

Bollinger, Bill & Meyer-Stoll, Christiane. Bill Bollinger. 2012. (ENG., Illus.). 256p. 59.95 ***(978-3-86335-058-1(8))*** Verlag der Buchhandlung Walther Konig DEU. Dist: D.A.P./Distributed Art Pubs.

Bonami, Francesco, ed. & contrib. by. Jeff Koons. 2008. (ENG., Illus.). 136p. 45.00 *(978-0-300-14194-8(7))* Yale Univ. Pr.

Bonet, Eugeni. Parallel: Benet Rossell. 2010. 256p. pap. 54.95 *(978-84-92505-42-5(7))* Museu d'Art Contemporani de Barcelona ESP. Dist: Actar Birkhauser Distribution.

Bonevardi, Gustavo & Bennett, John, eds. Bonevardi: Chasing Shadows, Constructing Art. 2007. (ENG., Illus.). 448p. 60.00 *(978-0-292-71436-6(X))* Univ. of Texas Pr.

Bookbinder, Judith. First Hand: Civil War Era Drawings from the Becker Collection. Gallagher, Sheila, ed. 2010. (Illus.). 200p. pap. 50.00 *(978-1-892850-15-7(X))* McMullen Museum of Art, Boston College.

Botha, Ted. The Girl with the Crooked Nose. 2012. (ENG., Illus.). 384p. (gr. 12). pap. 15.00 ***(978-0-425-24683-2(3),*** Berkley Trade) Penguin Group (USA) Inc.

Bovier, Lionel, ed. Justin Lieberman. 2009. (ENG., Illus.). 64p. 35.00 *(978-3-03764-008-1(1))* JRP Ringier Kunstverlag AG CHE. Dist: D.A.P./Distributed Art Pubs.

Bovier, Lionel & Taylor, Kelly, eds. Jonathan Horowitz: And/or. 2009. (ENG., Illus.). 192p. pap. 55.00 *(978-3-03764-018-0(9))* JRP Ringier Kunstverlag AG CHE. Dist: D.A.P./Distributed Art Pubs.

Boyden, Frank. Coexistence with Fire: Wood-Fired Ceramics by Frank Boyden, 1985-2006. 2008. (Illus.). 245p. *(978-0-9816728-2-3(5))* American Museum of Ceramic Art.

Bradshaw, Richard Lee. Thomas Bradshaw: A Georgian Politician in the Time of the American Revolution. 2011. 162p. 29.99 ***(978-1-4653-4478-6(0))***; pap. 19.99 ***(978-1-4653-4477-9(2))*** Xlibris Corp.

Braun, Marta. Eadweard Muybridge. 2010. (Reaktion Books - Critical Lives Ser.). (ENG., Illus.). 208p. pap. 16.95 (978-1-86189-760-2(X)) Reaktion Bks., Ltd. GBR. Dist: Chicago Distribution Ctr.

Braziel, Jana Evans. Artists, Performers, & Black Masculinity in the Haitian Diaspora. 2008. (Blacks in the Diaspora Ser.). (ENG., Illus.). 312p. 65.00 (978-0-253-35139-5(1), 0253351391); pap. 24.95 (978-0-253-21978-7(7), 025321978?) Indiana Univ. Pr.

Brennan, Virginia. Gasoline Gypsies: David & Virginia's Life on the Road. 2009. 132p. pap. 14.95 (978-1-4327-0391-2(9)) Outskirts Pr., Inc.

Bright, Susan. Flash Forward 2007: Emerging photographers from Canada, the United Kingdom & the United States. 2007. (ENG.). 192p. 25.00 (978-0-9739739-2-1(7)) Magenta Publishing for the Arts CAN. Dist: Consortium Bk. Sales & Distribution.

Briney, S. Self Portrait. 2010. 192p. pap. 15.99 (978-1-4490-6161-6(3)) AuthorHouse.

Brittin, Charles. Charles Brittin: West & South. 2011. (ENG., Illus.). 216p. 60.00 (978-3-7757-2836-2(8)) Hatje Cantz Verlag GmbH & Co KG DEU. Dist: D.A.P./Distributed Art Pubs.

Brown, Anne. Brother Me! Lifetime of Making Art. 2009. (Illus.). 236p. 65.00 (978-0-578-03493-5(X)) Arts Co. Pr., The.

Brown, Betty Ann & White, John M., contrib. by. Lifelines: John M. White: A Retrospective Exhibition of Performance, Installation, Sculpture, Painting & Drawing. 2011. (ENG., Illus.). 56p. pap. 25.00 (978-0-9833385-0-5(7)) Armory Ctr. for the Arts.

Brown, Harrison Bird & Routhier, Jessica Skwire. Vividly True to Nature: Harrison Bird Brown, 1831-1915. 2007. (Illus.). 32p. pap. (978-0-916857-47-9(6)) Portland Museum of Art.

Brown, Jeffrey. Little Things: A Memoir in Slices. 2008. (ENG., Illus.). 352p. pap. 14.00 (978-1-4165-4946-8(3), Touchstone) Touchstone.

Buckley, Annie, text. Marnie Weber: Sing Me a Western Song. 2007. (Illus.). 40p. lib. bdg. 50.00 (978-0-9778848-6-5(4)) Patrick Painter, Inc.

Burnet, Mary O. Art & Artists in Indiana. (Illus.). 448p. reprint ed. lib. bdg. 98.00 (978-0-7222-0857-1(X)) Library Reprints, Inc.

Burr, Tom. Tom Burr: Extrospective: Works 1994-2006, 1 vol. Derieux, Florence, ed. 2006. (FRE & ENG., Illus.). 160p. pap. 45.00 (978-3-905701-82-1(0)) JRP Ringier Kunstverlag AG CHE. Dist: D.A.P./Distributed Art Pubs.

Burton, Johanna, et al. Sherrie Levine: Mayhem. 2012. (ENG., Illus.). 216p. 60.00 (978-0-300-17596-7(5)) Yale Univ. Pr.

Buscema, John & Soltero, Emilio. John Buscema: A Life in Sketches. 2008. (Illus.). 104p. (978-0-9741332-3-2(X)) Pearl Pr.

Byrne, David, et al, texts. New York Noise: Art & Music from the New York Underground 1978-88, 1 vol. 2007. (ENG., Illus.). 208p. pap., pap. 39.95 (978-0-9554817-0-3(6)) Soul Jazz Records GBR. Dist: D.A.P./Distributed Art Pubs.

Caffery, Debbie Fleming, photos by. Debbie Fleming Caffery: The Spirit & the Flesh. 2009. (ENG., Illus.). 96p. 60.00 (978-1-934435-14-4(7)) Radius Bks.

Calit2, Gallery. Overheard. 2010. 48p. pap. 28.51 (978-0-578-05311-0(X)) gallery@calit2.

Cameron, Peter Saul. 2008. (ENG., Illus.). 160p. 55.00 (978-3-7757-2204-9(1)) Hatje Cantz Verlag GmbH & Co KG DEU. Dist: D.A.P./Distributed Art Pubs.

Cameron, Evelyn, photos by. Evelyn Cameron: Montana's Frontier Photographer. 2007. (ENG., Illus.). 120p. pap. 14.95 (978-1-56037-465-7(9)) Farcountry Pr.

Campello, F. Lennox. 100 Artists of Washington, D. C. 2011. (Illus.). 224p. (978-0-7643-3778-9(5), Schiffer Publishing Ltd) Schiffer Publishing, Ltd.

Caramelle, Ernst. Ernst Caramelle. 2009. pap. 20.00 (978-1-883597-08-5(0)) Markey, Lawrence Inc.

Carr, Cynthia. Fire in the Belly: The Life & Times of David Wojnarowicz. 2012. (ENG., Illus.). 624p. 35.00 (978-1-59691-533-6(1), 226195) Bloomsbury Publishing.

Carson, Anne, et al, texts. Elliott Hundley. 2012. (ENG., Illus.). 84p. pap. 39.95 (978-1-881390-50-3(0)) Ohio State Univ., Wexner Ctr. for the Arts.

Carter, Christopher. Stalwart: The Art of Christopher Carter. 2009. (ENG., Illus.). 44p. 19.95 (978-0-9773399-5-2(5)) Channel Photographics.

Castagno, John. American Artists II: Signatures & Monograms from 1800. 2007. (ENG.). 548p. 275.00 (978-0-8108-5895-4(9)) Scarecrow Pr., Inc.

—American Artists III: Signatures & Monograms from 1800. 2009. (ENG.). 596p. 250.00 (978-0-8108-6382-8(0)) Scarecrow Pr., Inc.

Celaya, Enrique Martínez. Enrique Martínez Celaya, 1990-2010: Collected Writings & Interviews. 2010. (ENG., Illus.). 272p. pap. 19.95 (978-0-8032-3474-1(0)) Univ. of Nebraska Pr.

Champney, Benjamin. Sixty Years' Memories of Art & Artists. 2010. 224p. pap. 25.75 (978-1-178-07509-0(5)) BiblioBazaar.

—Sixty Years' Memories of Art & Artists. 2010. 68p. pap. 20.00 (978-1-151-81929-1(8)) General Bks. LLC.

Chaudhuri, Shubh & Gomez-Pena, Guillermo. Conversations Across Borders. Seeger, Anthony, ed. 2011. (Seagull Books - Enactments Ser.). (ENG., Illus.). 360p. 40.00 (978-1-906497-50-7(8)) Seagull Bks. London Ltd. GBR. Dist: Chicago Distribution Ctr.

Chavez, Nicolasa. A Century of Masters: The NEA National Heritage Fellows of New Mexico. 2009. pap. (978-1-890689-43-8(2), Rio Grande Bks.) LPD Pr.

Chihuly Bellagio, 1 Disc with Book. 2nd rev. ed. 2007. (Illus.). 78p. 25.00 (978-1-57684-160-0(X)) Portland Pr., Inc.

Chihuly, Dale. Chihuly - 365 Days. 2008. (ENG., Illus.). 744p. 32.50 (978-0-8109-7088-5(0)) Abrams.

Chihuly, Dale, contrib. by. Team Chihuly. 2007. (Illus.). 240p. 50.00 (978-1-57684-163-1(4)) Portland Pr., Inc.

Christenberry, William. William Christenberry's Black Belt. 2nd ed. 2007. (ENG., Illus.). 64p. 25.00 (978-0-8173-1567-2(5)) Univ. of Alabama Pr.

Christman, Jill. Darkroom: A Family Exposure. 2011. (Association of Writers & Writing Programs Award for Creative Nonfiction Ser.). (ENG., Illus.). 264p. pap. 19.95 (978-0-8203-4174-3(6)) Univ. of Georgia Pr.

Chronicle Books Staff & Choe, David. David Choe. 2010. (ENG., Illus.). 288p. 45.00 (978-0-8118-6953-9(9)) Chronicle Bks. LLC.

Chueh, Luke. The Art of Luke Chueh. Gallery 1988, ed. 2012. (ENG., Illus.). 192p. 34.95 (978-0-85768-927-6(4), Titan Bks.) Titan Bks. Ltd. GBR. Dist: Random Hse., Inc.

Clark, Garth. Ian Ingram: Divining. 2010. (Illus.). 40p. 30.00 (978-0-9826397-0-2(8)) Friedman, Barry Ltd.

Clark, Robin Lee. Phenomenal: California Light, Space, Surface. 2011. (ENG.). 240p. 39.95 (978-0-520-27060-2(6)) Univ. of California Pr.

Clarkson, Millie. Edna Hibel: An Artist's Story of Love & Compassion, 1 vol. 2006. (ENG., Illus.). 176p. 60.00 (978-1-58980-427-2(9)) Pelican Publishing Co., Inc.

Clemente, Chiara & text. Our City Dreams. 2010. (ENG., Illus.). 120p. pap. 39.95 (978-88-8158-749-0(1)) Charta ITA. Dist: D.A.P./Distributed Art Pubs.

Cobb, Jeffrey. Stanley Matthew Mitruk. 2009. 175p. pap. 59.95 (978-0-615-24210-1(3)) Antgman1 Publishing.

Coblentz, Cassandra. Kirsten Everberg: Looking for Edendale. Neff, Terry Ann R., ed. 2011. pap. (978-0-9798936-3-6(1)) Scottsdale Museum of Contemporary Art.

Cohn, Damian A. Artists in the Workforce: Trends & Data. 2009. (Professions - Training, Education & Demographics Ser.). 79.00 (978-1-60741-484-1(8)) Nova Science Pubs., Inc.

Comis, Guido & Francioli, Marco. Man Ray. 2011. (ENG., Illus.). 330p. 70.00 (978-88-572-0974-6(1)) Skira Editore ITA. Dist: Random Hse., Inc.

Condit, Cecelia. Cecelia Condit. 2008. pap. 0.00 (978-0-9797964-6-3(6)) CUE Art Foundation.

Conley, Cort. Idaho Artists. 2011. pap. 29.95 (978-0-932129-48-2(X), Idaho Ctr. for the Bk.) Hemingway Western Studies Ctr.

Connor, Linda, photos by. Odyssey: the Photographs of Linda Connor. 2009. (ENG.). 180p. 50.00 (978-0-8118-6966-7(1)) Chronicle Bks. LLC.

Convis, Charles. Frontier Artists & Photographers. 2007. pap. 8.95 (978-1-892156-23-5(7)) Pioneer Pr.

Cooke, Lynne, ed. Martin Ramirez. 2010. (Illus.). 208p. 49.95 (978-3-7913-5048-6(X)) Prestel Publishing.

Cooke, Lynne & Crimp, Douglas, eds. Mixed Use, Manhattan: Photography & Related Practices, 1970s to the Present. 2010. (ENG., Illus.). 303p. (gr. 17). 49.95 (978-0-262-01482-3(3)) MIT Pr.

Cooper, Chris. Idle Hands: The Art of Coop. 2011. (ENG., Illus.). 208p. 50.00 (978-1-61404-002-6(8)) Baby Tattoo Bks.

Cooper, Edward. Vinnie Ream: An american Sculptor. 2009. (ENG., Illus.). 300p. pap. 18.95 (978-0-89733-589-8(9)) Academy Chicago Pubs., Ltd.

Copley, William. William N. Copley: Cply X-Rated. 2011. (ENG., Illus.). 140p. 65.00 (978-0-9829433-1-1(8)) Paul Kasmin Gallery.

Cortez, Constance. Carmen Lomas Garza. 2010. (Ver Ser.). (ENG., Illus.). 108p. 60.00 (978-0-89551-124-9(X)); pap. 24.95 (978-0-89551-125-6(8)) Univ. of Minnesota Pr.

Cosmic Debris Etc., Inc. Staff & Chwast, Seymour. Seymour: The Obsessive Images of Seymour Chwast. Heller, Steven & Scher, Paula, eds. 2009. (ENG., Illus.). 272p. 40.00 (978-0-8118-6546-3(0)) Chronicle Bks. LLC.

Couch, N. C. Christopher. Jerry Robinson: Ambassador of Comics. 2010. (ENG., Illus.). 128p. 35.00 (978-0-8109-7764-8(8)) Abrams.

Coyne, Petah & Lloyd, Ann Wilson. Petah Coyne: Vermilion Fog. 2008. (ENG., Illus.). 88p. 39.95 (978-88-8158-684-4(3)) Charta ITA. Dist: D.A.P./Distributed Art Pubs.

Cozzolino, Robert, text. Narcissus in the Studio: Artist Portraits & Self-Portraits. 2011. (ENG., Illus.). 128p. pap. 30.00 (978-0-943836-36-2(0)) Pennsylvania Academy of the Fine Arts.

Crawford, Ralston, illus. Ralston Crawford & Jazz. 2011. 262p. pap. 24.95 (978-1-891442-77-3(5)) Virginia Publishing Corp.

Crawford, Tad. Legal Guide for the Visual Artist. 5th ed. 2010. (ENG., Illus.). 304p. pap. 29.95 (978-1-58115-742-0(8), 115742, Allworth Pr.) Skyhorse Publishing Co., Inc.

Cross, Susan M. & Markonish, Denise, eds. Sol Lewitt: 100 Views. 2009. (ENG., Illus.). 272p. pap. 45.00 (978-0-300-15282-1(5)) Yale Univ. Pr.

Crumb, Sophie & Crumb, R. Sophie Crumb: Evolution of a Crazy Artist. Kominsky-Crumb, Aline, ed. 2010. (ENG., Illus.). 304p. 35.00 (978-0-393-08014-8(5), 8014) Norton, W. W. & Co., Inc.

Crumb, Sophie & Crumb, Robert. Sophie Crumb: Evolution of a Crazy Artist. Kominsky-Crumb, Aline, ed. 2010. (ENG., Illus.). 272p. 27.95 (978-0-393-07996-8(1), 7996) Norton, W. W. & Co., Inc.

Crump, Robert L. Minnesota Prints & Printmakers, 1900-1945. 2009. (ENG., Illus.). 208p. 49.95 (978-0-87351-635-8(4)) Minnesota Historical Society Pr.

Crutchfield, Margo A. Beyond the Line: The Art of Diana Cooper, 1 vol. 2008. (ENG., Illus.). 120p. per. 29.99 (978-1-880353-37-0(7)) Cleveland Ctr. for Contemporary Art.

Cummings, Hildegard. Charles Ethan Porter: African-American Master of Still Life. Barr, Pamela, ed. 2008. (Illus.). 112p. per. 35.00 (978-0-9724497-6-2(0)) New Britain Museum of American Art.

Cunningham, C. C., ed. Art in New England: The Arts & Crafts of New England & A Survey of the Taste of Its People. 2011. 616p. 64.95 (978-1-258-08854-5(1)) Literary Licensing, LLC.

Curtis, Judith A. Rocky Neck Art Colony, 1850-1950. 2008. (Illus.). 160p. 34.95 (978-0-9794505-0-1(0)) Rocky Neck Art Colony, Inc., The.

Cutler, Amy. Amy Cutler: Turtle Fur, 1 vol. 2011. (ENG., Illus.). 160p. 60.00 (978-3-7757-2809-6(0)) Hatje Cantz Verlag GmbH & Co KG DEU. Dist: D.A.P./Distributed Art Pubs.

Czestochowski, Joseph S., et al. Associated American Artists: Catalogue Raisonne, 1934-2000. 2010. (978-0-9716408-6-3(6)) International Arts.

Dailey, Meghan & Rosenthal, Norman. USA Today: New American Art from the Saatchi Gallery. 2007. (ENG., Illus.). 400p. 55.00 (978-1-903973-96-7(1)) Royal Academy of Arts GBR. Dist: Hachette Bk. Group.

Daniel, Malcolm. Stieglitz, Steichen, Strand: Masterworks from the Metropolitan Museum of Art. 2010. (Illus.). 180p. 35.00 (978-0-300-16901-0(9)) Yale Univ. Pr.

Danto, Ginger. The Art of George Rodrigue. 2012. (ENG., Illus.). 256p. pap. 40.00 (978-1-4197-0317-1(X)) Abrams.

David & Chie Hammons. 2008. (Illus.). 22p. 35.00 (978-0-9790942-4-8(0)) L & M Arts.

David, Catherine, ed. Hassan Sharif: Works 1973-2010. 2011. (ENG., Illus.). 320p. pap. 60.00 (978-3-7757-2824-9(4)) Hatje Cantz Verlag GmbH & Co KG DEU. Dist: D.A.P./Distributed Art Pubs.

Davies, Hugh M. & Irwin, Robert, contrib. by. Robert Irwin: Primaries & Secondaries, 1 vol. 2008. (ENG., Illus.). 220p. 65.00 (978-0-934418-67-6(5)) Museum of Contemporary Art, San Diego.

De Balincourt, Jules. Jules de Balincourt: Malpais. 2009. (ENG., Illus.). 48p. pap. 30.00 (978-2-910055-32-5(9)) Galerie Thaddaeus Ropac FRA. Dist: D.A.P./Distributed Art Pubs.

De Kwiatkowski, Lulu. Lulu: Popular Edition. 2010. 192p. 49.95 (978-1-934429-45-7(7)) AMMO Bks., LLC.

Deitch, Jeffrey & Gruen, Julia. Keith Haring. Geiss, Suzanne, ed. 2008. (ENG., Illus.). 522p. 60.00 (978-0-8478-3139-5(6)) Rizzoli International Pubns., Inc.

Deja-Vu 10: Robert Mapple. pap. 25.00 (978-4-309-90330-9(4)) Fiction, Inc. JPN. Dist: D.A.P./Distributed Art Pubs.

Deja-Vu 13: Larry Clark. pap. 25.00 (978-4-309-90333-0(9)) Fiction, Inc. JPN. Dist: D.A.P./Distributed Art Pubs.

Deja-Vu 7: Emmet Gowin. pap. 25.00 (978-4-309-90327-9(4)) Fiction, Inc. JPN. Dist: D.A.P./Distributed Art Pubs.

Deja-Vu 9: Nan Goldin. pap. 25.00 (978-4-309-90329-3(0)) Fiction, Inc. JPN. Dist: D.A.P./Distributed Art Pubs.

DeLong, Lea Rosson. Christian Petersen: Urban Artist, 1900-1934. 2007. (Illus.). 208p. 20.00 (978-0-9777494-1-6(X)) Iowa State Univ., College of Design.

Denenberg, Thomas Andrew, et al. Call of the Coast: Art Colonies of New England. 2009. (ENG., Illus.). 128p. pap. 29.95 (978-0-300-15162-6(4)) Yale Univ. Pr.

Denevan, Jim. Jim Denevan: Lake Baikal. 2011. (ENG., Illus.). 176p. 65.00 (978-1-934435-43-4(0)) Radius Bks.

Dennis, James M. Robert Koehler's The Strike: The Improbable Story of an Iconic 1886 Painting of Labor Protest. 2011. (Illus.). 176p. E-Book (978-0-299-25133-8(0)) Univ. of Wisconsin Pr.

—Robert Koehler's the Strike: The Improbable Story of an Iconic 1886 Painting of Labor Protest. 2011. (Studies in American Thought & Culture Ser.). (ENG., Illus.). 176p. pap. 24.95 (978-0-299-25134-5(9)) Univ. of Wisconsin Pr.

DePastino, Todd. Bill Mauldin: A Life up Front. 2009. (ENG., Illus.). 384p. pap. 16.95 (978-0-393-33488-3(0), 33488) Norton, W. W. & Co., Inc.

Derks, Scott, ed. Working Americans, 1880-2011 Vol. 12: Artists & Musicians. 2011. 500p. 150.00 (978-1-59237-762-6(9)) Grey Hse. Publishing.

Deyber, Robert & Gladstone, Valerie. Robert Deyber: A Language All His Own. 2008. (Illus.). 126p. (978-0-9814577-2-7(X)) Wellspring Communications, Inc.

Di Suvero, Mark. Mark Di Suvero: Sculpture & Drawings: January 28-March 12, 2011. 2011. (Illus.). 48p. (978-0-9794823-3-5(X)) Tasende Gallery.

Diane, Michener. Diana Michener: Figure Studies, 1 vol. 2011. (ENG.). 64p. pap. 39.50 (978-3-86930-213-3(5)) Steidl, Gerhard Druckerei und Verlag DEU. Dist: Innovative Logistics.

Díaz Royo, Antoni T. Martorell la Aventura de la Creación. 2007. 89.95 (978-0-8477-0427-9(0)) Univ. of Puerto Rico Pr.

Dibenedetto, Steve. Steve Dibenedetto: Recent Paintings & Drawings, 1 vol. 2006. (ENG., Illus.). 46p. 40.00 (978-0-9771714-9-1(3)) Nolan, David Gallery.

Dine, Jim. Jim Dine: Aldo et Moi, 1 vol. 2008. (ENG., Illus.). 224p. 50.00 (978-3-86521-461-4(4)) Steidl, Gerhard Druckerei und Verlag DEU. Dist: Innovative Logistics.

Dine, Jim, photos by. This Is How I Remember Now: Portraits; Photographs, 1 vol. 2008. (ENG., Illus.). 328p. 70.00 (978-3-86521-603-8(X)) Steidl, Gerhard Druckerei und Verlag DEU. Dist: Innovative Logistics.

DiPaola, Kathrin, ed. Nicolaus Schmitt: Breakin' the City. 2011. (ENG., Illus.). 160p. pap. 44.95 (978-3-86678-453-6(8)) Kerber Verlag DEU. Dist: D.A.P./Distributed Art Pubs.

Dituri, Frank. Dräite au Méure. 2007. 35.00 (978-0-9762983-3-5(3)) El Leon Literary Arts.

Doerr, Nathan & Musgrave, Judy. The Life & Art of Bernard P. Thomas: Paint, Passion & Preservation. 2007. (Illus.). 104p. 24.95 (978-0-9792871-0-7(3)) Sherlan County Historical Society Pr.

Donato, Gerald. Gerald Donato: Reinventing the Game. 2007. (Illus.). 62p. (978-0-935519-30-3(0)) Anderson Gallery.

Donnelly, Trisha. Trisha Donnelly. 2008. (ENG., Illus.). 64p. pap. 25.00 (978-0-88454-114-1(2)) Univ. of Pennsylvania, Institute of Contemporary Art.

Dorrill, Lisa. Seven Lively Artists: Fifty Years of ARt. 2006. 47p. lib. bdg. 10.00 (978-0-9785645-0-6(2)) Cumberland County Historical Society.

Dover. Kiowa & Pueblo Art: Watercolor Paintings by Native American Artists. 2009. (ENG., Illus.). 112p. pap. 19.95 (978-0-486-46441-1(5)) Dover Pubns., Inc.

Dowdy, Joanne Kilgour. Artful Stories: The Teacher, the Student, & the Muse. 2012. E-Book (978-1-4539-0524-1(3)); xxiii, 149p. (C). pap. 139.95 (978-1-4331-1407-6(0)); (C). pap. 34.95 (978-1-4331-1408-3(9)) Lang, Peter Publishing, Inc.

Dower, Darwin. The Wood Sculpturing of Darwin Dower: Sculptured stories of the past through incredible Detail. 2006. (Illus.). 80p. lib. bdg. (978-0-9754460-3-4(7)) Publisher's Place.

Droz, Dwight. The Art of the Midnight Poet. 2007. 152p. pap. 24.95 (978-0-9706357-9-2(5)) Scandia Patch Pr.

Drutt, Matthew. Anna Gaskell: Half Life. 2007. (ENG.). 96p. 40.00 (978-0-300-12475-0(9)) Yale Univ. Pr.

Duboff. Art Law. 2010. pap., stu. ed. 145.00 (978-0-7355-9658-0(1), Aspen Pubs.) Wolters Kluwer Law & Business.

Dunham, Carroll, illus. Carroll Dunham: Index! Who Is Pointing at Who - & Why - in Carroll Dunham's Drawings, 1 vol. 2007. (ENG.). 315p. 57.00 (978-3-86560-070-7(0)) Verlag der Buchhandlung Walther Konig DEU. Dist: D.A.P./Distributed Art Pubs.

Dunlap, William. Dunlap. 2006. (ENG., Illus.). 144p. 200.00 (978-1-57806-911-8(4)) Univ. Pr. of Mississippi.

Dunlap, William & Bayley, Frank W. A History of the Rise & Progress of the Arts of Design in the United States, 3 vols. (Illus.). reprint ed. lib. bdg. 375.00 (978-0-7222-4674-0(9)) Library Reprints, Inc.

Durham, Jimmie. Jimmie Durham: Amoxohtli: A Road Book. 2011. (ENG., Illus.). 228p. pap. 55.00 (978-3-86560-920-5(1)) Verlag der Buchhandlung Walther Konig DEU. Dist: D.A.P./Distributed Art Pubs.

Duty, Michael & McGarry, Susan Hallsten. Texas Traditions: Contemporary Artists of the Lone Star State. 2010. (ENG., Illus.). 240p. 85.00 (978-1-934491-24-9(1)) Fresco Fine Art Pubns., LLC.

Dwyer, Dennis E. God, Country & Tattoos. 2011. 268p. pap. 16.99 (978-1-61215-798-6(X)) Xulon Pr., Inc.

Eakins, Thomas. The Paris Letters of Thomas Eakins. Homer, William Innes, ed. 2009. (ENG., Illus.). 392p. 35.00 (978-0-691-13808-4(7)) Princeton Univ. Pr.

Eckhardt, Joseph P. So Bravely & So Well: The Life & Art of William T. Trego. 2011. (Illus.). 208p. 39.95 (978-1-879636-30-9(1)); pap. 39.95 (978-1-879636-24-8(7)) Univ. of Pennsylvania Pr.

The Economic & Employment Impact of the Arts & Music Industry: Hearing Before the Committee on Education & Labor, U.S. House of Representatives, One Hundred Eleventh Congress, First Session, Hearing Held in Washington, DC, March 26, 2009. 2009. (Illus.). iii, 70p. (978-0-16-083562-9(3), 552-070-39280-7) United States Government Printing Office.

Edmier, Keith. Keith Edmier 1991-2007. 2008. (ENG., Illus.). 176p. 125.00 (978-1-86154-303-5(4)) Booth-Clibborn Editions GBR. Dist: Hachette Bk. Group.

Eggers, Dave, et al, texts. Thomas Demand: L'Esprit D'Escalier, 1 vol. 2007. (ENG., Illus.). 224p. 85.00 (978-3-86560-210-7(X)) Verlag der Buchhandlung Walther Konig DEU. Dist: D.A.P./Distributed Art Pubs.

Elger, Dietmar. Allan McCollum: Natural Copies. (ENG & GER., Illus.). 36p. 34.95 (978-3-89322-805-8(5)) Edition Cantz DEU. Dist: D.A.P./Distributed Art Pubs.

Ellsworth, Angela & Campbell, Rebecca. Seeing Is Believing: Rebecca Campbell & Angela Ellsworth. 2011. (Illus.). 80p. pap. 24.99 (978-0-9844081-9-1(3)) Phoenix Art Museum.

Enany, Sarah, tr. Daniel Joseph Martinez: The Fully Enlightened Earth Radiates Disaster Triumphant, 1 vol. 2007. (ENG., Illus.). 96p. vinyl bd. 30.00 (978-0-89090-147-2(3)) Museum of Contemporary Art, Chicago.

Engelmann, Ines Janet. Jackson Pollock & Lee Krasner. 2007. (Pegasus Library). (Illus.). 95p. pap. 14.95 (978-3-7913-3882-8(X)) Prestel Publishing.

Erdosi, Aniko, et al, texts. Alina & Jeff Bliumis, Receiving the Stranger. 2007. (Illus.). 112p. pap. 25.00 (978-0-9797248-0-0(5)) CheckOff Art Pr.

Eshoo, Amy, ed. 560 Broadway: A New York Drawing Collection at Work, 1991-2006. 2008. (ENG., Illus.). 200p. 45.00 (978-0-300-13539-8(4)) Yale Univ. Pr.

Evans, Cerith Wyn. Parkett No. 87: Cerith Wyn Evans, Katarina Fritsch, Annette Kelm, Kelly Walker. 2010. (ENG., Illus.). 300p. pap. 32.00 (978-3-907582-47-3(0)) Parkett Verlag AG CHE. Dist: D.A.P./Distributed Art Pubs.

Everett, Deborah & Zorn, Elayne. Encyclopedia of Native American Artists, 1 vol. 2008. (Artists of the American Mosaic Ser.). (Illus.). 304p. 74.95 (978-0-313-33762-8(4), GR3762, Greenwood Pr.) Greenwood Publishing Group, Inc.

Ewing, William A. & Brandow, Todd. Edward Steichen: In High Fashion, the Condé Nast Years, 1923-37. 2008. (ENG., Illus.). 288p. 75.00 (978-0-393-06677-7(0), 6677) Norton, W. W. & Co., Inc.

Fahlman, Betsy. The Cowboy's Dream: The Mythic Life & Art of Lon Megargee. (Illus.). 144p. pap. 35.00 (978-0-87842-497-9(0), 1525) Mountain Pr. Publishing Co., Inc.

Fairey, Shepard. May Day. 2011. (Illus.). 133p. (978-1-58423-428-9(8)) Gingko Pr., Inc.

Falckenberg, Harald & Weibel, Peter, eds. Paul Thek: Artist's Artist. 2009. (ENG., Illus.). 550p. (gr. 17). 75.00 (978-0-262-01254-6(5)) MIT Pr.

Farrar, J. Maurice. Mary Anderson. 2007. 68p. per. (978-1-4065-1688-3(0)) Dodo Pr.

Feiffer, Jules. Backing into Forward: A Memoir. 2012. (ENG.). 456p. pap. 19.00 (978-0-226-24035-0(5)) Univ. of Chicago Pr.

Felix, Jason, illus. Savaged: The Art of Jason Felix. 2008. (ENG.). 160p. 35.00 *(978-1-933784-33-5(4))* Palace Publishing Group, LP.

Ferraris, Carlo, illus. Carlo Ferraris. 2008. (ENG.). 72p. per. 29.95 *(978-88-8158-665-3(7))* Charta ITA. Dist: D.A.P./Distributed Art Pubs.

Finch, Richard D. & Rives, Veda M., eds. Marks from the Matrix: Normal Editions Workshop Collaborative Limited Edition Prints 1976-2006. 2007. (Illus.). 196p. *(978-0-9795884-0-2(5))*; (ENG., pap. *(978-0-9795884-1-9(3))* Normal Editions Workshop Illinois State Univ.

Fingeroth, Danny. Disguised as Clark Kent: Jews, Comics, & the Creation of the Superhero. 2008. (ENG., Illus.). 216p. pap. 22.95 *(978-0-8264-3014-4(7))* Continuum International Publishing Group, Ltd. GBR. Dist: National Bk. Network.

Firmin, Sandra Q. Art Park, 1974-1984. 2010. (ENG., Illus.). 256p. 45.00 *(978-1-61689-019-3(3))* Princeton Architectural Pr.

Fish, Jeremy. Rome-Antic Delusions. 2008. (ENG., Illus.). 96p. pap. 29.00 *(978-88-88493-31-2(X))* Drago Arts & Communication ITA. Dist: SCB Distributors.

Fishback, Kurt Edward. Portrait of an Artist. 2010. 62p. pap. 32.80 *(978-1-4357-5429-4(8))* Lulu Enterprises Inc.

Fisher, Jennifer, ed. Technologies of Intuition. 2007. (ENG., Illus.). 288p. pap. 26.95 *(978-0-920397-43-5(3))* Y Y Z Artists Outlet CAN. Dist: LitDistCo.

Fitzgerald, Paul. Will Eisner & PS Magazine. 2008. (Illus.). 320p. pap. 29.99 *(978-1-932563-01-6(6))* Hermes Pr.

Fitzpatrick, Tony. The Wonder Vol. 3: Portraits of a Remembered City: City of Monsters, City of Ghosts. 2008. (Illus.). 128p. 30.00 *(978-0-86719-696-2(3))* Last Gasp of San Francisco.

Fleming, Geoffrey K., et al. A Shared Aesthetic: Artists of Long Island's North Fork. 2008. (ENG., Illus.). 250p. 50.00 *(978-1-55595-300-3(X))* Hudson Hills Pr. LLC.

Flett, George. George Flett: Ledger Art. 2008. (ENG., Illus.). vii, 81p. 69.00 *(978-0-923910-25-9(5))* New Media Ventures, Inc.

Folk, Thomas C. New Hope Impressions: George J. Stengel 1866-1937: George J. Stengel 1866-1937. 2008. 84p. 29.95 *(978-1-889097-76-3(4))* Hard Pr. Editions.

Fraenkel, Jeffrey, ed. Mel Bochner: Photographs & Not Photographs. 2010. (ENG., Illus.). 80p. 45.00 *(978-1-881337-28-7(6))* Fraenkel Gallery.

Frank, Robert & Banier, Francois-Marie, eds. Henry Frank - Father Photographer, 1890-1976, 1 vol. 2009. (ENG, FRE & GER., Illus.). 88p. 28.00 *(978-3-86521-814-8(8))* Steidl, Gerhard Druckerei und Verlag DEU. Dist: Innovative Logistics.

Fredericq, Suzanne. Oval Drawings by Eugene J Martin: 1971-1974. 2009. 106p. pap. 39.50 *(978-0-615-32215-5(8))* Lulu Enterprises Inc.

Freeman, Mark Philip. Finding the Muse: A Sociopsychological Inquiry into the Conditions of Artistic Creativity. 2007. (ENG.). 344p. pap. 69.00 *(978-0-521-04479-0(0))* Cambridge Univ. Pr.

Friedrich, Julia & K#xF6;nig, Kasper, eds. Wüste, Meer und Sterne: Desert, Sea & Stars. 2011. (GER & ENG., Illus.). 152p. 55.00 ***(978-3-86560-971-7(6))*** Verlag der Buchhandlung Walther Konig DEU. Dist: D.A.P./Distributed Art Pubs.

Friends, text. A Woman's Journey: The Life & Work of Artis Lane. 2007. (Illus.). 96p. pap. 29.99 *(978-0-9789818-1-5(2))* Friends, the Foundation of the CAAM.

Gallegos, Randy R. The Art of Gallegos: Dreaming in Black & White. 2007. (Illus.). 64p. per. 19.95 *(978-0-9797025-1-8(6))* Daydream Graphics.

Gámez, Omar. Omar Gamez: the Dark Book. 2010. (ENG., Illus.). 72p. 29.95 *(978-84-92480-70-8(X))* RM Verlag, S.L. ESP. Dist: D.A.P./Distributed Art Pubs.

Ganchan, Leigh N., et al. Immigration Options for Artists & Entertainers. 2007. (Illus.). x, 161p. *(978-1-57370-206-5(4)*, 918 F Street NW, Washington, DC 20004) American Immigration Lawyers Assn.

Garcia, Camille Rose. Tragic Kingdom: The Magical Art of Camille Rose Garcia. 2007. (ENG., Illus.). 131p. 39.95 *(978-0-86719-683-2(1))* Last Gasp of San Francisco.

Garcia, Erin C. & Man Ray. Man Ray in Paris. 2011. (ENG., Illus.). 128p. 24.95 *(978-1-60606-060-5(0)*, J. Paul Getty Museum) Getty Pubns.

Garelick, Rhonda & Garelick, Rhonda K. Electric Salome: Loie Fuller's Performance of Modernism. 2009. (ENG., Illus.). 288p. (C). pap. 26.95 *(978-0-691-14109-1(6))* Princeton Univ. Pr.

Gastman, Roger, ed. Tools of Criminal Mischief. 2011. (Illus.). 24.95 *(978-1-58423-438-8(5))* Gingko Pr., Inc.

Gerstenblith, Patty. Art, Cultural Heritage, & the Law: Cases & Materials. 2nd ed. 2008. 1142p. 110.00 *(978-1-59460-543-7(2))* Carolina Academic Pr.

Ghaffari, Michelle, ed. Multiple Vantage Points Southern California Women Artists 1980-2006. 2007. 30.00 *(978-0-9793187-0-2(X))* Southern California Womens Caucus For Art & Southern California Council of the National Museum of Women in the Arts.

Giannetto, David F. The Decoy Artist: America's Last Hunter-Carver, 1 vol. 2010. (ENG., Illus.). 208p. 39.95 *(978-1-58980-768-6(5))* Pelican Publishing Co., Inc.

Giant, Mike. Muerte. 2007. (ENG., Illus.). 96p. pap. 29.00 *(978-88-88493-19-0(0))* Drago Arts & Communication ITA. Dist: SCB Distributors.

Gilbert, Wally. Catalog of the BAAK Gallery Show of Wally Gilbert. 2008. 48p. pap. 28.50 *(978-1-4357-0243-1(3))* Lulu Enterprises Inc.

Gille, Don. Monster Revolt! The Art of Dirty Donny. 2011. (Illus.). 160p. *(978-1-58423-427-2(X))* Gingko Pr., Inc.

Glaser, Milton. Art Is Work. 2008. (ENG.). 272p. (gr. 12). pap. 50.00 *(978-1-59020-006-3(9))* Overlook Pr., The.

Gleissner, Stephen. Sue Jean Covacovich: Pioneer Kansas Abstract Artist. 2006. (Illus.). 36p. 15.00 *(978-0-939324-52-1(0))* Wichita Art Museum.

Goldberg, Phyllis. Phyllis Goldberg. 2007. pap. 8.00 *(978-0-9791843-5-2(5))* CUE Art Foundation.

Golec, Michael J. The Brillo Box Archive: Aesthetics, Design, & Art. 2008. (Interfaces: Studies in Visual Culture Ser.). (ENG., Illus.). 144p. pap. 25.00 *(978-1-58465-701-9(4)*, Dartmouth College Press) Univ. Pr. of New England.

Gonzalez, Jennifer A. Subject to Display: Reframing Race in Contemporary Installation Art. 2008. (ENG., Illus.). 320p. (gr. 17). 31.95 *(978-0-262-07286-1(6))* MIT Pr.

González, Jennifer A. Subject to Display: Reframing Race in Contemporary Installation Art. 2011. (ENG., Illus.). 320p. (gr. 17). pap. 17.95 *(978-0-262-51602-0(0))* MIT Pr.

Goodman, Wendy & Vanderbilt, Gloria. The World of Gloria Vanderbilt. 2010. (ENG., Illus.). 224p. 40.00 *(978-0-8109-9592-5(1))* Abrams.

Goodman, Wendy & Wilkinson, Hutton. Tony Duquette. 2007. (ENG., Illus.). 368p. 80.00 *(978-0-8109-9413-3(5))* Abrams.

Gotkin, Michael. Artists' Handmade Houses. 2011. (ENG., Illus.). 240p. 60.00 *(978-0-8109-9584-0(0))* Abrams.

Graham. Aura Rosenberg: Who am I?, What am I?, Where am I? 2009. (ENG., Illus.). 200p. 60.00 *(978-3-7757-2255-1(6))* Hatje Cantz Verlag GmbH & Co KG DEU. Dist: D.A.P./Distributed Art Pubs.

Graham, David. Almost Paradise. 2008. (ENG.). 80p. 29.95 *(978-0-9761955-4-2(2))* Pond Pr.

Grams, Diane. Producing Local Color: Art Networks in Ethnic Chicago. 2010. (ENG., Illus.). 328p. 40.00 *(978-0-226-30517-2(1))* Univ. of Chicago Pr.

Graphic Artists Guild Staff, ed. Graphic Artist's Guild Handbook of Pricing & Ethical Guidelines. 13th ed. 2010. (ENG., Illus.). 352p. pap. 39.99 *(978-0-932102-15-7(8))* Graphic Artists Guild.

Green, Renée. Renee Green: Endless Dreams & Time-Based Streams. 2011. (ENG., Illus.). 144p. pap. 35.00 *(978-0-9826789-0-9(8))* Yerba Buena Ctr. for the Arts.

Greene, C. & Koehler, J. Woven Color: The Tapestry Art of James Koehler. 2010. pap. 98.95 *(978-1-4507-1443-3(9))* Independent Pub.

Greene, Joshua & Greene, Amy. But That's Another Story: A Photographic Retrospective of Milton H. Greene. 2008. (ENG., Illus.). 268p. 75.00 *(978-1-57687-454-7(0))* powerHouse Cultural Entertainment, Inc.

Greenwold, Mark & contrib. by. Mark Greenwold: A Moment of True Feeling: 1997-2007, 1 vol. 2008. (ENG., Illus.). 64p. 30.00 *(978-0-9774965-8-7(9))* DC Moore Gallery.

Greenwood, Tim & Vardanyan, Edda. Hakob's Gospels: The Life & Work of an Armenian Artist of the Sixteenth Century. 2006. (Sam Fogg Ser.). (ENG., Illus.). 80p. pap. 35.00 *(978-0-9549014-7-9(9))* Sam, Fogg Rare Books GBR. Dist: Univ. of Washington Pr.

Gregory, Schaaf. Hopi Katsina: 1,600 Artist Biographies, 20 vols., Vol. 7. 2008. (American Indian Art Ser.). (ENG., Illus.). 342p. 65.00 *(978-0-9776652-1-1(6))* Ctr. for Indigenous Arts & Cultures (CIAC Pr.).

Grimly, Gris. Atrum Secretum: 13 Years of Hidden Truths. 2011. (ENG., Illus.). 180p. 44.00 ***(978-1-61404-000-2(1))*** Baby Tattoo Bks.

Groth, Gary. The Comics Journal. 2008. (Comics Journal Ser.). (ENG.). No. 291. 216p. pap. 11.99 *(978-1-56097-937-1(2)*, 56937)No. 292. 200p. pap. 11.99 *(978-1-56097-938-8(0)*, 56938) Fantagraphics Bks.

Gunzelman, Todd. Allan Linder 20th century & Beyond. 2010. 180p. pap. 68.50 *(978-0-557-07998-8(5))* Lulu Enterprises Inc.

Gurganus, Allan, text. James Castle. 2007. (Illus.). 72p. per. 30.00 *(978-1-883597-07-8(2))* Markey, Lawrence Inc.

Hagerty, Donald J. The Art of Maynard Dixon, 1 vol. 2010. (ENG.). 256p. 75.00 *(978-1-4236-0380-1(X))* Gibbs Smith, Publisher.

Haller, Robert A. Flesh into Light: The Films of Amy Greenfield. 2012. (Illus.). 100p. pap. 30.00 *(978-1-84150-488-9(2))* Intellect, Ltd. GBR. Dist: Chicago Distribution Ctr.

Hamilton, Ann. Ann Hamilton: An Inventory of Objects, 1 vol. 2006. (ENG., Illus.). 264p. 60.00 *(978-0-9743648-5-8(1))* Miller, Gregory & Co.

Hamilton, Vijali. World Wheel: One Woman's Quest for Peace. 2007. (Illus.). xii, 237p. *(978-0-9789055-1-4(2))* World Wheel Pr.

Han, Heng-Gil & Ho, Christopher K. Jamaica Flux: Workspaces & Windows 2010: Art As Action, April 10, 2010-June 12, 2010. 2010. *(978-0-9762853-7-3(1))* Jamaica Ctr. for Arts & Learning.

Hansl, Art. Flashbacks. 2009. 280p. 25.95 *(978-1-935125-27-3(3))* Robertson Publishing.

Hanson, Dian, ed. Bob's World: The Life & Boys of AMG's Bob Mizer. 2009. (ENG.). 288p. 59.99 *(978-3-8365-1230-5(0))* TASCHEN DEU. Dist: Ingram Pub. Services.

Harrison, Holly. Mixed-Media Collage: An Exploration of Contemporary Artists, Methods, & Materials. 2007. (ENG., Illus.). 128p. pap. 24.99 *(978-1-59253-316-9(7)*, 1592533167, Rockport Publishers) Quayside.

Haruko Tanaka. 2007. 8.00 *(978-0-9791843-0-7(4))* CUE Art Foundation.

Harvey, Doug & Fernandez, Veronica. Sean Duffy. 2011. (Front Forty Press - Front Forty Profiles Ser.). (Illus.). 122p. pap. 25.00 *(978-0-615-40146-1(5))* Front Forty Pr.

Haspiel, Dean & Irving, Christopher. Graphic NYC Presents: Dean Haspiel: The Early Years. 2010. (Illus.). 192p. pap. 19.99 *(978-1-60010-825-9(3))* Idea & Design Works, LLC.

Hassink, Jacqueline. The Power Book. 2009. (ENG., Illus.). 164p. 60.00 *(978-1-905712-07-6(3))* Boot, Chris GBR. Dist: D.A.P./Distributed Art Pubs.

Hausler, Christa & Hausler, Wolfgang, eds. Judy Ledgerwood. 2010. (ENG., Illus.). 160p. 60.00 *(978-3-7757-2421-0(4))* Hatje Cantz Verlag GmbH & Co KG DEU. Dist: D.A.P./Distributed Art Pubs.

Head, John J. & Newton, Richard. With Brush & Bridle - Richard Newton, Jr. - Artist & Equestrain. 2006. 55.00 *(978-0-9785686-0-3(5))* Head, John.

Healy, Patrick. Virgil Grotfeldt. 2007. 208p. *(978-2-87909-818-0(1))*; (Illus.). *(978-3-87909-818-7(2))* Wienand GmbH, Druck- & Verlagshaus.

Hearn, Marcus. The Art of Hammer: The Official Poster Collection from the Archive of Hammer Films. 2010. (ENG., Illus.). 192p. 34.95 *(978-1-84856-737-5(5)*, Titan Bks.) Titan Bks. Ltd. GBR. Dist: Random Hse., Inc.

Hedlund, Ann Lane. Gloria F. Ross & Modern Tapestry. 2010. (ENG., Illus.). 378p. 65.00 *(978-0-300-16635-4(4))* Yale Univ. Pr.

Held, Peter, ed. The Art of Toshiko Takaezu: In the Language of Silence. 2011. (ENG., Illus.). 160p. 40.00 *(978-0-8078-3482-4(3))* Univ. of North Carolina Pr.

Hemley, Robin. Twirl/Run. Nilson, Greger Ulf, ed. 2009. (ENG., Illus.). 88p. 40.00 *(978-1-57687-518-6(0)*, powerHouse Bks.) powerHouse Cultural Entertainment, Inc.

Heyes-Moore, Balshaw. Mary Kelly: Projects, 1973-2010. Heyse-Moore, Dominique, ed. 2011. (ENG., Illus.). 140p. pap. 39.95 *(978-0-7190-8628-1(0))* Manchester Univ. Pr. GBR. Dist: Macmillan.

Hicks, Bob, et al. Beth Van Hoesen: Catalogue Raisonne of Limited-Edition Prints, Books, & Portfolios. 2011. (ENG., Illus.). 592p. 95.00 ***(978-1-55595-344-7(1))*** Hudson Hills Pr. LLC.

Hignite, Todd. In the Studio: Visits with Contemporary Cartoonists. 2007. (ENG., Illus.). 320p. pap. 19.95 *(978-0-300-13387-5(1))* Yale Univ. Pr.

Hills, Patricia, et al, contrib. by. Perfectly American: The Art-Union & Its Artists. 2011. (ENG., Illus.). 200p. 39.95 *(978-0-9819799-2-2(0))*; pap. 24.95 *(978-0-9819799-3-9(9))* Gilcrease Museum.

Hirsch, Deborah. Iaia Filiberti & Debora Hirsch: Framed 100 Round Trips to Hollywood. 2010. (ENG., Illus.). 248p. pap. 47.50 *(978-88-8158-786-5(6))* Charta ITA. Dist: D.A.P./Distributed Art Pubs.

Historical Society of Cheshire County, creator. Steps to Great Art: Barry Faulkner & the Art of the Muralist. 2007. (Illus.). 28p. 12.50 *(978-0-9724478-7-4(3))* Historical Society of Cheshire Cty.

Hitchcock, Barbara. Sanctuary: Anna Tomczak Photography. 2008. (ENG., Illus.). 75p. pap. 40.00 *(978-1-934491-06-5(3))* Fresco Fine Art Pubns., LLC.

Hobbs, Robert. André Ethier: André Ethier's Knowing Naiveté. 2007. (Illus.). 48p. pap. 25.00 *(978-0-9779002-1-3(5))* Derek Eller Gallery, Inc.

Hoffmann, Jens, text. Chris Johanson. 2012. (ENG., Illus.). 160p. pap. 45.00 ***(978-0-7148-5694-0(0))*** Phaidon Pr., Inc.

Hoffmann, Jens & Fletcher, Harrell, texts. People's Biennial 2010: A Guide to America's Most Amazing Artists. 2011. (ENG., Illus.). 136p. 35.00 ***(978-0-916365-83-7(2))*** Independent Curators International.

Holl, Jim. Jim Holl the Landscape Painter. 2009. (ENG., Illus.). 128p. pap. 37.95 *(978-88-8158-729-2(7))* Charta ITA. Dist: D.A.P./Distributed Art Pubs.

Holzer, Jenny. Jenny Holzer: Retro. 2011. (ENG., Illus.). 68p. 30.00 ***(978-1-61623-719-6(8))*** Independent Pub.

Holzwarth, Hans Werner. Jeff Koons. 2008. (ENG.). 606p. 4500.00 *(978-3-8228-4944-6(8))* TASCHEN DEU. Dist: Ingram Pub. Services.

Holzwarth, Hans Werner, ed. Christoper Wool: With an Original Artwork. 2008. (Illus.). 500p. 0.03 *(978-3-8365-0361-7(1))* TASCHEN DEU. Dist: Ingram Pub. Services.

—Christopher Wool. 2009. (FRE, GER & ENG., Illus.). 500p. 1500.00 *(978-3-8228-0851-1(2))* TASCHEN DEU. Dist: Ingram Pub. Services.

Hopps, Walter & Bockris, Victor. Dennis Hopper - Trade Edition: Photographs 1961-1967. 2011. (ENG, GER & FRE., Illus.). 544p. 69.99 *(978-3-8365-2726-2(X))* TASCHEN DEU. Dist: Ingram Pub. Services.

Horn, Roni. Doubt Box Bks. IX: To Place, 1 vol. 1000th ltd. ed. 2009. (ENG., Illus.). 28p. lthr. 100.00 *(978-3-86521-276-4(X))* Steidl, Gerhard Druckerei und Verlag DEU. Dist: Innovative Logistics.

Houston, David. The making of an Exhibition. 2008. pap. *(978-0-9772544-4-6(5))* Ogden Museum of Southern Art, The.

—George Dunbar: Southern Masters Series. 2007. (Illus.). pap. 19.95 *(978-0-9772544-2-2(9))* Ogden Museum of Southern Art, The.

Howell, Andy. Art, Skateboarding & Life. 2007. (Illus.). pap. 29.95 *(978-1-58423-261-2(7))* Gingko Pr., Inc.

Hugo, Mario. I've Got Something I'd Like to Show You. 2007. (Illus.). 59p. pap. *(978-84-611-8356-2(8)*, LearnVerbs.com) Tsunami Systems S. L.

Hull, Roger. Henk Pander: Memory & Modern Life. 2011. (ENG., Illus.). 136p. (C). pap. 29.95 *(978-1-930957-63-3(7))* Ford, Hallie Museum of Art.

Hultberg, John. Vagabondage, a Paris Odyssey (1953-1955) The Memoir of John P. Hultberg, Painter (1922-2005) 2011. ***(978-1-936658-09-1(7))*** QCC Art Gallery.

Hunsicker. Roger Hane: Art, Times & Tragedy, 1 vol. 2009. (ENG.). 272p. pap. 34.95 *(978-1-934331-26-2(0))* Vanguard Productions.

Hunsicker, Robert C. Roger Hane: Art, Times & Tragedy, 1 vol. 2009. (ENG.). 272p. 49.95 *(978-1-934331-25-5(2))* Vanguard Productions.

Hurewitz, Daniel. Bohemian Los Angeles: And the Making of Modern Politics. (Illus.). 367p. 2008. pap. 21.95 *(978-0-520-25623-1(9))* 2007. 45.00 *(978-0-520-24925-7(9))* Univ. of California Pr.

Hushka, Rock & Adams, Victoria. Where Sky Meets Earth: The Luminous Landscapes of Victoria Adams. 2010. (ENG., Illus.). 80p. pap. 21.95 *(978-0-924335-30-3(0))* Tacoma Art Museum.

Hussey, Deborah. Monumental: The Reimagined World of Kevin O'Callaghan. 2010. (ENG., Illus.). 240p. 40.00 *(978-0-8109-8953-5(0))* Abrams.

Huxley, Geralyn & Wrbican, Matt. Andy Warhol Treasures. 2009. (Illus.). 128p. *(978-1-84796-004-7(9))* Carlton Bks., Ltd.

Iles, Chrissie. Sharon Hayes. 2012. (ENG., Illus.). 88p. pap. 24.95 ***(978-0-300-18037-4(3))*** Yale Univ. Pr.

Iles, Chrissie, et al. A Decade in Conversation: A Ten-Year Celebration of the Bucksbaum Award, 2000-2010 - With Interviews with Paul Pfeiffer, Irit Batsry, Raymond Pettibon, Mark Bradford, & Omer Fast. 2010. (Illus.). 88p. 19.95 *(978-0-300-16755-9(5))* Yale Univ. Pr.

Indiana Artists' Club Staff. Biographical Directory of Indiana Artists. 38p. reprint ed. lib. bdg. 88.00 *(978-0-7222-0590-7(2))* Library Reprints, Inc.

Indij, Guido, ed. MVD: Montevideo Popular Graphics. 2008. (ENG., Illus.). 120p. pap. 15.00 *(978-950-889-147-1(5))* La Marca ARG. Dist: D.A.P./Distributed Art Pubs.

Irving, Christopher. Comics Introspective Volume 1: Peter Bagge, Vol. 1. 2007. (Comics Introspective Ser.). (Illus.). 128p. pap. 16.95 *(978-1-893905-83-2(7))* TwoMorrows Publishing.

—Comics Introspective Volume Two: Dean Haspiel. 2008. 128p. pap. 16.95 *(978-1-893905-90-0(X))* TwoMorrows Publishing.

Jasmine Justice. 2007. 8.00 *(978-0-9791843-4-5(7))* CUE Art Foundation.

Jazzar, Bernard N. & Nelson, Harold B. Painting with Fire: Masters of Enameling in America, 1930-1980. 2006. 75.00 *(978-0-9712772-8-1(1))*; (Illus.). 288p. pap. 55.00 *(978-0-9712772-5-0(7))* Long Beach Museum of Art.

Jean, James. Rebus. 2011. (ENG., Illus.). 240p. 45.00 *(978-0-8118-7125-9(8))* Chronicle Bks. LLC.

Jenkins, Bruce. Gordon Matta-Clark: Conical Intersect. 2011. (Afterall Ser.). (ENG., Illus.). 112p. (gr. 17). pap. 16.00 *(978-1-84638-073-0(1))* Afterall Publishing GBR. Dist: MIT Pr.

—Gordon Matta-Clark: Conical Intersect. 2011. (Afterall Ser.). (ENG., Illus.). 112p. 35.00 *(978-1-84638-072-3(3))* MIT Pr.

Joe Novak. Something to Do with Wings: A Memoir. 2010. 360p. pap. 23.95 *(978-1-4401-9778-9(4))* iUniverse, Inc.

Johanson, George. Equivalents: Portraits of Oregon Artists. pap. *(978-1-883124-13-7(1))* Portland Art Museum.

John Legend - Evolver. 2009. (ENG.). 96p. pap. 19.99 *(978-1-60378-109-1(9)*, 1603781099) Cherry Lane Music Co.

Johns, Barbara. Paul Horiuchi: East & West. 2008. (Samuel & Althea Stroum Bks.). (ENG., Illus.). 128p. pap. 29.95 *(978-0-295-98795-8(2))* Univ. of Washington Pr.

Johnson, Robert Flynn & McCall Smith, Alexander. The Face in the Lens: Anonymous Photographs. 2011. 208p. pap. 29.95 *(978-0-520-26982-8(9))* Univ. of California Pr.

Jonas, Joan & Kim, Sung Hwan. Sung Hwan Kim: Source Book 6. 2010. (ENG., Illus.). 96p. pap. 15.00 *(978-90-73362-86-4(5))* Witte De With Centre for Contemporary Art NLD. Dist: D.A.P./Distributed Art Pubs.

Jonathan Elderfield. 2007. 8.00 *(978-0-9791843-3-8(9))* CUE Art Foundation.

Jones, Marian & Clough, Linda Jones, intros. Stroke of Genius: A Collection of Paintings & Musings on Life, Love & Art by Chuck Jones. deluxe ed. 2007. 75.00 *(978-0-615-13746-9(6))* Jones, Linda Enterprises, Inc.

Joseph. A Gifted Man: Memoir of an Artist. 2007. 184p. per. 16.95 *(978-0-595-45156-2(X))* iUniverse, Inc.

Jude, Ron, photos by. Ron Jude: Other Nature. 2008. (ENG., Illus.). 80p. 30.00 *(978-0-9776481-6-0(8))* Ice Plant, The.

Junker, Patricia A. & Bierstadt, Albert. Albert Bierstadt: Puget Sound on the Pacific Coast. 2011. (ENG., Illus.). 64p. pap. 19.95 *(978-0-295-99124-5(0))* Univ. of Washington Pr.

Kadour, Ric Kasini. Women. 2008. (Illus.). 50p. pap. 20.00 *(978-0-9771397-4-3(3))* Kasini Hse.

Kadour, Ric Kasini, ed. Vermont Contemporary Art Annual 2008. 2008. pap. 25.00 *(978-0-9771397-5-0(1))* Kasini Hse.

Kanevsky, Alexander & Khutoryansky, Nathalie. Kanevsky: Genius of Vision. 2010. 468p. pap. 134.00 *(978-1-4520-7658-4(8))* AuthorHouse.

Kaplan, Peter, comment. Arthur Carter: Sculptures - Paintings - Drawings. 2009. (ENG., Illus.). 208p. 50.00 *(978-0-8109-0595-5(7))* Abrams.

Karen Azoulay. 2007. 8.00 *(978-0-9791843-1-4(2))* CUE Art Foundation.

Kass, Deborah. Deborah Kass: More Feel Good Paintings for Feel Bad Times. 2011. (ENG., Illus.). 32p. pap. 25.00 *(978-0-9829433-0-4(X))* Kasmin, Paul Gallery.

Katheryn Webb. Apprentice to Master. 2010. 312p. pap. 18.95 *(978-1-4269-2506-1(9))* Trafford Publishing.

Katz, Vincent & Bittencourt, Vivien, eds. Kiki Smith: The Venice Story, 1 vol. 2007. (ENG., Illus.). 132p. pap. 34.95 *(978-88-8158-627-1(4))* Charta ITA. Dist: D.A.P./Distributed Art Pubs.

Kellein, Thomas. The Dream of Fluxus: George Maciunas: an Artist's Biography. 2007. (ENG., Illus.). 160p. 45.00 *(978-0-500-97665-4(1))* Thames & Hudson.

Kelly, James Edward & Styple, William B. Tell Me of Lincoln: Memories of Abraham Lincoln, the Civil War, & Life in Old New York. 2009. (Illus.). 326p. *(978-1-883926-23-6(8))* Belle Grove Publishing Co.

Kenan, Patrick Dan. Brighter Leaves: Celebrating the Arts in Durham, North Carolina. 2008. (Illus.). xiii, 301p. *(978-0-9615577-4-4(5))* Historic Preservation Society of Durham, Inc.

Kennedy Fine Art & California Artists. Best of California Artists & Artisans, Vol. 1. 2007. per. *(978-0-9796358-1-6(0))* Kennedy Publishing.

Kennedy, Michael Stephen. The Life & Times of Olaf C Seltzer, 1877-1957: Meticulous Montana Frontier Artist. 2011. 30p. 35.95 ***(978-1-258-05274-4(1))*** Literary Licensing, LLC.

Kennedy, Roger G. When Art Worked: The New Deal, Art, & Democracy. 2009. (Illus.). 368p. 75.00 *(978-0-8478-3089-3(6))* Rizzoli International Pubns., Inc.

Kenny, Peter, et al. Duncan Phyfe: Master Cabinetmaker in New York. 2011. (ENG., Illus.). 312p. 65.00 *(978-0-300-15511-2(5))* Yale Univ. Pr.

Kent, Brittany. Miley Cyrus: This Is Her Life. 2008. (ENG.). 176p. (gr. 12-18). 16.00 *(978-0-425-22538-7(0)*, Berkley Trade) Penguin Group (USA) Inc.

Ketchie, Cotton. A Country Boy's Education. 2007. 345p. pap. 17.95 *(978-0-7414-4338-0(4))* Infinity Publishing.

Kiedrowski, Thomas. New York City: Five Walks, Uptown to Downtown. 2011. (ENG., Illus.). 144p. pap. 14.95 *(978-1-892145-93-2(6))* Little Bookroom.

Kienholz, Lyn. L. A. Rising: SoCal Artists Before 1980. Betinski, Elizabeta & Nelson, Corinne, eds. 2011. (Illus.). 516p. 75.00 net. *(978-0-917571-13-8(4))* California/International Arts Foundation.

Kinney, Troy. Selected Letters of Troy Kinney to Doris Niles. 2011. 84p. 37.95 ***(978-1-258-04007-9(7))*** Literary Licensing, LLC.

Kipniss, Robert. Robert Kipniss: A Working Artist's Life. 2011. (Illus.). 304p. 29.95 *(978-1-61168-004-1(2))* Univ. Pr. of New England.

Kirwin, Liza & Lord, Joan. Artists in Their Studios: Images from the Smithsonian's Archives of American Art. 2007. (Illus.). 192p. 35.00 *(978-0-06-115012-8(6)*, Collins Design) HarperCollins Pubs.

—With Love: Artists' Letters & Illustrated Notes. 2008. (Illus.). 128p. 19.95 *(978-0-06-144150-9(3)*, Collins Design) HarperCollins Pubs.

Kirwin, Liza & Princeton Architectural Press Staff. Lists: To-Dos, Illustrated Inventories, Collected Thoughts, & Other Artists' Enumerations from the Smithsonian's Archives of American Art. 2010. (ENG., Illus.). 208p. 24.95 *(978-1-56898-888-7(5))* Princeton Architectural Pr.

Kitchen, Denis & Buhle, Paul. The Art of Harvey Kurtzman: The Mad Genius of Comics. 2009. (ENG., Illus.). 256p. 45.00 *(978-0-8109-7296-4(4))* Abrams.

Klein, Mason. Alias Man Ray. 2009. (ENG., Illus.). 256p. 50.00 *(978-0-300-14683-7(3))* Yale Univ. Pr.

Kotynek, Roy & Cohassey, John. American Cultural Rebels: Avant-Garde & Bohemian Artists, Writers & Musicians from the 1850s Through the 1960s. 2008. (ENG.). 262p. per. 39.95 *(978-0-7864-3709-2(X))* McFarland & Co., Inc. Pubs.

Kouwenhoven, Bill. Michael Itkoff: Street Portraits. 2009. (ENG., Illus.). 64p. pap. 24.95 *(978-88-8158-690-5(8))* Charta ITA. Dist: D.A.P./Distributed Art Pubs.

Kozloff, Joyce. China Is Near, 1 vol. 2010. (ENG., Illus.). 96p. pap. 37.50 *(978-88-8158-787-2(4))* Charta ITA. Dist: D.A.P./Distributed Art Pubs.

Kozloff, Joyce, et al. Tony Robbin. 2011. (ENG., Illus.). 120p. 45.00 *(978-1-55595-367-6(0))* Hudson Hills Pr. LLC.

Krass, Peter. Portrait of War: The U. S. Army's First Combat Artists & the Doughboys' Experience in WWI. 2006. (ENG., Illus.). 352p. 30.00 *(978-0-471-67023-0(5)*, Wiley) Wiley, John & Sons, Inc.

Krimko, Stuart, ed. Tobias Putrih: 99-07. 2008. (ENG., Illus.). 180p. 37.00 *(978-3-905770-71-1(7))* JRP Ringier Kunstverlag AG CHE. Dist: D.A.P./Distributed Art Pubs.

Kroeger, Michael. Paul Rand: Conversations with Students. 2008. (ENG., Illus.). 96p. pap. 19.95 *(978-1-56898-725-5(0))* Princeton Architectural Pr.

Krone, Larry. Larry Krone: Artist/Entertainer, 1 vol. 2006. (ENG., Illus.). 56p. lthr. 75.00 *(978-0-9777528-0-5(1))* Contemporary Art Museum St. Louis.

Kwon, Sue, photos by. Bibbidi, Bobbidi, Boo!, 1 vol. 2006. (ENG & GER., Illus.). 100p. 35.00 *(978-3-938821-35-0(3))* Verlag fur Moderne Kunst DEU. Dist: D.A.P./Distributed Art Pubs.

Lagerfeld, Karl. Body Freedom, 2 vols. 2011. (ENG., Illus.). 88p. pap. 58.00 *(978-3-86930-260-7(7))* Steidl, Gerhard Druckerei und Verlag DEU. Dist: Innovative Logistics.

Laichas, William D., ed. New Mexico Millennium Collection: A Twenty-First Century Celebration of Fine Art in New Mexico. 2007. (ENG., Illus.). 160p. 45.00 *(978-0-9679034-0-8(8))* New Mexico Millennium Collection, LLC.

Lamberton, Daniel, comment. On the River Through the Valley of Fire: The Collaborative Ceramics of Frank Boyden & Tom Coleman. 2008. (Illus.). 141p. *(978-0-9816728-1-6(7))* American Museum of Ceramic Art.

Landers, Sean. Sean Landers: [sic]. 2010. (ENG., Illus.). 454p. pap. 25.00 *(978-0-9820747-8-7(6))* Horowitz, Glenn Bookseller, Inc.

Lange, Sami Lynn, ed. Bob Nugent. Elizabetsky, Roberto, tr. 2007. (ENG.). 160p. pap. 35.00 *(978-0-9794809-1-1(4))*; (Illus.). 55.00 *(978-0-9794809-0-4(6))* Abandoned Pr.

Lanker, Brian & Newnham, Nicole. They Drew Fire: Combat Artists of World War II. (Illus.). 192p. 54.90 incl. VHS. 39.95 Public Broadcasting Service (PBS).

Lapthisophon, Stephen. Writing Art Cinema 1988-2010. 2011. 103p. pap. 12.00 *(978-1-4507-4210-8(6))* Green Lantern Pr.

Lass, Anne, et al. In Unserer Zeit: Die Fotografische Fixierung Eines Zeitgefühls. 2010. (GER & ENG., Illus.). 84p. pap. 28.00 *(978-3-422-06932-9(1)*, Art Stock Bks. Ltd/Csi) Continental Sales, Inc.

Lauren, Ralph. Ralph Lauren Deluxe. 2007. (ENG., Illus.). 512p. 400.00 *(978-0-8478-3106-7(X))* Rizzoli International Pubns., Inc.

Lawless, Debra. Provincetown: A History of Artists & Renegades in a Fishing Village. 2011. 144p. pap. 19.99 *(978-1-60949-025-6(8))* History Pr., The.

Lazarus, Marvin. Perfect Timing: Artists in New York, 19581962. 2010. (ENG.). 144p. 39.95 *(978-0-9794727-7-0(6))* Five Ties Publishing.

Lea, Tom. The Two Thousand Yard Stare: Tom Lea's World War II. Greeley, Brendan M., Jr., ed. 2008. (Military History Ser.: No. 119). (ENG., Illus.). 256p. 40.00 *(978-1-60344-008-0(9))* Texas A&M Univ. Pr.

Lecercle, Jean-Jacques & Kral, Françoise. Architecture & Philosophy: New Perspectives on the Work of Arakawa & Madeline Gins. 2010. (Illus.). 233p. pap. 64.00 *(978-90-420-3189-0(1))* Rodopi.

Lechaux, Bleuwenn & Roussel, Violaine, eds. Voicing Dissent: American Artists & the War on Iraq. 2009. (Routledge Studies in Law, Society & Popular Culture Ser.). (ENG., Illus.). 320p. 125.00 *(978-0-415-80058-7(7))* Routledge.

Lee, Jim & Baker, Bill. Icons: The DC Comics & Wildstorm Art of Jim Lee. 2010. (Illus.). 296p. 39.95 *(978-1-84576-519-4(2)*, Titan Bks.) Titan Bks. Ltd. GBR. Dist: Random Hse., Inc.

Leiter, Saul, photos by. Saul Leiter, 1 vol. 2008. (ENG., Illus.). 152p. 45.00 *(978-3-86521-587-1(4))* Steidl, Gerhard Druckerei und Verlag DEU. Dist: D.A.P./Distributed Art Pubs.

Lenore, Malen. Lenore Malen: The New Society for Universal Harmony. 2007. pap. 8.00 *(978-0-9791843-6-9(3))* CUE Art Foundation.

Levin, Bob. Most Outrageous: The Trials & Trespasses of Dwaine Tinsley & Chester the Molester. 2008. (ENG., Illus.). 200p. pap. 19.99 *(978-1-56097-919-7(4)*, 56919) Fantagraphics Bks.

Levin, Gail. Edward Hopper: An Intimate Biography. 2007. (ENG., Illus.). 780p. 15.00 *(978-0-8478-2930-9(8))* Rizzoli International Pubns., Inc.

Levy, Stu. Grid-Portraits. 2010. (Illus.). ***(978-1-59005-307-2(9))*** Nazraeli Pr.

Lewis, Adam. Billy Baldwin: The Great American Decorator. 2010. (ENG., Illus.). 256p. 65.00 *(978-0-8478-3367-2(4))* Rizzoli International Pubns., Inc.

Lewitt, Sol. Sol LeWitt: Cuaderno de Artista. 2012. (ENG & SPA., Illus.). 24p. pap. 65.00 ***(978-84-95471-81-9(7))*** La Fabrica ESP. Dist: D.A.P./Distributed Art Pubs.

Lichtenstein, Roy & Cowart, Jack. Lichtenstein in Process. 2009. (Illus.). 44p. *(978-0-915171-77-4(5))* Katonah Gallery.

Light, Michael, photos by. Michael Light: la Day, la Night. 2011. (ENG., Illus.). 72p. 60.00 *(978-1-934435-30-4(9))* Radius Bks.

Ligon, Glenn. Yourself in the World: Selected Writings & Interviews. Rothkopf, Scott, ed. 2011. (ENG., Illus.). 208p. pap. 24.95 *(978-0-300-16909-6(4))* Yale Univ. Pr.

Ligon, Glenn & Rothkopf, Scott. Yourself in the World: Selected Writings & Interviews. 2011. E-Book *(978-0-300-17257-7(5))* Yale Univ. Pr.

Lin, Maya. Boundaries. 2006. (ENG., Illus.). 224p. pap. 25.00 *(978-0-7432-9959-6(0))* Simon & Schuster.

Lippard, Lucy. Michelle Stuart: Sculptural Objects. 2011. (ENG., Illus.). 184p. pap. 45.00 ***(978-88-8158-803-9(X))*** Charta ITA. Dist: D.A.P./Distributed Art Pubs.

Littleton, Harvey & Byrd, Joan Falconer. Harvey K. Littleton: A Life in Glass: Founder of America's Studio Glass Movement. 2012. (ENG., Illus.). 208p. 45.00 ***(978-0-8478-3818-9(8)***, Skira) Rizzoli International Pubns., Inc.

Lozano, Lee. Lee Lozano. 2010. (ENG., Illus.). 272p. pap. 60.00 *(978-3-7757-2567-5(9))* Hatje Cantz Verlag GmbH & Co KG DEU. Dist: D.A.P./Distributed Art Pubs.

Lubben, Kristen, ed. Susan Meiselas: In History, 1 vol. 2009. (ENG., Illus.). 356p. 75.00 *(978-3-86521-685-4(4))* Steidl, Gerhard Druckerei und Verlag DEU. Dist: Innovative Logistics.

Lucas, Charlie & Windham, Ben. Tin Man. 2nd ed. 2009. (ENG., Illus.). 192p. 49.95 *(978-0-8173-1681-5(7))* Univ. of Alabama Pr.

Luie-Smith, Edward. Margaret Evageline. 2010. pap. 25.00 *(978-0-578-05783-5(2))* Evangeline Studio.

Lynch, Megan, et al. ArtNOW: The Guide to Kansas City Artists. 2007. (Illus.). 200p. pap. 19.95 *(978-0-9722657-2-0(4))* Kansas City Artists Coalition.

Lyne-Winkler, Layla, ed. Plastic Antinomy Number 3: Blue/Green Issue. 2009. 48p. pap. 8.00 *(978-0-86719-728-0(5))* Last Gasp of San Francisco.

Lynn, J. A Worst Case Scenario: Art, Death, & Asperger's. 2009. 368p. 34.95 *(978-1-4401-5779-0(0))*; pap. 24.95 *(978-1-4401-5777-6(4))* iUniverse, Inc.

Muller-Westermann, Iris, ed. & text. Jutta Koether. 2011. (ENG & SWE., Illus.). 96p. pap. 34.95 ***(978-3-86560-981-6(3))*** Verlag der Buchhandlung Walther Konig DEU. Dist: D.A.P./Distributed Art Pubs.

Macomber, Ben. The Jewel City. 2008. 204p. 24.99 *(978-0-554-31731-1(1))* 2008. 204p. 27.99 *(978-0-554-22428-2(3))* 2007. (ENG.). 190p. pap. 19.99 *(978-1-4264-2329-1(2))* 2007. (ENG.). 202p. pap. 22.99 *(978-1-4264-2377-2(2))* BiblioBazaar.

Madden, David, et al. Richard Anuskiewicz: Paintings & Sculptures 1945-2001. 2011. (ENG., Illus.). 272p. 85.00 *(978-88-7038-483-3(7))* Centro Di ITA. Dist: Antique Collectors' Club.

Madson, Jerry. Bog Walk Pitcher Plants Meet Implicate Polysynthesis. 2007. 100p. pap. 44.50 *(978-1-4303-2883-4(5))* Lulu Enterprises Inc.

Maiman, Ohad. Theory of Wants. 2008. (ENG., Illus.). 160p. 50.00 *(978-88-6208-059-0(X))* Damiani ITA. Dist: D.A.P./Distributed Art Pubs.

Mangold, Robert & Dreishpoon, Douglas. Beyond the Line: Paintings & Project, 2000-2008. 2009. (ENG., Illus.). 128p. 150.00 *(978-0-8109-5487-8(7))* Abrams.

Mann, Sally, photos by. Proud Flesh. 2009. (ENG., Illus.). 64p. 80.00 *(978-1-59711-135-5(X))* Aperture Foundation, Inc.

Marah, Bertie Stroup. Born with a Rusty Spoon: An Artist's Memoir. 2010. 192p. pap. 22.95 *(978-1-935514-66-4(0))* Plain View Pr.

Marcus, Cora & Kyer, Libby. Today's Botanical Artists. 2008. (Illus.). 160p. 29.95 *(978-0-7643-2905-0(7))* Schiffer Publishing, Ltd.

Margetts, Martina. Tord Boontje. 2007. (ENG., Illus.). 224p. 75.00 *(978-0-8478-2929-3(4))* Rizzoli International Pubns., Inc.

Marquis Who's Who, creator. Who's Who in American Art. 30th ed. 2009. (Who's Who in American Art Ser.). 1665p. 371.25 *(978-0-8379-6309-9(5))* Marquis Who's Who, LLC.

Marquis Who's Who Staff. Who's Who in American Art 2008. 28th ed. 2007. 1512p. 297.00 *(978-0-8379-6307-5(9))* Marquis Who's Who, LLC.

Martell, Nevin. Looking for Calvin & Hobbes: The Unconventional Story of Bill Watterson & His Revolutionary Comic Strip. (ENG., Illus.). 272p. 2010. pap. 16.95 *(978-1-4411-0685-8(5))* 2009. 27.95 *(978-0-8264-2984-1(X))* Continuum International Publishing Group, Ltd. GBR. Dist: National Bk. Network.

Martin, George W. Verdi in America: Oberto Through Rigoletto. 2011. (Eastman Studies in Music Ser.: Volume 86). (Illus.). 494p. 75.00 *(978-1-58046-388-1(6))* Univ. of Rochester Pr.

Martin, Terry Lynn. Children, Dogs & Sunflowers. 2011. 216p. pap. 29.99 ***(978-1-936688-05-0(0))*** AKA:yoLa.

Marzio, Peter C. Robert Frank, 1 vol. 2009. (ENG., Illus.). 112p. pap. 30.00 *(978-3-86521-013-5(9))* Steidl, Gerhard Druckerei und Verlag DEU. Dist: Innovative Logistics.

Masten, April F. Art Work: Women Artists & Democracy in Mid-Nineteenth-Century New York. 2008. (Arts & Intellectual Life in Modern America Ser.). (Illus.). 312p. (C). 59.95 *(978-0-8122-4071-9(5))* Univ. of Pennsylvania Pr.

Mathews, Nancy Mowll & Cantor, Jay E. Mary Cassatt: Friends & Family. 2008. pap. *(978-0-939384-34-1(5))* Shelburne Museum, Inc.

Matt, Gerald, et al, eds. Andro Wekua: Pink Wave Hunter, 3 Volumes. 2011. (ENG., Illus.). 388p. pap. 49.95 ***(978-3-86560-961-8(9))*** Verlag der Buchhandlung Walther Konig DEU. Dist: D.A.P./Distributed Art Pubs.

Matt, Gerald & Genzmer, Synne, texts. Clifton Childree: Fuck that Chicken from Popeyes. 2011. (ENG., Illus.). 120p. pap. 30.00 ***(978-3-86984-201-1(6))*** Verlag fur Moderne Kunst DEU. Dist: D.A.P./Distributed Art Pubs.

Mattioli, Laura, ed. Barry X Ball: Portraits & Masterpieces. 2011. (ITA & ENG., Illus.). 148p. 49.95 ***(978-88-8158-812-1(9))*** Charta ITA. Dist: D.A.P./Distributed Art Pubs.

Maurer, Christopher & Iglesias, Maria Estrella. Dreaming in Clay on the Coast of Mississippi: Love & Art at Shearwater. 2010. (ENG., Illus.). 358p. pap. 25.00 *(978-1-60473-459-1(0))* Univ. Pr. of Mississippi.

McBride, Rita. Rita Mcbride. 2010. (ENG & GER., Illus.). 144p. 60.00 *(978-3-941263-14-7(5))* Richter Verlag DEU. Dist: D.A.P./Distributed Art Pubs.

McCarthy, Laurette E. The Paintings of Walter Pach. 2011. (Illus.). 88p. pap. 45.00 ***(978-0-9800556-8-9(7))*** Naumann, Francis M. Fine Art, LLC.

McCarthy, Paul. Head Shop/Shop Head: Works, 1966-2006, 1 vol. 2008. (ENG., Illus.). 688p. pap. 50.00 *(978-3-86521-300-6(6))* Steidl, Gerhard Druckerei und Verlag DEU. Dist: Innovative Logistics.

MCD. The Land of the Number Zero: Art & Text. 2007. (Illus.). 141p. 54.99 *(978-1-4363-1566-1(2))* Xlibris Corp.

McFetridge, Geoff. Geoff Mcfetridge. 2008. 160p. 35.00 *(978-0-8109-9446-1(1))* Abrams.

McGarry, Susan Hallsten. Freedom of Expression: The Art of Charles W. Thwaites. 2008. (ENG., Illus.). 119p. pap. 35.00 *(978-1-934491-08-9(X))* Fresco Fine Art Pubns., LLC.

—John Nieto: Forces of Color & Spirit. 2010. (ENG., Illus.). 180p. 125.00 *(978-1-934491-15-7(2))* Fresco Fine Art Pubns., LLC.

McGee, Julie L. Artist & Scholar. 2006. (Illus.). 216p. 45.00 *(978-0-7649-3747-7(2)*, A127) Pomegranate Communications, Inc.

McGee, Micki, ed. Yaddo: Making American Culture. 2008. (ENG., Illus.). 184p. (gr. 17). 90.00 *(978-0-231-14736-1(8))* Columbia Univ. Pr.

McGinness, Ryan & Halley, Byrne et al. Ryan McGinness Works: Paintings, Sculptures, Sketches, Drawings, Installations, Editions & Other Stuff. 2009. (Illus.). 296p. 55.00 *(978-0-8478-3196-8(5))* Rizzoli International Pubns., Inc.

McGowin, Ed. Name Change: One Artist - Twelve Personas - Thirty-Five Years. 2006. (ENG., Illus.). 100p. 30.00 *(978-1-57806-970-5(X))* Univ. Pr. of Mississippi.

McIver, Beverly, et al. Reflections: Portraits by Beverly McIver. 2011. pap. ***(978-0-88259-997-7(6))*** North Carolina Museum of Art.

McPhee, Laura. River of No Return: Photographs by Laura McPhee. 2008. (ENG., Illus.). 132p. 60.00 *(978-0-300-14100-9(9))* Yale Univ. Pr.

McQuarrie, Ralph. The Art of Ralph Mcquarrie. 2007. 125.00 *(978-0-9791580-0-1(1))* dreams and visions pr.

Melton Art Reference Library. Directory of Oklahoma Artists. 2007. 50.00 *(978-0-9640163-3-0(8))* Melton Art Reference Library.

Merali, Shaheen. New York States of Mind: Art in the City. Merali, Shaheen, ed. 2007. (ENG., Illus.). 320p. 29.95 *(978-0-86356-681-3(2))* Saqi Bks. GBR. Dist: Consortium Bk. Sales & Distribution.

Merrill, C. S. Weekends with O'Keeffe. 2010. (ENG., Illus.). 246p. 24.95 *(978-0-8263-4928-6(5))* Univ. of New Mexico Pr.

Micheal Turner Tribute. 2008. 80p. (YA). pap. 8.99 *(978-0-9774821-7-7(0))* Aspen MLT, Inc.

Michels, Caroll. How to Survive & Prosper As an Artist: Selling Yourself Without Selling Your Soul. 6th ed. 2009. (ENG.). 400p. pap. 21.99 *(978-0-8050-8848-9(2)*, Owl Bks.) Holt, Henry & Co.

Miller, Sandro. Imagine Cuba: 1999-2007. 2009. (ENG., Illus.). 160p. 59.95 *(978-88-8158-692-9(4))* Charta ITA. Dist: D.A.P./Distributed Art Pubs.

Millidge, Judith. Charles Marion Russell. 2009. (ENG.). 192p. 24.99 *(978-0-7858-2535-7(5)*, 0785825355, Chartwell) Book Sales, Inc.

Milner, Richard. Charles R. Knight: The Artist Who Saw Through Time. 2012. (ENG., Illus.). 180p. 40.00 *(978-0-8109-8479-0(2))* Abrams.

Minter, Marilyn. Marilyn Minter. 2010. (ENG., Illus.). 240p. 60.00 *(978-1-61623-496-6(2))* Miller, Gregory & Co.

Moffatt, Frederick C. The Life, Art, & Times of Joseph Delaney, 1904-1991. 2009. (ENG.). 44.95 *(978-1-57233-676-6(5))* Univ. of Tennessee Pr.

Molesworth, Helen & Horrigan, Bill, texts. Dust, 1 vol. 2007. (ENG., Illus.). 64p. per. 19.95 *(978-1-881390-44-2(6))* Ohio State Univ., Wexner Ctr. for the Arts.

Monahan, Matthew. Matthew Monahan. 2012. (ENG., Illus.). 248p. 60.00 ***(978-3-7757-3164-5(4))*** Hatje Cantz Verlag GmbH & Co KG DEU. Dist: D.A.P./Distributed Art Pubs.

Moon, Michael. Darger's Resources. 2012. (ENG., Illus.). 184p. 79.95 ***(978-0-8223-5142-9(0))***; pap. 22.95 ***(978-0-8223-5156-6(0))*** Duke Univ. Pr.

Moore, Alan. Art Gangs: Postmodern Artists - Collectives in New York City. 2011. 256p. pap. 17.95 ***(978-1-57027-237-0(9))*** Autonomedia.

Morano, Cohen. Rest Is up to You: A Boy Named Cohen Morano, 118 Artists, & a Watercolor Revolution. 2009. (ENG., Illus.). 176p. (J). (gr. -1-17). pap. 24.95 *(978-0-8118-6859-4(1))* Chronicle Bks. LLC.

Morgan, Anne Lee. Oxford Dictionary of American Art & Artists. 2008. (Oxford Paperback Reference Ser.). (ENG.). 560p. pap. 17.95 *(978-0-19-537321-9(9))* Oxford Univ. Pr., Inc.

Morioka, Michiyo. An American Artist in Tokyo: Frances Blakemore, 1906-1997. 2008. (Illus.). 199p. 35.00 *(978-0-295-98773-6(1))* Univ. of Washington Pr.

Morris, Brian. Ernest Thompson Seton, Founder of the Woodcraft Movement 1860-1946: Apostle of Indian Wisdom & Pioneer Ecologist. 2006. 360p. 119.95 *(978-0-7734-5474-3(8))* Mellen, Edwin Pr., The.

Morrow, John. Kirby Five-Oh! Celebrating 50 Years of the King of Comics. 2008. (Illus.). 168p. pap. 19.95 *(978-1-893905-89-4(6))* TwoMorrows Publishing.

Moure, Gloria. Dan Graham: Works, & Collected Writings. 2009. (ENG., Illus.). 295p. 75.00 *(978-84-343-1201-2(8))* Polígrafa, Ediciones, S. A. ESP. Dist: D.A.P./Distributed Art Pubs.

Moure, Nancy Dustin Wall. Index to Articles on California Art & Artists found in Newspapers published in Laguna Beach (C. 1920-1945), Hollywood (C. 1911-1936) & Pasadena (C. 1900-1940) 2006. (Publications in Southern California Art: 8). 735p. 80.00 *(978-0-9614622-8-4(0))* Dustin Pubns.

Mulcahy, Susan, et al. Drawing Fashion: The Art of Kenneth Paul Block. 2008. (ENG., Illus.). 216p. 95.00 *(978-0-9777875-4-8(0))* Pointed Leaf Pr.

Munder, Heike & Seifermann, Ellen, eds. Rachel Harrison: If I Did It. 2008. (GER & ENG., Illus.). 144p. per. 49.00 *(978-3-905770-56-8(3))* JRP Ringier Kunstverlag AG CHE. Dist: D.A.P./Distributed Art Pubs.

Murphy, Kevin, et al. Three Fragments of a Lost Tale - Sculpture & Story by John Frame. 2011. (ENG.). 112p. pap. 24.95 *(978-0-87328-245-1(0))* Huntington Library Pr.

Museum of Fine Arts, Houston Staff, contrib. by. Core: Artists & Critics in Residence. 2008. (Illus.). 206p. *(978-0-89090-162-5(7))* Museum of Fine Arts, Houston.

Nadel, Dan. Where Demented Wented: The Art & Comics of Rory Hayes. Pouncey, Glenn & Bray, Glenn, eds. 2008. (Illus.). 144p. pap. 22.99 *(978-1-56097-923-4(2))* Fantagraphics Bks.

Nagel, Isolde, ed. José Salinas: Disembodiment. 2010. (ENG., Illus.). 144p. pap. 28.00 *(978-3-939633-97-6(6))* Jovis Verlag GmbH DEU. Dist: D.A.P./Distributed Art Pubs.

Needles, Belverd E., Jr. & Stephens, Rachel. A Democratic Age in American Printmaking: 1935-1941. 2007. (Illus.). 48p. per. 29.99 *(978-0-9763375-1-5(7))* PrintsAmerica.

Neumeyer, Peter F., ed. Floating Worlds: The Letters of Edward Gorey & Peter F. Neumeyer. 2011. (Illus.). 256p. 35.00 *(978-0-7649-5947-9(6))* Pomegranate Communications, Inc.

Nguyen, Hoang, illus. Memories Lost: The Art of Hoang Nguyen. 2007. 48p. 24.95 net. *(978-0-9787222-1-0(3))* LiquidBrush Productions.

Nilson, Greger Ulf. CDG/JHE, 1 vol. 2008. (ENG., Illus.). 112p. 48.00 *(978-3-86521-538-3(6))* Steidl, Gerhard Druckerei und Verlag DEU. Dist: Innovative Logistics.

Nogueras Cuevas, Celina, ed. Frescos: 50 Puerto Rican Artists Under 35. 2011. (ENG & SPA.). 350p. *(978-0-9815255-8-7(X))* Actar Birkhauser Distribution.

Nolen-Weathington, Eric. Modern Masters Volume 14: Frank Cho, Vol. 14. 2010. (Modern Masters Ser.). (Illus.). 120p. pap. 15.95 *(978-1-893905-84-9(5))* TwoMorrows Publishing.

—Modern Masters Volume 15: Mark Schultz. 2008. (Modern Masters Ser.: Vol. 15). (Illus.). 128p. pap. 14.95 *(978-1-893905-85-6(3))* TwoMorrows Publishing.

—Modern Masters Volume 16: Mike Allred. 2008. (Modern Masters Ser.). (Illus.). 120p. pap. 14.95 *(978-1-893905-86-3(1))* TwoMorrows Publishing.

Nutting, Wallace. Wallace Nutting's Biography. 2011. 302p. 48.95 ***(978-1-258-09503-1(3))*** Literary Licensing, LLC.

Nye, Tim, ed. Tim Hawkinson, 1 vol. 2007. (ENG., Illus.). 96p. 55.00 *(978-1-934171-03-5(4))* Thread Waxing Space.

Obrist, Hans Ulrich, ed. Hans Ulrich Obrist & Jeff Koons: the Conversation Series. 2012. (ENG., Illus.). 158p. pap. 29.95 *(978-3-86560-635-8(0))* Verlag der Buchhandlung Walther Konig DEU. Dist: D.A.P./Distributed Art Pubs.

—Hans Ulrich Obrist & Yoko Ono: the Conversation Series. 2010. (ENG., Illus.). 96p. pap. 27.00 *(978-3-86560-652-5(0))* Verlag der Buchhandlung Walther Konig DEU. Dist: D.A.P./Distributed Art Pubs.

Obrist, Hans Ulrich & Baldessari, John. John Baldessari / Hans Ulrich Obrist: The Conversation Series: 18. 2010. (ENG., Illus.). 242p. pap. 26.00 *(978-3-86560-500-9(1))* Verlag der Buchhandlung Walther Konig DEU. Dist: D.A.P./Distributed Art Pubs.

Ochsner, Jeffrey Karl. Lionel H. Pries: Architect, Artist, Educator: from Arts & Crafts to Modern Architecture. 2007. (Illus.). 384p. 60.00 *(978-0-295-98698-2(0))* Univ. of Washington Pr.

Oglesby, Christopher J. Fire in the Water, Earth in the Air: Legends of West Texas Music. 2006. (Brad & Michele Moore Roots Music Ser.). (ENG., Illus.). 302p. mass mkt. 22.95 *(978-0-292-71434-2(3))* Univ. of Texas Pr.

Okon, Yoshua. Yoshua Okon: US. 2011. (ENG., Illus.). 198p. pap. 25.00 *(978-0-9826789-1-6(6))* Yerba Buena Ctr. for the Arts.

Oldham, Todd. Charley Harper: An Illustrated Life. (ENG., Illus.). 420p. 2011. 29.95 *(978-1-934429-82-2(1))* 2009. 49.95 *(978-1-934429-37-2(6))* AMMO Bks., LLC.

—Wayne White: Maybe Now I'll Get the Respect I So Richly Deserve Popular Edition. 2010. (ENG.). 432p. lib. bdg. 29.95 (978-1-934429-67-9(8)) AMMO Bks., LLC.

Oldknow, Tina & Russell, Cristine. Voices of Contemporary Glass: The Heineman Collection. 2009. (ENG., Illus.). 382p. 85.00 (978-1-55595-314-0(X)) Hudson Hills Pr. LLC.

Oppenheim, Dennis. Dennis Oppenheim. 2012. (ENG & FRE., Illus.). 136p. pap. 30.00 (978-88-366-2044-9(2)) Silvana ITA. Dist: D.A.P./Distributed Art Pubs.

Ortiz, Luis. Infinity x Two: The Life & Art of Ed & Carol Emshwiller. 2007. (ENG., Illus.). 176p. 39.95 (978-1-933065-08-3(7)) Nonstop Pr.

Ottmann, Klaus, text. Joan Snyder: ... & seeking the Sublime. 2008. pap. 20.00 (978-0-9713548-5-2(5)) Nielsen Gallery.

Oursler, Tony. Tony Oursler: Thinking Gaze. 2009. (ENG & SPA., Illus.). 198p. 40.00 (978-84-7506-834-3(0)) Turner, Ediciones S.A. ESP. Dist: D.A.P./Distributed Art Pubs.

Padgett, Ron. Joe: A Memoir of Joe Brainard. 2008. (ENG., Illus.). 357p. 30.00 (978-1-56689-160-8(4)) Coffee Hse. Pr.

Paine, Roxy & Schall, Jan. Roxy Paine: Ferment. 2011. (978-0-615-43782-8(6)) Nelson-Atkins Museum of Art, The.

Panter, Gary, intro. Matt Leines: You Are Forgiven. 2008. (ENG., Illus.). 144p. 45.00 (978-0-9776523-5-8(1)) Heartworm Pr.

Panza di Biumo, Giuseppe, et al, texts. Phil Sims: Color in My Mind, 1 vol. 2009. (ENG.). 144p. 65.00 (978-3-937572-91-8(0)) Richter Verlag DEU. Dist: D.A.P./Distributed Art Pubs.

Paolini, Judy & Trueworthy, Nance, photos by. The Inspired Garden: 24 Artists Share Their Vision. 2009. (ENG.). 160p. 35.00 (978-0-89272-737-7(3)) Down East Bks.

Papanikolas, Zeese. American Silence. 2007. (ENG., Illus.). 222p. 29.95 (978-0-8032-3756-8(1)) Univ. of Nebraska Pr.

Parille, Ken & Cates, Isaac, eds. Daniel Clowes: Conversations. 2010. (Conversations with Comics Artists Ser.). (ENG., Illus.). 240p. 50.00 (978-1-60473-440-9(X)); pap. 22.00 (978-1-60473-441-6(8)) Univ. Pr. of Mississippi.

Park, Yeon Hwan. Tae Kwon Do: My Life & Philosophy. 2009. 176p. pap. 16.95 (978-0-8160-7797-7(5), Checkmark Bks.) Facts On File, Inc.

Parkhouse, Nick. 101 Forgotten Pop Hits of The 1980s. 2010. (Illus.). 312p. pap. 15.49 (978-1-4490-9847-6(9)) AuthorHouse.

Patterson, Dan. Gil Cohen: Aviation Artist. 2009. (ENG., Illus.). 144p. 49.95 (978-1-55046-512-9(0)) Boston Mills Pr. CAN. Dist: Firefly Bks., Ltd.

Pauwels, Wim. Lionel Jadot: An Autobiography. 2010. (ENG., Illus.). 256p. (978-90-8944-058-7(5), Beta-Plus (Acc)) Antique Collectors' Club.

Peake, Michael A. Blood Shed in This War: Civil War Illustrations by Captain Adolph Metzner, 32nd Indiana. 2010. 34.95 (978-0-87195-269-1(6)) Indiana Historical Society.

Peixotto, Ernest D. Ernest Clifford Peixotto: American Artist: A Biography, 1 vol. 2010. 460p. pap. 29.95 (978-1-61582-747-3(1)) PublishAmerica, Inc.

Peltomäki, Kirsi & Asher, Michael. Situation Aesthetics: The Work of Michael Asher. 2010. (ENG., Illus.). 240p. (gr. 17). 27.95 (978-0-262-01368-0(1)) MIT Pr.

Perry, Robert. Uprising: Woody Crumbo's Indian Art. 2009. (ENG.). 256p. (C). 36.00 (978-0-9797858-5-6(5)) Chickasaw Pr., The.

Peterman, Robert Leonard. Gillie: A Retrospective Biography of Robert Mcgill Mackall, Artist, 1889 - 1982. 2011. 354p. pap. 29.95 (978-1-4626-2094-4(9)) PublishAmerica, Inc.

Peterson, Charles, photos by. Cypher. 2008. (ENG., Illus.). 136p. 35.00 (978-1-57687-456-1(7)) powerHouse Cultural Entertainment, Inc.

Peterson, Larry. Philip R. Goodwin. 2007. 388p. 95.00 (978-0-87842-540-2(3)) Mountain Pr. Publishing Co., Inc.

Peterson, Larry Len & Russell, Charles M. Charles M. Russell: Printed Rarities from Private Collections. 2008. (Illus.). x, 213p. 70.00 (978-0-87842-550-1(0)); pap. 45.00 (978-0-87842-551-8(9)) Mountain Pr. Publishing Co., Inc.

Petrucci, Lisa. Kickass Kuties: the Art of Lisa Petrucci: The Art of Lisa Petrucci. 2009. (Illus.). 112p. 22.95 (978-1-59582-252-9(6)) Dark Horse Comics.

Phelps, Andrew. Higley. 2007. (ENG., Illus.). 144p. 54.00 (978-3-939583-33-2(2)) Kehrer Verlag Heidelberg, Klaus Kehrer DEU. Dist: Consortium Bk. Sales & Distribution.

Pirtle, Jim. Jim Pirtle. 2008. pap. 0.00 (978-0-9797964-7-0(4)) CUE Art Foundation.

Plain, Nancy & Russell, Charles M. Sagebrush & Paintbrush: The Story of Charlie Russell, the Cowboy Artist. 2006. (978-1-59336-715-2(5)) Mondo Publishing.

Plunkett, S. The World of a Wayward Comic Book Artist: The Private Sketchbooks of S. Plunkett. 2010. (ENG.). 224p. 55.00 (978-0-8040-1124-2(9)); pap. 24.95 (978-0-8040-1125-9(7)) Swallow Pr.

Podwal, Mark. Doctored Drawings. 2007. (ENG., Illus.). 80p. 22.00 (978-1-934137-02-4(2)) Bellevue Literary Pr.

Pogue, Stephanie E., et al. Arabesque: The Art of Stephanie E. Pogue. 2008. (Illus.). 48p. pap. (978-0-9819093-0-1(2)) Univ. of Maryland, David C. Driskell Ctr.

Pontegnie, Anne, ed. Mike Kelley: Educational Complex Onwards 1995-2008. 2010. (ENG., Illus.). 344p. 70.00 (978-3-905829-80-8(0)) JRP Ringier Kunstverlag AG CHE. Dist: D.A.P./Distributed Art Pubs.

Powell, Stephen Rolfe. Stephen Rolfe Powell: Glassmaker. 2007. (ENG., Illus.). 228p. 75.00 (978-0-8131-2464-3(6)) Univ. Pr. of Kentucky.

Prestel. Jasper Johns. 4.95 (978-3-7913-1767-0(9)) Prestel Publishing.

Price, C. s. C S Price, the Man & the Artist, 1874-1950. 2011. 26p. 35.95 (978-1-258-06938-4(5)) Literary Licensing, LLC.

Price, Con & Britzman, H. E. Trails I Rode. 2011. 270p. 47.95 (978-1-258-10451-1(2)) Literary Licensing, LLC.

Prince, Richard. Richard Prince Four Cowboys. 2010. (ENG., Illus.). 20p. pap. 90.00 (978-1-906957-02-5(9)) Abrams.

Princenthal, Nancy, ed. Joyce Kozloff: Co-Ordinates. 2009. (ENG., Illus.). 132p. 45.00 (978-0-9768488-8-2(0)) Dickinson College, The Trout Gallery.

Printz, Neil, et al. Catalogue Raisonn? Vol. 3: Paintings & Sculptures, 1970-1974. 2010. (ENG., Illus.). 544p. 495.00 (978-0-7148-5698-8(3)) Phaidon Pr., Inc.

Putterman, Florence. Entwined Metaphors. 2009. (978-1-933153-11-7(3), Northern Liberties Pr.) Old City Publishing, Inc.

Pyne, Kathleen A. & O'Keeffe, Georgia. Modernism & the Feminine Voice: O'Keeffe & the Women of the Stieglitz Circle. (Illus.). 339p. 2007. per. 36.95 (978-0-520-24190-9(8)) 2006. 65.00 (978-0-520-24189-3(4)) Univ. of California Pr.

Quilter, Jenni. Max Gimblett Workspace. 2010. (ENG., Illus.). 144p. 47.95 (978-88-8158-776-6(9)) Charta ITA. Dist: D.A.P./Distributed Art Pubs.

Rabottini, Alessandro, ed. Sterling Ruby. 2009. (ENG., Illus.). 168p. pap. 55.00 (978-3-03764-010-4(3)) JRP Ringier Kunstverlag AG CHE. Dist: D.A.P./Distributed Art Pubs.

Rajs, Jake, photos by. Beyond the Dunes: A Portrait of the Hamptons. 2008. (ENG., Illus.). 240p. (gr. 12). 60.00 (978-1-58093-203-5(7)) Monacelli Pr., Inc.

Raskin, David. Donald Judd. 2010. (Illus.). 220p. 55.00 (978-0-300-16276-9(6)) Yale Univ. Pr.

Reardon, Michael T. Foxo Reardon. 2008. 260p. pap. 24.95 (978-1-59393-149-0(2)) BearManor Media.

Reid, Sheila. A Place Between Thoughts: The Art of Sheila Reid. ltd. ed. 2010. 173p. pap. (978-0-9646268-2-9(9)) Rush Editions.

Reidel, James. Vanished Act: The Life & Art of Weldon Kees. 2007. (ENG., Illus.). 448p. pap. 19.95 (978-0-8032-5977-5(8)) Univ. of Nebraska Pr.

Reilly, Maura & Gerdts, William H. Patricia Cronin: Harriet Hosmer - Lost & Found. 2009. (ENG., Illus.). 104p. 39.95 (978-88-8158-732-2(7)) Charta ITA. Dist: D.A.P./Distributed Art Pubs.

Renzi, Jen & Neumann, Vera. Vera. 2010. 40.00 (978-0-8109-8904-7(2)) Abrams.

Richter, Carl. The Crumb Compendium. 2012. (ENG., Illus.). 320p. pap. 29.99 (978-1-60699-501-3(4), 699501) Fantagraphics Bks.

Rider, Alistair. Carl Andre: Things in Their Elements. 2011. (ENG., Illus.). 272p. 75.00 (978-0-7148-4922-5(7)) Phaidon Pr., Inc.

Riley, Peter Jason. New Tax Guide for Writers, Artists, Performers & other Creative People. rev. ed. 2012. (ENG., Illus.). 184p. (C). pap. 19.95 (978-1-58510-469-7(8)) Focus Publishing/R. Pullins Co., Inc.

Riley, Peter Jason. New Tax Guide for Writers, Artists, Performers, & Other Creative People. 2nd ed. 2009. (ENG.). 224p. pap. 16.95 (978-1-58510-345-4(4)) Focus Publishing/R. Pullins Co., Inc.

Ritchie, Matthew. More Than the Eye. 2008. (ENG., Illus.). 272p. 75.00 (978-0-8478-3108-1(6)) Rizzoli International Pubns., Inc.

Robert Seydel. 2007. 8.00 (978-0-9791843-2-1(0)) CUE Art Foundation.

Roberts, Holly. Holly Roberts: Works 2000 to 2009. 2010. (Illus.). 70p. (978-1-59005-258-7(7)) Nazraeli Pr.

Robertson, Edna, et al. Artists of the Canyons & Caminos: Santa Fe: Early Twentieth Century, 1 vol. 2006. (ENG., Illus.). 176p. per. 19.95 (978-1-4236-0114-2(9)) Gibbs Smith, Publisher.

Robertson, Mary. Watch the Right Lock: A Car & His Family in the Fifties. 2008. 216p. 24.99 (978-1-4389-1930-0(1)) AuthorHouse.

Rogaishio, Edward R. Midnight to Infinity: The Humor & History of a Mischievous Artist. 2009. (978-1-58982-504-8(7)) American Bk. Publishing Group.

Rogak, Lisa. Boy Named Shel: The Life & Times of Shel Silverstein. 2nd ed. 2009. (ENG., Illus.). 256p. pap. 16.99 (978-0-312-53931-3(2), St. Martin's Griffin) St. Martin's Pr.

Rogers, James G., Jr., et al. The Art of Downing Barnitz: A Retrospective Exhibition. 2007. 18.00 (978-0-9714065-1-3(0)) Florida Southern College, Melvin Art Gallery.

Rohrbach, John. Accommodating Nature: The Photographs of Frank Gohlke. 2007. (Center for American Places - Center Books on American Places Ser.). (Illus.). 176p. pap. 35.00 (978-1-930066-65-6(1)) Ctr. for American Places, Inc.

Rohrbach, John & Gohlke, Frank. Accommodating Nature: The Photographs of Frank Gohlke. 2007. (Center for American Places - Center Books on American Places Ser.). (Illus.). 176p. 65.00 (978-1-930066-66-3(X)) Ctr. for American Places, Inc.

Rojas, Clare, photos by. Everything Flowers. 2011. (ENG., Illus.). 96p. 22.95 (978-0-8118-7151-8(7)) Chronicle Bks. LLC.

Roma, Thomas, photos by. Dear Knights & Dark Horses. 2010. (ENG., Illus.). 100p. 24.95 (978-1-57687-553-7(9)) powerHouse Cultural Entertainment, Inc.

Romer, Grant B., et al. Young America: The Daguerreotypes of Southworth & Hawes, 1 vol. 2008. (ENG., Illus.). 356p. 120.00 (978-3-86521-066-1(X)) Steidl, Gerhard Druckerei und Verlag DEU. Dist: Innovative Logistics.

Rondinone, Ugo. Ugo Rondinone: The Night of Lead. 2010. (ENG & SPA., Illus.). 384p. 90.00 (978-3-03764-145-3(2)) JRP Ringier Kunstverlag AG CHE. Dist: D.A.P./Distributed Art Pubs.

Rooney, E. Ashley. 100 Artists of New England. 2011. (Illus.). 224p. 45.00 (978-0-7643-3665-2(7)) Schiffer Publishing, Ltd.

—100 Artists of the Mid-Atlantic. 2011. (Illus.). 224p. (978-0-7643-3734-5(3), Schiffer Publishing Ltd) Schiffer Publishing, Ltd.

Rosa, Joseph. Young Chicago. 2007. (A+D Ser.). (ENG., Illus.). 104p. pap. 16.95 (978-0-300-12067-7(2)) Art Institute of Chicago.

Ross, Alex. Rough Justice: The DC Comics Sketches of Alex Ross. Kidd, Chip, ed. 2012. (ENG., Illus.). 224p. pap. 24.95 (978-0-307-37878-1(0), Pantheon) Knopf Doubleday Publishing Group.

Roszkiewicz, Ron. To Turn the Perfect Wooden Bowl: The Lifelong Quest of Bob Stocksdale. 2009. (ENG., Illus.). 146p. pap. 24.95 (978-1-56523-388-1(3)) Fox Chapel Publishing Co., Inc.

Rothkopf, Scott. Glenn Ligon: America. 2011. (ENG., Illus.). 304p. 65.00 (978-0-300-16847-1(0)) Yale Univ. Pr.

Rowe, M. Jessica. Albert Paley: Portals & Gates. 2007. (Illus.). 143p. 35.00 (978-0-9798111-0-4(4)) Iloa State Univ., Univ. Museum.

Rubio, Agustín, ed. Terence Koh: 1980-2008. 2009. (ENG., Illus.). 208p. 55.00 (978-3-7757-2308-4(0)) Hatje Cantz Verlag GmbH & Co KG DEU. Dist: D.A.P./Distributed Art Pubs.

Ruf, Beatrix, ed. Sean Landers. 2008. (ENG., Illus.). 160p. pap. 55.00 (978-3-905829-87-7(8)) JRP Ringier Kunstverlag AG CHE. Dist: D.A.P./Distributed Art Pubs.

Ryan, Jay. 100 Posters / 134 Squirrels: A Decade of Hot Dogs, Large Mammals, & Independent Rock: the Handcrafted Art of Jay Ryan. 2010. (ENG., Illus.). 120p. pap. 22.95 (978-1-936070-68-5(5)) Akashic Bks.

Sacco, David C. David C. Sacco: An American Master. Goldman, Rita, ed. (Illus.). 48p. 25.00 (978-0-9638842-0-6(4)) Master Touch Gallery.

Sacco, Kevin. The Plane Story. 2011. (Illus.). 128p. (YA). pap. 19.99 (978-1-60010-867-9(9)) Idea & Design Works, LLC.

Sachs, Tom. Islandia: Tom Sachs, 1 vol. 2007. (ENG., Illus.). 68p. pap. 30.00 (978-0-9790499-1-0(1)) Sachs, Tom.

Sal Buscema: Comic's Fast & Furious Artist. 2010. 192p. (YA). pap. 46.95 (978-1-60549-022-9(9)) TwoMorrows Publishing.

Sans, Jerome. Stray Alchemists: Matt Bryans, Amy Granat, Lim Tzay Chuen, Takeshi Murata, Robin Rhode, Sterling Ruby, Fowle, Kate, ec. 2009. (ENG., Illus.). 140p. pap. 23.00 (978-988-17521-3-0(2)) Timezone 8 Ltd. HKG. Dist: D.A.P./Distributed Art Pubs.

SASSpeedis. Horse Trails Have No Ends. 2011. 160p. 25.00 (978-1-4567-6823-2(9)); pap. 11.70 (978-1-4567-6824-9(7)) AuthorHouse.

Savage, Jeff. Tito Ortiz. 2012. (Xtreme Athletes Ser.). (Illus.). 111p. (YA). (gr. 7-12). 28.95 (978-1-59935-184-1(6)) Reynolds, Morgan Inc.

Savides, Nick. Nick Savides: New York/Paris. 2009. (Illus.). 28p. pap. 10.00 (978-0-9747030-6-0(0)) Nabi Pr.

Schelly, Bill. Man of Rock: A Biography of Joe Kubert. 2008. (ENG., Illus.). 320p. pap. 19.99 (978-1-56097-928-9(3), 56928) Fantagraphics Bks.

Scherman, Tony & Dalton, David. Pop: The Genius of Andy Warhol. 2010. (ENG.). 528p. pap. 17.99 (978-0-06-093663-1(0)) HarperCollins Pubs.

Schilling, Richard. Portraits of the Prairie: The Land That Inspired Willa Cather. 2011. (ENG., Illus.). 176p. 44.95 (978-0-8032-2260-1(2)) Univ. of Nebraska Pr.

Schmitt, Anne-Florence. Karl Lagerfeld: Trait par Trait, 1 vol. 2011. (ENG., Illus.). 144p. pap. 25.00 (978-3-86521-552-9(1)) Steidl, Gerhard Druckerei und Verlag DEU. Dist: Innovative Logistics.

Schmuckli, Claudia, frwd. Bitter, Black Thoughts. 2011. (ENG., Illus.). 104p. pap. 29.99 (978-0-941193-48-1(9)) Blaffer Art Museum.

Schnabel, Julian. Julian Schnabel: Art & Film, 1 vol. 2010. (ENG., Illus.). 448p. pap. 40.00 (978-1-894243-66-7(8)) Art Gallery of Ontario CAN. Dist: D.A.P./Distributed Art Pubs.

Schneemann, Carolee. Split Decision, 1 vol. 2008. (ENG., Illus.). 96p. per. 29.95 (978-0-939784-26-4(2)) CEPA Gallery.

Schneemann, Carolee & Stiles, Kristine, eds. Correspondence Course: An Epistolary History of Carolee Schneemann & Her Circle. 2010. (ENG., Illus.). 576p. 99.95 (978-0-8223-4500-8(5)); pap. 29.95 (978-0-8223-4511-4(0)) Duke Univ. Pr.

Schneider, Tim, ed. Peter Wegner. 2007. (Illus.). (978-0-9704427-6-5(9)) Griffin, W. L. Editions.

Schoeller, Martin. Female Bodybuilders. 2008. (ENG.). 96p. 50.00 (978-0-9761955-3-5(4)) Pond Pr.

Schoenfeld, Wayne, photos by. Through This World but Once. 2007. (Illus.). 40p. pap. 30.00 (978-0-9798631-1-0(2)) Great Circle Bks.

Schoonmaker, Trevor, ed. Barkley L. Hendricks: Birth of the Cool. 2008. (ENG., Illus.). 140p. 39.95 (978-0-938989-31-8(6)) Duke Univ. Pr.

Schorr, Todd. American Surreal. 2009. (Illus.). 100p. 39.95 (978-0-86719-709-9(9)) Last Gasp of San Francisco.

Schrag, Ariel. Awkward & Definition: The High School Comic Chronicles of Ariel Schrag. 2008. (ENG., Illus.). 144p. pap. 16.95 (978-1-4165-5231-4(6), Touchstone) Touchstone.

Schroth, Sarah, ed. Irwin Kremen: Beyond Black Mountain, 1966-2006. 2007. (ENG., Illus.). 72p. pap. 24.95 (978-0-938989-29-5(4)) Duke Univ. Pr.

Schwabsky, Barry, et al. Suzanne McClelland: Rock & Shift. 2010. (ENG., Illus.). 86p. 39.95 (978-1-889097-75-6(6)) Hard Pr. Editions.

Schweizer, Nicole, ed. Renee Green: Ongoing Becomings. Retrospective 1989-2009. 2009. (ENG., Illus.). 160p. pap. 55.00 (978-3-03764-031-9(6)) JRP Ringier Kunstverlag AG CHE. Dist: D.A.P./Distributed Art Pubs.

Seeking Heaven, Eyeone. Lost: Graffiti in the City of Angels: Collection 0001: 1998-2008. 2008. (Illus.). 224p. spiral bd. 30.00 (978-0-9792356-0-3(X)) Laboratorios Margen.

Seid, Susan. Vera: The Art & Life of an Icon. 2010. (ENG., Illus.). 208p. 35.00 (978-0-8109-9604-5(9)) Abrams.

Sellen, Betty-Carol. Art Centers: American Studios & Galleries for Artists with Developmental or Mental Disabilities. 2008. (ENG., Illus.). 212p. pap. 49.95 (978-0-7864-4140-2(2)) McFarland & Co., Inc. Pubs.

Serra, Richard. Richard Serra. Drawings. Work comes out of work. 2008. (GER & ENG., Illus.). 234p. 90.00 (978-3-86560-416-3(1)) Kunsthaus Bregenz AUT. Dist: D.A.P./Distributed Art Pubs.

Shaffer, Stan, photos by. You Should Have Been with Me. 2010. (Illus.). 256p. 98.00 (978-3-8327-9425-5(5)) teNeues Publishing Co.

Shawhan, Dorothy Sample & Norris, Carolyn. Spirit of the Delta: The Art of Carolyn Norris. 2011. (ENG., Illus.). 128p. 35.00 (978-1-60473-992-3(4)) Univ. Pr. of Mississippi.

Sheskin, David. The Art of David Sheskin. 2011. (Illus.). 316p. pap. 69.95 (978-1-59594-447-4(8), Wingspan Pr.) WingSpan Publishing.

Shiner, Eric. Making a Home. 2007. (Illus.). 223p. 45.00 (978-0-913304-60-0(3)) Japan Society Gallery.

Shopsin, Tamara. Tamara Shopsin: C'est le Pied II. 2009. (ENG., Illus.). 96p. pap. 14.95 (978-0-9823653-0-4(6)) Ice Plant, The.

Shore, Stephen, photos by. A Road Trip Journal. 2008. (ENG., Illus.). 256p. 300.00 (978-0-7148-4801-3(8)) Phaidon Pr., Inc.

Siegel, Jerry. Facing South: Portraits of Southern Artists. 3rd ed. 2012. (ENG., Illus.). 232p. 29.95 (978-0-8173-1758-4(9)) Univ. of Alabama Pr.

Sietsema, Paul. Figure 3. 2009. (ENG., Illus.). 80p. pap. 29.95 (978-0-87070-776-6(0)) Museum of Modern Art.

Simon, Joan & Faxon, Susan C. Sheila Hicks: 50 Years. 2010. (ENG., Illus.). 256p. 65.00 (978-0-300-12164-3(4)) Yale Univ. Pr.

Simon, Joe. Joe Simon: My Life in Comics - The Illustrated Autobiography. 2011. (ENG., Illus.). 256p. 24.95 (978-1-84576-930-7(9), Titan Bks.) Titan Bks. Ltd. GBR. Dist: Random Hse., Inc.

Simpson, Bennett & Iles, Chrissie, eds. Dan Graham: Beyond. 2009. (ENG., Illus.). 348p. (gr. 17). pap. 44.95 (978-1-933751-12-2(6)) MIT Pr.

Sischy, Ingrid. Koons, Jeff: With an Original Artwork. Holzwarth, Hans Werner, ed. 2008. 606p. 9000.00 (978-3-8365-0070-8(1)) TASCHEN DEU. Dist: Ingram Pub. Services.

Skinner, Alice Blackmer. Stay by Me, Roses: The Life of American Artist Alice Archer Sewall James (1870-1955) 2011. (Illus.). 288p. pap. (978-0-87785-338-1(X)) Swedenborg Foundation, Inc.

Skinner, Tina. 100 Artists of the West Coast II. 2009. (Illus.). 224p. bds. 39.99 (978-0-7643-3271-5(6)) Schiffer Publishing, Ltd.

Slager, Daniel, ed. The Suspension of Time: Reflections on Simon Dinnerstein & the Fulbright Triptych. 2011. (ENG., Illus.). 360p. pap. 35.00 (978-1-57131-326-3(5)) Milkweed Editions.

Sliva, Jiri. Jam Session. 2009. (ENG.). 112p. 19.95 (978-80-7391-016-7(0), Art Stock Bks. Ltd/Csi) Continental Sales, Inc.

Slobodkina Foundation. Esphyr Slobodkina: Rediscovering a Pioneer of American Abstraction. 2008. pap. (978-0-9793620-0-2(8)) Slobodkina Foundation, The.

Small, David. Stitches: A Memoir. 2010. (ENG., Illus.). 329p. pap. 16.95 (978-0-393-33896-6(7), 33896) Norton, W. W. & Co., Inc.

Smith, Edward Lucie & Nahas, Dominique. Margaret Evangeline. 2011. (ENG., Illus.). 160p. 47.50 (978-88-8158-808-4(0)) Charta ITA. Dist: D.A.P./Distributed Art Pubs.

Smith, Zak. We Did Porn: Memoir & Drawings. 2009. (ENG., Illus.). 488p. 49.95 (978-0-9820539-2-8(4)) Tin Hse. Bks., LLC.

Sokolowski, Thomas. Rene Santos: Suspension of the Law. (Illus.). 76p. pap. 30.00 (978-0-934349-14-7(2)) Grey Art Gallery & Study Ctr., New York Univ.

Solis Betancourt, Jose, et al. Essential Elegance: The Interiors of Solis Betancourt. 2010. (ENG., Illus.). 248p. 50.00 (978-1-58093-278-3(9)) Monacelli Pr., Inc.

Sollins, Marybeth, ed. Art21: Art in the Twenty-First Century 5, 5 vols., Vol. 5. 2009. (Illus.). 224p. 45.00 (978-0-615-30836-4(8)) Art21, Incorporated.

Sorren, Joe. Joe Sorren. 2011. (978-1-58423-430-2(X)) Gingko Pr., Inc.

Souter, Gerry. American Realism. 2009. (Temporis Ser.). (ENG., Illus.). 256p. 39.95 (978-1-84484-575-0(3)) Parkstone International GBR. Dist: Ingram Pub. Services.

Spector, Nancy, ed. Richard Prince, 1 vol. 2007. (ENG., Illus.). 368p. 60.00 (978-0-89207-363-4(2)) Guggenheim, Solomon R. Museum.

Speed, Julie. Speed Art, 2003-2009. 2009. (ENG., Illus.). 188p. 55.00 (978-0-292-71994-1(9)) Univ. of Texas Pr.

Spring, Justin. Wolf Kahn. rev. ed. 2011. (ENG., Illus.). 196p. 55.00 (978-0-8109-9790-5(8)) Abrams.

Spurlock. Echoes: Drawings of Michael Wm Kaluta Hc, 1 vol. 2007. (ENG.). 112p. 27.95 (978-1-887591-13-3(3)) Vanguard Productions.

—Echoes: Drawings of Michael Wm Kaluta Pb, 1 vol. 2009. (ENG.). 111p. pap. 14.95 (978-1-887591-14-0(1)) Vanguard Productions.

St. Gaudens, Homer. The American Artist & His Times. 2011. 414p. 54.95 (978-1-258-10519-8(5)) Literary Licensing, LLC.

Stadtlander, Becca. The Little Otsu Living Things Series Volume 6: Winged Creatures of the Natural World. 2011. (Illus.). 16p. 6.95 (978-1-934378-27-4(5)) Little Otsu.

Stamey, Emily. The Prints of Roger Shimomura: A Catalogue Raisonne, 1968-2005. 2007. (Jacob Lawrence Series on American Artists). (ENG., Illus.). 152p. pap. 28.95 (978-0-295-98672-2(7)) Univ. of Washington Pr.

Stamos, Theodoros & Richardson, R. Sarah. Theodoros Stamos: A Communion with Nature. 2010. (Illus.). 104p. pap. (978-0-9800745-5-0(X)) Taggart, Hollis Galleries.

Stein, Sally. John Gutmann: The Photographer at Work. 2009. (Illus.). 180p. 50.00 (978-0-300-12331-9(0)) Yale Univ. Pr.

Stella, Frank. Frank Stella: Painting into Architecture. 2007. (ENG., Illus.). 40p. per. 16.95 (978-0-300-13148-2(8)) Yale Univ. Pr.

Stelmach, Augelina. Crossing Boundaries: The Art of Lee Waisler. 2006. (ENG., Illus.). 144p. 50.00 (978-1-890206-34-5(2)) Mapin Publishing Pvt. Ltd IND. Dist: National Bk. Network.

Stern Fotografie Portfolio 48. Mark Seliger. 2007. (Illus.). 94p. per. 22.95 (978-3-570-19734-9(4)) teNeues Publishing Co.

Stewart, Lizzy. The Little Otsu Annual Volume 6. 2011. (Illus.). 144p. spiral bd. 18.00 (978-1-934378-28-1(3)) Little Otsu.

Stice, Mike. Wolfgang Bloch: The Colors of Coincidence. 2008. (ENG., Illus.). 176p. 40.00 (978-0-8118-6101-4(5)) Chronicle Bks. LLC.

Stingel, Rudolf. Rudolf Stingel. 2011. (ENG., Illus.). 84p. 80.00 (978-3-7913-4581-9(8)) Prestel Publishing.

Stolfa, Sarah. The Regulars. 2009. (ENG., Illus.). 96p. 22.95 (978-1-57965-402-3(9), 1579654029) Artisan.

Storr, Robert, et al. Gary Panter. 2008. (ENG., Illus.). 700p. 95.00 (978-0-9794153-1-9(4)) PictureBox, Inc.

Stout, William. William Stout: Prehistoric Life Murals. 2008. (ENG.). 176p. 39.95 (978-1-933865-10-2(5)) Flesk Pubns.

Stroun, Fabrice & Bovier, Lionel, eds. Jim Shaw: My Mirage. 2011. (ENG., Illus.). 240p. pap. 55.00 (978-3-03764-187-3(8)) JRP Ringier Kunstverlag AG CHE. Dist: D.A.P./Distributed Art Pubs.

Struzan, Drew. The Art of Drew Struzan. 2010. (Illus.). 160p. reprint ed. 34.95 (978-1-84856-619-4(0), Titan Bks.) Titan Bks. Ltd. GBR. Dist: Random Hse., Inc.

Stuhlman, Jonathan, ed. Double Solitaire. 2011. (ENG., Illus.). 104p. pap. 40.00 (978-0-9831942-1-7(1)) Mint Museum, The.

Sugarman, Tracy. Drawing Conclusions: An Artist Discovers His America. 2008. (Illus.). 179p. 29.95 (978-0-8156-0871-4(3)) Syracuse Univ. Pr.

Swoon, Swoon. 2010. (ENG., Illus.). 192p. 35.00 (978-0-8109-8485-1(7)) Abrams.

Sylvia Beckman Warner, Her Life & Art. 2007. 50.00 net. (978-0-9796438-0-4(5)) Bishop, Anne.

Taft, Robert. Artists & Illustrators of the Old West, 1850-1900. 2008. 500p. pap. 42.00 (978-1-59740-587-4(6)) ACLS Humanities E-Book.

—Artists & Illustrators of the Old West, 1850-1900. 2011. 492p. 58.95 (978-1-258-01515-2(3)) Literary Licensing, LLC.

Tannenbaum, Allen. New York in The 70s. 2009. (ENG., Illus.). 272p. (gr. 12-18). 45.00 (978-1-59020-172-5(8)) Overlook Pr., The.

Tannenbaum, Judith. Wunderground: Providence, 1995 to the Present. 2006. (Illus.). 104p. per. 24.95 (978-1-58423-262-9(5)) Gingko Pr., Inc.

Taylor, Al. Al Taylor, 1 vol. 2008. (ENG., Illus.). 142p. 65.00 (978-3-86521-636-6(6)) Steidl, Gerhard Druckerei und Verlag DEU. Dist: Innovative Logistics.

Taylor, Anna Heyward, et al, eds. Selected Letters of Anna Heyward Taylor: South Carolina Artist & World Traveler. 2010. (Women's Diaries & Letters of the South Ser.). 39.95 (978-1-57003-945-4(3)) Univ. of South Carolina Pr.

Taylor, Michael & Chimes, Thomas. Thomas Chimes: Adventures in Pataphysics. 2007. (Illus.). xi, 255p. (978-0-87633-253-5(X)); (978-0-87633-252-8(1)) Philadelphia Museum of Art.

Tedeschi, Martha & Dahm, Kristi. John Marin's Watercolors: A Medium for Modernism. 2011. (ENG., Illus.). 192p. 50.00 (978-0-300-16637-8(0)) Art Institute of Chicago.

Telfair Museum of Art Staff. Picturing Savannah: The Art of Christopher A. D. Murphy. 2008. (ENG., Illus.). 120p. pap. 29.95 (978-0-933075-07-8(3)) Telfair Museum of Art.

Thomas, Roy & Amash, Jim. John Romita... & All That Jazz! 2007. 208p. 44.95 (978-1-893905-76-4(4)) TwoMorrows Publishing.

Thompson, Jerry, photos by. In the Street, 1 vol. 2010. (ENG., Illus.). 47p. 58.00 (978-3-86521-919-0(5)) Steidl, Gerhard Druckerei und Verlag DEU. Dist: Innovative Logistics.

Thompson, Mimi. Robert Rauschenberg: Prints from Universal Limited Art Editions, 1962-2008. 2011. (Illus.). 120p. pap. (978-0-9717187-8-4(4)) Jones Jr., Fred Museum of Art.

Tierney, Tom. ¿Attitude¿ Revisited: An Adult Paper Doll Book. 2008. (Illus.). 80p. bds. 29.99 (978-0-7643-2985-2(5)) Schiffer Publishing, Ltd.

Trela, Christopher, ed. The Autobiography & Sex Life of Andy Warhol. 2010. (ENG., Illus.). 256p. 45.00 (978-0-9706126-1-8(3)) Trela.

Trese, Daniel, photos by. Walking Backwards. 2007. 64p. per. 16.00 (978-0-9747238-0-8(0)) Adolescent Bks.

Tretiack, Philippe. Warhol's America. 2008. pap. (978-2-7594-0312-7(2)) Assouline.

Tsai, Eugenie & Biggers, Sanford. Sanford Biggers: Sweet Funk — an Introspective. 2011. (978-0-87273-169-1(3)) Brooklyn Museum, The.

Turck, W. C. Everything for Love: A memoir of love & War. 2009. 292p. pap. 21.95 (978-1-4401-3292-6(5)) iUniverse, Inc.

Ulysses; Departures, Journeys, & Returns: The Artwork of Andrew Schoultz. 3000th ed. 2007. (Illus.). 180p. 29.00 (978-0-9788739-0-5(4)) Paper Museum Pr.

Umberger, Leslie, ed. Sublime Spaces & Visionary Worlds: Built Environments of Vernacular Artists. 2007. (ENG., Illus.). 416p. 65.00 (978-1-56898-728-6(5)) Princeton Architectural Pr.

Umberto Allemandi and Company Staff. Noguchi: Between East & West. 2011. (ENG., Illus.). 176p. 49.00 (978-88-422-1876-0(6)) Allemandi, Umberto & Co. GBR. Dist: Antique Collectors' Club.

Ungerer, Tomi. Far Out Isn't Far Enough: Life in the Back of Beyond. 2011. (ENG., Illus.). 170p. 29.95 (978-0-7148-6077-0(8)) Phaidon Pr., Inc.

Vallejo, Boris & Bell, Julie. Boris Vallejo & Julie Bell: The Ultimate Illustrations. 2009. (ENG.). 192p. pap. 24.99 (978-0-06-115173-6(4), Collins Design) HarperCollins Pubs.

Van Hamersveld, John. My Art, My Life. Clucas, David Lynn, ed. 2010. (ENG., Illus.). 176p. 100.00 (978-1-58731-523-7(8)); pap. 23.00 (978-1-58731-524-4(6)) St. Augustine's Pr., Inc.

Varney, Carleton. Houses in My Heart: An International Decorator's Colorful Journey. 2008. (ENG., Illus.). 224p. 95.00 (978-0-9777875-5-5(9)) Shannongrove Pr.

Venet, Diane, ed. From Picasso to Jeff Koons - The Artist As Jeweler. 2011. (ENG., Illus.). 240p. 70.00 (978-88-572-1156-5(8)) Skira Editore ITA. Dist: Random Hse., Inc.

Victore, James & Bierut, Michael. Victore or, Who Died & Made You Boss? 2010. (ENG., Illus.). 208p. 40.00 (978-0-8109-9591-8(3)) Abrams.

Vincent, Lawrence M. In Search of Motif No. 1: The History of A Fish Shack. 2011. 160p. pap. 21.99 (978-1-60949-382-0(6)) History Pr., The.

von Amelunxen, Hubertus, et al, eds. Gordon Matta-Clark: Moment to Moment: Space. 2012. (ENG., Illus.). 224p. pap. 60.00 (978-3-86984-138-0(9)) Verlag fur Moderne Kunst DEU. Dist: D.A.P./Distributed Art Pubs.

Von D, Kat. High Voltage Tattoo. 2009. (ENG., Illus.). 144p. 29.99 (978-0-06-168438-8(4), Collins Design) HarperCollins Pubs.

Vos, Judith, ed. Josephine Powell 1919-2007. 2009. (Bulletins of the Royal Tropical Institute Ser.). (Illus.). 120p. pap. 35.00 (978-90-6832-698-7(8)) Royal Tropical Institute Pr. (KIT (Koninklijk Instituut voor de Tropen) NLD. Dist: Stylus Publishing, LLC.

Walker, Butch & Diehl, Matt. Drinking with Strangers: Music Lessons from a Teenage Bullet Belt. 2011. (ENG.). 304p. 25.99 (978-0-06-178731-7(0), Morrow, William & Co.) HarperCollins Pubs.

Walker, Hollis. Zink: The Language of Enchantment. 2006. (New Mexico Magazine Artist Ser.: No. 6). (ENG., Illus.). 96p. 19.95 (978-0-937206-90-4(3)) New Mexico Magazine.

Wang, ShiPu. Becoming American? The Art & Identity Crisis of Yasuo Kuniyoshi. 2011. (Illus.). xii, 191p. 56.00 (978-0-8248-3418-0(6)) Univ. of Hawaii Pr.

Wardlaw, Alvia J. & Hess, Aimee. Margaret Meade. 2007. (David C. Driskell Series of African American Art Ser.: 6). (Illus.). 64p. 12.95 (978-0-7649-3766-8(9)) Pomegranate Communications, Inc.

Warhol, Andy, et al. POPism: The Warhol Sixties. 2006. (ENG., Illus.). 400p. pap. 14.00 (978-0-15-603111-0(6), Mariner Bks.) Houghton Mifflin Harcourt Trade & Reference Pubs.

Warkel, Harriet G. Paper to Paint: Edward Hopper's Hotel Lobby. 2008. (ENG., Illus.). 60p. pap. 14.95 (978-0-936260-84-6(X)) Indianapolis Museum of Art.

Warmus, William, et al. Dan Dailey. Rapone, Joe, ed. 2007. (ENG., Illus.). 384p. 60.00 (978-0-8109-9319-8(8)) Abrams.

Washburn, Phoebe, illus. Phoebe Washburn: Regulated Fool's Milk Meadow, 1 vol. 2007. (ENG.). 72p. pap. 40.00 (978-0-89207-365-8(9)) Guggenheim, Solomon R. Museum.

Waters, John. Role Models, 1 vol. 2011. (ENG., Illus.). 320p. pap. 15.00 (978-0-374-53286-4(9)) Farrar, Straus & Giroux.

Watson, Daryl. Gifts to the Prairie: The Work of Pioneer Nurserymen & the Art of the Prestele Family. 2008. (Illus.). 32p. 15.00 (978-0-943788-34-0(X)) McLean County Historical Society.

Weber, Bruce. All-American VI: Larger Than Life. 2006. (Illus.). 192p. mass mkt. 155.00 net. (978-0-9787124-1-9(2), Little Bear Pr.) Little Bear, Inc.

—All-American VII: An Anthem for the South: 'till I Get It Right. 2007. 192p. pap. (978-0-9787124-2-6(0), Little Bear Pr.) Little Bear, Inc.

Webster, Kyle T. Deadline Drawings: Volume 1. 2007. 78p. pap. 29.95 (978-0-615-17063-3(3)) Webster, Kyle T.

Weems, Jason & Coir, Mark. James Scripps Booth: Artist, Engineer, Polymath. Weems, Jason, ed. 2008. pap. 25.00 (978-0-933691-10-0(6)) Univ. of Michigan-Dearborn.

Weems, Miriam. Mostly Mississippi. 2007. (Illus.). 112p. 39.95 (978-1-934193-07-5(0)) Quail Ridge Pr., Inc.

Weibel, Peter & Blase, Christoph, eds. Record Again! 40jahrevideokunst.de - Teil 2. 2011. (ENG., Illus.). 536p. pap. 55.00 (978-3-7757-2522-4(9)) Hatje Cantz Verlag GmbH & Co KG DEU. Dist: D.A.P./Distributed Art Pubs.

Weiner, Lawrence. Lawrence Weiner: If in Fact There Is A Context. 2011. (ENG., Illus.). 24p. pap. 10.00 (978-3-7757-2857-7(0)) Hatje Cantz Verlag GmbH & Co KG DEU. Dist: D.A.P./Distributed Art Pubs.

Weisbeck, Markus, ed. William Forsythe: Suspense. 2008. (ENG & GER., Illus.). 148p. pap. 55.00 (978-3-905829-75-4(4)) JRP Ringier Kunstverlag AG CHE. Dist: D.A.P./Distributed Art Pubs.

Weisman, Mary-Lou. Al Jaffee's Mad Life: A Biography. 2010. (ENG., Illus.). 240p. 27.99 (978-0-06-186448-3(X)) HarperCollins Pubs.

Welling, James. Light Sources, 1992-2005, 1 vol. 2011. (ENG., Illus.). 144p. 55.00 (978-3-86521-859-9(8)) Steidl, Gerhard Druckerei und Verlag DEU. Dist: Innovative Logistics.

Welsh, Caroline M., et al. The Adirondack World of A. F. Tait. 2011. (Illus.). 102p. pap. 24.95 (978-0-910020-53-4(1)) Adirondack Museum, The.

Werbel, Amy. Thomas Eakins: Art, Medicine, & Sexuality in Nineteenth-Century Philadelphia. 2007. (ENG., Illus.). 208p. 60.00 (978-0-300-11655-7(1)) Yale Univ. Pr.

Wertz, Julia. Drinking at the Movies. 2010. (ENG., Illus.). 192p. pap. 15.00 (978-0-307-59183-8(2), Three Rivers Pr.) Crown Publishing Group.

Weschler, Lawrence. Seeing Is Forgetting the Name of the Thing One Sees: Expanded Edition. exp. ed. 2009. (ENG., Illus.). 336p. pap. 26.95 (978-0-520-25609-5(3)) Univ. of California Pr.

—Seeing Is Forgetting the Name of the Thing One Sees: Over Thirty Years of Conversations with Robert Irwin. exp. ed. 2009. (Illus.). 352p. 50.00 (978-0-520-25608-8(5)) Univ. of California Pr.

Weschler, Lawrence & Hockney, David. True to Life: Twenty-Five Years of Conversations with David Hockney. 2009. (Illus.). 272p. pap. 26.95 (978-0-520-25879-2(7)) Univ. of California Pr.

Westfall, Stephen, text. Judith Rothschild: Paintings of The 1940s. 2008. (Illus.). 23p. per. 15.00 (978-0-9777686-9-1(4)) Carberry, Valerie Gallery, Inc.

Whalen, Nomi. She Collects Collections. 2009. 96p. pap. 28.99 (978-1-4389-4354-1(7)) AuthorHouse.

What the World Needs Now Is Peter Max. 2007. 39.95 (978-0-06-115011-1(8), Collins Design) HarperCollins Pubs.

Whitburn, Joel. The Billboard Book of Top 40 Hits: Complete Chart Information about America's Most Popular Songs & Artists, 1955-2009. 9th ed. 2010. (ENG.). 912p. pap. 25.00 (978-0-8230-8554-5(6), Billboard Bks.) Watson-Guptill Pubns., Inc.

Whiticar, George Curtis. Whiticar Waterway Tales: A Personal Narrative. 2007. (Illus.). 100p. pap. 18.95 (978-0-615-17770-0(0)) Darvill, Laura Kay.

Whitmer, Kathleen. The Glory in a Story: A Joyful Journey Through Memories. 2008. (Illus.). 198p. pap. 23.95 (978-0-9661079-5-1(0)) Peach Pubns., Inc.

Whittaker, Richard. The Conversations: Interviews with Sixteen Contemporary Artists. 2007. (Working Bks.). (ENG., Illus.). 240p. per. 18.95 (978-0-9673608-8-1(9)) Whale & Star Pr.

Wickersham, Sheldon. Randall Made Knives: A Timeline - the Quick Reference Guide. 3rd ed. 2007. 20.00 (978-0-9740474-3-0(0)) Blue Star Knives.

Wieder, John, ed. Nick Mauss & Ken Okiishi: A Fair to Meddling Story. 2008. (ENG., Illus.). 84p. pap. 28.00 (978-3-905829-33-4(9)) JRP Ringier Kunstverlag AG CHE. Dist: D.A.P./Distributed Art Pubs.

William, Maria J. Chimaera: the art of Maria J. William. 2007. 49p. pap. 24.50 (978-0-615-15271-4(6)) William, Maria J.

Wilmers, Gertrude de G. & Sloan, Julie L. Frederic Crowninshield: A Renaissance Man in Gilded Age. 2010. (Illus.). 448p. 39.95 (978-1-55849-864-8(8)) Univ. of Massachusetts Pr.

Witkin, Joel-Peter, photos by. Joel-Peter Witkin. 2007. (Illus.). 96p. 25.00 (978-88-88359-25-0(7)) Photology ITA. Dist: D.A.P./Distributed Art Pubs.

Witt, David L. & Seton, Ernest Thompson. Ernest Thompson Seton: The Life & Legacy of an Artist & Conservationist, 1 vol. 2010. (ENG., Illus.). 192p. 40.00 (978-1-4236-0391-7(5)) Gibbs Smith, Publisher.

Witz, Dan. Dan Witz - in Plain View: 30 Years of Artworks Illegal & Otherwise. 2009. (Illus.). 216p. 39.95 (978-1-58423-304-6(4)) Gingko Pr., Inc.

Wolf, Vicente. Lifting the Curtain on Design. 2010. (ENG., Illus.). 224p. 50.00 (978-1-58093-267-7(3)) Monacelli Pr., Inc.

Wood, Margaret. Remembering Miss O'Keefe. 2012. (ENG., Illus.). 64p. 19.95 (978-0-89013-546-4(0)) Museum of New Mexico Pr.

Wood, Paul. Kauai Art & Creative People. (Illus.). pap. 14.95 (978-0-9614443-1-0(2)) Jungle Pr.

Woodman, Francesca, photos by. Francesca Woodman's Notebook. 2011. (ENG., Illus.). 24p. pap. 49.95 (978-88-366-2117-0(1)) Silvana ITA. Dist: D.A.P./Distributed Art Pubs.

Wright, Chely. Like Me: Confessions of a Heartland Country Singer. 2010. (ENG., Illus.). 304p. 25.95 (978-0-307-37886-6(1), Pantheon) Knopf Doubleday Publishing Group.

Wright-Correll, Arlene. Who's Who in Kentucky Arts & Crafts 2006 Edition. 2007. 87p. pap. 33.50 (978-0-615-14755-0(0)) Trade Resources Unlimited.

—Who's Who in Kentucky Arts & Crafts 2007 Edition. 2008. 53p. pap. 29.50 (978-0-615-18494-4(4)) Trade Resources Unlimited.

Wright, David Gilmore. The Life & Art of Peter Moran, Painter-Etcher, 2 vols., Vol. 1. 1000th ed. 2010. (Illus.). 280p. 60.00 net. (978-0-9789779-6-2(3)) Creo Pr.

Wyeth, Andrew. Andrew Wyeth: Autobiography. 184p. 17.98 (978-1-56852-654-6(7), Konecky & Konecky) Konecky, William S. Assocs., Inc.

Wyeth, Andrew, illus. Andrew Wyeth: Autobiography. 2008. (ENG.). 168p. 50.00 (978-1-4379-5304-6(2)) DIANE Publishing Co.

Wyeth, Betsy James, ed. The Wyeths the Letters of N. C. Wyeth, 1901-1945. 2008. (Illus.). 904p. pap. (978-0-9795872-3-8(9)) Brandywine River Museum.

Yarnall, James L. John la Farge A Biographical & Critical Study. 2012. (Illus.). 384p. 99.95 (978-1-4094-1172-7(9)) Ashgate Publishing Co.

Yeager, Bunny. Striptease Artists of The 1950s. 2008. (Illus.). 160p. pap. 24.95 (978-0-7643-2800-8(X)) Schiffer Publishing, Ltd.

Zeleznik, John & Siembieda, Kevin. Rifts & the Megaverse: The Art of John Zeleznik. 2007. (Illus.). 128p. (978-1-57457-163-9(X)) Palladium Bks., Inc.

Zkm. William Forsythe: Improvisation Technologies: A Tool for the Analytical Dance Eye. 2012. (ENG.). 45.00 (978-3-7757-2184-4(3)) Hatje Cantz Verlag GmbH & Co KG DEU. Dist: D.A.P./Distributed Art Pubs.

Zybok, Oliver, ed. The Mage's Pantry. 2008. (ENG., Illus.). 104p. 45.00 (978-3-7757-2107-3(X)) Hatje Cantz Verlag GmbH & Co KG DEU. Dist: D.A.P./Distributed Art Pubs.

ARTISTS—WALES

Alston, David. Into Painting: The Work of Brendan Stuart Burns. 2007. (ENG., Illus.). 100p. pap. 17.95 (978-1-85411-446-4(8)) Seren Bks. GBR. Dist: Independent Pubs. Group.

Chamberlain, Brenda. A Rope of Vines: Journal from a Greek Island. Smith, Dai, ed. 2009. (Library of Wales Ser.). (ENG., Illus.). 148p. pap. 12.95 (978-1-905762-86-6(0)) Parthian Bks. GBR. Dist: Independent Pubs. Group.

Sinnott, Kevin. Behind the Canvas. 2009. (ENG., Illus.). 160p. pap. 29.95 (978-1-85411-445-7(X)) Seren Bks. GBR. Dist: Independent Pubs. Group.

ARTISTS, AFRICAN AMERICAN

see African American Artists

ARTISTS, BLACK

see Black Artists

ARTISTS, INSANE

see Art and Mental Illness

ARTISTS, JEWISH

see Jewish Artists

ARTISTS, WOMEN

see Women Artists

ARTISTS' BOOKS

Here are entered books which are produced by artists and intended as visual art objects as well as works about such books. Works about books richly illustrated with original prints by well known artists and published in limited editions are entered under Artists' Illustrated Books.

Abeyta, Rob, Jr. Compliments Of. 2007. (Illus.). 96p. 19.95 (978-0-9790862-0-5(5)) Upper Playground Pubng.

Again the Metaphor Problem & Other Engaged Critical Discourses about Art: A Conversation between John Baldessari, Liam Gillick & Lawrence Weiner, moderated by Beatrix Ruf. 2006. (GER & ENG., Illus.). 141p. pap. 25.00 (978-3-211-29821-3(5), 3211298215) Springer Wien AUT. Dist: Actar Birkhauser Distribution.

Albee, Edward, text. John Beech & Edward Albee: Obscure-Reveal. 2009. (ENG., Illus.). 104p. 225.00 (978-0-935875-23-2(9)) Blum, Peter Edition.

Ambrosio, Maddalena. Maddalena Ambrosio: Super Maddy: Explorations, 1 vol. 2006. (ENG., Illus.). 24p. 35.00 (978-88-8158-597-7(9)) Charta ITA. Dist: D.A.P./Distributed Art Pubs.

Amar, Anna Sigridur. The Book as Instrument: Stephane Mallarme, the Artist's Book, & the Transformation of Print Culture. 2011. (ENG., Illus.). 428p. 45.00 (978-0-226-02701-2(5)) Univ. of Chicago Pr.

Atkinson, Nora. The Book Borrowers. 2009. (Illus.). 49p. (978-0-942342-19-2(4)) Bellevue Arts Museum.

Auster, Paul, told to. Double Game, 1 vol. 2007. (ENG., Illus.). 296p. 39.95 (978-1-933045-69-6(8)) D.A.P./Distributed Art Pubs.

Badger, Gerry & Parr, Martin. The Photobook Vol. 1: A History. 2010. 320p. pap. 39.95 (978-0-7148-5743-5(2)) Phaidon Pr., Inc.

Baldessari, John & Cesarco, Alejandro. Retrospective: Baldessari/Cesarco. 2008. (ENG., Illus.). 24p. pap. 19.95 (978-3-86560-344-9(0)) Verlag der Buchhandlung Walther Konig DEU. Dist: D.A.P./Distributed Art Pubs.

Barney, Matthew. Matthew Barney: Cremaster 4. (Illus.). 100p. pap. 40.00 (978-2-86925-051-2(7)) D.A.P./Distributed Art Pubs.

Barr, Glenn. Sparrow: Glenn Barr. Glenn Barr. 2008. (Illus.). 48p. 11.99 (978-1-60010-325-4(1)) Idea & Design Works, LLC.

Becker, Olaf Otto, photos by. Olaf Otto Becker - Broken Line: Greenland 2003-2006, 1 vol. 2007. (ENG., Illus.). 144p. 95.00 (978-3-7757-1972-8(5)) Hatje Cantz Verlag GmbH & Co KG DEU. Dist: D.A.P./Distributed Art Pubs.

Bernadette Corporation. Eine Pinot Grigio, Bitte. 2007. (Illus.). 152p. pap. 24.95 (978-1-933128-17-7(8)) Sternberg Pr.

Berry, John. Herman Miller: The Purpose of Design. rev. ed. 2009. (ENG., Illus.). 260p. 60.00 (978-0-8478-3265-1(1)) Rizzoli International Pubns., Inc.

Blachly, Jimbo & Shaw, Lytle. The Chadwick Family Papers. 2008. (Illus.). 176p. 35.00 (978-1-934772-90-4(9)) Periscope Publishing.

Blaufuks, Daniel, photos by. Terezín: Terezín, 1 vol. 2010. (ENG., Illus.). 192p. 65.00 (978-3-86521-699-1(4)) Steidl, Gerhard Druckerei und Verlag DEU. Dist: Innovative Logistics.

Bonvicini, Monica & Bidner, Stefan. Cut. 2008. (ENG., Illus.). 52p. 38.00 (978-3-86560-378-4(5)) Verlag der Buchhandlung Walther Konig DEU. Dist: D.A.P./Distributed Art Pubs.

Bourgeois, Louise. Nothing to Remember, 1 vol. 2009. (ENG., Illus.). 56p. 150.00 (978-3-86521-659-5(5)) Steidl, Gerhard Druckerei und Verlag DEU. Dist: Innovative Logistics.

Breytenbach, Breyten. Intimate Stranger. 2009. (ENG.). 248p. pap. 15.00 (978-0-9800330-9-0(8)) Archipelago Bks.

Brock, Charles, des. Small Hotel. 2011. pap. 40.00 (978-1-4276-5157-0(4)) Aardvark Global Publishing.

Bronson, A. A. & Hobbs, Peter. AA Bronson & Peter Hobbs: Queer Spirits. 2011. (ENG., Illus.). 176p. 34.95 (978-1-928570-14-1(3)) Creative Time.

Cameron, Julia. The Artist's Way: Creative Kingdom Collection. 2011. (Artist's Way Ser.). (ENG.). 1p. (gr. 12). 59.95 (978-1-58542-927-1(9), Tarcher) Penguin Group (USA) Inc.

Cendrars, Blaise. Prose du Transsiberien et de la Petite Jehanne de France. 2010. (FRE., Illus.). 35.00 (978-0-300-16414-5(9)) Yale Univ. Pr.

Cho, Michael. Back Alleys & Urban Landscapes. 2012. (ENG., Illus.). 80p. pap. 19.95 (978-1-77046-080-5(2)) Drawn & Quarterly Pubns. CAN. Dist: Macmillan.

Cianciusi, Walter. Event Scores. 2007. 64p. pap. 13.50 (978-1-84753-568-9(2)) Lulu Enterprises Inc.

Coggins, David. Eden: Summer Collages. 2008. (Illus.). 110p. 40.00 (978-0-9788225-1-4(X)) Cobalt Pr.

Collishaw, Mat. Mat Collishaw. Beard, Jason, ed. 2008. (ENG., Illus.). 176p. pap. 70.00 (978-1-904212-15-7(8)) Other Criteria GBR. Dist: Hachette Bk. Group.

Colored People. 100th ltd. ed. 2008. (Illus.). 50p. (978-0-9792486-2-7(0)) C & C Pr.

Cowboy Junkies. XX. 2007. (ENG., Illus.). 148p. 45.00 (978-0-9673608-7-4(0)) Whale & Star Pr.

Deho, Valerio, et al. Children's Corner, 1 vol. 2008. (ENG., Illus.). 152p. pap. 45.00 (978-88-7570-112-3(1)) Corraini ITA. Dist: D.A.P./Distributed Art Pubs.

Dibiasio, Rick. The Affluent Artist: How Creative Could You Be If Money Wasn't an Issue? the Money Book for Creative People. 2008. (ENG.). pap. 19.95 *(978-1-60037-478-4(6))* Morgan James Publishing.

Diehn, Gwen. The Decorated Journal: Creating Beautifully Expressive Journal Pages. 2006. (Illus.). 128p. pap. 14.95 *(978-1-57990-956-7(6))* Lark Bks.

Dietl, Richard. I Was Write All Along: The Need to Write Came Early. 2009. (Illus.). 208p. pap. 14.95 *(978-1-4327-5061-9(5))* Outskirts Pr., Inc.

Dooley, David. Reflections. (Illus.). 104p. *(978-1-878044-15-0(X))* Mayhaven Publishing, Inc.

DuBasky, Valentina. The Cambodian Journal: Drawings 1994-1998. 2009. (Illus.). 68p. pap. 25.00 *(978-0-9823480-1-7(0),* Abingdon Square) Abingdon Square Publishing, Ltd.

Eliasson, Olafur & text. Olafur Eliasson: Printed Matter. 2010. (ENG & ITA., Illus.). 142p. pap. 49.95 *(978-3-86560-700-3(4))* Verlag der Buchhandlung Walther Konig DEU. Dist: D.A.P./Distributed Art Pubs.

Ellis, Elsi Vassdal & Rogers, Bertha, comments. Book Arts 2010, the Word & Image Gallery, Bright Hill Literary Center. 2010. 140p. pap. 16.00 *(978-1-892471-63-5(9))* Bright Hill Pr.

Feldman, Hans Peter, photos by. Birgit, 1 vol. 2007. (ENG., Illus.). 96p. pap. 30.00 *(978-0-920751-95-4(4))* Verlag der Buchhandlung Walther Konig DEU. Dist: D.A.P./Distributed Art Pubs.

Fietzek, Gerti, ed. Maria Eichhorn: the Artist's Contract. 2009. (ENG., Illus.). 336p. pap. 49.95 *(978-3-86560-421-7(8))* Verlag der Buchhandlung Walther Konig DEU. Dist: D.A.P./Distributed Art Pubs.

Fischer, Lucy Rose. I'm New at Being Old. 2010. 80p. pap. 19.95 *(978-0-615-33519-3(5))* Temuna Pr.

Foer, Jonathan Safran. Tree of Codes. 2010. (ENG.). 285p. pap. 40.00 *(978-0-9565692-1-9(8))* Visual Editions GBR. Dist: Perseus-PGW.

Frank, Fiona & Coyle, Judith. Hannah Frank: Footsteps on the Sands of Time; A Hundredth Birthday Celebration Gallimaufry. 2008. (Illus.). 148p. pap. *(978-1-904999-73-7(5))* Kennedy & Boyd.

Frazer, Colin, et al. Things, All Books May Be Recalled after 7 Days: Date Due, Apr. 9 2011. 2011. (Illus.). 82p. ***(978-0-615-47612-4(0))*** Brown, John Carter Library.

Friedman, Mildred. The Houses. 2009. (Illus.). 320p. 85.00 *(978-0-8478-3060-2(8))* Rizzoli International Pubns., Inc.

Ga, Ellie. Classification of a Spit Stain. 2009. (ENG., Illus.). 64p. 25.00 *(978-1-933254-45-6(9))* Ugly Duckling Presse.

Gabriel, Tricia, ed. Another Kind of Record: The Merger, the Indictment & the Girl. 2008. (ENG., Illus.). 96p. pap. 30.00 *(978-0-9776481-5-3(X))* Ice Plant, The.

Gander, Ryan & Bailey, Stuart. Appendix Appendix: A Proposal for a TV Series, 1 vol. 2007. (ENG., Illus.). 160p. per. 29.00 *(978-3-905770-19-3(9))* JRP Ringier Kunstverlag AG CHE. Dist: D.A.P./Distributed Art Pubs.

Gelitin. Gelitin: das Kakabet. 2008. (ENG., Illus.). 240p. 299.00 *(978-3-86560-233-6(9))* Verlag der Buchhandlung Walther Konig DEU. Dist: D.A.P./Distributed Art Pubs.

Gerken, Jonathan. Apples I Have Eaten. 2010. (ENG., Illus.). 108p. 14.95 *(978-0-8118-7459-5(1))* Chronicle Bks. LLC.

Gersin. New Orleans Sojourn: Premiers Pas à la Nouvelle Orleans. 2011. 45.00 ***(978-1-935754-09-1(2))*** Univ. of Louisiana at Lafayette Pr.

Giralt-Miracle, Daniel & A'taio, Vicenc. Visualkultur. Cat: Art/Design/Books. 2007. (Illus.). 339p. per. *(978-84-96540-93-4(6))* Actar Birkhauser Distribution.

Green, Maureen. Papermaking at Hayle Mill 1810-1987. 2008. (Illus.). 72p. 800.00 *(978-0-9792834-1-3(8))* Janus Pr., The.

Guyton, Wade. Wade Guyton. Zeichnungen für ein großes Bild: Ausstellungskatalog Museum Ludwig Köln 23.April - 22.August 2010. 2011. (ENG., Illus.). 128p. pap. 49.95 *(978-3-86560-814-7(0))* Verlag der Buchhandlung Walther Konig DEU. Dist: D.A.P./Distributed Art Pubs.

Hale, Julie & Lark Books Staff. Masters: Book Arts: Major Works by Leading Artists. 2011. (Masters Ser.). (ENG., Illus.). 330p. pap. 24.95 *(978-1-60059-497-7(2))* Lark Bks.

Hanmer, Karen & Rogers, Bertha, comments. Book Arts 2007, Bright Hill Center. 2007. 80p. pap. 16.00 *(978-1-892471-47-5(7))* Bright Hill Pr.

Hansgen, Karen & Schellong, Rüdiger. Schmatz! Lunches at Steidl, 1 vol. 2010. (ENG., Illus.). 176p. 22.95 *(978-3-86521-911-4(X))* Steidl, Gerhard Druckerei und Verlag DEU. Dist: Innovative Logistics.

Hardy, Ed. Ed Hardy - Art of Life: Pop Culture. 2009. 19.95 *(978-3-8327-9324-1(0))* teNeues Publishing Co.

Hayuk, Maya. Just Good Vibes. 2007. (Illus.). 96p. 19.95 *(978-0-9790862-4-3(8))* Upper Playground Pubng.

Hell, Richard & Wool, Christopher. Psychopts; Richard Hell, Christopher Wool. 2008. (Illus.). 128p. 400.00 *(978-0-9795077-4-8(X))*; (ENG., pap. 45.00 *(978-0-9795077-5-5(8))* Horowitz, Glenn Bookseller, Inc.

Hermant, Sydney, et al. Aunt Maud's Scrapbook, 1 vol. 2007. (ENG., Illus.). 112p. pap. 29.00 *(978-3-905770-03-2(2))* JRP Ringier Kunstverlag AG CHE. Dist: D.A.P./Distributed Art Pubs.

Hirst, Damien. Corpus: Drawings 1981-2006. Beard, Jason, ed. aut. ed. 2008. (ENG., Illus.). 410p. 450.00 *(978-1-904212-28-7(X))* Other Criteria GBR. Dist: Hachette Bk. Group.

Hoeniger, David. Concord of Sweet Sounds: Musical Instruments in Shakespeare. 2009. (ENG., Illus.). 64p. pap. 16.95 *(978-0-88984-316-5(3))* Porcupine's Quill, Inc. CAN. Dist: Univ. of Toronto Pr.

Horrigan, Terry. Whispers. 2009. 8p. pap. 155.00 *(978-0-9762829-3-8(3))* Protean Pr.

Howard, Rachel. Can't Breathe Without You. 2008. (ENG., Illus.). 48p. 30.00 *(978-0-9545949-0-9(8))* Other Criteria GBR. Dist: Hachette Bk. Group.

—Fiction/Fear/Fact. Beard, Jason, ed. 2008. (ENG., 56p. Illus.). 50.00 *(978-1-904212-22-5(0))*; 120.00 *(978-1-904212-34-8(4))* Other Criteria GBR. Dist: Hachette Bk. Group.

Howard, Rachel & Orre, Deborah J. Can't Breathe Without You. 2008. (ENG.). 48p. 60.00 *(978-1-904212-33-1(6))* Other Criteria GBR. Dist: Hachette Bk. Group.

Isaacs, John. In Advance of the Institution. 2008. (ENG., Illus.). 188p. 140.00 *(978-1-904212-16-4(6))* Other Criteria GBR. Dist: Hachette Bk. Group.

—In Advance of the Institution. Beard, Jason, ed. 2008. (ENG.). 188p. 190.00 *(978-1-904212-29-4(8))* Other Criteria GBR. Dist: Hachette Bk. Group.

Jack Pierson: All of a Sudden. (Illus.). 192p. 175.00 *(978-1-881616-59-7(2))* D.A.P./Distributed Art Pubs.

Jacob, Luis, photos by. Luis Jacob. 7 Pictures of Nothing Repeated Four Times, In Gratitude. 2010. (ENG., Illus.). 120p. pap. 49.00 *(978-3-86560-667-9(9))* Verlag der Buchhandlung Walther Konig DEU. Dist: D.A.P./Distributed Art Pubs.

Jacob, Mary Jane & Grabner, Michelle, eds. The Studio Reader: On the Space of Artists. 2010. (ENG., Illus.). 328p. 68.00 *(978-0-226-38959-2(6))*; pap. 25.00 *(978-0-226-38961-5(8))* Univ. of Chicago Pr.

Jacques, David. Por Convencion Ferrer: The Northwest of England, Anarchosyndicalism & Time Travel. 2009. (ENG., Illus.). 128p. 39.95 *(978-1-84631-206-9(X))* Liverpool Univ. Pr. GBR. Dist: Chicago Distribution Ctr.

Johnson, Cathy. Artist's Journal Workshop: Creating Your Life in Words & Pictures. 2011. (ENG., Illus.). 144p. pap. 22.99 *(978-1-4403-0868-0(3),* North Light Bks.) F&W Media, Inc.

Johnson-Freeman, Ronda, illus. One Peace. Date not set. 49p. *(978-0-9651384-0-6(2))* Piper Rain Pr.

Jury, David, ed. Book Art Object. 2010. (ENG., Illus.). 448p. 155.00 *(978-0-9817914-0-1(9))* Codex Foundation.

K#xFC;ng, Moritz, ed. Peter Downsbrough: the Books, 1968-2010. 2011. (ENG., Illus.). 332p. 45.00 ***(978-3-7757-2833-1(3))*** Hatje Cantz Verlag GmbH & Co KG DEU. Dist: D.A.P./Distributed Art Pubs.

K#xF6;hler, Thomas, pref. Susanne Kriemann. 2011. (ENG., Illus.). 96p. 45.00 ***(978-3-86678-466-6(X))*** Kerber Verlag DEU. Dist: D.A.P./Distributed Art Pubs.

Kabakov, Ilia Iosifovich & Haldemann, Matthias. Ilya Kabakov: Künstlerbücher 1958-2009. Werkverzeichnis. 2011. (GER & ENG., Illus.). 552p. 175.00 *(978-3-86678-372-0(8))* Kerber Verlag DEU. Dist: D.A.P./Distributed Art Pubs.

Keegan, Matt & Rafferty, Sara, eds. North Drive Press: NDP No. 4, 1 vol. 2008. (ENG., Illus.). 50.00 *(978-1-933045-71-9(X))* D.A.P./Distributed Art Pubs.

Keller, Christoph, ed. Not Made Visible. 2008. (ENG., Illus.). 192p. per. 37.00 *(978-3-905770-92-6(X))* JRP Ringier Kunstverlag AG CHE. Dist: D.A.P./Distributed Art Pubs.

—Peter Piller: Nijverdal/Hellendoorn. 2008. (ENG., Illus.). 90p. 30.00 *(978-3-905770-18-6(0))* JRP Ringier Kunstverlag AG CHE. Dist: D.A.P./Distributed Art Pubs.

Keller, Christoph, et al, eds. Activity. 2011. (ENG., Illus.). 420p. pap. 39.95 *(978-3-03764-161-3(4))* JRP Ringier Kunstverlag AG CHE. Dist: D.A.P./Distributed Art Pubs.

Kelly, Ellsworth. Drawings on a Bus: Sketchbook 23, 1954, 1 vol. 2008. (ENG., Illus.). 48p. 30.00 *(978-3-86521-415-7(0))* Steidl, Gerhard Druckerei und Verlag DEU. Dist: Innovative Logistics.

Kinmont, Ben. Ben Kinmont: Prospectus 1988-2010: Forty-two Works. 2011. (ENG., Illus.). 128p. pap. 37.50 ***(978-3-03764-169-9(X))*** JRP Ringier Kunstverlag AG CHE. Dist: D.A.P./Distributed Art Pubs.

Kirby, Don, et al. Grasslands. 2009. (Illus.). 79p. ***(978-1-59005-264-8(1))*** Nazraeli Pr.

Klein, Steven, photos by. Visionaire No. 55: Surprise. 2008. (ENG., Illus.). 250.00 *(978-1-888645-75-0(X))* Visionaire Publishing.

Klein, Yves. Yves Klein: Works, Writings, Interviews. 2010. (ENG., Illus.). 160p. 45.00 *(978-84-343-1210-4(7))* Poligrafa, Ediciones, S. A. ESP. Dist: D.A.P./Distributed Art Pubs.

Kuhl, Nancy, ed. Erica Van Horn: the Book Remembers Everything. 2011. (ENG., Illus.). 122p. 20.00 *(978-1-887123-79-2(2))* Granary Bks., Inc.

La Pietra, Ugo, ed. Gio Ponti. 2009. (ENG., Illus.). 408p. 85.00 *(978-0-8478-3270-5(8))* Rizzoli International Pubns., Inc.

Lacoste, compiled by. Visionaire No. 54: Sport No. 1, Knight / Lagerfeld / Stipe. 2008. (ENG., Illus.). bds. 250.00 *(978-1-888645-70-5(9))* Visionaire Publishing.

—Visionaire No. 54: Sport No. 2, Van Lambsveerde & Matadin with M/M Paris / Demand / Byrne. 2008. (ENG., Illus.). bds. 250.00 *(978-1-888645-72-9(5))* Visionaire Publishing.

—Visionaire No. 54: Sport No. 3, Lindburgh / Ruff / Almodovar. 2008. (ENG., Illus.). bds. 250.00 *(978-1-888645-73-6(3))* Visionaire Publishing.

—Visionaire No. 54: Sport No. 4, Phillips / Wilcox / Poynter. 2008. (ENG., Illus.). bds. 250.00 *(978-1-888645-74-3(1))* Visionaire Publishing.

Laib, Wolfgang. Wolfgang Laib. 2010. (ENG.). 136p. 45.00 *(978-88-7757-243-1(4))* Hopefulmonster Editore ITA. Dist: D.A.P./Distributed Art Pubs.

Laliberte, Mark. Brickbrickbrick. 2010. (ENG., Illus.). 128p. pap. 18.00 *(978-1-897388-57-0(8))* BookThug CAN. Dist: SPD-Small Pr. Distribution.

Landert, Markus, ed. Olaf Nicolai. Mirador: Mirador. 2011. (ENG., Illus.). 80p. pap. 45.00 *(978-3-86984-033-8(1))* Verlag fur Moderne Kunst DEU. Dist: D.A.P./Distributed Art Pubs.

LeBar, Georges. Six inches Away. 2007. 52p. pap. 29.95 *(978-1-4303-2768-4(5))* Lulu Enterprises Inc.

Lee, Tim, et al. Modern Optical Experiements in Typography: Univers Ultra Light Oblique (1968), 1 vol. 2007. (ENG., Illus.). 1028p. pap. 29.00 *(978-3-905770-04-9(0))* JRP Ringier Kunstverlag AG CHE. Dist: D.A.P./Distributed Art Pubs.

Lemke, Helmut. Helmut Lemke: The Site the Sound Requires. 2009. (GER & ENG., Illus.). 120p. 48.00 *(978-3-86678-126-9(1))* Kerber Verlag DEU. Dist: D.A.P./Distributed Art Pubs.

Lewis, C. J. Power of Reflections. 2008. 44p. pap. 24.95 *(978-1-4092-2638-3(7))* Lulu Enterprises Inc.

Lintault, M. Joan. Connecting Quilts, Art & Textiles. 2008. (ENG., Illus.). 128p. per. 29.95 *(978-0-9641201-4-3(3))* Dragon Threads.

Lippy, Tod, ed. Esopus 13. 2010. (ENG., Illus.). 152p. pap. 14.00 *(978-0-9815745-2-3(1))* Esopus Foundation Ltd.

—Esopus 14: Projects. 2010. (ENG., Illus.). 200p. pap. 20.00 *(978-0-9815745-3-0(X))* Esopus Foundation Ltd.

Lister, Anthony. Tales of White Trash Prophecy. 2008. (Illus.). 96p. 19.95 *(978-1-934991-01-5(5))* Upper Playground Pubng.

Lurie, Samuel. Love & Art. 2009. (ENG.). 168p. 40.00 incl. cd-rom *(978-0-615-21834-2(2))* Eagle Art Publishing, Inc.

Lyons, Joan. Artists' Books: Visual Studies Workshop Press, 1971-2008. 2009. *(978-0-89822-126-8(9))* Visual Studies Workshop.

Maffei, Giorgio. Books by Ettore Sottsass. Maffei, Giorgio & Tonini, Bruno, eds. 2011. (ENG., Illus.). 296p. pap. 45.00 ***(978-88-7570-276-2(4))*** Corraini ITA. Dist: D.A.P./Distributed Art Pubs.

Maffei, Giorgio. Sol Lewitt: Artist's Books. Maffei, Giorgio & De Donno, Emanuele, eds. 2010. (ENG., Illus.). 144p. pap. 40.00 *(978-88-903459-2-0(6))* Corraini ITA. Dist: D.A.P./Distributed Art Pubs.

Maffei, Giorgio & Picciau, Maura, eds. The Book As A Work of Art, 1 vol. 2007. (ENG., Illus.). 160p. pap. 55.00 *(978-88-7570-037-9(0))* Corraini ITA. Dist: D.A.P./Distributed Art Pubs.

Malone, Meredith & von Lowtzow, Dirk. Cosima von Bonin: Character Appropriation. 2011. (Illus.). 48p. pap. 10.00 ***(978-0-936316-33-8(0))*** Washington Univ., Mildred Lane Kemper Art Museum.

Manghetti, Gloria & Porto, Silvia, eds. Bruciamo le biblioteche... il libro futurista nelle collezioni pubbliche Fiorentine - Album, 1909-1994. 2009. (ITA., Illus.). 92p. (C). pap. 27.00 *(978-88-596-0591-1(1))* Polistampa ITA. Dist: Brown, David Bk. Co., The.

March, Guillem. Cover Girls HC. 2012. (Illus.). 80p. 16.99 ***(978-1-60706-491-6(X))*** Image Comics.

Massey, Richard J., et al. John Newsom: Crescendo. 2012. (ENG., Illus.). 64p. 24.95 ***(978-88-8158-827-5(7))*** Charta ITA. Dist: D.A.P./Distributed Art Pubs.

McChesney, Charles. Fantasy Land. 2009. 48p. pap. 28.40 *(978-0-557-11264-7(8))* Lulu Enterprises Inc.

McClure, Nikki, illus. Things to Make & Do. 2007. (ENG.). 160p. pap. 16.95 *(978-1-57061-564-1(0))* Sasquatch Bks.

Meier, Richard. Richard Meier, Architect, Vol. 5. 2009. (ENG., Illus.). 432p. 80.00 *(978-0-8478-3069-5(1))*; pap. 55.00 *(978-0-8478-3273-6(2))* Rizzoli International Pubns., Inc.

Michener, Diana, photos by. Sweethearts, 1 vol. 2010. (ENG., Illus.). 216p. pap. 22.00 *(978-3-86521-713-4(3))* Steidl, Gerhard Druckerei und Verlag DEU. Dist: Innovative Logistics.

Miller, George Bures & Cardiff, Janet. Janet Cardiff & George Bures Miller: the Murder of Crows. 2011. (ENG., Illus.). 112p. 60.00 ***(978-3-7757-3177-5(6))*** Hatje Cantz Verlag GmbH & Co KG DEU. Dist: D.A.P./Distributed Art Pubs.

Minsky, Richard. The Book Art of Richard Minsky. 2011. (ENG., Illus.). 148p. 34.95 *(978-0-8076-1606-2(0),* 761606) Braziller, George Inc.

Moireau, Fabrice. Loire Sketchbook. Date not set. pap. *(978-0-312-31935-9(5))*; mass mkt. *(978-0-312-99250-7(5))* St. Martin's Pr. (St. Martin's Paperbacks).

Moreno, Felicidad. Felicidad Moreno, 1 vol. 2007. (ENG., Illus.). 212p. 40.00 *(978-84-7506-761-2(1))* Turner, Ediciones S.A. ESP. Dist: D.A.P./Distributed Art Pubs.

Morstad, Julie. Milk Teeth. 2011. (ENG., Illus.). 104p. pap. 16.95 *(978-1-897299-45-6(1))* Drawn & Quarterly Pubns. CAN. Dist: Macmillan.

Multiple. Transfer - Feininger zeichnet: Hommage an einen großen Künstler und Weltbürger. Homage to a great artist & cosmopolitan. 2009. (ENG.). 120p. pap. 29.95 *(978-3-939964-31-5(X),* Art Stock Bks. Ltd/Csi) Continental Sales, Inc.

Munder, Heike, ed. Henrik Olesen: Some Faggy Gestures. 2009. (ENG., Illus.). 198p. pap. 59.00 *(978-3-905829-46-4(0))* JRP Ringier Kunstverlag AG CHE. Dist: D.A.P./Distributed Art Pubs.

Noble, Tim & Webster, Sue. Polymorphous Perverse. 2008. (ENG., Illus.). 56p. 75.00 *(978-1-904212-24-9(7))* Other Criteria GBR. Dist: Hachette Bk. Group.

—Polymorphous Perverse. Beard, Jason, ed. aut. ed. 2008. (ENG., Illus.). 56p. 130.00 *(978-1-904212-39-3(5))* Other Criteria GBR. Dist: Hachette Bk. Group.

Nunez, Jose Arturo Rodriguez. Four Decades of Books & Publications of Spanish Artists. Ortiz, Diego, ed. 2008. 272p. pap. *(978-84-96933-15-6(6))* Actar Birkhauser Distribution.

Oino, Espen. Luxury Toys Mega Yachts. 2008. 1300.00 *(978-3-8327-9253-4(8))* teNeues Publishing Co.

Oldfield Ford, Laura. Savage Messiah. 2011. (ENG., Illus.). 464p. pap. 29.95 *(978-1-84467-747-4(8),* 844747) Verso Bks. GBR. Dist: Norton, W. W. & Co., Inc.

Ono, Yoko. The Other Rooms. 2010. (ENG., Illus.). 252p. 39.95 *(978-88-8158-755-1(6))* Charta ITA. Dist: D.A.P./Distributed Art Pubs.

Parkett, compiled by. Art Works - 25 Years: The 200 Editions Made for Parkett since 1984. 2009. (ENG., Illus.). 517p. pap. 45.00 *(978-3-907582-25-1(X))* Parkett Verlag AG CHE. Dist: D.A.P./Distributed Art Pubs.

Parr, Martin & Badger, Gerry. The Photobook Vol. 2, Vol. 2. rev. ed. 2006. (ENG., Illus.). 336p. 90.00 *(978-0-7148-4433-6(0))* Phaidon Pr., Inc.

Past, Ambar, ed. Incantations: Songs, Spells & Images by Mayan Women. 2009. (ENG., Illus.). 230p. pap. 26.95 *(978-1-933693-09-5(6))* Cinco Puntos Pr.

Pestriniero, Renato, text. Faces (boxed set W/CD) Volti Truccati Del Carnevale Veneziano. 2006. (ENG.). 180p. 90.00 *(978-88-7200-214-8(1))* Vianello Libri ITA. Dist: National Bk. Network.

Pisano, Falke & text. Figures of Speech: Falke Pisano. 2010. (ENG., Illus.). 144p. pap. 39.95 *(978-3-03764-110-1(X))* JRP Ringier Kunstverlag AG CHE. Dist: D.A.P./Distributed Art Pubs.

Plunkett, S. The World of a Wayward Comic Book Artist: The Private Sketchbooks of S. Plunkett. 2010. (ENG.). 224p. 55.00 *(978-0-8040-1124-2(9))*; pap. 24.95 *(978-0-8040-1125-9(7))* Swallow Pr.

Prince, Richard. Richard Prince: 3rd Place. 2008. (ENG., Illus.). 82p. pap. 30.00 *(978-3-86560-492-7(7))* Verlag der Buchhandlung Walther Konig DEU. Dist: D.A.P./Distributed Art Pubs.

Prince, Richard, illus. Lynn Valley, 1 vol. 2007. (ENG.). 46p. pap. 35.00 *(978-0-920293-72-0(7))* Verlag der Buchhandlung Walther Konig DEU. Dist: D.A.P./Distributed Art Pubs.

Productions, Platte. Amazing Pencil Portraits. 2009. 80p. pap. 34.99 *(978-0-557-13322-2(X))* Lulu Enterprises Inc.

Reeves, Keanu. Ode to Happiness. 2011. (ENG., Illus.). 40p. 55.00 *(978-3-86930-209-6(7))* Steidl, Gerhard Druckerei und Verlag DEU. Dist: Innovative Logistics.

Rogers, Bertha & Smith, Keith A. Book Arts 2008, Bright Hill Center. 2008. 80p. pap. 16.00 *(978-1-892471-56-7(6))* Bright Hill Pr.

Roma, Thomas, photos by. Pictures for Books: Photographs by Thomas Roma, 1 vol. 2010. (ENG., Illus.). 136p. pap. 35.00 *(978-1-884919-25-1(1))* Columbia Univ., The Miriam & Ira D. Wallach Art Gallery.

Roth, Andrew & Aarons, Philip, eds. In Numbers. 2010. (ENG., Illus.). 504p. 90.00 *(978-3-03764-085-2(5))* JRP Ringier Kunstverlag AG CHE. Dist: D.A.P./Distributed Art Pubs.

Rothman, Julia, et al. The Exquisite Book: 100 Artists Play a Collaborative Game. 2010. (ENG., Illus.). 144p. 29.95 *(978-0-8118-7090-0(1))* Chronicle Bks. LLC.

Ruf, Beatrix, ed. General Idea: FILE Megazine. 2008. (ENG., Illus.). 2024p. 280.00 *(978-3-905829-21-1(5))* JRP Ringier Kunstverlag AG CHE. Dist: D.A.P./Distributed Art Pubs.

Runge, Gailen. A Beginner's Guide to Creating Beautiful Board Books: Inspiration, Instruction, Ideas. 2007. *(978-1-57120-424-0(5))* C & T Publishing.

Ryan, Rob. This Is for You. 2009. (ENG.). 64p. 16.95 *(978-0-8118-6841-9(9))* Chronicle Bks. LLC.

—This Is for You. 2007. (ENG., Illus.). 64p. *(978-0-340-93367-1(4),* Hodder & Stoughton) Hodder General Publishing Div. GBR. Dist: Independent Pubs. Group.

Salamony, Sandra, et al. 1,000 Artists' Books: A Showcase of Fine Hand-Bound Structures. 2012. (1000 Ser.). (ENG., Illus.). 320p. pap. 25.00 ***(978-1-59253-774-7(X),*** 159253774X) Quayside.

Schorr, Collier, photos by. Blumen, 1 vol. 2010. (ENG., Illus.). 102p. 50.00 *(978-3-86521-687-8(0))* Steidl, Gerhard Druckerei und Verlag DEU. Dist: Innovative Logistics.

Scott, Sam. Encounters with Beauty: Excerpts from an Artist's Journal, 1963-2006. 2007. (ENG., Illus.). 120p. 35.00 *(978-0-9679034-4-6(0))* Fresco Fine Art Pubns., LLC.

Shabout, Nada M. Dafatir: Contemporary Iraqi Book Art. 2007. pap. *(978-1-889886-08-4(4))* Univ. of North Texas Art Gallery.

Sharbonno, Riley & Rezac, Matthew, texts. Monica Haller: Riley & His Story. 2009. (ENG., Illus.). 480p. 55.00 *(978-2-915359-38-1(5))* Onestar Pr. FRA. Dist: D.A.P./Distributed Art Pubs.

Simpson, Jane & Groos, Ulrike. Jane Simpson: Fresh Fresher. Beard, Jason, ed. 2008. (ENG., Illus.). 104p. 45.00 *(978-1-904212-01-0(8))* Other Criteria GBR. Dist: Hachette Bk. Group.

Slade, Kathy, ed. Andrew Dadson: Visible Heavens From 1850-2008. 2008. (ENG., Illus.). 168p. 35.00 *(978-3-905829-68-6(1))* JRP Ringier Kunstverlag AG CHE. Dist: D.A.P./Distributed Art Pubs.

—Selected Standards: Euan MacDonald. 2008. (ENG., Illus.). 176p. pap. 30.00 *(978-3-905770-80-3(6))* JRP Ringier Kunstverlag AG CHE. Dist: D.A.P./Distributed Art Pubs.

Sligh & Sligh, Clarissa T. Wrongly Bodied: Documenting Transition from Female to Male. 2009. (Illus.). 159p. *(978-1-60743-932-5(8))* Independent Pub.

Smets, Coen. Zimmer Frei! 2010. 92p. pap. *(978-3-8383-7396-6(0))* Lambert Academic Publishing.

Smith, Michael. Baby Ikki at the Museum. 2012. (ENG., Illus.). 26p. 9.95 ***(978-0-300-18104-3(3))*** Yale Univ. Pr.

Smith, Ray & Dorling Kindersley Publishing Staff. Artist's Handbook. 3rd ed. 2009. (ENG.). 384p. pap. 21.95 *(978-0-7566-5722-2(9))* Dorling Kindersley Publishing, Inc.

Sorensen, Bodil & Hellesen, Sidsel. Rolf Nesch: The Complete Graphic Works. 2009. (ENG., Illus.). 584p. 280.00 *(978-88-572-0051-4(5))* Skira Editore ITA. Dist: Random Hse., Inc.

Starr, Sean. The Artist's Tao: 44 Principles for an Artist's Life. 2008. (Illus.). 100p. pap. 9.99 *(978-0-9799194-1-1(X))* Subculture Bks.

Stern Fotografie Portfolio 48. Mark Seliger. 2007. (Illus.). 94p. per. 22.95 *(978-3-570-19734-9(4))* teNeues Publishing Co.

Stewart, Garrett. Bookwork: Medium to Object to Concept to Art. 2011. (ENG., Illus.). 272p. 65.00 *(978-0-226-77391-9(4))* Univ. of Chicago Pr.

Tan, Fiona. Fiona Tan, Vox Populi: Switzerland. 2011. (ENG, FRE, GER & ITA., Illus.). 125p. pap. ***(978-1-906012-28-1(8))*** Book Works.

Testa, Melanie. Dreaming from the Journal Page: Transforming the Sketchbook to Art. 2012. (ENG., Illus.). 128p. pap. 24.99 ***(978-1-4403-1434-6(9)***, North Light Bks.) F&W Media, Inc.

Thomas, Peter & Thomas, Donna. More Making Books by Hand: Exploring Miniature Books, Alternative Structures, & Found Objects. 2007. (Illus.). 142p. pap. 19.00 *(978-1-4223-6592-2(1))* DIANE Publishing Co.

Thompson, Matthew, text. Kris Martin: Idiot. 2009. (ENG., Illus.). 1496p. pap. 15.00 *(978-0-934324-45-8(X))* Aspen Art Museum.

Trefonides, Steven. Trefonides Sketchbooks: Paris & Brussels 1986. 2008. (Illus.). 110p. 45.54 *(978-0-929228-10-5(3))* Static Image Pr.

—Trefonides Sketchbooks: Paris & Brussels 1986. 2008. (Illus.). 110p. pap. 40.75 *(978-0-929228-11-2(1))* Static Image Pr.

Trout. Diana. Journal Spilling: Mixed-Media Techniques for Free Expression. 2009. (ENG., Illus.). 128p. pap. 22.99 *(978-1-60061-319-7(5)*, North Light Bks.) F&W Media, Inc.

Upper Playground, creator. Upper Playground, Volume 1. 2007. (Illus.). 19.95 *(978-0-9790862-2-9(1))* Upper Playground Pubng.

Ursprung, Philip, text. Jürgen Mayer H. Wirrwarr. 2011. (ENG., Illus.). 216p. 300.00 *(978-3-7757-2779-2(5))* Hatje Cantz Verlag GmbH & Co KG DEU. Dist: D.A.P./Distributed Art Pubs.

Violette. Journal Bliss: Creative Prompts to Unleash Your Inner Eccentric. 2009. (ENG., Illus.). 128p. pap. 22.99 *(978-1-60061-189-6(3)*, North Light Bks.) F&W Media, Inc.

Visionaire, ed. Visionaire No. 56: Solar. 2009. (ENG., Illus.). 28p. 250.00 *(978-1-888645-77-4(6))* Visionaire Publishing.

Von Szombathy, Chris. Fire Away. 2008. (ENG., Illus.). 96p. pap. *(978-1-897299-49-4(4))* Drawn & Quarterly Pubns.

Vorkoeper, Ute, ed. Anna Oppermann Ensembles 1968-1992, 1 vol. 2007. (ENG., Illus.). 288p. pap. 50.00 *(978-3-7757-1995-7(4))* Hatje Cantz Verlag GmbH & Co KG DEU. Dist: D.A.P./Distributed Art Pubs.

Vuitton, Louis. Louis Vuitton: Art, Fashion & Architecture. 2009. (ENG., Illus.). 404p. 85.00 *(978-0-8478-3338-2(0))* Rizzoli International Pubns., Inc.

Walker, Nick. A Sequence of Events. 2009. (Illus.). 96p. pap. 29.00 *(978-88-88493-46-6(8))* Drago Arts & Communication ITA. Dist: SCB Distributors.

Wasserman, Krystyna. The Book As Art: Artists' Books from the National Museum of Women in the Arts. 2nd ed. 2006. (ENG., Illus.). 208p. 55.00 *(978-1-56898-609-8(2))* Princeton Architectural Pr.

—The Book As Art: Artists' Books from the National Museum of Women in the Arts. 2nd ed. 2011. (ENG., Illus.). 208p. pap. 34.95 *(978-1-56898-992-1(X))* Princeton Architectural Pr.

Weber, Bruce, et al. Visionaire # 49: Decades, 1 vol. 2006. (ENG., Illus.). 125p. lthr. 175.00 *(978-1-888645-59-0(8))* Visionaire Publishing.

Weiner, Lawrence. Lawrence Weiner: Something to put something On, 1 vol. 2008. (ENG., Illus.). 44p. (J). 35.00 *(978-3-86521-491-1(6))* Steidl, Gerhard Druckerei und Verlag DEU. Dist: Innovative Logistics.

Weiner, Lawrence & text. Henry the navigator in a sea of sand/enrique el navegante en un mar de Arena. 2006. (ENG & SPA., Illus.). 48p. pap. 40.00 *(978-1-883597-05-4(6))* Markey, Lawrence Inc.

Westwood, Martin. Martin Westwood. Beard, Jason, ed. aut. ed. 2008. (ENG.). 88p. pap. 95.00 *(978-1-904212-09-6(3))* Other Criteria GBR. Dist: Hachette Bk. Group.

Whiting, Lindsay. Living into Art: Journeys Through Collage. 2008. (Illus.). 192p. pap. 24.95 *(978-0-615-18294-0(1))* Paper Lantern.

Wiehager, Renate, ed. Charlotte Posenenske. 2009. (ENG., Illus.). 216p. 85.00 *(978-3-7757-2363-3(3))* Hatje Cantz Verlag GmbH & Co KG DEU. Dist: D.A.P./Distributed Art Pubs.

Woodman, Francesca, photos by. Francesca Woodman's Notebook. 2011. (ENG., Illus.). 24p. pap. 49.95 ***(978-88-366-2117-0(1))*** Silvana ITA. Dist: D.A.P./Distributed Art Pubs.

Yilmaz, Dziewior & Laure, Hoptman, eds. The Art of Tomorrow. 2010. (GER & ENG., Illus.). 340p. 60.00 *(978-3-89955-406-9(X))* Die Gestalten Verlag DEU. Dist: Prestel Publishing.

ARTISTS' ILLUSTRATED BOOKS

Here are entered works about books richly illustrated with original prints by well known artists and published in limited editions. Books which are produced by artists and intended as visual art objects as well as works about such books are entered under Artists' Books.

Afanador, Ruven. Mil Besos: One Thousand Kisses. 2009. (ENG., Illus.). 240p. 75.00 *(978-0-8478-3339-9(9))* Rizzoli International Pubns., Inc.

Andre, Thomas & Laqua, Carsten. The Life & Times of Walt Kelly. 2009. (Illus.). 208p. 49.99 *(978-1-932563-05-4(9))* Hermes Pr.

Dubia, Christopher. Welcome Home. num. ed. 2006. (ENG., Illus.). 72p. per. 30.00 *(978-0-9787480-0-5(X))* Bonnacon Pr.

Enaday, Imelda Cajipe. Society of Philippine American Artist Book 2: Selected Works. 2009. *(978-1-61584-052-6(4))* Independent Pub.

Endaya, Imelda Cajipe-, ed. Society of Phillippine American Artists Book 2: Selected Wroks. 2009. pap. *(978-1-61623-680-9(9))* Independent Pub.

Fryer, Paul. Radiations. Beard, Jason, ed. 2008. (Illus.). 96p. (ENG.). 70.00 *(978-1-904212-19-5(0))*; 120.00 *(978-1-904212-38-6(7))* Other Criteria GBR. Dist: Hachette Bk. Group, Abrams.

Gardner, Mark, et al. Habits, Patterns, Algorithms, 1998-2008. Ojeda, Oscar, ed. 2009. (ENG., Illus.). 424p. 75.00 *(978-0-9795395-2-7(8))* Oro Editions.

Gordon, Kim. Performing - Guzzling. 2010. (ENG., Illus.). 144p. 60.00 *(978-0-8478-3341-2(0))* Rizzoli International Pubns., Inc.

Hoy, Anne, et al. The Best of Both Worlds: Finely Printed Livres D'artistes, 1910-2010. 2011. (Illus.). 192p. 45.00 *(978-1-56792-431-2(X))* Godine, David R. Pub.

Janjigian, Robert & Corzine, Nancy. Glamour at Home. 2009. (Illus.). 224p. 50.00 *(978-0-8478-3340-5(2))* Rizzoli International Pubns., Inc.

Llorca, Enriqueta, contrib. by. 6am. 2010. 124p. 29.95 *(978-84-613-7605-6(6))* Ico López-Rienda ESP. Dist: Actar Birkhauser Distribution.

Manco, Tristan. Street Sketchbook: Journeys. 2010. (ENG.). 272p. 35.00 *(978-0-8118-7728-2(0))* Chronicle Bks. LLC.

Margiela, Maison Martin. Maison Martin Margiela. 2009. (ENG., Illus.). 368p. 100.00 *(978-0-8478-3188-3(4))* Rizzoli International Pubns., Inc.

Moore, Derry, photos by. In House. 2009. (Illus.). 256p. 60.00 *(978-0-8478-3349-8(6))* Rizzoli International Pubns., Inc.

Munder, Heike, ed. & text. Tadeusz Kantor, 1 vol. 2009. (ENG.). 156p. 55.00 *(978-3-03764-022-7(7))* JRP Ringier Kunstverlag AG CHE. Dist: D.A.P./Distributed Art Pubs.

Ortiz, Luis. Outermost: The Art & Life of Jack Gaughan. 2010. (ENG., Illus.). 176p. 39.95 *(978-1-933065-16-8(8))* Nonstop Pr.

Pittel, Christine & Kasler, Suzanne. Inspired Interiors. 2009. (ENG., Illus.). 224p. 50.00 *(978-0-8478-3220-0(1))* Rizzoli International Pubns., Inc.

Prats, Fernando & Ruibal, Miguel. Objects Subjects. 2009. 40p. pap. 19.95 *(978-1-4452-1060-5(6))* Lulu Enterprises Inc.

Rabin, Randy & Bassett, Jackie. Drawing on Brilliance. 2009. 176p. pap. 39.95 *(978-1-4389-9223-5(8))* AuthorHouse.

Ranalli, George. George Ranalli: Saratoga. Ojeda, Oscar Riera, ed. 2009. (ENG., Illus.). 112p. 29.95 *(978-0-9814628-8-2(X))* Oro Editions.

Richardson, John, et al, contrib. by. Picasso Mosqueteros: The Late Works, 1962-1972. 2009. (ENG., Illus.). 300p. 100.00 *(978-0-8478-3299-6(6))* Rizzoli International Pubns., Inc.

Riera Ojeda, Oscar, ed. Peter Forbes: Seal Harbor. 2008. (Illus.). 112p. 25.00 *(978-0-9795395-4-1(4))* Oro Editions.

Roth, Dieter. Dieter Roth: The Rings of Dieter Roth. 2010. 144p. pap. 22.00 *(978-3-907474-33-4(3))* Periferia, Edizioni, Poschiavo / Lucerna CHE. Dist: D.A.P./Distributed Art Pubs.

Roth, Dieter & text. Dieter Roth, Inserate: Advertisements 1971-1972. 2010. (ENG., Illus.). 280p. pap. 19.00 *(978-3-907474-77-8(5))* Periferia, Edizioni, Poschiavo / Lucerna CHE. Dist: D.A.P./Distributed Art Pubs.

Scheibitz, Thomas. Film, Music & Novel. Beard, Jason, ed. 2008. (ENG., 256p. Illus.). 100.00 *(978-1-904212-11-9(5))*; 155.00 *(978-1-904212-35-5(2))* Other Criteria GBR. Dist: Hachette Bk. Group.

Simpson, Jane & Groos, Ulrike. Fresh, Fresher. Beard, Jason, ed. 2008. (ENG.). 104p. pap. 90.00 *(978-1-904212-36-2(0))* Other Criteria GBR. Dist: Hachette Bk. Group.

Smith, Valerie, et al, texts. Generation 1. 5. 2009. (ENG., Illus.). 176p. 24.95 *(978-1-929641-13-0(3))* Queens Museum of Art.

Stosuy, Brandon, ed. Mirror Me. 2010. (ENG., Illus.). 174p. pap. 12.00 *(978-0-9788697-7-9(X))* Primary Information.

Tait, Neal. Neal Tait. 2008. (ENG., Illus.). 176p. pap. 100.00 *(978-1-904212-08-9(5))* Other Criteria GBR. Dist: Hachette Bk. Group.

—Neal Tait. Beard, Jason, ed. 2008. (ENG.). 176p. pap. 155.00 *(978-1-904212-43-0(3))* Other Criteria GBR. Dist: Hachette Bk. Group.

Trachtenberg, Amy. Amy Trachtenberg: Groundwork. 2008. (ENG., Illus.). 64p. pap. 16.95 *(978-0-9814628-0-6(4))* Oro Editions.

Van Eeghen, Hester & Gannij, Joan. Bag & Shoe Design. 2009. (ENG., Illus.). 160p. 49.00 *(978-90-6369-199-8(8))* Bis B.V., Uitgeverij(BIS Publishers) NLD. Dist: Consortium Bk. Sales & Distribution.

ARTISTS IN LITERATURE

Betjemann, Peter. Talking Shop: The Language of Craft in an Age of Consumption. 2011. (Illus.). ix, 267p. E-Book *(978-0-8139-3169-2(X))*; (ENG., 280p. (gr. 17). 35.00 *(978-0-8139-3121-0(5))* Univ. Pr. of Virginia.

Binding, Paul. With Vine-Leaves in His Hair: The Role of the Artist in Ibsen's Plays. 2007. (NOR & ENG.). 230p. per. 42.95 *(978-1-870041-67-6(4))* Norvik Pr. GBR. Dist: Dufour Editions, Inc.

Birkner, Nina. Vom Genius zum Medienästheten: Modelle des Kanstlerdramas im 20. Jahrhundert. 2009. (Studien zur deutschen Literatur Ser.).Tr. of From Genius to Media Aesthete. Models of the Kanstlerdrama in the 20th Century. (GER.). VII, 306p. 168.00 ***(978-3-11-173197-1(9))*** De Gruyter, Walter Inc.

Birkner, Nina. Vom Genius zum Medienästheten: Modelle des Künstlerdramas im 20. Jahrhundert. 2009. (Studien zur deutschen Literatur Ser.).Tr. of From Genius to Media Aesthete. Models of the Kanstlerdrama in the 20th Century. (GER.). VII, 306p. pap. *(978-3-484-18192-2(3))* Verlag Max Niemeyer.

Brams, Koen, ed. The Encyclopedia of Fictional Artists, 2 vols. 2011. (ENG., Illus.). 700p. pap. 55.00 *(978-3-03764-123-1(1))* JRP Ringier Kunstverlag AG CHE. Dist: D.A.P./Distributed Art Pubs.

Demel, Julie Anne. Die Kunst: ein Entwurf zur Welt: Ein Vergleich zwischen den Werken Alte Meister von Thomas Bernhard und Schlafes Bruder von Robert Schneider. 2009. (Europäische Hochschulschriften. Reihe 1: Deutsche Sprache und Literatur Ser.). (GER.). 154p. pap. 49.95 *(978-3-631-58374-6(5))* Lang, Peter GmbH, Europaischer Verlag der Wissenschaften DEU. Dist: Lang, Peter.

Doll, Eileen J. El Papel Del Artista en la Dramaturgia de Jerónimo López Mozo: Juegos Temporales e Intermediales. 2008. (SPA.). 205p. pap. 29.80 *(978-84-8489-427-8(4))* Iberoamericana Vervuert Publishing Corp.

Gibson, William. Art & Money in the Writings of Tobias Smollett. 2006. (Bucknell Studies in Eighteenth-Century Literature & Culture). (Illus.). (C). *(978-0-8387-5637-9(9))* Bucknell Univ. Pr.

McLaren, Stephen. Reframing 'A Portrait of the Artist' James Joyce's Evolution in Design. 2010. (ENG.). 256p. 74.95 *(978-1-84519-313-3(X))* Sussex Academic Pr. GBR. Dist: International Specialized Bk. Services.

Parker, Fred. The Devil as Muse: Blake, Byron, & the Adversary. 2011. (Making of the Christian Imagination Ser.). (ENG., Illus.). 215p. 29.95 *(978-1-60258-269-9(6))* Baylor Univ. Pr.

Potter, Martin / Gabriel. Three Great Artists Reflecting on the Spiritual Purpose of Art: A Study of Goethe's Wilhelm Meisters Lehrjahre, Keller's der Grune Heinrich, & Thomas Mann's Doktor Faustus. 2009. vii, 301p. *(978-0-7734-3854-5(8))* Mellen, Edwin Pr., The.

ARTISTS' MARKS

Benezit, Emmanuel. Benezit Dictionnaire des Peintres, Sculpteurs, Dessinateurs, et Graveurs, 14 vols. 2010. (ENG., Illus.). 13440p. 2995.00 *(978-0-19-977379-4(3))* Oxford Univ. Pr., Inc.

Castagno, John. Abstract Artists: Signatures & Monograms, an International Directory. 2007. (ENG., Illus.). 496p. 275.00 *(978-0-8108-5897-8(5))* Scarecrow Pr., Inc.

—American Artists II: Signatures & Monograms from 1800. 2007. (ENG.). 548p. 275.00 *(978-0-8108-5895-4(9))* Scarecrow Pr., Inc.

—American Artists III: Signatures & Monograms from 1800. 2009. (ENG.). 596p. 250.00 *(978-0-8108-6382-8(0))* Scarecrow Pr., Inc.

—Artists' Monograms & Indiscernible Signatures II: An International Directory from 1800. 2007. (ENG.). 308p. 200.00 *(978-0-8108-5898-5(3))* Scarecrow Pr., Inc.

—Artists' Monograms & Indiscernible Signatures III: An International Directory from 1800. 2009. (ENG.). 232p. 150.00 *(978-0-8108-6383-5(9))* Scarecrow Pr., Inc.

—Australian, British & Irish Artists: Signatures & Monograms from 1800. 2009. (ENG.). 524p. 225.00 *(978-0-8108-6384-2(7))* Scarecrow Pr., Inc.

—European Artists II: Signatures & Monograms from 1800: A Comprehensive Directory. 2007. (ENG., Illus.). 416p. 250.00 *(978-0-8108-5896-1(7))* Scarecrow Pr., Inc.

—Old Masters II: Signatures & Monograms. 2009. (ENG.). 152p. 125.00 *(978-0-8108-6385-9(5))* Scarecrow Pr., Inc.

LeBlanc, Steven A. & Henderson, Lucia R. Symbols in Clay: Seeking Artists' Identities in Hopi Yellow Ware Bowls. 2009. (Papers of the Peabody Museum Ser.: 84). (Illus.). 184p. pap. 35.00 *(978-0-87365-212-4(6))* Peabody Museum of Archaeology & Ethnology, Harvard Univ., Pubns. Dept.

Van De Velde, Ronny. Artists' Handbook: George Wittenborn's Guestbook, with 21st Century Additions. 2008. (ENG.). 624p. (C). 125.00 *(978-90-5544-719-0(6))* Ludion BEL. Dist: D.A.P./Distributed Art Pubs.

ARTISTS' MATERIALS

see also Plastics As Art Material

Altavilla, Claudia & Ciliberto, Enrico. Cultural Heritage Materials: An XPS Approach. 2011. (Materials Science & Technologies Ser.). 78p. pap. 47.00 ***(978-1-61324-651-1(X))*** Nova Science Pubs., Inc.

Carlyle, Leslie. The Artist's Assistant: Oil Painting Instruction Manuals & Handbooks in Britain, 1800-1900 with Reference to Selected Eighteenth Century Sources. 2007. (ENG., Illus.). 590p. 180.00 *(978-1-873132-16-6(6))* Archetype Pubns. GBR. Dist: National Bk. Network.

Clarke, Mark. The Art of All Colours: Mediaeval Recipe Books for Painters & Illuminators. 2007. (ENG., Illus.). 152p. pap. 50.00 *(978-1-873132-72-2(7))* Archetype Pubns. GBR. Dist: National Bk. Network.

Corbeil, Marie-Claude, et al. Jean Paul Riopelle: The Artist's Materials. 2011. (ENG., Illus.). 96p. pap. 40.00 ***(978-1-60606-086-5(4)***, Getty Conservation Institute, The) Getty Pubns.

Crabtree, Susan & Beudert, Peter. Scenic Art for the Theatre. 3rd ed. 2011. (ENG., Illus.). 448p. pap. 49.95 ***(978-0-240-81290-8(5)***, Focal Pr.) Elsevier Science & Technology Bks.

Fuga, Antonella. Artists' Techniques & Materials. 2006. (Guide to Imagery Ser.). (Illus.). 384p. pap. 24.95 *(978-0-89236-860-0(8))* Oxford Univ. Pr., Inc.

Haus, Andreas, et al. Material IM Prozess: Strategien Aesthetischer Produktivitaet. (GER & ENG., Illus.). 301p. *(978-3-496-01227-6(7))* Reimer, Dietrich.

Hermens, Erma & Townsend, Joyce. Sources & Serendipity: Testimonies of Artists' Practice. 2010. (ENG., Illus.). 208p. pap. 75.00 *(978-1-904982-52-4(2))* Archetype Pubns. GBR. Dist: National Bk. Network.

Heydenreich, Gunnar. Lucas Cranach the Elder: Painting Materials, Techniques & Workshop Practice. 2007. (Illus.). 464p. pap. *(978-90-5356-745-6(3)*, Leiden Univ. Pr.) Amsterdam Univ. Pr.

Jaitly, Jaya. Crafting Nature - Incredible India. (Illus.). 102p. 34.95 *(978-81-8328-070-9(6))* Wisdom Tree IND. Dist: SCB Distributors.

Krug, Margaret. An Artist's Handbook: Materials & Techniques. 2012. (ENG., Illus.). 256p. pap. 24.95 ***(978-1-85669-523-7(9))*** King, Laurence Publishing GBR. Dist: Hachette Bk. Group.

Lake, Susan F. Willem de Kooning: The Artist's Materials. 2010. (ENG., Illus.). 112p. pap. 40.00 *(978-1-60606-021-6(X)*, Getty Conservation Institute, The) Getty Pubns.

Learner, Tom, et al. From Start to Finish: De Wain Valentine's Gray Column. 2011. ***(978-0-9834922-1-4(2)***, Getty Conservation Institute, The) Getty Pubns.

Marley, Christopher. Pheromone: The Insect Artwork of Christopher Marley. 2008. (Illus.). 256p. 75.00 *(978-0-7649-4619-6(6))* Pomegranate Communications, Inc.

Michel, Karen. Green Guide for Artists: Nontoxic Recipes, Green Art Ideas, & Resources for the Eco-Conscious Artist. 2009. (ENG., Illus.). 128p. pap. 22.99 *(978-1-59253-518-7(6)*, 1592535186) Quayside.

Ouwerkerk, Annemick & Costaras, Nicola, eds. Looking Through Paintings: The Study of Painting Techniques & Materials in Support of Art Historical Research. 2007. (Leids Kunsthistorisch Jaarboek Ser.). (ENG., Illus.). 520p. 190.00 *(978-1-876132-56-9(6))* Archetype Pubns. GBR. Dist: National Bk. Network.

Pickering Rothamel, Susan. The Art of Paper Collage. 2008. (ENG., Illus.). 132p. pap. 17.95 *(978-1-4027-5613-9(5)*, Chapelle) Sterling Publishing Co., Inc.

Pogue, Dwight W. Printmaking Revolution: New Advancements in Technology, Safety, & Sustainability. 2012. (ENG., Illus.). 240p. 40.00 ***(978-0-8230-0812-4(6))*** Watson-Guptill Pubns., Inc.

Roccaforte, Marianne. Bridges in the Mind: An Artist's Handbook for Everyday Living. 2010. 216p. pap. 16.95 *(978-0-9815163-5-6(1))* Benu Pr.

Roy, Ashok. National Gallery Technical Bulletin, Vol. 28. 2007. (National Gallery Technical Bulletin Ser.). (ENG., Illus.). 96p. pap. 70.00 *(978-1-85709-372-8(0))* Yale Univ. Pr.

Roy, Ashok, ed. The National Gallery Technical Bulletin, Vol. 29. 2009. (ENG., Illus.). 80p. pap. 70.00 *(978-1-85709-419-0(0))* Yale Univ. Pr.

Simpson, Pamela H. Corn Palaces & Butter Queens: A History of Crop Art & Dairy Sculpture. 2012. (Illus.). 264p. 90.00 ***(978-0-8166-7619-4(4))***; pap. 29.95 ***(978-0-8166-7620-0(8))*** Univ. of Minnesota Pr.

Son, Kyong-Suk. Tongyang Hoehwa Ui Chaeryo Wa Kipop. 2010. (KOR., Illus.). 218p. pap. *(978-89-26-81145-0(X))*; E-Book *(978-89-26-81146-7(8))* Korean Studies Information Co., Ltd.

Stephenson, Jonathan. Paint with the Impressionists: Their Methods & Materials for Today's Artists. 2010. (ENG., Illus.). 160p. pap. 19.95 *(978-0-500-28878-8(X)*, 528878) Thames & Hudson.

—Paint with the Watercolor Masters. 2010. (ENG., Illus.). 160p. pap. 19.95 *(978-0-500-28879-5(8)*, 528879) Thames & Hudson.

Takahashi, Kaoru, ed. Design Texture: Unique Materials & Finishes for Graphic Design. 2010. (ENG & JPN., Illus.). 192p. 75.00 *(978-4-7562-4021-7(6)*, PIE Bks.) Rizzoli International Pubns., Inc.

Tauchid, Rheni. New Acrylics Essential Sourcebook: Materials, Techniques & Contemporary Applications for Today's Artist. 2009. (ENG., Illus.). 192p. pap. 24.95 *(978-0-8230-9926-9(1))* Watson-Guptill Pubns., Inc.

Tung, Lisa & Zaug, Chloé. "Crafty" Elaine Bradford, Nick Cave, Rob Conger ... 2007. (Illus.). 75p. *(978-0-9771419-2-0(6))* Massachusetts College of Art.

van de Wetering, Ernst. Rembrandt: The Painter at Work. 2nd rev. ed. 2009. (ENG.). 354p. pap. 41.95 *(978-0-520-25884-6(3))* Univ. of California Pr.

Van De Wettering. Rembrandt. 2009. (Illus.). 356p. pap. *(978-90-8964-033-8(9))* Amsterdam Univ. Pr.

Ward, Gerald W. R. The Grove Encyclopedia of Materials & Techniques in Art. 2008. (ENG., Illus.). 864p. 160.00 *(978-0-19-531391-8(7))* Oxford Univ. Pr., Inc.

Waterfield, Giles, ed. The Artist's Studio. 2010. (Illus.). 128p. pap. 30.00 *(978-0-9554063-3-1(1))* Univ. of Washington Pr.

Zhijie, Qiu, et al. A Question of Evidence. 2009. (ENG., Illus.). 190p. pap. 32.00 *(978-3-86560-569-6(9))* Verlag der Buchhandlung Walther Konig DEU. Dist: D.A.P./Distributed Art Pubs.

ARTISTS' MODELS

Allard, Sebastien, et al. Citizens & Kings: Portraits in the Age of Enlightenment. 2007. (ENG., Illus.). 368p. 85.00 *(978-1-903973-23-3(6))* Royal Academy of Arts GBR. Dist: Hachette Bk. Group.

Bocquet, José-Louis & Catel. Kiki de Montparnasse: The Graphic Biography. 2012. (ENG., Illus.). 416p. pap. 24.95 ***(978-1-906838-25-6(9)***, SelfMadeHero) Metro Media Ltd. GBR. Dist: Abrams.

Butler, Ruth. Hidden in the Shadow of the Master: The Model-Wives of Cezanne, Monet, & Rodin. 2010. (ENG., Illus.). 376p. pap. 22.00 *(978-0-300-16450-3(5))* Yale Univ. Pr.

Johnson, Maureen & Johnson, Douglas. Art Models 6: The Female Figure in Shadow & Light. 2011. (Art Models Ser.). (ENG., Illus.). 128p. 36.95 *(978-0-9816249-7-6(9))* Live Model Bks.

Marshall, Thomas Carroll. Kissing the Sun. 2006. 35.00 *(978-0-9789419-0-1(X))* San Diego Beachlife Pr.

Perkins, Michelle. Professional Portrait Posing: Techniques & Images from Master Photographers. 2007. (Photo Pro Workshop Ser.). (ENG., Illus.). 128p. pap. 34.95 *(978-1-58428-211-2(8))* Amherst Media, Inc.

Royal Academy of Arts, creator. Modigliani & His Models. 2006. (ENG., Illus.). 160p. 65.00 *(978-1-903973-81-3(3))* Royal Academy of Arts GBR. Dist: Hachette Bk. Group.

Steiner, Wendy. The Real Real Thing: The Model in the Mirror of Art. 2010. (Illus.). 240p. 32.50 *(978-0-226-77219-6(5))* Univ. of Chicago Pr.

ARTISTS' MODELS—BIOGRAPHY

Burnim, Kalman A. & Baskett, John. Brief Lives: Biographies of Sitters & Artists in the Garrick Club Collection. 2006. (ENG., Illus.). 192p. 65.00 *(978-0-906290-73-6(2))* Unicorn Pr., London GBR. Dist: National Bk. Network.

James, Russell. The Pocket Guide to Victorian Artists & Their Models. 2011. (Illus.). 240p. pap. 19.95 *(978-1-84468-095-5(9))* Pen & Sword Bks. Ltd. GBR. Dist: Casemate Pubs. & Bk. Distributors, LLC.

Marsh, Jan. The Legend of Elizabeth Siddal. 2010. (ENG.). 256p. pap. 20.00 *(978-0-7043-7193-4(6))* Quartet Bks., Ltd. GBR. Dist: Interlink Publishing Group, Inc.

Phillips, Sarah R. Modeling Life: Art Models Speak about Nudity, Sexuality, & the Creative Process. 2006. (Illus.). 147p. per. 19.95 *(978-0-7914-6908-8(5))* State Univ. of New York Pr.

Rooney, Kathleen. Live Nude Girl: My Life as an Object. 2010. 200p. pap. 15.95 *(978-1-55728-949-0(2))* Univ. of Arkansas Pr.

—Live Nude Girl: My Life As an Object. 2009. 168p. 22.50 *(978-1-55728-891-2(7))* Univ. of Arkansas Pr.

Zimmerman, Jean. Love, Fiercely: A Gilded Age Romance. 2012. (ENG., Illus.). 336p. 26.00 *(978-0-15-101447-7(7))* Houghton Mifflin Harcourt Trade & Reference Pubs.

ARTISTS' SPOUSES

Bona, Dominique. Gala. (SPA.). 346p. *(978-84-7223-964-7(0)*, 6020); (Illus.). 400p. *(978-84-8310-937-3(9))* Tusquets Editores.

Butler, Ruth. Hidden in the Shadow of the Master: The Model-Wives of Cezanne, Monet, & Rodin. 2010. (ENG., Illus.). 376p. pap. 22.00 *(978-0-300-16450-3(5))* Yale Univ. Pr.

Carolyn Carter-Kennedy. The Lucille Armstrong Story: A Lady with a Vision. 2010. 80p. pap. 13.95 *(978-1-4401-8469-7(0))* iUniverse, Inc.

Carter Cash, John. Anchored in Love. 2007. (Illus.). 224p. pap. 14.99 ***(978-0-8499-1907-7(X))*** Nelson, Thomas Inc.

Heslewood, Juliet. Lover: Portraits by 40 Great Artists. 2011. (ENG., Illus.). 96p. 19.95 *(978-0-7112-3108-5(7))* Lincoln, Frances Ltd. GBR. Dist: Perseus-PGW.

Levin, Gail. Lee Krasner: A Biography. (ENG., 2012. Illus.). 400p. pap. 16.99 *(978-0-06-184527-7(2)*, William Morrow Paperbacks) 2011. 400p. 30.00 *(978-0-06-184525-3(6)*, Morrow, William & Co.) 2011. 884p. pap. 30.00 *(978-0-06-201779-6(9)*, HarperLuxe) HarperCollins Pubs.

Roberts, Joan. Joan & Goodridge: My Life with Goodridge Roberts. 2010. (ENG., Illus.). 160p. pap. 19.95 *(978-1-55065-262-8(1))* Vehicule Pr. CAN. Dist: Independent Pubs. Group.

Rowland, Katharine Lollar. Katherine's World. 2009. (Illus.). x, 133p. *(978-1-933197-53-0(3))* Orange Frazer Pr.

Thirlwell, Angela. Into the Frame: The Four Loves of Ford Madox Brown. (ENG., Illus.). 2011. 336p. pap. 23.95 ***(978-1-84413-914-9(X))*** 2010. 328p. 39.95 *(978-0-7011-7902-1(3)*, Chatto & Windus) Random Hse. GBR. Dist: Independent Pubs. Group.

ARTS

Here are entered works on the arts in general, including the visual arts, literature and the performing arts. Works limited to the visual arts (architecture, painting, sculpture, etc.) are entered under Art. Works on special themes in the arts are entered under phrase headings of the type (Subject) in art, e.g. Automobiles in Art.

see also Artists; People with Disabilities and the Arts; Performing Arts

Barndt, Deborah. ¡viva! 2011. (Illus.). 240p. 75.00 ***(978-1-4384-3767-5(6)***, Suny Pr.) State Univ. of New York Pr.

Barrett, Estelle & Bolt, Barbara, eds. Practice as Research: Approaches to Creative Arts Enquiry. 2007. (ENG., Illus.). 224p. 85.00 *(978-1-84511-432-9(9))* I. B. Tauris & Co., Ltd. GBR. Dist: Macmillan.

Bartscherer, Thomas & Coover, Roderick. Switching Codes: Thinking Through Digital Technology in the Humanities & the Arts. 2011. (ENG., Illus.). 448p. 85.00 *(978-0-226-03830-8(0))* Univ. of Chicago Pr.

Bartscherer, Thomas & Coover, Roderick, eds. Switching Codes: Thinking Through Digital Technology in the Humanities & the Arts. 2011. (ENG., Illus.). 448p. pap. 30.00 *(978-0-226-03831-5(9))* Univ. of Chicago Pr.

Baudelaire, Charles. Essence of Laughter & Other Essays, Journals & Love Letters. Quennell, Peter, ed. 2011. 224p. 44.95 ***(978-1-258-02431-4(4))*** Literary Licensing, LLC.

Becker, Carol. Thinking in Place: Art, Action, & Cultural Production, 1 vol. 184p. 2009. pap. 36.95 *(978-1-59451-597-2(2))* 2008. (Illus.). (C). 125.00 *(978-1-59451-596-5(4))* Paradigm Pubs.

Beezley, William H. Latin American Popular Culture since Independence: An Introduction. 2nd ed. 2011. (ENG.). 368p. pap. 37.95 ***(978-1-4422-1255-8(1))*** Rowman & Littlefield Publishers, Inc.

Beezley/Curcio-Nagy. Latin American Popular Culture since Independence: An Introduction. 2nd ed. 2011. (ENG.). 368p. 95.00 ***(978-1-4422-1254-1(3))*** Rowman & Littlefield Publishers, Inc.

Bernadette Corporation. Bernadette Corporation: the Complete Poem. 2011. (ENG., Illus.). 172p. pap. 39.95 *(978-3-86560-870-3(1))* Verlag der Buchhandlung Walther Konig DEU. Dist: D.A.P./Distributed Art Pubs.

Bevolo, Marco. The Golden Crossroads: Multidisciplinary Findings for Business Success from the Worlds of Fine Arts, Design & Culture. 2009. (ENG., Illus.). 256p. 49.00 *(978-0-230-22418-6(0))* Palgrave Macmillan.

Biggs, Michael & Karlsson, Henrik, eds. The Routledge Companion to Research in the Arts. (ENG., Illus.). 488p. (C). 2012. pap. 49.95 ***(978-0-415-69794-1(8))*** 2010. 200.00 *(978-0-415-58169-1(9))* Routledge.

Bishop, Philip E. A Beginner's Guide to the Humanities. 3rd ed. 2009. (ENG.). 176p. (C). pap. 38.00 *(978-0-205-66514-3(4)*, Prentice Hall) Prentice Hall PTR.

Bolt, Barbara & Barrett, Estelle, eds. Practice as Research: Approaches to Creative Arts Enquiry. 2010. (ENG., Illus.). 224p. pap. 32.50 *(978-1-84885-301-0(7))* I. B. Tauris & Co., Ltd. GBR. Dist: Macmillan.

Brooke, Stephanie L. The Creative Therapies & Eating Disorders. 2008. 304p. 0.00 *(978-0-398-07758-7(4))*; pap. 0.00 *(978-0-398-07759-4(2))* Thomas, Charles C. Pub., Ltd.

Bruner, Michael Lane. Repressive Regimes, Aesthetic States, & Arts of Resistance. 2012. ***(978-1-4331-0108-3(4))*** Lang, Peter Publishing, Inc.

Bruter, Claude P., ed. Mathematics & Art: Mathematical Visualization in Art & Education. 2010. (Mathematics & Visualization Ser.). (Illus.). x, 337p. pap. 189.00 *(978-3-642-07782-1(X)*, 364207782X) Springer.

Caduff, Corina, et al, eds. Art & Artistic Research: Music, Visual Art, Design, Literature, Dance. 2010. (Verlag Scheidegger & Spiess-Zurich University of the Arts Yearbook Ser.). (GER & ENG., Illus.). 320p. 60.00 *(978-3-85881-293-3(5))* Scheidegger und Spiess AG, Verlag CHE. Dist: Antique Collectors' Club.

Carroll, Jerome, et al. Aesthetics & Modernity from Schiller to the Frankfurt School. 2011. (ENG.). 369p. pap. 71.95 ***(978-3-0343-0217-3(7))*** Lang, Peter AG GBR. Dist: Lang, Peter.

Celma, Òscar. Music Recommendation & Discovery: The Long Tail, Long Fail, & Long Play in the Digital Music Space. 2010. (ENG., Illus.). xvi, 194p. 49.95 *(978-3-642-13286-5(3)*, 3642132863) Springer.

Chaturvedi, Ravi, ed. Theatre & Democracy. 2008. (Illus.). 200p. 40.00 *(978-81-316-0199-0(4))* Rawat Pubns. IND. Dist: International Specialized Bk. Services.

Christine M., Unwin. The Artistic Touch 5. 2012. (Artistic Touch Ser.). 172p. 35.00 *(978-0-9642712-6-5(5))* Creative Art Pr.

Clapp, Edward P. 20under40: Re-Inventing the Arts & Arts Education for the 21st Century. 2010. 400p. 29.95 *(978-1-4520-6739-1(2))*; pap. 19.95 *(978-1-4520-6738-4(4))* AuthorHouse.

Coessens, Kathleen, et al. The Artistic Turn: A Manifesto. 2010. (Orpheus Research Centre in Music Ser.). 192p. pap. 39.50 *(978-94-90389-00-0(5))* Leuven Univ. Pr. BEL. Dist: Cornell Univ. Pr.

Cram101 Textbook Reviews & Cram101 Textbook Reviews. Outlines & Highlights for Reality Through the Arts by Dennis J Sporre. 2011. 360p. pap. 34.95 ***(978-1-61830-923-5(4))*** Cram101 Inc.

Day, Lewis Foreman. Every-Day Art. 2009. 150p. pap. *(978-0-217-47511-2(6))* Books LLC.

—Every-Day Art. 2008. 300p. pap. *(978-1-906600-07-5(4))* Mills, Jeremy Publishing.

Dean, Roger T. & Smith, Hazel, eds. Practice-Led Research, Research-Led Practice in the Creative Arts. 2009. (Research Methods for the Arts & Humanities Ser.). (ENG., Illus.). 288p. (gr. 17). 95.00 *(978-0-7486-3628-0(5))*; pap. 32.50 *(978-0-7486-3629-7(3))* Edinburgh Univ. Pr. GBR. Dist: Columbia Univ. Pr.

Degges-White, Suzanne & Davis, Nancy L. Integrating the Expressive Arts into Counseling Practice: Theory-Based Interventions. 2010. *(978-0-8261-0606-3(4))* Springer.

Doble, Rick. Experimental Digital Photography. 2010. (Lark Photography Book Ser.). (ENG., Illus.). 192p. pap. 24.95 *(978-1-60059-517-2(0)*, Pixiq) Sterling Publishing Co., Inc.

Dodds, Jack. Dodds Ready Reference Handbook Fourth Edition Plus Coleman Making Sensesecond Edition. 4th ed. 2007. (YA). pap. 95.96 *(978-0-547-09077-1(3)*, 1044101) CENGAGE Learning.

Elkins, James. On Pictures & the Words That Fail Them. 2011. (ENG., Illus.). 346p. pap. 39.99 *(978-0-521-62499-2(1))* Cambridge Univ. Pr.

Elkins, James & DeLue, Rachael Ziady. Landscape Theory. Elkins, James & Delue, Rachael Ziady, eds. 2007. (Art Seminar Ser.). (Illus.). 366p. 125.00 *(978-0-415-96053-3(3))*; per. 32.95 *(978-0-415-96054-0(1))* Routledge.

Feagin, Susan L., ed. Global Theories of the Arts & Aesthetics. 2006. (Journal of Aesthetics & Art Criticism Ser.). (ENG., Illus.). 140p. pap. 43.95 *(978-1-4051-7355-1(6)*, Wiley-Blackwell) Wiley, John & Sons, Inc.

Flabpohler, Svenja, et al, eds. Kipfiguren der Wiederholung: Interdisziplinare Untersuchungen Zur Figu der Wiederholung in Literatur, Kunst und Wissenschaft. (GER., Illus.). 151p. pap. 32.95 *(978-3-631-55955-0(0))* Lang, Peter GmbH, Europaischer Verlag der Wissenschaften DEU. Dist: Lang, Peter Publishing, Inc.

Fowler, Susan. Sensory Stimulation: Sensory-Focused Activities for People with Physical & Multiple Disabilities. 2006. (ENG., Illus.). 176p. per. *(978-1-84310-455-1(5))* Kingsley, Jessica Ltd.

Frampton, Hollis. On the Camera Arts & Consecutive Matters: The Writings of Hollis Frampton. Jenkins, Bruce, ed. & intro. by. 2009. (Writing Art Ser.). (ENG., Illus.). 360p. (gr. 17). 41.95 *(978-0-262-06276-3(3))* MIT Pr.

Geismar, Haidy & Herle, Anita. Moving Images: John. 2010. 308p. 90.00 *(978-0-8248-3503-3(4))* Univ. of Hawaii Pr.

Gladding, Samuel T. The Creative Arts in Counseling. 4th ed. 2011. *(978-1-55620-314-5(4))* American Counseling Assn.

Hamer, Mary. Signs of Cleopatra: Reading an Icon Historically. (Illus.). 192p. 2008. 90.00 *(978-0-85989-826-3(1))* 2nd ed. 2009. pap. 32.95 *(978-0-85989-809-6(1))* Univ. of Exeter Pr. GBR. Dist: Chicago Distribution Ctr.

Hyde, Lewis. Common as Air: Revolution, Art, & Ownership, 1 vol. (ENG., Illus.). 2011. 352p. pap. 16.00 *(978-0-374-53279-6(6))* 2010. 320p. 26.00 *(978-0-374-22313-7(0))* Farrar, Straus & Giroux.

—Trickster Makes This World. 2008. (Illus.). 432p. pap. *(978-1-84767-225-4(6))* Canongate Bks.

—Trickster Makes This World: Mischief, Myth, & Art. 2010. (ENG., Illus.). 432p. pap. 18.00 *(978-0-374-53255-0(9))* Farrar, Straus & Giroux.

International Directory of Arts 2011: [Print + EBookPLUS]. 35th ed. 2010. *(978-3-11-023040-6(2))* Saur, K. G. Verlag GmbH & Co.

Isar, Yudhishthir Raj & Anheier, Helmut K., eds. Cultural Expression, Creativity & Innovation. 2010. (Cultures & Globalization Ser.). (Illus.). 488p. (C). 142.00 *(978-1-4129-2085-8(X)*, B2085XC); pap. 50.00 *(978-1-4129-2086-5(8)*, B2085XP) SAGE Pubns., Ltd. GBR. Dist: SAGE Pubns., Inc.

Jaeger, C. Stephen. Enchantment: On Charisma & the Sublime in the Arts of the West. 2012. (Haney Foundation Ser.). (Illus.). 440p. (C). 69.95 ***(978-0-8122-4329-1(3))*** Univ. of Pennsylvania Pr.

Jarman, Derek. Chroma: A Book of Color. 2010. (ENG.). 160p. pap. 18.95 *(978-0-8166-6593-8(1))* Univ. of Minnesota Pr.

Jeffers, Alison. Performing Global Identities: Refugees, Theatre & Crisis. 2011. (Performance Interventions Ser.). (ENG., Illus.). 216p. 85.00 ***(978-0-230-24747-5(4))*** Palgrave Macmillan.

Kermode, Frank. Forms of Attention: Botticelli & Hamlet. 2011. (ENG.). 112p. pap. 16.00 *(978-0-226-43175-8(4))* Univ. of Chicago Pr.

Khatchadourian, Haig A. Music, Film, & Art. 2010. 234p. pap. 26.00 *(978-1-60899-572-1(0)*, Wipf and Stock) Wipf & Stock Pubs.

Kimball, Roger. Counterpoints: 25 Years of the New Criterion on Culture & the Arts. 2008. (ENG.). 512p. pap. 22.50 *(978-1-56663-805-0(4))* Dee, Ivan R. Pub.

Kramer, Hilton, ed. Counterpoints: 25 Years of the New Criterion on Culture & the Arts. 2007. (ENG.). 512p. 35.00 *(978-1-56663-706-0(6))* Dee, Ivan R. Pub.

Kronegger, M., ed. The Orchestration of the Arts-A Creative Symbiosis of Existential Powers: The Vibrating Interplay of Sound, Color, Image, Movement, Rhythm, Fragrance, Word, Touch. 2010. (Analecta Husserliana Ser.). 488p. pap. 299.00 *(978-90-481-5335-0(2)*, 9048153352) Springer.

Lazzara, Michael J. Chile in Transition: The Poetics & Politics of Memory. 2011. (ENG., Illus.). 224p. pap. 25.95 *(978-0-8130-3568-0(6))* Univ. Pr. of Florida.

Lee, Alexander, ed. Renaissance? Perceptions of Continuity & Discontinuity in Europe, C. 1300- C. 1550. (Illus.). 384p. *(978-90-04-18334-6(5))* BRILL.

Levinson, Jerrold. Contemplating Art. 2006. 432p. 165.00 *(978-0-19-920618-6(X))* Oxford Univ. Pr., Inc.

—Contemplating Art: Essays in Aesthetics. 2006. (ENG.). 432p. per. 55.00 *(978-0-19-920617-9(1))* Oxford Univ. Pr., Inc.

Louw, Ruud. Het Nederlands hoger Onderwijsrecht: Een thematisch commentaar op de Wet op het hoger onderwijs en wetenschappelijk Onderzoek. 2011. (LUP Dissertaties Ser.). (DUT.). 800p. pap. ***(978-90-8728-132-8(3)***, Leiden Univ. Pr.) Amsterdam Univ. Pr.

Maeder, Beverly. The Seeming & the Seen: Essays in Modern Visual & Literary Culture. 2006. (Illus.). 373p. pap. 68.95 *(978-3-03910-997-5(9))*; pap. 60.95 *(978-0-8204-8373-3(7))* Lang, Peter Publishing, Inc.

Malchiodi, Cathy A., ed. Handbook of Art Therapy. 2nd rev. ed. 2011. (ENG., Illus.). 496p. 65.00 *(978-1-60918-975-4(2))* Guilford Pubns., Inc.

Malesky, Kee. All Facts Considered: The Essential Library of Inessential Knowledge. 2010. (ENG., Illus.). 288p. 19.95 *(978-0-470-55965-9(9)*, Wiley) Wiley, John & Sons, Inc.

Manghani, Sunil, et al, eds. Image: A Reader. 2006. (Illus.). 352p. (C). 124.00 *(978-1-4129-0044-7(1)*, B00441C) SAGE Pubns., Ltd. GBR. Dist: SAGE Pubns., Inc.

—Images: A Reader. 2006. (Illus.). 352p. (C). per. 60.00 *(978-1-4129-0045-4(X)*, B00441P) SAGE Pubns., Ltd. GBR. Dist: SAGE Pubns., Inc.

Martin, F. David & Jacobus, Lee A. Humanities through the Arts. 8th ed. 2010. (ENG., Illus.). 496p. (C). pap. 133.33 *(978-0-07-337663-9(9)*, 0073376639) McGraw-Hill Cos., The.

Mathieu, Chris, ed. Careers in Creative Industries. 2011. (Routledge Advances in Management & Business Studies). (ENG., Illus.). 312p. (C). 125.00 ***(978-0-415-80826-2(X))*** Routledge.

Maxwell, Robert A., ed. Representing History, 900-1300: Art, Music, History. 2010. (ENG.). 296p. 79.95 *(978-0-271-03636-6(2))* Pennsylvania State Univ. Pr.

Mazzoni, Cristina. She-Wolf: The Story of a Roman Icon. 2010. (ENG., Illus.). 304p. (C). 85.00 *(978-0-521-19456-3(3))*; pap. 24.99 *(978-0-521-14566-4(X))* Cambridge Univ. Pr.

McAlpine, Jim, et al. Faces of Man No. 2: The Arts. Date not set. tchr. ed. 8.95 *(978-0-910857-66-6(0)*, 066-OAP) Educational Impressions.

McGonigal, Mike, ed. Yeti 10. 2010. (ENG.). 176p. 11.95 *(978-0-9829819-0-0(2)*, Yeti Publishing) Verse Chorus Pr.

McLagan, Meg & McKee, Yates. Sensible Politics: The Visual Culture of Nongovernmental Activism. 2012. ***(978-1-935408-24-6(0))*** Zone Bks.

McLeese, Don. The New York Times Reader: Arts & Culture, 00 vols. rev. ed. 2010. 296p. pap. 28.00 *(978-1-60426-480-7(2))* CQ Pr.

McNiff, Shaun. Integrating the Arts in Therapy: History, Theory, & Practice. 2009. 280p. 59.95 *(978-0-398-07868-3(8))*; pap. 39.95 *(978-0-398-07869-0(6))* Thomas, Charles C. Pub., Ltd.

O'Donnell, Timothy. Sketchbook: Conceptual Drawings from the World's Most Influential Designers. 2011. (ENG., Illus.). 192p. pap. 25.00 *(978-1-59253-734-1(0)*, 1592537340) Quayside.

Oosterling, Henk & Ziarek, Ewa Ponowska. Intermedialities: Philosophy, Arts, Politics. 2010. (TEXTURES: Philosophy / Literature / Culture Ser.). (ENG., Illus.). 242p. 75.00 *(978-0-7391-2735-3(7))*; pap. 29.95 *(978-0-7391-2736-0(5))* Lexington Bks.

O'reilly, Daragh & Kerrigan, Finola, eds. Marketing the Arts: A Fresh Approach. 2010. (ENG., Illus.). 328p. (C). 150.00 *(978-0-415-49685-8(3))*; pap. 55.95 *(978-0-415-49686-5(1))* Taylor & Francis Group GBR. (Routledge). Dist: Taylor & Francis Group.

Pajaczkowska, Claire & Ward, Ivan. Shame & Sexuality: Psychoanalysis & Visual Culture. Pajaczkowska, Claire & Ward, Ivan, eds. 2008. (ENG., Illus.). 256p. (C). 110.00 *(978-0-415-42011-2(3))*; pap. 37.50 *(978-0-415-42012-9(1))* Routledge.

Pater, Walter. The Renaissance: Studies in Art & Poetry. 2009. 140p. pap. 6.99 *(978-1-60450-652-5(0)*, Serenity Pubs.) Arc Manor.

—The Renaissance: Studies in Art & Poetry. lt. ed. 2007. 158p. pap. 19.99 *(978-1-4346-1779-8(3))*; (ENG.). 174p. pap. 21.99 *(978-1-4346-1948-8(6))* BiblioBazaar.

—The Renaissance: Studies in Art & Poetry. 2007. 148p. per. *(978-1-4065-4139-7(7))* Dodo Pr.

Paxson, Pat. Art & Intuition: Borderlines & Boundaries. 2011. 160p. 29.99 ***(978-1-4628-6210-8(1))***; pap. 19.99 ***(978-1-4628-6209-2(8))*** Xlibris Corp.

Phillips, Ron. Arts Entrepreneurship & Economic Development: Can Every City Be ¿Austintatious¿? 2011. (ENG., Illus.). 84p. pap. 65.00 net. *(978-1-60198-412-8(X))* Now Pubs.

Plate, Liedeke & Smelik, Anneke, eds. Technologies of Memory in the Arts. 2009. (ENG., Illus.). 256p. 89.00 *(978-0-230-57567-7(6))* Palgrave Macmillan.

Rebay-Salisbury, Katharina & Sorensen, Marie L. S. Embodied Knowledge: Historical Perspectives on Belief & Technology. 2012. (ENG., Illus.). 176p. (C). 60.00 ***(978-1-84217-490-6(8))*** Oxbow Bks., Ltd. GBR. Dist: Brown, David Bk. Co., The.

Reinstädler, Janett, et al. El Andar Tierras, Deseos y Memorias: Homenaje a Dieter Ingenschay. 2008. (POR, GER, ENG & SPA., Illus.). 749p. pap. 120.00 *(978-84-8489-408-7(8))* Iberoamericana Vervuert Publishing Corp.

Rice, Boyd. Standing in Two Circles: The Collected Works of Boyd Rice. Clark, Brian M., ed. 2008. (ENG., Illus.). 288p. pap. 22.95 *(978-1-84068-118-5(7))* Creation Bks. GBR. Dist: SCB Distributors.

Rogers, J. Earl, ed. The Art of Grief: The Use of Expressive Arts in a Grief Support Group. 2007. (Series in Death, Dying, & Bereavement). (ENG., Illus.). 224p. per. 34.95 *(978-0-415-95535-5(1))* Routledge.

Ross, Malcolm. Cultivating the Arts in Education & Therapy. 2011. (ENG., Illus.). 228p. 128.00 *(978-0-415-60365-2(X))* Routledge.

—Cultivating the Habit of Art: A Framework for the Arts in Education & Therapy. 2011. (ENG., Illus.). 228p. pap. 39.95 *(978-0-415-60366-9(8))* Routledge.

Rossing, Thomas D., ed. The Science of String Instruments. 2010. (ENG., Illus.). viii, 470p. 79.95 *(978-1-4419-7109-8(2)*, 1441971092) Springer.

Rozik, Eli. The Fictional Arts: An Inter-Art Journey from Theatre Theory to the Arts. 2011. 304p. 74.95 *(978-1-84519-425-3(X))*; (ENG.). pap. 37.95 *(978-1-84519-426-0(8))* Sussex Academic Pr. GBR. Dist: International Specialized Bk. Services.

Salter, Chris. Entangled: Technology & the Transformation of Performance. 2010. (ENG., Illus.). 504p. (gr. 17). 42.00 *(978-0-262-19588-1(7))* MIT Pr.

Samarth, Aditi. Global Arts & Cultures. rev. ed. 2011. (ENG.). 270p. pap. 61.95 ***(978-0-7575-8932-4(4))*** Kendall Hunt Publishing Co.

Schama, Simon. Scribble, Scribble, Scribble: Writing on Politics, Ice Cream, Churchill, & My Mother. 2011. (ENG.). 448p. 27.99 *(978-0-06-200986-9(9)*, Ecco) HarperCollins Pubs.

Schama, Simon. Scribble, Scribble, Scribble: Writing on Politics, Ice Cream, Churchill, & My Mother. 2012. (ENG.). 448p. pap. 16.99 ***(978-0-06-200987-6(7)***, Ecco) HarperCollins Pubs.

Scheer, Edward & Klich, Rosemary. Multimedia Performance. 2011. (ENG., Illus.). 240p. (C). pap. 85.00 ***(978-0-230-57468-7(8))*** Palgrave Macmillan.

Scheer, Edward, et al. Multimedia Performance. 2011. (ENG., Illus.). 240p. (C). pap. 27.00 ***(978-0-230-57467-0(X))*** Palgrave Macmillan.

Schiuma, Giovanni. The Value of Arts for Business. 2011. (ENG., Illus.). 304p. 90.00 *(978-0-521-76951-8(5))* Cambridge Univ. Pr.

Segre, Erica. Intersected Identities: Strategies of Visualisation in 19th & 20th Century Mexican Culture. 2007. (Remapping Cultural History Ser.). (Illus.). 304p. (C). 90.00 *(978-1-84545-291-9(7))* Berghahn Bks., Inc.

Shan, Gongbing & Visentin, Peter, eds. Arts Biomechanics - an Infant Science: Its Challenges & Future. 2010. (Biomechanics - Theory & Applications Ser.). (Illus.). 93p. pap. 43.00 *(978-1-60876-809-7(0))* Nova Science Pubs., Inc.

Shumate, A. Michael. Success in the Arts: What It Takes to Make It in Creative Fields. 2007. 128p. per. 10.95 *(978-0-9739333-5-2(6))* Elfstone Press CAN. Dist: AtlasBooks Distribution.

Sisson, Elaine & King, Linda, eds. Ireland, Design & Visual Culture: Negotiating Modernity 1922-1992. 2011. (Illus.). 320p. 49.00 *(978-1-85918-472-1(3))* Cork Univ. Pr. IRL. Dist: Stylus Publishing, LLC.

Smarandache, Florentin. Experimental paradoxist Linguistics (Florentin's Lexicon) 2008. pap. 9.90 *(978-1-59973-057-8(X))* Multimedia Larga.

Smelik, Anneke, ed. The Scientific Imaginary in Visual Culture. 2010. (Interfacing Science, Literature, & the Humanities Ser.). (GER & ENG., Illus.). 198p. (C). 51.00 *(978-3-89971-756-3(2))* Vandenhoeck & Ruprecht GmbH & Co. KG DEU. Dist: ISD.

Southern Quarterly Review, Set. reprint ed. lib. bdg. 2295.00 *(978-0-404-19557-1(1))* AMS Pr., Inc.

Sporre, Dennis J. Reality Through the Arts. 8th rev. ed. 2012. (ENG.). 432p. (C). pap. 128.40 ***(978-0-205-85822-4(8)***, Prentice Hall) Prentice Hall PTR.

—Reality Through the Arts, Books a la Carte Edition. 8th ed. 2012. (ENG.). 432p. (C). ring bd. 84.00 ***(978-0-205-85823-1(6)***, Prentice Hall) Prentice Hall PTR.

—Reality Through the Arts, Books a la Carte Plus MySearchLab. 8th ed. 2012. (ENG.). (C). ring bd. 90.67 ***(978-0-205-85824-8(4)***, Prentice Hall) Prentice Hall PTR.

Stojkov, Teresa R., ed. Critical Views: Essays on the Humanities & the Arts. 2011. (Townsend Papers in the Humanities Ser.). 275p. pap. 24.95 *(978-0-9823294-3-6(1))* Townsend Ctr. For The Humanities.

Story, William Wetmore. Excursions in Art & Letters. 2009. 304p. pap. 29.75 *(978-1-116-15074-2(3))* BiblioBazaar.

—Excursions in Art & Letters. 2009. 180p. pap. *(978-0-217-47237-1(0))* Books LLC.

—Excursions in Art & Letters. 2009. 304p. 43.95 *(978-1-104-16378-5(0))*; pap. 28.95 *(978-1-104-12537-0(4))* Kessinger Publishing, LLC.

Symons, Arthur. Studies in Seven Arts. 2010. 410p. pap. 34.75 *(978-1-178-24642-1(6))*; (ENG.). 406p. pap. 34.75 *(978-1-178-01856-1(3))*; 410p. pap. 34.75 *(978-1-146-74042-5(5))*; 412p. pap. 34.75 *(978-1-145-08927-3(5))*; 410p. pap. 34.75 *(978-1-141-98005-5(3))*; 404p. pap. 34.75 *(978-1-142-23987-9(X))*; 412p. pap. 34.75 *(978-1-143-03208-0(X))* BiblioBazaar.

—Studies in Seven Arts. 2009. 118p. pap. *(978-1-150-70766-7(6))* Books LLC.

—Studies in Seven Arts. 2007. (ENG.). 400p. 49.95 *(978-0-548-15257-7(8))*; 404p. per. 34.95 *(978-1-4304-4629-3(3))* Kessinger Publishing, LLC.

Thomas, Bonnie. Creative Expression Activities for Teens: Exploring Identity through Art, Craft & Journaling. 2010. (ENG., Illus.). 178p. pap. *(978-1-84905-842-1(3))* Kingsley, Jessica Ltd.

Tolstoy, Leo. What Is Art & Essays on Art. 2008. 360p. *(978-1-4437-3934-4(0)*, Obscure Pr.) 2008. 360p. *(978-1-4437-2390-9(8)*, Hesperides Pr.) 2006. 356p. per. *(978-1-4067-2567-4(6)*, Hesperides Pr.) Read Bks.

Townley, Barbara & Beech, Nic, eds. Managing Creativity: Exploring the Paradox. 2011. (ENG., Illus.). 364p. pap. 45.00 ***(978-1-107-40373-4(1))*** Cambridge Univ. Pr.

Ullrich, Ferdinand. Waldo Bien: Bildersien mit Virgil Grotfeld. 2007. 256p. 120.00 *(978-3-87909-711-1(9))* Wienand GmbH, Druck- & Verlagshaus DEU. Dist: Independent Pubs. Group.

Ulrich, Matthias, ed. Aleksandra Mir. Triumph: Triumph. 2009. (ENG., Illus.). 64p. pap. 28.00 *(978-3-86560-576-4(1))* Verlag der Buchhandlung Walther Konig DEU. Dist: D.A.P./Distributed Art Pubs.

van Steden, Ronald, ed. Strategieën van lokale Veiligheid: Een achtergrondstudie en drie Reflecties. 2011. (Nicis Ser.). (DUT.). pap. *(978-90-8964-323-0(0))* Amsterdam Univ. Pr.

Vinceneau. Art of Spectacle. pap. *(978-0-304-70254-1(4))* Continuum International Publishing Group, Ltd.

Walters, Thomas A. The Arts: A Comparative Approach to the Arts of Painting, Sculpture, Architecture, Music & Drama. 2011. 114p. 29.99 ***(978-1-4628-7382-1(0))***; pap. 19.99 ***(978-1-4628-7381-4(2))*** Xlibris Corp.

Warner, Marina. Monuments & Maidens: The Allegory of the Female Form. 2008. (ENG.). 417p. pap. 27.00 *(978-1-4379-5218-6(6))* DIANE Publishing Co.

Williams, Abayomi. Black Love: The Melancholy Bible. 2007. 272p. pap. 4.40 *(978-0-615-13891-6(8))* Williams, Abayomi.

Williams, Lesley Duggins & Atkins, Sally S. Sourcebook in Expressive Arts Therapy. 2007. (Illus.). 134p. per. 24.95 *(978-1-933251-37-0(9))* Parkway Pubs., Inc.

1997 Fine Arts. (Auction Records Ser.). (Illus.). 500p. pap. 59.95 *(978-957-99189-2-3(9))* Chinese Art Bks. Cultural Enterprise Co., Ltd. TWN. Dist: Art Media Resources, Inc.

1998 Fine Arts. (Auction Records Ser.). (Illus.). 500p. pap. 59.95 *(978-957-99189-4-7(5))* Chinese Art Bks. Cultural Enterprise Co., Ltd. TWN. Dist: Art Media Resources, Inc.

1999 Fine Arts. (Auction Records Ser.). (Illus.). 500p. pap. 59.95 *(978-957-99189-6-1(1))* Chinese Art Bks. Cultural Enterprise Co., Ltd. TWN. Dist: Art Media Resources, Inc.

ARTS—CRITICISM

see Art Criticism

ARTS—DATA PROCESSING

Bast, Gerald, ed. Julie Monaco 19972011. 2011. (GER.). 200p. 49.95 ***(978-3-7091-0434-7(3))*** Springer Wien AUT. Dist: Actar Birkhauser Distribution.

Bowen, Jonathan P., et al, eds. EVA London 2011: Electronic Visualisation & the Arts. 2011. 290p. pap. 75.00 ***(978-1-906124-88-5(4))*** British Computer Society, The GBR. Dist: Turpin Distribution Services Ltd.

Cashen, Trish, et al, eds. Futures Past: Thirty Years of Arts Computing. 2008. (Computers & the History of Art Ser.). (Illus.). 128p. per. 40.00 *(978-1-84150-168-0(9))* Intellect, Ltd. GBR. Dist: Chicago Distribution Ctr.

Hamill, Andrew. Learning Ict in the Arts. 2006. (Teaching ICT through the Primary Curriculum Ser.). (Illus.). CXXIVp. 41.95 *(978-1-84312-313-2(4))* Fulton, David Pubs. GBR. Dist: Taylor & Francis Group.

Poggiani Keller, Raffaella, et al, eds. Rock Art Data Base. 2009. (ENG., Illus.). 76p. (C). pap. 67.50 *(978-1-4073-0530-1(1))* British Archaeological Reports Ltd. GBR. Dist: Brown, David Bk. Co., The.

Reas, Casey & Fry, Ben. Getting Started with Processing. 2010. (ENG., Illus.). 210p. pap. 19.99 *(978-1-4493-7980-3(X))* O'Reilly Media, Inc.

Smarandache, Florentin. Quantum cyberart {the world of Micro-infinity}. 2007. (Illus.). 108p. 89.95 *(978-1-59973-022-6(7))* Multimedia Larga.

ARTS—DIRECTORIES

Creative Handbook 1997. *(978-0-611-00878-7(5))* Reed Information Services Ltd.

Europa Publications Staff, contrib. by. International Who's Who in Classical Music 2008. 24th rev. ed. 2008. 960p. 430.00 *(978-1-85743-455-2(2))* Taylor & Francis Group GBR. Dist: Taylor & Francis Group.

International Directory of Arts. 34th ed. 2009. (ENG & GER., Illus.). XXVI, 2960p. *(978-3-598-23120-9(2))* Saur, K. G. Verlag GmbH & Co.

International Directory of Arts: Print + EBookPLUS. 34th ed. 2009. *(978-3-598-23121-6(0))* Saur, K. G. Verlag GmbH & Co.

International Directory of Arts 2012, 3 vols. 36th ed. 2011. (ENG., Illus.). XXIV, 2954p. ***(978-3-11-023488-6(2))*** Saur, K. G. Verlag GmbH & Co.

Peterson's. College Guide for Visual Arts Majors 2009: Real-World Admission Guide for All Fine Arts, Design, & Media Majors. Oram, Fern, ed. 3rd ed. 2008. (ENG., Illus.). 416p. pap. 24.95 *(978-0-7689-2564-7(9))* Peterson's.

ARTS—ECONOMIC ASPECTS

Arts, Sciences, & Economics: A Historical Safari. 2010. (ENG., Illus.). xii, 193p. pap. 129.00 *(978-3-642-07076-1(0)*, 3642070760) Springer.

Bendixen, Peter. Managing Art: An Introduction into Principles & Conceptions. 2011. (ENG., Illus.). 256p. pap. 34.95 *(978-3-643-50063-2(7))* Lit Verlag DEU. Dist: Transaction Pubs.

Brault, Simon. No Culture, No Future. Kaplansky, Jonathan, tr. from FRE. 2010. (ENG.). 200p. 21.00 *(978-1-897151-76-1(4))* Cormorant Bks. Inc. CAN. Dist: Univ. of Toronto Pr.

Cram101 Textbook Reviews & Cram101 Textbook Reviews. Outlines & Highlights for a Textbook of Cultural Economics by Ruth Towse. 2011. 316p. pap. 33.95 ***(978-1-61830-245-8(0))*** Cram101 Inc.

De Bruin, Anne. Entrepreneurship & the Creative Economy: Process, Practice & Policy. Henry, Colette, ed. 2011. (Illus.). 240p. 110.00 ***(978-1-84844-769-1(8))*** Elgar, Edward Publishing, Inc.

de Bruyne, Paul & Gielen, Pascal, eds. Arts in Society. 2010. (ENG., Illus.). 206p. pap. 32.00 *(978-90-5662-711-9(2))* NAi Uitgevers / Publishers Stichting NLD. Dist: D.A.P./Distributed Art Pubs.

Graw, Isabelle. Der große Preis: Kunst zwischen Markt und Celebrity. 2008. (GER., Illus.). 255p. pap. *(978-3-8321-9007-1(4))* DuMont.

Hutter, Michael & Throsby, David, eds. Beyond Price: Value in Culture, Economics, & the Arts. (Murphy Institute Studies in Political Economy Ser.). (ENG., Illus.). 334p. 2011. pap. 45.00 ***(978-0-521-18300-0(6))*** 2007. 96.00 *(978-0-521-86223-3(X))* Cambridge Univ. Pr.

Ivey, Bill. Arts, Inc: How Greed & Neglect Have Destroyed Our Cultural Rights. 2010. (ENG., Illus.). 368p. pap. 17.95 *(978-0-520-26792-3(3))* Univ. of California Pr.

Julier, Guy & Moor, Liz. Design & Creativity: Policy, Management & Practice. 2009. (ENG., Illus.). 1p. 99.95 *(978-1-84788-307-0(9))*; pap. 39.95 *(978-1-84788-306-3(0))* Berg Pubs. GBR. Dist: Macmillan.

Kozul-Wright, Zeljka & Barrowclough, Diana, eds. Creative Industries & Developing Countries: Voice, Choice & Economic Growth. 2007. (Routledge Studies in Contemporary Political Economy Ser.). (ENG., Illus.). 352p. (C). 150.00 *(978-0-415-39138-2(5))* Routledge.

Leger, Marc James, ed. Culture & Contestation in the New Century. 2011. (ENG., Illus.). 220p. pap. 40.00 *(978-1-84150-426-1(2))* Intellect, Ltd. GBR. Dist: Chicago Distribution Ctr.

Liberatori, Ellen. Guide to Getting Arts Grants. 2006. (ENG.). 272p. per. 19.95 *(978-1-58115-456-6(9)*, 115456, Allworth Pr.) Skyhorse Publishing Co., Inc.

McKinlay, Alan & Smith, Chris, eds. Creative Labour: Working in the Creative Industries. 2009. (ENG., Illus.). 230p. pap. 49.00 *(978-0-230-22200-7(5))* Palgrave Macmillan.

Potts, Jason. Creative Industries & Economic Evolution. (New Horizons in Institutional & Evolutionary Economics Ser.). 240p. 2012. pap. 39.95 ***(978-0-85793-192-4(X))*** 2011. 110.00 *(978-1-84720-662-6(X))* Elgar, Edward Publishing, Inc.

Schuman. Economic Pressures & the Future. 2007. (ENG.). 112p. pap. 10.95 *(978-1-4165-7754-6(8)*, Free Pr.) Free Pr.

Sickels, Robert C., ed. The Business of Entertainment [Three Volumes], 3 vols. 2008. (Illus.). 752p. 300.00 *(978-0-275-99838-7(X)*, C9838, Praeger Pubs.) Greenwood Publishing Group, Inc.

Singh, J. P. Globalized Arts: The Entertainment Economy & Cultural Identity. 2010. (ENG., Illus.). 240p. (gr. 17). 39.50 *(978-0-231-14718-7(X))* Columbia Univ. Pr.

Snowball, Jeanette D. Measuring the Value of Culture: Methods & Examples in Cultural Economics. 2007. (ENG., Illus.). xi, 230p. 129.00 *(978-3-540-74355-2(3)*, 3540743553) Springer.

Towse, Ruth. A Textbook of Cultural Economics. 2010. (ENG., Illus.). 626p. (C). 134.00 *(978-0-521-88872-1(7))*; pap. 59.00 *(978-0-521-71702-1(7))* Cambridge Univ. Pr.

Twitchell & Singh, J. P. Globalized Arts: The Entertainment Economy & Cultural Identity. 2010. (Illus.). 256p. E-Book 31.99 *(978-0-231-51919-9(2))* Columbia Univ. Pr.

Yi, Tong-Yon. Munhwa Chabon Ui Sidae: Han'guk Munhwa Chabon Ui Hyongsong Wolli. 2010. (KOR., Illus.). 367p. *(978-89-86598-92-6(2))* Munhwagwahagsa Publishing Co.

Zakaras, Laura & Lowell, Julia F. Cultivating Demand for the Arts: Arts Learning, Arts Engagement, & State Arts Policy. 2008. 172p. pap. 30.50 *(978-0-8330-4184-5(3)*, mg-640) RAND Corp., The.

Zander, Ivo & Scherdin, Mikael. Art Entrepreneurship. Zander, Ivo & Scherdin, Mikael, eds. 2011. (Illus.). 208p. 110.00 *(978-1-84844-369-3(2))* Elgar, Edward Publishing, Inc.

ARTS—FEDERAL AID

see Federal Aid to the Arts

ARTS—FINANCE

see also Federal Aid to the Arts

Bendixen, Peter. Managing Art: An Introduction into Principles & Conceptions. 2011. (ENG., Illus.). 256p. pap. 34.95 *(978-3-643-50063-2(7))* Lit Verlag DEU. Dist: Transaction Pubs.

Georgiou, Danielle. The Politics of State Public Arts Funding: Examining the Factors & Changes in State-Level Funding for the Arts. 2008. 192p. pap. *(978-3-639-09583-8(9))* VDM Verlag Dr. Mueller e.K.

Hinsley, Matthew. Creativity to Community: Arts Nonprofit Success One Coffee at a Time. 2011. 224p. 33.95 ***(978-0-557-54392-2(4))*** Lulu Enterprises Inc.

McCarthy, Kevin F., et al. Arts & Culture in the Metropolis: Strategies for Sustainability. 2007. (Illus.). 156p. per. 25.00 *(978-0-8330-3890-6(7)*, MG-477) RAND Corp., The.

ARTS—GOVERNMENT POLICY

see Art and State

ARTS—HISTORY

see also Art Criticism

Barter, Judith A., ed. & contrib. by. Apostles of Beauty: Arts & Crafts from Britian to Chicago. 2009. (ENG., Illus.). 208p. 45.00 *(978-0-300-14113-9(0))* Art Institute of Chicago.

Beasley, Rebecca. Ezra Pound & the Visual Culture of Modernism. 2010. 236p. pap. 34.99 *(978-0-521-15267-9(4))* Cambridge Univ. Pr.

Becker, Cynthia. Amazigh Arts in Morocco: Women Shaping Berber Identity. 2006. (ENG., Illus.). 239p. pap. 25.00 *(978-0-292-72137-1(4))* Univ. of Texas Pr.

Benton & Diyanni & Cram101 Textbook Reviews Staff. Arts & Culture: An Introduction to the Humanities. 2007. 116p. per. 11.95 *(978-1-4288-2610-6(6))*; (ENG.). 60p. per. 9.95 *(978-1-4288-2614-4(9))* Cram101 Inc.

Benton, Janetta Rebold & DiYanni, Robert. Arts & Culture: An Introduction to the Humanities. 4th ed. 2011. (ENG.). 688p. (C). pap. 127.40 *(978-0-205-81667-5(3)*, Prentice Hall) Prentice Hall PTR.

—Arts & Culture: An Introduction to the Humanities, Volume 1, Books a la Carte Plus MyHumanitiesKit. 4th ed. 2011. (ENG.). (C). ring bd. 84.67 ***(978-0-205-23313-7(9)***, Prentice Hall) Prentice Hall PTR.

—Arts & Culture: An Introduction to the Humanities, Volume I & MyHumanitiesKit — Valuepack Access Card Package. 4th ed. 2011. (ENG.). (C). pap. 119.80 ***(978-0-205-17922-0(3)***, Prentice Hall) Prentice Hall PTR.

—Arts & Culture: An Introduction to the Humanities, Volume II, Books a la Carte Edition. 4th ed. 2011. (ENG.). 512p. (C). ring bd. 78.00 ***(978-0-205-03471-0(3)***, Prentice Hall) Prentice Hall PTR.

—Arts & Culture Vol. 1: An Introduction to the Humanities. 4th rev. ed. 2010. (ENG.). 480p. (C). pap. 119.80 *(978-0-205-81660-6(6)*, Prentice Hall) Prentice Hall PTR.

—Arts & Culture Vol. II: An Introduction to the Humanities. 4th ed. 2011. (ENG.). (C). 512p. pap. 119.80 *(978-0-13-213496-5(9))*; ring bd. 84.67 *(978-0-205-03472-7(1))* Prentice Hall PTR. (Prentice Hall).

Berman, Eleanor Davidson. Thomas Jefferson among the Arts. *(978-0-8022-0111-9(3))* Philosophical Library, Inc.

Bruno, Giuliana. Atlas of Emotion: Journeys in Art, Architecture, & Film. 2007. (ENG., Illus.). 496p. pap. 44.95 *(978-1-85984-133-4(3)*, 859133) Verso Bks. GBR. Dist: Norton, W. W. & Co., Inc.

Bucker, Andreas, et al, eds. Resonances: Historical Essays on Continuity & Change. 2011. (Ritus et Artes Ser.). (ENG., Illus.). 266p. (C). 116.00 *(978-2-503-53493-0(7))* Brepols Pubs. BEL. Dist: ISD.

Carson, Anne, et al, texts. Elliott Hundley. 2012. (ENG., Illus.). 84p. pap. 39.95 ***(978-1-881390-50-3(0))*** Ohio State Univ., Wexner Ctr. for the Arts.

Cashen, Trish, et al, eds. Futures Past: Thirty Years of Arts Computing. 2008. (Computers & the History of Art Ser.). (Illus.). 128p. per. 40.00 *(978-1-84150-168-0(9))* Intellect, Ltd. GBR. Dist: Chicago Distribution Ctr.

Cram101 Textbook Reviews. Outlines & Highlights for Arts & Culture: An Introduction to the Humanities, Combined Volume by Janetta Rebold Benton. 2011. 662p. pap. 41.95 ***(978-1-61905-112-6(5))*** Cram101 Inc.

—Outlines & Highlights for Arts & Culture, Combined by Janetta Rebold Benton, Isbn: 9780132283915 0132283913 9780132321716 9780131578616. 2011. 502p. pap. 37.95 ***(978-1-61812-323-7(8))*** Cram101 Inc.

Cram101 Textbook Reviews Staff. Outlines & Highlights for the Creative Impulse: An Introduction to the Arts by Dennis J. Sporre, ISBN. 2009. 140p. pap. 28.95 *(978-1-4288-9218-7(4))* Cram101 Inc.

Eleey, Peter, et al, texts. The Quick & the Dead. 2009. (ENG., Illus.). 352p. 45.00 *(978-0-935640-93-9(2))* Walker Art Ctr.

ELKINS, James, ed. The Contemporary Visual Studies Reader. 2011. 560p. (C). 150.00 *(978-0-415-87793-0(8))*; pap. 60.00 *(978-0-415-87794-7(6))* Routledge.

Frank, Patrick L., et al. Prebles' Artforms, Books a la Carte Edition. 10th ed. 2010. (ENG.). 504p. (C). ring bd. 98.00 *(978-0-205-01148-3(9)*, Prentice Hall) Prentice Hall PTR.

Gere, Cathy. Knossos & the Prophets of Modernism. 2009. (Illus.). 288p. 27.50 *(978-0-226-28953-3(2))* Univ. of Chicago Pr.

Kal, Hong. Aesthetic Constructions of Korean Nationalism: Spectacle, Politics & History. 2011. (Asia's Transformations Ser.). (ENG., Illus.). 184p. (C). 133.00 *(978-0-415-60256-3(4))* Routledge.

Kang, Minsoo & Woodson-Boulton, Amy, eds. Visions of the Industrial Age 1830-1914: Modernity & the Age of Representation in Europe. 2008. (Illus.). 394p. 144.95 *(978-0-7546-6488-8(0))* Ashgate Publishing Co.

Kearns, James. Théophile Gautier, Orator to the Artists: Art Journalism in in the Second Republic. 2007. (Legenda Main Ser.). (Illus.). 200p. (C). 79.50 *(978-1-904350-88-0(7))* European Humanities Research Ctr. GBR. Dist: Brown, David Bk. Co., The.

McLerran, Jennifer. A New Deal for Native Art: Indian Arts & Federal Policy, 1933-1943. 2009. (ENG., Illus.). 312p. 59.95 *(978-0-8165-2766-3(0))* Univ. of Arizona Pr.

Min, Shen. Bamboo in China: Arts, Crafts & a Cultural History. Lee, Yawtsong, tr. 2011. (ENG., Illus.). 128p. 16.95 *(978-1-60220-132-3(3))* BetterLink Pr., Inc.

Muther, Richard. The History of Modern Painting. 2010. 432p. pap. 33.45 *(978-1-4455-6485-2(8))* Audubon Pr. & Christian Bk. Service.

Safina, Carl & Longobardi, Pam. Pam Longobardi: Drifters. 2010. (ENG., Illus.). 96p. pap. 29.95 *(978-88-8158-770-4(X))* Charta ITA. Dist: D.A.P./Distributed Art Pubs.

Sharp, Charles. The Sovereignty of Art: Two Discourses Delivered in the Liverpool. 2007. pap. 18.95 *(978-1-4304-9294-8(5))* Kessinger Publishing, LLC.

Sidorenko, Irina. Private Art Collecting in St Petersburg Around 1900. 2008. 104p. pap. *(978-3-639-03017-4(6))* VDM Verlag Dr. Mueller e.K.

Sporre, Dennis J. The Creative Impulse: An Introduction to the Arts. 8th ed. 2008. (ENG., Illus.). 640p. (C). pap. 138.00 *(978-0-13-603493-3(4)*, Prentice Hall) Prentice Hall PTR.

—Reality Through the Arts. 7th ed. 2009. (ENG.). 432p. (C). pap. 128.40 *(978-0-205-66048-3(7)*, Prentice Hall) Prentice Hall PTR.

Watson, William & Ho, Chumei. The Arts of China after 1620. 2007. (Pelican History of Art Ser.). (ENG., Illus.). 320p. 65.00 *(978-0-300-10735-7(8))* Yale Univ. Pr.

ARTS—MANAGEMENT

Abruzzo, James. Arts Leadership. (ENG.). 312p. (C). 2012. 145.00 *(978-0-415-77927-2(8))* 2010. pap. 51.95 *(978-0-415-77928-9(6))* Routledge.

Bendixen, Peter. Managing Art: An Introduction into Principles & Conceptions. 2011. (ENG., Illus.). 256p. pap. 34.95 *(978-3-643-50063-2(7))* Lit Verlag DEU. Dist: Transaction Pubs.

Brindle, Meg & DeVereaux, Constance, eds. The Arts Management Handbook: New Directions for Students & Practitioners. 2011. (ENG., Illus.). 368p. (C). 89.95 *(978-0-7656-1741-5(2))* Sharpe, M.E. Inc.

Brindle, Meg & Devereaux, Constance, eds. The Arts Management Handbook: New Directions for Students & Practitioners. 2011. (ENG., Illus.). 368p. (C). pap. 45.95 ***(978-0-7656-1742-2(0))*** Sharpe, M.E. Inc.

Byrnes, William. Management & the Arts. 4th ed. 2008. (ENG., Illus.). 496p. pap. 48.95 *(978-0-240-81004-1(X)*, Focal Pr.) Elsevier Science & Technology Bks.

Carpenter, Gaylene, et al. Arts & Cultural Programming: A Leisure Perspective. 2008. (ENG., Illus.). 264p. (C). (gr. 13-16). pap. 39.00 *(978-0-7360-6564-1(4))* Human Kinetics Pubs.

Carter, Terrell, text. Machiavellian Arts Management: Timeless Advice for 21st Century Arts Managers, 1. 2006. 142p. per. 15.00 *(978-0-9792443-0-8(7))* CCD Publishing.

Chen, Katherine K. Enabling Creative Chaos: The Organization Behind the Burning Man Event. 2009. (ENG., Illus.). 272p. 75.00 *(978-0-226-10237-5(8))*; pap. 25.00 *(978-0-226-10238-2(6))* Univ. of Chicago Pr.

Chong. Arts Management. 2nd rev. ed. 2010. (ENG., Illus.). 264p. (C). pap. 54.95 *(978-0-415-42391-5(0))* Routledge.

Chong, Derrick. Arts Management. 2nd rev. ed. 2010. (ENG., Illus.). 264p. (C). 160.00 *(978-0-415-42390-8(2))* Routledge.

Henry, Colette, ed. Entrepreneurship in the Creative Industries: An International Perspective. 2008. (Illus.). 224p. (C). 119.00 *(978-1-84542-610-1(X))* Elgar, Edward Publishing, Inc.

Heo, Soonran. The Potential of the Internet in Arts Management: Online & Offline Integrated Arts Management. 2008. 296p. pap. *(978-3-639-09446-6(8))* VDM Verlag Dr. Mueller e.K.

Holden, John & Hewison, Robert. The Cultural Leadership Handbook: How to Run a Creative Organization. 2011. (Illus.). 222p. 74.95 *(978-0-566-09176-6(3)*, Gower Publishing Co., Ltd.) Ashgate Publishing, Ltd. GBR. Dist: Ashgate Publishing Co.

Kaiser, Michael M. Leading Roles: 50 Questions Every Arts Board Should Ask. 2010. (Illus.). 192p. 24.95 *(978-1-58465-906-8(8)*, Brandeis University Press) Univ. Pr. of New England.

Lake, Anthony S. Leading the Creative Mind. 2011. 134p. pap. ***(978-1-86335-976-4(1))*** Common Ground Publishing Pty, Ltd.

Munoz-Seca, Beatriz & Riverola, Josep, eds. When Business Meets Culture: Ideas & Experiences for Mutual Profit. 2011. (ENG., Illus.). 304p. 100.00 *(978-0-230-28016-8(1))* Palgrave Macmillan.

Quigg, Anne-Marie. Bullying in the Arts: Vocation, Exploitation & Abuse of Power. 2011. (Illus.). 266p. 124.95 *(978-1-4094-0482-8(X)*, Gower Publishing Co., Ltd.) Ashgate Publishing, Ltd. GBR. Dist: Ashgate Publishing Co.

Rauhe, Hermann & Demmer, Christine, eds. Kulturmanagement: Theorie und Praxis einer professionellen Kunst. (GER.). X, 594p. 210.00 ***(978-3-11-178564-6(5))*** De Gruyter, Walter Inc.

Sacramento, Nuno & Zeiske, Claudia, contrib. by. ARTocracy: Art, Informal Space, & Social Consequence: a curatorial handbook in collaborative practice. 2011. (ENG., Illus.). 192p. pap. 35.00 *(978-3-86859-064-7(1))* Jovis Verlag GmbH DEU. Dist: D.A.P./Distributed Art Pubs.

Smith, Melanie Kay. Cultural Planning for Urban Regeneration. 2010. 208p. pap. *(978-3-8383-9203-5(5))* Lambert Academic Publishing.

Volz, Jim. How to Run a Theater: Creating, Leading & Managing Professional Theater. 2nd ed. 2011. (ENG.). 192p. pap. 19.95 *(978-1-4081-3474-0(8)*, Methuen Drama) A & C Black GBR. Dist: Bloomsbury Publishing Plc.

Williams, Theo Stephan. The Interior Designer's Guide to Pricing, Estimating, & Budgeting. 2nd ed. 2010. (ENG., Illus.). 256p. pap. 24.95 *(978-1-58115-718-5(5)*, 115718, Allworth Pr.) Skyhorse Publishing Co., Inc.

Zan, Luca. Managerial Rhetoric & Arts Organizations. 2006. (ENG., Illus.). 192p. 121.00 *(978-0-230-00022-3(3))* Palgrave Macmillan.

Zander, Ivo & Scherdin, Mikael. Art Entrepreneurship. Zander, Ivo & Scherdin, Mikael, eds. 2011. (Illus.). 208p. 110.00 *(978-1-84844-369-3(2))* Elgar, Edward Publishing, Inc.

ARTS—PHILOSOPHY

Andina, Tiziana. Confini Sfumati: I Problemi Dell'arte, le Soluzioni Della Percezione. 2009. (ITA., Illus.). 199p. *(978-88-8483-852-0(5))* Mimesis.

Ardar, Cubitt, et al. 3rd Text Reader on Art/Culture/Theory. 2007. (Illus.). 400p. *(978-0-8254-9643-0(1))* Continuum International Publishing Group, Ltd.

Ascott, Roy, et al, eds. New Realities: Being Syncretic - Consciousness Reframed - The Planetary Collegium's 4th International Research Conference. 2008. (Edition Angewandte Ser.). (ENG., Illus.). 360p. 49.95 *(978-3-211-78890-5(5)*, 3211788905) Springer.

Bamford, Kiff. Lyotard & the Figural in Performance, Art & Writing. 2012. (Continuum Studies in Continental Philosophy Ser.). (ENG.). 224p. 120.00 ***(978-1-4411-6707-1(2))*** Continuum International Publishing Group, Ltd. GBR. Dist: National Bk. Network.

—Lyotard & the Figural in Performance, Art, & Writing. 2012. ***(978-1-4411-0875-3(0))*** Continuum International Publishing Group, Ltd.

Bell, Charles. The Anatomy & Philosophy of Expression As Connected with the Fine Arts. 2010. 136p. pap. *(978-1-151-88304-9(2))* Books LLC.

—The Anatomy & Philosophy of Expression As Connected with the Fine Arts. 2007. (ENG.). 312p. 45.95 *(978-0-548-10649-5(5))* Kessinger Publishing, LLC.

Benedetto, Stephen Di. The Provocation of the Senses in Contemporary Theatre. 2010. (Routledge Advances in Theatre & Performance Studies). (ENG.). 252p. (C). 125.00 *(978-0-415-87267-6(7))* Routledge.

Berlekamp, Persis. Wonder, Image, & Cosmos in Medieval Islam. 2011. (ENG., Illus.). 224p. 65.00 *(978-0-300-17060-3(2))* Yale Univ. Pr.

Butcher, S. H. Aristotle's Theory of Poetry & Fine Art. 2008. 464p. pap. *(978-1-4097-8247-6(6))* Read Bks.

Carrier, David. Proust/Warhol: Analytical Philosophy of Art. 2008. (American University Studies XX: Fine Arts Ser.). 142p. (C). 58.95 *(978-1-4331-0433-6(4))* Lang, Peter Publishing, Inc.

Carroll, Noel. Living in an Art World. 2008. (ENG.). 272p. 20.95 *(978-0-415-91938-8(X))*; 74.95 *(978-0-415-91937-1(1))* Routledge.

Cixous, Hélène. Poetry in Painting: Writings on Contemporary Arts & Aesthetics. Segarra, Marta & Masó, Joana, eds. 2012. (Frontiers of Theory Ser.). (ENG., Illus.). 224p. (gr. 17). 105.00 ***(978-0-7486-4744-6(9))*** Edinburgh Univ. Pr. GBR. Dist: Columbia Univ. Pr.

Clancy, Patrick & Dill, David D., eds. The Research Mission of the University: Policy Reforms & Institutional Response. 2009. 226p. *(978-90-8790-996-3(9))*; pap. *(978-90-8790-995-6(0))* Sense Pubs.

Cram101 Textbook Reviews. Outlines & Highlights for Perceiving the Arts by Dennis J Sporre. 2011. 216p. pap. 30.95 ***(978-1-4672-7001-4(6))*** Cram101 Inc.

Davis, James W. Image As Idea: The Arts in Global Cultures. 2nd rev. ed. 2009. (ENG., Illus.). 290p. pap. 81.00 *(978-0-7575-6027-9(X))* Kendall Hunt Publishing Co.

De Bolla, Peter. Aesthetics & the Work of Art: Adorno, Kafka, Richter. De Bolla, Peter & Uhlig, Stefan H., eds. 2008. (Language, Discourse, Society Ser.). (ENG., Illus.). 280p. 100.00 *(978-0-230-54919-7(5))* Palgrave Macmillan.

Feige, Daniel Martin & Köppe, Tilmann, eds. Funktionen von Kunst. 2009. (GER & ENG.). 224p. pap. 56.95 *(978-3-631-57838-4(5))* Lang, Peter GmbH, Europaischer Verlag der Wissenschaften DEU. Dist: Lang, Peter.

Finger, Anke K. & Follett, Danielle, eds. The Aesthetics of the Total Artwork: On Borders & Fragments. 2010. (Rethinking Theory Ser.). (ENG., Illus.). 480p. (gr. 17). 90.00 *(978-0-8018-9582-1(0))* Johns Hopkins Univ. Pr.

Giannachi, Gabriella. The Politics of New Media Theatre. 2009. (Illus.). 152p. pap. 34.00 *(978-0-415-54409-2(2))* Routledge.

Grosz, Elizabeth. Chaos, Territory, Art: Deleuze & the Framing of the Earth. 2008. (Wellek Library Lectures). (ENG., Illus.). 136p. (gr. 17). 24.00 *(978-0-231-14518-3(7))* Columbia Univ. Pr.

Hinderliter, Beth, et al, eds. Communities of Sense: Rethinking Aesthetics & Politics. 2009. (ENG., Illus.). 384p. 94.95 *(978-0-8223-4497-1(1))*; pap. 26.95 *(978-0-8223-4513-8(7))* Duke Univ. Pr.

Holland, Eugene W. Gilles Deleuze: Image & Text. Smith, Daniel W. & Stivale, Charles J., eds. 2009. (ENG., Illus.). 288p. 34.95 *(978-0-8264-3923-9(3))*; 130.00 *(978-0-8264-0832-7(X))* Continuum International Publishing Group, Ltd. GBR. Dist: National Bk. Network.

Holler, Christian. Time Action Vision. 2010. (ENG., Illus.). 222p. pap. 29.95 *(978-3-03764-124-8(X))* JRP Ringier Kunstverlag AG CHE. Dist: D.A.P./Distributed Art Pubs.

Houlgate, Stephen, ed. Hegel & the Arts. 2007. (Topics in Historical Philosophy Ser.). (ENG.). 382p. 79.95 *(978-0-8101-2361-8(4))*; per. 34.95 *(978-0-8101-2362-5(2))* Northwestern Univ. Pr.

Jaeger, Stephen. Magnificence & the Sublime in Medieval Aesthetics: Art, Architecture, Literature, Music. Jaeger, Stephen, ed. 2010. (New Middle Ages Ser.). (ENG., Illus.). 320p. 84.00 *(978-0-230-61898-5(7))* Palgrave Macmillan.

Jdey, Adnen & Kuhn, Rolf, eds. Michel Henry et l'affect de L'art: Recherches sur l'esthétique de la phénoménologie Matérielle. 2010. (Studies in Contemporary Phenomenology Ser.). *(978-90-04-18633-0(6))* BRILL.

Krause, Günter, ed. L' Autre: création et Médiation: Actes du colloque international du CERCI, Université de Nantes, Novembre/décembre 2006. 2008. 349p. pap. *(978-3-03911-652-2(5))* Lang, Peter.

Kraut, Robert. Artworld Metaphysics. (ENG.). 2010. 208p. pap. 35.00 *(978-0-19-958742-1(6))* 2007. 176p. 75.00 *(978-0-19-922812-6(4))* Oxford Univ. Pr., Inc.

Lamarque, Peter. Work & Object: Explorations in the Metaphysics of Art. (ENG.). 2012. 264p. pap. 35.00 ***(978-0-19-965549-6(9))*** 2010. 256p. 65.00 *(978-0-19-957746-0(3))* Oxford Univ. Pr., Inc.

Madson, Jerry. Bog Walk Pitcher Plants Meet Implicate Polysynthesis. 2007. 100p. pap. 44.50 *(978-1-4303-2883-4(5))* Lulu Enterprises Inc.

Melberg, Arne, ed. Aesthetics at Work. 2007. 176p. (C). pap. 29.00 *(978-82-7477-294-6(6)*, Oslo Academic Pr.) Unipub forlag NOR. Dist: International Specialized Bk. Services.

Senyshyn, Yaroslav. The artist in crisis: kierkegaard's philosophy of the aesthetic stage of existence & live musical Performance. 2010. 204p. 39.99 *(978-0-557-56093-6(4))*; 206p. pap. 25.99 *(978-0-557-52344-3(3))* Lulu Enterprises Inc.

Short, Christopher. The Art Theory of Wassily Kandinsky, 1909-1928: The Quest for Synthesis. 2009. (Illus.). xiv, 241p. 61.95 *(978-3-03911-399-6(2))* Lang, Peter AG GBR. Dist: Lang, Peter.

Sporre & Sporre, Dennis J. Perceiving the Arts: An Introduction to the Humanities with Music for the Humanities CD. 10th ed. 2011. (ENG.). (C). pap. 66.60 incl. cd-rom ***(978-0-205-23406-6(2)***, Prentice Hall) Prentice Hall PTR.

Sporre, Dennis J. Perceiving the Arts: An Introduction to the Humanities. 10th rev. ed. 2011. (ENG.). 272p. (C). pap. 66.60 *(978-0-205-09655-8(7)*, Prentice Hall) Prentice Hall PTR.

Thomson, Iain D. Heidegger, Art, & Postmodernity. 2011. (ENG., Illus.). 266p. 90.00 *(978-1-107-00150-3(1))*; 264p. pap. 27.99 *(978-0-521-17249-3(7))* Cambridge Univ. Pr.

van Eck, Caroline, et al, eds. The Question of Style in Philosophy & the Arts. 2010. (Cambridge Studies in Philosophy & the Arts Ser.). (ENG.). 258p. pap 37.00 *(978-0-521-15441-3(3))* Cambridge Univ. Pr.

Zeller, Christoph. Ästhetik des Authentischen: Literatur und Kunst Um 1970. 2010. (Spectrum Literaturwissenschaft / spectrum Literature Ser.).Tr. of Aesthetics of the Authentic. (GER., Illus.). IX, 333p. 140.00 *(978-3-11-022720-8(7))* De Gruyter, Walter Inc.

ARTS—PSYCHOLOGY

Becker, Howard S. Art Worlds. 25th ed. 2008. (Illus.). 408p. pap. 26.95 *(978-0-520-25636-1(0))* Univ. of California Pr.

Cram101 Textbook Reviews & Cram101 Textbook Reviews. Outlines & Highlights for Humanities Through the Arts by F David Martin. 2011. 400p. pap. 35.95 ***(978-1-61830-675-3(8))*** Cram101 Inc.

Faulkner, Barbara. A Way of Seeing & the Spiritual Search for Visual Truth in Painting. 2007. 172p. per. *(978-3-8364-2978-8(0))* VDM Verlag Dr. Mueller e.K.

Greene, David B. Styles in Art That Suddenly Disappear: An Unanswered Problem in Art History. 2008. (Illus.). 208p. 109.95 *(978-0-7734-5139-1(0))* Mellen, Edwin Pr., The.

Herding, Klaus & Gehrig, Gerlinde. Orte des Unheimlichen: Die Faszination verborgenen Grauens in Literatur und bildender Kunst. 2006. (Schriften D. sigmund-freud-inst. reihe 2: psychoanalyse im interdisziplinaren Dialog Ser.). (GER., Illus.). 300p. (C). pap. 42.00 *(978-3-525-45176-2(8))* Vandenhoeck & Ruprecht GmbH & Co. KG DEU. Dist: ISD.

Martin, F. David & Jacobus, Lee A. Telecourse Guide for Humanities through the Arts. 8th ed. 2010. (ENG.). 384p. (C). pap. 65.67 *(978-0-07-733326-3(8)*, 0077333268) McGraw-Hill Cos., The.

Milbrath, Consta. Arts & Human Development. 2009. (Jean Piaget Symposia Ser.). (ENG., Illus.). 304p. 84.95 *(978-0-415-96553-8(5)*, Psychology Press) Taylor & Francis Group GBR. Dist: Taylor & Francis Group.

Rowland, Susan. Psyche & the Arts: Jungian Approaches to Music, Architecture, Literature, Film & Painting. Rowland, Susan, ed. 2008. (ENG., Illus.). 216p. (C). 110.00 *(978-0-415-43835-3(7))* Routledge.

Rowland, Susan, ed. Psyche & the Arts: Jungian Approaches to Music, Architecture, Literature, Painting & Film. 2008. (ENG., Illus.). 216p. (C). 42.50 *(978-0-415-43836-0(5))* Routledge.

Zhu, Shouxing. Wen Yi Xin Li Fa Sheng Lun: Ren Wen Shi Ye Zhong de Wen Yi Xin Li Xue Yan Jiu. 2009. (CHI., Illus.). *(978-7-5601-5183-0(3))* Jilin Univ. Pr.

ARTS—SCHOLARSHIPS, FELLOWSHIPS, ETC.

Burkholder, Preethi. Finding the Money: The Complete Guide to Financial Aid for Students, Actors, Musicians & Artists. 2009. (ENG.). 268p. pap. 35.00 *(978-0-7864-3692-7(1))* McFarland & Co., Inc. Pubs.

ARTS—STUDY AND TEACHING

Abbs, Peter. Living Powers(Rle Edu K) 2012. (Routledge Library Editions: Education Ser.). (ENG.). 248p. 115.00 ***(978-0-415-69580-0(5))*** Routledge.

Albers, Peggy & Sanders, Jennifer, eds. Literacies, the Arts, & Multimodality. 2010. pap. *(978-0-8141-3214-2(6))* National Council of Teachers of English.

Allen, Felicity. Education. 2011. (Whitechapel: Documents of Contemporary Art Ser.). (ENG.). 240p. (gr. 17). pap. 24.95 *(978-0-262-51636-5(5))* MIT Pr.

Bartalot, Sally. Art Alive! A Fresh Approach to the Basics, the Teaching Techniques of Sally Bartalot. 2010. (ENG., Illus.). 144p. pap. 35.00 *(978-1-934491-20-1(9))* Fresco Fine Art Pubns., LLC.

Best, David. The Rationality of Feeling (Rle Edu K) 2012. (Routledge Library Editions: Education Ser.). (ENG.). 232p. 115.00 ***(978-0-415-69784-2(0))*** Routledge.

Beyerbach, Barbara. Activist Art in Social Justice Pedagogy: Engaging Students in Glocal Issues through the Arts. 2011. (Illus.). xii, 223p. (C). pap. 34.95 ***(978-1-4331-1231-7(0))***; 139.95 ***(978-1-4331-1230-0(2))*** Lang, Peter Publishing, Inc.

Boutin, Pierre. Les Arts, les Autres, Etc: éducation, Culture et Territoires en Savoie. 2008. (FRE., Illus.). 127p. *(978-2-84562-132-9(9))* La Passe du vent.

Bresler, L., ed. International Handbook of Research in Arts Education, 2 vols. 2007. (Springer International Handbooks of Education Ser.: Vol. 16). (Illus.). XXXVIII, 1627p. (C). 889.00 *(978-1-4020-2998-1(5)*, 1402029985) Springer London, Ltd. GBR. Dist: Springer.

Bresler, Liora, ed. International Handbook of Research in Arts Education, 2 vols. 2007. (Springer International Handbooks of Education Ser.). (Illus.). xlii, 1634p. pap. 129.00 *(978-1-4020-4857-9(2))* Springer.

Buck, Kavin & Schoenberg, Ed. A Guide to College Choices for the Performing & Visual Arts. 2008. 66p. pap. 17.95 *(978-1-4357-1857-9(7))* Lulu Enterprises Inc.

Burnard, Pamela & Hennessy, Sarah. Reflective Practices in Arts Education. Burnard, Pamela & Hennessy, Sarah, eds. 2006. (Landscapes: the Arts, Aesthetics, & Education Ser.). (Illus.). xvii, 199p. 169.00 *(978-1-4020-4702-2(9)*, 1402047029) Springer.

Burnard, Pamela & Hennessy, Sarah, eds. Reflective Practices in Arts Education. 2008. (Landscapes: the Arts, Aesthetics, & Education Ser.). (ENG., Illus.). xviii, 202p. pap. 59.95 *(978-1-4020-9565-8(1)*, 1402095651) Springer.

Campana, D. M. Teacher of Pottery, Clay Modeling, Casting, Sculpturing, Wood Carving. (Illus.). 9.50 *(978-0-939608-10-2(3))* Campana Art Co.

Cannatella, Howard. The Richness of Art Education. 2008. 136p. *(978-90-8790-608-5(0))*; pap. *(978-90-8790-607-8(2))* Sense Pubs.

Corbett, H. Dickson, et al. Creating & Sustaining Arts-Based School Reform: The A+ Schools Program. 2008. CXCVIII, 10p. 45.95 *(978-0-8058-6149-5(1))* Erlbaum, Lawrence Assocs., Inc.

Cornett, Claudia E. Creating Meaning Through Literature & the Arts: Arts Integration for Classroom Teachers. 4th ed. (ENG., 432p. 2011. Illus.). pap. ***(978-0-13-215359-1(9))*** 2010. (C). pap. 91.60 *(978-0-13-704832-8(7))* Allyn & Bacon, Inc.

Cornett, Claudia E. Creating Meaning through Literature & the Arts: Arts Integration for Classroom Teachers (with MyEducationLab) 4th ed. 2010. (ENG.). 432p. (C). pap. 98.27 *(978-0-13-138142-1(3))* Allyn & Bacon, Inc.

Cram101 Textbook Reviews. Outlines & Highlights for Power of Art by Richard L Lewis, Isbn: 9780534641030. 2010. 388p. pap. 34.95 *(978-1-61698-094-8(X))* Cram101 Inc.

Cram101 Textbook Reviews & Cram101 Textbook Reviews. Outlines & Highlights for Creative Arts: A Process Approach for Teachers & Children by Linda Carol Edwards, ISBN. 2011. 118p. pap. 28.95 ***(978-1-61744-898-0(2))*** Cram101 Inc.

—Outlines & Highlights for Power of Art by Richard L Lewis, Isbn: 9780495501916 0495501913. 2011. 450p. pap. 36.95 ***(978-1-61490-681-0(5))*** Cram101 Inc.

Davis, Jessica Hoffmann. Why Our High Schools Need the Arts. 2011. (ENG.). 160p. pap. 23.95 ***(978-0-8077-5286-9(X))*** Teachers College Pr., Teachers College, Columbia Univ.

Delle, Suzanne. Fitting the Arts into Education. 2010. 68p. pap. *(978-3-8383-1244-6(9))* Lambert Academic Publishing.

Denver Museum of Art Staff, ed. West Point Points West. 2008. (ENG.). 80p. pap. 10.95 *(978-0-8061-9968-9(7))* Denver Art Museum.

Department of Art and Media Staff & Schiesser, Giaco. Practices of Experimentation: Research & Teaching in the Arts Today. 2012. (Verlag Scheidegger & Spiess-Zurich University of the Arts Yearbook Ser.). (GER & ENG., Illus.). 304p. 60.00 *(978-3-85881-259-9(5))* Scheidegger und Spiess AG, Verlag CHE. Dist: Antique Collectors' Club.

Edwards, Linda Carol. The Creative Arts: A Process Approach for Teachers & Children. 5th ed. 2009. (ENG.). 384p. (C). pap. 74.80 *(978-0-13-715163-9(2)*, Prentice Hall) Prentice Hall PTR.

—The Creative Arts: A Process Approach for Teachers & Children (with MyEducationLab) 5th ed. 2009. (ENG.). 384p. (C). pap. 81.47 *(978-0-13-610109-3(7)*, Prentice Hall) Prentice Hall PTR.

Fleming, Mike. The Arts in Education: An Introduction to Aesthetics, Theory & Pedagogy. 2012. (ENG., Illus.). 152p. (C). pap. 40.95 *(978-0-415-62029-1(5))* Routledge.

—An Introduction to the Arts in Education: Aesthetics, theory & Pedagogy. 2012. (ENG., Illus.). 152p. (C). 160.00 *(978-0-415-62028-4(7))* Routledge.

Freestyle Academy of Communication Arts and Technology, compiled by. Glimpse. 2008. (Illus.). 84p. pap. 0.00 *(978-0-9801675-3-5(1))* Robertson Publishing.

Gelineau, Phyllis. Integrating the Arts Across the Elementary School Curriculum. 2nd ed. 2011. (Whatâ€(tm)s New in Education Ser.). (ENG.). 216p. (C). pap. 102.95 *(978-1-111-30126-2(3))* Wadsworth.

Goldberg, Merryl. Arts Integration: Teaching Subject Matter Through the Arts in Multicultural Settings. 4th rev. ed. 2011. (ENG.). 288p. (C). pap. 76.80 *(978-0-13-256556-1(0))* Allyn & Bacon, Inc.

Gore, Elaine Clift. Talent Knows No Color: The History of an Arts Magnet High School. 2007. (Research in Curriculum & Instruction Ser.). (ENG.). 196p. (C). *(978-1-59311-762-7(0))*; per. *(978-1-59311-761-0(2))* Information Age Publishing, Inc.

Hamill, Andrew. Learning Ict in the Arts. 2006. (Teaching ICT through the Primary Curriculum Ser.). (Illus.). CXXIVp. 41.95 *(978-1-84312-313-2(4))* Fulton, David Pubs. GBR. Dist: Taylor & Francis Group.

Hemphill, Brian K. The Elements of Creative & Expressive Artistry: A Philosophy for Creating Everything Artistic. 2011. 600p. 43.95 ***(978-1-4620-0584-0(5))*** iUniverse, Inc.

Hendrick, Becky. About & Through the Arts: Lessons & Activities for Creative Teaching & Learning. 2nd rev. ed. 2010. (ENG.). 194p. pap. 58.76 *(978-0-7575-6062-0(8))* Kendall Hunt Publishing Co.

Hyams, Leigh. How Painting Holds Me on the Earth. 2008. 132p. pap. 16.00 *(978-0-557-01285-5(6))* Lulu Enterprises Inc.

Ibraheem, Remi & Swift, Jordan. For Yourself: Professional Exploration in the Arts. rev. ed. 2010. (ENG., Illus.). 174p. spiral bd. 60.30 *(978-0-7575-8332-2(6))* Kendall Hunt Publishing Co.

Johnice, Deshannee'. Everybody Else's Guide to Careers in the Arts. 2007. (Illus.). 39p. (YA). 10.99 *(978-0-9797177-0-3(1))* Spring4th Publishing.

Joubert, Lindy, ed. Educating in the Arts: The Asian Experience, Twenty-Four Essays. 2008. (Education in the Asia-Pacific Region: Issues, Concerns & Prospects Ser.). (Illus.). 300p. 179.00 *(978-1-4020-6386-2(5))* Springer.

Kincheloe, Joe L., frwd. Assessment in Arts Education. 2006. 192p. (J). (gr. k-8). per. 31.25 *(978-0-325-00795-3(0)*, E00795) Heinemann.

Kohl, Herbert & Oppenheim, Tom, eds. The Muses Go to School: Conversations about the Necessity of Arts in Education. 2012. (ENG., Illus.). 240p. 26.95 *(978-1-59558-539-4(7))* New Pr., The.

Kohl, MaryAnn F., et al. First Art for Toddlers & Twos: Open-Ended Art Experiences. rev. ed. 2012. (ENG., Illus.). 128p. pap. 19.95 ***(978-0-87659-399-8(6))*** Gryphon Hse., Inc.

Korn-Bursztyn, Carol. Young Children & the Arts: Nurturing Imagination & Creativity. 2012. ***(978-1-61735-744-2(8))***; pap. ***(978-1-61735-743-5(X))*** Information Age Publishing, Inc.

Krensky, Beth & Steffen, Seana Lowe. Engaging Classrooms & Communities Through Art: A Guide to Designing & Implementing Community-Based Art Education. 2008. (ENG., Illus.). 204p. 75.00 *(978-0-7591-1067-0(0))*; pap. 29.95 *(978-0-7591-1068-7(9))* AltaMira Pr.

Lubawy, Joy. Visions of Creativity in Early Childhood: Connecting Theory, Practice, & Reflection. 2010. (ENG.). 264p. pap. 59.95 *(978-1-60554-038-2(2))* Redleaf Pr.

Macintyre Latta, Margaret & Chan, Elaine. Teaching the Arts to Engage English Language Learners. 2010. (ENG., Illus.). 264p. 135.00 *(978-0-415-87385-7(1))*; pap. 36.95 *(978-0-415-87386-4(X))* Routledge.

Martin, F. David & Jacobus, Lee A. Telecourse Guide for Humanities through the Arts. 8th ed. 2010. (ENG.). 384p. (C). pap. 65.67 *(978-0-07-733326-3(8)*, 0077333268) McGraw-Hill Cos., The.

McGee, Brenda & McGee, Tom. Reader's Theater & So Much More! 2007. 112p. pap. 19.95 *(978-1-59363-241-0(X))* Prufrock Pr.

Millette, Lynn. The Experience of Artmaking. 2010. 164p. pap. *(978-3-8383-0343-7(1))* Lambert Academic Publishing.

Mullen, Cathy. Viewfinding: Perspectives on New Media Curriculum in the Arts. 2010. (Minding the Media: Critical Issues for Learning & Teaching Ser.). 256p. (C). 129.95 *(978-1-4331-0849-5(6))*; pap. 34.95 *(978-1-4331-0850-1(X))* Lang, Peter Publishing, Inc.

Naidus, Beverly. Arts for Change: Teaching Outside the Frame. 2009. (ENG., Illus.). 256p. pap. 17.95 *(978-0-9815593-0-8(1))* New Village Pr.

Narey, Marilyn. Making Meaning: Constructing Multimodal Perspectives of Language, Literacy, & Learning Through Arts-Based Early Childhood Education. 2008. (Educating the Young Child Ser.). (ENG., Illus.). viii, 258p. 159.00 *(978-0-387-87537-8(9)*, 0387875379) Springer.

Narey, Marilyn, ed. Making Meaning: Constructing Multimodal Perspectives of Language, Literacy, & Learning Through Arts-Based Early Childhood Education. 2008. (Educating the Young Child Ser.). (Illus.). viii, 258p. pap. 49.95 *(978-0-387-87690-0(1))* Springer.

Peterson's. College Guide for Visual Arts Majors 2009: Real-World Admission Guide for All Fine Arts, Design, & Media Majors. Oram, Fern, ed. 3rd ed. 2008. (ENG., Illus.). 416p. pap. 24.95 *(978-0-7689-2564-7(9))* Peterson's.

—Graduate Programs in the Humanities, Arts & Social Sciences 2009. Oram, Fern, ed. 43rd ed. 2008. (ENG.). 1776p. 54.95 *(978-0-7689-2566-1(5))* Peterson's.

Peterson's & Everett, Carole J. College Guide for Performing Arts Majors: The Real-World Admission Guide for Dance, Music, & Theater Majors. Schwartz, Jill, ed. 15th ed. 2009. (ENG.). 464p. (YA). pap. 24.95 *(978-0-7689-2698-9(X))* Peterson's.

Peterson's Guides Staff. College Guide for Visual Arts Majors. Schwartz, Jill, ed. 15th ed. 2009. (ENG.). 416p. (YA). pap. 24.95 *(978-0-7689-2699-6(8))* Peterson's.

Peterson's Guides Staff, creator. Peterson's Graduate Programs in the Humanities, Arts & Social Sciences, Bk. 2. 41st ed. 2006. (ENG.). 1800p. 54.00 *(978-0-7689-2158-8(9))* Peterson's.

Pigrum, Derek. Teaching Creativity: Multi-mode Transitional Practices. 2009. (Continuum Studies in Educational Research Ser.). (ENG., Illus.). 216p. 140.00 *(978-1-84706-038-9(2))* Continuum International Publishing Group, Ltd. GBR. Dist: National Bk. Network.

Rudman, Jack. Social Studies, Literature & Fine Arts. (National Teacher Examination Ser.: NC-4). pap. 23.95 *(978-0-8373-8404-7(4)*, Passbooks) National Learning Corp.

Savage, Jonathan & Fautley, Martin. Cross-Curricular Teaching & Learning in the Secondary School! - The Arts: Drama, Visual Art, Music & Design. 2011. (ENG., Illus.). 192p. (C). 128.00 *(978-0-415-55044-4(0))* Fulton, David Pubs. GBR. Dist: Taylor & Francis Group.

—Cross-Curricular Teaching & Learning in the Secondary School! - The Arts: Drama, Visual Art, Music & Design. 2011. (ENG., Illus.). 192p. (C). pap. 35.95 *(978-0-415-55045-1(9))* Routledge.

Selwyn, Douglas. Living History in the Classroom: Integrative Arts Activities for Making Social Studies Meaningful. 2008. (ENG., Illus.). 224p. (gr. 5-12). pap. 29.95 *(978-1-59363-336-3(X))* Prufrock Pr.

Sikes, Michael. Building Parent Involvement Through the Arts: Activities & Projects That Enrich Classrooms & Schools. 2007. (Illus.). 168p. 76.95 (978-1-4129-3682-8(9), B36829C); per. 33.95 (978-1-4129-3683-5(7), B36829P) Corwin Pr.

Sinclair, Christine, et al, eds. Education in the Arts: Principles & Practices for Teaching. 2008. (ENG., Illus.). 215p. pap. 75.00 (978-0-19-556056-5(6)) Oxford Univ. Pr., Inc.

Smith, Tom. The Other Blocking: Teaching & Performing Improvisation. rev. ed. 2009. (ENG.). 144p. pap. 44.24 (978-0-7575-6071-2(7)) Kendall Hunt Publishing Co.

Spencer, Tracy. The Arts in Every Day: A Practical Introduction. rev. ed. 2010. (ENG.). 68p. pap. 62.17 (978-0-7575-4203-9(4)) Kendall Hunt Publishing Co.

Taylor, Rod & Andrews, Glennis. The Arts in the Primary School (Rle Edu O) 2011. (Routledge Library Editions: Education Ser.). (ENG.). 232p. 115.00 **(978-0-415-68986-1(4))** Routledge.

The Mailbox Books Staff. Arts & Crafts for Favorite Themes: PreK-1. 2010. (Illus.). 144p. 19.95 (978-1-56234-935-6(X), Mailbox Bks., The) Education Ctr., Inc.

Tickle, Les, ed. The Arts in Education(Rle Edu O) 2011. (Routledge Library Editions: Education Ser.). (ENG.). 312p. 130.00 **(978-0-415-68988-5(0))** Routledge.

Tickner, Lisa. Hornsey 1968: The Art School Revolution. 2008. (ENG., Illus.). 208p. pap. 24.95 (978-0-7112-2874-0(4)) Lincoln, Frances Ltd. GBR. Dist: Perseus-PGW.

Using Digital Information in Teaching & Learning in the Visual Arts. Date not set. (Visual Arts Data Service Ser.). pap. (978-1-84217-039-7(2)) Oxbow Bks., Ltd. GBR. Dist: Brown, David Bk. Co., The.

Wankel, Charles. Teaching Arts & Science with the New Social Media. 2011. (Cutting-Edge Technologies in Higher Education Ser.: Vol. 3). (Illus.). 405p. 79.99 (978-0-85724-781-0(6)) Emerald Group Publishing Ltd. GBR. Dist: Turpin Distribution Services Ltd.

Weiss, Cynthia. AIM Print: New Relationship in the Arts & Learning. Weiss, Cynthia & Lichtenstein, Amanda Leigh, eds. 2007. (Illus.). 332p. pap. 27.50 (978-0-929911-22-9(9)) Ctr. for American Places, Inc.

Wilson, Olivia M., ed. Arts Education: Assessment & Access. 2010. (Education in a Competitive & Globalizing World Ser.). 208p. 115.00 (978-1-61728-266-9(9)) Nova Science Pubs., Inc.

Wynne, Sharon. CSET Art Sample Subtest 140. 2008. (Xam Cset Ser.). (ENG.). 76p. pap. 16.50 (978-1-58197-397-6(7)) XAMonline, Inc.

Yeh, Lily. Awakening Creativity: Dandelion School Blossoms. 2011. (ENG., Illus.). 224p. 34.95 (978-0-9815593-7-7(9)) New Village Pr.

Zakaras, Laura & Lowell, Julia F. Cultivating Demand for the Arts: Arts Learning, Arts Engagement, & State Arts Policy. 2008. 172p. pap. 30.50 (978-0-8330-4184-5(3), mg-640) RAND Corp., The.

ARTS—AFRICA

Deacon, Janette, contrib. by. Some Views on Rock Paintings in the Cederberg. 2nd ed. (Illus.). (978-1-875012-25-1(7)) National Monuments Council.

Faber, Paul & Floor, Rob. African Signs. 2010. (Illus.). 210p. 45.00 (978-94-6022-080-7(0)) Royal Tropical Institute Pr. (KIT (Koninklijk Instituut voor de Tropen) NLD. Dist: Stylus Publishing, LLC.

Falola, Toyin & Ngom, Fallou. Facts, Fiction, & African Creative Imaginations. Falola, Toyin & Ngom, Fallou, eds. 2009. (Routledge African Studies). (ENG., Illus.). 348p. 125.00 (978-0-415-80316-8(0)) Routledge.

Gerdes, Paulus. African Basketry: A Gallery of Twill-Plaited Designs & Patterns. 2008. 220p. pap. 19.95 (978-1-4357-2625-3(1)) Lulu Enterprises Inc.

Kellner, Clive & Gonzalez, Sergio-Albio, eds. Thami Mnyele + Medu: Art Ensemble Retrospective. 2010. (ENG., Illus.). 264p. pap. 45.00 (978-1-77009-688-2(4)) Jacana Media ZAF. Dist: Independent Pubs. Group.

MacGonagle, Elizabeth. Crafting Identity in Zimbabwe & Mozambique. 2007. (Rochester Studies in African History & the Diaspora Ser.: Volume 30). (Illus.). 205p. 80.00 (978-1-58046-257-0(X)) Univ. of Rochester Pr.

Morel, Julien & Pinto, Alberto. Alberto Pinto Today. 2011. (ENG., Illus.). 256p. 65.00 (978-2-08-020074-7(7)) Flammarion et Cie FRA. Dist: Random Hse., Inc.

Okagbue, Osita. African Theatres & Performances. 2012. (ENG., Illus.). 208p. pap. 42.95 **(978-0-415-54085-8(2))** Routledge.

Okagbue, Osita, ed. 'African Performance Practices: Views & Insights (African Performance Review, Vol 2 No 1) 2008. 108p. pap. (978-1-906704-14-8(7)) Adonis & Abbey Publishers Ltd.

Riccio, Thomas. Performing Africa: Remixing Tradition, Theatre, & Culture. 2007. (Illus.). 256p. (C). 70.95 (978-0-8204-8899-8(2)) Lang, Peter Publishing, Inc.

Simak, Evelyn & Dreibelbis, Carl. African Beads: Jewels of a Continent. Liechty, Jacob, ed. 2010. (Illus.). 216p. 69.95 (978-0-9816267-2-7(6)) Africa Direct.

ARTS—AUSTRALIA

English, Bonnie & Pomazan, Liliana, eds. Australian Fashion Unstitched: The Last 60 Years, 1 vol. 2010. (Illus.). 312p. pap. 45.00 (978-0-521-75649-5(9)) Cambridge Univ. Pr.

Ennis, Helen. Photography & Australia. 2007. (Reaktion Books - Exposures Ser.). (ENG., Illus.). 144p. pap. 29.95 (978-1-86189-323-9(X)) Reaktion Bks., Ltd. GBR. Dist: Chicago Distribution Ctr.

Featherstone, Don. Creative Spirits: An Insight into the Life & Work of Some Extraordinary Australians. (Illus.). 148p. pap. (978-0-86806-610-3(9), Hale & Iremonger) GHR Pr., The.

Gilbert, Helen & Lo, Jacqueline. Performance & Cosmopolitics: Cross-Cultural Transactions in Australasia. 2009. (Studies in International Performance Ser.). (ENG., Illus.). 256p. pap. 32.00 (978-0-230-23402-4(X)) Palgrave Macmillan.

Sherman Contemporary Art Foundation Ltd. Contemporary Art & Philanthropy No. 7: Exploring the Foundations. Smith, Terry, ed. 2007. (ENG.). 104p. pap. (978-0-86840-951-1(0), UNSW Press) NewSouth Publishing AUS. Dist: Independent Pubs. Group.

Systems Design Limited, creator. Jeremyville Sessions: An Inside Look at Collaborations with over 300 International Artists & Companies. 2007. (Illus.). 304p. (978-988-98992-3-3(X)) Systems Design, Ltd.

Walker, David & Tampke, Jyrgen, eds. From Berlin to Burdekin. (Illus.). 300p. (978-0-86840-332-8(6), UNSW Press) NewSouth Publishing.

ARTS—CANADA

Blomberg, Nancy J. Action & Agency: Advancing the Dialogue on Native Performance Art. 2010. (978-0-914738-65-7(8)) Denver Art Museum.

Bourduas, Paul-Emile, et al. Total Refusal - Refus Global: The Complete 1948 Manifesto of the Montreal Automatists. 2010. (Exile Classics Ser.). (ENG., Illus.). 140p. pap. 18.95 (978-1-55096-107-2(1)) Exile Editions, Ltd. CAN. Dist: Independent Pubs. Group.

Brault, Simon. No Culture, No Future. Kaplansky, Jonathan, tr. from FRE. 2010. (ENG.). 200p. 21.00 (978-1-897151-76-1(4)) Cormorant Bks. Inc. CAN. Dist: Univ. of Toronto Pr.

Cho, Michael. Back Alleys & Urban Landscapes. 2012. (ENG., Illus.). 80p. pap. 19.95 **(978-1-77046-080-5(2))** Drawn & Quarterly Pubns. CAN. Dist: Macmillan.

Cronin, J. Keri & Robertson, Kirsty, eds. Imagining Resistance: Visual Culture & Activism in Canada. 2010. (Cultural Studies). (ENG., Illus.). 294p. (C). pap. 39.95 (978-1-55458-257-0(1)) Wilfrid Laurier Univ. Pr. CAN. Dist: Univ. of Toronto Pr.

Davidson, Sherrie. Quilts of Prince Edward Island: The Fabric of Rural Life, 1 vol. 2011. (ENG., Illus.). 228p. pap. 35.00 (978-1-55109-768-8(0)) Down East Bks.

Dumontier, Michael & Farber, Neil. Constructive Abandonment. 2011. (ENG., Illus.). 64p. 15.95 (978-1-77046-045-4(4)) Drawn & Quarterly Pubns. CAN. Dist: Macmillan.

Evans, Michael Robert. Isuma: Inuit Video Art. 2008. (McGill-Queen's Native & Northern Ser.). (ENG.). 256p. (C). pap. (978-0-7735-3378-3(8)) McGill-Queen's Univ. Pr.

Grace, Sherrill E. On the Art of Being Canadian. 2009. (ENG., Illus.). 224p. **(978-0-7748-1578-9(7))** Univ. of British Columbia Pr.

Hockenhull, Oliver & MacKenzie, Alex, eds. Damp: Contemporary Vancouver Media Art. 2008. (ENG., Illus.). 144p. 40.00 (978-1-895636-89-5(2)) Anvil Pr. CAN. Dist: Univ. of Toronto Pr.

Jennings, Sarah. Art & Politics: The History of the National Arts Centre. 2009. (ENG., Illus.). 426p. 50.00 (978-1-55002-886-7(3), Dundurn Pr.) Dundurn CAN. Dist: Ingram Pub. Services.

Kunard, Andrea. The Cultural Work of Photography in Canada. Payne, Carol, ed. 2011. (McGill-Queen's/Beaverbrook Canadian Foundation Studies in Art History Ser.). (ENG., Illus.). 296p. (C). (978-0-7735-3861-0(5)) McGill-Queen's Univ. Pr.

Mannani, Manijeh & Thompson, Veronica, eds. Selves & Subjectivities: Reflections on Canadian Arts & Culture. 2011. (ENG.). 280p. (C). pap. 32.95 **(978-1-926836-49-2(9))** Athabasca University Pr. CAN. Dist: Univ. of Washington Pr.

Morris, David. Matrix: A Collection of British Seals. 2012. (ENG., Illus.). 288p. (C). 148.00 **(978-0-9570102-0-8(6))** Whyteleaf.

Pepall, Rosalind & Charbonneau, Diane, eds. Decorative Arts & Design: The Montreal Museum of Fine Arts' Collection: Volume II. 2012. (ENG., Illus.). 400p. 60.00 **(978-2-89192-359-0(6))** Distribution General.

Slade, Kathy, ed. Andrew Dadson: Visible Heavens From 1850-2008. 2008. (ENG., Illus.). 168p. 35.00 (978-3-905829-68-6(1)) JRP Ringier Kunstverlag AG CHE. Dist: D.A.P./Distributed Art Pubs.

Steiner, Rudolf. Christmas: An Introductory Reader. 2007. (Pocket Library of Spiritual Wisdom Ser.). 160p. per. (978-1-85584-189-5(4)) Steiner, Rudolf Pr.

Vance, Jonathan F. A History of Canadian Culture. 2011. (ENG., Illus.). 512p. 24.95 (978-0-19-544422-3(1)) Oxford Univ. Pr., Inc.

ARTS—CHINA

Beauty of Stone Windows: A Cultural Interpretation of Stone Windows of Sanmen. 2012. **(978-1-931907-79-8(X))** Homa & Sekey Bks.

Christense, Karen, adapted by. Kailun Zodiac Collection: Designs from China for the Year of the Monkey. 2007. pap. 12.95 (978-1-933782-30-0(7)) Berkshire Publishing Group.

Christensen, Karen, adapted by. Kailun Zodiac Collection: Books 1-12. 2007. pap. 120.00 (978-1-933782-39-3(0)) Berkshire Publishing Group.

—Kailun Zodiac Collection: Designs from China for the Year of the Dog. 2007. pap. 12.95 (978-1-933782-31-7(5)) Berkshire Publishing Group.

—Kailun Zodiac Collection: Designs from China for the Year of the Dragon. 2007. pap. 12.95 (978-1-933782-38-6(2)) Berkshire Publishing Group.

—Kailun Zodiac Collection: Designs from China for the Year of the Goat. 2007. pap. 12.95 (978-1-933782-29-4(3)) Berkshire Publishing Group.

—Kailun Zodiac Collection: Designs from China for the Year of the Horse. 2007. pap. 12.95 (978-1-933782-28-7(5)) Berkshire Publishing Group.

—Kailun Zodiac Collection: Designs from China for the Year of the Ox. 2007. pap. 12.95 (978-1-933782-35-5(8)) Berkshire Publishing Group.

—Kailun Zodiac Collection: Designs from China for the Year of the Pig. 2007. pap. 12.95 (978-1-933782-33-1(1)) Berkshire Publishing Group.

—Kailun Zodiac Collection: Designs from China for the Year of the Rabbit. 2007. pap. 12.95 (978-1-933782-37-9(4)) Berkshire Publishing Group.

—Kailun Zodiac Collection: Designs from China for the Year of the Rooster. 2007. pap. 12.95 (978-1-933782-32-4(3)) Berkshire Publishing Group.

—Kailun Zodiac Collection: Designs from China for the Year of the Tiger. 2007. pap. 12.95 (978-1-933782-36-2(6)) Berkshire Publishing Group.

—Kailun Zodiac Collection: Designs from China for the Year of TheRat. 2007. pap. 12.95 (978-1-933782-34-8(X)) Berkshire Publishing Group.

Cody, Jeffrey & Terpak, Frances, eds. Brush & Shutter: Early Photography in China. 2011. (ENG., Illus.). 220p. 45.00 (978-1-60606-054-4(6)) Getty Pubns.

Daguang, Zhou, compiled by. Fine Brush Painting Art. 215p. 75.95 (978-7-119-01973-4(2)) Beijing, Foreign Languages Press CHN. Dist: China Bks. & Periodicals, Inc.

Fok, Siu-Har Silvia. Zhongguo Xing Wei Yi Shu: Shen Ti Yu Chang Yu = Performance Art in China: Site & the Body. 2010. (CHI., Illus.). 159p. (978-986-6565-81-6(5)) Artist Publishing Co.

Forsyth, Angus & McElney, Brian S. Jades from China. (Illus.). 423p. (ENG.). 125.00 (978-1-897734-03-2(4)); pap. 95.00 (978-1-897734-04-9(2)) Museum of East Asian Art GBR. Dist: Art Media Resources, Inc., China Bks. & Periodicals, Inc.

Hay, Jonathan. Sensuous Surfaces: The Decorative Object in Early Modern China. 2010. 272p. (C). 63.00 (978-0-8248-3361-9(9)) Univ. of Hawaii Pr.

Hu, Chunsheng & Hu, Hua. Wenzhou Jian Zhi. 2010. (Illus.). (978-7-80686-809-6(7)) Zhejiang Photographic Pr.

Koretsky, Elaine. Killing Green: An Account of Hand Papermaking in China. 2009. (ENG., Illus.). 217p. 35.00 (978-0-9797974-1-5(1)) Legacy Pr., The.

Lee, De-Nin D. The Night Banquet: A Chinese Scroll Through Time. 2010. (ENG., Illus.). 172p. (C). 40.00 (978-0-295-99072-9(4)) Univ. of Washington Pr.

Lin, James C. S. The Immortal Stone: Chinese Jades from the Neolithic Period to the Twentieth Century. 2009. (Illus.). 160p. 60.00 (978-1-85759-581-9(5)) Scala Pubs., Ltd. GBR. Dist: Antique Collectors' Club.

Liuming, Ma, photos by. Ma Liuming: Performances, Paintings, Sculptures. 2008. (ENG., Illus.). 232p. 50.00 (978-88-6208-001-9(8)) Damiani ITA. Dist: D.A.P./Distributed Art Pubs.

Long, Laurent. La Bonne Pierre. 2010. (Bar S Ser.). (CHI, FRE & ENG., Illus.). 110p. (C). pap. 77.50 (978-1-4073-0561-5(1)) British Archaeological Reports Ltd. GBR. Dist: Brown, David Bk. Co., The.

Miller, Tony & Hui, Humphrey K. F. Elegance in Relief: Carved Porcelain from Jingdezhen of the 19th to early 20th Centuries. (CHI & ENG., Illus.). 358p. 55.00 (978-962-7101-75-8(3)) Art Media Resources, Inc.

Mittler, Barbara. A Continuous Revolution: Making Sense of Cultural Revolution Culture. 2012. (Harvard East Asian Monographs: 343). (ENG., Illus.). 500p. 59.95 **(978-0-674-06581-9(6))** Harvard Univ., Asia Ctr.

Mroz, Daniel. The Dancing Word: An Embodied Approach to the Preparation of Performers & the Composition of Performances. 2011. (ENG., Illus.). 219p. pap. 64.00 (978-90-420-3330-6(4)) Rodopi.

Pang, Laikwan. The Distorting Mirror: Visual Modernity in China. 2007. (Illus.). 280p. 57.00 (978-0-8248-3093-9(8)) Univ. of Hawaii Pr.

Peng, Lu. A History of Art in 20th Century China. 2010. (ENG., Illus.). 1288p. 180.00 (978-88-8158-779-7(3)) Charta ITA. Dist: D.A.P./Distributed Art Pubs.

Piao, Wenying. Ke Si. 2009. (CHI., Illus.). (978-7-81137-424-7(2)) Suzhou Univ. Pr.

Sans, Jérôme, ed. Art China Now: And Tomorrow. 2012. (ENG., Illus.). 528p. pap. 50.00 **(978-988-19912-1-8(8))** Timezone 8 Ltd. HKG. Dist: D.A.P./Distributed Art Pubs.

Sans, Jerome & Xiaoyan, Guo, texts. Qui Zhijie: Breaking the Ice, a History. 2010. (ENG., Illus.). 288p. 50.00 (978-988-18034-0-5(3)) Timezone 8 Ltd. HKG. Dist: D.A.P./Distributed Art Pubs.

Shiqiang, Gao. Gao Shiqiang: the Other There. 2010. (ENG., Illus.). 350p. 90.00 (978-988-18034-7-4(0)) Timezone 8 Ltd. HKG. Dist: D.A.P./Distributed Art Pubs.

Sui, Jie, et al. Wuqiang Nian Hua. 2009. (CHI., Illus.). 146p. (978-7-03-023804-7(4)) Science Pr.

Sullivan, Michael. The Arts of China. 5th rev. exp. ed. 2009. (ENG., Illus.). 352p. 65.00 (978-0-520-25568-5(2)) Univ. of California Pr.

Sun, Peilan. Wu Di Su Xiu. 2009. (Illus.). (978-7-81137-427-8(7)) Suzhou Univ. Pr.

Tchou, Kang. China & the Humanities: At the Crossroads of the Human & the Humane. 2011. pap. (978-1-86335-851-4(X)) Common Ground Publishing Pty, Ltd.

Tong, Shaosu. Folk Culture in China's Zhejiang Province, Illustrated: The Flowing Mother River. 2009. pap. (978-1-931907-62-0(5)) Homa & Sekey Bks.

Tongcheng Shi bo wu guan Staff & Tongcheng Shi wen wu guan li suo Staff, contrib. by. Tongcheng Wen Wu Jing Hua, 2 vols. 2009. (CHI., Illus.). 371p. (978-7-5398-1292-2(3)) Anhui Fine Arts Publishing Hse.

van Elzen, Sus, text. Dragon & Rose Garden. 2010. (ENG., Illus.). 208p. pap. 19.95 (978-90-814503-0-0(1)) Timezone 8 Ltd. HKG. Dist: D.A.P./Distributed Art Pubs.

Watson, William & Ho, Chumei. The Arts of China after 1620. 2007. (Pelican History of Art Ser.). (ENG., Illus.). 320p. 65.00 (978-0-300-10735-7(8)) Yale Univ. Pr.

Wen, Zhu. Chinese Style: Interiors, Furniture, Details. 2011. (ENG., Illus.). 192p. 29.95 (978-1-60220-007-4(6)) BetterLink Pr., Inc.

White, Julia M. Mahjong: Art, Film, & Change in China. 2008. (ENG., Illus.). 100p. pap. 25.00 (978-0-9719397-7-6(2)) Univ. of California, Berkeley Art Museum & Pacific Film Archive.

Xu, Songhua, et al. A Computational Approach to Digital Chinese Painting & Calligraphy. 2009. (Advanced Topics in Science & Technology in China Ser.). (ENG., Illus.). 380p. 159.00 (978-3-540-88147-6(6)) Springer.

Zhang, Xiumin. The History of Chinese Printing: (Illustrated) 2009. pap. (978-1-931907-61-3(7)) Homa & Sekey Bks.

Zhao, Jianlei, et al. Zhongguo Min Jian ni Su Ji Fa. 2009. (CHI., Illus.). 166p. (978-7-5045-8022-1(8)) China Labour and Social Security Publishing Hse.

ARTS—EUROPE

Adamson, Walter. Embattled Avant-Gardes: Modernism's Resistance to Commodity Culture in Europe. 2007. 448p. 60.00 (978-0-520-25270-7(5)) Univ. of California Pr.

Ades, Dawn & Baker, Simon. Undercover Surrealism: Georges Bataille & Documents. 2006. (Illus.). 271p. pap. (978-0-262-51197-1(5)); (ENG., 272p. (gr. 17). pap. 40.00 (978-0-262-01230-0(8)) MIT Pr.

Arsovska, Tamara. Vleznica Za Idninata. 2008. 198p. (978-9989-163-52-4(9)) Metanoja.

Baichtal, John & Meno, Joe. The Cult of LEGO. 2011. (ENG., Illus.). 304p. 39.95 **(978-1-59327-391-0(6))** No Starch Pr., Inc.

Barnett, Dennis. Theatre & Performance in Eastern Europe: The Changing Scene. Skelton, Arthur, ed. 2007. (ENG.). 290p. per. 65.00 (978-0-8108-6023-0(6)) Scarecrow Pr., Inc.

Beekman, Klaus & Vries, Jan De, eds. Avant-Garde & Criticism. 2007. (Avant Garde Critical Studies: 21). (ENG., Illus.). 368p. 95.00 (978-90-420-2152-5(7)) Rodopi.

Belozerskaya, Marina. Rethinking the Renaissance: Burgundian Arts across Europe. 2012. (ENG., Illus.). 398p. (C). pap. 50.00 **(978-1-107-60544-2(X))** Cambridge Univ. Pr.

Bergemann, Uta-Christiane. Europäische Stickereien 1250-1650: Katalog des Deutschen Textilmuseums Krefeld, Band 3. 2010. (GER., Illus.). 399p. (978-3-7954-2399-5(6)) Schnell und Steiner GmbH, Verlag.

Berger, et al, eds. Narrating the Nation: Representations in History, Media & the Arts. 2011. (MSH Ser.). (ENG.). 360p. pap. 37.95 (978-0-85745-173-6(1)) Berghahn Bks., Inc.

Block, E. C., et al, eds. Profane Imagery in Marginal Arts of the Middle Ages. 2009. (Profane Arts of the Middle Ages Ser.). (ENG & FRE., Illus.). 420p. (C). pap. 102.00 (978-2-503-51599-1(1)) Brepols Pubs. BEL. Dist: ISD.

Bradatan, Costica, ed. Philosophy Geography Fragility. 2012. (ENG.). 232p. (C). 125.00 **(978-0-415-69919-8(3))** Routledge.

Brooker, Peter & Thacker, Andrew. The Oxford Critical & Cultural History of Modernist Magazines: Volume I: Britain & Ireland 1880-1955. 2012. (ENG., Illus.). 976p. pap. 65.00 **(978-0-19-965429-1(8))** Oxford Univ. Pr., Inc.

Brooks, Lynn, ed. Women's Work: Making Dance in Europe Before 1800. 2007. (Studies in Dance History Ser.). (Illus.). 288p. 65.00 (978-0-299-22530-8(5)) Univ. of Wisconsin Pr.

Buchhart, Dieter & Erritzoe, Marie Louise, eds. Red Faction. 2008. (GER & ENG.). 160p. 40.00 (978-3-939583-80-6(4)) Kehrer Verlag Heidelberg, Klaus Kehrer DEU. Dist: Consortium Bk. Sales & Distribution.

Campbell, Gordon. The Grove Encyclopedia of Northern Renaissance Art, 3 vols. 2009. (Grove Art Ser.). (ENG., Illus.). 1300p. (C). 357.00 (978-0-19-533467-8(1)) Oxford Univ. Pr., Inc.

Campbell, Thomas P. & Cleland, Elizabeth A. H. Tapestry in the Baroque: New Aspects of Production & Patronage. 2010. 14.95 (978-1-58839-397-5(6)) Metropolitan Museum of Art, The.

Campbell, Thomas P. & Cleland, Elizabeth A. H., eds. Tapestry in the Baroque: New Aspects of Production & Patronage. 2011. (ENG., Illus.). 368p. pap. 40.00 (978-0-300-15514-3(X)) Yale Univ. Pr.

Cavanaugh, Alden. Performing the "Everyday" The Culture of Genre in the Eighteenth Century. 2007. (ENG., Illus.). 151p. 57.50 (978-0-87413-970-9(8)) Univ. of Delaware Pr.

Cherix, Christophe. In & Out of Amsterdam. Cherix, Christophe, ed. 2009. (ENG., Illus.). 178p. 55.00 (978-0-87070-753-7(1)) Museum of Modern Art.

Clarke, John R. Looking at Laughter: Humor, Power, & Transgression in Roman Visual Culture, 100 B. C. -A. D. 250. 2007. (Illus.). 321p. 60.00 (978-0-520-23733-9(1)) Univ. of California Pr.

Cohen, Matthew Isaac. Performing Otherness: Java & Bali on International Stages, 1905-1952. 2010. (Studies in International Performance Ser.). (ENG., Illus.). 304p. 89.00 (978-0-230-22462-9(8)) Palgrave Macmillan.

Cohen, Simona. Animals as Disguised Symbols in Renaissance Art. 2008. 352p. (C). (978-90-04-17101-5(0)) BRILL.

Creative Handbook 1997. (978-0-611-00878-7(5)) Reed Information Services Ltd.

Endedijk, Leo & Dumas, Charles E. Masters of Mils: From Rembrandt to Mondriaan. 2007. (ENG., Illus.). 232p. pap. 35.00 (978-90-400-8291-7(X)) Waanders B.V., Uitgeverij NLD. Dist: National Bk. Network.

Epica. Europe's Best Advertising, Bk. 23. 2010. (ENG., Illus.). 400p. 65.00 (978-2-88479-108-3(6)) Ava Publishing SA CHE. Dist: Ingram Pub. Services.

Facos, Michelle. Symbolist Art in Context. 2009. (ENG., Illus.). 304p. pap. 31.95 (978-0-520-25582-1(8)) Univ. of California Pr.

Facos, Michelle & Facos, M. Symbolist Art in Context. 2009. (ENG., Illus.). 304p. 70.00 (978-0-520-25499-2(6)) Univ. of California Pr.

Feller, Carol. Contemporary Irish Knits. 2011. (ENG., Illus.). 160p. pap. 24.99 (978-0-470-88924-4(1), Wiley) Wiley, John & Sons, Inc.

Fill, Louise & Apatoff, Lise. Italianissimo: The Quintessential Guide to What Italians Do Best. 2008. (ENG., Illus.). 112p. 19.95 (978-1-892145-54-3(5)) Little Bookroom.

Fox, Celina. The Arts of Industry in the Age of Enlightenment. 2010. (Paul Mellon Centre for Studies in Britis Ser.). (Illus.). 576p. 95.00 (978-0-300-16042-0(9)) Yale Univ. Pr.

Frank, Robert. Building the European Public Sphere: History & the Global Perspective. 2010. (ENG & FRE., Illus.). 257p. pap. 52.95 (978-90-5201-629-0(1)) PIE - Peter Lang BEL. Dist: Lang, Peter.

Göttler, Christine & Neuber, Wolfgang, eds. Spirits Unseen: The Representation of Subtle Bodies in Early Modern European Culture. 2007. (Intersections Ser.). (Illus.). 384p. (978-90-04-16396-6(4)) BRILL.

Gura, Judith. Sourcebook of Scandinavian Furniture: Designs for the Twenty-First Century. 2012. (ENG., Illus.). 320p. pap. 60.00 (978-0-393-73387-7(4), 73387) Norton, W. W. & Co., Inc.

Hall, Marcia B. The Sacred Image in the Age of Art: Titian, Tintoretto, Barocci, el Greco, Caravaggio. 2011. (ENG., Illus.). 352p. 75.00 (978-0-300-16967-6(1)) Yale Univ. Pr.

Hanaor, Ziggy, ed. Graphic Europe. 2010. (ENG., Illus.). 288p. pap. 29.99 (978-0-9562053-0-8(5)) Cicada Bks. GBR. Dist: D.A.P./Distributed Art Pubs.

Hart, Clive & Stevenson, Kay Gilliland. Heaven & the Flesh: Imagery of Desire from the Renaissance to the Rococo. 2008. (ENG., Illus.). 256p. pap. 37.99 (978-0-521-07094-2(5)) Cambridge Univ. Pr.

Johnson, Donald-Brian & Pina, Leslie. Deco Decor: Porcelain, Glass, & Metal Accessories for the Home. 2009. (Illus.). 240p. bds. 69.99 (978-0-7643-3176-7(7)) Schiffer Publishing, Ltd.

Jooss, Birgit. Lebende Bilder: Koerperliche Nachahmungen von Kunstwerken in der Goethezeit. (GER., Illus.). 484p. (978-3-496-01197-2(1)) Reimer, Dietrich.

Kang, Minsoo & Woodson-Boulton, Amy, eds. Visions of the Industrial Age 1830-1914: Modernity & the Age of Representation in Europe. 2008. (Illus.). 394p. 144.95 (978-0-7546-6488-8(0)) Ashgate Publishing Co.

Karraker, D. Gene. Looking at European Frames: A Guide to Terms, Styles, & Techniques. 2010. (Looking at Ser.). (Illus.). 88p. pap. 18.95 (978-0-89236-981-2(7)) Oxford Univ. Pr., Inc.

Klaic, Dragan & Klaic, Gragan. Mobility of Imagination: A Companion Guide to International Cultural Cooperation. 2007. (ENG.). 172p. pap. 21.95 (978-963-9776-06-7(8)) Central European Univ. Pr.

Krpan, Jurij. Original: 20 years BJCEM. 2007. (Illus.). 272p. pap. 75.00 (978-88-370-5763-3(6)) Electa ITA. Dist: Trans-Atlantic Pubns., Inc.

Malgouyres, Philippe. Ivories: From the Renaissance to the Modern Era. 2011. (FRE & ENG., Illus.). 384p. 90.00 (978-2-35340-086-7(8)) Gourcuff Gradenigo FRA. Dist: National Bk. Network.

McKitterick, Rosamond. Charlemagne: The Formation of Carolingian Identity. 2008. (ENG., Illus.). 478p. (C). 88.00 (978-0-521-88672-7(4)) Cambridge Univ. Pr.

Milevska, Suzana. Gender Difference in the Balkans. 2010. 248p. pap. (978-3-639-20032-4(2)) VDM Verlag Dr. Mueller e.K.

Neri, Janice. The Insect & the Image: Visualizing Nature in Early Modern Europe, 1500-1700. 2011. (ENG., Illus.). 280p. 82.50 (978-0-8166-6764-2(0)); pap. 27.50 (978-0-8166-6765-9(9)) Univ. of Minnesota Pr.

Nilson, Micheline. Architecture in Nineteenth Century Photographs: Essays on Reading A Collection. 2011. (Visual Culture in Early Modernity Ser.). (Illus.). 216p. 104.95 (978-1-4094-0904-5(X)) Ashgate Publishing Co.

Olevska, Irina. Peculiarities of Legal Regulation of Fine Art Prints. 2010. 100p. pap. (978-3-8383-5312-8(9)) Lambert Academic Publishing.

Orta, Lucy, ed. Mapping the Invisible: EU-Roma Gypsies. 2010. (ENG., Illus.). 192p. pap. 29.95 (978-1-906155-91-9(7)) Black Dog Publishing Ltd. GBR. Dist: Perseus Distribution.

Patrakova, Iryna. Traditional Embroidery in Telemark & Crimea. 2011. 156p. pap. (978-3-8454-0792-0(1)) Lambert Academic Publishing.

Pinson. The Fools' Journey, a Myth of Obsession in Northern Renaissance Art. 2009. (ENG., Illus.). 226p. (C). pap. 152.00 (978-2-503-52612-6(8)) Brepols Pubs. BEL. Dist: ISD.

Ray, Gene. Terror & the Sublime in Art & Critical Theory: From Auschwitz to Hiroshima to September 11 & Beyond. 2011. (Studies in European Culture & History Ser.). (ENG.). 256p. pap. 28.00 (978-0-230-11048-9(7)) Palgrave Macmillan.

Rittersma, Rengenier C., ed. Luxury in the Low Countries: Miscellaneous Reflections on Netherlandish Material Culture, 1500 to the Present. 2011. 272p. pap. 34.95 (978-90-5487-797-4(9)) VUB Univ. Pr. BEL. Dist: Independent Pubs. Group.

Roman, Denise. Fragmented Identities: Popular Culture, Sex, & Everyday Life in Postcommunist Romania. rev. ed. 2007. (ENG., Illus.). 192p. pap. 27.50 (978-0-7391-2118-4(9)) Lexington Bks.

Roper, Lyndal. The Witch in the Western Imagination. 2012. E-Book (978-0-8139-3300-9(5)); (ENG., Illus.). 248p. (gr. 17). 39.50 (978-0-8139-3297-2(1)) Univ. Pr. of Virginia.

Sanguinetti, Alessandra. The Adventures of Guille & Belinda & the Enigmatic Meaning of Their Dreams. 2010. (Illus.). 120p. (978-1-59005-269-3(2)) Nazraeli Pr.

Sanudo, Marino. Venice, Città Excelentissima: Selections from the Renaissance Diaries of Marin Sanudo. Labalme, Patricia H. & Sanguineti White, Laura, eds. Carroll, Linda L., tr. from ITA. 2008. (ENG., Illus.). 640p. (gr. 17). 54.00 (978-0-8018-8765-9(8)) Johns Hopkins Univ. Pr.

Schmidt, Suzanne Karr & Nichols, Kimberly. Altered & Adorned: Using Renaissance Prints in Daily Life. 2011. (ENG., Illus.). 112p. 35.00 (978-0-300-16911-9(6)) Art Institute of Chicago.

Skowski, Christine. Incorrect: Prix Leica 2007. 2009. (ENG., Illus.). 111p. 30.00 (978-3-86678-125-2(3)) Kerber Verlag DEU. Dist: D.A.P./Distributed Art Pubs.

Steiger, Johann Anselm & Heinen, Ulrich. Golgatha in den Konfessionen und Medien der Frühen Neuzeit. 2010. (Arbeiten zur Kirchengeschichte Ser.). (GER., Illus.). VIII, 510p. 182.00 (978-3-11-022557-0(3)) De Gruyter, Walter Inc.

Storey, Martin. Aran Knits: 25 Contemporary Designs Using Classic Cable Patterns. 2012. (ENG., Illus.). 136p. pap. 24.99 (978-0-312-64221-1(0), St. Martin's Griffin) St. Martin's Pr.

Suntrup, Rudolf & Veenstra, Jan R., eds. Himmel auf Erden Heaven on Earth. 2009. (Medieval to Early Modern Culture / Kultureller Wandel vom Mittelalter zur Frühen Neuzeit Ser.). (ENG & GER.). 222p. pap. 57.95 (978-3-631-56420-2(1)) Lang, Peter GmbH, Europaischer Verlag der Wissenschaften DEU. Dist: Lang, Peter.

Takahashi, Kaoru, ed. Shop Image Graphics in Scandinavia. 2011. (ENG., Illus.). 192p. 75.00 (978-4-7562-4046-0(1)) Rizzoli International Pubns., Inc.

Theisen, Maria. History buech Reimenweise: Geschichte, Bildprogramm und Illuminatoren des Wilhelm-Codex Konig Wenzels IV. von Bohmen. Osterreichische Nationalbibliothek, Ser. nov. 2643, Kunsthistorische Studien zur Buchmalerei. 2010. (Denkschriften der Phil. -Hist. Klasse Ser.). (Illus.). 270p. (C). pap. 94.00 (978-3-7001-6058-8(5)) Austrian Academy of Sciences Press AUT. Dist: Brown, David Bk. Co., The.

Trouve, Tatiana, text. Tatiana Trouve: il Grande Ritratto. 2010. (ENG & GER., Illus.). 150p. pap. 49.95 (978-3-86560-753-9(5)) Verlag der Buchhandlung Walther Konig DEU. Dist: D.A.P./Distributed Art Pubs.

Van der Wee, Herman & Jacobs, Stephen. Bozar LXXX. 2009. (FRE, DUT & ENG., Illus.). 400p. (978-90-209-7984-8(1), Lannoo Pubs. (Acc)) Antique Collectors' Club.

Van Eck, Caroline. Classical Rhetoric & the Visual Arts in Early Modern Europe. 2007. (ENG., Illus.). 240p. 83.99 (978-0-521-84435-2(5)) Cambridge Univ. Pr.

Van Santvoort, Linda, et al, eds. Sources of Regionalism in the Nineteenth Century: Architecture, Art, & Literature. 2008. (KADOC Artes Ser.). (Illus.). 200p. 65.00 (978-90-5867-649-8(8)) Leuven Univ. Pr. BEL. Dist: Cornell Univ. Pr.

Verlag, Hirmer & Hirmer Verlag. Meisterwerke mittelalterlicher Kunst au dem Nationalmuseum Warschau. 2006. (GER., Illus.). 192p. (C). pap. 42.00 (978-3-7774-3275-5(X)) Hirmer Verlag GmbH DEU. Dist: Brown, David Bk. Co., The.

Weisberg, Gabriel, ed. & text. Illusions of Reality. 2011. (ENG., Illus.). 224p. 50.00 (978-90-6153-941-4(2)) Mercatorfonds N. V. BEL. Dist: D.A.P./Distributed Art Pubs.

Whitfield, Niamh. Design & Techniques in Early Medieval Celtic Metalwork. 2013. (ENG., Illus.). 580p. (C). 300.00 (978-1-904597-33-9(5)) Pindar Pr. GBR. Dist: Brown, David Bk. Co., The.

Wilkinson, Jane. Performing the Local & the Global: The Theatre Festivals of Lake Constance. 2007. (Illus.). 286p. pap. 69.95 (978-3-03911-047-6(0)) Lang, Peter Publishing, Inc.

Zeller, Christoph. Ästhetik des Authentischen: Literatur und Kunst Um 1970. 2010. (Spectrum Literaturwissenschaft / spectrum Literature Ser.).Tr. of Aesthetics of the Authentic. (GER., Illus.). IX, 333p. 140.00 (978-3-11-022720-8(7)) De Gruyter, Walter Inc.

ARTS—FRANCE

Bade, Patrick. Edgar Degas. 2012. (Best Of Ser.). (ENG., Illus.). 200p. 19.95 (978-1-906981-38-9(8)) Parkstone Pr. USA, Ltd.

Bajac, Quentin & Chéroux, Clément, eds. Collection Photographs, 1 vol. 2008. (ENG., Illus.). 468p. 85.00 (978-3-86521-480-5(0)) Steidl, Gerhard Druckerei und Verlag DEU. Dist: Innovative Logistics.

Bajac, Quentin, et al. 100 Chefs-D'uvre de la Photographie. 2010. (FRE., Illus.). 119p. (978-2-84426-476-3(X)) Centre National d'Art et de Culture Georges Pompidou.

Baker, George. The Artwork Caught by the Tail: Francis Picabia & Dada in Paris. 2010. (October Bks.). (ENG., Illus.). 496p. (gr. 17). pap. 24.95 (978-0-262-51486-6(9)) MIT Pr.

Barnhill, Georgia B., ed. With a French Accent: American Lithography to 1860. 2012. (ENG., Illus.). pap. 25.00 (978-1-929545-67-4(3)) American Antiquarian Society.

Barstow, Philippa & Waterhouse, Alan. French Polishing. 2012. (ENG., Illus.). 176p. (C). pap. 36.00 (978-0-85442-106-0(8)) Stobart Davies, Ltd. GBR. Dist: Brown, David Bk. Co., The.

Boutin, Pierre. Les Arts, les Autres, Etc: éducation, Culture et Territoires en Savoie. 2008. (FRE., Illus.). 127p. (978-2-84562-132-9(9)) La Passe du vent.

Camard, Florence. Ruhlmann. 2011. (ENG., Illus.). 512p. 150.00 (978-0-8478-5799-9(9)) Rizzoli International Pubns., Inc.

Charlesworth, Michael. Landscape & Vision in Nineteenth-Century Britain & France. 2008. (Illus.). 218p. 124.95 (978-0-7546-5664-7(0)) Ashgate Publishing Co.

Cole, Arthur Harrison & Watts, George Byron. The Handicrafts of France: As Recorded in the Descriptions des Arts et Metiers, 1761-1788. 2011. 50p. 36.95 (978-1-258-10329-3(X)) Literary Licensing, LLC.

Cowen, Pamela. A Fanfare for the Sun King: Unfolding Fans for Louis XIV. 2006. (ENG., Illus.). per. 45.00 (978-1-903942-20-8(9), Third Millenium Pub Ltd) Antique Collectors' Club GBR. Dist: National Bk. Network.

De, Conihout Isabelle. Mazarin. 2010. (FRE., Illus.). 480p. (978-2-903824-53-2(3)) Hayot, Monelle, Editions d'art.

Desdemaines-Hugon, Christine. Stepping-Stones: A Journey through the Ice Age Caves of the Dordogne. 2010. (Illus.). 272p. 30.00 (978-0-300-15266-1(3)) Yale Univ. Pr.

Diepois, Aline & Gizolme, Thomas, photos by. Dust Book, 1 vol. 2009. (ENG., Illus.). 104p. 49.00 (978-3-86521-818-6(0)) Steidl, Gerhard Druckerei und Verlag DEU. Dist: Innovative Logistics.

Dover. French Ornamental Ironwork Designs. 2012. (Dover Pictorial Archive Ser.). (ENG.). 112p. pap. 16.95 (978-0-486-48600-0(1)) Dover Pubns., Inc.

Dressendorfer, Werner. va-Vilmorin, The Vegetable Garden. 2012. (ENG., Illus.). 136p. 59.99 (978-3-8365-3599-1(8)) TASCHEN DEU. Dist: Ingram Pub. Services.

Duchamp, Marcel. Étant Donnés. rev. ed. 2009. (Illus.). 76p. 40.00 (978-0-300-14980-7(8)) Yale Univ. Pr.

Dulac, Edmund. An Edmund Dulac Treasury: XX Color Illustrations. Menges, Jeff A., ed. 2011. (Dover Fine Art, History of Art Ser.). (ENG., Illus.). 128p. pap. 19.95 (978-0-486-47911-8(0)) Dover Pubns., Inc.

Durozoi, Gérard & Bouvet, Vincent. Paris Between the Wars, 1919-1939: Art, Life & Culture. 2010. (ENG., Illus.). 416p. 50.00 (978-0-86565-252-1(X)) Vendome Pr., The.

Feneon, Felix. Félix Fénéon. Sante, Luc, tr. from FRE. 2010. (ENG.). 128p. 24.95 (978-0-9841906-6-9(X)) Batty, Mark Pub., LLC.

Frogier, Larys, text. Adel Abdessemed. 2011. (ENG., Illus.). 160p. pap. 55.00 (978-3-03764-108-8(8)) JRP Ringier Kunstverlag AG CHE. Dist: D.A.P./Distributed Art Pubs.

Game, Jerome, ed. Porous Boundaries: Texts & Images in Twentieth-Century French Culture. (Illus.). 164p. pap. 49.95 (978-3-03910-568-7(X)) Lang, Peter Publishing, Inc.

Garcia, Carmela. Carmela Garcia: Constelacion. 2008. (ENG., Illus.). 110p. 45.00 (978-84-7506-820-6(0)) Turner, Ediciones S.A. ESP. Dist: D.A.P./Distributed Art Pubs.

Gluck, Mary. Popular Bohemia: Modernism & Urban Culture in Nineteenth-Century Paris. 2008. (Illus.). 238p. per. 25.50 (978-0-674-02731-2(0)) Harvard Univ. Pr.

Goldstein, Carl. Print Culture in Early Modern France: Abraham Bosse & the Purposes of Print. 2012. (ENG., Illus.). 234p. 99.00 (978-1-107-01214-1(7)) Cambridge Univ. Pr.

Heinich, Nathalie. Guerre Culturelle et Art Contemporain: Une Comparaison Franco-Américaine. 2010. (FRE.). 170p. (978-2-7056-7063-4(7)) Hermann.

Heyer, John Hajdu, ed. Jean-Baptiste Lully & the Music of the French Baroque: Essays in Honor of James R. Anthony. 2008. (ENG.). 348p. pap. 48.00 (978-0-521-08196-2(3)) Cambridge Univ. Pr.

Jones, Kimberly. Impressionist & Post-Impressionist Masterpieces from the National Gallery of Art. 2011. (ENG., Illus.). 192p. 49.95 (978-3-7913-5104-9(4)) Prestel Publishing.

Jones, Kimberly, et al. In the Forest of Fontainebleau: Painters & Photographers from Corot to Monet. 2008. (ENG., Illus.). 220p. 60.00 (978-0-300-13897-9(0)) Yale Univ. Pr.

Kahng, Eik, et al. Picasso & Braque: The Cubist Experiment, 1910-1912. 2011. (Illus.). 136p. 30.00 (978-0-300-16971-3(X)) Kimbell Art Museum.

Kearns, James. Théophile Gautier, Orator to the Artists: Art Journalism in in the Second Republic. 2007. (Legenda Main Ser.). (Illus.). 200p. (C). 79.50 (978-1-904350-88-0(7)) European Humanities Research Ctr. GBR. Dist: Brown, David Bk. Co., The.

Kisluk-Grosheide, Danielle O. & Munger, Jeffrey H. The Wrightsman Galleries for French Decorative Arts, the Metropolitan Museum of Art. 2010. (Illus.). xii, 259p. 40.00 (978-1-58839-366-1(6)) Metropolitan Museum of Art, The.

Klemettila. Epitomes of Evil Representations of Executioners in Northern France & the Low Countri. 2006. (Studies in European Urban History (1100-1800) Ser.). (ENG.). 388p. (C). pap. 94.00 (978-2-503-52278-4(5)) Brepols Pubs. BEL. Dist: ISD.

Lamonaca, Marianne, et al. Liberty, Equality, & Fraternity. Lamonaca, Marianne, ed. 2011. (ENG.). pap. 50.00 (978-0-9677359-4-8(7)) Wolfsonian-Florida International Univ., The.

Lichtenstein, Therese & Lichtenstein, T. Twilight Visions: Surrealism & Paris. 2009. (ENG., Illus.). 224p. 45.00 (978-0-520-26081-8(3)) Univ. of California Pr.

Lillich, Meredith Parsons. The Gothic Stained Glass of Reims Cathedral. 2011. (ENG.). 400p. 59.95 (978-0-271-03777-6(6)) Pennsylvania State Univ. Pr.

Loyaute, Benjamin. Madeleine Vionnet. Golbin, Pamela, ed. 2009. (ENG., Illus.). 304p. 75.00 (978-0-8478-3278-1(3)) Rizzoli International Pubns., Inc.

Lyford, Amy. Surrealist Masculinities: Gender Anxiety & the Aesthetics of Post-World War I Reconstruction in France. 2007. (Illus.). 237p. 55.00 (978-0-520-24640-9(3)) Univ. of California Pr.

Malgouyres, Philippe. Ivories: From the Renaissance to the Modern Era. 2011. (FRE & ENG., Illus.). 384p. 90.00 (978-2-35340-086-7(8)) Gourcuff Gradenigo FRA. Dist: National Bk. Network.

Marchesano, Louis & Michel, Christian. Printing the Grand Manner: Charles le Brun & Monumental Prints in the Age of Louis XIV. 2010. (ENG., Illus.). 120p. 50.00 (978-0-89236-980-5(9)) Getty Pubns.

McCully, Marilyn, et al. Picasso in Paris, 1900-1907. 2011. (ENG., Illus.). 256p. 60.00 (978-0-86565-269-9(4)) Vendome Pr., The.

McWilliam, Neil, ed. A Bibliography of Salon Criticism in Paris from the Ancien Régime to the Restoration, 1699-1827, Vol. 1. 2008. (Cambridge Studies in the History of Art Ser.). (ENG.). 284p. pap. 38.99 (978-0-521-06914-4(9)) Cambridge Univ. Pr.

Mouchel, Christian & Nativel, Colette, eds. Republique des Lettres, Republique des Arts: Melanges en l'honneur de Marc Fumaroli, de l'Academie Francaise. 2008. (Travaux d'Humanisme et Renaissance Umanisme Ser.). (FRE.). 760p. (C). pap. 181.00 (978-2-600-01193-8(5)) Droz, Librairie CHE. Dist: Brown, David Bk. Co., The.

Nash, Susie. No Equal in Any Land: Andre Beauneveu, Artist to the Courts of France & Flanders. 2008. (Illus.). 216p. pap. 60.00 (978-1-903470-66-4(8)) Holberton, Paul Publishing GBR. Dist: Casemate Pubs. & Bk. Distributors, LLC.

Nolan, Kathleen D. & Nolan, Kathleen. Queens in Stone & Silver: The Creation of a Visual Imagery of Queenship in Capetian France. 2009. (New Middle Ages Ser.). (ENG., Illus.). 300p. 95.00 (978-1-4039-6990-3(6)) Palgrave Macmillan.

Nord, Philip G. France's New Deal: From the Thirties to the Postwar Era. 2010. (ENG.). 480p. (C). 42.00 (978-0-691-14297-5(1)) Princeton Univ. Pr.

Provence: Art, Architecture, Landscape. 2008. 49.95 (978-0-8416-0398-1(7)) American Map Corp.

Rocamora, Agnes. Fashioning the City: Paris, Fashion & the Media. 2009. (ENG., Illus.). 232p. pap. 32.00 (978-1-84511-897-6(9)) I. B. Tauris & Co., Ltd. GBR. Dist: Macmillan.

Rosenberg, P. Pierre Jean Mariette: Catalogue Raisonn. 2011. (ITA, ENG & FRE., Illus.). 464p. 120.00 (978-88-370-7170-7(1)) Electa ITA. Dist: National Bk. Network.

Ryan, Zoe, et al. Matali Crasset: Works. 2012. (ENG., Illus.). 320p. 75.00 (978-0-8478-3582-9(0)) Rizzoli International Pubns., Inc.

Santrot, Jacques, et al. Goudji, le Magicien D'or. 2008. (FRE & ENG., Illus.). 128p. pap. 45.00 (978-2-35340-022-5(1)) Gourcuff Gradenigo FRA. Dist: National Bk. Network.

Shepherd, Simon & Donger, Simon, eds. Orlan: A Hybrid Body of Artworks. 2010. (ENG., Illus.). 240p. 115.00 (978-0-415-56233-1(3)); pap. 40.95 (978-0-415-56234-8(1)) Taylor & Francis Group GBR. (Routledge). Dist: Taylor & Francis Group.

Sheriff, Mary D. Moved by Love: Inspired Artists & Deviant Women in Eighteenth-Century France. 2008. (Illus.). 320p. pap. 22.50 (978-0-226-75288-4(7)) Univ. of Chicago Pr.

Smith, Patrick. Chronicle of a Phantom. 2010. 188p. pap. (978-3-639-28592-5(1)) VDM Verlag Dr. Mueller e.K.

Soulié, David. Louvre: 400 Masterpieces. 2008. (ENG., Illus.). 544p. 45.00 (978-0-8109-7116-5(X)) Abrams.

Thomson, Richard, et al. Toulouse-Lautrec & Montmartre. 2006. (Illus.). 293p. pap. 39.50 (978-0-691-12904-4(5)) Princeton Univ. Pr.

Tondini, Gilles. Cataphiles: Artists Beneath Paris. 2012. (ENG.). 128p. 27.95 (978-1-935613-54-1(5)) Batty, Mark Pub., LLC.

Viollet-le-Duc, Eugene-Emmanuel & Ouradou, Maurice. Designs & Ornaments from the Chapels of Notre Dame. 2011. (Dover Pictorial Archive Ser.). (ENG., Illus.). 80p. pap. 16.95 (978-0-486-47538-7(7)) Dover Pubns., Inc.

Waanders Editors. Visions: Gauguin & His Time - Van Gogh Studies 3. 2010. (ENG., Illus.). 208p. 85.00 (978-90-400-7659-6(6)) Waanders B.V., Uitgeverij NLD. Dist: National Bk. Network.

Wakefield, David. The French Romantics: Literature & the Visual Arts 1800-1840. 2007. 240p. 50.00 (978-1-904495-91-8(5)) Chaucer Pr. GBR. Dist: International Publishers Marketing.

Wiethege, Katrin. Henri Matisse Jazz. 2009. (FRE & ENG., Illus.). 176p. 75.00 (978-3-7913-4277-1(0)) Prestel Publishing.

ARTS—GERMANY

Ay, Andreas. Nachts: Göthe gelesen: Heinrich Wölfflin und seine Goethe-Rezeption. 2010. (GER., Illus.). 453p. (C). 80.00 (978-3-89971-581-1(0)) Vandenhoeck & Ruprecht GmbH & Co. KG DEU. Dist: ISD.

Bergemann, Uta-Christiane. Europäische Stickereien 1250-1650: Katalog des Deutschen Textilmuseums Krefeld, Band 3. 2010. (GER., Illus.). 399p. (978-3-7954-2399-5(6)) Schnell und Steiner GmbH, Verlag.

Beuerlein, Katharina. Arts Sponsorship in the Usa & Germany. 2007. 96p. per. (978-3-8364-1745-7(6)) VDM Verlag Dr. Mueller e.K.

Beuys, Joseph, et al. Beuys, Pourquoi Faites-Vous des Multiples? 2010. (FRE & ENG., Illus.). 96p. pap. 40.00 (978-2-35340-030-0(2)) Gourcuff Gradenigo FRA. Dist: National Bk. Network.

Bierhals, Christine. City Fashion Berlin. 2011. (ENG., Illus.). 216p. pap. 19.99 (978-3-8331-6062-2(4)) h.f.ullmann DEU. Dist: Innovative Logistics.

—City Fashion Paris, 1 vol. 2011. (ENG., Illus.). 216p. 19.99 (978-3-8331-6066-0(7)) h.f.ullmann DEU. Dist: Innovative Logistics.

Braun, Matthias. Kulturinsel und Machtinstrument: Die Akademie der Künste, die Partei und die Staatssicherheit. 2007. (Analysen und Dokumente. Wissenschaftliche Reihe der Bundesbeauftragten fur die Unterlagen des Staatssicherheitsdienstes der ehemaligen Deutschen Demokratischen Republik (BStU) Ser.). (GER., Illus.). 480p. (C). 44.00 (978-3-525-35049-2(X)) Vandenhoeck & Ruprecht GmbH & Co. KG DEU. Dist: ISD.

Hedler, Ernst & Ulrich, Ralf E. SED Design. Volk, Annick, ed. 25th ed. 2008. (FRE, GER & ENG., Illus.). 160p. 14.99 (978-3-8365-0836-0(2)) TASCHEN DEU. Dist: Ingram Pub. Services.

Huener. The Arts in Nazi Germany: Continuity, Conformity, Change. 2007. (Illus.). 236p. 27.50 (978-1-84545-359-6(X)) Berghahn Bks., Inc.

Kirkpatrick, Gail, et al, eds. Josephine Meckseper. 2009. (ENG., Illus.). 114p. 35.00 (978-3-03764-047-0(2)) JRP Ringier Kunstverlag AG CHE. Dist: D.A.P./Distributed Art Pubs.

Lorenz, Detlef. Reklamekunst um 1900 - Kuenstlerlexikon fuer Sammelbilder. (GER., Illus.). 237p. (978-3-496-01220-7(X)) Reimer, Dietrich.

Nicosia, Francis R. & Huener, Jonathan, eds. The Arts in Nazi Germany: Continuity Conformity Change. 2006. (Illus.). 236p. (C). 90.00 (978-1-84545-209-4(7)) Berghahn Bks., Inc.

Pese, Claus. Jugendstil aus Nürnberg: Handwerk zwischen Kunst und Industriekultur. 2007. (ENG., Illus.). 264p. 75.00 (978-3-89790-236-7(2)) Arnoldsche Art Pubs. DEU. Dist: Antique Collectors' Club.

Richter, Frank & Friedrich, Caspar David. Caspar David Friedrich: Spurensuche im Dresdner Umland und in der Sächsischen Schweiz. 2009. (GER., Illus.). 143p. pap. *(978-3-86530-115-4(0))* Verlag der Kunst.

Rossler, Patrick, text. The Bauhaus at the Newsstand / Das Bauhaus am Kiosk: die neue linie 1929-1943. 2010. (ENG & GER., Illus.). 160p. pap. 46.50 *(978-3-86678-282-2(9))* Kerber Verlag DEU. Dist: D.A.P./Distributed Art Pubs.

Schneider, Gregor, photos by. Gregor Schneider. End. 2010. (ENG & GER., Illus.). 216p. 55.00 *(978-3-86560-422-4(6))* Verlag der Buchhandlung Walther Konig DEU. Dist: D.A.P./Distributed Art Pubs.

Sibeth, Achim, ed. Being Object, Being Art, 1 vol. 2010. (ENG.). 324p. 75.00 *(978-3-8030-3338-3(1))* Wasmuth, Ernst J. Verlag GmbH & Co. DEU. Dist: D.A.P./Distributed Art Pubs.

Sieg, Katrin. Ethnic Drag: Performing Race, Nation, Sexuality in West Germany. 2009. (Social History, Popular Culture, & Politics in Germany Ser.). (ENG., Illus.). 296p. pap. 27.95 *(978-0-472-03362-1(X))* Univ. of Michigan Pr.

Sistenich, Frank & Theobald, Christine. Malakhov's Sleeping Beauty. 2007. (ENG.). 160p. 50.00 *(978-3-7957-0557-2(6)*, 3795705576) Schott Music Corp.

Wolberg, Benjamin. Graffiti Berlin. 2007. 96p. 27.95 *(978-0-9790486-0-9(5))* Batty, Mark Pub., LLC.

Wood, Christopher. Forgery, Replica, Fiction: Temporalities of German Renaissance Art. 2008. (ENG., Illus.). 416p. 55.00 *(978-0-226-90597-6(7))* Univ. of Chicago Pr.

Zigrosser, Carl. The Expressionists: A Survey of Their Graphic Art. 2011. 144p. 40.95 ***(978-1-258-04564-7(8))*** Literary Licensing, LLC.

ARTS—GREAT BRITAIN

Armstrong, Isobel. Victorian Glassworlds: Glass Culture & the Imagination 1830-1880. 2008. (ENG., Illus.). 400p. 65.00 *(978-0-19-920520-2(5))* Oxford Univ. Pr., Inc.

Les Artistes Anglo-Américains et la Méditerranée. 2010. (FRE.). 174p. *(978-2-35692-046-1(3))* Houdiard, Michel, Editeur.

Aslet, Clive. The Arts & Crafts Country House: From the Archives of Country Life. 2012. (Country Life Ser.). (ENG., Illus.). 192p. 75.00 ***(978-1-84513-680-2(2))*** Aurum Pr., Ltd. GBR. Dist: Independent Pubs. Group.

Barton, Paulette E. Mercy & the Misericord in Late Medieval England: Cathedral Theology & Architecture. 2009. (Illus.). 272p. 109.95 *(978-0-7734-4841-4(1))* Mellen, Edwin Pr., The.

Beevers, David, ed. Chinese Whispers: Chinoiserie in Britain 1650-1930. 2009. (ENG., Illus.). 144p. pap. *(978-0-948723-71-1(8)*, Royal Pavilion Libraries & Mus) Antique Collectors' Club.

Bennett, Susan. Cultivating the Human Faculties: James Barry (1741-1806) & the Society of Arts. 2009. (Illus.). 168p. 57.50 *(978-0-934223-96-6(3))* Lehigh Univ. Pr.

—Cultivating the Human Faculties: James Barry, 1741-1806 & the Society of Arts. 2009. (ENG.). 1p. 57.50 *(978-1-61146-049-0(2))* Lehigh Univ. Pr.

Betts, Ian & Weinstein, Rosemary. Tin-Glazed Tiles from London. 2010. (ENG., Illus.). 222p. (C). 78.00 *(978-1-901992-90-8(X))* Museum of London Archaeology Service GBR. Dist: Brown, David Bk. Co., The.

Bindman, David, ed. The History of British Art, Volume 2: 1600-1870. 2009. (ENG., Illus.). 248p. 50.00 *(978-0-300-11671-7(3))* Yale Ctr. for British Art.

Bindman, David & Ayers, Tim, eds. The History of British Art, Volume 1: 600-1600. 2009. (ENG., Illus.). 296p. 50.00 *(978-0-300-11670-0(5))* Yale Ctr. for British Art.

Bindman, David & Stephens, Chris, eds. The History of British Art, Volume 3: 1870-Now. 2009. (ENG., Illus.). 256p. 50.00 *(978-0-300-11672-4(1))* Yale Ctr. for British Art.

Boettcher, Graham C. The Look of Love: Eye Miniatures from the Skier Collection. Boettcher, Graham C., ed. 2012. (ENG., Illus.). 208p. 35.00 ***(978-1-907804-01-4(3))*** Giles, D. Ltd. GBR. Dist: Antique Collectors' Club.

Bracewell, Michael. The Complete Postcard Art of Gilbert & George, 2 vols. 2011. (Illus.). 1081p. 65.00 *(978-3-7913-5116-2(8))* Prestel Publishing.

British Design & Art Direction. 89.95 incl. audio compact disk *(978-0-06-018583-1(X))* HarperCollins Pubs.

Brockington, Grace. Above the Battlefield: Modernism & the Peace Movement in Britain, 1900-1918. 2011. (Paul Mellon Centre for Studies in Britis Ser.). (Illus.). 244p. 75.00 *(978-0-300-15195-4(0))* Yale Univ. Pr.

Charlesworth, Michael. Landscape & Vision in Nineteenth-Century Britain & France. 2008. (Illus.). 218p. 124.95 *(978-0-7546-5664-7(0))* Ashgate Publishing Co.

Comentale, Edward P. Modernism, Cultural Production, & the British Avant-garde. 2009. (ENG., Illus.). 272p. pap. 38.99 *(978-0-521-12097-5(7))* Cambridge Univ. Pr.

Davison, Betsy & Davison, Elizabeth. The Furniture of John Shearer, 1790-1820: 'A True North Britain' in the Southern Backcountry. 2011. (ENG.). 240p. 99.00 *(978-0-7591-1954-3(6))* AltaMira Pr.

Dimbleby, David. Seven Ages of Britain. 2010. (ENG., Illus.). 256p. 42.95 *(978-0-340-99408-5(8))* Murray, John GBR. Dist: Independent Pubs. Group.

Doherty, Willie. Fuera de Posición: Out of Position, 1 vol. 2007. (SPA & ENG., Illus.). 102p. pap. 20.00 *(978-968-9056-03-4(4))* Turner, Ediciones S.A. ESP. Dist: D.A.P./Distributed Art Pubs.

Don, Sarah. Fair Isle Knitting. 2007. (Dover Knitting, Crochet, Tatting, Lace Ser.). (ENG., Illus.). 128p. per. 12.95 *(978-0-486-45754-3(0))* Dover Pubns., Inc.

Dover. Tiffany. 2010. (Dover Postcards Ser.). (ENG., Illus.). 24p. pap. 6.95 *(978-0-486-48075-6(5))* Dover Pubns., Inc.

Dunmore, Simon. An Actor's Guide to Getting Work. 5th ed. 2012. (ENG.). 256p. (C). pap. 22.95 ***(978-1-4081-4554-8(5)***, Methuen Drama) A & C Black GBR. Dist: Macmillan.

Edelstein, Teri, et al. Art for All: British Posters for Transport. 2010. (Illus.). 280p. 50.00 *(978-0-300-15297-5(3))* Yale Univ. Pr.

Eisenman, Stephen. Design in the Age of Darwin: From William Morris to Frank Lloyd Wright. 2008. (ENG., Illus.). 140p. pap. 36.95 *(978-0-8101-5204-5(5))* Northwestern Univ. Pr.

Fawcett, Hilary, ed. Made in Newcastle: Visual Culture. 2007. (ENG., Illus.). 200p. pap. 15.95 *(978-1-904794-26-4(2))* Northumbria University Press GBR. Dist: Independent Pubs. Group.

Gowing, Robert & Pender, Robyn, eds. All Manner of Murals: The History, Techniques & Conservation of Secular Wall Paintings. 2007. (ENG., Illus.). 256p. 90.00 *(978-1-904982-11-1(5))* Archetype Pubns. GBR. Dist: National Bk. Network.

Hamill, Andrew. Learning Ict in the Arts. 2006. (Teaching ICT through the Primary Curriculum Ser.). (Illus.). CXXIVp. 41.95 *(978-1-84312-313-2(4))* Fulton, David Pubs. GBR. Dist: Taylor & Francis Group.

Harrison, Colin. The Pre-Raphaelites & Italy. 2010. 200p. pap. 35.00 *(978-1-85444-250-5(3))* Ashmolean Museum GBR. Dist: National Bk. Network.

Hart, Imogen. Arts & Crafts Objects. 2010. (Studies in Design & Material Culture Ser.). (ENG., Illus.). 288p. 89.95 *(978-0-7190-7971-9(3))*; pap. 34.95 *(978-0-7190-7972-6(1))* Manchester Univ. Pr. GBR. Dist: Macmillan.

Johns, Catherine. The Jewellery of Roman Britain: Celtic & Classical Traditions. 2012. (ENG.). 246p. pap. 44.95 ***(978-0-415-51612-9(9))*** Routledge.

Jones, Yvonne. Japanned Papier Mâché & Tinware C. 1740-1940. 2012. (ENG., Illus.). 336p. 89.50 ***(978-1-85149-686-0(6))*** Antique Collectors' Club.

Keay, Anna. The Crown Jewels. 2011. (ENG., Illus.). 192p. 200.00 ***(978-0-500-51603-4(0)***, 551603) Thames & Hudson.

Lloyd-Morgan, Ceridwen. Welsh Manuscripts & English Manuscripts in Wales. 2011. (Index of images in english Manuscripts). (ENG & WEL., Illus.). 128p. (C). pap. 94.00 ***(978-1-905375-81-3(6))*** Brepols Pubs. BEL. Dist: Brown, David Bk. Co., The.

Luxford, Julian M. The Art & Architecture of English Benedictine Monasteries, 1300-1540: A Patronage History. 2008. (Studies in the History of Medieval Religion Ser.: Volume 25). (Illus.). 346p. 90.00 *(978-1-84383-153-2(8)*, Boydell Press) Boydell & Brewer, Ltd. GBR. Dist: Boydell & Brewer, Inc.

Marsden, Jonathan, ed. Victoria & Albert: Art & Love. 2010. (Illus.). 480p. 59.95 *(978-1-905686-21-6(8))* Royal Collection Enterprises Ltd. GBR. Dist: Chicago Distribution Ctr.

McMinn, Joseph. Jonathan Swift & the Arts. 2010. (Illus.). 187p. 46.00 *(978-0-87413-068-3(9))*; (ENG.). 46.00 *(978-1-61149-125-8(8))* Univ. of Delaware Pr.

Miller, Lesley, ed. Princely Treasures: European Masterpieces 1600-1800, from the Victoria & Albert Museum. 2011. (ENG., Illus.). 192p. 30.00 *(978-1-85177-633-7(8))* V & A Pubns. GBR. Dist: Hachette Bk. Group.

O'Kane, Martin, ed. Bible, Art, Gallery. 2011. 220p. ***(978-1-906055-63-9(7))*** Sheffield Phoenix Pr.

Oliver, Jeff & Neal, Tim, eds. Wild Signs: Graffiti in Archaeology & History. 2010. (Bar S Ser.). (ENG., Illus.). 103p. (C). pap. 75.00 *(978-1-4073-0635-3(9))* British Archaeological Reports Ltd. GBR. Dist: Brown, David Bk. Co., The.

O'Neill, Morna & Hatt, Michael, eds. The Edwardian Sense: Art, Design, & Performance in Britain, 1901-1910. 2010. (Studies in British Art Ser.). (Illus.). 336p. 65.00 *(978-0-300-16335-3(5))* Yale Ctr. for British Art.

Page, Sophie, ed. The Unorthodox Imagination in Late Medieval Britain. 2011. (ENG., Illus.). 272p. 95.00 *(978-0-7190-7835-4(0))* Manchester Univ. Pr. GBR. Dist: Macmillan.

Parlanti, Steve. The Parlantis - Art Bronze Founders of Fulham. 2010. (ENG., Illus.). 100p. pap. *(978-1-84876-461-3(8))* Troubadour Publishing Ltd.

Potvin, John & Myzelev, Alla, eds. Material Cultures, 1740-1920: The Meanings & Pleasures of Collecting. 2009. (Illus.). 250p. 124.95 *(978-0-7546-6144-3(X))* Ashgate Publishing Co.

Purtle, Jennifer & Thomsen, Hans Bjarne. Looking Modern: East Asian Visual Culture from Treaty Ports to World War II. 2009. *(978-1-58886-105-4(8))* Art Media Resources, Inc.

Quigg, Anne-Marie. Bullying in the Arts: Vocation, Exploitation & Abuse of Power. 2011. (Illus.). 266p. 124.95 *(978-1-4094-0482-8(X)*, Gower Publishing Co., Ltd.) Ashgate Publishing, Ltd. GBR. Dist: Ashgate Publishing Co.

Read, Dennis M. R. H. Cromek Engraver Editor & Entrepreneur. 2011. (Illus.). 194p. 99.95 *(978-0-7546-6399-7(X))* Ashgate Publishing Co.

Reed, Talbot Baines. A History of the Old English Letter Foundries: With Notes, Historical & Bibliographical, on the Rise & Progress of English Typography. 2010. (Cambridge Library Collection - Printing & Publishing History Ser.). (ENG., Illus.). 432p. pap. 32.99 *(978-1-108-01297-3(3))* Cambridge Univ. Pr.

Roms, Heike. What's Welsh for Performance - an Oral History of Performance Art in Wales 1968 - 2008. 2008. (WEL & ENG., Illus.). 200p. per. *(978-0-9553927-2-6(1))* Nute Publishing, Ltd.

Schulz, Max F. Paradise Preserved: Recreations in Eden in Eighteenth- & Nineteenth-Century England. 2009. 388p. pap. 42.00 *(978-0-521-11892-7(1))* Cambridge Univ. Pr.

Shave, Stuart, ed. Eva Rothschild. 2011. (ENG., Illus.). 137p. 75.00 *(978-3-86560-910-6(4))* Verlag der Buchhandlung Walther Konig DEU. Dist: D.A.P./Distributed Art Pubs.

Smith, Lindsay. Victorian Photography, Painting & Poetry: The Enigma of Visibility in Ruskin, Morris & the Pre-Raphaelites. 2008. (Cambridge Studies in Nineteenth-Century Literature & Culture Ser.). (ENG., Illus.). 264p. pap. 37.99 *(978-0-521-05468-3(0))* Cambridge Univ. Pr.

Smith, Melanie Kay. Cultural Planning for Urban Regeneration. 2010. 208p. pap. *(978-3-8383-9203-5(5))* Lambert Academic Publishing.

Sotelano, Martin & Sotelano, Karen. Sacred Sites, Profane Body. 2010. 44p. pap. 31.50 *(978-1-4461-4341-4(4))* Lulu Enterprises Inc.

Spalding, Frances. The Bloomsbury Group. 2006. (National Portrait Gallery Insights Ser.). (Illus.). 108p. 19.95 *(978-1-85514-351-7(8))* National Portrait Gallery Pubns. GBR. Dist: Antique Collectors' Club.

Strand, Clare, photos by. Clare Strand: A Photoworks Monograph, 1 vol. 2009. (ENG., Illus.). 112p. 55.00 *(978-3-86521-838-4(5))* Steidl, Gerhard Druckerei und Verlag DEU. Dist: Innovative Logistics.

Takahashi, Kaoru, ed. Hello! UK Graphics: Graphic Design in the UK since The 1980s. 2011. (ENG., Illus.). 208p. pap. 39.95 *(978-4-7562-4036-1(4))* Rizzoli International Pubns., Inc.

Taylor, Rod & Andrews, Glennis. The Arts in the Primary School (Rle Edu O) 2011. (Routledge Library Editions: Education Ser.). (ENG.). 232p. 115.00 ***(978-0-415-68986-1(4))*** Routledge.

Temperley, Alice & D'Souza, Christa. True British: Alice Temperley. 2011. (ENG., Illus.). 272p. 65.00 *(978-0-8478-3674-1(6))* Rizzoli International Pubns., Inc.

Tickle, Les, ed. The Arts in Education(Rle Edu O) 2011. (Routledge Library Editions: Education Ser.). (ENG.). 312p. 130.00 ***(978-0-415-68988-5(0))*** Routledge.

Tusa, John. Engaged with the Arts: Writings from the Frontline. 2007. (ENG.). 232p. 52.00 *(978-1-84511-424-4(8))* I. B. Tauris & Co., Ltd. GBR. Dist: Macmillan.

Webster, Leslie. Anglo-Saxon Art. 2011. 256p. pap. 29.95 ***(978-0-8014-7766-9(2))*** Cornell Univ. Pr.

Webster, Leslie. The Franks Casket. 2012. (Objects in Focus Ser.). (ENG., Illus.). 64p. (C). pap. 10.00 *(978-0-7141-2818-4(X))* British Museum Pr. GBR. Dist: Brown, David Bk. Co., The.

ARTS—INDIA

Banerjee, Utpal K. Millennium Glimpses of Indian Performing Arts. 2007. (Illus.). 358p. *(978-81-8290-092-9(1))* Shubji Pubns.

Brown, Rebecca M. Art for a Modern India, 1947-1980. 2009. (Objects/Histories Ser.). (ENG., Illus.). 224p. pap. 22.95 *(978-0-8223-4375-2(4))*; 79.95 *(978-0-8223-4355-4(X))* Duke Univ. Pr.

Granoff, Phyllis. Victorious Ones: Jain Images of Perfection. 2010. (Illus.). 308p. pap. 75.00 *(978-0-944142-83-7(4))* Grantha Corp.

Menon, Rekha. Seductive Aesthetics of Postcolonialism. 2010. (Illus.). xi, 118p. *(978-1-57273-972-7(X))*; pap. *(978-1-57273-973-4(8))* Hampton Pr., Inc.

Peterson, Indira Viswanathan & Soneji, Devesh. Performing Pasts: Reinventing the Arts in Modern South India. Peterson, Indira Vishwanathan & Soneji, Davesh, eds. 2008. (ENG., Illus.). 352p. 50.00 *(978-0-19-569084-2(2))* Oxford Univ. Pr., Inc.

Ranjan, Aditi & Ranjan, M. P., eds. Handmade in India: A Geographic Encyclopedia of India Handicrafts. 2009. (ENG., Illus.). 579p. 65.00 *(978-0-7892-1047-0(9))* Abbeville Pr., Inc.

ARTS—JAPAN

Amberlyn, J. C. Drawing Manga Animals, Chibis, & Other Adorable Creatures. 2009. (ENG., Illus.). 160p. pap. 21.99 *(978-0-8230-9533-9(9))* Watson-Guptill Pubns., Inc.

Azur Corporation Editors. Logo & Marks in Japan. 2010. (ENG & JPN., Illus.). 416p. 85.00 *(978-4-568-50399-9(X))* Azur Corp. JPN. Dist: Antique Collectors' Club.

Carter, Murray. Bladesmithing with Murray Carter: Modern Application of Traditional Techniques. 2011. (ENG., Illus.). 160p. pap. 27.99 *(978-1-4402-1838-5(2))* Krause Pubns.

Carter, Robert E. The Japanese Arts & Self-Cultivation. 2007. 185p. 53.50 *(978-0-7914-7253-8(1))*; per. 24.95 *(978-0-7914-7254-5(X))* State Univ. of New York Pr.

Chronicle Books Staff. Woolly Embroidery: Crewelwork, Stump Work, Canvas Work, & More! 2008. (ENG., Illus.). 80p. pap. 14.95 *(978-0-8118-6086-4(8))* Chronicle Bks. LLC.

Davey, H. E. & Kameoka, Ann H. The Japanese Way of the Artist: Living the Japanese Arts & Ways/Brush Meditation/the Japanese Way of the Flower. 2007. (Michi: Japanese Arts & Ways Ser.). (ENG., Illus.). 512p. per. 19.95 *(978-1-933330-07-5(4))* Stone Bridge Pr.

Farameh, Patrice. New on the Catwalk: Emerging Fashion Labels. 2011. (ENG., Illus.). 400p. 95.00 *(978-3-942597-15-9(2))* DAAB Media Gmbh DEU. Dist: Innovative Logistics.

Fraleigh, Sondra Horton. Dancing into Darkness: Butoh, Zen, & Japan. 2010. (Illus.). 288p. pap. 24.95 *(978-0-8229-6115-4(6))* Univ. of Pittsburgh Pr.

Galindo, Michelle. Japanese Interior Design. 2011. (Interior Design Ser.). (ENG., Illus.). 208p. 49.95 *(978-3-03768-076-6(8)*, Braun Publish,Csi) Continental Sales, Inc.

Graham, Patricia Jane. Faith & Power in Japanese Buddhist Art, 1600-2005. 2007. (Illus.). 353p. (C). pap. 33.00 *(978-0-8248-3191-2(8))* Univ. of Hawaii Pr.

Gray, Julia D. Traditional Japanese Embroidery, 2009. (ENG., Illus.). 96p. spiral bd. 21.95 *(978-1-84448-422-5(X))* Search Pr., Ltd. GBR. Dist: Independent Pubs. Group.

Hirota, Morio. Grand Opening Design Collection. 2008. (ENG., Illus.). 228p. 60.00 *(978-4-568-50325-8(6))* Azur Corp. JPN. Dist: Antique Collectors' Club.

Johnson Jaffe Staff. Performing Japan. 2007. (Illus.). 240p. (C). *(978-1-905246-31-1(5))* BRILL.

Jones, Richard & Santillan, Jorge. Manga Monsters. 2012. (Learn to Draw Manga Ser.). (ENG.). 32p. (J). (gr. 4-6). pap. 11.75 ***(978-1-4488-7947-2(7))***; (Illus.). lib. bdg. 26.50 ***(978-1-4488-7876-5(4))*** Rosen Publishing Group, Inc., The. (PowerKids Pr.).

Kamikaze Factory & Factory, Kamikaze. Manga Master Class: Gotik & Punk. Minguet, Josep, ed. 2011. (Kamikaze Factory Studio Ser.). (SPA., Illus.). 112p. pap. 32.50 ***(978-84-15223-23-8(4))*** Instituto Monsa de Ediciones, S.A. ESP. Dist: Trans-Atlantic Pubns., Inc.

—Manga Master Class: Kawaii. Minguet, Josep, ed. 2011. (Kamikaze Factory Studio Ser.). (SPA., Illus.). 112p. pap. 32.50 ***(978-84-15223-24-5(2))*** Instituto Monsa de Ediciones, S.A. ESP. Dist: Trans-Atlantic Pubns., Inc.

Matsuo, Mikio, photos by. Zuancho in Kyoto: Textile Design Books for the Kimono Trade. 2008. (Illus.). 34p. *(978-0-911221-41-7(2))* Stanford Univ. Libraries.

McCormick, Melissa & Tokyo National Museum Staff. Elegant Perfection: Masterpieces of Courtly & Religious Art from the Tokyo National Museum. 2012. (ENG., Illus.). 128p. 45.00 *(978-0-300-17593-6(0))* Museum of Fine Arts, Houston.

Nara, Hiroshi. Inexorable Modernity: Japan's Grappling with Modernity in the Arts. 2007. (ENG., Illus.). 284p. 94.50 *(978-0-7391-1841-2(2))* Lexington Bks.

Nobuyoshi, Araki. Deja-Vu 15: Tokyo Diaries. pap. 25.00 *(978-4-309-90335-4(5))* Fiction, Inc. JPN. Dist: D.A.P./Distributed Art Pubs.

Ono, Mari. The Simple Art of Japanese Papercrafts. 2011. (ENG., Illus.). 96p. pap. 19.95 *(978-1-907563-08-9(3))* CICO Bks. GBR. Dist: Ryland Peters & Small.

Saito, Kaori, ed. Girl, Illustrated: Japanese Manga, Anime & Video Game Characters. 2010. (JPN & ENG., Illus.). 208p. pap. 29.95 *(978-4-7562-4008-8(9)*, PIE Bks.) Rizzoli International Pubns., Inc.

Sas, Miryam B. Experimental Arts in Postwar Japan: Moments of Encounter, Engagement, & Imagined Return. 2011. (Harvard East Asian Monographs: 329). (Illus.). 300p. 39.95 *(978-0-674-05340-3(0))* Harvard Univ., Asia Ctr.

Shirane, Haruo, ed. Envisioning the Tale of Genji: Media, Gender, & Cultural Production. 2008. (ENG., Illus.). 416p. (gr. 17). 84.50 *(978-0-231-14236-6(6))*; pap. 32.50 *(978-0-231-14237-3(4))* Columbia Univ. Pr.

Southgate, Anna & Sparrow, Keith. Drawing Manga Girls. 2011. 32p. pap. 14.05 *(978-1-4488-4802-7(4))*; lib. bdg. 31.95 *(978-1-4488-4798-3(2))* Rosen Publishing Group, Inc., The. (Rosen Central).

Stainback, Charles & Berger, Maurice. Striking Resemblance: The Portrait as Muse. Stainback, Charles, ed. 2008. (Illus.). 126p. *(978-0-943411-46-0(7))* Norton Museum of Art.

Tiampo, Ming. Gutai: Decentering Modernism. 2011. (ENG., Illus.). 264p. 99.00 *(978-0-226-80165-0(9))*; pap. 39.00 *(978-0-226-80166-7(7))* Univ. of Chicago Pr.

Tinios, Ellis. Japanese Prints Ukiyo-E in Edo, 1700-1900. 2010. (Illus.). 144p. 60.00 *(978-1-84822-076-8(6)*, Lund Humphries Pubs.) Ashgate Publishing, Ltd. GBR. Dist: Ashgate Publishing Co.

Van Assche, Annie. Fashioning Kimono: Dress & Modernity in Early Twentieth-Century Japan: The Montgomery Collection. 2008. *(978-0-88397-149-9(6))* Art Services International.

Various. Pixiv Almanac. 2012. (Illus.). 258p. (YA). pap. 39.99 ***(978-1-926778-35-8(9))*** URON Entertainment Corp. CAN. Dist: Diamond Bk. Distributors.

Yamazaki, Saori & Chronicle Books Staff. Fuzzy Felted Friends. 2008. (JPN & ENG., Illus.). 80p. pap. 14.95 *(978-0-8118-6066-6(3))* Chronicle Bks. LLC.

ARTS—SOVIET UNION

Bowlt, John E. Moscow & St. Petersburg 1900-1920: Art, Life, & Culture of the Russian Silver Age. 2008. *(978-0-86565-191-3(4))* Vendome Pr., The.

Dorontchenkov. Russian & Soviet Views of Modern Western Art. 2009. (Documents of Twentieth-Century Art Ser.). (Illus.). xv, 347p. 65.00 *(978-0-520-22103-1(6))* Univ. of California Pr.

Gurianova, Nina. The Aesthetics of Anarchy: Art & Ideology in the Early Russian Avant-Garde. 2012. (ENG., Illus.). 343p. 49.95 ***(978-0-520-26876-0(8))*** Univ. of California Pr.

Ioffe, Dennis G. & White, Frederick, eds. The Russian Avant-Garde & Radical Modernism: An Introductory Reader. (Cultural Syllabus Ser.). (ENG.). 350p. 2012. 59.00 *(978-1-936235-29-2(3))* 2011. pap. 29.00 *(978-1-936235-45-2(5))* Academic Studies Pr.

Kachurin, Pamela Jill. Soviet Textiles: Designing the Modern Utopia, 1 vol. 2006. (ENG., Illus.). 96p. pap. 24.95 *(978-0-87846-703-7(3))* Museum of Fine Arts, Boston.

King, David. Red Star over Russia: A Visual History of the Soviet Union from the Revolution to the Death of Stalin. 2009. (ENG., Illus.). 352p. 50.00 *(978-0-8109-8279-6(X))* Abrams.

Schmelz, Peter John. Such Freedom, If Only Musical: Unofficial Soviet Music During the Thaw. 2009. (ENG., Illus.). 432p. 65.00 *(978-0-19-534193-5(7))* Oxford Univ. Pr., Inc.

Thomson, Boris. Lot's Wife & the Venus of Milo: Conflicting Attitudes to the Cultural Heritage in Modern Russia. 2010. (ENG.). 178p. pap. 26.99 *(978-0-521-15790-2(0))* Cambridge Univ. Pr.

Traisman, Yuri, ed. Ode to Joy. 2009. (ENG., Illus.). 260p. bds. 150.00 *(978-0-615-24715-1(6))* Traisman, Yuri.

ARTS—SPAIN

Abrantes, Ricardo, et al. Arte Español para Extranjeros. Cámara, Alicia, ed. 4th ed. 2006. (SPA., Illus.). 256p. pap. 36.95 ***(978-84-89569-36-2(3))*** Nerea Editorial ESP. Dist: Independent Pubs. Group.

Actar, creator. From I to J: Isabel Coixet/John Berger. 2009. (Illus.). 89p. *(978-84-96954-85-4(4))* Actar Birkhauser Distribution.

Actar & Cla-Se, creators. Esc: Enter Spanish Creativity. 2008. (Illus.). *(978-84-96954-00-7(5))* Actar Birkhauser Distribution.

Brooksbank Jones, Anny & Jones, Anny. Visual Culture in Spain & Mexico. 2007. (ENG., Illus.). 224p. 84.00 *(978-0-7190-5678-9(0))* Manchester Univ. Pr. GBR. Dist: Macmillan.

Cantero, Leonardo, photos by. Leonardo Cantero: PHotoBolsillo. 2010. (ENG., Illus.). 112p. pap. 20.00 *(978-84-92498-91-8(9))* La Fabrica ESP. Dist: D.A.P./Distributed Art Pubs.

Colita. Colita: PHotoBolsillo. 2010. (ENG., Illus.). 112p. pap. 20.00 *(978-84-92841-20-2(6))* La Fabrica ESP. Dist: D.A.P./Distributed Art Pubs.

Hughes, Robert. Barcelona the Great Enchantress. 2007. (Directions Ser.). (ENG., Illus.). 192p. per. 12.95 *(978-1-4262-0131-8(1)*, National Geographic) National Geographic Society.

Llatzer, Moix & Moix Puig, Llàtzer. Barcelona: The City of Gaudi, 1 vol. 2008. (ENG.). 240p. pap. 17.95 *(978-84-8478-316-9(2))* Triangle Postals, S.L. ESP. Dist: Innovative Logistics.

Mariné, Óscar. Design Is Everything. 2011. (SPA & ENG., Illus.). 280p. 52.00 *(978-84-92441-09-9(7)*, T.F. Editores, S.L.C.) Antique Collectors' Club GBR. Dist: National Bk. Network.

Morales, Andrés & Garriga Vela, Jose Antonio. Casabermeja: El Centro Del Mundo. 2003. (SPA., Illus.). 147p. *(978-84-7785-468-5(8))* Diputacion Provincial de Malaga. Centro de Ediciones de la Diputacion.

Offl. OFFF, Year Zero: Artwork & Designs from the OFFF Festival. 2011. (ENG., Illus.). 400p. pap. 60.00 *(978-1-935613-29-9(4))* Batty, Mark Pub., LLC.

Roca, Marcel-Li Antunez. Metamembrana. 2009. (ENG, FRE & SPA., Illus.). 127p. pap. *(978-84-96954-87-8(0))* Actar Birkhauser Distribution.

Sala, Marius. Identity Made in Spain. 2007. (SPA & ENG., Illus.). 354p. (Orig.). pap. 45.00 *(978-84-96309-46-3(0))* Index Bks., Spain ESP. Dist: Gingko Pr., Inc.

Santos, Cidras, ed. Benicassim. 2008. 174p. *(978-84-96954-27-4(7))* Actar Birkhauser Distribution.

Umberto Allemandi and Company Staff. Discover the Dalí Theatre-Museum in Figures. 2011. (ENG., Illus.). 16p. pap. 12.50 *(978-88-422-1727-5(1))* Allemandi, Umberto & Co. GBR. Dist: Antique Collectors' Club.

Universidad de Acalá, Museo Luis González Robles Staff, contrib. by. 60 Artistas Del Museo Luis González Robles en Los 500 Años Del Primer Curso Académico de la Universidad de Alcalá: Una Mirada a la Colección. 2009. (SPA., Illus.). 97p. *(978-84-8138-838-1(6))* Universidad de Alcala de Henares. Servicio de Publicaciones.

Uroz, Chu. Barcelona Brand New Fashion Designers. 2008. (Illus.). 320p. *(978-84-96954-65-6(X))* Actar Birkhauser Distribution.

Watson McCarthy, Courtney. Gaudi Pop-Ups. 2012. (ENG., Illus.). 16p. 29.95 ***(978-0-500-51650-8(2)***, 551650) Thames & Hudson.

ARTS—SWITZERLAND

Art Basel Miami Beach 2011. 2011. (ENG., Illus.). 650p. pap. 65.00 ***(978-3-7757-3139-3(3))*** Hatje Cantz Verlag GmbH & Co KG DEU. Dist: D.A.P./Distributed Art Pubs.

Büro, Destruct. Büro Destruct II. 2009. (GER & ENG., Illus.). 224p. pap. *(978-3-89955-260-7(1))* Die Gestalten Verlag.

Burri, Monika & Graf, Nicole. Die Welt Im Taschenformat. Gasser, Michael, ed. 2012. (Pictorial Worlds. Photographs from the ETH-Bibliothek's Image Archive (vol. 1) Ser.). Orig. Title: The World in Pocket-Size Format. (GER & ENG., Illus.). 136p. 75.00 ***(978-3-85881-339-8(7))*** Scheidegger und Spiess AG, Verlag CHE. Dist: Antique Collectors' Club.

Department of Art and Media Staff & Schiesser, Giaco. Practices of Experimentation: Research & Teaching in the Arts Today. 2012. (Verlag Scheidegger & Spiess-Zurich University of the Arts Yearbook Ser.). (GER & ENG., Illus.). 304p. 60.00 *(978-3-85881-259-9(5))* Scheidegger und Spiess AG, Verlag CHE. Dist: Antique Collectors' Club.

Doswald, Christoph, ed. Hanspeter Hofmann: Bonheur Automatique II. 2008. (ENG., Illus.). 180p. 28.00 *(978-3-905829-81-5(9))* JRP Ringier Kunstverlag AG CHE. Dist: D.A.P./Distributed Art Pubs.

Haldemann, Anita. Les yeux enchantés: Zeichnungen und Druckgraphik des Surrealismus. 2008. (GER., Illus.). 150p. *(978-3-86678-144-3(X))* Kerber Verlag.

Klee, Paul. Klee: Hand Puppets, 1 vol. 2006. (ENG., Illus.). 128p. 40.00 *(978-3-7757-1740-3(4))* Hatje Cantz Verlag GmbH & Co KG DEU. Dist: D.A.P./Distributed Art Pubs.

Koella, Rudolf, et al, texts. The Arthur & Hedy Hahnloser Collection: An Eye for Art Shared with Artists. 2011. (ENG., Illus.). 384p. 75.00 ***(978-1-935202-63-9(4))*** D.A.P./Distributed Art Pubs.

Nefkens, Han. Pipilotti Rist: Friendly game: Electronic Feelings. 2010. (CAT, SPA & ENG., Illus.). 152p. 34.95 *(978-84-92861-56-9(8))*, Fundacio Joan Miro ESP. Dist: Actar Birkhauser Distribution.

Passion Bild: Russische Kunst seit 1970. 2010. (Illus.). 280p. 171.00 ***(978-3-85881-199-8(8))*** Scheidegger und Spiess AG, Verlag CHE. Dist: Antique Collectors' Club.

Richter, Frank & Friedrich, Caspar David. Caspar David Friedrich: Spurensuche im Dresdner Umland und in der Sächsischen Schweiz. 2009. (GER., Illus.). 143p. pap. *(978-3-86530-115-4(0))* Verlag der Kunst.

Rüegg, Arthur. Le Corbusier. Furniture & Interiors 1905-1965. 2012. (ENG., Illus.). 352p. 195.00 ***(978-3-85881-728-0(7))*** Scheidegger und Spiess AG, Verlag CHE. Dist: Antique Collectors' Club.

Schubiger, Irene, ed. & text. Reconstructing Swiss Video Art: From the 1970s & 1980s. 2010. (ENG., Illus.). 184p. pap. 50.00 *(978-3-03764-054-8(5))* JRP Ringier Kunstverlag AG CHE. Dist: D.A.P./Distributed Art Pubs.

Stutzer, Beat, et al. The Unseen Giacometti: Unknown Photographs & Drawings. Stutzer, Beat, ed. 2011. (ENG., Illus.). 255p. 99.00 *(978-3-85881-726-6(0))* Scheidegger und Spiess AG, Verlag CHE. Dist: Antique Collectors' Club.

Szymczyk, Adam, text. Kilian Rüthemann: Double Rich. 2010. (ENG., Illus.). 4036p. 55.00 *(978-3-7757-2674-0(8))* Hatje Cantz Verlag GmbH & Co KG DEU. Dist: D.A.P./Distributed Art Pubs.

Ursprung, Philip, et al, texts. L/B: Beautiful Book. 2009. (ENG., Illus.). 164p. 35.00 *(978-3-905829-90-7(8))* JRP Ringier Kunstverlag AG CHE. Dist: D.A.P./Distributed Art Pubs.

Weber, Heidi. Heidi Weber 50 Years Ambassador for Le Corbusier 1958-2008: Heidi Weber 50 Jahre Botschafterin für Le Corbusier 1958-2008. 2009. (Illus.). 205p. pap. *(978-3-0346-0249-5(9))* Birkhauser Verlag AG.

ARTS—UNITED STATES

see also African American Arts

ACE (Adult and Continuing Education). Arts & Societal Learning No. 116: Transforming Communities Socially, Politically, & Culturally - New Directions for Adult & Continuing Education. Hayes, Sandra & Yorks, Lyle, eds. 2007. (J-B ACE Single Issue Adult & Continuing Education Ser.: 91). (ENG.). 96p. pap. 29.00 *(978-0-470-27852-9(8)*, Jossey-Bass) Wiley, John & Sons, Inc.

Adrian, Matt. The Mincing Mockingbird Guide to Troubled Birds: The Paintings of the Mincing Mockingbird. 2nd ed. 2012. (ENG.). 64p. (C). pap. 13.99 *(978-0-615-35804-8(7))* Mincing Mockingbird, The.

Adz, King. Street Knowledge. 2011. (ENG.). 320p. (gr. 12). 35.00 *(978-1-59020-477-1(8))* Overlook Pr., The.

Amalfitano, Lelia & Fox, Judith Hoos. The Strange Life of Objects: The Art of Annette Lemieux. 2011. (ENG., Illus.). 232p. 49.00 *(978-1-883015-45-9(6))* Krannert Art Museum.

Andera, Margaret & Stone, Lisa. Accidental Genius: Art from the Anthony Petullo Collection. 2012. (Illus.). 215p. pap. ***(978-3-7913-6405-6(7))*** Milwaukee Art Museum.

Antliff, Allan. Anarchist Modernism: Art, Politics, & the First American Avant-Garde. 2007. (Illus.). 314p. per. 45.00 *(978-0-226-02104-1(1))* Univ. of Chicago Pr.

Les Artistes Anglo-Américains et la Méditerranée. 2010. (FRE.). 174p. *(978-2-35692-046-1(3))* Houdiard, Michel, Editeur.

Baldessari, John & Cesarco, Alejandro. Retrospective: Baldessari/Cesarco. 2008. (ENG., Illus.). 24p. pap. 19.95 *(978-3-86560-344-9(0))* Verlag der Buchhandlung Walther Konig DEU. Dist: D.A.P./Distributed Art Pubs.

Banta, Martha. One True Theory & the Quest for an American Aesthetic. 2007. (ENG.). 336p. (C). 38.00 *(978-0-300-12297-8(7))* Yale Univ. Pr.

Barber, Edwin Atlee. Tulip Ware of the Pennsylvania-German Potters: An Historical Sketch of the Art of Slip-Decoration in the United States. 2011. (ENG.). 242p. pap. 20.95 ***(978-0-271-05240-3(6)***, Metalmark) Pennsylvania State Univ. Pr.

Barndt, Deborah, ed. ¡viva! Community Arts & Popular Education in the Americas. 2011. (Illus.). 240p. pap. 24.95 ***(978-1-4384-3766-8(8)***, Suny Pr.) State Univ. of New York Pr.

Barnhill, Georgia B., ed. With a French Accent: American Lithography to 1860. 2012. (ENG., Illus.). pap. 25.00 ***(978-1-929545-67-4(3))*** American Antiquarian Society.

Barter, Judith A., ed. & contrib. by. Apostles of Beauty: Arts & Crafts from Britian to Chicago. 2009. (ENG., Illus.). 208p. 45.00 *(978-0-300-14113-9(0))* Art Institute of Chicago.

Bell, Esther & Gere, Charlotte. Studying Nature: Oil Sketches from the Thaw Collection. 2011. ***(978-0-87598-160-4(7))*** Pierpont Morgan Library.

Bennett, Shelley M., et al. French Art of the Eighteenth Century at the Huntington. Bennett, Shelley M. & Sargentson, Carolyn, eds. 2008. (Illus.). 555p. 125.00 *(978-0-300-13594-7(7))* Yale Univ. Pr.

Berman, Marshall. On the Town: One Hundred Years of Spectacle in Times Square. 2nd ed. 2009. (ENG., Illus.). 320p. pap. 18.95 *(978-1-84467-397-1(9)*, 844397) Verso Bks. GBR. Dist: Norton, W. W. & Co., Inc.

Bernstein, Lee. America Is the Prison: Arts & Politics in Prison in the 1970s. 2010. (Illus.). xi, 244p. pap. *(978-0-8078-7117-1(6))* Univ. of North Carolina Pr.

Beuerlein, Katharina. Arts Sponsorship in the Usa & Germany. 2007. 96p. per. *(978-3-8364-1745-7(6))* VDM Verlag Dr. Mueller e.K.

Blomberg, Nancy J. Action & Agency: Advancing the Dialogue on Native Performance Art. 2010. *(978-0-914738-65-7(8))* Denver Art Museum.

Boyle Collins, Amy, ed. A Streetcar Named Inspire: Coffee Table Book. 2009. (Illus.). 152p. 45.00 *(978-0-615-29168-0(6))* Young Leadership Council.

Brilliant, Virginia. The John & Mable Ringling Museum of Art: Curator's Choice. 2010. (ENG., Illus.). 80p. pap. 9.95 *(978-1-85759-643-4(9))* Scala, Editions FRA. Dist: National Bk. Network.

Brown, Kendall H. Deco Japan: Shaping Art & Culture, 1920-1945. 2012. ***(978-0-88397-157-4(7))*** Art Services International.

Brunalti, Carla Ginelli & Brunalti, Roberto. American Costume Jewelry: Art & Industry, 1935-1950, A-M. 2008. (Illus.). 256p. bds. 59.99 *(978-0-7643-2982-1(0))* Schiffer Publishing, Ltd.

—American Costume Jewelry: Art & Industry, 1935-1950, N-Z. 2008. (Illus.). 256p. bds. 59.99 *(978-0-7643-2983-8(9))* Schiffer Publishing, Ltd.

Burke, Robert E. Handicrafts in Indiana. (Illus.). 30p. reprint ed. lib. bdg. 88.00 *(978-0-7222-0571-6(6))* Library Reprints, Inc.

Burns, Cherie. Searching for Beauty: The Life of Millicent Rogers. 2011. (ENG., Illus.). 384p. 27.99 *(978-0-312-54724-0(2))* St. Martin's Pr.

Burzlaff Bostic, Mary, ed. 2012 Artist's & Graphic Designer's Market. 37th ed. 2011. (ENG., Illus.). 672p. pap. 34.99 *(978-1-4403-1418-6(7)*, North Light Bks.) F&W Media, Inc.

Byrnes, Jennifer P., ed. Public Participation in the Arts & the Role of Technology. 2011. *(978-1-61209-744-2(8))* Nova Science Pubs., Inc.

Byrnes, William. Management & the Arts. 4th ed. 2008. (ENG., Illus.). 496p. pap. 48.95 *(978-0-240-81004-1(X)*, Focal Pr.) Elsevier Science & Technology Bks.

Carson, Andrea, frwd. Flash Forward 2008: Emerging Photographers from Canada, the United Kingdom & the United States. 2008. (ENG.). 192p. 30.00 *(978-0-9739739-6-9(X))* Magenta Publishing for the Arts CAN. Dist: Consortium Bk. Sales & Distribution.

Castronovo, Russ. Beautiful Democracy: Aesthetics & Anarchy in a Global Era. 2007. (Illus.). 272p. 65.00 *(978-0-226-09628-5(9))*; per. 27.50 *(978-0-226-09629-2(7))* Univ. of Chicago Pr.

Cathers, David & Parry, Linda. Arts & Crafts Rugs for Craftsman Interiors: The Crab Tree Farm Collection. 2009. (ENG., Illus.). 168p. 45.00 *(978-0-393-73320-4(3)*, 73320) Norton, W. W. & Co., Inc.

Chavez, Nicolasa. A Century of Masters: The NEA National Heritage Fellows of New Mexico. 2009. pap. *(978-1-890689-43-8(2)*, Rio Grande Bks.) LPD Pr.

Cherbo, Joni Maya, et al, eds. Understanding the Arts & Creative Sector in the United States. 2008. (Rutgers Series on the Public Life of the Arts). (ENG., Illus.). 224p. 68.00 *(978-0-8135-4307-9(X))*; pap. 26.95 *(978-0-8135-4308-6(8))* Rutgers Univ. Pr.

Cohen, Matthew Isaac. Performing Otherness: Java & Bali on International Stages, 1905-1952. 2010. (Studies in International Performance Ser.). (ENG., Illus.). 304p. 89.00 *(978-0-230-22462-9(8))* Palgrave Macmillan.

Cohn, Damian A. Artists in the Workforce: Trends & Data. 2009. (Professions - Training, Education & Demographics Ser.). 79.00 *(978-1-60741-484-1(8))* Nova Science Pubs., Inc.

Columbia Musuem of Art. Carolina Collects. 2011. (Distributed for the South Carolina State Museum Ser.). 44p. pap. 14.95 ***(978-0-9818064-0-2(6))*** Univ. of South Carolina Pr.

Couch, Dale L. Neighboring Voices: The Decorative Culture of Our Southern Cousins: The Fifth Henry D. Green Symposium of the Decorative Arts: Georgia Museum of Art, Athens, Georgia, January 29 & 30, 2010. 2011. ***(978-0-915977-76-5(1))*** Univ. of Georgia, Georgia Museum of Art.

Craven, David & Winkenweder, Brian, eds. Dialectical Conversions: Donald Kuspit's Art Criticism. 2011. (Liverpool University Press - Value-Art-Politics Ser.). (ENG., Illus.). 276p. 95.00 *(978-1-84631-479-7(8))* Liverpool Univ. Pr. GBR. Dist: Chicago Distribution Ctr.

Davis, Anita Price. New Deal Art in Virginia: The Oils, Murals, Reliefs & Frescoes & Their Creators. 2009. (ENG., Illus.). 223p. pap. 45.00 *(978-0-7864-4185-3(2))* McFarland & Co., Inc. Pubs.

Decker, Christof. Visuelle Kulturen der USA: Zur Geschichte von Malerei, Fotografie, Film, Fernsehen und Neuen Medien in Amerika. 2010. (GER., Illus.). 363p. pap. *(978-3-8376-1043-7(8))* Transcript Verlag.

Denver Museum of Art Staff, ed. Sweet on the West: How Candy Built a Colorado Treasure. 2008. (ENG.). 80p. pap. 10.95 *(978-0-8061-9969-6(5))* Denver Art Museum.

Deputy Director of Curatorial Affairs Staff & Departmental Curators of the Museum Staff. Cincinnati Art Museum: Collection Highlights. 2009. (ENG., Illus.). 392p. 49.95 *(978-1-904832-53-9(9))* Giles, D. Ltd. GBR. Dist: Antique Collectors' Club.

Dietz, Donald, photos by. Celebrating West Side Story: North Carolina School of the Arts A 50th Anniversary Production. 2007. (Illus.). 144p. 50.00 *(978-0-9617507-0-1(7))*; (ENG., Illus.). pap. 30.00 *(978-0-9617507-1-8(5))* North Carolina Schl. of the Arts Foundation, Inc.

Dotz, Warren & Husain, Masud. Ad Boy: Vintage Advertising with Character. 2009. (ENG., Illus.). 176p. pap. 16.99 *(978-1-58008-984-5(4))* Ten Speed Pr.

Dreiser, Theodore. Art, Music, & Literature, 1897-1902. Hakutani, Yoshinobu, ed. 2007. (Illus.). 336p. per. 21.00 *(978-0-252-07398-4(3))* Univ. of Illinois Pr.

Drew, Ned, et al. Purity of Aim: The Book Jackets of Alvin Lustig. 2010. (Illus.). 88p. 21.95 *(978-1-933360-48-5(8)*, RIT Cary Graphic Arts Pr.) Rochester Institute of Technology, Cary Graphic Arts Pr.

Duffus, R. L. The American Renaissance. 2011. 330p. 50.95 ***(978-1-258-04153-3(7))*** Literary Licensing, LLC.

Everett, Carole B. College Guide for Performing Arts Majors 2009: Real-World Admission Guide for All Dance, Music, & Theater Majors. Oram, Fern, ed. 14th ed. 2008. (ENG., Illus.). 467p. pap. 24.95 *(978-0-7689-2563-0(0))* Peterson's.

Fagaly, William A., ed. Ancestors of Congo Square: African Art in the New Orleans Museum of Art. 2011. (Illus.). 376p. 75.00 *(978-1-85759-698-4(6))* Scala, Editions FRA. Dist: National Bk. Network.

Fer, Briony, et al, texts. James Castle: Show & Store. 2011. (ENG., Illus.). 224p. 55.00 ***(978-1-935202-70-7(7))*** D.A.P./Distributed Art Pubs.

Fred L. Emerson Gallery Staff, contrib. by. The Best Kind of Life: Edward W. Root As Teacher, Collector, & Naturalist, Emerson Gallery, Hamilton College, September 27, 2007-January 6, 2008. 2007. (Illus.). 55p. *(978-1-880640-11-1(2))* Hamilton College, Emerson Gallery.

Gastman, Roger & Teri, Sonja, eds. Los Angeles Graffiti. 2007. (ENG., Illus.). 128p. 27.95 *(978-0-9790486-1-6(3))* Batty, Mark Pub., LLC.

Getty, J. Paul. The Joys of Collecting. 2011. (ENG., Illus.). 80p. pap. 9.95 ***(978-1-60606-087-2(2)***, J. Paul Getty Museum) Getty Pubns.

Glancy, Michael. Michael Glancy: Infinite Obsessions. 2011. (Illus.). 228p. ***(978-0-9826397-2-6(4))*** Arnoldsche Art Pubs.

Goodwin, James. Modern American Grotesque: Literature & Photography. 2009. (ENG.). 264p. 61.95 *(978-0-8142-1108-3(9))*; cd-rom 14.95 *(978-0-8142-9205-1(4))* Ohio State Univ. Pr.

Goodyear, Frank H. Zaida Ben-Yusuf: New York Portrait Photographer. 2008. (Illus.). 240p. 59.95 *(978-1-85894-439-5(2))* Merrell Pubs. Ltd. GBR. Dist: Perseus Distribution.

Gooseberry Patch. Gooseberry Patch Halloween. 2010. (ENG., Illus.). 208p. pap. 18.95 *(978-0-8487-3391-9(6))* Oxmoor Hse., Inc.

Gore, Elaine Clift. Talent Knows No Color: The History of an Arts Magnet High School. 2007. (Research in Curriculum & Instruction Ser.). (ENG.). 198p. (C). *(978-1-59311-762-7(0))*; per. *(978-1-59311-761-0(2))* Information Age Publishing, Inc.

Görner, Veit. One Hundred Fish Fountain. Moll, Frank-Thorsten, ed. 2008. (GER & ENG., Illus.). 80p. 36.00 *(978-3-939583-64-6(2))* Kehrer Verlag Heidelberg, Klaus Kehrer DEU. Dist: Consortium Bk. Sales & Distribution.

Graham's Magazine, Set, Vols. 1-53. reprint ed. lib. bdg. 3960.00 *(978-0-404-19521-2(0))* AMS Pr., Inc.

Grams, Diane, ed. Entering Cultural Communities: Diversity & Change in the Nonprofit Arts. 2008. (Rutgers Series - the Public Life of the Arts Ser.). (ENG.). 292p. (C). pap. 24.95 *(978-0-8135-4217-1(0))* Rutgers Univ. Pr.

Grams, Diane & Farrell, Betty, eds. Entering Cultural Communities: Diversity & Change in the Nonprofit Arts. 2008. (Rutgers Series - the Public Life of the Arts Ser.). (ENG., Illus.). 292p. (C). 70.00 *(978-0-8135-4216-4(2))* Rutgers Univ. Pr.

Guyton, Tyree. Connecting the Dots: Tyree Guyton's Heidelberg Project. 2007. (Painted Turtle Book Ser.). 60.00 *(978-0-8143-3320-4(6))* Wayne State Univ. Pr.

Haeg, Fritz & Wakefield, Stacy, eds. The Sundown Salon Unfolding Archive. 2009. (ENG., Illus.). 380p. 150.00 *(978-0-9763355-1-1(4))* Evil Twin Pubns.

Han, Heng-Gil, et al. Jamaica Flux: Workspaces & Windows 2007. 2008. (ENG., Illus.). 194p. 39.95 *(978-0-9762853-6-6(3))* Jamaica Ctr. for Arts & Learning.

Harris, Neil. The Chicagoan: A Lost Magazine of the Jazz Age. 2008. (ENG., Illus.). 400p. 65.00 *(978-0-226-31761-8(7))* Univ. of Chicago Pr.

Harrison, Jefferson C., et al. Collecting with Vision: Treasures from the Chrysler Museum of Art. 2007. (Illus.). 160p. *(978-0-940744-72-1(4))* Chrysler Museum, The.

Heinich, Nathalie. Guerre Culturelle et Art Contemporain: Une Comparaison Franco-Américaine. 2010. (FRE.). 170p. *(978-2-7056-7063-4(7))* Hermann.

Hemy, Ed, et al, contrib. by. Berkeley Bohemia: Artist & Visionaries of the Early 20th Century, 1 vol. 2008. (ENG., Illus.). 208p. 24.99 *(978-1-4236-0085-5(1))* Gibbs Smith, Publisher.

Hildebrand, Grant. Elegant Explorations: The Designs of Philip Jacobson. 2007. (ENG., Illus.). 80p. pap. 25.00 *(978-0-295-98719-4(7))* Univ. of Washington Pr.

Hinsley, Matthew. Creativity to Community: Arts Nonprofit Success One Coffee at a Time. 2011. 224p. 33.95 ***(978-0-557-54392-2(4))*** Lulu Enterprises Inc.

Hischak, Thomas S. The Oxford Companion to the American Musical: Theatre, Film, & Television. 2008. (ENG., Illus.). 592p. (C). 39.95 *(978-0-19-533533-0(3))* Oxford Univ. Pr., Inc.

Holladay, Wilhelmina Cole. A Museum of Their Own: The National Museum of Women in the Arts, 1987-2007. 2008. (ENG., Illus.). 240p. 50.00 *(978-0-7892-1003-6(7))* Abbeville Pr., Inc.

Hull, Brent & Franck, Christine G. H. Traditional American Rooms: Celebrating Style, Craftsmanship, & Historic Woodwork. 2008. (Illus.). 179p. *(978-1-56523-445-1(6))* Fox Chapel Publishing Co., Inc.

Ivey, Bill. Arts, Inc: How Greed & Neglect Have Destroyed Our Cultural Rights. 2010. (ENG., Illus.). 368p. pap. 17.95 *(978-0-520-26792-3(3))* Univ. of California Pr.

Ivey, Bill & Tepper, Steven J., eds. Engaging Art: The Next Great Transformation of America's Cultural Life. 2007. (ENG., Illus.). 408p. 131.00 *(978-0-415-96041-0(X))* Routledge.

Ivey, Bill J. Arts, Inc: How Greed & Neglect Have Destroyed Our Cultural Rights. 2008. (Illus.). 342p. 40.00 *(978-0-520-24112-1(6))* Univ. of California Pr.

J. Paul Getty Museum Staff, contrib. by. The Antiquities Collection. 2nd ed. 2010. *(978-0-89236-997-3(3)*, J. Paul Getty Museum) Getty Pubns.

Jacob, Mary Jane & Baas, Jacquelynn, eds. Chicago Makes Modern: How Creative Minds Changed Society. 2012. (ENG., Illus.). 304p. pap. 35.00 ***(978-0-226-38956-1(1))*** Univ. of Chicago Pr.

Johnson, Dominic. Glorious Catastrophe: Jack Smith, Performance & Visual Culture. 2012. (ENG., Illus.). 272p. 95.00 ***(978-0-7190-8299-3(4))*** Manchester Univ. Pr. GBR. Dist: Macmillan.

Johnston, Ella Bond. A History of the Art Association of Richmond, Indiana. (Illus.). 48p. reprint ed. lib. bdg. 88.00 *(978-0-7222-0601-0(1))* Library Reprints, Inc.

Jusko, Joe. Art of Joe Jusko. 2012. (Illus.). 328p. 49.99 ***(978-1-61377-096-2(0))*** Idea & Design Works, LLC.

Kaiser, Michael M. Leading Roles: 50 Questions Every Arts Board Should Ask. 2010. (Illus.). 192p. 24.95 *(978-1-58465-906-8(8)*, Brandeis University Press) Univ. Pr. of New England.

Kim, Clara, et al. Snake River: Charles Gaines & Edgar Arceneaux: Roy & Edna Disney/CalArts Theater. Kim, Clara, ed. 2006. (ENG.). pap. 40.00 *(978-0-9749831-5-8(2))* California Institute of the Arts.

Kinnison, William A. Modern Wittenberg. 2011. 402p. 34.99 ***(978-1-4628-6058-6(3))***; pap. 23.99 ***(978-1-4628-6057-9(5))*** Xlibris Corp.

Kious, Kevin. Breweriana. 2012. (Shire Library). (ENG., Illus.). 56p. pap. 9.95 ***(978-0-7478-1044-5(3))*** Shire Pubns., Ltd. GBR. Dist: Random Hse., Inc.

Klin, Richard. Something to Say: Thoughts on Art & Politics in America. 2011. (ENG., Illus.). 168p. pap. 14.95 ***(978-1-935248-19-4(7))*** Leapfrog Pr.

Kotz, Liz. Words to Be Looked At: Language in 1960s Art. (ENG., Illus.). 344p. (gr. 17). 2010. pap. 17.95 *(978-0-262-51403-3(6))* 2007. 31.95 *(978-0-262-11308-3(2))* MIT Pr.

Kreisman, Lawrence & Mason, Glenn. The Arts & Crafts Movement in the Pacific Northwest. 2007. (ENG., Illus.). 400p. 24.95 (978-0-88192-849-5(6), 0881928496) Timber Pr., Inc.

Krensky, Beth & Steffen, Seana Lowe. Engaging Classrooms & Communities Through Art: A Guide to Designing & Implementing Community-Based Art Education. 2008. (ENG., Illus.). 204p. 75.00 (978-0-7591-1067-0(0)); pap. 29.95 (978-0-7591-1068-7(9)) AltaMira Pr.

Krill, Rosemary Troy. Early American Decorative Arts, 1620-1860: A Handbook for Interpreters. 2010. (American Association for State & Local History Ser.). (ENG.). 278p. 100.00 incl. cd-rom (978-0-7591-1944-4(9)); pap. 49.95 incl. cd-rom (978-0-7591-1945-1(7)) AltaMira Pr.

Logsdon, Gene. The Mother of All Arts: Agrarianism & the Creative Impulse. 2007. (Culture of the Land Ser.). (ENG., Illus.). 344p. 40.00 (978-0-8131-2443-8(3)) Univ. Pr. of Kentucky.

Loveland, Elaina. Creative Colleges: A Guide for Student Actors, Artists, Dancers, Musicians & Writers. 3rd ed. 2010. (ENG.). 320p. pap. 19.95 (978-1-932662-46-7(4)) SuperCollege LLC.

Macomber, Ben. The Jewel City. 2008. 204p. 24.99 (978-0-554-31731-1(1)) 2008. 204p. 27.99 (978-0-554-22428-2(3)) 2007. (ENG.). 190p. pap. 19.99 (978-1-4264-2329-1(2)) 2007. (ENG.). 202p. pap. 22.99 (978-1-4264-2377-2(2)) BiblioBazaar.

Markowitz, Yvonne & Karlin, Elyse Zorn, texts. Imperishable Beauty. 2008. (ENG., Illus.). 176p. 45.00 (978-0-87846-734-1(3)) Museum of Fine Arts, Boston.

Marshall, Traute M. Art Museums PLUS: Cultural Excursions in New England. 2009. (ENG., Illus.). 400p. pap. 24.95 (978-1-58465-621-0(2)) Univ. Pr. of New England.

Martignette, Charles G. & Meisel, Louis K. Elvgren, Pin Ups: 25 Jahre TASCHEN. 25th ed. 2008. (FRE, GER & ENG., Illus.). 271p. 14.99 (978-3-8365-0305-1(0)) TASCHEN DEU. Dist: Ingram Pub. Services.

Mayer-Thurman, Christa C. & Wayne, June. June Wayne's Narrative Tapestries: Tidal Waves, DNA, & the Cosmos. 2010. (Illus.). 36p. pap. (978-0-86559-243-8(8)) Art Institute of Chicago.

Mazaroff, Stanley. Henry Walters & Bernard Berenson: Collector & Connoisseur. 2010. (ENG., Illus.). 248p. (gr. 17). 40.00 (978-0-8018-9512-8(X)) Johns Hopkins Univ. Pr.

McCarthy, Kevin F., et al. Arts & Culture in the Metropolis: Strategies for Sustainability. 2007. (Illus.). 156p. per. 25.00 (978-0-8330-3890-6(7), MG-477) RAND Corp., The.

McInnis, Maurie D. Slaves Waiting for Sale: Abolitionist Art & the American Slave Trade. 2011. (ENG., Illus.). 280p. 40.00 (978-0-226-55933-9(5)) Univ. of Chicago Pr.

Merrill, Linda, et al. Picturing America: Teachers Resource Book. 2008. (978-0-615-20793-3(6)) National Endowment for the Humanities.

Meyer, Regina G., ed. Live & Local: A Study of U. S. Outdoor Arts Festivals. 2011. (Fine Arts, Music & Literature Ser.). 190p. 89.00 (978-1-61209-825-8(8)) Nova Science Pubs., Inc.

Miller, Tyrus. Singular Examples: Artistic Politics & the Neo-Avant-Garde. 2009. (Avant-Garde & Modernism Studies). (ENG.). 270p. pap. 34.95 (978-0-8101-2512-4(9)); (Illus.). 69.95 (978-0-8101-2511-7(0)) Northwestern Univ. Pr.

Montgomery Museum of Fine Arts Staff, contrib. by. Adventures in Collecting Art: American Paintings from the Collections of Charles & Babette Wampold & the Montgomery Museum of Fine Arts. 2006. (978-0-89280-050-6(X)) Montgomery Museum of Fine Arts.

Mumford, Lewis. Mumford on Modern Art in The 1930s. Wojtowicz, Robert, ed. 2006. (Illus.). 265p. 45.00 (978-0-520-24858-8(9)) Univ. of California Pr.

The National Endowment for the Humanities & the National Endowment for the Arts: Overview of Programs & National Impact: Hearing Before the Subcommittee on Healthy Families & Communities, Committee on Education & Labor, U.S. House of Representatives, One Hundred Tenth Congress, Second Session, Hearing Held in Washington, DC, May 8, 2008. 2008. iii, 46p. (978-0-16-081545-4(2), 552-070-37888-0) United States Government Printing Office.

Nelson, Mike. Mike Nelson: A Psychic Vacuum. 2010. (ENG., Illus.). 196p. 39.95 (978-1-928570-11-0(9)) Creative Time.

New York Festivals Staff. New York Festivals 17. 2011. (ENG., Illus.). 500p. 65.00 (978-0-9774930-3-6(2), Collins Design) HarperCollins Pubs.

Nichol, John. European History, Literature, & Art, from A.d. 200 to 1888, & of American History, Literature, & Art. reprint ed. 150.00 (978-0-7222-7265-7(0)) Library Reprints, Inc.

Noever, Peter, ed. How Many Billboards? 2010. (ENG., Illus.). 160p. pap. 40.00 (978-3-86984-039-0(0)) Verlag der Buchhandlung Walther Konig DEU. Dist: D.A.P./Distributed Art Pubs.

North Carolina Central University, Museum of Art Staff. Hum 2420 Arts & Humanities Ii: The Impact of American Culture on the Arts & Humanities 1896-Present. rev. ed. 2010. 784p. pap. 98.38 (978-0-7575-2250-5(5)) Kendall Hunt Publishing Co.

Oakes, Kaya. Slanted & Enchanted: The Evolution of Indie Culture. 2009. (ENG.). 256p. pap. 14.00 (978-0-8050-8852-6(0), Holt Paperback) Holt, Henry & Co.

Oliver, Jeff & Neal, Tim, eds. Wild Signs: Graffiti in Archaeology & History. 2010. (Bar S Ser.). (ENG., Illus.). 103p. (C). pap. 75.00 (978-1-4073-0635-3(9)) British Archaeological Reports Ltd. GBR. Dist: Brown, David Bk. Co., The.

Ono, Yoko. Yoko Ono: Touch Me. 2009. (ENG., Illus.). 72p. 37.95 (978-88-8158-696-7(7)) Charta ITA. Dist: D.A.P./Distributed Art Pubs.

Overton, Patrick, intro. Grassroots & Mountain Wings: The Arts in Rural & Small Communities. 135p. reprint ed. pap. (978-0-9639060-1-4(1)) Columbia College, Ctr. for Community & Cultural Studies.

Pasternak, Anne. Creative Time. Peltason, Ruth, ed. 2008. (ENG., Illus.). 288p. pap. 35.00 (978-1-56898-804-7(4)) Princeton Architectural Pr.

—Creative Time: 33 Years of Public Art in New York. Peltason, Ruth A. & Peltason, Ruth, eds. 2007. (ENG., Illus.). 288p. pap. 50.00 (978-1-56898-696-8(3)) Princeton Architectural Pr.

Patterson, Cynthia Lee. Art for the Middle Classes: America's Illustrated Magazines of the 1840s. 2010. (ENG.). 176p. 50.00 (978-1-60473-736-3(0)) Univ. Pr. of Mississippi.

Peterson's. College Guide for Visual Arts Majors 2009: Real-World Admission Guide for All Fine Arts, Design, & Media Majors. Oram, Fern, ed. 3rd ed. 2008. (ENG., Illus.). 416p. pap. 24.95 (978-0-7689-2564-7(9)) Peterson's.

Pfeifer, Mario, et al. Mario Pfeifer: Reconsidering the New Industrial Parks near Irvine, California by Lewis Baltz 1974. 2011. (ENG., Illus.). 93p. pap. 19.95 (978-1-934105-29-0(5)) Sternberg Pr.

Preserving the American Spirit in the DAR Museum. 2006. (Illus.). 64p. (978-1-57864-356-1(2)) Donning Co. Pubs.

Rapaport, Brooke Kamin, et al. Houdini: Art & Magic. 2010. (Illus.). 280p. 39.95 (978-0-300-14684-4(1)) Yale Univ. Pr.

Raussert, Wilfried & Jones, John Miller, eds. Traveling Sounds: Music, Migration, & Identity in the U. S. & Beyond. 2011. (ENG., Illus.). 360p. pap. 51.50 (978-3-8258-1328-4(2)) Lit Verlag DEU. Dist: Transaction Pubs.

Rawlinson, Mark. American Visual Culture. 2009. (ENG., Illus.). 1p. 109.95 (978-1-84520-216-3(3)); 256p. pap. 29.95 (978-1-84520-217-0(1)) Berg Pubs. GBR. Dist: Macmillan.

Rhie, Marylin M. & Thurman, Robert A. F. A Shrine for Tibet: The Alice S. Kandell Collection. 2009. (978-0-9670115-7-8(4)) Overlook Pr., The.

Richard Tuttle. 75.00 (978-90-12-06665-5(4)) S. D. U. Uitgeverij NLD. Dist: D.A.P./Distributed Art Pubs.

Rinker, H. Dinnerware, Silver 20Th Cent. 2010. 512p. pap. 19.95 (978-0-375-72084-0(7)) Random Hse., Inc.

Roberts, Phillip. Waikiki Tiki. 2010. 264p. 22.95 (978-1-57306-311-1(8)) Bess Pr., Inc.

Rosbe, Judith Westlund. Marion in the Golden Age. 2009. 21.99 (978-1-59629-634-3(8)) History Pr., The.

Roselione-Valadez, Juan, ed. Beg Borrow & Steal: Rubell Family Collection. 2011. (ENG., Illus.). 272p. pap. 49.95 (978-0-9821195-2-5(6)) Rubell Family Collection.

Sante, Luc. Kill All Your Darlings: Pieces, 1990-2005. 2007. (ENG., Illus.). 300p. pap. 17.95 (978-1-891241-53-6(2)) Verse Chorus Pr.

Schiffer, Margaret B. Historical Needlework of Pennsylvani. 2011. 170p. 41.95 (978-1-258-08142-3(3)) Literary Licensing, LLC.

Schuman. Economic Pressures & the Future. 2007. (ENG.). 112p. pap. 10.95 (978-1-4165-7754-6(8), Free Pr.) Free Pr.

Schwartz, Constance. ¡Latinas! Latin American Women in Art. 2010. (Illus.). pap. (978-0-9815644-6-3(1)) Nassau County Museum of Art.

See, Sarita Echavez. The Decolonized Eye: Filipino American Art & Performance. 2009. (ENG., Illus.). 232p. 75.00 (978-0-8166-5318-6(6)); pap. 25.00 (978-0-8166-5319-5(4)) Univ. of Minnesota Pr.

Seidel, Matthias, et al. Egyptian Art: The Walters Art Museum. 2009. (ENG., Illus.). 192p. 45.00 (978-1-904832-57-7(1)) Giles, D. Ltd. GBR. Dist: Antique Collectors' Club.

Sherry, Michael S. Gay Artists in Modern American Culture: An Imagined Conspiracy. 2007. (ENG., Illus.). 304p. 34.95 (978-0-8078-3121-2(2)) Univ. of North Carolina Pr.

Siddall, Laura. The Adventures of Madder: My First 5000 Years. 2008. (Illus.). 76p. (YA). per. 29.95 (978-0-9797092-8-9(8)) Billings, Judith.

Sidorenko, Irina. Private Art Collecting in St Petersburg Around 1900. 2008. 104p. pap. (978-3-639-03017-4(6)) VDM Verlag Dr. Mueller e.K.

Siegmann, William. African Art: A Century at the Brooklyn Museum. 2009. (Illus.). 296p. pap. (978-0-87273-163-9(4)) Brooklyn Museum, The.

Sikes, Michael. Building Parent Involvement Through the Arts: Activities & Projects That Enrich Classrooms & Schools. 2007. (Illus.). 168p. 76.95 (978-1-4129-3682-8(9), B36829C); per. 33.95 (978-1-4129-3683-5(7), B36829P) Corwin Pr.

Slavick, Ann. Hour Chicago: Twenty-Five Self-Guided 60-Minute Tours of Chicago's Great Architecture & Art. 2008. (ENG., Illus.). 272p. pap. 16.95 (978-1-56663-743-5(0)) Dee, Ivan R. Pub.

Smith, David A. Money for Art: The Tangled Web of Art & Politics in American Democracy. 2008. (ENG.). 320p. 27.50 (978-1-56663-768-8(6)) Dee, Ivan R. Pub.

Sotiropoulos, Karen. Staging Race: Black Performers in Turn of the Century America. 2008. (Illus.). 304p. per. 22.50 (978-0-674-02760-2(4)) Harvard Univ. Pr.

Stewart, Jack. Graffiti Kings: New York City Mass Transit Art of the 1970s. 2009. (ENG., Illus.). 224p. 32.50 (978-0-8109-7526-2(2)) Abrams.

Stones, Alison. Studies in Arthurian Illustration. 2012. (ENG., Illus.). 560p. (C). 300.00 (978-1-904597-37-7(8)) Pindar Pr. GBR. Dist: Brown, David Bk. Co., The.

Tepper, Stephen & Ivey, Bill, eds. Engaging Art: The Next Great Transformation of America's Cultural Life. 2007. (ENG., Illus.). 408p. pap. 36.95 (978-0-415-96042-7(8)) Routledge.

Tepper, Steven J. Not Here, Not Now, Not That! Protest over Art & Culture in America. 2011. (ENG., Illus.). 384p. 90.00 (978-0-226-79286-6(2)); pap. 30.00 (978-0-226-79287-3(0)) Univ. of Chicago Pr.

Traugott, Joseph. New Mexico Art Through Time: Prehistory to the Present. 2012. (ENG., Illus.). 244p. 50.00 (978-0-89013-545-7(2)) Museum of New Mexico Pr.

Tucker, Daniel, footn. Visions for Chicago. 2011. 143p. pap. 10.00 (978-1-4507-7523-6(3)) Green Lantern Pr.

Tunzi, Joseph A. Elvis: Portraits. 2008. (Illus.). 110p. (978-1-888464-18-4(6)) JAT Publishing.

—Elvis Concerts. 2008. (Illus.). 111p. (978-1-888464-20-7(8)) JAT Publishing.

Vanderbeek, Stan, et al. Amazement Park: Stan, Sara, & Johannes VanDerBeek, 1 vol. 2012. (ENG.). 224p. 39.95 (978-3-7913-5208-4(3)) Prestel Publishing.

Velásquez, Luis Carlos. The Artwork of Luis Carlos Velásquez. 2011. 112p. pap. 33.95 (978-1-61764-854-0(X)) Palibrio.

Vine, Richard. Travis Conrad Erion: Paintings & Drawings. 2011. (ENG., Illus.). 178p. 45.00 (978-0-9626881-2-6(6)) Fredrick, Rose Fine Art Publishing.

Walker, Jo Ann. Emrys in Full Flower. 2008. lib. bdg. (978-0-9773516-2-6(9)) Emrys Pr. of the Emrys Foundation, The.

Watts, Jennifer A. & Bohn-Spector, Cludia. This Side of Paradise: Body & Landscape in Los Angeles Photography. 2008. (Illus.). 240p. 75.00 (978-1-85894-434-0(1)) Merrell Pubs. Ltd. GBR. Dist: Perseus Distribution.

Wild, David. Jazzpaths: An American Photomemento. 2012. (ENG., Illus.). 112p. 35.00 (978-0-907259-45-9(6)) Hyphen Pr. GBR. Dist: Hachette Bk. Group.

Willoughby, Bob, photos by. Audrey Hepburn: Photographs 1953 - 1966. collector's ed. 2010. (ENG.). 282p. 1000.00 (978-3-8365-1889-5(9)) TASCHEN DEU. Dist: Ingram Pub. Services.

Wixom, William, et al. The Ronald S. Lauder Collection: Selections from the 3rd Century BC to the 20th Century, 1 vol. 2011. (ENG.). 540p. 75.00 (978-3-7913-5164-3(8)) Prestel Publishing.

Wolohojian, Stephan. Harvard Art Museum Handbook. Wolohojian, Stephan, ed. 2008. (Harvard Art Museum Ser.). (Illus.). 288p. pap. 24.95 (978-1-891771-50-7(7)) Harvard Univ. Art Museums.

Writer's Digest Books Editors. 2010 Artist's & Graphic Designer's Market. 34th ed. 2009. (ENG.). 560p. pap. 29.99 (978-1-58297-583-2(3), Writer's Digest Bks.) F&W Media, Inc.

Writer's Digest Books Editors, et al, eds. 2011 Artist's & Graphic Designer's Market. 35th ed. 2010. (ENG., Illus.). 576p. pap. 34.99 (978-1-58297-955-7(3), Writer's Digest Bks.) F&W Media, Inc.

Wroth, William & Gavin, Robin Farwell, eds. Converging Streams: Art of the Hispanic & Native American Southwest from Preconquest Times to the Twentieth Century. 2010. (ENG.). 256p. 60.00 (978-0-89013-568-6(1)); pap. (978-0-89013-570-9(3)) Museum of New Mexico Pr.

Zakaras, Laura & Lowell, Julia F. Cultivating Demand for the Arts: Arts Learning, Arts Engagement, & State Arts Policy. 2008. 172p. pap. 30.50 (978-0-8330-4184-5(3), mg-640) RAND Corp., The.

Zoglin, Richard. Comedy at the Edge: How Stand-Up in the 1970s Changed America. 2009. (ENG.). 256p. pap. 15.00 (978-1-58234-625-0(9)) Bloomsbury Publishing.

Zwick, Jim. Inuit Entertainers in the United States: From the Chicago World's Fair through the Birth of Hollywood. 2006. 217p. pap. 18.95 (978-0-7414-3488-3(1)) Infinity Publishing.

ARTS, AFRICAN AMERICAN

see African American Arts

ARTS, DECORATIVE

see Art, Decorative; Art Industries and Trade; Arts and Crafts Movement; Decoration and Ornament; Design, Decorative; Handicraft; Interior Decoration also subjects referred to under these headings

ARTS, FINE

see Art; Arts

ARTS, GRAPHIC

see Graphic Arts

ARTS, MODERN

see also Art, Modern; Gothic Revival (Art); Postmodernism

Acocella, Joan. Twenty-Eight Artists & Two Saints. 2008. (Vintage Ser.). (ENG., Illus.). 560p. pap. 18.95 (978-0-307-27576-9(0), Vintage) Knopf Doubleday Publishing Group.

Ades, Dawn, ed. The Dada Reader: A Critical Anthology. 2006. (ENG., Illus.). 320p. 70.00 (978-0-226-00697-0(2)) Univ. of Chicago Pr.

—The Dada Reader - A Critical Anthology. 2006. (Illus.). 320p. pap. 30.00 (978-0-226-00698-7(0)) Univ. of Chicago Pr.

Aguilera, Steven. A New Perspective #8213; Photography & Filmmaking Edition. 2008. 120p. pap. 24.95 (978-0-578-00039-8(3)) Artistech Bks.

Anderson, Laurie. Night Life, 1 vol. 2009. (ENG., Illus.). 96p. 35.00 (978-3-86521-339-6(1)) Steidl, Gerhard Druckerei und Verlag DEU. Dist: Innovative Logistics.

Armstrong, Carol & de Zegher, Catherine, eds. Women Artists at the Millennium. 2006. (October Bks.). (ENG., Illus.). 472p. (gr. 17). 42.00 (978-0-262-01226-3(X)) MIT Pr.

Aspley, Keith. Historical Dictionary of Surrealism. 2010. E-Book 125.00 (978-0-8108-7499-2(7)); (ENG.). 574p. 125.00 (978-0-8108-5847-3(9)) Scarecrow Pr., Inc.

Asselin, Olivier, et al. Precarious Visualities: New Perspectives on Identification in Contemporary Art & Visual Culture. 2008. (ENG., Illus.). 448p. (C). (978-0-7735-3385-1(0)); pap. (978-0-7735-3390-5(7)) McGill-Queen's Univ. Pr.

Auping, Michael. 30 Years: Interviews & Outtakes. 2007. (Illus.). 286p. (978-0-929865-27-0(8)) Modern Art Museum of Fort Worth.

Babka, Anna & Hochreiter, Susanne. Queer Reading in den Philologien: Modelle und Anwendungen. 2008. (GER., Illus.). 296p. (C). pap. 37.00 (978-3-89971-387-9(7)) Vandenhoeck & Ruprecht GmbH & Co. KG DEU. Dist: ISD.

Basting, Anne Davis. Hiding Places: Memory in the Arts. 2011. (978-0-9710703-3-2(4)) Kohler, John Michael Arts Ctr.

Benjamin, Walter. The Work of Art in the Age of Its Technological Reproducibility, & Other Writings on Media. Jennings, Michael W. et al, eds. Jephcott, Edmund & Livingstone, Rodney, trs. from GER. 2008. (Illus.). 448p. pap. 18.95 (978-0-674-02445-8(1), Belknap Pr.) Harvard Univ. Pr.

Berghaus, Günter, ed. International Futurism in Arts & Literature. (European Cultures Ser.). (ENG., Illus.). X, 647p. 388.00 (978-3-11-188154-6(7)) De Gruyter, Walter Inc.

Bernier, Rosamond. Some of My Lives: A Scrapbook Memoir, 1 vol. 2011. (ENG., Illus.). 304p. 30.00 (978-0-374-26661-5(1)) Farrar, Straus & Giroux.

Bourduas, Paul-Emile, et al. Total Refusal - Refus Global: The Complete 1948 Manifesto of the Montreal Automatists. 2010. (Exile Classics Ser.). (ENG., Illus.). 140p. pap. 18.95 (978-1-55096-107-2(1)) Exile Editions, Ltd. CAN. Dist: Independent Pubs. Group.

Cabinet, creator. Magic: Quarterly of Art & Culture, 1 vol. 2007. (ENG., Illus.). 112p. pap. 10.00 (978-1-932698-22-0(1)) Cabinet.

Carr, C. On Edge: Performance at the End of the Twentieth Century. rev. ed. 2008. (ENG., Illus.). 392p. pap. 28.95 (978-0-8195-6888-5(0)) Wesleyan Univ. Pr.

Carroll, Noel. On Criticism. 2008. (Thinking in Action Ser.). (ENG.). 224p. 125.00 (978-0-415-39620-2(4)); pap. 21.95 (978-0-415-39621-9(2)) Routledge.

Cheng, Anne Anlin & Baker, Josephine. Second Skin: Josephine Baker & the Modern Surface, 1 vol. 2011. (ENG., Illus.). 224p. 24.95 (978-0-19-538705-6(8)) Oxford Univ. Pr., Inc.

Childs, Peter. Modernism. 2nd rev. ed. (New Critical Idiom Ser.). (ENG.). 248p. (C). 2008. 95.00 (978-0-415-41544-6(6)) 2007. 22.95 (978-0-415-41546-0(2)) Routledge.

Connelly, Frances S. Modern Art & the Grotesque. Connelly, Frances S., ed. 2009. (ENG., Illus.). 336p. pap. 42.00 (978-0-521-11576-6(0)) Cambridge Univ. Pr.

Corn, Wanda M. & Latimer, Tirza True. Seeing Gertrude Stein - Five Stories. 2011. (ENG., Illus.). 320p. 45.00 (978-0-520-27002-2(9)) Univ. of California Pr.

Cram101 Textbook Reviews. Outlines & Highlights for Humanistic Tradition, Book: Modernism, Globalism, & the Information Age by Gloria K. Fiero, ISBN. 2011. 100p. pap. 27.95 (978-1-61812-447-0(1)) Cram101 Inc.

Delville, Michel. Food, Poetry, & the Aesthetics of Consumption: Eating the Avant-Garde. 2007. (Routledge Studies in Twentieth-Century Literature Ser.). (ENG., Illus.). 160p. 125.00 (978-0-415-95831-8(8)) Routledge.

Dickerman, Leah. Dada: Zurich, Berlin, Hannover, Cologne, New York, Paris, 1 vol. 2008. (ENG., Illus.). 536p. pap. 29.95 (978-0-89468-313-8(6)) National Gallery of Art.

Dixon, Steve. Digital Performance: A History of New Media in Theater, Dance, Performance Art, & Installation. 2007. (Leonardo Bks.). (ENG., Illus.). 832p. (gr. 17). 58.00 (978-0-262-04235-2(5)) MIT Pr.

Doherty, Claire, ed. Situation. 2009. (Documents of Contemporary Art Ser.). (ENG.). 238p. (gr. 17). pap. 24.95 (978-0-262-51305-0(6)) MIT Pr.

Ehrlich, Ken & LaBelle, Brandon, eds. Surface Tension Supplement No. 3. 2009. (ENG., Illus.). 70p. pap. 19.00 (978-0-9772594-7-2(1)) Errant Bodies Pr.

Erman, Michel, ed. Le goût dans tous Ses états. 2009. (Littératures de langue française Ser.). (FRE.). 136p. pap. (978-3-03911-753-6(X)) Lang, Peter.

Eshelman, Raoul. Performatism, or the End of Postmodernism. 2008. (ENG., Illus.). 284p. pap. 27.00 (978-1-888570-41-0(5)) Davies Group Pubs., The.

Featherstone, Don. Creative Spirits: An Insight into the Life & Work of Some Extraordinary Australians. (Illus.). 148p. pap. (978-0-86806-610-3(9), Hale & Iremonger) GHR Pr., The.

Fiorentini, Erna. Observing Nature — Representing Experience: The Osmotic Dynamics of Romanticism, 1800-1850. 2009. (ENG., Illus.). 244p. 75.00 (978-3-496-02803-1(3), Art Stock Bks. Ltd/Csi) Continental Sales, Inc.

Foundation for International Arts and Education Staff, et al, contrib. by. American Artists from the Russian Empire: Paintings & Sculptures from Museums, Galleries in the U.S. & Private Collections. 2008. (Illus.). 286p. (978-3-940761-19-4(2)) Kiblitsky, Joseph Palace Editions.

Galenson, David W. Old Masters & Young Geniuses: The Two Life Cycles of Artistic Creativity. 2007. (ENG., Illus.). 256p. (C). per. 22.95 (978-0-691-13380-5(8)) Princeton Univ. Pr.

Gay, Peter. Modernism: The Lure of Heresy. 2010. (ENG.). 640p. pap. 21.95 (978-0-393-33396-1(5), 33396) Norton, W. W. & Co., Inc.

—Modernism: The Lure of Heresy from Baudelaire to Beckett & Beyond. 2007. (ENG., Illus.). 640p. 35.00 (978-0-393-05205-3(2), 5205) Norton, W. W. & Co., Inc.

Graham, Beryl & Cook, Sarah. Rethinking Curating: Art after New Media. 2010. (Leonardo Bks.). (ENG., Illus.). 376p. (gr. 17). 36.95 (978-0-262-01388-8(6)) MIT Pr.

Grey House Publishing Staff & Bass, Jennifer Durham. World Cultural Leaders of the Twentieth & Twenty-First Centuries, 2 vols., Set. 2nd ed. 2007. 800p. 175.00 (978-1-59237-118-1(3)) Grey Hse. Publishing.

Hemus, Ruth. Dada's Women. 2009. (ENG., Illus.). 250p. 60.00 (978-0-300-14148-1(3)) Yale Univ. Pr.

Higgie, Jennifer, ed. The Artist's Joke. 2007. (Documents of Contemporary Art Ser.). (ENG.). 238p. (gr. 17). per. 24.95 (978-0-262-58274-2(0)) MIT Pr.

Hinderliter, Beth, et al, eds. Communities of Sense: Rethinking Aesthetics & Politics. 2009. (ENG., Illus.). 384p. 94.95 *(978-0-8223-4497-1(1))*; pap. 26.95 *(978-0-8223-4513-8(7))* Duke Univ. Pr.
Huyssen, Andreas. After the Great Divide: Modernism, Mass Culture, Postmodernism. 2008. 260p. pap. 26.00 *(978-1-59740-555-3(8))* ACLS Humanities E-Book.
Hyvärinen, Matti & Muszynski, Lisa, eds. Terror & the Arts: Artistic, Literary, & Political Interpretations of Violence from Dostoyevsky to Abu Ghraib. 2008. (ENG., Illus.). 272p. 95.00 *(978-0-230-60671-5(7))* Palgrave Macmillan.
Jana, Reena & Tribe, Mark. New Media Art. 2009. (25 Ser.). (ENG., Illus.). 96p. 14.99 *(978-3-8365-1413-2(3))* TASCHEN DEU. Dist: Ingram Pub. Services.
Jones, Amelia. Seeing Differently. 2012. (ENG.). 288p. (C). 130.00 ***(978-0-415-54382-8(7))***; pap. 39.95 ***(978-0-415-54383-5(5))*** Routledge.
Joseph-Hunter, Galen, et al. Transmission Arts: Artists & Airwaves. 2011. (Art + Performance Ser.). (ENG., Illus.). 200p. pap. 19.95 *(978-1-55554-151-4(8))* PAJ Pubns.
Kastner, Jeffrey. Land & Environmental Art. 2006. (SPA.). 49.95 *(978-0-7148-9829-2(5))* Phaidon Pr., Inc.
Kreuzer, Stefanie. Katastrophe als Ubergangsmodus Kultureller Systeme im 20. Jahrhundert und das Phanomen des Ubergangs bei Wolfgang Max Faust. (Europaische Hochschulschriften Ser.). (GER., Illus.). 203p. 37.95 *(978-3-631-38167-0(0))* Lang, Peter Publishing, Inc.
Le Feuvre, Lisa. Failure. 2010. (Documents of Contemporary Art Ser.). (ENG.). 238p. (gr. 17). pap. 24.95 *(978-0-262-51477-4(X))* MIT Pr.
Lippy, Tod, ed. Esopus 10. 2008. (ENG., Illus.). 158p. pap. 10.00 *(978-0-9761641-7-3(5))* Esopus Foundation Ltd.
—Esopus 11. 2009. (ENG., Illus.). 172p. pap. 14.00 *(978-0-9815745-0-9(5))* Esopus Foundation Ltd.
—Esopus 12. 2009. (ENG., Illus.). 154p. pap. 14.00 *(978-0-9815745-1-6(3))* Esopus Foundation Ltd.
Matthews, Roy, et al. The Humanistic Tradition Bk. 4: Faith, Reason, & Power in the Early Modern World. 6th ed. 2010. (ENG., Illus.). 192p. (C). pap. 45.67 *(978-0-07-734626-3(2)*, 0077346262) McGraw-Hill Cos., The.
Meisel, Perry. The Myth of Popular Culture: From Dante to Dylan. 2010. (Blackwell Manifestos Ser.: 28). (ENG.). 224p. 99.95 *(978-1-4051-9933-9(4))*; pap. 33.95 *(978-1-4051-9934-6(2))* Wiley, John & Sons, Inc. (Wiley-Blackwell).
Mennel, Barbara. Cities & Cinema. 2008. (Routledge Critical Introductions to Urbanism & the City Ser.). (Illus.). 245p. 180.00 *(978-0-415-36445-4(0))*; pap. 49.95 *(978-0-415-36446-1(9))* Routledge.
Mercer, Kobena, ed. Pop Art & Vernacular Cultures. 2007. (Annotating Art's Histories: Cross-Cultural Perspectives in the Visual Arts Ser.). (ENG., Illus.). 232p. (gr. 17). pap. 27.00 *(978-0-262-63350-5(7))* MIT Pr.
Mercurio, Gianni & Paparoni, Demetrio, eds. Timer: Contemporary Art after Nine Eleven. 2008. (ITA & ENG., Illus.). 320p. pap. 50.00 *(978-88-6130-190-0(8))* Skira Editore ITA. Dist: Random Hse., Inc.
Mirzoeff, Nicholas, ed. The Visual Culture Reader. 3rd rev. ed. 2012. (ENG.). 720p. (C). 130.00 *(978-0-415-62055-0(4))*; pap. 49.95 *(978-0-415-78262-3(7))* Routledge.
Moore, Lisa L. Sister Arts: The Erotics of Lesbian Landscapes. 2011. (Illus.). 264p. 90.00 *(978-0-8166-7013-0(7))*; pap. 29.95 *(978-0-8166-7014-7(5))* Univ. of Minnesota Pr.
Murray, Graeme, ed. Poiesis. (Illus.). 112p. 35.00 *(978-0-947912-00-0(2))* Fruitmarket Gallery GBR. Dist: D.A.P./Distributed Art Pubs.
Neumark, Norie, et al. Voice: Vocal Aesthetics in Digital Arts & Media. 2010. (Leonardo Bks.). (ENG., Illus.). 440p. (gr. 17). 40.00 *(978-0-262-01390-1(8))* MIT Pr.
Painter, Karen & Crow, Thomas, eds. Late Thoughts: Reflections on Artists & Composers at Work. 2006. (Issues & Debates Ser.: Vol. 14). (Illus.). 264p. pap. 40.00 *(978-0-89236-813-6(6))* Oxford Univ. Pr., Inc.
Palenzuela, Nilo. Moradas Del Interprete. 2007. (Tierra Firme Ser.). (SPA.). 190p. pap. *(978-84-375-0601-2(8))* Fondo de Cultura Economica.
Powell, Jim. Postmodernism for Beginners. 2007. (For Beginners Ser.). (ENG., Illus.). 176p. per. 14.95 *(978-1-934389-09-6(9)*, For Beginners) Steerforth Pr.
Ros, Xon de. Primitivismo y Modernismo: El Legado de Maria Blanchard. 2007. (Hispanic Studies Ser.: Vol. 5). (SPA., Illus.). 250p. pap. 63.95 *(978-3-03910-937-1(5))* Lang, Peter Publishing, Inc.
Rothschild, Deborah, ed. Making It New: The Art & Style of Sara & Gerald Murphy. 2007. (Illus.). 237p. 60.00 *(978-0-520-25238-7(1))*; pap. 36.95 *(978-0-520-25240-0(3))* Univ. of California Pr.
Said, Edward W. On Late Style: Music & Literature Against the Grain. 2007. (Vintage Ser.). (ENG.). 208p. pap. 14.95 *(978-0-375-72633-0(0)*, Vintage) Knopf Doubleday Publishing Group.
Salter, Chris. Entangled: Technology & the Transformation of Performance. 2010. (ENG., Illus.). 504p. (gr. 17). 42.00 *(978-0-262-19588-1(7))* MIT Pr.
Satz, Aura & Wood, Jon. Articulate Objects: Voice, Sculpture & Performance. 2009. (Illus.). 300p. 54.95 *(978-3-03910-747-6(X))* Lang, Peter AG GBR. Dist: Lang, Peter.
Shifrin, Susan. Re-Framing Representations of Women: Figuring, Fashioning, Portraiting, & Telling in the 'Picturing' Women Project. Shifrin, Susan, ed. 2008. (Illus.). 354p. 149.95 *(978-0-7546-6077-4(X))* Ashgate Publishing Co.
Soltes, Ori Z. The Ashen Rainbow: Essays on the Arts & the Holocaust. 2007. (Illus.). 278p. per. *(978-0-935437-37-9(1))* Bartleby Pr.
Tojner, Poul Erik & Wilmes, Ulrich, eds. Per Kirkeby: Louisiana 2008. 2009. (ENG., Illus.). 192p. 40.00 *(978-87-91607-57-8(4))* Louisana DNK. Dist: D.A.P./Distributed Art Pubs.
Touchon, Cecil. The Neoist Manifesto - Documents of Neoism - the Neoist Society. 2009. 174p. pap. 24.96 *(978-0-615-25881-2(6))* Ontological Museum Pubns.
Tzara, Tristan. Seven Dada Manifestos & Lampisteries. Wright, Barbara, tr. 2011. (ENG.). 128p. pap. 14.95 *(978-0-7145-4450-2(7))* Alma Classics GBR. Dist: Independent Pubs. Group.
Versluis, Arthur, ed. Esotericism, Art, & Imagination. 2008. (ENG., Illus.). 327p. (C). pap. 29.95 *(978-0-87013-819-5(7))* Michigan State Univ. Pr.
Walz, Robin. Modernism. 2008. (Short Histories of Big Ideas Ser.). (ENG., Illus.). 216p. pap. 24.95 *(978-1-4058-3259-5(2))* Longman Publishing Group.
Wark, McKenzie. 50 Years of Recuperation: Of the Situationist International. 2008. (ENG., Illus.). 80p. 24.95 *(978-1-56898-789-7(7))* Princeton Architectural Pr.
Warr, Tracey. Artist's Body. 2006. (SPA.). 49.95 *(978-0-7148-9837-7(6))* Phaidon Pr., Inc.
White, Edmund. Arts & Letters. 2006. (ENG.). 376p. per. 15.95 *(978-1-57344-248-0(8))* Cleis Pr.
Williams, Raymond. Politics of Modernism: Against the New Conformists. 2007. (Radical Thinkers Ser.: Vol. 23). (ENG.). 208p. per. 12.95 *(978-1-84467-580-7(7)*, 844580) Verso Bks. GBR. Dist: Norton, W. W. & Co., Inc.
Willis, Deborah, ed. Black Venus 2010: They Called Her Hottentot. 2010. (ENG., Illus.). 256p. 81.50 *(978-1-4399-0204-2(6))*; pap. 35.95 *(978-1-4399-0205-9(4))* Temple Univ. Pr.
Wollen, Peter. Raiding the Icebox: Reflections on Twentieth-Century Culture, New Edition. rev. ed. 2008. (ENG.). 224p. 95.00 *(978-1-84467-274-5(3)*, 844274); pap. 26.95 *(978-1-84467-250-9(6)*, 844250) Verso Bks. GBR. Dist: Norton, W. W. & Co., Inc.
Zeller, Christoph. Ästhetik des Authentischen: Literatur und Kunst Um 1970. 2010. (Spectrum Literaturwissenschaft / spectrum Literature Ser.).Tr. of Aesthetics of the Authentic. (GER., Illus.). IX, 333p. 140.00 *(978-3-11-022720-8(7))* De Gruyter, Walter Inc.

ARTS, USEFUL
see Industrial Arts; Technology

ARTS AND CRAFTS MOVEMENT
see also Bookbinding; China Painting; Decoration and Ornament; Embroidery; Enamel and Enameling; Folk Art; Furniture; Furniture, Mission; Hand Weaving; Handicraft; Illumination of Books and Manuscripts; Lace and Lace Making; Lacquer and Lacquering; Manual Training; Metal-Work; Modeling; Pottery

Accossato, Katia & Probst, Nicola. Ivano Gianola: Buildings & Projects = Edifici e Progetti. 2008. (ENG & ITA., Illus.). 240p. 108.00 *(978-3-930698-97-4(8))* Edition Axel Menges GmbH DEU. Dist: National Bk. Network.
Addison, Julia de Wolf Gl. Arts & Crafts in the Middle Ages. 2008. 308p. 28.99 *(978-0-554-33203-1(5))* 2008. 308p. 29.99 *(978-0-554-23900-2(0))* 2006. (ENG.). 272p. pap. 21.99 *(978-1-4264-5135-5(0))* 2006. (ENG.). 304p. pap. 24.99 *(978-1-4264-5436-3(8))* BiblioBazaar.
Ashbee, Charles Robert. Where the Great City Stands. 2008. 256p. pap. *(978-1-905217-96-0(X))* Mills, Jeremy Publishing.
Aslet, Clive. The Arts & Crafts Country House: From the Archives of Country Life. 2012. (Country Life Ser.). (ENG., Illus.). 192p. 75.00 ***(978-1-84513-680-2(2))*** Aurum Pr., Ltd. GBR. Dist: Independent Pubs. Group.
Baker, Derek. The Flowers of William Morris. 2006. (ENG., Illus.). 25.00 *(978-1-899531-03-5(3))* Barn Elms Publishing GBR. Dist: National Bk. Network.
Bialecki, Matthew, et al. The New Bungalow, 1 vol. 2008. (ENG., Illus.). 160p. pap. 19.99 *(978-1-4236-0435-8(0))* Gibbs Smith, Publisher.
Bishop, Claire, ed. Participation. 2006. (Documents of Contemporary Art Ser.). (ENG., Illus.). 208p. (gr. 17). pap. 24.95 *(978-0-262-52464-3(3))* MIT Pr.
Blakesley, Rosalind P. Arts & Crafts Movement. 2009. (ENG., Illus.). 272p. pap. 49.95 *(978-0-7148-4967-6(7))* Phaidon Pr., Inc.
Boehn, Max Von. An Illustrated Guide to the Doll As Used in Fashion. 2011. (Illus.). 28p. pap. 6.95 ***(978-1-4465-4188-3(6))*** Research Pr.
Brandt, Beverly K. The Craftsman & the Critic: Defining Usefulness & Beauty in Arts & Crafts ERA Boston. 2009. (Illus.). 520p. 65.00 *(978-1-55849-677-4(7))* Univ. of Massachusetts Pr.
Cathers, David. Gustav Stickley. 2011. (ENG., Illus.). 240p. pap. 45.00 *(978-0-7148-6111-1(1))* Phaidon Pr., Inc.
Cathers, David & Parry, Linda. Arts & Crafts Rugs for Craftsman Interiors: The Crab Tree Farm Collection. 2009. (ENG., Illus.). 168p. 45.00 *(978-0-393-73320-4(3)*, 73320) Norton, W. W. & Co., Inc.
Cobden-Sanderson, T. J. Ecce Mundus: Industrial Ideals & the Book Beautiful. 2011. 40p. 35.95 ***(978-1-258-05742-8(5))*** Literary Licensing, LLC.
Day, Lewis F. Art in Needlework. 2009. (Illus.). 148p. pap. *(978-1-4068-2924-2(2))* Echo Library.
Doig, Alan. Theo Van Doesburg: Painting into Architecture, Theory into Practice. 2010. (ENG.). 280p. pap. 42.00 *(978-0-521-12981-7(8))* Cambridge Univ. Pr.
Domini, Mathias. Return Forecasting in the Art Market. 2011. 76p. pap. ***(978-3-8443-9805-2(8))*** Lambert Academic Publishing.
Dresser, Christopher. Dresser's Victorian Ornamentation: 150 Designs. 2008. (Dover Pictorial Archive Ser.). (ENG., Illus.). 64p. pap. 8.95 *(978-0-486-45564-8(5))* Dover Pubns., Inc.
Dueck, Pamela. Modern Crochet for the Beach Babe Goddess. 2011. 100p. pap. 51.99 ***(978-1-4568-6399-9(1))*** Xlibris Corp.
Edwards, Jason & Hart, Imogen. Rethinking the Interior, C.1867-1896: Aestheticism & Arts & Crafts. 2010. (Illus.). 294p. 124.95 *(978-0-7546-6817-6(7))* Ashgate Publishing Co.
Fiell, Charlotte & Fiell, Peter. Decorative Art 50s. 25th ed. 2008. (FRE, GER & ENG., Illus.). 575p. per. 14.99 *(978-3-8365-0310-5(7))* TASCHEN DEU. Dist: Ingram Pub. Services.
Gannett, William C. The House Beautiful. 2007. (ENG.). 108p. 34.95 *(978-0-548-12356-0(X))* Kessinger Publishing, LLC.
Gannett, William C., et al. The House Beautiful: A Book Designed by Frank Lloyd Wright. 2006. (Illus.). 80p. 25.00 *(978-0-7649-3764-4(2)*, A130) Pomegranate Communications, Inc.
Gladu, Christian. Small Bungalows, 1 vol. 2007. (ENG., Illus.). 112p. 21.99 *(978-1-4236-0098-5(3))* Gibbs Smith, Publisher.
Gordon, Catherine. Cotswolds Arts & Crafts Architecture. 2009. (ENG., Illus.). 192p. 37.95 *(978-1-86077-548-2(9))* History Pr. Ltd.,The GBR. Dist: Independent Pubs. Group.
Greensted, Mary. The Arts & Crafts Movement in Britain. 2010. (Shire History Ser.). (ENG., Illus.). 128p. pap. 19.95 *(978-0-7478-0782-7(5))* Shire Pubns., Ltd. GBR. Dist: Random Hse., Inc.
Hamerton, Ian, ed. W. A. S. Benson: Arts & Crafts Luminary & Pioneer of Modern Design. 2007. (ENG., Illus.). 352p. *(978-1-85149-476-7(6)*, Antique Collectors Club Dist) Antique Collectors' Club.
Hart, Imogen. Arts & Crafts Objects. 2010. (Studies in Design & Material Culture Ser.). (ENG., Illus.). 288p. 89.95 *(978-0-7190-7971-9(3))*; pap. 34.95 *(978-0-7190-7972-6(1))* Manchester Univ. Pr. GBR. Dist: Macmillan.
Heppner, Richard, ed. & intro. Woodstock Years II - Publications of the Historical Society of Woodstock. 2007. (Illus.). 76p. per. 12.00 *(978-0-9790298-0-6(5))* Historical Society of Woodstock.
Higgins, Rob & Robinson, Christopher Stolbert. William de Morgan: Arts & Crafts Potter. 2010. (Shire Library). (ENG., Illus.). 56p. pap. 13.95 *(978-0-7478-0738-4(8))* Shire Pubns., Ltd. GBR. Dist: Random Hse., Inc.
Holzwarth Hans Werner. T25 Modern Art, 2 vols. 2011. (25 Ser.). (ENG., Illus.). 680p. 59.99 *(978-3-8365-2730-9(8))* TASCHEN DEU. Dist: Ingram Pub. Services.
Johnson, Bruce. Grove Park Inn Arts & Crafts Furniture. 2009. (ENG., Illus.). 176p. 35.00 *(978-1-55870-849-5(9)*, Popular Woodworking Bks.) F&W Media, Inc.
Kreisman, Lawrence & Mason, Glenn. The Arts & Crafts Movement in the Pacific Northwest. 2007. (ENG., Illus.). 400p. 24.95 *(978-0-88192-849-5(6)*, 0881928496) Timber Pr., Inc.
Labau, Peter. The New Bungalow Kitchen. 2007. (ENG., Illus.). 216p. 30.00 *(978-1-56158-862-6(8)*, Taunton) Taunton Pr., Inc.
Lang, Robert W. Shop Drawings for Greene & Greene Furniture: 23 American Arts & Crafts Masterpieces. 2007. (ENG., Illus.). 159p. pap. 22.95 *(978-1-892836-29-8(7))* Fox Chapel Publishing Co., Inc.
Lang, Robert W., et al. Popular Woodworking's Arts & Crafts Furniture Projects: 25 Designs for Every Room in Your Home. 2008. (ENG., Illus.). 206p. pap. 29.99 *(978-1-55870-846-4(4)*, Popular Woodworking Bks.) F&W Media, Inc.
Lemos, Pedro J. & Lemos, Reta A. Arts & Crafts Era Concrete Projects. 2008. (Illus.). 192p. bds. 24.95 *(978-0-7643-2833-6(6))* Schiffer Publishing, Ltd.
Lombardi, Laura. From Realism to Art Nouveau. 2009. (ENG., Illus.). 192p. pap. 14.95 *(978-1-4027-5926-0(6))* Sterling Publishing Co., Inc.
Lucie-Smith, Edward. Movimiento Artistico Desde, 1945. Mariani, Hugo, tr. 4th ed. (SPA., Illus.). 288p. pap. 54.95 *(978-84-233-2057-8(X)*, DE057) Ediciones Destino ESP. Dist: Continental Bk. Co., Inc.
Macaulay, James. Charles Rennie Mackintosh - A Biography. 2010. (ENG., Illus.). 256p. 65.00 *(978-0-393-05175-9(7)*, 5175) Norton, W. W. & Co., Inc.
Malik, Anne E. A New & Native Beauty: The Art & Craft of Greene & Greene. Bosley, Edward R., ed. 2008. (Illus.). 272p. 75.00 *(978-1-85894-452-4(X))* Merrell Pubs. Ltd. GBR. Dist: Perseus Distribution.
Mathias, David. Greene & Greene Furniture: Poems of Wood & Light. 2010. (ENG., Illus.). 176p. 35.00 *(978-1-4403-0299-2(5)*, Popular Woodworking Bks.) F&W Media, Inc.
Menz, Christopher. Morris & Co. 2007. (Illus.). 188p. 55.00 *(978-0-7308-3029-0(2))* Art Gallery of South Australia AUS. Dist: Antique Collectors' Club.
Morris, William. Hopes & Fears for Art. 2008. 224p. 24.99 *(978-0-559-41285-1(1))* 2008. 224p. pap. 24.75 *(978-0-559-41283-7(5))* 2008. 160p. 25.99 *(978-0-554-29487-2(7))* 2008. 160p. 22.99 *(978-0-554-38790-1(5))* 2007. (ENG.). 140p. per. 18.99 *(978-1-4346-7746-4(X))* BiblioBazaar.
—Hopes & Fears for Art. 2007. 136p. per. *(978-1-4065-4601-9(1))* Dodo Pr.
—Hopes & Fears for Art. 2010. (ENG.). 228p. pap. 25.75 *(978-1-171-79903-0(9))* 2010. 228p. pap. 25.75 *(978-1-176-70644-6(6))* 2010. 232p. pap. 25.75 *(978-1-177-16945-5(2))* 2010. 230p. pap. 25.75 *(978-1-177-16955-4(X))* 2010. 232p. pap. 25.75 *(978-1-177-16951-6(7))* 2010. 232p. pap. 25.75 *(978-1-145-73986-4(5))* 2009. 226p. 28.99 *(978-1-110-85688-6(1))* 2009. (ENG.). 224p. pap. 22.99 *(978-1-110-85683-1(0)*, BiblioLife) 2009. (ENG.). 224p. pap. 20.99 *(978-1-110-85682-4(2)*, BiblioLife) 2009. 226p. pap. 24.75 *(978-1-110-85686-2(5))* BiblioBazaar.
—Hopes & Fears for Art. 2009. 98p. pap. *(978-1-151-72064-1(X))*; pap. *(978-1-151-35236-1(5))* Books LLC.
—Hopes & Fears for Art. 2010. (Illus.). 92p. pap. 20.00 *(978-1-153-62923-2(2))* General Bks. LLC.
—Hopes & Fears for Art. 2010. 122p. 28.76 *(978-1-169-25130-4(7))*; pap. 16.76 *(978-1-162-66668-6(4))*; 35.95 *(978-1-161-43533-7(6))* Kessinger Publishing, LLC.
—Hopes & Fears for Art. 2009. (ENG.). 132p. pap. 10.95 *(978-1-4385-2586-0(9)*, Book Jungle) Standard Pubns., Inc.
—Hopes & Fears for Art. Lt. ed. 2007. (ENG.). 156p. per. 21.99 *(978-1-4346-7747-1(8))* BiblioBazaar.
O'Donnell, Anne. Motawi Tileworks: Contemporary Handcrafted Tiles in the Arts & Crafts Tradition. 2008. 112p. 29.95 *(978-0-7649-4598-4(X))* Pomegranate Communications, Inc.
Rees, Diana. Grace Helen Mowat & the Making of Cottage Craft. 2009. (ENG., Illus.). 220p. pap. 16.95 *(978-0-86492-532-9(8))* Goose Lane Editions CAN. Dist: Univ. of Toronto Pr.
Robinson, Michael. Arts & Crafts. 480p. pap. 10.98 *(978-1-56852-554-9(0)*, Konecky & Konecky) Konecky, William S. Assocs., Inc.
Roth, Linda H. & Kornhauser, Elizabeth Mankin, eds. At Home with Gustav Stickley: Arts & Crafts from the Stephen Gray Collection. 2008. (ENG., Illus.). 120p. 50.00 *(978-0-918333-24-7(5))* Wadsworth Atheneum.
Ruskin, John. Works. 2010. 500p. pap. 38.75 *(978-1-142-69549-1(2))* BiblioBazaar.
—Works. 2009. 412p. pap. *(978-0-217-14448-3(9))*; 266p. pap. *(978-0-217-65721-1(4))*; 236p. pap. *(978-0-217-14506-0(X))*; 182p. pap. *(978-0-217-65875-1(X))* Books LLC.
—Works. 2009. 150p. pap. 19.99 *(978-1-4589-5493-0(5))* General Bks. LLC.
Sanchez, Sonia. I'm Black When I'm Singing, I'm Blue When I Ain't & Other Plays. Wood, Jacqueline, ed. 2010. (ENG.). 196p. 69.95 *(978-0-8223-4757-6(1))*; pap. 19.95 *(978-0-8223-4778-1(4))* Duke Univ. Pr.
Sommer, Petr & Klapste, Jan, eds. Arts & Crafts in Medieval Rural Environment. 2007. (Ruralia Ser.). (ENG, FRE & GER., Illus.). 411p. (C). pap. 109.00 *(978-2-503-51994-4(6))* Brepols Pubs. BEL. Dist: ISD.
Spencer, Amy. The Crafter Culture: Making It Yourself. 2006. (ENG., Illus.). 400p. per., instr.'s hndbk. ed. 17.95 *(978-0-7145-3128-1(6))* Boyars, Marion Pubs., Inc.
Stickley, Gustav. Gustav Stickley's Craftsman Homes & Bungalows. 2009. (ENG., Illus.). 576p. pap. 19.95 *(978-1-60239-303-5(6)*, 239303) Skyhorse Publishing Co., Inc.
Todd, Pamela. The Arts & Crafts Companion. 2008. (ENG.). 320p. pap. 24.95 *(978-0-9553046-7-5(9))* Palazzo Editions, Ltd. GBR. Dist: Independent Pubs. Group.
Triggs, Oscar Lovell. Arts & Crafts. 2009. (Art of Century Ser.). (ENG., Illus.). 200p. 19.95 *(978-1-84484-622-1(9))* Parkstone International GBR. Dist: Ingram Pub. Services.
Tucker, Kevin W. Gustav Stickley & the American Arts & Crafts Movement. 2010. (Illus.). 272p. 60.00 *(978-0-300-11802-5(3))* Yale Univ. Pr.
Weller, Alan & Dover Staff. Arts & Crafts. 2012. (Dover Pictura Electronic Clip Art Ser.). (ENG., Illus.). 128p. pap. 39.95 *(978-0-486-99031-6(1))* Dover Pubns., Inc.
Wilde, Oscar. Essays & Lectures. 2008. 140p. 21.99 *(978-0-554-30771-8(5))* 2008. 140p. 24.99 *(978-0-554-21468-9(7))* 2006. (ENG.). 144p. pap. 18.99 *(978-1-4264-0073-5(X))* 2006. (ENG.). 138p. pap. 19.99 *(978-1-4264-0202-9(3))* BiblioBazaar.
—Essays & Lectures. 2008. 132p. pap. *(978-1-4099-3412-7(8))* Dodo Pr.
Woodworker's Journal Editors. Craftsman Furniture Projects: Timeless Designs & Trusted Techniques from Woodworking's Top Experts. 2007. (Best of Woodworker's Journal Ser.). (ENG., Illus.). 159p. pap. 19.95 *(978-1-56523-324-9(7))* Fox Chapel Publishing Co., Inc.
Yorke, Trevor. Arts & Crafts House Styles. 2011. (ENG., Illus.). 64p. pap. 14.95 *(978-1-84674-230-9(7))* Countryside Bks. GBR. Dist: Brown, David Bk. Co., The.
Zipf, Catherine W. Professional Pursuits: Women & the American Arts & Crafts Movement. 2009. (ENG.). pap. 24.95 *(978-1-57233-685-8(4))* Univ. of Tennessee Pr.

ARTS AND OLDER PEOPLE

Korevaar, Gerbrand & Vogelaar, Christiaan. Rembrandt's Mother: Myth & Reality. 2006. (ENG., Illus.). 288p. 85.00 *(978-90-400-8163-7(8))* Waanders B.V., Uitgeverij NLD. Dist: National Bk. Network.

ARTS AND PEOPLE WITH DISABILITIES
see People with Disabilities and the Arts

ARTS AND SOCIETY

ACE (Adult and Continuing Education). Arts & Societal Learning No. 116: Transforming Communities Socially, Politically, & Culturally - New Directions for Adult & Continuing Education. Hayes, Sandra & Yorks, Lyle, eds. 2007. (J-B ACE Single Issue Adult & Continuing Education Ser.: 91). (ENG.). 96p. pap. 29.00 *(978-0-470-27852-9(8)*, Jossey-Bass) Wiley, John & Sons, Inc.
Allen, Nicholas. Modernism, Ireland & Civil War. 2009. (ENG., Illus.). 240p. 86.00 *(978-0-521-48995-9(4))* Cambridge Univ. Pr.
Araeen. Third Text. 2007. 49.95 *(978-0-415-44118-6(8))* Taylor & Francis Group.
Araeen, Rasheed & Sardar, Ziauddin, eds. Third Text. 2007. (ENG.). 10p. 49.95 *(978-0-415-44120-9(X)*, Taylor & Francis) Taylor & Francis Group GBR. Dist: Taylor & Francis Group.
Ardar, Cubitt, et al. 3rd Text Reader on Art/Culture/Theory. 2007. (Illus.). 400p. *(978-0-8264-9643-0(1))* Continuum International Publishing Group, Ltd.
Arriola, Magali, et al. Equilibrio Dinámico: En Busca de un Terreno Público. 2007. (SPA & ENG., Illus.). 247p. *(978-0-9642554-7-0(2))* Installation Gallery.
Bal, Mieke, et al. Digital & Other Virtualities: Renegotiating the Image. Pollock, Griselda, ed. 2010. (New Encounters: Arts, Cultures, Concepts Ser.). (ENG., Illus.). 320p. 85.00 *(978-1-84511-567-8(8))* I. B. Tauris & Co., Ltd. GBR. Dist: Macmillan.
Bán, Zsófia. Exposed Memories: Family Pictures in Private & Collective Memory. Turai, Hedvig, ed. 2010. (ENG., Illus.). 200p. 40.00 *(978-963-9776-70-8(X))* Central European Univ. Pr.

Barone, Tom & Eisner, Elliot W. Arts Based Research. 2011. 208p. (C). pap. 47.00 *(978-1-4129-8247-4(2)*, B82474P) SAGE Pubns., Inc.

Barruol, Guy. La France Médiévale. (FRE., Illus.). 431p. *(978-2-7424-0469-8(4))* Les Nouveaux loisirs.

Belfiore, Eleonora & Bennett, Oliver. The Social Impact of the Arts: An Intellectual History. (ENG.). 248p. 2010. pap. 29.00 *(978-0-230-27351-1(3))* 2008. 89.00 *(978-0-230-57255-3(3))* Palgrave Macmillan.

Bennett, Philippa & Miles, Rosie, eds. William Morris in the Twenty-First Century. 2010. (Illus.). 287p. pap. 68.95 *(978-3-0343-0106-0(5))* Lang, Peter AG GBR. Dist: Lang, Peter.

Bennett, Robert. Deconstructing Post-Wwii New York City. 2011. 142p. pap. 39.95 ***(978-0-415-80689-3(5))*** Routledge.

Bernstein, Lee. America Is the Prison: Arts & Politics in Prison in The 1970s. 2010. (ENG., Illus.). 240p. 35.00 *(978-0-8078-3387-2(8))* Univ. of North Carolina Pr.

—America Is the Prison: Arts & Politics in Prison in the 1970s. 2010. (Illus.). xi, 244p. pap. *(978-0-8078-7117-1(6))* Univ. of North Carolina Pr.

Blake, Casey Nelson, ed. The Arts of Democracy: Art, Public Culture, & the State. 2009. (Arts & Intellectual Life in Modern America Ser.). (Illus.). 384p. (C). pap. 26.50 *(978-0-8122-2001-8(3))* Univ. of Pennsylvania Pr.

Bradley, Patricia. Making American Culture: A Social History, 1900-1920. 2010. (ENG.). 264p. pap. 29.00 *(978-0-230-10584-3(X))* Palgrave Macmillan.

Brault, Simon. No Culture, No Future. Kaplansky, Jonathan, tr. from FRE. 2010. (ENG.). 200p. 21.00 *(978-1-897151-76-1(4))* Cormorant Bks. Inc. CAN. Dist: Univ. of Toronto Pr.

Bredohl, Thomas M. & Zimmermann, Michael, eds. Berlin's Culturescape in the 20th Century. 2009. (Ur Ser.). (GER & ENG.). 274p. pap. 29.95 *(978-0-88977-224-3(X))* Canadian Plains Research Ctr. CAN. Dist: Univ. of Toronto Pr.

Browne, Ray B. & Kreiser, Lawrence A., eds. Popular Culture Values & the Arts: Essays on Elitism versus Democratization. 2009. (ENG.). 230p. pap. 39.95 *(978-0-7864-3944-7(0))* McFarland & Co., Inc. Pubs.

Cheng, Anne Anlin & Baker, Josephine. Second Skin: Josephine Baker & the Modern Surface, 1 vol. 2011. (ENG., Illus.). 224p. 24.95 *(978-0-19-538705-6(8))* Oxford Univ. Pr., Inc.

Cherbo, Joni Maya, et al, eds. Understanding the Arts & Creative Sector in the United States. 2008. (Rutgers Series on the Public Life of the Arts). (ENG., Illus.). 224p. 68.00 *(978-0-8135-4307-9(X))*; pap. 26.95 *(978-0-8135-4308-6(8))* Rutgers Univ. Pr.

Chevallier, François. La Société du Mépris de Soi: De L'Urinoir de Duchamp Aux Suicidés de France Télécom. 2010. (FRE., Illus.). 119p. *(978-2-07-013148-8(3))* Gallimard, Editions.

Ch'oe, Yol. Misul Kwa Sahoe: Ch'oe Yol Pip'yong Chonso, 1976-2008. 2009. (KOR., Illus.). 468p. *(978-89-7278-279-7(3))* Cheong-nyeonsa.

Cleveland, William & Shifferd, Patricia Allen. Between Grace & Fear: The Role of the Arts in a Time of Change. 2010. (Illus.). xii, 416p. pap. *(978-1-86335-737-1(8))* Common Ground Publishing Pty, Ltd.

Coetzee, Mark, ed. Keith Haring: Against All Odds. 2009. (ENG., Illus.). 288p. 60.00 *(978-0-9821195-0-1(X))* Rubell Family Collection.

Cooke, Lynne & Crimp, Douglas, eds. Mixed Use, Manhattan: Photography & Related Practices, 1970s to the Present. 2010. (ENG., Illus.). 303p. (gr. 17). 49.95 *(978-0-262-01482-3(3))* MIT Pr.

Cope, Bill & Kalantzis, Mary, eds. The International Journal of the Arts in Society: Volume 5, Number 5. 2011. 334p. 0.00 ***(978-1-86335-920-7(6))*** Common Ground Publishing Pty, Ltd.

—The International Journal of the Arts in Society: Volume 5, Number 6. 2011. 360p. 0.00 ***(978-1-86335-991-7(5))*** Common Ground Publishing Pty, Ltd.

Costabile-Heming, Carol Anne, et al, eds. Berlin - the Symphony Continues: Orchestrating Architectural, Social & Artistic Change in Germany's New Capital. (ENG.). X, 328p. 210.00 ***(978-3-11-180273-2(6))*** De Gruyter, Walter Inc.

Cummings, Denise K., ed. Visualities: Perspectives on Contemporary American Indian Film & Art. 2011. (American Indian Studies). (ENG., Illus.). 340p. pap. 29.95 *(978-0-87013-999-4(1))* Michigan State Univ. Pr.

de Bruyne, Paul & Gielen, Pascal, eds. Arts in Society. 2010. (ENG., Illus.). 206p. pap. 32.00 *(978-90-5662-711-9(2))* NAi Uitgevers / Publishers Stichting NLD. Dist: D.A.P./Distributed Art Pubs.

De Vries, Annette, ed. Cultural Mediators: Artists & Writers at the Crossroads of Tradition, Innovation & Reception in the Low Countries & Italy 1450-1650. 2008. (Groningen Studies in Cultural Change Ser.). (ENG.). 234p. (C). 66.00 *(978-90-429-2043-9(2))* Peeters Pubs. & Booksellers BEL. Dist: Brown, David Bk. Co., The.

Dempsey, Charles. The Early Renaissance & Vernacular Culture. 2012. (Bernard Berenson Lectures on the Italian Renaissance Delivered at Villa I Tatti Ser.). (ENG., Illus.). 398p. 39.95 *(978-0-674-04952-9(7))* Harvard Univ. Pr.

Design2context. Des-/Orientierung, Dis-/Orientation, Dés-/Orientation 2. 2010. 384p. pap. 50.00 *(978-3-03778-158-6(0))* Lars Muller Pubs. CHE. Dist: Prestel Publishing.

Dillon, Sheila & Welch, Katherine E., eds. Representations of War in Ancient Rome. 2009. (ENG., Illus.). 380p. (C). pap. 40.99 *(978-0-521-13083-7(2))* Cambridge Univ. Pr.

DiMaggio, Paul & Fernandez-Kelly, Patricia, eds. Art in the Lives of Immigrant Communities in the United States. 2010. (Rugers Series on the Public Life of the Arts Ser.). (ENG., Illus.). 320p. pap. 22.95 *(978-0-8135-4758-9(X))* Rutgers Univ. Pr.

DiMaggio, Paul & Fernández-Kelly, Patricia, eds. Art in the Lives of Immigrant Communities in the United States. 2010. (Rugers Series on the Public Life of the Arts Ser.). (ENG., Illus.). 320p. 75.00 *(978-0-8135-4757-2(1))* Rutgers Univ. Pr.

Dissanayake, Ellen. Art & Intimacy: How the Arts Began. 2012. (ENG., Illus.). 268p. (C). pap. 25.00 ***(978-0-295-99196-2(8))*** Univ. of Washington Pr.

Douglas, Robert L. Resistance, Insurgence, & Identity: The Art of Mari Evans, Nelson Stevens, & the Black Arts Movement. 2008. *(978-1-59221-564-5(5))*; 376p. pap. *(978-1-59221-565-2(3))* Africa World Pr.

Elkins, James. Visual Cultures. 2010. (Illus.). 160p. pap. 25.00 *(978-1-84150-307-3(X))* Intellect, Ltd. GBR. Dist: Chicago Distribution Ctr.

Esche, Charles, et al, eds. Citizens & Subjects: The Netherlands, for Example, 1 vol. 2007. (ENG., Illus.). 336p. pap. 29.00 *(978-3-905770-73-5(3))* JRP Ringier Kunstverlag AG CHE. Dist: D.A.P./Distributed Art Pubs.

Estraikh, Gennady & Krutikov, Mikhail, eds. Yiddish in Weimar Berlin: An Ivory Tower at the Crossroads of Diaspora Politics & Culture. 2010. (Legenda Studies in Yiddish Ser.). (ENG., Illus.). 286p. (C). 89.50 *(978-1-906540-70-8(5))* European Humanities Research Ctr. GBR. Dist: Brown, David Bk. Co., The.

Eyerman, Ron & McCormick, Lisa. Myth, Meaning, & Performance: Toward a New Cultural Sociology of the Arts. 2006. (Yale Cultural Sociology Ser.). (ENG., Illus.). 172p. per. 39.95 *(978-1-59451-215-5(9))* Paradigm Pubs.

Feigel, Lara & Harris, Alexandra, eds. Modernism on Sea: Art & Culture at the British Seaside. (Peter Lang Ltd. Ser.). (Illus.). 2009. 280p. 38.95 *(978-1-906165-24-6(6))* 2nd rev. ed. 2011. (ENG., 272p. pap. 26.95 ***(978-1-906165-40-6(8))*** Lang, Peter AG GBR. Dist: Lang, Peter.

Finch, L. Boyd. Legacies of Camelot: Stewart & Lee Udall, American Culture, & the Arts. 2008. (ENG., Illus.). 208p. 24.95 *(978-0-8061-3879-4(3))* Univ. of Oklahoma Pr.

Flajsman, Bozidar. Likovna Dejavnost in Ekolosko Ozavescanje. 2009. (SLV., Illus.). 224p. *(978-961-6525-61-9(1))* Debora, spol. s r.o.

Folin, Marco, ed. Courts & Courtly Arts in Renaissance Italy: Arts, Culture & Politics, 1395-1530. 2010. (ENG., Illus.). 444p. 95.00 *(978-1-85149-643-3(2))* Antique Collectors' Club.

Fraterrigo, Elizabeth. Playboy & the Making of the Good Life in Modern America, 1 vol. (Illus.). 2011. 308p. pap. 21.95 ***(978-0-19-983245-3(5))*** 2009. (ENG., 320p. 29.95 *(978-0-19-538610-3(8))* Oxford Univ. Pr., Inc.

Genter, Robert. Late Modernism: Art, Culture, & Politics in Cold War America. 2010. (Arts & Intellectual Life in Modern America Ser.). 384p. (C). 49.95 *(978-0-8122-4264-5(5))* Univ. of Pennsylvania Pr.

Gibson, Chris, ed. Creativity in Peripheral Places. 2011. (ENG., Illus.). 168p. (C). 125.00 ***(978-0-415-69668-5(2))*** Routledge.

Gleiniger, Andrea, et al, eds. Transdiscourse 1. 2010. (Illus.). 216p. pap. 49.95 *(978-3-7091-0287-9(1)*, 3709102871) Springer Wien AUT. Dist: Springer.

Gluck, Mary. Popular Bohemia: Modernism & Urban Culture in Nineteenth-Century Paris. 2008. (Illus.). 238p. per. 25.50 *(978-0-674-02731-2(0))* Harvard Univ. Pr.

Goldstein, Carl. Print Culture in Early Modern France: Abraham Bosse & the Purposes of Print. 2012. (ENG., Illus.). 234p. 99.00 ***(978-1-107-01214-1(7))*** Cambridge Univ. Pr.

Goriunova, Olga. Art Platforms & Cultural Production on the Internet. 2011. (Routledge Research in Cultural & Media Studies). (ENG., Illus.). 176p. (C). 125.00 *(978-0-415-89310-7(0))* Routledge.

Greene, David B. The Imagining of Community in the Arts of Guatemala: Weaving, Folk Tales, Marimba Performance, Contemporary Painting. 2010. (Illus.). viii, 182p. *(978-0-7734-1311-5(1))* Mellen, Edwin Pr., The.

Harris, Jonathan. Identity Theft: The Cultural Colonization of Contemporary Art. Harris, Jonathan, ed. 2009. (ENG., Illus.). 272p. 85.00 *(978-1-84631-103-1(9))* Liverpool Univ. Pr. GBR. Dist: Chicago Distribution Ctr.

Harris, Jonathan, ed. Identity Theft: The Cultural Colonisation & Contemporary Art. 2009. (Liverpool University Press - Tate Liverpool Critical Forum Ser.). (ENG., Illus.). 272p. pap. 39.95 *(978-1-84631-102-4(0))* Liverpool Univ. Pr. GBR. Dist: Chicago Distribution Ctr.

Harris, Jonathan & Williams, Richard, eds. Regenerating Culture & Society: Architecture, Art & Urban Style Within the Global Politics of City-Branding. 2011. (Liverpool University Press - Tate Liverpool Critical Forum Ser.). (ENG., Illus.). 347p. pap. 85.00 *(978-1-84631-640-1(5))* Liverpool Univ. Pr. GBR. Dist: Chicago Distribution Ctr.

Hauser, Arnold. The Sociology of Art (Routledge Revivals) 2011. (Routledge Revivals Ser.). (ENG.). 802p. 250.00 ***(978-0-415-69994-5(0))*** Routledge.

Hesmondhalgh, David. The Cultural Industries. 2nd ed. 2007. (Illus.). 360p. (C). 125.00 *(978-1-4129-0807-8(8)*, B08078C) SAGE Pubns., Ltd. GBR. Dist: SAGE Pubns., Inc.

Huener. The Arts in Nazi Germany: Continuity, Conformity, Change. 2007. (Illus.). 236p. 27.50 *(978-1-84545-359-6(X))* Berghahn Bks., Inc.

Hutter, Michael & Throsby, David, eds. Beyond Price: Value in Culture, Economics, & the Arts. (Murphy Institute Studies in Political Economy Ser.). (ENG., Illus.). 334p. 2011. pap. 45.00 ***(978-0-521-18300-0(6))*** 2007. 96.00 *(978-0-521-86223-3(X))* Cambridge Univ. Pr.

Hutzel, Karen, et al, eds. Transforming City Schools Through Art: Approaches to Meaningful K-12 Learning. 2012. (ENG., Illus.). 192p. 64.00 ***(978-0-8077-5293-7(2))***; pap. 29.95 ***(978-0-8077-5292-0(4))*** Teachers College Pr., Teachers College, Columbia Univ.

IUsupova, G. M., et al. Iskusstvo I Sotsialnaia Pamiat. 2009. (RUS.). 382p. *(978-5-98287-015-5(3))* Gosudarstvennyj institut iskusstvoznanija.

JACKSON, Shannon. Social Works: Peroming Arts, Supporting Publics. 2011. (ENG., Illus.). 320p. pap. 35.95 *(978-0-415-48601-9(7))* Routledge.

Jacobs, Robert. Filling the Hole in the Nuclear Future: Art & Popular Culture Respond to the Bomb. 2010. (AsiaWorld Ser.). (ENG., Illus.). 290p. pap. 34.99 *(978-0-7391-3557-0(0))* Lexington Bks.

—Filling the Hole in the Nuclear Future - Art & Popular Culture Respond to the Bomb. 2010. (AsiaWorld Ser.). (ENG., Illus.). 290p. 83.99 *(978-0-7391-3556-3(2))* Lexington Bks.

Jain, Jyotindra. India's Popular Culture: Iconic Spaces & Fluid Images. 2008. (Illus.). 128p. 65.00 *(978-81-85026-81-7(5))* Marg Pubns. IND. Dist: National Bk. Network.

Jolivette, Catherine. Landscape, Art & Identity in 1950s Britain. 2009. (Illus.). 190p. 114.95 *(978-0-7546-6363-8(9))* Ashgate Publishing Co.

Kalantzis, Mary & Cope, Bill, eds. The International Journal of the Arts in Society: Volume 4, Number 1. 2009. 376p. 0.00 *(978-1-86335-668-8(1))* Common Ground Publishing Pty, Ltd.

—The International Journal of the Arts in Society: Volume 4, Number 2. 2009. 496p. 0.00 *(978-1-86335-700-5(9))* Common Ground Publishing Pty, Ltd.

Kang, Minsoo & Woodson-Boulton, Amy, eds. Visions of the Industrial Age 1830-1914: Modernity & the Age of Representation in Europe. 2008. (Illus.). 394p. 144.95 *(978-0-7546-6488-8(0))* Ashgate Publishing Co.

Kavka, Misha, et al, eds. Gothic NZ: The Darker Side of Kiwi Culture. 2006. (Illus.). 176p. (C). pap. 39.95 *(978-1-877372-23-0(4))* Otago University Pr. NZL. Dist: International Specialized Bk. Services.

Koepnick, Lutz P. Framing Attention: Windows on Modern German Culture. 2006. (Parallax: Re#45;visions of Culture & Society Ser.). (ENG., Illus.). 312p. (gr. 17). 55.00 *(978-0-8018-8489-4(6))* Johns Hopkins Univ. Pr.

Kretzschmar, Dirk. Identitat Statt Differenz: Zum Verhaltnis von Kunsttheorie und Gesellschaftsstruktur in Russland im 18. und 19. Jahrhundert. (Slavische Literaturen - Texte und Abhandlungen Ser.: Bd. 26). (GER.). 405p. 53.95 *(978-3-631-39241-6(9))* Lang, Peter Publishing, Inc.

Kuppers, Petra. Disability Culture & Community Performance: Find a Strange & Twisted Shape. 2011. (ENG., Illus.). 296p. 85.00 *(978-0-230-29827-9(3))* Palgrave Macmillan.

Levy, Allison, ed. Sex Acts in Early Modern Italy: Practice, Performance, Perversion, Punishment. 2010. (Visual Culture in Early Modernity Ser.). (Illus.). 302p. 124.95 *(978-0-7546-6748-3(0))* Ashgate Publishing Co.

Lord, Barry & Dexter, Gail. Artists, Patrons, & the Public: Why Culture Changes. 2010. (ENG., Illus.). 226p. 49.95 *(978-0-7591-1848-5(5))* AltaMira Pr.

Lürzer, Walter. Art Diary International 2009 2010. 2009. (ENG., Illus.). 624p. pap. 35.00 *(978-88-7816-148-1(9))* Politi, Giancarlo Editore ITA. Dist: D.A.P./Distributed Art Pubs.

Lymberopoulou, Angeliki. Images of the Byzantine World: Visions Messages & Meanings. 2011. (Illus.). 272p. 124.95 *(978-1-4094-0776-8(4))* Ashgate Publishing Co.

Marrinan, Michael. Romantic Paris: Histories of a Cultural Landscape, 1800-1850. 2009. (ENG., Illus.). 488p. 85.00 *(978-0-8047-5062-2(9))*; pap. 35.00 *(978-0-8047-6151-2(5))* Stanford Univ. Pr.

McCaughan, Edward J. Art & Social Movements: Cultural Politics in Mexico & Aztlán. 2012. (ENG., Illus.). 240p. pap. 23.95 ***(978-0-8223-5182-5(X))*** Duke Univ. Pr.

—Artists & Social Movements: Cultural Politics in Mexico & Aztlán. 2012. (ENG., Illus.). 240p. 84.95 ***(978-0-8223-5168-9(4))*** Duke Univ. Pr.

McGraw, Richard. Confronting Modernity: Art & Society in Louisiana. 2008. (ENG., Illus.). 304p. 55.00 *(978-1-57806-417-5(1))* Univ. Pr. of Mississippi.

Miller, Tyrus. Singular Examples: Artistic Politics & the Neo-Avant-Garde. 2009. (Avant-Garde & Modernism Studies). (ENG.). 270p. pap. 34.95 *(978-0-8101-2512-4(9))*; (Illus.). 69.95 *(978-0-8101-2511-7(0))* Northwestern Univ. Pr.

Morley, Simon, ed. The Sublime. 2010. (Documents of Contemporary Art Ser.). (ENG.). 237p. (gr. 17). pap. 24.95 *(978-0-262-51391-3(9))* MIT Pr.

Mraz, John. Looking for Mexico: Modern Visual Culture & National Identity. 2009. (ENG., Illus.). 360p. 94.95 *(978-0-8223-4429-2(7))*; pap. 25.95 *(978-0-8223-4443-8(2))* Duke Univ. Pr.

Najafi, Sina, ed. Shame: A Quarterly of Art & Culture. 2008. (ENG., Illus.). 112p. pap. 12.00 *(978-1-932698-29-9(9))* Cabinet.

Nind, Sarah. Painting As Metaphor. Schirmacher, Wolfgang, ed. 2010. 184p. pap. 21.95 *(978-0-9827067-0-1(7))* Atropos Pr.

Njogu, Kimani & Oluoch-Olunya, G. Cultural Production & Social Change in Kenya: Building Bridges. 2007. (Illus.). 272p. pap. *(978-9966-9743-7-2(7))* Michigan State Univ. Pr.

Oakes, Kaya. Slanted & Enchanted: The Evolution of Indie Culture. 2009. (ENG.). 256p. pap. 14.00 *(978-0-8050-8852-6(0)*, Holt Paperback) Holt, Henry & Co.

O'Neill, Morna & Hatt, Michael, eds. The Edwardian Sense: Art, Design, & Performance in Britain, 1901-1910. 2010. (Studies in British Art Ser.). (Illus.). 336p. 65.00 *(978-0-300-16335-3(5))* Yale Ctr. for British Art.

Pang, Laikwan. The Distorting Mirror: Visual Modernity in China. 2007. (Illus.). 280p. 57.00 *(978-0-8248-3093-9(8))* Univ. of Hawaii Pr.

Papanikolas, Theresa. Anarchism & the Advent of Paris Dada: Art & Criticism, 1914-1924. 2010. (Illus.). 206p. 99.95 *(978-0-7546-6626-4(3))* Ashgate Publishing Co.

Peixoto. Paisagens Urbanas. (POR., Illus.). 347p. *(978-85-85578-92-3(0))* Servico Nacional de Aprendizagem Comercial, Senac.

Peponi, Anastasia-Erasmia. Frontiers of Pleasure: Models of Aesthetic Response in Archaic & Classical Greek Thought. 2nd ed. 2012. (ENG., Illus.). 224p. 74.00 ***(978-0-19-979832-2(X))*** Oxford Univ. Pr., Inc.

Poggi, Christine. Inventing Futurism: The Art & Politics of Artificial Optimism. 2008. (ENG., Illus.). 392p. (C). 46.95 *(978-0-691-13370-6(0))* Princeton Univ. Pr.

Purtle, Jennifer & Thomsen, Hans Bjarne. Looking Modern: East Asian Visual Culture from Treaty Ports to World War II. 2009. *(978-1-58886-105-4(8))* Art Media Resources, Inc.

Rawlinson, Mark. American Visual Culture. 2009. (ENG., Illus.). 1p. 109.95 *(978-1-84520-216-3(3))*; 256p. pap. 29.95 *(978-1-84520-217-0(1))* Berg Pubs. GBR. Dist: Macmillan.

Sardar, Ziauddin & Rasheed, Araeen, eds. Third Text: Critical Perspectives on Contemporary Art & Culture. 2007. (Illus.). 112p. per. 49.95 *(978-0-415-44117-9(X))* Taylor & Francis Group.

Segre, Erica. Intersected Identities: Strategies of Visualisation in 19th & 20th Century Mexican Culture. 2007. (Remapping Cultural History Ser.). (Illus.). 304p. (C). 90.00 *(978-1-84545-291-9(7))* Berghahn Bks., Inc.

Shirane, Haruo, ed. Envisioning the Tale of Genji: Media, Gender, & Cultural Production. 2008. (ENG., Illus.). 416p. (gr. 17). 84.50 *(978-0-231-14236-6(6))*; pap. 32.50 *(978-0-231-14237-3(4))* Columbia Univ. Pr.

Sloan, Johanne, ed. Urban Enigmas: Montreal, Toronto, & the Problem of Comparing Cities. 2007. (Culture of Cities Ser.). (ENG.). 312p. (C). pap. *(978-0-7735-3182-6(3))* McGill-Queen's Univ. Pr.

Smock, William. Bauhaus Ideal: Then & Now. 2009. (ENG., Illus.). 150p. pap. 19.95 *(978-0-89733-590-4(2))* Academy Chicago Pubs., Ltd.

Snickare, Mårten. Performativity & Performance in Baroque Rome. Gillgren, Peter, ed. 2012. (Visual Culture in Early Modernity Ser.). (Illus.). 280p. 124.95 ***(978-1-4094-2099-6(X))*** Ashgate Publishing Co.

Solterer, Helen & Cohen, Gustave. Medieval Roles for Modern Times: Theater & the Battle for the French Republic. 2010. (ENG.). 256p. 80.00 *(978-0-271-03614-4(1))* Pennsylvania State Univ. Pr.

Syme, Alison & Sargent, John Singer. A Touch of Blossom: John Singer Sargent & the Queer Flora of Fin-de-Siècle Art. 2010. (ENG.). 328p. 74.95 *(978-0-271-03622-9(2))* Pennsylvania State Univ. Pr.

Taylor, Rabun. The Moral Mirror of Roman Art. 2008. (ENG., Illus.). 288p. 103.00 *(978-0-521-86612-5(X))* Cambridge Univ. Pr.

Terry-Fritsch, Allie, et al. Beholding Violence in Medieval & Early Modern Europe. 2012. (Illus.). 250p. ***(978-1-4094-4286-8(1))*** Ashgate Publishing, Ltd.

Thurman, Chris. At Large: Reviewing the Arts in South Africa. 2011. pap. ***(978-1-86335-927-6(3))*** Common Ground Publishing Pty, Ltd.

Towse, Ruth. A Textbook of Cultural Economics. 2010. (ENG., Illus.). 626p. (C). pap. 59.00 *(978-0-521-71702-1(7))* Cambridge Univ. Pr.

TransAct: Transnational Activities in the Cultural FieldInterventionen zur Lage in Österreichmuseum in progress. 2009. 513p. 49.95 *(978-3-211-99800-7(4))* Springer Wien AUT. Dist: Actar Birkhauser Distribution.

Trojanowska, Tamara. New Perspectives on Polish Culture: Personal Encounters, Public Affairs. 2012. 396p. pap. 24.95 ***(978-0-940962-73-6(X))*** Polish Institute of Arts & Sciences of America, Inc., The.

Turner, Frederick. Culture of Hope: A New Birth of the Classical Spirit. 2007. (ENG.). 300p. pap. 20.95 *(978-1-4165-7685-3(1)*, Free Pr.) Free Pr.

Wexler, Alice & Wexler, Alice J. Art & Disability: The Social & Political Struggles Facing Education. 2009. (ENG., Illus.). 272p. 89.00 *(978-0-230-60629-6(6))* Palgrave Macmillan.

Wexler, Alice J. Art & Disability: The Social & Political Struggles Facing Education. 2011. (ENG., Illus.). 266p. pap. 28.00 *(978-0-230-11485-2(7))* Palgrave Macmillan.

White, Geogina. Light Fantastic: Dance Floor Courtship in New Zealand. 2007. (Illus.). 207p. pap. *(978-1-86950-619-3(7))* HarperCollins Pubs. Australia.

White, Julia M. Mahjong: Art, Film, & Change in China. 2008. (ENG., Illus.). 100p. pap. 25.00 *(978-0-9719397-7-6(2))* Univ. of California, Berkeley Art Museum & Pacific Film Archive.

Wollen, Peter. Raiding the Icebox: Reflections on Twentieth-Century Culture, New Edition. rev. ed. 2008. (ENG.). 224p. 95.00 *(978-1-84467-274-5(3)*, 844274); pap. 26.95 *(978-1-84467-250-9(6)*, 844250) Verso Bks. GBR. Dist: Norton, W. W. & Co., Inc.

Wood, Sharon & Bigliazzi, Silvia, eds. Collaboration in the Arts from the Middle Ages to the Present. 2006. (Studies in European Cultural Transition). (Illus.). 234p. 110.00 *(978-0-7546-5512-1(1))* Ashgate Publishing Co.

Wyman, Max. The Defiant Imagination: Why Culture Matters. pap. 22.95 *(978-1-55365-007-2(7))* D&M Pubs. Inc. CAN. Dist: Perseus-PGW.

Young, James O. Cultural Appropriation & the Arts. 2nd ed. (New Directions in Aesthetics Ser.). (ENG.). 192p. 2010. pap. 32.95 *(978-1-4443-3271-1(6))* 2008. (Illus.). 87.95 *(978-1-4051-7656-9(3))* Wiley, John & Sons, Inc. (Wiley-Blackwell).

Zuidervaart, Lambert. Art in Public: Politics, Economics, & a Democratic Culture. 2010. (ENG.). (C). 352p. 85.00 *(978-0-521-11274-1(5))*; 344p. pap. 28.99 *(978-0-521-13017-2(4))* Cambridge Univ. Pr.

ARTS AND TECHNOLOGY

see Technology and the Arts

ARTS AND THE AGED

see Arts and Older People

ARTS IN THE CHURCH

see Art and Religion; Christian Art and Symbolism

ARTSCHWAGER, RICHARD, 1923-

Artschwager, Richard. Richard Artschwager: Objects As Images of Objects. 2010. (ENG., Illus.). 128p. 55.00 *(978-0-9771714-4-6(2))* Nolan, David Gallery.

Richard Artschwager. 2008. (ENG., Illus.). *(978-1-932598-66-7(9))* Gagosian Gallery.

ARUBA

Colón, Christina Paulette. Frommer's Portable Aruba, Bonaire & Curacao. 6th ed. 2011. (Frommer's Portable Ser.: 274). (ENG.). 216p. pap. 12.99 *(978-1-118-07472-5(6),* Frommers) Wiley, John & Sons, Inc.

Holloway, Beth. Loving Natalee: A Mother's Testament of Hope & Faith. 2007. (Illus.). 256p. 24.95 *(978-0-06-145227-7(0),* HarperOne) HarperCollins Pubs.

—Loving Natalee: The True Story of the Aruba Kidnapping & Its Aftermath. 2009. (ENG.). 272p. mass mkt. 7.99 *(978-0-06-146879-7(7))* HarperCollins Pubs.

Pulitzer, Lisa & Thompson, Cole. Portrait of a Monster: Joran van der Sloot, a Murder in Peru, & the Natalee Holloway Mystery. (ENG.). 2012. 352p. mass mkt. 7.99 ***(978-1-250-01185-5(X),*** St. Martin's Paperbacks) 2011. (Illus.). 288p. 25.99 *(978-0-312-35921-8(7))* St. Martin's Pr.

ARUBA—DESCRIPTION AND TRAVEL

Brushaber, Susan & Greenberg, Arnold. Aruba, Bonaire & Curacao: Alive Guide. 2nd ed. (Illus.). 380p. pap. 18.99 *(978-1-58843-259-9(9))* Hunter Publishing, Inc.

Croes, Robertico. Anatomy of Demand in International Tourism. 2010. 216p. pap. *(978-3-8383-4945-9(8))* Lambert Academic Publishing.

Fodor's Travel Publications, Inc. Staff. Fodor's in Focus Aruba, 3rd Edition. 2012. (In Focus-Color Ser.). (ENG.). 184p. pap. 11.99 *(978-0-307-92791-0(1),* Fodor's) Fodor's Travel Pubns.

Jackson, Jack. Dive Aruba, Bonaire & Curacao: Complete Guide to Diving & Snorkeling. 2007. (Dive Ser.). (ENG., Illus.). 176p. pap. 20.00 *(978-1-56656-707-7(6))* Interlink Publishing Group, Inc.

Nausbaum, Donald. Aruba, Bonnaire & Curacao. 2006. (ENG., Illus.). 220p. pap. 40.00 *(978-1-4050-6565-8(6))* Macmillan Caribbean GBR. Dist: Interlink Publishing Group, Inc.

Sullivan, Lynne M. Adventure Guide to Aruba, Bonaire & Curacao. 2nd rev. ed. 2008. (Illus.). 285p. per. 18.99 *(978-1-58843-572-9(5))* Hunter Publishing, Inc.

ARUM MACULATUM

Bown, Deni. Aroids: Plants of the Arum Family. 2010. (ENG.). 468p. pap. 34.95 *(978-1-60469-201-3(4),* 1604692014) Timber Pr., Inc.

ARUNDEL, THOMAS HOWARD, EARL OF, 1585-1646

Vickers, Michael. The Arundel & Pomfret Marbles: In Oxford. 2007. (Ashmolean Handbooks). (ENG., Illus.). 22.95 *(978-1-85444-208-6(2))* Ashmolean Museum GBR. Dist: Antique Collectors' Club.

ARUNTA (AUSTRALIAN PEOPLE)

see Aranda (Australian People)

ARV (VIRUSES)

see HIV (Viruses)

ARYAMAN (HINDU DEITY)

Ranganath, Rangi. Hijacking Gods, Religions & Customs. 2009. (Illus.). 238p. pap. *(978-0-7552-0492-2(1))* Authors OnLine, Ltd.

ARYAN ANTIQUITIES

see Indo-European Antiquities

ARYAN LANGUAGES

see Indo-European Languages

ARYAN PHILOLOGY

see Indo-European Philology

ARYANS

see Indo-Europeans

AS-400 (COMPUTER)

see IBM AS-400 (Computer)

ASAF JAH I, NIZAM OF HYDERABAD, 1671-1748

Husain, Yusuf. First Nizam. 2006. 284p. per. *(978-1-4067-1793-8(2),* Hesperides Pr.) Read Bks.

ASANTE (AFRICAN PEOPLE)

see Ashanti (African People)

ASANTE LANGUAGE

see Twi Language

ASBESTOS

Anderson, Eskil. Asbestos & Jade in the Kobuk River Region of Alaska. (Shorey Prospecting Ser.). 26p. reprint ed. pap. 10.00 *(978-0-8466-0037-4(4),* S37) Shorey's Bookstore.

Committee for the Review of the NIOSH Research Roadmap on Asbestos Fibers and Other Elongate Mineral Particles, et al. A Review of the NIOSH Roadmap for Research on Asbestos Fibers & Other Elongate Mineral Particles. 2009. (ENG.). 134p. pap. 21.00 *(978-0-309-14015-7(3))* National Academies Pr.

Hammar, Samuel P. & Dodson, Ronald F., eds. Asbestos: Risk Assessment, Epidemiology, & Health Effects. 2nd rev. ed. 2011. (ENG., Illus.). 679p. 159.95 *(978-1-4398-0968-6(2),* CRC Press) Taylor & Francis Group GBR. Dist: Taylor & Francis Group.

McCulloch, Jock & Tweedale, Geoffrey. Defending the Indefensible: The Global Asbestos Industry & its Fight for Survival. 2008. (ENG., Illus.). 336p. 55.00 *(978-0-19-953485-2(3))* Oxford Univ. Pr., Inc.

Oversight of Federal Efforts to Clean up Asbestos in Lincoln County, MT: Hearing Before the Committee on Environment & Public Works, United States Senate, One Hundred Tenth Congress, First Session, April 5, 2007, Libby, MT. 2007. (Illus.). iii, 138p. ***(978-0-16-086965-5(X),*** 552-070-41831-8) United States Government Printing Office.

ASBESTOS—CARCINOGENICITY

Gibbs, Allen R. & Craighead, John E., eds. Asbestos & its Diseases. 2008. (ENG., Illus.). 650p. 79.99 *(978-0-19-517869-2(6))* Oxford Univ. Pr., Inc.

Roggli, Victor L., et al, eds. Pathology of Asbestos-Associated Diseases. 2nd ed. 2010. (Illus.). xvi, 424p. pap. 225.00 *(978-1-4419-1894-9(9),* 1441918949) Springer.

ASBESTOS—ENVIRONMENTAL ASPECTS

Bowker, Michael. Fatal Deception: The Untold Story of Asbestos: Why It Is Still Legal & Still Killing US. 2006. (Illus.). 323p. reprint ed. pap. 25.00 *(978-1-4223-5563-3(2))* DIANE Publishing Co.

Examining the Human Health Effects of Asbestos & the Methods of Mitigating Such Impacts: Hearing Before the Committee on Environment & Public Works, United States Senate, One Hundred Tenth Congress, First Session, June 12, 2007. 2011. (Illus.). iv, 214p. ***(978-0-16-089523-4(5),*** 552-070-43482-8) United States Government Printing Office.

Waldman, Linda. The Politics of Asbestos: Understandings of Risk, Disease & Protest. 2011. (Pathways to Sustainability Ser.). (ENG., Illus.). 232p. 125.00 *(978-1-84971-107-4(0));* pap. 36.95 *(978-1-84971-108-1(9))* Routledge.

ASBESTOS—HEALTH ASPECTS

Asbestos: Still Lethal/Still Legal: The Need to Better Protect the Health of American Workers & Their Families: Hearing Before the Subcommittee on Employment & Workplace Safety of the Committee on Health, Education, Labor, & Pensions, United States Senate, One Hundred Tenth Congress, First Session, on Examining Asbestos, Focusing on Efforts to Better Protect the Health of American Workers & Their Fa. 2007. (Illus.). iii, 60p. *(978-0-16-078931-1(1),* 552-070-36058-1) United States Government Printing Office.

Bowker, Michael. Fatal Deception: The Untold Story of Asbestos: Why It Is Still Legal & Still Killing US. 2006. (Illus.). 323p. reprint ed. pap. 25.00 *(978-1-4223-5563-3(2))* DIANE Publishing Co.

Examining the Human Health Effects of Asbestos & the Methods of Mitigating Such Impacts: Hearing Before the Committee on Environment & Public Works, United States Senate, One Hundred Tenth Congress, First Session, June 12, 2007. 2011. (Illus.). iv, 214p. ***(978-0-16-089523-4(5),*** 552-070-43482-8) United States Government Printing Office.

Gibbs, Allen R. & Craighead, John E., eds. Asbestos & its Diseases. 2008. (ENG., Illus.). 650p. 79.99 *(978-0-19-517869-2(6))* Oxford Univ. Pr., Inc.

Institute of Medicine Staff, creator. Asbestos: Selected Cancers. 2006. (ENG., Illus.). 340p. per. 55.00 *(978-0-309-10169-1(7))* National Academies Pr.

Sanderson, Bill. Asbestos for Surveyors. 2nd rev. ed. 2007. (ENG., Illus.). 120p. per. 48.95 *(978-0-7282-0512-3(2))* Estates Gazette, Ltd. GBR. Dist: Taylor & Francis Group.

Waldman, Linda. The Politics of Asbestos: Understandings of Risk, Disease & Protest. 2011. (Pathways to Sustainability Ser.). (ENG., Illus.). 232p. 125.00 *(978-1-84971-107-4(0));* pap. 36.95 *(978-1-84971-108-1(9))* Routledge.

ASBESTOS—LAW AND LEGISLATION

Asbestos: Still Lethal/Still Legal: The Need to Better Protect the Health of American Workers & Their Families: Hearing Before the Subcommittee on Employment & Workplace Safety of the Committee on Health, Education, Labor, & Pensions, United States Senate, One Hundred Tenth Congress, First Session, on Examining Asbestos, Focusing on Efforts to Better Protect the Health of American Workers & Their Fa. 2007. (Illus.). iii, 60p. *(978-0-16-078931-1(1),* 552-070-36058-1) United States Government Printing Office.

Barnes, Jeb. Dust-Up: Asbestos Litigation & the Failure of Commonsense Policy Reform. 2011. (Illus.). 152p. pap. 24.95 *(978-1-58901-765-5(8))* Georgetown Univ. Pr.

Bartrip, Peter. Beyond the Factory Gates: Asbestos & Health in Twentieth Century America. 2006. (ENG.). 260p. 160.00 *(978-0-8264-8836-7(6))* Continuum International Publishing Group, Ltd. GBR. Dist: National Bk. Network.

Dixon, Lloyd & McGovern, Geoffrey. Asbestos Bankruptcy Trusts: An Overview of Trust Structure & Activity with Detailed Reports on the Largest Trusts, 1 vol. 2010. (Illus.). 208p. pap. 26.00 *(978-0-8330-5037-3(0),* tr-872) RAND Corp., The.

Dixon, Lloyd & McGovern, Geoffrey. Asbestos Bankruptcy Trusts & Tort Compensation, 1 vol. 2011. (Illus.). 108p. (C). pap. 27.50 ***(978-0-8330-5834-8(7))*** RAND Corp., The.

Kaminsky, Alan & Campbell, Karen L. The Lawyer's Guide to Lead Paint, Asbestos, & Chinese Drywall Litigation. 2011. (ENG.). 209p. pap. 99.95 *(978-1-60442-918-3(6))* American Bar Assn.

S. 742 & Draft Legislation to Ban Asbestos in Products: Hearing Before the Subcommittee on Environment & Hazardous Materials of the Committee on Energy & Commerce, House of Representatives, One Hundred Tenth Congress, Second Session, February 28, 2008. 2008. (Illus.). vi, 287p. *(978-0-16-082713-6(2),* 552-070-38730-7) United States Government Printing Office.

United States, Congress Senate Committee on the Judiciary Staff, contrib. by. The Fairness in Asbestos Injury Resolution ACT: Hearing Before the Committee on the Judiciary, United States Senate, One Hundred Ninth Congress, First Session, January 11, 2005. 2007. (Illus.). iv, 171p. *(978-0-16-078369-2(0),* 552-070-35674-6) United States Government Printing Office.

ASBESTOS—TOXICOLOGY

Examining the Human Health Effects of Asbestos & the Methods of Mitigating Such Impacts: Hearing Before the Committee on Environment & Public Works, United States Senate, One Hundred Tenth Congress, First Session, June 12, 2007. 2011. (Illus.). iv, 214p. ***(978-0-16-089523-4(5),*** 552-070-43482-8) United States Government Printing Office.

Soto, Antonio & Salazar, Gael. Asbestos: Risks, Environment & Impact. 2009. 129.00 *(978-1-60692-053-4(7))* Nova Science Pubs., Inc

ASBESTOS IN BUILDING—SAFETY MEASURES

Sanderson, Bill. Asbestos for Surveyors. 2nd rev. ed. 2007. (ENG., Illus.). 120p. per. 48.95 *(978-0-7282-0512-3(2))* Estates Gazette, Ltd. GBR. Dist: Taylor & Francis Group.

ASBESTOSIS

Gibbs, Allen R. & Craighead, John E., eds. Asbestos & its Diseases. 2008. (ENG., Illus.). 650p. 79.99 *(978-0-19-517869-2(6))* Oxford Univ. Pr., Inc.

Roggli, Victor L., et al, eds. Pathology of Asbestos-Associated Diseases. 2nd ed. 2010. (Illus.). xvi, 424p. pap. 225.00 *(978-1-4419-1894-9(9),* 1441918949) Springer.

Stallard, Eric, et al. Forecasting Product Liability Claims: Epidemiology & Modeling in the Manville Asbestos Case. 2010. (Statistics for Biology & Health Ser.). (Illus.). xxix, 394p. pap. 139.00 *(978-1-4419-2860-3(X),* 144192860X) Springer.

ASBURY, FRANCIS, 1745-1816

Asbury, Francis. The Journal of the Rev. Francis Asbury: Bishop of the Methodist Episcopal Church. 2009. (Amer Philosophy, Religion Ser.). (ENG.). 408p. pap. 25.95 *(978-1-4290-1789-3(9))* Applewood Bks.

—The Journal of the Rev. Francis Asbury, Bishop of the Methodist Episcopal Church, from Aug. 7, 1781, to Dec. 7, 1815 Set, 3 vols. reprint ed. lib. bdg. 375.00 *(978-0-7222-4824-9(5))* Library Reprints, Inc.

Asbury, Francis & Clark, Elmer T. The Journal & Letters of Francis Asbury. 2011. 28p. 35.95 ***(978-1-258-04450-3(1))*** Literary Licensing, LLC.

Journal of Francis Asbury. (Great Devotional Classics Ser.). pap. 1.85 *(978-0-687-60580-4(6))* Abingdon Pr.

Leslie, Mark. Midnight Rider for the Morning Star: From the life & times of Francis Asbury. 2008. 256p. pap. 14.95 *(978-0-915143-10-8(0))* Francis Asbury Society.

Nygaard, Norman E. Bishop on Horseback: The Story of Francis Asbury. 2011. 182p. 42.95 ***(978-1-258-06854-7(0))*** Literary Licensing, LLC.

Smith, George G. Life & Labors of Francis Asbury: Bishop of the Methodist Episcopal Church in America. (Illus.). 311p. reprint ed. lib. bdg. 98.00 *(978-0-7222-0985-1(1))* Library Reprints, Inc.

Strickland, W. P. (William Peter). The Pioneer Bishop. 2006. 500p. per. 29.99 *(978-1-4255-5605-1(1))* MPublishing.

Tipple, Ezra Squier. Francis Asbury the Prophet of the Long R. 2006. pap. 33.95 *(978-1-4286-5093-0(8))* Kessinger Publishing, LLC.

Wigger, John. American Saint: Francis Asbury & the Methodists. 2009. (ENG., Illus.). 560p. 39.95 *(978-0-19-538780-3(5))* Oxford Univ. Pr., Inc.

ASCENDED MASTERS

Morel, John Henry. The Transparency of Others. 2009. 124p. pap. 19.99 *(978-1-935436-71-3(6))* Rodaian Pr.

ASCENDING PATHWAYS

see Afferent Pathways

ASCENSION ISLAND (ATLANTIC OCEAN)

Ritsema, Alex. A Dutch Castaway on Ascension Island in 1725. 2010. 179p. (ENG.). 26.00 *(978-1-4461-8993-1(7));* pap. 12.00 *(978-1-4461-8986-3(4))* Lulu Enterprises Inc.

ASCENSION OF CHRIST

see Jesus Christ—Ascension

ASCETICAL THEOLOGY

see Asceticism

ASCETICISM

see also Fasting; Flagellants; Flagellation; Hedonism; Martyrdom; Meditation; Monastic and Religious Life; Monastic and Religious Life of Women; Monasticism and Religious Orders; Mysticism; Spiritual Direction; Vows; Wilderness (Theology)

al-Qurtubi, Muhammad & al-Qurtubi, Imam. The Secrets of Ascetism: Being the Third Part of Al-Qasr Al-Hirs. al-Adani, Abu Salif Ahmed Ali, tr. 2008. (ENG.). 131p. pap. 24.95 *(978-0-9552359-6-2(0))* Amal Pr. GBR. Dist: Independent Pubs. Group.

Ayyangar, T. R. Srinivasa. The Samanya Vedanta Upanisad-s. 2007. 570p. per. 60.00 *(978-0-89581-983-3(X))* Jain Publishing Company, Inc.

Baillie, John. Western Asceticism. Chadwick, Owen, ed. 2011. 364p. 51.95 ***(978-1-258-01411-7(4))*** Literary Licensing, LLC.

Barsanuphius, et al. Letters: Barsanuphius & John: Volume 1, 2 vols. 2006. (Fathers of the Church Ser.: Vol. 113). 344p. im. lthr. 39.95 *(978-0-8132-0113-9(6))* Catholic Univ. of America Pr.

Budge, E. A. Wallis, intro. The Paradise or Garden of the Holy Fathers. 2010. 259.60 *(978-1-61143-101-8(8));* 259.60 *(978-1-61143-100-1(X))* Gorgias Pr., LLC.

Campany, Robert Ford. Making Transcendents: Ascetics & Social Memory in Early Medieval China. 2009. 336p. (C). 48.00 *(978-0-8248-3333-6(3))* Univ. of Hawaii Pr.

Chediath, Geevarghese, intro. Mar Babai the Great: Some Useful Counsels on the Ascetical Life. 2010. 88.64 *(978-1-61143-567-2(6))* Gorgias Pr., LLC.

Chryssavgis, John, tr. from GEC. Barsanuphius & John: Letters, Volume 2, 2 vols., Vol. 2. 2007. (Fathers of the Church Ser.). 346p. 39.95 *(978-0-8132-0114-6(4))* Catholic Univ. of America Pr.

Coakley, Sarah. New Asceticism: Sexuality, Gender & the Quest for God. 2013. (ENG.). 200p. pap. 19.95 *(978-1-4411-0322-2(8))* Continuum International Publishing Group, Ltd. GBR. Dist: National Bk. Network.

Darling Young, Robin & Blanchard, Monica J., eds. To Train His Soul in Books: Syriac Asceticism in Early Christianity. 2011. (SPA.). 248p. 34.95 *(978-0-8132-1732-1(6))* Catholic Univ. of America Pr.

Demacopoulos, George E. Five Models of Spiritual Direction in the Early Church. 2006. 256p. per. 30.00 *(978-0-268-02590-8(8))* Univ. of Notre Dame Pr.

Duffey, Felix D. Psychiatry & Asceticism. 2011. 142p. 40.95 ***(978-1-258-03577-8(4))*** Literary Licensing, LLC.

Endsjo, Dag Øistein & Endsjo, Dag Øistein. Primordial Landscapes, Incorruptible Bodies: Desert Asceticism & the Christian Appropriation of Greek Ideas on Geography, Bodies & Immortality. 2007. (American University Studies VII: Theology & Religion Ser.). 208p. (C). 66.95 *(978-1-4331-0181-6(5))* Lang, Peter Publishing, Inc.

Finn, Richard. Asceticism in the Graeco-Roman World. 2009. (Key Themes in Ancient History Ser.). (ENG.). 194p. (C). 87.00 *(978-0-521-86281-3(7));* pap. 30.99 *(978-0-521-68154-4(5))* Cambridge Univ. Pr.

Flügel, Peter & Houtman, Gustaaf, eds. Asceticism & Power in South & Southeast Asia. 2013. (Royal Asiatic Society Bks.). (ENG., Illus.). 336p. (C). 145.00 *(978-0-415-42384-7(8))* Routledge.

Francis, James A. Subversive Virtue. 2008. pap. 24.95 *(978-0-271-03425-6(4))* Pennsylvania State Univ. Pr.

Freiberger, Oliver. Der Askesediskurs in der Religionsgeschichte: Eine vergleichende Untersuchung brahmanischer und fruhchristlicher Texte. 2009. (Studies in Oriental Religions Ser.). (GER.). 283p. (C). 72.00 *(978-3-447-05869-8(2))* Harrassowitz, Otto Verlag DEU. Dist: ISD.

Freiberger, Oliver, ed. Asceticism & Its Critics: Historical Accounts & Comparative Perspectives. 2006. (AAR Cultural Criticism Ser.). (ENG.). 268p. 99.00 *(978-0-19-530791-7(7))* Oxford Univ. Pr., Inc.

Fussell, Ronald. The Nature & Purpose of the Ascetic Ideal. 2011. 40p. 35.95 ***(978-1-258-01012-6(7))*** Literary Licensing, LLC.

Goodrich, Richard J. Contextualizing Cassian: Aristocrats, Asceticism, & Reformation in Fifth-Century Gaul. 2008. (Oxford Early Christian Studies). (ENG., Illus.). 320p. 125.00 *(978-0-19-921313-9(5))* Oxford Univ. Pr., Inc.

Hausner, Sondra L. Wandering with Sadhus: Ascetics in the Hindu Himalayas. 2007. (Contemporary Indian Studies Ser.). (ENG., Illus.). 272p. 50.00 *(978-0-253-34983-5(4),* 0253349834); per. 22.95 *(978-0-253-21949-7(3),* 0253219493) Indiana Univ. Pr.

Hayward, C. J. S. Doxology. 2010. 318p. 40.00 *(978-0-557-34650-9(9))* Lulu Enterprises Inc.

Hunt, Hannah. Clothed in the Body Asceticism the Body & the Spiritual in the Late Antique Era. 2012. (Ashgate Studies in Philosophy & Theology in Late Antiquity Ser.). 224p. 99.95 ***(978-1-4094-0914-4(7))*** Ashgate Publishing Co.

Isaac. The Ascetical Homilies of Saint Isaac the Syrian. 2nd ed. 2011. (Illus.). 607p. ***(978-0-943405-16-2(5))*** Holy Transfiguration Monastery.

Isherwood, Lisa. The Fat Jesus: Christianity & Body Image. 2008. 176p. per. 20.00 *(978-1-59627-094-7(2),* Seabury Bks.) Church Publishing, Inc.

Kessel, G. & Pinggera, K. A Bibliography of Syriac Ascetic & Mystical Literature. 2011. (Eastern Christian Studies). (ENG & MUL.). 224p. (C). pap. 70.00 *(978-90-429-2457-4(8))* Peeters Pubs. & Booksellers BEL. Dist: Brown, David Bk. Co., The.

Kestens, Adolph. Spiritual Guidance V1: Fundamentals of Ascetical Theology Based on the Franciscan Ideal. Stoffel, Elmer, ed. 2011. 652p. 68.95 ***(978-1-258-00772-0(X))*** Literary Licensing, LLC.

Kroschel, Simone. Wenig verlangt die Natur: Naturgemäß leben, Einfachheit und Askese im antiken Denken. 2008. (PRISMATA. Beiträge zur Altertumswissenschaft Ser.). 198p. pap. 56.95 *(978-3-631-58066-0(5))* Lang, Peter GmbH, Europaischer Verlag der Wissenschaften DEU. Dist: Lang, Peter.

Makarios, et al. The Philokalia: Writings of Holy Mystic Fathers in Which Is Explained How the Mind Is Purified, Illumined, & Perfected Through Practical & Contemplative Ethical Philosophy. 2008. (Illus.). 340p. *(978-1-884729-79-9(7))* Institute for Byzantine & Modern Greek Studies, Inc.

Malone, Edward E. The Monk & the Martyr: The Monk As the Successor of the Martyr. Quasten, Johannes, ed. 2011. 182p. 42.95 ***(978-1-258-05360-4(8))*** Literary Licensing, LLC.

Marriott, George L. The Messalians & the Discovery of Their Ascetic Book: The Harvard Theological Review V19, No. 2, April 1926. Moore, George F., ed. 2011. 12p. pap. 35.95 ***(978-1-258-05472-4(8))*** Literary Licensing, LLC.

Molle, et al, eds. Beyond Pleasure: Cultures of Modern Asceticism. 2011. (Illus.). 260p. 95.00 *(978-1-84545-773-0(0))* Berghahn Bks., Inc.

Nayar, Kamala E., et al. The Socially Involved Renunciate: Guru Nanak's Discourse to the Nath Yogis. 2007. xvi, 181p. pap. 24.95 *(978-0-7914-7214-9(0))* State Univ. of New York Pr.

O'Brien, Elmer. Ascetical & Mystical Theology, 1954-1955. 2011. 32p. 35.95 ***(978-1-258-00197-1(7))*** Literary Licensing, LLC.

Olivelle, Patrick. Ascetics & Brahmins: Studies in Ideologies & Institutions. 2011. (Cultural, Historical & Textual Studies of Religions Ser.). (Illus.). 328p. 99.00 ***(978-0-85728-432-7(0))*** Anthem Pr. GBR. Dist: Books International, Inc.

Parente, Pascal P. The Ascetical Life. 2011. 280p. 47.95 ***(978-1-258-10266-1(8))*** Literary Licensing, LLC.

Röcke, Werner & Weitbrecht, Julia, eds. Askese und Identität in Spätantike, Mittelalter und Früher Neuzeit. 2010. (Transformationen der Antike Ser.).Tr. of Asceticism & Identity in Late Antiquity & the Middle Ages. (GER., Illus.). VI, 307p. 112.00 *(978-3-11-022836-6(X))* De Gruyter, Walter Inc.

Rousseau, Philip. Ascetics, Authority, & the Church in the Age of Jerome & Cassian. 2nd ed. 2010. (ENG.). 304p. pap. 30.00 *(978-0-268-04029-1(X))* Univ. of Notre Dame Pr.

Rozenberg, Guillaume. Renunciation & Power: The Quest for Sainthood in Contemporary Burma. Hackett, Jessica, tr. from FRE. 2010. (Monograph Series, Yale Southeast Asia Studies: 59). pap. 20.00 *(978-0-938692-92-8(5))*; (ENG.). lib. bdg. 35.00 *(978-0-938692-93-5(3))* Yale Univ. Southeast Asia Studies.

Rudolph, Lloyd I. & Rudolph, Susanne Hoeber. Postmodern Gandhi & Other Essays: Gandhi in the World & at Home. 2010. (Oxford India Paperbacks Ser.). (ENG.). 264p. 24.95 *(978-0-19-806411-4(X))* Oxford Univ. Pr., Inc.

—Postmodern Gandhi & Other Essays: Gandhi in the World & at Home. 2006. (ENG.). 272p. 47.50 *(978-0-226-73123-0(5))*; per. 20.00 *(978-0-226-73124-7(3))* Univ. of Chicago Pr.

Ruffner, Henry. The Fathers of the Desert. 2006. 316p. per. 23.99 *(978-1-4255-3078-5(8))* MPublishing.

Sandhu, Jaswinder Singh & Nayar, Kamala Elizabeth. The Socially Involved Renunciate: Guru Nanak's Discourse to the Nath Yogis. 2007. (Illus.). 181p. 60.00 *(978-0-7914-7213-2(2))* State Univ. of New York Pr.

Schweig, Graham M. Asceticism, Identity, & Pedagogy in Dharma Traditions. 2006. (Illus.). xxix, 189p. *(978-0-937194-50-8(6))*, Deepak Heritage Bks.) Deepak, A Publishing.

Sherwood, Polycarp. St Maximus the Confessor: The Ascetic Life, the Four Centuries on Charity. Sherwood, Polycarp, tr. 2011. 292p. 48.95 ***(978-1-258-00798-0(3))*** Literary Licensing, LLC.

Smith, Matthew J. W. Practical Ascetics for the Use of Seminarians, Novices, Religious, Priests, & the Laity. 2011. 202p. 44.95 ***(978-1-258-05668-1(2))*** Literary Licensing, LLC.

Thornton, Martin. Pastoral Theology. 2010. 288p. pap. 33.00 *(978-1-60899-744-2(8)*, Wipf and Stock) Wipf & Stock Pubs.

Tinsley, David F. The Scourge & the Cross: Ascetic Mentalities of the Later Middle Ages. 2010. (Mediaevalia Groningana New Ser.). (ENG.). 217p. (C). pap. 81.00 *(978-90-429-2184-9(6))* Peeters Pubs. & Booksellers BEL. Dist: Brown, David Bk. Co., The.

Valantasis, Richard. The Making of the Self: Ancient & Modern Asceticism. 2008. (ENG.). 336p. pap. 53.00 *(978-0-227-17281-0(7))* Clarke, James Co., Ltd. GBR. Dist: Brown, David Bk. Co., The.

—The Making of the Self: Ancient & Modern Asceticism. 2008. 336p. pap. 37.00 *(978-1-55635-286-7(7))* Wipf & Stock Pubs.

Watts, Edward Jay. Riot in Alexandria: Tradition & Group Dynamics in Late Antique Pagan & Christian Communities. 2010. (Transformation of the Classical Heritage Ser.). (Illus.). 312p. 55.00 *(978-0-520-26207-2(7))* Univ. of California Pr.

Wiltshire, Martin G. Ascetic Figures before & in Early Buddhism: The Emergence of Gautama as the Buddha. (Religion & Reason Ser.). (ENG.). XXXVI, 338p. 314.00 ***(978-3-11-176316-3(1))*** De Gruyter, Walter Inc.

ASCIDIACEA

see Sea Squirts

ASCIDIANS

see Sea Squirts

ASCITES

Gerbes, A. L., ed. Ascites, Hyponatremia & Hepatorenal Syndrome: Progress in Treatment. 2010. (Frontiers of Gastrointestinal Research Ser.). (ENG., Illus.). 212p. *(978-3-8055-9591-9(3))* Karger, S. AG.

ASCOMYCETES

see also Discomycetes

Egel, Richard, ed. The Molecular Biology of Schizosaccharomyces Pombe: Genetics, Genomics & Beyond. 2010. (Illus.). xxviii, 450p. pap. 399.00 *(978-3-642-05631-4(8)*, 3642056318) Springer.

Egel, Richard & Lankenau, Dirk-Henner. Recombination & Meiosis: Models, Means, & Evolution. 2010. (Genome Dynamics & Stability Ser.). (Illus.). xxii, 390p. pap. 299.00 *(978-3-642-08850-6(3)*, 3642088503) Springer.

Fink, Bruce. The Ascomycetes of Ohio. 2009. 56p. pap. *(978-0-217-57108-1(5))* Books LLC.

Hohmann, Stefan & Mager, Willem H. Yeast Stress Responses. 2010. (Topics in Current Genetics Ser.). (ENG., Illus.). xiii, 389p. pap. 279.00 *(978-3-642-07875-0(3)*, 3642078753) Springer.

Schuller, Dorit-Elisabeth. Saccharomyces Cerevisiae Strains for Winemaking. 2009. 144p. pap. *(978-3-639-17174-7(8))* VDM Verlag Dr. Mueller e.K.

ASCORBIC ACID

see Vitamin C

ASDIC

see Sonar

ASEAN

see Association of Southeast Asian Nations

ASEPSIS AND ANTISEPSIS

Cram101 Textbook Reviews. Outlines & Highlights for Cottones Practical Infection Control in Dentistry by John a Molinari, Isbn: 9780781765329 0781765323. 2011. 338p. pap. 27.95 ***(978-1-61490-326-0(3))*** Cram101 Inc.

Dixon, John. Enviro Mon Aseptic Enviro. 2006. (Drugs & the Pharmaceutical Sciences Ser.: Vol. 164). (ENG., Illus.). 230p. 230.00 *(978-0-8247-2359-0(7)*, Informa Healthcare) Taylor & Francis Group GBR. Dist: Taylor & Francis Group.

Johnston, Mike & Gricar, Jeff. Sterile Products & Aseptic Techniques for the Pharmacy Technician. 2nd ed. 2010. (ENG.). 192p. (C). pap. 46.60 *(978-0-13-510964-9(7)*, Prentice Hall) Prentice Hall PTR.

Minor, Scott Duesterhaus & Minor, Mary Alice Duesterhaus. Patient Care Skills. 6th ed. 2009. (ENG.). 480p. (C). spiral bd. 86.27 *(978-0-13-208234-1(9)*, Prentice Hall) Prentice Hall PTR.

Molinari, John A. & Harte, Jennifer A., eds. Practical Infection Control in Dentistry. 3rd rev. ed. 2009. (ENG., Illus.). 400p. pap. 53.99 *(978-0-7817-6532-9(3))* Lippincott Williams & Wilkins.

Pankhurst, Caroline, et al. Infection Prevention & Control in Dentistry. 2009. (Basic Guide Dentistry Ser.: 2). (ENG., Illus.). 192p. pap. 47.99 *(978-1-4051-7662-0(8)*, Wiley-Blackwell) Wiley, John & Sons, Inc.

ASEXUAL REPRODUCTION

see Reproduction, Asexual

ASH (COMBUSTION PRODUCT)

see also Coal Ash

Goodyear, Norman & Hope-Simpson, Maggie. Utilization of Circulating Fluidized Bed Ash - As an Agricultural Soil Amendment. 2009. 212p. pap. *(978-3-639-04153-8(4))* VDM Verlag Dr. Mueller e.K.

ASHANTI (AFRICAN PEOPLE)

Adams, Frank Kwesi. Odwira & the Gospel: A Study of the Asante Odwira Festival & Its Significance for Christianity in Ghana. 2011. (Regnum Studies in Mission Ser.). 256p. pap. 28.00 ***(978-1-61097-439-4(5)***, Wipf and Stock) Wipf & Stock Pubs.

Kaminski, Joseph S. Asante Ivory Trumpet Music in Ghana: Culture Tradition & Sound Barrage. 2012. (Illus.). 220p. ***(978-1-4094-2684-4(X))*** Ashgate Publishing, Ltd.

Rattray, Robert S. Religion & Art in Ashanti. reprint ed. 34.50 *(978-0-404-15878-1(1))* AMS Pr., Inc.

Unglaub, Erich. Panther und Aschanti: Rilke-Gedichte in Kulturwissenschaftlicher Sicht. (GER., Illus.). 184p. 36.95 *(978-3-631-53791-6(3))* Lang, Peter GmbH, Europaischer Verlag der Wissenschaften DEU. Dist: Lang, Peter Publishing, Inc.

ASHANTI (AFRICAN PEOPLE)—HISTORY

Akyeampong, E., et al. 'the History of Ashanti Kings & the Whole Country Itself' & Other Writings, by Otumfuo, Nana Agyeman Prempeh I. Akyeampong, E. et al, eds. 2008. (Fontes Historiae Africanae, New Series: Sources of African History Ser.). (ENG., Illus.). 234p. pap. 39.95 *(978-0-19-726415-7(8))* Oxford Univ. Pr., Inc.

Wächter, Fenna. Tarnishing the Golden Stool. 2011. 88p. pap. ***(978-3-8454-0029-7(3))*** Lambert Academic Publishing.

ASHANTI LANGUAGE

see Twi Language

ASHANTIS (AFRICAN PEOPLE)

see Ashanti (African People)

ASHBERY, JOHN, 1927-

Blasing, Mutlu Konuk. Politics & Form in Postmodern Poetry: O'Hara, Bishop, Ashbery, & Merrill. 2009. (Cambridge Studies in American Literature & Culture Ser.). (ENG.). 236p. pap. 36.00 *(978-0-521-10613-9(3))* Cambridge Univ. Pr.

Blazer, Alex E. I Am Otherwise: The Romance Between Poetry & Theory after the Death of the Subject. 2007. (Dalkey Archive Scholarly Ser.). (ENG.). 246p. per. 34.95 *(978-1-56478-458-2(4))* Dalkey Archive Pr.

DuBois, Andrew Lee. Ashbery's Forms of Attention. 2006. (Modern & Contemporary Poetics Ser.). (Illus.). 192p. 60.00 *(978-0-8173-1489-7(X))*; per. 34.00 *(978-0-8173-5271-4(6))* Univ. of Alabama Pr.

Herd, David. John Ashbery & American Poetry. 2009. (ENG.). 245p. pap. 26.00 *(978-0-7190-8059-3(2))* Manchester Univ. Pr. GBR. Dist: Macmillan.

—John Ashbery & American Poetry: Fit to Cope with Our Occasions. (Illus.). 208p. *(978-0-7190-5597-3(0))* Manchester Univ. Pr.

Hickman, Ben. John Ashbery & English Poetry. 2012. (ENG.). 256p. (gr. 17). 105.00 ***(978-0-7486-4475-9(X))*** Edinburgh Univ. Pr. GBR. Dist: Columbia Univ. Pr.

Levy, Ellen. Criminal Ingenuity: Moore, Cornell, Ashbery, & the Struggle Between the Arts, 1 vol. 2011. (Modernist Literature & Culture Ser.). (ENG., Illus.). 304p. 49.95 *(978-0-19-974635-4(4))* Oxford Univ. Pr., Inc.

Reddy, Srikanth. Changing Subjects: Digressions in Modern American Poetry, 1 vol. 2012. (ENG.). 208p. 35.00 ***(978-0-19-979102-6(3))*** Oxford Univ. Pr., Inc.

Vincent, John Emil. John Ashbery & You: His Later Books. 2007. (ENG.). 208p. 44.95 *(978-0-8203-2973-4(8))* Univ. of Georgia Pr.

ASHEVILLE (N.C.)

Ballew, Bill. A History of Professional Baseball in Asheville. 2007. (Illus.). 126p. pap., per. 19.99 *(978-1-59629-176-8(1))* History Pr., The.

Chase, Nan K. Asheville: A History. 2007. (Contributions to Southern Appalachian Studies). (ENG., Illus.). 291p. per. 35.00 *(978-0-7864-3176-2(8))* McFarland & Co., Inc. Pubs.

Clark, Ethan. Leaning with Intent to Fall: A Memoir. 2007. (ENG., Illus.). 200p. per. 14.95 *(978-1-891053-04-7(3))* Garrett County Pr.

Davis, Jennifer Pharr. Five-Star Trails: Asheville: Your Guide to the Area's Most Beautiful Hikes. 2011. (Five-Star Trails Ser.). (ENG., Illus.). 240p. pap. 15.95 *(978-0-89732-920-0(1))* Menasha Ridge Pr., Inc.

Hansley, Richard. Asheville's Historic Architecture. 2011. (Illus.). 176p. pap. 19.99 *(978-1-60949-107-9(6))* History Pr., The.

Harshaw, Lou. Asheville: Mountain Majesty. 2007. (ENG., Illus.). 368p. pap. 29.00 *(978-0-914875-35-2(3))* Bright Mountain Bks., Inc.

Hinshaw, Jane. Biltmore: Our Table to Yours: Chef's Selection Cookbook. 2007. (Illus.). 184p. *(978-1-885378-20-0(3))* Biltmore Co.

Levin, Rob. Asheville: A Photographic Portrait. 2007. *(978-1-883987-32-9(6))* Riverbend Bks., Ltd.

Neufeld, Rob & Neufeld, Henry. Asheville's River Arts District. 2008. (Images of America Ser.). (ENG., Illus.). 128p. pap. 19.99 *(978-0-7385-5426-6(X))* Arcadia Publishing.

Pantas, Lee James. The Ultimate Guide to Asheville & the Western North Carolina Mountains: Including Hendersonville & more than 50 other mountain cities & Towns. 3rd exp. rev. ed. 2006. per. 18.00 *(978-0-9678061-0-5(0))* Brent, R. and Co., Inc.

Schatz, Bob, photos by. Asheville Impressions. 2008. (Illus.). 80p. pap. 9.95 *(978-1-56037-432-9(2))* Farcountry Pr.

ASHKENAZIM

Jaehn, Tomas, ed. Jewish Pioneers of New Mexico. (Illus.). 112p. 27.50 *(978-0-89013-467-2(7))*; (ENG., 1p. 39.95 *(978-0-89013-466-5(9))* Museum of New Mexico Pr.

Kriwaczek, Paul. Yiddish Civilisation: The Rise & Fall of a Forgotten Nation. 2006. (Vintage Ser.). (ENG., Illus.). 400p. pap. 16.95 *(978-1-4000-3377-5(2)*, Vintage) Knopf Doubleday Publishing Group.

Litt, Stefan. Pinkas, Kahal, & the Mediene: The Records of Dutch Ashkenazi Communities in the Eighteenth Century As Historical Sources. 2008. (Studies in Jewish History & Culture: Vol. 19). (Illus.). *(978-90-04-16773-5(0))* BRILL.

Madmoni-Gerber, Shoshana & Madmoni-gerber, Shoshana. Israeli Media & the Framing of Internal Conflict: The Yemenite Babies Affair. 2009. (ENG., Illus.). 240p. 89.00 *(978-0-230-61346-1(2))* Palgrave Macmillan.

Malkiel, David & Malkiel, David Joshua. Reconstructing Ashkenaz: The Human Face of Franco-German Jewry, 1000-1250. 2008. (Stanford Studies in Jewish History & C Ser.). (ENG.). 376p. 65.00 *(978-0-8047-5950-2(2))* Stanford Univ. Pr.

Matut, Diana. Dichtung und Musik Im Frühneuzeitlichen Aschkenas. 2010. (GER.). *(978-90-04-18194-6(6))* BRILL.

van Ditzhuijzen, Jeannette. A Shteti under the Sun. 2011. (Illus.). 248p. 45.00 ***(978-94-6022-157-6(2))*** Royal Tropical Institute Pr. (KIT (Koninklijk Instituut voor de Tropen) NLD. Dist: Stylus Publishing, LLC.

van Luit, R. T. Mediene Remnants: Yiddish Sources in the Netherlands Outside of Amsterdam. 2009. 146p. *(978-90-04-15625-8(9))* BRILL.

Zimmerman, Deena R. Mi Dor le Dor Genetics & Genetic Diseases: Jewish Legal & Ethical Perspectives. 2012. ***(978-1-60280-163-9(0))*** Ktav Publishing Hse., Inc.

ASHURNASIRPAL II, KING OF ASSYRIA, FL. 885-860 B.C.

Cohen, Ada & Kangas, Steven E., eds. Assyrian Reliefs from the Palace of Ashurnasirpal II: A Cultural Biography. 2010. (Illus.). 294p. pap. 40.00 *(978-1-58465-817-7(7))* Hood Museum of Art.

ASIA

Here are entered works on the entire continent that extends from Europe and Africa to the Pacific Ocean, including Siberia, Japan, Taiwan, the Philippines, and Indonesia (excluding Irian Jaya).

see also Asia, Central; Orient

Hammond World Atlas Corporation Staff. Asia, 6 vols., Vol. 1. 2nd ed. (FRE, SPA & ENG.). pap. 8.55 *(978-92-2-001666-4(4)*, ILO250) Bernan Assocs.

Robertson, Lawrence R., ed. Russia & Eurasia: Facts & Figures. 468p. 77.00 *(978-0-87569-185-5(4))* Academic International Pr.

Townsend, Meredith. Asia & Europe. 2008. 412p. 49.95 *(978-1-4365-6717-6(3))* 2007. (ENG.). 416p. per. 34.95 *(978-0-548-76314-8(3))* Kessinger Publishing, LLC.

ASIA—ANTIQUITIES

Adams, William Y. The Road from Frijoles Canyon: Anthropological Adventures on Four Continents. 2009. (ENG., Illus.). 371p. 45.00 *(978-0-8263-4787-9(8))* Univ. of New Mexico Pr.

Artin, Gassia. La "Necropole Eneolithique" de Byblos. 2009. (FRE & ENG., Illus.). 219p. (C). pap. 100.00 *(978-1-4073-0527-1(1))* British Archaeological Reports Ltd. GBR. Dist: Brown, David Bk. Co., The.

Bacus, Elisabeth A., et al. 50 Years of Archaeology in Southeast Asia: Essays in Honour of Ian Glover. Bellina, Bérénice, ed. 2010. (ENG., Illus.). 320p. pap. 35.00 *(978-616-7339-02-3(3))* River Bks. THA. Dist: Antique Collectors' Club.

Bar-Yosef, Ofer & Kozlowski, J. K., eds. Eurasian Prehistory 6:1 (2008) A Journal for Primary Archaeological Data. 2010. (Eurasian Prehistory Ser.). (ENG., Illus.). 300p. (C). pap. 25.00 *(978-83-923259-2-5(3))* Instytut Archeologii, UJ POL. Dist: Brown, David Bk. Co., The.

—A Journal for Primary Archaeological Data 2008, Vol. 6, Pt. 2. 2010. (Eurasian Prehistory Ser.). (ENG., Illus.). 189p. (C). pap. 25.00 *(978-83-923259-3-2(1))* Instytut Archeologii, UJ POL. Dist: Brown, David Bk. Co., The.

Bixio, Ani Roberto, et al. Ani 2004: Surveys on the Underground Settlements. 2009. (Bar S Ser.). (ITA & ENG., Illus.). 82p. (C). pap. 67.50 *(978-1-4073-0424-3(0))* British Archaeological Reports Ltd. GBR. Dist: Brown, David Bk. Co., The.

Blakely, Jeffrey A., et al, eds. The Joint Expedition to Caesarea Maritima: Excavation Reports, American School of Oriental Research Excavation Reports. 179.95 *(978-0-88946-376-9(X))* Mellen, Edwin Pr., The.

Dearborn, Lynne M. & Stallmeyer, John C. Inconvenient Heritage: Erasure & Global Tourism in Luang Prabang. 2010. (Heritage, Tourism & Community Ser.). (ENG., Illus.). 168p. 79.00 *(978-1-59874-435-4(6))* Left Coast Pr., Inc.

Dennell, Robin. The Palaeolithic Settlement of Asia. 2008. (Cambridge World Archaeology Ser.). (ENG., Illus.). 572p. 95.00 *(978-0-521-84866-4(0))*; pap. 52.99 *(978-0-521-61310-1(8))* Cambridge Univ. Pr.

Dexter, Miriam Robbins & Mair, Victor H. Sacred Display: Divine & Magical Female Figures of Eurasia. 2010. 218p. *(978-1-60497-674-8(8))* Cambria Pr.

Dotan, Yossi. Watercraft on World Coins Vol. 2: America & Asia, 1800-2008. 2010. (ENG., Illus.). 360p. pap. 79.95 *(978-1-898595-50-2(X)*, Alpha Pr.) Sussex Academic Pr. GBR. Dist: International Specialized Bk. Services.

Douglas, Janet G., et al, told to. Scientific Research in the Field of Asian Art: Proceedings of the First Forbes Symposium at the Feer Gallery of Art. 2007. (ENG., Illus.). 208p. 120.00 *(978-1-873132-38-8(7))* Archetype Pubns. GBR. Dist: National Bk. Network.

Evans, Ivor H. N. Papers on the Ethnology & Archaeology of the Malay Peninsula. 2011. (ENG.). 228p. pap. 22.99 *(978-1-107-60065-2(0))* Cambridge Univ. Pr.

Fleagle, John G., ed. Out of Africa I: The First Hominin Colonization of Eurasia. 2010. (Vertebrate Paleobiology & Paleoanthropology Ser.). (ENG., Illus.). x, 540p. 139.00 *(978-90-481-9035-5(5)*, 9048190355) Springer.

Frachetti, Michael David. Pastoralist Landscapes & Social Interaction in Bronze Age Eurasia. 2009. (ENG., Illus.). 232p. 50.00 *(978-0-520-25689-7(1))* Univ. of California Pr.

Gheorghiu, Dragos, ed. Neolithic & Chalcolithic Archaeology in Eurasia: Building Techniques & Spatial Organisation. 2010. (Bar S Ser.). (ENG., Illus.). 172p. (C). pap. 92.50 *(978-1-4073-0573-8(5))* British Archaeological Reports Ltd. GBR. Dist: Brown, David Bk. Co., The.

Hardy, Andrew, et al. Champa & the Archaeology of My Sn (Vietnam) (Illus.). xxxiv, 440p. 28.00 *(978-9971-69-451-7(4))* National Univ. of Singapore Pr. SGP. Dist: Univ. of Hawaii Pr.

Higham, C. F. W. & Kijngam, A. The Origins of the Civilization of Angkor, Volume 4: The Excavation of Ban Non Wat. Part II: the Neolithic Occupation. 2012. (ENG., Illus.). 223p. (C). 100.00 *(978-974-417-389-8(0))* Fine Arts Dept., The THA. Dist: Brown, David Bk. Co., The.

Hulsbosch, Marianne, et al, eds. Asian Material Culture. 2010. (ICAS Publications Ser.). (ENG., Illus.). 232p. pap. *(978-90-8964-090-1(8))* Amsterdam Univ. Pr.

Jordan, Peter & Zvelebil, Marek, eds. Ceramics Before Farming: The Dispersal of Pottery among Prehistoric Eurasian Hunter-Gatherers. 2011. (Univ col london inst arch Pub Ser.). (ENG., Illus.). 589p. pap. 46.95 ***(978-1-61132-789-2(X))*** Left Coast Pr., Inc.

Kohl, Philip L. The Making of Bronze Age Eurasia. 2009. (Cambridge World Archaeology Ser.). (ENG.). 322p. pap. 30.99 *(978-0-521-13015-8(8))* Cambridge Univ. Pr.

Kunst- und Ausstellungshalle der Bundesrepublik De, ed. Gandhara: Das buddhistische Erbe Pakistans. Legenden, Klöster und Paradiese. 2008. (Illus.). 384p. (C). 68.00 *(978-3-8053-3916-2(X))* Zabern, Philipp von Verlag, GmbH DEU. Dist: Brown, David Bk. Co., The.

Laufer, Berthold. Precious Materials in Asian History: Essays on Turquoise, Amber, Ivory, Diamond & Gold. 2012. (ENG., Illus.). 275p. pap. 45.00 *(978-974-524-109-1(1))* Orchid Pr. THA. Dist: National Bk. Network.

Lenz, Timothy. Gandharan Avadanas: British Library Kharosthi Fragments 1-3 & 21 & Supplementary Fragments A-C. 2010. (Gandharan Buddhist Texts, Volume 6 Ser.). (SAN & ENG., Illus.). 192p. 85.00 *(978-0-295-99013-2(9))* Univ. of Washington Pr.

March, Charles. Spatial & Religious Transformations in the Late Antique Polis: A Multi-Disciplinary Analysis with a Case-Study of the City of Gerasa. 2009. (Bar S Ser.). (ENG., Illus.). 202p. (C). pap. 100.00 *(978-1-4073-0513-4(1))* British Archaeological Reports Ltd. GBR. Dist: Brown, David Bk. Co., The.

Marriner, Nick. Geoarchaeology of Lebanon's Ancient Harbours. 2009. (ENG., Illus.). 314p. (C). pap. 125.00 *(978-1-4073-0436-6(4))* British Archaeological Reports Ltd. GBR. Dist: Brown, David Bk. Co., The.

Mouton, Michel. Péninsule d'Oman de la Fin de l'Age du Fer au Début de la Période Sassanide (250 Av. - 350 Ap. Jc) 2008. (Bar S Ser.). (FRE & ENG., Illus.). 500p. (C). pap. 137.50 *(978-1-4073-0264-5(7))* British Archaeological Reports Ltd. GBR. Dist: Brown, David Bk. Co., The.

Mrazek, Jan, ed. What's the Use of Art? Asian Visual & Material Culture in Context. 2007. (Illus.). 313p. 60.00 *(978-0-8248-3063-2(6))* Univ. of Hawaii Pr.

Muehlenbruch, Tobias. Die Synchronisierung der nördlichen Levante und Kilikiens mit der agaischen Spatbronzezeit. 2010. (Denkschriften der Gesamtakademie Ser.). (GER.). 174p. (C). pap. 95.00 *(978-3-7001-6552-1(8))* Austrian Academy of Sciences Press AUT. Dist: Brown, David Bk. Co., The.

Rabett, Ryan J. Human Adaptation in the Asian Palaeolithic: Hominin Dispersal & Behaviour during the Late Quaternary. 2012. (ENG., Illus.). 350p. 99.00 ***(978-1-107-01829-7(3))*** Cambridge Univ. Pr.

Robinson, David. New Greek Inscriptions from Attica, Achaia, Lydia. 2009. pap. 19.48 *(978-1-60724-647-3(3))* Gorgias Pr., LLC.

Salvatori, Sandro, et al, eds. The Archaeological Map of the Murghab Delta Vol. 2: The Bronze Age & Early Iron Age in the Margiana Lowlands. 2008. (Bar S Ser.). (ENG., Illus.). 237p. (C). pap. 100.00 *(978-1-4073-0293-5(0))* British Archaeological Reports Ltd. GBR. Dist: Brown, David Bk. Co., The.

Schweyer, Anne-Valerie. Ancient Vietnam: History & Archaeology. 2012. (ENG., Illus.). 280p. pap. 25.00 *(978-974-9863-75-5(5))* River Bks. THA. Dist: Antique Collectors' Club.

Siméon, M. Pierre. Étude Du Matériel de Hulbuk, de la Conquête islamique Jusqu'au Milieu Du XIe Siècle. 2009. (Bar S Ser.). (FRE & ENG., Illus.). 428p. (C). pap. 155.00 *(978-1-4073-0425-0(9))* British Archaeological Reports Ltd. GBR. Dist: Brown, David Bk. Co., The.

Strickert, Frederick M. Philip's City: From Bethsaida to Julias. 2011. 39.95 *(978-0-8146-5752-2(4))*; E-Book *(978-0-8146-8008-7(9))* Liturgical Pr.

Winter, John, ed. Scientific Research on the Pictorial Arts of Asia: Proceedings of the Second Forbes Symposium at the Freer Gallery of Art. 2007. (ENG., Illus.). 166p. 120.00 *(978-1-873132-74-6(3))* Archetype Pubns. GBR. Dist: National Bk. Network.

Yoffee, Norman & Crowell, Bradley L. Excavating Asian History: Interdisciplinary Studies in Archaeology & History. 2006. (ENG., Illus.). 368p. 55.00 *(978-0-8165-2418-1(1))* Univ. of Arizona Pr.

Zvelebil, Marek. Hunters in Transition: Mesolithic Societies of Temperate Eurasia & their Transition to Farming. 2009. (New Directions in Archaeology Ser.). (ENG.). 204p. pap. 31.99 *(978-0-521-10957-4(4))* Cambridge Univ. Pr.

ASIA—BIBLIOGRAPHY

The Asia Society Reprint Collection. 428.00 *(978-0-405-06551-4(5),* 394) Ayer Co. Pubs., Inc.

Earle Zeigler. International & Comparative Physical Education & Sport. 2009. 356p. pap. 24.37 *(978-1-4269-0643-5(9))* Trafford Publishing.

Ghazareans, Ara. The Armenian Review: A Bibliography & Index (1948-2008) 2010. *(978-0-9674621-9-6(3))* Armenian Cultural Foundation.

Toyo Bunko (Japan) Staff, contrib. by. Catalogue of the Asiatic Library of Dr. G. E. Morrison, Now a Part of the Oriental Library, Tokyo, Japan, 2 vols. 2009. (MUL & ENG.). 250.00 *(978-1-57898-735-1(0))* Martino Publishing.

ASIA—BIOGRAPHY

Aas, Martha Andrea. Pearls on a String: One Woman's Journey to the Past. 2007. (Illus.). vi, 214p. pap. *(978-1-887317-78-8(3))* X-communication.

Ahmadifar, Joe G. Six Plus One Worker #199459. 2011. 96p. 24.99 ***(978-1-4653-5794-6(7))***; pap. 15.99 ***(978-1-4653-5793-9(9))*** Xlibris Corp.

Angelroth, Dirk. The White Lady in the Tree. Mahesh, Hem, tr. 2011. 216p. pap. ***(978-0-9531827-2-5(X))*** Aaranya Pubs.

Anuar Nik Mahmud, et al. Biografi Tun Abdul Razak: Negarawan Dan Patriot. 2011. (MAY., Illus.). 413p. *(978-967-942-948-0(2))*; pap. *(978-967-942-956-5(3))* Penerbit Univ. Kebangsaan Maylasia.

Aquino, Paolo Benigno A. & Verzosa, Jake. Young Southeast Asia: 40 Inspiring Youths. 2008. (Illus.). 238p. pap. 20.00 *(978-971-93896-3-7(X))* Artpostasia Inc. PHL. Dist: National Bk. Network.

Armbrecht, Ann. Thin Places: A Pilgrimage Home. 2008. (ENG., Illus.). 296p. (gr. 17). 35.00 *(978-0-231-14652-4(3))* Columbia Univ. Pr.

Baramki, Gabriel. Peaceful Resistance: Building a Palestinian University under Occupation, 1 vol. 2009. (ENG., Illus.). 224p. 80.00 *(978-0-7453-2932-1(2))*; pap. 29.95 *(978-0-7453-2931-4(4))* Pluto Pr. GBR. Dist: Macmillan.

Beng, Ooi & Oo, Kee Beng. The Reluctant Politician: Tun Dr. Ismail & His Time. 2007. (Illus.). 372p. *(978-981-230-425-4(8))* Institute of Southeast Asian Studies.

Benians, E. A., ed. Captain John Smith: Travels, History of Virginia: The True Travels, Adventures & Observations of Captain John Smith in Europe, Asia, Africa & America & the General History of Virginia, New England & the Summer Isles, Books I-III. 2012. (ENG.). 260p. pap. 35.99 ***(978-1-107-69811-6(1))*** Cambridge Univ. Pr.

Beshara, Adel, ed. The Origins of Syrian Nationhood: Histories, Pioneers & Identity. 2011. (Routledge Studies in Middle Eastern History Ser.). (ENG.). 408p. (C). 125.00 *(978-0-415-61504-4(6))* Routledge.

Biggs, Chester M. Behind the Barbed Wire: Memoir of a World War II U. S. Marine Captured in North China in 1941 & Imprisoned by the Japanese Until 1945. alt. ed. 2011. (ENG., Illus.). 232p. pap. 25.00 ***(978-0-7864-6722-8(3))*** McFarland & Co., Inc. Pubs.

Bolt, Sydney. Pseudo Sahib. 2006. (Illus.). xiv, 269p. pap. *(978-1-84382-183-0(4))* Hardinge Simpole Publishing.

DAAB Media Staff, ed. Young Asian Graphic Designers, 1 vol. 2008. (ITA, FRE, GER, SPA & ENG., Illus.). 381p. 37.95 *(978-3-86654-012-5(4))* DAAB Media GmbH DEU. Dist: Innovative Logistics.

Davidson, Peter D. Bulldozing the Way: New Guinea to Japan. 2009. 163p. pap. 19.92 *(978-0-557-11199-2(4))* Lulu Enterprises Inc.

Eade, Philip. Sylvia, Queen of the Headhunters: An Outrageous Englishwoman & Her Lost Kingdom. 2008. (ENG., Illus.). 408p. pap. 17.95 *(978-0-7538-2381-1(0))* Orion Publishing Group, Ltd. GBR. Dist: Independent Pubs. Group.

Enthoven, Victor & Murdoch, Steve, eds. The Navigator: The Log of John Anderson, VOC Pilot-Major, 1640-1643. 2010. (European Expansion & Indigenous Response Ser.). (Illus.). 240p. *(978-90-04-18931-7(9))* BRILL.

Evans, Corothy. He Led All the Way. 2007. 276p. per. 15.99 *(978-1-60266-644-3(X))* Xulon Pr., Inc.

Frost, Mark Ravinder & Balasingamchow, Yu-Mei. Singapore: A Biography. 2009. (ENG., Illus.). 456p. (gr. 17). 35.00 *(978-988-8028-17-7(0))* Hong Kong Univ. Pr. HKG. Dist: Columbia Univ. Pr.

Habib, Randa. Hussein & Abdullah: Inside the Jordanian Royal Family. 2010. (ENG., Illus.). 244p. 24.95 *(978-0-86356-656-4(7))* Saqi Bks. GBR. Dist: Consortium Bk. Sales & Distribution.

Haigh, Ken. Under the Holy Lake: A Memoir of Eastern Bhutan. 2008. (Wayfarer Ser.). (ENG., Illus.). 296p. pap. 29.95 *(978-0-88864-492-3(2))* Univ. of Alberta Pr. CAN. Dist: Michigan State Univ. Pr.

Hasan, Ahmad Mujtaba. Bukhari: Makers of Islamic Civilization. 2008. (Makers of Islamic Civilization Ser.). (ENG.). 160p. pap. 18.00 *(978-1-84511-095-6(1))* I. B. Tauris & Co., Ltd. GBR. Dist: Macmillan.

Hughes, Richard. Foreign Devil: Thirty Years of Reporting in the Far East. 2008. (ENG.). 336p. per. 18.95 *(978-1-933698-17-5(9))* 1500 Bks.

Irving, Sarah. Leila Khaled: Icon of Palestinian Liberation, 1 vol. 2012. (ENG., Illus.). 168p. lib. bdg. 75.00 ***(978-0-7453-2952-9(7))*** Pluto Pr. GBR. Dist: Macmillan.

Joseph, Stephen C. River of Stone, River of Sand: A Story of Medicine & Adventure. 2012. 220p. pap. ***(978-0-86534-845-5(6))*** Sunstone Pr.

Jumper, Roy Davis Linville. Ruslan of Malaysia: The Man Behind the Domino That Didn't Fall. 2007. (Illus.). xiv, 427p. *(978-0-9780562-0-9(5))* CDR Pr.

Learning, Linda. Married to Bhutan: How One Woman Got Lost, Said 'I Do', & Found Bliss. 2011. (ENG.). 256p. pap. 14.95 *(978-1-4019-2846-9(3))* Hay Hse., Inc.

Malkin, A. Richard. A Glimpse into the Past. 2007. 80p. per. 10.00 *(978-1-4257-6612-2(9))* Xlibris Corp.

Malone, Desmond. Turbulent Times in the Far East: The Story of the Malone Family, 1893-1946. 2006. (Illus.). 204p. pap. *(978-1-84401-702-7(8))* Athena Pr.

Markham, Ian S. & Birinci, Suendam. An Introduction to Said Nursi: Non-Violent & Engaged Islam. 2011. 206p. 99.95 *(978-1-4094-0769-0(1))*; pap. 29.95 *(978-1-4094-0771-3(3))* Ashgate Publishing Co.

McNeil, Judith L. The Girl with the Cardboard Port. 2010. (ENG.). 245p. (Orig.). pap. 21.00 *(978-0-908988-80-8(X),* Hourglass) Exisle Publishing Ltd. NZL. Dist: BookMasters Distribution Services (BDS).

Metayo, Paul. Comparison of My Life Experience in South East Asia & North Americ. 2011. 84p. pap. 19.95 ***(978-1-4560-1176-5(6))*** PublishAmerica, Inc.

Nathan, S. R. Road to the Presidency. 2012. (ENG., Illus.). 592p. 40.00 ***(978-981-4260-73-2(8),*** Didier Millet,Csi) Continental Sales, Inc.

Nicolle, David. Saladin: The Background, Strategies, Tactics & Battlefield Experiences of the Greatest Commanders of History. 2011. (Command Ser.). (ENG., Illus.). 64p. pap. 18.95 *(978-1-84908-317-1(7))* Osprey Publishing, Ltd. GBR. Dist: Random Hse., Inc.

Nui, Chan King. From Poor Migrant to Millionaire: Chan Wing 1873-1947. 2010. (Illus.). 157p. pap. 25.00 *(978-967-978-966-9(7))* Pelanduk Pubns. Malaysia Sdn. Bhd MYS. Dist: Coronet Bks.

O'Malley, Vincent J. Saints of Asia: 1500 to the Present. 2007. (Illus.). 221p. per. 14.95 *(978-1-59276-173-9(9))* Our Sunday Visitor, Publishing Div.

Ooi, Kee Beng. Serving a New Nation: Baey Lian Peck's Singapore Story. 2011. xiv, 141p. ***(978-981-4345-42-2(3))*** Institute of Southeast Asian Studies.

Ove, Robert. In the Shadow of Everest. 2011. pap. 26.99 ***(978-1-61663-923-5(7))*** Tate Publishing & Enterprises, LLC.

Parton. The Fork Once Taken: From the British Crown Colony of North Borneo to the Federated State of Sabah, East Malaysia: 1963¿1965: A Creative Memoir. 2008. 199p. pap. 24.95 *(978-1-60610-087-5(4))* PublishAmerica, Inc.

Prister, Louise. From Jerusalem to Jerusalem. 2008. 229p. pap. 24.95 *(978-1-60610-640-2(6))* PublishAmerica, Inc.

Rabbula, et al. The Rabbula Corpus: Comprising the Life of Rabbula, His Correspondence, a Homily Delivered in Constantinople, Canons, & Hymns: With Texts in Syriac & Latin, English Translations, Notes, & Introduction. 2010. *(978-1-58983-127-6(6))* Society of Biblical Literature.

Rashidzada, Babur, tr. I Am Timour, World Conqueror: Autobiography of a 14th Century Central Asian Ruler. 2009. 504p. 39.95 *(978-1-59858-679-4(3))* Dog Ear Publishing, LLC.

Robinson, Francis. The Mughal Emperors: And the Islamic Dynasties of India, Iran & Central Asia, 1206-1925. 2007. (ENG., Illus.). 240p. 45.00 *(978-0-500-25134-8(7))* Thames & Hudson.

Sapet, Kerrily. Jimmy Choo. 2011. (Profiles in Fashion Ser.). (Illus.). 112p. 28.95 *(978-1-59935-151-3(X),* 1320454) Reynolds, Morgan Inc.

Shennan, Margaret. Our Man in Malaya: John Davis CBE, DSO, Force 136 SOE & Post-War Counter-Insurgency. 2008. (ENG., Illus.). 320p. 46.95 *(978-0-7509-4710-7(1))* Sutton Publishing.

—Our Man in Malaya: John Davis, CBE, DSO, Force 136 SOE & Postwar Counter-Insurgency. 2009. (ENG., Illus.). 320p. pap. 32.95 *(978-0-7524-5053-7(0))* History Pr. Ltd., The GBR. Dist: Independent Pubs. Group.

Sitchin, Zecharia. The Earth Chronicles Expeditions: Journeys to the Mythical Past. 2007. (ENG., Illus.). 1p. pap. 16.00 *(978-1-59143-076-6(3))* Bear & Co.

Sober, Melody. Vova Story. 2010. 108p. pap. 10.99 *(978-1-4490-5679-7(2))* AuthorHouse.

Tan, Terry. Stir-Fried & Not Shaken: A Nostalgic Trip down Singapore's Memory Lane. 2008. (ENG., Illus.). 256p. pap. 15.95 *(978-981-08-0705-4(8))* Monsoon Bks. Pte. Ltd.

Thesbjerg, Marie. Women of Buddha, Nuns in Bhutan. 2008. (ENG.). 136p. 49.00 *(978-87-92241-08-5(5))* Ajour DNK. Dist: Independent Pubs. Group.

Thorp, Michael. Elephants, Tigers & Tappers. 2010. (Illus.). 22' p. pap. *(978-981-261-746-0(9))* Marshall Cavendish.

Wain, Barry. Malaysian Maverick: Mahathir Mohamad in Turbulent Times. 2010. (Critical Studies of the Asia-Pacific Ser.). (ENG., Illus.). 366p. 110.00 *(978-0-230-23873-2(4))* Palgrave Macmillan.

Winkler, Ken. The Winter Line: A Memoir & Observations of Asia. 2010. 304p. pap. 15.49 *(978-1-4490-9461-4(9))* AuthorHouse.

Wong, Samuel. A Chinese from Singapore. 2009. 616p. 34.99 *(978-1-4415-0198-1(3))*; pap. 23.99 *(978-1-4415-0197-4(5))* Xlibris Corp.

ASIA—BOUNDARIES

Bashir, Shahzad & Crews, Robert D., eds. Under the Drones: Modern Lives in the Afghanistan-Pakistan Borderlands. 2012. (ENG., Illus.). 336p. 27.95 ***(978-0-674-06561-1(1))*** Harvard Univ. Pr.

Evans, Chris. Eurasia. 2007. (ENG.). 52p. per. *(978-1-4065-3374-3(2))* Dodo Pr.

Ewans, Martin. Securing the Indian Frontier in Central Asia: Confrontation & Negotiation, 1865-1895. 2010. (Central Asian Studies). (ENG., Illus.). 208p. (C). 140.00 *(978-0-415-49681-0(0))* Routledge.

Myint-U, Thant. Where China Meets India: Burma & the New Crossroads of Asia. 2011. (ENG., Illus.). 384p. 27.00 *(978-0-374-29907-1(2))* Farrar, Straus & Giroux.

National Defense University (U.S.), et al, eds. The Borderlands of Southeast Asia: Geopolitics, Terrorism & Globalization: Geopolitics, Terrorism & Globalization. 2011. (ENG.). 276p. pap. 25.00 ***(978-0-16-088678-2(3),*** National Defense University) United States Government Printing Office.

Sturgeon, Janet C. Border Landscapes: The Politics of Akha Land Use in China & Thailand. 2007. (Culture, Place, & Nature Ser.). (ENG., Illus.). 264p. per. 22.50 *(978-0-295-98763-7(4))* Univ. of Washington Pr.

Tkachenko, B. I. Kurilskaia Problema: Istoriia, Pravo, Politika I Ekonomika. 2009. (RUS., Illus.). 311p. *(978-5-8343-0506-4(7))* Dal'nevostocnaja gosudarstvennaja morskaja akademija im. admirala G.I. Nevel'skogo.

ASIA—CIVILIZATION

Archetype Books. Metallurgy & Civilisation. 2009. (ENG., Illus.). 208p. pap. 110.00 *(978-1-904982-49-4(2))* Archetype Pubns. GBR. Dist: National Bk. Network.

Barlow, Tani E. Positions: 20 Years After. 2012. (ENG., Illus.). 175p. pap. 14.00 ***(978-0-8223-6765-9(3))*** Duke Univ. Pr.

Boric, Dusan. Archaeology & Memory. Boric, Dusan, ed. 2010. (ENG., Illus.). 215p. (C). 110.00 *(978-1-84217-363-3(4))* Oxbow Bks., Ltd. GBR. Dist: Brown, David Bk. Co., The.

Callieri, Pierfrancesco & Colliva, Luca. South Asian Archaeology 2007, Vol. 2. 2010. (Bar S Ser.). (ENG., Illus.). 375p. (C). pap. 140.00 *(978-1-4073-0674-2(X))* British Archaeological Reports Ltd. GBR. Dist: Brown, David Bk. Co., The.

Chen, Kuan-Hsing & Huat, Chua Beng. The Inter-Asia Cultural Studies Reader. 2007. 624p. 140.00 *(978-0-415-43134-7(4))* Routledge.

Chen, Kuan-Hsing & Huat, Chua Beng, eds. Inter-Asia Cultural Studies Reader. 2007. 624p. per. 43.95 *(978-0-415-43135-4(2))* Routledge.

Chiekova, Dobrinka. Cultes et vie religieuse des cités grecques du Pont gauche (VIIe-Ier siècles avant J.-C.) 2008. (Europäische Hochschulschriften. Reihe 38: Archäologie Ser.). (FRE & GEC., Illus.). 340p. pap. *(978-3-03911-448-1(4))* Lang, Peter.

Clarke, Joanne. On the Margins of Southwest Asia: Cyprus During the 6th to 4th Millennia BC. 2007. (Illus.). 160p. (C). 90.00 *(978-1-84217-281-0(6))* Oxbow Bks., Ltd. GBR. Dist: Brown, David Bk. Co., The.

Corr, Kendra. The U. S. & W. W. I: I Think: U. S. History. 2011. (ENG.). 100p. (YA). pap. 29.95 *(978-1-933558-17-2(2))* InspirEd Educators.

Couteau, Ph.D., Jean. Bali Inspires: The Rudana Art Collection. 2011. (ENG., Illus.). 310p. 49.95 *(978-602-95704-1-0(2))* Tuttle Publishing.

Cram101 Textbook Reviews. Outlines & Highlights for Why Europe? the Rise of the West in World History 1500-1850 by Jack a Goldstone, Isbn: 9780072848014. 2011. 88p. pap. 27.95 ***(978-1-61812-490-6(0))*** Cram101 Inc.

Cultureshock Staff, ed. Cultureshock Jakarta, 1 vol. 2010. (ENG., Illus.). 240p. pap. 15.95 *(978-0-7614-5873-9(5))* Marshall Cavendish Corp.

—Cultureshock Laos, 1 vol. 2010. (ENG., Illus.). 240p. pap. 15.95 *(978-0-7614-5871-5(9))* Marshall Cavendish Corp.

—Cultureshock Syria, 1 vol. 2010. (ENG., Illus.). 240p. pap. 15.95 *(978-0-7614-5880-7(8))* Marshall Cavendish Corp.

Das, Veena. South Asian Culture & Society. 2010. (Illus.). 480p. (C). instr.'s hndbk. ed. 199.00 *(978-0-415-77557-1(4))* Routledge.

Diener, Alexander & Diener, Alexander C. One Homeland or Two? The Nationalization & Transnationalization of Mongolia's Kazakhs. 2009. (ENG., Illus.). 408p. 60.00 *(978-0-8047-6191-8(4))* Stanford Univ. Pr.

Druce, Stephen C. The Lands West of the Lakes. 2010. 394p. pap. 38.00 *(978-90-6718-331-4(8))* KITLV Pr. NLD. Dist: Univ. of Hawaii Pr.

Dube, Saurabh. Modern Makeovers: Handbook of Modernity in South Asia. 2011. (ENG.). 304p. 60.00 ***(978-0-19-807404-5(2))*** Oxford Univ. Pr., Inc.

Durand, J. M. & Jacquet, Antoine. Centre et Périphérie: Approches Nouvelles des Orientalistes: Actes du Colloque Organisé Par L'Institut du Proche-Orient Ancien du Collège de France, la Société Asiatique et le CNRS (UMR 7192) les 31 Mai et 1er Juin 2006, Paris, Collège de France. 2009. (FRE., Illus.). vii, 420p. *(978-2-7200-1161-0(4),* Spotlight Poets) Maisonneuve, Jean Editions d'Amerique et d'Orient.

Dutton, George Edson, et al. Sources of Vietnamese Tradition. 2012. 640p. E-Book ***(978-0-231-51110-0(8))*** Columbia Univ. Pr.

Ellavala Medhananda. Lova Vata Hela Handa. 2010. (Illus.). 207p. *(978-955-551-799-7(1),* Library of Congress — New Delhi Overseas Office) Dayawansa Jayakody & Co.

Eltsov, Piotr Andreevich. From Harappa to Hastinapura: A Study of the Earliest South Asian City & Civilization. 2007. (American School of Prehistoric Research Monograph Ser.). (Illus.). 244p. *(978-90-04-16060-6(4))* BRILL.

Finkbeiner, Uwe & Sakal, Ferhan, eds. Emar after the closure of the Tabqa Dam. the Syrian-German Excavations 1996 - 2002. Volume I: Late Roman & Medieval Cemeteries & Environmental Studies. 2010. (Subartu Ser.). (ENG., Illus.). 266p. (C). pap. 102.00 *(978-2-503-53320-9(5))* Brepols Pubs. BEL. Dist: ISD.

Geiger, Danilo. Frontier Encounters: Indigenous Communities & Settlers in Asia & Latin America. Geiger, Danilo, ed. 2008. 554p. pap. 40.00 *(978-87-91563-15-7(1))* IWGIA DNK. Dist: Transaction Pubs.

Gordon, Stewart. When Asia Was the World: Traveling Merchants, Scholars, Warriors, & Monks Who Created the Riches of the East. 2009. (ENG.). 256p. pap. 17.00 *(978-0-306-81739-7(X))* Perseus Bks. Group.

Grigoriadis, Ioannis N. Trials of Europeanization: Turkish Political Culture & the European Union. 2008. (ENG., Illus.). 248p. 95.00 *(978-0-230-61215-0(6))* Palgrave Macmillan.

Gullette, David. The Genealogical Construction of the Kyrgyz Republic: Kinship, State & Tribalism. 2010. (Inner Asia Book Ser.). (ENG., Illus.). 272p. *(978-1-906876-10-4(X))* BRILL.

Haigh, Ken. Under the Holy Lake: A Memoir of Eastern Bhutan. 2008. (Wayfarer Ser.). (ENG., Illus.). 296p. pap. 29.95 *(978-0-88864-492-3(2))* Univ. of Alberta Pr. CAN. Dist: Michigan State Univ. Pr.

Harris, Jonathan. Constantinople: Capital of Byzantium. 2009. (ENG., Illus.). 312p. 24.95 *(978-0-8264-3086-1(4))* Continuum International Publishing Group, Ltd. GBR. Dist: National Bk. Network.

Harrison, Rachel & Jackson, Peter A. The Ambiguous Allure of the West: Traces of the Colonial in Thailand. 2010. (Illus.). 292p. *(978-962-209-121-4(0))*; pap. *(978-962-209-123-8(7))* Hong Kong Univ. Pr.

Harrison, Rachel V. & Jackson, Peter A. The Ambiguous Allure of the West: Traces of the Colonial in Thailand. 2010. (Illus.). 292p. ***(978-988-220-749-3(9))*** Hong Kong Univ. Pr.

Harrison, Rachel V. & Jackson, Peter A., eds. The Ambiguous Allure of the West: Traces of the Colonial in Thailand. 2010. 292p. 46.95 *(978-0-87727-607-4(2))*; pap. 23.95 *(978-0-87727-608-1(0))* Hong Kong Univ. Pr. HKG. Dist: Cornell Univ. Pr.

Hartley, Charles W., et al. The Archaeology of Power & Politics in Eurasia: Regimes & Revolutions. 2012. (ENG., Illus.). 400p. 99.00 ***(978-1-107-01652-1(5))*** Cambridge Univ. Pr.

He, Xirong. Cultural Tradition & Social Progress. 2009. *(978-1-56518-266-0(9))* Council for Research in Values & Philosophy.

Hegewald, Julia A. B. & Mitra, Subrata K., eds. Re-Use: The Art of Politics of Integration & Anxiety. 2012. (Illus.). 360p. (C). 60.00 ***(978-81-321-0655-5(5),*** B06555C) SAGE Pubns., Inc.

Higham, Charles & Thosarat, Rachanee. Early Thailand: From Prehistory to Sukhothai. 2012. (ENG., Illus.). 268p. pap. 25.00 ***(978-974-9863-91-6(7))*** River Bks. THA. Dist: Antique Collectors' Club.

Holt, John Clifford, ed. The Sri Lanka Reader: History, Culture, Politics. 2011. (World Readers Ser.). (ENG., Illus.). 792p. pap. 34.95 *(978-0-8223-4982-2(5))*; 109.95 *(978-0-8223-4967-9(1))* Duke Univ. Pr.

Howe, Leo. The Changing World of Bali. 2009. 164p. pap. 39.95 *(978-0-415-54674-4(5))* Routledge.

Hu, Tze-yue G. Frames of Anime: Culture & Image-Building. 2010. (CHI., Illus.). 256p. ***(978-988-220-772-1(3))*** Hong Kong Univ. Pr.

—Frames of Anime: Culture & Image-Building. 2010. (ENG., Illus.). 256p. (gr. 17). 55.00 *(978-962-209-097-2(4))*; pap. 28.00 *(978-962-209-098-9(2))* Hong Kong Univ. Pr. HKG. Dist: Columbia Univ. Pr.

Jayasuriya, Shihan de S. The African Diaspora in Asian Trade Routes & Cultural Memories. 2010. (Illus.). viii, 198p. 109.95 *(978-0-7734-3651-0(0))* Mellen, Edwin Pr., The.

Jones, Jeremy & Ridout, Nicholas Peter. Oman, Culture & Diplomacy. 2012. (ENG., Illus.). 304p. (gr. 17). 95.00 ***(978-0-7486-4295-3(1))*** Edinburgh Univ. Pr. GBR. Dist: Columbia Univ. Pr.

Khalek, Nancy A. Damascus after the Muslim Conquest: Text & Image in Early Islam, 1 vol. 2011. (ENG., Illus.). 224p. 74.00 *(978-0-19-973651-5(0))* Oxford Univ. Pr., Inc.

Kunst- und Ausstellungshalle der Bundesrepublik De, ed. Gandhara: Das buddhistische Erbe Pakistans. Legenden, Klöster und Paradiese. 2008. (Illus.). 384p. (C). 68.00 *(978-3-8053-3916-2(X))* Zabern, Philipp von Verlag, GmbH DEU. Dist: Brown, David Bk. Co., The.

Kwai-Cheung, Lo. Excess & Masculinity in Asian Cultural Productions. 2010. (SUNY series in Global Modernity Ser.). (ENG., Illus.). 288p. 75.00 *(978-1-4384-3209-0(7))* State Univ. of New York Pr.

Lemoy, Christian. Across the Pacific: From Ancient Asia to Precolombian America. 2011. 250p. pap. 25.95 ***(978-1-59942-582-5(3))*** Universal Pubs.

Lindquist, Steven E., ed. Religion & Identity in South Asia & Beyond: Essays in Honor of Patrick Olivelle. 2011. (Cultural, Historical & Textual Studies of Religions Ser.). (Illus.). 392p. 99.00 ***(978-0-85728-790-8(7))*** Anthem Pr. GBR. Dist: Books International, Inc.

Lo, Kwai-Cheung. Excess & Masculinity in Asian Cultural Productions. 2011. 251p. pap. 24.95 ***(978-1-4384-3208-3(9),*** Suny Pr.) State Univ. of New York Pr.

Mazumdar, Sucheta. From Orientalism to Postcolonialism: Asia-Europe & the Lineages of Difference. 2009. (Routledge Contemporary Asia Ser.). (ENG.). 256p. 130.00 *(978-0-415-54740-6(7))* Routledge.

Mazumdar, Sucheta, et al. From Orientalism to Postcolonialism. 2011. 256p. pap. 42.95 ***(978-0-415-67169-9(8))*** Routledge.

Milam, William B. Bangladesh & Pakistan: Flirting with Failure in South Asia. 2011. (Columbia/Hurst Ser.). (ENG.). 256p. (gr. 17). pap. 26.50 *(978-0-231-70067-2(9))* Columbia Univ. Pr.

Milner, Anthony. The Malays. 2010. (Peoples of South-East Asia & the Pacific Ser.: 5). (ENG., Illus.). 312p. pap. 30.95 *(978-1-4443-3903-1(6),* Wiley-Blackwell) Wiley, John & Sons, Inc.

Moorthy, Shanti & Jamal, Ashraf, eds. Indian Ocean Studies: Cultural, Social, & Political Perspectives. 2009. (Routledge Indian Ocean Ser.). (ENG., Illus.). 454p. 125.00 *(978-0-415-80390-8(X))* Routledge.

O'Hara, Randolph. The Golden Land: A Burmese Romance. 2009. (ENG.). 132p. pap. 14.95 *(978-974-524-101-5(6))* Orchid Pr. THA. Dist: National Bk. Network.

Ortayl, Ilber. Discovering the Ottomans. 2010. (ENG., Illus.). 192p. pap. 16.50 (978-1-84774-008-3(1)) Kube Publishing Ltd. GBR. Dist: Consortium Bk. Sales & Distribution.

Petraglia, Michael D. & Allchin, Bridget, eds. The Evolution & History of Human Populations in South Asia: Inter-Disciplinary Studies in Archaeology, Biological Anthropology, Linguistics & Genetics. 2007. (Vertebrate Paleobiology & Paleoanthropology Ser.). (Illus.). 464p. 129.00 (978-1-4020-5561-4(7)) Springer.

Raud. Japan & Asian Modernities. 2012. (ENG.). 256p. pap. 42.95 (978-0-415-54152-7(2)) Routledge.

Reichle, Natasha. Bali: Art Ritual Performance. 2011. (ENG., Illus.). 376p. 49.50 (978-0-939117-55-0(X)) Asian Art Museum of San Francisco.

Rennie, Frank & Mason, Robin. Bhutan: Ways of Knowing. 2008. (978-1-59311-735-1(3)); pap. (978-1-59311-734-4(5)) Information Age Publishing, Inc.

Robinson, Carl. Mongolia: Nomad Empire of the Eternal Blue Sky. 2010. (ENG., Illus.). 536p. pap. 29.95 (978-962-217-808-3(1), 217808) Airphoto International/Odyssey HKG. Dist: Norton, W. W. & Co., Inc.

Russell, Francis. Places in Turkey: A Pocket Grand Tour. 2010. (ENG., Illus.). 352p. pap. 24.95 (978-0-7112-3061-3(7)) Lincoln, Frances Ltd. GBR. Dist: Perseus-PGW.

Rybatzki, Volker & Rachewiltz, Igor de. The Early Mongols: Language, Culture & History. 2009. (ITA, FRE, GER & ENG., Illus.). xxxiii, 217p. (978-0-933070-57-8(8)) Research Institute for Inner Asian Studies, Indiana Univ.

Sasaki, Komei. La Estructura Múltiple de la Cultura Japonesa: Repensando la Cultura Japonesa Desde una Perspectiva Asiática. 2009. (Estudios de Asia y África Ser.). (SPA., Illus.). 328p. pap. 41.99 (978-607-462-089-4(X)) El Colegio de México, A.C., Biblioteca Miguel Cosio Villegas MEX. Dist: Fondo de Cultura Economica USA.

Sedyawati, Edi. Keindonesiaan Dalam Budaya. 2007. (IND & ENG., Illus.). (978-979-3258-74-4(8)); (978-979-3258-76-8(4)) Wedatana Widya Sastra.

Spivak, Gayatri Chakravorty. Other Asias. 2008. (ENG., Illus.). 376p. 104.95 (978-1-4051-0206-3(3)); pap. 37.95 (978-1-4051-0207-0(1)) Wiley, John & Sons, Inc. (Wiley-Blackwell).

Squarcini, Federico. Tradition, Veda & Law: Studies on South Asian Classical Intellectual Traditions. 2011. (Cultural, Historical & Textual Studies of Religions Ser.). 178p. 99.00 (978-0-85728-436-5(3)) Anthem Pr. GBR. Dist: Books International, Inc.

Stanton, Andrea L., et al, eds. Cultural Sociology of the Middle East, Asia, & Africa: An Encyclopedia. 2012. 1976p. 495.00 (978-1-4129-8176-7(X), B81767C) SAGE Pubns., Inc.

Stunkel, Kenneth R. Ideas & Art in Asian Civilizations: India, China, & Japan. 2011. (ENG.). 320p. (C). pap. 42.95 (978-0-7656-2541-0(5)); (Illus.). 99.95 (978-0-7656-2540-3(7)) Sharpe, M.E. Inc. (East Gate Bk.).

Suvorova, Anna. Lahore: Topophilia of Space & Place. 2012. (ENG., Illus.). 230p. 35.00 (978-0-19-906355-0(9)) Oxford Univ. Pr., Inc.

Tolz, Vera. Russia's Own Orient: The Politics of Identity & Oriental Studies in the Late Imperial & Early Soviet Periods. 2011. (ENG., Illus.). 224p. 99.00 (978-0-19-959444-3(9)) Oxford Univ. Pr., Inc.

Torres, Evangelista Evangelista. The Americanization of Manila, 1898-1921. 2010. (Illus.). viii, 255p. (978-971-542-613-8(1)) Univ. of the Philippines Pr.

Uitz, Martin. Hidden Bhutan: Entering the Kingdom of the Thunder Dragon. 2012. (Armchair Traveller Ser.). (ENG.). 101p. pap. 11.95 (978-1-907973-16-1(8)) Haus Publishing GBR. Dist: Consortium Bk. Sales & Distribution.

Vaswani, T. L. Secret of Asia. 2006. 96p. per. (978-1-4067-3096-8(3), Hesperides Pr.) Read Bks.

Vo, Nghia M., et al. War & Remembrance: SACEI Forum # 6. 2009. 234p. pap. 17.95 (978-1-4327-4624-7(3)) Outskirts Pr., Inc.

Watt, John. Rhetoric & Philosophy from Greek into Syriac. 2010. (Variorum Collected Studies). 330p. 154.95 (978-1-4094-0020-2(4)) Ashgate Publishing Co.

Wee, C. J. Wan-Ling. The Asian Modern: Culture, Capitalist Development, Singapore. 2007. (Illus.). 224p. (978-9971-69-392-3(5)) Hong Kong Univ. Pr.

Werner, Jayne, et al. Sources of Vietnamese Tradition. 2012. (Introduction to Asian Civilizations Ser.). (ENG.). 640p. (gr. 17). 105.00 (978-0-231-13862-8(8)); pap. 35.00 (978-0-231-13863-5(6)) Columbia Univ. Pr.

Wilson, Constance M. The Middle Mekong River Basin: Studies in Tai History & Culture. 2009. 412p. 28.00 (978-1-891134-30-2(2)) Southeast Asia Pubns.

ASIA—CLIMATE

Clift, Peter & Plumb, R. Alan. The Asian Monsoon: Causes, History & Effects. 2008. (ENG., Illus.). 288p. 137.00 (978-0-521-84799-5(0)) Cambridge Univ. Pr.

Gutman, Garik & Reissell, Anni, eds. Eurasian Arctic Land Cover & Land Use in a Changing Climate. 2010. (ENG., Illus.). xxiii, 306p. 129.00 (978-90-481-9117-8(3), 9048191173) Springer.

United Nations. Asia & the Pacific Prespectives on Climate Change & Low Carbon Development Pathways. 2012. (ENG.). pap. 12.00 (978-92-1-120601-2(4)) United Nations Pubns.

ASIA—COMMERCE

Aggarwal, Vinod & Koo, Min Gyo, eds. Asia's New Institutional Architecture: Evolving Structures for Managing Trade & Security Relations. 2008. (Political Economy of the Asia Pacific Ser.). 275p. pap. 59.95 (978-3-540-74887-8(3), 3540748873) Springer.

Athukorala, Prema-Chandra, ed. The Rise of Asia: Trade & Investment in Global Perspective. 2010. (Routledge Studies in the Growth Economies of Asia Ser.). (ENG., Illus.). 384p. (C). 138.00 (978-0-415-55686-6(4)) Routledge.

Backman, Michael. The Asian Insider: Unconventional Wisdom for Asian Business. annot. ed. 2006. (ENG.). 352p. pap. 40.00 (978-0-230-00021-6(5)) Palgrave Macmillan.

Backman, Michael & Buttler, Charlotte. Big in Asia: 30 Strategies for Business Success. 2nd rev. ed. 2007. (ENG., Illus.). 380p. pap. 41.00 (978-0-230-00027-8(4)) Palgrave Macmillan.

BAI Staff, ed. A Passage to Asia: 35 Centuries of Exchange Between Asia & Europe, 1 vol. 2010. (ENG.). 271p. 60.00 (978-90-8586-565-0(4)) Exhibitions International BEL. Dist: Innovative Logistics.

Baladi, Joseph. The Brutal Truth about Asian Branding: And How to Break the Vicious Cycle. 2011. (ENG., Illus.). 250p. 29.95 (978-0-470-82647-8(9), Wiley) Wiley, John & Sons, Inc.

Beveridge, Albert Jeremiah. The Russian Advance. 2009. 506p. 32.99 (978-1-116-39897-7(4)); pap. 39.75 (978-1-116-39898-4(2)); 43.99 (978-1-116-39896-0(6)); pap. 38.75 (978-1-116-39899-1(0)) BiblioBazaar.

—The Russian Advance. 2009. 318p. pap. (978-1-4590-4840-9(7)); pap. (978-1-4590-4833-1(4)) Books LLC.

BIA. Essential Kyrgyz Manufacturers: Food, Textile, Clothing, & Chemical Companies. 6th rev. ed. 2006. 180p. (J). pap. 219.00 (978-1-4187-4195-2(7)) Business Information Agency.

—Major Wholesalers & Retailers in Asia. 6th rev. ed. 2006. 250p. (J). pap. 249.00 (978-1-4187-4295-9(3)) Business Information Agency.

Boomgaard, Peter & Kooiman, Dic. Linking Destinies. 2010. 284p. pap. 31.00 (978-90-6718-320-8(2)) KITLV Pr. NLD. Dist: Univ. of Hawaii Pr.

Bosrock, Mary Murray. Asian Business Customs & Manners: A Country-by-Country Guide. 2007. (Illus.). 450p. pap. (978-0-88166-525-3(8)) Meadowbrook Pr.

Bowen, H. V. The Business of Empire: The East India Company & Imperial Britain, 1756-1833. 2008. (ENG., Illus.). 320p. pap. 42.00 (978-0-521-08982-1(4)) Cambridge Univ. Pr.

Bowen, Huw, et al. Monsoon Traders: The Maritime World of the East India Company. 2011. (ENG., Illus.). 192p. 60.00 (978-1-85759-675-5(7)) Scala, Editions FRA. Dist: National Bk. Network.

Boyajian, James C. Portuguese Trade in Asia under the Habsburgs, 1580-1640. 2007. (ENG., Illus.). 360p. (gr. 17). pap. 37.00 (978-0-8018-8754-3(2)) Johns Hopkins Univ. Pr.

Brooks, Douglas H. & Hummels, David. Infrastructure's Role in Lowering Asia's Trade Costs: Building for Trade. 2009. (Illus.). 288p. 127.00 (978-1-84844-162-0(2)) Elgar, Edward Publishing, Inc.

Brooks, Douglas H. & Menon, Jayant, eds. Infrastructure & Trade in Asia. 2008. 256p. (C). 119.00 (978-1-84720-941-2(6)) Elgar, Edward Publishing, Inc.

Burgess, John & Connell, Julia, eds. Globalisation & Work in Asia. 2007. (Chandos Asian Studies). (ENG., Illus.). 342p. 110.00 (978-1-84334-217-5(0), Chandos Publishing) Woodhead Publishing Ltd. GBR. Dist: Ingram Pub. Services.

Chatterjee, Samir R., et al. Asian Management in Transition: Emerging Themes. 2006. (ENG., Illus.). 352p. pap. 56.00 (978-0-230-00774-1(0)) Palgrave Macmillan.

Chaudhury, Sushil & Morineau, Michel, eds. Merchants, Companies & Trade: Europe & Asia in the Early Modern Era. 2007. (Studies in Modern Capitalism Ser.). (ENG., Illus.). 344p. pap. 69.00 (978-0-521-03747-1(6)) Cambridge Univ. Pr.

Cheung, Yin-Wong & Ma, Guonan. Asia & China in the Global Economy. 2011. 300p. 84.00 (978-981-4335-26-3(6)) World Scientific Publishing Co., Inc.

Chow, Peter C. Y. Trade & Industrial Development in East Asia: Catching up or Falling Behind. 2012. 424p. 185.00 (978-1-84980-482-0(6)) Elgar, Edward Publishing, Inc.

Chu, Richard T. Chinese & Chinese Mestizos of Manila: Family, Identity, & Culture, 1860s-1930s. 2010. (Chinese Overseas Ser.). (Illus.). 451p. (978-90-04-17339-2(0)) BRILL.

Conway, Ida M., ed. Trade Barriers in Asia & Oceania. 2008. (C). 98.00 (978-1-60021-955-9(1)) Nova Science Pubs., Inc.

De Run, Ernest Cyril, et al. Readings on Business. 2008. 192p. pap. (978-3-639-07009-5(7)) VDM Verlag Dr. Mueller e.K.

Dent, Christopher M. & Dent, Christophe M. New Free Trade Agreements in the Asia-Pacific. 2006. (ENG., Illus.). 328p. 116.00 (978-0-230-00486-3(5)) Palgrave Macmillan.

Doing Business in Asia. Date not set. (Doing Business in Regions & Countries Around the World Ser.). (978-1-882390-82-3(2)) Training Management Corp.

Euromonitor International Staff, ed. Asian Marketing Data & Statistics. 5th ed. 2011. (Asia Marketing Data & Statistics Ser.). (ENG.). 382p. lib. bdg. (978-1-84264-547-5(1)) Euromonitor International PLC.

Eyraud, Francois & Lee, Sang-Heon. Globalization, Flexibilization & Working Conditions in Asia & the Pacific. Eyraud, Francois & Lee, Sangheon, eds. 2008. (ENG., Illus.). 320p. 120.00 (978-92-2-120029-1(9)) International Labour Office.

Githinji, Mwangi wa. Is That a Dragon or Elephant on Your Ladder: The Potential Impact of China & India on Export Led Growth in African Countries? 2009. (NAI Discussion Papers). 40p. pap. 12.95 (978-91-7106-646-6(2)) Nordiska Afrikainstitutet SWE. Dist: Stylus Publishing, LLC.

Guan, Yeoh. Penang & Its Neighbors. 260p. pap. 28.00 (978-9971-69-423-4(9)) National Univ. of Singapore Pr. SGP. Dist: Univ. of Hawaii Pr.

Gulati, Ashok & Dixon, John, eds. Maize in Asia: Changing Markets & Incentives. 2008. (ENG., Illus.). 488p. 69.95 (978-81-7188-663-0(9)) Academic Foundation IND. Dist: Independent Pubs. Group.

Haghirian, Parissa. Multinationals & Cross-Cultural Management: The Transfer of Knowledge Within Multinational Corporations. 2010. (Routledge International Business in Asia Ser.). (ENG., Illus.). 192p. (C). 150.00 (978-0-415-44931-1(6)) Routledge.

Ibp, Usa. Thailand Industrial & Business Directo. 2006. (Illus.). pap. 99.95 (978-0-7397-9761-7(1)) International Business Pubns., USA.

Kaminski, Bartlomiej & Mitra, Saumya. Borderless Bazaars & Border Trade in Central Asia: Emerging patterns of trade & cross-border Cooperation. 2012. (Directions in Development Ser.). (ENG.). 208p. pap. 25.95 (978-0-8213-9471-7(1), 9780821394717) World Bank Pubns.

Kaminski, Bartomiej & Mitra, Saumya. Borderless Bazaars & Regional Integration in Central Asia: Emerging Patterns of Trade & Cross- Border Cooperation. 2012. (978-0-8213-9472-4(X)) World Bank Pubns.

Kawai, Masahiro & Wignaraja, Ganeshan, eds. Asia's Free Trade Agreements: How Is Business Responding? 2011. (Illus.). 304p. 125.00 (978-1-84980-386-1(2)) Elgar, Edward Publishing, Inc.

Kelegama, Saman. South Asia in the WTO. 2008. 296p. (C). 55.95 (978-0-7619-3614-5(9), B36145C) SAGE Pubns., Inc.

Kerr, Gordon. Historical Researches into the Politics. 2006. 464p. per. (978-1-4067-1055-7(5), Hesperides Pr.) Read Bks.

Koo, Min Gyo & Aggarwal, Vinod K., eds. Asia's New Institutional Architecture: Evolving Structures for Managing Trade, Financial, & Security Relations. 2007. (Political Economy of the Asia Pacific Ser.). (Illus.). 321p. 179.00 (978-3-540-72388-2(9)) Springer.

La Croix, Sumner & Petri, Peter, eds. Challenges to the Global Trading System: Adjustment to Globalization in the Asia-Pacific Region. 2011. (ENG.). 256p. pap. 42.95 (978-0-415-66641-1(4)) Routledge.

Laptashvili, Natia. Modern Law of Contracts & Sales in Eastern Europe & Central Asia. 2011. 322p. 97.50 (978-94-90947-20-0(2)) Eleven International Publishing NLD. Dist: International Specialized Bk. Services.

Latham, A. J. H. Intra-Asian Trade & Industrialization: Essays in Memory of Yasukichi Yasuba. Kawakatsu, Heita, ed. 2009. (Routledge Explorations in Economic History Ser.). (ENG., Illus.). 254p. 150.00 (978-0-415-48501-2(0)) Routledge.

Latham, John. Intra-Asian Trade & the World Market. 2009. 248p. pap. 39.95 (978-0-415-54692-8(3)) Routledge.

Li, Kui Wai. Trade & Capital Flow among Asian Economies. Rowley, Chris, ed. 2007. (Illus.). 240p. 140.00 (978-0-415-44553-5(1)) Routledge.

Lim, Jason. Linking an Asian Trans-Regional Commerce in Tea: Overseas Chinese Merchants in the Fujian-Singapore Trade, 1920-1960. 2010. (Illus.). 280p. (978-90-04-18243-1(8)) BRILL.

Liu, Xinru. The Silk Road in World History. 2010. (New Oxford World History Ser.). (ENG., Illus.). 176p. pap. 19.95 (978-0-19-533810-2(3)) Oxford Univ. Pr., Inc.

Liu, Xinru & Shaffer, Lynda Norene. Connections Across Eurasia: Transportation, Communication, & Cultural Exchange on the Silk Roads. 2007. (ENG., Illus.). 272p. (C). per. 33.00 (978-0-07-284351-4(9), 0072843519) McGraw-Hill Cos., The.

Marquez, Jaime. Estimating Trade Elasticities. 2010. (Advanced Studies in Theoretical & Applied Econometrics Ser.). 152p. pap. 119.00 (978-1-4419-5300-1(0), 1441953000) Springer.

Meller, Susan. Russian Textiles: Printed Cloth for the Bazaars of Central Asia. 2nd ed. 2007. (ENG., Illus.). 208p. 55.00 (978-0-8109-9381-5(3)) Abrams.

Morrison, Terri & Conaway, Wayne A. Kiss, Bow, or Shake Hands - Asia: How to Do Business in 12 Asian Countries. 2006. (ENG., Illus.). 256p. pap. 14.95 (978-1-59869-216-7(X)) Adams Media Corp.

New Delhi, Centre for Trade and Development. South Asian Yearbook of Trade & Development: Harnessing Gains from Trade: Domestic Challenges & Beyond. 2009. (ENG.). 290p. pap. 99.95 (978-81-7188-743-9(0)) Academic Foundation IND. Dist: Independent Pubs. Group.

Ooi. Survivng War Talent Asia. 2009. (ENG.). 216p. pap. 29.99 (978-0-13-700951-0(8)) Pearson Education.

Palacios. Multinational Corporations & the Emerging Network Economy in Asia & the Pacific. 2007. (PAFTAD (Pacific Trade & Development Conference Series) Ser.). (ENG., Illus.). 336p. (C). 178.00 (978-0-415-43332-7(0)) Routledge.

Paliwoda, Stanley, et al, eds. Marketing Management in Asia. 2012. (Routledge Studies in International Business & the World Economy Ser.). (ENG., Illus.). 192p. (C). 125.00 (978-0-415-52317-2(6)) Routledge.

Petri, Peter A. & La Croix, Sumner J., eds. Challenges to the Global Trading System: Adjustment to Globalization in the Asia-Pacific Region. 2007. (Pacific Trade & Development Conference Ser.). (Illus.). 234p. 160.00 (978-0-415-42986-3(2)) Routledge.

Robert E. Flemchak. U. S. -Singapore Free Trade Agreement after Five Years. 2011. (Series: Trade Issues, Policies & Laws Ser.). 195.00 (978-1-61122-350-7(4)) Nova Science Pubs., Inc.

Sally, Razeen. New Frontiers in Free Trade: Globalization's Future & Asia's Rising Role. 2008. (ENG., Illus.). 124p. 18.95 (978-1-933995-21-2(1)) Cato Institute.

SEARO. Implications of SAFTA on Tobacco Trade & Public Health in the SAARC Region. 2009. (SEARO Nonserial Publication Ser.). (ENG.). 58p. pap. 12.00 (978-92-9022-316-0(2)) World Health Organization.

Shand & Rajan, Ramkishen S. Singapore: Trade, Investment & Economic Performance. 2009. 112p. 73.00 (978-981-4273-13-8(9)) World Scientific Publishing Co., Inc.

Siddique, M. A. B. Regionalism, Trade & Economic Development in the Asia-Pacific Region. 2007. (Illus.). 256p. (C). 127.00 (978-1-84542-503-6(0)) Elgar, Edward Publishing, Inc.

Um, Nancy. Merchant Houses of Mocha: Trade & Architecture in an Indian Ocean Port. 2009. (ENG., Illus.). 272p. 75.00 (978-0-295-98910-5(6)); pap. 30.00 (978-0-295-98911-2(4)) Univ. of Washington Pr.

United Nations. Agricultural Trade Reform & Poverty in the Asia-Pacific: A Survey & Some New Results. 2009. (UNESCAP Working Papers Ser.). (ENG.). 44p. pap. 12.00 (978-92-1-120556-5(5)) United Nations Pubns.

—Asia-Pacific Trade & Investment Report 2009: Trade-led Recovery & Beyond. 2010. (ENG.). 346p. pap. 55.00 (978-92-1-120586-2(7)) United Nations Pubns.

—Review of Information & Communications Technology & Development in Western Asia. 2007. (ARA.). 32p. pap. 17.00 (978-92-1-628061-1(1)) United Nations Pubns.

—Statistical Abstract of the ESCWA Region, 26th Issue. 2008. (MUL.). 260p. pap. 45.00 (978-92-1-128308-2(6)) United Nations Pubns.

—Trade Facilitation Beyond the Multilateral Trade Negotiations: Regional Practices, Customs Valuation & other Emerging Issues. 2008. (ENG., Illus.). 334p. pap. 60.00 (978-92-1-120539-8(5)) United Nations Pubns.

—Trade Facilitation in Selected Landlocked Countries in Asia. 2007. (Studies in Trade & Investment Ser.). (ENG.). 160p. pap. 29.00 (978-92-1-120493-3(3)) United Nations Pubns.

United Nations Staff. Asia-Pacific Trade & Investment Review 2008. 2009. (ENG.). 206p. pap. 55.00 (978-92-1-120572-5(7)) United Nations Pubns.

Vierra, Kimberly & Vierra, Brian. Vietnam Business Guide: Getting Started in Tomorrow's Market Today. 2010. (ENG., Illus.). 224p. pap. 27.95 (978-0-470-82452-8(2), Wiley) Wiley, John & Sons, Inc.

Wenzlhuemer, Roland. From Coffee to Tea Cultivation in Ceylon, 1880-1900: An Economic & Social History. 2008. (Brill's Indological Library Ser.). (Illus.). 336p. (978-90-04-16361-4(1)) BRILL.

Witt, Michael B., ed. Asian Business & Management, 8 vols. 2012. (SAGE Library in Business & Management Ser.). 3064p. 1500.00 (978-1-4462-0025-4(6), B00254C) SAGE Pubns., Ltd. GBR. Dist: SAGE Pubns., Inc.

Woolcock, Stephen, et al. The Rise of Bilateralism: Comparing American, European & Asian Approaches to Preferential Trade Agreements. 2009. (ENG., Illus.). 276p. pap. 34.00 (978-92-808-1162-9(2)) United Nations Univ. Pr. JPN. Dist: Brookings Institution Pr.

Yeung, Henry Wai-Chung, ed. Handbook of Research on Asian Business. 2007. (Elgar Original Reference Ser.). (Illus.). 512p. (C). 248.00 (978-1-84376-960-6(3)) Elgar, Edward Publishing, Inc.

Yoo, Youngjin, et al. Trends in Mobile Technology & Business in the Asia-Pacific Region. 2008. (Chandos Asian Studies). (ENG.). 280p. 110.00 (978-1-84334-224-3(3), Chandos Publishing) Woodhead Publishing Ltd. GBR. Dist: Ingram Pub. Services.

Yue Zhang, Marina & Dodgson, Mark. High-Tech Entrepreneurship in Asia: Innovation, Industry & Institutional Dynamics in Mobile Payments. 2007. (Illus.). 352p. (C). 150.00 (978-1-84720-056-3(7)) Elgar, Edward Publishing, Inc.

Yueh, Linda. Future Asian Trade: Economic Development with the Emergence of China. 2010. (Routledge Studies in the Growth Economies of Asia Ser.). (ENG., Illus.). 464p. 145.00 (978-0-415-36811-7(1)) Routledge.

ASIA—DEFENSES

Chapman, Dennis P. Security Forces of Kurdistan Regional Government. 2011. (978-1-56859-281-7(7)) Mazda Pubs., Inc.

Contracts for Afghan National Police Training: Hearing Before the Ad Hoc Subcommittee on Contracting Oversight of the Committee on Homeland Security & Governmental Affairs, United States Senate, One Hundred Eleventh Congress, Second Session, April 15, 2010. 2011. iii, 130p. (978-0-16-088620-1(1), 552-070-42789-9) United States Government Printing Office.

Goswami, Namrata & Lele, Ajey, eds. Imagining Asia in 2030: Tends, Scenarios & Alternatives. 2011. 580p. 89.95 (978-81-7188-870-2(4)) Academic Foundation IND. Dist: Independent Pubs. Group.

Jacoby, Tami A. & Jacoby, Tami Amanda. Bridging the Barrier: Israeli Unilateral Disengagement. 2007. (Illus.). 172p. 114.95 (978-0-7546-4969-4(5)) Ashgate Publishing Co.

Marshall, Frederick Henry. The Second Athenian Confederacy. 2009. 148p. 35.95 (978-1-120-06245-1(4)) Kessinger Publishing, LLC.

Muni, S. D., ed. IDSA Asian Strategic Review 2008. 2009. (ENG.). 378p. 55.95 (978-81-7188-712-5(0)) Academic Foundation IND. Dist: Independent Pubs. Group.

Nick, Bisley. Building Asias Security. 2010. (Adelphi Ser.). (Illus.). 159p. pap. 19.95 (978-0-415-58266-7(0), Routledge) Taylor & Francis Group GBR. Dist: Taylor & Francis Group.

Sebata, Takao. Japan's Defense Policy & Bureaucratic Politics, 1976-2007. 2010. (ENG.). 540p. pap. 62.99 (978-0-7618-5081-6(3)) Univ. Pr. of America, Inc.

Singh, R. S. N. Asian Strategic & Military Perspective. 2008. (Illus.). 423p. (978-81-7062-245-1(X)) Lancer International, Lancer Pr.

Tellis, Ashley J., et al, eds. Strategic Asia 2008-09: Challenges & Choices. 2008. (Illus.). pap. 34.95 (978-0-9713938-9-9(3)) National Bureau of Asian Research, The.

Tellis, Ashley J., et al. Strategic Asia 2011-12: Asia Responds to Its Rising Powers — China & India. Tellis, Ashley J. et al, eds. 2011. (Strategic Asia Ser.). (Illus.). pap. 34.95 ***(978-0-9818904-2-5(3))*** National Bureau of Asian Research, The.
Verma, Bharat. Indain Defence Review January/March 2011. 2011. (Illus.). 192p. pap. 18.95 ***(978-81-7062-214-7(X))*** Lancer International, Lancer Pr. IND. Dist: Casemate Pubs. & Bk. Distributors, LLC.

ASIA—DESCRIPTION AND TRAVEL

Allen, David. The Sky above the Kingdom Below: In the Footsteps of Thomas Coryate. 2008. (Armchair Traveller Ser.). (ENG., Illus.). 200p. 19.95 *(978-1-905791-30-9(5))* Haus Publishing GBR. Dist: Consortium Bk. Sales & Distribution.
Atkins, Gary. Imagining Gay Paradise: Bali, Bangkok, & Cyber-Singapore. 2011. 300p. ***(978-988-8053-89-6(2))*** Hong Kong Univ. Pr.
Bahr, Iris. Dork Whore: My Travels Through Asia as a Twenty-Year-Old Pseudo-Virgin. 2007. (ENG.). 224p. pap. 13.95 *(978-1-59691-234-2(0))* Bloomsbury Publishing.
Bald, Margaret. From the Sahara to Samarkand: The Remarkabke Journeys of Rosita Forbes. 2010. (ENG.). 369p. pap. 15.00 *(978-1-60419-030-4(2))* Axios Pr.
Baring, Rose. Meetings with Remarkable Muslims. Rogerson, Barnaby, ed. 2006. (ENG.). 312p. per. 33.95 *(978-0-9550105-0-7(0))* Local Ireland IRL. Dist: Dufour Editions, Inc.
Beisler, Jerry. The Bandit of Kabul: Counterculture Adventures along the Hashish Trail & Beyond ... 2nd ed. 2012. (ENG., Illus.). 288p. 24.95 *(978-1-936296-02-6(0))* Trine Day.
Belliveau, Denis & O'Donnell, Francis. In the Footsteps of Marco Polo: A Companion to the Public Television Film. 2008. (ENG.). 288p. 29.95 *(978-0-7425-5683-6(2))* Rowman & Littlefield Publishers, Inc.
Bergreen, Laurence. Marco Polo: From Venice to Xanadu. 2008. (Vintage Ser.). (ENG., Illus.). 432p. pap. 18.00 *(978-1-4000-7880-6(6)*, Vintage) Knopf Doubleday Publishing Group.
Bird, Isabella. The Golden Chersonese & the Way Thither. 2010. (Cambridge Library Collection - Travel & Exploration Ser.). (ENG., Illus.). 432p. pap. 32.99 *(978-1-108-01473-1(9))* Cambridge Univ. Pr.
Brennecke, Detlef, et al. K2. 2011. (ENG., Illus.). 144p. 30.00 *(978-88-544-0121-1(8))* White Star ITA. Dist: Random Hse., Inc.
Brummett, Palmira Johnson. The "Book" of Travels: Genre, Ethnology, & Pilgrimage, 1250-1700. 2009. *(978-90-04-17498-6(2))* BRILL.
Büscher, Wolfgang. Asian Absences: Searching for Shangri-La. 2011. (Armchair Traveller Ser.). (ENG.). 220p. 19.95 *(978-1-906598-76-1(2))* Haus Publishing GBR. Dist: Consortium Bk. Sales & Distribution.
Cassell, Coles. Letters to the Folks. 2011. 76p. 37.95 ***(978-1-258-10233-3(1))*** Literary Licensing, LLC.
Clinch, Nicholas & Clinch, Elizabeth. Through a Land of Extremes: The Littledales of Central Asia. 2009. (ENG., Illus.). 336p. pap. 24.95 *(978-0-7509-4783-1(7))* History Pr. Ltd.,The GBR. Dist: Independent Pubs. Group.
Cochrane, Janet, ed. Asian Tourism: Growth & Change. 2008. (ENG., Illus.). 416p. 115.00 *(978-0-08-045356-9(2))* Routledge.
Colley, Linda. The Ordeal of Elizabeth Marsh: A Woman in World History. 2008. (ENG., Illus.). 400p. pap. 16.95 *(978-0-385-72149-3(8)*, Anchor) Knopf Doubleday Publishing Group.
Cool, Catherine. Vivid Air: Travels to a Further Shore. 2006. 345p. pap. *(978-0-7414-3697-9(3))* Infinity Publishing.
Dalrymple, William. In Xanadu. 2012. (Vintage Ser.). (ENG., Illus.). 352p. pap. 15.95 ***(978-0-307-94888-5(9)***, Vintage) Knopf Doubleday Publishing Group.
Danziger, Nick. Danziger's Travels. (Illus.). 448p. pap. 17.99 *(978-0-586-08706-0(0)*, Collins) HarperCollins Pubs. Ltd. GBR. Dist: Trafalgar Square Publishing.
De Windt, Harry. From Pekin to Calais by Land. 2008. 408p. 49.95 *(978-1-4372-6468-5(9))*; 406p. pap. 34.95 *(978-1-4371-3807-8(1))* Kessinger Publishing, LLC.
Duncan, Nancy. The Nail That Sticks Up: An American Woman in Asia & Africa. 2007. 436p. per. 29.95 *(978-1-4241-7539-0(9))* PublishAmerica, Inc.
Enthoven, Victor & Murdoch, Steve, eds. The Navigator: The Log of John Anderson, VOC Pilot-Major, 1640-1643. 2010. (European Expansion & Indigenous Response Ser.). (Illus.). 240p. *(978-90-04-18931-7(9))* BRILL.
Ewans. George Nathaniel Curzon: Collected Writings V2, 5 vols. 2008. (Illus.). 400p. *(978-0-415-45612-8(6))* Routledge.
—George Nathaniel Curzon: Collected Writings V3, 5 vols. 2008. (Illus.). 400p. *(978-0-415-45613-5(4))* Routledge.
—George Nathaniel Curzon: Collected Writings V4, 5 vols. 2008. (Illus.). 400p. *(978-0-415-45614-2(2))* Routledge.
—George Nathaniel Curzon: Collected Writings V5, 5 vols. 2008. (Illus.). 400p. *(978-0-415-45615-9(0))* Routledge.
Ewans, Martin, ed. George Nathaniel Curzon: Collected Writings, 5 vols. 2008. (Illus.). 2200p. (C). 1225.00 *(978-0-415-41690-0(6))* Routledge.
—George Nathaniel Curzon: Collected Writings V1: Collection 1: Asian Travels, 5 vols. 2008. (Illus.). 400p. *(978-0-415-45611-1(8))* Routledge.
Favell Lee Mortimer. Far Off. 2006. (ENG.). 200p. pap. 19.99 *(978-1-4264-6563-5(7))* BiblioBazaar.
Fawcett, Charles & Burn, Richard, eds. The Travels of the Abbe Carre in India & the near East 1672-1674. 2010. (Hakluyt Society, Second Ser.). 1088p. 180.00 *(978-1-4094-2489-5(8))* Hakluyt Society GBR. Dist: Ashgate Publishing Co.
—The Travels of the Abbé Carré in India & the near East, 1672 To 1674: From Bijapur to Madras & St Thom. Account of the capture of Trincomalee Bay & St Thomé by de la Haye, & of the siege of St Thomé by the Golconda army & hostilities with the Dutch. 2010. (Hakluyt Society, Second Ser.). 384p. 69.95 *(978-1-4094-1462-9(0))* Hakluyt Society GBR. Dist: Ashgate Publishing Co.
—The Travels of the Abbé Carré in India & the near East, 1672 To 1674: From France through Syria, Iraq & the Persian Gulf to Surat, Goa, & Bijapur, with an account of his grave illness. 2010. (Hakluyt Society, Second Ser.). 372p. 69.95 *(978-1-4094-1461-2(2))* Hakluyt Society GBR. Dist: Ashgate Publishing Co.
—The Travels of the Abbé Carré in India & the near East, 1672 To 1674: Return Journey to France, with an account of the Sicilian revolt against Spanish rule at Messina. 2010. (Hakluyt Society, Second Ser.). 332p. 69.95 *(978-1-4094-1463-6(9))* Hakluyt Society GBR. Dist: Ashgate Publishing Co.
Fay, Eliza. Original Letters from India. 2010. (ENG., Illus.). 304p. pap. 16.95 *(978-1-59017-336-7(8)*, NYRB Classics) New York Review of Bks., Inc., The.
Giles, H. A., tr. from CHI. The Travels of Fa-hsien (399-414 A. D.), or Record of the Buddhistic Kingdoms. 2012. (ENG.). 116p. pap. 33.99 ***(978-1-107-68532-1(X))*** Cambridge Univ. Pr.
Gonzflez de Clavijo, Ruy. Narrative of the Embassy of Ruy. Gonzflez de Clavijo to the court of Timour, at Samarcand, A. D. 1403-6. Markham, Clements R., tr. 2010. (Cambridge Library Collection - Travel & Exploration Ser.). (ENG., Illus.). 276p. pap. 23.99 *(978-1-108-01058-0(X))* Cambridge Univ. Pr.
Gordon, Stewart. When Asia Was the World: Traveling Merchants, Scholars, Warriors, & Monks Who Created the Riches of the East. 2009. (ENG.). 256p. pap. 17.00 *(978-0-306-81739-7(X))* Perseus Bks. Group.
Graceffo, Antonio. Warrior Odyssey: The Travels of a Martial Artist in Asia. 2010. (ENG.). 200p. pap. 16.95 *(978-0-89750-190-3(X))* Black Belt Communications, Inc.
Green, J. W. Fistful of Promises: Trying to Help Tuva's Children. 2011. 184p. 26.95 ***(978-1-4620-0693-9(0))***; pap. 16.95 ***(978-1-4620-1656-3(1))*** iUniverse, Inc.
Haigh, Ken. Under the Holy Lake: A Memoir of Eastern Bhutan. 2008. (Wayfarer Ser.). (ENG., Illus.). 296p. pap. 29.95 *(978-0-88864-492-3(2))* Univ. of Alberta Pr. CAN. Dist: Michigan State Univ. Pr.
Hansen, Valerie. The Silk Road: A New History. 2012. (ENG., Illus.). 320p. 34.95 ***(978-0-19-515931-8(4))*** Oxford Univ. Pr., Inc.
Harris, John. The Backpacker. 2011. (ENG.). 384p. pap. 14.95 ***(978-1-84024-771-8(1))*** Summerdale Pubs. GBR. Dist: Independent Pubs. Group.
Jackson, Peter, tr. from LAT. & intro. The Mission of Friar William of Rubruck: His Journey to the Court of the Great Khan Möngke, 1253-1255. 2009. 328p. pap. 14.95 *(978-0-87220-981-7(4))* Hackett Publishing Co., Inc.
Jaynes, G. Come Hell or High Water. pap. 13.00 *(978-0-86547-534-2(2)*, North Point Pr.) Farrar, Straus & Giroux.
Jonson, Ben. The Travels of Marco Polo: The Venetian. 2007. (ENG.). 474p. 52.95 *(978-0-548-07183-0(7))* Kessinger Publishing, LLC.
Jordanus, Catalani. Mirabilia Descripta: The Wonders of the East. Yule, Henry, tr. 2010. (Cambridge Library Collection - Hakluyt First Ser.). 104p. pap. 21.00 *(978-1-108-01057-3(1))* Cambridge Univ. Pr.
Kemp, Hans, ed. Catch. 2009. (Illus.). 200p. 16.95 *(978-962-85637-6-0(9))* Visionary World, Ltd. HKG. Dist: AtlasBooks Distribution.
Kinvig, Noel. Beyond the Cabbage Tree. 2009. (Illus.). 240p. pap. 60.99 *(978-1-4490-1575-6(1))* AuthorHouse.
Kipling, Rudyard. From Sea to Sea & Other Sketches, 2. reprint ed. lib. bdg. 196.00 *(978-0-7426-2846-5(9))* Classic Bks.
Kipling, Rudyard. From Sea to Sea & Other Sketches: Letters of Travel. 2011. (Cambridge Library Collection - Travel & Exploration Ser.). (ENG.). 456p. pap. 34.99 ***(978-1-108-03369-5(5))***; 520p. pap. 37.99 ***(978-1-108-03368-8(7))*** Cambridge Univ. Pr.
Kyte-Coles, Robin, photos by. The Spirit of Buddha. 2009. 45.00 *(978-3-8327-9315-9(1))* teNeues Publishing Co.
Liu, Dalai. Nguyen Huu Dan. 2011. pap. ***(978-0-9799180-4-9(9))*** Asia Pub.
Locken, E. Travel Journal Brunei. 2010. 192p. pap. 19.99 *(978-0-557-43277-6(4))* Lulu Enterprises Inc.
Lopez, Robert Sabatino. European Merchants in the Medieval Indies. 2011. 82.64 *(978-1-61143-878-9(0))* Gorgias Pr., LLC.
Mandeville, John. The Book of Marvels & Travels. Bale, Anthony, tr. 2012. (ENG., Illus.). 224p. pap. 14.95 ***(978-0-19-960060-1(0))*** Oxford Univ. Pr., Inc.
McNamara, Helen K. Strange Places, New Faces: Privately Printed Letters of Helen K. Mcnamara. 2011. 186p. 42.95 ***(978-1-258-04178-6(2))*** Literary Licensing, LLC.
Meredith, Richard. Driven Together: Historic First Crossing of Asia's New Highway to the West. 2008. (Illus.). 224p. *(978-0-9541432-4-4(8))* Mercury Bks.
Mirante, Edith. Down the Rat Hole: Adventures Underground on the Burma Frontier. 2006. (ENG., Illus.). 200p. pap. 21.95 *(978-974-524-050-6(8))* Orchid Pr. THA. Dist: National Bk. Network.
Morin, France, et al. Shirin Neshat: Games of Desire. 2010. (ENG & FRE., Illus.). 72p. pap. 34.95 *(978-88-8158-759-9(9))* Charta ITA. Dist: D.A.P./Distributed Art Pubs.
Mortimer, Favell Lee. Far Off. 2008. 224p. 24.99 *(978-0-554-33773-9(8))* 2008. 224p. 27.99 *(978-0-554-24470-9(5))* 2006. (ENG.). 222p. pap. 22.99 *(978-1-4264-6622-9(6))* BiblioBazaar.
—Far Off. 2009. 228p. pap. *(978-0-217-83521-3(X))* Books LLC.
Murray, Hugh. Historical Account of Discoveries & Travels in Asia, from the Earliest Ages to the Present Time, 3 vols. reprint ed. lib. bdg. 55.00 *(978-0-404-09570-3(4))* AMS Pr., Inc.
—Historical Account of Discoveries & Travels in Asia, from the Earliest Ages to the Present Time. 2009. 554p. 37.99 *(978-1-115-56978-1(3))*; pap. 41.75 *(978-1-115-56980-4(5))* BiblioBazaar.
—Historical Account of Discoveries & Travels in Asia, from the Earliest Ages to the Present Time. 2010. 196p. pap. *(978-1-152-76498-9(5))*; pap. *(978-1-152-76494-1(2))* Books LLC.
Neelis, Jason Emmanuel. Early Buddhist Transmission & Trade Networks: Mobility & Exchange Within & Beyond the Northwestern Borderlands of South Asia. 2010. xviii, 371p. *(978-90-04-18159-5(8))* BRILL.
Norell, Mark, et al. Traveling the Silk Road: Ancient Pathway to the Modern World. 2011. (ENG., Illus.). 260p. 40.00 *(978-1-4027-8137-7(7)*, Sterling Signature) Sterling Publishing Co., Inc.
Omrani, Bijan. Asia Overland: Tales of Travel on the Trans-Siberian & Silk Road. 2010. (ENG., Illus.). 544p. pap. 29.95 *(978-962-217-811-3(1)*, 217811) Airphoto International/Odyssey HKG. Dist: Norton, W. W. & Co., Inc.
O'Shea, Barbara. Postcards from Elsewhere: Travels in a Changing World. 2008. (ENG.). 320p. pap. *(978-1-903582-58-9(X))* Merlin Publishing, Dublin.
Parfitt, Troy. Notes from the Other China: Adventures in Asia. 2007. 34.95 *(978-0-87586-583-6(6))*; pap. 22.95 *(978-0-87586-582-9(8))* Algora Publishing.
Peltenburg-Brechneff, Christian. Homage — Deluxe Edition: Encounters with the East. 2009. (ENG.). 144p. 300.00 *(978-0-9793384-1-0(7))* Glitterati, Inc.
Polo, Marco. The Book of Ser Marco Polo, the Venetian: Concerning the Kingdoms & Marvels of the East. 2010. (Cambridge Library Collection - Travel & Exploration Ser.). (ENG.). 570p. pap. 39.99 *(978-1-108-02207-1(3))*; (Illus.). 612p. pap. 43.00 *(978-1-108-02206-4(5))* Cambridge Univ. Pr.
—Marco Polo the Description of the World A. C. Moule & Paul Pelliot Volume 1. 2010. 604p. pap. 49.95 *(978-4-87187-308-6(0))* Ishi Pr. International.
—Travels. Wright, T., ed. Marsden, tr. (Bohn's Antiquarian Library). reprint ed. 57.00 *(978-0-404-50023-8(4))* AMS Pr., Inc.
—Travels of Marco Polo. 2006. (ENG.). 26.95 *(978-1-60206-024-1(X)*, Cosimo Classics) Cosimo, Inc.
—Travels of Marco Polo. 2009. (ENG.). 285p. pap. 20.00 *(978-1-4379-6616-9(0))* DIANE Publishing Co.
—The Travels of Marco Polo. Harris, Peter, ed. 2008. (ENG., Illus.). 472p. 26.00 *(978-0-307-26913-3(2)*, Everyman's Library) Knopf Doubleday Publishing Group.
Polo, Marco & Yule, Henry. The Travels of Marco Polo. 2012. (ENG., Illus.). 400p. 40.00 ***(978-1-4027-9630-2(7)***, Sterling Signature) Sterling Publishing Co., Inc.
Prideaux, Bruce. Cultural & Heritage Tourism in Asia & the Pacific. 2008. pap. 40.00 *(978-0-415-49486-1(9))* Routledge.
Raney, Bill & Raney, JoAnne Walker. Letters to Zerky: A Father's Legacy to a Lost Son & a Road Trip Around the World. 2011. (ENG., Illus.). 436p. pap. 14.95 *(978-0-9821384-1-0(5))* Nickelodeon Pr.
Raney, JoAnne Walker & Raney, Bill. Letters to Zerky: A Father's Legacy to a Lost Son ... & a Road Trip Around the World. 2009. (ENG., Illus.). 436p. 27.00 *(978-0-9821384-0-3(7))* Nickelodeon Pr.
Rawson, R. R. The Monsoon Lands of Asia. 2007. (ENG., Illus.). 256p. pap. 24.95 *(978-0-202-30942-2(8))* Aldine Transaction.
Rockhill, William Woodville, ed. The Journey of William of Rubruck to the Eastern Parts of the World, 1253-55. 2010. (Hakluyt Society, Second Ser.). 392p. 69.95 *(978-1-4094-1371-4(3))* Hakluyt Society GBR. Dist: Ashgate Publishing Co.
Roerich, Nicholas. Heart of Asia. 2006. (ENG., Illus.). 88p. reprint ed. per. 24.95 *(978-0-9753093-5-3(8))* Ancient Wisdom Pubns.
Romb, Anselm M. Mission to Cathay: The Biography of Blessed Odoric of Pordenone. 2011. 166p. 41.95 ***(978-1-258-09160-6(7))*** Literary Licensing, LLC.
Ruysbroeck, Willem van, et al. The Mission of Friar William of Rubruck: His Journey to the Court of the Great Khan Möngke, 1253-1255. 2009. *(978-0-87220-982-4(2))* Hackett Publishing Co., Inc.
Saad, Rana. William of Rubruck's Account of the Mong. 2007. 129p. pap. 29.41 *(978-1-4116-5876-9(0))* Lulu Enterprises Inc.
Scalapino, Robert A. From Leavenworth to Lhasa: Living in a Revolutionary ERA. 2009. *(978-1-55729-092-2(X)*, Univ. of California, Institute of East Asian Studies.
Schwartz, Daniel. Travelling Through the Eye of History. 2009. (ENG., Illus.). 304p. 60.00 *(978-0-500-54290-3(2)*, 554290) Thames & Hudson.
Shea, Gerald P. Jerry, Catch Your Plane on Time: Travels to the Middle East & Beyond. 2009. 88p. pap. 10.95 *(978-1-4401-1200-3(2))* iUniverse, Inc.
Shidooka. Victorian Lady Travellers in Asia: A Collection of Travel Writings. 2007. (Illus.). 2150p. 990.00 *(978-4-86166-027-6(0))* Synapse, Edition JPN. Dist: Taylor & Francis Group.
Singh, Shalini, ed. Domestic Tourism in Asia: Diversity & Divergence. 2009. (ENG.). 368p. 117.00 *(978-1-84407-660-4(1))* Routledge.
Sochaczewski, Paul S. Sultan & Mermaid Queen. 2009. (ENG., Illus.). 256p. pap. 13.95 *(978-981-4217-74-3(3)*, Didier Millet,Csi) Continental Sales, Inc.
Stark, Freya. A Winter in Arabia: A Journey Through Yemen. 2010. (Freya Stark Collection). (ENG., Illus.). 336p. pap. 17.00 *(978-1-84885-192-4(8)*, Tauris Parke Paperbacks) I. B. Tauris & Co., Ltd. GBR. Dist: Macmillan.
Stoddard, John L. John L. Stoddard's Lectures, 10. l.t. ed. 2007. (ENG.). 268p. pap. 23.99 *(978-1-4264-8740-8(1))* BiblioBazaar.
—John L. Stoddard's Lectures Volume 10. 2007. (ENG.). 228p. pap. 20.99 *(978-1-4264-8685-2(5))* BiblioBazaar.
Sulaiman Haji Duraman. Kenali Negara Kita. 2009. (MAY., Illus.). v, 64p. *(978-99917-0-638-2(0))* Dewan Bahasa Dan Pustaka.
Tan, Soon Keat & Huang, Zhenhua. Asian & Pacific Coasts 2009: Proceedings of the 5th International Conference on APAC 2009, 4 vols. 2009. (Illus.). 1680p. pap. 483.00 *(978-981-4287-94-4(6))* World Scientific Publishing Co., Inc.
Tayler, Jeffrey. Murderers in Mausoleums: Riding the Back Roads of Empire Between Moscow & Beijing. 2009. (ENG., Illus.). 320p. 24.00 *(978-0-618-79991-6(5))* Houghton Mifflin Harcourt Publishing Co.
Theroux, Paul. Ghost Train to the Eastern Star: On the Tracks of the Great Railway Bazaar. (ENG.). 512p. 2009. pap. 15.95 *(978-0-547-23793-0(6)*, Mariner Bks.) 2008. (Illus.). 28.00 *(978-0-618-41887-9(3))* Houghton Mifflin Harcourt Trade & Reference Pubs.
Von Lossberg, Ann. 1089 Nights: An Odyssey Through the Middle East, Africa & Asia. 2008. 316p. pap. 18.95 *(978-1-4401-0520-3(0))* iUniverse, Inc.
Wagner, David. Unpaved Roads. 2007. 190p. per. 15.95 *(978-0-9766340-8-9(2))* Inkwell Productions, LLC.
Wangchuck, Ashi Dori Wangmo. Treasures of the Thunder Dragon: A Portrait of Bhutan. 2007. (ENG., Illus.). 224p. (gr. 12-18). 19.95 *(978-0-670-99901-9(6)*, Penguin Global) Penguin Group (USA) Inc.
Watkins, Inc. Staff, ed. Marco Polo's Silk Road: The Art of the Journey - an Italian at the Court of Kublai Khan. 2011. (Art of Wisdom Ser.). (ENG., Illus.). 272p. 24.95 *(978-1-78028-015-8(7)*, Watkins Publishing) Duncan Baird Pubs. GBR. Dist: Sterling Publishing Co., Inc.
Weis, Janet. Tourific: Travels in Asia, Africa, & Europe. 2007. 160p. 25.00 *(978-0-8387-5695-9(6))* Bucknell Univ. Pr.
White, Daniel. Cambodia & Laos. 2010. (Frommer's Complete Guides: 729). (ENG., Illus.). 352p. pap. 21.99 *(978-0-470-49778-4(5)*, Frommers) Wiley, John & Sons, Inc.
Winter, Tim. Asia on Tour: Exploring the Rise of Asian Tourism. Chang, T. C. & Teo, Peggy, eds. 2008. (ENG., Illus.). 376p. (C). 170.00 *(978-0-415-46085-9(9))*; pap. 44.95 *(978-0-415-46086-6(7))* Routledge.
Wolf, Vicente. Crossing Boundaries: A Global Vision of Design. 2006. (ENG., Illus.). 232p. 50.00 *(978-1-58093-181-6(2))* Monacelli Pr., Inc.
Wriggins, Sally Hovey. Asia on My Mind: From Ceylon to the Silk Road. 2008. (Illus.). 284p. pap. 22.95 *(978-1-4327-2180-0(1))* Outskirts Pr., Inc.
Yamashita, Michael, photos by. Marco Polo: A Photographer's Journey. 2011. (ENG., Illus.). 536p. 24.95 *(978-88-544-0587-5(6))* White Star ITA. Dist: Sterling Publishing Co., Inc.
Zacharias, Claudia And Keith. Our Cruise Through Asi: A Pictorial Review from Australia to Japan. 2009. 108p. pap. 30.49 *(978-1-4490-1882-5(3))* AuthorHouse.

ASIA—DESCRIPTION AND TRAVEL—VIEWS

see Asia—Pictorial Works

ASIA—DIRECTORIES

Asia Law and Practice Staff. Asia Law Profiles 2001: The Definitive Guide to Asia's Leading Law Firms. 125.00 *(978-962-936-089-4(6))* Asia Law & Practice Ltd. HKG. Dist: Book Clearing Hse.
BIA. Major Electronic & Electrical Equipment Manufacturers of Asia. 6th rev. ed. 2006. 300p. (J). pap. 249.00 *(978-1-4187-4284-3(8))* Business Information Agency.
—Major Manufacturers of Asia: Food, Textile, Clothing, & Chemical Companies. 6th rev. ed. 2006. 400p. (J). pap. 249.00 *(978-1-4187-4192-1(2))* Business Information Agency.
—Major Manufacturers of Azerbaijan, Armenia, & Georgia: Food, Textile, Clothing, & Chemical Companies. 6th rev. ed. 2006. 200p. (J). pap. 219.00 *(978-1-4187-4199-0(X))* Business Information Agency.
—Major Manufacturers of Kazakhstan: Food, Textile, Clothing, & Chemical Companies. 6th rev. ed. 2006. 250p. (J). pap. 249.00 *(978-1-4187-4404-5(2))* Business Information Agency.
Europa Publications, ed. South Asia 2012. 9th rev. ed. 2011. (ENG.). 848p. 815.00 ***(978-1-85743-624-2(5))*** Routledge.
Europa Publications Staff, ed. South Asia 2010. 7th rev. ed. 2009. (ENG.). 808p. 695.00 *(978-1-85743-534-4(6))* Routledge.
Ibp, Usa. Vietnam Industrial & Business Director. 2006. (Illus.). pap. 99.95 *(978-0-7397-9919-2(3))* Internatonal Business Pubns., USA.
O'Brien, Jillian. South Asia 2007. 4th rev. ed. 2006. (Illus.). 704p. 495.00 *(978-1-85743-393-7(9))* Routledge.
South Asia 2011. 8th rev. ed. 2010. (ENG., Illus.). 856p. 720.00 *(978-1-85743-572-6(9))* Routledge.

ASIA—ECONOMIC CONDITIONS

Acharya, Amitav. Asia Rising: Who Is Leading? 2008. 191p. pap. 37.00 *(978-981-277-133-9(6))* World Scientific Publishing Co., Inc.
Agénor, Pierre-Richard, et al, eds. The Asian Financial Crisis: Causes, Contagion & Consequences. 2006. (Global Economic Institutions Ser.). (ENG., Illus.). 448p. pap. 58.00 *(978-0-521-02900-1(7))* Cambridge Univ. Pr.
Al. The New Dynamics of Growth & Change in. , 2011. 270p. 93.00 *(978-981-279-156-6(6))* World Scientific Publishing Co., Inc.
Allen, Joseph Boots. What about the Locals? 2010. 316p. pap. *(978-3-8383-0288-1(5))* Lambert Academic Publishing.
Amineh, M. Parvizi, ed. State, Society & International Relations in Asia. 2010. (ICAS Publications Ser.). (Illus.). 307p. pap. *(978-90-5356-794-4(1))* Amsterdam Univ. Pr.
Andreosso-O'callaghan, Bernadette, ed. The Transformation of Asia in A Global Changing Environment. 2011. (Global Economic Studies). 95.00 ***(978-1-61470-873-5(8))*** Nova Science Pubs., Inc.
Andreosso-O'Callaghan, Bernadette & Zolin, M. Bruna, eds. Current Issues in Economic Integration: Can Asia Inspire the West? 2010. (Illus.). 268p. 114.95 *(978-0-7546-7956-1(X))* Ashgate Publishing Co.

Asian Development Bank. Asian Economic Cooperation & Integration: Progress, Prospects, Challenges. 2006. (ENG., Illus.). 388p. pap. *(978-971-561-549-5(X))* Asian Development Bank PHL. Dist: Independent Pubs. Group.

—Assessing the Impact of Transport & Energy Infrastructure on Poverty Reduction. 2006. (ENG.). 262p. pap. *(978-971-561-580-8(5))* Asian Development Bank PHL. Dist: Independent Pubs. Group.

Backman, Michael. Asia Future Shock: Business Crisis & Opportunity in the Coming Years. 2007. (ENG.). 200p. 59.00 *(978-0-230-00677-5(9))* Palgrave Macmillan.

—The Asian Insider: Unconventional Wisdom for Asian Business. annot. ed. 2006. (ENG.). 352p. pap. 40.00 *(978-0-230-00021-6(5))* Palgrave Macmillan.

Barth, James R., et al, eds. Asia's Debt Capital Markets: Prospects & Strategies for Devel. 2006. (Milken Institute Series on Financial Innovation & Economic Growth Ser.). (Illus.). XII, 322p. 209.00 *(978-0-387-25089-2(1)*, 0387250891) Springer.

Beeson, Mark. Institutions of the Asia-Pacific: ASEAN, APEC, & Beyond. 2008. (Illus.). XVI, 136p. pap. 28.95 *(978-0-415-46504-5(4))* Routledge.

Bengtsson, Tommy, et al. Life under Pressure: Mortality & Living Standards in Europe & Asia, 1700-1900. 2009. (Eurasian Population & Family History Ser.). (ENG., Illus.). 552p. (gr. 17). pap. 23.00 *(978-0-262-51243-5(2))* MIT Pr.

Berkshire Encyclopedia of Sustainability Vol. 9: Afro-Eurasia: Assessing Sustainability. 2010. 512p. lib. bdg. 150.00 *(978-1-933782-19-5(6))* Berkshire Publishing Group.

Bezbaruah, Madhurjya Prasad. Indo-Myanmar Cross-Border Trade. 2010. 124p. pap. *(978-3-639-26188-2(7))* VDM Verlag Dr. Mueller e.K.

BIA. Essential Kyrgyz Manufacturers: Food, Textile, Clothing, & Chemical Companies. 6th rev. ed. 2006. 180p. (J). pap. 219.00 *(978-1-4187-4195-2(7))* Business Information Agency.

—Key Banking, Financial, & Insurance Companies of Asia. 6th rev. ed. 2006. 180p. (J). pap. 219.00 *(978-1-4187-4375-8(5))* Business Information Agency.

Boyer, Robert & Uemura, Hiroyasu, eds. Diversity & Transformations of Asian Capitalisms: A de Facto Regional Integration. 2011. (Routledge Studies in the Modern World Economy Ser.). (ENG., Illus.). 416p. (C). 171.00 *(978-0-415-60440-6(0))* Routledge.

Brooks, Douglas H. & Menon, Jayant, eds. Infrastructure & Trade in Asia. 2008. 256p. (C). 119.00 *(978-1-84720-941-2(6))* Elgar, Edward Publishing, Inc.

Brooks, Douglas H. & Stone, Susan F. Trade Facilitation & Regional Cooperation in Asia. Brooks, Douglas H. & Stone, Susan F., eds. 2010. (Illus.). 208p. 112.00 *(978-1-84844-986-2(0))* Elgar, Edward Publishing, Inc.

Burgess, John & Connell, Julia, eds. Globalisation & Work in Asia. 2007. (Chandos Asian Studies). (ENG., Illus.). 342p. 110.00 *(978-1-84334-217-5(0)*, Chandos Publishing) Woodhead Publishing Ltd. GBR. Dist: Ingram Pub. Services.

Cabanda, Emilyn. Privatisation & Performance of Asian Telecommunications. 2010. 136p. pap. *(978-3-8383-6072-0(9))* Lambert Academic Publishing.

Carney, Richard. Lessons from the Asian Financial Crisis. 2008. (Routledge Contemporary Asia Ser.). (ENG., Illus.). 288p. (C). 150.00 *(978-0-415-48190-8(2))* Routledge.

Carney, Richard, ed. Lessons from the Asian Financial Crisis. 2011. (ENG., Illus.). 276p. pap. 42.95 ***(978-0-415-66710-4(0))*** Routledge.

Chaze, Aaron. The Asian Investor: Charting a Course Through Asia's Emerging Markets. 2010. (ENG., Illus.). 250p. 34.95 *(978-0-470-82529-7(4)*, Wiley) Wiley, John & Sons, Inc.

Cheung, Yin-Wong, et al. The Evolving Role of Asia in Global Finance. 2011. (Frontiers of Economics & Globalization Ser.: Vol. 9). (Illus.). 410p. 154.95 *(978-0-85724-745-2(X))* Emerald Group Publishing Ltd. GBR. Dist: Turpin Distribution Services Ltd.

Chin, Felix, ed. Political & Economic Developments in Asia. 2011. (Asian Political, Economic & Security Issues Ser.). 309p. 129.00 *(978-1-61209-783-1(9))* Nova Science Pubs., Inc.

Chin, Felix, ed. Politics & Economics of Northern & Western Asia. 2011. (Asian Political, Economic & Security Issues Ser.). 185.00 ***(978-1-61470-460-7(0))*** Nova Science Pubs., Inc.

Chong, Terence, ed. Globalization & Its Counter-Forces in Southeast Asi. 2008. 432p. *(978-981-230-488-9(6))* Institute of Southeast Asian Studies.

Choudhary, K. N. Rural Women Workers in Asia. 2010. 255p. 59.50 *(978-81-7533-309-3(X))* M. D. Pubns. Pvt. Ltd. IND. Dist: Coronet Bks.

Chowdhury. Handbook on the Asian Economies - Southeast Asia & Northeast Asia. 2007. (Elgar Original Reference Ser.). 352p. (C). 210.00 *(978-1-84376-989-7(1))* Elgar, Edward Publishing, Inc.

Chu. China's Accession to the Wto & Its Impact on Asian Economies. 2007. 304p. *(978-1-84542-842-6(0))* Elgar, Edward Publishing, Inc.

Chu, Ming-Chin Monique. The East Asian Computer Chip War. 2012. (Routledge Studies on the Chinese Economy Ser.). (ENG.). 192p. (C). 130.00 *(978-0-415-56552-3(9))* Routledge.

Clifford, Mark L. & Pau, Janet. Through the Eyes of Tiger Cubs: Views of Asia's Next Generation. 2011. (ENG., Illus.). 224p. pap. 27.95 ***(978-1-118-09463-1(8)***, Wiley) Wiley, John & Sons, Inc.

Columbus, Frank, ed. Asian Economic & Political Issues, Volume 13. 2010. (Asian Economic & Political Issues Ser.). 89.00 *(978-1-61668-015-2(6))* Nova Science Pubs., Inc.

Constable, Nicole. Migrant Domestic Workers in Asia: Distant Divides, Intimate Connections. 2010. (Illus.). 232p. (C). *(978-0-415-57814-1(0)*, Routledge) Taylor & Francis Group.

Corr, Kendra. The U. S. & W. W. I: I Think: U. S. History. 2011. (ENG.). 100p. (YA). pap. 29.95 *(978-1-933558-17-2(2))* InspirEd Educators.

Cortinhas, Carlos. Prospects for Monetary Integration in Asean. 2009. 172p. pap. *(978-3-639-20742-2(4))* VDM Verlag Dr. Mueller e.K.

Daniels, P. W. & Harrington, J. W., eds. Services & Economic Development in the Asia-Pacific. 2007. (Dynamics of Economic Space Ser.). (Illus.). 262p. 124.95 *(978-0-7546-4859-8(1))* Ashgate Publishing Co.

Daniels, Peter W., et al, eds. New Economic Spaces in Asian Cities: From Industrial Restructuring to the Cultural Turn. 2012. (Routledge Studies in Human Geography Ser.). (ENG., Illus.). 320p. (C). 160.00 *(978-0-415-56773-2(4))* Routledge.

Das, Dilip K. The Asian Economy: Spearheading the Recovery from the Global Financial Crisis. 2011. (ENG., Illus.). 200p. (C). 140.00 *(978-0-415-66553-7(1))*; pap. 47.95 *(978-0-415-66554-4(X))* Routledge.

Das-Gupta, Dilip K. Asian Economy & Finance: A Post-Crisis Perspective. 2010. (Innovations in Financial Markets & Institutions Ser.). (Illus.). xxiv, 309p. pap. 219.00 *(978-1-4419-3619-6(X)*, 144193619X) Springer.

Debes Rasmussen, Britt. The Impacts of Water Scarcity on the Prospects for Poverty Alleviation. 2011. 120p. pap. ***(978-3-8443-8006-4(X))*** Lambert Academic Publishing.

Dezan Shira & Associates, et al, eds. China's Neighbors: Who Is Influencing China & Who China Is Influencing in the New Emerging Asia. 3rd ed. 2012. (China Briefing Ser.). (ENG., Illus.). viii, 87p. pap. 49.95 ***(978-3-642-27614-9(8)***, 3642276148) Springer.

Dimitriou. Motorization & Sustainable Develpt. 2008. 256p. pap. 150.00 *(978-0-415-33187-6(0))* Routledge.

Diokno, Maria. The Mekong Arranged & Rearranged. Chinh, Nguyen Van, ed. 2007. (Mekong Press Ser.). (ENG.). 228p. pap. 14.95 ***(978-974-94804-9-6(X))*** Silkworm Bks. THA. Dist: Univ. of Washington Pr.

Donald Wood Staff. Economic Development, Integration, & Morality in Asia & the Americas. 2009. (Illus.). x, 429p. 154.95 *(978-1-84855-542-6(3))* Emerald Group Publishing Ltd. GBR. Dist: Turpin Distribution Services Ltd.

Dong, Lisheng & Heiduk, Günter. The EU's Experience in Integration: A Model for ASEAN+3? (Illus.). 358p. pap. 68.95 *(978-3-03911-429-0(8))* Lang, Peter Publishing, Inc.

Douglas, Peter. Hedge Funds in Asia. 2006. (Wiley Finance Ser.). 250p. 60.00 *(978-0-470-82191-6(4))* Wiley, John & Sons, Inc.

Dowling, John Malcolm & Rana, Pradumna Bickram. Asia & the Global Economic Crisis: Challenges in a Financially Integrated World. 2010. (ENG., Illus.). 320p. 110.00 *(978-0-230-27363-4(7))* Palgrave Macmillan.

Drysdale & Terada. Asia-Pacific Economic Co-Operation: Critical Perspectives on the World Economy, 4 vols. 2007. (Critical Perspectives on the World Economy Ser.). (ENG., Illus.). 1968p. (C). 1680.00 *(978-0-415-31098-7(9))* Routledge.

Economic and Social Commission for Asia and the Pacific Staff. , Vol. 32, No. 2. 123p. pap. 11.00 United Nations Pubns.

Empson, Rebecca M. Harnessing Fortune: Personhood, Memory & Place in Northeast Mongolia. 2011. (ENG., Illus.). 398p. 115.00 *(978-0-19-726473-7(5))* Oxford Univ. Pr., Inc.

Eriksson, Sören. Global Shift in the Aircraft Industry: A Study of Airframe Manufacturing with Special Reference to the Asian NIEs. (Illus.). 244p. *(978-91-86472-21-4(6))* Goteborgs Universitet, Kulturgeografiska Institutionen.

Euromonitor International Staff, ed. Asian Marketing Data & Statistics. 5th ed. 2011. (Asia Marketing Data & Statistics Ser.). (ENG.). 382p. lib. bdg. ***(978-1-84264-547-5(1))*** Euromonitor International PLC.

Falloux, Francois & Talbot, Lee M. Aid & Development, Set. 2009. (Earthscan Library Collection). (ENG.). 3794p. 1390.00 *(978-1-84971-039-8(2))* Routledge.

Fang, Xiaomin. Lander ohne Marktwirtschaft im Antidumpingrecht der EG: Unter Besonderer Berucksichtigung der Praxis Gegenuber China. (Europaische Hochschulschriften Ser.: Vol. 3473). (GER., Illus.). 254p. 35.95 *(978-3-631-39804-3(2))* Lang, Peter Publishing, Inc.

Felipe, Jesus. Inclusive Growth, Full Employment, & Structural Change: Implications & Policies for Developing Asia, Second Edition. 2nd rev. ed. 2010. (Anthem-Asian Development Bank Series the Anthem-European Union Ser.). (ENG., Illus.). 368p. 99.00 *(978-0-85728-958-2(6))* Anthem Pr. GBR. Dist: Books International, Inc.

Francois, Joseph, et al, eds. National Strategies for Regional Integration: South & East Asian Case Studies. 2009. (Anthem Studies in Development & Globalization Ser.). (ENG., Illus.). 583p. 130.00 *(978-1-84331-789-0(3))* Anthem Pr. GBR. Dist: Books International, Inc.

Francois, Joseph F. & Wignaraja, Ganeshan. Pan-Asian Integration: Linking East & South Asia. Francois, Joseph F. & Wignaraja, Ganeshan, eds. Rana, Pradumna Bickram, ed. 2009. (ENG., Illus.). 320p. 121.00 *(978-0-230-22178-9(5))* Palgrave Macmillan.

Frost, Ellen L. Asia's New Regionalism. 2008. 275p. (C). pap. 25.00 *(978-1-58826-579-1(X))*; lib. bdg. 65.00 *(978-1-58826-554-8(4))* Rienner, Lynne Pubs.

Fujita, Masahisa. Economic Integration in Asia & India. Fujita, Masahisa, ed. 2008. (ENG., Illus.). 208p. 105.00 *(978-0-230-52085-1(5))* Palgrave Macmillan.

Fujita, Masahisa, et al, eds. The Economics of East Asian Integration: A Comprehensive Introduction to Regional Issues. 2011. (Illus.). 552p. 210.00 ***(978-0-85793-011-8(7))*** Elgar, Edward Publishing, Inc.

Gale. Consumer Asia Pacific & Australasia. 19th ed. 2011. (Consumer Asia Pacific & Australasia Ser.). (ENG.). 342p. ***(978-1-84264-552-9(8))*** Euromonitor International PLC.

Garon, Sheldon. Beyond Our Means: Why America Spends While the World Saves. 2011. (ENG., Illus.). 448p. 29.95 ***(978-0-691-13599-1(1))*** Princeton Univ. Pr.

Garon, Sheldon & MacLachlan, Patricia L., eds. The Ambivalent Consumer: Questioning Consumption in East Asia & the West. 2006. (Illus.). 314p. per. 29.95 *(978-0-8014-7302-9(0))* Cornell Univ. Pr.

Garon, Sheldon M. & MacLachlan, Patricia L. The Ambivalent Consumer: Questioning Consumption in East Asia & the West. 2006. (Illus.). 328p. 72.50 *(978-0-8014-4487-6(X))* Cornell Univ. Pr.

Gill, Sucha Singh, et al, eds. Economic & Environmental Sustainability of the Asian Region. 2010. (ENG., Illus.). xxvi, 461p. (C). 95.00 *(978-0-415-58144-8(3)*, Routledge India) Taylor & Francis Group GBR. Dist: Taylor & Francis Group.

Gipouloux, François, ed. Gateways to Globalisation: Asia's International Trading & Finance Centres. 2011. (Illus.). 288p. 115.00 ***(978-0-85793-424-6(4))*** Elgar, Edward Publishing, Inc.

Githinji, Mwangi wa. Is That a Dragon or Elephant on Your Ladder: The Potential Impact of China & India on Export Led Growth in African Countries? 2009. (NAI Discussion Papers). 40p. pap. 12.95 *(978-91-7106-646-6(2))* Nordiska Afrikainstitutet SWE. Dist: Stylus Publishing, LLC.

Glassman, Jim. Bounding the Mekong: The Asian Development Bank, China, & Thailand. 2010. 280p. 55.00 *(978-0-8248-3444-9(5))* Univ. of Hawaii Pr.

Goswami, Namrata & Lele, Ajey, eds. Imagining Asia in 2030: Tends, Scenarios & Alternatives. 2011. 580p. 89.95 *(978-81-7188-870-2(4))* Academic Foundation IND. Dist: Independent Pubs. Group.

Gubry El At., Patrick, ed. The Vietnamese City in Transition. 2010. 364p. pap. *(978-981-230-825-2(3))* Institute of Southeast Asian Studies.

Haryono, Endi. Dilema Mahathir: Kebijakan Ekonomi Politik Malaysia Dalam Menghadapi Krisis Ekonomi Asia. 2010. (IND.). xviii, 222p. *(978-979-1262-29-3(2))* Tiara Wacana.

Hiratsuka, Daisake. East Asia's de Facto Economic Integration. Hiratsuka, Daisuke, ed. 2007. (ENG., Illus.). 288p. 110.00 *(978-0-230-00782-6(1))* Palgrave Macmillan.

Hobbes, Marieke. Figuring Rural Development: Concepts & cases of land use, sustainability & integrative Indicators. 2010. (LUP Dissertaties Ser.). 232p. pap. *(978-90-8728-078-9(5)*, Leiden Univ. Pr.) Amsterdam Univ. Pr.

Holloway, Richard, ed. Doing Development: Government, NGOs & the Rural Poor in Asia. 2009. (Aid & Development Set Ser.). (ENG.). 250p. 110.00 *(978-1-84971-043-5(0))* Routledge.

Hossain, A. Central Banking & Monetary Policy in the Asia-Pacific. 2009. (Illus.). 368p. 173.00 *(978-1-84720-372-4(8))* Elgar, Edward Publishing, Inc.

Hossain, Aliar. Sustainable Development Handbook- A South Asian Perspective. 2011. 152p. pap. 17.23 *(978-1-4567-7197-3(3))* AuthorHouse.

Hossain, Moazzem & Selvanathan, Antony, eds. Climate Change & Growth in Asia. 2011. (Illus.). 288p. 125.00 *(978-1-84844-245-0(9))* Elgar, Edward Publishing, Inc.

Hou, Gary G., ed. Asian Noodles: Science, Technology, & Processing. 2010. (ENG., Illus.). 447p. 205.00 *(978-0-470-17922-2(8)*, Wiley) Wiley, John & Sons, Inc.

Icon Group International, Inc. Staff, compiled by. The 2006 Economic & Product Market Databook for Ashgabat, Turkmenistan. 2006. 618p. ring bd. 95.00 *(978-0-497-80092-5(6))* Icon Group International, Inc.

—The 2006 Economic & Product Market Databook for Bishkek, Kyrgyzstan. 2006. 618p. ring bd. 95.00 *(978-0-497-80204-2(X))* Icon Group International, Inc.

—The 2006 Economic & Product Market Databook for Darhan, Mongolia. 2006. 618p. ring bd. 95.00 *(978-0-497-79978-6(2))* Icon Group International, Inc.

—The 2006 Economic & Product Market Databook for Dhamar, Yemen. 2006. 618p. ring bd. 95.00 *(978-0-497-80456-5(5))* Icon Group International, Inc.

—The 2006 Economic & Product Market Databook for Kuala Belait, Brunei. 2006. 618p. ring bd. 95.00 *(978-0-497-80774-0(2))* Icon Group International, Inc.

—The 2006 Economic & Product Market Databook for Kyzyl-Kiya, Kyrgyzstan. 2006. 618p. ring bd. 95.00 *(978-0-497-80795-5(5))* Icon Group International, Inc.

—The 2006 Economic & Product Market Databook for Male, Maldives. 2006. 618p. ring bd. 95.00 *(978-0-497-80931-7(1))* Icon Group International, Inc.

—The 2006 Economic & Product Market Databook for Monywa, Burma. 2006. 618p. ring bd. 95.00 *(978-0-497-81054-2(9))* Icon Group International, Inc.

—The 2006 Economic & Product Market Databook for Moulmein, Burma. 2006. 618p. ring bd. 95.00 *(978-0-497-81065-8(4))* Icon Group International, Inc.

—The 2006 Economic & Product Market Databook for Nalayh, Mongolia. 2006. 618p. ring bd. 95.00 *(978-0-497-82028-2(5))* Icon Group International, Inc.

—The 2006 Economic & Product Market Databook for Phuntsholing, Bhutan. 2006. 618p. ring bd. 95.00 *(978-0-497-81221-8(5))* Icon Group International, Inc.

—The 2006 Economic & Product Market Databook for Przhevalsk, Kyrgyzstan. 2006. 618p. ring bd. 95.00 *(978-0-497-81293-5(2))* Icon Group International, Inc.

—The 2006 Economic & Product Market Databook for Punakha, Bhutan. 2006. 618p. ring bd. 95.00 *(978-0-497-81299-7(1))* Icon Group International, Inc.

—The 2006 Economic & Product Market Databook for Qandahar, Afghanistan. 2006. 618p. ring bd. 95.00 *(978-0-497-81312-3(2))* Icon Group International, Inc.

—The 2006 Economic & Product Market Databook for Qonduz, Afghanistan. 2006. 618p. ring bd. 95.00 *(978-0-497-81314-7(9))* Icon Group International, Inc.

—The 2006 Economic & Product Market Databook for Sittwe, Burma. 2006. 618p. ring bd. 95.00 *(978-0-497-81545-5(1))* Icon Group International, Inc.

—The 2006 Economic & Product Market Databook for Taizz, Yemen. 2006. 618p. ring bd. 95.00 *(978-0-497-81624-7(5))* Icon Group International, Inc.

—The 2006 Economic & Product Market Databook for Ulaanbaatar, Mongolia. 2006. 618p. ring bd. 95.00 *(978-0-497-81744-2(6))* Icon Group International, Inc.

—The 2006 Economic & Product Market Databook for Ulaangom, Mongolia. 2006. 618p. ring bd. 95.00 *(978-0-497-81745-9(4))* Icon Group International, Inc.

—The 2006 Economic & Product Market Databook for Uliastay, Mongolia. 2006. 618p. ring bd. 95.00 *(978-0-497-81746-6(2))* Icon Group International, Inc.

—The 2006 Economic & Product Market Databook for Vacoas-Phoenix, Mauritius. 2006. 618p. ring bd. 95.00 *(978-0-497-81765-7(9))* Icon Group International, Inc.

—The 2006 Economic & Product Market Databook for Yangon, Burma. 2006. 618p. ring bd. 95.00 *(978-0-497-81837-1(X))* Icon Group International, Inc.

Inomata, Satoshi. Asia Beyond the Global Economic Crisis: The Transmission Mechanism of Financial Shocks. Inomata, Satoshi, ed. 2011. (Illus.). 224p. 110.00 *(978-1-84980-764-7(7))* Elgar, Edward Publishing, Inc.

International Monetary Fund Staff, ed. Regional Economic Outlook - Asia & Pacific: 2008. 2008. (World Economic & Financial Surveys Ser.). 50p. pap. 31.00 *(978-1-58906-710-3(X))* International Monetary Fund.

Ito, Takatoshi. A Basket Currency for Asia. 2006. (Routledge Studies in the Growth Economies of Asia: Vol. 65). (Illus.). 203p. 180.00 *(978-0-415-38376-9(5))* Routledge.

Jarvis, Darryl S. L., ed. International Business Risk: A Handbook for the Asia-Pacific Region. 2011. (ENG., Illus.). 498p. pap. 39.99 *(978-0-521-17551-7(8))* Cambridge Univ. Pr.

Jeffries, Ian. Mongolia: A Guide to Economic & Political Developments. 2012. (Guides to Economic & Political Developments in Asia Ser.). (ENG., Illus.). 224p. (C). pap. 42.95 ***(978-0-415-54174-9(3))*** Routledge.

Jerve, Alf Morten. Aid Relationships in Asia: Exploring Ownership in Japanese & Nordic Aid. Jerve, Alf Morten et al, eds. 2008. (ENG., Illus.). 288p. 110.00 *(978-0-230-00495-5(4))* Palgrave Macmillan.

Johnson, Steve, et al. Afganistan: The Mirage of Peace. 2nd ed. 2008. (ENG., Illus.). 272p. pap. 26.95 *(978-1-84277-956-9(7))* Zed Bks., Ltd. GBR. Dist: Macmillan.

Kanke, Yoko. A Comparative Analysis of Eu & Asean. 2010. 88p. pap. *(978-3-8383-4233-7(X))* Lambert Academic Publishing.

Kawai, M., et al, eds. Monetary & Currency Policy Management in Asia: Implications of the Global Financial Crisis. 2012. 320p. 135.00 ***(978-0-85793-334-8(5))*** Elgar, Edward Publishing, Inc.

Kawai, Masahiro & Prasad, Eswar S., eds. Asian Perspectives on Financial Sector Reforms & Regulation. 2011. (ENG., Illus.). 350p. pap. 34.95 ***(978-0-8157-2210-6(9))*** Brookings Institution Pr.

Kawai, Masahiro, et al. Asian Regionalism in the World Economy: Engine for Dynamism & Stability. 2010. (Illus.). 544p. 160.00 *(978-1-84844-854-4(6))* Elgar, Edward Publishing, Inc.

Kawakami, Momoko. The Dynamics of Local Learning in Global Value Chains: Experiences from East Asia. 2011. (IDE-JETRO Ser.). (ENG., Illus.). 272p. 100.00 *(978-0-230-23849-7(1))* Palgrave Macmillan.

Keller, William W. & Rawski, Thomas G., eds. China's Rise & the Balance of Influence in Asia. 2007. (Pitt Security Continuum Ser.). (Illus.). 284p. 65.00 *(978-0-8229-4312-9(3))* Univ. of Pittsburgh Pr.

Khondker, Habibul Haque & Therborn, Goran, eds. Asia & Europe in Globalization: Continents, Regions & Nations. 2006. (Social Sciences in Asia Ser.: Vol. 8). (Illus.). 313p. pap. *(978-90-04-15350-9(0))* BRILL.

Kohli, Harinder S. & Sharma, Ashok. A Resilient Asia Amidst Global Financial Crisis: From Crisis Management to Global Leadership. 2010. (Illus.). 456p. (C). 49.95 *(978-81-321-0516-9(8)*, B05169C) SAGE Pubns., Inc.

Kuroda, Masahiro, et al. Productivity in Asia: Economic Growth & Competitiveness. Jorgenson, Dale et al, eds. Motohashi, Kazuyuki et al, eds. 2007. (Illus.). 256p. (C). 119.00 *(978-1-84720-399-1(X))* Elgar, Edward Publishing, Inc.

Lee, Yoong Yoong. Asean Matters: Reflecting on the Association of Southeast Asian Nations. 2011. (Illus.). 180p. pap. 35.00 *(978-981-4335-06-5(1))* World Scientific Publishing Co., Inc.

Li, Kui Wai. Trade & Capital Flow among Asian Economies. Rowley, Chris, ed. 2007. (Illus.). 240p. 140.00 *(978-0-415-44553-5(1))* Routledge.

Lim, Mah Hui & Lim, Chin. Nowhere to Hide: The Great Financial Crisis & Challenges for Asia. 2010. (Illus.). xxiv, 174p. pap. *(978-981-4279-73-4(0))* Institute of Southeast Asian Studies.

Lo, Chi. Asia & the Subprime Crisis: Lifting the Veil on the 'Financial Tsunami' 2009. (ENG., Illus.). 250p. 100.00 *(978-0-230-23619-6(7))* Palgrave Macmillan.

MacDonald, Scott B. & Lemco, Jonathan. Asia's Rise in the 21st Century. 2011. E-Book ***(978-0-313-39371-6(0)***, Praeger Pubs.) Greenwood Publishing Group, Inc.

Maddison, Angus. Asia Libecohis, 6 vols., Set C. 2006. 181p. 1095.00 *(978-0-415-38110-9(X))* Routledge.

Madumarov, Eldar. External Factors of Economic Growth. 2008. 260p. pap. *(978-3-639-07643-1(5))* VDM Verlag Dr. Mueller e.K.

Manoranjan Dutta Staff. The Asian Economy & Asian Money. 2009. (Illus.). xxxiv, 328p. 144.95 *(978-1-84855-260-9(2))* Emerald Group Publishing Ltd. GBR. Dist: Turpin Distribution Services Ltd.

Marek, David A., ed. Asian Economic & Political Issues. Volume 14. 2009. (Asian Economic & Political Issues Ser.). (Illus.). 267p. 103.50 (978-1-61728-019-1(4)) Nova Science Pubs., Inc.
MasterCard International Staff & Hedrick-Wong, Yuwa. The Future & Me: Power of the Youth Market in Asia. 2008. (ENG., Illus.). 200p. pap. 22.95 (978-0-470-82208-1(2), Wiley) Wiley, John & Sons, Inc.
Mazumdar, Krishna, ed. Performances of Asia-pacific Countries: A New Approach. 2009. (Global Economic Studies). 89.00 (978-1-60876-174-6(6)) Nova Science Pubs., Inc.
McKee, Chris, ed. International Country Risk Guide Annual - 2006 Vol. 6: Asia & the Pacific. 2006. (C). per. (978-1-933539-25-6(9)) PRS Group Inc., The.
Menkhoff, Thomas, et al, eds. Beyond the Knowledge Trap: Developing Asia's Knowledge-Based Economies. 2011. (ENG., Illus.). 444p. 88.00 (978-981-4343-87-1(6)) World Scientific Publishing Co., Inc.
Moller, J. Ørstrom. How Asia Can Shape the World: From the ERA of Plenty to the ERA of Scarcities. 2010. xiv, 540p. pap. (978-981-4311-33-5(2)) Institute of Southeast Asian Studies.
Morioka, Tohru, et al, eds. Establishing a Resource-Circulating Society in Asia: Challenges & Opportunities. 2011. (ENG.). 375p. pap. 37.00 (978-92-808-1182-7(7)) United Nations Univ. Pr. JPN. Dist: Brookings Institution Pr.
Mudupadi Peddadu, Ashveen. Exploring the Dynanism of the Freeport Sector in Mauritius. 2010. 120p. pap. (978-3-639-18312-2(6)) VDM Verlag Dr. Mueller e.K.
Munakata, Naoko. Transforming East Asia: The Evolution of Regional Economic Integration. 2006. (ENG., Illus.). 258p. per. 26.95 (978-0-8157-5887-7(1)) Brookings Institution Pr.
Nair, Chandran. Consumptionomics: Asia's Role in Reshaping Capitalism & Saving the Planet. 2011. (ENG.). 256p. 27.95 (978-0-470-82857-1(9), Wiley) Wiley, John & Sons, Inc.
Nakagawa, Junji, ed. Multilateralism & Regionalism in Global Economic Governance. 2011. (Routledge Studies in the Modern World Economy Ser.). (ENG., Illus.). 216p. (C). 152.00 (978-0-415-59569-8(X)) Routledge.
Naranhuu, Bolor. Studies on Poverty in Mongoli. 2008. 112p. pap. (978-3-639-07660-8(5)) VDM Verlag Dr. Mueller e.K.
Nath, Pabloo Pratim. My Mba Journey-A Global Experience with an Asian Perspective. 2011. 100p. pap. (978-3-8383-2543-9(5)) Lambert Academic Publishing.
Nathan, Dev, et al. Markets & Indigenous Peoples in Asia: Lessons from Development Projects. 2012. (ENG.). 246p. 40.00 (978-0-19-807895-1(1)) Oxford Univ. Pr., Inc.
Nault, Derrick M. Development in Asia: Interdisciplinary, Post-Neoliberal, & Transnational Perspectives. 2008. 276p. pap. 25.95 (978-1-59942-488-0(6), Brown Walker Pr.) Universal Pubs.
Neopaney, Kritika. Impacts of Rural Electrification in the Lives of Bhutanese Women. 2011. 128p. pap. (978-3-8443-2143-2(8)) Lambert Academic Publishing.
Nordell, Emelie & Stark, Caroline. Diversifying in the Integrated Markets of Asean+3. 2010. 84p. pap. (978-3-8383-9430-5(5)) Lambert Academic Publishing.
Oga, Toru. Discourses on Asianisation: The Asian Financial Crisis & Rediscovering Asianness. 2008. 308p. pap. (978-3-639-09294-3(5)) VDM Verlag Dr. Mueller e.K.
Omar, Norman & Danto, Arthur C. Responsible Development: Asia Ten Years after the Crisis. 2010. (Routledge Studies in the Growth Economies of Asia Ser.). (ENG., Illus.). 256p. (C). 145.00 (978-0-7103-1348-5(9)) Routledge.
Ooi. Surviving War Talent Asia. 2009. (ENG.). 216p. pap. 29.99 (978-0-13-700951-0(8)) Pearson Education.
Organisation for Economic Co-operation and Development Staff. Legal & Institutional Reforms of Asian Insolvency Systems. 2007. pap. 78.00 (978-92-64-03832-5(9)) Organization for Economic Cooperation & Development.
Osbeck, Maria & Wojciechowska-Shibuya, Marisha. Forest Partnerships: Enhancing Local Livelihoods & Protecting the Environment in Southeast Asia & the Pacific. 2007. (Illus.). 49p. pap. 15.00 (978-2-8317-1011-2(1)) International League of Conservation Photographers.
Ozawa, Terutomo. The Rise of Asia: The 'Flying-Geese' Theory of Tandem Growth & Regional Agglomeration. (New Horizons in International Business Ser.). (Illus.). 256p. 2011. pap. 45.00 (978-0-85793-590-8(9)) 2009. 127.00 (978-1-84720-815-6(0)) Elgar, Edward Publishing, Inc.
Park, Yung Chul & Wyplosz, Charles. Monetary & Financial Integration in East Asia: The Relevance of European Experience. 2010. (ENG., Illus.). 192p. 80.00 (978-0-19-958712-4(4)) Oxford Univ. Pr., Inc.
Parthasarathi, Prasannan. Why Europe Grew Rich & Asia Did Not: Global Economic Divergence, 1600-1850. 2011. (ENG., Illus.). 384p. 90.00 (978-1-107-00030-8(0)); pap. 29.99 (978-0-521-16824-3(4)) Cambridge Univ. Pr.
Peterson, Erik R. & Posner, Rachel, eds. Water & Energy Futures in an Urbanized Asia: Sustaining the Tiger. 2007. (Illus.). 64p. pap. 17.95 net. (978-0-89206-521-9(4), CSIS Pr., The) Ctr. for Strategic & International Studies.
Petrov, A. M. Mezhdunarodnoe Ekonomicheskoe Obshchenie V Istorii Vostoka. 2010. (RUS., Illus.). 205p. (978-5-93136-123-9(5)) Kljuc-S, Izdatel'skij dom.
Raa. Input-Output Economics: Theory & Appl. . 2009. 135.00 (978-981-283-366-2(6)) World Scientific Publishing Co., Inc.
Rahimli, Rovshan. The Case of Azerbaijan. 2011. 92p. pap. (978-3-8443-9181-7(9)) Lambert Academic Publishing.
Rahman, Sultan Hafeez, et al. Regional Integration & Economic Development in South Asia. Khatri, Sunil P., ed. 2012. (Illus.). 448p. 195.00 (978-1-78100-327-5(0)) Elgar, Edward Publishing, Inc.
Rajan, Ramkishen S., ed. Emerging Asia: Essays on Crises, Capital Flows, FDI & Exchange Rate. 2011. (ENG., Illus.). 208p. 90.00 (978-0-230-23845-9(9)) Palgrave Macmillan.
Rakesh, Raman. Weaker Sex Stronger Endeavour: Women in Economic Development of Bhutan. 2011. 124p. pap. (978-3-639-32942-1(2)) VDM Verlag Dr. Mueller e.K.
Rana, Pradumna Bickram. Renaissance of Asia: Evolving Economic Relations Between South Asia & East Asia. 2012. 276p. 108.00 (978-981-4366-50-2(1)) World Scientific Publishing Co., Inc.
Redman, Nicholas & Dodge, Toby. The Future of Afghanistan After 2014. 2012. (Adelphi Ser.). (ENG.). 300p. (C). pap. 24.99 (978-0-415-69642-5(9)) Routledge.
ROCHE. Private Equity in Asia. 2007. 208p. pap. 44.95 (978-0-415-36238-2(5), RU62385) Routledge.
Rondinelli, Dennis A. & Heffron, John M., eds. Globalization & Change in Asia. 2007. 265p. (C). pap. 24.50 (978-1-58826-497-8(1)); lib. bdg. 59.95 (978-1-58826-473-2(4)) Rienner, Lynne Pubs.
Rosefielde, Steven. Two Asias: The Emerging Postcrisis Divide. 2011. 472p. 140.00 (978-981-4366-26-7(9)) World Scientific Publishing Co., Inc.
Rowley, Chris & Harry, Wes. Managing People Globally: An Asian Perspective. 2011. (Chandos Asian Studies). (ENG.). 200p. 135.00 (978-1-84334-223-6(5), Chandos Publishing) Woodhead Publishing Ltd. GBR. Dist: Ingram Pub. Services.
Schiff, Jerald Alan, et al. Regional Economic Outlook: Asia & Pacific. 2008. (World Economic & Financial Surveys Ser.). (Illus.). ix, 57p. (978-1-58906-761-5(4)) International Monetary Fund.
Schlevogt, Kai-Alexander. Brave New Saw Wave World: Emerging & Submerging Asia in the Global Environment. 2011. 176p. (C). pap. 34.99 (978-81-317-5403-0(0)) FT Press.
Schommers, Thomas. An Outlook on Asian Integration- Are the Development of Fdi & Fta Between Japan, China, Republic of Korea & Asean Indicators for Further Integrati. 2007. 88p. per. (978-3-8364-4615-0(4), VDM Verlag Dr. Mueller e.K.
Sengupta, Jati K. Technology, Innovations & Growth. 2010. (ENG., Illus.). 196p. 95.00 (978-0-230-28550-7(3)) Palgrave Macmillan.
Sharma, Ashok, et al, eds. Asia 2050: Realizing the Asian Century. 2011. 412p. (C). 70.00 (978-81-321-0756-9(X), B07569C) SAGE Pubns., Inc.
Shimizu, Yoshinori, ed. Economic Dynamism of Asia in the New Millennium. 2007. (Advanced Research in Asian Economic Studies). (Illus.). 399p. 150.00 (978-981-256-898-4(0)) World Scientific Publishing Co., Inc.
Siengthai, Sununta, et al, eds. The Multi-Dimension of Industrial Relations in the Asian Knowledge-Based Economies. 2010. (Chandos Asian Studies). (Illus.). 288p. 120.00 (978-1-84334-264-9(2), Chandos Publishing) Woodhead Publishing Ltd. GBR. Dist: Ingram Pub. Services.
Simone & Cram101 Textbook Reviews Staff. The Asian Pacific: Political & Economic Development in a Global Context. 2007. 60p. per. 9.95 (978-1-4288-2166-8(X)) Cram101 Inc.
Sims-Williams, Nicholas. Bactrian Documents, Part II. 2007. (Studies in the Khalili Collections). 328p. (C). (978-1-874780-90-8(0), Khalili Collections) I. B. Tauris & Co., Ltd.
Singh, N. K. Eastern & Cross Cultural Management. 2012. (Management for Professionals Ser.). (ENG., Illus.). 184p. 99.00 (978-81-322-0471-8(9), 8132204719) Springer (India) Private Ltd. IND. Dist: Springer.
Smyth, Russell & Vicziany, Marika, eds. Business in Asia. 2008. 240p. (C). pap. 29.95 (978-1-876924-53-9(5), Monash Univ. Pr.) Monash Univ. Publishing AUS. Dist: International Specialized Bk. Services.
Srinivasan, Ancha, et al, eds. Transition to Low Carbon & Climate Resilient Economies in Asia: Challenges & Opportunities. 2012. (ENG., Illus.). 272p. 145.00 (978-1-84407-861-5(2)); pap. 44.95 (978-1-84407-862-2(0)) Routledge.
Stiftung, Bertelsmann, ed. Asia: Changing the World. 2008. (ENG., Illus.). 250p. 30.00 (978-3-89204-977-7(7)) Bertelsmann Stiftung DEU. Dist: Brookings Institution Pr.
Sugiharso, Safuan. Macroeconomic Interdependence & Contagion: Evidence for the Asian Crisis. 2011. 196p. pap. (978-3-639-30899-0(9)) VDM Verlag Dr. Mueller e.K.
Tai, Pih Nee & Sek, Siok Kun. The Dynamic of Interest Rate Pass-Through. 2011. 80p. pap. (978-3-8454-0185-0(0)) Lambert Academic Publishing.
Technology Research Editors, ed. Asian Economic Crisis: Impact on the Global Metal Industry, 2007 Ed. 2007. pap. 68.50 (978-1-60030-262-6(9), Search-In-Print) CSA Journal Division.
Tellis, Ashley J., et al, eds. Strategic Asia 2008-09: Challenges & Choices. 2008. (Illus.). pap. 34.95 (978-0-9713938-9-9(3)) National Bureau of Asian Research, The.
Tellis, Ashley J. & Wills, Michael, eds. Strategic Asia 2007-08: Domestic Political Change & Grand Strategy. 2007. (Strategic Asia Ser.). (Illus.). pap. 29.95 (978-0-9713938-8-2(5)) National Bureau of Asian Research, The.
Tellis, Ashley J., et al. Strategic Asia 2011-12: Asia Responds to Its Rising Powers — China & India. Tellis, Ashley J. et al, eds. 2011. (Strategic Asia Ser.). (Illus.). pap. 34.95 (978-0-9818904-2-5(3)) National Bureau of Asian Research, The.
Teng. Bioscience Entrepreneurship in Asia. 2008. 320p. 60.00 (978-981-270-020-9(X)) World Scientific Publishing Co., Inc.
Thomas, Nicholas & Nicholas Thomas. Governance & Regionalism in Asia. Thomas, Nicholas, ed. 2009. (Politics in Asia Ser.). (Illus.). 368p. 160.00 (978-0-415-45699-9(1)) Routledge.
Thomas, Pradip. Intellectual Property Rights & Communications in Asia: Conflicting Traditions. Servaes, Jan, ed. 2006. (Illus.). 264p. (C). 78.00 (978-0-7619-3498-1(7), B34987C) SAGE Pubns., Inc.
Till, Geoffrey, et al. Globalization & Defence in the Asia-Pacific: Arms Across Asia. Till, Geoffrey et al, eds. 2008. (Contemporary Security Studies). (ENG., Illus.). 288p. (C). 140.00 (978-0-415-44048-6(3)) Routledge.
Trichur, Ganesh K., ed. Asia & the Transformation of the World-System, 1 vol. (Political Economy of the World-System Annuals Ser.). 176p. 2010. pap. 31.95 (978-1-59451-742-6(8)) 2009. 125.00 (978-1-59451-741-9(X)) Paradigm Pubs.
Tselichtchev, Ivan & Debroux, Philippe. Asia's Turning Point: An Introduction to Asia's Dynamic Economies at the Dawn of the New Century. 2009. (ENG.). 350p. 34.95 (978-0-470-82360-6(7), Wiley) Wiley, John & Sons, Inc.
Tsuya, Noriko O., et al. Prudence & Pressure: Reproduction & Human Agency in Europe & Asia, 1700-1900. 2010. (Eurasian Population & Family History Ser.). (ENG., Illus.). 406p. (gr. 17). 40.00 (978-0-262-01352-9(5)) MIT Pr.
United Nations. Annual Report of the Economic & Social Commission for Asia & the Pacific 2010. 2011. (ENG.). 62p. pap. 13.00 (978-92-1-880188-3(0)) United Nations Pubns.
—Asia-Pacific Development Journal, December 2007. 2009. (ENG.). 138p. cd-rom 23.20 (978-92-1-120532-9(8)) United Nations Pubns.
—Asia-Pacific Development Journal, December 2010. 2011. (ENG.). 158p. pap. 33.00 (978-92-1-120619-7(7)) United Nations Pubns.
—Asia-Pacific Development Journal, June 2008. 2009. (ENG.). 164p. pap. 29.00 (978-92-1-120561-9(1)) United Nations Pubns.
—Asia-Pacific Development Journal, June 2009. 2010. (ENG.). 162p. pap. 33.00 (978-92-1-120583-1(2)) United Nations Pubns.
—Asia Pacific Development Journal June 2010. 2011. (ENG.). 168p. pap. 33.00 (978-92-1-120610-4(3)) United Nations Pubns.
—A Future Within Reach 2008: Regional Partnerships for the Millennium Developments Goals in Asia & the Pacific (Folder set includes book, overview booklet, CD-ROM & Delivering as One: Asia-Pacific Regional MDG Road Map 2008-2015) 2009. (ENG.). 172p. pap. 75.00 (978-92-1-120547-3(6)) United Nations Pubns.
—Key Economic Developments & Prospects in the Asia-Pacific Region 2008. 2008. (ENG.). 36p. pap. 16.00 (978-92-1-120523-7(9)) United Nations Pubns.
—Logistics Sector Developments: Planning Models for Enterprises & Logistics Clusters. 2009. (ENG.). 154p. pap. 52.00 (978-92-1-120517-6(4)) United Nations Pubns.
—Longer Combination Vehicles (LCV) for Asia & the Pacific Region: Some Economic Implications. 2007. (UNESCAP Working Papers Ser.) (ENG.). 34p. pap. 12.00 (978-92-1-120510-7(7)) United Nations Pubns.
—National Accounts Studies of the ESCWA Region, Bulletin No. 26. 2007. (ENG, FRE & MUL.). 104p. pap. 15.00 (978-92-1-128311-2(6)) United Nations Pubns.
—National Accounts Studies of the ESCWA Region, Bulletin No. 27. 2008. (MUL.). 104p. pap. 15.00 (978-92-1-128317-4(5)) United Nations Pubns.
—Statistical Abstract of the ESCWA Region, 26th Issue. 2008. (MUL.). 260p. pap. 45.00 (978-92-1-128308-2(6)) United Nations Pubns.
—TC Yearbook 2006: Technical Cooperation. 2007. (ENG.). 72p. pap. 38.00 (978-92-1-120506-0(9)) United Nations Pubns.
—Urban Safety & Poverty in Asia & the Pacific. 2012. (ENG.). pap. 18.00 (978-92-1-120589-3(1)) United Nations Pubns.
United Nations. Workers' Remittances, Economic Growth & Poverty in Developing Asia & the Pacific Countries. 2007. (UNESCAP Working Papers Ser.). (ENG.). 28p. pap. 12.00 (978-92-1-120509-1(3)) United Nations Pubns.
United Nations Development Programme. Power,Voice, & Rights: A Turning Point for Gender Equality in Asia & the Pacific. 2010. 260p. pap. 20.00 (978-92-1-126286-5(0)) United Nations Pubns.
United Nations Development Programme, creator. Indigenous Peoples & the Human Rights-Based Approach to Development: Engaging in Dialogue. 2007. (Illus.). 127p. per. 30.00 (978-92-1-126205-6(4)) United Nations Pubns.
United Nations Economic and Social Commission for Asia and the Pacific. Sustainable Infrastructure in Asia: Overview & Proceedings, Seoul Initiative Policy Forum on Sustainable Infrastructure, Seoul, Republic of Korea, 6-8 September 2006. 2007. (ENG.). 216p. pap. 40.00 (978-92-1-120507-7(7)) United Nations Pubns.
United Nations, Economic and Social Commission for Asia and the Pacific Staff. Economic & Social Survey of Asia & the Pacific 2009. 2009. (ENG., Illus.). 228p. pap. 80.00 (978-92-1-120577-0(8)) United Nations Pubns.
United Nations Publications Staff, ed. Development of Health Systems in the Context of Enhancing Growth Towards achieving the Millenium Developments Goals in Asia & the Pacific. 2007. (ENG.). 172p. pap. 45.00 (978-92-1-120505-3(0)) United Nations Pubns.
United Nations Staff. Asia-Pacific Development Journal, December 2008. 2009. (ENG.). 130p. pap. 29.00 (978-92-1-120567-1(0)) United Nations Pubns.
U.S. Promotion of the Afghan Economy: Impediments & Opportunities: Hearing Before the Subcommittee on National Security & Foreign Affairs of the Committee on Oversight & Government Reform, House of Representatives, One Hundred Eleventh Congress, First Session, July 14, 2009. 2010. (Illus.). iii, 83p. (978-0-16-086454-4(2), 552-070-41511-4) United States Government Printing Office.
Uzan, Marc, ed. The Macroeconomics of Global Imbalances: European & Asian Perspectives. 2008. (Routledge Studies in the Modern World Economy Ser.). (ENG., Illus.). 160p. (C). 130.00 (978-0-415-77469-7(1)) Routledge.
Varma, Arup & Budhwar, Pawan S., eds. Managing Human Resources in Asia-Pacific, 2E. 2012. (Global HRM Ser.). (ENG., Illus.). 325p. 120.00 (978-0-415-89864-5(1)); pap. 59.95 (978-0-415-89865-2(X)) Routledge.
Vo, Thanh Tri. International Institutions & Economic Development in Asia. 2010. (PAFTAD (Pacific Trade & Development Conference Series) Ser.). (ENG., Illus.). 240p. (C). 130.00 (978-0-415-49754-1(X), Routledge) Taylor & Francis Group GBR. Dist: Taylor & Francis Group.
Warner, Malcolm, ed. Managing Across Diverse Cultures in East Asia. 2012. (ENG., Illus.). 288p. (C). pap. 49.95 (978-0-415-68090-5(5)) Routledge.
Watkins, Kevin. Economic Growth with Equity: Lessons from East Asia. (Oxfam Insight Ser.). (ENG., Illus.). 128p. pap. 14.35 (978-0-85598-384-0(1)) Oxfam Publishing GBR. Dist: Stylus Publishing, LLC.
Wong, Poh Kam. Academic Entrepreneurship in Asia: The Role & Impact of Universities in National Innovation Systems. 2012. (New Horizons in Entrepreneurship Ser.). (Illus.). 360p. 135.00 (978-1-84980-307-6(2)) Elgar, Edward Publishing, Inc.
World Bank & Coulibaly, Souleymane. Trade Expansion through Market Connection: Trade Expansion through Market Connection: the Central Asian Markets of Kazakhstan, Kyrgyz Republic, & Tajikistan. 2011. (World Bank Studies). (ENG.). 96p. pap. 15.00 (978-0-8213-8788-7(X), 9780821387887) World Bank Pubns.
World Bank Staff, contrib. by. Mongolia Economic Retrospective. 2010. (World Bank Studies). (ENG., Illus.). 60p. pap. 15.00 (978-0-8213-8540-1(2), 9780821385401) World Bank Pubns.
Wouters, Thomas L., ed. Progress in Economics Research, Vol. 20. 2010. (Progress in Economics Research Ser.). 165.00 (978-1-61761-112-4(3)) Nova Science Pubs., Inc.
Wu, Guang. USA - United States of Asia. 2010. (Asian Political, Economic, & Security Issues Ser.). 99p. 43.00 (978-1-60876-180-7(0)) Nova Science Pubs., Inc.
Yahya, Mir Abdul Rahim. The Afghan Marble. 2010. 120p. pap. (978-3-639-23504-3(5)) VDM Verlag Dr. Mueller e.K.
Yeung, Henry Wai-Chung, ed. Handbook of Research on Asian Business. 2007. (Elgar Original Reference Ser.). (Illus.). 512p. (C). 248.00 (978-1-84376-960-6(3)) Elgar, Edward Publishing, Inc.
Yueh, Linda. Future Asian Trade: Economic Development with the Emergence of China. 2010. (Routledge Studies in the Growth Economies of Asia Ser.). (ENG., Illus.). 464p. 145.00 (978-0-415-36811-7(1)) Routledge.
Zhai, Fan. From Growth to Convergence: Asia's Next Two Decades. 2009. (ENG., Illus.). 304p. 126.00 (978-0-230-22176-5(9)) Palgrave Macmillan.
Zhang, Xiaoke. The Political Economy of Capital Market Reforms in South East Asia. 2011. (International Political Economy Ser.). (ENG., Illus.). 272p. 85.00 (978-0-230-25282-0(6)) Palgrave Macmillan.
Zhuang, Juzhong, ed. Poverty, Inequality, & Inclusive Growth in Asia: Measurement, Policy Issues, & Country Studies. 2010. (Anthem Studies in Development & Globalization Ser.). (ENG., Illus.). 492p. 99.00 (978-1-84331-845-3(8)) Anthem Pr. GBR. Dist: Books International, Inc.

ASIA—ECONOMIC POLICY

Adhikari, Chandra Mani. International Taxation: Comparative Analysis of UK, USA, India & Nepal. 2010. 592p. pap. (978-3-639-20723-1(8)) VDM Verlag Dr. Mueller e.K.
Aggarwal, Vinod & Koo, Min Gyo, eds. Asia's New Institutional Architecture: Evolving Structures for Managing Trade & Security Relations. 2008. (Political Economy of the Asia Pacific Ser.). 275p. pap. 59.95 (978-3-540-74887-8(3), 3540748873) Springer.
Ahmed, Sadiq, et al. Promoting Economic Cooperation in South Asia: Beyond SAFTA. 2010. (Illus.). 472p. (C). 39.95 (978-81-321-0311-0(4), B03110C) SAGE Pubns., Inc.
Arinto, Patricia B. & Akhtar, Shahid. Digital Review of Asia Pacific 2009-2010. 4th ed. 2009. (Illus.). 392p. (C). pap. 49.95 (978-81-321-0084-3(0), B00843P) SAGE Pubns., Inc.
Armstrong, Shiro, ed. The Politics & the Economics of Integration in Asia & the Pacific. 2011. (PAFTAD (Pacific Trade & Development Conference Series) Ser.). (ENG., Illus.). 232p. 125.00 (978-0-415-69042-3(0)) Routledge.
Arner, Douglas W., et al, eds. Asia's Debt Capital Markets: Prospects & Strategies for Development. 2010. (Milken Institute Series on Financial Innovation & Economic Growth Ser.). (Illus.). xii, 322p. pap. 209.00 (978-1-4419-2041-6(2), 1441920412) Springer.
Athukorala. Multinational Enterprises in Asian Development. 2007. (Illus.). 304p. (C). 137.00 (978-1-84720-102-7(4)) Elgar, Edward Publishing, Inc.
Athukorala, Prema-Chandra, ed. The Rise of Asia: Trade & Investment in Global Perspective. 2010. (Routledge Studies in the Growth Economies of Asia Ser.). (ENG., Illus.). 384p. (C). 138.00 (978-0-415-55686-6(4)) Routledge.
Azam, Muhammad, et al. The Impact of Political Risk & Policy Uncertainty on Fdi. 2011. 72p. pap. (978-3-8433-9119-1(X)) Lambert Academic Publishing.
Aziz, Farooq. Pakistan Economics for B. Com. II: 2009-10 Edition. 2011. (ENG.). 240p. 14.95 (978-0-19-547911-9(4)) Oxford Univ. Pr., Inc.
Barro, Robert J. & Lee, Jong-Wha, eds. Costs & Benefits of Economic Integration in Asia, 1 vol. 2011. (Illus.). 320p. 49.95 (978-0-19-975398-7(9)) Oxford Univ. Pr., Inc.
Batra, Amita. Preferential Trading Agreements in Asia: Towards an Asian Economic Community. Batra, Amita, ed. 2008. (ENG., Illus.). 244p. 45.95

(978-81-7188-630-2(2)) Academic Foundation IND. Dist: Independent Pubs. Group.

Boyd, Ricard, et al, eds. Political Conflict & Development in East Asia & Latin America. 2006. (Illus.). 293p. 168.00 *(978-0-415-36318-1(7))* Routledge.

Brooks, Douglas H. & Stone, Susan F. Trade Facilitation & Regional Cooperation in Asia. Brooks, Douglas H. & Stone, Susan F., eds. 2010. (Illus.). 208p. 112.00 *(978-1-84844-986-2(0))* Elgar, Edward Publishing, Inc.

Broome, André. The Currency of Power: The IMF & Monetary Reform in Central Asia. 2010. (International Political Economy Ser.). (ENG., Illus.). 256p. 89.00 *(978-0-230-24005-6(4))* Palgrave Macmillan.

Cavoli, Tony & Rajan, Ramkishen S. Exchange Rate Regimes & Macroeconomic Management in Asia. 2009. (ENG., Illus.). 248p. (gr. 17). 60.00 *(978-962-209-053-8(2))* Hong Kong Univ. Pr. HKG. Dist: Columbia Univ. Pr.

Chand, Ramesh. Free Trade Area in Asia. 2006. (ENG., Illus.). 130p. 45.95 *(978-81-7188-422-3(9))* Academic Foundation IND. Dist: Independent Pubs. Group.

Chauhan, Pradeep. Asian Economic & Financial Integration in Global Framework. 2009. 357p. 58.50 *(978-81-7708-224-1(8))* New Century Publications IND. Dist: International Specialized Bk. Services.

Cheung, Yin-Wong & Ma, Guonan. Asia & China in the Global Economy. 2011. 300p. 84.00 ***(978-981-4335-26-3(6))*** World Scientific Publishing Co., Inc.

Cheung, Yin-Wong, et al. The Evolving Role of Asia in Global Finance. 2011. (Frontiers of Economics & Globalization Ser.: Vol. 9). (Illus.). 410p. 154.95 *(978-0-85724-745-2(X))* Emerald Group Publishing Ltd. GBR. Dist: Turpin Distribution Services Ltd.

Chin, Felix. Asian Economic & Political Developments. 2011. (Series: Asian Political, Economic & Security Issues Ser.). 295.00 *(978-1-61122-470-2(5))* Nova Science Pubs., Inc.

—Economic, Political & Social Issues of Asia. 2011. (Series: Asian Political, Economic & Security Issues Ser.). (Illus.). xiii, 415p. 295.00 *(978-1-61122-471-9(3))* Nova Science Pubs., Inc.

Columbus, Alexandra M. Asian Economic & Political Issues. 2011. (Series: Asian Economic & Political Issues Ser.). 238p. 185.00 *(978-1-61324-239-1(5))* Nova Science Pubs., Inc.

Columbus, Frank H., ed. Asian Economic & Political Issues. 226p. 69.00 *(978-1-56072-598-5(2))* Nova Science Pubs., Inc.

Cram101 Textbook Reviews & Cram101 Textbook Reviews. Outlines & Highlights for Fiscal Policy & Management in East Asia by Takatoshi Ito, Isbn: 9780226386812. 2011. 128p. pap. 27.95 ***(978-1-4288-6483-2(0))*** Cram101 Inc.

Daniere, Amrita & Luong, Hy Van, eds. Social Capital & Civic Engagement in Asia: Vibrant Societies. 2012. (Routledge Contemporary Asia Ser.). (ENG., Illus.). 272p. (C). 125.00 *(978-0-415-67869-8(2))* Routledge.

Dargin, Justin & Lim, Tai Wei. Energy, Trade & Finance in Asia: A Political & Economic Analysis, 1 vol. 2011. (Perspectives in Economic & Social History Ser.). (ENG., Illus.). 264p. 99.00 *(978-1-84893-155-8(7))* Pickering & Chatto Pubs., Ltd. GBR. Dist: Ashgate Publishing Co.

D'Costa, Anthony, ed. Globalization & Economic Nationalism in Asia. 2012. (ENG., Illus.). 304p. 99.00 ***(978-0-19-964621-0(X))*** Oxford Univ. Pr., Inc.

Dee, Philippa & Dee, Philippa S. Institutions for Economic Reform in Asia. 2009. (Routledge Studies in the Growth Economies of Asia Ser.). (ENG., Illus.). CCXXXVIII, 18p. 135.00 *(978-0-415-55021-5(1))* Routledge.

Dervis, Kemal, et al, eds. Asia & Policymaking for the Global Economy. 2011. (ENG., Illus.). 200p. pap. 19.95 *(978-0-8157-0421-8(6))* Brookings Institution Pr.

Devereux, Michael, et al, eds. Global & Regional Financial Market Integration. 2011. (Routledge Studies in the Modern World Economy Ser.). (ENG., Illus.). 352p. (C). 180.00 *(978-0-415-59551-3(7))* Routledge.

Dew, Philip. Doing Business with Jordan. 2nd ed. 2007. (Doing Business With Ser.). (ENG.). 277p. 115.00 *(978-1-84673-054-2(6)*, GMB Publishing Ltd.) Blue Ibex Ltd. GBR. Dist: Ingram Pub. Services.

Diokno, Maria. The Mekong Arranged & Rearranged. Chinh, Nguyen Van, ed. 2007. (Mekong Press Ser.). (ENG.). 228p. pap. 14.95 ***(978-974-94804-9-6(X))*** Silkworm Bks. THA. Dist: Univ. of Washington Pr.

Dowling, John Malcolm & Rana, Pradumna Bickram. Asia & the Global Economic Crisis: Challenges in a Financially Integrated World. 2010. (ENG., Illus.). 320p. 110.00 *(978-0-230-27363-4(7))* Palgrave Macmillan.

Erik. International Economic Integration. . (V3) 2006. (Advanced Research in Asian Economic Studies). 124.00 *(978-981-256-757-4(7))* World Scientific Publishing Co., Inc.

Fang, Yen-Po. The Developing of Emerging Integrated Currency. 2008. 84p. pap. *(978-3-639-00172-3(9))* VDM Verlag Dr. Mueller e.K.

Fatemi, Khosrow. Globalization & East Asia: Opportunities & Challenges. 2006. (ENG., Illus.). 326p. 110.00 *(978-0-7890-2743-6(7))* Routledge.

Fatemi, Khosrow, ed. Globalization & East Asia: Opportunities & Challenges. 2006. (ENG., Illus.). 326p. per. 54.95 *(978-0-7890-2744-3(5))* Routledge.

Felipe, Jesus. Inclusive Growth, Full Employment, & Structural Change: Implications & Policies for Developing Asia, Second Edition. 2nd rev. ed. 2010. (Anthem-Asian Development Bank Series the Anthem-European Union Ser.). (ENG., Illus.). 368p. 99.00 *(978-0-85728-958-2(6))* Anthem Pr. GBR. Dist: Books International, Inc.

Freeman, Charles W., 3rd & Goodman, Matthew. Crafting U. S. Economic Strategy toward Asia: Lessons Learned from 30 Years of Experience. 2008. 44p. pap. 14.95 *(978-0-89206-554-7(0)*, CSIS Pr., The) Ctr. for Strategic & International Studies.

Gill, Sucha Singh, et al, eds. Economic & Environmental Sustainability of the Asian Region. 2010. (ENG., Illus.). xxvi, 461p. (C). 95.00 *(978-0-415-58144-8(3)*, Routledge India) Taylor & Francis Group GBR. Dist: Taylor & Francis Group.

Harriss-White, Barbara & Heyer, Judith, eds. The Comparative Political Economy of Development. 2012. (ENG., Illus.). 358p. (C). pap. 44.95 ***(978-0-415-80995-5(9))*** Routledge.

Harriss-white, Barbara & Heyer, Judith, eds. The Comparative Political Economy of Development: Africa & South Asia. 2010. (Routledge Studies in Development Economics Ser.). (ENG., Illus.). 384p. (C). 145.00 *(978-0-415-55288-2(5))* Routledge.

Heshmati, Almas & Tausch, Arno. Roadmap to Bangalore? Globalization, the EU's Lisbon Process & the Structures of Global Inequality. 2007. (C). 79.00 *(978-1-60021-478-3(9))* Nova Science Pubs., Inc.

Hinnebusch, Raymond, et al. Agriculture & Reform in Syria. 2010. (Illus.). 120p. (C). pap. 17.95 *(978-0-9559687-7-8(1))* Rienner, Lynne Pubs.

Hira, Anil. An east asian model for latin american Success: The new Path. 2007. (International Political Economy of New Regionalisms Ser.). 210p. 114.95 *(978-0-7546-7108-4(9))* Ashgate Publishing Co.

Hoa, Tran Van & Harvie, Charles, eds. Regional Trade Agreements in Asia. 2008. 296p. (C). 127.00 *(978-1-84720-061-7(3))* Elgar, Edward Publishing, Inc.

Hughes, Helen, ed. Achieving Industrialization in East Asia. 2009. (Trade & Development Ser.). (ENG., Illus.). 396p. pap. 42.00 *(978-0-521-11191-1(9))* Cambridge Univ. Pr.

Ichimura, Shinichi & Bahl, Roy, eds. Decentralization Policies in Asian Development. 2008. 310p. 133.00 *(978-981-281-863-8(4))* World Scientific Publishing Co., Inc.

Icon Group International, Inc. Staff, compiled by. The 2006 Economic & Product Market Databook for Bandar Seri Begawan, Brunei. 2006. 618p. ring bd. 95.00 *(978-0-497-80132-8(9))* Icon Group International, Inc.

Intarakumnerd, Patarapong & Lecler, Yveline. Sustainability of Thailand's Competitiveness: The Policy Challenges. 2010. (Illus.). xvii, 331p. pap. ***(978-981-4279-47-5(1))*** Institute of Southeast Asian Studies.

Ito, Takatoshi & Hahn, Chin Hee. The Rise of China & Structural Changes in Korea & Asia. Ito, Takatoshi & Hahn, Chin Hee, eds. 2010. (Illus.). 352p. 155.00 *(978-1-84844-855-1(4))* Elgar, Edward Publishing, Inc.

Jeffries, Ian. Mongolia: A Guide to Economic & Political Developments. (Guides to Economic & Political Developments in Asia Ser.). (ENG., Illus.). 224p. (C). 2012. pap. 42.95 ***(978-0-415-54174-9(3))*** 2007. 150.00 *(978-0-415-42545-2(X))* Routledge.

Jha, Raghbendra, ed. Routledge Handbook of South Asian Economics. 2011. (ENG., Illus.). 352p. (C). 220.00 *(978-0-415-55397-1(0))* Routledge.

Kawai, M., et al, eds. Monetary & Currency Policy Management in Asia: Implications of the Global Financial Crisis. 2012. 320p. 135.00 ***(978-0-85793-334-8(5))*** Elgar, Edward Publishing, Inc.

Kawai, Masahiro & Lamberte, Mario B. Managing Capital Flows: The Search for a Framework. 2011. (Illus.). 464p. 185.00 *(978-1-84844-787-5(6))* Elgar, Edward Publishing, Inc.

Khondker, Habibul Haque & Therborn, Goran, eds. Asia & Europe in Globalization: Continents, Regions & Nations. 2006. (Social Sciences in Asia Ser.: Vol. 8). (Illus.). 313p. pap. *(978-90-04-15350-9(0))* BRILL.

Kohli, Harinder S. & Sharma, Ashok. A Resilient Asia Amidst Global Financial Crisis: From Crisis Management to Global Leadership. 2010. (Illus.). 456p. (C). 49.95 *(978-81-321-0516-9(8)*, B05169C) SAGE Pubns., Inc.

Koo, Min Gyo & Aggarwal, Vinod K., eds. Asia's New Institutional Architecture: Evolving Structures for Managing Trade, Financial, & Security Relations. 2007. (Political Economy of the Asia Pacific Ser.). (Illus.). 321p. 179.00 *(978-3-540-72388-2(9))* Springer.

Kresl, Peter Karl. Economic Strategies for Mature Industrial Economies. 2011. (Illus.). 304p. 135.00 *(978-1-84980-404-2(4))* Elgar, Edward Publishing, Inc.

Lieberman, Ira W. & Kopf, Daniel J., eds. Privatization in Transition Economies: The Ongoing Story. 2007. 384p. 134.95 *(978-0-7623-1463-8(X))* Emerald Group Publishing Ltd. GBR. Dist: Turpin Distribution Services Ltd.

Lim, Mah Hui & Lim, Chin. Nowhere to Hide: The Great Financial Crisis & Challenges for Asia. 2010. (Illus.). xxiv, 174p. pap. *(978-981-4279-73-4(0))* Institute of Southeast Asian Studies.

Lim, Tai-Wei. Economic Recession, Integration & Regionalism in East Asia: A Constructivist Political Economic Survey & Comparative Macro Policy Analysis. 2010. 250p. pap. 77.00 *(978-981-4304-70-2(0))* World Scientific Publishing Co., Inc.

Lo, Chi. Phantom of the China Economic Threat: Shadow of the Next Asian Crisis DISTRIBUTION CANCELLED. 2008. (ENG.). 204p. pap. 42.50 *(978-0-230-51544-4(4))* Palgrave Macmillan.

Maluste, Rajiv G. Endogenous Origins of Economic Reforms in India & Chin: The Role of Attitudinal Changes. 2011. 368p. pap. 29.95 ***(978-1-61233-753-1(8)***, Dissertation.com) Universal Pubs.

Manoranjan Dutta Staff. The Asian Economy & Asian Money. 2009. (Illus.). xxxiv, 328p. 144.95 *(978-1-84855-260-9(2))* Emerald Group Publishing Ltd. GBR. Dist: Turpin Distribution Services Ltd.

McGuire, James W. Wealth, Health, & Democracy in East Asia & Latin America. 2010. (ENG., Illus.). 424p. pap. 30.00 *(978-0-521-13934-2(1))* Cambridge Univ. Pr.

Moller, J. Ørstrom. How Asia Can Shape the World: From the ERA of Plenty to the ERA of Scarcities. 2010. xiv, 540p. pap. ***(978-981-4311-33-5(2))*** Institute of Southeast Asian Studies.

Montgomery, John D. & Rondinelli, Dennis A., eds. Beyond Reconstruction in Afghanistan: Lessons from Development Experience. 2007. (ENG., Illus.). 256p. pap. 32.00 *(978-0-230-60220-5(7))* Palgrave Macmillan.

Morrison, Charles & Pedrosa, Eduardo, eds. An Apec Trade Agenda? the Political Economy of a Free Trade Area of the Asia-Pacific. 2007. 264p. per. *(978-981-230-460-5(6))* Institute of Southeast Asian Studies.

Nadkarni, Vidya. Strategic Partnerships in Asia: Balancing Without Alliances. 2010. (ENG., Illus.). 272p. (C). pap. 44.95 *(978-0-415-77775-9(5)*, Routledge) Taylor & Francis Group GBR. Dist: Taylor & Francis Group.

Nair, Chandran. Consumptionomics: Asia's Role in Reshaping Capitalism & Saving the Planet. 2011. (ENG.). 256p. 27.95 *(978-0-470-82857-1(9)*, Wiley) Wiley, John & Sons, Inc.

Nissanke, Machiko. Globalization & the Poor in Asia: Can Shared Growth Be Sustained? Nissanke, Machiko & Thorbecke, Erik, eds. 2008. (ENG., Illus.). 340p. 116.00 *(978-0-230-20188-0(1))* Palgrave Macmillan.

Omar, Norman & Danto, Arthur C. Responsible Development: Asia Ten Years after the Crisis. 2010. (Routledge Studies in the Growth Economies of Asia Ser.). (ENG., Illus.). 256p. (C). 145.00 *(978-0-7103-1348-5(9))* Routledge.

Organisation for Economic Co-operation and Development Staff. Oecd Territorial Reviews Oecd Territorial Reviews: Trans-Border Urban Cooperation in the Pan Yellow Sea Region 2009. 2009. pap. 63.00 *(978-92-64-07611-2(5))* Organization for Economic Cooperation & Development.

Organisation for Economic Co-operation and Development: Development Centre. Competitiveness & Private Sector Development: Central Asia 2011; Competitiveness Outlook. 2011. (Illus.). 160p. pap. 67.00 ***(978-92-64-09727-8(9))*** Organization for Economic Cooperation & Development.

Otsuka, Keijiro. Rural Poverty & Income Dynamics in Asia & Africa. Estudillo, Jonna P. & Sawada, Yasuyuki, eds. 2008. (Routledge Studies in Development Economics Ser.). (Illus.). XXIV, 232p. 160.00 *(978-0-415-48009-3(4))* Routledge.

Park, Yung Chul. Economic Liberalization & Integration in East Asia: A Post-Crisis Paradigm. 2007. (ENG.). 296p. 45.00 *(978-0-19-921521-8(9))* Oxford Univ. Pr., Inc.

Pempel, T. J., et al, eds. Political Economy of Northeast Asian Regionalism: Political Conflict & Economic Integration. 2008. (Illus.). 192p. 119.00 *(978-1-84720-891-0(6))* Elgar, Edward Publishing, Inc.

—Regionalism, Economic Integration & Security in Asia: A Political Economy Approach. 2011. (Illus.). 192p. 110.00 *(978-0-85793-126-9(1))* Elgar, Edward Publishing, Inc.

Petri, Peter A., ed. Inclusive, Balanced, Sustained Growth in the Asia-Pacific. 2010. 150p. pap. *(978-981-230-966-2(7))* Institute of Southeast Asian Studies.

Preston, Peter W. National Pasts in Europe & East Asia. 2012. (ENG.). 362p. (C). pap. 44.95 ***(978-0-415-62550-0(5))*** Routledge.

Previts, Gary, et al, eds. A Global History of Accounting, Financial Reporting & Public Policy: Asia & Oceania, 3 vols., Vol. 14. 2011. (Studies in the Development of Accounting Thought Ser.). (Illus.). 205p. ***(978-0-85724-813-8(8))*** Emerald Group Publishing Ltd.

Rajan, Ramkishen S. & Rongala, Sunil. Asia in the Global Economy: Finance, Trade & Investment. 2008. (Illus.). 260p. 86.00 *(978-981-270-573-0(2))* World Scientific Publishing Co., Inc.

Reddy, Sangay G. & United Nations Development Programme: Regional Centre in Colombo. Pro-poor macroeconomic policy, lessons from the Asia-Pacific Region: A synthesis paper based on country case studies on the macroeconomics of poverty Reduction. 2008. (Illus.). 47p. pap. 10.00 *(978-92-1-126218-6(6))* United Nations Pubns.

Richardson, Harry Ward, et al. Reshaping Regional Policy. Richardson, Harry Ward et al, eds. 2011. (Illus.). 384p. 150.00 *(978-1-84980-280-2(7))* Elgar, Edward Publishing, Inc.

Rodan, Garry & Hewison, Kevin, eds. Neoliberalism & Conflict in Asia After 9/11. 2009. 254p. pap. 39.95 *(978-0-415-56839-5(0))* Routledge.

Roy, Devesh & Gulati, Ashok. Liberalizing Foodgrains Markets: Experiences, Impacts & Lessons from South Asia. Ganesh-Kumar, A., ed. 2010. (ENG., Illus.). 304p. 49.95 *(978-0-19-806695-8(3))* Oxford Univ. Pr., Inc.

Roy, K. C. & Chatterjee, Srikanta. Growth, Development & Poverty Alleviation in the Asia-Pacific A Volume in Readings in World Development Series. 2007. ("Readings in World Development" Ser.). 221p. (C). 145.00 *(978-1-59454-931-1(1))* Nova Science Pubs., Inc.

Santos-Paulino, Amelia U. & Wan, Guanghua. Southern Engines of Global Growth. 2010. (ENG., Illus.). 300p. 90.00 *(978-0-19-958060-6(X))* Oxford Univ. Pr., Inc.

Schuman, Michael. The Miracle: The Epic Story of Asia's Quest for Wealth. 464p. 2010. (ENG.). pap. 16.99 *(978-0-06-134669-9(1))* 2009. (Illus.). 29.99 *(978-0-06-134668-2(3))* HarperCollins Pubs. (Collins).

Sek, Siok Kun. The Formation of Monetary Policy in the Emerging East-Asian Countries. 2010. 296p. pap. *(978-3-639-22481-8(7))* VDM Verlag Dr. Mueller e.K.

Sharma, Ashok, et al, eds. Asia 2050: Realizing the Asian Century. 2011. 412p. (C). 70.00 ***(978-81-321-0756-9(X)***, B07569C) SAGE Pubns., Inc.

Shaw, Daigee & Liu, Bih Jane. The Impact of the Economic Crisis on East Asia: Policy Responses from Four Economies. 2011. (Illus.). 232p. 110.00 ***(978-0-85793-169-6(5))*** Elgar, Edward Publishing, Inc.

Siddique, M. A. B. Regionalism, Trade & Economic Development in the Asia-Pacific Region. 2007. (Illus.). 256p. (C). 127.00 *(978-1-84542-503-6(0))* Elgar, Edward Publishing, Inc.

Siddiqui, Anjum, ed. India & South Asia: Economic Developments in the Age of Globalization. 2007. (ENG., Illus.). 448p. 129.95 *(978-0-7656-1452-0(9))* Sharpe, M.E. Inc.

Sng, Hui Ying & Chia, Wai Mun. Singapore & Asia: Impact of the Global Financial Tsunami & Other Economic Issues. 2009. 94.00 *(978-981-4280-46-4(1))*; (Illus.). 224p. 81.00 *(978-981-4280-45-7(3))* World Scientific Publishing Co., Inc.

Stiftung, Bertelsmann, ed. Asia: Changing the World. 2008. (ENG., Illus.). 250p. 30.00 *(978-3-89204-977-7(7))* Bertelsmann Stiftung DEU. Dist: Brookings Institution Pr.

Tellis, Ashley J., et al. Strategic Asia 2011-12: Asia Responds to Its Rising Powers — China & India. Tellis, Ashley J. et al, eds. 2011. (Strategic Asia Ser.). (Illus.). pap. 34.95 ***(978-0-9818904-2-5(3))*** National Bureau of Asian Research, The.

Thangavelu. Globalization, Technology & Issues of Labour Market in Asia & Singapore. 2011. 96.00 *(978-981-4289-20-7(5))* World Scientific Publishing Co., Inc.

Tianbiao, Zhu. The Origin & Transformation of Northeast Asian Developmentalism: Consistent Threat, Political-Economic Institutions, & the Developmental States in Taiwan & South Korea. 2011. 208p. pap. ***(978-3-639-34162-1(7))*** VDM Verlag Dr. Mueller e.K.

Tipton, Frank B. Asian Firms: History, Institutions, & Management. 2007. (Illus.). 432p. (C). 165.00 *(978-1-84064-334-3(X))* Elgar, Edward Publishing, Inc.

Ulrich, Dave. Leadership in Asia: Challenges, Opportunities, & Strategies from Top Global Leaders. 2010. (ENG., Illus.). 288p. 29.95 *(978-0-07-174384-6(7)*, 0071743847) McGraw-Hill Cos., The.

United Nations. Asia-Pacific Trade & Investment Report 2009: Trade-led Recovery & Beyond. 2010. (ENG.). 346p. pap. 55.00 *(978-92-1-120586-2(7))* United Nations Pubns.

United Nations. Implementation of the Brussels Programme of Action for the Least Developed Countries in Asia & the Pacific. 2012. (ENG.). pap. 42.00 ***(978-92-1-120624-1(3))*** United Nations Pubns.

United Nations, Economic and Social Commission for Asia and the Pacific Staff. Economic & Social Survey of Asia & the Pacific 2009. 2009. (ENG., Illus.). 228p. pap. 80.00 *(978-92-1-120577-0(8))* United Nations Pubns.

United Nations Staff. Asia-Pacific Trade & Investment Review 2008. 2009. (ENG.). 206p. pap. 55.00 *(978-92-1-120572-5(7))* United Nations Pubns.

Volz, Ulrich. Prospects for Monetary Cooperation & Integration in East Asia. 2010. (ENG., Illus.). 338p. (gr. 17). 40.00 *(978-0-262-01399-4(1))* MIT Pr.

World Bank Staff, contrib. by. Mongolia Economic Retrospective. 2010. (World Bank Studies). (ENG., Illus.). 60p. pap. 15.00 *(978-0-8213-8540-1(2)*, 9780821385401) World Bank Pubns.

Yi. Singapore & Asia in a Globalized World. 2008. (Illus.). viii, 222p. 81.00 *(978-981-281-557-6(0))* World Scientific Publishing Co., Inc.

Zhang, Xiaoke. The Political Economy of Capital Market Reforms in South East Asia. 2011. (International Political Economy Ser.). (ENG., Illus.). 272p. 85.00 ***(978-0-230-25282-0(6))*** Palgrave Macmillan.

Zhu, Zhiqun. Understanding East Asia's Economic Miracles. 2009. pap. *(978-0-924304-54-5(5))* Assn. for Asian Studies, Inc.

Zhuang, Juzhong, ed. Poverty, Inequality, & Inclusive Growth in Asia: Measurement, Policy Issues, & Country Studies. 2011. (Anthem-Asian Development Bank Ser.). (Illus.). 492p. pap. 40.00 *(978-0-85728-414-3(2))* Anthem Pr. GBR. Dist: Books International, Inc.

ASIA—EMIGRATION AND IMMIGRATION

Abushouk, Ahmed Ibrahim & Ibrahim, Hassan Ahmed, eds. Hadhrami Diaspora in Southeast Asia: Identity Maintenance or Assimilation? 2009. (Social, Economic & Political Studies of the Middle East Ser.). 297p. *(978-90-04-17231-9(9))* BRILL.

Ahmad, Ali Nobil. Masculinity Sexuality & Illegal Migration: Human Smuggling from Pakistan to Europe. 2011. (Studies in Migration & Diaspora Ser.). 230p. 99.95 ***(978-1-4094-0975-5(9))*** Ashgate Publishing Co.

Al-Shahi, Ahmed. Middle East & North African Immigrants in Europe. 2009. 298p. pap. 39.95 *(978-0-415-56832-6(3))* Routledge.

Alfaro-Velcamp, Theresa. So Far from Allah, So Close to Mexico: Middle Eastern Immigrants in Modern Mexico. 2007. (ENG., Illus.). 286p. pap. 24.95 *(978-0-292-71641-4(9))* Univ. of Texas Pr.

Ali, Syed. Dubai: Gilded Cage. 2010. (ENG., Illus.). 360p. pap. 20.00 *(978-0-300-15217-3(5))* Yale Univ. Pr.

Amrith, Sunil S. Migration & Diaspora in Modern Asia. 2011. (New Approaches to Asian History Ser.). (ENG., Illus.). 240p. (C). 85.00 *(978-0-521-89835-5(8))*; pap. 27.99 *(978-0-521-72702-0(2))* Cambridge Univ. Pr.

Babar, Zahra. Migrant Labor in the Persian Gulf. Kamrava, Mehran, ed. 2012. (Columbia/Hurst Ser.). (ENG.). 276p. (gr. 17). 40.00 ***(978-0-231-70364-2(3))*** Columbia Univ. Pr.

Baldoz, Rick. The Third Asiatic Invasion: Migration & Empire in Filipino America, 1898-1946. 2011. (ENG.). 336p. 79.00 *(978-0-8147-9108-0(5))*; pap. 25.00 *(978-0-8147-9109-7(3))* New York Univ. Pr.

Banerjee, Sukanya, et al, eds. New Routes for Diaspora Studies. 2012. (21st Century Studies). (ENG., Illus.). 252p. 85.00 ***(978-0-253-00217-4(6)***, 0253002176); pap. 30.00 ***(978-0-253-00210-5(9)***, 0253002109) Indiana Univ. Pr.

Barde, Robert Eric. Immigration at the Golden Gate: Passenger Ships, Exclusion, & Angel Island, 1 vol. 2008. (Illus.). 304p. 49.95 *(978-0-313-34782-5(4)*, C34782, Praeger Pubs.) Greenwood Publishing Group, Inc.

Basu, Sibaji Pratim, ed. The Fleeing People of South Asia: Selections from Refugee Watch. 2009. (Anthem Press India Ser.). (ENG.). 464p. 100.00 *(978-81-905835-7-2(3))* Anthem Pr. GBR. Dist: Books International, Inc.

Brown, Gillian, et al. The Malaysia-Indonesia Remittance Corridor: Making Formal Transfers the Best Option for Women & Undocumented Migrants. 2008.

(World Bank Working Papers: 149). (ENG.). 122p. (C). pap. 20.00 (978-0-8213-7577-8(6), 9780821375778) World Bank Pubns.

Curley, Melissa & Wong, Siu-Lun, eds. Security & Migration in Asia. 2009. 200p. pap. 39.95 (978-0-415-57431-0(5)) Routledge.

—Security & Migration in Asia: The Dynamics of Securitisation. 2008. (Politics in Asia Ser.). (Illus.). 224p. 150.00 (978-0-415-40055-8(4)) Routledge.

de Silva Jaysuriya, Shihan. African Identity in Asia: Cultural Effects of Forced Migration. 2009. (Illus.). xiv, 164p. 89.95 (978-1-55876-471-2(2)); 260p. pap. 28.95 (978-1-55876-472-9(0)) Wiener, Markus Pubs., Inc.

Endo, Isaku & Afram, Gabi G. The Qatar-Nepal Remittance Corridor: Enhancing the Impact & Integrity of Remittance Flows by Reducing Inefficiencies in the Migration Process. 2011. (World Bank Studies). (ENG.). 64p. pap. 20.00 (978-0-8213-7050-6(2), 9780821370506) World Bank Pubns.

Fechter, Anne-Meike. Transnational Lives: Expatriates in Indonesia. 2007. 190p. 114.95 (978-0-7546-4743-0(9)) Ashgate Publishing Co.

Freitag, Ulrike & Oppen, Achim Von. Translocality: The Study of Globalising Processes from a Southern Perspective. 2010. (978-90-04-18116-8(4)) BRILL.

Gender & Labour Migration in Asia. 2009. 356p. pap. (978-92-9068-453-4(4)) International Organization for Migration (IOM).

Ghosh. Partition & the South Asian Diaspora. 2007. (ENG.). 308p. (C). 110.00 (978-0-415-42409-7(7), Routledge India) Taylor & Francis Group GBR. Dist: Taylor & Francis Group.

Hasegawa, Koichi & Yoshihara, Naoki, eds. Globalization, Minorities & Civil Society: Perspectives from Asian & European Cities. 2008. 244p. (C). 94.95 (978-1-876843-79-3(9)); pap. 34.95 (978-1-876843-85-4(3)) Trans Pacific Pr. AUS. Dist: International Specialized Bk. Services.

Hemmings, Hilary. Remittances, Recession — Returning Home? The Effects of the 2008 Economic Crisis on Tajik Migrant Labor in Moscow. 2010. (Illus.). 48p. (978-1-933549-82-8(3)) Woodrow Wilson Interantional Ctr. fo Scholars.

Hewison, Kevin, ed. Transnational Migration & Work in Asi. 2009. 244p. pap. 39.95 (978-0-415-54678-2(8)) Routledge.

Hinnells, John R., ed. Religious Reconstruction in the South Asian Diasporas: From One Generation to Another. 2007. (Migration, Minorities & Citizenship Ser.). (ENG., Illus.). 272p. 110.00 (978-0-333-77401-4(9)) Palgrave Macmillan.

Hodder, R. N. W. Overseas Chinese & Trade Between the Philippines & China: The Intertwining of Family, Social, & Business Interests in Promoting Trade. 2006. (Illus.). 328p. 119.95 (978-0-7734-5793-5(3)) Mellen, Edwin Pr., The.

Horstmann, Alexander & Wadley, Reed L., eds. Centering the Margin: Agency & Narrative in Southwest Asia Borderlands. 2008. 248p. 27.95 (978-1-84545-591-0(6)) Berghahn Bks., Inc.

Hwang, Cindy, photos by. Kyopo. 2011. (ENG., Illus.). 500p. 75.00 (978-1-884157-90-4(X)) Umbrage Editions.

Immigration Law Client Strategies in the Asia-Pacific: Leading Lawyers on Navigating Recent Changes, Analyzing Key Laws, & Looking Ahead to Emerging Trends (Inside the Minds) 2009. 376p. pap. 100.00 (978-0-314-23132-1(3)) Aspatore Bks.

International Organization for Migration. Migration, Development & Natural Disasters: Insights from the Indian Ocean Tsunami. 2007. (IOM Migration Research Ser.). 92p. pap. 16.00 (978-92-1-103657-2(7)) International Organization for Migration (IOM) CHE. Dist: United Nations Pubns.

International Research and Training Institute for the Advancement of Women. Gender, Remittances & Development: The Case of Filipino Migration to Italy. 2009. 40p. pap. 7.00 (978-92-1-127063-1(4)) United Nations Pubns.

Kee, Pookong & Yoshimatsu, Hidetaka. Global Movements in the Asia Pacific. 2009. 144.00 (978-981-283-374-7(9)) World Scientific Publishing Co., Inc.

Kibria, Nazli. Muslims in Motion: Islam & National Identity in the Bangladeshi Diaspora. 2011. (ENG., Illus.). 208p. (C). 72.00 (978-0-8135-5055-8(6)); pap. 24.95 (978-0-8135-5056-5(4)) Rutgers Univ. Pr.

Kim, Hyejin. International Ethnic Networks & Intra-Ethnic Conflict: Koreans in China. 2010. (ENG., Illus.). 212p. 89.00 (978-0-230-10252-1(2)) Palgrave Macmillan.

Knudsen, John Chr. Capricious Worlds: Vietnamese Life Journeys. 2007. (Comparative Anthropological Studies in Society, Cosmology & Politics Ser.). (ENG.). 304p. (gr. 11). pap. 39.95 (978-3-8258-8108-5(3)) Lit Verlag DEU. Dist: Transaction Pubs.

Kuhn, Philip A. Chinese among Others: Emigration in Modern Times. 2009. (State & Society East Asia Ser.). (ENG.). 452p. pap. 39.95 (978-0-7425-6749-8(4)) Rowman & Littlefield Publishers, Inc.

Kumar, P. Pratap, ed. Religious Pluralism in the Diaspora. 2006. (Illus.). 315p. pap. (978-90-04-15250-2(4)) BRILL.

Le, Cuong Nguyen. Asian American Assimilation: Ethnicity, Immigration, & Socioeconomic Attainment. 2007. (New Americans). 260p. 65.00 (978-1-59332-175-8(9)) LFB Scholarly Publishing LLC.

Leong, Chan-Hoong. Intercultural Relations in Asia: Migration & Work Effectiveness. 2009. 296p. 96.00 (978-981-283-786-8(8)) World Scientific Publishing Co., Inc.

Ley, David. Millionaire Migrants: Trans-Pacific Life Lines. 2010. (RGS-IBG Book Ser.: 38). (ENG., Illus.). 328p. pap. 39.95 (978-1-4051-9292-7(5)); 94.95 (978-1-4051-9291-0(7)) Wiley, John & Sons, Inc. (Wiley-Blackwell).

Li, Wei. From Urban Enclave to Ethnic Suburb: New Asian Communities in Pacific Rim Countries. 2006. (Illus.). 278p. 56.00 (978-0-8248-2911-7(5)) Univ. of Hawaii Pr.

Ma, Sheng-mei. Asian Diaspora Literature & Visual Culture. 2010. (Routledge Contemporary Asia Ser.). (ENG.). 192p. (C). 125.00 (978-0-415-59426-4(X)) Routledge.

McKeown, Adam M. Melancholy Order: Asian Migration & the Globalization of Borders. 2011. (Columbia Studies in International & Global History Ser.). (ENG., Illus.). 472p. (gr. 17). pap. 26.50 (978-0-231-14077-5(0)) Columbia Univ. Pr.

Meng, Xin, et al, eds. The Great Migration: Rural-Urban Migration in China & Indonesia. 2010. (Illus.). 288p. 125.00 (978-1-84844-644-1(6)) Elgar, Edward Publishing, Inc.

Moukarbel. Sri Lankan Housemaids in Lebanon. 2009. (IMISCOE Dissertations Ser.). pap. (978-90-8964-051-2(7)) Amsterdam Univ. Pr.

Mursheda Farhana, Khandaker. Illegal Migration & Trafficking of the Adivasi Women & Children. 2011. 164p. pap. (978-3-8443-2660-4(X)) Lambert Academic Publishing.

Myung, April, ed. Korean-American Chronicles: As Recounted by Korean High School Leaders. 2010. (Illus.). pap. 25.00 (978-1-59689-100-5(9), Hermit Kingdom Pr., The) Hermit Kingdom Pr., The.

—Korean-American Chronicles: As Recounted by Korean High School Leaders (Color) 2010. (Illus.). 212p. 70.00 (978-1-59689-098-5(3)); (ENG., pap. 40.00 (978-1-59689-107-4(6)) Hermit Kingdom Pr., The. (Hermit Kingdom Pr., The).

Peyrouse, Sébastien. The Russian Minority in Central Asia: Migration, Politics, & Language. 2008. 28p. (978-1-933549-32-3(7)) Woodrow Wilson Interantional Ctr. fo Scholars.

Pho, Tuyet-Lan, et al, eds. Southeast Asian Refugees & Immigrants in the Mill City: Changing Families, Communities, Institutions — Thirty Years Afterward. 2008. (Illus.). 250p. 50.00 (978-1-58465-662-3(X)) Univ. Pr. of New England.

Pohlmann, Markus, et al, eds. Citizenship & Migration in the Era of Globalization: The Flow of Migrants & the Perception of Citizenship in Asia & Europe. 2012. (Transcultural Research â€" Heidelberg Studies on Asia & Europe in a Global Context Ser.). (ENG.). 250p. 139.00 (978-3-642-19738-3(8), 3642197388) Springer.

Rahman, Mizanur. Domestic Workers & Remittances. 2010. 140p. pap. (978-3-8383-5499-6(0)) Lambert Academic Publishing.

—In Quest of Golden Deer. 2009. 280p. pap. (978-3-639-16217-2(X)) VDM Verlag Dr. Mueller e.K.

Rahman, Shafiqur. The Bangladeshi Diaspora in the United States After 9/11: From Obscurity to High Visibility. 2011. (ENG.). 70.00 (978-1-59332-405-6(7)) LFB Scholarly Publishing LLC.

Rai, Rajesh & Reeves, Peter, eds. The South Asian Diaspora: Transnational Networks & Changing Identities. 2008. (Routledge Contemporary South Asia Ser.). (ENG., Illus.). 224p. (C). 170.00 (978-0-415-45691-3(6)) Routledge.

Rios, Roger Rodriguez, ed. Migration Perspectives: Eastern Europe & Central Asia. 2006. 147p. pap. (978-92-9068-250-9(7)) International Organization for Migration (IOM).

Rodriguez, Robyn Magalit. Migrants for Export: How the Philippine State Brokers Labor to the World. 2010. (Illus.). 208p. (ENG.). 67.50 (978-0-8166-6527-3(3)); pap. 22.50 (978-0-8166-6528-0(1)) Univ. of Minnesota Pr.

Sadiq, Kamal. Paper Citizens: How Illegal Immigrants Acquire Citizenship in Developing Countries, 1 vol. 2010. (ENG., Illus.). 296p. pap. 19.95 (978-0-19-976463-1(8)) Oxford Univ. Pr., Inc.

Sanchez-Mazas, Alicia, et al, eds. Past Human Migrations in East Asia: Matching Archaeology, Linguistics & Genetics. 2012. (Routledge Studies in the Early History of Asia Ser.). (ENG., Illus.). 504p. (C). pap. 42.95 (978-0-415-54188-6(3)) Routledge.

Sardar, Ziauddin. Balti Britain: A Journey Through the British Asian Experience. 2009. (ENG.). 392p. pap. 16.95 (978-1-84708-082-0(0)) Granta Bks. GBR. Dist: Independent Pubs. Group.

Sassoon, Joseph. The Iraqi Refugees: The New Crisis in the Middle-East. 2009. (ENG., Illus.). 256p. 79.00 (978-1-84511-919-5(3)) I. B. Tauris & Co., Ltd. GBR. Dist: Macmillan.

Schwekendiek, Daniel. Korean Migration to the Wealthy West. 2011. (Asian Political, Economic & Security Issues Ser.). 140.00 (978-1-61470-369-3(8)) Nova Science Pubs., Inc.

Shephard, Ben. The Long Road Home: The Aftermath of the Second World War. 2011. (ENG., Illus.). 512p. 35.00 (978-1-4000-4068-1(X), Knopf) Knopf Doubleday Publishing Group.

Stowell, Jacob I. Immigration & Crime: The Effects of Immigration on Criminal Behavior. 2007. (New Americans). 184p. 58.00 (978-1-59332-204-5(6)) LFB Scholarly Publishing LLC.

Ullah, A. K. M. Ahsan, ed. Population Migration & Asia: Theories & Practice. 2010. (Asian Political, Economic & Security Issues Ser.). 147p. 69.00 (978-1-61668-962-9(5)) Nova Science Pubs., Inc.

Ullah, Akm Ahsan. Rationalizing Migration Decisions: Labour Migrants in East & South-East Asia. 2010. (Illus.). 276p. 99.95 (978-1-4094-0513-9(3)) Ashgate Publishing Co.

United Nations. Perspectives on Gender & Migration: From the Regional Seminar on Strengthening the Capacity of National Machineries for Gender Equality to Shape Migration Policies & Protect Migrant Women, Bangkok (22-24 November 2006) 2009. (ENG.). 160p. pap. 40.00 (978-92-1-120521-3(2)) United Nations Pubns.

van Schendel, Willem, et al, eds. Labour Migration & Human Trafficking: Critical Perspectives from Southeast Asia. 2012. (Routledge Contemporary Southeast Asia Ser.). (ENG., Illus.). 192p. (C). 130.00 (978-0-415-66563-6(9)) Routledge.

World Bank Staff, contrib. by. The Qatar-Nepal Remittance Corridor: Enhancing the Impact & Integrity of Remittance Flows Through Reducing Inefficiencies in the Migration Process. 2011. (978-0-8213-8787-0(1)) World Bank Pubns.

Yang, Philip Q. Asian Immigration to the United States. 2011. (PIMS - Polity Immigration & Society Ser.: 3). (ENG., Illus.). 192p. 59.95 (978-0-7456-4502-5(X)); pap. 22.95 (978-0-7456-4503-2(8)) Polity Pr. GBR. Dist: Wiley, John & Sons, Inc.

Yeoh, Brenda & Huang, Shirlena, eds. The Cultural Politics of Talent Migration in East Asia. 2012. (ENG.). 208p. (C). 135.00 (978-0-415-52813-9(5)) Routledge.

Yin, Jun. The Economic Assimilation of South Asian Immigrants in Norway. 2010. 104p. pap. (978-3-8383-5905-2(4)) Lambert Academic Publishing.

Yo. Global Movements in the Asia Pacific. 2009. 350p. 111.00 (978-981-283-373-0(0)) World Scientific Publishing Co., Inc.

ASIA—ENVIRONMENTAL CONDITIONS

Abdul Kadir, Aeslina. Leachate Treatment in Constructed Wetlands. 2010. 136p. pap. (978-3-8383-6925-9(4)) Lambert Academic Publishing.

Acharya, Keya & Noronha, Frederick N. J., eds. The Green Pen: Environmental Journalism in India & South Asia. 2010. 324p. (C). pap. 29.95 (978-81-321-0301-1(7), B03011P) SAGE Pubns., Inc.

Adams, Colleen. The Pakistan Earthquake. 2009. (Nature in the News Ser.). 32p. (gr. 3-4). 42.50 (978-1-61514-823-3(X), PowerKids Pr.) Rosen Publishing Group, Inc., The.

Agoramoorthy, Govindasamy, et al. The Formosan Macaques of Mt Longevity. 2011. 168p. pap. (978-3-8433-9228-0(5)) Lambert Academic Publishing.

Ahmad, Habib, et al. Pollution in Kabul River. 2010. 100p. pap. (978-3-639-08924-0(3)) VDM Verlag Dr. Mueller e.K.

Ahmed, Asib. Environmental Impact Assessment of Eastern Bypass in Bangladesh. 2011. 72p. pap. (978-3-8443-1964-4(6)) Lambert Academic Publishing.

—Landuse-Environment Nexus. 2011. 144p. pap. (978-3-8443-1394-0(2)) Lambert Academic Publishing.

Ainuddin, Syed & Kumar Routray, Jayant. Earthquake Risks in Baluchistan. 2010. 96p. pap. (978-3-8383-8659-1(0)) Lambert Academic Publishing.

Al Madhoun, Wesam, et al. Non Methane Hydrocarbons Trends in Malaysi. 2011. 196p. pap. (978-3-8454-0060-0(9)) Lambert Academic Publishing.

Adrian, Edvin. Indonesian Rainfall. 2007. 172p. per. (978-3-8364-0913-1(5)) VDM Verlag Dr. Mueller e.K.

Amin, Md. Nurul & Amin, Nurul. Aquatic Invasion in Mongla Sea Port, Bangladesh. 2011. 60p. pap. (978-3-8443-9282-1(3)) Lambert Academic Publishing.

Anceschi, Luca & Symons, Jonathan, eds. Energy Security in the Era of Climate Change: The Asia-Pacific Experience. 2012. (Energy, Climate & the Environment Ser.). (ENG., Illus.). 320p. 95.00 (978-0-230-27987-2(2)) Palgrave Macmillan.

Antara, Zareen & Abu, Sumon. Biophysical Characterization & Economic Evaluation of Wetland Resource: Common Pool Natural Resources Management Otions for Ecologically Critical Areas of Bangladesh. 2011. 176p. pap. (978-3-639-32542-3(7)) VDM Verlag Dr. Mueller e.K.

Anwar, Muhammad Mushahid. An Investigation of Public Parks & Life Quality inKarachi, Pakistan: Urban Ecology 2008. 252p. pap. (978-3-8364-8705-4(5)) VDM Verlag Dr. Mueller e.K.

Aryal, Bimal. Adaptation to Climate Change. 2011. 112p. pap. (978-3-8443-2243-9(4)) Lambert Academic Publishing.

Asia Business Council. Building Energy Efficiency: Why Green Buildings Are Key to Asia's Future. 2007. 324p. per. 36.00 (978-988-99565-1-6(9), Inkstone Bks.

Asiful, Basar. Climate Change, Man-Made Destruction & the Loss of Rural Livelihoods: A Story from Coastal Bangladesh. 2011. 72p. pap. (978-3-639-32829-5(9)) VDM Verlag Dr. Mueller e.K.

Bajracharya, Leena. Biodiversity Conservation in Buffer Zone - Problems & Opportunities. 2011. 104p. pap. (978-3-8433-8447-6(9)) Lambert Academic Publishing.

Basnet, Kedar. Population Pressure & Responses in Terrace Cultivation in Nepal. 2011. 248p. pap. (978-3-8454-1217-7(8)) Lambert Academic Publishing.

Behnke, Roy H. The Socio-Economic Causes & Consequences of Desertification in Central Asia. 2008. (NATO Science for Peace & Security Series C: Environmental Security Ser.). (Illus.). 300p. spiral bd. 109.00 (978-1-4020-8543-7(5)); 249.00 (978-1-4020-8542-0(7), 1402085427) Springer.

Bhatti, Muhammad Tousif. Strategic Analysis of Water Quality. 2010. 188p. pap. (978-3-639-26451-7(7)) VDM Verlag Dr. Mueller e.K.

Bhowmik, Avit. Relocation of Hazaribagh Tannery: Myth or Reality? 2011. 96p. pap. (978-3-8443-2274-3(4)) Lambert Academic Publishing.

Biggs, David. Quagmire: Nation-Building & Nature in the Mekong Delta. (ENG., Illus.). 320p. 2012. (C). pap. 25.00 (978-0-295-99199-3(2)) 2011. 35.00 (978-0-295-99067-5(8)) Univ. of Washington Pr.

Boomgaard, Peter. A World of Water: Rain, Rivers & Seas in Southeast Asian Histories. 2010. (Illus.). 376p. pap. 44.00 (978-90-6718-294-2(X)) KITLV Pr. NLD. Dist: Univ. of Hawaii Pr.

Campbell, Ian Charles, ed. The Mekong: Biophysical Environment of an International River Basin. 2009. (Aquatic Ecology Ser.). (ENG., Illus.). 464p. 92.95 (978-0-12-374026-7(6), Academic Pr.) Elsevier Science & Technology Bks.

Chandrappa, Ramesha, et al. Coping with Climate Change: Principles & Asian Context. 2011. (ENG., Illus.). xxi, 370p. 179.00 (978-3-642-19673-7(X), 364219673X) Springer.

Chellaney, Brahma. Water: Asia's New Battleground. 2011. (Illus.). 400p. 29.95 (978-1-58901-771-9(4)) Georgetown Univ. Pr.

Chuanpongpanich, Supatchaya. Application of Weather Radar for Rainfall Forecasting. 2011. 212p. pap. (978-3-8433-8277-9(8)) Lambert Academic Publishing.

Clift, P. D., et al, eds. Monsoon Evolution & Tectonics-Climate Linkage in East Asia. 2010. (Special Publication Ser.). (Illus.). 352p. (978-1-86239-310-3(9)) Geological Society Publishing Hse.

Colopy, Cheryl. Dirty, Sacred Rivers: Confronting South Asia's Water Crisis. 2012. (ENG., Illus.). 416p. 34.95 (978-0-19-984501-9(8)) Oxford Univ. Pr., Inc.

Corlett, Richard T. The Ecology of Tropical East Asia. 2009. (ENG., Illus.). 288p. (C). 150.00 (978-0-19-953245-2(1)); pap. 65.00 (978-0-19-953246-9(X)) Oxford Univ. Pr., Inc.

De Alwis Karunarathne, Enoka Chandrakumara. Bioaccumulation of Heavy Metals in Freshwater Macrophytes: A Study of Apanogeton Sp. & Nelumbo Nucifera. 2011. 64p. pap. (978-3-639-32693-2(8)) VDM Verlag Dr. Mueller e.K.

Dhakal, Shiva Ram & Ram, Krishna. Environment & Sustainable Development in Nepal. 2010. 132p. pap. (978-3-639-22371-2(3)) VDM Verlag Dr. Mueller e.K.

Ellen, Roy, ed. Modern Crises & Traditional Strategies: Local Ecological Knowledge in Island Southeast Asia. 2011. (EAE Ser.). 288p. 34.95 (978-0-85745-145-3(6)) Berghahn Bks., Inc.

Elliott, Lorraine & Caballero-Anthony, Mely, eds. Human Security & Climate Change in Southeast Asia. 2012. (Routledge Security in Asia Pacific Ser.). (ENG., Illus.). 208p. (C). 145.00 (978-0-415-68489-7(7)) Routledge.

Fernández-Giménez, María Edith. Restoring Community Connections to the Land: Building Resilience Through Community-Based Rangeland Management in China & Mongolia. 2012. (Illus.). 272p. 125.00 (978-1-84593-894-9(1)); pap. 55.00 (978-1-84593-895-6(X)) CABI GBR. Dist: Stylus Publishing, LLC.

Fu, Congbin, et al, eds. Changes in the Human-Monsoon System of East Asia in the Context of Global Change. 2008. (Monsoon Asia Integrated Regional Study on Global Change Ser.). (Illus.). 369p. 112.00 (978-981-283-241-2(6)) World Scientific Publishing Co., Inc.

Fukushi, K., ed. Southeast Asian Water Environment 2. 2007. (Southeast Asian Water Environment Ser.). (Illus.). 346p. (C). pap. (978-1-84339-124-1(4)) IWA Publishing.

Fukushi, Kensuke. Southeast Asian Water Environment 4. 2010. (Southeast Asian Water Environment Ser.). (Illus.). 280p. (C). pap. (978-1-84339-362-7(X)) IWA Publishing.

Fuller, Linda K. Tsunami Communication: (Inter)personal/Intercultural, Mass Media, & Philanthropic Responses: Historical, Technical, Ethical, & Development Communication. 2010. (Illus.). 312p. (978-1-57273-817-1(0)); pap. (978-1-57273-818-8(9)) Hampton Pr., Inc.

Fung, Tung, et al, eds. Facility Siting in the Asia-Pacific: Perspectives on Knowledge Production & Application. 2009. (ENG.). 320p. (gr. 17). 49.00 (978-962-996-406-1(6)) Chinese Univ. of Hong Kong, The HKG. Dist: Columbia Univ. Pr.

Ghulam, Mujtaba Shah, et al. Plants & Plant Resources of Siran Valley, Mansehra, NWFP, Pakistan: Ethnobotany & Conservation. 2011. 380p. pap. (978-3-639-31706-0(8)) VDM Verlag Dr. Mueller e.K.

Gilbert, Jeremy I. Climate Change in Southeast Asia & the Pacific Islands. 2011. (Climate Change & its Causes, Effects & Prediction Ser.). 89.00 (978-1-61122-852-6(2)) Nova Science Pubs., Inc.

Gill, Sucha Singh, et al, eds. Economic & Environmental Sustainability of the Asian Region. 2010. (ENG., Illus.). xxvi, 461p. (C). 95.00 (978-0-415-58144-8(3), Routledge India) Taylor & Francis Group GBR. Dist: Taylor & Francis Group.

Green, Michael J., et al. Green Dragons: The Politics of Climate Change in Asia: A Report of the CSIS Asian Regionalism Initiative. 2010. (Illus.). 108p. pap. (978-0-89206-605-6(9), CSIS Pr., The) Ctr. for Strategic & International Studies.

Guneratne, Arjun, ed. Culture & the Environment in the Himalaya. 2012. (ENG., Illus.). 256p. (C). pap. 42.95 (978-0-415-53314-0(7)) Routledge.

Hajiyeva, Sevil. Municipal Solid Waste Management in Azerbaijan. 2009. 128p. pap. (978-3-639-22108-4(7)) VDM Verlag Dr. Mueller e.K.

Hamblyn, Richard. Terra: Tales of the Earth - Four Events That Changed the World. 2010. (ENG., Illus.). 304p. pap. 19.95 (978-0-330-49074-0(5), Picador) Pan Macmillan GBR. Dist: Trans-Atlantic Pubns., Inc.

Han, Chin-Hui, et al. Responding to Climate Change: Global Experiences & the Korean Perspective. 2012. (KDI/EWC series on Economic Policy Ser.). 240p. 110.00 (978-0-85793-995-1(5)) Elgar, Edward Publishing, Inc.

Haque, A. K. Enamul, et al. Environmental Valuation in South Asia. 2011. (Illus.). 506p. (978-1-107-00714-7(3)) Cambridge Univ. Pr.

Haruyama, Shigeko, ed. Hydro Gis: Theory & Lessons from the Vietnamese Delta. 2009. (Environmental Science, Engineering & Technology Ser.). 79.00 (978-1-60876-156-2(8)) Nova Science Pubs., Inc.

Hasan, Zaheed. Public Understanding of Climate Change in Urban Bangladesh. 2011. 80p. pap. (978-3-8443-9689-8(6)) Lambert Academic Publishing.

Haslinger, Josef. Phi Phi Island: Ein Bericht. 2007. (GER.). 203p. (978-3-10-030059-1(9)) Fischer, S. Verlag.

—Tsunami: A Report from Phi Phi Island. 2011. 151p. pap. (978-1-57241-176-0(7)) Ariadne Pr.

Ho, Peter. Leapfrogging Development in Emerging Asia: Caught Between Greening & Pollution. 2008. 79.00 *(978-1-60456-410-5(5))* Nova Science Pubs., Inc.

Hobbes, Marieke. Figuring Rural Development: Concepts & cases of land use, sustainability & integrative Indicators. 2010. (LUP Dissertaties Ser.). 232p. pap. *(978-90-8728-078-9(5)*, Leiden Univ. Pr.) Amsterdam Univ. Pr.

Huq, S., et al, eds. Vulnerability & Adaptation to Climate Change for Bangladesh. 2010. (Illus.). 164p. pap. 92.00 *(978-90-481-5160-8(0)*, 9048151600) Springer.

Hussain, Dr. Raja Rizwan, et al. Pakistan's Water. 2011. 80p. pap. ***(978-3-8454-1686-1(6))*** Lambert Academic Publishing.

Islam, Rafiqul, et al. Environmental Impacts of Sewage Pollution on Karnafully River. 2011. 104p. pap. ***(978-3-8443-8899-2(0))*** Lambert Academic Publishing.

Japan Environmental Council Staff. The State of the Environment in Asia 2006/2007. 2010. (ENG., Illus.). 352p. pap. 36.00 *(978-92-808-1187-2(8))* United Nations Univ. Pr. JPN. Dist: Brookings Institution Pr.

Jayasuriya, Sisira & McCawley, Peter. The Asian Tsunami: Aid & Reconstruction after a Disaster. 2011. (Illus.). 288p. 115.00 *(978-1-84844-692-2(6))* Elgar, Edward Publishing, Inc.

Jean, Jiin-Shuh, et al. The Taiwan Crisis: A Showcase of the Global Arsenic Problem. 2010. (Arsenic in the Environment Ser.). (ENG., Illus.). 234p. 89.95 *(978-0-415-58510-1(4)*, CRC Press) Taylor & Francis Group GBR. Dist: Taylor & Francis Group.

Jiang, Guibin, et al, eds. Persistent Organic Pollutants in Asia: Sources, Distributions, Transport & Fate. 2007. (Developments in Environmental Science Ser.: 7). (ENG., Illus.). 842p. 225.00 *(978-0-08-045132-9(2)*, Elsevier Science) Elsevier Science & Technology Bks.

Jitendra, Priya & V.K.Anand, . The Oedogoniales of Jammu , Indi. 2011. 448p. pap. ***(978-3-8383-9763-4(0))*** Lambert Academic Publishing.

Kameyama, Yasuko & United Nations University Staff. Climate Change in Asia: Perspectives on the future climate Regime. Sari, Agus P., ed. 2008. (ENG., Illus.). 260p. pap. 34.00 *(978-92-808-1152-0(5))* United Nations Univ. Pr. JPN. Dist: Brookings Institution Pr.

Karnawati, Dwikorita. The Yogyakarta Earthquake of May 27, 2006. 2008. (Illus.). *(978-0-89863-304-7(4))* Star Publishing Co.

Karpal Singh, Harkiranpal Singh. Beyond the Kyoto Protocol. 2010. 88p. pap. *(978-3-8383-7786-5(9))* Lambert Academic Publishing.

Khadka, Sarba Raj. Biodiversity Conservation in Nepal. 2011. 344p. pap. ***(978-3-8433-8576-3(9))*** Lambert Academic Publishing.

King, S. A., et al, eds. Seismic Hazard & Building Vulnerability in Post-Soviet Central Asian Republics. 2010. (Nato Science Partnership Subseries: 2 (closed) Ser.). (ENG.). 276p. pap. 219.00 *(978-90-481-5176-9(7)*, 9048151767) Springer.

Koh, Kheng-Lian. Asean Environmental Law, Policy & Governance: Selected Documents. 2011. 800p. 188.00 *(978-981-4329-58-3(4))*; 307.00 *(978-981-4338-91-2(5))* World Scientific Publishing Co., Inc.

—Crucial Issues in Climate Change & the Kyoto Protocol: Asia & the World. 2009. 596p. 111.00 *(978-981-4277-52-5(5))* World Scientific Publishing Co., Inc.

Kohyama, Takashi, et al, eds. Forest Ecosystems & Environments: Scaling up from Shoot Module to Watershed. 2010. (Illus.). viii, 160p. pap. 149.00 *(978-4-431-99810-5(1)*, 4431998101) Springer.

Koirala, Rishi Raj. Assessment of Policy Measures in Controlling the Vehicular Pollution. 2011. 120p. pap. ***(978-3-8443-2737-3(1))*** Lambert Academic Publishing.

Kulasena, Nayomi & Dahanayake, Kapila. Recent- & Paleo-Tsunami Sediments of Sri Lank. 2010. 104p. pap. *(978-3-8383-5475-0(3))* Lambert Academic Publishing.

Kumaran (Sanath), Sanar & A. N., Ainuddin. Hydrometeorology of Tropical Montane Rainforests in West Malaysi. 2010. 312p. pap. *(978-3-639-24167-9(3))* VDM Verlag Dr. Mueller e.K.

Kunstadter, Peter. Pesticides in Southeast Asia: Environmental, Biomedical, & Economic Uses & Effects. 2007. (ENG.). 286p. (C). 55.00 ***(978-974-9511-20-6(4))*** Silkworm Bks. THA. Dist: Univ. of Washington Pr.

Lal, Rattan. Climate Change & Food Security in South Asia. Lal, Rattan et al, eds. 2010. (ENG., Illus.). xxii, 600p. 209.00 *(978-90-481-9515-2(2)*, 9048195152) Springer.

Lal, Rattan, et al, eds. Climate Change & Terrestrial Carbon Sequestration in Central As. 2007. (ENG., Illus.). 512p. 172.95 *(978-0-415-42235-2(3)*, Taylor & Francis) Taylor & Francis Group GBR. Dist: Taylor & Francis Group.

Lasco, Rodel D., et al. Assessing Climate Change Impacts, Vulnerability & Adaptation the Case of Pantabangan-Carranglan Watershed. 2011. pap. *(978-1-61122-132-9(3))* Nova Science Pubs., Inc.

Lestari, Rosbintarti Kartika. Mechanisms of Seasonal March of Precipitation over Maritime Continent. 2010. 108p. pap. *(978-3-639-25569-0(0))* VDM Verlag Dr. Mueller e.K.

—Numerical Study on the Southeast Asian Summer Monsoon. 2010. 76p. pap. *(978-3-639-25930-8(0))* VDM Verlag Dr. Mueller e.K.

Lin Erda, et al, eds. Climate Change Vulnerability & Adaptation in Asia & the Pacific. 2010. 260p. pap. 141.00 *(978-90-481-4745-8(X)*, 904814745X) Springer.

Macauslan, Robert. Air Pollution Policy in Singapore, Dalian, & Hong Kong: Contemporary Case Studies Examining the Role of Political Will in Policy Development & Enforcement. 2008. 92p. pap. *(978-3-639-10307-6(6))* VDM Verlag Dr. Mueller e.K.

Madsen, David B., ed. Entering America: Northeast Asia & Beringia Before the Last Glacial Maximum. 2010. (ENG., Illus.). 492p. pap. 30.00 *(978-1-60781-057-5(3))* Univ. of Utah Pr.

Mamun, Abu Hena Mohammad. Feasibility Study for the Establishment of Waste Reception Facility: In Context of Seaports in South Asian Countries. 2011. 144p. pap. ***(978-3-639-31430-4(1))*** VDM Verlag Dr. Mueller e.K.

Miah, Md Danesh, et al. Forests to Climate Change Mitigation: Clean Development Mechanism in Bangladesh. 2010. (Environmental Science & Engineering Ser.). (ENG., Illus.). xcviii, 15p. 129.00 *(978-3-642-13252-0(9)*, 3642132529) Springer.

Mitra, A. P. & Sharma, C., eds. Global Environmental Changes in South Asia: A Regional Perspective. 2010. (ENG., Illus.). vi, 394p. 169.00 *(978-1-4020-9912-0(6)*, 1402099126) Springer.

Mustaeva, Nailya. Mountain Environment & Climate Change. 2009. 72p. pap. *(978-3-639-09216-5(3))* VDM Verlag Dr. Mueller e.K.

Nielsen, Kenneth Bo. Imagining & Encountering the Indian State. 2011. 152p. pap. ***(978-3-8454-2463-7(X))*** Lambert Academic Publishing.

Nüsser, Marcus, ed. Large Dams in Asia: Contested Environments between Hydro-Power & Resistance. 2012. (Advances in Asian Human-Environmental Research Ser.). (ENG., Illus.). 250p. 139.00 ***(978-94-007-2797-7(6)***, 9400727976) Springer.

O'Driscoll, Kieran. A 3D regional model of the Indonesian Seas circulation. 2008. 176p. pap. *(978-3-639-08796-3(8))* VDM Verlag Dr. Mueller e.K.

Ofori, George. Sustainability Matters: Environmental Management in Asia. 2010. 652p. 138.00 *(978-981-4322-90-4(3))* World Scientific Publishing Co., Inc.

Omar, Nasr Y. M. Environmental Pollution Analysis. 2009. 132p. pap. *(978-3-639-19227-8(3))* VDM Verlag Dr. Mueller e.K.

Pariatamby, Agamuthu. Landfill Cover Systems Modelling for Tropical Climate. 2009. 172p. pap. *(978-3-639-17377-2(5))* VDM Verlag Dr. Mueller e.K.

Pattazhy, Sainudeen. Impact of Electromagnetic Radiation on the Density of Honeybees. 2011. 152p. pap. ***(978-3-8454-1023-4(X))*** Lambert Academic Publishing.

Paul, Delia. The Living Mekong. 2009. (ENG., Illus.). 156p. 35.00 *(978-974-9511-67-1(0))* Silkworm Bks. THA. Dist: Univ. of Washington Pr.

Paul J., Thomassin & Kakali, Mukhopadhyay. Economic & Environmental Impact of Free Trade Agreement in East & South East Asia. 2010. (ENG., Illus.). xix, 209p. 129.00 *(978-90-481-3506-6(0)*, 9048135060) Springer.

Phan, Kongkea & Kim, Kyoung-Woong. Arsenic & Trace Element Calamities in Cambodi. 2011. 56p. pap. ***(978-3-8383-2371-8(8))*** Lambert Academic Publishing.

Ritzema, Henk. Drain for gain: making water management worth its Salt: Subsurface drainage practices in irrigated agriculture in semi-arid & arid Regions. 2009. (ENG., Illus.). 224p. 69.95 *(978-0-415-49857-9(0)*, CRC Press) Taylor & Francis Group GBR. Dist: Taylor & Francis Group.

Roy, Sajal & Mongalom, Kumar. Environmental Management Scenario: A Study in Satkhira. 2011. 76p. pap. ***(978-3-8443-8988-3(1))*** Lambert Academic Publishing.

Salman, Aneel. A Coastal Ecosystem & a People in Peril. 2011. 232p. pap. ***(978-3-8454-0056-3(0))*** Lambert Academic Publishing.

Schwela, Dieter, et al. Urban Air Pollution in Asian Cities: Status, Challenges & Management. 2006. (ENG., Illus.). 296p. 146.00 *(978-1-84407-375-7(0))* Routledge.

Shah, Fatima & Ranghieri, Federica. A Workbook on Planning for Urban Resilience in the Face of Disasters: Adapting Experiences from Vietnam to Other Cities. 2012. (World Bank Training Ser.). (ENG.). 176p. pap. 20.00 ***(978-0-8213-8878-5(9)***, 9780821388785) World Bank Pubns.

Sharma, Deepshikha, et al. Wastewater Management in National Capital Territory of Indi. 2011. 92p. pap. ***(978-3-8443-9752-9(3))*** Lambert Academic Publishing.

Sharma, Vinay. Water Jet System for Mining under Indian Environment. 2011. 292p. pap. ***(978-3-8443-9506-8(7))*** Lambert Academic Publishing.

Shaw, Rajib, et al. Climate Change Adaptation & Disaster Risk Reduction: An Asian Perspective. 2010. (Community, Environment & Disaster Risk Ser.: Vol. 5). (Illus.). 471p. *(978-0-85724-485-7(X))* Emerald Group Publishing Ltd. GBR. Dist: Turpin Distribution, Inc.

Shrestha, Ravi Kumar. Designing Community Based Adaptation Plan to Climate Change. 2011. 96p. pap. ***(978-3-8454-0813-2(8))*** Lambert Academic Publishing.

Siddiqui, Muhammad Tahir. Fertilizer Requirements & Nutrient Dynamics in Teak Plantations. 2010. 184p. pap. *(978-3-639-27534-6(9))* VDM Verlag Dr. Mueller e.K.

Sivaperuman, C. Faunal Ecology & Conservation of the Great Indian Desert. 2008. (ENG., Illus.). xviii, 222p. 199.00 *(978-3-540-87408-9(9)*, 3540874089) Springer.

Skidmore, Monique & Wilson, Trevor, eds. Myanmar: The State, Community & the Environment. 2007. (Illus.). (C). pap. *(978-0-7315-3811-9(0))* Asia Pacific Pr.

Sodhi, Navjot S. & Brook, Barry W. Southeast Asian Biodiversity in Crisis. 2011. (Cambridge Tropical Biology Ser.). (ENG.). 204p. pap. 60.00 ***(978-1-107-40313-0(8))*** Cambridge Univ. Pr.

Subedi, Deepak Raj. Informal Settlements in Kathmandu. 2011. 124p. pap. ***(978-3-8454-1557-4(6))*** Lambert Academic Publishing.

Sultana, Haque. Environmental Management of Municipality in Bangladesh. 2011. 204p. pap. ***(978-3-8454-2284-8(X))*** Lambert Academic Publishing.

Takizawa, S. Groundwater Management in Asian Cities: Technology & Policy for Sustainability. 2008. (CSUR-UT Series: Library for Sustainable Urban Regeneration Ser.). (Illus.). 334p. 109.00 *(978-4-431-78398-5(9))* Springer.

Tarigan, Balaman. Kontribusi Perkebunan Kelapa Sawit Dalam Perekonomian Dan Lingkungan Hidup Sumatera Utara. 2011. (IND., Illus.). 128p. *(978-979-493-314-5(7))* Institut Pertanian Bogor Press, IPB-Press.

Thampanya, Udomluck. Mangroves & Sediment Dynamics along the Coasts of Southern Thailand. 2006. (ENG., Illus.). 116p. (C). per. 89.95 *(978-0-415-38486-5(9)*, Taylor & Francis) Taylor & Francis Group GBR. Dist: Taylor & Francis Group.

Timotius, Kris H., et al, eds. Ecology of Insular Southeast Asia: The Indonesian Archipelago. 2006. (ENG., Illus.). 568p. 195.00 *(978-0-444-52739-4(7)*, Elsevier Science) Elsevier Science & Technology Bks.

Tiwari, Ravi Mohan & Bharat Babu Shrestha. Community Structure & Regeneration of Sub-Alpine Abies Spectabilis. 2011. 56p. pap. ***(978-3-8433-9226-6(9))*** Lambert Academic Publishing.

Toyota, Tomoyo & Fujikura, Ryo, eds. Climate Change Mitigation & Development Cooperation. 2012. (ENG., Illus.). 264p. (C). 135.00 ***(978-0-415-50864-3(9))***; pap. 60.95 ***(978-0-415-50865-0(7))*** Routledge.

United Nations Development Programme. One Planet to Share: Sustaining Human Progress in a Changing Climate: UNDP Asia-Pacific Human Development Report. 2012. (ENG.). pap. 45.00 ***(978-0-415-62570-8(X))*** United Nations Pubns.

United Nations, Economic Commission for Europe Staff, contrib. by. Environmental Indicators & Indicator-Based Assessment Reports: Eastern Europe, Caucasus & Central Asia. 2007. (ENG., Illus.). 104p. pap. 20.00 *(978-92-1-116961-4(5))* United Nations Pubns.

United Nations Environment Programme Staff. Lebanon: Post-Conflict Environmental Assessment. 2007. (Illus.). 181p. pap. 25.00 *(978-92-807-2794-4(X))* United Nations Environment Programme KEN. Dist: United Nations Pubns.

United Nations Staff. Tsunami Early Warning Systems in the Indian Ocean & Southeast Asia: Report on Regional Unmet Needs. 2009. (ENG.). 50p. pap. 12.00 *(978-92-1-120580-0(8))* United Nations Pubns.

Unsworth, Richard K. F. Marine Research & Conservation in the Coral Triangle. Clifton, Julian, ed. 2010. (Environmental Science, Engineering & Technology Ser.). 274p. 89.00 *(978-1-61668-473-0(9))* Nova Science Pubs., Inc.

Urfi, Abdul Jamil. The Painted Stork: Ecology & Conservation. 2011. (Illus.). xvii, 163p. ***(978-1-4419-8468-5(2))*** Springer.

Vincent, Peter. Saudi Arabia: An Environmental Overview. 2008. (ENG., Illus.). 332p. (C). 164.95 *(978-0-415-41387-9(7)*, Taylor & Francis) Taylor & Francis Group GBR. Dist: Taylor & Francis Group.

Voulvouli, Aimilia. From Environmentalism to Transenvironmentalism: The Ethnography of an Urban Protest in Modern Istanbul. 2009. (ENG., Illus.). 216p. pap. 44.95 *(978-3-03911-947-9(8))* Lang, Peter AG GBR. Dist: Lang, Peter.

Weng, Yu-Chi. Towards Sustainable Municipal Solid Waste Management. 2010. 168p. pap. *(978-3-8383-5269-5(6))* Lambert Academic Publishing.

Wijeyeratne, Mokshana. Environmentally Sound Management of Municipal Solid Waste. 2011. 132p. pap. ***(978-3-8443-9222-7(X))*** Lambert Academic Publishing.

Wolanski, Eric, ed. The Environment in Asia Pacific Harbours. 2008. (Illus.). 497p. pap. 109.00 incl. cd-rom *(978-1-4020-6566-8(3))* Springer London, Ltd. GBR. Dist: Springer.

Yaacob, Mohd Rafi. Environmental Management in the Malaysian Palm Oil Industry. 2010. 408p. pap. *(978-3-8383-5698-3(5))* Lambert Academic Publishing.

Yadav, Ramesh Kumar. Variability, Teleconnections & Lrf of Nw India Winter Precipitation. 2011. 136p. pap. ***(978-3-8443-3105-9(0))*** Lambert Academic Publishing.

Yusup, Yusri. Turbulence & Dispersion in the Lowest Atmospheric Layer. 2011. 176p. pap. ***(978-3-8443-8722-3(6))*** Lambert Academic Publishing.

Zaman, Sheikh. Electricity from Poultry Waste in Bangladesh. 2011. 124p. pap. ***(978-3-8443-0100-7(3))*** Lambert Academic Publishing.

ASIA—FOREIGN RELATIONS

Acharya, Amitav. Asia Rising: Who Is Leading? 2008. 191p. pap. 37.00 *(978-981-277-133-9(6))* World Scientific Publishing Co., Inc.

—Whose Ideas Matter? Agency & Power in Asian Regionalism. 2011. (Cornell Studies in Political Economy Ser.). (Illus.). 200p. pap. 21.95 *(978-0-8014-7708-9(5))* Cornell Univ. Pr.

Acharya, Amitav & Buzan, Barry, eds. Non-Western International Relations Theory: Perspectives from Asia. 2010. (ENG., Illus.). 248p. 150.00 *(978-0-415-47473-3(6))* Routledge.

—Non-Western International Relations Theory: Perspectives on & Beyond Asia. 2010. (ENG., Illus.). 256p. (C). 49.95 *(978-0-415-47474-0(4))* Routledge.

Aggarwal, Vinod & Koo, Min Gyo, eds. Asia's New Institutional Architecture: Evolving Structures for Managing Trade & Security Relations. 2008. (Political Economy of the Asia Pacific Ser.). 275p. pap. 59.95 *(978-3-540-74887-8(3)*, 3540748873) Springer.

Akita, Shigru & White, Nicholas J. The International Order of Asia in the 1930s & 1950s. 2010. (Modern Economic & Social History Ser.). (Illus.). 332p. 124.95 *(978-0-7546-5341-7(2))* Ashgate Publishing Co.

Alam, Anwar, ed. India & West Asia in the Era of Globalisation. 2008. 327p. 49.50 *(978-81-7708-154-1(3))* New Century Publications IND. Dist: International Specialized Bk. Services.

Allen, Michael J. Until the Last Man Comes Home: POWs, MIAs, & the Unending Vietnam War. 2009. (ENG., Illus.). 448p. 32.00 *(978-0-8078-3261-5(8))* Univ. of North Carolina Pr.

Amineh, M. Parvizi, ed. State, Society & International Relations in Asia. 2010. (ICAS Publications Ser.). (Illus.). 307p. pap. *(978-90-5356-794-4(1))* Amsterdam Univ. Pr.

Ampiah, Kweku. The Political & Moral Imperatives of the Bandung Conference of 1955: The Reactions of the US, UK & Japan. 2007. 252p. *(978-1-905246-40-3(4))* BRILL.

Andreosso-O'Callaghan, Bernadette, et al, eds. The Economic Relations Between Asia & Europe: Organisations, Trade & Investment. 2007. (Chandos Asian Studies). (ENG., Illus.). 264p. 110.00 *(978-1-84334-311-0(8)*, Chandos Publishing) Woodhead Publishing Ltd. GBR. Dist: Ingram Pub. Services.

Andreosso-O'Callaghan, Bernadette & Zolin, M. Bruna, eds. Current Issues in Economic Integration: Can Asia Inspire the West? 2010. (Illus.). 268p. 114.95 *(978-0-7546-7956-1(X))* Ashgate Publishing Co.

Aris, Stephen. Eurasian Regionalism: The Shanghai Cooperation Organisation. 2011. (Critical Studies of the Asia-Pacific Ser.). (ENG., Illus.). 224p. 85.00 *(978-0-230-28527-9(9))* Palgrave Macmillan.

Asia Foundation Staff, contrib. by. America's Role in Asia: Asian & American Views: Recommendations for U.S. Policy from Both Sides of the Pacific. 2008. vii, 310p. *(978-1-892325-08-2(X))* Asia Foundation, The.

Asia Overview: Protecting American Interests in China & Asia: Hearing Before the Subcommittee on Asia & the Pacific of the Committee on Foreign Affairs, House of Representatives, One Hundred Twelfth Congress, First Session, March 31, 2011. 2011. (Illus.). iii, 106p. ***(978-0-16-088856-4(5)***, 552-070-42976-0) United States Government Printing Office.

Asian Development Bank. Asian Economic Cooperation & Integration: Progress, Prospects, Challenges. 2006. (ENG., Illus.). 388p. pap. *(978-971-561-549-5(X))* Asian Development Bank PHL. Dist: Independent Pubs. Group.

Athukorala, Prema-Chandra, ed. The Rise of Asia: Trade & Investment in Global Perspective. 2010. (Routledge Studies in the Growth Economies of Asia Ser.). (ENG., Illus.). 384p. (C). 138.00 *(978-0-415-55686-6(4))* Routledge.

Baddeley, John F. Russia, Mongolia, China: Being Some Record of the Relations Between Them from the Beginning of the XVIIth Century to the Death of the Tsar Alexei Mikhailovich, A. D. 1602-1676, Rendered Mainly in the Form of Narratives Dictated or Written by the Envoys Sent by the Russian Tsars, or Their Voevodas in Siberia to the Kalmuk & Mongol Khans & Princes: & to the Emperors of China: with Introductions, Historical & Geograp, 2 vols. 2008. (Illus.). 350.00 *(978-1-57898-641-5(9))* Martino Publishing.

Balci, Bayram, et al, eds. China & India in Central Asia: A New Great Game? 2010. (Sciences Po Series in International Relations & Political Economy Ser.). (ENG., Illus.). 268p. 89.00 *(978-0-230-10356-6(1))* Palgrave Macmillan.

Balme, Richard & Bridges, Brian, eds. Europe-Asia Relations: Building Multilateralisms. 2008. (Palgrave studies in European Union Politics Ser.). (ENG., Illus.). 288p. 103.00 *(978-0-230-55067-4(3))* Palgrave Macmillan.

Beeson, Mark & Stubbs, Richard, eds. Routledge Handbook of Asian Regionalism. 2011. (ENG., Illus.). 512p. (C). 200.00 *(978-0-415-58054-0(4))* Routledge.

Bersick, Sebastian & van der Velde, Paul, eds. The Asia-Europe Meeting: Contributing to a New Global Governance Architecture: The Eighth ASEM Summit in Brussels (2010) 2012. (IIAS Publications Ser.). 264p. pap. *(978-90-8964-343-8(5))* Amsterdam Univ. Pr.

Blank, Stephen. U. S. Interests in Central Asia & the Challenges to Them. 2007. vi, 47p. pap. *(978-1-58487-283-2(7))* Strategic Studies Institute, U.S. Army War College Commandant (AWCC-DSI/Pubns.).

Blank, Stephen J. Challenges & Opportunities for the Obama Administration in Central Asia. 2009. *(978-1-58487-391-4(4))* Strategic Studies Institute, U.S. Army War College Commandant (AWCC-DSI/Pubns.).

Blank, Stephen J., ed. Central Asian Security Trends: Views from Europe & Russia. 2011. (ENG.). 94p. ***(978-1-58487-487-4(2))*** Strategic Studies Institute, U.S. Army War College Commandant (AWCC-DSI/Pubns.).

Breslin, Shaun & Higgott, Richard A., eds. The International Relations of the Asia-Pacific, 4 vols. 2010. (SAGE Library of International Relations Ser.). (Illus.). 1608p. 995.00 *(978-1-4129-4783-1(9)*, B47831C) SAGE Pubns., Ltd. GBR. Dist: SAGE Pubns., Inc.

Brewster, David. India as an Asia Pacific Great Power. 2011. (Routledge Security in Asia Pacific Ser.). (ENG.). 240p. (C). 145.00 *(978-0-415-61761-1(8))* Routledge.

Broadbridge, Anne F. Kingship & Ideology in the Islamic & Mongol Worlds. 2010. (Cambridge Studies in Islamic Civilization Ser.). (ENG., Illus.). 250p. pap. 39.99 *(978-0-521-17449-7(X))* Cambridge Univ. Pr.

Burke, Anthony. Fear of Security: Australia's Invasion Anxiety. 2008. (ENG.). 304p. (C). pap. 29.99 *(978-0-521-71427-3(3))* Cambridge Univ. Pr.

Butler, Jeffrey T. The Influence of Politics, Technology, & Asia on the Future of US Missile Defense. 2007. (Illus.). xiv, 81p. pap. *(978-1-58566-167-1(8))* Air University Pr.

Campi, Alicia & Baason, Ragchaa. The Impact of China & Russia on United States-Mongolian Political Relations in the Twentieth Century. 2009. (ENG., Illus.). 625p. 149.95 *(978-0-7734-4753-0(9))* Mellen, Edwin Pr., The.

Carey, Kevin, et al. Sub-Saharan Africa: Forging New Trade Links with Asia. 2007. (Illus.). vii, 55p. *(978-1-58906-667-0(7))* International Monetary Fund.

Chaban, Natalia & Holland, Martin, eds. Europe & Asia: Perceptions from Afar. 2012. 200p. pap. 43.00 *(978-3-8329-5417-8(1))* Nomos Verlagsgesellschaft DEU. Dist: International Specialized Bk. Services.

Chaban, Natalia & Holland, Martin, eds. The European Union & the Asia-Pacific: Media, Public & Elite Perceptions of the EU. 2011. (ENG., Illus.). 256p. pap. 42.95 ***(978-0-415-66397-7(0))*** Routledge.

Chin, Felix. Asian Economic & Political Developments. 2011. (Series: Asian Political, Economic & Security Issues Ser.). 295.00 *(978-1-61122-470-2(5))* Nova Science Pubs., Inc.

—Economic, Political & Social Issues of Asia. 2011. (Series: Asian Political, Economic & Security Issues Ser.). (Illus.). xiii, 415p. 295.00 *(978-1-61122-471-9(3))* Nova Science Pubs., Inc.

Chin, Felix, ed. Political & Economic Developments in Asia. 2011. (Asian Political, Economic & Security Issues Ser.). 309p. 129.00 *(978-1-61209-783-1(9))* Nova Science Pubs., Inc.

Cho, Yong-Gwan & Yi, Si-Yong. Chungang Asia Kukkadul Ui Nongop Chongch'aek Kwa Han, Chungang Asia Nongop Hyomyok Hwaktae Pangan: K'ajahusut'an, Ujubek'isut'an, K'irugijusut'an Ui Chungsim Uro. 2010. (KOR., Illus.). 90p. *(978-89-322-2174-8(X))* Korea Institute for International Economic Policy.

Christensen, Thomas J. Worse Than A Monolith - Alliance Politics & Problems of Coercive Diplomacy in Asia. 2011. (Princeton Studies in International History & Politics Ser.). (ENG.). 318p. (C). 70.00 *(978-0-691-14260-9(2))* Princeton Univ. Pr.

—Worse Than A Monolith - Alliance Politics & Problems of Coercive Diplomacy in Asia. 2011. (Princeton Studies in International History & Politics Ser.). (ENG.). 318p. (C). pap. 24.95 *(978-0-691-14261-6(0))* Princeton Univ. Pr.

Clarke, Colin, et al, eds. South Asians Overseas: Migration & Ethnicity. 2010. (Comparative Ethnic & Race Relations Ser.). (ENG.). 396p. pap. 47.00 *(978-0-521-12965-7(6))* Cambridge Univ. Pr.

Clarke, Michael, ed. China, Xinjiang & Central Asia: History, Transition & Crossborder Interaction into the 21st Century. 2009. (Routledge Contemporary China Ser.). (Illus.). 256p. 150.00 *(978-0-415-45317-2(8))* Routledge.

Collins, Kathleen. Clan Politics & Regime Transition in Central Asia. 2009. (ENG., Illus.). 400p. (C). pap. 36.99 *(978-0-521-11466-0(7))* Cambridge Univ. Pr.

Columbus, Alexandra M. Asian Economic & Political Issues. 2011. (Series: Asian Economic & Political Issues Ser.). 238p. 185.00 *(978-1-61324-239-1(5))* Nova Science Pubs., Inc.

Columbus, Frank, ed. Asian Economic & Political Issues, Volume 13. 2010. (Asian Economic & Political Issues Ser.). 89.00 *(978-1-61668-015-2(6))* Nova Science Pubs., Inc.

Connors. The New Global Politics of the Asia. 2nd rev. ed. 2011. (ENG., Illus.). 288p. (C). 145.00 *(978-0-415-46496-3(X))* Routledge.

Constancinos, Andreas. Britain & the Cyprus Crisis Of 1974. 2011. 60p. pap. ***(978-3-8443-0920-1(9))*** Lambert Academic Publishing.

Cooley, Alexander. Great Games, Local Rules: The New Great Power Contest in Central Asia. 2012. (ENG., Illus.). 272p. 29.95 ***(978-0-19-992982-5(3))*** Oxford Univ. Pr., Inc.

Council for Asia-Europe Cooperation Staff. Rationale & Common Agenda for Asia-Europe Cooperation. 95p. pap. 12.00 *(978-4-88907-022-4(2))* Japan Ctr. for International Exchange JPN. Dist: Brookings Institution Pr.

Crisis in Kyrgyzstan: Fuel, Contracts, & Revolution along the Afghan Supply Chain: Hearing Before the Subcommittee on National Security & Foreign Affairs of the Committee on Oversight & Government Reform, House of Representatives, One Hundred Eleventh Congress, Second Session, April 22, 2010. 2011. iii, 79p. ***(978-0-16-089068-0(3)***, 552-070-43100-4) United States Government Printing Office.

Crosston, Matthew D. Fostering Fundamentalism: Terrorism, Democracy & American Engagement in Central Asia. 2006. (US Foreign Policy & Conflict in the Islamic World Ser.). (Illus.). 194p. 120.00 *(978-0-7546-4632-7(7))* Ashgate Publishing Co.

Dallin, David J. Rise of Russia in Asia. 2006. (ENG.). 304p. per. *(978-1-4067-2919-1(1)*, Hesperides Pr.) Read Bks.

Dargin, Justin & Lim, Tai Wei. Energy, Trade & Finance in Asia: A Political & Economic Analysis, 1 vol. 2011. (Perspectives in Economic & Social History Ser.). (ENG., Illus.). 264p. 99.00 *(978-1-84893-155-8(7))* Pickering & Chatto Pubs., Ltd. GBR. Dist: Ashgate Publishing Co.

de Sales Marques, José Luis, et al, eds. Asia & Europe: Dynamics of Inter- & Intra-Regional Dialogues. 2009. 441p. pap. 86.00 *(978-3-8329-3960-1(1))* Nomos Verlagsgesellschaft DEU. Dist: International Specialized Bk. Services.

Dellecker, Adrian & Gomart, Thomas, eds. Russian Energy Security & Foreign Policy. 2011. (Routledge/GARNET Ser.). (ENG., Illus.). 272p. (C). 135.00 *(978-0-415-54733-8(4))* Routledge.

Denoon, David B. H. & Denoon, David B. The Economic & Strategic Rise of China & India: Asian Realignments after the 1997 Financial Crisis. 2007. (ENG., Illus.). 228p. 95.00 *(978-1-4039-8200-1(7))* Palgrave Macmillan.

Devare, Sudhir T., et al, eds. Emerging China: Prospects of Partnership in Asia. 2012. (ENG.). (C). 95.00 ***(978-0-415-50236-8(5)***, Routledge India) Taylor & Francis Group GBR. Dist: Taylor & Francis Group.

Dosch, Jörn & Jacob, Olaf, eds. Asia & Latin America: Political, Economic & Multilateral Relations. 2010. (Routledge Contemporary Asia Ser.). (ENG., Illus.). 272p. (C). 130.00 *(978-0-415-55650-7(3)*, Routledge) Taylor & Francis Group GBR. Dist: Taylor & Francis Group.

Doyle, Randall. Roots of War in the 21st Century: Geography, Hegemony, & Politics in Asia-Pacific. 2009. (ENG.). 170p. pap. 28.50 *(978-0-7618-4630-7(1))* Univ. Pr. of America, Inc.

The Emerging Importance of the U.S.-Central Asia Partnership: Hearing Before the Subcommittee on Asia, the Pacific, & the Global Environment of the Committee on Foreign Affairs, House of Representatives, One Hundred Eleventh Congress, Second Session, November 17, 2010. 2010. iii, 51p. ***(978-0-16-087765-0(2)***, 552-070-42276-5) United States Government Printing Office.

Emerson, Michael & Boonstra, Jos. Into EurAsia: Monitoring the EU's Central Asia Strategy. 2010. (ENG.). 143p. pap. 30.00 *(978-92-9079-966-5(8))* Ctr. for European Policy Studies BEL. Dist: Brookings Institution Pr.

Emmott, Bill. Rivals: How the Power Struggle Between China, India & Japan Will Shape Our Next Decade. 2008. (ENG., Illus.). 352p. 26.00 *(978-0-15-101503-0(1))* Houghton Mifflin Harcourt Trade & Reference Pubs.

—Rivals: How the Power Struggle Between China, India, & Japan Will Shape Our Next Decade. 2009. (ENG.). 352p. pap. 15.95 *(978-0-15-603362-6(3)*, Mariner Bks.) Houghton Mifflin Harcourt Trade & Reference Pubs.

Faure, Guy. New Dynamics Between China & Japan in Asia: How to Build the Future from the Past? 2010. (Illus.). 368p. 108.00 *(978-981-4313-66-7(1))* World Scientific Publishing Co., Inc.

Fernandes, Clinton, ed. Hot Spot: Asia & Oceania, 1 vol. 2008. (Hot Spot Histories Ser.). (Illus.). 328p. 65.00 *(978-0-313-35412-0(X)*, GR5412, Greenwood Pr.) Greenwood Publishing Group, Inc.

Freedman, Craig F. & Hatakeyama, Kyoko. Snow on the Pine: Japan's Quest for a Leadership Role in Asia. 2010. 512p. 124.00 *(978-981-4289-99-3(X))* World Scientific Publishing Co., Inc.

Friedberg, Aaron L. A Contest for Supremacy: China, America, & the Struggle for Mastery in Asia. 2011. (ENG., Illus.). 384p. 27.95 *(978-0-393-06828-3(5)*, 6828) Norton, W. W. & Co., Inc.

Fujita, Masahisa. Economic Integration in Asia & India. Fujita, Masahisa, ed. 2008. (ENG., Illus.). 208p. 105.00 *(978-0-230-52085-1(5))* Palgrave Macmillan.

Gaens, Bart, ed. Europe-Asia Interregional Cooperation: A Decade of ASEM. 2008. (International Political Economy of New Regionalisms Ser.). (Illus.). 222p. 114.95 *(978-0-7546-7142-8(9))* Ashgate Publishing Co.

Ganguly, Sumit & Thompson, William, eds. Asian Rivalries: Conflict, Escalation, & Limitations on Two-Level Games. 2011. (ENG., Illus.). 272p. 80.00 *(978-0-8047-7595-3(8))* Stanford Univ. Pr.

Ganguly, Sumit & Thompson, William R. Asian Rivalries: Conflict, Escalation, & Limitations on Two-Level Games. 2011. (ENG., Illus.). 272p. pap. 24.95 *(978-0-8047-7596-0(6))* Stanford Univ. Pr.

Githinji, Mwangi wa. Is That a Dragon or Elephant on Your Ladder: The Potential Impact of China & India on Export Led Growth in African Countries? 2009. (NAI Discussion Papers). 40p. pap. 12.95 *(978-91-7106-646-6(2))* Nordiska Afrikainstitutet SWE. Dist: Stylus Publishing, LLC.

Goldman, Minton F. Rivalry in Eurasia: Russia, the United States, & the War on Terror, 1 vol. 2009. (Illus.). 261p. 39.95 *(978-0-275-97752-8(8)*, C7752); E-Book *(978-0-313-38153-9(4))*; pap. 19.95 *(978-0-275-97753-5(6)*, B7753) Greenwood Publishing Group, Inc. (Praeger Pubs.).

Green, Michael J. & Gill, Bates. Asia's New Multilateralism: Cooperation, Competition, & the Search for Community. Green, Michael J. & Gill, Bates, eds. 2009. (ENG., Illus.). 400p. (gr. 17). 89.50 *(978-0-231-14442-1(3))* Columbia Univ. Pr.

Greenaway, David, ed. The World Economy: Global Trade Policy 2009. 2010. (World Economy Special Issues Ser.: 7). (ENG.). 176p. pap. 39.95 *(978-1-4051-9704-5(8)*, Wiley-Blackwell) Wiley, John & Sons, Inc.

Habib, Randa. Hussein & Abdullah: Inside the Jordanian Royal Family. 2010. (ENG., Illus.). 244p. 24.95 *(978-0-86356-684-4(7))* Saqi Bks. GBR. Dist: Consortium Bk. Sales & Distribution.

Hanami, Andrew K. The U. S. , Japan, & Asia in International Politics. 2009. (Illus.). 200p. (C). pap. 36.95 *(978-1-934269-85-5(9))* Univ. Readers.

Hanks, Reuel R. Global Security Watch — Central Asia. 2010. (Illus.). xii, 225p. E-Book *(978-0-313-35423-6(5)*, Praeger Pubs.) Greenwood Publishing Group, Inc.

—Global Security Watch-Central Asia. 2010. (Global Security Watch Ser.). (Illus.). 225p. instr.'s hndbk. ed. 49.95 *(978-0-313-35422-9(7)*, C35422, Praeger Pubs.) Greenwood Publishing Group, Inc.

Hara, Kimie. Northern Territories, Asia-Pacific Regional Conflicts & the Aland Experience: Untying the Kurillian Knot. Hara, Kimie & Jukes, Geoffrey, eds. 2009. (Routledge Studies in Asia's Transformations Ser.). (ENG., Illus.). 152p. 140.00 *(978-0-415-48409-1(X))* Routledge.

Hermann, Werner & Linn, Johannes. Central Asia & the Caucasus: At the Crossroads of Eurasia in the 21st Century. 2011. (Illus.). 262p. (C). 40.00 ***(978-81-321-0743-9(8)***, B07439C) SAGE Pubns., Inc.

Holland, et al. The European Union & the Asia-Pacific: Media, Public, & Elite Perceptions of the EU. Chaban, Natalia, ed. 2008. (Routledge/UACES Contemporary European Studies). (Illus.). 208p. 160.00 *(978-0-415-42138-6(1))* Routledge.

Holland, Martin. The Eu Through the Eyes of Asia Vol. 2: New Cases, New Findings. 2009. 284p. 86.00 *(978-981-4289-81-8(7))* World Scientific Publishing Co., Inc.

Hotta, Eri. Pan-Asianism & Japan's War, 1931-1945. 2007. (Palgrave Macmillan Series in Transnational History Ser.). (ENG.). 304p. 100.00 *(978-0-230-60103-1(0))* Palgrave Macmillan.

Jacobs, Seth. The Universe Unraveling. 2012. (United States in the World Ser.). (ENG., Illus.). 336p. 35.00 ***(978-0-8014-4547-7(7))*** Cornell Univ. Pr.

Karrar, Hasan H. The New Silk Road Diplomacy: China's Central Asian Foreign Policy since the Cold War. 2010. (ENG., Illus.). 272p. (C). pap. 35.95 *(978-0-7748-1693-9(7))* UBC Pr. CAN. Dist: Univ. of Washington Pr.

—The New Silk Road Diplomacy: China's Central Asian Foreign Policy since the Cold War. 2009. (ENG.). 272p. ***(978-0-7748-1692-2(9))*** Univ. of British Columbia Pr.

Kavalski, Emilian. India & Central Asia: The Mythmaking & International Relations of a Rising Power. 2010. (Library of International Relations Ser.). (ENG.). 288p. 89.50 *(978-1-84885-124-5(3)*, Tauris Academic Studies) I. B. Tauris & Co., Ltd. GBR. Dist: Macmillan.

—The New Central Asia: The Regional Impact of International Actors. 2010. 364p. 99.00 *(978-981-4287-56-2(3))* World Scientific Publishing Co., Inc.

Kee, Pookong & Yoshimatsu, Hidetaka. Global Movements in the Asia Pacific. 2009. 144.00 *(978-981-283-374-7(9))* World Scientific Publishing Co., Inc.

Kim, Heungchong & Park, Sung-Hoon, eds. Regional Integration in Europe & Asia: Legal, Economic, & Political Perspectives. 2009. 279p. pap. 49.00 *(978-3-8329-4336-3(6))* Nomos Verlagsgesellschaft DEU. Dist: International Specialized Bk. Services.

Kim, Jodi. Ends of Empire: Asian American Critique & the Cold War. 2010. (Critical American Studies). (ENG., Illus.). 344p. 75.00 *(978-0-8166-5591-5(X))*; pap. 25.00 *(978-0-8166-5592-2(8))* Univ. of Minnesota Pr.

Klintworth, Gary, ed. Taiwan & the Asia-Pacific in the 1990s. 3rd ed. 312p. mass mkt. 24.95 *(978-1-86373-594-0(1))* Allen & Unwin AUS. Dist: Paul & Co. Pubs. Consortium, Inc.

Koo, Min Gyo & Aggarwal, Vinod K., eds. Asia's New Institutional Architecture: Evolving Structures for Managing Trade, Financial, & Security Relations. 2007. (Political Economy of the Asia Pacific Ser.). (Illus.). 321p. 179.00 *(978-3-540-72388-2(9))* Springer.

Larulle, Marlene & Peyrouse, Sébastien. Mapping Central Asia: Indian Perceptions & Strategies. 2011. (Illus.). 262p. 99.95 ***(978-1-4094-0985-4(6))*** Ashgate Publishing Co.

Lester, Anne E., ed. Central Asia: Background, Issues & U. S. Interests. 2010. (Countries, Regional Studies, Trading Blocks, Unions, World Organizations Ser.). 115.00 *(978-1-61728-880-7(2))* Nova Science Pubs., Inc.

Levi, Werner. Free India in Asia. 2009. (ENG.). 170p. pap. 40.00 *(978-0-8166-5989-0(3))* Univ. of Minnesota Pr.

Li, Mingjiang, ed. China's International Relations in Asia, 4 vols. 2010. (Critical Issues in Modern Politics Ser.). (ENG., Illus.). 1618p. 1075.00 *(978-0-415-47691-1(7))* Routledge.

—China's International Relations in Asia V1, 4 vols. 2010. (Illus.). 406p. *(978-0-415-48482-4(0))* Routledge.

—China's International Relations in Asia V2, 4 vols. 2010. (Illus.). 404p. *(978-0-415-48483-1(9))* Routledge.

—China's International Relations in Asia V3, 4 vols. 2010. (Illus.). 388p. *(978-0-415-48484-8(7))* Routledge.

—China's International Relations in Asia V4, 4 vols. 2010. (Illus.). 420p. *(978-0-415-48485-5(5))* Routledge.

Lim, Hua Sing. Japan & China in East Asian Integration. 5th ed. 2008. (Illus.). xxxvii, 371p. pap. *(978-981-230-744-6(3))* Institute of Southeast Asian Studies.

Liu, Xiaoyuan. Reins of Liberation: An Entangled History of Mongolian Independence, Chinese Territoriality, & Great Power Hegemony, 1911-1950. 2006. (ENG., Illus.). 506p. 70.00 *(978-0-8047-5426-2(8))* Stanford Univ. Pr.

Mahbubani, Kishore. The New Asian Hemisphere: The Irresistible Shift of Global Power to the East. 2009. (ENG.). 336p. pap. 16.95 *(978-1-58648-671-6(3))* PublicAffairs.

Marek, David A., ed. Asian Economic & Political Issues. Volume 14. 2009. (Asian Economic & Political Issues Ser.). (Illus.). 267p. 103.50 *(978-1-61728-019-1(4))* Nova Science Pubs., Inc.

Marketos, Thrassy N. China's Energy Geopolitics. 2010. pap. 39.95 *(978-0-415-58617-7(8))* Routledge.

Melvin, Neil J., ed. Engaging Central Asia: The European Union's New Strategy in the Heart of Eurasia. 2008. (ENG., Illus.). 200p. pap. 30.00 *(978-92-9079-707-4(X))* Ctr. for European Policy Studies BEL. Dist: Brookings Institution Pr.

Michael, Michàlis S., et al, eds. Asia-Pacific Geopolitics: Hegemony vs Human Security. 2007. 264p. (C). 127.00 *(978-1-84720-098-3(2))* Elgar, Edward Publishing, Inc.

Miller, Alice Lyman & Wich, Richard. Becoming Asia: Change & Continuity in Asian International Relations since World War II. 2011. (ENG., Illus.). 336p. 80.00 *(978-0-8047-7150-4(2))*; pap. 29.95 *(978-0-8047-7151-1(0))* Stanford Univ. Pr.

Mishra, Pankaj. The Revolt Against the West: The Rise of Asia & the Remaking of the Modern World. 2012. (ENG., Illus.). 320p. 27.00 ***(978-0-374-24959-5(8))*** Farrar, Straus & Giroux.

Mullerson, Rein. Central Asia. 2012. (ENG.). 256p. pap. 42.95 ***(978-0-415-54102-2(6))*** Routledge.

Mullerson, Rein. Central Asia: A Chessboard & Player in the New Great Game. 2007. (Kegan Paul Library of Central Asia Ser.). (Illus.). 370p. 150.00 *(978-0-7103-1316-4(0))* Taylor & Francis Group.

Murphy, Derrick & Wells, Mike. The USA & the Cold War in Asia, 1945-1975. 2009. (Illus.). 80p. pap., stu. ed. 22.50 *(978-0-340-99040-7(6))* Hodder Education GBR. Dist: Trans-Atlantic Pubns., Inc.

Nair-Venugopal, Shanta, ed. The Gaze of the West & Framings of the East. 2012. (ENG., Illus.). 288p. 85.00 ***(978-0-230-30292-1(0))*** Palgrave Macmillan.

Nanda, Swati Sucharita. Locating the State in Women's Lives in South Asi. 2010. 176p. pap. *(978-3-639-27025-9(8))* VDM Verlag Dr. Mueller e.K.

Newberg, Paula R. Countries Without Nations: Domestic Politics & Foreign Policies in Southwest & Central Asia. 200p. pap. 17.00 *(978-0-8157-0635-9(9))* Brookings Institution Pr.

Nichol, Jim. Central Asia: Security, Internal Affairs & U. S. Interests. 2008. 135p. 69.00 *(978-1-60456-848-6(8))* Nova Science Pubs., Inc.

Pang, Eul-Sco. The US-Singapore Free Trade Agreement: An American Perspective on Power, Trade & Security in the Asia Pacific. 2011. 250p. pap. ***(978-981-4311-99-1(5))*** Institute of Southeast Asian Studies.

Paramonov, Vladimir, et al. Russia in Central Asia: Policy, Security & Economics. 2009. (Illus.). xvii, 118p. 79.00 *(978-1-60692-880-6(5))* Nova Science Pubs., Inc.

Park, Yung Chul. Economic Liberalization & Integration in East Asia: A Post-Crisis Paradigm. 2007. (ENG.). 296p. 45.00 *(978-0-19-921521-8(9))* Oxford Univ. Pr., Inc.

Peimani, Hooman. Conflict & Security in Central Asia & the Caucasus, 1 vol. 2009. (Illus.). 373p. 95.00 *(978-1-59884-054-4(1)*, CEASCA1C) ABC-CLIO, LLC.

Petrov, Marcus A., ed. Jordan: Background & Issues. 2010. (Countries, Regional Studies, Trading Blocks, Unions, World Organizations Ser.). (Illus.). 174p. 130.00 *(978-1-61668-947-6(1))* Nova Science Pubs., Inc.

Pike, Francis. Empires at War: A Short History of Modern Asia since World War II. 2011. (ENG.). 896p. pap. 32.00 *(978-1-84885-865-7(5))* I. B. Tauris & Co., Ltd. GBR. Dist: Macmillan.

Pollack, Jonathan D., ed. Asia Eyes America: Regional Perspectives on U.S. Asia-Pacific Strategy in the Twenty-First Century. 2008. (ENG.). 262p. pap. 21.00 *(978-1-884733-43-7(3)*, Dept. of the Navy) United States Government Printing Office.

Principles of U.S. Engagement in Asia: Hearing Before the Subcommittee on East Asian & Pacific Affairs of the Committee on Foreign Relations, United States Senate, One Hundred Eleventh Congress, Second Session, January 21, 2010. 2010. iii, 52p. ***(978-0-16-087471-0(8)***, 552-070-42159-9) United States Government Printing Office.

Qassem, Ahmad Shayeq. Afghanistan's Political Stability: A Dream Unrealised. 2009. 226p. 114.95 *(978-0-7546-7940-0(3))* Ashgate Publishing Co.

Rajan, Ramkishen S., ed. Emerging Asia: Essays on Crises, Capital Flows, FDI & Exchange Rate. 2011. (ENG., Illus.). 208p. 90.00 *(978-0-230-23845-9(9))* Palgrave Macmillan.

Rana, Kishan S. Asian Diplomacy: The Foreign Ministries of China, India, Japan, Singapore, & Thailand. 2008. (ENG.). 268p. (gr. 17). pap. 29.95 *(978-0-8018-9196-0(5))* Johns Hopkins Univ. Pr.

Rappa, Antonio L. Globalization: Power, Authority, & Legitimacy in Late Modernity. 2nd ed. 2011. xxii, 348p. pap. ***(978-981-4279-99-4(4))*** Institute of Southeast Asian Studies.

Rasgotra, Maharajakrishna, ed. The New Asian Power Dynamic. 2007. 308p. (C). 69.00 *(978-0-7619-3572-8(X)*, B3572XC) SAGE Pubns., Inc.

Redwood, John. Superpower Struggles: Mighty America, Faltering Europe, Rising Asia. 2006. (ENG.). 208p. pap. 40.00 *(978-1-4039-9078-5(6))* Palgrave Macmillan.

Reid, Anthony & Zheng, Yangwen. Negotiating Asymmetry: China's Place in Asia. 2009. (C). pap. 28.00 *(978-0-8248-3412-8(7))* Univ. of Hawaii Pr.

Reynolds, Julius David Alexander. The Construction of Regional Security in Eurasi. 2009. 80p. pap. *(978-3-639-17535-6(2))* VDM Verlag Dr. Mueller e.K.

Roach, Stephen. Stephen Roach on the Next Asia: Opportunities & Challenges for a New Globalization. 2010. (ENG., Illus.). 414p. pap. 16.95 *(978-0-470-64604-5(7)*, Wiley) Wiley, John & Sons, Inc.

Robertson, Justin. US-Asia Economic Relations: A Political Economy of Crisis & the Rise of New Business Actors. 2008. (Routledge/City University of Hong Kong Southeast Asia Ser.). (Illus.). 272p. 150.00 *(978-0-415-46951-7(1))* Routledge.

Robles, Alfredo C. The Asia-Europe Meeting: The Theory & Practice of Interregionalism. (Routledge Contemporary Asia Ser.). (ENG., Illus.). 224p. (C). 2012. pap. 42.95 ***(978-0-415-54091-9(7))*** 2007. 168.00 *(978-0-415-45223-6(6))* Routledge.

Roland, Alan. JOURNEYS to FOREIGN SELVES Asians & Asian Americans in a Global Era JOURNEYS to FOREIGN SELVES: Asians & Asian Americans in a Global Era. 2011. (ENG.). 248p. 34.99 *(978-0-19-806946-1(4))* Oxford Univ. Pr., Inc.

Rosefielde, Steven. Two Asias: The Emerging Postcrisis Divide. 2011. 472p. 140.00 ***(978-981-4366-26-7(9))*** World Scientific Publishing Co., Inc.

Rozman, Gilbert. Chinese Strategic Thought Toward Asia. 2010. (Strategic Thought in Northeast Asia Ser.). (ENG.). 272p. 89.00 *(978-1-4039-7551-5(5))* Palgrave Macmillan.

Rozman, Gilbert, et al. Japanese Strategic Thought Toward Asia. annot. ed. 2007. (Strategic Thought in Northeast Asia Ser.). (ENG.). 288p. 89.00 *(978-1-4039-7553-9(1))* Palgrave Macmillan.

—Russian Strategic Thought Toward Asia. Ferguson, Joseph, ed. 2006. (Strategic Thought in Northeast Asia Ser.). (ENG., Illus.). 272p. 89.00 *(978-1-4039-7554-6(X))* Palgrave Macmillan.

Ruland, Jurgen, et al, eds. Asian-European Relations: Building Blocks for Global Governance? 2008. (Illus.). 320p. 160.00 *(978-0-415-45057-7(8))* Routledge.

Rumer, Eugene, et al. Central Asia: Views from Washington, Moscow, & Beijing. 2007. 223p. per. 32.95 *(978-0-7656-1995-2(4))* Sharpe, M.E. Inc.

Sahni, Kalpana. Crucifying the Orient: Russian Orientalism & the Colonization of Caucasus & Central Asia. 2006. (Institute for Comparative Research in Human Culture Ser.). (ENG., Illus.). 39.00 *(978-974-8299-50-1(3))* Orchid Pr THA. Dist: National Bk. Network.

Sanders, Vivienne. USA in Asia, 1945-75. 2010. (Illus.). 241p. pap. 19.99 *(978-1-4441-1009-8(8))* Hodder Education GBR. Dist: Oxford Univ. Pr., Inc.

Santhanam, K. & Dwivedi, Ramakant. India-Tajikistan Cooperation: Perspectives & Prospects. 2007. xxii, 187p. *(978-81-88342-06-8(8))* Anamaya Publishers.

Seekins, Donald M. Burma & Japan Since 1940: From Co-Prosperity to Quiet Dialogue. 2006. (Nordic Institute of Asian Studies Monograph Ser.). (Illus.). 181p. 27.00 *(978-87-91114-98-4(5))* Nordic Institute of Asian Studies DNK. Dist: Univ. of Hawaii Pr.

Seidelmann, Reimund & Vasilache, Andreas, eds. European Union & Asia: A Dialogue on Regionalism & Interregional Cooperation. 2008. 363p. (C). pap. 74.00 *(978-3-8329-3433-0(2))* Nomos Verlagsgesellschaft DEU. Dist: International Specialized Bk. Services.

Seliger, Bernhard & Pascha, Werner, eds. Towards a Northeast Asian Security Community: Implications for Korea's Growth & Economic Development. 2011. (Political Economy of the Asia Pacific Ser.). (Illus.). xiv, 262p. 139.00 *(978-1-4419-9656-5(7),* 1441996567) Springer.

Sengupta, Anita. Heartlands of Eurasia: The Geopolitics of Political Space. 2009. (ENG., Illus.). 220p. 68.50 *(978-0-7391-3606-5(2))* Lexington Bks.

Shambaugh, David & Yahuda, Michael. International Relations of Asia. 2008. (Asia in World Politics Ser.). (ENG., Illus.). 392p. pap. 39.95 *(978-0-7425-5696-6(4))* Rowman & Littlefield Publishers, Inc.

—International Relations of Asia. 2008. (Asia in World Politics Ser.). (ENG., Illus.). 402p. 90.00 *(978-0-7425-5695-9(6))* Rowman & Littlefield Publishers, Inc.

Singh, Daljit. By Design or Accident: Reflections on Asian Security. 2010. 176p. ***(978-981-4279-71-0(4))*** Institute of Southeast Asian Studies.

Sisodia, N. S. & Krishnappa, V., eds. Global Power Shifts & Strategic Transition in Asia. 2009. (ENG., Illus.). 394p. 79.95 *(978-81-7188-751-4(1))* Academic Foundation IND. Dist: Independent Pubs. Group.

Sosland, Jeffrey K. Cooperating Rivals: The Riparian Politics of the Jordan River Basin. 2007. (SUNY Series in Global Politics). (Illus.). 294p. (C). 80.00 *(978-0-7914-7201-9(9))* State Univ. of New York Pr.

Sutter, Robert G. The United States in Asia. 2008. (ENG.). 330p. 90.00 *(978-0-7425-5648-5(4));* pap. 34.95 *(978-0-7425-5649-2(2))* Rowman & Littlefield Publishers, Inc.

Swaine, Michael D. America's Challenge: Engaging a Rising China in the Twenty-First Century. 2011. (ENG.). 673p. 49.95 *(978-0-87003-258-5(5));* pap. 19.95 *(978-0-87003-257-8(7))* Carnegie Endowment for International Peace.

Tay, Simon S. C. Asia Alone: The Dangerous Post-Crisis Divide from America. 2010. (ENG., Illus.). 256p. pap. 24.95 *(978-0-470-82582-2(0),* Wiley) Wiley, John & Sons, Inc.

Taylor, Brendan. American Sanctions in the Asia-Pacific. (C). 2012. (ENG.). 192p. pap. 44.95 ***(978-0-415-62492-3(4))*** 2010. ix, 170p. 130.00 ***(978-0-203-86681-8(9))*** Routledge.

Taylor, Brendan, ed. Australia as an Asia-Pacific Regional Power: Friendships in Flux? 2012. (Routledge Security in Asia Pacific Ser.). (ENG.). 224p. (C). pap. 42.95 ***(978-0-415-54092-6(5))*** Routledge.

Tellis, Ashley J., et al, eds. Strategic Asia 2008-09: Challenges & Choices. 2008. (Illus.). pap. 34.95 *(978-0-9713938-9-9(3))* National Bureau of Asian Research, The.

Tellis, Ashley J. & Wills, Michael, eds. Strategic Asia 2006-07: Trade, Interdependence, & Security. 2006. (Illus.). xiv, 423p. pap. 24.95 *(978-0-9713938-7-5(7))* National Bureau of Asian Research, The.

—Strategic Asia 2007-08: Domestic Political Change & Grand Strategy. 2007. (Strategic Asia Ser.). (Illus.). 2p. pap. 29.95 *(978-0-9713938-8-2(5))* National Bureau of Asian Research, The.

Thomas, Nicholas & Nicholas Thomas. Governance & Regionalism in Asia. Thomas, Nicholas, ed. 2009. (Politics in Asia Ser.). (ENG.). 368p. 160.00 *(978-0-415-45699-9(1))* Routledge.

United Nations. Statistical Abstract of the ESCWA Region, 26th Issue. 2008. (MUL.). 260p. pap. 45.00 *(978-92-1-128308-2(6))* United Nations Pubns.

Velde, Paul Van Der. Multiregionalism & Multilateralism: Asian-European Relations in a Global Context. Bersick, Sebastian & Stokhof, Wim, eds. 2007. (ICAS Publications Ser.). 192p. pap. *(978-90-5356-929-0(4),* Leiden Univ. Pr.) Amsterdam Univ. Pr.

Welfens, Paul J. J., et al, eds. EU - ASEAN: Facing Economic Globalisation. 2008. (ENG., Illus.). xvi, 246p. 129.00 *(978-3-540-87388-4(0),* 3540873880) Springer.

Wishnick, Elizabeth. Russia, China, & the United States in Central Asia: Prospects for Great Power Competition & Cooperation in the Shadow of the Georgian Crisis. 2009. *(978-1-58487-379-2(5))* Strategic Studies Institute, U.S. Army War College Commandant (AWCC-DSI/Pubns.).

Womack, Brantly. China among Unequals: Asymmetric Foreign Relationships in Asia. 2010. (Illus.). 552p. 130.00 *(978-981-4295-27-7(2))* World Scientific Publishing Co., Inc.

Wunderlich, Uwe. Regionalisation Globalisation & International Order: Europe & the Asia-Pacific. 2008. (International Political Economy of New Regionalisms Ser.). 222p. 114.95 *(978-0-7546-4845-1(1))* Ashgate Publishing Co.

Yo. Global Movements in the Asia Pacific. 2009. 350p. 111.00 *(978-981-283-373-0(0))* World Scientific Publishing Co., Inc.

Zandvliet, Kees. The Dutch Encounter with Asia: 1600-1950. 2006. (Illus.). 464p. (C). 50.00 *(978-90-400-8717-2(2))* Waanders B.V., Uitgeverij NLD. Dist: Antique Collectors' Club.

Zheng, Yangwen, et al. The Cold War in Asia: The Battle for Hearts & Minds. 2010. 268p. *(978-90-04-17537-2(7))* BRILL.

ASIA—GUIDEBOOKS

Asian Geographic Magazine, creator. Asian Geographic Journal: 101 Things to Do in Asia. 2007. (Illus.). 168p. pap. *(978-981-05-8165-7(3))* Monsoon Bks. Pte. Ltd.

Dixon, Paul. Borneo: Travel Guide to Borneo. 3rd ed. 2010. (Footprint - Handbooks Ser.). (ENG., Illus.). 352p. (Orig.). 25.95 *(978-1-907263-06-4(3))* Footprint Handbooks GBR. Dist: Globe Pequot Pr., The.

Explorer. Oman. 3rd ed. 2008. (ENG.). 315p. pap. 24.95 *(978-976-8182-83-8(0))* Explorer Publishing UAE. Dist: Globe Pequot Pr., The.

INSIGHT. Singapore Insight City Guide. 12th ed. 2011. (City Guide Ser.). (Illus.). 288p. pap. 19.99 *(978-981-282-374-8(3))* APA Publications Services SGP. Dist: Ingram Pub. Services.

Kunz, Martin N. Cool Hotels Asia/Pacific. 2009. 220p. pap. 19.95 *(978-3-8327-9332-6(1))* teNeues Publishing Co.

Lamberti, Stefania. Maldives. 7th ed. 2011. (Globetrotter Travel Packs Ser.). (ENG., Illus.). 128p. 14.95 *(978-1-84773-898-1(2),* Globetrotter) New Holland Pubs., Ltd. GBR. Dist: Globe Pequot Pr., The.

LaPlante, John Guy. Around Asia in 80 Days. Oops, 83! 2007. 284p. pap. 18.95 *(978-0-7414-4252-9(3))* Infinity Publishing.

Lonely Planet Staff. Asia & India. 2nd rev. ed. 2008. (Healthy Travel Ser.). (ENG., Illus.). 432p. pap. 8.99 *(978-1-74059-144-7(5))* Lonely Planet Pubns.

Lonely Planet Staff, creator. Asia: 10 Essential Languages for City Breaks. 2008. (Fast Talk Ser.). (MUL & ENG., Illus.). 128p. pap. 6.99 *(978-1-74179-142-6(1))* Lonely Planet Pubns.

Lonely Planet Staff & Richmond, Simon. Malaysia Singapore & Brunei. 11th rev. ed. 2010. (Country Guide Ser.). (ENG., Illus.). 652p. pap. 24.99 *(978-1-74104-887-2(7))* Lonely Planet Pubns.

Lonely Planet Staff, et al. The Asia Book: A Journey Through Every Country in the Continent. 2007. (General Pictorial Ser.). (ENG., Illus.). 256p. 40.00 *(978-1-74104-601-4(7))* Lonely Planet Pubns.

Munan, Heidi. Borneo: A Survival Guide to Customs & Etiquette. 2009. 264p. pap. 15.95 *(978-0-7614-5659-9(7))* Marshall Cavendish Corp.

Museyon Guides, ed. Film + Travel Asia, Oceania, Africa: Traveling the World Through Your Favorite Movies. 2009. (Film+ Ser.). (ENG., Illus.). 164p. pap. 15.95 *(978-0-9822320-1-9(2))* Museyon Inc.

Phillips, Matt & Lonely Planet Staff. The Africa Book: A Journey Through Every Country in the Continent. 2007. (General Pictorial Ser.). (ENG., Illus.). 264p. 40.00 *(978-1-74104-602-1(5))* Lonely Planet Pubns.

Pommaret, Françoise. Bhutan: Himalayan Mountain Kingdom. 6th ed. 2009. (ENG., Illus.). 320p. pap. 23.95 *(978-962-217-810-6(3),* 217810) Airphoto International/Odyssey HKG. Dist: Norton, W. W. & Co., Inc.

Reader, Lesley, et al. First-Time Asia. 5th ed. 2010. (ENG., Illus.). 416p. 18.99 *(978-1-84836-474-5(1))* Rough Guides, Ltd. GBR. Dist: Dorling Kindersley Publishing, Inc.

Reiter, Christiane. Asia. Taschen, Angelika, ed. 25th ed. 2009. (FRE, GER & ENG., Illus.). 360p. pap. 19.99 *(978-3-8365-1481-1(8))* TASCHEN DEU. Dist: Ingram Pub. Services.

Ridge, Gerald. 12 Things I Learned While Trying to Retire in Asia. 2009. 229p. pap. 16.62 *(978-0-557-07575-1(0))* Lulu Enterprises Inc.

Robinson, Daniel. Borneo. 2nd rev. ed. 2011. (Regional Guide Ser.). (ENG., Illus.). 332p. (Orig.). pap. 24.99 *(978-1-74179-215-7(0))* Lonely Planet Pubns.

Scott, Chris. Overlanders' Handbook: Worldwide Route & Planning Guide - Car, 4wd, Van, Truck. 2011. (ENG., Illus.). 672p. 39.95 *(978-1-905864-07-2(8))* Trailblazer Pubns. GBR. Dist: Globe Pequot Pr., The.

Seki, Akihiko & Brooke, Elizabeth Heilman. Asian Resorts. 2009. (ENG., Illus.). 192p. 34.95 *(978-0-8048-4055-2(5))* Tuttle Publishing.

Szepesi, Stefan. Walking Palestine: 25 Journeys in the West Bank. 2012. (ENG.). 272p. pap. 22.95 ***(978-1-56656-860-9(9),*** Interlink Bks.) Interlink Publishing Group, Inc.

teNeues. Cool Hotels Best of Asia. 2009. (ENG.). 95.00 *(978-3-8327-9238-1(4))* teNeues Publishing Co.

Trojanow, Ilija. Mumbai to Mecca: A Pilgrimage to the Holy Sites of Islam. Morrison, Rebecca, tr. from GER. 2007. (Armchair Traveller Ser.). (ENG., Illus.). 266p. 19.95 *(978-1-904950-29-5(9))* Haus Publishing GBR. Dist: Consortium Bk. Sales & Distribution.

Wilson, Paul. The Silk Roads: Routes Through Syria, Turkey, Iran, Turkmenistan, Uzbekistan, Kyrgyzstan, Pakistan & China. 3rd rev. ed. 2011. (ENG., Illus.). 384p. pap. 24.95 *(978-1-905864-32-4(9))* Trailblazer Pubns. GBR. Dist: Globe Pequot Pr., The.

ASIA—HISTORICAL GEOGRAPHY

Atlas of Korea History. 2009. 56.00 *(978-981-08-0785-6(6))* World Scientific Publishing Co., Inc.

Barjamovic, Gojko. Historical Geography of Anatolia in the Old Assyrian Colony Period. 2011. (Illus.). 537p. 183.00 *(978-87-635-3645-5(5))* Museum Tusculanum Pr. DNK. Dist: Chicago Distribution Ctr.

Bretschneider, Emil. Mediaeval Researches. 2010. 164.48 *(978-1-61719-425-2(5))* Gorgias Pr., LLC.

Brunn, Stanley D. & Toops, Stanley W. The Routledge Atlas of Central Eurasian Affairs. 2012. (ENG., Illus.). 240p. 145.00 *(978-0-415-49750-3(7));* pap. 42.95 *(978-0-415-49752-7(3))* Routledge.

Cram101 Textbook Reviews Staff. Outlines & Highlights for Dragons & Tigers: Geography of South, East, & Southeast Asia by Weightman, ISBN. 2009. 64p. pap. 27.95 *(978-1-4288-9499-0(3))* Cram101 Inc.

Kaplony, Andreas & Forêt, Philippe. The Journey of Maps & Images on the Silk Road. Forêt, Phillipe & Kaplony, Andreas, eds. 2008. (Brill's Inner Asian Library Ser.). (Illus.). 234p. (C). 134.00 *(978-90-04-17165-7(7))* BRILL.

Le Strange, G. The Lands of the Eastern Caliphate. 2011. (Illus.). 598p. pap. 43.00 *(978-1-107-60014-0(6))* Cambridge Univ. Pr.

Pletcher, Kenneth, ed. The Geography of China: Sacred & Historic Places. 2010. (Understanding China Ser.). (Illus.). 384p. (YA). 106.00 *(978-1-61530-185-0(2))* Rosen Publishing Group, Inc., The.

Ramsay, W. M. The Historical Geography of Asia Minor. 2010. (Cambridge Library Collection - History Ser.). (ENG., Illus.). 576p. pap. 39.99 *(978-1-108-01453-3(4))* Cambridge Univ. Pr.

Rumney, Thomas A. The Geography of Southeast Asia: A Scholarly Bibliography & Guide. 2010. (ENG.). 514p. instr.'s gde. ed. 97.99 *(978-0-7618-5008-3(2));* pap., instr.'s gde. ed. 62.99 *(978-0-7618-5009-0(0))* Univ. Pr. of America, Inc.

Starr, S. Frederick, ed. Ferghana Valley: The Heart of Central Asia. 2011. (Studies of Central Asia & the Caucasus Ser.). (ENG., Illus.). 464p. 104.95 *(978-0-7656-2998-2(4))* Sharpe, M.E. Inc.

ASIA—HISTORIOGRAPHY

Aiken, Edwin James. Scriptural Geography: Portraying the Holy Land. 2009. (ENG., Illus.). 256p. 89.50 *(978-1-84511-818-1(9))* I. B. Tauris & Co., Ltd. GBR. Dist: Macmillan.

Bretelle-Establet, Florence, ed. Looking at it from Asia: the Processes that Shaped the Sources of History of Science: The Processes that Shaped the Sources of History of Science. 2010. (Boston Studies in the Philosophy of Science Ser.). (ENG., Illus.). 400p. 219.00 *(978-90-481-3675-9(X),* 904813675X) Springer.

Jordan, Peter, ed. Landscape & Culture in Northern Eurasia. 2010. (Univ col london inst arch Pub Ser.). (ENG., Illus.). 356p. 99.95 *(978-1-59874-244-2(2))* Left Coast Pr., Inc.

Kemper, Michael & Conermann, Stephan, eds. The Heritage of Soviet Oriental Studies. 2011. (Routledge Contemporary Russia & Eastern Europe Ser.). (ENG., Illus.). 352p. (C). 150.00 *(978-0-415-59977-1(6))* Routledge.

Paksoy, Hasan B. Central Asian Monuments. 2011. 128.80 *(978-1-61143-110-0(7))* Gorgias Pr., LLC.

Richter, Stefanie. Contested Views of a Common Past: Revisions of History in Contemporary East Asia. 2008. (Illus.). 350p. pap. 59.00 *(978-3-593-38548-8(1))* Campus Verlag GmbH DEU. Dist: Chicago Distribution Ctr.

Shin, Gi-Wook & Sneider, Daniel, eds. History Textbooks & the Wars in Asia: Divided Memories. 2011. (Routledge Contemporary Asia Ser.). (ENG.). 312p. (C). 148.00 *(978-0-415-60303-4(X))* Routledge.

Subrahmanyam, Sanjay. From Tagus to the Ganges: Explorations in Connected History. 2012. (ENG., Illus.). 276p. pap. 24.95 ***(978-0-19-807716-9(5))*** Oxford Univ. Pr., Inc.

ASIA—HISTORY

Adelaar, K. Alexander & Himmelmann, Nikolaus, eds. The Austronesian Languages of Asia & Madagascar. 2011. (Routledge Language Family Ser.). 864p. (C). pap. 71.95 *(978-0-415-68153-7(7))* Routledge.

Alam, Muzaffar & Subrahmanyam, Sanjay. Indo-Persian Travels in the Age of Discoveries, 1400-1800. 2007. (ENG., Illus.). 416p. 126.00 *(978-0-521-78041-4(1))* Cambridge Univ. Pr.

Amitai, Reuven. From Holy War to Reconciliation: Mamluk-Mongol Relations 1260-1335. 2012. (Miroir de l'orient Musulman Ser.). (ENG., Illus.). 279p. (C). 87.00 *(978-2-503-53152-6(0))* Brepols Pubs. BEL. Dist: ISD.

Asia II. tchr. ed. 41.95 *(978-0-382-44544-6(9))* Cobblestone Publishing Co.

Auerbach, Ernest. Blue Villa & Other Vietnam Stories. 2008. 61p. *(978-1-4401-1403-8(X))* iUniverse, Inc.

Biran, Michal. The Empire of the Qara Khitai in Eurasian History: Between China & the Islamic World. 2008. (Cambridge Studies in Islamic Civilization Ser.). (ENG., Illus.). 300p. pap. 42.00 *(978-0-521-06602-0(6))* Cambridge Univ. Pr.

Bogaerts, Els & Raben, Remco. Beyond Empire & Nation. 2010. 250p. pap. 31.00 *(978-90-6718-289-8(3))* KITLV Pr. NLD. Dist: Univ. of Hawaii Pr.

Bonhomme, Brian. Russian Exploration, from Siberia to Space: A History. 2012. (ENG., Illus.). 232p. pap. 55.00 ***(978-0-7864-6687-0(1))*** McFarland & Co., Inc. Pubs.

Broadbridge, Anne F. Kingship & Ideology in the Islamic & Mongol Worlds. 2008. (Cambridge Studies in Islamic Civilization Ser.). (ENG., Illus.). 256p. 100.00 *(978-0-521-85265-4(X))* Cambridge Univ. Pr.

Brown, Robin. Marco Polo: Journey to the End of the Earth. 2008. (ENG., Illus.). 320p. pap. 14.95 *(978-0-7509-3421-3(2))* History Pr. Ltd., The GBR. Dist: Independent Pubs. Group.

Cabestan, Jean-Pierre & PavkoviÄ‡, Aleksandar, eds. Secessionism & Separatism in Europe & Asia: To Have a State of One's Own. 2012. (Politics in Asia Ser.). (ENG., Illus.). 272p. (C). 135.00 *(978-0-415-66774-6(7))* Routledge.

Calichman, Richard & Kim, John Namjun, eds. The Politics of Culture: Around the Work of Naoki Sakai. 2010. (Routledge/Leiden Series in Modern East Asian History & Politics Ser.). (ENG.). 272p. (C). 138.00 *(978-0-415-56216-4(3))* Routledge.

Carstens, Anne Marie. Karia & the Hekatomnids: The Creation of a Dynasty. 2009. (ENG., Illus.). 168p. (C). pap. 87.50 *(978-1-4073-0423-6(2))* British Archaeological Reports Ltd. GBR. Dist: Brown, David Bk. Co., The.

Chaudhuri, K. N. The Trading World of Asia & the English East India Company: 1660-1760. 2006. (ENG., Illus.). 652p. pap. 116.00 *(978-0-521-03159-2(1))* Cambridge Univ. Pr.

Chomsky, Noam. A New Generation Draws the Line: Kosovo, East Timor, & the Responsibility to Protect Today. rev. exp. ed. 2011. (ENG.). 176p. pap. 18.95 ***(978-1-61205-074-4(3))*** Paradigm Pubs.

—A New Generation Draws the Line: Kosovo, East Timor, & the Responsibility to Protect Today, Updated & Expanded Edition. 2011. 176p. 91.00 ***(978-1-61205-073-7(5))*** Paradigm Pubs.

Clements, Jonathan. Marco Polo. 2007. (Life&Times Ser.). (ENG., Illus.). 178p. pap. 15.95 *(978-1-905791-05-7(4))* Haus Publishing GBR. Dist: Consortium Bk. Sales & Distribution.

Clinch, Nicholas & Clinch, Elizabeth. Through a Land of Extremes: The Littledales of Central Asia. 2009. (ENG., Illus.). 336p. pap. 24.95 *(978-0-7509-4783-1(7))* History Pr. Ltd., The GBR. Dist: Independent Pubs. Group.

Cole, Roger & Belfield, Richard. SAS Operation Storm: Nine Men Against Four Hundred in Britain's Secret War. 2011. (ENG., Illus.). 320p. 29.95 ***(978-1-4447-2695-4(1),*** Hodder & Stoughton) Hodder General Publishing Div. GBR. Dist: Independent Pubs. Group.

Corr, Kendra. The U. S. & W. W. I: I Think: U. S. History. 2011. (ENG.). 100p. (YA). pap. 29.95 *(978-1-933558-17-2(2))* InspirEd Educators.

Cotterell, Arthur. Asia: A Concise History. 2011. (ENG.). 450p. pap. 29.95 *(978-0-470-82504-4(9),* Wiley) Wiley, John & Sons, Inc.

—Western Power in Asia: Its Slow Rise & Swift Fall, 1415-1999. 2009. (ENG., Illus.). 448p. pap. 29.95 *(978-0-470-82489-4(1),* Wiley) Wiley, John & Sons, Inc.

Cram101 Textbook Reviews. Outlines & Highlights for History of Asia by Rhoads Murphey, Isbn: 9780205649167. 2010. 338p. pap. 33.95 *(978-1-61654-191-0(1))* Cram101 Inc.

Cram101 Textbook Reviews & Cram101 Textbook Reviews. Outlines & Highlights for History of Asia by Rhoads Murphey, Isbn: 9780321340542 032134054x. 2011. 166p. pap. 29.95 ***(978-1-61490-877-7(X))*** Cram101 Inc.

Crump, Thomas. Asia-Pacific: A History of Empire & Conflict. 2008. (ENG., Illus.). 400p. 29.95 *(978-1-84725-222-7(2),* Hambledon Continuum) Continuum International Publishing Group, Ltd. GBR. Dist: National Bk. Network.

Crump, Thomas & Crump. Asia-Pacific: A History of Empire & Conflict. 2007. (ENG., Illus.). 400p. 65.00 *(978-1-85285-518-5(5),* Hambledon Continuum) Continuum International Publishing Group, Ltd. GBR. Dist: National Bk. Network.

Dadayan, Khachatur. Aproyan Gerdastani Patmutyun: XVId.-XXd. Arajin Karord. 2010. (ARM., Illus.). 207p. *(978-99941-2-443-5(9))* Gasprint Ltd., Publishing Hse.

Davidson, Peter D. Bulldozing the Way: New Guinea to Japan. 2009. 163p. pap. 19.92 *(978-0-557-11199-2(4))* Lulu Enterprises Inc.

De Wilde, Jaap & Den Boer, Monica. Viability of Human Security. 2008. 272p. pap. *(978-90-5356-796-8(8),* Leiden Univ. Pr.) Amsterdam Univ. Pr.

Diokno, Maria. The Mekong Arranged & Rearranged. Chinh, Nguyen Van, ed. 2007. (Mekong Press Ser.). (ENG.). 228p. pap. 14.95 ***(978-974-94804-9-6(X))*** Silkworm Bks. THA. Dist: Univ. of Washington Pr.

Duchhardt, Heinz, ed. Russland, der Ferne Osten und die Deutschen. 2009. (Veroffentlichungen des Instituts fur Europaische Geschichte Mainz - Beihefte Abendlandische Religionsgeschichte Ser.). (GER., Illus.). 123p. (C). 41.00 *(978-3-525-10092-9(2))* Vandenhoeck & Ruprecht GmbH & Co. KG DEU. Dist: ISD.

Durand, J. M. & Jacquet, Antoine. Centre et Périphérie: Approches Nouvelles des Orientalistes: Actes du Colloque Organisé Par L'Institut du Proche-Orient Ancien du Collège de France, la Société Asiatique et le CNRS (UMR 7192) les 31 Mai et 1er Juin 2006, Paris, Collège de France. 2009. (FRE., Illus.). vii, 420p. *(978-2-7200-1161-0(4),* Spotlight Poets) Maisonneuve, Jean Editions d'Amerique et d'Orient.

Duus, Peter, et al, eds. Japanese Wartime Empire, 1931-1945. 2010. (ENG., Illus.). 426p. (C). pap. 28.95 *(978-0-691-14506-8(7))* Princeton Univ. Pr.

Ewans. George Nathaniel Curzon: Collected Writings V2, 5 vols. 2008. (Illus.). 400p. *(978-0-415-45612-8(6))* Routledge.

—George Nathaniel Curzon: Collected Writings V3, 5 vols. 2008. (Illus.). 400p. *(978-0-415-45613-5(4))* Routledge.

—George Nathaniel Curzon: Collected Writings V4, 5 vols. 2008. (Illus.). 400p. *(978-0-415-45614-2(2))* Routledge.

—George Nathaniel Curzon: Collected Writings V5, 5 vols. 2008. (Illus.). 400p. *(978-0-415-45615-9(0))* Routledge.

Ewans, Martin, ed. George Nathaniel Curzon: Collected Writings, 5 vols. 2008. (Illus.). 2200p. (C). 1225.00 *(978-0-415-41690-0(6))* Routledge.

—George Nathaniel Curzon: Collected Writings V1: Collection 1: Asian Travels, 5 vols. 2008. (Illus.). 400p. *(978-0-415-45611-1(8))* Routledge.

Fernandes, Clinton. The Independence of East Timor: Multi-Dimensional Perspectives - Occupation, Resistance, & International Political Activism. 2011. 274p. pap. 34.95 ***(978-1-84519-491-8(8))*** Sussex Academic Pr. GBR. Dist: International Specialized Bk. Services.

Frye. Hoc Golden Age of Persia. (Illus.). 304p. pap. 29.99 *(978-0-297-81393-4(5),* Weidenfeld & Nicolson) Orion Publishing Group, Ltd. GBR. Dist: Trafalgar Square Publishing.

Ghosh. Partition & the South Asian Diaspora. 2007. (ENG.). 308p. (C). 110.00 *(978-0-415-42409-7(7),* Routledge India) Taylor & Francis Group GBR. Dist: Taylor & Francis Group.

Gomes, Jules. The Sanctuary of Bethel & the Configuration of Israelite Identity. 2006. (Beihefte Zur Zeitschrift Für Die Alttestamentliche Wissenschaft Ser.). (ENG.). XX, 303p. 133.00 *(978-3-11-018993-3(3))* De Gruyter, Walter Inc.

Gomes, Jules Francis. The Sanctuary of Bethel & the Configuration of Israelite Identity. (Beihefte zur Zeitschrift far die alttestamentliche Wissenschaft Ser.). (ENG.). XX, 303p. 225.00 ***(978-3-11-182965-4(0))*** De Gruyter, Walter Inc.

Goody, Jack. Eurasian Miracle. 2009. (ENG.). 200p. 64.95 *(978-0-7456-4793-7(6))* Polity Pr. GBR. Dist: Wiley, John & Sons, Inc.

—The Eurasian Miracle. 2009. (ENG.). 200p. pap. 19.95 *(978-0-7456-4794-4(4))* Polity Pr. GBR. Dist: Wiley, John & Sons, Inc.

Harding, John. Roads to Nowhere: A South Arabian Odyssey, 1960-1965. 2009. (ENG., Illus.). 336p. (C). 60.00 *(978-0-9558894-2-4(1))* Arabian Publishing, Ltd. GBR. Dist: Brown, David Bk. Co., The.

Hardy, Andrew, et al. Champa & the Archaeology of My Sn (Vietnam) (Illus.). xxxiv, 440p. 28.00 *(978-9971-69-451-7(4))* National Univ. of Singapore Pr. SGP. Dist: Univ. of Hawaii Pr.

Howorth, Henry Hoyle. History of the Mongols from the 9th to the 19th Century, 4 vols. reprint ed. 625.00 *(978-0-7222-2485-4(0))* Library Reprints, Inc.

Hunt, Michael H. & Levine, Steven I. Arc of Empire: America's Wars in Asia from the Philippines to Vietnam. 2012. (ENG., Illus.). 360p. 35.00 ***(978-0-8078-3528-9(5))*** Univ. of North Carolina Pr.

A Journey Through Africa, Asia, & the Pacific Realm Program Kit: All program components for A Journey Through Africa, 1 vol. 2009. 149.95 *(978-1-4236-0729-8(5))* Gibbs Smith, Publisher.

Katsiaficas, George. Asia's Unknown Uprisings Volume 2: People Power in the Philippines, Burma, Tibet, China, Taiwan, Bangladesh, Nepal, Thailand & Indonesia 1947-2009. 2nd ed. 2012. (ENG., Illus.). 400p. pap. 26.95 ***(978-1-60486-488-5(5))*** PM Pr.

Kellogg, Samuel. The Light of Asia & the Light of the World. 2007. (ENG.). 410p. 49.95 *(978-0-548-05216-7(6))* Kessinger Publishing, LLC.

Kerr, Gordon. Historical Researches into the Politics. 2006. 464p. per. *(978-1-4067-1055-7(5)*, Hesperides Pr.) Read Bks.

Kudaisya, Gyanesh & Yong, Tan Tai, eds. Partition & Post-Colonial South Asia Set: A Reader, 3 vols. 2008. (Illus.). 1233p. 850.00 *(978-0-415-35954-2(6))* Routledge.

Kyrgyzstan's Revolution: Causes & Consequences: Hearing Before the Commission on Security & Cooperation in Europe, One Hundred Ninth Congress, First Session, April 7, 2005. 2007. iii, 44p. *(978-0-16-078436-1(0)*, 552-070-35727-1) United States Government Printing Office.

Le Fleur, Blanche, et al. Torn Apart: The True Story of Two Sisters Who Found Each Other after Sixty-Five Years. 2009. (ENG., Illus.). 224p. 15.95 *(978-1-84596-470-2(5))* Mainstream Publishing Co., Ltd. GBR. Dist: Independent Pubs. Group.

Leng, Loh Wei, ed. Multicultural Organizations in Asia. 2006. (ENG.). 192p. 130.00 *(978-0-415-36868-1(5))* Routledge.

Liu, Xinru. The Silk Road in World History. 2010. (New Oxford World History Ser.). (ENG., Illus.). 176p. pap. 19.95 *(978-0-19-533810-2(3))* Oxford Univ. Pr., Inc.

Lone, Stewart, ed. Daily Lives of Civilians in Wartime Asia: From the Taiping Rebellion to the Vietnam War, 1 vol. 2007. (Greenwood Press Daily Life Through History Ser.). (Illus.). 280p. 65.00 *(978-0-313-33684-3(9)*, GR3684, Greenwood Pr.) Greenwood Publishing Group, Inc.

Lung, Haha. The Sinister Mind. 2011. (ENG., Illus.). 1p. 14.95 *(978-0-8065-3428-2(1)*, Citadel Pr.) Kensington Publishing Corp.

Magalhães, António Barbedo de, et al. Timor-Leste: Interesses Internacionais e Actores Locais, 3 vols. 2007. (POR., Illus.). 59p. *(978-972-36-0935-6(5))* Edicoes Afrontamento.

Marat, Erica. The Tulip Revolution: Kyrgyzstan One Year after: March 15, 2005 — March 24 2006. 2006. 150p. per. 16.95 *(978-1-933556-52-9(8))* Brookings Institution Pr.

Marozzi, Justin. Tamerlane: Sword of Islam, Conqueror of the World. 2007. (ENG., Illus.). 496p. per. 18.00 *(978-0-306-81543-0(5))* Da Capo Pr., Inc.

Marshall, Alex. The Russian General Staff & Asia, 1860-1917. 2012. (ENG., Illus.). 264p. (C). pap. 44.95 *(978-0-415-54583-9(8))* Routledge.

Merali, Shaheen, ed. Re-Imagining Asia: A Thousand Years of Separation. 2008. (ENG., Illus.). 364p. pap. 29.95 *(978-0-86356-653-0(7))* Saqi Bks. GBR. Dist: Consortium Bk. Sales & Distribution.

Metraux, Daniel A. The Asian Writings of Jack London: Essays, Letters, Newspaper Dispatches, & Short Fiction by Jack London. 2010. ix, 322p. *(978-0-7734-3812-5(2))* Mellen, Edwin Pr., The.

Mishra, Pankaj. The Revolt Against the West: The Rise of Asia & the Remaking of the Modern World. 2012. (ENG., Illus.). 320p. 27.00 ***(978-0-374-24959-5(8))*** Farrar, Straus & Giroux.

Moffett, Samuel Hugh. A History of Christianity in Asia: Volume II: 1500-1900. 2007. (American Society of Missiology Ser.). 742p. per. 40.00 *(978-1-57075-701-3(1))* Orbis Bks.

Moore, Jacqueline M. & Wendelken, Rebecca Woodward, eds. Teaching the Silk Road: A Guide for College Teachers. 2010. (SUNY series in Asian Studies Development Ser.). (Illus.). 256p. 75.00 *(978-1-4384-3103-1(1))*; pap. 24.95 *(978-1-4384-3102-4(3))* State Univ. of New York Pr.

Murphey, Rhoads. A History of Asia. 6th ed. 2008. (ENG., Illus.). 552p. (C). pap. 105.20 *(978-0-205-64916-7(5))* Longman Publishing Group.

Olson, Gregory Allen. Landmark Speeches on the Vietnam War. 2010. (Landmark Speeches: A Book Ser.). (ENG.). 208p. 44.00 *(978-1-60344-164-3(6))*; 160p. pap. 22.00 *(978-1-60344-181-0(6))* Texas A&M Univ. Pr.

Panikkar, K. M. Asia & Western Dominance: A Survey of the Vasco Da Gama Epoch of Asian History, 1498-1945. 2008. 376p. pap. 35.00 *(978-1-59740-601-7(5))* ACLS Humanities E-Book.

Pekar, Harvey. Not the Israel My Parents Promised Me, 1 vol. 2012. (ENG., Illus.). 176p. 24.95 ***(978-0-8090-9482-0(7)***, Hill & Wang) Farrar, Straus & Giroux.

Philips, C. H. Handbook of Oriental History. 273p. 17.50 *(978-0-901050-16-8(4))* Brown, David Bk. Co., The.

Pike, Francis. Empires at War: A Short History of Modern Asia since World War II. 2011. (ENG.). 896p. pap. 32.00 *(978-1-84885-865-7(5))* I. B. Tauris & Co., Ltd. GBR. Dist: Macmillan.

Raverty, H. G. Tabakat-i-Nasiri. 2010. pap. 246.72 *(978-1-61719-755-0(6))*; pap. 246.72 *(978-1-61719-753-6(X))*; pap. 246.72 *(978-1-61719-754-3(8))* Gorgias Pr., LLC.

Reinhard, Wolfgang. A Short History of Colonialism. 2011. (ENG., Illus.). 336p. 100.00 ***(978-0-7190-8327-3(3))***; pap. 38.95 ***(978-0-7190-8328-0(1))*** Manchester Univ. Pr. GBR. Dist: Macmillan.

Sakhuja, Vijay. Asian Maritime Power in the 21st Century: Strategic Transactions: China, India, & Southeast Asia. 2011. xv, 363p. pap. ***(978-981-4311-09-0(X))*** Institute of Southeast Asian Studies.

Salter, Christopher L. South & East Asia & the Pacific. 2009. (Holt Social Studies). (ENG., Illus.). 304p. (gr. 6-8). 20.15 *(978-0-03-099540-8(X))* Houghton Mifflin Harcourt Publishing Co.

Schwarz-Friesel, Monika, et al, eds. Aktueller Antisemitismus - Ein Phänomen der Mitte. 2010.Tr. of Anti-Semitism Today â¿¿ A Mainstream Phenomenon. (GER., Illus.). VI, 254p. 70.00 *(978-3-11-023010-9(0))* De Gruyter, Walter Inc.

Smith, Kirby Flower. The Tale of Gyges & the King of Lydia. 2009. pap. 21.88 *(978-1-60724-625-1(2))* Gorgias Pr., LLC.

Subrahmanyam, Sanjay. The Portuguese Empire in Asia, 1500-1700: A Political & Economic History. 2nd ed. 2012. (ENG.). 360p. 99.95 ***(978-0-470-67291-4(9)***, Wiley-Blackwell) Wiley, John & Sons, Inc.

Sylas, Eluma Ikemefuna. Terrorism: A Global Scourge. 2011. (ENG.). 484p. pap. 22.95 ***(978-1-4327-7923-8(0))*** Outskirts Pr., Inc.

Tikhonov, Vladimir & Brekke, Torkel, eds. Violent Buddhism. 2012. (Routledge Studies in Religion Ser.). (ENG., Illus.). 264p. (C). 125.00 ***(978-0-415-53696-7(0))*** Routledge.

Tsitsishvili, Nino & Arutiunov, Sergey. Cultural Archetypes & Political Change in the Caucasus. 2009. (Caucasus Region Political, Economic, & Security Issues Ser.). 79.00 *(978-1-60741-739-2(1))* Nova Science Pubs., Inc.

Uitz, Martin. Hidden Bhutan: Entering the Kingdom of the Thunder Dragon. 2012. (Armchair Traveller Ser.). (ENG.). 101p. pap. 11.95 ***(978-1-907973-16-1(8))*** Haus Publishing GBR. Dist: Consortium Bk. Sales & Distribution.

Um, Nancy. Merchant Houses of Mocha: Trade & Architecture in an Indian Ocean Port. 2009. (ENG., Illus.). 272p. 75.00 *(978-0-295-98910-5(6))*; pap. 30.00 *(978-0-295-98911-2(4))* Univ. of Washington Pr.

Vang, Thomas. A History of the Hmong: from Ancient Times to the Modern Diaspora. 2008. 484p. 64.24 *(978-1-4357-0932-4(2))* Lulu Enterprises Inc.

Verma, Som Prakash. 1857: An Illustrated History. 2008. (ENG., Illus.). 160p. 80.00 *(978-0-19-569577-9(1))* Oxford Univ. Pr., Inc.

Wade, Geoffrey, ed. Asian Expansions: The Historical Experiences of Polity Expansion in Asia. 2012. (Routledge Studies in the Early History of Asia Ser.). (ENG.). 256p. (C). 125.00 *(978-0-415-58995-6(9))* Routledge.

Weinrib, Laura M. & Weinrib, Estee. Nitzotz: The Spark of Resistance in Kovno Ghetto & Dachau-Kaufering Concentration Camp. 2009. 34.95 *(978-0-8156-3233-7(9))* Syracuse Univ. Pr.

Wetzel, Klaus. Kirchengeschichte Asiens. 2010. 682p. pap. *(978-3-941750-25-8(9))* VTR Verlag fur Theologie und Religionswissenschaft.

Wu, Hung. The Art of the Yellow Springs: Understanding Chinese Tombs. 2010. 272p. (C). 50.00 *(978-0-8248-3426-5(7))* Univ. of Hawaii Pr.

Zhang, Weiyuan, ed. Theories, Policy, & Practice of Lifelong Learning in East Asia. 2009. (ENG., Illus.). 112p. (C). 125.00 *(978-0-415-56042-9(X))* Routledge.

ASIA—HISTORY—SOURCES

Yoffee, Norman & Crowell, Bradley L. Excavating Asian History: Interdisciplinary Studies in Archaeology & History. 2006. (ENG., Illus.). 368p. 55.00 *(978-0-8165-2418-1(1))* Univ. of Arizona Pr.

ASIA—HISTORY, MILITARY

Abbott, Peter & Heath, Ian. Rivals of the Raj: Non-British Colonial Armies in Asia 1497-1941. 2010. (Illus.). 200p. 63.00 *(978-1-901543-19-3(6))* Foundry Bks. GBR. Dist: Casemate Pubs. & Bk. Distributors, LLC.

Allen, William Edward David & Muratoff, Paul. Caucasian Battlefields: A History of the Wars on the Turco-Caucasian Border 1828-1921. 2010. (Cambridge Library Collection - History Ser.). (Illus.). 716p. pap. 48.00 *(978-1-108-01335-2(X))* Cambridge Univ. Pr.

Bodley Scott, Richard. Colonies & Conquest: Asia 1494-1698. 2011. (Field of Glory Renaissance Ser.). (ENG., Illus.). 100p. pap. 24.95 *(978-1-84908-231-0(6))* Osprey Publishing, Ltd. GBR. Dist: Random Hse., Inc.

Bunn, Mike & Williams, Clay. Battle for the Southern Frontier: The Creek War & the War of 1812. 2008. pap. 22.99 *(978-1-59629-371-7(3))* History Pr., The.

Burton, Reginald. Railway of Hell: War Captivity & Forced Labour at the Hands of the Japanese. 2010. (Illus.). 192p. pap. 24.95 *(978-1-84884-299-1(6))* Pen & Sword Bks. Ltd. GBR. Dist: Casemate Pubs. & Bk. Distributors, LLC.

Commission on Wartime Contracting: Interim Findings & Path Forward: Hearing Before the Subcommittee on National Security & Foreign Affairs of the Committee on Oversight & Government Reform, House of Representatives, One Hundred Eleventh Congress, First Session, June 10, 2009. 2009. (Illus.). iii, 178p. *(978-0-16-084279-5(4)*, 552-070-39844-9) United States Government Printing Office.

de Matos, Christine & Ward, Rowena, eds. Gender, Power, & Military Occupations: Asia Pacific & the Middle East since 1945. 2012. (Routledge Research in Gender & History Ser.). (ENG., Illus.). 264p. (C). 125.00 *(978-0-415-89183-7(3))* Routledge.

Ehrhart, W. D. In the Shadow of Vietnam: Essays, 1977-1991. alt. ed. 2011. (ENG.). 208p. pap. 19.99 ***(978-0-7864-6727-3(4))*** McFarland & Co., Inc. Pubs.

Gardner, Gerald B. Keris & Other Malay Weapons. 2010. (ENG., Illus.). 144p. pap. 30.00 *(978-974-8304-29-8(9))* Orchid Pr. THA. Dist: National Bk. Network.

Gates, Scott & Roy, Kaushik. Critical Essays Warfare in South Asia 1947 to the Present, 3 vols., Set. 2011. (Critical Essays on Warfare in South Asia, 1947 to the Present Ser.). 1270p. 750.00 *(978-0-7546-2978-8(3))* Ashgate Publishing Co.

Gates, Scott & Roy, Kaushik, eds. Conventional Warfare in South Asia 1947 to Present. 2011. (Critical Essays on Warfare in South Asia, 1947 to the Present Ser.). 446p. 250.00 *(978-0-7546-2975-7(9))* Ashgate Publishing Co.

—The Nuclear Shadow over South Asia 1947 to Present. 2011. (Critical Essays on Warfare in South Asia, 1947 to the Present Ser.). 418p. 250.00 *(978-0-7546-2976-4(7))* Ashgate Publishing Co.

—Unconventional Warfare in South Asia 1947 to Present. 2011. (Critical Essays on Warfare in South Asia, 1947 to the Present Ser.). (Illus.). 406p. 250.00 *(978-0-7546-2977-1(5))* Ashgate Publishing Co.

Girardet, Edward. Killing the Cranes: A Reporter's Journey Through Three Decades of War in Afghanistan. 2011. (ENG.). 416p. 27.95 *(978-1-60358-342-8(4))* Chelsea Green Publishing.

Herbert, Edwin. Risings & Rebellions 1919-39: Organisation, Warfare, Dress & Weapons. Interwar Colonial Campaigns in Africa, Asia, & the Americas. 2007. (Armies of the Twentieth Century Ser.). (Illus.). 192p. 63.00 *(978-1-901543-12-4(9))* Foundry Bks. GBR. Dist: Casemate Pubs. & Bk. Distributors, LLC.

Juhary, Jowati. A Military Learning Environment. 2010. 100p. pap. *(978-3-8383-7521-2(1))* Lambert Academic Publishing.

Kelly, Ltc David M. The Kunar Adt & the Afghan Coin Fight: How National Guard Agribusiness Development Teams Support Battle Space Commander's COunter INsurgency Operati. 2011. 488p. 30.79 ***(978-1-4567-5304-7(5))***; pap. 22.50 ***(978-1-4567-5303-0(7))*** AuthorHouse.

Lebra-Chapman, Joyce. Japanese-Trained Armies in Southeast Asia. 2010. 226p. pap. *(978-981-4279-44-4(7))* Institute of Southeast Asian Studies.

Lord, Cliff & Birtles, David. The Armed Forces of Aden & the Protectorate 1839-1967: Revised & Expanded Edition. 2010. (Illus.). 160p. pap. 79.95 *(978-1-906033-96-5(X))* Helion & Co., Ltd. GBR. Dist: Casemate Pubs. & Bk. Distributors, LLC.

Lorge, Peter A. The Asian Military Revolution: From Gunpowder to the Bomb. 2008. (New Approaches to Asian History Ser.). (ENG., Illus.). 200p. (C). 78.99 *(978-0-521-84682-0(X))*; pap. 24.99 *(978-0-521-60954-8(2))* Cambridge Univ. Pr.

MacRory, Patrick. Retreat from Kabul: The Catastrophic British Defeat in Afghanistan 1842. 2007. (ENG.). 288p. pap. 16.95 *(978-1-59921-177-0(7)*, Lyons Pr.) Globe Pequot Pr., The.

Magyar, Karl P. Prolonged Wars: A Post-Nuclear Challenge. Danopo, Constantine P., ed. 475p. pap. 27.00 *(978-1-58566-056-8(6))* Air University Pr.

Marston, Daniel P. & Sundaram, Chandar S., eds. A Military History of India & South Asia: From the East India Company to the Nuclear Era, 1 vol. 2006. (Praeger Security International Ser.). (Illus.). 256p. 49.95 *(978-0-275-98570-7(9)*, C8570, Praeger Pubs.) Greenwood Publishing Group, Inc.

—A Military History of India & South Asia: From the East India Company to the Nuclear Era. 2008. (ENG., Illus.). 256p. pap. 24.95 *(978-0-253-21999-2(X)*, 025321999X) Indiana Univ. Pr.

Matthews, Matt. An Ever Present Danger: A Concise History of British Military Operations on the North-West Frontier, 1849-1947. 2010. *(978-0-9841901-3-3(9))* United States Government Printing Office.

Matthews, Matt. We Have Not Learned How to Wage War There: The Soviet Approach in Afghanistan 1979-1989. 2011. ***(978-0-9841901-9-5(8))*** Combat Studies Institute Pr.

McGoldrick, James & McCaffrie, Jack. Navies of South-East Asia: A Comparative Study. 2012. (Cass Series: Naval Policy & History Ser.). (ENG., Illus.). 288p. (C). 135.00 ***(978-0-415-80942-9(8))*** Routledge.

Oliker, Olga. Building Afghanistan's Security Forces in Wartime: The Soviet Experience, 1 vol. 2011. (ENG.). 126p. (C). pap. 20.00 ***(978-0-8330-5168-4(7))*** RAND Corp., The.

Porajska, Barbara. From the Steppes to the Savannah. 2010. (ENG.). 137p. pap. 11.95 *(978-0-557-50429-9(5))* Lulu Enterprises Inc.

Reed, Graham F. Walks in Waziristan: A Young Officer's Guide to Dealing with Cock-Ups on the Front Line. 2010. 244p. pap. 16.95 *(978-1-4520-2616-9(5))* AuthorHouse.

Rieffel, Lex & Pramodhawardani, Jaleswari. Out of Business & on Budget: The Challenge of Military Financing in Indonesia. 2007. (ENG., Illus.). 147p. per. 18.95 *(978-0-8157-7447-1(8))* Brookings Institution Pr.

Roy, Kaushik. War, Culture & Society in Early Modern South Asia, 1740-1849. 2011. (Asian States & Empires Ser.). (ENG., Illus.). 256p. (C). 145.00 *(978-0-415-58767-9(0))* Routledge.

Salik, Naeem. The Genesis of South Asian Nuclear Deterrence: Pakistan's Perspective. 2010. 336p. 35.00 *(978-0-19-547716-0(2))* Oxford Univ. Pr., Inc.

Scott, Richard & Gaukroger, Nik. Empires of the Dragon: The Far East at War. 2009. (Field of GLory Ser.). (ENG., Illus.). 100p. pap. 24.95 *(978-1-84603-690-3(9))* Osprey Publishing, Ltd. GBR. Dist: Random Hse., Inc.

Shin, Gi-Wook & Sneider, Daniel, eds. History Textbooks & the Wars in Asia: Divided Memories. 2011. (Routledge Contemporary Asia Ser.). (ENG.). 312p. (C). 148.00 *(978-0-415-60303-4(X))* Routledge.

Sloan, Bill. The Darkest Summer: Pusan & Inchon 1950 - The Battles That Saved South Korea - And the Marines - From Extinction. 2010. (ENG., Illus.). 400p. pap. 16.00 *(978-1-4165-7175-9(2))* Simon & Schuster.

Swope, Kenneth M. A Dragon's Head & a Serpent's Tail: Ming China & the First Great East Asian War, 1592-1598. 2009. (Campaigns & Commanders Ser.). (ENG.). 432p. 34.95 *(978-0-8061-4056-8(9))* Univ. of Oklahoma Pr.

Tanner, Stephen. Afghanistan: A Military History from Alexander the Great to the War Against the Taliban. rev. ed. 2009. (ENG., Illus.). 392p. pap. 17.95 *(978-0-306-81826-4(4))* Da Capo Pr., Inc.

Thompson, Julian. Forgotten Voices of Burma: The Second World War's Forgotten Conflict. 2010. (ENG., Illus.). 412p. pap. 14.95 *(978-0-09-193237-4(8))* Ebury Publishing GBR. Dist: Independent Pubs. Group.

Thompson, Warren & McLaren, David. Mig Alley - Sabres vs. Migs over Korea: Pilot Accounts & the Complete Combat Record of the F-86 Sabre 1950-53. 2010. (Illus.). 288p. 69.95 *(978-1-906033-97-2(8))* Helion & Co., Ltd. GBR. Dist: Casemate Pubs. & Bk. Distributors, LLC.

Tupper, Benjamin. Greetings from Afghanistan, Send More Ammo: Dispatches from Taliban Country. 2010. (ENG., Illus.). 272p. (gr. 12). 24.95 *(978-0-451-23143-7(0)*, N A L Hardcover) Penguin Group (USA) Inc.

Weiss, Mitch & Maurer, Kevin. No Way Out: A Story of Valor in the Mountains of Afghanistan. 2012. (ENG., Illus.). 336p. (gr. 12). 26.95 ***(978-0-425-24526-2(8)***, Berkley Hardcover) Penguin Group (USA) Inc.

Wilhite, Usar James. We Answered the Call: Building the Crown Jewel of Afghanistan. 2010. pap. 18.99 *(978-1-61566-779-6(2))* Tate Publishing & Enterprises, LLC.

Wylly, Harold Carmichael. From the Black Mountain to Waziristan. 2009. 310p. pap. *(978-1-4590-9894-7(3))* Books LLC.

Yoshihara, Toshi & Holmes, James R., eds. Asia Looks Seaward: Power & Maritime Strategy, 1 vol. 2007. (Praeger Security International Ser.). (Illus.). 232p. 49.95 *(978-0-275-99403-7(1)*, C9403, Praeger Security International) Greenwood Publishing Group, Inc.

ASIA—LANGUAGES

see also Oriental Languages

Adelaar, Alexander. Siraya: Retrieving the Phonology, Grammar & Lexicon of a Dormant Formosan Language. 2012. (Trends in Linguistics. Documentation [TiLDOC] Ser.). (ENG., Illus.). XVI, 413p. (gr. 17). E-Book 280.00 ***(978-3-11-219171-2(4))*** De Gruyter, Mouton DEU. Dist: de Gruyter, Walter GmbH & Co. KG.

Ananda, Lalith. The Focus Construction in Sinhal. 2011. 192p. pap. ***(978-3-8443-1022-1(3))*** Lambert Academic Publishing.

Bolton, Kingsley & Kachru, Braj B. Asian Englishes, 5 vols. (Illus.). 2007. 528p. *(978-0-415-41474-6(1))* 2006. 320p. *(978-0-415-41471-5(7))* 2006. 432p. *(978-0-415-41470-8(9))* 2006. 432p. *(978-0-415-41472-2(5))* 2006. 464p. *(978-0-415-41473-9(3))* Routledge.

Bolton, Kingsley & Kachru, Braj B., eds. Asian Englishes, Vols. 1-5., Set. 2006. (History & Development of World Englishes Ser.). (Illus.). 2176p. 1600.00 *(978-0-415-37456-6(3))* Routledge.

Breitenbach, Sandra. Missionary Linguistics in East Asia: The Origins of Religious Language in the Shaping of Christianity? 2008. 222p. pap. 56.95 *(978-3-631-50441-3(1))* Lang, Peter GmbH, Europaischer Verlag der Wissenschaften DEU. Dist: Lang, Peter.

Christensen, Matthew B. & Warnick, J. Paul. Performed Culture: An Approach to East Asian Language Pedagogy. 2006. (Pathways to Advanced Skills Ser.). *(978-0-87415-307-1(7))* Foreign Language Pubns.

David, Maya Khemlani & McLellan, James, eds. Code Switching in Malaysia. 2009. (Duisburger Arbeiten zur Sprach- und Kulturwissenschaft. Duisburg Papers on Research in Language & Culture Ser.). 246p. 72.95 *(978-3-631-59564-0(6))* Lang, Peter GmbH, Europaischer Verlag der Wissenschaften DEU. Dist: Lang, Peter.

Deterding, David. Singapore English. Beal, Joan et al, eds. 2007. (Dialects of English Ser.). (ENG., Illus.). 160p. (gr. 17). 100.00 *(978-0-7486-2544-4(5))* Edinburgh Univ. Pr. GBR. Dist: Columbia Univ. Pr.

Euro Talk. Talk Now! Pashto. 2008. 29.99 *(978-1-84352-404-5(X))* TOPICS Entertainment.

Ferrara, Silvia. Cypro-Minoan Inscriptions: Volume 1: Analysis. 2012. (ENG., Illus.). 320p. 125.00 ***(978-0-19-960757-0(5))*** Oxford Univ. Pr., Inc.

Heinrich, Patrick & Galan, Christian. Language Life in Japan. 2010. (Routledge Contemporary Japan Ser.). (ENG., Illus.). 272p. (C). 140.00 *(978-0-415-58722-8(0))* Routledge.

Icon Group International, Inc. Staff, compiled by. Webster's Burushaski - English Thesaurus Dictionary. 2008. 72p. ring bd. 28.95 incl. audio compact disk *(978-0-497-83456-2(1))* Icon Group International, Inc.

Jahani, Carina, et al, eds. The Baloch & Others: Linguistic, historical & socio-political perspectives on pluralism in Balochistan. 2008. (ENG.). 399p. (C). 100.00 *(978-3-89500-591-6(6))* Reichert, Ludwig Dr. DEU. Dist: Brown, David Bk. Co., The.

Kàdàr, Dàniel Z. & Mills, Sara, eds. Politeness in East Asia. 2011. (ENG., Illus.). 328p. 105.00 *(978-1-107-00706-2(2))* Cambridge Univ. Pr.

Kaplan, Robert B. & Baldauf, Richard B., Jr., eds. Language Planning & Policy in Asia Vol. 1: Japan, Nepal & Taiwan & Chinese Characters. 2008. (Language Planning & Policy Ser.). (ENG., Illus.). 320p. 89.95 *(978-1-84769-095-1(5))* Multilingual Matters GBR. Dist: Univ. of Toronto Pr.

Kaye, Alan S. Morphologies of Asia & Africa. 2007. (C). 175.00 *(978-1-57506-109-2(0))*; *(978-1-57506-110-8(4))*; *(978-1-57506-111-5(2))* Eisenbrauns, Inc.

Koh, Ernest. Singapore Stories: Language, Class, & the Chinese of Singapore, 1945-2000. 2010. *(978-1-60497-677-9(2))* Cambria Pr.

Kondo-Brown, Kimi. Heritage Language Development: Focus on East Asian Immigrants. (Studies in Bilingualism: Vol. 32). (Illus.). vi, 281p. (C). 138.00 *(978-90-272-4143-6(0))* Benjamins, John Publishing Co.

Landau, Jacob M. & Kellner-Heinkele, Barbara. Language Politics in Contemporary Central Asia: National & Ethnic Identity & the Soviet Legacy. 2012. (International Library of Central Asia Studies: No. 5). (ENG., Illus.). 256p. 92.00 ***(978-1-84885-820-6(5))*** I. B. Tauris & Co., Ltd. GBR. Dist: Macmillan.

Lee, Chungmin, et al, eds. The Handbook of East Asian Psycholinguistics: Volume 3, Korean, 3 vols. 2009. (ENG., Illus.). 658p. 185.00 *(978-0-521-83335-6(3))* Cambridge Univ. Pr.

Levy, Indra, ed. Translation in Modern Japan. 2010. (Routledge Contemporary Japan Ser.). (ENG., Illus.). 304p. (C). 125.00 *(978-0-415-57391-7(2)*, Routledge) Taylor & Francis Group GBR. Dist: Taylor & Francis Group.

Lim, Lisa, et al, eds. English in Singapore: Modernity & Management. 2010. (Asian Englishes Today Ser.). 324p. ***(978-988-220-693-9(X))*** Hong Kong Univ. Pr.

—English in Singapore: Modernity & Management. 2010. (Asian Englishes Today Ser.). (ENG.). 324p. (gr. 17). 50.00 *(978-988-8028-42-9(1))*; pap. 30.00 *(978-988-8028-43-6(X))* Hong Kong Univ. Pr. HKG. Dist: Columbia Univ. Pr.

Lonely Planet Staff, creator. Asia: 10 Essential Languages for City Breaks. 2008. (Fast Talk Ser.). (MUL & ENG., Illus.). 128p. pap. 6.99 *(978-1-74179-142-6(1))* Lonely Planet Pubns.

Lonely Planet Staff & Rudelson, Justin Jon. Central Asia. 2nd rev. ed. 2008. (Phrasebook Ser.). (MUL & ENG., Illus.). 244p. pap. 8.99 *(978-1-74059-114-0(3))* Lonely Planet Pubns.

Lustig, Anton. A Grammar & Dictionary of Zaiwa (2 vol. Set), 2 vols. 2010. (Brill's Tibetan Studies Library). (KAC, ENG & SIT., Illus.). 1500p. *(978-90-04-18489-3(9))* BRILL.

Morgenstierne, George. Report on a Linguistic Mission to North-Western India. 2006. per. 14.95 net. *(978-0-923891-14-5(5))* Ishi Pr. International.

Notices of the Monosyllabic Languages of South Eastern Asia. 2010. pap. 18.76 *(978-1-61143-195-7(6))* Gorgias Pr., LLC.

Paksoy, Hasan B. Central Asian Monuments. 2011. 128.80 *(978-1-61143-110-0(7))* Gorgias Pr., LLC.

Perera, Wathsala. Leveraging Ict Penetration in Sri Lanka Using Local Language. 2011. 84p. pap. ***(978-3-8443-0725-2(7))*** Lambert Academic Publishing.

Price, Fiona Swee-Lin. Success with Asian Names: A Practical Guide for Business & Everyday Life. 2007. (ENG.). 176p. per. 19.95 *(978-1-85788-378-7(0))* Ebsco Publishing.

Rasul, Sarwet. Code-ing & Hybridization in Pakistan. 2009. 360p. pap. *(978-3-639-14766-7(9))* VDM Verlag Dr. Mueller e.K.

Sanchez-Mazas, Alicia, et al, eds. Past Human Migrations in East Asia: Matching Archaeology, Linguistics & Genetics. 2012. (Routledge Studies in the Early History of Asia Ser.). (ENG., Illus.). 504p. (C). pap. 42.95 ***(978-0-415-54188-6(3))*** Routledge.

Simpson, Andrew, ed. Language & National Identity in Asia. 2007. (ENG., Illus.). 480p. 199.00 *(978-0-19-926748-4(0))*; pap. 60.00 *(978-0-19-922648-1(2))* Oxford Univ. Pr., Inc.

Stroud, Christopher & Wee, Lionel. Style, Identity & Literacy: English in Singapore. 2011. (Critical Language & Literacy Studies). (ENG.). 240p. 159.95 ***(978-1-84769-596-3(5))***; pap. 49.95 ***(978-1-84769-595-6(7))*** Multilingual Matters GBR. Dist: Univ. of Toronto Pr.

Tranter, Nicolas. The Languages of Japan & Korea. 2012. (Routledge Language Family Ser.). (ENG., Illus.). 544p. (C). 360.00 *(978-0-415-46287-7(8))* Routledge.

Vaish, Viniti. Globalization of Language & Culture in Asia: The Impact of Globalization Processes on Language. 2012. (ENG.). 256p. pap. 44.95 ***(978-1-4411-3165-2(5))*** Continuum International Publishing Group, Ltd. GBR. Dist: National Bk. Network.

Woodard, Roger D., ed. The Ancient Languages of Asia & the Americas. 2008. (ENG., Illus.). 296p. pap. 48.00 *(978-0-521-68494-1(3))* Cambridge Univ. Pr.

Yang, Bo & Deterding, David. Singapore English. 2007. (Dialects of English Ser.). (ENG., Illus.). 160p. (gr. 17). pap. 34.00 *(978-0-7486-2545-1(3))* Edinburgh Univ. Pr. GBR. Dist: Columbia Univ. Pr.

Yap, Foong Ha, et al. Nominalization in Asian Languages: Diachronic & Typological Perpsectives. 2011. *(978-90-272-8724-3(4))*; (Illus.). xvi, 796p. *(978-90-272-0677-0(5))* Benjamins, John Publishing Co.

ASIA—MILITARY POLICY

Alagappa, Muthiah, ed. The Long Shadow: Nuclear Weapons & Security in 21st Century Asia. 2008. (ENG.). 592p. 75.00 *(978-0-8047-6086-7(1))*; (Illus.). pap. 29.95 *(978-0-8047-6087-4(X))* Stanford Univ. Pr.

Barak, Oren. The Lebanese Army: A National Institution in a Divided Society. 2010. (Illus.). 288p. pap. 25.95 *(978-0-7914-9346-5(6)*, Suny Pr.) State Univ. of New York Pr.

Chakma, Bhumitra. Pakistan's Nuclear Weapons. 2010. (ENG.). pap. 39.95 *(978-0-415-59032-7(9))* Routledge.

—South Asia's Nuclear Security. 2010. (Routledge Security in Asia Pacific Ser.). (ENG.). 240p. 145.00 *(978-0-415-49449-6(4))* Routledge.

Cole, Bernard. Taiwan's Security: History & Prospects. 2008. 272p. 39.95 *(978-0-415-46082-8(4))* Routledge.

Cordesman, Anthony H. & Gagel, Andrew. The Korean Military Balance: Comparative Korean Forces & the Forces of Key Neighboring States: Main Report. 2011. pap. ***(978-0-89206-632-2(6))*** Ctr. for Strategic & International Studies.

De Mel, Neloufer. Militarizing Sri Lanka: Popular Culture, Memory & Narrative in the Armed Conflict. 2007. 330p. (C). pap. 34.95 *(978-0-7619-3635-0(1)*, B36350P) SAGE Pubns., Inc.

Ganguly, Sumit. Nuclear Proliferation in South Asia: Crisis Behaviour & the Bomb. Kapur, S. Paul, ed. 2008. (Asian Security Studies). (Illus.). 272p. 140.00 *(978-0-415-44049-3(1))* Routledge.

Gupta, Amit, ed. Strategic Stability in Asia. 2008. 184p. 114.95 *(978-0-7546-7243-2(3))* Ashgate Publishing Co.

Hanks, Reuel R. Global Security Watch-Central Asia. 2010. (Global Security Watch Ser.). (Illus.). 225p. instr.'s hndbk. ed. 49.95 *(978-0-313-35422-9(7)*, C35422, Praeger Pubs.) Greenwood Publishing Group, Inc.

Hedrick, Brian K. India's Strategic Defense Transformation: Expanding Global Relationships. 2009. (Letort Papers). *(978-1-58487-414-0(7))* Strategic Studies Institute, U.S. Army War College Commandant (AWCC-DSI/Pubns.).

Kapur, S. Paul. Dangerous Deterrent: Nuclear Weapons Proliferation & Conflict in South Asia. 2007. (Studies in Asian Security Ser.). (ENG.). 280p. 65.00 *(978-0-8047-5549-8(3))* Stanford Univ. Pr.

Marshall, Frederick Henry. The Second Athenian Confederacy. 2009. 148p. 35.95 *(978-1-120-06245-1(4))* Kessinger Publishing, LLC.

McDermott, Roger N. Kazakhstan's Defense Policy: An Assessment of the Trends. 2009. *(978-1-58487-377-8(9))* Strategic Studies Institute, U.S. Army War College Commandant (AWCC-DSI/Pubns.).

Mufti, Malik. Daring & Caution in Turkish Strategic Culture: Republic at Sea. 2009. (ENG., Illus.). 240p. 95.00 *(978-0-230-23638-7(3))* Palgrave Macmillan.

Pakistan at the Crossroads; Afghanistan in the Balance: Hearing Before the Subcommittee on National Security & Foreign Affairs of the Committee on Oversight & Government Reform, House of Representatives, One Hundred Tenth Congress, First Session, July 12, 2007. 2009. iii, 61p. *(978-0-16-083701-2(4)*, 552-070-39408-7) United States Government Printing Office.

Sadri, Houman A. The Caucasus States. 2010. (Global Security Watch Ser.). (Illus.). 270p. 49.95 *(978-0-313-37980-2(7)*, A2036C, Praeger Pubs.) Greenwood Publishing Group, Inc.

Sagan, Scott D., ed. Inside Nuclear South Asia. 2009. (ENG., Illus.). 296p. 75.00 *(978-0-8047-6238-0(4))* Stanford Univ. Pr.

Sagan, Scott Douglas, ed. Inside Nuclear South Asia. 2009. (ENG., Illus.). 296p. pap. 27.95 *(978-0-8047-6239-7(2))* Stanford Univ. Pr.

Sokolski, Henry D., ed. Pakistan's Nuclear Future: Worries Beyond War. 2008. lib. bdg. *(978-1-58487-333-4(7))* Strategic Studies Institute, U.S. Army War College Commandant (AWCC-DSI/Pubns.).

Tellis, Ashley J. & Wills, Michael, eds. Strategic Asia 2007-08: Domestic Political Change & Grand Strategy. 2007. (Strategic Asia Ser.). (Illus.). pap. 29.95 *(978-0-9713938-8-2(5))* National Bureau of Asian Research, The.

Verma, Bharat. Indian Defence Review. 2009. 128p. pap. 18.95 *(978-81-7062-164-5(X))* Lancer International, Lancer Pr. IND. Dist: Casemate Pubs. & Bk. Distributors, LLC.

—Indian Defence Review: Apr-Jun 2010. 2011. (Vol. 25. 2 Ser.). 152p. pap. 18.95 *(978-81-7062-178-2(X))* Lancer International, Lancer Pr. IND. Dist: Casemate Pubs. & Bk. Distributors, LLC.

—Indian Defence Review: Jul-Sep 2008. 2009. (Vol 23. 3 Ser.). 128p. pap. 18.95 *(978-81-7062-163-8(1))* Lancer International, Lancer Pr. IND. Dist: Casemate Pubs. & Bk. Distributors, LLC.

Verma, Bharat. Indian Defence Review October 2010. 2011. (Illus.). 188p. pap. 18.95 ***(978-81-7062-182-9(8))*** Lancer International, Lancer Pr. IND. Dist: Casemate Pubs. & Bk. Distributors, LLC.

Verma, Bharat, ed. Indian Defence Review. 2010. (Vol 24. 4 Ser.). 144p. pap. 18.95 *(978-81-7062-173-7(9))* Lancer International, Lancer Pr. IND. Dist: Casemate Pubs. & Bk. Distributors, LLC.

Younossi, Obaid, et al. The Long March: Building an Afghan National Army. 2009. 92p. pap. 31.00 *(978-0-8330-4668-0(3)*, mg-845) RAND Corp., The.

ASIA—MAPS

Abazov, Rafis. The Palgrave Concise Historical Atlas of Central Asia. 2008. (ENG., Illus.). 144p. pap. 23.00 *(978-1-4039-7542-3(6))* Palgrave Macmillan.

Asien 1: 8 000 000: Kontinentkarte mit Themenkarten. (Illus.). spiral bd. 25.99 *(978-3-8327-1025-5(6))* teNeues Publishing Co.

Atlas of Korea History. 2009. 56.00 *(978-981-08-0785-6(6))* World Scientific Publishing Co., Inc.

Bennett, Lindsay. Dubai. 2008. (The Globetrotter Travel Ser.). (ENG., Illus.). 128p. 14.95 *(978-1-84773-164-7(3))* New Holland Pubs., Ltd. GBR. Dist: Globe Pequot Pr., The.

Campbell, Rusty & Porter, Malcolm. Atlas of Asia. 2010. (Illus.). 48p. (YA). pap. 11.75 *(978-1-4358-9112-8(0)*, Rosen Central) Rosen Publishing Group, Inc., The.

Gauldie, Robin. Thailand. 6th ed. 2007. (Globetrotter Travel Atlas Ser.). (ENG., Illus.). 72p. pap. 12.95 *(978-1-84330-755-6(3))* New Holland Pubs., Ltd. GBR. Dist: Globe Pequot Pr., The.

Kaplony, Andreas & Forêt, Philippe. The Journey of Maps & Images on the Silk Road. Forêt, Phillipe & Kaplony, Andreas, eds. 2008. (Brill's Inner Asian Library Ser.). (Illus.). 234p. (C). *(978-90-04-17165-7(7))* BRILL.

Mapping Asia: Grades 5-9. (Illus.). 82p. tchr. ed., spiral bd. 19.95 incl. trans. *(978-0-382-40818-2(7))* Cobblestone Publishing Co.

Olason, Eric, creator. Expressive Map: Illustrated Map of Bangkok Including the Old City, Chao Phraya Riverside & Greater Metropolitan Bangkok, 001. collector's ed. 2007. (Illus.). mass mkt. 3.75 *(978-0-9794819-0-1(2))* Olason Cartographic Artistry.

ASIA—PICTORIAL WORKS

Brambilla, Stefano. Vanishing Wilderness of Asia. 2010. (Illus.). 272p. 39.95 *(978-88-544-0460-1(8))* White Star ITA. Dist: Random Hse., Inc.

Crane, Christina & Brown, Denise Scott. Asia Beyond Growth: Urbanization in the World's Fastest-Changing Continent. AECOM Consult, Inc Staff, ed. 2010. (ENG., Illus.). 400p. pap. 40.00 *(978-0-9795395-1-0(X))* Oro Editions.

Davaa, Byambasuren & Reisch, Lisa. The Cave of the Yellow Dog. Spencer, Sally-Ann, tr. 2008. (ENG., Illus.). 192p. pap. 15.95 *(978-1-84408-456-2(6))* Little, Brown Bk. Group Ltd. GBR. Dist: Independent Pubs. Group.

Dobson, Sebastian. Art & Artifice: Japanese Photographs of the Meiji Era. 2009. (ENG.). 95p. pap. 17.00 *(978-1-4379-6793-7(0))* DIANE Publishing Co.

Fields, Charles. Vietnam Journeys. 2011. (Illus.). 224p. 50.00 *(978-0-9823196-7-3(3))* Fields Publishing.

Follmi, Olivier. Asia. 2008. (ENG., Illus.). 352p. 65.00 *(978-0-8109-7121-9(6))* Abrams.

Friedlander, Lee. Cherry Blossom Time in Japan: The Complete Works, 1 vol. 2006. (ENG., Illus.). 156p. 65.00 *(978-1-881337-20-1(0))* Fraenkel Gallery.

Grace Zhang. Kirk Pedersen: Urban Asia Photos. 2007. (Illus.). 36p. pap. *(978-0-9778184-1-9(1))* Pedersen, Kirk.

Grant, Colesworthy. Rough Pencillings of a Rough Trip to Rangoon In 1846. 2006. (Itineraria Asiatica: Burma Ser.). (ENG., Illus.). pap. 20.00 *(978-974-8299-79-2(1))* Orchid Pr. THA. Dist: National Bk. Network.

Hwang, Cindy, photos by. Kyopo. 2011. (ENG., Illus.). 500p. 75.00 ***(978-1-884167-90-4(X))*** Umbrage Editions.

Lacoste, Anne, et al. Felice Beato: A Photographer on the Eastern Road. 2010. (ENG., Illus.). 208p. 39.95 *(978-1-60606-035-3(X)*, J. Paul Getty Museum) Getty Pubns.

Lambray, Maureen, photos by. War Remnants of the Khmer Rouge. 2011. (ENG., Illus.). 136p. 60.00 ***(978-1-884167-31-7(4))*** Umbrage Editions.

Leboutillier, Kris. On the Iron Rails of the Orient: Train Journeys in Thailand, Cambodia, Vietnam & Tibet, 1 vol. 2008. (ENG.). 128p. 29.95 *(978-981-261-217-5(3))* Marshall Cavendish International (Asia) Private Ltd. SGP. Dist: Marshall Cavendish Corp.

London, Mkemo Zaire. Portrait of Asia. 2007. 72p. pap. 26.98 *(978-0-615-14834-2(4))* London, Mkemo.

Morelli, Marcello. Royal Palaces. 2008. (ENG & ITA., Illus.). 304p. 19.99 *(978-88-544-0046-7(7))* White Star ITA. Dist: Book Sales, Inc.

Murphy, Stephen. Connections: Portraits of Asia. 2007. (ENG., Illus.). 96p. 29.95 *(978-0-9793314-1-1(2)*, Imago) LawyersWriting.

Oba, Yoshiyuki, ed. Heroes & Heroines. 2012. (ENG., Illus.). 208p. pap. 29.95 ***(978-4-7562-4169-6(7))*** Rizzoli International Pubns., Inc.

Oertel, F.O. Note on a Tour in Burma in March & April 1892. 2006. (Itineraria Asiatica: Burma Ser.). (ENG., Illus.). pap. 20.00 *(978-974-8299-73-0(2))* Orchid Pr. THA. Dist: National Bk. Network.

Oppenheim, Felix. Reflections. 2008. 120p. pap. 35.00 *(978-0-9792451-6-9(8))* White River Pr.

Paul, Delia. The Living Mekong. 2009. (ENG., Illus.). 156p. 35.00 *(978-974-9511-67-1(0))* Silkworm Bks. THA. Dist: Univ. of Washington Pr.

Reiter, Christiane. Asia. Taschen, Angelika, ed. 25th ed. 2009. (FRE, GER & ENG., Illus.). 360p. pap. 19.99 *(978-3-8365-1481-1(8))* TASCHEN DEU. Dist: Ingram Pub. Services.

Roberts, Fredric & Roberts, Frederic. Humanitas II: The People of Gujarat. 2007. (ENG., Illus.). 158p. 60.00 *(978-0-7892-0949-8(7))* Abbeville Pr., Inc.

Sethi, Sunil. Inside Asia Box: 25 Jahre TASCHEN, 2 vols. 2011. (25 Ser.). (ENG., Illus.). 840p. 59.99 ***(978-3-8365-3176-4(3))*** TASCHEN DEU. Dist: Ingram Pub. Services.

Suvanto, Mari. Images of Japan & the Japanese. 2008. 140p. pap. *(978-3-639-08571-6(X))* VDM Verlag Dr. Mueller e.K.

van Ham, Peter & Van Ham, Peter. Indiens Tibet - Tibets Indien: Das kulturelle Vermächtnis des West-Himalaja. Begleit-Ausstellungen: St. Gallen 05.09.2009-18.04.2010 Historisches und Völkerkundemuseum. 2009. (GER., Illus.). 240p. (C). 72.00 *(978-3-7774-2221-3(5))* Hirmer Verlag GmbH DEU. Dist: Brown, David Bk. Co., The.

Wardale, David & Haslbeck, Gunther. Steam on 4 Continents: Asia, Vol. 3. (GER & ENG., Illus.). 128p. 34.95 *(978-3-925314-02-5(4))* Arnoldsche Art Pubs. DEU. Dist: Antique Collectors' Club.

ASIA—POLITICS AND GOVERNMENT

see also Afro-Asian Politics

Abhyankar, Rajendra M., ed. West Asia & the Region: Defining India's Role. 2009. (ENG.). 760p. 89.95 *(978-81-7188-616-6(7))* Academic Foundation IND. Dist: Independent Pubs. Group.

Acharya, Amitav. Asia Rising: Who Is Leading? 2008. 191p. pap. 37.00 *(978-981-277-133-9(6))* World Scientific Publishing Co., Inc.

—Whose Ideas Matter? Agency & Power in Asian Regionalism. 2011. (Cornell Studies in Political Economy Ser.). (Illus.). 200p. pap. 21.95 *(978-0-8014-7708-9(5))* Cornell Univ. Pr.

Ali, S. Mahmud. Asia-Pacific Security Dynamics in the Obama Era: A New World Emerging. 2011. (Politics in Asia Ser.). (ENG., Illus.). 240p. (C). 125.00 *(978-0-415-67054-8(3))* Routledge.

Amineh, M. Parvizi, ed. State, Society & International Relations in Asia. 2010. (ICAS Publications Ser.). (Illus.). 307p. pap. *(978-90-5356-794-4(1))* Amsterdam Univ. Pr.

Antje, Flachter & Richter, Susan, eds. Structures on the Move: Technologies of Governance in Transcultural Encounters between Asia & Europe (16th-20th Century) 2011. (Transcultural Research ndash; Heidelberg Studies on Asia & Europe in a Global Context Ser.). 400p. 179.00 *(978-3-642-19287-6(4)*, 3642192874) Springer.

Antons, Christoph & Gessner, Volkmar, eds. Globalisation & Resistance: Law Reform in Asia since the Crisis. 2007. (ENG.). 316p. (C). 48.00 *(978-1-84113-681-3(6))*; 100.00 *(978-1-84113-680-6(8))* Hart Publishing Ltd. GBR. Dist: International Specialized Bk. Services.

Anttiroiko, A-V., et al, eds. Innovative Trends in Public Governance in Asia. 2011. (Innovation & the Public Sector Ser.). (Illus.). 252p. E-Book 170.00 ***(978-1-60750-729-1(3))*** IOS Pr., Inc.

Anttiroiko, Ari-Veikko, et al. Innovative Trends in Public Governance in Asia. 2011. (Illus.). 252p. 170.00 ***(978-1-60750-728-4(5))*** IOS Pr., Inc.

Armstrong, Shiro, ed. The Politics & the Economics of Integration in Asia & the Pacific. 2011. (PAFTAD (Pacific Trade & Development Conference Series) Ser.). (ENG., Illus.). 232p. 125.00 ***(978-0-415-69042-3(0))*** Routledge.

Asia Business & Political Handbook: Companies-Products-Services. (Illus.). 600p. (Orig.). pap. 2400.00 *(978-0-7605-1337-8(6))* Rector Pr., Ltd.

Asia Foundation Staff, contrib. by. America's Role in Asia: Asian & American Views: Recommendations for U.S. Policy from Both Sides of the Pacific. 2008. vii, 310p. *(978-1-892325-08-2(X))* Asia Foundation, The.

Aspalter, Christian, et al, eds. Health Care Systems in Asia & Europe. 2011. (Routledge Studies in Social Welfare in Asia Ser.). (ENG., Illus.). 216p. (C). 145.00 *(978-0-415-67168-2(X))* Routledge.

Ayaz, Aazar & Fleschenberg, Andrea, eds. The Gender Face of Asian Politics. 2009. (ENG., Illus.). 350p. 24.95 *(978-0-19-547516-6(X))* Oxford Univ. Pr., Inc.

Aydin, Cemil. The Politics of Anti-Westernism in Asia: Visions of World Order in Pan-Islamic & Pan-Asian Thought. annot. ed. 2007. (Columbia Studies in International & Global History Ser.). (ENG.). 320p. (gr. 17). 40.00 *(978-0-231-13778-2(8))* Columbia Univ. Pr.

Bagshaw, Dale. Mediation in the Asia-Pacific Region: Transforming Conflicts & Building Peace. Bagshaw, Dale & Porter, Elisabeth, eds. 2009. (Routledge Advances in International Relations & Global Politics Ser.). (ENG.). 240p. 128.00 *(978-0-415-48967-6(9))* Routledge.

Behuria, Ashok K. & Sisodia, N. S., eds. West Asia in Turmoil: Implications for Global Security. 2007. (ENG., Illus.). 480p. 69.95 *(978-81-7188-626-5(4))* Academic Foundation IND. Dist: Independent Pubs. Group.

Bercovitch, Jacob & Oishi, Mikio. International Conflict in the Asia-Pacific: Patterns, Consequences & Management. 2012. (ENG., Illus.). 224p. (C). pap. 39.95 ***(978-0-415-53261-7(2))*** Routledge.

—International Conflict in the Asia-Pacific: Patterns, Consequences & Management. 2010. (Routledge Global Security Studies). (ENG., Illus.). 224p. (C). 130.00 *(978-0-415-58004-5(8)*, Routledge) Taylor & Francis Group GBR. Dist: Taylor & Francis Group.

Bertrand, Jacques & Laliberte, Andre, eds. Multination States in Asia: Accommodation or Resistance. 2010. (ENG., Illus.). 352p. 95.00 *(978-0-521-19434-1(2))*; pap. 32.99 *(978-0-521-14363-9(2))* Cambridge Univ. Pr.

Biswas, Asit K. & Tortajada, Cecilia, eds. Asian Perspectives on Water Policy. 2012. (ENG., Illus.). 192p. (C). 125.00 ***(978-0-415-69726-2(3))*** Routledge.

Blondel, Jean & Inoguchi, Takashi. Political Cultures in Asia & Europe: Citizens, States & Societal Values. 2006. (Politics in Asia Ser.). (Illus.). 189p. 160.00 *(978-0-415-40415-0(0))* Routledge.

Blum, Isa. Chaos in Yemen: Societal Collapse & the New Authoritarianism. 2012. (ENG., Illus.). 208p. (C). pap. 42.95 ***(978-0-415-62575-3(0))*** Routledge.

Bowonwatthana, Phitthaya & Wescott, Clay, eds. Comparative Governance Reform in Asia: Democracy, Corruption, & Government Trust. 2008. (Research in Public Policy Analysis Ser.). (Illus.). 253p. 99.95 *(978-1-84663-996-8(4))* Emerald Group Publishing Ltd. GBR. Dist: Turpin Distribution Services Ltd.

Boyd, Richard & Ngo, Tak-Wing, eds. State Making in Asia. 2009. 208p. pap. 39.95 *(978-0-415-54681-2(8))* Routledge.

Bradshaw, Michael J., et al. Natural Gas in Asia: The Challenges of Growth in China, India, Japan & Korea. Stern, Jonathan, ed. 2008. (ENG., Illus.). 432p. 125.00 *(978-0-19-954141-6(8))* Oxford Univ. Pr., Inc.

Bridges, Brian & Ho, Lok-Sang. Public Governance in Asia & the Limits of Electoral Democracy. Bridges, Brian & Ho, Lok-Sang, eds. 2010. 320p. 140.00 *(978-1-84844-628-1(4))* Elgar, Edward Publishing, Inc.

Burke, Anthony. Critical Security in the Asia-Pacific. McDonald, Matt, ed. 2007. (New Approaches to Conflict Analysis Ser.). (ENG.). 320p. 94.00 *(978-0-7190-7304-5(9))* Manchester Univ. Pr. GBR. Dist: Macmillan.

Burke, Anthony & McDonald, Matt, eds. Critical Security in the Asia-Pacific. 2007. (New Approaches to Conflict Analysis Ser.). (ENG.). 320p. pap. 31.00 *(978-0-7190-7305-2(7))* Manchester Univ. Pr. GBR. Dist: Macmillan.

Calichman, Richard & Kim, John Namjun, eds. The Politics of Culture: Around the Work of Naoki Sakai. 2010. (Routledge/Leiden Series in Modern East Asian History & Politics Ser.). (ENG.). 272p. (C). 138.00 *(978-0-415-56216-4(3))* Routledge.

Carlson, Matthew & Inoguchi, Takashi, eds. Governance & Democracy in Asia. 2006. 201p. 79.95 *(978-1-876843-37-3(3))*; pap. 34.95 *(978-1-876843-38-0(1))* Trans Pacific Pr. AUS. Dist: International Specialized Bk. Services.

Chatterji, Joya & Washbrook, David, eds. Handbook of the South Asian Diaspora. 2012. (ENG., Illus.). 464p. (C). 175.00 *(978-0-415-48010-9(8))* Routledge.

Cheema, G. Shabbir, et al, eds. Cross-Border Governance in Asia: Regional Issues & Mechanisms. 2011. (ENG.). 300p. pap. 35.00

(978-92-808-1193-3(2)) United Nations Univ. Pr. JPN. Dist: Brookings Institution Pr.

Cheema, G. Shabbir & Popovski, Vesselin, eds. Building Trust in Government: Innovations in Governance Reform in Asia. 2010. (ENG., Illus.). 296p. pap. 35.00 (978-92-808-1189-6(4)) United Nations Univ. Pr. JPN. Dist: Brookings Institution Pr.

Chellaney, Brahma. Water: Asia's New Battleground. 2011. (Illus.). 400p. 29.95 (978-1-58901-771-9(4)) Georgetown Univ. Pr.

Chin, Felix. Asian Economic & Political Developments. 2011. (Series: Asian Political, Economic & Security Issues Ser.). 295.00 (978-1-61122-470-2(5)) Nova Science Pubs., Inc.

Chin, Felix, ed. Political & Economic Developments in Asia. 2011. (Asian Political, Economic & Security Issues Ser.). 309p. 129.00 (978-1-61209-783-1(9)) Nova Science Pubs., Inc.

Chin, Felix, ed. Politics & Economics of Northern & Western Asia. 2011. (Asian Political, Economic & Security Issues Ser.). 185.00 **(978-1-61470-460-7(0))** Nova Science Pubs., Inc.

Choi, Jungug. Governments & Markets in East Asia: The Politics of Economic Crises. 2006. (Routledge Malaysian Studies: Vol. 3). (Illus.). 140p. 160.00 (978-0-415-39902-9(5)) Routledge.

Choi, Jungug. Votes, Party Systems & Democracy in Asia. 2012. (Politics in Asia Ser.). (ENG., Illus.). 192p. (C). 145.00 **(978-0-415-69069-0(2))** Routledge.

Chong, Terence, ed. Globalization & Its Counter-Forces in Southeast Asi. 2008. 432p. (978-981-230-488-9(6)) Institute of Southeast Asian Studies.

Chouvy, Pierre-Arnaud. Opium: Uncovering the Politics of the Poppy. 2010. (Illus.). 272p. 27.95 (978-0-674-05134-8(3)) Harvard Univ. Pr.

Chowdhury. Handbook on the Asian Economies - Southeast Asia & Northeast Asia. 2007. (Elgar Original Reference Ser.). 352p. (C). 210.00 (978-1-84376-989-7(1)) Elgar, Edward Publishing, Inc.

Collet, Christian & Lien, Pei-Te, eds. The Transnational Politics of Asian Americans. 2009. (Asian American History & Culture Ser.). (ENG., Illus.). 252p. 76.50 (978-1-59213-860-9(8)); pap. 30.95 (978-1-59213-861-6(6)) Temple Univ. Pr.

Columbus, Alexandra M. Asian Economic & Political Issues. 2011. (Series: Asian Economic & Political Issues Ser.). 238p. 185.00 (978-1-61324-239-1(5)) Nova Science Pubs., Inc.

Columbus, Frank, ed. Asian Economic & Political Issues, Volume 13. 2010. (Asian Economic & Political Issues Ser.). 89.00 (978-1-61668-015-2(6)) Nova Science Pubs., Inc.

Cook, Sarah & Kabeer, Naila, eds. Social Protection as Development Policy. 2010. (ENG.). 396p. (C). 95.00 (978-0-415-58573-6(2), Routledge India) Taylor & Francis Group GBR. Dist: Taylor & Francis Group.

Corr, Kendra. The U. S. & W. W. I: I Think: U. S. History. 2011. (ENG.). 100p. (YA). pap. 29.95 (978-1-933558-17-2(2)) InspirEd Educators.

Cox, Dan G., et al. Terrorism, Instability, & Democracy in Asia & Africa. 2009. (Northeastern Series on Democratization & Political Development Ser.). (Illus.). (ENG.) 244p. (C). lib. bdg. 60.00 (978-1-55553-705-0(7)); 240p. (C). lib. bdg. 65.00 (978-1-58465-753-8(7)); (ENG., 240p. pap. 21.95 (978-1-58465-754-5(5)) Univ. Pr. of New England. (Northeastern University Pr.).

Crisis in Kyrgyzstan: Fuel, Contracts, & Revolution along the Afghan Supply Chain: Hearing Before the Subcommittee on National Security & Foreign Affairs of the Committee on Oversight & Government Reform, House of Representatives, One Hundred Eleventh Congress, Second Session, April 22, 2010. 2011. iii, 79p. **(978-0-16-089068-0(3)**, 552-070-43100-4) United States Government Printing Office.

Crump, Thomas. Asia-Pacific: A History of Empire & Conflict. 2008. (ENG., Illus.). 400p. 29.95 (978-1-84725-222-7(2), Hambledon Continuum) Continuum International Publishing Group, Ltd. GBR. Dist: National Bk. Network.

Cummings, Sally N. Domestic & International Perspectives on Kyrgyzstan's 'Tulip Re: Motives, Mobilization & Meanings. 2009. (ThirdWorlds Ser.). (ENG., Illus.). 176p. (C). 133.00 (978-0-415-49190-7(8)) Routledge.

Daniere, Amrita. The Politics of Civic Space in Asia: Building Urban Communities. Douglass, Mike, ed. 2008. (Illus.). XVI, 240p. 160.00 (978-0-415-46460-4(9)) Routledge.

Danzan Narantuya & Danzan, Narantuya. Religion in 20th Century Mongolia: Social Changes & Popular Practices. 2008. 168p. pap. (978-3-639-09465-7(4)) VDM Verlag Dr. Mueller e.K.

de Sales Marques, José Luis, et al, eds. Asia & Europe: Dynamics of Inter- & Intra-Regional Dialogues. 2009. 441p. pap. 86.00 (978-3-8329-3960-1(1)) Nomos Verlagsgesellschaft DEU. Dist: International Specialized Bk. Services.

DeKrey, Steve. Learning from Leaders in Asia: The Lessons of Experience. 2010. (ENG., Illus.). 256p. pap. 27.95 (978-0-470-82509-9(X), Wiley) Wiley, John & Sons, Inc.

Dieter, Heribert, ed. The Evolution of Regionalism in Asia: Economic & Security Issues. 2011. (ENG., Illus.). 224p. pap. 42.95 **(978-0-415-66400-4(4))** Routledge.

Dosch, Jorn, et al. The New Global Politics of the Asia Pacific. 2nd rev. ed. 2011. (ENG., Illus.). 288p. (C). pap. 42.95 (978-0-415-46497-0(8)) Routledge.

Doyle, Randall. Roots of War in the 21st Century: Geography, Hegemony, & Politics in Asia-Pacific. 2009. (ENG.). 170p. pap. 28.50 (978-0-7618-4630-7(1)) Univ. Pr. of America, Inc.

—The Roots of War in the 21st Century: Geography, Hegemony, & Politics in Asia-Pacific. 2009. (ENG.). 170p. 52.50 (978-0-7618-4629-1(8)) Univ. Pr. of America, Inc.

Dressel, Bjö, ed. The Judicialization of Politics in Asia. 2012. (Routledge Law in Asia Ser.). (ENG., Illus.). 240p. (C). 150.00 (978-0-415-67410-2(7)) Routledge.

Emirates Center for Strategic Studies and Research Staff & Tauris, I. B. China, India & the United States: Competition for Energy Resources. 2009. (ENG., Illus.). 612p. pap. 51.00 (978-9948-00-929-0(0), Emirates Center for Strategic Studies) I. B. Tauris & Co., Ltd. GBR. Dist: Macmillan.

—China, India & the United States: Competition for Energy Resources. 2009. (ENG., Illus.). 612p. 102.00 (978-9948-00-930-6(4), Emirates Center for Strategic Studies) I. B. Tauris & Co., Ltd. GBR. Dist: Macmillan.

Empson, Rebecca M. Harnessing Fortune: Personhood, Memory & Place in Northeast Mongolia. 2011. (ENG., Illus.). 398p. 115.00 (978-0-19-726473-7(5)) Oxford Univ. Pr., Inc.

Er. The Rise of China & India. 2009. viii, 169p. 90.00 (978-981-4280-33-4(X)) World Scientific Publishing Co., Inc.

Fernandes, Clinton. The Independence of East Timor: Multi-Dimensional Perspectives - Occupation, Resistance, & International Political Activism. 2011. 274p. pap. 34.95 **(978-1-84519-491-8(8))**; (ENG.). 240p. 69.95 (978-1-84519-428-4(4)) Sussex Academic Pr. GBR. Dist: International Specialized Bk. Services.

Fernandes, Clinton, ed. Hot Spot: Asia & Oceania, 1 vol. 2008. (Hot Spot Histories Ser.). (Illus.). 328p. 65.00 (978-0-313-35412-0(X), GR5412, Greenwood Pr.) Greenwood Publishing Group, Inc.

Fong, Jack. Revolution As Development: The Karen Self-Determination Struggle Against Ethnocracy from 1949-2004. 2008. 376p. pap. (978-1-59942-994-6(2)) Universal Pubs.

Fornari, Emanuela. Modernity Out of Joint: Democracy & Asian Values in Jürgen Habermas & Amartya K. Sen. 2007.Tr. of Modernità Fuori Luogo. (ENG.). 230p. pap. 24.00 (978-1-888570-39-7(3)) Davies Group Pubs., The.

Freeman, Charles W., 3rd & Goodman, Matthew. Crafting U. S. Economic Strategy toward Asia: Lessons Learned from 30 Years of Experience. 2008. 44p. pap. 14.95 (978-0-89206-554-7(0), CSIS Pr., The) Ctr. for Strategic & International Studies.

Frost, Ellen L. Asia's New Regionalism. 2008. 275p. (C). pap. 25.00 (978-1-58826-579-1(X)); lib. bdg. 65.00 (978-1-58826-554-8(4)) Rienner, Lynne Pubs.

Gadzhiev, K. S. "Bolshaia Igra" Na Kavkaze: Vchera, Segodnia, Zavtra. 2010. 339p. (978-5-7133-1366-1(2)) Mezhdunarodnye Otnosheniya.

Ganguly, Sumit. Handbook of Asian Security Studies. 2010. (ENG., Illus.). 336p. 210.00 (978-0-415-77781-0(X)) Routledge.

Ganguly, Sumit & Thompson, William, eds. Asian Rivalries: Conflict, Escalation, & Limitations on Two-Level Games. 2011. (ENG., Illus.). 272p. 80.00 (978-0-8047-7595-3(8)) Stanford Univ. Pr.

Ganguly, Sumit & Thompson, William R. Asian Rivalries: Conflict, Escalation, & Limitations on Two-Level Games. 2011. (ENG., Illus.). 272p. pap. 24.95 (978-0-8047-7596-0(6)) Stanford Univ. Pr.

Ghosh, Lipi. Minorities, Community Rights & Political Governance: South & South-East Asian Scenario. 2009. (ENG., Illus.). xlii, 349p. (C). 110.00 (978-0-415-55071-0(8), Routledge India) Taylor & Francis Group GBR. Dist: Taylor & Francis Group.

Ginsburg, Tom. Administrative Law & Governance in Asia: Comparative Perspectives. Chen, Albert H. Y., ed. 2008. (Routledge Law in Asia Ser.). (ENG., Illus.). 400p. (C). 190.00 (978-0-415-77683-7(X)) Routledge.

Gong, Ting & Ma, Stephen K. Preventing Corruption in Asia: Institutional Design & Policy Capacity. Gong, Ting & Ma, Stephen K., eds. 2009. (Routledge Contemporary Asia Ser.). (ENG., Illus.). 250p. 150.00 (978-0-415-48408-4(1)) Routledge.

Goodall, et al. Water, Sovereignty & Borders in Asia & Oceania. 2008. (Routledge Studies in Physical Geography & Environment Ser.). (Illus.). 240p. 170.00 (978-0-415-43726-4(1)) Routledge.

Guo, Rongxing. The Land & Maritime Boundary Disputes of Asia. 2009. (Asian Political, Economic, & Security Issues Ser.). pap. 89.00 (978-1-60741-629-6(8)) Nova Science Pubs., Inc.

Gupta, Amit, ed. Strategic Stability in Asia. 2008. 184p. 114.95 (978-0-7546-7243-2(3)) Ashgate Publishing Co.

Haacke, Jürgen. Cooperative Security in the Asia-Pacific: The ASEAN Regional Forum. Morada, Noel M., ed. 2009. (Asian Security Studies). (ENG.). 288p. 130.00 (978-0-415-46052-1(2)) Routledge.

Haan, Arjan de. Towards a New Poverty Agenda in Asia: Social Policies & Economic Transformation. 2010. (Illus.). 284p. (C). 39.95 (978-81-321-0504-6(4), B05046C) SAGE Pubns., Inc.

Harris, VanDra & Goldsmith, Andrew John, eds. Security, Development & Nation-Building in Timor-Leste: A Cross-Sectoral Assessment. 2011. (Routledge Contemporary Southeast Asia Ser.). (ENG., Illus.). 288p. (C). 140.00 (978-0-415-60124-5(X)) Routledge.

Hasan, Samiul & Onyx, Jenny. Comparative Third Sector Governance in Asia: Structure, Process, & Political Economy. Hasan, Samiul & Onyx, Jenny, eds. 2008. (Nonprofit & Civil Society Studies). (Illus.). XIV, 341p. (C). 119.00 (978-0-387-75566-3(7), 0387755667) Springer.

He, Baogang. Political Parties & Democracy Vol. 3: Post-Soviet & Asian Political Parties. Lawson, Kay & Kulik, Anatoly, eds. 2010. (Political Parties in Context Ser.). (Illus.). 299p. 44.95 (978-0-313-38060-0(0), A2218C, Praeger Pubs.) Greenwood Publishing Group, Inc.

He, Baogang, et al, eds. Federalism in Asia. 352p. 2009. pap. 58.00 (978-1-84844-798-1(1)) 2007. (C). 150.00 (978-1-84720-140-9(7)) Elgar, Edward Publishing, Inc.

Heng, Siam-Heng Michael & Ten, Chin Liew. State & Secularism: Perspectives from Asia. 2009. 300p. 94.00 (978-981-4282-37-6(5)) World Scientific Publishing Co., Inc.

Heo, Seunghoon Emilia. Reconciling Enemy States in Europe & Asia. 2012. (International Relations & Development Ser.). (ENG., Illus.). 208p. 85.00 **(978-0-230-29543-8(6))** Palgrave Macmillan.

Hesse, Joachim, et al, eds. The Public Sector in Transition: East Asia & European Union Compared. 2008. 372p. pap. 61.00 (978-3-8329-3302-9(6)) Nomos Verlagsgesellschaft DEU. Dist: International Specialized Bk. Services.

Hua, Shiping. Islam & Democratization in Asia. 2009. (978-1-60497-632-8(2)) Cambria Pr.

Ishkanian, Armine. Democracy Building & Civil Society in Post-Soviet Armenia. 2008. (Routledge Contemporary Russia & Eastern Europe Ser.). (ENG.). 216p. (C). 160.00 (978-0-415-43601-4(X)) Routledge.

Jaffrelot, Christophe & Gayer, Lauren, eds. Armed Militias of South Asia: Fundamentalists, Maoists, & Separatists. 2009. (Columbia/Hurst Ser.). (ENG.). 356p. (gr. 17). 45.00 (978-0-231-70110-5(1)) Columbia Univ. Pr.

Jarvis, Darryl. ASEAN Industries & the Challenge from China: The Dragon & Tiger Cubs. Welch, Anthony, ed. 2011. (ENG., Illus.). 272p. 90.00 (978-0-230-54234-1(4)) Palgrave Macmillan.

Jayasuriya. Asian Regional Governance: Crisis & Change. 2008. pap. 39.95 (978-0-415-47011-7(0)) Routledge.

Jeffries, Ian. Mongolia: A Guide to Economic & Political Developments. 2012. (Guides to Economic & Political Developments in Asia Ser.). (ENG., Illus.). 224p. (C). pap. 42.95 **(978-0-415-54174-9(3))** Routledge.

Kane, John, et al, eds. Dissident Democrats: The Challenge of Democratic Leadership in Asia. 2008. (Palgrave Series in Asian Governance Ser.). (ENG.). 324p. 100.00 (978-0-230-60266-3(5)) Palgrave Macmillan.

Katsiaficas, George. Asia's Unknown Uprisings Volume 2: People Power in the Philippines, Burma, Tibet, China, Taiwan, Bangladesh, Nepal, Thailand & Indonesia 1947-2009. 2nd ed. 2012. (ENG., Illus.). 400p. pap. 26.95 **(978-1-60486-488-5(5))** PM Pr.

Katsumata, Hiro. Asean's Cooperative Security Enterprise: Norms & Interests in the ASEAN Regional Forum. 2010. (Critical Studies of the Asia-Pacific Ser.). (ENG., Illus.). 240p. 89.00 (978-0-230-22929-7(8)) Palgrave Macmillan.

Kawai, M., et al, eds. Implications of the Global Financial Crisis for Financial Reform & Regulation in Asia. 2012. 304p. 125.00 **(978-0-85793-471-0(6))** Elgar, Edward Publishing, Inc.

Khan, Tahira S. Beyond Honour: A Historical Materialist Explanation of Honour Related Violence. 2006. (ENG.). 384p. 55.00 (978-0-19-597902-2(8)) Oxford Univ. Pr., Inc.

Kim, Nam-Kook. Globalization & Regional Integration in Europe & Asia. 2009. (Illus.). 196p. 114.95 (978-0-7546-7613-3(7)) Ashgate Publishing Co.

Krieger, Heike, ed. East Timor & the International Community: Basic Documents. 2011. (Cambridge International Documents Ser.). (ENG.). 524p. pap. 90.00 (978-0-521-39979-1(3)) Cambridge Univ. Pr.

Kyrgyzstan's Revolution: Causes & Consequences: Hearing Before the Commission on Security & Cooperation in Europe, One Hundred Ninth Congress, First Session, April 7, 2005. 2007. iii, 44p. (978-0-16-078436-1(0), 552-070-35727-1) United States Government Printing Office.

Laine, Arthur T. Economic, Political & Social Issues of the Caucasus Region. 2011. (Series: Caucasus Region Political, Economic, & Security Issues Ser.). 129.00 (978-1-61122-553-2(1)) Nova Science Pubs., Inc.

Lam. Japan's Peace Building Diplomacy in Asia. 2009. (Routledge Security in Asia Pacific Ser.). (ENG., Illus.). 192p. (C). 150.00 (978-0-415-41320-6(6)) Routledge.

Loy, Hui-Chieh, et al, eds. Political Legitimacy in Asia: New Leadership Challenges. 2011. (Palgrave Series on Asian Goverance Ser.). (ENG., Illus.). 304p. 90.00 **(978-0-230-33753-4(8))** Palgrave Macmillan.

Lye, Liang Fook & Hofmeister, Wilhelm, eds. Parliaments in Asia: Institution Building & Political Development. 2012. (Politics in Asia Ser.). (ENG.). 256p. (C). 140.00 (978-0-415-68158-2(8)) Routledge.

Macauslan, Robert. Air Pollution Policy in Singapore, Dalian, & Hong Kong: Contemporary Case Studies Examining the Role of Political Will in Policy Development & Enforcement. 2008. 92p. pap. (978-3-639-10307-6(6)) VDM Verlag Dr. Mueller e.K.

Marek, David A., ed. Asian Economic & Political Issues. Volume 14. 2009. (Asian Economic & Political Issues Ser.). (Illus.). 267p. 103.50 (978-1-61728-019-1(4)) Nova Science Pubs., Inc.

McDougall, Derek. Asia Pacific in World Politics. 2006. (Illus.). 325p. (C). pap. 24.50 (978-1-58826-170-0(0)); lib. bdg. 59.95 (978-1-58826-194-6(8)) Rienner, Lynne Pubs.

McGrath, Conor. Interest Groups & Lobbying in Latin America, Africa, the Middle East, & Asia: Essays on Drug Trafficking, Chemical Manufacture, Exchange Rates, & Women's Interests. McGrath, Conor, ed. 2009.Tr. of Essays on Drug Trafficking, Chemical Manufacture, Exchange Rates, & Women's Interests. (Illus.). 432p. 129.95 (978-0-7734-4694-6(X)) Mellen, Edwin Pr., The.

Michael Hsiao, Hsin-Huang, ed. Democracy or Alternative Political Systems in Asia: After the Strongmen. 2013. (Routledge Contemporary Asia Ser.). (ENG.). 240p. (C). 125.00 (978-0-415-67725-7(4)) Routledge.

Midgley, James & Mitsuhiko, Hosaka, eds. Grassroots Social Security in Asia: Mutual Associations, Microinsurance & Social Welfare. 2011. (Routledge Research on Public & Social Policy in Asia Ser.). (ENG., Illus.). 176p. (C). 133.00 (978-0-415-49306-2(4)) Routledge.

Miller, Alice Lyman & Wich, Richard. Becoming Asia: Change & Continuity in Asian International Relations since World War II. 2011. (ENG., Illus.). 336p. 80.00 (978-0-8047-7150-4(2)); pap. 29.95 (978-0-8047-7151-1(0)) Stanford Univ. Pr.

Mishra, Pankaj. The Revolt Against the West: The Rise of Asia & the Remaking of the Modern World. 2012. (ENG., Illus.). 320p. 27.00 **(978-0-374-24959-5(8))** Farrar, Straus & Giroux.

Morozova, Irina Y. Socialist Revolutions in Asia: The Social History of Mongolia in the 20th Century. 2012. (ENG., Illus.). 172p. (C). pap. 42.95 **(978-0-415-62748-1(6))** Routledge.

Moyo, Sam & Yeros, Paris, eds. Reclaiming the Nation: The Return of the National Question in Africa, Asia & Latin America, 1 vol. 2011. (ENG., Illus.). 288p. 38.00 (978-0-7453-3082-2(7)); lib. bdg. 115.00 (978-0-7453-3083-9(5)) Pluto Pr. GBR. Dist: Macmillan.

Murzaeva, Dinara. Transition to Democracy in Post-Soviet Kyrgyzstan. 2011. 360p. pap. **(978-3-8454-0065-5(X))** Lambert Academic Publishing.

Nick, Bisley. Building Asias Security. 2010. (Adelphi Ser.). (Illus.). 159p. pap. 19.95 (978-0-415-58266-7(0), Routledge) Taylor & Francis Group GBR. Dist: Taylor & Francis Group.

Oga, Toru. Discourses on Asianisation: The Asian Financial Crisis & Rediscovering Asianness. 2008. 308p. pap. (978-3-639-09294-3(5)) VDM Verlag Dr. Mueller e.K.

Organisation for Economic Co-operation and Development Staff. Enforcement of Corporate Governance in Asia: The Unfinished Agenda. 2009. 120p. pap. 63.00 (978-92-64-03550-8(8)) Organization for Economic Cooperation & Development.

Overholt, William H. Asia & America: The Coming Transformation of Asian Geopolitcs. 2007. (Illus.). xl, 322p. pap. (978-0-8330-4175-3(4)) RAND Corp., The.

Panikkar, K. M. The Afro-Asian States & their Problems. 2011. (ENG.). 128p. 90.00 (978-0-415-60141-2(X)) Routledge.

Pedersen, Morten Axel. Not Quite Shamans: Spirit Worlds & Political Lives in Northern Mongolia. 2011. (Culture & Society after Socialism Ser.). (Illus.). 272p. 69.95 (978-0-8014-4910-9(3)); pap. 28.95 (978-0-8014-7620-4(8)) Cornell Univ. Pr.

Pempel, T. J., et al, eds. Political Economy of Northeast Asian Regionalism: Political Conflict & Economic Integration. 2008. (Illus.). 192p. 119.00 (978-1-84720-891-0(6)) Elgar, Edward Publishing, Inc.

Petersen, Alexandros. The World Island: Eurasian Geopolitics & the Fate of the West, 1 vol. 2011. (Praeger Security International Ser.). 176p. (Illus.). 34.95 (978-0-313-39137-8(8), A3189C); E-Book (978-0-313-39138-5(6)) Greenwood Publishing Group, Inc. (Praeger Pubs.).

Pike, Francis. Empires at War: A Short History of Modern Asia since World War II. 2011. (ENG.). 896p. pap. 32.00 (978-1-84885-865-7(5)) I. B. Tauris & Co., Ltd. GBR. Dist: Macmillan.

Quah, Jon S. T. Combating Corruption Singapore-Style: Lessons for Other Asian Countries. 2007. 56p. (978-1-932330-19-9(4)) Maryland Series in Contemporary Studies.

Quah, Stella R. Crisis Preparedness: Asia & the Global Governance of Epidemics. 2007. (ENG., Illus.). 165p. per. 24.95 (978-1-931368-09-4(0)) Shorenstein, Walter H. Asia-Pacific Research Ctr.

Radu, Michael. Islamism & Terrorist Groups in Asia. (Major Muslim Nations Ser.). (YA). 2010. 112p. (gr. 5-18). lib. bdg. 25.95 (978-1-4222-1404-6(4)) 2008. pap. 14.95 (978-1-4222-1434-3(6)) Mason Crest Pubs.

Ramesh, M. & Fritzen, Scott. Transforming Asian Governance: Rethinking Assumptions, Challenging Practices. Fritzen, Scott, ed. 2009. (Routledge Research on Public & Social Policy in Asia Ser.). (ENG., Illus.). 256p. (C). 158.00 (978-0-415-47478-8(7)) Routledge.

Reiter, Erich & Hazdra, Peter, eds. The Impact of Asian Powers on Global Developments. 2010. (ENG., Illus.). xii, 209p. pap. 104.00 (978-3-7908-2454-4(2), 3790824542) Physica-Verlag DEU. Dist: Springer.

Rodan, Garry & Hewison, Kevin, eds. Neoliberalism & Conflict in Asia After 9/11. 2009. 254p. pap. 39.95 (978-0-415-56839-5(0)) Routledge.

Rossabi, Mary, tr. from MON. Herdsman to Statesman: The Autobiography of Jamsrangiin Sambuu of Mongolia. 2010. (ENG.). 168p. 75.00 (978-1-4422-0750-9(7)) Rowman & Littlefield Publishers, Inc.

Sadri, Houman A. The Caucasus States. 2010. (Global Security Watch Ser.). (Illus.). 270p. 49.95 (978-0-313-37980-2(7), A2036C, Praeger Pubs.) Greenwood Publishing Group, Inc.

Sambuu, Zh. Herdsman to Statesman: The Autobiography of Jamsrangiin Sambuu of Mongolia. 2010. 69.00 (978-1-4422-0752-3(3)) Rowman & Littlefield Publishers, Inc.

Sethi, Rumina. The Politics of Postcolonialism: Globalisation & the Nation-State, 1 vol. 2011. (ENG.). 216p. lib. bdg. 90.00 (978-0-7453-2364-0(2)) Pluto Pr. GBR. Dist: Macmillan.

Shambaugh, David & Yahuda, Michael. International Relations of Asia. 2008. (Asia in World Politics Ser.). (ENG., Illus.). 392p. pap. 39.95 (978-0-7425-5696-6(4)) Rowman & Littlefield Publishers, Inc.

—International Relations of Asia. 2008. (Asia in World Politics Ser.). (ENG., Illus.). 402p. 90.00 (978-0-7425-5695-9(6)) Rowman & Littlefield Publishers, Inc.

Sharma, Ashok, et al, eds. Asia 2050: Realizing the Asian Century. 2011. 412p. (C). 70.00 **(978-81-321-0756-9(X)**, B07569C) SAGE Pubns., Inc.

Shin, Gi-Wook & Sneider, Daniel C. Cross Currents: Regionalism & Nationalism in Northeast Asia. Shin, Gi-Wook & Sneider, Daniel C., eds. 2007. (ENG., Illus.). 312p. per. 24.95 (978-1-931368-10-0(4)) Shorenstein, Walter H. Asia-Pacific Research Ctr.

Shoup, Brian. Conflict & Cooperation in Multi-Ethnic States: Institutional Incentives, Myths & Counter-Balancing. 2007. (Asian Security Studies). (Illus.). 208p. 170.00 *(978-0-415-43391-4(6))* Routledge.

Singh, Bilveer. The Talibanization of Southeast Asia: Losing the War on Terror to Islamist Extremists, 1 vol. 2007. (Praeger Security International Ser.). (Illus.). 264p. 49.95 *(978-0-275-99995-7(5)*, C9995, Praeger Security International) Greenwood Publishing Group, Inc.

Sisodia, N. S., et al, eds. Proliferation & Emerging Nuclear Order in the Twenty-First Century. 2009. (ENG.). 122p. 34.95 *(978-81-7188-752-1(X))* Academic Foundation IND. Dist: Independent Pubs. Group.

Sleeboom, Margaret & Sleeboom-Faulkner, Margaret. Human Genetic Biobanks in Asia: Politics of Trust & Scientific Advancement. 2008. (Routledge Contemporary Asia Ser.). (ENG., Illus.). 224p. (C). 190.00 *(978-0-7103-1341-6(1))* Routledge.

Spiegel, Steven, ed. Conflict Management in the Middle East. (Illus.). 250p. *(978-1-85567-059-4(3)*, Burns & Oates) Continuum International Publishing Group, Ltd.

Stewart, Sarah & Curtis, Vesta Sarkhosh, eds. The Age of the Parthians. 2007. (Idea of Iran Ser.). (ENG., Illus.). 192p. 79.00 *(978-1-84511-406-0(X))* I. B. Tauris & Co., Ltd. GBR. Dist: Macmillan.

Strauss, Julia C. & O'Brien, Donal Cruise, eds. Staging Politics: Power & Performance in Asia & Africa. 2007. (International Library of Political Studies). (ENG., Illus.). 288p. 89.00 *(978-1-84511-367-4(5))* I. B. Tauris & Co., Ltd. GBR. Dist: Macmillan.

Tan, See Seng. The Role of Knowledge Communities in Constructing Asia-Pacific Security: How Thought & Talk Make War & Peace. 2006. 276p. 109.95 *(978-0-7734-5442-2(X))* Mellen, Edwin Pr., The.

Tarling, Nicholas. Corruption & Good Governance in Asia. 2009. 286p. pap. 39.95 *(978-0-415-54666-9(4))* Routledge.

Taylor, Robert H. The State in Myanmar. 2008. (C). pap. 28.00 *(978-0-8248-3362-6(7))* Univ. of Hawaii Pr.

Tellis, Ashley J., et al, eds. Strategic Asia 2008-09: Challenges & Choices. 2008. (Illus.). pap. 34.95 *(978-0-9713938-9-9(3))* National Bureau of Asian Research, The.

Tellis, Ashley J. & Wills, Michael, eds. Strategic Asia 2006-07: Trade, Interdependence, & Security. 2006. (Illus.). xiv, 423p. pap. 24.95 *(978-0-9713938-7-5(7))* National Bureau of Asian Research, The.

—Strategic Asia 2007-08: Domestic Political Change & Grand Strategy. 2007. (Strategic Asia Ser.). (Illus.). pap. 29.95 *(978-0-9713938-8-2(5))* National Bureau of Asian Research, The.

Tellis, Ashley J., et al. Strategic Asia 2011-12: Asia Responds to Its Rising Powers — China & India. Tellis, Ashley J. et al, eds. 2011. (Strategic Asia Ser.). (Illus.). pap. 34.95 ***(978-0-9818904-2-5(3))*** National Bureau of Asian Research, The.

Terao, Tadayoshi & Otsuka, Kenji, eds. Development of Environmental Policy in Japan & Asian Countries. 2007. (ENG.). 304p. 126.00 *(978-0-230-00470-2(9))* Palgrave Macmillan.

Thomas, Nicholas, ed. Governance & Regionalism in Asia. 2011. (Illus.). 368p. pap. 42.95 ***(978-0-415-66715-9(1))*** Routledge.

Thomas, Nicholas & Nicholas Thomas. Governance & Regionalism in Asia. Thomas, Nicholas, ed. 2009. (Politics in Asia Ser.). (Illus.). 368p. 160.00 *(978-0-415-45699-9(1))* Routledge.

Thornton, William H. & Thornton, Songok Han. Development Without Freedom: The Politics of Asian Globalization. 2008. 246p. 114.95 *(978-0-7546-7227-2(1))* Ashgate Publishing Co.

Till, Geoffrey, et al. Globalization & Defence in the Asia-Pacific: Arms Across Asia. Till, Geoffrey et al, eds. 2008. (Contemporary Security Studies). (ENG., Illus.). 288p. (C). 140.00 *(978-0-415-44048-6(3))* Routledge.

Tow, William T., ed. Security Politics in the Asia-Pacific: A Regional-Global Nexus? 2009. (ENG., Illus.). 386p. 108.00 *(978-0-521-76535-0(8))*; pap. 35.00 *(978-0-521-75882-6(3))* Cambridge Univ. Pr.

Trichur, Ganesh K., ed. Asia & the Transformation of the World-System. 2009. (Political Economy of the World-System Annuals Ser.). 176p. 125.00 *(978-1-59451-741-9(X))* Paradigm Pubs.

Tun, Sai Aung. History of the Shan State: From Its Origins To 1962. 2008. (ENG., Illus.). 680p. (C). pap. 52.00 ***(978-974-9511-43-5(3))*** Silkworm Bks. THA. Dist: Univ. of Washington Pr.

Ulziikhutag, Odgerel. E-Government Policy in Mongoli. 2011. 136p. pap. ***(978-3-8443-0931-7(4))*** Lambert Academic Publishing.

United Nations. Climate Change Action in Asia & the Pacific: Lessons Learned & Policy Implications - A Guide to Clean Development Mechanism Projects Related to Municipal Solid Waste Management. 2008. (ENG.). 52p. pap. 12.00 *(978-92-1-120529-9(8))* United Nations Pubns.

—Social Services Policies & Family Well-being in the Asian & Pacific Region. 2009. (ENG.). 124p. pap. 37.00 *(978-92-1-120570-1(0))* United Nations Pubns.

—Statistical Abstract of the ESCWA Region, 26th Issue. 2008. (MUL.). 260p. pap. 45.00 *(978-92-1-128308-2(6))* United Nations Pubns.

United States, Congress Senate Committee on Foreign Relations Subcommittee on East Asian and Pacific Affairs Staff, contrib. by. Asian Adoptions in the United States: Hearing Before the Subcommittee on East Asian & Pacific Affairs of the Committee on Foreign Relations, United States Senate, One Hundred Ninth Congress, Second Session, June 8, 2006. 2007. iii, 45p. *(978-0-16-078380-7(1)*, 552-070-35685-1) United States Government Printing Office.

Wade, Geoffrey, ed. Asian Expansions: The Historical Experiences of Polity Expansion in Asia. 2012. (Routledge Studies in the Early History of Asia Ser.). (ENG.). 256p. (C). 125.00 *(978-0-415-58995-6(9))* Routledge.

Warikoo, K., ed. Religion & Security in South & Central Asia. 2010. (Central Asia Research Forum Ser.). (ENG., Illus.). 232p. (C). 130.00 *(978-0-415-57590-4(7)*, Routledge) Taylor & Francis Group GBR. Dist: Taylor & Francis Group.

Wescott, Clay, et al, eds. The Many Faces of Public Management Reform in the Asia-Pacific Region. 2009. (Research in Public Policy Analysis Ser.). 392p. 144.95 *(978-1-84950-639-7(6))* Emerald Group Publishing Ltd. GBR. Dist: Turpin Distribution Services Ltd.

White, Lynn. Political Booms Vol. 16: Local Money & Power in Taiwan, East China, Thailand, & the Philippines. 2009. (Illus.). 748p. 84.00 *(978-981-283-681-6(0))*; pap. 48.00 *(978-981-283-682-3(9))* World Scientific Publishing Co., Inc.

Whitson, Sarah Leah & Gorvin, Ian. Group Denial: Repression of Kurdish Political & Cultural Rights in Syria. 2009. (Illus.). 63p. pap. ***(978-1-56432-560-0(1))*** Human Rights Watch.

Wiessala, Georg. Re-Orienting the Fundamentals: Human Rights & New Connections in EU-Asia Relations. 2006. 198p. 120.00 *(978-0-7546-4363-0(8))* Ashgate Publishing Co.

Wignaraja, Ponna, et al, eds. Economic Democracy through Pro Poor Growth. 2009. (Illus.). 376p. (C). 49.95 *(978-81-7829-849-8(X)*, B98498C) SAGE Pubns., Inc.

Wilkinson, John Craven. The Imamate Tradition of Oman. 2009. (Cambridge Middle East Library). (ENG.). 428p. pap. 46.00 *(978-0-521-10614-6(1))* Cambridge Univ. Pr.

Wilnat, Lars. Political Communication in Asia. Aw, Annette, ed. 2009. (Routledge Communication Ser.). (ENG., Illus.). 248p. 125.00 *(978-0-415-96284-1(6))* Routledge.

Willnat, Lars & Aw, Annette, eds. Political Communication in Asia. 2009. (Routledge Communication Ser.). (ENG., Illus.). 248p. pap. 34.95 *(978-0-415-96285-8(4))* Routledge.

Wirsing, Robert G. & Ahrari, Ehsan M., eds. Fixing Fractured Nations: The Challenge of Ethnic Separatism in the Asia-Pacific. 2010. (Critical Studies of the Asia-Pacific Ser.). (ENG., Illus.). 272p. 89.00 *(978-0-230-23659-2(6))* Palgrave Macmillan.

Wu, Guang. USA - United States of Asia. 2010. (Asian Political, Economic, & Security Issues Ser.). 99p. 43.00 *(978-1-60876-180-7(0))* Nova Science Pubs., Inc.

Yi-Chong, Xu. Nuclear Energy Development in Asia: Problems & Prospects. 2011. (Energy, Climate & the Environment Ser.). (ENG., Illus.). 272p. 85.00 *(978-0-230-24024-7(0))* Palgrave Macmillan.

Yoshihara, Toshi & Holmes, James R. Red Star over the Pacific: China's Rise & the Challenge to U.S. Maritime Strategy. 2010. (Illus.). xii, 292p. *(978-1-59114-390-1(X))* Naval Institute Pr.

Zheng, Yangwen, et al. The Cold War in Asia: The Battle for Hearts & Minds. 2010. 268p. *(978-90-04-17537-2(7))* BRILL.

ASIA—POPULATION

Abbasi-Shavazi, Mohammad Jalal, et al. The Fertility Transition in Iran: Revolution & Reproduction. 2009. (ENG., Illus.). xxiv, 196p. 159.00 *(978-90-481-3197-6(9)*, 9048131979) Springer.

Antobam, Samuel Kojo. Sex Differentials in Child Mortality. 2010. 68p. pap. *(978-3-639-28140-8(3))* VDM Verlag Dr. Mueller e.K.

Bengtsson, Tommy, et al. Life under Pressure: Mortality & Living Standards in Europe & Asia, 1700-1900. 2009. (Eurasian Population & Family History Ser.). (ENG., Illus.). 552p. (gr. 17). pap. 23.00 *(978-0-262-51243-5(2))* MIT Pr.

Goodman, Roger & Harper, Sarah, eds. Aging in Asia. 2007. (Illus.). 128p. 160.00 *(978-0-415-44583-2(3))* Routledge.

Jones, Gavin & Douglass, Michael. Mega-urban Regions in Pacific Asia. (Illus.). 416p. pap. 28.00 *(978-9971-69-379-4(8))* National Univ. of Singapore Pr. SGP. Dist: Univ. of Hawaii Pr.

Laurent, Clint. Tomorrow's Asia: Exploding Asia's Population Myths. 2012. (ENG.). 256p. 24.95 *(978-0-470-82471-9(9)*, Wiley) Wiley, John & Sons, Inc.

Newson, Linda A. Conquest & Pestilence in the Early Spanish Philippines. 2009. (Illus.). 464p. 56.00 *(978-0-8248-3272-8(8))* Univ. of Hawaii Pr.

Nitisastro, Widjojo. Population Trends in Indonesia. 2010. (Illus.). 292p. pap. 29.95 *(978-979-3780-43-6(6))* Equinox Publishing IDN. Dist: Univ. of Hawaii Pr.

Petraglia, Michael D. & Allchin, Bridget, eds. The Evolution & History of Human Populations in South Asia: Inter-disciplinary Studies in Archaeology, Biological Anthropology, Linguistics & Genetics. 2010. (Vertebrate Paleobiology & Paleoanthropology Ser.). xiii, 464p. pap. 129.00 *(978-90-481-7394-5(9)*, 9048173949) Springer.

Richell, Judith. Disease & Demography in Colonial Burma. 2006. (Illus.). 327p. per. 32.00 *(978-9971-69-301-5(1))* National Univ. of Singapore Pr. SGP. Dist: Univ. of Hawaii Pr.

Sanchez-Mazas, Alicia, et al, eds. Past Human Migrations in East Asia: Matching Archaeology, Linguistics & Genetics. 2012. (Routledge Studies in the Early History of Asia Ser.). (ENG., Illus.). 504p. (C). pap. 42.95 ***(978-0-415-54188-6(3))*** Routledge.

Ullah, A. K. M. Ahsan, ed. Population Migration & Asia: Theories & Practice. 2010. (Asian Political, Economic & Security Issues Ser.). 147p. 69.00 *(978-1-61668-962-9(5))* Nova Science Pubs., Inc.

United Nations. Asia-Pacific Population Journal: 20th Anniversary Special. 2007. (ENG.). 112p. pap. 12.50 *(978-92-1-120489-6(5))* United Nations Pubns.

—Asia-Pacific population journal, April 2006. 2007. (ENG.). 110p. pap. 12.50 *(978-92-1-120472-8(0))* United Nations Pubns.

—Asia-Pacific Population Journal, April 2007. 2007. (ENG.). 76p. pap. 12.50 *(978-92-1-120508-4(5))* United Nations Pubns.

—Asia-Pacific Population Journal, April 2008. 2009. (ENG.). 116p. pap. 12.50 *(978-92-1-120549-7(2))* United Nations Pubns.

—Asia-Pacific Population Journal, August 2006. 2007. (ENG.). 84p. pap. 12.50 *(978-92-1-120483-4(6))* United Nations Pubns.

—Asia-Pacific Population Journal, August 2007. 2008. (ENG.). 132p. pap. 12.50 *(978-92-1-120527-5(1))* United Nations Pubns.

—Asia-Pacific Population Journal, August 2008. 2009. (ENG.). 108p. pap. 12.50 *(978-92-1-120558-9(1))* United Nations Pubns.

—Asia-Pacific Population Journal, December 2006. 2007. (Air Pollution Studies). (ENG.). 140p. pap. 12.50 *(978-92-1-120498-8(4))* United Nations Pubns.

—Asia-Pacific Population Journal, December 2007. 2008. (ENG.). 96p. pap. 12.50 *(978-92-1-120543-5(3))* United Nations Pubns.

—Asia-Pacific Population Journal, December 2008. 2009. (ENG.). 120p. pap. 12.50 *(978-92-1-120566-4(2))* United Nations Pubns.

United Nations. Asia-Pacific Population Journal, December 2010. 2012. (ENG.). 142p. pap. 15.00 ***(978-92-1-120627-2(8))*** United Nations Pubns.

ASIA—RELATIONS

Aktar, Ayhan Turhan. Nationalism in the Troubled Triangle: Cyprus, Greece & Turkey. Kizilyurek, Niyazi & Ozkirimli, Umut, eds. 2010. (New Perspectives on South-East Europe Ser.). (ENG.). 288p. 100.00 *(978-0-230-57915-6(9))* Palgrave Macmillan.

Alpers, Edward A. East Africa & the Indian Ocean. 2008. 240p. (ENG.). pap. 28.95 *(978-1-55876-453-8(4))*; (Illus.). 86.95 *(978-1-55876-452-1(6))* Wiener, Markus Pubs., Inc.

Chung, Chien-Peng. China's Multilateral Co-Operation in Asia & the Pacific: Institutionalizing Beijing's 'Good Neighbour Policy' 2010. (Politics in Asia Ser.). (ENG., Illus.). 192p. (C). 130.00 *(978-0-415-56914-9(1)*, Routledge) Taylor & Francis Group GBR. Dist: Taylor & Francis Group.

Cooney, Kevin J. The Rise of China & International Security: America & Asia Respond. 2009. pap. 39.95 *(978-0-415-55876-1(X))* Routledge.

Delanty, Gerard, ed. Europe & Asia beyond East & West. 2012. (Routledge/ESA Studies in European Societies Ser.). (ENG., Illus.). 320p. (C). pap. 42.95 ***(978-0-415-51165-0(8))*** Routledge.

Delanty, Gerard, ed. Europe & Asia Beyone East & West. 2006. (Routledge/European Sociological Association Studies in Europ Ser.). (Illus.). 322p. 190.00 *(978-0-415-37947-2(4))* Routledge.

Dent, Christopher M., ed. China, Japan & Regional Leadership in East Asia. 2008. 328p. (C). 150.00 *(978-1-84720-749-4(9))* Elgar, Edward Publishing, Inc.

Dharamdasani, M. D. Asia's Role in Global Politics. 2007. (Illus.). 262p. *(978-81-89741-40-2(3))* SBS Publishers.

Fojas, Camilla & Guevarra, Rudy P., Jr., eds. Transnational Crossroads: Remapping the Americas & the Pacific. 2012. (Borderlands & Transcultural Studies). (ENG., Illus.). 496p. pap. 45.00 ***(978-0-8032-3795-7(2))*** Univ. of Nebraska Pr.

Garrison, Jean A. China & the Energy Equation in Asia: The Determinants of Policy Choice. 2009. (Illus.). 200p. 59.95 *(978-1-935049-05-0(4))* FirstForumPress.

Goody, Jack. Eurasian Miracle. 2009. (ENG.). 200p. 64.95 *(978-0-7456-4793-7(6))* Polity Pr. GBR. Dist: Wiley, John & Sons, Inc.

—The Eurasian Miracle. 2009. (ENG.). 200p. pap. 19.95 *(978-0-7456-4794-4(4))* Polity Pr. GBR. Dist: Wiley, John & Sons, Inc.

—Renaissances: The One or the Many? 2009. (ENG., Illus.). 332p. 78.00 *(978-0-521-76801-6(2))* Cambridge Univ. Pr.

Hamanaka, Shintaro. Asian Regionalism & Japan: The Politics of Membership in Regional Diplomatic, Financial & Trade Groups. 2010. (Sheffield Centre for Japanese Studies/Routledge Ser.). (ENG., Illus.). 256p. (C). 130.00 *(978-0-415-55304-9(0))* Routledge.

Happel, Jorn. Nomadische Lebenswelten und zarische Politik: Der Aufstand in Zentralasien 1916. 2011. (Quellen und Studien zur Geschichte des ostlichen Europa Ser.). (GER., Illus.). 378p. (C). pap. 84.00 *(978-3-515-09771-0(6))* Steiner, Franz Verlag Wiesbaden GmbH DEU. Dist: Brown, David Bk. Co., The.

Ilias, M.H. & Vincent, P. J., eds. India - West Asia Relations: Understanding Cultural Interplays. 2007. 236p. (C). 41.50 *(978-81-7708-139-8(X))* New Century Publications IND. Dist: International Specialized Bk. Services.

Jarvis, Darryl. ASEAN Industries & the Challenge from China: The Dragon & Tiger Cubs. Welch, Anthony, ed. 2011. (ENG., Illus.). 272p. 90.00 *(978-0-230-54234-1(4))* Palgrave Macmillan.

Kim, Hyejin. International Ethnic Networks & Intra-Ethnic Conflict: Koreans in China. 2010. (ENG., Illus.). 212p. 89.00 *(978-0-230-10252-1(2))* Palgrave Macmillan.

Kohn, Hans. Western Civilization in the Near East. Dickes, E. W., tr. reprint ed. 20.00 *(978-0-404-03739-0(9))* AMS Pr., Inc.

Lee, Christopher, ed. Making a World after Empire: The Bandung Moment & Its Political Afterlives. 2010. (Ohio RIS Global Ser.). (ENG., Illus.). 280p. pap. 29.95 *(978-0-89680-277-3(9))* Ohio Univ. Pr.

Lee, Christopher J. Making a World after Empire: The Bandung Moment & Its Political Afterlives. 2010. 280p. *(978-0-89680-468-5(2))* Ohio Univ. Pr.

Mackerras, Colin & Clarke, Michael, eds. China Xinjiang & Central Asia. 2011. (ENG., Illus.). 212p. pap. 42.95 ***(978-0-415-67333-4(X))*** Routledge.

Malik, V. P. & Crome, Erhard, eds. Europe & Asia: Perspectives on the Emerging International Order. 2008. 210p. *(978-81-7062-247-5(6))* Lancer International, Lancer Pr.

Mills, Cynthia, et al. East-West Interchanges in American Art: "A Long & Tumultuous Relationship" 2011. ***(978-1-935623-08-3(7))*** Smithsonian Institution Scholarly Pr.

Ruland, Jurgen, et al, eds. Asian-European Relations. 2009. (Illus.). 294p. pap. 39.95 *(978-0-415-57423-5(4))* Routledge.

Sardar, Ziauddin. Balti Britain: Journeys Through the British Asian Experience. 2008. (ENG.). 416p. 37.95 *(978-1-86207-931-1(5))* Granta Bks. GBR. Dist: Independent Pubs. Group.

Sathasivam, Kanishkan. Keeping up with the Joneses. 2009. 204p. pap. *(978-3-639-20217-5(1))* VDM Verlag Dr. Mueller e.K.

Schwartz, Barry. Northeast Asia's Difficult Past: Essays in Collective Memory. Kim, Mikyoung, ed. 2010. (Palgrave Macmillan Memory Studies). (ENG., Illus.). 320p. 95.00 *(978-0-230-23747-6(9))* Palgrave Macmillan.

Tang, Shiping, et al. Living with China: Regional States & China Through Crises & Turning Points. Tang, Shiping et al, eds. 2009. (ENG.). 288p. 105.00 *(978-0-230-61670-7(4))* Palgrave Macmillan.

Wiessala, Georg. Enhancing Asia-Europe Co-Operation Through Educational Exchange. 2011. (Routledge Contemporary Asia Ser.). (ENG., Illus.). 272p. (C). 133.00 *(978-0-415-48194-6(5))* Routledge.

ASIA—RELIGION

Ahlstrand, Kajsa & Gunner, Goran. Non-Muslims in Muslim Majority Societies: With Focus on the Middle East & Pakistan. 2011. (ENG.). 176p. pap. 36.25 *(978-0-7188-9244-9(5))* Lutherworth Pr., The GBR. Dist: Printondemand-worldwide.com.

Ahmed, Ishtiaq, ed. The Politics of Religion in South & Southeast Asia. 2011. (Routledge Contemporary Asia Ser.). (ENG., Illus.). 288p. (C). 148.00 *(978-0-415-60227-3(0))* Routledge.

Amaladoss, Sj, Michael. Life in Freedom: Liberation Theologies from Asia. 2010. 192p. pap. 22.00 *(978-1-60899-409-0(0)*, Wipf and Stock) Wipf & Stock Pubs.

Amaladoss, Michael. The Asian Jesus. 2006. 180p. per. 25.00 *(978-1-57075-661-0(9))* Orbis Bks.

App, Urs. The Birth of Orientalism. 2010. (Encounters with Asia Ser.). (Illus.). 568p. (C). 79.95 *(978-0-8122-4261-4(0))* Univ. of Pennsylvania Pr.

Balzer, Marjorie Mandelst. Shamans, Spirituality, & Cultural Revitalization: Explorations in Siberia & Beyond. 2011. (Contemporary Anthropology of Religion Ser.). (ENG.). 304p. 85.00 *(978-0-230-11091-5(6))* Palgrave Macmillan.

Bautista, Julius. Christianity & the State in Asia: Complicity & Conflict. Gee, Francis Lim Khek, ed. 2009. (ENG., Illus.). 240p. 145.00 *(978-0-415-48069-7(8))* Routledge.

Bautista, Julius & Khek Gee Lim, Francis, eds. Christianity & the State in Asia: Complicity & Conflict. 2012. (ENG., Illus.). 240p. (C). pap. 42.95 ***(978-0-415-62742-9(7))*** Routledge.

Blair, Sara G. The Song of Life: A Correlation of Ancient Eastern Science & Modern Western Science. 2011. 192p. 42.95 ***(978-1-258-09643-4(9))*** Literary Licensing, LLC.

Blée, Fabrice, et al. The Third Desert: The Story of Monastic Interreligious Dialogue. 2011. 24.95 *(978-0-8146-3357-1(9))*; E-Book *(978-0-8146-3949-8(6))* Liturgical Pr.

Boivin, Michel. Artefacts of Devotion: A Sufi Repertoire of the Qalandariyya in Sehwan Sharif, Sindh, Pakistan. 2012. (ENG., Illus.). 180p. 60.00 ***(978-0-19-906321-5(4))*** Oxford Univ. Pr., Inc.

Brannigan, Michael C. Striking a Balance: A Primer in Traditional Asian Values. 2009. (ENG.). 238p. pap. 31.50 *(978-0-7391-3846-5(4))* Lexington Bks.

Bresnan, Patrick. Awakening: An Introduction to the History of Eastern Thought. 3rd rev. ed. 2006. (Illus.). 397p. per. 71.00 *(978-0-13-243691-5(4)*, Prentice Hall) Prentice Hall PTR.

Bresnan, Patrick S. Awakening: An Introduction to the History of Eastern Thought. 4th ed. 2009. (ENG.). 400p. (C). pap. 84.40 *(978-0-205-73909-7(1)*, Prentice Hall) Prentice Hall PTR.

Bubandt, Nils Ole & Van Beek, Martijn, eds. Varieties of Secularism in Asia: Anthropological Explorations of Religion, Politics & the Spiritual. 2011. (Anthropology of Asia Ser.). (ENG., Illus.). 272p. (C). 145.00 *(978-0-415-61672-0(7))* Routledge.

Chenique, François & Rangdreul, Christian. Souvenirs Métaphysiques D'Orient et D'Occident. 2009. (FRE.). 233p. *(978-2-296-08564-0(4))* Harmattan Pr.

Chiekova, Dobrinka. Cultes et vie religieuse des cités grecques du Pont gauche (VIIe-Ier siècles avant J. -C.) 2008. (Europäische Hochschulschriften. Reihe 38: Archäologie Ser.). (FRE & GEC., Illus.). 340p. pap. *(978-3-03911-448-1(4))* Lang, Peter.

Chung, Paul S., et al, eds. Asian Contextual Theology for the Third Millenium: Theology of Minjung in Fourth-Eye Formation. 2010. (ENG.). 372p. pap. 58.00 *(978-0-227-17331-2(7))* Clarke, James Co., Ltd. GBR. Dist: Brown, David Bk. Co., The.

—Asian Contextual Theology for the Third Millennium: A Theology of Minjung in Fourth-Eye Formation. Chung, Paul S., tr. 2006. (Princeton Theological Monographs). 372p. pap. 35.00 *(978-1-55635-044-3(9)*, Pickwick Pubns.) Wipf & Stock Pubs.

Chung, S. & Chung, Paul S. Constructing Irregular Theology: Bamboo & Minjung in East Asian Perspective. 2009. (Studies in Systematic Theology Ser.). *(978-90-04-17417-7(6))* BRILL.

Cormack, Don. Killing Fields Living Fields. 2009. (ENG., Illus.). 464p. 13.99 *(978-1-84550-511-0(5))* Christian Focus Pubns. GBR. Dist: STL Distribution North America.

Coward, Harold, et al. Readings in Eastern Religions: 2nd Edition. 2nd rev. ed. 2006. (ENG.). 414p. (C). pap. 42.95 (978-0-88920-435-5(7)) Wilfrid Laurier Univ. Pr. CAN. Dist: Univ. of Toronto Pr.

Danzan Narantuya & Danzan, Narantuya. Religion in 20th Century Mongolia: Social Changes & Popular Practices. 2008. 168p. pap. (978-3-639-09465-7(4)) VDM Verlag Dr. Mueller e.K.

De Neui, Paul H. Family & Faith in Asia: The Missional Impact of Social Networks. 2009. (978-0-87808-022-9(8)) Carey, William Library Pubs.

DuBois, Thomas David. Casting Faiths: Imperialism & the Transformation of Religion in East & Southeast Asia. DuBois, Thomas David & DuBois, Thomas, eds. 2009. (ENG., Illus.). 320p. 100.00 (978-0-230-22158-1(0)) Palgrave Macmillan.

Dy, Jason K., illus. Eastern Wisdom for Western Minds. 2007. 176p. per. 16.00 (978-1-57075-738-9(0)) Orbis Bks.

Eng, Ah Lai, ed. Religious Diversity in Singapore. 2008. 780p. (978-981-230-754-5(0)) Institute of Southeast Asian Studies.

Esposito, John L., et al. Religions of Asia Today. 2nd ed. 2011. (ENG.). 480p. (C). pap. 59.95 **(978-0-19-975949-1(9))** Oxford Univ. Pr., Inc.

Evans, I. H. N. The Religion of the Tempasuk Dusuns of North Borneo. 2012. (ENG.). 624p. pap. 45.99 **(978-1-107-64603-2(0))** Cambridge Univ. Pr.

Fitch, Florence Mary. Their Search for God: Ways of Worship in the Orient. 2007. (ENG.). 160p. 36.95 (978-0-548-07237-0(X)) Kessinger Publishing, LLC.

Fjelstad, Karen & Hien, Nguyen Thi. Spirits without Borders: Vietnamese Spirit Mediums in a Transnational Age. 2011. (Contemporary Anthropology of Religion Ser.). (ENG., Illus.). 230p. 85.00 (978-0-230-11493-7(8)) Palgrave Macmillan.

Freiberger, Oliver, ed. Asceticism & Its Critics: Historical Accounts & Comparative Perspectives. 2006. (AAR Cultural Criticism Ser.). (ENG.). 268p. 99.00 (978-0-19-530791-7(7)) Oxford Univ. Pr., Inc.

Goto, Shoji. The Philosophy of Emerson & Thoreau: Orientals Meet Occidentals. 2007. 208p. 109.95 (978-0-7734-5351-7(2)) Mellen, Edwin Pr., The.

Harrison, Mycroft R., ed. Religious Freedom Issues in Iraq. 2010. (Religion & Spirituality Ser.). 94p. pap. 43.00 (978-1-60741-988-4(2)) Nova Science Pubs., Inc.

Hegarty, James. Religion Narrative & Public Imagination in South Asia. 2011. (Routledge Hindu Studies Ser.). (ENG., Illus.). 240p. (C). 135.00 (978-0-415-55863-1(8)) Routledge.

Heirman, Ann & Bumbacher, Stephan Peter, eds. The Spread of Buddhism. 2007. (Handbook of Oriental Studies). 450p. (978-90-04-15830-6(8)) BRILL.

Hilgers, Irene. Why Do Uzbeks Have to Be Muslims? Exploring Religiosity in the Ferghana Valley. 2011. (Illus.). 192p. pap. 49.95 **(978-3-643-10176-7(7))** Lit Verlag DEU. Dist: Transaction Pubs.

Hunt, Stephen, ed. Religions of the East. 2010. (Library of Essays on Sexuality & Religion Ser.). (Illus.). 542p. 225.00 (978-0-7546-2922-1(8)) Ashgate Publishing Co.

Jenkins, John Philip. The Lost History of Christianity: The Thousand-Year Golden Age of the Church in the Middle East, Africa, & Asia — And How It Died. 2009. (ENG.). 304p. pap. 15.99 (978-0-06-147281-7(6), HarperOne) HarperCollins Pubs.

Jones, David, ed. Asian Texts - Asian Contexts: Encounters with Asian Philosophies & Religions. Klein, E. R., tr. 2010. (SUNY series in Asian Studies Development Ser.). (Illus.). 240p. 68.50 (978-1-4384-2675-4(5)) State Univ. of New York Pr.

—Asian Texts - Asian Contexts: Encounters with Asian Philosophy & Religions. Klein, E. R., tr. 2010. (SUNY series in Asian Studies Development Ser.). (Illus.). 240p. pap. 21.95 (978-1-4384-2676-1(3)) State Univ. of New York Pr.

Jongeneel, Jan A. B. & Liu, Jiafeng, eds. Christian Presence & Progress in North-East Asia: Historical & Comparative Studies. 2011. (IC - Studien zur interkulturellen Geschichte des Christentums. Etudes d'histoire interculturelle de christianisme. Studies in the Intercultural History of Christianity Ser.). 256p. 69.95 (978-3-631-61115-9(3)) Lang, Peter GmbH, Europaischer Verlag der Wissenschaften DEU. Dist: Lang, Peter.

Jorgensen, Jonas Adelin. Jesus Imandars & Christ Bhaktas: Two Case Studies of Interreligious Hermeneutics & Identity in Global Christianity. 2008. xii, 481p. pap. 107.95 (978-3-631-58486-6(5)) Lang, Peter GmbH, Europaischer Verlag der Wissenschaften DEU. Dist: Lang, Peter.

Kelly, James W., ed. Religions of South Vietnam in Faith & Fact. 2007. 97p. reprint ed. pap. 20.00 (978-1-4223-1590-3(8)) DIANE Publishing Co.

Keul, István, ed. Transformations & Transfer of Tantra in Asia & Beyond. 2012. (Religion & Society Ser.). (ENG.). X, 531p. 168.00 (978-3-11-025810-3(2)) De Gruyter, Walter Inc.

Kim, Heup Young, et al, eds. Asian & Oceanic Christianities in Conversation: Exploring Theological Identities at Home & in Diaspora. 2011. (ENG., Illus.). 239p. pap. 67.00 (978-90-420-3298-9(7)) Rodopi.

Kim, Sebastian C. H., ed. Christian Theology in Asia. 2008. (ENG.). 310p. (C). 88.00 (978-0-521-86308-7(2)); pap. 33.99 (978-0-521-68183-4(9)) Cambridge Univ. Pr.

Kitiarsa, Pattana, ed. Religious Commodifications in Asia: Marketing Gods. 2008. (Illus.). XIV, 274p. 160.00 (978-0-415-43738-7(5)) Routledge.

Kitinov, Baatr U. The Spread of Buddhism among Western Mongolian Tribes Between the 13th & 18th Centuries: Tibetan Buddhism in the Politics & Ideology of the Oirat People. 2010. 324p. 119.95 (978-0-7734-1434-1(7)) Mellen, Edwin Pr., The.

Koen, Benjamin D. Beyond the Roof of the World: Music, Prayer, & Healing in the Pamir Mountains, 1 vol. 2011. (ENG., Illus.). 240p. pap. 29.95 (978-0-19-979621-6(4)) Oxford Univ. Pr., Inc.

König, Andrea, ed. Christliche Existenz in einer überwiegend nicht-christlichen Umgebung: Situationsbeschreibung, Initiativen und Perspektiven für die Zukunft. 2008. (Glaube und Denken. Jahrbuch der Karl-Heim-Gesellschaft Ser.). (GER & ENG., Illus.). 420p. pap. 99.95 (978-3-631-58300-5(1)) Lang, Peter GmbH, Europaischer Verlag der Wissenschaften DEU. Dist: Lang, Peter.

Koschorke, Klaus, et al, eds. A History of Christianity in Asia, Africa, & Latin America, 1450-1990: A Documentary Sourcebook. 2007. 426p. per. 35.00 (978-0-8028-2889-7(2)) Eerdmans, William B. Publishing Co.

Kupperman, Joel J. Classic Asian Philosophy: A Guide to the Essential Texts. 2nd rev. ed. 2006. (ENG.). 208p. per. 29.99 (978-0-19-518981-0(7)) Oxford Univ. Pr., Inc.

Lecomte-Tilouine, Marie, ed. Nature, Culture & Religion at the Crossroads of Asia. 2010. (SSP Ser.). 386p. 90.00 (978-81-87358-46-6(7)) Berghahn Bks., Inc.

Lee, Chanseok. The Christological Perspectives of Panikkar & Byungmu Ahn - Toward an Asian Christology. 2008. 216p. pap. (978-3-639-03856-9(8)) VDM Verlag Dr. Mueller e.K.

Lim, F. K. G., ed. Mediating Piety: Technology & Religion in Contemporary Asia. 2009. (Social Sciences in Asia Ser.). 224p. pap. (978-90-04-17839-7(2)) BRILL.

Lim, Swee Hong. Giving Voice to Asian Christians. 2008. 344p. pap. (978-3-639-06074-4(1)) VDM Verlag Dr. Mueller e.K.

Lipinski, E., ed. Resheph: A Syro-Canaanite Deity. 2009. (Orientalia Lovaniensia Analecta Ser.). (ENG & MUL., Illus.). 295p. (C). 109.00 (978-90-429-2107-8(2)) Peeters Pubs. & Booksellers BEL. Dist: Brown, David Bk. Co., The.

Lumsdaine, David Halloran. Evangelical Christianity & Democracy in Asia. 2009. (ENG., Illus.). 352p. pap. 29.95 (978-0-19-530825-9(5)) Oxford Univ. Pr., Inc.

Lyall, Alfred Comyn. Asiatic Studies: Religious & Social. 2010. (ENG.). 348p. pap. 32.75 (978-1-171-74482-5(X)); 364p. pap. 32.75 (978-1-176-51204-7(8)) BiblioBazaar.

Lynch, Jerry & Huang, Chungliang Al. Spirit of the Dancing Warrior: Asian Wisdom for Peak Performance in Athletics & Life. 2010. pap. 16.95 (978-1-60237-364-8(7)) Amber Lotus Publishing.

Mathiesen, Gaylan Kent. A Theology of Mission: Examining the Challenges & Opportunities in Northeast Asia. 2007. (ENG.). 224p. pap. 16.00 (978-1-932688-26-9(9), Lutheran Univ. Pr.) Kirk Hse. Pubs.

McCheyne, Murray. Siete Iglesias de Asia: Seven Churches of Asia. (SPA.). (978-84-7645-114-4(8), 223168) Clie, Editorial.

McFarlane, Stewart, ed. East Asian Religion: Themes & Issues. (Illus.). 224p. pap. (978-0-304-33845-0(1), Burns & Oates) Continuum International Publishing Group, Ltd.

—Themes & Issues in East Asian Religions. (Illus.). 224p. (978-0-304-33844-3(3), Burns & Oates) Continuum International Publishing Group, Ltd.

Merton, Thomas. On Eastern Meditation. Thurston, Bonnie, ed. 2012. (ENG.). 80p. pap. 13.95 **(978-0-8112-1994-5(1)**, 21994) New Directions Publishing Corp.

Moffett, Samuel Hugh. A History of Christianity in Asia: Volume II: 1500-1900. 2007. (American Society of Missiology Ser.). 742p. per. 40.00 (978-1-57075-701-3(1)) Orbis Bks.

Morgan, Kenneth W. Reaching for the Moon: On Asian Religious Paths. 2010. (ENG.). 207p. (gr. 17). pap. 34.00 (978-0-231-15789-6(4)) Columbia Univ. Pr.

Mountcastle, William W. The Secret Ministry of Jesus: Pioneer Prophet of Interfaith Dialogue. 2007. (ENG.). 120p. per. 26.50 (978-0-7618-3833-3(3)) Univ. Pr. of America, Inc.

Naher, Ainoon. Gender, Religion & Development in Rural Bangladesh. 2008. 244p. pap. (978-3-8364-8312-4(2)) VDM Verlag Dr. Mueller e.K.

Nelson, Sarah Milledge. Shamanism & the Origins of States: Spirit, Power, & Gender in East Asia. 2008. (ENG., Illus.). 303p. 89.00 (978-1-59874-132-2(2)); pap. 29.95 (978-1-59874-133-9(0)) Left Coast Pr., Inc.

Ng, Andrew Hock-Soon. Intimating the Sacred: Religion in Malaysian Fiction. 2011. **(978-988-8053-88-9(4))** Hong Kong Univ. Pr.

Noll, Mark A. & Nystrom, Carolyn. Clouds of Witnesses: Christian Voices from Africa & Asia. 2011. (ENG.). 286p. 25.00 (978-0-8308-3834-9(1), IVP Bks.) InterVarsity Pr.

Noor, Farish A., et al, eds. Madrasa in Asia: Political Activism & Transnational Linkages. 2009. (ISIM Series on Contemporary Muslim Societies Ser.). 270p. pap. (978-90-5356-710-4(0), Leiden Univ. Pr.) Amsterdam Univ. Pr.

Oldmeadow, Harry. Light from the East: Eastern Wisdom for the Modern West. 2007. (ENG.). 352p. per. 23.95 (978-1-933316-22-2(5)) World Wisdom, Inc.

Orzech, Charles D., et al. Esoteric Buddhism & the Tantras in East Asia. 2010. (Illus.). 850p. (978-90-04-18491-6(0)) BRILL.

Peters, George W. El Despertamiento en Indonesia: Indonesia Revival: Focus on Timor. (SPA.). (978-84-7228-171-4(X), 220275) Clie, Editorial.

Phan, Peter C., ed. Christianities in Asia. 2010. (Blackwell Guides to Global Christianity Ser.: 1). (ENG., Illus.). 290p. 94.95 (978-1-4051-6089-6(6)); 288p. pap. 37.95 (978-1-4051-6090-2(X)) Wiley, John & Sons, Inc. (Wiley-Blackwell).

Pianciola, Niccolo & Stamatopulos, Paolo Sartori Costas. Kazakhstan: Religions & Society of Central Eurasia. Bonora, Gian Luca, ed. 2010. (ENG., Illus.). 272p. 86.00 (978-88-422-1755-8(7)) Allemandi, Umberto & Co. GBR. Dist: Antique Collectors' Club.

Poon. Pilgrims & Citizens. 2007. 228p. pap. 18.00 (978-1-920691-58-5(8)) ATF Pr. AUS. Dist: International Publishers Marketing.

Reimer, Reg. Vietnam's Christians: A Century of Growth in Adversity. 2011. (Illus.). xxii, 122p. **(978-0-87808-304-6(9))** Carey, William Library Pubs.

Ring, George C. Religions of the Far East Their History. 2006. pap. 33.95 (978-1-4286-5482-2(8)) Kessinger Publishing, LLC.

Saggs, Henry W. Ancient Near Eastern Religion. Date not set. 240p. (C). (978-0-485-11436-2(4), Burns & Oates) Continuum International Publishing Group, Ltd.

Showalter, Richard & Showalter, Jewel. A Silk Road Pilgrimage: Discovering the Church of the East. 2009. pap. 12.99 (978-0-8361-9477-7(2)) Herald Pr.

Sidky, H. Haunted by the Archaic Shaman: Himalayan Jhakris & the Discourse on Shamanism. 2008. (ENG., Illus.). 270p. 78.99 (978-0-7391-2621-9(0)) Lexington Bks.

Sinha, Vineeta. Religion & Commodification: 'Merchandizing' Diasporic Hinduism. 2010. (Routledge Research in Religion, Media & Culture Ser.). (ENG., Illus.). 242p. (C). 125.00 (978-0-415-87363-5(0)) Routledge.

—Religion-State Encounters in Hindu Domains: From the Straits Settlements to Singapore. 2011. (ARI - Springer Asia Ser.). (Illus.). xix, 284p. 139.00 (978-94-007-0886-0(6), 9400708866) Springer.

Sit, Kwan-Yuk Claire. The Lord's Prayer: An Eastern Perspective. 2008. 192p. pap. 20.00 (978-0-88010-596-5(8)) SteinerBooks, Inc.

Soon-Ng, Andrew Hock. Intimating the Sacred: Religion in English Language Malaysian Fiction. 2011. (ENG.). 292p. (gr. 17). pap. 25.00 (978-988-8083-21-3(X)) Hong Kong Univ. Pr. HKG. Dist: Columbia Univ. Pr.

Squarcini, Federico. Tradition, Veda & Law: Studies on South Asian Classical Intellectual Traditions. 2011. (Cultural, Historical & Textual Studies of Religions Ser.). 178p. 99.00 **(978-0-85728-436-5(3))** Anthem Pr. GBR. Dist: Books International, Inc.

Steenbrink, K. A.; . & Aritonang, J. S, eds. A History of Christianity in Indonesia. 2008. (Studies in Christian Mission Ser.). (Illus.). 960p. (978-90-04-17026-1(X)) BRILL.

Takenaka, Masao. God Is Rice. 2009. 90p. pap. 13.00 (978-1-60608-892-0(0), Wipf and Stock) Wipf & Stock Pubs.

Tan-Chow, Mayling. Pentecostal Theology for the Twenty-First Century: Engaging with Multi-Faith Singapore. 2007. (Ashgate New Critical Thinking in Religion, Theology & Biblical Studies Ser.). 224p. 99.95 (978-0-7546-5718-7(3)) Ashgate Publishing Co.

Taylor, Philip, ed. Modernity & Re-Enchantment: Religion in Post-Revolutionary Vietnam. 2008. (AsiaWorld Ser.). (ENG., Illus.). 504p. 99.99 (978-0-7391-2739-1(X)) Lexington Bks.

Thompson, Ashley. Engendering the Buddhist State: Reconstructions of Cambodian History. 2012. (Routledge Critical Studies in Buddhism Ser.). (ENG.). 240p. (C). 140.00 (978-0-415-67772-1(6)) Routledge.

Tiwari, Ramakant. Changing Religious Roles in Pre-Modern Asia. 2010. 271p. 47.50 (978-81-7533-254-6(9)) M. D. Pubns. Pvt, Ltd. IND. Dist: Coronet Bks.

Topley, Marjorie. Cantonese Society in Hong Kong & Singapore: Gender, Religion, Medicine & Money. DeBernardi, Jean, ed. 2011. (Royal Asiatic Society Hong Kong Studies). (CHI., Illus.). 624p. **(978-988-220-657-1(3))** Hong Kong Univ. Pr.

Van Gulik, Robert H. Hayagriva: The Mantrayanic Aspect of Horse-Cult in China & Japan. 2006. (ENG., Illus.). 104p. 40.00 (978-974-524-074-2(5)) Orchid Pr. THA. Dist: National Bk. Network.

Wang, Youru. Deconstruction & the Ethical in Asian Thought. 2007. (Illus.). 251p. 160.00 (978-0-415-77016-3(5)) Routledge.

Wetzel, Klaus. Kirchengeschichte Asiens. 2010. 682p. pap. (978-3-941750-25-8(9)) VTR Verlag fur Theologie und Religionswissenschaft.

Wheelock, Wade. Considering the Asian Religions: A Guide to Understanding, Evaluating, & Appreciating. 2007. 392p. pap. 19.95 (978-1-57258-501-0(3)) TEACH Services, Inc.

Williams, Paul & Ladwig, Patrice, eds. Buddhist Funeral Cultures of Southeast Asia & China. 2012. (ENG., Illus.). 312p. 99.00 **(978-1-107-00386-0(1))** Cambridge Univ. Pr.

Winkler, Dietmar & Tang, Li, eds. Hidden Treasures & Intercultural Encounters: Studies on East Syriac Christianity in China & Central Asia. 2011. (ENG.). 400p. pap. 39.95 (978-3-643-50045-8(9)) Lit Verlag DEU. Dist: Transaction Pubs.

ASIA—RURAL CONDITIONS

Balisacan, Arsenio & Fuwa, Nobuhiko, eds. Reasserting the Rural Development Agenda: Lessons Learned & Emerging Challenges in Asia. 2007. 436p. (978-981-230-412-4(6)) Institute of Southeast Asian Studies.

Cho, George. The Malaysian Economy (Routledge Revivals) 2012. (ENG.). 334p. pap. 42.95 **(978-0-415-61404-7(X))** Routledge.

Cho, George. The Malaysian Economy (Routledge Revivals) Spatial Perspectives. 2011. (Routledge Revivals Ser.). (ENG.). 334p. 130.00 (978-0-415-61250-0(0)) Routledge.

Connell, John & Waddell, Eric, eds. Environment, Development & Change in Rural Asia-Pacific. 2006. (Routledge Pacific Rim Geographies Ser.: Vol. 6). (Illus.). 264p. 190.00 (978-0-415-40414-3(2)) Routledge.

Dillon, Andrew, et al. Estimating the Impact of Access to Infrastructure & Extension Services in Rural Nepal. 2011. **(978-0-89629-188-1(X))** International Food Policy Research Institute.

Falloux, Francois & Talbot, Lee M. Aid & Development, Set. 2009. (Earthscan Library Collection). (ENG.). 3794p. 1390.00 (978-1-84971-039-8(2)) Routledge.

Hinnebusch, Raymond, et al. Agriculture & Reform in Syria. 2010. (Illus.). 120p. (C). pap. 17.95 (978-0-9559687-7-8(1)) Rienner, Lynne Pubs.

Holloway, Richard, ed. Doing Development: Government, NGOs & the Rural Poor in Asia. 2009. (Aid & Development Set Ser.). (ENG.). 250p. 110.00 (978-1-84971-043-5(0)) Routledge.

ASIA—SOCIAL CONDITIONS

Abeysuriya, Kumudini. A Pathway to Sustainability in Urban Sanitation. 2010. 276p. pap. (978-3-639-22026-1(9)) VDM Verlag Dr. Mueller e.K.

Agergaard, Jytte. Rural-Urban Dynamics: Livelihoods, Mobility & Markets in African & Asian Frontiers. 2009. (Routledge Studies in Human Geography Ser.). (ENG., Illus.). 212p. 150.00 (978-0-415-47562-4(7)) Routledge.

Agergaard, Jytte, et al. Rural-Urban Dynamics: Livelihoods, Mobility & Markets in African & Asian Frontiers. 2009. (Illus.). xx, 212p. (C). 140.00 (978-0-203-87394-6(7)) Routledge.

Al-Budaiwi, Dalal. Freedom of Expression in Kuwait. 2011. 68p. pap. **(978-3-8443-2722-9(3))** Lambert Academic Publishing.

Ali, Kamran Asdar. Gendering Urban Space in the Middle East, South Asia, & Africa. Rieker, Martina & Ali, Kamran Asdar, eds. 2008. (ENG.). 248p. 95.00 (978-1-4039-7523-2(X)) Palgrave Macmillan.

Aryal, Sanjaya. Use of Child Soldiers in Nepal. 2011. 116p. pap. **(978-3-8433-9438-3(5))** Lambert Academic Publishing.

Askari, Hossein, et al. Corruption & Its Manifestation in the Persian Gulf. 2010. (Illus.). 168p. 112.00 (978-1-84720-612-1(3)) Elgar, Edward Publishing, Inc.

Atkins, Gary. Imagining Gay Paradise: Bali, Bangkok, & Cyber-Singapore. 2012. (ENG.). 320p. (gr. 17). 50.00 (978-988-8083-23-7(6)); pap. 25.00 (978-988-8083-24-4(4)) Hong Kong Univ. Pr. HKG. Dist: Columbia Univ. Pr.

Aung-Thwin, Michael & Aung-Thwin, Maitrii. A History of Myanmar: Traditions & Transformations. 2012. (Illus.). 304p. 39.00 **(978-1-86189-901-9(7))** Reaktion Bks., Ltd. GBR. Dist: Chicago Distribution Ctr.

B#xE9;har, Yves, frwd. Material Change: Design Thinking & the Social Entrepreneurship Movement, 1 vol. 2011. (ENG., Illus.). 160p. pap. 30.00 **(978-1-935202-45-5(6)**, Metropolis Bks.) D.A.P./Distributed Art Pubs.

Beall, Jo, et al, eds. Urbanization & Development in Asia: Multidimensional Perspectives. 2012. (ENG.). 336p. 55.00 **(978-0-19-807853-1(6))** Oxford Univ. Pr., Inc.

Bernardo, Allan B. I., et al, eds. The Self, Relationships, & Subjective Well-Being in Asia: Psychological, Social, & Cultural Perspectives. 2008. (Progress in Asian Social Psychology Ser.). (Illus.). 352p. 50.00 (978-89-25-40073-0(1)) Univ. of Hawaii Pr.

Bernstein, Richard. The East, the West, & Sex: A History of Erotic Encounters. 2010. (Vintage Ser.). (ENG., Illus.). 336p. pap. 16.00 (978-0-375-71389-7(1), Vintage) Knopf Doubleday Publishing Group.

Bertrand, Jacques & Laliberte, Andre, eds. Multination States in Asia: Accommodation or Resistance. 2010. (ENG., Illus.). 352p. 95.00 (978-0-521-19434-1(2)); pap. 32.99 (978-0-521-14363-9(2)) Cambridge Univ. Pr.

Bhandari, Om. Social & Economic Impacts of Rural Electrification in Bhutan. 2010. 120p. pap. (978-3-639-25211-8(X)) VDM Verlag Dr. Mueller e.K.

Blackwood, Evelyn & Bhaiya, Abha. Women's Sexualities & Masculinities in a Globalizing Asia. Wieringa, Saskia E., ed. 2009. (Comparative Feminist Studies). (ENG.). 296p. pap. 33.00 (978-0-230-61748-3(4)) Palgrave Macmillan.

Blackwood, Evelyn & Wieringa, Saskia E. Women's Sexualities & Masculinities in a Globalizing Asia. Blackwood, Evelyn et al, eds. 2007. (Comparative Feminist Studies). (ENG., Illus.). 296p. 89.00 (978-1-4039-7768-7(2)) Palgrave Macmillan.

Blum, Isa. Chaos in Yemen: Societal Collapse & the New Authoritarianism. 2012. (ENG., Illus.). 208p. (C). pap. 42.95 **(978-0-415-62575-3(0))** Routledge.

Brigg, Morgan & Bleiker, Roland. Mediating Across Differ Cl. 2010. (Illus.). 264p. 52.00 (978-0-8248-3459-3(3)) Univ. of Hawaii Pr.

—Mediating Across Differ Pa. 2010. 264p. pap. 28.00 (978-0-8248-3519-4(0)) Univ. of Hawaii Pr.

Brooks, Ann. Social Theory in Contemporary Asia. 2010. (Routledge Studies in Social & Political Thought Ser.). (ENG.). 160p. (C). 130.00 (978-0-415-55109-0(9), Routledge) Taylor & Francis Group GBR. Dist: Taylor & Francis Group.

Brooks, Ann & Devasahayam, Theresa. Gender, Emotions & Labour Markets: Asian & Western Perspectives. 2011. (ASAA Women in Asia Ser.). (ENG., Illus.). 160p. (C). 130.00 (978-0-415-56389-5(5)) Routledge.

Bullough, Oliver. Let Our Fame Be Great: Journeys among the Defiant People of the Caucasus. 2012. (ENG.). 528p. (gr. 9). pap. 19.99 **(978-0-465-02904-4(3))** Basic Bks.

Cao, Huhua, ed. Ethnic Minorities & Regional Development in Asia: Reality & Challenges. 2009. (ICAS Publications Ser.). (ENG.). 252p. pap. (978-90-8964-091-8(6)) Amsterdam Univ. Pr.

Chacon, Richard J. & Mendoza, Rubén G., eds. The Ethics of Anthropology & Amerindian Research: Reporting on Environmental Degradation & Warfare. 2011. (ENG., Illus.). xvi, 521p. 179.00 **(978-1-4614-1064-5(9)**, 1461410649) Springer.

Chadha, Radha & Husband, Paul. The Cult of the Luxury Brand: Inside Asia's Love Affair with Luxury. 2006. (ENG., Illus.). 300p. 39.95 (978-1-904838-05-0(7)) Ebsco Publishing.

Chaikin, David, et al. Corruption & Money Laundering: A Symbiotic Relationship. 2009. (Palgrave Series on Asian Governance Ser.). (ENG.). 256p. 100.00 (978-0-230-61360-7(8)) Palgrave Macmillan.

Chan, Phil C. W., ed. Equality in Asia-Pacific. 2007. (ENG.). 272p. 160.00 (978-0-415-37329-6(8)) Routledge.

Chapagai Chaulagai, Pratima. Child Labour in Domestic Affairs, Nepal. 2010. 64p. pap. (978-3-639-26648-1(X)) VDM Verlag Dr. Mueller e.K.

Chinese Academy of Social Sciences, et al. Preparing for the Challenges of Population Aging in Asia: Strengthening the Scientific Basis of Policy Development. 2010. (ENG., Illus.). 28p. pap. 15.00 *(978-0-309-15937-1(7))* National Academies Pr.

Chong, Terence, ed. Globalization & Its Counter-Forces in Southeast Asi. 2008. 432p. *(978-981-230-488-9(6))* Institute of Southeast Asian Studies.

Choudhary, K. N. Rural Women Workers in Asia. 2010. 255p. 59.50 *(978-81-7533-309-3(X))* M. D. Pubns. Pvt, Ltd. IND. Dist: Coronet Bks.

Chung, Irene & Shibusawa, Tazuko. Contemporary Clinical Practice with Asian Immigrants: A Relational Framework with Culturally Responsive Approaches. 2012. (ENG.). 224p. 115.00 ***(978-0-415-78342-2(9))*** Routledge.

Clifford, Mark L. & Pau, Janet. Through the Eyes of Tiger Cubs: Views of Asia's Next Generation. 2011. (ENG., Illus.). 224p. pap. 27.95 ***(978-1-118-09463-1(8)***, Wiley) Wiley, John & Sons, Inc.

Combating Human Trafficking in Asia: Hearing Before the Subcommittee on East Asian & Pacific Affairs of the Committee on Foreign Relations, United States Senate, One Hundred Twelfth Congress, First Session, April 7, 2011. 2011. iii, 28p. ***(978-0-16-089367-4(4)***, 552-070-43351-1) United States Government Printing Office.

Constable, Nicole. Migrant Domestic Workers in Asia: Distant Divides, Intimate Connections. 2010. (Illus.). 232p. (C). *(978-0-415-57814-1(0)*, Routledge) Taylor & Francis Group.

Cook, Sarah & Kabeer, Naila, eds. Social Protection as Development Policy. 2010. (ENG.). 396p. (C). 95.00 *(978-0-415-58573-6(2)*, Routledge India) Taylor & Francis Group GBR. Dist: Taylor & Francis Group.

Cox, Dan G., et al. Terrorism, Instability, & Democracy in Asia & Africa. 2009. (Northeastern Series on Democratization & Political Development Ser.). (Illus.). 240p. (C). lib. bdg. 65.00 *(978-1-58465-753-8(7))*; (ENG., pap. 21.95 *(978-1-58465-754-5(5))* Univ. Pr. of New England. (Northeastern University Pr.).

Cram101 Textbook Reviews. Outlines & Highlights for Why Europe? the Rise of the West in World History 1500-1850 by Jack a Goldstone, Isbn: 9780072848014. 2011. 88p. pap. 27.95 ***(978-1-61812-490-6(0))*** Cram101 Inc.

Culas, Christian. Inter-Ethnic Dynamics in Asia: Considering the Other Through Ethnonyms, Territories & Rituals. Robinne, François, ed. 2010. (Routledge Contemporary Asia Ser.). (Illus.). 240p. 130.00 *(978-0-415-55936-2(7))* Routledge.

Dam, Nikolaos van. The Struggle for Power in Syria: Politics & Society under Asad & the Ba'th Party. 4th rev. ed. 2011. (ENG., Illus.). 288p. pap. 25.00 *(978-1-84885-760-5(8))* I. B. Tauris & Co., Ltd. GBR. Dist: Macmillan.

Das, Chaitali. British-Indian Adult Children of Divorce: Context Impact & Coping. 2011. (Illus.). 204p. 99.95 *(978-1-4094-0824-6(8))* Ashgate Publishing Co.

Davaa, Byambasuren & Reisch, Lisa. The Cave of the Yellow Dog. Spencer, Sally-Ann, tr. 2008. (ENG., Illus.). 192p. pap. 15.95 *(978-1-84408-456-2(6))* Little, Brown Bk. Group Ltd. GBR. Dist: Independent Pubs. Group.

De Borchgrave, Arnaud, et al. Conflict, Community, & Criminality in Southeast Asia & Australia: Assessments from the Field. 2009. pap. 21.95 *(978-0-89206-583-7(4)*, CSIS Pr., The) Ctr. for Strategic & International Studies.

Devkota, Bhimsen. A Case Study of Rebel Health Services in Nepal. 2011. 308p. pap. ***(978-3-8443-8049-1(3))*** Lambert Academic Publishing.

Earnest, Jaya, et al, eds. Rebuilding Education & Health in a Post Conflict Transitional Nation: Case Studies from Timor-Leste. 2008. 232p. pap. *(978-90-8790-307-7(3))* Sense Pubs.

Emerson, Geoffrey Charles. Hong Kong Internment, 1942 To 1945: Life in the Japanese Civilian Camp at Stanley. 2008. (Royal Asiatic Society Hong Kong Studies Ser.). (ENG., Illus.). 268p. (gr. 17). 45.00 ***(978-988-8028-53-5(7))*** Hong Kong Univ. Pr. HKG. Dist: Columbia Univ. Pr.

Fernandes, Clinton, ed. Hot Spot: Asia & Oceania, 1 vol. 2008. (Hot Spot Histories Ser.). (Illus.). 328p. 65.00 *(978-0-313-35412-0(X)*, GR5412, Greenwood Pr.) Greenwood Publishing Group, Inc.

Fink, Christina. Living Silence in Burma: Surviving under Military Rule. 2nd ed. 2009. (ENG., Illus.). 320p. 120.95 *(978-1-84813-271-9(9))*; pap. 26.95 *(978-1-84813-272-6(7))* Zed Bks., Ltd. GBR. Dist: Macmillan.

Fong, Jack. Revolution As Development: The Karen Self-Determination Struggle Against Ethnocracy from 1949-2004. 2008. 376p. pap. *(978-1-59942-994-6(2))* Universal Pubs.

Fu, Tsung-Hsi & Hughes, Rhidian, eds. Ageing in East Asia. 2011. (ENG.). 204p. pap. 42.95 ***(978-0-415-66981-8(2))*** Routledge.

Gadzhiev, K. S. "Bolshaia Igra" Na Kavkaze: Vchera, Segodnia, Zavtra. 2010. 339p. *(978-5-7133-1366-1(2))* Mezdunarodnye Otnosheniya.

Gill, Sucha Singh, et al, eds. Economic & Environmental Sustainability of the Asian Region. 2010. (ENG., Illus.). xxvi, 461p. (C). 95.00 *(978-0-415-58144-8(3)*, Routledge India) Taylor & Francis Group GBR. Dist: Taylor & Francis Group.

Gillan, Michael & Pokrant, Bob, eds. Trade, Labour & Transformation of Community in Asia. 2010. (ENG., Illus.). 304p. 116.00 *(978-0-230-22249-6(8))* Palgrave Macmillan.

Goodman, Roger. Ageing in Asia: Asia's Position in the New Global Demography. Harper, Sarah, ed. 2008. (ENG.). 256p. (C). pap. 41.95 *(978-0-415-46426-0(9))* Routledge.

Grennan, Conor. Little Princes: One Man's Promise to Bring Home the Lost Children of Nepal. 2011. (ENG.). 304p. pap. 14.99 ***(978-0-06-193006-5(7)***, William Morrow Paperbacks); 25.99 *(978-0-06-193005-8(9)*, Morrow, William & Co.) HarperCollins Pubs.

—Little Princes: One Man's Promise to Bring Home the Lost Children of Nepal. l.t. ed. 2011. (ENG.). 505p. 31.99 *(978-1-4104-3527-9(X))* Thorndike Pr.

Grossman, David L., et al, eds. Citizenship Curriculum in Asia & the Pacific. 2010. (CERC Studies in Comparative Education Ser.). xii, 268p. pap. 189.00 *(978-90-481-7976-3(9)*, 9048179769) Springer.

Guan, Lee Hock, ed. Ageing in Southeast & East Asi: Family, Social Protection, Policy Challenges. 2008. (Illus.). 264p. *(978-981-230-766-8(4))* Institute of Southeast Asian Studies.

Gullette, David. The Genealogical Construction of the Kyrgyz Republic: Kinship, State & Tribalism. 2010. (Inner Asia Book Ser.). (ENG., Illus.). 272p. *(978-1-906876-10-4(X))* BRILL.

Gyamtsho, Sonam. Gross National Happiness & Social Progress. 2011. 120p. pap. ***(978-3-8443-0053-6(8))*** Lambert Academic Publishing.

Hangartner, Judith. The Constitution & Contestation of Darhad Shaman's Power in Contemporary Mongolia. 2010. (Illus.). 256p. *(978-1-906876-11-1(8))* BRILL.

Hangen, Susan. The Rise of Ethnic Politics in Nepal: Democracy in the Margins. 2010. (Routledge Contemporary South Asia Ser.). (ENG., Illus.). 208p. (C). 130.00 *(978-0-415-77884-8(0))* Routledge.

Harriss-white, Barbara & Heyer, Judith, eds. The Comparative Political Economy of Development: Africa & South Asia. 2010. (Routledge Studies in Development Economics Ser.). (ENG., Illus.). 384p. (C). 145.00 *(978-0-415-55288-2(5))* Routledge.

Hayton, Bill. Vietnam: Rising Dragon. 2011. (ENG., Illus.). 272p. pap. 22.00 *(978-0-300-17814-2(X))* Yale Univ. Pr.

Herath, Gamini & Sharma, Kishor, eds. Child Labour in South Asia. 2007. (Contemporary Employment Relations Ser.). (Illus.). 202p. 114.95 *(978-0-7546-7004-9(X))* Ashgate Publishing Co.

Hertzog, Esther. Patrons of Women: Literacy Projects & Gender Development in Rural Nepal. 2011. (Illus.). 278p. 95.00 *(978-1-84545-768-6(4))* Berghahn Bks., Inc.

Holland, Martin. The Eu Through the Eyes of Asia Vol. 2: New Cases, New Findings. 2009. 284p. 86.00 *(978-981-4289-81-8(7))* World Scientific Publishing Co., Inc.

Howard, Elizabeth, ed. The Changing Face of Retailing in the Asia Pacific. 2009. (ENG., Illus.). 158p. (C). 125.00 *(978-0-415-48342-1(5))* Routledge.

Hua, Shiping. Islam & Democratization in Asia. 2009. *(978-1-60497-632-8(2))* Cambria Pr.

Inoguchi, Takashi & Blondel, Jean. Citizens & the State: Attitudes in Western Europe & East & Southeast Asia. 2007. (Routledge Innovations in Political Theory Ser.). (Illus.). 208p. 150.00 *(978-0-415-45191-8(4))* Routledge.

Jackson, Stevi, et al, eds. East Asian Sexualities: Modernity, Gender & New Sexual Cultures. 2008. (ENG.). 256p. 117.95 *(978-1-84277-888-3(9))*; pap. 36.95 *(978-1-84277-889-0(7))* Zed Bks., Ltd. GBR. Dist: Macmillan.

Jahani, Carina, et al, eds. The Baloch & Others: Linguistic, historical & socio-political perspectives on pluralism in Balochistan. 2008. (ENG.). 399p. (C). 100.00 *(978-3-89500-591-6(6))* Reichert, Ludwig Dr. DEU. Dist: Brown, David Bk. Co., The.

Jeffrey, Robin, et al, eds. Diminishing Conflicts in Asia & the Pacific. 2012. (Routledge Advances in Asia-Pacific Studies). (ENG., Illus.). 256p. (C). 145.00 *(978-0-415-67031-9(4))* Routledge.

Jones, Gavin & Douglass, Michael. Mega-urban Regions in Pacific Asia. (Illus.). 416p. pap. 28.00 *(978-9971-69-379-4(8))* National Univ. of Singapore Pr. SGP. Dist: Univ. of Hawaii Pr.

Kahlert, Heike & SchäFer, Sabine, eds. Engendering Transformation: Post-Socialist Experiences on Work, Politics & Culture: Gender Special Issue, Vol. 1. 2011. 200p. pap. 36.95 ***(978-3-86649-422-0(X))*** Budrich-Esser, Barbara DEU. Dist: International Specialized Bk. Services.

Kazimi, Nibras. Syria Through Jihadist Eyes: A Perfect Enemy. 2010. (Hoover inst press Publication). (ENG.). 66p. pap. 9.95 *(978-0-8179-1075-4(1))* Hoover Institution Pr.

Kazimi, Nibras. Syria Through Jihadist Eyes: A Perfect Enemy. 2010. (Hoover Inst Press Publication Ser.). xvi, 123p. E-Book 9.95 ***(978-0-8179-1076-1(X))*** Hoover Institution Pr.

Khondker, Habibul Haque & Therborn, Goran, eds. Asia & Europe in Globalization: Continents, Regions & Nations. 2006. (Social Sciences in Asia Ser.: Vol. 8). (Illus.). 313p. pap. *(978-90-04-15350-9(0))* BRILL.

Kidokoro, Tetsuo. Vulnerable Cities: Realities, Innovations & Strategies. 2008. (CSUR-UT Series: Library for Sustainable Urban Regeneration Ser.). (Illus.). xii, 330p. 109.00 *(978-4-431-78148-6(X))* Springer.

Kim, Heungchong & Park, Sung-Hoon, eds. Regional Integration in Europe & Asia: Legal, Economic, & Political Perspectives. 2009. 279p. pap. 49.00 *(978-3-8329-4336-3(6))* Nomos Verlagsgesellschaft DEU. Dist: International Specialized Bk. Services.

Kim, Saehoon. How Connected Is Connected? 2010. 96p. pap. *(978-3-8383-2118-9(9))* Lambert Academic Publishing.

Kim, Youna, ed. Media Consumption & Everyday Life in Asia. 2008. (Routledge Advances in Internationalizing Media Studies). (ENG., Illus.). 250p. 125.00 *(978-0-415-96245-2(5))* Routledge.

Kim, Youna, ed. Women & the Media in Asia: The Precarious Self. 2012. (ENG., Illus.). 256p. 85.00 ***(978-0-230-29272-7(0))*** Palgrave Macmillan.

Koirala, Anusha. A Comparative Study of Working Capital Management. 2011. 144p. pap. ***(978-3-8454-0229-1(6))*** Lambert Academic Publishing.

Kreutzmann, Hermann, ed. Pastoral Practices in High Asia: Agency of 'Development' Effected by Modernisation, Resettlement & Transformation. 2012. (Advances in Asian Human-Environmental Research Ser.). (ENG., Illus.). xv, 350p. 129.00 ***(978-94-007-3845-4(5)***, 9400738455) Springer.

Kudaisya, Gyanesh & Yong, Tan Tai, eds. Partition & Post-Colonial South Asia Set: A Reader, 3 vols. 2008. (Illus.). 1233p. 850.00 *(978-0-415-35954-2(6))* Routledge.

Kupatadze, Alexander. Organized Crime, Political Transitions & State Formation in Post-Soviet Eurasia. 2012. (Transnational Crime, Crime Control & Security Ser.). (ENG., Illus.). 272p. 85.00 ***(978-0-230-29980-1(6))*** Palgrave Macmillan.

Kyi, Aung San Suu. Letters from Burma. rev. ed. 2010. (ENG., Illus.). 224p. (gr. 12). pap. 16.00 *(978-0-14-104144-5(7)*, Penguin (Non-Classics)) Penguin Group (USA) Inc.

Lam. Japan's Peace Building Diplomacy in Asia. 2009. (Routledge Security in Asia Pacific Ser.). (ENG., Illus.). 192p. (C). 150.00 *(978-0-415-41320-6(6))* Routledge.

Laurent, Clint. Tomorrow's Asia: Exploding Asia's Population Myths. 2012. (ENG.). 256p. 24.95 *(978-0-470-82471-9(9)*, Wiley) Wiley, John & Sons, Inc.

Lee, Sang-Heon. Globalization, Flexibilization & Working Conditions in Asia & the Pacific. Lee, Sangheon & Eyraud, Francois, eds. 2008. (Chandos Asian Studies). (ENG., Illus.). 480p. 100.00 *(978-1-84334-330-1(4)*, Chandos Publishing) Woodhead Publishing Ltd. GBR. Dist: Ingram Pub. Services.

Lim, F. K. G. Imagining the Good Life: Negotiating Culture & Development in Nepal Himalaya. 2008. (Social Sciences in Asia Ser.). 225p. *(978-90-04-16787-2(0))* BRILL.

Liu, James H., et al, eds. Casting the Individual in Societal & Cultural Contexts: Social & Societal Psychology for Asia & the Pacific. 2007. (Progress in Asian Social Psychology Ser.). (Illus.). 375p. 50.00 *(978-89-25-40079-2(0))* Univ. of Hawaii Pr.

Lone, Stewart, ed. Daily Lives of Civilians in Wartime Asia: From the Taiping Rebellion to the Vietnam War, 1 vol. 2007. (Greenwood Press Daily Life Through History Ser.). (Illus.). 280p. 65.00 *(978-0-313-33684-3(9)*, GR3684, Greenwood Pr.) Greenwood Publishing Group, Inc.

Luong, Hy V. Tradition, Revolution, & Market Economy in a North Vietnamese Village, 1925-2006. 2010. (Illus.). (C). 62.00 *(978-0-8248-3370-1(8))*; pap. 28.00 *(978-0-8248-3423-4(2))* Univ. of Hawaii Pr.

Lyall, Alfred Comyn. Asiatic Studies: Religious & Social. 2010. (ENG.). 348p. pap. 32.75 *(978-1-171-74482-5(X))*; 364p. pap. 32.75 *(978-1-176-51204-7(8))* BiblioBazaar.

MACINTYRE, STIVENS MACKIE. Human Rights & Gender Politics: Asia-Pacific Perspectives. 2006. CCLVIp. 54.95 *(978-0-415-19174-6(2))* Routledge.

Mackintosh, Maureen, et al, eds. Promoting Innovation, Productivity & Industrial Growth & Reducing Poverty. 2008. VI, 202p. 150.00 *(978-0-415-46528-1(1))* Routledge.

Majumdar, Nivedita, ed. The Other Side of Terror: An Anthology of Writings on Terrorism in South Asia. 2009. (ENG., Illus.). 368p. 49.95 *(978-0-19-569696-7(4))* Oxford Univ. Pr., Inc.

Mangan, J. A., et al, eds. The Triple Asian Olympics: Asia Rising - The Pursuit of National Identity, International Recognition & Global Esteem. 2012. (Sport in the Global Society - Historical Perspectives Ser.). (ENG.). 224p. (C). 140.00 ***(978-0-415-52988-4(3))*** Routledge.

Martin, Fran, et al, eds. AsiaPacifiQueer: Rethinking Genders & Sexualities. 2008. (ENG., Illus.). 288p. 70.00 *(978-0-252-03307-0(8))* Univ. of Illinois Pr.

Mausch, Kai. Poverty, Inequality & the Non-farm Economy: the Case of Rural Vietnam: The Case of Rural Vietnam. 2010. 175p. pap. *(978-3-8325-2461-6(4))* Logos Verlag Berlin.

McCaskill, Don, et al, eds. Living in a Globalized World. 2008. (ENG., Illus.). 386p. (C). pap. 36.95 *(978-974-8276-63-2(5))* Silkworm Bks. THA. Dist: Univ. of Washington Pr.

Midgley, James & Mitsuhiko, Hosaka, eds. Grassroots Social Security in Asia: Mutual Associations, Microinsurance & Social Welfare. 2011. (Routledge Research on Public & Social Policy in Asia Ser.). (ENG., Illus.). 176p. (C). 133.00 *(978-0-415-49306-2(4))* Routledge.

Miller, Donald Eugene, et al, eds. Overcoming Violence in Asia: The Role of the Church in Seeking Cultures of Peace. 2011. 294p. pap. 23.95 *(978-1-931038-89-8(9))* Cascadia Publishing Hse., LLC.

Moller, J. Ørstrom. How Asia Can Shape the World: From the ERA of Plenty to the ERA of Scarcities. 2010. xiv, 540p. pap. ***(978-981-4311-33-5(2))*** Institute of Southeast Asian Studies.

Montiel, Cristina Jayme & Noor, Noraini M., eds. Peace Psychology in Asia. 2010. (Peace Psychology Book Ser.). (ENG., Illus.). xvi, 337p. pap. 189.00 ***(978-1-4419-3198-6(8)***, 1441931988) Springer.

Montiel, Cristina Jayme & Noor, Noraini N., eds. Peace Psychology in Asia. 2009. (Peace Psychology Book Ser.). (ENG., Illus.). xvi, 337p. 189.00 *(978-1-4419-0142-2(6))* Springer.

Muniappan, Rangaswamy, et al. Arthropod Pests of Horticultural Crops in Tropical Asia. 2012. (Illus.). 208p. 145.00 ***(978-1-84593-951-9(4))*** CABI GBR. Dist: Stylus Publishing, LLC.

Nag, Chitta Ranjan. Mizo Society in Transition. (C). 28.00 *(978-0-7069-6963-4(4))* Vikas Publishing Hse. Private, Ltd. IND. Dist: South Asia Bks.

Naguib, Nefissa. Women, Water & Memory: Recasting Lives in Palestine. 2009. (Women & Gender: The Middle East & the Islamic World Ser.). 196p. (C). pap. *(978-90-04-16778-0(1))* BRILL.

Nathan, Dev, et al. Markets & Indigenous Peoples in Asia: Lessons from Development Projects. 2012. (ENG.). 246p. 40.00 ***(978-0-19-807895-1(1))*** Oxford Univ. Pr., Inc.

Nault, Derrick M. Development in Asia: Interdisciplinary, Post-Neoliberal, & Transnational Perspectives. 2008. 276p. pap. 25.95 *(978-1-59942-488-0(6)*, Brown Walker Pr.) Universal Pubs.

Neopaney, Kritika. Impacts of Rural Electrification in the Lives of Bhutanese Women. 2011. 128p. pap. ***(978-3-8443-2143-2(8))*** Lambert Academic Publishing.

Oanh, Nguyen Thi Kim. Integrated Air Quality Mangement. 2012. (ENG., Illus.). 434p. 129.95 *(978-1-4398-6225-4(7)*, CRC Press) Taylor & Francis Group GBR. Dist: Taylor & Francis Group.

Oo, Thet Su. Violin Teaching for Young Beginners in Myanmar. 2010. 120p. pap. *(978-3-8383-1852-3(8))* Lambert Academic Publishing.

Organisation for Economic Co-Operation and Development & Asian Development Bank. The Criminalisation of Bribery in Asia & the Pacific: Frameworks & Practices in 28 Jurisdictions; Thematic Review - Final Report. 2011. (Illus.). 522p. pap. ***(978-92-64-09743-8(0))*** Organization for Economic Cooperation & Development.

Özbilgin, M. F. Diversity Management in Asia: A Research Companion. Syed, J., ed. 2010. (Illus.). 296p. 165.00 *(978-1-84720-644-2(1))* Elgar, Edward Publishing, Inc.

Paman, Alex. Asian Supernatural: Including Hawai'i & the Pacific. 2010. (ENG., Illus.). 288p. pap. 18.95 *(978-1-56647-924-0(X))* Mutual Publishing LLC.

Pawar, Manohar & Pawar, Manohar S. Community Development in Asia & the Pacific. 2009. (Routledge Studies in Development & Society Ser.). (ENG., Illus.). 244p. 125.00 *(978-0-415-99874-1(3))* Routledge.

Pham, Phu, et al. Livelihood Outcomes in the Residential Cluster & Dyke Programme. 2010. 112p. pap. *(978-3-639-26750-1(8))* VDM Verlag Dr. Mueller e.K.

Poudel. Dealing with Hidden Issues. 2011. 292p. pap. ***(978-3-8443-9021-6(9))*** Lambert Academic Publishing.

Powell, Jason L. & Cook, Ian G. Aging in Asia. 2009. (Aging Issues, Health & Financial Alternatives Ser.). (Illus.). 219p. 79.00 *(978-1-60741-649-4(2))* Nova Science Pubs., Inc.

Purewal, Navtej. Son Preference: Sex Selection, Gender & Culture in South Asia. 2010. (ENG.). 192p. 99.95 *(978-1-84520-467-9(0))*; pap. 29.95 *(978-1-84520-468-6(9))* Berg Pubs. GBR. Dist: Macmillan.

Quah, Stella R. Families in Asia: Home & Kin. 2nd rev. ed. 2008. (ENG., Illus.). 232p. (C). pap. 43.95 *(978-0-415-45570-1(7))*; 178.00 *(978-0-415-45568-8(5))* Routledge.

Rabinowitz, Alan. Life in the Valley of Death: The Fight to Save Tigers in a Land of Guns, Gold, & Greed. 2010. (ENG., Illus.). 248p. pap. 26.00 *(978-1-59726-824-0(0)*, Shearwater Bks.) Island Pr.

Reddy, Dr. D. Raja & Reddy, D. Raja. Endemic Skeletal Fluorosis. 2011. 180p. pap. ***(978-3-8454-1303-7(4))*** Lambert Academic Publishing.

Robinson, Kathryn, ed. Asian & Pacific Cosmopolitans: Self & Subject in Motion. 2007. (ENG., Illus.). 260p. 110.00 *(978-0-230-01330-8(9))* Palgrave Macmillan.

Rondinelli, Dennis A. & Heffron, John M., eds. Globalization & Change in Asia. 2007. 265p. (C). pap. 24.50 *(978-1-58826-497-8(1))*; lib. bdg. 59.95 *(978-1-58826-473-2(4))* Rienner, Lynne Pubs.

Rowley, Chris & Truong, Quang, eds. The Changing Face of Vietnamese Management. 2009. (Working in Asia Ser.). (ENG & CHI., Illus.). XXVI, 278p. 135.00 *(978-0-415-47604-1(6))* Routledge.

Roy, Ananya & Ong, Aihwa, eds. Worlding Cities: Asian Experiments & the Art of Being Global. 2011. (Studies in Urban & Social Change Ser.: 31). (ENG., Illus.). 376p. 89.95 *(978-1-4051-9277-4(1)*, Wiley-Blackwell) Wiley, John & Sons, Inc.

Rydstrom, Helle. Gendered Inequalities in Asia: Configuring, Contesting & Recognizing Women & Men. (Illus.). 336p. pap. 37.00 *(978-87-7694-047-8(0))* Nordic Institute of Asian Studies DNK. Dist: Univ. of Hawaii Pr.

SEARO. Regional Report on Status of Road Safety: The South-East Asia Region. 2010. (SEARO Publication). 103p. pap. 24.00 *(978-92-9022-355-9(3))* World Health Organization.

Shagdarsuren, Oyuntuya. Tackling Isolation in Rural Mongoli. 2009. 68p. pap. *(978-3-639-19919-2(7))* VDM Verlag Dr. Mueller e.K.

Sharma, Ashok, et al, eds. Asia 2050: Realizing the Asian Century. 2011. 412p. (C). 70.00 ***(978-81-321-0756-9(X)***, B07569C) SAGE Pubns., Inc.

Shaunak, Mir Fahim & Chowdhury, Sabrin. Inclusion of Disabled People in Transport Facilities. 2011. 84p. pap. ***(978-3-8443-2360-3(0))*** Lambert Academic Publishing.

Shaw, Rajib & Nguyen, Huy, eds. Droughts in Asian Monsoon Region. 2011. (Community, Environment & Disaster Risk Management Ser.). 206p. ***(978-0-85724-863-3(4))*** Emerald Group Publishing Ltd.

Shaw, Rajib, et al. Urban Risk Reduction: An Asian Perspective. 2009. (Illus.). 230p. 144.95 *(978-1-84855-906-6(2))* Emerald Group Publishing Ltd. GBR. Dist: Turpin Distribution Services Ltd.

Shaw, Victor N. Crime & Social Control in Asia & the Pacific: A Cross-Border Study. 2007. (ENG.). 358p. 83.99 *(978-0-7618-3679-7(9))*; per. 52.50 *(978-0-7618-3680-3(2))* Univ. Pr. of America, Inc.

Sleeboom-Faulkner, Margaret, ed. Frameworks of Choice: Predictive & Genetic Testing in Asia. 2010. (IIAS Publications Ser.). (Illus.). 288p. pap. *(978-90-8964-165-6(3))* Amsterdam Univ. Pr.

Sleeboom-Faulkner, Margaret, ed. Human Genetic Biobanks in Asia: Politics of trust & scientific Advancement. 2012. (Routledge Contemporary Asia Ser.). (ENG.). 224p. (C). pap. 42.95 ***(978-0-415-54141-7(7))*** Routledge.

Srivastava, Anil K. Gender & Slum Culture in Asia. 2010. 277p. 47.50 *(978-81-7533-260-7(3))* M. D. Pubns. Pvt, Ltd. IND. Dist: Coronet Bks.

Streeten, Paul. Essays in Social & Economic Development. 2010. 385p. 93.75 (978-81-7708-232-6(9)) New Century Publications IND. Dist: International Specialized Bk. Services.
Sylas, Eluma Ikemefuna. Terrorism: A Global Scourge. 2011. (ENG.). 484p. pap. 22.95 (978-1-4327-7923-8(0)) Outskirts Pr., Inc.
Teh Cheng Guan, Benny, ed. Human Security: Securing East Asia's Future. 2012. (ENG.). xiii, 255p. 139.00 (978-94-007-1798-5(9), 9400717989) Springer.
Tong, Chee Kiong. Identity & Ethnic Relations in Southeast Asia: Racializing Chineseness. 2010. (ENG.). viii, 274p. 189.00 (978-90-481-8908-3(X), 904818908X) Springer.
Tooker, Deborah E. Space & the Production of Cultural Difference among the Akha Prior to Globalization: Channeling the Flow of Life. 2012. (ICAS Publications Ser.). (ENG.). 372p. pap. (978-90-8964-325-4(7)) Amsterdam Univ. Pr.
Trichur, Ganesh K., ed. Asia & the Transformation of the World-System. 2009. (Political Economy of the World-System Annuals Ser.). 176p. 125.00 (978-1-59451-741-9(X)) Paradigm Pubs.
Tsai, Lucetta. The Impact of Western Culture on Women's Leisure in Taiwan. 2011. 412p. pap. (978-3-8443-1613-1(2)) Lambert Academic Publishing.
Tsuya, Noriko O., et al. Prudence & Pressure: Reproduction & Human Agency in Europe & Asia, 1700-1900. 2010. (Eurasian Population & Family History Ser.). (ENG., Illus.). 406p. (gr. 17). 40.00 (978-0-262-01352-9(5)) MIT Pr.
Tun, Sai Aung. History of the Shan State: From Its Origins To 1962. 2008. (ENG., Illus.). 680p. (C). pap. 52.00 (978-974-9511-43-5(3)) Silkworm Bks. THA. Dist: Univ. of Washington Pr.
Turner, Bryan S. & Yangwen, Zheng, eds. The Body in Asia. 2009. (Illus.). 240p. 90.00 (978-1-84545-550-7(9)) Berghahn Bks., Inc.
United Nations. Annual Report of the Economic & Social Commission for Asia & the Pacific 2010. 2011. (ENG.). 62p. pap. 13.00 (978-92-1-880188-3(0)) United Nations Pubns.
—Greening Growth in Asia & the Pacific: Follow-up to the World Summit on Sustainable Development - Taking action on the Regional Implementation Plan for Sustainable Development in Asia & the Pacific, 2006-2010. 2009. (ENG.). 76p. pap. 36.00 (978-92-1-120571-8(9)) United Nations Pubns.
—Regional Workshop on the Empowerment of Persons with Intellectual Disabilities & their Families in Asia & the Pacific. 2009. (ENG.). 26p. pap. 20.00 (978-92-1-120555-8(7)) United Nations Pubns.
—Statistical Abstract of the ESCWA Region, 26th Issue. 2008. (MUL.). 260p. pap. 45.00 (978-92-1-128308-2(6)) United Nations Pubns.
—TC Yearbook 2006: Technical Cooperation. 2007. (ENG.). 72p. pap. 38.00 (978-92-1-120506-0(9)) United Nations Pubns.
United Nations Development Programme. Power,Voice, & Rights: A Turning Point for Gender Equality in Asia & the Pacific. 2010. 260p. pap. 20.00 (978-92-1-126286-5(0)) United Nations Pubns.
Werbner, Pnina & Johnson, Mark, eds. Diasporic Journeys Ritual & Normativity among Asian Migrant Women. 2011. (ENG.). 264p. (C). 125.00 (978-0-415-59201-7(1)) Routledge.
WHO Regional Office for the Western Pacific. HIV/AIDS Care & Treatment for People Who Inject Drugs in Asia & the Pacific. 2009. (WPRO Nonserial Publication Ser.). (ENG.). 64p. pap. 12.00 (978-92-9061-320-6(3)) World Health Organization.
Wilson, Constance M. The Middle Mekong River Basin: Studies in Tai History & Culture. 2009. 412p. 28.00 (978-1-891134-30-2(2)) Southeast Asia Pubns.
Wu, Guang. USA - United States of Asia. 2010. (Asian Political, Economic, & Security Issues Ser.). 99p. 43.00 (978-1-60876-180-7(0)) Nova Science Pubs., Inc.
Xiao, Xinhuang. East Asian Middle Classes in Comparative Perspective: Konqueror, KDevelop, Opera, Calligra Suite, Skype, Amarok, KDE Software Compilation 4, VLC media player, Kontact, K3b, Scribus, Digikam, KTorrent, Rekonq, Clementine, Doxygen, KVIrc, MuseScore, Konversation, Umbrello, KGet, Kopete. (Illus.). x, 497p. pap. (978-957-671-623-2(3)) Academia Sinica.
Yea, Sallie & Kitiarsa, Pattana, eds. Human Trafficking in Asia. 2012. (Routledge Contemporary Asia Ser.). (ENG.). 256p. (C). 135.00 (978-0-415-52182-6(3)) Routledge.
Yew, Leong, ed. Alterities in Asia: Reflections on Identity & Regionalism. 2010. (Routledge Contemporary Asia Ser.). (ENG., Illus.). 240p. (C). 140.00 (978-0-415-58750-1(6)) Routledge.
Yip, Paul S. F. Suicide in Asia: Causes & Prevention. 2008. (ENG., Illus.). 176p. (gr. 17). 50.00 (978-962-209-942-5(4)); pap. 19.50 (978-962-209-943-2(2)) Hong Kong Univ. Pr. HKG. Dist: Columbia Univ. Pr.
Zhang, Yanchun. Progress in Www Research & Development. 2008. (Lecture Notes in Computer Science / Information Systems & Applications, incl. Internet/Web, & HCI Ser.). (Illus.). pap. 129.00 (978-3-540-78848-5(4), 3540788484) Springer.
Zittrain, Jonathan. Access Contested: Security, Identity, & Resistance in Asian Cyberspace. Deibert, Ronald et al, eds. 2011. (Information Revolution & Global Politics Ser.). (ENG., Illus.). 432p. (gr. 17). 48.00 (978-0-262-01678-0(8)); pap. 24.00 (978-0-262-51680-8(2)) MIT Pr.

ASIA—SOCIAL LIFE AND CUSTOMS

Anderson, Edward F. Plants & People of the Golden Triangle: Ethnobotany of the Hill Tribes of Northern Thailand. 2009. (ENG.). 356p. pap. 49.95 (978-1-60469-081-1(X), 160469081X) Timber Pr., Inc.
Anderson, Sean. Flames of Devotion: Oil Lamps from South & Southeast Asia & the Himalayas. 2006. (ENG., Illus.). 112p. pap. (978-0-9748729-3-3(8)) Univ. of California, Los Angeles, Fowler Museum of Cultural History.
Bala, Arun, ed. Asia, Europe, & the Emergence of Modern Science: Knowledge Crossing Boundaries. 2012. (ENG., Illus.). 304p. 90.00 (978-1-137-03172-3(7)) Palgrave Macmillan.
Bald, Margaret. From the Sahara to Samarkand: The Remarkabke Journeys of Rosita Forbes. 2010. (ENG.). 369p. pap. 15.00 (978-1-60419-030-4(2)) Axios Pr.
Baldeck, Andrea. Himalaya: Land of the Snow Lion. 2008. (Illus.). 244p. 34.95 (978-1-934536-09-4(1), Univ. of Pennsylvania Museum of Archaeology & Anthropology) Univ. Museum Pubns.
Bates, Chris & Bates, Ling-Li. Taiwan, 1 vol. 2008. (CultureShock! Ser.). (ENG., Illus.). 304p. pap. 15.95 (978-0-7614-5497-7(7)) Marshall Cavendish Corp.
Berkwitz, Stephen C., et al. Buddhist Manuscript Cultures: Knowledge, Ritual & Art. Berkwitz, Stephen C. et al, eds. 2009. (Routledge Critical Studies in Buddhism Ser.). (Illus.). 222p. 170.00 (978-0-415-77616-5(3)) Routledge.
Bose, Sugata & Jalal, Ayesha, eds. Modern South Asia: A Sourcebook & Reader. 2012. (ENG.). 384p. (C). 135.00 (978-0-415-77940-1(5)); pap. 39.95 (978-0-415-77941-8(3)) Routledge.
Bosrock, Mary Murray. Asian Business Customs & Manners: A Country-by-Country Guide. McGinnis, Megan, ed. 2007. (ENG.). 450p. per. 16.00 (978-0-684-05200-7(8)) Meadowbrook Pr.
Cheah, Hwei-Fe'N. Phoenix Rising: Cl. 2010. (Illus.). 400p. 78.00 (978-9971-69-516-3(2)) National Univ. of Singapore Pr. SGP. Dist: Univ. of Hawaii Pr.
—Phoenix Rising: Pa. 2010. (Illus.). 400p. pap. 58.00 (978-9971-69-468-5(9)) National Univ. of Singapore Pr. SGP. Dist: Univ. of Hawaii Pr.
Chen, Kuan-Hsing & Huat, Chua Beng. The Inter-Asia Cultural Studies Reader. 2007. 624p. 140.00 (978-0-415-43134-7(4)) Routledge.
Chen, Kuan-Hsing & Huat, Chua Beng, eds. Inter-Asia Cultural Studies Reader. 2007. 624p. per. 43.95 (978-0-415-43135-4(2)) Routledge.
Cheung. Food & Foodways in Asia. 2007. (Illus.). 240p. 180.00 (978-0-415-39213-6(6)) Routledge.
Cheung, Sidney C. H., ed. Food & Foodways in Asi. 2009. 216p. pap. 39.95 (978-0-415-54704-8(0)) Routledge.
Corr, Kendra. The U. S. & W. W. I: I Think: U. S. History. 2011. (ENG.). 100p. (YA). pap. 29.95 (978-1-933558-17-2(2)) InspirEd Educators.
Cravath, Paul. Earth in Flower: The Divine Mystery of the Cambodian Dance Drama. 2008. (Illus.). 544p. 128.00 (978-1-934431-28-3(1)) DatASIA.
Cytryn-Silverman, Katia. The Road Inns (Khans) in Bilad Al-Sham. 2010. (Bar S Ser.). (ENG., Illus.). 290p. (C). pap. 145.00 (978-1-4073-0671-1(5)) British Archaeological Reports Ltd. GBR. Dist: Brown, David Bk. Co., The.
Czaplicka, Marie Antoinette. The Turks of Central Asia in History & at the Present Day: An Ethnological Inquiry into the Pan-Turanian Problem, & Bibliographical Material Relating to the Early Turks & the Present Turks of Central Asia. 2006. (Illus.). 242p. 55.00 (978-1-57898-535-7(8)) Martino Publishing.
Daguan, Zhou. A Record of Cambodia: The Land & Its People. Harris, Peter, tr. from CHI. 2007. (ENG., Illus.). 184p. (C). pap. 26.95 (978-974-9511-24-4(7)) Silkworm Bks. THA. Dist: Univ. of Washington Pr.
Danzan Narantuya & Danzan, Narantuya. Religion in 20th Century Mongolia: Social Changes & Popular Practices. 2008. 168p. pap. (978-3-639-09465-7(4)) VDM Verlag Dr. Mueller e.K.
Das, Veena. South Asian Culture & Society. 2010. (Illus.). 480p. (C). instr.'s hndbk. ed. 199.00 (978-0-415-77557-1(4)) Routledge.
De Bary, William Theodore. Sources of East Asian Tradition Vol. 1: Premodern Asia, 2 vols., vol. 1. de Bary, Wm. Theodore, ed. 2008. (Introduction to Asian Civilizations Ser.). (ENG.). 936p. (gr. 17). pap. 35.00 (978-0-231-14305-9(2)) Columbia Univ. Pr.
de Bary, Wm. Theodore. Sources of East Asian Tradition Vol. 2: The Modern Period, 2 vols., vol. 2. 2008. (Introduction to Asian Civilizations Ser.). (ENG.). 1192p. (gr. 17). 99.50 (978-0-231-14322-6(2)); pap. 35.00 (978-0-231-14323-3(0)) Columbia Univ. Pr.
de Bary, Wm. Theodore, ed. Sources of East Asian Tradition Vol. 1: Premodern Asia, 2 vols., vol. 1. 2008. (Introduction to Asian Civilizations Ser.). (ENG., Illus.). 936p. (gr. 17). 99.50 (978-0-231-14304-2(4)) Columbia Univ. Pr.
Doron, Assa & Broom, Alex, eds. Health, Culture & Religion in South Asia: Critical Social Science Perspectives. 2010. (Routledge South Asian History & Culture Ser.). (ENG., Illus.). 164p. (C). 125.00 (978-0-415-55609-5(0)) Routledge.
Duncan, Nancy. The Nail That Sticks Up: An American Woman in Asia & Africa. 2007. 436p. per. 29.95 (978-1-4241-7539-0(9)) PublishAmerica, Inc.
Farkas, Barbara. Chinesische Einwanderer in Penang. 2009. (GER.). 145p. pap. 49.95 (978-3-631-58327-2(3)) Lang, Peter GmbH, Europaischer Verlag der Wissenschaften DEU. Dist: Lang, Peter.
Fijn, Natasha. Living with Herds: Human-Animal Co-Existence in Mongolia. 2011. (ENG., Illus.). 273p. 90.00 (978-1-107-00090-2(4)) Cambridge Univ. Pr.
Fisher, Aaron. The Way of Tea: Reflections on a Life with Tea. 2010. (ENG., Illus.). 192p. 19.95 (978-0-8048-4032-3(6)) Tuttle Publishing.
Freiberger, Oliver, ed. Asceticism & Its Critics: Historical Accounts & Comparative Perspectives. 2006. (AAR Cultural Criticism Ser.). (ENG.). 268p. 99.00 (978-0-19-530791-7(7)) Oxford Univ. Pr., Inc.
Goody, Jack. Food & Love: A Cultural History of East & West. 2010. (ENG.). 240p. pap. 24.95 (978-1-84467-438-1(X), 844438) Verso Bks. GBR. Dist: Norton, W. W. & Co., Inc.
Grehan, James. Everyday Life & Consumer Culture in Eighteenth-Century Damascus. 2007. (ENG., Illus.). 310p. 50.00 (978-0-295-98676-0(X)) Univ. of Washington Pr.
Guirdham, Maureen. Culture & Business in Asia. 2009. (ENG., Illus.). 320p. pap. 56.00 (978-0-230-51808-7(7)) Palgrave Macmillan.
Haigh, Ken. Under the Holy Lake: A Memoir of Eastern Bhutan. 2008. (Wayfarer Ser.). (ENG., Illus.). 296p. pap. 29.95 (978-0-88864-492-3(2)) Univ. of Alberta Pr. CAN. Dist: Michigan State Univ. Pr.
Harris, Lisa Ohlen. Through the Veil. 2010. pap. (978-1-59128-070-5(2)) Canon Pr.
Hipsher, Scott A. Expatriates in Asia: Breaking Free from the Colonial Paradigm. 2008. (Illus.). 224p. (978-1-84334-422-3(X), Chandos Publishing) Woodhead Publishing Ltd.
—Expatriates in Asia: Breaking Free from the Colonial Paradigm. 2008. (Chandos Asian Studies). (ENG., Illus.). 222p. pap. 70.00 (978-1-84334-421-6(1), Chandos Publishing) Woodhead Publishing Ltd. GBR. Dist: Ingram Pub. Services.
Ho, Chi-Tang & Shahidi, Fereidoon. Functional Foods of the East. Shi, John, ed. 2010. (Nutraceutical Science & Technology Ser.). (ENG., Illus.). 502p. 169.95 (978-1-4200-7192-4(0), CRC Press) Taylor & Francis Group GBR. Dist: Taylor & Francis Group.
Hua, Shiping. Islam & Democratization in Asia. 2009. (978-1-60497-632-3(2)) Cambria Pr.
Idris, Wan Irma Sabrina. Wayang Kulit Online Game. 2009. 144p. pap. (978-3-639-18842-4(X)) VDM Verlag Dr. Mueller e.K.
Imady, Elaine Rippey. Road to Damascus. 2009. (ENG., Illus.). 276p. pap. 19.95 (978-1-933455-13-6(6)) M S I Pr.
Jacobsen, Knut A. South Asian Religions on Display: Religious Processions in South Asia & in the Diaspora. 2009. (Illus.). 228p. pap. 39.95 (978-0-415-54489-4(0)) Routledge.
James, David. Sixteen Seasons: Stories from a Missionary Family in Tajikstan. 2011. (978-0-87808-473-9(8)) Carey, William Library Pubs.
Jordan, Peter, ed. Landscape & Culture in Northern Eurasia. 2010. (Univ col london inst arch Pub Ser.). (ENG., Illus.). 356p. 99.95 (978-1-59874-244-2(2)) Left Coast Pr., Inc.
Jung, Sun. Korean Masculinities & Transcultural Consumption: Yonsama, Rain, Oldboy. 2010. (TransAsia: Screen Cultures Ser.). (ENG & CHI., Illus.). 232p. (gr. 17). 50.00 (978-988-8028-66-5(9)) Hong Kong Univ. Pr. HKG. Dist: Columbia Univ. Pr.
—Korean Masculinities & Transcultural Consumption: Yonsama, Rain, Oldboy, K-Pop Idols. 2010. (TransAsia: Screen Cultures Ser.). (ENG., Illus.). 232p. (gr. 17). pap. 28.00 (978-988-8028-67-2(7)) Hong Kong Univ. Pr. HKG. Dist: Columbia Univ. Pr.
Keul, István, ed. Transformations & Transfer of Tantra in Asia & Beyond. 2012. (Religion & Society Ser.). (ENG., Illus.). X, 531p. (gr. 17). E-Book 252.00 (978-3-11-220396-5(8)) De Gruyter, Walter Inc.
Khan, Ashfaq,;MBA. Experience Intelligent Eating. 2009. (ENG.). 97p. pap. 34.99 (978-0-557-20648-3(0)) Lulu Enterprises Inc.
Kociejowski, Marius. The Pigeon Wars of Damascus. 2011. (ENG., Illus.). 328p. 25.95 (978-1-897231-97-5(0)); pap. 17.95 (978-1-926845-02-9(1)) Biblioasis CAN. Dist: Consortium Bk. Sales & Distribution.
Lattimore, Owen. Nomads & Commissars: Mongolia Revisited. 2011. 272p. 47.95 (978-1-258-08610-7(7)) Literary Licensing, LLC.
Lawrence, T. E. Revolt in the Desert: The Abridged Edition of Seven Pillars of Wisdom. 2011. (ENG., Illus.). 352p. 18.00 (978-1-84885-665-3(2), Tauris Parke Paperbacks) I. B. Tauris & Co., Ltd. GBR. Dist: Macmillan.
Leaming, Linda. Married to Bhutan: How One Woman Got Lost, Said 'I Do', & Found Bliss. 2011. (ENG.). 256p. pap. 14.95 (978-1-4019-2846-9(3)) Hay Hse., Inc.
Lee, Chanseok. The Christological Perspectives of Panikkar & Byungmu Ahn - Toward an Asian Christology. 2008. 216p. pap. (978-3-639-03856-9(8)), VDM Verlag Dr. Mueller e.K.
Lee, G. Y. & Tapp, Nicholas. Culture & Customs of the Hmong. 2010. E-Book (978-0-313-34527-2(9), Greenwood Pr.) Greenwood Publishing Group, Inc.
Lee, Gary & Tapp, Nicholas. Culture & Customs of the Hmong, 1 vol. 2010. (Culture & Customs of Asia Ser.). (Illus.). 241p. 49.95 (978-0-313-34526-5(0), GR4526) Greenwood Publishing Group, Inc.
Leong-Salobir, Cecilia. Food Culture in Colonial Asia. 2011. (Routledge Studies in the Modern History of Asia Ser.). (ENG.). 208p. (C). 148.00 (978-0-415-60632-5(2)) Routledge.
Limbert, Mandana. In the Time of Oil: Piety, Memory, & Social Life in an Omani Town. 2010. (ENG., Illus.). 264p. 65.00 (978-0-8047-5626-6(0)); pap. 24.95 (978-0-8047-5627-3(9)) Stanford Univ. Pr.
Low, Kelvin E. Y. & Kalekin-Fishman, Devorah, eds. Everyday Life in Asia: Social Perspectives on the Senses. 2010. (Illus.). 224p. 99.95 (978-0-7546-7994-3(2)) Ashgate Publishing Co.
Lyall, Alfred Comyn. Asiatic Studies: Religious & Social. 2010. (ENG.). 348p. pap. 32.75 (978-1-171-74482-5(X)); 364p. pap. 32.75 (978-1-176-51204-7(8)) BiblioBazaar.
Manners, David. In the Shadow of Crows. 2010. (ENG., Illus.). 352p. pap. (978-1-906702-06-9(3)) Reportage Pr.
Manners, David Charles. In the Shadow of Crows. 2011. (ENG.). 336p. pap. (978-1-904955-92-4(4)) Signal Bks.
Michaels, Axel, ed. Ritual Dynamics & the Science of Ritual: I: Grammars & Morphologies of Ritual Practices in Asia. 2010. (ENG.). 591p. (C). 147.00 (978-3-447-06201-5(0)) Harrassowitz, Otto Verlag DEU. Dist: ISD.
—Ritual Dynamics & the Science of Ritual: II: Body, Performance, Agency & Experience. 2010. (ENG.). 583p. (C). 147.00 (978-3-447-06202-2(9)) Harrassowitz, Otto Verlag DEU. Dist: ISD.
—Ritual Dynamics & the Science of Ritual: III: State, Power & Violence. 2010. (ENG.). 831p. (C). 177.00 (978-3-447-06203-9(7)) Harrassowitz, Otto Verlag DEU. Dist: ISD.
—Ritual Dynamics & the Science of Ritual: IV: Reflexivity, Media & Visuality. 2011. (ENG.). 723p. (C). 162.00 (978-3-447-06204-6(5)) Harrassowitz, Otto Verlag DEU. Dist: ISD.
—Ritual Dynamics & the Science of Ritual (5 volume Set), 5 vols. 2010. (ENG.). 3200p. (C). 588.00 (978-3-447-06206-0(1)) Harrassowitz, Otto Verlag DEU. Dist: ISD.
Ming-Yuet, Kee. Peranakan Chinese Porcelain: Vibrant Festive Ware of the Straits Chinese. 2009. (ENG., Illus.). 256p. 65.00 (978-0-8048-4007-1(5)) Tuttle Publishing.
Mirante, Edith. Down the Rat Hole: Adventures Underground on the Burma Frontier. 2006. (ENG., Illus.). 200p. pap. 21.95 (978-974-524-050-6(6)) Orchid Pr. THA. Dist: National Bk. Network.
Mooney, Peter. A Servant of Sarawak: Reminiscences of a Crown Counsel in 1950s Borneo. 2012. (ENG., Illus.). 272p. pap. 15.95 (978-981-4358-37-8(1)) Monsoon Bks. Pte. Ltd.
Morgan, Kenneth W. Reaching for the Moon: On Asian Religious Paths. 2010. (ENG.). 207p. (gr. 17). pap. 34.00 (978-0-231-15789-6(4)) Columbia Univ. Pr.
Munan, Heidi. Borneo: A Survival Guide to Customs & Etiquette. 2009. 264p. pap. 15.95 (978-0-7614-5659-9(7)) Marshall Cavendish Corp.
—Malaysia, 1 vol. 2008. (CultureShock! Ser.). (ENG., Illus.). 272p. pap. 15.95 (978-0-7614-5491-5(8)) Marshall Cavendish Corp.
Murphy, Stephen. Connections: Portraits of Asia. 2007. (ENG., Illus.). 96p. 29.95 (978-0-9793314-1-1(2), Imago) LawyersWriting.
Naguib, Nefissa. Women, Water & Memory: Recasting Lives in Palestine. 2009. (Women & Gender: The Middle East & the Islamic World Ser.). 196p. (C). pap. (978-90-04-16778-0(1)) BRILL.
Ngcheong-Lum, Roseline. Mauritius: A Survival Guide to Customs & Etiquette. 2009. 312p. pap. 15.95 (978-0-7614-5668-1(6)) Marshall Cavendish Corp.
Ngcheong-Lum, Roseline & Cavendish, Marshall. Cultureshock! Mauritius, 1 vol. 2007. (Cultureshock Mauritius: A Survival Guide to Customs & Etiquette Ser.). (ENG., Illus.). 32p. pap. 15.95 (978-0-7614-2501-4(2)) Marshall Cavendish Corp.
Osborne, Milton. Phnom Penh: A Cultural History. 2008. (CityScapes Ser.). (ENG., Illus.). 256p. 60.00 (978-0-19-534247-5(X)); pap. 16.95 (978-0-19-534248-2(8)) Oxford Univ. Pr., Inc.
Peletz, Michael G. Gender, Sexuality, & Body Politics in Modern Asia. 2007. pap. (978-0-924304-50-7(2)) Assn. for Asian Studies, Inc.
Raj, Selva J. & Harman, William P., eds. Dealing with Deities: The Ritual Vow in South Asia. 2007. (Illus.). 287p. per. 31.95 (978-0-7914-6708-4(2)) State Univ. of New York Pr.
Saul, Jamie. The Naga of Burma: Their Festivals, Customs, & Way of Life. 2006. (ENG., Illus.). 212p. pap. 36.00 (978-974-524-065-0(6)) Orchid Pr. THA. Dist: National Bk. Network.
Shannon, Jonathan. Among the Jasmine Trees: Music & Modernity in Contemporary Syria. 2009. (Music Culture Ser.). (ENG., Illus.). 288p. pap. 24.95 (978-0-8195-6944-8(5)) Wesleyan Univ. Pr.
Shih, Fang-Long. Rewriting Culture in Taiwan. Thompson, Stuart & Tremlett, Paul, eds. 2008. (Asia's Transformations Ser.). (ENG., Illus.). 240p. (C). 150.00 (978-0-415-46666-0(0)) Routledge.
Sinha, Babli, ed. South Asian Transnationalisms: Cultural Exchange in the Twentieth Century. 2012. (Routledge South Asian History & Culture Ser.). (ENG.). 160p. (C). 125.00 (978-0-415-55618-7(X)) Routledge.
Skeat, Walter William. Malay Magic: Being an Introduction to the Folklore & Popular Religion of the Malay Peninsula. 2007. (ENG.). 740p. 66.95 (978-0-548-10918-2(4)) Kessinger Publishing, LLC.
Sochaczewski, Paul S. Sultan & Mermaid Queen. 2009. (ENG., Illus.). 256p. pap. 13.95 (978-981-4217-74-3(3), Didier Millet,Csi) Continental Sales, Inc.
Steinpichler, Constantin K. Asian Business Culture & Management: A Deconstruction of Intercultural Management Research Approaches on the Asian Business Region 2008. 128p. pap. (978-3-8364-3126-2(2)) VDM Verlag Dr. Mueller e.K.
Stevenson, Dominic. Monkey House Blues. 2010. (ENG., Illus.). 240p. pap. 18.95 (978-1-84596-566-2(3)) Mainstream Publishing Co., Ltd. GBR. Dist: Independent Pubs. Group.
Stewart, Pamela J. & Strathern, Andrew, eds. Asian Ritual Systems: Syncretisms & Ruptures. 2007. (Ritual Studies Monograph). pap. 40.00 (978-1-59460-157-6(7)) Carolina Academic Pr.
Sung, Kyu-taik. Respect & Care for the Elderly: The East Asian Way. 2007. (ENG., Illus.). 347p. 78.99 (978-0-7618-3789-3(2)); per. 51.50 (978-0-7618-3790-9(6)) Univ. Pr. of America, Inc.
Terhune, Molly. The Multinational Significance of Yog. 2009. 112p. pap. (978-3-639-17728-2(2)) VDM Verlag Dr. Mueller e.K.
Timothy, Dallen J., et al, eds. Cultural & Heritage Tourism in Asia & the Pacific. 2008. (Illus.). VIII, 336p. 125.00 (978-0-415-36673-1(9)) Routledge.
Trzcionka, Silke. Magic & the Supernatural in Fourth Century Syria. 2006. 240p. 34.95 (978-0-415-39242-6(X)) Routledge.
Tun, Sai Aung. History of the Shan State: From Its Origins To 1962. 2008. (ENG., Illus.). 680p. (C). pap. 52.00 (978-974-9511-43-5(3)) Silkworm Bks. THA. Dist: Univ. of Washington Pr.
Vaidya, Kalyan. Not for $ Anymore. 2010. 143p. pap. (978-81-223-1114-3(8)) Mahal, Pustak Pubs., Booksellers & Order Suppliers.
Vaish, Viniti. Globalization of Language & Culture in Asia: The Impact of Globalization Processes on Language. Vaish, Viniti, ed. 2010. (Advances in Sociolinguistics Ser.). (ENG., Illus.). 256p. 140.00 (978-1-84706-183-6(4))

Continuum International Publishing Group, Ltd. GBR. Dist: National Bk. Network.

van Ham, Peter & Van Ham, Peter. Indiens Tibet - Tibets Indien: Das kulturelle Vermächtnis des West-Himalaja. Begleit-Ausstellungen: St. Gallen 05.09.2009-18.04.2010 Historisches und Völkerkundemuseum. 2009. (GER., Illus.). 240p. (C). 72.00 *(978-3-7774-2221-3(5))* Hirmer Verlag GmbH DEU. Dist: Brown, David Bk. Co., The.

Wilson, Constance M. The Middle Mekong River Basin: Studies in Tai History & Culture. 2009. 412p. 28.00 *(978-1-891134-30-2(2))* Southeast Asia Pubns.

Witham, Lynn. Kuala Lumpur, 1 vol. 2008. (CultureShock! Ser.). (ENG.). 352p. pap. 15.95 *(978-0-7614-5508-0(6))* Marshall Cavendish Corp.

Zurick, David. The Himalaya: Encounters with the Roof of the World. 2011. (Center for American Places - Center Books on American Places Ser.). (ENG., Illus.). 192p. 39.95 *(978-1-930066-96-0(1))* Ctr. for American Places, Inc.

ASIA—STATISTICS

Abbasi-Shavazi, Mohammad Jalal, et al. The Fertility Transition in Iran: Revolution & Reproduction. 2009. (ENG., Illus.). xxiv, 196p. 159.00 *(978-90-481-3197-6(9)*, 9048131979) Springer.

Beeson, Mark. Far East & Australasia 2010. Europa Publications Staff, ed. 41st ed. 2009. 1588p. 810.00 *(978-1-85743-533-7(8))* Routledge.

Belay, Tekabe A. Building on Early Gains in Afghanistan's Health, Nutrition, & Population Sector: Challenges & Options. 2010. (Directions in Development Ser.). (ENG., Illus.). 224p. pap. 35.00 *(978-0-8213-8335-3(3)*, 9780821383353) World Bank Pubns.

Engelen, Theo, et al, eds. Death at the Opposite Ends of Eurasian Continent: Mortality Trends in Taiwan & the Netherlands. 2012. (Life at the Extremes Ser.). 400p. pap. *(978-90-5260-379-7(0))* Amsterdam Univ. Pr.

Euromonitor International Staff, ed. Asian Marketing Data & Statistics. 5th ed. 2011. (Asia Marketing Data & Statistics Ser.). (ENG.). 382p. lib. bdg. ***(978-1-84264-547-5(1))*** Euromonitor International PLC.

Europa Publications, ed. The Far East & Australasia 2012. 43rd rev. ed. 2011. (ENG.). 1608p. 880.00 ***(978-1-85743-630-3(X))*** Routledge.

—South Asia 2012. 9th rev. ed. 2011. (ENG.). 848p. 815.00 ***(978-1-85743-624-2(5))*** Routledge.

Gale. Consumer Asia Pacific & Australasia. 19th ed. 2011. (Consumer Asia Pacific & Australasia Ser.). (ENG.). 342p. ***(978-1-84264-552-9(8))*** Euromonitor International PLC.

Mitchell, Brian. Africa, Asia & Oceania, 1750-2005, 3 vols. 6th rev. ed. 2007. (ENG.). 1152p. 400.00 *(978-0-230-00515-0(2))* Palgrave Macmillan.

Rahman, Rejaur. Urban Spatial Growth Analysis of Khulna City. 2010. 68p. pap. *(978-3-639-25864-6(9))* VDM Verlag Dr. Mueller e.K.

Shin, Doh Chull & Inoguchi, Takashi, eds. The Quality of Life in Confucian Asia: From Physical Welfare to Subjective Well-Being. 2010. (Social Indicators Research Ser.). (ENG., Illus.). vi, 254p. 159.00 *(978-90-481-3482-3(X)*, 904813482X) Springer.

South Asia 2011. 8th rev. ed. 2010. (ENG., Illus.). 856p. 720.00 *(978-1-85743-572-6(9))* Routledge.

United Nations. National Accounts Studies of the ESCWA Region, Bulletin No. 26. 2007. (ENG, FRE & MUL.). 104p. pap. 15.00 *(978-92-1-128311-2(6))* United Nations Pubns.

—Statistical Abstract of the ESCWA Region: 27th Issue. 2008. (MUL.). 220p. pap. 40.00 *(978-92-1-128319-8(1))* United Nations Pubns.

United Nations Publications Staff. Yearbook for Asia & the Pacific 2007. 2008. (ENG.). 206p. pap. 90.00 *(978-92-1-019241-5(9))* United Nations Pubns.

WHO Regional Office for the Western Pacific. Road Safety in the Western Pacific Region: Call for Action. 2010. (WPRO Publication). 109p. pap. 18.00 *(978-92-9061-449-4(8))* World Health Organization.

ASIA—STUDY AND TEACHING

American Geographical Society of New York Staff. Oriental Explorations & Studies, 6 vols. , Set. reprint ed. 438.00 *(978-0-404-60230-7(4))* AMS Pr., Inc.

AMS Asian Studies, 3 vols. *(978-0-404-61550-5(3))* AMS Pr., Inc.

Asia I. tchr. ed. 41.95 *(978-0-382-40658-4(3))* Cobblestone Publishing Co.

Chen, Kuan-Hsing. Asia as Method: Toward Deimperialization. 2010. (ENG., Illus.). 344p. pap. 24.95 *(978-0-8223-4676-0(1))* Duke Univ. Pr.

—Asia as Method: Towards De-Imperialization. 2010. (ENG., Illus.). 344p. 89.95 *(978-0-8223-4664-7(8))* Duke Univ. Pr.

Dew, Nicholas. Orientalism in Louis XIV's France. 2009. (Oxford Historical Monographs). (ENG.). 352p. 120.00 *(978-0-19-923484-4(1))* Oxford Univ. Pr., Inc.

Dodson, Michael S. Orientalism, Empire & National Culture. 2007. (ENG., Illus.). 288p. 100.00 *(978-1-4039-8645-0(2))* Palgrave Macmillan.

Ganim, John M. Medievalism & Orientalism: Three Essays on Literature, Architecture & Cultural Identity. 2008. (New Middle Ages Ser.). (ENG.). 170p. pap. 30.00 *(978-0-230-60245-8(2))* Palgrave Macmillan.

Hock, Saw & Wong, eds. Southeast Asian Studies in China. 2006. 220p. *(978-981-230-404-9(5))* Institute of Southeast Asian Studies.

Irwin, Robert. Dangerous Knowledge: Orientalism & Its Discontents. (ENG.). (gr. 12). 2008. 416p. per. 16.95 *(978-1-59020-017-9(9))* 2006. 376p. 35.00 *(978-1-58567-835-8(X))* Overlook Pr., The.

Joubert, Lindy, ed. Educating in the Arts: The Asian Experience: Twenty-Four Essays. 2010. (Education in the Asia-Pacific Region: Issues, Concerns & Prospects Ser.). xxii, 358p. pap. 179.00 *(978-90-481-7621-2(2)*, 9048176212) Springer.

Kemper, Michael & Conermann, Stephan, eds. The Heritage of Soviet Oriental Studies. 2011. (Routledge Contemporary Russia & Eastern Europe Ser.). (ENG., Illus.). 352p. (C). 150.00 *(978-0-415-59977-1(6))* Routledge.

Kokusai Koryu Kikin Staff, contrib. by. Directory of Japan Specialists & Japanese Studies Institutions in the United States & Canada: Japanese Studies in the United States, 3 vols. 2006. *(978-0-8248-3143-1(8))*; *(978-0-8248-3144-8(6))*; *(978-0-8248-3142-4(X))* Japan Foundation, The.

Marchand, Suzanne L. German Orientalism in the Age of Empire: Religion, Race, & Scholarship. (Publications of the German Historical Institute Ser.). (ENG., Illus.). 560p. 2010. pap. 34.99 *(978-0-521-16907-3(0))* 2009. 60.00 *(978-0-521-51849-9(0))* Cambridge Univ. Pr.

Nietupski, Paul K. Reading Asian Art & Artifacts: Windows to Asia on American College Campuses. 2011. (ENG.). 240p. pap. 32.95 *(978-1-61146-071-1(9))* Lehigh Univ. Pr.

Nietupski, Paul K. & O'Mara, Joan. Reading Asian Art & Artifacts: Windows to Asia on American College Campuses. 2011. (ENG.). 240p. 80.00 *(978-1-61146-070-4(0))* Lehigh Univ. Pr.

Saito, Shiro. Japanese Contributions to Southeast Asian Studies: A Research Guide. 2006. *(978-0-924304-47-7(2))* Assn. for Asian Studies, Inc.

Scalapino, Robert A. From Leavenworth to Lhasa: Living in a Revolutionary ERA. 2009. *(978-1-55729-092-2(X))* Univ. of California, Institute of East Asian Studies.

Shin, Gi-Wook & Sneider, Daniel, eds. History Textbooks & the Wars in Asia: Divided Memories. 2011. (Routledge Contemporary Asia Ser.). (ENG.). 312p. (C). 148.00 *(978-0-415-60303-4(X))* Routledge.

South & Southeast Asia Studies, 55 titles in 57 vols., Set. (AMS Press Reprint Ser.). reprint ed. *(978-0-404-54800-1(8))* AMS Pr., Inc.

Stremmelaar, Josine & Van Der Velde, Paul, eds. What about Asia? Revisiting Asian Studies. 2007. 200p. per. *(978-90-5356-959-7(6)*, Leiden Univ. Pr.) Amsterdam Univ. Pr.

Tolz, Vera. Russia's Own Orient: The Politics of Identity & Oriental Studies in the Late Imperial & Early Soviet Periods. 2011. (ENG., Illus.). 224p. 99.00 *(978-0-19-959444-3(9))* Oxford Univ. Pr., Inc.

Varisco, Daniel Martin. Reading Orientalism: Said & the Unsaid. 2007. (Publications on the near East Ser.). (ENG.). 512p. 90.00 *(978-0-295-98758-3(8))* Univ. of Washington Pr.

Wesley-Smith, Terence & Goss, Jon D. Remaking Area Studies: Teaching & Learning Across Asia & the Pacific. 2010. (C). 45.00 *(978-0-8248-3321-3(X))* Univ. of Hawaii Pr.

ASIA, CENTRAL

Here are entered works on the inland part of Asia, extending from the Caspian Sea in the west to, and including, northwestern China and Mongolia in the east, and from southern Siberia in the north to, and including, northern Iran and Afghanistan in the south, as well as works limited to the republics of former Soviet Central Asia treated collectively.

Marvin, Charles. The Eye-Witnesses' Account of the Disastrous Russian Campaign Against the Akhal Tekke Turcomans. 2007. (ENG.). 428p. 51.95 *(978-0-548-33286-3(X))*; per. 36.95 *(978-1-4326-9173-8(2))* Kessinger Publishing, LLC.

Shafi, Mohammad. Central Asia: Economy, Environment, & Culture. 2007. (Illus.). 224p. 30.00 *(978-81-316-0060-3(2))* Rawat Pubns. IND. Dist: International Specialized Bk. Services.

Spalding, Henry. Khiva & Turkestan. 2009. 268p. 24.99 *(978-1-103-70326-5(9))*; 24.99 *(978-1-103-46285-8(7))*; pap. 18.99 *(978-1-103-70324-1(2))*; pap. 18.99 *(978-1-103-46282-7(2))* BiblioBazaar.

Spalding, Henry, tr. Khiva & Turkestan. 2008. 262p. 42.95 *(978-1-4372-2398-9(2))*; pap. 27.95 *(978-1-4370-9523-4(2))* Kessinger Publishing, LLC.

ASIA, CENTRAL—ANTIQUITIES

Baimatowa, Nasiba S. 5000 Jahre Architektur in Mittelasien: Lehmziegelgewölbe vom 4. 3. Jt. V. Chr. bis zum Ende des 8. Jhs. N. Chr. 2008. (Archäologie in Iran und Turan Ser.). (GER., Illus.). 492p. (C). 102.00 *(978-3-8053-3906-3(2))* Zabern, Philipp von Verlag, GmbH DEU. Dist: Brown, David Bk. Co., The.

Barnard, Hans & Wendrich, Willeke, eds. The Archaeology of Mobility: Old & New World Nomadism. 2008. (Cotsen Advanced Seminars Ser.). (ENG., Illus.). 614p. (C). 89.95 *(978-1-931745-50-5(1))*; pap. 55.00 *(978-1-931745-49-9(8))* Cotsen Institute of Archaeology at UCLA.

Baumer, Christoph. Traces in the Desert: Journeys of Discovery Across Central Asia. 2008. (ENG., Illus.). 240p. 42.00 *(978-1-84511-337-7(3))* I. B. Tauris & Co., Ltd. GBR. Dist: Macmillan.

Fihl, Esther & Nicolaisen, Ida. Exploring Central Asia: From the Steppes to the High Pamirs, 1896-1899. 2010. (ENG., Illus.). 736p. 125.00 *(978-0-295-99000-2(7))* Univ. of Washington Pr.

Harris, David R. Origins of Agriculture in Western Central Asia: An Environmental-Archaeological Study. 2010. (Illus.). 328p. (C). 65.00 *(978-1-934536-16-2(4)*, Univ. of Pennsylvania Museum of Archaeology & Anthropology) Univ. Museum Pubns.

Herrmann, Georgina & Cribb, Joe, eds. After Alexander: Central Asia Before Islam. 2007. (Proceedings of the British Academy Ser.). (ENG., Illus.). 500p. 165.00 *(978-0-19-726384-6(4))* Oxford Univ. Pr., Inc.

Holt, Frank Lee. Lost World of the Golden King: In Search of Ancient Afghanistan. 2012. (Hellenistic Culture & Society Ser.). (ENG.). 304p. 39.95 ***(978-0-520-27342-9(7))*** Univ. of California Pr.

Neva, Elena. Iskusstvo Drevnykh Yuvelirov. Levin, Vladimir, ed. 2008. (RUS., Illus.). 124p. pap. *(978-1-934881-05-7(8)*, M-Graphics) M-Graphics Publishing.

Stark, Sören. Die Alttürkenzeit in Mittel- und Zentralasien: Archäologische und historische Studien. 2009. (Nomaden und Sesshafte Ser.). (GER., Illus.). 608p. (C). 150.00 *(978-3-89500-532-9(0))* Reichert, Ludwig Dr. DEU. Dist: Brown, David Bk. Co., The.

Wegener, Rebecca. Sauromatisches und Sarmatisches Fundgut Nordöstlich und Östlich des Kaspischen Meeres. 2010. (Bar S Ser.). (GER & ENG., Illus.). 260p. (C). pap. 112.50 *(978-1-4073-0633-9(2))* British Archaeological Reports Ltd. GBR. Dist: Brown, David Bk. Co., The.

ASIA, CENTRAL—BIOGRAPHY

Clinch, Nicholas & Clinch, Elizabeth. Through a Land of Extremes: The Littledales of Central Asia. 2011. (ENG.). 324p. pap. 21.95 *(978-1-59485-514-6(5))* Mountaineers Bks., The.

Farr, Saffia. Revolution Baby. 2007. 300p. per. *(978-1-897312-50-6(4))* Adlibbed Ltd.

Fleming, Tom. Taxi to Tashkent: Two Years with the Peace Corps in Uzbekistan. 2007. xii, 343p. E-Book ***(978-0-595-87338-8(3)***, iUniverse, Inc.) iUniverse, Inc.

Gonzlez de Clavijo, Ruy. Narrative of the Embassy of Ruy. Gonzlez de Clavijo to the court of Timour, at Samarcand, A. D. 1403-6. Markham, Clements R., tr. 2010. (Cambridge Library Collection - Travel & Exploration Ser.). (ENG., Illus.). 276p. pap. 23.99 *(978-1-108-01058-0(X))* Cambridge Univ. Pr.

Heron, Joan. Chai Budesh? Anyone for Tea? A Peace Corps Memoir of Turkmenistan. 2008. 332p. pap. 29.95 *(978-1-60672-557-3(2))* PublishAmerica, Inc.

Shayakhmetov, Mukhamet. The Silent Steppe: The Memoir of a Kazakh Nomad under Stalin. Butler, Jan, tr. 2007. (ENG., Illus.). 360p. (gr. 12). 35.00 *(978-1-58567-955-3(0))* Overlook Pr., The.

ASIA, CENTRAL—CIVILIZATION

Baumer, Christoph. Traces in the Desert: Journeys of Discovery Across Central Asia. 2008. (ENG., Illus.). 240p. 42.00 *(978-1-84511-337-7(3))* I. B. Tauris & Co., Ltd. GBR. Dist: Macmillan.

Golden, Peter B. Central Asia in World History, 1 vol. 2011. (New Oxford World History Ser.). (ENG., Illus.). 176p. pap. 19.95 *(978-0-19-533819-5(7))* Oxford Univ. Pr., Inc.

Holt, Frank Lee. Lost World of the Golden King: In Search of Ancient Afghanistan. 2012. (Hellenistic Culture & Society Ser.). (ENG.). 304p. 39.95 ***(978-0-520-27342-9(7))*** Univ. of California Pr.

Levi, Scott C. & Sela, Ron, eds. Islamic Central Asia: An Anthology of Historical Sources. 2009. (ENG., Illus.). 338p. 75.00 *(978-0-253-35385-6(8)*, 0253353858); pap. 29.00 *(978-0-253-22140-7(4)*, 0253221404) Indiana Univ. Pr.

May, Timothy Michael. Culture & Customs of Mongolia, 1 vol. 2008. (Culture & Customs of Asia Ser.). (Illus.). 204p. 49.95 *(978-0-313-33983-7(X)*, GR3983, Greenwood Pr.) Greenwood Publishing Group, Inc.

McChesney, Robert. The Cambridge History of Inner Asia: The Chinggisid Age. Di Cosmo, Nicola et al, eds. 2009. (ENG., Illus.). 516p. 205.00 *(978-0-521-84926-5(8))* Cambridge Univ. Pr.

ASIA, CENTRAL—DESCRIPTION AND TRAVEL

Alam, Muzaffar & Subrahmanyam, Sanjay. Indo-Persian Travels in the Age of Discoveries, 1400-1800. 2010. (ENG.). 416p. pap. 47.00 *(978-0-521-12955-8(9))* Cambridge Univ. Pr.

Atkinson, Thomas Witlam. Oriental & Western Siberia. 2009. 438p. pap. *(978-0-217-73799-9(4))* Books LLC.

Baumer, Christoph. Traces in the Desert: Journeys of Discovery Across Central Asia. 2008. (ENG., Illus.). 240p. 42.00 *(978-1-84511-337-7(3))* I. B. Tauris & Co., Ltd. GBR. Dist: Macmillan.

Biderman, Stan. Bullet Trains to Yaks: Glimpses into Art, Politics, & Culture in China & Tibet. 2011. 144p. pap. 24.95 ***(978-0-9832636-0-9(4))*** Irony Pr.

Bonavia, Judy. The Silk Road: From Xi'an to Kashgar. 8th rev. ed. 2007. (Odyssey Illustrated Guides). (Illus.). 367p. pap. 24.95 *(978-962-217-761-1(1))* Odyssey Pubns., Ltd. HKG. Dist: Norton, W. W. & Co., Inc.

Bonvalot, Gabriel. Across Thibet; Being a Translation of de Paris Au Tonkin a Travers le Tibet Inconnu. 2011. 432p. pap. 33.45 ***(978-1-4460-6805-2(6))*** Audubon Pr. & Christian Bk. Service.

Bullough, Oliver. Let Our Fame Be Great: Journeys among the Defiant People of the Caucasus. 2012. (ENG.). 528p. (gr. 9). pap. 19.99 ***(978-0-465-02904-4(3))*** Basic Bks.

Burnaby, Fred. A Ride to Khiva: Travels & Adventures in Central Asia. 2011. (Cambridge Library Collection - Travel & Exploration Ser.). (ENG., Illus.). 524p. pap. 39.99 ***(978-1-108-03758-7(5))*** Cambridge Univ. Pr.

Burnaby, Frederick. A Ride to Khiva: Travels & Adventures in Central Asia. 2007. (ENG.). 332p. per. 16.95 *(978-1-60206-396-9(6))* Cosimo, Inc.

Burnes, Alexander. Travels into Bokhara. 2009. 166p. pap. *(978-0-217-64733-5(2))* Books LLC.

—Travels into Bokhara. 2009. 172p. pap. 19.99 *(978-1-4589-8814-0(7))*; 216p. pap. 19.99 *(978-0-217-30157-2(6))* General Bks. LLC.

Burnes, Alexander. Travels into Bokhara: A Voyage up the Indus to Lahore & a Journey to Cahool, Tartary & Persia. Hopkirk, Kathleen, ed. 2012. (ENG., Illus.). xii, 240p. pap. 29.95 ***(978-1-906011-71-0(0))*** Eland Bks. GBR. Dist: Dufour Editions, Inc.

Christie, Ella Robertson. Khiva to Samarkand - the Remarkable Story of a Woman's Adventurous Journey Alone Through the Deserts of Central Asia to the Heart of Turkestan. 2009. 318p. pap. *(978-1-906393-17-5(6))* Trotamundas Pr., Ltd.

Clinch, Nicholas & Clinch, Elizabeth. Through a Land of Extremes: The Littledales of Central Asia. 2011. (ENG.). 324p. pap. 21.95 *(978-1-59485-514-6(5))* Mountaineers Bks., The.

Colegrave, Bill. Halfway House to Heaven: Unravelling the Mystery of the Majestic River Oxus. 2011. (ENG., Illus.). 176p. pap. 22.95 *(978-1-903071-28-1(3))* Bene Factum Publishing, Ltd. GBR. Dist: Independent Pubs. Group.

Davis-Kimball, Jeannine. Nomads of the Altai Mountains: The Mongols: Ancient Traditions in a Modern World. 2010. (Illus.). 65p. ***(978-1-885979-09-4(6))*** Zinat Pr.

Etherton, P T. Across the Roof of the World: A Record of Sport & Travel Through Kashmir, Gilgit, Hunza, the Pamirs, Chinese Turkestan, Mongolia & Siberia. 2007. *(978-1-57898-676-7(1))* Martino Publishing.

Fadlan, Ibn & Ghamātī, Al. Ibn Fadlan & the Land of Darkness: Arab Travellers in the Far North. Lunde, Paul & Stone, Caroline, trs. from ARA. 2012. (ENG.). 256p. (gr. 12). 16.00 ***(978-0-14-045507-6(8)***, Penguin Classics) Penguin Group (USA) Inc.

Fihl, Esther & Nicolaisen, Ida. Exploring Central Asia: From the Steppes to the High Pamirs, 1896-1899. 2010. (ENG., Illus.). 736p. 125.00 *(978-0-295-99000-2(7))* Univ. of Washington Pr.

Fleming, Peter. To Peking: A Forgotten Journey from Moscow to Manchuria. 2009. (ENG., Illus.). 200p. pap. 16.00 *(978-1-84511-996-6(7)*, Tauris Parke Paperbacks) I. B. Tauris & Co., Ltd. GBR. Dist: Macmillan.

Frye, Richard, ed. & tr. from ARA. Ibn Fadlan's Journey to Russia: A Tenth-Century Traveler from Baghad to the Volga River. 2007. (Illus.). 174p. pap. *(978-1-55876-366-1(X))* Wiener, Markus Pubs., Inc.

Hamilton, Angus. Afghanistan. 2009. 344p. 32.99 *(978-1-113-61130-7(8))*; pap. 31.75 *(978-1-113-61128-4(6))*; pap. 32.75 *(978-1-113-61129-1(4))* BiblioBazaar.

—Afghanistan. 2009. 180p. pap. *(978-0-217-67676-2(6))* Books LLC.

Ibn Batuta & Ibrahimovich, Ibrahimov Nematulla. The Travels of Ibn Battuta to Central Asia. 2010. (ARA & ENG.). *(978-1-55876-522-1(0))* Wiener, Markus Pubs., Inc.

Ibrahimovich, Ibrahimov N. Travels of Ibn Battuta in Central Asia. 2009. (ARA & ENG.). 200p. pap. 28.95 *(978-1-55876-523-8(9))* Wiener, Markus Pubs., Inc.

Jacobson, Jessica. Roaming Kyrgyzstan: Beyond the Tourist Track. 2008. 216p. pap. 17.95 *(978-0-595-52686-4(1))* iUniverse, Inc.

Knee, Roman, Beyer. Kirgistan: Ein Bildband über Talas. 2007. 224p. 75.00 *(978-3-7774-3805-4(7))* Hirmer Verlag GmbH DEU. Dist: Chicago Distribution Ctr.

Lansdell, Henry. Chinese Central Asia: A Ride to Little Tibet. 2006. *(978-1-57898-627-9(3))* Martino Publishing.

—Chinese Central Asia; a Ride to Little Tibet. 2009. 304p. pap. *(978-1-4590-4130-1(5))* Books LLC.

Locken, E. Travel Journal Kyrgyzstan. 2010. 192p. pap. 19.99 *(978-0-557-43650-7(8))* Lulu Enterprises Inc.

Lonely Planet Staff, et al. Central Asia. 5th rev. ed. 2010. (Multi Country Guide Ser.). (ENG., Illus.). 556p. pap. 32.99 *(978-1-74179-148-8(0))* Lonely Planet Pubns.

MacGahan, J. A. Campaigning on the Oxus & the Fall of Khiva. 2007. *(978-1-57898-635-4(4))* Martino Publishing.

Maclean, Fitzroy. A Person from England. 2012. 400p. pap. ***(978-1-4482-0524-0(7)***, 146216, Bloomsbury Reader) Bloomsbury Publishing Plc.

MacLean, Rory. Magic Bus: On the Hippie Trail from Istanbul to India. 2009. (ENG.). 240p. pap. 14.95 *(978-0-9788431-9-9(3))* Ig Publishing, Inc.

Marshall Cavendish Corporation Staff, contrib. by. World & Its Peoples. 2006. *(978-0-7614-7582-8(6))*; *(978-0-7614-7581-1(8))*; *(978-0-7614-7628-3(8))*; *(978-0-7614-7579-8(6))*; *(978-0-7614-7578-1(8))*; *(978-0-7614-7626-9(1))*; *(978-0-7614-7575-0(3))*; *(978-0-7614-7625-2(3))*; *(978-0-7614-7574-3(5))*; *(978-0-7614-7572-9(9))*; *(978-0-7614-7573-6(7))* Marshall Cavendish Corp.

Olufsen, O. The Emir of Bokhara & His Country: Journeys & Studies in Bokhara (with a Chapter on My Voyage on the Amu Darya to Kiva) 2008. 110.00 *(978-1-57898-710-8(5))* Martino Publishing.

—Through the Unknown Pamirs: The Second Danish Pamir Expedition 1898-99. 2007. (ENG.). 258p. 42.95 *(978-0-548-18843-9(2))*; 260p. per. 27.95 *(978-1-4304-9246-7(5))* Kessinger Publishing, LLC.

—Through the Unknown Pamirs: The Second Danish Pamir Expedition 1898-99. 2008. (Illus.). 75.00 *(978-1-57898-693-4(1))* Martino Publishing.

Richie, Donald. Travels in the East. 2007. (ENG., Illus.). 160p. per. 14.95 *(978-1-933330-61-7(9))* Stone Bridge Pr.

Rickmers, W. Rickmer. The Duab of Turkestan: A Physiographic Sketch & Account of Some Travels. 2010. (Cambridge Library Collection - Travel & Exploration Ser.). (Illus.). 596p. pap. 43.00 *(978-1-108-01066-5(0))* Cambridge Univ. Pr.

Rutstein, Harry. The Marco Polo Odyssey: In the Footsteps of a Merchant Who Changed the World. 2008. (Illus.). 296p. 27.95 *(978-0-9802076-0-6(6))* Marco Polo Foundation, Inc.

Scheffer, Martin. In Post-Communist Worlds: Living & Teaching in Estonia, Lithuania, Ukraine & Uzbekistan. 2009. 432p. pap. 25.95 *(978-0-595-48519-2(7))* iUniverse, Inc.

Stewart, Rowan & Weldon, Susie. Kyrgyz Republic: Heart of Central Asia, 3rd ed. 2008. (Odyssey Illustrated Guides). (ENG.). 320p. pap. 24.95 *(978-962-217-791-8(3)*, 217791) Airphoto International/Odyssey HKG. Dist: Norton, W. W. & Co., Inc.

Sykes, Ella & Sykes, Percy. Through Deserts & Oases of Central Asia. 2007. (ENG., Illus.). 356p. per. 31.95 *(978-1-4325-3574-2(9))* Kessinger Publishing, LLC.

Sykes, Ella & Sykes, Percy M. Through Deserts & Oases of Central Asia. 2007. (Illus.). 345p. 85.00 *(978-1-57898-600-2(1))* Martino Publishing.

Thubron, Colin. The Lost Heart of Asia. 2008. (P. S. Ser.). 400p. pap. 15.99 (978-0-06-157767-3(7), HarperPerennial) HarperCollins Pubs.

—Shadow of the Silk Road. (P. S. Ser.). 2008. 400p. pap. 15.99 (978-0-06-123177-3(0), HarperPerennial) 2007. 384p. 25.95 (978-0-06-123172-8(X)) HarperCollins Pubs.

Valikhanov, Ch Ch & Veniukov, M. The Russians in Central Asia: Their Occupation of the Kirghiz Steppe & the Line of the Syr-Daria: Their Political Relations with Khiva, Bokhara, & Kokan: Also Descriptions of Chinese Turkestan & Dzungaria. 2007. (Illus.). 575p. 85.00 (978-1-57898-643-9(5)) Martino Publishing.

Vambery, Arminius. Sketches of Central Asia: Additional Chapters on My Travels, Adventures, & on the Ethnology of Central Asia. 2007. 450p. 75.00 (978-1-57898-634-7(6)) Martino Publishing.

Watson, Claire Burges. Silk Route Adventure: On Horseback in the Heart of Asia. 2007. (ENG., Illus.). 352p. 50.00 (978-0-7090-8061-9(1)) Hale, Robert Ltd. GBR. Dist: Independent Pubs. Group.

Wolff, Joseph. Narrative of a Mission to Bokhara, in the Years 1843-1845, to Ascertain the Fate of Colonel Stoddart & Captain Conolly. 2010. 322p. pap. (978-1-151-74964-2(8)) 2010. 158p. pap. (978-1-151-74968-0(0)) 2009. 176p. pap. (978-1-150-74893-6(1)) Books LLC.

—Narrative of a Mission to Bokhara, in the Years 1843-1845, to Ascertain the Fate of Colonel Stoddart & Captain Conolly. 2008. 540p. pap. (978-1-4086-8877-9(8)) Read Bks.

ASIA, CENTRAL—ECONOMIC CONDITIONS

Ahrens, Joachim & Hoen, Herman W., eds. Institutional Reform in Central Asia: Politico-Economic Challenges. 2012. (Central Asian Studies). (ENG., Illus.). 272p. (C). 130.00 (978-0-415-60200-6(9)) Routledge.

Bruun, Ole. Precious Steppe: Mongolian Nomadic Pastoralists in Pursuit of the Market. 2008. (Asiaworld Ser.). (ENG., Illus.). 262p. pap. 31.50 (978-0-7391-2807-7(8)) Lexington Bks.

Chin, Felix, ed. Politics & Economics of South, Southeastern & Central Asia. 2011. (Asian Political, Economic & Security Issues Ser.). 140.00 **(978-1-61470-461-4(9))** Nova Science Pubs., Inc.

Eastern Europe, Russia & Central Asia 2011. 11th rev. ed. 2011. (ENG.). 808p. 775.00 (978-1-85743-569-6(9)) Routledge.

Europa Publications, ed. Eastern Europe Russia & Central Asia 2012. 12th rev. ed. 2011. (ENG.). 816p. 815.00 **(978-1-85743-627-3(X))** Routledge.

Europa Publications Staff. Eastern Europe, Russia & Central Asia 2007. 7th rev. ed. 2006. (Illus.). 750p. 575.00 (978-1-85743-378-4(5)) Routledge.

Europa Publications Staff, ed. Eastern Europe, Russia & Central Asia 2009. 9th rev. ed. 2008. (ENG.). 776p. 700.00 (978-1-85743-473-6(0)) Routledge.

Goldberg, Itzhak, et al. Growth through Innovation or Technology Absorption? Strategies for Eastern Europe & Central Asia. 2011. (Eastern Europe & Central Asia Reports). (ENG., Illus.). 184p. pap. 20.00 **(978-0-8213-8740-5(5)**, 9780821387405) World Bank Pubns.

Hanson, Philip, et al. Eastern Europe, Russia & Central Asia 2010. Europa Publications Staff, ed. 10th rev. ed. 2009. (ENG.). 804p. 750.00 (978-1-85743-531-3(1)) Routledge.

Icon Group International, Inc. Staff, compiled by. The 2006 Economic & Product Market Databook for Baghlan, Afghanistan. 2006. 618p. ring bd. 95.00 (978-0-497-80118-2(3)) Icon Group International, Inc.

—The 2006 Economic & Product Market Databook for Bumthang, Bhutan. 2006. 618p. ring bd. 95.00 (978-0-497-80268-4(6)) Icon Group International, Inc.

—The 2006 Economic & Product Market Databook for Dzhalal-Abad, Kyrgyzstan. 2006. 618p. ring bd. 95.00 (978-0-497-80495-4(6)) Icon Group International, Inc.

—The 2006 Economic & Product Market Databook for Erdenedalay, Mongolia. 2006. 618p. ring bd. 95.00 (978-0-497-79985-4(5)) Icon Group International, Inc.

—The 2006 Economic & Product Market Databook for Ghazni, Afghanistan. 2006. 618p. ring bd. 95.00 (978-0-497-80595-1(2)) Icon Group International, Inc.

—The 2006 Economic & Product Market Databook for Herat, Afghanistan. 2006. 618p. ring bd. 95.00 (978-0-497-81896-8(5)) Icon Group International, Inc.

—The 2006 Economic & Product Market Databook for Jalalabad, Afghanistan. 2006. 618p. ring bd. 95.00 (978-0-497-81942-2(2)) Icon Group International, Inc.

—The 2006 Economic & Product Market Databook for Kabul, Afghanistan. 2006. 618p. ring bd. 95.00 (978-0-497-81962-0(7)) Icon Group International, Inc.

—The 2006 Economic & Product Market Databook for Mazar-e-Sharif, Afghanistan. 2006. 618p. ring bd. 95.00 (978-0-497-80987-4(7)) Icon Group International, Inc.

—The 2006 Economic & Product Market Databook for Meymaneh, Afghanistan. 2006. 618p. ring bd. 95.00 (978-0-497-81017-7(4)) Icon Group International, Inc.

—The 2006 Economic & Product Market Databook for Naryn, Kyrgyzstan. 2006. 618p. ring bd. 95.00 (978-0-497-81103-7(0)) Icon Group International, Inc.

—The 2006 Economic & Product Market Databook for Osh, Kyrgyzstan. 2006. 618p. ring bd. 95.00 (978-0-497-81173-0(1)) Icon Group International, Inc.

—The 2006 Economic & Product Market Databook for Pol-e-Khomri, Afghanistan. 2006. 618p. ring bd. 95.00 (978-0-497-81268-3(1)) Icon Group International, Inc.

International Monetary Fund Staff. Regional Economic Outlook: Middle East & Central Asia, May 2008. 2008. 62p. pap. 31.00 (978-1-58906-715-8(0)) International Monetary Fund.

Jeffries, Ian. Mongolia: A Guide to Economic & Political Developments. 2007. (Guides to Economic & Political Developments in Asia Ser.). (ENG., Illus.). 224p. (C). 150.00 (978-0-415-42545-2(X)) Routledge.

Kaminski, Bartlomiej & Mitra, Saumya. Borderless Bazaars & Border Trade in Central Asia: Emerging patterns of trade & cross-border Cooperation. 2012. (Directions in Development Ser.). (ENG.). 208p. pap. 25.95 **(978-0-8213-9471-7(1)**, 9780821394717) World Bank Pubns.

Kaminski, Bartlomiej & Mitra, Saumya. Borderless Bazaars & Regional Integration in Central Asia: Emerging Patterns of Trade & Cross- Border Cooperation. 2012. **(978-0-8213-9472-4(X))** World Bank Pubns.

Kaplonski, Christopher. Mongolia: Democracy on the Steppe. 2008. (Postcommunist States & Nations Ser.). 192p. 130.00 (978-0-415-27437-1(0)) Routledge.

Laine, Arthur T. Economic, Political & Social Issues of the Caucasus Region. 2011. (Series: Caucasus Region Political, Economic, & Security Issues Ser.). 129.00 (978-1-61122-553-2(1)) Nova Science Pubs., Inc.

Laruelle, Marlène & Peyrouse, Sébastien. The Chinese Factor in Central Asia: Domestic Order, Social Change, & the Chinese Factor. 2012. (Columbia/Hurst Ser.). (ENG.). 224p. (gr. 17). 60.00 **(978-0-231-70304-8(X))** Columbia Univ. Pr.

Liu, Morgan Y. Under Solomon's Throne: Uzbek Visions of Renewal in Osh. 2012. (Central Eurasia in Context Ser.). (ENG.). 328p. pap. 29.95 **(978-0-8229-6177-2(6))** Univ. of Pittsburgh Pr.

MacDonald, Scott B. & Lemco, Jonathan. Asia's Rise in the 21st Century. 1 vol. 2011. 200p. 37.00 (978-0-313-39370-9(2), A3372C) Greenwood Publishing Group, Inc.

Manscor, Ali & Quillin, Bryce, eds. Migration & Remittances: Eastern Europe & the Former Soviet Union. 2006. (Eastern Europe & Central Asia Reports). (ENG., Illus.). 224p. per. 30.00 (978-0-8213-6233-4(X), 9780821362334) World Bank Pubns.

McTernan, Benedict, ed. Political Risk Yearbook - 2007 Vol. 8: Central & South Asia. 2007. per. (978-1-933539-36-2(4)) PRS Group Inc., The.

Myant, Martin & Drahokoupil, Jan. Transition Economies: Political Economy in Russia, Eastern Europe, & Central Asia. 2010. (ENG., Illus.). 391p. (C). 92.95 (978-0-470-59619-7(8), Wiley) Wiley, John & Sons, Inc.

Nasritdinov, Emil & O'Connor, Kevin. Regional Change in Kyrgyzstan. 2010. 178p. pap. (978-3-8383-0093-1(9)) Lambert Academic Publishing.

Nove, Alec. The Soviet Middle East (Routledge Revivals) 2012. (Routledge Revivals Ser.). (ENG.). 164p. 110.00 **(978-0-415-68241-1(X))** Routledge.

Organisation for Economic Co-operation and Development Staff. Black Sea & Central Asia: Promoting Work & Well Being. 2008. (Illus.). 149p. pap. 63.00 (978-92-64-04729-7(8)) Organization for Economic Cooperation & Development.

—Perspectives éConomiques de l'Asie Centrale et la réGion de la Mer Noire. 2008. 164p. pap. 63.00 (978-92-64-04731-0(X)) Organization for Economic Cooperation & Development.

Organisation for Economic Co-operation and Development: Development Centre. Competitiveness & Private Sector Development: Central Asia 2011; Competitiveness Outlook. 2011. (Illus.). 160p. pap. 67.00 **(978-92-64-09727-8(9))** Organization for Economic Cooperation & Development.

Özcan, Gül Berna. Building States & Markets: Enterprise Development in Central Asia. 2010. (ENG., Illus.). 256p. 100.00 (978-1-4039-9161-4(8)) Palgrave Macmillan.

Pomfret, Richard. The Central Asian Economies since Independence. 2006. (ENG., Illus.). 256p. (C). 90.00 (978-0-691-12465-0(5)) Princeton Univ. Pr.

Routledge Staff, creator. Eastern Europe, Russia & Central Asia 2008. 8th rev. ed. 2008. (Eastern Europe, Russia & Central Asia Ser.). (Illus.). 776p. 640.00 (978-1-85743-424-8(2)) Routledge.

Tiongson, Erwin R., et al. The Crisis Hits Home: Stress-Testing Households in Europe & Central Asia. 2009. (ENG., Illus.). 104p. pap. 20.00 (978-0-8213-8222-6(5), 9780821382226) World Bank Pubns.

United Nations. Implementation of the Brussels Programme of Action for the Least Developed Countries in Asia & the Pacific. 2012. (ENG.). pap. 42.00 **(978-92-1-120624-1(3))** United Nations Pubns.

Wooden, Amanda E. & Stefes, Christoph H., eds. The Politics of Transition in Central Asia & the Caucasus: Enduring Legacies & Emerging Challenges. 2012. (ENG., Illus.). 288p. (C). pap. 44.95 **(978-0-415-62539-5(4))** Routledge.

World Bank, et al. Fiscal Policy & Economic Growth: Lessons for Eastern Europe & Central Asia. Lane, Tracey, ed. 2007. (Books Ser.). (ENG., Illus.). 356p. pap. 35.00 (978-0-8213-7181-7(9), 9780821371817) World Bank Pubns.

ASIA, CENTRAL—ETHNIC RELATIONS

Barrett, Tracy C. The Chinese Diaspora in South-East Asia: The Overseas Chinese in Indo-China. 2012. (Library of China Studies). (ENG., Illus.). 256p. 95.00 **(978-1-78076-134-3(1))** I. B. Tauris & Co., Ltd. GBR. Dist: Macmillan.

Bruun, Ole. Precious Steppe: Mongolian Nomadic Pastoralists in Pursuit of the Market. 2008. (Asiaworld Ser.). (ENG., Illus.). 262p. pap. 31.50 (978-0-7391-2807-7(8)) Lexington Bks.

Canfield, Robert L. & Rasuly-Paleczek, Gabriele, eds. Ethnicity & Authority in Central Asia: New Games Great & Small. 2010. (Central Asian Studies). (ENG., Illus.). 272p. (C). 140.00 (978-0-415-78069-8(1), Routledge) Taylor & Francis Group GBR. Dist: Taylor & Francis Group.

Daiya, Kavita. Violent Belongings: Partition, Gender, & National Culture in Postcolonial India. 2011. (ENG., Illus.). 274p. pap. 27.95 (978-1-59213-744-2(X)) Temple Univ. Pr.

Ganguly, Rajat. Autonomy & Ethnic Conflict in South & South-East Asia. 2012. (Asian Security Studies). (ENG.). 176p. (C). 135.00 (978-0-415-57016-9(6)) Routledge.

Holst, Frederik. Ethnicization & Identity Politics in Malaysia. 2012. (Routledge Malaysian Studies Ser.). (ENG., Illus.). 256p. (C). 145.00 **(978-0-415-69913-6(4))** Routledge.

Hsieh, Jolan. Collective Rights of Indigenous Peoples. 2010. 156p. 39.95 (978-0-415-88252-1(4)) Routledge.

Human Rights Watch (Organization) Staff, contrib. by. Appeasing China: Restricting the Rights of Tibetans in Nepal. 2008. (Illus.). 60p. pap. (978-1-56432-365-1(X)) Human Rights Watch.

Lee, Joann Faung Jean. Asian Americans in the Twenty-First Century: Oral Histories of First- to Fourth- Generation Americans from China, Japan, India, Korea, the Philippines, Vietnam, & Laos. 2008. (ENG., Illus.). 277p. 24.95 (978-1-59558-152-5(9)) New Pr., The.

Levi, Tomer. The Jews of Beirut: The Rise of a Levantine Community, 1860s-1930s. 2012. 244p. (C). 82.95 **(978-1-4331-1709-1(6))**; E-Book **(978-1-4539-0235-6(X))** Lang, Peter Publishing, Inc.

Liu, Morgan Y. Under Solomon's Throne: Uzbek Visions of Renewal in Osh. 2012. (Central Eurasia in Context Ser.). (ENG.). 328p. pap. 29.95 **(978-0-8229-6177-2(6))** Univ. of Pittsburgh Pr.

Rais, Rasul, et al. Recovering the Frontier State: War, Ethnicity, & the State in Afghanistan. 2009. (ENG.). 238p. pap. 31.50 (978-0-7391-3701-7(8)) Lexington Bks.

Shoup, Brian. Conflict & Cooperation in Multi-Ethnic States: Institutional Incentives, Myths & Counter-Balancing. 2007. (Asian Security Studies). (Illus.). 208p. 170.00 (978-0-415-43391-4(6)) Routledge.

Thawnghmung, Ardeth Maung. Other Karen in Myanmar: Ethnic Minorities & the Struggle without Arms. 2011. (AsiaWorld Ser.). (ENG., Illus.). 232p. (gr. 17). 60.00 **(978-0-7391-6852-3(5))** Lexington Bks.

—The "Other" Karen in Myanmar: Ethnic Minorities & the Struggle Without Arms. 2011. (Illus.). xxxii, 197p. **(978-0-7391-7107-3(0))** Lexington Bks.

ASIA, CENTRAL—HISTORY

Abazov, Rafis. Culture & Customs of the Central Asian Republics, 1 vol. 2006. (Culture & Customs of Asia Ser.). (Illus.). 324p. 49.95 (978-0-313-33656-0(3), GR3656, Greenwood Pr.) Greenwood Publishing Group, Inc.

—The Palgrave Concise Historical Atlas of Central Asia. 2008. (ENG., Illus.). 144p. pap. 23.00 (978-1-4039-7542-3(6)) Palgrave Macmillan.

Barthold, W. Turkestan down to the Mongol Invasion. 2008. 616p. pap. 60.00 (978-1-59740-450-1(0)) ACLS Humanities E-Book.

Beckwith, Christopher. Empires of the Silk Road - A History of Central Eurasia from the Bronze Age to the Present. 2011. (ENG., Illus.). 504p. pap. 16.95 (978-0-691-15034-5(6)) Princeton Univ. Pr.

Beckwith, Christopher I. Empires of the Silk Road: A History of Central Eurasia from the Bronze Age to the Present. 2009. (ENG., Illus.). 504p. (C). 35.00 (978-0-691-13589-2(4)) Princeton Univ. Pr.

Beckwith, Christopher I. Warriors of the Cloisters: The Central Asian Origins of Science in the Medieval World. 2012. (ENG.). 192p. (C). 29.95 **(978-0-691-15531-9(3))** Princeton Univ. Pr.

Brunn, Stanley D. & Toops, Stanley W. The Routledge Atlas of Central Eurasian Affairs. 2012. (ENG., Illus.). 240p. 145.00 (978-0-415-49750-3(7)); pap. 42.95 (978-0-415-49752-7(3)) Routledge.

Central Asia: History of Civilization. (Illus.). 535p. (978-1-57205-627-5(4)) Rector Pr., Ltd.

Clements, Jonathan. A Brief History of Khubilai Khan. 2010. (ENG.). 352p. pap. 13.95 (978-0-7624-3987-4(4)) Running Pr. Bk. Pubs.

Colegrave, Bill. Halfway House to Heaven: Unravelling the Mystery of the Majestic River Oxus. 2011. (ENG., Illus.). 176p. pap. 22.95 (978-1-903071-28-1(3)) Bene Factum Publishing, Ltd. GBR. Dist: Independent Pubs. Group.

Cummings, Sally N. Understanding Central Asia. 2012. (ENG., Illus.). 256p. (C). pap. 44.95 (978-0-415-29703-5(6)) Routledge.

Ewans. Britain & Russia in Central Asia 18801907, 6 vols. 2007. (Illus.). 350p. (978-0-415-44357-9(1)); 350p. (978-0-415-44359-3(8)); 350p. (978-0-415-44362-3(8)); 2100p. (978-0-415-44358-6(X)) Routledge.

Ewans, Martin. Securing the Indian Frontier in Central Asia: Confrontation & Negotiation, 1865-1895. (ENG., Illus.). 208p. (C). 2012. pap. 42.95 **(978-0-415-62746-7(X))** 2010. 140.00 (978-0-415-49681-0(0)) Routledge.

Ewans, Martin, ed. Britain & Russia in Central Asia 18801907, 6 vols. 2007. (Illus.). 350p. (978-0-415-44361-6(X)); (978-0-415-44360-9(1)) Routledge.

Farr, Saffia. Revolution Baby. 2007. 300p. per. (978-1-897312-50-6(4)) Adlibbed Ltd.

Ferdinand, Peter. New Central Asia. (Illus.). 128p. pap. (978-1-85567-139-3(5), Burns & Oates) Continuum International Publishing Group, Ltd.

Fihl, Esther & Nicolaisen, Ida. Exploring Central Asia: From the Steppes to the High Pamirs, 1896-1899. 2010. (ENG., Illus.). 736p. 125.00 (978-0-295-99000-2(7)) Univ. of Washington Pr.

Golden, Peter B. Central Asia in World History, 1 vol. 2011. (New Oxford World History Ser.). (ENG., Illus.). 176p. pap. 19.95 (978-0-19-533819-5(7)) Oxford Univ. Pr., Inc.

—Turks & Khazars: Origins, Institutions, & Interactions in Pre-Mongol Eurasia. 2010. (Variorum Collected Studies). (Illus.). 380p. 154.95 (978-1-4094-0003-5(4)) Ashgate Publishing Co.

The Great Game: From Mid-Century Through the Second Anglo-Afghan. 2006. 2100p. (978-0-415-39356-0(6), Routledge) Taylor & Francis Group.

Gumilev, Lev Nikolaevich. Searches for an Imaginary Kingdom: The Legend of the Kingdom of Prester John. Smith, R. E. F., tr. from RUS. 2009. (Past & Present Publications). (ENG., Illus.). 428p. pap. 53.00 (978-0-521-10879-9(9)) Cambridge Univ. Pr.

Hannigan, Tim. Murder in the Hindu Kush: George Hayward & the Great Game. 2011. (ENG., Illus.). 256p. 34.95 (978-0-7524-5886-1(8)) History Pr. Ltd.,The GBR. Dist: Independent Pubs. Group.

Happel, Jorn. Nomadische Lebenswelten und zarische Politik: Der Aufstand in Zentralasien 1916. 2011. (Quellen und Studien zur Geschichte des ostlichen Europa Ser.). (GER., Illus.). 378p. (C). pap. 84.00 (978-3-515-09771-0(6)) Steiner, Franz Verlag Wiesbaden GmbH DEU. Dist: Brown, David Bk. Co., The.

Haydar Mirza, et al. A History of the Moghuls of Central Asia: Being the Tarikh-I-Rashidi of Mirza Muhammad Haidar, Dughlát. 2008. (978-1-57898-694-1(X)) Martino Publishing.

Hellwald, Friedrich von. The Russians in Central Asia: A Critical Examination down to the Present Time of the Geography & History of Central Asia. 2008. (978-1-57898-698-9(2)) Martino Publishing.

Hermann, Georgina & Cribb, Joe, eds. After Alexander: Central Asia Before Islam. 2007. (Proceedings of the British Academy Ser.). (ENG., Illus.). 500p. 165.00 (978-0-19-726384-6(4)) Oxford Univ. Pr., Inc.

Hiro, Dilip. Inside Central Asia. 2009. (Illus.). 448p. (978-0-7156-3877-4(7)) Overlook Pr., The.

—Inside Central Asia: A Political & Cultural History of Uzbekistan, Turkmenistan, Kazakhstan, Kyrgyzstan, Tajikistan, Turkey, & Iran. 2009. (ENG., Illus.). 480p. (gr. 12-18). 35.00 (978-1-59020-221-0(X)) Overlook Pr., The.

—Inside Central Asia: A Political & Cultural History of Uzbekistan, Turkmenistan, Kazakhstan, Kyrgyzstan, Tajikstan Turky, & Iran. 2011. (ENG.). 464p. (gr. 12). pap. 20.00 (978-1-59020-333-0(X)) Overlook Pr., The.

Ibn Batuta & Ibrahimovich, Ibrahimov Nematulla. The Travels of Ibn Battuta to Central Asia. 2010. (ARA & ENG.). (978-1-55876-522-1(0)) Wiener, Markus Pubs., Inc.

Kuzmina, E E. The Prehistory of the Silk Road. Mair, Victor H., ed. 2007. (Encounters with Asia Ser.). (Illus.). 264p. (C). 65.00 (978-0-8122-4041-2(3)) Univ. of Pennsylvania Pr.

Lester, Anne E., ed. Central Asia: Background, Issues & U. S. Interests. 2010. (Countries, Regional Studies, Trading Blocks, Unions, World Organizations Ser.). 115.00 (978-1-61728-880-7(2)) Nova Science Pubs., Inc.

Levi, Scott C & Sela, Ron, eds. Islamic Central Asia: An Anthology of Historical Sources. 2009. (ENG., Illus.). 338p. 75.00 (978-0-253-35385-8(8), 0253353858); pap. 29.00 (978-0-253-22140-7(4), 0253221404) Indiana Univ. Pr.

Maclean, Fitzroy. A Person from England. 2012. 400p. pap. **(978-1-4482-0524-0(7)**, 146216, Bloomsbury Reader) Bloomsbury Publishing Plc.

McChesney, Robert. The Cambridge History of Inner Asia: The Chinggisid Age. Di Cosmo, Nicola et al, eds. 2009. (ENG., Illus.). 516p. 205.00 (978-0-521-84926-5(8)) Cambridge Univ. Pr.

Peyrouse, Sebastien. The Russian Minority in Central Asia: Migration, Politics, & Language. 2008. 28p. (978-1-933549-32-3(7)) Woodrow Wilson International Ctr. fo Scholars.

Prinsep, Henry Thoby. Note on the Historical Results Deducible from Recent Discoveries in Afghanistan. 2011. (Cambridge Library Collection - History Ser.). (ENG., Illus.). 156p. pap. 19.99 (978-1-108-02871-4(3)) Cambridge Univ. Pr.

Roudik, Peter L. The History of the Central Asian Republics, 1 vol. 2007. (Greenwood Histories of the Modern Nations Ser.). (Illus.). 240p. 45.00 (978-0-313-34013-0(7), GR4013) Greenwood Publishing Group, Inc.

Roy, Olivier. The New Central Asia: Geopolitics & the Birth of Nations. 2007. (ENG.). 248p. pap. 23.00 (978-0-8147-7609-4(4)) New York Univ. Pr.

Rutstein, Harry. The Marco Polo Odyssey: In the Footsteps of a Merchant Who Changed the World. 2008. (Illus.). 296p. 27.95 (978-0-9802076-0-6(6)) Marco Polo Foundation, Inc.

Starr, S. Frederick. Ferghana Valley: The Heart of Central Asia. 2011. (ENG., Illus.). 464p. pap. 39.95 **(978-0-7656-2999-9(2))** Sharpe, M.E. Inc.

Starr, S. Frederick, ed. Ferghana Valley: The Heart of Central Asia. 2011. (Studies of Central Asia & the Caucasus Ser.). (ENG., Illus.). 464p. 104.95 (978-0-7656-2998-2(4)) Sharpe, M.E. Inc.

Wheeler, James Talboys. Journey of a Voyage up the Irrawaddy to Mandalay & Bhamo. 2006. (Itineraria Asiatica: Burma Ser.). (ENG., Illus.). pap. 16.00 (978-974-8299-67-9(8)) Orchid Pr. THA. Dist: National Bk. Network.

Zonn, Igor S., et al. The Caspian Sea Encyclopedia. 2010. (ENG., Illus.). xii, 540p. 229.00 (978-3-642-11523-3(3), 3642115233) Springer.

ASIA, CENTRAL—POLITICS AND GOVERNMENT

Ahrens, Joachim & Hoen, Herman W., eds. Institutional Reform in Central Asia: Politico-Economic Challenges. 2012. (Central Asian Studies). (ENG., Illus.). 272p. (C). 130.00 (978-0-415-60200-6(9)) Routledge.

Becks, Carleton. The Security Situation in Central Asi. 2011. 96p. pap. **(978-3-8443-1228-7(5))** Lambert Academic Publishing.

Beeson, Mark & Stubbs, Richard, eds. Routledge Handbook of Asian Regionalism. 2011. (ENG., Illus.). 512p. (C). 200.00 (978-0-415-58054-0(4)) Routledge.

Behnke, Roy H. The Socio-Economic Causes & Consequences of Desertification in Central Asia. 2008. (NATO Science for Peace & Security Series C: Environmental Security Ser.). (Illus.). 300p. spiral bd. 109.00

A

(978-1-4020-8543-7(5)); 249.00 (978-1-4020-8542-0(7), 1402085427) Springer.

Biryukov, Vadim. Clans' State Capture & Regime Durability. 2010. 60p. pap. (978-3-8383-3720-3(4)) Lambert Academic Publishing.

Blank, Stephen J., ed. Central Asian Security Trends: Views from Europe & Russia. 2011. (ENG.). 94p. **(978-1-58487-487-4(2))** Strategic Studies Institute, U.S. Army War College Commandant (AWCC-DSI/Pubns.).

Brunn, Stanley D. & Toops, Stanley W. The Routledge Atlas of Central Eurasian Affairs. 2012. (ENG., Illus.). 240p. 145.00 (978-0-415-49750-3(7)); pap. 42.95 (978-0-415-49752-7(3)) Routledge.

Buxton, Charles. The Struggle for Civil Society in Central Asia: Crisis & Transformation. 2011. (Illus.). 256p. 75.00 (978-1-56549-300-1(1)); pap. 24.95 (978-1-56549-299-8(4)) Stylus Publishing, LLC.

Chin, Felix. Economic, Political & Social Issues of Asia. 2011. (Series: Asian Political, Economic & Security Issues Ser.). (Illus.). xiii, 415p. 295.00 (978-1-61122-471-9(3)) Nova Science Pubs., Inc.

Chin, Felix, ed. Politics & Economics of South, Southeastern & Central Asia. 2011. (Asian Political, Economic & Security Issues Ser.). 140.00 **(978-1-61470-461-4(9))** Nova Science Pubs., Inc.

Collins, Kathleen. Clan Politics & Regime Transition in Central Asia. 2009. (ENG., Illus.). 400p. (C). pap. 36.99 (978-0-521-11466-0(7)) Cambridge Univ. Pr.

Crews, Robert D. For Prophet & Tsar: Islam & Empire in Russia & Central Asia. 2009. (Illus.). 480p. pap. 20.00 (978-0-674-03223-1(3)) Harvard Univ. Pr.

Cummings, Sally N. Understanding Central Asia. 2012. (ENG., Illus.). 256p. (C). pap. 44.95 (978-0-415-29703-5(6)) Routledge.

Cummings, Sally N., ed. Symbolism & Power in Central Asia: Politics of the Spectacular. 2010. (ENG., Illus.). 268p. (C). 125.00 (978-0-415-57567-6(2), Routledge) Taylor & Francis Group GBR. Dist: Taylor & Francis Group.

Cummings, Sally N. & Hinnebusch, Raymond, eds. Sovereignty after Empire: Comparing the Middle East & Central Asia. 2011. (ENG.). 344p. (gr. 17). 105.00 (978-0-7486-4304-2(4)) Edinburgh Univ. Pr. GBR. Dist: Columbia Univ. Pr.

Dave. Politics of Modern Central Asia, 4 vols. 2010. (Illus.). Vol. 3. 390p. (978-0-415-47299-9(7)) Vol. 4. 376p. (978-0-415-47298-2(9)) Routledge.

Dave, Bhavna. Politics of Modern Central Asia, 4 vols. 2010. (Critical Issues in Modern Politics Ser.). (Illus.). (ENG.). 1776p. 1075.00 (978-0-415-46826-8(4)); Vol. 2. 486p. (978-0-415-47300-2(4)) Routledge.

Dave, Bhavna, ed. Politics of Modern Central Asia, 4 vols., Vol. 1. 2010. (Illus.). 476p. (978-0-415-47301-9(2)) Routledge.

Dillinger, William. Poverty & Regional Development in Eastern Europe & Central Asia. 2007. (World Bank Working Papers: 118). (ENG., Illus.). 76p. per. 15.00 (978-0-8213-7161-9(4), 9780821371619) World Bank Pubns.

The Emerging Importance of the U.S.-Central Asia Partnership: Hearing Before the Subcommittee on Asia, the Pacific, & the Global Environment of the Committee on Foreign Affairs, House of Representatives, One Hundred Eleventh Congress, Second Session, November 17, 2010. 2010. iii, 51p. **(978-0-16-087765-0(2)**, 552-070-42276-5) United States Government Printing Office.

F. Woode, Amanda. The Politics of Transition in Central Asia & the Caucasus: Enduring Legacies & Emerging Challenges. Stefes, Christoph H., ed. 2009. (Central Asian Studies). (ENG., Illus.). 272p. 135.00 (978-0-415-36813-1(8)) Routledge.

Hanks, Reuel R. Global Security Watch — Central Asia. 2010. (Illus.). xii, 225p. E-Book (978-0-313-35423-6(5), Praeger Pubs.) Greenwood Publishing Group, Inc.

—Global Security Watch-Central Asia. 2010. (Global Security Watch Ser.). (Illus.). 225p. instr.'s hndbk. ed. 49.95 (978-0-313-35422-9(7), C35422, Praeger Pubs.) Greenwood Publishing Group, Inc.

—Handbook of Central Asian Politics. 2012. (ENG., Illus.). 368p. (C). instr.'s hndbk. ed. 200.00 (978-0-415-77676-9(7)) Routledge.

Hiro, Dilip. Inside Central Asia. 2009. (Illus.). 448p. (978-0-7156-3877-4(7)) Overlook Pr., The.

—Inside Central Asia: A Political & Cultural History of Uzbekistan, Turkmenistan, Kazakhstan, Kyrgyzstan, Tajikstan Turky, & Iran. 2011. (ENG.). 464p. (gr. 12). pap. 20.00 (978-1-59020-333-0(X)) Overlook Pr., The.

Jeffries, Ian. Mongolia: A Guide to Economic & Political Developments. 2007. (Guides to Economic & Political Developments in Asia Ser.). (ENG., Illus.). 224p. (C). 150.00 (978-0-415-42545-2(X)) Routledge.

Johnson, Rob. Oil, Islam, & Conflict: Central Asia Since 1945. 2007. (Reaktion Books - Contemporary Worlds Ser.). (ENG., Illus.). 240p. per. 25.00 (978-1-86189-339-0(6)) Reaktion Bks., Ltd. GBR. Dist: Chicago Distribution Ctr.

Kaplonski, Christopher. Mongolia: Democracy on the Steppe. 2008. (Postcommunist States & Nations Ser.). 192p. 130.00 (978-0-415-27437-1(0)) Routledge.

Karagiannis, Emmanuel. Political Islam in Central Asia. 2011. (ENG., Illus.). 192p. pap. 42.95 **(978-0-415-67375-4(5))** Routledge.

Karagiannis, Emmanuel. Political Islam in Central Asia: The Challenge of Hizb Ut-Tahrir. 2010. (ENG., Illus.). 176p. 140.00 (978-0-415-55399-5(7)) Routledge.

Lester, Anne E., ed. Central Asia: Background, Issues & U. S. Interests. 2010. (Countries, Regional Studies, Trading Blocks, Unions, World Organizations Ser.). 115.00 (978-1-61728-880-7(2)) Nova Science Pubs., Inc.

Lewis, David. The Temptations of Tyranny in Central Asia. 2008. (Columbia/Hurst Ser.). (ENG.). 224p. (gr. 17). 31.00 (978-0-231-70025-2(3)) Columbia Univ. Pr.

Liu, Morgan Y. Under Solomon's Throne: Uzbek Visions of Renewal in Osh. 2012. (Central Eurasia in Context Ser.). (ENG.). 328p. pap. 29.95 **(978-0-8229-6177-2(6))** Univ. of Pittsburgh Pr.

Macfadyen. Russian Culture in Uzbekistan: One Language in the Middle of Nowhere. 2006. (Central Asian Studies Ser.). (Illus.). 208p. 160.00 (978-0-415-34134-9(5), RU42338) Routledge.

Mackerras, Colin & Clarke, Michael, eds. China Xinjiang & Central Asia. 2011. (ENG., Illus.). 212p. pap. 42.95 **(978-0-415-67333-4(X))** Routledge.

MacLean, Rory. Magic Bus: On the Hippie Trail from Istanbul to India. 2009. (ENG.). 240p. pap. 14.95 (978-0-9788431-9-9(3)) Ig Publishing, Inc.

Marat, Erica. The Military & the State in Central Asia: From Red Army to Independence. (ENG.). 176p. (C). 2012. pap. 44.95 **(978-0-415-62538-8(6))** 2009. 138.00 (978-0-415-49347-5(1)) Routledge.

McTernan, Benedict, ed. Political Risk Yearbook - 2007 Vol. 8: Central & South Asia. 2007. per. (978-1-933539-36-2(4)) PRS Group Inc., The.

Mullerson, Rein. Central Asia. 2012. (ENG.). 256p. pap. 42.95 **(978-0-415-54102-2(6))** Routledge.

Mullerson, Rein. Central Asia: A Chessboard & Player in the New Great Game. 2007. (Kegan Paul Library of Central Asia Ser.). (Illus.). 370p. 150.00 (978-0-7103-1316-4(0)) Taylor & Francis Group.

Nichol, Jim. Central Asia: Security, Internal Affairs & U. S. Interests. 2008. 135p. 69.00 (978-1-60456-848-6(8)) Nova Science Pubs., Inc.

OECD Staff, ed. Asset Declarations for Public Officials: A Tool to Prevent Corruption. 2011. (Fighting Corruption in Eastern Europe & Central Asia Ser.). pap. **(978-92-64-09527-4(6))** Organization for Economic Cooperation & Development.

Organisation for Economic Co-operation and Development Staff. The Istanbul Anti-Corruption Action Plan: Progress & Challenges. 2008. 96p. pap. 63.00 (978-92-64-04697-9(6)) Organization for Economic Cooperation & Development.

Özdemir Çolak, Aysel. Soviet Legacy in Central Asi. 2011. 84p. pap. **(978-3-8443-9099-5(5))** Lambert Academic Publishing.

Paramonov, Vladimir, et al. Russia in Central Asia: Policy, Security & Economics. 2009. (Illus.). xvii, 118p. 79.00 (978-1-60692-880-6(5)) Nova Science Pubs., Inc.

Peimani, Hooman. Conflict & Security in Central Asia & the Caucasus, 1 vol. 2009. (Illus.). 373p. 95.00 (978-1-59884-054-4(1), CEASCA1C) ABC-CLIO, LLC.

Reeves, Madeleine, ed. Contested Trajectories. 2012. (ThirdWorlds Ser.). (ENG.). 216p. (C). 155.00 **(978-0-415-50353-2(1))** Routledge.

Rumer, Eugene, et al. Central Asia: Views from Washington, Moscow, & Beijing. 2007. 223p. per. 32.95 (978-0-7656-1995-2(4)) Sharpe, M.E. Inc.

Sengupta, Anita. Heartlands of Eurasia: The Geopolitics of Political Space. 2009. (ENG., Illus.). 220p. 68.50 (978-0-7391-3606-5(2)) Lexington Bks.

Sneath, David. The Headless State: Aristocratic Orders, Kinship Society, & Misrepresentations of Nomadic Inner Asia. 2007. (ENG., Illus.). 288p. (gr. 17). 60.00 (978-0-231-14054-6(1)) Columbia Univ. Pr.

Tentas, James C., ed. Security & Internal Affairs of Central Asia. 2010. (Countries, Regional Studies, Trading Blocks, Unions, World Organizations Ser.). 159p. 98.00 (978-1-61728-846-3(2)) Nova Science Pubs., Inc.

The World Bank. Trends in Corruption & Regulatory Burden in Eastern Europe & Central Asia. 2011. (World Bank Studies). (ENG.). 98p. pap. 15.00 (978-0-8213-8671-2(9), 9780821386712) World Bank Pubns.

Wooden, Amanda E. & Stefes, Christoph H., eds. The Politics of Transition in Central Asia & the Caucasus: Enduring Legacies & Emerging Challenges. 2012. (ENG., Illus.). 288p. (C). pap. 44.95 **(978-0-415-62539-5(4))** Routledge.

Zhao, Huasheng, et al. Central Asia: Views from Washington, Moscow, & Beijing. 2007. (ENG.). 232p. 97.95 (978-0-7656-1994-5(6)) Sharpe, M.E. Inc.

ASIA, CENTRAL—RELIGION

Foltz, Richard C. Religions of the Silk Road: Premodern Patterns of Globalization. 2nd rev. ed. 2010. (ENG., Illus.). 208p. pap. 26.00 (978-0-230-62125-1(2)) Palgrave Macmillan.

Karagiannis, Emmanuel. Political Islam in Central Asia. 2011. (ENG., Illus.). 192p. pap. 42.95 **(978-0-415-67375-4(5))** Routledge.

Mingana, Alphonse. The Early Spread of Christianity in Central Asia & the Far East. 2010. pap. 25.12 (978-1-61719-589-1(8)) Gorgias Pr., LLC.

Zertural, Zekine & Wilkens, Jens. Der östliche Manichäismus - Gattungs- und Werksgeschichte: Vorträge des Göttinger Symposiums vom 4./5. März 2010. 2011. (Abhandlungen der Akademie der Wissenschaften zu Göttingen. Neue Folge Ser.). (GER., Illus.). X, 237p. 140.00 **(978-3-11-026137-0(5))** De Gruyter, Walter Inc.

Van Gorder, Christian. Muslim-Christian Relations in Central Asia. 2008. (Illus.). XIV, 210p. 170.00 (978-0-415-77608-0(2)) Routledge.

Varghese, Baby. Baptism & Chrismation in the Syriac Tradition. 2011. pap. 31.10 **(978-1-4632-0049-7(8))** Gorgias Pr., LLC.

Zieme, P., ed. Aspects of Research into Central Asian Buddhism: In Memoriam Kogi Kudara. 2008. (Silk Road Studies). (ENG & GER.). 483p. (C). pap. 94.00 (978-2-503-52751-2(5)) Brepols Pubs. BEL. Dist: ISD.

ASIA, CENTRAL—SOCIAL CONDITIONS

Alexander, Catharine, et al, eds. Urban Life in Post-Soviet Asia. 2012. (ENG., Illus.). 224p. (C). pap. 42.95 **(978-0-415-53316-4(3))** Taylor & Francis Group GBR. Dist: Taylor & Francis Group.

Alexander, Catherine. Urban Life in Post-Soviet Central Asia. Humphrey, Caroline et al, eds. 2006. (Illus.). XII, 212p. 160.00 (978-1-84472-115-3(9), Routledge) Taylor & Francis Group GBR. Dist: Taylor & Francis Group.

Amsler, Sarah. The Politics of Knowledge in Central Asia: Science Between Marx & the Market. 2007. (Central Asia Research Forum Ser.). (ENG.). 208p. (C). 160.00 (978-0-415-41334-3(6)) Routledge.

Becks, Carleton. The Security Situation in Central Asi. 2011. 96p. pap. **(978-3-8443-1228-7(5))** Lambert Academic Publishing.

Bruun, Ole. Precious Steppe: Mongolian Nomadic Pastoralists in Pursuit of the Market. 2008. (Asiaworld Ser.). (ENG., Illus.). 262p. pap. 31.50 (978-0-7391-2807-7(8)) Lexington Bks.

Collins, Kathleen. Clan Politics & Regime Transition in Central Asia. 2009. (ENG., Illus.). 400p. (C). pap. 36.99 (978-0-521-11466-0(7)) Cambridge Univ. Pr.

Gupta, Ramanika. Adivasi Kauna. 2008. (HIN.). 203p. (978-81-8361-219-7(9), Library of Congress — New Delhi Overseas Office) Radha Krishna Prakashan Pvt Ltd.

Kaplonski, Christopher. Mongolia: Democracy on the Steppe. 2008. (Postcommunist States & Nations Ser.). 192p. 130.00 (978-0-415-27437-1(0)) Routledge.

Kirmse, Stefan B., ed. Youth in the Former Soviet South: Everyday Lives between Experimentation & Regulation. 2011. (ThirdWorlds Ser.). (ENG., Illus.). 184p. (C). 148.00 (978-0-415-68099-8(9)) Routledge.

Liu, Morgan Y. Under Solomon's Throne: Uzbek Visions of Renewal in Osh. 2012. (Central Eurasia in Context Ser.). (ENG.). 328p. pap. 29.95 **(978-0-8229-6177-2(6))** Univ. of Pittsburgh Pr.

Mullerson, Rein. Central Asia. 2012. (ENG.). 256p. pap. 42.95 **(978-0-415-54102-2(6))** Routledge.

Mullerson, Rein. Central Asia: A Chessboard & Player in the New Great Game. 2007. (Kegan Paul Library of Central Asia Ser.). (Illus.). 370p. 150.00 (978-0-7103-1316-4(0)) Taylor & Francis Group.

Nasritdinov, Emil & O'Connor, Kevin. Regional Change in Kyrgyzstan. 2010. 176p. pap. (978-3-8383-0093-1(9)) Lambert Academic Publishing.

Nove, Alec. The Soviet Middle East (Routledge Revivals) 2012. (Routledge Revivals Ser.). (ENG.). 164p. 110.00 **(978-0-415-68241-1(X))** Routledge.

Omelicheva, Mairya Y. Counterterrorism Policies in Central Asia. 2010. (Central Asian Studies). (ENG., Illus.). 192p. (C). 130.00 (978-0-415-77981-4(2)) Routledge.

Organisation for Economic Co-operation and Development Staff. Black Sea & Central Asia: Promoting Work & Well Being. 2008. (Illus.). 149p. pap. 63.00 (978-92-64-04729-7(8)) Organization for Economic Cooperation & Development.

Organisation for Economic Co-operation and Development: Development Centre. Competitiveness & Private Sector Development: Central Asia 2011; Competitiveness Outlook. 2011. (Illus.). 160p. pap. 67.00 **(978-92-64-09727-8(9))** Organization for Economic Cooperation & Development.

Peimani, Hooman. Conflict & Security in Central Asia & the Caucasus, 1 vol. 2009. (Illus.). 373p. 95.00 (978-1-59884-054-4(1), CEASCA1C) ABC-CLIO, LLC.

Pirie, F. & Huber, T., eds. Conflict & Social Order in Tibet & Inner Asia. 2008. 250p. (978-90-04-15817-7(0)) BRILL.

Reeves, Madeleine, ed. Contested Trajectories. 2012. (ThirdWorlds Ser.). (ENG.). 216p. (C). 155.00 **(978-0-415-50353-2(1))** Routledge.

Starr, S. Frederick. Ferghana Valley: The Heart of Central Asia. 2011. (ENG., Illus.). 464p. pap. 39.95 **(978-0-7656-2999-9(2))** Sharpe, M.E. Inc.

Starr, S. Frederick, ed. Ferghana Valley: The Heart of Central Asia. 2011. (Studies of Central Asia & the Caucasus Ser.). (ENG., Illus.). 464p. 104.95 (978-0-7656-2998-2(4)) Sharpe, M.E. Inc.

Stern, Jessica. These Everyday Humiliations: Violence Against Lesbians, Bisexual Women, & Transgender Men in Kyrgyzstan. 2008. 45p. (978-1-56432-381-1(1)) Human Rights Watch.

Sultanova, Razia. From Shamanism to Sufism: Women, Islam & Culture in Central Asia. 2011. (International Library of Central Asia Studies). (ENG., Illus.). 256p. 90.00 (978-1-84885-309-6(2)) I. B. Tauris & Co., Ltd. GBR. Dist: Macmillan.

United Nations. Paths to 2015 Mdg Priorities in Asia & the Pacific. 2011. (ENG.). 68p. pap. 12.00 **(978-92-1-120618-0(9))** United Nations Pubns.

World Bank Staff, contrib. by. Trends in Corruption & Regulatory Burden: Eastern Europe & Central Asia. 2011. (978-0-8213-8696-5(4)) World Bank Pubns.

ASIA, CENTRAL—SOCIAL LIFE AND CUSTOMS

Abazov, Rafis. Culture & Customs of the Central Asian Republics, 1 vol. 2006. (Culture & Customs of Asia Ser.). (Illus.). 324p. 49.95 (978-0-313-33656-0(3), GR3656, Greenwood Pr.) Greenwood Publishing Group, Inc.

Alexander, Aslan. A Carpet Ride to Khiva. 2010. (ENG., Illus.). 336p. 14.95 **(978-1-84831-149-7(4))** Totem Bks. GBR. Dist: Consortium Bk. Sales & Distribution.

Baumer, Christoph. Traces in the Desert: Journeys of Discovery Across Central Asia. 2008. (ENG., Illus.). 240p. 42.00 (978-1-84511-337-7(3)) I. B. Tauris & Co., Ltd. GBR. Dist: Macmillan.

Clark, Ruby. Central Asian Ikats: From the Rau Collection. 2007. (ENG., Illus.). 96p. pap. 35.00 (978-1-85177-525-5(0)) V & A Pubns. GBR. Dist: Hachette Bk. Group.

Davis-Kimball, Jeannine. Nomads of the Altai Mountains: The Mongols: Ancient Traditions in a Modern World. 2010. (Illus.). 65p. **(978-1-885979-09-4(6))** Zinat Pr.

Farr, Saffia. Revolution Baby. 2007. 300p. per. (978-1-897312-50-6(4)) Adlibbed Ltd.

Foltz, Richard C. Religions of the Silk Road: Premodern Patterns of Globalization. 2nd rev. ed. 2010. (ENG., Illus.). 208p. pap. 26.00 (978-0-230-62125-1(2)) Palgrave Macmillan.

Günther, Olaf. Die dorboz im Ferghanatal: Erkundungen im Alltag und der Geschichte einer Gauklerkultur. 2008. (Europäische Hochschulschriften. Reihe 27: Asiatische und Afrikanische Studien Ser.). 378p. pap. 81.95 (978-3-631-57801-8(6)) Lang, Peter GmbH, Europaischer Verlag der Wissenschaften DEU. Dist: Lang, Peter.

Kehl-Bodrogi, Krisztina. Religion Is Not So Strong Here: Muslim Religious Life in Khorezm after Socialism. 2011. (Illus.). 272p. pap. 36.95 (978-3-8258-9909-7(8)) Lit Verlag DEU. Dist: Transaction Pubs.

Knee, Roman, Beyer. Kirgistan: Ein Bildband über Talas. 2007. 224p. 75.00 (978-3-7774-3805-4(7)) Hirmer Verlag GmbH DEU. Dist: Chicago Distribution Ctr.

Lent, John A. & Fitzsimmons, Lorna, eds. Asian Popular Culture in Transition. 2012. (Routledge Contemporary Asia Ser.). (ENG., Illus.). 208p. (C). 125.00 **(978-0-415-69284-7(9))** Routledge.

Lewin, Ted & Lewin, Betsy. Horse Song: The Naadam of Mongolia. 2008. (Illus.). 56p. (J). (gr. 1-5). 19.95 (978-1-58430-277-3(1)) Lee & Low Bks., Inc.

Macfadyen. Russian Culture in Uzbekistan: One Language in the Middle of Nowhere. 2006. (Central Asian Studies Ser.). (Illus.). 208p. 160.00 (978-0-415-34134-9(5), RU42338) Routledge.

May, Timothy Michael. Culture & Customs of Mongolia, 1 vol. 2008. (Culture & Customs of Asia Ser.). (Illus.). 204p. 49.95 (978-0-313-33983-7(X), GR3983, Greenwood Pr.) Greenwood Publishing Group, Inc.

Musakeev, Temirbek & Antipina, Claudia. Kyrgyzstan. 2007. (ENG., Illus.). 224p. 65.00 (978-88-8491-970-0(3)) Skira Editore ITA. Dist: Random Hse., Inc.

Nasritdinov, Emil & O'Connor, Kevin. Regional Change in Kyrgyzstan. 2010. 176p. pap. (978-3-8383-0093-1(9)) Lambert Academic Publishing.

Sahadeo, Jeff & Zanca, Russell, eds. Everyday Life in Central Asia: Past & Present. 2007. (Illus.). (ENG.). 424p. pap. 24.95 (978-0-253-21904-6(3), 0253219043); 401p. 65.00 (978-0-253-34883-8(8)) Indiana Univ. Pr.

Watson, Claire Burges. Silk Route Adventure: On Horseback in the Heart of Asia. 2007. (ENG., Illus.). 352p. 50.00 (978-0-7090-8061-9(1)) Hale, Robert Ltd. GBR. Dist: Independent Pubs. Group.

ASIA, EAST

see East Asia

ASIA, EASTERN

see East Asia

ASIA, SOUTH

see South Asia

ASIA, SOUTHEAST

see Southeast Asia

ASIA, SOUTHEASTERN

see Southeast Asia

ASIA, SOUTHWEST

see Middle East

ASIA, WESTERN

see Middle East

ASIA-AFRICA CONFERENCE, BANDUNG, JAVA, 1955

Ampiah, Kweku. The Political & Moral Imperatives of the Bandung Conference of 1955: The Reactions of the US, UK & Japan. 2007. 252p. (978-1-905246-40-3(4)) BRILL.

Lee, Christopher, ed. Making a World after Empire: The Bandung Moment & Its Political Afterlives. 2010. (Ohio RIS Global Ser.). (ENG., Illus.). 280p. pap. 29.95 (978-0-89680-277-3(9)) Ohio Univ. Pr.

Lee, Christopher J. Making a World after Empire: The Bandung Moment & Its Political Afterlives. 2010. 280p. (978-0-89680-468-5(2)) Ohio Univ. Pr.

ASIA MINOR

see Turkey

ASIA PACIFIC ECONOMIC COOPERATION (ORGANIZATION)

Cheema, G. Shabbir, et al, eds. Cross-Border Governance in Asia: Regional Issues & Mechanisms. 2011. (ENG.). 300p. pap. 35.00 (978-92-808-1193-3(2)) United Nations Univ. Pr. JPN. Dist: Brookings Institution Pr.

Drysdale & Terada. Asia-Pacific Economic Co-Operation: Critical Perspectives on the World Economy, 4 vols. 2007. (Critical Perspectives on the World Economy Ser.). (ENG., Illus.). 1968p. (C). 1680.00 (978-0-415-31098-7(9)) Routledge.

—Asia-Pacific Economic Cooperation, 5 vols., Vol. 1. 2007. (Illus.). 368p. (978-0-415-31099-4(7)) Routledge.

—Asia-Pacific Economic Cooperation: Critical Pers Wld Econ, 5 vols. 2007. (Illus.). Vol. 3. 368p. (978-0-415-31101-4(2)) Vol. 4. 480p. (978-0-415-31102-1(0)) Routledge.

—Asia-Pacific Economic Cooperative: Critica Persp Wld Econ, 5 vols., Vol. 2. 2007. (Illus.). 352p. (978-0-415-31100-7(4)) Routledge.

Drysdale, Peter & Terada, Takashi. Asia-Pac Econ Coop Vol. 5, 5 vols. 2007. (Illus.). 400p. (978-0-415-41575-0(6)) Routledge.

The Future of APEC: Hearing Before the Subcommittee on Asia, the Pacific, & the Global Environment of the Committee on Foreign Affairs, House of Representatives, One Hundred Eleventh Congress, First Session, October 14, 2009. 2009. iii, 53p. (978-0-16-084834-6(2), 552-070-40235-7) United States Government Printing Office.

Ho, Lok Sang & Wong, John. Apec & the Rise of China. 2011. 248p. 85.00 (978-981-4329-40-8(1)) World Scientific Publishing Co., Inc.

Pue, W. Wesley. Pepper in Our Eyes: The Apec Affair. 276p. pap. *(978-0-7748-0780-7(6))* Univ. of British Columbia Pr.

ASIAN-AFRICAN POLITICS

see Afro-Asian Politics

ASIAN AMERICAN ART

Asian American Women Artists Association Staff, contrib. by. Cheers to Muses: Contemporary Works by Asian American Women. 2007. (Illus.). 128p. pap. 24.95 *(978-0-9787359-0-6(0))* AAWAA Pr.

Chang, Alexandra, text. Envisioning Diaspora, Asian American Visual Arts Collectives. 2009. (ENG., Illus.). 266p. pap. 35.00 *(978-988-17522-3-9(X))* Timezone 8 Ltd. HKG. Dist: D.A.P./Distributed Art Pubs.

Chiu, Melissa, et al, eds. One Way or Another: Asian American Art Now. 2006. (ENG., Illus.). 127p. pap. 29.95 *(978-0-300-12059-2(1))* Yale Univ. Pr.

Dariotis, Wei Ming. War Baby / Love Child: Mixed Race Asian American Art. Kina, Laura, ed. 2012. (ENG., Illus.). 304p. pap. 45.00 ***(978-0-295-99225-9(5))*** Univ. of Washington Pr.

Lyuh, Soo Jin. Cross-Cultural, Cross-Institutional Collaborative Art Project. 2008. 68p. pap. *(978-3-639-03774-6(X))* VDM Verlag Dr. Mueller e.K.

Machida, Margo. Unsettled Visions: Contemporary Asian American Artists & the Social Imaginary. 2009. (Objects/Histories Ser.). (ENG., Illus.). 384p. 99.95 *(978-0-8223-4187-1(5))*; pap. 27.95 *(978-0-8223-4204-5(9))* Duke Univ. Pr.

Spain, Sharon. Asian American Art: A History, 1850-1970. Chang, Gordon H. et al, eds. 2008. (Asian America Ser.). (ENG.). 576p. pap. 39.95 *(978-0-8047-5752-2(6))*; (Illus.). 80.00 *(978-0-8047-5751-5(8))* Stanford Univ. Pr. (Stanford General Bks.).

ASIAN AMERICAN LITERATURE (ENGLISH)

see American Literature—Asian American Authors

ASIAN AMERICANS

Alban Institute Action Research Team on Conflict Management. Pacific Asian American Ministry in a Time of Shifting Paradigms: The Example of Asian American Conflict Management. pap. 7.50 *(978-1-56699-163-6(3)*, OD117) Alban Institute, Inc.

Alvarez, Alvin. Asian American Psychology: Current Perspectives. Alvarez, Alvin N. & Tewari, Nita, eds. 2008. (ENG., Illus.). 704p. pap. 74.95 *(978-0-8058-6008-5(8)*, Psychology Press) Taylor & Francis Group GBR. Dist: Taylor & Francis Group.

Alvarez, Alvin N. & Alvarez, Alvin. Asian American Psychology: Current Perspectives. Alvarez, Alvin N., ed. 2008. (ENG. Illus.). 704p. 131.95 *(978-1-84169-769-7(9)*, Psychology Press) Taylor & Francis Group GBR. Dist: Taylor & Francis Group.

Ancheta, Angelo N. Race, Rights & the Asian American Experience. 2nd annot. ed. 2006. (ENG.). 232p. per. 24.95 *(978-0-8135-3902-7(1))* Rutgers Univ. Pr.

Aoki, Andrew L. & Takeda, Okiyoshi. Asian American Politics. 2009. (UMP - US Minority Politics Ser.: 1). (ENG., Illus.). 224p. 64.95 *(978-0-7456-3446-3(X))* Polity Pr. GBR. Dist: Wiley, John & Sons, Inc.

Aoki, Andrew L., et al. Asian American Politics. 2009. (UMP - US Minority Politics Ser.: 2). (ENG., Illus.). 224p. pap. 26.95 *(978-0-7456-3447-0(8))* Polity Pr. GBR. Dist: Wiley, John & Sons, Inc.

Asian American Women Artists Association Staff, contrib. by. Cheers to Muses: Contemporary Works by Asian American Women. 2007. (Illus.). 128p. pap. 24.95 *(978-0-9787359-0-6(0))* AAWAA Pr.

Asian Americans: A Statistical Sourcebook. 2006. (Asian Americans: A Statistical Sourcebook Ser.). (Illus.). 231p. 70.00 *(978-0-929960-40-1(8)*, AA05CL) Information Pubns., Inc.

Asian & Pacific Islander Student Challenges/GAO. 2008. pap. 50.00 *(978-1-60456-754-0(6))* Nova Science Pubs., Inc.

Bascara, Victor. Model-Minority Imperialism. 2006. 232p. per. 22.50 *(978-0-8166-4512-1(4))* Univ. of Minnesota Pr.

Bateman, William B., et al. Praeger Handbook of Asian American Health: Taking Notice & Taking Action, 2 vols. 2009. 800p. 195.00 *(978-0-313-34701-6(8)*, C34701, Praeger Pubs.) Greenwood Publishing Group, Inc.

Bow, Leslie. Partly Colored: Asian Americans & Racial Anomaly in the Segregated South. 2010. (ENG., Illus.). 304p. 75.00 *(978-0-8147-9132-5(8))*; pap. 25.00 *(978-0-8147-9133-2(6))* New York Univ. Pr.

Brooks, Charlotte & Brooks, C. Alien Neighbors, Foreign Friends: Asian Americans, Housing, & the Transformation of Urban California. 2009. (Historical Studies of Urban America Ser.). (Illus.). 352p. 40.00 *(978-0-226-07597-6(4))* Univ. of Chicago Pr.

Brown, Michael S. Victorio Acosta Velasco: An American Life. 2007. (ENG.). 152p. pap. 31.50 *(978-0-7618-3800-5(7))* Hamilton Bks.

Chang, Yoonmee. Writing the Ghetto: Class, Authorship, & the Asian American Ethnic Enclave. 2011. (Mellon-ALI Ser.). (ENG., Illus.). 252p. pap. 24.95 ***(978-0-8135-5175-3(7))*** Rutgers Univ. Pr.

Chen, Carolyn & Jeung, Russell. Sustaining Faith Traditions: Race, Ethnicity, & Religion among the Latino & Asian American Second Generation. 2012. (ENG.). 304p. 80.00 ***(978-0-8147-1735-6(7))***; pap. 28.00 ***(978-0-8147-1736-3(5))*** New York Univ. Pr.

Chen, Edith W. & Yoo, Grace J., eds. Encyclopedia of Asian American Issues Today, 2 vols. 2009. (Illus.). 1005p. 180.00 *(978-0-313-34749-8(2)*, GR4749) Greenwood Publishing Group, Inc.

Chen, Thomas C., ed. Asian American Studies Now: A Critical Reader. 2010. (ENG.). 672p. (C). pap. 37.50 *(978-0-8135-4575-2(7))* Rutgers Univ. Pr.

Chew, Ron. Remembering Silme Domingo & Gene Viernes: The Legacy of Filipino American Labor Activism. 2012. (ENG.). 125p. pap. 17.95 ***(978-0-295-99190-0(9)***, Alaskero Foundation) Univ. of Washington Pr.

Chi, Sang & Robinson, Emily Moberg. Voices of the Asian American & Pacific Islander Experience, 2 vols. 2012. 700p. 189.00 ***(978-1-59884-354-5(0)***, A2635C) Greenwood Publishing Group, Inc.

—Voices of the Asian American Experience. 2012. E-Book ***(978-1-59884-355-2(9)***, Greenwood Pr.) Greenwood Publishing Group, Inc.

Chiang, Mark. The Cultural Capital of Asian American Studies: Autonomy & Representation in the University. 2009. (ENG.). 272p. 78.00 *(978-0-8147-1700-4(4))*; pap. 23.00 *(978-0-8147-1701-1(2))* New York Univ. Pr.

ChiHa. U. S Portland Radio Station Harassments. 2007. 120p. per. 9.95 *(978-1-4327-0697-5(7))* Outskirts Pr., Inc.

Ching, Doris & Agbayani, Amefil, eds. Asian Americans & Pacific Islanders in Higher Education: Research & Perspectives on Identity, Leadership, & Success. 2012. (ENG.). 400p. 39.95 ***(978-0-931654-60-2(2))*** National Assn. of Student Personnel Administrators, Inc.

Chiu, Monica, ed. Asian Americans in New England: Culture & Community. 2009. (Revisiting New England Ser.). (ENG., Illus.). 276p. lib. bdg. 50.00 *(978-1-58465-794-1(4))* Univ. Pr. of New England.

Cho, In Nam. On Life Satisfaction of Ethnic Minority Older Adults- the Differences Between Korean American & Korean Older Adults. 2007. 204p. per. *(978-3-8364-2820-0(2))* VDM Verlag Dr. Mueller e.K.

Choi, Ariel Raimundo, ed. Korean-American Stories: Collection of Autobiographies. 2011. (KOR & ENG., Illus.). 100.00 ***(978-1-59689-167-8(X)***, Hermit Kingdom Pr., The) Hermit Kingdom Pr., The.

Chou, Rosalind S. & Feagin, Joe R. The Myth of the Model Minority: Asian Americans Facing Racism. 2008. 264p. pap. 29.95 *(978-1-59451-587-3(5))* Paradigm Pubs.

Choua, Mouavangsou. Traditional Hmong Marriage Ceremony Values. 2010. pap. 24.00 *(978-1-55605-400-6(9))* Wyndham Hall Pr.

Chung, Hye Seung. Hollywood Asian: Philip Ahn & the Politics of Cross-Ethnic Performance. 2006. (Illus.). 248p. 72.50 *(978-1-59213-515-8(3))*; pap. 25.95 *(978-1-59213-516-5(1))* Temple Univ. Pr.

Collet, Christian & Lien, Pei-Te, eds. The Transnational Politics of Asian Americans. 2009. (Asian American History & Culture Ser.). (ENG., Illus.). 252p. 76.50 *(978-1-59213-860-9(8))*; pap. 30.95 *(978-1-59213-861-6(6))* Temple Univ. Pr.

Conant, Py Kim. Sex Secrets of an American Geisha: How to Attract, Satisfy, & Keep Your Man. 2006. (Positively Sexual Ser.). (ENG., Illus.). 240p. per. 13.95 *(978-0-89793-490-9(3))* Hunter Hse., Inc.

Das Gupta, Monisha. Unruly Immigrants: Rights, Activism, & Transnational South Asian Politics in the United States. 2006. (ENG., Illus.). 336p. (C). 89.95 *(978-0-8223-3858-1(0))* Duke Univ. Pr.

Dasgupta, Shamita D., ed. Body Evidence: Intimate Violence Against South Asian Women in America. 2007. (ENG.). 320p. (C). 72.00 *(978-0-8135-3981-2(1))* Rutgers Univ. Pr.

—Body Evidence: Intimate Violence Against South Asian Women in America. 2007. (ENG.). 320p. per. 29.95 *(978-0-8135-3982-9(X))* Rutgers Univ. Pr.

Davis, Rocio G. Relative Histories: Mediating History in Asian American Family Memoirs. 2011. xi, 183p. 39.00 *(978-0-8248-3458-6(5))* Univ. of Hawaii Pr.

Duffy, John M. Writing from These Roots: Literacy in a Hmong-American Community. 2011. 256p. pap. 21.00 ***(978-0-8248-3615-3(4))*** 2007. 241p. 47.00 *(978-0-8248-3095-3(4))* Univ. of Hawaii Pr.

Dumas, Firoozeh. Laughing Without an Accent: Adventures of a Global Citizen. 2009. (ENG.). 256p. pap. 15.00 *(978-0-345-49957-8(3)*, Random Hse. Trade Paperbacks) Random House Publishing Group.

Eng, David L. The Feeling of Kinship: Queer Liberalism & the Racialization of Intimacy. 2010. (ENG., Illus.). 268p. 84.95 *(978-0-8223-4715-6(6))* Duke Univ. Pr.

—The Feeling of Kinship: Queer Liberalism & the Racialization of Intimacy. 2010. (ENG., Illus.). 268p. pap. 23.95 *(978-0-8223-4732-3(6))* Duke Univ. Pr.

Espiritu, Yen Le. Asian American Women & Men: Labor, Laws, & Love. 2nd ed. 2007. (Gender Lens Ser.). (ENG.). 160p. 70.00 *(978-0-7425-6060-4(0))*; per. 22.95 *(978-0-7425-6061-1(9))* Rowman & Littlefield Publishers, Inc.

—Asian American Women & Men: The Gender Lens. 2006. pap. 8.95 *(978-1-4288-1584-1(8))* Cram101 Inc.

Feagin, Joe R. & Chou, Rosalind S. The Myth of the Model Minority: Asian Americans Facing Racism. 2008. 264p. (C). 125.00 *(978-1-59451-586-6(7))* Paradigm Pubs.

Fong, Timothy P. The Contemporary Asian American Experience: Beyond the Model Minority. 3rd ed. 2007. (ENG.). 400p. (C). per. 79.40 *(978-0-13-185061-3(X)*, Prentice Hall) Prentice Hall PTR.

Foo, Lora Jo. Asian American Women: Issues, Concerns, & Responsive Human & Civil Rights Advocacy. 2007. 264p. (ENG.). 29.95 *(978-0-595-90115-9(8))*; per. 19.95 *(978-0-595-45299-6(X))* iUniverse, Inc.

Franks, Joel. Crossing Sidelines Crossing Cultures: Sport & Asian Pacific American Cultural Citizenship. 2nd ed. 2009. (ENG.). 322p. pap. 41.99 *(978-0-7618-4744-1(8))* Univ. Pr. of America, Inc.

Franks, Joel S. Asian Pacific Americans & Baseball: A History. 2008. (ENG., Illus.). 224p. pap. 29.95 *(978-0-7864-3291-2(8))* McFarland & Co., Inc. Pubs.

Fujii, Daryl. The Neuropsychology of Asian-Americans. 2010. (Studies on Neuropsychology, Neurology & Cognition Ser.). (ENG., Illus.). 324p. 89.95 *(978-1-84169-784-0(2)*, Psychology Press) Taylor & Francis Group GBR. Dist: Taylor & Francis Group.

Fujikane, Candace & Okamura, Jonathan Y. Asian Settler Colonialism: From Local Governance to the Habits of Everyday Life in Hawai'i. 2008. (Illus.). 318p. (C). pap. 25.00 *(978-0-8248-3300-8(7))* Univ. of Hawaii Pr.

—Asian Settler Colonialism: From Local Governance to the Habits of Everyday Life in Hawaii. 2008. (Illus.). xiv, 318p. 55.00 *(978-0-8248-3015-1(6))* Univ. of Hawaii Pr.

Fujino, Diane C. Samurai among Panthers: Richard Aoki on Race, Resistance, & a Paradoxical Life. 2012. (Critical American Studies). 496p. 75.00 ***(978-0-8166-7786-3(7))***; pap. 24.95 ***(978-0-8166-7787-0(5))*** Univ. of Minnesota Pr.

Fujiwara, Lynn. Mothers Without Citizenship: Asian Immigrant Families & the Consequences of Welfare Reform. 2008. (Illus.). 272p. 67.50 *(978-0-8166-5075-0(6))*; pap. 22.50 *(978-0-8166-5076-7(4))* Univ. of Minnesota Pr.

Garrod, Andrew & Kilkenny, Robert, eds. Balancing Two Worlds: Asian American College Students Tell Their Life Stories. 2007. (Illus.). 270p. 66.95 *(978-0-8014-4595-8(7))*; per. 19.95 *(978-0-8014-7384-5(5))* Cornell Univ. Pr.

Gatewood, James V. Contemporary Asian America: A Multidisciplinary Reader. Zhou, Min, ed. 2nd ed. 2007. (ENG., Illus.). 550p. (C). 85.00 *(978-0-8147-9712-9(1))*; pap. 30.00 *(978-0-8147-9713-6(X))* New York Univ. Pr.

Hallmark, Kara Kelley. Encyclopedia of Asian American Artists, 1 vol. 2007. (Artists of the American Mosaic Ser.). (Illus.). 312p. 85.00 *(978-0-313-33451-1(X)*, GR3451, Greenwood Pr.) Greenwood Publishing Group, Inc.

Hertig, Young Lee & Sun, Chloe, eds. Mirrored Reflections. 2010. 166p. pap. 19.00 *(978-1-60899-593-6(3)*, Wipf and Stock) Wipf & Stock Pubs.

Hess, Mary Anne, et al. Once They Hear My Name: Korean Adoptees & Their Journeys Toward Identity. 2008. (ENG., Illus.). 200p. pap. 14.95 *(978-0-9793756-0-6(6))* Tamarisk Bks. LLC.

Ho, Fred & Mullen, Bill V., eds. Afro Asia: Revolutionary Political & Cultural Connections Between African Americans & Asian Americans. 2008. (ENG., Illus.). 416p. 94.95 *(978-0-8223-4258-8(8))*; pap. 26.95 *(978-0-8223-4281-6(2))* Duke Univ. Pr.

Ho, Fred Wei-Han & Fujino, Diane C. Wicked Theory, Naked Practice: A Fred Ho Reader. 2009. (ENG., Illus.). 384p. pap. 24.95 *(978-0-8166-5685-1(1))* Univ. of Minnesota Pr.

Ho, Fred Wei-Han & Mullen, Bill V. Wicked Theory, Naked Practice: A Fred Ho Reader. Fujino, Diane C., ed. 2009. (ENG., Illus.). 384p. 75.00 *(978-0-8166-5684-4(3))* Univ. of Minnesota Pr.

Hoskins, Bruce Calvin. Asian American Racial Realities in Black & White. 2011. 150p. 58.50 *(978-1-935049-39-5(9))* FirstForumPress.

Huang, Tiffany. Taiwan Tiff. 2009. 93p. pap. 11.97 *(978-0-557-07819-6(9))* Lulu Enterprises Inc.

Huie, Wing Young. Looking for Asian America: An Ethnocentric Tour. 2007. (Illus.). 136p. pap. 39.95 *(978-0-8166-4672-2(4))* Univ. of Minnesota Pr.

Information Publications, creator. Asian Americans: A Statistical Sourcebook. 2007. (Asian Americans: A Statistical Sourcebook Ser.). (Illus.). 278p. 104.25 *(978-0-929960-43-2(2))* Information Pubns., Inc.

Information Publications, ed. Asian Americans 2008: A Statistical Sourcebook & Guide to Government Data. 2008. 300p. per. 77.00 *(978-0-929960-48-7(3))* Information Pubns., Inc.

Irwin, Wallace. Seed of the Sun. 2010. 356p. pap. 32.75 *(978-1-178-43101-8(0))* BiblioBazaar.

—Seed of the Sun. 2009. 250p. pap. *(978-0-217-04590-2(1))* Books LLC.

—Seed of the Sun. 2010. 354p. pap. 25.56 *(978-1-163-28724-8(5))* 2007. (ENG.). 352p. 46.95 *(978-0-548-25504-9(0))* 2007. (ENG.). 356p. per. 31.95 *(978-1-4326-5845-8(X))* Kessinger Publishing, LLC.

Jain, Anupama. How to Be South Asian in America: Narratives of Ambivalence & Belonging. 2011. (ENG.). 288p. pap. 26.95 *(978-1-4399-0303-2(4))* Temple Univ. Pr.

jain, anupama. How to Be South Asian in America: Narratives of Ambivalence & Belonging. 2011. (ENG.). 288p. 68.50 *(978-1-4399-0302-5(6))* Temple Univ. Pr.

Jasser, M. Zuhdi. A Battle for the Soul of Islam: An American Muslim Patriot's Fight to Save His Faith. 2012. (ENG.). 304p. 26.00 ***(978-1-4516-5794-4(3)***, Threshold Editions) Threshold Editions.

—A Battle for the Soul of Islam: An American-Muslim Patriot's Fight to Save His Faith. 2012. pap. ***(978-1-4516-5796-8(X)***, Threshold Editions) Threshold Editions.

Johnson, Mark Dean, et al. Asian American Modern Art: Shifting Currents, 1900-1970. Cornell, Daniel & Johnson, Mark Dean, eds. 2008. (ENG., Illus.). 168p. 50.00 *(978-0-520-25864-8(9))* Univ. of California Pr.

Jun, Helen. Race for Citizenship: Black Orientalism & Asian Uplift from Pre-Emancipation to Neoliberal America. 2011. (ENG.). 208p. 70.00 *(978-0-8147-4297-6(1))*; pap. 22.00 *(978-0-8147-4298-3(X))* New York Univ. Pr.

Jung, Moon-Ho. Coolies & Cane: Race, Labor, & Sugar in the Age of Emancipation. 2008. (ENG., Illus.). 288p. (gr. 17). pap. 27.00 *(978-0-8018-9082-6(9))* Johns Hopkins Univ. Pr.

Kang, Hye-Kyung Stella. Cultural Citizenship & Immigrant Community Identity: Constructing a Multi-Ethnic Asian American Community. 2010. (New Americans). 200p. 62.00 *(978-1-59332-343-1(3))* LFB Scholarly Publishing LLC.

Kang, Miliann. The Managed Hand: Race, Gender, & the Body in Beauty Service Work. 2010. (ENG., Illus.). 275p. 60.00 *(978-0-520-26258-4(1))*; pap. 26.95 *(978-0-520-26260-7(3))* Univ. of California Pr.

Kato, Julius-Kei. How Immigrant Christians Living in Mixed Cultures Interpret Their Religion: Asian-American Diasporic Hybridity & Its Implications for Hermeneutics. 2011. 372p. 129.95 ***(978-0-7734-3919-1(6))*** Mellen, Edwin Pr., The.

Kawahara, Debra M. & Espin, Oliva M. Feminist Reflections on Growth & Transformation: Asian American Women in Therapy. 2007. (ENG.). 266p. 50.50 *(978-0-7890-3434-2(4))* Routledge.

Kawahara, Debra M. & Espin, Oliva M., eds. Feminist Reflections on Growth & Transformation: Asian American Women in Therapy. 2007. (ENG., Illus.). 266p. 125.00 *(978-0-7890-3433-5(6))* Routledge.

Khang, Kathy, et al. More Than Serving Tea: Asian American Women on Expectations, Relationships, Leadership & Faith. Toyama, Nikki A. et al, eds. 2006. (ENG., Illus.). 208p. per. 16.00 *(978-0-8308-3371-9(4)*, IVP Bks.) InterVarsity Pr.

Kim, Bryan, et al. Counseling & Diversity: Counseling Asian Americans. 2010. (ENG.). 112p. (C). pap. 16.95 *(978-0-618-47037-2(9))* Wadsworth.

Kim, Jodi. Ends of Empire: Asian American Critique & the Cold War. 2010. (Critical American Studies). (ENG., Illus.). 344p. 75.00 *(978-0-8166-5591-5(X))*; pap. 25.00 *(978-0-8166-5592-2(8))* Univ. of Minnesota Pr.

Kim, Jung Ha, et al, eds. Off the Menu: Asian & Asian North American Women's Religion & Theology. 2007. (ENG.). 341p. per. 40.00 *(978-0-664-23140-8(3))* Westminster John Knox Pr.

Kim, Matthew D. Preaching to Second Generation Korean Americans: Towards a Possible Selves Contextual Homiletic. 2007. (American University Studies VII: Theology & Religion Ser.). 244p. (C). 70.95 *(978-1-4331-0004-8(5))* Lang, Peter Publishing, Inc.

Kim, Thomas P. The Racial Logic of Politics: Asian Americans & Party Competition. 2006. (Illus.). 208p. per. 25.95 *(978-1-59213-549-3(8))*; 75.50 *(978-1-59213-548-6(X))* Temple Univ. Pr.

King, C. Richard, ed. Asian Americans in Sport & Society. 2012. (Routledge Research in Sport, Culture & Society Ser.). (ENG.). 208p. 125.00 *(978-0-415-87491-5(2))* Routledge.

Kulkarni, Veena S. Asians in the United States Labor Market. 2009. 216p. pap. *(978-3-639-13616-6(0))* VDM Verlag Dr. Mueller e.K.

Kwak, U. k. Are There Real Asian American Women in Hollywood Movies? 2010. 64p. pap. *(978-3-639-25491-4(0))* VDM Verlag Dr. Mueller e.K.

Kwoh, Stewart & Leong, Russell C. Untold Civil Rights Stories: Asian Americans Speak Out for Justice. 2009. (Illus.). 160p. (YA). pap. 20.00 *(978-0-934052-43-6(3))* Univ. of California, Los Angeles, Asian American Studies Ctr.

Kyne, Peter B. The Pride of Palomar. 2007. (ENG.). 282p. pap. 21.99 *(978-1-4346-0229-9(X))*; 312p. pap. 24.99 *(978-1-4346-0303-6(2))* BiblioBazaar.

—The Pride of Palomar. 2007. (ENG., Illus.). 340p. per. *(978-1-4065-3663-8(6))* Dodo Pr.

—The Pride of Palomar. 2007. (ENG.). 382p. 48.95 *(978-0-548-02576-5(2))* Kessinger Publishing, LLC.

Lai, James S. Asian American Political Action: Suburban Transformations. 2010. (Illus.). 300p. 62.50 *(978-1-58826-724-5(5))* Rienner, Lynne Pubs.

Le, Cuong Nguyen. Asian American Assimilation: Ethnicity, Immigration, & Socioeconomic Attainment. 2007. (New Americans). 260p. 65.00 *(978-1-59332-175-8(9))* LFB Scholarly Publishing LLC.

Lee, Esther Kim. A History of Asian American Theatre. 2006. (Cambridge Studies in American Theatre & Drama Ser.). (ENG., Illus.). 282p. 106.00 *(978-0-521-85051-3(7))* Cambridge Univ. Pr.

Lee, Inn. Passage to the Real Self: The Development of Self Integration for Asian American Women. 2009. (ENG.). 190p. pap. 31.50 *(978-0-7618-4473-0(2))* Univ. Pr. of America, Inc.

Lee, Inn Sook. Passage to the Real Self: The Development of Self Integration for Asian American Women. 2009. ix, 185p. ***(978-0-7618-4474-7(0))*** Univ. Pr. of America, Inc.

Lee, Inn Sook & Son, Timothy D., eds. Asian Americans & Christian Ministry. 2009. 338p. pap. 37.00 *(978-1-60608-546-2(8)*, Wipf and Stock) Wipf & Stock Pubs.

Lee, JoAnn. Asian Americans in the Twenty-first Century: Oral Histories of First- to Fourth-Generation Americans from China, Japan, India, Korea, the Philippines, Vietnam, & Laos. 2009. (ENG.). 288p. pap. 15.95 *(978-1-59558-478-6(1))* New Pr., The.

Lee, Jonathan H. X. & Nadeau, Kathleen G. Encyclopedia of Asian American Folklore & Folklife, 3 vols. 2010. (Illus.). xl, 1254p. E-Book *(978-0-313-35067-2(1))* ABC-CLIO, LLC.

Lee, Stacey J. Unraveling the "Model Minority" Stereotype: Listening to Asian American Youth. 2nd ed. 2009. (ENG.). 176p. pap. 24.95 *(978-0-8077-4973-9(7))* Teachers College Pr., Teachers College, Columbia Univ.

Leon, Frederick T. L. Asian American & Pacific Islander Children & Mental Health. 2011. E-Book *(978-0-313-38301-4(4)*, Praeger Pubs.) Greenwood Publishing Group, Inc.

Leong, Frederick T., et al, eds. Asian American & Pacific Islander Children & Mental Health Vols. 1 & 2: Development & Context. 2011. (Child Psychology & Mental Health Ser.). (Illus.). 518p. 104.95 *(978-0-313-38300-7(6)*, A2698C, Praeger Pubs.) Greenwood Publishing Group, Inc.

—Handbook of Asian American Psychology. 2nd rev. ed. 2006. (Racial Ethnic Minority Psychology Ser.). (Illus.). 528p. 135.00 *(978-1-4129-4133-4(4)*, B24677C) SAGE Pubns., Inc.

Leong, Frederick T. L., et al, eds. Handbook of Asian American Psychology. 2nd rev. ed. 2006. (Racial Ethnic Minority Psychology Ser.). (Illus.). 528p. pap. 84.00 *(978-1-4129-2467-2(7)*, B24677P) SAGE Pubns., Inc.

Li, Guofang & Wang, Lihshing. Model Minority Myth Revisited: An Interdisciplinary Approach to Demystifying Asian American Educational Experiences. 2008. (Chinese American Educational Research & Development Association Book Ser.). (Illus.). 356p. (C). (978-1-59311-951-5(8)); pap. (978-1-59311-950-8(X)) Information Age Publishing, Inc.

Lin, M. & Nakanishi, Don. Beyond Myths: The Growth & Diversity of Asian American College Freshman, 1971-2005. Chang, Mitchell J. & Park, Julie, eds. 2011. 63p. pap. 19.95 (978-1-878477-42-2(0)) UCLA Higher Education Research Institute.

Ling, Huping. Emerging Voices: Experiences of Underrepresented Asian Americans. Ling, Huping, ed. 2008. (ENG.). 344p. pap. 25.95 (978-0-8135-4342-0(8)) Rutgers Univ. Pr.

—Voices of the Heart: Asian American Women on Immigration, Work, & Family. 2007. (Illus.). 424p. pap. 34.95 (978-1-931112-68-0(1)) Truman State Univ. Pr.

Ling, Huping, ed. Emerging Voices: Experiences of Underrepresented Asian Americans. 2008. (ENG.). 344p. 70.00 (978-0-8135-4341-3(X)) Rutgers Univ. Pr.

Ling, Huping, ed. & contrib. by. Asian America: Forming New Communities, Expanding Boundaries. 2009. (ENG., Illus.). 304p. (C). 72.00 (978-0-8135-4486-1(6)); pap. 25.95 (978-0-8135-4487-8(4)) Rutgers Univ. Pr.

Ling, Huping & Austin, Allan W., eds. Asian American History & Culture: An Encyclopedia, 2 vols., Set. 2009. (ENG., Illus.). 800p. 229.00 (978-0-7656-8077-8(7), Sharpe Reference) Sharpe, M.E. Inc.

Liu, Michael, et al. The Snake Dance of Asian American Activism: Community, Vision, & Power. 2008. (ENG., Illus.). 260p. pap. 34.99 (978-0-7391-2720-9(9)) Lexington Bks.

—The Snake Dance of Asian American Activism: Community, Vision, & Power in the Struggle for Social Justice, 1945-2000. 2008. (ENG., Illus.). 260p. 78.99 (978-0-7391-2719-3(5)) Lexington Bks.

Liu, William, ed. Culturally Responsive Counseling with Asian American Men. 2010. (Routledge Series on Counseling & Psychotherapy with Boys & Men Ser.). (ENG., Illus.). 367p. 125.00 (978-0-415-80007-5(2)) Routledge.

Liu, William, et al, eds. Culturally Responsive Counseling with Asian American Men. 2010. (Routledge Series on Counseling & Psychotherapy with Boys & Men Ser.). (ENG., Illus.). 367p. pap. 37.95 (978-0-415-80008-2(0), Routledge) Taylor & Francis Group GBR. Dist: Taylor & Francis Group.

Lobb, Nancy. 16 Extraordinary Asian Americans. 2nd ed. 2007. (gr. 6-12). pap., tchr. ed. 25.00 (978-0-8251-6280-0(7)) Walch Education.

Louie, Steven G. & Omatsu, Glenn K., eds. Asian Americans: The Movement & the Moment. 352p. (978-0-934052-35-1(2)) Univ. of California, Los Angeles, Asian American Studies Ctr.

Madan-Bahel, Anvita. Sexual Health & Bollywood Films: A Culturally-Based Program for South Asian Teenage Girls. 2007. 104.95 (978-1-934043-81-3(8)) Cambria Pr.

Maeda, Daryl. Introducing the Asian American Movement. 2011. (American Social & Political Movements of the 20th Century Ser.). (ENG., Illus.). 200p. (C). 130.00 (978-0-415-80081-5(1)); pap. 26.95 (978-0-415-80082-2(X)) Routledge.

Maeda, Daryl J. Chains of Babylon: The Rise of Asian America. 2009. (Critical American Studies). (ENG., Illus.). 248p. pap. 20.00 (978-0-8166-4891-7(3)) Univ. of Minnesota Pr.

Maira, Sunaina Marr. Missing: Youth, Citizenship, & Empire After 9/11. 2009. (ENG.). 352p. 97.95 (978-0-8223-4391-2(6)) Duke Univ. Pr.

—Missing: Youth, Citizenship, & Empire After 9/11. 2009. (ENG.). 352p. pap. 25.95 (978-0-8223-4409-4(2)) Duke Univ. Pr.

Mao, LuMing & Young, Morris, eds. Representations: Doing Asian American Rhetoric. 2008. (ENG.). 324p. (C). pap. 29.95 (978-0-87421-724-7(5), Utah State Univ. Pr.) Univ. Pr. of Colorado.

Maséquesmay, Gina & Metzger, Sean. Embodying Asian/American Sexualities. 2009. (ENG.). 196p. 68.50 (978-0-7391-2903-6(1)) Lexington Bks.

Masequesmay/Metzger. Embodying Asian/American Sexualities. 2010. (ENG.). 198p. pap. 29.95 (978-0-7391-2904-3(X)) Lexington Bks.

Matsuoka, Fumitaka. Learning to Speak a New Tongue: Imagining a Way that Holds People TogetherNtide;an Asian American Conversation. 2011. 154p. pap. 18.00 (978-1-60899-828-9(2), Pickwick Pubns.) Wipf & Stock Pubs.

Matsuoka, Fumitaka. Out of Silence: Emerging Themes in Asian American Churches. 2009. 178p. (Orig.). pap. 20.00 (978-1-60608-161-7(6), Wipf and Stock) Wipf & Stock Pubs.

McKeown, Adam M. & McKeown, Adam. Melancholy Order: Asian Migration & the Globalization of Borders. 2008. (Columbia Studies in International & Global History Ser.). (ENG., Illus.). 472p. (gr. 17). 40.00 (978-0-231-14076-8(2)) Columbia Univ. Pr.

ME.O. 2Journey: Crossing the Bridge Volume One. 2007. 82p. pap. 10.00 (978-0-8059-7225-2(0)) Dorrance Publishing Co., Inc.

Mercado, Nestor J., et al. Voices from Colorado: Perspectives of Asian Pacific Americans. 2008. (Illus.). 312p. pap. 17.95 (978-0-615-20213-6(6)) Mercado Information & Business Services.

Mimura, Glen M. Ghostlife of Third Cinema: Asian American Film & Video. 2009. (ENG., Illus.). 216p. 67.50 (978-0-8166-4830-6(1)) Univ. of Minnesota Pr.

Mimura, Glen M. & Mimura. Ghostlife of Third Cinema: Asian American Film & Video. 2009. (ENG., Illus.). 216p. pap. 22.50 (978-0-8166-4831-3(X)) Univ. of Minnesota Pr.

Mui, Ada C. & Shibusawa, Tazuko. Asian American Elders in the Twenty-First Century: Key Indicators of Well-Being. 2008. (ENG., Illus.). 224p. (gr. 17). 45.00 (978-0-231-13590-0(4)) Columbia Univ. Pr.

Nadal, Kevin L. Filipino American Psychology: A Collection of Personal Narratives. 2010. 360p. (ENG.). 44.99 (978-1-4520-0189-0(8)); pap. 34.99 (978-1-4520-0188-3(X)) AuthorHouse.

Nadeau, Kathleen M. & Lee, Jonathan H. X., eds. Encyclopedia of Asian American Folklore & Folklife, 3 vols. 2010. (Illus.). 1254p. 265.00 (978-0-313-35066-5(3), GR5066) ABC-CLIO, LLC.

Nair, Ajay & Balaji, Murali. Desi Rap: Hip-Hop & South Asian America. Nair, Ajay & Balaji, Murali, eds. 2008. (ENG.). 202p. pap. 22.99 (978-0-7391-2722-3(5)) Lexington Bks.

Narayan, Anjana & Purkayastha, Bandana. Living Our Religions: Hindu & Muslim South Asian-American Women Narrate Their Experiences. 2008. 348p. pap. 29.50 (978-1-56549-270-7(6)) Stylus Publishing, LLC.

Nemoto, Kumiko. Racing Romance: Love, Power, & Desire among Asian American White Couples. 2009. (ENG.). 208p. (C). pap. 23.95 (978-0-8135-4533-2(1)) Rutgers Univ. Pr.

—Racing Romance: Love, Power, & Desire among Asian American/White Couples. 2009. (ENG.). 208p. (C). 68.00 (978-0-8135-4532-5(3)) Rutgers Univ. Pr.

New Strategist Staff. Asians, Who We Are. 2007. 233p. pap. 89.95 (978-1-933588-79-7(9)) New Strategist Pubns., Inc.

Nguyen, Mimi Thi & Tu, Thuy Linh Nguyen, eds. Alien Encounters: Popular Culture in Asian America. 2007. (ENG., Illus.). 376p. 94.95 (978-0-8223-3910-6(2)); per. 25.95 (978-0-8223-3922-9(6)) Duke Univ. Pr.

Nguyen, Tuyen D. Domestic Violence in Asian-American Communities: A Cultural Overview. 2007. (ENG.). 154p. pap. 26.50 (978-0-7391-2358-4(0)) Lexington Bks.

Numrich, Paul, et al. Buddhists, Hindus, & Sikhs in America: A Short History. 2007. (Religion in American Life Ser.). (ENG., Illus.). 168p. per. 12.95 (978-0-19-533311-4(X)) Oxford Univ. Pr., Inc.

O'Brien, Eileen. The Racial Middle: Latinos & Asian Americans Living Beyond the Racial Divide. 2008. (ENG.). 272p. pap. 24.00 (978-0-8147-6215-8(8)); (Illus.). 75.00 (978-0-8147-6214-1(X)) New York Univ. Pr.

Ono, Kent A. & Pham, Vincent. Asian Americans & the Media. 2008. (MM - Media & Minorities Ser.: 1). (ENG., Illus.). 216p. 69.95 (978-0-7456-4273-4(X)); pap. 26.95 (978-0-7456-4274-1(8)) Polity Pr. GBR. Dist: Wiley, John & Sons, Inc.

Ordona, Trinity A. Coming Out Together: An Ethnohistory of the Asian & Pacific Isl. 2012. (Studies in Asian Americans Ser.). (ENG.). 256p. 125.00 (978-0-415-97808-8(4)) Routledge.

Pacis, Dina. Asian Females in Educational Leadership. 2008. 132p. pap. (978-3-639-06821-4(1)) VDM Verlag Dr. Mueller e.K.

Park, Andrew Sung. Triune Atonement: Christ's Healing for Sinners, Victims, & the Whole Creation. 2009. (ENG.). 152p. pap. 20.00 (978-0-664-23347-1(3)) Westminster John Knox Pr.

Park, Clara C. Asian American Education Acculturation, Literacy Development, & Learning. 2007. (Research on the Education of Asian & Pacific Americans Ser.). (ENG.). 232p. (C). (978-1-59311-723-8(X)); per. (978-1-59311-722-1(1)) Information Age Publishing, Inc.

Park, Clara C., et al, eds. New Perspectives on Asian American Parents, Students, & Teacher Recruitment. 2009. (Illus.). 236p. 85.99 (978-1-60752-092-4(3)); pap. 45.99 (978-1-60752-091-7(5)) Information Age Publishing, Inc.

Philip, Cheri L. Asian American Identity: Racial & Ethnic Identity Issues in the Twenty-First Century. 2007. (ENG.). 236p. (C). 99.95 (978-1-934043-62-2(1)) Cambria Pr.

Pho, Tuyet-Lan, et al, eds. Southeast Asian Refugees & Immigrants in the Mill City: Changing Families, Communities, Institutions — Thirty Years Afterward. 2008. (Illus.). 250p. 50.00 (978-1-58465-662-3(X)) Univ. Pr. of New England.

Phu, Thy. Picturing Model Citizens: Civility in Asian American Visual Culture. 2012. E-Book (978-1-4399-0722-1(6)) 2012. (ENG., Illus.). 218p. 86.50 (978-1-4399-0720-7(X)) 2011. (ENG., Illus.). 218p. pap. 28.95 (978-1-4399-0721-4(8)) Temple Univ. Pr.

Poon-McBrayer, Kim Fong. Partnership Challenges with Asian Immigrant Parents. 2011. 68p. pap. (978-3-8443-1461-8(X)) Lambert Academic Publishing.

Reyes, Angela. Language, Identity, & Stereotype among Southeast Asian American Youth: The Other Asian. 2006. (ENG., Illus.). 192p. 95.00 (978-0-8058-5539-5(4)) Routledge.

Reyes, Angela & Lo, Adrienne. Beyond Yellow English: Toward a Linguistic Anthropology of Asian Pacific America. Reyes, Angela & Lo, Adrienne, eds. 2008. (Oxford Studies in Sociolinguistics Ser.). (ENG., Illus.). 448p. pap. 29.95 (978-0-19-532736-6(5)) Oxford Univ. Pr., Inc.

Reyes, Angela & Lo, Adrienne, eds. Beyond Yellow English: Toward a Linguistic Anthropology of Asian Pacific America. 2008. (Oxford Studies in Sociolinguistics Ser.). (ENG., Illus.). 448p. 99.00 (978-0-19-532735-9(7)) Oxford Univ. Pr., Inc.

Richard, Levi. Opinion Leadership for Ethnic Products. 2010. 224p. pap. (978-3-639-23173-1(2)) VDM Verlag Dr. Mueller e.K.

Risse, Guenter B. Plague, Fear, & Politics in San Francisco's Chinatown. 2012. (ENG., Illus.). 392p. (gr. 17). 39.95 (978-1-4214-0510-0(5)) Johns Hopkins Univ. Pr.

Robles, Rowena. Asian Americans & the Shifting Politics of Race: The Dismantling of Affirmative Action at an Elite Public High School. 2009. 194p. 39.95 (978-0-415-80575-9(9)) Routledge.

Robles, Rowena A. Asian Americans & the Shifting Politics of Race: The Dismantling of Affirmative Action at an Elite Public High School. 2006. (Studies in Asian Americans Ser.). 191p. 128.00 (978-0-415-97632-9(4)) Routledge.

Roland, Alan. JOURNEYS to FOREIGN SELVES Asians & Asian Americans in a Global Era JOURNEYS to FOREIGN SELVES: Asians & Asian Americans in a Global Era. 2011. (ENG.). 248p. 34.99 (978-0-19-806946-1(4)) Oxford Univ. Pr., Inc.

Rondilla, Joanne L. & Spickard, Paul. Is Lighter Better? Skin-Tone Discrimination among Asian Americans. 2007. (ENG., Illus.). 158p. 84.00 (978-0-7425-5493-1(7)) Rowman & Littlefield Publishers, Inc.

Rong, Xue Lan & Endo, Russell. Asian American Education: Asian American Identities, Racial Issues, & Languages. 2011. 236p. (978-1-61735-462-5(7)); 236p. pap. (978-1-61735-461-8(9)); E-Book (978-1-61735-463-2(5)) Information Age Publishing, Inc.

Russell, Stephen T., et al, eds. Asian American Adolescents & Their Parents: Cultural Factors in Parenting & Family Relationships. 2010. (Advancing Responsible Adolescent Development Ser.). (ENG., Illus.). x, 136p. 149.00 (978-1-4419-5727-6(8), 1441957278) Springer.

Sara, Atienza. Breaking down the Homogenized View of Asian American Academic Success: Exploring the Educational Aspirations & Attainment of Asian American High School Students. 2011. 60p. pap. (978-3-639-32751-9(9)) VDM Verlag Dr. Mueller e.K.

Schlund-Vials, Cathy. Modeling Citizenship: Jewish & Asian American Writing. 2011. (ENG.). 248p. 68.50 (978-1-4399-0317-9(4)); pap. 24.95 (978-1-4399-0318-6(2)) Temple Univ. Pr.

Shimizu, Celine. Straitjacket Sexualities: Unbinding Asian American Manhoods in the Movies. 2012. (Asian America Ser.). (ENG., Illus.). 296p. pap. 22.95 (978-0-8047-7301-0(7)) Stanford Univ. Pr.

Shimizu, Celine Parreñas. The Hypersexuality of Race: Performing Asian/American Women on Screen & Scene. 2007. (ENG., Illus.). 352p. 94.95 (978-0-8223-4012-6(7)); pap. 25.95 (978-0-8223-4033-1(X)) Duke Univ. Pr.

Snow, Jennifer. Protestant Missionaries, Asian Immigrants, & Ideologies of Race in America, 1850-1924. 2006. (Studies in Asian Americans Ser.). (ENG.). 176p. 136.00 (978-0-415-95583-6(1)) Routledge.

Snow, Jennifer. Protestant Missionaries, Asian Immigrants, & Ideologies of Race in America, 1850ndash;1924. 2012. (Studies in Asian Americans Ser.). (ENG.). 176p. pap. 42.95 (978-0-415-54201-2(4)) Routledge.

So, Christine. Economic Citizens: A Narrative of Asian American Visibility. 2009. (ENG.). 190p. pap. 27.95 (978-1-59213-585-1(4)) Temple Univ. Pr.

Steen, Shannon, et al. AfroAsian Encounters: Culture, History, Politics. Raphael-Hernandez, Heike, ed. 2006. (ENG., Illus.). 336p. 75.00 (978-0-8147-7580-6(2)) New York Univ. Pr.

Stone, Jin. Asian Masculinity, American Identity: Asian American Citizenship through Interracial Relations. 2008. 116p. pap. (978-3-639-07174-0(3)) VDM Verlag Dr. Mueller e.K.

Stone, Jon R. & Piar, Carlos R. Readings in American Religious Diversity. rev. ed. 2012. (ENG.). 588p. pap. 94.80 (978-0-7575-4091-2(0)) Kendall Hunt Publishing Co.

Stowell, Jacob I. Immigration & Crime: The Effects of Immigration on Criminal Behavior. 2007. (New Americans). 184p. 58.00 (978-1-59332-204-5(6)) LFB Scholarly Publishing LLC.

Sukrungruang, Ira. Talk Thai: The Adventures of Buddhist Boy. 2010. (ENG.). 184p. 24.95 (978-0-8262-1889-6(X)) Univ. of Missouri Pr.

Sun, Wei. Minority Invisibility: An Asian American Experience. 2007. (ENG.). 112p. per. 26.50 (978-0-7618-3780-0(9)) Univ. Pr. of America, Inc.

Tan, Jonathan Y. Introducing Asian American Theologies. 2008. (Introducing Ser.). (Illus.). 210p. pap. 24.00 (978-1-57075-768-6(2)) Orbis Bks.

Teranishi, Robert T. Asians in the Ivory Tower: Dilemmas of Racial Inequality in American Higher Education. 2010. (Multicultural Education Ser.). (ENG., Illus.). 216p. 68.00 (978-0-8077-5131-2(6)); pap. 31.95 (978-0-8077-5130-5(8)) Teachers College Pr., Teachers College, Columbia Univ.

Thatchenkery, Tojo & Sugiyama, Keimei. Making the Invisible Visible: Understanding Leadership Contributions of Asian Minorities in the Workplace. 2011. (ENG., Illus.). 224p. 90.00 (978-0-230-10306-1(5)) Palgrave Macmillan.

Tintiangco-Cubales, Allyson. Pinay Educational Partnerships: A Filipina/o American Studies Sourcebook, Volume I: Philippine & Filipina/o American History, 2 vols. Tintiangco-Cubales, Allyson, ed. 2007. per. 39.95 (978-0-9779438-0-7(1)) Phoenix Publishing Hse. International.

TIYM Publishing Company, Inc. Staff, ed. Asian American Yearbook: The Resource & Referral Guide for & about Asian Pacific Americans 2006/2007. 3rd ed. 2007. 256p. 29.95 (978-0-9777254-1-0(3)) TIYM Publishing Co., Inc.

Toyota, Tritia. Envisioning America: New Chinese Americans & the Politics of Belonging. 2009. (Asian America Ser.). (ENG.). 256p. 65.00 (978-0-8047-6241-0(4)); pap. 21.95 (978-0-8047-6242-7(2)) Stanford Univ. Pr.

Trinh, Nhi-Ha. Handbook of Mental Health in Asian Americans: Families, Acculturation & Resilience. 2009. (Current Clinical Psychiatry Ser.). (Illus.). 292p. 109.00 (978-1-60327-436-4(7)) Humana Pr.

Trinh-Shevrin, Chau, et al, eds. Asian American Communities & Health: Context, Research, Policy, & Action. 2009. (Public Health/Vulnerable Populations Ser.: 19). (ENG., Illus.). 736p. pap. 85.00 (978-0-7879-9829-5(X), Jossey-Bass) Wiley, John & Sons, Inc.

Ty, Eleanor Rose. Unfastened: Globality & Asian North American Narratives. 2010. (Illus.). 216p. 67.50 (978-0-8166-6507-5(9)); (ENG., pap. 22.50 (978-0-8166-6508-2(7)) Univ. of Minnesota Pr.

Ung, Loung. Lulu in the Sky: A Daughter of Cambodia Finds Love, Healing, & Double Happiness. 2012. (P. S. Ser.). (ENG.). 368p. pap. 15.99 (978-0-06-209191-8(3), HarperPerennial) HarperCollins Pubs.

Wang, Chi. A Compelling Journey from Peking to Washington: Building a New Life in America. 2011. (ENG.). 210p. 65.00 (978-0-7618-5497-5(5)) Hamilton Bks.

Wang, Susan. Outstanding: Growing up Asian. 2nd ed. 2010. (Illus.). 182p. (YA). pap. 9.95 (978-0-9822137-6-6(X)) Shidai Zhuanji Chinese Literary Collections, Inc.

Watkins, Rychetta. Black Power, Yellow Power, & the Making of Revolutionary Identities. 2012. (ENG.). 176p. 55.00 (978-1-61703-161-8(5)) Univ. Pr. of Mississippi.

Who We Are. 2007. (Who We Are Ser.). 468p. 245.00 (978-1-933588-30-8(6)) New Strategist Pubns., Inc.

Wong, Janelle. Asian American Political Participation: Emerging Constituents & Their Political Identities. 2011. pap. (978-0-87154-962-4(X)); E-Book (978-1-61044-755-3(7)) Russell Sage Foundation.

Wong, Yutian. Choreographing Asian America. 2010. (ENG.). 280p. (C). 75.00 (978-0-8195-6702-4(7)); pap. 27.95 (978-0-8195-6703-1(5)) Wesleyan Univ. Pr.

Wu, H. Denis & Lee, Tien-Tsung. Media, Politics, & Asian Americans. 2008. (978-1-57273-870-6(7)); pap. (978-1-57273-871-3(5)) Hampton Pr., Inc.

Wu, Jean Yu-wen Shen & Chen, Thomas C., eds. Asian American Studies Now: A Critical Reader. 2010. (ENG.). 672p. (C). 80.00 (978-0-8135-4574-5(9)) Rutgers Univ. Pr.

Yee, Russell. Worship on the Way: Exploring Asian North American Christian Experience. 2012. (ENG.). 256p. pap. 17.99 (978-0-8170-1707-1(0)) Judson Pr.

Yoo, Grace J., et al, eds. Handbook of Asian American Health. 2012. (ENG., Illus.). xxviii, 463p. 349.00 (978-1-4614-2226-6(4), 1461422264) Springer.

Yoshihara, Mari. Musicians from a Different Shore: Asians & Asian Americans in Classical Music. 2008. (ENG., Illus.). 288p. pap. 24.95 (978-1-59213-333-8(9)) Temple Univ. Pr.

Zane, Nolan & Kim, Bryan. Readings in Asian American Psychology. rev. ed. 2008. (ENG.). 942p. pap. 101.32 (978-0-7575-1688-7(2)) Kendall Hunt Publishing Co.

Zhao, Xiaojian. Asian American Chronology: Chronologies of the American Mosaic, 1 vol. 2009. (Illus.). 152p. 85.00 (978-0-313-34875-4(8), GR4875, Greenwood Pr.) Greenwood Publishing Group, Inc.

—Comparative Asian American History. rev. ed. 2010. (ENG.). 260p. pap. 46.47 (978-0-7575-6021-7(0)) Kendall Hunt Publishing Co.

ASIAN AMERICANS IN LITERATURE

Chang, Yoonmee. Writing the Ghetto: Class, Authorship, & the Asian American Ethnic Enclave. (Mellon-ALI Ser.). (ENG., Illus.). 252p. 2011. pap. 24.95 (978-0-8135-5175-3(7)) 2010. 45.00 (978-0-8135-4801-2(2)) Rutgers Univ. Pr.

Huang, Betsy. Contesting Genres in Contemporary Asian American Fiction. 2010. (ENG.). 192p. 79.00 (978-0-230-10831-8(8)) Palgrave Macmillan.

Huang, Guiyou, ed. The Greenwood Encyclopedia of Asian American Literature, 3 vols. 2008. 1256p. 299.95 (978-0-313-34157-1(5), GR4157, Greenwood Pr.) Greenwood Publishing Group, Inc.

Kim, Taehyung. Incompatible Sufferings. 2010. 168p. pap. (978-3-639-02666-5(7)) VDM Verlag Dr. Mueller e.K.

Lee, Christopher. The Semblance of Identity: Aesthetic Mediation in Asian American Literature. 2012. (Asian America Ser.). (ENG.). 208p. 50.00 (978-0-8047-7870-1(1)) Stanford Univ. Pr.

Lee, Julia. Interracial Encounters: Reciprocal Representations in African & Asian American Literatures, 1896-1937. 2011. (ENG.). 228p. 75.00 (978-0-8147-5255-5(1)); pap. 23.00 (978-0-8147-5256-2(X)) New York Univ. Pr.

Lee, Julia H. Interracial Encounters: Reciprocal Representations in African American & Asian American Literatures, 1896-1937. 2011. E-Book (978-0-8147-5328-6(0)); E-Book (978-0-8147-5257-9(8)) New York Univ. Pr.

Mani, Bakirathi. Aspiring to Home: South Asians in America. 2012. (Asian America Ser.). (ENG.). 328p. 85.00 (978-0-8047-7799-5(3)); pap. 27.95 (978-0-8047-7800-8(0)) Stanford Univ. Pr.

Neudecker, Claudia. Implanting Foreignness: The Literacy Construction of Korean/American Realities. 226p. pap. 47.95 (978-3-631-54859-2(1)) Lang, Peter Publishing, Inc.

Oh, Seiwoong. Encyclopedia of Asian American Literature. 2007. (Encyclopedia of American Ethnic Literature Ser.). 400p. (C). (gr. 9). 75.00 (978-0-8160-6086-3(X)) Facts On File, Inc.

Oh, Seung Ah. Recontextualizing Asian American Domesticity: From Madame Butterfly to My American Wife. 2008. (ENG.). 208p. 68.50 (978-0-7391-2278-5(9)) Lexington Bks.

Rody, Caroline. The Interethnic Imagination: Roots & Passages in Contemporary Asian American Fiction. 2009. (Imagining the Americas Ser.). (ENG.). 216p. 65.00 (978-0-19-537736-1(2)) Oxford Univ. Pr., Inc.

Saed, Zohra & Muradi, Sahar, eds. One Story, Thirty Stories: An Anthology of Contemporary Afghan American Literature. 2010. (ENG.). 290p. 65.00 (978-1-55728-946-9(8)); pap. 24.95 (978-1-55728-945-2(X)) Univ. of Arkansas Pr.

So, Christine. Economic Citizens: A Narrative of Asian American Visibility. 2009. (ENG.). 190p. pap. 27.95 (978-1-59213-585-1(4)) 2007. 192p. 51.00 (978-1-59213-584-4(6)) Temple Univ. Pr.

Ty, Eleanor Rose. Unfastened: Globality & Asian North American Narratives. 2010. (Illus.). 216p. 67.50 (978-0-8166-6507-5(9)); (ENG., pap. 22.50 (978-0-8166-6508-2(7)) Univ. of Minnesota Pr.

Xu, Wenying. Eating Identities: Reading Food in Asian American Literature. 2008. 259p. per. 31.00 *(978-0-8248-3195-0(0))* Univ. of Hawaii Pr.

ASIAN AND PACIFIC COUNCIL COUNTRIES
see Pacific Area

ASIAN ARCHITECTURE
see Architecture—Asia

ASIAN ART
see Art, Asian

ASIAN COOKING
see Cooking, Asian

ASIAN DEVELOPMENT BANK

Glassman, Jim. Bounding the Mekong: The Asian Development Bank, China, & Thailand. 2010. 280p. 55.00 *(978-0-8248-3444-9(5))* Univ. of Hawaii Pr.

ASIAN LITERATURE
see Oriental Literature

ASIAN MYTHOLOGY
see Mythology, Asian

ASIAN NATIONAL CHARACTERISTICS
see National Characteristics, Asian

ASIAN PAINTING
see Painting, Asian

ASIAN POTBELLIED PIG
see Potbellied Pig

ASIAN SCULPTURE
see Sculpture—Asia

ASIAN STATESMEN
see Statesmen—Asia

ASIAN STUDIES
see Asia—Study and Teaching

ASIAN STUDIES SPECIALISTS
see Orientalists

ASIANS
see also names of individual races, e.g. East Indians, Mongols

Amrith, Sunil S. Migration & Diaspora in Modern Asia. 2011. (New Approaches to Asian History Ser.). (ENG., Illus.). 240p. (C). 85.00 *(978-0-521-89835-5(8))*; pap. 27.99 *(978-0-521-72702-0(2))* Cambridge Univ. Pr.

Charney, Michael W., et al, eds. Asian Migrants & Education: The Tensions of Education in Immigrant Societies & among Migrant Groups. 2010. (Education in the Asia-Pacific Region: Issues, Concerns & Prospects Ser.). 248p. pap. 179.00 *(978-90-481-6302-1(1)*, 9048163021) Springer.

Chatterji, Joya & Washbrook, David, eds. Handbook of the South Asian Diaspora. 2012. (ENG., Illus.). 464p. (C). 175.00 *(978-0-415-48010-9(8))* Routledge.

Chitty, Gina Ismene & Chitty, Gina. Public Postures, Private Positions. 2010. 248p. pap. *(978-3-639-24546-2(6))* VDM Verlag Dr. Mueller e.K.

Fujikane, Candace & Okamura, Jonathan Y. Asian Settler Colonialism: From Local Governance to the Habits of Everyday Life in Hawai'i. 2008. (Illus.). 318p. (C). pap. 25.00 *(978-0-8248-3300-8(7))* Univ. of Hawaii Pr.

—Asian Settler Colonialism: From Local Governance to the Habits of Everyday Life in Hawaii. 2008. (Illus.). xiv, 318p. 55.00 *(978-0-8248-3015-1(6))* Univ. of Hawaii Pr.

Gothard, Jan, ed. Asian Orientations. (Studies in Western Australian History: Vol. XVI). pap. *(978-0-86422-435-4(4))* UWA Publishing AUS. Dist: International Specialized Bk. Services.

Hardcastle, Leonie. Big Picture, Small Picture. 2010. 364p. pap. *(978-3-8383-4378-5(6))* Lambert Academic Publishing.

Khoo, Tseen, ed. Locating Asian Australian Cultures. 2007. (ENG.). 256p. 150.00 *(978-0-415-41148-6(3))* Routledge.

Kwok, Siu-ming & Kwok, Siu-Ming. Coping with a Spoiled Self. 2009. 148p. pap. *(978-3-639-14645-5(X))* VDM Verlag Dr. Mueller e.K.

Law, Edmond H. F. & Nieveen, Nienke, eds. Schools As Curriculum Agencies: Asian & European Perspectives on School-Based Curriculum Development. 2010. 306p. *(978-94-6091-280-1(X))*; pap. *(978-94-6091-279-5(6))* Sense Pubs.

Li, Xiaoping. Voices Rising: Asian Canadian Cultural Activism. 2007. (ENG., Illus.). 320p. pap. *(978-0-7748-1222-1(2))* Univ. of British Columbia Pr.

Ma, Sheng-mei. Asian Diaspora Literature & Visual Culture. 2010. (Routledge Contemporary Asia Ser.). (ENG.). 192p. (C). 125.00 *(978-0-415-59426-4(X))* Routledge.

—Diaspora Literature & Visual Culture: Asia in Flight. 2011. 183p. (C). 125.00 *(978-0-203-84077-1(1))* Routledge.

Neame, Lawrence E. The Asiatic Danger in the Colonies. 192p. reprint ed. 88.00 *(978-0-7222-9814-5(5))* Library Reprints, Inc.

Palriwala, Rajni & Uberoi, Patricia, eds. Marriage, Migration & Gender. 2008. (Women & Migration in Asia Ser.). 364p. (C). pap. 34.95 *(978-0-7619-3675-6(0)*, B42551P) SAGE Pubns., Inc.

Pathomvanich, Damkerng & Imagawa, Kenichiro, eds. Hair Restoration Surgery in Asians. 2010. (ENG., Illus.). xvi, 266p. 189.00 *(978-4-431-99658-3(3)*, 4431996583) Springer.

Pung, Alice. Unpolished Gem: My Mother, My Grandmother, & Me. 2009. (ENG.). 304p. (gr. 12-18). 16.00 *(978-0-452-29000-6(7)*, Plume) Penguin Group (USA) Inc.

Saaler, Sven. Pan-Asianism: A Documentary History, 2 vols, Set. 2011. (Asia/Pacific/Perspectives Ser.). (ENG.). 768p. 125.00 *(978-1-4422-0602-1(0))* Rowman & Littlefield Publishers, Inc.

Shimizu, Celine Parreñas. The Hypersexuality of Race: Performing Asian/American Women on Screen & Scene. 2007. (ENG., Illus.). 352p. 94.95 *(978-0-8223-4012-6(7))*; pap. 25.95 *(978-0-8223-4033-1(X))* Duke Univ. Pr.

Simpson, Bertram L. The Conflict of Colour: A Detailed Examination of Racial Problems Throughout the World with Special Reference to the English-Speaking Peoples. 340p. reprint ed. 98.00 *(978-0-7222-9702-5(5))* Library Reprints, Inc.

Stephenson, Peta. The Outsiders Within: Telling Australia's Indigenous-Asian Story. 2007. (ENG., Illus.). 256p. per. 35.95 *(978-0-86840-836-1(0)*, UNSW Press) NewSouth Publishing AUS. Dist: Independent Pubs. Group.

Tay, Yong-Kwang & Chan, Yuin-Chew. Textbook of Laser & Light Dermatology in the Asian Skin. 2011. 156p. 112.00 *(978-981-4338-86-8(9))* World Scientific Publishing Co., Inc.

Um, Hae-Kyung. Diasporas & Interculturalism in Asian. 2006. (Illus.). 256p. 39.95 *(978-0-415-40591-1(2))* Routledge.

Zhang, Benzi. Asian Diaspora Poetry in North America. 2007. (Literary Criticism & Cultural Theory Ser.). (ENG.). 194p. 125.00 *(978-0-415-95717-5(6))* Routledge.

ASIANS—GREAT BRITAIN

Bains & Joha. Corner Flags & Corner Shops. 252p. pap. 22.99 *(978-0-575-06636-6(9))* Gollancz, Victor Ltd. GBR. Dist: Trafalgar Square Publishing.

Bhopal, Kalwant. Asian Women in Higher Education: Shared Communities. 2010. 148p. pap. 34.95 *(978-1-85856-469-2(7))* Trentham Bks. Ltd. GBR. Dist: Stylus Publishing, LLC.

Burdsey, Daniel. British Asians & Football: Culture, Identity, Exclusion. 2008. 192p. 49.95 *(978-0-415-45553-4(7))* 2007. 185p. 168.00 *(978-0-415-39500-7(3))* Routledge.

Chambers. Black & Asian Theatre in Britain. 2011. (ENG., Illus.). 304p. pap. 39.95 *(978-0-415-37598-6(3))* Routledge.

Clark, Ken & Drinkwater, Stephen. Ethnic Minorities in the Labour Market: Dynamics & Diversity. 2007. (Illus.). 76p. (C). pap. 23.95 *(978-1-86134-959-0(9))* Policy Pr. GBR. Dist: Chicago Distribution Ctr.

Dadswell, Edward. British South Asian Theatres: A Documented History. Ley, Graham & Dadswell, Sarah, eds. 2012. (University of Exeter Press - Exeter Performance Studies). (Illus.). 265p. 105.00 *(978-0-85989-832-4(6))* Univ. of Exeter Pr. GBR. Dist: Chicago Distribution Ctr.

Dhaliwal, Spinder. Making a Fortune: Learning from the Asian Phenomenon. 2008. (ENG., Illus.). 206p. pap. 29.95 *(978-1-84112-799-6(X)*, Capstone) Wiley, John & Sons, Inc.

Fisher, Michael H., et al. South-Asian History of Britain: Four Centuries of Peoples from the Indian Sub-Continent. 2007. (Illus.). 250p. 49.95 *(978-1-84645-008-2(X)*, GWP008) Greenwood Publishing Group, Inc.

Harris, Roxy. New Ethnicities & Language Use. 2009. (Language & Globalization Ser.). (ENG.). 210p. pap. 37.00 *(978-0-230-58007-7(6))* Palgrave Macmillan.

Innes, C. L. A History of Black & Asian Writing in Britain. 2nd ed. 2008. (ENG., Illus.). 330p. pap. 28.99 *(978-0-521-71968-1(2))* Cambridge Univ. Pr.

Kureishi, Hanif. My Ear at His Heart: Reading My Father. 2010. (ENG., Illus.). 208p. 24.00 *(978-1-4165-7212-1(0)*, Scribner) Scribner.

Ley, Graham & Dadswell, Sarah, eds. British South Asian Theatres: A Documented History. 2012. (University of Exeter Press - Exeter Performance Studies). (Illus.). 320p. 37.25 *(978-0-85989-833-1(4))* Univ. of Exeter Pr. GBR. Dist: Chicago Distribution Ctr.

McLoughlin, Sean, et al, eds. Diaspora & Multi-Locality in British Asian Cities. 2011. (Routledge Contemporary South Asia Ser.). (ENG.). 256p. (C). 130.00 *(978-0-415-59024-2(8))* Routledge.

Murphy, Neil & Sim, Wai-chew. British Asian Fiction: Framing the Contemporary. 2008. 119.95 *(978-1-60497-541-3(5))* Cambria Pr.

Rasinger, Sebastian M. Bengali-English in East London: A Study in Urban Multilingualism. (Contemporary Studies in Descriptive Linguistics Ser.: Vol. 11). (Illus.). 270p. pap. 57.95 *(978-3-03911-036-0(5))* Lang, Peter CHE. Dist: Lang, Peter Publishing, Inc.

Sardar, Ziauddin. Balti Britain: A Journey Through the British Asian Experience. 2009. (ENG.). 392p. pap. 16.95 *(978-1-84708-082-0(0))* Granta Bks. GBR. Dist: Independent Pubs. Group.

—Balti Britain: Journeys Through the British Asian Experience. 2008. (ENG.). 416p. 37.95 *(978-1-86207-931-1(5))* Granta Bks. GBR. Dist: Independent Pubs. Group.

Upstone, Sara. British Asian Fiction: Twenty-First Century Voices. 2011. (ENG.). 240p. 84.95 *(978-0-7190-7832-3(6))* Manchester Univ. Pr. GBR. Dist: Macmillan.

ASIANS—UNITED STATES
see also Asian Americans

Alban Institute Action Research Team on Conflict Management. Pacific Asian American Ministry in a Time of Shifting Paradigms: The Example of Asian American Conflict Management. pap. 7.50 *(978-1-56699-163-6(3)*, OD117) Alban Institute, Inc.

Barde, Robert Eric. Immigration at the Golden Gate: Passenger Ships, Exclusion, & Angel Island, 1 vol. 2008. (Illus.). 304p. 49.95 *(978-0-313-34782-5(4)*, C34782, Praeger Pubs.) Greenwood Publishing Group, Inc.

Choe, Justin. A Reflection of Western Psychotherapy in the Eastern Cultures. 2010. 88p. pap. *(978-3-8383-5913-7(5))* Lambert Academic Publishing.

Li, Wei. From Urban Enclave to Ethnic Suburb: New Asian Communities in Pacific Rim Countries. 2006. (Illus.). 278p. 56.00 *(978-0-8248-2911-7(5))* Univ. of Hawaii Pr.

Rahman, Shafiqur. The Bangladeshi Diaspora in the United States After 9/11: From Obscurity to High Visibility. 2011. (ENG.). 70.00 *(978-1-59332-405-6(7))* LFB Scholarly Publishing LLC.

Thornton, Meg Malpaya, ed. Asian American & Pacific Islander Community Directory: For Los Angeles & Orange Counties 2008. 10th ed. 2008. (ENG.). 360p. pap. 20.00 *(978-0-934052-44-3(1))* Univ. of California, Los Angeles, Asian American Studies Ctr.

Ung, Loung. Lucky Child. 2007. *(978-0-7322-8348-3(5)*, HarperPerennial) HarperCollins Pubs. Australia.

Yang, Philip Q. Asian Immigration to the United States. 2011. (PIMS - Polity Immigration & Society Ser.: 3). (ENG., Illus.). 192p. 59.95 *(978-0-7456-4502-5(X))*; pap. 22.95 *(978-0-7456-4503-2(8))* Polity Pr. GBR. Dist: Wiley, John & Sons, Inc.

ASIATIC CHOLERA
see Cholera

ASIATIC ZOOLOGICAL EXPEDITION OF THE AMERICAN MUSEUM OF NATURAL HISTORY TO CHINA, 1916-1917

Andrews, Roy Chapman & Yvette Borup Andrews. Camps & Trails in China: A Narrative of Exploration Adventure & Sport I. 2007. (ENG.). 266p. pap. 21.99 *(978-1-4264-5930-6(0))*; 292p. pap. 23.99 *(978-1-4264-5998-6(X))* BiblioBazaar.

ASL (AMERICAN SIGN LANGUAGE)
see American Sign Language

ASMAT

Pouwer, Jan. Gender, Ritual & Social. 2010. 312p. pap. 44.00 *(978-90-6718-325-3(3))* KITLV Pr. NLD. Dist: Univ. of Hawaii Pr.

ASMONEANS
see Maccabees

ASOKA, KING OF MAGADHA, FL. 259 B.C.

Asoka, King of Magadha. The Edicts of Asoka. reprint ed. 34.50 *(978-0-404-17219-0(9))* AMS Pr., Inc.

Burnouf, Eugene. Legends of Indian Buddhism. 2007. 128p. 35.95 *(978-0-548-11234-2(7))* Kessinger Publishing, LLC.

Chakrabarti, Dilip K. Royal Messages by the Wayside: Historical Geography of the Asokan Edicts. 2011. (Illus.). xvi, 184p. *(978-81-7305-411-2(8)*, Library of Congress — New Delhi Overseas Office) Aryan Bks. International.

Olivelle, Patrick, et al, eds. Reimagining Asoka: Memory & History. 2012. (ENG., Illus.). 512p. 85.00 ***(978-0-19-807800-5(5))*** Oxford Univ. Pr., Inc.

Rich, Bruce. To Uphold the World: A Call for a New Global Ethic from Ancient India. 2010. (ENG.). 256p. pap. 23.00 *(978-0-8070-0613-9(0))* Beacon Pr.

Smith, Vincent A. Edicts of Asoka. 2006. pap. 19.95 *(978-1-4286-4431-1(8))* Kessinger Publishing, LLC.

Smith, Vincent Arthur. Asoka, the Buddhist Emperor of India. 3rd enl. rev. ed. reprint ed. 37.50 *(978-0-404-17378-4(0))* AMS Pr., Inc.

Stephens, Winifred. Legends of Indian Buddhism. 2008. 132p. pap. *(978-1-4437-0361-1(3))* Read Bks.

Thapar, Romila. Asoka & the Decline of the Mauryas. 3rd ed. 2012. (ENG., Illus.). 392p. pap. 27.95 ***(978-0-19-807724-4(6))*** Oxford Univ. Pr., Inc.

ASP (COMPUTER PROGRAM)
see Active Server Pages (Computer Program)

ASPARTAME

Kruppa, Carole. Free & Equal Cookbook: Over 160 Quick & Delicious No Sugar Added Recipes 2nd rev. l.t. ed. 2010. (ENG.). 236p. 31.95 *(978-1-4104-2324-5(7))* Thorndike Pr.

ASPECT-ORIENTED PROGRAMMING

Association for Computing Machinery (ACM) Staff, compiled by. Early Aspects at ICSE: Workshop in Aspect-Oriented Workshop in Aspect-Oriented & Architecture Design (EA'06) 2007. 66p. pap. 50.00 *(978-1-60423-064-2(9))* Curran Assocs., Inc.

—1st Workshop on Virtual Machines & Intermediate Languages for Emerging Modularization Mechanisms (VMIL '07) 2007. (ACM International Conference Proceedings Ser.). 32p. pap. 50.00 *(978-1-60423-025-3(8))* Curran Assocs., Inc.

—2nd Workshop on Best Practices in Applying Aspect-Oriented Software Development (BPAOSD '07) 2007. (ACM International Conference Proceedings Ser.). 25p. pap. 50.00 *(978-1-60423-024-6(X))* Curran Assocs., Inc.

—2nd Workshop on Testing Aspect-Oriented Programs (WTAOP 2006) 2007. 41p. pap. 50.00 *(978-1-60423-166-3(1))* Curran Assocs., Inc.

—3rd Workshop on Testing Aspect-Oriented Programs (WTAOP '07) 2007. (ACM International Conference Proceedings Ser.). 27p. pap. 50.00 *(978-1-60423-023-9(1))* Curran Assocs., Inc.

—5th International Conference on Aspect-Oriented Software Development (AOSD '06) 2007. 237p. pap. 93.00 *(978-1-60423-016-1(9))* Curran Assocs., Inc.

—5th Workshop on Software Engineering Properties of Languages & Aspect Technologies (SPLAT 2007) 2007. (ACM International Conference Proceedings Ser.). 60p. pap. 50.00 *(978-1-60423-026-0(6))* Curran Assocs., Inc.

—6th International Conference on Aspect-Oriented Software Development (AOSD 2007) 2007. (ACM International Conference Proceedings Ser.). 328p. pap. 93.00 *(978-1-60423-021-5(5))* Curran Assocs., Inc.

—6th Workshop on Foundations of Aspect-Oriented Languages (FOAL 2007) 2007. 74p. pap. 62.00 *(978-1-60423-020-8(7))* Curran Assocs., Inc.

—10th International Workshop on Aspect-Oriented Modeling (AOM @ AOSD '07) 2007. (ACM International Conference Proceedings Ser.). 56p. pap. 50.00 *(978-1-60423-022-2(3))* Curran Assocs., Inc.

Charfi, Anis. Aspect-Oriented Workflow Management. 2008. 208p. pap. *(978-3-8364-5638-8(9))* VDM Verlag Dr. Mueller e.K.

De Meuter, Wolfgang. Advances in SmallTalk: 14th International SmallTalk Conference, ISC 2006, Prague, Czech Republic, September 4-8, 2006, Revised Selected Papers. 2007. (Lecture Notes in Computer Science Ser.). (Illus.). 157p. pap. 69.95 *(978-3-540-71835-2(4))* Springer.

Georgieva, Konstantina. Testing of Aspect Oriented Programs. 2010. 144p. pap. *(978-3-8383-3408-0(6))* Lambert Academic Publishing.

Grundy, John, ed. Early Aspects: Current Challenges & Future Directions: 10th International Workshop, Vancouver, Canada, March 13, 2007, Revised Selected Papers. 2008. (Lecture Notes in Computer Science Ser.). (Illus.). 198p. pap. 69.95 *(978-3-540-76810-4(6))* Springer.

Katz, Shmuel & Mezini, Mira. Transactions on Aspect-Oriented Software Development VII: A Common Case Study for Aspect-Oriented Modeling. 2010. (Lecture Notes in Computer Science / Transactions on Aspect-Oriented Software Development Ser.). xv, 423p. pap. 129.00 *(978-3-642-16085-1(9)*, 3642160859) Springer.

Katz, Shmuel & Ossher, Harold. Transactions on Aspect-Oriented Software Development VI: Special Issue on Aspects & Model-Driven Engineering. 2009. (Lecture Notes in Computer Science / Transactions on Aspect-Oriented Software Development Ser.). xiii, 267p. pap. 99.00 *(978-3-642-03763-4(1)*, 3642037631) Springer.

Leonardo, Cole & Paulo, Borba. Deriving Refactorings for AspectJ: An Approach to Refactoring Aspect-Oriented Applications Using Composed Programming Laws. 2011. 100p. pap. ***(978-3-639-32561-4(3))*** VDM Verlag Dr. Mueller e.K.

Rashid, Awais. Aspect-Oriented Database Systems. 2010. (ENG.). xv, 176p. pap. 79.95 *(978-3-642-05669-7(5)*, 3642056695) Springer.

Rashid, Awais, et al, eds. Aspect-Oriented, Model-Driven Software Product Lines: The AMPLE Way. 2011. (ENG., Illus.). 470p. 75.00 *(978-0-521-76722-4(9))* Cambridge Univ. Pr.

Rashid, Awais & Ossher, Harold. Transactions on Aspect-Oriented Software Development V. 2009. (Lecture Notes in Computer Science / Transactions on Aspect-Oriented Software Development Ser.). ix, 265p. pap. 99.00 *(978-3-642-02058-2(5)*, 3642020585) Springer.

Robinson, David. Aspect-Oriented Programming with the e Verification Language: A Pragmatic Guide for Testbench Developers. 2007. (Systems on Silicon Ser.). (ENG., Illus.). 264p. per. 79.95 *(978-0-12-374210-0(2)*, Morgan Kaufmann) Elsevier Science & Technology Bks.

Safonov, Vladimir O. Using Aspect-Oriented Programming for Trustworthy Software Development. 2008. (ENG., Illus.). 338p. 117.00 *(978-0-470-13817-5(3)*, Wiley-Interscience) Wiley, John & Sons, Inc.

Tasiran, Serdar, ed. Runtime Verification. 2008. (Lecture Notes in Computer Science Ser.). (Illus.). 213p. pap. 69.95 *(978-3-540-77394-8(0))* Springer.

Wloka, Jan. Tool-Supported Refactoring of Aspect-Oriented Programs - Why Aspect-Oriented Programming Prevents Developers from Using Their Favorite Refactoring Too. 2008. 204p. pap. *(978-3-8364-8999-7(6))* VDM Verlag Dr. Mueller e.K.

ASPEN (COLO.)

Andersen, Paul. Aspen's Rugged Splendor: Exploring the Human & Natural Histories of the Maroon & Castle Creek Valleys. 2007. (Illus.). 200p. 44.95 *(978-1-882426-25-6(8))* Peoples Pr., LLC.

Pellow, David & Park, Lisa Sun-Hee. The Slums of Aspen: Immigrants vs. the Environment in America's Eden. 2011. (ENG., Illus.). 284p. 30.00 ***(978-0-8147-6803-7(2))*** New York Univ. Pr.

Pfaffmann, Garrick. Mountain Biking Aspen to Glenwood. 2008. (ENG., Illus.). 144p. pap. 19.95 *(978-1-882426-27-0(4))* Peoples Pr., LLC.

ASPERGILLUS

Barakat, Hassan, et al. Application for the Antifungal Protein from Aspergillus Giganteus. 2010. 220p. pap. *(978-3-639-27174-4(2))* VDM Verlag Dr. Mueller e.K.

Goldman, Gustavo H. & Osmani, Stephen A., eds. The Aspergilli: Genomics, Medical Applications, Biotechnology & Research Methods. 2007. (Mycology Ser.). (ENG., Illus.). 576p. 154.95 *(978-0-8493-9080-7(X)*, CRC Press) Taylor & Francis Group GBR. Dist: Taylor & Francis Group.

Haddad, Ziad. Monocytic Cell Responses to Aspergillus Fumigatus. 2008. 124p. pap. *(978-3-639-06994-5(3))* VDM Verlag Dr. Mueller e.K.

Kumar, Adepu Kiran. Characteristics & Applications of a Novel Alcohol Oxidase. 2011. 152p. pap. ***(978-3-8443-3187-5(5))*** Lambert Academic Publishing.

Latgé, Jean-Paul & Steinbach, William J. Aspergillus Fumigatus & Aspergillosis. 2008. (Illus.). 592p. 205.00 *(978-1-55581-438-0(7))* ASM Pr.

Samson, Robert, ed. Advances in Penicillium & Aspergillus Systematics. 2010. pap. 224.00 *(978-1-4419-3204-4(6)*, 1441932046) Springer.

Varga, János & Samson, Robert A., eds. Aspergillus in the genomic Era. 2008. 334p. 152.00 *(978-90-8686-065-4(6))* Wageningen Academic Publishers NLD. Dist: Enfield Publishing & Distribution Co., Inc.

ASPHALT
see also Asphalt Concrete; Pavements, Asphalt

Aema. Basic Asphalt Emulsion Manual. 4th ed. 2009. (Illus.). 97p. pap. 60.00 *(978-1-934154-56-4(3))* Asphalt Institute.

Ancheyta, Jorge, et al. Asphaltenes: Chemical Transformation During Hydroprocessing of Heavy Oils. 2010. (Chemical Industries Ser.). (ENG., Illus.). 461p. 169.95 *(978-1-4200-6630-2(7)*, CRC Press) Taylor & Francis Group GBR. Dist: Taylor & Francis Group.

Anderson, R. Michael. Ms-26 the Asphalt Binder Handbook. Butler, Kendal, ed. 2011. 242p. pap. 90.00 ***(978-1-934154-63-2(6))*** Asphalt Institute.

Asphalt Institute, creator. Asphalt Binder Testing: Technician's Manual for Specification Testing of Asphalt Binders. 2nd ed. 2009. (Illus.). 184p. pap. 130.00 *(978-1-934154-57-1(1))* Asphalt Institute.

—The Asphalt Handbook. 7th ed. 2007. (Illus.). 788p. per. 120.00 *(978-1-934154-27-4(X))* Asphalt Institute.

—Asphalt in Pavement Preservation & Maintenance. 4th ed. 2009. (Illus.). 155p. pap. 60.00 *(978-1-934154-58-8(X))* Asphalt Institute.

Brown, Alton. Feasting on Asphalt: The River Run. 2008. (ENG., Illus.). 208p. 30.00 *(978-1-58479-681-7(2))* Stewart, Tabori & Chang.

Mullins, Oliver C., et al. Asphaltenes, Heavy Oils, & Petroleomics. 2006. (ENG., Illus.). xxi, 669p. 139.00 *(978-0-387-31734-2(1)*, 0387317341) Springer.

Prowell, Brian D. Validating the Fatigue Endurance Limit for Hot Mix Asphalt. 2010. (Illus.). 128p. pap. ***(978-0-309-11821-7(2))*** Transportation Research Board.

Wang, Linbing. Mechanics of Asphalt: Microstructure & Micromechanics. 2010. (ENG., Illus.). 480p. (C). 115.00 *(978-0-07-149854-8(0)*, 0071498540) McGraw-Hill Professional Publishing.

Zaumanis, Martins. Asphalt Is Going Green. 2011. 112p. pap. ***(978-3-8443-0018-5(X))*** Lambert Academic Publishing.

ASPHALT CONCRETE

Kim, Y. Richard. Modeling of Asphalt Concrete. 2008. (ENG., Illus.). 460p. 115.00 *(978-0-07-146462-8(X)*, 007146462X) McGraw-Hill Professional Publishing.

Si, Zhiming. Characterization of Asphalt Concrete Tures. 2009. 180p. pap. *(978-3-639-18545-4(5))* VDM Verlag Dr. Mueller e.K.

Wang, Linbing. Mechanics of Asphalt: Microstructure & Micromechanics. 2010. (ENG., Illus.). 480p. (C). 115.00 *(978-0-07-149854-8(0)*, 0071498540) McGraw-Hill Professional Publishing.

ASPHALT EMULSION MIXTURES

West, Randy C. Mixing & Compaction Temperatures of Asphalt Binders in Hot-Mix Asphalt. 2010. (Illus.). pap. ***(978-0-309-11825-5(5))*** Transportation Research Board.

ASPERGER'S SYNDROME

Adams, Lynn. Autism & Asperger Syndrome: Busting the Myths. 2007. (Illus.). 117p. per. 24.95 *(978-1-59756-083-2(9))* Plural Publishing, Inc.

Adreon, Diane, et al. Simple Strategies That Work! Helpful Hints for All Educators of Students with Asperger Syndrome, High-Functioning Autism, & Related Disabilities. 2006. (Illus.). 40p. pap. 19.95 *(978-1-931282-99-4(4))* Autism Asperger Publishing Co.

Angermeier, Patricia, et al. Learning in Motion: 101+ Sensory Activities for the Classroom. 2nd ed. 2009. (ENG., Illus.). 350p. pap. 39.95 *(978-1-932565-90-4(6))* Future Horizons, Inc.

Ariel, Cindy. Loving Someone with Asperger's Syndrome: Understanding & Connecting with your Partner. 2012. (New Harbinger Loving Someone Ser.). (ENG.). 216p. pap. 18.95 ***(978-1-60882-077-1(7))*** New Harbinger Pubns.

Ariel, Cindy N. Loving Someone with Asperger's Syndrome: Understanding & Connecting with Your Partner. 2012. ***(978-1-60882-079-5(3))*** New Harbinger Pubns.

Arwood, Ellyn Lucas, et al. Visual Thinking Strategies for Individuals with Autism Spectrum Disorders - the Language of Pictures. 2009. (Illus.). 199p. pap. 24.95 *(978-1-934575-50-5(X))* Autism Asperger Publishing Co.

Ashley, Susan. The Asperger's: The Top 300 Questions Parents Ask. 2006. (ENG., Illus.). 320p. per. 14.95 *(978-1-4022-0807-2(3))* Sourcebooks, Inc.

Aspy, Ruth & Grossman, Barry. * Designing Comprehensive Interventions for High-Functioning Individuals with Autism Spectrum Disorders: The Ziggurat Model-Release 2. 0. 2011. 246p. pap. 59.00 ***(978-1-934575-96-3(8))*** Autism Asperger Publishing Co.

—UCC-CL Assessment Booklets (contains 1 manual & 20 Forms) 2007. pap. 24.95 *(978-1-931282-46-8(3))* Autism Asperger Publishing Co.

—Underlying Characteristics Checklists (UCC) User Manual. 2011. 19.00 ***(978-1-934575-98-7(4))*** Autism Asperger Publishing Co.

—The Ziggurat Model: A Framework for Designing Comprehensive Interventions for Individuals with High-Functioning Autism & Asperger Syndrome. 390p. 49.95 *(978-1-934575-43-7(7))* Autism Asperger Publishing Co.

Aspy, Ruth & Grossman, Barry. The Ziggurat Model ¿ A Framework for Designing Comprehensive Interventions for Individuals with High-Functioning Autism & Asperger Syndrome Updated & Expanded Edition. 2011. 340p. pap. 49.95 ***(978-1-934575-94-9(1))*** Autism Asperger Publishing Co.

Aspy, Ruth, et al. * Underlying Characteristics Checklist — Early Intervention (UCC-EI) 2011. 24.95 ***(978-1-934575-95-6(X))*** Autism Asperger Publishing Co.

Aston, Jude, ed. Asperger Syndrome: Complete Handbook. 2009. 166p. pap. 19.95 *(978-0-9822136-2-9(X))* Rapid Publishing LLC.

Attwood, Tony. Asperger's Syndrome. 2008. (ENG., Illus.). 400p. pap. *(978-1-84310-669-2(8))* Kingsley, Jessica Ltd.

Attwood, Tony, et al. Asperger's & Girls. 2006. (ENG.). 152p. per. 19.95 *(978-1-932565-40-9(X))* Future Horizons, Inc.

Baron-Cohen, Simon. Autism & Asperger Syndrome. 2nd ed. 2008. (Facts Ser.). (ENG., Illus.). 160p. 19.95 *(978-0-19-850490-0(X))* Oxford Univ. Pr., Inc.

Barrett Mann, Lisa, ed. More Than Little Professors: Children with Asperger Syndrome: in Their Own Words. 2008. pap. 18.95 *(978-1-934575-25-3(9))* Autism Asperger Publishing Co.

Beardon, Luke & Edmonds, Genevieve, eds. Asperger Syndrome & Employment: Adults Speak Out about Asperger Syndrome. 2008. (Adults Speak Out about Asperger Syndrome Ser.). (ENG.). 160p. pap. *(978-1-84310-648-7(5))* Kingsley, Jessica Ltd.

Bentley, Katrin. Alone Together: Making an Asperger Marriage Work. 2007. (ENG., Illus.). 128p. per. *(978-1-84310-537-4(3))* Kingsley, Jessica Ltd.

Betts, Stacey W. Asperger Syndrome in the Inclusive Classroom: Advice & Strategies for Teachers. 2007. (ENG.). 16p. per. *(978-1-84310-840-5(2))* Kingsley, Jessica Ltd.

Bliss, Veronica E. & Edmonds, Genevive. A Self Determined Future with Asperger Syndrome: Solution Focused Approaches. 2007. (ENG., Illus.). 16p. pap. *(978-1-84310-513-8(6))* Kingsley, Jessica Ltd.

Boushey, Ann. Talking Teenagers: Information & Inspiration for Parents of Teenagers with Autism or Asperger's Syndrome. 2007. (ENG.). 192p. per. *(978-1-84310-844-3(5))* Kingsley, Jessica Ltd.

Bowler, Dermot. Autism Spectrum Disorders: Psychological Theory & Research. 2006. (ENG., Illus.). 318p. per. 62.95 *(978-0-470-02686-1(3)*, Wiley) Wiley, John & Sons, Inc.

Boyd, Brenda & Newsone, Elizabeth. Appreciating Asperger Syndrome: Looking at the Upside - With 300 Positive Points. 2009. (ENG., Illus.). 240p. pap. *(978-1-84310-625-8(6))* Kingsley, Jessica Ltd.

Breeding, Travis E. I Want to be Like You: Life with Asperger's Syndrome. 2011. pap. 21.99 *(978-1-61663-918-1(0))* Tate Publishing & Enterprises, LLC.

Bromfield, Richard. Doing Therapy with Children & Adolescents with Asperger Syndrome. 2010. (ENG.). 240p. 40.00 *(978-0-470-54025-1(7)*, Wiley) Wiley, John & Sons, Inc.

Carley, Michael John & Carley, Michael. Asperger's from the Inside Out: A Supportive & Practical Guide for Anyone with Asperger's Syndrome. 2008. (ENG.). 272p. (gr. 12-18). 14.95 *(978-0-399-53397-6(4)*, Perigee Trade) Penguin Group (USA) Inc.

Clark Brack, Jenny. Learn to Move, Moving up! Sensorimotor Elementary-School Activity Themes. 2009. pap. 34.95 *(978-1-934575-38-3(0))* Autism Asperger Publishing Co.

Clark, Julie. Asperger's in Pink: A Mother & Daughter Guidebook for Raising (Or Being!) a Girl with Asperger's. 2010. (ENG.). 200p. pap. 14.95 *(978-1-935274-10-0(4))* Future Horizons, Inc.

Colby, Dane E. 101 Choices on My Path to Well-Being. 2009. 126p. pap. 14.50 *(978-0-557-04134-3(1))* Lulu Enterprises Inc.

Cooper, Barbara & Widdows, Nancy. Knowing Yourself, Knowing Others: A Workbook for Children with Asperger's Disorder, Nonverbal Learning Disorder, & Other Social-Skill Problems. 2008. (Instant Help Ser.). 130p. pap. 16.95 *(978-1-931704-36-6(8))* Play2Grow.

Cooper, Barbara, et al. Social Success Workbook for Te. 2008. 136p. pap. 16.95 *(978-1-931704-43-4(0))* Play2Grow.

Cresswell, Paul. Childhood Autism & Asperger's Syndrome. 2009. 94p. pap. 20.95 *(978-1-4092-6408-8(4))* Lulu Enterprises Inc.

Cumine, Val, et al. Asperger Syndrome: A Practical Guide for Teachers. 2nd ed. 2009. (Illus.). (ENG.). 116p. 37.95 *(978-0-415-48371-1(9))*; xi, 112p. 37.95 ***(978-0-203-86486-9(7))*** Routledge.

Cumpata, JoEllen & Fell, Susan. A Quest for Social Skills for Students with Autism or Asperger's: Ready-to-use lessons with games, role-play activities, & More! 2010. (Illus.). 300p. pap. 24.95 *(978-1-935274-11-7(2))* Future Horizons, Inc.

Davies, Joshua. Between the Lines of Autism. 2011. 34p. pap. ***(978-1-906236-48-9(8))*** SilverWood Bks.

DeLong, Janet. Think: ... & into my Life. 2011. 348p. pap. 19.95 *(978-1-4520-9057-3(2))* AuthorHouse.

Denault, Jeanne. Sucking up Yellow Jackets: Raising an Undiagnosed Asperger Syndrome Son Obsessed with Explosives. 2010. (ENG.). 259p. pap. 24.95 *(978-1-84694-384-3(1))* Hunt, John Publishing Ltd. GBR. Dist: National Bk. Network.

Docter, Melinda & Naqvi, Syed. Asperger's Syndrome: A Guide to Helping Your Child Thrive at Home & at School. 2010. (ENG., Illus.). 224p. pap. 16.95 *(978-0-470-14014-7(3)*, Wiley) Wiley, John & Sons, Inc.

Dubin, Nick. Asperger Syndrome & Anxiety: A Guide to Successful Stress Management. 2009. (ENG.). 224p. pap. *(978-1-84310-895-5(X))* Kingsley, Jessica Ltd.

—Asperger Syndrome & Bullying: Strategies & Solutions. 2007. (ENG.). 16p. per. *(978-1-84310-846-7(1))* Kingsley, Jessica Ltd.

Edmonds, Genevieve. Asperger Syndrome & Social Relationships. Beardon, Luke, ed. 2008. (Adults Speak Out about Asperger Syndrome Ser.). (ENG.). 160p. pap. *(978-1-84310-647-0(7))* Kingsley, Jessica Ltd.

Edmonds, Genevieve & Worton, Dean. The Asperger Social Guide: How to Relate with Confidence to Anyone in Any Social Situation as an Adult with Asperger's Syndrome. 2006. (Lucky Duck Bks.). (Illus.). 120p. 69.00 *(978-1-4129-2023-0(X)*, B2023XC); per. 26.95 *(978-1-4129-2024-7(8)*, B2023XP) SAGE Pubns., Ltd. GBR. Dist: SAGE Pubns., Inc.

Engel Fisher, Jennifer & Price, Janet. Take Control of Asperger's Syndrome: The Official Strategy Guide for Teens with Asperger's Syndrome & Nonverbal Learning Disorder. 2010. (ENG.). 200p. (gr. 5-10). pap. 16.95 *(978-1-59363-405-6(6))* Prufrock Pr.

Faehn-Sheehan, Emily & Faehn, Parker. My Mom & Me Together We Dance Simply Living with Aspergers & Tourettes: My Son & I the Dances We Do. 2009. 52p. pap. 12.95 *(978-1-4401-1519-6(2))* iUniverse, Inc.

Faherty, Catherine. Communication: What Does It Mean to Me? A Contract for Communication that will promote understanding between individuals with autism or Asperger's & their families, teachers, therapists, co-workers, & many More! 2010. (ENG., Illus.). 118p. pap. 19.95 *(978-1-935274-17-9(1))* Future Horizons, Inc.

—Understanding Death & Illness & What They Teach about Life: A Practical Guidebook for People with Autism or Aspergers, & Their Loved Ones. 2008. (ENG., Illus.). 341p. pap. 24.95 *(978-1-932565-56-0(6))* Future Horizons, Inc.

Fattig, Michelle. Taming Tommy's Tantrums. 2007. 76p. pap. 10.99 *(978-0-9795805-7-4(9))* Flower by the Water Publishing.

Finch, David. The Journal of Best Practices: A Memoir of Marriage, Asperger Syndrome, & One Man's Quest to Be a Better Husband. 2012. (ENG.). 320p. pap. 16.00 ***(978-1-4391-8974-0(9))***; 240p. 25.00 *(978-1-4391-8971-9(4))* Scribner. (Scribner).

Fitzgerald, Michael. Genius Genes: How Asperger Talents Changed the World. 2007. (Illus.). 309p. per. 24.95 *(978-1-931282-44-4(7))* Autism Asperger Publishing Co.

Gallegos, Elena M. & Shallenberger, Jill M. Autism Methodology Cases to Live By: Legal Guidance for Practical Program Strategies. 2008. *(978-1-57834-100-9(0))* LRP Pubns.

Gaus, Valerie L. Cognitive-Behavioral Therapy for Adult Asperger Syndrome. 2007. (Guides to Individualized Evidence-Based Treatment Ser.). (ENG., Illus.). 244p. 35.00 *(978-1-59385-497-3(8))* Guilford Pubns., Inc.

—Living Well on the Spectrum: How to Use Your Strengths to Meet the Challenges of Asperger Syndrome/High-Functioning Autism. 2011. (ENG.). 383p. pap. 21.95 *(978-1-60623-634-5(2))* Guilford Pubns., Inc.

Giler, Janet Z. Socially ADDept: Teaching Social Skills to Children with ADHD, LD, & Asperger's. rev. ed. 2011. (ENG., Illus.). 224p. pap. 29.95 *(978-0-470-59683-8(X)*, Jossey-Bass) Wiley, John & Sons, Inc.

Gillard, Arthur, ed. Asperger Syndrome. 2011. (Perspectives on Diseases & Disorders Ser.). (Illus.). 144p. (YA). (gr. 9-12). 37.10 *(978-0-7377-5771-2(X))* Cengage Gale.

Gomez, Joan. Living with Asperger Syndrome. 2006. 128p. pap. *(978-0-85969-935-8(8)*, Sheldon Press) SPCK Publishing.

Goodyear, Billy & Goodyear, Bill. Coaching People with Asperger's Syndrome: Family Coaching. 2008. (Illus.). 225p. pap. 41.00 *(978-1-85575-413-3(4))* Karnac Bks. GBR. Dist: Stylus Publishing, LLC.

Grandin, Temple. The Way I See It: A Personal Look at Autism & Asperger's. 2nd rev. exp. ed. 2011. (ENG., Illus.). 339p. pap. 19.95 *(978-1-935274-21-6(X))* Future Horizons, Inc.

Grandin, Temple & Duffy, Kate. Developing Talents: Careers for Individuals with Asperger Syndrome & High-Functioning Autism. 2008. 153p. pap. 21.95 *(978-1-934575-28-4(3))* Autism Asperger Publishing Co.

Griffiths, Jonathan. Asperger Meets Girl: Happy Endings for Asperger Boys. 2008. (ENG., Illus.). 96p. per. *(978-1-84310-630-2(2))* Kingsley, Jessica Ltd.

Grossberg, Blythe. Asperger's Rules! How to Make Sense of School & Friends. 2012. 14.95 ***(978-1-4338-1128-9(6))***; pap. 9.95 ***(978-1-4338-1127-2(8))*** American Psychological Assn. (Magination Pr.).

Gutstein, Steven, ed. The Relationship Development Intervention Program & Education. 2007. 259p. per. 22.50 *(978-0-9777186-1-0(1))* Connections Center.

Hagland, Carol. Getting to Grips with Asperger Syndrome: Understanding Adults on the Autism Spectrum. 2009. (ENG.). 240p. pap. *(978-1-84310-977-8(8))* Kingsley, Jessica Ltd.

Haldane, Carol. Dannie's Dilemma. 2008. 68p. pap. *(978-1-84747-676-0(7))* Chipmunkapublishing.

Hartley, Dustin. The Sky Is Falling. 2009. 162p. 26.96 *(978-0-578-00337-5(6))* Hartley Bks.

—The Sky Is Falling - Revised & with Bonus Material. 2010. 191p. pap. 12.65 *(978-0-557-37573-8(8))* Lulu Enterprises Inc.

Hendrickx, Sarah. Asperger Syndrome & Employment: What People with Asperger Syndrome Really Really Want. 2008. (ENG.). 144p. pap. *(978-1-84310-677-7(9))* Kingsley, Jessica Ltd.

—Love, Sex & Long-Term Relationships: What People with Asperger Syndrome Really Really Want. 2008. (ENG.). 160p. pap. *(978-1-84310-605-0(1))* Kingsley, Jessica Ltd.

Hendrickx, Sarah & Newton, Keith. Asperger Syndrome: A Love Story. 2007. (ENG., Illus.). 176p. per. *(978-1-84310-540-4(3))* Kingsley, Jessica Ltd.

Hubbard, Kristi. Unwrapping the Mysteries of Asperger's: The Search for Truth & Discovery of Solutions - Guide for Girls & Women with Asperger's Syndrome. 2010. 324p. 29.45 *(978-1-4490-9488-1(0))*; (ENG.). pap. 19.95 *(978-1-4490-9489-8(9))* AuthorHouse.

Hull, Kevin B. Play Therapy & Asperger's Syndrome: Helping Children & Adolescents Grow, Connect, & Heal through the Art of Play. 2011. (ENG.). 174p. 60.00 ***(978-0-7657-0856-4(6)***, Aronson, Jason) Rowman & Littlefield Publishers, Inc.

Jeanette D. Harmon. The Other Normal: Understanding Asperger's. 2011. 216p. pap. 24.95 ***(978-1-4560-6048-0(1))*** PublishAmerica, Inc.

Johnston-Tyler, Jan. Mom's Guide to Asperger Syndrome & Related Disorders. 2007. pap. 21.95 *(978-1-931282-42-0(0))* Autism Asperger Publishing Co.

Kaufman, Nancy & Lord Larson, Vicki. Asperger Syndrome. 2007. (C). per. 38.00 *(978-1-58650-729-9(X))* Super Duper Pubns.

Kennedy-Kline, Tara. Stop Raising Einstein: Discover the Unique Brilliance in Your Child... & You. 2009. (ENG.). 180p. pap. 15.99 *(978-1-59932-151-6(3))* Advantage Media Group.

—Stop Raising Einstein Journal: Kids Journal. 2009. (ENG.). 126p. (gr. -1-12). pap. 10.99 *(978-1-59932-173-8(4))* Advantage Media Group.

Koeneman, Quinn. Marching Out of Time. 2008. 122p. pap. 13.95 *(978-0-557-03075-0(7))* Lulu Enterprises Inc.

Kraus, J. d. & Kraus, J. D. The Aspie Teen's Survival Guide: Candid Advice for Teens, Tweens, Parents, & Educators, from a Young Man with Asperger's Syndrome. 2010. (ENG.). 214p. pap. 19.95 *(978-1-935274-16-2(3))* Future Horizons, Inc.

Krug, David. Young Adults with Asperger's: a Handbook for Parents, Teachers. 2006. (ENG.). 76p. per. 35.95 *(978-1-4327-0157-4(6))* Outskirts Pr., Inc.

Lawrence, Clare. How to Make School Make Sense: A Parents' Guide to Helping the Child with Asperger Syndrome. 2008. (ENG.). 128p. pap. *(978-1-84310-664-7(7))* Kingsley, Jessica Ltd.

—Successful School Change & Transition for the Child with Asperger Syndrome: A Parents' Guide to Smooth School Transition for the Child with Asperger Syndrome. 2010. (ENG.). 160p. pap. *(978-1-84905-052-4(X))* Kingsley, Jessica Ltd.

Lawton, Suzanne C. Asperger Syndrome: Natural Steps Toward a Better Life. 2007. (Complementary & Alternative Medicine Ser.). 200p. 44.95 *(978-0-275-99178-4(4)*, C9178, Praeger Pubs.) Greenwood Publishing Group, Inc.

LaZebnik, Claire & Koegel, Lynn Kern. Growing up on the Spectrum: A Guide to Life, Love, & Learning for Teens & Young Adults with Autism & Asperger's. 2010. (ENG.). 400p. (gr. 12-18). 16.00 *(978-0-14-311666-0(5)*, Penguin (Non-Classics)) Penguin Group (USA) Inc.

Lesko, Anita A. Asperger's Syndrome: When Life Hands You Lemons, Make Lemonade. 2011. 204p. pap. 24.95 ***(978-1-4620-3052-1(1))*** iUniverse, Inc.

Lester, Barbara R. My Parent has an Autism Spectrum Disorder: A Workbook for Children & Teens. 2011. (ENG.). 128p. pap. ***(978-1-84905-835-3(0))*** Kingsley, Jessica Ltd.

Levine, Karen & Chedd, Naomi. Replays: Using Play to Enhance Emotional & Behavioral Development for Children with Autism Spectrum Disorders. 2006. (ENG., Illus.). 16p. per. *(978-1-84310-832-0(1))* Kingsley, Jessica Ltd.

Likens, Aaron. Finding Kansas: Living & Decoding Asperger's Syndrome. 2012. (ENG.). 240p. (gr. 12). 16.00 ***(978-0-399-53733-2(3)***, Perigee Trade) Penguin Group (USA) Inc.

Lucan, Dawn. Practical Asperger Syndrome Manual. 2010. 80p. pap. 16.95 *(978-0-557-72875-6(4))* Lulu Enterprises Inc.

Lynch, Jack. I Am Not a MacHine Book III: Rethinking Cognitive Psychology. 2007. 300p. per. 16.95 *(978-1-59330-482-9(X))* Aventine Pr.

Lynn, George T. The Asperger Plus Child: How to Identify & Help Children with Asperger Syndrome & Seven Common Co-Existing Conditions. 2007. 280p. per. 29.95 *(978-1-931282-33-8(1))* Autism Asperger Publishing Co.

Lynn, J. A Worst Case Scenario: Art, Death, & Asperger's. 2009. 368p. 34.95 *(978-1-4401-5779-0(0))*; pap. 24.95 *(978-1-4401-5777-6(4))* iUniverse, Inc.

MacBroom, Helen. Derek: Dublin's Gentle Giant. 2008. (Illus.). 80p. per. *(978-1-84748-251-8(1))* Athena Pr.

Marlin, Brigid. A Meaning for Danny. 2012. 286p. pap. 15.95 ***(978-0-7414-6692-1(9))*** Infinity Publishing.

Marshack, Kathy J. Life with a Partner or Spouse with Asperger Syndrome: Going over the Edge? Practical Steps to Saving You & Your Relationship. 2009. pap. 21.95 *(978-1-934575-47-5(X))* Autism Asperger Publishing Co.

Martin, Rosemary. Top Tips for Asperger Students: How to Get the Most Out of University & College. 2010. (ENG., Illus.). 144p. pap. *(978-1-84905-140-8(2))* Kingsley, Jessica Ltd.

McManmon, Michael P. Made for Good Purpose: What Every Parent Needs to Know to Help Their Adolescent with Asperger's, High Functioning Autism or a Learning Difference Become an Independent Adult. 2012. (ENG., Illus.). 240p. pap. ***(978-1-84905-863-6(6))*** Kingsley, Jessica Ltd.

Mitchell, Chris. Asperger's Syndrome & Mindfulness: Taking Refuge in the Buddha. 2008. (ENG.). 144p. pap. *(978-1-84310-686-9(8))* Kingsley, Jessica Ltd.

Moreno, Susan, et al. The Partner's Guide to Asperger Syndrome. 2011. (ENG.). 240p. pap. ***(978-1-84905-878-0(4))*** Kingsley, Jessica Ltd.

Moyer, Sherry. The ECLIPSE Model: Teaching Self-Regulation, Executive Function, Attribution, & Sensory Awareness to Students with Asperger Syndrome, High Functioning Autism, & Related Disorders. 2009. (Illus.). 290p. (C). pap. 24.95 *(978-1-934575-37-6(2))* Autism Asperger Publishing Co.

Muggleton, Joshua. Raising Martians - From Crash-Landing to Leaving Home: How to Help a Child with Asperger Syndrome or High-Functioning Autism. 2012. (ENG.). 240p. pap. ***(978-1-84905-002-9(3))*** Kingsley, Jessica Ltd.

Musarra, Nancy & Ford, Rodney. Working Memory & Individuals with Asperger's Disorder: A Comparison Between the Working Memory Capacity of Typical Boys & Boys Who Meet Criteria for Asperger's Disorder 2008. 132p. pap. *(978-3-639-08374-3(1))* VDM Verlag Dr. Mueller e.K.

Myers, Jennifer McIlwee. How to Teach Life Skills to Kids with Autism or Asperger's. 2010. (ENG.). 322p. pap. 19.95 *(978-1-935274-13-1(9))* Future Horizons, Inc.

Nembhard, Kynda. Robots & Rainbows: Our Story of Asperger's Syndrome. 2009. 188p. pap. 17.50 *(978-1-4389-3374-0(6))* AuthorHouse.

Norall, Cynthia La Brie & Brust, Beth Wagner. Quirky, Yes - Hopeless, No: Practical Tips to Help Your Child with Asperger's Syndrome Be More Socially

Accepted. 2009. (ENG.). 384p. pap. 16.99 *(978-0-312-55849-9(X)*, St. Martin's Griffin) St. Martin's Pr.

Notbohm, Ellen & Zysk, Veronica. 1001 Great Ideas for Teaching & Raising Children with Autism Spectrum Disorders, 2nd Edition. 2nd rev. ed. 2010. (ENG.). 320p. pap. 24.95 *(978-1-935274-06-3(6))* Future Horizons, Inc.

Ortiz, John M. The Myriad Gifts of Asperger's Syndrome. 2008. (ENG.). 144p. pap. *(978-1-84310-883-2(6))* Kingsley, Jessica Ltd.

Osborne, Lawrence. American Normal: The Hidden World of Asperger Syndrome. 2010. (ENG.). xvi, 224p. pap. 27.50 *(978-1-4419-2946-4(0)*, 1441929460) Springer.

O'Toole, Jennifer Cook. Asperkids: An Insider's Guide to Loving, Understanding, & Teaching Children with Asperger Syndrome. 2012. (ENG., Illus.). 192p. pap. ***(978-1-84905-902-2(0))*** Kingsley, Jessica Ltd.

Ottinger, Becky, ed. Tictionary. (Illus.). 260p. pap. 29.95 *(978-1-931282-16-1(1))* Autism Asperger Publishing Co.

Page, Tim. Parallel Play: Growing up with Undiagnosed Asperger's. 2010. (Illus.). 208p. pap. 15.00 *(978-0-7679-2969-1(1)*, Anchor) Knopf Doubleday Publishing Group.

Paradiz, Valerie. Elijah's Cup: A Family's Journey into the Community & Culture of High-Functioning Autism & Asperger's Syndrome. 2007. (ENG.). 256p. pap. 17.95 *(978-1-4165-6776-9(3)*, Free Pr.) Free Pr.

Paradiz, Valerie, et al. * Lesson Plan a la Carte¿: Integrated Planning for Students with Special Needs. 2011. 91p. pap. 21.95 ***(978-1-934575-92-5(5))*** Autism Asperger Publishing Co.

Patrick, Nancy J. Social Skills for Teenagers & Adults with Asperger's Syndrome: A Practical Guide to Day-to-Day Life. 2008. (ENG.). 208p. pap. *(978-1-84310-876-4(3))* Kingsley, Jessica Ltd.

Phillips-Goodnight, Dee. My Silent Scream: Finding Hope & Grace to Endure: Inside a Mother's Struggle to Raise a Child with OCD, ADHD, & Asperger's Syndrome. 2011. (ENG., Illus.). 148p. pap. 10.99 ***(978-0-936314-54-6(1))*** Word & Spirit Resources, LLC.

Rathwell, Richard. Quicker & Deader. 2011. 173p. pap. 16.50 ***(978-1-889960-23-4(3))*** First Intensity Pr.

Rausch, Jeffrey L., et al, eds. Asperger's Disorder. 2008. (Medical Psychiatry Ser.: Vol. 40). (ENG., Illus.). 400p. 200.00 *(978-0-8493-8360-1(9)*, Informa Healthcare) Taylor & Francis Group GBR. Dist: Taylor & Francis Group.

Robison, John Elder. Be Different: Adventures of a Free-Range Aspergian with Practical Advice for Aspergians, Misfits, Families & Teachers. 2011. (ENG.). 304p. 24.00 *(978-0-307-88481-7(3)*, Crown) Crown Publishing Group.

—Be Different: My Adventures with Asperger's & My Advice for Fellow Aspergians, Misfits, Families, & Teachers. 2012. (ENG.). 304p. pap. 14.00 ***(978-0-307-88482-4(1))*** Broadway Bks.

Robison, John Elder. Look Me in the Eye: My Life with Asperger's. (ENG.). 2008. 320p. pap. 14.95 *(978-0-307-39618-1(5)*, Three Rivers Pr.) 2007. 304p. 25.95 *(978-0-307-39598-6(7)*, Crown) Crown Publishing Group.

—Look Me in the Eye: My Life with Asperger's. l.t. ed. 2007. (Thorndike Biography Ser.). 461p. 31.95 *(978-1-4104-0306-3(8))* Thorndike Pr.

Romanowski, Patricia. The Parents' Guide to Teaching Kids with Asperger Syndrome & Similar ASDs Real-Life Skills for Independence. 2011. (ENG., Illus.). 400p. pap. 16.00 *(978-0-307-58895-1(5)*, Three Rivers Pr.) Crown Publishing Group.

Rubinyi, Susan. Natural Genius: The Gift of Aspreger's Syndrome. 2007. (ENG.). 12p. per. *(978-1-84310-784-2(8))* Kingsley, Jessica Ltd.

Rubio, Ron. Mind/Body Techniques for Asperger's Syndrome: The Way of the Pathfinder. 2008. (ENG., Illus.). 152p. pap. *(978-1-84310-875-7(5))* Kingsley, Jessica Ltd.

Sainsbury, Clare. Martian in the Playground: Understanding the Schoolchild with Asperger's Syndrome. 2009. (Lucky Duck Bks.). 144p. pap. 34.00 *(978-1-84920-000-4(9)*, B00004P) SAGE Pubns., Ltd. GBR. Dist: SAGE Pubns., Inc.

Santomauro, Josie. Autism All-Stars: How We Use Our Autism & Asperger Traits to Shine in Life. Santomauro, Josie, ed. 2012. (ENG., Illus.). 192p. pap. ***(978-1-84310-188-8(2))*** Kingsley, Jessica Ltd.

Saperstein, Jesse A. Atypical: Life with Asperger's in 20 1/3 Chapters. 2010. (ENG.). 240p. (gr. 12-18). 14.00 *(978-0-399-53572-7(1)*, Perigee Trade) Penguin Group (USA) Inc.

Schilling, Shonda & Schilling, Curt. The Best Kind of Different: Our Family's Journey with Asperger's Syndrome. 2011. (ENG.). 256p. pap. 14.99 *(978-0-06-198684-0(4)*, Harper Paperbacks) 2010. 240p. 25.99 *(978-0-06-198683-3(6)*, Morrow, William & Co.) HarperCollins Pubs.

Schneider, Cindy B. Acting Antics: A Theatrical Approach to Teaching Social Understanding to Kids & Teens with Asperger Syndrome. 2007. (ENG., Illus.). 224p. per. *(978-1-84310-845-0(3))* Kingsley, Jessica Ltd.

Schultz, Tori. Zach & Asperger Syndrome: A Sister's View of Her Brother. 2011. 20p. (gr. 1-2). pap. 13.00 ***(978-1-4567-5044-2(5))*** AuthorHouse.

Seach, Diana. Interactive Play & Creative Activities for Children with Autism. 2015. (ENG.). 112p. pap. 35.95 *(978-0-415-48154-0(6))* Routledge.

Shapiro, Bruce K. & Accardo, Pasquale J., eds. Autism Frontiers: Clinical Issues & Innovations. 2008. (Illus.). 256p. 49.95 *(978-1-55766-957-5(0))* Brookes, Paul H. Publishing Co.

Shepherd, Neil. Wired up Right - Further Adventures with Asperger Syndrome. 2010. 196p. pap. 25.50 *(978-1-4452-6150-8(2))* Lulu Enterprises Inc.

Sicile-Kira, Chantal. What Is Autism? Understanding Life with Autism or Asperger's. rev. ed. 2012. (ENG.). 174p. pap. 14.95 ***(978-1-59652-842-0(7))*** Turner Publishing Co.

Sicile-Kira, Chantal. 41 Things to Know about Autism. 2010. (Good Things to Know Ser.). (ENG.). 211p. pap. 9.99 *(978-1-59652-583-2(5))* Turner Publishing Co.

Silverman, Stephan M. & Weinfeld, Rich. School Success for Children with Asperger's Syndrome. 2007. (ENG.). 229p. pap. 16.95 *(978-1-59363-215-1(0))* Prufrock Pr.

Simone, Rudy. Asperger's on the Job: Must-have Advice for People with Asperger's or High Functioning Autism, & their Employers, Educators, & Advocates. 2010. 200p. pap. 19.95 *(978-1-935274-09-4(0))* Future Horizons, Inc.

—Aspergirls: Empowering Females with Asperger Syndrome. 2010. 240p. pap. 18.95 *(978-1-84905-826-1(1))* Kingsley, Jessica Ltd GBR. Dist: Books International, Inc.

—22 Things a Woman Must Know If She Loves a Man with Asperger's Syndrome. 2009. (Illus.). 112p. pap. *(978-1-84905-803-2(2))* Kingsley, Jessica Ltd.

Simone, Rudy. 22 Things a Woman with Asperger's Syndrome Wants Her Partner to Know. 2012. (ENG., Illus.). 144p. pap. ***(978-1-84905-883-4(0))*** Kingsley, Jessica Ltd.

Simpson, Richard L. & Myles, Brenda Smith. Asperger Syndrome & Higher Functioning Autism Spectrum Disorders: A Guide for Effective Practice. 3rd ed. 2010. (Illus.). viii, 279p. 38.00 *(978-1-4164-0489-7(9))* PRO-ED, Inc.

Smith, John E., et al. Create a Reward Plan for Your Child with Asperger Syndrome. 2008. (ENG., Illus.). 96p. per. *(978-1-84310-622-7(1))* Kingsley, Jessica Ltd.

Sofronoff. Making Babies the Hard Way: Living with Infertility & Treatment. 2007. (ENG.). 192p. pap. *(978-1-84310-311-0(7))* Kingsley, Jessica Ltd.

Stanford, Ashley. Business for Aspies: 42 Best Uses of Asperger Syndrome Traits in the Workplace. 2011. (ENG.). 240p. pap. *(978-1-84905-845-2(8))* Kingsley, Jessica Ltd.

Stewart, Kathryn. Helping a Child with Nonverbal Learning Disorder or Asperger's Disorder: A Parent's Guide. 2nd rev. ed. 2007. (ENG., Illus.). 256p. per. 18.95 *(978-1-57224-526-6(3))* New Harbinger Pubns.

Stillman, William. The Everything Parent's Guide to Children with Asperger's Syndrome: The sound advice & reliable answers you need to help your child Succeed. 2nd ed. 2010. (ENG.). 320p. pap. 14.95 *(978-1-4405-0354-8(X))* Adams Media Corp.

Stillman, William. When Your Child Has ... Asperger's Syndrome: Get the Right Diagnosis - Understand Treatment Options - Help Your Child Cope. 2008. (ENG.). 224p. pap. 6.95 *(978-1-59869-667-7(X))* Adams Media Corp.

Stoddart, Kevin, et al. Asperger Syndrome in Adulthood: A Comprehensive Guide for Clinicans. 2012. (ENG.). 352p. 32.00 *(978-0-393-70550-8(1)*, 70550) Norton, W. W. & Co., Inc.

Stuart-Hamilton, Ian. An Asperger Dictionary of Everyday Expressions. 2nd ed. 2007. (ENG.). 256p. per. *(978-1-84310-518-3(7))* Kingsley, Jessica Ltd.

Summers, Sophia. Asperger's-If You Only Knew: A Family's Struggle with Asperger's Syndrome. 2007. 152p. per. 14.95 *(978-0-595-44932-3(8))* iUniverse, Inc.

Swavely, Terri. Move, Move, Move: Alex's Story! 2009. 24p. pap. 14.95 *(978-1-4389-8070-6(1))* AuthorHouse.

Tantam, Digby. Can the World Afford Autistic Spectrum Disorder? Nonverbal Communication, Asperger Syndrome & the Interbrain. 2009. (ENG., Illus.). 256p. *(978-1-84310-694-4(9))* Kingsley, Jessica Ltd.

Thompson, Barrie. Counseling for Asperger Couples. 2008. (ENG., Illus.). 144p. pap. *(978-1-84310-544-2(6))* Kingsley, Jessica Ltd.

Tickle, Anna & Stott, Bettina. Exploring Bullying with Adults with Autism & Asperger Syndrome: A Photocopiable Workbook. 2010. (ENG., Illus.). 320p. pap. *(978-1-84905-035-7(X))* Kingsley, Jessica Ltd.

Tinsley, Matthew & Hendrickx, Sarah. Asperger Syndrome & Alcohol: Drinking to Cope? 2008. (ENG.). 160p. pap. *(978-1-84310-609-8(4))* Kingsley, Jessica Ltd.

Tubbs, Janet. Creative Therapy for Children with Autism, Add, & Asperger's: Using Artistic Creativity to Reach, Teach, & Touch Our Children. 2008. (ENG.). 224p. pap. 18.95 *(978-0-7570-0300-4(1))* Square One Pubs.

Uhlenkamp, Jeannie. The Guide to Dating for Teenagers with Asperger Syndrome. 2009. (Illus.). xii, 129p. (YA). pap. 19.95 *(978-1-934575-53-6(4))* Autism Asperger Publishing Co.

Van Der Post, Anna. Children & Teenagers with Aspergers. 2009. 356p. pap. *(978-1-84747-904-4(9))* Chipmunkapublishing.

Verbout, Scott. An Asperger Journey: My Lifelong Battle with Autism. 2011. 76p. pap. 10.95 *(978-1-4502-9535-2(5))* iUniverse, Inc.

Wagner, Sheila. Inclusive Programming for High School Students with Autism or Asperger's Syndrome: A Guide for Parents & Teachers. 2009. (ENG., Illus.). 392p. pap. 24.95 *(978-1-932565-57-7(4))* Future Horizons, Inc.

Wahlberg, Timothy. Finding the Gray: The Black & White World of Asperger's & Autism. 2010. pap. 19.95 *(978-0-615-35704-1(0))* Wahlberg & Assocs.

Walker, Antoinette & Fitzgerald, Michael. Unstoppable Brilliance: Irish Geniuses & Asperger's Syndrome. (ENG.). 336p. 2008. pap. 31.95 *(978-1-905483-28-0(7))* 2006. 45.95 *(978-1-905483-03-7(1))* Liberties Pr. IRL. Dist: Dufour Editions, Inc.

Weiss, Mary Jane. Practical Solutions for Educating Young Children with High Functioning Autism & Asperger Syndrome. 2007. (Illus.). 242p. pap. 21.95 *(978-1-934575-14-7(3))* Autism Asperger Publishing Co.

West, Bryan. Aspergers, God & Me. 2008. 136p. pap. 18.49 *(978-1-4092-4394-6(X))* Lulu Enterprises Inc.

—Asperger's, God & Me (Australian Edition) 2008. 136p. pap. 18.44 *(978-1-4092-4709-8(0))* Lulu Enterprises Inc.

Weston, Louise. Connecting with Your Asperger Partner: Negotiating the Maze of Intimacy 2010. (Illus.). 208p. pap. *(978-1-84905-130-9(5))* Kingsley, Jessica Ltd.

White, Susan Williams. Social Skills Training for Children with Asperger Syndrome & High-Functioning Autism. 2011. (Practitioner Guides in Child Psychotherapy Ser.). (ENG., Illus.). 182p. 30.00 *(978-1-60918-209-0(X))* Guilford Pubns., Inc.

Willey, Liane Holliday. Safety Skills for Asperger Women: How to Save a Perfectly Good Female Life. 2011. 160p. pap. *(978-1-84905-836-0(9))* Kingsley, Jessica Ltd.

Wolf, Lorraine E., et al. Students with Asperger Syndrome: A Guide for College Personnel. 2009. (Illus.). xiv, 337p. pap. *(978-1-934575-39-0(9))* Autism Asperger Publishing Co.

Worton, Dean & Edmonds, Genevieve. The Asperger Personal Guide: Raising Self-Esteem & Making the Most of Yourself As an Adult with Asperger's Syndrome. 2006. (Lucky Duck Bks.). 128p. per. 31.00 *(978-1-4129-2257-9(7)*, B22577P) SAGE Pubns., Ltd. GBR. Dist: SAGE Pubns., Inc.

Yoshida, Yuko. Raising Children with Asperger's Syndrome & High-Functioning Autism: Championing the Individual. Sanders, Esther & Hirano, Cathy, trs. from JPN. 2012. (ENG., Illus.). 256p. pap. ***(978-1-84905-317-4(0))*** Kingsley, Jessica Ltd.

Young, Ronnie. Asperger Syndrome Pocketbook. 2008. (Illus.). 128p. pap. *(978-1-903776-99-5(6)*, Teachers' Pocketbooks) Management Pocketbooks GBR. Dist: Ware-Pak, Inc.

ASPHYXIA

see also Anoxemia; Artificial Respiration; Drowning; Gases, Asphyxiating and Poisonous

Elsner, Robert & Gooden, Brett. Diving & Asphyxia: A Comparative Study of Animals & Man. 2009. (Monographs of the Physiological Society Ser.). (ENG.). 180p. pap. 29.99 *(978-0-521-11289-5(3))* Cambridge Univ. Pr.

Laoutaris, Joanne. Olive Branch. 2011. 84p. pap. 12.10 ***(978-1-4567-7551-3(0))*** AuthorHouse.

ASPHYXIATING GASES

see Gases, Asphyxiating and Poisonous

ASPIRATION LEVEL

see Level of Aspiration

ASPIRATIONS, VOCATIONAL

see Vocational Interests

ASPIRIN

Demir, Dilan M. Aspirin: Therapeutic Uses, Adverse Effects & Pharmacokinetics. 2011. (Pharmacology - Research, Safety Testing & Regulation Ser.). (Illus.). 228p. 95.00 *(978-1-61324-578-1(5))* Nova Science Pubs., Inc.

Keith, Souter. An Aspirin A Day. 2012. (ENG., Illus.). 224p. pap. 12.95 ***(978-1-84317-632-9(7))*** O'Mara, Michael Bks., Ltd. GBR. Dist: Independent Pubs. Group.

Millwood, Charles L. New Research on Aspirin & Health. 2006. (Nova Biomedical Ser.). (Illus.). 263p. 89.00 *(978-1-60021-244-4(1)*, Nova Biomedica Bks.) Nova Science Pubs., Inc.

Quinn, Paul . Aspirin & Health Research Progress. 2008. (C). 129.00 *(978-1-60456-164-7(5))* Nova Science Pubs., Inc.

Schrör, Karsten. Acetylsalicylic Acid. 2009. (ENG., Illus.). 390p. 99.95 *(978-3-527-32109-4(8)*, Wiley-VCH) Wiley, John & Sons, Inc.

ASQUITH, H. H. (HERBERT HENRY), 1852-1928

Bates, Stephen. H H Asquith. 2006. (British Prime Ministers of the 20th Century Ser.). (ENG., Illus.). 176p. pap. 16.95 *(978-1-904950-57-8(4))* Haus Publishing GBR. Dist: Consortium Bk. Sales & Distribution.

Neate, Bobbie. Conspiracy of Secrets. 2012. (ENG., Illus.). 356p. 27.95 ***(978-1-84353-372-1(0))*** Blake, John Publishing, Ltd. GBR. Dist: Independent Pubs. Group.

ASQUITH, MARGOT, 1864-1945

Asquith, Margot. The Autobiography of Margot Asquith. (Best Sellers of 1921 Ser.). reprint ed. lib. bdg. 48.00 *(978-0-7426-1360-7(7))* Classic Bks.

—Margot Asquith Vols. 1-2: An Autobiography. l.t. ed. 2006. 284p. pap. 23.99 *(978-1-4264-1472-5(2))* BiblioBazaar.

—Margot Asquith an Autobiography. 2008. 288p. 28.99 *(978-0-554-22006-2(7))*; 25.99 *(978-0-554-31309-2(X))* BiblioBazaar.

—Margot Asquith, an Autobiography. 2009. 308p. 25.99 *(978-1-103-92012-9(X))* 2009. 308p. pap. 19.99 *(978-1-103-92006-8(5))* Vol. 2 in 1. 2006. (ENG.). 292p. pap. 21.99 *(978-1-4264-1456-5(0))* BiblioBazaar.

ASSAD, HAFEZ AL, 1928-2000

Dam, Nikolaos van. The Struggle for Power in Syria: Politics & Society under Asad & the Ba'th Party. 4th rev. ed. 2011. (ENG., Illus.). 288p. pap. 25.00 *(978-1-84885-760-5(8))* I. B. Tauris & Co., Ltd. GBR. Dist: Macmillan.

ASSAM (INDIA)

Barman, Prateeti. Changing Perception of Freedom: Civil Society & Its Response to United Liberation Front of Asom. 2010. (Illus.). xii, 127p. *(978-81-8370-244-7(9)*, Library of Congress — New Delhi Overseas Office) Akansha Publishing House.

Bhuyan, Suryya K. Anglo-Assamese Relations: Seventeen Seventy-One to Eighteen Twenty-Six. reprint ed. 46.00 *(978-0-404-16795-0(0))* AMS Pr., Inc.

Bhuyan, Suryya Kumar & Buragohain, Romesh. Copper-Plate & Stone Inscriptions of Ancient & Medieval Assam. 2010. 84p. *(978-81-85921-68-6(7))* LBS Pubns.

Borgohain, Parijat. Managing Home & Work: Role of Dual Career Couples in Guwahati City. 2010. 296p. pap. *(978-3-8383-7799-5(0))* Lambert Academic Publishing.

Borgohain, Parijat. Socio-Economic Disparities in Guwahati City, Indi. 2011. 128p. pap. ***(978-3-8454-0732-6(8))*** Lambert Academic Publishing.

Butler, John. Travels & Adventures in the Province of Assam: During A Residence of Fourteen Years (1855) 2008. 292p. 43.95 *(978-1-4374-3524-5(6))*; pap. 28.95 *(978-1-4373-5598-7(6))* Kessinger Publishing, LLC.

Graham, Ralph & Bean, Robert. Rhino! Rhino! 2011. 24p. 35.95 ***(978-1-258-03769-7(6))*** Literary Licensing, LLC.

Kakati, Kashmira. Impact of Forest Fragmentation on the Hoolock Gibbon in Assam, Indi. 2010. 240p. pap. *(978-3-8383-7897-8(0))* Lambert Academic Publishing.

Rabha, Bipul Kumar. Community Based Forest Management in Assam. 2010. 96p. pap. *(978-3-639-26625-2(0))* VDM Verlag Dr. Mueller e.K.

Sharma, Jayeeta. Empire's Garden: Assam & the Making of India. 2011. (Radical Perspectives Ser.). (ENG., Illus.). 344p. 94.95 *(978-0-8223-5032-3(7))* Duke Univ. Pr.

Sharma, Jayeeta, et al. Empire's Garden: Assam & the Making of India. 2011. (Radical Perspectives Ser.). (ENG., Illus.). 344p. pap. 25.95 *(978-0-8223-5049-1(1))* Duke Univ. Pr.

ASSAMESE LANGUAGE

Baruah, Manjeet. Frontier Cultures. 2012. (ENG.). 220p. (C). 95.00 ***(978-0-415-50080-7(X)***, Routledge India) Taylor & Francis Group GBR. Dist: Taylor & Francis Group.

Bronson, Miles. A Dictionary in Assamese & English. 2009. (ASM & ENG.). 624p. pap. 44.75 *(978-1-113-68341-0(4))* BiblioBazaar.

Euro Talk. Talk Now! Assamese. 2008. 29.99 *(978-1-84352-353-6(1))* TOPICS Entertainment.

Haddad, Youssef A. Control into Conjunctive Participle Clauses: The Case of Assamese. 2011. (Trends in Linguistics. Studies & Monographs [TiLSM] Ser.). (ENG., Illus.). XII, 226p. 210.00 ***(978-3-11-218799-9(7))***; 140.00 ***(978-3-11-023824-2(1))*** De Gruyter, Mouton DEU. Dist: de Gruyter, Walter GmbH & Co. KG.

ASSAMESE LITERATURE—HISTORY AND CRITICISM

Baruah, Manjeet. Frontier Cultures. 2012. (ENG.). 220p. (C). 95.00 ***(978-0-415-50080-7(X)***, Routledge India) Taylor & Francis Group GBR. Dist: Taylor & Francis Group.

ASSANGE, JULIAN, 1971-

Ball, James & Beckett, Charlie. WikiLeaks: News in the Networked Era. 2012. (ENG.). 180p. pap. 19.95 ***(978-0-7456-5976-3(4))*** Polity Pr. GBR. Dist: Wiley, John & Sons, Inc.

Domscheit-Berg, Daniel. Inside WikiLeaks: My Time with Julian Assange at the World's Most Dangerous Website. 2011. (ENG.). 304p. 23.00 *(978-0-307-95191-5(X)*, Crown) Crown Publishing Group.

Fowler, Andrew. The Most Dangerous Man in the World: A Definitive Account of Julian Assange & WikiLeaks. 2011. (ENG.). 288p. 24.95 *(978-1-61608-489-9(8)*, 608489) Skyhorse Publishing Co., Inc.

Leigh, David, et al. WikiLeaks: Inside Julian Assange's War on Secrecy. 2011. (ENG., Illus.). 352p. pap. 15.99 *(978-1-61039-061-3(X))* PublicAffairs.

Qin, Yue. Weiji Jie Mi Dang An: Chong Xin Ren Shi Zhongguo Jue Ce Zhe. 2011. (CHI., Illus.) 518p. ***(978-1-935981-11-4(0))*** Mirror Bks. USA.

Rademecker, Sophie & Guichaoua, Valerie. Julian Assange - WikiLeaks: Warrior for Truth. 2011. 400p. 24.95 *(978-1-926893-55-6(7))* Cogito Media Grp. CAN. Dist: Midpoint Trade Bks., Inc.

ASSASSINATION

see also Murder; Terrorism

Bellany, Alastair & Cogswell, Tom. England's Assassin: John Felton & the Killing of the Duke of Buckingham. 2007. (ENG., Illus.). 336p. 35.00 *(978-0-300-11849-0(X))* Yale Univ. Pr.

Bellfield, Richard. A Brief History of Hitmen & Assassinations. 2011. (ENG.). 420p. pap. 13.95 *(978-0-7624-4100-6(3))* Running Pr. Bk. Pubs.

Blanford, Nicholas. Killing Mr. Lebanon: The Assassination of Rafik Hariri & Its Impact on the Middle East. (ENG., Illus.). 2008. 248p. pap. 16.95 *(978-1-84511-854-9(5))* 2006. 256p. 29.95 *(978-1-84511-202-8(4))* I. B. Tauris & Co., Ltd. GBR. Dist: Macmillan.

Borgonovo, John & O'Halpin, Eunan. Spies, Informers & the 'Anti-Sinn Fein Society' The Intelligence War in Cork City, 1919-1921. 2007. 198p. (C). 75.00 *(978-0-7165-2832-6(0))* Irish Academic Pr. IRL. Dist: International Specialized Bk. Services.

Boudjedra, Rachid. Lettres Algériennes. (FRE.). 205p. *(978-2-246-49091-3(X))* Grasset et Fasquello.

Clarke, James W. Defining Danger: American Assassins & the New Domestic Terrorists. 2012. (ENG.). 456p. pap. 34.95 ***(978-1-4128-4590-8(4))*** Transaction Pubs.

Davies, Nicholas. Diana the Killing of a Princess. 2006. 291p. pap. *(978-1-905621-48-4(5))* Pen Pr. Pubs., Ltd.

Diebel, Linda. Betrayed: The Assassination of Digna Ochoa. 2007. (ENG., Illus.). 512p. per. 17.95 *(978-0-7867-1876-4(5))* Basic Bks.

Donnelley, Paul. Assassins & Assassinations. 2008. (ENG., Illus.). 192p. 24.95 *(978-1-84537-940-7(3))* New Holland Pubs., Ltd. GBR. Dist: National Bk. Network.

Dutta. Political Assassinations & International Politics. 2008. (Cass Series on Political Violence Ser.). 208p. 130.00 *(978-0-415-41800-3(3))* Routledge.

Establishing the House Democracy Assistance Commission for the 110th Congress; & Calling on the Government of the UK to Immediately Establish a

Full, Independent, & Public Judicial Inquiry into the Murder of Northern Ireland Defense Attorney Patrick Finucane in Order to Move Forward on the Northern Ireland Peace Process: Markup Before the Committee on Foreign Affairs, House of Representatives, One Hundred Tenth Congress, First Session, on H. Res. 24 & H. con. Res 20, January 23, 2007. 2007. iii, 20p. *(978-0-16-078672-3(X)*, 552-070-35902-8) United States Government Printing Office.

Eyerman, Ron. The Cultural Sociology of Political Assassination: From MLK & RFK to Fortuyn & van Gogh. 2011. (Cultural Sociology Ser.). (ENG., Illus.). 208p. 90.00 *(978-0-230-11822-5(4))*; pap. 32.00 *(978-0-230-11823-2(2))* Palgrave Macmillan.

Falk, Gerhard. An Encyclopedia of Assassinations & Terrorism in World History: Cases of Anarchism from Tutankamen to Wikileaks. 2011. 119.95 *(978-0-7734-1478-5(9))* Mellen, Edwin Pr., The.

Goldman, Francisco. Art of Political Murder: Who Killed the Bishop? 2008. (ENG.). 416p. pap. 15.00 *(978-0-8021-4385-3(7)*, Grove Pr.) Grove/Atlantic, Inc.

Greig, Charlotte. Cold Blooded Killings: Hits, Assassinations, & near Misses That Shook the World. 2009. (ENG.). 208p. 9.99 *(978-1-84193-405-1(4)*, 1841934054, Chartwell) Book Sales, Inc.

Haas, Jeffrey. The Assassination of Fred Hampton: How the FBI & the Chicago Police Murdered a Black Panther. 2011. (ENG.). 384p. pap. 16.95 *(978-1-56976-709-2(2))* 2009. (Illus.). 424p. 26.95 *(978-1-55652-765-4(9))* Chicago Review Pr., Inc. (Hill, Lawrence Bks.).

Hakakian, Roya. Assassins of the Turquoise Palace. 2011. (ENG.). 320p. 25.00 *(978-0-8021-1911-7(5)*, Grove Pr.) Grove/Atlantic, Inc.

Hernon, Ian. Assassin! 200 Years of British Political Murder. 2007. (ENG., Illus.). 266p. per. 29.00 *(978-0-7453-2715-0(X))*; 272p. 84.00 *(978-0-7453-2716-7(8))* Pluto Pr. GBR. Dist: Macmillan.

Hudson, Miles. Assassination. 2011. (Illus.). 208p. 39.95 *(978-1-84884-363-9(1))* Pen & Sword Bks. Ltd. GBR. Dist: Casemate Pubs. & Bk. Distributors, LLC.

Jardine, Lisa. The Awful End of Prince William the Silent: The First Assassination of a Head of State with a Handgun. 2007. (Making History Ser.). (Illus.). 176p. per. 12.99 *(978-0-06-083836-2(1)*, HarperPerennial) HarperCollins Pubs.

Kennerk, Barry. Shadow of the Brotherhood: The Temple Bar Shootings. unabr. ed. 2011. (ENG., Illus.). 352p. pap. 23.95 *(978-1-85635-677-0(9))* Mercier Pr., Ltd., The IRL. Dist: Dufour Editions, Inc.

Kiefer, Michael. Democrat Down. 2008. 230p. pap. 21.95 *(978-1-4357-4514-8(0))* Lulu Enterprises Inc.

Larson, Kate Clifford. The Assassin's Accomplice: Mary Surratt & the Plot to Kill Abraham Lincoln. 2010. (ENG.). 288p. (gr. 9). pap. 16.95 *(978-0-465-01893-2(9))* Basic Bks.

Lenoe, Matthew E. The Kirov Murder & Soviet History. 2010. (Annals of Communism Ser.). (ENG., Illus.). 872p. 85.00 *(978-0-300-11236-8(X))* Yale Univ. Pr.

Levine, Steve & LeVine, Steve. Putin's Labyrinth: Spies, Murder, & the Dark Heart of the New Russia. 2009. (ENG., Illus.). 240p. 16.00 *(978-0-8129-7841-4(2)*, Random Hse. Trade Paperbacks) Random House Publishing Group.

McGovern, Glenn. Protective Operations: A Handbook for Security & Law Enforcement. 2011. (ENG., Illus.). 224p. 79.95 *(978-1-4398-5171-5(9)*, CRC Press) Taylor & Francis Group GBR. Dist: Taylor & Francis Group.

—Targeted Violence: A Statistical & Tactical Analysis of Assassinations, Contract Killings, & Kidnappings. 2010. (ENG., Illus.). 331p. 89.95 *(978-1-4398-2512-9(2)*, CRC Press) Taylor & Francis Group GBR. Dist: Taylor & Francis Group.

Melchionda, Achille. Piombo Contro la Giustizia: Mario Amato e I Magistrati Assassinati Dai Terroristi. 2010. (ITA.). 362p. *(978-88-8342-864-7(1))* Palandech Pubns. Group, Inc.

Melville, Lewis & Hargreaves, Reginald. Famous Duels & Assassinations. 320p. 2008. 45.95 *(978-1-4366-8477-4(3))* 2007. (ENG.). per. 30.95 *(978-1-4325-1417-4(2))* Kessinger Publishing, LLC.

Mirabal, Dede. Vivas en Su Jardin: La Verdadera Historial de las Hermanas Mirabal y Su Lucha por la Libertad. 2009. (Vintage Espanol Ser.). (SPA.). 368p. pap. 15.00 *(978-0-307-47453-7(4)*, Vintage) Knopf Doubleday Publishing Group.

Molony, Senan. The Phoenix Park Murders: Conspiracy, Betrayal & Retribution. 2006. (ENG., Illus.). 285p. pap. 20.95 *(978-1-85635-511-7(X))* Mercier Pr., Ltd., The IRL. Dist: Dufour Editions, Inc.

Newman, John. Oswald & the CIA: The Documented Truth about the Unknown Relationship Between the U. S. Government & the Alleged Killer of JFK. 2008. (ENG., Illus.). 680p. pap. 16.95 *(978-1-60239-253-3(6)*, 239253) Skyhorse Publishing Co., Inc.

Pace, Mary & Pecorelli, Mino. Mino Pecorelli: Il Delitto Irrisolto. 2009. (ITA.). 303p. *(978-88-95049-53-3(5))* Armando Curcio Editore spa.

Parissien, Steven. Assassinated! 50 Notorious Assassinations. 2009. (ENG.). 208p. 12.99 *(978-1-84724-190-0(5)*, 1847241905) Quercus GBR. Dist: Book Sales, Inc.

Porter, Lindsay. Assassination: A History of Political Murder. 2010. (ENG.). 192p. (gr. 12). 35.00 *(978-1-59020-348-4(8))* Overlook Pr., The.

Root, Neil. Who Killed Rosemary Nelson? 2011. (ENG., Illus.). 288p. pap. 23.95 *(978-1-84358-317-2(8))* Blake, John, Publishing, Ltd. GBR. Dist: Independent Pubs. Group.

Schmitt, Michael N. Essays on Law & War at the Fault Lines. 2011. (ENG., Illus.). xii, 637p. 239.00 *(978-90-6704-739-5(2)*, 9067047392) T.M.C. Asser Pr. NLD. Dist: Springer.

Schmitz-Elvenich, Heiko F. Targeted Killing: Die völkerrechtliche Zulässigkeit der gezielten Tötung von Terroristen im Ausland. 2008. (Kölner Schriften zu Recht und Staat Ser.). 298p. pap. 74.95 *(978-3-631-57646-5(3))* Lang, Peter GmbH, Europaischer Verlag der Wissenschaften DEU. Dist: Lang, Peter.

Sides, Hampton. Hellhound on His Trail: The Stalking of Martin Luther King, Jr. & the International Hunt for His Assassin. 2010. (ENG., Illus.). 480p. 28.95 *(978-0-385-52392-9(0)*, Doubleday) Knopf Doubleday Publishing Group.

—Hellhound on His Trail: The Stalking of Martin Luther King, Jr. & the International Hunt for His Assassin. l.t. ed. 2010. (ENG.). 720p. pap. 29.00 *(978-0-7393-7757-4(4))* Random Hse. Large Print.

Swanson, James L. Manhunt. 2011. 15.12 *(978-0-7848-3544-9(6)*, Everbind) Marco Bk. Co.

—Manhunt: The 12-Day Chase for Lincoln's Killer. 2007. (P. S. Ser.). (ENG., Illus.). 496p. pap. 15.99 *(978-0-06-051850-9(2)*, William Morrow Paperbacks) HarperCollins Pubs.

Time-Life Books Staff, contrib. by. Assasination. (Illus.). 192p. 20.00 *(978-1-84447-107-2(1))* Time Life Value GBR. Dist: Mercury Bks. Ltd.

Vasksberg, Arkadi. Toxic Politics: The Secret History of the Kremlin's Poison Laboratory - From the Special Cabinet to the Death of Litvinenko. 2011. 218p. 44.95 *(978-0-313-38746-3(X)*, A3176C, Praeger Pubs.) Greenwood Publishing Group, Inc.

Volodarsky, Boris. KGB's Poison Factory: From Lenin to Litvinenko. 2010. (ENG., Illus.). 256p. 25.00 *(978-0-7603-3753-0(5)*, 0760337535, Zenith Pr.) MBI Publishing Co. LLC.

Von Boeselager, Philip Freiherr. Valkyrie: The Story of the Plot to Kill Hitler, by Its Last Member. Rendall, Steven, tr. from FRE. 2010. (Vintage Ser.). (ENG., Illus.). 224p. pap. 15.00 *(978-0-307-45497-3(5)*, Vintage) Knopf Doubleday Publishing Group.

Waterkeyn, Xavier & Waterkeyn, Xavier. Assassination: Political Murder Through the Ages. 2007. (ENG., Illus.). 256p. pap. 14.95 *(978-1-74110-566-7(8))* New Holland Pubs. Pty, Ltd. AUS. Dist: Tuttle Publishing.

Wilcox, Robert. Target Patton: The Plot to Assassinate General George S. Patton. 2008. (ENG., Illus.). 444p. 27.95 *(978-1-59698-579-7(8))* Regnery Publishing, Inc., An Eagle Publishing Co.

Wilcox, Robert K. Target: Patton: The Plot to Assassinate General George S. Patton. 2010. (ENG.). 454p. pap. 18.95 *(978-1-59698-606-0(9))* Regnery Publishing, Inc., An Eagle Publishing Co.

Woolf, Greg. Et Tu, Brute? The Murder of Caesar & Political Assassination. 2007. (Profiles in History Ser.). (Illus.). 224p. 19.95 *(978-0-674-02684-1(5))* Harvard Univ. Pr.

ASSASSINS

Assassins: Vocal Selections. 2010. (ENG.). 88p. pap. 16.99 *(978-1-4234-7286-5(1)*, 1423472861) Leonard, Hal Corp.

Ayton, Mel. The Forgotten Terrorist: Sirhan Sirhan & the Assassination of Robert F. Kennedy. (Illus.). 356p. 2008. pap. 19.95 *(978-1-59797-080-8(8))* 2007. 29.95 *(978-1-59797-079-2(4))* Potomac Bks., Inc.

Baddeley, Gavin & Woods, Paul. God's Assassins: The Medieval Roots of Terrorism. 2009. (ENG., Illus.). 256p. pap. 24.95 *(978-0-7110-3409-9(5))* Allan, Ian Publishing GBR. Dist: BookMasters Distribution Services (BDS).

Bell, Graham. Murder, Inc: The Mafia's Hit Men in New York City. 2010. (True Crime Ser.). (ENG., Illus.). 128p. pap. 16.99 *(978-1-60949-135-2(1))* History Pr., The.

Bellany, Alastair & Cogswell, Tom. England's Assassin: John Felton & the Killing of the Duke of Buckingham. 2007. (ENG., Illus.). 336p. 35.00 *(978-0-300-11849-0(X))* Yale Univ. Pr.

Bowden, Charles & Molloy, Molly, eds. El Sicario: The Autobiography of a Mexican Assassin. 2011. (ENG.). 224p. (gr. 9). pap. 15.99 *(978-1-56858-658-8(2))* Basic Bks.

Chamlee, Roy Z. Lincoln's Assassins: A Complete Account of Their Capture, Trial, & Punishment, 2 vols. alt. ed. 2008. (ENG.). 634p. pap. 49.95 *(978-0-7864-4088-7(0))* McFarland & Co., Inc. Pubs.

Clarke, James W. Defining Danger: American Assassins & the New Domestic Terrorists. (ENG.). 2012. 456p. pap. 34.95 ***(978-1-4128-4590-8(4))*** 2006. 436p. (gr. 11). 39.95 *(978-0-7658-0341-2(0))* Transaction Pubs.

Fabijancic, Tony. Bosnia: In the Footsteps of Gavrilo Princip. 2010. (Wayfarer Ser.). (ENG., Illus.). 264p. pap. 29.95 *(978-0-88864-519-7(8))* Univ. of Alberta Pr. CAN. Dist: Michigan State Univ. Pr.

Fiennes, Ranulph. Killer Elite. 2011. 400p. mass mkt. 7.99 *(978-0-345-52808-7(5)*, Ballantine Bks.) Random House Publishing Group.

Flynn, Ray. Confessions of a Mob Hitman. 2009. 170p. pap. 24.95 *(978-1-60653-013-9(5))* High Hill Pr.

Greig, Charlotte. Cold Blooded Killings: Hits, Assassinations, & near Misses That Shook the World. 2009. (ENG.). 208p. 9.99 *(978-1-84193-405-1(4)*, 1841934054, Chartwell) Book Sales, Inc.

Hanrahan, David C. The Assassination of the Prime Minister: John Bellingham & the Murder of Spencer Perceval. 2008. (ENG., Illus.). 256p. 34.95 *(978-0-7509-4400-7(5))* History Pr. Ltd., The GBR. Dist: Independent Pubs. Group.

Hartranft, John F. The Lincoln Assassination Conspirators: Their Confinement & Execution, As Recorded in the Letterbook of John Frederick Hartranft. Steers, Edward, Jr. & Holzer, Harold, eds. 2009. 200p. 24.95 *(978-0-8071-3396-5(5))* Louisiana State Univ. Pr.

Holzer, Harold, et al, eds. The Lincoln Assassination: Crime & Punishment, Myth & Memory A Lincoln Forum Book. 2010. (North's Civil War Ser.). (ENG.). 256p. 29.00 *(978-0-8232-3226-0(3))* Fordham Univ. Pr.

Hunt, Jim & Risch, Bob. Cuba on My Mind. 2011. (ENG., Illus.). 336p. 25.99 *(978-0-7653-2863-2(1)*, Forge Bks.) Doherty, Tom Assocs., LLC.

Hunter, Stephen & Bainbridge, John, Jr. American Gunfight: The Plot to Kill President Truman - And the Shoot-Out That Stopped It. 2007. (ENG., Illus.). 384p. pap. 15.99 *(978-0-7432-6069-5(4))* Simon & Schuster.

Jampoler, Andrew. Last Lincoln Conspirator. 2009. (Illus.). 288p. pap. 18.95 *(978-1-59114-408-3(6))* Naval Institute Pr.

Jampoler, Andrew C. A. The Last Lincoln Conspirator: John Surratt's Flight from the Gallows. 2008. (Illus.). 288p. 29.95 *(978-1-59114-407-6(8))* Naval Institute Pr.

Marinovich, Greg & Silva, Joao. The Bang-Bang Club: Snapshots from a Hidden War. 2nd movie tie-in ed. 2011. (ENG., Illus.). 296p. (gr. 9). pap. 16.99 *(978-0-465-01978-6(1))* Basic Bks.

Moorhouse, Roger. Killing Hitler: The Plots, the Assassins, & the Dictator Who Cheated Death. 2007. (ENG., Illus.). 384p. pap. 16.00 *(978-0-553-38255-6(1)*, Bantam) Random House Publishing Group.

Oliver, Willard & Marion, Nancy. Killing the President: Assassinations, Attempts, & Rumored Attempts on U. S. Commanders-in-Chief, 1 vol. 2010. (Illus.). 235p. 44.95 *(978-0-313-36474-7(5)*, C36474, Praeger Pubs.) Greenwood Publishing Group, Inc.

Oliver, Willard M. & Marion, Nancy E. Assassinations, Attempts, & Rumored Attempts on U.S. Commanders-In-Chief. 2010. (Illus.). xiii, 235p. E-Book *(978-0-313-36475-4(3)*, Praeger Pubs.) Greenwood Publishing Group, Inc.

Parissien, Steven. Assassinated! 50 Notorious Assassinations. 2009. (ENG.). 208p. 12.99 *(978-1-84724-190-0(5)*, 1847241905) Quercus GBR. Dist: Book Sales, Inc.

Pitch, Anthony S. They Have Killed Papa Dead! The Road to Ford's Theatre, Abraham Lincoln's Murder, & the Rage for Vengeance. (ENG., Illus.). 2009. 560p. 19.99 *(978-1-58642-162-5(X))* 2008. 512p. 29.95 *(978-1-58642-158-8(1))* Steerforth Pr.

Spieler, Geri. Taking Aim at the President: The Remarkable Story of the Woman Who Shot at Gerald Ford. 2008. (ENG., Illus.). 256p. 24.95 *(978-0-230-61023-1(4))* Palgrave Macmillan.

Stonor Saunders, Frances. The Woman Who Shot Mussolini. 2010. (ENG., Illus.). 400p. 30.00 *(978-0-8050-9121-2(1)*, Metropolitan Bks.) Holt, Henry & Co.

Thallon, Wayne. Devil Incarnate: A Depraved Mercenary's Lifelong Swathe of Destruction. 2007. (ENG., Illus.). 336p. per. 19.95 *(978-1-84596-206-7(0))* Mainstream Publishing Co., Ltd. GBR. Dist: Independent Pubs. Group.

Time-Life Books Staff, contrib. by. Assasination. (Illus.). 192p. 20.00 *(978-1-84447-107-2(1))* Time Life Value GBR. Dist: Mercury Bks. Ltd.

Titone, Nora. My Thoughts Be Bloody: The Bitter Rivalry That Led to the Assassination of Abraham Lincoln. 2011. (ENG.). 496p. pap. 16.00 *(978-1-4165-8606-7(7)*, Free Pr.) Free Pr.

Townsend, George Alfred. Life Crime & Capture of John Wilkes Bo. 2006. pap. *(978-1-4068-0987-9(X))* Echo Library.

—The Life, Crime & Capture of John Wilkes Booth. 2009. 140p. 21.99 *(978-0-559-09801-7(4))*; 24.99 *(978-0-559-09787-4(5))*; pap. 20.99 *(978-0-559-09792-8(1))*; pap. 15.99 *(978-0-559-09796-6(4))* BiblioBazaar.

Townsend, George Alfred. The Life, Crime, & Capture of John Wilkes Booth, with a Full Sketch of the Conspiracy of Which He Was the Leader, & the Pursuit, Trial & Executi. 2011. 84p. pap. 14.99 ***(978-1-4255-0344-4(6))*** MPublishing.

ASSASSINS (ISMAILITES)

see also Nosairians

Bartlett, W. B. The Assassins: The Story of Medieval Islam's Secret Sect. 2009. (ENG., Illus.). 336p. pap. 23.95 *(978-0-7524-5205-0(3))* History Pr. Ltd., The GBR. Dist: Independent Pubs. Group.

Campbell, Anthony. The Assassins of Alamut. 2008. 142p. pap. 15.95 *(978-1-4092-0863-1(X))* Lulu Enterprises Inc.

Madden, Richard Robert. The Turkish Empire V2: In Its Relations with Christianity & Civilization. 2007. pap. 38.95 *(978-1-4304-5000-9(2))* Kessinger Publishing, LLC.

Waterson, James. Ismail: Assassins. 2008. (Illus.). 256p. 39.95 *(978-1-84832-505-0(3))* Pen & Sword Bks. Ltd. GBR. Dist: Casemate Pubs. & Bk. Distributors, LLC.

ASSATEAGUE ISLAND (MD. AND VA.)

Assateague Island. 175p. pap. 170.00 *(978-0-16-003501-2(5)*, Interior Dept.) United States Government Printing Office.

Cherrix, Myrna J. Assateague Island. 2011. (Images of America Ser.). (ENG., Illus.). 128p. pap. 21.99 ***(978-0-7385-8779-0(6))*** Arcadia Publishing.

Kavanagh, James. Assateague/Chincoteague Seashore Life: An Introduction to Familiar Species. 2007. (Pocket Naturalist - Waterford Press Ser.). (ENG., Illus.). 1p. 5.95 *(978-1-58355-336-7(3))* Waterford Pr., Inc.

ASSAULT, CRIMINAL

see Rape

ASSAULT AND BATTERY

see also Poisoning

Braun, Christian. Self Defense. 2008. (Illus.). 256p. pap. 19.95 *(978-1-84126-246-8(3))* Meyer & Meyer Sport, Ltd. GBR. Dist: Cardinal Pubs. Group.

—Self-Defense Against Knife Attacks. 2006. (Illus.). 287p. pap. 19.95 *(978-1-84126-198-0(X))* Meyer & Meyer Sport, Ltd. GBR. Dist: Cardinal Pubs. Group.

Hanna, Cheryl & Dalton, Clare. Domestic Violence & the Law: Theory & Practice. 2nd ed. 2008. (Illus.). xlv, 997p. pap. *(978-1-58778-417-0(3)*, Foundation Pr.) West.

Hoffer, Williamjames. The Caning of Charles Sumner: Honor, Idealism, & the Origins of the Civil War. 2010. (Witness to History Ser.). (ENG., Illus.). 160p. 50.00 *(978-0-8018-9468-8(9))* Johns Hopkins Univ. Pr.

Hoffer, Williamjames Hull. The Caning of Charles Sumner: Honor, Idealism, & the Origins of the Civil War. 2010. (Witness to History Ser.). (ENG., Illus.). 160p. (C). (gr. 13-17). pap. 19.95 *(978-0-8018-9469-5(7))* Johns Hopkins Univ. Pr.

Smith, Trisha. Holiday in Hell. 2009. 257p. (YA). *(978-0-9731379-6-5(7))* Asteroid Publishing, Inc.

Stationary Battery: 1993 Edition. 224p. 97.00 *(978-1-55937-363-0(6)*, SH16725) IEEE.

ASSAYING

see also classes of metals, and names of specific metals

Miller, Alfred Stanley. Assaying Manual - Fire Assay of Gold, Silver & Lead. 2008. 164p. pap. 29.95 *(978-1-934939-20-8(X))* Wexford College Pr.

Overman, Frederick. Practical Mineralogy, Assaying & Mining: With A Description of the Useful Minerals, & instructions for Assaying & Mining According to the Simple. 2006. 232p. per. 20.99 *(978-1-4255-1965-0(2))* MPublishing.

Rose, T. K. The Metallurgy of Gold - Mining & Mineral Processing. 2008. 640p. 59.95 *(978-1-934939-24-6(2))* Wexford College Pr.

Shepard, Orson Cutler & Dietrich, Waldemar F. Fire Assaying. 2007. 277p. pap. *(978-0-9799765-0-6(2))* Legend, Inc.

ASSEMBLAGE (ART)

see also Collage

Bauermeister, Mary, et al. Welten in der Schachtel / Worlds in a Box: Mary Bauermeister und die experimentelle Kunst der 1960er Jahre / Mary Bauermeister & the Experimental Art of the Sixties. 2011. (GER & ENG., Illus.). 176p. 55.00 *(978-3-86678-449-9(X))* Kerber Verlag DEU. Dist: D.A.P./Distributed Art Pubs.

Charlwood, Lindsay & Tilton, Connie Rogers, eds. L. A. Object & David Hammons Body Prints. 2011. (ENG., Illus.). 424p. 65.00 *(978-1-4276-1374-5(5))* Tilton Gallery.

Cornell, Joseph & Hartigan, Lynda Roscoe. Joseph Cornell: Navigating the Imagination. 2008. (Illus.). 391p. *(978-0-87577-211-0(0))* Peabody Essex Museum.

Doedens, Bruno. Temporary Landscapes. 2009. (DUT & ENG., Illus.). 192p. 50.00 *(978-90-78964-33-9(2)*, Thieme Art (Acc)) Antique Collectors' Club GBR. Dist: National Bk. Network.

Fredman, Stephen. Contextual Practice: Assemblage & the Erotic in Postwar Poetry & Art. 2010. (ENG., Illus.). 240p. 55.00 *(978-0-8047-6358-5(5))* Stanford Univ. Pr.

Lockhart, Annie. Objects of Reflection: A Soulful Journey Through Assemblage. 2010. (ENG., Illus.). 128p. pap. 22.99 *(978-1-60061-331-9(4)*, North Light Bks.) F&W Media, Inc.

Maurer-Mathison, Diane V. Collage, Assemblage, & Altered Art: Creating Unique Images & Objects. 2008. (ENG., Illus.). 144p. pap. 19.95 *(978-0-8230-7113-5(8))* Watson-Guptill Pubns., Inc.

Munder, Heike, ed. & text. Tadeusz Kantor, 1 vol. 2009. (ENG.). 156p. 55.00 *(978-3-03764-022-7(7))* JRP Ringier Kunstverlag AG CHE. Dist: D.A.P./Distributed Art Pubs.

Oliveau, Tally & Molina, Julie. Mixed-Media Dollhouses: Techniques & Ideas for Doll-Size Assemblages. 2010. (ENG., Illus.). 128p. pap. 24.99 *(978-1-59253-588-0(7)*, 1592535887, Quarry Books) Quayside.

Orta, Lucy & Orta, Jorge. Lucy & Jorge Orta: Clouds, Versailles. 2012. (ENG & FRE., Illus.). 224p. pap. 40.00 ***(978-88-6208-216-7(9))*** Damiani ITA. Dist: D.A.P./Distributed Art Pubs.

Perrella, Lynne. Art Making, Collections, & Obsessions: An Intimate Exploration of the Mixed-Media Work & Collections of 35 Artists. 2010. (ENG., Illus.). 160p. pap. 17.99 *(978-1-59253-626-9(3)*, 1592536263) Quayside.

Skov, Mara Holt & Holt, Steven Skov. Manufractured: The Conspicuous Transformation of Everyday Objects. 2008. (ENG., Illus.). 144p. 35.00 *(978-0-8118-6509-8(6))* Chronicle Bks. LLC.

Slominski, Andreas. Andreas Slominski, 1 vol. 2006. (ENG., Illus.). 224p. pap. 85.00 *(978-88-87029-34-5(2))* Fondazione Prada ITA. Dist: D.A.P./Distributed Art Pubs.

Umberger, Leslie. Messages & Magic: 100 Years of Collage & Assemblage in American Art. 2008. (Illus.). 78p. *(978-0-9710703-7-0(7))* Kohler, John Michael Arts Ctr.

Whiteley, Gillian. Junk: Art & the Politics of Trash. (ENG., Illus.). 192p. 2011. pap. 26.00 *(978-1-84885-413-0(7))* 2010. 85.00 *(978-1-84885-412-3(9))* I. B. Tauris & Co., Ltd. GBR. Dist: Macmillan.

Wynn, Jane. Altered Curiosities: Assemblage Techniques & Projects. 2007. (ENG., Illus.). 128p. pap. 22.99 *(978-1-58180-972-5(7)*, North Light Bks.) F&W Media, Inc.

ASSEMBLER LANGUAGE (COMPUTER PROGRAM LANGUAGE)

Cram101 Textbook Reviews & Cram101 Textbook Reviews. Outlines & Highlights for Assembly Language for X86 Processors by Kip R Irvine, Isbn: 9780136022121. 2011. 260p. pap. 31.95 ***(978-1-61461-746-4(5))*** Cram101 Inc.

—Outlines & Highlights for Principles of Computer Organization & Assembly Language by Patrick Juola, Isbn: 9780131486836 0131486837. 2011. 342p. pap. 33.95 ***(978-1-61490-693-3(9))*** Cram101 Inc.

Dandamudi, Sivarama P. Guide to RISC Processors: For Programmers & Engineers. 2010. (Illus.). xv, 387p. pap. 99.00 *(978-1-4419-1935-9(X)*, 144191935X) Springer.

—Introduction to Assembly Language Programming: For Pentium & RISC Processors. 2nd ed. 2010. (Texts in Computer Science Ser.). (Illus.). xxiv, 696p. pap. 109.00 *(978-1-4419-1921-2(X)*, 144191921X) Springer.

Detmer, Richard C. Essentials of 80x86 Assembly Language. 2nd ed. 2011. 286p. pap. 62.95 *(978-1-4496-4092-7(3))* Jones & Bartlett Learning, LLC.

—Introduction to 80x86 Assembly Language & Computer Architecture. 2nd rev. ed. 2009. (Illus.). 386p. 156.95 *(978-0-7637-7223-9(2))* Jones & Bartlett Learning, LLC.

Duntemann, Jeff. Assembly Language Step-by-Step: Programming with Linux. 3rd ed. 2009. (ENG., Illus.). 648p. pap. 65.00 *(978-0-470-49702-9(5)*, Wiley) Wiley, John & Sons, Inc.

Gibson, J. R. ARM Assembly Language - an Introduction. 2007. 244p. pap. 41.95 *(978-1-84753-696-9(4))* Lulu Enterprises Inc.

Gibson, J. r. & Gibson, J. R. Arm Assembly Language - an Introduction. 2011. 262p. pap. 46.50 ***(978-1-4477-1715-7(5))*** Lulu Enterprises Inc.

Hohl, William. ARM Assembly Language: Fundamentals & Techniques. 2009. (ENG., Illus.). 371p. 82.95 *(978-1-4398-0610-4(1)*, CRC Press) Taylor & Francis Group GBR. Dist: Taylor & Francis Group.

Hyde, Randall. The Art of Assembly Language. 2nd ed. 2010. (ENG., Illus.). 760p. pap. 59.95 *(978-1-59327-207-4(3))* No Starch Pr., Inc.

Irvine, Kip R. Assembly Language for X86 Processors. 6th ed. 2010. (ENG.). 768p. (C). 151.00 *(978-0-13-602212-1(X)*, Prentice Hall) Prentice Hall PTR.

Juola, Patrick. Principles of Computer Organization & Assembly Language: Using the Java Virtual Machine. 2006. (ENG., Illus.). 439p. (C). per. 137.00 *(978-0-13-148683-6(7)*, Prentice Hall) Prentice Hall PTR.

Mahout, V. Assembly Language Programming: Arm Cortex-M3. 2012. (Iste Ser.: 595). (ENG.). 256p. 95.00 ***(978-1-84821-329-6(8)**,* Wiley-ISTE) Wiley, John & Sons, Inc.

Margush, Timothy S. Some Assembly Required: Assembly Language Programming with the AVR Processor. 2011. (ENG., Illus.). 643p. 89.95 *(978-1-4398-2064-3(3)*, CRC Press) Taylor & Francis Group GBR. Dist: Taylor & Francis Group.

Mazidi, Muhammad Ali, et al. AVR Microcontroller & Embedded Systems: Using Assembly & C. 2010. (ENG.). 792p. (C). 133.00 *(978-0-13-800331-9(9)*, Prentice Hall) Prentice Hall PTR.

Rafiquzzaman, Mohamed. Microcontroller Theory & Applications with the PIC18F. 2011. (ENG., Illus.). 478p. (C). 133.95 *(978-0-470-94769-2(1)*, Wiley) Wiley, John & Sons, Inc.

Streib, James T. Guide to Assembly Language: A Concise Introduction. 2011. (ENG.). xiv, 256p. 69.95 *(978-0-85729-270-4(6)*, 0857292706) Springer.

Summerville, Douglas. Embedded Systems Interfacing for Engineers using the Freescale HCS08 Microcontroller: Assembly Language Programming. 2009. (Synthesis Lectures on Digital Circuits & Systems Ser.). 151p. pap. 40.00 *(978-1-60845-005-3(8))* Morgan & Claypool Pubs.

Wagner, Roger. Assembly Lines the Book. 2nd rev. ed. (Illus.). 273p. reprint ed. pap. 19.95 *(978-0-927796-99-6(6))* Wagner, Roger Publishing, Inc.

ASSEMBLIES OF GOD

African Gifts of the Spirit: Pentecostalism & the Rise of a Zimbabwean Transnational Religious Movement. 2006. (Illus.). 320p. 90.00 *(978-0-85255-965-9(8))*; pap. 34.95 *(978-0-85255-966-6(6))* Boydell & Brewer, Ltd. GBR. (Currey, James). Dist: Boydell & Brewer, Inc.

Alexander, Paul. Peace to War: Shifting Allegiances in the Assemblies of God. 2009. (C. Henry Smith Ser.: 9). 432p. pap. 26.95 *(978-1-931038-58-4(9))* Cascadia Publishing Hse., LLC.

Burke, Bob. Like a Prairie Fire: A History of the Assemblies of God in Oklahoma. Cunningham, Robert C. & Womack, David A., eds. (Illus.). 518p. 12.00 *(978-0-9641325-0-4(8))* Oklahoma District Council of the Assemblies of God.

Clifton & Clifton, Shane. Pentecostal Churches in Transition: Analysing the Developing Ecclesiology of the Assemblies of God in Australia. 2009. (Global Pentecostal & Charismatic Studies). (Illus.). ix, 249p. *(978-90-04-17526-6(1))* BRILL.

Dresselhaus, Richard L. Deacon Ministry: Empowering Volunteers. 2009. 122p. pap. 5.95 *(978-0-88243-851-1(4))* Gospel Publishing Hse.

Duncan, Londa. Touching Lives. 2008. 288p. per. 15.99 *(978-1-60477-122-0(4))* Xulon Pr., Inc.

Feuerstahler, Michael T. A Lutheran Looks at the Assemblies of God. 2009. pap. *(978-0-8100-2092-4(0))* Northwestern Publishing Hse.

Grams, Rollin G. Stewards of Grace: A Reflective, Mission Biography of Eugene & Phyllis Grams in South Africa, 1951-1962. 2010. 222p. pap. 24.00 *(978-1-60899-552-3(6)*, Wipf and Stock) Wipf & Stock Pubs.

Ma, Julie C. When the Spirit Meets the Spirits: Pentecostal Ministry among the Kankana-Ey Tribe in the Philippines. 2010. 274p. pap. 30.00 *(978-1-60899-464-9(3)*, Wipf and Stock) Wipf & Stock Pubs.

Malcomson, Keith. Pentecostal Pioneers Remembered. 2008. 480p. 35.99 *(978-1-60477-691-1(9))* Xulon Pr., Inc.

—Pentecostal Pioneers Remembered: British & Irish Pioneers of Pentecost. 2008. 480p. pap. 23.99 *(978-1-60477-690-4(0))* Xulon Pr., Inc.

Maxwell, David. African Gifts of the Spirit: Pentecostalism & the Rise of Zimbabwean Transnational Religious Movement. 2007. (Illus.). 272p. 55.00 *(978-0-8214-1737-9(1))*; (ENG., per. 26.95 *(978-0-8214-1738-6(X))* Ohio Univ. Pr.

Nelson, P. c. & Nelson, Peter Christopher. Bible Doctrines: Discover Profound Truths for Everyday Living. 75th ed. 2009. 144p. pap. *(978-0-88243-858-0(1))* Gospel Publishing Hse.

Newman, Joe. Race & the Assemblies of God Church: The Journey from Azusa Street to the "Miracle of Memphis" 2007. (ENG.). 240p. (C). 99.95 *(978-1-934043-55-4(9))* Cambria Pr.

Olena, Lois E. & Gannon, Raymond L. Stanley M. Horton: Shaper of Pentecostal Theology. 2009. (Illus.). 318p. pap. 5.00 *(978-0-88243-768-2(2))* Gospel Publishing Hse.

Pollard, T. Dale. I Knew There Was More. 2008. 256p. pap. 16.99 *(978-1-60647-907-0(5))* Xulon Pr., Inc.

Poloma, Margaret & Green, John. The Assemblies of God: Godly Love & the Revitalization of American Pentecostalism. 2010. (ENG.). 272p. 47.00 *(978-0-8147-6793-2(4))* New York Univ. Pr.

Venn-Brown, Anthony. A Life of Unlearning: A Journey to Find the Truth. rev. ed. 2007. (ENG.). 400p. pap. 14.95 *(978-1-74110-546-5(3))* New Holland Pubs. Pty, Ltd. AUS. Dist: Tuttle Publishing.

Ward, C. M. Asking No Question for Conscience Sake. 2011. 28p. 35.95 ***(978-1-258-06486-0(3))*** Literary Licensing, LLC.

ASSEMBLY, RIGHT OF

see also Freedom of Association; Freedom of Speech; Public Meetings; Riots

Cornelisse, Galina. Immigration Detention & Human Rights: Rethinking Territorial Sovereignty. 2010. (Immigration & Asylum Law & Policy in Europe Ser.). ix, 388p. *(978-90-04-17370-5(6))* BRILL.

Human Rights Watch (Organization) Staff, contrib. by. The Islamic Republic at 31: Post-Election Abuses Show Serious Human Rights Crisis. 2010. 19p. pap. ***(978-1-56432-601-0(2))*** Human Rights Watch.

Inazu, John D. Liberty's Refuge: The Forgotten Freedom of Assembly. 2012. (ENG.). 288p. 55.00 *(978-0-300-17315-4(6))* Yale Univ. Pr.

Merino, No'l, ed. Freedom of Assembly & Association. 2012. (Teen Rights & Freedoms Ser.). (ENG., Illus.). 176p. (gr. 10-12). lib. bdg. 37.10 ***(978-0-7377-5828-3(7)**,* Greenhaven Pr., Inc.) Cengage Gale.

Russell, Margaret. Freedom of Assembly & Petition: The First Amendment - Its Constitutional History & the Contemporary Debate. Oppenheimer, David, ed. 2010. (ENG.). 290p. pap. 19.00 *(978-1-59102-777-5(2))* Prometheus Bks., Pubs.

Sajó, András, ed. Free to Protest: Constituent Power & Street Demonstration. 2009. 274p. 96.00 *(978-90-77596-64-7(X))* Eleven International Publishing NLD. Dist: International Specialized Bk. Services.

Zick, Timothy. Speech Out of Doors: Preserving First Amendment Liberties in Public Places. 2008. (ENG., Illus.). 362p. 100.00 *(978-0-521-51730-0(3))*; pap. 30.99 *(978-0-521-73196-6(8))* Cambridge Univ. Pr.

ASSEMBLY, SCHOOL

see Schools—Exercises and Recreations

ASSEMBLY INDUSTRY, OFFSHORE

see Offshore Assembly Industry

ASSEMBLY LANGUAGE (COMPUTER PROGRAM LANGUAGE)

see Assembler Language (Computer Program Language)

ASSEMBLY-LINE METHODS

see also Automation

Birmingham, Fletcher & Jelinek, Jim. Quick Changeover Simplified: The Manager's Guide to Increasing Profits with SMED. 2007. (ENG., Illus.). 128p. per. 35.95 *(978-1-56327-349-0(7))* Productivity Pr.

Cutting, Robert. King of Wheels. 2007. (Timeline Ser.). (Illus.). 48p. pap. 8.99 *(978-1-4190-4396-3(X))* Houghton Mifflin Harcourt Supplemental Pubs.

Glucksmann, Miriam. Women on the Line. 2009. (ENG., Illus.). 232p. (C). pap. 35.95 *(978-0-415-47642-3(9))* Routledge.

Glucksmann, Miriam & Glucksmann Aka Ruth Ca, Miriam. Women on the Line. 2009. (ENG., Illus.). 232p. (C). 140.00 *(978-0-415-47641-6(0))* Routledge.

Heitmann, Silvia. Job-Shop Scheduling with Limited Buffer Capacities - Models, Solution Representations, Heuristics. 2007. 120p. per. *(978-3-8364-4745-4(2))* VDM Verlag Dr. Mueller e.K.

Ihara, Ryoji. Toyota's Assembly Line: A View from the Factory Floor. 2007. 258p. 79.95 *(978-1-876843-36-6(5))* Trans Pacific Pr. AUS. Dist: International Specialized Bk. Services.

—Toyota's Assembly Line: A View from the Factory Floor. Clarke, Hugh, tr. 2007. 258p. pap. 34.95 *(978-1-876843-42-7(X))* Trans Pacific Pr. AUS. Dist: International Specialized Bk. Services.

Kolisch, Rainer. Make-to-Order Assembly Management. 2010. (Illus.). xi, 260p. pap. 149.00 *(978-3-642-07431-8(6)*, 3642074316) Springer.

Lee, Sukhan, et al, eds. Frontiers of Assembly & Manufacturing: Selected papers from ISAM'09. 2010. (Illus.). 275p. 129.00 *(978-3-642-14115-7(3)*, 3642141153) Springer.

Lotter, Bruno & Wiendahl, Hans-Peter, eds. Montage in der industriellen Produktion: Optimierte Abläufe, rationelle Automatisierung. (VDI-Buch Ser.). (GER., Illus.). XVIII, 532p. 199.00 *(978-3-540-21413-7(5)*, 3540214135) Springer.

Mcgovern, Seamus M. & Gupta, Surendra M. The Disassembly Line: Balancing & Modeling. 2010. (ENG., Illus.). 398p. 130.00 *(978-0-07-162287-5(X)*, 007162287X) McGraw-Hill Professional Publishing.

Niederstadt, Joseph. Standardized Work for Noncyclical Processes. 2010. (ENG., Illus.). 120p. pap. 39.95 *(978-1-4398-2550-1(5))* Productivity Pr.

Papadopoulos, Chrissoleon T., et al. Analysis & Design of Discrete Part Production Lines. 2009. (Springer Optimization & Its Applications Ser.). (ENG., Illus.). xx, 279p. 119.00 *(978-0-387-89493-5(4)*, 0387894934) Springer.

Ratchev, Svetan, ed. Micro-Assembly Technologies & Applications: IFIP TC5 WG5. 5 Fourth International Precision Assembly Seminar (IPAS'2008) Chamonix, France, February 10-13 2008. 2010. (IFIP Advances in Information & Communication Technology Ser.). viii, 416p. pap. 149.00 *(978-1-4419-4591-4(1)*, 1441945911) Springer.

—Precision Assembly Technologies for Mini & Micro Products: Proceedings of the IFIP TC5 WG5. 5 Third International Precision Assembly Seminar (IPAS'2006), 19-21 February 2006, Bad Hofgastein, Austria. 2010. (IFIP Advances in Information & Communication Technology Ser.). xii, 336p. pap. 155.00 *(978-1-4419-4063-6(4)*, 1441940634) Springer.

Rekiek, Brahim & Delchambre, Alain. Assembly Line Design: The Balancing of Mixed-Model Hybrid Assembly Lines with Genetic Algorithms. 2010. (Springer Series in Advanced Manufacturing Ser.). (Illus.). xviii, 160p. pap. 169.00 *(978-1-84996-555-2(2)*, 1849965552) Springer.

Sawik, Tadeusz. Scheduling in Supply Chains Using Mixed Integer Programming. 2011. (ENG., Illus.). 492p. 125.00 *(978-0-470-93573-6(1)*, Wiley) Wiley, John & Sons, Inc.

Singh, Bikram Jit. Set-up Time Reduction. 2011. 112p. pap. ***(978-3-8454-0520-9(1))*** Lambert Academic Publishing.

Walker, Charles Rumford & Guest, Robert H. The Man on the Assembly Line. 2011. 202p. 44.95 ***(978-1-258-08641-1(7))*** Literary Licensing, LLC.

ASSER, JOHN, D. 909

Hart, Cyril. Byrhtferth's east anglian Chronicle: A Comparative Edition & Translation of the Latin Annals / the Early Chronicles of England, Volume III. 2006. (Early Chronicles of England Ser.: Vol. 3). (ANG, ENG & LAT, Illus.). 344p. *(978-0-7734-5545-0(0))* Mellen, Edwin Pr., The.

ASSERTIVENESS (PSYCHOLOGY)

Alberti, Robert E. & Emmons, Michael L. Your Perfect Right: Assertiveness & Equality in Your Life & Relationships. 9th ed. 2008. 312p. 24.95 *(978-1-886230-86-6(2))*; (Illus.). pap. *(978-1-886230-85-9(4))* Impact Pubs., Inc.

Atlantic Publishing Group Staff & Manresa, Maritza. Learning How to Say No When You Usually Say Yes: Everything You Need to Know Explained Simply. 2011. 288p. pap. 24.95 *(978-1-60138-384-6(3))* Atlantic Publishing Co.

Babcock, Linda & Laschever, Sara. Ask for It: How Women Can Use the Power of Negotiation to Get What They Really Want. 2009. (ENG.). 336p. pap. 16.00 *(978-0-553-38455-0(4))* Random House Publishing Group.

Bishop, Sue. Develop Your Assertiveness. 2nd ed. 2010. (Creating Success Ser.). (ENG.). 144p. pap. 14.95 *(978-0-7494-6042-6(3))*; pap. 14.95 *(978-0-7494-6001-3(6))* Kogan Page, Ltd. GBR. Dist: Ingram Pub. Services.

Boothman, Nicholas. How to Make People Like You in 90 Seconds or Less. 2008. (ENG., Illus.). 203p. pap. 11.95 *(978-0-7611-4946-0(5)*, 0761149465) Workman Publishing Co., Inc.

Carr, Dannie Lu. Brilliant Assertiveness: What the Most Assertive People Know, Do & Say. 2012. (ENG.). 248p. pap. ***(978-0-273-76867-8(0))*** Prentice Hall PTR.

Casey, Karen. Let Go Now: Embracing Detachment. 2010. (ENG.). 224p. pap. 14.95 *(978-1-57324-466-4(X)*, Conari Pr.) Red Wheel/Weiser.

Cheek, Don. Assertive Black... Puzzled White: A Black Perspective on Assertive Behavior. 2010. (Illus.). 168p. pap. 14.95 *(978-1-4327-5574-4(9))* Outskirts Pr., Inc.

Crant, John. Self-Recruiter Changing the Rules: How to Be Your Own Recruiter & Ride the Economic Crisis to Your Next Career Challenge. Crant, John, ed. 2009. (Illus.). 130p. pap. 19.95 *(978-0-9819592-0-7(2))* Provident Resource, Inc.

Eggert, Max A. The Assertiveness Pocketbook. 2nd rev. ed. 2011. (Illus.). 128p. pap. *(978-1-906610-36-4(3))* Management Pocketbooks GBR. Dist: Ware-Pak, Inc.

Evans-Ware, Keeronica. The Art of Bitchcraft: The Only Guidebook to the Magic of GETTING WHAT YOU WANT. 2007. (ENG., Illus.). 96p. per. 9.95 *(978-1-4022-0881-2(X)*, Sourcebooks Hysteria) Sourcebooks, Inc.

Fehr, Martha & Fehr, Wes. The Two Sides of the Golden Rule: Living Assertively Is Living Biblically. 2011. 256p. pap. 19.95 *(978-1-4497-1317-1(3)*, WestBow Pr.) Author Solutions, Inc.

Gartrell, Nanette. My Answer Is No — If That's Okay with You: How Women Can Say No with Confidence. 2009. (ENG., Illus.). 272p. pap. 17.99 *(978-1-4165-4695-5(2)*, Free Pr.) Free Pr.

Grado, Rebecca & Whitman, Christy. Taming Your Alpha Bitch: How to Be Fierce & Feminine (And Get Everything You Want!) 2012. (ENG.). 224p. pap. 14.95 *(978-1-936661-15-2(2))* BenBella Bks.

Hadfield, Sue & Hasson, Gill. How to Be Assertive in Any Situation. 2010. (ENG.). 224p. pap. *(978-0-273-73849-7(5))* Prentice Hall PTR.

Hartley, Mary. The Assertiveness Handbook. 2006. 128p. *(978-0-85969-941-9(2)*, Sheldon Press) SPCK Publishing.

Hawkins, David. When Pleasing Others Is Hurting You: Finding God's Patterns for Healthy Relationships. 2010. 240p. pap. 12.99 *(978-0-7369-2778-9(6))* Harvest Hse. Pubs.

Hayman, Suzie. Be More Assertive: A Teach Yourself Guide. 2011. (Teach Yourself: General Reference Ser.). (ENG.). 224p. pap. 15.00 *(978-0-07-176958-7(7)*, 0071769587) McGraw-Hill Cos., The.

Hilts, Elizabeth. The Bitch in the Bedroom: Your Inner Bitch Guide to Men & Relationships. 2006. (Illus.). 193p. per. 10.95 *(978-1-4022-0795-2(6)*, Sourcebooks Hysteria) Sourcebooks, Inc.

Kotzman, Anne & Kotzman, Mandy. Listen to Me, Listen to You: A Step-by-Step Guide to Communication Skills Training. 2008. 134p. spiral bd. 59.95 *(978-0-86431-864-0(2))* ACER Pr. AUS. Dist: International Specialized Bk. Services.

Luecke, Richard A. & McIntosh, Perry. Increase Your Influence at Work: Simple Solutions for Busy People, 1 vol. 2010. (ENG.). 112p. pap. 14.00 *(978-0-8144-1601-3(2))* Amacom.

Mansfield, Harvey Claflin, Jr. Manliness. 2007. (ENG.). 304p. per. 17.00 *(978-0-300-12254-1(3))* Yale Univ. Pr.

Meyer, Joyce. Approval Addiction: Overcoming Your Need to Please Everyone. 2008. (ENG.). 272p. pap. 13.99 *(978-0-446-50490-4(4))* FaithWords.

Michelli, Dena. Successful Assertiveness: Learn in a Week, What the Leading Experts Learn in a Lifetime. 2012. (Teach Yourself Ser.). (ENG., Illus.). 128p. pap. 12.00 ***(978-1-4441-5871-7(6)**,* 1444158716) McGraw-Hill Cos., The.

Moon, Jenny A., et al. Achieving Success Through Academic Assertiveness: Real Life Strategies for Today's Higher Education Students. 2008. (ENG., Illus.). 216p. 140.00 *(978-0-415-99142-1(0))*; pap. 49.95 *(978-0-415-99143-8(9))* Routledge.

Munroe, Megan. Bitch, Please: How Nice Girls Can Succeed in a Bitch's World. 2011. (ENG.). 236p. 24.95 *(978-1-59652-806-2(0))* Turner Publishing Co.

O'Keeffe, Julie. 10 Critical Strategies for Finding Fulfillment in a Hectic World. 2011. 64p. pap. 10.99 ***(978-1-4567-5626-0(5))*** AuthorHouse.

Potts, Suzanne & Potts, Conrad. Entitled to Respect: How to Be Confident & Assertive in the Workplace. 2010. (ENG., Illus.). 207p. pap. 26.00 *(978-1-84528-421-3(6))* How To Books GBR. Dist: Parkwest Pubns., Inc.

Rezvani, Selena. Pushback: How Smart Women Ask — And Stand Up — For What They Want. 2012. (ENG.). 224p. 26.95 ***(978-1-118-10490-3(0)**,* Jossey-Bass) Wiley, John & Sons, Inc.

Smith, Jackie, et al. Personal Impact: What it takes to make a Difference. 2008. (ENG., Illus.). 288p. pap. *(978-0-273-72032-4(5))* Prentice Hall PTR.

Townend, Anni. Assertiveness & Diversity. 2007. (ENG., Illus.). 256p. 59.00 *(978-1-4039-9344-1(0))* Palgrave Macmillan.

Vinkler, Henry. Speaking the Truth in Love: A Christian Approach to Assertiveness. 2009. 220p. pap. 15.99 *(978-1-61579-414-0(X))* Xulon Pr., Inc.

Zondervan Publishing Staff & Townsend, John. Limites Con los Adolecentes: How to Say Yes, How to Say No, 1 vol. 2006. (SPA.). 272p. pap. 12.99 *(978-0-8297-4629-7(3))* Vida Pubs.

ASSERTIVENESS TRAINING

Bavister, Steve & Vickers, Amanda. Assert Yourself. 2012. (Bullet Guides). (ENG.). 128p. pap. 6.95 ***(978-1-4441-4430-7(8)**,* Hodder & Stoughton) Hodder General Publishing Div. GBR. Dist: Independent Pubs. Group.

Bishop, Sue. Develop Your Assertiveness. 2nd ed. 2010. (Sunday Times Creating Success Ser.). (ENG.). 144p. pap. 14.95 *(978-0-7494-6001-3(6))*; pap. 14.95 *(978-0-7494-6042-6(3))* Kogan Page, Ltd. GBR. Dist: Ingram Pub. Services.

Kaizer, Sherryll. 10 Days to a Bully-Proof Child: The Proven Program to Build Confidence & Stop Bullies for Good. 2007. (ENG.). 240p. per. 14.95 *(978-1-56924-253-7(4))* Da Capo Pr., Inc.

ASSESSMENT

Here are entered works on tax assessment. Works on the technique of property valuation for other than taxation purposes are entered under specific headings with subdivision Valuation, e.g. Real Property—Valuation. Works on assessment in a particular field of taxation are entered under the heading covering taxation in that field, e.g. Real Property Tax.

see also Real Property—Valuation; Taxation, Exemption From; Valuation

American Society of Mechanical Engineers Staff, ed. Associated Lists. 32p. 35.00 *(978-0-7918-2437-5(3))* ASME Pr.

Assessment Update Staff. Assessment Update, November-December 2008, Volume 19. Banta, Trudy W., ed. 2009. (J-B AU Single Issue Assessment Update Ser. 113). (ENG.). 16p. pap. 29.00 *(978-0-470-45246-1(9)*, Jossey-Bass) Wiley, John & Sons, Inc.

Banta, Trudy W., ed. A Bird's-Eye View of Assessment: Selections from Editor's Notes. 2011. (Assessment Update Special Collections: 6). (ENG.). 96p. pap. 14.95 *(978-1-118-09966-7(4)*, Jossey-Bass) Wiley, John & Sons, Inc.

Bird, Richard M., et al. A Tale of Two Taxes: Property Tax Reform in Ontario. 2012. 288p. pap. 30.00 ***(978-1-55844-225-2(1))*** Lincoln Institute of Land Policy.

Bishop, John A. & Howitt, Idelle A. Federal Tax Valuation Digest. annuals. per. 175.00 *(978-0-7913-0157-9(5))* Warren, Gorham & Lamont, Inc.

Daubert, Erik J. & Daubert. The Annual Campaign. 2009. (AFP/Wiley Fund Development Ser.: 183). (ENG., Illus.). 284p. pap. 49.95 *(978-0-470-43863-3(0)*, Wiley) Wiley, John & Sons, Inc.

Denning, Shea. Guide to the Listing, Assessment, & Taxation of Property in North Carolina. 2009. 300p. pap. 50.00 *(978-1-56011-602-8(1)*, Schl. of Government.

Drummond, Mary Jane. Assessing Childrens Learning. (ENG., Illus.). 192p. (C). 2012. pap. 40.95 *(978-0-415-68673-0(3))* 2011. 155.00 *(978-0-415-68672-3(5))* Routledge.

Haveman, Mark & Sexton, Terri A. Property Tax Assessment Limits: Lessons from Thirty Years of Experience. 2008. (ENG.). 44p. pap. 15.00 *(978-1-55844-167-5(0))* Lincoln Institute of Land Policy.

Jaughin, Gordon. Oral Assessment from the Learner's Perspective - the Experience of Oral Assessment in Post-Compulsory Education. 2008. 144p. pap. *(978-3-639-00182-2(6))* VDM Verlag Dr. Mueller e.K.

Kábrtová, Jana. Effective Tax Rate Measures. 2010. 112p. pap. *(978-3-8383-6485-8(6))* Lambert Academic Publishing.

Kaufman, Roger & Roger Kauffman & Associates. The Assessment Book. 2008. 130p. pap. 29.95 *(978-1-59996-126-6(8))* Human Resource Development Pr.

Kwako, Joan. Assessment Task Design: Developing Mathematics Teaching Assistants\\\ Conceptions of Assessment 2008. 164p. pap. *(978-3-8364-8698-9(9))* VDM Verlag Dr. Mueller e.K.

Larson, Joni. Valuation Handbook. 2010. *(978-1-4224-0676-2(8))* LexisNexis Matthew Bender.

Metzer, Patricia Ann & Finkel, Robert M. Real Estate Tax Abatement Practice & Procedure. 2009. (ENG.). 174p. pap. 125.00 *(978-1-57589-550-5(1))* Massachusetts Continuing Legal Education, Inc.

New York (State) Laws, Statutes, etc. Staff. State Laws Relative to the Making & Perfecting Assessments, Applicable to the City of New York to Which Is Appended a Compilation of the Laws Of. 2006. 428p. per. 26.99 *(978-1-4255-4673-1(0))* MPublishing.

Oecd Publishing, Publishing & Organisation for Economic Co-Operation and Development. Implementing the Tax Transparency Standards: A Handbook for Assessors & Jurisdictions. 2010. (Illus.). 219p. pap. 63.00 *(978-92-64-08800-9(8))* Organization for Economic Cooperation & Development.

Paik, J. K. & Melchers, R. E., eds. Condition assessment of aged Structures. 2008. (Illus.). 384p. 269.95 *(978-1-4200-9304-9(5))* CRC Pr. LLC.

Thompson, Randy. The Teaming Assessment: A Diagnostic Tool for Assessing the Effectiveness of Academic Teams. 2008. (Illus.). pap. 6.99 *(978-0-86530-712-4(1))* Incentive Pubns., Inc.

Zuschlag, Daniela. Die pauschalierte Gewerbesteueranrechnung nach § 35 EStG. 2009. (Bochumer Schriften zum Steuerrecht Ser.). (GRE.). 370p. pap. 81.95 *(978-3-631-58549-8(7))* Lang, Peter GmbH, Europaischer Verlag der Wissenschaften DEU. Dist: Lang, Peter.

ASSESSMENT, CURRICULUM-BASED

see Curriculum-Based Assessment

ASSESSMENT, NURSING

see Nursing Assessment

ASSESSMENT, RISK

see Risk Assessment

ASSESSMENT CENTERS (PERSONNEL MANAGEMENT PROCEDURE)

Here are entered works on the procedure of using multiple assessment techniques to evaluate employees for selection, development, promotion and training in managerial positions.

see also Executives—Rating of; Executives—Training of

Biech, Elaine, ed. The 2009 Pfeiffer Annual: Training. annuals 2008. (J-B Pfeiffer Annual Vol1 Ser.: 39). (ENG.). 336p. 95.00 *(978-0-470-37142-8(0)*, Pfeiffer) Wiley, John & Sons, Inc.

Coleman, John L. Police Assessment Testing: An Assessment Center Handbook for Law Enforcement Personnel. 4th ed. 2010. 298p. *(978-0-398-07921-5(8))*; pap. *(978-0-398-07922-2(6))* Thomas, Charles C. Pub., Ltd.

Elearn. Project Management Revised Edition: Management Extra. 2007. (Management Extra Ser.). (ENG., Illus.). 120p. (C). pap. 49.95 *(978-0-08-048989-6(3))* Routledge.

Hale, Charles D. The Assessment Center Handbook for Police & Fire Personnel. 3rd ed. 2010. (Illus.). 238p. spiral bd. *(978-0-398-07948-2(X))* Thomas, Charles C. Pub., Ltd.

Hay, Julie. Simulations for Assessment, Training, & Development. 2009. 597p. spiral bd. 149.95 *(978-1-59996-169-9(5))* Human Resource Development Pr.

Jackson, Duncan, et al, eds. The Psychology of Assessment Centers. 2012. (ENG., Illus.). 360p. 84.95 ***(978-0-415-87814-2(4)***, Routledge) Taylor & Francis Group GBR. Dist: Taylor & Francis Group.

Kabagabe Byarugaba, Jolly, et al. Manager Development & Self Efficacy in Public Universities in Ugand. 2011. 84p. pap. ***(978-3-8433-9112-2(2))*** Lambert Academic Publishing.

Michelson, Rick & Maher, Pat. Assessment Centers for Public Safety. 2009. pap. *(978-1-61584-457-9(0))* Independent Pub.

Povah, Nigel & Povah, Lucy. Succeeding at Assessment Centres for Dummies. 2012. (ENG., Illus.). 320p. pap. 16.95 ***(978-0-470-72101-8(4)***, For Dummies) Wiley, John & Sons, Inc.

Povah, Nigel & Thornton, George. Assessment Centres & Global Talent Management. 2011. (Illus.). 526p. 175.00 ***(978-1-4094-0386-9(6)***, Gower Publishing Co., Ltd.) Ashgate Publishing, Ltd. GBR. Dist: Ashgate Publishing Co.

Sponton, John & Wright, Stewart. Managing Assessment Centres. 2009. (Illus.). 112p. pap. *(978-1-906610-05-0(3))* Management Pocketbooks GBR. Dist: Ware-Pak, Inc.

Suzuki, Lisa A. & Ponterotto, Joseph G., eds. Handbook of Multicultural Assessment: Clinical, Psychological, & Educational Applications. 3rd ed. 2007. (Wiley Desktop Editions Ser.). (ENG., Illus.). 736p. 100.00 *(978-0-7879-8703-9(4)*, Jossey-Bass) Wiley, John & Sons, Inc.

Terpak, Michael A. Assessment Center Strategy & Tactics. 2008. 138p. 49.00 *(978-1-59370-142-0(X))* PennWell Corp.

Tolley, Harry & Wood, Robert. How to Succeed at an Assessment Centre: Essential Preparation for Psychometric Tests, Group & Role-Play Exercises, Panel Interviews & Presentations. 3rd rev. ed. 2011. (ENG.). 224p. pap. 19.95 *(978-0-7494-6229-1(9))* Kogan Page, Ltd. GBR. Dist: Ingram Pub. Services.

Woodruffe, Charles. Development & Assessment Centres. 2007. (ENG.). 356p. per. *(978-0-9554488-0-5(8))* Human Assets, Ltd.

ASSESSMENT OF MEDICAL CARE NEEDS

see Medical Care—Needs Assessment

ASSESSMENT OF NEEDS

see Needs Assessment

ASSESSMENT OF BEHAVIOR

see also Behavioral Assessment

Bar-On, Reuven, et al. Emotional Intelligence Skills Assessment Facilitator Guide. 2009. 136p. pap. 50.00 *(978-0-470-24863-8(7)*, Pfeiffer) Wiley, John & Sons, Inc.

Multi Health Systems, et al. Emotional Intelligence Skills Assessment (EISA) Self. 2009. (ENG.). 16p. pap. 20.00 *(978-0-470-24865-2(3)*, Pfeiffer) Wiley, John & Sons, Inc.

ASSESSMENT OF PERSONALITY

see Personality Assessment

ASSET-BACKED FINANCING

Balzacq, Thierry, ed. Securitization Theory: How Security Problems Emerge & Dissolve. 2010. (PRIO New Security Studies). (ENG., Illus.). 272p. 145.00 *(978-0-415-55627-9(9)*, Routledge) Taylor & Francis Group GBR. Dist: Taylor & Francis Group.

Bergström, Maria, et al, eds. Securitization, Accountability & Risk Management: Transforming the Public Security Domain. 2012. (PRIO New Security Studies). (ENG., Illus.). 192p. (C). 130.00 *(978-0-415-68014-1(X))* Routledge.

Bluhm Christian & Overbeck Ludger. Structured Credit Portfolio Analysis, Baskets & CDOs. 2006. (Chapman & Hall/CRC Financial Mathematics Ser.). (ENG., Illus.). 376p. 92.95 *(978-1-58488-647-1(1)*, Chapman & Hall/CRC) CRC Pr. LLC.

Burgess, J. Peter & Balzacq, Thierry, eds. Securitization Theory: How Security Problems Emerge & Dissolve. 2010. (PRIO New Security Studies). (ENG., Illus.). 272p. pap. 39.95 *(978-0-415-55628-6(7))* Routledge.

Bussian, Jörg Christoph. Die Verantwortung der Organe einer Aktiengesellschaft bei Fehlinformation des Sekundärmarkts. 2009. (Schriftenreihe zum Gesellschafts- und Kapitalmarktrecht Ser.). (GER.). 364p. 89.95 *(978-3-631-58906-9(9))* Lang, Peter GmbH, Europaischer Verlag der Wissenschaften DEU. Dist: Lang, Peter.

Campbell, John Y. Asset Prices & Monetary Policy. Campbell, John Y., ed. 2008. (National Bureau of Economic Research Conference Report). (ENG., Illus.). 440p. 85.00 *(978-0-226-09211-9(9))* Univ. of Chicago Pr.

Caselli, Stefano & Gatti, Stefano, eds. Structured Finance: Techniques, Products & Market. 2010. (ENG., Illus.). x, 206p. pap. 119.00 *(978-3-642-06454-8(X)*, 364206454X) Springer.

Choudhry, Moorad. Bank Asset & Liability Management: Strategy, Trading, Analysis. 2007. (ENG., Illus.). 1440p. 115.00 *(978-0-470-82135-0(3)*, Wiley) Wiley, John & Sons, Inc.

Choudhry, Moorad & Fabozzi, Frank J. The Mechanics of Securitization: Structuring & Closing Asset-Backed Security Transactions. 2012. (Frank J. Fabozzi Ser.). (ENG.). 256p. instr.'s gde. ed. 85.00 *(978-0-470-60972-9(9)*, Wiley) Wiley, John & Sons, Inc.

Congressional Oversight Panel May Oversight Report: Reviving Lending to Small Businesses & Families & the Impact of TALF. 2009. (Illus.). iii, 160p. *(978-0-16-083326-7(4)*, 552-070-39150-9) United States Government Printing Office.

Covered Bonds: Potential Uses & Regulatory Issues: Hearing Before the Committee on Banking, Housing, & Urban Affairs, United States Senate, One Hundred Eleventh Congress, Second Session, on Examining Covered Bonds, Their Potential Uses, & Regulatory Issues, September 15, 2010. 2011. (Illus.). iii, 198p. ***(978-0-16-088600-3(7)***, 552-070-42776-7) United States Government Printing Office.

Covered Bonds: Prospects for a U.S. Market Going Forward: Hearing Before the Committee on Financial Services, U.S. House of Representatives, One Hundred Eleventh Congress, First Session, December 15, 2009. 2010. (Illus.). iii, 80p. *(978-0-16-085976-2(X)*, 552-070-41167-4) United States Government Printing Office.

de Servigny, Arnaud & Jobst, Norbert. The Handbook of Structured Finance. 2007. (ENG., Illus.). 500p. 129.95 *(978-0-07-146864-0(1)*, 0071468641) McGraw-Hill Cos., The.

De Vries Robbe, Jan Job. Securitization Law & Practice in the Face of the Credit Crunch. 2008. (Illus.). xxxix, 426p. 198.00 *(978-90-411-2715-0(1))* Wolters Kluwer Law & Business.

Dermine, Jean. Asset & Liability Management: The Banker's Guide to Value Creation & Risk Control. 2nd rev. ed. 2007. (Illus.). 208p. pap. 250.00 incl. cd-rom *(978-0-273-71001-1(X))* Financial Times/Prentice Hall.

Fabozzi, Frank J. & Drake, Pamela Peterson. Finance: Capital Markets, Financial Management, & Investment Management. 2009. (Frank J. Fabozzi Ser.: 178). (ENG., Illus.). 811p. 125.00 *(978-0-470-40735-6(2)*, Wiley) Wiley, John & Sons, Inc.

Fabozzi, Frank J. & Kothari, Vinod. Introduction to Securitization. 2008. (Frank J. Fabozzi Ser.: 174). (ENG., Illus.). 366p. 80.00 *(978-0-470-37190-9(0)*, Wiley) Wiley, John & Sons, Inc.

Fabozzi, Frank J., et al. Introduction to Structured Finance. 2006. (Frank J. Fabozzi Ser.: 148). (ENG., Illus.). 400p. 85.00 *(978-0-470-04535-0(3)*, Wiley) Wiley, John & Sons, Inc.

Fattor, Anna & Grammenidis, Ackis. Zero Impact or Zero Reliability? 2010. 144p. pap. *(978-3-8383-8612-6(4))* Lambert Academic Publishing.

Filomeni, Stefano. Securitisation: Financial Stability after Financial Crisis? 2011. 108p. pap. ***(978-3-8443-9455-9(9))*** Lambert Academic Publishing.

Giurgea, Florentin Catalin. Receivables Financing in the Context of Abs Securitization. 2010. 88p. pap. *(978-3-639-24474-8(5))* VDM Verlag Dr. Mueller e.K.

Gumpert, Benjamin, et al. Securitisation Handbook. Koonin, Eugene V., ed. 2010. 250.00 *(978-0-85308-636-9(2))* Jordan Publishing, Ltd. GBR. Dist: International Specialized Bk. Services.

Heller, Peter W., ed. Innovative Funding Mechanisms for Social Change. 2009. 141p. pap. 33.00 *(978-3-8329-3948-9(2))* Nomos Verlagsgesellschaft DEU. Dist: International Specialized Bk. Services.

Herring, Richard J., et al, eds. Prudent Lending Restored: Securitization after the Mortgage Meltdown. 2009. (ENG., Illus.). 326p. pap. 32.95 *(978-0-8157-0336-5(8))* Brookings Institution Pr.

Hu, Joseph C. Asset Securitization: Theory & Practice. 2011. (Wiley Finance Ser.: 679). (ENG.). 256p. 99.00 *(978-0-470-82603-4(7)*, Wiley) Wiley, John & Sons, Inc.

Kalani, Gautam. Making Benevolence Profitable. 2010. 56p. pap. *(978-3-639-24001-6(4))* VDM Verlag Dr. Mueller e.K.

Krebsz, Markus. Securitisation & Structured Finance Post Credit Crunch: A Best Practice Deal Lifecycle Guide. 2011. (Wiley Finance Ser.: 2). (ENG., Illus.). 480p. 95.00 *(978-0-470-71391-4(7)*, Wiley) Wiley, John & Sons, Inc.

Locke, Natania. Aspects of Traditional Securitisation in South African Law. 2010. 416p. pap. *(978-3-8383-4814-8(1))* Lambert Academic Publishing.

Lucas, Douglas J. Developments in Collateralized Debt Obligations: New Products & Insights with Collateralized Debt Obligations 2E Set: New Products & Insights with Collateralized Debt Obligations 2E Set. 2007. (ENG.). 144.00 *(978-0-470-17982-6(1)*, Wiley) Wiley, John & Sons, Inc.

Lucas, Douglas J., et al. Developments in Collateralized Debt Obligations: New Products & Insights. 2007. (Frank J. Fabozzi Ser.: 154). (ENG., Illus.). 287p. 80.00 *(978-0-470-13554-9(9)*, Wiley) Wiley, John & Sons, Inc.

Nowell, Peter B. & Nowell, Peter. Asset-Backed Credit Derivatives: Products, Applications & Markets. 2008. (Illus.). 236p. *(978-1-904339-97-7(2))* Risk Bks.

Parizek, Tomas. Death Bonds. 2010. 80p. pap. *(978-3-8383-5741-6(8))* Lambert Academic Publishing.

Ramos-Munoz, David & Ingram, Kevin. The Law of Transnational Securitization. 2010. (ENG.). 528p. 364.50 *(978-0-19-958392-8(7))* Oxford Univ. Pr., Inc.

Robbe. Structured Finance: On from the Credit Crunch - The Road to Recovery. 2009. (Illus.). xxiv, 308p. 185.00 *(978-90-411-2787-7(9))* Wolters Kluwer Law & Business.

Robbe, Jan Job de Vries. Innovations in Securitisation, Yearbook 2006. 2006. (International Banking, Finance & Economic Law Series Set Ser.). (Illus.). 340p. *(978-90-411-2533-0(7))* Kluwer Law International.

Samet, Joseph. Recent Developments in Distressed Debt, Restructurings & Workouts: Fallout from the Credit Crunch 2008. 2008. (Illus.). 674p. pap. *(978-1-4024-1188-5(X))* Practising Law Institute.

Schaber, Albert. Collateralized Debt Obligations: First Loss Piece Retention, Combination Notes, & Tranching. 2009. (Europäische Hochschulschriften. Reihe 5: Volks- und Betriebswirtschaft Ser.). 180p. pap. 57.95 *(978-3-631-58795-9(3))* Lang, Peter GmbH, Europaischer Verlag der Wissenschaften DEU. Dist: Lang, Peter.

Securitization of Assets: Problems & Solutions: Hearing Before the Subcommittee on Securities, Insurance, & Investment of the Committee on Banking, Housing, & Urban Affairs, United States Senate, One Hundred Eleventh Congress, First Session, on Examining the Securitization of Mortgages & Other Assets, October 7, 2009. 2010. (Illus.). iii, 77p. *(978-0-16-086137-6(3)*, 552-070-41242-5) United States Government Printing Office.

Shipoli, Erdoan A. International Securitization. 2010. 140p. pap. *(978-3-8383-4352-5(2))* Lambert Academic Publishing.

Tavakoli, Janet M. Structured Finance & Collateralized Debt Obligations: New Developments in Cash & Synthetic Securitization. 2nd ed. 2008. (Wiley Finance Ser.: 461). (ENG., Illus.). 480p. 90.00 *(978-0-470-28894-8(9)*, Wiley) Wiley, John & Sons, Inc.

Trafkowski, Uwe. Kreditderivate und Versicherungsderivate als Risikotransferverträge. 2008. (Schriftenreihe zum Gesellschafts- und Kapitalmarktrecht Ser.). 336p. pap. 81.95 *(978-3-631-57943-5(8))* Lang, Peter GmbH, Europaischer Verlag der Wissenschaften DEU. Dist: Lang, Peter.

Von Troschke, Otto. Asset-Backed Securities & Commercial Mortgage-Backed Securities. 2008. 96p. pap. *(978-3-8364-6306-5(7))* VDM Verlag Dr. Mueller e.K.

Vries, De. Innovations in Securitization Yearbook 2007. 2007. (Illus.). *(978-90-411-2661-0(9))* Kluwer Law International.

ASSETS (ACCOUNTING)

Abbink, John B. Alternative Assets & Strategic Allocation: Rethinking the Institutional Approach. 2010. (Bloomberg Ser.: 94). (ENG., Illus.). 509p. 85.00 *(978-1-57660-368-0(7)*, Bloomberg Pr.) Wiley, John & Sons, Inc.

Ahmed, J. U. Asset Quality & Non-Performing Assets of Commercial Banks. 2008. (Illus.). 234p. 43.50 *(978-81-7533-146-4(1))* M. D. Pubns. Pvt, Ltd. IND. Dist: Coronet Bks.

Berman, Bruce. From Assets to Profits: Competing for IP Value & Return. 2nd ed. 2008. (Intellectual Property-General, Law, Accounting & Finance, Management, Licensing, Special Topics Ser.: 33). (ENG., Illus.). 320p. 45.00 *(978-0-470-22538-7(6)*, Wiley) Wiley, John & Sons, Inc.

CCH Editors. CCH Accounting for Financial Assets & Liabilities. 2007. 820p. pap. 210.00 *(978-0-8080-9117-2(4))* Toolkit Media Group.

Childers, J. J. Trump University Asset Protection 101: Tax & Legal Strategies of the Rich. 2007. (ENG., Illus.). 288p. 24.95 *(978-0-470-17464-7(1)*, Wiley) Wiley, John & Sons, Inc.

Congressional Oversight Panel August Oversight Report: The Global Context & International Effects of the TARP. 2010. (Illus.). iii, 127p. *(978-0-16-086606-7(5)*, 552-070-41594-7) United States Government Printing Office.

Darst, David M. The Little Book That Saves Your Assets: What the Rich Do to Stay Wealthy in up & down Markets. 2008. (Little Books. Big Profits Ser.: 19). (ENG., Illus.). 240p. 19.95 *(978-0-470-25004-4(6)*, Wiley) Wiley, John & Sons, Inc.

Fraser-Sampson, Guy. Private Equity As an Asset Class. 2nd ed. 2010. (Wiley Finance Ser.: 509). (ENG., Illus.). 280p. 60.00 *(978-0-470-66138-3(0)*, Wiley) Wiley, John & Sons, Inc.

Funston, Frederick D., et al. Surviving & Thriving in Uncertainty: Creating the Risk Intelligent Enterprise. 2010. (ENG., Illus.). 368p. 39.95 *(978-0-470-24788-4(6)*, Wiley) Wiley, John & Sons, Inc.

Halligan, R. Mark & Weyand, Richard F. Trade Secret Asset Management: An Executive's Guide to Information Asset Management, Including Sarbanes-Oxley Accounting Requirements for Trade Secrets. 2006. 246p. per. 124.95 *(978-1-59622-560-2(2))* Aspatore Bks.

HDR Engineering. Asset Management Research Needs Roadmap. 2008. (Illus.). 272p. pap. *(978-1-60573-015-8(7))* Water Research Foundation.

Herder, Paulien, et al, eds. Asset Management: The State of the Art in Europe from a Life Cycle Perspective. 2012. (Topics in Safety, Risk, Reliability & Quality Ser.). (ENG., Illus.). xiv, 172p. 129.00 ***(978-94-007-2723-6(2)***, 9400727232) Springer.

Höglund, Thomas & H_glund, Thomas. Mathematical Asset Management. 2008. (ENG., Illus.). 222p. 111.00 *(978-0-470-23287-3(0)*, Wiley-Interscience) Wiley, John & Sons, Inc.

Ineichen, Alexander M. Asymmetric Returns: The Future of Active Asset Management. 2006. (Wiley Finance Ser.: 369). (ENG., Illus.). 352p. 75.00 *(978-0-470-04266-3(4)*, Wiley) Wiley, John & Sons, Inc.

Jarvis, Christopher R. & Mandell, David B. Wealth Secrets of the Affluent: Keys to Fortune Building & Asset Protection. 2008. (ENG., Illus.). 376p. 39.95 *(978-0-470-13979-0(X)*, Wiley) Wiley, John & Sons, Inc.

Joehnk, Michael D., et al, eds. Candidate Study Notes, Level 1, Volume 3: CFA Exam Review; Economics, Derivatives, Alternative Investments. 2nd ed. 2009. (Illus.). 240p. pap. 141.95 *(978-0-324-78362-9(0)*, South-Western) Cengage South-Western.

Kirwan, Adam O. The Asset Protection Guide for Florida Physicians 2007. 357p. per. 39.95 *(978-0-9745459-0-5(2))* Pocat Publishing, LLC.

Leibowitz, Martin L., et al. Modern Portfolio Management: Active Long/Short 130/30 Equity Strategies. 2009. (Wiley Finance Ser.: 488). (ENG., Illus.). 511p. 95.00 *(978-0-470-39853-1(1)*, Wiley) Wiley, John & Sons, Inc.

Lifetime Investment Advice: Human Capital, Asset Allocation, & Insurance. 2007. pap. 25.00 *(978-0-943205-94-6(8))* Research Foundation of CFA Institute.

Malo-Alain, Alaa. Fixed Assets Accounting. 2010. 364p. pap. *(978-3-639-24411-3(7))* VDM Verlag Dr. Mueller e.K.

McKinsey, et al. CAPEX Excellence: Optimizing Fixed Asset Investments. 2009. (ENG., Illus.). 232p. 75.00 *(978-0-470-77967-5(5)*, Wiley) Wiley, John & Sons, Inc.

Mendell, Ronald L. How to Do Financial Asset Investigations: A Practical Guide for Private Investigators, Collections Personnel, & Asset Recovery Specialists. (Illus.). 3rd ed. 2006. 240p. 54.95 *(978-0-398-07672-6(3))* 3rd ed. 2006. 240p. pap. 34.95 *(978-0-398-07673-3(1))* 4th ed. 2011. 292p. 59.95 *(978-0-398-08660-2(5))* 4th ed. 2011. 292p. pap. 39.95 *(978-0-398-08661-9(3))* Thomas, Charles C. Pub., Ltd.

Michael, Justin Nelson. Non Performing Assets in C0-0perative Banks. 2011. 264p. pap. ***(978-3-8443-9681-2(0))*** Lambert Academic Publishing.

Moser, Caroline, ed. Reducing Global Poverty: The Case for Asset Accumulation. 2007. (ENG., Illus.). 305p. per. 24.95 *(978-0-8157-5857-0(X))* Brookings Institution Pr.

Moser, Caroline O. N. Asset-based Approaches to Poverty Reduction in a Globalized Context: An introduction to asset accumulation policy & summary of workshop Findings. 2006. 0.00 *(978-0-9790376-0-3(3))* Brookings Global Economy & Development.

Ramsebner, Katrin. Asset Management & University Endowments. 2010. 88p. pap. *(978-3-639-26978-9(0))* VDM Verlag Dr. Mueller e.K.

Schmautz, Matthias. Asset-Liability-Management und Eigentümerorientierung bei Schadenversicherungsunternehmen. 2008. (Europäische Hochschulschriften. Reihe 5: Volks- und Betriebswirtschaft Ser.). 298p. pap. 74.95 *(978-3-631-57199-6(2))* Lang, Peter GmbH, Europaischer Verlag der Wissenschaften DEU. Dist: Lang, Peter.

Snow, Marian. Stop Sitting on Your Assets: How to Safely Leverage the Equity Trapped in Your Home & Transform It into a Constant Flow of Wealth & Security. 2nd ed. 2008. (Illus.). 354p. 24.95 *(978-0-9790142-0-8(4))* Madison, Ethan Publishing.

Stapelberg, Rudolph Frederick. Research into the Development & Application of Asset Management. 2010. 468p. pap. *(978-3-8383-8866-3(6))* Lambert Academic Publishing.

Stewart, John E., et al. CCH Accounting for Financial Assets & Liabilities: Sales, Transfers, & Extinguishments: Interpretations of FASB Statement No. 140, Accounting for Transfers & Servicing of Financial Assets & Extinguishments of Liabilities — A Replacement of FASB Statement No. 125. 2007th rev. ed. 2006. (Illus.). 786p. per. 211.00 *(978-0-8080-9057-1(7))* Toolkit Media Group.

Zenios, Stavros A. & Ziemba, William T. Handbook of Asset & Liability Management - Set. 2007. (ENG.). 1634p. 275.00 *(978-0-444-53248-0(X)*, North Holland) Elsevier Science & Technology Bks.

ASSETS, LIQUID

see Liquidity (Economics)

ASSIGNATS

White, Andrew Dickson. Flat Money Inflation in France. 2008. Orig. Title: Paper Money Inflation in France. 72p. pap. (978-1-4065-2213-6(9)) Dodo Pr.

—Paper-Money Inflation in France. 2009. 48p. pap. (978-1-151-68446-2(5)) Books LLC.

ASSIGNMENTS

Bryant. Complete Guide to Federal & State Garnishment 2011. 2010. pap. (978-0-7355-9177-6(6), Aspen Pubs.) Wolters Kluwer Law & Business.

Ikeda, Masao. Saiken Joto to Denshika Kokusaika. 2010. (Illus.). xvi, 480p. (978-4-335-35456-4(8)) Kobundo.

Smith, Marcus. The Law of Assignment: The Creation & Transfer of Choses in Action. 2nd ed. 2012. (ENG.). 996p. 335.00 (978-0-19-958508-3(3)) Oxford Univ. Pr., Inc.

ASSIMILATION (SOCIOLOGY)

see also Acculturation; Americanization; Discrimination; Emigration and Immigration; Ethnic Relations; Indians of North America—Cultural Assimilation; Marginality, Social; Minorities

Abi-Mershed, Osama. Apostles of Modernity: Saint-Simonians & the Civilizing Mission in Algeria. 2010. (ENG., Illus.). 344p. 60.00 (978-0-8047-6909-9(5)) Stanford Univ. Pr.

Alba, Richard D. The Next Generation: Immigrant Youth in a Comparative Perspective. Waters, Mary C. & Alba, Richard, eds. 2011. (ENG., Illus.). 382p. 75.00 (978-0-8147-0742-5(4)) New York Univ. Pr.

Alba, Richard D. & Waters, Mary C. The Next Generation: Immigrant Youth in a Comparative Perspective. 2011. E-Book (978-0-8147-0762-3(9)) New York Univ. Pr.

Alba, Richard D. & Waters, Mary C., eds. The Next Generation: Immigrant Youth in a Comparative Perspective. 2011. (ENG., Illus.). 382p. pap. 25.00 (978-0-8147-0743-2(2)) New York Univ. Pr.

Antrop-González, Rene. Schools As Radical Sanctuaries: Decolonizing Urban Education Through the Eyes of Latina/O Youth. 2012. **(978-1-61735-591-2(7))**; pap. **(978-1-61735-590-5(9))**; xiv, 117p. E-Book **(978-1-61735-592-9(5))** Information Age Publishing, Inc.

Baber, H. E. The Multicultural Mystique: The Liberal Case Against Diversity. 2008. (ENG.). 271p. 26.98 (978-1-59102-553-5(2)) Prometheus Bks., Pubs.

Barkan, Elliott Robert, ed. Immigration, Incorporation & Transnationalism. 2007. (ENG., Illus.). 260p. (gr. 11). pap. 29.95 (978-0-7658-0386-3(0)) Transaction Pubs.

Barth, Kelly. Assimilation. 2009. (At ISSUE Ser.). (ENG.). 128p. 22.50 (978-0-7377-4641-9(6)); (Illus.). pap. 31.80 (978-0-7377-4640-2(8)) Cengage Gale. (Greenhaven Pr., Inc.).

Bedolla, Lisa Garcia. Introduction to Latino Politics in the U. S. 2009. (UMP - US Minority Politics Ser.: 3). (ENG., Illus.). 288p. 74.95 (978-0-7456-3384-8(6)); pap. 26.95 (978-0-7456-3385-5(4)) Polity Pr. GBR. Dist: Wiley, John & Sons, Inc.

Bell, Sinclair & Hansen, Inge Lyse. Role Models in the Roman World: Identity & Assimilation. 2008. (Supplements to the Memoirs of the American Academy in Rome Ser.). (ENG., Illus.). 328p. 90.00 (978-0-472-11589-1(8)) Univ. of Michigan Pr.

Berglund, Barbara. Making San Francisco American: Cultural Frontiers in the Urban West, 1846-1906. (Illus.). 294p. 2010. pap. 19.95 (978-0-7006-1722-7(1)) 2007. 34.95 (978-0-7006-1530-8(X)) Univ. Pr. of Kansas.

Bernard, Richard M. The Melting Pot & the Altar: Marital Assimilation in Early Twentieth-Century Wisconsin. 2009. (ENG.). 192p. pap. 40.00 (978-0-8166-5707-0(6)) Univ. of Minnesota Pr.

Boatwright, Mary Taliaferro. Peoples of the Roman World. 2012. (Cambridge Introduction to Roman Civilization Ser.). (ENG.). 258p. 90.00 **(978-0-521-84062-0(7))**; (Illus.). pap. 25.99 **(978-0-521-54994-3(9))** Cambridge Univ. Pr.

Bonfil, Robert. Cultural Change among the Jews of Early Modern Italy. 2010. (Variorum Collected Studies). (Illus.). 342p. 149.95 (978-1-4094-0016-5(6)) Ashgate Publishing Co.

Brubaker, Rogers. Ethnicity Without Groups. 2006. (Illus.). 296p. per. 28.50 (978-0-674-02231-7(9)) Harvard Univ. Pr.

Bump, Micah & Gozdziak, Elzbieta M. New Immigrants, Changing Communities: Best Practices for a Better America. 2008. (ENG.). 134p. pap. 18.99 (978-0-7391-0637-2(6)) Lexington Bks.

Butcher, Melissa. Managing Cultural Change: Reclaiming Synchronicity in a Mobile World. 2011. (Global Connections Ser.). (Illus.). 164p. 99.95 **(978-1-4094-2510-6(X))** Ashgate Publishing Co.

Chung, Erin Aeran. Immigration & Citizenship in Japan. 2010. (ENG., Illus.). 224p. 75.00 (978-0-521-51404-0(5)) Cambridge Univ. Pr.

Comprehensive Immigration Reform: Becoming Americans: U.S. Immigrant Integration (Continued): Hearing Before the Subcommittee on Immigration, Citizenship, Refugees, Border Security, & International Law of the Committee on the Judiciary, House of Representatives, One Hundred Tenth Congress, First Session, May 23, 2007. 2007. iii, 87p. (978-0-16-079523-7(0), 552-070-36501-0) United States Government Printing Office.

Cram101 Textbook Reviews Staff. Outlines & Highlights for Yucatecans in Dallas, Texas: Breaching the Border, Bridging the Distance by Adler, ISBN. 2009. 80p. pap. 10.95 (978-1-4288-6649-2(3)) Cram101 Inc.

Davidson, Lawrence. Cultural Genocide. 2012. (Genocide, Political Violence, Human Rights Ser.). (ENG.). 162p. 68.00 **(978-0-8135-5243-9(5))**; (Illus.). pap. 23.95 **(978-0-8135-5349-8(0))** Rutgers Univ. Pr.

Donato, Katharine M., et al, eds. Continental Divides: International Migration in the Americas: International Migration in the Americas. 2010. (ANNALS of the American Academy of Political & Social Science Ser.: 630). (Illus.). 324p. (C). 47.00 (978-1-4129-9186-5(2), 295630C); pap. 34.95 (978-1-4129-9187-2(0), 295630P) SAGE Pubns., Inc.

Easton-Brooks, Donald. African Americanæs Academic Outcomes. 2008. 152p. pap. (978-3-639-04586-4(6)) VDM Verlag Dr. Mueller e.K.

Fancy, Richard. Values Patterns Across Cultures. 2008. 324p. pap. (978-3-639-03018-1(4)) VDM Verlag Dr. Mueller e.K.

Feagin, Joe R. & Feagin, Clairece Booher. Racial & Ethnic Relations. 7th ed. 2006. pap. 10.95 (978-1-4288-1722-7(0)) Cram101 Inc.

Fernandez, Ronald. America Beyond Black & White: How Immigrants & Fusions Are Helping Us Overcome the Racial Divide. 2008. (Contemporary Political & Social Issues Ser.). (ENG., Illus.). 296p. pap. 23.95 (978-0-472-03320-1(4)) Univ. of Michigan Pr.

Fog Olwig, Karen, et al, eds. Migration Family & the Welfare State. 2012. (ENG.). 192p. (C). 125.00 **(978-0-415-50759-2(6))** Routledge.

Franks, Joel. Crossing Sidelines Crossing Cultures: Sport & Asian Pacific American Cultural Citizenship. 2nd ed. 2009. (ENG.). 322p. pap. 41.99 (978-0-7618-4744-1(8)) Univ. Pr. of America, Inc.

Gozdziak, Elzbieta M. & Bump, Micah. New Immigrants, Changing Communities: Best Practices for a Better America. 2008. (ENG.). 134p. 52.50 (978-0-7391-0634-1(1)) Lexington Bks.

Gutiérrez, David G. & Hondagneu-Sotelo, Pierrette, eds. Nation & Migration: Past & Future. 2009. (Special Issue of American Quarterly Ser.). (ENG., Illus.). 392p. (C). (gr. 13-17). pap. 25.00 (978-0-8018-9281-3(3)) Johns Hopkins Univ. Pr.

Hanley, Lisa M., et al, eds. Immigration & Integration in Urban Communities: Renegotiating the City. 2008. (ENG., Illus.). 336p. (gr. 17). 55.00 (978-0-8018-8841-0(7)) Johns Hopkins Univ. Pr.

Haselwanter, Stephanie. Immigration & the Politics of Identity in the European Union. 2010. 124p. pap. (978-3-639-23967-6(9)) VDM Verlag Dr. Mueller e.K.

Heffelfinger, Chris. Radical Islam in America: Salafism's Journey from Arabia to the West. 2011. 182p. 29.95 (978-1-59797-302-1(5)) Potomac Bks., Inc.

Huang, Pei. Reorienting the Manchus. 2011. (ENG., Illus.). xxiv, 374p. 45.00 **(978-1-933947-52-5(7))** Cornell Univ. East Asia Program.

Iceland, John. Where We Live Now: Immigration & Race in the United States. 2009. (ENG., Illus.). 240p. 50.00 (978-0-520-25762-7(6)) Univ. of California Pr.

Iceland, John & Iceland, J. Where We Live Now: Immigration & Race in the United States. 2009. (ENG., Illus.). 200p. pap. 24.95 (978-0-520-25763-4(4)) Univ. of California Pr.

Iyall Smith, Keri E. & Leavy, Patricia, eds. Hybrid Identities: Theoretical & Empirical Examinations. 2008. 354p. (978-90-04-17039-1(1)) BRILL.

Jansen, Stef & Löfving, Staffan. Struggles for Home: Violence, Hope & the Movement of People. Jansen, Stef & Lofving, Staffan, eds. 2008. 200p. (C). 70.00 (978-1-84545-523-1(1)) Berghahn Bks., Inc.

Jansen, Stef & Löfving, Staffan, eds. Struggles for Home: Violence, Hope & the Movement of People. 2011. (Disl Ser.). 200p. 25.00 (978-0-85745-150-7(2)) Berghahn Bks., Inc.

Jenkins, Richard. Being Danish - Paradoxes of Identity in Everyday Life. 2011. (Illus.). 371p. pap. 48.00 (978-87-635-2603-6(4)) Museum Tusculanum Pr. DNK. Dist: Chicago Distribution Ctr.

Kü, et a . Fremde in der Fremde: Berufliche und soziale Integration von Zuwanderern im historischen Rückblick. 2009. (GER.). 182p. pap. (978-3-7639-3698-4(X)) Bertelsmann, W., Verlag GmbH & Co. KG.

Khan-Svik, Gabriele. Assimilation - Integration - Segregation? Migrantinnen und Migranten aus Indien, Pakistan oder Bangladesch in Europa. 2010. 144p. pap. (978-3-639-21699-8(7)) VDM Verlag Dr. Mueller e.K.

Kilar, Jeremy W. Germans in Michigan. 2008. (Discovering the Peoples of Michigan Ser.). (ENG., Illus.). 58p. pap. 12.95 (978-0-87013-619-1(4)) Michigan State Univ. Pr.

Kuh, George D., et al. Piecing Together the Student Success Puzzle: Research, Propositions, & Recommendations: ASHE Higher Education Report. 2007. (J-B ASHE Higher Education Report Series (AEHE) Ser.: 116). (ENG.). 200p. pap. 29.00 (978-0-7879-9776-2(5), Jossey-Bass) Wiley, John & Sons, Inc.

Lai, Him Ma. Becoming Chinese American. 2008. (ENG.). 182p. pap. 29.95 (978-0-7591-0454-9(9)) AltaMira Pr.

Laoire, Caitríona Ní, et al. Childhood & Migration in Europe: Portraits from Contemporary Ireland. 2011. (Studies in Migration & Diaspora Ser.). (Illus.). 212p. 99.95 (978-1-4094-0109-4(X)) Ashgate Publishing Co.

Laurence, Jonathan. The Emancipation of Europe's Muslims: The State's Role in Minority Integration. 2011. (Princeton Studies in Muslim Politics Ser.). (ENG., Illus.). 392p. (C). 80.00 **(978-0-691-14421-4(4))** Princeton Univ. Pr.

—The Emancipation of Europe's Muslims - The State's Role in Minority Integration. 2011. (Princeton Studies in Muslim Politics Ser.). (ENG., Illus.). 392p. (C). pap. 29.95 **(978-0-691-14422-1(2))** Princeton Univ. Pr.

Lee, Inn Sook. Passage to the Real Self: The Development of Self Integration for Asian American Women. 2009. ix, 185p. **(978-0-7618-4474-7(0))** Univ. Pr. of America, Inc.

Lev Ari, Lilach. The American Dream — for Men Only Gender, Immigration, & the Assimilation of Israelis in the United States. 2008. (New Americans). 200p. 62.00 (978-1-59332-268-7(2)) LFB Scholarly Publishing LLC.

Louie, Vivian S. Keeping the Immigrant Bargain: The Costs & Rewards of Success in America. 2012. pap. **(978-0-87154-564-0(0))** Russell Sage Foundation.

Lowenstein, Tom. Ultimate Americans: Point Hope, Alaska, 1826-1909. (ENG., Illus.). 368p. 2010. pap. 36.95 (978-1-60223-038-5(2)) 2009. 49.95 (978-1-60223-027-9(7)) Univ. of Alaska Pr.

Mansouri, Fethi, ed. Youth Identity & Migration: Culture, values & social Connectedness. 2009. 244p. pap. 30.00 (978-1-86335-621-3(5)) Common Ground Publishing Pty, Ltd.

Massey & Sanchez. Brokered Boundaries: Creating Immigrant Identity in Anti Immigrant Times. 2010. (Illus.). 305p. (978-0-87154-579-4(9)) Russell Sage Foundation.

Masten, Ann S., et al, eds. The Potential of Immigrant Youth. 2012. (Jacobs Foundation Series on Adolescence Ser.). (ENG., Illus.). 400p. (C). 99.00 **(978-1-107-01950-8(8))** Cambridge Univ. Pr.

Middleton & Cram101 Textbook Reviews Staff. The Challenge of Human Diversity Mirrors, Bridges, & Chasms. 2007. 80p. per. 10.95 (978-1-4288-2674-8(2)) Cram101 Inc.

Morris-Reich, Amos. The Quest for Jewish Assimilation in Modern Social Science. 2007. (Routledge Studies in Social & Political Thought Ser.). (ENG.). 206p. 125.00 (978-0-415-96089-2(4)) Routledge.

Murray, Meredyth. How New York City Saved My Life. 2011. 232p. pap. 15.95 **(978-1-60976-791-4(8)**, Eloquent Bks.) AEG Literary Publishing Services, Inc.

Mushaben, Joyce Marie. The Changing Faces of Citizenship: Integration & Mobilization among Ethnic Minorities in Germany. 2008. 364p. (C). 100.00 (978-1-84545-453-1(7)) Berghahn Bks., Inc.

—The Changing Faces of Citizenship Social Integration & Political Mobilization among Ethnic Minorities. 2008. 304p. pap. (978-1-84545-468-5(5)) Berghahn Bks., Inc.

Musterd, S., et al. Multi-Ethnic Metropolis: Patterns & Policies: Patterns & Policies. 2010. (GeoJournal Library). (Illus.). 224p. pap. 159.00 (978-90-481-4950-6(9), 9048149509) Springer.

Olson, Sherry & Thornton, Patricia. Peopling the North American City: Montreal, 1840-1900. 2011. (Carleton Library Ser.). (ENG., Illus.). 544p. (C). (978-0-7735-3830-6(5)); pap. (978-0-7735-3831-3(3)) McGill-Queen's Univ. Pr.

Pulido, James. Resistance to Learning by Latino Males Students. 2008. 156p. pap. (978-3-639-06406-3(2)) VDM Verlag Dr. Mueller e.K.

Rozbicki, Michal Jan & Ndege, George O. Cross-Cultural History & the Domestication of Otherness. 2011. (ENG., Illus.). 242p. 85.00 **(978-0-230-33997-2(2))** Palgrave Macmillan.

Sandin, Lyn Di Iorio. Killing Spanish: Literary Essays on Ambivalent U. S. Latino - A Identity. 2009. (ENG.). 208p. pap. 32.00 (978-0-230-61751-3(4)) Palgrave Macmillan.

Schneider, Jens & Crul, Maurice, eds. Theorising Integration & Assimilation. 2012. (Ethnic & Racial Studies). (ENG., Illus.). 144p. (C). 125.00 (978-0-415-68002-8(6)) Routledge.

Sherman, John & Wolin, Jeffrey A. New Faces at the Crossroads: The World in Central Indiana. 2007. (ENG., Illus.). 96p. 29.95 (978-0-253-35068-8(9), 0253350689) Indiana Univ. Pr.

Smokowski, Paul & Bacallao, Martica. Becoming Bicultural: Risk, Resilience, & Latino Youth. 2011. (ENG., Illus.). 256p. 75.00 (978-0-8147-4089-7(8)); pap. 24.00 (978-0-8147-4090-3(1)) New York Univ. Pr.

Somerville, Margaret, et al, eds. Landscapes & Learning: Place Studies for a Global World. 2009. 236p. (978-94-6091-082-1(3)); pap. (978-94-6091-081-4(5)) Sense Pubs.

Streissguth, Tom. Welcome to America? A Pro/con Debate over Immigration. 2008. (Issues in Focus Today Ser.). (Illus.). 112p. (J). (gr. k-6). lib. bdg. 31.93 (978-0-7660-2912-5(3)) Enslow Pubs., Inc.

Sycamore, Matt Bernstein & Counterpoint Staff. That's Revolting! Queer Strategies for Resisting Assimilation. Sycamore, Mattilda Bernstein, ed. 2nd rev. ed. 2008. (ENG., Illus.). 360p. pap. 19.95 (978-1-59376-195-0(3), Soft Skull Pr.) Counterpoint LLC.

Tara M. Johnson. Acculturation: Implications for Individuals, Families & Societies. 2011. (Series: Social Issues, Justice & Status Ser.). xii, 246p. 89.00 (978-1-61122-525-9(6)) Nova Science Pubs., Inc.

Thompson, Gordon E. The Assimilationist Impulse in Four African American Narratives: Frederic Douglas, James Weldon Johnson, Richard Wright, & Leroi Jones. 2011. 248p. 119.95 (978-0-7734-1555-3(6)) Mellen, Edwin Pr., The.

Thompson, Kenneth. The Early Sociology of Race & Ethnicity. 2007. 2400p. 1845.00 (978-0-415-45702-6(5)) RoutledgeFalmer GBR. Dist: Taylor & Francis Group.

Thompson, Shirley Elizabeth. Exiles at Home: The Struggle to Become American in Creole New Orleans. 2009. (Illus.). 400p. 54.50 (978-0-674-02351-2(X)) Harvard Univ. Pr.

Trundle, Catherine. Local Lives: Migration & the Politics of Place. Bönisch-Brednich, Brigitte, ed. 2010. (Studies in Migration & Diaspora Ser.). 218p. 99.95 (978-1-4094-0103-2(0)) Ashgate Publishing Co.

Vigdor, Jacob L. From Immigrants to Americans: The Rise & Fall of Fitting In. 2010. (ENG., Illus.). 232p. 40.00 (978-1-4422-0136-1(3)) Rowman & Littlefield Publishers, Inc.

Warikoo, Natasha Kumar. Balancing Acts: Youth Culture in the Global City. 2011. (ENG.). 296p. 55.00 (978-0-520-26210-2(7)); pap. 21.95 (978-0-520-26211-9(5)) Univ. of California Pr.

Wertheimer, Jack. Imagining the American Jewish Community. 2007. (Brandeis Series in American Jewish History, Culture, & Life). (Illus.). xiii, 346p. (978-1-58465-669-2(7)) Univ. Pr. of New England.

Westphalen, Linda. An Anthropological & Literary Study of Two Australian Aboriginal Women's Life Histories: The Impacts of Enforced Child Removal & Policies of Assimilation. 2012. 480p. 159.95 **(978-0-7734-1593-5(9))** Mellen, Edwin Pr., The.

White, Michael J. & Glick, Jennifer E. Achieving Anew: How New Immigrants Do in American Schools, Jobs, & Neighborhoods. 2011. (ENG., Illus.). 226p. pap. 29.95 **(978-0-87154-926-6(3))** 2009. (978-0-87154-920-4(4)) Russell Sage Foundation.

Yoshino, Kenji. Covering: The Hidden Assault on Our Civil Rights. 2007. (ENG.). 304p. pap. 15.95 (978-0-375-76021-1(0), Random Hse. Trade Paperbacks) Random House Publishing Group.

ASSINIBOIN INDIANS

see Indians of North America—West (U.S.)

ASSISI (ITALY)

Galli, Mark. Francis of Assisi & His World. 2011. (IVP Histories Ser.). (ENG., Illus.). 190p. pap. 16.00 (978-0-8308-2354-3(9), IVP Bks.) InterVarsity Pr.

ASSISI (ITALY)—DESCRIPTION AND TRAVEL

Art & History of Assisi. 128p. pap. (978-88-7009-460-2(X)) Casa Editrice Bonechi.

Goodburn, Raymond. A Pilgrim's Guide to Rome & Assisi. 2010. (Pilgrim's Guides Ser.: 4). (Illus.). 96p. pap. 16.95 (978-0-9532511-4-8(4)) Pilgrim Bk. Services, Ltd. GBR. Dist: AtlasBooks Distribution.

National Education Association of the United States. The Sun & Moon over Assisi: A Personal Encounter with Francis & Clare. 2008. (Illus.). 614p. pap. 24.95 (978-0-86716-856-3(0)) Franciscan Media.

Richmond, W. B. Assisi: Impressions of Half A Century. 2007. (ENG.). 292p. 43.95 (978-0-548-04714-9(6)) Kessinger Publishing, LLC.

ASSISI (ITALY)—SAN FRANCESCO (CHURCH)

see San Francesco (Church: Assisi, Italy)

ASSISTANCE IN EMERGENCIES

see also First Aid in Illness and Injury; Necessity (Law)

Ahern, Jerry. Survive! The Disaster, Crisis & Emergency Handbook. 2010. (ENG.). 240p. pap. 19.99 (978-1-4402-1112-6(4)) Krause Pubns.

Broder, James F. & Tucker, Gene. Risk Analysis & the Security Survey. 4th ed. 2012. (ENG.). 368p. 69.95 **(978-0-12-382233-8(5)**, Butterworth-Heinemann) Elsevier Science & Technology Bks.

Burau, Carolina. Answering 911: Life in the Hot Seat. 2006. 216p. 19.95 (978-0-87351-569-6(2), Borealis Bk.) Minnesota Historical Society Pr.

Burau, Caroline. Answering 911: Life in the Hot Seat. 2007. (ENG.). 216p. per. 15.95 (978-0-87351-602-0(8), Borealis Bk.) Minnesota Historical Society Pr.

Canton, Lucien G. Emergency Management: Concepts & Strategies for Effective Programs. 2006. (ENG., Illus.). 368p. 99.95 (978-0-471-73487-1(X), Wiley-Interscience) Wiley, John & Sons, Inc.

Crawford, James. Fire Prevention Organization & Management. 2010. (ENG.). 272p. (C). 75.33 (978-0-13-508784-8(8), Prentice Hall) Prentice Hall PTR.

Emergency Service Dive Team - Standards & Procedures Manual. 50p. pap. 15.95 (978-0-943155-02-9(9)) California Investigative Academy.

Emergency Service Diver - Instructor's Guide. (Illus.). 50p. pap. 15.95 (978-0-943155-16-6(9)) California Investigative Academy.

Fabre, Cécile. Whose Body Is it Anyway? Justice & the Integrity of the Person. 2008. (ENG.). 256p. pap. 39.95 (978-0-19-953229-2(X)) Oxford Univ. Pr., Inc.

Jackson, Brian A., et al. Evaluating the Reliability of Emergency Response Systems for Large-Scale Incident Operations. 2010. 224p. pap. 53.00 (978-0-8330-5005-2(2), mg-994) RAND Corp., The.

Leveraging Mutual Aid for Effective Emergency Response: Hearing Before the Subcommittee on Emergency Communications, Preparedness & Response of the Committee on Homeland Security, House of Representatives, One Hundred Tenth Congress, First Session, November 15, 2007. 2009. (Illus.). iii, 74p. (978-0-16-084836-0(9), 552-070-40237-3) United States Government Printing Office.

Marzilli, Alan. Disaster Relief. 2007. (Point/Counterpoint Ser.). (Illus.). 128p. (YA). (gr. 9-12). lib. bdg. 35.00 (978-0-7910-9554-6(1)) Facts On File, Inc.

Office of the Federal Register (U.S.), ed. Code of Federal Regulations, Title 44, Emergency Management & Assistance, Revised as of October 1 2011. rev. ed. 2012. (ENG.). 682p. pap. 56.00 **(978-0-16-089567-8(7)**, Office of the Federal Register) United States Government Printing Office.

Rescue Diver Instructor Slates. 2007. (YA). (978-1-931451-53-6(2)) International Training, Inc.

Rescue Diver Slates. 2007. (978-1-931451-54-3(0)) International Training, Inc.

Sheppard, Al. E-Man: Life in the NYPD Emergency Service Unit. 2007. (Illus.). 189p. per. 18.95 (978-1-60008-050-0(2), Rooftop Publishing) AuthorHouse.

Sheppard, Al & Schmetterer, Jerry. E-Man: Life in the NYPD Emergency Service Unit. 2009. (Illus.). 208p. pap. 18.95 (978-1-935278-26-9(6), iUniverse Star); xviii, 189p. E-Book (978-1-935278-27-6(4)) iUniverse, Inc.

ASSISTANCE TO UNDERDEVELOPED AREAS

see Technical Assistance

ASSISTANT TEACHERS

see Teachers' Assistants

ASSISTED SUICIDE

see also Euthanasia

Ball, Howard. At Liberty to Die: The Battle for Death with Dignity in America. 2012. (ENG.). 224p. 30.00 **(978-0-8147-9104-2(2))** New York Univ. Pr.

Battiny, Margaret Pabst. The Least Worst Death: Essays in Bioethics on the End of Life. 2006. 305p. reprint ed. pap. 30.00 (978-1-4223-5526-8(8)) DIANE Publishing Co.

Benzenhö, et al. Der gute Tod? Geschichte der Euthanasie und Sterbehilfe. 2009. (GER.). 224p. (C). 27.00 *(978-3-525-30162-3(6))* Vandenhoeck & Ruprecht GmbH & Co. KG DEU. Dist: ISD.

Birnbacher, Dieter & Dahl, Edgar, eds. Giving Death a Helping Hand. 2008. (International Library of Ethics, Law, & the New Medicine Ser.). XII, 160p. (C). 169.00 *(978-1-4020-6495-1(0)*, 1402064950) Springer.

Bonelli, Johannes & Prat, Enrique H., eds. Leben, Sterben, Euthanasie? (Medizin und Ethik Ser.). (GER.). XI, 178p. pap. 32.00 *(978-3-211-83525-8(3)*, 3211835253) Springer.

Chamberlain, Paul. Final Wishes: A Cautionary Tale on Death, Dignity, & Physician-Assisted Suicide. 2009. 216p. pap. 24.00 *(978-1-60608-445-8(3)*, Wipf and Stock) Wipf & Stock Pubs.

The Consequences of Legalized Assisted Suicide & Euthanasia: Hearing Before the Subcommittee on the Constitution, Civil Rights & Property Rights of the Committee on the Judiciary, United States Senate, One Hundred Ninth Congress, Second Session, May 25, 2006. 2008. iii, 124p. *(978-0-16-082554-5(7)*, 552-070-38582-7) United States Government Printing Office.

Ekland-Olson, Sheldon & Aseltine, Elyshia. How Ethical Systems Change: Tolerable Suffering & Assisted Dying. 2011. (Framing 21st Century Social Issues Ser.). (ENG.). 64p. pap. 9.95 ***(978-0-415-50516-1(X))*** Routledge.

Ferry, Luc & Kahn, Axel. Faut-Il Légaliser L'euthanasie? 2010. 143p. *(978-2-7381-2576-7(X))* Jacob, Odile.

friedman, Lauri S. Assisted Suicide. 2008. (Compact Research Ser.). (YA). (gr. 7-12). lib. bdg. 25.95 *(978-1-60152-048-7(4))* ReferencePoint Pr., Inc.

Friedman, Mark D. Assisted Suicide. 2011. (Hot Topics Ser.). (ENG.). 56p. (gr. 7-8). 33.50 *(978-1-4329-4867-2(9))*; (Illus.). pap. 9.99 *(978-1-4329-6202-9(7))* Heinemann-Raintree. (NA-h).

Gilderdale, Kay. One Last Goodbye: Sometimes Only a Mother's Love Can Help End the Pain. 2011. (ENG., Illus.). 336p. pap. 12.95 ***(978-0-09-193914-4(3))*** Ebury Publishing GBR. Dist: Independent Pubs. Group.

Gorsuch, Neil M. Future of Assisted Suicide & Euthanasia. 2006. (New Forum Bks.). (ENG., Illus.). 328p. (C). 46.95 *(978-0-691-12458-2(2))* Princeton Univ. Pr.

Gorsuch, Neil M. & Gorsuch, Neil M. The Future of Assisted Suicide & Euthanasia. 2009. (New Forum Bks.). (ENG., Illus.). 328p. (C). pap. 26.95 *(978-0-691-14097-1(9))* Princeton Univ. Pr.

Greene, Barbara & Howard, Vanessa. A Mother's Love. 2010. (ENG.). 304p. pap. 13.95 ***(978-1-84916-998-1(5))*** Quercus GBR. Dist: Independent Pubs. Group.

Habicht, Annekatrin. Sterbehilfe - Wandel in der Terminologie: Eine integrative Betrachtung aus der Sicht von Medizin, Ethik und Recht. 2009. (Recht & Medizin Ser.). (GER.). 212p. pap. 56.95 *(978-3-631-58305-0(2))* Lang, Peter GmbH, Europaischer Verlag der Wissenschaften DEU. Dist: Lang, Peter.

Holody, Kyle J. Framing Death - the Use of Frames in Newspaper Coverage of & Press Releases about Death with Dignity. 2008. 104p. per. *(978-3-8364-5370-7(3))* VDM Verlag Dr. Mueller e.K.

Jones, Robert P. Liberalism's Troubled Search for Equality: Religion & Cultural Bias in the Oregon Physician-Assisted Suicide Debates. 2007. 352p. per. 30.00 *(978-0-268-03267-8(X))* Univ. of Notre Dame Pr.

Langwith, Jacqueline, ed. Suicide. 2008. (Opposing Viewpoints Ser.). (ENG.). 268p. (YA). (gr. 7-12). 27.50 *(978-0-7377-4013-4(2))*; (Illus.). pap. 39.70 *(978-0-7377-4012-7(4))* Cengage Gale. (Greenhaven Pr., Inc.).

Lewis, Penney. Assisted Dying & Legal Change. 2007. (ENG.). 256p. 139.95 *(978-0-19-921287-3(2))* Oxford Univ. Pr., Inc.

Lewy, Guenter. Assisted Death in Europe & America: Four Regimes & Their Lessons, 1 vol. 2010. (ENG.). 256p. 49.95 *(978-0-19-974641-5(9))* Oxford Univ. Pr., Inc.

Lillie, Timothy & Werth, James L. End-Of-Life Issues & Persons with Disabilities. 2007. *(978-1-4164-0263-3(2))* PRO-ED, Inc.

Marneghani, Jussi Raafael. Der mutmaßliche Wille als Kriterium für den ärztlichen Behandlungsabbruch bei entscheidungsunfähigen Patienten und sein Verhältnis zum Betreuungsrecht. 2010. (Recht & Medizin Ser.). (GER.). 236p. pap. 61.95 *(978-3-631-58519-1(5))* Lang, Peter GmbH, Europaischer Verlag der Wissenschaften DEU. Dist: Lang, Peter.

Marcus, Eric. Why Suicide? Questions & Answers about Suicide, Suicide Prevention, & Coping with the Suicide of Someone You Know. 2010. (ENG.). 240p. pap. 14.99 *(978-0-06-200391-1(7)*, HarperOne) HarperCollins Pubs.

McKhann, Charles F. A Time to Die: The Place for Physician Assistance. 2006. 268p. reprint ed. pap. 20.00 *(978-1-4223-5363-9(X))* DIANE Publishing Co.

McLean, Sheila A. M. Assisted Dying: Reflections on the Need for Law Reform. 2006. (Biomedical Law & Ethics Library). (ENG.). 224p. (C). per. 57.50 *(978-1-84472-054-5(3)*, Routledge Cavendish); 213p. 200.00 *(978-1-84472-055-2(1)*, Routledge) Taylor & Francis Group GBR. Dist: Taylor & Francis Group.

Merino, No'l, ed. Assisted Suicide. 2012. (Current Controversies Ser.). (ENG.). 240p. (gr. 10-12). pap. 40.90 ***(978-0-7377-5613-5(6)***, Greenhaven Pr., Inc.); (YA). (gr. 9-12). lib. bdg. 28.35 ***(978-0-7377-5612-8(8))*** Cengage Gale.

Mitchell, John B. Understanding Assisted Suicide: Nine Issues to Consider. 2007. (ENG.). 232p. pap. 23.95 *(978-0-472-06996-5(9))* Univ. of Michigan Pr.

Novak, David. The Sanctity of Human Life. (ENG.). 208p. 2009. pap. 29.95 *(978-1-58901-504-3(5))* 2007. 34.95 *(978-1-58901-176-2(7))* Georgetown Univ. Pr.

Paterson, Craig. Assisted Suicide & Euthanasia: A Natural Law Ethics Approach. 2008. (Live Questions in Ethics & Moral Philosophy Ser.). 228p. 99.95 *(978-0-7546-5745-3(0))*; pap. 39.95 *(978-0-7546-5746-0(9))* Ashgate Publishing Co.

Prado, Carlos. Coping with Choices to Die. 2010. (ENG.). 206p. 85.00 *(978-0-521-11476-9(4))*; pap. 27.99 *(978-0-521-13248-0(7))* Cambridge Univ. Pr.

Purdy, Debbie. It's Not Because I Want to Die. 2010. (ENG., Illus.). 292p. 13.95 *(978-0-00-735798-7(2))* HarperCollins Pubs. Ltd. GBR. Dist: Independent Pubs. Group.

Shavelson, Lonny. A Chosen Death: The Dying Confront Assisted Suicide. 2006. (Illus.). 240p. reprint ed. 23.00 *(978-1-4223-5752-1(X))* DIANE Publishing Co.

Sumner, L. W. Assisted Death: A Study in Ethics & Law. 2011. (ENG.). 248p. 65.00 *(978-0-19-960798-3(2))* Oxford Univ. Pr., Inc.

Viers, Kenneth G. Discourses of Assisted Dying. 2010. 220p. pap. *(978-3-8383-8354-5(0))* Lambert Academic Publishing.

Vöhringer, Caroline. Tötung auf Verlangen: Die Abgrenzung des § 216 StGB zur straflosen Beihilfe zum Suizid sowie das Verhältnis von privilegierenden zu qualifizierenden Tötungsumständen. 2008. (Würzburger Schriften zur Kriminalwissenschaft Ser.). 338p. pap. 81.95 *(978-3-631-57091-3(0))* Lang, Peter GmbH, Europaischer Verlag der Wissenschaften DEU. Dist: Lang, Peter.

Warnock, Mary & Macdonald, Elisabeth. Easeful Death: Is There a Case for Assisted Dying? 2009. (ENG.). 176p. pap. 18.95 *(978-0-19-956184-1(2))* Oxford Univ. Pr., Inc.

West, John. The Last Goodnights: Assisting My Parents with Their Suicides. (ENG.). 272p. 2010. pap. 15.95 *(978-1-58243-557-2(X))* 2009. 25.00 *(978-1-58243-448-3(4))* Basic Bks. GBR. (Counterpoint Pr.). Dist: Perseus-PGW.

Wester-Mittan, Candle M. Physician-Assisted Death: Four Views on the Issue of Legalizing PAD: A Legal Research Guide. 2009. (Illus.). xviii, 58p. *(978-0-8377-1698-5(5))* Hein, William S. & Co., Inc.

Williams, Glenys O. Intention & Causation in Medical Non-Killing: The Impact of Criminal Law Concepts on Euthanasia & Assisted Suicide. 2007. (Biomedical Law & Ethics Library). (ENG.). 248p. (C). per. 59.95 *(978-0-415-42302-1(3)*, Routledge Cavendish) Taylor & Francis Group GBR. Dist: Taylor & Francis Group.

Youngner, Stuart & Kimsma, Gerrit K., eds. Physician-Assisted Death in Perspective: Assessing the Dutch Experience. 2012. (ENG., Illus.). 424p. 99.00 ***(978-1-107-00756-7(9))*** Cambridge Univ. Pr.

ASSISTIVE TECHNOLOGY

see Self-Help Devices for People with Disabilities

ASSOCIACION LATINOAMERICANA DE LIBRE COMMERCIO

Yudelman, Montague & Howard, Frederic. Agricultural Development & Economic Integration in Latin America. 2011. (ENG.). 336p. 115.00 *(978-0-415-59436-3(7))* Routledge.

ASSOCIATED PRESS

Graff, Chris. Dateline Vermont: Covering & Uncovering the Newsworthy Stories that Shaped a State — & Influenced a Nation. 2006. (Illus.). 240p. 24.95 *(978-0-9705511-3-9(4))* Thistle Hill Pubns.

Kennedy, Ed. Ed Kennedy's War: V-E Day, Censorship, & the Associated Press. Cochran, Julia Kennedy, ed. 2012. (From Our Own Correspondent Ser.). (Illus.). 248p. 34.95 ***(978-0-8071-4525-8(4))*** Louisiana State Univ. Pr.

Reporters of the Associated Press. Breaking News: How the Associated Press Has Covered War, Peace, & Everything Else. 2007. (ENG., Illus.). 432p. 35.00 *(978-1-56898-689-0(0))* Princeton Architectural Pr.

ASSOCIATION

see Social Groups

ASSOCIATION, FREEDOM OF

see Freedom of Association

ASSOCIATION FOOTBALL

see Soccer

ASSOCIATION OF IDEAS

see also Conditioned Response; Paired-Association Learning

De Ley, Gerd & Potter, David. The Big Book of Business Advice: A Great Resource for Insightful Ideas & Amusing Quotations from the Famous & Infamous. rev. ed. 2011. (ENG.). 188p. pap. 21.95 *(978-1-61110-010-5(0))* Global Management Enterprises.

Ferguson, Alexander. Consciousness & Feedback - Explaining the Coherence of Content. 2008. 84p. pap. *(978-3-639-01121-0(X))* VDM Verlag Dr. Mueller e.K.

Franko, Mark, ed. Ritual & Event. 2009. (Illus.). 204p. pap. 34.00 *(978-0-415-54411-5(4))* Routledge.

Freud, Sigmund. Zur Psychopathologie des Alltagslebens: Über Vergessen, Versprechen, Vergreifen, Aberglaube und Irrtum. 2008. 116p. pap. *(978-1-4099-2300-8(2))* Dodo Pr.

—Zur Psychopathologie des Alltagslebens: Über Vergessen, Versprechen, Vergreifen, Aberglaube und Irrtum. 2008. 80p. pap. *(978-1-4068-7331-3(4))* Echo Library.

Grimaldi, Gesualdo. The Market for Errors. 2010. 120p. pap. *(978-3-639-23076-5(0))* VDM Verlag Dr. Mueller e.K.

Kent, Grace Helen & Rosanoff, A. J. A Study of Association in Insanity. 2007. 644p. per. *(978-1-4065-1902-0(2))* Dodo Pr.

Kent, Grace Helen & Rosanoff, Aaron Joshua. A Study of Association in Insanity. 2009. 144p. 35.95 *(978-1-120-21644-1(3))*; pap. 20.95 *(978-1-120-13147-8(2))* Kessinger Publishing, LLC.

Warren, Howard C. A History of the Association Psychology. 2007. (ENG.) 336p. 45.95 *(978-0-548-19996-1(5))*; 340p. per. 30.95 *(978-1-4325-0936-1(5))* Kessinger Publishing, LLC.

Zhao, Yanchang, et al, eds. Post-Mining of Association Rules: Techniques for Effective Knowledge Extraction. 2009. (Illus.). 394p. 195.00 *(978-1-60566-404-0(9))* IGI Global.

ASSOCIATION OF SOUTHEAST ASIAN NATIONS

Acharya, Amitav. Constructing a Security Community in Southeast Asia: ASEAN & the Problem of Regional Order. 2nd rev. ed. (Politics in Asia Ser.). (Illus.). 2009. (ENG.). 352p. (C). 190.00 *(978-0-415-41428-9(8))* 2008. 256p. 44.95 *(978-0-415-41429-6(6))* Routledge.

—The Making of Southeast Asia: International Relations of a Region. 2011. (Cornell Studies in Political Economy Ser.). (Illus.). 240p. pap. 22.95 *(978-0-8014-7736-2(0))* Cornell Univ. Pr.

Asean Studies Center. Asean-Canada Forum 2008. 2010. 278p. pap. *(978-981-4279-14-7(5))* Institute of Southeast Asian Studies.

—The Global Economic Crisis: Implications for ASEAN. 2010. (Illus.). 164p. pap. *(978-981-4279-41-3(2))* Institute of Southeast Asian Studies.

Ba, Alice & Ba, Alice D. (Re)Negotiating East & Southeast Asia: Region, Regionalism, & the Association of Southeast Asian Nations. 2009. (Studies in Asian Security Ser.). (ENG., Illus.). 344p. 75.00 *(978-0-8047-6069-0(1))*; pap. 29.95 *(978-0-8047-6070-6(5))* Stanford Univ. Pr.

Beeson, Mark. Institutions of the Asia-Pacific: ASEAN, APEC, & Beyond. 2008. (Illus.). XVI, 136p. pap. 28.95 *(978-0-415-46504-5(4))* Routledge.

Bhasin, Balbir. Doing Business in the ASEAN Countries. 2011. (ENG.). 175p. pap. 25.00 *(978-1-60649-108-9(3))* Business Expert Pr.

Chairas, Ira Yuta & E.D. Radianto, Wirawan. Accounting Harmonization in Asean. 2010. 148p. pap. *(978-3-639-25457-0(0))* VDM Verlag Dr. Mueller e.K.

Chufrin, Gennadii Illarionovich & Hong, Mark. Russia-ASEAN Relations: New Directions. 2007. xx, 142p. *(978-981-230-736-1(2))* Institute of Southeast Asian Studies.

Collins, Alan. Building a People-Oriented Security Community the ASEAN Way. 2012. (Routledge Contemporary Southeast Asia Ser.). (ENG.). 208p. (C). 135.00 *(978-0-415-60868-8(6))* Routledge.

Cortinhas, Carlos. Prospects for Monetary Integration in Asean. 2009. 172p. pap. *(978-3-639-20742-2(4))* VDM Verlag Dr. Mueller e.K.

Cram101 Textbook Reviews Staff. Outlines & Highlights for International Relations in Southeast Asi: The Struggle for Autonomy by Donald Weatherbee, Ralf Emmers, ISBN. 2009. 108p. pap. 27.95 *(978-1-4288-7779-5(7))* Cram101 Inc.

Curley, Melissa G. & Thomas, Nick, eds. Advancing East Asian Regionalism. 2006. (Politics in Asia Ser.). (ENG., Illus.). 320p. (C). 180.00 *(978-0-415-34909-3(5)*, RU42437) Routledge.

Doidge, Mathew. The European Union & Interregionalism: Patterns of Engagement. 2011. (Illus.). 234p. 99.95 *(978-0-7546-7927-1(6))* Ashgate Publishing Co.

Dong, Lisheng & Heiduk, Günter. The EU's Experience in Integration: A Model for ASEAN+3? (Illus.). 358p. pap. 68.95 *(978-3-03911-429-0(8))* Lang, Peter Publishing, Inc.

Emmers, Ralf, ed. ASEAN & the Institutionalization of East Asia. 2011. (Routledge Security in Asia Pacific Ser.). (ENG., Illus.). 248p. (C). 140.00 *(978-0-415-61434-4(1))* Routledge.

Emmers, Ralf, et al. The East Asia Summit & the Regional Security Architecture. 2010. 52p. ***(978-1-932330-32-8(1))*** Univ. of Maryland, Schl. of Law.

Emmerson, Donald K., ed. & contrib. by. Hard Choices: Security, Democracy, & Regionalism in Southeast Asia. 2008. (ENG.). 320p. pap. 28.95 *(978-1-931368-13-1(9))* Shorenstein, Walter H. Asia-Pacific Research Ctr.

Erik. International Economic Integration. . (V3) 2006. (Advanced Research in Asian Economic Studies). 124.00 *(978-981-256-757-4(7))* World Scientific Publishing Co., Inc.

Feigenbaum, Evan A. & Manning, Robert A. The United States in the New Asia: Council Special Report No. 50, November 2009. 2009. (ENG.). 56p. 10.00 *(978-0-87609-469-3(8))* Council on Foreign Relations.

Fort, Bertrand & Webber, Douglas, eds. Regional Integration in East Asia & Europe: Convergence or Divergence? 2008. 352p. 41.95 *(978-0-415-47974-5(6))* Routledge.

Gugler, Philippe & Chaisse, Julien, eds. Competitiveness of the ASEAN Countries: Corporate & Regulatory Drivers. 2010. (New Horizons in International Business Ser.). 336p. 139.00 *(978-1-84980-124-9(X))* Elgar, Edward Publishing, Inc.

Gulyás, Viktor. Totalitary Regimes in Security Regionalism. 2008. 56p. pap. *(978-3-639-02722-8(1))* VDM Verlag Dr. Mueller e.K.

Haacke, Jurgen. ASEAN's Diplomatic & Security Culture: Origins, Development & Prospects. 2009. 298p. pap. 39.95 *(978-0-415-54632-4(X))* Routledge.

Haacke, Jürgen. Cooperative Security in the Asia-Pacific: The ASEAN Regional Forum. Morada, Noel M., ed. 2009. (Asian Security Studies). (ENG.). 288p. 130.00 *(978-0-415-46052-1(2))* Routledge.

Hew, Denis. Brick by Brick: The Building of an ASEAN Economic Community. 2007. (Illus.). xx, 250p. pap. *(978-0-7315-3814-0(5))* Asia Pacific Pr.

—Brick by Brick: The Building of an ASEAN Economic Community. 2007. (Illus.). xx, 250p. *(978-981-230-733-0(8))* Institute of Southeast Asian Studies.

Hongyi, Lai & Seng, Lim Tin, eds. Harmony & Development: ASEA - China Relations. 2007. 164p. 84.00 *(978-981-270-970-7(3))* World Scientific Publishing Co., Inc.

Hund, Markus. Asean & Asean Plus Three - Manifestations of Collective Identities in Southeast & East Asia? 2007. 428p. per. *(978-3-8364-5045-4(3))* VDM Verlag Dr. Mueller e.K.

Institute of Southeast Asian Studies Staff, contrib. by. Economic Integration & the Investment Climates in ASEAN Countries: Perspectives from Taiwan Investors. 2009. (Illus.). viii, 95p. pap. *(978-981-230-998-3(5))* Institute of Southeast Asian Studies.

—Know Your ASEAN. 2007. (Illus.). vi, 50p. pap. *(978-981-230-487-2(8))* Institute of Southeast Asian Studies.

Iseas, Asc. Asean Community: Unblocking the Roadblocks. 2008. 112p. pap. *(978-981-230-843-6(1))* Institute of Southeast Asian Studies.

Jones, Lee. ASEAN, Sovereignty & Intervention in Southeast Asia. 2012. (Critical Studies of the Asia-Pacific Ser.). (ENG., Illus.). 280p. 85.00 ***(978-0-230-31926-4(2))*** Palgrave Macmillan.

Jones, Nick. Asean & East Asian International Relations Regional Delusion. 2007. 288p. pap. 58.00 *(978-1-84720-086-0(9))* Elgar, Edward Publishing, Inc.

Kanke, Yoko. A Comparative Analysis of Eu & Asean. 2010. 88p. pap. *(978-3-8383-4233-7(X))* Lambert Academic Publishing.

Katsumata, Hiro. Asean's Cooperative Security Enterprise: Norms & Interests in the ASEAN Regional Forum. 2010. (Critical Studies of the Asia-Pacific Ser.). (ENG., Illus.). 240p. 89.00 *(978-0-230-22929-7(8))* Palgrave Macmillan.

Keyuan, Zou. China-Asean Relations & International Law. 2011. (Chandos Asian Studies). (ENG., Illus.). 250p. 110.00 *(978-1-84334-438-4(6)*, Chandos Publishing) Woodhead Publishing Ltd. GBR. Dist: Ingram Pub. Services.

Kirkpatrick, Andy. English as a Lingua Franca in ASEAN: A Multilingual Model. 2010. (Asian Englishes Today Ser.). (ENG., Illus.). 236p. (gr. 17). 50.00 *(978-988-8028-78-8(2))*; pap. 30.00 *(978-988-8028-79-5(0))* Hong Kong Univ. Pr. HKG. Dist: Columbia Univ. Pr.

Koh, Tommy, et al, eds. The Making of the Asean Charter. 2009. 180p. 51.00 *(978-981-283-390-7(0))* World Scientific Publishing Co., Inc.

Lall, Ashish. Facets of Competitiveness: Narratives from Asean. 2011. 350p. 85.00 *(978-981-4324-11-3(6))* World Scientific Publishing Co., Inc.

Lee, Yoong Yoong. Asean Matters: Reflecting on the Association of Southeast Asian Nations. 2011. (Illus.). 180p. pap. 35.00 *(978-981-4335-06-5(1))* World Scientific Publishing Co., Inc.

Li, Mingjiang & Kwa, Chong Guan. China-ASEAN Sub-Regional Cooperation: Progress, Problems & Prospect. 2011. xiii, 172p. ***(978-981-4340-42-7(1))*** World Scientific Publishing Co., Inc.

Lim, Hua Sing. Japan & China in East Asian Integration. 5th ed. 2008. (Illus.). xxxvii, 371p. pap. *(978-981-230-744-6(3))* Institute of Southeast Asian Studies.

Montesano, Michael J. Regional Outlook: Southeast Asia 2011-2012. Montesano, Michael J. & Onn, Lee Poh, eds. 2011. 200p. pap. ***(978-981-4311-00-7(6))*** Institute of Southeast Asian Studies.

Nguitragool, Paruedee. Environmental Cooperation in Southeast Asia. 2010. (Routledge Contemporary Southeast Asia Ser.). (ENG., Illus.). 208p. (C). 130.00 *(978-0-415-58214-8(8)*, Routledge) Taylor & Francis Group GBR. Dist: Taylor & Francis Group.

Nishikawa, Yukiko. Human Security in Southeast Asia. 2012. (ENG.). 224p. (C). pap. 44.95 ***(978-0-415-62548-7(3))*** Routledge.

Nordell, Emelie & Stark, Caroline. Diversifying in the Integrated Markets of Asean+3. 2010. 84p. pap. *(978-3-8383-9430-5(5))* Lambert Academic Publishing.

Pavin Chachavalpongpun. The Road to Ratification & Implementation of the ASEAN Charter. 2008. xi, 70p. pap. *(978-981-230-898-6(9))* Institute of Southeast Asian Studies.

Plummer. Asean-Economic Development & Integ. . (V5) 2009. (Illus.). ix, 343p. 100.00 *(978-981-256-910-3(3))* World Scientific Publishing Co., Inc.

Roberts, Christopher. Asean Regionalism: Co-Operation, Values & Institutionalisation. 2011. (Routledge Security in Asia Pacific Ser.). (ENG., Illus.). 280p. (C). 155.00 *(978-0-415-49001-6(4))* Routledge.

Seng. Harmony & Development. 2007. pap. 1.00 *(978-981-270-971-4(1))* World Scientific Publishing Co., Inc.

Severino, et al. Southeast Asia in a New ERA: Ten Countries, One Region in ASEAN. (Illus.). xx, 281p. pap. *(978-981-230-957-0(8))* Institute of Southeast Asian Studies.

Severino, C. Southeast Asia in Search of an Asean Community. 2006. (Illus.). 520p. *(978-981-230-389-9(8))* Institute of Southeast Asian Studies.

Severino, Rodolfo. ASEAN. 2008. (Illus.). v, 111p. *(978-981-230-750-7(8))* Institute of Southeast Asian Studies.

Simon, Sheldon W. ASEAN & Its Security Offspring: Facing New Challenges. 2007. (Global Security Challenges to U.S. Interests Ser.). *(978-1-58487-306-8(X))* Strategic Studies Institute, U.S. Army War College Commandant (AWCC-DSI/Pubns.).

Storey, Ian. Asean & the Rise of China. 2011. (Routledge Security in Asia Ser.). (ENG., Illus.). 384p. 145.00 *(978-0-415-32621-6(4))* Routledge.

—The United States & ASEAN-China Relations: All Quiet on the Southeast Asian Front. 2007. (Global Security Challenges to U.S. Interests Ser.). *(978-1-58487-320-4(5))* Strategic Studies Institute, U.S. Army War College Commandant (AWCC-DSI/Pubns.).

Tan, See Seng. Regionalism in Asia, 4 vols. 2009. (Illus.). 392p. *(978-0-415-47825-0(1))*; *(978-0-415-47824-3(3))*; *(978-0-415-47827-4(8))*; *(978-0-415-47826-7(X))* Routledge.

Thompson, Eric C. & Chulanee Thianthai. Attitudes & Awareness Towards ASEAN: Findings of a Ten-Nation Survey. 2008. (Illus.). xiii, 98p. pap. *(978-981-230-869-6(5))* Institute of Southeast Asian Studies.

Tiwari, S., ed. Asean: Life after the Charter. 2010. (Illus.). 186p. *(978-981-4279-56-7(0))* Institute of Southeast Asian Studies.

United Nations. Striving Together: ASEAN & the United Nations. 2009. (ENG.). 92p. pap. 32.00 *(978-92-1-120565-7(4))* United Nations Pubns.

Weatherbee, Donald & Emmers, Ralf. International Relations in Southeast Asia: The Struggle for Autonomy. 2nd ed. 2008. (Asia in World Politics Ser.). (ENG.). 348p. 100.00 *(978-0-7425-5681-2(6))*; pap. 34.95 *(978-0-7425-5682-9(4))* Rowman & Littlefield Publishers, Inc.

Welfens, Paul J. J., et al, eds. Integration in Asia & Europe: Historical Dynamics, Political Issues, & Economic Perspectives. 2010. (ENG., Illus.). vi, 284p. pap. 129.00 *(978-3-642-06685-6(2),* 3642066852) Springer.

Yuzawa, Takeshi. Japan's Security Policy & the ASEAN Regional Forum: The Search for Multilateral Security in the Asia-Pacific. 2007. (Sheffield Centre for Japanese Studies/Routledge Ser.). 219p. 170.00 *(978-0-415-40337-5(5))* Routledge.

ASSOCIATIONS (LAW)

see Unincorporated Societies

ASSOCIATIONS, EMPLOYERS'

see Employers' Associations

ASSOCIATIONS, INSTITUTIONS, ETC.

see also Charities; Clubs; Committees; Community Life; Cooperation; Freedom of Association; Learned Institutions and Societies; Nonprofit Organizations; Public Institutions; Religious Institutions; Social Group Work; Societies; Trade and Professional Associations; Voluntarism

also subdivision Societies, etc. under topical headings; subdivision Societies and Clubs under classes of persons; and names of individual associations, institutions, etc.

American Society of Association Executives Staff & Center for Association Leadership Staff, contrib. by. 7 Measures of Success: What Remarkable Associations Do That Others Don't. 2006. (Illus.). xxii, 138p. *(978-0-88034-272-8(2))* American Society of Assn. Executives.

Anderson, Ray S. Minding GodÕs Business. 2008. (Ray S. Anderson Collection Ser.). 164p. pap. 19.00 *(978-1-60608-219-5(1),* Wipf and Stock) Wipf & Stock Pubs.

Ariño Villarroya, Antoni, et al. Asociacionismo y Voluntariado en España: Una Perspectiva General. 2007. (SPA., Illus.). 670p. *(978-84-8456-960-2(8))* Tirant lo Blanch.

Arts, Bas & Leroy, Pieter, eds. Institutional Dynamics in Environmental Governance. 2010. (Environment & Policy Ser.). xiv, 292p. pap. 149.00 *(978-90-481-7277-1(2),* 9048172772) Springer.

Ascough, Richard S., et al. Associations in the Greco-Roman World: A Sourcebook. 2012. (ENG., Illus.). 430p. (C). pap. 39.95 ***(978-1-60258-374-0(9))*** Baylor Univ. Pr.

Bano, Masooda. Breakdown in Pakistan: How Aid Is Eroding Institutions for Collective Action. 2012. (ENG.). 240p. 45.00 ***(978-0-8047-8132-9(X),*** Stanford Economics & Finance) Stanford Univ. Pr.

Bergendorff, Steen. Simple Lives, Cultural Complexity: Rethinking Culture in Terms of Complexity Theory. 2009. (ENG., Illus.). 208p. 62.99 *(978-0-7391-2897-8(3))* Lexington Bks.

Bimber, Bruce A., et al. Collective Action in Organizations: Interaction & Engagement in an ERA of Technological Change. 2012. (Communication, Society & Politics Ser.). (ENG., Illus.). 240p. 99.00 ***(978-0-521-19172-2(6))***; pap. 29.99 ***(978-0-521-13963-2(5))*** Cambridge Univ. Pr.

Bird, Frederick & Westley, Frances. Voices from the Voluntary Sector: Perspectives on Leadership Challenges. 2010. (Illus.). 448p. pap. *(978-0-8020-9661-6(1))* Univ. of Toronto Pr.

Bradley, Joseph. Voluntary Associations in Tsarist Russia: Science, Patriotism, & Civil Society. 2009. (Illus.). 384p. 58.00 *(978-0-674-03279-8(9))* Harvard Univ. Pr.

Braveboy-Wagner, Jacqueline Anne. Institutions of the Global South: Third World. 2009. (Global Institutions Ser.). (Illus.). 192p. 26.95 *(978-0-415-36591-8(0))* Routledge.

—Institutions of the Global South/Third World. 2008. (Global Institutions Ser.). (Illus.). XX, 252p. 140.00 *(978-0-415-36590-1(2))* Routledge.

Brinckerhoff, Peter C. Generations: The Challenge of a Lifetime for Your Nonprofit. 2007. (ENG.). 232p. pap. 35.95 *(978-0-940069-55-8(5),* Fieldstone Alliance) Turner Publishing Co.

Brown, Craig. Working in the Voluntary Sector: How to Find Rewarding & Fulfilling Work in Charities & Voluntary Organisations. 4th ed. 2008. 180p. pap. 20.00 *(978-1-84528-007-9(5))* How To Books GBR. Dist: Parkwest Pubns., Inc.

Cameron, David R. & Simeon, Richard, eds. Language Matters: How Canadian Voluntary Associations Manage French & English. 2010. (ENG.). 232p. pap. 32.95 *(978-0-7748-1504-8(3))* Univ. of Washington Pr.

Carlson, Mim & Donohoe, Margaret. The Executive Director's Guide to Thriving as a Nonprofit Leader. 2nd ed. 2010. (Jossey-Bass Nonprofit Guidebook Ser.: 7). (ENG., Illus.). 352p. pap. 38.00 *(978-0-470-40749-3(2),* Jossey-Bass) Wiley, John & Sons, Inc.

Cnaan, Ram A. & Milofsky, Carl. Handbook of Community Movements & Local Organizations. 2008. (Handbooks of Sociology & Social Research Ser.). (Illus.). 436p. pap. 89.95 *(978-0-387-75729-2(5),* 0387757295) Springer.

Cohen, Susan. The Women's Institute. 2011. (Shire Library). (ENG., Illus.). 64p. pap. 12.95 *(978-0-7478-1046-9(X))* Shire Pubns., Ltd. GBR. Dist: Random Hse., Inc.

College Board Staff. Scholarship Handbook 2011. 2010. (ENG.). 620p. pap. 28.99 *(978-0-87447-906-5(1))* College Board, The.

Comerford, R. V. & Kelly, Jennifer, eds. Associational Culture in Ireland & Abroad. 2010. (Illus.). 236p. 74.95 *(978-0-7165-3078-7(3))* Irish Academic Pr. IRL. Dist: International Specialized Bk. Services.

Consumer Sourcebook. 25th ed. 2011. pap. 505.00 *(978-1-4144-4589-2(X))* Cengage Gale.

Cope, Bill & Kalantzis, Mary, eds. The International Journal of Knowledge, Culture & Change Management: Volume 10, Number 1. 2010. 602p. 0.00 *(978-1-86335-822-4(6))* Common Ground Publishing Pty, Ltd.

—The International Journal of Knowledge, Culture & Change Management: Volume 10, Number 7. 2011. 180p. 0.00 ***(978-1-86335-910-8(9))*** Common Ground Publishing Pty, Ltd.

—The International Journal of Knowledge, Culture & Change Management: Volume 10, Number 8. 2011. 134p. 0.00 ***(978-1-86335-923-8(0))*** Common Ground Publishing Pty, Ltd.

—The International Journal of Knowledge, Culture & Change Management: Volume 10, Number 9. 2011. 118p. 0.00 ***(978-1-86335-926-9(5))*** Common Ground Publishing Pty, Ltd.

Cope, Bill & Kalantzis, Mary, eds. The International Journal of Knowledge, Culture & Change Management: Volume 9, Number 12. 2010. 188p. 0.00 *(978-1-86335-753-1(X))* Common Ground Publishing Pty, Ltd.

Corcoran, Mary P., et al. Suburban Affiliations: Social Relations in the Greater Dublin Area. 2010. (Illus.). 328p. *(978-0-8156-3214-6(2))* Syracuse Univ. Pr.

Cram101 Textbook Reviews & Cram101 Textbook Reviews. Outlines & Highlights for Groups, Representation & Democracy: Between Promise & Practice by Darren R. Halpin, ISBN. 2011. 72p. pap. 27.95 ***(978-1-61461-137-0(8))*** Cram101 Inc.

De Warren, Robert. Destiny's Waltz, in Step with Giants. 2009. 412p. 36.50 *(978-1-60860-457-9(8),* Eloquent Bks.) AEG Literary Publishing Services, Inc.

Djordjevic, Nenad. Old Shanghai Clubs & Associations: A Directory of the Rich Life of Foreigners in Shanghai from the 1840s to the 1950s. 2010. (ENG., Illus.). 340p. 29.99 *(978-988-17621-9-1(7))* Earnshaw Bks. HKG. Dist: Independent Pubs. Group.

Dolfsma, Wilfred. Institutions, Communication & Values. 2009. (ENG., Illus.). 184p. 100.00 *(978-0-230-22379-0(6))* Palgrave Macmillan.

Doner, Richard F. Explaining Institutional Innovation: Case Studies from Latin America & East Asia. 2010. (ENG., Illus.). 120p. (gr. 17). pap. 15.00 *(978-0-9790772-7-2(3))* Social Science Research Council, The.

Eek, Nat, et al. Discovering a New Audience for Theatre: The History of ASSITEJ, the International Association of Theatre for Children & Youth. 2008. 348p. pap. 26.95 *(978-0-86534-660-4(7))* Sunstone Pr.

Encyclopedia of Medical Organizations & Agencies, 3.0. 23rd ed. 2011. pap. 584.00 *(978-1-4144-5902-8(5))* Cengage Gale.

Feldman, Sharon G. In the Eye of the Storm: Contemporary Theater in Barcelona. 2009. (Illus.). 411p. 82.50 *(978-0-8387-5722-2(7))* Bucknell Univ. Pr.

Fernández Christlieb, Federico & García Zambrano, Ángel Julián. Territorialidad y Paisaje en el Altepetl Del Siglo XVI. 2007. (Historia Ser.). (SPA., Illus.). 580p. pap. *(978-968-16-7981-1(4))* Fondo de Cultura Economica.

Fernández Christlieb, Federico & García Zambrano, Julián Ángel. Territorialidad y Paisaje en el Altepetl del Siglo. 2007. (Historia Ser.). (SPA., Illus.). 580p. pap. 39.95 *(978-968-16-8328-3(5))* Fondo de Cultura Economica USA.

Ferry, Darren. Uniting in Measures of Common Good: The Construction of Liberal Identities in Central Canada, 1830-1900. 2008. (ENG., Illus.). 448p. (C). *(978-0-7735-3423-0(7))* McGill-Queen's Univ. Pr.

Fleishman, Joel, et al. Casebook for the Foundation: A Great American Secret. 2007. (ENG.). 354p. pap. 30.00 *(978-1-58648-488-0(5))* PublicAffairs.

Fleishman, Joel L. The Foundation: A Great American Secret; How Private Wealth Is Changing the World. 2009. (ENG., Illus.). 464p. pap. 19.95 *(978-1-58648-702-7(7))* PublicAffairs.

Gale Editor, ed. Consumer Sourcebook, 3 vols. 26th ed. 2011. pap. 530.00 *(978-1-4144-5849-6(5))* Cengage Gale.

Gallagher, Brian P., et al. CMMI-ACQ: Guidelines for Improving the Acquisition of Products & Services. 2008. (SEI Series in Software Engineering Ser.). (ENG., Illus.). 576p. 69.99 *(978-0-321-58035-1(4))* Addison Wesley Professional.

Gaudefroy-Demombynes, Maurice. Muslim Institutions. 2007. 224p. 175.00 *(978-0-415-44062-2(9))* Routledge.

Ghose, Tandra & Palmer, Stephen E. The Role Played by Extremal Edges in Figure-Ground Organization. 2008. 84p. pap. *(978-3-8364-8406-0(4))* VDM Verlag Dr. Mueller e.K.

Hajnal, Peter I. The G8 System & the G20: Evolution, Role & Documentation. 2nd rev. ed. 2007. (Global Finance Ser.). 296p. 124.95 *(978-0-7546-4550-4(9))* Ashgate Publishing Co.

Hensley, Jeremiah. Katrina That Bitch! The Drama Continues. 2006. per. 14.95 *(978-0-9774336-6-7(8))* Parallel View Publishing.

Hopkins, Bruce R. The Tax Law of Associations. 2009. (ENG.). 496p. pap. 75.00 *(978-0-470-45548-7(9),* Wiley) Wiley, John & Sons, Inc.

Hopper, Earl, ed. Trauma & Organizations. 2012. (New International Library of Group Analysis Ser.). 336p. pap. 44.95 *(978-1-85575-779-0(6))* Karnac Bks. GBR. Dist: Stylus Publishing, LLC.

Institute of Economic Growth (India) Staff, contrib. by. Ieg at Fifty: Recollections, Retrospect & Prospect. 2008. (ENG., Illus.). 238p. 39.95 *(978-81-7188-675-3(2))* Academic Foundation IND. Dist: Independent Pubs. Group.

Jamal, Amaney. Barriers to Democracy: The Other Side of Social Capital in Palestine & the Arab World. 2009. (ENG., Illus.). 192p. (C). pap. 20.95 *(978-0-691-14099-5(5))* Princeton Univ. Pr.

Jamal, Amaney A. Barriers to Democracy: The Other Side of Social Capital in Palestine & the Arab World. 2007. (ENG., Illus.). 192p. (C). 46.95 *(978-0-691-12727-9(1))* Princeton Univ. Pr.

Kalantzis, Mary & Cope, Bill, eds. The International Journal of Knowledge, Culture & Change Management: Volume 9, Number 1. 2009. 260p. 0.00 *(978-1-86335-640-4(1))* Common Ground Publishing Pty, Ltd.

Kapitza, Mathias. Untersuchungen zur Markenrechtsfähigkeit der BGB-Gesellschaft. 2008. (Studien zum Europäischen und Internationalen Wirtschaftsrecht. Studies in European & International Economic Law Ser.). 110p. pap. 35.95 *(978-3-631-58213-8(7))* Lang, Peter GmbH, Europäischer Verlag der Wissenschaften DEU. Dist: Lang, Peter.

Kavanagh, Donncha, et al. Organisation in Play. 2011. 225p. pap. ***(978-3-0343-0213-5(4))*** Lang, Peter Publishing, Inc.

Kenis, P. N., et al, eds. Temporary Organizations: Prevalence, Logic & Effectiveness. 2009. (Illus.). 304p. 137.00 *(978-1-84844-085-2(5))* Elgar, Edward Publishing, Inc.

Kirton, John, et al. Making Global Economic Governance Effective: Hard & Soft Law Institutions in a Crowded World. 2010. (Global Finance Ser.). (Illus.). 366p. 119.95 *(978-0-7546-7671-3(4))* Ashgate Publishing Co.

Kitching, Laurence Patrick Anthony. Das Deutschsprachige Theater Im Baltischen Raum, 1630-1918: The German-Language Theatre in the Baltic, 1630-1918. 2011. (GER.). 213p. *(978-0-8204-3507-7(4))* Lang, Peter Publishing, Inc.

Kloppenborg, John S. & Ascough, Richard S. Attica, Central Greece, Macedonia, Thrace. 2011. (Beihefte zur Zeitschrift für die neutestamentliche Wissenschaft und die Kunde der älteren Kirche Ser.). (ENG., XXXVI, 488p. Illus.). 252.00 ***(978-3-11-219069-2(6))***; 168.00 ***(978-3-11-025345-0(3))*** De Gruyter, Walter Inc.

Kolcio, Katja. Movable Pillars: Organizing Dance, 1956-1978. 2010. (ENG., Illus.). 240p. pap. 26.95 *(978-0-8195-6911-0(9))* Wesleyan Univ. Pr.

Koppelman, Andrew & Wolff, Tobias Barrington. A Right to Discriminate? How the Case of Boy Scouts of America V. James Dale Warped the Law of Free Association. 2009. (ENG.). 192p. 38.00 *(978-0-300-12127-8(X))* Yale Univ. Pr.

Koschnik, Albrecht. Let a Common Interest Bind Us Together: Associations, Partisanship, & Culture in Philadelphia, 1775-1840. 2007. (Jeffersonian America Ser.). (ENG., Illus.). 384p. (gr. 17). 45.00 *(978-0-8139-2648-3(3))* Univ. Pr. of Virginia.

Kott, Alexander. Information Warfare & Organizational Decision-Making. 2007. (Artech House Information Warfare Library). (Illus.). 273p. 129.00 *(978-1-59693-079-7(9))* Artech Hse., Inc.

Levitt, Tom. Partners for Good: Business Government & the Third Sector. 2012. 180p. 94.95 ***(978-1-4094-3437-5(0),*** Gower Publishing Co., Ltd.) Ashgate Publishing, Ltd. GBR. Dist: Ashgate Publishing Co.

Lewis, David, ed. International Perspectives on Voluntary Action: Reshaping the third Sector. 2009. (Earthscan Library Collection: Aid & Development Set Ser.). (ENG.). 292p. 110.00 *(978-1-84971-045-9(7))* Earthscan LLC.

Maloney, William A. Social Capital & Associations in European Democracies: A Comparative Analysis. 2009. 312p. pap. 37.50 *(978-0-415-54340-8(1))* Routledge.

Mars, Laura, ed. Educators Resource Directory. 2011. 2500p. pap. 145.00 *(978-1-59237-743-5(2))* Grey Hse. Publishing.

Mayer, Starr. When Bad Things Happen to Good Organizations: How Effective Manager's Prepare for Crisis. 2011. (ENG.). 162p. pap. 14.95 *(978-1-60037-861-4(7))* Morgan James Publishing.

Menuez, Douglas. Transcendent Spirit: The Orphans of Uganda. 2008. (Illus.). 156p. 35.00 *(978-0-8253-0585-6(3))* Beaufort Bks., Inc.

Morton, Graeme, et al. Civil Society, Associations, & Urban Places: Class, Nation, & Culture in Nineteenth-Century Europe. 2006. (Historical Urban Studies). (Illus.). 234p. 130.00 *(978-0-7546-5247-2(5))* Ashgate Publishing Co.

Moxley, David. Beyond Oversight: Developing Grassroots Nonprofit Boards for Community & Institutional Change. 2011. 39.99 *(978-0-87101-401-6(7),* NASW Pr.) National Assn. of Social Workers/NASW Pr.

Mulcahy, Lisa. Building the Successful Theater Company. 2nd ed. 2011. (ENG.). 256p. pap. 24.95 *(978-1-58115-761-1(4),* 115761, Allworth Pr.) Skyhorse Publishing Co., Inc.

Nambiar, Shankaran, ed. Sen's Capability Approach & Institutions. 2010. (Education in a Competitive & Globalizing World Ser.). 160.00 *(978-1-61668-508-9(5))* Nova Science Pubs., Inc.

Nanami, Akiko. Non-Governmental Organisations in Japanese Foreign Aid Strategy - Partners or Challengers? 2008. 304p. pap. *(978-3-639-02565-1(2))* VDM Verlag Dr. Mueller e.K.

Pekkanen, Robert. Japan's Dual Civil Society: Members Without Advocates. 2006. (East-West Center Series on Contemporary Issues in Asia & the Pacific). (ENG., Illus.). 280p. 70.00 *(978-0-8047-5428-6(4))* Stanford Univ. Pr.

Pendgracs, Doreen. Before You Say Yes ... A Guide to the Pleasures & Pitfalls of Volunteer Boards. 2010. (ENG.). 152p. pap. 19.99 *(978-1-55488-703-3(8))* Dundurn CAN. Dist: Ingram Pub. Services.

Poetter, Thomas. The Art & Science of Partnership: Catalytic Cases of School, University, & Community Renewal. 2008. (ENG., Illus.). 236p. pap. 38.99 *(978-0-7618-4399-3(X))* Univ. Pr. of America, Inc.

Porcheddu, Andrea. La Storia e la Visione: 60 Anni Dell'Accademia Nazionale Di Danza. 2010. (ITA., Illus.). 208p. pap. 60.00 *(978-88-492-1569-4(X))* Gangemi ITA. Dist: International Publishers Marketing.

Porter, Paula. Seven Steps in Researching & Writing an Apa Paper. 2009. 178p. pap. 36.95 *(978-1-935551-68-3(X))* Univ. Readers.

Rasmussen, Morten & Knudsen, Ann-Christina L., eds. The Road to a United Europe: Interpretations of the Process of European Integration. 2009. 380p. pap. 58.95 *(978-90-5201-560-6(0))* PIE - Peter Lang BEL. Dist: Lang, Peter.

Rebecca, Leet. Message Matters: Succeeding at the Crossroads of Mission & Market. 2007. (ENG.). 160p. per. 26.95 *(978-0-940069-63-3(6),* Fieldstone Alliance) Turner Publishing Co.

Rhodes, R. A. W., et al, eds. The Oxford Handbook of Political Institutions. 2008. (Oxford Handbooks Ser.). (ENG., Illus.). 840p. pap. 49.95 *(978-0-19-954846-0(3))* Oxford Univ. Pr., Inc.

Rickard, John. Air safety group: a brief History. 2010. 58p. pap. 16.95 *(978-1-4457-6276-0(5))* Lulu Enterprises Inc.

Rossteutscher, Sigrid, ed. Social Capital & Associations in European Democracies: A Comparative Analysis. 2006. (Routledge Research in Comparative Politics Ser.). (Illus.). 336p. 150.00 *(978-0-415-41053-3(3))* Routledge.

S., Padmamma. Role & Responsibilities of Women Associations for Women Development: In India. 2010. 116p. pap. *(978-3-8383-5687-6(5))* Lambert Academic Publishing.

Salehyan, Idean, et al. Rebels Without Borders: Transnational Insurgencies in World Politics. 2009. (Illus.). 216p. 39.95 *(978-0-8014-4744-0(5))* Cornell Univ. Pr.

Satyanarayana, G. Voluntary Effort & Rural Development. 2007. 312p. 32.00 *(978-81-316-0086-3(6))* Rawat Pubns. IND. Dist: International Specialized Bk. Services.

Schaut, Scott. Historic Mansfield: A Bicentennial History. 2010. (Illus.). 140p. *(978-1-935377-12-2(4))* Historical Publishing Network.

Schwabenland, Christina. Stories, Visions & Values in Voluntary Organisations. 2006. (Corporate Social Responsibility Ser.). (Illus.). 232p. 130.00 *(978-0-7546-4462-0(6))* Ashgate Publishing Co.

Scott, W. Richard & Davis, Gerald F. Organizations & Organizing: Rational, Natural & Open Systems Perspectives. 6th rev. ed. 2006. (ENG., Illus.). 464p. (C). per. 105.00 *(978-0-13-195893-7(3),* Prentice Hall) Prentice Hall PTR.

Sheridan, Valerie S., et al, eds. National Trade & Professional Associations of the United States. 45th ed. 2010. (National Trade & Professional Associations Ser.). 1615p. pap. 299.00 *(978-1-880873-81-6(8))* Columbia Bks. Inc., Pubs.

Sidel, Mark. Regulation of the Voluntary Sector: Freedom & Security in an Era of Uncertainty. 2009. (Critical Approaches to Law Ser.). (ENG.). 168p. 125.00 *(978-0-415-42424-0(0),* Routledge Cavendish) Taylor & Francis Group GBR. Dist: Taylor & Francis Group.

Siegel, Marcia B. Mirrors & Scrims: The Life & Afterlife of Ballet. 2010. (ENG., Illus.). 416p. (C). lib. bdg. 85.00 *(978-0-8195-6875-5(9))*; pap. 27.95 *(978-0-8195-6926-4(7))* Wesleyan Univ. Pr.

Sine, Wesley D. & David, Robert J., eds. Institutions & Entrepreneurship. 2010. (Research in the Sociology of Work Ser.). (Illus.). 392p. *(978-0-85724-239-6(3))* Emerald Group Publishing Ltd.

Sridhar, Devi, ed. Anthropologists Inside Organisations: South Asian Case Studies. 2008. 228p. (C). 29.95 *(978-81-7829-886-3(4),* B98863C) SAGE Pubns., Inc.

Stubbs, Mike & Newman, Karen, eds. We Are the Real-Time Experiment: 20 Years of FACT. 2010. (Liverpool University Press - Foundation for Art Creative Technology Ser.). (ENG., Illus.). 208p. 29.95 *(978-1-84631-229-8(9))* Liverpool Univ. Pr. GBR. Dist: Chicago Distribution Ctr.

Thornton, Patricia H., et al. The Institutional Logics Perspective: A New Approach to Culture, Structure, & Process. 2012. (ENG.). 304p. 99.00 ***(978-0-19-960193-6(3))*** Oxford Univ. Pr., Inc.

—The Institutional Logics Perspective: A New Approach to Culture, Structure & Process. 2012. (ENG.). 304p. pap. 35.00 ***(978-0-19-960194-3(1))*** Oxford Univ. Pr., Inc.

Tiepelmann, Klaus & Beek, Gregor von der, eds. Theorie der Parafiski. (GER.). VII, 198p. 210.00 ***(978-3-11-177843-3(6))*** De Gruyter, Walter Inc.

Trade Associations & Professional Bodies of the United Kingdom & Eire 20th Ed: 2010. 20th rev. ed. 2009. 365.00 *(978-1-86099-581-1(0))* Graham & Whiteside, Ltd. GBR. Dist: Cengage Gale.

Tuntalp, Deniz. The Recursive Dualism of Technology. 2009. 228p. pap. *(978-3-639-12915-1(6))* VDM Verlag Dr. Mueller e.K.

Unger, Jonathan, ed. Associations & the Chinese State: Contested Spaces. 2008. (ENG.). 288p. 93.95 *(978-0-7656-1325-7(5))*; pap. 43.95 *(978-0-7656-1326-4(3))* Sharpe, M.E. Inc. (East Gate Bk.).

Verma, Niraj, ed. Institutions & Planning. 2007. (Current Research in Urban & Regional Studies). (Illus.). 233p. 152.95 *(978-0-08-044931-9(X))* Emerald Group Publishing Ltd. GBR. Dist: Turpin Distribution Services Ltd.

Webb, Janette. Organisations, Identities & the Self. 2006. (ENG., Illus.). 216p. 130.00 *(978-0-333-80487-2(2))*; pap. 39.00 *(978-0-333-80488-9(0))* Palgrave Macmillan.

Westley, Frances & Bird, Frederick. Voices from the Voluntary Sector: Perspectives on Leadership Challenges. 2010. (Illus.). 448p. *(978-0-8020-9101-7(6))* Univ. of Toronto Pr.

Worth, Steven. The Association Guide to Going Global: New Strategies for a Changing Economic Landscape. 2010. (ENG.). 208p. 49.95 *(978-0-470-58789-8(X),* Wiley) Wiley, John & Sons, Inc.

Yu, Jianxing & Guo, Sujian, eds. Civil Society & Governance in China. 2012. (ENG., Illus.). 254p. 85.00 ***(978-0-230-34096-1(2))*** Palgrave Macmillan.

ASSOCIATIONS, INSTITUTIONS, ETC.—DIRECTORIES

Commonwealth Secretariat Staff. Commonwealth Ministers Reference Book 2008. 2008. (Commonwealth Ministers Reference Books Ser.). 266p. pap. 68.00 *(978-0-9554408-4-7(X))* Henley Media Group, Ltd. GBR. Dist: Stylus Publishing, LLC.

Davis, Mitchell, compiled by. Yearbook of Experts, Authorities & Spokespesons. 2007. 504p. per. 39.95 *(978-0-934333-57-3(2))* Broadcast Interview Source, Inc.

Davis, Mitchell P., ed. Yearbook of Experts 2008. 2008. 488p. per. 39.95 *(978-0-934333-59-7(9))* Broadcast Interview Source, Inc.

—Yearbook of Experts, Authorities & Spokespersons, 28th Final. 2008. 504p. pap. 39.95 *(978-0-934333-65-8(3))* Broadcast Interview Source, Inc.

Directory of Business Information Resources. 14th ed. 2007. (Directory of Business Information Resources Ser.). 1747p. per. 195.00 *(978-1-59237-146-4(9))* Grey Hse. Publishing.

Ency Assn 23. 23rd ed. 2011. (ENG.). 265.00 *(978-1-4144-4650-9(0))*; (ENG.). 265.00 *(978-1-4144-4646-2(2))*; 1065.00 *(978-1-4144-4645-5(4))*; (ENG.). 265.00 *(978-1-4144-4649-3(7))*; (ENG.). 265.00 *(978-1-4144-4648-6(9))* Cengage Gale.

Ency Assn 50. 50th ed. 2011. 988.00 *(978-1-4144-4657-8(8))* Cengage Gale.

Encyclopedia of Associations, 3 vols., Set. 48th rev. ed. 2010. (ENG.). 289p. 778.00 *(978-1-4144-4033-0(2))* Cengage Gale.

Encyclopedia of Associations: International Organizations, 3.0. 50th ed. 2011. 1133.00 *(978-1-4144-5895-3(9))* Cengage Gale.

Encyclopedia of Associations: National Organizations of the U. S. - An Associations Unlimited Reference Geographic & Executive Indexes. 50th ed. 2011. 770.00 *(978-1-4144-4661-5(6))* Cengage Gale.

Encyclopedia of Associations: Regional State Local, 5 vols. 10th ed. Date not set. 585.00 *(978-0-7876-3357-8(7))* Cengage Gale.

The Europa International Foundation Directory 2007. 15th rev. ed. 2007. (ENG., Illus.). 744p. 425.00 *(978-1-85743-430-9(7))* Routledge.

The Europa International Foundation Directory 2009. 18th rev. ed. 2009. (ENG.). 728p. 495.00 *(978-1-85743-523-8(0))* Routledge.

The Europa International Foundation Directory 2011. 20th rev. ed. 2011. (ENG.). 692p. 540.00 *(978-1-85743-605-1(9))* Routledge.

Europa Publications, ed. The Europa International Foundation Directory 2012. 21st rev. ed. 2012. (ENG.). 696p. 565.00 ***(978-1-85743-647-1(4))*** Routledge.

Europa Publications Staff. The Europa International Foundation Directory 2008. 17th rev. ed. 2008. 744p. 465.00 *(978-1-85743-463-7(3))* Europa Pubns.

Europa Publications Staff, ed. The Europa International Foundation Directory 2011. 19th rev. ed. 2010. 712p. 510.00 *(978-1-85743-559-7(1))* Routledge.

Gale Editor, ed. Encyclopedia of Associations: National Organizations of the U. S. 50th ed. 2011. pap. 817.00 *(978-1-4144-4662-2(4))* Cengage Gale.

Gale Research Staff. Encyclopedia of Associations: National Organizations of the U. S., 3 pts., Vol. 1. 38th ed. 4600p. 560.00 *(978-0-7876-4819-0(1)*, GML00502-114863) Cengage Gale.

—Encyclopedia of Associations Vol. 2: Geographic & Executive Indexes. 38th ed. 770p. 440.00 *(978-0-7876-4828-2(0)*, GML00502-114872) Cengage Gale.

Gottlieb, Richard, ed. Educators Resource Directory 2007/08. 7th ed. 2007. (Educators Resource Directory ser.). 615p. pap. 145.00 *(978-1-59237-179-2(5))* Grey Hse. Publishing.

Henley Media Group Limited, creator. Commonwealth Ministers Reference Book 2006. 2007. (Commonwealth Ministers Reference Books Ser.). (Illus.). 224p. per. 65.00 *(978-0-9546572-6-0(8))* Commonwealth Secretariat GBR. Dist: Stylus Publishing, LLC.

Lang, Robert, ed. Associations Canada. 2011. 1600p. 365.00 *(978-1-59237-764-0(5))* Grey Hse. Publishing.

MacKenzie, Leslie & Gottlieb, Richard, eds. The Directory of Business Information Resources. 15th ed. 2008. (Directory of Business Information Resources Ser.). 1747p. per. 195.00 *(978-1-59237-193-8(0))* Grey Hse. Publishing.

Mars, Laura. Associations Canada 2010. Lang, Robert, ed. 2010. 365.00 *(978-1-59237-570-7(7))* Grey Hse. Publishing.

Mars-Proietti, Laura. Associations Canada. 29th ed. 2008. 1600p. 315.00 *(978-1-59237-277-5(5))* Grey Hse. Publishing.

—Washington Associations Contacts Directory: Associations, Executives & Publications in the DC Area. 2008. 400p. pap. 150.00 *(978-1-59237-394-9(1))* Grey Hse. Publishing.

Mars-Proietti, Laura, ed. Associations Canada: 2007. 2007. 1600p. 315.00 *(978-1-59237-219-5(8))* Grey Hse. Publishing.

—Associations Canada: 2009. 2009. 1600p. 325.00 *(978-1-59237-401-4(8))* Grey Hse. Publishing.

—Directory of Business Information Resources: 2009. 16th rev. ed. 2009. 1800p. pap. 195.00 *(978-1-59237-399-4(2))* Grey Hse. Publishing.

—Washington Associations Contacts Directory: 2009. 2009. 400p. pap. 150.00 *(978-1-59237-409-0(3))* Grey Hse. Publishing.

McMillon, Bill, et al. Volunteer Vacations: Short-Term Adventures That Will Benefit You & Others. (ENG., 464p. 10th ed. 2009. Illus.). pap. 18.95 *(978-1-55652-784-5(5))* 11th ed. 2012. pap. 18.95 *(978-1-56976-841-9(2))* Chicago Review Pr., Inc.

National Faculty Directory. 41st rev. ed. 2010. (ENG.). 548.00 *(978-1-4144-2145-2(1))* Cengage Gale.

National Scholarship Research Service & Cassidy, Daniel J. The Scholarship Book, 13th Edition: The Complete Guide to Private-Sector Scholarships, Fellowships, Grants, & Loans for the Undergraduate. 13th ed. 2008. (ENG.). 720p. (gr. 12-18). 32.50 *(978-0-7352-0427-0(6))* Prentice Hall Pr.

Omnigraphics, creator. Web Site Source Book: A Guide to Major U. S. Businesses, Organizations, Agencies, Institutions, & Other Information Resources on the World Wide Web. 13th ed. 2007. 2127p. pap. 194.00 *(978-0-7808-1024-2(4))* Omnigraphics, Inc.

O'Phelan, Ann Marie. How to Go to College on a Shoe String: Grants, Scholarships, Cheap Books, Fellowships, & Other Financial Aid Secrets. 2008. (ENG., Illus.). 288p. pap. 24.95 *(978-1-60138-020-3(8))* Atlantic Publishing Co.

Pybus, Victoria. International Voluntary Work. 10th ed. 2007. (International Voluntary Work Ser.). (Illus.). 366p. per. 19.95 *(978-1-85458-354-3(9)*, Vacation Work Pubns.) Crimson Publishing, Ltd. GBR. Dist: National Bk. Network.

Regional, State & Local Organizations. 23rd ed. 2011. 265.00 *(978-1-4144-4647-9(0))* Cengage Gale.

Wyszomierski, Sara, ed. Guide to Funding for International & Foreign Programs. 9th ed. 2008. (Guide to Funding for International & Foreign Programs Ser.). 791p. pap. 173.75 *(978-1-59542-182-1(3))* Foundation Ctr., The.

Yearbook Plus. 6th ed. incl. cd-rom *(978-3-598-40454-2(9))* Saur, K. G. Verlag GmbH & Co.

ASSOCIATIONS, INSTITUTIONS, ETC.—MEMBERSHIP

A Fresh Approach to Member Loyality. 2007. 125.00 *(978-1-932795-09-7(X))* Filene Research Institute, Inc.

Löwer, Sandra. Inhaltskontrolle von Nutzungs- und Leistungsbeziehungen zwischen dem Idealverein und seinen Mitgliedern. 2008. (Schriften zum Handels- und Wirtschaftsrecht Ser.). 326p. pap. 81.95 *(978-3-631-57167-5(4))* Lang, Peter GmbH, Europaischer Verlag der Wissenschaften DEU. Dist: Lang, Peter.

Sladek, Sarah/L. The New Recruit: What your association needs to know about X, Y, & Z. 2007. *(978-1-931945-66-0(7))* Expert Publishing, Inc.

ASSOCIATIONS, INTERNATIONAL

see International Agencies

ASSOCIATIVE ALGEBRAS

Aprodu, Marian & Nagel, Jan. Koszul Cohomology & Algebraic Geometry. 2009. (University Lecture Ser.). 125p. pap. 39.00 *(978-0-8218-4964-4(6))* American Mathematical Society.

Borceux, F. & Vandenbossche, G. Algebra in a Localic Topos with Applications to Ring Theory. 2008. (Lecture Notes in Mathematics Ser.). pap. 59.95 *(978-3-540-12711-6(9))* Springer.

Dito, Giuseppe, et al, eds. Poisson Geometry in Mathematics & Physics. 2008. (Contemporary Mathematics Ser.). (Illus.). 311p. (C). pap. 92.00 *(978-0-8218-4423-6(7))* American Mathematical Society.

Dlab, V. Representation Theory I. Proceedings of the Fourth International Conference on Representations of Algebras, held in Ottawa, Canada, August 16-25, 1984: Finite Dimensional Algebras. 2008. (Lecture Notes in Mathematics Ser.). pap. 46.00 *(978-3-540-16432-6(4))*; pap. 46.00 *(978-3-540-16433-3(2))* Springer.

Dlab, V. & Scott, Leonard, eds. Finite Dimensional Algebras & Related Topics. 2010. (NATO Science Series C: (closed) Ser.). 408p. pap. 389.00 *(978-90-481-4377-1(2)*, 9048143772) Springer.

Gekhtman, Michael, et al. Cluster Algebra & Poisson Geometry. 2010. (Mathematical Surveys & Monographs). (Illus.). 246p. 82.00 *(978-0-8218-4972-9(7))* American Mathematical Society.

Girard, Patrick R. Quaternions, Clifford Algebras & Relativistic Physics. 2007. (ENG., Illus.). xii, 179p. per. 49.95 *(978-3-7643-7790-8(9)*, 3764377909) Birkhauser Verlag AG CHE. Dist: Springer.

Kotchetov, Mikhail. Polynomial Identities of Hopf Algebras. 2009. 132p. pap. *(978-3-639-20808-5(0))* VDM Verlag Dr. Mueller e.K.

Lluis, Puig. Frobenius Categories Versus Brauer Blocks. 2009. (Progress in Mathematics Ser.). 498p. 129.00 *(978-3-7643-9997-9(X))* Birkhauser Verlag AG CHE. Dist: Springer.

Milies, Cesar Polcino, ed. Groups, Algebras, & Applications. 2011. (Contemporary Mathematics Ser.). 324p. pap. 105.00 *(978-0-8218-5239-2(6))* American Mathematical Society.

Oystaeyen, F. van. Prime Spectra in Non-Commutative Algebr. 2008. (Lecture Notes in Mathematics Ser.). 140p. pap. 26.00 *(978-3-540-07146-4(6))* Springer.

Ratliff, L. J. Jr. Chain Conjectures in Ring Theory: An Exposition of Conjectures on Catenary Chains. 2008. (Lecture Notes in Mathematics Ser.). 144p. pap. 39.95 *(978-3-540-08758-8(3))* Springer.

Reiner, I. & Roggenkamp, K.W. Integral Representations: Topics in Integral Representation Theory. Integral Representations & Presentations of Finite Groups by Roggenkamp, K. W. 2008. (Lecture Notes in Mathematics Ser.). 284p. pap. 46.00 *(978-3-540-09546-0(2))* Springer.

Reviews in Ring Theory, 1960-1984: Reviews in Ring Theory, 1960-1979; Reviews in Ring Theory, 1980-1984, 2 vols. pap. 372.00 *(978-0-8218-0147-5(3)*, REVRNG/60/84C) American Mathematical Society.

Simson, D. & Skowronski, Andrzej. Elements of the Representation Theory of Associative Algebras Vol. 3: Representation-Infinite Tilted Algebras, 3 vols. 2007. (London Mathematical Society Student Texts). (ENG., Illus.). 464p. 136.99 *(978-0-521-88218-7(4))* Cambridge Univ. Pr.

Simson, Daniel & Skowronski, Andrzej. Elements of the Representation Theory of Associative Algebras: Representation-Infinite Tilted Algebras, 3 vols. 2007. (London Mathematical Society Student Texts). (ENG., Illus.). 464p. per. 58.99 *(978-0-521-70876-0(1))* Cambridge Univ. Pr.

—Elements of the Representation Theory of Associative Algebras: Tubes & Concealed Algebras of Euclidean Type, 3 vols. 2007. (London Mathematical Society Student Texts). (ENG., Illus.). 320p. 145.00 *(978-0-521-83610-4(7))* Cambridge Univ. Pr.

—Elements of the Representation Theory of Associative Algebras: Volume 2: Tubes & Concealed Algebras of Euclidean Type, 3 vols. 2007. (London Mathematical Society Student Texts). (ENG., Illus.). 320p. per. 60.99 *(978-0-521-54420-7(3))* Cambridge Univ. Pr.

Vanoystaeyen, F. & Verschoren, A., eds. Brauer Groups in Ring Theory & Algebraic Geometry: Proceedings, University of Antwerp U.I.A., Belgium, August 17-28, 1981. 2008. (Lecture Notes in Mathematics Ser.). pap. 59.95 *(978-3-540-11216-7(2))* Springer.

Zelinsky, D., ed. Brauer Groups: Proceedings of the Conference held at Evanston, October 11-15, 1975. 2008. (Lecture Notes in Mathematics Ser.). 192p. pap. 26.00 *(978-3-540-07989-7(0))* Springer.

ASSOCIATIVE LEARNING

see Paired-Association Learning

ASSOCIATIVE RINGS

Andersen, Jorgen E., et al, eds. Chern-Simons Gauge Theory: 20 Years After. 2011. (Ams/Ip Studies in Advanced Mathematics Ser.). (Illus.). 446p. pap. 130.00 ***(978-0-8218-5353-5(8))*** American Mathematical Society.

Arnold, D. M. Finite Rank Torsion Free Abelian Groups & Rings. 2008. (Lecture Notes in Mathematics Ser.). pap. 39.95 *(978-3-540-11557-1(9))* Springer.

Baba, Yoshitomo & Oshiro, Kiyoichi. Classical Artinian Rings & Related Topics. 2009. 96.00 *(978-981-4287-24-1(5))* World Scientific Publishing Co., Inc.

Bass, Hyman, ed. Algebraic K-Theory I. Proceedings of the Conference Held at the Seattle Research Center of Battelle Memorial Institute, August 28 - September 8, 1972: Higher K-Theories. 2008. (Lecture Notes in Mathematics Ser.). pap. 59.95 *(978-3-540-06434-3(6))* Springer.

Borceux, F. & Vandenbossche, G. Algebra in a Localic Topos with Applications to Ring Theory. 2008. (Lecture Notes in Mathematics Ser.). pap. 59.95 *(978-3-540-12711-6(9))* Springer.

Breiar, Matej, et al. Functional Identities. 2007. (Frontiers in Mathematics Ser.). 272p. pap. 59.95 *(978-3-7643-7795-3(X))* Birkhauser Verlag AG CHE. Dist: Springer.

Bruns & Gubeladze. Polytopes, Rings, & K-Theory. 2008. (Springer Monographs in Mathematics Ser.). (Illus.). 362p. 139.00 *(978-0-387-76355-2(4))* Springer.

Chapman, S. T. & Glaz, Sarah, eds. Non-Noetherian Commutative Ring Theory. 2010. (Mathematics & Its Applications Ser.). 492p. pap. 289.00 *(978-1-4419-4835-9(X)*, 144194835X) Springer.

Chebotar, Mikhail, et al, eds. Rings & Nearrings: Proceedings of the International Conference of Algebra in Memory of Kostia Beidar, Tainan, Taiwan, March 6-12 2005. 2007. (De Gruyter Proceedings in Mathematics Ser.). (ENG., 167p. Illus.). 196.00 *(978-3-11-019952-9(1))*; 293.00 ***(978-3-11-180255-8(8))*** De Gruyter, Walter Inc.

Cozzens, J. H. & Sandomierski, F. L., eds. Noncommutative Ring Theory: Papers Presented at the Internation Conference held at Kent State University April 4-5, 1975. 2008. (Lecture Notes in Mathematics Ser.). 220p. pap. 46.00 *(978-3-540-07985-9(8))* Springer.

Dicks, W. Groups, Trees & Projective Modules. 2008. (Lecture Notes in Mathematics Ser.). ix, 127p. pap. 39.95 *(978-3-540-09974-1(3))* Springer.

Faith, Carl. Lectures on Injective Modules & Quotient Rings. 2007. (Lecture Notes in Mathematics Ser.). 160p. per. 39.95 *(978-3-540-03920-4(1))* Springer.

Faith, Carl Clifton & Osofsky, Barbara. Rings, Modules, & Representations. Dung, Nguyen Viet et al, eds. 2009. (Contemporary Mathematics Ser.). (Illus.). 361p. pap. 99.00 *(978-0-8218-4370-3(2))* American Mathematical Society.

Faticoni, Theodore G. Modules over Endomorphism Rings. 2009. (Encyclopedia of Mathematics & its Applications Ser.). (ENG., Illus.). 392p. 124.00 *(978-0-521-19960-5(3))* Cambridge Univ. Pr.

Fossum, R. M., et al. Trivial Extensions of Abelian Categories. 2008. (Lecture Notes in Mathematics Ser.). 140p. pap. 26.00 *(978-3-540-07159-4(8))* Springer.

Haley, D. K. Equational Compactness in Rings: With Applications to the Theory of Topological Rings. 2008. (Lecture Notes in Mathematics Ser.). 172p. pap. 26.00 *(978-3-540-09548-4(9))* Springer.

Handelman, D. & Lawrence, J., eds. Ring Theory, Waterloo 1978: Proceedings, University of Waterloo, Canada, 12-16 June, 1978. 2008. (Lecture Notes in Mathematics Ser.). 372p. pap. 46.00 *(978-3-540-09529-3(2)*, 3540095292) Springer.

Hofmann, Karl H. Tulane University Ring & Operator Theory Year, 1970-1971. 2008. (Lecture Notes in Mathematics Ser.). 804p. pap. 59.00 *(978-3-540-05729-1(3))* Springer.

Hofmann, Karl H., ed. Tulane University Ring & Operator Theory Year, 1970-1971. 2008. (Lecture Notes in Mathematics Ser.). 328p. pap. 46.00 *(978-3-540-05714-7(5)*, 3540057145) Springer.

Jain, S. R. Non-Commutative Ring Theory: Proceedings of a Conference held in Athens, Ohio, Sept. 29-30, 1989. 2008. (Lecture Notes in Mathematics Ser.). pap. 39.95 *(978-3-540-53164-7(5))* Springer.

Jespers, Eric & Okninski, Jan. Noetherian Semigroup Algebras. (Algebra & Applications Ser.). vii, 366p. 2010. pap. 119.00 *(978-90-481-7448-5(1)*, 9048174481) 2008. 119.00 *(978-1-4020-5809-7(8))* Springer.

Kiechle, Hubert, et al, eds. Nearrings & Nearfields: Proceedings of the Conference on Nearrings & Nearfields, Hamburg, Germany July 27 - August 3 2003. 2010. xiv, 319p. pap. 119.00 *(978-90-481-6850-7(3)*, 9048168503) Springer.

Levy, Lawrence S. & Robson, J. Chris. Hereditary Noetherian Prime Rings & Idealizers. 2011. (Mathematical Surveys & Monographs). (Illus.). 228p. 84.00 *(978-0-8218-5350-4(3))* American Mathematical Society.

Matson, Johnny L., et al, eds. Treating Childhood Psychopathology & Developmental Disabilities. 2010. x, 457p. pap. 89.95 *(978-1-4419-8141-7(1)*, 1441981411) Springer.

Nastasescu, C. & Oystaeyen, F. van. Graded & Filtered Rings & Modules. 2008. (Lecture Notes in Mathematics Ser.). 164p. pap. 39.95 *(978-3-540-09708-2(2))* Springer.

Oystaeyen, F. van. Prime Spectra in Non-Commutative Algebr. 2008. (Lecture Notes in Mathematics Ser.). 140p. pap. 26.00 *(978-3-540-07146-4(6))* Springer.

Oystaeyen, F. van, ed. Ring Theory, Antwerp 1980: Proceedings, University of Antwerp, U.I.A., Antwerp, Belgium, May 6-9, 1980. 2008. (Lecture Notes in Mathematics Ser.). 224p. pap. 46.00 *(978-3-540-10246-5(9))* Springer.

Petrich, M. Rings & Semigroups. 2008. (Lecture Notes in Mathematics Ser.). 200p. pap. 39.95 *(978-3-540-06730-6(2))* Springer.

Reviews in Ring Theory, 1960-1984: Reviews in Ring Theory, 1960-1979; Reviews in Ring Theory, 1980-1984, 2 vols. pap. 372.00 *(978-0-8218-0147-5(3)*, REVRNG/60/84C) American Mathematical Society.

Stenström, B. Rings & Modules of Quotients. 2008. (Lecture Notes in Mathematics Ser.). 148p. pap. 39.95 *(978-3-540-05690-4(4)*, 3540056904) Springer.

Tuganbaev, A. A. Rings Close to Regular. 2010. (Mathematics & Its Applications Ser.). 368p. pap. 146.00 *(978-90-481-6116-4(9)*, 9048161169) Springer.

ASSUMPTION

see Hypothesis

ASSUMPTION OF THE BLESSED VIRGIN MARY

see Mary, Blessed Virgin, Saint—Assumption

ASSURANCE (INSURANCE)

see Insurance

ASSURANCE (THEOLOGY)

see also Antinomianism; Inner Light; Perseverance (Theology)

Bass, Christopher David. That You May Know: Assurance of Salvation in 1 John. 2008. (New American Commentary Studies in Bible & Theology Ser.). (ENG.). 256p. 24.99 *(978-0-8054-4761-3(X)*, B&H Academic) B&H Publishing Group.

Cassady, David. Unconditional Eternal Security. 2008. 88p. pap. 9.99 *(978-1-60647-624-6(6))* Xulon Pr., Inc.

Dunham, Philip W. Sure Salvation: You Can Know You Have Eternal Life. 2007. 13.99 *(978-0-8163-2178-0(7))* Pacific Pr. Publishing Assn.

Embry, Adam. Keeper of the Great Seal of Heaven: Sealing of the Spirit in the Life & Thought of John Flavel. 2011. (ENG.). pap. 18.00 ***(978-1-60178-154-3(7))*** Reformation Heritage Bks.

Gromacki, Robert Glenn. Salvation Is Forever. 2007. 188p. pap. *(978-1-59402-471-9(5))* Regular Baptist Pr.

Haile, Bill & Haile, Bill, Sr. A Walk in Assurance: Sustained by Faith. 2006. 113p. per. 10.99 *(978-1-59886-647-6(8))* Tate Publishing & Enterprises, LLC.

Hoskinson, Matthew C. Assurance of Salvation: Implications of a New Testament Theology of Hope. 2009. *(978-1-60682-044-5(3))* BJU Pr.

MacGregor, Kirk R. & Mattis, Kevaughn. Perspectives on Eternal Security: Biblical, Historical, & Philosophical Perspectives. 2011. (ENG.). 238p. pap. 37.50 *(978-0-227-17373-2(2))* Clarke, James Co., Ltd. GBR. Dist: Brown, David Bk. Co., The.

Morgan, Christopher W. & Peterson, Robert A., eds. Faith Comes by Hearing: A Response to Inclusivism. 2008. (ENG.). 270p. per. 23.00 *(978-0-8308-2590-5(8)*, IVP Acad.) InterVarsity Pr.

Parsons, Burk. Assured by God: Living in the Fullness of God's Grace. 2006. 200p. 18.00 *(978-1-59638-029-5(2))* 2nd ed. 2007. 204p. pap. *(978-1-59638-101-8(9))* P & R Publishing.

Patton, William J. Pardon & Assurance: How to Know for Certain Your Sins Are Forgiven. 2009. (Illus.). 258p. pap. 20.00 *(978-1-59925-209-4(0))* Solid Ground Christian Bks.

Peterson, Robert A. Our Secure Salvation: Preservation & Apostasy. 2009. pap. *(978-1-59638-043-1(8))* P & R Publishing.

Pink, Arthur W. Studies on Saving Faith. 2011. 154p. pap. 14.99 ***(978-1-61203-333-4(4))*** Bottom of the Hill Publishing.

Pink, Arthur Walkington & Kistler, Don. Studies on Saving Faith. 2010. viii, 209p. *(978-0-9826155-1-5(5))* Northampton Pr., The.

Sproul, R. C. Can I Be Sure I'm Saved? 2010. *(978-1-56769-208-2(7))* Reformation Pubs.

Stanley, Charles F. Understanding Eternal Security: Secure in God's Unconditional Love, 0 vols. 2008. (Life Principles Study Ser.). 128p. per. 9.99 *(978-1-4185-2814-0(5))* Nelson, Thomas Inc.

Tchividjian, Tullian. Do I Know God? Finding Certainty in Life's Most Important Relationship. (ENG.). 224p. 2009. pap. 13.99 *(978-1-60142-218-7(0))* 2007. 16.99 *(978-1-59052-936-2(7))* Doubleday Religious Publishing Group, The. (Multnomah).

Whidden, Woodrow W. The Judgment & Assurance: The Dynamics of Personal Salvation. 2011. *(978-0-8280-2565-2(7))* Review & Herald Publishing Assn.

ASSYRIA

Abbeloos, J. B. Acta Mar Kardaghi, Assyriae Praefecti. 2010. 94.16 *(978-1-61719-447-4(6))* Gorgias Pr., LLC.

Anderson, Clive. Face2face Sennacherib: Encountering Assyrias great & terrifying Ruler. 2007. (Face2face With Ser.). 96p. 9.00 *(978-1-84625-076-7(5))* DayOne Pubns. GBR. Dist: STL Distribution North America.

Azize, Joseph & Weeks, Noel. Gilgamesh & the World of Assyria: Proceedings of the Conference Held at the Mandelbaum House, the University of Sydney,

21-23 July 2004. Azize, J. & Weeks, N., eds. 2007. (Ancient near Eastern Studies: Vol. 21). (ENG.). 242p. (C). 122.00 *(978-90-429-1802-3(0))* Peeters Pubs. & Booksellers BEL. Dist: Brown, David Bk. Co., The.

British Museum, Department of Egyptian and Assyrian Art Staff. Annals of the Kings of Assyria. (Ancient Mesopotamian Texts & Studies). reprint ed. 95.00 *(978-0-404-18165-9(1))* AMS Pr., Inc.

Budge. Annals of the Kings of Assyria. 2012. (ENG.). 256p. pap. 42.95 ***(978-0-415-54089-6(5))*** Routledge.

Budge, E. A. Wallis. tr. The History of Esarhaddon (Son of Sennacherib) King of Assyria, B. C. 681-688: Translated from the Cuneiform Inscriptions upon Cylinders & Tablets in the British Museum Collection, Together with Original Texts. 2010. (Cambridge Library Collection - Archaeology Ser.). (ENG.). 184p. pap. 21.00 *(978-1-108-01710-7(X))* Cambridge Univ. Pr.

De Lafayette, Maximillien. ANUNNAKI ULEMA BARIDU TECHNIQUE: How to zoom into an astral body or in the Double. 2010. 55p. pap. 13.49 *(978-0-557-56368-5(2))* Lulu Enterprises Inc.

—Anunnaki Ulema Bisho-barkadari: How to block negative vibes & bad thoughts aimed at You. 2010. 52p. pap. 13.49 *(978-0-557-56114-8(0))* Lulu Enterprises Inc.

—Anunnaki Ulema Cadari-Rou'yaa: How to Read Others' Thoughts & Feelings. 2010. 50p. pap. 12.50 *(978-0-557-56243-5(0))* Lulu Enterprises Inc.

—Anunnaki Ulema Chabariduri: How to Develop Your Remote Viewing Faculty. 2010. 50p. pap. 12.50 *(978-0-557-56251-0(1))* Lulu Enterprises Inc.

—Anunnaki Ulema Da-Irat Technique: How to Self Energize your Mind & Body. 2010. 52p. pap. 11.49 *(978-0-557-56276-3(7))* Lulu Enterprises Inc.

—Anunnaki Ulema Daemat-Afnah Technique: How to stay & look 37 for Ever. 2010. 55p. pap. 13.49 *(978-0-557-56069-1(1))* Lulu Enterprises Inc.

—Book of Ramadosh:13 Anunnaki Ulema Techniques to Live Longer,Happier, Healthier,Wealthier. 8th Edition. 2010. 330p. pap. 25.99 *(978-0-557-52978-0(6))* Lulu Enterprises Inc.

Esarhaddon & Leichty, Erle. The Royal Inscriptions of Esarhaddon, King of Assyria (680-669 BC) 2011. (AKK & ENG.). *(978-1-57506-209-9(7))* Eisenbrauns, Inc.

Evans, Paul S. The Invasion of Sennacherib in the Book of Kings: A Source-Critical & Rhetorical Study of 2 Kings 18-19. 2009. 240p. *(978-90-04-17596-9(2))* BRILL.

Galil, Gershon. The Lower Stratum Families in the Neo-Assyrian Period. 2007. (Culture & History of the Ancient near East Ser.). (Illus.). 403p. *(978-90-04-15512-1(0))* BRILL.

Goodspeed, George Stephen. A History of the Babylonians & Assyrians. 2009. 572p. pap. *(978-0-217-42615-2(6))* Books LLC.

Grayson, A. Kirk. Assyrian & Babylonian Chronicles. 2008. (Texts from Cuneiform Sources Ser.: Vol. 5). 300p. 79.50 *(978-1-57506-049-1(3))* Eisenbrauns, Inc.

Green, Douglas J. I Undertook Great Works: The Ideology of Domestic Achievements in West Semitic Royal Inscriptions. 2010. (Illus.). 368p. pap. 147.50 *(978-3-16-150168-5(3))* Mohr Siebeck GmbH & Co. KG DEU. Dist: Coronet Bks.

Johns, C. H. W. Ancient Assyria. 2012. (ENG., Illus.). 210p. pap. 19.99 ***(978-1-107-62967-7(5))*** Cambridge Univ. Pr.

Johns, Claude H., ed. An Assyrian Doomsday Book, or, Liber Censualis of the District Round Harran in the Seventh Century B.C. (Ancient Mesopotamian Texts & Studies). reprint ed. 27.50 *(978-0-404-18179-6(1))* AMS Pr., Inc.

Maximillien de Lafayette, Germain Lumiere/. Description & Explanation of Anunnaki, Babylonian, Sumerian, Akkadian, Assyrian, Phoenician Slabs, Seals, Inscriptions, Statues, Tablets & Secret Symbols. 2010. 400p. pap. 29.50 *(978-0-557-44178-5(1))* Lulu Enterprises Inc.

Olmstead, Albert Ten Eyck. Assyrian Historiography. 2007. (ENG.). 68p. per. *(978-1-4065-3199-2(5))* Dodo Pr.

—Assyrian Historiography. 2007. pap. *(978-1-4068-3619-6(2))* Echo Library.

Olsmstead, Albert Ten Eyck. Assyrian Historiography: A Source Study. 2008. 66p. pap. 6.00 *(978-1-60608-303-1(1),* Wipf and Stock) Wipf & Stock Pubs.

Ragozin, Zénaïde Alexeïevna. Media Babylon & Persia. 2006. 476p. per. *(978-1-4067-2215-4(4),* Hesperides Pr.) Read Bks.

Rawlinson, George. Seven Great Monarchies of the Ancient Ea. 2006. pap. 54.95 *(978-1-4286-4794-7(5))*; pap. 54.95 *(978-1-4286-4792-3(9))* Kessinger Publishing, LLC.

—The Seven Great Monarchies of the Ancient Eastern World: Media: Media. 2007. (ENG.). 142p. pap. 18.99 *(978-1-4346-0109-4(9))*; 154p. pap. 21.99 *(978-1-4346-0118-6(8))* BiblioBazaar.

—The Seven Great Monarchies of the Ancient Eastern World, Part I. 2007. (Illus.). 180p. per. *(978-1-4065-4248-6(2))* Dodo Pr.

Rizza, Alfredo. Assyrians & Babylonians: History & Treasures of an Ancient Civilization. 2010. (ENG.). 19.98 *(978-88-544-0457-1(8))* White Star ITA. Dist: Random Hse., Inc.

Tadmor, Hayim, et al. The Royal Inscriptions of Tiglath-Pileser III (744-727 BC) & Shalmaneser V (726-722 BC), Kings of Assyria. 2011. ***(978-1-57506-220-4(8))*** Eisenbrauns, Inc.

ASSYRIA—ANTIQUITIES

Anastasio, Stefano. Atlas of the Assyrian Pottery of the Iron Age. 2010. (Subartu Ser.). (ENG., Illus.). 197p. (C). pap. 95.00 *(978-2-503-53288-2(8))* Brepols Pubs. BEL. Dist: ISD.

Biggs, Robert D., et al. Proceedings of the 51st Recontre Assyriologique Internationale, Held at the Oriental Institute of the University of Chicago, July 18-22, 2005: Held at the Oriental Institute of the University of Chicago July 18-22 2005. Biggs, Robert D. et al, eds. 2008. (Studies in Ancient Oriental Civilization Ser.). (ENG., Illus.). 432p. (C). 80.00 *(978-1-885923-54-7(6))* Oriental Institute of the Univ. of Chicago, The.

Bonavia, E. The Flora of the Assyrian Monuments. 2009. (ENG.). 250p. 32.99 *(978-1-117-15634-7(6))*; 252p. pap. 25.75 *(978-1-117-15635-4(4))* BiblioBazaar.

Cohen, Ada & Kangas, Steven E., eds. Assyrian Reliefs from the Palace of Ashurnasirpal II: A Cultural Biography. 2010. (Illus.). 294p. pap. 40.00 *(978-1-58465-817-7(7))* Hood Museum of Art.

Collins, Paul. Assyrian Palace Sculptures. 2009. (ENG., Illus.). 144p. 45.00 *(978-0-292-72169-2(2))* Univ. of Texas Pr.

Foster, Benjamin & Foster, Karen Polinger. Civilizations of Ancient Iraq. 2011. (ENG., Illus.). 312p. (C). pap. 16.95 *(978-0-691-14997-4(6))* Princeton Univ. Pr.

Foster, Benjamin R. & Foster, Karen Polinger. Civilizations of Ancient Iraq. 2009. (ENG., Illus.). 312p. (C). 26.95 *(978-0-691-13722-3(6))* Princeton Univ. Pr.

Gadd, Cyril J. The Stones of Assyria. reprint ed. 110.00 *(978-0-404-20104-3(0))* AMS Pr., Inc.

Hilprecht, H. V. Drought, Famine, Plague & Pestilence. 2009. 294p. pap. *(978-1-4590-7310-4(X))* Books LLC.

—Drought, Famine, Plague & Pestilence. 2007. (Gorgias Classic Archaeological Reprints Ser.: 9). 88.00 *(978-1-59333-640-0(3))*; 2 of 2. 44.00 *(978-1-59333-650-9(0))* Gorgias Pr., LLC.

Hilprecht, H. V. & Robertson, Warren. Drought, Famine, Plague & Pestilence, 1 of 2. 2010. (Gorgias Classic Archaeological Reprints Ser.: 9). pap. 130.00 *(978-1-59333-649-3(7))* Gorgias Pr., LLC.

Hilprecht, Hermann Vollrat, ed. The Excavations in Assyria & Babylonia. 2011. (Cambridge Library Collection - Archaeology Ser.). (Illus.). 688p. pap. 48.00 *(978-1-108-02564-5(1))* Cambridge Univ. Pr.

Postgate, J. Nicholas & Postgate, J. N. The Land of Assur & the Yoke of Assur: Studies on Assyria, 1971-2005. 2007. (ENG., Illus.). 368p. (C). 110.00 *(978-1-84217-216-2(6))* Oxbow Bks., Ltd. GBR. Dist: Brown, David Bk. Co., The.

Rizza, Alfredo. Assyrians & Babylonians: History & Treasures of an Ancient Civilization. 2010. (ENG.). 19.98 *(978-88-544-0457-1(8))* White Star ITA. Dist: Random Hse., Inc.

ASSYRIAN LANGUAGE

see Akkadian Language

ASSYRIANS

see also Nestorians

Aboona, Hirmis. Assyrians, Kurds, & Ottomans: Intercommunal Relations on the Periphery of the Ottoman Empire. 2008. 344p. 109.95 *(978-1-60497-583-3(0))* Cambria Pr.

Allen Bonck, Bonck & Allen Bonck. Asshur the Assyrian. 2009. 120p. 22.95 *(978-1-4401-6275-6(1))*; pap. 12.95 *(978-1-4401-6273-2(5))* iUniverse, Inc.

Aprim, Frederick A. Assyrians: From Bedr Khan to Saddam Hussein. 2nd ed. 2007. per. *(978-0-9771873-1-7(4))*; kivar *(978-0-9771873-2-4(2))* Pearlida Publishing.

Austin, H. The Baqubah Refugee Camp: An Account of Work on Behalf of the Persecuted Assyrian Christians. 2006. 48.00 *(978-1-59333-401-7(X))* Gorgias Pr., LLC.

Betgivargis-McDaniel, Maegan. Assyrians of New Britain. 2007. (Images of America Ser.). (ENG., Illus.). 128p. per. 19.99 *(978-0-7385-5012-1(4))* Arcadia Publishing.

De Lafayette, Maximillien. Anunnaki & Ulema-Anunnaki Vault of Forbidden Knowledge & Universe Greatest Secrets. Book 2. 2010. 300p. pap. 25.50 *(978-0-557-53908-6(0))* Lulu Enterprises Inc.

—Anunnaki & Ulema-Anunnaki Vault of Forbidden Knowledge & Universe Greatest Secrets. Book 3. 2010. 318p. pap. 25.97 *(978-0-557-53914-7(5))* Lulu Enterprises Inc.

—Anunnaki Genetic Creation of the Human Races, Demons & Spirits. 3rd Edition. 2010. 282p. pap. 24.51 *(978-0-557-64421-6(6))* Lulu Enterprises Inc.

—Anunnaki Ulema Baaniradu: How to Acquire a Healing Touch (Lesson & Technique) 2010. 60p. pap. 14.51 *(978-0-557-56100-1(0))* Lulu Enterprises Inc.

—Ba'ab: The Anunnaki Stargate. 2010. 100p. pap. 17.50 *(978-0-557-67629-7(3))* Lulu Enterprises Inc.

—Baalbeck: The Anunnaki's City & Afrit Undergound. 2010. 80p. pap. 16.49 *(978-0-557-62407-2(X))* Lulu Enterprises Inc.

—Description & Explanation of Anunnaki, Babylonian, Sumerian, Akkadian, Assyrian, Phoenician Slabs, Seals, Inscriptions, Statues, Tablets & Secret Symbols. 4th Edition. 2010. 400p. pap. 29.50 *(978-0-557-45240-8(6))* Lulu Enterprises Inc.

—Description,Translation,Explanation of Babylonian,Sumerian,Akkadian,Assyrian,Ugaritic,Anunnaki,Phoenician Cylinder Seals,Slabs,Inscriptions,Tablets,Symbols. 2010. 402p. pap. 29.49 *(978-0-557-53697-9(9))* Lulu Enterprises Inc.

—Mind Blowing Dialogues with Anunnaki Ulema Masters Living among Us. 3rd Edition. Revelations of the Greatest Information, Secrets & Mysteries of UFOs, Extraterrestrials, Time Space Travel, Parallel Dimensions, Occult & Life after Death. 2010. 272p. pap. 23.97 *(978-0-557-44725-1(9),* Lulu Enterprises Inc.

—Mind Blowing Dialogues with Anunnaki Ulema Masters Living among Us. 5th Edition. 2010. 272p. pap. 23.97 *(978-0-557-52997-1(2))* Lulu Enterprises Inc.

Heazell, F. N., et al, eds. Kurds & Christians. 2010. 115.76 *(978-1-61719-842-7(0))* Gorgias Pr., LLC.

Hom, Mary Katherine Y. H. The Characterisation of the Assyrians in Isaiah: Synchronic & Diachronic Perspectives. 2012. (Library Hebrew Bible/Old Testament Studies). (ENG., Illus.). 256p. 130.00 ***(978-0-567-63471-8(0),*** T&T Clark Int'l) Continuum International Publishing Group, Ltd. GBR. Dist: National Bk. Network.

Ishaya, Arianne. New Lamps for Old. 2009. pap. 48.00 *(978-1-60724-585-8(X))* Gorgias Pr., LLC.

Khan, G. The Neo-Aramaic Dialect of Barwar, 3 vols. 2008. (ARC & ENG., Illus.). xxxviii, 2175p. *(978-90-04-16765-0(X))* BRILL.

Malik, Mirza Dawid Gewargis. The Throne of Saliq: The Condition of Assyrianism in the Era of the Incarnation of Our Lord, & Notes on the History of Assyria. 2006. 78.00 *(978-1-59333-406-2(0))* Gorgias Pr., LLC.

Olmstead, A. T. The Assyrian Chronicle. 2010. pap. 19.00 *(978-1-61719-553-2(7))* Gorgias Pr., LLC.

Stavridis, Stavros & Chibo, David, eds. The Assyrians in Australian Archives. 2010. 140.00 *(978-1-60724-993-1(6))* Gorgias Pr., LLC.

Vaschalde, Arthur. The Monks of Rabban Hormizd. 2010. pap. 17.92 *(978-1-61143-585-6(4))* Gorgias Pr., LLC.

Werda, Joel E. & Burgess, Thomas. The Flickering Light of Asia. 2011. 92.96 *(978-1-61143-914-4(0))* Gorgias Pr., LLC.

ASSYRIOLOGY

Cathcart, Kevin J., ed. The Correspondence of Edward Hincks, 1818-1849, Vol. 1. 2008. (ENG.). 364p. 104.95 *(978-1-904558-70-5(4))* Univ. College Dublin Pr. IRL. Dist: Dufour Editions, Inc.

—Correspondence of Edward Hincks, 1857-1866, 3 vols., Vol. 3. 2010. (ENG.). 396p. 120.00 *(978-1-904558-72-9(0))* Univ. College Dublin Pr. IRL. Dist: Dufour Editions, Inc.

Clay, Albert T. Light on the Old Testament from Babel. 2007. (Ancient near East: Classic Studies: Ser.). (Illus.). 484p. pap. 44.00 *(978-1-59752-717-0(3),* Wipf and Stock) Wipf & Stock Pubs.

Damrosch, David. The Buried Book: The Loss & Rediscovery of the Great Epic of Gilgamesh. 2007. (ENG., Illus.). 336p. pap. 16.99 *(978-0-8050-8725-3(7),* Holt Paperback) Holt, Henry & Co.

Fleming, Daniel E. & Milstein, Sara J. The Buried Foundation of the Gilgamesh Epic: The Akkadian Huwawa Narrative. 2010. (Cuneiform Monographs). *(978-90-04-17848-9(1))* BRILL.

Holloway, Steven. Orientalism Assyriology & the Bible. 2006. (Illus.). 592p. *(978-1-905048-37-3(8))* Sheffield Phoenix Pr.

Holloway, Steven, ed. Orientalism, Assyriology & the Bible. 2007. 592p. per. *(978-1-906055-33-2(5))* Sheffield Phoenix Pr.

Holloway, Steven, et al, eds. In the Wake of Tikva Frymer-Kensky. 2009. 105.00 *(978-1-59333-977-7(1))* Gorgias Pr., LLC.

Roth, Martha T., et al, eds. Studies Presented to Robert D. Biggs, June 4 2004. 2007. (From the Workshop of the Chicago Assyrian Dictionary Ser.). (ENG., Illus.). 362p. (C). pap. 40.00 *(978-1-885923-44-8(9))* Oriental Institute of the Univ. of Chicago, The.

Weisberg, David B. Leaders & Legacies in Assyriology & Bible: The Collected Essays of David B. Weisberg. 2012. ***(978-1-57506-230-3(5))*** Eisenbrauns, Inc.

ASSYRO-BABYLONIAN ART

see Art, Assyro-Babylonian

ASSYRO-BABYLONIAN CHRONOLOGY

see Chronology, Assyro-Babylonian

ASSYRO-BABYLONIAN CIVILIZATION

see Civilization, Assyro-Babylonian

ASSYRO-BABYLONIAN HYMNS

see Hymns, Assyro-Babylonian

ASSYRO-BABYLONIAN INSCRIPTIONS

see Cuneiform Inscriptions

ASSYRO-BABYLONIAN LANGUAGE

see Akkadian Language

ASSYRO-BABYLONIAN LAW

see Law—Assyria; Law—Iraq—Babylonia

ASSYRO-BABYLONIAN LETTERS

Alexander, James B. Early Babylonian Letters & Economic Texts. (Babylonian Inscriptions in the Collection of James B. Nies Ser.: 7). reprint ed. 45.00 *(978-0-404-60137-9(5))* AMS Pr., Inc.

Clay, Albert T. Letters & Transactions from Cappadocia. (Babylonian Inscriptions in the Collection of James B. Nies Ser.: 4). reprint ed. 30.00 *(978-0-404-60134-8(0))* AMS Pr., Inc.

Keiser, Clarence E. Letters & Contracts from Erech Written in the Neo-Babylonian Period. (Babylonian Inscriptions in the Collection of James B. Nies Ser.: 1). reprint ed. 27.50 *(978-0-404-60131-7(6))* AMS Pr., Inc.

King, L. W., ed. The Letters & Inscriptions of Hammurabi, King of Babylon About. 2006. (ENG.). 444p. per. 36.95 *(978-1-4286-3423-7(1))* Kessinger Publishing, LLC.

Lutz, Henry Frederick. Early Babylonian Letters from Larsa. 2008. 188p. pap. 22.95 *(978-1-4368-2725-6(6))* Kessinger Publishing, LLC.

Parpola, Simo, et al. Letters from Assyrian Scholars to the Kings Esarhaddon & Ashurbanipal, 2 vols. 2007. (Illus.). 85.00 *(978-1-57506-137-5(6))*; 110.00 *(978-1-57506-138-2(4))*; 169.00 *(978-1-57506-139-9(2))* Eisenbrauns, Inc.

Pfeiffer, Robert H. State Letters of Assyria: A Transliteration & Translation of 355 Official Assyrian Letters Dating from the Sargonid Period, 722-625 B. C. Brown, W. Norman & Shryock, John K., eds. 2011. 280p. 47.95 ***(978-1-258-04413-8(7))*** Literary Licensing, LLC.

Stephens, Ferris J. Old Assyrian Letters & Business Documents. (Babylonian Inscriptions in the Collection of James B. Nies Ser.: No. 6). reprint ed. 30.00 *(978-0-404-60136-2(7))* AMS Pr., Inc.

Ungnad, Arthur. Alt Babylonische Briefe aus dem Museum zu Philadelphia. (Ancient Mesopotamian Texts & Studies). reprint ed. 34.50 *(978-0-404-18226-7(7))* AMS Pr., Inc.

—Babylonische Breife aus der Zeit der Hammurapidynastic. (Ancient Mesopotamian Texts & Studies). reprint ed. 45.00 *(978-0-404-18227-4(5))* AMS Pr., Inc.

ASSYRO-BABYLONIAN LITERATURE

Clay, Albert T. Epics, Hymns, Omens & Other Texts. (Babylonian Records in the Library of J. Pierpont Morgan: 4). reprint ed. 30.00 *(978-0-404-60124-9(3))* AMS Pr., Inc.

—Origin of Biblical Traditions Hebrew Leg. 2006. pap. 26.95 *(978-1-4286-4379-6(6))* Kessinger Publishing, LLC.

de Jong, Matthijs J. Isaiah among the Ancient near Eastern Prophets: A Comparative Study of the Earliest Stages of the Isaiah Tradition & the Neo-Assyrian Prophecies. 2007. (Vetus Testamentum Supplements Ser.). (Illus.). 522p. *(978-90-04-16161-0(9))* BRILL.

Hurowitz, Victor. I Have Built You an Exalted House: Temple Building in the Bible in Light of Mesopotamian & North-West Semitic Writings. 2009. (Library of Hebrew Bible/Old Testament Studies, the Ser.). (ENG.). 398p. 65.00 *(978-0-567-02988-1(3),* T&T Clark) Continuum International Publishing Group, Ltd. GBR. Dist: National Bk. Network.

Johns, Claude H., ed. Assyrian Deeds & Documents, 4 vols., Set. (Ancient Mesopotamian Texts & Studies). reprint ed. 195.00 *(978-0-404-18180-2(5))* AMS Pr., Inc.

Keel, Othmar & Schroer, Silvia. Schöpfung: Biblische Theologien im Kontext altorientalischer Religionen. 2008. (GER., Illus.). 303p. (C). pap. 54.00 *(978-3-525-53500-4(7))* Vandenhoeck & Ruprecht GmbH & Co. KG DEU. Dist: ISD.

Langdon, Stephen H. Babylonian Liturgies. (Ancient Mesopotamian Texts & Studies) (Illus.). reprint ed. 37.50 *(978-0-404-18191-8(0))* AMS Pr., Inc.

Mack, Russell. Neo-Assyrian Prophecy & the Hebrew Bible: Nahum, Habakkuk, & Zephaniah. 2011. 160.30 ***(978-1-4632-0077-0(3))*** Gorgias Pr., LLC.

Oppenheim, A. Leo. The Interpretation of Dreams in the Ancient near East: With a New Introduction by Scott Noegel. 2007. 204p. 125.00 *(978-1-59333-733-9(7))* Gorgias Pr., LLC.

Oppenheim, A. Leo. The Interpretation of Dreams in the Ancient near East, with a Translation of an Assyrian Dream Book. 2011. 198p. 44.95 ***(978-1-258-10419-1(9))*** Literary Licensing, LLC.

Poebel, Amo. Historical & Grammatical Texts. 2009. 256p. pap. 27.95 *(978-1-104-76559-0(4))* Kessinger Publishing, LLC.

Rogers, Robert William. Cuneiform Parallels to the Old Testament. 2009. 596p. 30.99 *(978-1-103-02092-8(7))*; pap. 24.99 *(978-1-103-02089-8(7))* BiblioBazaar.

Sayce, A. H. Babylonian Literature. 2009. 90p. pap. 8.00 *(978-1-60608-827-2(0),* Wipf and Stock) Wipf & Stock Pubs.

Strassmaier Johann N., ed. Babylonische Texte, 5 vols., Set. Incl. Vol. 1. Inschriften von Nabuchodnosor. 32.50 *(978-0-404-61451-5(5))*; Vol. 2. Inschriften von Nabonidus. 57.50 *(978-0-404-61452-2(3))*; Vol. 3. Inschriften von Cyrus. 30.00 *(978-0-404-61453-9(1))*; Vol. 4. Inschriften von Cambyses. 32.50 *(978-0-404-61454-6(X))*; Vol. 5. Inschriften von Darius. 40.00 *(978-0-404-61455-3(8))*; (Ancient Mesopotamian Texts & Studies). reprint ed. 192.50 *(978-0-404-61450-8(7))* AMS Pr., Inc.

Ungnad, Arthur. Selected Babylonian Business & Legal Terms of the Hammurabi Period. 2009. 106p. pap. 9.00 *(978-1-60608-381-9(3),* Wipf and Stock) Wipf & Stock Pubs.

Viel, H.-Dieter. The New Complete Code of Hammurabi. 2011. (ENG.). 794p. 120.00 ***(978-0-7618-5656-6(0))*** Univ. Pr. of America, Inc.

ASSYRO-BABYLONIAN LITERATURE—HISTORY AND CRITICISM

Anthonioz, Stéphanie. L'eau, Enjeux Politiques et Théologiques, de Sumer à la Bible. 2009. (FRE.). *(978-90-04-17898-4(8))* BRILL.

Clifford, Richard J. Wisdom Literature in Mesopotamia & Israel. 2007. (SBL - Symposium Ser.). 118p. *(978-90-04-15108-6(7))* BRILL.

—Wisdom Literature in Mesopotamia & Israel. 2007. (ENG.). 132p. per. 19.95 *(978-1-58983-219-0(1))* Society of Biblical Literature.

Fleming, Daniel E. & Milstein, Sara J. The Buried Foundation of the Gilgamesh Epic: The Akkadian Huwawa Narrative. 2010. (Cuneiform Monographs). *(978-90-04-17848-9(1))* BRILL.

George, A. R. Babylonian Literary Texts in the Schoyen Collection. 2009. *(978-1-934309-09-4(5),* CDL Pr.) Univ. Pr. of Maryland.

Hunt, Joel H. Mesopotamian Suilla Prayers to Ea, Marduk, & Nabu: Exegetical Studies. 2010. ii, 253p. 109.95 *(978-0-7734-3652-7(9))* Mellen, Edwin Pr., The.

Petter, Donna Lee. The Book of Ezekiel & Mesopotamian City Laments. 2011. (Orbis Biblicus et Orientalis Ser.). (GER & ENG.). 207p. (C). 75.00 *(978-3-525-54367-2(0))* Vandenhoeck & Ruprecht GmbH & Co. KG DEU. Dist: ISD.

Sanders, Seth L. The Invention of Hebrew. (Traditions Ser.). (ENG., Illus.). 280p. 2011. pap. 35.00 ***(978-0-252-07835-4(7))*** 2009. 50.00 *(978-0-252-03284-4(5))* Univ. of Illinois Pr.

Stackert, Jeffrey, et al. Gazing on the Deep: Ancient near Eastern & Other Studies in Honor of Tsvi Abusch. 2010. *(978-1-934309-26-1(5))*, CDL Pr.) Univ. Pr. of Maryland.

Vanstiphout, H. L. J. Approaches to Sumerian Literature: Studies in Honor of Stip (H.L.J. Vanstiphout) Michalowski, Piotr & Veldhuis, Niek, trs. 2006. (Illus.). 250p. *(978-90-04-15325-7(X))* BRILL.

ASSYRO-BABYLONIAN MAGIC

see Magic, Assyro-Babylonian

ASSYRO-BABYLONIAN MYTHOLOGY

see Mythology, Assyro-Babylonian

ASSYRO-BABYLONIAN RELIGION

Barta, Heinz, et al, eds. Recht und Religion: Menschliche und gottliche Gerechtigkeitsvorstellungen in den Antiken Welten. 2008. (Philippika Ser.). (GER., Illus.). 207p. (C). pap. 72.00 *(978-3-447-05733-2(5))* Harrassowitz, Otto Verlag DEU. Dist: ISD.

Boscawen, W. St. Chad. Bible & the Monuments the Primitive He. 2006. pap. 26.95 *(978-1-4286-3630-9(7))* Kessinger Publishing, LLC.

Curtiss, Samuel. Primitive Semitic Religion Today. 2007. (ENG.). 342p. 46.95 *(978-0-548-05192-4(5))* Kessinger Publishing, LLC.

Gray, Clifton D., ed. The Samas Religious Texts Classified in the British Museum Catalogue As Hymns, Prayers, & Incantations. (Ancient Mesopotamian Texts & Studies). reprint ed. 29.50 *(978-0-404-18176-5(7))* AMS Pr., Inc.

Groneberg, Brigitte, et al. Die Welt der Gotterbilder. 2007. (Beihefte Zur Zeitschrift Für Die Alttestamentliche Wissenschaft Ser.). (GER & ENG., Illus.). VIII, 380p. 154.00 *(978-3-11-019463-0(5))* De Gruyter, Walter Inc.

Hackman, George G., ed. Temple Documents of the Third Dynasty of Ur from Umma. (Babylonian Inscriptions in the Collection of James B. Nies Ser.: No. 5). reprint ed. 28.50 *(978-0-404-60135-5(9))* AMS Pr., Inc.

Jastrow, Morris. Aspects of Religious Belief & Practice. 2006. pap. 45.95 *(978-1-4286-4772-5(4))* Kessinger Publishing, LLC.

—The Religion of Babylonia & Assyria. 2007. 680p. per. 49.95 *(978-1-4065-2734-6(3))* Dodo Pr.

—The Religion of Babylonia & Assyria. 2007. (ENG.). 796p. per. 54.95 *(978-1-4304-4302-5(2))* Kessinger Publishing, LLC.

Jeremias, Alfred. The Babylonian Conception of Heaven & Hell. 2009. 60p. pap. 6.00 *(978-1-60608-421-2(6)*, Wipf and Stock) Wipf & Stock Pubs.

King, L. W. Babylonian Religion & Mythology. 2008. 240p. pap. *(978-1-4097-8515-6(7))* Read Bks.

Langdon, Stephen H. Tammuz & Ishtar. (Ancient Mesopotamian Texts & Studies). reprint ed. 34.50 *(978-0-404-18193-2(7))* AMS Pr., Inc.

Lenzi, Alan. Akkadian Prayers & Hymns: A Reader. 2011. ***(978-1-58983-595-5(6))***; (AKK & ENG.). ***(978-1-58983-596-2(4))*** Society of Biblical Literature.

Mann, Thomas W. Divine Presence & Guidance in Israelite Traditions: The Typology of Exaltation. 2010. 320p. pap. 35.00 *(978-1-60899-718-3(9)*, Wipf and Stock) Wipf & Stock Pubs.

Mercer, Samuel A. B. Religious & Moral Ideas in Babylonia & Assyria. 2007. pap. 20.95 *(978-1-4304-5243-0(9))* Kessinger Publishing, LLC.

Rogers, Robert William. Cuneiform Parallels to the Old Testament. 2009. 596p. 30.99 *(978-1-103-02092-8(7))*; pap. 24.99 *(978-1-103-02089-8(7))* BiblioBazaar.

Sayce, A. H. The Hibbert Lectures 1887: Lectures on the Origin & Growth of Religion as Illustrated by the Religion of the Ancient Babylonians 1897. 2007. (ENG.). 564p. 58.95 *(978-0-548-05656-1(0))* Kessinger Publishing, LLC.

—The Origin & Growth of Religion: As Illustrated by the Religion of the Ancient Babylonians. 2007. (Gorgias Theological Library: 25). 98.00 *(978-1-59333-740-7(X))* Gorgias Pr., LLC.

Thompson, R. Campbell. The Devils & Evil Spirits of Babylonia, Being Babylonian & Assyrian Incantations Against the Demons, Ghouls, Vampires, Hobgoblins, Ghosts, & Kin. 2009. 276p. pap. 29.45 *(978-1-4437-9143-4(1))* Barclay Pr., Inc.

ASSYRO-BABYLONIAN SCULPTURE

see Sculpture, Assyro-Babylonian

ASSYRO-BABYLONIAN STUDIES

see Assyria—Antiquities; Assyriology

ASTAIRE, FRED, 1899-1987

Astaire, Fred. Steps in Time: An Autobiography. 2008. (ENG., Illus.). 384p. pap. 13.99 *(978-0-06-156756-8(6))* HarperCollins Pubs.

Croce, Arlene. The Fred Astaire & Ginger Rogers Book. 2010. (ENG., Illus.). 191p. pap. 24.95 *(978-1-934849-32-3(4))* Zip Publishing.

Epstein, Joseph. Fred Astaire. 2009. (Icons of America Ser.). (ENG., Illus.). 224p. pap. 15.00 *(978-0-300-15844-1(0))* Yale Univ. Pr.

Epstein, Joseph & Miller, Mark Crispin. Fred Astaire. 2008. (Icons of America Ser.). (ENG., Illus.). 224p. 22.00 *(978-0-300-11695-3(0))* Yale Univ. Pr.

Mueller, John. Astaire Dancing: The Musical Films. 2nd ed. 2010. (ENG., Illus.). 446p. pap. 69.95 *(978-1-934849-31-6(6))* Zip Publishing.

Riley, Kathleen. The Astaires: Fred & Adele, 1 vol. 2012. (ENG., Illus.). 266p. 27.95 ***(978-0-19-973841-0(6))*** Oxford Univ. Pr., Inc.

ASTATINE

Elgqvist, Jörgen. Astatine-211 Radioimmunotherapy of Ovarian Cancer. 2010. 172p. pap. *(978-3-8383-1721-2(1))* Lambert Academic Publishing.

ASTELL, MARY, 1666-1731

Kolbrener, William & Michelson, Michal, eds. Mary Astell: Reason, Gender, Faith. 2007. 230p. 99.95 *(978-0-7546-5264-9(5))* Ashgate Publishing Co.

ASTEROIDEA

see Starfishes

ASTEROIDS

Adushkin, V. V & Nemchinov, I. V., eds. Catastrophic Events Caused by Cosmic Objects. 2007. (Illus.). 316p. 139.00 *(978-1-4020-6451-7(9)*, 1402064519) Springer.

Adushkin, Vitaly & Nemchinov, Ivan, eds. Catastrophic Events Caused by Cosmic Objects. 2010. (Illus.). xii, 358p. pap. 139.00 *(978-90-481-7644-1(1)*, 9048176441) Springer.

Belton, Michael J. S., et al, eds. Mitigation of Hazardous Comets & Asteroids. 2011. (ENG., Illus.). 438p. pap. 55.00 *(978-0-521-17332-2(9))* Cambridge Univ. Pr.

Blasius, Ralf & Podbregar, Nadja. Armageddon: Die längste Nacht. 2007. (Illus.). IV, 268p. 39.95 *(978-3-540-37656-9(9)*, 3540376569) Springer.

Bobrowsky, Peter T. & Rickman, Hans, eds. Comet/Asteroid Impacts & Human Society: An Interdisciplinary Approach. (ENG., Illus.). xxvi, 546p. 2010. pap. 189.00 *(978-3-642-06924-6(X)*, 364206924X) 2007. 189.00 *(978-3-540-32709-7(6)*, 3540327096) Springer.

Bond, Alan & Hempsell, Mark. A Sumerian Observation of the Köfels' Impact Event. 2008. (Illus.). 128p. per. *(978-1-904623-64-9(6))* WritersPrintShop.

Busch, Michael W. Shapes & Spins of near-Earth Asteroids. 2010. 126p. pap. 19.95 *(978-1-59942-322-7(7)*, Dissertation.com) Universal Pubs.

Committee to Review Near-Earth Object Surveys and Hazard Mitigation Strategies & National Research Council Staff. Near-Earth Object Surveys & Hazard Mitigation Strategies: Interim Report. 2009. (ENG.). 40p. pap. 21.00 *(978-0-309-14361-5(6))* National Academies Pr.

Dementieva, Akilina & Ostrogorsky, Danilo. Meteorites & Asteroids: Classification, Geology, & Exploration. 2012. *(978-1-61942-115-8(1))* Nova Science Pubs., Inc.

Di Martino, M. The Asteroid Hazard: Evaluating & Avoiding the Threat of Asteroid Impacts. 2009. (Illus.). 324p. *(978-92-9221-403-6(9))* European Space Agency.

Dvorak, Rudolf & Ferraz-Mello, Sylvio, eds. A Comparison of the Dynamical Evolution of Planetary Systems: Proceedings of the Sixth Alexander von Humboldt Colloquium on Celestial Mechanics Bad Hofgastein (Austria), 21-27 March 2004. 2010. vi, 302p. pap. 129.00 *(978-90-481-7077-7(X)*, 904817077X) Springer.

Dvorak, Rudolf & Henrard, Jacques, eds. New Developments in the Dynamics of Planetary Systems. 2010. (Illus.). 400p. pap. 189.00 *(978-90-481-5702-0(1)*, 9048157021) Springer.

Dymock, Roger. Asteroids & Dwarf Planets & How to Observe Them. 2010. (Astronomers' Observing Guides). (Illus.). xiii, 248p. pap. 39.95 *(978-1-4419-6438-0(X)*, 144196438X) Springer.

Dypvik, Henning, et al. The Mjolnir Impact Event: Geology & Geophysics of a Late Jurassic/Early Cretaceous Submarine Impact Structure. 2010. (Impact Studies). (ENG.). 400p. 179.00 *(978-3-540-88259-6(6)*, 3540882596) Springer.

Edberg, Stephen J. & Levy, David H. Observing Comets, Asteroids, Meteors, & the Zodiacal Light. 2008. (Practical Astronomy Handbooks Ser.). (ENG., Illus.). 260p. pap. 41.00 *(978-0-521-06627-3(1))* Cambridge Univ. Pr.

Elkins-Tanton, Linda T. Asteroids, Meteorites, & Comets. 2nd rev. ed. 2010. (Solar System Ser.). 288p. (gr. 6-12). 39.50 *(978-0-8160-7696-3(0))* Facts On File, Inc.

Farquhar, Robert. Fifty Years on the Space Frontier: Halo Orbits, Comets, Asteroids, & More. 2011. 459p. 86.95 ***(978-1-4327-5927-8(2))*** Outskirts Pr., Inc.

Farquhar, Robert W. Fifty Years on the Space Frontier: Halo Orbits, Comets, Asteroids, & More. 2011. 459p. pap. 28.95 ***(978-1-4327-7606-0(1))***; (ENG.). pap. 35.95 ***(978-1-4327-7721-0(1))*** Outskirts Pr., Inc.

Gainsburg, Adam. Chiron: The Wisdom of a Deeply Open Heart. 2006. per. 13.95 *(978-0-9788535-2-5(0))* Soulsign Publishing.

Kortenkamp, Steve. Asteroids, Comets, & Meteorites. 2007. (Solar System Ser.). (ENG.). 24p. (gr. 1-2). 24.65 *(978-1-4296-0059-0(4)*, First Facts) Capstone Pr., Inc.

Lang-Wescott, Martha. Mechanics of the Future: Asteroids. rev. ed. (Illus.). 244p. 22.95 *(978-0-9619852-1-9(6))* Treehouse Mountain.

Lang-Wescott, Martha, ed. Asteroid Mechanics, 1925-2006, 2 vols., Vol. II. (Asteroid Ephemerides Ser.). 80p. 15.95 *(978-0-9619852-4-0(0))* Treehouse Mountain.

Norton, O. Richard. Rocks from Space: Meteorites & Meteorite Hunters. 2nd ed. (Illus.). 467p. pap. 55.00 *(978-0-87842-438-2(5)*, 334) Mountain Pr. Publishing Co., Inc.

Palmer, Trevor. Perilous Planet Earth: Catastrophes & Catastrophism through the Ages. 2010. 536p. pap. 50.00 *(978-0-521-17464-0(3))* Cambridge Univ. Pr.

Pottenger, Rique. The Asteroid Ephemeris 1900 to 2050. 2008. 220p. pap. 26.95 *(978-1-934976-00-5(8))* Starcrafts LLC.

Rivkin, Andrew S. Asteroids, Comets, & Dwarf Planets, 1 vol. 2009. (Greenwood Guides to the Universe Ser.). (Illus.). 206p. (gr. 9-18). 65.00 *(978-0-313-34432-9(9)*, GR4432) Greenwood Publishing Group, Inc.

Rzoska, Sylwester J. Soft Matter under Exogenic Impacts. 2007. (NATO Science Series II). 504p. 269.00 *(978-1-4020-5870-7(5))*; (ENG.). per. 139.00 *(978-1-4020-5871-4(3))* Springer.

Scheeres, Daniel J. Orbital Motion in Strongly Perturbed Environments: Applications to Asteroid & Comet Orbiters. 2011. (Springer Praxis Books / Astronautical Engineering Ser.). (ENG.). 300p. 129.00 *(978-3-642-03255-4(9)*, 3642032559) Springer.

Schmadel, L. D. & Schmadel, Lutz D. Dictionary of Minor Planet Names: Addendum to Fifth Edition: 2003 - 2005. 2006. (Illus.). x, 343p. 159.00 *(978-3-540-34360-8(1)*, 3540343601) Springer.

Schmadel, Lutz D. Dictionary of Minor Planet Names. 5th ed. 2006. XVI, 992p. 209.00 *(978-3-540-33631-0(1)*, 3540336311) Springer.

—Dictionary of Minor Planet Names + Addendum. 2007. X, 343p. 373.00 *(978-3-540-36748-2(9)*, 3540367489) Springer.

Shustov, B. M. & Rykhlova, L. V. Asteroidno-Kometnaia Opasnost: Vchera, Segodnia, Zavtra. 2010. (RUS., Illus.). 383p. *(978-5-9221-1241-3(4))* Fiziko-Matematiceskaja Literatura.

Steves, B. A. & Roy, Archie E., eds. The Dynamics of Small Bodies in the Solar System: A Major Key to Solar Systems Studies: A Major Key to Solar Systems Studies. 2010. (NATO Science Series C: (closed) Ser.). 624p. pap. 469.00 *(978-90-481-5133-2(3)*, 9048151333) Springer.

Wescott, Martha, ed. Asteroid Mechanics, 1925-2006, Vol. I. (Asteroid Ephemerides Ser.). 80p. 15.95 *(978-0-9619852-6-4(7))* Treehouse Mountain.

Yabushita, Shin & Henrard, Jacques, eds. Dynamics of Comets & Asteroids & Their Role in Earth History. 2010. 304p. pap. 182.00 *(978-90-481-5081-6(7)*, 9048150817) Springer.

ASTHMA

Acevedo-Nieves, Rose. Influence of Acculturation on Asthma Outcomes in Hispanic Children - the Influence of Acculturation & Other Family Characteristics on Asthma Outcome. 2008. 108p. pap. *(978-3-639-04228-3(X))* VDM Verlag Dr. Mueller e.K.

Adams, Francis V. The Asthma Sourcebook. 3rd rev. ed. 2006. (Sourcebooks Ser.). (ENG., Illus.). 256p. per. 16.95 *(978-0-07-147652-2(0)*, 0071476520) McGraw-Hill Cos., The.

Al-Afaleg, Nouf. Oxidative Stress & Antioxidant Status in Saudi Asthmatic Patients. 2010. 88p. pap. *(978-3-639-24452-6(4))* VDM Verlag Dr. Mueller e.K.

Alexatos, Michael S. Biography of Captain Michael S. Alexatos USN (Ret.) 2010. 56p. pap. 10.49 *(978-1-4520-3025-8(1))* AuthorHouse.

American Academy of Pediatrics. Your Child's Allergies & Asthma: The American Academy of Pediatrics Guide to Breathing Easy & Bringing up Healthy, Active Children. Welch, Michael J., ed. 2nd ed. 2010. (What Every Parent Needs to Know Ser.). (ENG.). 200p. pap. 14.95 *(978-1-58110-445-5(6))* American Academy of Pediatrics.

Anna Murphy Staff. Asthma in Focus. 2006. (Illus.). 286p. 49.99 *(978-0-85369-647-6(0))* Pharmaceutical Pr. GBR. Dist: Smith Fulfillment Services.

Arshad, S. Hasan & Babu, K. Suresh. Asthma. 2008. (ENG., Illus.). 208p. pap. 19.95 *(978-0-19-921126-5(4))* Oxford Univ. Pr., Inc.

Bansal, Ranju, et al. Asthma - Molecular Basis & Treatment Approaches. 2011. 60p. pap. ***(978-3-8433-9167-2(X))*** Lambert Academic Publishing.

Barnes, Peter J., et al, eds. Asthma & COPD: Basic Mechanisms & Clinical Management. 2nd ed. 2008. (ENG., Illus.). 896p. 165.00 *(978-0-12-374001-4(0)*, Academic Pr.) Elsevier Science & Technology Bks.

Bee, Peta. I Have Asthma. 2010. (Taking Care of Myself Ser.). (ENG.). 32p. (gr. 3-6). lib. bdg. 26.60 *(978-1-4339-3851-1(0)*, Stevens, Gareth Learning Library) Stevens, Gareth Publishing LLLP.

Berger, William E. Asthma. 2009. (Oxford American Respiratory Library). (ENG., Illus.). 112p. pap. 24.95 *(978-0-19-538439-0(3))* Oxford Univ. Pr., Inc.

Berger, William E. Asthma for Dummies 2011. 2nd ed. 2011. 144p. pap. 4.99 ***(978-1-118-09718-2(1)***, For Dummies) Wiley, John & Sons, Inc.

Bernstein, David I. Occupational Asthma, an Issue of Immunology & Allergy Clinics. 2011. (Clinics: Internal Medicine Ser.: 31-4). (ENG., Illus.). 240p. 110.00 ***(978-1-4557-1104-8(7)***, Saunders) Elsevier - Health Sciences Div.

Blaser, K., ed. T Cell Regulation in Allergy, Asthma & Atopic Skin Diseases. 2008. (Chemical Immunology & Allergy Ser.). (Illus.). 226p. *(978-3-8055-8628-3(0))* Karger, S. AG.

Borm Bruckmeier Publishing LLC, ed. Asthma - COPD Pockettool. 2007. 9.95 *(978-1-59103-802-3(2))* Bruckmeier, Borm Publishing, LLC.

Bos, Gerrit & McVaugh, Michael R., trs. On Asthma, Volume II: Critical Editions of Hebrew & Latin Medieval Translations, Vol. 2. 2008. (C). 100.00 *(978-0-8425-2705-7(2)*, Brigham Young Univ. Pr.) Brigham Young Univ.

Bradley, Dinah & Clifton-Smith, Tania. Breathing Works for Asthma. (Illus.). 120p. pap. 19.95 *(978-1-85626-494-5(7))* Cathie, Kyle Ltd. GBR. Dist: Graphic Arts Ctr. Publishing Co.

Brewer, Sarah. Overcoming Asthma: The Complete Complementary Health Program. 2009. (Natural Health Guru Ser.). (ENG., Illus.). 180p. pap. 14.95 *(978-1-84483-727-4(0))* Duncan Baird Pubs. GBR. Dist: Sterling Publishing Co., Inc.

Briner, William & American College of Sports Medicine Staff. Action Plan for Allergies. 2006. (ENG., Illus.). 200p. per. 17.95 *(978-0-7360-6279-4(3))* Human Kinetics Pubs.

Brown, E. S., ed. Asthma: Social & Psychological Factors & Psychosomatic Syndromes, Vol. 24. (Advances in Psychosomatic Medicine Ser.: Vol. 24). (Illus.). *(978-3-8055-7579-9(3))* Karger, S. AG.

Brown, Phil. Toxic Exposures: Contested Illnesses & the Environmental Health Movement. 2007. (ENG., Illus.). 392p. (gr. 17). 32.00 *(978-0-231-12948-0(3))* Columbia Univ. Pr.

Brown, Sandra, ed. Asthma & Allergy: Handbook for Patient & Family. 2009. 176p. pap. 19.95 *(978-0-9822136-0-5(3))* Rapid Publishing LLC.

Cantani, Arnaldo. Pediatric Allergy, Asthma & Immunology. 2008. Orig. Title: Allergologia e immunologia pediatrica - Dall' Infanzia All'Adolescenza. (Illus.). XXXII, 1619p. 809.00 *(978-3-540-20768-9(6)*, 3540207686) Springer.

Castro, Mario & Kraft, Monica. Clinical Asthma. 2008. (ENG., Illus.). 532p. 152.00 *(978-0-323-04289-5(9)*, Mosby) Elsevier - Health Sciences Div.

Chidekel, Aaron. Curbside Consultation in Pediatric Asthma: 49 Clinical Questions. 2012. (ENG.). 250p. pap. 79.95 ***(978-1-55642-987-3(8))*** SLACK, Inc.

Chillemi, Stacey. How to Live Comfortably with Asthma. 2009. 205p. pap. 23.95 *(978-0-557-07430-3(4))* Lulu Enterprises Inc.

Chung, K. Fan & Adcock, Ian, eds. Asthma. 2010. (Methods in Molecular Medicine Ser.). (Illus.). 360p. pap. 149.00 *(978-1-61737-103-5(3)*, 1617371033) Humana Pr.

Clark, Margaret A. Asthma. rev. ed. 2010. 174p. pap. 49.95 *(978-0-7637-7854-5(0))* Jones & Bartlett Learning, LLC.

Colectivo de Medicina Natural. La Curacion Natural del Asma y las Alergias.Tr. of Natural Cure for Asthma & Alergies. (SPA., Illus.). 368p. *(978-84-7927-200-5(7))* Robinbk., Ediciones S.L.

Crameri, Reto, ed. Allergy & Asthma in Modern Scoiety Vol. 91: A Scientific Approach: Dedicated to Kurt Blaser. (Chemical Immunology & Allergy Ser.: Vol. 91). (Illus.). *(978-3-8055-8000-7(2))* Karger, S. AG.

Cram101 Textbook Reviews. Outlines & Highlights for Allergy & Asthm: Practical Diagnosis & Management by Massoud Mahmoudi, ISBN. 2011. 116p. pap. 28.95 ***(978-1-61461-466-1(0))*** Cram101 Inc.

—Outlines & Highlights for Asthma & Copd: Basic Mechanisms & Clinical Management by Peter Barnes, ISBN. 2011. 262p. pap. 31.95 ***(978-1-61461-450-0(4))*** Cram101 Inc.

Currie, Graeme & Baker, John. Asthma. 2nd ed. 2012. (ENG., Illus.). 160p. pap. 24.99 ***(978-0-19-963891-8(8))*** Oxford Univ. Pr., Inc.

Currie, Graeme P., ed. Asthma. 2008. (Oxford Respiratory Medicine Library). (ENG., Illus.). 112p. pap. 24.95 *(978-0-19-953956-7(1))* Oxford Univ. Pr., Inc.

Cutler, Ellen W. Live Free from Asthma & Allergies: Use the BioSET System to Detoxify & Desensitize Your Body. 2007. (ENG., Illus.). 304p. pap. 19.95 *(978-1-58761-301-2(8)*, Celestial Arts) Ten Speed Pr.

Denburg, Judah A., ed. Allergy & Allergic Diseases: The New Mechanisms & Therapeutics. 2010. (ENG.). 608p. pap. 175.00 *(978-1-61737-026-7(6)*, 1617370266) Humana Pr.

Douglas, J. Graham & Zeitz, Howard. Asthma: Clinician's Desk Reference. 2010. (ENG., Illus.). 128p. 69.95 *(978-1-84076-082-8(6))* Manson Publishing, Ltd. GBR. Dist: Thieme Medical Pubs., Inc.

Eckersley, Jill. Coping with Childhood Asthma. 128p. *(978-0-85969-907-5(2)*, Sheldon Press) SPCK Publishing.

Ehrlich, Paul & Chiaramonte, Larry. Asthma Allergies Children: A Parent's Guide. 2010. 311p. pap. 18.95 *(978-0-9843832-0-7(4))* Third Avenue Bks.

Fanta, Christopher H., et al. The Asthma Educator's 2007. (ENG., Illus.). 432p. (C). pap., instr.'s hndbk. ed. 64.00 *(978-0-07-144737-9(7)*, 0071447377) McGraw-Hill Professional Publishing.

Firshein, Richard N. Your Asthma - Free Child: The Revolutionary 7-Step Breath of Life Program. 2006. 148p. reprint ed. pap. 12.00 *(978-1-4223-5705-7(8))* DIANE Publishing Co.

Galant, Stanley P. What to Do for Kids with Asthma: Easy to Read, Easy to Use. 2011. (Illus.). ix, 145p. pap. ***(978-0-9720148-6-1(1))*** Institute for Healthcare Advancement.

Gershwin, M. Eric & Albertson, Timothy E., eds. Bronchial Asthma: A Guide for Practical Understanding & Treatment. 6th ed. 2011. (Illus.). xiii, 350p. 119.00 ***(978-1-4419-6835-7(0)***, 1441968350) Springer.

Gomieiro, Ludmila Taís Yazbek. Breathing Exercises for Asthmatics Elderly. 2010. 200p. pap. *(978-3-639-22170-1(2))* VDM Verlag Dr. Mueller e.K.

Greally, Dr Peter & Greally, Peter. Childhood Asthma: Your Questions Answered. 2011. (ENG.). 160p. pap. 22.95 ***(978-1-907593-00-0(4))*** Liberties Pr. IRL. Dist: Dufour Editions, Inc.

Harver, Andrew & Kotses, Harry, eds. Asthma, Health & Society: From the Clinic to the Public. 2009. 400p. 179.00 *(978-0-387-78284-3(2))* Springer.

Holgate, Stephen & Douglass, Jo. Fast Facts: Fast Facts. 3rd rev. ed. 2010. (Illus.). 108p. pap. 25.00 ***(978-1-905832-66-8(4))*** Health Pr., Ltd. GBR. Dist: BookMasters Distribution Services (BDS).

Hooper, James. James Hooper Buteyko Training Kit. 2007. *(978-1-921183-08-9(X))* One-on-One Learning Centre.

Jackson, Mark. Asthma: The Biography. 2009. (Biographies of Diseases Ser.). (ENG., Illus.). 256p. 24.95 *(978-0-19-923795-1(6))* Oxford Univ. Pr., Inc.

Jakob, Michael. Asthma Pocketcard Set. 2008. 69.50 *(978-1-59103-146-8(X))* Bruckmeier, Borm Publishing, LLC.

Jeyanthi, G. P., et al. Hepatoprotective Potential of Euphorbia Hirt. 2010. 220p. pap. *(978-3-8383-8201-2(3))* Lambert Academic Publishing.

Jing, Yi. Epithelial Mechanisms in Airway Responses Induced by Hyperosmolarity. 2009. 168p. pap. *(978-3-639-19868-3(9))* VDM Verlag Dr. Mueller e.K.

Johansson, S. G. O. & Haahtela, Tari, eds. Prevention of Allergy & Allergic Asthma Vol. 84: World Allergy Organization Project Report & Guidelines. (Chemical Immunology & Allergy Ser.: Vol. 84). (Illus.). 20.212p. *(978-3-8055-7810-3(5))* Karger, S. AG.

Jones, Lon. No More Allergies, Asthma or Sinus Infections: The Revolutionary Approach. 2011. (ENG.). 160p. pap. 15.95 *(978-1-893910-88-1(1))* Freedom Pr., Inc., The.

Judd, Sandra, ed. Asthma Sourcebook. 3rd rev. ed. 2011. (Health Reference Ser.). lib. bdg. 95.00 *(978-0-7808-1224-6(7))* Omnigraphics, Inc.

Kavuru, Mani S. Diagnosis & Management of Asthma. 2007. (ENG.). 288p. pap. 24.95 *(978-1-932610-38-3(3))* Professional Communications, Inc.

Kay, A. Barry, et al, eds. Allergy & Allergic Diseases, 2 vols., Set. 2nd ed. 2008. (ENG., Illus.). 2184p. 469.95 *(978-1-4051-5720-9(8)*, Wiley-Blackwell) Wiley, John & Sons, Inc.

Lee, Peter N. & Forey, Barbara. Exacerbation of Asthma: Epidemiological Evidence in Children. 2008. pap. 35.00 *(978-1-60692-083-1(9))* Nova Science Pubs., Inc.

—The Role of Environmental Tobacco Smoke in Asthma Induction & Exacerbation in Children & Adults. 2007. 120.00 *(978-1-60021-872-9(5))* Nova Science Pubs., Inc.

Lindberg, Malou. Asthma Nurse Practice in Primary Health Care. 2011. 108p. pap. ***(978-3-8443-9349-1(8))*** Lambert Academic Publishing.

Mahmoudi, Massoud. Allergy & Asthma: Practical Diagnosis & Management. 2007. (LANGE Clinical Medicine Ser.). (ENG., Illus.). 400p. per. 58.00 *(978-0-07-147173-2(1)*, 0071471731) McGraw-Hill Professional Publishing.

Maimonides, Moses, et al. On Asthma: Articles from the FARMS Review & the Journal of Book of Mormon Studies. 2008. (Brigham Young University - Medical Works of Moses Maimonides Ser.). (ARA., Illus.). 798p. 74.95 *(978-0-8425-2690-6(0)*, F. A. R. M. S.) Brigham Young Univ.

Makino, S. et al, eds. Asthma Prevention & Management Guidelines [Bibliography & Price Not Definite] Vol. 136: 2003, Japan (JGL 2003): English Summary. (Illus.). *(978-3-8055-7943-8(8))* Karger, S. AG.

Martin, Colin R. & Preedy, Victor R., eds. Scientific Basis of Healthcare. 2012. (ENG., Illus.). 210p. 69.95 ***(978-1-57808-731-0(7))*** BIOS Scientific Publishers Ltd. GBR. Dist: Taylor & Francis Group.

Martin, Richard & Sutherland, E. Rand, eds. Asthma & Infections. 2009. (ENG., Illus.). 218p. 250.00 *(978-1-4200-9299-8(5)*, Informa Healthcare) Taylor & Francis Group.

McConville, Brigid. Combat Asthma Through Diet: A Collection of 50 Low-Allergen Recipes to Beat the Symptoms of Asthma, Eczema & Hayfever. Expert Dietary Advice, Shown in More Than 400 Step-by-Step Photographs. 2009. (ENG., Illus.). 96p. pap. 14.99 *(978-1-84476-675-8(6))* Anness Publishing GBR. Dist: National Bk. Network.

Miller, Thomas, ed. Allergy: Complete Handbook. 2011. 124p. pap. 14.95 ***(978-1-937354-08-4(3))*** Rapid Publishing LLC.

Mohapatra, Shyam & Hellermann, Gary. Viral Infections in Asthma, an Issue of Immunology & Allergy Clinics. 2010. (Clinics: Internal Medicine Ser.: 30-4). (ENG., Illus.). xviii, 454p. 105.00 *(978-1-4377-2459-2(0)*, Saunders) Elsevier - Health Sciences Div.

Novozhilov, Andrey. Living without Asthma. 2007. 68p. pap. 39.50 *(978-1-84753-536-8(4))* Lulu Enterprises Inc.

Oates, James Mitchum. Life 101 - a True Life Story. 2011. 156p. pap. 19.99 ***(978-1-4535-3153-2(X))*** Xlibris Corp.

Pabst, Reinhard, ed. Animal Models for Asthma: Workshop on Asthma in Animal Models, Hannover, January 2003. (Pathobiology Ser.: Vol. 70, No. 5). (Illus.). 56p. *(978-3-8055-7589-8(0))* Karger, S. AG.

Page, Clive P. & Barnes, Peter J. Pharmacology & Therapeutics of Asthma & COPD. 2010. (Handbook of Experimental Pharmacology Ser.). (Illus.). x, 376p. pap. 449.00 *(978-3-642-05590-4(7)*, 3642055907) Springer.

Patterson, Alina V. & Yeager, Pauline N., eds. Asthma: Etiology, Pathogenesis & Treatment. 2008. 98.00 *(978-1-60456-891-2(7))* Nova Science Pubs., Inc.

Pescatore, Fred. The Allergy & Asthma Cure: A Complete 8-Step Nutritional Program. 2008. (ENG.). 272p. pap. 15.95 *(978-0-470-27541-2(3)*, Wiley) Wiley, John & Sons, Inc.

Plottel, Claudia S. Asthma. 2nd rev. ed. 2010. 316p. pap. 22.95 *(978-0-7637-8091-3(X))* Jones & Bartlett Learning, LLC.

Plottel, Claudia S. & Feldman, B. Robert. 100 Questions & Answers about Your Child's Asthma. 2007. 284p. pap. 22.95 *(978-0-7637-3917-1(0))* Jones & Bartlett Learning, LLC.

Postma, Dirkje S. & Weiss, Scott T., eds. Genetics of Asthma & Chronic Obstructive Pulmonary Disease. 2007. (Lung Biology in Health & Disease Ser.: Vol. 218). (ENG., Illus.). 414p. 250.00 *(978-0-8493-6966-7(5))* Taylor & Francis Group.

Priftis, K. N. & Chrousos, G. P., eds. Neuroimmunomodulation in Asthma: Focus on the Hypothalamic-Pituitary-Adrenal Axis. 2009. (Illus.). 104p. pap. *(978-3-8055-9200-0(0))* Karger, S. AG.

Ravikovich, Felix. L' Asthme et les Allergies: Le Complot du Siecle. Charland, Caroline, tr. from ENG. 2008. (FRE.). 534p. pap. *(978-2-922969-14-6(2))* Editions le mieux-etre CAN. Dist: AtlasBooks Distribution.

Rees, John, et al. ABC of Asthma. 6th ed. 2010. (ENG., Illus.). 104p. pap. 41.95 *(978-1-4051-8596-7(1))* Wiley, John & Sons, Inc.

Roberts, Ron. Asthma Controlled Naturally: Techniques That Work. 2008. (ENG., Illus.). 240p. pap. 19.95 *(978-1-74110-594-0(3))* New Holland Pubs. Pty, Ltd. AUS. Dist: Tuttle Publishing.

Sander, Nancy J. Consumer Update on Asthma. 2nd ed. (Illus.). 49p. pap. *(978-1-885543-00-4(X))* Allergy & Asthma Network-Mothers of Asthmatic, Inc.

Sebastian, L. Johnston & O'Byrne, Paul, eds. Exacerbations of Asthma. 2007. (ENG., Illus.). 388p. 240.00 *(978-1-84214-318-6(2)*, Informa Healthcare) Taylor & Francis Group GBR. Dist: Taylor & Francis Group.

Shafer. Asthma Free in 21 Days. Date not set. 256p. pap. 14.00 *(978-0-06-251719-7(8)*, Harper San Francisco) HarperCollins Pubs.

Shahzad, Muhammad. Immunomodulatory Role of Black Seed Oil. 2010. 84p. pap. *(978-3-639-21677-6(6))* VDM Verlag Dr. Mueller e.K.

Sigsgaard, Torben & Heederik, Dick. Occupational Asthma. 2009. (Progress in Inflammation Research Ser.). (Illus.). 350p. 219.00 *(978-3-7643-8555-2(3))* Birkhauser Boston.

Simmons, Janice C. Everything Parent's Guide to Children with Asthma: Professional Advice to Help Your Child Manage Symptoms, Be More Active, & Breathe Better. 2008. (ENG.). 304p. pap. 14.95 *(978-1-59869-430-7(8))* Adams Media Corp.

Sjöbring, U. & Taylor, J. D., eds. Models of Exacerbations in Asthma & COPD [Bibliography & Price not Definite.]. 2007. (Contributions to Microbiology Ser.). (Illus.). 146p. *(978-3-8055-8332-9(X))* Karger, S. AG.

Sorensen Allacci, Maryann. Neighborhood Characteristics & Asthma Emergency Visits. 2009. 144p. pap. *(978-3-639-13407-0(9))* VDM Verlag Dr. Mueller e.K.

Stauth, Cameron & Bock, Kenneth. Healing the New Childhood Epidemics: Autism, ADHD, Asthma, & Allergies: The Groundbreaking Program for the 4-A Disorders. 2008. (ENG., Illus.). 480p. pap. 16.00 *(978-0-345-49451-1(2)*, Ballantine Bks.) Random House Publishing Group.

Stshl, Elisabeth. Health-Related Quality of Life in Copd & Asthma - Discriminative & Evaluative Aspects. 2008. 76p. pap. *(978-3-639-07971-5(X))* VDM Verlag Dr. Mueller e.K.

Tuomisto, Leena. Asthma Programme in Finland: Management of Adult Asthma as Reflected by Referral Letters. 2010. (Acta Universitatis Tamperensis Ser.). 149p. pap. 79.50 *(978-951-44-8075-1(9))* Tampere Univ. Pr. FIN. Dist: Coronet Bks.

Vatcher, James Gordon. Secret Cures for Asthma & Heartburn. 2011. 48p. 24.99 ***(978-1-4628-5208-6(4))***; pap. 15.99 ***(978-1-4628-5207-9(6))*** Xlibris Corp.

Wadhwa, Vinod. Asthma. 2007. (Your Family Doctor Ser.). (Illus.). 91p. pap. 6.95 *(978-81-8328-033-4(1))* Wisdom Tree IND. Dist: SCB Distributors.

Waldron, Jill. Asthma Care in the Community. 2007. (ENG., Illus.). 200p. per. 60.99 *(978-0-470-03000-4(3)*, Wiley-Interscience) Wiley, John & Sons, Inc.

Wang, Chengbo. Hyperpolarized Helium-3 Diffusion Magnetic Resonance Imaging in Human Lungs. 2008. 188p. per. *(978-3-8364-6366-9(0))* VDM Verlag Dr. Mueller e.K.

Wohlenhaus, Kim, ed. Asthma Information for Teens. 2nd rev. ed. 2010. (Teen Health Ser.). (YA). lib. bdg. 69.00 *(978-0-7808-1086-0(4))* Omnigraphics, Inc.

World Health Organization Staff, et al, contrib. by. Principles & Methods for Assessing Autoimmunity Associated with Exposure to Chemicals. 2006. (Environmental Health Criteria Series,No. 236 Ser.). (ENG., Illus.). 359p. pap. 60.00 *(978-92-4-157236-1(1))* World Health Organization.

Young, Stephen. How to Inhale the Universe without Wheezing. 2008. 120p. pap. 13.95 *(978-1-4357-1510-3(1))* Lulu Enterprises Inc.

Youngson, R. M. Living with Asthma. xii, 147p. *(978-0-85969-892-4(0)*, Sheldon Press) SPCK Publishing.

ASTHMA—CHEMOTHERAPY

Ali Mahmoud Elgaher, Walid. New Theophylline Derivatives. 2011. 204p. pap. ***(978-3-8454-0133-1(8))*** Lambert Academic Publishing.

Hansel, T. T. & Barnes, P. J., eds. New Drugs & Targets for Asthma & COPD. 2010. (Progress in Respiratory Research Ser.). (Illus.). 310p. *(978-3-8055-9566-7(2))* Karger, S. AG.

Hansel, Trevor T. & Barnes, Peter J., eds. New Drugs for Asthma, Allergy & COPD, Vol. 31. (Progress in Respiratory Research Ser.: Vol. 31). (Illus.). *(978-3-8055-6862-3(2))* Karger, S. AG.

Lotvall, Jan & Busse, William, eds. Advances in Combination Therapy for Asthma & COPD. 2012. (ENG., Illus.). 364p. 129.95 ***(978-0-470-72702-7(0)***, Wiley) Wiley, John & Sons, Inc.

ASTON MARTIN AUTOMOBILE

Autocar Staff, contrib. by. Aston Martin since 1994. 2008. (Autocar Collection). (ENG., Illus.). 176p. 39.95 *(978-1-84425-445-3(3)*, 1844254453) Haynes Publishing PLC GBR. Dist: MBI Distribution Services/Quayside Distribution.

Clarke, R. M., ed. Aston Martin, 1948-1968. 2007. (Ultimate Portfolio Ser.). (ENG., Illus.). 208p. pap. 37.95 *(978-1-85520-722-6(2)*, 1855207222) Brooklands Bks. GBR. Dist: MBI Distribution Services/Quayside Distribution.

—Aston Martin, 1968-1980. 2007. (Ultimate Portfolio Ser.). (ENG., Illus.). 208p. per. 37.95 *(978-1-85520-723-3(0)*, 1855207230) Brooklands Bks. GBR. Dist: MBI Distribution Services/Quayside Distribution.

—Aston Martin, 1981-1993. 2007. (Ultimate Portfolio Ser.). (ENG., Illus.). 192p. pap. 37.95 *(978-1-85520-724-0(9)*, 1855207249) Brooklands Bks. GBR. Dist: MBI Distribution Services/Quayside Distribution.

—Aston Martin Gold Portfolio, 1921-1947. 2007. (Gold Portfolio Ser.). (ENG., Illus.). 176p. per. 32.95 *(978-1-85520-721-9(4)*, 1855207214) Brooklands Bks. GBR. Dist: MBI Distribution Services/Quayside Distribution.

—Aston Martin Ultimate Portfolio, 1994-2006. 2007. (Ultimate Portfolio Ser.). (ENG., Illus.). 224p. pap. 37.95 *(978-1-85520-725-7(7)*, 1855207257) Brooklands Bks. GBR. Dist: MBI Distribution Services/Quayside Distribution.

Dowsey, David. Aston Martin: Power, Beauty & Soul. 2nd ed. 2010. (ENG., Illus.). 352p. 45.00 *(978-1-86470-424-2(1)*, Images Publishing Dist Ac) Antique Collectors' Club GBR. Dist: National Bk. Network.

Noakes, Andrew. Aston Martin: Model by Model, 1 vol. 2012. (ENG., Illus.). 208p. 39.95 ***(978-1-84797-322-1(1)***, 1847973221) Crowood Pr., Ltd. GBR. Dist: MBI Distribution Services/Quayside Distribution.

Noakes, Andrew. Aston Martin DB7: The Complete Story. 2007. (ENG., Illus.). 176p. 34.95 *(978-1-86126-823-5(8)*, 1861268238) Crowood Pr., Ltd. GBR. Dist: MBI Distribution Services/Quayside Distribution.

Presland, Willi & Presland, William A. Aston Martin V8. 2009. (ENG., Illus.). 208p. 44.95 *(978-1-84797-066-4(4)*, 1847970664) Crowood Pr., Ltd. GBR. Dist: MBI Distribution Services/Quayside Distribution.

Pritchard, Anthony. Aston Martin: A Racing History. 2006. (ENG., Illus.). 272p. 60.00 *(978-1-84425-241-1(8)*, 1844252418) Haynes Publishing PLC GBR. Dist: MBI Distribution Services/Quayside Distribution.

Raby, Philip. The Little Book of Aston Martin. 2007. (Little Book Ser.). (ENG., Illus.). 128p. 11.99 *(978-1-905828-87-6(X)*, 190582887X) G2 Entertainment Ltd. GBR. Dist: BookMasters Distribution Services (BDS).

Schlegeimilch, Rainer W., et al. Aston Martin. 2008. (Transportation Ser.). (Illus.). 279p. 49.95 *(978-0-8416-0273-1(5))* American Map Corp.

Schlegelmilch, Rainer W., et al. Aston Martin. 2010. (ENG, FRE & GER., Illus.). 280p. spiral bd. 19.99 *(978-3-8331-5137-8(4))* h.f.ullmann DEU. Dist: Innovative Logistics.

ASTOR, BROOKE, 1902-2007

Gordon, Meryl. Mrs. Astor Regrets: The Hidden Betrayals of a Family Beyond Reproach. (ENG., Illus.). 2009. 368p. pap. 14.95 *(978-0-547-24798-4(2)*, Mariner Bks.) 2008. 336p. 28.00 *(978-0-618-89373-7(3))* Houghton Mifflin Harcourt Trade & Reference Pubs.

Kiernan, Frances. Last Mrs. Astor. 2007. 24.95 *(978-0-7930-5720-7(5))* Norton, W. W. & Co., Inc.

—The Last Mrs. Astor: A New York Story. (ENG., Illus.). 2008. 352p. pap. 15.95 *(978-0-393-33160-8(1)*, 33160) 2007. 320p. 24.95 *(978-0-393-05720-1(8)*, 5720) Norton, W. W. & Co., Inc.

ASTOR, JOHN JACOB, 1763-1848

Astor, John Jacob. A Journey in Other Worlds. 2008. 292p. 28.99 *(978-0-554-26424-0(2))*; 25.99 *(978-0-554-35727-0(5))* BiblioBazaar.

—A Journey in Other Worlds. 2009. 218p. pap. *(978-0-217-42725-8(1))* Books LLC.

—A Journey in Other Worlds. 2006. (ENG.). pap. *(978-1-4065-1105-5(6))* Dodo Pr.

Derbyshire, Wyn. Six Tycoons: Lives of John Astor, Vanderbilt, Carnegie, Henry Ford & J. D. Rockefeller. 2008. (Illus.). 251p. 36.95 *(978-1-904905-84-4(6))* Spiramus Pr. GBR. Dist: International Specialized Bk. Services.

Irving, Washington. Astoria: Anecdotes of an enterprise beyond the rocky Mountains. 2008. (ENG.). 316p. pap. 23.99 *(978-1-4264-0031-5(4))* BiblioBazaar.

ASTOR, NANCY WITCHER LANGHORNE ASTOR, VISCOUNTESS, 1879-1964

Harrison, Rosina. Rose: My Life in Service to Lady Astor. 2011. (ENG.). 368p. (gr. 12). 15.00 ***(978-0-14-312086-5(7)***, Penguin (Non-Classics)) Penguin Group (USA) Inc.

McCray, James. Ebb Tide: Nancy Astor's Greatest Challenge. 2008. 24.95 *(978-0-9814650-9-8(9))* G Publishing LLC.

ASTOR FAMILY

Gordon, Meryl. Mrs. Astor Regrets: The Hidden Betrayals of a Family Beyond Reproach. 2008. (ENG., Illus.). 336p. 28.00 *(978-0-618-89373-7(3))* Houghton Mifflin Harcourt Trade & Reference Pubs.

Kaplan, Justin. When the Astors Owned New York: Blue Bloods & Grand Hotels in a Gilded Age. 2007. (ENG., Illus.). 208p. (gr. 12-18). 15.00 *(978-0-452-28858-4(4)*, Plume) Penguin Group (USA) Inc.

ASTORIA (OR.)

Brick, Jason. Astoria: A Guide to Oregon's Gate to the Sea. 2012. (Tourist Town Guides). 192p. pap. 14.95 *(978-1-935455-08-0(7))* Channel Lake, Inc.

Franchere, Gabriel. Narrative of a Voyage to the Northwest Coast of America: In the years 1811 1812 1813 & 1814 or the Fir. 2007. (ENG.). 198p. pap. 19.99 *(978-1-4264-9098-9(4))*; 216p. pap. 22.99 *(978-1-4264-9152-8(2))* BiblioBazaar.

Franchere, Gabriel & Huntington, Jedediah. Franchere's Narrative of a Voyage. 2007. (Travel in America Ser.). (ENG.). 232p. 49.95 *(978-1-4290-0306-3(5))*; per. 24.95 *(978-1-4290-0307-0(3))* Applewood Bks.

Irving, Washington. Astoria. (ENG.). 2009. 676p. pap. 32.99 *(978-1-117-41398-3(5)*, BiblioLife) 2009. 528p. pap. 30.99 *(978-1-117-41401-0(9)*, BiblioLife) 2008. 394p. pap. 25.99 *(978-1-4264-0160-2(4))* BiblioBazaar.

—Astoria. 2007. (ENG.). 328p. per. *(978-1-4068-3804-6(7))* Echo Library.

—Astoria: Anecdotes of an enterprise beyond the rocky Mountains. 2008. (ENG.). 316p. pap. 23.99 *(978-1-4264-0031-5(4))* BiblioBazaar.

—Astoria, or, Anecdotes of an Enterprise Beyond the Rocky Mountains. 2007. 424p. per. *(978-1-4065-3429-0(3))* Dodo Pr.

Kirtley, Karen, ed. Astorians, Eccentric & Extraordinary. 2010. 224p. pap. 19.95 *(978-0-87071-632-4(8))* Oregon State Univ. Pr.

—Eminent Astorians. 2010. 272p. pap. 19.95 *(978-0-87071-631-7(X))* Oregon State Univ. Pr.

Ross, Alexander. Adventures of the First Settlers on the Columbia River. 2006. pap. 31.95 *(978-1-4286-4998-9(0))* Kessinger Publishing, LLC.

Smith, Jeffrey H. Astoria. 2011. (Images of America Ser.). (ENG., Illus.). 128p. pap. 21.99 *(978-0-7385-7527-8(5))* Arcadia Publishing.

ASTRAGALUS (PLANTS)

Jan, Saleem. Cycloartane Triterpenoids. 2010. 164p. pap. *(978-3-639-26203-2(4))* VDM Verlag Dr. Mueller e.K.

Welsh, Stanley L. North American Species of Astragalus. 2006. (Illus.). (C). *(978-0-8425-2662-3(5)*, Brigham Young Univ. Pr.) Brigham Young Univ.

ASTRAL PROJECTION

Adair, Joseph B., told to. My Strange Experiences: UFO Contacts, Visions & Out of Body Travels. 2010. (Illus.). 130p. pap. 12.00 *(978-0-615-36659-3(7))* Crosstimbers Pr.

Barton, Mary. Soul Sight: Projections of Consciousness & Out of Body Epiphanies. 2008. 177p. pap. 12.95 *(978-0-557-02163-5(4))* Lulu Enterprises Inc.

Battersby, H. F. Prevost. Man Outside Himself: The Methods of Astral Projection. 2007. (ENG.). 108p. 33.95 *(978-0-548-05602-8(1))* Kessinger Publishing, LLC.

Belanger, Michelle. Psychic Dreamwalking: Explorations at the Edge of Self. 2006. (ENG.). 1p. per. 14.95 *(978-1-57863-386-9(9)*, Weiser Bks.) Red Wheel/Weiser.

Belzebuub. A Course in Astral Travel & Dreams. 2010. (Illus.). 293p. pap. 12.95 *(978-0-9789864-4-5(X))* Absolute Publishing Pr.

Braschler, Von. Seven Secrets of Time Travel: Mystic Voyages of the Energy Body. 2012. (ENG.). 1p. pap. ***(978-1-59477-447-8(1)***, Destiny Bks.) Inner Traditions International, Ltd.

Bruce, Robert. Astral Dynamics: The Complete Book of Out-of-Body Experiences, 1 vol. rev. ed. 2009. (ENG., Illus.). 392p. pap. 24.95 *(978-1-57174-616-0(1))* Hampton Roads Publishing Co., Inc

Conway, D. J. A Witch's Travel Guide to Astral Realms. 2009. (ENG.). 224p. pap. 14.95 *(978-0-7387-1545-2(X))* Llewellyn Pubns.

Craze, Richard. Astral Projection: Beginners Guide. (Illus.). 92p. pap. 11.95 *(978-0-340-73755-2(7)*, Hodder & Stoughton) Hodder General Publishing Div. GBR. Dist: Trafalgar Square Publishing.

Crookall, Robert. The Study & Practice of Astral Projection. 2011. 246p. 46.95 ***(978-1-258-00883-3(1))*** Literary Licensing, LLC.

Draganic, Ivan. Open Your Mind to See. 2011. 134p. 29.99 ***(978-1-4568-6903-8(5))***; pap. 19.99 ***(978-1-4568-6902-1(7))*** Xlibris Corp.

Glaskin, G. M. Windows of the Mind: Consciousness Beyond the Body. 208p. pap. *(978-0-907061-81-6(8))* Prism Pr. GBR. Dist: APG Sales & Distribution Services.

Gold, E. J. Astral Projection Made Easy. 2011. (ENG., Illus.). 216p. pap. 24.95 *(978-0-89556-173-2(5))* Gateways Bks. & Tapes.

Gordon-Delee, Marjorie A. Redemption from Sin: A Memoir. 2008. 168p. pap. 14.99 *(978-1-4343-8244-3(3))* AuthorHouse.

Guiden. Traveling: an Accidental Experts How: To Leave Your Body Handbook. 2009. 160p. pap. 21.95 *(978-1-904658-33-7(4))* Aeon Bks. Ltd. GBR. Dist: Stylus Publishing, LLC.

Gustus, Sandie. Less Incomplete: A Guide to Experiencing the Human Condition beyond the Physical Body. 2011. (ENG., Illus.). 332p. pap. 26.95 *(978-1-84694-351-5(5))* Hunt, John Publishing Ltd. GBR. Dist: National Bk. Network.

Holy, Monica. Fringe Dweller on the Night Shift: True Stories from an Afterlife Paramedic. 2009. (ENG.). 1p. pap. 16.95 *(978-1-57863-468-2(7)*, Weiser Bks.) Red Wheel/Weiser.

Johnson, Debbie. Soul Travel to Find God's Love. 2007. (Illus.). 143p. per. *(978-1-57043-233-0(3))* Eckankar.

Kraalingen, Elleke van. Love Beyond Death. 2010. (ENG.). 296p. pap. 24.95 *(978-1-84694-379-9(5))* Hunt, John Publishing Ltd. GBR. Dist: National Bk. Network.

Laszlo, Ervin, frwd. The Out of Body Experience: The History & Science of Astral Travel. 2011. (ENG.). 240p. pap. 14.95 *(978-1-78028-021-9(1)*, Watkins Publishing) Duncan Baird Pubs. GBR. Dist: Sterling Publishing Co., Inc.

Leadbeater, C. W. The Astral Plane. 2010. (Illus.). 58p. pap. 20.00 *(978-1-153-75920-5(9))* General Bks. LLC.

—The Astral Plane: Its Scenery, Inhabitants & Phenomena. 2007. (ENG.). 108p. 34.95 *(978-0-548-28127-7(0))* Kessinger Publishing, LLC.

Marrs, Jim. PSI Spies: The True Story of America's Psychic Warfare Program. 2007. (ENG., Illus.). 1p. pap. 15.99 *(978-1-56414-960-2(9)*, New Page Bks.) Career Pr., Inc.

Marsh, Michael N. Out-of-Body & near-Death Experiences: Brain-State Phenomena or Glimpses of Immortality? 2010. (Oxford Theological Monographs). (ENG., Illus.). 272p. 110.00 *(978-0-19-957150-5(3))* Oxford Univ. Pr., Inc.

McMoneagle, Joseph. Remote Viewing Secrets: The Handbook for Developing & Extending Your Psychic Abilities. 2011. (ENG., Illus.). 296p. pap. 16.95 *(978-1-57174-159-2(3))* Hampton Roads Publishing Co., Inc.

Minero, Luis. Demystifying the Out-of-Body Experience: A Practical Manual for Exploration & Personal Evolution. 2012. (ENG.). 408p. pap. 19.99 ***(978-0-7387-3079-0(3))*** Llewellyn Pubns.

Murray, Criag D. Psychological Scientific Perspectives on Out of Body & near Death Experiences. 2009. (Psychology Research Progress Ser.). 79.00 *(978-1-60741-705-7(7))* Nova Science Pubs., Inc.

Nicholls, Graham. Navigating the Out-of-Body Experience: Radical New Techniques. 2012. (ENG.). 264p. pap. 15.95 ***(978-0-7387-2761-5(X))*** Llewellyn Pubns.

Oakford, David. Journey Through the World of Spirit: God, Gaia, & Guardian Angels. 2007. (ENG.). 136p. pap. 17.95 *(978-0-9791750-9-1(7))* Reality Pr.

Ophiel. The Art & Practice of Astral Projection. 2011. 136p. 40.95 ***(978-1-258-10225-8(0))*** Literary Licensing, LLC.

Phinn, Gordon. More Adventures in Eternity: From Henry to Higher Self. 2008. (ENG.). 240p. per. 22.95 *(978-1-84694-081-1(8))* Hunt, John Publishing Ltd. GBR. Dist: National Bk. Network.

Puhalo, Lazar. Out-of-Body Experiences. Date not set. 32p. pap. 4.00 *(978-1-879038-64-6(1)*, 9034) Synaxis Pr.

—Soul, Body & Death. Date not set. 94p. pap. 8.00 *(978-1-879038-68-4(4)*, 9038) Synaxis Pr.

Raduga, Michael. School of Out-of-Body Travel. 2010. 229p. pap. 35.00 *(978-1-4457-6671-3(X))* Lulu Enterprises Inc.

Redding, Ann & Campbell, Ann. Tails from Beyond. 2008. 180p. pap. 36.95 *(978-1-4327-0237-3(8))* Outskirts Pr., Inc.

Russell, Ronald. The Journey of Robert Monroe: From Out-of-Body Explorer to Consciousness Pioneer. 2007. (ENG., Illus.). 408p. 24.95 (978-1-57174-533-0(5)) Hampton Roads Publishing Co., Inc.

Schrock, Marilyn. Wake Up, Church! The Enemy Is Within Your Gates - Astral Projection & the Church. 2009. (ENG.). 80p. 10.99 (978-1-59979-852-3(2), Creation Hse.) Charisma Media.

Sorrell, Stephanie. Astral Projection Made Easy. 2012. (ENG.). 80p. pap. 12.95 **(978-1-84694-611-0(5))** Hunt, John Publishing Ltd. GBR. Dist: National Bk. Network.

Stavish, Mark. Between the Gates: Lucid Dreaming, Astral Projection, & the Body of Light in Western Esotericism. 2008. (ENG., Illus.). 1p. per. 18.95 (978-1-57863-396-8(6), Weiser Bks.) Red Wheel/Weiser.

Stead, William T. Glue Sniffing & Out of Body Experiences. 2009. 264p. pap. 14.49 (978-1-4389-7987-8(8)) AuthorHouse.

Tyson, Donald. Soul Flight: Astral Projection & the Magical Universe. 2007. (ENG.). 360p. per. 18.95 (978-0-7387-1087-7(3)) Llewellyn Pubns.

Weschcke, Carl Llewellyn & Slate, PhD, Joe H. Astral Projection for Psychic Empowerment: The Out-of-Body Experience, Astral Powers, & their Practical Application. 2012. (ENG.). 528p. pap. 24.95 **(978-0-7387-3029-5(7))** Llewellyn Pubns.

Willson, Terrill. How I Learned Soul Travel: The True Experiences of a Student in Eckankar, the Ancient Science of Soul Travel. 2006. vi, 193p. pap. (978-1-57043-235-4(X)) Eckankar.

Wraithe, William. Watt. 2010. 169p. pap. 44.99 (978-0-557-01017-2(9)) Lulu Enterprises Inc.

Wylie, Alison. First Flight. 2009. 48p. pap. 9.98 (978-1-4092-6448-4(3)) Lulu Enterprises Inc.

ASTRIONICS

see also Astronautics—Communication Systems; Ground Support Systems (Astronautics); Space Vehicles—Guidance Systems

IEEE Staff. 2008 IEEE Aerospace Conference. 2008. pap. 562.00 (978-1-4244-1487-1(3)) IEEE.

IEEE, Standards Office Staff, ed. 2007 IEEE Aerospace Conference. 2007. pap. 4430.00 (978-1-4244-0524-4(6), TH8903) IEEE.

Mitchell, John M. Communications Pioneer. Janson, Bobbi, ed. 2008. 212p. pap. 24.95 (978-1-889131-79-5(2)) Janson Media Group.

Petersen, Edward. Single Event Effects in Aerospace. 2011. (ENG., Illus.). 520p. 135.00 (978-0-470-76749-8(9), Wiley-IEEE Pr.) Wiley, John & Sons, Inc.

ASTROBIOLOGY

see Exobiology; Space Biology

ASTROCYTES

Alzate, Oscar. Neuroproteomics. Alzate, Oscar, ed. 2009. (Frontiers in Neuroscience Ser.). (ENG., Illus.). 354p. 164.95 (978-1-4200-7625-7(6), CRC Press) Taylor & Francis Group GBR. Dist: Taylor & Francis Group.

Cram101 Textbook Reviews. Outlines & Highlights for Astrocytes in Physiology of the Nervous System by Vladimir Parpura, Isbn: 9780387794914 0387794913. 2011. 94p. pap. 27.95 **(978-1-61490-437-3(5))** Cram101 Inc.

Malva, Joao, ed. Interaction Between Neurons & Glia in Aging & Disease. 2010. (ENG., Illus.). x, 521p. pap. 179.00 (978-1-4419-4360-6(9), 1441943609) Springer.

Milner, Richard, ed. Astrocytes: Methods & Protocols. 2011. (Methods in Molecular Biology Ser.). (ENG., Illus.). xiv, 575p. 159.00 **(978-1-61779-451-3(1)**, 1617794511) Humana Pr.

Nguyen, Khoa. Distribution of Glast & Na+/K+-Atpase Activity in Astrocytes. 2009. 208p. pap. (978-3-639-13132-1(0)) VDM Verlag Dr. Mueller e.K.

Parpura, Vladimir & Haydon, Philip G. Astrocytes in (Patho)Physiology of the Nervous System. 2008. (ENG., Illus.). xx, 700p. 171.00 (978-0-387-79491-4(3), 0387794913) Springer.

Rego, Ana Cristina, et al, eds. Interaction Between Neurons & Glia in Aging & Disease. 2007. (ENG., Illus.). x, 521p. 179.00 (978-0-387-70829-4(4), 0387708294) Springer.

Scemes, Eliana & Spray, David C., eds. Astrocytes. 2011. (Frontiers in Neuroscience Ser.). (ENG., Illus.). 440p. 149.95 (978-1-4398-2584-6(X), CRC Press) Taylor & Francis Group GBR. Dist: Taylor & Francis Group.

ASTRODIAGNOSIS

see Medical Astrology

ASTRODYNAMICS

see also Artificial Satellites—Orbits; Astronautics; Navigation (Astronautics); Orbital Mechanics; Space Flight; Space Trajectories

Astrodynamics 2007: Proceedings of the AAS/AIAA Astrodynamics Conference, held Aug. 19-23, 2007, Mackinac Island, MI. 2008. (Illus.). 2892p. 520.00 incl. cd-rom (978-0-87703-543-5(1)) Univelt, Inc.

Belbruno, Edward. Fly Me to the Moon: An Insider's Guide to the New Science of Space Travel. 2007. (ENG., Illus.). 176p. (C). 19.95 (978-0-691-12822-1(7)) Princeton Univ. Pr.

Chobotov, Vladimir A. Spacecraft Attitude Dynamics & Control. 2009. 161p. pap. 94.00 (978-0-89464-069-8(0)) Krieger Publishing Co.

Coffey, Shannon L., et al, eds. The Kyle T. Alfriend Astrodynamics Symposium. 2011. (Illus.). 544p. 150.00 **(978-0-87703-565-7(2))**; cd-rom 100.00 **(978-0-87703-566-4(0))** Univelt, Inc. (American Astronautical Society).

Gao, Lin. Behavior & Relative Velocity of Debris near Geostationary Orbit. 2011. 76p. pap. **(978-3-8443-1629-2(9))** Lambert Academic Publishing.

Guptil, P. Modern Astrodynamics. 2006. (C). 150.00 (978-0-7506-8157-5(8)) Elsevier Science & Technology Bks.

Gurfil, Pini. Modern Astrodynamics. 2006. (Elsevier Astrodynamics Ser.: 1). (ENG., Illus.). 336p. 148.00 (978-0-12-373562-1(9), Butterworth-Heinemann) Elsevier Science & Technology Bks.

Ley, Wilfried, et al, eds. Handbook of Space Technology. 2009. (Illus.). 882p. 139.95 (978-1-60086-701-9(4)) American Institute of Aeronautics & Astronautics.

New Trends in Astrodynamics & Applications III. 2007. (AIP Conference Proceedings Ser.). (Illus.). 336p. 144.00 (978-0-7354-0389-5(9)) American Institute of Physics.

Rauschenbakh, V., et al. Essential Spaceflight Dynamics & Magnetospherics. 2010. (Space Technology Library). 420p. pap. 229.00 (978-90-481-6194-2(0), 9048161940) Springer.

Tewari, Ashish. Atmospheric & Space Flight Dynamics: Modeling & Simulation with MATLAB & Simulink. 2006. (Modeling & Simulation in Science, Engineering & Technology Ser.). (Illus.). 556p. per. 59.95 (978-0-8176-4373-7(7), 0817643737) Birkhauser Boston.

Vallado, David A. Fundamentals of Astrodynamics & Applications. 3rd rev. ed. 2007. (Space Technology Library). (Illus.). 1055p. 229.00 (978-0-387-71831-6(1)) Springer.

ASTROGATION

see Navigation (Astronautics)

ASTROGEOLOGY

Bar-Cohen, Yoseph & Zacny, Kris, eds. Drilling in Extreme Environments: Penetration & Sampling on Earth & Other Planets. 2009. (ENG., Illus.). 827p. 220.00 (978-3-527-40852-8(5), Wiley-VCH) Wiley, John & Sons, Inc.

Breger, Michel, ed. Communications in Asteroseismology, Volume 160 (2010) 2010. (Communications in Asteroseismology Ser.). (ENG.). 91p. (C). pap. 15.00 (978-3-7001-6871-3(3)) Austrian Academy of Sciences Press AUT. Dist: Brown, David Bk. Co., The.

Chahine, Moustafa T., et al, eds. Comparative Planetology with an Earth Perspective. 2010. 236p. pap. 229.00 (978-90-481-4636-9(4), 9048146364) Springer.

Cram101 Textbook Reviews & Cram101 Textbook Reviews. Outlines & Highlights for Introduction to Planetary Science: The Geological Perspective by Faure, ISBN. 2011. 216p. pap. 30.95 **(978-1-61461-669-6(8))** Cram101 Inc.

De Lafayette, Maximillien. Mind-Bending Black Operations, Weapons Systems & Experiments by Extraterrestrials, Grays & Governments. 5th Edition. 2010. 320p. pap. 25.94 (978-0-557-46051-9(4)) Lulu Enterprises Inc.

Di Mauro, Maria Pia, et al, eds. Synergies between Solar & Stellar Modelling. 2010. (Illus.). xvi, 360p. 259.00 (978-90-481-9197-0(1), 9048191971) Springer.

Dikpati, Mausumi, et al. Solar-Stellar Dynamos As Revealed by Helio- & Asteroseismology: GONG 2008. 2009. (Illus.). xxi, 597p. **(978-1-58381-713-1(1)); (978-1-58381-712-4(3))** Astronomical Society of the Pacific, The.

Faure, Gunter & Mensing, Teresa M. Introduction to Planetary Science: The Geological Perspective. 2007. (ENG., Illus.). xx, 526p. 99.00 (978-1-4020-5233-0(2), 1402052332) Springer.

Fishbaugh, Kathryn E., et al, eds. Geology & Habitability of Terrestrial Planets. 2007. (Space Sciences Series of ISSI Ser.). (Illus.). 304p. 199.00 (978-0-387-74287-8(5)) Springer.

Gizon, Laurent, et al, eds. Helioseismology, Asteroseismology, & MHD Connections. (ENG.). vi, 638p. 2010. pap. 199.00 (978-1-4419-2796-5(4), 1441927964) 2009. 199.00 (978-0-387-89481-2(0), 0387894810) Springer.

Handler, Gerald & Schuh, Sonja, eds. Communications in Asteroseismology Volume 159 2009: JENAM 2008 Symposium N. 4: Asteroseismology & Stellar Evolution; Vienna, 8 - 12 September 2008. 2009. (Communications in Asteroseismology Ser.). 134p. (C). pap. 14.95 (978-3-7001-6625-2(7)) Austrian Academy of Sciences Press AUT. Dist: Brown, David Bk. Co., The.

Henning, Thomas, ed. Astromineralogy. 2010. (Lecture Notes in Physics Ser.). (ENG., Illus.). ix, 281p. pap. 129.00 (978-3-642-07932-0(6), 3642079326) Springer.

Norton, O. Richard & Chitwood, Lawrence. Field Guide to Meteors & Meteorites. 2008. (Patrick Moore's Practical Astronomy Ser.). (Illus.). XVI, 288p. pap. 39.95 (978-1-84800-156-5(8), 1848001568) Springer.

Pappalardo, Robert T., et al, eds. Europa. 2009. (Space Science Ser.). (ENG.). 720p. 85.00 (978-0-8165-2844-8(6)) Univ. of Arizona Pr.

Seager, Sara. Exoplanet Atmospheres: Physical Processes. 2010. (Princeton Series in Astrophysics Ser.). (ENG., Illus.). 264p. (C). 89.50 (978-0-691-11914-4(7)); pap. 45.00 (978-0-691-14645-4(4)) Princeton Univ. Pr.

Yabushita, Shin & Henrard, Jacques, eds. Dynamics of Comets & Asteroids & Their Role in Earth History. 2010. 304p. pap. 182.00 (978-90-481-5081-6(7), 9048150817) Springer.

Zima, Wolfgang. Communications in Asteroseismology, Volume 155 (October 2008) 2008. (Communications in Asteroseismology Ser.). (Illus.). 121p. (C). pap. 15.00 (978-3-7001-6634-4(6)) Austrian Academy of Sciences Press AUT. Dist: Brown, David Bk. Co., The.

ASTROLABES

Borelli, Arianna. Aspects of the Astrolabe: 'architectonica Ratio' in Tenth- & Eleventh-Century Europe. 2008. (Sudhoffs Archiv - Beihefte (SAr-B) Ser.). (ENG., Illus.). 272p. (C). pap. 67.00 (978-3-515-09129-9(7)) Steiner, Franz Verlag Wiesbaden GmbH DEU. Dist: Brown, David Bk. Co., The.

Chaucer, Geoffrey. A Treatise on the Astrolabe. 2010. 204p. pap. 28.45 (978-1-4455-3745-0(1), Kent Pr.) Kent Communications, Ltd.

King, David A. Astrolabes from Medieval Europe. 2011. (Variorum Collected Studies). (Illus.). 422p. 190.00 (978-1-4094-2593-9(2)) Ashgate Publishing Co.

King, David A., contrib. by. Astrolabes & Angels, Epigrams & Enigmas: From Regiomontanus' Acrostic for Cardinal Bessarion to Piero Della Francesca's Flagellation of Christ. 2007. (Boethius. Texte und Abhandlungen zur Geschichte der Mathematik und der Naturwissenschaften Ser.). (ENG., Illus.). 348p. (C). 117.00 (978-3-515-09061-2(4)) Steiner, Franz Verlag Wiesbaden GmbH DEU. Dist: Brown, David Bk. Co., The.

Pingree, David E. Eastern Astrolabes: Historic Scientific Instruments of the Adler Planetarium & Astronomy Museum, Volume II. Chandler, Bruce, ed. 2009. (Historic Scientific Instruments of the Adler Planetarium Ser.: Vol. 2). (ENG., Illus.). 268p. 75.00 (978-1-891220-02-9(0)) Adler Planetarium & Astronomy Museum.

ASTROLOGY

see also Bible and Astrology; Hindu Astrology; Horary Astrology; Horoscopes; Indian Astrology; Maya Astrology; Medical Astrology; Zodiac

ABBEresearchDiv. Astrology in History, Medicine & Science — with Index & Medical Analysis of New Research Informatin for All Nations, 2 vols., Vol. 2. 2006. (Illus.). 160p. 69.95 (978-0-7883-4632-3(6), 07883-46326) ABBE Pubs. Assn. of Washington, D.C.

Ackermann, Silke. Sternstunden am Kaiserhof: Michael Scotus und sein Buch von den Bildern und Zeichen des Himmels. 2010. (Illus.). 642p. 141.95 (978-3-631-59489-6(5)) Lang, Peter GmbH, Europaischer Verlag der Wissenschaften DEU. Dist: Lang, Peter.

Adam, C. G. M. Fresh Sidelights on Astrology: An Elemen. 2006. pap. 12.75 (978-1-59605-909-2(5), Cosimo Classics) Cosimo, Inc.

Adams, Ruth. Tu Signo del Zodiaco. (SPA.). 160p. (978-84-7927-428-3(X)) Robinbk., Ediciones S.L. ESP. Dist: Lectorum Pubns., Inc.

Aerts, C., et al. Asteroseismology. 2008. (Astronomy & Astrophysics Library). (Illus.). 350p. 159.00 (978-1-4020-5178-4(6), 1402051786) Springer.

Agrippa, Henry Cornelius. Astrology & the Mystery of Numbers. 2006. pap. 9.95 (978-1-4286-6502-6(1)) Kessinger Publishing, LLC.

—Of the Virtue of Places & What Places Are Suitable to Every Star. 2006. pap. 9.95 (978-1-4286-6496-8(3)) Kessinger Publishing, LLC.

Aharoni, Ruth. Karmic Astrology: Past Lives, Present Loves. 2007. (ENG., Illus.). 192p. per. 16.95 (978-0-7387-0967-3(0)) Llewellyn Pubns.

Ahern, CHT, Donata, MSW. The Medicine Wheel: Path of the Heart. 2009. 176p. pap. 19.99 (978-0-557-07594-2(7)) Lulu Enterprises Inc.

Allen, Don Cameron. The Star-Crossed Renaissance: The Quarrel about Astrology & Its Influence in England. 2011. 292p. 48.95 **(978-1-258-05402-1(7))** Literary Licensing, LLC.

Alpheus, A. Were You Born under a Lucky Star? 2006. (ENG.). pap. 17.95 (978-1-59605-900-9(1), Cosimo Classics) Cosimo, Inc.

—Were You Born under a Lucky Star? 2007. (ENG.). 220p. 39.95 (978-0-548-09937-7(5)) Kessinger Publishing, LLC.

Alvina. Visions, Wishes & Dreams... Oh My! pap. 16.95 (978-0-9707786-0-4(0)) Esmio Properties, Ltd.

Anderson, Karl. Proof That the Ancients Knew the Sun to Be the Grand Central Orb - 2006. pap. 12.95 (978-1-4286-6591-0(9)) Kessinger Publishing, LLC.

—The Signification, Nature, Quality & Description of the 12 Houses - 2006. pap. 12.95 (978-1-4286-6589-7(7)) Kessinger Publishing, LLC.

—The Wisdom & What It Is: Astrology Divine & Inspired of God And. 2006. pap. 9.95 (978-1-4286-6588-0(9)) Kessinger Publishing, LLC.

Anrias, David. Adepts of the Five Elements: An occult survey of past & future Problems. 2007. (Illus.). per. 14.95 (978-0-9792665-1-5(3)) Ancient Wisdom Pubns.

Antepara, Robin. Aspects: A New Approach to Understanding the Planetary Relationships in Your Chart. 2006. (Special Topics in Astrology Ser.: 6). (ENG., Illus.). 192p. per. 16.95 (978-0-7387-0928-4(X)) Llewellyn Pubns.

Arcane Astrology. 2008. (Illus.). 264p. lib. bdg. 30.00 net. (978-0-9707430-0-8(9)) Clover Pr.

Arroyo, Stephen. Astrologia, karma y Transformacion. 2006. 413p. pap. 22.90 (978-950-17-0432-7(7)) Kier ARG. Dist: LD Bks., Inc.

—Person-to-Person Astrology: Energy Factors in Love, Sex & Compatability. 2007. (ENG., Illus.). 440p. pap. 18.95 (978-1-58394-204-8(1), Frog Ltd.) North Atlantic Bks.

Ashe (Editor), Steven. The Picatrix - the Goal of the Wise. 2007. 435p. 52.50 (978-1-84753-738-6(3)) Lulu Enterprises Inc.

Ashe, Steven. The Picatrix Â Ãiyat al Hakim - the Goal of the Wise. 2010. 98p. pap. 25.50 (978-1-4461-7475-3(1)) Lulu Enterprises Inc.

Ayre, A. K. Football Aims for the Stars: How the constellations can affect planet Football. 2010. (ENG., Illus.). 212p. pap. **(978-1-84876-457-6(X))** Troubadour Publishing Ltd.

Bacher, Elman. Studies in Astrology V2. 2011. 106p. 39.95 **(978-1-258-07590-3(3))** Literary Licensing, LLC.

—Studies in Astrology V3. 2011. 96p. 38.95 **(978-1-258-07604-7(7))** Literary Licensing, LLC.

Bailey, Alice A. Esoteric Astrology. 2008. (Treatise on the Seven Rays Ser.: Vol. III). (ENG.). 46.00 (978-0-85330-020-5(8)) Lucis Publishing Co.

Bailey, E. The Prenatal Epoch. 2007. 244p. per. 23.95 (978-1-933303-24-6(7)) Astrology Ctr. Of America, The.

Bailey, E. H. Astrological Basis of Cards. 2006. pap. 9.95 (978-1-4286-6960-4(4)) Kessinger Publishing, LLC.

Bannerman-Phillips, E. Ivy A. Amulets & Birthstones: Their Astrological Significance. 2011. 60p. 36.95 **(978-1-258-00969-4(2))** Literary Licensing, LLC.

Barley, Alfred H. The Practicability of Astrological Symbolism. 2006. pap. 9.95 (978-1-4286-7009-9(2)) Kessinger Publishing, LLC.

Beck, Roger. A Brief History of Ancient Astrology. 2006. (Brief Histories of the Ancient World Ser.). (ENG., Illus.). 176p. per. 31.95 (978-1-4051-1074-7(0)); 99.95 (978-1-4051-1087-7(2)) Wiley, John & Sons, Inc. (Wiley-Blackwell).

Beim, Margarete. Aquarius (Super Horoscopes 2013) 2012. (ENG.). 256p. (gr. 12). 9.99 **(978-0-425-24643-6(4)**, Berkley Trade) Penguin Group (USA) Inc.

—Aries (Super Horoscopes 2013) 2012. (ENG.). 256p. (gr. 12). 9.99 **(978-0-425-24633-7(7)**, Berkley Trade) Penguin Group (USA) Inc.

—Cancer (Super Horoscopes 2013) 2012. (ENG.). 256p. (gr. 12). 9.99 **(978-0-425-24636-8(1)**, Berkley Trade) Penguin Group (USA) Inc.

—Capricorn (Super Horoscopes 2013) 2012. (ENG.). 256p. (gr. 12). 9.99 **(978-0-425-24642-9(6)**, Berkley Trade) Penguin Group (USA) Inc.

—Leo (Super Horoscopes 2012) 2011. (Super Horoscopes Ser.). (ENG.). 256p. (gr. 12). 9.99 (978-0-425-23939-1(X), Berkley Trade) Penguin Group (USA) Inc.

—Leo (Super Horoscopes 2013) 2012. (ENG.). 256p. (gr. 12). 9.99 **(978-0-425-24637-5(X)**, Berkley Trade) Penguin Group (USA) Inc.

—Libra Super Horoscopes 2012. 2011. (Super Horoscopes Ser.). (ENG.). 256p. (gr. 12). 9.99 (978-0-425-23941-4(1), Berkley Trade) Penguin Group (USA) Inc.

—Libra (Super Horoscopes 2013) 2012. (ENG.). 256p. (gr. 12). 9.99 **(978-0-425-24639-9(6)**, Berkley Trade) Penguin Group (USA) Inc.

—Pisces (Super Horoscopes 2013) 2012. (ENG.). 256p. (gr. 12). 9.99 **(978-0-425-24644-3(2)**, Berkley Trade) Penguin Group (USA) Inc.

—Virgo (Super Horoscopes 2013) 2012. (ENG.). 256p. (gr. 12). 9.99 **(978-0-425-24638-2(8)**, Berkley Trade) Penguin Group (USA) Inc.

Benjamine, Elbert & Zain, C. C. Astrological Lore of All Ages. 2010. 144p. 28.76 (978-1-163-34810-9(4)) 2010. 144p. pap. 16.76 (978-1-162-73203-9(2)) 2007. (ENG.). 142p. 35.95 (978-0-548-03682-2(9)) Kessinger Publishing, LLC.

—How to Use Modern Ephemerides: Computed for Midnight, Noon, Greenwich & Other Places. 2011. 66p. 36.95 **(978-1-258-01768-2(7))** Literary Licensing, LLC.

—The Influence of the Planet Pluto: Including Ephemeris of Pluto, 1840-1960. 2011. 26p. 35.95 **(978-1-258-00699-0(5))** Literary Licensing, LLC.

Benjamine, Elbert & Zain, C. C. Stellar Dietetics the Astrological Road Map to Diet & Health. 2007. (ENG.). 108p. 33.95 (978-0-548-03681-5(0)) Kessinger Publishing, LLC.

Bennett, Sidney Kimball. Astrology: Science of Prediction 1945. 2007. (ENG.). 314p. 45.95 (978-0-548-05604-2(8)) Kessinger Publishing, LLC.

Berg, Philip S. Ten Luminous Emmanations. (SPA.). 224p. (C). Vol. I. pap. (978-0-943688-14-5(0)) Vol. II. pap. (978-0-943688-15-2(9)) Research Centre of Kabbalah.

Berg, Rav P. S. Kabbalistic Astrology: And the Meaning of Our Lives. 2nd ed. 2006. (ENG.). 204p. per. 14.95 (978-1-57189-556-1(6)) Research Centre of Kabbalah.

Berlinski, David. The Secrets of the Vaulted Sky: Astrology & the Art of Prediction. 2009. (ENG., Illus.). 320p. pap. 14.00 (978-0-15-603006-9(3), Mariner Bks.) Houghton Mifflin Harcourt Trade & Reference Pubs.

The Best of Al H. Morrison: Selected & Edited by Karen Christino. 2006. per. 21.95 (978-0-9725117-1-1(7)) Stella Mira Bks.

Bharadwaj, Monisha. The Indian Luck Book. 2006. (Illus.). 256p. reprint ed. pap. 17.00 (978-1-4223-5675-3(2)) DIANE Publishing Co.

Bild Buch Staff. Was Macht der Sterne: Horoskope fuer jedes Tierkreiszeichen. (GER.). 128p. pap. (978-3-548-42028-8(1)) Ullstein-Taschenbuch-Verlag DEU. Dist: International Bk. Import Service, Inc.

Birkbeck, Lyn. Do It Yourself Astrology: A User-Friendly Guide to Your Personality. 2009. (ENG., Illus.). 380p. 12.99 (978-0-7858-2421-3(9), 0785824219, Castle Bks., Inc.) Book Sales, Inc.

—Do It Yourself Relationship Astrology. 2009. (ENG., Illus.). 530p. 12.99 (978-0-7858-2423-7(5), 0785824235, Castle Bks., Inc.) Book Sales, Inc.

—The Watkins Astrology Handbook: The Practical System of DIY Astrology. 2006. (Illus.). 389p. per. 19.95 (978-1-84293-167-7(9)) Sterling Publishing Co., Inc.

Black, Milton. Capricorn 2010. 2009. (ENG.). 144p. pap. 3.95 (978-1-74110-880-4(2)) New Holland Pubs. Pty, Ltd. AUS. Dist: Tuttle Publishing.

—Gemini. 2009. (ENG.). 144p. pap. 3.95 (978-1-74110-873-6(X)) New Holland Pubs. Pty, Ltd. AUS. Dist: Tuttle Publishing.

—Leo. 2009. (ENG.). 144p. pap. 3.95 (978-1-74110-875-0(6)) New Holland Pubs. Pty, Ltd. AUS. Dist: Tuttle Publishing.

—Libra 2010. 2009. (ENG.). 144p. pap. 3.95 (978-1-74110-877-4(2)) New Holland Pubs. Pty, Ltd. AUS. Dist: Tuttle Publishing.

—Pisces 2010. 2009. (ENG.). 144p. pap. 3.95 (978-1-74110-882-8(9)) New Holland Pubs. Pty, Ltd. AUS. Dist: Tuttle Publishing.

—Sagittarius: 22 November-21 December. 2009. (ENG.). 144p. pap. 3.95 (978-1-74110-879-8(9)) New Holland Pubs. Pty, Ltd. AUS. Dist: Tuttle Publishing.

—Scorpio: 23 October-21 November 2009. (ENG.). 144p. pap. 3.95 (978-1-74110-878-1(0)) New Holland Pubs. Pty, Ltd. AUS. Dist: Tuttle Publishing.

—Taurus 2010: 21 April-20 May 2009. (ENG.). 144p. pap. 3.95 (978-1-74110-872-9(1)) New Holland Pubs. Pty, Ltd. AUS. Dist: Tuttle Publishing.

—Virgo: 23 August-22 September 2009. (ENG.). 144p. pap. 3.95 *(978-1-74110-876-7(4))* New Holland Pubs. Pty, Ltd. AUS. Dist: Tuttle Publishing.
Blake, Linden. Discover Your True Wealth Using Astrology. 2011. 144p. pap. 15.95 ***(978-1-4575-0143-2(0))*** Dog Ear Publishing, LLC.
Blaschke, Robert P. Holographic Transits. 2006. (Astrology: A Language of Life Ser.). (Illus.). 256p. per. 21.95 *(978-0-9668978-5-2(4))* Earthwalk Schl. of Astrology.
Blaze, Chrissie. Baby Star Signs. 2008. (ENG.). 320p. pap. 19.95 *(978-1-84694-124-5(5))* Hunt, John Publishing Ltd. GBR. Dist: National Bk. Network.
—Mercury Retrograde: Your Survival Guide to Astrology's Most Precarious Time of Year! 2008. (ENG., Illus.). 256p. per. 19.95 *(978-1-84694-073-6(7))* Hunt, John Publishing Ltd. GBR. Dist: National Bk. Network.
—Superstar Signs: Sun Signs of Heroes, Celebrities & You. 2008. (ENG.). 320p. pap. 19.95 *(978-1-84694-125-2(3))* Hunt, John Publishing Ltd. GBR. Dist: National Bk. Network.
Bobrick, Benson. The Fated Sky: Astrology in History. 2006. (ENG., Illus.). 384p. pap. 15.00 *(978-0-7432-6895-0(4))* Simon & Schuster.
Bohannon, Cynthia. North & South Nodes: Guideposts of the Spirit. 2011. 102p. pap. 14.95 ***(978-0-86690-622-7(3))*** American Federation of Astrologers, Inc.
Bold, Ulrich. Evolutionary Astrology Practical Text & Handbook. 2009. 236p. pap. *(978-3-8370-9202-8(X))* Books on Demand GmbH.
Bonaddio, T. L. Celtic Astrology. 2011. (ENG.). 144p. 5.95 *(978-0-7624-3969-0(6)*, Running Pr.) Running Pr. Bk. Pubs.
Bonatus, Guido & Lilly, William. The Astrologer's Guide. 2010. 154p. 36.95 *(978-1-161-37691-3(7))* Kessinger Publishing, LLC.
Booth, Janet. Janet's Plan-its 2007 Celestial Planner: Easy-to-Use Astrology Calendar. 2006. 60p. 12.95 *(978-0-9711903-5-1(6))* Astrology Booth, LLC.
—2008 Janet's Plan-its Celestial Planner: Easy-to-Use Astrology Calendar. Wolf, Ilene, ed. 2007. 64p. 14.95 *(978-0-9711903-6-8(4))* Astrology Booth, LLC.
Borax, Mark. 2012: Crossing the Bridge to the Future. 2008. (ENG.). 264p. pap. 16.95 *(978-1-58394-208-6(4)*, Frog Ltd.) North Atlantic Bks.
Bracho, Kitty. Horoscopo 2011. 2010. (SPA.). 240p. pap. 12.95 *(978-607-07-0511-3(4))* Editorial Planeta, S. A. ESP. Dist: Perseus Distribution.
Bradley, Donald A. Profession & Birth Date. 2011. 126p. 40.95 ***(978-1-258-03819-9(6))*** Literary Licensing, LLC.
Brady, Bernadette. Astrology a Place in Chaos. 2006. pap. *(978-1-902405-21-6(8))* Wessex Astrologer Ltd., The.
—Star & Planet Combinations. 2008. 280p. pap. *(978-1-902405-30-8(7))* Wessex Astrologer Ltd., The.
Brittain, Patti Tobin. Planetary Powers: The Morin Method. 2011. 126p. pap. 16.95 ***(978-0-86690-616-6(9))*** American Federation of Astrologers, Inc.
Bryan, Gwyneth. Houses: A Contemporary Guide. 2006. (Special Topics in Astrology Ser.: 4). (ENG., Illus.). 192p. per. 16.95 *(978-0-7387-0868-3(2))* Llewellyn Pubns.
Buchan, Vivian. Vivian's Original Cat Astrology. 2007. (Illus.). 120p. pap. 12.95 *(978-1-932043-42-5(X))* Penfield Bks.
Burgoyne, Thomas. Light of Egypt. 2008. 156p. 22.99 *(978-0-554-30722-0(7))*; 25.99 *(978-0-554-21419-1(9))* BiblioBazaar.
Burgoyne, Thomas & Wagner, Henry & Belle. Light of Egypt. 2006. (ENG.). 164p. pap. 19.99 *(978-1-4264-0017-9(9))*; 152p. pap. 21.99 *(978-1-4264-0146-6(9))* BiblioBazaar.
Burgoyne, Thomas H. The Mystical Chain or the Union of the Soul & the Stars - 2006. pap. 12.95 *(978-1-4286-7609-1(0))* Kessinger Publishing, LLC.
—The Soul Its Nature & Attributes. 2006. pap. 9.95 *(978-1-4286-7598-8(1))* Kessinger Publishing, LLC.
—The Triumph of the Human Soul. 2006. pap. 12.95 *(978-1-4286-7612-1(0))* Kessinger Publishing, LLC.
Burk, Kevin. Astrological Relationship Workbook. 2007. 408p. per. 37.95 *(978-0-9758692-9-1(9)*, Serendipity Pr.) Burk, Kevin B.
Butler, Hiram E. Solar Biology. 2010. 534p. 44.76 *(978-1-163-21039-0(0))*; pap. 32.75 *(978-1-162-63659-7(9))* Kessinger Publishing, LLC.
—Solar Biology Is a Lamp to the Mind & an Aide to the Intuitions - 2006. pap. 9.95 *(978-1-4286-7640-4(6))* Kessinger Publishing, LLC.
Campion, Nicholas. Astrology & Popular Religion: Prophecy Cosmology & the New Age Movement. 2012. 224p. 99.95 ***(978-1-4094-3514-3(8))*** Ashgate Publishing Co.
—History of Western Astrology Vol. 1: The Ancient & Classical Worlds. 2009. (ENG., Illus.). 400p. 32.95 *(978-1-4411-2737-2(2))* Continuum International Publishing Group, Ltd. GBR. Dist: National Bk. Network.
—History of Western Astrology Vol. 2: The Medieval & Modern Worlds, 2 vols. 2009. (ENG., Illus.). 392p. 120.00 *(978-1-84725-224-1(9))* Continuum International Publishing Group, Ltd. GBR. Dist: National Bk. Network.
—What Do Astrologers Believe? 2006. (What Do We Believe? Ser.). (ENG., Illus.). 100p. pap. 12.95 *(978-1-86207-838-3(6))* Granta Bks. GBR. Dist: Independent Pubs. Group.
Cappucci, Serina. Basic Astrology Direct & to the Point. 2011. 116p. 25.00 ***(978-1-4567-3578-4(0))***; pap. 15.00 ***(978-1-4567-3580-7(2))*** AuthorHouse.
Capricorn. pap. 2.95 Grand Central Publishing.
Carelli, Adriano. The 360 Degrees of the Zodiac. 2011. 212p. 44.95 ***(978-1-258-04348-3(3))*** Literary Licensing, LLC.
Cartledge, Anthony. Planetary Types: The Science of Celestial Influence. 2009. 254p. pap. *(978-1-906834-03-6(2))* Bardic Pr.
Cayce, Edgar. Planetary Influences & Sojourns. 2010. 192p. pap. 15.95 *(978-0-87604-602-9(2))* A.R.E. Pr.
Cehovet, Bonnie. Tarot, Birth Cards, & You: Keys to Empowering Yourself. 2011. (Illus.). 192p. pap. 19.99 ***(978-0-7643-3902-8(8)***, Schiffer Publishing Ltd) Schiffer Publishing, Ltd.
Cervantes, Sasha. Consequences. 2010. 272p. (ENG.). 25.99 *(978-1-4490-4415-2(8))*; pap. 17.49 *(978-1-4490-4414-5(X))* AuthorHouse.
Champion, Maude Houghton. Rectification & Prediction. 2006. pap. 15.95 *(978-1-4286-3731-3(1))* Kessinger Publishing, LLC.
Chasen, Jill. Clinking to Love: A Coffee Klatch Read... Tips of Compatibility to Meet Your Perfect Mate. 2010. 56p. pap. 9.95 *(978-1-4502-4591-3(9))* iUniverse, Inc.
Cheiro. When Were You Born? 2007. 132p. per. 15.95 *(978-1-60206-225-2(0))* Cosimo, Inc.
Chester-Lambert, Alison. The Future in the Stars: The Astrological Message for 2012 & Beyond. 2010. (ENG.). 208p. pap. 16.95 *(978-1-84409-505-6(3))* Findhorn Pr. GBR. Dist: Independent Pubs. Group.
Christino, Karen. Your Wedding Astrologer: How to Plan a Marriage Made in the Heavens. 2008. (ENG.). 256p. pap. 9.95 *(978-1-59869-630-1(0))* Adams Media Corp.
Clancy, Paul G. What They Mean: A Lesson in Astrology for Those Who Can Erect A Horoscope but Cannot Read It. 2011. 28p. 35.95 ***(978-1-258-05992-7(4))*** Literary Licensing, LLC.
Clark, I. Edward. Ancient Hebrew Calendar. 2006. pap. 9.95 *(978-1-4286-7830-9(1))* Kessinger Publishing, LLC.
—The Antiquity of Freemasonry & the Royal Secret. 2006. pap. 9.95 *(978-1-4286-7828-6(X))* Kessinger Publishing, LLC.
—Astronomical & Astrological Triple Taus. 2006. pap. 9.95 *(978-1-4286-7827-9(1))* Kessinger Publishing, LLC.
—AUM & Is It the Lost Word. 2006. pap. 9.95 *(978-1-4286-7831-6(X))* Kessinger Publishing, LLC.
—The Egyptians & Their Worship of the Visible & Invisible. 2006. pap. 9.95 *(978-1-4286-7835-4(2))* Kessinger Publishing, LLC.
—The Judgment of the Dead or Amenti & Isis. 2006. pap. 9.95 *(978-1-4286-7814-9(X))* Kessinger Publishing, LLC.
—The Masonic Ark. 2006. pap. 9.95 *(978-1-4286-7825-5(5))* Kessinger Publishing, LLC.
—Masonic Legend of the Lost Word. 2006. pap. 9.95 *(978-1-4286-7824-8(7))* Kessinger Publishing, LLC.
—Masonic Significance of the Macrocosm & Microcosm. 2006. pap. 9.95 *(978-1-4286-7819-4(0))* Kessinger Publishing, LLC.
—Masonic Symbolism of the Checkered Floor. 2006. pap. 9.95 *(978-1-4286-7816-3(6))* Kessinger Publishing, LLC.
—Masonic Symbolism of the Cornucopia, Beehive, Hourglass, Keystone. 2006. pap. 9.95 *(978-1-4286-7841-5(7))* Kessinger Publishing, LLC.
—Masonic Symbolism of the Lion, Clock, Man, Eagle, Royal Arch. 2006. pap. 9.95 *(978-1-4286-7833-0(6))* Kessinger Publishing, LLC.
—Masonic Symbolism of the Number Seven. 2006. pap. 9.95 *(978-1-4286-7826-2(3))* Kessinger Publishing, LLC.
—Masonic Symbolism of the Triple Tau & the Crux Ansata. 2006. pap. 9.95 *(978-1-4286-7834-7(4))* Kessinger Publishing, LLC.
—Master of the Royal Secret Versus He Who Is Not. 2006. pap. 9.95 *(978-1-4286-7820-0(4))* Kessinger Publishing, LLC.
—Occult Symbolism of the Swastika. 2006. pap. 9.95 *(978-1-4286-7817-0(4))* Kessinger Publishing, LLC.
—The Rite of Circumambulation & the Royal Secret. 2006. pap. 9.95 *(978-1-4286-7815-6(8))* Kessinger Publishing, LLC.
—The Royal Secret: The Mystery of the Burning Bush Explained. 2006. pap. 9.95 *(978-1-4286-7822-4(0))* Kessinger Publishing, LLC.
—The Secrets of the Hebrew Alphabet, Qabalistic Numbers, & the Sacred Cross. 2006. pap. 9.95 *(978-1-4286-7844-6(1))* Kessinger Publishing, LLC.
—The Symbolism of the Circle & Bordered by Two Parallel Lines Or. 2006. pap. 9.95 *(978-1-4286-7838-5(7))* Kessinger Publishing, LLC.
—Symbolism of the Masonic Northeast Corner & the Cornerstone - 2006. pap. 9.95 *(978-1-4286-7840-8(9))* Kessinger Publishing, LLC.
—The Ways of the Cross. 2006. pap. 9.95 *(978-1-4286-7829-3(8))* Kessinger Publishing, LLC.
—What Is Astrology? 2006. pap. 9.95 *(978-1-4286-7836-1(0))* Kessinger Publishing, LLC.
—What Is Masonic Truth? 2006. pap. 9.95 *(978-1-4286-7821-7(2))* Kessinger Publishing, LLC.
—What the Ancients Knew about Astronomy & Astrology. 2006. pap. 9.95 *(978-1-4286-7823-1(9))* Kessinger Publishing, LLC.
—The 47th Problem of Euclid & Freemasonry. 2006. pap. 9.95 *(978-1-4286-7818-7(2))* Kessinger Publishing, LLC.
—The 49th Chapter of Genesis & Its Esoteric Meaning. 2006. pap. 9.95 *(978-1-4286-7837-8(9))* Kessinger Publishing, LLC.
Clement, Stephanie Jean. Aspect Patterns: What They Reveal & How They Are Triggered. 2007. (Special Topics in Astrology Ser.: 7). (ENG., Illus.). 216p. per. 17.95 *(978-0-7387-0782-2(1))* Llewellyn Pubns.
—The Astrology of Development. 2009. 152p. pap. 22.95 *(978-0-86690-596-1(0))* American Federation of Astrologers, Inc.
Clifton, Lucille. The Lucky Stone. 12.85 *(978-0-8124-4711-8(5))* Perfection Learning Corp.
Close, Jeffrey Sayer. Self-Evident Astrology. 2009. 104p. pap. 13.95 *(978-0-86690-592-3(8))* American Federation of Astrologers, Inc.
Coley, Henry. Clavis Astrologie Elimata Set: Key to the Whole Art of Astrology, 3 vols. Wiggers, Carol A., ed. Cochran, Kathleen R., tr. Incl. Vol. 3. Clavis Astrologie Elimata: Key to the Whole Art of Astrology. 441p. pap. 30.00 *(978-1-878935-28-1(3))*; Vol. 1. 134p. pap. 15.00 *(978-1-878935-26-7(7))*; Vol. 2. 220p. pap. 20.00 *(978-1-878935-27-4(5))*; (Illus.). 1996. 75.00 *(978-1-878935-29-8(1))* JustUs & Assocs.
Collins Publishers Staff. Zodiac Signs (Collins Gem) 2007. 256p. pap. 7.95 *(978-0-06-119811-3(0))* HarperCollins Pubs.
Colville, W. J. Libra & It's Significance in the Universal Zodiac. 2006. pap. 12.95 *(978-1-4286-7986-3(3))* Kessinger Publishing, LLC.
—Taurus & It's Significance in the Universal Zodiac. 2006. pap. 12.95 *(978-1-4286-7985-6(5))* Kessinger Publishing, LLC.
Committee on the Societal and Economic Impacts of Severe Space Weather Events: A Workshop & National Research Council. Severe Space Weather Events — Understanding Societal & Economic Impacts: A Workshop Report. 2008. (ENG.). 144p. pap. 35.00 *(978-0-309-12769-1(6))* National Academies Pr.
Committee on the Societal and Economic Impacts of Severe Space Weather Events: A Workshop & National Research Council Staff. Severe Space Weather Events — Understanding Societal & Economic Impacts: A Workshop Report - Extended Summary. 2009. (ENG.). 32p. pap. 15.00 *(978-0-309-13811-6(6))* National Academies Pr.
The Complete Guide to Astrology. 2008. 96p. *(978-1-4075-1130-6(0))* Parragon, Inc.
Cooksley, J. Compton. Believe It or Not. 2010. 120p. pap. 10.99 *(978-1-4490-9351-8(5))* AuthorHouse.
Coppa, Max. Does Your Love Life Add Up? How to Use Numbers to Find Your Perfect Relationship. 2008. (ENG.). 176p. mass mkt. 17.95 ***(978-1-74175-415-5(1))*** Allen & Unwin AUS. Dist: Independent Pubs. Group.
Costello, Priscilla. The Weiser Concise Guide to Practical Astrology. Wasserman, James, ed. 2008. (Weiser Concise Guides). (ENG., Illus.). 1p. pap. 12.95 *(978-1-57863-423-1(7)*, Weiser Bks.) Red Wheel/Weiser.
Covington, S. R. Sensual Astrology for the African American Man. 2011. (ENG., Illus.). 304p. 6.99 *(978-1-60162-320-1(3))* Urban Bks.
—Sensual Astrology for the African-American Man: Everything You Need to Know about Your Woman Through Her Sun Sign. 2008. (ENG., Illus.). 288p. 14.95 *(978-1-60162-116-0(7))* Urban Bks.
—Sensual Astrology for the African American Woman. 2011. (ENG., Illus.). 304p. 6.99 *(978-1-60162-321-8(5))* Urban Bks.
—Sensual Astrology for the African-American Woman: Everything You Need to Know about Your Man Through His Sun Sign. 2008. (ENG., Illus.). 300p. 14.95 *(978-1-60162-117-7(5))* Urban Bks.
Cox, Susie. Susie's Sun Signs: How to Truly Understand Your Lover, Family, Friends, Pets, & Yourself Using Astrology. 2011. (ENG., Illus.). 272p. pap. 14.95 *(978-1-4027-7495-9(8))* Sterling Publishing Co., Inc.
Cragin, Sally. The Astrological Elements: How Fire, Earth, Air & Water Influence Your Life. 2010. (ENG.). 216p. pap. 18.95 *(978-0-7387-1871-2(8))* Llewellyn Pubns.
Cragin, Sally. Astrology on the Cusp: Birthdays on the Edge of Two Signs. 2012. (ENG., Illus.). 240p. pap. 17.95 ***(978-0-7387-3154-4(4))*** Llewellyn Pubns.
Cramer, Frederick H. Astrology in Roman Law & Politics: Memoirs of the American Philosophical Society, V37. 2011. 302p. 48.95 ***(978-1-258-10474-0(1))*** Literary Licensing, LLC.
Crane, Joseph. Hellenistic Legacy. 2007. 336p. per. *(978-1-902405-24-7(2))* Wessex Astrologer Ltd., The.
—A Practical Guide to Traditional Astrology. 2007. 110p. per. 20.00 *(978-0-9662266-1-4(5))* Arhat Media, Inc.
Cress, Juel. Perfection & Deception: Virgo, the Virgin, Volume 1. 2007. 388p. per. 29.95 *(978-1-4241-7093-7(1))* PublishAmerica, Inc.
Cumont, Franz. Astrology & Religion among the Greeks. 2006. pap. 16.95 *(978-1-59605-896-5(X)*, Cosimo Classics) Cosimo, Inc.
—Astrology & Religion among the Greeks & Romans. 2010. 240p. 32.99 *(978-1-140-06100-7(3))* 2010. 240p. pap. 26.75 *(978-1-140-06101-4(1))* 2008. 148p. 24.99 *(978-0-554-30264-5(0))* 2008. 148p. 21.99 *(978-0-554-39567-8(3))* 2007. (ENG.). 130p. per. 18.99 *(978-1-4346-9689-2(8))* 2007. (ENG.). 148p. per. 19.99 *(978-1-4346-9690-8(1))* BiblioBazaar.
—Astrology & Religion among the Greeks & Romans. 2010. 238p. 41.95 *(978-1-161-35282-5(1))* Kessinger Publishing, LLC.
Curth, Louise Hill & Curth, Louise. English Almanacs, Astrology & Popular Medicine, 1550-1700. 2008. (ENG., Illus.). 288p. 89.00 *(978-0-7190-6928-4(9))* Manchester Univ. Pr. GBR. Dist: Macmillan.
Das, Tapan. Why Astrology Is Science: Five Good Reasons. 2009. 192p. 26.95 *(978-1-4401-3373-2(5))*; pap. 16.95 *(978-1-4401-3371-8(9))* iUniverse, Inc.
Davies, Erik, et al. A Briefer History of Time. 2008. (ENG., Illus.). 176p. pap. 22.00 *(978-0-553-38546-5(1)*, Bantam) Random House Publishing Group.
Davis, Rowan. The Ex-Boyfriend Book: A Zodiac Guide to Your Former Flames. 2008. (ENG., Illus.). 216p. per. 12.95 *(978-0-7387-1143-0(8))* Llewellyn Pubns.
De Fontbrune, Jean-Charles. Nostradamus 2000-2025 Guerra O Paz? (SPA.). 322p. *(978-84-7927-575-4(8))* Robinbk., Ediciones S.L. ESP. Dist: Lectorum Pubns., Inc.
DE LARCHE, Jean. Ceres. 2009. 246p. pap. 23.95 *(978-1-4092-6931-1(0))* Lulu Enterprises Inc.
Deluce, Robert. Complete Method of Prediction from Genethliac Astrology According to the Western Systems. 2011. 202p. 44.95 ***(978-1-258-01649-4(4))*** Literary Licensing, LLC.
d'Este, Sorita & Rankine, David. Practical Planetary Magick. 2007. 220p. per. *(978-1-905297-01-6(7))* Avalonia.
Devos, Trix. Astrological Indications for Your Own Horoscope 1922. 2007. (ENG.). 108p. 33.95 *(978-0-548-05353-9(7))* Kessinger Publishing, LLC.
Digitalis, Raven. Planetary Spells & Rituals: Practicing Dark & Light Magick Aligned with the Cosmic Bodies. 2010. (ENG., Illus.). 336p. pap. 19.95 *(978-0-7387-1971-9(4))* Llewellyn Pubns.
Discepolo, Ciro. Transits & Solar Returns. 2007. (ENG., Illus.). 556p. per. 25.00 *(978-0-9814620-0-4(6))* Ricerca '90.
Dixon-Cooper, Hazel. Friends on a Rotten Day: The Astrology of Friendships. 2008. (ENG., Illus.). 1p. per. 12.95 *(978-1-57863-412-5(1)*, Weiser Bks.) Red Wheel/Weiser.
Doane, Doris Chase, ed. Astrology: 30 Years Research. 2007. (ENG.). 328p. 45.95 *(978-0-548-07712-2(6))* Kessinger Publishing, LLC.
Dobyns, Zipporah Pottenger. The Node Book. 2010. 122p. pap. 14.95 *(978-0-86690-606-7(1))* American Federation of Astrologers, Inc.
Dobyns, Zipporah Pottenger. Progressions Directions & Rectification. 2011. 114p. pap. 14.95 ***(978-0-86690-612-8(6))*** American Federation of Astrologers, Inc.
Dorsan, Jacques. The Clockwise House System: A True Foundation for Sidereal & Tropical Astrology. Powell, Robert & Farrants, Wain, eds. 2011. Orig. Title: Le véritable sens des maisons Astrologiques. (ENG.). 256p. pap. 30.00 *(978-1-58420-095-6(2)*, Lindisfarne Bks.) SteinerBooks, Inc.
Durbin, Deborah. Simply Native American Astrology. 2007. (Simply Ser.). (ENG., Illus.). 160p. pap. 9.95 *(978-1-4027-2697-2(X)*, Sterling/Zambezi) Sterling Publishing Co., Inc.
—Simply Native American Astrology: Learn to Use This Ancietn & Mysterious Technique. 2007. (Illus.). 160p. pap. *(978-1-903065-52-5(6))* Sterling Publishing Co., Inc.
Ebertin, Elsbeth. Astrology & Romance 1936. 2007. (ENG.). 124p. 35.95 *(978-0-548-05352-2(9))* Kessinger Publishing, LLC.
Ebertin, Reinhold. The Annual Diagram. 2010. 130p. pap. 18.95 *(978-0-86690-605-0(3))* American Federation of Astrologers, Inc.
Edut, Ophira & Edut, Tali. The Astrotwins' Love Zodiac: The Essential Astrology Guide for Women. 2008. (ENG.). 448p. pap. 15.99 *(978-1-4022-1359-5(X)*, Sourcebooks Casablanca) Sourcebooks, Inc.
Elwell, Dennis. Cosmic Loom: The New Science of Astrology. 2008. 300p. pap. *(978-1-902405-31-5(5))* Wessex Astrologer Ltd., The.
English, Mary. How to Believe in a Sagittarius: Real life guidance on how to get on & be friends with the ninth sign of the Zodiac. 2012. (ENG.). 103p. pap. 14.95 ***(978-1-84694-861-9(4))*** Hunt, John Publishing Ltd. GBR. Dist: National Bk. Network.
—How to Bond with an Aquarius. 2011. (ENG.). 118p. pap. 14.95 *(978-1-84694-433-8(3))* Hunt, John Publishing Ltd. GBR. Dist: National Bk. Network.
—How to Cheer up a Capricorn: Real Life Guidance on How to Get Along & Be Friends with the 10th sign of the Zodiac. 2011. (ENG.). 109p. pap. 14.95 *(978-1-84694-664-6(6))* Hunt, John Publishing Ltd. GBR. Dist: National Bk. Network.
—How To Survive a Pisces. 2010. (ENG., Illus.). 103p. pap. 16.95 *(978-1-84694-252-5(7))* Hunt, John Publishing Ltd. GBR. Dist: National Bk. Network.
Ensworth, Heather M. Finding Our Center: An Astrological & Cosmological View of our Time. 2009. 156p. pap. 14.95 *(978-1-4401-8392-8(9))* iUniverse, Inc.
Esoteric Technologies Pty Ltd. Solar Fire Gold, v 7 User Guide. 2008. 360p. pap. 15.00 *(978-0-87199-151-5(9))* Astrolabe, Inc.
Fagan, Cyril. Zodiacs Old & New: A Probe into Antiquity & What Was Found. 2011. 82p. 37.95 ***(978-1-258-06696-3(3))*** Literary Licensing, LLC.
Fagan, Cyril & Firebrace, Roy. Primer of Sidereal Astrology. 2008. (Moray Ser.: No. 1). (Illus.). 160p. pap. 21.95 *(978-0-86690-427-8(1))* American Federation of Astrologers, Inc.
Farnell, Kim. Flirting with the Zodiac. 2007. 256p. per. *(978-1-902405-23-0(4))* Wessex Astrologer Ltd., The.
—Star Crossed. 2010. 300p. pap. 25.00 *(978-0-557-55886-5(7))* Lulu Enterprises Inc.
Fitch, Ben. Science of Astrology. 2010. 100p. pap. 11.95 *(978-1-4502-1139-0(9))* iUniverse, Inc.
Flynn, Beverly Ann. Astrology & Weight Control: The Jupiter/Pluto Connection. 2nd ed. 2009. (Illus.). vi, 136p. pap. *(978-1-934976-07-4(5))* Starcrafts LLC.
Forrest, Jodie. The Ascendant. 2007. 240p. pap. 15.95 *(978-0-9790677-0-9(7))* Seven Paws Pr.
Foulsham, creator. Old Moore's Horoscope: Aquarius. 2007. (Old Moore's Horoscope & Astral Diary Ser.). (ENG., Illus.). 1p. per. 5.95 *(978-0-572-03348-4(6))* Foulsham, W. Co., Ltd. GBR. Dist: APG Sales & Distribution Services.
—Old Moore's Horoscope: Aries. 2007. (Old Moore's Horoscope & Astral Diary Ser.). (ENG., Illus.). 1p. per. 5.95 *(978-0-572-03350-7(8))* Foulsham, W. Co., Ltd. GBR. Dist: APG Sales & Distribution Services.
—Old Moore's Horoscope: Capricorn. 2007. (Old Moore's Horoscope & Astral Diary Ser.). (ENG., Illus.). 1p. per. 5.95 *(978-0-572-03359-0(1))* Foulsham, W. Co., Ltd. GBR. Dist: APG Sales & Distribution Services.
—Old Moore's Horoscope: Gemini. 2007. (Old Moore's Horoscope & Astral Diary Ser.). (ENG., Illus.). 1p. per. 5.95 *(978-0-572-03352-1(4))* Foulsham, W. Co., Ltd. GBR. Dist: APG Sales & Distribution Services.

A

—Old Moore's Horoscope: Leo. 2007. (Old Moore's Horoscope & Astral Diary Ser.). (ENG., Illus.). 1p. per. 5.95 (978-0-572-03354-5(0)) Foulsham, W. Co., Ltd. GBR. Dist: APG Sales & Distribution Services.
—Old Moore's Horoscope: Libra. 2007. (Old Moore's Horoscope & Astral Diary Ser.). (ENG., Illus.). 1p. per. 5.95 (978-0-572-03356-9(7)) Foulsham, W. Co., Ltd. GBR. Dist: APG Sales & Distribution Services.
—Old Moore's Horoscope: Pisces. 2007. (Old Moore's Horoscope & Astral Diary Ser.). (ENG., Illus.). 1p. per. 5.95 (978-0-572-03349-1(4)) Foulsham, W. Co., Ltd. GBR. Dist: APG Sales & Distribution Services.
—Old Moore's Horoscope: Taurus. 2007. (Old Moore's Horoscope & Astral Diary Ser.). (ENG., Illus.). 1p. per. 5.95 (978-0-572-03351-4(6)) Foulsham, W. Co., Ltd. GBR. Dist: APG Sales & Distribution Services.
—Raphael's 151-Year Ephemeris 1900-2050. 2007. (Raphael's Astronomical Ephemeris of the Planets' Places Ser.). (Illus.). 1840p. 99.95 (978-0-572-02583-0(1)) Foulsham, W. Co., Ltd. GBR. Dist: APG Sales & Distribution Services.
Foulsham Editors, ed. Raphael's 101-Year Ephemeris, 1950-2050. 2007. (Raphael's Astronomical Ephemeris of the Planets' Places Ser.). (ENG., Illus.). 1240p. pap. (978-0-572-03363-7(X)) Foulsham, W. Co., Ltd.
—Raphael's 51-Year Ephemeris, 2000-2050. 2007. (Raphael's Astronomical Ephemeris of the Planets' Places Ser.). (ENG., Illus.). 640p. pap. 39.95 (978-0-572-03362-0(1)) Foulsham, W. Co., Ltd. GBR. Dist: APG Sales & Distribution Services.
—Raphael's Ephemeris 2011. 2010. 48p. pap. 8.95 (978-0-572-03572-3(1)) Foulsham, W. Co., Ltd. GBR. Dist: APG Sales & Distribution Services.
Franz Cumont. Astrology & Religion among the Greeks & Romans. 2009. 236p. pap. 9.95 (978-1-60386-174-8(2), Merchant Bks.) Rough Draft Printing.
Frederick, Nancy. The Astro Tutor. 2008. 216p. pap. 24.95 (978-0-86690-579-4(0)) American Federation of Astrologers, Inc.
Frederick, Sue. I See Your Dream Job: A Career Intuitive Shows You How to Discover What You Were Put on Earth to Do. 2010. (ENG.). 272p. pap. 13.99 (978-0-312-55421-7(4), St. Martin's Griffin) St. Martin's Pr.
Freed, Jennifer. A New Moon. 2009. 108p. pap. 45.50 (978-0-557-04095-7(7)) Lulu Enterprises Inc.
Furst, Dan. Surfing Aquarius: How to Ace the Wave of Change. 2011. (ENG.). 1p. pap. 21.95 (978-1-57863-501-6(2), Weiser Bks.) Red Wheel/Weiser.
Gainsburg, Adam. Chiron: The Wisdom of a Deeply Open Heart. 2006. per. 13.95 (978-0-9788535-2-5(0)) Soulsign Publishing.
Garrett, Helen Adams. Relationships. 2011. 82p. pap. 13.95 (978-0-86690-621-0(5)) American Federation of Astrologers, Inc.
Garrison, Cal. The Astrology of 2012 & Beyond. 2009. (ENG.). 1p. pap. 16.95 (978-1-57863-445-3(8), Weiser Bks.) Red Wheel/Weiser.
Gaston, Wilber. First Principles of Astrology 1927. 2007. (ENG.). 202p. 39.95 (978-0-548-05354-6(5)) Kessinger Publishing, LLC.
Geffner, Gayle. Creative Step-Parenting. 2009. 188p. pap. 23.95 (978-0-86690-593-0(6)) American Federation of Astrologers, Inc.
George, Demetra. Astrology & the Authentic Self: Integrating Traditional & Modern Astrology to Uncover the Essence of the Birth Chart. 2008. (ENG., Illus.). 1p. pap. 24.95 (978-0-89254-149-2(0)) Nicolas-Hays, Inc.
George, Linda. Sun Signs & Soul Mates: An Astrological Guide to Relationships. 2009. (ENG.). 240p. pap. 17.95 (978-0-7387-1558-2(1)) Llewellyn Pubns.
George, Llewellyn. The Astrologer's Searchlight. 2007. (ENG.). 176p. 37.95 (978-0-548-08279-9(0)) Kessinger Publishing, LLC.
George, Llewellyn. How to Succeed in the Study & Practice of Astrology. 2011. 48p. 35.95 (978-1-258-02418-5(7)) Literary Licensing, LLC.
Gerwick-Brodeur, Madeline & Lenard, Lisa. Astrology. 4th ed. 2007. (Complete Idiot's Guide Ser.). (ENG., Illus.). 384p. (gr. 12-18). 18.95 (978-1-59257-581-7(1), Alpha Bks.) Penguin Group (USA) Inc.
Gerwick, Madeline C. Good Timing Guide 2007: An Astrological Business Planner. 2010. spiral bd. 24.50 (978-1-60070-011-8(X), Elite Bks.) Author's Publishing Cooperative.
Gibson, Walter. Astrology Explained. 2011. 194p. 42.95 (978-1-258-06604-8(1)) Literary Licensing, LLC.
Gillett, Roy. The Secret Language of Astrology: The Illustrated Key to Unlocking the Secrets of Your Star Sign - Create Your Own Birth Chart & Discover What It Means. 2011. (ENG., Illus.). 176p. pap. 19.95 (978-1-78028-027-1(0), Watkins Publishing) Duncan Baird Pubs. GBR. Dist: Sterling Publishing Co., Inc.
Gillman, Kennet. One after Another. 2010. 429p. pap. 32.50 (978-0-557-43517-3(X)) Lulu Enterprises Inc.
Glovanna. La Guia Astrologica: 2002.Tr. of Astrological Guide for Two Thousand Two. (SPA.). 22.48 (978-970-05-1388-1(2)) Grijalbo, Editorial MEX. Dist: Continental Bk. Co., Inc.
Goddard, Gerry. Transpersonal Theory & the Astrological Mandal: An Evolutionary Model. 2009. 688p. pap. 39.50 (978-1-4269-1211-5(0)) Trafford Publishing.
Golding, Rohan "G-Money". Warrior Life. 2010. 108p. 22.95 (978-1-4502-1060-7(0)) iUniverse, Inc.
Goldstein-Jacobson, Ivy M. Here & There in Astrology: And What Is the Nature of This Event? 2011. 224p. 44.95 (978-1-258-02491-8(8)) Literary Licensing, LLC.
Gottheil, Richard J. H. A Fragment on Astrology from the Genizah. 2010. (ARA.). pap. 17.92 (978-1-61143-327-2(4)) Gorgias Pr., LLC.
Grant, R. Russell Grant's Zodiac Baby Names. 2009. 240p. (978-1-84850-024-2(6), 792) Hay Hse. UK, Ltd. GBR. Dist: Grantham Bk. Services.
Grant, Russell. Zodiac Baby Names: The Complete Book of Baby Names Defined by Star Sign. 2009. (ENG.). 432p. pap. 12.95 (978-1-4019-2326-6(7)) Hay Hse., Inc.
Graubard, Mark. Astrology & Alchemy: Two Fossil Sciences. 2011. 394p. 53.95 (978-1-258-00162-9(4)) Literary Licensing, LLC.
Green, H. S. Theoretical Astrology. 2007. (ENG.). 108p. 34.95 (978-0-548-08445-8(9)) Kessinger Publishing, LLC.
Green, Jonathan. Printing & Prophecy: Prognostication & Media Change, 1450-1550. 2011. (Cultures of Knowledge in the Early Modern World Ser.). (ENG.). 280p. (C). 70.00 (978-0-472-11783-3(1)); E-Book (978-0-472-02758-3(1)) Univ. of Michigan Pr.
Greene, Liz. Astrology for Lovers. 2009. (ENG.). 1p. pap. 18.95 (978-1-57863-426-2(1), Weiser Bks.) Red Wheel/Weiser.
—Saturn: A New Look at an Old Devil. 2011. (ENG.). 1p. pap. 18.95 (978-1-57863-507-8(1), Weiser Bks.) Red Wheel/Weiser.
Gros, Michel. In Tune with the Moon 2011: The Complete Day-by-Day Moon Planner for Growing & Living In 2011. 2010. (ENG., Illus.). 114p. pap. 15.00 (978-1-84409-527-8(4)) Findhorn Pr. GBR. Dist: Independent Pubs. Group.
—In Tune with the Moon 2012: The Complete Day-by-Day Moon Planner for Growing & Living In 2012. 2011. (ENG., Illus.). 114p. pap. 15.00 (978-1-84409-573-5(8)) Findhorn Pr. GBR. Dist: Independent Pubs. Group.
Gross, Ruth W. Astrology in Everyday Life. 2011. 182p. 42.95 (978-1-258-07219-3(X)) Literary Licensing, LLC.
Gullfoss, Per Henrik. The Complete Book of Spiritual Astrology. 2008. (ENG.). 264p. pap. 24.95 (978-0-7387-1258-1(2)) Llewellyn Pubns.
Haanel, Charles. You. 2007. pap. (978-0-9783883-2-4(1)) Ishtar Publishing.
Hakim, Nasir. Nations Are Destroyed Because Men Forget. 2008. (ENG.). 68p. pap. 13.95 (978-1-884855-41-2(5)) Secretarius MEMPS Pubns.
Hall, Judy. The Crystal Zodiac: Use Birthstones to Enhance Your Life. 2006. (ENG., Illus.). 320p. pap. 17.95 (978-1-84181-241-0(2), Godsfield Press) Octopus Publishing Group GBR. Dist: Hachette Bk. Group.
Hall, Manly P. Astrological Essays. 2011. 62p. 36.95 (978-1-258-00125-4(X)) Literary Licensing, LLC.
—Astrological Essays. 4.95 (978-0-89314-302-2(2)) Philosophical Research Society, Inc.
—Astrology & Reincarnation. 2011. 48p. 35.95 (978-1-258-00154-4(3)) Literary Licensing, LLC.
—Pluto in Libra. pap. 4.95 (978-0-89314-342-8(1)) Philosophical Research Society, Inc.
—The Story of Astrology. 14.95 (978-0-89314-525-5(4)) Philosophical Research Society, Inc.
Hall, Manly Palmer. The Horoscope of the United States: Based on Mr. Hall's Original Research. 2011. 22p. 35.95 (978-1-258-00736-2(3)) Literary Licensing, LLC.
—The Piscean Age: A System of World Prophecy. 2011. 46p. 35.95 (978-1-258-00757-7(6)) Literary Licensing, LLC.
Hall, Molly. Knack Astrology: A Complete Illustrated Guide to the Zodiac. 2010. (Knack: Make It Easy Ser.). (ENG., Illus.). 256p. pap. 19.95 (978-1-59921-623-2(X), Knack) Globe Pequot Pr., The.
Hampar, Joann. Astrology for Beginners: A Simple Way to Read Your Chart. 2007. (For Beginners Ser.). (ENG., Illus.). 240p. per. 14.95 (978-0-7387-1106-5(3)) Llewellyn Pubns.
Hansen, John M. Astrological Comments. 2010. 108p. pap. 17.50 (978-0-557-36103-8(6)) Lulu Enterprises Inc.
Harris, Janet. Astrology for Everyday Living. 2011. 194p. 42.95 (978-1-258-06362-7(X)) Literary Licensing, LLC.
Hazelrigg, John. Astrosophic Principles. 2010. 132p. 35.95 (978-1-161-35496-6(4)) Kessinger Publishing, LLC.
—Fundamentals of Hermetic Science. 2007. (ENG.). 142p. 35.95 (978-0-548-00720-4(9)) Kessinger Publishing, LLC.
Heindel, Max. The Message of the Stars. 2006. pap. 24.95 (978-1-59605-902-3(8), Cosimo Classics) Cosimo, Inc.
—Simplified Scientific Astrology. 2009. 98p. pap. (978-0-217-87579-0(3)) Books LLC.
—Simplified Scientific Astrology. 2006. (ENG.). pap. 9.95 (978-1-59605-919-1(2), Cosimo Classics) Cosimo, Inc.
—Simplified Scientific Astrology. 2007. (ENG.). 212p. 39.95 (978-0-548-00411-1(0)) Kessinger Publishing, LLC.
Hendrix, Scott E. How Albert the Great's Speculum Astronomiae Was Interpreted & Used by Four Centuries of Readers: A Study in Late Medieval Medicine, Astronomy, & Astrology. 2010. iii, 326p. 119.95 (978-0-7734-3635-0(9)) Mellen, Edwin Pr., The.
Herring, Amy. Astrology of the Moon: An Illuminating Journey Through the Signs & Houses. 2010. (ENG.). 312p. pap. 21.95 (978-0-7387-1896-5(3)) Llewellyn Pubns.
Hickey, Isabel M. Astrology, A Cosmic Science: The Classic Work on Spiritual Astrology. 4th rev. ed. 2011. (ENG., Illus.). 356p. pap. 22.95 (978-0-916360-63-4(6)) CRCS Pubns.
Hill, J. Astral Worship. 2007. 80p. per. 12.99 (978-1-59547-790-3(X)) NuVision Pubns., LLC.
Hill, Judith A. The Lunar Nodes: Your Key to Excellent Chart Interpretation. 2009. 154p. pap. 24.95 (978-1-883376-33-8(5)) Stellium Pr.
Ho, Kyun. Sibiji Ui Munhwasa. 2010. (KOR., Illus.). 176p. (978-89-7199-372-9(3)) Dolbegae Publishing Co.
Holden, James H. Journal of Research of the American Federation of Astrologers. Holden, James H. & Brandt Riske, Kris, eds. 2010. 154p. pap. 89.95 (978-0-86690-607-4(X)) American Federation of Astrologers, Inc.
Hooft. Playing with Planets. 2008. (Illus.). 200p. 51.00 (978-981-279-307-2(0)); pap. 24.00 (978-981-279-020-0(9)) World Scientific Publishing Co., Inc.
Horrocks, Thomas A. Popular Print & Popular Medicine: Almanacs & Health Advice in Early America. 2008. (Illus.). 224p. (ENG.). pap. 29.95 (978-1-55849-657-6(2)); lib. bdg. 80.00 (978-1-55849-656-9(4)) Univ. of Massachusetts Pr.
House, Chuck. The Journey of the Sun. 2008. 164p. pap. 15.95 (978-0-595-52024-4(3)) iUniverse, Inc.
Howard, Nona. Follow Your Lucky Stars: A Handbook for Student Astrologers. 2007. (ENG.). 192p. 37.95 (978-0-548-12291-4(1)) Kessinger Publishing, LLC.
Howell, Irene C. Cyclic Astrology, As Interpreted by the Point of Self System. 2011. 74p. 36.95 (978-1-258-01531-2(5)) Literary Licensing, LLC.
Howells, R. G. The Zodiac & You: Your Character Revealed. 2011. 142p. 40.95 (978-1-258-05623-0(2)) Literary Licensing, LLC.
Huber, Bruno & Huber, Louise. Astrolog I: Life & Meaning. 2008. (Illus.). 328p. per. (978-0-9547680-7-2(8)) HopeWell.
—Transformation: Astrology as a Spiritual Path. 2008. 228p. pap. (978-0-9547680-8-9(6)) HopeWell.
Husson, Mark S. LoveScopes: What Astrology Knows about You & the Ones You Love. 2009. (ENG.). 384p. pap. 15.95 (978-1-4019-2004-3(7)) Hay Hse., Inc.
—Power Peek 2008: A Daily Astrological Companion. 2007. (ENG., Illus.). 460p. per. 16.95 (978-1-4019-1157-7(9)) Hay Hse., Inc.
Hyde, Stella. Darkside Zodiac at Work. 2007. (ENG., Illus.). 1p. pap. 16.95 (978-1-57863-402-6(4), Weiser Bks.) Red Wheel/Weiser.
—Darkside Zodiac in Love. 2007. (ENG., Illus.). 1p. pap. 16.95 (978-1-57863-415-6(6), Weiser Bks.) Red Wheel/Weiser.
Idel, Moshe. Saturn's Jews: On Witches' Sabbat & Sabbateanism. 2011. 208p. E-Book (978-1-4411-0502-8(6)) Continuum International Publishing Group, Ltd.
—Saturn's Jews: On Witches' Sabbat & Sabbateanism. 2011. (Robert & Arlene Kogod Library Judaic Studies). (ENG.). 216p. 140.00 (978-1-4411-2144-8(7)) Continuum International Publishing Group, Ltd. GBR. Dist: National Bk. Network.
The Inner Sky: How to Make Wiser Choices for a More Fulfilling Life. 2007. 303p. pap. 18.95 (978-0-9790677-1-6(5)) Seven Paws Pr.
Jaks, Anton. Astrology Handbook. 2010. 155p. pap. 29.97 (978-0-557-53457-9(7)) Lulu Enterprises Inc.
Jay, Delphine Gloria. Lilith Ephemeris 2000-2050. 2011. 114p. pap. 23.95 (978-0-86690-613-5(4)) American Federation of Astrologers, Inc.
Jayne, Charles A. Preface to Prenatal Charts. 2011. 84p. pap. 13.95 (978-0-86690-620-3(7)) American Federation of Astrologers, Inc.
—Progressions & Directions. 2011. 112p. pap. 14.95 (978-0-86690-615-9(0)) American Federation of Astrologers, Inc.
Jensen, Magnus. Everybody's Astrology. 2009. (Illus.). 48p. pap. (978-1-4099-6896-2(0)) Dodo Pr.
Jim Maynard's Astrologer's Datebook 2002: Pacific & Eastern. (Illus.). 176p. 7.95 (978-0-930356-20-0(9)) Quicksilver Productions.
Jim Maynard's Celestial Guide 2002: Pacific & Eastern. (Illus.). 176p. spiral bd. 9.95 (978-0-930356-29-3(2)) Quicksilver Productions.
Jim Maynard's Celestial Influences 2002: Pacific Time. (Illus.). 48p. 10.95 (978-0-930356-02-6(0)) Quicksilver Productions.
Jim Maynard's Pocket Astrologer 2002: Pacific Time. (Illus.). 64p. 5.95 (978-0-930356-55-2(1)) Quicksilver Productions.
Johndro, L. Edwards. The Stars: How & Where They Influence. 2007. (ENG.). 132p. 35.95 (978-0-548-09602-4(3)) Kessinger Publishing, LLC.
Jones, Marc Edmund. The Sabian Symbols in Astrology: Illustrated by 1,000 Horoscopes of Well-Known People. 2011. 448p. 56.95 (978-1-258-06117-3(1)) Literary Licensing, LLC.
Jones, Marie D. & Jones, Marie. 2013: The End of Days or a New Beginning? Envisioning the World after the Evens of 2012. 2008. (ENG.). 1p. pap. 15.99 (978-1-60163-007-0(7), New Page Bks.) Career Pr., Inc.
Kaldera, Raven. Moon Phase Astrology. 2011. (ENG., Illus.). 1p. pap. 19.95 (978-1-59477-401-0(3)) Inner Traditions International, Ltd.
—Pagan Astrology: Spell-Casting, Love Magic, & Shamanic Stargazing. 2010. (ENG.). 1p. pap. 18.95 (978-1-59477-302-0(5), Destiny Bks.) Inner Traditions International, Ltd.
Kaleta, Ján. Introduction to Aquarian Astrology. 2010. 238p. pap. 26.95 (978-1-4457-1479-0(5)) Lulu Enterprises Inc.
Kaley, Joan. Astrology Sun Sign Secrets Money Love Sex: Astrology Sun Sign Secrets. 2008. 214p. (978-0-9744528-0-7(7)) New Minerva Pr.
Karen, Michelle. Astrology for Enlightenment. 2008. (ENG.). 432p. pap. 25.99 (978-1-4165-8085-0(9), Beyond Words/Atria Bks.) Atria Bks.
Katzenberg, Michael A. The Astrology of Whole Relationships. 2009. 336p. pap. 17.99 (978-1-4490-0223-7(4)) AuthorHouse.
Kent, April Elliott. The Essential Guide to Practical Astrology. 2011. (ENG.). 432p. (gr. 12). 18.95 (978-1-61564-093-5(2), Alpha Bks.) Penguin Group (USA) Inc.
—Star Guide to Weddings: Your Horoscope for Living Happily Ever After. 2008. (ENG., Illus.). 264p. per. 12.95 (978-0-7387-1169-0(1)) Llewellyn Pubns.
Kepler, Johann. Concerning the More Certain Fundamentals of Astrology. 2010. 36p. 30.95 (978-1-161-36663-1(6)) Kessinger Publishing, LLC.
Kerston, Kathy. Balancing Your Orbit. 2008. 72p. pap. 10.95 (978-0-595-47717-3(8)) iUniverse, Inc.
Kimmel, Eleonora. Altered & Unfinished Lives. 2006. (ENG.). 220p. per. 21.95 (978-0-86690-568-8(5)) American Federation of Astrologers, Inc.
KING, R. O. N. S. Love & sex, astrologically Speaking. 2009. 264p. pap. 18.50 (978-1-4452-0101-6(1)) Lulu Enterprises Inc.
KING, RON S. Astrology; houses of the rising Sun. 2007. 333p. pap. 21.95 (978-1-84799-096-9(7)) Lulu Enterprises Inc.
Kirk, Eleanor. The Influence of the Zodiac upon Human L. 2006. pap. 16.95 (978-1-59605-901-6(X), Cosimo Classics) Cosimo, Inc.
—The Influence of the Zodiac upon Human Life. 2009. 80p. pap. 14.85 (978-0-217-92512-9(X)) General Bks. LLC.
—The Influence of the Zodiac upon Human Life. 2007. (ENG.). 196p. 37.95 (978-0-548-00045-8(X)) Kessinger Publishing, LLC.
Knapp, Emeline. More Than You Know about Yourself: A Manual of the Triple Sciences. 2006. 116p. per. 14.95 (978-1-59605-878-1(1)) Cosimo, Inc.
Kochunas, Brad Hiljanen. The Astrological Imagination: Where Psyche & Cosmos Meet. 2008. 132p. pap. 13.95 (978-0-595-53108-0(3)) iUniverse, Inc.
Kosarin, Jenni. The Everything Love Signs Book: Use astrology to find your perfect Partner! 2nd ed. 2012. (ENG.). 304p. pap. 12.95 (978-1-4405-2819-4(5)) Adams Media Corp.
—He's Just Not in the Stars: Wicked Astrology & Uncensored Advice for Getting the (Almost) Perfect Guy. 2006. (Illus.). 304p. 17.95 (978-0-06-088728-5(1)) HarperCollins Pubs.
—Love Is in the Stars: Wicked & Uncensored Astrology Advice for Getting the (Almost) Perfect Guy. 2008. (ENG.). 320p. pap. 13.95 (978-0-06-088729-2(X), William Morrow Paperbacks) HarperCollins Pubs.
Kuman, Maria. Connected to the Stars - Pleiades or Orion? pap. 20.00 (978-1-893637-33-7(6)) Health & Happiness Bks.
Lachman, Gary. Jung the Mystic: The Esoteric Dimensions of Carl Jung's Life & Teachings. 2010. (ENG.). 272p. (gr. 12). 24.95 (978-1-58542-792-5(6), Tarcher) Penguin Group (USA) Inc.
Lamb, Myrna. The Astrology of Great Gay Sex: The Ultimate Guide to Finding Mr. Right & Avoiding Mr. Wrong. 2008. (ENG., Illus.). 304p. pap. 16.95 (978-1-57174-575-0(0)) Hampton Roads Publishing Co., Inc.
—The Astrology of Great Sex: Discover Your Lover's-and Your Own-Deepest Desires. rev. ed. 2006. (ENG., Illus.). 312p. per. 17.95 (978-1-57174-509-5(2)) Hampton Roads Publishing Co., Inc.
Landwehr, Joe. Tracking the Soul with an Astrology of Consciousness. 2007. (Illus.). xxviii, 470p. per. (978-0-9747626-1-6(X)) Ancient Tower Pr.
Lang-Wescott, Martha. The Orders of Light. (Illus.). 320p. 25.00 (978-0-9619852-3-3(2)) Treehouse Mountain.
Lash, John. Quest for the Zodiac: The Cosmic Code Beyond Astrology. 2007. (ENG.). 240p. pap. 29.95 (978-1-933392-93-6(2)) Marion Institute.
Lavoie, Alphee & Lavoie, Carol. Life Lessons Through the Sun Signs. Date not set. pap. (978-0-9645621-2-7(X)) AIR Software.
Ledo, Michael. The Bible Astrology Handbook. 2010. 48p. pap. 11.99 (978-0-557-38010-7(3)) Lulu Enterprises Inc.
Lehman, J. Lee. Astrology of Sustainability. 2011. (Illus.). 304p. (978-0-7643-3805-2(6), Schiffer Publishing Ltd) Schiffer Publishing, Ltd.
Lehoux, Daryn. Astronomy, Weather, & Calendars in the Ancient World: Parapegmata & Related Texts in Classical & near-Eastern Societies. 2007. (ENG., Illus.). 580p. 140.00 (978-0-521-85181-7(5)) Cambridge Univ. Pr.
Lennox, Psyd & Terry Oleson. Astrology & Personality. 2010. 68p. pap. (978-3-8383-0138-9(2)) Lambert Academic Publishing.
Leo, Alan. The Art of Synthesis. 2010. 310p. 43.95 (978-1-161-36965-6(1)) Kessinger Publishing, LLC.
—Astrology for All. 2009. 86p. pap. (978-1-4590-8109-3(9)) Books LLC.
—Astrology for All. 2006. (ENG.). pap. 16.95 (978-1-59605-924-5(9), Cosimo Classics) Cosimo, Inc.
—Casting the Horoscope. 2010. 384p. 48.95 (978-1-161-36961-8(9)) Kessinger Publishing, LLC.
—Horary Astrology. 2006. pap. 15.95 (978-1-59605-911-5(7), Cosimo Classics) Cosimo, Inc.
—Jupiter the Preserver. 2007. (ENG.). 108p. 34.95 (978-0-548-00199-8(5)) Kessinger Publishing, LLC.
—The Key to Your Own Nativity. 2006. (ENG.). pap. 16.95 (978-1-59605-923-8(0), Cosimo Classics) Cosimo, Inc.
—The Progressed Horoscope. 2007. (ENG.). 372p. per. 29.95 (978-1-933303-23-9(9)) Astrology Ctr. Of America, The.
Letorney, Mary A. Discover the Universe Within You: Through the Metaphysical Science of Astrology. 2007. (Illus.). 266p. per. 14.50 (978-1-886940-96-3(7)) Ozark Mountain Publishing, Inc.
Levacy, William R. Beneath a Vedic Sun: Discover Your Life Purpose with Vedic Astrology. 2006. (ENG., Illus.). 400p. 23.95 (978-1-4019-0717-4(2)) Hay Hse., Inc.
—Vedic Astrology Simply Put: An Illustrated Guide to the Astrology of Ancient India. 2007. (ENG., Illus.). 350p. 19.95 (978-1-4019-0718-1(0)) Hay Hse., Inc.
Levine, Joyce. Breakthrough Astrology: Transform Yourself & Your World. 2006. (ENG., Illus.). 1p. per. 21.95 (978-1-57863-357-9(5), 1255857, Weiser Bks.) Red Wheel/Weiser.
Levine, Rick & Jawer, Jeff. Your Astrology Guide 2012. 2011. (ENG., Illus.). 448p. pap. 12.95 (978-1-4027-7939-8(9)) Sterling Publishing Co., Inc.
—Your Personal Astrology Guide 2012 Aquarius January 20-February 18. 2011. (ENG., Illus.). 160p. pap. 4.95 (978-1-4027-7942-8(9)) Sterling Publishing Co., Inc.
—Your Personal Astrology Planner 2009: Aries. 2008. (ENG.). 160p. pap. 4.95 (978-1-4027-5025-0(0)) Sterling Publishing Co., Inc.
—Your Personal Astrology Planner 2009: Capricorn. 2008. (ENG.). 160p. pap. 4.95 (978-1-4027-5027-4(7)) Sterling Publishing Co., Inc.

—Your Personal Astrology Planner 2011: Aquarius. 2010. (ENG.). 160p. pap. 4.95 *(978-1-4027-7483-6(4))* Sterling Publishing Co., Inc.
—Your Personal Astrology Planner 2011: Aries. 2010. (ENG.). 160p. pap. 4.95 *(978-1-4027-7473-7(7))* Sterling Publishing Co., Inc.
—Your Personal Astrology Planner 2011: Cancer. 2010. (ENG.). 160p. pap. 4.95 *(978-1-4027-7476-8(1))* Sterling Publishing Co., Inc.
—Your Personal Astrology Planner 2011: Capricorn. 2010. (ENG.). 160p. pap. 4.95 *(978-1-4027-7482-9(6))* Sterling Publishing Co., Inc.
—Your Personal Astrology Planner 2011: Gemini. 2010. (ENG.). 160p. pap. 4.95 *(978-1-4027-7475-1(3))* Sterling Publishing Co., Inc.
—Your Personal Astrology Planner 2011: Leo. 2010. (ENG.). 160p. pap. 4.95 *(978-1-4027-7477-5(X))* Sterling Publishing Co., Inc.
—Your Personal Astrology Planner 2011: Libra. 2010. (ENG.). 160p. pap. 4.95 *(978-1-4027-7479-9(6))* Sterling Publishing Co., Inc.
—Your Personal Astrology Planner 2011: Pisces. 2010. (ENG.). 160p. pap. 4.95 *(978-1-4027-7484-3(2))* Sterling Publishing Co., Inc.
—Your Personal Astrology Planner 2011: Sagittarius. 2010. (ENG.). 160p. pap. 4.95 *(978-1-4027-7481-2(8))* Sterling Publishing Co., Inc.
—Your Personal Astrology Planner 2011: Scorpio. 2010. (ENG.). 160p. pap. 4.95 *(978-1-4027-7480-5(X))* Sterling Publishing Co., Inc.
—Your Personal Astrology Planner 2011: Taurus. 2010. (ENG.). 160p. pap. 4.95 *(978-1-4027-7474-4(5))* Sterling Publishing Co., Inc.
—Your Personal Astrology Planner 2012 Aries. 2011. (ENG., Illus.). 160p. pap. 4.95 *(978-1-4027-7943-5(7))* Sterling Publishing Co., Inc.
—Your Personal Astrology Planner 2012 Cancer. 2011. (ENG., Illus.). 160p. pap. 4.95 *(978-1-4027-7944-2(5))* Sterling Publishing Co., Inc.
—Your Personal Astrology Planner 2012 Capricorn. 2011. (ENG., Illus.). 160p. pap. 4.95 *(978-1-4027-7945-9(3))* Sterling Publishing Co., Inc.
—Your Personal Astrology Planner 2012 Gemini. 2011. (ENG., Illus.). 160p. pap. 4.95 *(978-1-4027-7946-6(1))* Sterling Publishing Co., Inc.
—Your Personal Astrology Planner 2012 Leo. 2011. (ENG., Illus.). 160p. pap. 4.95 *(978-1-4027-7947-3(X))* Sterling Publishing Co., Inc.
—Your Personal Astrology Planner 2012 Libra. 2011. (ENG., Illus.). 160p. pap. 4.95 *(978-1-4027-7948-0(8))* Sterling Publishing Co., Inc.
—Your Personal Astrology Planner 2012 Pisces. 2011. (ENG., Illus.). 160p. pap. 4.95 *(978-1-4027-7949-7(6))* Sterling Publishing Co., Inc.
—Your Personal Astrology Planner 2012 Sagittarius. 2011. (ENG., Illus.). 160p. pap. 4.95 *(978-1-4027-7950-3(X))* Sterling Publishing Co., Inc.
—Your Personal Astrology Planner 2012 Scorpio. 2011. (ENG., Illus.). 160p. pap. 4.95 *(978-1-4027-7951-0(8))* Sterling Publishing Co., Inc.
—Your Personal Astrology Planner 2012 Taurus. 2011. (ENG., Illus.). 160p. pap. 4.95 *(978-1-4027-7952-7(6))* Sterling Publishing Co., Inc.
—Your Personal Astrology Planner 2012 Virgo. 2011. (ENG., Illus.). 160p. pap. 4.95 *(978-1-4027-7953-4(4))* Sterling Publishing Co., Inc.
Lewis, James R. The Astrology Book: The Encyclopedia of Heavenly Influences. 2nd ed. (Illus.). 889p. *(978-1-57859-182-4(1))* Visible Ink Pr.
Lilly, William. Christian Astrology Modestly Treated of. 2006. (ENG.). pap. 36.95 *(978-1-4286-4519-6(5))*; pap. 36.95 *(978-1-4286-4518-9(7))* Kessinger Publishing, LLC.
Lilly, William & Coley, Henry. The Astrologer's Guide: Anima Astrologia. Wiggers, Carol A., ed. Date not set. (C). wbk. ed. 18.00 *(978-1-878935-24-3(0))* JustUs & Assocs.
Linacre, Vivian T. & Batchelor, Richard A., eds. Megalithic Measures & Rhythms: Sacred Knowledge of the Ancient Britons. 2006. (Illus.). 254p. 40.00 *(978-0-86315-554-3(5))* Floris Bks. GBR. Dist: SteinerBooks, Inc.
Lionnet, Annie. Astrology Directory. 224p. 12.99 *(978-0-7858-1630-0(5))* Book Sales, Inc.
Llewellyn. Llewellyn's 2012 Moon Sign Book: Conscious Living by the Cycles of the Moon. 2011. (Annuals - Moon Sign Book Ser.). (ENG., Illus.). 360p. pap. 10.99 *(978-0-7387-1208-6(6))* Llewellyn Pubns.
—Llewellyn's 2013 Moon Sign Book: Conscious Living by the Cycles of the Moon. 2012. (Annuals - Moon Sign Book Ser.). (ENG.). 312p. pap. 10.99 ***(978-0-7387-1513-1(1))*** Llewellyn Pubns.
—Llewellyn's 2013 Sun Sign Book: Horoscopes for Everyone. 2012. (Annuals - Sun Sign Book Ser.). (ENG.). 312p. pap. 10.99 ***(978-0-7387-1514-8(X))*** Llewellyn Pubns.
Llewellyn, George. Astrological Chats. 2007. (ENG.). 128p. 35.95 *(978-0-548-08198-3(0))* Kessinger Publishing, LLC.
—Lectures on Astrology. 2007. (ENG.). 108p. 34.95 *(978-0-548-09716-8(X))* Kessinger Publishing, LLC.
—Powerful Planets Astrologically Considered 1931. 2007. (ENG.). 224p. 39.95 *(978-0-548-05660-8(9))* Kessinger Publishing, LLC.
—Student Chart Reader of Horoscope Indications 1934. 2007. (ENG.). 314p. 45.95 *(978-0-548-05355-3(3))* Kessinger Publishing, LLC.
Llewellyn Publications Staff. Pagan Anthology of Short Fiction: 13 Prize Winning Tales. 2008. (ENG.). 240p. pap. 18.95 *(978-0-7387-1269-7(8))* Llewellyn Pubns.
Lonsdale, Ellias & Borax, Mark. Cosmic Weather Report: Notes from the Edge of the Universe. 2010. (ENG.). 256p. pap. 16.95 *(978-1-55643-942-1(3))* North Atlantic Bks.
Loomis, Benjamin. Science & Religion. 2006. 344p. per. 16.95 *(978-1-59605-922-1(2))* Cosimo, Inc.
Louis, Anthony. The Art of Forecasting Using Solar Returns. 2008. 302p. pap. *(978-1-902405-29-2(3))* Wessex Astrologer Ltd., The.
Luntz, Charles E. Vocational Guidance by Astrology. 2007. (ENG.). 208p. 39.95 *(978-0-548-08462-5(9))* Kessinger Publishing, LLC.
Lutin, Michael. Sunshines: The Astrology of Being Happy. 2006. (ENG., Illus.). 496p. pap. 16.95 *(978-0-7432-7726-6(0)*, Touchstone) Touchstone.
Lyons, Tim. Astrology Beyond Ego. 2010. 164p. pap. 24.95 *(978-0-86690-603-6(7))* American Federation of Astrologers, Inc.
MacGregor, Trish. Sydney Omarr's Astrological Guide for You In 2013. 2012. (ENG.). 336p. (gr. 12). 7.99 ***(978-0-451-23742-2(0)***, Signet) Penguin Group (USA) Inc.
MacGregor, Trish & MacGregor, Rob. Sydney Omarr's Day-by-Day Astrological Guide For - Sagittarius 2011: November 22-December 21 - 18 Months of Daily Horoscopes from July 2010 to December 2011. 2010. (ENG.). 320p. (gr. 12). 7.99 *(978-0-451-23041-6(8)*, Signet) Penguin Group (USA) Inc.
—Sydney Omarr's Day-by-Day Astrological Guide for Leo 2011: 18 Months of Daily Horoscopes from July 2010 to December 2011. 2010. (ENG.). 320p. (gr. 12). 7.99 *(978-0-451-23036-2(1)*, Signet) Penguin Group (USA) Inc.
—Sydney Omarr's Day-by-Day Astrological Guide for Leo 2013: 18 Months of Daily Horoscopes from July 2012 to December 2013. 2012. (ENG.). 320p. (gr. 12). 7.99 ***(978-0-451-23723-1(4)***, Signet) Penguin Group (USA) Inc.
—Sydney Omarr's Day-by-Day Astrological Guide for the Year 2011: Aquarius. 2010. (ENG.). 320p. (gr. 12). 7.99 *(978-0-451-23030-0(2)*, Signet) Penguin Group (USA) Inc.
—Sydney Omarr's Day-by-Day Astrological Guide for the Year 2011: Aries. 2010. (ENG.). 320p. (gr. 12). 7.99 *(978-0-451-23033-1(7)*, Signet) Penguin Group (USA) Inc.
—Sydney Omarr's Day-by-Day Astrological Guide for the Year 2011: Capricorn. 2010. (ENG.). 320p. (gr. 12). 7.99 *(978-0-451-23040-9(X)*, Signet) Penguin Group (USA) Inc.
—Sydney Omarr's Day-by-Day Astrological Guide for the Year 2011: Gemini. 2010. (ENG.). 320p. (gr. 12). 7.99 *(978-0-451-23034-8(5)*, Signet) Penguin Group (USA) Inc.
—Sydney Omarr's Day-by-Day Astrological Guide for the Year 2011: Libra. 2010. (ENG.). 320p. (gr. 12). 7.99 *(978-0-451-23038-6(8)*, Signet) Penguin Group (USA) Inc.
—Sydney Omarr's Day-by-Day Astrological Guide for the Year 2011: Pisces. 2010. (ENG.). 320p. (gr. 12). 7.99 *(978-0-451-23031-7(0)*, Signet) Penguin Group (USA) Inc.
—Sydney Omarr's Day-by-Day Astrological Guide for the Year 2011: Scorpio. 2010. (ENG.). 320p. (gr. 12). 7.99 *(978-0-451-23039-3(6)*, Signet) Penguin Group (USA) Inc.
—Sydney Omarr's Day-by-Day Astrological Guide for the Year 2011 - Cancer. 2010. (ENG.). 320p. (gr. 12). 7.99 *(978-0-451-23035-5(3)*, Signet) Penguin Group (USA) Inc.
—Sydney Omarr's Day-by-Day Astrological Guide for the Year 2011 - Taurus. 2010. (ENG.). 320p. (gr. 12). 7.99 *(978-0-451-23032-4(9)*, Signet) Penguin Group (USA) Inc.
—Sydney Omarr's Day-by-Day Astrological Guide for the Year 2013: Aquarius. 2012. (ENG.). 320p. (gr. 12). 7.99 ***(978-0-451-23717-0(X)***, Signet) Penguin Group (USA) Inc.
—Sydney Omarr's Day-by-Day Astrological Guide for the Year 2013: Aries. 2012. (ENG.). 320p. (gr. 12). 7.99 ***(978-0-451-23720-0(X)***, Signet) Penguin Group (USA) Inc.
—Sydney Omarr's Day-by-Day Astrological Guide for the Year 2013: Capricorn. 2012. (ENG.). 320p. (gr. 12). 7.99 ***(978-0-451-23727-9(7)***, Signet) Penguin Group (USA) Inc.
—Sydney Omarr's Day-by-Day Astrological Guide for the Year 2013: Gemini. 2012. (ENG.). 320p. (gr. 12). 7.99 ***(978-0-451-23721-7(8)***, Signet) Penguin Group (USA) Inc.
—Sydney Omarr's Day-by-Day Astrological Guide for the Year 2013: Pisces. 2012. (ENG.). 320p. (gr. 12). 7.99 ***(978-0-451-23718-7(8)***, Signet) Penguin Group (USA) Inc.
—Sydney Omarr's Day-by-Day Astrological Guide for the Year 2013: Sagittarius. 2012. (ENG.). 320p. (gr. 12). 7.99 ***(978-0-451-23728-6(5)***, Signet) Penguin Group (USA) Inc.
—Sydney Omarr's Day-by-Day Astrological Guide for the Year 2013: Taurus. 2012. (ENG.). 320p. (gr. 12). 7.99 ***(978-0-451-23719-4(6)***, Signet) Penguin Group (USA) Inc.
—Sydney Omarr's Day-by-Day Astrological Guide for the Year 2013 - Libra. 2012. (ENG.). 320p. (gr. 12). 7.99 ***(978-0-451-23725-5(0)***, Signet) Penguin Group (USA) Inc.
—Sydney Omarr's Day-by-Day Astrological Guide for the Year 2013 - Scorpio. 2012. (ENG.). 320p. (gr. 12). 7.99 ***(978-0-451-23726-2(9)***, Signet) Penguin Group (USA) Inc.
—Sydney Omarr's Day-by-Day Astrological Guide for the Year 2013: Cancer: Cancer. 2012. (ENG.). 320p. (gr. 12). 7.99 ***(978-0-451-23722-4(6)***, Signet) Penguin Group (USA) Inc.
—Sydney Omarr's Day-by-Day Astrological Guide for the Year 2013: Virgo: Virgo. 2012. (ENG.). 320p. (gr. 12). 7.99 ***(978-0-451-23724-8(2)***, Signet) Penguin Group (USA) Inc.
MacGregor, Trish & MacGregor, Rob. Sydney Omarr's Day-by-Day Astrological Guide for Virgo 2011: 18 Months of Daily Horoscopes from July 2010 to December 2011. 2010. (ENG.). 320p. (gr. 12). 7.99 *(978-0-451-23037-9(X)*, Signet) Penguin Group (USA) Inc.
MacGregor, Trish, et al. Sydney Omarr's Astrological Guide for You In 2011. 2010. (ENG.). 336p. (gr. 12). 7.99 *(978-0-451-23069-0(8)*, Signet) Penguin Group (USA) Inc.
—Sydney Omarr's Astrological Guide for You In 2012. 2011. (ENG.). 336p. (gr. 12). 7.99 *(978-0-451-23403-2(0)*, Signet) Penguin Group (USA) Inc.
—Sydney Omarr's Day-by-Day Astrological Guide for the Year 2012: Cancer. 2011. (ENG.). 320p. (gr. 12). 7.99 *(978-0-451-23367-7(0)*, Signet) Penguin Group (USA) Inc.
—Sydney Omarr's Day-by-Day Astrological Guide for the Year 2012: Capricorn. 2011. (ENG.). 320p. (gr. 12). 7.99 *(978-0-451-23372-1(7)*, Signet) Penguin Group (USA) Inc.
—Sydney Omarr's Day-by-Day Astrological Guide for the Year 2012: Gemini. 2011. (ENG.). 320p. (gr. 12). 7.99 *(978-0-451-23366-0(2)*, Signet) Penguin Group (USA) Inc.
—Sydney Omarr's Day-by-Day Astrological Guide for the Year 2012: Scorpio. 2011. (ENG.). 320p. (gr. 12). 7.99 *(978-0-451-23371-4(9)*, Signet) Penguin Group (USA) Inc.
—Sydney Omarr's Day-by-Day Astrological Guide for the Year 2012 - Aquarius. 2011. (ENG.). 320p. (gr. 12). 7.99 *(978-0-451-23362-2(X)*, Signet) Penguin Group (USA) Inc.
—Sydney Omarr's Day-by-Day Astrological Guide for the Year 2012 - Aries. 2011 (ENG.). 320p. (gr. 12). 7.99 *(978-0-451-23365-3(4)*, Signet) Penguin Group (USA) Inc.
—Sydney Omarr's Day-by-Day Astrological Guide for the Year 2012 - Leo. 2011. (ENG.). 320p. (gr. 12). 7.99 *(978-0-451-23368-4(9)*, Signet) Penguin Group (USA) Inc.
—Sydney Omarr's Day-by-Day Astrological Guide for the Year 2012 - Libra. 2011. (ENG.). 320p. (gr. 12). 7.99 *(978-0-451-23370-7(0)*, Signet) Penguin Group (USA) Inc.
—Sydney Omarr's Day-by-Day Astrological Guide for the Year 2012 - Sagittarius. 2011. (ENG.). 320p. 7.99 *(978-0-451-23373-8(5)*, Signet) Penguin Group (USA) Inc.
—Sydney Omarr's Day-by-Day Astrological Guide for the Year 2012 - Taurus. 2011. (ENG.). 320p. (gr. 12). 7.99 *(978-0-451-23364-6(6)*, Signet) Penguin Group (USA) Inc.
Macphail, Jamie. Astrology & the Causes of War. 2006. pap. *(978-1-902405-19-3(6))* Wessex Astrologer Ltd., The.
MacPherson, Johanna. The Way of the Zodiac: A Guide to Health & Well-Bieng using Astrology. 2011. 120p. pap. 19.99 ***(978-1-4653-5014-5(4))*** Xlibris Corp.
Maerz, John. TAROT: the Astrological Layout. 2009. 90p. pap. 14.99 *(978-0-557-20251-5(5))* Lulu Enterprises Inc.
Magnus, Hugo. Superstition in Medicine. 2009. 220p. 23.99 *(978-1-103-01593-1(1))*; pap. 17.99 *(978-1-103-01583-7(5))* BiblioBazaar.
—Superstition in Medicine. Salinger, Julius L., tr. 2007. (ENG.). 216p. 39.95 *(978-0-548-08709-1(1))* Kessinger Publishing, LLC.
Mancuso, P. Shabbatai Donnolo's Sefer Hakhmoni: Introduction, Critical Text, & Annotated English Translation. 2009. (Studies in Jewish History & Culture Ser.). 432p. *(978-90-04-16762-9(5))* BRILL.
Manning, Marguerite. Cosmic Karma: Understanding Your Contract with the Universe. 2007. (ENG.). 216p. per. 15.95 *(978-0-7387-1054-9(7))* Llewellyn Pubns.
March, Marion D. & McEvers, Joan. The Only Way to Learn Astrology. 2nd ed. 2008. (Illus.). *(978-1-934976-03-6(2))*; pap. *(978-1-934976-01-2(6))*; ***(978-1-934976-04-3(0))***; ***(978-1-934976-05-0(9))***; ***(978-1-934976-06-7(7))*** ACS Pubns.
March, Marion D., et al. The Only Way to Learn Astrology. 3rd ed. 2009. (Illus.). *(978-1-934976-02-9(4))* ACS Pubns.
Marks, Tracy. Art of Chart Interpretation: A Step-by-Step Method for Analyzing, Synthesizing, & Understanding the Birth Chart. 2008. (ENG., Illus.). 1p. pap. 15.95 *(978-0-89254-142-3(3))* Nicolas-Hays, Inc.
—Astrology of Self-Discovery: An In-Depth Exploration of the Potentials Revealed in Your Birth Chart. 2008. (ENG.). 1p. pap. 18.95 *(978-0-89254-136-2(9))* Nicolas-Hays, Inc.
—Your Secret Self: Illuminating the Mysteries of the Twelfth House. rev. ed. 2010. (ENG., Illus.). 1p. (Orig.). pap. 24.95 *(978-0-89254-161-4(X))* Nicolas-Hays, Inc.
Martin Davis Staff. From Here to There. 2007. pap. *(978-1-902405-27-8(7))* Wessex Astrologer Ltd., The.
Massey, Anne. Venus: Her Cycles, Symbols & Myths. 2006. (Special Topics in Astrology Ser.: 5). (ENG., Illus.). 264p. pap. 17.95 *(978-0-7387-0991-8(3))* Llewellyn Pubns.
Mata, Tara. Astrological World Cycles - Original First Edition, Copyright 1933. 2008. 100p. pap. 11.50 *(978-0-615-18500-2(2))* Noble New, The.
Mathis, Holiday. Rock Your Stars: Your Astrological Guide to Getting It All. 2007. (ENG., Illus.). 220p. per. 15.95 *(978-1-58005-217-7(7))* Seal Pr.
Maury, L. -F -Alfred. La Magie et l'Astrologie dans l'Antiquité et au Moyen #194;ge: Ou, #201;tude sur les Superstitions Pa#239;ennes que se sont Perpétuées Jusqu'a Nos Jours. 2011. (Cambridge Library Collection - Spiritualism & Esoteric Knowlege Ser.). (FRE.). 460p. pap. 34.99 *(978-1-108-07306-6(9))* Cambridge Univ. Pr.
Maxwell-Stuart, P. G. Astrology: From Ancient Babylon to the Present Day. 2010. (ENG., Illus.). 288p. 29.95 *(978-1-84868-107-1(0))* Amberley Publishing GBR. Dist: Casemate Pubs. & Bk. Distributors, LLC.
Maynard, Jim. Astrologer's Datebook 2012: An Astrological Week-at-a-Glance Engagement Calendar. 2011. (Illus.). 176p. pap. 8.95 ***(978-1-935482-17-8(3))*** Quicksilver Productions.
—Celestial Guide 2012: An Astrological Week-at-a-Glance Engagement Calendar. 2011. (Illus.). 176p. spiral bd. 11.95 ***(978-1-935482-16-1(5))*** Quicksilver Productions.
—Pocket Astrologer 2012 Eastern Time: An Astrological Almanac, Ephemeris & Calendar. 2011. (Illus.). 64p. 6.95 ***(978-1-935482-14-7(9))*** Quicksilver Productions.
—Pocket Astrologer 2012 Pacific Time: An Astrological Almanac, Ephemeris & Calendar. 2011. (Illus.). 64p. 6.95 ***(978-1-935482-15-4(7))*** Quicksilver Productions.
Mayo, Margaret. Our Fate & the Zodiac. 2006. (ENG.). pap. 14.25 *(978-1-59605-914-6(1)*, Cosimo Classics) Cosimo, Inc.
McBroom, Don. Midpoints: Identify & Integrate Midpoints into Horoscope Synthesis. 2007. (Special Topics in Astrology Ser.: 8). (ENG., Illus.). 240p. per. 19.95 *(978-0-7387-0983-3(2))* Llewellyn Pubns.
McCaffery, Ellen. Graphic Astrology: The Astrological Home Study Course. 2007. (ENG.). 318p. 45.95 *(978-0-548-08045-0(3))* Kessinger Publishing, LLC.
McGerr, Angela. The Angel Almanac: An Inspirational Guide to Healing & Harmony. 2008. (Illus.). 256p. 19.95 incl. audio compact disk *(978-1-84400-640-3(9))* Quadrille Publishing, Ltd. GBR. Dist: Ingram Pub. Services.
McGriff, Jennye. Bits of Stardust. 2011. 62p. 36.95 ***(978-1-258-06671-0(8))*** Literary Licensing, LLC.
Mcwhirter, Louise. Mcwhirter Theory of Stock Market Forecasting. 2008. 208p. pap. 39.95 *(978-0-86690-585-5(5))*, American Federation of Astrologers, Inc.
Mercado, Walter. El Mundo Secreto de Walter Mercado. 2010. (SPA & ENG.). 512p. pap. 16.99 *(978-0-06-178005-9(7)*, Rayo) HarperCollins Pubs.
Michell, John & Sweetman, John. The Dambusters. 2013. (ENG., Illus.). 288p. pap. 15.95 *(978-0-349-12323-3(3))* Little, Brown Bk. Group Ltd. GBR. Dist: Independent Pubs. Group.
Michelsen, Neil. The American Heliocentric Ephemeris 2001-2050. 2007. 312p. per. 34.95 *(978-0-9762422-5-3(7))* Starcrafts LLC.
—The American Sidereal Ephemeris 2001-2025. 2007. 312p. per. 32.95 *(978-0-9762422-6-0(5))* Starcrafts LLC.
—Tables of Planetary Phenomen. 2007. 260p. per. 32.95 *(978-0-9762422-4-6(9))* Starcrafts LLC.
Michelsen, Neil & Pottenger, Rique. The American Ephemeris 1950 - 2050 at Noon: Trans-Century Edition. 2011. 624p. pap. 29.95 ***(978-1-934976-27-2(X))*** Starcrafts LLC.
Michelsen, Neil F. & Pottenger, Rique. The Michelsen Book of Tables. 2nd ed. 2009. 174p. ***(978-1-934976-12-8(1))*** ACS Pubns.
Miller, Laurel. Astro-Psychology. 2006. pap. 14.75 *(978-1-59605-915-3(X)*, Cosimo Classics) Cosimo, Inc.
Milligan, V. A. Astrological Birthday Readings and, Book. 2006. pap. 16.95 *(978-1-59605-895-8(1)*, Cosimo Classics) Cosimo, Inc.
Milovidov, Grigorii. Energiia Zhizni V Tvolkh Rukakh: Ezotericheskaia Anatomiia I Fiziologiia Cheloveka, Znakomstvo S Ezotericheskoi Astrologiei I Khirologiei Mudry. 2008. (RUS., Illus.). v, 315p. pap. *(978-0-9791791-9-8(X))* Seagul Pr.
Mitton, Jacqueline. The Zodiac: Celestial Circle of the Sun. 2008. (ENG., Illus.). 40p. (J). pap. 7.95 *(978-1-84507-279-7(0))* Lincoln, Frances Ltd. GBR. Dist: Perseus-PGW.
Mitz, Phyllis F. Astrology's Secrets to Hot Romance: How to Find True Compatibility & the One Who's Right for You. 2007. (ENG., Illus.). 531p. pap. 15.95 *(978-0-7573-0490-3(7))* Health Communications, Inc.
Monaghan, Patricia. Das Buro-Orakel. (GER.). *(978-3-612-26721-4(3))* Econ-Verlag GmbH DEU. Dist: International Bk. Import Service, Inc.
Moore, Francis. Aquarius. 2008. (ENG.). 160p. pap. 6.95 *(978-0-572-03460-3(1))* Foulsham, W. Co., Ltd. GBR. Dist: APG Sales & Distribution Services.
—Aries. 2008. (ENG.). 160p. pap. 6.95 *(978-0-572-03462-7(8))* Foulsham, W. Co., Ltd. GBR. Dist: APG Sales & Distribution Services.
—Capricorn. 2008. (ENG.). 160p. pap. 6.95 *(978-0-572-03471-9(7))* Foulsham, W. Co., Ltd. GBR. Dist: APG Sales & Distribution Services.
—Gemini. 2008. (ENG.). 160p. pap. 6.95 *(978-0-572-03464-1(4))* Foulsham, W. Co., Ltd. GBR. Dist: APG Sales & Distribution Services.
—Leo. 2008. (ENG.). 160p. pap. 6.95 *(978-0-572-03466-5(0))* Foulsham, W. Co., Ltd. GBR. Dist: APG Sales & Distribution Services.
—Libra. 2008. (ENG.). 160p. pap. 6.95 *(978-0-572-03468-9(7))* Foulsham, W. Co., Ltd. GBR. Dist: APG Sales & Distribution Services.
—Old Moore's 2008 Astral Diaries: Cancer. 2007. (ENG.). 1p. 5.95 *(978-0-572-03353-8(2))* Foulsham, W. Co., Ltd. GBR. Dist: APG Sales & Distribution Services.
—Old Moore's 2008 Astral Diaries: Scorpio. 2007. (ENG.). 1p. 5.95 *(978-0-572-03357-6(5))* Foulsham, W. Co., Ltd. GBR. Dist: APG Sales & Distribution Services.
—Old Moore's 2008 Astral Diaries: Virgo. 2007. (ENG.). 1p. 5.95 *(978-0-572-03355-2(9))* Foulsham, W. Co., Ltd. GBR. Dist: APG Sales & Distribution Services.
—Old Moore's 2012 Astral Diaries: Aries. 2011. (ENG.). 160p. pap. 6.95 ***(978-0-572-03652-2(3))*** Foulsham, W. Co., Ltd. GBR. Dist: APG Sales & Distribution Services.
—Old Moore's Horoscope & Daily Astral Diary 2005: Capricorn. 189p. *(978-0-572-02993-7(4))* Foulsham, W. Co., Ltd.
—Old Moore's Horoscope: Sagittarius: November 23-December 21. 2007. (Old Moore's Horoscope & Astral Diary Ser.). (ENG., Illus.). 1p. per. 5.95 *(978-0-572-03358-3(3))* Foulsham, W. Co., Ltd. GBR. Dist: APG Sales & Distribution Services.
—Pisces. 2008. (ENG.). 160p. pap. 6.95 *(978-0-572-03461-0(X))* Foulsham, W. Co., Ltd. GBR. Dist: APG Sales & Distribution Services.
—Sagittarius. 2008. (ENG.). 160p. pap. 6.95 *(978-0-572-03470-2(9))* Foulsham, W. Co., Ltd. GBR. Dist: APG Sales & Distribution Services.
—Sagittarius. pap. 2.95 Grand Central Publishing.
—Scorpio. 2008. (ENG.). 160p. pap. 6.95 *(978-0-572-03469-6(5))* Foulsham, W. Co., Ltd. GBR. Dist: APG Sales & Distribution Services.

A

—Taurus. 2008. (ENG.). 160p. pap. 6.95 (978-0-572-03463-4(6)) Foulsham, W. Co., Ltd. GBR. Dist: APG Sales & Distribution Services.

Moorey, Teresa. Sex Signs: Beginners Guide. (Illus.). iv, 107p. pap. 11.95 (978-0-340-73066-9(8), Hodder & Stoughton) Hodder General Publishing Div. GBR. Dist: Trafalgar Square Publishing.

Morel, John Henry. The Astrology of Man. 2009. 80p. pap. 24.99 (978-1-935436-55-3(4)) Rodaian Pr.

Morin, Jean-Baptiste. Astrologia Gallica Book. Holden, James Herschel, tr. 2008. 144p. pap. 21.95 (978-0-86690-583-1(9)); 168p. pap. 21.95 (978-0-86690-582-4(0)) American Federation of Astrologers, Inc.

—Astrologia Gallica Book 25. Holden, James Herschel, tr. 2008. 260p. pap. 24.95 (978-0-86690-584-8(7)) American Federation of Astrologers, Inc.

—Astrologia Gallica Books 13, 14, 15. Holden, James, tr. 2007. 308p. per. 24.95 (978-0-86690-571-8(5)) American Federation of Astrologers, Inc.

Morningstar, Sally. Astrology & Fortune Telling: Including Tarot, Palmistry, I Ching & Dream Interpretation. (ENG., Illus.). 2011. 264p. pap. 12.99 **(978-1-78019-039-6(5))** 2010. 256p. pap. 24.99 (978-1-84476-921-6(6)) Anness Publishing GBR. Dist: National Bk. Network.

Morris, Grace K. How to Choose Stocks to Out Perform the Market 2008. 2007. 100p. 80.00 (978-0-9673224-8-3(0)) Astro Economics, Inc.

—How to Choose Stocks to Outperform the Market 2007. 2006. 90p. 80.00 (978-0-9673224-7-6(2)) Astro Economics, Inc.

Mosbakk, Brynjar. Forecast & trade the financial markets. Patterns. Leaders. the business Cycle. 2008. 96p. pap. 48.96 (978-1-84753-612-9(3)) Lulu Enterprises Inc.

Mother Tongue Ink Staff, ed. We'Moon '01: Gaia Rhythms for Womyn. Date not set. 240p. spiral bd. 15.95 (978-1-890931-07-0(1)) Mother Tongue Ink.

Mott, Francis J. The Meaning of the Zodiac 1941. 2007. (ENG.). 234p. 41.95 (978-0-548-05357-7(X)) Kessinger Publishing, LLC.

Muir, Ada. The Book of the Nodes & the Part of Fortune: Astrology & Health, No. 4. 2011. 50p. 35.95 **(978-1-258-04400-8(5))** Literary Licensing, LLC.

Murray, Don. Astrology. 2010. 166p. pap. 19.99 (978-1-4535-3465-6(2)) Xlibris Corp.

Naiman, Ingrid. Lunar Consciousness. 2nd ed. Date not set. 120p. pap. 25.00 (978-1-882834-00-6(3)) Seventh Ray Pr.

Naylor, R. H. Astrology Reveals How the Stars Can Guide You to the Right Jobs - 2006. pap. 12.95 (978-1-4304-1462-9(6)) Kessinger Publishing, LLC.

—Astrology Reveals What Type of Woman Makes the Best Wife - 2006. pap. 9.95 (978-1-4304-1460-5(X)) Kessinger Publishing, LLC.

Neugebauer, Otto & Van Hoesen, H. B. Greek Horoscopes. 2011. 242p. 46.95 **(978-1-258-02359-1(8))** Literary Licensing, LLC.

Newman, Paul. Declination in Astrology. 2006. (Illus.). 198p. pap. (978-1-902405-22-3(6)) Wessex Astrologer Ltd., The.

Neylon, Margaret. Perfect Timing: How to Make the Right Decisions at the Right Time. 2011. 98p. pap. 10.50 **(978-1-60976-848-5(5)**, Eloquent Bks.) AEG Literary Publishing Services, Inc.

Nichols, Steve. The Hellenic Mystery Tarot of Hermes. 2009. 88p. pap. 51.50 (978-1-4092-3758-7(3)) Lulu Enterprises Inc.

Noel, Kristie. How to Have a Harmonious Workforce? A Quick Reference & Survival Guide for Ev. 2011. 78p. 24.99 **(978-1-4628-6182-8(2))**; pap. 15.99 **(978-1-4628-6181-1(4))** Xlibris Corp.

Nordhaus-Bike, Anne M. Follow the Sun: A Simple Way to Use Astrology for Living in Harmony. 2011. 112p. pap. 39.95 **(978-1-4567-5931-5(0))** AuthorHouse.

North, John D. Cosmos: An Illustrated History of Astronomy & Cosmology. 2008. (Illus.). 736p. pap. 39.00 (978-0-226-59441-5(6)) Univ. of Chicago Pr.

Nunn, Richard. Cosmic Guessing. 2008. 54p. pap. 13.95 (978-1-84799-283-3(8)) Lulu Enterprises Inc.

Oestmann, Günther, et al, eds. Horoscopes & Public Spheres: Essays on the History of Astrology. (Religion & Society Ser.). (ENG., Illus.). VIII, 290p. 225.00 **(978-3-11-182831-2(X))** De Gruyter, Walter Inc.

of Carinthia, Hermann. The Search of the Heart: Consultation Charts, Interpreting Thoughts & Calculating Victors in Traditional Astrology. Dykes, Benjamin, tr. 2011. (Illus.). 240p. pap. 24.99 (978-1-934586-18-1(8)) Cazimi Pr., The.

Ohotto, Robert. Transforming Fate into Destiny: A New Dialogue with Your Soul. 2008. (ENG.). 240p. per. 14.95 (978-1-4019-1155-3(2)) Hay Hse., Inc.

Oken, Alan. Alan Oken's Complete Astrology: The Classic Guide to Modern Astrology. 2006. (ENG., Illus.). 1p. per. 29.95 (978-0-89254-125-6(3)) Nicolas-Hays, Inc.

—Houses of the Horoscope: An Introduction. 2009. (ENG.). 1p. pap. 15.95 (978-0-89254-156-0(3)) Nicolas-Hays, Inc.

—Rulers of the Horoscope. 2008. (ENG., Illus.). 1p. pap. 19.95 (978-0-89254-135-5(0)) Nicolas-Hays, Inc.

—Soul-Centered Astrology: A Key to Your Expanding Self. 2008. (ENG., Illus.). 1p. pap. 22.95 (978-0-89254-134-8(2)) Nicolas-Hays, Inc.

Omarr, Sidney. Truth about Astrology. 2011. 52p. 36.95 **(978-1-258-05593-6(7))** Literary Licensing, LLC.

Ophira, Edut & Edut, Tali. Shoestrology: Discover Your Birthday Shoe. 2012. (ENG., Illus.). 384p. 17.95 **(978-0-307-98504-0(0)**, Potter Style) Crown Publishing Group.

Orion, Rae. Astrology for Dummies. 2nd rev. ed. 2007. (ENG., Illus.). 408p. per. 19.99 (978-0-470-09840-0(6), For Dummies) Wiley, John & Sons, Inc.

Ormsby, F. E., ed. Planets & People 1897. 2007. (ENG.). 432p. 51.95 (978-0-548-05349-2(9)) Kessinger Publishing, LLC.

Pagan, Isabelle M. From Pioneer to Poet or the Twelve Great Gates: An Expansion of the Signs of the Zodiac Analyzed. 2011. 342p. 51.95 **(978-1-258-02074-3(2))** Literary Licensing, LLC.

Palmer, Lynne. Astrological Almanac For 2007. 2006. 208p. pap. 20.00 (978-0-9709498-9-9(8)) Palmer, Lynne.

—Astrological Almanac for 2008. 2007. 208p. pap. 20.00 (978-0-9709498-3-7(9)) Palmer, Lynne.

Parker, Derek & Parker, Julia. Parker's Encyclopedia of Astrology: Everything You Ever Wanted to Know about Astrology. 2009. (ENG.). 320p. pap. 19.95 (978-1-905857-85-2(3), Watkins Publishing) Duncan Baird Pubs. GBR. Dist: Sterling Publishing Co., Inc.

Parker, E. & Goedhart, Coba. Astrology & Its Practical Application. 2010. 212p. 39.95 (978-1-161-35535-2(9)) Kessinger Publishing, LLC.

Parkyn, Chetan. Human Design: Discover the Person You Were Born to Be. 2010. (ENG., Illus.). 304p. pap. 24.95 (978-1-57731-941-2(9)) New World Library.

Paul, Lacquanna & Powell, Robert. Cosmic Dances of the Planets. 2006. pap. (978-1-59731-150-2(2)) Perennis, Sophia.

Payton, Michelle A. Birth Mix Patterns & Loving Relationships: Using Astrology, Numerology & Birth Order. 2007. 134p. pap. 12.95 (978-0-9719804-4-0(6)) Left Side, The.

Pearce, Alfred. The Text-Book of Astrology. 2006. 516p. 44.95 (978-0-86690-560-2(X)) American Federation of Astrologers, Inc.

Perkins, Elizabeth. Star Guide to Guys: How to Live Happily with Him... or Without Him. 2007. (ENG., Illus.). 240p. per. 12.95 (978-0-7387-0954-3(9)) Llewellyn Pubns.

Perry, Wendell C. Saturn Cycles: Mapping Changes in Your Life. 2009. (ENG., Illus.). 336p. pap. 27.95 (978-0-7387-1493-6(3)) Llewellyn Pubns.

Petulengro, Claire. Life Signs: Let the Power of the Stars Guide You to Success. (ENG., Illus.). 2010. 352p. pap. 11.95 (978-0-330-46064-4(1)) 2009. 320p. pap. 19.95 (978-0-330-46063-7(3)) Macmillan Pubs., Ltd. GBR. Dist: Independent Pubs. Group.

Phelps, J. R. Birthday Horoscopes. 2007. 156p. 24.95 (978-1-4344-9610-2(4)); per. 14.95 (978-1-4344-9609-6(0)) Wildside Pr., LLC.

Phuvanatnaranubala, Thirachai. Know Your Future: Thai Astrology Step by Step. 2010. (ENG., Illus.). 280p. pap. 22.95 (978-1-84694-340-9(X)) Hunt, John Publishing Ltd. GBR. Dist: National Bk. Network.

Place, Robert. Astrology & Divination. Gulley, Rosemary, ed. 2008. (Mysteries, Legends, & Unexplained Phenomena Ser.). 136p. (gr. 6-12). pap. 10.95 (978-1-60413-315-8(5), Checkmark Bks.) Facts On File, Inc.

Popescu, Andrei. Astropsychology of Human Birthdates, Social Metaphysics of Frustrations & Blood Groups: Connections with the astrological signs of the Zodiac. 2010. (Illus.). 552p. pap. 23.49 (978-1-4389-8501-5(0)) AuthorHouse.

Pottenger, Milton A. How All of Our Thoughts, Acts, & Deeds Are Forever Recorded In. 2006. pap. 9.95 (978-1-4304-1741-5(2)) Kessinger Publishing, LLC.

—A Qabalistic Chart & How Geometry & Masonry Are One - 2006. pap. 9.95 (978-1-4304-1742-2(0)) Kessinger Publishing, LLC.

—Symbolism of the Four Great Emblems & the Esoteric Meaning Of. 2006. pap. 9.95 (978-1-4304-1743-9(9)) Kessinger Publishing, LLC.

Pottenger, Rique. The Asteroid Ephemeris 1900 to 2050. 2008. 220p. pap. 26.95 (978-1-934976-00-5(8)) Starcrafts LLC.

—The New American Ephemeris for the 20th Century, 1900-2000 at Midnight. 2008. 620p. pap. 29.95 (978-0-9762422-9-1(X)) Starcrafts LLC.

—The New American Ephemeris for the 21st Century, 2000-2100 at Midnight: Michelsen Memorial Edition. 2006. (Illus.). 624p. per. 29.95 (978-0-9762422-3-9(0)) Starcrafts LLC.

Pottenger, Rique & Michelsen, Neil. The New American Midpoint Ephemeris 2006-2020. 2007. 188p. per. 21.95 (978-0-9762422-7-7(3)) Starcrafts LLC.

Powell, Robert. The Sign of the Son of Man in Heaven: Sophia & the New Star Wisdom. 2007. (978-1-59731-161-8(8)); pap. (978-1-59731-159-5(6)) Perennis, Sophia.

Powell, Robert & Dann, Kevin. The Astrological Revolution: Unveiling the Science of the Stars as a Science of Reincarnation & Karma, 1 vol. 2010. (ENG., Illus.). 234p. pap. 25.00 (978-1-58420-083-3(9), Lindisfarne Bks.) SteinerBooks, Inc.

Powell, Robert A. Hermetic Astrology: Towards a New Wisdom of the Stars. 2nd ed. 2006. (978-1-59731-156-4(1)); (978-1-59731-158-8(8)); (978-1-59731-155-7(3)); (978-1-59731-157-1(X)) Perennis, Sophia.

Powers, Kathleen. Using Astrology to Find your Luck159: What Works? 2008. 159p. pap. 19.99 (978-1-893012-01-1(8)) Newage Enterprises Worldwide.

Ramesey, William. Astrologia Restaurata: Astrology Restored, 4 vols., Set. Wiggers, Carol A., ed. Cochran, Kathleen R., tr. Incl. Vol. 1. 39p. pap. 15.00 (978-1-878935-30-4(5)); Vol. 2. 72p. pap. 15.00 (978-1-878935-31-1(3)); Vol. 3. 90p. pap. 15.00 (978-1-878935-32-8(1)); Vol. 4. 141p. pap. 30.00 (978-1-878935-33-5(X)); (Illus.). 1996. 75.00 (978-1-878935-34-2(8)) JustUs & Assocs.

Randall, Sidney. The Abc of the Old Science of Astrology. 2006. pap. 12.95 (978-1-59605-920-7(6), Cosimo Classics) Cosimo, Inc.

Raphael. Raphaels Ephemeris 2009. 2008. (ENG.). 48p. 8.95 (978-0-572-03404-7(0)) Foulsham, W. Co., Ltd. GBR. Dist: APG Sales & Distribution Services.

—Raphaels Ephemeris 2010: Astronomical Ephemeris of the Planets' Places for 2010. Foulsham Publishers Staff, ed. 2009. (ENG.). 120p. 8.95 (978-0-572-03496-2(2)) Foulsham, W. Co., Ltd. GBR. Dist: APG Sales & Distribution Services.

Raphael. Raphael's Famous Key to Astrology. 2011. 120p. 39.95 **(978-1-258-03828-1(5))** Literary Licensing, LLC.

Raphael, David, et al. Raphael's Private Instructions in Genethliacal Astrology: Adapted for Those Advanced in the Study of Astrology. 2011. 62p. 36.95 **(978-1-258-04074-1(3))** Literary Licensing, LLC.

Raphael, Edwin. Raphaels Ephemeris 2008. 2007. (ENG.). 48p. pap. 8.95 (978-0-572-03298-2(6)) Foulsham, W. Co., Ltd. GBR. Dist: APG Sales & Distribution Services.

Regulous Astrology LLC. A Rectification Manual: The American Presidency. 2007. 796p. pap. 59.95 (978-0-9801856-0-7(2)) Regulus Astrology LLC.

Reid, Lori. Love Signs. 2007. (ENG., Illus.). 128p. 17.95 (978-1-84483-325-2(9)) Duncan Baird Pubs. GBR. Dist: Sterling Publishing Co., Inc.

—Sun Signs Moon Signs: Discover Your Destiny. 2009. (ENG., Illus.). 128p. pap. (978-1-84483-475-4(1)) Duncan Baird Pubs. GBR. Dist: Sterling Publishing Co., Inc.

Ricci, Sabra. Lobster for Leos, Cookies for Capricorns: An Astrology Lover's Cookbook. 2012. (ENG., Illus.). 288p. pap. 15.99 **(978-1-250-00213-6(3)**, St. Martin's Griffin) St. Martin's Pr.

Richardson, Alan AA. The Magician's Tables: A Complete Book of Correspondences. 2006. (ENG., Illus.). 320p. 27.95 (978-1-84181-235-9(8), Godsfield Press) Octopus Publishing Group GBR. Dist: Hachette Bk. Group.

Richmond, Arline L. The Checkers King: How Olney H Richmond Won the World. 2006. pap. 9.95 (978-1-4304-2016-3(2)) Kessinger Publishing, LLC.

—A Mysterious Tale: Olney H Richmond Tells How He Became a Member of the Magi. 2006. pap. 12.95 (978-1-4304-2017-0(0)) Kessinger Publishing, LLC.

Righter, Carroll. Astrology & You. 224p. 2010. 31.96 (978-1-163-38630-9(8)) 2007. (ENG.). 39.95 (978-0-548-07713-9(4)) Kessinger Publishing, LLC.

Riske, Kris Brandt. Llewellyn's Complete Book of Astrology: The Easy Way to Learn Astrology. 2007. (ENG., Illus.). 336p. per. 18.95 (978-0-7387-1071-6(7)) Llewellyn Pubns.

—Llewellyn's Complete Book of Predictive Astrology: The Easy Way to Predict Your Future. 2011. (ENG., Illus.). 288p. pap. 18.95 (978-0-7387-2755-4(5)) Llewellyn Pubns.

Rochberg, Francesca. The Heavenly Writing: Divination, Horoscopy, & Astronomy in Mesopotamian Culture. 2007. (ENG., Illus.). 360p. pap. 31.99 (978-0-521-71661-1(6)) Cambridge Univ. Pr.

Rodriguez, Felix. Love Astrology To Go Kit. 2008. 274p. pap. 12.95 (978-1-4199-8040-4(8)) Ellora's Cave Publishing, Inc.

Rohan "G-Money" Golding. Warrior Life. 2010. 108p. pap. 12.95 (978-1-4502-1058-4(9)) iUniverse, Inc.

Roig, Olga. El Arte de Echar las Cartas. (SPA.). 160p. (978-84-7927-502-0(2)) Robinbk., Ediciones S.L. ESP. Dist: Lectorum Pubns., Inc.

Rose, Edwin. Generational Patterns Using Astrology. 2011. (ENG.). 263p. pap. 24.95 (978-1-84694-446-8(5)) Hunt, John Publishing Ltd. GBR. Dist: National Bk. Network.

Rose, Sioux. Moon Dance: The Feminine Dimensions of Time. 2009. 316p. pap. 22.95 (978-1-4401-2839-4(1)) iUniverse, Inc.

Rosenbaum, Stephanie. The Astrology Cookbook: A Cosmic Guide to Feasts of Love. 2009. (ENG.). 128p. (gr. 9). pap. 16.95 (978-1-933149-26-4(4)) Manic D Pr.

Ross, Alex C. Astrology Understood, Mythology Explained 1946. 2007. (ENG.). 448p. 51.95 (978-0-548-05360-7(X)) Kessinger Publishing, LLC.

Royal-Holt, Lyssa & Priest, Keith. The Prism of Lyra: An Exploration of Human Galactic Heritage. 2011. 176p. pap. 16.95 **(978-1-891824-87-6(2))** Light Technology Publishing, LLC.

Rubino, Jennifer. As Different As Night & Day: A Complete Guide to Astrology. 2009. 76p. pap. 10.95 (978-1-4401-7455-1(5)) iUniverse, Inc.

Rudhyar, Dane. The Astrology of Transformation a Multilevel Approach. 230p. 14.00 (978-0-943358-49-9(3)) Aurora Pr., Inc.

—Gifts of the Spirit. 2007. (ENG.). 144p. 35.95 (978-0-548-07797-9(5)) Kessinger Publishing, LLC.

Ruiz. Interpreting Empty Houses. 2006. 208p. per. 19.95 (978-0-86690-569-5(3)) American Federation of Astrologers, Inc.

Ryan, Anita. Moon Goddess - Manifest Your Dreams. 2006. 88p. pap. 12.95 (978-1-84728-869-1(3)) Lulu Enterprises Inc.

Ryan, Michael A. A Kingdom of Stargazers: Astrology & Authority in the Late Medieval Crown of Aragon. 2011. 232p. 45.00 (978-0-8014-4984-0(7)) Cornell Univ. Pr.

Sachs, Robert. Nine Star Ki: Feng Shui Astrology for Deepening Self-Knowledge & Enhancing Relationships, Health, & Prosperity. 2008. 356p. pap. 22.95 (978-0-595-53139-4(3)) iUniverse, Inc.

Sakoian, Frances & Acker, Louis. The Transiting Planets. 2009. 264p. pap. 24.95 (978-0-86690-597-8(9)) American Federation of Astrologers, Inc.

Samso, Julio. Astronomy & Astrology in al-Andalus & the Maghrib. 2007. (Variorum Collected Studies). (Illus.). 382p. 170.00 (978-0-7546-5934-1(8)) Ashgate Publishing Co.

Santoni, Francis, et al. The Black Moon Book. 126p. pap. 12.00 (978-0-9629352-2-0(0)) Sum Pr.

Sasportas, Howard. The Gods of Change. 2007. (Illus.). vii, 321p. pap. (978-1-902405-25-4(0)) Wessex Astrologer Ltd., The.

Sasson, Gahl. Cosmic Navigator: Design Your Destiny with Astrology & Kabbalah. 2008. (ENG., Illus.). 1p. pap. 21.95 (978-1-57863-420-0(2), Weiser Bks.) Red Wheel/Weiser.

Schick, Tom. Major Tom's Tarot of Marseilles. 2007. (Illus.). pap. 24.95 (978-0-7643-2760-5(7)) Schiffer Publishing, Ltd.

Schiemenz, Siegfried. The Positions of Planets & the Human Spirit: The real background of astrology. 2008. 156p. pap. (978-3-8334-4335-0(9)) Books on Demand GmbH.

Scofield, Bruce. The Circuitry of the Self: Astrology & the Developmental Model. 192p. pap. 12.95 (978-0-9628031-7-8(0)) One Reed Pubns.

—Cómo Practicar la Astrología Maya: El Calendario Tzolkin y su Sendero en la Vida. 2009. (ENG.). 1p. pap. 19.95 (978-1-59477-300-6(9)) Inner Traditions International, Ltd.

Scofield, Bruce C. & Orr, Barry C. How to Practice Mayan Astrology: The Tzolkin Calendar & Your Life Path. 2006. (ENG., Illus.). 1p. per. 20.00 (978-1-59143-064-3(X)) Inner Traditions International, Ltd.

Scott, Randall. Christos Sun Meditations: Following the Eightfold Path Through the Decans of the Zodiac. 2009. pap. (978-1-59731-501-2(X)) Perennis, Sophia.

Sela, Shlomo, ed. Abraham Ibn Ezra the Book of Reasons: A Parallel Hebrew-English Critical Edition of the Two Versions of the Text. 2007. (Études Sur le Judaïsme Médiéval Ser.). 368p. (978-90-04-15764-4(6)) BRILL.

—Abraham Ibn Ezra's Sefer ha'Olam (Book of the World) A Parallel Hebrew English Critical Edition of the Two Versions of the Text (Abraham Ibn Era's Astrological Writings, Volume 2) 2009. (Études Sur le Judaïsme Médiéval Ser.). (ENG & HEB.). (978-90-04-17914-1(3)) BRILL.

Sellwood, Debbie. Centaury for Virgo Rock Rose for Pisces. 2007. (ENG., Illus.). 288p. pap. 19.95 (978-1-905398-13-3(1)) Polair Publishing GBR. Dist: SCB Distributors.

Sepharial. The Law of Values: An Exposition of the Primary Causes of Stock & Share Fluctuations. 2007. 56p. per. 12.95 (978-1-60206-108-8(4)) Cosimo, Inc.

—Law of Values; Silver Key; Arcana or Stock & Share Key. 2007. 144p. per. 19.95 (978-1-933303-22-2(0)) Astrology Ctr. Of America, The.

—Theory of Geodetic Equivalents in Relati. 2006. pap. 16.95 (978-1-4286-3816-7(4)) Kessinger Publishing, LLC.

Sette, Ray. The Planets Align So Rare: Twelve Dimensions to the Human Potential. 2006. (ENG.). 264p. 24.95 (978-1-59800-720-6(3)) Outskirts Pr., Inc.

Sette, Ray & DeCarlo, Carlo. The Planets Align So Rare: Twelve Dimensions to the Human Potential. 2007. (ENG.). 264p. per. 19.95 (978-1-59800-928-6(1)) Outskirts Pr., Inc.

Seva, Blissful P. The Hindu Book of Astrology. 2006. pap. 13.95 (978-1-59605-913-9(3), Cosimo Classics) Cosimo, Inc.

Seward, Alfred. Humanity & the Zodiac. 2006. pap. 15.95 (978-1-59605-899-6(4), Cosimo Classics) Cosimo, Inc.

Shesso, Renna. A Magical Tour of the Night Sky: Use the Planets & Stars for Personal & Sacred Discovery. 2011. (ENG.). 1p. pap. 19.95 (978-1-57863-495-8(4), Weiser Bks.) Red Wheel/Weiser.

Shiozawa, Fumio. Divining the Asian Zodiac: Ancient Guide to Life & Love. 2007. (ENG., Illus.). 128p. per. 18.95 (978-0-89346-949-8(1)) Heian International Publishing, Inc.

Simms, Maria Kay. Moon Tides, Soul Passages: Your Astrological Cycles for Personal & Spiritual Development. 2nd rev. exp. ed. 2006. (Illus.). xiv, 313p. per. 22.95 (978-0-9762422-1-5(4)) Starcrafts LLC.

Skinner, Stephen & Karr, Don. Liber Lunae: Book of the Moon & Sepher Ha-Levanah. 2012. (ENG.). 296p. 65.00 **(978-0-7387-3139-1(0))** Llewellyn Pubns.

Slozberg, Miriam. Stars Behind the Tortured Soul. 2011. 336p. pap. 18.95 **(978-1-935340-76-8(X))** Worthy Shorts.

Sparke, Maggie. The Tarot a Channel. 2009. (Illus.). 92p. pap. 30.49 (978-1-4389-2346-8(5)) AuthorHouse.

Spencer, Katharine Q. The Zodiac Looks Westward: A Complete History of the World as Written in the Stars 1943. 2007. (ENG.). 118p. 34.95 (978-0-548-05362-1(6)) Kessinger Publishing, LLC.

Spiller, Jan. Cosmic Love: Secrets of the Astrology of Intimacy Revealed. 2007. (ENG., Illus.). 480p. pap. 18.00 (978-0-553-38311-9(6), Bantam) Random House Publishing Group.

Spiller, Jan & McCoy, Karen. Spiritual Astrology: A Path to Divine Awakening. 2010. (ENG., Illus.). 448p. pap. 16.00 (978-1-4165-9951-7(7), Touchstone) Touchstone.

Spirit, Free. 2012 Meeting the Star Beings the Healing of Humanity. 2010. (ENG.). 308p. pap. 14.00 (978-1-4538-0494-0(3)) CreateSpace.

Star, Sharita. It's All in the Name: The Hidden Power within Words. 2011. 308p. pap. 18.00 **(978-0-9831984-0-6(3))** Portal Bks.

Star Wolf, Linda. Shamanic Egyptian Astrology. 2010. (ENG.). 1p. pap. 16.00 (978-1-59143-113-8(1)) Bear & Co.

St.Clair, Michael. LIGHT-SEEDS Futures of Planet Earth. 2008. 580p. 51.61 (978-1-4092-0386-5(7)) Lulu Enterprises Inc.

Stubbs, Chris. When Scorpio Ruled the World. 2011. 180p. pap. **(978-1-4269-6028-4(X))** Trafford Publishing (UK) Ltd.

Stubbs, David. Our Birth on Earth. 2009. 100p. pap. 14.99 (978-1-4251-8588-6(6)) Trafford Publishing.

Suskin, Rod. Synastry: Understanding the Astrology of Relationships. 2008. (ENG., Illus.). 264p. per. 21.95 (978-0-7387-1255-0(8)) Llewellyn Pubns.

Sutton, Komilla. Personal Panchanga & the Five Sources of Light. 2007. (Illus.). 208p. per. (978-1-902405-26-1(9)) Wessex Astrologer Ltd., The.

Swami Ram Charran. 100 Year Patra: Vedic Charts, Life Paths, Life Cycles & Planetary Tracking. 2009. 828p. pap. 99.99 (978-1-4389-2189-1(6)) AuthorHouse.

T., Kiki. The Celestial Sexpot's Handbook: Astrological Tips for Satisfying Seduction & Ultimate Love. 2007. (ENG.). 320p. per. 14.99 (978-0-446-69695-1(1)) Grand Central Publishing.

Tamas, Richard. Cosmos & Psyche: Intimations of a New World View. 2007. (ENG., Illus.). 592p. (gr. 12-18). pap. 20.00 *(978-0-452-28859-1(2)*, Plume) Penguin Group (USA) Inc.
Teal, Celeste. Lunar Nodes: Discover Your Soul's Karmic Mission. 2008. (ENG., Illus.). 240p. pap. 27.95 *(978-0-7387-1337-3(6))* Llewellyn Pubns.
—Predicting Events with Astrology. 2009. (ENG.). 360p. pap. 26.95 *(978-0-7387-1553-7(0))* Llewellyn Pubns.
Tebbs, Carol A. The Complete Book of Chart Rectification. 2008. (ENG., Illus.). 240p. pap. 34.95 *(978-0-7387-1308-3(2))* Llewellyn Pubns.
Tenzin-Dolma, Lisa. Take Control with Astrology. 3rd ed. 2010. (Teach Yourself: Health & New Age Ser.). (ENG.). 224p. pap. 14.95 *(978-0-07-166504-9(8)*, 0071665048) McGraw-Hill Cos., The.
Terry, Gisele. The Progressed Moon Around the Zodiac. 2011. 128p. pap. 22.95 ***(978-0-86690-617-3(7))*** American Federation of Astrologers, Inc.
Thompson, Gerry Maguire & Thompson, Gerry. Sudoku Astrology: Creating Happiness & Succeeding in Love, Sex, & Relationships. 2009. (ENG., Illus.). 144p. pap. 9.95 *(978-1-4027-5136-3(2))* Sterling Publishing Co., Inc.
Tresemer, David. The Venus Eclipse of the Sun: A Rare Celestial Event, 1 vol. 2011. (ENG.). 172p. pap. 15.00 ***(978-1-58420-074-1(X)***, Lindisfarne Bks.) SteinerBooks, Inc.
Tsuji, Mariko. Go Beyond 22: The Adventure in the Cosmic Library. 2009. 227p. pap. 14.95 *(978-1-934140-04-8(X))* Natural Spirit Internation Inc.
Tucker, William J. The Principles of Scientific Astrology 1938. 2007. (ENG.). 326p. 45.95 *(978-0-548-05363-8(4))* Kessinger Publishing, LLC.
Turi, Louis. And God Created the Stars. 384p. 30.00 *(978-0-9667312-7-9(1))* Startheme Pubns.
—Beyond the Secret. 2007. 372p. per. 30.00 *(978-0-9745209-3-3(4))* Startheme Pubns.
—I Know All about You. 248p. 25.00 *(978-0-9667312-4-8(7))* Startheme Pubns.
Valby, Mary. The Quotable Capricorn: Capricorn Traits Described by Capricorns. 2011. (ENG.). 224p. pap. 12.95 ***(978-1-936998-10-4(6))*** Quotable Zodiac Publishing.
—The Quotable Libra: Libra Traits Described by Librans. 2011. (ENG.). 224p. pap. 12.95 ***(978-1-936998-07-4(6))*** Quotable Zodiac Publishing.
—The Quotable Sagittarius: Sagittarius Traits Described by Sagittarians. 2011. (ENG.). 224p. pap. 12.95 ***(978-1-936998-09-8(2)***, Quotable Zodiac Publishing.
—The Quotable Scorpio: Scorpio Traits Described by Scorpios. 2011. (ENG.). 224p. pap. 12.95 ***(978-1-936998-08-1(4))*** Quotable Zodiac Publishing.
Valentin Brenda. Astrología: Una Guía Simple para el éxito Personal y el Autoconocimiento. 2006. (SPA., Illus.). 192p. per. 10.95 *(978-0-7387-0993-2(X)*, Llewellyn Espanol) Llewellyn Pubns.
Valeria, Andrea. El Sexo y las Estrellas: Armoniza Cósmicamente tu Relación de Pareja. 2009. (SPA.). 288p. pap. 14.99 *(978-0-06-171363-7(5)*, Rayo) HarperCollins Pubs.
Van Norstrand, Frederic. Gabriel, Angel of Birth, of Dreams & Aspirations: The Influence of the Moon in the Twelve Signs of the Zodiac. 2011. 114p. 39.95 ***(978-1-258-02406-2(3))*** Literary Licensing, LLC.
Van Wingerden, Bastiaan & van Wingerden, Bastiaan. The Northern Moon Node: The Message from the Beyond. 2008. 441p. 29.95 *(978-90-807155-4-7(9))* Lilalith uitgeverij NLD. Dist: AtlasBooks Distribution.
Vega, Phyllis. Erotic Astrology: The Sex Secrets of Your Horoscope Revealed. 2009. (ENG.). 256p. pap. 12.95 *(978-1-60550-056-0(9))* Adams Media Corp.
—Lovestrology: Astonishingly Accurate Romantic Profiles & Compatibility Matchups for Every Birthday. 2007. (ENG., Illus.). 512p. per. 19.95 *(978-1-59233-235-9(8)*, 1592332358, Fair Winds Press) Quayside.
—What Your Birthday Reveals about You: 366 Days of Astonishingly Accurate Revelations about Your Future, Your Secrets, & Your Strengths. 2009. (ENG., Illus.). 480p. 12.99 *(978-0-7858-2238-7(0)*, 0785822380, Castle Bks., Inc.) Book Sales, Inc.
—What Your Birthday Reveals about Your Sex Life: Your Key to the Heavenly Sex Life You Were Born to Have. 2011. (ENG.). 384p. pap. 16.95 *(978-1-4405-0596-6(9))* Adams Media Corp.
Verdarluz. Codex of the Soul: Astrology, Archetypes, & Your Sacred Blueprint. 2012. (ENG., Illus.). 320p. pap. 18.95 ***(978-1-58394-449-3(4))*** North Atlantic Bks.
Vernar, Alexander & Swami Brahma. How to Know Your Future. reprint ed. pap. 2.00 *(978-0-911662-29-0(4))* Yoga Pubn. Society.
Vickers, A. S. The Cosmic Key of Life: Self Realization 1930. 2007. (ENG.). 216p. 39.95 *(978-0-548-05578-6(5))* Kessinger Publishing, LLC.
Vickers, Roderic & Lee, Tom. For Love of the Stars. Date not set. 44p. pap. 8.95 *(978-1-886956-04-9(9))* Star Concepts, Ltd.
Vitale, Judi. Babystrology: The Astrological Guide to Your Little Star. 2012. (ENG.). 224p. 15.95 ***(978-1-4405-3888-9(3))*** Adams Media Corp.
Vitale, Judi. Lovecasts: The Astrological Guide to Finding Lasting Love. 2010. (ENG.). 304p. pap. 14.95 *(978-1-4405-1101-1(2))* Adams Media Corp.
Vorel, Iris. Be Your Own Astrologer. 2007. (ENG.). 156p. 36.95 *(978-0-548-07717-7(7))* Kessinger Publishing, LLC.
Voss, Angela, ed. Marsilio Ficino. 2006. (Western Esoteric Masters Ser.). (ENG., Illus.). 272p. pap. 18.95 *(978-1-55643-560-7(6))* North Atlantic Bks.
Vyvadil, Doris. Astrologie und kognitive Fähigkeiten: Naturwissenschaftliche Untersuchung zur Aussagekraft astrologischer Konstellationen. 2010. 300p. pap. *(978-3-639-22893-9(6))* VDM Verlag Dr. Mueller e.K.
Walther, Bridgett. Conquer the Cosmos: Use the Power of Astrology to Attract the Man, Money, & Happiness You Deserve. 2010. (ENG.). 272p. (gr. 12-18). 15.00 *(978-0-452-29585-8(8)*, Plume) Penguin Group (USA) Inc.
Warnock, Christopher. Mansions of the Moon: A Lunar Zodiac for Astrology & Magic. 2010. 194p. pap. 29.95 *(978-0-557-56078-3(0))* Lulu Enterprises Inc.
—Secrets of Planetary Magic 3rd Edition. 2010. 105p. pap. 19.95 *(978-0-557-36626-2(7))* Lulu Enterprises Inc.
Warnock, Christopher & Greer, John. Picatrix Books I & II: Astrological Magic. 2009. 140p. pap. 54.95 *(978-0-557-12899-0(4))* Lulu Enterprises Inc.
Warriar, P. Krishna, et al. 1994 Sidereal Astrological Almanac. Date not set. 118p. (Orig.). pap. 14.00 *(978-0-9618070-7-8(5))* Personal Insight Data Services.
—1995 Sidereal Astrological Almanac. Date not set. 118p. (Orig.). pap. 14.00 *(978-0-9618070-8-5(3))* Personal Insight Data Services.
Watters, Barbara H. Sex & the Outer Planets. 2010. 130p. pap. 19.95 *(978-0-86690-604-3(5))* American Federation of Astrologers, Inc.
Wedel, Theodore Otto. The Mediaeval Attitude Toward Astrology, Particularly in England. 2009. 178p. 37.95 *(978-1-104-67912-5(4))*; pap. 22.95 *(978-1-104-66152-6(7))* Kessinger Publishing, LLC.
Westman, Robert S. The Copernican Question: Prognostication, Skepticism, & Celestial Order. 2011. (ENG., Illus.). 720p. 95.00 *(978-0-520-25481-7(3))* Univ. of California Pr.
Weston, L. H. Fixed Stars in Astrology. 2006. pap. 19.95 *(978-1-4286-4378-9(8))* Kessinger Publishing, LLC.
White, Maya. Easy Astrology Oracle Cards: Unlock Your Inner Guide. 2008. (ENG.). 15.95 *(978-1-4019-2193-4(0))* Hay Hse., Inc.
White, Susanne. Astrology Advantage. Date not set. *(978-0-312-25257-1(9))* St. Martin's Pr.
White, Suzanne. The New Chinese Astrology. 2009. (ENG.). 624p. 27.99 *(978-0-312-58644-7(2)*, Dunne, Thomas Bks.) St. Martin's Pr.
Wildfeuer, Sherry. Stella Natura 2008: Working with Cosmic Rhythms: Inspiration & Practical Advice for Home Gardeners & Professional Growers. 2007. (Illus.). 40p. pap. 14.95 *(978-0-9795530-0-4(8))* Growing Biodynamics, LLC.
Williams, Mark. Fiery Shapes: Celestial Portents & Astrology in Ireland & Wales 650-1650. 2010. (ENG., Illus.). 256p. 110.00 *(978-0-19-957184-0(8))* Oxford Univ. Pr., Inc.
Wilson, William. Astrology: An Effort at Simplification 1928. 2007. (ENG.). 186p. 37.95 *(978-0-548-05457-4(6))* Kessinger Publishing, LLC.
Wolf, Stacey. Never Throw Rice at a Pisces: The Bride's Astrology Guide to Planning Your Wedding, Choosing Your Honeymoon, & Loving Every Second of It, No Matter What Your Sign. 2007. (ENG.). 256p. pap. 15.99 *(978-0-312-35918-8(7)*, St. Martin's Griffin) St. Martin's Pr.
Woolfolk, Joanna. Aquarius: Joanna Woolfolk's Sun Sign Series. 2011. (Sun Sign Ser.). (ENG.). 96p. pap. 6.95 *(978-1-58979-563-1(6))* Taylor Trade Publishing.
—Aries: Joanna Woolfolk's Sun Sign Series. 2011. (Sun Sign Ser.). (ENG.). 96p. pap. 6.95 *(978-1-58979-553-2(9))* Taylor Trade Publishing.
—Cancer: Joanna Woolfolk's Sun Sign Series. 2011. (Sun Sign Ser.). (ENG.). 96p. pap. 6.95 *(978-1-58979-556-3(3))* Taylor Trade Publishing.
—Capricorn: Joanna Woolfolk's Sun Sign Series. 2011. (Sun Sign Ser.). (ENG.). 96p. pap. 6.95 *(978-1-58979-562-4(8))* Taylor Trade Publishing.
—Gemini: Joanna Woolfolk's Sun Sign Series. 2011. (Sun Sign Ser.). (ENG.). 96p. pap. 6.95 *(978-1-58979-555-6(5))* Taylor Trade Publishing.
—Leo: Joanna Woolfolk's Sun Sign Series. 2011. (Sun Sign Ser.). (ENG.). 96p. pap. 6.95 *(978-1-58979-557-0(1))* Taylor Trade Publishing.
—Libra: Joanna Woolfolk's Sun Sign Series. 2011. (Sun Sign Ser.). (ENG.). 96p. pap. 6.95 *(978-1-58979-559-4(8))* Taylor Trade Publishing.
—Only Astrology Book Youll Ever Need. 2012. (ENG.). 504p. pap. 19.95 incl. cd-rom *(978-1-58979-653-9(5))* Taylor Trade Publishing.
—Pisces: Joanna Woolfolk's Sun Sign Series. 2011. (Sun Sign Ser.). (ENG.). 96p. pap. 6.95 *(978-1-58979-564-8(4))* Taylor Trade Publishing.
—Sagittarius: Joanna Woolfolk's Sun Sign Series. 2011. (Sun Sign Ser.). (ENG.). 96p. pap. 6.95 *(978-1-58979-561-7(X))* Taylor Trade Publishing.
—Scorpio: Joanna Woolfolk's Sun Sign Series. 2011. (Sun Sign Ser.). (ENG.). 96p. pap. 6.95 *(978-1-58979-560-0(1))* Taylor Trade Publishing.
—Taurus: Joanna Woolfolk's Sun Sign Series. 2011. (Sun Sign Ser.). (ENG.). 96p. pap. 6.95 *(978-1-58979-554-9(7))* Taylor Trade Publishing.
—Virgo: Joanna Woolfolk's Sun Sign Series. 2011. (Sun Sign Ser.). (ENG.). 96p. pap. 6.95 *(978-1-58979-558-7(X))* Taylor Trade Publishing.
Woolfolk, Joanna Martine. Aquarius. 2011. ***(978-1-58979-538-9(5))*** Taylor Trade Publishing.
—Aries. 2011. *(978-1-58979-528-0(8))* Taylor Trade Publishing.
—Cancer. 2011. *(978-1-58979-531-0(8))* Taylor Trade Publishing.
—Capricorn. 2011. ***(978-1-58979-537-2(7))*** Taylor Trade Publishing.
—Gemini. 2011. *(978-1-58979-530-3(X))* Taylor Trade Publishing.
—Leo. 2011. *(978-1-58979-532-7(6))* Taylor Trade Publishing.
—Libra. 2011. *(978-1-58979-534-1(2))* Taylor Trade Publishing.
—The Only Astrology Book You'll Ever Need. 2008. (ENG.). 100p. pap. 19.95 incl. lp *(978-1-58979-377-4(3))* Taylor Trade Publishing.
—Pisces. 2011. ***(978-1-58979-539-6(3))*** Taylor Trade Publishing.
—Sagittarius. 2011. *(978-1-58979-536-5(9))* Taylor Trade Publishing.
—Scorpio. 2011. *(978-1-58979-535-8(0))* Taylor Trade Publishing.
—Taurus. 2011. *(978-1-58979-529-7(6))* Taylor Trade Publishing.
—Virgo. 2011. *(978-1-58979-533-4(4))* Taylor Trade Publishing.
Wrey, A. M. The Reading of the Stars for Those Who L. 2006. pap. 9.95 *(978-1-59605-879-8(X)*, Cosimo Classics) Cosimo, Inc.
Wyss, Phoebe. Hercules' Labours. 2007. (Illus.). xvi, 191p. pap. *(978-0-9546099-6-2(4))* Tree Tongue.
—Virtual Lives. 2008. 320p. pap. *(978-0-9546099-8-6(0))* Tree Tongue.
Your Birthday, Your Card: The Secrets of Life, Love & Destiny in A Deck of Playing Cards. 2008. 256p. pap. 14.95 *(978-1-4022-1292-5(5))* Sourcebooks, Inc.
Zain, C. C. & Benjamine, Elbert. Chart Your Future. 2011. 66p. 36.95 ***(978-1-258-00172-8(1))*** Literary Licensing, LLC.
Zain, C. c., et al. Weather Predicting: Brotherhood of Light V15, Serial No. 190-196. 2011. 226p. 44.95 ***(978-1-258-00199-5(3))*** Literary Licensing, LLC.
Zambelli, P. The Speculum Astronomiae & its Enigma: Astrology, Theology & Science in Albertus Magnus & his Contemporaries. 2010. (Boston Studies in the Philosophy of Science Ser.). 384p. pap. 254.00 *(978-90-481-4098-5(6)*, 9048140986) Springer.
Zambelli, Paola. Astrology & Magic from the Medieval Islamic World to Renaissance Europe: Theories & Approaches. 2012. (Variorum Collected Studies). 306p. 144.95 ***(978-1-4094-2514-4(2))*** Ashgate Publishing Co.
Zerner, Amy & Farber, Monte. The Enchanted Birthday Book: Discover the Meaning & Magic of Your Birthday. 2011. (ENG.). 376p. pap. 19.95 *(978-1-4027-8121-6(0))* Sterling Publishing Co., Inc.
Zodiac International Publisher. Star Guide to Your Relations with Others. 2011. 98p. 38.95 ***(978-1-258-06296-5(8))*** Literary Licensing, LLC.

ASTROLOGY—DICTIONARIES

Leo, Alan & Robson, Vivian E. Alan Leo's Dictionary of Astrology. 2010. 222p. 39.95 *(978-1-161-36959-5(7))* Kessinger Publishing, LLC.
Taeger, Hans M. Internationales Horoscope Lexikon, 3 vols., Set. (ENG & GER.). 450.00 *(978-0-7859-8455-9(0)*, 3762603855) French & European Pubns., Inc.
Tognetti, Arlene, et al. Astrology Dictionary. 2010. (Complete Idiot's Guide Ser.). (ENG.). 416p. (gr. 12). 18.95 *(978-1-59257-987-7(6)*, Alpha Bks.) Penguin Group (USA) Inc.
Wilson, James & Goold, Oliver Ames. A Complete Dictionary of Astrology. 2010. 444p. 51.95 *(978-1-161-37634-0(8))* Kessinger Publishing, LLC.

ASTROLOGY—EARLY WORKS TO 1800

Ackermann, Silke. Sternstunden am Kaiserhof: Michael Scotus und sein Buch von den Bildern und Zeichen des Himmels. 2010. (Illus.). 642p. 141.95 *(978-3-631-59489-6(5))* Lang, Peter GmbH, Europaischer Verlag der Wissenschaften DEU. Dist: Lang, Peter.
Fell Smith, Charlotte. Qabalah - John Dee 1527 - 1608 - the Secret Life of Queen Elizabeth I's Astrologer Royal. 2008. 155p. pap. 16.50 *(978-1-4092-2856-1(8))* Lulu Enterprises Inc.
Habner, Wolfgang. Manilius, Astronomica Buch V: Einfahrung, Text, Ðbersetzung und Kommentar. 2011. (Sammlung wissenschaftlicher Commentare (SWC) Ser.).Tr. of Manilius, Astronomica Volume V. Introduction, Edition, Translation, & Commentary. (GER & GEC., Illus.). XIV, 760p. 377.00 ***(978-3-11-173099-8(9))*** De Gruyter, Walter Inc.
Housman, A. E. & Manilii, M. Astronomicon Liber Qvartus. 2010. 150p. 28.99 *(978-1-140-37866-2(X))*; pap. 21.75 *(978-1-140-37967-9(8))* BiblioBazaar.
Hübner, Wolfgang. Manilius. Astronomica Buch V: Einfahrung, Text, Ã_bersetzung und Kommentar. 2010. (Sammlung wissenschaftlicher Commentare (SWC) Ser.).Tr. of Manilius, Astronomica Volume V. (GER, MUS & GEC., Illus.). XIV, 760p. 249.00 *(978-3-11-020670-8(6))* De Gruyter, Walter Inc.
MacKinnell, Terry. The Dawning. 2011. 398p. 29.99 ***(978-1-4568-8254-9(6))***; pap. 19.99 ***(978-1-4568-8253-2(8))*** Xlibris Corp.
Manilii, M. Astronomicon Vol. 1: Liber Primus. Housman, A. E., ed. 2011. 204p. pap. 19.99 *(978-0-521-16937-0(2))* Cambridge Univ. Pr.
Manilius, M. Astronomicon: Volume 2, Liber Secundus. Housman, A. e., ed. 2nd rev. ed. 2011. (ENG.). 174p. pap. 19.99 *(978-1-107-64808-1(4))* Cambridge Univ. Pr.
—Astronomicon: Volume 3, Liber Tertius. Housman, A. e., ed. 2nd rev. ed. 2011. (ENG.). 112p. pap. 19.99 *(978-1-107-64807-4(6))* Cambridge Univ. Pr.
—Astronomicon: Volume 4, Liber Quartus. Housman, A. e., ed. 2nd rev. ed. 2011. (ENG.). 164p. pap. 19.99 *(978-1-107-64806-7(8))* Cambridge Univ. Pr.
—Astronomicon: Volume 5, Liber Quintus. Housman, A. e., ed. 2nd rev. ed. 2011. (ENG.). 190p. pap. 19.99 *(978-1-107-64805-0(X))* Cambridge Univ. Pr.
Manilius, Marcus. Astronomicon. Housman, A. E., ed. 2011. (Cambridge Library Collection - Classics Ser.). (LAT.). 162p. pap. 19.99 *(978-1-108-12758-5(4))*; 186p. pap. 19.99 *(978-1-108-04047-1(0))*; 154p. pap. 19.99 *(978-1-108-03054-0(8))*; 108p. pap. 19.99 *(978-1-108-17063-5(3))* Cambridge Univ. Pr.
—Astronomicon. Housman, A. e., ed. 2011. (Cambridge Library Collection - Classics Ser.). (LAT.). 254p. pap. 23.99 *(978-1-108-03796-9(8))* Cambridge Univ. Pr.
—Astronomicon. Bentleii, Richardi, ed. 166p. 2010. 29.56 ***(978-1-165-96197-9(0))*** 2009. 36.95 *(978-1-104-67736-7(9))* 2009. pap. 21.95 *(978-1-104-61944-2(X))* Kessinger Publishing, LLC.
—Astronomicon, Book. Jacob, Fredrick, ed. 252p. 2010. 33.56 *(978-1-166-08914-6(2))* 2009. 41.95 *(978-1-104-80453-4(0))* 2009. pap. 26.95 *(978-1-104-72302-6(6))* Kessinger Publishing, LLC.
—Astronomicon Ex Recensione Richardi Bentleii Adjecta Est in Calce Cujusque Paginae Lection Vulgat. 2010. 172p. pap. 21.75 *(978-1-149-91053-6(0))* BiblioBazaar.
Manilius, Marcus & Housman, A. e. 1859-1936. Astronomicon; Recensuit et Enarravit a E Housman. 2010. 166p. pap. 21.75 *(978-1-175-03197-6(6))* BiblioBazaar.
Manilius, Marcus & Housman, Alfred Edward. Astronomicon. 2009. (LAT.). 103p. pap. 18.99 *(978-1-115-42846-0(2))*; pap. 19.99 *(978-1-115-42848-4(9))* BiblioBazaar. (BiblioLife).
Manilius, Marcus & Pithou, Pierre. Astronomicon Liber Primus[-Quintus]. 2010. 240p. pap. 26.75 *(978-1-175-04259-0(5))* BiblioBazaar.
Manilius, Marcus & Scaligeri, Joseph. Astronomicon a Iosepho Scaligero Ex Vetusto Codice Gemblacendi Infinitis Mendis Repurgarum. 664p. 2010. pap. 39.16 ***(978-1-166-07022-9(0))*** 2009. 63.95 *(978-1-104-83331-2(X))* 2009. pap. 48.95 *(978-1-104-72303-3(4))* Kessinger Publishing, LLC.
Maternus, Julius Firmicus. Mathesis. Holden, James Herschel, tr. 2011. 620p. pap. 59.95 ***(978-0-86690-619-7(3))*** American Federation of Astrologers, Inc.
Michael. The Book of Michael of Rhodes Vol. 2: A Fifteenth-Century Maritime Manuscript. Stahl, Alan M. et al, eds. Rossi, Franco, tr. from ITA. 2009. (ITA & ENG., Illus.). 732p. (gr. 17). 75.00 *(978-0-262-19590-4(9))* MIT Pr.
Sela, Shlomo. Abraham Ibn Ezra on Elections, Interrogations, & Medical Astrology: A Parallel Hebrew-English Critical Edition of the Book of Elections (3 Versions), the Book of Interrogations (3 Versions), & the Book of the Luminaries. 2011. (Études Sur le Judaïsme Médiéval Ser.). (HEB & ENG., Illus.). XII, 660p. ***(978-90-04-21220-6(5))*** BRILL.
Seva, Bhakti. The Hindu Book of Astrology. 2009. 72p. pap. *(978-1-4099-6903-7(7))* Dodo Pr.

ASTROLOGY, CHINESE

Aylward, Thomas F. The Imperial Guide to Feng Shui & Chinese Astrology: The Only Authentic Translation from the Original Chinese. 2007. (ENG., Illus.). 336p. pap. 17.95 *(978-1-84293-176-9(8)*, Watkins Publishing) Duncan Baird Pubs. GBR. Dist: Sterling Publishing Co., Inc.
Christense, Karen, adapted by. Kailun Zodiac Collection: Designs from China for the Year of the Monkey. 2007. pap. 12.95 *(978-1-933782-30-0(7))* Berkshire Publishing Group.
Christensen, Karen, adapted by. Kailun Zodiac Collection: Books 1-12. 2007. pap. 120.00 *(978-1-933782-39-3(0))* Berkshire Publishing Group.
—Kailun Zodiac Collection: Designs from China for the Year of the Dog. 2007. pap. 12.95 *(978-1-933782-31-7(5))* Berkshire Publishing Group.
—Kailun Zodiac Collection: Designs from China for the Year of the Dragon. 2007. pap. 12.95 *(978-1-933782-38-6(2))* Berkshire Publishing Group.
—Kailun Zodiac Collection: Designs from China for the Year of the Goat. 2007. pap. 12.95 *(978-1-933782-29-4(3))* Berkshire Publishing Group.
—Kailun Zodiac Collection: Designs from China for the Year of the Horse. 2007. pap. 12.95 *(978-1-933782-28-7(5))* Berkshire Publishing Group.
—Kailun Zodiac Collection: Designs from China for the Year of the Ox. 2007. pap. 12.95 *(978-1-933782-35-5(8))* Berkshire Publishing Group.
—Kailun Zodiac Collection: Designs from China for the Year of the Pig. 2007. pap. 12.95 *(978-1-933782-33-1(1))* Berkshire Publishing Group.
—Kailun Zodiac Collection: Designs from China for the Year of the Rabbit. 2007. pap. 12.95 *(978-1-933782-37-9(4))* Berkshire Publishing Group.
—Kailun Zodiac Collection: Designs from China for the Year of the Rooster. 2007. pap. 12.95 *(978-1-933782-32-4(3))* Berkshire Publishing Group.
—Kailun Zodiac Collection: Designs from China for the Year of the Snake. 2007. pap. 12.95 *(978-1-933782-27-0(7))* Berkshire Publishing Group.
—Kailun Zodiac Collection: Designs from China for the Year of the Tiger. 2007. pap. 12.95 *(978-1-933782-36-2(6))* Berkshire Publishing Group.
—Kailun Zodiac Collection: Designs from China for the Year of TheRat. 2007. pap. 12.95 *(978-1-933782-34-8(X))* Berkshire Publishing Group.
Lau, Laura & Lau, Theodora. Wedding Feng Shui: The Chinese Horoscopes Guide to Planning Your Wedding. 2010. (ENG.). 288p. pap. 16.99 *(978-0-06-199053-3(1)*, Harper Paperbacks) HarperCollins Pubs.
Lau, Theodora & Lau, Laura. The Handbook of Chinese Horoscopes. (ENG., (Orig.). 6th ed. 2007. Illus.). 464p. pap. 18.99 *(978-0-06-143263-7(6))* 7th ed. 2010. 400p. pap., instr.'s hndbk. ed. 18.99 *(978-0-06-199091-5(4)*, HarperPerennial) HarperCollins Pubs.
Morgan, Harry Titterton. Chinese Astrology. 2011. 20p. pap. 35.95 ***(978-1-258-01524-4(2))*** Literary Licensing, LLC.
Somerville, Neil. Your Chinese Horoscope 2010: What the Year of the Tiger Holds in Store for You. 2009. (ENG.). 384p. 14.95 *(978-0-00-728146-6(3))* HarperCollins Pubs. Ltd. GBR. Dist: Independent Pubs. Group.
Walters, Derek. Chinese Astrology Bible: The Definitive Guide to Using the Chinese Zodiac. 2009. (ENG., Illus.). 400p. pap. 14.95 *(978-1-4027-6622-0(X))* Sterling Publishing Co., Inc.
—The Complete Guide to Chinese Astrology: The Most Comprehensive Study of the Subject Ever Published in the English Language. 4th ed. 2006. (ENG., Illus.). 416p. pap. 17.95 *(978-1-84293-111-0(3)*, Watkins Publishing) Duncan Baird Pubs. GBR. Dist: Sterling Publishing Co., Inc.
Williams Griffin, Linda. The Dragon's Head: 2011 Astrology Almanac. 2010. 104p. pap. 21.50 *(978-0-557-73003-2(1))* Lulu Enterprises Inc.
Wu, Master Zhongxian. The 12 Chinese Animals: Create Harmony in Your Daily Life Through Ancient Chinese Wisdom. 2010. (Illus.). 160p. *(978-1-84819-031-3(X))* Singing Dragon.
Wu, Shelly. Chinese Sexual Astrology: Eastern Secrets to Mind-Blowing Sex. 2006. (ENG., Illus.). 1p. per. 14.99 *(978-1-56414-921-3(8))* Career Pr., Inc.
Wu Shelly & Wu, Shelly. Definitive Book of Chinese Astrology. 2009. (ENG., Illus.). 1p. 18.99 *(978-1-60163-078-0(6)*, 1301928, New Page Bks.) Career Pr., Inc.
Yoshikawa, Takashi. The Chinese Birthday Book: How to Use the Secrets of Ki-Ology to Find Love, Happiness, & Success. 2008. (ENG., Illus.). 1p. per. 19.95 *(978-1-57863-392-0(3)*, Weiser Bks.) Red Wheel/Weiser.

ASTROLOGY, HINDU

see Hindu Astrology

ASTROLOGY, HORARY

see Horary Astrology

ASTROLOGY, INDIC

Misra, Ram Bilas. Influence of Celestial Bodies on Human Lives. 2011. 60p. pap. ***(978-3-8383-2259-9(2))*** Lambert Academic Publishing.

ASTROLOGY, MAYA
see Maya Astrology
ASTROLOGY AND MEDICINE
see Medical Astrology
ASTROLOGY AND THE BIBLE
see Bible and Astrology
ASTROMETRY

Alfonso, C., ed. Transiting Extrasolar Planets Workshop. 2007. (Astronomical Society of the Pacific Conference Ser.). 342p. 77.00 *(978-1-58381-234-1(2))* Astronomical Society of the Pacific, The.

Budding, Edwin & Demircan, Osman. Introduction to Astronomical Photometry. 2nd rev. ed. 2007. (Cambridge Observing Handbooks for Research Astronomers). (ENG., Illus.). 450p. 103.00 *(978-0-521-84711-7(7))* Cambridge Univ. Pr.

Jin, Wenjing, et al, eds. A Giant Step: from Milli- to Micro- Arcsecond Astrometry (IAU S248) 2008. (Proceedings of the International Astronomical Union Symposia & Colloquia Ser.). (ENG., Illus.). 610p. 127.00 *(978-0-521-87470-0(X))* Cambridge Univ. Pr.

Kovalevsky, Jean. Modern Astrometry. 2nd ed. 2010. (Astronomy & Astrophysics Library). (Illus.). xvi, 375p. pap. 139.00 *(978-3-642-07619-0(X)*, 364207619X) Springer.

Kovalevsky, Jean & Seidelmann, P. Kenneth. Fundamentals of Astrometry. 2010. (ENG., Illus.). 422p. pap. 75.00 *(978-0-521-17331-5(0))* Cambridge Univ. Pr.

Labeyrie, A., et al. An Introduction to Optical Stellar Interferometry. 2006. (ENG., Illus.). 360p. 102.00 *(978-0-521-82872-7(4))* Cambridge Univ. Pr.

Perryman, Michael. Astronomical Applications of Astrometry: Ten Years of Exploitation of the Hipparcos Satellite Data. 2008. (ENG., Illus.). 692p. 132.00 *(978-0-521-51489-7(4))* Cambridge Univ. Pr.

—The Making of History's Greatest Star Map. 2010. (Astronomers' Universe Ser.). (Illus.). x, 275p. 29.95 *(978-3-642-11601-8(9)*, 3642116019) Springer.

Peterson, Bradley M., et al, eds. Co-evolution of Central Black Holes & Galaxies (IAU S267) 2010. (Proceedings of the International Astronomical Union Symposia & Colloquia Ser.). (Illus.). 494p. 125.00 *(978-0-521-76502-2(1))* Cambridge Univ. Pr.

Pont, Frédéric & Holman, Matthew. Transiting Planets. Queloz, Didier & Sasselov, Dimitar, eds. 2009. (Proceedings of the International Astronomical Union Symposia & Colloquia Ser.). (ENG., Illus.). 590p. 130.00 *(978-0-521-88984-1(7))* Cambridge Univ. Pr.

Van Leeuwen, Floor. Hipparcos, the New Reduction of the Raw Data. 2007. (Astrophysics & Space Science Library). (Illus.). 449p. 209.00 *(978-1-4020-6341-1(5))* Springer.

van Leeuwen, Floor. Hipparcos, the New Reduction of the Raw Data. 2010. (Astrophysics & Space Science Library). xxxii, 449p. pap. 209.00 *(978-90-481-7612-0(3)*, 9048176123) Springer.

ASTRONAUTICAL ACCIDENTS
see Astronautics—Accidents
ASTRONAUTICAL INSTRUMENTS
see also Artificial Satellites—Attitude Control Systems; Astrionics; Astronautics—Communication Systems; Spectrograph
also headings for special astronautical vehicles with subdivisions for instruments or instrument systems, e.g. Space vehicles—Guidance systems

Colangeli, Luigi, et al, eds. The New ROSETTA Targets: Observations, Simulations & Instrument Performances. 2010. (Astrophysics & Space Science Library). xi, 315p. pap. 169.00 *(978-90-481-6683-1(7)*, 9048166837) Springer.

Cram101 Textbook Reviews & Cram101 Textbook Reviews. Outlines & Highlights for Deep Space Craft by Dave Doody. 2011. 146p. pap. 29.95 ***(978-1-61830-857-3(2))*** Cram101 Inc.

Doody, Dave. Deep Space Craft. 2009. (Springer Praxis Books / Astronautical Engineering Ser.). (ENG., Illus.). xxiv, 440p. 99.00 *(978-3-540-89509-1(4))* Springer.

Ellerbroek, Brent L. & Calia, Domenico Bonaccini. Advances in Adaptive Optics II: 24-31 May, 2006, Orlando, Florida, USA, 3 vols. 2006. (Proceedings of SPIE Ser.). (Illus.). 1874p. pap. 250.00 *(978-0-8194-6337-1(X))* SPIE.

Gough. Spacecraft & Space Instruments. 2009. (Illus.). 33.95 *(978-0-7484-0771-2(5))* Taylor & Francis Group.

Radioisotope Power Systems Committee & National Research Council Staff. Radioisotope Power Systems: An Imperative for Maintaining U. S. Leadership in Space Exploration. 2009. (ENG.). 68p. pap. 21.00 *(978-0-309-13857-4(4))* National Academies Pr.

Sakurai, Takashi. The Hinode Mission. 2008. (ENG., Illus.). iv, 208p. 179.00 *(978-0-387-88738-8(5)*, 0387887385) Springer.

ASTRONAUTICAL RESEARCH
see Astronautics—Research
ASTRONAUTICS
Here are entered general works on the scientific, technological, and engineering disciplines needed for the exploration of outer space. Works on the physics and technical details of locomotion beyond earth's atmosphere are entered under Space Flight.
see also Aerothermodynamics; Artificial Satellites; Astrodynamics; Astronauts; Interplanetary Voyages; Interstellar Travel; Manned Space Flight; Navigation (Astronautics); Outer Space; Outer Space—Exploration; Project Gemini (U.S.); Project Mercury (U.S.); Rocketry; Space Flight; Space Ships; Space Stations; Space Vehicles; Space Vehicles—Atmospheric Entry; Unidentified Flying Objects

Aerospace Engineering Workbook. 2011. (ENG.). 128p. (C). spiral bd. 24.95 *(978-1-4354-4754-7(9))* Delmar Cengage Learning.

American Institute of Aeronautics and Astronautics Staff, contrib. by. Managing the Use of Commercial off the Shelf (COTS) Software Components for Mission-Critical Systems: AIAA G-118-2006 Guide. 2006. *(978-1-56347-915-1(X))* American Institute of Aeronautics & Astronautics.

Arnould, Jacques. Icarus' Second Chance: The Basis & Perspectives of Space Ethics. 2011. (Studies in Space Policy Ser.). (ENG., Illus.). xi, 202p. 129.00 *(978-3-7091-0711-9(3)*, 3709107113) Springer.

Astronautics & Aeronautics. (Illus.). reprint ed. lib. bdg. *(978-0-7222-3104-3(0))* Library Reprints, Inc.

Ball, Andrew, et al. Planetary Landers & Entry Probes. 2010. (ENG.). 364p. pap. 67.00 *(978-0-521-12958-9(3))* Cambridge Univ. Pr.

Bizony, Piers. The Space Shuttle: Celebrating Thirty Years of NASA's First Space Plane. 2011. (ENG., Illus.). 300p. 40.00 *(978-0-7603-3941-1(4)*, 0760339414, Zenith Pr.) MBI Publishing Co. LLC.

Brennan, Louis & Vecchi, Alessandra. The Business of Space: The Next Frontier of International Competition. 2011. (ENG., Illus.). 256p. 40.00 *(978-0-230-23173-3(X))* Palgrave Macmillan.

Buckbee, Ed. 50 Years of Rockets & Spacecraft: NASA-Marshall Space Flight Center Commemorative History. 2009. 44.95 *(978-1-935001-17-1(5))* Acclaim Pr., Inc.

Bugheim, Robert W. Space Handbook: Aeronautics & Its Applications. 2007. 348p. pap. 32.50 *(978-0-8330-4223-1(8)*, CB-136-1) RAND Corp., The.

Callmers, William N. Space Policy & Exploration. 2008. 69.00 *(978-1-60456-448-8(2))* Nova Science Pubs., Inc.

The Case for Space: Examining the Value: Hearing Before the Subcommittee on Science & Space of the Committee on Commerce, Science, & Transportation, United States Senate, One Hundred Eleventh Congress, First Session, October 21, 2009. 2010. iii, 40p. *(978-0-16-086159-8(4)*, 552-070-12591-0) United States Government Printing Office.

Challenges & Opportunities in the NASA Fiscal Year 2011 Budget Proposal: Hearing Before the Subcommittee on Science & Space of the Committee on Commerce, Science, & Transportation, United States Senate, One Hundred Eleventh Congress, Second Session, February 24, 2010. 2010. iii, 63p. ***(978-0-16-088123-7(4)***, 552-070-42543-8) United States Government Printing Office.

Claessens, Marline. Detecting Extrasolar Planets from Space. 2010. 288p. pap. *(978-3-8383-4944-2(X))* Lambert Academic Publishing.

Collins, Martin J. & Collins, Martin. After Sputnik: 50 Years of the Space Age. 2007. (Illus.). 256p. 35.00 *(978-0-06-089781-9(3))* Smithsonian Institution Pr.

Correno, Sophia C., ed. NASA's Future & it's Pursuits. 2010. (Space Science, Exploration & Policies Ser.). 234p. 115.00 *(978-1-61668-999-5(4))* Nova Science Pubs., Inc.

Cox, Joseph L., et al. Space Missions & Technologies: 5-6 April 2010, Orlando, Florida, United States. 2010. (Proceedings of SPIE Ser.). (Illus.). 160p. pap. 70.00 ***(978-0-8194-8155-9(6))*** SPIE.

Cram101 Textbook Reviews Staff. Outlines & Highlights for Understanding Space: An Introduction to Astronautics by Sellers, ISBN. 2009. 276p. pap. 32.95 *(978-1-4288-6724-6(4))* Cram101 Inc.

Cruzen, Craig A., ed. Space Operations: Exploration, Scientific Utilization, & Technology Development. 2011. 589p. 119.95 ***(978-1-60086-817-7(7))*** American Institute of Aeronautics & Astronautics.

Curtis, Howard, et al. Aerospace Engineering Desk Reference. 2009. (ENG., Illus.). 704p. 103.00 *(978-1-85617-575-3(8)*, Butterworth-Heinemann) Elsevier Science & Technology Bks.

Darrin, Ann Garrison & O'Leary, Beth Laura, eds. Handbook of Space Engineering, Archaeology, & Heritage. 2009. (Advances in Engineering Ser.). (ENG., Illus.). 1035p. 164.95 *(978-1-4200-8431-3(3)*, CRC Press) Taylor & Francis Group GBR. Dist: Taylor & Francis Group.

Dougherty, Michele, et al, eds. Saturn from Cassini-Huygens. 2009. (ENG., Illus.). viii, 805p. 119.00 *(978-1-4020-9216-9(4)*, 1402092164) Springer.

Duggins, Pat. Final Countdown: NASA & the End of the Space Shuttle Program. 2009. (ENG., Illus.). 264p. pap. 19.95 *(978-0-8130-3384-6(5))* Univ. Pr. of Florida.

Eckel, Hans-Albert & Scharring, Stefan, eds. Beamed Energy Propulsion: Seventh International Symposium. 2012. (AIP Conference Proceedings / Accelerators, Beams, & Instrumentations Ser.: 1402). (ENG.). 510p. 191.00 ***(978-0-7354-0982-8(X)***, 073540982X, AIP Pr.) Springer.

El-Genk, Mohamed S. Space Technology & Applications International Forum, STAIF 2008: 12th Conference on Thermophysics Applications in Microgravity: 1st Symposium on Space Resource Utilization: 25th Symposium on Space Nuclear Power & Propulsion: 6th Conference on Human/Robotic Technology & the Vision for Space Exploration: 6th Symposium on Space Colonization: 5th Symposium on New Frontiers & Future Concepts: Albuquerque, New Mexico, 10-14 February 2008. 2008. (AIP Conference Proceedings Ser.). (Illus.). xxiv, 1174p. 299.00 *(978-0-7354-0486-1(0))* American Institute of Physics.

El-Genk, Mohamed S., ed. Space Technology & Applications International Forum - STAIF 2008: 12th Conference on Thermophysics Applications in Microgravity. 2008. (AIP Conference Proceedings Ser.). cd-rom 145.00 *(978-0-7354-0487-8(9))* American Institute of Physics.

—Space Technology & Applications International Forum-STAIF 2007: 11th Conference on Thermophysics Applications in Microgravity 24th Symposium on Space Nuclear Power & Propulsion 5th Symposium on Space Colonization 4th Symposium on New Frontiers & Future Concepts. 2007. (AIP Conference Proceedings Ser.). 1254p. 286.00 *(978-0-7354-0386-4(4))* American Institute of Physics.

Evans, Ben. Escaping the Bonds of Earth: Prehistory Through the Sixties. 2009. (Springer Praxis Books / Space Exploration Ser.). (ENG., Illus.). xviii, 494p. pap. 39.95 *(978-0-387-79093-0(4)*, Springer-Praxis) Springer.

Feuerbacher, Berndt & Stoewer, Heinz, eds. Utilization of Space: Today & Tomorrow. 2010. (Illus.). xx, 410p. pap. 109.00 *(978-3-642-06437-1(X)*, 364206437X) Springer.

Fink, Wolfgang. Space Exploration Technologies: 17-18 March 2008, Orlando, Florida, USA. 2008. (Proceedings of SPIE Ser.). (Illus.). 226p. pap. 70.00 *(978-0-8194-7151-2(8))* SPIE.

—Space Exploration Technologies II: 13 April 2009, Orlando, Florida, United States. 2009. (Proceedings of SPIE Ser.). (Illus.). 98p. pap. 70.00 *(978-0-8194-7597-8(1))* SPIE.

Fox, Bernard, et al. Guidelines & Metrics for Assessing Space System Cost Estimates. 2007. 279p. pap. 35.50 *(978-0-8330-4023-7(5)*, tr418) RAND Corp., The.

Gilster, Paul. Centauri Dreams: Imagining & Planning Interstellar Exploration. 2012. (ENG.). xvii, 302p. pap. 25.00 *(978-1-4419-1818-5(3)*, 1441918183) Springer.

Gruzdeva, Maria, photos by. Direction-Space! 2011. (ENG., Illus.). 96p. 48.00 ***(978-1-907893-05-6(9))*** Lewis, Dewi Publishing GBR. Dist: Consortium Bk Sales & Distribution.

Haerens, Margaret, ed. NASA. 2012. (Opposing Viewpoints Ser.). (ENG., Illus.). 240p. (gr. 10-12). pap. 41.70 ***(978-0-7377-5746-0(9)***, Greenhaven Pr., Inc.); (YA). (gr. 9-12). lib. bdg. 28.90 ***(978-0-7377-5745-3(0))*** Cengage Gale.

Hamkins, Jon & Simon, Marvin K., eds. Autonomous Software-Defined Radio Receivers for Deep Space Applications. 2006. (JPL Deep-Space Communications & Navigation Ser.: 13). (ENG., Illus.). 435p. 197.00 *(978-0-470-08212-6(7)*, Wiley-Interscience) Wiley, John & Sons, Inc.

Harvey, Brian & Harland, David M. Space Exploration. 2007. (Springer Praxis Books / Space Exploration Ser.). (Illus.). 183p. per. 32.95 *(978-0-387-71667-1(X)*, 038771667X, Springer-Praxis) Springer.

Häuplik-Meusburger, Sandra. Architecture for Astronauts: An Activity-Based Approach. 2011. (Springer Praxis Bks.). xiv, 316p. 129.00 *(978-3-7091-0666-2(4)*, 3709106664) Springer.

Hemmati, Hamid. Free-Space Laser Communication Technologies XXIII. 2011. (Proceedings of SPIE Ser.). 206p. pap. 70.00 ***(978-0-8194-8460-4(1))*** SPIE.

Hickman, John. Reopening the Space Frontier. 2010. pap. *(978-1-86335-800-2(5))* Common Ground Publishing Pty, Ltd.

Institute of Electrical and Electronics Engineers Staff, contrib. by 2007 3rd International Conference on Recent Advances in Space Technologies. 2007. pap. 340.00 *(978-1-4244-1056-9(8)*, 07EX1710) IEEE.

International Symposium on Photoelectronic Detection & Imaging 2011: Space Exploration Technologies & Applications. 2011. (Proceedings of SPIE Ser.). 682p. pap. 130.00 ***(978-0-8194-8837-4(2))*** SPIE.

Johnson, Stephen B. The Secret of Apollo: Systems Management in American & European Space Programs. 2006. (New Series in NASA History Ser.). (ENG., Illus.). 312p. (gr. 17). per. 27.00 *(978-0-8018-8542-6(6))* Johns Hopkins Univ. Pr.

Jones, Morris. The New Moon Race. 2009. (Illus.). 184p. 49.95 *(978-1-877058-82-0(3))* Rosenberg Publishing Pty, Ltd. AUS. Dist: International Specialized Bk. Services.

Koll, Hilary & Mills, Steve. Using Math on a Space Mission. 2006. (Mathworks! Ser.). 32p. (gr. 2-6). pap. 10.50 *(978-0-8368-6770-1(X)*, Stevens, Gareth Learning Library) Stevens, Gareth Publishing LLLP.

Koll, Hilary, et al. Using Math on a Space Mission. 2006. (Mathworks!). (Illus.). 32p. (gr. 2-6). lib. bdg. 26.00 *(978-0-8368-6763-3(7)*, Stevens, Gareth Learning Library) Stevens, Gareth Publishing LLLP.

Larson, Wiley, et al. Applied Space Systems Engineering (Space Technology Series) 2009. (ENG.). 920p. (C). pap. 63.33 *(978-0-07-340886-6(7)*, 0073408867) McGraw-Hill Cos., The.

Ley, Wilfried, et al, eds. Handbook of Space Technology. 2009. (Illus.). 882p. 139.95 *(978-1-60086-701-9(4))* American Institute of Aeronautics & Astronautics.

—Handbook of Space Technology. 2009. (Aerospace Ser.). (ENG., Illus.). 908p. 185.00 *(978-0-470-69739-9(3)*, Wiley) Wiley, John & Sons, Inc.

Liebergot, Sy & Harland, David M. Apollo EECOM: Journey of a Lifetime. 2nd ed. 2008. (Apogee Books Space Ser.). (ENG., Illus.). 216p. pap. 21.95 *(978-1-894959-88-9(4))* Collector's Guide Publishing, Inc. CAN. Dist: Independent Pubs. Group.

Lojdahl, Franz, ed. Future U. S. Space Launch Capabilities. 2010. (Space Science, Exploration & Policies Ser.). 69.00 *(978-1-60741-384-4(1))* Nova Science Pubs., Inc.

Long, K. F. Deep Space Propulsion: A Roadmap to Interstellar Flight. 2011. (Astronomers' Universe Ser.). (ENG., Illus.). xxi, 367p. pap. 44.95 ***(978-1-4614-0606-8(4)***, 1461406064) Springer.

Maguire, Dillon S. Exploring the Final Frontier: Issues, Plans & Funding for NASA. 2010. (Space Science, Exploration & Policies Ser.). 115.00 *(978-1-60876-080-0(4))* Nova Science Pubs., Inc.

Majumdar, Arun K. & Davis, Christopher C. Free-Space Laser Communications VI. 2006. (Proceedings of SPIE Ser.). (Illus.). 550p. pap. 130.00 *(978-0-8194-6383-8(3))* SPIE.

Mari, Christopher. The Next Space Age. 2008. (Illus.). ix, 187p. *(978-0-8242-1082-3(4))* Wilson, H.W.

Mari, Christopher. U.S. National Debate Topic 2011-2012: American Space Exploration & Development. 2011. ***(978-0-8242-1109-7(X))*** Wilson, H.W.

McCurdy, Howard E. Space & the American Imagination. 2nd ed. 2011. (ENG., Illus.). 408p. (C). (gr. 13-17). 60.00 *(978-0-8018-9867-9(6))*; pap. 30.00 *(978-0-8018-9868-6(4))* Johns Hopkins Univ. Pr.

McElyea, Tim. Project Constellation: Moon, Mars & Beyond. 2007. (Pocket Space Guides: 9). (ENG., Illus.). 96p. per. 9.95 *(978-1-894959-49-0(3)*, Apogee Bks.) Collector's Guide Publishing, Inc. CAN. Dist: Independent Pubs. Group.

Meskin, Nader & Khorasani, Khashayar. Fault Detection & Isolation: Multi-Vehicle Unmanned Systems. 2011. (ENG., Illus.). xix, 166p. 139.00 *(978-1-4419-8392-3(9)*, 1441983929) Springer.

Mindell, David A. Digital Apollo: Human & Machine in Spaceflight. (ENG., Illus.). 384p. (gr. 17). 2008. 29.95 *(978-0-262-13497-2(7))* 2011. pap. 16.95 *(978-0-262-51610-5(1))* MIT Pr.

Mughal, Umair & Iqbal, Muhammad. Break-Even Analysis of Sky Sail for Pakistan Maritime. 2010. 84p. pap. *(978-3-8383-6013-3(3))* Lambert Academic Publishing.

Myrabo, Leik N., et al. Lightcraft Flight Handbook LTI-20: Hypersonic Flight Transport for an Era Beyond Oil. 2009. (ENG., Illus.). 304p. pap., instr.'s hndbk. ed. 29.95 *(978-1-926592-03-9(4))* Collector's Guide Publishing, Inc. CAN. Dist: Independent Pubs. Group.

NASA at 50: Past Accomplishments & Future Opportunities & Challenges: Hearing Before the Committee on Science & Technology, House of Representatives, One Hundred Tenth Congress, Second Session, July 30, 2008. 2008. (Illus.). iii, 59p. *(978-0-16-082104-2(5)*, 552-070-38251-8) United States Government Printing Office.

NASA's Fiscal Year 2008 Budget Request: Hearing Before the Committee on Science & Technology, House of Representatives, One Hundred Tenth Congress, First Session, March 15, 2007. 2007. (Illus.). iv, 87p. *(978-0-16-079522-0(2)*, 552-070-36500-1) United States Government Printing Office.

NASA'S Fiscal Year 2010 Budget Request: Hearing Before the Committee on Science & Technology, House of Representatives, One Hundred Eleventh Congress, First Session, May 19, 2009. 2009. (Illus.). iii, 90p. *(978-0-16-084990-9(X)*, 552-070-40369-8) United States Government Printing Office.

NASA's Space Science Programs: Review of Fiscal Year 2008 Budget Request & Issues: Hearing Before the Subcommittee on Space & Aeronautics, Committee on Science & Technology, House of Representatives, One Hundred Tenth Congress, First Session, May 2, 2007. 2007. (Illus.). iv, 125p. *(978-0-16-079210-6(X)*, 552-070-36316-5) United States Government Printing Office.

National Research Council. United States Civil Space Policy: Summary of a Workshop. 2008. (ENG.). 42p. pap. 15.00 *(978-0-309-12014-2(4))* National Academies Pr.

Newell, Homer E., Jr. Beyond the Atmosphere: Early Years of Space Science. 2010. (Dover Books on Astronomy Ser.). (ENG.). 528p. pap. 24.95 *(978-0-486-47464-9(X))* Dover Pubns., Inc.

Pellegrino, Sergio & Guest, Simon D., eds. IUTAM-IASS Symposium on Deployable Structures: Theory & Applications: Theory & Applications. 2010. (Solid Mechanics & Its Applications Ser.). 512p. pap. 359.00 *(978-90-481-5539-2(8)*, 9048155398) Springer.

Pelt, Michel Van. Space Tourism: Adventures in Earth Orbit & Beyond. 2010. (ENG., Illus.). xvi, 224p. pap. 27.50 *(978-1-4419-2314-1(4)*, 1441923144) Springer.

Pelton, Joseph N. Space Exploration & Astronaut Safety. 2006. (Illus.). xi, 386p. *(978-1-56347-844-4(7))* American Institute of Aeronautics & Astronautics.

Pelton, Joseph N. & Jakhu, Ram, eds. Space Safety Regulations & Standards. 2010. (ENG., Illus.). 544p. 175.00 *(978-1-85617-752-8(1)*, Butterworth-Heinemann) Elsevier Science & Technology Bks.

Phillips, Cynthia, et al. Space Exploration for Dummies. 2009. (ENG., Illus.). 392p. pap. 19.99 *(978-0-470-44573-0(4)*, For Dummies) Wiley, John & Sons, Inc.

Phipps, Claude R., et al, eds. Beamed Energy Propulsion: 6th International Symposium. 2010. (AIP Conference Proceedings / Accelerators, Beams, & Instrumentations Ser.). 424p. 227.00 *(978-0-7354-0774-9(6)*, 0735407746, AIP Pr.) Springer.

Pillet, V. Mártinez, et al, eds. Payload & Mission Definition in Space Sciences. 2011. 403p. pap. 50.00 *(978-0-521-18245-4(X))* Cambridge Univ. Pr.

Piombo, Akbar Del. Is That You Simon? a Cosmic Dram. 2011. 94p. 38.95 ***(978-1-258-08420-2(1))*** Literary Licensing, LLC.

Proulx, Tom, ed. Advanced Aerospace Applications, Volume 1: Proceedings of the 29th IMAC, A Conference on Structural Dynamics 2011. 2011. (Conference Proceedings of the Society for Experimental Mechanics SeriesPublishing Ser.). (Illus.). ix, 368p. 259.00 *(978-1-4419-9301-4(0)*, 1441993010) Springer.

Rapp, Donald. Human Missions to Mars: Enabling Technologies for Exploring the Red Planet. (Springer Praxis Books / Astronautical Engineering Ser.). 2010. xxxiv, 520p. pap. 169.00 *(978-3-642-09201-5(2)*, 3642092012) 2007. (Illus.). 520p. 169.00 *(978-3-540-72938-9(0))* Springer.

Razani, Mohammad. Information Communication & Space Technology. 2012. (ENG., Illus.). 280p. 129.95 ***(978-1-4398-4163-1(2)***, CRC Press) Taylor & Francis Group GBR. Dist: Taylor & Francis Group.

Sadeh, Eligar. The Politics of Space: A Survey. 2010. (ENG., Illus.). 320p. 230.00 *(978-1-85743-419-4(6)*, Routledge) Taylor & Francis Group GBR. Dist: Taylor & Francis Group.

Schrogl, Kai-Uwe, et al. Yearbook on Space Policy 2006/2007: New Impetus for Europe. 2010. (Yearbook on Space Policy Ser.). (Illus.). xxvi, 330p. pap. 189.00 *(978-3-211-99932-5(9)*, 3211999329) Springer.

Schwartz, David L. Those Who Wait Below. 2007. 173p. pap. 12.95 *(978-0-7414-3477-7(6))* Infinity Publishing.

Seedhouse, Erik. Prepare for Launch: The Astronaut Training Process. 2010. (Springer Praxis Books / Space Exploration Ser.). (ENG., Illus.). 250p. pap. 34.95 *(978-1-4419-1349-4(1)*, 1441913491, Springer-Praxis) Springer.

Sellers, Jerry Jon, et al. Understanding Space: An Introduction to Astronautics + Website. 3rd ed. 2007. (ENG.). 792p. (C). 74.00 *(978-0-07-723030-2(2)*, 0077230302) McGraw-Hill Cos., The.

Sgobba, Tommaso, et al. Safety Design for Space Systems. 2009. (ENG., Illus.). 992p. 215.00 *(978-0-7506-8580-1(8)*, Butterworth-Heinemann) Elsevier Science & Technology Bks.

Shayler, David J. & Shayler, David. Space Rescue: Ensuring the Safety of Manned Spacecraft. 2008. (Springer Praxis Books / Space Exploration Ser.). (Illus.). 500p. pap. 39.95 *(978-0-387-69905-9(8)*, 0387699058, Springer-Praxis) Springer.

Space Directory: The Complete Guide to World Space Programmes & Operators. 510.00 *(978-0-7106-2330-0(5))* Jane's Information Group, Inc.

Space Operations: Mission Management, Technologies, & Current Applications. 2007. (Illus.). 662p. 109.95 *(978-1-56347-919-9(2))* American Institute of Aeronautics & Astronautics.

Spagnulo, Marcello, et al, eds. Space Program Management: Methods & Tools. 2012. (Space Technology Library: 28). (ENG., Illus.). xi, 331p. 129.00 ***(978-1-4614-3754-3(7))***, 1461437547) Springer.

Spitzmiller, Ted. Astronautics - Dawn of the Space Age Bk. 1: A Historical Perspective of Mankind's Efforts to Conquer the Cosmos. 2007. (Apogee Books Space Ser.). (ENG., Illus.). 232p. per. 24.95 *(978-1-894959-63-6(9))* Collector's Guide Publishing, Inc. CAN. Dist: Independent Pubs. Group.

Stott, Carole & Dorling Kindersley Publishing Staff. Space: From Earth to the Edge of the Universe. 2010. (ENG., Illus.). 360p. 40.00 *(978-0-7566-6738-2(0))* Dorling Kindersley Publishing, Inc.

Strengthening NASA's Technology Development Programs: Hearing Before the Subcommittee on Space & Aeronautics, Committee on Science & Technology, House of Representatives, One Hundred Eleventh Congress, First Session, October 22, 2009. 2010. (Illus.). iv, 63p. *(978-0-16-085953-3(0)*, 552-070-41144-5) United States Government Printing Office.

Sweetman, Bill & Ebner, Kimberley, eds. Jane's Space Systems & Industry. 23rd rev. ed. 2007. (Jane's Space Directory Ser.). (Illus.). 487p. *(978-0-7106-2813-8(7))* Jane's Information Group.

Ulivi, Paolo & Harland, David. Robotic Exploration of the Solar System: Part II: Hiatus & Renewal, 1983-1996. 2008. (Springer Praxis Books / Space Exploration Ser.). (Illus.). 400p. pap. 39.95 *(978-0-387-78904-0(9)*, 0387789049) Springer.

Walter, Ulrich. Astronautics. 2007. (ENG., Illus.). 508p. pap. 150.00 *(978-3-527-40685-2(9)*, Wiley-VCH) Wiley, John & Sons, Inc.

Walter Ulrich. Astronautics: The Physics of Space Flight. 2nd ed. 2012. (ENG.). 596p. 160.00 ***(978-3-527-41065-1(1))***; pap. 95.00 ***(978-3-527-41035-4(X))*** Wiley, John & Sons, Inc. (Wiley-VCH).

Warren, Derek A. & Conway, Bridget D., eds. Future of U. S. Human Spaceflight: Background & Issues. 2010. (Space Science, Exploration & Policies Ser.). (Illus.). x, 245p. 115.00 *(978-1-61668-774-8(6))* Nova Science Pubs., Inc.

Wolfe Tom. The Right Stuff. rev. ed. 2008. (ENG.). 368p. pap. 16.00 *(978-0-312-42756-6(5))* Picador.

Wu, Weiren. Shen Zhou Fei Chuan He Tan Yue Gong Cheng. 2008. (Illus.). 92p. *(978-7-5085-1355-3(X))* China Intercontinental Communication Ctr.

Zaehringer, Alfred & Whitfield, Steve. Rocket Science. 2008. (Apogee Books Space Ser.). (ENG.). 214p. pap. 21.95 *(978-1-894959-86-5(8))* Collector's Guide Publishing, Inc. CAN. Dist: Independent Pubs. Group.

Zhong yang dian shi tai (Beijing, China), "Bai jia jiang tan" lan mu zu Staff, contrib. by. Shen Zhou Fei Tian: Zhongguo Hang Tian de Cheng Jiu Yu Zhan Wang. 2008. (Illus.). 186p. *(978-7-300-09788-6(X))* China Renmin Univ.Pr.

ASTRONAUTICS—ACCIDENTS

Burns, Christopher. Deadly Decisions: How False Knowledge Sank the Titanic, Blew up the Shuttle, & Led America into War. 2008. (ENG., Illus.). 340p. bds. 26.98 *(978-1-59102-660-0(1))* Prometheus Bks., Pubs.

Cabbage, Michael & Harwood, William. Comm Check... The Final Flight of Shuttle Columbia. 2008. (ENG., Illus.). 336p. pap. 22.95 *(978-1-4391-0176-6(0)*, Free Pr.) Free Pr.

Chan, F. Kenneth. Spacecraft Collision Probability. 2007. 79.95 *(978-1-884989-18-6(7))* Aerospace Pr.

Ensuring the Safety of Human Spaceflight: Hearing Before the Subcommittee on Space & Aeronautics, Committee on Science & Technology, House of Representatives, One Hundred Eleventh Congress, First Session, December 2, 2009. 2010. (Illus.). iv, 138p. ***(978-0-16-087975-3(2)***, 552-070-42426-1) United States Government Printing Office.

Gordon, R. Michael. The Space Shuttle Program: How NASA Lost Its Way. 2008. (ENG., Illus.). 354p. pap. 45.00 *(978-0-7864-3434-3(1))* McFarland & Co., Inc. Pubs.

Ivanovich, Grujica & Ivanovich, Grujica S. Salyut: The First Space Station: Triumph & Tragedy. 2008. (Springer Praxis Books / Space Exploration Ser.). (Illus.). 300p. pap. 34.95 *(978-0-387-73585-6(2)*, 0387735852, Springer-Praxis) Springer.

Jones, Chris. Out of Orbit: The True Story of How Three Astronauts Found Themselves Hundreds of Miles above the Earth with No Way Home. 2008. (ENG., Illus.). 304p. pap. 15.00 *(978-0-7679-1991-3(2))* Broadway Bks.

Marshall, Albert C., et al. Space Nuclear Safety. 2008. (Illus.). *(978-0-89464-061-2(5))* Krieger Publishing Co.

Waterkeyn, Xavier. Air & Space Disasters of the World. 2009. (ENG.). 320p. 39.95 *(978-1-74110-550-6(1))* New Holland Pubs. Pty, Ltd. AUS. Dist: Tuttle Publishing.

ASTRONAUTICS—BIBLIOGRAPHY

Chapman, Albert T. & Chapman, Bert. Space Warfare & Defense: A Historical Encyclopedia & Research Guide, 1 vol. 2008. (Illus.). 403p. 95.00 *(978-1-59884-006-3(1)*, SPWADE1C) ABC-CLIO, LLC.

Nasa, ed. Space Scientists & Engineers: Selected Biographical & Bibliographical Listing, 1957-1961. 2011. 338p. 50.95 ***(978-1-258-10404-7(0))*** Literary Licensing, LLC.

Wilkinson, Ronald S., et al. Aeronautical & Astronautical Resources of the Library of Congress: A Comprehensive Guide. 2007. (Illus.). 463p. *(978-0-8444-1160-6(4))* Library of Congress.

ASTRONAUTICS—BIOGRAPHY

Billings, Richard N. & Schirra, Wally. Schirra's Space. (Bluejacket Bks.). (Illus.). 240p. pap. 19.95 *(978-1-55750-792-1(9))* Naval Institute Pr.

Chertok, Boris E. Rockets & People Vol. 2: Creating a Rocket Industry. 2006. (NASA History Ser.). (ENG., Illus.). 698p. 25.00 *(978-0-16-076672-5(9)*, U. S. National Aeronautics & Space Administration) United States Government Printing Office.

Hasday, Judy L. Ellen Ochoa. 2006. (Great Hispanic Heritage Ser.). (Illus.). 112p. (gr. 6-12). lib. bdg. 35.00 *(978-0-7910-8842-5(1)*, Chelsea Hse.) Facts On File, Inc.

Mudgway, Douglas J. William H. Pickering: America's Deep Space Pioneer: America's Deep Space Pioneer. rev. ed. 2008. (ENG., Illus.). 271p. 25.00 *(978-0-16-081536-2(3)*, History Office) United States Government Printing Office.

Mullane, Mike. Riding Rockets: The Outrageous Tales of a Space Shuttle Astronaut. 2007. (ENG., Illus.). 400p. pap. 16.99 *(978-0-7432-7683-2(3)*, Scribner) Scribner.

Neufeld, Michael. Von Braun: Dreamer of Space, Engineer of War. 2008. (Vintage Ser.). (ENG., Illus.). 624p. pap. 21.00 *(978-0-307-38937-4(5)*, Vintage) Knopf Doubleday Publishing Group.

O'Donoghue, Aileen. The Sky Is Not a Ceiling: An Astronomer's Faith. 2007. (Illus.). 180p. pap. 18.00 *(978-1-57075-703-7(8))* Orbis Bks.

Schoneberger, William A. Aeronautic Pathfinders: Celebrating Thirty-Three Years of Honoring Aeronautic & Space Pioneers with the Howard Hughes Memorial Award of the Aero Club of Southern California. 2012. pap. ***(978-1-57864-740-8(1))*** Donning Co. Pubs.

ASTRONAUTICS—COMMUNICATION SYSTEMS

Brambilla, Andrea. Artificial Intelligence in Space Systems. 2010. 116p. pap. *(978-3-8383-6888-7(6))* Lambert Academic Publishing.

Burns, Christopher. Deadly Decisions: How False Knowledge Sank the Titanic, Blew up the Shuttle, & Led America into War. 2008. (ENG., Illus.). 340p. bds. 26.98 *(978-1-59102-660-0(1))* Prometheus Bks., Pubs.

Maccone, Claudio. Deep Space Flight & Communications: Exploiting the Sun as a Gravitational Lens. (Springer Praxis Books / Astronautical Engineering Ser.). 2010. (ENG.). 416p. pap. 159.00 *(978-3-642-09202-2(0)*, 3642092020) 2009. 500p. 159.00 *(978-3-540-72942-6(9))* Springer.

National Research Council (U.S.), Committee to Review NASA's Space Communication Program Staff & United States, National Aeronautics and Space Administration Staff, contrib. by. Review of the Space Communications Program of NASA's Space Operations Mission Directorate. 2007. (ENG., Illus.). 98p. pap. 21.00 *(978-0-309-10297-1(9))* National Academies Pr.

Otoshi, Tom Y. Noise Temperature Theory & Applications for Deep Space Communications Antenna Systems. 2008. (Illus.). 300p. 145.00 *(978-1-59693-377-4(1))* Artech Hse., Inc.

Reid, Macgregor S. Low-Noise Systems in the Deep Space Network. 2008. (JPL Deep-Space Communications & Navigation Ser.: 15). (ENG., Illus.). 424p. 195.00 *(978-0-470-40228-3(8)*, Wiley) Wiley, John & Sons, Inc.

2007 International Workshop on Satellite & Space Communication. 2007. pap. 212.00 *(978-1-4244-0938-9(1)*, 07EX1664) IEEE.

ASTRONAUTICS—DATA PROCESSING

Ciriani, Tito A., et al, eds. Operations Research in Space & Air. 2010. (Applied Optimization Ser.). 464p. pap. 339.00 *(978-1-4419-5242-4(X)*, 144195242X) Springer.

Taylor, Brian J., ed. Methods & Procedures for the Verification & Validation of Artificial Neural Networks. 2010. (ENG., Illus.). xi, 277p. pap. 155.00 *(978-1-4419-3935-7(0)*, 1441939350) Springer.

ASTRONAUTICS—DICTIONARIES

Dickson, Paul. A Dictionary of the Space Age. 2009. (New Series in NASA History Ser.). (ENG.). 288p. (gr. 17). 52.00 *(978-0-8018-9115-1(5))* Johns Hopkins Univ. Pr.

Guilbert, Louis. Le Vocabulaire de l'Astronautique: Enquete Linguistique a l'Occasion de 5 Exploits de Cosmonautes. (FRE.). 33.95 *(978-0-8288-7795-4(5)*, F135670) French & European Pubns., Inc.

Gunston, Bill. The Cambridge Aerospace Dictionary. 2nd rev. ed. (Cambridge Aerospace Ser.). (ENG.). 816p. (C). 2011. pap. 50.00 *(978-0-521-27967-3(4))* 2009. 160.00 *(978-0-521-19165-4(3)*, Cambridge Univ. Pr.

McKenna-Lawlor, Susan M. P. & Ó Muirí, Damien, eds. An English-Irish Lexicon of Scientific & Technological Space-Related Terminology. 2010. 145p. 39.95 *(978-1-84682-269-8(6))* Four Courts Pr. IRL. Dist: International Specialized Bk. Services.

Williamson, Mark. The Cambridge Dictionary of Space Technology. 2010. (ENG., Illus.). 476p. pap. 36.99 *(978-0-521-14231-1(8))* Cambridge Univ. Pr.

ASTRONAUTICS—ECONOMIC ASPECTS

Seedhouse, Erik. Astronauts for Hire: The Emergence of a Commercial Astronaut Corps. 2012. (Springer Praxis Books / Space Exploration Ser.). (ENG., Illus.). xxv, 243p. pap. 34.95 ***(978-1-4614-0519-1(X)***, 146140519X) Springer.

ASTRONAUTICS—HISTORY

Andrews, James T. Red Cosmos: K. E. Tsiolkovskii, Grandfather of Soviet Rocketry. 2009. (Centennial of Flight Ser.). (ENG.). 166p. 49.00 *(978-1-60344-117-9(4))* Texas A&M Univ. Pr.

Barbree, Jay. Live from Cape Canaveral: Covering the Space Race, from Sputnik to Today. 2008. (Illus.). 336p. pap. 15.95 *(978-0-06-123393-7(5)*, Harper Paperbacks) HarperCollins Pubs.

Billings, Richard N. & Schirra, Wally. Schirra's Space. (Bluejacket Bks.). (Illus.). 240p. pap. 19.95 *(978-1-55750-792-1(9))* Naval Institute Pr.

Brodsky, Robert F. & Brodsky, Robert. On the Cutting Edge: Tales of a Cold War Engineer at the Dawn of the Nuclear, Guided Missile, Computer & Space Ages. 2006. (ENG., Illus.). 216p. pap. 18.00 *(978-1-884092-62-6(4))* Altschuler, Richard & Assocs., Inc.

Brzezinski, Matthew. Red Moon Rising: Sputnik & the Hidden Rivalries That Ignited the Space Age. 2008. (ENG., Illus.). 336p. pap. 17.00 *(978-0-8050-8858-8(X)*, Holt Paperback) Holt, Henry & Co.

—Red Moon Rising: Sputnik & the Hidden Rivalries That Ignited the Space Age. l.t. ed. 2007. (Thorndike Nonfiction Ser.). (Illus.). 629p. 29.95 *(978-1-4104-0279-0(7))* Thorndike Pr.

Cadbury, Deborah. Space Race: The Epic Battle Between America & the Soviet Union for Dominion of Space. 2007. (ENG., Illus.). 400p. per. 15.95 *(978-0-06-117628-9(1)*, HarperPerennial) HarperCollins Pubs.

Dean, James D. & Ulrich, Bertram. NASA/ART: 50 Years of Exploration. 2008. (ENG., Illus.). 176p. 40.00 *(978-0-8109-7287-2(5))* Abrams.

Dick, Steven J., ed. Remembering the Space Age: Proceedings of the 50th Anniversary Conference. 2009. (ENG., Illus.). 478p. 55.00 *(978-0-16-081723-6(4)*, U. S. National Aeronautics & Space Administration) United States Government Printing Office.

Dick, Steven J. & National Aeronautics and Space Administration, eds. Nasa's First 50 Years: Historical Perspectives - NASA 50th Anniversary Proceedings. 2010. (ENG., Illus.). 776p. 79.00 *(978-0-16-084965-7(9)*, U. S. National Aeronautics & Space Administration) United States Government Printing Office.

Dick, Steven J., et al. America in Space: NASA's First Fifty Years. 2007. (ENG., Illus.). 352p. 55.00 *(978-0-8109-9373-0(2))* Abrams.

Doran, Jamie & Bizony, Piers. Starman: The Truth Behind the Legend of Yuri Gagarin. 2011. (ENG., Illus.). 256p. pap. 16.00 *(978-0-8027-7950-2(6))* Walker & Co.

Dougherty, Kerrie & Elder, Donald C., eds. History of Rocketry & Astronautics: Proceedings of the Thirty-Second History Symposium of. 2007. (AAS History Ser.: Vol. 27). 416p. pap. 70.00 *(978-0-87703-536-7(9))* Univelt, Inc.

Eisman, Gene & Hardesty, Von. Epic Rivalry: The Inside Story of the Soviet & American Space Race. 2007. (ENG., Illus.). 304p. 28.00 *(978-1-4262-0119-6(2)*, National Geographic) National Geographic Society.

Elder, Donald C. & Dougherty, Kerrie. History of Rocketry & Astronautics: Proceedings of the Thirty-Second History Symposium of the International Academy of Astronautics: Melbourne, Australia, 1998. 2007. (AAS History Symposia Ser.: Vol. 27). (Illus.). xii, 403p. *(978-0-87703-535-0(0))* Univelt, Inc.

Erickson, Lance. Space Flight: History, Technology, & Operations. 2010. (ENG., Illus.). 668p. 25.00 *(978-0-86587-419-0(0))* Government Institutes.

Erickson, Lance K. Space Flight: History, Technology, & Operations. 2010. (ENG., Illus.). 668p. pap. 85.00 *(978-1-60590-685-0(9))* Government Institutes.

Evans, Ben. At Home in Space: The Eighties. 2011. (Springer Praxis Books / Space Exploration Ser.). (Illus.). 500p. pap. 39.95 *(978-1-4419-8809-6(2)*, 1441988092) Springer.

—Foothold in the Heavens: The Seventies. 2010. (Springer Praxis Books / Space Exploration Ser.). (Illus.). xv, 533p. pap. 44.95 *(978-1-4419-6341-3(3)*, 1441963413, Springer-Praxis) Springer.

Frank, Graham. Lunatrick. 2009. 432p. 32.25 *(978-1-60860-113-4(7)*, Strategic Bk. Publishing) AEG Literary Publishing Services, Inc.

French, Francis & Burgess, Colin. In the Shadow of the Moon: A Challenging Journey to Tranquility, 1965-1969. (Outward Odyssey: A People's History of S Ser.). (ENG., Illus.). 2010. 464p. pap. 22.95 *(978-0-8032-2979-2(8)*, Bison Bks.) 2007. 448p. 29.95 *(978-0-8032-1128-5(7))* Univ. of Nebraska Pr.

—Into That Silent Sea: Trailblazers of the Space Era, 1961-1965. 2009. (Outward Odyssey: A People's History of S Ser.). (ENG., Illus.). 440p. pap. 22.95 *(978-0-8032-2639-5(X)*, Bison Bks.) Univ. of Nebraska Pr.

Gainor, Chris. To a Distant Day: The Rocket Pioneers. 2008. (Outward Odyssey: A People's History of Spaceflight Ser.). (ENG., Illus.). 264p. 29.95 *(978-0-8032-2209-0(2))* Univ. of Nebraska Pr.

Hardesty, Von & Eisman, Gene. Epic Rivalry: The Inside Story of the Soviet & American Space Race. 2008. (ENG., Illus.). 304p. 16.95 *(978-1-4262-0321-3(7)*, National Geographic) National Geographic Society.

Jenkins, Dennis R. & Frank, Jorge R. Servicing the Hubble Space Telescope: Space Shuttle Atlantis - 2008. 2009. 120p. pap. 22.95 *(978-1-58007-138-3(4))* Specialty Pr. Pubs. & Wholesalers, Inc.

Johnson, Stephen B. Space Exploration & Humanity: A Historical Encyclopedia, 2 vols. 2010. (Illus.). E-Book *(978-1-85109-519-3(5))* ABC-CLIO, LLC.

Kranz, Gene. Failure Is Not an Option: Mission Control from Mercury to Apollo 13 & Beyond. 2009. (ENG., Illus.). 416p. pap. 16.00 *(978-1-4391-4881-5(3))* Simon & Schuster.

Liepack, Otfrid G., ed. History of Rocketry & Astronautics: 34th Proceedings of the History of Astronautics Symposia 2000, 1, 30. 2009. (ENG., Illus.). 346p. 80.00 *(978-0-87703-549-7(0)*, American Astronautical Society) Univelt, Inc.

Lipartito, Kenneth & Butler, Orville R. A History of the Kennedy Space Center. 2007. (ENG., Illus.). 496p. 39.95 *(978-0-8130-3069-2(2))* Univ. Pr. of Florida.

Madders, Kevin. A New Force at a New Frontier: Europe's Development in the Space Field in the Light of its Main Actors, Policies, Law & Activities from its Beginnings up to the Present. 2006. (ENG., Illus.). 632p. pap. 116.00 *(978-0-521-03022-9(6))* Cambridge Univ. Pr.

McDougall, Walter A. The Heavens & the Earth: A Political History of the Space Age. 2008. 580p. pap. 58.00 *(978-1-59740-428-0(4))* ACLS Humanities E-Book.

Moltz, James Clay. The Politics of Space Security: Strategic Restraint & the Pursuit of National Interests. 2008. (ENG.). 384p. 70.00 *(978-0-8047-5914-4(6))*; pap. 35.00 *(978-0-8047-6010-2(1))* Stanford Univ. Pr.

Moulin, Herve, ed. History of Rocketry & Astronautics: IAA History Symposia 1967-2000 Abstracts & Index, 1, 31. 2009. (ENG.). 386p. pap. 80.00 incl. cd-rom *(978-0-87703-552-7(0))*; (Illus.). 95.00 incl. cd-rom *(978-0-87703-551-0(2))* Univelt, Inc. (American Astronautical Society).

Nelson, Craig. Rocket Men: The Epic Story of the First Men on the Moon. 2010. (ENG.). 416p. (gr. 12). 17.00 *(978-0-14-311716-2(5)*, Penguin (Non-Classics)) Penguin Group (USA) Inc.

—Rocket Men: The Epic Story of the First Men on the Moon. l.t. ed. 2009. 616p. 31.95 *(978-1-4104-1854-8(5))* Thorndike Pr.

Powell, Joel W. & Lebrun, Art. Go for Launch: An Illustrated History of Cape Canaveral. 2010. (ENG., Illus.). 320p. pap. 29.95 *(978-1-926592-13-8(1))* Collector's Guide Publishing, Inc. CAN. Dist: Independent Pubs. Group.

Prelinger, Megan. Another Science Fiction: Advertising the Space Race 1957-1962. 2010. (ENG., Illus.). 240p. pap. 29.95 *(978-0-922233-35-9(7))* Blast Bks.

Pyne, Stephen J. Voyager: Exploration, Space, & the Third Great Age of Discovery. 2011. (ENG.). 464p. (gr. 12). 17.00 *(978-0-14-311959-3(1)*, Penguin (Non-Classics)) Penguin Group (USA) Inc.

—Voyager: Seeking Newer Worlds in the Third Great Age of Discovery. 2010. (ENG., Illus.). 464p. (gr. 12). 29.95 *(978-0-670-02183-3(0)*, Viking Adult) Penguin Group (USA) Inc.

Rinard, Judith E. Book of Flight: The Smithsonian National Air & Space Museum. 2nd ed. 2007. (ENG., Illus.). 128p. (J). (gr. 5-12). 24.95 *(978-1-55407-292-7(1))*; pap. 16.95 *(978-1-55407-275-0(1))* Firefly Bks., Ltd.

Skoog, A. Ingemar, ed. History of Rocketry & Astronautics (AAS History Series, Volume 35) 2011. 544p. pap. 75.00 ***(978-0-87703-568-8(7)***, American Astronautical Society) Univelt, Inc.

Winter, Frank H., ed. History of Rocketry & Astronautics: History Symposium of the International Academy of Astronautics (23d: 1999: Amsterdam, the Netherlands), 28. 2007. (AAS History Ser.: Vol. 28). (ENG.). 544p. pap. 70.00 *(978-0-87703-540-4(7)*, American Astronautical Society) Univelt, Inc.

—History of Rocketry & Astronautics: Proceedings of the Thirty-Third History Symposium of the International Academy of Astronautics (IAA) Amsterdam, the Netherlands, 28. 2007. (ENG., Illus.). 560p. 95.00 *(978-0-87703-539-8(3)*, American Astronautical Society) Univelt, Inc.

ASTRONAUTICS—INTERNATIONAL COOPERATION

Ezell, Edward Clinton & Ezell, Linda Neuman. The Partnership: A History of the Apollo-Soyuz Test Project. 2011. (Dover Books on Astronomy Ser.). (ENG., Illus.). 584p. pap. 29.95 *(978-0-486-47889-0(0))* Dover Pubns., Inc.

Jamison, David E., ed. The International Space Station. 2008. 69.00 *(978-1-60692-322-1(6))* Nova Science Pubs., Inc.

Manber, Jeffrey. Selling Peace: Inside the Soviet Conspiracy That Transformed the U. S. Space Program. 2010. (Apogee Books Space Ser.). (ENG.). 332p. pap. 28.95 *(978-1-926592-03-4(5))* Collector's Guide Publishing, Inc. CAN. Dist: Independent Pubs. Group.

National Aeronautics and Space Administration, compiled by. Reference Guide to the International Space Station. 2007. (ENG., Illus.). cd-rom 18.00 *(978-0-16-077627-4(9)*, U. S. National Aeronautics & Space Administration) United States Government Printing Office.

United Nations. Highlights in Space 2010. 2011. (ENG.). cd-rom 15.00 ***(978-92-1-101236-1(8))*** United Nations Pubns.

ASTRONAUTICS—JUVENILE LITERATURE

Bailey, Gerry. Space Challenge. 2011. (Planet SOS Ser.). (Illus.). 48p. (J). (gr. 3-6). lib. bdg. 31.95 *(978-1-4339-4982-1(2)*, Stevens, Gareth Learning Library) Stevens, Gareth Publishing LLLP.

ASTRONAUTICS—LAW AND LEGISLATION

see Space Law

ASTRONAUTICS—OPTICAL COMMUNICATION SYSTEMS

see also Lasers

Hemmati, Hamid. Free-Space Laser Communication Technologies XXI: 28-29 January 2009, San Jose, California, USA. 2009. (Proceedings of SPIE Ser.). (Illus.). 240p. pap. 70.00 *(978-0-8194-7445-2(2))* SPIE.

Hemmati, Hamid. Free-Space Laser Communication Technologies XXII: 26-28 January 2010, San Francisco, California, United States. 2010. (Proceedings of SPIE Ser.). (Illus.). 328p. pap. 80.00 ***(978-0-8194-7983-9(7))*** SPIE.

A

Ismail, Norhazwani Hanis. Free Space Optics. 2011. 80p. pap. (978-3-8443-0299-8(9)) Lambert Academic Publishing.

Majumdar, Arun K. & Davis, Christopher C. Free-Space Laser Communications IX: 2-3 August 2009, San Diego, California, United States. 2009. (Proceedings of SPIE Ser.). (Illus.). 340p. pap. 80.00 (978-0-8194-7754-5(0)) SPIE.

—Free-Space Laser Communications VII: 28-30 August 2007, San Diego, California, USA. 2007. (Proceedings of SPIE Ser.). (Illus.). 488p. pap. 105.00 (978-0-8194-6857-4(6)) SPIE.

—Free-Space Laser Communications VIII: 10-12 August 2008, San Diego, California, USA. 2008. (Proceedings of SPIE Ser.). (Illus.). 298p. pap. 80.00 (978-0-8194-7311-0(1)) SPIE.

Majumdar, Arun K. & Ricklin, Jennifer C., eds. Free-Space Laser Communications: Principles & Advances. 2010. (Optical & Fiber Communications Reports). (Illus.). xii, 418p. pap. 199.00 (978-1-4419-2108-6(7), 1441921087) Springer.

Mecherle, G. Stephen. Free-Space Laser Communication Technologies XX: 24 January 2008, San Jose, California, USA. 2008. (Proceedings of SPIE Ser.). (Illus.). 208p. pap. 70.00 (978-0-8194-7052-2(X)) SPIE.

Mecherle, G. Stephen & Korotkova, Olga. Free-Space Laser Communication Technologies XIX & Atmospheric Propagation of Electromagnetic Waves: 24-25 January 2007, San Jose, California, USA. 2007. (Proceedings of SPIE Ser.). (Illus.). 270p. pap. 70.00 (978-0-8194-6573-3(9)) SPIE.

Ricklin, Jennifer C. Free-Space Laser Communications: Principles & Advances. Majumdar, Arun, ed. 2007. (Optical & Fiber Communications Reports). (Illus.). 432p. 199.00 (978-0-387-28652-5(7), 0387286527) Springer.

ASTRONAUTICS—POPULAR WORKS

Grego, Peter. Voyage Through Space. 2008. (Qeb Space Guides). (Illus.). 32p. (J). (gr. 3-7). lib. bdg. 19.95 (978-1-59566-385-6(1)) QEB Publishing Inc.

Prochnow, Dave. 101 Outer Space Projects for the Evil Genius. 2007. (Evil Genius Ser.). (ENG., Illus.). 300p. per. 24.95 (978-0-07-148548-7(1), 0071485481, TAB/Electronics) McGraw-Hill Professional Publishing.

Swinerd, Graham. How Spacecraft Fly: Spaceflight Without Formulae. (ENG., Illus.). xvi, 272p. 2010. pap. 27.50 (978-1-4419-2629-6(1), 1441926291) 2008. 27.50 (978-0-387-76571-6(9), 0387765719, Copernicus) Springer.

Teacher Created Resources Staff. Voyage Through Space. 2008. (Qeb Space Guides). (ENG., Illus.). 32p. (gr. 4-13). pap. 6.99 (978-1-4206-8276-2(8)) Teacher Created Resources, Inc.

ASTRONAUTICS—PSYCHOLOGY

see Space Flight—Psychological Aspects

ASTRONAUTICS—RESEARCH

Committee on the Assessment of NASA Laboratory Capabilities & National Research Council. Capabilities for the Future: An Assessment of NASA Laboratories for Basic Research. 2010. (ENG., Illus.). 112p. pap. 29.75 (978-0-309-15351-5(4)) National Academies Pr.

Committee to Review NASA's Exploration Technology Development Program & National Research Council. Review of NASA's Exploration Technology Development Program — an Interim Report. 2008. (ENG.). 74p. pap. 21.00 (978-0-309-11943-6(X)) National Academies Pr.

Denis, John H. & Aldridge, Paul D., eds. Space Exploration Research. 2009. 129.00 (978-1-60692-264-4(5)) Nova Science Pubs., Inc.

External Perspectives on the Fiscal Year 2010 NASA Budget Request & Related Issues: Hearing Before the Subcommittee on Space & Aeronautics, Committee on Science & Technology, House of Representatives, One Hundred Eleventh Congress, First Session, June 18, 2009. 2010. (Illus.). iv, 102p. (978-0-16-086307-3(4), 552-070-41394-1) United States Government Printing Office.

Hall, Loretta. Out of This World: New Mexico's Contributions to Space Travel. 2011. pap. 19.95 (978-1-890689-79-7(3), Rio Grande Bks.) LPD Pr.

Kuchemann, D. Progress in Aerospace Sciences (Incorporating Progress in Astronautical Sciences), Vol. 8. pap. Franklin Bk. Co., Inc.

Montluc, Bertrand de. A New International Strategic Context for Space Policies. 2011. (Space Science, Exploration & Policies Ser.). (Illus.). viii, 99p. pap. 43.00 (978-1-61761-607-5(9), Nova Novinka) Nova Science Pubs., Inc.

NASA's Science Programs: Fiscal Year 2009 Budget Request & Issues: Hearing Before the Subcommittee on Space & Aeronautics, Committee on Science & Technology, House of Representatives, One Hundred Tenth Congress, Second Session, March 13, 2008. 2008. (Illus.). iii, 103p. (978-0-16-081797-7(8), 552-070-38003-5) United States Government Printing Office.

ASTRONAUTICS—STUDY AND TEACHING

Arthurs, Susan. Aerospace Activities - Ideas & Resources Grades 7-12, 1. 2007. cd-rom 49.00 (978-0-9792025-8-2(2)) Arthurs, S Enterprises, LLC.

—Aerospace Activities - Ideas & Resources Grades K-3. 2007. 60p. cd-rom 49.00 (978-0-9792025-6-8(6)) Arthurs, S Enterprises, LLC.

—Aerospace Education - Activities & Ideas Grades 7-12. 2006. 95p. spiral bd. (978-0-9792025-5-1(8)); cd-rom 45.00 (978-0-9792025-4-4(X)) Arthurs, S Enterprises, LLC.

Arthurs, Susan, compiled by. Aerospace Activities - Ideas & Resources Grades 4-6, 1. 2007. 86p. cd-rom 49.00 (978-0-9792025-7-5(4)) Arthurs, S Enterprises, LLC.

Committee for the Review and Evaluation of NASA's Precollege Education Program & National Research Council. NASA's Elementary & Secondary Education Program: Review & Critique. Quinn, Helen R. et al, eds. 2008. (ENG.). 162p. pap. 38.25 (978-0-309-11551-3(5)) National Academies Pr.

Rodgers, June Scobee. Silver Linings: My Life Before & after Challenger 7. 2010. (Illus.). 334p. 28.00 (978-1-57312-570-3(9)) Smyth & Helwys Publishing, Inc.

ASTRONAUTICS—SYSTEMS ENGINEERING

Aguirre, Miguel R. Introduction to Space Systems: Design & Synthesis. 2012. (Space Technology Library). (ENG., Illus.). xx, 586p. 129.95 (978-1-4614-3757-4(1), 1461437571) Springer.

Swinerd, Graham, et al, eds. Spacecraft Systems Engineering. 4th ed. 2011. (Aerospace Ser.: 25). (ENG., Illus.). 724p. 75.00 (978-0-470-75012-4(X), Wiley) Wiley, John & Sons, Inc.

ASTRONAUTICS—EUROPE

Chabás, José & Goldstein, Bernard R., eds. The Astronomical Tables of Giovanni Bianchini. 2009. (Illus.). 160p. (978-90-04-17615-7(2)) BRILL.

Geppert, Alexander C. T., ed. Imagining Outer Space: European Astroculture in the Twentieth Century. 2012. (ENG., Illus.). 416p. 105.00 (978-0-230-23172-6(1)) Palgrave Macmillan.

Johnson, Stephen B. The Secret of Apollo: Systems Management in American & European Space Programs. 2006. (New Series in NASA History Ser.). (ENG., Illus.). 312p. (gr. 17). per. 27.00 (978-0-8018-8542-6(6)) Johns Hopkins Univ. Pr.

Madders, Kevin. A New Force at a New Frontier: Europe's Development in the Space Field in the Light of its Main Actors, Policies, Law & Activities from its Beginnings up to the Present. 2006. (ENG., Illus.). 632p. pap. 116.00 (978-0-521-03022-9(6)) Cambridge Univ. Pr.

Mosley, Adam. Bearing the Heavens: Tycho Brahe & the Astronomical Community of the Late Sixteenth Century. 2011. (ENG.). 370p. pap. 45.00 (978-1-107-40365-9(0)) Cambridge Univ. Pr.

ASTRONAUTICS—SOVIET UNION

Andrews, James T. Red Cosmos: K. E. Tsiolkovskii, Grandfather of Soviet Rocketry. 2009. (Centennial of Flight Ser.). (ENG., Illus.). 168p. pap. 23.00 (978-1-60344-168-1(9)) Texas A&M Univ. Pr.

Andrews, James T. & Siddiqi, Asif A., eds. Into the Cosmos: Space Exploration & Soviet Culture. 2011. (Pitt Russian East European Ser.). (ENG., Illus.). 336p. pap. 27.95 (978-0-8229-6161-1(X)) Univ. of Pittsburgh Pr.

Cadbury, Deborah. Space Race: The Epic Battle Between America & the Soviet Union for Dominion of Space. 2007. (ENG., Illus.). 400p. per. 15.95 (978-0-06-117628-9(1), HarperPerennial) HarperCollins Pubs.

Doran, Jamie & Bizony, Piers. Starman: The Truth Behind the Legend of Yuri Gagarin. 2011. (ENG., Illus.). 256p. pap. 16.00 (978-0-8027-7950-2(6)) Walker & Co.

Eisman, Gene & Hardesty, Von. Epic Rivalry: The Inside Story of the Soviet & American Space Race. 2007. (ENG., Illus.). 304p. 28.00 (978-1-4262-0119-6(2), National Geographic) National Geographic Society.

Gordon, Yefim. Soviet Rocket Fighters. 2010. (Red Star Ser.). (ENG., Illus.). 127p. pap. 36.95 (978-1-85780-245-0(4)) Allan, Ian Publishing GBR. Dist: BookMasters Distribution Services (BDS).

Hardesty, Von & Eisman, Gene. Epic Rivalry: The Inside Story of the Soviet & American Space Race. 2008. (ENG., Illus.). 304p. 16.95 (978-1-4262-0321-3(7), National Geographic) National Geographic Society.

Harvey, Brian. The Rebirth of the Russian Space Program: 50 Years after Sputnik, New Frontiers. 2007. (Springer Praxis Books / Space Exploration Ser.). (Illus.). 355p. per. 44.95 (978-0-387-71354-0(9), 0387713549) Springer.

—Russian Planetary Exploration: History, Development, Legacy, Prospects. 2007. (Springer Praxis Books / Space Exploration Ser.). (Illus.). 351p. per. 44.95 (978-0-387-46343-8(7)) Springer.

Huntress, Wesley T., Jr. & Marov, Mikhail Ya. Soviet Robots in the Solar System: Mission Technologies & Discoveries. 2011. (Springer Praxis Books / Space Exploration Ser.). (ENG., Illus.). xx, 453p. pap. 44.95 (978-1-4419-7897-4(6), 1441978976) Springer.

Ivanovich, Grujica & Ivanovich, Grujica S. Salyut: The First Space Station: Triumph & Tragedy. 2008. (Springer Praxis Books / Space Exploration Ser.). (Illus.). 300p. pap. 34.95 (978-0-387-73585-6(2), 0387735852, Springer-Praxis) Springer.

Manber, Jeffrey. Selling Peace: Inside the Soviet Conspiracy That Transformed the U.S. Space Program. 2010. (Apogee Books Space Ser.). (ENG.). 332p. pap. 28.95 (978-1-926592-08-4(5)) Collector's Guide Publishing, Inc. CAN. Dist: Independent Pubs. Group.

Moltz, James. The Politics of Space Security: Strategic Restraint & the Pursuit of National Interests, Second Edition. 2011. (ENG.). 400p. pap. 35.00 (978-0-8047-7858-9(2)) Stanford Univ. Pr.

Moltz, James Clay. The Politics of Space Security: Strategic Restraint & the Pursuit of National Interests. 2008. (ENG.). 384p. 70.00 (978-0-8047-5914-4(6)); pap. 35.00 (978-0-8047-6010-2(1)) Stanford Univ. Pr.

Siddiqi, Asif A. The Red Rockets' Glare: Spaceflight & the Soviet Imagination, 1857-1957. 2010. (Cambridge Centennial of Flight Ser.). (ENG., Illus.). 414p. 89.00 (978-0-521-89760-0(2)) Cambridge Univ. Pr.

ASTRONAUTICS, ELECTRONICS IN

see Astrionics

ASTRONAUTICS, MILITARY

Chapman, Albert T. & Chapman, Bert. Space Warfare & Defense: A Historical Encyclopedia & Research Guide, 1 vol. 2008. (Illus.). 403p. 95.00 (978-1-59884-006-3(1), SPWADE1C) ABC-CLIO, LLC.

Chirila, Abel. Military Satellites: Issues, Goals & Challenges. 2009. (Defense, Security & Strategy Ser.). (Illus.). 117p. 79.00 (978-1-60741-238-0(1)) Nova Science Pubs., Inc.

Coletta, Damon & Pilch, Frances T., eds. Space & Defense Policy. 2009. pap. 39.95 (978-0-415-77879-4(4)) Routledge.

Fergusson, James & Wong, Wilson W. S. Military Space Power: A Guide to the Issues, 1 vol. Fergusson, James & Wong, Wilson W. S., eds. 2010. (Contemporary Military, Strategic, & Security Issues Ser.). (Illus.). 158p. instr.'s hndbk. ed. 34.95 (978-0-313-35680-3(7), C35680, Praeger Pubs.) Greenwood Publishing Group, Inc.

Gillen, Cale M. Alternatives for Military Space Radar. 2010. (Defense, Security & Strategies Ser.). 174p. 79.00 (978-1-60741-485-8(6)) Nova Science Pubs., Inc.

Gillespie, Paul G. & Weller, Grant T. Harnessing the Heavens: National Defense Through Space. 2008. xii, 235p. (978-1-879176-45-4(9)) Imprint Pubns., Inc.

Hays, Peter L. Space & Security: A Reference Handbook, 1 vol. 2011. (Contemporary World Issues Ser.). 289p. 55.00 (978-1-59884-421-4(0), A2855C); E-Book (978-1-59884-422-1(9)) ABC-CLIO, LLC.

—The US Military & Outer Space: Perspectives, Plans & Programs. 2013. (Space Power & Politics Ser.). (ENG.). 240p. (C). 130.00 (978-0-415-36654-0(2)) Routledge.

Hearing on National Defense Authorization ACT for Fiscal Year 2007 & Oversight of Previously Authorized Programs Before the Committee on Armed Services, House of Representatives, One Hundred Ninth Congress, Second Session: Strategic Forces Subcommittee Hearing on Budget Request for Space Activities, Hearing Held, March 16, 2006. 2007. iii, 108p. (978-0-16-079571-8(0), 552-070-36538-9) United States Government Printing Office.

Hearing on National Defense Authorization ACT for Fiscal Year 2008 & Oversight of Previously Authorized Programs Before the Committee on Armed Services, House of Representatives, One Hundred Tenth Congress, First Session: Strategic Forces Subcommittee Hearing on Budget Request for Military Space Activities, Hearing Held, March 23, 2007. 2008. iii, 105p. (978-0-16-082401-2(X), 552-070-38446-4) United States Government Printing Office.

Hearing on National Defense Authorization ACT for Fiscal Year 2009 & Oversight of Previously Authorized Programs Before the Committee on Armed Services, House of Representatives, One Hundred Tenth Congress, Second Session: Strategic Forces Subcommittee Hearing on Budget Request & Status of Space Activities, Hearing Held, March 5, 2008. 2009. iii, 97p. (978-0-16-083346-5(9), 552-070-39170-3) United States Government Printing Office.

IDSA-Indian Pugwash Society Working Group on Space Security Staff, et al, contrib. by. Space Security: Need for a Proactive Approach: Report of the IDSA-Indian Pugwash Society Working Group on Space Security. 2011. (Illus.). 112p. 35.95 (978-81-7188-762-0(7)) Academic Foundation IND. Dist: Independent Pubs. Group.

Johnson, Stephen B. The Secret of Apollo: Systems Management in American & European Space Programs. 2006. (New Series in NASA History Ser.). (ENG., Illus.). 312p. (gr. 17). per. 27.00 (978-0-8018-8542-6(6)) Johns Hopkins Univ. Pr.

Kalic, Sean N. US Presidents & the Militarization of Space, 1946-1967. 2012. (Centennial of Flight Ser.). (ENG.). 224p. 40.00 (978-1-60344-691-4(5)) Texas A&M Univ. Pr.

Klein, John J. Space Warfare. 2006. 39.95 (978-0-415-40796-0(6)) Routledge.

Lele, Ajey & Singh, Gunjan, eds. Space Security & Global Cooperation. 2009. (ENG., Illus.). 264p. 59.95 (978-81-7188-741-5(4)) Academic Foundation IND. Dist: Independent Pubs. Group.

Lloyd, Richmond M. & Naval War College Press (U.S.) Staff, eds. American Foreign Policy: Regional Perspectives: Proceedings, a Workshop Sponsored by the William B. Ruger Chair of National Security Economics, Newport, Rhode Island, 13-15 May 2009. 2009. (William B. Ruger Chair of National Security Economics Papers). (ENG., Illus.). 303p. pap. 29.00 (978-1-884733-70-3(0), Dept. of the Navy) United States Government Printing Office.

Manzo, Vincent A., et al. Toward a Theory of Spacepower: Selected Essays. Lutes, Charles D. et al, eds. 2011. (ENG.). 366p. pap. 33.00 (978-0-16-087786-5(5), National Defense University) United States Government Printing Office.

McCartney, Forrest, et al. National Security Space Launch Report. 2006. (Illus.). 110p. pap. 65.00 (978-0-8330-3959-0(8), mg503) RAND Corp., The.

Norris, Pat. Spies in the Sky: Surveillance Satellites in War & Peace. 2007. (Springer Praxis Books / Space Exploration Ser.). (Illus.). 220p. per. 34.95 (978-0-387-71672-5(6), 0387716726, Springer-Praxis) Springer.

Pekkanen, Saadia M. & Kallender-Umezu, Paul. In Defense of Japan: From the Market to the Military in Space Policy. 2010. (ENG., Illus.). 408p. 55.00 (978-0-8047-0063-4(X)) Stanford Univ. Pr.

Pilch, Frances. Space & Defense Policy. Coletta, Damon, ed. 2009. (Space Power & Politics Ser.). (ENG., Illus.). 368p. (C). 150.00 (978-0-415-77732-2(1)) Routledge.

The Posture of the U.S. Strategic Command (USSTRATCOM) Hearing Before the Strategic Forces Subcommittee of the Committee on Armed Services, House of Representatives, One Hundred Tenth Congress, First Session, Hearing Held, March 8, 2007. 2008. iii, 71p. (978-0-16-081824-0(9), 552-070-38022-1) United States Government Printing Office.

Shannon, Christopher C., et al. Finding the Shape of Space. 2011. (978-1-58566-208-1(9)) Air University Pr.

Smith, M. V. Ten Propositions Regarding Space Power. 2011. 156p. pap. 21.36 (978-1-60888-060-7(5)) Nimble Bks. LLC.

Snyder, Don, et al. Sustaining Air Force Space Systems: A Model for the Global Positioning System. 2007. (Illus.). 66p. pap. 23.00 (978-0-8330-4044-2(8)) RAND Corp., The.

Space & U.S. National Power: Hearing Before the Strategic Forces Subcommittee of the Committee on Armed Services, House of Representatives, One Hundred Ninth Congress, Second Session, Hearing Held, June 21, 2006. 2007. iii, 93p. (978-0-16-079191-8(X), 552-070-36278-9) United States Government Printing Office.

Space & U.S. Security: Hearing Before the Strategic Forces Subcommittee of the Committee on Armed Services, House of Representatives, One Hundred Eleventh Congress, First Session, Hearing Held March 18, 2009. 2010. iii, 62p. (978-0-16-085908-3(5), 552-070-41104-6) United States Government Printing Office.

Space Systems Acquisition & the Industrial Base: Hearing Before the Strategic Forces Subcommittee of the Committee on Armed Services, House of Representatives, One Hundred Eleventh Congress, First Session, Hearing Held, April 30, 2009. 2010. (Illus.). iii, 73p. (978-0-16-085924-3(7), 552-070-41120-8) United States Government Printing Office.

Thomas, Kenneth S. & McMann, Harold J. U. S. Spacesuits. 2nd ed. 2011. (Springer Praxis Books / Space Exploration Ser.). (ENG., Illus.). xxxv, 472p. pap. 44.95 (978-1-4419-9565-0(X), 144199565X) Springer.

Tripp, Robert S. Space Command Sustainment Review: Improving the Balance Between Current & Future Capabilities. 2007. 166p. pap. 26.50 (978-0-8330-4014-5(6), mg-518) RAND Corp., The.

ASTRONAUTICS AND CIVILIZATION

see also Religion and Astronautics; Space Law

Bainum, Peter M., et al, eds. Applications of Space Technology for Humanity (Volume 138 of the Advances in the Astronautical Sciences Series) Twelfth ISCOPS (formerly PISSTA) AAS/JRS/CSA Symposium 2010, Vol.138. 2010. (Illus.). 762p. 190.00 incl. cd-rom (978-0-87703-562-6(8)) Univelt, Inc.

Geppert, Alexander C. T., ed. Imagining Outer Space: European Astroculture in the Twentieth Century. 2012. (ENG., Illus.). 416p. 105.00 (978-0-230-23172-6(1)) Palgrave Macmillan.

Johnson, Stephen B. Space Exploration & Humanity: A Historical Encyclopedia, 2 vols. 2010. (Illus.). E-Book (978-1-85109-519-3(5)) ABC-CLIO, LLC.

McCray, W. Patrick. Keep Watching the Skies! The Story of Operation Moonwatch & the Dawn of the Space Age. 2008. (ENG., Illus.). 324p. (C). 31.95 (978-0-691-12854-2(5)) Princeton Univ. Pr.

Olla, Phillip. Space Technologies for the Benefit of Human Society & Earth. 2009. (ENG., Illus.). xxx, 554p. 229.00 (978-1-4020-9572-6(4), 1402095724) Springer.

Olla, Phillip, ed. Commerce in Space: Infrastructures, Technologies & Applications. 2007. (Premier Reference Source Ser.). (Illus.). 400p. 180.00 (978-1-59904-624-2(5)) IGI Global.

Sadeh, Eligar, ed. Space Strategy in the 21st Century: Theory & Policy. 2012. (Space Power & Politics Ser.). (ENG.). 272p. (C). 135.00 (978-0-415-62211-0(5)) Routledge.

Sheldon, John. Theory of Space Power: The Perils of Strategic Analogy. 2013. (Space Power & Politics Ser.). (ENG.). 224p. (C). 130.00 (978-0-415-47715-4(8)) Routledge.

Smith, M. V. Ten Propositions Regarding Space Power. 2011. 156p. pap. 21.36 (978-1-60888-060-7(5)) Nimble Bks. LLC.

Woodmansee, Laura S. Sex in Space. 2006. (Apogee Books Space Ser.: 59). (ENG., Illus.). 136p. per. 17.95 (978-1-894959-44-5(2), Apogee Bks.) Collector's Guide Publishing, Inc. CAN. Dist: Independent Pubs. Group.

ASTRONAUTICS AND RELIGION

see Religion and Astronautics

ASTRONAUTICS AND STATE

Andrews, James T. & Siddiqi, Asif A., eds. Into the Cosmos: Space Exploration & Soviet Culture. 2011. (Pitt Russian East European Ser.). (ENG., Illus.). 336p. pap. 27.95 (978-0-8229-6161-1(X)) Univ. of Pittsburgh Pr.

Brünner, Christian & Soucek, Alexander, eds. Outer Space in Society, Politics & Law. 2011. (Studies in Space Policy Ser.). (ENG., Illus.). xxi, 876p. 279.00 (978-3-7091-0663-1(X), 370910663X) Springer.

The Case for Space: Examining the Value: Hearing Before the Subcommittee on Science & Space of the Committee on Commerce, Science, & Transportation, United States Senate, One Hundred Eleventh Congress, First Session, October 21, 2009. 2010. iii, 40p. (978-0-16-086159-8(4), 552-070-1259-0) United States Government Printing Office.

Coletta, Damon & Pilch, Frances T., eds. Space & Defense Policy. 2009. pap. 39.95 (978-0-415-77879-4(4)) Routledge.

Dickson, Paul. Sputnik: The Shock of the Century. 2011. (ENG., Illus.). 320p. pap. 16.00 (978-0-8027-7951-9(4)) Walker & Co.

Dorai, Luigi, et al, eds. Rethinking European Spatial Policy as a Hologram: Actions, Institutions & Discourses. 2006. (Urban & Regional Planning & Development Ser.). (Illus.). 338p. 130.00 (978-0-7546-4548-1(7)) Ashgate Publishing Co.

The Growth of Global Space Capabilities: What Is Happening & Why It Matters: Hearing Before the Subcommittee on Space & Aeronautics, Committee on Science & Technology, House of Representatives, One Hundred Eleventh Congress, First Session, November 19, 2009. 2010. (Illus.). iv, 81p. (978-0-16-086079-9(2), 552-070-41191-7) United States Government Printing Office.

Harding, Robert C. Space Policy in Developing Countries: Security & Development on the Final Frontier. 2012. (Space Power & Politics Ser.). (ENG., Illus.). 248p. (C). 135.00 (978-0-415-53845-9(9)) Routledge.

Harvey, Brian, et al. Emerging Space Powers: The New Space Programs of Asia, the Middle East & South-America. 2010. (Springer Praxis Books / Space Exploration Ser.). (ENG., Illus.). 732p. pap. 44.95 (978-1-4419-0873-5(0), 1441908730, Springer-Praxis) Springer.

Hays, Peter L. Space & Security: A Reference Handbook. 1 vol. 2011. (Contemporary World Issues Ser.). 289p. 55.00 (978-1-59884-421-4(0), A2855C); E-Book (978-1-59884-422-1(9)) ABC-CLIO, LLC.

Hearing on National Defense Authorization ACT for Fiscal Year 2007 & Oversight of Previously Authorized Programs Before the Committee on Armed Services, House of Representatives, One Hundred Ninth Congress, Second Session: Strategic Forces Subcommittee Hearing on Budget Request for Space Activities, Hearing Held, March 16, 2006. 2007. iii, 108p. (978-0-16-079571-8(0), 552-070-36538-9) United States Government Printing Office.

Hearing on National Defense Authorization ACT for Fiscal Year 2008 & Oversight of Previously Authorized Programs Before the Committee on Armed Services, House of Representatives, One Hundred Tenth Congress, First Session: Strategic Forces Subcommittee Hearing on Budget Request for Military Space Activities, Hearing Held, March 23, 2007. 2008. iii, 105p. (978-0-16-082401-2(X), 552-070-38446-4) United States Government Printing Office.

Hearing on National Defense Authorization ACT for Fiscal Year 2009 & Oversight of Previously Authorized Programs Before the Committee on Armed Services, House of Representatives, One Hundred Tenth Congress, Second Session: Strategic Forces Subcommittee Hearing on Budget Request & Status of Space Activities, Hearing Held, March 5, 2008. 2009. iii, 97p. (978-0-16-083346-5(9), 552-070-39170-3) United States Government Printing Office.

Hogan, Thor. Mars Wars: the Rise & Fall of the Space Exploration Initiative: The Rise & Fall of the Space Exploration Initiative. National Aeronautics and Space Administration, ed. 2009. (ENG.). 194p. pap. 15.00 (978-0-16-083157-7(1), U. S. National Aeronautics & Space Administration) United States Government Printing Office.

Institute of Electrical and Electronics Engineers Staff, contrib. by. 2007 3rd International Conference on Recent Advances in Space Technologies. 2007. pap. 340.00 (978-1-4244-1056-9(8), 07EX1710) IEEE.

Jamison, David E., ed. The International Space Station. 2008. 69.00 (978-1-60692-322-1(6)) Nova Science Pubs., Inc.

Johnson-Freese, Joan. Heavenly Ambitions: America's Quest to Dominate Space. 2009. 192p. (C). 32.50 (978-0-8122-4169-3(X)) Univ. of Pennsylvania Pr.

Key Issues & Challenges Facing NASA: Views of the Agency's Watchdogs: Hearing Before the Subcommittee on Space & Aeronautics, Committee on Science & Technology, House of Representatives, One Hundred Eleventh Congress, Second Session, February 3, 2010. 2010. iv, 73p. (978-0-16-086201-4(9), 552-070-41299-9) United States Government Printing Office.

Li, Zhen & Handberg, Roger. Chinese Space Policy: A Study in Domestic & International Politics. 2006. (Space Power & Politics Ser.). (Illus.). 202p. 170.00 (978-0-415-36582-6(1)) Routledge.

Logsdon, John M. John F. Kennedy & the Race to the Moon. 2010. (Palgrave Studies in the History of Science & Technology Ser.). (ENG., Illus.). 308p. 37.00 (978-0-230-11010-6(X)) Palgrave Macmillan.

Ludwig, George H. Opening Space Research Dreams, Technology, & Scientific Discovery. 2011. (978-0-87590-733-8(4)) American Geophysical Union.

McCartney, Forrest, et al. National Security Space Launch Report. 2006. (Illus.). 110p. pap. 65.00 (978-0-8330-3959-0(8), mg503) RAND Corp., The.

McCurdy, Howard E. Space & the American Imagination. 2nd ed. 2011. (ENG., Illus.). 408p. (C). (gr. 13-17). 60.00 (978-0-8018-9867-9(6)); pap. 30.00 (978-0-8018-9868-6(4)) Johns Hopkins Univ. Pr.

—The Space Station Decision: Incremental Politics & Technological Choice. 2007. (New Series in NASA History Ser.). (ENG., Illus.). 290p. (gr. 17). pap. 27.00 (978-0-8018-8749-9(6)) Johns Hopkins Univ. Pr.

McDougall, Walter A. The Heavens & the Earth: A Political History of the Space Age. 2008. 580p. pap. 58.00 (978-1-59740-428-0(4)) ACLS Humanities E-Book.

Moltz, James. The Politics of Space Security: Strategic Restraint & the Pursuit of National Interests, Second Edition. 2011. (ENG.). 400p. pap. 35.00 (978-0-8047-7858-9(2)) Stanford Univ. Pr.

Moltz, James Clay. Asia's Space Race: National Motivations, Regional Rivalries, & International Risks. 2011. (Contemporary Asia in the World Ser.). (ENG.). 283p. (gr. 17). 35.00 (978-0-231-15688-2(X)) Columbia Univ. Pr.

Montluc, Bertrand de. A New International Strategic Context for Space Policies. 2011. (Space Science, Exploration & Policies Ser.). (Illus.). viii, 99p. pap. 43.00 (978-1-61761-607-5(9), Nova Novinka) Nova Science Pubs., Inc.

Moore, Mike. Twilight War: The Folly of U. S. Space Dominance. 2008. (ENG.). 416p. 24.95 (978-1-59813-018-8(8)) Independent Institute, The.

NASA's Exploration Initiative: Status & Issues: Hearing Before the Subcommittee on Space & Aeronautics, Committee on Science & Technology, House of Representatives, One Hundred Tenth Congress, Second Session, April 3, 2008. 2008. iii, 108p. (978-0-16-081715-1(3), 552-070-37939-8) United States Government Printing Office.

National Aeronautics and Space Administration, compiled by. Leadership in Space: Selected Speeches of NASA Administrator Michael Griffin, May 2005 - October 2008. 2008. (ENG., Illus.). 141p. 43.00 (978-0-16-081565-2(7), U. S. National Aeronautics & Space Administration) United States Government Printing Office.

Olivea, Andrew E., ed. United States in Space: National Security Strategy & National Space Policy. 2011. (Series: Space Science, Exploration & Policies Ser.). 80p. pap. 47.00 (978-1-61324-303-9(0)) Nova Science Pubs., Inc.

Options & Issues for NASA's Human Space Flight Program: Report of the "Review of U.S. Human Space Flight Plans" Committee: Hearing Before the Committee on Science & Technology, House of Representatives, One Hundred Eleventh Congress, First Session, September 15, 2009. 2010. (Illus.). iv, 132p. (978-0-16-086607-4(3), 552-070-41595-5) United States Government Printing Office.

Pekkanen, Saadia M. & Kallender-Umezu, Paul. In Defense of Japan: From the Market to the Military in Space Policy. 2010. (ENG., Illus.). 408p. 55.00 (978-0-8047-0063-4(X)) Stanford Univ. Pr.

Pilch, Frances. Space & Defense Policy. Coletta, Damon, ed. 2009. (Space Power & Politics Ser.). (ENG., Illus.). 368p. (C). 150.00 (978-0-415-77732-2(1)) Routledge.

Pollpeter, Kevin. Building for the Future: China's Progress in Space Technology during the Tenth 5-Year Plan & the U. S. Response. 2008. (978-1-58487-347-1(7)) Strategic Studies Institute, U.S. Army War College Commandant (AWCC-DSI/Pubns.).

Ramos, John P. Space Policy & its Ramifications. 2011. (Space Science, Exploration & Policies Ser.). 129.00 (978-1-61761-555-9(2)) Nova Science Pubs., Inc.

Sadeh, Eligar. The Politics of Space: A Survey. 2010. (ENG., Illus.). 320p. 230.00 (978-1-85743-419-4(6), Routledge) Taylor & Francis Group GBR. Dist: Taylor & Francis Group.

Schrogl, Kai-Uwe, et al, eds. Yearbook on Space Policy 2007/2008: From Policies to Programmes. 2012. (Yearbook on Space Policy Ser.). (ENG., Illus.). xxiii, 311p. pap. 189.00 (978-3-211-99949-3(3), 3211999493) Springer.

—Yearbook on Space Policy 2009/2010: Space for Society. 2011. (Yearbook on Space Policy Ser.). (ENG., Illus.). xxii, 357p. 179.00 (978-3-7091-0941-0(8), 3709109418) Springer.

Schrogl, Kai-Uwe, et al. Threats, Risks & Sustainability - Answers by Space: Answers by Space. 2009. (Studies in Space Policy Ser.). (ENG., Illus.). x, 321p. 189.00 (978-3-211-87449-3(6)) Springer.

Shannon, Christopher C., et al. Finding the Shape of Space. 2011. (978-1-58566-208-1(9)) Air University Pr.

Sheehan, Michael. The International Politics of Space: No Final Frontier. 2007. (Space Power & Politics Ser.). (Orig.). 238p. per. 43.95 (978-0-415-39917-3(3)); 248p. 170.00 (978-0-415-39807-7(X)) Routledge.

Smith, Lesley Jane & Baumann, Ingo. Contracting for Space: Contract Practice in the European Space Sector. 2011. (Illus.). 456p. 180.00 (978-1-4094-1923-5(1)) Ashgate Publishing Co.

Smith, M. V. Ten Propositions Regarding Space Power. 2011. 156p. pap. 21.36 (978-1-60888-060-7(5)) Nimble Bks. LLC.

Space & U.S. National Power: Hearing Before the Strategic Forces Subcommittee of the Committee on Armed Services, House of Representatives, One Hundred Ninth Congress, Second Session, Hearing Held, June 21, 2006. 2007. iii, 93p. (978-0-16-079191-8(X), 552-070-36278-9) United States Government Printing Office.

Tyson, Neil deGrasse & Lang, Avis. Space Chronicles: Facing the Ultimate Frontier. 2012. (ENG.). 240p. 26.95 (978-0-393-08210-4(5), 8210) Norton, W. W. & Co., Inc.

ASTRONAUTICS IN ASTRONOMY

see also Space Astronomy

Cram101 Textbook Reviews. Outlines & Highlights for the Sun from Space by Kenneth R Lang. 2011. 110p. pap. 28.95 (978-1-61490-117-4(1)) Cram101 Inc.

Jenkins, Dennis R. & Frank, Jorge R. Servicing the Hubble Space Telescope: Space Shuttle Atlantis - 2008. 2009. 120p. pap. 22.95 (978-1-58007-138-3(4)) Specialty Pr. Pubs. & Wholesalers, Inc.

Lang, Kenneth R. The Sun from Space. 2nd ed. 2008. (Astronomy & Astrophysics Library). (Illus.). 410p. 109.00 (978-3-540-76952-1(8)) Springer.

Strong, Avaine. Deployment/Stationkeeping Dynamics of N Body Orbiting Sat Constellation. 2009. 264p. pap. (978-3-639-12555-9(X)) VDM Verlag Dr. Mueller e.K.

Vulpetti, Giovanni, et al. Solar Sails: A Novel Approach to Interplanetary Travel. 2008. (ENG., Illus.). xvi, 256p. 27.50 (978-0-387-34404-1(7), 0387344047) Springer.

ASTRONAUTICS IN EARTH SCIENCES

Committee on Scientific Accomplishments of Earth Observations from Space & National Research Council. Earth Observations from Space: The First 50 Years of Scientific Achievements. 2007. (ENG.). 144p. pap. 34.75 (978-0-309-11095-2(5)) National Academies Pr.

Li, Deren, et al. International Conference on Earth Observation Data Processing & Analysis (ICEODPA) 28-30 December 2008, Wuhan, China, 3 vols. 2008. (Proceedings of SPIE Ser.). (Illus.). 1764p. pap. 250.00 (978-0-8194-7545-9(9)) SPIE.

ASTRONAUTICS IN GEODESY

Plag, Hans-Peter & Pearlman, Michael, eds. Global Geodetic Observing System: Meeting the Requirements of a Global Society on a Changing Planet in 2020. 2009. (ENG., Illus.). xliv, 332p. 209.00 (978-3-642-02686-7(9), 3642026869) Springer.

ASTRONAUTICS IN METEOROLOGY

see also Artificial Satellites; Meteorological Satellites

Conway, Erik M. Atmospheric Science at NASA: A History. 2008. (New Series in NASA History Ser.). (ENG., Illus.). 416p. (gr. 17). 57.00 (978-0-8018-8984-4(7)) Johns Hopkins Univ. Pr.

ASTRONAUTICS IN OCEANOGRAPHY

Barale, Vittorio, et al, eds. Oceanography from Space. 2010. (ENG., Illus.). xvi, 361p. 179.00 (978-90-481-8680-8(3), 9048186803) Springer.

ASTRONAUTS

ABBE Scientist Research Division Staff. Aerospace Medicine & Astronaut Health in Space: Index, Reference & Medical Analysis of New Research Information for All Nations. 2008. (Illus.). 160p. ring bd. 69.95 (978-0-7883-3865-6(X)) ABBE Pubs. Assn. of Washington, D.C.

Aldrin, Buzz, Jr. & Abraham, Ken. Magnificent Desolation: The Long Journey Home from the Moon. (ENG., Illus.). 2010. 352p. pap. 16.00 (978-0-307-46346-3(X), Three Rivers Pr.) 2009. 336p. 27.00 (978-0-307-46345-6(1), Harmony) Crown Publishing Group.

Ansari, Anousheh & Hickam, Homer. My Dream of Stars: From Daughter of Iran to Space Pioneer. (ENG., Illus.). 256p. 2011. pap. 16.00 (978-0-230-11221-6(8)) 2010. 25.00 (978-0-230-61993-7(2)) Palgrave Macmillan.

Burgess, Colin. First Soviet Cosmonaut Team. 2008. (Springer Praxis Books / Space Exploration Ser.). (Illus.). 356p. pap. 39.95 (978-0-387-84823-5(1), Springer-Praxis) Springer.

—Selecting the Mercury Seven: The Search for America's First Astronauts. 2011. (Springer Praxis Books / Space Exploration Ser.). (ENG., Illus.). xxv, 371p. pap. 44.95 (978-1-4419-8404-3(6), 1441984046) Springer.

Burgess, Colin & Shayler, David J. NASA's Scientist-Astronauts. 2006. (Springer Praxis Books / Space Exploration Ser.). (Illus.). 543p. per. 52.95 (978-0-387-21897-7(1), 0387218971, Springer-Praxis) Springer.

Carpenter, Scott M., et al. We Seven: By the Astronauts Themselves. 2010. (ENG., Illus.). 352p. pap. 15.00 (978-1-4391-8103-4(9)) Simon & Schuster.

Cezzar, Juliette. Paper Astronaut: The Paper Spacecraft Mission Manual. 2009. (ENG., Illus.). 208p. pap. 9.95 (978-0-7893-1881-7(4)) Universe Publishing.

Chaikin, Andrew & Kohl, Victoria. Voices from the Moon: Apollo Astronauts Describe Their Lunar Experiences. 2009. (ENG., Illus.). 224p. (gr. 12-18). 29.95 (978-0-670-02078-2(8), Studio) Penguin Group (USA) Inc.

Chen, Shanguang. Fei Tian Yao Lan: Tai Kong Xing Zou Hang Tian Yuan Shi Zen Yang Lian Cheng de: Cradle to Space. 2008. (Illus.). 173p. (978-7-5357-5468-4(6)) Hunan Science & Technology Press, China.

Chien, Philip. Columbia: Final Voyage. 2010. (ENG., Illus.). x, 454p. pap. 27.50 (978-1-4419-2092-8(7), 1441920927) Springer.

Chouker, Alexander, ed. Stress Challenges & Immunity in Space: From Mechanisms to Monitoring & Preventive Strategies. 2012. (ENG., Illus.). xiii, 469p. 239.00 (978-3-642-22271-9(4), 3642222714) Springer.

Christopher, John. The Apollo Story. 2010. (Story Ser.). (ENG., Illus.). 128p. 16.95 (978-0-7524-5173-2(1)) History Pr. Ltd., The GBR. Dist: Independent Pubs. Group.

—The Shuttle Story. 2010. (Story Ser.). (ENG., Illus.). 128p. 16.95 (978-0-7524-5174-9(X)) History Pr. Ltd., The GBR. Dist: Independent Pubs. Group.

Collins, Michael. Carrying the Fire: An Astronaut's Journeys. 40th ed. 2009. (ENG., Illus.). 512p. pap. 16.00 (978-0-374-53194-2(3)) Farrar, Straus & Giroux.

Committee for Evaluation of Space Radiation Cancer Risk Model, et al. Technical Evaluation of the NASA Model for Cancer Risk to Astronauts Due to Space Radiation. 2012. (ENG.). 86p. pap. 36.00 (978-0-309-25305-5(5)) National Academies Pr.

Committee on Human Spaceflight Crew Operations & National Research Council. Preparing for the High Frontier: The Role & Training of NASA Astronauts in the Post- Space Shuttle Era. 2011. (ENG.). 104p. pap. 37.00 (978-0-309-21869-6(1)) National Academies Pr.

Cooper Jr, L. Gordon, et al. The Astronauts: Pioneers in Space. 2011. 92p. 38.95 (978-1-258-04364-3(5)) Literary Licensing, LLC.

Cunningham, Walter. The All American Boys. 2009. (ENG.). 448p. pap. 7.99 (978-1-59687-408-4(2)) IBks., Inc.

—The All American Boys. 2011. (ENG.). 448p. pap. 16.95 (978-1-59687-345-2(0)) IBks., Inc.

Downey, Craig A. Six Steps to the Moon. 2009. (Illus.). x, 175p. (978-1-4415-6566-2(3)) Xlibris Corp.

Enders, Lawrence J. Surviving Serendipity. 2011. 212p. 29.99 (978-1-4628-5667-1(5)); pap. 19.99 (978-1-4628-5666-4(7)) Xlibris Corp.

Fanning, Diane. Out There: The In-Depth Story of the Astronaut Love Triangle Case That Shocked America. 2007. (ENG., Illus.). 272p. mass mkt. 6.99 (978-0-312-94930-3(8), St. Martin's Paperbacks) St. Martin's Pr.

Foster, Amy E. Integrating Women into the Astronaut Corps: Politics & Logistics at NASA, 1972-2004. 2011. (ENG., Illus.). 224p. (gr. 17). 55.00 (978-1-4214-0195-9(9)) Johns Hopkins Univ. Pr.

French, Francis & Burgess, Colin. Into That Silent Sea: Trailblazers of the Space Era, 1961-1965. 2009. (Outward Odyssey: A People's History of S Ser.). (ENG., Illus.). 440p. pap. 22.95 (978-0-8032-2639-5(X), Bison Bks.) Univ. of Nebraska Pr.

Giffords, Gabrielle & Kelly, Mark. Gabby: A Story of Courage & Hope. 2011. (ENG.). 320p. 26.99 (978-1-4516-6106-4(1), Scribner) Scribner.

—Gabby: Una Historia de Valor y Esperanza. 2012. (SPA., Illus.). 352p. pap. 18.00 (978-1-4516-8271-7(9), Scribner) Scribner.

Giffords, Gabrielle & Kelly, Mark E. Gabby: A Story of Courage & Hope. 2012. (ENG., Illus.). 320p. pap. 16.00 (978-1-4516-6107-1(X), Scribner) Scribner.

Giffords, Gabrielle, et al. Gabby: A Story of Courage & Hope. 2011. (978-1-4104-4538-4(0)) 2012. (ENG.). pap. 16.99 (978-1-59413-564-4(9), Large Print Pr.) Thorndike Pr.

Graveline, Duane. From Laika with Love. 2008. 192p. pap. 20.00 (978-1-4243-3870-2(0)) Graveline, Duane E.

Hansen, James R. First Man: The Life of Neil A. Armstrong. 2008. (ENG.). 769p. 30.00 (978-1-4223-9334-5(8)) DIANE Publishing Co.

—First Man: The Life of Neil A. Armstrong. 2006. (ENG., Illus.). 784p. pap. 18.00 (978-0-7432-5751-0(0)) Simon & Schuster.

Harrison Publishing. The Edge of Time: The Authoritative Biography of Kalpana Chawla. 2011. (ENG., Illus.). 242p. 34.95 (978-0-9768279-0-0(5)) Harrison Publishing.

Heiken, Grant & Jones, Eric. On the Moon: The Apollo Journals. 2007. (Springer Praxis Books / Space Exploration Ser.). (Illus.). xiv, 498p. pap. 39.95 (978-0-387-48939-1(8), 0387489398) Springer.

Jenks, Andrew L. The Cosmonaut Who Couldn't Stop Smiling: The Life & Legend of Yuri Gagarin. 2012. (Illus.). (ENG.). 318p. 35.00 (978-0-87580-447-7(0)); (978-1-60909-052-4(7)) Northern Illinois Univ. Pr.

Jones, Thomas D. Sky Walking: An Astronaut's Memoir. 2007. (ENG., Illus.). 288p. pap. 14.99 (978-0-06-088436-5(3), HarperPerennial) HarperCollins Pubs.

McPhee, Jancy C. & Charles, John B. Human Health & Performance Risks of Space Exploration Missions: Evidence Reviewed by the NASA Human Research Program. 2009. (Illus.). vi, 389p. pap. (978-0-16-084634-2(X), 033-000-01335-3) Library of Congress.

Melady, John. Canadians in Space: The Forever Frontier. 2009. (ENG., Illus.). 232p. pap. 27.99 (978-1-55002-940-6(1), Dundurn Pr.) Dundurn CAN. Dist: Ingram Pub. Services.

Miles, Charles A. Argosy: The Imaginary Memoirs of an Astronaut. 2011. 124p. 40.95 (978-1-258-06399-3(9)) Literary Licensing, LLC.

Mitchell, Edgar D. The Way of the Explorer: An Apollo Astronaut's Journey Through the Material & Mystical Worlds. rev. ed. 2008. (ENG.). 1p. per. 16.99 (978-1-56414-977-0(3), New Page Bks.) Career Pr., Inc.

Moseley, Willie G. Smoke Jumper, Moon Pilot: The Remarkable Life of Apollo 14 Astronaut Stuart A. Roosa. 2011. (978-1-935001-76-8(0)) Acclaim Pr., Inc.

Mullane, Mike. Riding Rockets: The Outrageous Tales of a Space Shuttle Astronaut. 2007. (ENG., Illus.). 400p. pap. 16.99 (978-0-7432-7683-2(3), Scribner) Scribner.

National Council on Radiation Protection and Measurements Staff, contrib. by. Information Needed to Make Radiation Protection Recommendations for Space Missions Beyond Low-Earth Orbit. 2006. (NCRP Reports: No. 153). (Illus.). xii, 427p. (978-0-929600-90-1(8)) National Council on Radiation Protection & Measurements.

National Council on Radiation Protection and Measurements Staff, contrib. by. Potential Impact of Individual Genetic Susceptibility & Previous Radiation Exposure on Radiation Risk for Astronauts. 2011. (978-0-9823843-5-0(1)) National Council on Radiation Protection & Measurements.

National Research Council Staff. Space Radiation Hazards & the Vision for Space Exploration: Report of a Workshop. 2006. (ENG., Illus.). 104p. pap. 28.25 (978-0-309-10264-3(2)) National Academies Pr.

Pogue, William R. But for the Grace of God: An Autobiography of an Aviator & Astronaut. 2011. 338p. pap. 35.00 (978-0-9814756-6-0(3)) Soar With Eagles.

Pyle, Rod. Destination Moon: The Apollo Missions in the Astronauts' Own Words. 2007. (Illus.). 192p. per. 14.95 (978-0-06-087350-9(7), HarperPerennial) HarperCollins Pubs.

Rockwell, Carey & Ley, Willy. On the Trail of the Space Pirates: A Tom Corbett Space Cadet Adventure. 2011. 220p. 44.95 (978-1-258-09703-5(6)) Literary Licensing, LLC.

—Sabotage in Space: A Tom Corbett Space Cadet Adventure. 2011. 222p. 44.95 (978-1-258-09513-0(0)) Literary Licensing, LLC.

Scantamburlo, Luca. Apollo 20. the Disclosure. 2010. 191p. pap. 21.50 (978-1-4452-7397-6(7)) Lulu Enterprises Inc.

Seedhouse, Erik. Astronauts for Hire The Emergence of a Commercial Astronaut Corps. 2012. (Springer Praxis Books / Space Exploration Ser.). (ENG., Illus.). xxv, 243p. pap. 34.95 (978-1-4614-0519-1(X), 146140519X) Springer.

—Prepare for Launch: The Astronaut Training Process. 2010. (Springer Praxis Books / Space Exploration Ser.). (ENG., Illus.). 250p. pap. 34.95 (978-1-4419-1349-4(1), 1441913491, Springer-Praxis) Springer.

—Trailblazing Medicine: Sustaining Explorers During Interplanetary Missions. 2011. (Springer Praxis Books / Space Exploration Ser.). (ENG., Illus.). xxvi, 182p. pap. 34.95 (978-1-4419-7828-8(3), 1441978283) Springer.

Shayler, David J. Around the World in 84 Days: The Authorized Biography of Skylab Astronaut Jerry Carr. 2008. (Apogee Books Space Ser.: 63). (ENG., Illus.). 272p. pap. 31.95 (978-1-894959-40-7(X), Apogee Bks.) Collector's Guide Publishing, Inc. CAN. Dist: Independent Pubs. Group.

Smith, Andrew. Moondust: In Search of the Men Who Fell to Earth. 2006. (Illus.). 384p. pap. 14.99 (978-0-00-715542-2(5), HarperPerennial) HarperCollins Pubs.

Smith, Scott M., et al. Nutritional Biochemistry of Space Flight. 2009. (Space Science, Exploration & Policies Ser.). 89.00 (978-1-60741-641-8(7)) Nova Science Pubs., Inc.

Sprekelmeyer, Linda. These We Honor: The International Aerospace Hall of Fame. 2006. (Illus.). 78p. (978-1-57864-397-4(X)) Donning Co. Pubs.

Whitfield, Steve, ed. Aurora 7: The Three Orbits of M. Scott Carpenter: the NASA Mission Reports. 2011. (Apogee Books Space Ser.). (ENG., Illus.). 192p. pap. 24.95 *(978-1-926592-21-3(2))* Collector's Guide Publishing, Inc. CAN. Dist: Independent Pubs. Group.

Wolfe, Tom. The Right Stuff. rev. ed. 2008. (ENG.). 368p. pap. 16.00 *(978-0-312-42756-6(5))* Picador.

Worden, Al & French, Francis. Falling to Earth: An Apollo 15 Astronaut's Journey to the Moon. 2011. (ENG., Illus.). 312p. 29.95 ***(978-1-58834-309-3(X))*** Smithsonian Institution Pr.

ASTRONAUTS—JUVENILE LITERATURE

Adamson, Heather. The Challenger Explosion. 2006. (Graphic Library: Disasters in History Ser.). (ENG., Illus.). 32p. (gr. 3-4). per. 7.95 *(978-0-7368-6873-0(9),* Graphic Library) Capstone Pr., Inc.

Wearing, Judy. Roberta Bondar: Canada's First Woman in Space. 2010. (Crabtree Groundbreaker Biographies Ser.). (ENG., Illus.). 112p. (J). pap. *(978-0-7787-2549-7(9))* Crabtree Publishing Co.

ASTRONAVIGATION

see Navigation (Astronautics)

ASTRONOMERS

Airy, George Biddell. Autobiography of Sir George Biddell Airy. 2008. 392p. 31.99 *(978-0-554-21546-4(2));* 29.99 *(978-0-554-30849-4(5))* BiblioBazaar.

—Autobiography of Sir George Biddell Airy. Airy, Wilfrid, ed. 2006. (ENG.). 394p. pap. 25.99 *(978-1-4264-0336-1(4));* 388p. pap. 26.99 *(978-1-4264-0387-3(9))* BiblioBazaar.

—Autobiography of Sir George Biddell Airy. 2009. 324p. pap. *(978-0-217-68659-4(1))* Books LLC.

—Autobiography of Sir George Biddell Airy. Airy, Wilfred, ed. 2010. (Cambridge Library Collection - Physical Sciences Ser.). (Illus.). 436p. pap. 32.99 *(978-1-108-00894-5(1))* Cambridge Univ. Pr.

—Autobiography of Sir George Biddell Airy. 2008. 344p. pap. 12.95 *(978-1-4385-0495-7(0),* Book Jungle) Standard Pubns., Inc.

Aughton, Peter. The Story of Anatomy: From Babylonian Stargazers to the Search for the Big Bang. 2009. (ENG., Illus.). 256p. 14.99 *(978-1-84724-186-3(7),* 1847241867) Quercus GBR. Dist: Book Sales, Inc.

Aughton, Peter. The Transit of Venus: The Brief, Brilliant Life of Jeremiah Horrocks, Father of British Astronomy. 2012. (Illus.). 256p. pap. 13.95 ***(978-1-85936-214-3(1))*** International Publishers Marketing.

Bailey, Solon I. Biographical Memoir of Edward Charles Pickering, 1846-1919: National Academy of Sciences, Biographical Memoirs, V15, Fifth Memoir. 2011. 26p. 35.95 ***(978-1-258-07172-1(X))*** Literary Licensing, LLC.

Ball, R S. Great Astronomers. 2010. 196p. 30.36 *(978-1-169-28395-4(0));* pap. 18.36 *(978-1-162-66489-7(4))* Kessinger Publishing, LLC.

Ball, R. s. & Ball, R S. Great Astronomers. 2010. 196p. 37.95 *(978-1-161-43354-8(6))* Kessinger Publishing, LLC.

Ball, Robert S. Great Astronomers. 2010. 394p. pap. 33.75 *(978-1-177-75973-1(X));* (ENG.). 388p. pap. 33.75 *(978-1-174-88311-8(1))* BiblioBazaar.

—Great Astronomers. 2010. (Illus.). 156p. pap. 24.39 *(978-1-153-62514-2(8))* General Bks. LLC.

Ball, Robert Stawell. Great Astronomers. 2010. 394p. pap. 33.75 *(978-1-145-45429-3(1))* 2008. 264p. 28.99 *(978-0-554-26797-5(7))* 2008. 264p. 25.99 *(978-0-554-36100-0(0))* 2007. (ENG.). 262p. pap. 23.99 *(978-1-4346-1915-0(X))* BiblioBazaar.

—Great Astronomers. 2009. 180p. pap. *(978-1-150-34787-0(2))* Books LLC.

Becker, Barbara J. Unravelling Starlight: William & Margaret Huggins & the Rise of the New Astronomy. 2011. (ENG., Illus.). 400p. 110.00 *(978-1-107-00229-6(X))* Cambridge Univ. Pr.

Bergland, Renée. Maria Mitchell & the Sexing of Science: An Astronomer among the American Romantics. 2008. (ENG., Illus.). 320p. 29.95 *(978-0-8070-2142-2(3))* Beacon Pr.

Bracher, Katherine, et al. The Biographical Encyclopedia of Astronomers, 2 vols. Hockey, Thomas et al, eds. Bolt, Marvin et al, eds. 2007. (Springer Reference Ser.). (Illus.). xciv, 1341p. 499.00 *(978-0-387-31022-0(3),* 0387310223) Springer.

Braude, S. Ya., et al, eds. A Brief History of Radio Astronomy in the USSR: A Collection of Scientific Essays. 2012. (Astrophysics & Space Science Library). Orig. Title: The History of Radio Astronomy in the USSR. (ENG., Illus.). 276p. 129.00 ***(978-94-007-2833-2(6),*** 9400728336) Springer.

Brown, Ernest W. Biographical Memoir of George William Hill, 1838-1914: National Academy of Sciences, Biographical Memoirs, V9. 2011. 40p. 35.95 ***(978-1-258-07188-2(6))*** Literary Licensing, LLC.

Brück, M. T. Agnes Mary Clerke & the Rise of Astrophysics. 2008. (ENG., Illus.). 288p. pap. 36.00 *(978-0-521-05579-6(2))* Cambridge Univ. Pr.

Campbell, W. w. & Campbell, W. W. Biographical Memoir of Edward Singleton Holden, 1846-1914: National Academy of Sciences, Biographical Memoirs, V8. 2011. 32p. 35.95 ***(978-1-258-07189-9(4))*** Literary Licensing, LLC.

Cannon, Annie J. Biographical Memoir of Solon Irving Bailey, 1854-1931: National Academy of Sciences, Biographical Memoirs, V15, Sixth Memoir. 2011. 18p. 35.95 ***(978-1-258-07167-7(3))*** Literary Licensing, LLC.

Clark, Stuart. The Sun Kings: The Unexpected Tragedy of Richard Carrington & the Tale of How Modern Astronomy Began. 2007. (ENG., Illus.). 224p. (C). 24.95 *(978-0-691-12660-9(7))* Princeton Univ. Pr.

Comstock, George C. Biographical Memoir of John Huntington Crane Coffin, 1815-1890: National Academy of Sciences, Biographical Memoirs, V8. 2011. 12p. pap. 35.95 ***(978-1-258-07185-1(1))*** Literary Licensing, LLC.

Contopoulos, George. Adventures in Order & Chaos: A Scientific Autobiography. 2010. (Astrophysics & Space Science Library). x, 199p. pap. 129.00 *(978-90-481-6773-9(6),* 9048167736) Springer.

Drake, Stillman. Galileo. 2010. (Brief Insights Ser.). (ENG.). 192p. 14.95 *(978-1-4027-6886-6(9))* Sterling Publishing Co., Inc.

Egeland, Alv & Burke, William J. Kristian Birkeland: The First Space Scientist. 2010. (Astrophysics & Space Science Library). ix, 221p. pap. 169.00 *(978-90-481-6830-9(9),* 9048168309) Springer.

Fahie, John. Galileo His Life & Work. 2007. (ENG.). 500p. 53.95 *(978-0-548-04962-4(9))* Kessinger Publishing, LLC.

Ferguson, James. Life of James Ferguson, F. R. S. In a Brief Autobiographical Account, & Further Extended Memoir. Henderson, Ebenezer, ed. 2010. (Cambridge Library Collection - Physical Sciences Ser.). (Illus.). 530p. pap. 37.99 *(978-1-108-02126-5(3))* Cambridge Univ. Pr.

Field, Eugene. The House: An Episode in the Lives of Reuben Baker, Astronomer, & of His Wife Alice. l.t. ed. 2007. (ENG.). 158p. pap. 21.99 *(978-1-4346-4286-8(0))* BiblioBazaar.

Foerstner, Abigail. James Van Allen: The First Eight Billion Miles. 2009. (ENG., Illus.). 396p. pap. 24.95 *(978-1-58729-795-3(7))* Univ. of Iowa Pr.

Frost, Edwin B. Biographical Memoir of Charles Augustus Young, 1834-1908: National Academy of Sciences, Biographical Memoirs, V7, No. 3, June 1911. 2011. 30p. 35.95 ***(978-1-258-07179-0(7))*** Literary Licensing, LLC.

GARY, Bruce L. Misanthrope's Holiday: Vignettes & Stories. 2007. (Illus.). 220p. pap. 15.00 *(978-0-9798446-1-4(4))* Reductionist Publications.

Ginenthal, A. Charles & Rose, Lynn E. Pillars of the Past: Mesopotamian, Anatolian, Mycenaean, Minoan & Harrappan Chronology. 2008. 671p. pap. 27.95 *(978-0-9639759-0-4(0))* Ginenthal, Charles Ivy Pr. Bks.

Hall, Angelo. An Astronomers Wife: the Biography of Angeline Hall. 2007. (ENG.). 128p. per. 20.95 *(978-1-4304-4269-1(7))* Kessinger Publishing, LLC.

Heilbron, John. Galileo. 2010. (ENG., Illus.). 352p. 34.95 *(978-0-19-958352-2(8))* Oxford Univ. Pr., Inc.

Heilbron, John L. Galileo. 2012. (ENG., Illus.). 528p. pap. 24.95 ***(978-0-19-965598-4(7))*** Oxford Univ. Pr., Inc.

Henden, Arne E. Variable Stars & How to Observe Them. 2011. (Astronomers' Observing Guides). (Illus.). 232p. pap. 34.95 *(978-0-387-85352-9(9),* 0387853529) Springer.

Hockey, Thomas, et al, eds. The Biographical Encyclopedia of Astronomers, 2 vols. 2007. (Illus.). 2000p. 629.00 *(978-0-387-33628-2(1),* 0387336281) Springer.

Holden, Edward S. Biographical Memoir of William H C Bartlett, 1804-1893: National Academy of Sciences, Biographical Memoirs, V7, No. 6, June 1911. 2011. 26p. 35.95 ***(978-1-258-07182-0(7))*** Literary Licensing, LLC.

Hooks, James A. My Wayward Winds. 2011. 262p. 29.99 ***(978-1-4628-8841-2(0));*** pap. 19.99 ***(978-1-4628-8842-9(9))*** Xlibris Corp.

Hoskin, Michael. The Construction of the Heavens: William Herschel's Cosmology. 2012. (ENG., Illus.). 214p. 105.00 ***(978-1-107-01838-9(2))*** Cambridge Univ. Pr.

Hoskin, Michael. Discoverers of the Universe: William & Caroline Herschel. 2011. (ENG., Illus.). 272p. 29.95 *(978-0-691-14833-5(3))* Princeton Univ. Pr.

Impey, Chris, ed. Talking about Life: Conversations on Astrobiology. 2010. (ENG., Illus.). 418p. 29.99 *(978-0-521-51492-7(4))* Cambridge Univ. Pr.

Launay, Françoise. The Astronomer Jules Janssen: A Globetrotter of Celestial Physics. 2011. (Astrophysics & Space Science Library). (ENG., Illus.). xxix, 220p. 129.00 ***(978-1-4614-0696-9(X),*** 146140696X) Springer.

Mitchell, Maria. Maria Mitchell: Life, Letters, & Journals. 2007. (ENG.). 222p. pap. 20.99 *(978-1-4264-4029-8(4))* 2006. 246p. pap. 22.99 *(978-1-4264-4088-5(X))* BiblioBazaar.

Mitton, Simon. Conflict in the Cosmos: Fred Hoyle's Life in Science. 2006. (Illus.). 401p. per. 18.95 *(978-0-309-10200-1(6))* National Academies Pr.

—Fred Hoyle: A Life in Science. 2011. (Illus.). 384p. pap. 36.99 *(978-0-521-18947-7(0))* Cambridge Univ. Pr.

Moore, Patrick. Watchers of the Stars: The Story of a Revolution. 3rd ed. 2009. (ENG.). 200p. pap. 25.00 *(978-1-904275-44-2(3),* Horwood Publishing, Ltd.) Woodhead Publishing Ltd. GBR. Dist: Ingram Pub. Services.

Naess, Atle. Galileo Galilei - When the World Stood Still. Anderson, J., tr. 2010. (ENG., Illus.). viii, 222p. pap. 44.95 *(978-3-642-06024-3(2),* 3642060242) Springer.

Newcomb, Simon. The Reminiscences of an Astronomer. 2008. 308p. 28.99 *(978-0-554-36809-2(9))* 2008. 308p. 29.99 *(978-0-554-27506-2(6))* 2007. (ENG.). 274p. pap. 21.99 *(978-1-4346-3366-8(7))* BiblioBazaar.

—The Reminiscences of an Astronomer. 2010. (Cambridge Library Collection - Physical Sciences Ser.). (ENG.). 444p. pap. 32.99 *(978-1-108-01391-8(0))* Cambridge Univ. Pr.

—The Reminiscences of an Astronomer. 2007. (ENG.). 264p. per. *(978-1-4065-3096-4(4))* Dodo Pr.

—The Reminiscences of an Astronomer. 2008. 436p. 51.95 *(978-0-548-96554-2(4))* 2007. (ENG.). 440p. per. 36.95 *(978-0-548-64104-0(8))* Kessinger Publishing, LLC.

—Reminiscences of an Astronomer. 2007. (ENG.). pap. *(978-1-4068-3517-5(X))* Echo Library.

—The Reminiscences of an Astronomer. l.t. ed. 2007. (ENG.). 304p. pap. 24.99 *(978-1-4346-3367-5(5))* BiblioBazaar.

North, John & North. God's Clockmaker: Richard of Wallingford & the Invention of Time. 2007. (ENG., Illus.). 464p. 75.00 *(978-1-85285-571-0(1),* Hambledon Continuum) Continuum International Publishing Group, Ltd. GBR. Dist: National Bk. Network.

O'Donoghue, Aileen. The Sky Is Not a Ceiling: An Astronomer's Faith. 2007. (Illus.). 180p. pap. 18.00 *(978-1-57075-703-7(8))* Orbis Bks.

Ogilvie, Marilyn Bailey. Searching the Stars: The Story of Caroline Herschel. 2008. (ENG., Illus.). 240p. pap. 27.95 *(978-0-7524-4277-8(5))* History Pr. Ltd.,The GBR. Dist: Independent Pubs. Group.

Pagano, Sergio. Galileo Galilei: Lo splendore e le pene di un divin Uomo. 2009. (ITA., Illus.). 256p. (C). 64.00 *(978-88-564-0088-5(X))* Polistampa ITA. Dist: Brown, David Bk. Co., The.

Proudfoot, William Jardine. Biographical Memoir of James Dinwiddie, L. L. D., Astronomer in the British Embassy to China, 1792, '3, '4, Afterwards Professor of Natural Philosophy in the College of Fort William, Bengal. 2010. (Cambridge Library Collection - Travel & Exploration Ser.). (ENG.). 152p. pap. 21.00 *(978-1-108-01379-6(1))* Cambridge Univ. Pr.

Quarmby, David. Planetary Pioneers: The Mapping of Our Solar System. 2011. (Illus.). 56p. 20.00 ***(978-1-84624-548-0(6))*** Book Guild, Ltd. GBR. Dist: Trans-Atlantic Pubns., Inc.

Repcheck, Jack. Copernicus' Secret: How the Scientific Revolution Began. 2008. (ENG., Illus.). 256p. pap. 16.99 *(978-0-7432-8952-8(8))* Simon & Schuster.

Robert S. Sir, Ball. Great Astronomers. 2007. (ENG.). 238p. pap. 20.99 *(978-1-4346-1746-0(7))* BiblioBazaar.

Rogers, Gordon. My Heavens! The Adventures of a Lonely Stargazer Building an over-the-Top Observatory. 2008. (Patrick Moore's Practical Astronomy Ser.). (Illus.). 180p. per. 34.95 *(978-0-387-73781-2(2))* Springer.

Sobel, Dava. Galileo's Daughter: A Historical Memoir of Science, Faith, & Love. 2011. (Illus.). 432p. pap. 17.00 *(978-0-8027-7965-6(4))* Walker & Co.

Spangenburg, Ray & Moser, Kit. Carl Sagan: A Biography. 2008. (ENG., Illus.). 145p. 16.98 *(978-1-59102-658-7(X))* Prometheus Bks., Pubs.

Strauss, David, ed. Percival Lowell: Collected Writings on Japan & Asia. 2007. 1650p. 990.00 *(978-4-901481-48-9(7))* Synapse, Edition JPN. Dist: Taylor & Francis Group.

Struve, Otto & Frost, Edwin Brant. Biographical Memoir of Edwin Brant Frost, 1866-1935. 2011. 34p. 35.95 ***(978-1-258-06492-1(8))*** Literary Licensing, LLC.

Thoren, Victor E. The Lord of Uraniborg: A Biography of Tycho Brahe. 2007. (ENG., Illus.). 536p. pap. 100.00 *(978-0-521-03307-7(1))* Cambridge Univ. Pr.

Trimble, Virginia. The Biographical Encyclopedia of Astronomers, 2 vols. 2009. (ENG., Illus.). xciv, 1341p. pap. 99.00 *(978-0-387-35133-9(7))* Springer.

Wali, Kameshwar. A Scientific Autobiography: S. Chandrasekhar: with Selected Correspondence. 2010. 350p. 85.00 *(978-981-4299-57-2(X));* pap. 42.00 *(978-981-4299-58-9(8))* World Scientific Publishing Co., Inc.

Wendt, Guenter & Still, Russell. Unbroken Chain. 2nd ed. 2009. (ENG., Illus.). 200p. pap. 22.95 *(978-1-926592-01-5(8))* Collector's Guide Publishing, Inc. CAN. Dist: Independent Pubs. Group.

Whatton, Arundell Blount & Horrox, Jeremiah. Memoir of the Life & Labors of the Rev. Jeremiah Horrox: To Which Is Appended a Translation of his Celebrated Discourse upon the Transit of Venus Across the Sun. 2010. (Cambridge Library Collection - Physical Sciences Ser.). (ENG., Illus.). 248p. pap. 22.99 *(978-1-108-01441-0(0))* Cambridge Univ. Pr.

Wootton, David. Galileo: Watcher of the Skies. 2010. (Illus.). 354p. 35.00 *(978-0-300-12536-8(4)); (978-83-00-12536-4(1))* Yale Univ. Pr.

Yount, Lisa. Modern Astronomy: Expanding the Universe. 2006. (Milestones in Discovery & Invention Ser.). (Illus.). 224p. (YA). (gr. 7-12). 35.00 *(978-0-8160-5746-7(X))* Facts On File, Inc.

Zimmerman, Robert. The Universe in a Mirror: The Saga of the Hubble Space Telescope & the Visionaries Who Built It. 2008. (ENG., Illus.). 320p. (C). 29.95 *(978-0-691-13297-6(6))* Princeton Univ. Pr.

ASTRONOMICAL CLOCKS

Hoppes, Ronald R. The Most Important Clock in America: The David Rittenhouse Astronomical Musical Clock at Drexel University. 2009. *(978-1-60618-992-4(1))* American Philosophical Society.

Marchant, Jo. Decoding the Heavens: A 2,000-Year-Old-Computer — And the Century-Long Search to Discover Its Secrets. 2010. (ENG.). 344p. pap. 15.95 *(978-0-306-81861-5(2))* Da Capo Pr., Inc.

Needham, Joseph, et al. Heavenly Clockwork: The Great Astronomical Clocks of Medieval China. 2nd rev. ed. 2008. (ENG.). 324p. pap. 36.99 *(978-0-521-08716-2(3))* Cambridge Univ. Pr.

Turgenev, Ivan. First Love. 16.95 *(978-0-88411-445-1(7))* Amereon LTD.

ASTRONOMICAL GEOGRAPHY

see also Mathematical Geography; Seasons

Ozima, Minoru, et al. The Earth: Its Birth & Growth. 2nd rev. ed. 2012. (ENG., Illus.). (C). 164p. 95.00 ***(978-0-521-76025-6(9));*** 168p. pap. 42.99 ***(978-1-107-60076-8(6))*** Cambridge Univ. Pr.

Poynting, J. H. The Earth: Its Shape, Size, Weight & Spin. 2012. (ENG.). 150p. pap. 19.99 ***(978-1-107-60604-3(7))*** Cambridge Univ. Pr.

ASTRONOMICAL INSTRUMENTS

see also Astrolabes; Astronomical Photography; Spectroscope; Telescopes

Ageorges, N. & Dainty, C., eds. Laser Guide Star Adaptive Optics for Astronomy. 2010. (NATO Science Series C: (closed) Ser.). 364p. pap. 229.00 *(978-90-481-5492-0(8),* 9048154928) Springer.

Alloin, D. M. & Mariotti, Jean-Marie, eds. Adaptive Optics for Astronomy. 2010. (NATO Science Series C: (closed) Ser.). (Illus.). 360p. pap. 329.00 *(978-90-481-4375-7(6),* 9048143756) Springer.

Amico, P. & Beletic, James W., eds. Scientific Detectors for Astronomy: The Beginning of a New Era. 2010. (Astrophysics & Space Science Library). 668p. pap. 439.00 *(978-90-481-6506-3(7),* 9048165067) Springer.

Angeli, George Z. & Cullum, M. J. Modeling, Systems Engineering, & Project Management for Astronomy III: 26-28 June 2008, Marseille, France. 2008. (Proceedings of SPIE Ser.). (Illus.). 644p. pap. 130.00 *(978-0-8194-7227-4(1))* SPIE.

Angeli, George Z. & Dierickx, PhiSlippe. Modeling, Systems Engineering, & Project Management for Astronomy IV: 27-29 June & 1 July 2010. 2010. (Proceedings of SPIE Ser.). (Illus.). 754p. pap. 140.00 ***(978-0-8194-8228-0(5))*** SPIE.

Argyle, Robert W., et al. Astronomical Data & Analysis Software & Systems XVII. 2008. (Illus.). xxxvii, 757p. *(978-1-58381-658-5(5)); (978-1-58381-659-2(3))* Astronomical Society of the Pacific, The.

Atad-Ettedgui, Eli. Modern Technologies in Space- & Ground-Based Telescopes & Instrumentation: 27 June-2 July 2010, San Diego, California, United States. 2010. (Proceedings of SPIE Ser.). (Illus.). 1736p. pap. 245.00 ***(978-0-8194-8229-7(3))*** SPIE.

Bell, Jim. Mars 3-D: A Rover's-Eye View of the Red Planet. 2008. (ENG., Illus.). 160p. 19.95 *(978-1-4027-5620-7(8))* Sterling Publishing Co., Inc.

Brandner, Wolfgang & Kasper, Markus E., eds. Science with Adaptive Optics: Proceedings of the ESO Workshop Held at Garching, Germany, 16-19 September 2003. 2010. (ESO Astrophysics Symposia Ser.). xix, 387p. pap. 74.95 *(978-3-642-06406-7(X),* 364206406X) Springer.

Breckinridge, Jim B. Basic Optics for the Astronomical Sciences. 2011. (Press Monographs). 400p. 86.00 *(978-0-8194-8366-9(4));* 250p. pap. 61.00 ***(978-0-8194-8204-4(8))*** SPIE.

Burriesci, Lawrence G. & Heaney, James B. Cryogenic Optical Systems & Instruments XII: 26-27 August 2007, San Diego, California, USA. 2007. (Proceedings of SPIE Ser.). (Illus.). 240p. pap. 80.00 *(978-0-8194-6840-6(1))* SPIE.

Chambers, George Frederick. A Handbook of Descriptive & Practical Astronomy. 2010. (Cambridge Library Collection - Physical Sciences Ser.). (Illus.). 644p. pap. 43.00 *(978-1-108-01475-5(5))* Cambridge Univ. Pr.

Fineschi, Silvano & Fennelly, Judy A. Solar Physics & Space Weather Instrumentation III: 4-6 August 2009, San Diego, California, United States. 2009. (Proceedings of SPIE Ser.). (Illus.). 348p. pap. 90.00 *(978-0-8194-7728-6(1))* SPIE.

Fineschi, Silvano & Viereck, Rodney A. Solar Physics & Space Weather Instrumentation II: 26-27 August 2007, San Diego, California, USA. 2007. (Proceedings of SPIE Ser.). (Illus.). 348p. pap. 80.00 *(978-0-8194-6837-6(1))* SPIE.

Finkbeiner, Ann K. A Grand & Bold Thing: An Extraordinary New Map of the Universe Ushering in a New Era of Discovery. 2010. (ENG., Illus.). 240p. 27.00 *(978-1-4165-5216-1(2),* Free Pr.) Free Pr.

Garcia, Paulo J. V., et al, eds. The Very Large Telescope Interferometer - Challenges for the Future. 2010. 332p. pap. 130.00 *(978-90-481-6379-3(X),* 904816379X) Springer.

The Geometry of Light: Galileo's Telescope, Kepler's Optics. 2008. (Illus.). 128p. pap. 10.95 *(978-0-9819416-0-8(5))* Gerald Rottman.

Grycewicz, Thomas J., et al. Focal Plane Arrays for Space Telescopes III: 27-28 August 2007, San Diego, California, USA. 2007. (Proceedings of SPIE Ser.). (Illus.). 258p. pap. 70.00 ***(978-0-8194-6838-3(X))*** SPIE.

Holland, Andrew D. & Dorn, David A. High Energy, Optical, & Infrared Detectors for Astronomy IV: 27-30 June 2010, San Diego, California United States. 2010. (Proceedings of SPIE Ser.). (Illus.). 750p. pap. 160.00 ***(978-0-8194-8232-7(3))*** SPIE.

Hubin, Norbert, et al. Adaptive Optics Systems: 23-28 June 2008, Marseille, France. 2008. (Proceedings of SPIE Ser.). (Illus.). 2130p. pap. 310.00 ***(978-0-8194-7225-0(5))*** SPIE.

Kaufer, Andreas & Kerber, Florian, eds. The 2007 ESO Instrument Calibration Workshop: Proceedings of the ESO Workshop held in Garching, Germany, 23-26 January 2007. 2010. (ESO Astrophysics Symposia Ser.). (Illus.). xxviii, 616p. pap. 149.00 *(978-3-642-09566-5(6),* 3642095666) Springer.

Kennedy, E. S., tr. The Planetary Equatorium of Jamshid Ghiyath Al-Din Al-Kashi. 2011. 282p. 48.95 ***(978-1-258-05732-9(8))*** Literary Licensing, LLC.

Kissler-Patig, Markus, et al, eds. Science Perspectives for 3D Spectroscopy: Proceedings of the ESO Workshop held in Garching, Germany, 10-14 October 2005. 2010. (ESO Astrophysics Symposia Ser.). (Illus.). xviii, 402p. pap. 129.00 *(978-3-642-09259-6(4),* 3642092594) Springer.

Kopilovich, L. E. & Sodin, L. G. Multielement System Design in Astronomy & Radio Science. 2010. (Astrophysics & Space Science Library). 200p. pap. 129.00 *(978-90-481-5846-1(X),* 904815846X) Springer.

Labeyrie, A., et al. An Introduction to Optical Stellar Interferometry. 2006. (ENG., Illus.). 360p. 102.00 *(978-0-521-82872-7(4))* Cambridge Univ. Pr.

Lashley, Jeff. The Radio Sky & How to Observe It. 2010. (Astronomers' Observing Guides). (ENG., Illus.). xiv, 246p. pap. 34.95 *(978-1-4419-0882-7(X),* 144190882X) Springer.

Lemaître, Gérard René. Astronomical Optics & Elasticity Theory. 2008. (Astronomy & Astrophysics Library). (Illus.). 380p. 129.00 *(978-3-540-68904-1(4))* Springer.

Lena, Pierre, et al. Observational Astrophysics. Lyle, S., tr. 2nd ed. 2010. (Astronomy & Astrophysics Library). (Illus.). xv, 512p. pap. 135.00 *(978-3-642-08336-5(6),* 3642083366) Springer.

Léna, Pierre, et al. Observational Astrophysics. Lyle, Stephen, tr. from FRE. 3rd ed. 2012. (Astronomy & Astrophysics Library). (ENG., Illus.). xv, 719p. 179.00 ***(978-3-642-21814-9(8),*** 3642218148) Springer.

MacEwen, Howard A. & Breckinridge, James B. UV/Optical/IR Space Telescopes: Innovative Technologies & Concepts II: 26-29 August 2007, San Diego, California, USA. 2007. (Proceedings of SPIE Ser.). (Illus.). 508p. pap. 105.00 *(978-0-8194-6835-2(5))* SPIE.

MacEwen, Howard A. & Breckinridge, Jim B. UV/Optical/IR Space Telescopes: Innovative Technologies & Concepts IV: 3 August 2009, San Diego, California, United States. 2009. (Proceedings of SPIE Ser.). (Illus.). 268p. pap. 70.00 *(978-0-8194-7726-2(5))* SPIE.

Maui Economic Development Board Staff, compiled by. Advanced Maui Optical & Space Surveillance Technologies Conference (AMOS 2005) 2007. 883p. pap. 118.00 *(978-1-60423-995-9(6))* Curran Assocs., Inc.

—Advanced Maui Optical & Space Surveillance Technologies Conference (AMOS 2006) 2007. 1008p. pap. 118.00 *(978-1-60423-996-6(4))* Curran Assocs., Inc.

McLean, Ian S. Electronic Imaging in Astronomy: Detectors & Instrumentation. 2nd ed. (Springer Praxis Books / Astronomy & Planetary Sciences Ser.). (Illus.). 2010. xi, 552p. pap. 99.00 *(978-3-642-09532-0(1)*, 3642095321) 2008. XI, 552p. (C). 99.00 *(978-3-540-76582-0(4)*, 3540765824) Springer.

McLean, Ian S. & Casali, Mark M. Ground-Based & Airborne Instrumentation for Astronomy II: 23-28 June 2008, Marseille, France. 2008. (Proceedings of SPIE Ser.). (Illus.). 2806p. pap. 335.00 ***(978-0-8194-7224-3(7))*** SPIE.

McLean, Ian S., et al. Ground-Based & Airborne Instrumentation for Astronomy III: 27 June-2 July 2010, San Diego, California, United States, 4 vols. 2010. (Proceedings of SPIE Ser.). (Illus.). 3206p. pap. 360.00 ***(978-0-8194-8225-9(0))*** SPIE.

Meek, Andrew, et al, eds. SEM & Microanalysis: The Study of Historical Technology, Materials & Conservation. 2012. (ENG.). 228p. pap. 100.00 *(978-1-904982-65-4(4))* Archetype Pubns. GBR. Dist: National Bk. Network.

Mobberley, Martin. Cataclysmic Cosmic Events & How to Observe Them. 2008. (Astronomers' Observing Guides). (Illus.). 225p. pap. 34.95 *(978-0-387-79945-2(1))* Springer.

Morris, W. J. The Nautical Sextant. 2010. pap. 39.95 *(978-0-939837-89-2(7))* Paradise Cay Pubns.

Pugh, Philip. Observing the Messier Objects with a Small Telescope: In the Footsteps of a Great Observer. 2011. (Patrick Moore's Practical Astronomy Ser.). (ENG., Illus.). 224p. pap. 44.95 *(978-0-387-85356-7(1)*, 0387853561) Springer.

Radziwill, Nicole M. & Bridger, Alan. Software & Cyberinfrastructure for Astronomy: 27-30 June 2010, San Diego, California, United States, 2 vols. 2010. (Proceedings of SPIE Ser.). (Illus.). 1302p. pap. 200.00 ***(978-0-8194-8230-3(7))*** SPIE.

Reeves, Eileen. Galileo's Glassworks: The Telescope & the Mirror. 2008. (Illus.). 240p. 21.95 *(978-0-674-02667-4(5))* Harvard Univ. Pr.

Richichi, Andrea, et al, eds. The Power of Optical/IR Interferometry: Recent Scientific Results & 2nd Generation Instrumentation: Proceedings of the ESO Workshop held in Garching, Germany, 4-8 April 2005. 2010. (ESO Astrophysics Symposia Ser.). (Illus.). xxx, 604p. pap. 139.00 *(978-3-642-09360-9(4)*, 3642093604) Springer.

Riva, Marco. Smart Structures in Instrumentation for Astronomy. 2011. 144p. pap. ***(978-3-8443-1038-2(X))*** Lambert Academic Publishing.

Romano, Antonio. Geometric Optics: Theory & Design of Astronomical Optical Systems Using Mathematica(r). 2009. (Modeling & Simulation in Science, Engineering & Technology Ser.). (ENG., Illus.). xii, 224p. 99.00 *(978-0-8176-4871-8(2)*, 0817648712) Birkhauser Verlag AG CHE. Dist: Springer.

Siegmund, Oswald. UV, X-Ray, & Gamma-Ray Space Instrumentation for Astronomy XVI. 2009. (Proceedings of SPIE Ser.). 200p. pap. 80.00 ***(978-0-8194-7725-5(7))*** SPIE.

Siegmund, Oswald H. W. UV, X-Ray, & Gamma-Ray Space Instrumentation for Astronomy XV: 26-27 August, 2007, San Diego, California, USA. 2007. (Proceedings of SPIE Ser.). (Illus.). 376p. pap. 90.00 *(978-0-8194-6834-5(7))* SPIE.

Tyson, Robert K. & Lloyd-Hart, Michael. Astronomical Adaptive Optics Systems & Applications III: 29-30 August 2007, San Diego, California, USA. 2007. (Proceedings of SPIE Ser.). (Illus.). 234p. pap. 70.00 *(978-0-8194-6839-0(8))* SPIE.

Van Dam, Marcos. Wave-Front Sensing for Adaptive Optics in Astronomy. 2008. 244p. pap. *(978-3-639-02445-6(1))* VDM Verlag Dr. Mueller e.K.

Warren, Penny G. Astronomical & Space Optical Systems: 2-3 August 2009, San Diego, California, United States. 2009. (Proceedings of SPIE Ser.). (Illus.). 440p. pap. 90.00 *(978-0-8194-7729-3(X))* SPIE.

Yount, Lisa. Modern Astronomy: Expanding the Universe. 2006. (Milestones in Discovery & Invention Ser.). (Illus.). 224p. (YA). (gr. 7-12). 35.00 *(978-0-8160-5746-7(X))* Facts On File, Inc.

ASTRONOMICAL OBSERVATORIES

see also names of individual observatories

Angeli, George Z. & Cullum, M. J. Modeling, Systems Engineering, & Project Management for Astronomy III: 26-28 June 2008, Marseille, France. 2008. (Proceedings of SPIE Ser.). (Illus.). 644p. pap. 130.00 *(978-0-8194-7227-4(1))* SPIE.

Angeli, George Z. & Dierickx, Philippe. Modeling, Systems Engineering, & Project Management for Astronomy IV: 27-29 June & 1 July 2010. 2010. (Proceedings of SPIE Ser.). (Illus.). 754p. pap. 140.00 ***(978-0-8194-8228-0(5))*** SPIE.

Arditti, David. Setting-up a Small Observatory: From Concept to Construction. 2007. (Patrick Moore's Practical Astronomy Ser.). (Illus.). 235p. per. 29.95 *(978-0-387-34521-5(3)*, 0387345213) Springer.

Brandl, Bernhard R., et al, eds. 400 Years of Astronomical Telescopes: A review of History, Science & Technology. 2009. (ENG., Illus.). xvi, 516p. 149.00 *(978-90-481-2232-5(5)*, 9048122325) Springer.

Bridle, Alan H., et al. Frontiers of Astrophysics: A Celebration of NRAO's 50th Anniversary: Proceedings of a Symposium Held at National Radio Astronomy Observatory, Charlottesville, Virginia, USA, 18-21 June 2007. 2008. (Astronomical Society of the Pacific Conference Ser.: Vol. 395). (Illus.). xx, 390p. *(978-1-58381-660-8(7))* Astronomical Society of the Pacific, The.

Brissenden, R. J. V. & Silva, David R. Observatory Operations: Strategies, Processes, & Systems II: 24-26 May, 2008, Marseille, France. 2008. (Proceedings of SPIE Ser.). (Illus.). 722p. pap. 130.00 *(978-0-8194-7226-7(3))* SPIE.

Cesarsky, Catherine & Salama, Alberto, eds. ISO Science Legacy: A Compact Review of ISO Major Achievements. 2010. (ENG.) viii, 448p. pap. 179.00 *(978-90-481-6979-5(8)*, 9048169798) Springer.

Dick, Steven J. Sky & Ocean Joined: The U. S. Naval Observatory 1830-2000. 2007. (ENG., Illus.). 624p. pap. 122.00 *(978-0-521-03750-1(6))* Cambridge Univ. Pr.

Doressoundiram, A. & Lellouch, Emmanuel. At the Edge of the Solar System: Icy New Worlds Unveiled. 2009. (Springer Praxis Books / Popular Astronomy Ser.). (ENG., Illus.). x, 214p. pap. 34.95 *(978-1-4419-0864-3(1)*, 1441908641, Springer-Praxis) Springer.

GARY, Bruce L. Exoplanet Observing for Amateurs. 2007. (Illus.). 170p. per. 22.00 *(978-0-9798446-3-8(0))* Reductionist Publications.

Gordon, M. A. Recollections of Tucson Operations: The Millimeter-Wave Observatory of the National Radio Astronomy Observatory. 2010. (Astrophysics & Space Science Library). xvii, 221p. pap. 179.00 *(978-90-481-6822-4(8)*, 9048168228) Springer.

Harrington, Philip S. Cosmic Challenge: The Ultimate Observing List for Amateurs. 2010. (ENG., Illus.). 488p. (C). 45.00 *(978-0-521-89936-9(2))* Cambridge Univ. Pr.

Haubold, Hans J. International Heliophysical Year 2007: the United Nations Report: The United Nations Report. 2009. (Studies in Space Policy Ser.). (ENG., Illus.). xv, 371p. 239.00 *(978-3-211-99179-4(4)*, 3211991794) Springer.

Haubold, Hans J. & Mathai, A. M., eds. Proceedings of the Third un/ESA/NASA Workshop on the International Heliophysical Year 2007 & Basic Space Science: National Astronomical Observatory of Japan. 2009. (Astrophysics & Space Science Proceedings Ser.). (ENG., Illus.). viii, 190p. 219.00 *(978-3-642-03323-0(7)*, 3642033237) Springer.

Heck, André, ed. The Multinational History of Strasbourg Astronomical Observatory. 2010. (Astrophysics & Space Science Library). viii, 310p. pap. 169.00 *(978-90-481-6918-4(6)*, 9048169186) Springer.

Hicks, John. Building a Roll-off Roof Observatory. 2008. (Patrick Moore's Practical Astronomy Ser.). (Illus.). 163p. 59.95 *(978-0-387-76603-4(0)*, 0387766030) Springer.

Isbell, Douglas & Strom, Stephen E. Observatories of the Southwest: A Guide for Curious Skywatchers. 2009. (ENG., Illus.). 192p. pap. 21.95 *(978-0-8165-2641-3(9))* Univ. of Arizona Pr.

Kerrod, Robin & Stott, Carole. Hubble: The Mirror on the Universe. rev. ed. 2007. (ENG., Illus.). 192p. 35.00 *(978-1-55407-316-0(2))* Firefly Bks., Ltd.

MacEwen, Howard A. & Breckinridge, James B. UV/Optical/IR Space Telescopes: Innovative Technologies & Concepts II: 26-29 August 2007, San Diego, California, USA. 2007. (Proceedings of SPIE Ser.). (Illus.). 508p. pap. 105.00 *(978-0-8194-6835-2(5))* SPIE.

McLean, Ian S. & Casali, Mark M. Ground-Based & Airborne Instrumentation for Astronomy II: 23-28 June 2008, Marseille, France. 2008. (Proceedings of SPIE Ser.). (Illus.). 2806p. pap. 335.00 ***(978-0-8194-7224-3(7))*** SPIE.

McLean, Ian S., et al. Ground-Based & Airborne Instrumentation for Astronomy III: 27 June-2 July 2010, San Diego, California, United States, 4 vols. 2010. (Proceedings of SPIE Ser.). (Illus.). 3206p. pap. 360.00 ***(978-0-8194-8225-9(0))*** SPIE.

Penprase, Bryan E. The Power of Stars: How Celestial Observations Have Shaped Civilization. 2010. (Illus.). xii, 348p. 39.95 *(978-1-4419-6802-9(4)*, 1441968024) Springer.

Rogers, Gordon. My Heavens! The Adventures of a Lonely Stargazer Building an over-the-Top Observatory. 2008. (Patrick Moore's Practical Astronomy Ser.). (Illus.). 180p. per. 34.95 *(978-0-387-73781-2(2))* Springer.

Siegmund, Oswald H. W. UV, X-Ray, & Gamma-Ray Space Instrumentation for Astronomy XV: 26-27 August, 2007, San Diego, California, USA. 2007. (Proceedings of SPIE Ser.). (Illus.). 376p. pap. 90.00 *(978-0-8194-6834-5(7))* SPIE.

Silva, David R., et al. Observatory Operations: Strategies, Processes, & Systems III: 30 June-2 July 2010, San Diego, California, United States. 2010. (Proceedings of SPIE Ser.). (Illus.). 752p. pap. 160.00 ***(978-0-8194-8227-3(7))*** SPIE.

Stepp, Larry M. & Gilmozzi, Roberto. Ground-Based & Airborne Telescopes II: 23-28 June 2008, Marseille, France, 3 vols. 2008. (Proceedings of SPIE Ser.). (Illus.). 1756p. pap. 230.00 *(978-0-8194-7222-9(0))* SPIE.

Tubbs, Robert. Lucky Exposures. 2008. 152p. pap. *(978-3-8364-9769-5(7))* VDM Verlag Dr. Mueller e.K.

Udías, Agustín. Searching the Heavens & the Earth: the History of Jesuit Observatories: The History of Jesuit Observatories. 2010. (Astrophysics & Space Science Library). 388p. pap. 269.00 *(978-90-481-6252-9(1)*, 9048162521) Springer.

Weiler, Edward. Hubble: A Journey Through Space & Time. Brown, Dwayne et al, eds. 2010. (ENG., Illus.). 144p. 29.95 *(978-0-8109-8997-9(2))* Abrams.

Williams, Thomas R. & Saladyga, Michael. Advancing Variable Star Astronomy: The Centennial History of the American Association of Variable Star Observers. 2011. (ENG., Illus.). 448p. 99.00 *(978-0-521-51912-0(8))* Cambridge Univ. Pr.

Wise, George. Civic Astronomy: Albany's Dudley Observatory, 1852-2002. 2010. (Astrophysics & Space Science Library). x, 215p. pap. 169.00 *(978-90-481-6702-9(7)*, 9048167027) Springer.

ASTRONOMICAL PHOTOGRAPHY

see also Space Photography; Spectrograph

Barnard, Edward Emerson. A Photographic Atlas of Selected Regions of the Milky Way. 2011. (Illus.). 372p. (C). 125.00 *(978-0-521-19143-2(2))* Cambridge Univ. Pr.

Birdlebough, John. Practical Guide to Astrophotography. 2011. (Patrick Moore's Practical Astronomy Ser.). (Illus.). 224p. pap. 29.95 *(978-0-387-68122-1(1))* Springer.

Buick, Tony & Pugh, Philip. How to Photograph the Moon & Planets with Your Digital Camera. 2nd ed. 2011. (Patrick Moore's Practical Astronomy Ser.). (ENG., Illus.). xix, 345p. pap. 39.95 *(978-1-4419-5827-3(4)*, 1441958274) Springer.

Covington, Michael A. Digital SLR Astrophotography. 2007. (ENG., Illus.). 234p. per. 48.00 *(978-0-521-70081-8(7))* Cambridge Univ. Pr.

Dickinson, Terence & Dyer, Alan. The Backyard Astronomer's Guide. 3rd rev. ed. 2008. (ENG., Illus.). 368p. 49.95 *(978-1-55407-344-3(8))* Firefly Bks., Ltd.

Dragesco, Jean. High Resolution Astrophotography. McKim, Richard, tr. from FRE. 2011. (Practical Astronomy Handbooks Ser.). (ENG., Illus.). 174p. pap. 36.99 *(978-1-107-40273-7(5))* Cambridge Univ. Pr.

Folberg, Neil. Celestial Nights: Visions of an Ancient Land. 2008. (ENG., Illus.). 62p. 45.00 *(978-0-7892-0954-2(3))* Abbeville Pr., Inc.

Gendler, Robert. Capturing the Stars: Astrophotography by the Masters. 2009. (ENG., Illus.). 160p. 30.00 *(978-0-7603-3500-0(1)*, 0760335001, Voyageur Pr) MBI Publishing Co. LLC.

Ireland, R. Scott. Photoshop Astronomy: Includes Full Res Tutorial Images on DVD. 2nd ed. 2009. *(978-0-943396-91-0(3))* Willmann-Bell, Inc.

Keeney, L. Douglas. The Lights of Mankind: The Earth at Night As Seen from Space. 2011. (ENG., Illus.). 288p. 32.50 *(978-0-7627-7755-6(9))*, Lyons Pr.) Globe Pequot Pr., The.

Kier, Ruben. The 100 Best Astrophotography Targets: A Monthly Guide for CCD Imaging with Amateur Telescopes. 2009. (Patrick Moore's Practical Astronomy Ser.). (ENG., Illus.). xxi, 360p. pap. 34.95 *(978-1-4419-0602-1(9)*, 1441906029) Springer.

Malin, David. Ancient Light: A Portrait of the Universe. 2009. (ENG., Illus.). 128p. 49.95 *(978-0-7148-4932-4(4))* Phaidon Pr., Inc.

Massey, Steve & Quirk, Steve. Deep-Sky Video Astronomy. 2009. (Patrick Moore's Practical Astronomy Ser.). (ENG., Illus.). xvi, 185p. pap. 34.95 *(978-0-387-87611-5(1))* Springer.

Milone, Eugene F. & Sterken, C., eds. Astronomical Photometry: Past, Present, & Future. 2011. (Astrophysics & Space Science Library). (ENG., Illus.). xii, 217p. 129.00 *(978-1-4419-8049-6(0)*, 1441980490) Springer.

Osborn, Wayne & Robbins, Lee. Preserving Astronomy's Photographic Legacy: Current State & the Future of North American Astronomical Plates: Included Are the Proceedings of a Workshop Held at the Pisgah Astronomical Research Institute, Rosman, North Carolina, USA, 1-3 November 2007. 2009. (Illus.). vii, 202p. *(978-1-58381-700-1(X))*; *(978-1-58381-701-8(8))* Astronomical Society of the Pacific, The.

Parker, Greg. Making Beautiful Deep-Sky Images: Astrophotography with Affordable Equipment & Software. 2007. (Patrick Moore's Practical Astronomy Ser.). (Illus.). 177p. pap. 34.95 *(978-0-387-71352-6(2)*, 0387713522) Springer.

Parker, Greg & Carboni, Noel. Star Vistas: A Collection of Fine Art Astrophotography. 2009. (ENG., Illus.). x, 158p. 39.95 *(978-0-387-88435-6(1))* Springer.

Privett, Grant. Creating & Enhancing Digital Astro Images. 2007. (Patrick Moore's Practical Astronomy Ser.). (Illus.). 142p. pap. 44.95 *(978-1-84628-580-6(1)*, 1846285801) Springer.

Reeves, Robert. Introduction to Digital Astrophotography: Imaging the Universe with a Digital Camera. 2nd ed. 2011. ***(978-0-943396-94-1(8))*** Willmann-Bell, Inc.

Riese, Uta, ed. Trevor Paglen: A Compendium of secrets. 2011. (ENG., Illus.). 64p. 37.50 *(978-3-86678-436-9(8))* Kerber Verlag DEU. Dist: D.A.P./Distributed Art Pubs.

Roberts, Isaac. Photographs of Stars, Star-Clusters & Nebulae Vol. 1: Together with Information Concerning the Instruments & the Methods Employed in the Pursuit of Celestial Photography. 2010. (Cambridge Library Collection - Physical Sciences Ser.). (ENG., Illus.). 168p. pap. 22.99 *(978-1-108-01522-6(0))* Cambridge Univ. Pr.

—Photographs of Stars, Star-Clusters & Nebulae: Volume 2: Together with Records of Results Obtained in the Pursuit of Celestial Photography. 2010. (Cambridge Library Collection - Physical Sciences Ser.). (ENG., Illus.). 196p. pap. 22.99 *(978-1-108-01523-3(9))* Cambridge Univ. Pr.

Seip, Stefan. Digital Astrophotography: A Guide to Capturing the Cosmos. 2007. (ENG., Illus.). 162p. per. 29.95 *(978-1-933952-16-1(4))* Rocky Nook.

Smith, Gregory Hallock, et al. Telescopes, Eyepieces, & Astrographs: Design, Analysis, & Performance of Modern Astronomical Optics. 2012. ***(978-0-943396-96-5(4))*** Willmann-Bell, Inc.

Tubbs, Robert. Lucky Exposures. 2008. 152p. pap. *(978-3-8364-9769-5(7))* VDM Verlag Dr. Mueller e.K.

ASTRONOMICAL PHOTOMETRY

see Photometry, Astronomical

ASTRONOMICAL PHYSICS

see Astrophysics

ASTRONOMICAL RESEARCH

see Astronomy—Research

ASTRONOMICAL SPECTROSCOPY

Blain, Andrew W., et al. The Cold Universe: Saas-Fee Advanced Course 32, 2002. Swiss Society for Astrophysics & Astronomy. Pfenniger, Daniel & Revaz, Yves, eds. 2010. (Saas-Fee Advanced Courses Ser.). xiv, 308p. pap. 129.00 *(978-3-642-07407-3(3)*, 3642074073) Springer.

Dimitrijevic, Milan S., ed. Spectral Line Shapes in Astrophysics: VI Serbian Conference on Spectral Line Shapes in Astrophysics (VI SCSLSA) 2007. (AIP Conference Proceedings / Astronomy & Astrophysics Ser.). (Illus.). 310p. 145.00 *(978-0-7354-0449-6(6))* American Institute of Physics.

Finkbeiner, Ann K. A Grand & Bold Thing: An Extraordinary New Map of the Universe Ushering in a New Era of Discovery. 2010. (ENG., Illus.). 240p. 27.00 *(978-1-4165-5216-1(2)*, Free Pr.) Free Pr.

Hagen, Nathan. Snapshot Imaging Spectropolarimetry. 2009. 176p. pap. *(978-3-639-16395-7(8))* VDM Verlag Dr. Mueller e.K.

Hapke, Bruce. Theory of Reflectance & Emittance Spectroscopy. 2nd ed. 2012. (ENG., Illus.). 528p. 90.00 ***(978-0-521-88349-8(0))*** Cambridge Univ. Pr.

Harrison, Ken M. Astronomical Spectroscopy for Amateurs. 2011. (Patrick Moore's Practical Astronomy Ser.). (ENG., Illus.). xii, 241p. 34.95 *(978-1-4419-7238-5(2)*, 1441972382) Springer.

Harrison, Ken M. Grating Spectroscopes & How to Use Them. 2012. (Patrick Moore's Practical Astronomy Ser.). (ENG., Illus.). xvii, 167p. pap. 34.95 ***(978-1-4614-1396-7(6)***, 1461413966) Springer.

Hubeny, Ivan, et al, eds. Recent Directions in Astrophysical Quantitative Spectroscopy & Radiation Hydrodynamics: Proceedings of the International Conference in Honor of Dimitri Mihalas for His Lifetime Scientific Contributions on the Occasion of His 70th Birthday. 2009. (AIP Conference Proceedings / Astronomy & Astrophysics Ser.). (ENG., Illus.). 378p. pap. 159.00 *(978-0-7354-0710-7(X)*, 073540710X) American Institute of Physics.

Kaufer, Andreas & Kerber, Florian, eds. The 2007 ESO Instrument Calibration Workshop: Proceedings of the ESO Workshop held in Garching, Germany, 23-26 January 2007. 2010. (ESO Astrophysics Symposia Ser.). (Illus.). xxviii, 616p. pap. 149.00 *(978-3-642-09566-5(6)*, 3642095666) Springer.

Käufl, Hans Ulrich, et al, eds. High Resolution Infrared Spectroscopy in Astronomy: Proceedings of an ESO Workshop Held at Garching, Germany, 18-21 November 2003. 2010. (ESO Astrophysics Symposia Ser.). xx, 559p. pap. 89.95 *(978-3-642-06440-1(X)*, 364206440X) Springer.

Kazantsev, Sergi & Henoux, J. C. Polarization Spectroscopy of Ionized Gases. 2010. (Astrophysics & Space Science Library). (Illus.). 216p. pap. 199.00 *(978-90-481-4550-8(3)*, 9048145503) Springer.

Martin, Jack. A Spectroscopic Atlas of Bright Stars. 2009. (Astronomer's Pocket Field Guide Ser.). (Illus.). 205p. pap. 29.95 *(978-1-4419-0704-2(1)*, 1441907041) Springer.

Mediavilla, Evencio, et al, eds. 3D Spectroscopy in Astronomy. (Canary Islands Winter School of Astrophysics Ser.). (ENG., Illus.). 288p. 2011. pap. 55.00 ***(978-1-107-40347-5(2))*** 2010. 115.00 *(978-0-521-89541-5(3))* Cambridge Univ. Pr.

Paradijs, Jan Van & Bleeker, Johan A. M., eds. X-Ray Spectroscopy in Astrophysics: Lectures Held at the Astrophysics School X Organized by the European Astrophysics Doctoral Network (EADN) in Amsterdam, the Netherlands, September 22 - October 3 1997. 2010. (Lecture Notes in Physics Ser.). xv, 530p. pap. 99.00 *(978-3-642-08486-7(9)*, 3642084869) Springer.

Phelan, Don. High Time Resolution Astrophysics. 2008. (AIP Conference Proceedings Ser.: No. 984). 147.00 *(978-0-7354-0503-5(4))* American Institute of Physics.

Pradhan, Anil K. Atomic Astrophysics & Spectroscopy. Date not set. (Illus.). 400p. 75.00 *(978-0-521-82536-8(9))* Cambridge Univ. Pr.

Santos, Nuno C., et al, eds. Precision Spectroscopy in Astrophysics: Proceedings of the ESO/Lisbon/Aveiro Conference Held in Aveiro, Portugal, 11-15 September 2006. 2008. (Eso Astrophysics Symposia Ser.). (Illus.). 328p. 109.00 *(978-3-540-75484-8(9))* Springer.

Sterken, Christiaan, ed. Conference on the Future of Photometric, Spectrophotometric & Polarimetric: Blankenberge, Belgium - 2006, Vol. 364. 2007. (Astronomical Society of the Pacific Conference Ser.: Vol. 364). 633p. 77.00 *(978-1-58381-232-7(6))* Astronomical Society of the Pacific, The.

Tennyson, Jonathan. Astronomical Spectroscopy: An Introduction to the Atomic & Molecular Physics of Astronomical Spectra. 2nd rev. ed. 2011. (Illus.). 236p. 65.00 *(978-981-4291-96-5(X))*; pap. 40.00 *(978-981-4291-97-2(8))* World Scientific Publishing Co., Inc.

ASTRONOMY

see also Astrogeology; Astronautics in Astronomy; Astrophysics; Calendar; Constellations; Cosmology; Galaxies; Geodesy; Hindu Astronomy; Infrared Astronomy; Maya Astronomy; Meteors; Moon; Nautical Almanacs; Nutation; Outer Space; Plurality of Worlds; Quasars; Radar in Astronomy; Radio Astronomy; Seasons; Sky; Space Astronomy; Space Sciences; Spherical Astronomy; Stars; Statistical Astronomy; Transits; X-ray Astronomy; Zodiac

Accomazzi, Alberto & Heck, André, eds. Future Professional Communication in Astronomy II. 2011. (Astrophysics & Space Science Proceedings Ser.). (ENG., Illus.). xvi, 162p. 199.00 *(978-1-4419-8368-8(6)*, 1441983686) Springer.

Adamson, Thomas K. Saturn [Scholastic]: Revised Edition. 2010. (Exploring the Galaxy Ser.). 24p. pap. 0.49 *(978-1-4296-5814-0(2)*, Pebble Plus) Capstone Pr., Inc.

Afonso, Fiona. 2005: Past Meets Present in Astronomy... 2006. (Illus.). 120 ppp. 100.00 *(978-981-256-887-8(5))* World Scientific Publishing Co., Inc.

Ahad, A. The Midnight Stars. 2011. 40p. pap. 16.95 ***(978-1-4626-2961-9(X))*** PublishAmerica, Inc.

Alcaniz, Jailson, et al, eds. Graduate School in Astronomy: XI Special Courses at the National Observatory of Rio de Janeiro. 2007. (AIP Conference Proceedings / Astronomy & Astrophysics Ser.). (Illus.). 125p. 69.00 *(978-0-7354-0440-3(2))* American Institute of Physics.

Alexander, David. The Sun, 1 vol. Jones, Lauren V. & Slater, Timothy F., eds. 2009. (Greenwood Guides to the Universe Ser.). 228p. 65.00 *(978-0-313-34077-2(3)*, GR4077, Greenwood Pr.) Greenwood Publishing Group, Inc.

Ali Rahoma, Walid, et al. Binary System with Varying Mass. 2011. 120p. pap. ***(978-3-8443-1582-0(9))*** Lambert Academic Publishing.

Alvarez, Ted, et al. Instant Egghead Guide: Universe. 2009. (ENG., Illus.). 240p. pap. 16.99 *(978-0-312-38637-5(0)*, St. Martin's Griffin) St. Martin's Pr.

Anderson, Warren, et al. Gravitational-Wave Physics & Astronomy: An Introduction to Theory, Experiment & Data Analysis. 2011. (ENG., Illus.). 381p. 155.00 *(978-3-527-40886-3(X)*, Wiley-VCH) Wiley, John & Sons, Inc.

Annual Review of Astronomy & Astrophysics. 2006. 85.00 *(978-0-8243-0944-2(8))* Annual Reviews, Inc.

Argyle, Robert W., et al. Astronomical Data & Analysis Software & Systems XVII. 2008. (Illus.). xxxvii, 757p. *(978-1-58381-659-2(3))*; *(978-1-58381-658-5(5))* Astronomical Society of the Pacific, The.

Arnaud, Keith, et al, eds. Handbook of X-ray Astronomy. 2011. (Cambridge Observing Handbooks for Research Astronomers Ser.). (ENG., Illus.). 206p. 60.00 ***(978-0-521-88373-3(0))*** Cambridge Univ. Pr.

Arny, Thomas & Schneider, Step. Explorations INTRO to Astronom. 2007. 608p. pap. 86.75 *(978-0-07-331598-0(2))*; 5th ed. pap. 86.75 *(978-0-07-294360-3(2))* McGraw-Hill Professional Publishing.

Arny, Thomas & Schneider, Stephen. Exploration: An Introduction to Astronomy, Vol. 2. 6th ed. 2009. (ENG.). (C). pap. 87.67 *(978-0-07-739529-2(8)*, 0077395298, McGraw-Hill Science, Engineering & Mathematics) McGraw-Hill Higher Education.

—Explorations: Introduction to Astronomy. 6th ed. 2009. (ENG.). (C). pap., pap. 157.67 *(978-0-07-734509-9(6)*, 0077345096, McGraw-Hill Science, Engineering & Mathematics) McGraw-Hill Higher Education.

—Explorations: Introduction to Astronomy (NASTA Hardcover Reinforced High School Binding) 6th ed. 2009. (ENG.). (C). 144.19 *(978-0-07-893547-3(4)*, 0078935474) McGraw-Hill Higher Education.

—Explorations Volume 1: Solar System (Ch 1-12) 6th ed. 2009. (ENG.). (C). pap. 87.67 *(978-0-07-738953-6(0)*, 0077389530, McGraw-Hill Science, Engineering & Mathematics) McGraw-Hill Higher Education.

—Looseleaf for Explorations: Introduction to Astronomy. 6th ed. 2010. (ENG.). (C). ring bd. 110.67 *(978-0-07-749772-9(4)*, 0077497724, McGraw-Hill Science, Engineering & Mathematics) McGraw-Hill Higher Education.

Arny, Thomas T. & Schneider, Stephen E. Explorations: An Introduction to Astronomy. 5th ed. 2007. (Illus.). 594p. 126.88 *(978-0-07-334723-3(X)*, 9780073347233); pap. 126.88 incl. cd-rom *(978-0-07-334722-6(1)*, 9780073347226) McGraw-Hill Higher Education. (McGraw-Hill Science, Engineering & Mathematics).

Asada, Hideki, et al. Equations of Motion in General Relativity. 2011. (International Series of Monographs on Physics Ser.). (ENG., Illus.). 168p. 98.50 *(978-0-19-958410-9(9))* Oxford Univ. Pr., Inc.

Aschwanden, Markus J. Self-Organized Criticality in Astrophysics: The Statistics of Nonlinear Processes in the Universe. 2011. (Springer Praxis Books / Astronomy & Planetary Sciences Ser.). (Illus.). xiv, 420p. 169.00 *(978-3-642-15000-5(4)*, 3642150004) Springer.

Ashworth, William B., Jr. Out of This World: The Golden Age of the Celestial Atlas. 2007. (ENG.). per. 20.00 *(978-0-9763590-1-2(4))* Linda Hall Library.

Die Astronomie (Astronomy) (Schulerduden Ser.) (ENG & GER.). 27.95 *(978-3-411-02220-5(5)*, B2220) Bibliographisches Institut & F. A. Brockhaus AG DEU. Dist: Continental Bk. Co., Inc.

Astronomy & Astrophysics. Date not set. *(978-0-387-91525-8(7))* Springer.

Aveni, Anthony F., ed. Archaeoastronomy in the New World: American Primitive Astronomy. 2009. 232p. pap. 36.99 *(978-0-521-12547-5(2))* Cambridge Univ. Pr.

—Foundations of New World Cultural Astronomy: A Reader with Commentary. 2008. (ENG., Illus.). 728p. pap. 34.95 *(978-0-87081-900-1(3))* Univ. Pr. of Colorado.

Axelrod, Alan & De Pree, Christopher. The Complete Idiot's Guide to Astronomy. 4th ed. 2008. (Complete Idiot's Guide Ser.). (ENG., Illus.). 336p. (gr. 12-18). 20.95 *(978-1-59257-719-4(9)*, Alpha Bks.) Penguin Group (USA) Inc.

Backman, Dana & Seeds, Michael A. Astronomy: The Solar System & Beyond. 7th ed. 2011. (Textbooks Available with Cengage YouBook Ser.). (ENG.). 528p. (C). pap. 179.95 *(978-1-111-42567-8(1))* Brooks/Cole.

—Horizons: Exploring the Universe. 12th ed. 2011. (Textbooks Available with Cengage YouBook Ser.). (ENG.). 528p. (C). pap. 168.95 *(978-1-111-43020-7(9))* Brooks/Cole.

Backman, Dana E. & Seeds, Michael A. Astro. 2011. (Illus.). xi, 342p. *(978-0-538-49591-2(X))* Brooks/Cole.

Bahrami, Bahram. The Mystery of the Origin of the Universe. 2011. 174p. pap. 38.90 ***(978-3-8423-4710-6(3))*** Bks. on Demand.

Baker, Andrew J., ed. From Z-Machines to Alma: Sub Millimeter Spectroscopy of Galaxies. 2007. (Astronomical Society of the Pacific Conference Ser.). 310p. 77.00 *(978-1-58381-311-9(X))* Astronomical Society of the Pacific, The.

Bakich, Michael E. 1001 Celestial Wonders to See Before You Die: The Best Sky Objects for Star Gazers. 2010. (Patrick Moore's Practical Astronomy Ser.). (ENG., Illus.). xiii, 479p. pap. 44.95 *(978-1-4419-1776-8(4)*, 1441917764) Springer.

Ball, Andrew, et al. Planetary Landers & Entry Probes. 2007. (ENG., Illus.). 362p. 174.00 *(978-0-521-82002-8(2))* Cambridge Univ. Pr.

Ball, Robert S. The Story of the Heavens. 2010. (Cambridge Library Collection - Physical Sciences Ser.). (ENG., Illus.). 608p. pap. 43.00 *(978-1-108-01414-4(3))* Cambridge Univ. Pr.

Bally, John & Reipurth, Bo. The Birth of Stars & Planets. 2006. (ENG., Illus.). 306p. 56.00 *(978-0-521-80105-8(2))* Cambridge Univ. Pr.

Barbieri, C. Fundamentals of Astronomy. 2006. (ENG., Illus.). 366p. (C). per. 75.95 *(978-0-7503-0886-1(9)*, IP294, Taylor & Francis) Taylor & Francis Group GBR. Dist: Taylor & Francis Group.

BarCharts, Inc. Astronomy: Stargazing. 2011. (ENG.). 6p. 6.95 *(978-1-4232-1634-6(2))* Barcharts, Inc.

Barstow, Martin A. & Holberg, Jay B. Extreme Ultraviolet Astronomy. 2007. (Cambridge Astrophysics Ser.). (ENG.). 412p. (C). pap. 87.00 *(978-0-521-03906-2(1))* Cambridge Univ. Pr.

Baski. Elementary Astronomy: PHYS 103L, Spring 2007. 2007. (C). per. *(978-1-60036-061-9(0))* Academx Publishing Services, Inc.

—Elementary Astronomy: PHYZ 103L, Fall 2006. 2006. (C). per. *(978-1-60036-047-3(5))* Academx Publishing Services, Inc.

Bastieri, Denis & Rando, Riccardo, eds. Science with the New Generation of High Energy Gamma-Ray Experiments: Proceedings of the 6th Edition: Bridging the Gap Between GeV & TeV. 2009. (AIP Conference Proceedings / Astronomy & Astrophysics Ser.). (ENG.). 252p. 118.00 *(978-0-7354-0649-0(9))* American Institute of Physics.

Bennett, Clinton. The Cosmic Perspective. 4th ed. 736p. (YA). (gr. 11-12). tchr. ed. 18.97 *(978-0-8053-9284-5(X))* Addison-Wesley Educational Pubs., Inc.

Bennett, G. G. & Freislich, J. G. Field Astronomy Surveyor. 247p. pap. *(978-0-86840-080-8(7)*, UNSW Press) NewSouth Publishing.

Bennett, Jeffrey. The Cosmic Perspective. 6th ed. 2009. *(978-0-321-63656-0(2))* Addison-Wesley Longman, Inc.

Bennett, Jeffrey O. The Essential Cosmic Perspective. 4th ed. (Illus.). 2007. xxix, 735p. *(978-0-8053-9283-8(1))* 2007. *(978-0-321-49186-2(6))* 2007. *(978-0-321-49971-4(9))* 2007. xxix, 735p. *(978-0-8053-9210-4(6))* 2007. xxix, 735p. *(978-0-8053-9296-8(3))* 2006. *(978-0-8053-4792-0(5))* Addison-Wesley Longman, Inc.

Bennett, Jeffrey O., et al. The Books a la Carte for Essential Cosmic Perspective. 6th ed. 2011. (ENG.). 624p. (C). ring bd. 85.67 ***(978-0-321-72440-3(2))*** Benjamin-Cummings Publishing Co.

—The Cosmic Perspective: Media Update. 4th ed. 2007. pap. *(978-0-8053-7248-9(2))* Addison-Wesley Longman, Inc.

—The Cosmic Perspective: Stars, Galaxies, & Cosmology. 6th ed. 2009. (ENG.). 624p. (C). pap. 90.60 *(978-0-321-64270-7(8))* Benjamin-Cummings Publishing Co.

—The Cosmic Perspective: Stars, Galaxies & Cosmology (text Component) 5th ed. 2008. (Illus.). xxviii, 759p. pap. *(978-0-321-50320-6(1))* Addison-Wesley Longman, Inc.

—The Cosmic Perspective: The Solar System. 6th ed. 2009. (ENG.). 560p. (C). pap. 90.60 *(978-0-321-64269-1(4))* Benjamin-Cummings Publishing Co.

—The Cosmic Perspective: The Solar System (text Component) 5th ed. 2008. pap. *(978-0-321-50318-3(X))* Addison-Wesley Longman, Inc.

—The Cosmic Perspective Fundamentals. 2009. (ENG.). 320p. (C). pap. 84.27 incl. cd-rom *(978-0-321-56695-9(5))* Benjamin-Cummings Publishing Co.

—The Cosmic Perspective Fundamentals. 2009. (ENG., Illus.). 320p. (C). pap. 84.27 *(978-0-321-56704-8(8))* Benjamin-Cummings Publishing Co.

—Cosmic Perspective Media Update P-Copy, the (text Component) 5th ed. 2009. (Illus.). pap. incl. cd-rom *(978-0-321-55820-6(0))* Addison-Wesley Longman, Inc.

—The Cosmic Perspective P-copy (text Component) 5th ed. 2008. 736p. pap. *(978-0-321-46099-8(5))* Addison-Wesley Longman, Inc.

—The Cosmic Perspective (text Component) 5th ed. 2008. (Illus.). 736p. pap. *(978-0-321-50618-4(9))* Addison-Wesley Longman, Inc.

—The Essential Cosmic Perspective. 5th ed. 2009. (ENG.). 624p. (C). pap. 140.60 *(978-0-321-58088-7(5))* Addison-Wesley Longman, Inc.

—The Essential Cosmic Perspective. (ENG., (C). 5th ed. 2009. Illus.). 624p. pap. 140.60 incl. cd-rom *(978-0-321-56694-2(7))* 6th ed. 2011. ring bd. 95.67 *(978-0-321-77546-7(5))* 6th ed. 2009. 832p. pap. 152.47 *(978-0-321-63366-8(0))* 6th rev. ed. 2010. 624p. pap. 142.73 *(978-0-321-71823-5(2))* 6th rev. ed. 2010. (Illus.). 624p. pap. 142.73 *(978-0-321-71536-4(5))* Benjamin-Cummings Publishing Co.

—Essential Cosmic Perspective P-Copy, the (text Component) 5th ed. 2009. 624p. pap. incl. cd-rom *(978-0-321-58089-4(3))* Addison-Wesley Longman, Inc.

Bereder, Antoine. The Photographic Atlas of Acupuncture. 2011. (ENG., Illus.). 576p. 149.00 *(978-1-84409-538-1(4))* Findhorn Pr. GBR. Dist: Independent Pubs. Group.

Bhaumik, Mani. The Cosmic Detective. 2009. 130p. 19.95 *(978-3-527-40965-5(3))* Wiley, John & Sons, Inc.

Billing, Ronald. The New Universe & Origins of the Stars. 2011. 40p. pap. 21.99 ***(978-1-4568-3132-5(1))*** Xlibris Corp.

Blackwell, Richard J. Behind the Scenes at Galileo's Trial: Including the First English Translation of Melchior Inchofer's Tractatus Syllepticus. 2008. (ENG.). 264p. pap. 28.00 *(978-0-268-02210-5(0))* Univ. of Notre Dame Pr.

Blake, J. L. Conversations on Natural Philosophy: in Which the Elements of That. 2006. (ENG.). 336p. per. 30.95 *(978-1-4286-5398-6(8))* Kessinger Publishing, LLC.

Blandford, Roger. Annual Review of Astronomy & Astrophysics, Vol. 45. 2007th ed. 2007. 701p. pap. 197.00 *(978-0-8243-0945-9(6))* Annual Reviews, Inc.

Block, David L., et al, eds. Galaxies & their Masks: A Conference in Honour of K. C. Freeman, FRS. 2010. (ENG., Illus.). xxxiv, 479p. 259.00 *(978-1-4419-7316-0(8)*, 1441973168) Springer.

Blondel, Philippe & Mason, John, eds. Solar System Update. 2010. (Springer Praxis Books / Geophysical Sciences Ser.). xx, 329p. pap. 219.00 *(978-3-642-06537-8(6)*, 3642065376) Springer.

Blumenthal, George, et al. 21st Century Astronomy. 3rd ed. 2010. (ENG., Illus.). 651p. (C). pap. 144.14 *(978-0-393-93198-3(6)*, 93198) Norton, W. W. & Co., Inc.

Bobrowsky, Peter T. & Rickman, Hans, eds. Comet/Asteroid Impacts & Human Society: An Interdisciplinary Approach. 2007. (ENG., Illus.). xxvi, 546p. 189.00 *(978-3-540-32709-7(6)*, 3540327096) Springer.

Bonatti, Guido. Book of Astronomy. unabr. ed. 2007. Orig. Title: Liber Astronomiae. (Illus.). 736p. kivar 149.98 *(978-1-934586-00-6(5))* Cazimi Pr., The.

—Book of Astronomy, 2, 2. 2007. Orig. Title: Liber Astronomiae. (Illus.). 29p. kivar 149.98 *(978-1-934586-01-3(3))* Cazimi Pr., The.

Bone, Neil. Aurora: Observing & Recording Nature's Spectacular Light Show. 2007. (Patrick Moore's Practical Astronomy Ser.). (Illus.). 182p. per. 39.95 *(978-0-387-36052-2(2)*, 0387360522) Springer.

Bordeleau, André G. Flags of the Night Sky: Why Some National Symbols Carry Heavenly Signs. 2012. (ENG., Illus.). 220p. pap. 34.95 ***(978-1-4614-0928-1(4)***, 1461409284) Springer.

Borgia, Michael. Human Vision & the Night Sky: How to Improve Your Observing Skills. 2006. (Patrick Moore's Practical Astronomy Ser.). (Illus.). 289p. per. 29.95 *(978-0-387-30776-3(1)*, 0387307761) Springer.

Bowen, Alan C. & Wildberg, Christian. New Perspectives on Aristotle's De Caelo. 2009. *(978-90-04-17376-7(5))* BRILL.

Brekke, Pal. Our Explosive Sun: A Visual Feast of Our Source of Light & Life. 2012. (ENG., Illus.). x, 158p. 29.95 ***(978-1-4614-0570-2(X)***, 146140570X) Springer.

Broxton, Tony. Our Sun. 2011. 228p. pap. 18.95 ***(978-1-4620-5570-8(2))*** iUniverse, Inc.

Bryan, Margaret. Lectures on Natural Philosophy: The Result of Many Years' Practical Experience of the Facts Elucidated. 2011. (Cambridge Library Collection - Women's Writing Ser.). (ENG., Illus.). 470p. pap. 34.99 ***(978-1-108-03808-9(5))*** Cambridge Univ. Pr.

Buchheim, Robert K. The Sky Is Your Laboratory: Advanced Astronomy Projects for Amateurs. 2007. (Springer Praxis Books / Popular Astronomy Ser.). (Illus.). 299p. per. 39.95 *(978-0-387-71822-4(2)*, 038771822X, Springer-Praxis) Springer.

Bullinger, E. W. The Witness of the Stars. 2007. 296p. 29.95 *(978-1-60206-783-7(X))* Cosimo, Inc.

—The Witness of the Stars. 2011. 298p. pap. 9.45 ***(978-1-61427-078-2(3))*** Martino Publishing.

Bullinger, Ethelbert. The Witness of the Stars. 2007. 296p. per. 10.95 *(978-1-60206-046-3(0))* Cosimo, Inc.

Buta, Ronald J., et al. The de Vaucouleurs Atlas of Galaxies. 2007. (ENG., Illus.). 356p. 197.00 *(978-0-521-82048-6(0))* Cambridge Univ. Pr.

Carina Software, x. x. Voyager: SkyGazer v4. 0 College Edition CD-ROM. 6th ed. 2009. (ENG., Illus.). xxviii, 725p. (C). cd-rom 15.47 *(978-0-321-66162-3(1))* Benjamin-Cummings Publishing Co.

—Voyager: SkyGazer v4. 0 College Edition CD-ROM (component) 5th ed. 2009. cd-rom *(978-0-321-55626-4(7))* Addison-Wesley Longman, Inc.

Carina Software, x. x. & Bennett, Jeffrey O. The Essential Cosmic Perspective: SkyGazer College Edition v3. 7 CD-ROM. 4th ed. 2008. (Illus.). cd-rom *(978-0-321-50700-6(2))* Addison-Wesley Longman, Inc.

Caswell, Alexis. Address Before the American Association for the Advancement of Science. 2011. 34p. pap. 11.99 ***(978-1-4181-9469-7(7))*** MPublishing.

Cavin, Jerry. The Amateur Astronomer's Guide to the Deep-Sky Catalogs. 2011. (Patrick Moore's Practical Astronomy Ser.). (ENG., Illus.). x, 380p. pap. 39.95 ***(978-1-4614-0655-6(2)***, 1461406552) Springer.

Cecchi, Claudia, et al, eds. Science with the New Generation of High Energy Gamma-Ray Experiments: Proceedings of the 7th Workshop on Gamma-Ray Physics in the LHC Era. 2010. (AIP Conference Proceedings / Mathematical & Statistical Phsyics Ser.). 272p. 114.00 *(978-0-7354-0767-1(3)*, 0735407673, AIP Pr.) Springer.

Chabrier, Gilles, ed. Structure Formation in Astrophysics. (Cambridge Contemporary Astrophysics Ser.). (ENG.). 2011. 456p. pap. 55.00 *(978-0-521-18274-4(3))* 2009. (Illus.). 454p. 139.00 *(978-0-521-88779-3(8))* Cambridge Univ. Pr.

Chaisson & McMillan. Astronomy Today. 5th ed. 800p. (YA). (gr. 11-12). stu. ed. 70.97 *(978-0-13-192492-5(3))* Prentice Hall (Schl. Div.).

Chaisson, et al. Astronomy Today. 7th ed. 2010. (ENG.). 850p. (C). 152.47 *(978-0-321-69623-6(9))* Benjamin-Cummings Publishing Co.

—Astronomy Today Vol. 1: The Solar System. 7th ed. 2010. (ENG.). (C). pap. 90.80 *(978-0-321-71864-8(X))* Benjamin-Cummings Publishing Co.

—Astronomy Today Vol. 2: Stars & Galaxies. 7th ed. 2010. (ENG.). (C). pap. 90.80 *(978-0-321-71865-5(8))* Benjamin-Cummings Publishing Co.

—Astronomy Today Volume 1: The Solar System, 2 vols. 7th ed. 3911. (ENG., Illus.). 480p. (C). pap. 90.80 *(978-0-321-71862-4(3))* Benjamin-Cummings Publishing Co.

—Astronomy Today Volume 2: Stars & Galaxies, 2 vols. 7th ed. 2010. (ENG., Illus.). 544p. (C). pap. 90.80 *(978-0-321-71863-1(1))* Benjamin-Cummings Publishing Co.

Chaisson, Eric & McMillan, S. Astronomy: A Beginner's Guide to the Universe. 6th ed. 2010. (Illus.). *(978-0-321-64964-5(8))* Addison-Wesley Longman, Inc.

—Astronomy Today. 7th ed. 2011. (Illus.). *(978-0-321-70471-9(1))*; *(978-0-13-212006-7(2))* Addison-Wesley Longman, Inc.

Chaisson, Eric & McMillan, Steve. Astronomy: A Beginner's Guide to the Universe. 6th ed. 2009. (ENG.). 592p. (C). pap. 142.73 *(978-0-321-59876-9(8))*; (Illus.). pap. 142.73 *(978-0-321-60510-8(1))* Benjamin-Cummings Publishing Co.

—Astronomy Today. 6th ed. 2008. (Illus.). 848p. pap. *(978-0-321-49535-8(7))* Addison-Wesley Longman, Inc.

—Astronomy Today. 2010. (ENG.). (C). 6th ed. 825p. ring bd. 105.20 *(978-0-321-73235-4(9))* 7th ed. 880p. 152.47 *(978-0-321-69143-9(1))* Benjamin-Cummings Publishing Co.

—Astronomy Today, 2 vols. 6th ed. 2007. (ENG., Illus.). 848p. (C). 150.20 *(978-0-13-240085-5(5)*, Prentice Hall) Prentice Hall PTR.

Chaisson, Eric & Mcmillan, Steve. Astronomy Today. 7th ed. 2010. (ENG.). 850p. (C). 57.20 *(978-0-321-70597-6(1))* Benjamin-Cummings Publishing Co.

Chaisson, Eric & McMillan, Steve. Books a la Carte for Astronomy Today. 7th ed. 2010. (ENG.). 880p. (C). ring bd. 91.53 *(978-0-321-69850-6(9))* Benjamin-Cummings Publishing Co.

Chaisson, Eric, et al. Astronomy Today. 7th ed. 2010. (ENG.). 850p. (C). E-Book, E-Book 96.00 *(978-0-321-70598-3(X))* Benjamin-Cummings Publishing Co.

—Astronomy Today: The Solar System, 2 vols. 6th ed. 2007. (ENG., Illus.). 480p. (C). per. 89.40 *(978-0-13-615549-2(9)*, Prentice Hall) Prentice Hall PTR.

Chalmers, Thomas. Discourses on the Christian Revelation V. 2006. pap. 26.99 *(978-1-4255-3752-4(9))* MPublishing.

—A Series of Discourses on the Christian Revelation. 2009. (Cambridge Library Collection - Religion Ser.). 280p. pap. 23.99 *(978-1-108-00527-2(6))* Cambridge Univ. Pr.

Chambers, George Frederick. A Handbook of Descriptive & Practical Astronomy. 2010. (Cambridge Library Collection - Physical Sciences Ser.). (Illus.). 644p. pap. 43.00 *(978-1-108-01475-5(5))* Cambridge Univ. Pr.

Chaplin, William James. Music of the Sun: The Story of Helioseismology. 2006. (ENG., Illus.). 288p. 29.95 *(978-1-85168-451-9(4))* Oneworld Pubns. GBR. Dist: National Bk. Network.

Chapman, Samuel L. A Mirror Image of the Universe. 2010. 216p. 27.95 *(978-1-4502-5003-0(3))*; pap. 17.95 *(978-1-4502-5001-6(7))* iUniverse, Inc.

Chávez Dagostino, Miguel, et al, eds. New Quests in Stellar Astrophysics II: Ultraviolet Properties of Evolved Stellar Populations. 2009. (Astrophysics & Space Science Proceedings Ser.). (Illus.). xvii, 346p. 159.00 *(978-0-387-87620-7(0))* Springer.

Cheng, K. S. & Romero, Gustavo E., eds. Cosmic Gamma-Ray Sources. 2010. (Astrophysics & Space Science Library). pap. 239.00 *(978-90-481-6625-1(X)*, 904816625X) Springer.

—Multiwavelength Approach to Unidentified Gamma-Ray Sources: A Second Workshop on the Nature of the High-Energy Unidentified Sources. 2010. (ENG.). xvi, 440p. pap. 219.00 *(978-90-481-6816-3(3)*, 9048168163) Springer.

Clancy, Paul, et al. Looking for Life, Searching the Solar System. 2009. (ENG., Illus.). 384p. pap. 36.99 *(978-0-521-12454-6(9))* Cambridge Univ. Pr.

Clark, Alan T., et al. Observing Projects Using Starry Night Enthusiast. 8th ed. 2008. (ENG.). 300p. (C). pap. 31.95 *(978-1-4292-1866-5(5))* Freeman, W. H. & Co.

Clark, John D. Measure Solar System Objects & Their Movements for Yourself! 2009. (Patrick Moore's Practical Astronomy Ser.). (ENG., Illus.). xv, 173p. pap. 34.95 *(978-0-387-89560-4(4))* Springer.

Clark, Stuart & Clark, S. The Sun Kings: The Unexpected Tragedy of Richard Carrington & the Tale of How Modern Astronomy Began. 2009. (ENG., Illus.). 224p. (C). pap. 18.95 *(978-0-691-14126-8(6))* Princeton Univ. Pr.

Clark, T. Alan, et al. Observing Projects Using Starry Night Enthusiast. 8th ed. 2007. (ENG., Illus.). 300p. (C). per. 38.95 *(978-1-4292-0074-5(X))* Freeman, W. H. & Co.

Clerke, Agnes Mary, et al. The Concise Knowledge Astronomy. 2011. (Cambridge Library Collection - Physical Sciences Ser.). (Illus.). 602p. pap. 43.00 *(978-1-108-02388-7(6))* Cambridge Univ. Pr.

Colpi, Monica. Physics of Relativistic Objects in Compact Binaries: From Birth to Coalescence. 2009. (Astrophysics & Space Science Library). (Illus.). 604p. 199.00 *(978-1-4020-9263-3(6))* Springer.

Comins, Neil F Discovering the Essential Universe. (ENG.). (C). 4th ed. 2009. 500p. 55.95 *(978-1-4292-3952-3(2))* 4th ed. 2008. 438p. pap. 85.95 *(978-1-4292-1797-2(9))* 5th ed. 2012. 300p. pap. 85.95 ***(978-1-4292-5519-6(6))*** Freeman, W. H. & Co.

Comins, Neil F. & Kaufmann, William J. Discovering the Universe. 8th ed. 2008. (ENG., Illus.). 544p. (C). pap. 137.95 *(978-1-4292-0519-1(9))* 9th ed. 2012. (Illus.). xxv, 583p. ***(978-1-4292-8451-6(X))*** 9th ed. 2011 (ENG.). 544p. (C). pap. 124.95 *(978-1-4292-5520-2(X))* Freeman, W. H. & Co.

—Discovering the Universe: From the Stars to the Planets. 2008. (ENG.). 624p. (C). pap. 106.95 *(978-1-4292-3042-1(8))* Freeman, W. H. & Co.

—Discovering the Universe (Loose Leaf) 9th ed. 2011. (ENG.). 544p. (C). 80.95 *(978-1-4292-7145-5(0))* Freeman, W. H. & Co.

Compton, William David & Benson, Charles D. Living & Working in Space: A NASA History of Skylab. 2011. (Dover Books on Astronomy Ser.). (ENG., Illus.). 464p. pap. 24.95 *(978-0-486-48218-7(9))* Dover Pubns., Inc.

Cooke, Antony. Make Time for the Stars: Fitting Astronomy into Your Busy Life. 2009. (Patrick Moore's Practical Astronomy Ser.). (ENG., Illus.). xii, 259p. pap. 34.95 *(978-0-387-89340-2(7))* Springer.

Corwin, Harold G., Jr., et al. The Historically Corrected New General Catalogue - (NGC 2000 thru NGC 3999), Vol. 2. 2006. spiral bd. *(978-0-9785526-1-9(X))* NGC/IC Project LLC, The.

—The Historically Corrected New General Catalogue - (NGC 4000 thru NGC 5999), Vol. 3. 2006. spiral bd. *(978-0-9785526-2-6(8))* NGC/IC Project LLC, The.

Corwin, Harold G., Jr., frwd. The Historically Corrected New General Catalogue - (NGC 1 thru NGC 1999), Vol. 1. 2006. spiral bd. *(978-0-9785526-0-2(1))* NGC/IC Project LLC, The.

Cram101 Textbook Reviews. Outlines & Highlights for 21st Century Astronomy: Stars & Galaxies by Jeff Hester, ISBN. 2011. 544p. pap. 39.95 ***(978-1-61812-066-3(2))*** Cram101 Inc.

—Outlines & Highlights for Cosmic Perspective: Stars, Galaxies & Cosmology by Bennett, ISBN. 2011. 268p. pap. 31.95 ***(978-1-61812-148-6(0))*** Cram101 Inc.

—Outlines & Highlights for Discovering the Essential Universe: With Scientific American by Neil F. Comins, ISBN. 2010. 652p. pap. 41.95 *(978-1-4288-5388-1(X))* Cram101 Inc.

—Outlines & Highlights for Extreme Ultraviolet Astronomy by Martin a Barstow, Isbn: 9780521039062. 2011. 104p. pap. 28.95 ***(978-1-61812-042-7(5))*** Cram101 Inc.

—Outlines & Highlights for Perspectives on Astronomy by Michael a Seeds. 2010. 244p. pap. 31.95 *(978-1-4288-5255-6(7))* Cram101 Inc.

Cram101 Textbook Reviews. Outlines & Highlights for the New Cosmos: An Introduction to Astronomy & Astrophysics by Albrecht Unsold, ISBN. 2011. 548p. pap. 38.95 ***(978-1-61812-084-7(0))*** Cram101 Inc.

Cram101 Textbook Reviews & Cram101 Textbook Reviews. Outlines & Highlights for Astronomy: A Beginners Guide to the Universe by Eric Chaisson, ISBN. 2011. 632p. pap. 40.95 ***(978-1-61490-420-5(0))*** Cram101 Inc.

—Outlines & Highlights for Astronomy: Journey to the Cosmic Frontier by John D. Fix, ISBN. 2011. 450p. pap. 36.95 ***(978-1-61490-308-6(5))*** Cram101 Inc.

—Outlines & Highlights for Astronomy Today by Eric Chaisson. 2011. 592p. pap. 39.95 ***(978-1-61830-556-5(5))*** Cram101 Inc.

—Outlines & Highlights for Foundations of Astronomy by Michael a Seeds, Isbn: 9781439050354. 2011. 444p. pap. 36.95 ***(978-1-61490-451-9(0))*** Cram101 Inc.

—Outlines & Highlights for Pathways to Astronomy by Stephen Schneider, Isbn: 9780073512136. 2011. 536p. pap. 38.95 ***(978-1-61490-031-3(0))*** Cram101 Inc.

—Outlines & Highlights for Universe: Stars & Galaxies by Roger A. Freedman. 2011. 314p. pap. 33.95 ***(978-1-61830-543-5(3))*** Cram101 Inc.

Cram101 Textbook Reviews Staff. Outlines & Highlights for Astronomy: A Beginners Guide to the Universe by Eric Chaisson, Steve Mcmillan, ISBN. 2009. 368p. pap. 34.95 *(978-1-4288-4182-6(2))* Cram101 Inc.

—Outlines & Highlights for Astronomy: Journey to the Cosmic Frontier — Galaxies (VOLUME 2) by Fix, ISBN. 2009. 408p. pap. 35.95 *(978-1-4288-6719-2(8))* Cram101 Inc.

—Outlines & Highlights for Astronomy: Journey to the Cosmic Frontier — Solar System (VOLUME 1) by Fix, ISBN. 2009. 420p. pap. 35.95 *(978-1-4288-6722-2(8))* Cram101 Inc.

—Outlines & Highlights for Astronomy: Journey to the Cosmic Frontier by Fix, ISBN. 2009. 416p. pap. 35.95 *(978-1-4288-6717-8(1))*; 392p. pap. 35.95 *(978-1-4288-6721-5(X))* Cram101 Inc.

—Outlines & Highlights for Astronomy: Journey to the Cosmic Frontier, Volume 1 (Solar System) by Fix, ISBN. 2009. 312p. pap. 33.95 *(978-1-4288-6718-5(X))* Cram101 Inc.

—Outlines & Highlights for Astronomy: Physical Perspective by Kutner, Marc, ISBN. 2009. 382p. pap. 34.95 *(978-1-4288-7596-8(4))* Cram101 Inc.

—Outlines & Highlights for Astronomy: The Solar System & Beyond by Michael A. Seeds, ISBN. 2009. 300p. pap. 32.95 *(978-1-4288-2107-1(4))* Cram101 Inc.

—Outlines & Highlights for Astronomy for the Utterly Confused by Jones, Isbn: 9780071471589. 2009. 184p. pap. 12.95 *(978-1-4288-6660-7(4))* Cram101 Inc.

—Outlines & Highlights for Astronomy Today by Eric Chaisson, Isbn: 9780132400855. 2009. 124p. pap. 28.95 *(978-1-4288-9624-6(4))* Cram101 Inc.

—Outlines & Highlights for Astronomy Today, Volume 1 by Chaisson, Eric / Mcmillan Steve, Isbn: 9780136155492. 2009. 414p. pap. 35.95 *(978-1-4288-7798-6(3))* Cram101 Inc.

—Outlines & Highlights for Astronomy Today, Volume 2 by Chaisson, Isbn: 9780136155508. 2009. 400p. pap. 35.95 *(978-1-4288-8640-7(0))* Cram101 Inc.

—Outlines & Highlights for Cosmic Perspective by Bennett, Jeffrey O , Isbn: 9780321505675. 2009. 676p. pap. 41.95 *(978-1-4288-8633-9(8))* Cram101 Inc.

—Outlines & Highlights for Cosmos: Astronomy in the New Millennium by Pasachoff, Jay M. / Filippenko, Alex, ISBN. 2009. 356p. pap. 34.95 *(978-1-4288-7593-7(X))* Cram101 Inc.

—Outlines & Highlights for Discovering the Essential Universe by Neil F Comins, Isbn: 9780716745952. 2009. 398p. pap. 35.95 *(978-1-4288-4057-7(5))*; 84p. pap. 27.95 *(978-1-4288-9817-2(4))* Cram101 Inc.

—Outlines & Highlights for Discovering the Universe: From STARS-PLANETS by COMINS, ISBN. 2009. 308p. pap. 32.95 *(978-1-4288-7590-6(5))* Cram101 Inc.

—Outlines & Highlights for Discovering the Universe: Starry Night Enthusiast & AstroPortal by Neil F. Comins, ISBN. 2009. 384p. pap 34.95 *(978-1-4288-3387-6(0))* Cram101 Inc.

—Outlines & Highlights for Discovering the Universe by Comins, Neil F / Kaufmann, William J , Isbn: 9781429205191. 2009. 334p. pap. 33.95 *(978-1-4288-8639-1(7))* Cram101 Inc.

—Outlines & Highlights for Essential Cosmic Perspective with Masteringastronomy, the by Jeffrey Bennett, Isbn: 9780321566942. 2009. 472p. pap. 36.95 *(978-1-4288-9079-4(3))* Cram101 Inc.

—Outlines & Highlights for Explorations: An Introduction to Astronomy by Arny, ISBN. 2009. 384p. pap. 34.95 *(978-1-4288-6720-8(1))*; 280p. pap. 15.95 *(978-1-4288-6661-4(2))* Cram101 Inc.

—Outlines & Highlights for Explorations: An Introduction to Astronomy, Volume 1 (Solar System) by Arny, ISBN. 2009. 288p. pap. 32.95 *(978-1-4288-6726-0(0))* Cram101 Inc.

—Outlines & Highlights for Explorations: An Introduction to Astronomy, Volume 2 (Stars & Galaxies) by Arny, ISBN. 2009. 324p. pap. 33.95 *(978-1-4288-6725-3(2))* Cram101 Inc.

—Outlines & Highlights for Explorations, Stars & Galaxies by Arny, Isbn: 9780073125862. 2009. 284p. pap. 32.95 *(978-1-4288-6723-9(6))* Cram101 Inc.

—Outlines & Highlights for Foundations of Astronomy by Michael a Seeds, Isbn: 9780495387244. 2009. 474p. pap. 36.95 *(978-1-4288-4186-4(5))* Cram101 Inc.

—Outlines & Highlights for in Quest of the Universe by Kuhn & Koupelis, Isbn: 0763708100. 2009. 296p. pap. 32.95 *(978-1-4288-7656-9(1))* Cram101 Inc.

—Outlines & Highlights for Pathways to Astronomy by Schneider, Isbn: 0072499656. 2009. 356p. pap. 34.95 *(978-1-4288-6716-1(3))* Cram101 Inc.

—Outlines & Highlights for Pathways to Astronomy by Schneider, Stephen / Thomas, Amy, Isbn: 9780073404455. 2009. 692p. pap. 42.95 *(978-1-4288-7647-7(2))* Cram101 Inc.

—Outlines & Highlights for Pathways to Astronomy Col1 Vl1 by Stephen Schneider, Isbn: 9780077315771. 2009. 408p. pap. 35.95 *(978-1-4288-9070-1(X))* Cram101 Inc.

—Outlines & Highlights for Universe: Stars & Galaxies by Roger Freedman, ISBN. 2009. 706p. pap. 42.95 *(978-1-4288-4024-9(9))* Cram101 Inc.

—Outlines & Highlights for Universe by Roger Freedman, William J Kaufmann, Isbn: 9780716785842. 2009. 480p. pap. 37.95 *(978-1-4288-7800-6(9))* Cram101 Inc.

—Outlines & Highlights for Voyages Through the Universe by Fraknoi, Andrew / Morrison, David / Wolff, Sidney, Isbn: 9780495017899. 2009. 482p. pap. 37.95 *(978-1-4288-7802-0(5))* Cram101 Inc.

Cristiani, S., et al, eds. Deep Fields: Proceedings of the ESO Workshop Held at Garching, Germany, 9-12 October 2000. 2010. (ESO Astrophysics Symposia Ser.). (ENG.). xxvi, 379p. pap. 59.95 *(978-3-642-07673-2(4)*, 3642076734) Springer.

Critchlow, Keith. Time Stands Still: New Light on Megalithic Science, 1 vol. 2nd rev. ed. 2007. (ENG., Illus.). 240p. pap. *(978-0-86315-587-1(1))* Floris Bks.

Cuntz, Manfred, et al. Practical Universe: Observations, Experiments, Exercises. rev. ed. 2010. (ENG.). 404p. pap. 56.72 *(978-0-7575-4633-4(1))* Kendall Hunt Publishing Co.

Cutsforth, Norma. Keeping Starwatch. 2006. 340p. pap. 29.95 *(978-1-4241-5013-7(2))* PublishAmerica, Inc.

Daflon, Simone, et al, eds. Graduate School in Astronomy: X Special Courses at the National Observatory of Rio de Janeiro (X CCE) 2006. (AIP Conference Proceedings Ser.: No. 843). (Illus.). 169p. 125.00 *(978-0-7354-0336-9(8)*, 0735403368) American Institute of Physics.

Dahmke, Mark. The Prairie Astronomy Club: Fifty Years of Amateur Astronomy. 2010. 566p. pap. 27.99 *(978-0-557-34865-7(X))* Lulu Enterprises Inc.

Darwin, George Howard. The Scientific Papers of Sir George Darwin: Figures of Equilibrium of Rotating Liquid & Geophysical Investigations. 2009. (Cambridge Library Collection - Physical Sciences Ser.). (ENG., Illus.). 548p. pap. 39.99 *(978-1-108-00445-9(8))* Cambridge Univ. Pr.

—The Scientific Papers of Sir George Darwin: Oceanic Tides & Lunar Disturbance of Gravity. 2009. (Cambridge Library Collection - Physical Sciences Ser.). (ENG., Illus.). 488p. pap. 35.99 *(978-1-108-00442-8(3))* Cambridge Univ. Pr.

—The Scientific Papers of Sir George Darwin: Periodic Orbits & Miscellaneous Papers. 2009. (Cambridge Library Collection - Physical Sciences Ser.). (ENG., Illus.). 628p. pap. 43.00 *(978-1-108-00447-3(4))* Cambridge Univ. Pr.

—The Scientific Papers of Sir George Darwin: Supplementary Volume. Stratton, F. J. M. & Jackson, J., eds. 2009. (Cambridge Library Collection - Physical Sciences Ser.). (ENG., Illus.). 148p. pap. 19.99 *(978-1-108-00448-0(2))* Cambridge Univ. Pr.

—The Scientific Papers of Sir George Darwin: Tidal Friction & Cosmogony. 2009. (Cambridge Library Collection - Physical Sciences Ser.). (ENG., Illus.). 540p. pap. 39.99 *(978-1-108-00443-5(1))* Cambridge Univ. Pr.

David, Gary A. The Orion Zone: Ancient Star Cities of the American Southwest. 2007. (Illus.). 343p. per. 19.95 *(978-1-931882-65-1(7))* Adventures Unlimited Pr.

Davies, Jonathan I. & Disney, Michael J., eds. Dark Galaxies & Lost Baryons. 2008. (Proceedings of the International Astronomical Union Symposia & Colloquia Ser.). (ENG., Illus.). 420p. 127.00 *(978-0-521-87466-3(1))* Cambridge Univ. Pr.

Davis, Diane A. Fusion energy ~ the public's Guide: Volume ii: harnessing celestial starpower - an introduction to the dream & Technology. 2008. (Illus.). 608p. pap. 25.95 *(978-0-9800166-4-2(9))* Fusion Energy & The Environment Publishing Co.

de Grijs, Richard & Cartwright, Susan. An Introduction to Distance Measurement in Astronomy. 2011. (ENG., Illus.). 326p. 130.00 ***(978-0-470-51179-4(6)***, Wiley) Wiley, John & Sons, Inc.

de Grijs, Richard & Heron. An Introduction to Distance Measurement in Astronomy. 2011. (ENG., Illus.). 326p. pap. 55.00 ***(978-0-470-51180-0(X)***, Wiley) Wiley, John & Sons, Inc.

De Laet, Rony. The Casual Sky Observer's Guide: Stargazing with Binoculars & Small Telescopes. 2011. (Astronomer's Pocket Field Guide Ser.). (ENG., Illus.). xiv, 292p. pap. 39.95 ***(978-1-4614-0594-8(7)***, 1461405947) Springer.

De Lafayette, Maximillien. The whole truth about Nibiru "Ne. Be. Ru"-Ashtari: How the Anunnaki live on their Planet. 2010. 104p. pap. 17.52 *(978-0-557-66995-0(2))* Lulu Enterprises Inc.

DeBlieu, Jan. Year of the Comets: A Journey from Sadness to the Stars. 2006. (ENG.). 208p. per. 15.00 *(978-1-59376-121-9(X))* Counterpoint LLC.

Deeg, Hans, et al, eds. Extrasolar Planets. 2007. (Canary Islands Winter School of Astrophysics Ser.). (ENG., Illus.). 282p. 142.00 *(978-0-521-86808-2(4))* Cambridge Univ. Pr.

Derham, W. Astro-Theology or, a Demonstration of the Being & Attributes Of. 2007. (ENG.). 336p. per. 30.95 *(978-1-4304-4684-2(6))* Kessinger Publishing, LLC.

Desch, Steve. Starry Night Workbook with Starry Night College Software: For 21st Century Astronomy, Third Edition. 2nd ed. 2010. (ENG.). 104p. (C). pap. 33.00 net. *(978-0-393-11660-1(3)*, 11660) Norton, W. W. & Co., Inc.

Dickinson, Terence. NightWatch: A Practical Guide to Viewing the Universe. 4th rev. exp. ed. 2006. (ENG., Illus.). 192p. (gr. 5-12). spiral bd. 35.00 *(978-1-55407-147-0(X))* Firefly Bks., Ltd.

Diego, J. M., et al, eds. Highlights of Spanish Astrophysics V. 2010. (Astrophysics & Space Science Proceedings Ser.). lxx, 566p. 299.00 *(978-3-642-11249-2(8)*, 3642112498) Springer.

Diehl, Roland, et al, eds. Astronomy with Radioactivities. 2010. (Lecture Notes in Physics Ser.). (Illus.). xii, 564p. pap. 119.00 *(978-3-642-12697-0(9)*, 3642126979) Springer.

Dodd, Richard. Using SI Units in Astronomy. 2011. (ENG., Illus.). 246p. 55.00 ***(978-0-521-76917-4(5))*** Cambridge Univ. Pr.

Domienik, Robert. The Secret of Life. 2009. (Illus.). 52p. pap. 10.49 *(978-1-4389-7531-3(7))* AuthorHouse.

Donahue, Megan O., et al. The Cosmic Perspective. 6th ed. 2009. (ENG.). 832p. (C). pap. 152.47 incl. cd-rom *(978-0-321-52090-3(9))* Benjamin-Cummings Publishing Co.

Dorling Kindersley Publishing Staff. The Night Sky Month by Month. 2011. (ENG.). 128p. 18.00 *(978-0-7566-7148-8(5))* Dorling Kindersley Publishing, Inc.

—Practical Astronomer. 2010. (ENG., Illus.). 256p. 19.95 *(978-0-7566-6210-3(9))* Dorling Kindersley Publishing, Inc.

Dunkin, Edwin. The Midnight Sky: Familiar Notes on the Stars & Planets. 2010. (Cambridge Library Collection - Physical Sciences Ser.). (ENG., Illus.). 344p. pap. 28.99 *(978-1-108-01745-9(2))* Cambridge Univ. Pr.

DUNN. Astronomy 2 Student Handbook. 3rd ed. 2009. (ENG.). (C). pap. 66.80 *(978-0-558-38133-2(2))* Pearson Learning Solutions.

—Astronomy 5 Student Handbook. 3rd ed. 2009. (ENG.). (C). pap. 63.60 *(978-0-558-38134-9(0))* Pearson Learning Solutions.

Dupke, Renato, et al, eds. Graduate School in Astronomy: XIV Special Courses at the National Observatory of Rio de Janeiro. 2010. (AIP Conference Proceedings / Astronomy & Astrophysics Ser.). (Illus.). 150p. 99.00 *(978-0-7354-0817-3(3)*, 0735408173, AIP Pr.) Springer.

Eales, Stephen. Origins: How the Planets, Stars, Galaxies, & the Universe Began. 2006. (Astronomers' Universe Ser.). (Illus.). 284p. 32.95 *(978-1-84628-401-4(5)*, 1846284015) Springer.

Engvold, Oddbjorn, ed. Reports on Astronomy: Transactions of the International Astronomical Union. 2007. (Proceedings of the International Astronomical Union Symposia & Colloquia Ser.). (ENG., Illus.). 408p. 124.99 *(978-0-521-85604-1(3))* Cambridge Univ. Pr.

Erdmann, Robert E., Jr., compiled by & creator. The Historically Corrected New General Catalogue - (Historical & Observing Notes), Vol. 5. 2006. spiral bd. *(978-0-9785526-4-0(4))* NGC/IC Project LLC, The.

—The Historically Corrected New General Catalogue - (NGC 6000 thru NGC 7840), Vol. 4. 2006. spiral bd. *(978-0-9785526-3-3(6))* NGC/IC Project LLC, The.

Everett, Edward. The Uses of Astronomy. 2009. 52p. pap. *(978-1-4068-5208-0(2))* Echo Library.

—The Uses of Astronomy: An Oration Delivered at Albany on the 28th of July, 1856. 2007. 60p. per. *(978-1-4065-3384-2(X))* Dodo Pr.

Faccioli, Lorenzo. Circularization & Tidal Dissipation in EclipsingBinary Stars: Results for early type binaries in the MagellanicClouds from the MACHO project. 2008. 204p. pap. *(978-3-639-08588-4(4))* VDM Verlag Dr. Mueller e.K.

Fadul, Jose A. Un Cielo tan Claro como el Zafiro. 2009. 70p. pap. 11.95 *(978-0-557-07918-6(7))* Lulu Enterprises Inc.

Filippenko, Alex. Understanding the Universe: An Introduction to Astronomy, 8 bks. 2nd ed. 2007. 124.95 *(978-1-59803-275-8(5))* Teaching Co., LLC, The.

Firefly Planisphere: Latitude 42 Degrees North. 2nd rev. ed. 2010. (ENG., Illus.). 19.95 *(978-1-55407-778-6(8))* Firefly Bks., Ltd.

Fischer, Daniel & Duerbeck, Hilmar. Hubble Renewed: New Tools, New Science, New Vistas. 2006. (Illus.). 240p. 45.00 *(978-0-387-02619-0(3)*, 0387026193) Springer.

Fisher, David G. & Erickson, Richard R. The Solar System. 2009. 121.00 *(978-1-58765-533-3(0))*; 121.00 *(978-1-58765-531-9(4))*; 121.00 *(978-1-58765-532-6(2))* Salem Pr., Inc.

Fisher, David G. & Erickson, Richard R., eds. The Solar System. 2nd ed. 2009. 1056p. 364.00 *(978-1-58765-530-2(6))* Salem Pr., Inc.

Fix, John. Astronomy. 5th ed. 2007. 752p. 88.00 *(978-0-07-305002-7(4))* McGraw-Hill Professional Publishing.

Fix, John D. Astronomy: Journey to the Cosmic Frontier. 5th ed. 2007. (ENG.). (C). 79.00 *(978-0-07-723463-8(4)*, 0077234634); (Illus.). 768p. 136.25 *(978-0-07-334721-9(3)*, 0073347213) McGraw-Hill Higher Education. (McGraw-Hill Science, Engineering & Mathematics).

Freedman, Roger & Kaufmann, William J. Universe. 8th ed. 2007. (ENG., Illus.). 864p. (C). pap. 144.95 *(978-0-7167-8584-2(6))* Freeman, W. H. & Co.

Freedman, Roger, et al. Universe. 9th rev. ed. 2010. (ENG.). 800p. (C). pap. 130.95 *(978-1-4292-3153-4(X))* Freeman, W. H. & Co.

Freedman, Roger, et al. Universe: Stars & Galaxies. 4th rev. ed. 2010. (ENG., Illus.). 800p. (C). pap. 88.95 ***(978-1-4292-4015-4(6))*** Freeman, W. H. & Co.

Gainer, Michael K. Real Astronomy with Small Telescopes: Step-by-Step Activities for Discovery. 2006. (Patrick Moore's Practical Astronomy Ser.). (Illus.). 148p. per. 29.95 *(978-1-84628-478-6(3)*, 1846284783) Springer.

Gallego, Jesús, et al, eds. Highlights of Spanish Astrophysics III. 2010. 548p. pap. 229.00 *(978-90-481-6323-6(4)*, 9048163234) Springer.

Gator, William J. H. The Cosmic Keyhole: How Astronomy Is Unlocking the Secrets of the Universe. 2009. (Astronomers' Universe Ser.). (ENG., Illus.). xix, 228p. 29.95 *(978-1-4419-0512-3(X)*, 144190512X) Springer.

Gendler, Robert, et al. Treasures of the Southern Sky. 2011. (ENG., Illus.). xxx, 190p. 44.95 ***(978-1-4614-0627-3(7)***, 1461406277) Springer.

Gibson, Charles R. The Stars & Their Mysteries an Interestingly Written Account of the Wonders of Astronomy Told in Simple Language. 2007. (ENG.). 258p. 42.95 *(978-0-548-03353-1(6))* Kessinger Publishing, LLC.

Gibson, Walter B., ed. The Key to Astronomy. 2011. 98p. 38.95 ***(978-1-258-05014-6(5))*** Literary Licensing, LLC.

Giobbi, Giuliana, et al, eds. Probing Stellar Populations Out to the Distant Universe: CEFALU 2008, Proceedings of the International Conference. 2009. (AIP Conference Proceedings / Astronomy & Astrophysics Ser.). 674p. 319.00 *(978-0-7354-0648-3(0))* American Institute of Physics.

Glindemann, Andreas. Principles of Stellar Interferometry. 2011. (Astronomy & Astrophysics Library). (ENG., Illus.). xvii, 342p. 124.00 *(978-3-642-15027-2(6)*, 3642150276) Springer.

Goldwater, David. Astronomy 101 Student Supplement. rev. ed. 2011. (ENG.) 100p. spiral bd. 33.73 *(978-0-7575-6990-6(0))* Kendall Hunt Publishing Co.

Gómez de Castro, Ana I. & Wamsteker, Willem, eds. Fundamental Questions in Astrophysics: Guidelines for Future UV Observatories: Guidelines for Future UV Observatories. 2010. iv, 172p. pap. 139.00 *(978-90-481-7208-5(X)*, 904817208X) Springer.

Gonzalo, Julio A. Cosmic Paradoxes. 2011. 180p. 72.00 ***(978-981-4355-61-2(5))***; pap. 34.00 ***(978-981-4355-11-7(9))*** World Scientific Publishing Co., Inc.

Gorgas, Javier & Zamorano, Jaime, eds. Highlights of Spanish Astrophysics I. 2010. 428p. pap. 229.00 *(978-90-481-5288-9(7)*, 9048152887) Springer.

Gottheil, Richard J. H. A Further Astronomic Fragment from the Genziah. 2010. (ARA.). pap. 17.92 *(978-1-61143-330-2(4))* Gorgias Pr., LLC.

—A Further Fragment on Astrology from the Genizah. 2010. (ARA.). pap. 18.04 *(978-1-61143-329-6(0))* Gorgias Pr., LLC.

Grace, Charles H. Astronomy: Selected Topics. 2010. 224p. 22.99 *(978-1-4269-3443-8(2))* Trafford Publishing.

Greene, Candace S. & Thornton, Russell, eds. The Year the Stars Fell: Lakota Winter Counts at the Smithsonian. 2007. (ENG., Illus.). 377p. 45.00 *(978-0-8032-2211-3(4))* Univ. of Nebraska Pr.

Grego, Peter. Discovering the Solar System. 2008. (QEB Space Guides Ser.) (Illus.). 32p. (J). (gr. 3-7). lib. bdg. 19.95 *(978-1-59566-382-5(7))* QEB Publishing Inc.

Gregoriades, P. & Gregoriades, P. D. The Creation of Prototypes: World Civilization & Human Progress: the Minoan Calendar Today. 2010. (History of Mechanism & Machine Science Ser.). (Illus.). iv, 196p. 139.00 *(978-90-481-9721-7(X)*, 904819721X) Springer.

A

Gribbin, John & Gribbin, Mary. From Here to Infinity: A Beginner's Guide to Astronomy. (ENG., Illus.). 256p. 2011. pap. 14.95 *(978-1-4027-8824-6(X))* 2009. 24.95 *(978-1-4027-6501-8(0))* Sterling Publishing Co., Inc.

—From Here to Infinity: The Royal Observatory Greenwich Guide to Astronomy. 2008. (Illus.). 256p. pap. 29.00 *(978-0-948065-78-1(8))* National Maritime Museum GBR. Dist: Independent Pubs. Group.

—From Here to Infinity: The Royal Observatory Greenwich Guide to Astronomy. 2007. (Illus.). pap. 15.00 *(978-0-9802965-6-3(0))* UWA Publishing AUS. Dist: International Specialized Bk. Services.

Gros, Michel. In Tune with the Moon 2010: The Complete Day-by-Day Moon Planner for Growing & Living In 2010. 2009. (ENG., Illus.). 114p. pap. 15.00 *(978-1-84409-178-2(3))* Findhorn Pr. GBR. Dist: Independent Pubs. Group.

Gummere, John. An Elementary Treatise on Astronomy; in Two Parts the First Containing a Clear & Compendious View of the Theory; the Second, a Number of Practical. 2006. 500p. pap. 29.99 *(978-1-4255-5584-9(5))*; 484p. per. 29.99 *(978-1-4255-5360-9(5))* MPublishing.

Hale, George Ellery. The New Heavens. 2009. 92p. pap. 18.75 *(978-0-559-06880-5(8))*; pap. 18.75 *(978-0-559-06887-4(5))* BiblioBazaar.

—The New Heavens. 2009. 48p. pap. *(978-0-217-12345-7(7))* Books LLC.

—The New Heavens. 2007. (Illus.). 84p. per. *(978-1-4065-1574-9(4))* Dodo Pr.

—The New Heavens. 2007. (ENG.). 108p. per. 19.95 *(978-0-548-76345-2(3))* Kessinger Publishing, LLC.

Hall. Stellar Astronomy: A Customized Version of Contemporary Activities in Astronomy by Darrel B. Hoff & Jeffrey A. Wilkinson Designed Specifically for Georgiana Hall at Fiu. 2nd rev. ed. 2011. (ENG.). 118p. spiral bd., lab manual ed. 61.00 ***(978-0-7575-9577-6(4))*** Kendall Hunt Publishing Co.

Hamilton, Ross. Star Mounds: Legacy of a Native American Mystery. 2012. (ENG., Illus.). 336p. pap. 29.95 ***(978-1-58394-446-2(X))*** North Atlantic Bks.

Hamilton, Thomas Wm. Useful Star Names: With Nebulas & other Celestial Features. 2011. 76p. pap. 12.97 ***(978-1-61204-614-3(2)***, Strategic Bk. Publishing) AEG Literary Publishing Services, Inc.

Handy, Richard, et al. Astronomical Sketching: A Step-by-Step Introduction. 2007. (Patrick Moore's Practical Astronomy Ser.). (Illus.). 195p. pap. 44.95 *(978-0-387-26240-6(7)*, 0387262407) Springer.

Hanisch, Nadine. Spare Parts Logistics for Sofi. 2009. 112p. pap. *(978-3-639-16553-1(5))* VDM Verlag Dr. Mueller e.K.

Hasinger, Günther, ed. Status & Prospects of Astronomy in Germany 2003-2016: Memorandum. 2008. (Denkschrift (DFG) Ser.: 3). (ENG., Illus.). 244p. pap. 90.00 *(978-3-527-31910-7(7)*, Wiley-VCH) Wiley, John & Sons, Inc.

Haubold, Hans J. International Heliophysical Year 2007: the United Nations Report: The United Nations Report. 2009. (Studies in Space Policy Ser.). (ENG., Illus.). xv, 371p. 239.00 *(978-3-211-99179-4(4)*, 3211991794) Springer.

Hearnshaw, John & Martinez, Peter, eds. Astronomy for the Developing World (IAU XXVI GA SPS5) 2007. (Proceedings of the International Astronomical Union Symposia & Colloquia Ser.). (ENG., Illus.). 346p. 166.99 *(978-0-521-87657-5(5))* Cambridge Univ. Pr.

Heggie, D. C. Archaeoastronomy in the Old World. 2009. (ENG.). 292p. pap. 42.00 *(978-0-521-12530-7(8))* Cambridge Univ. Pr.

Hendrie, Michael. Times Night Sky 2005. (Illus.). 32p. pap. 9.99 *(978-0-00-718997-7(4))* HarperCollins Pubs. Ltd. GBR. Dist: Trafalgar Square Publishing.

Heritage House Publishing Co. Ltd. Staff & Shadick, Stan. Skywatchers 2012: A Celestial-Events Calendar by Stan Shadick, 1 vol. 2011. (ENG.). 24p. pap. 14.95 *(978-1-926936-57-4(4))* Heritage Hse. CAN. Dist: TNT Media Group, Inc.

Herschel, John F. W. A Treatise on Astronomy. 2009. (Cambridge Library Collection - Life Sciences Ser.). 444p. pap. 32.99 *(978-1-108-00554-8(3))* Cambridge Univ. Pr.

Herschel, John Frederick William. Outlines of Astronomy. 2010. (Cambridge Library Collection - Physical Sciences Ser.). (Illus.). 696p. pap. 48.00 *(978-1-108-01377-2(5))* Cambridge Univ. Pr.

Hesperid, Laura. Como Nos Influye la Luna? (SPA., Illus.). 256p. *(978-84-7927-587-7(1))* Robinbk., Ediciones S.L. ESP. Dist: Lectorum Pubns., Inc.

Hester. Astronomy: The Solar System. 3rd ed. 2010. (ENG.). 436p. (C). pap. 67.00 net. *(978-0-393-93284-3(2)*, 93284) Norton, W. W. & Co., Inc.

Hester, Jeff, et al. 21St Century Astronomy 3E: Stars & Galaxies. 3rd ed. 2010. (ENG.). 445p. (C). pap. 67.00 net. *(978-0-393-93285-0(0)*, 93285) Norton, W. W. & Co., Inc.

Hetherington, Edith W. & Hetherington, Norriss S. Astronomy & Culture, 1 vol. 2009. (Greenwood Guides to the Universe Ser.). 231p. 65.00 *(978-0-313-34536-4(8)*, GR4536, Greenwood Pr.) Greenwood Publishing Group, Inc.

Hirshfeld, Alan W. Astronomy Activity & Laboratory Manual. 2008. 136p. pap. 46.95 *(978-0-7637-6019-9(6))* Jones & Bartlett Learning, LLC.

Ho, L. C. & Wang, Jian-Min. The Central Engine of Active Galactic Nuclei: Proceedings of a Workshop Held at Xi'an Jiaotong University, Xi'an, China, 16-21 October, 2006. 2007. (Astronomical Society of the Pacific Conference Ser.: Vol. 373). (Illus.). xxxiii, 772p. 77.00 *(978-1-58381-307-2(1))* Astronomical Society of the Pacific, The.

Hoard, Donald W., ed. White Dwarf Atmospheres & Circumstellar Environments. 2011. (ENG., Illus.). 244p. 140.00 ***(978-3-527-41031-6(7)***, Wiley-VCH) Wiley, John & Sons, Inc.

Hofstadter, Dan. The Earth Moves: Galileo & the Roman Inquisition. 2010. (Great Discoveries Ser.). (ENG., Illus.). 240p. pap. 14.95 *(978-0-393-33820-1(7)*, 33820) Norton, W. W. & Co., Inc.

Holbrook, Jarita, et al, eds. African Cultural Astronomy: Current Archaeoastronomy & Ethnoastronomy research in Africa. 2010. (Astrophysics & Space Science Proceedings Ser.). viii, 260p. pap. 169.00 *(978-90-481-7687-8(5)*, 9048176875) Springer.

Hooft. Playing with Planets. 2008. (Illus.). 200p. 51.00 *(978-981-279-307-2(0))*; pap. 24.00 *(978-981-279-020-0(9))* World Scientific Publishing Co., Inc.

Horkheimer, Jack & O'Meara, Stephen J. Stargazing with Jack Horkheimer: Cosmic Comics for the Sky Watcher. 2007. (ENG., Illus.). 96p. (J). (gr. 3-9). 19.95 *(978-0-8126-7933-5(4))* Cricket Bks.

Hotakainen, Markus. GAstronomical Cookbook. 2011. (Illus.). 136p. 39.95 *(978-1-4419-6925-5(X)*, 144196925X) Springer.

Houpis. Astronomy 10 Student Handbook. 2nd ed. 2008. (ENG.). (C). pap. 80.00 *(978-0-555-01188-1(7))* Pearson Learning Solutions.

—Astronomy 2 Student Handbook. 2nd ed. 2008. (ENG.). (C). pap. 78.60 *(978-0-555-01679-4(X))* Pearson Learning Solutions.

—Astronomy 5 Student Handbook. 2nd ed. 2008. (ENG.). (C). pap. 80.00 *(978-0-555-01189-8(5))* Pearson Learning Solutions.

Houston, Walter Scott. Deep-Sky Wonders. O'Meara, Stephen James, ed. 2007. (ENG.). 320p. pap. 19.95 *(978-1-931559-23-2(6))* Sky Publishing.

Hutchins, Paul. The Secret Doorway: Beyond Imagination. 2009. (Illus.). 213p. pap. 24.95 *(978-0-9817123-4-5(7))* Imagination Publishing-Orlando.

Hyginus. De Astronomia. Viré, Ghislaine, ed. (Bibliotheca scriptorum Graecorum et Romanorum Teubneriana (BT) Ser.). (LAT.). LIX, 176p. 135.00 ***(978-3-11-181239-7(1))*** De Gruyter, Walter Inc.

Isaksson, Eva, et al. Library & Information Services in Astronomy VI: 21st Century Astronomy Librarianship, from New Ideas to Action, Proceedings of a Conference Held at IUCAA & NCRA, Pune, Maharashtra, India, 14 - 17 February 2010. 2010. (Illus.). xxii, 359p. ***(978-1-58381-746-9(8))***; E-Book ***(978-1-58381-747-6(6))*** Astronomical Society of the Pacific, The.

Islam, Jamal N. The Ultimate Fate of the Universe. 2009. (ENG.). 168p. pap. 39.99 *(978-0-521-11312-0(1))* Cambridge Univ. Pr.

Jeanloz, Raymond, ed. Annual Review of Earth & Planetary Sciences, Vol. 35. 2007. 807p. pap. 216.00 *(978-0-8243-2035-5(2))* Annual Reviews, Inc.

Jeans, James. Astronomy & Cosmogony. 2nd ed. 2009. (Cambridge Library Collection - Physical Sciences Ser.). (ENG.). 476p. pap. 45.99 *(978-1-108-00562-3(4))* Cambridge Univ. Pr.

—Stars in Their Courses. 2009. (Cambridge Library Collection - Physical Sciences Ser.). (ENG.). 260p. pap. 34.99 *(978-1-108-00570-8(5))* Cambridge Univ. Pr.

—The Stars in Their Courses 1931. 2007. (ENG.). 236p. 41.95 *(978-0-548-05589-2(0))* Kessinger Publishing, LLC.

—Through Space & Time. 2009. (Cambridge Library Collection - Physical Sciences Ser.). (ENG.). 300p. pap. 36.99 *(978-1-108-00571-5(3))* Cambridge Univ. Pr.

Joardar, S., et al. Astronomy & Astrophysics. (Illus.). 2008. 364p. 103.95 *(978-1-934015-05-6(9))* 2009. vi, 364p. 82.95 *(978-0-7637-7786-9(2))* Jones & Bartlett Learning, LLC.

Jones, Antonius. Universal Truth through Simple Observation. 2008. 49p. pap. 14.99 *(978-1-4116-1583-0(2))* Lulu Enterprises Inc.

Jones, Terry Jay & Hanson, Jeanne K. Astronomy for the Utterly Confused. 2006. (Utterly Confused Ser.). (ENG., Illus.). 352p. per. 18.95 *(978-0-07-147158-9(8)*, 0071471588) McGraw-Hill Cos., The.

Jordan, Thomas. Necessary Tools for Introductory Astronomy: Aka How to Pass My Astronomy Course! rev. ed. 2010. (ENG.). 300p. ring bd. 30.00 *(978-0-7575-6998-2(6))* Kendall Hunt Publishing Co.

Joseph, Lawrence E. The Sun Factor: How the Sun Shaped Our Past & Determines Our Future. 2012. (ENG.). 288p. 25.99 ***(978-0-06-206192-8(5)***, HarperOne) HarperCollins Pubs.

Kambic, Bojan. Observing the Northern Skies Using Binoculars & Small Telescopes. 2009. (Patrick Moore's Practical Astronomy Ser.). (ENG., Illus.). 448p. pap. 39.95 *(978-0-387-85354-3(5))* Springer.

Karttunen, H., et al, eds. Fundamental Astronomy. 5th rev. ed. 2007. (Illus.). 510p. 69.95 *(978-3-540-34143-7(9)*, 3540341439) Springer.

Keane, Evan Francis. The Transient Radio Sky. 2011. (Springer Theses Ser.). (ENG., Illus.). xiii, 190p. 129.00 *(978-3-642-19626-3(8)*, 3642196268) Springer.

Keeney, L. Douglas. The Lights of Mankind: The Earth at Night As Seen from Space. 2011. (ENG., Illus.). 288p. 32.50 *(978-0-7627-7755-6(9)*, Lyons Pr.) Globe Pequot Pr., The.

Kerrod, Robin & Stott, Carole. Hubble: The Mirror on the Universe. rev. ed. 2007. (ENG., Illus.). 192p. 35.00 *(978-1-55407-316-0(2))* Firefly Bks., Ltd.

Khomich, Vladislav Yu, et al. Airglow as an Indicator of Upper Atmospheric Structure & Dynamics. 2010. (ENG., Illus.). xvi, 740p. pap. 289.00 *(978-3-642-09500-9(3)*, 3642095003) Springer.

King, David A. Astrolabes from Medieval Europe. 2011. (Variorum Collected Studies). (Illus.). 422p. 190.00 *(978-1-4094-2593-9(2))* Ashgate Publishing Co.

Kiss, Zoltán. Quantum Energy & Mass Balance. 2009. 160p. pap. 21.21 *(978-1-4251-9157-3(6))* Trafford Publishing.

Kitchin, Chris. Exoplanets: Finding, Exploring, & Understanding Alien Worlds. 2011. (Astronomers' Universe Ser.). (ENG., Illus.). xvi, 281p. pap. 29.95 ***(978-1-4614-0643-3(9)***, 1461406439) Springer.

Klioner, Sergei A., et al, eds. Relativity in Fundamental Astronomy (IAU S261) Dynamics, Reference Frames, & Data Analysis. 2010. (Proceedings of the International Astronomical Union Symposia & Colloquia Ser.). (ENG., Illus.). 450p. 125.00 *(978-0-521-76481-0(5))* Cambridge Univ. Pr.

Kohl, John L. & Cranmer, Steven R., eds. Coronal Holes & Solar Wind Acceleration. 2010. 368p. pap. 204.00 *(978-90-481-5267-4(4)*, 9048152674) Springer.

Koribalski, Bärbel Silvia & Jerjen, H. Galaxies in the Local Volume. 2008. (Astrophysics & Space Science Proceedings Ser.). (ENG., Illus.). 360p. 199.00 *(978-1-4020-6932-1(4)*, 1402069324) Springer.

Koribalski, Bärbel Silvia & Jerjen, H., eds. Galaxies in the Local Volume. 2010. (Astrophysics & Space Science Proceedings Ser.). 360p. pap. 199.00 *(978-90-481-7769-1(3)*, 9048177693) Springer.

Koupelis. In Quest of the Universe 6E International Version. 6th rev. ed. 2010. pap. 117.95 *(978-0-7637-9366-1(3))* Jones & Bartlett Learning, LLC.

Koupelis, Theo. In Quest of the Universe. 6th rev. ed. 2010. 614p. pap. 151.95 *(978-0-7637-6858-4(8))* Jones & Bartlett Learning, LLC.

Koupelis, Theo & Kuhn, Karl F. In Quest of the Universe. 5th rev. ed. 2007. (Illus.). 648p. pap. 154.95 *(978-0-7637-4387-1(9))* Jones & Bartlett Learning, LLC.

Krautter, Joachim. Meyers Handbuch Weltall. 7th ed. (GER., Illus.). 674p. *(978-3-411-07757-1(3))* Bibliographisches Institut & F. A. Brockhaus AG DEU. Dist: i. b. d., Ltd.

Kurtz, J. H. (Johann Heinrich). History of the Old Covenant. 2006. 540p. per. 29.99 *(978-1-4255-5985-4(9))*; 524p. per. 29.99 *(978-1-4255-5838-3(0))*; 440p. per. 26.99 *(978-1-4255-4807-0(5))* MPublishing.

Lang, Kenneth R. Sun, Earth & Sky. 2nd rev. ed. 2006. (ENG., Illus.). xvi, 284p. 69.95 *(978-0-387-30456-4(8)*, 0387304568) Springer.

Langdon, Roger & Langdon, Ellen. The Life of Roger Langdon: Told by Himself, with Additions by his Daughter. 2010. (Cambridge Library Collection - Physical Sciences Ser.). (ENG.). 110p. pap. 19.99 *(978-1-108-02164-7(6))* Cambridge Univ. Pr.

Lankford, George E. Reachable Stars: Patterns in the Ethnoastronomy of Eastern North America. 2007. (ENG., Illus.). 368p. 61.25 *(978-0-8173-1568-9(3))*; per. 38.50 *(978-0-8173-5428-2(X))* Univ. of Alabama Pr.

Larson, Shane. Guidestars: Projects & Activities for Seeing & Learning the Sky. rev. ed. 2011. (ENG.). 192p. spiral bd. 48.00 ***(978-0-7575-8962-1(6))*** Kendall Hunt Publishing Co.

Lasota, Jean-Pierre, ed. Astronomy at the Frontiers of Science. 2011. (Integrated Science & Technology Program Ser.). (ENG., Illus.). xxi, 357p. 179.00 *(978-94-007-1657-5(5)*, 9400716575) Springer.

Launay, Françoise. The Astronomer Jules Janssen: A Globetrotter of Celestial Physics. 2011. (Astrophysics & Space Science Library). (ENG., Illus.). xxix, 220p. 129.00 ***(978-1-4614-0696-9(X)***, 146140696X) Springer.

Leavitt, C. Franklin. Mental & Physical Ease & Supremacy: Being A Practical Adaptation of Leavitt Science to Individual Use. 2007. (ENG.). 360p. 46.95 *(978-0-548-04565-7(8))* Kessinger Publishing, LLC.

Lehoux, Daryn. Astronomy, Weather, & Calendars in the Ancient World: Parapegmata & Related Texts in Classical & near-Eastern Societies. 2007. (ENG., Illus.). 580p. 140.00 *(978-0-521-85181-7(5))* Cambridge Univ. Pr.

Lemonick, Michael D. The Georgian Star. 2008. (Great Discoveries Ser.). (ENG., Illus.). 224p. 23.95 *(978-0-393-06574-9(X)*, 6574) Atlas & Co.

León, Manuel de, et al, eds. Mathematics & Astronomy: A Joint Long Journey: Proceedings of the International Conference. 2011. (AIP Conference Proceedings / Astronomy & Astrophysics Ser.). 350p. pap. 167.00 *(978-0-7354-0837-1(8)*, 0735408378, AIP Pr.) Springer.

Leverington, David. Babylon to Voyager & Beyond: A History of Planetary Astronomy. 2007. (ENG., Illus.). 572p. pap. 81.00 *(978-0-521-00461-9(6))* Cambridge Univ. Pr.

Levy, David H. David Levy's Guide to Eclipses, Transits, & Occultations. 2010. (ENG., Illus.). 184p. pap. 25.99 *(978-0-521-16551-8(2))* Cambridge Univ. Pr.

—Skywatching. 2007. (Illus.). 288p. 14.98 *(978-1-74089-578-1(9))* Fog City Pr.

Lew, Kristi. The Expanding Universe. 2011. (Science Foundations Ser.). 102p. (gr. 6-12). 35.00 *(978-1-60413-292-2(2)*, Chelsea Hse.) Facts On File, Inc.

Lewellen, John Bryan. My Easy-to-Read True Book of Moon, Sun & Stars. 2011. 44p. 35.95 ***(978-1-258-10139-8(4))*** Literary Licensing, LLC.

Lewis, Simon. Two Faced Moon. 2007. 104p. pap. 17.39 *(978-1-4251-2076-4(8))* Trafford Publishing.

Lewis, W. Scott. Astronomical Rambles. 2011. 52p. 36.95 ***(978-1-258-01663-0(X))*** Literary Licensing, LLC.

—In the Depths of Space. 2011. 52p. 36.95 ***(978-1-258-02453-6(5))*** Literary Licensing, LLC.

Liderbach, Daniel. MYST of the Elegant Universe. 2007. 136p. pap. *(978-1-905868-07-0(3))* Foxwell & Davies, Ltd.

Lieu, R. & Mittaz, Jonathan, eds. Soft X-Ray Emission from Clusters of Galaxies & Related Phenomena. 2010. (Astrophysics & Space Science Library). x, 200p. pap. 149.00 *(978-90-481-6681-7(0)*, 9048166810) Springer.

Livio, Mario & Brown, Thomas M., eds. The Local Group as an Astrophysical Laboratory: Proceedings of the Space Telescope Science Institute Symposium, Held in Baltimore, Maryland May 5-8 2003. 2011. (Space Telescope Science Institute Symposium Ser.). (ENG.). 238p. pap. 39.99 *(978-0-521-17533-3(X))* Cambridge Univ. Pr.

Lockyer, Joseph Norman. Elements of Astronomy: Accompanied with Numerous Illustration, A Colored Representation of the Solar, Stellar, & Nebular Spectra, & Celestial Char. 2006. 316p. per. 23.99 *(978-1-4255-3124-9(5))* MPublishing.

Loomis, Elias. The Recent Progress of Astronomy: Especially in the United States. 2010. (Cambridge Library Collection - Physical Sciences Ser.). (ENG.). 402p. pap. 31.99 *(978-1-108-01393-2(7))* Cambridge Univ. Pr.

—A Treatise on Astronomy by Elias Loomis. 2006. 356p. per. 26.99 *(978-1-4255-3814-9(2))* MPublishing.

LoPresto, Michael. Astronomy Media Workbook. 6th ed. 2009. 200p. pap. *(978-0-321-55627-1(5))* Addison-Wesley Longman, Inc.

Lopresto, Michael. Cycles in the Sky. 3rd rev. ed. 2009. (ENG.). 150p. pap. 58.92 *(978-0-7575-5704-0(X))* Kendall Hunt Publishing Co.

Lowell, Anna C. (Anna Cabot). The Elements of Astronomy; or, the World As It Is, & As It Appears by the Author of Theory of Teaching, Edward's First Lessons in Grammar, Etc. 2006. 380p. per. 26.99 *(978-1-4255-3982-5(3))* MPublishing.

Lubbock, John. The Beauties of Nature. 2009. 198p. pap. *(978-0-217-62185-4(6))* Books LLC.

—The Beauties of Nature. 2009. (Illus.). 168p. pap. *(978-1-4068-2933-4(1))* Echo Library.

—The Beauties of Nature & the Wonders of the World We Live In. 2009. 196p. pap. *(978-0-217-29054-8(X))*; 190p. pap. *(978-0-217-37892-5(7))*; 206p. pap. *(978-0-217-62189-2(9))* Books LLC.

—The Beauties of Nature & the Wonders of the World We Live In. 2007. (ENG.). 464p. 52.95 *(978-0-548-05274-7(3))* Kessinger Publishing, LLC.

Macchetto, F. Duccio, ed. The Impact of HST on European Astronomy. 2010. (Astrophysics & Space Science Proceedings Ser.). (ENG., Illus.). xxiv, 312p. 249.00 *(978-90-481-3399-4(8)*, 9048133998) Springer.

Malville, McKim. Guide to Prehistoric Astronomy in the Southwest. rev. ed. 2008. 160p. pap. 18.00 *(978-1-55566-414-5(8))* Johnson Bks.

Mammana, Dennis, et al. National Geographic Backyard Guide to the Night Sky. 2009. (ENG., Illus.). 288p. pap. 21.95 *(978-1-4262-0281-0(4)*, National Geographic) National Geographic Society.

Maran, Stephen P. Astronomy for Dummies(r). 3rd ed. 2012. (ENG.). 384p. pap. 22.99 ***(978-1-118-37697-3(8)***, For Dummies) Wiley, John & Sons, Inc.

Maran, Stephen P. & Marschall, Laurence A. Galileo's New Universe: The Revolution in Our Understanding of the Cosmos. 2009. (ENG.). 174p. pap. 14.95 *(978-1-933771-59-5(3))* BenBella Bks.

Maran, Stephen P. & Marschall, Laürence A. Pluto Confidential: An Insider Account of the Ongoing Battles over the Status of Pluto. 2009. (ENG.). 232p. pap. 14.95 *(978-1-933771-80-9(1))* BenBella Bks.

Martinez, Leonardo. My First Encounter with Astronomy. rev. ed. 2009. (ENG.). 274p. pap. 69.84 *(978-0-7575-6259-4(0))* Kendall Hunt Publishing Co.

Massey, Steve, et al. Video Astronomy. rev. ed. 2007. (Sky & Telescope Observer's Guides). (ENG.). 214p. per. 24.95 *(978-1-931559-09-6(0))* Sky Publishing.

May, Brian. A Survey of Radial Velocities in the Zodiacal Dust Cloud. 2008. (Illus.). 300p. 89.95 *(978-0-387-77705-4(9))* Springer.

May, Nadine. Vanishing Worlds. 2011. 458p. pap. ***(978-0-9870048-5-7(9))*** Kima Global Pubs.

McLean, Ian S., et al, eds. Planets, Stars & Stellar Systems, 2 vols. 2012. (ENG., Illus.). 4760p. 3750.00 *(978-90-481-8852-9(0)*, 9048188520); 3000.00 *(978-90-481-8817-8(2)*, 9048188172) Springer.

Meadows, A. J. The Future of the Universe. 2010. (Astronomers' Universe Ser.). (Illus.). x, 175p. pap. 32.95 *(978-1-84996-968-0(X)*, 184996968X) Springer.

Meadows, Jack. The Future of the Universe. 2006. (Astronomers' Universe Ser.). (Illus.). 175p. 32.95 *(978-1-85233-946-3(2)*, 1852339462) Springer.

Mebarki, N. & Mimouni, J., eds. The Third Algerian Workshop on Astronomy & Astrophysics. 2011. (AIP Conference Proceedings / Astronomy & Astrophysics Ser.). 304p. pap. 157.00 *(978-0-7354-0852-4(1)*, 0735408521, AIP Pr.) Springer.

Meeus, Jean. Mathematical Astronomy Morsels IV. 2007. 374p. *(978-0-943396-87-3(5))* Willmann-Bell, Inc.

—Mathematical Astronomy Morsels V. 2009. *(978-0-943396-92-7(1))* Willmann-Bell, Inc.

Melville, Henry. Astronomy & Freemasonry Revealed by Means of the Median And. 2006. pap. 9.95 *(978-1-4304-1300-4(X))* Kessinger Publishing, LLC.

Michelson, Peter & Meegan, Charles A., eds. The First Glast Symposium. 2007. (AIP Conference Proceedings / Astronomy & Astrophysics Ser.). (Illus.). 613p. 151.00 *(978-0-7354-0431-1(3))* American Institute of Physics.

Mitchel, O. M. (Ormsby MacKnight). The Astronomy of the Bible by O M Mitchel with a Biographical Sketch. 2006. 336p. per. 23.99 *(978-1-4255-3385-4(X))* MPublishing.

—Popular Astronomy a Concise Elementary Treatise on the Sun, Planets, Satellites & Comets. 2006. 396p. per. 26.99 *(978-1-4255-4233-7(6))* MPublishing.

Mitchel, Ormsby M. The Planetary & Stellar Worlds: A Popular Exposition of the Great Discoveries & Theories of Modern Astronomy. 2007. (ENG.). 340p. 45.95 *(978-0-548-35379-0(4))*; per. 30.95 *(978-0-548-29632-5(4))* Kessinger Publishing, LLC.

Moché, Dinah L. Astronomy. 7th ed. 2009. (Wiley Self-Teaching Guides: 190). (ENG., Illus.). 388p. pap. 19.95 *(978-0-470-23083-1(5)*, Wiley) Wiley, John & Sons, Inc.

Monteiro, Mário J. P. F. G., ed. The Unsolved Universe: Challenges for the Future: Jenam 2002. 2010. 150p. pap. 66.00 *(978-90-481-6447-9(8)*, 9048164478) Springer.

Moore, Patrick. The Amateur Astronomer. 12th ed. 2010. (ENG., Illus.). xiii, 293p. pap. 69.95 *(978-1-84996-941-3(8)*, 1849969418) Springer.

—Astronomy. 2nd ed. 2008. (Teach Yourself: Math & Science Ser.). (ENG., Illus.). 256p. pap. 12.95 *(978-0-07-155009-3(7)*, 0071550097) McGraw-Hill Cos., The.

—Atlas of the Universe. (Illus.). 288p. *(978-0-540-08707-5(6))* Octopus Publishing Group.

—Our Universe: An Introduction. 2007. (ENG., Illus.). 128p. 8.95 *(978-1-904332-41-1(2))* AAPPL Artists & Photographers Pr., Ltd. GBR. Dist: Sterling Publishing Co., Inc.

—Yearbook of Astronomy 2010. Mason, John, ed. 2010. (ENG., Illus.). 384p. pap. 29.95 *(978-0-230-73605-4(X))* Macmillan Pubs., Ltd. GBR. Dist: Independent Pubs. Group.

Moore, Patrick & Mason, John. Patrick Moore's Yearbook of Astronomy 2012. 50th ed. 2011. (ENG., Illus.). 544p. 32.95 ***(978-0-230-75984-8(X))*** Macmillan Pubs., Ltd. GBR. Dist: Independent Pubs. Group.

Moore, Patrick & Rees, Robin. Patrick Moore's Data Book of Astronomy. 2nd ed. 2011. (Illus.). 586p. 55.00 *(978-0-521-89935-2(4))* Cambridge Univ. Pr.

Morison, Ian. Introduction to Astronomy & Cosmology. 2008. (ENG., Illus.). 360p. 179.00 *(978-0-470-03333-3(9))*; pap. 65.00 *(978-0-470-03334-0(7))* Wiley, John & Sons, Inc. (Wiley).

Nautical Almanac Office (U.S.), compiled by. Astronomical Phenomena for the Year 2011. 2008. (ENG.). 82p. pap. 9.00 *(978-0-16-082126-4(6)*, Dept. of the Navy) United States Government Printing Office.

Nevarez, David S. Our Universe, the Greatest Story Ever Told, 1 vol. 2010. 58p. pap. 16.95 *(978-1-4512-9225-1(2))* PublishAmerica, Inc.

Newcomb, Simon. Astronomy for Everybody. 2009. 174p. pap. 19.99 *(978-1-150-64227-2(0))* General Bks. LLC.

—Elements of Astronomy. 2008. 242p. 41.95 *(978-1-4366-0737-7(X))*; (ENG.). 244p. per. 26.95 *(978-0-548-81667-7(0))* Kessinger Publishing, LLC.

—Popular Astronomy. 2009. 602p. pap. *(978-1-4588-4386-9(6))*; 536p. pap. *(978-0-217-03233-9(8))*; 566p. pap. *(978-0-217-86754-2(5))* Books LLC.

—Popular Astronomy. 2011. (Cambridge Library Collection - Physical Sciences Ser.). (ENG., Illus.). 598p. pap. 43.00 ***(978-1-108-03773-0(9))*** Cambridge Univ. Pr.

—Popular Astronomy. 2009. 594p. pap. 26.90 *(978-0-217-86762-7(6))* General Bks. LLC.

—Popular Astronomy. (ENG.). 2007. 600p. 59.95 *(978-0-548-13858-8(3))* 2006. pap. 44.95 *(978-1-4286-5030-5(X))* Kessinger Publishing, LLC.

—Popular Astronomy. 2007. (ENG.). 584p. per. *(978-1-4067-4574-0(X))*; 608p. per. *(978-1-4067-6845-9(6))* Read Bks.

—Side-Lights on Astronomy & Kindred Fields of Popular Science. 2008. 244p. 27.99 *(978-0-554-21943-1(3))* 2008. 244p. 24.99 *(978-0-554-31246-0(8))* 2006. 254p. pap. 21.99 *(978-1-4264-1302-5(5))* 2006. (ENG.). 240p. pap. 22.99 *(978-1-4264-1326-1(2))* BiblioBazaar.

—Side-Lights on Astronomy & Kindred Fields of Popular Science. 2009. 228p. pap. *(978-0-217-87485-4(1))* Books LLC.

—Side-Lights on Astronomy & Kindred Fields of Popular Science. 2007. (ENG.). 236p. per. *(978-1-4065-3097-1(2))* Dodo Pr.

Nigro, Nick. Knack Night Sky: Decoding the Solar System, from Constellations to Black Holes. 2010. (Knack: Make It Easy Ser.). (ENG., Illus.). 256p. pap. 19.95 *(978-1-59921-955-4(7)*, Knack) Globe Pequot Pr., The.

North, John D. Cosmos: An Illustrated History of Astronomy & Cosmology. 2008. (Illus.). 736p. 95.00 *(978-0-226-59440-8(8))*; pap. 39.00 *(978-0-226-59441-5(6))* Univ. of Chicago Pr.

Norton, William A. (William Augustus). A Treatise on Astronomy, Spherical & Physica ; with Astronomical Problems, & Solar, Lunar, & Other Astronomical Tables for the Use of Colleges. 2006. 624p. per. 34.99 *(978-1-4255-6580-0(8))* MPublishing.

Nouveau Ciel, Nouvelle Terre: La Révolution Copernicienne Dans L'Allemagne de la Réforme (1530-1630) 2009. (FRE, GER & ENG., Illus.). 448p. (C). pap. 56.00 ***(978-2-251-42037-0(1))*** Societe d'edition Les Belles lettres FRA. Dist: ISD.

O'Dell, Stephen L. & Pareschi, Giovanni. Optics for EUV, X-Ray, & Gamma-Ray Astronomy III: 29-30 August 2007, San Diego, California, USA. 2007. (Proceedings of SPIE Ser.). (Illus.). 466p. pap. 105.00 *(978-0-8194-6836-9(3))* SPIE.

Oglesby, Shannon M. The Human Planet: Unraveling the Mysteries of God's Light Within the Soul, Spirit, & Body. 2009. 144p. pap. 37.99 *(978-1-4490-1699-9(5))* AuthorHouse.

Olcott, William Tyler. A Field Book of the Stars. 2009. 180p. 22.99 *(978-1-103-97755-0(5))*; 148p. 24.99 *(978-0-559-13029-8(5))*; 148p. 21.99 *(978-0-559-13045-8(7))*; 180p. pap. 16.99 *(978-1-103-97745-1(8))*; 148p. pap. 21.75 *(978-0-559-13031-1(7))*; 148p. pap. 20.75 *(978-0-559-13041-0(4))* BiblioBazaar.

—A Field Book of the Stars. 2008. 180p. pap. *(978-1-4086-6937-2(4))* Read Bks.

Olmsted, Denison. An Introduction to Astronomy: Designed As A Text-Book for the Use of Students in College. by Denison Olmsted ... 2006. 348p. per. 23.99 *(978-1-4255-3516-2(X))* MPublishing.

—Letters on Astronomy, in Which the Elements of the Science Are Familiarly [!] Explained with Numerous Engravings by Denison Olmsted, LI D. 2006. 456p. per. 29.99 *(978-1-4255-5059-2(2))* MPublishing.

Opstbaum, Roger. Astronomy Notes Esc 111. rev. ed. 2010. (ENG.). 104p. ring bd. 26.07 *(978-0-7872-9163-1(3))* Kendall Hunt Publishing Co.

Ormathwaite, John Benn Walsh. Astronomy & Geology Compared by Lord Ormathwaite. 2006. 180p. per. 18.99 *(978-1-4255-1481-5(2))* MPublishing.

Padmanabhan, Thanu, ed. Astronomy in India: A Historical Perspective. 2010. 250p. 129.00 *(978-81-8489-997-9(1))* Springer.

Palen, Stacy E., et al. Understanding Our Universe. 2011. (ENG.). 485p. (C). pap. 75.00 net. *(978-0-393-91210-4(8)*, 91210) Norton, W. W. & Co., Inc.

Panel on Implementing Recommendations from New Worlds, New Horizons Decadal Survey & National Research Council. Report of the Panel on Implementing Recommendations from the New Worlds, New Horizons Decadal Survey. 2012. (ENG.). 36p. pap. 15.00 *(978-0-309-16373-6(0))* National Academies Pr.

Pankenier, David W., et al. Historical Observational Records of Comets & Meteor Showers from China, Japan & Korea. 2008. 776p. 159.95 *(978-1-60497-587-1(3))* Cambria Pr.

Papantonopoulos, Lefteris, ed. The Invisible Universe: Dark Matter & Dark Energy: Dark Matter & Dark Energy. 2010. (Lecture Notes in Physics Ser.). (Illus.). xiv, 436p. pap. 129.00 *(978-3-642-09004-2(4)*, 3642090044) Springer.

Pedersen, Olaf. A Survey of the Almagest: With Annotation & New Commentary by Alexander Jones. Jones, Alexander, ed. 2010. (Sources & Studies in the History of Mathematics & Physical Sciences Ser.). Orig. Title: Survey of the Almagest. (Illus.). x, 468p. 149.00 *(978-0-387-84825-9(8)*, 0387848258) Springer.

Pellegrini, Paulo. Graduate School in Astronomy. 2008. (AIP Conference Proceedings / Astronomy & Astrophysics Ser.). 105.00 *(978-0-7354-0587-5(5))* American Institute of Physics.

Pfeiffer. Descriptive Astronomy. Date not set. (Adaptable Courseware-Hardside Ser.) pap. 21.00 *(978-0-534-16051-7(4))* Wadsworth.

Plait, Philip. Death from the Skies! The Science Behind the End of the World. 2009. (ENG.). 336p. (gr. 12-18). 16.00 *(978-0-14-311604-2(5)*, Penguin (Non-Classics)) Penguin Group (USA) Inc.

Plionis, Manolis, et al, eds. A Pan-Chromatic View of Clusters of Galaxies & the Large-Scale Structure. 2008. (Lecture Notes in Physics Ser.). (Illus.). 471p. 109.00 *(978-1-4020-6940-6(5))* Springer.

Polster, Burkard, et al. Sciencia: Mathematics, Physics, Chemistry, Biology, & Astronomy for All. 2011. (Wooden Bks.). (ENG., Illus.). 416p. 20.00 *(978-0-8027-7899-4(2))* Walker & Co.

Poole, Jane S. Adam's Astronomy: The Original Zodiac. 2008. (Illus.). 78p. pap. 11.00 *(978-1-55635-528-8(9))* Wipf & Stock Pubs.

Prather, Edward E., et al. Lecture Tutorials for Introductory Astronomy. 2nd ed. 2007. (ENG., Illus.). 144p. (C). per. 42.87 *(978-0-13-239226-6(7))* Benjamin-Cummings Publishing Co.

Pratt, Orson. Wonders of the Universe: Or A Compilation of the Astronomical Writings of Orson Pratt. Lundwall, Nels B., ed. 2011. 366p. 53.95 ***(978-1-258-00856-7(4))*** Literary Licensing, LLC.

Proctor, Richard A. The Orbs Around Us. 2008. 352p. *(978-1-4437-2291-9(X)*, Hesperides Pr.) Read Bks.

Proctor, Richard A. (Richard Anthony). Half-Hours with the Telescope; Being a Popular Guide to the Use of the Telescope As a Means of Amusement & Instruction by Richard a Proctor Wi. 2006. 140p. per. 16.99 *(978-1-4255-0966-8(5))* MPublishing.

Proctor, Richard Anthony. Other Worlds Than Ours. 2009. (Cambridge Library Collection - Religion Ser.). 360p. pap. 29.99 *(978-1-108-00417-6(2))* Cambridge Univ. Pr.

Publications International Staff, ed. Electronic Time for Learning: Stars & Planets. 2010. 120p. 18.98 *(978-1-60553-154-0(5)*, PIL Kids) Publications International, Ltd.

Pudritz, Ralph, et al, eds. Planetary Systems & the Origins of Life. 2007. (Cambridge Astrobiology Ser.). (ENG., Illus.). 334p. 127.00 *(978-0-521-87548-6(X))* Cambridge Univ. Pr.

Pugh, Philip. Observing the Messier Objects with a Small Telescope: In the Footsteps of a Great Observer. 2011. (Patrick Moore's Practical Astronomy Ser.). (ENG., Illus.). 224p. pap. 44.95 *(978-0-387-85356-7(1)*, 0387853561) Springer.

Quanz, Sascha P. Circumstellar Disks & Envelopes Around Young Low-Mass Stars. 2008. 172p. pap. *(978-3-639-01015-2(9))* VDM Verlag Dr. Mueller e.K.

Ratcliffe, Martin. State of the Universe: New Images, Discoveries, & Events. 2006. (Springer Praxis Books / Popular Astronomy Ser.). (Illus.). 193p. 29.95 *(978-0-387-34178-1(1)*, 0387341781) Springer.

Richardson, David. Descriptive Astronomy. rev. ed. 2010. (ENG.). 60p. spiral bd. 49.00 *(978-0-7575-4446-0(0))* Kendall Hunt Publishing Co.

Ricketts, Sandra, et al, eds. Library & Information Services In Astronomy: Common Challenges, Uncommon Solutions. 2007. (Astronomical Society of the Pacific Conference Ser.). 436p. 77.00 *(978-1-58381-316-4(0))* Astronomical Society of the Pacific, The.

Rickey, Vern G. The Creation & the Extinction: Global Warming & Ice. 2009. 138p. pap. 13.99 *(978-1-4490-0788-1(0))* AuthorHouse.

Roach, F. The Light of the Night Sky. 2010. 144p. pap. 153.00 *(978-90-481-8339-5(1)*, 9048183391) Springer.

Robinson, Horatio N. (Horatio Nelson). A Treatise on Astronomy, Descriptive, Physical, & Practical Designed for Schools, Colleges, & Private Students by H N Robinson. 2006. 368p. per. 26.99 *(978-1-4255-3886-6(X))* MPublishing.

—A Treatise on Astronomy, Descriptive, Theoretical & Physical, Designed for Schools, Academies, & Private Students. 2006. 416p. per. 26.99 *(978-1-4255-4555-0(6))* MPublishing.

Robinson, John. The Universe We Live In. 2011. 294p. 48.95 ***(978-1-258-09773-8(7))*** Literary Licensing, LLC.

Rochberg, Francesca. The Heavenly Writing: Divination, Horoscopy, & Astronomy in Mesopotamian Culture. 2007. (ENG., Illus.). 360p. pap. 31.99 *(978-0-521-71661-1(6))* Cambridge Univ. Pr.

Roe, James. The Birth of Belief: Alien Alert! 2011. 28p. pap. 14.95 ***(978-1-4634-4052-7(9))*** AuthorHouse.

Roig, Fernando, et al, eds. XIII Special Courses at the National Observatory of Rio de Janeiro. 2009. (AIP Conference Proceedings / Astronomy & Astrophysics Ser.). 158p. 97.00 *(978-0-7354-0730-5(4)*, 0735407304, AIP Pr.) Springer.

Röser, Siegfried, ed. Cosmic Matter, Volume 20. 2008. (Reviews in Modern Astronomy Ser.: 10). (ENG., Illus.). 426p. 195.00 *(978-3-527-40820-7(7)*, Wiley-VCH) Wiley, John & Sons, Inc.

Roth, Dennis Morrow. Oozing the Moon: A Sky & Night Woods Guide to the Galaxy. 2006. 167p. per. 12.95 *(978-1-56474-460-9(4)*, Fithian Pr) Daniel & Daniel, Pubs., Inc.

Roth, Günter D., ed. Handbook of Practical Astronomy. 2008. (Illus.). 916p. 109.00 *(978-3-540-76377-2(5)*, 3540763775) Springer.

Roy, A. Astronomy: Structure of the Universe. 4th ed. 2009. 500p. 52.95 *(978-0-7503-0984-4(9))* Taylor & Francis Group.

Ruggles, Clive L. N., ed. Archaeoastronomy & Ethnoastronomy (IAU S278) Building Bridges between Cultures. 2011. (Proceedings of the International Astronomical Union Symposia & Colloquia Ser.). (ENG., Illus.). 430p. 125.00 ***(978-1-107-01978-2(8))*** Cambridge Univ. Pr.

Ryan, Jay. Signs & Seasons: Understanding the Elements of Classical Astronomy. 2007. (Illus.). 280p. (YA). 39.99 *(978-0-9792211-0-1(2))* Fourth Day Pr.

Saha, Swapan K. Diffraction-Limited Imaging with Large & Moderate Telescopes. 2007. (Illus.). 604p. 121.00 *(978-981-270-777-2(8))* World Scientific Publishing Co., Inc.

Sandy Andrew. Your Never-Ending Life: Book 1 of the Universal Learning Series. 2010. 144p. pap. 14.95 *(978-1-4401-8927-2(7))* iUniverse, Inc.

Saviane, Ivo, et al, eds. Groups of Galaxies in the Nearby Universe: Proceedings of the ESO Workshop held at Santiago de Chile, December 5 - 9 2005. 2010. (ESO Astrophysics Symposia Ser.). (Illus.). xxii, 400p. pap. 119.00 *(978-3-642-09026-4(5)*, 3642090265) Springer.

Scagell, Robin & Frydman, David. Stargazing with Binoculars. 3rd enl. ed. 2012. (ENG., Illus.). 208p. pap. 19.95 ***(978-1-77085-043-9(0))*** Firefly Bks., Ltd.

Schönfelder, Volker, ed. The Universe in Gamma Rays. 2011. (Astronomy & Astrophysics Library). (Illus.). xiv, 407p. pap. 149.00 *(978-3-642-08745-5(0)*, 3642087450) Springer.

Schindler, Karl. Physics of Space Plasma Activity. 2006. (ENG., Illus.). 522p. 88.00 *(978-0-521-85897-7(6))* Cambridge Univ. Pr.

Schmadel, Lutz D. Dictionary of Minor Planet Names: Addendum to Fifth Edition: 2006 - 2008. 2009. (ENG., Illus.). viii, 316p. 189.00 *(978-3-642-01964-7(1)*, 3642019641) Springer.

Schmitt, Andreas. Dense Matter in Compact Stars: A Pedagogical Introduction. 2010. (Lecture Notes in Physics Ser.). (Illus.). x, 147p. pap. 49.95 *(978-3-642-12865-3(3)*, 3642128653) Springer.

Schmude, Richard W. Comets, & How to Observe Them. 2010. (Illus.). xii, 254p. E-Book ***(978-1-4419-5790-0(1))*** Springer.

Schneider, Peter. Extragalactic Astronomy & Cosmology: An Introduction. (Illus.). 2010. xiv, 459p. pap. 89.95 *(978-3-642-06971-0(1)*, 3642069711) 2006. 459p. 89.95 *(978-3-540-33174-2(3)*, 3540331743) Springer.

Schneider, Step & Arny, Thomas. Pathways to Astronomy. 2nd ed. 2008. (Illus.). 800p. pap. 105.63 *(978-0-07-340445-5(4))* McGraw-Hill Professional Publishing.

Schneider, Stephen & Arny, Thomas. Loose Leaf Pathways to Astronomy. 3rd ed. 2011. (ENG.). (C). pap. 100.00 *(978-0-07-743135-8(9)*, 0077431359, McGraw-Hill Science, Engineering & Mathematics) McGraw-Hill Higher Education.

—Pathways to Astronomy. 2nd ed. 2009. (ENG.). (C). pap. 127.19 *(978-0-07-740183-2(2)*, 0077401832, McGraw-Hill Science, Engineering & Mathematics) McGraw-Hill Higher Education.

Schneider, Stephen E. & Arny, Thomas. Pathways to Astronomy. 3rd ed. 2011. (ENG., Illus.). 800p. (C). pap. 142.67 *(978-0-07-351213-6(3)*, 0073512133, McGraw-Hill Science, Engineering & Mathematics) McGraw-Hill Higher Education.

Schneider, Stephen E. & Arny, Thomas T. Pathways to Astronomy with Starry Nights Pro DVD, Version 5. 0. 2nd ed. 2008. (Illus.). (C). pap. 112.50 *(978-0-07-726311-9(1)*, 9780077263119, McGraw-Hill Science, Engineering & Mathematics) McGraw-Hill Higher Education.

Schneider Stephen E, et al. Explorations: An Introduction to Astronomy. 6th ed. 2009. *(978-0-07-351217-4(6))* McGraw-Hill Cos., The.

Schneider, Steven & Arny, Thomas T. Pathways to Astronomy. 2007. (ENG.). (C). pap. 113.75 *(978-0-07-334710-3(8)*, 0073347108, McGraw-Hill Science, Engineering & Mathematics) McGraw-Hill Higher Education.

Schrogl, Kai-Uwe, et al, eds. Yearbook on Space Policy 2008/2009: Setting New Trends. 2010. (Yearbook on Space Policy Ser.). (Illus.). xxvi, 364p. 189.00 *(978-3-7091-0317-3(7)*, 3709103177) Springer.

Scientific American Editors. Reality-Bending Black Holes. Rennie, John, ed. 2007. (ENG., Illus.). 92p. (C). per. 15.95 *(978-1-4292-1045-4(1))* Freeman, W. H. & Co.

Scott, Donald. The Electric Sky: A Challenge to the Myths of Modern Astronomy. Acheson, Mel, ed. 2006. (Illus.). 256p. per. 25.00 *(978-0-9772851-1-2(1))* Mikamar Publishing.

Scranton, Laird. The Science of the Dogon: Decoding the African Mystery Tradition. 2006. (ENG., Illus.). 1p. per. 18.95 *(978-1-59477-133-0(2))* Inner Traditions International, Ltd.

Seeds, Michael A. Astronomy: The Solar System & Beyond. 5th ed. 2007. (Illus.). 553p. *(978-0-495-01379-2(X))* 2006. 576p. (C). pap. 115.95 *(978-0-495-01378-5(1))* 2006. (ENG., Illus.). 576p. (C). pap. 198.95 *(978-0-495-01577-2(6))* Brooks/Cole.

—Foundations of Astronomy. 2007. (Illus.). 9th ed. 724p. *(978-0-495-01586-4(5))* 10th ed. (ENG., 688p. (C). 224.95 *(978-0-495-38724-4(X))* Brooks/Cole.

—Horizons: Exploring the Universe. 10th ed. (Illus.). 2008. (ENG.). 552p. (C). per. 184.95 *(978-0-495-11963-0(6))* 2008. xiii, 516p. *(978-0-495-19095-0(0))* 2007. (ENG., 552p. (C). pap. 184.95 *(978-0-495-11358-4(1))* Brooks/Cole.

—Horizons: Exploring the Universe. 11th ed. 2009. (ENG.). 448p. (C). pap. 75.95 *(978-1-4390-4602-9(6))* Brooks/Cole.

—The Solar System. 5th ed. 2007. (Illus.). xii, 721p. *(978-0-495-12655-3(1))* Brooks/Cole.

Seeds, Michael A. & Backman, Dana. Astro. 2010. (Textbooks Available with Cengage YouBook Ser.). (ENG.). 352p. pap. 77.95 *(978-0-538-73804-0(9))* Brooks/Cole.

—Foundations of Astronomy. 11th ed. 2010. (Textbooks Available with Cengage YouBook Ser.). (ENG.). 672p. (C). 232.95 *(978-1-4390-5035-4(X))* Brooks/Cole.

Seeds, Michael A. & Backman, Dana E. Perspectives on Astronomy. 2007. (Available 2010 Titles Enhanced Web Assign Ser.). (ENG.). 384p. (C). pap. 101.95 *(978-0-495-11352-2(2))*; (Illus.). per. 101.95 *(978-0-495-39273-6(1))* Brooks/Cole.

Seiss, Joseph. The Gospel in the Stars. 2007. 196p. 26.95 *(978-1-60206-916-9(6))* Cosimo, Inc.

Sela, Shlomo, ed. Abraham Ibn Ezra the Book of Reasons: A Parallel Hebrew-English Critical Edition of the Two Versions of the Text. 2007. (Études Sur le Judaisme Médiéval Ser.). 368p. *(978-90-04-15764-4(6))* BRILL.

Serviss, Garrett P. Curiosities of the Sky. 2008. 144p. pap. *(978-1-4099-1651-2(0))* Dodo Pr.

—Curiosities of the Sky. 2010. (Illus.). 90p. pap. 20.00 *(978-1-153-59831-6(0))* General Bks. LLC.

—Curiosities of the Sky. 2010. 114p. pap. 15.96 *(978-1-162-65900-8(9))*; 27.96 ***(978-1-169-24728-4(8))*** Kessinger Publishing, LLC.

Serviss, Garrett Putman & Serviss, Garrett P. Curiosities of the Sky. 2010. 114p. 34.95 *(978-1-161-42765-3(1))* Kessinger Publishing, LLC.

Serviss, Garrett Putnam. Curiosities of the Sky. 2008. 160p. 25.99 *(978-0-554-28059-2(0))* 2008. 160p. 22.99 *(978-0-554-37362-1(9))* 2007. (ENG.). 144p. pap. 18.99 *(978-1-4346-4607-1(6))* 2007. 158p. pap. 21.99 *(978-1-4346-4608-8(4))* BiblioBazaar.

Sharma, Rakesh & G.K.Upadhyaya, . Study of Dark Matter in Context of Recent Observations & Experiments. 2011. 232p. pap. ***(978-3-8433-8717-0(6))*** Lambert Academic Publishing.

Shaver, Peter A., et al, eds. Astronomy, Cosmology & Fundamental Physics: Proceedings of the ESO/CERN/ESA Symposium Held at Garching, Germany, 4-7 March 2002. 2010. (ESO Astrophysics Symposia Ser.). xxi, 501p. pap. 64.95 *(978-3-642-07281-9(X)*, 364207281X) Springer.

Shaw, Andrew M. Astrochemistry: From Astronomy to Astrobiology. 2006. (ENG., Illus.). 352p. 190.00 *(978-0-470-09136-4(3))*; per. 65.00 *(978-0-470-09137-1(1))* Wiley, John & Sons, Inc. (Wiley).

Shipsey, Ian & Coy, Jennifer. Introductory Astronomy Lab Man. 2008. 288p. pap. 44.38 *(978-0-07-340446-2(2))* McGraw-Hill Professional Publishing.

Shustov, Boris, et al, eds. UV Astronomy 2011. 2011. (ENG., Illus.). 343p. 169.00 ***(978-94-007-2572-0(8)***, 9400725728) Springer.

Sidgwick, J. B. Introductory Astronomy. *(978-0-8022-1567-3(X))* Philosophical Library, Inc.

Sion, E., et al, eds. White Dwarfs: Cosmological & Galactic Probes: Cosmological & Galactic Probes. 2010. (Astrophysics & Space Science Library). x, 267p. pap. 189.00 *(978-90-481-6932-0(1)*, 9048169321) Springer.

Sky and Telescope Magazine Staff. Night Sky Guide. 19.95 *(978-1-893770-01-0(X))* Lewers, Steven & Assocs.

Slater, Timothy F. & Jones, Lauren V., eds. Greenwood Guides to the Universe, 7 vols. 2009. (Greenwood Guides to the Universe Ser.). 1856p. 349.96 *(978-0-313-33873-1(6)*, GR3873) Greenwood Publishing Group, Inc.

Smart, Tim & Kunitzsch, Paul. A Dictionary of Modern Star Names: A Short Guide to 254 Star Names & Their Derivations. 2nd ed. 2007. (ENG., Illus.). 76p. per. 12.95 *(978-1-931559-44-7(9))* Sky Publishing.

Sofaer, Anna. Chaco Astronomy: An Ancient American Cosmology. 2007. *(978-0-943734-46-0(0))* Ocean Tree Bks.

Soltysiak, Arkadiusz, ed. Time & Astronomy in Past Cultures. 2010. 102.56 *(978-1-60724-668-8(6))* Gorgias Pr., LLC.

Sparrow, Giles. The Stargazer's Handbook. 2008. (Illus.). 272p. *(978-1-84724-145-0(X))* Quercus.

Spielberg, Nathan. (WCS)Seven Ideas that Shook the Universe. 3rd ed. 2006. (ENG.). 376p. (C). pap. 74.95 *(978-0-470-09660-4(8)*, Wiley) Wiley, John & Sons, Inc.

Spiritual Astronomy: Realize the Light. 2007. per. *(978-1-58916-999-9(9))* Great Year Pr.

Steele, Joel Dorman. Fourteen Weeks in Descriptive Astronomy by J Dorman Steele. 2006. 340p. per. 23.99 *(978-1-4255-3451-6(1))* MPublishing.

Steiner, Andrea, et al, eds. New Horizons in Occultation Research: Studies in Atmosphere & Climate. 2009. (ENG., Illus.). xv, 316p. 179.00 *(978-3-642-00320-2(6)*, 3642003206) Springer.

Stimets, Richard. Exploring the Universe. rev. ed. 2010. (ENG.). 216p. spiral bd. 37.33 *(978-0-7575-6070-5(9))* Kendall Hunt Publishing Co.

Stine, Peter. Introduction to Astronomy. rev. ed. 2010. (ENG.). 94p. pap. 72.11 *(978-0-7575-5378-3(8))* Kendall Hunt Publishing Co.

Stoyan, Ronald, et al. Atlas of the Messier Objects: Highlights of the Deep Sky. Schroeder, Klaus-Peter, tr. from GER. 2008. (ENG., Illus.). 370p. 62.00 *(978-0-521-89554-5(5))* Cambridge Univ. Pr.

Talcott, Richard. Astronomy. 2008. (Teach Yourself VISUALLY Consumer Ser.). (ENG., Illus.). 256p. pap. 24.99 *(978-0-470-34382-1(6)*, Visual) Wiley, John & Sons, Inc.

Telles, Eduardo, et al, eds. XV Special Courses at the National Observatory of Rio de Janeiro. 2011. (AIP Conference Proceedings / Astronomy & Astrophysics

Ser.). (ENG.). 178p. pap. 135.00 ***(978-0-7354-0950-7(1)***, 0735409501, AIP Pr.) Springer.

Thompson, Robert, et al. Illustrated Guide to Astronomical Wonders: From Novice to Master Observer. 2007. (DIY Science Ser.). (ENG., Illus.). 520p. per. 29.99 *(978-0-596-52685-6(7))* O'Reilly Media, Inc.

Traugott, William H. Ancient Astronomy: A Story of the Stars. 2011. 122p. pap. 19.95 ***(978-1-4560-4101-4(0))*** PublishAmerica, Inc.

Tsinganos, Kanaris C., et al. Advances in Hellenic Astronomy During the IYA09: 9th International Conference of the Hellenic Astronomical Society: Proceedings of a Conference Held at University of Athens, Athens, Greece, 20-24 September 2009. 2010. (Illus.). xxi, 515p. ***(978-1-58381-728-5(X))*** Astronomical Society of the Pacific, The.

Turfa, Jean MacIntosh. Divining the Etruscan World: The Brontoscopic Calendar & Religious Practice. 2012. (ENG., Illus.). 400p. 99.00 ***(978-1-107-00907-3(3))*** Cambridge Univ. Pr.

Ulmschneider, Peter. Intelligent Life in the Universe: Principles & Requirements Behind Its Emergence. 2nd rev. ed. 2006. (Advances in Astrobiology & Biogeophysics Ser.). (Illus.). xiv, 310p. (C). 129.00 *(978-3-540-32836-0(X)*, 354032836X) Springer.

Underwood, Deborah. Graphing the Universe. 2008. (Real World Data Ser.). (ENG.). 32p. pap. 7.99 *(978-1-4329-1546-9(0)*, NA-h) Heinemann-Raintree.

Unsöld, Albrecht & Baschek, Bodo. The New Cosmos: An Introduction to Astronomy & Astrophysics. Brewer, William D., tr. 5th ed. 2010. (Illus.). xiv, 557p. pap. 89.95 *(978-3-642-08746-2(9)*, 3642087469) Springer.

Urama, Johnson O., et al, eds. African Cultural Astronomy: Current Archaeoastronomy & Ethnoastronomy Research in Africa. 2008. (Astrophysics & Space Science Proceedings Ser.). (Illus.). 260p. 169.00 *(978-1-4020-6638-2(4))* Springer.

Valls-Gabaud, David & Boksenberg, Alec, eds. The Role of Astronomy in Society & Culture (IAU S260) 2011. (Proceedings of the International Astronomical Union Symposia & Colloquia Ser.). (ENG., Illus.). 816p. 125.00 *(978-0-521-76477-3(7))* Cambridge Univ. Pr.

Van Der Hucht, Karel, ed. Highlights of Astronomy, Vol. 14. 2008. (Proceedings of the International Astronomical Union Symposia & Colloquia Ser.). (ENG., Illus.). 752p. 121.00 *(978-0-521-89683-2(5))* Cambridge Univ. Pr.

van der Hucht, Karel A., ed. Reports on Astronomy, 2006-2009 (IAU XXVIIA) IAU Transactions XXVIIA. 2009. (Proceedings of the International Astronomical Union Symposia & Colloquia Ser.). (ENG., Illus.). 480p. 128.99 *(978-0-521-85605-8(1))* Cambridge Univ. Pr.

Van Loon, Jacco Th. & Oliveira, Joana M. The Magellanic System: Star, Gas, & Galaxies. Van Loon, Jacco Th., ed. 2009. (Proceedings of the International Astronomical Union Symposia & Colloquia Ser.). (ENG., Illus.). 540p. 135.00 *(978-0-521-88987-2(1))* Cambridge Univ. Pr.

von Berlepsch, Regina, ed. Reviews in Modern Astronomy Vol. 23: Zooming In - The Cosmos at High Resolution, Volume 23. 2011. (Reviews in Modern Astronomy Ser.). (ENG., Illus.). 276p. 155.00 ***(978-3-527-41113-9(5)***, Wiley-VCH) Wiley, John & Sons, Inc.

von Humboldt, Alexander. Cosmos: Sketch of a Physical Description of the Universe. Sabine, Edward, ed. 2010. (Cambridge Library Collection - Physical Sciences Ser.). (ENG.). 498p. pap. 35.99 *(978-1-108-01363-5(5))*; 514p. pap. 37.99 *(978-1-108-01364-2(3))* Cambridge Univ. Pr.

Vreede, Elizabeth. Astronomy & Spiritual Science: The Astronomical Letters of Elizabeth Vreede. 2007. 400p. pap. 45.00 *(978-0-88010-588-0(7))* SteinerBooks, Inc.

Wang, Xun. Kerr & Kerr-AdS Black Shells & Black Hole Entropy. 2008. 80p. pap. *(978-3-8364-8292-9(4))* VDM Verlag Dr. Mueller e.K.

Waxman, Gerald D. Astronomical Tidbits: A Layperson's Guide to Astronomy. 2010. 256p. pap. 10.99 *(978-1-4520-4836-9(3))* AuthorHouse.

Werner, Klaus & Rauch, Thomas, eds. 17th European White Dwarf Workshop. 2010. (AIP Conference Proceedings / Astronomy & Astrophysics Ser.). (Illus.). 627p. pap. 318.00 *(978-0-7354-0823-4(8)*, 0735408238, AIP Pr.) Springer.

Whalen, Daniel J., et al, eds. The First Stars & Galaxies: Challenges for the Next Decade. 2010. (AIP Conference Proceedings / Astronomy & Astrophysics Ser.). 314p. pap. 159.00 *(978-0-7354-0849-4(1)*, 0735408491, AIP Pr.) Springer.

Whewell, William. Astronomy & General Physics Considered with Reference to Natural Theology. 2009. (Cambridge Library Collection - Religion Ser.). (ENG.). 404p. pap. 31.99 *(978-1-108-00012-3(6))* Cambridge Univ. Pr.

—Astronomy & General Physics Considered with Reference to Natural Theology. 2007. (ENG.). 394p. 49.95 *(978-0-548-03613-6(6))* Kessinger Publishing, LLC.

—Astronomy & General Physics Considered with Reference to Natural Theology by William Whewell. 2006. 236p. per. 20.99 *(978-1-4255-2159-2(2))*; per. 20.99 *(978-1-4255-2100-4(2))* MPublishing.

Whiting, Alan B. Hindsight & Popular Astronomy. 2010. 288p. 41.00 *(978-981-4307-91-8(2))* World Scientific Publishing Co., Inc.

Wickramasinghe, N. C., et al, eds. Fred Hoyle's Universe. 2010. 308p. pap. 149.00 *(978-90-481-6339-7(0)*, 9048163390) Springer.

Wiley Visual Imprint. Visualizing Astronomy. 2006. 500p. pap. 76.95 *(978-0-471-76341-3(1))* Wiley, John & Sons, Inc.

Wilkins, Jamie & Dunn, Robert. 300 Astronomical Objects: A Visual Reference to the Universe. 2011. (ENG., Illus.). 264p. pap. 29.95 *(978-1-55407-812-7(1))* Firefly Bks., Ltd.

Wilkinson, John. The Moon in Close-up: A Next Generation Astronomer's Guide. 2011. (Patrick Moore's Practical Astronomy Ser.). (ENG., Illus.). xi, 310p. pap. 39.95 *(978-3-642-14804-0(2)*, 3642148042) Springer.

Willoughby, Shannon, et al. Mysteries of the Sky: Activities for Collaborative Groups. 2nd rev. ed. 2010. (ENG.). 234p. spiral bd. 49.69 *(978-0-7575-7822-9(5))* Kendall Hunt Publishing Co.

Wilson, James N. The Noon Fix: The simplest possible backup to GPS. the only battery required Is in the Watch. 2009. 72p. pap. 19.95 *(978-1-4389-5866-8(8))* AuthorHouse.

Winget, Donald & University of Texas. We're Texas Astronomy. rev. ed. 2012. (ENG.). 534p. pap. 69.00 ***(978-0-7575-9919-4(2))*** Kendall Hunt Publishing Co.

Winget-Hermes. We're Texas Astronomy. rev. ed. 2011. (ENG.). 534p. pap. 59.00 ***(978-0-7575-8995-9(2))*** Kendall Hunt Publishing Co.

Winnewisser, Gisbert & Yamada, Koichi M. T., eds. Interstellar Molecules: Their Laboratory & Interstellar Habitat. 2011. (Springer Tracts in Modern Physics Ser.). (ENG., Illus.). ix, 230p. 179.00 *(978-3-642-16267-1(3)*, 3642162673) Springer.

Wojcikiewicz, Andrew. Awakening the Pharaoh: How to Avoid World Cataclysm In 2012. 2009. 256p. 31.99 *(978-1-4490-3922-6(7))* AuthorHouse.

Wood, David A. A Cosmic Journey: Big Picture Ideas in Astronomy. rev. ed. 2010. (ENG.). 168p. spiral bd. 35.42 *(978-0-7575-3829-2(0))* Kendall Hunt Publishing Co.

Wood, Floris & Wood, Kenneth. Homer's Secret Iliad. (Illus.). x, 294p. 40.00 *(978-0-7195-5780-4(1))* Murray, John GBR. Dist: Trafalgar Square Publishing.

Young, Anthony H. Lunar & Planetary Rovers: The Wheels of Apollo & the Quest for Mars. 2006. (Springer Praxis Books / Space Exploration Ser.). (Illus.). 305p. per. 44.95 *(978-0-387-30774-9(5)*, 0387307745) Springer.

Zamorano, Jaime, et al, eds. Highlights of Spanish Astrophysics II. 2010. 432p. pap. 206.00 *(978-90-481-5705-1(6)*, 9048157056) Springer.

Zaslow, Harry. Life in the Universe. 2011. 116p. pap. 39.49 ***(978-1-4567-6256-8(7))*** AuthorHouse.

Zwack, Joseph Patrick. The Origin & Location of Our Universe: (We didn't begin with the Big Bang) 2008. (Illus.). 128p. pap. 12.95 *(978-0-9801734-0-6(X))* Cosmic Pr.

ASTRONOMY—ATLASES

see Stars—Atlases

ASTRONOMY—BIBLIOGRAPHY

Literature, Grade 6, Vol. 3. Bernan Assocs.

Literature, Grade 6. tchr. ed. 41.95 *(978-0-382-40672-0(9))* Cobblestone Publishing Co.

Luther, Paul. The Printed Catalogues of the Library of the Royal Astronomical Society: Books, Pamphlets, Journals & Manuscripts from 1450 to 1940. 2006. *(978-1-57898-586-9(2))* Martino Publishing.

ASTRONOMY—CHARTS, DIAGRAMS, ETC.

see also Moon—Photographs, Maps, Etc.; Stars—Atlases

Combes, Francoise, ed. Mapping the Galaxy & Nearby Galaxies. 2007. (Astrophysics & Space Science Proceedings Ser.). (Illus.). 392p. 219.00 incl. cd-rom *(978-0-387-72767-7(1))* Springer.

Finkbeiner, Ann K. A Grand & Bold Thing: An Extraordinary New Map of the Universe Ushering in a New Era of Discovery. 2010. (ENG., Illus.). 240p. 27.00 *(978-1-4165-5216-1(2)*, Free Pr.) Free Pr.

Karkoschka, E. The Observer's Sky Atlas: With 50 Star Charts Covering the Entire Sky. 3rd ed. 2007. (ENG., Illus.). 162p. pap. 34.95 *(978-0-387-48537-9(6)*, 0387485376) Springer.

Lacy, Jodi. Mapping the Universe. 2007. (ENG., Illus.). 104p. pap. 19.95 *(978-1-891220-05-0(5))* Adler Planetarium & Astronomy Museum.

Mobberley, Martin. The Caldwell Objects & How to Observe Them. 2009. (Astronomers' Observing Guides). (ENG., Illus.). xiv, 288p. pap. 34.95 *(978-1-4419-0325-9(9)*, 1441903259) Springer.

Monks, Neale. Go-to Telescopes under Suburban Skies. 2010. (Patrick Moore's Practical Astronomy Ser.). (Illus.). xxi, 260p. pap. 34.95 *(978-1-4419-6850-0(4)*, 1441968504) Springer.

Mullaney, James. The Cambridge Double Star Atlas. 2009. (ENG., Illus.). 154p. pap. 35.00 *(978-0-521-49343-7(9))* Cambridge Univ. Pr.

Nautical Almanac Office (U.S.), compiled by. Astronomical Almanac for the Year 2009 & Its Companion, the Astronomical Almanac Online: Data for Astronomy, Space Sciences, Geodesy, Surveying, Navigation, & other Applications. 2008. (ENG., Illus.). 596p. 42.00 *(978-0-11-887342-0(3)*, Dept. of the Navy) United States Government Printing Office.

O'Meara, Stephen James. Hidden Treasures. 2007. (ENG., Illus.). 602p. 46.00 *(978-0-521-83704-0(9))* Cambridge Univ. Pr.

Renzini, Alvio & Bender, Ralf, eds. Multiwavelength Mapping of Galaxy Formation & Evolution: Proceedings of the ESO Workshop Held at Venice, Italy, 13-16 October 2003. 2010. (ESO Astrophysics Symposia Ser.). xxv, 487p. pap. 89.95 *(978-3-642-06509-5(0)*, 3642065090) Springer.

Ridpath, Ian. The Monthly Sky Guide. 8th rev. ed. 2009. (ENG., Illus.). 72p. pap. 17.00 *(978-0-521-13369-2(6))* Cambridge Univ. Pr.

Sinnott, Roger W. Sky & Telescope's Pocket Sky Atlas. 2007. (ENG., Illus.). 110p. spiral bd. 19.95 *(978-1-931559-31-7(7))* Sky Publishing.

Van Gent, Robert H. The Finest Atlas of the Heavens: Harmonia Macrocosmica of 1660: The Finest Atlas of the Heavens. 2006. (FRE, GER & ENG., Illus.). 208p. 150.00 *(978-3-8228-5290-3(2))* TASCHEN DEU. Dist: Ingram Pub. Services.

ASTRONOMY—DATA PROCESSING

Astronomical Data Analysis Software & Systems; Proceedings. 2007. (Astronomical Society of the Pacific Conference Ser.: Vol. 376). 731p. 77.00 *(978-1-58381-314-0(4))* Astronomical Society of the Pacific, The.

Brissenden, R. J. V. & Silva, David R. Observatory Operations: Strategies, Processes, & Systems II: 24-26 May, 2008, Marseiile, France. 2008. (Proceedings of SPIE Ser.). (Illus.). 722p. pap. 130.00 *(978-0-8194-7226-7(3))* SPIE.

Evans, Ian N., ed. Astronomical Data Analysis Software & Systems XX (Asp Conference Series) 2011. 77.00 ***(978-1-58381-764-3(6))*** Astronomical Society of the Pacific, The.

Fairman, Randall S. (Randall Stuart). 3D Astronomy with Java: An Introduction to Computer Graphics. 2010. *(978-0-943396-93-4(X))* Willmann-Bell, Inc.

Heck, Andre, ed. Information Handling in Astronomy - Historical Vistas. 2010. (Astrophysics & Space Science Library). (ENG.). 312p. pap. 189.00 *(978-90-481-6245-1(9)*, 9048162459) Springer.

Jaschek, Carlos. Data in Astronomy. 2011. (ENG.). 214p. pap. 39.99 *(978-0-521-17728-3(6))* Cambridge Univ. Pr.

Radziwill, Nicole M. & Bridger, Alan. Software & Cyberinfrastructure for Astronomy: 27-30 June 2010, San Diego, California, United States, 2 vols. 2010. (Proceedings of SPIE Ser.). (Illus.). 1302p. pap. 200.00 ***(978-0-8194-8230-3(7))*** SPIE.

Ricketts, Sandra, et al. Library & Information Services in Astronomy V: Common Challenges, Uncommon Solutions: Proceedings of a Conference Co-Hosted by the Harvard-Smithsonian Center for Astrophysics & Massachusetts Institute of Technology, Cambridge, Massachusetts, USA, 18-21 June 2006. 2007. (Astronomical Society of the Pacific Conference Ser.: Vol. 377). (Illus.). xxv, 436p. *(978-1-58381-317-1(9))* Astronomical Society of the Pacific, The.

Seeds, Michael A., et al. TheSkyX Workbook. 2nd ed. 2010. (ENG.). 384p. (C). pap. 63.95 *(978-0-538-73852-1(9))* Brooks/Cole.

Silva, David R., et al. Observatory Operations: Strategies, Processes, & Systems III: 30 June-2 July 2010, San Diego, California, United States. 2010. (Proceedings of SPIE Ser.). (Illus.). 752p. pap. 160.00 ***(978-0-8194-8227-3(7))*** SPIE.

SPIE Europe Staff, et al, contrib. by. Advanced Software & Control for Astronomy II: 26-28 June 2008, Marseille, France, 2 vols. 2008. (Proceedings of SPIE Ser.). (Illus.). 1158p. pap. 190.00 ***(978-0-8194-7229-8(8))*** SPIE.

Starck, Jean-Luc & Murtagh, Fionn. Astronomical Image & Data Analysis. 2nd rev. ed. 2006. (Astronomy & Astrophysics Library). (Illus.). xiv, 335p. 159.00 *(978-3-540-33024-0(0)*, 3540330240) Springer.

Tsvetkov, M., ed. Virtual Observatory: Plate Content Digitization, Archive Mining & Image Sequence Processing: Proceedings of the International Workshop. 2006. (Illus.). 197.50 *(978-954-580-190-7(5))* Heron Pr. BGR. Dist: Coronet Bks.

Way, Michael J., et al, eds. Advances in Machine Learning & Data Mining for Astronomy. 2012. (Chapman & Hall/CRC Data Mining & Knowledge Discovery Ser.). (ENG., Illus.). 744p. 99.95 ***(978-1-4398-4173-0(X)***, Chapman & Hall/CRC) CRC Pr. LLC.

Zink, Burkhard. Ray-tracing Black Holes: Theory & Implementation. 2008. 136p. pap. *(978-3-639-02902-4(X))* VDM Verlag Dr. Mueller e.K.

ASTRONOMY—DICTIONARIES

Dorling Kindersley Publishing Staff, et al. Encyclopedia of Space. 2009. (ENG.). 304p. (J). (gr. 3-8). 21.99 *(978-0-7566-5157-2(3))* Dorling Kindersley Publishing, Inc.

Mitton, Jacqueline. Cambridge Illustrated Dictionary of Astronomy. 2008. (ENG., Illus.). 416p. 34.00 *(978-0-521-82364-7(1))* Cambridge Univ. Pr.

Ridpath, Ian. A Dictionary of Astronomy. 2nd rev. ed. 2012. (Oxford Paperback Reference Ser.). (ENG., Illus.). 544p. pap. 21.95 ***(978-0-19-960905-5(5))*** Oxford Univ. Pr., Inc.

Schmadel, Lutz D. Dictionary of Minor Planet Names. 5th ed. 2006. XVI, 992p. 209.00 *(978-3-540-33631-0(1)*, 3540336311) Springer.

Williamson, Mark. The Cambridge Dictionary of Space Technology. 2010. (ENG., Illus.). 476p. pap. 36.99 *(978-0-521-14231-1(8))* Cambridge Univ. Pr.

ASTRONOMY—DIRECTORIES

American Institute of Physics, ed. 2012 Graduate Programs in Physics, Astronomy, & Related Fields. 2011. (ENG.). 731p. pap. 79.00 ***(978-0-7354-0966-8(8)***, 0735409668, AIP Pr.) Springer.

ASTRONOMY—EARLY WORKS TO 1800

Aratus, et al. Phaenomena. Poochigian, Aaron, tr. from GEC. 2010. (Johns Hopkins New Translations from Antiquity Ser.). (ENG., Illus.). 112p. (C). (gr. 13-17). 50.00 *(978-0-8018-9465-7(4))*; pap. 25.00 *(978-0-8018-9466-4(2))* Johns Hopkins Univ. Pr.

Aristotle. On the Heavens. 2009. 148p. 24.99 *(978-0-559-06477-7(2))*; 21.99 *(978-0-559-06491-3(8))*; pap. 20.75 *(978-0-559-06488-3(8))*; pap. 21.75 *(978-0-559-06482-1(9))* BiblioBazaar.

Copernicus, Nicolaus. Three Copernican Treatises: The Commentariolus of Copernicus; the Letter Against Werner; the Narratio Prima of Rheticus. Rosen, Edward, tr. 2011. 228p. 46.95 ***(978-1-258-05702-2(6))*** Literary Licensing, LLC.

Drawnel, Henryk. The Aramaic Astronomical Book from Qumran: Text, Translation, & Commentary. 2011. (ARC & ENG., Illus.). 560p. 350.00 *(978-0-19-959043-8(5))* Oxford Univ. Pr., Inc.

Frova, Andrea & Marenzana, Mariapiera. Thus Spoke Galileo: The great scientist's ideas & their relevance to the present Day. 2011. (Illus.). 512p. pap. 34.95 *(978-0-19-960682-5(X))* Oxford Univ. Pr., Inc.

Galilei, Galileo. The Essential Galileo. Finocchiaro, Maurice A., ed. & tr. by. from ITA. 2008. 384p. (C). 39.95 *(978-0-87220-938-1(5))* Hackett Publishing Co., Inc.

—Galileo's Siderius Nuncius, or, A Sidereal Message. 2009. 14.95 *(978-0-88135-375-4(2)*, Science History Pubns./USA) Watson Publishing International, LLC.

Galilei, Galileo & Finocchiaro, Maurice A. The Essential Galileo. Finocchiaro, Maurice A., ed. 2008. (Illus.). 384p. (C). pap. 13.95 *(978-0-87220-937-4(7))* Hackett Publishing Co., Inc.

Galilei, Galileo, et al. Sidereus Nuncius, Ovvero, Avviso Sidereo. 2009. (ITA., Illus.). 179p. *(978-88-89736-84-5(4))* Marcianum Pr.

Galileo, et al. Selected Writings. 2012. (Oxford World's Classics Ser.). (ENG., Illus.). 480p. pap. 15.95 ***(978-0-19-958369-0(2))*** Oxford Univ. Pr., Inc.

Gingerich, Owen. The Book Nobody Read: In Pursuit of the Revolutions of Nicolaus Copernicus. 2006. (Illus.). 306p. reprint ed. 25.00 *(978-1-4223-5738-5(4))* DIANE Publishing Co.

Holden, James H. Five Medieval Astrologers. 2008. 164p. pap. 21.95 *(978-0-86690-578-7(2))* American Federation of Astrologers, Inc.

Housman, A. E. & Manilii, M. Astronomicon Liber Qvartus. 2010. 150p. 28.99 *(978-1-140-37866-2(X))*; pap. 21.75 *(978-1-140-37867-9(8))* BiblioBazaar.

Hübner, Wolfgang. Manilius. Astronomica Buch V: Einfahrung, Text, Ã_bersetzung und Kommentar. 2010. (Sammlung wissenschaftlicher Commentare (SWC) Ser.).Tr. of Manilius, Astronomica Volume V. (GER, MUS & GEC., Illus.). XIV, 760p. 249.00 *(978-3-11-020670-8(6))* De Gruyter, Walter Inc.

Manilii, M. Astronomicon Vol. 1: Liber Primus. Housman, A. E., ed. 2011. 204p. pap. 19.99 *(978-0-521-16937-0(2))* Cambridge Univ. Pr.

Manilius, M. Astronomicon: Volume 2, Liber Secundus. Housman, A. e., ed. 2nd rev. ed. 2011. (ENG.). 174p. pap. 19.99 *(978-1-107-64808-1(4))* Cambridge Univ. Pr.

—Astronomicon: Volume 3, Liber Tertius. Housman, A. e., ed. 2nd rev. ed. 2011. (ENG.). 112p. pap. 19.99 *(978-1-107-64807-4(6))* Cambridge Univ. Pr.

—Astronomicon: Volume 4, Liber Quartus. Housman, A. e., ed. 2nd rev. ed. 2011. (ENG.). 164p. pap. 19.99 *(978-1-107-64806-7(8))* Cambridge Univ. Pr.

—Astronomicon: Volume 5, Liber Quintus. Housman, A. e., ed. 2nd rev. ed. 2011. (ENG.). 190p. pap. 19.99 *(978-1-107-64805-0(X))* Cambridge Univ. Pr.

Manilius, Marcus. Astronomicon. Housman, A. E., ed. 2011. (Cambridge Library Collection - Classics Ser.). (LAT.). 162p. pap. 19.99 *(978-1-108-12758-5(4))*; 108p. pap. 19.99 *(978-1-108-17063-5(3))*; 154p. pap. 19.99 *(978-1-108-03054-0(8))* Cambridge Univ. Pr.

—Astronomicon. Housman, A. e., ed. 2011. (Cambridge Library Collection - Classics Ser.). (LAT.). 254p. pap. 23.99 *(978-1-108-03796-9(8))* Cambridge Univ. Pr.

—Astronomicon. Housman, A. E., ed. 2011. (Cambridge Library Collection - Classics Ser.). (LAT.). 186p. pap. 19.99 *(978-1-108-04047-1(0))* Cambridge Univ. Pr.

—Astronomicon. Bentleii, Richardi, ed. 166p. 2010. 29.56 ***(978-1-165-96197-9(0))*** 2009. 36.95 *(978-1-104-67736-7(9))* 2009. pap. 21.95 *(978-1-104-61944-2(X))* Kessinger Publishing, LLC.

—Astronomicon, Book. Jacob, Fredrick, ed. 252p. 2010. 33.56 *(978-1-166-08914-6(2))* 2009. 41.95 *(978-1-104-80453-4(0))* 2009. pap. 26.95 *(978-1-104-72302-6(6))* Kessinger Publishing, LLC.

—Astronomicon Ex Recensione Richardi Bentleii Adjecta Est in Calce Cujusque Paginae Lection Vulgat. 2010. 172p. pap. 21.75 *(978-1-148-91053-6(0))* BiblioBazaar.

Manilius, Marcus & Housman, A. e. 1859-1936. Astronomicon; Recensuit et Enarravit a E Housman. 2010. 166p. pap. 21.75 *(978-1-175-03197-6(6))* BiblioBazaar.

Manilius, Marcus & Housman, Alfred Edward. Astronomicon. 2009. (LAT.). 103p. pap. 19.99 *(978-1-115-42848-4(9))*; pap. 18.99 *(978-1-115-42846-0(2))* BiblioBazaar. (BiblioLife).

Manilius, Marcus & Pithou, Pierre. Astronomicon Liber Primus[-Quintus]. 2010. 240p. pap. 26.75 *(978-1-175-04259-0(5))* BiblioBazaar.

Manilius, Marcus & Scaligeri, Joseph. Astronomicon a Iosepho Scaligero Ex Vetusto Codice Gemblacendi Infinitis Mendis Repurgarum. 664p. 2010. pap. 39.16 ***(978-1-166-07022-9(0))*** 2009. 63.95 *(978-1-104-83331-2(X))* 2009. pap. 48.95 *(978-1-104-72303-3(4))* Kessinger Publishing, LLC.

McKinzie, Harry. Zthorg - God's Computer. 170p. (Orig.). pap. 24.00 *(978-0-86626-017-6(X))* AAIMS Pubs.

Michael. The Book of Michael of Rhodes Vol. 3: A Fifteenth-Century Maritime Manuscript. Stahl, Alan M. et al, eds. 2009. (ITA & ENG., Illus.). 384p. (gr. 17). 45.00 *(978-0-262-12308-2(8))* MIT Pr.

Michael, et al. The Book of Michael of Rhodes Vol. 1: A Fifteenth-Century Maritime Manuscript. McGee, David et al, eds. Stahl, Alan M., tr. fac. ed. 2009. (ITA & ENG., Illus.). 534p. (gr. 17). 65.00 *(978-0-262-13503-0(5))* MIT Pr.

Mueller, Ian, tr. from GEC. Simplicius: On Aristitle on the Heavens 3. 7-4. 6. 2009. (Ancient Commentators on Aristotle Ser.). 192p. 130.00 *(978-0-7156-3844-6(0))* Duckworth Publishers GBR. Dist: International Publishers Marketing.

—Simplicius: On the Heavens 3. 1-7. 2009. (Ancient Commentators on Aristotle Ser.). 192p. 130.00 *(978-0-7156-3843-9(2))* Duckworth Publishers GBR. Dist: International Publishers Marketing.

Sarma, K.V., et al. Ganita-Yukti-Bhasa (Rationales in Mathematical Astronomy) of Jyesthadeva: Volume I: MathematicsVolume II: Astronomy, 2 vols. 2009. (Sources & Studies in the History of Mathematics & Physical Sciences Ser.). (MAL & ENG., Illus.). lxviii, 1084p. 219.00 *(978-1-84882-072-2(0))* Springer.

Van Gent, Robert H. The Finest Atlas of the Heavens: Harmonia Macrocosmica of 1660: The Finest Atlas of the Heavens. 2006. (FRE, GER & ENG., Illus.). 208p. 150.00 *(978-3-8228-5290-3(2))* TASCHEN DEU. Dist: Ingram Pub. Services.

The check digit for ISBN-10 appears in parentheses after the full ISBN-13

Vollmann, William T. Uncentering the Earth: Copernicus & the Revolutions of the Heavenly Spheres. 2007. (Great Discoveries Ser.). (ENG., Illus.). 304p. per. 15.95 *(978-0-393-32918-6(6)*, 32918) Norton, W. W. & Co., Inc.

ASTRONOMY—EPHEMERIDES

see Ephemerides; Nautical Almanacs

ASTRONOMY—HISTORY

Ansari, S. M., ed. History of Oriental Astronomy. 2010. (Astrophysics & Space Science Library). 308p. pap. 249.00 *(978-90-481-6033-4(2)*, 9048160332) Springer.

Ashbrook, Joseph. The Astronomical Scrapbook: Skywatchers, Pioneers & Seekers in Astronomy. 2009. (ENG.). 484p. pap. 95.00 *(978-0-521-10604-7(4))* Cambridge Univ. Pr.

Ashworth, William B., Jr. Further Out: An Exhibition from the Collections of the Linda Hall Library. 2007. 10.00 *(978-0-9763590-3-6(0))* Linda Hall Library.

Aubin, David, et al, eds. The Heavens on Earth: Observatories & Astronomy in Nineteenth-Century Science & Culture. 2010. (Science & Cultural Theory Ser.). (ENG., Illus.). 400p. 94.95 *(978-0-8223-4628-9(1))*; pap. 26.95 *(978-0-8223-4640-1(0))* Duke Univ. Pr.

Aughton, Peter. The Story of Anatomy: From Babylonian Stargazers to the Search for the Big Bang. 2009. (ENG., Illus.). 256p. 14.99 *(978-1-84724-186-3(7)*, 1847241867) Quercus GBR. Dist: Book Sales, Inc.

Aughton, Peter. The Transit of Venus: The Brief, Brilliant Life of Jeremiah Horrocks, Father of British Astronomy. 2012. (Illus.). 256p. pap. 13.95 ***(978-1-85936-214-3(1))*** International Publishers Marketing.

Aveni, Anthony. People & the Sky: Our Ancestors & the Cosmos. 2008. (ENG., Illus.). 252p. 29.95 *(978-0-500-05152-8(6))* Thames & Hudson.

Ball, R S. Great Astronomers. 2010. 196p. 30.36 *(978-1-169-28395-4(0))*; pap. 18.36 *(978-1-162-66489-7(4))* Kessinger Publishing, LLC.

Ball, R. s. & Ball, R S. Great Astronomers. 2010. 196p. 37.95 *(978-1-161-43354-8(6))* Kessinger Publishing, LLC.

Ball, Robert S. Great Astronomers. 2010. 394p. pap. 33.75 *(978-1-177-75973-1(X))*; (ENG.). 388p. pap. 33.75 *(978-1-174-88311-8(1))* BiblioBazaar.

—Great Astronomers. 2010. (Illus.). 156p. pap. 24.39 *(978-1-153-62514-2(8))* Genera Bks. LLC.

Ball, Robert Stawell. Great Astronomers. 2010. 394p. pap. 33.75 *(978-1-145-45429-3(1))* 2008. 264p. 28.99 *(978-0-554-26797-5(7))* 2008. 264p. 25.99 *(978-0-554-36100-0(0))* BiblioBazaar.

—Great Astronomers. 2009. 180p. pap. *(978-1-150-34787-0(2))* Books LLC.

Barrow, John & Barrow, John D. Cosmic Imagery: Key Images in the History of Science. 2009. (ENG., Illus.). 624p. pap. 19.95 *(978-0-393-33799-0(5)*, 33799) Norton, W. W. & Co., Inc.

Bartusiak, Marcia. The Day We Found the Universe. (Vintage Ser.). (Illus.). 368p. 2010. (ENG.). pap. 16.95 *(978-0-307-27660-5(0)*, Vintage) 2009. 27.95 *(978-0-375-42429-8(6)*, Pantheon) Knopf Doubleday Publishing Group.

Baum, Richard. The Haunted Observatory: Curiosities from the Astronomer's Cabinet. 2007. (ENG., Illus.). 1p. 28.98 *(978-1-59102-512-2(5))* Prometheus Bks., Pubs.

Berry, Arthur. A Short History of Astronomy. 2009. 86p. pap. *(978-0-217-31049-9(4))* Books LLC.

Bolt, Marvin. Telescopes: Through the Looking Glass. 2009. (ENG., Illus.). 238p. pap. 19.95 *(978-1-891220-06-7(3)*, Adler Planetarium, Astronomy) Antique Collectors' Club GBR. Dist: National Bk. Network.

Borelli, Arianna. Aspects of the Astrolabe: 'architectonica Ratio' in Tenth- & Eleventh-Century Europe. 2008. (Sudhoffs Archiv - Beihefte (SAr-B) Ser.). (ENG., Illus.). 272p. (C). pap. 67.00 *(978-3-515-09129-9(7))* Steiner, Franz Verlag Wiesbaden GmbH DEU. Dist: Brown, David Bk. Co., The.

Brandl, Bernhard R., et al, eds. 400 Years of Astronomical Telescopes: A Review of History, Science & Technology. 2010. xvi, 516p. 149.00 *(978-90-481-8834-5(2)*, 9048188342) Springer.

Brück, M. T. Agnes Mary Clerke & the Rise of Astrophysics. 2008. (ENG., Illus.). 286p. pap. 36.00 *(978-0-521-05579-6(2))* Cambridge Univ. Pr.

Burl, Aubrey. Prehistoric Astronomy & Ritual. 2nd ed. 2008. (Shire Archaeology Ser.). (ENG., Illus.). 72p. pap. 13.95 *(978-0-7478-0614-1(4))* Shire Pubns., Ltd. GBR. Dist: Random Hse., Inc.

Campion, Nicholas. History of Western Astrology Volume II: The Medieval & Modern Worlds. 2009. (ENG.). 392p. 32.95 *(978-1-4411-8129-9(6))* Continuum International Publishing Group, Ltd. GBR. Dist: National Bk. Network.

Christensen, Lars Lindberg & Schilling, Govert. Eyes on the Skies: 400 Years of Telescopic Discovery. 2009. (ENG., Illus.). 132p. 31.95 *(978-3-527-40865-8(7)*, Wiley-VCH) Wiley, John & Sons, Inc.

Clerke, Agnes M. A Popular History of Astronomy During the Nineteenth Century. 2009. (Illus.). 384p. pap. *(978-1-4068-2922-8(6))* Echo Library.

—A Popular History of Astronomy During the Nineteenth Century. 2008. 604p. 59.95 *(978-0-548-99931-8(7))* 2007. (ENG.). 608p. per. 44.95 *(978-0-548-64721-9(6))* Kessinger Publishing, LLC.

Clerke, Agnes Mary. The Herschels & Modern Astronomy. 2010. (Cambridge Library Collection - Physical Sciences Ser.). (ENG., Illus.). 236p. pap. 24.00 *(978-1-108-01392-5(9))* Cambridge Univ. Pr.

—A Popular History of Astronomy During the Nineteenth Century. 2010. (Cambridge Library Collection - Physical Sciences Ser.). (ENG.). 488p. pap. 35.99 *(978-1-108-01432-8(1))* Cambridge Univ. Pr.

Cohen, Richard. Chasing the Sun: The Epic Story of the Star That Gives Us Life. 2011. (ENG., Illus.). 608p. pap. 20.00 *(978-0-8129-8092-9(1)*, Random Hse. Trade Paperbacks) Random House Publishing Group.

—Chasing the Sun: The Epic Story of the Star That Gives Us Life. 2010. (ENG., Illus.). 608p. 35.00 *(978-1-4000-6875-3(4))* Random Hse., Inc.

Consolmagno, Guy, ed. The Heavens Proclaim: Astronomy & the Vatican. 2009. (Illus.). 231p. 39.95 *(978-1-59276-645-1(5))* Our Sunday Visitor, Publishing Div.

Couper, Heather & Henbest, Nigel. The History of Astronomy. (ENG., Illus.). 288p. 2009. pap. 29.95 *(978-1-55407-537-9(8))* 2007. 59.95 *(978-1-55407-325-2(1))* Firefly Bks., Ltd.

De Padova, Thomas. Das Weltgeheimnis: Kepler, Galilei und die Vermessung des Himmels. 2009. (GER., Illus.). 351p. pap. *(978-3-492-25861-6(1))* Piper Verlag GmbH.

De Padova, Thomas & Padova, Thomas de. Das Weltgeheimnis: Kepler, Galilei und die Vermessung des Himmels. 2009. (GER., Illus.). 351p. *(978-3-492-05172-9(3))* Piper Verlag GmbH.

Dick, Steven J., et al, eds. Cosmos & Culture: Cultural Evolution in a Cosmic Context. 2010. (ENG., Illus.). 612p. (gr. 12). 61.00 *(978-0-16-083119-5(9)*, U. S. National Aeronautics & Space Administration) United States Government Printing Office.

Dreyer, J. L. E. History of the Planetary Systems from Thales to Kepler. 2007. 436p. per. 21.95 *(978-1-60206-441-6(5))* Cosimo, Inc.

Dunn, Richard. The Telescope: A Short History. 2009. (ENG., Illus.). 192p. 25.00 *(978-1-906367-04-6(3))* National Maritime Museum GBR. Dist: Independent Pubs. Group.

Dyson, Marianne J. Space & Astronomy: Decade by Decade. Cannon, William J., ed. 2007. (Twentieth-Century Science Ser.). (Illus.). 304p. (gr. 6-12). 49.50 *(978-0-8160-5536-4(X))* Facts On File, Inc.

Fahie, John. Galileo His Life & Work. 2007. (ENG.). 500p. 53.95 *(978-0-548-04962-4(9))* Kessinger Publishing, LLC.

Faintich, Marshall. Astronomical Symbols on Ancient & Medieval Coins. 2007. (ENG., Illus.). 232p. 55.00 *(978-0-7864-3178-6(4))* McFarland & Co., Inc. Pubs.

Giacconi, Riccardo. Secrets of the Hoary Deep: A Personal History of Modern Astronomy. 2008. (ENG., Illus.). 432p. (gr. 17). 45.00 *(978-0-8018-8809-0(3))* Johns Hopkins Univ. Pr.

Gingerich, Owen. The Book Nobody Read: In Pursuit of the Revolutions of Nicolaus Copernicus. 2006. (Illus.). 306p. reprint ed. 25.00 *(978-1-4223-5738-5(4))* DIANE Publishing Co.

Gingerich, Owen, ed. The General History of Astronomy: Volume 4, Astrophysics & Twentieth-Century Astronomy to 1950: Part A. 2010. (General History of Astronomy Ser.). (ENG.). 228p. pap. 27.99 *(978-0-521-13542-9(7))* Cambridge Univ. Pr.

Goddu, André. Copernicus & the Aristotelian Tradition: Education, Reading, & Philosophy in Copernicus's Path to Heliocentrism. 2010. *(978-90-04-18107-6(5))* BRILL.

Grant, Robert. History of Physical Astronomy. 2009. 694p. pap. *(978-0-217-22252-5(8))* Books LLC.

—History of Physical Astronomy: From the Earliest Ages to the Middle of the Nineteenth Century: Comprehending a Detailed Account of the Establishment of the Theory of Gravitation by Newton, & Its Development by His Successors: With an Exposition of the Progress of Research on All the Other Subjects of Celestial Physics. 2006. *(978-1-57898-574-6(9))* Martino Publishing.

Grego, Peter & Mannion, David. Galileo & 400 Years of Telescopic Astronomy. 2010. (Astronomers' Universe Ser.). (ENG., Illus.). xii, 170p. pap. 29.95 *(978-1-4419-5570-8(4)*, 1441955704) Springer.

Haynes, Raymond, et al. Explorers of the Southern Sky: A History of Australian Astronomy. 2010. (ENG., Illus.). 541p. pap. 50.00 *(978-0-521-14491-9(4))* Cambridge Univ. Pr.

Herschel, John F. W. Preliminary Discourse on the Study of Na. 2008. pap. 28.95 *(978-1-4286-3416-9(9))* Kessinger Publishing, LLC.

Hetherington, Norriss S. Planetary Motions: A Historical Perspective, 1 vol. 2006. (Greenwood Guides to Great Ideas in Science). (Illus.). 248p. 65.00 *(978-0-313-33241-8(X)*, GR3241, Greenwood Pr.) Greenwood Publishing Group, Inc.

Hoskin, Michael. The Construction of the Heavens: William Herschel's Cosmology. 2012. (ENG., Illus.). 214p. 105.00 ***(978-1-107-01838-9(2))*** Cambridge Univ. Pr.

Jardine, Nicholas, et al. La Guerre des Astronomes: La Querelle Au Sujet de L'origine du Système Géo-Héliocentrique à la Fin du XVIe Siècle. 2008. (LAT & FRE., Illus.). (C). 286p. pap. 60.00 ***(978-2-251-34513-0(2))***; 852p. pap. 128.00 ***(978-2-251-34512-3(4))*** Societe d'edition Les Belles lettres FRA. Dist: ISD.

Johns Hopkins University Press Staff. Aristotle Leads the Way. 2007. (Story of Science Ser.). (ENG.). 440p. pap. 49.95 *(978-1-58834-251-5(4))* Smithsonian Institution Pr.

Kragh, Helge. The Moon That Wasn't. 2008. (Science Networks. Historical Studies). (Illus.). 220p. 69.95 *(978-3-7643-8908-6(7))* Birkhauser Verlag AG CHE. Dist: Springer.

Lemonick, Michael. The Georgian Star: How William & Caroline Herschel Revolutionized Our Understanding of the Cosmos. 2009. (Great Discoveries Ser.). (ENG., Illus.). 208p. pap. 14.95 *(978-0-393-33709-9(X)*, 33709) Norton, W. W. & Co., Inc.

Linton, C. M. From Eudoxus to Einstein: A History of Mathematical Astronomy. 2007. (ENG., Illus.). 532p. pap. 69.00 *(978-0-521-04571-1(1))* Cambridge Univ. Pr.

Magli, Giulio. Mysteries & Discoveries of Archaeoastronomy: From Pre-History to Easter Island. 2009. (Illus.). 300p. 27.50 *(978-0-387-76564-8(6)*, 0387765646, Copernicus) Springer.

McCray, W. Patrick. Keep Watching the Skies! The Story of Operation Moonwatch & the Dawn of the Space Age. 2008. (ENG., Illus.). 324p. (C). 31.95 *(978-0-691-12854-2(5))* Princeton Univ. Pr.

Methuen, Charlotte. Science & Theology in the Reformation: Studies in Interpretations of Astronomical Observation in Sixteenth-Century Germany. 2008. (ENG.). 144p. 120.00 *(978-0-567-03271-3(X)*, T&T Clark Int'l) Continuum International Publishing Group, Ltd. GBR. Dist: National Bk. Network.

Milhorn, H. Thomas. The History of Astronomy & Astrophysics: A Biographical Approach. 2008. 340p. pap. 15.95 *(978-1-60264-258-4(3))* Virtualbookworm.com Publishing, Inc.

Mioc, Vasile. Exploring the Solar System & the Universe. Mioc, Vasile et al, eds. 2008. (AIP Conference Proceedings / Astronomy & Astrophysics Ser.). 452p. 229.00 *(978-0-7354-0571-4(9))* American Institute of Physics.

Moore, Patrick. Watchers of the Stars: The Story of a Revolution. 3rd ed. 2009. (ENG.). 200p. pap. 25.00 *(978-1-904275-44-2(3)*, Horwood Publishing, Ltd.) Woodhead Publishing Ltd. GBR. Dist: Ingram Pub. Services.

—Watchers of the Stars: The Story of a Revolution. 3rd rev. ed. 2009. (ENG., Illus.). 200p. 60.00 *(978-1-904275-36-7(2)*, Horwood Publishing, Ltd.) Woodhead Publishing Ltd. GBR. Dist: Ingram Pub. Services.

Moreno, Marco Arturo. Historia de la Astronomia en Mexico. (Ciencia para Todos Ser.). (SPA.). pap. 6.99 *(978-968-16-4808-4(0))* Fondo de Cultura Economica USA.

Mosley, Adam. Bearing the Heavens: Tycho Brahe & the Astronomical Community of the Late Sixteenth Century. 2011. (ENG.). 370p. pap. 45.00 ***(978-1-107-40365-9(0))*** Cambridge Univ. Pr.

Murdin, Paul. Mapping the Universe: The Interactive History of Astronomy. 2011. (ENG., Illus.). 124p. 39.95 *(978-1-84732-915-8(2))* Carlton Bks., Ltd. GBR. Dist: Sterling Publishing Co., Inc.

—Secrets of the Universe: How We Discovered the Cosmos. 2009. (ENG., Illus.). 342p. 49.00 *(978-0-226-55143-2(1))* Univ. of Chicago Pr.

Murphy, Anthony & Moore, Richard. Island of the Setting Sun: In Search of Ireland's Ancient Astronomers. 2nd rev. ed. 2009. (ENG., Illus.). 352p. pap. 47.95 *(978-1-905785-47-6(X))* Liffey Pr., The IRL. Dist: Dufour Editions, Inc.

Orchiston, Wayne, et al, eds. Highlighting the History of Astronomy in the Asia-Pacific Region: Proceedings of the ICOA-6 Conference. 2011. (Astrophysics & Space Science Proceedings Ser.). (ENG., Illus.). xv, 660p. 259.00 *(978-1-4419-8160-8(8)*, 1441981608) Springer.

Pecker, Jean-Claude. Understanding the Heavens: Thirty Centuries of Astronomical Ideas from Ancient Thinking to Modern Cosmology. 2010. (ENG., Illus.). xiii, 597p. pap. 79.95 *(978-3-642-08325-9(0)*, 3642083250) Springer.

Penprase, Bryan E. The Power of Stars: How Celestial Observations Have Shaped Civilization. 2011. (Illus.). xi, 347p. E-Book ***(978-1-4419-6803-6(2))*** Springer.

Rees, Tony. Arc of the Medicine Line: Mapping the World's Largest Undefended Border Across the Western Plains. 2007. (Illus.). 384p. *(978-1-55365-278-6(9))* D&M Pubs. Inc.

—Arc of the Medicine Line: Mapping the World's Longest Undefended Border Across the Western Plains. 2008. (ENG., Illus.). 426p. 29.95 *(978-0-8032-1791-1(9))* Univ. of Nebraska Pr.

Robert S. Sir, Ball. Great Astronomers. 2007. (ENG.). 238p. pap. 20.99 *(978-1-4346-1746-0(7))* BiblioBazaar.

Samso, Julio. Astronomy & Astrology in al-Andalus & the Maghrib. 2007. (Variorum Collected Studies). (Illus.). 382p. 170.00 *(978-0-7546-5934-1(8))* Ashgate Publishing Co.

Schilling, Govert. Atlas of Astronomical Discoveries. 2011. (ENG., Illus.). ix, 234p. 39.95 *(978-1-4419-7810-3(0)*, 1441978100) Springer.

—The Hunt for Planet X: New Worlds & the Fate of Pluto. (ENG., Illus.). xi, 281p. 2010. pap. 27.50 *(978-1-4419-2667-8(4)*, 1441926674) 2008. 27.50 *(978-0-387-77804-8(7)*, 0387778047) Springer.

Schultz, David. The Andromeda Galaxy & the Rise of Modern Astronomy. 2012. (Astronomers' Universe Ser.). (ENG., Illus.) xii, 271p. pap. 34.95 ***(978-1-4614-3048-3(8)***, 1461430488) Springer.

Sheehan, William. The Immortal Fire Within: The Life & Work of Edward Emerson Barnard. 2007. (ENG., Illus.). 444p. pap. 84.00 *(978-0-521-04601-5(7))* Cambridge Univ. Pr.

—A Passion for the Planets: Envisioning Other Worlds, from the Pleistocene to the Age of the Telescope. 2010. (ENG., Illus.). vi, 194p. pap. 34.95 *(978-1-4419-5970-6(X)*, 144195970X) Springer.

Shkodrov, V. Etiudi Po Istoriia Na Astronomiiata. 2010. (BUL., Illus.). 251p. *(978-954-322-366-4(1))* Drinov, Marin Akedem izdatelstvo.

Sobel, Dava. A More Perfect Heaven: How Copernicus Revolutionized the Cosmos. 2011. (ENG., Illus.). 288p. 25.00 *(978-0-8027-1793-1(4))* Walker & Co.

Steele, John M. Calendars & Years: Astronomy & Time in the Ancient near East. 2010. (ENG., Illus.). 176p. (C). per. 50.00 *(978-1-84217-302-2(2))* Oxbow Bks., Ltd. GBR. Dist: Brown, David Bk. Co., The.

Stetson, Harlan True. Man & the Stars. 2007. (ENG.). 260p. 42.95 *(978-0-548-08130-3(1))* Kessinger Publishing, LLC.

Taton, René & Wilson, Curtis, eds. The General History of Astronomy: Volume 2, Planetary Astronomy from the Renaissance to the Rise of Astrophysics. 2009. (General History of Astronomy Ser.). (ENG., Illus.). 296p. (C). pap. 46.00 *(978-0-521-12009-8(8))* Cambridge Univ. Pr.

Thoren, Victor E. The Lord of Uraniborg: A Biography of Tycho Brahe. 2007. (ENG., Illus.). 536p. pap. 100.00 *(978-0-521-03307-7(1))* Cambridge Univ. Pr.

Udías, Agustín. Searching the Heavens & the Earth: the History of Jesuit Observatories: The History of Jesuit Observatories. 2010. (Astrophysics & Space Science Library). 388p. pap. 269.00 *(978-90-481-6252-9(1)*, 9048162521) Springer.

Waerden, H. van der. Science Awakening Ii. 2010. 368p. pap. 299.00 *(978-90-481-8247-3(6)*, 9048182476) Springer.

Westman, Robert S. The Copernican Question: Prognostication, Skepticism, & Celestial Order. 2011. (ENG., Illus.). 720p. 95.00 *(978-0-520-25481-7(3))* Univ. of California Pr.

Wulf, Andrea. Chasing Venus: The Race to Measure the Heavens. 2012. (ENG., Illus.). 336p. 26.95 ***(978-0-307-70017-9(8)***, Knopf) Knopf Doubleday Publishing Group.

York, Donald G., et al, eds. The Astronomy Revolution: 400 Years of Exploring the Cosmos. 2011. (ENG., Illus.). 450p. 79.95 *(978-1-4398-3600-2(0)*, Taylor & Francis) Taylor & Francis Group GBR. Dist: Taylor & Francis Group.

Yount, Lisa. Modern Astronomy: Expanding the Universe. 2006. (Milestones in Discovery & Invention Ser.). (Illus.). 224p. (YA). (gr. 7-12). 35.00 *(978-0-8160-5746-7(X))* Facts On File, Inc.

ASTRONOMY—JUVENILE LITERATURE

Snedden, Robert. How Do Scientists Explore Space?, 1 vol. 2011. (Earth, Space, & Beyond Ser.). (ENG.). 48p. (gr. 3-9). pap. 8.99 *(978-1-4109-4182-4(5)*, Raintree Freestyle Express) Heinemann-Raintree.

ASTRONOMY—LABORATORY MANUALS

Gordon. Astronomy Online Laboratory - Text. 4th rev. ed. 2010. 186p. spiral bd. 43.14 *(978-0-7575-5011-9(8))* Kendall Hunt Publishing Co.

Hall, Georgiana. Solar Astronomy: A Customized Version of Contemporary Activities in Astronomy by Darrel B. Hoff & Jeffrey A. Wilkinson Designed Specifically for Georgiana Hall at Fiu. 2nd rev. ed. 2012. (ENG.). 94p. spiral bd., lab manual ed. 61.00 ***(978-0-7575-9576-9(6))*** Kendall Hunt Publishing Co.

Haogland, Margie. Astonomy 109 Lab Manual. 2007. 148p. (C). spiral bd. 27.03 *(978-0-7442-6413-5(8))* Montezuma Publishing.

Hoff, Darrel B. & Wilkerson, Jeffrey A. Contemporary Activities in Astronomy: A Process Approach. 4th rev. ed. 2011. (ENG.). 318p. spiral bd. 63.16 *(978-0-7575-6691-2(X))* Kendall Hunt Publishing Co.

Jandorf, Harold. Experiences in Astronomy Laboratory Manual. 3rd rev. ed. 2010. (ENG.). 234p. spiral bd. 74.03 *(978-0-7575-7003-2(8))* Kendall Hunt Publishing Co.

Jones, Lauren. Observation Exercises in Astronomy. 2010. (ENG.). 208p. (C). pap. 42.87 *(978-0-321-63812-0(3))* Benjamin-Cummings Publishing Co.

Kielkopf, John F. Introductory Astronomy Laboratory. 3rd rev. ed. 2010. (ENG.). 252p. spiral bd. 43.86 *(978-0-7575-4741-6(9))* Kendall Hunt Publishing Co.

Naylor, John. Out of the Blue: A 24-Hour Skywatcher's Guide. 2008. 360p. 40.00 *(978-1-4379-6362-5(5))* DIANE Publishing Co.

Regas, James L. Introductory Astronomy Laboratory Exercises. 8th rev. ed. 2008. 178p. spiral bd. 47.99 *(978-0-7575-4611-2(0))* Kendall Hunt Publishing Co.

Shaw, J. Scott & Dittmann, Mariam. Laboratory Textbook for Elementary Astronomy. 8th ed. (Illus.). 200p. (C). pap., lab manual ed. 27.95 *(978-0-89892-200-4(3))* Contemporary Publishing Co. of Raleigh, Inc.

Taylor, Gregory & Regas, James L. Introductory Astronomy Laboratory Exercises. 9th rev. ed. 2009. (ENG.). 98p. spiral bd. 41.99 *(978-0-7575-6150-4(0))* Kendall Hunt Publishing Co.

UNT. Astronomy 1051: Laboratory Experiments. 2007. (Illus.). (C). per. *(978-0-9774658-8-0(8))* Univ. of North Texas Copy Ctr.

—Astronomy 1061: Laboratory Experiments. 2007. (Illus.). (C). per. *(978-0-9774658-9-7(6))* Univ. of North Texas Copy Ctr.

Whitlock, Laura A. & Pulliam, Kiley. Listen Up! Laboratory Exercises for Introductory Radio Astronomy with a Small Radio Telescope. 2008. 60p. pap. 10.95 *(978-1-4401-0784-9(X)*, iUniverse, Inc.

Wilson, John. Astronomy: A Laboratory Textbook. 3rd ed. (Illus.). 200p. (C). pap. 32.95 *(978-0-89892-202-8(X))* Contemporary Publishing Co. of Raleigh, Inc.

ASTRONOMY—MISCELLANEA

Baum, Richard. The Haunted Observatory: Curiosities from the Astronomer's Cabinet. 2007. (ENG., Illus.). 1p. 28.98 *(978-1-59102-512-2(5))* Prometheus Bks., Pubs.

Bely, Pierre-Yves, et al. A Question & Answer Guide to Astronomy. 2010. (ENG., Illus.). 294p. pap. 28.99 *(978-0-521-18066-5(X))* Cambridge Univ. Pr.

Cardona, Dwardu. Primordial Star. 2009. 394p. pap. 85.51 *(978-1-4251-8850-4(8))* Trafford Publishing.

Faintich, Marshall. Astronomical Symbols on Ancient & Medieval Coins. (ENG., Illus.). 232p. 2007. 55.00 *(978-0-7864-3178-6(4))* 2012. pap. 25.00 ***(978-0-7864-6915-4(3))*** McFarland & Co., Inc. Pubs.

Flynn, Michael. Whitaker's Almanack Little Book of Astronomy. 2007. (Whitaker's Ser.). (ENG., Illus.). 144p. 16.95 *(978-0-7136-8237-3(X))* A & C Black GBR. Dist: Macmillan.

Fort, Charles. The Book of the Damned. 2008. 356p. 29.99 *(978-0-554-39390-2(5))* 2008. 356p. 31.99 *(978-0-554-30067-0(7))* 2007. (ENG.). 316p. per. 23.99 *(978-1-4346-9146-0(2))* BiblioBazaar.

—The Book of the Damned. 2009. 346p. pap. *(978-1-4099-8051-3(0))* Dodo Pr.

—The Book of the Damned. 2007. (ENG.). 420p. per. 12.99 *(978-1-59986-753-3(2))* Filiquarian Publishing, LLC.

—The Book of the Damned. 2011. 280p. 29.95 ***(978-1-4638-9700-0(6))***; pap. 15.95 ***(978-1-60664-445-4(9))*** Rodgers, Alan Bks.

—The Book of the Damned. 2009. (ENG.). 296p. pap. 18.95 *(978-1-4385-2446-7(3)*, Book Jungle) Standard Pubns., Inc.

—The Book of the Damned. 2007. (ENG.). 220p. per. 12.99 *(978-1-60459-107-1(2))* Wilder Pubns., Ltd.

—The Book of the Damned. 2007. (ENG.). 232p. 24.95 *(978-1-4344-8210-5(3))*; per. 14.95 *(978-1-4344-8209-9(X))* Wildside Pr., LLC.

—Book of the Damned. 2006. 31.95 *(978-1-60206-008-1(8)*, Cosimo Classics) Cosimo, Inc.

—The Book of the Damned. rev. ed. 2007. (ENG.). 354p. per. 26.99 *(978-1-4346-9147-7(0))* BiblioBazaar.

—The Charles Fort Reader: The Book of the Damned, New Lands, Wild Talents, Lo! 2008. 652p. pap. 24.95 *(978-1-60459-582-6(5))* Wilder Pubns., Ltd.

James, C. Renée. Seven Wonders of the Universe That You Probably Took for Granted. 2010. (ENG., Illus.). 256p. (C). (gr. 13-17). 70.00 *(978-0-8018-9797-9(1))*; pap. 25.00 *(978-0-8018-9798-6(X))* Johns Hopkins Univ. Pr.

Lebans, Jim. The Quirks & Quarks Guide to Space: 42 Questions (And Answers) about Life, the Universe, & Everything. 2008. (ENG., Illus.). 256p. per. 18.95 *(978-0-7710-5003-9(8)*, McClelland & Stewart) McClelland & Stewart CAN. Dist: Random Hse., Inc.

Levy, David H. Star Trails: 50 Favorite Columns from Sky & Telescope. 2007. (ENG., Illus.). 160p. pap. 24.95 *(978-1-931559-46-1(5))* Sky Publishing.

Liu, Charles. The Handy Astronomy Answer Book. 2nd ed. 2008. (Handy Answer Book Ser.). (ENG.). 352p. (gr. 7-18). pap. 21.95 *(978-1-57859-193-0(7))* Visible Ink Pr.

Nickell, Duane S. Guidebook for the Scientific Traveler: Visiting Astronomy & Space Exploration Sites Across America. 2008. (Scientific Traveler Ser.). (ENG., Illus.). 256p. pap. 21.95 *(978-0-8135-4374-1(6))* Rutgers Univ. Pr.

Ringwood, Steve. Astronomer's Anonymous: Getting Help with the Puzzles & Pitfalls of Practical Astronomy. 2010. (ENG., Illus.). xv, 222p. pap. 29.95 *(978-1-4419-5816-7(9)*, 1441958169) Springer.

Seargent, David A. J. Weird Astronomy: Tales of Unusual, Bizarre, & Other Hard to Explain Observations. 2010. (Astronomers' Universe Ser.). (Illus.). xiii, 304p. pap. 39.95 *(978-1-4419-6423-6(1)*, 1441964231) Springer.

Sims, Michael. Apollo's Fire: A Journey Through the Extraordinary Wonders of an Ordinary Day. 2008. (ENG.). 320p. (gr. 12-18). 16.00 *(978-0-14-311441-3(7)*, Penguin (Non-Classics)) Penguin Group (USA) Inc.

Whitaker, Anne. Jupiter Meets Uranus. 2009. 184p. pap. 23.95 *(978-0-86690-574-9(X))* American Federation of Astrologers, Inc.

ASTRONOMY—OBSERVATIONS

see also Astronomical Observatories

Atad-Ettedgui, Eli. Modern Technologies in Space- & Ground-Based Telescopes & Instrumentation: 27 June-2 July 2010, San Diego, California, United States. 2010. (Proceedings of SPIE Ser.). (Illus.). 1736p. pap. 245.00 ***(978-0-8194-8229-7(3))*** SPIE.

Barbosa, Domingos, et al, eds. 3K, SN's, Clusters: Hunting the Cosmological Parameters with Precision Cosmology: Hunting the Cosmological Parameters with Precision Cosmology. 2010. 232p. pap. 105.00 *(978-90-481-6546-9(6)*, 9048165466) Springer.

Bond, Alan & Hempsell, Mark. A Sumerian Observation of the Köfels' Impact Event. 2008. (Illus.). 128p. per. *(978-1-904623-64-9(6))* WritersPrintShop.

Chaisson, Eric. Starry Night Pro Activities & Observation & Research Projects for Astronomy Today. 6th ed. 2007. (ENG.). 320p. (C). pap. 36.20 *(978-0-13-240097-8(9))* Benjamin-Cummings Publishing Co.

Chromey, Frederick R. To Measure the Sky: An Introduction to Observational Astronomy. 2010. (ENG., Illus.). 460p. (C). 130.00 *(978-0-521-76386-8(X))*; pap. 58.00 *(978-0-521-74768-4(6))* Cambridge Univ. Pr.

Cracknell, A. P., et al, eds. Earth Observation Small Satellites for Remote Sensing Application. 2011. (ENG.). 320p. 139.00 *(978-0-415-54881-6(0)*, CRC Press) Taylor & Francis Group GBR. Dist: Taylor & Francis Group.

Cram101 Textbook Reviews. Outlines & Highlights for Observational Astronomy by D Scott Birney, Isbn: 9780521853705. 2011. 168p. pap. 29.95 ***(978-1-61812-029-8(8))*** Cram101 Inc.

Crossen, Craig & Tirion, Wil. Binocular Astronomy. 2nd ed. 2008. *(978-0-943396-88-0(3))* Willmann-Bell, Inc.

Crossley, Edward, et al. A Handbook of Double Stars: For the Use of Amateurs. 2011. (Cambridge Library Collection - Physical Sciences Ser.). (ENG., Illus.). 550p. pap. 39.99 ***(978-1-108-03977-2(4))*** Cambridge Univ. Pr.

Cuntz, Manfred, et al. Practical Universe: Observations Experiments Exercises. rev. ed. 2010. (ENG.). 406p. pap. 61.36 *(978-0-7575-7661-4(3))* Kendall Hunt Publishing Co.

Elena, Cenacchi. Full Stokes Polarimetry with the Effelsberg 100-M Radio Telescope: Application of the Jones & Stokes Formalism to the Effelsberg Telescope, Optimized to Obtained Accurate Full Stokes Measurements. 2011. 148p. pap. ***(978-3-639-31007-8(1))*** VDM Verlag Dr. Mueller e.K.

Evans, A. & et al. Rs Ophiuchi (2006) & the Recurrent Nova Phenomenon. 2009. 360p. 77.00 *(978-1-58381-674-5(7))* Astronomical Society of the Pacific, The.

Evans, Ian N., ed. Astronomical Data Analysis Software & Systems XX (Asp Conference Series) 2011. 77.00 ***(978-1-58381-764-3(6))*** Astronomical Society of the Pacific, The.

Garcia, Paulo & Ferreira, Joao, eds. Jets from Young Stars IV: From Models to Observations & Experiments. 2009. (Lecture Notes in Physics Ser.). (ENG., Illus.). viii, 252p. 89.95 *(978-3-642-02288-3(X)*, 364202288X) Springer.

Grego, Peter. Astronomical Cybersketching: Observational Drawing with PDAs & Tablet PCs. 2009. (Patrick Moore's Practical Astronomy Ser.). (ENG., Illus.). xviii, 222p. pap. 34.95 *(978-0-387-85350-5(2))* Springer.

Harrington, Philip S. Cosmic Challenge: The Ultimate Observing List for Amateurs. 2010. (ENG., Illus.). 488p. (C). 45.00 *(978-0-521-89936-9(2))* Cambridge Univ. Pr.

Jaschek, Carlos. Data in Astronomy. 2011. (ENG.). 214p. pap. 39.99 *(978-0-521-17728-3(6))* Cambridge Univ. Pr.

Lena, Pierre, et al. Observational Astrophysics. Lyle, S., tr. 2nd ed. 2010. (Astronomy & Astrophysics Library). (Illus.). xv, 512p. pap. 135.00 *(978-3-642-08336-5(6)*, 3642083366) Springer.

Léna, Pierre, et al. Observational Astrophysics. Lyle, Stephen, tr. from FRE. 3rd ed. 2012. (Astronomy & Astrophysics Library). (ENG., Illus.). xv, 719p. 179.00 ***(978-3-642-21814-9(8)***, 3642218148) Springer.

Levy, David H. Star Trails: 50 Favorite Columns from Sky & Telescope. 2007. (ENG., Illus.). 160p. pap. 24.95 *(978-1-931559-46-1(5))* Sky Publishing.

Malacara, Daniel. Telescopios y Estrellas. (Ciencia para Todos Ser.). (SPA.). pap. 6.99 *(978-968-16-2862-8(4))* Fondo de Cultura Economica USA.

Moore, Patrick. Watchers of the Stars: The Story of a Revolution. 3rd rev. ed. 2009. (ENG., Illus.). 200p. 60.00 *(978-1-904275-36-7(2)*, Horwood Publishing, Ltd.) Woodhead Publishing Ltd. GBR. Dist: Ingram Pub. Services.

Ockerl, Betty May. The Mysterious Lindsey Lights: One Family's True Encounters with Strange Lights in the Sky near Lindsey, Wisconsin. 2011. pap. 11.95 ***(978-0-533-16399-1(4))*** Vantage Pr., Inc.

O'Meara, James. Deep-Sky Companions: The Messier Objects. 34.95 *(978-0-933346-85-7(9))* Sky Publishing.

Ratcliff, Jessica. The Transit of Venus Enterprise in Victorian Britain, 1 vol., 1. 2008. (Science & Culture in the Nineteenth Century Ser.). (ENG., Illus.). 320p. 99.00 *(978-1-85196-541-0(6))* Pickering & Chatto Pubs., Ltd. GBR. Dist: Ashgate Publishing Co.

Sheehan, William. A Passion for the Planets: Envisioning Other Worlds, from the Pleistocene to the Age of the Telescope. 2010. (ENG., Illus.). vi, 194p. pap. 34.95 *(978-1-4419-5970-6(X)*, 144195970X) Springer.

Sims, Michael. Apollo's Fire: A Journey Through the Extraordinary Wonders of an Ordinary Day. 2008. (ENG.). 320p. (gr. 12-18). 16.00 *(978-0-14-311441-3(7)*, Penguin (Non-Classics)) Penguin Group (USA) Inc.

Sutton, Edmund C. Observational Astronomy: Techniques & Instrumentation. 2011. (ENG., Illus.). 428p. (C). 75.00 ***(978-1-107-01046-8(2))*** Cambridge Univ. Pr.

Tsvetkov, M., ed. Virtual Observatory: Plate Content Digitization, Archive Mining & Image Sequence Processing: Proceedings of the International Workshop. 2006. (Illus.). 197.50 *(978-954-580-190-7(5))* Heron Pr. BGR. Dist: Coronet Bks.

Wepster, Steven. Between Theory & Observations: Tobias Mayer's Explorations of Lunar Motion, 1751-1755. 2009. (Sources & Studies in the History of Mathematics & Physical Sciences Ser.). (ENG., Illus.). xiv, 246p. 139.00 *(978-1-4419-1313-5(0)*, 1441913130) Springer.

ASTRONOMY—OBSERVATORIES

see Astronomical Observatories

ASTRONOMY—OBSERVERS' MANUALS

Aranda, Ted. 3,000 Deep-Sky Objects: An Annotated Catalogue. 2011. (Patrick Moore's Practical Astronomy Ser.). (ENG., Illus.). xii, 563p. pap. 44.95 *(978-1-4419-9418-9(1)*, 1441994181) Springer.

Bratton, Mark. The Complete Guide to the Herschel Objects: Sir William Herschel's Star Clusters, Nebulae & Galaxies. 2011. (ENG., Illus.). 592p. (C). 70.00 ***(978-0-521-76892-4(6))*** Cambridge Univ. Pr.

Broxton, Tony. Solar Observer's Handbook. 2009. (Illus.). 132p. pap. 38.49 *(978-1-4389-1140-3(8))* AuthorHouse.

Brunowe, Marion J. A Famous Convent School. 2007. (ENG.). 172p. 37.95 *(978-0-548-04138-3(5))* Kessinger Publishing, LLC.

Consolmagno, Guy & Davis, Dan M. Turn Left at Orion: A Hundred Night Sky Objects for Beginners - And How to Find Them. 4th rev. ed. 2011. (ENG., Illus.). 256p. (C). spiral bd. 28.99 ***(978-0-521-15397-3(2))*** Cambridge Univ. Pr.

Denning, William Frederik. Telescopic Work for Starlight Evenings. 2010. (Cambridge Library Collection - Physical Sciences Ser.). (ENG., Illus.). 384p. pap. 31.99 *(978-1-108-01413-7(5))* Cambridge Univ. Pr.

Dickinson, Terence & Dyer, Alan. The Backyard Astronomer's Guide. 3rd rev. ed. 2008. (ENG., Illus.). 368p. 49.95 *(978-1-55407-344-3(8))* Firefly Bks., Ltd.

Farinacci, Jeff A. Guide to Observing Deep-Sky Objects: A Complete Global Resource for Astronomers. 2007. (Patrick Moore's Practical Astronomy Ser.). (Illus.). 196p. pap. 29.95 incl. cd-rom *(978-0-387-72850-6(3)*, 0387728503) Springer.

French, Sue. Celestial Sampler: 60 Small-Scope Tours for Starlit Nights. 2007. (Stargazing Ser.). (ENG., Illus.). 170p. per. 24.95 *(978-1-931559-28-7(7))* Sky Publishing.

—Deep-Sky Wonders: A Tour of the Universe with Sky & Telescope's Sue French. 2011. (Illus.). 320p. 39.95 *(978-1-55407-793-9(1))* Firefly Bks., Ltd.

Garlick, Mark A. Astronomy: A Visual Guide. 2009. (ENG., Illus.). 304p. pap. 27.95 *(978-1-55407-460-0(6))* Firefly Bks., Ltd.

Gendler, Robert. A Year in the Life of the Universe: A Seasonal Guide to Viewing the Cosmos. rev. ed. 2006. (ENG., Illus.). 160p. 24.95 *(978-0-7603-2642-8(8)*, 0760326428, Voyageur Pr) MBI Publishing Co. LLC.

Graun, Ken. What's Out Tonight? 50 Year Astronomy Field Guide, 2000 to 2050. 368p. pap. 29.95 *(978-1-928771-14-2(9))* Ken Pr.

Green, Jane. Astronomy Manual: The Complete Step-by-Step Guide. 2011. (Owners Workshop Manual Ser.). (ENG., Illus.). 160p. 34.95 *(978-1-84425-821-5(1)*, 1844258211) Haynes Publishing PLC GBR. Dist: MBI Distribution Services/Quayside Distribution.

Grego, Peter. Venus & Mercury, & How to Observe Them. 2007. (Astronomers' Observing Guides). (Illus.). 262p. pap. 34.95 *(978-0-387-74285-4(9)*, 0387742859) Springer.

Heim, Dan. Easy Field Guide to the Arizona Night Sky. 2006. (Easy Field Guides). (Illus.). 32p. pap. 1.75 *(978-0-935810-78-3(1)*, Primer Pubs.) American Traveler Pr.

—Easy Field Guide to the New Mexico Night Sky. 2006. (Easy Field Guides). (Illus.). 32p. pap. 1.75 *(978-0-935810-79-0(X)*, Primer Pubs.) American Traveler Pr.

Horkheimer, Jack & O'Meara, Stephen J. Stargazing with Jack Horkheimer: Cosmic Comics for the Sky Watcher. 2007. (ENG., Illus.). 96p. (J). (gr. 3-9). 19.95 *(978-0-8126-7933-5(4))* Cricket Bks.

Inglis, Michael D. A Field Guide to Deep-Sky Objects. 2nd ed. 2011. (Patrick Moore's Practical Astronomy Ser.). (ENG., Illus.). xvii, 261p. pap. 39.95 ***(978-1-4614-1265-6(X)***, 146141265X) Springer.

James, Mathew. The Original Prophecy. 2011. 156p. pap. 16.95 ***(978-1-60844-463-2(5))*** Dog Ear Publishing, LLC.

Kambic, Bojan. Viewing the Constellations with Binoculars: 250+ Wonderful Sky Objects to See & Explore. 2010. (Illus.). xiv, 518p. E-Book *(978-0-387-85355-0(3))* Springer.

Kinzer, Paul E. Stargazing Basics: Getting Started in Recreational Astronomy. 2008. (Illus.). 160p. pap. 18.99 *(978-0-521-72859-1(2))* Cambridge Univ. Pr.

Liller, William. The Cambridge Guide to Astronomical Discovery. 2010. (ENG., Illus.). 272p. pap. 38.99 *(978-0-521-12605-2(3))* Cambridge Univ. Pr.

Lynch, Mike. Canada Starwatch: The Essential Guide to Our Night Sky. rev. ed. 2007. (ENG., Illus.). 160p. spiral bd. 26.95 *(978-0-7603-3123-1(5)*, 0760331235, Voyageur Pr) MBI Publishing Co. LLC.

Martinez, Patrick, ed. The Observer's Guide to Astronomy, 2 vols. Dunlop, Storm, tr. 2008. (Practical Astronomy Handbooks Ser.). (Illus.). 272p. 90.00 *(978-0-521-38075-1(8))* Cambridge Univ. Pr.

Maunder, Michael, et al. Lights in the Sky: Identifying & Understanding Astronomical & Meteorological Phenomena. 2nd ed. 2007. (Patrick Moore's Practical Astronomy Ser.). (Illus.). 226p. pap. 29.95 *(978-1-84628-562-2(3)*, 1846285623) Springer.

Mobberley, Martin. The Caldwell Objects & How to Observe Them. 2009. (Astronomers' Observing Guides). (ENG., Illus.). xiv, 288p. pap. 34.95 *(978-1-4419-0325-9(9)*, 1441903259) Springer.

—Cataclysmic Cosmic Events & How to Observe Them. 2008. (Astronomers' Observing Guides). (Illus.). 225p. pap. 34.95 *(978-0-387-79945-2(1))* Springer.

Moore, Patrick. Patrick Moore's Astronomy. 2011. (Teach Yourself Ser.). (ENG., Illus.). 276p. pap. 15.95 *(978-1-4441-0313-7(X)*, Hodder & Stoughton) Hodder General Publishing Div. GBR. Dist: Independent Pubs. Group.

Mullaney, James. The Cambridge Double Star Atlas. 2009. (ENG., Illus.). 154p. pap. 35.00 *(978-0-521-49343-7(9))* Cambridge Univ. Pr.

—The Herschel Objects & How to Observe Them. 2007. (Astronomers' Observing Guides). (Illus.). 167p. per. 32.95 *(978-0-387-68124-5(8))* Springer.

O'Byrne, John, ed. Space: A Guide to Astronomy. 2007. (Illus.). 320p. reprint ed. pap. 15.00 *(978-1-4223-6799-5(1))* DIANE Publishing Co.

O'Meara, James. Deep-Sky Companions: The Messier Objects. 34.95 *(978-0-933346-85-7(9))* Sky Publishing.

O'Meara, Stephen James. Deep-Sky Companions: the Secret Deep. 2011. (ENG., Illus.). 498p. (C). 48.00 *(978-0-521-19876-9(3))* Cambridge Univ. Pr.

—Exploring the Solar System with Binoculars: A Beginner's Guide to the Sun, Moon & Planets. 2010. (ENG., Illus.). 166p. pap. 29.99 *(978-0-521-74128-6(9))* Cambridge Univ. Pr.

—Observing the Night Sky with Binoculars: A Simple Guide to the Heavens. 2008. (ENG., Illus.). 168p. pap. 29.99 *(978-0-521-72170-7(9))* Cambridge Univ. Pr.

O'Meara, Steve. The Herschel 400 Observing Guide. 2007. (ENG., Illus.). 380p. 67.00 *(978-0-521-85893-9(3))* Cambridge Univ. Pr.

Pfleger, Thomas. Eye & Telescope V3. 0: The Deep Sky Observing Planner. 2010. (C). 75.00 *(978-0-521-15115-3(5))* Cambridge Univ. Pr.

Plotner, Tammy. The Night Sky Companion: A Yearly Guide to Sky-Watching. Vogt, Ken, ed. 2007. (Patrick Moore's Practical Astronomy Ser.). (Illus.). 669p. pap. 29.95 *(978-0-387-71608-4(4)*, 0387716084) Springer.

—The Night Sky Companion: A Yearly Guide to Sky-Watching, 2009-2010. 2008. (Patrick Moore's Practical Astronomy Ser.). (Illus.). 368p. pap. 39.95 *(978-0-387-79508-9(1))* Springer.

Price, Fred W. The Moon Observer's Handbook. 2009. (ENG.). 332p. pap. 69.00 *(978-0-521-11315-1(6))* Cambridge Univ. Pr.

Ramotowski, Becky. Secrets of Stargazing: Skywatching Tips & Tricks. 2007. (ENG., Illus.). 96p. pap. 13.95 *(978-1-931559-40-9(6))* Sky Publishing.

Ratcliffe, Martin & Nix, Charles. The Night Sky Revealed. 2007. (Illus.). 105p. *(978-0-7607-9327-5(1))* Barnes & Noble, Inc.

Raymo, Chet. Three Hundred & Sixty Five Starry Nights: An Introduction to Astronomy for Every Night of the Year. 2006. (Illus.). 225p. reprint ed. pap. 16.00 *(978-1-4223-5229-8(3))* DIANE Publishing Co.

Reddy, Francis. Celestial Delights: The Best Astronomical Events Through 2020. 3rd ed. 2011. (Patrick Moore's Practical Astronomy Ser.). (ENG., Illus.). xv, 423p. pap. 44.95 ***(978-1-4614-0609-9(9)***, 1461406099) Springer.

Ridpath, Ian. The Monthly Sky Guide. 8th rev. ed. 2009. (ENG., Illus.). 72p. pap. 17.00 *(978-0-521-13369-2(6))* Cambridge Univ. Pr.

Scagell, Robin. Stargazing with a Telescope. 3rd rev. ed. 2009. (ENG., Illus.). 192p. pap. 19.95 *(978-1-55407-577-5(7))* Firefly Bks., Ltd.

Scagell, Robin & Frydman, David. Stargazing with Binoculars. 2nd rev. ed. 2011. (ENG., Illus.). 208p. pap. 19.95 *(978-1-55407-821-9(0))* Firefly Bks., Ltd.

Scalzi, John & Rough Guides Staff. The Universe. 2nd ed. 2008. (Rough Guide Reference Ser.). (ENG., Illus.). 1p. (gr. 12). pap. 16.99 *(978-1-84353-800-4(8))* Rough Guides, Ltd. GBR. Dist: Dorling Kindersley Publishing, Inc.

Schaaf, Fred. The Brightest Stars: Discovering the Universe Through the Sky's Most Brilliant Stars. 2008. (ENG., Illus.). 288p. pap. 19.95 *(978-0-471-70410-2(5)*, Wiley) Wiley, John & Sons, Inc.

—The 50 Best Sights in Astronomy & How to See Them: Observing Eclipses, Bright Comets, Meteor Showers, & Other Celestial Wonders. 2007. (ENG., Illus.). 288p. pap. 19.95 *(978-0-471-69657-5(9)*, Wiley) Wiley, John & Sons, Inc.

Schmude, Richard, Jr. Uranus, Neptune, & Pluto: And How to Observe Them. 2008. (Astronomers' Observing Guides). (Illus.). XII, 232p. pap. 34.95 *(978-0-387-76601-0(4)*, 0387766014) Springer.

Schneider, Howard. Backyard Guide to the Night Sky. 2009. (Illus.). 287p. *(978-1-4262-0539-2(2))*; *(978-1-4262-0538-5(4))* National Geographic Society.

Tirion, Wil & Heifetz, Milton D. A Walk Through the Southern Sky: A Guide to Stars & Constellations & Their Legends. 2nd rev. ed. 2007. (Illus.). 109p. per. 32.99 *(978-0-521-68945-8(7))* Cambridge Univ. Pr.

Tonkin, Stephen F. Binocular Astronomy. 2006. (Patrick Moore's Practical Astronomy Ser.). (Illus.). 284p. per. 32.95 *(978-1-84628-308-6(6)*, 1846283086) Springer.

Vamplew, Anton. Stargazing Secrets. 2008. (Illus.). 176p. pap. 17.95 *(978-0-06-143494-5(9))* HarperCollins Pubs.

Webb, Thomas William. Celestial Objects for Common Telescopes. 2010. (Cambridge Library Collection - Physical Sciences Ser.). (ENG., Illus.). 272p. pap. 23.99 *(978-1-108-01407-6(0))* Cambridge Univ. Pr.

Wilkins, Jamie & Dunn, Robert. 300 Astronomical Objects: A Visual Reference to the Universe. 2006. (ENG., Illus.). 528p. 29.95 *(978-1-55407-175-3(5))* Firefly Bks., Ltd.

Winterburn, Emily. The Stargazer's Guide: How to Read Our Night Sky. 2009. 288p. pap. 15.99 *(978-0-06-178969-4(0)*, HarperPerennial) HarperCollins Pubs.

ASTRONOMY—PHILOSOPHY

see also Cosmology

Henrich, Jö, et al. Die Fixierung des Modernen Wissenschaftsideals Durch Laplace. 2010. (GER., Illus.). 247p. *(978-3-05-004663-1(5))* Akademie Verlag.

Scantamburlo, Luca. The American Armageddon. 2009. (ITA.). 259p. pap. 23.95 *(978-1-4092-8120-7(5))* Lulu Enterprises Inc.

Tymieniecka, Anna-Teresa. Astronomy & Civilization in the New Enlightenment: Passions of the Skies. Tymieniecka, Anna-Teresa & Grandpierre, Attila, eds. 2010. (Analecta Husserliana Ser.). xvi, 315p. 139.00 *(978-90-481-9747-7(3)*, 9048197473) Springer.

York, Donald G., et al, eds. The Astronomy Revolution: 400 Years of Exploring the Cosmos. 2011. (ENG., Illus.). 450p. 79.95 *(978-1-4398-3600-2(0)*, Taylor & Francis) Taylor & Francis Group GBR. Dist: Taylor & Francis Group.

ASTRONOMY—PICTORIAL WORKS

Barrow, John & Barrow, John D. Cosmic Imagery: Key Images in the History of Science. 2009. (ENG., Illus.). 624p. pap. 19.95 *(978-0-393-33799-0(5)*, 33799) Norton, W. W. & Co., Inc.

Barrow, John D. Cosmic Imagery: Key Images in the History of Science. 2008. (ENG.). 624p. 39.95 *(978-0-393-06177-2(9)*, 6177) Norton, W. W. & Co., Inc.

Bell, Jim. Moon 3-D: The Lunar Surface Comes to Life. 2009. (ENG., Illus.). 160p. 19.95 *(978-1-4027-6551-3(7))* Sterling Publishing Co., Inc.

—Postcards from Mars: The First Photographer on the Red Planet. 2010. (ENG.). 208p. (gr. 12). 30.00 *(978-0-452-29674-9(9)*, Plume) Penguin Group (USA) Inc.

de Goursac, Olivier. Walking on the Moon: A New Photographic Experience of the NASA Lunar Explorations. 2010. (ENG.). 224p. 45.00 *(978-0-9794727-8-7(4))* Five Ties Publishing.

Dunlop, Storm. Sky. 2010. (ENG., Illus.). 160p. pap. 19.95 *(978-1-86108-660-0(1))* Guild of Master Craftsman Pubns., Ltd. GBR. Dist: Sterling Publishing Co., Inc.

Fadul, Jose A. Integration of Astronomy in the Rizal Course. 2009. 69p. pap. 26.50 *(978-0-557-06940-8(8))* Lulu Enterprises Inc.

Gendler, Robert. A Year in the Life of the Universe: A Seasonal Guide to Viewing the Cosmos. rev. ed. 2006. (ENG., Illus.). 160p. 24.95 *(978-0-7603-2642-8(8)*, 0760326428, Voyageur Pr) MBI Publishing Co. LLC.

Mailer, Norman & McCann, Colum. Moonfire: The Epic Journey of Apollo 11. ltd. ed. 2009. (ENG., Illus.). 350p. 1800.00 *(978-3-8365-1179-7(7))* TASCHEN DEU. Dist: Ingram Pub. Services.

Malin, David. Ancient Light: A Portrait of the Universe. 2009. (ENG., Illus.). 128p. 49.95 *(978-0-7148-4932-4(4))* Phaidon Pr., Inc.

Mortillaro, Nicole. Saturn: Exploring the Mystery of the Ringed Planet. 2010. (ENG., Illus.). 96p. 29.95 *(978-1-55407-649-9(8))* Firefly Bks., Ltd.

Osborn, Wayne & Robbins, Lee. Preserving Astronomy's Photographic Legacy: Current State & the Future of North American Astronomical Plates: Included Are the Proceedings of a Workshop Held at the Pisgah Astronomical Research Institute, Rosman, North Carolina, USA, 1-3 November 2007.

2009. (Illus.). vii, 202p. *(978-1-58381-700-1(X)); (978-1-58381-701-8(8))* Astronomical Society of the Pacific, The.
Parker, Greg & Carboni, Noel. Star Vistas: A Collection of Fine Art Astrophotography. 2009. (ENG., Illus.). x, 158p. 39.95 *(978-0-387-88435-6(1))* Springer.
Sollett, Rob. Space Tripping. 2008. 43p. pap. 19.95 *(978-1-4357-3691-7(5))* Lulu Enterprises Inc.
Sparrow, Giles. Cosmos Close-Up. 2011. (ENG., Illus.). 320p. 29.95 *(978-1-55407-891-2(1))* Firefly Bks., Ltd.

ASTRONOMY—POPULAR WORKS

Adair, Rick, ed. Scientific Information about the Universe & the Scientific Theories of the Evolution of the Universe: An Anthology of Current Thought. 2009. (Contemporary Discourse in the Field of Astronomy Ser.). (ENG.). 240p. (gr. 10-10). 63.90 *(978-1-61511-905-9(1))* Rosen Publishing Group, Inc., The.
Becan, Jeff. Astronomy for Beginners. 2008. (For Beginners Ser.). (ENG., Illus.). 160p. per. 16.99 *(978-1-934389-25-6(0),* For Beginners) Steerforth Pr.
Cooper, Chris. Everything You Need to Know about the Universe: The Big Bang, the Big Crunch & Everything in Between. 2012. (Everything You Need to Know Ser.). (ENG., Illus.). 224p. pap. 19.95 ***(978-1-60710-359-2(1)**,* Thunder Bay Pr.) Advantage Pubs. Group.
Dickinson, Terence. The Universe & Beyond. 5th rev. ed. 2010. (ENG., Illus.). 204p. 45.00 *(978-1-55407-640-6(4));* pap. 29.95 *(978-1-55407-748-9(6))* Firefly Bks., Ltd.
Ellyard, David & Tirion, Wil. The Southern Sky Guide. 3rd rev. ed. 2008. (ENG., Illus.). 104p. pap. 26.00 *(978-0-521-71405-1(2))* Cambridge Univ. Pr.
Garlick, Mark A. Astronomy: A Visual Guide. 2009. (ENG., Illus.). 304p. pap. 27.95 *(978-1-55407-460-0(6))* Firefly Bks., Ltd.
Glasby, John S. Boundaries of the Universe. 2008. (Routledge Library Editions: History & Philosophy of Science Ser.). (ENG.). 320p. (C). 150.00 *(978-0-415-47482-5(5))* Routledge.
Grego, Peter. Exploring the Earth. 2008. (Qeb Space Guides). (Illus.). 32p. (J). (gr. 3-7). lib. bdg. 19.95 *(978-1-59566-383-2(5))* QEB Publishing Inc.
—Voyage Through Space. 2008. (Qeb Space Guides). (Illus.). 32p. (J). (gr. 3-7). lib. bdg. 19.95 *(978-1-59566-385-6(1))* QEB Publishing Inc.
Heidorn, Keith C. & Whitelaw, Ian. The Field Guide to Natural Phenomena: The Secret World of Optical, Atmospheric & Celestial Wonders. 2010. (ENG., Illus.). 224p. pap. 24.95 *(978-1-55407-707-6(9))* Firefly Bks., Ltd.
Hockey, Thomas A. How We See the Sky: A Naked-Eye Tour of Day & Night. 2011. (ENG., Illus.). 224p. pap. 20.00 *(978-0-226-34577-2(7));* 60.00 *(978-0-226-34576-5(9))* Univ. of Chicago Pr.
Martin, Stephan. Cosmic Conversations. 2009. (ENG.). 1p. pap. 16.99 *(978-1-60163-077-3(8),* New Page Bks.) Career Pr., Inc.
Moore, Patrick & Lawrence, Pete. The 21st Century Astronomer: The Practical Guide to Observing & Photographing the Moon, Sun, Planets, Stars & Beyond in the Digital Imaging Age. 2012. (ENG., Illus.). 192p. 34.95 ***(978-1-78097-064-6(1))*** Carlton Bks., Ltd. GBR. Dist: Sterling Publishing Co., Inc.
Murdin, Paul. Mapping the Universe: The Interactive History of Astronomy. 2011. (ENG., Illus.). 124p. 39.95 *(978-1-84732-915-8(2))* Carlton Bks., Ltd. GBR. Dist: Sterling Publishing Co., Inc.
Nakagawa, Hitoshi. The World's Easiest Astronomy Book. 2009. (ENG., Illus.). 120p. pap. 12.95 *(978-0-9785084-4-9(0))* One Peace Bks., Inc.
Nickell, Duane S. Guidebook for the Scientific Traveler: Visiting Astronomy & Space Exploration Sites Across America. 2008. (Scientific Traveler Ser.). (ENG., Illus.). 256p. pap. 21.95 *(978-0-8135-4374-1(6))* Rutgers Univ. Pr.
Nordgren, Tyler. Stars Above, Earth Below: A Guide to Astronomy in the National Parks. 2010. (Springer Praxis Books / Popular Astronomy Ser.). (Illus.). 300p. pap. 29.95 *(978-1-4419-1648-8(2),* 1441916482, Springer-Praxis) Springer.
Ratcliffe, Martin. State of the Universe: Images, Discoveries, & Events. 2007. (Springer Praxis Books / Popular Astronomy Ser.). (Illus.). 183p. per. 29.95 *(978-0-387-71674-9(2),* 0387716742, Springer-Praxis) Springer.
Saber, Rogue. 2012 A Family Brief: "the Science Is all In" 2009. 464p. 34.99 *(978-1-4415-4825-2(4));* pap. 23.99 *(978-1-4415-4824-5(6))* Xlibris Corp.
Sidharth, B. G., ed. A Century of Ideas: Perspectives from Leading Scientists of the 20th Century. 2010. (Fundamental Theories of Physics Ser.). xi, 207p. pap. 149.00 *(978-90-481-7114-9(8),* 9048171148) Springer.
Swimme, Brian Thomas & Tucker, Mary Evelyn. Journey of the Universe. 2011. (ENG.). 175p. 25.00 *(978-0-300-17190-7(0))* Yale Univ. Pr.
Teacher Created Resources Staff. Voyage Through Space. 2008. (Qeb Space Guides). (ENG., Illus.). 32p. (gr. 4-13). pap. 6.99 *(978-1-4206-8276-2(8))* Teacher Created Resources, Inc.
Yount, Lisa. Modern Astronomy: Expanding the Universe. 2006. (Milestones in Discovery & Invention Ser.). (Illus.). 224p. (YA). (gr. 7-12). 35.00 *(978-0-8160-5746-7(X))* Facts On File, Inc.

ASTRONOMY—PROBLEMS, EXERCISES, ETC.

Amendola, Luca & Tsujikawa, Shinji. Dark Energy: Theory & Observations. 2010. (ENG., Illus.). 506p. 83.00 *(978-0-521-51600-6(5))* Cambridge Univ. Pr.
Duffett-Smith, Peter & Zwart, Jonathan. Practical Astronomy with Your Calculator or Spreadsheet. 4th rev. ed. 2011. (ENG., Illus.). 238p. spiral bd. 40.00 *(978-0-521-14654-8(2))* Cambridge Univ. Pr.
Fix, John D. Astronomy: Journey to the Cosmic Frontier. 6th ed. 2010. (ENG., Illus.). 768p. (C). 157.67 *(978-0-07-351218-1(4),* 0073512184, McGraw-Hill Science, Engineering & Mathematics) McGraw-Hill Higher Education.
Jones, Lauren. Observation Exercises in Astronomy. 2010. (ENG.). 208p. (C). pap. 42.87 *(978-0-321-63812-0(3))* Benjamin-Cummings Publishing Co.
LoPresto, Michael. Astronomy Media Workbook. 7th ed. 2011. (C). cd-rom 21.20 *(978-0-321-74124-0(2))* Benjamin-Cummings Publishing Co.
Seeds, Michael A., et al. TheSkyX Workbook. 2nd ed. 2010. (ENG.). 384p. (C). pap. 63.95 *(978-0-538-73852-1(9))* Brooks/Cole.

ASTRONOMY—RESEARCH

Chaisson, Eric. Starry Night Pro Activities & Observation & Research Projects for Astronomy Today. 6th ed. 2007. (ENG.). 320p. (C). pap. 36.20 *(978-0-13-240097-8(9))* Benjamin-Cummings Publishing Co.
Committee for a Decadal Survey of Astronomy and Astrophysics & National Research Council. New Worlds, New Horizons in Astronomy & Astrophysics. 2011. (ENG.). 324p. 54.95 *(978-0-309-15802-2(8));* pap. 39.95 *(978-0-309-15799-5(4))* National Academies Pr.
Committee on the Assessment of a Plan for U.S. Participation in Euclid, et al. Assessment of a Plan for U. S. Participation in Euclid. 2012. (ENG.). 60p. pap. 31.00 ***(978-0-309-25384-0(5))*** National Academies Pr.
Doressoundiram, A. & Lellouch, Emmanuel. At the Edge of the Solar System: Icy New Worlds Unveiled. 2009. (Springer Praxis Books / Popular Astronomy Ser.). (ENG., Illus.). x, 214p. pap. 34.95 *(978-1-4419-0864-3(1),* 1441908641, Springer-Praxis) Springer.
Figueras, Francesca, et al, eds. Highlights of Spanish Astrophysics IV: Proceedings of the VII Scientific Meeting of the Spanish Astronomical Society (SEA) held in Barcelona, Spain, September 12-15 2006. 2007. xx, 367p. 199.00 *(978-1-4020-5999-5(X))* Springer.
Frebel, Anna. New Horizons in Astronomy: Frank N. Bash Symposium 2007: Proceedings of a Workshop Held at the University of Texas, Austin, Texas, USA, 14-16 October 2007. 2008. (Astronomical Society of the Pacific Conference Ser.: Vol. 393). (Illus.). xx, 304p. *(978-1-58381-656-1(9))* Astronomical Society of the Pacific, The.
Garcia, Paulo & Ferreira, Joao, eds. Jets from Young Stars IV: From Models to Observations & Experiments. 2009. (Lecture Notes in Physics Ser.). (ENG., Illus.). viii, 252p. 89.95 *(978-3-642-02288-3(X),* 364202288X) Springer.
Gronich, Bruce J., et al. Wanderings among the Stars: Experiments in Elementary Astronomy. 3rd rev. ed. 2010. (ENG.). 100p. pap. 42.03 *(978-0-7575-6331-7(7))* Kendall Hunt Publishing Co.
Heck, André, ed. The Multinational History of Strasbourg Astronomical Observatory. 2010. (Astrophysics & Space Science Library). viii, 310p. pap. 169.00 *(978-90-481-6918-4(6),* 9048169186) Springer.
Heck, Andre, ed. Organizations & Strategies in Astronomy, Vol. 7. 2007. (Astrophysics & Space Science Library). (Illus.). xi, 594p. 249.00 *(978-1-4020-5300-9(2),* 1402053002) Springer.
Heck, André, ed. Organizations, People & Strategies in Astronomy. 2012. (Astrophysics & Space Science Library: 388). (ENG., Illus.). xviii, 278p. 169.00 ***(978-1-4614-2352-2(X)**,* 146142352X) Springer.
Israelian, Garik & Meynet, Georges, eds. The Metal-Rich Universe. 2008. (Cambridge Contemporary Astrophysics Ser.). (ENG., Illus.). 488p. 138.00 *(978-0-521-87998-9(1))* Cambridge Univ. Pr.
Livio, Mario & Casertano, Stefano, eds. Planets to Cosmology: Essential Science in the Final Years of the Hubble Space Telescope: Proceedings of the Space Telescope Science Institute Symposium, held in Baltimore, Maryland May 3-6 2004. 2011. (Space Telescope Science Institute Symposium Ser.). (ENG., Illus.). 215p. pap. 30.99 *(978-0-521-18244-7(1))* Cambridge Univ. Pr.
López Corredoira, M. & Castro Perelman, C. Against the Tide: A Critical Review by Scientists of How Physics & Astronomy Get Done. 2008. 268p. per. *(978-1-59942-993-9(4))* Universal Pubs.
Matsuoka, A. & Russell, C. T., eds. The Kaguya Mission to the Moon. 2010. (ENG.). iv, 348p. 169.00 *(978-1-4419-8121-9(7),* 1441981217) Springer.
Milani, Andrea, et al, eds. Near Earth Objects, our Celestial Neighbours (IAU S236) Opportunity & Risk. 2007. (Proceedings of the International Astronomical Union Symposia & Colloquia Ser.). (ENG., Illus.). 524p. 135.00 *(978-0-521-86345-2(7))* Cambridge Univ. Pr.
Mitnik, G. Donald. Death of a Trillion Dreams. 2009. 178p. pap. 20.12 *(978-0-557-15601-6(7))* Lulu Enterprises Inc.
Moran, Edward C., ed. Proceedings of the 2008 Undergraduate Symposium on Research in Astronomy. 2009. 82p. pap. *(978-1-882334-18-6(3))* Keck Northeast Astronomy Consortium.
Saber, Rogue. 2012 A Family Brief: "the Science Is all In" 2009. 464p. 34.99 *(978-1-4415-4825-2(4));* pap. 23.99 *(978-1-4415-4824-5(6))* Xlibris Corp.
Science Frontiers Panels, et al. Panel Reports — New Worlds, New Horizons in Astronomy & Astrophysics. 2011. (ENG.). 548p. pap. 55.00 *(978-0-309-15962-3(8))* National Academies Pr.
Stanford, Laura M. New Horizons in Astronomy: Frank N. Bash Symposium 2009: Proceedings of a Workshop Held at the University of Texas, Austin, Texas, USA, 18-20 October 2009. 2010. (Illus.). xvi, 276p. *(978-1-58381-744-5(1))* Astronomical Society of the Pacific, The.
Topper, David R. Quirky Sides of Scientists: True Tales of Ingenuity & Error from Physics & Astronomy. 2010. (ENG., Illus.). xiv, 210p. pap. 39.95 *(978-1-4419-2429-2(9),* 1441924299) Springer.
York, Donald G., et al, eds. The Astronomy Revolution: 400 Years of Exploring the Cosmos. 2011. (ENG., Illus.). 450p. 79.95 *(978-1-4398-3600-2(0),* Taylor & Francis) Taylor & Francis Group GBR. Dist: Taylor & Francis Group.
Zotti, Georg. Computer Graphics in Historical & Modern Sky Observations: Graphical Analysis, Visualisation, Modelling, & Image Processing. 2008. 192p. pap. *(978-3-8364-8936-2(8))* VDM Verlag Dr. Mueller e.K.

ASTRONOMY—STUDY AND TEACHING

American Institute of Physics, ed. Graduate Programs in Physics, Astronomy, & Related Fields. 2007. (Graduate Programs in Physics, Astronomy & Related Fields Ser.). (Illus.). 838p. per. 72.00 *(978-0-7354-0450-2(X))* American Institute of Physics.
—2010 Graduate Programs in Physics, Astronomy, & Related Fields. 2009. (ENG.). iv, 836p. pap. 76.00 *(978-0-7354-0717-6(7),* 0735407177) American Institute of Physics.
—2011 Graduate Programs in Physics, Astronomy, & Related Fields. 2010. 798p. pap. 79.00 *(978-0-7354-0840-1(8),* 0735408408, AIP Pr.) Springer.
American Institute of Physics, ed. 2012 Graduate Programs in Physics, Astronomy, & Related Fields. 2011. (ENG.). 731p. pap. 79.00 ***(978-0-7354-0966-8(8)**,* 0735409668, AIP Pr.) Springer.
Barnes, Jonathan. Science Education & Outreach: Forging a Path to the Future: Proceedings of a Conference Held at Milbrae, California, USA, 12-16 September 2009. 2010. (Illus.). xx, 553p. *(978-1-58381-742-1(5))* Astronomical Society of the Pacific, The.
Building Blocks of Science: Sky Watchers Teacher's Guide (Firsthand Learning) 2007. ring bd. *(978-1-4350-0000-1(5))* Carolina Biological Supply Co.
Gibbs, Michael G. Preparing for the 2009 International Year of Astronomy: A Hands-On Symposium: Proceedings of a Symposium & Related Workshops Held in St. Louis, Missouri, USA, 1-5 June 2008, in Conjunction with the 212th Meeting of the American Astronomical Society. 2008. (Illus.). xvii, 575p. *(978-1-58381-672-1(0)); (978-1-58381-673-8(9))* Astronomical Society of the Pacific, The.
Gibbs, Michael G., et al. Science Educators under the Stars: Amateur Astronomers Engaged in Education & Public Outreach. 2007. (Illus.). 120p. pap. *(978-1-58381-315-7(2))* Astronomical Society of the Pacific, The.
Gowdy, Robert H. Astronomy: Notes to Accompany the Online Textbook. 2nd rev. ed. 2009. (ENG.). 338p. pap., pupil's gde. ed. 48.69 *(978-0-7575-6219-8(1))* Kendall Hunt Publishing Co.
Graduate Programs in Physics, Astronomy, & Related Fields. 2006. (Graduate Programs in Physics, Astronomy & Related Fields Ser.). 834p. per. 69.00 *(978-0-7354-0358-1(9),* AIP Pr.) Springer.
Greathouse, Lisa E. The Wonder of Our Solar System: Earth & Space Science. 2007. (Science Readers Ser.). 32p. (gr. 3-4). pap. 8.99 *(978-0-7439-0561-9(X))* Shell Educational Publishing.
Hartmann, Roland Karl. Astronomy: The Cosmic Journey. Date not set. (Astronomy Ser.). pap., tchr. ed. *(978-0-534-01751-4(7))* Wadsworth.
Heck, Andre & Madsen, C., eds. Astronomy Communication. 2010. (Astrophysics & Space Science Library). 240p. pap. 189.00 *(978-90-481-6307-6(2),* 9048163072) Springer.
Holt, Geoff & West, Nancy W. Project Earth Science: Astronomy. 2nd ed. 2011. *(978-1-936137-33-6(X));* E-Book *(978-1-936137-52-7(6))* National Science Teachers Assn.
Hurt, John, narrated by. The Planets. (Expanding Universe Ser.). pap., tchr. ed. 29.95 incl. VHS *(978-1-930545-26-7(6),* 30005C) Choices, Inc.
—The Sun & Other Stars. (Expanding Universe Ser.). pap., tchr. ed. 29.95 incl. VHS *(978-1-930545-25-0(8),* 30005B) Choices, Inc.
Jensen, Joseph B., ed. Earth & Space Science, Making Connections in Education & Public Outreach, Proceedings. 2011. 493p. pap. 77.00 ***(978-1-58381-766-7(2))*** Astronomical Society of the Pacific, The.
Lawrence, Richard. Our Universe. 2006. (God's Design for Heaven & Earth Ser.). (Illus.). 134p. per. 22.99 *(978-1-893345-85-0(8))* Answers in Genesis Ministries.
Lawrence, Richard & Lawrence, Debbie. Our Universe. 3rd ed. 2008. (Illus.). 160p. *(978-1-60092-153-7(1))* Answers in Genesis Ministries.
Pasachoff, Jay M. & Percy, John R. Teaching & Learning Astronomy: Effective Strategies for Educators Worldwide. Pasachoff, Jay & Percy, John, eds. 2009. (ENG., Illus.). 284p. pap. 42.00 *(978-0-521-11539-1(6))* Cambridge Univ. Pr.
Pasachoff, Jay M., et al. Innovation in Astronomy Education. Pasachoff, Jay M. et al, eds. 2008. (ENG., Illus.). 384p. 131.00 *(978-0-521-88015-2(7))* Cambridge Univ. Pr.
Powers, Don & Beaver, John B. Astronomy: Our Solar System & Beyond. 2010. (Expanding Science Skills Ser.). (ENG., Illus.). 80p. (gr. 5-8). pap. 11.99 *(978-1-58037-528-3(6))* Twain, Mark Media, Inc. Pubs.
Seeds, Michael A., et al. TheSkyX Workbook. 2nd ed. 2010. (ENG.). 384p. (C). pap. 63.95 *(978-0-538-73852-1(9))* Brooks/Cole.
Slater, Timothy F., et al. Conducting Astronomy Education Research: A Primer. 2010. (ENG.). 150p. (C). pap. 19.95 *(978-1-4292-6409-9(8))* Freeman, W. H. & Co.
Wilson, David C. Easy Astronomy for Lazy Students! 2008. 48p. pap. 13.95 *(978-1-4357-5029-6(2))* Lulu Enterprises Inc.

ASTRONOMY—TABLES

Baker, Harry J. Reeds Astro Navigation Tables. 2006. (ENG., Illus.). 72p. pap. 26.95 *(978-0-7136-7824-6(0),* Adlard Coles) A & C Black GBR. Dist: MBI Distribution Services/Quayside Distribution.
Lee, Thos. J. (Thomas Jefferson). A Collection of Tables & Fromul Useful in Surveying, Geodesy, & Practical Astronomy. 2006. 268p. per. 23.99 *(978-1-4255-2394-7(3))* MPublishing.
—Tables & Formulae Useful in Surveying, Geodesy, & Practical Astronomy, Including Elements for the Projection of Maps, & Instructions for Field M. 2006. 324p. per. 23.99 *(978-1-4255-3185-0(7))* MPublishing.

ASTRONOMY—VOCATIONAL GUIDANCE

Heck, André, ed. Organizations, People & Strategies in Astronomy. 2012. (Astrophysics & Space Science Library: 388). (ENG., Illus.). xviii, 278p. 169.00 ***(978-1-4614-2352-2(X)**,* 146142352X) Springer.
Plotner, Tammy. Moonwalk with Your Eyes: A Pocket Field Guide. 2010. (Astronomer's Pocket Field Guide Ser.). (ENG., Illus.). x, 220p. pap. 34.95 *(978-1-4419-0645-8(2),* 1441906452) Springer.

ASTRONOMY, ANCIENT

see also Astronomy—Early Works to 1800

Aristotle. On the Heavens. 2009. 108p. 19.99 *(978-1-60459-777-6(1))* Wilder Pubns., Ltd.
Bond, Alan & Hempsell, Mark. A Sumerian Observation of the Köfels' Impact Event. 2008. (Illus.). 128p. per. *(978-1-904623-64-9(6))* WritersPrintShop.
Bullinger, Ethelbert W. The Witness of the Stars. (ENG.). 300p. 2007. 43.95 *(978-0-548-13851-9(6))* 2006. per. 28.95 *(978-1-4286-5022-0(9))* Kessinger Publishing, LLC.
Collins, Andrew. The Cygnus Mystery: Unlocking the Ancient Secret of Life's Origins in the Cosmos. (ENG.). 2010. 384p. pap. 19.95 *(978-1-906787-55-4(7))* 2007. (Illus.). 368p. 24.95 *(978-1-84293-202-5(0))* Duncan Baird Pubs. GBR. (Watkins Publishing). Dist: Sterling Publishing Co., Inc.
Corsini, Enrico Maria, ed. The Inspiration of Astronomical Phenomena VI Proceedings. 2011. 555p. pap. 77.00 ***(978-1-58381-762-9(X))*** Astronomical Society of the Pacific, The.
Falkner, David E. The Mythology of the Night Sky: An Amateur Astronomer's Guide to the Ancient Greek & Roman Legends. 2011. (Patrick Moore's Practical Astronomy Ser.). (ENG., Illus.). xiii, 238p. pap. 34.95 *(978-1-4614-0136-0(4),* 1461401364) Springer.
Fraser, Craig G. The Cosmos: A Historical Perspective, 1 vol. 2006. (Greenwood Guides to Great Ideas in Science) (Illus.). 200p. 65.00 *(978-0-313-33218-0(5),* GR3218, Greenwood Pr.) Greenwood Publishing Group, Inc.
Gage, Mary E. America's Stonehenge Deciphered, 1. 2006. (Illus.). 274p. per. 15.95 *(978-0-9717910-4-6(X))* Powwow River Bks.
Gee, Emma. Ovid, Aratus & Augustus: Astronomy in Ovid's Fasti. 2006. (Cambridge Classical Studies). (ENG., Illus.). 240p. pap. 34.99 *(978-0-521-10177-6(8))* Cambridge Univ. Pr.
Hubner, Wolfgang. Manilius, Astronomica Buch V: Einfahrung, Text, ßbersetzung und Kommentar. 2011. (Sammlung wissenschaftlicher Commentare (SWC) Ser.).Tr. of Manilius, Astronomica Volume V. Introduction, Edition, Translation, & Commentary. (GER & GEC., Illus.). XIV, 760p. 377.00 ***(978-3-11-173099-8(9))*** De Gruyter, Walter Inc.
Hübner, Wolfgang. Manilius, Astronomica Buch V: Einfahrung, Text, Ã_bersetzung und Kommentar. 2010. (Sammlung wissenschaftlicher Commentare (SWC) Ser.).Tr. of Manilius, Astronomica Volume V. (GER, MUS & GEC., Illus.). XIV, 760p. 249.00 *(978-3-11-020670-8(6))* De Gruyter, Walter Inc.
Kelley, David H. & Milone, Eugene F. Exploring Ancient Skies: A Survey of Ancient & Cultural Astronomy. 2nd ed. 2011. (Illus.). xxv, 614p. pap. 99.00 *(978-1-4419-7623-9(X),* 144197623X) Springer.
Partridge, A. e. & Partridge, A. E. The Story of the Heavens: How the Forty-Eight Ancient Constellations Got Their Names 5000 Years Ago. 2011. 50p. 35.95 ***(978-1-258-05411-3(6))*** Literary Licensing, LLC.
Powell, Robert. History of the Zodiac. 2007. *(978-1-59731-178-6(2))* 2007. pap. *(978-1-59731-177-9(4))* 2006. (ENG.). 224p. 37.95 *(978-1-59731-153-3(7))* 2006. 224p. per. 21.95 *(978-1-59731-152-6(9))* Perennis, Sophia.
Simplicius. Simplicius: on Aristotle on the Heavens 1. 3-4. Mueller, Ian, tr. from GEC. 2011. 224p. 130.00 *(978-0-7156-4063-0(1))* Duckworth Publishers GBR. Dist: International Publishers Marketing.
Steele, J. M. Observations & Predictions of Eclipse Times by Early Astronomers. 2010. (Archimedes Ser.). 336p. pap. 239.00 *(978-90-481-5454-8(5),* 9048154545) Springer.
Steele, John M. Ancient Astronomical Observations & the Study of the Moon's Motion (1691-1757) 2012. (Sources & Studies in the History of Mathematics & Physical Sciences Ser.). (ENG., Illus.). 174p. 124.00 ***(978-1-4614-2148-1(9)**,* 1461421489) Springer.
Waerden, H. van der. Science Awakening II. 2010. 368p. pap. 299.00 *(978-90-481-8247-3(6),* 9048182476) Springer.
Whitehouse, David. The Moon: A Biography. 2006. (Illus.). 312p. reprint ed. 26.00 *(978-1-4223-5339-4(7))* DIANE Publishing Co.
Wilson, John. The Lost Solar System of the Ancients Discovered. 2009. 220p. pap. 24.11 *(978-1-4589-2879-5(9))* General Bks. LLC.
—The Lost Solar System of the Ancients Discovered, 2 vols. 2006. (Illus.). 1125p. 110.00 *(978-1-57898-573-9(0))* Martino Publishing.

ASTRONOMY, ARABIC

Chabás, José & Goldstein, B. R. The Alfonsine Tables of Toledo. 2012. (Archimedes Ser.). (ENG.). 356p. pap. 219.00 *(978-90-481-6404-2(4),* 9048164044) Springer.
Holden, James H. Five Medieval Astrologers. 2008. 164p. pap. 21.95 *(978-0-86690-578-7(2))* American Federation of Astrologers, Inc.
Juste, David. Les Alchandreana Primitifs: Étude sur les plus anciens traités astrologiques latins d'origine arabe (Xe Siècle) 2007. (Brill's Studies in Intellectual History). 756p. *(978-90-04-15827-6(8))* BRILL.
Rashed, Roshdi, ed. Thabit ibn Qurra: Science & Philosophy in Ninth-Century Baghdad. 2009. (Scientia Graeco-Arabica Ser.).Tr. of Thabit ibn Qurra. Science & Philosophy in 9th-Century Bagdad. (ENG & FRE.). X, 789p. 182.00 *(978-3-11-022078-0(4));* 280.00 ***(978-3-11-173292-3(4))*** De Gruyter, Walter Inc.

Schmidl, Petra. Volkstümliche Astronomie im islamischen Mittelalter: Zur Bestimmung der Gebetszeiten und der Qibla bei al-A?ba??, Ibn Ra??q und Al-F?ris? 2006. 904p. *(978-90-04-15390-5(X))* BRILL.

Schmidl, Petra G., et al. Volkstümliche Astronomie Im Islamischen Mittelalter: Zur Bestimmung der Gebetszeiten und der Qibla Bei Al-Asbahi, Ibn Rahiq und Al-Farisi, 2 vols. 2006. (ARA & GER., Illus.). xxii, 857p. *(978-90-04-15418-6(3))*; *(978-90-04-15417-9(5))* BRILL.

Steele, John M. A Brief Introduction to Astronomy in the Middle East. 2008. (Brief Introduction Ser.). (ENG., Illus.). 140p. pap. 11.95 *(978-0-86356-428-4(3))* Saqi Bks. GBR. Dist: Consortium Bk. Sales & Distribution.

ASTRONOMY, CHINESE

Cullen, Christopher. Astronomy & Mathematics in Ancient China: The 'Zhou Bi Suan Jing' 2007. (Needham Research Institute Studies). (ENG.). 256p. pap. 53.00 *(978-0-521-03537-8(6))* Cambridge Univ. Pr.

Li, Zhen & Handberg, Roger. Chinese Space Policy: A Study in Domestic & International Politics. 2006. (Space Power & Politics Ser.). (Illus.). 202p. 170.00 *(978-0-415-36582-6(1))* Routledge.

Schafer, Edward H. Pacing the Void: T'ang Approaches to the Stars. 2006. (ENG.). 368p. pap. 50.00 *(978-1-891640-14-8(3))* Floating World Editions.

Sivin, Nathan. Granting the Seasons. 2008. (Sources & Studies in the History of Mathematics & Physical Sciences Ser.). (Illus.). 664p. 69.95 *(978-0-387-78955-2(3))* Springer.

—Granting the Seasons: The Chinese Astronomical Reform of 1280, with a Study of Its Many Dimensions & a Translation of its Records. 2010. (Sources & Studies in the History of Mathematics & Physical Sciences Ser.). (Illus.). vi, 664p. pap. 69.95 *(978-1-4419-2707-1(7)*, 1441927077) Springer.

ASTRONOMY, EGYPTIAN

Bauval, Robert. Egypt Code. 2008. (ENG.). 336p. 27.95 *(978-1-934708-00-2(3))* Disinformation Co. Ltd., The.

Bomhard, Anne-Sophie von. The Naos of the Decades: Underwater Archaeology in the Canopic region in Egypt. 2008. (OCMA Monograph Ser.). (ENG., Illus.). 300p. (C). 90.00 *(978-1-905905-04-1(1))* Oxford Univ. Schl. of Archaeology GBR. Dist: Brown, David Bk. Co., The.

Furlong, David. Hatshepsut's Mortuary Temple - Midwinter Solstice Alignment. 2010. (Illus.). 16p. 31.50 *(978-0-9559795-1-4(X))* Atlanta Bks. GBR. Dist: Lulu Enterprises Inc.

Gilligan, Gary. An Ancient World in Chaos. 2007. (Illus.). 402p. *(978-1-906510-00-8(8))* Troubadour Publishing Ltd.

Lockyer, J. Norman. Inquiries with Regard to the Stellar Temples of the Ancient. 2006. pap. 9.95 *(978-1-4304-0748-5(4))* Kessinger Publishing, LLC.

—Methods of Determining the Orientation of Egyptian Temples - 2006. pap. 9.95 *(978-1-4304-0747-8(6))* Kessinger Publishing, LLC.

Morel, John Henry. The Book of the Damned. 2010. 336p. 39.99 *(978-1-935436-41-6(4))* Rodaian Pr.

Neugebauer, Otto. Egyptian Planetary Texts: On Some Astronomical Papyri & Related Problems of Ancient Geography. 2011. 76p. 37.95 ***(978-1-258-02277-8(X))*** Literary Licensing, LLC.

Schumann-Antelme, Ruth & Rossini, Stéphane. Nout, le Cosmos des Pharaons. 2007. (FRE., Illus.). 426p. *(978-2-268-05674-6(0))* Editions du Rocher, Les.

Zitman, Willem H. Egypt: Image of Heaven: The Planisphere & the Lost Cradle. 2006. (Illus.). 311p. per. 19.95 *(978-1-931882-54-5(1))* Adventures Unlimited Pr.

ASTRONOMY, HINDU

see Hindu Astronomy

ASTRONOMY, MAYA

see Maya Astronomy

ASTRONOMY, MEDIEVAL

Aspden, Darren & Aspden, Diane. Lovestruck. 2011. 70p. ***(978-1-897472-00-2(5))*** Golden Meteorite Pr.].

Chabás, José & Goldstein, Bernard R., eds. The Astronomical Tables of Giovanni Bianchini. 2009. (Illus.). 160p. *(978-90-04-17615-7(2))* BRILL.

Eastwood, Bruce S. Ordering the Heavens: Roman Astronomy & Cosmology in the Carolingian Renaissance. 2007. (History of Science & Medicine Library). (Illus.). 472p. *(978-90-04-16186-3(4))* BRILL.

Grant, Edward. Planets, Stars, & Orbs Set: The Medieval Cosmos, 1200-1687, 2 vols. 2009. (ENG., Illus.). 842p. pap. 79.00 *(978-0-521-13868-0(X))* Cambridge Univ. Pr.

Holden, James H. Five Medieval Astrologers. 2008. 164p. pap. 21.95 *(978-0-86690-578-7(2))* American Federation of Astrologers, Inc.

Ibn Ezra, Abraham ben Meïr & Goodman, Mordechai S. The Sabbath Epistle of Rabbi Abraham Ibn Ezra: 'Iggeret Hashabbat. 2008. *(978-1-60280-111-0(8))* Ktav Publishing Hse., Inc.

Joseph, George Gheverghese. A Passage to Infinity: Medieval Indian Mathematics from Kerala & Its Impact. 2009. (Illus.). 236p. (C). 39.95 *(978-81-321-0168-0(5)*, B01680C) SAGE Pubns., Inc.

Mü, et al. Visuelle Weltaneignung: Astronomische und kosmologische Diagramme in Handschriften des Mittelalters. Historische Semantik 11. 2008. (Historische Semantik Ser.). (GER., Illus.). 438p. (C). 84.00 *(978-3-525-36711-7(2))* Vandenhoeck & Ruprecht GmbH & Co. KG DEU. Dist: ISD.

Mosley, Adam. Bearing the Heavens: Tycho Brahe & the Astronomical Community of the Late Sixteenth Century. 2007. (ENG., Illus.). 368p. 126.00 *(978-0-521-83866-5(5))* Cambridge Univ. Pr.

Qurra, Thabit B. & Carbody, Francis J. The Astronomical Works of Thabit B Qurr. 2011. 262p. 47.95 ***(978-1-258-05148-8(6))*** Literary Licensing, LLC.

Repcheck, Jack. Copernicus' Secret: How the Scientific Revolution Began. 2008. (ENG., Illus.). 256p. pap. 16.99 *(978-0-7432-8952-8(8))* Simon & Schuster.

Rodriguez, Jose Luis Mancha. Studies in Medieval Astronomy & Optics. 2006. (Variorum Collected Studies). (Illus.). 352p. 160.00 *(978-0-86078-996-3(9))* Ashgate Publishing Co.

Samso, Julio. Astronomy & Astrology in al-Andalus & the Maghrib. 2007. (Variorum Collected Studies). (Illus.). 382p. 170.00 *(978-0-7546-5934-1(8))* Ashgate Publishing Co.

Sivin, Nathan. Granting the Seasons. 2008. (Sources & Studies in the History of Mathematics & Physical Sciences Ser.). (Illus.). 664p. 69.95 *(978-0-387-78955-2(3))* Springer.

Steele, John M. A Brief Introduction to Astronomy in the Middle East. 2008. (Brief Introduction Ser.). (ENG., Illus.). 140p. pap. 11.95 *(978-0-86356-428-4(3))* Saqi Bks. GBR. Dist: Consortium Bk. Sales & Distribution.

Wedel, Theodore Otto. The Mediaeval Attitude Toward Astrology, Particularly in England. 2009. 178p. 37.95 *(978-1-104-67912-5(4))*; pap. 22.95 *(978-1-104-66152-6(7))* Kessinger Publishing, LLC.

ASTRONOMY, NAUTICAL

see Nautical Astronomy

ASTRONOMY, SPHERICAL AND PRACTICAL

see Spherical Astronomy

ASTRONOMY, STATISTICAL

see Statistical Astronomy

ASTRONOMY AS A PROFESSION

see Astronomy—Vocational Guidance

ASTROPHYSICS

see also Astrodynamics; Astronomical Spectroscopy; Celestial Mechanics; Cosmic Magnetic Fields; Dark Energy (Astronomy); Interstellar Matter; Nuclear Astrophysics; Radiative Transfer; Stars—Atmospheres

Abdo, Aous. Discovery of Localized Tev Gamma-Ray Sources & Diffuse Tev Gamma-Ray Emission. 2008. 240p. pap. *(978-3-8364-8676-7(8))* VDM Verlag Dr. Mueller e.K.

Abebe, Amare. Covariant Perturbations in F -Gravity of Multi-Fluid Cosmologies. 2011. 100p. pap. ***(978-3-8443-1404-5(0))*** Lambert Academic Publishing.

Abramowicz, Marek A., et al, eds. Theory of Black Hole Accretion Discs. 2010. (Cambridge Contemporary Astrophysics Ser.). (ENG., Illus.). 308p. pap. 39.99 *(978-0-521-15295-2(X))* Cambridge Univ. Pr.

Adams, Fred, et al. Cosmic Update: Dark Puzzles. Arrow of Time. Future History. Nekoogar, Farzad, ed. 2011. (Multiversal Journeys Ser.). (ENG., Illus.). xi, 138p. 69.95 *(978-1-4419-8293-3(0)*, 1441982930) Springer.

Adcock, Robert L. Two into the Blue. 2008. 144p. 29.99 *(978-1-4363-5021-1(2))*; pap. 19.99 *(978-1-4363-5020-4(4))* Xlibris Corp.

Adelman, Saul J., et al, eds. Hot Stars in the Galactic Halo: Proceedings of a Meeting, Held at Union College, Schenectady, New York November 4-6, 1993 in Honor of the 65th Birthday of A. G. Davis Philip. 2011. (ENG.). 406p. pap. 45.00 *(978-0-521-17492-3(9))* Cambridge Univ. Pr.

Adushkin, V. V & Nemchinov, I. V., eds. Catastrophic Events Caused by Cosmic Objects. 2007. (Illus.). 316p. 139.00 *(978-1-4020-6451-7(9)*, 1402064519) Springer.

Afonso, Fiona. 2005: Past Meets Present in Astronomy... 2006. (Illus.). 120 ppp. 100.00 *(978-981-256-887-8(5))* World Scientific Publishing Co., Inc.

Aharonian, F. A., et al, eds. High Energy Gamma-Ray Astronomy: Proceedings of the Fourth International Meeting on High Energy Gamma-Ray Astronomy. 2009. (AIP Conference Proceedings / Astronomy & Astrophysics Ser.). (ENG.). 932p. 329.00 *(978-0-7354-0616-2(2))* American Institute of Physics.

Aharonian, Felix A., et al, eds. 25th Texas Symposium on Relativistic Astrophysics (Texas 2010) 2011. (AIP Conference Proceedings / Astronomy & Astrophysics Ser.). (ENG.). 262p. pap. 140.00 ***(978-0-7354-0941-5(2)***, 0735409412, AIP Pr.) Springer.

Al. Astrophysics at Ultra-High Energies. 2007. (Science & Culture Ser.). 150.00 *(978-981-279-014-9(4))* World Scientific Publishing Co., Inc.

—Science with the New Generation of... 2007. 137.00 *(978-981-270-964-6(9))* World Scientific Publishing Co., Inc.

Al & Diamond, Patrick H. Relaxation Dynamics in Laboratory & Astrophysical Plasmas, Vol. 1. 2009. 336p. 97.00 *(978-981-4291-54-5(4))* World Scientific Publishing Co., Inc.

Alexander, David. The Sun, 1 vol. Jones, Lauren V. & Slater, Timothy F., eds. 2009. (Greenwood Guides to the Universe Ser.). 228p. 65.00 *(978-0-313-34077-2(3)*, GR4077, Greenwood Pr.) Greenwood Publishing Group, Inc.

Alfonso, C., ed. Transiting Extrasolar Planets Workshop. 2007. (Astronomical Society of the Pacific Conference Ser.). 342p. 77.00 *(978-1-58381-234-1(2))* Astronomical Society of the Pacific, The.

Alloin, D. M. & Mariotti, Jean-Marie, eds. Adaptive Optics for Astronomy. 2010. (NATO Science Series C: (closed) Ser.). (Illus.). 360p. pap. 329.00 *(978-90-481-4375-7(6)*, 9048143756) Springer.

Amelino-Camelia, Giovanni & Kowalski-Glikman, Jurek, eds. Planck Scale Effects in Astrophysics & Cosmology. 2010. (Lecture Notes in Physics Ser.). (Illus.). xvi, 413p. pap. 109.00 *(978-3-642-06441-8(8)*, 3642064418) Springer.

Andersen, Johannes, et al. The Galaxy Disk in Cosmological Context. Andersen, Johannes et al, eds. 2009. (Proceedings of the International Astronomical Union Symposia & Colloquia Ser.). (ENG., Illus.). 532p. 118.00 *(978-0-521-88985-8(5))* Cambridge Univ. Pr.

Anderson, Warren, et al. Gravitational-Wave Physics & Astronomy: An Introduction to Theory, Experiment & Data Analysis. 2011. (ENG., Illus.). 381p. 155.00 *(978-3-527-40886-3(X)*, Wiley-VCH) Wiley, John & Sons, Inc.

Annual Review of Astronomy & Astrophysics. 2006. 85.00 *(978-0-8243-0944-2(8))* Annual Reviews, Inc.

Anzalone, Charles E. Galactic Travel at Warp Speed in Imaginary Time. 2008. 168p. 29.99 *(978-1-4363-4682-5(7))*; pap. 19.99 *(978-1-4363-4681-8(9))* Xlibris Corp.

Ao, Xianzhi, et al, eds. Shock Waves in Space & Astrophysical Environments: 18th Annual International Astrophysics Conference. 2009. (AIP Conference Proceedings / Astronomy & Astrophysics Ser.). 238p. 159.00 *(978-0-7354-0724-4(X)*, 073540724X, AIP Pr.) Springer.

Aparicio, A., et al, eds. Stellar Astrophysics for the Local Group: VIII Canary Islands Winter School of Astrophysics. 2011. (Cambridge Contemporary Astrophysics Ser.). (ENG.). 623p. pap. 75.00 *(978-0-521-17630-9(1))* Cambridge Univ. Pr.

Armitage, Philip. Astrophysics of Planet Formation. 2009. (ENG., Illus.). 294p. 72.00 *(978-0-521-88745-8(3))* Cambridge Univ. Pr.

Aschenbach, Bernd, et al, eds. Relativistic Astrophysics & Cosmology - Einstein's Legacy: Proceedings of the MPE/USM/MPA/ESO Joint Astronomy Conference Held in Munich, Germany, 7-11 November 2005. 2010. (ESO Astrophysics Symposia Ser.). (Illus.). xxxiv, 506p. pap. 139.00 *(978-3-642-09417-0(1)*, 3642094171) Springer.

—Relativistic Physics & Cosmology - Einstein's Legacy: International Astrophysics Conference, Munich, 7-11 November 2005. 2007. (ESO Astrophysics Symposia Ser.). 530p. 139.00 *(978-3-540-74712-3(5)*, 3540747125) Springer.

Aschwanden, Markus J. Self-Organized Criticality in Astrophysics: The Statistics of Nonlinear Processes in the Universe. 2011. (Springer Praxis Books / Astronomy & Planetary Sciences Ser.). (Illus.). xiv, 420p. 169.00 *(978-3-642-15000-5(4)*, 3642150004) Springer.

Ashman, Keith M. & Zepf, Stephen E. Globular Cluster Systems. 2008. (Cambridge Astrophysics Ser.). (ENG., Illus.). 184p. pap. 46.00 *(978-0-521-08783-4(X))* Cambridge Univ. Pr.

Astbury, Alan. Fundamental Interactions. 2007. 222.00 *(978-981-277-609-9(5))* World Scientific Publishing Co., Inc.

Astbury, Alan, et al, eds. Fundamental Interactions: Proceedings of the 21st Lake Louise Winter Institute. 2007. (Illus.). 384p. 202.00 *(978-981-270-367-5(5))* World Scientific Publishing Co., Inc.

Astronomy & Astrophysics. Date not set. *(978-0-387-91525-8(7))* Springer.

Bacciotti, Francesca, et al. Jets from Young Stars II: Clues from High Angular Resolution Observations. 2007. (Lecture Notes in Physics Ser.). (Illus.). 291p. 99.00 *(978-3-540-68031-4(4))* Springer.

Backman, Dana & Seeds, Michael A. Astronomy: The Solar System & Beyond. 7th ed. 2011. (Textbooks Available with Cengage YouBook Ser.). (ENG.). 528p. (C). pap. 179.95 *(978-1-111-42567-8(1))* Brooks/Cole.

Barbosa, Domingos, et al, eds. 3K, SN's, Clusters: Hunting the Cosmological Parameters with Precision Cosmology: Hunting the Cosmological Parameters with Precision Cosmology. 2010. 232p. pap. 105.00 *(978-90-481-6546-9(6)*, 9048165466) Springer.

Baumjohann, Wolfgang. Basic Space Plasma Physics. 2012. 496p. 128.00 ***(978-1-84816-894-7(2))***; pap. 68.00 ***(978-1-84816-895-4(0))*** Imperial College Pr. GBR. Dist: World Scientific Publishing Co., Inc.

Becker, Barbara J. Unravelling Starlight: William & Margaret Huggins & the Rise of the New Astronomy. 2011. (ENG., Illus.). 400p. 110.00 *(978-1-107-00229-6(X))* Cambridge Univ. Pr.

Belusevic, Radoje. Relativity, Astrophysics & Cosmology, 2 vols., Set. 2008. (ENG., Illus.). 1122p. 495.00 *(978-3-527-40764-4(2)*, Wiley-VCH) Wiley, John & Sons, Inc.

Berger, A. L., et al, eds. Milankovitch & Climate: Understanding the Response to Astronomical Forcing. 2012. (NATO Science Series C: (closed) Ser.). (ENG.). 544p. pap. 289.00 *(978-90-481-8400-2(2)*, 9048184002) Springer.

Bertin, Giuseppe, et al, eds. Plasmas in the Laboratory & the Universe: Interactions, Patterns, & Turbulence. 2010. (AIP Conference Proceedings / Astronomy & Astrophysics Ser.). 378p. 219.00 *(978-0-7354-0787-9(8)*, 0735407878, AIP Pr.) Springer.

Beskin, Vassily, et al. Accretion Disks, Jets & High-Energy Phenomena in Astrophysics: Les Houches Session LXXVIII, July 29 - August 23 2002. 2010. (Houches - Ecole d'Ete de Physique Theorique Ser.). (Illus.). xxviii, 625p. pap. 219.00 *(978-3-642-05768-7(3)*, 3642057683) Springer.

Bhadra, Ed. Arunava. Exploring the Cosmos. 2011. 144p. pap. ***(978-3-8443-9165-7(7))*** Lambert Academic Publishing.

Bhardwaj, Anil. Advances in Geosciences: Planetary Science, 6 vols. 2010. 680p. 217.00 *(978-981-283-815-5(5))* World Scientific Publishing Co., Inc.

Bianco, Carlo Luciano & She-Sheng, Xue. Relativistic Astrophysics: 4th Italian-Sino Workshop, Pescara, Italy 20-28 July 2007. 2008. (AIP Conference Proceedings Ser.). (Illus.). xiii, 354p. 135.00 *(978-0-7354-0483-0(6))* American Institute of Physics.

Binetruy, P., et al, eds. The primordial universe - L'univers Primordial: 28 June - 23 July 1999. 2010. (Houches - Ecole d'Ete de Physique Theorique Ser.). (Illus.). xxxvi, 629p. pap. 159.00 *(978-3-642-07425-7(1)*, 3642074251) Springer.

Blandford, Roger. Annual Review of Astronomy & Astrophysics, Vol. 45. 2007th ed. 2007. 701p. pap. 197.00 *(978-0-8243-0945-9(6))* Annual Reviews, Inc.

Bliokh, P., et al. Dusty & Self-Gravitational Plasmas in Space. 2010. (Astrophysics & Space Science Library). 268p. pap. 229.00 *(978-90-481-4445-7(0)*, 9048144450) Springer.

Blumenthal, George, et al. 21st Century Astronomy. 3rd ed. 2010. (ENG., Illus.). 651p. (C). pap. 144.14 *(978-0-393-93198-3(6)*, 93198) Norton, W. W. & Co., Inc.

Bodenheimer, Peter, et al. Numerical Methods in Astrophysics: An Introduction. 2006. (Series in Astronomy & Astrophysics Ser.). (ENG., Illus.). 344p. (C). 92.95 *(978-0-7503-0883-0(4)*, Taylor & Francis) Taylor & Francis Group GBR. Dist: Taylor & Francis Group.

Bodo, Gianluigi. Jets from Young Stars III: Numerical MHD & Instabilities. 2008. (Lecture Notes in Physics Ser.). (Illus.). 188p. 79.95 *(978-3-540-76966-8(8))* Springer.

Borello, Domenic. Spce the Superconductor & the Hydrogen Cell & How the Pyramids Were Built. 2007. 48.00 *(978-0-8059-8858-1(0))* Dorrance Publishing Co., Inc.

Borisovich Dubovichenko, Sergey. Thermonuclear Processes of the Universe. 2012. ***(978-1-61942-552-1(1))*** Nova Science Pubs., Inc.

Bradt, Hale. Astrophysics Processes: The Physics of Astronomical Phenomena. 2008. (ENG., Illus.). 536p. (C). 80.00 *(978-0-521-84656-1(0))* Cambridge Univ. Pr.

Brahic, A. De Feu et de Glace: Ardentes Géantes. 2010. (FRE., Illus.). 395p. *(978-2-7381-2330-5(9))* Jacob, Odile.

Bray, R. J., et al. The Solar Granulation. 2nd rev. ed. 2009. (Cambridge Astrophysics Ser.). (ENG.). 276p. pap. 56.00 *(978-0-521-11551-3(5))* Cambridge Univ. Pr.

Bridle, Alan H., et al. Frontiers of Astrophysics: A Celebration of NRAO's 50th Anniversary: Proceedings of a Symposium Held at National Radio Astronomy Observatory, Charlottesville, Virginia, USA, 18-21 June 2007. 2008. (Astronomical Society of the Pacific Conference Ser.: Vol. 395). (Illus.). xx, 390p. *(978-1-58381-660-8(7))* Astronomical Society of the Pacific, The.

Brummell, Nic, et al, eds. Astrophysical Dynamics (IAU S271) From Stars to Galaxies. 2011. (Proceedings of the International Astronomical Union Symposia & Colloquia Ser.). (ENG., Illus.). 432p. 125.00 ***(978-0-521-19739-7(2))*** Cambridge Univ. Pr.

Burdyuzha, Vladimir, ed. The Future of Life & the Future of Our Civilization. 2006. (ENG., Illus.). xvii, 495p. 219.00 *(978-1-4020-4967-5(6)*, 1402049676) Springer.

Bureau, Martin, et al, eds. Formation & Evolution of Galaxy Bulges (IAU S245) 2008. (Proceedings of the International Astronomical Union Symposia & Colloquia Ser.). (ENG., Illus.). 500p. 121.00 *(978-0-521-87467-0(X))* Cambridge Univ. Pr.

Burrows, John P., et al, eds. The Remote Sensing of Tropospheric Composition from Space. 2011. (Physics of Earth & Space Environments Ser.). (ENG., Illus.). xv, 536p. 199.00 *(978-3-642-14790-6(9)*, 3642147909) Springer.

Buta, Ronald J., et al. The de Vaucouleurs Atlas of Galaxies. 2007. (ENG., Illus.). 356p. 197.00 *(978-0-521-82048-6(0))* Cambridge Univ. Pr.

Calle, Carlos I. The Universe: Order Without Design. 2009. (ENG., Illus.). 264p. 27.98 *(978-1-59102-714-0(4))* Prometheus Bks., Pubs.

Camenzind, Max. Compact Objects in Astrophysics: White Dwarfs, Neutron Stars & Black Holes. 2007. (Astronomy & Astrophysics Library). (Illus.). xxiv, 682p. 109.00 *(978-3-540-25770-7(5)*, 3540257705) Springer.

Capozziello, Salvatore & Faraoni, Valerio. Beyond Einstein Gravity: A Survey of Gravitational Theories for Cosmology & Astrophysics. 2010. (Fundamental Theories of Physics Ser.). (Illus.). xix, 448p. 169.00 *(978-94-007-0164-9(0)*, 9400701640) Springer.

Caprini, Chiara. The Observational Consequences of Primordial Fields. 2011. 192p. pap. ***(978-3-8433-7310-4(8))*** Lambert Academic Publishing.

Carroll, Bradley W. & Ostlie, Dale A. An Introduction to Modern Astrophysics. 2nd rev. ed. 2006. (ENG., Illus.). 1400p. (C). 188.80 *(978-0-8053-0402-2(9))* Benjamin-Cummings Publishing Co.

—An Introduction to Modern Galactic Astrophysics & Cosmology. 2nd ed. 2006. (Illus.). 769p. *(978-0-8053-0347-6(2))* Addison Wesley.

—An Introduction to Modern Stellar Astrophysics. 2nd ed. 2006. (ENG., Illus.). 800p. (C). 158.80 *(978-0-8053-0348-3(0))* Addison-Wesley Longman, Inc.

Casertano, Stefano, et al, eds. Warped Disks & Inclined Rings around Galaxies. 2006. (ENG., Illus.). 312p. pap. 61.00 *(978-0-521-03163-9(X))* Cambridge Univ. Pr.

Cassen, Patrick, et al. Extrasolar Planets: Saas Fee Advanced Course 31. Queloz, Didier et al, eds. 2010. (Saas-Fee Advanced Courses Ser.). (Illus.). xiv, 451p. pap. 129.00 *(978-3-642-06722-8(0)*, 3642067220) Springer.

Castell, Lutz & Ischebeck, Otfried, eds. Time, Quantum & Information. 2010. (Illus.). xiv, 476p. pap. 109.00 *(978-3-642-07892-7(3)*, 3642078923) Springer.

Castor, John I. Radiation Hydrodynamics. 2007. (Illus.). 367p. pap. 74.00 *(978-0-521-54062-9(3))* Cambridge Univ. Pr.

Cernicharo, José & Bachiller, Rafael, eds. The Molecular Universe (IAU S280) 2012. (Proceedings of the International Astronomical Union Symposia & Colloquia Ser.). (ENG., Illus.). 528p. 125.00 ***(978-1-107-01980-5(X))*** Cambridge Univ. Pr.

Chabrier, Gilles, ed. Structure Formation in Astrophysics. (Cambridge Contemporary Astrophysics Ser.). (ENG.). 2011. 456p. pap. 55.00 *(978-0-521-18274-4(3))* 2009. (Illus.). 454p. 139.00 *(978-0-521-88779-3(8))* Cambridge Univ. Pr.

Chakrabarti, Sandip K., et al, eds. Astrophysics & Cosmology after Gamow: Proceedings of the 4th Gamow International Conference on Astrophysics & Cosmology after Gamow & the 9th Gamow Summer School Astronomy & Beyond: Astrophysics, Cosmology, Radio Astronomy, High Energy Physics & Astrobiology. 2010. (AIP Conference Proceedings / Astronomy &

Astrophysics Ser.). (ENG.). 506p. pap. 274.00 *(978-0-7354-0743-5(6),* 0735407436, AIP Pr.) Springer.

Chandrasekhar, S. Eddington: The Most Distinguished Astrophysicist of his Time. 2009. (ENG., Illus.). 72p. pap. 27.99 *(978-0-521-12242-9(2))* Cambridge Univ. Pr.

Chapman, Jessica & Baan, Willem, eds. Astrophysical Masers & their Environments (IAU S242) 2008. (Proceedings of the International Astronomical Union Symposia & Colloquia Ser.). (ENG., Illus.). 540p. 121.00 *(978-0-521-87464-9(5))* Cambridge Univ. Pr.

Cheng, K. S., et al, eds. Stellar Astrophysics - A Tribute to Helmut A. Abt. 2011. (Astrophysics & Space Science Library). 352p. pap. 219.00 *(978-90-481-6452-3(4),* 9048164524) Springer.

Chernov, Gennady Pavlovich. Fine Structure of Solar Radio Bursts. 2011. (Astrophysics & Space Science Library). (Illus.). xv, 282p. 169.00 *(978-3-642-20014-4(1),* 3642200141) Springer.

Choudhary, Debi Prasad & Strassmeier, Klaus G., eds. Physics of Sun & Star Spots (IAU S273) 2011. (Proceedings of the International Astronomical Union Symposia & Colloquia Ser.). (ENG., Illus.). 526p. 125.00 ***(978-0-521-76062-1(3))*** Cambridge Univ. Pr.

Ciufolini, Ignazio & Matzner, Richard A., eds. General Relativity & John Archibald Wheeler. 2010. (Astrophysics & Space Science Library). (ENG., Illus.). 490p. 159.00 *(978-90-481-3734-3(9),* 9048137349) Springer.

Clarke, Cathie & Carswell, Bob. Principles of Astrophysical Fluid Dynamics. 2007. (ENG., Illus.). 336p. 87.00 *(978-0-521-85331-6(1))* Cambridge Univ. Pr.

Colpi, Monica. Physics of Relativistic Objects in Compact Binaries: From Birth to Coalescence. 2009. (Astrophysics & Space Science Library). (Illus.). 604p. 199.00 *(978-1-4020-9263-3(6))* Springer.

Comastri, A., et al, eds. X-Ray Astronomy 2009; Present Status, Multi-wavelength Approach & Future Perspectives: Proceedings of the International Conference. 2010. (AIP Conference Proceedings / Astronomy & Astrophysics Ser.). 646p. pap. 324.00 *(978-0-7354-0795-4(9),* 0735407959, AIP Pr.) Springer.

Committee for a Decadal Survey of Astronomy and Astrophysics & National Research Council. New Worlds, New Horizons in Astronomy & Astrophysics. 2011. (ENG.). 324p. 54.95 *(978-0-309-15802-2(8),*; pap. 39.95 *(978-0-309-15799-5(4))* National Academies Pr.

Committee on NASA's Suborbital Research Capabilities & National Research Council. Revitalizing Nasa's Suborbital Program: Advancing Science, Driving Innovation, & Developing Workforce. 2010. (ENG.). 100p. pap. 21.00 *(978-0-309-15083-5(3))* National Academies Pr.

Committee on the Planetary Science Decadal Survey & National Research Council. Vision & Voyages for Planetary Science in the Decade 2013-2022. 2011. (ENG.). 400p. 39.95 *(978-0-309-20954-0(4));* pap. 55.00 ***(978-0-309-22464-2(0))*** National Academies Pr.

Cooray, Asantha. Applications of Halo Approach to Non-Linear Large Scale Structure. 2010. 176p. pap. *(978-3-8383-3672-5(0))* Lambert Academic Publishing.

Cram101 Textbook Reviews. Outlines & Highlights for Galaxies & Cosmology by Francoise Combes, Isbn: 9783540419273. 2011. 186p. pap. 30.95 ***(978-1-61812-146-2(4))*** Cram101 Inc.

—Outlines & Highlights for Introduction to High-Energy Astrophysics by Stephan Rosswog, Isbn: 9780521857697. 2011. 156p. pap. 29.95 ***(978-1-61812-147-9(2))*** Cram101 Inc.

Cram101 Textbook Reviews & Cram101 Textbook Reviews. Outlines & Highlights for Astrophysics of Planet Formation by Philip J Armitage. 2011. 78p. pap. 27.95 ***(978-1-61830-442-1(9))*** Cram101 Inc.

—Outlines & Highlights for Astrophysics of the Diffuse Universe by Michael a Dopit. 2011. 116p. pap. 28.95 ***(978-1-61830-155-9(9))*** Cram101 Inc.

—Outlines & Highlights for Astrophysics Processes: The Physics of Astronomical Phenomena by Hale Bradt. 2011. 126p. pap. 28.95 ***(978-1-61830-125-2(X))*** Cram101 Inc.

—Outlines & Highlights for Numerical Methods in Astrophysics: An Introduction by Peter Bodenheimer. 2011. 60p. pap. 26.95 ***(978-1-61830-557-2(3))*** Cram101 Inc.

—Outlines & Highlights for Physics of the Sun: A First Course by Dermott J. Mullan. 2011. 72p. pap. 27.95 ***(978-1-61830-050-8(4))*** Cram101 Inc.

Cram101 Textbook Reviews Staff. Outlines & Highlights for Astronomy: The Solar System & Beyond by Michael A. Seeds, ISBN. 2009. 300p. pap. 32.95 *(978-1-4286-2107-1(4))* Cram101 Inc.

Cristiani, S., et al, eds. Deep Fields: Proceedings of the ESO Workshop Held at Garching, Germany, 9-12 October 2000. 2010. (ESO Astrophysics Symposia Ser.). (ENG.). xxvi, 379p. pap. 59.95 *(978-3-642-07673-2(4),* 3642076734) Springer.

Dark Matter, Neutrino, & Our Solar System. 2010. 133.00 *(978-981-4304-53-5(0));* pap. 77.00 *(978-981-4304-54-2(9))* World Scientific Publishing Co., Inc.

de Jong, R. S. Island Universes: Structure & Evolution of Disk Galaxies. 2006. (Astrophysics & Space Science Proceedings Ser.: Vol. 3). (Illus.). xxv, 584p. 219.00 *(978-1-4020-5572-0(2),* 1402055722) Springer.

del Toro Iniesta, Jose Carlos. Introduction to Spectropolarimetry. 2007. (ENG., Illus.). 244p. pap. 62.00 *(978-0-521-03648-1(8))* Cambridge Univ. Pr.

Demetriou, Paraskevi, et al, eds. Frontiers in Nuclear Structure, Astrophysics, & Reactions: FINUSTAR 3. 2012. (AIP Conference Proceedings / High Energy Physics Ser.: 1377). (ENG., Illus.). 500p. pap. 178.00 ***(978-0-7354-0937-8(4),*** 0735409374, AIP Pr.) Springer.

Demetriou, Vivian P. Frontiers in Nuclear Structure, Astrophysics & Reactions. 2003. (AIP Conference Proceedings Ser.). (Illus.). 478p. 199.00 *(978-0-7354-0532-5(8))* American Institute of Physics.

Dermer, C. D. High-Energy Radiation from Black Holes - Gamma Rays, Cosmic Rays, & Neutrinos. 2009. (Princeton Series in Astrophysics Ser.). (ENG., Illus.). 568p. (C). 125.00 *(978-0-691-13795-7(1));* pap. 78.50 *(978-0-691-14408-5(7))* Princeton Univ. Pr.

Di, Gesu Vito. Modeling & Simulation in Science. 2007. 167.00 *(978-981-277-944-1(2))* World Scientific Publishing Co., Inc.

Di Salvo, Tiziana, et al, eds. The Multicolored Landscape of Compact Objects & Their Explosive Origins -Week 1 And 2: Cefalu 2006. 2007. (AIP Conference Proceedings / Astronomy & Astrophysics Ser.). (Illus.). 249.00 *(978-0-7354-0434-2(8))* American Institute of Physics.

Dittus, Hansjörg, et al, eds. Lasers, Clocks & Drag-Free Key Technologies: Future High Precision Tests of General Relativity. 2007. (Astrophysics & Space Science Library). (Illus.). 670p. 189.00 *(978-3-540-34376-9(8),* 3540343768) Springer.

Doel, Ronald E. Solar System Astronomy in America: Communities, Patronage, & Interdisciplinary Science, 1920-1960. 2009. (ENG., Illus.). 316p. pap. 46.00 *(978-0-521-11568-1(X))* Cambridge Univ. Pr.

Dopita, Michael A. & Sutherland, Ralph S. Astrophysics of the Diffuse Universe. 2010. (Astronomy & Astrophysics Library). (Illus.). xiv, 439p. pap. 109.00 *(978-3-642-07771-5(4),* 3642077714) Springer.

Dormy, Emmanuel & Soward, Andrew M., eds. Mathematical Aspects of Natural Dynamos. 2007. (Fluid Mechanics of Astrophysics & Geophysics (CRC Press) Ser.). (ENG., Illus.). 504p. 157.95 *(978-1-58488-954-0(3),* Chapman & Hall/CRC) CRC Pr. LLC.

Draine, B. Physics of the Interstellar & Intergalactic Medium. 2010. (Princeton Series in Astrophysics Ser.). (ENG., Illus.). 568p. (C). pap. 65.00 *(978-0-691-12214-4(8))* Princeton Univ. Pr.

Draine, Bruce T. Physics of the Interstellar & Intergalactic Medium. 2010. (Princeton Series in Astrophysics Ser.). (ENG., Illus.). 568p. (C). 125.00 *(978-0-691-12213-7(X))* Princeton Univ. Pr.

Dumitrache, Cristiana, et al, eds. Fifty Years of Romanian Astrophysics. 2007. (AIP Conference Proceedings / Astronomy & Astrophysics Ser.). (Illus.). 352p. 144.00 *(978-0-7354-0400-7(3))* American Institute of Physics.

Dyson, J. E., et al. Diffuse Matter from Star Forming Regions to Active Galaxies: A Volume Honouring John Dyson. 2007. (Astrophysics & Space Science Proceedings Ser.). (Illus.). 342p. 239.00 *(978-1-4020-5424-2(6),* 1402054246) Springer.

Eggleton, Peter. Evolutionary Processes in Binary & Multiple Stars. 2006. (Cambridge Astrophysics Ser.: Vol. 40). (ENG., Illus.). 330p. 155.00 *(978-0-521-85557-0(8))* Cambridge Univ. Pr.

Elmegreen, Bruce G. & Palous, Jan, eds. Triggered Star Formation in a Turbulent Interstellar Medium: Proceedings of the 237th Symposium of the International Astronomical Union Held in Prague, Czech Republic August 14-18 2006. 2007. (Proceedings of the International Astronomical Union Symposia & Colloquia Ser.). (ENG., Illus.). 536p. 149.00 *(978-0-521-86346-9(5))* Cambridge Univ. Pr.

Eng, Elier. The Original Energy Theory: Photogenesis. 2011. 152p. 30.95 ***(978-1-61764-515-0(X))***; pap. 13.95 ***(978-1-61764-513-6(3))*** Palibrio.

Evans, A. & et al. Rs Ophiuchi (2006) & the Recurrent Nova Phenomenon. 2009. 360p. 77.00 *(978-1-58381-674-5(7))* Astronomical Society of the Pacific, The.

Evans, Charles Ross, et al. Frontiers in Numerical Relativity. 2011. (ENG.). 450p. pap. 55.00 ***(978-0-521-11595-7(7))*** Cambridge Univ. Pr.

Falgarone, Edith & Passot, Thierry, eds. Turbulence & Magnetic Fields in Astrophysics. 2010. (Lecture Notes in Physics Ser.). xi, 484p. pap. 159.00 *(978-3-642-05545-4(1),* 3642055451) Springer.

Farrell, Joseph P. The Cosmic War: Interplanetary Warfare, Modern Physics, & Ancient Texts: A Study in Non-Catastrophist Interpretations of Ancient Legends. 2007. (Illus.). 425p. per. 18.95 *(978-1-931882-75-0(4))* Adventures Unlimited Pr.

Federrath, Christoph. Modeling Molecular Cloud & Star Formation. 2010. 212p. pap. *(978-3-8383-6493-3(7))* Lambert Academic Publishing.

Ferreira, J., et al, eds. Jets from Young Stars: Models & Constraints. 2007. (Lecture Notes in Physics Ser.). (Illus.). 228p. 89.95 *(978-3-540-68033-8(0),* 3540680330) Springer.

Feuerbacher, Berndt & Messerschmid, Ernst. From Space to Earth: The Laboratory & Marketplace. 2011. (Illus.). 320p. *(978-0-7643-3776-5(9),* Schiffer Publishing Ltd) Schiffer Publishing, Ltd.

Figueras, Francesca, et al, eds. Highlights of Spanish Astrophysics IV: Proceedings of the VII Scientific Meeting of the Spanish Astronomical Society (SEA) held in Barcelona, September 12-15 2006. 2007. xx, 367p. 199.00 *(978-1-4020-5999-5(X))* Springer.

Fineschi, Silvano & Fennelly, Judy A. Solar Physics & Space Weather Instrumentation III: 4-6 August 2009, San Diego, California, United States. 2009. (Proceedings of SPIE Ser.). (Illus.). 348p. pap. 90.00 *(978-0-8194-7728-6(1))* SPIE.

Fineschi, Silvano & Viereck, Rodney A. Solar Physics & Space Weather Instrumentation II: 26-27 August 2007, San Diego, California, USA. 2007. (Proceedings of SPIE Ser.). (Illus.). 348p. pap. 80.00 *(978-0-8194-6837-6(1))* SPIE.

Foerstner, Abigail. James Van Allen: The First Eight Billion Miles. 2007. (ENG., Illus.). 396p. 37.50 *(978-0-87745-999-6(1))* Univ. of Iowa Pr.

Fridman, Alexei M., et al, eds. Progress in the Study of Astrophysical Discs: Collective & Stochastic Processes & Computational Tools. 2006. (Astrophysics & Space Science Library). (Illus.). xvi, 351p. 189.00 *(978-1-4020-4347-5(3),* 1402043473) Springer.

Frisch, P. C., ed. The Influence of Our Galactic Environment on the Sun, Heliosphere & Planetary System. 2006. (Astrophysics & Space Science Library). (Illus.). xxvi, 413p. 219.00 *(978-1-4020-4397-0(X),* 140204397X) Springer.

Funes, Jose G. & Corsini, Enrico Maria. Formation & Evolution of Galaxy Disks: Proceedings of a Conference Organized by the Vatican Observatory Held at the Centro Convegni Matteo Ricci in Rome, Italy, 1-5 October 2007. 2008. (Astronomical Society of the Pacific Conference Ser.: Vol. 396). (Illus.). xxx, 496p. *(978-1-58381-662-2(3))* Astronomical Society of the Pacific, The.

Futterman, J. A. H., et al. Scattering from Black Holes. 2009. (Cambridge Monographs on Mathematical Physics Ser.). (ENG.). 204p. pap. 48.00 *(978-0-521-11210-9(9))* Cambridge Univ. Pr.

Garcia, Paulo & Ferreira, Joao, eds. Jets from Young Stars IV: From Models to Observations & Experiments. 2009. (Lecture Notes in Physics Ser.). (ENG., Illus.). viii, 252p. 89.95 *(978-3-642-02288-3(X),* 364202288X) Springer.

Garcia, Paulo J. V. Physical Processes in Circumstellar Disks Around Young Stars. 2011. (ENG., Illus.). 440p. pap. 55.00 *(978-0-226-28229-9(5))* Univ. of Chicago Pr.

Garcia, Paulo J. V., ed. Physical Processes in Circumstellar Disks Around Young Stars. 2011. (ENG., Illus.). 440p. 150.00 *(978-0-226-28228-2(7))* Univ. of Chicago Pr.

Gargaud, Muriel, et al, eds. From Suns to Life: A Chronological Approach to the History of Life on Earth. 2006. (Illus.). 372p. 159.00 *(978-0-387-45082-7(3),* 0387450823) Springer.

Gilfanov, Marat, et al, eds. Lighthouses of the Universe: the Most Luminous Celestial Objects & Their Use for Cosmology: Proceedings of the MPA/ESO/MPE/USM Joint Astronomy Conference, Held in Garching, Germany, 6-10 August 2001. 2010. (ESO Astrophysics Symposia Ser.). (ENG.). xiv, 618p. pap. 117.00 *(978-3-642-07846-0(X),* 364207846X) Springer.

Ginzburg, Vladimir. Prime Elements of Ordinary Matter, Dark Matter & Dark Energy - Beyond Standard Model & String Theory. 2007. 401p. 44.95 *(978-1-4303-1874-3(0))* Lulu Enterprises Inc.

Ginzburg, Vladimir B. & Ginzburg, Tatyana V. Prime Elements of Ordinary Matter, Dark Matter & Dark Energy: Beyond Standard Model & String Theory. 2nd ed. 2007. (ENG.). 448p. per. *(978-1-58112-946-5(7))* Universal Pubs.

Giovannelli, Franco & Sabau-Graziati, Lola. The Impact of Space Experiments on Our Knowledge of the Physics of the Universe. 2010. 445p. pap. 219.00 *(978-90-481-6621-3(7),* 9048166217) Springer.

Glass, Ian. Revolutionaries of the Cosmos: The Astro-Physicists. 2008. (ENG., Illus.). 336p. pap. 39.95 *(978-0-19-955025-8(5))* Oxford Univ. Pr., Inc.

Glendenning. Our Place in the Universe. 2007. 85.00 *(978-981-270-068-1(4))* World Scientific Publishing Co., Inc.

Glendenning, Norman K. Our Place in the Universe. 2007. (Illus.). 223p. pap. 43.00 *(978-981-270-069-8(2))* World Scientific Publishing Co., Inc.

Gnedin, Yu N. & Natsvlishvili, T. M. Magnetic Fields of Stars: The Interaction Between Observations & Theory. (Astrophysics & Space Physics Reviews Ser.: Vol. 10, No. 3). 83p. (C). pap. 30.00 *(978-90-5823-063-8(5),* RX10275, Harwood Academic Pubs.) Gordon & Breach Publishing Group.

Golub, Leon & Pasachoff, Jay M. The Solar Corona. 2nd rev. ed. 2009. (ENG., Illus.). 404p. (C). 80.00 *(978-0-521-88201-9(X))* Cambridge Univ. Pr.

Gómez de Castro, Ana I. & Wamsteker, Willem, eds. Fundamental Questions in Astrophysics: Guidelines for Future UV Observatories: Guidelines for Future UV Observatories. 2010. iv, 172p. pap. 139.00 *(978-90-481-7208-5(X),* 904817208X) Springer.

Gonzalo. Intelligible Universe: An Overview of the Last Thirteen Billion Years. 2008. 108.00 *(978-981-279-410-9(7))* World Scientific Publishing Co., Inc.

Gonzalo, Julio A. Intelligible Universe: An Overview of the Last Thirteen Billion Years. 2nd ed. 2008. 350p. pap. 59.00 *(978-981-279-411-6(5))* World Scientific Publishing Co., Inc.

Gopalswamy, Nat, et al, eds. Heliophysical Processes. 2010. (Astrophysics & Space Science Proceedings Ser.). (ENG., Illus.). i, 310p. 299.00 *(978-3-642-11340-6(0),* 3642113400) Springer.

Goss, W. M. & McGee, Richard. Under the Radar: The First Woman in Radio Astronomy: Ruby Payne-Scott. 2009. (Astrophysics & Space Science Library). (ENG., Illus.). xxi, 354p. 159.00 *(978-3-642-03140-3(4),* 3642031404) Springer.

Gough, Douglas, ed. The Scientific Legacy of Fred Hoyle. 2011. (ENG.). 266p. pap. 50.00 *(978-1-107-40286-7(7))* Cambridge Univ. Pr.

Gouveia Dal Pino, Elisabete de. Advances in Plasma Astrophysics (IAU S274) Bonanno, Alfio & Kosovichev, Alexander G., eds. 2011. (Proceedings of the International Astronomical Union Symposia & Colloquia Ser.). (ENG., Illus.). 520p. 125.00 ***(978-0-521-19741-0(4))*** Cambridge Univ. Pr.

Gracia, Jose, et al, eds. Jets from Young Stars V: High Performance Computing & Applications. 2009. (Lecture Notes in Physics Ser.). (Illus.). xi, 227p. 89.95 *(978-3-642-03369-8(5),* 3642033695) Springer.

Gray, David F. The Observation & Analysis of Stellar Photospheres. 3rd rev. ed. 2008. (ENG., Illus.). 552p. (C). pap. 69.00 *(978-0-521-06681-5(6))* Cambridge Univ. Pr.

Gray, Malcolm. Maser Sources in Astrophysics. 2012. (Cambridge Astrophysics Ser.). (ENG., Illus.). 350p. 120.00 ***(978-0-521-87980-4(9))*** Cambridge Univ. Pr.

Gross, David, et al, eds. The Quantum Structure of Space & Time: Proceedings of the 23rd Solvay Conference on Physics. 2007. (Illus.). 272p. 150.00 *(978-981-256-952-3(9));* per. 82.00 *(978-981-256-953-0(7))* World Scientific Publishing Co., Inc.

Guillard, Pierre. Molecular Hydrogen Magie. 2011. 404p. pap. ***(978-3-8433-9405-5(9))*** Lambert Academic Publishing.

Gurevich, Alexandr, et al. Physics of the Pulsar Magnetosphere. 2006. (ENG., Illus.). 436p. pap. 79.00 *(978-0-521-03253-7(9))* Cambridge Univ. Pr.

Gurzadyan, V., et al, eds. VAAmbartsumian: Selected Papers. 2011. (Illus.). 450p. *(978-1-904868-26-2(6),* 4102) Cambridge Scientific Pubs. Ltd.

Guthmann, A. W., et al, eds. Relativistic Flows in Astrophysics. 2010. (Lecture Notes in Physics Ser.). xii, 260p. pap. 99.00 *(978-3-642-07804-0(4),* 3642078044) Springer.

Haas, Fernando. Quantum Plasmas: An Hydrodynamic Approach. 2011. (Springer Series on Atomic, Optical, & Plasma Physics Ser.). (ENG., Illus.). xiii, 206p. 129.00 *(978-1-4419-8200-1(0),* 1441982000) Springer.

Haisch. Zero-Point Field. Date not set. 27.50 *(978-0-8050-5448-4(0));* pap. 14.95 *(978-0-8050-5449-1(9),* Owl Bks.) Holt, Henry & Co.

Hanslmeier, A. & Messerotti, Mauro, eds. Motions in the Solar Atmosphere. 2010. (Astrophysics & Space Science Library). 286p. pap. 199.00 *(978-90-481-5151-6(1),* 9048151511) Springer.

Hanssen, Ramon F. Radar Interferometry: Data Interpretation & Error Analysis. 2010. (Remote Sensing & Digital Image Processing Ser.). 328p. pap. 139.00 *(978-90-481-5696-2(3),* 9048156963) Springer.

Haq, Sami Ul. Measurement of Oscillator Strengths & Photoionization Cross-Sections. 2010. 96p. pap. *(978-3-8383-4686-1(6))* Lambert Academic Publishing.

Hartkopf, William, et al, eds. Binary Stars As Critical Tools & Tests in Contemporary Astrophysics: Proceedings of the 240th Symposium of the International Astronomical Union, Held in Prague, Czech Republic August 22-25, 2006. Harmanec, Petr et al, trs. 2007. (Proceedings of the International Astronomical Union Symposia & Colloquia Ser.). (ENG., Illus.). 500p. 133.99 *(978-0-521-86348-3(1))* Cambridge Univ. Pr.

Hartmann, Lee. Accretion Processes in Star Formation. 2nd rev. ed. 2008. (Cambridge Astrophysics Ser.). (ENG., Illus.). 346p. pap. 85.00 *(978-0-521-53199-3(3))* Cambridge Univ. Pr.

Hartnett, J. G. & Abbott, P. C., eds. Frontiers of Fundamental & Computational Physics: 10th International Symposium. 2010. (AIP Conference Proceedings / Mathematical & Statistical Phsyics Ser.). 240p. pap. 138.00 *(978-0-7354-0793-0(2),* 0735407932, AIP Pr.) Springer.

Harutyunian, Haik, et al, eds. Ambartsumian's Legacy & Active Universe. 2011. (ENG., Illus.). xxiv, 192p. 129.00 *(978-1-4614-0181-0(X),* 146140181X) Springer.

Harwit, Martin. Astrophysical Concepts. 4th ed. (Astronomy & Astrophysics Library). (Illus.). 2010. xvi, 716p. pap. 99.00 *(978-1-4419-2199-4(0),* 1441921990) 2006. 714p. 99.00 *(978-0-387-32943-7(9),* 0387329439) Springer.

Hasan, S. S., et al, eds. Turbulence, Dynamos, Accretion Disks, Pulsars & Collective Plasma Processes: First Kodai-Trieste Workshop on Plasma Astrophysics held at the Kodaikanal Observatory, India, August 27 - September 7 2007. 2010. (Astrophysics & Space Science Proceedings Ser.). xvi, 344p. pap. 199.00 *(978-90-481-8011-0(2),* 9048180112) Springer.

Hasan, S. S. & Banerjee, D., eds. Kodai School on Solar Physics. 2007. (AIP Conference Proceedings / Astronomy & Astrophysics Ser.). 330p. 143.00 *(978-0-7354-0429-8(1))* American Institute of Physics.

Hawking, Stephen W. & Penrose, Roger. The Nature of Space & Time. 2010. (Princeton Science Library). (ENG., Illus.). 160p. pap. 15.95 *(978-0-691-14570-9(9))* Princeton Univ. Pr.

Haynes, Doug. Starlines to the Universe: Third Wave (Galactic) Airlines Book 3. 2011. 384p. pap. 29.95 ***(978-1-4512-2764-2(7))*** PublishAmerica, Inc.

Henriksen, Richard N. Practical Relativity: From First Principles to the Theory of Gravity. 2010. (ENG., Illus.). 288p. 165.00 *(978-0-470-74142-9(2));* pap. 65.00 *(978-0-470-74141-2(4))* Wiley, John & Sons, Inc. (Wiley).

Herndon, J. Marvin. Maverick's Earth & Universe. 2008. (Illus.). 273p. 27.00 *(978-1-4251-4132-5(3));* 276p. 45.00 *(978-1-4251-6831-5(0))* Trafford Publishing.

Hobson, Michael P., et al, eds. Bayesian Methods in Cosmology. 2009. (ENG., Illus.). 316p. 65.00 *(978-0-521-88794-6(1))* Cambridge Univ. Pr.

Hodge, P. The Spiral Galaxy M33. 2011. (Astrophysics & Space Science Library). (ENG., Illus.). xii, 158p. 139.00 ***(978-94-007-2024-4(6),*** 9400720246) Springer.

Horedt, Georg P. Polytropes: Applications in Astrophysics & Related Fields. 2010. (Astrophysics & Space Science Library). viii, 724p. pap. 269.00 *(978-90-481-6645-9(4),* 9048166454) Springer.

Howard, Timothy. Coronal Mass Ejections: An Introduction. 2011. (Astrophysics & Space Science Library). (Illus.). xxiii, 244p. 129.00 *(978-1-4419-8788-4(6),* 1441987886) Springer.

Hoyng, Peter. Relativistic Astrophysics & Cosmology: A Primer. 2010. (Astronomy & Astrophysics Library). (Illus.). xii, 293p. pap. 109.00 *(978-90-481-7141-5(5),* 9048171415) Springer.

Huebner, W. F., et al, eds. Solar Photo Rates for Planetary Atmospheres & Atmospheric Pollutants. 2010. (ENG.). 292p. pap. 236.00 *(978-90-481-4212-5(1),* 9048142121) Springer.

Hughes, D. W., et al, eds. The Solar Tachocline. 2007. (ENG., Illus.). 382p. 202.00 *(978-0-521-86101-4(2))* Cambridge Univ. Pr.

Hunter, G., et al, eds. Causality & Locality in Modern Physics. 2010. (Fundamental Theories of Physics Ser.). 508p. pap. 359.00 *(978-90-481-5092-2(2),* 9048150922) Springer.

Inglis, Mike. Astrophysics Is Easy! An Introduction for the Amateur Astronomer. 2007. (Patrick Moore's Practical Astronomy Ser.). (Illus.). XVIII, 206p. pap. 39.95 (978-1-85233-890-9(3), 1852338903) Springer.

Irwin, Judith A. Astrophysics: Decoding the Cosmos. 2007. (ENG., Illus.). 446p. per. 79.00 (978-0-470-01306-9(0), Wiley) Wiley, John & Sons, Inc.

Irwin, Judith Ann. Astrophysics: Decoding the Cosmos. 2007. (ENG., Illus.). 446p. 210.00 (978-0-470-01305-2(2), Wiley) Wiley, John & Sons, Inc.

Ishiwata. Physics of Self-Organization Systems. 2008. 124.00 (978-981-279-336-2(4)) World Scientific Publishing Co., Inc.

Joardar, S., et al. Astronomy & Astrophysics. (Illus.). 2008. 364p. 103.95 (978-1-934015-05-6(9)) 2009. vi, 364p. 82.95 (978-0-7637-7786-9(2)) Jones & Bartlett Learning, LLC.

Johnson, Les, et al. Paradise Regained: The Regreening of Earth. 2010. (ENG., Illus.). xxviii, 180p. 27.50 (978-0-387-79985-8(0), 0387799850) Springer.

Johnson, Stephen B. Space Exploration & Humanity: A Historical Encyclopedia, 2 vols. 2010. (Illus.). E-Book (978-1-85109-519-3(5)) ABC-CLIO, LLC.

Jong, R. S. de. Island Universes: Structure & Evolution of Disk Galaxies. 2010. (Astrophysics & Space Science Proceedings Ser.). xxiv, 584p. pap. 219.00 (978-90-481-7398-3(1), 9048173981) Springer.

Joshi, Pankaj S. Gravitational Collapse & Spacetime Singularities. 2007. (Cambridge Monographs on Mathematical Physics). (ENG., Illus.). 284p. 123.00 (978-0-521-87104-4(2)) Cambridge Univ. Pr.

Kadomsev, B. B. On the Pulsar. 2009. 148p. 28.00 (978-981-4289-72-6(8)); 150p. pap. 26.00 (978-981-4289-73-3(6)) World Scientific Publishing Co., Inc.

Kang, Young Woon. Seventh Pacific Rim Conference on Stellar Astrophysics. 2007. (Astronomical Society of the Pacific Conference Ser.: Vol. 362). 322p. 77.00 (978-1-58381-230-3(X)) Astronomical Society of the Pacific, The.

Karshenboim, Savely G. & Peik, Ekkehard, eds. Astrophysics, Clocks & Fundamental Constants. 2010. (Lecture Notes in Physics Ser.). (ENG., Illus.). xviii, 346p. pap. 169.00 (978-3-642-06025-0(0), 3642060250) Springer.

Khazanov, George V. Kinetic Theory of the Inner Magnetospheric Plasma. 2010. (Astrophysics & Space Science Library). (Illus.). xx, 581p. 229.00 (978-1-4419-6796-1(6), 1441967966) Springer.

Khlopov, Maxim Y & Rubin, Sergei G. Cosmological Pattern of Microphysics in the Inflationary Universe. 2010. (Fundamental Theories of Physics Ser.). xv, 291p. pap. 219.00 (978-90-481-6695-4(0), 9048166950) Springer.

Khomich, Vladislav Yu, et al. Airglow as an Indicator of Upper Atmospheric Structure & Dynamics. 2010. (ENG., Illus.). xvi, 740p. pap. 289.00 (978-3-642-09500-9(3), 3642095003) Springer.

Kieda, David B. & Gondolo, P. Proceedings of the 2009 Snowbird Particle Astrophysics & Cosmology Workshop (SNOWPAC 2009) Proceedings of a Workshop Held at Snowbird, Utah, USA, 1-7 February 2009. 2010. (Illus.). ix, 169p. (978-1-58381-733-9(6)); (978-1-58381-732-2(8)) Astronomical Society of the Pacific, The.

Kim, Dong-Woo & Pellegrini, Silvia, eds. Hot Interstellar Matter in Elliptical Galaxies. 2011. (Astrophysics & Space Science Library). (ENG., Illus.). vii, 282p. 129.00 (**978-1-4614-0579-5(3)**, 1461405793) Springer.

Kipping, David M. The Transits of Extrasolar Planets with Moons. 2011. (Springer Theses Ser.). (ENG., Illus.). xvii, 200p. 129.00 (**978-3-642-22268-9(4)**, 3642222684) Springer.

Kirk, J. G., et al. Plasma Astrophysics: Saas-Fee Advanced Course 24. Lecture Notes 1994. Swiss Society for Astrophysics & Astronomy. Benz, A. O. & Courvoisier, T. J. -L., eds. 2011. (Saas-Fee Advanced Courses Ser.). (ENG., Illus.). xii, 324p. pap. 79.95 (978-3-642-08202-3(5), 3642082025) Springer.

Kirk, J.G., et al. Plasma Astrophysics: Saas-Fee Advanced Course 24. Lecture Notes 1994. Swiss Society for Astrophysics & Astronomy. Benz, Arnold O. & Courvoisier, T.J.-L., eds. 2008. (Saas-Fee Advanced Courses Ser.). (Illus.). xii, 324p. 79.95 (978-3-540-58327-1(0)) Springer.

Kitchin, C. R. Astrophysical Techniques, Fifth Edition. 5th rev. ed. 2008. (ENG., Illus.). 592p. (C). 75.95 (978-1-4200-8243-2(4), CRC Press) Taylor & Francis Group GBR. Dist: Taylor & Francis Group.

Klapdor-kleingrothaus, Hans Volker. Dark Matter in Astrophysics & Particle Physics - Proceedings of the 7th International Heidelberg Conference on Dark 2009. 2009. 604p. 203.00 (978-981-4293-78-5(4)) World Scientific Publishing Co., Inc.

Klapdor-Kleingrothaus, Hans Volker & Arnowitt, Richard, eds. Dark Matter in Astro- & Particle Physics: Proceedings of the International Conference DARK 2004, College Station, USA, 3-9 October 2004. 2010. (ENG., Illus.). xx, 665p. pap. 389.00 (978-3-642-06581-1(3), 3642065813) Springer.

Klein, Ludwig, ed. Energy Conversion & Particle Acceleration in the Solar Corona. 2010. (Lecture Notes in Physics Ser.). x, 318p. pap. 109.00 (978-3-642-05546-1(X), 364205546X) Springer.

Knight, Christopher & Butler, Alan. Who Built the Moon? 2007. (ENG., Illus.). 272p. per. 19.95 (978-1-84293-163-9(6), Watkins Publishing) Duncan Baird Pubs. GBR. Dist: Sterling Publishing Co., Inc.

KODUKULA, Siva Prasad. Double relativity effect&film theory of the Universe. 2009. 67p. pap. 37.60 (978-0-557-07712-0(5)) Lulu Enterprises Inc.

Kogure, Tomokazu & Leung, Kam-Ching. The Astrophysics of Emission Line Stars. 2007. (Astrophysics & Space Science Library). (Illus.). xiv, 537p. 259.00 (978-0-387-34500-0(0), 0387345000) Springer.

Kolb, Ulrich. Extreme Environment Astrophysics. 2010. (ENG., Illus.). 288p. (C). 130.00 (978-0-521-19344-3(3)); pap. 59.99 (978-0-521-18785-5(0)) Cambridge Univ. Pr.

Krasinski, Andrzej. Inhomogeneous Cosmological Models. 2006. (ENG., Illus.). 336p. pap. 76.00 (978-0-521-03017-5(X)) Cambridge Univ. Pr.

Krawczynski, Henric, et al, eds. Relativistic Jets from Active Galactic Nuclei. 2012. (ENG., Illus.). 426p. 135.00 (**978-3-527-41037-8(6)**, Wiley-VCH) Wiley, John & Sons, Inc.

Kukovinets, O. S. Astrophysics & Condensed Matter, Vol. 262. 2008. (Horizons in World Physics Ser.). 149.00 (978-1-60456-332-0(X)) Nova Science Pubs., Inc.

Kunow, H., et al, eds. Coronal Mass Ejections. 2007. (Space Sciences Series of ISSI Ser.). (Illus.). vi, 484p. 229.00 (978-0-387-45086-5(6), 0387450866) Springer.

Kupka, Friedrich, et al. Convection in Astrophysics: Proceedings of the 239th Symposium of the International Astronomical Union Held in Prague, Czech Republic, 21-25 August 2006. Kupka, Friedrich et al, eds. 2007. (Proceedings of the International Astronomical Union Symposia & Colloquia Ser.). (ENG., Illus.). 550p. 133.00 (978-0-521-86349-0(X)) Cambridge Univ. Pr.

Kursunogammalu, Behram N., et al, eds. Physics of Mass. 2010. (ENG.). 300p. pap. 205.00 (978-1-4419-3305-8(0), 1441933050) Springer.

Kwok, Sun. The Origin & Evolution of Planetary Nebulae. 2007. (Cambridge Astrophysics Ser.). (ENG.). 260p. pap. 56.00 (978-0-521-03907-9(X)) Cambridge Univ. Pr.

—Physics & Chemistry of the Interstellar Medium. 2006. (Illus.). 569p. 92.59 (978-1-891389-46-7(7)) Univ. Science Bks.

Kyrala, George A., ed. High Energy Density Laboratory Astrophysics. 2010. (ENG.). viii, 404p. pap. 189.00 (978-90-481-6880-4(5), 9048168805) Springer.

Lämmerzahl, C., et al, eds. Gyros, Clocks, Interferometers.... Testing Relativistic Gravity in Space. 2010. (Lecture Notes in Physics Ser.). xvii, 507p. pap. 139.00 (978-3-642-07450-9(2), 3642074502) Springer.

Lang, Kenneth R. Parting the Cosmic Veil. 2006. (Illus.). 229p. 44.95 (978-0-387-30735-0(4), 0387307354) Springer.

Lang-Wescott, Martha, ed. Asteroid Mechanics, 1925-2006, 2 vols., Vol. II. (Asteroid Ephemerides Ser.). 80p. 15.95 (978-0-9619852-4-0(0)) Treehouse Mountain.

Lebedev, Sergey V., ed. High Energy Density Laboratory Astrophysics. 2010. vi, 346p. pap. 199.00 (978-90-481-7519-2(4), 9048175194) Springer.

LeBlanc, Francis. An Introduction to Stellar Astrophysics. 2010. (ENG., Illus.). 352p. 175.00 (978-0-470-69957-7(4)); pap. 60.00 (978-0-470-69956-0(6)) Wiley, John & Sons, Inc. (Wiley).

Lebost, Barry. The Universal Properties of Acceleration: Did Einstein Look the Wrong Way? 2008. (Illus.). 164p. pap. 48.00 (978-1-4389-1251-6(X)) AuthorHouse.

Lee, Da-Shin. Relativistic Astrophysics. 2008. (AIP Conference Proceedings Ser.: Vol. 1059). spiral bd. 125.00 (978-0-7354-0589-9(1)) American Institute of Physics.

Lee, Sabine. From Nuclei to Stars: Festschrift in Honor of Gerald E Brown. 2011. 400p. 110.00 (**978-981-4329-08-8(8)**) World Scientific Publishing Co., Inc.

Lena, Pierre, et al. Observational Astrophysics. Lyle, S., tr. 2nd ed. 2010. (Astronomy & Astrophysics Library). (Illus.). xv, 512p. pap. 135.00 (978-3-642-08336-5(6), 3642083366) Springer.

Lèna, Pierre, et al. Observational Astrophysics. Lyle, Stephen, tr. from FRE. 3rd ed. 2012. (Astronomy & Astrophysics Library). (ENG., Illus.). xv, 719p. 179.00 (**978-3-642-21814-9(8)**, 3642218148) Springer.

Letokhov, Vladilen & Johansson, Sveneric. Astrophysical Lasers. 2009. (ENG., Illus.). 304p. 125.00 (978-0-19-954827-9(7)) Oxford Univ. Pr., Inc.

LeVeque, Randall J., et al. Computational Methods for Astrophysical Fluid Flow: Saas-Fee Advanced Course 27. Lecture Notes 1997 Swiss Society for Astrophysics & Astronomy. Steiner, Oskar & Gautschy, A., eds. 2010. (Saas-Fee Advanced Courses Ser.). (ENG., Illus.). xiv, 508p. pap. 69.95 (978-3-642-08412-6(5), 3642084125) Springer.

Levin, E. M. Dynamic Analysis of Space Tether Missions. 2007. (Illus.). vii, 453p. (978-0-87703-537-4(7)) Univelt, Inc.

Levin, Eugene. Dynamic Analysis of Space Tether Missions. 2007. (Advances in the Astronautical Sciences Ser.: Vol. 126). 462p. pap. 110.00 (978-0-87703-538-1(5)) Univelt, Inc.

Liebergot, Sy & Harland, David M. Apollo EECOM: Journey of a Lifetime. 2nd ed. 2008. (Apogee Books Space Ser.). (ENG., Illus.). 216p. pap. 21.95 (978-1-894959-88-9(4)) Collector's Guide Publishing, Inc. CAN. Dist: Independent Pubs. Group.

Lipatov, Alexander S. The Hybrid Multiscale Simulation Technology: An Introduction with Application to Astrophysical & Laboratory Plasmas. 2010. (Scientific Computation Ser.). (Illus.). xviii, 403p. pap. 179.00 (978-3-642-07508-7(8), 3642075088) Springer.

Literature, Grade 6, Vol. 3. Beman Assocs.

Literature, Grade 6. tchr. ed. 41.95 (978-0-382-40672-0(9)) Cobblestone Publishing Co.

Lites, Bruce W. The Second Hinode Science Meeting: Beyond Discovery — Toward Understanding. 2009. (Illus.). xxvi, 465p. (978-1-58381-710-0(7)); (978-1-58381-711-7(5)) Astronomical Society of the Pacific, The.

Liu, Shuo. The Limiting Background in a Detector Testing Facility for Supercdms. 2011. 116p. pap. (**978-3-8443-8043-9(4)**) Lambert Academic Publishing.

Livio, Mario & Brown, Thomas M., eds. The Local Group as an Astrophysical Laboratory: Proceedings of the Space Telescope Science Institute Symposium, Held in Baltimore, Maryland May 5-8 2003. 2011. (Space Telescope Science Institute Symposium Ser.). (ENG.). 238p. pap. 39.99 (978-0-521-17533-3(X)) Cambridge Univ. Pr.

Livio, Mario & Koekemoer, Anton M., eds. Black Holes. 2011. (Space Telescope Science Institute Symposium Ser.). (ENG., Illus.). 332p. 115.00 (978-1-107-00553-2(1)) Cambridge Univ. Pr.

Loaiza, Pia, ed. Topical Workshop on Low Radioactivity Techniques: Lrt 2006. 2007. (AIP Conference Proceedings / Astronomy & Astrophysics Ser.). (Illus.). 152p. 160.00 (978-0-7354-0402-1(X)) American Institute of Physics.

Lobanov, A. P., et al, eds. Exploring the Cosmic Frontier: Astrophysical Instruments for the 21st Century. 2010. (ESO Astrophysics Symposia Ser.). (Illus.). xxviii, 271p. pap. 99.00 (978-3-642-07259-8(3), 3642072593) Springer.

Lobanov, Andrei, et al, eds. Exploring the Cosmic Frontier: Astrophysical Instruments for the 21st Century. 2006. (ESO Astrophysics Symposia Ser.). (Illus.). xxviii, 271p. 99.00 (978-3-540-39755-7(8), 3540397558) Springer.

Longair, Malcolm S. The Cosmic Century: A History of Astrophysics & Cosmology. 2006. (ENG., Illus.). 565p. 83.00 (978-0-521-47436-8(1)) Cambridge Univ. Pr.

Luo, Jun. Gravitation & Astrophysics - Proceedings of the Ninth Asia-Pacific International Conference. 2010. 372p. 108.00 (978-981-4307-66-6(1)) World Scientific Publishing Co., Inc.

Maccarone, Thomas J., et al, eds. From X-ray Binaries to Quasars: Black Holes on All Mass Scales: Black Holes on All Mass Scales. 2010. (Illus.). vi, 288p. pap. 149.00 (978-90-481-7037-1(0), 9048170370) Springer.

Machette, Michael N., et al. Terrestrial Cosmogenic-Nuclide Dating of Alluvial Fans in Death Valley, California. 2008. (Illus.). v, 44p. (978-1-4113-2187-8(1)) United States Geological Survey.

Macquart, J.-P. & Fender, R. P., eds. Circular Polarisation from Relativistic Jet Sources. 2010. 208p. pap. 85.00 (978-90-481-6439-4(7), 9048164397) Springer.

Maoz, Dan. Astrophysics in a Nutshell. 2007. (In a Nutshell Ser.). (ENG., Illus.). 268p. (C). 75.00 (978-0-691-12584-8(8)) Princeton Univ. Pr.

Mason, John, ed. Astrophysics Update 2. 2010. (Springer Praxis Books / Astronomy & Planetary Sciences Ser.). xiv, 398p. pap. 189.00 (978-3-642-06778-5(6), 3642067786) Springer.

Massaglia, Silvano, et al, eds. Virtual Astrophysical Jets. 2010. xvi, 269p. pap. 139.00 (978-90-481-5856-0(7), 9048158567) Springer.

Massardi, Marcella. The Extragalactic Sources at Mm Wavelengths. 2010. 168p. pap. (978-3-8383-6921-1(1)) Lambert Academic Publishing.

Matos, Tonatiuh, et al, eds. Solar, Stellar & Galactic Connections Between Particle Physics & Astrophysics. 2007. (Astrophysics & Space Science Proceedings Ser.). (Illus.). 303p. 239.00 (978-1-4020-5574-4(9), 1402055749) Springer London, Ltd. GBR. Dist: Springer.

McCutcheon, Mark. The Final Theory: Rethinking Our Scientific Legacy. 2nd ed. 2010. 470p. pap. (978-1-59942-866-6(0)) Universal Pubs.

Mebarki, N. & Mimouni, J., eds. The Third Algerian Workshop on Astronomy & Astrophysics. 2011. (AIP Conference Proceedings / Astronomy & Astrophysics Ser.). 304p. pap. 157.00 (978-0-7354-0852-4(1), 0735408521, AIP Pr.) Springer.

Mediavilla, Evencio, et al, eds. 3D Spectroscopy in Astronomy. 2010. (Canary Islands Winter School of Astrophysics Ser.). (ENG., Illus.). 288p. 115.00 (978-0-521-89541-5(3)) Cambridge Univ. Pr.

Meier, David L. Black Hole Astrophysics: The Engine Paradigm. 2012. (Springer Praxis Books / Astronomy & Planetary Sciences Ser.). (ENG., Illus.). 850p. 139.00 (978-3-642-01935-7(8), 3642019358) Springer.

Meinel, Reinhard, et al. Relativistic Figures of Equilibrium. 2008. (ENG., Illus.). 228p. 135.00 (978-0-521-86383-4(X)) Cambridge Univ. Pr.

Merrill, Ronald T. Our Magnetic Earth: The Science of Geomagnetism. 2010. (Illus.). 272p. 25.00 (978-0-226-52050-6(1)) Univ. of Chicago Pr.

Mészáros, Péter. The High Energy Universe: Ultra-High Energy Events in Astrophysics & Cosmology. 2010. (ENG., Illus.). 222p. (C). 59.00 (978-0-521-51700-3(1)) Cambridge Univ. Pr.

Metzger, Lenard. The Theories of Lenard Metzger. 2010. 184p. pap. 14.92 (978-0-557-51450-2(9)) Lulu Enterprises Inc.

Michelle, Harley. Radiation Recoil from Spinning Black Hole Mergers. 2010. 88p. pap. (978-3-8383-4008-1(6)) Lambert Academic Publishing.

Miglio, Andrea, et al, eds. Red Giants as Probes of the Structure & Evolution of the Milky Way. 2012. (Astrophysics & Space Science Proceedings Ser.). (ENG., Illus.). xiv, 182p. 199.00 (**978-3-642-18417-8(0)**, 3642184170) Springer.

Milhorn, H. Thomas. The History of Astronomy & Astrophysics: A Biographical Approach. 2008. 340p. pap. 15.95 (978-1-60264-258-4(3)) Virtualbookworm.com Publishing, Inc.

Miller, Ron & Furniss, Tim. Extreme Space. 2008. (Extreme Wonders Ser.). (Illus.). 224p. pap. 15.95 (978-0-06-089145-9(9)) HarperCollins Pubs.

Milone, Eugene F. & Wilson, William. Solar System Astrophysics: A Text for the Science of Planetary Systems, 2 vols. 2008. (Astronomy & Astrophysics Library). (Illus.). 1000p. 169.00 (978-0-387-73153-7(9)) Springer.

—Solar System Astrophysics Vol. 2: A Text for the Science of Planetary Systems, 2 vols. 2008. (Astronomy & Astrophysics Library). (Illus.). 500p. 119.00 (978-0-387-73156-8(3)) Springer.

Milone, Eugene F. & Wilson, William J. F. Solar System Astrophysics: Background Science & the Inner Solar System, 2 vols. 2008. (Astronomy & Astrophysics Library). (Illus.). 257p. 119.00 (978-0-387-73154-4(7)) Springer.

Miner, Ellis D., et al. Planetary Ring Systems. 2006. (Springer Praxis Books / Space Exploration Ser.). (Illus.). 234p. per. 52.95 (978-0-387-34177-4(3), 0387341773, Springer-Praxis) Springer.

Mioc, Vasile. Exploring the Solar System & the Universe. Mioc, Vasile et al, eds. 2008. (AIP Conference Proceedings / Astronomy & Astrophysics Ser.). 452p. 229.00 (978-0-7354-0571-4(9)) American Institute of Physics.

Mioc, Vasile, et al, eds. Flows, Boundaries, Interactions. 2007. (AIP Conference Proceedings / Astronomy & Astrophysics Ser.). (Illus.). 228p. 89.00 (978-0-7354-0445-8(3)) American Institute of Physics.

Mirza, Babur. Gravitoelectromagnetic Fields. 2009. 92p. pap. (978-3-639-14476-5(7)) VDM Verlag Dr. Mueller e.K.

Moffat, John W. Reinventing Gravity: A Physicist Dares to Take on Einstein. 2009. 272p. pap. 14.95 (978-0-06-117089-8(5)) HarperCollins Pubs.

Moitinho, André & Alves, João, eds. Star Clusters in the Era of Large Surveys: Proceedings of Symposium 5 of JENAM 2010. 2011. (Astrophysics & Space Science Proceedings Ser.). (ENG., Illus.). xiii, 266p. 199.00 (**978-3-642-22112-5(2)**, 3642221122) Springer.

Molokov, Sergei S., et al, eds. Magnetohydrodynamics: Historical Evolution & Trends. 2010. (Fluid Mechanics & Its Applications Ser.). x, 410p. pap. 179.00 (978-90-481-7205-4(5), 9048172055) Springer.

Monteiro, Mario Joao P. F. G, ed. Evolution & Seismic Tools for Stellar Astrophysics. 2008. (Illus.). vi, 262p. 229.00 (978-1-4020-9439-2(6)) Springer.

Monteiro, Mário J. P. F. G., ed. The Unsolved Universe: Challenges for the Future: Jenam 2002. 2010. 150p. pap. 66.00 (978-90-481-6447-9(8), 9048164478) Springer.

Moreau, R. J. Magnetohydrodynamics. 2010. (Fluid Mechanics & Its Applications Ser.). 336p. pap. 189.00 (978-90-481-4077-0(3), 9048140773) Springer.

Muindi, Damian. The Minimal Resolution Conjecture for Projective Space of Dimension. 2011. 64p. pap. (**978-3-8433-8937-2(3)**) Lambert Academic Publishing.

Mullan, Dermott J. Physics of the Sun: A First Course. 2009. (Pure & Applied Physics Ser.). (ENG., Illus.). 390p. (C). 83.95 (978-1-4200-8307-1(4), Chapman & Hall/CRC) CRC Pr. LLC.

Nagendra, K. N. & Stenflo, Jan Olof, eds. Solar Polarization. 2010. (Astrophysics & Space Science Library). (Illus.). 552p. pap. 379.00 (978-90-481-5261-2(5), 9048152615) Springer.

Narlikar, Jayant Vishnu. Violent Phenomena in the Universe. 2007. (Dover Science Bks.). (ENG., Illus.). 240p. per. 14.95 (978-0-486-45797-0(4)) Dover Pubns., Inc.

NASA Astrophysics Performance Assessment Committee & National Research Council. A Performance Assessment of NASA's Astrophysics Program. 2007. (ENG.). 60p. pap. 21.00 (978-0-309-10490-6(4)) National Academies Pr.

National Research Council Staff. Approaches to Future Space Cooperation & Competition in a Globalizing World: Summary of a Workshop. 2009. (ENG.). 68p. pap. 21.00 (978-0-309-13996-0(1)) National Academies Pr.

Nelson, Dennett Berg. Have Wavelength, Will Travel. 2009. 80p. pap. 8.95 (978-1-4401-4488-2(5)) iUniverse, Inc.

Nester, James M., et al, eds. Gravitation & Astrophysics: On the Occasion of the 90th Year of General Relativity: Proceedings of the VII Asia-Pacific International Conference: National Central University, Taiwan, 23-36 November 2005. 2006. (Illus.). 421p. 164.00 (978-981-256-950-9(2)) World Scientific Publishing Co., Inc.

Niemeyer, J. C. & Truran, J. W., eds. Type Ia Supernovae: Theory & Cosmology. 2010. (Cambridge Contemporary Astrophysics Ser.). (ENG., Illus.). 148p. pap. 32.99 (978-0-521-12653-3(3)) Cambridge Univ. Pr.

Novikov, I. & Frolov, V. Physics of Black Holes. Kisin, V. I. & Yankovsky, E. M., trs. 2010. (Fundamental Theories of Physics Ser.). 360p. pap. 379.00 (978-90-481-8448-4(7), 9048184487) Springer.

Pagels, Heinz R. Perfect Symmetry: The Search for the Beginning of Time. 2009. (ENG.). 400p. pap. 16.00 (978-1-4391-4888-4(0)) Simon & Schuster.

Panek, Richard. The 4 Percent Universe: Dark Matter, Dark Energy, & the Race to Discover the Rest of Reality. 2011. (ENG.). 320p. pap. 15.95 (978-0-547-57757-9(5), Mariner Bks.) Houghton Mifflin Harcourt Trade & Reference Pubs.

Panel on Implementing Recommendations from New Worlds, New Horizons Decadal Survey & National Research Council. Report of the Panel on Implementing Recommendations from the New Worlds, New Horizons Decadal Survey. 2012. (ENG.). 36p. pap. 15.00 (978-0-309-16373-6(0)) National Academies Pr.

Papaderos, Polychronis, et al, eds. Dwarf Galaxies: Keys to Galaxy Formation & Evolution: Proceedings of Symposium 3 of JENAM 2010. 2012. (Astrophysics & Space Science Proceedings Ser.). (ENG., Illus.). xxii, 319p. 259.00 (**978-3-642-22017-3(7)**, 3642220177) Springer.

Papantonopoulos, Lefteris. Physics of Black Holes. 2009. (Lecture Notes in Physics Ser.). (ENG., Illus.). xvi, 511p. 129.00 (978-3-540-88459-0(9)) Springer.

Parry, Dan. Moonshot: The Inside Story of Mankind's Greatest Adventure. 2009. (ENG., Illus.). 352p. pap. 22.95 (978-0-09-192837-7(0)) Ebury Publishing GBR. Dist: Independent Pubs. Group.

Partridge, R. B. 3k: The Cosmic Microwave Background Radiation. 2007. (Cambridge Astrophysics Ser.: Vol. 25). (ENG., Illus.). 396p. pap. 79.00 (978-0-521-35808-8(6)) Cambridge Univ. Pr.

Pazameta. An Introduction to Solar System Physics. 2011. 40.95 (978-0-7637-4680-3(0)) Jones & Bartlett Learning, LLC.

Perryman, Michael. Astronomical Applications of Astrometry: Ten Years of Exploitation of the Hipparcos Satellite Data. 2008. (ENG., Illus.). 692p. 132.00 (978-0-521-51489-7(4)) Cambridge Univ. Pr.

Phelan, Don. High Time Resolution Astrophysics. 2008. (AIP Conference Proceedings Ser.: No. 984). 147.00 (978-0-7354-0503-5(4)) American Institute of Physics.

Phelan, Don, et al, eds. High Time Resolution Astrophysics. (Astrophysics & Space Science Library). 2010. x, 350p. pap. 189.00 (978-90-481-7657-1(3), 9048176573) 2008. 300p. 189.00 (978-1-4020-6517-0(5)) Springer.

Plait, Philip C. Death from the Skies! These Are the Ways the World Will End ... 2008. (ENG.). 336p. (gr. 12-18). 25.95 *(978-0-670-01997-7(6)*, Viking Adult) Penguin Group (USA) Inc.

Plebanski, Jerzy & Krasinski, Andrzej. An Introduction to General Relativity & Cosmology. 2006. (ENG., Illus.). 554p. 116.00 *(978-0-521-85623-2(X))* Cambridge Univ. Pr.

Polk, Kevin Scott. Gaiome: Notes on Ecology, Space Travel & Becoming Cosmic Species. 2007. 300p. pap. 16.95 *(978-1-60145-242-9(X))* Booklocker.com, Inc.

Potter, Paul. Gravitational Manipulation of Domed Craft: UFO Propulsion Dynamics. 2008. (ENG.). 424p. pap. 20.00 *(978-1-931882-91-0(6))* Adventures Unlimited Pr.

Pozzoli, R., et al, eds. Collective Phenomena in Macroscopic Systems: Proceedings of the Conference. 2007. (Illus.). 303p. 124.00 *(978-981-270-705-5(0))* World Scientific Publishing Co., Inc.

Pradhan, Anil K. Atomic Astrophysics & Spectroscopy. Date not set. (Illus.). 400p. 75.00 *(978-0-521-82536-8(9))* Cambridge Univ. Pr.

Prialnik, Dina. An Introduction to the Theory of Stellar Structure & Evolution. 2nd rev. ed. 2009. (ENG., Illus.). 330p. (C). 80.00 *(978-0-521-86604-0(9))* Cambridge Univ. Pr.

Pringle, James E. & King, Andrew. Astrophysical Flows. 2007. (ENG., Illus.). 216p. 108.00 *(978-0-521-86936-2(6))* Cambridge Univ. Pr.

Prosper, Harrison B. & Danilov, Michael. Techniques & Concepts of High Energy Physics XII. 2003. (NATO Science Series II: Mathematics, Physics & Chemistry Ser.). (Illus.). 392p. 199.00 *(978-1-4020-1590-8(9))* Springer.

Puglielli, David. Galaxy Modelling Using Bayesian Statistics. 2010. 136p. pap. *(978-3-8383-1833-2(1))* Lambert Academic Publishing.

Rajantie, Arttu. Particles, Strings, & Cosmology. 2007. (AIP Conference Proceedings / High Energy Physics Ser.). (Illus.). xii, 477p. 167.00 *(978-0-7354-0471-7(2))* American Institute of Physics.

Randich, Sofia & Pasquini, Luca, eds. Chemical Abundances & Mixing in Stars in the Milky Way & its Satellites: Proceedings of the ESO Workshop held in Castiglione della Pescaia, Italy, 13-17 September 2004. 2006. (ESO Astrophysics Symposia Ser.). (Illus.). xxiv, 391p. 129.00 *(978-3-540-34135-2(8)*, 3540341358) Springer.

Ratcliffe, Martin. State of the Universe: Images, Discoveries, & Events. 2007. (Springer Praxis Books / Popular Astronomy Ser.). (Illus.). 183p. per. 29.95 *(978-0-387-71674-9(2)*, 0387716742, Springer-Praxis) Springer.

Redondi, Pietro, et al, eds. The Scientific Legacy of Beppo Occhialini. 2010. (ENG.). xii, 312p. pap. 109.00 *(978-3-642-07216-1(X)*, 364207216X) Springer.

Renzini, Alvio & Greggio, Laura. Stellar Populations: A User Guide from Low to High Redshift. 2011. (ENG., Illus.). 317p. 140.00 ***(978-3-527-40918-1(1)***, Wiley-VCH) Wiley, John & Sons, Inc.

Rickey, Vern G. The Creation & the Extinction: Global Warming & Ice. 2009. 138p. pap. 13.99 *(978-1-4490-0788-1(0))* AuthorHouse.

Ripa, Jakub. Statistical Analysis of the Observable Data of Gamma-Ray Bursts. 2011. 140p. pap. ***(978-3-8454-1241-2(0))*** Lambert Academic Publishing.

Ritter, Gordon. Planets, Stars, & Galaxies. 2007. (Physics in Action Ser.). (Illus.). 120p. (YA). (gr. 9-12). lib. bdg. 35.00 *(978-0-7910-8933-0(9))* Facts On File, Inc.

Romero, Gustavo E., et al, eds. Jets at All Scales (IAU S275) 2011. (Proceedings of the International Astronomical Union Symposia & Colloquia Ser.). (ENG., Illus.). 440p. 125.00 *(978-0-521-76607-4(9))* Cambridge Univ. Pr.

Röser, Siegfried, ed. Reviews in Modern Astronomy Vol. 21: Formation & Evolution of Cosmic Structures, Volume 21. 2009. (Reviews in Modern Astronomy Ser.: 11). (ENG., Illus.). 295p. 175.00 *(978-3-527-40910-5(6)*, Wiley-VCH) Wiley, John & Sons, Inc.

Ross, Ronald G., ed. Cryocoolers 13. 2010. xvi, 726p. pap. 289.00 *(978-1-4419-3670-7(X)*, 144193670X) Springer.

Ruffini, Remo & Vereshchagin, Gregory, eds. The Sun, the Stars, the Universe & General Relativity: International Conference in Honor of Ya. B. Zeldovich's 95th Anniversary. 2010. (AIP Conference Proceedings / Astronomy & Astrophysics Ser.). 216p. 179.00 *(978-0-7354-0742-8(8)*, 0735407428, AIP Pr.) Springer.

Russell, C. T. The Mars Plasma Environment. 2007. (Illus.). 501p. 169.00 *(978-0-387-70941-3(X))* Springer.

Ryden, Barbara & Peterson, Bradley M. Foundations of Astrophysics. 2009. (ENG., Illus.). 608p. (C). 160.00 *(978-0-321-59558-4(0))* Addison Wesley.

Saha, Swapan K. Aperture Synthesis: Methods & Applications to Optical Astronomy. 2011. (Illus.). xxiii, 466p. E-Book ***(978-1-4419-5710-8(3))*** Springer.

Saikia, D. J., et al. Fluid Flows to Black Holes: A Tribute to S. Chandrasekhar on His Birth Centenary. 2011. 312p. 108.00 ***(978-981-4374-76-7(8))*** World Scientific Publishing Co., Inc.

Sasselov, Dimitar. The Life of Super-Earths: How the Hunt for Alien Worlds & Artificial Cells Will Revolutionize Life on Our Planet. 2012. (ENG., Illus.). 240p. (gr. 9). 25.99 *(978-0-465-02193-2(X))* Basic Bks.

Sato, Katsuhiko & Hisano, Junji, eds. Energy Budget in the High Energy Universe: Proceedings of the International Workshop. 2007. (Illus.). 398p. 184.00 *(978-981-270-010-0(2))* World Scientific Publishing Co., Inc.

Saunders, William & Haas, George. The Martian Codex: More Reflections from Mars. 2009. (ENG., Illus.). 264p. pap. 19.95 *(978-1-55643-814-1(1))* North Atlantic Bks.

Saviane, Ivo, et al, eds. Groups of Galaxies in the Nearby Universe: Proceedings of the ESO Workshop held at Santiago de Chile, December 5 - 9 2005. 2010. (ESO Astrophysics Symposia Ser.). (Illus.). xxii, 400p. pap. 119.00 *(978-3-642-09026-4(5)*, 3642090265) Springer.

—Groups of Galaxies in the Nearby Universe: Proceedings of the ESO Workshop Held at Santiago de Chile, December 5-9 2005. 2007. (ESO Astrophysics Symposia Ser.). (Illus.). 398p. 119.00 *(978-3-540-71172-8(4)*, 3540711724) Springer.

Scharringhausen, Marco. Mesospheric & Thermospheric Magnesium Species. 2008. 212p. pap. *(978-3-8364-9164-8(6))* VDM Verlag Dr. Mueller e.K.

Schindler, Karl. Physics of Space Plasma Activity. 2006. (ENG., Illus.). 522p. 88.00 *(978-0-521-85897-7(6))* Cambridge Univ. Pr.

Schmadel, Lutz D. Dictionary of Minor Planet Names: Addendum to Fifth Edition: 2006 - 2008. 2009. (ENG., Illus.). viii, 316p. 189.00 *(978-3-642-01964-7(1)*, 3642019641) Springer.

Schmelcher, P. & Schweizer, W., eds. Atoms & Molecules in Strong External Fields. 2010. pap. 225.00 *(978-1-4419-3291-4(7)*, 1441932917) Springer.

Schrijver, C. J. & Zwaan, C. Solar & Stellar Magnetic Activity. 2008. (Cambridge Astrophysics Ser.). (Illus.). 400p. pap. 53.00 *(978-0-521-73986-3(1))* Cambridge Univ. Pr.

Schutz, Bernard. A First Course in General Relativity. 2nd ed. 2009. (ENG., Illus.). 410p. (C). 75.00 *(978-0-521-88705-2(4))* Cambridge Univ. Pr.

Science Frontiers Panels, et al. Panel Reports — New Worlds, New Horizons in Astronomy & Astrophysics. 2011. (ENG.). 548p. pap. 55.00 *(978-0-309-15962-3(8))* National Academies Pr.

Seager, Sara. Exoplanet Atmospheres: Physical Processes. 2010. (Princeton Series in Astrophysics Ser.). (ENG., Illus.). 264p. (C). 89.50 *(978-0-691-11914-4(7))*; pap. 45.00 *(978-0-691-14645-4(4))* Princeton Univ. Pr.

Seeds, Michael A. Horizons: Exploring the Universe. 11th ed. 2009. (ENG.). 448p. (C). pap. 75.95 *(978-1-4390-4602-9(6))* Brooks/Cole.

Shaposhnikov, Nikolai & Titarchuk, Lev. Bursting Neutron Stars. 2008. 160p. pap. *(978-3-639-06888-7(2))* VDM Verlag Dr. Mueller e.K.

Shaviv, Giora. The Life of the Stars: The Controversial Inception & Emergence of the Theory of Stellar Structure Theory. 2009. (ENG., Illus.). xiv, 504p. 129.00 *(978-3-642-02087-2(9)*, 3642020879) Springer.

Shore, S. N., et al. Interacting Binaries: Saas-Fee Advanced Course 22. Lecture Notes 1992. Swiss Society for Astrophysics & Astronomy. Nussbaumer, H. & Orr, Astrid, eds. 2010. (Saas-Fee Advanced Courses Ser.). (Illus.). xvi, 479p. pap. 79.95 *(978-3-642-08166-8(5)*, 3642081665) Springer.

Shore, Steven N. Astrophysical Hydrodynamics: An Introduction. 2nd ed. 2007. (ENG.). 472p. pap. 95.00 *(978-3-527-40669-2(7)*, Wiley-VCH) Wiley, John & Sons, Inc.

Shore, Steven N., et al. Interacting Binaries: Saas-Fee Advanced Course 22. Lecture Notes 1992. Swiss Society for Astrophysics & Astronomy. 2008. (Saas-Fee Advanced Courses Ser.). (Illus.). xvi, 479p. 79.95 *(978-3-540-57014-1(4))* Springer.

Sidharth, B.g. & Sidharth, B. G. Frontiers of Fundamental & Computational Physics: 9th International Symposium, Udine & Trieste, Italy, 7-9 January 2008. 2008. (AIP Conference Proceedings / Astronomy & Astrophysics Ser.). (Illus.). ix, 264p. 145.00 *(978-0-7354-0539-4(5))* American Institute of Physics.

Sidharth, Burra G., et al, eds. Frontiers of Fundamental Physics (FFP 8) Eighth International Symposium. 2007. (AIP Conference Proceedings / Astronomy & Astrophysics Ser.). 290p. 129.00 *(978-0-7354-0412-0(7))* American Institute of Physics.

Siegle, Gerald. Time & Everything. 2011. 96p. 24.99 ***(978-1-4568-3519-4(X))***; pap. 15.99 ***(978-1-4568-3518-7(1))*** Xlibris Corp.

Smarandache, Florentin & Christianto, Victor, eds. Quantization in Astrophysics, Brownian Motion, & Supersymmetry. 2007. (Illus.). 516p. per. 56.65 *(978-81-902190-9-9(X))* Multimedia Larga.

Smith, Michael D. Astrophysical Jets & Beams. 2012. (Cambridge Astrophysics Ser.). (ENG., Illus.). 240p. 105.00 ***(978-0-521-83476-6(7))*** Cambridge Univ. Pr.

Smith, Randall K., et al, eds. The Local Bubble & Beyond II: Proceedings of the International Conference. 2009. (AIP Conference Proceedings / Astronomy & Astrophysics Ser.). 326p. pap. 184.00 *(978-0-7354-0693-3(6)*, 0735406936) American Institute of Physics.

Solano Salinas, Carlos Javier, et al, eds. Cosmic Rays & Astrophysics: Proceedings of the 3rd School on Cosmic Rays & Astrophysics. 2009. (AIP Conference Proceedings / Astronomy & Astrophysics Ser.). 284p. pap. 118.00 *(978-0-7354-0659-9(6))* American Institute of Physics.

Somov, Boris V. Plasma Astrophysics Pt. I: Fundamentals & Practice, 2 vols. 2006. (Astrophysics & Space Science Library: Vol. 340). (Illus.). xi, 437p. (C). 219.00 *(978-0-387-34916-9(2)*, 0387349162) Springer.

—Plasma Astrophysics, Part I: Fundamentals & Practice. 2010. (Astrophysics & Space Science Library). (Illus.). xi, 437p. pap. 219.00 *(978-1-4419-2244-1(X)*, 144192244X) Springer.

—Plasma Astrophysics, Part II: Reconnection & Flares. (Astrophysics & Space Science Library). (Illus.). 2010. xii, 428p. pap. 209.00 *(978-1-4419-2245-8(8)*, 1441922458) 2006. 413p. 209.00 *(978-0-387-34948-0(0)*, 0387349480) Springer.

Soonthornthum, B. The Eighth Pacific Rim Conference on Stellar Astrophysics: A Tribute to Kam-Ching Leung: Proceedings of a Workshop Held at Merlin Beach Hotel, Phuket, Thailand, 5-9 May 2008. 2009. (Illus.). xxv, 374p. *(978-1-58381-685-1(2))*; *(978-1-58381-686-8(0))* Astronomical Society of the Pacific, The.

Sozzetti, Alessandro, et al, eds. The Astrophysics of Planetary Systems (IAU S276) Formation, Structure, & Dynamical Evolution. 2011. (Proceedings of the International Astronomical Union Symposia & Colloquia Ser.). (ENG., Illus.). 598p. 125.00 ***(978-0-521-19652-9(3))*** Cambridge Univ. Pr.

Sreekantan, B. V., ed. Remembering Einstein: Lectures on Physics & Astrophysics. 2010. (ENG., Illus.). 224p. 35.00 *(978-0-19-806449-7(7))* Oxford Univ. Pr., Inc.

Srinivasa Rao, Mynampati. Atmospheres of the Components of Close Binary Stars. 2010. 192p. pap. *(978-3-639-22553-2(8))* VDM Verlag Dr. Mueller e.K.

Stancliffe, Richard J., et al, eds. Unsolved Problems in Stellar Physics: A Conference in Honor of Douglas Gough. 2008. (AIP Conference Proceedings / Astronomy & Astrophysics Ser.). (Illus.). 465p. 187.00 *(978-0-7354-0462-5(3))* American Institute of Physics.

Stefan, V. Nonlinear Electromagnetic Radiation Plasma Interactions. 2008. pap. *(978-1-889545-88-2(0))* Stefan Univ. Pr., The.

Stefl, Stanislav, et al, eds. Active Ob-Stars: Laboratories for Stellar & Circumstellar Physics, CS 361. 2007. (ASP Conference Ser.). (Illus.). xxiv, 573p. 77.00 *(978-1-58381-229-7(6))* Astronomical Society of the Pacific, The.

Stepanov, Alexander, et al. Coronal Seismology: Waves & Oscillations in Stellar Coronae. 2012. (ENG.). 230p. 160.00 ***(978-3-527-40994-5(7)***, Wiley-VCH) Wiley, John & Sons, Inc.

Sterken, C. & Käufl, H. U., eds. Deep Impact as a World Observatory Event: Synergies in Space, Time, & Wavelength: Proceedings of the VUB/ESO Workshop held in Brussels, Belgium, August 7-10 2006. 2008. (ESO Astrophysics Symposia Ser.). 159.00 *(978-3-540-76958-3(7))* Springer.

Steves, B. A., et al, eds. Chaotic Worlds: From Order to Disorder in Gravitational N-Body Dynamical Systems. 2006. (NATO Science Ser.: Vol. 227). (Illus.). xiii, 344p. 189.00 *(978-1-4020-4704-6(5)*, 1402047045) Springer.

—Chaotic Worlds: from Order to Disorder in Gravitational N-Body Dynamical Systems: From Order to Disorder in Gravitational N-Body Dynamical Systems. 2006. (NATO Science Ser.: Vol. 227). (Illus.). XI, 342p. pap. 109.00 *(978-1-4020-4705-3(3)*, 1402047053) Springer.

Steves, B. A. & Roy, Archie E., eds. The Dynamics of Small Bodies in the Solar System: A Major Key to Solar Systems Studies: A Major Key to Solar Systems Studies. 2010. (NATO Science Series C: (closed) Ser.). 624p. pap. 469.00 *(978-90-481-5133-2(3)*, 9048151333) Springer.

Stewart, John, Jr. Science of Stonehenge. 2006. (Astronomers' Universe Ser.). 300p. pap. 39.95 *(978-1-85233-473-4(8)*, 1852334738) Springer.

Storrie-Lombardi, Lisa J. The Science Opportunities of the Warm Spitzer Mission Workshop. 2007. (AIP Conference Proceedings / Astronomy & Astrophysics Ser.). 95.00 *(978-0-7354-0457-1(7))* American Institute of Physics.

Straumann, Norbert. General Relativity: With Applications to Astrophysics. 2010. (Theoretical & Mathematical Physics Ser.). (Illus.). xii, 674p. pap. 109.00 *(978-3-642-06013-7(7)*, 3642060137) Springer.

Susa, Hajime, et al, eds. Tours Symposium on Nuclear Physics & Astrophysics - VII. 2010. (AIP Conference Proceedings / Astronomy & Astrophysics Ser.). (Illus.). 418p. 211.00 *(978-0-7354-0784-8(3)*, 0735407843, AIP Pr.) Springer.

Susskind, Leonard. The Cosmic Landscape: String Theory & the Illusion of Intelligent Design. 2006. (ENG., Illus.). 416p. per. 15.99 *(978-0-316-01333-8(1)*, Back Bay Bks.) Little Brown & Co.

Talbott, David & Thornhill, Wallace. The Electric Universe: A new view of the Earth, the Sun, & the Heavens. 2007. (Illus.). 132p. per. 25.00 *(978-0-9772851-3-6(8))* Mikamar Publishing.

Tamburini, Fabrizio. Aspects of Gravitation in Astrophysics. 2011. 248p. pap. ***(978-3-8443-2788-5(6))*** Lambert Academic Publishing.

Taton, René & Wilson, Curtis, eds. The General History of Astronomy: Volume 2, Planetary Astronomy from the Renaissance to the Rise of Astrophysics. 2009. (General History of Astronomy Ser.). (ENG., Illus.). 296p. (C). pap. 46.00 *(978-0-521-12009-8(8))* Cambridge Univ. Pr.

Tessema, Solomon Belay. Accretion Discs Around Magnetized Stars, in Particular Neutron Stars. 2011. 132p. pap. ***(978-3-8454-1736-3(6))*** Lambert Academic Publishing.

Thomas, John H. & Weiss, Nigel O. Sunspots & Starspots. 2008. (Cambridge Astrophysics Ser.). (ENG., Illus.). 296p. 121.00 *(978-0-521-86003-1(2))* Cambridge Univ. Pr.

Thompson, Ian J. & Nunes, Filomena M. Nuclear Reactions for Astrophysics: Principles, Calculation & Applications of Low-Energy Reactions. 2009. (ENG., Illus.). 480p. 85.00 *(978-0-521-85635-5(3))* Cambridge Univ. Pr

Thompson, Michael J. & Christensen-Dalsgaard, Jorgen, eds. Stellar Astrophysical Fluid Dynamics. 2008. (ENG., Illus.). 432p. pap. 64.00 *(978-0-521-05020-3(0))* Cambridge Univ. Pr.

Thronson, Harley A., et al. Astrophysics in the Next Decade: The James Webb Space Telescope & Concurrent Facilities. 2009. (Astrophysics & Space Science Proceedings Ser.). (ENG., Illus.). xii, 520p. 239.00 *(978-1-4020-9456-9(6))* Springer.

Tielens, Xander. The Physics & Chemistry of the Interstellar Medium. 2010. (Illus.). 509p. pap. 48.00 *(978-0-521-53372-0(4))* Cambridge Univ. Pr.

Treyer, Marie, et al. UP2010: Have Observations Revealed a Variable Upper End of the Initial Mass Function?: Proceedings of a Conference Held at Sedona, Arizona, USA, 20-25 June 2010. 2011. (Illus.). xviii, 416p. ***(978-1-58381-760-5(3))*** Astronomical Society of the Pacific, The.

Tsinganos, Kanaris, et al, eds. Protostellar Jets in Context. 2009. (Astrophysics & Space Science Proceedings Ser.). (Illus.). xxxii, 662p. 339.00 *(978-3-642-00575-6(6)*, 3642005756) Springer.

Turakulov, Zafar. Selected Problems of Celestial Mechanics & Astrophysics. 2011. 92p. pap. ***(978-3-8443-9491-7(5))*** Lambert Academic Publishing.

Turyshev. From Quantum to Cosmos. 2009. 160.00 *(978-981-4261-20-3(3))* World Scientific Publishing Co., Inc.

Vaas, Rüdiger, ed. Beyond the Big Bang: Prospects for an Eternal Universe. 2009. (Frontiers Collection). (Illus.). 600p. 89.95 *(978-3-540-71422-4(7)*, 3540714227) Springer.

Van Putten, Maurice H. P. M. & Levinson, Amir. Relativistic Astrophysics of the Transient Universe: Gravitation, Hydrodynamics & Radiation. 2012. (ENG., Illus.). 392p. 80.00 ***(978-1-107-01073-4(X))*** Cambridge Univ. Pr.

Vasconcellos Cesar, A. Zen. Astronomy & Relativistic Astrophysics: New Phenomena & New States of Matter in the Universe - Proceedings of the Third Workshop (Iwara07) 2010. 280p. pap. 99.00 *(978-931-4304-87-0(5))* World Scientific Publishing Co., Inc.

Vedrenne, Gilber & Atteia, Jean-Luc. Gamma-Ray Bursts. 2007. (Springer Praxis Books / Astronomy & Planetary Sciences Ser.). 189.00 *(978-3-540-39085-5(5)*, 3540390855) Springer.

Vietri, Mario. Foundations of High-Energy Astrophysics. 2008. (Theoretical Astrophysics Ser.). (Illus.). 568p. 75.00 *(978-0-226-85569-1(4))* Univ. of Chicago Pr.

Villard, Ray, ed. Changes Within Physical Systems and/or Conservation of Energy & Momentum: An Anthology of Current Thought. 2009. (Contemporary Discourse in the Field of Physics Ser.). 220p. (gr. 10-12). 63.90 *(978-1-61511-915-8(9))* Rosen Publishing Group, Inc., The.

Viollier, R. & Klapdor-Kleingrothaus, H. V. Physics Beyond the Standard Models of Particles, Cosmology & Astrophysics - Proceedings of the Fifth International Conference - Beyond 2010. 2011. 776p. 220.00 ***(978-981-4340-85-4(5))*** World Scientific Publishing Co., Inc.

Vozmischeva, T. G. Integrable Problems of Celestial Mechanics in Spaces of Constant Curvature. 2010. (Astrophysics & Space Science Library). 196p. pap. 149.00 *(978-90-481-6382-3(X)*, 904816382X) Springer.

Wadhawan, Vinod. Complexity Science. 2010. 312p. pap. *(978-3-8383-7754-4(0))* Lambert Academic Publishing.

Wamsteker, Willem, et al, eds. Developing Basic Space Science World-Wide: A Decade of un/ESA Workshops. 2010. (ENG.). 516p. pap. 175.00 *(978-90-481-6451-6(6)*, 9048164516) Springer.

Wamsteker, Willem & Gómez de Castro, Ana I., eds. Fundamental Questions in Astrophysics: Guidelines for Future UV Observatories. 2006. (Illus.). 170p. 139.00 *(978-1-4020-4838-8(6)*, 1402048386) Springer.

Willis, A. J. & Hartquist, T. W., eds. Astrophysical & Laboratory Plasmas: A Festschrift for Professor Sir Robert Wilson. 2010. 412p. pap. 232.00 *(978-90-481-4729-8(8)*, 9048147298) Springer.

Woerden, Hugo van, et al, eds. High-Velocity Clouds. 2010. (Astrophysics & Space Science Library). x, 406p. pap. 219.00 *(978-90-481-6685-5(3)*, 9048166853) Springer.

Yahya, Harun. The Creation of the Universe. 215p. *(978-1-894264-38-9(X))* Al-Attique Pubs., Inc.

Yerlikaya-Özkurt, Fatma. Cmars: A New Contribution to Nonparametric Regression with MARS. 2011. 212p. pap. ***(978-3-8443-0849-5(0))*** Lambert Academic Publishing.

Yuan, Ye-Fei. Astrophysics of Compact Objects. 2008. (AIP Conference Proceedings Ser.). (Illus.). xiii, 431p. 179.00 *(978-0-7354-0485-4(2))* American Institute of Physics.

Zank, Gary P., ed. Turbulence & Nonlinear Processes in Astrophysical Plasmas: 6th Annual International Astrophysics Conference Oahu, Hawaii 16-22 March 2007. 2007. (AIP Conference Proceedings / Astronomy & Astrophysics Ser.). (Illus.). 434p. 139.00 *(978-0-7354-0443-4(7))* American Institute of Physics.

Zharkova, Valentina & Jain, L. C. Artificial Intelligence in Recognition & Classification of Astrophysical & Medical Images. 2007. (Studies in Computational Intelligence: Vol. 46). (Illus.). xvi, 374p. 219.00 *(978-3-540-47511-8(7))* Springer.

Zharkova, Valentina & Jain, Lakhmi C., eds. Artificial Intelligence in Recognition & Classification of Astrophysical & Medical Images. 2010. (Studies in Computational Intelligence Ser.). (Illus.). xvi, 374p. pap. 219.00 *(978-3-642-08000-5(6)*, 3642080006) Springer.

Zhelyazkov, Ivan & Mishonov, Todor, eds. 3rd School & Workshop on Space Plasma Physics. 2011. (AIP Conference Proceedings / Astronomy & Astrophysics Ser.). 234p. pap. 148.00 ***(978-0-7354-0914-9(5)***, 0735409145, AIP Pr.) Springer.

Zheng, Ling. Wrinkling of Dielectric Elastomer Membranes. 2009. 184p. pap. *(978-3-639-13238-0(6))* VDM Verlag Dr. Mueller e.K.

Zirker, J. B. The Magnetic Universe: The Elusive Traces of an Invisible Force. 2009. (ENG., Illus.). 312p. (C). (gr. 13-17). 72.00 *(978-0-8018-9301-8(1))* Johns Hopkins Univ. Pr.

—The Magnetic Universe: The Elusive Traces of an Invisible Force. 2009. (ENG., Illus.). 312p. (C). (gr. 13-17). pap. 37.00 *(978-0-8018-9302-5(X))* Johns Hopkins Univ. Pr.

Zombeck, Martin. Handbook of Space Astronomy & Astrophysics. 2010. (ENG., Illus.). 780p. pap. 45.00 *(978-0-615-41392-1(7))* Zombeck, Martin.

Zombeck, Martin V. Handbook of Space Astronomy & Astrophysics. 3rd rev. ed. 2006. (ENG., Illus.). 780p. 126.00 *(978-0-521-78242-5(2))* Cambridge Univ Pr.

ASTROPHYSICS—BIBLIOGRAPHY

Babb, James F. Proceedings of the Dalgarno Celebratory Symposium: Contributions to Atomic, Molecular, & Optical Physics, Astrophysics, & Atmospheric Physics. 2009. 500p. 135.00 *(978-1-84816-469-7(6))* Imperial College Pr. GBR. Dist: World Scientific Publishing Co., Inc.

A

ASTROPHYSICS—DATA PROCESSING

Hagelstein, Peter L. Introduction to Numerical Modeling in Engineering & Applied Physics. 2013. (ENG., Illus.). 900p. 125.00 *(978-0-471-71574-0(3),* Wiley-Interscience) Wiley, John & Sons, Inc.

ASVAB

see Armed Services Vocational Aptitude Battery

ASYLUM, RIGHT OF

see also Extradition

Anker, Deborah E. The Law of Asylum in the United States. 4th ed. 2011. xxviii, 611p. pap. ***(978-0-314-90334-1(8))*** West Publishing Co., College & Schl. Div.

Bagaric, Mirko, et al. Migration & Refugee Law in Australia: Cases & Commentary. 2007. 499p. per. 107.00 *(978-0-521-69137-6(0))* Cambridge Univ. Pr.

Baldaccini, Anneliese & Guild, Elspeth, eds. Terrorism & the Foreigner: A Decade of Tension Around the Rule of Law in Europe. 2006. (Immigration & Asylum Law & Policy in Europe Ser.). 431p. *(978-90-04-15187-1(7))* BRILL.

Beyani, Chaloka. Protection of the Right to Seek & Obtain Asylum under African Human Rights System. 2012. (Refugees & Human Rights Ser.). (ENG., Illus.). 250p. ***(978-90-04-16341-6(7))*** BRILL.

Bohmer, Carol & Shuman, Amy. Rejecting Refugees: Political Asylum in the 21st Century. 2007. (Illus.). XII, 292p. 39.95 *(978-0-415-77376-8(8))*; 155.00 *(978-0-415-77375-1(X))* Routledge.

Brennan, Frank. Tampering with Asylum: A Universal Humanitarian Problem. rev. ed. 2007. (Illus.). 320p. (Orig.). *(978-0-7022-3581-8(4))* Univ. of Queensland Pr.

Briscoe, Lesley. Maternity Care for Asylum Seekers. 2009. 216p. pap. *(978-3-639-14644-8(1))* VDM Verlag Dr. Mueller e.K.

Burgess, Greg. Refuge in the Land of Liberty: France & Its Refugees, from the Revolution to the End of Asylum, 1787-1939. 2008. (ENG., Illus.). 300p. 100.00 *(978-0-230-50775-3(1))* Palgrave Macmillan.

Clayton, Gina. Textbook on Immigration & Asylum Law. (ENG., 4th ed. 2010. Illus.). 690p. 66.00 *(978-0-19-957408-7(1))* 5th ed. 2012. 704p. pap. 65.00 ***(978-0-19-969943-8(7))*** Oxford Univ. Pr., Inc.

Den Heijer, Maarten. Europe & Extraterritorial Asylum, 0 vols. 2012. (ENG.). 314p. 110.00 ***(978-1-84946-270-9(4))*** Hart Publishing Ltd. GBR. Dist: International Specialized Bk. Services.

Esibo, Simon Omaada. Conflict Between Right to Asylum & Security Concerns of Ugand. 2011. 120p. pap. ***(978-3-8433-5904-7(0))*** Lambert Academic Publishing.

Executive Office for Immigration Review: Hearing Before the Subcommittee on Immigration, Citizenship, Refugees, Border Security, & International Law of the Committee on the Judiciary, House of Representatives, One Hundred Eleventh Congress, Second Session, June 17, 2010. 2010. iii, 91p. *(978-0-16-086960-0(9),* 552-070-41826-1) United States Government Printing Office.

Flynn, Josephe Marie. Rescuing Regina: The Battle to Save a Friend from Deportation & Death. 2011. (ENG.). 352p. 26.95 *(978-1-56976-624-8(X),* Hill, Lawrence Bks.) Chicago Review Pr., Inc.

Freedman, Jane. Gendering the International Asylum & Refugee Debate. 2007. (ENG., Illus.). 240p. 100.00 *(978-0-230-00653-9(1))* Palgrave Macmillan.

Friedman, Edie & Klein, Reva. Reluctant Refuge: The Story of Asylum in Britain. 2008. (ENG.). 160p. pap. 30.00 *(978-0-7123-0887-8(3))* British Library, The GBR. Dist: Chicago Distribution Ctr.

Gammeltoft-Hansen, Thomas. Access to Asylum: International Refugee Law & the Globalisation of Migration Control. 2011. (Cambridge Studies in International & Comparative Law Ser.). (ENG.). 308p. 95.00 *(978-1-107-00347-7(4))* Cambridge Univ. Pr.

Goudappel, Flora A. N. J. & Zwaan, J. W. de. Freedom, Security & Justice in the European Union: Implementation of the Hague Programme. de Zwaan, Jaap W. & Goudappel, Flora A. N. J., eds. 2006. (ENG.). 308p. 99.00 *(978-90-6704-225-3(0))* T.M.C. Asser Pr. NLD. Dist: Springer.

Guild, Elspeth & Minderhoud, Paul, eds. The First Decade of EU Migration & Asylum Law. 2011. (Immigration & Asylum Law & Policy in Europe Ser.). xvi, 485p. ***(978-90-04-21203-9(5))*** BRILL.

Hellmann, Gunther, ed. Germany's EU Policy on Asylum & Defence: De-Europeanization by Default? 2006. (New Perspectives in German Studies). (ENG., Illus.). 224p. 105.00 *(978-1-4039-8798-3(X))* Palgrave Macmillan.

Hollenbach, David, ed. Refugee Rights: Ethics, Advocacy, & Africa. 2nd rev. ed. 2008. (ENG., Illus.). 272p. pap. 29.95 *(978-1-58901-202-8(X))* Georgetown Univ. Pr.

Hurwitz, Agnes. The Collective Responsibility of States to Protect Refugees. 2009. (Oxford Monographs in International Law Ser.). (ENG.). 300p. 132.00 *(978-0-19-927838-1(5))* Oxford Univ. Pr., Inc.

Hynes, Patricia. The Dispersal & Social Exclusion of Asylum Seekers: Between Liminality & Belonging. 2011. (Illus.). 240p. 99.00 *(978-1-84742-326-9(4))* Policy Pr. GBR. Dist: Chicago Distribution Ctr.

Kirkagac, Nevzat. Verdachtsausweisungen Im Deutschen Rechtsstaat. 2011. (Schriften zum internationalen und zum öffentlichen Recht Ser.). (GER.). 281p. 80.95 ***(978-3-631-62001-4(2))*** Lang, Peter GmbH, Europaischer Verlag der Wissenschaften DEU. Dist: Lang, Peter.

Koser, Khalid. Refugees, Transnationalism & the State. 2006. 150p. pap. 53.95 *(978-1-84472-009-5(8),* Routledge) Taylor & Francis Group GBR. Dist: Taylor & Francis Group.

Kotzeva, Anna & Tam, Robin. Asylum & Human Rights Handbook. Burnett, Ian, ed. 2008. (ENG.). 600p. pap. 135.00 *(978-0-19-928942-4(5))* Oxford Univ. Pr., Inc.

Leach, Daniel. Fugitive Ireland: European Minority Nationalists & Irish Political Asylum, 1937-2008. 2009. (Illus.). 285p. 65.00 *(978-1-84682-164-6(9))* Four Courts Pr. IRL. Dist: International Specialized Bk. Services.

Leach, Margery. Sanctuary in Phoenix! A Narrative History of the Valley Religious Task Force on Central America & Its Role in the Sanctuary Movement in Phoenix, Arizona from 1981-1998. 2008. (Illus.). xi, 39p. pap. *(978-1-60585-206-5(6))* Harvest Pubns.

Legras, B. Les Reclus grecs du Sarapieion de Memphis: Une enquete sur l'hellenisme Egyptien. 2011. (Studia Hellenistica Ser.). 320p. (C). pap. 105.00 *(978-90-429-2361-4(X))* Peeters Pubs. & Booksellers BEL. Dist: Brown, David Bk. Co., The.

Lillig, Marion. Identitätskonstruktionen von Exilantinnen: Aufgeben nur Pakete und Briefe, nicht und nie Mich. 2008. (Europäische Migrationsforschung Ser.). 246p. pap. 61.95 *(978-3-631-57714-1(1))* Lang, Peter GmbH, Europaischer Verlag der Wissenschaften DEU. Dist: Lang, Peter.

Lindahl, Hans, ed. A Right to Inclusion & Exclusion? Normative Fault Lines of the EU's Area of Freedom, Security & Justice. 2009. (ENG.). 285p. 104.00 *(978-1-84113-949-4(1))* Hart Publishing Ltd. GBR. Dist: International Specialized Bk. Services.

Lippert, Randy & Rehaag, Sean, eds. Sanctuary Practices in International Perspective: Migration, Citizenship & Social Movements. 2012. (ENG., Illus.). 272p. 125.00 *(978-0-415-67346-4(1))* Routledge.

Martin, David A. Forced Migration: Law & Policy. 2007. (American Casebook Ser.). (Illus.). iii, 770p. *(978-0-314-18041-4(9))* West Publishing Co., College & Schl. Div.

Menz, Georg. The Political Economy of Managed Migration: Nonstate Actors, Europeanization, & the Politics of Designing Migration Policies. (ENG.). 320p. 2011. pap. 35.00 *(978-0-19-959329-3(9))* 2009. (Illus.). 99.00 *(978-0-19-953388-6(1))* Oxford Univ. Pr., Inc.

Meyers, Eytan. International Immigration Policy: A Theoretical & Comparative Analysis. 2007. (ENG.). 304p. pap. 32.00 *(978-0-230-60224-3(X))* Palgrave Macmillan.

Mole, Nuala & Meredith, Catherine. Asylum & the European Convention on Human Rights. rev. ed. 2010. (Human Rights Files Ser.: 9). 283p. pap. 29.00 *(978-92-871-6819-1(9))* Council of Europe FRA. Dist: Manhattan Publishing Co.

Morris, Lydia. Asylum Welfare & the Cosmopolitan Ideal. 2011. 184p. pap. 53.95 *(978-0-415-60294-5(7),* Routledge Cavendish) Taylor & Francis Group GBR. Dist: Taylor & Francis Group.

—Asylum, Welfare & the Cosmopolitan Ideal: A Sociology of Rights. 2010. (ENG.). 184p. 125.00 *(978-0-415-49773-2(6),* Routledge Cavendish) Taylor & Francis Group GBR. Dist: Taylor & Francis Group.

Musalo, Karen, et al. Refugee Law & Policy: A Comparative & International Approach. 4th ed. 2011. 1220p. 100.00 *(978-1-59460-839-1(3))* Carolina Academic Pr.

—Refugee Law & Policy: A Comparative & International Approach, Third Edition. 3rd ed. 2006. 1234p. 95.00 *(978-1-59460-299-3(9))* Carolina Academic Pr.

O'Brien, Louisa. The Experience of Asylum Seekers Entering Greece. 2010. 72p. pap. *(978-3-639-22408-5(6))* VDM Verlag Dr. Mueller e.K.

O'Grady. Rome Reshaped (p) 2007. (ENG.). 224p. per. 29.95 *(978-0-8264-2961-2(0))* Continuum International Publishing Group, Ltd. GBR. Dist: National Bk. Network.

Peers, Steve & Rogers, Nicola, eds. EU Immigration & Asylum Law: Text & Commentary. 2006. 1040p. *(978-90-04-15374-5(8))* BRILL.

Price, Matthew & Price, Matthew E. Rethinking Asylum: History, Purpose & Limits. 2009. (ENG., Illus.). 290p. (C). pap. 33.99 *(978-0-521-70747-3(1))* Cambridge Univ. Pr.

Rabben, Linda. Give Refuge to the Stranger: The Past, Present, & Future of Sanctuary. 2011. (ENG., Illus.). 280p. 94.00 *(978-1-61132-029-9(1))*; pap. 29.95 *(978-1-61132-030-5(5))* Left Coast Pr., Inc.

Ramji-Nogales, Jaya, et al. Refugee Roulette: Disparities in Asylum Adjudication & Proposals for Reform. (ENG.). 354p. 2011. pap. 24.00 *(978-0-8147-4106-1(1))* 2009. (Illus.). 65.00 *(978-0-8147-4074-3(X))* New York Univ. Pr.

Schotel, Bas. On the Right of Exclusion: Law, Ethics & Immigration Policy. 2011. (ENG.). 232p. 125.00 *(978-0-415-57537-9(0))* Routledge.

Sharma, Parnesh. The Human Rights Act & the Assault on Liberty: Rights & Asylum in the UK. 2011. (ENG.). 316p. pap. 25.95 ***(978-1-908062-30-7(4))*** Nottingham Univ. Pr. GBR. Dist: Independent Pubs. Group.

Sicakkan, Hakan G. Do Our Citizenship Requirements Impede the Protection of Political Asylum Seekers? A Comparative Analysis of European Practices. 2008. (Illus.). 452p. 129.95 *(978-0-7734-5032-5(7))* Mellen, Edwin Pr., The.

Sidorenko, Olga Ferguson. The Common European Asylum System: Background, Current State of Affairs, Future Direction. 2007. (ENG.). 254p. 79.95 *(978-90-6704-236-9(6),* 9067042366) T.M.C. Asser Pr. NLD. Dist: Springer.

Son, Minjoon & Park, Jimin. Applying for Asylum: The U. S. System & Policies. 2011. (American Political, Economic, & Security Issues Ser.). 215.00 ***(978-1-61470-254-2(3))*** Nova Science Pubs., Inc.

Squire, Victoria. The Exclusionary Politics of Asylum. 2009. (Migration, Minorities & Citizenship Ser.). (ENG., Illus.). 272p. 100.00 *(978-0-230-21659-4(5))* Palgrave Macmillan.

Symes, Mark & Jorro, Peter. Asylum Law & Practice. 2nd rev. ed. 2010. 1254p. 215.00 *(978-1-84592-453-9(3),* Bloomsbury Professional) Bloomsbury Publishing Plc GBR. Dist: International Specialized Bk. Services.

Thomas, Robert. Administrative Justice & Asylum Appeals: A Study of Tribunal Adjudication. 2011. (ENG., Illus.). 342p. pap. 100.00 *(978-1-84113-936-4(X))* Hart Publishing Ltd. GBR. Dist: International Specialized Bk. Services.

Toner, Helen, et al. EU Immigration & Asylum Law & Policy: Whose Freedom, Security & Justice? 2007. 550p. (C). 156.00 *(978-1-84113-684-4(0))* Hart Publishing Ltd. GBR. Dist: International Specialized Bk. Services.

United States, Congress Senate Committee on the Judiciary Subcommittee on Immigration, Border Security, and Citizenship Staff, contrib. by. Oversight Hearing: U.S. Refugee Admissions & Policy: Hearing Before the Subcommittee on Immigration, Border Security, & Citizenship of the Committee on the Judiciary, United States Senate, One Hundred Ninth Congress, Second Session, September 27, 2006. 2007. iii, 108p. *(978-0-16-078119-3(1),* 552-070-35520 1) United States Government Printing Office.

Vrachnas, John, et al. Migration & Refugee Law. 3rd rev. ed. 2011. (ENG.). 382p. (C). pap. 90.00 *(978-1-107-62327-9(8))* Cambridge Univ. Pr.

—Migration & Refugee Law: Principles & Practice in Australia. 2nd rev. ed. 2008. (ENG.). 364p. pap. 72.00 *(978-0-521-71432-7(X))* Cambridge Univ. Pr.

ASYLUMS

see also Almshouses; Old Age Homes; Orphans; Poor; Psychiatric Hospitals

Coin-Delisle, Jean Baptiste César. Opinion of Messieurs Coin Delisle & Paillard de Villeneuve on the Validity of the Disposition Contained in the Will of the Late John D Fink Providing. 2011. 32p. pap. 11.99 ***(978-1-4181-9375-1(5))*** MPublishing.

The eye of Danvers: A History of a Former Massachusetts Asylum. 2008. (Illus.). 89p. pap. *(978-0-9765975-4-4(3))* ARTSHIP.

Fink, J. D. "Donnie". Yesterday's Asylum: Reflections of Lunacy. 2011. 24.95 ***(978-0-533-16383-0(8))*** Vantage Pr., Inc.

Francke, August Hermann. Faith's Work Perfected; or, Francke's Orphan House at Halle by a H Francke Edited & Translated by Wm L Gage. 2006. 120p. per. 16.99 *(978-1-4255-0834-0(0))* MPublishing.

Lael, Richard L., et al. Evolution of a Missouri Asylum: Fulton State Hospital, 1851-2006. 2007. (ENG., Illus.). 270p. (C). 44.95 *(978-0-8262-1689-2(7))* Univ. of Missouri Pr.

Leahy, Todd E. They Called It Madness: The Canton Asylum for Insane Indians 1899-1934. 2009. 272p. pap. 27.95 *(978-1-61546-418-0(2))* PublishAmerica, Inc.

Milner, James H. S. Refugees, the State & the Politics of Asylum in Africa. 2009. (St. Antony's Ser.). (ENG., Illus.). 288p. 95.00 *(978-0-230-21504-7(1))* Palgrave Macmillan.

Miron, Janet. As in a Menagerie. 2009. *(978-0-8020-9366-0(3))*; pap. *(978-0-8020-9513-8(5))* Univ. of Toronto Pr.

Parle, Julie. States of Mind: Searching for Mental Health in Natal & Zululand, 1868-1918. 2007. 350p. pap. 39.95 *(978-1-86914-098-4(2))* University of Kwazulu-Natal Press ZAF. Dist: International Specialized Bk. Services.

Price, Matthew & Price, Matthew E. Rethinking Asylum: History, Purpose, & Limits. 2009. (ENG., Illus.). 290p. (C). 87.00 *(978-0-521-88116-6(1))* Cambridge Univ. Pr.

Yanni, Carla. The Architecture of Madness: Insane Asylums in the United States. 2007. (Architecture, Landscape & Amer Culture Ser.). (Illus.). 256p. per. 27.50 *(978-0-8166-4940-2(5))* Univ. of Minnesota Pr.

ASYLUMS—GREAT BRITAIN

Ewing, Logan. A History of St Nicholas Hospital, Newcastle-upon-Tyne, England 1869-2001. 2009. (Illus.). 316p. pap. 17.49 *(978-1-4389-3754-0(7))* AuthorHouse.

Good, Anthony. Anthropology & Expertise in the Asylum Courts. 2006. (Illus.). 299p. per. 59.95 *(978-1-904385-55-4(9),* Routledge) Taylor & Francis Group GBR. Dist: Taylor & Francis Group.

—Anthropology & Expertise in the British Asylum Courts. 2006. (Illus.). 328p. 180.00 *(978-1-904385-56-1(7),* Routledge) Taylor & Francis Group GBR. Dist: Taylor & Francis Group.

Squire, Victoria. The Exclusionary Politics of Asylum. 2009. (Migration, Minorities & Citizenship Ser.). (ENG., Illus.). 272p. 100.00 *(978-0-230-21659-4(5))* Palgrave Macmillan.

Symes, Mark & Jorro, Peter. Asylum Law & Practice. 2nd rev. ed. 2010. 1254p. 215.00 *(978-1-84592-453-9(3),* Bloomsbury Professional) Bloomsbury Publishing Plc GBR. Dist: International Specialized Bk. Services.

ASYMMETRIC SYNTHESIS

Caprio, Vittorio & Williams, Jonathan M. J. Catalysis in Asymmetric Synthesis. 2nd ed. 2009. (Postgraduate Chemistry Ser.). (ENG., Illus.). 408p. pap. 75.00 *(978-1-4051-7519-7(2))*; 160.00 *(978-1-4051-9091-6(4))* Wiley, John & Sons, Inc. (Wiley-Blackwell).

Carreira, Erick M. & Kvaerno, Lisbet. Classics in Stereoselective Synthesis. 2009. (ENG., Illus.). 651p. 175.00 *(978-3-527-32452-1(6),* Wiley-VCH) Wiley, John & Sons, Inc.

Christmann, Mathias & Bräse, Stefan, eds. Asymmetric Synthesis: More Methods & Applications. 2012. (ENG.). 400p. 170.00 ***(978-3-527-32921-2(8),*** Wiley-VCH) Wiley, John & Sons, Inc.

Christmann, Mathias & Bräse, Stefan, eds. Asymmetric Synthesis: The Essentials. 2nd ed. 2007. (ENG.). 395p. pap. 159.00 *(978-3-527-32093-6(8),* Wiley-VCH) Wiley, John & Sons, Inc.

Cordova, Armando, ed. Catalytic Asymmetric Conjugate Reactions. 2010. (ENG., Illus.). 464p. 200.00 *(978-3-527-32411-8(9),* Wiley-VCH) Wiley, John & Sons, Inc.

Cram101 Textbook Reviews & Cram101 Textbook Reviews. Outlines & Highlights for Catalysis in Asymmetric Synthesis by Vittorio Caprio, Isbn: 9781405175197. 2011. 426p. pap. 35.95 ***(978-1-61461-493-7(8))*** Cram101 Inc.

Ding, Kuiling & Uozumi, Yasuhiro, eds. Handbook of Asymmetric Heterogeneous Catalysis. 2008. (ENG., Illus.). 466p. 235.00 *(978-3-527-31913-8(1),* Wiley-VCH) Wiley, John & Sons, Inc.

Gawley, Robert E. & Aubé, Jeffrey. Principles of Asymmetric Synthesis, 2E. 2nd ed. 2012. (ENG.). 514p. pap. 69.95 ***(978-0-08-044860-2(7))*** Elsevier Science & Technology Bks.

Gotor, Vicente, et al, eds. Asymmetric Organic Synthesis with Enzymes. 2008. (ENG., Illus.). 340p. 249.00 *(978-3-527-31825-4(9),* Wiley-VCH) Wiley, John & Sons, Inc.

Gruttadauria, Michelangelo & Giacalone, Francesco, eds. Catalytic Methods in Asymmetric Synthesis: Advanced Materials, Techniques, & Applications. 2011. (ENG., Illus.). 720p. 149.95 *(978-0-470-64136-1(3),* Wiley) Wiley, John & Sons, Inc.

Hayashi, Tamio & Shintani, Ryo, eds. Privileged Chiral Ligands in Asymmetric Catalysis. 2010. 450p. 215.00 *(978-3-527-32405-7(4),* Wiley-VCH) Wiley, John & Sons, Inc.

Jacobsen, Eric N., et al, eds. Comprehensive Asymmetric Catalysis: Supplement 1. 2010. (ENG., Illus.). xiv, 238p. pap. 279.00 *(978-3-642-05562-1(1),* 3642055621) Springer.

—Comprehensive Asymmetric Catalysis: Supplement 2. 2010. (ENG., Illus.). xvi, 135p. pap. 179.00 *(978-3-642-05901-8(5),* 3642059015) Springer.

Jaeger, Karl-Erich & Enders, Dieter, eds. Asymmetric Synthesis with Chemical & Biological Methods. 2007. (ENG., Illus.). 470p. 249.00 *(978-3-527-31473-7(3),* Wiley-VCH) Wiley, John & Sons, Inc.

Lemaire, Marc & Mangeney, Pierre. Chiral Diazaligands for Asymmetric Synthesis. 2010. (Topics in Organometallic Chemistry Ser.). (Illus.). x, 301p. pap. 349.00 *(978-3-642-06538-5(4),* 3642065384) Springer.

List, Benjamin, ed. Asymmetric Organocatalysis. 2010. (Topics in Current Chemistry Ser.). (ENG., Illus.). i, 400p. 389.00 *(978-3-642-02814-4(4),* 3642028144) Springer.

Ma, Shengming, ed. Asymmetric Catalysis from a Chinese Perspective. 2011. (Topics in Organometallic Chemistry Ser.). (ENG., Illus.). xii, 280p. 309.00 *(978-3-642-19471-9(0),* 3642194710) Springer.

Maruoka, Keiji, ed. Asymmetric Phase Transfer Catalysis. 2008. (ENG., Illus.). 228p. 175.00 *(978-3-527-31842-1(9),* Wiley-VCH) Wiley, John & Sons, Inc.

Oro, Luis A. & Claver, Carmen, eds. Iridium Complexes in Organic Synthesis. 2009. (ENG., Illus.). 424p. 245.00 *(978-3-527-31996-1(4),* Wiley-VCH) Wiley, John & Sons, Inc.

Patti, Angela. Green Approaches to Asymmetric Catalytic Synthesis. 2011. (SpringerBriefs in Molecular Science / Green Chemistry for Sustainability Ser.). (ENG., Illus.). xiv, 140p. pap. 49.95 *(978-94-007-1453-3(X),* 940071453X) Springer.

Pellissier, Hélène. Chiral Sulfur-Containing Ligands: Asymmetric Catalysis. 2009. (RSC Catalysis Ser.). (ENG., Illus.). 402p. (C). 224.00 *(978-1-84755-924-1(7))* Royal Society of Chemistry, The GBR. Dist: Ingram Pub. Services.

Pu, Lin. 1, 1'-Binaphthyl-Based Chiral Materials: Our Journey. 2009. (Illus.). 368p. 111.00 *(978-1-84816-411-6(4))* Imperial College Pr. GBR. Dist: World Scientific Publishing Co., Inc.

Reetz, Manfred, et al. Organocatalysis. 2010. (Ernst Schering Foundation Symposium Proceedings Ser.). (Illus.). xiv, 342p. pap. 149.00 *(978-3-642-09261-9(6),* 3642092616) Springer.

Reetz, Manfred T., et al. Organocatalysis. 2008. (Ernst Schering Foundation Symposium Proceedings Ser.). (Illus.). 256p. 149.00 *(978-3-540-73494-9(5),* 3540734945) Springer.

Riehl, James P. Mirror-Image Asymmetry: An Introduction to the Origin & Consequences of Chirality. 2010. (ENG., Illus.). 250p. pap. 52.95 *(978-0-470-38759-7(9),* Wiley) Wiley, John & Sons, Inc.

Royer, Jacques, ed. Asymmetric Synthesis of Nitrogen Heterocycles. 2009. (ENG., Illus.). 425p. 220.00 *(978-3-527-32036-3(9),* Wiley-VCH) Wiley, John & Sons, Inc.

Rudroff, Florian. Enzymatic Baeyer-Villiger Oxidation for Natural Product Synthesis. 2008. 200p. pap. *(978-3-639-02093-9(6))* VDM Verlag Dr. Mueller e.K.

Saluzzo, Christine. Asymmetric Heterogeneous Supported Catalysis: Use of Nitrogen-Containing Ligand. Guillarme, Stéphane, ed. 2012. (Polymer Science & Technology Ser.). 183p. 43.00 *(978-1-61668-680-2(4))* Nova Science Pubs., Inc.

Shams, Afaque. Numerical Simulation of Turbulent Shock-Induced Separated Flows. 2011. 248p. pap. ***(978-3-8443-1856-2(9))*** Lambert Academic Publishing.

Soloshonok, Vadim A. & Izawa, Kunisuke, eds. Asymmetric Synthesis & Application of Alpha-Amino Acids. 2009. (ACS Symposium Ser.). (ENG., Illus.). 504p. 195.00 *(978-0-8412-6974-3(2))* American Chemical Society.

Walsh, Patrick & Kozlowski, Marisa. Fundamentals of Asymmetric Catalysis. 2008. (Illus.). 750p. (C). 94.00 *(978-1-891389-54-2(8))* Univ. Science Bks.

Ward, Thomas R. Bio-Inspired Catalysts. 2008. (Topics in Organometallic Chemistry Ser.). (Illus.). ix, 115p. 179.00 *(978-3-540-87756-1(8))* Springer.

ASYMMETRY (LINGUISTICS)

Carlier, Anne, et al, eds. Passt et Parfait. 2008. 164p. pap. 38.00 *(978-90-420-1211-0(0))* Rodopi.

Hausman, Daniel M. Causal Asymmetries. 2008. (Cambridge Studies in Probability, Induction & Decision Theory Ser.). (ENG.). 320p. pap. 61.00 *(978-0-521-05242-9(4))* Cambridge Univ. Pr.
Junge, Kay & Postoutenko, Kirill, eds. Asymmetrical Concepts after Reinhart Koselleck: Historical Semantics & Beyond. 2011. (ENG.). 250p. pap. 40.95 *(978-3-8376-1589-0(8))* Transcript Verlag DEU. Dist: Transaction Pubs.
Lewandowska-Tomaszczyk, Barbara. Asymmetric Events. 2008. (C). *(978-90-272-3899-3(5))* Benjamins, John Publishing Co.
Mayes, David G. & Viren, Matti. Asymmetry & Aggregation in the Euro Area. 2011. (ENG., Illus.). 272p. 90.00 *(978-0-230-53808-5(8))* Palgrave Macmillan.
Nikolaeva, Elena & Leutin, Vitalii. Functional Brain Asymmetry: Myth & Reality. 2011. 352p. pap. ***(978-3-8433-8289-2(1))*** Lambert Academic Publishing.

ASYMPTOTES
see also Asymptotic Expansions
Cator, Eric, ed. Asymptotics; Particles, Processes & Inverse Problems. 2007. (Institute of Mathematical Statistics Lecture Notes Monograph: Vol. 55). 252p. pap. 120.00 *(978-0-940600-71-3(4))* Institute of Mathematical Statistics.
Smirnov, Vladimir A. Applied Asymptotic Expansions in Momenta & Masses. 2010. (Springer Tracts in Modern Physics Ser.). (Illus.). ix, 263p. pap. 269.00 *(978-3-642-07612-1(2),* 3642076122) Springer.

ASYMPTOTIC EXPANSIONS
Andrianov, Igor V., et al. Asymptotical Mechanics of Thin-Walled Structures: A Handbook. 2010. (Foundations of Engineering Mechanics Ser.). ii, 535p. pap. 229.00 *(978-3-642-07415-8(4),* 3642074154) Springer.
Barbe, Ph. & McCormick, W. P. Asymptotic Expansions for Infinite Weighted Convolutions of Heavy Tail Distributions & Applications. 2009. (Memoirs of the American Mathematical Society Ser.). 117p. pap. 67.00 *(978-0-8218-4259-1(5))* American Mathematical Society.
Bloom, C. O. & Kazarinoff, N. D. Short Wave Radiation Problems in Inhomogeneous Media: Asymptotic Solutions. 2008. (Lecture Notes in Mathematics Ser.). 112p. pap. 26.00 *(978-3-540-07698-8(0))* Springer.
Choudhury, Jayanta & Christov, Christo I. Stationary-Propagating Solutions of the Boussinesq Equation in 2d Numerical & Asymptotic Investigation of Localized Solutions Using Finite-Differen. 2009. 84p. pap. *(978-3-639-10818-7(3))* VDM Verlag Dr. Mueller e.K.
Costin, Ovidiu, et al, eds. Asymptotics in Dynamics, Geometry & PDEs; Generalized Borel Summation: Proceedings of the conference held in CRM Pisa, 12-16 October 2009. 2011. (Publications of the Scuola Normale Superiore / CRM Ser.). 450p. pap. 34.95 *(978-88-7642-374-1(5),* 8876423745) Scuola Normale Superiore ITA. Dist: Springer.
Costin, Ovidiu, et al, eds. Asymptotics in Dynamics, Geometry & PDEs; Generalized Borel Summation: Proceedings of the conference held in CRM Pisa, 12-16 October 2009, Vol. II. 2011. (Publications of the Scuola Normale Superiore / CRM Ser.). (ENG.). 274p. pap. 34.95 ***(978-88-7642-376-5(1),*** 8876423761) Scuola Normale Superiore ITA. Dist: Springer.
Costin, Ovidiu & Costin, O. Asymptotics & Borel Summability. 2008. (Monographs & Surveys in Pure & Applied Math Ser.). (ENG., Illus.). 256p. 97.95 *(978-1-4200-7031-6(2),* Chapman & Hall/CRC) CRC Pr. LLC.
Cousteix, Jean & Mauss, Jacques. Asymptotic Analysis & Boundary Layers. (Scientific Computation Ser.). (Illus.). xviii, 432p. 2010. pap. 149.00 *(978-3-642-07983-2(0),* 3642079830) 2007. 149.00 *(978-3-540-46488-4(3),* 3540464883) Springer.
Cram101 Textbook Reviews. Outlines & Highlights for from Finite Sample to Asymptotic Methods in Statistics by Pranab K Sen. 2011. 238p. pap. 31.95 ***(978-1-4672-6677-2(9))*** Cram101 Inc.
From Divergent Power Series to Analytic Functions. 2008. (Lecture Notes in Mathematics Ser.). pap. 39.95 *(978-3-540-58268-7(1))* Springer.
Gil Amparo, et al. Numerical Methods for Special Functions. 2007. (ENG., Illus.). 430p. pap. 99.00 *(978-0-89871-634-4(9))* Society for Industrial and Applied Mathematics.
Hirschman, I. I. Jr. & Hughes, D. E. Extreme Eigen Values of Toeplitz Operators. 2008. (Lecture Notes in Mathematics Ser.). 152p. pap. 26.00 *(978-3-540-07147-1(4))* Springer.
Immink, G. Asymptotics of Analytic Difference Equations. 2008. (Lecture Notes in Mathematics Ser.). pap. 39.95 *(978-3-540-13867-9(6))* Springer.
Ivrii, Victor. Microlocal Analysis & Precise Spectral Asymptotics. 2010. (Springer Monographs in Mathematics Ser.). xvi, 731p. pap. 179.00 *(978-3-642-08307-5(2),* 3642083072) Springer.
Ivrii, V. Precise Spectral Asymptotics for Elliptic Operators Acting in Fiberings over Manifolds with Boundary. 2008. (Lecture Notes in Mathematics Ser.). pap. 46.00 *(978-3-540-13361-2(5))* Springer.
Kaimanovich, V. & Lodkin, A., eds. Representation Theory, Dynamical Systems, & Asymptotic Combinatorics. 2006. (American Mathematical Society Translations Ser.: Vol. 58). (Illus.). 246p. 112.00 *(978-0-8218-4208-9(0))* American Mathematical Society.
Lagerstrom, P. A. Matched Asymptotic Expansions: Ideas & Techniques. 2010. (Applied Mathematical Sciences Ser.). (Illus.). xxii, 250p. pap. 89.95 *(978-1-4419-3086-6(8),* 1441930868) Springer.
Majima, H. Asymptotic Analysis for Integrable Connections with Irregular Singular Points. 2008. (Lecture Notes in Mathematics Ser.). pap. 39.95 *(978-3-540-13375-9(5))* Springer.
Mitropolsky, Yuri A. & Lopatin, A. K. Nonlinear Mechanics, Groups & Symmetry. 2010. (Mathematics & Its Applications Ser.). 388p. pap. 339.00 *(978-90-481-4517-1(1),* 9048145171) Springer.
Nonstandard Asymptotic Analysis. 2008. (Lecture Notes in Mathematics Ser.). pap. 39.95 *(978-3-540-17767-8(1))* Springer.
Oliveira, Paulo Eduardo. Asymptotics for Associated Random Variables. 2012. (ENG.). x, 194p. 79.95 ***(978-3-642-25531-1(0),*** 3642255310) Springer.
Ramnath, Rudrapatna V. Computation & Asymptotics. 2012. (SpringerBriefs in Applied Sciences & Technology / SpringerBriefs in Computational Mechanics Ser.). (ENG., Illus.). xv, 120p. pap. 49.95 ***(978-3-642-25748-3(8),*** 3642257488) Springer.
Reid, N. Applied Asymptotics: Case Studies in Small-Sample Statistics. 2007. (Cambridge Series in Statistical & Probabilistic Mathematics Ser.). (ENG., Illus.). 248p. 83.00 *(978-0-521-84703-2(6))* Cambridge Univ. Pr.
Ruggeri, T. & Sammartino, M., eds. Asymptotic Methods in Nonlinear Wave Phenomena: In Honor of the 65th Birthday of Antonio Greco. 228p. 113.00 *(978-981-270-782-6(4))* World Scientific Publishing Co., Inc.
Sen, Pranab K., et al. From Finite Sample to Asymptotic Methods in Statistics. 2nd ed. 2009. (Cambridge Series in Statistical & Probabilistic Mathematics Ser.). (ENG., Illus.). 398p. 72.00 *(978-0-521-87722-0(9))* Cambridge Univ. Pr.
Skorokhod, A. V. Asymptotic Methods in the Theory of Stochastic Differential Equations. 2009. (Translations of Mathematical Monographs Ser.). 339p. pap. 114.00 *(978-0-8218-4686-5(8))* American Mathematical Society.
Strong Asymptotics for Extremal Polynomials Associated with Weights on R. 2008. (Lecture Notes in Mathematics Ser.). pap. 26.00 *(978-3-540-18958-9(0))* Springer.
Sychev, Vladimir V., et al. Asymptotic Theory of Separated Flows. 2008. (ENG., Illus.). 348p. pap. 48.00 *(978-0-521-06587-0(9))* Cambridge Univ. Pr.
Vainikko, G. Multidimensional Weakly Singular Integral Equations. 2008. (Lecture Notes in Mathematics Ser.). 170p. pap. 39.95 *(978-3-540-56878-0(6))* Springer.
Widom, H. Asymptotic Expansions for Pseudodifferential Operators on Bounded Domains. 2008. (Lecture Notes in Mathematics Ser.). pap. 26.00 *(978-3-540-15701-4(8))* Springer.
Zeytounian, Radyadour. Asymptotic Modelling of Fluid Flow Phenomena. 2010. (Fluid Mechanics & Its Applications Ser.). 564p. pap. 229.00 *(978-90-481-5939-0(3),* 9048159393) Springer.

ASYNCHRONOUS CIRCUITS
El Astal, Mohammed Taha & Abu-Hudrouss, Ammar. Distributed Space Time Block Code in Asynchronous Cooperative Networks. 2011. 100p. pap. ***(978-3-8443-9268-5(8))*** Lambert Academic Publishing.
IEEE Computer Society Press Staff, ed. Asynchronous Circuits & Systems, 2008. ASYNC '08. 14th IEEE International Symposium on. 2008. 171p. pap. 180.00 *(978-0-7695-3107-6(5))* IEEE Computer Society Pr.
IEEE Computer Society Staff, contrib. by. 13th IEEE International Symposium on Asynchronous Circuits & Systems: [proceedings]: 12-14 March, 2007: Berkeley, California. 2007. (Illus.). xvi, 205p. *(978-0-7695-2771-0(X))* IEEE Computer Society Pr.
Nystrom, Mika M. & Martin, Alain. Asynchronous Pulse Logic. 2010. (ENG.). 232p. pap. 159.00 *(978-1-4419-5284-4(5),* 1441952845) Springer.
Sparsø, Jens & Furber, Steve, eds. Principles of Asynchronous Circuit Design: A Systems Perspective. 2010. 360p. pap. 229.00 *(978-1-4419-4936-3(4),* 1441949364) Springer.
Tranchero, Maurizio & M. Reyneri, Leonardo. Synthesis of Asynchronous Circuits from Simulink Specifications. 2010. 128p. pap. *(978-3-8383-6631-9(X))* Lambert Academic Publishing.
Yahya, Eslam, et al. Performance Modeling, Analysis & Optimization for Asynchronous Circuits:Static & Statistical Analysis Approaches: Static & Statistical Analysis Approaches. 2012. (ENG.). 200p. 129.00 ***(978-1-4614-0544-3(0),*** 1461405440) Springer.
Yakovlev, Alex, et al, eds. Hardware Design & Petri Nets. 2010. (ENG.). 344p. pap. 249.00 *(978-1-4419-4969-1(0),* 1441949690) Springer.
Yu, Zhiyi & Baas, Bevan. High Performance & Energy Efficient Many-core DSP Systems: An Asynchronous Array of Simple Processors. 2008. 172p. pap. *(978-3-639-09859-4(5))* VDM Verlag Dr. Mueller e.K.

ASYNCHRONOUS ELECTRIC MOTORS
see Electric Motors, Induction

ASYNCHRONOUS TRANSFER MODE
Ajax. 2006. cd-rom 99.95 *(978-1-933736-41-9(0))* VTC, Inc.
Asleson, Ryan & Schutta, Nathaniel T. Pro Ajax & Java Frameworks. 2006. (ENG., Illus.). 336p. per. 49.99 *(978-1-59059-677-7(3))* Apress L. P.
Holdener, Anthony T., III & Holdener, Anthony T. Ajax. 2008. (ENG., Illus.). 982p. pap. 49.99 *(978-0-596-52838-6(8))* O'Reilly Media, Inc.
IEEE Communications Society Staff, contrib. by. 2008 International Workshop on High Performance Switching & Routing (HPSR) Shanghai, China, 15-17 May 2008. 2008. (Illus.). 296p. *(978-1-4244-1982-1(4))* IEEE Computer Society Pr.
IEEE Staff. 2008 International Workshop on High Performance Switching & Routing. 2008. (Illus.). 296p. pap. 220.00 *(978-1-4244-1981-4(6))* IEEE.
Mahemoff, Michael. Ajax Design Patterns. 2006. (ENG., Illus.). 656p. per. 44.99 *(978-0-596-10180-0(5))* O'Reilly Media, Inc.
Morrison, Michael. Ajax Construction Kit: Building Plug-and-Play Ajax Applications. 2007. (Negus Live Linux Ser.). (ENG., Illus.). 312p. pap. 44.99 *(978-0-13-235008-2(4))* Prentice Hall PTR.
Odell, Dennis. Pro JavaScript RIA Techniques: Best Practices, Performance & Presentation. 2009. (ENG.). 400p. pap. 44.99 *(978-1-4302-1934-7(3))* Apress L. P.
Sambells, Jeffrey, et al. Beginning Google Maps Applications with Rails & Ajax. 2007. (Expert's Voice in Open Source Ser.). (ENG., Illus.). 365p. per. 34.99 *(978-1-59059-787-3(7))* Apress L. P.
Zakas, Nicholas C., et al. Professional Ajax. 2nd rev. ed. 2007. (ENG., Illus.). 624p. per. 39.99 *(978-0-470-10949-6(1),* Wrox) Wiley, John & Sons, Inc.
2007 Fourth International Conference on Broadband Communications, Networks & Systems. 2007. pap. 332.00 *(978-1-4244-1432-1(6),* 07EX1861) IEEE.

ATANASIO, SAINT, PATRIARCH OF ALEXANDRIA, D. 373
see Athanasius, Saint, Patriarch of Alexandria, d. 373

ATARACTIC DRUGS
see Tranquilizing Drugs

ATARI COMPUTER
see also Atari ST Computers; Atari XL Computers
Montfort, Nick & Bogost, Ian. Racing the Beam: The Atari Video Computer System. 2009. (Platform Studies). (ENG., Illus.). 192p. (gr. 17). 23.95 *(978-0-262-01257-7(X))* MIT Pr.

ATARI ST COMPUTERS
Steiner, Josef & Steiner, Gerhard. Gem for the Atari 520 ST. Dorn, Susan & Moore, Sean, eds. Kesten, Detlev, tr. from GER.Tr. of Gem Fur Dem Atari 520 ST. (Illus.). 325p. (Orig.). pap. 25.95 *(978-0-941689-04-5(2))* Progressive Peripherals & Software, Inc.

ATARI XL COMPUTERS
Evans, Carl M. Atari BASIC: Faster & Better. 300p. 19.95 *(978-0-936200-29-3(4))* Blue Cat.
Rowley, Thomas E. Atari BASIC: Learning by Using. 73p. 7.95 *(978-0-936200-35-4(9))* Blue Cat.
Wagner, H. C. Hackerbook for Your Atari Computer. 116p. 9.95 *(978-3-88963-172-5(X))* Blue Cat.

ATATURK, KEMAL, 1881-1938
Azak, Umut. Islam & Secularism in Turkey: Kemalism, Religion & the Nation State. 2010. (International Library of Twentieth Centruy History Ser.). (ENG., Illus.). 256p. 92.00 *(978-1-84885-263-1(0))* I. B. Tauris & Co., Ltd. GBR. Dist: Macmillan.
Bali, Rifat N. New Documents on Atatürk. 2010. 103.16 *(978-1-61719-139-8(6))* Gorgias Pr., LLC.
Bay, Austin. Ataturk: The Extraordinary Life & Achievements of the Greatest General of the Ottoman Empire. 2011. (World Generals Ser.). (ENG., Illus.). 224p. 23.00 *(978-0-230-10711-3(7))* Palgrave Macmillan.
Brockett, Gavin D. How Happy to Call Oneself a Turk: Provincial Newspapers & the Negotiation of a Muslim National Identity. (ENG., Illus.). 312p. 2012. pap. 30.00 ***(978-0-292-74400-4(5))*** 2011. 55.00 *(978-0-292-72359-7(8))* Univ. of Texas Pr.
Hanioglu, Sukru. Ataturk: An Intellectual Biography. 2011. (ENG., Illus.). 280p. 27.95 *(978-0-691-15109-0(1))* Princeton Univ. Pr.
Harris, George S. & Criss, Bilge. Studies in Atatürk's Turkey: The American Dimension. Harris, S. & Criss, N. B., eds. 2009. (Ottoman Empire & Its Heritage Ser.). (Illus.). 328p. *(978-90-04-17434-4(6))* BRILL.
Mango, Andrew. From the Sultan to Ataturk? Turkey -The Peace Conferences of 1919-23 & Their Aftermath. 2010. (Makers of the Modern World Ser.). (ENG., Illus.). 220p. 19.95 *(978-1-905791-65-1(8))* Haus Publishing GBR. Dist: Consortium Bk. Sales & Distribution.
Ozoglu, Ph.D., Hakan. From Caliphate to Secular State: Power Struggle in the Early Turkish Republic, 1 vol. 2011. 218p. 34.95 *(978-0-313-37956-7(4),* A2024C) Greenwood Publishing Group, Inc.
Rotberg, Robert I. Transformative Political Leadership: Making a Difference in the Developing World. 2012. (ENG.). 216p. 75.00 ***(978-0-226-72898-8(6))***; pap. 25.00 ***(978-0-226-72899-5(4))*** Univ. of Chicago Pr.
Sitki, Hatice. Myths, Symbols & Branding. 2009. 268p. pap. *(978-3-639-15905-9(5))* VDM Verlag Dr. Mueller e.K.
Zürcher, Erik J. The Young Turk Legacy & Nation Building: From the Ottoman Empire to Atatürk's Turkey. 2010. (Library of Modern Middle East Studies). (ENG.). 368p. pap. 30.00 *(978-1-84885-272-3(X))* I. B. Tauris & Co., Ltd. GBR. Dist: Macmillan.
—The Young Turk Legacy & National Awakening: From the Ottoman Empire to Atatürk's Turkey. 2010. (Library of Modern Middle East Studies). (ENG.). 368p. 99.00 *(978-1-84885-271-6(1))* I. B. Tauris & Co., Ltd. GBR. Dist: Macmillan.

ATAVISM
see also Heredity
Seitler, Dana. Atavistic Tendencies: The Culture of Science in American Modernity. 2008. (Illus.). 320p. pap. 22.50 *(978-0-8166-5124-5(8))* Univ. of Minnesota Pr.
Seitler, Dana & Seitler. Atavistic Tendencies: The Culture of Science in American Modernity. 2008. (Illus.). 320p. 67.50 *(978-0-8166-5123-8(X))* Univ. of Minnesota Pr.

ATCHISON, TOPEKA AND SANTA FE RAILWAY COMPANY
Brasher, Larry E. Santa Fe Locomotive Development: The Journey to Supreme Steam & Pioneer Diesels. 2006. (Illus.). 304p. 65.00 *(978-1-930013-20-9(5))* Signature Pr.
Glischinski, Steve. Santa Fe Railway. 2008. (MBI Railroad Color History Ser.). (ENG., Illus.). 160p. 37.00 *(978-0-7603-3335-8(1),* 0760333351, Voyageur Pr) MBI Publishing Co. LLC.
Kelly, John. Santa Fe Railway Photo Archive. 2010. (Photo Archive Ser.). (ENG., Illus.). 128p. pap. 32.95 *(978-1-58388-259-7(6),* 1583882596) Iconografix, Inc.
Marshall, James. Santa Fe: The Railroad That Built an Empire. 2011. 534p. 62.95 ***(978-1-258-03935-6(4))*** Literary Licensing, LLC.

ATELIERS
see Workshops

ATEN, IRA, 1862-1953
Alexander, Bob. Rawhide Ranger, Ira Aten: Enforcing Law on the Texas Frontier. 2011. (Frances B. Vick Ser.). (Illus.). 528p. 32.95 ***(978-1-57441-315-1(5))*** Univ. of North Texas Pr.

ATESO LANGUAGE
see Teso Language

ATGET, EUGENE, 1857-1927
Atget, Eugene, photos by. Atget: Photographe de Paris. 2009. (ENG., Illus.). 112p. 39.95 *(978-1-935004-00-4(X))* Errata Editions.
Gierstberg, Frits, et al. Eugène Atget: Paris 1898-1924. 2011. (ENG., Illus.). 320p. 71.00 ***(978-84-15253-03-7(6))*** T.F. Editores ESP. Dist: National Bk. Network.
Rauschenberg, Christopher & Atget, Eugène. Paris Changing: Revisiting Eugene Atget's Paris. 2007. (ENG., Illus.). 192p. 40.00 *(978-1-56898-680-7(7))* Princeton Architectural Pr.

ATHANASIAN CREED
Alwis, Anne P. Celibate Marriages in Late Antique & Byzantine Hagiography: The Lives of Saints Julian & Basilissa, Andronikos & Athanasia, & Galaktion & Episteme. 2011. (ENG.). 352p. 120.00 *(978-1-4411-1525-6(0))* Continuum International Publishing Group, Ltd. GBR. Dist: National Bk. Network.
Disney, John & Frend, William. Six Tracts, in Vindication of the Worship of One God. 2009. 224p. pap. 20.95 *(978-0-557-03694-3(1))* Lulu Enterprises Inc.
Tetz, Martin. Athanasiana: Zu Leben und Lehre des Athanasius. Geerlings, Wilhelm & Wyrwa, Dietmar, eds. (Beihefte zur Zeitschrift fur die neutestamentliche Wissenschaft und die Kunde der älteren Kirche Ser.). (GER.). 314p. 225.00 ***(978-3-11-179832-5(1))*** De Gruyter, Walter Inc.

ATHANASIUS, SAINT, PATRIARCH OF ALEXANDRIA, D. 373
DelCogliano, Mark, et al. Works on the Spirit: Athanasius's Letters to Serapion on the Holy Spirit, and, Didymus's on the Holy Spirit. 2011. ***(978-0-88141-379-3(8))*** St. Vladimir's Seminary Pr.
Donker, Gerald J. The Text of the Apostolos in Athanasius of Alexandria. 2011. 372p. ***(978-90-04-20254-2(4))*** BRILL.
—The Text of the Apostolos in Athanasius of Alexandria. 2011. ***(978-1-58983-551-1(4))***; pap. ***(978-1-58983-550-4(6))*** Society of Biblical Literature.
Ernest, James D. The Bible in Athanasius of Alexandria. 2010. *(978-1-58983-496-5(8))* Society of Biblical Literature.
Gwynn, David M. Athanasius of Alexandria: Bishop, Theologian, Ascetic, Father. 2012. (Christian Theology in Context Ser.). (ENG.). 256p. 110.00 ***(978-0-19-921096-1(9))***; pap. 35.00 ***(978-0-19-921095-4(0))*** Oxford Univ. Pr., Inc.
Gwynn, David M. The Eusebians: The Polemic of Athanasius of Alexandria & the Construction of the 'Arian Controversy' 2007. (Oxford Theological Monographs). (ENG.). 304p. 99.00 *(978-0-19-920555-4(8))* Oxford Univ. Pr., Inc.
HarperCollins Spiritual Classics Staff. Athanasius: The Life of Antony. Gregg, Robert C., tr. from GEC. 2006. (HarperCollins Spiritual Classics Ser.). (ENG.). 128p. pap. 11.99 *(978-0-06-075469-3(9),* HarperOne) HarperCollins Pubs.
Jones, Marvin D. Athanasius' Concept of Eternal Sonship as Revealed in Contra Arianos. 2006. 240p. *(978-0-7734-5644-0(9))* Mellen, Edwin Pr., The.
Piper, John. Contending for Our All: Defending Truth & Treasuring Christ in the Lives of Athanasius, John Owen, & J. Gresham Machen. 2011. (Swans Are Not Silent Ser.: Vol. 4). 192p. pap. 14.99 ***(978-1-4335-1928-4(3))*** Crossway.
Robertson, Jon M. Christ as Mediator: A Study of the Theologies of Eusebius of Caesarea, Marcellus of Ancyra, & Athanasius of Alexandria. 2007. (Oxford Theological Monographs). (ENG.). 245p. 135.00 *(978-0-19-921260-6(0))* Oxford Univ. Pr., Inc.
Stockhausen, Annette Von & Brennecke, Hanns Christof, eds. Von Arius zum Athanasianum: Studien zur Edition der 'Athanasius Werke' 2010. (Texte und Untersuchungen zur Geschichte der altchristlichen Literatur Ser.).Tr. of From Arius to Athanasian Creed. Studies on the Edition Athanasius Werke. (GER.). X, 318p. 126.00 *(978-3-11-021860-2(7))*; 196.00 ***(978-3-11-173206-0(1))*** De Gruyter, Walter Inc.
Weinandy, Thomas G. Athanasius: A Theological Introduction. 2007. (Great Theologians Ser.). 162p. 89.95 *(978-0-7546-1719-8(X))*; pap. 29.95 *(978-0-7546-1720-4(3))* Ashgate Publishing Co.

ATHAPASCAN LANGUAGES
see also Carrier Language; Navajo Language
Cook, Eung-Do & Rice, Keren D., eds. Athapaskan Linguistics: Current Perspectives on a Language Family. (Trends in Linguistics. State-of-the-Art Reports). (ENG.). VIII, 645p. 374.00 ***(978-3-11-179360-3(5))*** De Gruyter, Mouton DEU. Dist: de Gruyter, Walter GmbH & Co. KG.
Meek, Barbara A. We Are Our Language: An Ethnography of Language Revitalization in a Northern Athabascan Community. 2011. (First Peoples: New Directions in Indigenous Studies). (ENG., Illus.). 240p. 49.95 *(978-0-8165-2717-5(2))* Univ. of Arizona Pr.

ATHEISM
see also Agnosticism; God; Irreligion; Theism
Aikin, Scott F. & Talisse, Robert B. Reasonable Atheism: A Moral Case for Respectful Disbelief. 2011. (ENG.). 265p. pap. 20.00 *(978-1-61614-383-1(5))* Prometheus Bks., Pubs.

Alter, Torin Andrew & Howell, Robert J. The God Dialogues: A Philosophical Journey, 1 vol. 2010. (ENG.). 192p. (C). pap. 19.95 *(978-0-19-539559-4(X))* Oxford Univ. Pr., Inc.

Amarasingam, Amarnath. Religion & the New Atheism: A Critical Appraisal. 2010. (Studies in Critical Social Sciences Ser.). 268p. *(978-90-04-18557-9(7))* BRILL.

Amarasingam, Amarnath, ed. Religion & the New Atheism: A Critical Appraisal. 2012. (Studies in Critical Social Sciences Ser.). (ENG., Illus.). 256p. pap. 28.00 ***(978-1-60846-203-2(X))*** Haymarket Bks.

Antinoff, Steve. Spiritual Atheism. 2010. (ENG.). 120p. pap. 14.95 *(978-1-58243-564-0(2)*, Counterpoint Pr.) Basic Bks. GBR. Dist: Perseus-PGW.

Antony, Louise, ed. Philosophers without Gods: Meditations on Atheism & the Secular Life, 1 vol. 2010. (ENG.). 320p. pap. 17.95 *(978-0-19-974341-4(X))* Oxford Univ. Pr., Inc.

Antony, Louise M., ed. Philosophers Without Gods: Meditations on Atheism & the Secular Life. 2007. (ENG.). 352p. 74.00 *(978-0-19-517307-9(4))* Oxford Univ. Pr., Inc.

Armstrong, Karen. The Case for God: What Religion Really Means. (ENG.). 432p. 2010. pap. 16.95 *(978-0-307-38980-0(4)*, Anchor) 2009. 27.95 *(978-0-307-26918-8(3)*, Knopf) Knopf Doubleday Publishing Group.

Aronson, Ronald. Living Without God: New Directions for Atheists, Agnostics, Secularists, & the Undecided. 2009. (ENG.). 256p. pap. 15.95 *(978-1-58243-530-5(8)*, Counterpoint Pr.) Basic Bks. GBR. Dist: Perseus-PGW.

Avakian, Bob. Fuera con todos los dioses: Desencadenando la mente y cambiando radicalmente el mundo. 2009. (SPA.). pap. 12.95 *(978-0-615-27109-5(X))* JB Bks.

Bakunin, Mikhail. God & the State. 2009. pap. 8.75 *(978-0-9737827-7-6(3))* Black Cat Pr. CAN. Dist: AK Pr. Distribution.

Barker, Dan. Godless: How an Evangelical Preacher Became One of America's Leading Atheists. 2008. (ENG.). 392p. pap. 14.95 *(978-1-56975-677-5(5))* Ulysses Pr.

—The Good Atheist: Living a Purpose-Filled Life Without God. 2011. (ENG.). 240p. pap. 14.95 *(978-1-56975-846-5(8))* Ulysses Pr.

Baron d'Holbach, Paul-Henri Thiry, et al. Superstition in all Ages. 2010. 348p. pap. 24.95 *(978-0-557-35875-5(2))* Lulu Enterprises Inc.

Beres, Derek. Sound Against Flame: The Process of Yoga & Atheism in America. 2008. 260p. pap. 15.00 *(978-0-9817398-0-9(6))* Outside the Box Publishing, LLC.

Berg, Geoffrey. The Six Ways of Atheism: New Logical Disproofs of the Existence of God. 2009. 176p. pap. *(978-0-9543956-6-7(2))* Temple DPS, Ltd.

Berlinski, David. The Devil's Delusion: Atheism & its Scientific Pretensions. 2nd ed. 2009. (ENG.). 256p. pap. 15.95 *(978-0-465-01937-3(4))* Basic Bks.

Blackford, Russell & Schüklenk, Udo, eds. 50 Voices of Disbelief: Why We Are Atheists. 2009. (ENG.). 360p. 99.95 *(978-1-4051-9045-9(0))*; pap. 29.95 *(978-1-4051-9046-6(9))* Wiley, John & Sons, Inc. (Wiley-Blackwell).

Brooks, David. The Necessity of Atheism. 2007. 216p. per. 14.99 *(978-1-59547-784-2(5))* NuVision Pubns., LLC.

Brooks, David Marshall. The Necessity of Atheism. 2008. 284p. 25.99 *(978-0-554-37005-7(0))*; 28.99 *(978-0-554-27702-8(6))* BiblioBazaar.

—The Necessity of Atheism. 2008. 216p. 29.99 *(978-1-59547-724-8(1))* NuVision Pubns., LLC.

Brown, Arthur I. Footprints of God. 2007. (ENG.). 248p. 41.95 *(978-0-548-10805-5(6))* Kessinger Publishing, LLC.

Buchanan, James. Modern Atheism under Its Forms of Pantheism, Materialism, Secularism, Development, & Natural Laws. 2009. 384p. 31.99 *(978-0-559-09525-2(2))*; 29.99 *(978-0-559-09538-2(4))*; pap. 33.75 *(978-0-559-09531-3(7))*; pap. 32.75 *(978-0-559-09537-5(6))* BiblioBazaar.

—Modern Atheism under Its Forms of Pantheism, Materialism, Secularism, Development, & Natural Laws by James Buchanan. 2006. 436p. per. 26.99 *(978-1-4255-4787-5(7))* MPublishing.

Carroll, Richard. Death: An Alternate Lifestyle, 1 vol. 2010. 262p. pap. 27.95 *(978-1-60813-446-5(6))* PublishAmerica, Inc.

Chole, Alicia Britt. Finding an Unseen God: Reflections of a Former Atheist, 1 vol. 2009. 176p. pap. 13.99 *(978-0-7642-0602-3(8))* Bethany Hse. Pubs.

Cohen, Chapman. Theism or Atheism: The Great Alternative. 2008. 184p. pap. 24.95 *(978-1-60444-018-8(X))* IndoEuropeanPublishing.com.

Comfort, Ray. Nothing Created Everything: The Scientific Impossibility of Atheistic Evolution. 2009. 224p. 25.95 *(978-1-935071-23-5(8))* WND Bks, Inc.

Comte-Sponville, Andre. The Little Book of Atheist Spirituality. Huston, Nancy, tr. 2008. (ENG.). 224p. (gr. 12-18). 13.00 *(978-0-14-311443-7(3)*, Penguin (Non-Classics)) Penguin Group (USA) Inc.

Condell, Pat. Godless & Free. 2010. 272p. pap. 25.50 *(978-1-4452-2315-5(5))* Lulu Enterprises Inc.

Cook, Harry T. Asking. 2010. (Illus.). 138p. pap. 16.00 *(978-1-60899-426-7(0)*, Wipf and Stock) Wipf & Stock Pubs.

Corlett, J. Angelo. The Errors of Atheism. 2010. (ENG.). 272p. 110.00 *(978-1-4411-5187-2(7))*; pap. 29.95 *(978-1-4411-5893-2(6))* Continuum International Publishing Group, Ltd. GBR. Dist: National Bk. Network.

Cornwell, John. Darwin's Angel: An Angelic Riposte to the God Delusion. 2009. (ENG.). 176p. pap. 12.95 *(978-1-84668-065-6(4))* Profile Bks. Ltd. GBR. Dist: Consortium Bk. Sales & Distribution.

Covington, Nicholas. Atheism & Naturalism. 2010. 171p. pap. 13.99 *(978-0-557-07046-6(5))* Lulu Enterprises Inc.

Cudworth, Ralph. The True Intellectual System of the Universe. 2009. 512p. pap. *(978-0-217-11087-7(8))* Books LLC.

Curran, Mark. Atheism, Religion & Enlightenment in Pre-Revolutionary Europe. 2012. (Royal Historical Society Studies in History New Ser.: Volume 83). (Illus.). 222p. 90.00 *(978-0-86193-316-7(8))* Royal Historical Society GBR. Dist: Boydell & Brewer, Inc.

David Marshall Brooks. The Necessity of Atheism. 2007. (ENG.). 254p. pap. 21.99 *(978-1-4346-3804-5(9))*; 280p. pap. 23.99 *(978-1-4346-3805-2(7))* BiblioBazaar.

Dawkins, Richard. The God Delusion. (ENG.). 2008. 464p. pap. 15.95 *(978-0-618-91824-9(8)*, Mariner Bks.) 2006. 416p. 27.00 *(978-0-618-68000-9(4))* Houghton Mifflin Harcourt Trade & Reference Pubs.

Day, Vox. The Irrational Atheist: Dissecting the Unholy Trinity of Dawkins, Harris, & Hitchens. 2008. (ENG., Illus.). 305p. 24.95 *(978-1-933771-36-6(4))* BenBella Bks.

de Botton, Alain. Religion for Atheists: A Non-Believer's Guide to the Uses of Religion. 2012. (ENG., Illus.). 320p. 26.95 ***(978-0-307-37910-8(8)***, Pantheon) Knopf Doubleday Publishing Group.

de Sade, Marquis. Dialogue Between a Priest & a Dying Man. Heine, Maurice, ed. Putnam, Samuel, tr. 2011. 52p. 36.95 ***(978-1-258-02092-7(0))*** Literary Licensing, LLC.

Dembski, William A. & Wells, Jonathan. How to be an Intellectually Fulfilled Atheist (or Not) 2008. (ENG.). 150p. (C). pap. 12.00 *(978-1-933859-84-2(9))* ISI Bks.

D'Holbach, Paul Henri Thi. Good Sense. 2007. pap. *(978-1-4068-1357-9(5))* Echo Library.

Drachmann, A. B. Atheism in Pagan Antiquity. 2010. 178p. 30.36 *(978-1-169-72550-8(3))* Kessinger Publishing, LLC.

Drachman, A. b. & Drachman, A. B. Atheism in Pagan Antiquity. 2010. 178p. 37.95 *(978-1-161-37653-1(4))* Kessinger Publishing, LLC.

Drachmann, A. B. Atheism in Pagan Antiquity. Hill, George Francis, ed. Andersen, Ingeborg, tr. 2009. 136p. pap. *(978-1-4099-7639-4(4))* Dodo Pr.

—Atheism in Pagan Antiquity. 2010. 178p. 30.36 *(978-1-163-21159-5(1))*; pap. 18.36 *(978-1-162-76252-4(7))* Kessinger Publishing, LLC.

E A St Amant.com Publishers. Atheism, Scepticism & Philosophy. 2007. 262p. per. *(978-0-9780119-7-0(X))* eastamant.com.

Eller, David. Atheism Advanced: Further Thoughts of a Freethinker. 2007. (Illus.). 520p. pap. 22.00 *(978-1-57884-002-1(3))* American Atheist Pr.

Estes, Yolanda & Bowman, Curtis. Fichte & the Atheism Dispute (1798-1800) 2010. 316p. 124.95 *(978-0-7546-3688-5(7))* Ashgate Publishing Co.

Evans, Jill & Taliaferro, Charles. The Image in Mind: Theism, Naturalism, & the Imagination. 2010. (Continuum Studies in Philosophy of Religion Ser.). (ENG., Illus.). 224p. 130.00 *(978-1-84706-482-0(5))* Continuum International Publishing Group, Ltd. GBR. Dist: National Bk. Network.

Fernandes. The Atheist Delusion. 2009. 228p. pap. 15.99 *(978-1-60791-582-9(0))* Xulon Pr., Inc.

Feser, Edward. The Last Superstition. 2010. (ENG.). 312p. pap. 19.00 *(978-1-58731-452-0(5))* St. Augustine's Pr., Inc.

Flynn, Tom, ed. The New Encyclopedia of Unbelief. 2007. (ENG.). 800p. 199.98 *(978-1-59102-391-3(2))* Prometheus Bks., Pubs.

Frede, Victoria. Doubt, Atheism, & the Nineteenth-Century Russian Intelligentsia. 2011. (ENG., Illus.). 314p. pap. 26.95 ***(978-0-299-28444-2(1))*** Univ. of Wisconsin Pr.

Fuller, Alan. The GOSPEL PROPHECY: the Bible as Allegory. 2009. 206p. pap. 18.99 *(978-0-557-06033-7(8))* Lulu Enterprises Inc.

Ganssle, Gregory E. A Reasonable God: Engaging the New Face of Atheism. 2009. (ENG.). 165p. pap. 24.95 *(978-1-60258-241-5(6))* Baylor Univ. Pr.

Garrison, Becky. The New Atheist Crusaders & Their Unholy Grail: The Misguided Quest to Destroy Your Faith, 0 vols. 2008. 256p. pap. 14.99 *(978-0-8499-1972-5(X))* Nelson, Thomas Inc.

Garrod, , Victor, ThM. Did God Screw Up? 2010. 160p. pap. 19.51 *(978-0-557-46418-0(8))* Lulu Enterprises Inc.

Gefrom, Rolf A. Atheism ENDS NOW! 2008. 200p. pap. 14.95 *(978-0-557-02641-8(5))* Lulu Enterprises Inc.

Geroulanos, Stefanos. An Atheism That Is Not Humanist Emerges in French Thought. 2010. (Cultural Memory in the Present Ser.). (ENG.). 448p. 75.00 *(978-0-8047-6298-4(8))*; pap. 27.95 *(978-0-8047-6299-1(6))* Stanford Univ. Pr.

Graffin, Greg & Olson, Steve. Anarchy Evolution: Faith, Science, & Bad Religion in a World Without God. (ENG.). 304p. 2011. pap. 14.99 *(978-0-06-182851-5(3)*, HarperPerennial) 2010. 22.99 *(978-0-06-182850-8(5))* HarperCollins Pubs.

Grauds, Rozmarija. Diary of an Old World Pagan Atheist. 2006. pap. 10.00 *(978-1-4257-3164-9(3))* Xlibris Corp.

Grayling, A. C. Against All Gods: Six Polemics on Religion & an Essay on Kindness. 2010. (ENG.). 116p. pap. 18.95 *(978-1-84002-727-3(4))* Oberon Bks., Ltd. GBR. Dist: Consortium Bk. Sales & Distribution.

Hagglund, Martin. Radical Atheism: Derrida & the Time of Life. 2008. (Meridian: Crossing Aesthetics Ser.). (ENG.). 272p. 65.00 *(978-0-8047-0077-1(X))* Stanford Univ. Pr.

—Radical Atheism: Derrida & the Time of Life. 2008. (Meridian: Crossing Aesthetics Ser.). (ENG.). 272p. pap. 24.95 *(978-0-8047-0078-8(8))* Stanford Univ. Pr.

Hall, Roger G. For Heaven's Sake - It's Here Now. 2010. (Illus.). 50p. pap. *(978-1-84748-736-0(X))* Athena Pr.

Hanft, Frank. You Can Believe: A Lawyer's Brief on Christianity. 2011. 186p. 42.95 ***(978-1-258-08479-0(1))*** Literary Licensing, LLC.

Harding, Nick. How to Be a Good Atheist. 2008. (ENG.). 224p. 16.95 *(978-1-84243-237-2(0))* Oldcastle Bks., Ltd. GBR. Dist: Independent Pubs. Group.

Harwood, William. Dictionary of Contemporary Mythology Third Edition 2011. Strozier, M. Stefan & Torke, Kyle, eds. 2011. (Illus.). 602p. 45.00 ***(978-1-935444-78-7(6))*** World Audience Pubs.

Harwood, William. God Psychosis. Strozier, M. Stefan & Torke, Kyle, eds. 2009. 428p. pap. 20.00 *(978-1-935444-17-6(4))* World Audience Pubs.

Haught, James A. Honest Doubt: Essays on Atheism in a Believing Society. 2007. (ENG.). 1p. per. 20.98 *(978-1-59102-459-0(5))* Prometheus Bks., Pubs.

Haught, John F. God & the New Atheism: A Critical Response to Dawkins, Harris, & Hitchens. 2008. (ENG.). 124p. per. 17.00 *(978-0-664-23304-4(X))* Westminster John Knox Pr.

Hedges, Chris. I Don't Believe in Atheists. 2008. (ENG., Illus.). 224p. 25.00 *(978-1-4165-6795-0(X)*, Free Pr.) Free Pr.

—When Atheism Becomes Religion: America's New Fundamentalists. 2009. (ENG., Illus.). 224p. pap. 15.00 *(978-1-4165-7078-3(0)*, Free Pr.) Free Pr.

Hitchens, Christopher. The Portable Atheist: Essential Readings for the Nonbeliever. 2007. (ENG.). 528p. per. 17.95 *(978-0-306-81608-6(3))* Da Capo Pr., Inc.

Holden, Thomas. Spectres of False Divinity: Hume's Moral Atheism. (ENG.). 2012. 264p. pap. 29.95 ***(978-0-19-964594-7(9))*** 2010. 256p. 50.00 *(978-0-19-957994-5(6))* Oxford Univ. Pr., Inc.

Huberman, Jack. The Quotable Atheist: Ammunition for Nonbelievers, Political Junkies, Gadflies, & Those Generally Hell-Bound. 2006. (ENG.). 352p. pap. 15.95 *(978-1-56025-969-5(8)*, Nation Bks.) Basic Bks.

Huhn, Wilson R. Telling Right from Wrong Without the Help of God. 2008. 198p. pap. 22.00 *(978-1-59460-536-9(X))* Carolina Academic Pr.

Hurth, Elisabeth. Between Faith & Unbelief: American Transcendentalists & the Challenge of Atheism. 2007. (Studies in the History of Christian Traditions). 240p. *(978-90-04-16166-5(X))* BRILL.

Hyman, Gavin. A Short History of Atheism. 2010. (Library of Modern Religion Ser.). (ENG.). 232p. 85.00 *(978-1-84885-136-8(7))*; pap. 25.00 *(978-1-84885-137-5(5))* I. B. Tauris & Co., Ltd. GBR. Dist: Macmillan.

Jenman, Rodney. The Good Delusion: an Unethical Response to Richard Dawkins the God Delusion. 2010. 72p. pap. 11.98 *(978-1-4452-5700-6(9))* Lulu Enterprises Inc.

Johnson, Robert Bowie, Jr. Sowing Atheism: The National Academy of Sciences' Sinister Scheme to Teach Our Children They're Descended from Reptiles. 2008. (ENG., Illus.). 128p. pap. 12.95 *(978-0-9705438-5-1(9))* Solving Light Bks.

Joshi, S. T. Icons of Unbelief: Atheists, Agnostics, & Secularists, 1 vol. Joshi, S. T., ed. 2008. (Greenwood Icons Ser.). 476p. 75.00 *(978-0-313-34759-7(X)*, GR4759) Greenwood Publishing Group, Inc.

—The Unbelievers: The Evolution of Modern Atheism. 2011. (ENG.). 300p. pap. 19.00 *(978-1-61614-236-0(7))* Prometheus Bks., Pubs.

Kawaguchi, Dorothy Bible. Does God Exist? 2008. 112p. pap. 19.99 *(978-1-4257-9674-7(5))* Xlibris Corp.

Kearney, Richard. Anatheism: Returning to God after God. 2009. (Insurrections: Critical Studies in Religion, Politics, & Culture Ser.). (ENG., Illus.). 272p. (gr. 17). 29.50 *(978-0-231-14788-0(0))* Columbia Univ. Pr.

Kernohan, Andrew William. A Good Life Without God: Atheism & a Meaningful Life. 2009. ii, 187p. pap. *(978-0-557-04479-5(0))* Lulu Enterprises Inc.

King, Mike. Postsecularism: The Hidden Challenge to Extremism. 2009. (ENG.). 279p. pap. 53.00 *(978-0-227-17247-6(7))* Clarke, James Co., Ltd. GBR. Dist: Brown, David Bk. Co., The.

Klingman, Edwin E. The Atheist & the God Particle. 2008. (Illus.). x, 342p. pap. *(978-0-9791765-6-2(5))* Ekom Publishing.

Knowlton, Charles. Fruits of Philosophy. 2009. 52p. pap. *(978-1-4590-9912-8(5))* Books LLC.

Konner, Joan. The Atheist's Bible: An Illustrious Collection of Irreverent Thoughts. 2007. (ENG., Illus.). 208p. 16.95 *(978-0-06-134915-7(1)*, Ecco) HarperCollins Pubs.

Kreps, M. To the Devil with Religion! 2007. pap. *(978-0-9533505-6-8(8))* Cardinal Pr.

Lalli, Nica. Nothing: Something to Believe In. 2007. (ENG.). 1p. per. 18.98 *(978-1-59102-529-0(X))* Prometheus Bks., Pubs.

Lane, Dave. Isn't Religion weird? Quotations for Atheists. 2008. 133p. pap. 18.95 *(978-1-4092-1876-0(7))* Lulu Enterprises Inc.

Levy, Andrea. Faith in Faithlessness: An Anthology of Atheism. Roussopoulos, Dimitrios, ed. 2008. (ENG.). 440p. pap. 19.99 *(978-1-55164-312-0(X))* Black Rose Bks. CAN. Dist: Consortium Bk. Sales & Distribution.

Levy, Andrea & Roussopoulos, Dimitrios, eds. Faith in Faithlessness: An Anthology of Atheism. 2008. (ENG.). 440p. 48.99 *(978-1-55164-313-7(8))* Black Rose Bks. CAN. Dist: Consortium Bk. Sales & Distribution.

Lewis, Joseph. Atheism & Other Addresses. 2010. 162p. 29.56 *(978-1-163-31669-6(5))* 2007. (ENG.). 164p. 36.95 *(978-0-548-00408-1(0))* Kessinger Publishing, LLC.

Linker, Damon. The Religious Test: Why We Must Question the Beliefs of Our Leaders. 2010. (ENG.). 251p. 25.95 *(978-0-393-06795-8(5)*, 6795) Norton, W. W. & Co., Inc.

Loftus, John W. Why I Became an Atheist: A Former Preacher Rejects Christianity. (ENG.). 2012. 480p. pap. 21.00 ***(978-1-61614-577-4(3))*** 2008. 355p. pap. 19.98 *(978-1-59102-592-4(3))* Prometheus Bks., Pubs.

Luehrmann, Sonja. Secularism Soviet Style: Teaching Atheism & Religion in a Volga Republic. 2011. (New Anthropologies of Europe Ser.). (ENG., Illus.). 292p. 80.00 *(978-0-253-35698-7(9)*, 0253356989); pap. 27.95 *(978-0-253-22355-5(5)*, 0253223555) Indiana Univ. Pr.

Maisel, Eric. The Atheist's Way: Living Well Without Gods. 2009. (ENG.). 200p. pap. 14.00 *(978-1-57731-642-8(8))* New World Library.

Markham, Ian S. Against Atheism: Why Dawkins, Hitchens, & Harris Are Fundamentally Wrong. 2010. (ENG., Illus.). 176p. 94.95 *(978-1-4051-8964-4(9))*; pap. 27.95 *(978-1-4051-8963-7(0))* Wiley, John & Sons, Inc. (Wiley-Blackwell).

Martin, Michael, ed. The Cambridge Companion to Atheism. 2006. (Cambridge Companions to Philosophy Ser.). (ENG.). 352p. 97.00 *(978-0-521-84270-9(0))*; per. 29.99 *(978-0-521-60367-6(6))* Cambridge Univ. Pr.

McCabe, Joseph & Haldeman-Julius, E. The Blood of Martyrs. 2011. 34p. 35.95 ***(978-1-258-00873-4(4))*** Literary Licensing, LLC.

McGrath, Alister E. & McGrath, Joanna Collicutt. The Dawkins Delusion? Atheist Fundamentalism & the Denial of the Divine. annot. ed. 2007. (Veritas Bks.). (ENG.). 118p. 16.00 *(978-0-8308-3446-4(X)*, IVP Bks.) InterVarsity Pr.

Mehta, Hemant. I Sold My Soul on EBay: Viewing Faith through an Atheist's Eyes. 2007. (ENG.). 224p. pap. 13.99 *(978-1-4000-7347-4(2)*, WaterBrook Pr.) Doubleday Religious Publishing Group, The.

Meslier, Jean. Superstition in All Ages: Common Sense. 2007. (ENG.). 260p. pap. 21.99 *(978-1-4346-1174-1(4))*; 282p. pap. 23.99 *(978-1-4346-1245-8(7))* BiblioBazaar.

Miller, Darrow L. Emancipating the World: A Christian Response to Radical Islam & Fundamentalist Atheism. 2012. ***(978-1-57658-716-4(9))*** YWAM Publishing.

Mills, David. Atheist Universe: The Thinking Person's Answer to Christian Fundamentalism. 2006. (ENG., Illus.). 256p. per. 14.95 *(978-1-56975-567-9(1))* Ulysses Pr.

Munn, Gerald E. Congruent Parallels, Living Infinity~Living God: An Answer to Atheism. 2011. 206p. pap. 24.95 *(978-1-4327-6617-7(1))* Outskirts Pr., Inc.

Naville, Ernest. The Heavenly Father Lectures on Modern Atheism by Ernest Naville Tr from the French by Henry Downton. 2006. 392p. per. 26.99 *(978-1-4255-4189-7(5))* MPublishing.

Nicholls, Samuel. Losing My Religion. 2007. 208p. per. *(978-1-897312-08-7(3))* Adlibbed Ltd.

Obasi, Geoffrey. A Critique of Atheism. 2009. (ENG.). 292p. pap. *(978-1-85756-663-5(7))* Janus Publishing Co.

O'Malley, William J. Help My Unbelief. 2008. 160p. 15.00 *(978-1-57075-803-4(4))* Orbis Bks.

Onfray, Michel. Atheist Manifesto: The Case Against Christianity, Judaism, & Islam. 2011. (ENG.). 264p. pap. 14.95 *(978-1-61145-008-8(X)*, 611008, Arcade Publishing) Skyhorse Publishing Co., Inc.

Palmer, Michael. Atheism for Beginners. 2012. (ENG.). (C). pap. 30.00 ***(978-0-7188-9297-5(6))*** Lutherworth Pr., The GBR. Dist: Brown, David Bk. Co., The.

Paramore, Kiri. Ideology & Christianity in Japan. 2009. (Routledge/Leiden Series in Modern East Asian History & Politics Ser.). 240p. 150.00 *(978-0-415-44356-2(3))* Routledge.

Parker, Theodore. Sermons of Theism, Atheism, & the Popular Theology. 2008. 448p. 30.99 *(978-0-559-26078-0(4))*; pap. 35.75 *(978-0-559-26075-9(X))* BiblioBazaar.

—Sermons of Theism, Atheism, & the Popular Theology. 2009. 210p. pap. *(978-0-217-55385-8(0))* Books LLC.

—Sermons of Theism, Atheism, & the Popular Theology. 2006. 448p. per. 26.99 *(978-1-4255-4952-7(7))* MPublishing.

Pasquini, John J. Atheist Personality Disorder: Addressing A Distorted Mindset. 2009. 288p. pap. 15.49 *(978-1-4389-9279-2(3))* AuthorHouse.

Patterson, Robert. Fables of Infidelity & Facts of Faith. 2009. 484p. 31.99 *(978-0-559-05575-1(7))*; 33.99 *(978-0-559-05563-8(3))*; pap. 37.75 *(978-0-559-05568-3(4))*; pap. 36.75 *(978-0-559-05572-0(2))* BiblioBazaar.

—Fables of Infidelity & Facts of Faith. 2009. 360p. pap. *(978-0-217-71729-8(2))* Books LLC.

—Fables of Infidelity & Facts of Faith. 2006. 544p. per. 29.99 *(978-1-4255-6006-5(7))* MPublishing.

Paulos, John Allen, et al. Irreligion: A Mathematician Explains Why the Arguments for God Just Don't Add Up. 2009. (ENG., Illus.). 176p. pap. 14.00 *(978-0-8090-5918-8(5)*, Hill & Wang) Farrar, Straus & Giroux.

Pearl, Michael. Learning from the Atheists, 1. 2007. *(978-1-892112-96-5(5))* No Greater Joy Ministries, Inc.

Pearson, Thomas. The Evangelical Alliance Prize Essay on Infidelity Infidelity Dissected. 2006. 396p. per. 26.99 *(978-1-4255-4238-2(7))* MPublishing.

—Infidelity; Its, Aspects, Causes, & Agencies: Being the Prize Essay of the British organization of the Evangelical Alliance ... 2006. 632p. per. 34.99 *(978-1-4255-6603-6(0))* MPublishing.

Pius XI. Atheistic Communism: Divini Redemptoris. 50p. pap. 1.75 *(978-0-8198-0749-6(4)*, 332-005) Pauline Bks. & Media.

Reuben Stone, David. ATHEISM IS FALSE Richard Dawkins & the Improbability of God Delusion. 2007. 268p. pap. 19.95 *(978-1-4303-1230-7(0))* Lulu Enterprises Inc.

Reymond, Robert L. What Is God? An Investigation of the Perfections of God's Nature. 2007. (ENG.). 368p. per. 19.99 *(978-1-84550-228-7(0)*, Mentor) Christian Focus Pubns. GBR. Dist: STL Distribution North America.

Ricker, George A. Mere Atheism: No gods... no Problem! 2007. 144p. per. 14.95 *(978-0-595-47506-3(X))* iUniverse, Inc.

Robertson, David. The Dawkins Letters Revised Edition. 2010. (ENG.). 160p. mass mkt. 8.99 *(978-1-84550-597-4(2))* Christian Focus Pubns. GBR. Dist: STL Distribution North America.

Rosenberg, Alex. The Atheist's Guide to Reality: Enjoying Life Without Illusions. 2011. (ENG., Illus.). 368p. 25.95 (978-0-393-08023-0(4), 8023) Norton, W. W. & Co., Inc.
Rosenberg, Alex. The Atheist's Guide to Reality: Enjoying Life without Illusions. 2012. (ENG., Illus.). 368p. pap. 16.95 **(978-0-393-34411-0(8),** 34411) Norton, W. W. & Co., Inc.
Russell, Paul. The Riddle of Hume's Treatise: Skepticism, Naturalism, & Irreligion. 2008. (ENG., Illus.). 448p. 99.00 *(978-0-19-511033-3(1))* Oxford Univ. Pr., Inc.
Sabbath, Linda Miroslava. The Unveiling of God. 2010. 146p. pap. 12.95 *(978-0-557-35414-6(5))* Lulu Enterprises Inc.
Saltman, Roy G. Sacred Humanism Without Miracles: Responding to the New Atheists. 2012. (ENG., Illus.). 276p. 85.00 **(978-1-137-00361-4(8))** Palgrave Macmillan.
Scruton, Roger. The Face of God. 2012. (ENG.). 200p. 26.95 *(978-1-84706-524-7(4))* Continuum International Publishing Group, Ltd. GBR. Dist: National Bk. Network.
Sheiman, Bruce. An Atheist Defends Religion: Why Humanity Is Better off with Religion Than Without It. 2009. (ENG.). 256p. (gr. 12-18). pap. 14.95 *(978-1-59257-854-2(3),* Alpha Bks.) Penguin Group (USA) Inc.
Shelley, Percy Bysshe. The Necessity of Atheism. reprint ed. lib. bdg. 98.00 *(978-0-7426-2116-9(2))* Classic Bks.
Shelley, Percy Bysshe. The Necessity of Atheism: Selected Aphorisms. 2011. 26p. 35.95 **(978-1-258-05264-5(4))** Literary Licensing, LLC.
Sinnott-Armstrong, Walter. Morality Without God?, 1 vol. 2011. (Philosophy in Action Ser.). (ENG.). 192p. pap. 14.95 *(978-0-19-984135-6(7))* Oxford Univ. Pr., Inc.
Smith, Bruce A. The Path of Reason: A Philosophy of Nonbelief. 2007. 212p. 34.95 *(978-0-87586-580-5(1));* pap. 22.95 *(978-0-87586-579-9(8))* Algora Publishing.
Smith, John H. Dialogues Between Faith & Reason: The Death & Return of God in Modern German Thought. 2011. (Illus.). 328p. 85.00 *(978-0-8014-4927-7(8));* pap. 35.00 **(978-0-8014-7762-1(X))** Cornell Univ. Pr.
Southwell, Charles. An Apology for Atheism. 2008. 120p. 24.99 *(978-0-554-26642-3(3));* 21.99 *(978-0-554-35945-8(6))* BiblioBazaar.
—An Apology for Atheism. 2008. 100p. pap. *(978-1-4099-5731-5(6))* Dodo Pr.
Spiegel, James S. The Making of an Atheist: How Immorality Leads to Unbelief, 1 vol. 2010. (ENG.). 144p. pap. 12.99 *(978-0-8024-7611-1(2))* Moody Pubs.
Stahl, Philip A. Atheism: A Beginner's Handbook. 2007. 144p. per. 14.95 *(978-0-595-42737-6(5))* iUniverse, Inc.
—Dialectical Atheism. 2009. 188p. pap. 19.90 *(978-0-557-11111-5(5))* Lulu Enterprises Inc.
Staume, David. The Atheist Afterlife: The odds of an afterlife - reasonable, the odds of meeting God there - Nil. 2009. 176p. pap. *(978-1-897435-29-8(0))* Agio Publishing Hse.
Steele, David Ramsay & Carus Publishing Staff. Atheism Explained: From Folly to Philosophy. 2008. (Ideas Explained Ser.). (ENG.). 224p. pap. 29.95 *(978-0-8126-9637-0(9))* Open Court Publishing Co.
Stenger, Victor J. The Fallacy of Fine-Tuning: Why the Universe Is Not Designed for Us. 2011. (ENG., Illus.). 340p. 28.00 *(978-1-61614-443-2(2))* Prometheus Bks., Pubs.
—God: The Failed Hypothesis: How Science Shows That God Does Not Exist. (ENG., Illus.). 1p. 2008. pap. 18.98 *(978-1-59102-652-5(0))* 2007. 28.98 *(978-1-59102-481-1(1))* Prometheus Bks., Pubs.
Stewart, Robert B. The Future of Atheism: Alister Mcgrath & Daniel Dennett in Dialogue. 2008. 192p. (C). pap. 19.00 *(978-0-8006-6314-8(4),* Fortress Pr.) Augsburg Fortress, Pubs.
Sullivan, Clayton. The Impossibility of Atheism. 2010. 64p. pap. 10.99 *(978-1-61507-086-6(5))* Cross Bks. Publishing.
Tzanetakos, Christos. The Life & Work of an Atheist Pioneer. 2011. 236p. 28.95 **(978-1-4620-4498-6(0));** pap. 18.95 **(978-1-4620-4495-3(9))** iUniverse, Inc.
Uhl, Stephen Frederick. Imagine No Superstition: The Power to Enjoy Life with No Guilt, No Shame, No Blame. 2007. (ENG., Illus.). 190p. per. 18.95 *(978-0-9793169-0-6(1))* Golden Rule Pubs.
Vetter, Herbert F. Is God Necessary? No! & Yes! 2007. 121p. pap. 12.95 *(978-0-615-16046-7(8))* Harvard Square Library.
Walters, Kerry. Atheism. 2010. (Guides for the Perplexed Ser.). (ENG.). 208p. pap. 19.95 *(978-0-8264-2493-8(7))* Continuum International Publishing Group, Ltd. GBR. Dist: National Bk. Network.
—Atheism: A Guide for the Perplexed. 2010. (Guides for the Perplexed Ser.). (ENG.). 208p. 80.00 *(978-0-8264-4326-7(5))* Continuum International Publishing Group, Ltd. GBR. Dist: National Bk. Network.
Ward, Keith. Why There Almost Certainly Is a God: Doubting Dawkins. 2009. (ENG., Illus.). 160p. pap. 14.95 *(978-0-7459-5330-4(1))* Lion Hudson PLC GBR. Dist: Independent Pubs. Group.
Watkin, Christopher. Difficult Atheism: Post-Theological Thinking in Alain Badiou, Jean-Luc Nancy & Quentin Meillassoux. 2011. (Crosscurrents Ser.). (ENG.). 224p. (gr. 17). 105.00 *(978-0-7486-4057-7(6))* Edinburgh Univ. Pr. GBR. Dist: Columbia Univ. Pr.
Wilson, Gareth. The Plain Truths of Religion. 2010. 424p. (ENG.). 30.99 *(978-1-4520-0475-4(7));* pap. 20.49 *(978-1-4520-0474-7(9))* AuthorHouse.
Wolpe, David J. Why Faith Matters. 2009. (ENG.). 256p. pap. 14.99 *(978-0-06-163335-5(6),* HarperOne) HarperCollins Pubs.
Wright, Walter Henry. The Blind Atheist. 2009. 176p. pap. 11.99 *(978-1-4490-2211-2(1))* AuthorHouse.
Zindler, Frank R. Through Atheist Eyes: Religions & Scriptures: Scenes from a World That Won't Reason, 5 vols., Vol. 1. 2011. (Illus.). pap. *(978-1-57884-011-3(2))* American Atheist Pr.
Zuckerman, Phil. Faith No More: Why People Reject Religion, 1 vol. 2011. (ENG., Illus.). 224p. 24.95 *(978-0-19-974001-7(1))* Oxford Univ. Pr., Inc.
Zuckerman, Phil, ed. Atheism & Secularity, 2 vols. 2010. (Illus.). 514p. 104.95 *(978-0-313-35181-5(3),* C35181, Praeger Pubs.) Greenwood Publishing Group, Inc.

ATHEISM, CHRISTIAN

see Death of God Theology

ATHEISM AND CHRISTIANITY

see Christianity and Atheism

ATHELSTAN, KING OF ENGLAND, 895-940

Foot, Sarah. Aethelstan: The First King of England. 2011. (English Monarchs Ser.). (ENG., Illus.). 283p. 40.00 *(978-0-300-12535-1(6))* Yale Univ. Pr.
—Æthelstan: The First King of England. 2011. *(978-83-00-12535-7(3))* Yale Univ. Pr.

ATHENA (GREEK DEITY)

Cooley, Arthur. Athena Polias on the Acropolis of Athens. 2009. pap. 23.68 *(978-1-60724-488-2(8))* Gorgias Pr., LLC.
Deacy, Susan. Athena. (Gods & Heroes of the Ancient World Ser.). (Illus.). 2008. (ENG.). 200p. (C). pap. 28.95 *(978-0-415-30066-7(5))* 2007. CXC, 18p. 120.00 *(978-0-415-30065-0(7))* Routledge.
Dinsmoor, William. The Sculptured Parapet of Athena Nike. 2009. pap. 20.08 *(978-1-60724-457-8(8))* Gorgias Pr., LLC.
Graninger, Denver. Cult & Koinon in Hellenistic Thessaly. 2011. XII, 212p. **(978-90-04-20710-3(4))** BRILL.
Keesling, Katherine. The Votive Statues of the Athenian Acropolis. 2008. (ENG., Illus.). 292p. pap. 38.99 *(978-0-521-07126-0(7))* Cambridge Univ. Pr.

Ruskin, John. The Queen of the Air. 2009. 224p. 23.99 *(978-1-103-33145-1(0))* 2009. 224p. pap. 17.99 *(978-1-103-33142-0(6))* 2008. 144p. 21.99 *(978-0-554-33640-4(5))* 2008. 144p. 24.99 *(978-0-554-24337-5(7))* BiblioBazaar.
—The Queen of the Air. 2007. (ENG.). 120p. per. *(978-1-4065-6374-0(9))* Dodo Pr.
—The Queen of the Air. 2008. pap. *(978-1-84830-060-6(3),* Wildhern Pr.) Echo Library.
—The Queen of the Air: Being a Study of the Greek Myths of Cloud & Storm. 2009. 192p. 22.99 *(978-1-103-66018-6(7))* 2009. 192p. pap. 16.99 *(978-1-103-66012-4(8))* 2009. 192p. 22.99 *(978-1-103-38568-3(2))* 2009. 192p. pap. 16.99 *(978-1-103-38565-2(8))* 2007. 128p. pap. 18.99 *(978-1-4264-6203-0(4))* 2006. (ENG.). 140p. pap. 19.99 *(978-1-4264-6258-0(1))* BiblioBazaar.
Sergent, Bernard. Athéna et la Grande Déesse Indienne. 2008. (FRE.) 396p. (C). pap. 41.00 **(978-2-251-32443-2(7))** Societe d'edition Les Belles lettres FRA. Dist: ISD.

ATHENS (GA.)

Coleman, Kenneth L. Confederate Athens. 2009. (ENG.). 230p. pap. 24.95 *(978-0-8203-3438-7(3))* Univ. of Georgia Pr.
Doster, Emily Jean & Doster, Gary L. Athens. 2011. (Postcard History Ser.). (ENG., Illus.). 128p. pap. 21.99 **(978-0-7385-8792-9(3))** Arcadia Publishing.
Stegeman, John F. These Men She Gave: Civil War Diary of Athens, Georgia. 2009. (ENG.). 196p. pap. 22.95 *(978-0-8203-3458-5(8))* Univ. of Georgia Pr.
Thomas, Frances Taliaferro. A Portrait of Historic Athens & Clarke County. 2nd ed. 2009. (Wormsloe Foundation Publications Ser.). (ENG., Illus.). 376p. pap. 29.95 *(978-0-8203-3044-0(2))* Univ. of Georgia Pr.

ATHENS (GREECE)

Brüggenbrock, Christel. Die Ehre in Den Zeiten der Demokratie: Das Verhältnis Von Athenischer Polis und Ehre in Klassischer Zeit. 2006. (Historische Semantik Ser.). (GER.). 354p. (C). 63.00 *(978-3-525-36708-7(2))* Vandenhoeck & Ruprecht GmbH & Co. KG DEU. Dist: ISD.
Cooley, Arthur. Athena Polias on the Acropolis of Athens. 2009. pap. 23.68 *(978-1-60724-488-2(8))* Gorgias Pr., LLC.
Dinsmoor, William. Attic Building Accounts. 2009. pap. 30.28 *(978-1-60724-434-9(9))* Gorgias Pr., LLC.
Gabrielsen, Vincent. Financing the Athenian Fleet: Public Taxation & Social Relations. 2010. (ENG.). 328p. (gr. 17). pap. 35.00 *(978-0-8018-9815-0(3))* Johns Hopkins Univ. Pr.
Holland, Leicester. Erechtheum Papers. 2009. pap. 26.80 *(978-1-60724-454-7(3))* Gorgias Pr., LLC.
Hunt, Peter. War, Peace, & Alliance in Demosthenes' Athens: Debate & the Process of Decision-Making. 2010. (ENG.). 332p. 99.00 *(978-0-521-83551-0(8))* Cambridge Univ. Pr.
Johnson, David. Socrates & Athens. 2011. (Greece & Rome: Texts & Contexts Ser.). (ENG., Illus.). 164p. pap. 26.00 *(978-0-521-75748-5(7))* Cambridge Univ. Pr.
Miller, Walter. A History of the Akropolis of Athens. 2009. pap. 26.56 *(978-1-60724-498-1(5))* Gorgias Pr., LLC.
Noussia, Maria. Solon the Athenian, the Poetic Fragments. 2010. (Mnemosyne, Supplements Ser.). 550p. *(978-90-04-17478-8(8))* BRILL.
Tschumi. New Acropolis Museum - Greek Language. 2009. **(978-0-8478-3436-5(0))** Rizzoli International Pubns., Inc.

ATHENS (GREECE)—ANTIQUITIES

Artz, James. Natural Resources & 5th Century Athenian Foreign Policy. 2008. 72p. pap. *(978-3-639-08667-6(8))* VDM Verlag Dr. Mueller e.K.
Beard, Mary. The Parthenon, Revised Edition. 2010. (Wonders of the World Ser.). (Illus.). 240p. pap. 14.95 *(978-0-674-05563-6(2))* Harvard Univ. Pr.
Camp, John McK & Mauzy, Craig A. Agora Excavations, 1931-2006: A Pictorial History. 2006. (ENG., Illus.). 128p. pap. 15.00 *(978-0-87661-910-0(3))* American Schl. of Classical Studies at Athens.
Camp, John McK., II & Mauzy, Craig A. The Athenian Agora: Site Guide. 5th rev. ed. 2010. (Guides). (ENG., Illus.). 192p. (C). (gr. 13). pap. 19.95 *(978-0-87661-657-4(0))* American Schl. of Classical Studies at Athens.
Conwell, David H. Connecting a City to the Sea: The History of the Athenian Long Walls. 2008. (History & Archaeology of Classical Antiquity Ser.). (Illus.). 267p. *(978-90-04-16232-7(1))* BRILL.
Derrida, Jacques. Athens, Still Remains: The Photographs of Jean-François Bonhomme. Brault, Pascale-Anne & Naas, Michael, trs. from FRE. 2010. (ENG., Illus.). 88p. 70.00 *(978-0-8232-3205-5(0));* pap. 17.00 *(978-0-8232-3206-2(9))* Fordham Univ. Pr.
Gardner, Ernest A. Ancient Athens. 30.00 *(978-0-8196-2806-0(9))* Biblo & Tannen Booksellers & Pubs., Inc.
Goette, Hans Rupprecht. Athens, Attica & the Megarid: An Archaeological Guide. 2008. (Illus.). 416p. 39.95 *(978-0-415-48725-2(0))* Routledge.
Hayes, John W. Roman Pottery: Fine-Ware Imports. 2008. (Excavations in the Athenian Agora Ser.). (ENG., Illus.). 386p. 150.00 *(978-0-87661-232-3(X))* American Schl. of Classical Studies at Athens.
Kaltsas, Nikolaos, ed. Athens-Sparta. 2006. (ENG., Illus.). 319p. (C). pap. 30.00 *(978-0-9776598-1-4(X))* Onassis, Alexander S. Public Benefit Foundation (US).
—Athens-Sparta: Contributions to the Research on the History & Archaeology of the Two City-States. 2009. (Illus.). 96p. (C). pap. 20.00 *(978-0-9776598-5-2(2))* Onassis, Alexander S. Public Benefit Foundation (US).
Keesling, Katherine. The Votive Statues of the Athenian Acropolis. 2008. (ENG., Illus.). 292p. pap. 38.99 *(978-0-521-07126-0(7))* Cambridge Univ. Pr.
Lang, Mabel. The Athenian Citizen. Marathaki, Irini, tr. 2009. (Agora Picture Book Ser.). (ENG & GRE., Illus.). 32p. (C). (gr. 13). pap. 4.95 *(978-960-7067-04-3(5))* American Schl. of Classical Studies at Athens.
Lawton, Carol L. Marbleworkers in the Athenian Agora. 2006. (American School of Classical Studies at Athens Ser.: Vol. 27). (ENG., Illus.). 52p. pap. 4.95 *(978-0-87661-645-1(7))* American Schl. of Classical Studies at Athens.
Lynch, K. M. The Symposium in Context: Pottery from a Late Archaic House near the Classical Athenian Agora. 2011. (Hesperia Supplements Ser.). (ENG., Illus.). 400p. (C). pap. 75.00 *(978-0-87661-546-1(9))* American Schl. of Classical Studies at Athens.
Mauzy, Craig A. & Camp, John M. Agora Excavations, 1931-2006: A Pictorial History. 2006. (ENG., Illus.). 128p. pap. 15.00 *(978-960-7067-03-6(7))* American Schl. of Classical Studies at Athens.
Neils, Jenifer, ed. The Parthenon: From Antiquity to the Present. 2010. (ENG., Illus.). 454p. (C). pap. 32.99 *(978-0-521-16482-5(6))* Cambridge Univ. Pr.
Petsalis-Diomidis, Alexia. Truly Beyond Wonders: Aelius Aristides & the Cult of Asklepios. 2010. (Oxford Studies in Ancient Culture & Representation Ser.). (ENG., Illus.). 380p. 135.00 *(978-0-19-956190-2(7))* Oxford Univ. Pr., Inc.
Rotroff, Susan I. Hellenistic Pottery: The Plain Wares. 2006. (Athenian Agora Ser.: Vol. 33). (ENG., Illus.). 480p. 150.00 *(978-0-87661-233-0(8))* American Schl. of Classical Studies at Athens.
Silver, Vernon. The Lost Chalice: The Real-Life Chase for One of the World's Rarest Masterpieces - A Priceless 2,500-Year-Old Artifact Depicting the Fall of Troy. 2010. (ENG.). 352p. pap. 14.99 *(978-0-06-155829-0(X),* Harper Paperbacks) HarperCollins Pubs.
Stuart, James & Revett, Nicholas. The Antiquities of Athens. 2007. (ENG., Illus.). 496p. 125.00 *(978-1-56898-723-1(4))* Princeton Architectural Pr.

Vlachopoulos, Andreas G. Archaia Athena Kai Attike: Historike Topographia Tou Asteos Kai Tes Choras. 2010. (GRE., Illus.). 256p. (C). 70.00 **(978-960-204-301-1(6))** Ekdotikos Oikos Melissa GRC. Dist: ISD.
Walbank, Michael B. Fragmentary Inscriptions from the Athenian Agora. 2008. (Hesperia Supplements Ser.). (ENG.). 150p. pap. 45.00 *(978-0-87661-538-6(8))* American Schl. of Classical Studies at Athens.
Weinberg, Gladys D. & Stern, E. Marianne. Vessel Glass. 2010. (Excavations in the Athenian Agora Ser.). (ENG., Illus.). 248p. 150.00 *(978-0-87661-234-7(6))* American Schl. of Classical Studies at Athens.
Weller, Charles. The Pre-Periclean Propylon of the Acropolis at Athens. 2009. pap. 21.28 *(978-1-60724-509-4(4))* Gorgias Pr., LLC.
Williams, Tim & Kemp, Ann. The Parthenon: An Introduction, 1 bks., bk. 2nd abr. ed. 2010. (Illus.). 144p. pap. 12.95 *(978-0-615-39673-6(9))* Clinton Publishing.

ATHENS (GREECE)—DESCRIPTION AND TRAVEL

Athens. (Illus.). pap. *(978-3-8283-0054-5(5))* Hallwag Verlag GmbH DEU. Dist: Rand McNally.
Brugger, Eva Maria, et al. Lander und Stadte: Griechenland, Athen. (Bibliothek Ser.). (GER., Illus.). 530p. *(978-3-7653-7782-2(1))* Brockhaus, F. A., GmbH DEU. Dist: International Bk. Import Service, Inc.
Davenport, Coral & Foster, Jane. Top 10 Athens. 2012. (Eyewitness top 10 travel Guide Ser.). (ENG.). 160p. 14.00 **(978-0-7566-8462-4(5))** Dorling Kindersley Publishing, Inc.
Dubin, Marc & Dorling Kindersley Publishing Staff. Eyewitness Travel Guide - Greece Athens & the Mainland. 2011. (Eyewitness Travel Guides). (ENG.). 352p. 25.00 *(978-0-7566-7017-7(9))* Dorling Kindersley Publishing, Inc.
Fisher, John & Rough Guides Staff. Pocket Rough Guide Athens. 2011. (Rough Guide Pocket Guides). (ENG., Illus.). 176p. 12.99 *(978-1-84836-272-7(2))* Rough Guides, Ltd. GBR. Dist: Dorling Kindersley Publishing, Inc.
Gardner, Ernest A. Ancient Athens. 30.00 *(978-0-8196-2806-0(9))* Biblo & Tannen Booksellers & Pubs., Inc.
Gray, William. Athens. (Illus.). 128p. pap. 10.95 *(978-1-84330-644-3(1))* New Holland Pubs., Ltd. GBR. Dist: Globe Pequot Pr., The.
Harvard Student Agencies Inc. Staff & Avalon Travel Publishing Staff. Let's Go Istanbul, Athens & the Greek Islands: The Student Travel Guide. 2011. (Let's Go Ser.). (ENG., Illus.). 248p. pap. 14.95 *(978-1-59880-740-0(4),* Let's Go) Avalon Travel Publishing.
Johnson, G. M. Map Athens/Logan Jackson Southeast OH Cities Counties. 2010. 4.95 *(978-1-897359-61-7(6))* Johnson, G.M. &Assocs., Ltd. CAN. Dist: Langenscheidt Publishing Group.
Kakissis, Joanna. National Geographic Traveler: Athens & the Island. 2011. (ENG., Illus.). 272p. pap. 22.95 *(978-1-4262-0823-2(5),* National Geographic) National Geographic Society.
Knopf Guides Staff. Athens. 2009. (Knopf Mapguides Ser.). (ENG., Illus.). 48p. pap. 10.95 *(978-0-375-71090-2(6),* Knopf) Knopf Doubleday Publishing Group.
Kollias, Tania & Brewer, Stephen. Frommer's Athens Day by Day. 2nd ed. 2011. (Frommer's Day by Day - Pocket Ser.: 188). (ENG., Illus.). 192p. pap. 13.99 **(978-1-118-04596-1(3),** Frommers) Wiley, John & Sons, Inc.
Livingston. Athens: A University City. 2013. (Routledge Monographs in Classical Studies). (ENG.). 288p. 120.00 *(978-0-415-21296-0(0))* Routledge.
Locken, E. Travel Journal Athens. 2010. 192p. pap. 19.99 *(978-0-557-44294-2(X))* Lulu Enterprises Inc.
Lonely Planet Staff & Kyriakopoulos, Victoria. Athens. 2009. (Best Of Ser.). (ENG., Illus.). 160p. pap. 11.99 *(978-1-74104-991-6(1))* Lonely Planet Pubns.
Lucas, John. 92 Acharnon Street. 2009. (ENG., Illus.). 219p. 36.95 *(978-0-9550105-3-8(5))* Eland Bks. GBR. Dist: Dufour Editions, Inc.
Lucas, John. 92 Acharnon Street: A Year in Athens. 2nd rev. ed. 2011. (ENG., Illus.). 224p. pap. 29.95 **(978-1-906011-57-4(5))** Eland Bks. GBR. Dist: Dufour Editions, Inc.
Matyszak, Philip. Ancient Athens on Five Drachmas a Day. 2008. (Illus.). 136p. *(978-0-500-05157-3(7))* Thames & Hudson.
Speller, Elizabeth. Athens. 2007. (ENG., Illus.). 256p. per. 17.95 *(978-1-86207-830-7(0))* Granta Bks. GBR. Dist: Independent Pubs. Group.
Thames and Hudson Staff, creator. Athens. 2006. (Stylecity: Athens Ser.). (ENG., Illus.). 192p. pap. 24.95 *(978-0-500-21019-2(5))* Thames & Hudson.
Thomas Cook Publishing Staff. Athens Pocket Guide. 3rd ed. 2011. (Thomas Cook Pocket Guides). (ENG., Illus.). 160p. pap. 9.95 *(978-1-84848-346-0(5))* Cook, Thomas Publishing GBR. Dist: Globe Pequot Pr., The.
Time Out Guides Staff, creator. Time Out Athens. 3rd rev. ed. 2007. (Time Out Guides). (ENG., Illus.). 320p. per. 19.95 *(978-1-84670-032-3(9))* Time Out Guides Ltd. GBR. Dist: Perseus-PGW.
Wallpaper Magazine Editors, ed. Athens 2012 - Wallpaper City Guide. 2nd ed. 2011. (ENG., Illus.). 128p. pap., pap. 9.95 *(978-0-7148-6101-2(4))* Phaidon Pr., Inc.

ATHENS (GREECE)—DESCRIPTION AND TRAVEL—VIEWS

see Athens (Greece)—Pictorial Works

ATHENS (GREECE)—ECONOMIC CONDITIONS

Cassia, Paul Sant. The Making of the Modern Greek Family: Marriage & Exchange in Nineteenth-Century Athens. 2006. (Cambridge Studies in Social & Cultural Anthropology Ser.). (ENG., Illus.). 300p. pap. 61.00 *(978-0-521-02826-4(4))* Cambridge Univ. Pr.
Engen, Darel Tai. Honor & Profit: Athenian Trade Policy & the Economy & Society of Greece, 415-307 B. C. E. 2010. (ENG., Illus.). 410p. 85.00 *(978-0-472-11634-8(7))* Univ. of Michigan Pr.
Flament, C. Une economie Monetarisee: Athenes a l'epoque classique (440-338): Contribution a l'etude du phenomene monetaire en Grece Ancienne. 2008. (Collection d'Etudes Classiques Ser.). (FRE.). 329p. (C). pap. 70.00 *(978-90-429-1958-7(2))* Peeters Pubs. & Booksellers BEL. Dist: Brown, David Bk. Co., The.
French, A. Ancient Medieval & Early Modern, 10 vols., Set. 2006. (Routledge Library Editions). xii, 208p. 1725.00 *(978-0-415-37680-8(7))* Routledge.
Oliver, G. J. War, Food, & Politics in Early Hellenistic Athens. 2007. (ENG., Illus.). 384p. 155.00 *(978-0-19-928350-7(8))* Oxford Univ. Pr., Inc.
Shipton, K. Econ Classical Athens. 2013. pap. 80.00 **(978-0-415-24043-7(3))** Routledge.

ATHENS (GREECE)—HISTORY

Abbott, Evelyn. Pericles & the Golden Age of Athens. 2009. 280p. pap. *(978-1-4588-9664-3(1))* Books LLC.
—Pericles & the Golden Age of Athens. (ENG.). 2007. 536p. 57.95 *(978-0-548-13960-8(1))* 2006. pap. 42.95 *(978-1-4286-5142-5(X))* Kessinger Publishing, LLC.
Agoratsios, Emmanuel. Politics & Oracles. 2010. 140p. pap. *(978-3-8383-4665-6(3))* Lambert Academic Publishing.
Bates, Fred Orlando. The Five Post-Kleisthenean Tribes. 2008. 84p. pap. 18.75 *(978-0-559-63168-9(5))* BiblioBazaar.
—The Five Post-Kleisthenean Tribes. 2007. (Analecta Gorgiana Ser.: 34). per. 29.00 *(978-1-59333-629-5(2))* Gorgias Pr., LLC.
Beaumont, L. Childhood in Ancient Athens. 2012. (Routledge Monographs in Classical Studies). (ENG.). 272p. 115.00 *(978-0-415-24874-7(4))* Routledge.
Bilheimer, Albert. Amendments in Athenian Decrees. 2009. pap. 19.60 *(978-1-60724-477-6(2))* Gorgias Pr., LLC.
Bulwer-Lytton, Edward. Athens: Its Rise & Fall. 2009. 704p. 35.99 *(978-0-559-10179-3(1));* 39.99 *(978-0-559-10164-9(3));* pap. 47.75 *(978-0-559-10174-8(0));* pap. 48.75 *(978-0-559-10167-0(8))* BiblioBazaar.

—Athens: Its Rise & Fall. 2007. 656p. per. *(978-1-4065-5251-5(8))* Dodo Pr.
—Athens, Its Rise & Fall; with Views of the Literature, Philosophy, & Social Life of the Athenian People by Edward Lytton Bulwer. 2006. 276p. per. 23.99 *(978-1-4255-2534-7(2))*; (ENG.). 324p. per. 23.99 *(978-1-4255-3265-9(9))* MPublishing.
Butler, Howard. The Story of Athens. 2007. (ENG.). 552p. 57.95 *(978-0-548-05015-6(5))* Kessinger Publishing, LLC.
Chaline, Eric. The Traveler's Guide to the Ancient World, Greece: Athens in the Classical Age. 2011. (Illus.). 160p. pap. 16.95 *(978-0-7627-7049-6(X)*, Lyons Pr.) Globe Pequot Pr., The.
Church, A. J. The Fall of Athens: A Story of the Peloponnesian War. pap. 20.00 *(978-0-8196-0393-7(7))* Biblo & Tannen Booksellers & Pubs., Inc.
Conwell, David H. Connecting a City to the Sea: The History of the Athenian Long Walls. 2008. (History & Archaeology of Classical Antiquity Ser.). (Illus.). 267p. *(978-90-04-16232-7(1))* ERILL.
Dinsmoor, William. The Burning of the Opisthodomos at Athens. 2009. pap. 22.12 *(978-1-60724-467-7(5))* Gorgias Pr., LLC.
—The Date of the Older Parthenon. 2009. pap. 20.92 *(978-1-60724-469-1(1))* Gorgias Pr., LLC.
—The Gables of the Propylaea at Athens. 2009. pap. 21.28 *(978-1-60724-523-0(X))* Gorgias Pr., LLC.
Engen, Darel Tai. Honor & Profit: Athenian Trade Policy & the Economy & Society of Greece, 415-307 B. C. E. 2010. (ENG., Illus.). 410p. 85.00 *(978-0-472-11634-8(7))* Univ. of Michigan Pr.
French, A. Ancient Medieval & Early Modern, 10 vols., Set. 2006. (Routledge Library Editions). xii, 208p. 1725.00 *(978-0-415-37680-8(7))* Routledge.
Hale, John R. Lords of the Sea: The Epic Story of the Athenian Navy & the Birth of Democracy. 2010. (ENG.). 432p. (gr. 12). 17.00 *(978-0-14-311768-1(8)*, Penguin (Non-Classics)) Penguin Group (USA) Inc.
Harding & Harding, Phillip. The Story of Athens: The Fragments of the Local Chronicles of Attika. 2007. (Routledge Sourcebooks for the Ancient World Ser.). (ENG.). 272p. 32.95 *(978-0-415-33809-7(3))*; 145.00 *(978-0-415-33808-0(5))* Routledge.
Herman, Gabriel. Morality & Behaviour in Democratic Athens: A Social History. (ENG., Illus.). 496p. 2009. pap. 60.00 *(978-0-521-12535-2(9))* 2006. 141.00 *(978-0-521-85021-6(5))* Cambridge Univ. Pr.
Hughes, Bettany. The Hemlock Cup: Socrates, Athens, & the Search for the Good Life. 2011. (ENG., Illus.). 528p. 35.00 *(978-1-4000-4179-4(1)*, Knopf) Knopf Doubleday Publishing Group.
Jack Meyer. Alcibiades: Fact, Fiction, Farce. 2009. 176p. 30.00 *(978-1-4269-1834-6(8))*; pap. 20.00 *(978-1-4269-1833-9(X))* Trafford Publishing.
Judge, E. A. Jerusalem & Athens: Cultural Transformation in Late Antiquity. Nobbs, Alanna, ed. 2010. (Illus.). 364p. 197.50 *(978-3-16-150572-0(7))* Mohr Siebeck GmbH & Co. KG DEU. Dist: Coronet Bks.
Kaltsas, Nikolaos, ed. Athens-Sparta. 2006. (ENG., Illus.). 319p. (C). pap. 30.00 *(978-0-9776598-1-4(X))* Onassis, Alexander S. Public Benefit Foundation (US).
—Athens-Sparta: Contributions to the Research on the History & Archaeology of the Two City-States. 2009. (Illus.). 96p. (C). pap. 20.00 *(978-0-9776598-5-2(2))* Onassis, Alexander S. Public Benefit Foundation (US).
Kaltsas, Nikolaos & Shapiro, Alan, eds. The Feminine & the Sacred in Ancient Athens: Proceedings of the International Conference held at the Onassis Cultural Center on Saturday, May 2 2009. 2012. (ENG.). 150p. (C). pap. 20.00 *(978-0-9819666-1-8(5))* Onassis, Alexander S. Public Benefit Foundation (US).
Laracy, Bede. The Rule of Law in the Athenian Democracy. 2010. 140p. pap. *(978-3-8383-0246-1(X))* Lambert Academic Publishing.
Liddel, Peter. Civic Obligation & Individual Liberty in Ancient Athens. 2007. (Oxford Classical Monographs). (ENG.). 450p. 180.00 *(978-0-19-922658-0(X))* Oxford Univ. Pr., Inc.
Low, Polly. The Athenian Empire. 2008. (Edinburgh Readings on the Ancient World Ser.). (ENG., Illus.). 334p. (gr. 17). 150.00 *(978-0-7486-2585-7(2))* Edinburgh Univ. Pr. GBR. Dist: Columbia Univ. Pr.
Ma, John, et al, eds. Interpreting the Athenian Empire. 2011. (Illus.). 224p. pap. 39.95 *(978-0-7156-3784-5(3))* Duckworth Publishers GBR. Dist: International Publishers Marketing.
Matyszak, Philip. Ancient Athens on 5 Drachmas a Day. 2008. (Traveling On 5 Ser.). (ENG.). 144p. pap. 18.95 *(978-0-500-28765-1(1)*, 528765) Thames & Hudson.
—Ancient Athens on Five Drachmas a Day. 2008. (Illus.). 136p. *(978-0-500-05157-3(7))* Thames & Hudson.
Meritt, Benjamin. Tribute Assessments in the Athenian Empire from 454 to 440 B. C. 2009. pap. 20.56 *(978-1-60724-458-5(6))* Gorgias Pr., LLC.
Moreno, Alfonso. Feeding the Democracy: The Athenian Grain Supply in the Fifth & Fourth Centuries BC. (ENG., Illus.). 2012. 440p. pap. 55.00 *(978-0-19-965694-3(0))* 2007. 400p. 150.00 *(978-0-19-922840-9(X))* Oxford Univ. Pr., Inc.
Oliver, G. J. War, Food, & Politics in Early Hellenistic Athens. 2007. (ENG., Illus.). 384p. 155.00 *(978-0-19-928350-7(8))* Oxford Univ. Pr., Inc.
Osborne, Robin. Athens & Athenian Democracy. 2010. (ENG., Illus.). 482p. 99.00 *(978-0-521-84421-5(5))*; pap. 39.99 *(978-0-521-60570-0(9))* Cambridge Univ. Pr.
Osborne, Robin, ed. Debating the Athenian Cultural Revolution: Art, Literature, Philosophy, & Politics 430-380 BC. 2007. (ENG., Illus.). 358p. 109.99 *(978-0-521-87916-3(7))* Cambridge Univ. Pr.
PHILLIP HARDING. Fourth Century Athens & the Hellenistic City. 2012. (Routledge Monographs in Classical Studies). (ENG.). 304p. (C). 125.00 *(978-0-415-87392-5(4))* Routledge.
Pritchard, David M., ed. War, Democracy & Culture in Classical Athens. 2010. (ENG., Illus.). 478p. 110.00 *(978-0-521-19033-6(9))* Cambridge Univ. Pr.
Schmalz, Geoffrey C. R. Augustan & Julio-Claudian Athens: A New Epigraphy & Prosopography. 2008. (History & Archaeology of Classical Antiquity Ser.). (Illus.). 336p. *(978-90-04-17009-4(X))* BRILL.
Sewell, Richard C. In the Theatre of Dionysos: Democracy & Tragedy in Ancient Athens. 2007. (ENG.). 216p. per. 35.00 *(978-0-7864-2993-6(3))* McFarland & Co., Inc. Pubs.
Shear, Julia L. Polis & Revolution: Responding to Oligarchy in Classical Athens. 2011. (ENG., Illus.). 384p. 99.00 *(978-0-521-76044-7(5))* Cambridge Univ. Pr.
Sourvinou-Inwood, Christiane & Parker, Robert. Athenian Myths & Festivals: Aglauros, Erechtheus, Plynteria, Panathenaia, Dionysia. 2011. (ENG., Illus.). 400p. 150.00 *(978-0-19-959207-4(1))* Oxford Univ. Pr., Inc.
Steinbock, Bernd. Social Memory in Athenian Public Discourse: Uses & Meanings of the Past. 2012. (ENG., Illus.). 456p. 85.00 ***(978-0-472-11832-8(3))*** Univ. of Michigan Pr.
Sternberg, Rachel Hall. Tragedy Offstage: Suffering & Sympathy in Ancient Athens. 2009. (ENG.). 250p. pap. 25.00 *(978-0-292-72238-5(9))* Univ. of Texas Pr.
Stevens, Gorham. The East Wall of the Erechtheum. 2009. pap. 19.48 *(978-1-60724-513-1(2))* Gorgias Pr., LLC.
Taylor, Martha C. Thucydides, Pericles, & the Idea of Athens in the Peloponnesian War. 2009. (ENG., Illus.). 324p. (C). 88.00 *(978-0-521-76593-0(5))* Cambridge Univ. Pr.
Toepffer, Johannes. Attische Genealogie. 2010. 354p. pap. 32.75 *(978-1-144-86148-1(9))*; 340p. pap. 31.75 *(978-1-146-06612-9(0))* BiblioBazaar.
Tracy, Stephen V. Pericles: A Sourcebook & Reader. 2009. (ENG., Illus.). 204p. 50.00 *(978-0-520-25603-3(4))*; pap. 21.95 *(978-0-520-25604-0(2))* Univ. of California Pr.
Tyrrell, William Blake. The Sacrifice of Socrates: Athens, Plato, Girard. 2012. (Studies in Violence, Mimesis & Culture Ser.). (ENG.). pap. 29.95 ***(978-1-61186-054-2(7))*** Michigan State Univ. Pr.
Von Wilamowitz-Moellendorff, Ulrich. Aristoteles und Athen. 2010. 834p. pap. 56.75 *(978-1-149-87065-5(6))*; 438p. pap. 35.75 *(978-1-146-22608-0(X))*; 442p. pap. 35.75 *(978-1-142-27041-4(6))* BiblioBazaar.
Walton, W. S. The Demos at Dawn. 2008. 636p. 33.99 *(978-1-4343-9525-2(1))* AuthorHouse.
—The Demos at Dawn: Marathon, 490 BCE. 2008. 636p. pap. 23.49 *(978-1-4343-9524-5(3))* AuthorHouse.
Wilson, Douglas. Five Cities that Ruled the World: How Jerusalem, Athens, Rome, London, & New York Shaped Global History, 0 vols. 2009. 256p. pap. 14.99 *(978-1-59555-136-8(0))* Nelson, Thomas Inc.
Wohl, Victoria. Law's Cosmos: Juridicial Discourse in Athenian Forensic Oratory. 2010. (ENG.). 376p. 99.00 *(978-0-521-11074-7(2))* Cambridge Univ. Pr.
Worman, Nancy. Abusive Mouths in Classical Athens. 2011. (ENG.). 398p. pap. 50.00 *(978-0-521-18256-0(5))* Cambridge Univ. Pr.

ATHENS (GREECE)—PICTORIAL WORKS

Camp, John McK & Mauzy, Craig A. Agora Excavations, 1931-2006: A Pictorial History. 2006. (ENG., Illus.). 128p. pap. 15.00 *(978-0-87661-910-0(3))* American Schl. of Classical Studies at Athens.
Derrida, Jacques. Athens, Still Remains: The Photographs of Jean-François Bonhomme. Brault, Pascale-Anne & Naas, Michael, trs. from FRE. 2010. (ENG., Illus.). 88p. 70.00 *(978-0-8232-3205-5(0))*; pap. 17.00 *(978-0-8232-3206-2(9))* Fordham Univ. Pr.

ATHENS (GREECE)—POLITICS AND GOVERNMENT

Agoratsios, Emmanuel. Politics & Oracles. 2010. 140p. pap. *(978-3-8383-4665-6(3))* Lambert Academic Publishing.
Anna, Missiou. Literacy & Democracy in Fifth-Century Athens. 2011. (ENG., Illus.). 228p. (C). pap. 29.99 *(978-0-521-12876-6(5))* Cambridge Univ. Pr.
Anna, Missiou & Missiou, Anna. Literacy & Democracy in Fifth-Century Athens. 2011. (ENG., Illus.). 228p. (C). 85.00 *(978-0-521-11140-9(4))* Cambridge Univ. Pr.
Aristotle. Aristotle on the Constitution of Athens. 2009. 116p. 24.99 *(978-1-110-33885-6(6))*; pap. 19.75 *(978-1-110-33879-5(1))* BiblioBazaar.
—Aristotle on the Constitution of Athens. 2009. 112p. pap. *(978-1-4590-7972-4(8))* Books LLC.
—Aristotle on the Constitution of Athens. Kenyon, Frederic G., ed. 2007. (ENG.). 240p. 41.95 *(978-0-548-01303-8(9))* Kessinger Publishing, LLC.
—The Athenian Constitution. Kenyon, Frederic G., tr. 2008. 100p. pap. *(978-1-4099-2878-2(0))* Dodo Pr.
—The Athenian Constitution. Sir Frederic G. Kenyon, tr. 2009. 92p. pap. 3.95 *(978-1-60386-245-5(5)*, Merchant Bks.) Rough Draft Printing.
—Constitution of Athens. 2nd enl. rev. ed. (BCL Ser.: No. 1). reprint ed. 36.50 *(978-0-404-00368-5(0))* AMS Pr., Inc.
Artz, James. Natural Resources & 5th Century Athenian Foreign Policy. 2008. 72p. pap. *(978-3-639-08667-6(8))* VDM Verlag Dr. Mueller e.K.
Asmonti, Luca. Athenian Democracy: A Sourcebook. 2014. (Continuum Sources in Ancient History Ser.). (ENG., Illus.). 256p. pap. 39.95 *(978-1-4411-1371-9(1))* Continuum International Publishing Group, Ltd. GBR. Dist: National Bk. Network.
Bayliss, Andrew J. After Demosthenes: The Politics of Early Hellenistic Athens. 2011. (ENG.). 288p. 120.00 *(978-1-4411-1151-7(4))* Continuum International Publishing Group, Ltd. GBR. Dist: National Bk. Network.
Carawan, Edwin, ed. The Attic Orators. 2007. (Oxford Readings in Classical Studies). (ENG.). 480p. pap. 60.00 *(978-0-19-927993-7(4))* Oxford Univ. Pr., Inc.
Demosthenes. Demosthenes, Speeches 1-17. 2011. E-Book ***(978-0-292-73550-7(2))*** Univ. of Texas Pr.
Demosthenes. Demosthenes, Speeches 60 & 61, Prologues, Letters. Worthington, Ian, tr. 2006. (Oratory of Classical Greece Ser.: Vol. 10). (ENG & GEC.). 178p. mass mkt. 19.95 *(978-0-292-71332-1(0))* Univ. of Texas Pr.
Demosthenes. The Olynthiac, & Other Public Orations of Demosthenes Tr , with Notes, etc by Charles Rann Kennedy. 2006. 432p. per. 26.99 *(978-1-4255-4696-0(X))* MPublishing.
—The Oration of Demosthenes on the Crown. 2006. 280p. per. 23.99 *(978-1-4255-2537-8(7))* MPublishing.
Demosthenes. Orations, 60-61: Funeral Speech, Erotic Essay, Exordia & Letters. De Witt, N. W. & De Witt, N. J., trs. 2011. 400p. 54.95 ***(978-1-258-09562-8(9))*** Literary Licensing, LLC.
Demosthenes. The Orations of Demosthenes Tr , with Notes, Andc , by Charles Rann Kennedy. 2006. 332p. per. 23.99 *(978-1-4255-3300-7(0))* MPublishing.
Demosthenes. The Public Orations of Demosthenes, Vol. 2. 2007. (ENG.). 188p. pap. 19.99 *(978-1-4264-3379-5(4))* BiblioBazaar.
—The Public Orations of Demosthenes, Vol. 1. ARTHUR WALLACE PICKARD, tr. 2007. (ENG.). 206p. pap. 20.99 *(978-1-4264-3378-8(6))* BiblioBazaar.
—The Public Orations of Demosthenes, Vol. 1. Packard, Arthur Wallace, tr. l.t. ed. 2006. 232p. pap. 22.99 *(978-1-4264-3428-0(6))* BiblioBazaar.
—The Public Orations of Demosthenes, Vol. 2. l.t. ed. 2007. (ENG.). 252p. pap. 23.99 *(978-1-4264-3429-7(4))* BiblioBazaar.
Demosthenes. Select Popular Orations of Demosthenes, with Notes & a Chronological Table, by J T Champlin. 2006. 252p. per. 23.99 *(978-1-4255-2181-3(9))* MPublishing.
Demosthenes & Dilts, Mervin R. Orationes, 4 vols., Vol. 3. Dilts, Mervin R., ed. 2008. (Oxford Classical Texts). (GEC & ENG.). 258p. 85.00 *(978-0-19-872170-3(6))* Oxford Univ. Pr., Inc.
Dilts, Mervin R., ed. Demosthenis Orationes IV, 4 vols. 2010. (Oxford Classical Texts). (ENG & GEC.). 400p. 75.00 *(978-0-19-872171-0(4))* Oxford Univ. Pr., Inc.
Evans, Nancy. Civic Rites: Democracy & Religion in Ancient Athens. 2010. (ENG., Illus.). 296p. 60.00 *(978-0-520-26202-7(6))*; pap. 26.95 *(978-0-520-26203-4(4))* Univ. of California Pr.
Fritz, Kurt von & Kapp, Ernst, trs. Aristotle's Constitution of Athens & Related Texts. 2011. 248p. 46.95 ***(978-1-258-01833-7(0))*** Literary Licensing, LLC.
Fuks, Alexander. The Ancestral Constitution. 2009. 140p. 104.00 *(978-0-415-55565-4(5))* Routledge.
Garland, Robert. Introducing New Gods: The Politics of Athenian Religion. 2009. (Illus.). 256p. pap. 29.50 *(978-0-8014-7486-6(8))* Cornell Univ. Pr.
Haake, Matthias (Ed), et al, eds. Rollenbilder in der athenischen Demokratie: Medien, Gruppen, Raume im politischen und sozialen System. 2010. (GER., Illus.). 224p. (C). 100.00 *(978-3-89500-712-5(9))* Reichert, Ludwig Dr. DEU. Dist: Brown, David Bk. Co., The.
Harris, Edward M., tr. from GEC. Demosthenes, Speeches 20-22. 2008. (Oratory of Classical Greece Ser.). (ENG., Illus.). 245p. 55.00 *(978-0-292-71783-1(0))*; pap. 22.95 *(978-0-292-71784-8(9))* Univ. of Texas Pr.
Hesk, Jon. Deception & Democracy in Classical Athens. 2006. (ENG.). 348p. (C). pap. 50.00 *(978-0-521-02871-4(X))* Cambridge Univ. Pr.
Johnson, Allan Chester. The Creation of the Tribe Ptolemais at Athens. 2009. pap. 20.56 *(978-1-60724-653-4(8))* Gorgias Pr., LLC.
Jones, Nicholas F. Politics & Society in Ancient Greece, 1 vol. 2008. (Praeger Series on the Ancient World). 184p. 44.95 *(978-0-275-98765-7(5)*, C8765, Praeger Pubs.) Greenwood Publishing Group, Inc.
Lambert, Stephen D. Inscribed Athenian Laws & Decrees 352/1-322/1 BC: Epigraphical Essays. 2012. (Brill Studies in Greek & Roman Epigraphy Ser.). (ENG.). ***(978-90-04-20931-2(X))*** BRILL.
Lape, Susan. Race & Citizen Identity in the Classical Athenian Democracy. 2010. (ENG.). 356p. 90.00 *(978-0-521-19104-3(1))* Cambridge Univ. Pr.
Lewis, John. Solon the Thinker: Political Thought in Archaic Athens. 2006. (Illus.). 178p. 70.00 *(978-0-7156-3456-1(9))* Duckworth Publishers GBR. Dist: International Publishers Marketing.
Lewis, John David. Solon the Thinker: Political Thought in Archaic Athens. 2008. 192p. pap. 32.95 *(978-0-7156-3728-9(2))* Duckworth Publishers GBR. Dist: International Publishers Marketing.
Linforth, Ivan Mortimer. Solon the Athenian. 2009. 208p. pap. *(978-1-150-04890-6(5))* Books LLC.
—Solon the Athenian. 2009. 210p. pap. 19.99 *(978-1-150-28890-6(6))* General Bks. LLC.
Ma, John, et al, eds. Interpreting the Athenian Empire. 2011. (Illus.). 224p. pap. 39.95 *(978-0-7156-3784-5(3))* Duckworth Publishers GBR. Dist: International Publishers Marketing.
Missiou, Anna. The Subversive Oratory of Andokides: Politics, Ideology & Decision-Making in Democratic Athens. 2007. (Cambridge Classical Studies). (ENG.). 232p. pap. 51.00 *(978-0-521-03759-4(X))* Cambridge Univ. Pr.
Ober, Josiah. Athenian Legacies: Essays on the Politics of Going on Together. 2007. (ENG., Illus.). 288p. (C). per. 24.95 *(978-0-691-13394-2(8))* Princeton Univ. Pr.
—Democracy & Knowledge: Innovation & Learning in Classical Athens. 2010. (ENG., Illus.). 368p. (C). pap. 23.95 *(978-0-691-14624-9(1))* 2008. xvi, 342p. 29.95 *(978-0-691-13347-8(6))* Princeton Univ. Pr.
Osborne, Robin. Athens & Athenian Democracy. 2010. (ENG., Illus.). 482p. 99.00 *(978-0-521-84421-5(5))*; pap. 39.99 *(978-0-521-60570-0(9))* Cambridge Univ. Pr.
Parton, Sarah. Cleisthenes: Founder of Athenian Democracy. 2009. (Ancient Leaders Ser.). 112p. (gr. 5-8). 66.50 *(978-1-61511-421-4(1)*, Rosen Central) Rosen Publishing Group, Inc., The.
Pritchard, David M., ed. War, Democracy & Culture in Classical Athens. 2010. (ENG., Illus.). 478p. 110.00 *(978-0-521-19033-6(9))* Cambridge Univ. Pr.
Randall, Bernard. Solon: The Lawmaker of Athens. 2009. (Ancient Leaders Ser.). 112p. (gr. 5-8). 66.50 *(978-1-61511-429-0(7)*, Rosen Central) Rosen Publishing Group, Inc., The.
Recco, Gregory. Athens Victorious: Democracy in Plato's Republic. 2009. (ENG.). 262p. pap. 34.99 *(978-0-7391-2327-0(0))* Lexington Bks.
Saxonhouse, Arlene W. Free Speech & Democracy in Ancient Athens. 2008. (ENG.). 248p. pap. 25.99 *(978-0-521-72158-5(X))* Cambridge Univ. Pr.
Scafuro, Adele C., tr. from GEC. Demosthenes, Speeches 39-49. 2011. (ENG., Illus.). 434p. 55.00 *(978-0-292-72556-0(6))*; pap. 24.95 *(978-0-292-72641-3(4))* Univ. of Texas Pr.
Sideridis, Alexander B. & Patrikakis, Charalampos Z. Next Generation SocietyTechnological & Legal Issues: Third International Conference, e-Democracy 2009, Athens, Greece, September 23-25, 2009, Revised Selected Papers. 2010. (Lecture Notes of the Institute for Computer Sciences, Social-Informatics & Telecommunications Engineering Ser.). 454p. pap. 99.00 *(978-3-642-11629-2(9)*, 3642116299) Springer.
Taylor, Martha C. Thucydides, Pericles, & the Idea of Athens in the Peloponnesian War. 2009. (ENG., Illus.). 324p. (C). 88.00 *(978-0-521-76593-0(5))* Cambridge Univ. Pr.
Trevett, Jeremy, tr. from GEC. Demosthenes, Speeches 1-17. 2011. (ENG.). 352p. 55.00 *(978-0-292-72677-2(5))*; pap. 24.95 *(978-0-292-72909-4(X))* Univ. of Texas Pr.
Xenophon. The Polity of the Athenians & the Lacedaemonians. Dakyns, Henry G., tr. 2007. (ENG.). 68p. per. 11.95 *(978-1-4065-5573-8(8))* Dodo Pr.
Zumbrunnen, John. Silence & Democracy: Athenian Politics in Thucydides' History. 208p. 2010. pap. 28.95 *(978-0-271-03358-7(4))* 2008. (ENG.). (C). 45.00 *(978-0-271-03357-0(6))* Pennsylvania State Univ. Pr.

ATHENS (GREECE)—SOCIAL CONDITIONS

Jones, Nicholas F. Politics & Society in Ancient Greece, 1 vol. 2008. (Praeger Series on the Ancient World). 184p. 44.95 *(978-0-275-98765-7(5)*, C8765, Praeger Pubs.) Greenwood Publishing Group, Inc.
Strauss, Barry S. Fathers & Sons in Athens. 2011. 300p. pap. 42.95 ***(978-0-415-62021-5(X))*** Routledge.

ATHENS (GREECE)—SOCIAL LIFE AND CUSTOMS

Davidson, James N. Courtesans & Fishcakes: The Consuming Passions of Classical Athens. 2011. (ENG., Illus.). 400p. pap. 22.50 *(978-0-226-13743-8(0))* Univ. of Chicago Pr.
Davis, William Stearns. A Day in Old Athens. 2008. 200p. 22.99 *(978-0-554-31502-7(5))*; 25.99 *(978-0-554-22199-1(3))* BiblioBazaar.
—A Day in Old Athens. 2009. 358p. pap. *(978-0-217-15964-7(8))* Books LLC.
—A Day in Old Athens. 2008. (ENG.). 196p. pap. 15.45 *(978-1-60597-409-5(9)*, Book Jungle) Standard Pubns., Inc.
—A Day in Old Athens: A Picture of Athenian Life. 2007. (ENG.). 208p. pap. 20.99 *(978-1-4264-1820-4(5))* 2006. 198p. pap. 21.99 *(978-1-4264-1878-5(7))* BiblioBazaar.
—A Day in Old Athens: A Picture of Athenian Life. 2009. 200p. pap. *(978-1-4099-0475-5(X))* Dodo Pr.
Engen, Darel Tai. Honor & Profit: Athenian Trade Policy & the Economy & Society of Greece, 415-307 B. C. E. 2010. (ENG., Illus.). 410p. 85.00 *(978-0-472-11634-8(7))* Univ. of Michigan Pr.
Footsteps Through Athina: A Traveler's Guide to Athens. 2009. 260p. pap. 19.95 *(978-0-578-00019-0(9))* Palo Albums Inc.
Gibbon, J. Athenian Society. 2007. (Illus.). 85p. pap. 19.95 *(978-1-85399-499-9(5))* Bristol Classical Pr. GBR. Dist: International Publishers Marketing.
Herman, Gabriel. Morality & Behaviour in Democratic Athens: A Social History. (ENG., Illus.). 496p. 2009. pap. 60.00 *(978-0-521-12535-2(9))* 2006. 141.00 *(978-0-521-85021-6(5))* Cambridge Univ. Pr.
Judge, E. A. Jerusalem & Athens: Cultural Transformation in Late Antiquity. Nobbs, Alanna, ed. 2010. (Illus.). 364p. 197.50 *(978-3-16-150572-0(7))* Mohr Siebeck GmbH & Co. KG DEU. Dist: Coronet Bks.
Lucas, John. 92 Acharnon Street: A Year in Athens. 2nd rev. ed. 2011. (ENG., Illus.). 224p. pap. 29.95 ***(978-1-906011-57-4(5))*** Eland Bks. GBR. Dist: Dufour Editions, Inc.
McHardy, F. Revenge in Athenian Culture. 2007. 192p. (C). 110.00 *(978-0-7156-3569-8(7))* Duckworth Publishers GBR. Dist: International Publishers Marketing.
Omitowoju, Rosanna. Rape & the Politics of Consent in Classical Athens. 2009. (Cambridge Classical Studies). (ENG.). 264p. pap. 38.00 *(978-0-521-10026-7(7))* Cambridge Univ. Pr.
Parker, Robert. Polytheism & Society at Athens. 2007. (ENG., Illus.). 576p. per. 65.00 *(978-0-19-921611-6(8))* Oxford Univ. Pr., Inc.
Pickard, John. Dionysus en Limnais. 2009. pap. 19.24 *(978-1-60724-499-8(3))* Gorgias Pr., LLC.

Pritchard, David M., ed. War, Democracy & Culture in Classical Athens. 2010. (ENG., Illus.). 478p. 110.00 (978-0-521-19033-6(9)) Cambridge Univ. Pr.

William Stearns Davis. A Day in Old Athens - a Picture of Athenian Life. 2009. (Illus.). 264p. pap. 6.95 (978-1-60386-249-3(8), Merchant Bks.) Rough Draft Printing.

ATHEROSCLEROSIS

Ballantyne, Christie M., et al. Dyslipidemia Essentials 2008. 2008. 175p. pap. 24.95 (978-0-7637-6122-6(2)) Jones & Bartlett Learning, LLC.

Beisman, Mark. Guide to Rotational Atherectomy. Date not set. (Illus.). 317p. (C). pap. 59.95 (978-1-890114-02-2(2)) Physician's Pr.

Cho, Sungbo. Electrical Impedance Spectroscopy for Characterization of Vessel Wall. 2009. 156p. pap. (978-3-639-20741-5(6)) VDM Verlag Dr. Mueller e.K.

Drew, Angela F., ed. Atherosclerosis: Experimental Methods & Protocols. 2010. (Methods in Molecular Medicine Ser.). (Illus.). 256p. pap. 169.00 (978-1-61737-168-4(8), 1617371688) Humana Pr.

Fan, Meng. Role of CYBA Gene Polymorphisms in Atherosclerosis. 2009. (Acta Universitatis Tamperensis Ser.). 121p. pap. 82.50 (978-951-44-7927-4(0)) Tampere Univ. Pr. FIN. Dist: Coronet Bks.

Feinstein, Steven B., ed. Non-Invasive Surrogate Markers of Atherosclerosis. 2008. (ENG., Illus.). 320p. 120.00 (978-1-84184-635-4(X), Informa Healthcare) Taylor & Francis Group GBR. Dist: Taylor & Francis Group.

Gallos, Alice F. & Jones, Margaret L. Angina Pectoris: Etiology, Pathogenesis & Treatment. Gallo, Alice, ed. 2008. (C). 185.00 (978-1-60456-674-1(4)) Nova Science Pubs., Inc.

George, Sarah Jane & Johnson, Jason, eds. Atherosclerosis: Molecular & Cellular Mechanisms. 2010. (ENG., Illus.). 420p. 189.95 (978-3-527-32448-4(8), Wiley-VCH) Wiley, John & Sons, Inc.

Grundy, Scott M., ed. Atlas of Atherosclerosis & Metabolic Syndrome. 5th ed. 2010. (ENG., Illus.). cccxx, 320p. 179.00 (978-1-4419-5838-9(X), 144195838X) Springer.

Hernesniemi, Jussi. Role of Interleukin 18 Gene Polymorphism in the Development of Atherosclerosis. 2010. (Acta Universitatis Tamperensis Ser.). (Illus.). 238p. pap. 87.50 (978-951-44-8118-5(6)) Tampere Univ. Pr. FIN. Dist: Coronet Bks.

Holtzman, Jordan L., ed. Atherosclerosis & Oxidant Stress: A New Perspective. 2008. (ENG., Illus.). x, 247p. 139.00 (978-0-387-72345-7(5), 0387723455) Springer.

—Atherosclerosis & Oxidant Stress: A New Perspective: A New Perspective. 2010. (ENG., Illus.). x, 247p. pap. 139.00 (978-1-4419-4432-0(X), 144194432X) Springer.

Icon Health Publications Staff. Official Patients Sourcebook on Atherosc. 2006. 408p. per. 34.95 (978-0-497-11185-4(3)) Icon Group International, Inc.

Kaur, Sukhinder C., ed. Biochemistry of Atherosclerosis. (Illus.). xvi, 572p. 2010. (Advances in Biochemistry in Health & Disease Ser.). pap. 209.00 (978-1-4419-4061-2(8), 1441940618) 2006. (Advances in Biochemistry in Health Disease Ser.: Vol. 1). (ENG., 209.00 (978-0-387-31252-1(8), 0387312528) Springer.

Kepper, Karin F., ed. Frontiers in Atherosclerosis Research. 2006. (Illus.). 237p. (C). 169.00 (978-1-60021-371-7(5)) Nova Science Pubs., Inc.

Koivu, Tommi. Changes in Atherosclerosis Risk Factors Induced by Hormone Replacement Therapy or Ethanol Consumption. 2011. (Acta Universitatis Tamperensis Ser.). 114p. pap. 72.50 **(978-951-44-8577-0(7))** Tampere Univ. Pr. FIN. Dist: Coronet Bks.

Maki, Kevin & Toth, Peter P. Practical Lipid Management: Concepts & Controversies. 2008. (ENG., Illus.). 252p. 82.00 (978-0-470-05690-5(8), Wiley) Wiley, John & Sons, Inc.

Mirkhani, Amir Mansur. Bimari-I Sharayanha, Surkhragha, Siktah-I Qalbi Va Maghzi Va Fishar-I Khun: Shinakht Va Pishgiri: Majmuah-Yi Maqalat Va Sukhanranihayi. 2010. (PER., Illus.). 91p. **(978-1-59584-279-4(9))** Ketab Corp.

Mitrovska, Slavica, et al. Atherosclerosis: Understanding Pathogenesis & Challenge for Treatment. 2009. pap. 37.00 (978-1-60692-677-2(2)) Nova Science Pubs., Inc.

Miyazaki, Akira. New Frontiers in Lifestyle-Related Diseases. 2008. (ENG., Illus.). xxii, 160p. 79.95 (978-4-431-76427-4(5), 4431764275) Springer.

Miyazaki, Akira & Imawari, Michio, eds. New Frontiers in Lifestyle-Related Diseases. 2010. (ENG., Illus.). xxii, 160p. pap. 79.95 (978-4-431-99839-6(X), 443199339X) Springer.

Naghavi, Morteza, ed. Asymptomatic Atherosclerosis: Pathophysiology, Detection & Treatment. 2010. (Contemporary Cardiology Ser.). (ENG., Illus.). 624p. 279.00 (978-1-60327-178-3(3), 1603271783) Humana Pr.

Naghavi, Morteza, et al, eds. Asymptomatic Atherosclerosis: Pathophysiology, Detection & Treatment. 2011. (Contemporary Cardiology (Humana Press) Ser.). (ENG.). 737p. 239.00 **(978-1-61779-134-5(2))** Humana Pr.

Nicolaides, Andrew N., et al, eds. Ultrasound & Carotid Bifurcation Atherosclerosis. 2011. (ENG., Illus.). xvii, 649p. 239.00 (978-1-84882-687-8(7), 1848826877) Springer.

Roman, Richard. Arachidonic Acid Metabolites & Kidney Function. 2012. (Colloquium Series on Integrated Systems Physiology: from Molecule to Function Ser.). 100p. pap. 35.00 (978-1-61504-204-3(0)) Morgan & Claypool Life Science Publishers.

Safar, Michel & Frohlich, Edward D. Atherosclerosis, Large Arteries, & Cardiovascular Risk. (Advances in Cardiology Ser.: Vol. 44). (Illus.). viii, 359p. (978-3-8055-8176-9(9)) Karger, S. AG.

Shor, Allan. Chlamydia Atherosclerosis Lesion: Discovery, Diagnosis & Treatment. 2007. (ENG., Illus.). xii, 170p. 219.00 (978-1-84628-309-6(6), 1846288096) Springer.

Siplä, Kalle. Cardiometabolic & Genetic Risk Factors for Early Atherosclerosis. 2011. (Acta Universitatis Tamperensis Ser.). (Illus.). 167p. pap. 87.50 (978-951-44-8321-9(9)) Tampere Univ. Pr. FIN. Dist: Coronet Bks.

Suri, Jasjit S., et al, eds. Atherosclerosis Disease Management. 2010. (ENG., Illus.). xiv, 944p. 239.00 (978-1-4419-7221-7(8), 1441972218) Springer.

Tousoulis, Dimitris & Stefanadis, Christodoulos. Risk Factors & Vascular Endothelium. 2011. (Cardiology Research & Clinical Developments Ser.). (Illus.). 319p. 145.00 (978-1-61209-577-6(1)) Nova Science Pubs., Inc.

Tracy, R. E. The Role of Aging in Atherosclerosis: The Sequestration Hypothesis. 2010. 288p. pap. 124.00 (978-90-481-6265-9(3), 9048162653) Springer.

Uchiyama, Shinichiro & Yamaguchi, Takenori, eds. Antiplatelet Therapy in Atherothrombosis, Vol. 21. (Cerebrovascular Diseases Ser.). (Illus.). 40p. pap. (978-3-8055-8087-8(8)) Karger, S. AG.

Wick, Georg & Grundtman, Cecilia, eds. Inflammation & Atherosclerosis. 2011. (ENG., Illus.). ix, 631p. 239.00 (978-3-7091-0337-1(1), 3709103371) Springer.

ATHLETES

see also African American Athletes; Athletes with Disabilities; Athletic Ability; Gay Athletes; Jewish Athletes; Track and Field Athletes; Wrestlers

ABBE Scientist Research Division Staff. AIDS & HIV in Athletes: Index & Medical Analysis of New Clinical & Research Information. 2007. (Illus.). 160p. ring bd. 69.95 (978-0-7883-4776-4(4)) ABBE Pubs. Assn. of Washington, D.C.

Amidon, Stephen. Something Like the Gods: A Cultural History of the Athlete from Achilles to Lebron. 2012. (ENG.). 256p. 24.99 **(978-1-60961-123-1(3))** Rodale Pr., Inc.

Anderson, et al. Foundations of Athletic Training: Prevention, Assessment, & Management, 3 vols. 2009. (Illus.). (978-1-60831-632-8(7)) Lippincott Williams & Wilkins.

ANON. The Secret Olympian: The Inside story of the Olympic Experience. 2012. (ENG.). 224p. pap. 14.95 **(978-1-4081-5492-2(7))** A & C Black GBR. Dist: Macmillan.

Baker, Joseph J., et al. The Masters Athlete: Understanding the Role of Sport & Exercise in Optimizing Aging. Baker, Joseph (joe) et al, eds. 2009. (ENG., Illus.). 204p. pap. 51.95 (978-0-415-47657-7(7)) Routledge.

Barrell, James J. & Ryback, David. The Psychology of Champions: How to Win at Sports & Life with the Focus Edge of Super-Athletes. 2008. 240p. 44.95 (978-0-313-35436-6(7), C35436, Praeger Pubs.) Greenwood Publishing Group, Inc.

Basson, Tamsyn. Eap & the High Performance Athlete. 2008. 192p. per. (978-3-8364-3550-5(0)) VDM Verlag Dr. Mueller e.K.

Bayés de Luna, Antonio, et al, eds. Arrhythmias & Sudden Death in Athletes. 2010. (Developments in Cardiovascular Medicine Ser.). 176p. pap. 105.00 (978-90-481-5470-8(7), 9048154707) Springer.

Bean, Anita. Sports Nutrition for Young Athletes. 2012. (ENG., Illus.). 154p. pap. 24.95 **(978-1-77085-030-9(9))** Firefly Bks., Ltd.

Benn, Tansin, et al, eds. Muslim Women & Sport. 2010. (International Studies in Physical Education & Youth Sport Ser.). (ENG., Illus.). 296p. (C). 168.00 (978-0-415-49076-4(6)) Routledge.

Berkemeyer, Michael. Die Leihgabe von Berufssportlern. 2011. (Osnabrücker Schriften zum Unternehmens- und Wirtschaftsrecht Ser.). (GER.). 302p. 83.95 (978-3-631-60679-7(6)) Lang, Peter GmbH, Europaischer Verlag der Wissenschaften DEU. Dist: Lang, Peter.

Bommarito, Pete. Performance Training for Athletes. 2012. pap. 19.95 (978-0-7360-9933-2(6)) Human Kinetics Pubs.

Boone, Tommy. Sex Before Athletic Competition: Myth or Fact. 172p. 99.95 (978-0-7734-5137-7(4)) Mellen, Edwin Pr., The.

Bowden, Ken. Teeing Off: Players, Techniques, Characters, & Reflections from a Lifetime Inside Golf. 2008. (ENG.). 256p. 22.95 (978-1-60078-075-2(X)) Triumph Bks.

Boyle, Michael. Advances in Functional Training: Training Techniques for Athletes, Coaches & Personal Trainers. 2010. (Illus.). 320p. pap. 34.95 (978-1-931046-01-5(8)) On Target Pubns.

Bradley, Lloyd. The Rough Guide to Cult Sport. 2011. (ENG., Illus.). 304p. 14.99 (978-1-4053-8598-5(7)) Rough Guides, Ltd. GBR. Dist: Dorling Kindersley Publishing, Inc.

Branner, Toni. Care & Feeding of an Athlete: What You Need to Know to Rise to the Top of Your Game. 2007. (Illus.). 112p. (YA). pap. 8.95 (978-0-9796046-1-4(3)) Blue Water Pr., LLC.

Brown, Scott, ed. Treat Your Poker Like A Business: A Guide to Turning Your Hobby into Profit. 2009. pap. 39.95 (978-0-9843363-0-2(3)) Imagine Media.

Brown, Stewart. The Student Athlete's Guide to Getting Recruited: How to Win Scholarships, Attract Colleges & Excel as an Athlete. 2nd ed. 2011. (ENG.). 272p. pap. 16.95 (978-1-932662-99-3(5)) SuperCollege LLC.

Brunton, Henry. Journey to Excellence: The Young Golfer's Complete Guide to Achievement & Personal Growth. 2009. 147p. pap. 21.95 (978-0-615-30293-5(9)) Sea Script Co.

Bunbury, Turtle & Fennell, James. Sporting Legends of Ireland. 2010. (ENG., Illus.). 256p. 35.00 (978-1-84596-502-0(7)) Mainstream Publishing Co., Ltd. GBR. Dist: Independent Pubs. Group.

Buonpastore, Philip. Shifting Gears at 50: A Motorcycling Guide for New & Returning Riders. 2012. (ENG.). 195p. pap. 24.95 (978-1-935434-33-2(8)) BowTie Pr.

Byrd, Isaac. HOW to: Think Like a Pro, Act Like a Pro & Play Like a Pro: The 8 Principles that Bridge the Gap between Professional & Amateur Athletes. 2011. 134p. pap. 15.95 **(978-1-4327-5938-4(8))** Outskirts Pr., Inc.

Cantu, Robert & Hyman, Mark. Concussions & Our Kids: America's Leading Expert on How to Protect Young Athletes & Keep Sports Safe. 2012. (ENG., Illus.). 208p. 25.00 **(978-0-547-77394-0(3))** Houghton Mifflin Harcourt Trade & Reference Pubs.

Carmichael, Chris & Rutberg, Jim. The Time-Crunched Cyclist: Fit, Fast, & Powerful in 6 Hours a Week. 2nd ed. 2012. (Time-Crunched Athlete Ser.). (ENG., Illus.). 256p. pap. 19.95 **(978-1-934030-83-7(X))** VeloPress.

Carroll, Steve. Build to Break: The Rise of an Endurance Athlete. 2010. 218p. pap. 20.03 (978-0-557-26364-6(6)) Lulu Enterprises Inc.

Casa. Preventing Sudden Death in Sport & Physical Activity. rev. ed. 2011. 368p. pap. 86.95 (978-0-7637-8554-3(7)) Jones & Bartlett Learning, LLC.

Champions for Change: Athletes Making a World of Difference. 2009. (Illus.). 168p. (YA). pap. 24.95 (978-0-615-30479-3(6)) Global Sports Alliance USA.

Cissik, John. Strength & Conditioning: A Concise Introduction. 2011. (ENG., Illus.). 320p. 160.00 (978-0-415-66664-0(3)); pap. 44.95 (978-0-415-66666-4(X)) Routledge.

Coach Dean. Coach, I Didn't Run Because: Excuses not to Run. 2008. 84p. pap. 13.99 (978-1-4389-1602-6(7)) AuthorHouse.

Colucci, Michele. Sports Law in Italy. 2010. (Illus.). 152p. pap. (978-90-411-3304-5(6)) Kluwer Law International.

Cox, Richard. Sport Psychology: Concepts & Applications. 7th ed. 2011. (ENG., Illus.). 572p. (C). pap. 130.67 (978-0-07-802247-0(9), 0078022479) McGraw-Hill Cos., The.

Craig, Gary. EFT for Sports Performance. 2010. 200p. pap. 14.95 (978-1-60415-052-0(1)) Energy Psychology Pr.

Cram101 Textbook Reviews. Outlines & Highlights for Essentials of Sports Nutrition & Supplements by Jose Antonio, Isbn: 9781588296115 1588296113. 2011. 324p. pap. 33.95 **(978-1-61490-240-9(2))** Cram101 Inc.

—Outlines & Highlights for Sport Psychology by Gallucci, Isbn: 9781841694863 184169486x. 2011. 252p. pap. 31.95 **(978-1-4288-9405-1(5))** Cram101 Inc.

Cram101 Textbook Reviews & Cram101 Textbook Reviews. Outlines & Highlights for Foundations of Athletic Training by M Anderson. 2011. 266p. pap. 31.95 **(978-1-61830-688-3(X))** Cram101 Inc.

Davidson, Max. Fields of Courage: Great Tales of Sporting Heroism. 2011. (ENG., Illus.). 288p. 24.95 (978-1-4087-0216-1(9)) Little, Brown Bk. Group Ltd. GBR. Dist: Independent Pubs. Group.

Davidson, Max. Fields of Courage: The Bravest Chapters in Sport. 2012. (ENG., Illus.). 288p. pap. 15.95 **(978-0-349-12260-1(1))** Little, Brown Bk. Group Ltd. GBR. Dist: Independent Pubs. Group.

DeVenzio, Dick. Think Like a Champion: A Guide to Championship Performance for Student-Athletes. 2nd ed. 2006. (Illus.). 343p. per. 16.95 (978-1-933538-54-9(6)) Bridgeway Bks.

Duncanson, Neil. The Fastest Men on Earth: The Story of the Men's 100 Metre Champions. 2011. (ENG., Illus.). 352p. 35.00 **(978-0-233-00336-8(3))** Andre Deutsch GBR. Dist: Independent Pubs. Group.

Ederer, Dorothy K. The Golfer's Prayer Book: Walking the Fairway with the Master. 2010. 96p. 12.00 (978-1-58768-059-5(9), HiddenSpring) Paulist Pr.

Ellenbecker, Todd, et al. Effective Functional Progressions in Sport Rehabilitation. 2009. (ENG., Illus.). 248p. (C). pap. 44.00 (978-0-7360-6381-4(1)) Human Kinetics Pubs.

Emerson, Steven. Playing a Parochial Game: A Critical Analysis of the Leadership Lives of 12 Women Who Administer High School Athletic Programs. 2008. 124p. pap. (978-3-639-09992-8(3)) VDM Verlag Dr. Mueller e.K.

ET Training Systems, afterword by. It's All about SPEED: A Comprehensive Guide to the World of Speed. 2007. 4p. (YA). 19.95 (978-0-9798568-0-8(9)) ET Training Systems.

Etnier, Jennifer L. Bring Your A Game: A Young Athlete's Guide to Mental Toughness. 2009. (ENG., Illus.). 216p. 36.95 (978-0-8078-3347-6(9)); pap. 18.00 (978-0-8078-5990-2(7)) Univ. of North Carolina Pr.

Evening Standard Sports Writers Staff. Sporting Spite: Rebels & Rebellion in World Sport. (Illus.). 144p. pap. 14.95 (978-0-7063-7078-2(3)) Cassell P L C GBR. Dist: Sterling Publishing Co., Inc.

Ferraro, Jeffrey. Getting Recruited: A Strategic Look into the Collegiate Athletic Recruitment Process. 2011. pap. 10.99 **(978-1-61777-804-9(4))** Tate Publishing & Enterprises, LLC.

Fishpool, Sean & Keogh, Sean. The Complete Long Distance Runner's Manual: A Unique Training Guide for Long Distance Runners of All Abilities. 2009. (ENG.). 128p. pap. 14.99 (978-0-7641-4246-8(1)) Barron's Educational Series, Inc.

Friel, Joe. The Triathlete's Training Bible. 3rd ed. 2009. (ENG., Illus.). 386p. pap. 24.95 (978-1-934030-19-6(8)) VeloPress.

Gamble, Paul. Training for Sports Speed & Agility: An Evidence-Based Approach. 2011. (ENG., Illus.). 200p. (C). 155.00 (978-0-415-59125-6(2)); pap. 47.95 (978-0-415-59126-3(0)) Routledge.

Garrigues. Guide to Taxation of Sportspersons in Certain Relevant Jurisdict. 2008. 79.00 (978-90-411-2791-4(7)) Wolters Kluwer Law & Business.

Gerling, Ilona E & Pache, Alexander. The Ultimate Parkour & Freerunning. 2011. (Illus.). 320p. pap. 19.95 (978-1-84126-319-9(2)) Meyer & Meyer Sport, Ltd. GBR. Dist: Cardinal Pubs. Group.

Getty Images, Inc Staff, contrib. by. Visions of Sport. 2011. (ENG., Illus.). 204p. 25.95 **(978-1-907637-34-6(6))** Vision Sports Publishing GBR. Dist: SCB Distributors.

Gleason, Randy. In for the Long Run: A Firefighter's Marathon for Burn Survivors. 2007. per. 12.95 (978-0-9793994-4-2(0)) Bear Lodge Bks.

Golightly Marshall, Brian Leonard. Lawn bowls champions Secrets. 2008. 72p. pap. 41.50 (978-1-4092-1602-5(0)) Lulu Enterprises Inc.

—LAWN BOWLS the SECRET. 2008. 72p. 38.50 (978-1-4092-0594-4(0)) Lulu Enterprises Inc.

Granat & Chin, C. F. A. Who Will Win the Big Game? 50 Championship Characteristics a Psychological & Mathematical Method for Identifying Winning Players, Teams, & Coaches. Strozier, M. Stefan, ed. 2010. 130p. pap. 20.00 (978-1-935444-37-4(9)) World Audience Pubs.

Grand, David & Goldberg, Alan. This Is Your Brain on Sports: Beating Blocks, Slumps & Performance Anxiety for Good! 2011. 228p. pap. 24.95 **(978-1-60844-864-7(9))** Dog Ear Publishing, LLC.

Green Earth Publishers & Jones, Richard S. Doing Time. 2010. (C). 0.00 (978-0-9821120-0-7(9)) Green Earth Pubns.

Griffin, Geoff. Should College Athletes Be Paid? 2007. (At Issue Ser.). (ENG.). (gr. 10-12). 91p. pap. 22.50 (978-0-7377-3790-5(5)); (Illus.). 99p. pap. 31.80 (978-0-7377-3789-9(1)) Cengage Gale. (Greenhaven Pr., Inc.).

Grout, Jeff & Perrin, Sarah. Mind Games: Inspirational Lessons from the World's Finest Sports Stars. 2006. (ENG.). 304p. per. 15.95 (978-1-84112-739-2(6), Capstone) Wiley, John & Sons, Inc.

Hahn, Kathy. Are Athletes Good Role Models? 2010. (At Issue Ser.). 128p. pap. 21.85 (978-0-7377-4647-1(5)); (Illus.). 30.85 (978-0-7377-4646-4(7)) Cengage Gale. (Greenhaven Pr., Inc.).

Halbert, Sarah A. Athletes' perceptions of coaches' behaviors toward injured athletes: An exploratory study. 2008. 60p. pap. (978-3-639-10352-6(1)) VDM Verlag Dr. Mueller e.K.

Hallinan, Christopher J. & Judd, Barry, eds. Indigenous People, Race Relations & Australian Sport. 2012. (Sport in the Global Society â€" Contemporary Perspectives Ser.). (ENG., Illus.). 160p. (C). 125.00 (978-0-415-58269-8(5)) Routledge.

Heller, Peter. Kook: What Surfing Taught Me about Love, Life, & Catching the Perfect Wave. 2010. (ENG., Illus.). 336p. pap. 15.00 (978-0-7432-9420-1(3), Free Pr.) Free Pr.

Higgins, Rob. Higgins Hockey Fantasy Index: 2010-2011. 2010. (ENG., Illus.). 496p. pap. 19.99 (978-1-4391-6944-5(6), Touchstone) Touchstone.

Hurley, Michael. The World's Greatest Olympians. 2011. (Olympics Ser.). (ENG.). 32p. (gr. 3-5). 29.99 (978-1-4109-4122-0(1)); pap. 7.99 (978-1-4109-4128-2(0)) Heinemann-Raintree. (NA-h).

Isenberg, Marc. Money Players: A Guide to Success in Sports, Business & Life for Current & Future Pro Athletes. 2007. (Illus.). 250p. pap. 29.95 (978-0-9666764-1-9(6)) A-Game, LLC.

Jackson & Bauer, Jami Lynn. Sports for Life: The Fruits of Play & Competition for the Young & the Young at Heart. Adams, Loren, ed. 2010. 164p. pap. 14.95 (978-1-60844-679-7(4)) Dog Ear Publishing, LLC.

Jeffreys, Ian. Gamespeed: Movement Training for Superior Sports Performance. 2009. (Illus.). 216p. pap. 19.95 (978-1-60679-075-5(7)) Coaches Choice.

Jensen, Erik Norman. Body by Weimar: Athletes, Gender, & German Modernity. 1 vol. 2010. (ENG., Illus.). 256p. 50.00 (978-0-19-539564-8(6)) Oxford Univ. Pr., Inc.

Jeukendrup, A., ed. Current Issues in Sports Nutrition: Supplement Issue: Annals of Nutrition & Metabolism 2010, Vol. 57, Suppl. 2. 2011. (Illus.). 54p. pap. (978-3-8055-9709-8(6)) Karger, S. AG.

Jimenez, C. Mas Que Vencedores.Tr. of More Than Winners. (SPA.). 10.99 (978-0-7899-0206-1(0), 550048) Editorial Unilit.

Jones, Ryan. Play & Pay. 2008. 84p. pap. (978-3-639-10276-5(2)) VDM Verlag Dr. Mueller e.K.

Jonsson, Hjorleifur & Holthuysen, Jaime. Contests in Context: Readings in the Anthropology of Sports. 2012. (ENG.). 236p. pap. 72.00 **(978-0-7575-9942-2(7))** Kendall Hunt Publishing Co.

Journi, David. Rapsheets for Our Young Athletes. 2009. 28p. pap. 12.49 (978-1-4389-5790-6(4)) AuthorHouse.

Juan Gonzalez. The Athlete Whisperer: What It Takes to Make Her Great. 2009. 148p. pap. 11.99 (978-1-4389-5691-6(6)) AuthorHouse.

Kent, Richard. Writing on the Bus: Using Athletic Team Notebooks & Journals to Advance Learning & Performance in Sports. 2012. (Illus.). xvi, 194p. **(978-1-4331-1684-1(7))**; pap. **(978-1-4331-1651-3(0))** Lang, Peter GmbH, Europaischer Verlag der Wissenschaften.

Kimiecik, Jay C. & Newburg, Doug. Runner as Hero: The Inner Quest of Becoming an Athlete or Just about Anything... At Any Age. 2009. (ENG.). 164p. pap. 20.99 (978-0-7618-4795-3(2)) Univ. Pr. of America, Inc.

Klein, Aaron J. Striking Back: The 1972 Munich Olympics Massacre & Israel's Deadly Response. 2007. (ENG., Illus.). 288p. per. 16.00 (978-0-8129-7463-8(8), Random Hse. Trade Paperbacks) Random House Publishing Group.

Knapp, Fritz. The Book of Sports Virtues: Portraits from the Field of Play. 2008. (Illus.). 239p. pap. 14.95 (978-0-87946-348-9(1)) ACTA Pubns.

Knoetze-Raper, Jessica. Families with Adolescents Achieving in Sport. 2010. 200p. pap. (978-3-639-26818-8(0)) VDM Verlag Dr. Mueller e.K.

Konin, Jeff G. Rehabilitation from the Perspective of the Athletic Trainer/Physical Therapist: Clinics in Sports Medicine. 2010. (Clinics: Orthopedics Ser.: 29-1). (ENG., Illus.). xiv, 201p. 105.00 (978-1-4377-1873-7(6), Saunders) Elsevier - Health Sciences Div.

Konin, Jeff G., et al. Documentation for Athletic Training. 2nd ed. 2011. (ENG., Illus.). 320p. (C). pap. 49.95 (978-1-55642-982-8(7)) SLACK, Inc.

Kramer, Garret. Stillpower: Excellence with Ease in Sports & Life. 2012. (ENG.). 224p. 22.00 ***(978-1-58270-388-6(4)***, Beyond Words/Atria Bks.) Atria Bks.

—Stillpower: Find Your Inner Source of Excellence in Sports — And Life. 2012. pap. ***(978-1-58270-389-3(2))*** Beyond Words Publishing, Inc.

Krump, Jason. Identification of Athletes by Athletes at a Division I University. 2009. 72p. pap. *(978-3-639-16554-8(3))* VDM Verlag Dr. Mueller e.K.

Kuehl, Karl, et al. Mental Toughness: Baseball's Winning Edge. 2006. (ENG., Illus.). 304p. per. 15.95 *(978-1-56663-723-7(6))* Dee, Ivan R. Pub.

Kundzicz, Walter. Classic Male Nudes, 1 vol. 2011. (ENG., Illus.). 44p. pap. 24.95 ***(978-3-936709-61-2(0))*** Goliath DEU. Dist: SCB Distributors.

Kurmaskie, Joe. Metal Cowboy: Ten Years Further down the Road Less Pedaled. 2010. (ENG.). 304p. pap. 15.00 *(978-1-891369-86-5(5))* Breakaway Bks.

Ladefoged, Joachim. Mirror. 2008. (ENG.). 132p. 79.00 *(978-87-92241-06-1(9)*, Art Stock Bks. Ltd/Csi) Continental Sales, Inc.

Lamont, Daveda & Mango, Kirk. Becoming A True Champion: Achieving Athletic Excellence from the Inside Out. 2012. (ENG.). 264p. pap. 17.95 ***(978-1-4422-1406-4(6))*** Rowman & Littlefield Publishers, Inc.

Lapchick, Richar. 100 Trailblazers. 2009. (Leaders in Sprort (Fit) Ser.). 520p. pap. 24.95 *(978-1-885693-86-0(9))* Fitness Information Technology, Inc.

Large, David Clay. Munich 1972: Tragedy, Terror, & Triumph at the Olympic Games. 2012. E-Book ***(978-0-7425-6741-2(9))***; (ENG., Illus.). 396p. 29.95 ***(978-0-7425-6739-9(7))*** Rowman & Littlefield Publishers, Inc.

Latty, Franck. La Lex Sportiva: Recherche Sur le Droit Transnational. 2007. (Etudes de Droit Internationa Ser.). 849p. *(978-90-04-15697-5(6))* BRILL.

Laura Long. Olympknits: Knit 18 Champion Athletes & a Handsome Horse. 2012. (ENG., Illus.). 96p. pap. 9.99 ***(978-1-4463-0232-3(6))*** David & Charles Pubs. GBR. Dist: F&W Media, Inc.

Leifer, Neil. A Year in Sports: From the Rose Bowl to Figure Skating. 2006. (ENG., Illus.). 347p. 55.00 *(978-0-7892-0903-0(9))* Abbeville Pr., Inc.

Lewis, Gary. The Making of Champions: Roots of the Sporting Mind. 2008. (MacSci Ser.). (ENG., Illus.). 277p. 42.00 *(978-0-230-21016-5(3))* Palgrave Macmillan.

Lieberman, David C., ed. Aerobic Exercise & Athletic Performance: Types, Duration & Health Benefits. 2009. (Sports & Athletics Preparation, Performance, & Psychology Ser.). 195.00 *(978-1-60876-217-0(3)*, Nova Biomedical Bks.) Nova Science Pubs., Inc.

Magnuson, Mike. Bike Tribes: A Field Guide to Cyclists from Beach Cruisers to Cyclocrossers to the Fastest Slow Road Racers in the World. 2012. (ENG., Illus.). 224p. 18.99 ***(978-1-60961-743-1(6))*** Rodale Pr., Inc.

Mango, Kirk & Lamont, Daveda. Becoming a True Champion: Achieving Athletic Excellence from the Inside Out. 2012. E-Book ***(978-1-4422-1407-1(4))*** Rowman & Littlefield Publishers, Inc.

Mangum, George. 10 Traits of Winning Athletes, 1 vol. 2010. 54p. pap. 16.95 *(978-1-4489-4097-4(4))* PublishAmerica, Inc.

Martin, Nita A. Total Fitness: An Advanced Training Guide for the Sportsperson, 1 vol. 2010. (ENG., Illus.). 160p. 27.95 *(978-1-84797-186-9(5))* Crowood Pr., Ltd. GBR. Dist: Independent Pubs. Group.

McAuley, Jordan, ed. The Celebrity Black Book: Over 55,000 Accurate Celebrity Addresses. 17th ed. 2007. (Celebrity Black Book Ser.). 768p. per. 75.00 *(978-0-9707095-8-5(7))* Mega Niche Media, LLC.

McCarthy, Kevin. Gold, Silver & Green: The Irish Olympic Journey 1896-1924. 462p. 2011. pap. 34.95 ***(978-1-85918-488-2(X))*** 2010. (Illus.). 66.00 *(978-1-85918-458-5(8))* Cork Univ. Pr. IRL. Dist: Stylus Publishing, LLC.

Meehan, M.D., William P. Kids, Sports, & Concussion: A Guide for Coaches & Parents, 1 vol. 2011. (Praeger Series on Contemporary Health & Living Ser.). (Illus.). 192p. 34.95 *(978-0-313-38730-2(3)*, A3160C) Greenwood Publishing Group, Inc.

Meehan, William P. Kids, Sports, & Concussion: A Guide for Coaches & Parents. 2011. E-Book ***(978-0-313-38731-9(1)***, Praeger Pubs.) Greenwood Publishing Group, Inc.

Meldrum, Carol. Knitlympics: Knit Your Favourite Sports Star. 2012. (ENG., Illus.). 96p. pap. 12.95 ***(978-1-84340-670-9(5)***, Collins & Brown) Anova Bks. GBR. Dist: Sterling Publishing Co., Inc.

Merino, Noël. Sports & Athletes. 2010. (Introducing Issues with Opposing Viewpoints Ser.). (ENG., Illus.). 144p. 35.75 *(978-0-7377-4942-7(3)*, Greenhaven Pr., Inc.) Cengage Gale.

Molinari, Dave. Best in the Game. abr. ed. 15.95 incl. audio *(978-1-56703-012-9(2))* High-Top Publishing.

Moore, Cherie. Practical Nutrition for a Fit Life. rev. ed. 2009. (ENG.). 168p. pap. 37.10 *(978-0-7575-3754-7(5))* Kendall Hunt Publishing Co.

Moorman, Claude T., et al, eds. Praeger Handbook of Sports Medicine & Athlete Health, 3 vols. 2010. (Illus.). 915p. 154.95 *(978-0-313-35640-7(8)*, C35640, Praeger Pubs.) Greenwood Publishing Group, Inc.

Moorman, III, Claude T. Post-Operative Rehabilitation Controversies in Athletes: Clinics in Sports Medicine. 2010. (Clinics: Orthopedics Ser.: 29-2). (ENG., Illus.). x, 204p. 105.00 *(978-1-4377-1874-4(4)*, Saunders) Elsevier - Health Sciences Div.

Mujika, Iñigo. Tapering & Peaking for Optimal Performance. 2009. (ENG., Illus.). 224p. (C). pap. 27.95 *(978-0-7360-7484-1(8))* Human Kinetics Pubs.

Nathanson, Bob & Kimmel, Arthur. The College Athlete's Guide to Academic Success: Tips from Peers & Profs. 2007. (ENG., Illus.). 192p. (C). per. 36.40 *(978-0-13-237947-2(3)*, Prentice Hall) Prentice Hall PTR.

Nicholls, Adam R., ed. Coping in Sport: Theory, Methods, & Related Constructs. 2010. 125.00 *(978-1-60876-483-4(5))* Nova Science Pubs., Inc.

Nicholson, Nigel. Aristocracy & Athletics in Archaic & Classical Greece. 2011. (ENG.). 296p. (C). pap. 36.99 ***(978-1-107-40368-0(5))*** Cambridge Univ. Pr.

Norman, Matthew. You Cannot Be Serious! The 101 Most Infuriating Things in Sport. 2011. (ENG.). 300p. 16.95 ***(978-0-00-743873-0(7)***, Fourth Estate) HarperCollins Pubs. Ltd. GBR. Dist: Independent Pubs. Group.

Nye, Joe. Delaware Sports Legends: Blue Hens, Hornets, High Schools, & More. 2011. *(978-1-892142-49-8(X))* Cedar Tree Bks.

Ormezzano, Gian Paolo & Graham, Harriet. Fairy Tale Stories of Snow & Ice from the Winter Olympic Games: Snow, Ice & Olympic Fire. 2007. (ENG., Illus.). 224p. 65.00 *(978-88-422-1384-0(5))* Allemandi, Umberto & Co. GBR. Dist: Antique Collectors' Club.

Overman, Steven J. Living out of Bounds: The Male Athlete's Everyday Life, 1 vol. 2008. 256p. 44.95 *(978-0-313-34668-2(2)*, C34668, Praeger Pubs.) Greenwood Publishing Group, Inc.

Patel, Dilip R. & Greydanus, Donald E., eds. Adolescence & Sports. 2010. (Health & Human Development (Joav Merrick - Series Editor - National Institute of Child Health & Human Development, Ministry of Social Affairs, Jerusalem) Ser.). 157p. 89.00 *(978-1-60876-702-1(7))* Nova Science Pubs., Inc.

Pelé & do Nascimento, Pele Arantes. Pele 10: What Makes a Great Play from the Master. 2010. (ENG., Illus.). 208p. 29.95 *(978-0-85733-035-2(7)*, 0857330357) Haynes Publishing PLC GBR. Dist: MBI Distribution Services/Quayside Distribution.

Pire, Neal. Plyometrics for Athletes at All Levels: A Training Guide for Explosive Speed & Power. 2006. (ENG., Illus.). 144p. per. 15.95 *(978-1-56975-559-4(0))* Ulysses Pr.

Pitsiladis, Yannis, et al, eds. East African Running. 2006. (ENG., Illus.). 320p. (C). 200.00 *(978-0-415-37787-4(0))* Routledge.

—East African Running: Toward a Cross-Disciplinary Perspective. 2007. (ENG., Illus.). 320p. (C). per. 58.95 *(978-0-415-37788-1(9))* Routledge.

Powell, G. Lee. Speed for Soccer. 2010. 148p. pap. 19.95 *(978-0-557-46576-7(1))* Lulu Enterprises Inc.

Power, Chris. Shooting the Curl: The Best Surfers, the Best Waves by 15 of the Best Surf Photographers. 2010. (ENG., Illus.). 160p. pap. 29.95 *(978-0-9523646-8-9(9)*, 0952364689) Orca Pubns. Ltd., Newquay GBR. Dist: MBI Distribution Services/Quayside Distribution.

Pristine, Nancy. The Victory Dance: Placing Yourself in the Winner's Circle in Sports & in Life. 2010. *(978-1-61242-000-4(1))* Arc Manor.

—Victory Dancing for Teens: Smoth Moves for Getting to the Winner's Circle. 2010. *(978-1-61242-001-1(X))* Arc Manor.

Radcliffe, James C. Functional Training for Athletes at All Levels: Workouts for Agility, Speed & Power. 2007. (ENG., Illus.). 176p. per. 15.95 *(978-1-56975-584-6(1))* Ulysses Pr.

Raedeke, Thomas D. & Smith, Alan L. The Athlete Burnout Questionnaire Manual. 2009. 88p. 39.00 *(978-1-885693-88-4(5))* Fitness Information Technology, Inc.

Reeve, Simon. One Day in September: The Full Story of the 1972 Munich Olympics Massacre & the Israeli Revenge Operation Wrath of God. 2011. (ENG., Illus.). 352p. pap. 14.95 *(978-1-61145-035-4(7)*, 611035, Arcade Publishing) Skyhorse Publishing Co., Inc.

Reiter, Annette. Parenting an Athlete. 2011. pap. 9.99 ***(978-1-61777-401-0(4))*** Tate Publishing & Enterprises, LLC.

Richardson, Paul E. Running Is Flying: Aphorisms, Meditations, & Thoughts on a Running Life. 2012. (ENG., Illus.). 144p. 14.99 ***(978-1-60961-221-4(3))*** Rodale Pr., Inc.

Rough Guides. The Rough Guide to Cult Sport. 2011. 304p. 14.99 *(978-1-4053-8694-4(0))* Rough Guides, Ltd. GBR. Dist: Dorling Kindersley Publishing, Inc.

Rountree, Sage. The Athlete's Guide to Recovery: Rest, Relax, & Restore for Peak Performance. 2011. (Athlete's Guide Ser.). (ENG., Illus.). 248p. (gr. 12). pap. 18.95 *(978-1-934030-67-7(8))* VeloPress.

—The Athlete's Guide to Yoga: An Integrated Approach to Strength, Flexibility, & Focus. 2008. (Athlete's Guide Ser.). (ENG., Illus.). 251p. pap. 21.95 *(978-1-934030-04-2(X))* VeloPress.

—The Athlete's Pocket Guide to Yoga: 50 Routines for Flexibility, Balance, & Focus. 2009. (ENG., Illus.). 160p. spiral bd. 15.95 *(978-1-934030-41-7(4))* VeloPress.

Rubenstein, Lorne. This Round's on Me: Lorne Rubenstein on Golf. 2010. (ENG.). 296p. pap. 16.95 *(978-0-7710-7858-3(7)*, McClelland & Stewart) McClelland & Stewart CAN. Dist: Random Hse., Inc.

Ruxin, Robert H. An Athlete's Guide to Agents. 5th rev. ed. 2009. 258p. pap. 56.95 *(978-0-7637-7611-4(4))* Jones & Bartlett Learning, LLC.

Sance, T. S. Living Like a Champion: A Student Athlete¿s Survival Guide, 1 vol. 2009. 48p. pap. 16.95 *(978-1-4489-8867-9(5))* PublishAmerica, Inc.

Sandvoss, Cornel, et al. Bodies of Discourse: Sports Stardom & Celebrity in the Global Public Sphere. 2012. ***(978-1-4331-1173-0(X))***; E-Book ***(978-1-4539-0211-0(2))*** Lang, Peter GmbH, Europaischer Verlag der Wissenschaften.

Scally, John. 100 GAA Greats: From Christie Ring to Joe Canning. 2010. (ENG., Illus.). 336p. pap. 22.95 *(978-1-84596-564-8(7))* Mainstream Publishing Co., Ltd. GBR. Dist: Independent Pubs. Group.

Schoem, David & Kovacs, Shelly. College Knowledge for the Student Athlete. 2011. (ENG., Illus.). 200p. (C). pap. 18.95 ***(978-0-472-03454-3(5))*** Univ. of Michigan Pr.

Scott, Randall. Golf Etiquette: A Comprehensive & Short Guide to Expected Player Behavior. 2009. 52p. pap. 10.95 *(978-1-4327-4148-8(9))* Outskirts Pr., Inc.

Sears, Wallace, ed. Bobby Bowden - The 300th Win. Date not set. (Illus.). 39.95 *(978-0-9639505-8-1(4))* Pachyderm Pr., Inc.

Senft, Jean. Triumph on Ice: The New World of Figure Skating, 1 vol. 2011. (ENG., Illus.). 144p. 29.95 *(978-1-55365-657-9(1)*, Greystone Bks.) D&M Pubs. Inc. CAN. Dist: Perseus-PGW.

Sheard, Michael. Mental Toughness: The Mindset Behind Sporting Achievement. (ENG., Illus.). 2009. 160p. 59.95 *(978-0-415-49109-9(6))* 2009. 160p. pap. 29.95 *(978-0-415-49110-5(X))* 2nd rev. ed. 2012. 256p. 80.00 *(978-0-415-57895-0(7))* 2nd rev. ed. 2012. 256p. pap. 34.95 *(978-0-415-57896-7(5))* Routledge.

Shepherd, John. Sports Training: The Complete Guide. 2007. (ENG., Illus.). 225p. pap. 24.95 *(978-1-55407-329-0(4))* Firefly Bks., Ltd.

Silva, John M., et al. Training Professionals in the Practice of Sport Psychology. 2007. 224p. pap. 48.00 *(978-1-885693-76-1(1))* Fitness Information Technology, Inc.

Solotaroff, Paul. The Body Shop: Parties, Pills, & Pumping Iron - Or, My Life in the Age of Muscle. 2010. (ENG., Illus.). 304p. 24.99 *(978-0-316-01101-3(0))* Little Brown & Co.

Sporting News. Best by Number: Who Wore What... with Distinction. 2008. (ENG.). 224p. 24.99 *(978-0-7407-7370-9(4))* Andrews McMeel Publishing.

Street, Scott A. Life Skills for the Student-Athlete. 2007. (ENG., Illus.). 304p. (C). per. 79.00 *(978-0-07-245868-8(2)*, 0072458682) McGraw-Hill Cos., The.

Surf Girl Roxy (Custom) 2007. 35.00 *(978-0-8118-6125-0(2))* Chronicle Bks. LLC.

Vande Streek, Kevin & Bratt, Wallace. Strong & Courageous: Joshua's Lessons for Athletes (and the Cheering Section) 2011. 136p. pap. 10.00 ***(978-0-9832385-0-8(2))*** Calvin College Alumni Assn.

Walker, Isaiah Helekunihi. Waves of Resistance: Surfing & History in Twentieth-Century Hawaii. 2011. 55.00 *(978-0-8248-3462-3(3))*; pap. 24.99 *(978-0-8248-3547-7(6))* Univ. of Hawaii Pr.

Walker, Mick. Velocette: The Racing Story. 2010. (Illus.). 224p. 44.95 *(978-1-84797-072-5(9))* Crowood Pr., Ltd. GBR. Dist: MBI Distribution Services/Quayside Distribution.

Walls, Everson, et al. Gift for Ron: Friendship & Sacrifice on & off the Gridiron. 2010. (ENG., Illus.). 240p. pap. 16.95 *(978-0-7627-6375-7(2)*, Lyons Pr.) Globe Pequot Pr., The.

Watkins, Christine, ed. Child Athletes. 2007. (At Issue Ser.). (ENG.). (gr. 10-12). 91p. pap. 22.50 *(978-0-7377-3786-8(7))*; (Illus.). 123p. pap. 31.80 *(978-0-7377-3785-1(9))* Cengage Gale. (Greenhaven Pr., Inc.).

Watson, Lance. Triathlon: The Workouts that Worked. 2010. 160p. pap. 17.95 *(978-1-84126-119-5(X))* Meyer & Meyer Sport, Ltd. GBR. Dist: Cardinal Pubs. Group.

Wiggins, David K. & Rodgers, R. . Pierre, eds. Rivals: Legendary Matchups That Made Sports History. 2010. (Illus.). 491p. pap. 29.95 *(978-1-55728-921-6(2))* Univ. of Arkansas Pr.

Wiggins, Jonathan. In Pursuit of a Powerful Performance. 2010. (Illus.). 196p. pap. 38.00 *(978-90-382-1535-8(5))* Academia Pr. BEL. Dist: Univ. Pr. of New England.

Winch, Michael A. Conditioning for Marathon Runners & Endurance Athletes. 2006. (ENG., Illus.). 160p. pap. 29.95 *(978-1-86126-901-0(3))* Crowood Pr., Ltd. GBR. Dist: Independent Pubs. Group.

Witt, Richard. A Lifetime of Training for Just Ten Seconds: Olympians in Their Own Words. 2012. (ENG.). 192p. 15.95 ***(978-1-4081-6403-7(5))*** A & C Black GBR. Dist: Macmillan.

Yessis, Michael, ed. Block Periodization 2: Fundamental Concepts & Training Design. 2008. (Illus.). 221p. pap. 65.00 *(978-0-9817180-4-0(3))* Ultimate Athlete Concepts.

ATHLETES—BIOGRAPHY

Allen, Richard. When Football Was Football: Fulham: A Nostalgic Look at a Century of the Club. 2011. (ENG., Illus.). 208p. 29.95 *(978-0-85733-049-9(7)*, 0857330497) Haynes Publishing PLC GBR. Dist: MBI Distribution Services/Quayside Distribution.

Allred, Alexandra. Swingman: What a Difference a Decade Makes. Torke, Kyle & Strozier, M. Stefan, eds. 2010. 258p. pap. 20.00 *(978-1-935444-40-4(9))* World Audience Pubs.

American Indian Athletic Hall Of Fame. The American Indian Athletic Hall of Fame - 1972-2009. 2010. 360p. 34.95 *(978-1-4269-2380-7(5))* Trafford Publishing.

Antognoni, Giancarlo. Antognoni: 10 Modi per Dirti "Ti Amo" Calamai, Luca, ed. 2011. (Passaparola Ser.). (ITA., Illus.). 160p. (C). pap. 25.00 ***(978-88-564-0134-9(7))*** Polistampa ITA. Dist: Brown, David Bk. Co., The.

Athans, Sandra K. Tales from the Top of the World: Climbing Mount Everest with Pete Athans. 2012. lib. bdg. ***(978-0-7613-6506-8(0)***, Millbrook Pr.) Lerner Publishing Group.

Austin, Charles. Head Games: Life's Greatest Challenge. 2007. 108p. pap. 13.95 *(978-1-933538-98-3(8))* Hillcrest Publishing Group, Inc.

Axelrod, Jim. In the Long Run: A Father, a Son, & Unintentional Lessons in Happiness, 1 vol. 2011. (ENG.). 304p. 26.00 *(978-0-374-19211-2(1))* Farrar, Straus & Giroux.

Bagga, David. The Walk-on. 2009. 176p. 24.99 *(978-1-4490-3773-4(9))*; pap. 14.95 *(978-1-4490-3772-7(0))* AuthorHouse.

Bak, Richard. Mr. Weightlifting: Norbert Schemansky: History's Greatest Olympic & World Champion Heavyweight Lifter. 2007. (Illus.). xviii, 190p. *(978-0-9723637-8-5(5))* Immortal Investments Publishing.

Baldwin, Robert "Bummer". Onward Through the Fog: Conversations with Pappy, 1 vol. 2009. 184p. pap. 19.95 *(978-1-60813-236-2(6))* PublishAmerica, Inc.

Barbe, Penelope. Olympic Dream: The Pain & Glory of Figure Skating. 2010. 188p. *(978-1-926745-00-8(0))* Transit Publishing (Transit Editeur Inc.).

Bart Yasso. My Life on the Run: The Wit, Wisdom, & Insights of a Road Racing Icon. 2008. 17.50 *(978-1-60529-914-3(6))* Rodale Pr., Inc.

Batesel, Paul. Major League Baseball Players Of 1884: A Biographical Dictionary. 2010. (ENG., Illus.). 251p. pap. 39.95 *(978-0-7864-5905-6(0))* McFarland & Co., Inc. Pubs.

Beard, Amanda & Paley, Rebecca. In the Water They Can't See You Cry: A Memoir. 2012. (ENG., Illus.). 256p. 24.99 ***(978-1-4516-4437-1(X)***, Touchstone) Touchstone.

Belton, Brian. East End Heroes, Stateside Kings: The Amazing True Story of Three Football Players Who Changed the World. 2008. (ENG., Illus.). 288p. 29.95 *(978-1-84454-501-8(6))* Blake, John Publishing, Ltd. GBR. Dist: Independent Pubs. Group.

Benjey, Tom. Oklahoma's Carlisle Indian School Immortals. 2009. (ENG., Illus.). 192p. 24.99 *(978-0-9774486-8-5(1))* Tuxedo Pr.

—Wisconsin's Carlisle Indian School Immortals. (ENG., Illus.). 340p. 2011. pap. 19.95 *(978-1-936161-22-5(2))* 2010. 29.95 *(978-1-936161-21-8(4))* Tuxedo Pr.

Berger, Ronald J. Hoop Dreams on Wheels: Disability & the Dedicated Wheelchair Athlete. 2008. (Contemporary Sociological Perspectives Ser.). (Illus.). XIV, 170p. 135.00 *(978-0-415-96510-1(1))* Routledge.

Birken, Randy A. Her Longest Marathon: A Runner's Race to Survive. 2008. (Illus.). 164p. pap. 15.95 *(978-1-57733-226-8(1))* Blue Dolphin Publishing, Inc.

Bohn, Michael K. Heroes & Ballyhoo: How the Golden Age of the 1920s Transformed American Sports. 2009. (Illus.). 336p. 27.50 *(978-1-59797-412-7(9))* Potomac Bks., Inc.

Bolt, Usain. Usain Bolt: My Story - 9. 58 - Being the World's Fastest Man. 2010. (ENG., Illus.). 288p. 26.95 *(978-0-00-737139-6(X))* HarperCollins Pubs. Ltd. GBR. Dist: Independent Pubs. Group.

Botham, Ian. My Sporting Heroes: His 50 Greatest from Britain & Ireland. 2010. (ENG., Illus.). 320p. pap. 14.95 *(978-1-84596-598-3(1))*; 304p. 37.95 *(978-1-84596-487-0(X))* Mainstream Publishing Co., Ltd. GBR. Dist: Independent Pubs. Group.

Boyce, Lucas Daniel. Living Proof: From Foster Care to the White House & the NBA. 2011. (ENG.). 228p. pap. 16.99 *(978-1-59932-257-5(9))* Advantage Media Group.

Boyle, Brian & Katovsky, Bill. Iron Heart: The True Story of How I Came Back from the Dead. 2011. (ENG., Illus.). 256p. pap. 14.95 *(978-1-61608-360-1(3)*, 608360) Skyhorse Publishing Co., Inc.

Brant, John & Salazar, Alberto. 14 Minutes: A Running Legend's Life & Death & Life. 2012. (ENG., Illus.). 280p. 25.99 ***(978-1-60961-314-3(7))*** Rodale Pr., Inc.

Brody, Howard & Rhodes, Dusty. Dusty: Reflections of Wrestling's American Dream. 2012. (ENG., Illus.). 272p. pap. 14.95 ***(978-1-61321-096-3(5)***, 613096) Skyhorse Publishing Co., Inc.

Brown, David W. Philly Jocks: The Best Philadelphia Pro Athletes of Our Time. 2007. 334p. per. 19.95 *(978-1-933822-09-9(0))* Camino Bks., Inc.

Brown, Robert. Running for Fun: High School Runner, Jonathan Brown. 2009. (Illus.). 400p. pap. 17.95 *(978-1-4327-4120-4(9))* Outskirts Pr., Inc.

Budig, Gene A. & Gilman, Sander. Grasping the Ring II: Nine People Who Matter. 2010. (ENG., Illus.). 120p. pap. 14.95 *(978-0-8032-3400-0(7)*, Bison Bks.) Univ. of Nebraska Pr.

Buford, Kate. Native American Son: The Life & Sporting Legend of Jim Thorpe. 2010. (ENG., Illus.). 496p. 35.00 *(978-0-375-41324-7(3)*, Knopf) Knopf Doubleday Publishing Group.

—Native American Son: The Life & Sporting Legend of Jim Thorpe. 2012. (ENG., Illus.). 528p. pap. 24.95 ***(978-0-8032-4089-6(9)***, Bison Bks.) Univ. of Nebraska Pr.

Caduto, Tommy Jon. Fight or Die: The Vinny Paz Story. 2010. (ENG., Illus.). 240p. pap. 12.95 *(978-0-59921-967-7(0)*, Lyons Pr.) Globe Pequot Pr., The.

Calhoun, Skip. You Can't Lose If You Don't Quit: The Life & Times of Doyle Hall. 2008. 184p. 26.95 *(978-1-4401-0458-9(1))*; pap. 16.95 *(978-0-595-49085-1(9))* iUniverse, Inc.

Callow, Nick. The 100 Greatest Olympians & Paralympians. 2012. (ENG., Illus.). 224p. 34.95 ***(978-1-84732-701-7(X))*** Carlton Bks., Ltd. GBR. Dist: Sterling Publishing Co., Inc.

Cantor, George. Usain Bolt. 2011. (People in the News Ser.). 128p. (YA). (gr. 7-12). lib. bdg. 33.45 *(978-1-4205-0341-8(3))* Cengage Gale.

Carney, James M., Jr. Ultimate Tough Guy. 2009. (Illus.). 308p. pap. 22.00 *(978-0-578-01055-7(0))* Achill Publishing.

Carruthers, Kitty. British Olympic Heroes: The Best of British Gold Medallists. 2011. (Illus.). 132p. pap. 12.95 ***(978-1-906768-15-7(3)***, Stacey International) Stacey Publishing GBR. Dist: Midpoint Trade Bks., Inc.

Carter, Butch & Carter, Chris. Born to Believe. 232p. pap. *(978-1-894389-05-1(0))* Full Wits Publishing, Inc.

Carter, Rubin. The Sixteenth Round: From Number 1 Contender to Number 45472. 2011. (ENG.). 368p. pap. 16.95 *(978-1-56976-567-8(7))*, Hill, Lawrence Bks.) Chicago Review Pr., Inc.

Casey, John. Room for Improvement: Notes on a Dozen Lifelong Sports. 2011. (ENG.). 256p. 25.95 *(978-0-307-70002-5(X)*, Knopf) Knopf Doubleday Publishing Group.

Cejudo, Henry & Plaschke, Bill. American Victory: Wrestling, Dreams & a Journey Toward Home. 2011. (ENG.). 240p. (gr. 12). 15.00 *(978-0-451-23203-8(8)*, Celebra) Penguin Group (USA) Inc.

Chapman, Mike. The Life & Legacy of Frank Gotch: King of the Catch-As-Catch-Can Wrestlers. 2008. (Illus.). xi, 149p. 19.95 *(978-1-58160-646-1(X))* Paladin Pr.

—Oklahoma Shooter: The Dan Hodge Story. 2009. (Illus.). 198p. pap. 22.95 *(978-0-9819484-0-9(5))* Culture Hse.

Clark, Dan. Gladiator: A True Story of 'Roids, Rage, & Redemption. 2011. (ENG., Illus.). 256p. pap. 16.99 (978-1-4165-9733-9(6), Scribner) Scribner.

Clements, Frank. A Bike Ride Through My Life. 2011. 440p. 33.95 (978-1-4269-6317-9(3)); pap. 23.95 (978-1-4269-6266-0(5)) Trafford Publishing.

Clemons, Kortney & Briggs, Bill. Amped: A Soldier's Race for Gold in the Shadow of War. 2008. (ENG., Illus.). 288p. 24.95 (978-0-470-28137-6(5), Wiley) Wiley, John & Sons, Inc.

Comaneci, Nadia. Letters to a Young Gymnast. 2011. (ENG.). 192p. (gr. 9). pap. 14.99 (978-0-465-02505-3(6)) Basic Bks.

Connolly, Kevin Michael. Double Take: A Memoir. 2010. (ENG., Illus.). 240p. pap. 14.99 (978-0-06-179152-9(0), HarperPerennial) HarperCollins Pubs.

Considine, Bob. The Unreconstructed Amateur: A Pictorial Biography of Amos Alonzo Stagg. Cahn, Ralph, ed. 2011. 160p. 41.95 (978-1-258-10398-9(2)) Literary Licensing, LLC.

Cook, William A. Jim Thorpe: A Biography. 2011. (ENG., Illus.). 232p. pap. 29.95 (978-0-7864-6355-8(4)) McFarland & Co., Inc. Pubs.

Coppola, Sam. Silent Quarterback. 2010. 176p. pap. 19.95 (978-0-9766965-9-9(2)) Pull Your Own Weight Sports Marketing.

Cottier, Adam. Steven Gerrard. 2010. (World Cup Heroes Ser.). (ENG & ABK., Illus.). 128p. pap. 10.95 (978-1-84358-174-1(4)) Blake, John Publishing, Ltd. GBR. Dist: Independent Pubs. Group.

Cramer, Richard Ben. What Do You Think of Ted Williams Now? A Remembrance. 2011. (ENG.). 128p. pap. 10.99 (978-1-4516-4340-4(3)) Simon & Schuster.

Crum, Richard D. & Crum, Dax. Relentless. 2011. pap. 13.99 (978-1-59955-464-8(X), Bonneville Bks.) Cedar Fort, Inc./CFI Distribution.

Cruz, Victor & Schrager, Peter. Out of the Blue. 2012. 304p. (gr. 12). 26.95 (978-0-451-41615-5(5)) Penguin Group (USA) Inc.

—Out of the Blue (Spanish Edition) 2012. (SPA.). 320p. (gr. 12). pap. 17.00 (978-0-451-41616-2(3), Celebra) Penguin Group (USA) Inc.

Curll, Ronald. Wheels of Faith. 2007. 157p. pap. 15.95 (978-0-9796829-0-2(8)) Curll, Ronald.

Daly, Sherrie. Teed Off: My Life as a Player's Wife on the PGA Tour. 2011. (ENG., Illus.). 224p. 25.00 (978-1-4516-1012-3(2)) Gallery Pr., The IRL. Dist: Simon & Schuster, Inc.

Davidson, James West, et al. The Ledge: An Adventure Story of Friendship & Survival on Mount Rainier. 2011. (Illus.). 288p. 26.00 (978-0-345-52319-8(9), Ballantine Bks.) Random House Publishing Group.

Davies, Chris. Deadly Dimitar: The Biography of Superstriker Dimitar Berbatov. 2009. (ENG., Illus.). 264p. 34.95 (978-1-84454-569-8(5)) Blake, John Publishing, Ltd. GBR. Dist: Independent Pubs. Group.

Dawes, Susan Z. Run the Race: A Father's Legacy of Life Lessons. 2007. 140p. per. 13.95 (978-0-595-42942-4(4)) iUniverse, Inc.

Day, Frederick J. Dream Team: Saints & Gentle Souls from the World of Sports. 2007. 392p. (ENG.). 35.95 (978-0-595-70071-4(3)); per. 25.95 (978-0-595-45406-8(2)) iUniverse, Inc.

De La Hoya, Oscar & Springer, Steve. Un Sueno Americano: Mi Historia. 2009. (SPA.). 304p. pap. 12.99 (978-0-06-172542-5(0), Rayo) HarperCollins Pubs.

Delany, Ronnie. Ronnie Delany: Staying the Distance. (ENG., Illus.). 208p. 2006. 37.95 (978-0-86278-975-6(3)) 2nd rev. ed. 2007. pap. 23.95 (978-1-84717-044-6(7)) O'Brien Pr., Ltd., The IRL. Dist: Dufour Editions, Inc.

DeMarco, Tony & Zappala, Ellen. Nardo: Memoirs of a Boxing Champion. 2011. pap. (978-1-881901-82-2(3)); pap. (978-1-881901-81-5(5)) LEGAS.

DiBiase, Ted. Ted Dibiase: The Million Dollar Man. 2008. (Wwe Ser.). (ENG., Illus.). 256p. pap. 16.00 (978-1-4165-5890-3(X), World Wrestling Entertainment) World Wrestling Entertainment.

Doeden, Matt. Sports Illustrated Kids Greatest Sports Stars. 2010. (Sports Illustrated Kids Ser.). (ENG.). 112p. (gr. 3-4). pap. 12.95 (978-1-4296-5035-9(4)) Capstone Pr., Inc.

Donahue, Topher. Bugaboo Dreams: A Story of Skiers, Helicopters & Mountains, 1 vol. rev. ed. 2009. (ENG., Illus.). 296p. (978-1-897522-11-0(8)) Rocky Mountain Bks.

Doug Freedline. Summer Of 1977: A North American Bicycling Odyssey. 2009. 592p. 43.95 (978-1-4401-5093-7(1)); pap. 33.95 (978-1-4401-0020-8(9)) iUniverse, Inc.

Dugard, Martin. To Be a Runner: How Racing up Mountains, Running with the Bulls, or Just Taking on a 5-K Make You a Better Person (And the World a Better Place) 2011. (ENG.). 256p. 24.99 (978-1-60961-108-8(X)) Rodale Pr., Inc.

Duggan, Hacksaw Jim & Williams, Scott E. Hacksaw: The Jim Duggan Story. 2012. (ENG.). 240p. 22.95 (978-1-60078-686-0(3)) Triumph Bks.

Dunn, Robert. Houser-Pride of America. 2006. (ENG.). 236p. per. 14.95 (978-0-7414-3637-5(X)) Infinity Publishing.

Dwight, Eleanor. Tie Breaker: Jimmy Van Alen & Tennis in the 20th Century. 2010. (ENG.). 196p. pap. 25.00 (978-1-905377-40-4(1), Maria Teresa Train Mtt Scala) Antique Collectors' Club GBR. Dist: National Bk. Network.

Eastley, Matthew. From Bovril to Champagne: When the FA cup really mattered Part 1 - The 1970s. 2010. 348p. pap. 17.99 (978-1-4520-0582-9(6)) AuthorHouse.

Eben, Jeffrey. How Many Wins Have YOU Had Today? 2006. 204p. 20.00 (978-0-9777666-1-1(6)) Garden of Eben Publishing.

Egenolf, Douglas B. The Last Seasons: The Story of the Bird Hunter. 2008. 256p. pap. 14.95 (978-1-59858-791-3(9)) Dog Ear Publishing, LLC.

Estiarte, Manel. Todos MIS Hermanos. 2nd ed. 2009. (Plataforma Testimonio Ser.). (SPA., Illus.). 288p. pap. 26.95 (978-84-96981-37-9(1)) Plataforma Editorial SL ESP. Dist: Independent Pubs. Group.

Everett, Reg & Walker, Mick. Rocker to Racer. 2010. (ENG., Illus.). 240p. 34.95 (978-1-85983-679-8(8), 1859836798) DB Publishing GBR. Dist: MBI Distribution Services/Quayside Distribution.

Evison, Sue. Wayne Rooney. 2010. (World Cup Heroes Ser.). (ENG., Illus.). 124p. pap. 10.95 (978-1-84358-171-0(X)) Blake, John Publishing, Ltd. GBR. Dist: Independent Pubs. Group.

Faxon, Brad, intro. One Week in April: the Masters: Stories & Insights from Arnold Palmer, Phil Mickelson, Rick Reilly, Ken Venturi, Jack Nicklaus, Lee Trevino, & Many More about the Quest for the Famed Green Jacket. 2009. (ENG.). 400p. pap. 14.95 (978-1-4027-6537-7(1), Sterling Innovation) Sterling Publishing Co., Inc.

Fett, B. Michael. Beautiful Hardship: My Story. 2009. (978-1-58982-555-0(1)) American Bk. Publishing Group.

Fields, Truman. Remembering The 40's: In the Heart of Appalachia. 2009. 348p. pap. 20.00 (978-1-4389-9782-7(5)) AuthorHouse.

Fisher, Derek. Character Driven: Life, Lessons, & Basketball. 2012. (ENG., Illus.). 272p. pap. 14.99 (978-1-4516-7207-7(1), Howard Bks) Howard Books.

Foley, Mick. Countdown to Lockdown: A Hardcore Journal. 2011. (ENG., Illus.). 400p. mass mkt. 7.99 (978-0-446-56460-1(5)) Grand Central Publishing.

Foran, Charles. Maurice Richard. 2011. (ENG.). 208p. (gr. 12). 19.95 (978-0-670-06412-0(2), Penguin Global) Penguin Group (USA) Inc.

Foreman, Ken. A Coach's Journey: From a Sand Lot to the Olympic Stadium. 2010. pap. 17.99 (978-1-61566-910-3(8)) Tate Publishing & Enterprises, LLC.

Foster, Richard J. Mark Spitz: The Extraordinary Life of an Olympic Champion. 2008. (ENG., Illus.). 360p. 24.95 (978-1-59580-039-8(5)) Santa Monica Pr.

Fotheringham, William. Fallen Angel: The Passion of Fausto Coppi. 2010. (ENG., Illus.). 292p. pap. 16.95 (978-0-224-07450-6(4)) Random Hse. GBR. Dist: Independent Pubs. Group.

Friedman, Steve. The Agony of Victory: When Winning Isn't Enough. 2012. (ENG.). 288p. pap. 14.95 (978-1-61145-492-5(1), 611492, Arcade Publishing) Skyhorse Publishing Co., Inc.

Gaetjens, Lesly. The Shot Heard Around the World: the Joe Gaetjens Story. 2010. 116p. pap. 12.99 (978-0-557-61231-4(4)) Lulu Enterprises Inc.

Gaines, W. S. Blood on a Pew: Overcoming Tragedy through the Truth of Eternity. 2011. pap. 12.99 (978-1-61777-402-7(2)) Tate Publishing & Enterprises, LLC.

Gascoigne, Paul. Glorious: My Football World in Pictures. 2012. (ENG., Illus.). 256p. 32.95 (978-0-85720-448-6(3)) Simon & Schuster, Ltd. GBR. Dist: Independent Pubs. Group.

Gill, Dominic. Take a Seat: One Man, One Tandem & Twenty Thousand Miles of Possibilities. 2010. (ENG., Illus.). 288p. pap. 16.95 (978-0-7627-7069-4(4), Falcon Guides) Globe Pequot Pr., The.

Glanville, Doug. The Game from Where I Stand: From Batting Practice to the Clubhouse to the Best Breakfast on the Road, an Inside View of a Ballplayer's Life. 2011. (ENG.). 304p. pap. 14.99 (978-0-312-57309-6(X), St. Martin's Griffin) St. Martin's Pr.

Golus, Carrie. Jim Thorpe. 2007. (Sports Heroes & Legends Ser.). (Illus.). 106p. (YA). (gr. 7-12). lib. bdg. 29.27 (978-0-8225-7163-6(3)) Twenty First Century Bks.

Grey-Thompson, Tanni. Aim High. 2007. 96p. pap. (978-1-905170-89-0(0)) Accent Pr. Ltd.

Gruber, May. Sky Hooks & Track Shoes. Date not set. pap. 12.95 (978-0-931790-86-7(7)) Brick Hse. Publishing Co.

Hamill, Dorothy. A Skating Life. l.t. ed. 2007. (Thorndike Biography Ser.). (Illus.). 368p. 31.95 (978-0-7862-9965-2(7)) Thorndike Pr.

Hammond, James Herschel. What a Beautiful Sunset. 2007. 231p. pap. 13.99 (978-1-57399-372-2(7)) Mac Hammond Ministries.

Hanks, Bill. Five Minutes till Race Time. 2008. 74p. pap. 16.95 (978-1-60563-730-3(0)) PublishAmerica, Inc.

Harvey, Sean D. One Moment Changes Everything: The All-America Tragedy of Don Rogers. 2007. (Illus.). 243p. 24.95 (978-1-59670-231-8(1)) Sports Publishing, LLC.

Heits, Rudolph T. Jason Witten. 2009. (Superstars of Pro Football Ser.). 64p. (YA). (gr. 5-18). pap. 9.95 (978-1-4222-1986-7(0)) Mason Crest Pubs.

Helling, Steve. Tiger: The Real Story. 2010. (Illus.). 242p. pap. (978-0-306-81950-6(3)) Da Capo Pr., Inc.

Henderson, Jon. Best of British: Hendo's Sporting Heroes. 2007. (ENG., Illus.). 192p. 19.95 (978-0-224-08248-8(5)) Random Hse. GBR. Dist: Independent Pubs. Group.

Herlihy, David. The Lost Cyclist: The Epic Tale of an American Adventurer & His Mysterious Disappearance. 2011. (ENG., Illus.). 368p. pap. 14.95 (978-0-547-52198-5(7), Mariner Bks.) Houghton Mifflin Harcourt Trade & Reference Pubs.

Herlihy, David V. The Lost Cyclist: The Epic Tale of an American Adventurer & His Mysterious Disappearance. 2010. (ENG., Illus.). 336p. 26.00 (978-0-547-19557-5(5)) Houghton Mifflin Harcourt Trade & Reference Pubs.

Hide, Herbie. Nothing but Trouble? My Story. 2009. (ENG., Illus.). 260p. 28.95 (978-1-84454-706-7(X)) Blake, John Publishing, Ltd. GBR. Dist: Independent Pubs. Group.

Hignell, Andrew. Turnbull: A Welsh Sporting Hero. (Illus.). 287p. 45.00 (978-0-7524-2184-1(0)) History Pr. Ltd.,The GBR. Dist: Trafalgar Square Publishing.

Hogan, Jim. The Irishman Who Ran for England. 2008. (ENG., Illus.). 157p. pap. 28.95 (978-1-85607-958-7(9)) Columba Pr. IRL. Dist: Dufour Editions, Inc.

Holgate, Andy. Can't Swim, Can't Ride, Can't Run: My Triathlon Journey from Common Man to Ironman. 2011. (ENG., Illus.). 240p. pap. 19.95 (978-1-84818-743-6(2)) Pitch Publishing (Brighton) Ltd. GBR. Dist: Independent Pubs. Group.

Homan, Andrew M. Life in the Slipstream: The Legend of Bobby Walthour Sr. 2011. (Illus.). 280p. 26.95 (978-1-59797-685-5(7)) Potomac Bks., Inc.

Horowitz, Jeff. My First 100 Marathons: 2,620 Miles with an Obsessive Runner. 2008. 272p. 24.95 (978-1-60239-318-9(4)) Skyhorse Publishing Co., Inc.

Hosoi, Christian. Hosoi: My Life as a Skateboarder Junkie Inmate Pastor. 2012. (ENG.). 336p. 26.99 (978-0-06-202430-5(2), HarperOne) HarperCollins Pubs.

Hostetler, Will. A Runner's Journal: To Boston & Beyond. 2008. 326p. pap. 29.95 (978-1-4241-9862-7(3)) PublishAmerica, Inc.

Howard, Paul. Sex, Lies & Handlebar Tape: The Remarkable Life of Jacques Anquetil, the First Five-Times Winner of the Tour de France. (ENG., Illus.). 320p. 2011. pap. 16.95 (978-1-84596-461-0(6)) 2008. 34.95 (978-1-84596-301-9(6)) Mainstream Publishing Co., Ltd. GBR. Dist: Independent Pubs. Group.

Howard, Russ & Weeks, Bob. Hurry Hard: The Russ Howard Story. 2007. (ENG., Illus.). 296p. 34.95 (978-0-470-83955-3(4), Wiley) Wiley, John & Sons, Inc.

Hoy, Chris. Chris Hoy: The Autobiography. (ENG.). 352p. 2010. 18.95 (978-0-00-731134-7(6)) 2009. (Illus.). 29.95 (978-0-00-731131-6(1)) HarperCollins Pubs. Ltd. GBR. Dist: Independent Pubs. Group.

Hoyt, Dick. Devoted: The Story of a Father's Love for His Son. (ENG.). 2012. 232p. pap. 12.99 (978-0-306-82074-8(9)) 2010. (Illus.). 224p. 22.95 (978-0-306-81832-5(9)) Da Capo Pr., Inc.

HRH the Prince of Wales. Profiles in Polo: The Players Who Changed the Game. 2007. (978-0-7864-3702-3(2)) McFarland & Co., Inc. Pubs.

Hughes, Eric. Eric, or Little by Little. 2010. (Illus.). 168p. pap. 13.49 (978-1-4520-0937-7(6)) AuthorHouse.

Hungarian Long-Distance Runners: László Tábori, Sándor Iharos, Sándor Rozsnyói, Edit Bérces, Zoltán Káldy, Judit Földing-Nagy, Gyula Kellner. 2010. 44p. pap. 14.14 (978-1-157-53079-4(6)) General Bks. LLC.

Husher, John Durbin. Heroes Afar: How Eighty Athletes & Leaders Inspired the World. 2007. 328p. 32.95 (978-0-595-69313-9(X)); per. 22.95 (978-0-595-45253-8(1)) iUniverse, Inc.

Ironside, Len. When You're Ready Boys - Take Hold! My Grappling Story. 2011. 88p. pap. 12.10 (978-1-4520-8950-8(7)) AuthorHouse.

Jackson, Peter. Triumph & Tragedy: Welsh Sporting Legends. 2011. (ENG., Illus.). 272p. 34.95 (978-1-84596-776-5(3)) Mainstream Publishing Co., Ltd. GBR. Dist: Independent Pubs. Group.

Johnson, Rafer. Great Athletes. 2009. 85.00 (978-1-58765-474-9(1)); 85.00 (978-1-58765-486-2(5)); 85.00 (978-1-58765-485-5(7)); 85.00 (978-1-58765-484-8(9)); 85.00 (978-1-58765-483-1(0)); 85.00 (978-1-58765-482-4(2)); 85.00 (978-1-58765-475-6(X)); 170.00 (978-1-58765-476-3(8)); 85.00 (978-1-58765-477-0(6)); 85.00 (978-1-58765-478-7(4)); 170.00 (978-1-58765-479-4(2)); 85.00 (978-1-58765-480-0(6)); 85.00 (978-1-58765-481-7(4));Set. (Illus.). 1020.00 (978-1-58765-473-2(3)) Salem Pr., Inc.

Jones, Marion. On the Right Track: From Olympic Downfall to Finding Forgiveness & the Strength to Overcome & Succeed. 2011. (ENG., Illus.). 240p. pap. 14.99 (978-1-4516-2630-8(4), Howard Bks.) Howard Books.

Jones, Ryan. King James: The Buying & Selling of LeBron James. Date not set. mass mkt. (978-0-312-99376-4(5), St. Martin's Paperbacks) St. Martin's Pr.

Jordan, Darrell. Ving Tsun Foundation: A Personal Journey. Stein, Joel, ed. 2007. spiral bd., wbk. ed. 25.00 (978-0-9728825-0-7(2)) FLVTAA Publishing.

Jordan, Michael. Mi Filosofia del Triunfo.Tr. of My Philosophy of Life. (SPA.). 6.98 (978-968-403-868-4(2)) Selector, S.A. de C.V. MEX. Dist: AIMS International Bks., Inc.

Judah, Tim. Bikila. 2009. (ENG.). 176p. pap. (978-0-9558302-1-1(4)) Reportage Pr.

Kann, Bob & Hoffman, Caroline. Cindy Bentley: Spirit of a Champion. 2010. pap. (978-0-87020-457-9(2)); (ENG., Illus.). 96p. (J). pap. 12.95 (978-0-87020-456-2(4)) Wisconsin Historical Society.

Kanyon, Chris & Clark, Ryan. Wrestling Reality: The Life & Mind of Chris Kanyon Wrestling's Gay Superstar. 2011. (ENG., Illus.). 336p. pap. 18.95 (978-1-77041-028-2(7)) ECW Pr. CAN. Dist: Independent Pubs. Group.

Karnazes, Dean. Run! 26. 2 Stories of Blisters & Bliss. 2011. (ENG., Illus.). 272p. 24.99 (978-1-60529-279-3(6)) Rodale Pr., Inc.

Katchen, Alan S. Abel Kiviat, National Champion: Twentieth-Century Track & Field & the Melting Pot. 2009. (Sports & Entertainment Ser.). (Illus.). 320p. 34.95 (978-0-8156-0939-1(6)) Syracuse Univ. Pr.

Keane, Roy. Keane: The Autobiography. 2012. (ENG.). 336p. (gr. 12). pap. 15.00 (978-0-7181-9399-7(7), Penguin Global) Penguin Group (USA) Inc.

Keddie, John W. Running the Race: Eric Liddell — Olympic Champion & Missionary. 2007. (Illus.). 254p. per. (978-0-85234-665-5(4)) Evangelical Pr.

Keston, John. Expressions of Aging. 2011. 192p. pap. 15.95 (978-0-615-44684-4(1)) 42K Books.

King, Christopher. Where Has All the Glory Gone? The Chris King Story. 2007. 192p. per. 12.95 (978-1-4327-0755-2(8)) Outskirts Pr., Inc.

Kirkland, Richard. All American. Date not set. 25.95 (978-0-06-008308-3(5), Amistad) HarperCollins Pubs.

Kohl, Carol. The Match of a Lifetime. 2008. 156p. pap. 13.99 (978-1-60477-831-1(8)) Xulon Pr., Inc.

Kopek, Ray. The Kid & His Mountain: A Motivational & Inspiring Story about a Kid Who Ran up Pike's Peak. 2008. 84p. pap. 16.95 (978-1-60563-909-3(5)) PublishAmerica, Inc.

Kriegel, Mark. Good Son: The Life of Ray Boom Boom Mancini. 2012. (ENG., Illus.). 320p. 27.00 (978-0-7432-8635-0(9), Free Pr.) Free Pr.

Krohn, Marie. Louise Pound: The 19th Century Iconoclast Who Forever Changed America's Views about Women, Academics & Sports. 2008. 312p. pap. 17.95 (978-0-9796896-2-8(7)) American Legacy Historical Pr.

Kubiszyn, Lucy Stallworth. A Star Fell on Alabama the Jack Kubiszyn Story. 2009. pap. (978-1-61623-911-4(5)) Independent Pub.

Kurmaskie, Joe. Momentum Is Your Friend: The Metal Cowboy & His Pint-Sized Posse Take on America. 2011. (ENG., Illus.). 320p. pap. 15.00 (978-1-891369-93-3(8)) Breakaway Bks.

Kuttai, Heather. Maternity Rolls: Pregnancy, Childbirth & Disability. 2010. (ENG.). 144p. pap. 18.95 (978-1-55266-342-4(6)) Fernwood Publishing Co., Ltd. CAN. Dist: Independent Pubs. Group.

Lajoie, Roger & Henderson, Paul. The Goal of My Life: A Memoir. 2012. (ENG.). 304p. 29.99 (978-0-7710-4650-6(2), McClelland & Stewart) McClelland & Stewart CAN. Dist: Random Hse., Inc.

Lake, Paul. I'm Not Really Here. 2012. (ENG.). 256p. pap. 16.95 (978-0-09-955325-0(2)) Random Hse. GBR. Dist: Independent Pubs. Group.

Lapchick, Richard. 100 Campeones: Latino Groundbreakers Who Paved the Way in Sport. 2010. (Leaders in Sprort (Fit) Ser.). (Illus.). 555p. pap. 24.95 (978-1-935412-18-2(3)) Fitness Information Technology, Inc.

Laurinaitis, Joe & Wright, Andrew William. The Road Warriors: Danger, Death, & the Rush of Wrestling. 2011. (ENG., Illus.). 250p. 24.95 (978-1-60542-142-1(1), Gold Medallion) Medallion Pr., Inc.

Lawler, Jerry. It's Good to Be the King... Sometimes. 2007. (ENG.). 384p. pap. 25.95 (978-1-4165-7720-1(3)) Pocket Books.

Leonetti, Mike. Hockey's Original 6: Great Players of the Golden Era, 1 vol. 2011. (ENG., Illus.). 144p. 40.00 (978-1-55365-563-3(X), Greystone Bks.) D&M Pubs. Inc. CAN. Dist: Perseus-PGW.

Lesnar, Brock. Death Clutch: My Story of Determination, Domination, & Survival. (ENG., Illus.). 2012. 224p. pap. 16.99 (978-0-06-202311-7(X), William Morrow Paperbacks) 2011. 256p. 25.99 (978-0-06-202312-4(8), Morrow, William & Co.) HarperCollins Pubs.

Lewis, Chad. Surround Yourself with Greatness. 2009. 400p. 25.99 (978-1-60641-195-7(0), Shadow Mountain) Deseret Bk. Co.

Linda Prefontaine, Bree Donovan. Steve Prefontaine-Rocketman. 2008. 167p. pap. 14.95 (978-1-4357-1629-2(9)) Lulu Enterprises Inc.

Livingston, Bill. Above & Beyond: Tim Mack, the Pole Vault, & the Quest for Olympic Gold. 2008. (Illus.). 192p. 26.95 (978-0-87338-974-7(3)) Kent State Univ. Pr.

Livingston, David & Livingston, James. Blood over Water. 2011. (ENG.). 320p. 18.50 (978-1-4088-0119-2(1)) Bloomsbury Publishing.

Lloyd, Larry. Hard Man: Hard Game. 2008. (ENG., Illus.). 272p. 34.95 (978-1-84454-533-9(4)) Blake, John Publishing, Ltd. GBR. Dist: Independent Pubs. Group.

Long, Giles. Changing to Win: An Incredible Story of Courage & a Template for Success. 2008. (ENG.). 256p. pap. 21.95 (978-0-7499-0992-5(7)) Piatkus Bks. GBR. Dist: Independent Pubs. Group.

Long, Matt & Butler, Charles. The Long Run: A New York City Firefighter's Triumphant Comeback from Crash Victim to Elite Athlete. 2010. (ENG., Illus.). 264p. 25.99 (978-1-60529-246-5(X)) Rodale Pr., Inc.

Longs, Harold. God, are you mad at Me? 2007. per. 14.95 (978-0-9766666-6-0(9)) Arcadian Hse.

Lopez, Jean, et al. Family Power: The True Story of How the First Family of Taekwondo Made Olympic History. 2009. (ENG.). 272p. (gr. 12-18). 24.95 (978-0-451-22851-2(0)) Penguin Group (USA) Inc.

Ludwig, Scott. A Few Degrees from Hell: The 2003 Badwater Ultramarathon. 2010. 324p. pap. 22.95 (978-1-4502-6782-3(3)) iUniverse, Inc.

—A Passion for Running: Portraits of the Everyday Runner. 2009. 300p. pap. 21.95 (978-1-4401-7835-1(6)) iUniverse, Inc.

—Running Through My Mind: Confessions of an Every Day Runner. 2007. 452p. (ENG.). 37.95 (978-0-595-70322-7(4)); per. 27.95 (978-0-595-46523-1(4)) iUniverse, Inc.

Luman, Mikael D. 800 Meters: A Journey of Addiction, Recovery & Redemption. 2007. pap. 16.95 (978-0-9797374-0-4(0)) Generation Free Pr.

Lynch, Jack. Nice Row, Mit. 2008. 80p. per. 10.95 (978-1-59330-531-4(1)) Aventine Pr.

MacDougall, Paul. Distinction Earned: Cape Breton's Boxing Legends, 1946-1970, 1 vol. 2010. 178p. pap. (978-1-897009-48-2(8)) Cape Breton Univ. Pr.

MacGregor, Roy. Wayne Gretzky's Ghost: And Other Tales from a Lifetime in Hockey. 2012. (ENG.). 368p. pap. 17.95 (978-0-307-35742-7(2), Vintage Canada) Random Hse. of Canada, Ltd. CAN. Dist: Random Hse., Inc.

—Wayne Gretzky's Ghost: And Other Tales from a Lifetime in Hockey. 2011. (ENG., Illus.). 400p. 25.99 (978-0-307-35741-0(4), Random Hse CAN) Random Hse. of Canada, Ltd. CAN. Dist: Random Hse., Inc.

Maimon, Alan. Shane Victorino: The Flyin' Hawaiian. 2011. (ENG.). 230p. 24.95 (978-1-60078-542-9(5)) Triumph Bks.

Marchante, Frank. Sergio Oliva the Myth: Building the Ultimate Physique. 2007. (ENG., Illus.). 350p. pap. 29.95 (978-0-9779040-1-3(6)) Gras Publishing.

Martin, Paul. Drinking from My Leg: Lessons from a Blistered Optimist. 2010. 236p. pap. 18.95 (978-1-4502-1755-2(9)) iUniverse, Inc.

Masin, Robert G. Swede. 2009. 244p. 29.95 (978-1-4401-4435-6(4)) iUniverse, Inc.

—Swede: Weequahic's Gentle Giant. 2009. 244p. pap. 19.95 (978-1-4401-4433-2(8)) iUniverse, Inc.

Matthews, Ray. Me & My Shadow. 2012. (ENG.). 118p. pap. 11.99 (978-1-907728-35-8(X)) Pneuma Springs Publishing GBR. Dist: Lightning Source, Inc.

Maxwell, Michael, et al. What It Means to Be a Hawkeye: Kirk Ferentz & Iowa's Greatest Players. 2011. (What It Means to Be Ser.). (ENG., Illus.). 352p. 26.95 (978-1-60078-564-1(6)) Triumph Bks.

Maynard, Kyle. No Excuses: The True Story of a Congenital Amputee Who Became a Champion in Wrestling & in Life. 2006. (ENG., Illus.). 243p. per. 16.95 (978-1-59698-010-5(9)) Regnery Publishing, Inc., An Eagle Publishing Co.

McConnon, Andres & McConnon, Aili. Road to Valor: A True Story of World War II Italy, the Nazis, & the Cyclist Who Inspired a Nation. 2012. (ENG., Illus.). 336p. 25.00 (978-0-307-59064-0(X), Crown) Crown Publishing Group.

McCormack, Chris. I'm Here to Win: A World Champion's Advice for Peak Performance. 2011. (ENG., Illus.). 288p. 27.99 (978-1-4555-0267-7(7)) Center St.

McDiarmid, Mac. Joey Dunlop: His Authorised Biography. 2010. (ENG., Illus.). 208p. 44.95 (978-1-84425-940-3(4), 1844259404) Haynes Publishing PLC GBR. Dist: MBI Distribution Services/Quayside Distribution.

McDonell, Chris. Hockey's Greatest Stars: Legends & Young Lions. 3rd rev. ed. 2011. (ENG., Illus.). 192p. pap. 24.95 (978-1-55407-888-2(1)) Firefly Bks., Ltd.

McDougall, Christopher. Nacidos para Correr: Superatletas, una Tribu Oculta y la Carrera Más Grande Que el Mundo Nunca ha Visto. Salazar, Diego, tr. from ENG. 2011. (Vintage Espanol Ser.). (SPA & ENG.). 368p. pap. 15.95 (978-0-307-74129-5(X), Vintage) Knopf Doubleday Publishing Group.

McGarvey, Frank & Esplin, Ronnie. Totally Frank. 2008. (ENG., Illus.). 240p. 29.95 (978-1-84596-364-4(4)) Mainstream Publishing Co., Ltd. GBR. Dist: Independent Pubs. Group.

McQueen, Stephen. On the Precipice: A Story of Running, Kayaking & Heart Surgery. 2007. 212p. per. 24.95 (978-1-4241-6860-6(0)) PublishAmerica, Inc.

McShane, John. Didier Drogba - Portrait of a Hero. 2008. (ENG., Illus.). 335p. pap. 15.95 (978-1-84454-590-2(3)) Blake, John Publishing, Ltd. GBR. Dist: Independent Pubs. Group.

Mecklenburg, Karl. Heart of a Student Athlete: All-Pro Advice for Competitors & Their Families. 2009. 128p. pap. 14.95 (978-0-9841475-0-2(0)) Bernard Publishing.

Mee, Bob. Liston & Ali: The Ugly Bear & the Boy Who Would Be King. 2011. (ENG., Illus.). 336p. 24.95 (978-1-61608-369-4(7), 608369) Skyhorse Publishing Co., Inc.

Melrose, Barry & Vaughan, Roger. Dropping the Gloves: Inside the Fiercely Competitive World of Professional Hockey. 2012. (ENG., Illus.). 304p. 27.99 (978-0-7710-5694-9(X), McClelland & Stewart) McClelland & Stewart CAN. Dist: Random Hse., Inc.

Mendoza, Louis G. A Journey Around Our America: A Memoir on Cycling, Immigration, & the Latinoization of the U. S. 2012. (ENG.). 222p. pap. 25.00 (978-0-292-74387-8(4)); (Illus.). 55.00 (978-0-292-74208-6(8)) Univ. of Texas Pr.

Michael, Mitchell D. Sunrise 47. 2009. 188p. pap. 11.95 (978-1-4327-2376-7(6)) Outskirts Pr., Inc.

Millar, David. Racing Through the Dark: Crash. Burn. Coming Clean. Coming Back. 2012. (ENG., Illus.). 368p. 26.00 (978-1-4516-8268-7(9), Touchstone) Touchstone.

Miller, Joel. Damien Duff: The Biography. 2008. (ENG., Illus.). 288p. pap. 15.95 (978-1-84454-578-0(4)) Blake, John Publishing, Ltd. GBR. Dist: Independent Pubs. Group.

Minneapolis Star Tribune Staff. Favre a Viking. 2009. 144p. pap. 19.95 (978-0-615-33732-6(5)) Sport-Publishing llc.

Mitchell, Jane. One on One: My Journey with Hall of Famers, Fan Favorites & Rising Stars. 2010. (ENG.). 664p. 27.00 (978-0-9824461-7-1(9)) Sweet Dreams Publishing of Massachusetts.

Mitchell, Michael D. Road to Glory. 2006. (ENG.). 31.99 (978-1-4257-4021-4(9)); pap. 21.99 (978-1-4257-4020-7(0)) Xlibris Corp.

Montville, Leigh. Manute: The Center of Two Worlds. 2011. (ENG.). 240p. pap. 15.99 (978-1-4516-2072-6(1)) Simon & Schuster.

Moody, John. Kiss It Good-Bye: The Mystery, the Mormon, & the Moral of the 1960 Pittsburgh Pirates. 2010. (Illus.). 350p. 24.99 (978-1-60641-149-0(7), Shadow Mountain) Deseret Bk. Co.

Mooney, Maggie. Canada's Top 100: The Greatest Athletes of All Time, 1 vol. 2010. (ENG., Illus.). 144p. 27.95 (978-1-55365-557-2(5), Greystone Bks.) D&M Pubs. Inc. CAN. Dist: Perseus-PGW.

Moore, Joseph Thomas. Larry Doby: The Struggle of the American League's First Black Player. 2012. (Dover Baseball Ser.). (ENG., Illus.). 256p. pap. 12.95 (978-0-486-48337-5(1)) Dover Pubns., Inc.

Moore, Richard. In Search of Robert Millar: Unravelling the Mystery Surrounding Britain's Most Successful Tour de France Cyclist. 2008. (ENG., Illus.). 336p. pap. 17.95 (978-0-00-723502-5(X)) HarperCollins Pubs. Ltd. GBR. Dist: Independent Pubs. Group.

Moore, Richard. Slaying the Badger: Greg Lemond, Bernard Hinault, & the Greatest Tour de France. 2012. (ENG., Illus.). 304p. pap. 18.95 (978-1-934030-87-5(2)) VeloPress.

Mora, Manuel A. Stanley Ketchel: A Life of Triumph & Prophecy. 2010. 232p. pap. 15.99 (978-1-4343-2370-5(6)) AuthorHouse.

Morgan, Mal & Mount, Ron. Lawn Green to Gold: The Story of Paralympian Madge Morgan MBE. 2012. (Illus.). 106p. pap. 12.00 (978-1-84426-603-6(6), Fastprint Publishing) Upfront Publishing Ltd. GBR. Dist: Printondemand-worldwide.com.

Mortimer, Gavin. The Great Swim. 2009. (ENG., Illus.). 336p. pap. 16.00 (978-0-8027-1749-8(7)) Walker & Co.

Murakami, Haruki. What I Talk about When I Talk about Running. 2009. (Vintage International Ser.). (ENG.). 192p. pap. 14.95 (978-0-307-38983-1(9), Vintage) Knopf Doubleday Publishing Group.

Neethling, Ryk & van der Berg, Clinton. Chasing the Dream. 2009. 256p. pap. 20.00 (978-1-77022-030-0(5)) Struik Pubs. ZAF. Dist: International Publishers Marketing.

Newman, Jesse. Local Sports Hero: The Untold Story of Wesley B. Walker. 2009. 96p. pap. 24.95 (978-1-4389-9720-9(5)) AuthorHouse.

Nicholson, Lorna Schultz & Quinn, Pat. The Next Ones: Hockey's Future Stars. 2011. (ENG., Illus.). 268p. (gr. 6). pap. 19.95 (978-1-55168-380-5(6)) Key Porter Bks. CAN. Dist: Perseus-PGW.

Nwamu, Punchin' Pat. They're Just My Friends. 2008. pap. 17.00 (978-0-8059-8709-6(5)) Dorrance Publishing Co., Inc.

O'Brien, Dan & Botkin, Brad. Clearing Hurdles: The Quest to Be the World's Greatest Athlete. 2012. (ENG., Illus.). 256p. 22.95 (978-1-935628-08-8(9)) Blue River Pr.

O'Connor, Ian. The Captain: The Journey of Derek Jeter. 2012. (ENG., Illus.). 448p. pap. 14.95 (978-0-547-74760-6(8), Mariner Bks.) Houghton Mifflin Harcourt Trade & Reference Pubs.

O'Flynn, Niall. Irelands Olympians. 2008. (ENG.). 256p. 43.95 (978-1-905172-70-2(2)) Collins Pr., The IRL. Dist: Dufour Editions, Inc.

Ohno, Apolo Anton. Zero Regrets: Be Greater Than Yesterday. (ENG., Illus.). 304p. 2011. pap. 15.00 (978-1-4516-0907-3(8)) 2010. 26.00 (978-1-4516-0906-6(X)) Atria Bks. (Beyond Words/Atria Bks.).

Olverson, Eric. Eric on His Bike - a Home to Head For. 2011. (Illus.). 258p. pap. (978-0-7552-1343-6(2)) Authors OnLine, Ltd.

Olympic Wrestlers of Japan: Jumbo Tsuruta, Katsuhiko Nagata, Kyoko Hamaguchi, Saori Yoshida, Yuji Takada, Yojiro Uetake, Osamu Watanabe. 2010. 74p. pap. 19.99 (978-1-155-23625-4(4)) General Bks. LLC.

O'Neal, Lucille. Walk Like You Have Somewhere to Go: My Journey from Mental Welfare to Mental Health. 2010. (Illus.). 240p. 22.99 (978-1-59555-307-2(X)) Nelson, Thomas Inc.

Orlando, Alexandra. Breaking Through My Limits: An Olympian Uncovered. 2011. (ENG.). 200p. (YA). pap. 14.95 (978-1-927005-02-6(7)) Burman Books, Inc. CAN. Dist: Innovative Logistics.

Orloff, Kristin. American Wings, Iranian Roots. 2011. 330p. pap. 16.95 (978-1-57472-501-8(7)) Archer Ellison Publishing Co.

O'Sullivan, Ronnie. More Ronnie O'Sullivan: The Autobiography. 2013. (ENG., Illus.). 288p. 34.95 (978-0-7528-9880-3(9)) Orion Publishing Group, Ltd. GBR. Dist: Independent Pubs. Group.

Overman, Steven J. Living Out of Bounds: The Male Athlete's Everyday Life. 2010. (ENG.). 256p. pap. 18.95 (978-0-8032-3287-7(X), Bison Bks.) Univ. of Nebraska Pr.

Paisner, Daniel & McElwain, Jason J-Mac. The Game of My Life: A True Story of Challenge, Triumph, & Growing up Autistic. 2009. (ENG.). 256p. (gr. 12-18). 14.00 (978-0-451-22619-8(4), N A L Trade) Penguin Group (USA) Inc.

Park, Lowell R. Cylena of the Stadium Games. 2006. pap. 11.49 (978-1-4259-4875-7(8)) AuthorHouse.

Parker, Denise. Denise Parker: A Teenage Archer's Quest for Olympic Glory. 2008. (Illus.). 168p. per. 24.95 (978-0-9795131-1-4(1)) Woods N' Water Pr., Inc.

Parkin, Joe. Come & Gone: A True Story of Blue-Collar Bike Racing in America. 2010. (ENG., Illus.). 208p. pap. 21.95 (978-1-934030-54-7(6)) VeloPress.

—A Dog in a Hat: An American Bike Racer's Story of Mud, Drugs, Blood, Betrayal, & Beauty in Belgium. 2008. (ENG., Illus.). 205p. pap. 21.95 (978-1-934030-26-4(0)) VeloPress.

Pauly, Thomas H. Game Faces: Five Early American Champions & the Sports They Changed. 2012. (ENG., Illus.). 264p. pap. 25.00 (978-0-8032-3817-6(7)) Univ. of Nebraska Pr.

Peoples, John L. A Kiss to Remember. 2006. (YA). per. (978-0-9776332-5-8(X)) Salt City Books.

Perry, William. Promise Fulfilled the John Vrionis Story. 2010. 107p. pap. 15.00 (978-0-557-52884-4(4)) Lulu Enterprises Inc.

Peters, Jason. Aboriginal Sport Heroes: Atlantic Canada. 2011. (ENG.). 125p. pap. 14.95 (978-0-9865278-7-6(4)) DreamCatcher Publishing CAN. Dist: Univ. of Toronto Pr.

Petrucci, Dominic. A runner's Trail. 2009. 268p. 29.99 (978-1-4415-8540-0(0)); pap. 19.99 (978-1-4415-8539-4(7)) Xlibris Corp.

Phinney, Davis & Murphy, Austin. The Happiness of Pursuit: A Father's Courage, a Son's Love & Life's Steepest Climb. (ENG.). 2012. 256p. pap. 14.95 (978-0-547-75036-1(6), Mariner Bks.) 2011. (Illus.). 240p. 25.00 (978-0-547-31593-5(7)) Houghton Mifflin Harcourt Trade & Reference Pubs.

Pierson, Melissa Holbrook. The Man Who Would Stop at Nothing: Long-Distance Motorcycling's Endless Road. 2012. (ENG.). 208p. pap. 15.95 (978-0-393-34412-7(6), 34412) Norton, W. W. & Co., Inc.

Pipkin, James W. Sporting Lives: Metaphor & Myth in American Sports Autobiographies. 2008. (Sports & American Culture Ser.). (ENG.). 176p. (C). 29.95 (978-0-8262-1779-0(6)) Univ. of Missouri Pr.

Podnieks, Andrew. Retired Numbers: A Celebration of NHL Excellence. 2011. (ENG., Illus.). 256p. 40.00 (978-1-55168-347-8(4)) Key Porter Bks. CAN. Dist: Perseus-PGW.

Poulton, J. Alexander. Canadians in the Summer Olympics. 2008. (ENG.). 192p. pap. (978-1-897277-33-1(4), OverTime Bks.) Editions de la Montagne Verte, Inc. CAN. Dist: Lone Pine Publishing.

—Sidney Crosby. 3rd ed. 2011. (ENG., Illus.). 224p. pap. 14.95 (978-1-897277-69-0(5)) Editions de la Montagne Verte, Inc. CAN. Dist: Lone Pine Publishing.

Purvis, Andy. In the Company of Greatness. 2010. 402p. pap. 22.99 (978-1-60957-252-5(1)) Xulon Pr., Inc.

Rambali, Paul. Barefoot Runner: The Life of Marathon Champion Abebe Bikila. 2007. (ENG.). 320p. per. 20.00 (978-1-85242-904-1(6)) Serpent's Tail Ltd. GBR. Dist: Consortium Bk. Sales & Distribution.

Ramo, Joshua Cooper. No Visible Horizon: Surviving the World's Most Dangerous Sport. 2006. 273p. reprint ed. 24.00 (978-1-4223-5567-1(5)) DIANE Publishing Co.

Redgrave, Sheila. The Sonshine of Our Lives. 2010. (Illus.). 420p. 30.99 (978-1-4490-6879-0(0)) AuthorHouse.

Reed, Pam. The Extra Mile: One Woman's Personal Journey to Ultrarunning Greatness. 2007. (ENG., Illus.). 280p. pap. 15.99 (978-1-59486-730-9(5)) Rodale Pr., Inc.

Reed, Ted. Carl Furillo, Brooklyn Dodgers All-Star. 2010. (ENG., Illus.). 210p. pap. 29.95 (978-0-7864-4709-1(5)) McFarland & Co., Inc. Pubs.

Reinertsen, Sarah. In a Single Bound: Losing My Leg, Finding Myself, & Training for Life. 2009. (Illus.). 256p. (978-0-7627-5684-1(5)) Globe Pequot Pr., The.

Reinertsen, Sarah & Goldsher, Alan. In a Single Bound: Losing My Leg, Finding Myself, & Training for Life. (ENG., Illus.). 256p. 2010. pap. 16.95 (978-0-7627-6127-2(X), Lyons Pr.) 2009. 24.95 (978-0-7627-5143-3(6)) Globe Pequot Pr., The.

Reinisch, Nancy. Chemosabee. 2009. 234p. pap. 24.95 (978-0-615-22963-8(8)) NRR Publishing.

Rendell, Matt. The Death of Marco Pantani - A Biography. 2007. (ENG., Illus.). 320p. pap. 12.95 (978-0-7538-2203-6(2), Phoenix) Orion Publishing Group, Ltd. GBR. Dist: Sterling Publishing Co., Inc.

Rensin, David. All for a Few Perfect Waves: The Audacious Life & Legend of Rebel Surfer Miki Dora. 2009. (ENG.). 496p. pap. 15.99 (978-0-06-077333-5(2)) HarperCollins Pubs.

Riach, Steve. True Heroes of Sports: Discovering the Heart of a Champion, 0 vols. 2009. 160p. 15.99 (978-1-4041-8699-6(9)) Nelson, Thomas Inc.

Richards, Bob. The Heart of a Champion: Inspiring True Stories of Challenge & Triumph. 2009. 144p. reprint ed. pap. 10.99 (978-0-8007-3272-1(3)) Revell.

Robert, Alain. With Bare Hands: The true story of Alain Robert, the real-life Spiderman. 2010. (ENG.). 308p. pap. 16.95 (978-988-99799-2-8(6)) Blacksmith Bks. HKG. Dist: National Bk. Network.

Robert, Edwards. Henry Cooper - Authorised. 2012. (ENG., Illus.). 288p. 14.95 (978-1-84358-946-4(X)) Blake, John Publishing, Ltd. GBR. Dist: Independent Pubs. Group.

Roberts, Darren. How Triathlon Ruined My Life. 2007. (Illus.). 500p. per. (978-1-84426-469-8(6)) Upfront Publishing Ltd.

Roberts, Jeremy & Mysterio, Rey. Rey Mysterio: Behind the Mask. 2009. (Wwe Ser.). (ENG., Illus.). 368p. 27.00 (978-1-4165-9896-1(0), World Wrestling Entertainment) World Wrestling Entertainment.

Roberts, Les. From Wits' End to John O'Groats: A Journey by les Roberts. 2009. (Illus.). 116p. pap. 10.99 (978-1-4389-6835-3(3)) AuthorHouse.

Robinson, Chris. Maurice Richard: The Most Amazing Hockey Player Ever. 2011. (Amazing Stories Ser.). (ENG., Illus.). 128p. mass mkt. 9.95 (978-1-55277-900-2(9)) Lorimer, James & Co., Ltd., Pubs. CAN. Dist: Casemate Pubs. & Bk. Distributors, LLC.

Rowbottom, Mike. Usain Bolt: Fast As Lightning. 2011. (Blackamber Inspirations Ser.). (ENG.). 190p. pap. 14.95 (978-1-906413-82-7(5)) Arcadia Bks. Ltd. GBR. Dist: Dufour Editions, Inc.

Roynon, Gavin, ed. Home Fires Burning: The Great War Diaries of Georgina Lee. 2009. (Great War Diaries of Georgina Lee Ser.). (ENG., Illus.). 336p. pap. 24.95 (978-0-7524-5064-3(6)) History Pr. Ltd., The GBR. Dist: Independent Pubs. Group.

Rubino, Guido P. Italian Racing Bicycles: The People, the Products, the Passion. 2011. (ENG., Illus.). 192p. 39.95 (978-1-934030-66-0(X)) VeloPress.

Russell, Gwen. Arise Sir David Beckham. 2008. (ENG., Illus.). 288p. pap. 15.95 (978-1-84454-579-7(2)) Blake, John Publishing, Ltd. GBR. Dist: Independent Pubs. Group.

Russell, Simone. Diving Dream to Olympic Team. 2009. 316p. 32.95 (978-1-4401-3579-8(7)); pap. 22.95 (978-1-4401-3577-4(0)) iUniverse, Inc.

Sagert, Kelly Boyer. Icons of Women's Sport. 2012. (Illus.). E-Book (978-0-313-38549-0(1), Greenwood Pr.) Greenwood Publishing Group, Inc.

Sagert, Kelly Boyer & Overman, Steven J. Icons of Women's Sport, 2 vols. 2012. (Greenwood Icons Ser.). (Illus.). 623p. 173.00 (978-0-313-38548-3(3), A2992C) Greenwood Publishing Group, Inc.

Sandler, Michael & Wilson, Norries. Santonio Holmes & the Pittsburgh Steelers. 2009. (Super Bowl Superstars Ser.). (Illus.). 24p. (J). (gr. k-3). lib. bdg. 22.61 (978-1-59716-968-4(4)) Bearport Publishing Co., Inc.

Sansom, Kenny. Kenny Sansom: To Cap It All. 2011. (ENG., Illus.). 286p. pap. 13.95 (978-1-84358-274-8(0)) Blake, John Publishing, Ltd. GBR. Dist: Independent Pubs. Group.

—To Cap It All. 2009. (ENG., Illus.). 304p. pap. 16.95 (978-1-84454-758-6(2)) Blake, John Publishing, Ltd. GBR. Dist: Independent Pubs. Group.

Savage, Jeff. Brock Lesnar. 2012. (Xtreme Athletes Ser.). (Illus.). 112p. (YA). (gr. 7-12). 28.95 (978-1-59935-185-8(4)) Reynolds, Morgan Inc.

Savage, Robbie & Self, Janine. Savage! The Robbie Savage Autobiography. 2011. (ENG., Illus.). 272p. pap. 16.95 (978-1-84596-716-1(X)) Mainstream Publishing Co., Ltd. GBR. Dist: Independent Pubs. Group.

Schiller, Kay & Young, Christopher. The 1972 Munich Olympics & the Making of Modern Germany. 2010. (Weimar & Now: German Cultural Criticism Ser.). (ENG., Illus.). 342p. 65.00 (978-0-520-26213-3(1)); pap. 24.95 (978-0-520-26215-7(8)) Univ. of California Pr.

Schulian, John. Sometimes They Even Shook Your Hand: Portraits of Champions Who Walked among Us. 2011. (ENG.). 336p. pap. 19.95 (978-0-8032-3776-6(6), Bison Bks.) Univ. of Nebraska Pr.

Sears, Edward S. George Seward: America's First Great Runner. 2008. (ENG., Illus.). 242p. pap. 50.00 (978-0-8108-6133-6(X)) Scarecrow Pr., Inc.

Seeley, Colin. Colin Seeley: Racer ... & the Rest. 2007. (ENG., Illus.). 288p. 66.95 (978-0-9544357-1-4(0)) Redline Bks. GBR. Dist: MBI Distribution Services/Quayside Distribution.

Senda, Argentina & Higginbotham, Evelyn. That's Why I Run: The Story of Argentina Senda. 2011. (ENG., Illus.). 100p. pap. 11.95 (978-1-920222-33-8(2)) STE Pubs. ZAF. Dist: Independent Pubs. Group.

Seymour, Joey. San Diego's Finest Athletes: Five Exceptional Lives. 2009. pap. 17.95 (978-0-916251-99-4(3), Sunbelt Pictorial Bks.) Sunbelt Pubns., Inc.

Shalin, Mike. Donnie Baseball: The Definitive Biography of Don Mattingly. 2011. (ENG.). 224p. 24.95 (978-1-60078-536-8(0)) Triumph Bks.

Shapton, Leanne. Swimming Studies. 2012. (ENG., Illus.). 336p. (gr. 12). 30.00 (978-0-399-15817-9(0), Blue Rider Pr.) Penguin Group (USA) Inc.

Shields, Brian & Sullivan, Kevin. WWE Encyclopedia. 2nd ed. 2012. (ENG.). 400p. 45.00 (978-0-7566-9159-2(1)) Brady GAMES.

Skjoldager, Per & Nielsen, Jo Erik. Aron Nimzowitsch: On the Road to Chess Mastery, 1886-1924. 2012. (ENG.). 49.95 (978-0-7864-6539-2(5)) McFarland & Co., Inc. Pubs.

Smith, Robert C. Keeping Track: Success in Track & Field. 2007. (Illus.). 160p. pap. 15.95 (978-0-9729119-6-2(0)) Productivity Pubns.

Smith, Tommie, et al. Silent Gesture: The Autobiography of Tommie Smith. 2008. (Sporting Ser.). (ENG., Illus.). 288p. pap. 23.95 (978-1-59213-640-7(0)) Temple Univ. Pr.

Southerland, Phil & Hanc, John. Not Dead Yet: My Triumph over Type I Diabetes & the Race Across America. 2011. (ENG., Illus.). 336p. 25.99 (978-0-312-61023-4(8), Dunne, Thomas Bks.) St. Martin's Pr.

Stead, Marcus. In Bod We Trust: The Biography of Ireland's Greatest Rugby Hero. 2009. (ENG., Illus.). 288p. pap. 14.95 (978-1-84454-764-7(7)) Blake, John Publishing, Ltd. GBR. Dist: Independent Pubs. Group.

—Kevin Pietersen: Portrait of a Rebel. 2009. (ENG., Illus.). 296p. pap. 14.95 (978-1-84454-805-7(8)) Blake, John Publishing, Ltd. GBR. Dist: Independent Pubs. Group.

Stecher, Peter O. Legends in Archery: Adventurers with Bow & Arrow. 2010. (Illus.). 192p. 29.99 (978-0-7643-3575-4(8)) Schiffer Publishing, Ltd.

Steinberg, Jacques. You Are an Ironman: How Six Weekend Warriors Chased Their Dream of Finishing the World's Toughest Triathlon. (ENG.). (gr. 12). 2012. Illus.). 1p. pap. 16.00 (978-0-14-312207-4(X), Penguin (Non-Classics)) 2011. 304p. 27.95 (978-0-670-02302-8(7), Viking Adult) Penguin Group (USA) Inc.

Stout, Glenn. Young Woman & the Sea: How Trudy Ederle Conquered the English Channel & Inspired the World. 2009. (ENG., Illus.). 352p. 25.00 (978-0-618-85868-2(7)) Houghton Mifflin Harcourt Trade & Reference Pubs.

Stratton, W. K. Boxing Shadows. 2009. (ENG., Illus.). 195p. 24.95 (978-0-292-72129-6(3)) Univ. of Texas Pr.

—Floyd Patterson: The Fighting Life of Boxing's Invisible Champion. 2012. (ENG., Illus.). 288p. 25.00 (978-0-15-101430-9(2)) Houghton Mifflin Harcourt Trade & Reference Pubs.

Strickland, Bill. Tour de Lance: The Extraordinary Story of Cycling's Most Controversial Champion. 2011. (ENG., Illus.). 336p. pap. 16.00 (978-0-307-58995-8(1), Three Rivers Pr.) Crown Publishing Group.

Sutherland, Adam. Athletes. 2012. (Black History Makers Ser.). (ENG.). 24p. (J). (gr. 3-8). pap. 8.25 (978-1-4488-7058-5(5)); lib. bdg. 21.25 (978-1-4488-6640-3(5)) Rosen Publishing Group, Inc., The. (PowerKids Pr.).

Swanson, Terry. Lameness with Terry Swanson: Understanding & Managing the Equine Athlete. Barren, Jennifer, tr. 2009. (ENG., Illus.). 216p. pap. 21.95 (978-0-911647-74-7(0)) Western Horseman.

Talksport Staff & Bailey, Tom. The Talksport 100 Greatest British Sporting Legends. Borrows, Bill, ed. 2011. (ENG., Illus.). 208p. 29.95 (978-0-85720-093-8(3)) Simon & Schuster, Ltd. GBR. Dist: Independent Pubs. Group.

Tanas. From Glory Days. 2008. pap. 19.95 (978-0-615-18052-6(3)) Tanas & Assos., LLC.

Tectum, creator. A Rush of Blood to the Head: The Story of a Man Facing the Elements of Nature. 2006. (ENG, FRE & DUT., Illus.). 144p. (978-90-76886-30-5(X)) Tectum B.V.B.A.

Terry, Barbara. How Athletes Roll. 2010. 240p. 29.99 (978-1-935361-58-9(9)) Comfort Publishing Services, LLC.

Thesz, Lou. Hooker. Kenyon, J. Michael, ed. 2011. (Illus.). 320p. pap. 19.95 (978-0-9844090-4-4(1)) Crowbar Pr.

Thorburn, Ryan John. Lost Cowboys: The Story of Bud Daniel & Wyoming Baseball. Reich, Laurie Mansell, ed. 2010. 202p. pap. 18.00 (978-0-9841683-2-3(X), Burning Daylight) Peam & Assocs. Inc.

Thordarson, Eystein. Tenacity: My Journey Through Life. 2011. 132p. 22.95 (978-1-4401-9871-7(3)); pap. 12.95 (978-1-4401-9869-4(1)) iUniverse, Inc.

Tillman, Marie. The Letter: My Journey Through Love, Loss, & Life. 2012. (ENG.). 272p. 23.99 (978-0-446-57145-6(8)) Grand Central Publishing.

Tischendorf, Juanita. The Madman, the Marathoner: The Life of Marathoner Donald P. Mcnelly. 2010. pap. 23.99 (978-1-61566-594-5(3)) Tate Publishing & Enterprises, LLC.

Titus, Mark. Don't Put Me in, Coach: My Incredible NCAA Journey from the End of the Bench to the End of the Bench. 2012. (ENG., Illus.). 272p. 24.95 (978-0-385-53510-6(4), Doubleday) Knopf Doubleday Publishing Group.

Tomson, Shaun. Surfer's Code: 12 Simple Lessons for Riding Through Life. 2011. (ENG., Illus.). 184p. pap. 14.99 (978-1-4236-2227-7(8)) Gibbs Smith, Publisher.

Torres, Dara & Weil, Elizabeth. Age Is Just a Number: Achieve Your Dreams at Any Stage in Your Life. 2010. (ENG.). 240p. pap. 14.99 (978-0-7679-3191-5(2)) Broadway Bks.

Triche, Brandon. Balance: The Life of a Gay Gymnast. 2008. 132p. 29.99 (978-1-4363-2382-6(7)); pap. 19.99 (978-1-4363-2381-9(9)) Xlibris Corp.

Turner, Morrie. Black Sports Heroes: Past & Present. 2011. 148p. 25.00 (978-1-4269-7653-7(4)); pap. 15.00 (978-1-4269-7652-0(6)) Trafford Publishing.

Ulrich, Marshall. Running on Empty: An Ultramarathoner's Story of Love, Loss, & a Record-Setting Run Across America. 2011. (ENG.). 320p. (gr. 12). 26.00 (978-1-58333-423-2(8), Avery) Penguin Group (USA) Inc.

Vecsey, George. Stan Musial: An American Life. (ENG., Illus.). 416p. 2012. pap. 16.00 (978-0-345-51707-4(5)) 2011. 26.00 (978-0-345-51706-7(7)) ESPN Enterprises.

Virtue, Tessa, et al. Tessa & Scott: Our Journey from Childhood Dream to Gold, 1 vol. 2010. (ENG., Illus.). 208p. 24.95 (978-0-88784-273-3(9)) House of Anansi Pr. CAN. Dist: Perseus-PGW.

Waeschle, Amy. Chasing Waves: A Surfer's Tale of Obsessive Wandering. 2009. (ENG.). 160p. pap. 16.95 (978-1-59485-113-1(1)) Mountaineers Bks., The.

Walker, Chris. Stalker! Chris Walker: The Autobiography. (ENG., Illus.). 2008. 384p. pap. 15.95 (978-0-00-725986-1(7)) 2007. 352p. 34.95 (978-0-00-725985-4(9)) HarperCollins Pubs. Ltd. GBR. Dist: Independent Pubs. Group.

Walter, John C. & Iida, Malina, eds. Better Than the Best: Black Athletes Speak, 1920-2007. 2010. (V Ethel Willis White Bks.). (ENG., Illus.). 288p. pap. 24.95 (978-0-295-99053-8(8)) Univ. of Washington Pr.

Ward, Mark. Hammered. 2011. (ENG., Illus.). 334p. pap. 13.95 (978-1-84358-272-4(4)) Blake, John Publishing, Ltd. GBR. Dist: Independent Pubs. Group.

Waters, Mike. Game of My Life Syracuse. 2007. (Game of My Life Ser.). 256p. pap. 18.95 (978-1-59670-235-6(4)) Sports Publishing, LLC.

Watson, Alan. Athletes & Other Lower Types. 2010. 316p. pap. 24.95 (978-0-557-11724-6(0)) Lulu Enterprises Inc.

Weekley, Boo & Brown, Paul. True Boo: Gator Catchin', Orangutan Boxin', & My Wild Ride to the PGA Tour. (ENG.). 304p. 2012. pap. 15.99 (978-1-250-00206-8(0), St. Martin's Griffin) 2011. (Illus.). 24.99 (978-0-312-61729-5(1)) St. Martin's Pr.

Weidt, Klaus. Haile Gebrselassie - The Greatest Runner of All Time. 2011. (Illus.). 200p. pap. 18.95 (978-1-84126-323-6(0)) Meyer & Meyer Sport, Ltd. GBR. Dist: Cardinal Pubs. Group.

Weir, Johnny. Welcome to My World. 2011. (ENG., Illus.). 272p. pap. 15.00 (978-1-4516-1134-2(X)); 26.00 (978-1-4516-1026-4(9)) Gallery Pr., The IRL. Dist: Simon & Schuster, Inc.

Whatley, Anthony. Ghosts of the Fisher. 2007. (Illus.). 132p. per. 13.50 (978-1-84426-443-8(2)) Upfront Publishing Ltd. GBR. Dist: Printondemand-worldwide.com.

White, Jaclyn Weldon. The Greatest Champion That Never Was: The Life of W. L. "Young" Stribling. 2011. 320p. 30.00 (978-0-88146-252-4(7)) Mercer Univ. Pr.

White, Paul. East Coast NHLers: The stories of the lives & careers of players from the Maritimes & Newfoundland. 2011. (ENG.). 168p. 16.95 (978-0-88780-969-9(3)) Formac Publishing Co., Ltd. CAN. Dist: Casemate Pubs. & Bk. Distributors, LLC.

White, Richard. Wrestlers in History: Real People & Legends. 2010. 256p. pap. 16.00 (978-1-935271-45-1(8)) Published by Westview, Inc.

Wickham, Tracey & Meares, Peter. Treading Water: My Life in & Out of the Pool. 2010. (ENG.). 400p. pap. 26.95 (978-1-74166-951-0(0)) Random Hse. Australia AUS. Dist: Independent Pubs. Group.

Wiggins, Bradley. On Tour. 2010. (ENG., Illus.). 192p. pap. 26.95 (978-1-4091-3136-6(X)) Orion Publishing Group, Ltd. GBR. Dist: Independent Pubs. Group.

Wilcockson, John. Lance: The Making of the World's Greatest Champion. (ENG.). 2010. 432p. pap. 15.95 (978-0-306-81874-5(4)) 2009. (Illus.). 416p. 26.00 (978-0-306-81587-4(7)) Da Capo Pr., Inc.

Williams, Billy & Mitchell, Fred. Billy Williams: My Sweet-Swinging Lifetime with the Cubs. 2008. (ENG., Illus.). 256p. 24.95 (978-1-60078-050-9(4)) Triumph Bks.

Williams, Pat. How to Be Like Women Athletes of Influence: 32 Women at the Top of Their Game & How You Can Get There Too. 2007. (How to Be Like Ser.). (ENG.). 288p. pap. 14.95 (978-0-7573-0677-8(2)) Health Communications, Inc.

Wise, Bill. Silent Star: The Story of Deaf Major Leaguer William Hoy. 2012. (Illus.). 40p. (J). 18.95 (978-1-60060-411-9(0)) Lee & Low Bks., Inc.

Woodring, Kristen. Finding My Lifesaver - A Swimmer's Journey Through Success, Burnout, & Finding Balance. 2009. 122p. pap. 15.00 (978-0-557-07839-4(3)) Lulu Enterprises Inc.

Worrall, Frank. Andy Carroll the Biography. 2012. (ENG., Illus.). 288p. 24.95 (978-1-84358-411-7(5)) Blake, John Publishing, Ltd. GBR. Dist: Independent Pubs. Group.

Wright, John D. The Terror of Terre Haute: Bud Taylor & The 1920s. 2008. 332p. pap. 20.00 (978-1-59858-761-6(7)) Dog Ear Publishing, LLC.

Yasso, Bart. My Life on the Run: The Wit, Wisdom, & Insights of a Road Racing Icon. 2009. (ENG.). pap. 11.95 (978-1-60529-498-8(5)) Rodale Pr., Inc.

Yasso, Bart & Parrish, Kathleen. My Life on the Run: The Wit, Wisdom, & Insights of a Road Racing Icon. 2009. (ENG., Illus.). 288p. pap. 16.95 (978-1-60529-827-6(1)) Rodale Pr., Inc.

Zahab, Ray. Running for My Life: On the Extreme Road with Adventure Runner Ray Zahab. 2008. (ENG., Illus.). 248p. pap. (978-1-897178-44-7(1)) Insomniac Pr.

Zarnowski, Frank. American Decathletes: A 20th Century Who's Who. alt. ed. 2011. (ENG.). 326p. pap. 45.00 (978-0-7864-4930-9(6)) McFarland & Co., Inc. Pubs.

Zbyszko, Larry. Adventures in Larryland! Life in Professional Wrestling. 2008. (ENG., Illus.). 240p. pap. 19.95 (978-1-55022-826-7(9)) ECW Pr. CAN. Dist: Independent Pubs. Group.

Zirin, Dave & Carlos, John Wesley. John Carlos Story: The Sports Moment That Changed the World. 2011. (ENG., Illus.). 220p. 22.95 (978-1-60846-127-1(0)) Haymarket Bks.

Zuccaro, Ron. Heaven, Iron & I: The Ron Martinelli Story. 2010. (ENG., Illus.). 145p. pap. 15.95 (978-0-615-41750-9(7)) Tribute Hse. Publishing.

ATHLETES—DRUG USE

see also Doping in Sports

Aikens, Willie Mays & Jordan, Gregory. Willie Mays Aikens: Safe at Home. 2012. (ENG.). 224p. 25.95 (978-1-60078-696-9(0)) Triumph Bks.

"Body Building Products & Hidden Steroids: Enforcement Barriers": Hearing Before the Subcommittee on Crime & Drugs of the Committee on the Judiciary, United States Senate, One Hundred Eleventh Congress, First Session, September 29, 2009. 2010. iii, 207p. (978-0-16-086426-1(7), 552-070-41487-8) United States Government Printing Office.

Carroll, Will. The Juice: The Real Story of Baseball's Drug Problems. 2006. (ENG.). 272p. per. 14.95 (978-1-56663-720-6(1)) Dee, Ivan R. Pub.

DIMEO. History of Drug Use in Sport 1876-1976: Beyond Good & Evil. 2007. 168p. 54.95 (978-0-415-35772-2(1)) Routledge.

Dimeo, Paul. History of Drug Use in Sport 1876-1976: Beyond Good & Evil. 2007. 168p. 170.00 (978-0-415-35771-5(3)) Routledge.

Dimeo, Paul, ed. Drugs, Alchohol & Sport. 2006. (Sport in the Global Society Ser.). 187p. 150.00 (978-0-415-40016-9(3)) Routledge.

—Drugs Alcohol & Sport. 2009. 200p. pap. 39.95 (978-0-415-56848-7(X)) Routledge.

Drugs in Sports: Compromising the Health of Athletes & Undermining the Integrity of Competition: Hearing Before the Subcommittee on Commerce, Trade, & Consumer Protection of the Committee on Energy & Commerce, House of Representatives, One Hundred Tenth Congress, Second Session, February 27, 2008. 2008. vi, 181p. (978-0-16-085256-5(0), 552-070-40596-4) United States Government Printing Office.

Fett, B. Michael. Beautiful Hardship: My Story. 2009. (978-1-58982-555-0(1)) American Bk. Publishing Group.

Fourcroy, Jean L. Pharmacology Doping & Sports. 2010. (Illus.). xx, 216p. (C). pap. 49.95 (978-0-415-57822-6(1)) Routledge.

Ghigo, Ezio, et al, eds. Hormone Use & Abuse by Athletes. 2010. (Endocrine Updates Ser.). (Illus.). xii, 178p. 139.00 (978-1-4419-7013-8(4), 1441970134) Springer.

Gullo, Jim. Trading Manny: How a Father & Son Learned to Love Baseball Again. 2012. (ENG.). 272p. 23.00 (978-0-306-82017-5(X)) Da Capo Pr., Inc.

Hamidi, Mehrdad, et al, eds. Drug Abuse in Sport: Doping. 2011. (Sports & Athletics Preparation, Performance, & Psychology Ser.). 140.00 (978-1-61324-574-3(2)) Nova Science Pubs., Inc.

Harris, Michael. A Culture of Steroid Use among High School Athletes. 2008. 206p. pap. 20.99 (978-1-4357-4383-0(0)) Lulu Enterprises Inc.

Harvey, Sean D. One Moment Changes Everything: The All-America Tragedy of Don Rogers. 2007. (Illus.). 243p. 24.95 (978-1-59670-231-8(1)) Sports Publishing, LLC.

Haugen, David M., ed. Athletes & Drug Use. 2012. (Introducing Issues with Opposing Viewpoints Ser.). (ENG., Illus.). 144p. (gr. 7-10). lib. bdg. 36.80 (978-0-7377-6272-3(1), Greenhaven Pr., Inc.) Cengage Gale.

Herren, Chris & Reynolds, Bill. Basketball Junkie: A Memoir. 2011. (ENG., Illus.). 288p. 24.99 (978-0-312-65672-0(6)) St. Martin's Pr.

Hoch-Parker, Ben. The Impact of University Substance Abuse Programs on Athletes. 2009. 84p. pap. (978-3-639-14557-1(7)) VDM Verlag Dr. Mueller e.K.

Jones, Marion. On the Right Track: From Olympic Downfall to Finding Forgiveness & the Strength to Overcome & Succeed. 2010. (ENG., Illus.). 224p. 25.00 (978-1-4516-1082-6(3), Howard Bks.) Howard Books.

Kolar, Nicole. Detektion der Laktatkonzentration im maximalen Laktat-Steady-State: unter Einbeziehung herkömmlicher Stufentestverfahren. 2010. 148p. pap. (978-3-8364-6317-1(2)) VDM Verlag Dr. Mueller e.K.

Lee, Jason W. & Lee, Jeffrey C. Sport & Criminal Behavior. 2009. 300p. pap. 32.00 (978-1-59460-502-4(5)) Carolina Academic Pr.

McNamee, M. J. & Moller, Verner. Doping & Anti-Doping Policy in Sport. 2011. (Ethics & Sport Ser.). (ENG., Illus.). 264p. (C). 133.00 (978-0-415-61923-3(8)) Routledge.

Millar, David. Racing Through the Dark: Crash. Burn. Coming Clean. Coming Back. 2012. (ENG., Illus.). 368p. 26.00 (978-1-4516-8268-7(9), Touchstone) Touchstone.

The Mitchell Report: The Illegal Use of Steroids in Major League Baseball, Day 2: Hearing Before the Committee on Oversight & Government Reform, House of Representatives, One Hundred Tenth Congress, Second Session, February 13, 2008. 2008. (Illus.). iii, 162p. (978-0-16-081413-6(8), 552-070-37787-5) United States Government Printing Office.

Moore, Richard. In Search of Robert Millar: Unravelling the Mystery Surrounding Britain's Most Successful Tour de France Cyclist. 2008. (ENG., Illus.). 336p. pap. 17.95 (978-0-00-723502-5(X)) HarperCollins Pubs. Ltd. GBR. Dist: Independent Pubs. Group.

Mottram, David R., ed. Drugs in Sport. 5th rev. ed. 2010. (ENG., Illus.). 432p. (C). 54.95 (978-0-415-55087-1(4)) Routledge.

Piehl, Norah. Performance-Enhancing Drugs. 2010. (Social Issues Firsthand Ser.). (ENG.). 120p. 31.80 (978-0-7377-5011-9(1), Greenhaven Pr., Inc.) Cengage Gale.

Porterfield, Jason. Doping: Athletes & Drugs. 2009. (In the News Ser.). 64p. (gr. 6-6). 58.50 (978-1-61513-466-3(2)) Rosen Publishing Group, Inc., The.

Pound, Richard W. Inside Dope: How Drugs Are the Biggest Threat to Sports, Why You Should Care, & What Can Be Done about Them. 2006. (ENG.). 288p. 32.95 (978-0-470-83733-7(0), Wiley) Wiley, John & Sons, Inc.

Rendell, Matt. The Death of Marco Pantani - A Biography. 2007. (ENG., Illus.). 320p. pap. 12.95 (978-0-7538-2203-6(2), Phoenix) Orion Publishing Group, Ltd. GBR. Dist: Sterling Publishing Co., Inc.

Skirboll, Aaron. The Pittsburgh Cocaine Seven: How a Ragtag Group of Fans Took the Fall for Major League Baseball. 2010. (ENG., Illus.). 288p. 22.95 (978-1-56976-288-2(0)) Chicago Review Pr., Inc.

Soek, Janwillem. The Strict Liability Principle & the Human Rights of Athletes in Doping Cases. 2007. (ASSER International Sports Law Ser.). (ENG.). 478p. 129.00 (978-90-6704-226-0(9)) T.M.C. Asser Pr. NLD. Dist: Springer.

Teitelbaum, Stanley H. Athletes Who Indulge Their Dark Side: Sex, Drugs, & Cover-Ups, 1 vol. 2009. 179p. 44.95 (978-0-313-37756-3(1), C37756, Praeger Pubs.) Greenwood Publishing Group, Inc.

Walsh, David. From Lance to Landis: Inside the American Doping Controversy at the Tour de France. 2007. (ENG., Illus.). 352p. 24.95 (978-0-345-49962-2(X), Ballantine Bks.) Random House Publishing Group.

ATHLETES—JUVENILE LITERATURE

Stout, Glenn. Soldier Athletes. 2011. lib. bdg. 16.00 (978-0-606-23400-9(4), Turtleback) Turtleback Bks.

Thornley, Stew. Kobe Bryant: Champion Basketball Star. 2012. (Sports Star Champions Ser.). 48p. (J). (gr. 5-9). 23.93 (978-0-7660-4029-8(1)) Enslow Pubs., Inc.

ATHLETES—NUTRITION

Adele, Stephen & Jalali, Rehan. Sports Supplement Buyer's Guide: Complete Nutrition for Your Active Lifestyle, 1 vol. 2007. 320p. pap. 19.95 (978-1-59120-166-3(7)) Basic Health Pubns., Inc.

Al-Masri, Lilah & Bartlett, Simon. 100 Questions & Answers about Sports Nutrition. rev. ed. 2010. 256p. pap. 19.95 (978-0-7637-7886-6(9)) Jones & Bartlett Learning, LLC.

Alejo, Bob, et al. Double Play: Training & Nutrition Advice from the World's Experts in Baseball, 1 vol. 2008. (ENG., Illus.). 128p. pap. 14.95 (978-1-59120-180-9(2)) Basic Health Pubns., Inc.

Almada, Anthony L., ed. Sports, Fitness & Physique Foods & Beverages: Active Ingredients & Supplements. 2007. (Illus.). 304p. 99.99 (978-0-8138-0237-4(7), Wiley-Blackwell) Wiley, John & Sons, Inc.

Anderson, Dawn, et al. Nutrition for Health, Fitness & Sport. 10th ed. 2012. (ENG., Illus.). 672p. (C). pap. 133.00 (978-0-07-802132-9(4), 0078021324, McGraw-Hill Science, Engineering & Mathematics) McGraw-Hill Higher Education.

Angelillo, Michael P. The Hardcore Facts: What Every Athlete Needs to Know Today about Sports Nutrition for Peak Performance. 2009. 52p. pap. 9.95 (978-1-4401-5211-5(X)) iUniverse, Inc.

Antonio, Jose, et al, eds. Essentials of Creatine in Sports & Health. 2007. (Illus.). 249p. 109.00 (978-1-58829-690-0(3)) Humana Pr.

Austin, Krista & Seebohar, Bob. Performance Nutrition: Applying the Science of Nutrient Timing. 2011. (ENG., Illus.). 200p. pap. 24.95 (978-0-7360-7945-7(9)) Human Kinetics Pubs.

Averbuch, Gloria & Clark, Nancy. Food Guide for Soccer. 2010. 200p. pap. 18.95 (978-1-84126-288-8(9)) Meyer & Meyer Sport, Ltd. GBR. Dist: Cardinal Pubs. Group.

Beals, Katherine A., ed. Nutrition & the Female Athlete. 2012. (ENG., Illus.). 300p. 99.95 (978-1-4398-4938-5(2), CRC Press) Taylor & Francis Group GBR. Dist: Taylor & Francis Group.

Bean, Anita. Sports Nutrition. 5th ed. 2007. (Complete Guide To Ser.). (ENG., Illus.). 1p. per. (978-0-7136-7558-0(6)) A & C Black.

Benardot, Dan. Advanced Sports Nutrition-2nd Edition. 2nd ed. 2011. (Illus.). 424p. pap. 23.95 (978-1-4504-0161-6(9)) Human Kinetics Pubs.

Benardot, Dan & Thompson, Walter R. The Coaches' Guide to Sports Nutrition. 2007. (Illus.). 241p. per. 21.95 (978-1-58518-002-8(5)) Coaches Choice.

Berning, Jacqueline. Nutrition for Sport & Exercise. 3rd rev. ed. 2010. 72.95 (978-0-7637-3890-7(5)) Jones & Bartlett Learning, LLC.

Bonci, Leslie. Sport Nutrition for Coaches. 2009. (ENG., Illus.). 272p. pap. 26.95 (978-0-7360-6917-5(8)) Human Kinetics Pubs.

Burke, Louise. Practical Sports Nutrition. 2007. (ENG., Illus.). 544p. (C). 84.00 (978-0-7360-4695-4(X)) Human Kinetics Pubs.

Burke, Louise & Cox, Greg. The Complete Guide to Food for Sports Performance: Peak Nutrition for Your Sport. rev. ed. 2010. (ENG.). xxii, 522p. (Orig.). pap. 24.95 (978-1-74114-390-4(X)) Allen & Unwin AUS. Dist: Independent Pubs. Group.

Burke, Louise & Deakin, Vicki. Clinical Sports Nutrition. 4th ed. 2009. (ENG., Illus.). 850p. pap. 125.00 (978-0-07-027720-5(6), 0070277206) McGraw-Hill Australia AUS. Dist: McGraw-Hill Cos., The.

Cardwell, Glenn. Gold Medal Nutrition-5th Edition. 5th ed. 2012. (Illus.). 256p. pap. 24.95 (978-1-4504-1120-2(7)) Human Kinetics Pubs.

Clark, Nancy. Food Guide for Marathoners. 2007. (Illus.). 160p. (J). pap. 16.95 (978-1-84126-206-2(4)) Meyer & Meyer Sport, Ltd. GBR. Dist: Cardinal Pubs. Group.

—Nancy Clark's Food Guide for Marathoners. 4th ed. 2011. (Illus.). 168p. pap. 16.95 (978-1-84126-322-9(2)) Meyer & Meyer Sport, Ltd. GBR. Dist: Cardinal Pubs. Group.

—Sports Nutrition Guidebook. 4th ed. 2008. (ENG., Illus.). 472p. pap. 19.95 (978-0-7360-7415-5(5)) Human Kinetics Pubs.

Cram101 Textbook Reviews. Outlines & Highlights for Practical Applications in Sports Nutrition by Heather Hedrick Fink, Alan E Mikesky, Lisa a Burgoon, Isbn: 9780763754945. 2010. 98p. pap. 27.95 (978-1-61698-410-6(4)) Cram101 Inc.

Cram101 Textbook Reviews Staff. Outlines & Highlights for Practical Applications in Sports Nutrition by Heather Hedrick Fink, Alan E Mikesky, Lisa a Burgoon, Isbn: 9780763754945. 2009. 90p. pap. 27.95 (978-1-4288-8373-4(8)) Cram101 Inc.

Di Pasquale, Mauro G. Amino Acids & Proteins for the Athlete: The Anabolic Edge. 2nd rev. ed. 2007. (Nutrition in Exercise & Sport Ser.). (ENG., Illus.). 456p. 113.95 (978-1-4200-4380-8(3), CRC Press) Taylor & Francis Group GBR. Dist: Taylor & Francis Group.

Dieffenbach, Kristen & McCauley, Steve. Bike Racing for Juniors: A Guide for Riders, Parents, & Coaches. 2008. (ENG.). 392p. pap. 18.95 (978-1-934030-22-6(8)) VeloPress.

Dosil, Joaquin. Eating Disorders in Athletes. 2008. (ENG., Illus.). 230p. 159.95 (978-0-470-01169-0(6)); pap. 64.95 (978-0-470-01170-6(X)) Wiley, John & Sons, Inc. (Wiley-Interscience).

Driskell, Judy A. Nutrition & Exercise Concerns of Middle Age. 2009. (ENG., Illus.). 516p. 124.95 (978-1-4200-6601-2(3), CRC Press) Taylor & Francis Group GBR. Dist: Taylor & Francis Group.

Driskell, Judy A., ed. Sports Nutrition: Fats & Proteins. 2007. (ENG., Illus.). 400p. 113.95 (978-0-8493-9079-1(6), CRC Press) Taylor & Francis Group GBR. Dist: Taylor & Francis Group.

Driskell, Judy A. & Wolinsky, Ira. Nutritional Concerns in Recreation, Exercise, & Sport. 2009. (ENG., Illus.). 368p. 124.95 (978-1-4200-6815-3(6), CRC Press) Taylor & Francis Group GBR. Dist: Taylor & Francis Group.

Driskell, Judy A. & Wolinsky, Ira, eds. Nutritional Assessment of Athletes. 2nd rev. ed. 2010. (ENG., Illus.). 420p. 125.95 (978-1-4398-1821-3(5), CRC Press) Taylor & Francis Group GBR. Dist: Taylor & Francis Group.

Dunford, Marie. Fundamentals of Sport & Exercise Nutrition. 2010. (ENG., Illus.). 208p. (C). pap. 31.00 (978-0-7360-7631-9(X)) Human Kinetics Pubs.

Dunford, Marie & Doyle, J. Andrew. Nutrition for Sport & Exercise. 2nd ed. 2011. (ENG.). 560p. (C). pap. 163.95 (978-0-8400-6829-3(8)) Wadsworth.

Durkin, Todd, et al. The IMPACT! Body Plan: Build New Muscle, Flatten Your Belly, & Get Your Mind Right! 2010. (ENG., Illus.). 304p. 27.99 (978-1-60529-071-3(8)) Rodale Pr., Inc.

Eberle, Suzanne Girard. Endurance Sports Nutrition. 2nd rev. ed. 2007. (ENG., Illus.). 320p. per. 21.95 (978-0-7360-6471-2(0)) Human Kinetics Pubs.

Fink. Sports Nutrition Workbook & Assessments. rev. ed. 2009. 114p. pap. 45.95 (978-0-7637-6194-3(X)) Jones & Bartlett Learning, LLC.

Fink, Heather Hedrick, et al. Practical Applications in Sports Nutrition. (Illus.). 2nd rev. ed. 2008. 564p. pap. 111.95 (978-0-7637-5494-5(3)) 3rd ed. 2011. 570p. pap. 103.95 (978-1-4496-4643-1(3)) Jones & Bartlett Learning, LLC.

Fitzgerald, Matt. Racing Weight: How to Get Lean for Peak Performance. 2009. (ENG., Illus.). 224p. pap. 18.95 (978-1-934030-51-6(1)) VeloPress.

—Racing Weight Quick Start Guide: A 4-WeekWeight-Loss Plan for Endurance Athletes. 2011. (ENG., Illus.). 240p. (gr. 11). pap. 18.95 (978-1-934030-72-1(4)) VeloPress.

Germano, Carl. The Misled Athlete: Effective Nutritional & Training Strategies Without the Need for Steroids, Stimulants & Banned Substances. 2011. 180p. 26.95 (978-1-4502-9053-1(1)); pap. 16.95 (978-1-4502-9051-7(5)) iUniverse, Inc.

Greenwood, Mike, et al, eds. Nutritional Supplements in Sports & Exercise. 2010. (ENG., Illus.). xxix, 522p. pap. 69.95 (978-1-61737-834-8(8), 1617378348) Humana Pr.

Greenwood, Mike, et al. Nutritional Supplements in Sports & Exercise. 2008. (ENG., Illus.). xxix, 522p. 69.95 (978-1-58829-900-0(7), 1588299007) Humana Pr.

Haff, Gregory. Essentials of Sports Nutrition & Supplements Study Guide. 2007. 150p. pap. 24.95 (978-1-58829-650-4(4)) Humana Pr.

Houtkooper, Linda, et al. Winning Sports Nutrition. 2007. spiral bd. 199.00 (978-0-9790787-0-5(9)) Desert Southwest Fitness, Inc.

Jemni, Monèm, ed. The Science of Gymnastics. 2011. (ENG., Illus.). 224p. (C). 155.00 (978-0-415-54990-5(6)); pap. 54.95 (978-0-415-54991-2(4)) Routledge.

Jennings, Debbisowell & Steen, Suzanne Nelson. Play Hard, Eat Right: A Parents' Guide to Sports Nutrition for Children. 2006. (Illus.). 152p. reprint ed. pap. 11.00 (978-1-4223-5566-4(7)) DIANE Publishing Co.

Jeukendrup, Asker. Sports Nutrition. 2010. (Illus.). 200p. pap. 19.95 (978-1-84126-296-3(X)) Meyer & Meyer Sport, Ltd. GBR. Dist: Cardinal Pubs. Group.

Jeukendrup, Asker & Gleeson, Michael. Sport Nutrition. 2nd ed. 2009. (ENG., Illus.). 488p. (C). pap. 86.00 (978-0-7360-7962-4(9)) Human Kinetics Pubs.

Jurek, Scott & Friedman, Steve. Eat & Run: My Unlikely Journey to Ultramarathon Greatness. 2012. (ENG., Illus.). 272p. 26.00 (978-0-547-56965-9(3)) Houghton Mifflin Harcourt Trade & Reference Pubs.

A

Kang, Jie. Nutrition & Metabolism in Sports, Exercise & Health. 2012. (ENG., Illus.). 504p. (C). pap. 69.95 (978-0-415-57879-0(5)); 180.00 (978-0-415-57878-3(7)) Routledge.

Kelinson, Adam. The Athlete's Plate: Real Food for High Performance. 2009. (ENG., Illus.). 240p. pap. 24.95 (978-1-934030-46-2(5)) VeloPress.

Kerksick, Chad M., ed. Nutrient Timing. 2011. (ENG., Illus.). 373p. 79.95 (978-1-4398-3889-1(5), CRC Press) Taylor & Francis Group GBR. Dist: Taylor & Francis Group.

Kimmons, Cherie. Potluck Survival Guide: The Care & Feeding of the Athletic Supporter. 2008. 216p. pap. 24.95 (978-1-58985-073-6(4)) Five Star Pubns., Inc.

Kleiner, Susan & Greenwood-Robinson, Maggie. Power Eating. 3rd rev. ed. 2006. (ENG., Illus.). 328p. per. 16.95 (978-0-7360-6698-3(5)) Human Kinetics Pubs.

Larson-Meyer, D. Enette. Vegetarian Sports Nutrition. 2006. (ENG., Illus.). 272p. per. 18.95 (978-0-7360-6361-6(7)) Human Kinetics Pubs.

Lee, Yishane & Runner's World Magazine Editors. The Athlete's Palate Cookbook: Renowned Chefs, Delicious Dishes, & the Art of Fueling up While Eating Well. 2009. (ENG., Illus.). 224p. pap. 25.99 (978-1-60529-578-7(7)) Rodale Pr., Inc.

Lowery, Lonnie Michael & Antonio, Jose, eds. Dietary Protein & Resistance Exercise. 2012. (ENG., Illus.). 258p. 99.95 (978-1-4398-4456-4(9), CRC Press) Taylor & Francis Group GBR. Dist: Taylor & Francis Group.

Macedonio, Michele A. & Dunford, Marie. The Athlete's Guide to Making Weight. 2009. (ENG., Illus.). 272p. pap. 17.95 (978-0-7360-7586-2(0)) Human Kinetics Pubs.

MacLaren, Don. Nutrition & Sport. 2007. (Advances in Sport & Exercise Science Ser.). (ENG., Illus.). 272p. pap. 42.95 (978-0-443-10341-4(0), Churchill Livingstone) Elsevier - Health Sciences Div.

Manore, Melinda M., et al. Sport Nutrition for Health & Performance. 2nd ed. 2009. (ENG., Illus.). 560p. (C). 86.00 (978-0-7360-5295-5(X)) Human Kinetics Pubs.

Maughan, R. J. Nutrition & Football: The FIFA/FMARC Consensus on Sports Nutrition. 2006. (Illus.). 241p. 188.00 (978-0-415-41229-2(3)) Routledge.

National Strength and Conditioning Association Staff. NSCA's Guide to Sport & Exercise Nutrition. Campbell, Bill & Spano, Marie, eds. 2011. (ENG., Illus.). 320p. pap. 44.00 (978-0-7360-8349-2(9)) Human Kinetics Pubs.

Owen, Sarah. The Top 100 Fitness Foods: 100 Ways to Supercharge Your Life. 2010. (Top 100 Recipes Ser.). (ENG., Illus.). 128p. pap. 9.95 (978-1-84483-853-0(6), 1305357) Duncan Baird Pubs. GBR. Dist: Sterling Publishing Co., Inc.

Paluch, Kevin & Myers, Jennifer. Par for Life, the Front Nine. 2007. per. 19.95 (978-0-9794174-0-5(6)) Golf For Life, LLC.

Percy, Kate. Go Faster Food: Over 100 Energy-Boosting Recipes for Runners, Cyclists, Swimmers & Rowers. 2009. (ENG.). 280p. 24.95 (978-0-09-192932-9(6)) Random Hse. GBR. Dist: Independent Pubs. Group.

Perlus, Haley. The Ultimate Achievement Journal: Daily Inspiration for Peak Fitness Performance. 2009. (ENG.). 200p. 24.95 (978-1-60037-636-8(3)) Morgan James Publishing.

Pesta, Dominik. Non-Invasive Methods of Muscle Fibre Type Determination. 2010. 132p. pap. (978-3-639-23281-3(X)) VDM Verlag Dr. Mueller e.K.

Power, Will. Superfood Awakening. 2010. 116p. pap. 10.99 (978-1-4389-4274-2(5)) AuthorHouse.

Rehel. Nutrition Basics for Performance & Sport Customized Version. 3rd rev. ed. 2011. (ENG.). 350p. spiral bd. 80.00 (978-0-7575-9464-9(6)) Kendall Hunt Publishing Co.

Ryan, Monique. Sports Nutrition for Endurance Athletes. 2nd ed. 2007. (ENG., Illus.). 357p. per. 21.95 (978-1-931382-96-0(4)) VeloPress.

Ryan, Monique. Sports Nutrition for Endurance Athletes: Running Cycling Triathlon Swimming. 3rd ed. 2012. (ENG., Illus.). 432p. pap. 21.95 (978-1-934030-82-0(1)) VeloPress.

Seebohar, Bob. Nutrition Periodization for Athletes: Taking Traditional Sports Nutrition to the Next Level. 2nd ed. 2011. (ENG.). 304p. pap. 14.95 (978-1-933503-65-3(3)) Bull Publishing Co.

Smolin, Lori A. & Grosvenor, Mary B. Nutrition for Sports & Exercise. 2nd rev. ed. 2010. (Healthy Eating: A Guide to Nutrition Ser.). (Illus.). 192p. (C). (gr. 9). 35.00 (978-1-60413-804-7(1), Chelsea Hse.) Facts On File, Inc.

Stout, Jeffrey R., et al, eds. Essentials of Creatine in Sports & Health. 2010. (Illus.). x, 254p. pap. 109.00 (978-1-61737-719-8(8), 1617377198) Humana Pr.

Taylor IV, Lemuel W., ed. Nutritional Guidelines for Athletic Performance. 2012. (ENG., Illus.). 349p. 119.95 (978-1-4398-3936-2(0), CRC Press) Taylor & Francis Group GBR. Dist: Taylor & Francis Group.

Taylor Steven. Nutritional Solutions. 2011. 148p. pap. (978-1-907011-25-2(0)) Esteemworld Pubns.

Thomas, Biju & Lim, Allen. The Feed Zone Cookbook: Fast & Flavorful Food for Athletes. 2011. (ENG., Illus.). 320p. 24.95 (978-1-934030-76-9(7)) VeloPress.

Thomas, Donald Spiderman. New Jump Swing Healthy Aging & Athletic Nutrition Program. 2011. 208p. 29.99 (978-1-4628-8427-8(X)); pap. 19.99 (978-1-4628-8426-1(1)) Xlibris Corp.

Thompson, Ron & Sherman, Roberta. Eating Disorders in Sport. 2010. (ENG., Illus.). 300p. 51.95 (978-0-415-99836-9(0)) Routledge.

Volpe, Stella Lucia, et al. Fitness Nutrition for Special Dietary Needs. 2007. (ENG., Illus.). 200p. per. 37.95 (978-0-7360-4812-5(X)) Human Kinetics Pubs.

Whipple, Thomas J. & Eckhardt, Robert. The Endurance Paradox: Bone Health for the Endurance Athlete. 2011. (ENG.). 220p. 94.00 (978-1-59874-617-4(0)) Left Coast Pr., Inc.

Wienecke, E. Performance Explosion in Sports. 2011. (Illus.). 280p. pap. 24.95 (978-1-84126-330-4(3)) Meyer & Meyer Sport, Ltd. GBR. Dist: Cardinal Pubs. Group.

Willey, Warren. Better Than Steroids! 2007. (Illus.). 180p. per. 35.00 (978-1-4251-0339-2(1)) Trafford Publishing.

Wolinsky Ira Staff. Sports Nutrition Energy Metabolism & Exercise. 2nd rev. ed. 2007. (Nutrition in Exercise & Sport Ser.). (ENG., Illus.). 288p. 133.95 (978-0-8493-7950-5(4), CRC Press) Taylor & Francis Group GBR. Dist: Taylor & Francis Group.

Zahensky, Barbara A. Frequently Asked Questions about Athletes & Eating Disorders. (FAQ: Teen Life Ser.). 64p. 2009. (gr. 5-6). 58.50 (978-1-61512-563-0(9)) 2008. (Illus.). (YA). (gr. 7-12). lib. bdg. 29.25 (978-1-4042-1807-9(6)) Rosen Publishing Group, Inc., The.

ATHLETES—RELIGIOUS LIFE

Altrogge, Stephen. Game Day for the Glory of God: A Guide for Athletes, Fans, & Wannabes. 2008. (Illus.). 128p. pap. 9.99 (978-1-4335-0139-5(2)) Crossway.

Anderson-Facile, Doreen. Dueling Identities: The Christian Biker. 2007. (ENG.). 110p. 52.50 (978-0-7391-1587-9(1)) Lexington Bks.

Davis, Josh, compiled by. The Goal & the Glory: Christian Athletes Share Their Inspiring Stories. 2008. (ENG.). 224p. pap. 14.99 (978-0-8307-4600-2(5)) Gospel Light Pubns.

Evans, Tony & Evans, Jonathan. Get in the Game: An Athlete's Guide for the Spiritual Journey. 2006. (ENG.). 160p. per. 10.99 (978-0-8024-4406-6(7)) Moody Pubs.

Fellowship of Christian Athletes Staff. Excellence: The Heart & Soul in Sports. Britton, Dan, ed. 2009. (ENG.). 160p. pap. 12.99 (978-0-8307-4629-3(3)) Gospel Light Pubns.

Fellowship of Christian Athletes Staff, contrib. by. God's Game Plan. 2009. (Illus.). 1542p. pap. (978-1-4158-6718-1(6)) B&H Publishing Group.

Gray, Steven L. Athletes, are you Complete? 2009. pap. (978-1-61623-770-7(8)) Independent Pub.

Hutch, Richard. Sport As a Spiritual Practice: Mastery, Failure, & Transcendence in the Life of Athletes. 2011. 240p. 109.95 (978-0-7734-1472-3(X)) Mellen, Edwin Pr., The.

Johnson, Jere. One Day Better. 2009. (ENG.). 192p. pap. 12.99 (978-1-935416-14-2(6)); pap. 12.99 (978-1-935416-15-9(4)) Ellie Claire & Summerside Pr.

Krattenmaker, Tom. Onward Christian Athletes: Turning Ballparks into Pulpits & Players into Preachers. 2009. (ENG.). 228p. 22.95 (978-0-7425-6247-9(6)) Rowman & Littlefield Publishers, Inc.

Mahaney, C. J. Don't Waste Your Sports. 2010. 64p. pap. 4.99 (978-1-4335-2247-5(0)) Crossway.

Mangas, Alexandria & Mangas, Janet Hommel. Oxygen for the Swimmer. 2009. 132p. pap. 14.99 (978-1-60791-603-1(7)) Xulon Pr., Inc.

McFee, Marcia & Foster, Karen. Spiritual Adventures in the Snow: Skiing & Snowboarding as Renewal for Your Soul. 2009. 160p. pap. 16.99 (978-1-59473-270-6(1)) SkyLight Paths Publishing.

Ondov, Rebecca E. Horse Tales from Heaven: Reflections along the Trail with God. 2010. 240p. pap. 12.99 (978-0-7369-2758-1(1)) Harvest Hse. Pubs.

Page, Holly. God's Girls in Sports: Guiding Young Girls Through the Benefits & Pitfalls. 2009. (ENG.). 173p. pap. 14.99 (978-1-934068-83-0(7)) Authentic Media.

Penrice, James. Living the Eucharist Through Sports: A Guide for Catholic Athletes, Coaches, & Fans. 2009. (978-0-8189-1292-4(8), St. Pauls) St Pauls/Alba Hse. Pubs.

Rae, Malcom. Advice & Help for Christian Athletes. 2007. 152p. 25.79 (978-1-4251-2735-0(5)) Trafford Publishing.

Ray, David. Diamond Gems: Life Lessons between the Lines. 2008. 240p. pap. 15.99 (978-1-60647-855-4(9)) Xulon Pr., Inc.

Riach, Steve. True Heroes of Sports: Discovering the Heart of a Champion, 0 vols. 2009. 160p. 15.99 (978-1-4041-8699-6(9)) Nelson, Thomas Inc.

Sandrolini, Mike. All the Good in Sports: True Stories That Go Beyond the Headlines. 2007. (ENG., Illus.). 192p. per. 12.99 (978-0-8307-4474-9(6)) Gospel Light Pubns.

Snelling, Carolyn. Ace: One in Golf & One with God. 2010. (ENG.). 112p. 13.99 (978-1-61638-153-0(1), Creation Hse.) Charisma Media.

Tinley, Josh. Kneeling in the End Zone: Spiritual Lessons from the World of Sports. 2009. (978-0-8298-1842-0(1)) Pilgrim Pr., The/United Church Pr.

Wood, Gail. Saved Twice. 2009. 92p. pap. 10.99 (978-1-61579-434-8(4)) Xulon Pr., Inc.

ATHLETES—SCHOLARSHIPS, FELLOWSHIPS, ETC.

Czja, Nikolai. A Hip Pocket Guide to Athletic Recruiting & Scholarships. 2007. 174p. per. 13.95 (978-1-59824-458-8(2)) E-BookTime LLC.

Grimes, Christina. Student Athlete Handbook for the 21st Ce. 2007. 104p. pap. 14.95 (978-1-4303-0901-7(6)) Lulu Enterprises Inc.

Hastings, Penny & Caven, Todd. How to Win a Sports Scholarship. 2007. 182p. ring bd. 24.95 (978-0-9787132-2-5(2)) Redwood Creek Publishing.

Hiles, Gary. A Simple Guide to Getting an Athletic Scholarship. 2011. 180p. pap. 24.99 (978-1-60844-754-1(5)) Dog Ear Publishing, LLC.

Hornback, Joe. Next Level A Preps Guide to College Recr. 2006. pap. 11.95 (978-1-59330-427-0(7)) Aventine Pr.

Moniba, Clarence K. The Official Guidebook to a College Football Scholarship. 2011. 176p. 29.99 (978-1-4568-9813-7(2)); pap. 19.99 (978-1-4568-9812-0(4)) Xlibris Corp.

Patilla, Coach Lisimba Mba - Pmp. Guide to Athletic Recruiting & Career Education. 2010. 112p. 29.99 (978-1-4500-2846-2(2)); pap. 19.99 (978-1-4500-2845-5(4)) Xlibris Corp.

Poulton, Jeff & Poulton, Emily. My Softball Scholarship: Living the Dream of Earning a College Softball Scholarship. 2010. (Illus.). 142p. pap. 19.95 (978-1-4327-3707-8(4)) Outskirts Pr., Inc.

Richter, Laurie A. Put Me in, Coach: A Parent's Guide to Winning the Game of College Recruiting. Kearns, Gail, ed. 2009. 208p. pap. 16.95 (978-0-615-21333-0(2)) Right Fit Pr.

Spainhour, Dan. How to Get Your Child an Athletic Scholarship: the Parent's Ultimate Guide to Recruiting. 2007. 188p. pap. 19.95 (978-0-615-17570-6(8)) Educational Coaching & Business Communications.

Wheeler, Dion. Sports Scholarships Insider's Guide. 2nd ed. 2009. (ENG.). 384p. pap. 16.99 (978-1-4022-1884-2(2)) Sourcebooks, Inc.

ATHLETES—WOUNDS AND INJURIES

see Sports Injuries

ATHLETES—CANADA

Bisson, James. 100 Greatest Canadian Sports Moments. 2009. (ENG.). 160p. 39.95 (978-0-470-15543-1(4), Wiley) Wiley, John & Sons, Inc.

Clark, Doug. The Roaring Game: A Sweeping Saga of Curling. 2008. (ENG., Illus.). 288p. pap. 19.95 (978-1-55470-118-6(X)) Key Porter Bks. CAN. Dist: Perseus-PGW.

Donahue, Topher. Bugaboo Dreams: A Story of Skiers, Helicopters & Mountains, 1 vol. rev. ed. 2009. (ENG., Illus.). 296p. (978-1-897522-11-0(8)) Rocky Mountain Bks.

Howard, Russ & Weeks, Bob. Hurry Hard: The Russ Howard Story. 2007. (ENG., Illus.). 296p. 34.95 (978-0-470-83955-3(4), Wiley) Wiley, John & Sons, Inc.

Kuttai, Heather. Maternity Rolls: Pregnancy, Childbirth & Disability. 2010. (ENG.). 144p. pap. 18.95 (978-1-55266-342-4(6)) Fernwood Publishing Co., Ltd. CAN. Dist: Independent Pubs. Group.

Mellanby, Ralph & Brophy, Mike. Let the Games Begin: My Life with Olympians, Hockey Heroes, & Other Good Sports. 2009. (ENG., Illus.). 304p. 27.95 (978-1-55168-364-5(4)) Key Porter Bks. CAN. Dist: Perseus-PGW.

Mooney, Maggie. Canada's Top 100: The Greatest Athletes of All Time, 1 vol. 2010. (ENG., Illus.). 144p. 27.95 (978-1-55365-557-2(5), Greystone Bks.) D&M Pubs. Inc. CAN. Dist: Perseus-PGW.

Nicholson, Lorna Schultz & Quinn, Pat. The Next Ones: Hockey's Future Stars. 2011. (ENG., Illus.). 268p. (gr. 6). pap. 19.95 (978-1-55168-380-5(6)) Key Porter Bks. CAN. Dist: Perseus-PGW.

Orlando, Alexandra. Breaking Through My Limits: An Olympian Uncovered. 2011. (ENG.). 200p. (YA). pap. 14.95 (978-1-927005-02-6(7)) Burman Books, Inc. CAN. Dist: Innovative Logistics.

Poulton, J. Alexander. Canadians in the Summer Olympics. 2008. (ENG.). 192p. pap. (978-1-897277-33-1(4), OverTime Bks.) Editions de la Montagne Verte, Inc. CAN. Dist: Lone Pine Publishing.

—Sidney Crosby. 3rd ed. 2011. (ENG., Illus.). 224p. pap. 14.95 (978-1-897277-69-0(5)) Editions de la Montagne Verte, Inc. CAN. Dist: Lone Pine Publishing.

Robertson, Sheila Hurtig. Shattered Hopes: Canada's Boycott of the 1980 Olympics Games. 2012. (ENG.). pap. (978-1-927403-08-2(1)) Iguana Bks.

Shapton, Leanne. Swimming Studies. 2012. (ENG., Illus.). 336p. (gr. 12). 30.00 (978-0-399-15817-9(0), Blue Rider Pr.) Penguin Group (USA) Inc.

Sirois, Bob. Discrimination in the NHL: Quebec Hockey Players Sidelined. Snyder, Jacqueline, tr. from FRE. 2010. (ENG., Illus.). 250p. 22.95 (978-1-926824-01-7(6)) Baraka Bks. CAN. Dist: Independent Pubs. Group.

Tischendorf, Juanita. The Madman, the Marathoner: The Life of Marathoner Donald P. Mcnelly. 2010. pap. 23.99 (978-1-61566-594-5(3)) Tate Publishing & Enterprises, LLC.

Virtue, Tessa, et al. Tessa & Scott: Our Journey from Childhood Dream to Gold, 1 vol. 2010. (ENG., Illus.). 208p. 24.95 (978-0-88784-273-3(9)) House of Anansi Pr. CAN. Dist: Perseus-PGW.

Zahab, Ray. Running for My Life: On the Extreme Road with Adventure Runner Ray Zahab. 2008. (ENG., Illus.). 248p. pap. (978-1-897178-44-7(1)) Insomniac Pr.

ATHLETES—GREAT BRITAIN

Aird, Alisdair. Ally Mccoist - Portrait of a Hero. 2008. (ENG., Illus.). 384p. 34.95 (978-1-84454-568-1(7)) Blake, John Publishing, Ltd. GBR. Dist: Independent Pubs. Group.

Botham, Ian. My Sporting Heroes: His 50 Greatest from Britain & Ireland. 2010. (ENG., Illus.). 320p. pap. 14.95 (978-1-84596-598-3(1)); 304p. 37.95 (978-1-84596-487-0(X)) Mainstream Publishing Co., Ltd. GBR. Dist: Independent Pubs. Group.

Carruthers, Kitty. British Olympic Heroes: The Best of British Gold Medallists. 2011. (Illus.). 132p. pap. 12.95 (978-1-906768-15-7(3), Stacey International) Stacey Publishing GBR. Dist: Midpoint Trade Bks., Inc.

Cavendish, Mark. Boy Racer: My Journey to Tour de France Record-Breaker. 2010. (ENG., Illus.). 320p. pap. 21.95 (978-1-934030-64-6(3)) VeloPress.

Cloake, Martin & Powley, Adam. The Boys from White Hart Lane: White Hart Lane in the 80s. 2011. (ENG., Illus.). 256p. pap. 14.95 (978-1-907637-08-7(7)) Vision Sports Publishing GBR. Dist: SCB Distributors.

Days, Paul. Sunderland: A Nostalgic Look at a Century of the Club. 2011. (ENG., Illus.). 208p. 29.95 (978-1-84425-997-7(8), 1844259978) Haynes Publishing PLC GBR. Dist: MBI Distribution Services/Quayside Distribution.

Galvin, Robert & National Football Museum Staff. Football Hall of Fame: The Ultimate Guide to the Greatest Footballing Legends of All Time. 2008. (ENG., Illus.). 352p. 29.95 (978-1-906032-46-3(7)) Anova Bks. GBR. Dist: Independent Pubs. Group.

Gascoigne, Paul. Glorious: My Football World in Pictures. 2012. (ENG., Illus.). 256p. 32.95 (978-0-85720-448-6(3)) Simon & Schuster, Ltd. GBR. Dist: Independent Pubs. Group.

Giggs, Ryan. Ryan Giggs: My Life, My Story. 2011. (ENG., Illus.). 304p. 26.95 (978-0-7553-6142-7(3)) Headline Bk. Publishing GBR. Dist: Independent Pubs. Group.

Grey-Thompson, Tanni. Aim High. 2007. 96p. pap. (978-1-905170-89-0(0)) Accent Pr. Ltd.

Harris, Clive & Whippy, Julian. The Greater Game: Sporting Icons Who Fell in the Great War. 2008. (Illus.). 208p. 45.00 (978-1-84415-762-4(8)) Pen & Sword Bks. Ltd. GBR. Dist: Casemate Pubs. & Bk. Distributors, LLC.

Henderson, Jon. Best of British: Hendo's Sporting Heroes. 2007. (ENG., Illus.). 192p. 19.95 (978-0-224-08248-8(5)) Random Hse. GBR. Dist: Independent Pubs. Group.

Hide, Herbie. Nothing but Trouble? My Story. 2009. (ENG., Illus.). 260p. 28.95 (978-1-84454-706-7(X)) Blake, John Publishing, Ltd. GBR. Dist: Independent Pubs. Group.

Hildred, Stafford & Ewbank, Tim. Roy Keane: Portrait of a Legend. 2009. (ENG., Illus.). 270p. pap. 15.95 (978-1-84454-644-2(6)) Blake, John Publishing, Ltd. GBR. Dist: Independent Pubs. Group.

Howard, Paul. Eat, Sleep, Ride: How I Braved Bears, Badlands, & Big Breakfasts in My Quest to Cycle the Tour Divide, 1 vol. 2011. (ENG., Illus.). 272p. pap. 16.95 (978-1-55365-817-7(5), Greystone Bks.) D&M Pubs. Inc. CAN. Dist: Perseus-PGW.

Hoy, Chris. Chris Hoy: The Autobiography. 2010. (ENG., 352p. Illus.). pap. 14.95 (978-0-00-731132-3(X)); 18.95 (978-0-00-731134-7(6)) HarperCollins Pubs. Ltd. GBR. Dist: Independent Pubs. Group.

Lake, Paul. I'm Not Really Here. 2012. (ENG.). 256p. pap. 16.95 (978-0-09-955325-0(2)) Random Hse. GBR. Dist: Independent Pubs. Group.

Livingston, David & Livingston, James. Blood over Water. 2011. (ENG.). 320p. 18.50 (978-1-4088-0119-2(1)) Bloomsbury Publishing.

Macleay, Ian. Joe Cole. 2009. (ENG., Illus.). 338p. pap. 14.95 (978-1-84454-732-6(9)) Blake, John Publishing, Ltd. GBR. Dist: Independent Pubs. Group.

Marshall, Ian & MUFC. The Official Manchester United Book of Facts & Figures. 2011. (ENG.). 288p. pap. 16.95 (978-1-84737-920-7(6)) Simon & Schuster, Ltd. GBR. Dist: Independent Pubs. Group.

Matthews, Ray. Me & My Shadow. 2012. (ENG.). 118p. pap. 11.99 (978-1-907728-35-8(X)) Pneuma Springs Publishing GBR. Dist: Lightning Source, Inc.

McColl, Graham. Celtic: A Nostalgic Look at a Century of the Club. 2011. (ENG., Illus.). 208p. 29.95 (978-0-85733-034-5(9), 0857330349) Haynes Publishing PLC GBR. Dist: MBI Distribution Services/Quayside Distribution.

McGarvey, Frank & Esplin, Ronnie. Totally Frank. 2008. (ENG., Illus.). 240p. 29.95 (978-1-84596-364-4(4)) Mainstream Publishing Co., Ltd. GBR. Dist: Independent Pubs. Group.

Millar, David. Racing Through the Dark: Crash. Burn. Coming Clean. Coming Back. 2012. (ENG., Illus.). 368p. 26.00 (978-1-4516-8268-7(9), Touchstone) Touchstone.

Mitten, Andy. We're the Famous Man United: Old Trafford in the 80s. 2011. (ENG., Illus.). 376p. pap. 11.95 (978-1-907637-09-4(5)) Vision Sports Publishing GBR. Dist: SCB Distributors.

Moore, Richard. In Search of Robert Millar: Unravelling the Mystery Surrounding Britain's Most Successful Tour de France Cyclist. 2008. (ENG., Illus.). 336p. pap. 17.95 (978-0-00-723502-5(X)) HarperCollins Pubs. Ltd. GBR. Dist: Independent Pubs. Group.

Morgan, Mal & Mount, Ron. Lawn Green to Gold: The Story of Paralympian Madge Morgan MBE. 2012. (Illus.). 106p. pap. 12.00 (978-1-84426-603-6(6), Fastprint Publishing) Upfront Publishing Ltd. GBR. Dist: Printondemand-worldwide.com.

Moss, Simon. Paul Scholes: The Biography. 2009. (ENG., Illus.). 298p. 28.95 (978-1-84454-747-0(7)) Blake, John Publishing, Ltd. GBR. Dist: Independent Pubs. Group.

O'Sullivan, Ronnie. More Ronnie O'Sullivan: The Autobiography. 2013. (ENG., Illus.). 288p. 34.95 (978-0-7528-9880-3(9)) Orion Publishing Group, Ltd. GBR. Dist: Independent Pubs. Group.

Philip, Robert. Scottish Sporting Legends. 2011. (ENG., Illus.). 250p. pap. 17.95 (978-1-84596-770-3(4)) Mainstream Publishing Co., Ltd. GBR. Dist: Independent Pubs. Group.

Riddoch, Andrew & Kemp, John. When the Whistle Blows: The Story of the Footballers' Battalion in the Great War. 2011. (ENG., Illus.). 336p. pap. 14.95 (978-0-85733-103-8(5), 0857331035) Haynes Publishing PLC GBR. Dist: MBI Distribution Services/Quayside Distribution.

Roberts, Darren. How Triathlon Ruined My Life. 2007. (Illus.). 500p. per. (978-1-84426-469-8(6)) Upfront Publishing Ltd.

Russell, Dave & Wagg, Stephen, eds. Sporting Heroes of the North: Sport, Heroism & the North of England. 2010. (ENG., Illus.). 288p. pap. 14.95 (978-1-904794-29-5(7)) Northumbria University Press GBR. Dist: Independent Pubs. Group.

Russell, Gwen. Arise Sir David Beckham. 2008. (ENG., Illus.). 288p. pap. 15.95 (978-1-84454-579-7(2)) Blake, John Publishing, Ltd. GBR. Dist: Independent Pubs. Group.

Sansom, Kenny. Kenny Sansom: To Cap It All. 2011. (ENG., Illus.). 286p. pap. 13.95 (978-1-84358-274-8(0)) Blake, John Publishing, Ltd. GBR. Dist: Independent Pubs. Group.

—To Cap It All. 2009. (ENG., Illus.). 304p. pap. 16.95 (978-1-84454-758-6(2)) Blake, John Publishing, Ltd. GBR. Dist: Independent Pubs. Group.

Scott, Andrea. Working in Sports Medicine. 2011. 260p. pap. ***(978-3-8383-8670-6(1))*** Lambert Academic Publishing.

Scottish Institute of Sport Foundation Staff, et al. Be a Winner: Achieve Your Goals with Scotland's Sporting Heroes. 2008. (ENG., Illus.). 208p. pap. 19.95 *(978-1-84596-402-3(0))* Mainstream Publishing Co., Ltd. GBR. Dist: Independent Pubs. Group.

Seeley, Colin. Colin Seeley: Racer ... & the Rest. 2007. (ENG., Illus.). 288p. 66.95 *(978-0-9544357-1-4(0))* Redline Bks. GBR. Dist: MBI Distribution Services/Quayside Distribution.

Stead, Marcus. Kevin Pietersen: Portrait of a Rebel. 2009. (ENG., Illus.). 296p. pap. 14.95 *(978-1-84454-805-7(8))* Blake, John Publishing, Ltd. GBR. Dist: Independent Pubs. Group.

Swan, Peter. Swanny: Confessions of a Lower-League Legend. 2008. (ENG., Illus.). 282p. 29.95 *(978-1-84454-660-2(8))* Blake, John Publishing, Ltd. GBR. Dist: Independent Pubs. Group.

Talksport Staff & Bailey, Tom. The Talksport 100 Greatest British Sporting Legends. Borrows, Bill, ed. 2011. (ENG., Illus.). 208p. 29.95 *(978-0-85720-093-8(3))* Simon & Schuster, Ltd. GBR. Dist: Independent Pubs. Group.

Torrance, Sam. An Enduring Passion: My Ryder Cup Years. 2010. (ENG., Illus.). 240p. 29.95 *(978-1-84596-629-4(5))* Mainstream Publishing Co., Ltd. GBR. Dist: Independent Pubs. Group.

Walker, Chris. Stalker! Chris Walker: The Autobiography. (ENG., Illus.). 2008. 384p. pap. 15.95 *(978-0-00-725986-1(7))* 2007. 352p. 34.95 *(978-0-00-725985-4(9))* HarperCollins Pubs. Ltd. GBR. Dist: Independent Pubs. Group.

Walker, Mick. Derek Minter: King of Brands. 2008. (ENG., Illus.). 240p. *(978-1-85983-601-9(1)*, 1859836011) DB Publishing.

Ward, Mark. Hammered. 2011. (ENG., Illus.). 334p. pap. 13.95 *(978-1-84358-272-4(4))* Blake, John Publishing, Ltd. GBR. Dist: Independent Pubs. Group.

White, John & MUFC Staff. Irish Devils: The Official Story of Manchester United & the Irish. 2011. (ENG., Illus.). 272p. 26.95 ***(978-0-85720-644-2(3))*** Simon & Schuster, Ltd. GBR. Dist: Independent Pubs. Group.

Wiggins, Bradley. On Tour. 2010. (ENG., Illus.). 192p. pap. 26.95 ***(978-1-4091-3136-6(X))*** Orion Publishing Group, Ltd. GBR. Dist: Independent Pubs. Group.

Worrall, Frank. Andy Carroll the Biography. 2012. (ENG., Illus.). 288p. 24.95 ***(978-1-84358-411-7(5))*** Blake, John Publishing, Ltd. GBR. Dist: Independent Pubs. Group.

ATHLETES—GREECE

Golden, Mark. Sport in the Ancient World from A to Z. 2008. 208p. 39.95 *(978-0-415-48672-9(6))* Routledge.

Gouw, Patrick. Griekse atleten in de Romeinse Keizertijd: 31 V. Chr. - 400 N. Chr. 2009. (UvA Proefschriften Ser.). (DUT.). 442p. pap. *(978-90-5629-576-9(4)*, Vossiupers UvA) Amsterdam Univ. Pr.

Park, Lowell R. Cylena of the Stadium Games. 2006. pap. 11.49 *(978-1-4259-4875-7(8))* AuthorHouse.

ATHLETES—UNITED STATES

Abrams, Roger I. Sports Justice: The Law & the Business of Sports. 2010. (ENG., Illus.). 223p. 35.00 *(978-1-55553-700-5(6)*, Northeastern University Pr.) Univ. Pr. of New England.

Aikens, Willie Mays & Jordan, Gregory. Willie Mays Aikens: Safe at Home. 2012. (ENG.). 224p. 25.95 ***(978-1-60078-696-9(0))*** Triumph Bks.

Allen, Dwight. A Second Look at Sports: Behind-the-Scenes Interviews with Top American Athletes. 2008. 136p. pap. 14.95 *(978-0-9787268-0-5(4))* Power Publishing.

Austin, Charles. Head Games: Life's Greatest Challenge. 2007. 108p. pap. 13.95 *(978-1-933538-98-3(8))* Hillcrest Publishing Group, Inc.

Austin, Earl, Jr. The Phl in the Stl. 2009. 188p. pap. 19.95 *(978-0-9819913-0-6(0))* Prioritybooks Pubns.

Bak, Richard. Mr. Weightlifting: Norbert Schemansky: History's Greatest Olympic & World Champion Heavyweight Lifter. 2007. (Illus.). xviii, 190p. *(978-0-9723637-8-5(5))* Immortal Investments Publishing.

Balf, Todd. Major: A Black Athlete, a White Era, & the Fight to Be the World's Fastest Human Being. 2009. (ENG., Illus.). 320p. pap. 14.00 *(978-0-307-23659-3(5)*, Three Rivers Pr.) Crown Publishing Group.

Ballard, Chris. One Shot at Forever: A Small Town, an Unlikely Coach, & a Magical Baseball Season. 2012. (ENG.). 272p. 24.99 ***(978-1-4013-2438-4(X))*** Hyperion Pr.

Bart Yasso. My Life on the Run: The Wit, Wisdom, & Insights of a Road Racing Icon. 2008. 17.50 *(978-1-60529-914-3(6))* Rodale Pr., Inc.

Bergquist, Lee. Second Wind: The Rise of the Ageless Athlete. 2009. (ENG., Illus.). 216p. pap. 17.95 *(978-0-7360-7491-9(0))* Human Kinetics Pubs.

Bill, Althaus & Rich, Zvosec. For Tigers Fans Only! Wonderful Stories Celebrating the Incredible Fans of the Missouri Tigers. 2009. 240p. 24.95 *(978-0-9841130-1-9(0))* Ascend Bks., LLC.

Birken, Randy A. Her Longest Marathon: A Runner's Race to Survive. 2008. (Illus.). 164p. pap. 15.95 *(978-1-57733-226-8(1))* Blue Dolphin Publishing, Inc.

"Body Building Products & Hidden Steroids: Enforcement Barriers": Hearing Before the Subcommittee on Crime & Drugs of the Committee on the Judiciary, United States Senate, One Hundred Eleventh Congress, First Session, September 29, 2009. 2010. iii, 207p. ***(978-0-16-086426-1(7)***, 552-070-41487-8) United States Government Printing Office.

Bohn, Michael K. Heroes & Ballyhoo: How the Golden Age of the 1920s Transformed American Sports. 2009. (Illus.). 336p. 27.50 *(978-1-59797-412-7(9))* Potomac Bks., Inc.

Bollig, Jeff & Vance, Doug. What It Means to Be a Jayhawk. 2007. (What It Means to Be Ser.). (ENG.). 240p. 27.95 *(978-1-57243-981-8(5))* Triumph Bks.

Boy Scouts of America. The Best of Boys' Life. 2010. (ENG., Illus.). 192p. 21.95 *(978-1-59921-992-9(1)*, Lyons Pr.) Globe Pequot Pr., The.

Boyle, Brian & Katovsky, Bill. Iron Heart: The True Story of How I Came Back from the Dead. 2011. (ENG., Illus.). 256p. pap. 14.95 *(978-1-61608-360-1(3)*, 608360) Skyhorse Publishing Co., Inc.

Brinkley, Alan. The Unfinished Nation: A Concise History of the American People. 5th rev. ed. 2006. (ENG., Illus.). 1080p. (C). per. 89.69 *(978-0-07-351323-2(7)*, 0073513237) McGraw-Hill Cos., The.

Brown, David W. Philly Jocks: The Best Philadelphia Pro Athletes of Our Time. 2007. 334p. per. 19.95 *(978-1-933822-09-9(0))* Camino Bks., Inc.

Buford, Kate. Native American Son: The Life & Sporting Legend of Jim Thorpe. 2010. (ENG., Illus.). 496p. 35.00 *(978-0-375-41324-7(3)*, Knopf) Knopf Doubleday Publishing Group.

—Native American Son: The Life & Sporting Legend of Jim Thorpe. 2012. (ENG., Illus.). 528p. pap. 24.95 ***(978-0-8032-4089-6(9)***, Bison Bks.) Univ. of Nebraska Pr.

Calhoun, Skip. You Can't Lose If You Don't Quit: The Life & Times of Doyle Hall. 2008. 184p. pap. 16.95 *(978-0-595-49085-1(9))* iUniverse, Inc.

Carney, James M., Jr. Ultimate Tough Guy. 2009. (Illus.). 308p. pap. 22.00 *(978-0-578-01055-7(0))* Achill Publishing.

Casey, John. Room for Improvement: Notes on a Dozen Lifelong Sports. (Vintage Ser.). (ENG.). 256p. 2012. pap. 15.00 ***(978-0-307-74452-4(3)***, Vintage) 2011. 25.95 *(978-0-307-70002-5(X)*, Knopf) Knopf Doubleday Publishing Group.

Clemons, Kortney & Briggs, Bill. Amped: A Soldier's Race for Gold in the Shadow of War. 2008. (ENG., Illus.). 288p. 24.95 *(978-0-470-28137-6(5)*, Wiley) Wiley, John & Sons, Inc.

Community Colleges Staff. Student Athletes & Athletics No. 147: New Directions for Community Colleges. Horton, David & Hagedorn, Linda Serra, eds. 2009. (J-B CC Single Issue Community Colleges Ser.: 205). (ENG.). 112p. pap. 29.00 *(978-0-470-58221-3(9)*, Jossey-Bass) Wiley, John & Sons, Inc.

Connolly, Kevin Michael. Double Take: A Memoir. 2010. (ENG., Illus.). 240p. pap. 14.99 *(978-0-06-179152-9(0)*, HarperPerennial) HarperCollins Pubs.

Cook, William A. Jim Thorpe: A Biography. 2011. (ENG., Illus.). 232p. pap. 29.95 *(978-0-7864-6355-8(4))* McFarland & Co., Inc. Pubs.

Coppola, Sam. Silent Quarterback. 2010. 176p. pap. 19.95 *(978-0-9766965-9-9(2))* Pull Your Own Weight Sports Marketing.

Coughlin, Dan. Crazy, with the Papers to Prove It: Stories about the Most Unusual, Eccentric & Outlandish People I've Known in 45 Years as a Sports Journalist. 2010. (Illus.). 288p. pap. 14.95 *(978-1-59851-068-3(1))* Gray and Company, Publishers.

Crisafulli, Dave 'Agam'. Good Enough: An Autobiography of a Major Minor Local Athlete, 1 vol. 2009. 287p. pap. 27.95 *(978-1-60749-235-1(0))* PublishAmerica, Inc.

Cruz, Victor & Schrager, Peter. Out of the Blue. 2012. 304p. (gr. 12). 26.95 ***(978-0-451-41615-5(5))*** Penguin Group (USA) Inc.

—Out of the Blue (Spanish Edition) 2012. (SPA.). 320p. (gr. 12). pap. 17.00 ***(978-0-451-41616-2(3)***, Celebra) Penguin Group (USA) Inc.

Curl, Ronald. Wheels of Faith. 2007. 157p. pap. 15.95 *(978-0-9796829-0-2(8))* Curl, Ronald.

Day, Frederick J. Dream Team: Saints & Gentle Souls from the World of Sports. 2007. 392p. (ENG.). 35.95 *(978-0-595-70071-4(3))*; per. 25.95 *(978-0-595-45406-8(2))* iUniverse, Inc.

De La Hoya, Oscar & Springer, Steve. Un Sueno Americano: Mi Historia. 2009. (SPA.). 304p. pap. 12.99 *(978-0-06-172542-5(0)*, Rayo) HarperCollins Pubs.

DiBiase, Ted. Ted Dibiase: The Million Dollar Man. 2008. (Wwe Ser.). (ENG., Illus.). 256p. pap. 16.00 *(978-1-4165-5890-3(X)*, World Wrestling Entertainment) World Wrestling Entertainment.

Doeden, Matt. Sports Illustrated Kids Greatest Sports Stars. 2010. (Sports Illustrated Kids Ser.). (ENG.). 112p. (gr. 3-4). pap. 12.95 *(978-1-4296-5035-9(4))* Capstone Pr., Inc.

Drake, Geoff & Ochowicz, Jim. Team 7-Eleven: The Complete History of How an Unsing Band of American Cyclists Took on the World - & Won. 2011. (ENG., Illus.). 352p. 27.95 *(978-1-934030-53-0(8))* VeloPress.

Duggan, Hacksaw Jim & Williams, Scott E. Hacksaw: The Jim Duggan Story. 2012. (ENG.). 240p. 22.95 ***(978-1-60078-686-0(3))*** Triumph Bks.

Dunn, Robert. Houser-Pride of America. 2006. (ENG.). 236p. per. 14.95 *(978-0-7414-3637-5(X))* Infinity Publishing.

Dusterberg, Kurt. The Journeymen: 24 Bittersweet Tales of Short Major League Sports Careers. 2007. (Illus.). 237p. *(978-1-933197-36-4(6))* Orange Frazer Pr.

Eaton, Ron. Local Legends: 100 Years of Southwestern Indiana Sports History: the Stories Behind the Headlines. 2008. (Illus.). 312p. lib. bdg. 44.95 *(978-1-934729-10-6(8))* M.T. Publishing Co., Inc.

Farney, Steven Michael. Club 50. 2009. 170p. 24.95 *(978-0-9786644-1-1(8))* Full Crescent Pubns.

Fertman, Carl I. Student-Athlete Success: Meeting the Challenges of College Life. 2008. (ENG.). 243p. pap. 55.95 *(978-0-7637-5044-2(1))* Jones & Bartlett Learning, LLC.

Fielitz, Lynn. Recruiting Student-Athletes at the United States Military Academy. 2009. 140p. pap. *(978-3-639-17602-5(2))* VDM Verlag Dr. Mueller e.K.

Finkle, Matthew & Sullivan, Brittain. I Love My Bike. 2011. (ENG., Illus.). 160p. pap. 16.95 *(978-1-4521-0048-7(9))* Chronicle Bks. LLC.

Freedman, Lew. Lebron James: A Biography. 2008. (Greenwood Biographies Ser.). (Illus.). 155p. 35.00 *(978-0-313-34361-2(6)*, GR4361, Greenwood Pr.) Greenwood Publishing Group, Inc.

Golus, Carrie. Jim Thorpe. 2007. (Sports Heroes & Legends Ser.). (Illus.). 106p. (YA). (gr. 7-12). lib. bdg. 29.27 *(978-0-8225-7163-6(3))* Twenty First Century Bks.

Heits, Rudolph T. Jason Witten. 2009. (Superstars of Pro Football Ser.). 64p. (YA). (gr. 5-18). pap. 9.95 *(978-1-4222-1986-7(0))* Mason Crest Pubs.

Huddleston, Lindsay W. Unlikely Saviors: Realizing How Amateur & Professional Athletes Can Impact Society Through Philanthropy. 2012. ***(978-1-4675-0126-2(3))*** Independent Pub.

Kann, Bob & Hoffman, Caroline. Cindy Bentley: Spirit of a Champion. 2010. pap. *(978-0-87020-457-9(2))* Wisconsin Historical Society.

Kanyon, Chris & Clark, Ryan. Wrestling Reality: The Life & Mind of Chris Kanyon Wrestling's Gay Superstar. 2011. (ENG., Illus.). 336p. pap. 18.95 ***(978-1-77041-028-2(7))*** ECW Pr. CAN. Dist: Independent Pubs. Group.

Karzen, Jeff. Homer: A Smalltown Baseball Odyssey. 2008. pap. 14.95 *(978-0-9752706-5-3(6))* August Pubns.

Katchen, Alan S. Abel Kiviat, National Champion: Twentieth-Century Track & Field & the Melting Pot. 2009. (Sports & Entertainment Ser.). (Illus.). 320p. 34.95 *(978-0-8156-0939-1(6))* Syracuse Univ. Pr.

Kent, Pulliam. For Wildcats Fans Only! Wonderful Stories Celebrating the Incredible Fans of the Kansas State Wildcats. 2009. 240p. 24.95 *(978-0-9841130-0-2(2))* Ascend Bks., LLC.

King, C. Native Americans & Sport in North America: Other People's Games. 2007. pap. 40.00 *(978-0-415-49492-2(3))* Routledge.

King, Christopher. Where Has All the Glory Gone? The Chris King Story. 2007. 192p. per. 12.95 *(978-1-4327-0755-2(8))* Outskirts Pr., Inc.

Kopek, Ray. The Kid & His Mountain: A Motivational & Inspiring Story about a Kid Who Ran up Pike's Peak. 2008. 84p. pap. 16.95 *(978-1-60563-909-3(5))* PublishAmerica, Inc.

Krohn, Marie. Louise Pound: The 19th Century Iconoclast Who Forever Changed America's Views about Women, Academics & Sports. 2008. 312p. pap. 17.95 *(978-0-9796896-2-8(7))* American Legacy Historical Pr.

Kubiszyn, Lucy Stallworth. A Star Fell on Alabama the Jack Kubiszyn Story. 2009. pap. *(978-1-61623-911-4(5))* Independent Pub.

Kurmaskie, Joe. Momentum Is Your Friend: The Metal Cowboy & His Pint-Sized Posse Take on America. 2011. (ENG., Illus.). 320p. pap. 15.00 ***(978-1-891369-93-3(8))*** Breakaway Bks.

—Mud, Sweat, & Gears: A Rowdy Family Bike Adventure Across Canada on Seven Wheels. 2011. (ENG., Illus.). 304p. pap. 15.00 ***(978-1-891369-94-0(6))*** Breakaway Bks.

Laurinaitis, Joe & Wright, Andrew William. The Road Warriors: Danger, Death, & the Rush of Wrestling. 2011. (ENG., Illus.). 250p. 24.95 *(978-1-60542-142-1(1)*, Gold Medallion) Medallion Pr., Inc.

Lawler, Jerry. It's Good to Be the King... Sometimes. 2007. (ENG.). 384p. pap. 25.95 *(978-1-4165-7720-1(3))* Pocket Books.

Lee, Jason W. & Lee, Jeffrey C. Sport & Criminal Behavior. 2009. 300p. pap. 32.00 *(978-1-59460-502-4(5))* Carolina Academic Pr.

Lesnar, Brock. Death Clutch: My Story of Determination, Domination, & Survival. (ENG., Illus.). 2012. 224p. pap. 16.99 *(978-0-06-202311-7(X)*, William Morrow Paperbacks) 2011. 256p. 25.99 *(978-0-06-202312-4(8)*, Morrow, William & Co.) HarperCollins Pubs.

Livingston, Bill. Above & Beyond: Tim Mack, the Pole Vault, & the Quest for Olympic Gold. 2008. (Illus.). 192p. 26.95 *(978-0-87338-974-7(3))* Kent State Univ. Pr.

Longs, Harold. God, are you mad at Me? 2007. per. 14.95 *(978-0-9766666-6-0(9))* Arcadian Hse.

—God, Are You Mad at Me? 2009. 164p. 23.25 *(978-1-60693-776-1(6)*, Strategic Bk. Publishing) AEG Literary Publishing Services, Inc.

Luckman, Richard "Lucky". Champion by Choice: From Loser to Winner: A True Story. 2008. 149p. pap. 24.95 *(978-1-60563-210-0(4))* PublishAmerica, Inc.

Marchante, Frank. Sergio Oliva the Myth: Building the Ultimate Physique. 2007. (ENG., Illus.). 350p. pap. 29.95 *(978-0-9779040-1-3(6))* Gras Publishing.

Masin, Robert G. Swede. 2009. 244p. 29.95 *(978-1-4401-4435-6(4))* iUniverse, Inc.

—Swede: Weequahic's Gentle Giant. 2009. 244p. pap. 19.95 *(978-1-4401-4433-2(8))* iUniverse, Inc.

Maynard, Mark. Mark My Words: Tales of Brandon Webb, O. J. Mayo, & Other Sports Legends of Northeastern Kentucky. 2010. (Illus.). 400p. pap. *(978-1-931672-55-9(5))* Stuart, Jesse Foundation, The.

Minneapolis Star Tribune Staff. Favre a Viking. 2009. 144p. pap. 19.95 *(978-0-615-33732-6(5))* Sport-Publishing llc.

Mora, Manuel A. Stanley Ketchel: A Life of Triumph & Prophecy. 2010. 232p. pap. 15.99 *(978-1-4343-2370-5(6))* AuthorHouse.

Newman, Jesse. Local Sports Hero: The Untold Story of Wesley B. Walker. 2009. 96p. pap. 24.95 *(978-1-4389-9720-9(5))* AuthorHouse.

O'Brien, Dan & Botkin, Brad. Clearing Hurdles: The Quest to Be the World's Greatest Athlete. 2012. (ENG., Illus.). 256p. 22.95 ***(978-1-935628-08-8(9))*** Blue River Pr.

Ogden, David C. & Rosen, Joel Nathan, eds. Fame to Infamy: Race, Sport, & the Fall from Grace. 2010. (ENG., Illus.). 208p. 50.00 *(978-1-60473-751-6(4))* Univ. Pr. of Mississippi.

—Reconstructing Fame: Sport, Race, & Evolving Reputations. (ENG.). 176p. 2011. pap. 30.00 *(978-1-61703-043-7(0))* 2008. (Illus.). 65.00 *(978-1-60473-091-3(9))* Univ. Pr. of Mississippi.

Ohno, Apolo Anton. Zero Regrets: Be Greater Than Yesterday. 2011. (ENG., Illus.). 304p. pap. 15.00 *(978-1-4516-0907-3(8)*, Beyond Words/Atria Bks.) Atria Bks.

O'Neal, Lucille. Walk Like You Have Somewhere to Go: My Journey from Mental Welfare to Mental Health. 2010. (Illus.). 240p. 22.99 *(978-1-59555-307-2(X))* Nelson, Thomas Inc.

Parker, Denise. Denise Parker: A Teenage Archer's Quest for Olympic Glory. 2008. (Illus.). 168p. per. 24.95 *(978-0-9795131-1-4(1))* Woods N' Water Pr., Inc.

Parkin, Joe. Come & Gone: A True Story of Blue-Collar Bike Racing in America. 2010. (ENG., Illus.). 208p. pap. 21.95 *(978-1-934030-54-7(6))* VeloPress.

—A Dog in a Hat: An American Bike Racer's Story of Mud, Drugs, Blood, Betrayal, & Beauty in Belgium. 2008. (ENG., Illus.). 205p. pap. 21.95 *(978-1-934030-26-4(0))* VeloPress.

Pauly, Thomas H. Game Faces: Five Early American Champions & the Sports They Changed. 2012. (ENG., Illus.). 264p. pap. 25.00 ***(978-0-8032-3817-6(7))*** Univ. of Nebraska Pr.

Pellowski, Michael J. 50 Notable New Jersey Athletes. 2008. 200p. pap. 16.95 *(978-0-9705804-6-7(0))* Middle Atlantic Pr.

Pierson, Melissa Holbrook. The Man Who Would Stop at Nothing: Long-Distance Motorcycling's Endless Road. 2012. (ENG.). 208p. pap. 15.95 ***(978-0-393-34412-7(6)***, 34412) Norton, W. W. & Co., Inc.

Pipkin, James W. Sporting Lives: Metaphor & Myth in American Sports Autobiographies. 2008. (Sports & American Culture Ser.). (ENG.). 176p. (C). 29.95 *(978-0-8262-1779-0(6))* Univ. of Missouri Pr.

Pitoniak, Scott. Jewel of the Sports World: The Story of the Hickok Belt Award. 2010. (ENG., Illus.). 152p. pap. 24.95 *(978-1-933360-45-4(3)*, RIT Pr.) Rochester Institute of Technology, Cary Graphic Arts Pr.

Reed, Pam. The Extra Mile: One Woman's Personal Journey to Ultrarunning Greatness. 2007. (ENG., Illus.). 280p. pap. 15.99 *(978-1-59486-730-9(5))* Rodale Pr., Inc.

Regalado, Samuel & Iber, Jorge, eds. Mexican Americans & Sports: A Reader on the Athletics & Barrio Life. 2006. (ENG.). 272p. per. 18.95 *(978-1-58544-552-3(5))* Texas A&M Univ. Pr.

Reinertsen, Sarah & Goldsher, Alan. In a Single Bound: Losing My Leg, Finding Myself, & Training for Life. (ENG., Illus.). 256p. 2010. pap. 16.95 *(978-0-7627-6127-2(X)*, Lyons Pr.) 2009. 24.95 *(978-0-7627-5143-3(6))* Globe Pequot Pr., The.

Rensin, David. All for a Few Perfect Waves: The Audacious Life & Legend of Rebel Surfer Miki Dora. 2009. (ENG.). 496p. pap. 15.99 *(978-0-06-077333-5(2))* HarperCollins Pubs.

Riach, Steve. True Heroes of Sports: Discovering the Heart of a Champion, 0 vols. 2009. 160p. 15.99 *(978-1-4041-8699-6(9))* Nelson, Thomas Inc.

Rich, Bob. The Right Angle: Tales from a Sporting Life. 2011. (ENG.). 430p. 27.00 *(978-1-61614-427-2(0))* Prometheus Bks., Pubs.

Rickman, Rick & Wares, Donna. The Wonder Years: Portraits of Athletes Who Never Slow Down. 2009. (ENG., Illus.). 144p. 35.00 *(978-0-8118-6849-5(4))* Chronicle Bks. LLC.

Roberts, Jeremy & Mysterio, Rey. Rey Mysterio: Behind the Mask. 2009. (Wwe Ser.). (ENG., Illus.). 368p. 27.00 *(978-1-4165-9896-1(0)*, World Wrestling Entertainment) World Wrestling Entertainment.

Robertson, Oscar P. The Big O: My Life, My Times, My Game. 2010. (ENG., Illus.). 376p. pap. 19.95 *(978-0-8032-3463-5(5)*, Bison Bks.) Univ. of Nebraska Pr.

Russell, Simone. Diving Dream to Olympic Team. 2009. 316p. 32.95 *(978-1-4401-3579-8(7))*; pap. 22.95 *(978-1-4401-3577-4(0))* iUniverse, Inc.

Sack, Allen L. & Sack, Allen. Counterfeit Amateurs: An Athlete's Journey Through the Sixties to the Age of Academic Capitalism. 2008. (ENG., Illus.). 216p. 24.95 *(978-0-271-03368-6(1))* Pennsylvania State Univ. Pr.

Sandrolini, Mike. All the Good in Sports: True Stories That Go Beyond the Headlines. 2007. (ENG., Illus.). 192p. per. 12.99 *(978-0-8307-4474-9(6))* Gospel Light Pubns.

Savage, Jeff. Brock Lesnar. 2012. (Xtreme Athletes Ser.). (Illus.). 112p. (YA). (gr. 7-12). 28.95 ***(978-1-59935-185-8(4))*** Reynolds, Morgan Inc.

Schulian, John. Sometimes They Even Shook Your Hand: Portraits of Champions Who Walked among Us. 2011. (ENG.). 336p. pap. 19.95 *(978-0-8032-3776-6(6)*, Bison Bks.) Univ. of Nebraska Pr.

Sears, Edward S. George Seward: America's First Great Runner. 2008. (ENG., Illus.). 242p. pap. 50.00 *(978-0-8108-6133-6(X))* Scarecrow Pr., Inc.

Seymour, Joey. San Diego's Finest Athletes: Five Exceptional Lives. 2009. pap. 17.95 *(978-0-916251-99-4(3)*, Sunbelt Pictorial Bks.) Sunbelt Pubns., Inc.

Tanas. From Glory Days. 2008. pap. 19.95 *(978-0-615-18052-6(3))* Tanas & Assos., LLC.

Tanier, Mike. The Philly Fan's Code: The 50 Toughest, Craziest, Most Legendary Philadelphia Athletes of the Last 50 Years. 2011. (ENG.). 264p. pap. 14.95 *(978-1-4399-0599-9(1))* Temple Univ. Pr.

Teitelbaum, Stanley H. Sports Heroes, Fallen Idols. 2008. (ENG., Illus.). 304p. pap. 18.95 *(978-0-8032-1644-0(0)*, Bison Bks.) Univ. of Nebraska Pr.

Titus, Mark. Don't Put Me in, Coach: My Incredible NCAA Journey from the End of the Bench to the End of the Bench. 2012. (ENG., Illus.). 272p. 24.95 ***(978-0-385-53510-6(4)***, Doubleday) Knopf Doubleday Publishing Group.

Torres, Dara & Weil, Elizabeth. Age Is Just a Number: Achieve Your Dreams at Any Stage in Your Life. 2010. (ENG.). 240p. pap. 14.99 *(978-0-7679-3191-5(2))* Broadway Bks.

Trejo, Aaron. Rey Mysterio. 2011. (Pro Wrestling Champions Ser.). (ENG., Illus.). 24p. (J). (gr. 3-6). lib. bdg. 21.95 *(978-1-60014-639-8(2)*, Torque Bks.) Bellwether Media.

Turrini, Joseph M. The End of Amateurism in American Track & Field. 2nd ed. 2010. (Sport & Society Ser.). (ENG., Illus.). 280p. 80.00 *(978-0-252-03515-9(1))*; pap. 28.00 *(978-0-252-07707-4(5))* Univ. of Illinois Pr.

United States, Congress House Committee on the Judiciary Subcommittee on Commercial and Administrative Law Staff, contrib. by. Arbitration Process of the National Football League Players Association: Hearing Before the Subcommittee on Commercial & Administrative Law of the Committee on the Judiciary, House of Representatives, One Hundred Ninth Congress, Second Session, December 7, 2006. 2007. iii, 159p. *(978-0-16-077950-3(2)*, 552-070-35383-6) United States Government Printing Office.

Weekley, Boo & Brown, Paul. True Boo: Gator Catchin', Orangutan Boxin', & My Wild Ride to the PGA Tour. (ENG.). 304p. 2012. pap. 15.99 ***(978-1-250-00206-8(0)***, St. Martin's Griffin) 2011. (Illus.). 24.99 *(978-0-312-61729-5(1))* St. Martin's Pr.

Weinreb, Michael. Bigger Than the Game: Bo, Boz, the Punky QB, & How the '80s Created the Modern Athlete. 2011. (ENG.). 352p. (gr. 12). 16.00 *(978-1-59240-637-1(8)*, Gotham) Penguin Group (USA) Inc.

—Bigger Than the Game: Bo, Boz, the Punky QB, & the Making of the Modern Athlete. 2010. (ENG., Illus.). 352p. (gr. 12). 26.00 *(978-1-59240-559-6(2)*, Gotham) Penguin Group (USA) Inc.

Zbyszko, Larry. Adventures in Larryland! Life in Professional Wrestling. 2008. (ENG., Illus.). 240p. pap. 19.95 *(978-1-55022-826-7(9))* ECW Pr. CAN. Dist: Independent Pubs. Group.

Zuccaro, Ron. Heaven, Iron & I: The Ron Martinelli Story. 2010. (ENG., Illus.). 145p. pap. 15.95 ***(978-0-615-41750-9(7))*** Tribute Hse. Publishing.

ATHLETES, AFRICAN AMERICAN

see African American Athletes

ATHLETES IN ART

Duran, Tony, photos by. Dieux du Stade: Gods of the Stadium. 2010. (Illus.). 128p. 60.00 *(978-3-8327-9391-3(7))* teNeues Publishing Co.

McBride, Sue. Knitting for Gold. 2012. (ENG., Illus.). 64p. pap. 12.95 ***(978-1-84448-791-2(1))*** Search Pr., Ltd. GBR. Dist: Independent Pubs. Group.

Scullion, Jim. Drawing & Painting Sports Figures. 2012. (ENG., Illus.). 96p. pap. 29.95 ***(978-1-84448-773-8(3))*** Search Pr., Ltd. GBR. Dist: Independent Pubs. Group.

Skrypzak, Joann M. Sporting Modernity. 2008. 336p. pap. *(978-3-8364-6533-5(7))* VDM Verlag Dr. Mueller e.K.

ATHLETES IN LITERATURE

Neumann-Hartmann, Arlette. Epinikien und ihr Auffuehrungsrahmen. 2009. (Nikephorus - Beitraege zu Sport und Kultur Im Altertum Ser.: 17). (GER.). 360p. pap. 145.00 *(978-3-615-00369-7(1))* Olms, Georg Verlag AG DEU. Dist: Lubrecht & Cramer, Ltd.

ATHLETES WITH DISABILITIES

Abbott, Jim & Brown, Tim. Imperfect: An Improbable Life. 2012. (ENG., Illus.). 304p. 26.00 ***(978-0-345-52325-9(3)***, Ballantine Bks.) Random House Publishing Group.

Alexander, Eric. The Summit. 2010. pap. 14.99 *(978-0-89221-701-4(4)*, New Leaf Pr.) New Leaf Pr., Inc.

Bailey, Steve. Athlete First: A History of the Paralympic Movement. 2008. (ENG., Illus.). 302p. 115.00 *(978-0-470-05824-4(2)*, Wiley-Interscience) Wiley, John & Sons, Inc.

Beckerman, Debbie. Power & Movement: Portraits of Britain's Paralympic Athletes. 2012. (ENG., Illus.). 256p. 45.00 ***(978-1-119-97310-2(4)***, Wiley) Wiley, John & Sons, Inc.

Berger, Ronald J. Hoop Dreams on Wheels: Disability & the Competitive Wheelchair Athlete. 2008. (Contemporary Sociological Perspectives Ser.). (Illus.). XIV, 170p. 34.95 *(978-0-415-96509-5(8))* Routledge.

—Hoop Dreams on Wheels: Disability & the Dedicated Wheelchair Athlete. 2008. (Contemporary Sociological Perspectives Ser.). (Illus.). XIV, 170p. 135.00 *(978-0-415-96510-1(1))* Routledge.

Brittain, Ian. From Stoke Mandeville to Stratford: A History of the Summer Paralympic Games. 2012. ***(978-1-86335-986-3(9))***; pap. ***(978-1-86335-987-0(7))*** Common Ground Publishing Pty, Ltd.

Callow, Nick. The 100 Greatest Olympians & Paralympians. 2012. (ENG., Illus.). 224p. 34.95 ***(978-1-84732-791-7(X))*** Carlton Bks., Ltd. GBR. Dist: Sterling Publishing Co., Inc.

Centre of Excellence Defence Against Terrorism Staff & North Atlantic Treaty Organization, Public Diplomacy Division Staff, contrib. by. Amputee Sports for Victims of Terrorism. 2007. (Illus.). xii, 129p. *(978-1-58603-808-3(7))* IOS Pr., Inc.

Clemons, Kortney & Briggs, Bill. Amped: A Soldier's Race for Gold in the Shadow of War. 2008. (ENG., Illus.). 288p. 24.95 *(978-0-470-28137-6(5)*, Wiley) Wiley, John & Sons, Inc.

Grey-Thompson, Tanni. Aim High. 2007. 96p. pap. *(978-1-905170-89-0(0))* Accent Pr. Ltd.

Howe, P. David & Howe, David. The Cultural Politics of the Paralympic Movement: Through an Anthropological Lens. 2008. (Routledge Critical Studies in Sport Ser.). (Illus.). XII, 196p. 51.95 *(978-0-415-28887-3(8))*; 160.00 *(978-0-415-28886-6(X))* Routledge.

Jenifer, Trevon. Trevon Jenifer: From the Ground Up. 2006. (Illus.). 205p. 22.95 *(978-1-59670-143-4(9))* Sports Publishing, LLC.

Johnson, Jim. "Dummy" Hanson. 2008. pap. 22.95 *(978-1-59298-256-1(5))* Beaver's Pond Pr., Inc.

Johnson, Robin. Paralympic Sports Events. 2009. (Winter Olympic Sports Ser.). (ENG., Illus.). 32p. (J). (gr. 4-3). pap. *(978-0-7787-4044-5(7))* Crabtree Publishing Co.

Kuttai, Heather. Maternity Rolls: Pregnancy, Childbirth & Disability. 2010. (ENG.). 144p. pap. 18.95 *(978-1-55266-342-4(6))* Fernwood Publishing Co., Ltd. CAN. Dist: Independent Pubs. Group.

Martin, Paul. Drinking from My Leg: Lessons from a Blistered Optimist. 2010. 236p. pap. 18.95 *(978-1-4502-1755-2(9))* iUniverse, Inc.

Mastandrea, Linda & Czubernat, Donna. Sports & the Physically Challenged: An Encyclopedia of People, Events, & Organizations, 1 vol. 2006. (Illus.). 208p. 75.00 *(978-0-313-32453-6(0*, GR2453, Greenwood Pr.) Greenwood Publishing Group, Inc.

Morgan, Mal & Mount, Ron. Lawn Green to Gold: The Story of Paralympian Madge Morgan MBE. 2012. Illus.). 106p. pap. 12.00 ***(978-1-84426-603-6(6)***, Fastprint Publishing) Upfront Publishing Ltd. GBR. Dist: Printondemand-worldwide.com.

Reinertsen, Sarah & Goldsher, Alan. In a Single Bound: Losing My Leg, Finding Myself, & Training for Life. 2010. (ENG., Illus.). 256p. pap. 16.95 *(978-0-7627-6127-2(X)*, Lyons Pr.) Globe Pequot Pr., The.

Rigsby, Scott. Unthinkable: The True Story about the First Double Amputee to Complete the World-Famous Hawaiian Ironman Triathlon. 2009. (ENG.). 288p. pap. 14.99 *(978-1-4143-3314-4(5))* Tyndale Hse. Pubs.

Vanlandewijck, Yves & Thompson, Walter, eds. The Paralympic Athlete: Handbook of Sports Medicine & Science. 2011. (ENG., Illus.). 312p. pap. 59.95 *(978-1-4443-3404-3(2*, Wiley-Blackwell) Wiley, John & Sons, Inc.

Zupan, Mark & Swanson, Tim. Gimp: The Story Behind the Star of Murderball. 2007. (ENG., Illus.). 288p. per. 13.95 *(978-0-06-112769-4(8))* HarperCollins Pubs.

ATHLETIC ABILITY

Bam, B. P. Winning Habits: Techniques for Excellence in Sports. 2009. (ENG.). 260p. (C). 14.99 *(978-81-317-1028-9(9))* FT Press.

Bouchard, Claude & Hoffman, Eric P., eds. Genetic & Molecular Aspects of Sports Performance. 2011. (ENG., Illus.). 424p. 167.95 *(978-1-4443-3445-6(X)*, Wiley-Blackwell) Wiley, John & Sons, Inc.

Byrd, Isaac. HOW to: Think Like a Pro, Act Like a Pro & Play Like a Pro: The 8 Principles that Bridge the Gap between Professional & Amateur Athletes. 2011. 134p. pap. 15.95 ***(978-1-4327-5938-4(8))*** Outskirts Pr., Inc.

Edgette, Janet Sasson & Rupp, Beth Margolis. The Last Boys Picked: Helping Boys Who Don't Play Sports Survive Bullies & Boyhood. 2012. (ENG., Illus.). 304p. (gr. 12). 15.00 ***(978-0-425-24543-9(8)***, Berkley Trade) Penguin Group (USA) Inc.

Honeybourne, John. Acquiring Skill in Sport. 2006. (Student Sport Studies). (Illus.). 160p. 180.00 *(978-0-415-34935-2(4))* Routledge.

—Acquiring Skill in Sport: An Introduction. 2006. (Student Sport Studies). (Illus.). 142p. per. 54.95 *(978-0-415-34936-9(2))* Routledge.

It's All about Power, Bulk & Speed: A Comprehensive Guide to the World of Power, Bulk & Speed for Athleticism. 2008. 4p. (C). lib. bdg. 24.95 *(978-0-9798568-2-2(5))* ET Training Systems.

Lewis, Gary. The Making of Champions: Roots of the Sporting Mind. 2008. (MacSci Ser.). (ENG., Illus.). 277p. 42.00 *(978-0-230-21016-5(3))* Palgrave Macmillan.

Magdalinski, Tara. Performance Technologies: Reading Athletic Enhancement. 2008. (ENG., Illus.). 200p. (C). 164.00 *(978-0-415-37877-2(X))* Routledge.

—Sport, Technology & the Body: The Nature of Performance. 2008. (ENG., Illus.). 200p. (C). 55.95 *(978-0-415-37876-5(1))* Routledge.

Murray, Thomas H., et al, eds. Performance-Enhancing Technologies in Sports: Ethical, Conceptual, & Scientific Issues. 2009. (ENG., Illus.). 304p. (gr. 17). 53.00 *(978-0-8018-9361-2(5))* Johns Hopkins Univ. Pr.

Scottish Institute of Sport Foundation Staff, et al. Be a Winner: Achieve Your Goals with Scotland's Sporting Heroes. 2008. (ENG., Illus.). 208p. pap. 19.95 *(978-1-84596-402-3(0))* Mainstream Publishing Co., Ltd. GBR. Dist: Independent Pubs. Group.

ATHLETIC FIELDS

see also Baseball Fields; Playgrounds

The Field Guide Templates: CD-ROM. 2008. (Illus.). cd-rom 14.95 *(978-0-9800571-1-9(6))* Walnut Cracker Publishing, LLC.

Huws, Richard E. Football & Rugby Playing Fields of Wales. 2009. (ENG., Illus.). 336p. pap. 16.95 ***(978-1-84771-145-8(6))*** Y Lolfa GBR. Dist: Dufour Editions, Inc.

Nelson, Chris & Taylor, Demi. Around the Grounds: Full-Colour Lifestyle Guide to the 92 Clubs in the English Football League. 2010. (Footprint - Lifestyle Guides). (ENG., Illus.). 304p. pap. 24.95 *(978-1-906098-77-3(8))* Footprint Handbooks GBR. Dist: Globe Pequot Pr., The.

Puhalla, Jim, et al. Sports Fields: Design, Construction, & Maintenance. 2nd ed. 2010. (ENG., Illus.). 528p. 99.00 *(978-0-470-43893-0(2)*, Wiley) Wiley, John & Sons, Inc.

Thuma, Cynthia A. Sport Lauderdale: Big Names & Big Games. 2007. (Illus.). 127p. pap., per. 19.99 *(978-1-59629-145-4(1))* History Pr., The.

ATHLETIC GOODS

see Athletics—Equipment and Supplies

ATHLETIC INJURIES

see Sports Injuries

ATHLETIC MEDICINE

see Sports Medicine

ATHLETIC SCHOLARSHIPS

see Athletes—Scholarships, Fellowships, Etc.

ATHLETIC TRAINING

see Physical Education and Training

ATHLETICS

see also Boxing; College Sports; Fencing; Gymnastics; Jiu-Jitsu; Jumping; Olympics; Physical Education and Training; Professionalism in Sports; Rowing; Skating; Sports; Swimming; Track and Field; Walking; Weight Lifting also individual educational institutions, with or without subdivision Athletics

Arvanitis, Jim. The First Mixed Martial Art: Pankration from Myths to Modern Times. 2009. (ENG.). 230p. pap. 24.95 *(978-0-89750-182-8(9))* Black Belt Communications, Inc.

Athletic Sports for Boys: A Repository of Graceful Recreations for Youth. 2006. 192p. per. 18.99 *(978-1-4255-1513-3(4))* MPublishing.

Bakere, Samuel R., ed. Hot Topics in Sports & Athletics. 2008. (Illus.). xi, 170p. 89.00 *(978-1-60456-077-0(0)*, Nova Biomedical Bks.) Nova Science Pubs., Inc.

Bartlett, Roger, et al, eds. Encyclopedia of International Sports Studies. 2009. (ENG., Illus.). XLII, 1526p. pap. 79.95 *(978-0-415-56147-1(7))* Routledge.

Bostrom, Helene, ed. Pernilla Zetterman: Behave. 2010. (ENG., Illus.). 112p. 55.00 *(978-3-7757-2467-8(2))* Hatje Cantz Verlag GmbH & Co KG DEU. Dist: D.A.P./Distributed Art Pubs.

Caine, Dennis J., et al, eds. Epidemiology of Injury in Olympic Sports. 2009. (Encyclopaedia of Sports Medicine Ser.: 14). (ENG., Illus.). 536p. 220.95 *(978-1-4051-7364-3(5)*, Wiley-Blackwell) Wiley, John & Sons, Inc.

Edwardes, Dan & Parkour Generations. The Parkour & Freerunning Handbook. 2009. (ENG.). 144p. pap. 16.99 *(978-0-06-178367-8(6))* HarperCollins Pubs.

Gambetta, Vern. Athletic Development: The Art & Science of Functional Sports Conditioning. 2006. (ENG., Illus.). 312p. pap. 24.95 *(978-0-7360-5100-2(7))* Human Kinetics Pubs.

Gouw, Patrick. Griekse atleten in de Romeinse Keizertijd: 31 V. Chr. - 400 N. Chr. 2009. (UvA Proefschriften Ser.). (DUT.). 442p. pap. *(978-90-5629-576-9(4)*, Vossiupers UvA) Amsterdam Univ. Pr.

Hanson, Hans J. Be A Recruited Athlete-the Secret to College Recruiting: What Every Mom & Dad Should Know. 2010. 164p. 25.95 *(978-1-4502-4473-2(4))*; pap. 15.95 *(978-1-4502-4472-5(6))* iUniverse, Inc.

Holliday, H. E. Boys Transitioning fro Athletic Aggression to Academinc Affirmation. 2010. pap. 24.95 *(978-1-61623-862-9(3))* Independent Pub.

—Boys Transitioning from Athletic Aggression to Academic Affirmation. 2010. pap. 19.95 *(978-1-61623-559-8(4))* Independent Pub.

Humphrey, James H., ed. Sports & Athletics Developments. 2008. (Illus.). 118p. (C). 129.00 *(978-1-60456-205-7(6))* Nova Science Pubs., Inc.

Kevorkian, Meline. Tackling Bullying in Athletics: Best Practices for Modeling Appropriate Behavior. 2010. (ENG.). 100p. 60.00 *(978-1-60709-379-4(0))*; pap. 17.95 *(978-1-60709-380-0(4))* Rowman & Littlefield Education.

Kevorkian, Meline M. & D'Antona, Robin. Tackling Bullying in Athletics: Guidelines for Modeling Appropriate Behavior. 2010. 17.95 *(978-1-60709-381-7(2))* Rowman & Littlefield Publishers, Inc.

Kieblaso, J. Ultimate Speed & Agility. 2nd ed. 2011. 224p. pap. 19.95 ***(978-0-9762944-1-2(9))*** Crew Pr.

König, Jason. Athletics & Literature in the Roman Empire. 2008. (Greek Culture in the Roman World Ser.). (ENG., Illus.). 420p. pap. 55.00 *(978-0-521-07008-9(2))* Cambridge Univ. Pr.

Luebbers III, A m & Luebbers Iii, A. M. Annual Training Patterns & Success in Ironman-Distance Triathletes. 2010. 176p. pap. *(978-3-639-26019-9(8))* VDM Verlag Dr. Mueller e.K.

Murray, Jack L. & Watson, Emily O. Encyclopedia of Sports & Athletics. 2011. (Sports & Athletics Preparation, Performance, & Psychology Ser.). 663p. 195.00 *(978-1-61209-959-0(9))* Nova Science Pubs., Inc.

Prentice, William E. & Arnheim, Daniel D. Principles of Athletic Training: A Competency-Based Approach. 14th ed. 2010. (ENG., Illus.). 928p. (C). 172.67 *(978-0-07-352373-6(9)*, 0073523739) McGraw-Hill Cos., The.

Robinson, Patrick. Jamaican Athletics: A Model for 2012 Olympics & the World. 2009. (ENG., Illus.). 140p. pap. 26.95 *(978-1-906413-29-3(0)*, Black Amber) Arcadia Bks. Ltd. GBR. Dist: Dufour Editions, Inc.

Rodze, J. L. Meet Me There. 2011. 160p. pap. 19.99 ***(978-1-4653-4332-1(6))*** Xlibris Corp.

Rozzi, Susan L., et al. Study Guide for the Board of Certification, Inc. , Entry-Level Athletic Trainer Certification Examination. 4th rev. ed. 2010. (Illus.). 192p. pap. 54.95 *(978-0-8036-0020-1(8))* Davis, F. A. Co.

Schneider, Robert C. Ethics of Sport & Athletics: Theory, Issues, & Application. 2008. (ENG., Illus.). 400p. pap. 62.99 *(978-0-7817-8791-8(2))* Lippincott Williams & Wilkins.

Ungar, Ken. Ahead of the Game: What Every Athlete Needs to Know about Sports Business. 2007. (Illus.). 240p. pap. 22.95 *(978-0-9798830-3-3(2))* IBJ Custom Publishing.

Waldorf, James P. Advances in Sports & Athletics. Volume 1. 2011. (Advances in Sports & Athletics Ser.). 129.00 *(978-1-61122-824-3(7))* Nova Science Pubs., Inc.

ATHLETICS—COACHING

see Coaching (Athletics)

ATHLETICS—EQUIPMENT AND SUPPLIES

see also Sporting Goods

Chronicle Books Staff, et al. The Sneaker Coloring Book. 2010. (ENG., Illus.). 152p. pap. 19.95 *(978-1-85669-667-8(7))* King, Laurence Publishing GBR. Dist: Hachette Bk. Group.

Estivalet, Margaret. The Engineering of Sport 7: Vol. 2. Estivalet, Margaret & Brisson, Pierre, eds. 2008. (ENG.). xiii, 704p. 149.00 *(978-2-287-09412-5(1)*, 2287094121) Springer.

Estivalet, Margaret & Brisson, Pierre, eds. The Engineering of Sport 7: Vol. 1. 2009. (ENG., Illus.). xiii, 715p. pap. 109.00 *(978-2-287-99053-3(4))* Springer.

—The Engineering of Sport 7, Volume 1. 2008. (Engineering of Sport 7 Ser.). (Illus.). 715p. 179.00 *(978-2-287-09410-1(5))* Springer.

Hauser, Dan, et al. Antique Sports Uniforms & Equipment: 1840-1940, Baseball - Football - Basketball. 2008. (Illus.). 176p. bds. 49.99 *(978-0-7643-3018-6(7))* Schiffer Publishing, Ltd.

MacBain, MacBain. The Engineering of Sport 7: Vol. 2. Estivalet, Margaret, ed. 2009. (ENG.). xiii, 704p. pap. 109.00 *(978-2-287-99055-7(0)*, 2287990550) Springer.

Moritz, Eckehard & Haake, Steve, eds. Engineering of Sport 6: Volume 1: Developments for Sports. 2010. (ENG., Illus.). xliv, 445p. pap. 159.00 *(978-1-4419-2177-2(X)*, 144192177X) Springer.

—Engineering of Sport 6: Volume 2: Developments for Disciplines. 2010. (ENG., Illus.). xl, 329p. pap. 139.00 *(978-1-4419-2241-0(5)*, 1441922415) Springer.

—The Engineering of Sport 6: Volume 3: Developments for Innovation. 2010. (ENG., Illus.). xliv, 440p. pap. 149.00 *(978-1-4419-2242-7(3)*, 1441922423) Springer.

Peterson, Hal. Chucks! The Phenomenon of Converse Chuck Taylor All Stars. 2007. (ENG., Illus.). 160p. 14.95 *(978-1-60239-079-9(7)*, 239079) Skyhorse Publishing Co., Inc.

Talbot, Brian & Augustine, Grace. Russell Athletic Tries to Keep the Shirt on Its Back (A) 2010. (C). pap. 20.00 *(978-1-61674-312-3(3))* Davidson, William Institute At The Univ. of Michigan, The.

Talbot, Brian, et al. Russell Athletic Tries to Keep the Shirt on Its Back (B) 2010. (C). pap. 7.00 *(978-1-61674-314-7(X))* Davidson, William Institute At The Univ. of Michigan, The.

Wu, Yanwen. Sport Materials, Modelling & Simulation: Selected Peer Reviewed Papers from the 2011 International Conference on Sport Material, Modelling & Simulation (ICSMMS 2011), January 27-28, 2011, Shenzhen, P.R. China. 2011. (Illus.). xvi, 840p. pap. ***(978-3-03785-041-1(8))*** Trans Tech Pubns., Ltd.

ATHLETICS—HISTORY

Arrington, Larry W. The Dawn of A Sport: Roanoke College's Track & Field Athletics Program - 1895-1930. 2007. 136p. per. 10.95 *(978-1-4327-0367-7(6))* Outskirts Pr., Inc.

Iber, Jorge, et al. Latinos in U. S Sport: A History of Isolation, Cultural Identity, & Acceptance. 2011. (Illus.). 312p. (C). 59.00 *(978-0-7360-8726-1(5))* Human Kinetics Pubs.

Morrison, Pat. Walker County High School Athletics: 1920-2000. 2007. (Images of Sports Ser.). (Illus.). 127p. per. 19.99 *(978-0-7385-4434-2(5))* Arcadia Publishing.

Smith, Ronald A. Pay for Play: A History of Big-Time College Athletic Reform. 2010. (ENG.). 360p. 80.00 *(978-0-252-03587-6(9))*; pap. 30.00 *(978-0-252-07783-8(0))* Univ. of Illinois Pr.

Walter, John C. & Iida, Malina, eds. Better Than the Best: Black Athletes Speak, 1920-2007. 2010. (V Ethel Willis White Bks.). (ENG., Illus.). 288p. pap. 24.95 *(978-0-295-99053-8(8))* Univ. of Washington Pr.

Waring, Rob. The Olympians (US) 2008. (ENG.). 24p. (C). pap. 10.95 *(978-1-4240-4468-9(5))* Cengage Heinle.

Wilhelm, Robert. Ancient Athletic Games: Heracles & the Olympics. (Ancient Greek & Roman Resource Ser.). (Illus.). 100p. 24.95 *(978-1-56696-134-9(3))* Jackdaw Pubns.

Will-Weber, Mark. Run for the Diamonds: 100 Years of Footracing in Berwick, Pennsylvania. 2008. (ENG.). 360p. pap. 16.00 *(978-1-891369-78-0(4))* Breakaway Bks.

ATHLETICS—MEDICAL ASPECTS

see Sports Medicine

ATHLETICS—PUBLIC RELATIONS

see Sports—Public Relations

ATHLETICS—SCHOLARSHIPS, FELLOWSHIPS, ETC.

see Athletes—Scholarships, Fellowships, Etc.

ATHLETICS—GREECE

Golden, Mark. Greek Sport & Social Status. 2010. (ENG.). 232p. pap. 25.00 *(978-0-292-72153-1(6))* Univ. of Texas Pr.

Konig, Jason, ed. Greek Athletics. 2010. (Edinburgh Readings on the Ancient World Ser.). (ENG., Illus.). 320p. (gr. 17). 150.00 *(978-0-7486-3490-3(8))* Edinburgh Univ. Pr. GBR. Dist: Columbia Univ. Pr.

Miller, Stephen G. Ancient Greek Athletics. 2006. (ENG., Illus.). 304p. pap. 30.00 *(978-0-300-11529-1(6))* Yale Univ. Pr.

Newby, Zahra. Athletics in the Ancient World. 2006. (BCP Classical World Ser.). (Illus.). 128p. per. 19.95 *(978-1-85399-688-7(2))* Bristol Classical Pr. GBR. Dist: International Publishers Marketing.

Reid, Heather. Athletics & Philosophy in the Ancient World: Contests of Virtue. 2011. (Ethics & Sport Ser.). (ENG.). 136p. 125.00 *(978-0-415-66950-4(2))* Routledge.

ATHLETICS—UNITED STATES

Arrington, Larry W. The Dawn of A Sport: Roanoke College's Track & Field Athletics Program - 1895-1930. 2007. 136p. per. 10.95 (978-1-4327-0367-7(6)) Outskirts Pr., Inc.

Gomez, Ron & SHIPLEY, BERYL. Slam Dunked: The NCAA's Shameful Reaction to Athletic Integration in the Deep South. 2007. 272p. per. 19.95 (978-1-60008-077-7(4), Rooftop Publishing) AuthorHouse.

Gottlieb, Richard, ed. Sports Market Place Directory. 2007. (Sports Market Place Directory Ser.). (Illus.). 2219p. per. 225.00 (978-1-59237-189-1(2)) Grey Hse. Publishing.

Grey House Publishing Staff. Sports Market Place Directory. 2008. 1800p. pap. 225.00 (978-1-59237-348-2(8)) Grey Hse. Publishing.

Humphrey, James H. Contemporary Athletics Compendium, Volume 3. 2009. (Illus.). 315p. 95.00 (978-1-60741-561-9(5)) Nova Science Pubs., Inc.

Humphrey, James H., ed. Contemporary Athletics Research, 2 vols. 2008. (Illus.). 95.00 (978-1-60456-565-2(9)) Nova Science Pubs., Inc.

Mars, Laura, ed. Sports Market Place Directory. 2011. 1800p. pap. 225.00 (978-1-59237-752-7(1)) Grey Hse. Publishing.

—Sports Market Place Directory 2010. 8th rev. ed. 2010. pap. 225.00 (978-1-59237-552-3(9)) Grey Hse. Publishing.

Mars-Proietti, Laura, ed. Sports Market Place Directory: 2009. 7th rev. ed. 2009. 1800p. pap. 225.00 (978-1-59237-418-2(2)) Grey Hse. Publishing.

Mastripolito, Wendy. The ChesapeakeMan Ultra Triathlon. 2009. 84p. pap. 15.11 (978-0-557-08544-6(6)) Lulu Enterprises Inc.

Silver, Murray. Tech's Luck: The Story of Jim Luck: Wherein Goodness Springs Forth from Goodness, the Extraordinary Is Found & Sown. 2010. (Illus.). 240p. pap. 21.95 (978-0-9822583-4-7(8)) Continental Shelf Publishing.

Thuma, Cynthia A. Sport Lauderdale: Big Names & Big Games. 2007. (Illus.). 127p. pap., per. 19.99 (978-1-59629-145-4(1)) History Pr., The.

Waeschle, Amy. Chasing Waves: A Surfer's Tale of Obsessive Wandering. 2009. (ENG.). 160p. pap. 16.95 (978-1-59485-113-1(1)) Mountaineers Bks., The.

White, Alvin G. Education Is Not a Four-Letter Word. 2010. 118p. 24.95 (978-1-59594-397-2(8), Wingspan Pr.) WingSpan Publishing.

ATHOS (MONASTERIES)

della Dora, Veronica. Imagining Mount Athos: Visions of a Holy Place, from Homer to World War II. 2011. (ENG., Illus.). 336p. (C). (gr. 13-17). pap. 19.50 (978-0-8139-3259-0(9)); (gr. 17). 35.00 (978-0-8139-3085-5(5)) Univ. Pr. of Virginia.

Hasluck, F. W. Athos & its Monasteries. 2008. (Gorgias Classic Archaeological Reprints Ser.: 15). 74.00 (978-1-59333-767-4(1)) Gorgias Pr., LLC.

Rocha, Luiz. Mount Athos, a Journey of Self-Discovery. 2009. 104p. pap. 11.95 (978-1-4401-1753-4(5)) iUniverse, Inc.

ATHYMIA

see Dementia

ATKINSON, EDWARD, 1827-1905

Dalton, Marshall B. Edward Atkinson Patron of Engineering Sc. 2006. pap. 15.95 (978-1-4286-6068-7(2)) Kessinger Publishing, LLC.

Williamson, Harold Francis. Edward Atkinson: The Biography of an American Liberal, 1827-1905. 2011. 328p. 50.95 (978-1-258-07515-3(2)) Literary Licensing, LLC.

ATLANTA (GA.)

ADC, the Map People Staff. Atlanta Metro GA. 2010. 192p. spiral bd. 19.99 (978-0-6416-7184-3(2)) American Map Corp.

ATLANTA (GA.)—DESCRIPTION AND TRAVEL

Armstrong, Christopher. The Painted Valley: Artists along Alberta's Bow River, 1845-2000. 2007. (ENG., Illus.). 176p. per. 54.95 (978-1-55238-207-3(9)) Univ. of Calgary Pr. CAN. Dist: Chicago Distribution Ctr.

Atlanta. (Rand Mcnally Wall Maps Ser.). 229.00 (978-0-528-86121-5(2)) Rand McNally.

Butler, Tray. Moon Atlanta. 2009. (Moon Handbooks). (ENG., Illus.). 208p. pap. 16.95 (978-1-59880-219-1(4)) Avalon Travel Publishing.

Christian, Reese. Ghosts of Atlanta: Phantoms of the Phoenix City. 2008. pap. 19.99 (978-1-59629-544-5(9)) History Pr., The.

Crimmins, Timothy & Farrissee, Anne H. Democracy Restored: A History of the Georgia State Capitol. 2007. (ENG., Illus.). 200p. 39.95 (978-0-8203-2911-6(8)) Univ. of Georgia Pr.

Davis, Ren. Best Easy Day Hikes Atlanta. 2009. (Best Easy Day Hikes Ser.). (ENG., Illus.). 112p. pap. 9.95 (978-0-7627-5290-4(4), Falcon Guides) Globe Pequot Pr., The.

Davis, Ren & Davis, Helen. Atlanta Walks: A Comprehensive Guide to Walking, Running, & Bicycling the Area's Scenic & Historic Locales, 1 vol. 4th rev. ed. 2011. (ENG.). 416p. pap. 16.95 (978-1-56145-584-3(9)) Peachtree Pubs.

Dorgan, Theo. Time on the Ocean: A Viyage from Cape Horn to Cape Town. 2011. (ENG.). 298p. pap. 27.95 (978-1-84840-075-7(6)) New Island Books IRL. Dist: Dufour Editions, Inc.

Entertainment Publications, Inc. Staff, compiled by. Atlanta 2009 Entertainment Book. 2008. pap. 25.00 (978-1-59878-621-7(0)) Entertainment Pubns., Inc.

—Edmonton 2009 Entertainment Book. 2008. pap. 45.00 (978-1-59878-657-6(1)) Entertainment Pubns., Inc.

Felton, Carly, ed. A Marmac Guide to Atlanta, 1 vol. 11th ed. 2007. (Marmac Guide to Atlanta Ser.). (ENG., Illus.). 304p. pap. 17.95 (978-1-58980-499-9(6)) Pelican Publishing Co., Inc.

Foster Jones, Sharon. The Atlanta Exposition. 2010. (Images of America Ser.). (ENG., Illus.). 128p. pap. 21.99 (978-0-7385-6659-7(4)) Arcadia Publishing.

Golden, Randy & Golden, Pam. Easy Hikes Close to Home: Atlanta. 2009. (Easy Hikes Close to Home Ser.). (ENG.). 96p. pap. 8.95 (978-0-89732-726-8(8)) Menasha Ridge Pr., Inc.

—60 Hikes Within 60 Miles: Atlanta: Including Marietta, Lawrenceville, & Peachtree City. 2nd ed. 2008. (60 Hikes within 60 Miles Ser.). (ENG., Illus.). 252p. pap. 16.95 (978-0-89732-673-5(3)) Menasha Ridge Pr., Inc.

Hartle, Robert. The Highs & Lows of Little Five: A History of Little Five Points. 2010. (Brief History Ser.). (ENG., Illus.). 128p. pap. 19.99 (978-1-59629-874-3(X)) History Pr., The.

Joiner, Sean, et al. Fort Gordon. 2009. (Images of America Ser.). (ENG., Illus.). 128p. pap. 21.99 (978-0-7385-6812-6(0)) Arcadia Publishing.

Kyi, Tanya Lloyd & Kyi, Tanya Lloyd. Atlanta. 2010. (ENG., Illus.). 96p. 19.95 (978-1-55285-357-3(8)) Whitecap Bks., Ltd. CAN. Dist: Midpoint Trade Bks., Inc.

Marr, Christine V. & Jones, Sharon Foster. Inman Park. 2008. (Images of America Ser.). (ENG., Illus.). 128p. pap. 21.99 (978-0-7385-6731-0(0)) Arcadia Publishing.

McAuley, Jordan & Burkhalter, Matt. Atlanta. 2009. (Out Traveler Guides). (ENG., Illus.). 248p. pap. 15.95 (978-1-59350-102-0(1)) Alyson Pubns.

McDonald, Janice. Atlanta. 9th ed. 2010. (Insiders' Guide Ser.). (ENG., Illus.). 360p. pap. 18.95 (978-0-7627-5310-9(2), Insiders' Guide) Globe Pequot Pr., The.

—Day Trips from Atlanta: Getaway Ideas for the Local Traveler. 2011. (Day Trips Ser.). (ENG.). 320p. pap. 14.95 (978-0-7627-7305-3(7)) Globe Pequot Pr., The.

McDonald, Janice. The Varsity. 2011. (Images of America Ser.). (ENG., Illus.). 128p. pap. 21.99 (978-0-7385-8797-4(4)) Arcadia Publishing.

Mobil US City Gd. Atlanta 2009. 2009. (CITY GUIDE-DOMESTIC Ser.). 192p. 16.95 (978-0-8416-0740-8(0)) Langenscheidt Publishing Group.

Not For Tourists. Not for Tourists Guide to Atlanta, 6th Edition. 6th ed. 2011. (Not for Tourists Ser.). (ENG., Illus.). 384p. pap. 21.99 (978-0-9825951-3-8(1)) Not For Tourists, Inc.

NOT FOR TOURISTS, creator. Not for Tourists Guide to Atlanta: 2012. 2011. (ENG., Illus.). 384p. pap. 19.95 (978-1-61608-565-0(7), 608565, Not For Tourist) Skyhorse Publishing Co., Inc.

Not for Tourists Guide to Atlanta. 2nd ed. 2007. (Not for Tourists Guide to Atlanta Ser.). (Illus.). 373p. 16.95 (978-0-9778031-8-7(X), Not For Tourists) Not for Tourists, Inc.

Not For Tourists Staff. Not for Tourists Guide to Atlanta 2010. 5th ed. 2009. (Not for Tourists Ser.). (ENG., Illus.). 384p. pap. 19.99 (978-0-9795339-3-8(7)) Not For Tourists, Inc.

Not for Tourists Staff, creator. Not for Tourists Guide to Atlanta. 2008. (Not for Tourists Guide to Atlanta Ser.). (Illus.). 373p. 18.95 (978-0-9793945-9-1(7)) Not for Tourists, Inc.

Panache Partners LLC Staff, ed. Atlanta: An Architectural Perspective of Atlanta. 2008. (City by Design Ser.). (ENG., Illus.). 250p. 34.95 (978-1-933415-47-5(9)) Panache Partners, LLC.

Parr, Martin. Up & down Peachtree. 2012. (ENG., Illus.). 208p. 50.00 (978-88-6965-333-9(1)) Contrasto DUE ITA. Dist: Consortium Bk. Sales & Distribution.

Pashby, Christie. Frommer's Banff & the Canadian Rockies Day by Day. 2010. (Frommer's Day by Day - Pocket Ser.: 177). (ENG., Illus.). 184p. pap. 12.99 (978-0-470-73628-9(3), Frommers) Wiley, John & Sons, Inc.

Publications International Staff. Yesterday & Today: Atlanta. 2010. 192p. 24.95 (978-1-60553-900-3(7)) Publications International, Ltd.

Ridgeway, Benjamin C. Atlanta's Ebenezer Baptist Church. 2009. (Images of America Ser.). (ENG., Illus.). 128p. pap. 21.99 (978-0-7385-6798-3(1)) Arcadia Publishing.

Rose, Michael. Atlanta. 2008. (Then & Now Thunder Bay Ser.). (ENG., Illus.). 144p. pap. 12.95 (978-1-59223-874-3(2), Thunder Bay Pr.) Advantage Pubs. Group.

—Historic Photos of Atlanta. 2007. (Historic Photos Ser.). (ENG., Illus.). 205p. 39.95 (978-1-59652-404-0(9)) Turner Publishing Co.

Schemmel, William. Atlanta in Your Pocket: Your Guide to an Hour, a Day or a Weekend in the City. 2010. (Insiders' Guide Ser.). (ENG., Illus.). 120p. 10.95 (978-0-7627-5316-1(1), Insiders' Guide) Globe Pequot Pr., The.

Snyder, Karen K. Frommer's Atlanta. 12th ed. 2011. (Frommer's Complete Guides: 911). (ENG., Illus.). 256p. pap. 16.99 (978-0-470-88869-8(5), Frommers) Wiley, John & Sons, Inc.

Thalimer, Carol & Thalimer, Dan. Atlanta. 2008. (Great Destinations Atlanta Ser.). (ENG., Illus.). 344p. per. 18.95 (978-1-58157-086-1(4), 157086) Countryman Pr.

Time-Life Audiobooks Staff, contrib. by. Atlanta. (978-88-7009-616-3(5)) Casa Editrice Bonechi.

Underwood, Corrina. Haunted History: Atlanta & North Georgia. 2008. (Illus.). 160p. pap. 14.95 (978-0-7643-2854-1(9)) Schiffer Publishing, Ltd.

Wilcox, Walter. The Rockies of Canada: A Revised & Enlarged Edition of Camping in the Canadian Rockies, 1 vol. rev. ed. 2009. (Mountain Classics Collection). (ENG., Illus.). 216p. pap. (978-1-897522-14-1(2)) Rocky Mountain Bks.

Williford, William Bailey. Peachtree Street, Atlanta. 2010. (ENG.). 212p. pap. 22.95 (978-0-8203-3477-6(4)) Univ. of Georgia Pr.

Woolf, Marcus. Afoot & Afield Atlanta: A Comprehensive Hiking Guide. 2009. (Afoot & Afield Ser.). (ENG.). 298p. pap. 18.95 (978-0-89997-415-6(5)) Wilderness Pr.

Zagat Survey Staff. Atlanta Restaurants 2008/09. 2008. 208p. pap. 12.95 (978-1-57006-978-9(6)) Zagat Survey.

ATLANTA (GA.)—DIRECTORIES

Adams-Smith, Beth. Atlantic Cruising Club's Guide to Mid-Atlantic/ICW Marinas - Book with DVD: Hampton, Virginia to St. Mary's , Georgia (Including the Intra-Coastal Waterway, North Carolina Sounds & Bermuda) Smith, Richard Y., ed. 7th ed. 2010. (ENG., Illus.). 280p. pap. 39.95 incl. DVD (978-0-9664028-6-5(3), Atlantic Cruising Club) Atlantic Cruising Club at Jerawyn Publishing.

NOT FOR TOURISTS, creator. Not for Tourists Guide to Atlanta: 2012. 2011. (ENG., Illus.). 384p. pap. 19.95 (978-1-61608-565-0(7), 608565, Not For Tourist) Skyhorse Publishing Co., Inc.

Stout, Carol A. 101 Things for Kids in Atlanta: A Complete Family Directory. Date not set. (101 Things for Kids Ser.). 150p. pap. 14.95 (978-1-886161-04-7(6)) Millennium Marketing & Publishing.

ATLANTA (GA.)—ECONOMIC CONDITIONS

Business Information International Staff. Doing Business in Atlanta (Fulton Co.) Date not set. 600p. spiral bd. 299.95 (978-1-890631-00-0(0)) Business Information International.

Hartle, Robert. The Highs & Lows of Little Five: A History of Little Five Points. 2010. (Brief History Ser.). (ENG., Illus.). 128p. pap. 19.99 (978-1-59629-874-3(X)) History Pr., The.

Icon Group International, Inc. Staff, compiled by. The 2006 Economic & Product Market Databook for Atlanta , United States. 2006. 618p. ring bd. 95.00 (978-0-497-80104-5(3)) Icon Group International, Inc.

Sjoquist, David L. Past Trends & Future Prospects of the American City: The Dynamics of Atlanta. 2009. (ENG.). 342p. 89.50 (978-0-7391-3537-2(6)) Lexington Bks.

ATLANTA (GA.)—HISTORY

Armstrong, Christopher. The Painted Valley: Artists along Alberta's Bow River, 1845-2000. 2007. (ENG., Illus.). 176p. per. 54.95 (978-1-55238-207-3(9)) Univ. of Calgary Pr. CAN. Dist: Chicago Distribution Ctr.

Chenault, Wesley & Braukman, Stacy. Gay & Lesbian Atlanta. 2008. (Images of America Ser.). (ENG., Illus.). 128p. pap. 21.99 (978-0-7385-5377-1(8)) Arcadia Publishing.

Christian, Reese. Ghosts of Atlanta: Phantoms of the Phoenix City. 2008. pap. 19.99 (978-1-59629-544-5(9)) History Pr., The.

Cox, Jacob Dolson. Atlanta. (Campaigns of the Civil War Ser.). 274p. reprint ed. 98.00 (978-0-7222-8043-0(2)) Library Reprints, Inc.

Crater, Paul. Baseball in Atlanta. 2007. (Images of Baseball Ser.). (ENG., Illus.). 128p. per. 21.99 (978-0-7385-4380-2(2)) Arcadia Publishing.

Crimmins, Timothy & Farrissee, Anne H. Democracy Restored: A History of the Georgia State Capitol. 2007. (ENG., Illus.). 200p. 39.95 (978-0-8203-2911-6(8)) Univ. of Georgia Pr.

Darnell, Tim. The Crackers: Early Days of Atlanta Baseball. 2006. (Illus.). 224p. reprint ed. pap. 16.95 (978-1-58818-101-5(4)) Hill Street Pr., LLC.

Davis, Ren & Davis, Helen. Atlanta's Oakland Cemetery: An Illustrated History & Guide. 2012. (ENG., Illus.). 224p. pap. 24.95 (978-0-8203-4313-6(7)) Univ. of Georgia Pr.

Davis, Robert Scott. Atlanta in the Civil War. 2011. (Illus.). 128p. pap. 19.99 (978-1-59629-763-0(8)) History Pr., The.

Ecelbarger, Gary. Day Dixie Died: The Battle of Atlanta. 2010. (ENG., Illus.). 320p. 26.99 (978-0-312-56399-8(X), Dunne, Thomas Bks.) St. Martin's Pr.

Fleming, Ellen N., ed. Who's Who in Peoplestown - Historic Edition. 2008. 108p. 25.00 (978-0-9788571-8-9(6)) Thomas Max Publishing.

Foster Jones, Sharon. The Atlanta Exposition. 2010. (Images of America Ser.). (ENG., Illus.). 128p. pap. 21.99 (978-0-7385-6659-7(4)) Arcadia Publishing.

Garrett, Franklin M. Atlanta & Environs: A Chronicle of Its People & Events, 1820s-1870s. 2011. (ENG., Illus.). 992p. 74.95 (978-0-8203-3902-3(4)); pap. 64.95 (978-0-8203-3903-0(2)) Univ. of Georgia Pr.

—Atlanta & Environs: A Chronicle of Its People & Events, 1880s-1930s. 2011. (ENG.). 1080p. 74.95 (978-0-8203-3904-7(0)); pap. 64.95 (978-0-8203-3905-4(9)) Univ. of Georgia Pr.

Hammer, Charles. Of Love & War: 1864: A Civil War Novel for the North. 2010. 260p. pap. 15.00 (978-1-4520-6776-6(7)) AuthorHouse.

Hartle, Robert. Atlanta's Druid Hills: A Brief History. 2008. pap. 19.99 (978-1-59629-375-5(6)) History Pr., The.

—The Highs & Lows of Little Five: A History of Little Five Points. 2010. (Brief History Ser.). (ENG., Illus.). 128p. pap. 19.99 (978-1-59629-874-3(X)) History Pr., The.

Joiner, Sean, et al. Fort Gordon. 2009. (Images of America Ser.). (ENG., Illus.). 128p. pap. 21.99 (978-0-7385-6812-6(0)) Arcadia Publishing.

Jones, Sharon Foster. Atlanta's Ponce de Leon Avenue: A History. 2012. 128p. pap. 19.99 (978-1-60949-349-3(4)) History Pr., The.

Kaemmerlen, Cathy J. Historic Oakland Cemetery of Atlanta. 2007. 128p. pap. 19.99 (978-1-59629-330-4(6)) History Pr., The.

Marr, Christine V. & Jones, Sharon Foster. Inman Park. 2008. (Images of America Ser.). (ENG., Illus.). 128p. pap. 21.99 (978-0-7385-6731-0(0)) Arcadia Publishing.

Martin, Harold H. Atlanta & Environs: A Chronicle of Its People & Events, 1940s-1970s. 2011. (ENG., Illus.). 648p. 69.95 (978-0-8203-3906-1(7)); pap. 59.95 (978-0-8203-3907-8(5)) Univ. of Georgia Pr.

McDonald, Janice. The Varsity. 2011. (Images of America Ser.). (ENG., Illus.). 128p. pap. 21.99 (978-0-7385-8797-4(4)) Arcadia Publishing.

McKay, John. It Happened in Atlanta. 2011. (It Happened in Ser.). (ENG., Illus.). 208p. pap. 14.95 (978-0-7627-6439-6(2)) Globe Pequot Pr., The.

Ottley, James. Atlanta History for Cocktail Parties. 2009. 89p. pap. 12.00 (978-0-557-04658-4(0)) Lulu Enterprises Inc.

Publications International Staff. Yesterday & Today: Atlanta. 2010. 192p. 24.95 (978-1-60553-900-3(7)) Publications International, Ltd.

Reed, Wallace P., ed. History of Atlanta, Georgia. (Illus.). 702p. reprint ed. lib. bdg. 148.00 (978-0-7222-0872-4(3)) Library Reprints, Inc.

Ridgeway, Benjamin C. Atlanta's Ebenezer Baptist Church. 2009. (Images of America Ser.). (ENG., Illus.). 128p. pap. 21.99 (978-0-7385-6798-3(1)) Arcadia Publishing.

Rose, Michael. Atlanta. 2008. (Then & Now Thunder Bay Ser.). (ENG., Illus.). 144p. pap. 12.95 (978-1-59223-874-3(2), Thunder Bay Pr.) Advantage Pubs. Group.

—Historic Photos of Atlanta. 2007. (Historic Photos Ser.). (ENG., Illus.). 205p. 39.95 (978-1-59652-404-0(9)) Turner Publishing Co.

Sengkhounmany, Chay. The Lawyers Club of Atlanta. 2010. (978-0-88146-181-7(4)) Mercer Univ. Pr.

Wells, Jeffrey. The Atlanta Ripper: The Unsolved Story of the Gate City's Most Infamous Murders. 2011. 128p. pap. 19.99 (978-1-60949-381-3(8)) History Pr., The.

Wilkinson, Jack. 100 Things Braves Fans Should Know & Do Before They Die. 2011. (100 Things... Fans Should Know Ser.). (ENG.). 296p. pap. 14.95 (978-1-60078-555-9(7)) Triumph Bks.

ATLANTA (GA.)—POLITICS AND GOVERNMENT

Fleming, Ellen N., ed. Who's Who in Peoplestown - Historic Edition. 2008. 108p. 25.00 (978-0-9788571-8-9(6)) Thomas Max Publishing.

Goldhagen, Harold. Signal 63: Officer Needs Help. 2006. pap. (978-1-59526-408-4(6)) Aeon Publishing Inc.

Holmes, Robert A. Maynard Jackson: A Biography. 2009. (Illus.). 368p. 27.99 (978-0-9801744-0-3(6)) Barnhardt & Ashe Publishing, Inc.

Martin, Harold H. William Berry Hartsfield: Mayor of Atlanta. 2010. (ENG.). 266p. pap. 24.95 (978-0-8203-3544-5(4)) Univ. of Georgia Pr.

Parsons, Sara. From Southern Wrongs to Civil Rights: The Memoir of a White Civil Rights Activist. 2009. (ENG., Illus.). 216p. pap. 22.00 (978-0-8173-5558-6(8)) Univ. of Alabama Pr.

ATLANTA (GA.)—SOCIAL CONDITIONS

Greene, Melissa Fay. The Temple Bombing. 2006. (ENG., Illus.). 514p. per. 21.00 (978-0-306-81518-8(4)) Da Capo Pr., Inc.

Hartle, Robert. The Highs & Lows of Little Five: A History of Little Five Points. 2010. (Brief History Ser.). (ENG., Illus.). 128p. pap. 19.99 (978-1-59629-874-3(X)) History Pr., The.

McKay, John. It Happened in Atlanta. 2011. (It Happened in Ser.). (ENG., Illus.). 208p. pap. 14.95 (978-0-7627-6439-6(2)) Globe Pequot Pr., The.

Richards, Samuel Pearce. Sam Richards's Civil War Diary: A Chronicle of the Atlanta Home Front. Venet, Wendy Hamand, ed. 2009. (ENG.). 328p. 34.95 (978-0-8203-2999-4(1)) Univ. of Georgia Pr.

ATLANTA BRAVES (BASEBALL TEAM)

see also Boston Braves (Baseball Team); Milwaukee Braves (Baseball Team)

Frisch, Aaron. Atlanta Braves. 2009. (World Series Champions Ser.). (Illus.). 23p. (J). (gr. 2-3). 24.25 (978-1-58341-687-7(0), Creative Education) Creative Co., The.

Goodman, Michael E. The Story of the Atlanta Braves. 2007. (Baseball, the Great American Game Ser.). (Illus.). 48p. (YA). (gr. 4-7). lib. bdg. 32.80 (978-1-58341-479-8(7)) Creative Co., The.

Green, Ron, Jr. 101 Reasons to Love the Braves. 2008. (ENG., Illus.). 120p. 15.95 (978-1-58479-670-1(7)) Stewart, Tabori & Chang.

Lopez, Javy & Caruso, Gary. Behind the Plate: A Catcher's View of the Braves Dynasty. 2012. (ENG.). 208p. 25.95 (978-1-60078-653-2(7)) Triumph Bks.

Whitaker, Lang. In the Time of Bobby Cox: The Atlanta Braves, Their Manager, My Couch, Two Decades, & Me. 2011. (ENG.). 240p. 24.00 (978-1-4391-4838-9(4), Scribner) Scribner.

Wieren, Pete Van & Wilkinson, Jack. Of Mikes & Men: A Lifetime of Braves Baseball. 2010. (ENG.). 224p. 24.95 (978-1-60078-359-3(7)) Triumph Bks.

Wilkinson, Jack. Atlanta Braves. 2007. (Game of My Life Ser.). (Illus.). 216p. 24.95 (978-1-59670-099-4(8)) Sports Publishing, LLC.

—100 Things Braves Fans Should Know & Do Before They Die. 2011. (100 Things... Fans Should Know Ser.). (ENG.). 296p. pap. 14.95 (978-1-60078-555-9(7)) Triumph Bks.

ATLANTA CAMPAIGN, 1864

Bonds, Russell S. War Like the Thunderbolt: The Battle & Burning of Atlanta. (ENG., Illus.). 2010. 536p. pap. 18.95 (978-1-59416-127-8(5)) 2009. 544p. 29.95 (978-1-59416-100-1(3)) Westholme Publishing.

Cox, Jacob D. Atlanta. 2009. (ENG.). 287p. pap. 21.99 (978-1-117-57662-6(0), BiblioLife) BiblioBazaar.

—Atlanta. 2010. 286p. pap. 23.16 (978-1-163-94450-9(5)) 2008. 284p. 43.95 (978-0-548-95759-2(2)) 2007. (ENG.). 288p. per. 28.95 (978-0-548-63281-9(2)) Kessinger Publishing, LLC.

Davis, Robert Scott. Atlanta in the Civil War. 2011. (Illus.). 128p. pap. 19.99 (978-1-59629-763-0(8)) History Pr., The.

Key, Thomas J. & Campbell, Robert J. Two Soldiers: The Campaign Diaries of Thomas J. Key, & Robert J. Campbell. Cate, Wirt Armistead, ed. 2011. 298p. 48.95 (978-1-258-10194-7(7)) Literary Licensing, LLC.

Lepa, Jack H. Breaking the Confederacy: The Georgia & Tennessee Campaigns Of 1864. alt. ed. 2011. (ENG., Illus.). 244p. pap. 35.00 (978-0-7864-6098-4(9)) McFarland & Co., Inc. Pubs.

Luvaas, Jay & Nelson, Harold W. eds. Guide to the Atlanta Campaign: Rocky Face Ridge to Kennesaw Mountain. 2008. (U. S. Army War College Guides to Civil War Battles Ser.). (Illus.). 383p. 39.95 *(978-0-7006-1569-8(5))*; pap. 17.95 *(978-0-7006-1570-4(9))* Univ. Pr. of Kansas.

Scales, John R. Sherman Invades Georgia: Planning the North Georgia Campaign Using a Modern Perspective. 2006. (Illus.). 213p. 34.95 *(978-1-59114-815-9(4))* Naval Institute Pr.

Sherman, William T. The Capture of Atlanta & the March to the Sea: From Sherman's Memoirs. 2007. (Civil War Ser.). (ENG., Illus.). 240p. per. 10.95 *(978-0-486-45477-1(0))* Dover Pubns., Inc.

Williams, Hiram Smith. This War So Horrible: The Civil War Diary of Hiram Smith Williams, 40th Alabama Confederate Pioneer. Wynne, Lewis N. & Taylor, Robert A., eds. 2nd ed. 2006 (Illus.). 200p. per. 24.95 *(978-0-8173-5374-2(7))* Univ. of Alabama Pr.

Wilson, John P., ed. From Western Deserts to Carolina Swamps: A Civil War Soldier's Journals & Letters Home. 2012. (ENG., Illus.). 296p. 40.00 ***(978-0-8263-5142-5(5))*** Univ. of New Mexico Pr.

Wortman, Marc. The Bonfire: The Siege & Burning of Atlanta. 2010. (ENG., Illus.). 464p. pap. 15.95 *(978-1-58648-819-2(8))* PublicAffairs.

ATLANTA FALCONS (FOOTBALL TEAM)

Holley, Michael. War Room: The Legacy of Bill Belichick & the Art of Building the Perfect Team. 2012. (ENG.). 256p. pap. 15.99 ***(978-0-06-208240-4(X))*** HarperCollins Pubs.

ATLANTA METROPOLITAN AREA (GA.)

Futrell, Janae. Urban Mobility - Transference & Atlanta's Transit. 2008. 144p. per. *(978-3-8364-5962-4(0))* VDM Verlag Dr. Mueller e.K.

Konrad, Miriam. Transporting Atlanta: The Mode of Mobility under Construction. Konrad, Miriam, ed. 2010. 219p. pap. 24.95 *(978-1-4384-2678-5(X)*, Suny Pr.) State Univ. of New York Pr.

ATLANTIC, BATTLE OF THE, 1939-1945

see World War, 1939-1945—Campaigns—Atlantic Ocean

ATLANTIC ALLIANCE

see North Atlantic Treaty Organization

ATLANTIC CANADA

see Atlantic Provinces

ATLANTIC CITY (N.J.)

Bronson, Richard D. The War at the Shore: Steve Wynn, Donald Trump, & the Epic War to Save Atlantic City 2012. (ENG.). 224p. (gr. 12). 26.00 ***(978-1-4683-0046-8(6))*** Overlook Pr., The.

D'Amato, Grace Anselmo. Chance of a Lifetime: Nucky Johnson, Skinny D'Amato & how Atlantic City became the Naughty Queen of Resorts. 237p. pap. 16.95 *(978-1-59322-007-5(3))* Down The Shore Publishing.

Davis, Ed. Atlantic City Diary, 1880-1985: A Century of Memories. (Illus.). 172p. reprint ed. pap. 9.95 *(978-0-9622645-1-1(2))* Atlantic City News Publishing.

Dowey, Bill. Life with the Contraltos - a Tale of Atlantic City's Politics, Mob, & Casinos As Told by a Man with Sand in His Shoes. 2011. 298p. pap. 19.95 ***(978-1-257-79974-9(6))*** Lulu Enterprises Inc.

Johnson, Nelson. Boardwalk Empire: The Birth, High Times, & Corruption of Atlantic City. (ENG.). 2010. 312p. pap. 16.95 *(978-0-9666748-6-6(3))* 2009. 296p. pap. 17.95 *(978-0-9666748-5-9(5))* Plexus Publishing, Inc.

—The Northside: African Americans & the Creation of Atlantic City. 2010. 352p. 24.95 *(978-0-937548-73-8(1))* Plexus Publishing, Inc.

Karmel, James R. Gambling on the American Dream: Atlantic City & the Casino Era, 1 vol. 2008. (Financial History Ser.). (ENG., Illus.). 256p. 99.00 *(978-1-85196-926-5(8))* Pickering & Chatto Pubs., Ltd. GBR. Dist: Ashgate Publishing Co.

Liebowitz, Steve. Steel Pier, Atlantic City: Showplace of the Nation. 2009. (Illus.). 263p. 39.00 *(978-1-59322-036-5(7)*, Cormorant Bks.) Down The Shore Publishing.

Mauger, Edward Arthur. Atlantic City Then & Now. 2008. (Then & Now Thunder Bay Ser.). (ENG., Illus.). 144p. 19.95 *(978-1-59223-863-7(7)*, Thunder Bay Pr.) Advantage Pubs. Group.

Miller, Fred & Miller, Susan. Atlantic City, 1854-1954: An Illustrated History. 2009. (Illus.). 128p. pap. 24.99 *(978-0-7643-3187-9(6))* Schiffer Publishing, Ltd.

Porcelli, Richard V. Naval Air Station Atlantic City. 2012. (Images of Aviation Ser.). (ENG., Illus.). 128p. pap. 21.99 ***(978-0-7385-7670-1(0))*** Arcadia Publishing.

Raheem, Turiya S. A. Growing up in the Other Atlantic City: Wash's & the Northside. 2009. 122p. 29.99 *(978-1-4500-0755-9(4))*; pap. 19.99 *(978-1-4500-0754-2(6))* Xlibris Corp.

Ristine, James D. Atlantic City. 2008. (Postcard History Ser.). (ENG., Illus.). 128p. pap. 19.99 *(978-0-7385-5704-5(8))* Arcadia Publishing.

Sokolic, William H. & Ruffolo, Robert E., Jr. Atlantic City Revisited. 2006. (Images of America Ser.). (ENG., Illus.). 128p. per. 21.99 *(978-0-7385-4904-0(5))* Arcadia Publishing.

ATLANTIC COAST

Clarke, Ted. South of Boston: Tales from the Coastal Communities of Massachusetts Bay. 2010. 128p. pap. 19.99 *(978-1-60949-042-3(8))* History Pr., The.

Coast Guard (U.S.), compiled by. Light List, 2011, V. 1, Atlantic Coast, St. Croix River, Maine to Shrewsbury River, New Jersey. 2011. (ENG., Illus.). 380p. pap. 53.00 *(978-0-16-087112-2(3)*, Coast Guard) United States Government Printing Office.

Coast Guard (U.S.), ed. Light List, 2011, V. 2, Atlantic Coast, Toms River, New Jersey to Little River, South Carolina. 2011. (ENG., Illus.). 398p. pap. 53.00 *(978-0-16-087113-9(1)*, Coast Guard) United States Government Printing Office.

Coast Guard (U.S.), ed. Light List, 2011, V. 3, Atlantic & Gulf Coasts, Little River, South Carolina to Econfina River, Florida (Includes Puerto Rico & the U. S. Virgin Islands) 2011. (ENG., Illus.). 224p. pap. 33.00 ***(978-0-16-087114-6(X)***, Coast Guard) United States Government Printing Office.

de Balbín Behrmann, Rodrigo, et al, eds. Rock Carvings of the European & African Atlantic Façade. 2009. (FRE, SPA & ENG., Illus.). 349p. (C). pap. 135.00 *(978-1-4073-0619-3(7))* British Archaeological Reports Ltd. GBR. Dist: Brown, David Bk. Co., The.

D'Entremont, Jeremy. Great Shipwrecks of the Maine Coast. 2010. (Maritime Ser.). (Illus.). 128p. pap. 14.95 *(978-0-9819430-6-0(3))* Commonwealth Editions.

Donnelly, Mark P. & Diehl, Daniel. Pirates of New Jersey: Plunder & High Adventure on the Garden State Coastline. 2010. (ENG.). 144p. pap. 10.95 *(978-0-8117-0667-4(2))* Stackpole Bks.

Drake, Samuel. The Pine-tree Coast. 2010. 395p. pap. 24.95 *(978-1-4290-4059-4(9))* Applewood Bks.

Gannon, Michael. Operation Drumbeat: The Dramatic True Story of Germany's First U-Boat Attacks along the American Coast in World War II. 2009. (Illus.). 529p. pap. 22.95 *(978-1-59114-302-4(0))* Naval Institute Pr.

Gentile, Gary. The Kaiser's U-Boats in American Waters. 2010. (Illus.). 381p. pap. ***(978-1-883056-40-7(3)***, Bellerophon Bookworks) GGP.

Gratwick, Harry. Stories from the Maine Coast: Skippers, Ships & Storms. 2012. 128p. pap. 19.99 ***(978-1-60949-249-6(8))*** History Pr., The.

Hancock, David. Oceans of Wine: Madeira & the Emergence of American Trade & Taste. 2009. (Lewis Walpole Series in Eighteenth-C Ser.). (ENG., Illus.). 680p. 50.00 *(978-0-300-13605-0(6))* Yale Univ. Pr.

Hornsby, Stephen J. Surveyors of Empire: Samuel Holland, J. F. W. des Barres, & the Making of the Atlantic Neptune. 2011. (Carleton Library Ser.). (ENG., Illus.). 288p. (C). pap. ***(978-0-7735-3848-1(8))*** McGill-Queen's Univ. Pr.

International Marine, creator. Tidal Current Tables: Atlantic Coast of North America. 2006. (Tidal Current Tables: Atlantic Coast of North America Ser.). (Illus.). 269p. per. 13.95 *(978-0-07-147774-1(8)*, 9780071477741, International Marine/Ragged Mountain Pr.) McGraw-Hill Professional Publishing.

James D Snyder. A Light in the Wilderness: The Story of Jupiter Inlet Lighthouse & the Southeast Florida Frontier, 1. 2006. (ENG., Illus.). 287p. 27.95 *(978-0-9675200-1-8(0))* Pharos Bks.

Konstam, Angus. Blackbeard: America's Most Notorious Pirate. 2007. (ENG., Illus.). 336p. per. 15.95 *(978-0-470-12821-3(6)*, Wiley) Wiley, John & Sons, Inc.

Linderoth, Matthew. Prohibition on the North Jersey Shore: Gangsters on Vacation. 2010. (ENG., Illus.). 128p. pap. 19.99 *(978-1-60949-059-1(2))* History Pr., The.

Lippson, Robert L. & Lippson, Alice Jane. Life along the Inner Coast: A Naturalist's Guide to the Sounds, Inlets, Rivers, & Intracoastal Waterway from Norfolk to Key West. (ENG., Illus.). 472p. 2012. pap. 26.00 ***(978-0-8078-7227-7(X))*** 2009. 36.95 *(978-0-8078-3303-2(7))* Univ. of North Carolina Pr.

Marshall, Bill. The French Atlantic: Travels in Culture & History. 2010. (Liverpool University Press - Contemporary French & Francophone Cultures Ser.). (ENG., Illus.). 256p. pap. 35.00 *(978-1-84631-051-5(2))* Liverpool Univ. Pr. GBR. Dist: Chicago Distribution Ctr.

McCoy, Roger. On the Edge: Mapping North America's Coasts. 2012. (ENG., Illus.). 256p. 29.95 ***(978-0-19-974404-6(1))*** Oxford Univ. Pr., Inc.

Milner, Josh. Piracy in the Americas, 1775-1865: A Short History. 2010. pap. *(978-0-89824-597-4(4))* Royal Fireworks Publishing Co.

Milner, Nicky, et al. Shell Middens in Atlantic Europe. 2007. (Illus.). 336p. 70.00 *(978-1-84217-243-8(3))* Oxbow Bks., Ltd. GBR. Dist: Brown, David Bk. Co., The.

Neal, William J., et al. Atlantic Coast Beaches: A Guide to Ripples, Dunes, & Other Natural Features of the Seashore. 2007. (Illus.). 250p. per. 20.00 *(978-0-87842-534-1(9))* Mountain Pr. Publishing Co., Inc.

Proctor, Noble S. & Lynch, Patrick J. A Field Guide to the Southeast Coast & Gulf of Mexico: Coastal Habitats, Seabirds, Marine Mammals, Fish, & Other Wildlife. 2012. (ENG., Illus.). 386p. pap. 24.00 *(978-0-300-11328-0(5))* Yale Univ. Pr.

Robinson, J. Dennis. Maritime Portsmouth: The Sawtelle Collection. Candee, Richard M., ed. 2011. (Illus.). 212p. 35.00 ***(978-0-915819-38-6(4))*** Portsmouth Marine Society, The.

Sawyer, Roy T. America's Wetland: An Environmental & Cultural History of Tidewater Virginia & North Carolina. 2010. (ENG., Illus.). 272p. (gr. 17). 35.00 *(978-0-8139-2921-7(0))* Univ. Pr. of Virginia.

Simmons, Rick. Defending South Carolina's Coast: The Civil War from Georgetown to Little River. 2009. (Civil War Sesquicentennial Ser.). (ENG., Illus.). 192p. pap. 21.99 *(978-1-59629-780-7(8))* History Pr., The.

Snow, Edward Rowe. Pirates & Buccaneers of the Atlantic Coast. 2011. 350p. 51.95 ***(978-1-258-03489-4(1))*** Literary Licensing, LLC.

Urajner, Melvin C., ed. Coastal Sensitivity to Sea Level Rise - Focusing on the Mid-atlantic Region. 2009. (Climate Change & Its Causes, Effects & Prediction Ser.). 89.00 *(978-1-60741-440-7(6))* Nova Science Pubs., Inc.

ATLANTIC COAST—DESCRIPTION AND TRAVEL

Anderson, Tom. Chasing Dean: Surfing America's Hurricane States. 2011. (ENG., Illus.). 352p. pap. 12.95 ***(978-1-84024-741-1(X))*** Summerdale Pubs. GBR. Dist: Independent Pubs. Group.

Atlantic Coast: Continuous Coverage from Maine to Florida. 2nd ed. Date not set. pap. 39.95 *(978-0-930527-40-2(2))* Maptech, Inc.

Barth, Roland Sawyer. Tales of the Intracoastal Waterway: An Account of a Passage from the Florida Keys to Cape Cod on a Seventeen Foot Catboat. 2010. 124p. pap. 15.00 *(978-1-4490-5391-8(2))* AuthorHouse.

Bishop, Nathaniel Holmes. Voyage of the Paper Canoe: A geographical journey of 2500 miles from Quebec. 2007. (ENG.). 226p. pap. 20.99 *(978-1-4346-1441-4(7))* BiblioBazaar.

—Voyage of the Paper Canoe: A Geographical Journey of 2500 Miles from Quebec. l.t. ed. 2007. (ENG.). 246p. pap. 22.99 *(978-1-4346-1535-0(9))* BiblioBazaar.

Chestney, Linda. Bicycling New Hampshire's Seacoast. rev. ed. 2010. (Illus.). 160p. pap. 17.95 *(978-1-58465-871-9(1))* Univ. Pr. of New England.

Clayton, Sandra. Dolphins under My Bed. 2011. (ENG., Illus.). 288p. pap. 14.95 *(978-1-4081-3288-3(5))* A & C Black GBR. Dist: Macmillan.

D'Arcy, David. Civil War Tours of the Low Country: Beaufort, Hilton Head, & Bluffton, South Carolina. 2008. (Illus.). 144p. pap. 16.95 *(978-0-7643-2790-2(9))* Schiffer Publishing, Ltd.

Devereux, Antelo, Jr. Maine Coast Perspectives. 2008. (Illus.). 80p. pap. 9.99 *(978-0-7643-3015-5(2))* Schiffer Publishing, Ltd.

Eid, Joseph F., Jr. & Gummere, Barker. Streetcars of New Jersey Vol. 1: Atlantic Coast. 2007. (Illus.). 131p. 24.95 *(978-0-9801026-0-4(X))* Eid, Joseph.

Gimlette, John. Theatre of Fish: Travels Through Newfoundland & Labrador. 2006. (Vintage Departures Ser.). (ENG., Illus.). 400p. pap. 15.00 *(978-1-4000-7853-0(9)*, Vintage) Knopf Doubleday Publishing Group.

Githens, Katie. Moon Spotlight Virginia Coast. 2010. (Moon Spotlight Ser.). (ENG.). 90p. pap. 8.95 *(978-1-59880-682-3(3))* Avalon Travel Publishing.

Green, Michelin. Michelin Green Gd French Atlantic Coast. 6th rev. ed. 2010. (Green Guide Ser.). (ENG., Illus.). 480p. pap. 21.99 *(978-1-906261-79-5(2))* Michelin Travel & Lifestyle.

Holy, Norman. Deserted Ocean: A Social History of Depletion. 2009. 156p. 32.49 *(978-1-4389-6494-2(3))*; pap. 19.99 *(978-1-4389-6493-5(5))* AuthorHouse.

Jensen, Jamie. Road Trip USA Atlantic Coast. 2010. (Road Trip USA Ser.). (ENG.). 128p. pap. 9.95 *(978-1-59880-580-2(0))* Avalon Travel Publishing.

Kain, Tara & Kain, Len. DogFriendly. com's East Coast Dog Travel Guide: Premier Edition 6,000+ Dog-Friendly Places! 2008. (Illus.). 677p. pap. 21.95 *(978-0-9795551-2-1(4))* DogFriendly.com, Inc.

Langenscheidt Publishers Staff. Michelin Travel Guide French Atlantic Coast. 5th rev. ed. 2007. (Michelin Travel Guide French Atlantic Coast Ser.). (Illus.). 480p. 21.95 *(978-1-906261-17-7(2))* Michelin.

Leffman, David, et al. Iceland. 4th ed. 2010. (ENG., Illus.). 400p. 21.99 *(978-1-84836-461-5(X))* Rough Guides, Ltd. GBR. Dist: Dorling Kindersley Publishing, Inc.

Locken, E. Travel Journal Dakar. 2010. 192p. pap. 19.99 *(978-0-557-44758-9(5))* Lulu Enterprises Inc.

McCain, Diana Ross. Connecticut Coast: Our Stories in Words & Pictures. 2009. (ENG., Illus.). 288p. 29.95 *(978-0-7627-4723-8(4))* Globe Pequot Pr., The.

Petersen, Kim. Charting the Unknown: Family, Fear, & One Long Boat Ride. 2010. (ENG.). 306p. pap. 16.95 *(978-1-933016-63-4(9))* Behler Pubns., LLC.

Prieur, Benoit. Atlantic Canada. 4th ed. (Illus.). 304p. 17.95 *(978-2-89464-427-0(2))* Ulysses Travel Guides CAN. Dist: Hunter Publishing, Inc.

Rich, Nancy & Spectre, Peter H. Afloat on the Tide: Wooden Dinghies, Prams, Skiffs & Other Rowboats. 2009. (ENG., Illus.). 192p. pap. 29.95 *(978-1-57409-285-1(5))* Sheridan Hse., Inc.

Van Atten, Suzanne. San Juan & Puerto Rico's East Coast: Including Vieques & Culebra. 2010. (Moon Spotlight Ser.). (ENG.). 112p. pap. 7.95 *(978-1-59880-387-7(5))* Avalon Travel Publishing.

Vietze, Andrew. Insiders' Guide to the Maine Coast. 3rd ed. 2009. (Insiders' Guide Ser.). (ENG., Illus.). 328p. pap. 18.95 *(978-0-7627-5039-9(1)*, Insiders' Guide) Globe Pequot Pr., The.

Yow, John. The Armchair Birder Goes Coastal: The Secret Lives of Birds of the Southeastern Shore. 2012. (ENG., Illus.). 256p. 26.00 ***(978-0-8078-3561-6(7))*** Univ. of North Carolina Pr.

Zagat Survey Staff. 2011/12 New Jersey Shore Restaurants (Pocket Guide) 2011. (ZAGAT Pocket Guides). (ENG.). 80p. pap. 6.95 *(978-1-60478-356-8(7))* Zagat Survey.

Zepke, Terrance. Coastal North Carolina. 2nd ed. 2011. (ENG.). 264p. pap. 14.95 ***(978-1-56164-511-4(7))*** Pineapple Pr., Inc.

ATLANTIC COAST LINE RAILROAD

Langley, Albert M., Jr. Atlantic Coast Line Railroad Album. 2007. (Illus.). per. *(978-0-9615257-7-4(0))* Union Station, The.

ATLANTIC MONTHLY (MAGAZINE)

Austin, James C. Fields of the Atlantic Monthly: Letters to an Editor, 1861-1870. 2011. 456p. 57.95 ***(978-1-258-07494-4(X))*** Literary Licensing, LLC.

Goodman, Susan. Republic of Words: The Atlantic Monthly & Its Writers, 1857-1925. 2011. 356p. 29.95 *(978-1-58465-985-3(8))* Univ. Pr. of New England.

ATLANTIC OCEAN

Aller, Renate, photos by. Renate Aller: Oceanscapes. 2010. (ENG., Illus.). 96p. 50.00 *(978-1-934435-23-6(6))* Radius Bks.

Angus, Julie. Rowboat in a Hurricane: My Amazing Journey Across a Changing Atlantic Ocean, 1 vol. 2009. (ENG., Illus.). 272p. pap. 17.95 *(978-1-55365-337-0(8)*, Greystone Bks.) D&M Pubs. CAN. Dist: Perseus-PGW.

Araujo, Ana Lucia. Paths of the Atlantic Slave Trade: Interactions, Identities, & Images. 2011. *(978-1-60497-747-9(7))* Cambria Pr.

—Public Memory of Slavery: Victims & Perpetrators in the South Atlantic. 2010. *(978-1-60497-714-1(0))* Cambria Pr.

Bailyn, Bernard & Denault, Patricia L., eds. Soundings in Atlantic History: Latent Structures & Intellectual Currents, 1500-1830. 2009. (Illus.). 640p. 63.00 *(978-0-674-03276-7(4))* Harvard Univ. Pr.

Bailyn, Bernard, et al. Soundings in Atlantic History: Latent Structures & Intellectual Currents, 1500-1830. Denault, Patricia L., ed. 2011. (ENG., Illus.). 640p. pap. 29.95 *(978-0-674-06177-4(2))* Harvard Univ. Pr.

Beesley, Lawrence. The Loss of the S.S. Titanic: Its Story & Its Lessons. 2008. *(978-1-934941-31-7(X))* Red & Black Pubs.

Belaubre, Christophe & Dym, Jordana, eds. Napoleon's Atlantic: The Impact of Napoleonic Empire in the Atlantic World. (Atlantic World Ser.). (Illus.). 332p. *(978-90-04-18154-0(7))* BRILL.

Belluck, Pam. Island Practice: Cobblestone Rash, Underground Tom, & Other Adventures of a Nantucket Doctor. 2012. (ENG., Illus.). 288p. 25.99 *(978-1-58648-751-5(5))* PublicAffairs.

Biel, Steven. Down with the Old Canoe: A Cultural History of the Titanic Disaster. 2012. (ENG., Illus.). 320p. pap. 15.95 ***(978-0-393-34080-8(5)***, 34080) Norton, W. W. & Co., Inc.

Buchan, Alastair. The Atlantic Sailor's Handbook. 2010. (ENG., Illus.). 192p. pap. 29.95 *(978-1-4081-0011-0(8))* A & C Black GBR. Dist: Macmillan.

Butler, Daniel Allen. The Other Side of the Night: The Carpathia, the California & the Night the Titanic was Lost. 2009. (Illus.). 256p. 29.95 *(978-1-935149-02-6(4))* Casemate Pubs. & Bk. Distributors, LLC.

—The Other Side of the Night: The Carpathia, the Californian & the Night the Titanic was Lost. 2011. (Illus.). 264p. pap. 16.95 *(978-1-935149-85-9(7))* Casemate Pubs. & Bk. Distributors, LLC.

Canny, Nicholas & Morgan, Philip. The Oxford Handbook of the Atlantic World: 1450-1850. 2011. (Oxford Handbooks Ser.). (ENG., Illus.). 752p. 150.00 *(978-0-19-921087-9(X))* Oxford Univ. Pr., Inc.

Christopher, John. Transatlantic Airships. 2010. (ENG., Illus.). 192p. 37.95 *(978-1-84797-161-6(X))* Crowood Pr., Ltd. GBR. Dist: Independent Pubs. Group.

Clarke, James. Atlantic Pilot Atlas. 5th ed. 2011. (ENG., Illus.). 80p. spiral bd. 110.00 *(978-1-4081-2247-1(2))* A & C Black GBR. Dist: Macmillan.

Cramoisi, George. AIR CRASH INVESTIGATIONS: RUNNING OUT of FUEL, How Air Transat 236 Managed to Fly 100 Miles without Fuel & Land Safely. 2010. 196p. pap. 26.50 *(978-0-557-25070-7(6))* Lulu Enterprises Inc.

Cram101 Textbook Reviews. Outlines & Highlights for Atlantic World: History, 1400-1888 by Egerton / Alison / Landers / Lane / Wright, ISBN. 2011. 360p. pap. 34.95 ***(978-1-61812-395-4(5))*** Cram101 Inc.

Dal Lago, Enrico. American Slavery, Atlantic Slavery, & Beyond: The U.S. "Peculiar Institution" in International Perspective. 2012. pap. ***(978-1-59451-585-9(9))*** Paradigm Pubs.

Davenport-Hines, R. P. T. Titanic Lives: Atlantic Voyagers & the Worlds They Came From. 2012. pap. 25.99 ***(978-0-06-187686-8(0)***, Morrow, William & Co.) HarperCollins Pubs.

Davenport-Hines, Richard. Voyagers of the Titanic: Passengers, Sailors, Shipbuilders, Aristocrats, & the Worlds They Came From. 2012. (ENG.). 352p. 26.99 ***(978-0-06-187684-4(4)***, Morrow, William & Co.) HarperCollins Pubs.

—Voyagers of the Titanic: Passengers, Sailors, Shipbuilders, Aristocrats, & the Worlds They Came From. l.t. ed. 2012. (ENG.). 336p. pap. 26.99 ***(978-0-06-210705-3(4)***, HarperLuxe) HarperCollins Pubs.

Egerton, Douglas, et al. Atlantic World: A History, 1400-1888. 2007. (Illus.). 500p. pap. *(978-0-88295-245-1(5))* Davidson, Harlan Inc.

Falola, Toyin & Roberts, Kevin D., eds. The Atlantic World: 1450 — 2000. 2008. (Blacks in the Diaspora Ser.). (ENG., Illus.). 408p. pap. 24.95 *(978-0-253-21943-5(4)*, 0253219434) Indiana Univ. Pr.

Games, Alison & Rothman, Adam. Major Problems in Atlantic History: Documents & Essays. 2007. (Major Problems in American History Ser.). (ENG., Illus.). 512p. (C). per. 95.95 *(978-0-618-61114-0(2)*, 317739) Wadsworth.

Ghione, Sergio. Turtle Island. Date not set. pap. *(978-0-312-31096-7(X))* St. Martin's Pr.

Grannan, Dick. It Ain't over Yet! Big Seas in a Small Boat. 2010. 168p. pap. 19.36 *(978-1-4269-3512-1(9))* Trafford Publishing.

Gruesser, John Cullen. Confluences: Postcolonialism, African American Literary Studies, & the Black Atlantic. 2007. (ENG.). 192p. per. 22.95 *(978-0-8203-3026-6(4))* Univ. of Georgia Pr.

Heyer, Paul. Titanic Century: Media, Myth, & the Making of a Cultural Icon, 1 vol. 2012. (Illus.). 208p. 48.00 ***(978-0-313-39815-5(1)***, A3613C) Greenwood Publishing Group, Inc.

Hsu, K. J. & Weissert, H. J., eds. South Atlantic Paleoceanography. 2010. (ENG.). 364p. pap. 47.00 *(978-0-521-12973-2(7))* Cambridge Univ. Pr.

Hudson, Benjamin, ed. The Studies in the Medieval Atlantic. 2012. (New Middle Ages Ser.). (ENG., Illus.). 304p. 90.00 ***(978-0-230-12083-9(0))*** Palgrave Macmillan.

Karrasch, Werner. The Sea Stallion from Glendalough (Havhingsten fra Glendalough) Roskilde - Dublin 2007, Pictures of a Trial Voyage. 2008. (ENG & DAN., Illus.). 148p. (C). pap. 60.00 *(978-87-85180-45-2(9))* Vikingeskibsmuseet DNK. Dist: Brown, David Bk. Co., The.

Kupperman, Karen Ordahl. The Atlantic in World History. 2012. (New Oxford World History Ser.). (ENG.). 160p. pap. 19.95 ***(978-0-19-533809-6(X))***; (Illus.). 74.00 ***(978-0-19-516074-1(6))*** Oxford Univ. Pr., Inc.

Latymer, Crispin. Where the Ocean Meets the Sky: Solo into the Unknown. 2011. (ENG., Illus.). 224p. pap. 13.95 *(978-1-4081-1402-5(X))* A & C Black GBR. Dist: Macmillan.

Layton, J. Transatlantic Liners: 1899-2004. 2012. (Shire Library). (ENG., Illus.). 64p. pap. 11.95 ***(978-0-7478-1087-2(7))*** Shire Pubns., Ltd. GBR. Dist: Random Hse., Inc.

Lewis, Gwyneth. Two in a Boat: The True Story of a Marital Rite of Passage. 2007. (ENG., Illus.). 304p. pap. 13.95 *(978-0-06-082324-5(0),* HarperPerennial) HarperCollins Pubs.

Lobban, J. H., ed. Fielding: Journal of a Voyage to Lisbon. 2012. (ENG.). 134p. pap. 34.00 ***(978-1-107-60491-9(5))*** Cambridge Univ. Pr.

Locken, E. Travel Journal Antigua & Barbuda. 2010. 192p. pap. 19.99 *(978-0-557-43257-8(X))* Lulu Enterprises Inc.

Lugo-Ortiz, Agnes I. & Rosenthal, Angela. Slave Portraiture in the Atlantic World. 2012. (ENG., Illus.). 500p. 99.00 ***(978-1-107-00439-9(X))*** Cambridge Univ. Pr.

McNeil, D. R. Sex & Race in the Black Atlantic: Mulatto Devils & Multiracial Messiahs. 2009. (Routledge Studies on African & Black Diaspora Ser.). (ENG., Illus.). 204p. 125.00 *(978-0-415-87226-3(X))* Routledge.

Miller, William H. Floating Palaces. 2010. (Illus.). 96p. pap. 34.95 *(978-1-84868-698-4(6))* Amberley Publishing GBR. Dist: Casemate Pubs. & Bk. Distributors, LLC.

Moore, Rachel A. Forty Miles from the Sea: Xalapa, the Public Sphere, & the Atlantic World in Nineteenth-Century Mexico. 2011. (ENG., Illus.). 240p. 49.95 *(978-0-8165-2933-9(7))* Univ. of Arizona Pr.

Morozov, Eugene G., et al. Abyssal Channels in the Atlantic Ocean: Water Structure & Flows. 2010. (ENG., Illus.). xxii, 266p. 129.00 *(978-90-481-9357-8(5),* 9048193575) Springer.

Petersen, Kim. Charting the Unknown: Family, Fear, & One Long Boat Ride. 2010. (ENG.). 306p. pap. 16.95 *(978-1-933016-63-4(9))* Behler Pubns., LLC.

Racine, Karen. The Human Tradition in the Atlantic World, 1500-1850. 2010. (Human Tradition around the World Ser.). (ENG.). 283p. pap. 26.95 *(978-1-4422-0698-4(5))* Rowman & Littlefield Publishers, Inc.

Racine, Karen & Mamigonian, Beatriz G. The Human Tradition in the Atlantic World, 1500-1850. 2010. *(978-1-4422-0699-1(3))* Rowman & Littlefield Publishers, Inc.

Racine/Mamigonian. The Human Tradition in the Atlantic World, 1500D1850. 2010. (Human Tradition around the World Ser.). (ENG.). 286p. 75.00 *(978-1-4422-0697-7(7))* Rowman & Littlefield Publishers, Inc.

Roller, Duane W. Through the Pillars of Herakles: Greco-Roman Exploration of the Atlantic. 2008. pap. 39.95 *(978-0-415-48696-5(3))* Routledge.

Roussel, Mike & Warwick, Sam. Shipwrecks of the Cunard Line. 2012. (ENG., Illus.). 168p. 34.95 ***(978-0-7524-6578-4(3))*** History Pr. Ltd.,The GBR. Dist: Independent Pubs. Group.

Russell, Jane. The RCC Pilotage Foundation Atlantic Crossing Guide. 6th ed. 2010. (ENG., Illus.). 240p. 75.00 *(978-1-4081-1380-6(5))* A & C Black GBR. Dist: Macmillan.

Sandz, Victoria & Marx, Robert F. Encyclopedia of Western Atlantic Shipwrecks & Sunken Treasure. alt. ed. 2006. (ENG., Illus.). 240p. per. 49.95 *(978-0-7864-2902-8(X))* McFarland & Co., Inc. Pubs.

Sheil, Inger. Titanic Valour: The Life of Fifth Officer Harold Lowe. 2012. (ENG., Illus.). 160p. pap. 16.95 ***(978-0-7524-6996-6(7))*** History Pr. Ltd.,The GBR. Dist: Independent Pubs. Group.

Stemm, Greg & Kingsley, Sean A., eds. Oceans Odyssey: Deep-Sea Shipwrecks in the English Channel, Straits of Gibraltar & Atlantic Ocean. 2012. (Odyssey Marine Exploration Reports: 1). (ENG., Illus.). 300p. (C). 50.00 *(978-1-84217-415-9(0))* Oxbow Bks., Ltd. GBR. Dist: Brown, David Bk. Co., The.

—Oceans Odyssey II: Underwater Heritage Management & Deep-Sea Shipwrecks in the English Channel & Atlantic Ocean. 2011. (Odyssey Marine Exploration Reports: 2). (ENG., Illus.). 354p. (C). 50.00 *(978-1-84217-442-5(8))* Oxbow Bks., Ltd. GBR. Dist: Brown, David Bk. Co., The.

Suttles, Sherry A. & Atlantic Beach Historical Society. Atlantic Beach. 2009. (Images of America Ser.). (ENG., Illus.). 128p. pap. 21.99 *(978-0-7385-6820-1(1))* Arcadia Publishing.

Tibballs, Geoff. Voices from the Titanic: The Epic Story of the Tragedy from the People Who Were There. 2012. (ENG.). 526p. pap. 14.95 ***(978-1-61608-605-3(X)***, 608605) Skyhorse Publishing Co., Inc.

The Titanic Reports: The Official Conclusions of the 1912 Inquiries into the Titanic Disaster. 2008. *(978-1-934941-11-9(5))* Red & Black Pubs.

United States. Navy Dept. Report & Charts of the Cruise of the U S Brig Dolphin, Made under Direction of the Navy Department. 2006 152p. per. 18.99 *(978-1-4255-1152-4(X))* MPublishing.

Villiers, Alan. Wild Ocean: The Story of the North Atlantic & the Men Who Sailed It. 2011. 350p. 51.95 ***(978-1-258-06432-7(4))*** Literary Licensing, LLC.

Walker, Dylan, et al. Whales & Dolphins of the European Atlantic: The Bay of Biscay, English Channel, Celtic Sea & Coastal SW Ireland. 2nd ed. 2008. (Illus.). 88p. pap. 30.00 *(978-1-903657-31-7(8))* Trans-Atlantic Pubns., Inc.

Weatheritt, Les. Your First Atlantic Crossing: A Planning Guide for Passagemakers. 3rd ed. 2008. (ENG., Illus.). 192p. pap. 29.95 *(978-0-7136-8949-5(8))* A & C Black GBR. Dist: Macmillan.

Wels, Susan. Amelia Earhart: The Thrill of It. 2009. (ENG., Illus.). 224p. 35.00 *(978-0-7624-3763-4(4),* Running Pr.) Running Pr. Bk. Pubs.

Williams, Caroline A. Bridging the Early Modern Atlantic World: People, Products, & Practices on the Move. 2009. (Illus.). 276p. 124.95 *(978-0-7546-6681-3(6))* Ashgate Publishing Co.

Williams, Julie Hedgepeth. A Rare Titanic Family: The Caldwells' Story of Survival. 2011. (ENG.). 208p. pap. 21.95 ***(978-1-58838-282-5(6)***, NewSouth Bks.) NewSouth, Inc.

Wilson, Frances. How to Survive the Titanic: The Sinking of J. Bruce Ismay. 2012. (ENG.). 352p. pap. 15.99 ***(978-0-06-209455-1(6)***, HarperPerennial) HarperCollins Pubs.

Winchester, Simon. Atlantic: Great Sea Battles, Heroic Discoveries, Titanic Storms, & a Vast Ocean of a Million Stories. (P. S. Ser.). (ENG., 2011. Illus.). 512p. pap. 15.99 *(978-0-06-170262-4(5),* HarperPerennial) 2010. (Illus.). 320p. 27.99 *(978-0-06-170258-7(7))* 2010. 492p. pap. 27.99 *(978-0-06-200249-5(X),* HarperLuxe) HarperCollins Pubs.

Yerxa, Donald A. Recent Themes in the History of Africa & the Atlantic World: Historians in Conversation. Yerxa, Donald A., ed. 2008. (Historians in Conversation Ser.). 120p. pap. 21.95 *(978-1-57003-758-0(2))* Univ. of South Carolina Pr.

Young, Filson. Titanic. 2011. (Illus.). 304p. 24.95 ***(978-1-4456-0407-7(8))*** Amberley Publishing GBR. Dist: Casemate Pubs. & Bk. Distributors, LLC.

ATLANTIC PROVINCES

Here are entered works dealing with the provinces of Nova Scotia, New Brunswick, Prince Edward Island, and Newfoundland and Labrador.

see also Maritime Provinces

Carbert, Louise. Rural Women's Leadership in Atlantic Canada: First-Hand Perspectives on Local Public Life & Participation in Electoral Politics. 2006. (ENG., Illus.). 176p. *(978-0-8020-9125-3(3))* Univ. of Toronto Pr.

Eastern Atlantic Canada. pap. *(978-0-660-54775-6(9))* Canadian Government Publishing.

Fakhri, Mark. Community Economic Development in Atlantic Canad. 2010. 52p. pap. *(978-3-639-23662-0(9))* VDM Verlag Dr. Mueller e.K.

McKenna, Peter. Terminal Damage: The Politics of VLTs in Atlantic Canada. 2008. (ENG.). 240p. pap. 26.95 *(978-1-55266-264-9(0))* Fernwood Publishing Co., Ltd. CAN. Dist: Independent Pubs. Group.

Wyile, Herb. Anne of Tim Hortons: Globalization & the Reshaping of Atlantic-Canadian Literature. 2011. (Illus.). 294p. (C). pap. 42.95 *(978-1-55458-326-3(8))* Wilfrid Laurier Univ. Pr. CAN. Dist: Univ. of Toronto Pr.

ATLANTIC PROVINCES—DESCRIPTION AND TRAVEL

Chiang, Jack. Celebrating Atlantic Canada, 1 vol. 2006. (ENG., Illus.). 192p. 27.95 *(978-1-55041-347-2(3))* Fitzhenry & Whiteside, Ltd. CAN. Dist: Ingram Pub. Services.

Ernst, Chloe. Scenic Driving Atlantic Canada: Nova Scotia, New Brunswick, Prince Edward Island, Newfoundland, & Labrador. 2011. (Scenic Driving Ser.). (ENG., Illus.). 264p. pap. 15.95 *(978-0-7627-6481-5(3))* Globe Pequot Pr., The.

Fodor's Travel Publications, Inc. Staff. Nova Scotia & Atlantic Canada: With New Brunswick, Prince Edward Island, & Newfoundland & Labrador. 12th ed. 2012. (Fodor's Gold Guides). (ENG.). 320p. pap. 16.99 ***(978-0-307-92835-1(7)***, Fodor's) Fodor's Travel Pubns.

Karr, Paul. Nova Scotia, New Brunswick & Prince Edward Island. 8th ed. 2010. (Frommer's Complete Guides: 770). (ENG., Illus.). 352p. pap. 16.99 *(978-0-470-58250-3(2),* Frommers) Wiley, John & Sons, Inc.

Latymer, Crispin. Where the Ocean Meets the Sky: Solo into the Unknown. 2011. (ENG., Illus.). 224p. pap. 13.95 *(978-1-4081-1402-5(X))* A & C Black GBR. Dist: Macmillan.

Michelin Travel Publications Staff. Atlantic Canada. 2009. (Green Guide Ser.). (ENG., Illus.). 288p. pap. 19.95 *(978-1-906261-57-3(1))* Michelin Travel & Lifestyle.

Mowat, Farley. Bay of Spirits: A Love Story. 2007. (ENG., Illus.). 320p. 25.95 *(978-0-7867-1994-5(X))* Da Capo Pr., Inc.

—Bay of Spirits: A Love Story. 2007. (ENG., Illus.). 376p. pap. 18.95 *(978-0-7710-6505-7(1),* McClelland & Stewart) McClelland & Stewart CAN. Dist: Random Hse., Inc.

Rogers, Barbara Radcliffe & Rogers, Stillman. Travel Adventures Canada's Atlantic Provinces. 4th ed. 2009. 672p. pap. 25.99 *(978-1-58843-691-7(8))* Hunter Publishing, Inc.

ATLANTIC PROVINCES—HISTORY

de la Fuente, Alejandro. Havana & the Atlantic in the Sixteenth Century. 2008. (ENG., Illus.). 304p. 44.00 *(978-0-8078-3192-2(1))* Univ. of North Carolina Pr.

Dubois, Laurent & Rabinowitz, Richard. Revolution! The Atlantic World Reborn. Bender, Thomas, ed. 2011. (ENG., Illus.). 288p. 65.00 *(978-1-904832-94-2(6))* Giles, D. Ltd. GBR. Dist: Antique Collectors' Club.

Eaton, Doris. A Lifetime of Rug Hooking. 2011. (ENG., Illus.). 328p. pap. 26.95 ***(978-1-55109-846-3(6))*** Down East Bks.

Fitzpatrick, Deanne. Inspired Rug-Hooking: Turning Atlantic Canadian Life into Art, 1 vol. 2011. (ENG., Illus.). 144p. pap. 22.95 ***(978-1-55109-780-0(X))*** Down East Bks.

Fleming, Andrew. Bathroom Book of Atlantic Canada Trivia: Weird, Wacky & Wild. 2007. (ENG., Illus.). 168p. pap. *(978-1-897278-21-5(7))* Blue Bike Bks. CAN. Dist: Lone Pine Publishing.

Klooster, Wim. Revolutions in the Atlantic World: A Comparative History. 2009. (ENG., Illus.). 216p. pap. 22.00 *(978-0-8147-4789-6(2))* New York Univ. Pr.

Lord, Walter. The Crucible: 22 Related Readings. 2009. 9.89 *(978-0-9729765-1-0(5),* Everbind) Marco Bk. Co.

MacNeill, Tim. Life in a Cultural Economy. 2009. 140p. pap. *(978-3-639-11318-1(7))* VDM Verlag Dr. Mueller e.K.

McCain, Diana Ross. Connecticut Coast: Our Stories in Words & Pictures. 2009. (ENG., Illus.). 288p. 29.95 *(978-0-7627-4723-8(4))* Globe Pequot Pr., The.

McNeil, Daniel. Sex & Race in the Black Atlantic: Mulatto Devils & Multiracial Messiahs. 2011. (ENG., Illus.). 204p. pap. 39.95 ***(978-0-415-89391-6(7))*** Routledge.

Nelson, Mary. Shackles & Webs. 2009. 104p. pap. 12.99 *(978-1-4251-6250-4(9))* Trafford Publishing.

O'Reilly, William. The Atlantic World. 2011. (Illus.). 736p. (C). 236.00 *(978-0-415-46704-9(7))* Routledge.

Scott, Rebecca J. & Hébrard, Jean M. Freedom Papers: An Atlantic Odyssey in the Age of Emancipation. 2012. (ENG., Illus.). 288p. 35.00 ***(978-0-674-04774-7(5))*** Harvard Univ. Pr.

Summkoski, Corey. Inventing Atlantic Canada. 2011. ***(978-1-4426-4288-1(2))***; pap. ***(978-1-4426-1158-0(8))*** Univ. of Toronto Pr.

Varga, Darrell. Rain/Drizzle/Fog: Film & Television in Atlantic Canada. 2008. (Cinemas off-Centre: Ser.). (Illus.). 300p. pap. 34.95 *(978-1-55238-248-6(6))* Univ. of Calgary Pr. CAN. Dist: Michigan State Univ. Pr.

White, Paul. East Coast NHLers: The stories of the lives & careers of players from the Maritimes & Newfoundland. 2011. (ENG.). 168p. 16.95 ***(978-0-88780-969-9(3))*** Formac Publishing Co., Ltd. CAN. Dist: Casemate Pubs. & Bk. Distributors, LLC.

Yerxa, Donald A., ed. Recent Themes in the History of Africa & the Atlantic World: Historians in Conversation. 2008. (Historians in Conversation Ser.). (ENG.). 120p. 39.95 *(978-1-57003-757-3(4))* Univ. of South Carolina Pr.

ATLANTIC STATES

Haviland, Beverly. Henry James' Last Romance: Making Sense of the Past & the American Scene. 2009. (Cambridge Studies in American Literature & Culture Ser.). (ENG.). 300p. pap. 41.00 *(978-0-521-10996-3(5))* Cambridge Univ. Pr.

Kelton, Paul. Epidemics & Enslavement: Biological Catastrophe in the Native Southeast, 1492-1715. 2009. (Indians of the Southeast Ser.). (ENG., Illus.). 312p. pap. 24.95 *(978-0-8032-2791-0(4))* Univ. of Nebraska Pr.

Kettlewell, John. The Intracoastal Waterway Chartbook: Norfolk, Virginia to Miami, Florida. Kettlewell, Leslie, ed. 5th ed. 2008. (ENG., Illus.). 288p. spiral bd. 69.95 *(978-0-07-154579-2(4),* 0071545794, International Marine/Ragged Mountain Pr.) McGraw-Hill Professional Publishing.

Lindsay, Lisa A. Captives as Commodities: The Transatlantic Slave Trade. 2007. (Connections Series for World History Ser.). (ENG., Illus.). 208p. (C). per. 27.20 *(978-0-13-194215-8(8),* Prentice Hall) Prentice Hall PTR.

Military Historical Society of Massachusetts Staff. Operations on the Atlantic Coast 1861-1865, Virginia, 1862,1864, Vicksburg. (Papers of the Military Historical Society of Massachusetts Ser.). 585p. reprint ed. 98.00 *(978-0-7222-8099-7(8))* Library Reprints, Inc.

Nelson, Gil. Atlantic Coastal Plain Wildflowers: A Guide to Common Wildflowers of the Coastal Regions of Virginia, North Carolina, South Carolina, Georgia, & Northeastern Florida. 2006. (Falcon Guide Ser.). (ENG., Illus.). 272p. pap. 24.95 *(978-0-7627-3433-7(7),* Falcon Guides) Globe Pequot Pr., The.

Phillips, Joshua Daniel. 1,800 Miles: Striving to End Sexual Violence, One Step at a Time. 2010. (ENG.). 184p. pap. 14.95 *(978-1-60037-677-1(0))* Morgan James Publishing.

ATLANTIC STATES—DESCRIPTION AND TRAVEL

Alexander, James. Alexander's Transatlantic Sketches: Comprising Visits to the Most Interesting Scenes in North & South America, & the West Indies. with Notes on Negro Slavery. 2007. (Travel in America Ser.). (ENG.). 392p. 49.95 *(978-1-4290-0160-1(7))* Applewood Bks.

—Alexander's Transatlantic Sketches: Comprising Visits to the Most Interesting Scenes in North & South America, & the West Indies. with Notes on Negro Slavery & Canadian Emigration. 2007. (Travel in America Ser.). (ENG.). 392p. per. 24.95 *(978-1-4290-0161-8(5))* Applewood Bks.

Brooks, Elbridge Streeter. The Century Book of the American Revolution. 249p. reprint ed. 98.00 *(978-0-7222-7691-4(5))* Library Reprints, Inc.

Buckingham, James. America Vol. 1: Historical, Statistic, & Descriptive. 2007. (Travel in America Ser.). (ENG.). 660p. 49.95 *(978-1-4290-0222-6(0))*; 532p. 49.95 *(978-1-4290-0226-4(3))*; 584p. per. 49.95 *(978-1-4290-0224-0(7))*; 532p. per. 24.95 *(978-1-4290-0227-1(1))* Applewood Bks.

Buckingham, James Silk. America: Historical, Statistic, & Descriptive. 2011. (Cambridge Library Collection - Travel & Exploration Ser.). (ENG.). 584p. pap. 43.00 ***(978-1-108-03252-0(4))***; 530p. pap. 39.99 ***(978-1-108-03251-3(6))***; (Illus.). 634p. pap. 43.00 ***(978-1-108-03253-7(2))*** Cambridge Univ. Pr.

—America, Historical, Statistic, & Descriptive. 2010. (ENG.). 526p. pap. 40.75 *(978-1-177-50593-2(2))*; 534p. pap. 40.75 *(978-1-147-03250-5(5))*; 530p. pap. 40.75 *(978-1-145-08760-6(4))*; 530p. pap. 40.75 *(978-1-144-04365-8(4))*; 524p. pap. 40.75 *(978-1-142-62811-6(6))* BiblioBazaar.

—America, Historical, Statistic, & Descriptive. 2009. 452p. pap. *(978-1-4590-2629-2(2))*; 528p. pap. *(978-0-217-16444-3(7))*; 554p. pap. *(978-1-4588-0499-0(2))* Books LLC.

—America, Historical, Statistic, & Descriptive. 2010. (Illus.). 400p. pap. 28.70 *(978-1-154-62428-1(5))* General Bks. LLC.

—America, Historical, Statistic & Descriptive. 2010. 530p. pap. 40.75 *(978-1-177-39171-9(6))*; (ENG.). 634p. pap. 45.75 *(978-1-176-17661-4(7))* BiblioBazaar.

—America, Historical, Statistic & Descriptive. 2010. 308p. pap. *(978-1-151-87561-7(9))* Books LLC.

—America, Historical, Statistic & Descriptive. 2010. 262p. pap. 34.14 *(978-1-151-87555-6(4))* General Bks. LLC.

—America, Historical Statistic, & Descriptive. 2010. (ENG.). 530p. pap. 40.75 *(978-1-177-39217-4(8))* BiblioBazaar.

—America, Historical Statistic, & Descriptive. 2010. 444p. pap. *(978-1-151-87558-7(9))* Books LLC.

—America, historical, statistic, & descriptive. with a Portrait. 2011. (ENG.). 539p. pap. 40.75 *(978-1-240-91536-1(5))*; 593p. pap. 44.75 *(978-1-240-91435-7(0))* BiblioBazaar. (British Library, Historical Print Editions).

Chester, Greville. Chester's Transatlantic Sketches. 2007. (Travel in America Ser.). (ENG.). 432p. per. 24.95 *(978-1-4290-0417-6(7))* Applewood Bks.

—Chester's Transatlantic Sketches in the West Indies, South America, Canada, & the United States. 2007. (Travel in America Ser.). (ENG.). 432p. 49.95 *(978-1-4290-0416-9(9))* Applewood Bks.

Coke, E. A Subaltern's Furlough. 2007. (Travel in America Ser.). (ENG.). 428p. 49.95 *(978-1-4290-0146-5(1))* Applewood Bks.

—A Subaltern's Furlough: Descriptive of Scenes in Various Parts of the United States, Upper & Lower Canada, New-Brunswick, & Nova Scotia, During the Summer & Autumn of 1832. 2007. (Travel in America Ser.). (ENG.). 428p. per. 24.95 *(978-1-4290-0147-2(X))* Applewood Bks.

Finch, John. Finch's Travels in the United States. 2007. (Travel in America Ser.). (ENG.). 480p. 49.95 *(978-1-4290-0162-5(3))* Applewood Bks.

—Finch's Travels in the United States 1833: And Canada, Containing Some Account of Their Scientific Institutions, & a Few Notices of the Geology & Mineralogy of Those Countries. 2007. (Travel in America Ser.). (ENG.). 480p. per. 24.95 *(978-1-4290-0163-2(1))* Applewood Bks.

Finlayson, Archibald. A Trip to America. 2007. (Travel in America Ser.). (ENG.). 60p. per. 24.95 *(978-1-4290-0441-1(X))* Applewood Bks.

—A Trip to America: A Lecture. 2007. (Travel in America Ser.). (ENG.). 60p. 49.95 *(978-1-4290-0440-4(1))* Applewood Bks.

Karlin, Adam, et al. New York Washington DC & the Mid-Atlantic Trips. 2009. (Regional Guide Ser.). (ENG., Illus.). 354p. pap. 19.99 *(978-1-74179-731-2(4))* Lonely Planet Pubns.

Latham, Henry. Black & White: A Journal of a Three Months' Tour in the United States. 2007. (Travel in America Ser.). (ENG.). 324p. 49.95 *(978-1-4290-0406-0(1))*; per. 24.95 *(978-1-4290-0407-7(X))* Applewood Bks.

—Black & White: A Journal of a Three Months' Tour in the United States. 2009. (Cambridge Library Collection - History Ser.). 324p. pap. 24.99 *(978-1-108-00394-0(X))* Cambridge Univ. Pr.

Leviton, Alex, et al. The Carolinas, Georgia & the South Trips. 2009. (Regional Guide Ser.). (ENG., Illus.). 440p. pap. 19.99 *(978-1-74179-730-5(6))* Lonely Planet Pubns.

Lillard, David Edwin. Journey Through Hallowed Ground: The Official Guide to Where America Happened from Gettysburg to Monticello. 2006. (Capital Travels Ser.). (Illus.). 288p. pap. 20.00 *(978-1-933102-24-5(1))* Capital Bks., Inc.

Lyell, Charles. Lyell's Travels in North America. 2007. (Travel in America Ser.). (ENG.). 292p. 49.95 *(978-1-4290-0324-7(3))*; 340p. 49.95 *(978-1-4290-0326-1(X))* Applewood Bks.

—Lyell's Travels in North America. 2007. 180p. per. 11.95 *(978-1-59462-813-9(0),* Book Jungle) Standard Pubns., Inc.

—Lyell's Travels in North America, Canada, & Nova Scotia with Geological Observations. 2007. (Travel in America Ser.). (ENG.). 340p. per. 24.95 *(978-1-4290-0327-8(8))* Applewood Bks.

Mobil Travel Gd, ed. Mobil Travel Gd Coastal Se 2009. 2009. (Regional Guide Ser.). 208p. pap. 17.99 *(978-0-8416-1126-9(2))* Langenscheidt Publishing Group.

Molloy, Johnny. Beach & Coastal Camping in the Southeast. 2006. (ENG., Illus.). 208p. per. 18.95 *(978-0-8130-3000-5(5))* Univ. Pr. of Florida.

Nichols, Peter. Sea Change: Alone Across the Atlantic in a Wooden Boat, 1 vol. 2010. (ENG.). 256p. pap. 16.95 *(978-1-57409-292-9(8))* Sheridan Hse., Inc.

Perrier, Dianne. Interstate 95: The Road to Sun & Sand. 2010. (ENG., Illus.). 256p. pap. 24.95 *(978-0-8130-3480-5(9))* Univ. Pr. of Florida.

Posner, Stan & Phillips-Posner, Sandra. Drive I-95: Exit by Exit Info, Maps, History, & Trivia. 4th ed. 2007. (Illus.). 208p. pap. 23.95 *(978-1-894979-88-7(5))* Travelsmart Publishing CAN. Dist: Partners Bk. Distributing, Inc.

Royall, Anne. Mrs. Royall's America, 1828 to 1831, 7 vols. in 6. Incl. Pt. 2. Mrs. Royall's Pennsylvania: Or Travels Continued in the United States. 16.00 Pt. 3. Mrs. Royall's Southern Tour: Or Second Series of the Black Book. 16.00 reprint ed. 95.00 *(978-0-404-56830-6(0))* AMS Pr., Inc.

Wilson, Rufus. Rambles in Colonial Byways. 2007. (Travel in America Ser.). (ENG.). 316p. 49.95 *(978-1-4290-0532-6(7))*; 264p. 49.95 *(978-1-4290-0534-0(3))*; 264p. per. 24.95 *(978-1-4290-0535-7(1))* Applewood Bks.

ATLANTIS (LEGENDARY PLACE)

Ashe, Geoffrey. Atlantis. 2012. (Art & Imagination Ser.). (ENG., Illus.). 128p. pap. 14.95 ***(978-0-500-81051-4(6)***, 581051) Thames & Hudson.

Bramwell, James. Lost Atlantis. 2007. (ENG.). 286p. 43.95 *(978-0-548-00714-3(4))* Kessinger Publishing, LLC.

Brooks, Dennis. Atlantis Conspiracy: The Lost Continent: Help Solve the Mystery! Cayce's Predictions Explained. 2006. (Illus.). 264p. per. 15.50 *(978-1-60002-100-8(X),* 3946) Mountain Valley Publishing, LLC.

Cayce, Edgar. Atlantis. 2010. 166p. 15.95 *(978-0-87604-588-6(3))* A.R.E. Pr.

Cayce, Edgar Evans, et al. Mysteries of Atlantis. 2007. (Illus.). 210p. per. 14.95 *(978-0-87604-574-9(3))* A.R.E. Pr.

Cayce, Hugh Lynn. The Lost Continent of Atlantis: The Searchlight, V3, Nos. 13-14, May 1-15 1951. 2011. 20p. 35.95 ***(978-1-258-04883-9(3))*** Literary Licensing, LLC.
Chapman, Carol. Arrival of the Gods in Egypt: Hidden Mysteries of Soul & Myth Finally Revealed. Balsley, Clair, ed. 2008. (Illus.). 300p. pap. 16.95 *(978-0-9754691-5-6(0))* SunTopaz LLC.
Cooper, Diana. Discover Atlantis: A Guide to Reclaiming the Wisdom of the Ancients. 2007. (ENG., Illus.). 272p. per. 16.95 *(978-1-84409-104-1(X))* Findhorn Pr. GBR. Dist: Independent Pubs. Group.
Cox, Simon & Foster, Mark. An A to Z of Atlantis. 2008. (ENG., Illus.). 240p. pap. 15.95 *(978-1-84596-263-0(X))* Mainstream Publishing Co., Ltd. GBR. Dist: Independent Pubs. Group.
Danelek, J. Allan. Atlantis: Lessons from the Lost Continent. 2008. (ENG., Illus.). 264p. per. 15.95 *(978-0-7387-1162-1(4))* Llewellyn Pubns.
Donnelly, Ignatius. Atlantis: The Antediluvian World. 2nd rev. ed. 2006. (ENG., Illus.). 384p. per. 27.95 *(978-1-58509-268-0(1))* Book Tree, The.
—Atlantis: The Antediluvian World. 504p. 2009. 53.95 *(978-1-120-10748-0(2))* 2007. (ENG.). per. 38.95 *(978-0-548-38382-7(0))* Kessinger Publishing, LLC.
Donnelly, Ignatius. Atlantis - the Antediluvian World. 2011. 502p. pap. 16.95 ***(978-1-4474-0341-8(X))*** Thorndike Pr.
Drown, Ruth B. Wisdom from Atlantis. 152p. 2008. 36.95 *(978-1-4367-0967-5(9))* 2007. (ENG.). per. 21.95 *(978-1-4325-7756-8(5))* Kessinger Publishing, LLC.
Flem-Ath, Rand & Flem-Ath, Rose. Atlantis Beneath the Ice: The Fate of the Lost Continent. 2012. (ENG.). 240p. pap. ***(978-1-59143-137-4(9))*** Bear & Co.
Frazee, Charles. Atlantis. Miller, Zachary N., ed. 2007. (Ancient Greek Mystery Ser.). (J). pap. 4.95 *(978-1-58659-216-5(5))* Artesian Pr.
Godwin, Joscelyn. Atlantis & the Cycles of Time: Prophecies, Traditions, & Occult Revelations. 2011. (ENG.). 1p. pap. 19.95 *(978-1-59477-262-7(2))* Inner Traditions International, Ltd.
Gordon, J. S. The Rise & Fall of Atlantis: And the Mysterious Origins of Human Civilization. 2008. (ENG., Illus.). 384p. per. 19.95 *(978-1-905857-24-1(1)*, Watkins Publishing) Duncan Baird Pubs. GBR. Dist: Sterling Publishing Co., Inc.
Greer, John Michael. Atlantis: Ancient Legacy, Hidden Prophecy. 2007. (ENG.). 264p. 21.95 *(978-0-7387-0978-9(6))* Llewellyn Pubns.
Hall, Manly P. Atlantis: An Interpretation. 2011. 54p. 36.95 ***(978-1-258-00126-1(8))*** Literary Licensing, LLC.
Jakovljevic, Ranko. Atlantida U Srbiji. 2008. (Illus.). 264p. *(978-86-7540-091-2(8))* Pesic I Sinovi, Izdavacko Preduzece.
Joseph, Frank. Atlantis & 2012: The Science of the Lost Civilization & the Prophecies of the Maya. 2010. (ENG., Illus.). 1p. pap. 16.00 *(978-1-59143-112-1(3)*, 1309790) Bear & Co.
—Atlantis & Other Lost Worlds: New Evidence of Ancient Secrets. 2008. (Illus.). 208p. 12.99 *(978-0-7858-2431-2(6)*, Chartwell) Book Sales, Inc.
—La Destruccion de la Atlantida: Convincente Evidencia de la Precipitada Caida de la Legendaria Civilizacion. 2007. (SPA & ENG., Illus.). 1p. per. 18.00 *(978-0-89281-141-0(2)*, Healing Arts Pr.) Inner Traditions International, Ltd.
King, David. Finding Atlantis: A True Story of Genius, Madness, & an Extraordinary Quest for a Lost World. 2006. (ENG., Illus.). 320p. per. 13.95 *(978-1-4000-4753-6(6)*, Three Rivers Pr.) Crown Publishing Group.
Kuman, Maria. Atlantis. pap. 20.00 *(978-1-893637-19-1(0))* Health & Happiness Bks.
Lace, William W. & Abrams, Dennis. Atlantis. 2012. (Lost Worlds & Mysterious Civilizations Ser.). (gr. 6-12). 35.00 *(978-1-60413-969-3(2)*, Chelsea Hse.) Facts On File, Inc.
Luis, Espejo José. Los Hijos Del Edén. (SPA., Illus.). 672p. 34.95 *(978-84-666-4182-1(3))* Ediciones B ESP. Dist: Ediciones Urano S. A.
Menzies, Gavin. The Lost Empire of Atlantis: History's Greatest Mystery Revealed. (ENG.). 416p. 2012. pap. 16.99 ***(978-0-06-204949-0(6)***, William Morrow Paperbacks) 2011. 26.99 *(978-0-06-204948-3(8)*, Morrow, William & Co.) HarperCollins Pubs.
Past Eras Awaken II: Atlantis-the Realm of the Incas, Abd-Ru-Shin, Cassandra, John the Baptist, Jesus of Nazareth. 507p. pap. 20.00 *(978-1-898853-07-7(X))* Grail Foundation Pr.
Plaskett, Douglas. Talking to Heaven... Atlantis Again? 2009. 136p. pap. 16.99 *(978-0-557-08397-8(4))* Lulu Enterprises Inc.
Plato. Timaeus: And, Critias. 2011. 186p. pap. 9.99 ***(978-1-61720-106-6(5))*** Wilder Pubns., Ltd.
Santos, Arysio. Atlantis: The Lost Continent Finally Found. 2011. (ENG., Illus.). 368p. pap. 21.95 *(978-1-55643-956-8(3))* North Atlantic Bks.
Scott-Elliot, W. The Story of Atlantis. 2009. (ENG.). 82p. pap. 7.96 *(978-1-4385-2077-3(8)*, Book Jungle) Standard Pubns., Inc.
—The Story of Atlantis & the Lost Lemuri. 2007. 112p. per. 9.95 *(978-1-60312-365-5(2))*; (ENG.). 22.95 *(978-1-60312-703-5(8))* Aegypan.
—The Story of Atlantis & the Lost Lemuri. 2008. 140p. 21.99 *(978-0-554-37109-2(X))* BiblioBazaar.
—The Story of Atlantis & the Lost Lemuria. 2008. 140p. 24.99 *(978-0-554-27806-3(5))* 2007 122p. pap. 18.99 *(978-1-4346-4032-1(9))* 2007. 136p. pap. 19.99 *(978-1-4346-4079-6(5))* BiblioBazaar.
—The Story of Atlantis & the Lost Lemuria. 2007. 124p. per. *(978-1-4065-3909-7(0))* Dodo Pr.
Smit, Wolter. Was This Atlantis. 2011. 200p. pap. 23.95 ***(978-1-4475-2250-8(8))*** Lulu Enterprises Inc.
Spence, Lewis. The History of Atlantis. (Mystic Traveller & Atlantis Reprints Ser.). 238p. 16.95 *(978-0-932813-30-5(5))* Adventures Unlimited Pr.
—The History of Atlantis. 2007. (ENG.). 288p. per. 13.95 *(978-1-60206-835-3(6))* Cosimo, Inc.
Steiner, Rudolf. Atlantis: The Fate of a Lost Land & Its Secret Knowledge. 2007. (Pocket Library of Spiritual Wisdom Ser.). (Illus.). 102p. per. *(978-1-85584-194-9(0))* Steiner, Rudolf Pr.
Svadihatra, Julia. The Re-Birth of an Atlantean Queen. 2009. 444p. pap. 27.95 *(978-1-4401-4115-7(0))* iUniverse, Inc.
Sweeney, Emmet. Atlantis: The Evidence of Science. 2010. (Illus.). pap. 22.95 *(978-0-87586-771-7(5))*; 200p. pap. 32.95 *(978-0-87586-772-4(3))* Algora Publishing.
Vidal-Naquet. The Atlantis Story: A Short History of Plato's Myth. 2007. (C). pap. *(978-0-85989-804-1(0))* Univ. of Exeter Pr.
Vidal-Naquet, Pierre. The Atlantis Story: A Short History of Plato's Myth. Lloyd, Janet, tr. from FRE. 2007. (ENG., Illus.). 208p. (C). 40.00 *(978-0-85989-805-8(9))* Univ. of Exeter Pr. GBR. Dist: Brown, David Bk. Co., The.
Webb, Stuart. Atlantis & Other Lost Worlds. 2012. (Paranormal Files Ser.). (ENG.). 80p. (YA). (gr. 7-12). lib. bdg. 33.25 ***(978-1-4488-7173-5(5))*** Rosen Publishing Group, Inc., The.
Welch, Richard W. Roots of Cataclysm: Geopulsation & the Atlantis Supervolcano. 2009. 32.95 *(978-0-87586-733-5(2))*; 224p. pap. 22.95 *(978-0-87586-732-8(4))* Algora Publishing.
Wilson, Stewart & Prentis, Joanna. Atlantis & the New Consciousness. 2011. 172p. pap. 16.00 *(978-1-886940-20-8(7))* Ozark Mountain Publishing, Inc.
Wingate, Richard. Atlantis in the Amazon. 2011. (ENG., Illus.). 1p. pap. 16.00 *(978-1-59143-120-6(4))* Bear & Co.
Woyt, Barbara A. & Lewis, Ann. Searching for Atlantis. 2011. 77.70 *(978-1-4488-4775-4(3)*, Rosen Central); pap. 12.95 *(978-1-4488-4767-9(2)*, Rosen Central); (YA). (gr. 5-9). lib. bdg. 30.60 *(978-1-4488-4758-7(3))* Rosen Publishing Group, Inc., The.

ATLANTIS (WARSHIP)

Mohr, Ulrich & Sellwood, A.V. Ship: The Story of the Secret German Raider Atlantis. 2011. 262p. 47.95 ***(978-1-258-00715-7(0))*** Literary Licensing, LLC.
Wolfgang, Frank & Rogge, Bernhard. The German Raider Atlantis. Long, R. O. B., tr. 2011. 162p. 41.95 ***(978-1-258-01067-6(4))*** Literary Licensing, LLC.

ATLAS MOUNTAINS

Brown, Hamish. The Mountains Look on Marrakech. 2007. (Illus.). 256p. *(978-1-870325-29-5(X))* Whittles Publishing.
Harris, Walter B. Tafilet: The Narrative of a Journey of Exploration in the Atlas Mountains & the Oases of the North-West Sahara. 2009. 386p. pap. 39.95 *(978-1-85964-222-1(5))* Garnet Publishing, Ltd. GBR. Dist: International Publishers Marketing.

ATLASES

Here are entered geographical atlases of world coverage.
see also Bible—Geography; Children's Atlases
also subdivision Maps under names of countries, cities, etc., e.g. United States—Maps; London—Maps; also subdivision Atlases under subjects, e.g. Human Anatomy—Atlases

AAA Publishing. AAA Easy Reading Road Atlas 2012. 2011. (ENG.). 104p. pap. 9.95 *(978-1-59508-441-5(X))* AAA.
ADC. Atlas Cobb & North Fulton Ga Atlas. 2007. 108p. 12.95 *(978-0-87530-841-8(4))* ADC The Map People.
ADC, the Map People Staff, creator. ADC Berks County, Pennsylvania Street Atlas. 4th ed. 2007. (Illus.). 120p. 12.95 *(978-0-87530-913-2(5))* ADC The Map People.
—ADC Charles County Maryland Street Atlas. 16th ed. 2007. (Illus.). 56p. 12.95 *(978-0-87530-914-9(3))* ADC The Map People.
—ADC Charlotte Mecklenburg County North Carolina Street Atlas. 6th ed. 2007. (Illus.). 108p. 12.95 *(978-0-87530-908-8(9))* ADC The Map People.
—ADC Gloucester County, New Jersy Street Atlas. 3rd ed. 2007. (Illus.). 64p. 12.95 *(978-0-87530-906-4(2))* ADC The Map People.
—Frederick County, Maryland Street Atlas. 2007. (Illus.). 96p. 12.95 *(978-0-87530-915-6(1))* ADC The Map People.
—Gwinnett County, Georgia Street Atlas. 2007. (Illus.). 84p. 12.95 *(978-0-87530-850-0(3))* ADC The Map People.
Allen, John & Sutton, Christopher. Student Atlas of World Geography. 7th ed. 2011. (Student Atlas Ser.). (ENG., Illus.). 288p. (C). pap. 44.00 *(978-0-07-352762-8(9)*, 0073527629, McGraw-Hill/Dushkin) McGraw-Hill Higher Education.
Allen, John L. & Allen, John. World Geography. 6th ed. 2009. (Student Atlas Ser.). (ENG., Illus.). 336p. (C). pap. 44.00 *(978-0-07-352760-4(2)*, 0073527602, McGraw-Hill/Dushkin) McGraw-Hill Higher Education.
Anthem Press, compiled by. Modern World University Atlas: International Edition. 2009. (ENG., Illus.). 176p. (C). 19.95 *(978-1-84331-306-9(5))* Anthem Pr. GBR. Dist: Books International, Inc.
Arno, Peters. Peters World Atlas. Franz, Huber, ed. 2010. 228p. 29.99 *(978-0-8416-7156-0(7))* Langenscheidt Publishing Group.
Atlas Escolar Universal: Con Indice y Nomenclador Geografico. (SPA.). 112p. pap. 19.95 *(978-958-04-3049-0(7)*, NOR0497) Norma S.A. COL. Dist: Continental Bk. Co., Inc.
Atlas of the World. (Mini Children's Reference Ser.). 256p. *(978-1-4054-5894-8(1))* Parragon, Inc.
The Atlas of World Surfing. 2007. 256p. pap. *(978-0-7322-8643-9(3)*, HarperSports) HarperCollins Pubs. Australia.
Bassett, Thomas & Winter-Nelson, Alex. The Atlas of World Hunger. 2010. (Illus.). 216p. 45.00 *(978-0-226-03907-7(2))* Univ. of Chicago Pr.
Cambridge IGCSE Student World Atlas. 2012. (ENG., Illus.). 152p. (J). (gr. 7). pap. 17.95 ***(978-0-00-744305-5(6))*** HarperCollins Pubs. Ltd. GBR. Dist: Independent Pubs. Group.
Cambridge World Atlas Klett Edition. 2009. (ENG., Illus.). 344p. pap. 30.00 *(978-0-521-17815-0(0))* Cambridge Univ. Pr.
Cheng, P. C., et al. The Maize Atlas. 2010. (Illus.). 550p. 239.00 *(978-0-387-94303-9(X)*, 038794303X) Springer.
Collins. Student World Atlas. 4th ed. 2012. (ENG.). 200p. (YA). (gr. 9). pap. 16.95 ***(978-0-00-743781-8(1))*** HarperCollins Pubs. Ltd. GBR. Dist: Independent Pubs. Group.
—World Atlas. 4th ed. 2012. (ENG.). 192p. (YA). (gr. 9). 22.95 ***(978-0-00-743782-5(X))*** HarperCollins Pubs. Ltd. GBR. Dist: Independent Pubs. Group.
Collins Staff. World Atlas. 2010. (ENG., Illus.). 312p. 39.95 *(978-0-00-734718-6(9))* HarperCollins Pubs. Ltd. GBR. Dist: Independent Pubs. Group.
Collins World Atlas. ed. 2012. (ENG., Illus.). 240p. pap. 19.95 ***(978-0-00-745265-1(9))*** HarperCollins Pubs. Ltd. GBR. Dist: Independent Pubs. Group.
Comprehensive Atlas of the World. 2008. 584p. 250.00 *(978-0-19-537479-7(7))* Oxford Univ. Pr., Inc.
Cram101 Textbook Reviews. Outlines & Highlights for Color Atlas of Histology by Leslie P Gartner, James L Hiatt, Isbn: 9780781798280. 2010. 500p. pap. 37.95 *(978-1-61698-382-6(5))* Cram101 Inc.
Dorling Kindersley Publishing Staff. Atlas: 5th Edition. 2012. (ENG.). 432p. 11.95 ***(978-0-7566-8977-3(5))*** Dorling Kindersley Publishing, Inc.
—Compact Atlas of the World. 2012. (ENG.). 192p. 14.95 ***(978-0-7566-8984-1(8))*** Dorling Kindersley Publishing, Inc.
—Complete Atlas of the World, 2nd Edition. 2012. (ENG.). 432p. 75.00 *(978-0-7566-8972-8(4))* Dorling Kindersley Publishing, Inc.
—Concise Atlas of the World. 2011. (ENG.). 384p. (YA). (gr. 9). pap. 35.00 *(978-0-7566-7146-4(9))* Dorling Kindersley Publishing, Inc.
—Essential World Atlas. 2011. (ENG.). 256p. pap. 16.00 *(978-0-7566-7223-2(6))* Dorling Kindersley Publishing, Inc.
—Great World Atlas. 2008. (ENG.). 528p. (gr. 12-18). 100.00 *(978-0-7566-3984-6(0))* Dorling Kindersley Publishing, Inc.
—The Most Fantastic Atlas of the Whole World. 2008. (ENG.). 64p. (YA). (gr. 4-7). 19.99 *(978-0-7566-4009-5(1))* Dorling Kindersley Publishing, Inc.
—World Atlas. 8th ed. 2010. (ENG.). 384p. 50.00 *(978-0-7566-6746-7(1))* Dorling Kindersley Publishing, Inc.
Encyclopaedia Britannica & Collins Bartholomew, compiled by. Encyclopaedia Britannica World Atlas. 2010. (Illus.). 432p. (YA). (gr. 9). 89.95 *(978-1-61535-359-0(3))* Encyclopaedia Britannica, Inc.
Encyclopaedia Britannica Publishers, ed. Britannica World Atlas. 2008. (Illus.). 392p. (YA). (gr. 9). 89.95 *(978-1-59339-428-8(4))* Encyclopaedia Britannica, Inc.
Forbes, Scott, et al, eds. Geographica World Atlas & Encyclopedia. 2008. (Illus.). 610p. pap. 24.95 *(978-0-8416-0304-2(9))* American Map Corp.
Gilbert. Atlas of World since 1900. 2009. (Routledge Historical Atlases Ser.). (ENG., Illus.). 224p. 39.95 *(978-0-415-37248-0(8))*; pap. 26.95 *(978-0-415-37249-7(6))* Routledge.
Graham-Cumming, John & Graham-Cumming, J. The Geek Atlas: 128 Places Where Science & Technology Come Alive. 2009. (ENG., Illus.). 544p. pap. 29.99 *(978-0-596-52320-6(3))* O'Reilly Media, Inc.
Hammond, creator. The Comparative World Atlas. rev. ed. 2007. (Hammond Comparative World Atlas Ser.). (Illus.). 104p. per. 11.95 *(978-0-8437-0952-0(9))* Hammond World Atlas Corp.
Hammond World Atlas Corporation, creator. Essential World Atlas. 2008. (Hammond Ser.). (Illus.). 192p. 19.95 *(978-0-8437-0964-3(2))* Hammond World Atlas Corp.
Hammond World Atlas Corporation Staff, creator. Concise World Atlas. 5th rev. ed. 2007. (Illus.). 290p. 29.95 *(978-0-8437-0965-0(0))* Hammond World Atlas Corp.
—Scholastic New Headline World Atlas. rev. ed. 2007. (Illus.). 53p. 6.95 *(978-0-8437-0950-6(2))* Hammond World Atlas Corp.
—The World Almanac Compact Factfile: An A-Z Look at the World in Maps, Stats, & Facts. 2007. (World Almanac Ser.). (Illus.). 448p. 14.95 *(978-0-8437-0963-6(4))* Hammond World Atlas Corp.
—The World Almanac World Atlas. 2nd rev. ed. 2007. (World Almanac Ser.). (Illus.). 292p. 29.95 *(978-0-8437-0970-4(7))* Hammond World Atlas Corp.
—World Atlas. 5th rev. ed. 2007. (Hammond World Atlas Ser.). (Illus.). 408p. 59.95 *(978-0-8437-0967-4(7))* Hammond World Atlas Corp.
Hammond World Atlas Corporation Staff, ed. Cartografico Terrestre. 2008. 344p. pap. 29.95 *(978-0-8437-0996-4(0))* Hammond World Atlas Corp.
—Discovering Maps. 3rd rev. ed. 2008. 88p. (J). 9.95 *(978-0-8437-0975-9(8))* Hammond World Atlas Corp.
—World Atlas 2009. 3rd rev. ed. 2008. (World Almanac Ser.). 292p. pap. 29.95 *(978-0-8437-0997-1(9))* Hammond World Atlas Corp.
Hammonds World Atlas Corporate Staff. Hammond World Atlas. 2010. 464p. 59.99 *(978-0-8437-1560-6(X))* Hammond World Atlas Corp.
Hammonds World Atlas Corporation Staff. Hammond Concise World Atlas. 2010. 288p. 29.99 *(978-0-8437-1557-6(X))* Hammond World Atlas Corp.
HarperCollins Publishers Ltd. Staff. HarperCollins Student World Atlas, 2nd Edition: Changing Your Worldview. 2009. 240p. pap. 19.99 *(978-0-06-179376-9(0))* HarperCollins Pubs.
—Times Comprehensive Atlas of the World, Twelfth Edition. 2008. 544p. 285.00 *(978-0-06-146450-8(3))* HarperCollins Pubs.
Heilo, Arne, et al, eds. Atlas of Thyroid Lesions. 2010. (ENG., Illus.). vii, 267p. 189.00 *(978-1-4419-6009-2(0)*, 1441960090) Springer.
Hema Maps Staff. Concise Atlas of the World. (Illus.). pap. 29.95 *(978-1-86500-250-7(X))* Hema Maps Pty, Ltd. AUS. Dist: Map Link.
hf Ullmann, compiled by. Peters World Atlas: The Earth in Its True Proportions, 1 vol. 2010. (ENG., Illus.). 232p. pap. 29.99 *(978-3-8331-5560-4(4))* h.f.ullmann DEU. Dist: Innovative Logistics.
Horrabin, J. F. Atlas of Empire. 2006. 160p. per. *(978-1-4067-1112-7(8)*, Hesperides Pr.) Read Bks.
Ilaslan, Hakan & Sundaram, Murali. Pediatric & Adult MRI Atlas of Bone Marrow: Normal Appearances, Variants & Diffuse Disease States. 2013. (ENG., Illus.). 300p. 179.00 *(978-3-642-02739-0(3)*, 3642027393) Springer.
Irish Times. The Irish Times Desktop Atlas of the World. 2010. (ENG.). 256p. 27.95 *(978-0-00-731816-2(2))* HarperCollins Pubs. Ltd. GBR. Dist: Independent Pubs. Group.
Jackson, Jack, ed. Dive Atlas of the World, 2nd: An Illustrated Guide to the Best Sites. 2nd ed. 2010. (Illus.). 300p. 49.95 *(978-1-59228-953-0(3)*, Falcon Guides) Globe Pequot Pr., The.
Jacobs, Frank. Strange Maps: An Atlas of Cartographic Curiosities. 2009. (ENG., Illus.). 256p. (gr. 12-18). 30.00 *(978-0-14-200525-5(8)*, Studio) Penguin Group (USA) Inc.
Kemp, Richard. Atlas Visual del Mundo. (SPA.). 13.98 *(978-968-13-2157-4(X))* Editorial Diana, S.A. MEX. Dist: Continental Bk. Co., Inc.
Klett International Staff. Perthes World Atlas. Herb, Guntram H. et al, eds. 2006. (ENG., Illus.). 315p. (C). pap. 41.33 *(978-0-07-329073-7(4)*, 0073290734, McGraw-Hill Science, Engineering & Mathematics) McGraw-Hill Higher Education.
Krauss, Gregory L., et al, eds. The Johns Hopkins Atlas of Digital EEG: An Interactive Training Guide. 2nd ed. 2011. (ENG., Illus.). 448p. (gr. 17). 150.00 *(978-0-8018-9733-7(5))* Johns Hopkins Univ. Pr.
Larousse Staff. Gran Enciclopedia Larousse Atlas Geografico: Geographical Atlas. (SPA., Illus.). 125.00 *(978-0-8288-8247-7(9))* French & European Pubns., Inc.
Lavin, Stephen J., et al. Atlas of the Great Plains. 2011. (ENG., Illus.). 352p. 39.95 *(978-0-8032-1536-8(3))* Univ. of Nebraska Pr.
Limusa, ed. Atlas Universal Panorama 6a Ed. 6th ed. (SPA.). 108p. (C). *(978-968-18-6140-7(X)*, Limusa) Noriega Editores.
Lynn, Pamela. Lippincott's Atlas of Medication Administration, 2 vols. 3rd rev. ed. 2007. (Illus.). 80p. pap. 15.00 *(978-0-7817-6923-5(X))* Lippincott Williams & Wilkins.
The Macmillan School Atlas. 3rd ed. 140p. 22.95 *(978-0-7715-9092-4(X))* Nelson Education Ltd. CAN. Dist: CDG Bks. Canada, Inc.
Massow, Martin. Der Weiterbildungsatlas. (GER.). *(978-3-612-21340-2(7))* Econ-Verlag GmbH DEU. Dist: International Bk. Import Service, Inc.
Merriam-Webster, creator. Webster's International Atlas. 2009. (Illus.). 379p. (J). pap. 7.99 *(978-1-59695-019-1(6))* Federal Street Pr.
Meyers Grosser Weltatlas. *(978-3-411-08826-3(5))* Bibliographisches Institut & F. A. Brockhaus AG DEU. Dist: i. b. d., Ltd.
Monaco Books, compiled by. World Pocket Atlas Black. 2010. (ENG.). 256p. 13.95 *(978-3-89944-585-5(6)*, Monaco Bks.) Verlag Wolfgang Kunth GmbH & Co. KG DEU. Dist: Innovative Logistics.
—World Pocket Atlas Red. 2010. (ENG.). 256p. 13.95 *(978-3-89944-587-9(2)*, Monaco Bks.) Verlag Wolfgang Kunth GmbH & Co. KG DEU. Dist: Innovative Logistics.
Monaco Books, ed. World Pocket Atlas Green, 1 vol. 2010. (ENG.). 256p. 13.95 *(978-3-89944-588-6(0)*, Monaco Bks.) Verlag Wolfgang Kunth GmbH & Co. KG DEU. Dist: Innovative Logistics.
—World Pocket Atlas Navy, 1 vol. 2010. (ENG.). 256p. 13.95 *(978-3-89944-586-2(4)*, Monaco Bks.) Verlag Wolfgang Kunth GmbH & Co. KG DEU. Dist: Innovative Logistics.
National Geographic Society Staff. Concise Atlas of the World - National Geographic. 2nd rev. ed. 2007. (National Geographic Concise Atlas of the World Ser.). (ENG., Illus.). 160p. (gr. 9). pap. 24.95 *(978-1-4262-0196-7(6))* National Geographic Society.
—Family Reference Atlas of the World: Indispensable Information & More Than 1,000 Maps & Illustrations. 3rd ed. 2009. (ENG., Illus.). 384p. 65.00 *(978-1-4262-0543-9(0)*, National Geographic) National Geographic Society.
—National Geographic Collegiate Atlas of the World, Second Edition. 2nd ed. 2011. (ENG., Illus.). 400p. 40.00 *(978-1-4262-0839-3(1)*, National Geographic) National Geographic Society.
—National Geographic Visual Atlas of the World. 2008. (ENG., Illus.). 416p. 100.00 *(978-1-4262-0332-9(2)*, National Geographic) National Geographic Society.
National Geographic Society Staff, et al. National Geographic Atlas of the World-college, Second Edition. 2nd ed. 2010. (ENG.). (C). pap. 47.95 *(978-0-470-88887-2(3)*, Wiley) Wiley, John & Sons, Inc.
Ottersbach, John Philip. Micro Black Holes at the Lhc. 2010. 96p. pap. *(978-3-8383-7273-0(5))* Lambert Academic Publishing.
Ovenden, Mark. Railway Maps of the World. 2012. (ENG., Illus.). 144p. (gr. 12). pap. 25.00 ***(978-0-14-312240-1(1)***, Penguin (Non-Classics)) Penguin Group (USA) Inc.
Oxford, ed. Atlas of Exploration. 2nd ed. 2008. (ENG., Illus.). 256p. 50.00 *(978-0-19-534318-2(2))* Oxford Univ. Pr., Inc.

—Atlas of the World, 1 vol. (ENG., 448p. 18th ed. 2011. Illus.). 89.95 (978-0-19-982995-8(0)) 19th ed. 2012. 89.95 (978-0-19-993782-0(6)) Oxford Univ. Pr., Inc.
—Atlas of the World: Deluxe Edition, 1 vol. 2nd ed. 2011. (ENG., Illus.). 584p. 199.00 (978-0-19-982993-4(4)) Oxford Univ. Pr., Inc.
—Essential World Atlas, 1 vol. 6th ed. 2011. (ENG., Illus.). 208p. (Orig.). pap. 24.95 (978-0-19-982982-8(9)) Oxford Univ. Pr., Inc.
—New Concise World Atlas. 3rd ed. 2010. (ENG.). 288p. 39.95 (978-0-19-539329-3(5)) Oxford Univ. Pr., Inc.
—Pocket World Atlas. 6th ed. 2008. (ENG., Illus.). 240p. pap. 16.95 (978-0-19-537453-7(3)) Oxford Univ. Pr., Inc.
Palmer, Douglas. The Complete Earth: A Satellite Portrait of Our Planet. 2011. (ENG., Illus.). 224p. 39.95 (978-1-905204-31-1(0)) Quercus GBR. Dist: Independent Pubs. Group.
Philip's Maps and Atlases Staff & Nagle, Garrett. Philip's Interactive Modern School Atlas: For Whiteboards & Data Projectors. 2006. (Illus.). cd-rom 675.00 (978-0-340-91416-8(5), Hodder Murray) Hodder Education GBR. Dist: Trans-Atlantic Pubns., Inc.
Pracejus, Bernhard. The Ore Minerals under the Microscope: An Optical Guide. 2008. (Atlases in Geoscience Ser.: 3). (ENG., Illus.). 894p. 385.00 (978-0-444-52863-6(6), Elsevier Science) Elsevier Science & Technology Bks.
Rand McNally, creator. Rand Mcnally Deluxe Midsize Road Atlas. 2008. (Rand Mcnally Road Atlas Ser.). (Illus.). 192p. pap. 9.95 (978-0-528-94207-5(7)) Rand McNally.
—Rand Mcnally Manatee, Sarasota & Charlotte Counties Streetguide. 5th ed. 2008. (Illus.). pap. 19.95 (978-0-528-87409-3(8)) Rand McNally.
Rand McNally Staff. Goode's World Atlas. 22nd ed. 2009. (ENG.). 371p. (C). pap. 47.40 (978-0-321-65200-3(2), Prentice Hall) Prentice Hall PTR.
—Rand Mcnally Atlas of World Geography Single. 2010. pap. 13.50 (978-0-528-67809-7(4)) Rand McNally.
—Rand Mcnally Classroom Atlas Single. 2010. pap. 8.50 (978-0-528-67805-9(1)) Rand McNally.
—Rand Mcnally Goode's World Atlas Set. 22nd rev. ed. 2010. (C). 1015.95 (978-0-528-68391-6(8)) Rand McNally.
—Rand Mcnally Historical Atlas of the World Single. 2010. pap. 11.00 (978-0-528-67829-5(9)) Rand McNally.
—Rand Mcnally Junior Classroom Atlas Single. 2010. pap. 6.50 (978-0-528-67801-1(9)) Rand McNally.
—Rand Mcnally Junior Classroom Atlas Teacher's Guide & Activity Book. 2010. ring bd. 109.00 (978-0-528-67803-5(5)) Rand McNally.
—Rand Mcnally Our Government Big Book: People, Spaces, & Places. 2010. 29.00 (978-0-528-67749-6(7)) Rand McNally.
—Rand Mcnally Primary Atlas Big Book & Guide: People, Spaces, & Places. 2010. 29.00 (978-0-528-67770-0(5)) Rand McNally.
—Rand Mcnally Primary Atlas Single. 2010. pap. 6.00 (978-0-528-67769-4(1)) Rand McNally.
Random House Disney Staff, creator. Random House World Atlas & Encyclopedia. 1st ed. 2007. (ENG., Illus.). 448p. 35.00 (978-0-375-42610-0(8), Random House Reference) Random Hse. Information Group.
Robertson, Ian. An Atlas of the Peninsular War. 2010. (Illus.). 160p. 55.00 (978-0-300-14869-5(0)) Yale Univ. Pr.
School Atlas 1924: Climate, Population, Empires, Occupations, Industry, Economic, Commerce, Vegetation, Agriculture. 2008. 64p. 30.00 (978-1-873590-72-0(5)) Old Hse. Bks. GBR. Dist: Parkwest Pubns., Inc.
Shirley, Rodney. Courtiers & Cannibals, Angels & Amazons: The art of the decorative cartographic Titlepage. 2009. (Illus.). 272p. 89.00 (978-90-6194-060-9(5)) HES & DE GRAAF Pubs. BV NLD. Dist: Oak Knoll Pr.
Smith, Dan. The Penguin State of the World Atlas. 8th rev. ed. 2008. (ENG.). 144p. (gr. 12-18). 20.00 (978-0-14-311452-9(2), Penguin (Non-Classics)) Penguin Group (USA) Inc.
Smith, Dan. The Penguin State of the World Atlas: Ninth Edition. rev. ed. 2012. (ENG., Illus.). 144p. (gr. 12). pap. 22.00 (978-0-14-312265-4(7), Penguin (Non-Classics)) Penguin Group (USA) Inc.
Smith, Roswell Chamberlain. Smith's Atlas of Modern & Ancient Geography, Corrected & Enlarged, to Accompany Smith's Geography for Schools, Academies & Families by Roswell. 2011. 18p. pap. 11.99 (978-1-4181-8981-5(2)) MPublishing.
Srivastav, Nitendra, ed. Social, Economic & Natural Mini Atlas of World. 2007. (ENG.). 384p. (978-81-8386-048-2(6)) India Research Pr. IND. Dist: Independent Pubs. Group.
The Times. The Times Comprehensive Atlas of the World. (ENG., Illus.). 544p. 12th ed. 2007. 250.00 (978-0-00-723670-1(0)) 13th ed. 2011. 200.00 (978-0-00-741913-5(9)) HarperCollins Pubs. Ltd. GBR. Dist: Independent Pubs. Group.
Times Books. The Times Mini Atlas of the World. 6th ed. 2012. (ENG., Illus.). 256p. 10.95 (978-0-00-745241-5(1)) HarperCollins Pubs. Ltd. GBR. Dist: Independent Pubs. Group.
Times Books Staff. Atlas of the World. 11th ed. 2009. (ENG., Illus.). 452p. 145.00 (978-0-00-731199-6(0)) HarperCollins Pubs. Ltd. GBR. Dist: Independent Pubs. Group.
—The Times Mini Atlas of the World. 4th ed. 2009. (ENG., Illus.). 256p. 11.95 (978-0-00-727638-7(9)) HarperCollins Pubs. Ltd. GBR. Dist: Independent Pubs. Group.
Times Newspapers Limited Staff, contrib. by. The Times Concise Atlas of the World. 10th rev. ed. 2006. (ENG., Illus.). 416p. 125.00 (978-0-00-722906-2(2)) HarperCollins Pubs. Ltd. GBR. Dist: Independent Pubs. Group.
Times UK. The Times Desktop Atlas of the World. 3rd ed. 2012. (ENG., Illus.). 240p. 27.95 (978-0-00-745266-8(7)) HarperCollins Pubs. Ltd. GBR. Dist: Independent Pubs. Group.
Times UK Staff. The Times Atlas of Britain. 2010. (ENG., Illus.). 448p. 135.00 (978-0-00-734583-0(6)) HarperCollins Pubs. Ltd. GBR. Dist: Independent Pubs. Group.
—The Times Compact Atlas of the World. 5th rev. ed. 2010. (ENG.). 240p. 18.95 (978-0-00-731817-9(0)) HarperCollins Pubs. Ltd. GBR. Dist: Independent Pubs. Group.
Trident, ed. DICT THESAURUS & COLOR ATLAS. 2007. 1008p. 21.95 (978-1-58279-642-0(4)) Trident Pr. International.
—Q ref notebk world Atlas. 2007. 48p. pap. 4.95 (978-1-60081-100-5(0)) Trident Pr. International.
—Quick ref notebk us Atlas. 2007. 48p. pap. 4.95 (978-1-60081-101-2(9)) Trident Pr. International.
Tuggy, Michael & Garcia, Jorge. Atlas of Essential Procedures. 2010. (ENG., Illus.). 256p. 99.95 (978-1-4377-1499-9(4), Saunders) Elsevier - Health Sciences Div.
Ullmann, H. F., ed. Geographica. 2009. 640p. 29.95 (978-0-8416-0788-0(5)) American Map Corp.
Veregin. Rand Mcnally Goode's World Atlas. 22nd rev. ed. 2010. (C). 40.95 (978-0-528-87754-4(2)) Rand McNally.
Veregin & Rand McNally Staff. Rand Mcnally Goode's World Atlas. 22nd rev. ed. 2010. (C). pap. 29.95 (978-0-528-87753-7(4)) Rand McNally.
Veregin, Howard, ed. Goode's World Atlas. 2006. pap. incl. cd-rom (978-0-13-135125-7(7)); 21st ed. (Illus.). 371p. per. (978-0-13-612824-3(6), Prentice Hall) Pearson Education Canada.
Weltatlas. (GER., Illus.). 538p. (978-3-7653-1132-1(4)) Brockhaus, F. A., GmbH DEU. Dist: International Bk. Import Service, Inc.
Wheeler, Alina & Katz, Joel. Brand Atlas: Branding Intelligence Made Visible. 2011. (ENG., Illus.). 144p. 29.95 (978-0-470-43342-3(6), Wiley) Wiley, John & Sons, Inc.
Whitfield, Peter. Cities of the World: A History in Maps. 2010. 208p. pap. 35.00 (978-0-520-26599-8(8)) Univ. of California Pr.

ATLASES—BIBLIOGRAPHY

Phillips, Philip Lee & Le Gear, Clara Egli. A List of Geographical Atlases in the Library of Congress: With Bibliographical Notes. 2006. (978-1-57898-613-2(3)) Martino Publishing.

ATLASES—EARLY WORKS TO 1800

Blaeu, Joan & Krogt, P. C. J. van der. Joan Blaeu. Atlas Maior of 1665: 25 Jahre TASCHEN. 2010. (25 Ser.). (ENG., Illus.). 544p. 69.99 (978-3-8365-2411-7(2)) TASCHEN DEU. Dist: Ingram Pub. Services.
Ptolemy, Claudius. Geography of Claudius Ptolemy. Stevenson, Edward L., ed. reprint ed. 245.00 (978-0-404-05148-8(0)) AMS Pr., Inc.

ATLASES—JUVENILE LITERATURE

see Children's Atlases

ATLASES, ASTRONOMICAL

see Stars—Atlases

ATLASES, HISTORICAL

see Geography, Ancient—Maps; Historical Geography—Maps

ATLASES FOR CHILDREN

see Children's Atlases

ATLATL

see Throwing-Sticks

ATM (BANKING)

see Automated Tellers

ATM (DATA TRANSFER)

see Asynchronous Transfer Mode

ATMOSPHERE

see also Air; Biosphere; Ionosphere; Meteorology; Sky
also headings beginning with the word Atmospheric

Ackerman. Pac: meteorology 3E: understanding the atmosphere w/Ac. 3rd ed. 2011. 580p. pap. 145.95 (978-1-4496-3175-8(4)) Jones & Bartlett Learning, LLC.
Archibald, Douglas. The Story of the Earth's Atmosphere. 2009. 196p. 26.99 (978-1-110-53538-5(4)); pap. 22.75 (978-1-110-53537-8(6)) BiblioBazaar.
—The Story of the Earth's Atmosphere. 2009. 112p. pap. (978-0-217-89853-9(X)) Books LLC.
—The Story of the Earth's Atmosphere. 2008. 196p. 37.95 (978-0-548-97572-5(8)) 2007. (ENG.). 200p. per. 22.95 (978-0-548-67217-4(2)) Kessinger Publishing, LLC.
Bösenberg, Jens, et al, eds. Instrument Development for Atmospheric Research & Monitoring: Lidar Profiling, DOAS & Tunable Diode Laser Spectroscopy. 2010. (Transport & Chemical Transformation of Pollutants in the Troposphere Ser.). (ENG.). xix, 394p. pap. 239.00 (978-3-642-08291-7(2), 3642082912) Springer.
Berry, A. J. The Atmosphere. 2011. (ENG., Illus.). 156p. pap. 19.99 (978-1-107-40167-9(4)) Cambridge Univ. Pr.
Brutsaert, W. Evaporation into the Atmosphere: Theory, History & Applications. 2010. (Environmental Fluid Mechanics Ser.). 316p. pap. 319.00 (978-90-481-8365-4(0), 9048183650) Springer.
Bychkov, Vladimir, et al, eds. The Atmosphere & Ionosphere: Dynamics, Processes & Monitoring. 2009. (Physics of Earth & Space Environments Ser.). (ENG., Illus.). 362p. 199.00 (978-90-481-3211-9(8), 9048132118) Springer.
Bychkov, Vladimir, et al, eds. The Atmosphere & Ionosphere: Elementary Processes, Discharges & Plasmoids. 2012. (Physics of Earth & Space Environments Ser.: 0). (ENG., Illus.). xvi, 284p. 129.00 (978-94-007-2913-1(8), 9400729138) Springer.
Carbone, Greg. Exercises for Weather & Climate. 8th rev. ed. 2012. (ENG.). (C). 244p. pap., pap. 72.13 (978-0-321-83357-0(0)); 232p. pap. 72.13 (978-0-321-76965-7(1)) Prentice Hall PTR. (Prentice Hall).
Clarlet, Philippe G., contrib. by. Computational Methods for the Atmosphere & the Oceans: Special Volume. 2008. (Handbook of Numerical Analysis Ser.: 14). (ENG., Illus.). 784p. 220.00 (978-0-444-51893-4(2), Elsevier Science) Elsevier Science & Technology Bks.
Committee on Earth Science and Applications from Space: A Community Assessment and Strategy for the Future & National Research Council. Satellite Observations to Benefit Science & Society: Recommended Missions for the Next Decade. Henson, Robert, ed. 2008. (ENG.). 40p. pap. 15.00 (978-0-309-10903-1(5)) National Academies Pr.
Conway, Erik M. Atmospheric Science at NASA: A History. 2008. (New Series in NASA History Ser.). (ENG., Illus.). 416p. (gr. 17). 57.00 (978-0-8018-8984-4(7)) Johns Hopkins Univ. Pr.
Cram101 Textbook Reviews Staff. Outlines & Highlights for Atmosphere: An Introduction to Meteorology by Frederick K. Lutgens, ISBN. 2009. 168p. pap. 29.95 (978-1-4288-9076-3(9)) Cram101 Inc.
Demaison, Jean, et al, eds. Remote Sensing of the Atmosphere for Environmental Security. 2007. (NATO Science for Peace & Security Series / NATO Science for Peace & Security Series C: Environmental Security Ser.). (Illus.). 353p. 229.00 (978-1-4020-5088-6(7), 1402050887) Springer.
Diston, Dominic. Computational Modelling of Aircraft & the Environment. 2009. (Illus.). (978-1-60086-704-0(9)) American Institute of Aeronautics & Astronautics.
Doicu, Adrian, et al. Numerical Regularization for Atmospheric Inverse Problems. 2010. (Springer Praxis Books / Environmental Sciences Ser.). (ENG., Illus.). 400p. 199.00 (978-3-642-05438-9(2), 3642054382) Springer.
Doss-Hammel, Stephen M. Atmospheric Optics: 27-28 August, 2007, San Diego, California, USA. 2007. (Proceedings of SPIE Ser.). (Illus.). 312p. pap. 80.00 (978-0-8194-6856-7(8)) SPIE.
Doss-Hammel, Stephen M. & Kohnle, Anton. Atmospheric Optical Modeling, Measurement, & Simulation II: 15-16 August, 2006, San Diego, California, USA. 2006. (Proceedings of SPIE Ser.). (Illus.). 304p. pap. 80.00 (978-0-8194-6382-1(5)) SPIE.
Doss-Hammel, Stephen M., et al. Atmospheric Optics: Models, Measurements, & Target-In-The-Loop Propagation II: 12-13 August 2008, San Diego, California, USA. 2008. (Proceedings of SPIE Ser.). (Illus.). 152p. pap 70.00 (978-0-8194-7310-3(3)) SPIE.
Doss-Hammel, Stephen M., et al. Atmospheric Optics: Models Measurements, & Target-In-The-Loop Propagation III: 3-4 August 2009, San Diego, California, United States. 2009. (Proceedings of SPIE Ser.). (Illus.). 166p. pap. 60.00 (978-0-8194-7753-8(2)) SPIE.
Foelsche, Ulrich, et al, eds. Atmosphere & Climate: Studies by Occultation Methods. 2010. (ENG., Illus.). x, 336p. pap. 239.00 (978-3-642-07054-9(X), 364207054X) Springer.
Francis Emmanuel Mensah. Lidar Techniques & Remote Sensing in the Atmosphere: Understanding the use of laser light in the Atmosphere. 2009. 144p. 26.99 (978-1-4389-8273-1(9)) AuthorHouse.
Frederick, John E. Principles of Atmospheric Science. 2007. 211p. pap. 58.95 (978-0-7637-4089-4(6)) Jones & Bartlett Learning, LLC.
Goldberg, Mitchell D. Atmospheric & Environmental Remote Sensing Data Processing & Utilization IV: Readiness for GEOSS II: 12-14 August 2008, San Diego, California, USA. 2008. (Proceedings of SPIE Ser.). (Illus.). 236p. pap. 105.00 (978-0-8194-7305-9(7)) SPIE.
Goldberg, Mitchell D. & Bloom, Hal J. Atmospheric & Environmental Remote Sensing Data Processing & Utilization V: Readiness for GEOSS III: 5-6 August 2009, San Diego, California, United States. 2009. (Proceedings of SPIE Ser.). (Illus.). 210p. pap. 90.00 (978-0-8194-7746-0(X)) SPIE.
Goldberg, Mitchell David. Atmospheric & Environmental Remote Sensing Data Processing & Utilization III: Readiness for GEOSS: 27-28 & 30 August 2007, San Diego, California, USA. 2007. (Proceedings of SPIE Ser.). (Illus.). 410p. pap. 105.00 (978-0-8194-6832-1(0)) SPIE.
Goldberg, Mitchell David & Bloom, Hal J. Atmospheric & Environmental Remote Sensing Data Processing & Utilization VI: Readiness for GEOSS IV: 1 August 2010, San Diego, California, United States. 2010. (Proceedings of SPIE Ser.). (Illus.). 98p. pap. 70.00 (978-0-8194-8307-2(9)) SPIE.
Gottwald, Manfred & Bovensmann, Heinrich, eds. SCIAMACHY - Exploring the Changing Earth's Atmosphere. 2010. (Illus.). x, 240p. 129.00 (978-90-481-9895-5(X), 904819895X) Springer.
Grainger, Roy Gordan. Atmospheric Remote Sounding. 2013. (ENG., Illus.). 500p. 139.95 (978-0-8493-7250-6(X), CRC Press) Taylor & Francis Group GBR. Dist: Taylor & Francis Group.
Heard, Dwayne, ed. Analytical Techniques for Atmospheric Measurement. 2006. (ENG., Illus.). 528p. 240.00 (978-1-4051-2357-0(5), Wiley-Blackwell) Wiley, John & Sons, Inc.
Kgabi, Nnenesi. Toxic Metals of Atmospheric Particulate Matter. 2011. 204p. pap. (978-3-8443-0188-5(7)) Lambert Academic Publishing.
Kirchengast, Gottfried, et al, eds. Occultations for Probing Atmosphere & Climate. 2010. (ENG., Illus.). x, 408p. pap. 229.00 (978-3-642-06108-0(7), 3642061087) Springer.
Kokhanovsky, Alexander A. & Chylek, Petr. Remote Sensing of the Atmosphere from Space. 2010. (Springer Praxis Books / Environmental Sciences Ser.). (ENG., Illus.). xxvii, 549p. 169.00 (978-3-642-10411-4(8), 3642104118) Springer.
Krishnamurti, T. N., et al. Remote Sensing & Modeling of the Atmosphere, Oceans, & Interactions: 13-16 November, 2006, Goa, India. 2006. (Proceedings of SPIE Ser.). (Illus.). 322p. pap. 105.00 (978-0-8194-6511-5(9)) SPIE.
—Remote Sensing & Modeling of the Atmosphere, Oceans, & Interactions: 19-20 November, 2008, Noumea, New Caledonia. 2008. (Proceedings of SPIE Ser.). (Illus.). 102p. pap. 70.00 (978-0-8194-7390-5(1)) SPIE.
Krishnamurti, Tiruvalam, et al. Remote Sensing & Modeling of the Atmosphere, Oceans, & Interactions III. 2010. (Proceedings of SPIE Ser.). 128p. pap. 70.00 (978-0-8194-8386-7(9)) SPIE.
Levin, Iosif M. Current Research on Remote Sensing, Laser Probing, & Imagery in Natural Waters. 2007. (Proceedings of SPIE Ser.). (Illus.). 226p. pap. 70.00 (978-0-8194-6756-0(1)) SPIE.
Lutgens, Frederick K. & Tarbuck, Edward J. The Atmosphere: An Introduction to Meteorology. 11th ed. 2009. (ENG.). (C). 30.00 (978-0-321-59524-9(6), Prentice Hall) Prentice Hall PTR.
Lutgens, Frederick K., et al. The Atmosphere: An Introduction. 12th ed. 2012. (ENG.). 528p. (C). E-Book 60.00 (978-0-321-81551-4(3), Prentice Hall) Prentice Hall PTR.
—The Atmosphere: An Introduction to Meteorology. (ENG., Illus.). 528p. (C). 11th ed. 2009. 143.40 (978-0-321-58733-6(2)) 12th rev. ed. 2011. 143.40 (978-0-321-75631-2(2)) Prentice Hall PTR. (Prentice Hall).
—The Atmosphere: An Introduction to Meteorology, Books a la Carte Edition. 12th ed. 2012. (ENG.). 528p. (C). ring bd. 86.07 (978-0-321-78034-8(5), Prentice Hall) Prentice Hall PTR.
—The Atmosphere: An Introduction to Meteorology, Books a la Carte Plus NEW MyMeteorologyLab#8482; 12th ed. 2012. (ENG.). (C). ring bd. 86.07 (978-0-321-82207-9(2), Prentice Hall) Prentice Hall PTR.
Lutgens, Tarbuck & Cram101 Textbook Reviews Staff. The Atmosphere. 2007. 236p. per. 14.95 (978-1-4288-3306-7(4)) Cram101 Inc.
Marzano, Frank S. & Visconti, Guido, eds. Remote Sensing of Atmosphere & Ocean from Space: Models, Instruments & Techniques: Models, Instruments & Techniques. 2010. (Advances in Global Change Research Ser.). 256p. pap. 135.00 (978-90-481-6151-5(7), 9048161517) Springer.
Maurette, M. Micrometeorites & the Mysteries of Our Origins. 2010. (Advances in Astrobiology & Biogeophysics Ser.). (Illus.). xvi, 330p. pap. 109.00 (978-3-642-06520-0(1), 3642065201) Springer.
P Thakker and W Shiroma, et al. Emergence of Pico- & Nanosatellites for Atmospheric Research & Technology Testing. 2010. (Illus.). xvi, 391p. (978-1-60086-768-2(5)) American Institute of Aeronautics & Astronautics.
Perrin-Baland, Agnès, et al, eds. Remote Sensing of the Atmosphere for Environmental Security. 2006. (NATO Science for Peace & Security Series / NATO Science for Peace & Security Series C: Environmental Security Ser.). XI, 353p. pap. 139.00 (978-1-4020-5089-3(5), 1402050895) Springer.
Rafferty, John P., ed. Storms, Violent Winds, & Earth's Atmosphere. 2010. (Dynamic Earth Ser.). 256p. (YA). (ENG.). lib. bdg. 45.00 (978-1-61530-114-0(3)); (Illus.). 90.00 (978-1-61530-191-1(7)) Rosen Publishing Group, Inc., The.
Rehrl, Christoph. Mesospheric Temperature & Ozone Sounding Based on Solar Occultation Data- Retrieval Processing System & Performance Analysis. 2008. 156p. pap. 79.00 (978-3-8364-7101-5(9)) VDM Verlag Dr. Mueller e.K.
Schneider, Tapio & Sobel, Adam H., eds. Global Circulation of the Atmosphere. 2007. (ENG., Illus.). 400p. (C). 82.50 (978-0-691-12181-9(8)) Princeton Univ. Pr.
Sherman, Joe. Gasp! The Swift & Terrible Beauty of Air. 2007. (ENG., Illus.). 416p. per. 16.95 (978-1-59376-140-0(6)) Counterpoint LLC.
Singh, Upendra N. Lidar Technologies, Techniques, & Measurements for Atmospheric Remote Sensing II: 13-14 September, 2006, Stockholm, Sweden. 2006. (Proceedings of SPIE Ser.). (Illus.). 298p. pap. 80.00 (978-0-8194-6462-0(7)) SPIE.
Singh, Upendra N. & Pappalardo, Gelsomina. Lidar Technologies, Techniques, & Measurements for Atmospheric Remote Sensing IV: 16-18 September 2008, Cardiff, Wales, United Kingdom. 2008. (Proceedings of SPIE Ser.). (Illus.). 170p. pap. 80.00 (978-0-8194-7342-4(1)) SPIE.
—Lidar Technologies, Techniques, & Measurements for Atmospheric Remote Sensing V: 31 August-1 September 2009, Berlin, Germany. 2009. (Proceedings of SPIE Ser.). (Illus.). 234p. pap. 80.00 (978-0-8194-7784-2(2)) SPIE.
Singh, Upendra N. & Pappalardo, Gelsomina. Lidar Technologies, Techniques, & Measurements for Atmospheric Remote Sensing VI: 20-21 September 2010, Toulouse, France. 2010. (Proceedings of SPIE Ser.). (Illus.). 256p. pap. 80.00 (978-0-8194-8349-2(4)) SPIE.
Stephens, Graeme L. & Nakajima, Takashi. Remote Sensing of the Atmosphere & Clouds II: 18 November 2008, Noumea, New Caledonia. 2008. (Proceedings of SPIE Ser.). (Illus.). 158p. pap. 70.00 (978-0-8194-7394-3(4)) SPIE.

A

Tammemagi, Hans. Air: Our Planet's Ailing Atmosphere. 2009. (ENG., Illus.). 256p. 27.95 *(978-0-19-543007-3(7))* Oxford Univ. Pr., Inc.
Tsay, Si Chee. Remote Sensing of the Atmosphere & Clouds: 13-16 November, 2006, Goa, India. 2006. (Proceedings of SPIE Ser.). (Illus.). 350p. pap. 130.00 *(978-0-8194-6515-3(1))* SPIE.
V., Madhu & Mohanakumar, K. Role of Stratosphere in Weather & Climate. 2010. 236p. pap. *(978-3-639-26561-3(0))* VDM Verlag Dr. Mueller e.K.
Valinia, Azita, et al. Microwave Remote Sensing of the Atmosphere & Environment V: 15-16 November, 2006, Goa, India. 2006. (Proceedings of SPIE Ser.). (Illus.). 300p. pap. 90.00 *(978-0-8194-6517-7(8))* SPIE.
—Microwave Remote Sensing of the Atmosphere & Environment VI: 19-20 November, 2008, Noumea, New Caledonia. 2008. (Proceedings of SPIE Ser.). (Illus.). 132p. pap. 70.00 *(978-0-8194-7396-7(0))* SPIE.
Van Eijk, Alexander M. & Hammel Stephen. Atmospheric Optics IV: Turbulence & Propagation. 2011. (Proceedings of SPIE Ser.). 170p. pap. 70.00 ***(978-0-8194-8771-1(6))*** SPIE
Walker, Gabrielle. An Ocean of Air: Why the Wind Blows & Other Mysteries of the Atmosphere. (ENG., Illus.). 288p. 2008. pap. 17.95 *(978-0-15-603414-2(X)*, Mariner Bks.) 2007. 25.00 *(978-0-15-101124-7(9))* Houghton Mifflin Harcourt Trade & Reference Pubs.
Ward, Peter. Out of Thin Air: Dinosaurs, Birds, & Earth's Ancient Atmosphere. 2006. (ENG., Illus.). 296p. 27.95 *(978-0-309-10061-8(5)*, Joseph Henry Pr.) National Academies Pr.
Yang, Chih-Hao, ed. Atmospheric Science Research Progress. 2008. (Illus.). xi, 230p. 98.00 *(978-1-60456-439-6(3))* Nova Science Pubs., Inc.
Yassin, Mohamed F. Study on Pollutant Dispersion Within Urban Are. 2010. 204p. pap. *(978-3-639-27279-6(X))* VDM Verlag Dr. Mueller e.K.
Yusoff, Nooryusmiza. Statistical Analyses of Ozone Temporal Trends - an Application of Multivariate Geostatistics. 2008. 196p. pap. *(978-3-639-02793-8(0))* VDM Verlag Dr. Mueller e.K.

ATMOSPHERE-OCEAN INTERACTION
see Ocean-Atmosphere Interaction

ATMOSPHERE, UPPER
see also Airglow; Jet Stream; Magnetosphere; Stratosphere
Abdu, Mangalathayil Ali & Pancheva, Dora, eds. Aeronomy of the Earth's Atmosphere & Ionosphere. 2011. (IAGA Special Sopron Book Ser.). (ENG., Illus.). xxi, 480p. 179.00 *(978-94-007-0325-4(2)*, 9400703252) Springer.
Bauer, Siegfried & Lammer, Helmut. Planetary Aeronomy: Atmosphere Environments in Planetary Systems. 2010. (Physics of Earth & Space Environments Ser.). (ENG., Illus.). viii, 207p. pap. 179.00 *(978-3-642-05990-2(2)*, 3642059902) Springer.
Cram101 Textbook Reviews & Cram101 Textbook Reviews. Outlines & Highlights for Atmospheric Thermodynamics: Elementary Physics & Chemistry by Gerald R. North. 2011. 110p. pap. 28.95 ***(978-1-61830-098-0(9))*** Cram101 Inc.
Darrouzet, F., et al, eds. The Earth's Plasmasphere: A CLUSTER & IMAGE Perspective. 2009. (ENG., Illus.). iv, 296p. 149.00 *(978-1-4419-1322-7(X)*, 144191322X) Springer.
Ghosh, S. N. The Neutral Upper Atmosphere. 2010. (Astrophysics & Space Science Library). 296p. pap. 219.00 *(978-90-481-5513-2(4)*, 9048155134) Springer.
Kamide, Yohsuke & Chian, Abraham C. -L, eds. Handbook of the Solar-Terrestrial Environment. 2010. (Illus.). xiv, 539p. pap. 279.00 *(978-3-642-07968-9(7)*, 3642079687) Springer.
Khomich, Vladislav Yu, et al. Airglow As an Indicator of Upper Atmospheric Structure & Dynamics. 2008. (ENG., Illus.). xvi, 740p. 289.00 *(978-3-540-75832-7(1)*, 3540758321) Springer London, Ltd. GBR. Dist: Springer.
Kondrat&apos, et al. The Thermal State of Upper Atmospheric Layers: Technical Translation F-103. 2011. 412p. 54.95 ***(978-1-258-05462-5(0))*** Literary Licensing, LLC.
Krishnappa, Nagaraju. Spectropolarimetry of Active Regions on the Sun. 2010. 144p. pap. *(978-3-8383-7004-0(X))* Lambert Academic Publishing.
Nagy, Andrew F. Comparative Aeronomy. 2009. (Space Sciences Series of ISSI Ser.). 209.00 *(978-0-387-87824-3(6))* Springer.
Nagy, Andrew F., et al, eds. Comparative Aeronomy. 2010. (Space Sciences Series of ISSI Ser.). (ENG.). iv, 456p. pap. 209.00 *(978-1-4419-2772-9(7)*, 1441927727) Springer.
North, Gerald R., et al. Atmospheric Thermodynamics: Elementary Physics & Chemistry. 2009. (ENG., Illus.). 280p. 76.00 *(978-0-521-89963-5(X))* Cambridge Univ. Pr.
Prölss, Gerd. Physics of the Earth's Space Environment: An Introduction. Bird, Michael Keith, tr. 2010. (ENG., Illus.). xv, 514p. pap. 129.00 *(978-3-642-05979-7(1)*, 3642059791) Springer.
Wang, Jian'guo. Gao Kong He Bao Zha Xiao Ying Can Shu Shou Ce. 2010. (CHI., Illus.). vii, 272p. *(978-7-5022-4667-9(3))* Atomic Energy Pr.

ATMOSPHERIC ABSORPTION OF SOLAR RADIATION
see Solar Radiation

ATMOSPHERIC CHEMISTRY
American Society for Testing and Materials Staff, contrib. by. ASTM Standards Related to Environmental Site Characterization: ENVSIT06. 2006. *(978-0-8031-4475-0(X))* American Society for Testing & Materials.
Barnes, I. & Kharytonov, M. M. Simulation & Assessment of Chemical Processes in a Multiphase Environment. 2008. (NATO Science for Peace & Security Series C: Environmental Security Ser.). (ENG., Illus.). xxv, 540p. 319.00 *(978-1-4020-8844-5(2)*, 1402088442) Springer.
Bösenberg, Jens, et al, eds. Instrument Development for Atmospheric Research & Monitoring: Lidar Profiling, DOAS & Tunable Diode Laser Spectroscopy. 2010. (Transport & Chemical Transformation of Pollutants in the Troposphere Ser.). (ENG.). xix, 394p. pap. 239.00 *(978-3-642-08291-7(2)*, 3642082912) Springer.
Bemmerer, Daniel. Experimental Study of the Carbon-Nitrogen-Oxygen Cycle at Low Energy. 2008. 100p. pap. *(978-3-8364-7343-9(7))* VDM Verlag Dr. Mueller e.K.
Berner, Elizabeth & Berner, Robert. Global Enviroment - Water, Air, & Geochemical Cycles 2e. 2nd ed. 2012. (ENG., Illus.). 480p. (C). 85.00 ***(978-0-691-13678-3(5))*** Princeton Univ. Pr.
Berry, A. J. The Atmosphere. 2011. (ENG., Illus.). 156p. pap. 19.99 *(978-1-107-40167-9(4))* Cambridge Univ. Pr.
Calvert, Jack G., et al. Mechanisms of Atmospheric Oxidation of the Alkanes. 2008. (Illus.). 1008p. 125.00 *(978-0-19-536581-8(X))* Oxford Univ. Pr., Inc.
—The Mechanisms of Atmospheric Oxidation of the Oxygenates, 1 vol. 2011. (ENG., Illus.). 1328p. 350.00 *(978-0-19-976707-6(6))* Oxford Univ. Pr., Inc.
Carbon Capture & Storage Technologies: Hearing Before the Subcommittee on Energy of the Committee on Energy & Natural Resources, United States Senate, One Hundred Tenth Congress, Second Session, to Receive Testimony on the Challenges Associated with Rapid Deployment of Large-Scale Carbon Capture & Storage Technologies, Bismarck, ND, March 26, 2008. 2008. iii, 66p. *(978-0-16-081514-0(2)*, 552-070-37870-7) United States Government Printing Office.
Ellis, Andrew M. & Monks, Paul S. Proton Transfer Reaction Mass Spectrometry & Related Techniques. 2013. (ENG.). 328p. 160.00 *(978-1-4051-7668-2(7)*, Wiley) Wiley, John & Sons, Inc.
Frederick, John E. Principles of Atmospheric Science. 2007. 211p. pap. 58.95 *(978-0-7637-4089-4(6))* Jones & Bartlett Learning, LLC.
Gautier, Catherine & Fellous, Jean-Louis, eds. Facing Climate Change Together. 2008. (ENG., Illus.). 280p. 73.00 *(978-0-521-89682-5(7))* Cambridge Univ. Pr.
Gerondeau, Christian. Climate: the Great Delusion: A Study of the Climatic, Economic & Political Unrealities. 2010. 256p. pap. 18.00 ***(978-1-906768-41-6(2)***, Stacey International) Stacey Publishing GBR. Dist: Midpoint Trade Bks., Inc.
Granier, Claire, et al, eds. Emissions of Atmospheric Trace Compounds. 2010. (Advances in Global Change Research Ser.). 560p. pap. 299.00 *(978-90-481-6605-3(5)*, 9048166055) Springer.
Grobe, M., et al. Carbon Dioxide Sequestration in Geological Media - State of the Science. 2009. (Illus.). xi, 715p. ***(978-0-89181-066-7(8))*** American Assn. of Petroleum Geologists.
Hayden, Howard C. A Primer on CO2 & Climate. 2007. (Illus.). 66p. per. 13.95 *(978-0-9714845-5-9(4))* Vales Lake Publishing, LLC.
Hoffmann, Elvira S. Pipelines for Carbon Sequestration: Background & Issues. 2010. (Environmental Science, Engineering & Technology Ser.). 233p. 69.00 *(978-1-60741-383-7(3))* Nova Science Pubs., Inc.
Huebner, W. F., et al, eds. Solar Photo Rates for Planetary Atmospheres & Atmospheric Pollutants. 2010. (ENG.). 292p. pap. 236.00 *(978-90-481-4212-5(1)*, 9048142121) Springer.
Jacobson, Mark Z. Air Pollution & Global Warming: History, Science, & Solutions. 2nd ed. 2012. (ENG., Illus.). 406p. (C). pap. 85.00 ***(978-1-107-69115-5(X))*** Cambridge Univ. Pr.
Khalil, Mohammad Aslam Khan, ed. Atmospheric Methane: Its Role in the Global Environment. 2010. (Illus.). viii, 352p. pap. 339.00 *(978-3-642-08451-5(6)*, 3642084516) Springer.
Kharytonov, M. M. & Barnes, Ian, eds. Simulation & Assessment of Chemical Processes in a Multiphase Environment. 2008. (NATO Science for Peace & Security Series C: Environmental Security Ser.). (ENG., Illus.). xxv, 540p. pap. 139.00 *(978-1-4020-8845-2(0)*, 1402088450) Springer.
Kondratyev, Kirill Ya, et al. Atmospheric Aerosol Properties: Formation, Processes & Impacts. 2010. (Springer Praxis Books / Environmental Sciences Ser.). xxxiv, 572p. pap. 319.00 *(978-3-642-06577-4(5)*, 3642065775) Springer.
Krivolutsky, A. & Repnev, A. I. Vozdeistvie Kosmicheskikh Faktorov Na Ozonosferu Zemli. 2009. (RUS., Illus.). 382p. *(978-5-89118-488-6(5))* GEOS.
Lehmann, Christopher. Atmospheric Deposition Monitoring: Assessing Trends for the Continental United States. 2008. 408p. pap. *(978-3-639-04614-4(5))* VDM Verlag Dr. Mueller e.K.
Li, Zachary & Feng, Christopher, eds. Handbook of Radon: Properties, Applications & Health. 2012. ***(978-1-62100-177-5(6))*** Nova Science Pubs., Inc.
Muller, Rolf, ed. Stratospheric Ozone Depletion & Climate Change. 2011. (ENG., Illus.). 346p. 200.00 ***(978-1-84973-002-0(4))*** Royal Society of Chemistry, The GBR. Dist: Ingram Pub. Services.
Panel to Review CCSP Draft Synthesis and Assessment Product 5.3: Decision-Support Experiments and Evaluations Using Seasonal to Interannual Forecasts and Observational Data & National Research Council. Review of CCSP Draft Synthesis & Assessment Product 5. 3: Decision-Support Experiments & Evaluations Using Seasonal to Interannual Forecasts & Observational Data. 2007. (ENG.). 56p. pap. 21.00 *(978-0-309-11568-1(X))* National Academies Pr.
Parlar, Harun & Greim, Helmut, eds. Air Monitoring Methods, Vol. 11, Pt. 3. 2009. (MAK-Collection for Occupational Health & Safety. Part III: Air Monitoring Methods (DFG) Ser.). (ENG.). 196p. 179.00 *(978-3-527-31959-6(X)*, Wiley-VCH) Wiley, John & Sons, Inc.
Platt, Ulrich & Stutz, Jochen. Differential Optical Absorption Spectroscopy: Principles & Applications. 2008. (Physics of Earth & Space Environments Ser.). (Illus.). 500p. 179.00 *(978-3-540-21193-8(4))* Springer.
—Differential Optical Absorption Spectroscopy: Principles & Applications. 2010. (Physics of Earth & Space Environments Ser.). (Illus.). xvi, 597p. pap. 179.00 *(978-3-642-05946-9(5)*, 3642059465) Springer.
Quéré, Corinne Le & Saltzman, Eric S. Surface Ocean-Lower Atmosphere Processes. 2009. *(978-0-87590-477-1(7))* American Geophysical Union.
Rudolph, J. & Koppmann, R., eds. Atmospheric Measurements during POPCORN - Characterisation of the Photochemistry over a Rural Area. 2010. 256p. pap. 121.00 *(978-90-481-5158-5(9)*, 9048151589) Springer.
Schafer, Karina. Water & Carbon Relations under Ambient & Elevated Atmospheric Co2. 2009. 144p. pap. *(978-3-639-12075-2(2))* VDM Verlag Dr. Mueller e.K.
Seinfeld, John H. & Pandis, Spyros N. Atmospheric Chemistry & Physics: From Air Pollution to Climate Change. 2nd ed. 2006. 1360p. 150.00 *(978-0-470-04626-5(0))*; 1360p. 150.00 *(978-0-470-03902-1(7))*; (ENG., Illus.). 1232p. pap. 144.00 *(978-0-471-72018-8(6))* Wiley, John & Sons, Inc. (Wiley-Interscience).
Sokhi, Ranjeet S. World Atlas of Atmospheric Pollution. 2008. (Anthem Atlas & Reference Ser.). (ENG., Illus.). 144p. 250.00 *(978-1-84331-289-5(1))* Anthem Pr. GBR. Dist: Books International, Inc.
Sokhi, Ranjeet S., ed. World Atlas of Atmospheric Pollution. 2011. (Anthem Environmental Studies). (ENG., Illus.). 144p. pap. 50.00 *(978-1-84331-891-0(1))* Anthem Pr. GBR. Dist: Books International, Inc.
Sportisse, Bruno. Fundamentals in Air Pollution: From Processes to Modelling. 2009. (ENG., Illus.). x, 299p. 89.95 *(978-90-481-2969-0(9)*, 9048129699) Springer.
Sportisse, Bruno, ed. Air Pollution Modelling & Simulation. 2010. (ENG., Illus.). xiv, 592p. pap. 259.00 *(978-3-642-07637-4(8)*, 3642076378) Springer.
Stevens, Carly. The Impact of Atmospheric Nitrogen Deposition on Grasslands. 2009. 148p. pap. *(978-3-639-14414-7(7))* VDM Verlag Dr. Mueller e.K.
Valsaraj, Kalliat T. & Kommalapati, Raghava R. Atmospheric Aerosols: Characterization, Chemistry, Modelingand Climate. 2009. (ACS Symposium Ser.). (ENG., Illus.). 216p. 150.00 *(978-0-8412-6973-6(4))* American Chemical Society.
Visconti, Guido, et al, eds. Observing Systems for Atmospheric Composition: Satellite, Aircraft, Sensor Web & Ground-Based Observational Methods & Strategies. (ENG., Illus.). xii, 244p. 2010. pap. 159.00 *(978-1-4419-2147-5(8)*, 1441921478) 2006. 159.00 *(978-0-387-30719-0(2)*, 0387307192) Springer.
Warneck, Peter & Williams, Jonathan. The Atmospheric Chemist's Companion: Numerical Data for Use in the Atmospheric Sciences. 2012. (ENG., Illus.). x, 432p. 229.00 ***(978-94-007-2274-3(5)***, 9400722745) Springer.
Wayne, Richard P. & Holloway, Ann M. Atmospheric Chemistry. 2010. (ENG., Illus.). 288p. (C). 42.00 *(978-1-84755-807-7(0))* Royal Society of Chemistry, The GBR. Dist: Ingram Pub. Services.

ATMOSPHERIC ELECTRICITY
see also Auroras; Ionization of Gases; Lightning; Sporadic E (Ionosphere)
Betz, Hans Dieter, et al, eds. Lightning: Principles, Instruments & Applications - Review of Modern Lightning Research. 2009. (ENG., Illus.). xv, 641p. 229.00 *(978-1-4020-9078-3(1)*, 1402090781) Springer.
Milne, Antony. Fireballs, Skyquakes & Hums. 2012. (ENG., Illus.). 288p. 27.95 ***(978-0-7090-9278-0(4))*** Hale, Robert Ltd. GBR. Dist: Independent Pubs. Group.
Pulinets, Sergey & Boyarchuk, Kyrill. Ionospheric Precursors of Earthquakes. 2010. (ENG., Illus.). xiv, 316p. pap. 179.00 *(978-3-642-05876-9(0)*, 3642058760) Springer.
Talbott, David & Thornhill, Wallace. The Electric Universe: A new view of the Earth, the Sun, & the Heavens. 2007. (Illus.). 132p. per. 25.00 *(978-0-9772851-3-6(8))* Mikamar Publishing.

ATMOSPHERIC ENTRY PROBLEMS
see Space Vehicles—Atmospheric Entry

ATMOSPHERIC HUMIDITY
see Humidity

ATMOSPHERIC NUCLEATION
see also Condensation (Meteorology); Ionization of Gases
O'Dowd, Colin & Wagner, Paul, eds. Nucleation & Atmospheric Aerosols: 17th International Conference, Galway, Ireland 2007. 2007. 1010p. 339.00 *(978-1-4020-6474-6(8)*, 1402064748) Springer.

ATMOSPHERIC OPTICS
see Meteorological Optics

ATMOSPHERIC OZONE
Bakker, Sem H. Ozone Depletion, Chemistry, & Impacts. 2008. 98.00 *(978-1-60692-007-7(3))* Nova Science Pubs., Inc.
Barrett, John P. Ozone: Earth's Doctor. 2010. pap. 18.95 *(978-1-61584-984-0(X))* Independent Pub.
Committee on Estimating Mortality Risk Reduction Benefits from Decreasing Tropospheric Ozone Exposure & National Research Council. Estimating Mortality Risk Reduction & Economic Benefits from Controlling Ozone Air Pollution. 2008. (ENG.). 226p. pap. 49.00 *(978-0-309-11994-8(4))* National Academies Pr.
Committee to Review the U.S. Climate Change Science Program's Draft Synthesis and Assessment Product 2.4 & National Research Council. Review of the U. S. Climate Change Science Program's Draft Synthesis & Assessment Product 2.4: Trends in Emissions of Ozone Depleting Substances, Ozone Layer Recovery, & Implications for Ultraviolet Radiation Exposure. 2007. (ENG.). 76p. pap. 21.00 *(978-0-309-11525-4(6))* National Academies Pr.
EPA's New Ozone Standards: Hearing Before the Committee on Oversight & Government Reform, House of Representatives, One Hundred Tenth Congress, Second Session, May 20, 2008. 2009. (Illus.). iii, 284p. *(978-0-16-082949-9(6)*, 552-070-38861-3) United States Government Printing Office.
Isikwue, Bernadette. Solar Dynamic Effects on Stratospheric Ozone Variations in the Tropics. 2011. 80p. pap. ***(978-3-8443-1442-7(3))*** Lambert Academic Publishing.
Karl, Tom, et al, eds. Global Climate Change Impacts in the United States. 2009. (ENG., Illus.). 192p. pap. 51.99 *(978-0-521-14407-0(8))* Cambridge Univ. Pr.
Krivolutsky, A. & Repnev, A. I. Vozdeistvie Kosmicheskikh Faktorov Na Ozonosferu Zemli. 2009. (RUS., Illus.). 382p. *(978-5-89118-488-6(5))* GEOS.
Martins, John. Ultraviolet Danger: Holes in the Ozone Layer. 2006. 68p. (gr. 8-12). pap. 29.25 *(978-1-4358-3770-6(3))* Rosen Publishing Group, Inc., The.
Rosser, Kevin. Study of the Planetary Boundary Layer. 2010. 128p. pap. *(978-3-8383-1879-0(X))* Lambert Academic Publishing.
Wu, Shiliang. Global Change & Ozone Air Quality. 2008. 116p. pap. *(978-3-639-07993-7(0))* VDM Verlag Dr. Mueller e.K.

ATMOSPHERIC PHYSICS
Here are entered works on the physical rather than chemical or dynamical aspects of the atmosphere of the earth and other planets.
see also Acoustic Phenomena in Nature; Auroras; Cloud Physics; Meteorological Optics
Adeeb, Farah. Near-Surface Ozone Concentrations in the City of Auckland, New Zealand. 2010. 316p. pap. *(978-3-8383-4608-3(4))* Lambert Academic Publishing.
Aguado, Burt & Cram101 Textbook Reviews Staff. Understanding Weather & Climate. 2007. 220p. per. 13.95 *(978-1-4288-3330-2(7))* Cram101 Inc.
Aguado, Edward & Burt, James E. Understanding Weather & Climate. (ENG., (C). 5th ed. 2009. Illus.). 608p. pap. 139.27 *(978-0-321-59550-8(5))* 6th ed. 2012. 608p. ring bd. 93.60 ***(978-0-321-81960-4(8))*** 6th rev. ed. 2012. 576p. pap. 139.27 ***(978-0-321-76963-3(5))*** Prentice Hall PTR. (Prentice Hall).
Aguado, Edward & Burt, James E. Understanding Weather & Climate, Books a la Carte Edition. 6th ed. 2012. (ENG.). 576p. (C). ring bd. 83.60 ***(978-0-321-77322-7(5)***, Prentice Hall) Prentice Hall PTR.
Andrews, David G. An Introduction to Atmospheric Physics. 2nd rev. ed. 2010. (ENG., Illus.). 248p. (C). pap. 65.00 *(978-0-521-69318-9(7))* Cambridge Univ. Pr.
Barry, Roger G., et al. Atmosphere, Weather & Climate. 9th ed. 2009. (ENG., Illus.). 536p. (C). 200.00 *(978-0-415-46569-4(9))*; pap. 76.95 *(978-0-415-46570-0(2))* Routledge.
Behrens, Jö. Adaptive Atmospheric Modeling: Key Techniques in Grid Generation, Data Structures, & Numerical Operations with Applications. 2006. (Lecture Notes in Computational Science & Engineering Ser.: Vol. 52). (Illus.). xi, 214p. pap. 139.00 *(978-3-540-33382-1(7)*, 3540333827) Springer.
Berry, A. J. The Atmosphere. 2011. (ENG., Illus.). 156p. pap. 19.99 *(978-1-107-40167-9(4))* Cambridge Univ. Pr.
Boeker, Egbert & van Grondelle, Rienk. Environmental Physics: Sustainable Energy & Climate Change. 3rd ed. 2011. (ENG., Illus.). 456p. 175.00 ***(978-0-470-66675-3(7))***; pap. 65.00 ***(978-0-470-66676-0(5))*** Wiley, John & Sons, Inc. (Wiley).
Bohren, Craig F. What Light Through Yonder Window Breaks? More Experiments in Atmospheric Physics. 2006. (Dover Science Bks.). (ENG., Illus.). 208p. per. 12.95 *(978-0-486-45336-1(7))* Dover Pubns., Inc.
Borghese, Ferdinando, et al. Scattering from Model Nonspherical Particles: Theory & Applications to Environmental Physics. 2nd ed. (Physics of Earth & Space Environments Ser.). (Illus.). xx, 348p. 2010. pap. 219.00 *(978-3-642-07221-5(6)*, 3642072216) 2006. 219.00 *(978-3-540-37413-8(2)*, 3540374132) Springer.
Brown, Timothy J. & Mielke Jr., Paul W., eds. Statistical Mining & Data Visualization in Atmospheric Sciences. 2010. 84p. pap. 133.00 *(978-1-4419-4974-5(7)*, 1441949747) Springer.
Budisulistiorini, Sri Hapsari. Evaluation of Air Quality Management Plans for PM10Control: Jakarta Case Study. 2008. 132p. pap. *(978-3-639-09778-8(5))* VDM Verlag Dr. Mueller e.K.
Bychkov, Vladimir, et al, eds. The Atmosphere & Ionosphere: Elementary Processes, Discharges & Plasmoids. 2012. (Physics of Earth & Space Environments Ser.: 0). (ENG., Illus.). xvi, 284p. 129.00 ***(978-94-007-2913-1(8)***, 9400729138) Springer.
Cram101 Textbook Reviews. Outlines & Highlights for the Earth's Atmosphere: Its Physics & Dynamics by Kshudiram Saha. 2011. 76p. pap. 27.95 ***(978-1-61905-278-9(4))*** Cram101 Inc.
Cram101 Textbook Reviews & Cram101 Textbook Reviews. Outlines & Highlights for Exercises in Environmental Physics by Valerio Faraoni. 2011. 166p. pap. 29.95 ***(978-1-61830-089-8(X))*** Cram101 Inc.
—Outlines & Highlights for Weather Studies by Joseph M Moran, Isbn: 9781878220745 1878220748. 2011. 320p. pap. 33.95 ***(978-1-61490-481-6(2))*** Cram101 Inc.
Cram101 Textbook Reviews Staff. Outlines & Highlights for Understanding Weather & Climate by Edward Aguado, James E Burt, Isbn: 9780131496965. 2009. 118p. pap. 28.95 *(978-1-4288-7404-6(6))* Cram101 Inc.

Dorman, Lev. Cosmic Rays in Magnetospheres of the Earth & other Planets. 2009. (Astrophysics & Space Science Library). (Illus.). xxxiv, 770p. 249.00 *(978-1-4020-9238-1(5))* Springer.

Faraoni, Valerio. Exercises in Environmental Physics. (ENG.). xv, 330p. 2010. pap. 84.95 *(978-1-4419-2222-9(9)*, 1441922229) 2006. (Illus.). 84.95 *(978-0-387-33912-2(4)*, 0387339124) Springer.

Frederick, John E. Principles of Atmospheric Science. 2007. 211p. pap. 58.95 *(978-0-7637-4089-4(6))* Jones & Bartlett Learning, LLC.

Guzzi, Rodolfo. Exploring the Atmosphere by Remote Sensing Techniques. 2010. (Lecture Notes in Physics Ser.). xii, 370p. pap. 139.00 *(978-3-642-05636-9(9)*, 3642056369) Springer.

Haapala, Ilmari, ed. From the Earth's Core to Outer Space. 2012. (Lecture Notes in Earth Sciences Ser.). (ENG., Illus.). xi, 340p. 139.00 ***(978-3-642-25549-6(3)***, 3642255493) Springer.

Hewitt, C. Nick & Jackson, Andrea V. Atmospheric Science for Environmental Scientists. 2009. (ENG., Illus.). 320p. 174.95 *(978-1-4051-8542-4(2)*, Wiley-Blackwell) Wiley, John & Sons, Inc.

Hewitt, C. Nick, et al. Atmospheric Science for Environmental Scientists. 2009. (ENG., Illus.). 320p. pap. 99.95 *(978-1-4051-5690-5(2)*, Wiley-Blackwell) Wiley, John & Sons, Inc.

Hoeppe, Gotz. Why the Sky Is Blue: Discovering the Color of Life. Stewart, John, tr. from GER. 2007. (ENG., Illus.). 368p. (C). 29.95 *(978-0-691-12453-7(1))* Princeton Univ. Pr.

Kamide, Yohsuke & Chian, Abraham C. -L, eds. Handbook of the Solar-Terrestrial Environment. 2010. (Illus.). xiv, 539p. pap. 279.00 *(978-3-642-07968-9(7)*, 3642079687) Springer.

Khazanov, George V. Kinetic Theory of the Inner Magnetospheric Plasma. 2010. (Astrophysics & Space Science Library). (Illus.). xx, 581p. 229.00 *(978-1-4419-6796-1(6)*, 1441967966) Springer.

Kittler, Richard, et al. Daylight Science & Daylighting Technology. 2011. (ENG., Illus.). xxii, 341p. 169.00 *(978-1-4419-8815-7(7)*, 1441988157) Springer.

Larsen, Michael. Discrete Fluctuations in Atmospheric Physics. 2008. 220p. pap. *(978-3-8364-6939-0(8))* VDM Verlag Dr. Mueller e.K.

Liou, K N & Chou, M D. Recent Progress in Atmospheric Sciences. 2008. 496p. 150.00 *(978-981-281-890-4(1))* World Scientific Publishing Co., Inc.

Lynch, Amanda H. & Cassano, John J. Applied Atmospheric Dynamics. 2006. (ENG., Illus.). 290p. 209.95 *(978-0-470-86172-1(X)*, Wiley) Wiley, John & Sons, Inc.

Mak, Mankin. Atmospheric Dynamics. 2011. (ENG., Illus.). 500p. 80.00 *(978-0-521-19573-7(X))* Cambridge Univ. Pr.

Marshall, John & Plumb, R. Alan. Atmosphere, Ocean & Climate Dynamics: An Introductory Text. 2007. (International Geophysics Ser.). (ENG., Illus.). 344p. (C). 79.95 *(978-0-12-558691-7(4)*, Academic Pr.) Elsevier Science & Technology Bks.

Matvienko, G. G. & Banakh, V. A. Fourteenth International Symposium on Atmospheric & Ocean Optics/Atmospheric Physics: 24-30 June 2007, Buryatia, Russia. 2008. (Proceedings of SPIE Ser.). (Illus.). 546p. pap. 120.00 *(978-0-8194-7123-9(2))* SPIE.

Matvienko, G. G. & Ponomarev, IU N. Fifteenth International Symposium on Atmospheric & Ocean Optics/Atmospheric Physics: 22-28 June 2008, Krasnoyarsk, Russian Federation. 2009. (Proceedings of SPIE Ser.). (Illus.). 190p. pap. 70.00 *(978-0-8194-7558-9(0))* SPIE.

Mecherle, G. Stephen. Free-Space Laser Communication Technologies XX: 24 January 2008, San Jose, California, USA. 2008. (Proceedings of SPIE Ser.). (Illus.). 208p. pap. 70.00 ***(978-0-8194-7052-2(X))*** SPIE.

Mozdzynski. Use of High Performance Computing in... 2007. 274.00 *(978-981-277-588-7(9))* World Scientific Publishing Co., Inc.

Müller, Peter. Computer Modelling in Atmospheric & Oceanic Sciences: Building Knowledge. 2010. (ENG., Illus.). xvi, 304p. pap. 179.00 *(978-3-642-05795-3(0)*, 3642057950) Springer.

National Research Council (U.S.), Committee on Strategic Guidance for the NSF's Support of the Atmospheric Sciences Staff & National Academies Press (U.S.) Staff, contrib. by. Strategic Guidance for the National Science Foundation's Support of the Atmospheric Sciences. 2007. (ENG.). 216p. pap. 47.25 *(978-0-309-10349-7(5))* National Academies Pr.

North, Gerald R., et al. Atmospheric Thermodynamics: Elementary Physics & Chemistry. 2009. (ENG., Illus.). 280p. 76.00 *(978-0-521-89963-5(X))* Cambridge Univ. Pr.

Oh, Jai Ho. Advances in Geosciences Vol. 16, Set: Atmospheric Science, 6 vols. 2010. 200p. 124.00 *(978-981-283-809-4(0))* World Scientific Publishing Co., Inc.

Oliver, John E., et al. Climatology: An Atmospheric Science. 3rd ed. 2009. (ENG.). 408p. (C). 116.40 *(978-0-321-60205-3(6)*, Prentice Hall) Prentice Hall PTR.

Raschke, Ehrhard, ed. Radiation & Water in the Climate System: Remote Measurements. 2010. (NATO asi Series / Global Environmental Change Ser.). xii, 614p. pap. 149.00 *(978-3-642-08261-0(0)*, 3642082610) Springer.

Ray, Pallav. The Madden-Julian Oscillation. 2009. 156p. pap. *(978-3-639-13054-6(5))* VDM Verlag Dr. Mueller e.K.

Saha, Kshudiram. The Earth's Atmosphere: Its Physics & Dynamics. (ENG., Illus.). xxii, 370p. 2010. pap. 239.00 *(978-3-642-09717-1(0)*, 3642097170) 2008. 239.00 *(978-3-540-78426-5(8)*, 3540784238) Springer.

Salby, Murry L. Physics of the Atmosphere & Climate. 2nd rev. ed. 2012. (ENG., Illus.). 718p. (C). 90.00 ***(978-0-521-76718-7(0))*** Cambridge Univ. Pr.

Seargent, David A. J. Weird Weather: Tales of Astronomical & Atmospheric Anomalies. 2012. (Astronomers' Universe Ser.). (ENG., Illus.). xv, 360p. pap. 39.95 ***(978-1-4614-3069-8(0)***, 1461430690) Springer.

Seinfeld, John H. & Pandis, Spyros N. Atmospheric Chemistry & Physics: From Air Pollution to Climate Change. 2nd ed. 2006. 1360p. 150.00 *(978-0-470-04626-5(0))*; 1360p. 150.00 *(978-0-470-03902-1(7))*; (ENG., Illus.). 1232p. pap. 144.00 *(978-0-471-72018-8(3))* Wiley, John & Sons, Inc. (Wiley-Interscience).

Singh, Upendra N. Lidar Technologies, Techniques, & Measurements for Atmospheric Remote Sensing II: 13-14 September, 2006, Stockholm, Sweden. 2006. (Proceedings of SPIE Ser.). (Illus.). 298p. pap. 80.00 *(978-0-8194-6462-0(7))* SPIE.

Singh, Upendra N. & Pappalardo, Gelsomina. Lidar Technologies, Techniques, & Measurements for Atmospheric Remote Sensing IV: 16-18 September 2008, Cardiff, Wales, United Kingdom. 2008. (Proceedings of SPIE Ser.). (Illus.). 170p. pap. 80.00 *(978-0-8194-7342-4(1))* SPIE.

—Lidar Technologies, Techniques, & Measurements for Atmospheric Remote Sensing V: 31 August-1 September 2009, Berlin, Germany. 2009. (Proceedings of SPIE Ser.). (Illus.). 234p. pap. 30.00 *(978-0-8194-7784-2(2))* SPIE.

Singh, Upendra N. & Pappalardo, Gelsomina. Lidar Technologies, Techniques, & Measurements for Atmospheric Remote Sensing VI: 20-21 September 2010, Toulouse, France. 2010. (Proceedings of SPIE Ser.). (Illus.). 256p. pap. 80.00 ***(978-0-8194-8349-2(4))*** SPIE.

Sonmez, Ibrahim. Determination of the Proper Site Spacing Density. 2009. 136p. pap. *(978-3-639-19184-4(6))* VDM Verlag Dr. Mueller e.K.

Sportisse, Bruno, ed. Air Pollution Modelling & Simulation. 2010. (ENG., Illus.). xiv, 532p. pap. 259.00 *(978-3-642-07637-4(8)*, 3642076378) Springer.

Trenberth, Kevin E., ed. Climate System Modeling. 2010. (ENG., Illus.). 820p. pap. 73.00 *(978-0-521-12837-7(4))* Cambridge Univ. Pr.

Tsonis, Anastasios A. An Introduction to Atmospheric Thermodynamics. 2nd rev. ed. 2007. (ENG., Illus.). 198p. (C). per. 66.00 *(978-0-521-69628-9(3))* Cambridge Univ. Pr.

Turner, D. Bruce & Schulze, Richard H., eds. A Practical Guide for Atmospheric Dispersion Modeling. 2007. *(978-0-923204-92-1(X))* Air & Waste Management Assn.

United Nations. Hemispheric Transport Air Pollution 2010: Part D - Answers to Policy-Relevant Questions. 2011. (Air Pollution Studies). (ENG.). 56p. pap. 15.00 ***(978-92-1-117047-4(8))*** United Nations Pubns.

—Hemispheric Transport of Air Pollution 2010. 2011. (Air Pollution Studies). (ENG.). 256p. pap. 43.00 ***(978-92-1-117045-0(1))***; 212p. pap. 38.00 ***(978-92-1-117044-3(3))*** United Nations Pubns.

—Hemispheric Transport of Air Pollution 2010: Part A - Tropospheric Ozone & Particulate Matter. 2011. (Air Pollution Studies). (ENG.). 304p. pap. 46.00 ***(978-92-1-117043-6(5))*** United Nations Pubns.

Warneck, Peter & Williams, Jonathan. The Atmospheric Chemist's Companion: Numerical Data for Use in the Atmospheric Sciences. 2012. (ENG., Illus.). x, 432p. 229.00 ***(978-94-007-2274-3(5)***, 9400722745) Springer.

Wells, Neil C. The Atmosphere & Ocean: A Physical Introduction. 3rd ed. 2012. (Advancing Weather & Climate Science Ser.). (ENG., Illus.). 424p. pap. 99.95 ***(978-0-470-69468-8(8)***, Wiley) Wiley, John & Sons, Inc.

—The Atmosphere & Ocean: A Physical Introduction. 3rd ed. 2012. (Advancing Weather & Climate Science Ser.). (ENG., Illus.). 424p. 149.95 ***(978-0-470-69469-5(6)***, Wiley) Wiley, John & Sons, Inc.

Wilks, Daniel S. Statistical Methods in the Atmospheric Sciences. 3rd ed. 2011. (International Geophysics Ser.: 100). (ENG., Illus.). 704p. 99.95 *(978-0-12-385022-5(3)*, Academic Pr.) Elsevier Science & Technology Bks.

ATMOSPHERIC PRESSURE

Donner, Leo, et al, eds. The Development of Atmospheric General Circulation Models: Complexity, Synthesis & Computation. 2010. (ENG., Illus.). 272p. 85.00 *(978-0-521-19006-0(1))* Cambridge Univ. Pr.

Herrera, Lisandra Cubero. Mass Spectrometry of Polycyclic Aromatic Compounds from Petroleum. 2008. 260p. pap. *(978-3-639-06765-1(7))* VDM Verlag Dr. Mueller e.K.

Kogoma, Masuhiro, et al, eds. Generation & Application of Atmospheric Pressure Plasmas. 2011. (Physics Research & Technology Ser.). (Illus.). 358p. 129.00 *(978-1-61209-717-6(0))* Nova Science Pubs., Inc.

Pelliccia, Fabrizio & Bonafoni, Stefania. Atmospheric Profiling by Gps Radio Occultation. 2011. 80p. pap. ***(978-3-8443-0871-6(7))*** Lambert Academic Publishing.

ATMOSPHERIC RADIATION

Here are entered works on the infrared radiation emitted by or propagated through the atmosphere.

Duvall, James. IRS Circular E-2003 Edition/UPDATE 2009: Master study guide & Workbook. 2009. (ENG.). stu. ed., wbk. ed. *(978-0-9769489-9-5(0))* Ficus Tree Publishing, LLC.

Grieder, Peter K. F. Exentsive Air Showers & High Energy Phenomena, 2 vols. 2010. (Astrophysics & Space Science Library). (ENG., Illus.). xxviii, 1115p. 469.00 *(978-3-540-76940-8(4)*, 3540769404) Springer.

Marshak, Alexander & Davis, Anthony, eds. 3D Radiative Transfer in Cloudy Atmospheres. 2010. (Physics of Earth & Space Environments Ser.). (Illus.). xii, 686p. pap. 129.00 *(978-3-642-06303-9(9)*, 3642063039) Springer.

Melnikova, Irina, et al. Remote Sensing of the Environment & Radiation Transfer: An Introductory Survey. 2012. (ENG., Illus.). xiii, 185p. 79.95 *(978-3-642-14898-9(0)*, 3642148980) Springer.

Nakajima, Teruyuki & Yamasoe, Marcia Akemi, eds. Current Problems in Atmospheric Radiation (IRS 2008) Proceedings of the International Radiation Symposium (IRC/IAMAS) 2009. (AIP Conference Proceedings Ser.). (ENG.). 696p. 396.00 *(978-0-7354-0635-3(9))* American Institute of Physics.

Picard, Richard, et al. Remote Sensing of Clouds & the Atmosphere XV. 2010. (Proceedings of SPIE Ser.). 404p. pap. 105.00 ***(978-0-8194-8344-7(3))*** SPIE.

Picard, Richard H. Remote Sensing of Clouds & the Atmosphere XIII: 15-17 September 2008, Cardiff, Wales, United Kingdom. 2008. (Proceedings of SPIE Ser.). (Illus.). 356p. pap. 90.00 *(978-0-8194-7338-7(3))* SPIE.

—Remote Sensing of Clouds & the Atmosphere XIV: 31 August-1 September 2009, Berlin, Germany. 2009. (Proceedings of SPIE Ser.). (Illus.). 468p. pap. 120.00 *(978-0-8194-7780-4(X))* SPIE.

Raschke, Ehrhard, ed. Radiation & Water in the Climate System: Remote Measurements. 2010. (NATO asi Series / Global Environmental Change Ser.). xii, 614p. pap. 149.00 *(978-3-642-08261-0(0)*, 3642082610) Springer.

Slusser, James Robert, et al. Remote Sensing of Clouds & the Atmosphere XI: 11-14 September, 2006, Stockholm, Sweden. 2006. (Proceedings of SPIE Ser.). (Illus.). 648p. pap. 165.00 *(978-0-8194-6457-6(0))* SPIE.

Wendisch, Manfred & Yang, Ping. Theory of Atmospheric Radiative Transfer: A Comprehensive Introduction. 2012. (ENG., Illus.). 366p. pap. 105.00 ***(978-3-527-40836-8(3)***, Wiley-VCH) Wiley, John & Sons, Inc.

ATMOSPHERIC TEMPERATURE

Feudale, Laura. Large Scale Extreme Events of Temperature During 1950-2003. 2008. 196p. pap. *(978-3-8364-8953-9(8))* VDM Verlag Dr. Mueller e.K.

Kondrat'es, et al. The Thermal State of Upper Atmospheric Layers: Technical Translation F-103. 2011. 412p. 54.95 ***(978-1-258-05462-5(0))*** Literary Licensing, LLC.

National Research Council (U.S.), Committee on Surface Temperature Reconstructions for the Last 2,000 Years Staff, contrib. by. Surface Temperature Reconstructions for the Last 2,000 Years. 2006. (ENG., Illus.). 160p. pap. 40.00 *(978-0-309-10225-4(1))* National Academies Pr.

Przybylak, Rajmund. Variability of Air Temperature & Atmospheric Precipitation in the Arctic. Kearns, John, tr. 2010. (Atmospheric & Oceanographic Sciences Library). 352p. pap. 149.00 *(978-90-481-6153-9(3)*, 9048161533) Springer.

Strangeways, Ian C. Measuring Global Temperatures: Analysis & Interpretation. 2009. (ENG., Illus.). 252p. (C). 118.00 *(978-0-521-89848-5(X))* Cambridge Univ. Pr.

ATMOSPHERIC TURBULENCE

Businger, S. & Cherubini, T., eds. Seeing Clearly: The Impact of Atmospheric Turbulence on the Propagation of Extraterrestrial Radiation. 2011. 212p. 39.95 ***(978-1-60264-698-8(8))*** Virtualbookworm.com Publishing, Inc.

Dritschel, David, ed. Iutam Symposium on Turbulence in the Atmosphere & Oceans: Proceedings of the Iutam Symposium on Turbulence in the Atmosphere & Oceans, Cambridge, UK, December 8-12 2008. 2010. (IUTAM Bookseries Ser.). (ENG., Illus.). xxi, 302p. 139.00 *(978-94-007-0359-9(7)*, 9400703597) Springer.

Fedorovich, Evgeni, et al, eds. Atmospheric Turbulence & Mesoscale Meteorology: Scientific Research Inspired by Doug Lilly. 2010. (ENG.). 300p. pap. 45.00 *(978-0-521-18392-5(8))* Cambridge Univ. Pr.

Gualtieri, Carlo & Mihailovic, Dragutin T., eds. Fluid Mechanics of Environmental Interfaces: Second Edition. 2nd rev. ed. 2012. (ENG.). 450p. (C). 139.95 ***(978-0-415-62156-4(9)***, Taylor & Francis) Taylor & Francis Group GBR. Dist: Taylor & Francis Group.

Kohnle, Anton & Stein, Karin. Optics in Atmospheric Propagation & Adaptive Systems IX: 11-13 September 2006, Stockholm, Sweden. 2006. (Proceedings of SPIE Ser.). (Illus.). 178p. pap. 70.00 *(978-0-8194-6459-0(7))* SPIE.

Kohnle, Anton, et al. Optics in Atmospheric Propagation & Adaptive Systems X: 17-18 September 2007, Florence, Italy. 2007. (Proceedings of SPIE Ser.). (Illus.). 282p. pap. 80.00 ***(978-0-8194-6905-2(X))*** SPIE.

—Optics in Atmospheric Propagation & Adaptive Systems XI: 16-18 September 2008, Cardiff, Wales, United Kingdom. 2008. (Proceedings of SPIE Ser.). (Illus.). 206p. pap. 70.00 ***(978-0-8194-7339-4(1))*** SPIE.

—Optics in Atmospheric Propagation & Adaptive Systems XII. 2009. (Proceedings of SPIE Ser.). 202p. pap. 70.00 ***(978-0-8194-7781-1(8))*** SPIE.

Korotkova, Olga. Partially Coherent Beam Propagation in Turbulent Atmosphere. 2009. 150p. pap. *(978-3-639-18490-7(4))* VDM Verlag Dr. Mueller e.K.

Lang, Peter R. & Lombargo, Frank S., eds. Atmospheric Turbulence, Meteorological Modeling & Aerodynamics. 2010. 738p. 129.00 *(978-1-60741-091-1(5))* Nova Science Pubs., Inc.

Le Pichon, Alexis, et al. Infrasound Monitoring for Atmospheric Studies. 2010. (ENG., Illus.). xix, 735p. 269.00 *(978-1-4020-9507-8(4)*, 1402095074) Springer.

Li, Dalong. Restoration of Atmospheric Turbulence Degraded Video. 2008. (Illus.). 116p. per. *(978-3-8364-6089-7(0))* VDM Verlag Dr. Mueller e.K.

Masciadri, Elena & Sarazin, Marc. Optical Turbulence: Astronomy Meets Meteorology - Proceedings of the Optical Turbulence Characterization for Astronomical Applications. 2009. 416p. 133.00 *(978-1-84816-485-7(8))* Imperial College Pr. GBR. Dist: World Scientific Publishing Co., Inc.

Mehta, Kishor C. & Coulbourne, William L. Wind Loads: Guide to the Wind Load Provisions of ASCE 7-05. 2010. 163p. pap. 65.00 *(978-0-7844-0858-2(0)*, ASCE Pr.) American Society of Civil Engineers.

Moreira, Davidson, ed. Air Pollution & Turbulence: Modeling & Applications. 2009. (ENG., Illus.). 354p. 129.95 *(978-1-4398-1144-3(X)*, CRC Press) Taylor & Francis Group GBR. Dist: Taylor & Francis Group.

Patel, Chinmay. Energy Extraction from Atmospheric Turbulence to Improve Aircraft Performance. 2008. 132p. pap. *(978-3-8364-8036-9(0))* VDM Verlag Dr. Mueller e.K.

Sasiela, Richard J. Electromagnetic Wave Propogation in Turbulence: Evaluation & Application of Mellin Transforms. 2nd rev. ed. 2007. (Press Monographs). 386p. 91.00 *(978-0-8194-6728-7(6))* SPIE.

Stein, Karin & Gonglewski, John D. Optics in Atmospheric Propagation & Adaptive Systems XIII: 20-21 September 2010, Toulouse, France. 2010. (Proceedings of SPIE Ser.). (Illus.). 226p. pap. 70.00 ***(978-0-8194-8345-4(1))*** SPIE.

Tuck, Adrian. Atmospheric Turbulence: A Molecular Dynamics Perspective. 2008. (ENG., Illus.). 184p. 99.00 *(978-0-19-923653-4(4))* Oxford Univ. Pr., Inc.

Wyngaard, John C. Turbulence in the Atmosphere. 2010. (ENG., Illus.). 406p. 83.00 *(978-0-521-88769-4(0))* Cambridge Univ. Pr.

ATMS (BANKING)

see Automated Tellers

ATOLLS

see Coral Reefs and Islands

ATOM BOMB

see Atomic Bomb

ATOMIC BLASTING

see Nuclear Excavation

ATOMIC BOMB

see also Hydrogen Bomb; Radioactive Fallout

Abernathy, Jack N. We Called Ourselves Sailgers. 2010. 60p. pap. 10.49 *(978-1-4490-7158-5(9))* AuthorHouse.

Asada, Sadao. Culture Shock & Japanese-American Relations: Historical Essays. 2011. (ENG., Illus.). 304p. (C). (gr. 13). pap. 35.00 *(978-0-8262-1953-4(5))* Univ. of Missouri Pr.

Baggott, Jim. The First War of Physics: The Secret History of the Atom Bomb, 1939-1949. 2011. (ENG., Illus.). 584p. pap. 17.95 *(978-1-60598-197-0(4)*, 605197) Pegasus Bks.

—The First War of Physics: The Secret History of the Atomic Bomb, 1939-1949. 2010. (ENG., Illus.). 584p. 35.00 *(978-1-60598-084-3(6)*, 605084) Pegasus Bks.

Cassidy, David C. Beyond Uncertainty: Heisenberg, Quantum Physics, & the Bomb. (ENG.). 480p. 2010. pap. 18.95 *(978-1-934137-28-4(6))* 2009. 29.00 *(978-1-934137-13-0(8))* Bellevue Literary Pr.

—J. Robert Oppenheimer & the American Century. 2009. (ENG., Illus.). 496p. (gr. 17). pap. 25.00 *(978-0-8018-9317-9(8))* Johns Hopkins Univ. Pr.

Clearwater, John. Broken Arrow #1: The World's First Lost Atomic Bomb. 2008. (Illus.). 160p. pap. 14.95 ***(978-0-88839-596-2(5))*** Hancock Hse. Pubs.

Connell, Francis J. Morality & the Atom Bomb. 2011. 16p. pap. 35.95 ***(978-1-258-04108-3(1))*** Literary Licensing, LLC.

Craig, Campbell, et al. The Atomic Bomb & the Origins of the Cold War. 2008. (ENG.). 232p. 27.00 *(978-0-300-11028-9(6))* Yale Univ. Pr.

Fandel, Jennifer. The Atomic Bomb. 2007. (What in the World? Ser.). (Illus.). 48p. (J). (gr. 4-7). lib. bdg. 32.80 *(978-1-58341-555-9(6)*, Creative Education) Creative Co., The.

Farish, Matthew. The Contours of America's Cold War. 2010. (ENG., Illus.). 368p. 75.00 *(978-0-8166-4842-9(5))*; pap. 25.00 *(978-0-8166-4843-6(3))* Univ. of Minnesota Pr.

Feifer, George. The Battle of Okinawa: The Blood & the Bomb. 2011. (ENG.). 528p. pap. 19.95 *(978-0-7627-7279-7(4)*, Lyons Pr.) Globe Pequot Pr., The.

Flank, Lenny. Hell's Fire: A Documentary History of the American Atomic & Thermonuclear Weapons Programs: From Hiroshima to the Cold War & the War on Terror. 2008. *(978-1-934941-10-2(7))* Red & Black Pubs.

Fraser, Gordon. The Quantum Exodus: Jewish Fugitives, the Atomic Bomb, & the Holocaust. 2012. (ENG., Illus.). 264p. 45.00 ***(978-0-19-959215-9(2))*** Oxford Univ. Pr., Inc.

Gallagher, Thomas. Assault in Norway: Sabotaging the Nazi Nuclear Program. 2010. (ENG.). 208p. pap. 16.95 *(978-1-59921-912-7(3)*, Lyons Pr.) Globe Pequot Pr., The.

Giangreco, D. M. Hell to Pay: Operation Downfall & the Invasion of Japan, 1945-47. 2009. (Illus.). 416p. 36.95 *(978-1-59114-316-1(0))* Naval Institute Pr.

Glynn, Paul. A Song for Nagasaki: The Story of Takashi Nagai - Scientist, Convert, & Survivor of the Atomic Bomb. 2009. 300p. pap. 16.95 *(978-1-58617-343-2(X))* Ignatius Pr.

Gordin, Michael D. Five Days in August: How World War II Became a Nuclear War. 2007. (ENG., Illus.). 226p. (C). 24.95 *(978-0-691-12818-4(9))* Princeton Univ. Pr.

Hargittai, Istvan. Judging Edward Teller: A Closer Look at One of the Most Influential Scientists of the Twentieth Century. 2010. (ENG., Illus.). 650p. 32.00 *(978-1-61614-221-6(9))* Prometheus Bks., Pubs.

Hersey, John. Hiroshima. 2010. (Illus.). 132p. pap. 19.95 *(978-0-923891-65-7(X))* Ishi Pr. International.

Hornblum, Allen M. The Invisible Harry Gold: The Man Who Gave the Soviets the Atom Bomb. 2010. (Illus.). 464p. 32.50 *(978-0-300-15676-8(6))* Yale Univ. Pr.

Hunner, Jon. J. Robert Oppenheimer, the Cold War, & the Atomic West. 2009. (Oklahoma Western Biography Ser.). (ENG.). 272p. 24.95 *(978-0-8061-4046-9(1))* Univ. of Oklahoma Pr.

Jacobs, Robert. The Dragon's Tail: American Nuclear Narratives. 2009. (Illus.). 176p. pap. 24.95 net. *(978-1-55849-727-6(7))*; lib. bdg. 80.00 net. *(978-1-55849-726-9(9))* Univ. of Massachusetts Pr.

—Filling the Hole in the Nuclear Future: Art & Popular Culture Respond to the Bomb. 2010. (AsiaWorld Ser.). (ENG., Illus.). 290p. pap. 34.99 (978-0-7391-3557-0(0)) Lexington Bks.
—Filling the Hole in the Nuclear Future - Art & Popular Culture Respond to the Bomb. 2010. (AsiaWorld Ser.). (ENG., Illus.). 290p. 83.99 (978-0-7391-3556-3(2)) Lexington Bks.
Joseph, Timothy. Historic Photos of the Manhattan Project. 2009. (Historic Photos Ser.). (ENG.). 205p. 39.95 (978-1-59652-521-4(5)) Turner Publishing Co.
Kelly, Cynthia C., ed. The Manhattan Project: The Birth of the Atomic Bomb in the Words of Its Creators, Eyewitnesses & Historians. 2007. (ENG., Illus.). 400p. 24.95 (978-1-57912-747-3(9), 1579127479) Black Dog & Leventhal Pubs., Inc.
—The Manhattan Project: The Birth of the Atomic Bomb in the Words of Its Creators, Eyewitnesses, & Historians. 2009. (ENG., Illus.). 496p. pap. 17.95 (978-1-57912-808-1(4), 1579128084) Black Dog & Leventhal Pubs., Inc.
Kuran, Peter. How to Photograph an Atomic Bomb. 2007. 142p. (ENG.). pap. 24.95 (978-1-889054-19-3(4)); (Illus.). 39.95 (978-1-889054-11-7(9)) VCE, Inc.
Makhijani, Arjun. Target Japan: Why American's Nuclear Bombs Fell on Japan Instead of Germany. 2007. (Illus.). 240p. pap. 17.95 (978-1-57143-165-3(9)) RDR Bks.
Mariner, Rosemary B. & Piehler, G. Kurt, eds. The Atomic Bomb & American Society: New Perspectives. 2009. (ENG.). 470p. 42.00 (978-1-57233-648-3(X)) Univ. of Tennessee Pr.
Masters, Dexter & Way, Katharine, eds. One World or None: A Report to the Public on the Full Meaning of the Atomic Bomb. 2007. (ENG.). 240p. 23.95 (978-1-59558-227-0(4)) New Pr., The.
Mowat, Farley. Eastern Passage. (ENG.). 224p. 2011. pap. 19.95 (978-0-7710-6492-0(6), Emblem Edns) 2010. 27.95 (978-0-7710-6491-3(8), McClelland & Stewart) McClelland & Stewart CAN. Dist: Random Hse., Inc.
Numerof, Paul. In August 1945: A Memoir. 2006. (Illus.). 118p. (978-0-941232-35-7(2)) Los Alamos Historical Society.
O'Neal, Michael J. The Atomic Bomb. 39.00 (978-1-56696-102-8(5)) Jackdaw Pubns.
O'Neill, Dan. The Firecracker Boys: H-Bombs, Inupiat Eskimos, & the Roots of the Environmental Movement. 2007. (ENG., Illus.). 448p. pap. 16.95 (978-0-465-00348-8(6)) Basic Bks.
Porter, Jeff. Oppenheimer Is Watching Me: A Memoir. 2007. (Sightline Bks.). (ENG.). 150p. 24.95 (978-1-58729-616-1(0)) Univ. of Iowa Pr.
Preston, Diana. Before the Fallout: From Marie Curie to Hiroshima. 2009. (ENG.). 400p. 27.00 (978-1-4379-6605-3(5)) DIANE Publishing Co.
Rotter, Andrew J. Hiroshima: The World's Bomb. 2009. (ENG., Illus.). 384p. pap. 19.95 (978-0-19-956976-2(2)) Oxford Univ. Pr., Inc.
Sheinkin, Steve. Bomb: The Race to Build — And Steal — The World's Most Dangerous Weapon. 2012. (ENG., Illus.). 272p. (J). 19.99 (978-1-59643-487-5(2)) Roaring Brook Pr.
Smyth, Henry De Wolf. Atomic Energy for Military Purposes; the Official Report on the Development of the Atomic Bomb under the Auspices of the United States. 2010. 154p. pap. 24.11 (978-1-153-44365-4(1)) General Bks. LLC.
Swedin, Eric G., ed. Survive the Bomb: The Radioactive Citizen's Guide to Nuclear Survival. 2011. (ENG., Illus.). 192p. 17.00 (978-0-7603-4031-8(5), 0760340315, Zenith Pr.) MBI Publishing Co. LLC.
van Wyck, Peter. The Highway of the Atom. 2010. (ENG., Illus.). 288p. (C). (978-0-7735-3783-5(X)) McGill-Queen's Univ. Pr.
Wainstock, Dennis D. The Decision to Drop the Atomic Bomb: Hiroshima & Nagasaki: August 1945. 2008. (ENG.). 224p. pap. 19.00 (978-1-929631-76-6(6)) Enigma Bks.
Wainstock, Dennis D. Decision to Drop the Atomic Bomb: Hiroshima & Nagasaki: August 1945. 2011. (ENG., Illus.). 224p. pap. 19.00 (978-1-936274-00-0(0)) Enigma Bks.
Williams, Hill. Made in Hanford: The Bomb that Changed the World. 2011. (ENG., Illus.). 181p. pap. 22.95 (978-0-87422-307-1(5)) Washington State Univ. Pr.
Wills, Garry. Bomb Power: The Modern Presidency & the National Security State. 2011. (ENG.). 288p. (gr. 12). 16.00 (978-0-14-311868-8(4), Penguin (Non-Classics)) Penguin Group (USA) Inc.

ATOMIC BOMB—JUVENILE LITERATURE

Sonneborn, Liz. The Manhattan Project: Development of the Atomic Bomb. 2011. (Milestones in Modern World History Ser.). (Illus.). 128p. (C). (gr. 9). 35.00 (978-1-60413-410-0(0), Chelsea Hse.) Facts On File, Inc.
Vander Hook, Sue. The Manhattan Project. 2011. (Essential Events Set 6 Ser.). (Illus.). 112p. (YA). (gr. 7-12). 34.22 (978-1-61714-767-8(2)) ABDO Publishing Co.

ATOMIC BOMB—MORAL AND ETHICAL ASPECTS

Malloy, Sean L. Atomic Tragedy: Henry L. Stimson & the Decision to Use the Bomb against Japan. 2010. (Illus.). 248p. pap. 19.95 (978-0-8014-7629-7(1)) Cornell Univ. Pr.
Miscamble, Wilson D. The Most Controversial Decision: Truman, the Atomic Bombs, & the Defeat of Japan. 2011. (Cambridge Essential Histories Ser.). (ENG., Illus.). 192p. (C). 85.00 (978-0-521-51419-4(3)); pap. 24.99 (978-0-521-73536-0(X)) Cambridge Univ. Pr.
Schweber, Silvan S. In the Shadow of the Bomb: Oppenheimer, Bethe, & the Moral Responsibility of the Scientist. 2006. (Princeton Series in Physics). (ENG., Illus.). 288p. (C). per. 26.95 (978-0-691-12785-9(9)) Princeton Univ. Pr.

ATOMIC BOMB—PHYSIOLOGICAL EFFECT

see also Radioactivity—Physiological Effect

Oe, Kenzaburo. Hiroshima Notes. 192p. pap. 22.95 (978-0-7145-3025-3(5)) Boyars, Marion Pubs., Inc.

ATOMIC BOMB (INTERNATIONAL LAW)

see Nuclear Weapons (International Law)

ATOMIC BOMB AND DISARMAMENT

see Nuclear Disarmament

ATOMIC BOMB VICTIMS

Here are entered works on victims of atomic bomb warfare. Works on victims of nuclear weapons tests are entered under Nuclear Weapons Testing Victims.

Hayashi, Kyoko & Otake, Eiko. From Trinity to Trinity. Atake, Eiko, tr. from JPN. 2010. 100p. pap. 12.95 (978-1-58177-117-6(7)) Barrytown/Station Hill Pr.
Hersey, John. Hiroshima. 2010. (Illus.). 132p. pap. 19.95 (978-0-923891-65-7(X)) Ishi Pr. International.
Keiji, Nakazawa. Hiroshima: The Autobiography of Barefoot Gen. 2010. (Asian Voices Ser.). (ENG.). 216p. 39.95 (978-1-4422-0747-9(7)) Rowman & Littlefield Publishers, Inc.
Oe, Kenzaburo. Hiroshima Notes. 192p. pap. 22.95 (978-0-7145-3025-3(5)) Boyars, Marion Pubs., Inc.
Okuda, Sadako & Vergun, Pamela B. A Dimly Burning Wick: Memoir from the Ruins of Hiroshima. 2008. 180p. 29.95 (978-0-87586-561-4(5)); (Illus.). pap. 22.95 (978-0-87586-560-7(7)) Algora Publishing.
Rizzuto, Rahna Reiko. Hiroshima in the Morning. 2010. (ENG.). 320p. pap. 16.95 (978-1-55861-667-7(5)) Feminist Pr. at The City Univ. of New York.
Roose, Diana Wickes. Teach Us to Live: Stories from Hiroshima & Nagasaki. 2007. (Illus.). 143p. pap. 15.95 (978-0-9648042-8-9(X)) Intentional Productions.

Smith, Jeffrey K. Fire in the Sky: The Story of the Atomic Bomb. 2010. 136p. 25.00 (978-1-4490-9265-8(9)); (ENG.). pap. 21.00 (978-1-4490-9266-5(7)) AuthorHouse.

ATOMIC COLLISIONS

see Collisions (Nuclear Physics)

ATOMIC DAMAGES, LIABILITY FOR

see Liability for Nuclear Damages

ATOMIC ENERGY

see Nuclear Energy

ATOMIC ENERGY COMMISSION

see United States—Atomic Energy Commission

ATOMIC ENERGY INDUSTRIES

see Nuclear Industry

ATOMIC FUEL

see Nuclear Fuels

ATOMIC INDUSTRY

see Nuclear Industry

ATOMIC MASS

see also Mass Transfer

Altarelli, Guido & Winter, Klaus, eds. Neutrino Mass. 2010. (Springer Tracts in Modern Physics Ser.). (Illus.). xii, 248p. pap. 219.00 (978-3-642-07313-7(1), 3642073131) Springer.
Ferroni, F., et al. Measurements of Neutrino Mass. 2009. (Illus.). 459p. 260.00 (978-1-60750-038-4(8)) IOS Pr., Inc.
Kursunogammalu, Behram N., et al, eds. Physics of Mass. 2010. (ENG.). 300p. pap. 205.00 (978-1-4419-3305-8(0), 1441933050) Springer.
Lunney, David, et al, eds. Atomic Physics at Accelerators: Mass Spectrometry: Mass Spectrometry. 2012. (ENG.). 556p. pap. 260.00 (978-90-481-5825-6(7), 9048158257) Springer.

ATOMIC MEDICINE

see Nuclear Medicine

ATOMIC NUCLEI

see Nuclear Physics

ATOMIC ORBITALS

Anisimov, Vladmimir & Izyumov, Yuri. Electronic Structure of Strongly Correlated Materials. 2010. (Springer Series in Solid-State Sciences Ser.). (ENG., Illus.). xiii, 288p. 179.00 (978-3-642-04825-8(0), 3642048250) Springer.
Evarestov, Robert A. Quantum Chemistry of Solids: The LCAO First Principles Treatment of Crystals. 2010. (Springer Series in Solid-State Sciences Ser.). (Illus.). xiv, 560p. pap. 289.00 (978-3-642-08022-7(7), 3642080227) Springer.
Hopersky, Alexey N. & Yavna, Victor A. Scattering of Photons by Many-Electron Systems. 2009. (Springer Series on Atomic, Optical, & Plasma Physics Ser.). (Illus.). xi, 133p. 129.00 (978-3-642-04255-3(4), 3642042554) Springer.
Wilson, Angela K. & Peterson, Kirk A., eds. Electron Correlation Methodology. 2007. (ACS Symposium Ser.). (ENG., Illus.). 228p. (C). 155.00 (978-0-8412-3843-5(X)) American Chemical Society.

ATOMIC PILES

see Nuclear Reactors

ATOMIC PLANES

see Nuclear Aircraft

ATOMIC POWER

see Nuclear Energy

ATOMIC POWER ENGINEERING

see Nuclear Engineering

ATOMIC POWER INDUSTRY

see Nuclear Industry

ATOMIC POWER PLANTS

see Nuclear Power Plants

ATOMIC-POWERED VEHICLES

see Nuclear Propulsion

ATOMIC RESEARCH

see Nuclear Energy—Research

ATOMIC RESEARCH LABORATORIES

see Nuclear Energy—Research—Laboratories

ATOMIC SUBMARINES

see Nuclear Submarines

ATOMIC SPECTRA

see also Triplet State

Avery. Generalized Sturmians & Atomic Spectra. 2006. (Illus.). 113.00 (978-981-256-806-9(9)) World Scientific Publishing Co., Inc.
Child, M. S. Theory of Molecular Rydberg States. 2011. (Cambridge Molecular Science Ser.). (ENG., Illus.). 330p. 125.00 (978-0-521-76995-2(7)) Cambridge Univ. Pr.
Herzberg, Gerhard. Atomic Spectra & Atomic Structure. 2007. (ENG.). 288p. per. (978-1-4067-5322-6(X)) Read Bks.
IAtsenko, A. S. & Shalagin, Anatolii Mikhailovich. Opticheskie Spektry B- I C-Podobnykh Ionov. 2007. (RUS., Illus.). 203p. (978-5-02-023178-8(9)) Nauka.
López de Recalde, Andrea. Alkali atomic Spectra. 2008. 268p. pap. 29.90 (978-1-4357-1097-9(5)) Lulu Enterprises Inc.
Marciak-Kozowska, Janina & Kozowski, Mirosaw. From Femto-to Attoscience & Beyond. 2009. (Illus.). 191p. 79.00 (978-1-60741-164-2(4)) Nova Science Pubs., Inc.
Stebbings, R. F. & Dunning, F. B., eds. Rydberg States of Atoms & Molecules. 2011. (ENG.). 526p. pap. 60.00 (978-0-521-18973-6(X)) Cambridge Univ. Pr.

ATOMIC SPECTROSCOPY

Afanas'ev, Valery V. Internal Photoemission Spectroscopy: Principles & Applications. 2007. (ENG., Illus.). 312p. 200.00 (978-0-08-045145-9(4), Elsevier Science) Elsevier Science & Technology Bks.
Blaszczak, Z., et al, eds. Laser 2009: Proceedings of the 8th International Workshop on Application of Laers & Storage Devices in Atomic Nuclei Research: Recent Achievements & Future Prospects (LASER 2009) held in Poznan, Poland, 22 June - 25 June 2009. 2010. (ENG.). x, 342p. 259.00 (978-3-642-12285-9(X), 364212285X) Springer.
Gershberg, Roald E. Solar-Type Activity in Main-Sequence Stars. Knyazeva, Svetlana, tr. 2010. (Astronomy & Astrophysics Library). (Illus.). xii, 494p. pap. 159.00 (978-3-642-05953-7(8), 3642059538) Springer.
Kogure, Tomokazu & Leung, Kam-Ching. The Astrophysics of Emission-Line Stars. 2010. (Astrophysics & Space Science Library). (Illus.). xiv, 537p. pap. 259.00 (978-1-4419-2236-6(9), 1441922369) Springer.
Kurfürst, Ulrich, ed. Solid Sample Analysis: Direct & Slurry Sampling using GF-AAS & ETV-ICP. 2012. (ENG., Illus.). xix, 423p. pap. 329.00 (978-3-642-08290-0(4), 3642082904) Springer.
Letokhov, V. S. Laser Control of Atoms & Molecules. (ENG., Illus.). 328p. 2012. pap. 58.50 (978-0-19-969713-7(2)) 2007. 135.00 (978-0-19-852816-6(7)) Oxford Univ. Pr., Inc.
Markov, B., et al, eds. LASER 2006: Proceedings of the 7th International Workshop on Application of Lasers in Atomic Nuclei Research Nuclear Ground & Isometric State Properties (LASER 2006) held in Poznan, Poland, May 29-June 01 2006. 2007. (ENG., Illus.). viii, 262p. 179.00 (978-3-540-71112-4(0), 3540711120) Springer.
Murray-Krezan, Jeremy. Probing Stark Atoms. 2008. 176p. per. (978-3-8364-5787-3(3)) VDM Verlag Dr. Mueller e.K.
Noll, Reinhard. Laser-Induced Breakdown Spectroscopy: Fundamentals & Applications. 2012. (ENG., Illus.). x, 543p. 199.00 (978-3-642-20667-2(0), 3642206670) Springer.
Rudzikas, Zenonas Bronislovaitis. Theoretical Atomic Spectroscopy. 2007. (Cambridge Monographs on Atomic, Molecular & Chemical Physics). (ENG., Illus.). 456p. pap. 74.00 (978-0-521-02622-2(9)) Cambridge Univ. Pr.
Shevelko, V. P. Atoms & Their Spectroscopic Properties. 2010. (Springer Series on Atomic, Optical, & Plasma Physics Ser.). (Illus.). x, 202p. pap. 259.00 (978-3-642-08274-0(2), 3642082742) Springer.
Steenberg, Michael Van, et al, eds. Future Directions in Ultraviolet Spectroscopy: A Conference Inspired by the Accomplishments of the Far Ultraviolet Spectroscopic Explorer Mission. 2009. (AIP Conference Proceedings / Astronomy & Astrophysics Ser.). (ENG.). 360p. 198.00 (978-0-7354-0672-8(3), 0735406723) American Institute of Physics.
Tomás-Morer, Xavier, et al. Basic Chemometric Techniques in Atomic Spectroscopy. Andrade-Garda, Jose M. et al, eds. 2009. (RSC Analytical Spectroscopy Ser.). (ENG., Illus.). 314p. (C). 213.00 (978-0-85404-159-6(1)) Royal Society of Chemistry, The GBR. Dist: Ingram Pub. Services.
Torres, Diego F. & Rea, Nanda, eds. High-Energy Emission from Pulsars & their Systems: Proceedings of the first session of the Sant Cugat Forum on High-Energy & Particle Astrophysics. 2011. (Astrophysics & Space Science Proceedings Ser.). (Illus.). xxxv, 641p. 349.00 (978-3-642-17250-2(4), 3642172504) Springer.
Verma, Hem Raj. Atomic & Nuclear Analytical Methods: XRF, Mössbauer, XPS, NAA & Ion-Beam Spectroscopic Techniques. 2010. (ENG., Illus.). xiv, 376p. pap. 219.00 (978-3-642-06773-0(5), 3642067735) Springer.
Zachariadis, George. Inductively Coupled Plasma Atomic Emission Spectrometry: A Model Multi-Elemental Technique for Modern Analytical Laboratory. 2012. (978-1-61942-693-1(5)) Nova Science Pubs., Inc.

ATOMIC STRUCTURE

see also Electronic Structure

Bartík-Pártay, Albert. The Gaussian Approximation Potential: An Interatomic Potential Derived from First Principles Quantum Mechanics. 2010. (Springer Theses Ser.). (Illus.). xiii, 88p. 129.00 (978-3-642-14066-2(1), 3642140661) Springer.
Boeyens, Jan C. A. & Levendis, Demetrius C. Number Theory & the Periodicity of Matter. 2010. (ENG., Illus.). xvi, 374p. pap. 159.00 (978-90-481-7692-2(1), 9048176921) Springer.
Boeyens, Jan C. A. & Levendis, Demetrius C. Number Theory & the Periodicity of Matter. 2007. (ENG., Illus.). xvi, 374p. 159.00 (978-1-4020-6659-7(7), 1402066597) Springer.
Cram101 Textbook Reviews & Cram101 Textbook Reviews. Outlines & Highlights for Atomic Structure Theory: Lectures on Atomic Physics by Walter R. Johnson. 2011. 60p. pap. 26.95 (978-1-61830-506-0(9)) Cram101 Inc.
Grant, Ian P. Relativistic Quantum Theory of Atoms & Molecules: Theory & Computation. 2010. (Springer Series on Atomic, Optical, & Plasma Physics Ser.). (Illus.). xxiv, 800p. pap. 289.00 (978-1-4419-2240-3(7), 1441922407) Springer.
Ham & Yang, Fujia. Modern Atomic & Nuclear Physics. rev. ed. 2009. (Illus.). 750p. 128.00 (978-981-283-678-6(0)); pap. 75.00 (978-981-283-679-3(9)) World Scientific Publishing Co., Inc.
Herzberg, Gerhard. Atomic Spectra & Atomic Structure. 2007. (ENG.). 288p. per. (978-1-4067-5322-6(X)) Read Bks.
Hubac, Ivan & Wilson, Stephen. Brillouin-Wigner Methods for Many-Body Systems. 2009. (Progress in Theoretical Chemistry & Physics Ser.). (Illus.). xx, 235p. 359.00 (978-90-481-3372-7(6), 9048133726) Springer.
Johnson, Rebecca L. Atomic Structure. 2007. (Great Ideas of Science Ser.). (Illus.). 80p. (YA). (gr. 9-12). lib. bdg. 27.93 (978-0-8225-6602-1(8)) Twenty First Century Bks.
Johnson, Walter R. Atomic Structure Theory: Lectures on Atomic Physics. (ENG., Illus.). xii, 312p. 2010. pap. 109.00 (978-3-642-08762-2(0), 3642087620) 2007. 109.00 (978-3-540-68010-9(1), 3540680101) Springer.
Katz, Nevin. Atomic Structure & Chemical Reactions: Middle & High School. 2007. (Dr. Birdley Teaches Science Ser.). (Illus.). 94p. per. 12.99 (978-0-86530-537-3(4)) Incentive Pubns., Inc.
Kolessin, Rangel. Nuclear Structure. 2010. 114p. pap. 7.56 (978-0-557-19504-6(7)) Lulu Enterprises Inc.
Lannoo, Michel & Friedel, Paul. Atomic & Electronic Structure of Surfaces: Theoretical Foundations. 2010. (Springer Series in Surface Sciences Ser.). (Illus.). xii, 256p. pap. 137.00 (978-3-642-08094-4(4), 3642080944) Springer.
Leitner, Michael. Studying Atomic Dynamics with Coherent X-rays. 2012. (Springer Theses Ser.). (ENG., Illus.). x, 96p. 129.00 (978-3-642-24120-8(4), 3642241204) Springer.
Metaferia, Wondwosen Tilahun. Nano-Photonics & the Clausius-Mossotti Relation. 2010. 84p. pap. (978-3-639-23939-3(3)) VDM Verlag Dr. Mueller e.K.
Rau, A. R. Astronomy-Inspired Atomic & Molecular Physics. 2010. (Astrophysics & Space Science Library). (Illus.). 256p. pap. 149.00 (978-90-481-5951-2(2), 9048159512) Springer.
Trsic, Milan & da Silva, Alberico B. F. Electronic, Atomic & Molecular Calculations: Applying the Generator Coordinate Method. 2007. (ENG., Illus.). 320p. 250.00 (978-0-444-52781-3(8), Elsevier Science) Elsevier Science & Technology Bks.
Xu, Kunming, ed. The Law of Nature: Spherical Quantity in Dynamic Calculus. 2010. 95.00 (978-1-61668-345-0(7)) Nova Science Pubs., Inc.
Yang, Fujia. Modern Atomic & Nuclear Physics (Revised Edition) Problems & Solutions Manual. 2010. 104p. pap. 19.00 (978-981-4307-68-0(8)) World Scientific Publishing Co., Inc.

ATOMIC THEORY

see also Atomic Structure; Atomism

Atkins, Peter. Reactions: The Private Life of Atoms. 2011. (ENG., Illus.). 256p. 24.95 (978-0-19-969512-6(1)) Oxford Univ. Pr., Inc.
Barysz, Maria. Relativistic Methods for Chemists. 2010. (Challenges & Advances in Computational Chemistry & Physics Ser.). (ENG., Illus.). xiv, 613p. 319.00 (978-1-4020-9974-8(6), 1402099746) Springer.
Bohr, Niels. Atomic Theory & the Description of Nature: Four Essays with an Introductory Survey. 2011. (ENG.). 128p. pap. 24.99 (978-1-107-62805-2(9)) Cambridge Univ. Pr.
—The Theory of Spectra & Atomic Constitution: Three Essays. 2011. (ENG.). 150p. pap. 24.99 (978-1-107-66981-9(2)) Cambridge Univ. Pr.
Burkhardt, Charles E. & Leventhal, Jacob J. Topics in Atomic Physics. 2010. (ENG., Illus.). xiv, 288p. pap. 69.95 (978-1-4419-2068-3(4), 1441920684) Springer.
Carolina Biological Staff, compiled by. Reconstructing Atomic Theory. 2009. (Inquiries in Science Chemistry Ser.). (978-1-4350-0386-6(1)) Carolina Biological Supply Co.
Chalmers, Alan. The Scientist's Atom & the Philosopher's Stone: How Science Succeeded & Philosophy Failed to Gain Knowledge of Atoms. 2010. (Boston Studies in the Philosophy of Science Ser.). (Illus.). xii, 288p. pap. 49.95 (978-94-007-0533-3(6), 9400705336) Springer.

Dalton, John. A New System of Chemical Philosophy. 2010. (Cambridge Library Collection - Physical Sciences Ser.). 376p. pap. 29.99 *(978-1-108-01968-2(4))* Cambridge Univ. Pr.
—A New System of Chemical Philosophy Set, 3 vols. reprint ed. lib. bdg. 375.00 *(978-0-7222-3059-6(1))* Library Reprints, Inc.
Genes, Claudiu. Atomic Entanglement & Decoherence. 2008. 180p. per. *(978-3-8364-6393-5(8))* VDM Verlag Dr. Mueller e.K.
Ghanbari, Saeed. Cold Atoms & Permanent Magnetic Lattices. 2010. 152p. pap. *(978-3-8383-2121-9(9))* Lambert Academic Publishing.
Jeans, James. Atomicity & Quanta. 2009. (Cambridge Library Collection - Physical Sciences Ser.). (ENG.). 72p. pap. 19.99 *(978-1-108-00563-0(2))* Cambridge Univ. Pr.
Lastow, Orest. Electrohydrodynamic Atomisation of Aqueous Liquids. 2010. 224p. pap. *(978-3-8383-6420-9(1))* Lambert Academic Publishing.
Roscoe, Henry E. A New View of the Origin of Dalton's Atomic Theory. 2009. 102p. pap. *(978-1-4432-9163-7(3))* Books LLC.
Scully, Marlan O. & Scully, Robert J. The Demon & the Quantum: From the Pythagorean Mystics to Maxwell's Demon & Quantum Mystery. 2nd ed. 2010. (ENG., Illus.). 275p. pap. 24.95 *(978-3-527-40983-9(1),* Wiley-VCH) Wiley, John & Sons, Inc.
Smirnov, Boris M. Reference Data on Atomic Physics & Atomic Processes. 2008. (Springer Series on Atomic, Optical, & Plasma Physics Ser.). (Illus.). 145p. 169.00 *(978-3-540-79362-5(3))* Springer.
Veitch, John. Lucretius & the Atomic Theory. 2009. 96p. pap. 18.75 *(978-1-110-69055-8(X))* BiblioBazaar.
—Lucretius & the Atomic Theory. 2007. (ENG.). 108p. 33.95 *(978-0-548-05129-0(1))* Kessinger Publishing, LLC.
Woolfson, Michael M. Materials, Matter & Particles: A Brief History. 2009. (Illus.). 328p. pap. 39.00 *(978-1-84816-460-4(2))* Imperial College Pr. GBR. Dist: World Scientific Publishing Co., Inc.

ATOMIC UNDERGROUND EXPLOSIONS
see Underground Nuclear Explosions

ATOMIC WARFARE
see Nuclear Warfare

ATOMIC WEAPONS
see Nuclear Weapons

ATOMIC WEAPONS (INTERNATIONAL LAW)
see Nuclear Weapons (International Law)

ATOMIC WEAPONS TESTING VICTIMS
see Nuclear Weapons Testing Victims

ATOMIC WEIGHTS
see also Molecular Weights
Clarke, Frank Wigglesworth. The Constants of Nature, Part: A Recalculation of the Atomic Weights (1910) 2009. 552p. pap. 42.95 *(978-1-104-48599-3(0))* Kessinger Publishing, LLC.

ATOMISM
Gemelli Marciano, M. Laura. Democrito e L'Accademia: Studi Sulla Trasmissione Dell'atomismo Antico Da Aristotele a Simplicio. 2007. (Studia Praesocratica Ser.). (ITA & GEC.). XII, 376p. 147.00 *(978-3-11-018542-3(3))* De Gruyter, Walter Inc.
Grellard, Christophe & Robert, Aurelelen, eds. Atomism in Late Medieval Philosophy & Theology. 2009. (History of Science & Medicine Library). (Illus.). 288p. *(978-90-04-17217-3(3))* BRILL.
Kuczynski, John-Michael. Conceptual Atomism & the Computational Theory of Mind: A Defense of Content-Internalism & Semantic Externalism. (C). 138.00 *(978-90-272-5205-0(X))* Benjamins, John Publishing Co.
Leucippus, et al. The Atomists, Leucippus & Democritus: Fragments - A Text & Translation with a Commentary. 2010. (GEC & ENG.). xii, 308p. pap. ***(978-1-4426-1212-9(6))*** Univ. of Toronto Pr.
Mudry, Joseph. The Philosophy of Atomic Physics. 2011. 144p. 40.95 ***(978-1-258-07165-3(7))*** Literary Licensing, LLC.
Sethy, Satya. Meaning Atomism vs. Meaning Holism. 2010. 280p. pap. *(978-3-639-26263-6(8))* VDM Verlag Dr. Mueller e.K.
Vicario, Michael A. Shelley's Intellectual System & Its Epicurean Background. 2007. (Studies in Major Literary Authors Ser.). 303p. 131.00 *(978-0-415-98143-9(3))* Routledge.
Whyte, Lancelot Law. Essay on Atomism: From Democritus To 1960. 2011. 116p. 39.95 ***(978-1-258-00558-0(1))*** Literary Licensing, LLC.

ATOMISM (LOGIC)
see Logical Atomism

ATOMIZATION
see also Aerosols; Spraying
Nasr, Ghasem G., et al. Industrial Sprays & Atomization: Design, Analysis & Applications. 2010. (ENG., Illus.). xviii, 502p. pap. 279.00 *(978-1-84996-875-1(6),* 1849968756) Springer.
Sirignano, William. Fluid Dynamics & Transport of Droplets & Sprays. 2nd ed. 2010. (ENG., Illus.). 480p. (C). 115.00 *(978-0-521-88489-1(6))* Cambridge Univ. Pr.

ATOMS
see also Atomic Mass; Electrons; Magnetic Resonance, Matter; Neutrons; Nuclear Shell Theory; Protons; Transmutation (Chemistry)
Ahmed Alvi, Shahbaz. Modelling Hyperfine Interaction. 2011. 80p. pap. ***(978-3-8443-1784-8(8))*** Lambert Academic Publishing.
Alonso, Julio A. Structure & Properties of Atomic Nanoclusters (2nd Edition) 2011. 492p. 150.00 ***(978-1-84816-733-9(4))*** Imperial College Pr. GBR. Dist: World Scientific Publishing Co., Inc.
Angelo, Joseph A. Quantifying Matter. 2011. (States of Matter Ser.). (Illus.). 248p. (C). (gr. 9). 45.00 *(978-0-8160-7609-3(X))* Facts On File, Inc.
Arimondo, Ennio, et al. Advances in Atomic, Molecular, & Optical Physics. (ENG.). 2010. 304p. 225.00 *(978-0-12-381021-2(3))* 2010. 376p. 225.00 *(978-0-12-381029-8(9))* 2009. 312p. 225.00 *(978-0-12-374799-0(6))* 2008. 368p. 225.00 *(978-0-12-374290-2(0))* Vol. 55. 2007. (Illus.). 498p. 225.00 *(978-0-12-373710-6(9))* Elsevier Science & Technology Bks. (Academic Pr.).
Auzinsh, Marcis, et al. Optically Polarized Atoms: Understanding Light-Atom Interactions. 2010. (ENG., Illus.). 380p. 79.95 *(978-0-19-956512-2(0))* Oxford Univ. Pr., Inc.
Bailey, Alice A. The Consciousness of the Atom. 2008. 76p. pap. 9.99 *(978-1-60459-444-7(6))* Wilder Pubns., Ltd.
Berman, Paul R., et al. Advances in Atomic, Molecular, & Optical Physics. 2011. (ENG.). 560p. 225.00 ***(978-0-12-385508-4(X),*** Academic Pr.) Elsevier Science & Technology Bks.
Bernotas, Andrius, et al, eds. 7th International Conference on Atomic & Molecular Data & Their Applications - ICAMDATA-2010. 2011. (AIP Conference Proceedings / Astronomy & Astrophysics Ser.). 268p. pap. 134.00 ***(978-0-7354-0900-2(5),*** 0735409005, AIP Pr.) Springer.
Bishop, Mark. An Introduction to Chemistry - Atoms First. 2009. (Illus.). 812p. (C). 79.95 *(978-0-9778105-9-8(3))* Chiral Publishing Co.
Bohr, Niels. Niels Bohr on the Application of the Quantum Theory to Atomic Structure, Part 1, the Fundamental Postulates. 2011. (ENG.). 48p. pap. 21.99 *(978-1-107-68158-3(8))* Cambridge Univ. Pr.
Braterman, Paul S. From Stars to Stalagmites: How Everything Connects. 2012. 250p. pap. 38.00 ***(978-981-4324-97-7(3))*** World Scientific Publishing Co., Inc.
Burdge, Julia. Chemistry: Atoms First 2011. (ENG.). (C). 238.66 *(978-0-07-746841-5(4),* 0077468414, McGraw-Hill Science, Engineering & Mathematics) McGraw-Hill Higher Education.
Burdge, Julia R. & Overby, Jason. Chemistry: Atoms First. 2011. (ENG., Illus.). 1128p. (C). 229.67 *(978-0-07-351116-0(1),* 0073511161, McGraw-Hill Science, Engineering & Mathematics) McGraw-Hill Higher Education.
Connerade, J. P. Latest Advances in Atomic Cluster Collisions: Structure & Dynamics from the Nuclear to the Biological Scale. Solov'Yov, Andrey, ed. 2008. (Illus.). xvii, 442p. 159.00 *(978-1-84816-237-2(5))* Imperial College Pr. GBR. Dist: World Scientific Publishing Co., Inc.
Controlling Steady-State & Dynamical Properties of Atomic Optical Bistability. 2011. 97.00 *(978-981-4307-55-0(6))* World Scientific Publishing Co., Inc.
Coskuner, Orkid, et al. Metallic Systems: A QuantumChemists Perspective. 2011. (ENG., Illus.). 432p. 149.95 *(978-1-4200-6077-5(5),* CRC Press) Taylor & Francis Group GBR. Dist: Taylor & Francis Group.
Cram101 Textbook Reviews. Outlines & Highlights for Atoms, Radiation, & Radiation Protection by James E Turner, Isbn: 9783527406067. 2010. 140p. pap. 28.95 *(978-1-61698-045-0(1))* Cram101 Inc.
Cram101 Textbook Reviews & Cram101 Textbook Reviews. Outlines & Highlights for the Physics of Atoms & Quant: Introduction to Experiments & Theory by Hermann Haken. 2011. 430p. pap. 35.95 ***(978-1-61830-485-8(2))*** Cram101 Inc.
Drake, Gordon W. F., ed. Springer Handbook of Atomic, Molecular, & Optical Physics. 2nd ed. 2007. (Illus.). LVIII, 1506p. 249.00 *(978-0-387-33634-3(6),* 0387336346) Springer.
Elsersawi, Amin. The Atom & the Universe. 2009. 120p. 29.99 *(978-1-4415-5492-5(0));* pap. 19.99 *(978-1-4415-5491-8(2))* Xlibris Corp.
Fehlner, Thomas, et al. Molecular Clusters: A Bridge to Solid-State Chemistry. 2007. (Cambridge Molecular Science Ser.). (ENG., Illus.). 390p. 170.00 *(978-0-521-85236-4(6))* Cambridge Univ. Pr.
Fornel, Frédérique de. Evanescent Waves: From Newtonian Optics to Atomic Optics. 2010. (Springer Series in Optical Sciences Ser.). (Illus.). xviii, 268p. pap. 199.00 *(978-3-642-08513-0(X),* 364208513X) Springer.
Friedrich, Harald Siegfried. Theoretical Atomic Physics. 3rd ed. 2010. (ENG., Illus.). xiv, 506p. pap. 109.00 *(978-3-642-06503-3(1),* 3642065031) Springer.
Ghanbari, Saeed. Cold Atoms & Permanent Magnetic Lattices. 2010. 152p. pap. *(978-3-8383-2121-9(9))* Lambert Academic Publishing.
Grant, I. P. Relativistic Quantum Theory of Atoms & Molecules: Theory & Computation. 2006. (Springer Series on Atomic, Optical, & Plasma Physics: Vol. 40). (Illus.). 797p. 289.00 *(978-0-387-34671-7(6),* 0387346716) Springer.
Gregersen, Erik. The Britannica Guide to the Atom. 2011. (Physics Explained Ser.) (ENG.). 344p. (YA). lib. bdg. 64.65 *(978-1-61530-319-9(7))* Rosen Publishing Group, Inc., The.
Gregersen, Erik, ed. The Britannica Guide to Matter. 2011. (Physics Explained Ser.). (Illus.). 296p. (YA). 129.30 *(978-1-61530-425-7(8))* Rosen Publishing Group, Inc., The.
—The Britannica Guide to the Atom. 2011. (Physics Explained Ser.). (Illus.). 344p. (YA). 129.30 *(978-1-61530-429-5(0))* Rosen Publishing Group, Inc., The.
Guet, C., et al, eds. Atomic clusters & nanoparticles. Agregats atomiques et Nanoparticules: Les Houches Session LXXIII 2-28 July 2000. 2010. (Houches - Ecole d'Ete de Physique Theorique Ser.). (ENG & FRE., Illus.). xxxv, 585p. pap. 219.00 *(978-3-642-07687-9(4),* 3642076874) Springer.
Haken, Hermann & Wolf, Hans-Christoph. The Physics of Atoms & Quanta: Introduction to Experiments & Theory. Brewer, W. D., tr. 7th ed. 2010. (Advanced Texts in Physics Ser.).Tr. of Atom- und Quantenphysik. (Illus.). xx, 517p. pap. 139.00 *(978-3-642-05871-4(X),* 364205871X) Springer.
Hellmann, Andreas. Polymer Films with Embedded Metal Nanoparticles. 2010. (Springer Series in Materials Science Ser.). (Illus.). x, 216p. pap. 219.00 *(978-3-642-07729-6(3),* 3642077293) Springer.
Hertel, Ingolf V. & Schulz, C. -P. Atom-, Moleküle und Optische Physik. 2008. (Springer-Lehrbuch Ser.). (Illus.). XVIII, 511p. pap. 69.95 *(978-3-540-30613-9(7),* 3540306137) Springer.
Hill, Wendell T. & Lee, Chi H. Light-Matter Interaction: Atoms & Molecules in External Fields & Nonlinear Optics. 2007. (ENG., Illus.). 325p. pap. 95.00 *(978-3-527-40661-6(1),* Wiley-VCH) Wiley, John & Sons, Inc.
Jaksch, Dieter & Clark, Stephen A. Cold Atoms in Optical Lattices. 2011. (ENG.). iv, 300p. 129.00 *(978-90-481-8688-4(9),* 9048186889) Springer.
Kaiser, R., et al, eds. Coherent atomic matter waves - Ondes de matiere Coherentes: 27 July - 27 August 1999. 2010. (Houches - Ecole d'Ete de Physique Theorique Ser.). (ENG & FRE., Illus.). xxxvi, 717p. pap. 229.00 *(978-3-642-07426-4(X),* 364207426X) Springer.
Karshenboim, Savely G., ed. Precision Physics of Simple Atoms & Molecules. (Lecture Notes in Physics Ser.). (Illus.). xiv, 286p. 2010. pap. 109.00 *(978-3-642-09472-9(4),* 3642094724) 2007. (ENG.), 109.00 *(978-3-540-75478-7(4),* 3540754784) Springer.
Karshenboim, Savely G. & Smirnov, Valery B. Precision Physics of Simple Atomic Systems. 2010. (Lecture Notes in Physics Ser.). (Illus.). xiii, 217p. pap. 99.00 *(978-3-642-07344-1(1),* 3642073441) Springer.
Kawazoe, Y., et al. Clusters & Nanomaterials: Theory & Experiment. 2010. (Springer Series in Cluster Physics Ser.). (Illus.). xv, 345p. pap. 159.00 *(978-3-642-07522-3(3),* 3642075223) Springer.
Kirkland, Kyle. Atoms & Materials. 2007. (Physics in Our World Ser.). (Illus.). 160p. (gr. 6-12). 35.00 *(978-0-8160-6115-0(7))* Facts On File, Inc.
Kreibig, Uwe & Vollmer, Michael. Optical Properties of Metal Clusters. 2010. (Springer Series in Materials Science Ser.). (Illus.). xx, 532p. pap. 129.00 *(978-3-642-08191-0(6),* 3642081916) Springer.
Krems, Roman, et al. Cold Molecules: Theory, Experiment, Applications. 2009. (ENG., Illus.). 753p. 154.95 *(978-1-4200-5903-8(3),* CRC Press) Taylor & Francis Group GBR. Dist: Taylor & Francis Group.
Lambert, R. M. & Pacchioni, Gianfranco, eds. Chemisorption & Reactivity on Supported Clusters & Thin Films: Towards an Understanding of Microscopic Processes in Catalysis. 2010. (NATO Science Series E: (closed) Ser.). 526p. pap. 449.00 *(978-90-481-4807-3(3),* 9048148073) Springer.
Langmuir, Irving. Phenomena, Atoms & Molecules. *(978-0-8022-0922-1(X))* Philosophical Library, Inc.
Lichtenberg, Don. The Universe & the Atom. 2007. (Illus.). 311p. 82.00 *(978-981-270-606-5(2));* pap. 41.00 *(978-981-270-561-7(9))* World Scientific Publishing Co., Inc.
Lin, Chun C., et al. Advances in Atomic, Molecular, & Optical Physics. 2006. (Advances in Atomic, Molecular, & Optical Physics Ser.). (ENG., Illus.). 748p. 225.00 *(978-0-12-003854-1(4),* Academic Pr.) Elsevier Science & Technology Bks.
Machette, Michael N., et al. Terrestrial Cosmogenic-Nuclide Dating of Alluvial Fans in Death Valley, California. 2008. (Illus.). v, 44p. *(978-1-4113-2187-8(1))* United States Geological Survey.
Meystre, Pierre. Atom Optics. 2010. (Springer Series on Atomic, Optical, & Plasma Physics Ser.). (Illus.). xvi, 311p. pap. 104.00 *(978-1-4419-2930-3(4),* 1441929304) Springer.
Mitchell, Allan C. G. & Zemansky, Mark W. Resonance Radiation & Excited Atoms. 2009. (ENG.). 356p. pap. 69.00 *(978-0-521-11482-0(9))* Cambridge Univ. Pr.
National Academies Press, creator. Controlling the Quantum World: The Science of Atoms, Molecules, & Photons. 2007. (ENG., Illus.). 244p. per. 54.00 *(978-0-309-10270-4(7))* National Academies Pr.
Perrin, Jean. Atoms. 2010. 236p. (ENG.). pap. 26.75 *(978-1-178-01723-6(0));* pap. 26.75 *(978-1-177-79771-9(2));* pap. 25.75 *(978-1-144-08319-7(2))* BiblioBazaar.
—Atoms. 2010. 136p. pap. *(978-1-151-90315-0(9))* Books LLC.
—Atoms. Hammick, D. L., tr. 2008. 226p. 41.95 *(978-1-4365-1437-8(1))* 2007. (ENG.). 228p. per. 26.95 *(978-0-548-69352-0(8))* Kessinger Publishing, LLC.
Piecuch, Piotr, et al, eds. Advances in the Theory of Atoms, Molecular Systems & Condensed Matter, 2 vols. 2009. (Progress in Theoretical Chemistry & Physics Ser.). (ENG., Illus.). xiv, 450p. 389.00 *(978-90-481-2595-1(2),* 9048125952) Springer.
—Advances in the Theory of Atoms, Molecular Systems & Condensed Matter II, 2 vols. 2009. (Progress in Theoretical Chemistry & Physics Ser.). (ENG., Illus.). xii, 300p. 299.00 *(978-90-481-2984-3(2),* 9048129842) Springer.
Prigogine, Ilya, et al. Advances in Chemical Physics, Volume 137. 2008. (Advances in Chemical Physics Ser.: 133). (ENG.). 253p. 233.00 *(978-0-471-43573-0(2),* Wiley-Interscience) Wiley, John & Sons, Inc.
Rempe, Gerhard & Scully, Marlan O. Advances in Atomic, Molecular, & Optical Physics. 2006. (Advances in Atomic, Molecular, & Optical Physics Ser.). (ENG., Illus.). 484p. 225.00 *(978-0-12-003853-4(6),* Academic Pr.) Elsevier Science & Technology Bks.
Roueff, Evelyne, ed. Atomic & Molecular Data & Their Applications: 5th International Conference on Atomic & Molecular Data & Their Applications (ICAMDATA) 2007. (AIP Conference Proceedings / Atomic, Molecular, Chemical Physics Ser.). (Illus.). XV, 268p. 127.00 *(978-0-7354-0407-6(0),* 0735404070) American Institute of Physics.
Sattler, Klaus, ed. Nanophysics: Clusters & Fullerenes, 7 vols. 2010. (ENG., Illus.). 909p. instr.'s hndbk. ed. 139.95 *(978-1-4200-7554-0(3),* CRC Press) Taylor & Francis Group GBR. Dist: Taylor & Francis Group.
Singer, Stephanie Frank. Linearity, Symmetry, & Prediction in the Hydrogen Atom. 2010. (Undergraduate Texts in Mathematics Ser.). (Illus.). xiv, 398p. pap. 59.95 *(978-1-4419-2035-5(8),* 1441920358) Springer.
Sinha, Chandana & Bhattacharyya, Shibshankar, eds. Current Topics in Atomic, Molecular & Optical Physics: Invited Lectures Delivered at the Conference on Atomic Molecular & Optical Physics (TC2005), 13th-15th December, 2005, Indian Association for the Cultivatoin of Science, Kolkata, India. 2006. (Illus.). 274p. 124.00 *(978-981-270-379-8(9))* World Scientific Publishing Co., Inc.
Smirnov, Boris M. Nanoclusters & Microparticles in Gases & Vapors. 2012. (De Gruyter Studies in Mathematical Physics Ser.: 6). (ENG., Illus.). XIV, 249p. (gr. 17-17). 154.00 ***(978-3-11-027390-8(X))*** De Gruyter, Walter Inc.
Smirnov, Boris M. Physics of Atoms & Ions. 2012. (Graduate Texts in Contemporary Physics Ser.). (ENG., Illus.). xiii, 442p. pap. 159.00 *(978-1-4419-3051-4(5),* 1441930515) Springer.
Stolterfoht, Nikolaus, et al. Electron Emission in Heavy Ion-Atom Collisions. 2010. (Springer Series on Atomic, Optical, & Plasma Physics Ser.). (Illus.). xii, 264p. pap. 189.00 *(978-3-642-08322-8(6),* 3642083226) Springer.
Tao, Jianmin. Density Functional Theory of Atoms, Molecules, & Solids. 2010. 136p. pap. *(978-3-639-27858-3(5))* VDM Verlag Dr. Mueller e.K.
Wales, D. Intermolecular Forces & Clusters I. 2010. (Structure & Bonding Ser.). xvi, 206p. pap. 239.00 *(978-3-642-06644-3(5),* 3642066445) Springer.
—Intermolecular Forces & Clusters II. 2010. (Structure & Bonding Ser.). (ABK.). xvi, 158p. pap. 219.00 *(978-3-642-06642-9(9),* 3642066429) Springer.
Zhu, Shaoping & Yan, Jun, eds. Icamdata-2008: Sixth International Conference on Molecular Data & Their Applications. 2009. (AIP Conference Proceedings / Atomic, Molecular, Chemical Physics Ser.). (ENG., Illus.). 255p. 132.00 *(978-0-7354-0661-2(8),* 0735406618) American Institute of Physics.

ATOMS—SPACE ARRANGEMENT
see Stereochemistry

ATOMS—SPECTRA
see Atomic Spectra

ATOMS, NUCLEI OF
see Nuclear Physics

ATONALITY
see Tonality

ATONEMENT
see also Jesus Christ—Priesthood; Redemption; Servant of Jehovah
Adams, Joseph. A Christian Science Exposition of the Atonement. 2007. (ENG.). 92p. per. 18.95 *(978-1-4304-4590-6(4))* Kessinger Publishing, LLC.
Andross, E. E. A More Excellent Ministry. 2008. 130p. pap. 12.95 *(978-1-57258-527-0(7))* TEACH Services, Inc.
Baadsgaard, Janene Wolsey. Healing from Abuse: How the Atonement of Jesus Christ Can Heal Broken Lives & Broken Hearts. 2007. pap. 16.95 *(978-1-59038-714-6(7))* Deseret Bk. Co.
Baker, Mark D., ed. Proclaiming the Scandal of the Cross: Contemporary Images of the Atonement. 2006. 208p. (C). pap. 22.00 *(978-0-8010-2742-0(X))* Baker Academic.
Barnes, Albert. The Atonement. 2009. 172p. pap. *(978-0-217-62070-3(1))* Books LLC.
Beecher, Edward. The Conflict of Ages; or, the Great Debate on the Moral Relations of God & Man. 2006. 572p. per. 32.99 *(978-1-4255-6246-5(9,)* MPublishing.
Beilby, James K. & Eddy, Paul R., eds. The Nature of the Atonement: Four Views. 2006. (Spectrum Multiview Book Ser.). (ENG.). 208p. per. 20.00 *(978-0-8308-2570-7(3),* IVP Acad.) InterVarsity Pr.
Belousek, Darrin W. Snyder. Atonement, Justice, & Peace: The Message of the Cross & the Mission of the Church. 2011. pap. 55.00 ***(978-0-8028-6642-4(5))*** Eerdmans, William B. Publishing Co.
Berkhof, Louis. Vicarious Atonement Through Christ. 2011. 184p. 42.95 ***(978-1-258-05859-3(6))*** Literary Licensing, LLC.
Boettner, Loraine. The Atonement. 2011. 136p. 40.95 ***(978-1-258-05091-7(3))*** Literary Licensing, LLC.
Bushnell, Horace. Forgiveness & Law, Grounded in Principles Interpreted by Human Analogies. 2009. 144p. pap. *(978-0-217-72565-1(1))* Books LLC.
—Forgiveness & Law, Grounded in Principles Interpreted by Human Analogies. 2006. 268p. per. 23.99 *(978-1-4255-2391-6(9))* MPublishing.
—God in Christ. 2011. (ENG.). 358p. pap. 21.95 ***(978-1-4585-0153-0(1))*** Univ. of Michigan Library.
—God in Christ Three Discourses Delivered at New Haven, Cambridge, & Andover, with a Preliminary Dissertation on Language by Horace Bushnell. 2006. 360p. per. 26.99 *(978-1-4255-3727-2(8))* MPublishing.
—The Vicarious Sacrifice, Grounded in Principles of Universal Obligation: By Horace Bushnell. 2006. 556p. per. 32.99 *(978-1-4255-6130-7(6))* MPublishing.
Buswell Jr., J. Oliver. Sin & Atonement V3: The Lamb of God. 2011. 114p. 39.95 ***(978-1-258-03606-5(1))*** Literary Licensing, LLC.
Callister, Tad R. The Infinite Atonement. 2006. 368p. im. lthr. 25.95 *(978-1-59038-671-2(X))* Deseret Bk. Co.
Campbell, John McLeod. Nature of the Atonement & Its Relation. 2006. pap. 37.95 *(978-1-4286-4862-3(3))* Kessinger Publishing, LLC.
Cole, Graham A. God the Peacemaker: How Atonement Brings Shalom, 1 vol. 2009. (New Studies in Biblical Theology Ser.: Volume 25). (ENG.). 296p. pap. 26.00 *(978-0-8308-2626-1(2),* IVP Acad.) InterVarsity Pr.

Cousineau, Phil. Beyond Forgiveness: Reflections on Atonement. 2011. (ENG.). 272p. pap. 19.95 *(978-0-470-90773-3(8)*, Jossey-Bass) Wiley, John & Sons, Inc.

de de Jong, Mayke. The Penitential State: Authority & Atonement in the Age of Louis the Pious, 814-840. (ENG.). 340p. 2011. pap. 43.00 *(978-0-521-20520-7(4))* 2009. (Illus.). 103.99 *(978-0-521-88152-4(8))* Cambridge Univ. Pr.

Denney, James. Atonement & the Modern Mind. 2006. pap. 21.95 *(978-1-4286-3744-3(3))* Kessinger Publishing, LLC.

—The Death of Christ, Abridged. Tasker, R. V. G., ed. 2008. 208p. pap. 23.00 *(978-1-55635-777-0(X)*, Wipf and Stock) Wipf & Stock Pubs.

Dewey, Simon. My Redeemer Lives: Remembering His Atonement & Resurrection. 2009. (Illus.). 89p. *(978-1-59811-789-9(0))* Covenant Communications.

Elliott, Charles. Memory & Salvation. 352p. pap. *(978-0-232-52141-2(7))* South Asia Bks.

Finlan, Stephen. Options on Atonement in Christian Thought. 2007. (Michael Glazier Bks.). 160p. per. 17.95 *(978-0-8146-5986-1(1))* Liturgical Pr.

Florell, J. M. The Atonement. 2011. 66p. 36.95 ***(978-1-258-05890-6(1))*** Literary Licensing, LLC.

Fluhrer, Gabriel N. E. Atonement. 2010. pap. *(978-1-59638-178-0(7))* P & R Publishing.

Ford, Juanita. Life in the Blood. 2009. 36p. pap. 16.99 *(978-1-4490-3843-4(3))* AuthorHouse.

Gibbons, Ted. Be Not Afraid. 2009. pap. 12.99 *(978-1-59955-274-3(4))* Cedar Fort, Inc./CFI Distribution.

Goldingay. Atonement Today. 304p. 32.95 *(978-0-281-04894-6(0))* International Publishers Marketing.

Grensted, L. W. The Atonement in History & in Life. 2007. 344p. per. *(978-1-4067-8857-0(0)*, Pomona Pr.) Read Bks.

Hafen, Bruce. Broken Heart. 2008. 320p. pap. 15.95 *(978-1-59038-885-3(2))* Deseret Bk. Co.

Hayden, Clarence B. Baptism in Relation to the Atonement. 2011. 98p. 38.95 ***(978-1-258-07137-0(1))*** Literary Licensing, LLC.

Heim, S. Mark. Saved from Sacrifice: A Theology of the Cross. 2006. 346p. per. 27.00 *(978-0-8028-3215-3(6))* Eerdmans, William B. Publishing Co.

Hoeksema, Herman. The Death of the Son of God: The Heidelberg Catechism, the Triple Knowledge, V3. 2011. 276p. 47.95 ***(978-1-258-04322-3(X))*** Literary Licensing, LLC.

Holzapfel, Richard Neitzel & Jackson, Kent P., eds. To Save the Lost: An Easter Celebration. 2009. (Illus.). 138p. *(978-0-8425-2726-6(1)*, Brigham Young Univ. Religious Studies Ctr.) Brigham Young Univ.

Hovey, Alvah. God with Us; 2006. 288p. per. 23.99 *(978-1-4255-2667-2(5))* MPublishing.

Huntsman, Eric D. God So Loved the World: The Final Days of the Savior's Life. 2011. 112p. 21.99 *(978-1-60641-975-5(7))* Deseret Bk. Co.

Jeffery, Steve, et al. Pierced for Our Transgressions: Rediscovering the Glory of Penal Substitution. 2007. 384p. pap. 25.00 *(978-1-4335-0108-1(2))* Crossway.

Jersak, Brad & Hardin, Michael. Stricken by God? Nonviolent Identification & the Victory of Christ. Jersak, Brad & Hardin, Michael, eds. 2007. 527p. per. 32.00 *(978-0-8028-6287-7(X))* Eerdmans, William B. Publishing Co.

Johnson, Adam J. God's Being in Reconciliation: The Theological Basis of the Unity & Diversity of the Atonement in the Theology of Karl Barth. 2012. (ENG.). 240p. 120.00 ***(978-0-567-63833-5(2)***, T&T Clark Int'l) Continuum International Publishing Group, Ltd. GBR. Dist: National Bk. Network.

Johnson, Jeffrey D. God's Passion: A Look at the Cross. 2007. 16p. pap. 3.00 *(978-1-55635-080-1(5)*, Wipf and Stock) Wipf & Stock Pubs.

Kirkwood, James. Unlimited Grace. 2006. pap. 13.99 *(978-1-60034-528-9(X))* Xulon Pr., Inc.

Knight, George R. The Cross of Christ: God's Work for Us. 2008. *(978-0-8280-2067-1(1))* Review & Herald Publishing Assn.

Knox, John. The Death of Christ: The Cross in New Testament History & Faith. 2011. 190p. 42.95 ***(978-1-258-08634-3(4))*** Literary Licensing, LLC.

Kotsko, Adam. Politics of Redemption: The Social Logic of Salvation. 2010. (ENG.). 224p. 34.95 *(978-0-567-18566-2(4))*; 120.00 *(978-0-567-52588-8(0))* Continuum International Publishing Group, Ltd. GBR. (T&T Clark Int'l). Dist: National Bk. Network.

Lidgett, J. Scott. Spiritual Principle of the Atonement As. 2006. pap. 40.95 *(978-1-4286-3963-8(2))* Kessinger Publishing, LLC.

Lofthouse, William F. Ethics & Atonement. 2007. (ENG.). 320p. 45.95 *(978-0-548-08792-3(X))* Kessinger Publishing, LLC.

Love, Gregory Anderson. Love, Violence, & the Cross: How the Nonviolent God Saves Us Through the Cross of Christ. 2010. 316p. pap. 35.00 *(978-1-60899-042-9(7)*, Cascade Bks.) Wipf & Stock Pubs.

Mathews, Shailer. The Atonement & the Social Process. 2011. 212p. 44.95 ***(978-1-258-04502-9(8))*** Literary Licensing, LLC.

Maxwell, L. E. Born Crucified, 1 vol. 2010. (Moody Classics Ser.). (ENG.). 224p. pap. 7.99 *(978-0-8024-5456-0(9))* Moody Pubs.

McDowall, Stewart A. Evolution & the Need of Atonement. 2nd rev. ed. 2012. (ENG.). 204p. pap. 44.00 ***(978-1-107-60521-3(0))*** Cambridge Univ. Pr.

McKnight, Scot. A Community Called Atonement. Jones, Tony, ed. 2007. (Living Theology Ser.). 177p. per. 18.00 *(978-0-687-64554-1(9))* Abingdon Pr.

—Jesus & His Death: Historiography, the Historical Jesus, & Atonement Theory. 2006. 590p. pap. 39.95 *(978-1-932792-79-9(1))*; 54.95 *(978-1-932792-29-4(5))* Baylor Univ. Pr.

Mikkelsen, Hans Vium. Reconciled Humanity: Karl Barth in Dialogue. 2010. pap. 30.00 *(978-0-8028-6363-8(9))* Eerdmans, William B. Publishing Co.

Miyamoto, Arata. Embodied Cross: Intercontextual Reading of Theologia Crucis. 2010. 166p. pap. 19.00 *(978-1-60899-149-5(0)*, Wipf and Stock) Wipf & Stock Pubs.

Moberly, Robert C. Atonement & Personality. 2007. (ENG.). 448p. 51.95 *(978-0-548-12443-7(4))* 2006. pap. 36.95 *(978-1-4286-3400-8(2))* Kessinger Publishing, LLC.

Morris, Chad. New Light on the Atonement: Revelations of the Prophet Joseph Smith on the Atonement of Christ. 2006. 145p. per. 11.99 *(978-1-55517-980-9(0))* Cedar Fort, Inc./CFI Distribution.

Neie, Herbert. The Doctrine of the Atonement in the Theology of Wolfhart Pannenberg. (Theologische Bibliothek Töpelmann Ser.). (ENG.). IX, 237p. 196.00 ***(978-3-11-176060-5(X))*** De Gruyter, Walter Inc.

Nygren, Anders. Essence of Christianity: Two Essays. Watson, Philip S., tr. 2009. 128p. pap. 16.00 *(978-1-60608-716-9(9)*, Wipf and Stock) Wipf & Stock Pubs.

Packer, J. I. & Dever, Mark. In My Place Condemned He Stood: Celebrating the Glory of the Atonement. 2008. 192p. pap. 16.99 *(978-1-4335-0200-2(3))* Crossway.

Park, Andrew Sung. Triune Atonement: Christ's Healing for Sinners, Victims, & the Whole Creation. 2009. (ENG.). 152p. pap. 20.00 *(978-0-664-23347-1(3))* Westminster John Knox Pr.

Parry, Donald & Parry, Jay A. Symbols & Shadows: Unlocking a Deeper Understanding of the Atonement. 2009. 29.95 *(978-1-60641-129-2(2))* Deseret Bk. Co.

Peacore, Linda D. The Role of Women's Experience in Feminist Theologies of Atonement. 2010. (Princeton Theological Monographs). 254p. pap. 28.00 *(978-1-55635-803-6(2)*, Pickwick Pubns.) Wipf & Stock Pubs.

Peterson, David, ed. Where Wrath & Mercy Meet. 2007. (ENG.). 193p. pap. 16.99 *(978-1-84227-079-0(6)*, Paternoster) Authentic Media.

Phillips, Richard D. Precious Blood: The Atoning Work of Christ. 2009. 240p. *(978-1-4335-0923-0(7))* Crossway.

—What Is the Atonement? 2010. 44p. pap. *(978-1-59638-168-1(X))* P & R Publishing.

Phillips, Richard D., et. & contrib. by. Precious Blood: The Atoning Work of Christ. 2009. 240p. pap. 16.99 *(978-1-4335-0921-6(0))* Crossway.

Pink, Arthur W. The Satisfaction of Christ, Studies in the Atonement. 2011. 208p. pap. 16.99 ***(978-1-61203-214-6(1))*** Bottom of the Hill Publishing.

Porter, Bruce D. The King of Kings. 2007. pap. 15.95 *(978-1-59038-815-0(1))* Deseret Bk. Co.

Prince, Derek. Bought with Blood: The Divine Exchange at the Cross. 2007. 240p. pap. 16.99 *(978-0-8007-9424-8(9))* Chosen Bks.

Pringle, Phil. Dead for Nothing? What the Cross Has Done for You. 2007. 140p. per. 12.99 *(978-1-57794-931-2(5))* Harrison House Pubs.

Radzik, Linda. Making Amends: Atonement in Morality, Law, & Politics, 1 vol. 2011. (ENG.). 256p. pap. 29.95 *(978-0-19-976725-0(4))* Oxford Univ. Pr., Inc.

Rea, Michael C., ed. Oxford Readings in Philosophical Theology: Volume 1: Trinity, Incarnation, & Atonement, 2 vols. 2009. (ENG.). 384p. 175.00 *(978-0-19-923747-0(6))* Oxford Univ. Pr., Inc.

Riswold, Caryn D. Coram Deo: Human Life in the Vision of God. 2006. (Princeton Theological Monographs). 174p. pap. 21.00 *(978-1-59752-598-5(7)*, Pickwick Pubns.) Wipf & Stock Pubs.

Robinson, H. Wheeler. Suffering, Human & Divine. 2011. 252p. 46.95 ***(978-1-258-04180-9(4))*** Literary Licensing, LLC.

Rowley, Derek G. By Man Least Understood: Repentance, Agency, Restoration, Atonement & the Everlasting Covenant. 2007. 131p. per. 12.99 *(978-1-55517-940-3(1))* Cedar Fort, Inc./CFI Distribution.

Sanders, John, ed. Atonement & Violence: A Theological Conversation. 2006. 170p. pap. 25.00 *(978-0-687-34294-5(5))* Abingdon Pr.

Sangar, James Mortimer. The Redeemed. 2007. 80p. per. *(978-1-4067-8835-8(X)*, Pomona Pr.) Read Bks.

Scherrer, Steven. The Vicarious, Sacrificial, Atoning Death of Jesus Christ: How We Benefit from the Death of Jesus Christ. 2010. 196p. (ENG.). 26.95 *(978-1-4502-2408-6(3))*; pap. 16.95 *(978-1-4502-2406-2(7))* iUniverse, Inc.

Schramm, Jan-Melissa. Atonement & Self-Sacrifice in Nineteenth-Century Narrative. 2012. (ENG.). 304p. 99.00 ***(978-1-107-02126-6(X))*** Cambridge Univ. Pr.

Shelton, R. Larry. Cross & Covenant: Interpreting the Atonement for 21st Century Mission. 2006. (ENG.). 288p. per. 24.99 *(978-1-932805-67-3(2)*, Paternoster) Authentic Media.

Stalker, James. The Atonement. 2008. 157p. pap. 19.95 *(978-0-557-00807-0(7))* Lulu Enterprises Inc.

Steiner, Rudolf. Karma or Destiny; Fatalism; Redemption; & Christ's Atonement - 2006. pap. 9.95 *(978-1-4304-2522-9(9))* Kessinger Publishing, LLC.

Stroud, William. Treatise on the Physical Cause of the de. 2006. pap. 40.95 *(978-1-4286-3997-3(7))* Kessinger Publishing, LLC.

Sweat, Anthony. I'm Not Perfect, Can I Still Go to Heaven? Finding Hope for the Celestial Kingdom Through the Atonement of Christ. 2010. *(978-1-60641-231-2(0))* Deseret Bk. Co.

Sykes, S. W., ed. Sacrifice & Redemption: Durham Essays in Theology. 2007. (ENG.). 352p. pap. 74.00 *(978-0-521-04460-8(X))* Cambridge Univ. Pr.

Tanner, Jacob. Atonement & Forgiveness: A Reorientation. 2011. 126p. 40.95 ***(978-1-258-01397-4(5))*** Literary Licensing, LLC.

Taylor, Vincent. The Atonement in New Testament Teaching. 2009. 222p. pap. 24.00 *(978-1-60608-726-8(6)*, Wipf and Stock) Wipf & Stock Pubs.

Tidball, Derek. The Atonement Debate, 1 vol. 2008. (ENG.). 368p. pap. 18.99 *(978-0-310-27339-4(0))* Zondervan.

Todd, James Henry. The Cross of Christ: Eternal Glory from Dark Calvary. 2011. 130p. 40.95 ***(978-1-258-08633-6(6))*** Literary Licensing, LLC.

Torrance, Thomas F. Atonement: The Person & Work of Christ. Walker, Robert T., ed. 2009. (ENG.). 489p. 40.00 *(978-0-8308-2892-0(3)*, IVP Acad.) InterVarsity Pr.

Tucker, Henry St George. Providence & the Atonement: Being the Bishop Paddock Lectures For 1933. 2011. 182p. 42.95 ***(978-1-258-03764-2(5))*** Literary Licensing, LLC.

Vandagriff, David P. I Need Thee Every Hour: Applying the Atonement in Everyday Life. 2010. 180p. *(978-1-59811-910-7(9))* Covenant Communications.

Vandagriff, G. G., et al. Deliverance from Depression: Finding Hope & Healing Through the Atonement of Christ. 2008. 100p. *(978-1-59811-648-9(7)*, Debolsillo) Covenant Communications, Inc.

Vorster, Nico. Created in the Image of God: Understanding GodÕs Relationship with Humanity. 2011. (Princeton Theological Monographs). 196p. pap. 23.00 ***(978-1-61097-223-9(6)***, Pickwick Pubns.) Wipf & Stock Pubs.

Weaver, J. Denny. The Nonviolent Atonement, Second Edition. 2nd ed. 2011. 376p. pap. 28.00 *(978-0-8028-6437-6(6))* Eerdmans, William B. Publishing Co.

Wilcox, Brad. The Continuous Atonement. 2009. 224p. 21.95 *(978-1-60641-037-0(7))* Deseret Bk. Co.

Zahl, Paul F. M. Who Will Deliver Us? The Present Power of the Death of Christ. 2008. 94p. pap. 13.00 *(978-1-60608-212-6(4)*, Wipf and Stock) Wipf & Stock Pubs.

ATONEMENT—BIBLICAL TEACHING

Banks, Robert & Banks, Robert, Jr., eds. Reconciliation & Hope: New Testament Essays on Atonement & Eschatology. 2006. 318p. pap. 32.00 *(978-1-59752-989-1(3)*, Wipf and Stock) Wipf & Stock Pubs.

Barnes, Tom. Atonement Matters: A Call to Declare the Biblical View of the Atonement. 2008. (Emmaus Ser.). 342p. pap. *(978-0-85234-660-0(3))* Evangelical Pr.

Boda, Mark J. A Severe Mercy: Sin & Its Remedy in the Old Testament. 2009. x, 622p. 59.50 *(978-1-57506-164-1(3))* Eisenbrauns, Inc.

Bridges, Jerry & Bevington, Bob. The Great Exchange: My Sin for His Righteousness. 2007. 304p. pap. 15.99 *(978-1-58134-927-6(0))* Crossway.

Dever, Mark & Lawrence, Michael. It Is Well: Expositions on Substitutionary Atonement. 2010. (IXMarks Ser.). 224p. pap. 17.99 *(978-1-4335-1476-0(1))* Crossway.

Eberhart, Christian A. The Sacrifice of Jesus: Understanding Atonement Biblically. 2011. (Facets Ser.). 184p. pap. 9.99 *(978-0-8006-9738-9(3)*, Fortress Pr.) Augsburg Fortress, Pubs.

Goligher, Liam. The Jesus Gospel: Recovering the Lost Message. 2006. (ENG.). 176p. per. 14.99 *(978-1-85078-698-6(4))* Authentic Media.

Lofthouse, W. F. Ethics & Atonement (1906) 2007. 320p. per. *(978-1-4067-8853-2(8)*, Pomona Pr.) Read Bks.

Morey, Robert A. Journal of Biblical Apologetics: Vol. 10, No. 1, Vol. 10. 2007. (ENG.). per. 25.00 *(978-0-9796640-0-7(4))* California Biblical Univ. and Seminary.

—Studies in the Atonement. rev. ed. 320p. reprint ed. pap. *(978-0-925703-07-1(9))* Crown Pubns., Inc.

Morris, Leon. The Cross in the New Testament. 2006. 454p. pap. 47.00 *(978-1-59752-695-1(9)*, Wipf and Stock) Wipf & Stock Pubs.

Rodriguez, Angel M. Spanning the Abyss: How the Atonement Brings Humanity & God Together. 2008. 10.99 *(978-0-8280-2357-3(3))* Review & Herald Publishing Assn.

Schwartz. Perspectives on Purity & Purification in the Bible. Wright, David, ed. 2008. (Library of Hebrew Bible/Old Testament Studies, the Ser.). (ENG.). 128p. *(978-0-567-02832-7(1)*, T&T Clark Int'l) Continuum International Publishing Group, Ltd.

Skinner, Andrew C., et al. Parables of Redemption: The Restored Doctrine of the Atonement as Taught in the Parables of Jesus Christ. 2007. 104p. per. 9.99 *(978-0-88290-834-2(0))* Cedar Fort, Inc./CFI Distribution.

Smith, C. Ryder. The Bible Doctrine of Salvation. 2009. 280p. pap. 32.00 *(978-1-60608-715-2(0)*, Wipf and Stock) Wipf & Stock Pubs.

—The Bible Doctrine of Salvation - A Study of the Atonement. 2007. 280p. per. *(978-1-4067-8886-0(4)*, Pomona Pr.) Read Bks.

Stevenson, Peter K. & Wright, Stephen I. Preaching the Atonement. 2009. (ENG.). 224p. pap. 25.00 *(978-0-664-23328-0(7))* Westminster John Knox Pr.

Thomas, G. M. The Extent of the Atonement: A Dilemma for Reformed Theology from Calvin to the Consensus (1536Ð1675) 2007. (Studies in Christian History & Thought: Ser.). 296p. pap. 35.00 *(978-1-59752-742-2(4)*, Wipf and Stock) Wipf & Stock Pubs.

ATONEMENT—HISTORY OF DOCTRINES

Gupta, Nijay K. Worship that Makes Sense to Paul: A New Approach to the Theology & Ethics of Paul's Cultic Metaphors. 2011. (Beihefte zur Zeitschrift fur die neutestamentliche Wissenschaft und die Kunde der älteren Kirche Ser.). (ENG., Illus.). X, 263p. 154.00 ***(978-3-11-173045-5(X))*** De Gruyter, Walter Inc.

Hengel, Martin. The Atonement: The Origins of the Doctrine in the New Testament. 2007.Tr. of Zur Entstehung der Vorstellung vom Stellvertretenden Suhnetod Jesu. 132p. pap. 16.00 *(978-1-55635-231-7(X)*, Wipf and Stock) Wipf & Stock Pubs.

McAvoy, Jane Ellen. The Satisfied Life: Medieval Women Mystics on Atonement. 2009. 152p. pap. 17.00 *(978-1-60608-759-6(2)*, Wipf and Stock) Wipf & Stock Pubs.

Morey, Robert A. Journal of Biblical Apologetics: Vol. 10, No. 1, Vol. 10. 2007. (ENG.). per. 25.00 *(978-0-9796640-0-7(4))* California Biblical Univ. and Seminary.

—Studies in the Atonement. rev. ed. 320p. reprint ed. pap. *(978-0-925703-07-1(9))* Crown Pubns., Inc.

Scott, Waldron Byron. What about the Cross? Exploring Models of the Atonement. 2007. 228p. per. 18.95 *(978-0-595-46894-2(2))* iUniverse, Inc.

Seaich, Eugene. A Great Mystery, the Secret of the Jerusalem Temple: The Embracing Cherubim & at-One-Ment with the Divine. 2008. (Deities & Angels of the Ancient World Ser.: 1). 125.00 *(978-1-59333-840-4(6))* Gorgias Pr., LLC.

Spence, Alan. Promise of Peace: A Unified Theory of Atonement. 2007. (ENG.). 144p. 100.00 *(978-0-567-03117-4(9)*, T&T Clark Int'l) Continuum International Publishing Group, Ltd. GBR. Dist: National Bk. Network.

Spence, Alan & Spence. Promise of Peace: A Unified Theory of Atonement. 2007. (ENG.). 144p. 29.95 *(978-0-567-03118-1(7)*, T&T Clark Int'l) Continuum International Publishing Group, Ltd. GBR. Dist: National Bk. Network.

Stevenson, Peter Kenneth. God in our Nature: The Incarnational Theology of John Mcleod Campbell. 2007. (Studies in Evangelical History & Thought: Ser.). 490p. pap. 51.00 *(978-1-59752-735-4(1)*, Wipf and Stock) Wipf & Stock Pubs.

Yamaguchi, Miho. George MacDonald's Challenging Theology of the Atonement, Suffering, & Death. 2007. (ENG.). 160p. per. 14.95 *(978-1-58736-798-4(X))* Wheatmark.

ATONEMENT, DAY OF

see Yom Kippur

ATP (BIOCHEMISTRY)

see Adenosine Triphosphate

ATROCITIES

see also Massacres; Persecution; Political Atrocities

also subdivision Atrocities under names of wars, e.g. World War, 1939-1945—Atrocities

Adam, Heribert, ed. Hushed Voices: Unacknowledged Atrocities of the 20th Century. 2011. 240p. pap. 25.00 *(978-1-907784-03-3(9))*; 60.00 *(978-1-907784-00-2(4))* Berkshire Academic Pr., Ltd. GBR. Dist: International Specialized Bk. Services.

Batchen, Geoffrey, et al, eds. Picturing Atrocity: Photography in Crisis. 2012. (Illus.). 256p. pap. 30.00 *(978-1-86189-872-2(X))* Reaktion Bks., Ltd. GBR. Dist: Chicago Distribution Ctr.

Black, David R. & Williams, Paul D., eds. The International Politics of Mass Atrocities: The Case of Darfur. 2010. (Security & Governance Ser.). (ENG., Illus.). 288p. (C). 43.95 *(978-0-415-55903-4(0))* Routledge.

—The International Politics of Mass Atrocities: The Case of Darfur. 2010. (Security & Governance Ser.). (ENG., Illus.). 288p. (C). 145.00 *(978-0-415-55902-7(2)*, Routledge) Taylor & Francis Group GBR. Dist: Taylor & Francis Group.

Brudholm, Thomas & Cushman, Thomas, eds. The Religious in Responses to Mass Atrocity: Interdisciplinary Perspectives. 2009. (ENG., Illus.). 296p. 88.00 *(978-0-521-51885-7(7))* Cambridge Univ. Pr.

Burroughs. Travel Writing & Atrocities: Eyewitness Accounts of Slavery in the Congo, Angola & the Putumayo. 2010. (Routledge Research in Travel Writing Ser.). (ENG., Illus.). 230p. (C). 125.00 *(978-0-415-99238-1(9))* Routledge.

Burroughs, Robert M. Travel Writing & Atrocities: Eyewitness Accounts of Colonialism in the Congo, Angola, & the Putumayo. 2010. (Illus.). xiv, 215p. 95.00 *(978-0-203-84916-3(7))* Routledge.

Cohen, Stanley. States of Denial: Knowing about Atrocities & Suffering. 2nd ed. 2015. (ENG.). 380p. 69.95 ***(978-0-7456-4468-4(6))***; pap. 29.95 ***(978-0-7456-4469-1(4))*** Polity Pr. GBR. Dist: Wiley, John & Sons, Inc.

Cox, Caroline, et al. Heroes & Zeros: Bible Discovery for Families. 2010. (Illus.). 48p. (J). pap. *(978-1-873166-79-6(6))* Good Bk. Co.

Current Situation in Darfur: Hearing Before the Committee on Foreign Affairs, House of Representatives, One Hundred Tenth Congress, First Session, April 19, 2007. 2007. iii, 55p. *(978-0-16-078961-8(3)*, 552-070-36079-4) United States Government Printing Office.

Dawes, James. That the World May Know: Bearing Witness to Atrocity. 2007. 304p. 19.95 *(978-0-674-02623-0(3))* Harvard Univ. Pr.

Del Boca, Angelo. Mohamed Fekini & the Fight to Free Libya. Shugaar, Antony, tr. from ITA. 2010. (Italian & Italian American Studies). (ENG., Illus.). 248p. 89.00 *(978-0-230-10886-8(5))* Palgrave Macmillan.

Drumbl, Mark A. Atrocity, Punishment, & International Law. 2007. (ENG., Illus.). 320p. 83.99 *(978-0-521-87089-4(5))*; 316p. per. 33.99 *(978-0-521-69138-3(9))* Cambridge Univ. Pr.

Dwyer, Philip G. & Ryan, Lyndall, eds. Theatres of Violence: Massacre, Mass Killing & Atrocity throughout History. 2012. (War & Genocide Ser.). (ENG.). 350p. 120.00 ***(978-0-85745-299-3(1))*** Berghahn Bks., Inc.

Evans, Gareth. The Responsibility to Protect: Ending Mass Atrocity Crimes Once & for All. (ENG.). 349p. 2009. pap. 19.95 *(978-0-8157-0334-1(1))* 2008. (Illus.). 36.95 *(978-0-8157-2504-6(3))* Brookings Institution Pr.

Genser, Jared & Cotler, I. The Responsibility to Protect: The Promise of Stopping Mass Atrocities in Our Time, 1 vol. 2011. (ENG., Illus.). 420p. ***(978-0-19-979776-9(5))*** Oxford Univ. Pr., Inc.

Goodman, Jordan. The Devil & Mr. Casement: One Man's Battle for Human Rights in South America's Heart of Darkness. 2011. (ENG., Illus.). 336p. pap. 18.00 *(978-0-312-68058-9(9))* Picador.

Gove, Michael. Celsius 7/7: How the West's Policy of Appeasement Has Provoked yet More Fundamentalist Terror - & What Has to Be Done Now. 2007. (Phoenix Press Ser.). 160p. pap. 14.95 *(978-0-7538-2195-4(8),* Phoenix) Orion Publishing Group, Ltd. GBR. Dist: Sterling Publishing Co., Inc.

H.R. 180, the Darfur Accountability & Divestment ACT of 2007: Hearing Before the Subcommittee on Domestic & International Monetary Policy, Trade, & Technology of the Committee on Financial Services, U.S. House of Representatives, One Hundred Tenth Congress, First Session, March 20, 2007. 2007. iv, 82p. *(978-0-16-079103-1(0),* 552-070-36200-2) United States Government Printing Office.

Hughes, Edel, et al, eds. Atrocities & International Accountability: Beyond Transnational Justice. 2008. (ENG., Illus.). 297p. pap. 32.00 *(978-92-808-1141-4(X))* United Nations Pubns.

Jamail, Dahr. Beyond the Green Zone: Dispatches from an Unembedded Journalist in Occupied Iraq. 2008. (ENG., Illus.). 330p. pap. 16.00 *(978-1-931859-61-5(2))* Haymarket Bks.

Kassimeris, George, ed. The Barbarization of Warfare. 2006. (ENG.). 200p. 65.00 *(978-0-8147-4796-4(5))*; pap. 21.00 *(978-0-8147-4797-1(3))* New York Univ. Pr.

Kazi, Gregorio. Subjetividad y Contexto: Matar la Muerte. 2009. (SPA.). 171p. *(978-987-1231-53-9(9))* Asociacion Madres de Plaza de Mayo.

Kennedy, Carmel. The Masters of Hope. 2011. 252p. 28.99 ***(978-1-4670-7096-6(3))***; pap. 19.95 ***(978-1-4670-7097-3(1))*** AuthorHouse.

Lary, Diana, et al, eds. The Scars of War: The Impact of Warfare on Modern China. (ENG., Illus.). 224p. *(978-0-7748-0840-8(3))* Univ. of British Columbia Pr.

McCullum, Hugh. Africa's Broken Heart: The Land the World Forgot. 2006. (Risk Book Ser.: No. 115). (Illus.). 116p. pap. 13.00 *(978-2-8254-1506-1(5))* World Council of Churches/Conseil Oecumenique des Eglises CHE. Dist: International Specialized Bk. Services.

Mitchell, Neil J. Democracy's Blameless Leaders: From Dresden to Abu Ghraib, How Leaders Evade Accountability for Abuse, Atrocity, & Killing. 2012. E-Book ***(978-0-8147-6337-7(5))***; E-Book ***(978-0-8147-6338-4(3))*** New York Univ. Pr.

Mitchell, Neil James. Democracy's Blameless Leaders: From Dresden to Abu Ghraib, How Leaders Evade Accountability for Abuse, Atrocity, & Killing. 2012. (ENG.). 256p. 39.00 ***(978-0-8147-6144-1(5))*** New York Univ. Pr.

Mithander, Conny, et al, eds. Collective Traumas: Memories of War & Conflict in 20th-Century Europe. 2007. (Multiple Europes Ser.: Vol. 38). 268p. pap. *(978-90-5201-068-7(4))* Lang, Peter AG.

Narwani, G. S. Atrocities Against Scheduled Castes & Scheduled Tribes. 2011. 198p. 40.00 ***(978-81-316-0362-8(8))*** Rawat Pubns. IND. Dist: International Specialized Bk. Services.

Norlock, Kathryn J. Evil, Political Violence, & Forgiveness: Essays in Honor of Claudia Card. Veltman, ed. 2009. (ENG.). 238p. 68.50 *(978-0-7391-3650-8(X))* Lexington Bks.

Othman, Mohamed. Accountability for International Humanitarian Law Violations: the Case of Rwanda & East Timor: The Case of Rwanda & East Timor. 2010. (ENG.). xiv, 384p. pap. 219.00 *(978-3-642-06544-6(9),* 3642065449) Springer.

Ratner, Steven R., et al. Accountability for Human Rights Atrocities in International Law: Beyond the Nuremberg Legacy. 3rd ed. 2009. (ENG.). 480p. 203.50 *(978-0-19-954666-4(5))*; pap. 66.00 *(978-0-19-954667-1(3))* Oxford Univ. Pr., Inc.

Rice, Andrew. The Teeth May Smile but the Heart Does Not Forget: Murder & Memory in Uganda. 2010. (ENG., Illus.). 384p. pap. 17.00 *(978-0-312-42973-7(8))* Picador.

Rotberg, Robert I., ed. Mass Atrocity Crimes: Preventing Future Outrages. 2010. (ENG., Illus.). 255p. pap. 28.95 *(978-0-8157-0471-3(2))* Brookings Institution Pr.

Savelsberg, Joachim J. & King, Ryan D. American Memories: Atrocities & the Law. 2011. ***(978-0-87154-736-1(8))***; E-Book ***(978-1-61044-749-2(2))*** Russell Sage Foundation.

Sliwinski, Sharon. Human Rights in Camera. 2011. (ENG., Illus.). 192p. 65.00 *(978-0-226-76275-3(0))*; pap. 22.50 *(978-0-226-76276-0(9))* Univ. of Chicago Pr.

Smith, Patti, contrib. by. Double Blind: War in Lebanon 2006. 2007. (Illus.). 128p. pap. 39.95 *(978-1-904563-57-0(0))* Trolley GBR. Dist: Prestel Publishing.

Sriram, Chandra Lekha. Globalizing Justice for Mass Atrocities: A Revolution in Accountability. Gow, James & Kerr, Rachel, eds. 2009. 208p. pap. 39.95 *(978-0-415-54490-0(4))* Routledge.

Taithe, Bertrand. The Killer Trail: A Colonial Scandal in the Heart of Africa. 2009. (ENG., Illus.). 304p. 34.95 *(978-0-19-923121-8(4),* Oxford Univ. Pr., Inc.

Van Woudenberg, Anneke, et al. Trail of Death: LRA Atrocities in Northeastern Congo. 2010. (Illus.). 67p. pap. ***(978-1-56432-614-0(4))*** Human Rights Watch.

Walker, Alice. Overcoming Speechlessness: A Poet Encounters the Horror in Rwanda, Eastern Congo, & Palestine/Israel. 2010. (ENG.). 64p. pap. 9.95 *(978-1-58322-917-0(5))* Seven Stories Pr.

Whiteman, Dennis. The Resonant Factor. 2010. 586p. pap. 39.96 *(978-1-4452-1776-5(7))* Lulu Enterprises Inc.

Williams, Paul. Memorial Museums: The Global Rush to Commemorate Atrocities. 2008. (ENG., Illus.). 1p. 104.95 *(978-1-84520-488-4(3))*; 224p. pap. 35.95 *(978-1-84520-489-1(1))* Berg Pubs. GBR. Dist: Macmillan.

ATROPHY, MUSCULAR

see Muscular Atrophy

ATTACHES

see Military Attaches

ATTACHMENT AND GARNISHMENT

Botti, James P. Ohio Creditors' Rights. 2007. (Illus.). pap. 84.00 *(978-1-59345-452-4(X))* LexisNexis Matthew Bender.

Bryant. Complete Guide to Federal & State Garnishment 2011. 2010. pap. *(978-0-7355-9177-6(6),* Aspen Pubs.) Wolters Kluwer Law & Business.

Bryant, Amorette Nelson. Complete Guide to Federal & State Garnishment 2010. 2009. pap. 285.00 *(978-0-7355-8201-9(7))* Wolters Kluwer Law & Business.

Casher, Dana E. Collecting Civil Judgments. 2009. 192p. pap. 125.00 *(978-1-57589-560-4(9))* Massachusetts Continuing Legal Education, Inc.

González Cano, Ma Isabel & Cano, María Isabel González. Embargo de Bienes y Derechos en la Ley de Enjuiciamiento Civil. 2009. (SPA., Illus.). 201p. *(978-84-9876-484-0(X))* Tirant lo Blanch.

Hunt, Colin A.G. Carbon Sinks & Climate Change: Forests in the Fight against Global Warming. 2011. (Advances in Ecological Economics Ser.). (Illus.). 256p. pap. 40.00 *(978-0-85793-385-0(X))* Elgar, Edward Publishing, Inc.

Khanal, Yajnamurti. Valuation of Carbon Sequestration & Water Supply Services. 2010. 68p. pap. *(978-3-8383-7854-1(7))* Lambert Academic Publishing.

Mohoney, Beatrice V., ed. Suits Against Terrorist States by Victims of Terrorism. 2009. pap. 43.00 *(978-1-60692-835-6(X))* Nova Science Pubs., Inc.

Nath. Aircraft Repossession Enforcement Practical Aspects Volume II. 2010. xxiv, 471p. *(978-90-411-3251-2(1))* Kluwer Law International.

Rackley, Steve. Carbon Capture & Storage: Engineering Technologies. 2009. (ENG., Illus.). 408p. 155.00 *(978-1-85617-636-1(3),* Butterworth-Heinemann) Elsevier Science & Technology Bks.

Waples, Rufus. A Treatise on Attachment & Garnishment. 2009. 708p. 40.99 *(978-1-116-19872-0(X))*; pap. 48.75 *(978-1-116-19874-4(6))*; pap. 49.75 *(978-1-116-19873-7(8))* BiblioBazaar.

—A Treatise on Attachment & Garnishment. 2009. 506p. pap. *(978-0-217-15490-1(5))* Books LLC.

ATTACHMENT BEHAVIOR

see also Dependency (Psychology); Imprinting (Psychology)

Arnold, Elaine. Working with Families of African Caribbean Origin: Understanding Issues Around Immigration & Attachment. 2011. (ENG., Illus.). 144p. pap. ***(978-1-84310-992-1(1))*** Kingsley, Jessica Ltd.

Becker-Weidman, Arthur, ed. Creating Capacity for Attachment: Dyadic Developmental Psychotherapy in the Treatment of Trauma-Attachment Disorders. 2008. (ENG.). 334p. pap. 34.95 net. *(978-0-9822883-2-0(8))* Ctr. For Family Development.

Benamer, Sarah & White, Kate, eds. Trauma & Attachment. 2008. (Illus.). 110p. pap. 24.95 *(978-1-85575-666-3(8))* Karnac Bks. GBR. Dist: Stylus Publishing, LLC.

Bennett, Susanne & Nelson, Judith Kay. Adult Attachment in Clinical Social Work Practice: Practice, Research, & Policy. 2nd ed. 2010. (Essential Clinical Social Work Ser.). xiii, 271p. E-Book ***(978-1-4419-6241-6(7))*** Springer.

Bennett, Susanne & Nelson, Judith Kay, eds. Adult Attachment in Clinical Social Work: Practice, Research, & Policy. 2011. (Essential Clinical Social Work Ser.). (ENG., Illus.). xiii, 300p. pap. 49.95 ***(978-1-4614-1455-1(5),*** 1461414555) Springer.

Bifulco, Antonia & Thomas, Geraldine. Understanding Adult Attachment in Family Relationships. 2012. (ENG., Illus.). 352p. (C). 155.00 ***(978-0-415-59432-5(4))***; pap. 53.95 ***(978-0-415-59433-2(2))*** Routledge.

Brandell, Jerrold R. & Ringel, Shoshana. Attachment & Dynamic Practice: An Integrative Guide for Social Workers & Other Clinicians. 2007. (ENG.). 224p. (gr. 17). pap. 29.00 *(978-0-231-13391-3(X))*; (Illus.). 90.00 *(978-0-231-13390-6(1))* Columbia Univ. Pr.

Brink, Andrew. Desire & Avoidance in Art: Psychobiographical Studies with Attachment Theory of Pablo Picasso, Hans Bellmer, Balthus, & Joseph Cornell. 2007. (Illus.). 222p. (C). 68.95 *(978-0-8204-9721-1(5))* Lang, Peter Publishing, Inc.

Carr, Sam. Attachment in Sport, Exercise & Wellness. 2011. (Routledge Research in Sport & Exercise Science Ser.). (ENG.). 168p. (C). 125.00 ***(978-0-415-57858-5(2))*** Routledge.

Cassidy, Jude & Shaver, Phillip R., eds. Handbook of Attachment: Theory, Research, & Clinical Applications. 2nd rev. ed. 2010. (ENG., Illus.). 1020p. 65.00 *(978-1-60623-028-2(X))* Guilford Pubns., Inc.

—Handbook of Attachment, Second Edition: Theory, Research, & Clinical Applications. 2nd rev. ed. 2008. (ENG., Illus.). 1020p. 125.00 *(978-1-59385-874-2(4))* Guilford Pubns., Inc.

Cicchetti, Dante & Roisman, Glenn I. Minnesota Symposia on Child Psychology Vol. 36: The Origins & Organization of Adaptation & Maladaptation. 2011. (Minnesota Symposia on Child Psychology Ser.: 2). (ENG., Illus.). 496p. 132.00 *(978-0-470-42273-1(4),* Wiley) Wiley, John & Sons, Inc.

Cozolino, Louis. The Neuroscience of Human Relationships: Attachment & the Developing Social Brain. 2006. (Norton Series on Interpersonal Neurobiology Ser.). (ENG., Illus.). 272p. 35.00 *(978-0-393-70454-9(8),* 70454) Norton, W. W. & Co., Inc.

Cozolino, Louis. The Social Neuroscience of Education: Optimizing Attachment & Learning in the Classroom. 2012. (ENG.). 304p. 37.50 ***(978-0-393-70609-3(5),*** 70609) Norton, W. W. & Co., Inc.

Cram101 Textbook Reviews & Cram101 Textbook Reviews. Outlines & Highlights for Attachment in Adulthood: Structure, Dynamics, & Change by Mario Mikulincer. 2011. 68p. pap. 27.95 ***(978-1-61830-460-5(7))*** Cram101 Inc.

Crittenden, Patricia McKinsey & Landini, Andrea. The Assessing Adult Attachment: A Dynamic-Maturational Approach to Discourse Analysis. 2011. (ENG., Illus.). 304p. 42.50 *(978-0-393-70667-3(2),* 70667) Norton, W. W. & Co., Inc.

Dallos, Rudi & Vetere, Arlene. Systemic Therapy & Attachment Narratives: Applications in a Range of Clinical Settings. 2009. (ENG., Illus.). 232p. (C). 95.00 *(978-0-415-41657-3(4))*; pap. 34.95 *(978-0-415-41658-0(2))* Routledge.

Diamond, Diana, pseud, et al, eds. Attachment & Sexuality. 2007. (Psychoanalytic Inquiry Book Ser.: No. 21). (ENG.). 288p. 46.95 *(978-0-88163-466-2(2))* Routledge.

Du Plessis, Karin, et al. Attachment & Conflict in Close Relationships. 2011. 304p. pap. ***(978-3-8443-0288-2(3))*** Lambert Academic Publishing.

Dutton, Donald G. The Abusive Personality: Violence & Control in Intimate Relationships. 2nd rev. ed. 2006. (ENG., Illus.). 262p. 55.00 *(978-1-59385-371-6(8))* Guilford Pubns., Inc.

Epstein, Badouk, et al, eds. Ritual Abuse & Mind Control: The Manipulation of Attachment Needs. 2011. (Illus.). 200p. pap. 34.95 *(978-1-85575-839-1(3))* Karnac Bks. GBR. Dist: Stylus Publishing, LLC.

Farnfield, Steve. A Practical Guide to Using Attachment Theory & Research with Children & Young People. 2008. 240p. pap. *(978-1-84310-100-0(9))* Kingsley, Jessica Ltd.

Flores, Philip J. Addiction as an Attachment Disorder. 2011. (ENG.). 364p. pap. 38.99 ***(978-0-7657-0905-9(8),*** Aronson, Jason) Rowman & Littlefield Publishers, Inc.

Fonagy, Peter. Attachment Theory & Psychoanalysis. 2006. (ENG., Illus.). 272p. pap. 32.00 *(978-1-892746-70-2(0))* Other Pr., LLC.

Fricchione, Gregory L. Compassion & Healing in Medicine & Society: On the Nature & Use of Attachment Solutions to Separation Challenges. 2011. (ENG., Illus.). 552p. (gr. 17). 65.00 *(978-1-4214-0220-8(3))* Johns Hopkins Univ. Pr.

George, Carol & West, Malcolm L. The Adult Attachment Projective Picture System: Attachment Theory & Assessment in Adults. 2012. (ENG.). 304p. 45.00 ***(978-1-4625-0425-1(6))*** Guilford Pubns., Inc.

Golding, Kim S. Nurturing Attachments: Supporting Children Who Are Fostered or Adopted. 2007. (ENG., Illus.). 240p. (C). pap. *(978-1-84310-614-2(0))* Kingsley, Jessica Ltd.

Golding, Kim S. & Hughes, Daniel A. Creating Loving Attachments: Parenting with PACE to Nurture Confidence & Security in the Troubled Child. 2012. (Illus.). 240p. pap. ***(978-1-84905-227-6(1))*** Kingsley, Jessica Ltd.

Goodman, Geoff. Therapeutic Attachment Relationships: Interaction Structures & the Processes of Therapeutic Change. 2009. (ENG.). 144p. 47.50 *(978-0-7657-0745-1(4),* Aronson, Jason) Rowman & Littlefield Publishers, Inc.

—Transforming the Internal World & Attachment Vol. 1: Theoretical & Empirical Perspectives. 2009. (ENG.). 342p. 78.99 *(978-0-7657-0538-9(9),* Aronson, Jason) Rowman & Littlefield Publishers, Inc.

—Transforming the Internal World & Attachment Vol. 2: Clinical Applications. 2nd ed. 2009. (ENG.). 210p. 57.99 *(978-0-7657-0709-3(8),* Aronson, Jason) Rowman & Littlefield Publishers, Inc.

Gray, Deborah D. Attaching in Adoption: Practical Tools for Today's Parents. 2012. (ENG., Illus.). 400p. pap. ***(978-1-84905-890-2(3))*** Kingsley, Jessica Ltd.

Green, Marci, ed. Risking Human Security: Attachment & Public Life. 2008. (Illus.). 210p. (C). pap. 43.95 *(978-1-85575-597-0(1))* Karnac Bks. GBR. Dist: Stylus Publishing, LLC.

Hart, Susan. Brain, Attachment, Personality: An Introduction to Neuroaffective Development. Silver, Dorte A., tr. from DAN. 2008. (Illus.). 398p. (C). pap. 58.50 *(978-1-85575-588-8(2))* Karnac Bks. GBR. Dist: Stylus Publishing, LLC.

—The Impact of Attachment. 2010. (Norton Series on Interpersonal Neurobiology Ser.). (ENG., Illus.). 448p. 42.50 *(978-0-393-70662-8(1),* 70662) Norton, W. W. & Co., Inc.

Heard & Lake. Challenge of Attachment Caregiving. 2009. 240p. pap. 34.95 *(978-1-85575-728-8(1))* Karnac Bks. GBR. Dist: Stylus Publishing, LLC.

Heard, Dorothy, et al. Attachment Therapy for Adolescents & Adults. 2009. (Illus.). 270p. pap. 36.95 *(978-1-85575-522-2(X))* Karnac Bks. GBR. Dist: Stylus Publishing, LLC.

Hill, John. At Home in the World: Sounds & Symmetries of Belonging. 2010. 288p. pap. 26.95 *(978-1-935528-00-5(9))* Spring Journal.

Holmes, Jeremy. Exploring in Security: Towards an Attachment-Informed Psychoanalytic Psychotherapy. 2009. (ENG.). 216p. (C). 36.95 *(978-0-415-55415-2(2))*; 95.00 *(978-0-415-55414-5(4))* Routledge.

Hopkins, Peter. Young People, Place & Identity. 2010. (ENG., Illus.). 336p. (C). 180.00 *(978-0-415-45437-7(9))* Routledge.

Howe, David. Attachment Across the Lifecourse: A Brief Introduction. 2011. (ENG., Illus.). 272p. pap. 24.00 *(978-0-230-29359-5(X))* Palgrave Macmillan.

Hughes, Daniel. Building the Bonds of Attachment: Awakening Love in Deeply Troubled Children. 2nd ed. 2006. (ENG.). 272p. per. 46.50 *(978-0-7657-0404-7(8),* Aronson, Jason) Rowman & Littlefield Publishers, Inc.

Hughes, Daniel A. Attachment-focused Family Therapy. 2007. 32.00 *(978-0-7937-0526-9(6))* Norton, W. W. & Co., Inc.

—Attachment-Focused Family Therapy. 2007. (ENG.). 288p. wbk. ed. 32.00 *(978-0-393-70526-3(9),* 70526) Norton, W. W. & Co., Inc.

—Attachment-Focused Family Therapy Workbook. 2011. (ENG.). 256p. pap. 29.95 *(978-0-393-70649-9(4),* 70649) Norton, W. W. & Co., Inc.

—Attachment-Focused Parenting: Effective Strategies to Care for Children. 2009. (ENG.). 272p. 29.95 *(978-0-393-70555-3(2),* 70555) Norton, W. W. & Co., Inc.

Hughes, Daniel A. & Baylin, Jonathan. Brain-Based Parenting: The Neuroscience of Caregiving for Healthy Attachment. 2012. (ENG.). 256p. 27.95 ***(978-0-393-70728-1(8),*** 70728) Norton, W. W. & Co., Inc.

James, Beverly. Handbook for Treatment of Attachment Problems in Children. 2008. (ENG.). 308p. pap. 20.95 *(978-1-4391-4300-1(5),* Free Pr.) Free Pr.

Kernberg, Paulina F. Beyond the Reflection: The Role of the Mirror Paradigm in Clinical Practice. 2007. (ENG., Illus.). 232p. pap. 26.00 *(978-1-59051-071-1(2))* Other Pr., LLC.

Klein, Barbara. Alone in the Mirror: Twins in Therapy. 2012. (ENG.). 218p. 36.95 *(978-0-415-89340-4(2))* Routledge.

Knox, Jean. Self-Agency in Psychotherapy: Attachment, Autonomy, & Intimacy. 2010. (Norton Series on Interpersonal Neurobiology Ser.). (ENG., Illus.). 256p. 35.00 *(978-0-393-70559-1(5),* 70559) Norton, W. W. & Co., Inc.

Leonard, Erin. Adolescents with HIV: Attachment, Depression, & Medication 2008. 136p. 89.95 *(978-1-60497-533-8(4))* Cambria Pr.

Levine, Amir & Heller, Rachel. Attached: The New Science of Adult Attachment & How It Can Help You Find - And Keep - Love. (ENG.). 304p. (gr. 12). 2012. 15.95 ***(978-1-58542-913-4(9))*** 2010. 24.95 *(978-1-58542-848-9(5))* Penguin Group (USA) Inc. (Tarcher).

Ludlam, Molly & Nyberg, Viveka, eds. Couple Attachments: Theoretical & Clinical Studies. 2008. (Illus.). 290p. per. 45.00 *(978-1-85575-452-2(5))* Karnac Bks. GBR. Dist: Stylus Publishing, LLC.

Mawson, Anthony R. Mass Panic & Social Attachment. 2007. (Illus.). 336p. 124.95 *(978-0-7546-4880-2(X))* Ashgate Publishing Co.

Mayseless, Ofra & Scharf, Miri, eds. Attachment in Adolescence: Reflections & New Angles. 2007. (J-B CAD Single Issue Child & Adolescent Development Ser.: 87). (ENG., Illus.). 128p. per. 29.00 *(978-0-470-22560-8(2),* Jossey-Bass) Wiley, John & Sons, Inc.

Mikulincer, Mario & Shaver, Phillip R. Attachment in Adulthood: Structure, Dynamics, & Change. (ENG., Illus.). 578p. 2010. pap. 50.00 *(978-1-60623-610-9(5))* 2007. 75.00 *(978-1-59385-457-7(9))* Guilford Pubns., Inc.

Muller, Robert T. Trauma & the Avoidant Client: Attachment-Based Strategies for Healing. 2010. (ENG.). 304p. 27.95 *(978-0-393-70573-7(0),* 70573) Norton, W. W. & Co., Inc.

Music, Graham. Nurturing Natures: Attachment & Children's Emotional, Sociocultural & Brain Development. 2010. (ENG., Illus.). 336p. 105.00 *(978-1-84872-052-7(1))*; pap. 46.99 *(978-1-84872-057-2(2))* Taylor & Francis Group GBR. (Psychology Press). Dist: Taylor & Francis Group.

Nelson, Judith Kay. Laughter in Psychotherapy: An Attachment Perspective. 2012. (ENG.). 232p. 125.00 ***(978-0-415-99832-1(8))***; pap. 41.95 ***(978-0-415-99833-8(6))*** Routledge.

Obegi, Joseph H. & Berant, Ety, eds. Attachment Theory & Research in Clinical Work with Adults. (ENG., 529p. 2010. Illus.). pap. 40.00 *(978-1-60623-928-5(7))* 2008. 65.00 *(978-1-59385-998-5(8))* Guilford Pubns., Inc.

Oppenheim, David & Goldsmith, Douglas F., eds. Attachment Theory in Clinical Work with Children: Bridging the Gap Between Research & Practice. (ENG.). 256p. 2011. pap. 27.00 *(978-1-60918-482-7(3))* 2007. (Illus.). 50.00 *(978-1-59385-448-5(X))* Guilford Pubns., Inc.

Parkes, Colin Murray. Love & Loss: The Roots of Grief & Its Complications. 2006. (ENG., Illus.). 448p. (C). 69.95 *(978-0-415-39041-5(9),* RU0419) Routledge.

Perl, Elizabeth. Psychotherapy with Adolescent Girls & Young Women: Fostering Autonomy through Attachment. 2008. (ENG.). 198p. 30.00 *(978-1-59385-651-9(2))* Guilford Pubns., Inc.

Peterkin, Allan. The Flyaway Blanket. 2011. (Illus.). 32p. (J). pap. 9.95 ***(978-1-4338-1046-6(8),*** Magination Pr.) American Psychological Assn.

Raicar, Alexandra Maeja. Child-Centred Attachment Therapy. 2009. (United Kingdom Council for Psychotherapy Ser.). (Illus.). 152p. pap. 36.95 *(978-1-85575-505-5(X))* Karnac Bks. GBR. Dist: Stylus Publishing, LLC.

Read, Veronica. Developing Attachment in Early Years Settings: Nurturing Secure Relationships from Birth to Five Years. 2009. (ENG., Illus.). 144p. 33.95 *(978-0-415-49164-8(9))*; XII, 132p. 105.00 *(978-0-415-49163-1(0))* Fulton, David Pubs. GBR. Dist: Taylor & Francis Group.

Redman, Peter. Attachment: Sociology & Social Worlds. Redman, Peter, ed. 2008. (ENG., Illus.). 224p. pap. 41.00 *(978-0-7190-7812-5(1))* Manchester Univ. Pr. GBR. Dist: Macmillan.

Riley, Philip. Attachment Theory & the Teacher-Student Relationship. 2010. (ENG., Illus.). 188p. (C). 130.00 *(978-0-415-56261-4(9))* Routledge.

—Attachment Theory & the Teacher-Student Relationship: A Practical Guide for Teachers, Teacher Educators & School Leaders. 2010. (ENG., Illus.). 188p. (C). pap. 47.95 *(978-0-415-56262-1(7))* Routledge.

Roberts, Donald D. & Roberts, Deanda S. Another Chance to Be Real: Attachment & Object Relations Treatment of Borderline Personality Disorder. 2007. (ENG.). 186p. 89.50 *(978-0-7657-0553-2(2))*; per. 41.99 *(978-0-7657-0554-9(0))* Rowman & Littlefield Publishers, Inc. (Aronson, Jason).

Schofield, John, et al. Local Heritage Global Context: Cultural Perspectives on Sense of Place. 2010. (Heritage, Culture & Identity Ser.). (Illus.). 230p. 99.95 *(978-0-7546-7829-8(6))* Ashgate Publishing Co.

Schulkin, Jay. Adaptation & Well-Being: Social Allostasis. 2011. (ENG., Illus.). 212p. 75.00 *(978-0-521-50992-3(0))* Cambridge Univ. Pr.

Segal, Jeanne. The Language of Emotional Intelligence: The Five Essential Tools for Building Powerful & Effective Relationships. 2008. (ENG., Illus.). 240p. pap. 16.95 *(978-0-07-154455-9(0),* 0071544550) McGraw-Hill Cos., The.

Shemmings, David & Shemmings, Yvonne. Understanding Disorganized Attachment: Theory & Practice for Working with Children & Adults. 2011. (ENG., Illus.). 240p. pap. *(978-1-84905-044-9(9))* Kingsley, Jessica Ltd.

Solomon, Judith & George, Carol C., eds. Disorganized Attachment & Caregiving. 2011. (ENG., Illus.). 427p. 55.00 *(978-1-60918-128-4(X))* Guilford Pubns., Inc.

Steele, Howard & Steele, Miriam, eds. Clinical Applications of the Adult Attachment Interview. 2008. (ENG., Illus.). 501p. 60.00 *(978-1-59385-696-0(2))* Guilford Pubns., Inc.

Stoller, John L. Parenting other People's Children: Understanding & Repairing Reactive Attachment Disorder. 2006. (ENG.). 243p. pap. 15.95 *(978-0-533-15322-0(0))* Vantage Pr., Inc.

Thomas Nelson Publishing Staff. Attachments, 0 vols. 2009. 316p. pap. 15.99 *(978-0-7852-9737-6(5))* Nelson, Thomas Inc.

Thompson Ncc Lpc Lmft, Jill M. Rebuilding the Foundation for Attachment: A Guide to Social-Emotional-Behavioral Well-Being. 2008. 128p. per. 18.95 *(978-1-4327-1945-6(9))* Outskirts Pr., Inc.

Tyksinski, Rosemary Bannon. Disorganized Romantic Attachment. 2009. 288p. pap. *(978-3-639-12323-4(9))* VDM Verlag Dr. Mueller e.K.

van der Horst, Frank C. P. John Bowlby - From Psychoanalysis to Ethology: Unravelling the Roots of Attachment Theory. 2011. (ENG., Illus.). 210p. 99.95 *(978-0-470-68364-4(3)*, Wiley) Wiley, John & Sons, Inc.

Wake. Role of Brief Therapy in Attachment: Disorders. 2010. (Illus.). 210p. pap. 36.95 *(978-1-85575-697-7(8))* Karnac Bks. GBR. Dist: Stylus Publishing, LLC.

Wallin, David J. Attachment in Psychotherapy. 2007. (ENG.). 366p. 50.00 *(978-1-59385-456-0(0))* Guilford Pubns., Inc.

Wilkinson, Margaret. Changing Minds in Therapy: Emotion, Attachment, Trauma & Neurobiology. 2010. (Norton Series on Interpersonal Neurobiology Ser.). (ENG., Illus.). 248p. 32.00 *(978-0-393-70561-4(7)*, 70561) Norton, W. W. & Co., Inc.

Williams, Damian "JB". I thought You said You Loved Me?? 2010. 52p. pap. 11.00 *(978-0-557-12477-0(8))* Lulu Enterprises Inc.

Woodward, Joan. The Lone Twin: Understanding Twin Bereavement & Loss. 2nd rev. ed. 2010. 187p. pap. 34.95 *(978-1-85343-200-2(8))* Free Assn. Bks. Ltd. GBR. Dist: International Specialized Bk. Services.

ATTACK AND DEFENSE (MILITARY SCIENCE)

see Defensive (Military Science); Offensive (Military Science); Siege Warfare

ATTEMPTED SUICIDE

see Suicidal Behavior

ATTENDANCE, CHURCH

see Church Attendance

ATTENDANCE, SCHOOL

see School Attendance

ATTENTION

see also Abstraction; Boredom; Interest (Psychology); Listening; Vigilance (Psychology)

Almaas, A. H. The Unfolding Now: Realizing Your True Nature Through the Practice of Presence. 2008. (ENG.). 272p. pap. 18.95 *(978-1-59030-559-1(0))* Shambhala Pubns., Inc.

Arvidson, P. Sven. The Sphere of Attention: Context & Margin. 2010. (Contributions to Phenomenology Ser.). xi, 214p. pap. 169.00 *(978-90-481-6901-6(1)*, 9048169011) Springer.

Bays, Jan Chozen. How to Train a Wild Elephant: And Other Adventures in Mindfulness. 2011. (ENG.). 224p. pap. 14.00 *(978-1-59030-817-2(4))* Shambhala Pubns., Inc.

Braza, Jerry. The Seeds of Love: Growing Mindful Relationships. 2011. (ENG., Illus.). 192p. pap. 14.95 *(978-0-8048-4169-6(1))* Tuttle Publishing.

Briscoe, William P. Focus on Cognitive Disorder Research. 2006. 240p. 225.00 *(978-1-60021-482-0(7))* Nova Science Pubs., Inc.

Brownell, Judi & Wolvin, Andrew D. What Every Student Should Know about Listening. 2009. (ENG.). 64p. (C). pap. 9.80 *(978-0-205-77807-2(0))* Allyn & Bacon, Inc.

Bruya, Brian, ed. & intro. Effortless Attention: A New Perspective in the Cognitive Science of Attention & Action. 2010. (ENG., Illus.). 464p. (gr. 17). 80.00 *(978-0-262-01384-0(3))*; pap. 42.00 *(978-0-262-51395-1(1))* MIT Pr.

Bundesen, Claus & Habekost, Thomas. Principles of Visual Attention: Linking Mind & Brain. 2008. (Oxford Psychology Ser.). (ENG., Illus.). 284p. pap. 75.00 *(978-0-19-857070-7(8))* Oxford Univ. Pr., Inc.

Burack, Jacob A., et al. Cognitive Science, Development, & Psychopathology: Typical & Atypical Developmental Trajectories of Attention. 2012. (ENG.). 320p. 85.00 ***(978-0-19-531545-5(6))*** Oxford Univ. Pr., Inc.

Bush, David V. Concentration Made Effective & Easy. 2007. (ENG.). 488p. 53.95 *(978-0-548-08987-3(6))* Kessinger Publishing, LLC.

Cram101 Textbook Reviews & Cram101 Textbook Reviews. Outlines & Highlights for Attention & Associative Learning: From Brain to Behaviour by Chris Mitchell, ISBN. 2011. 108p. pap. 28.95 ***(978-1-4288-2499-7(5))*** Cram101 Inc.

Csikszentmihalyi, Mihaly. Flow: The Psychology of Optimal Experience. 2008. (P. S. Ser.). (ENG.). 336p. pap. 15.99 *(978-0-06-133920-2(2)*, HarperPerennial) HarperCollins Pubs.

Cusimano, Addie. Auditory Memory in Context Instructional Workbook: For the Development of Attention, Listening, Processing & Recall of Sentences & Paragraphs. 2012. 86p. (J). 15.00 ***(978-0-9727762-8-8(1))*** Achieve Pubns.

Davidson, Cathy N. Now You See It: How Technology & Brain Science Will Transform Schools & Business for the 21st Century. 2012. (ENG.). 352p. (gr. 12). pap. 16.00 ***(978-0-14-312126-8(X)***, Penguin (Non-Classics)) Penguin Group (USA) Inc.

Davidson, Cathy N. Now You See It: How the Brain Science of Attention Will Transform the Way We Live, Work, & Learn. 2011. (ENG.). 352p. (gr. 12). 27.95 *(978-0-670-02282-3(9)*, Viking Adult) Penguin Group (USA) Inc.

Davis, Alison & Brown, Paul. Your Attention Please: How to Appeal to Today's Distracted, Disinterested, Disengaged, Disenchanted, & Busy Consumer. 2006. (ENG., Illus.). 256p. per. 14.95 *(978-1-59337-687-1(1))* Adams Media Corp.

de Laurence, L. W. The Abolition of Worry & the Acquisition of Serenity & Mind. 2006. pap. 9.95 *(978-1-4286-8369-3(0))* Kessinger Publishing, LLC.

De Laurence, L. W. The Master Key. 2007. 428p. per. 19.95 *(978-1-60206-660-1(4))* Cosimo, Inc.

de Laurence, L. W. The Master Key. 2007. (ENG.). 428p. per. 36.95 *(978-1-4209-2937-9(2))* Digireads.com.

—The Master Key. 2007. (ENG.). 428p. per. 14.45 *(978-1-59462-743-9(6)*, Book Jungle) Standard Pubns., Inc.

—Secrets of the Cultivation of Memory. 2006. pap. 12.95 *(978-1-4286-8400-3(X))* Kessinger Publishing, LLC.

—Unconscious Concentration. 2006. pap. 9.95 *(978-1-4286-8354-9(2))* Kessinger Publishing, LLC.

—Will Culture & Mind Training. 2006. pap. 12.95 *(978-1-4286-8399-0(2))* Kessinger Publishing, LLC.

DuBois, Andrew Lee. Ashbery's Forms of Attention. 2006. (Modern & Contemporary Poetics Ser.). (Illus.). 192p. 60.00 *(978-0-8173-1489-7(X))*; per. 34.00 *(978-0-8173-5271-4(6))* Univ. of Alabama Pr.

Dumon, Theron. The Power of Concentration. 2007. 112p. per. 14.99 *(978-1-59547-861-0(2))* NuVision Pubns., LLC.

Dumont, Theron. The Power of Concentration. 2008. 132p. 24.99 *(978-0-554-21422-1(9))*; 21.99 *(978-0-554-30725-1(1))* BiblioBazaar.

—The Power of Concentration. 2007. 160p. 19.99 *(978-1-59986-733-5(8))* Filiquarian Publishing, LLC.

Dumont, Theron & Atkinson, William. The Power of Concentration. 2007. 108p. per. 8.99 *(978-1-60459-051-7(3))* Wilder Pubns., Ltd.

Dumont, Theron Q. The Power of Concentration. 2010. 278p. pap. 27.75 *(978-1-141-20305-5(7))* 2008. 140p. 21.99 *(978-0-554-35423-1(3))* 2008. 140p. 24.99 *(978-0-554-26120-1(0))* 2007. (ENG.). 136p. pap. 18.99 *(978-1-4264-0020-9(9))* 2007. (ENG.). 124p. pap. 18.99 *(978-1-4346-0475-0(6))* 2007. (ENG.). 136p. pap. 19.99 *(978-1-4346-0508-5(6))* BiblioBazaar.

—The Power of Concentration. 2010. 112p. pap. 9.99 ***(978-1-935785-23-1(0))*** Bottom of the Hill Publishing.

—The Power of Concentration. 2009. 128p. pap. *(978-1-4099-6999-0(1))* Dodo Pr.

—The Power of Concentration. 2008. (ENG.). 88p. per. *(978-1-4068-2660-9(X))* Echo Library.

—The Power of Concentration. 2007. (ENG.). pap. 9.99 *(978-1-59986-908-7(X)*, FQ Classics) Filiquarian Publishing, LLC.

—The Power of Concentration. 2010. (Illus.). 70p. pap. 20.00 *(978-1-153-71737-3(9))* General Bks. LLC.

—The Power of Concentration. 2010. 100p. pap. *(978-1-4076-1484-7(3))* HardPr.

—The Power of Concentration. 2010. 188p. 30.36 *(978-1-169-27973-5(2))*; pap. 18.36 ***(978-1-162-63009-0(4))***; 37.95 *(978-1-161-41092-1(9))* Kessinger Publishing, LLC.

—The Power of Concentration. 2008. 100p. pap. *(978-1-4097-2619-7(3))* Read Bks.

—Power of Concentration. reprint ed. 15.00 *(978-0-911662-39-9(1))* Yoga Pubn. Society.

—The Power of Concentration - Complete Text of Dumont's Classic. 2008. 132p. pap. 7.99 *(978-1-60450-171-1(5))* Arc Manor.

Elkins, James. How to Use Your Eyes. 2008. (ENG., Illus.). 272p. pap. 45.00 *(978-0-415-99363-0(6))* Routledge.

Fabio, Rosa Angela. Relationship Between Automatic & Controlled Processes of Attention & Leading to Complex Thinking. 2009. (Neuroscience Research Progress Ser.). 89.00 *(978-1-60741-810-8(X))* Nova Science Pubs., Inc.

Forrester, Daniel & Patrick, Daniel. Consider: Harnessing the Power of Reflective Thinking in Your Organization. 2010. (ENG.). 256p. 30.00 *(978-0-230-10607-9(2))* Palgrave Macmillan.

Gallagher, Winifred. Rapt: Attention & the Focused Life. 2010. (ENG.). 256p. (gr. 12-18). 15.00 *(978-0-14-311690-5(8)*, Penguin (Non-Classics)) Penguin Group (USA) Inc.

Gibson, Bradley S., et al, eds. Attentional Capture: A Special Issue of Visual Cognition. 2009. (Special Issues of Visual Cognition Ser.). (ENG.). 264p. 80.99 *(978-1-84169-849-6(0)*, Psychology Press) Taylor & Francis Group GBR. Dist: Taylor & Francis Group.

Hanh, Thich Nhat. Planting Seeds: Practicing Mindfulness with Children. 2011. (ENG., Illus.). 240p. pap. 28.95 *(978-1-935209-80-5(9))* Parallax Pr.

Harp, David. Mindfulness to Go: How to Meditate While You're on the Move. 2011. (ENG.). 224p. pap. 16.95 *(978-1-57224-989-9(7))* New Harbinger Pubns.

Hick, Steven F. & Bien, Thomas, eds. Mindfulness & the Therapeutic Relationship. (ENG.). 2010. 240p. pap. 25.00 *(978-1-60918-019-5(4))* 2008. 50.00 *(978-1-59385-820-9(5))* Guilford Pubns., Inc.

Hill, Napoleon. Law of Success Volume Xii Xiii Concentr. 2006. 88p. per. *(978-956-291-208-2(6))* Editorial Benei Noaj.

Jackson, Maggie. Distracted: The Erosion of Attention & the Coming Dark Age. (ENG.). 2009. 327p. pap. 18.00 *(978-1-59102-748-5(9))* 2008. 320p. 25.98 *(978-1-59102-623-5(7))* Prometheus Bks., Pubs.

Jo. A Cross in the Sky, 1 vol. 2009. 96p. pap. 16.95 *(978-1-60703-500-8(6))* PublishAmerica, Inc.

Kabat-Zinn, Jon. Mindfulness for Beginners: Reclaiming the Present Moment—and Your Life. 2011. 120p. 21.95 incl. audio compact disk ***(978-1-60407-658-5(5))*** Sounds True, Inc.

Kemp, Sally L. & Korkman, Marit. Essentials of NEPSY-II Assessment. 2010. (Essentials of Psychological Assessment Ser.: 69). (ENG., Illus.). 496p. pap. 38.95 *(978-0-470-43691-2(3)*, Wiley) Wiley, John & Sons, Inc.

Klingberg, Torkel. The Overflowing Brain: Information Overload & the Limits of Working Memory. 2008. (ENG., Illus.). 224p. 21.95 *(978-0-19-537288-5(3))* Oxford Univ. Pr., Inc.

Kramer, Arthur F., et al. Attention: From Theory to Practice. 2006. (Human Technology Interaction Ser.: Vol. 4). (ENG., Illus.). 288p. 85.00 *(978-0-19-530572-2(8))* Oxford Univ. Pr., Inc.

Krummenacher, Joseph & Muller, Hermann J., eds. Visual Search & Attention: A Special Issue of Visual Cognition. 2006. (Special Issues of Visual Cognition Ser.). (ENG., Illus.). 664p. (C). 199.50 *(978-1-84169-806-9(7)*, Psychology Press) Taylor & Francis Group GBR. Dist: Taylor & Francis Group.

Kühlewind, Georg & Bamford, Christopher. The Light of the I: Guidelines for Meditation. 2008. 68p. pap. 12.00 *(978-1-58420-059-8(6)*, Lindisfarne Bks.) SteinerBooks, Inc.

Lampert, Martina. Attention & Recombinance: A Cognitive-Semantic Investigation into Morphological Compositionality in English. 2009. 446p. 109.95 *(978-3-631-59276-2(0))* Lang, Peter GmbH, Europaischer Verlag der Wissenschaften DEU. Dist: Lang, Peter.

Lane, Kenneth. Visual Attention in Children: Theories & Activities. 2012. (ENG.). 240p. (C). pap. 49.95 *(978-1-55642-956-9(8))* SLACK, Inc.

Lawson, Wendy. The Passionate Mind: How People with Autism Learn. 2010. (ENG., Illus.). 224p. pap. *(978-1-84905-121-7(6))* Kingsley, Jessica Ltd.

Lubow, R. E. Latent Inhibition & Conditioned Attention Theory. 2009. (Problems in the Behavioural Sciences Ser.). (ENG., Illus.). 336p. pap. 61.00 *(978-0-521-10257-5(X))* Cambridge Univ. Pr.

Lund, Nick. Attention. 2012. (ENG.). 200p. 69.95 ***(978-0-415-59210-9(0))***; pap. 27.50 ***(978-0-415-59214-7(3))*** Routledge.

Mangun, George R., ed. Neuroscience of Attention: Attention Control & Selection. 2012. (ENG., Illus.). 296p. 98.50 ***(978-0-19-533436-4(1))*** Oxford Univ. Pr., Inc.

Marchetti, Giorgio. Consciousness, Attention & Meaning. 2010. (Psychology Research Progress Ser.). (Illus.). xi, 219p. 145.00 *(978-1-61668-960-5(9))* Nova Science Pubs., Inc.

McCown, Donald & Micozzi, Marc S. New World Mindfulness. 2012. 208p. pap. 16.95 ***(978-1-59477-424-9(2))*** Inner Traditions International, Ltd.

McGee, Margaret D. Sacred Attention: A Spiritual Practice for Finding God in the Moment. 2007. 176p. 19.99 *(978-1-59473-232-4(9))* SkyLight Paths Publishing.

McLeod, Alison. Listening to Children: A Practitioner's Guide. 2008. (Illus.). 224p. pap. *(978-1-84310-549-7(7))* Kingsley, Jessica Ltd.

Militz, Annie Rix. Concentration. 2011. 76p. pap. 9.99 ***(978-1-61203-280-1(X))*** Bottom of the Hill Publishing.

Mitchell, Chris. Asperger's Syndrome & Mindfulness: Taking Refuge in the Buddha. 2008. (ENG.). 144p. pap. *(978-1-84310-686-9(8))* Kingsley, Jessica Ltd.

Mitchell, Chris & Le Pelley, Mike. Attention & Associative Learning: From Brain to Behaviour. 2010. (ENG., Illus.). 424p. 79.95 *(978-0-19-955053-1(0))* Oxford Univ. Pr., Inc.

Mole, Christopher. Attention Is Cognitive Unison: An Essay in Philosophical Psychology, 1 vol. 2011. (Philosophy of Mind Ser.). (ENG.). 224p. 49.95 *(978-0-19-538452-9(0))* Oxford Univ. Pr., Inc.

Mole, Christopher, et al, eds. Attention: Philosophical & Psychological Essays, 1 vol. 2011. (ENG., Illus.). 416p. 74.00 *(978-0-19-975923-1(5))* Oxford Univ. Pr., Inc.

Nobre, Kia & Coull, Jennifer. Attention & Time. Nobre, Anna C., ed. 2010. (ENG., Illus.). 472p. 89.95 *(978-0-19-956345-6(4))* Oxford Univ. Pr., Inc.

Oakley, Todd. From Attention to Meaning: Explorations in Semiotics, Linguistics, & Rhetoric. 2009. (Illus.). 268p. pap. *(978-3-03911-442-9(5))* Lang, Peter.

Paletta, Lucas. Attention in Cognitive Systems Theories & Systems from an Interdisciplinary Viewpoint. 2008. (Lecture Notes in Computer Science / Lecture Notes in Artificial Intelligence Ser.). spiral bd. 99.00 *(978-3-540-77342-9(8)*, 3540773428) Springer.

Palladino, Lucy Jo. Find Your Focus Zone: An Effective New Plan to Defeat Distraction & Overload. 2011. (ENG., Illus.). 304p. pap. 19.99 *(978-1-4165-3201-9(3)*, Free Pr.) Free Pr.

Pillsbury, W. B. Attention. 2007. (ENG.). 360p. 46.95 *(978-0-548-13346-0(8))* 2006. pap. 31.95 *(978-1-4286-4440-3(7))* Kessinger Publishing, LLC.

Posner, Michael I. Attention in a Social World, 1 vol. 2012. (Social Cognition & Social Neuroscience Ser.). (ENG.). 240p. 59.99 ***(978-0-19-979121-7(X))*** Oxford Univ. Pr., Inc.

Posner, Michael I., ed. Cognitive Neuroscience of Attention, Second Edition. 2nd rev. ed. 2011. (ENG., Illus.). 514p. 85.00 ***(978-1-60918-985-3(X))*** Guilford Pubns., Inc.

Posner, Michael I. & Rothbart, Mary K. Educating the Human Brain. 2006. (Illus.). 263p. 39.95 *(978-1-59147-381-7(0))* American Psychological Assn.

Prinz, Jesse J. The Conscious Brain: How Attention Engenders Experience. 2012. (ENG.). 288p. ***(978-0-19-531459-5(X))*** Oxford Univ. Pr., Inc.

Proctor, Robert W. & Read, Lenore E., eds. Attention, 4 vols. 2009. (SAGE Library of Cognitive & Experimental Psychology Ser.). (Illus.). 1504p. 995.00 *(978-1-84787-269-2(7)*, B72692C) SAGE Pubns., Ltd. GBR. Dist: SAGE Pubns., Inc.

Proulx, Michael J. The Strategic Control of Attention in Visual Search- Top-down & Bottom-up Processes. 2007. 132p. per. *(978-3-8364-2249-9(2))* VDM Verlag Dr. Mueller e.K.

Quarrick, Gene. Our Sweetest Hours: Recreation & the Mental State of Absorption. alt. ed. 2012. (ENG.). 256p. pap. 25.00 ***(978-0-7864-6714-3(2))*** McFarland & Co., Inc. Pubs.

Ribot, Theodule Armand. The Psychology of Attention. 2007. (ENG.). 136p. 35.95 *(978-0-548-11402-5(1))* Kessinger Publishing, LLC.

Robbins, Jim & Fehmi, Les. The Open-Focus Brain: Harnessing the Power of Attention to Heal Mind & Body. 2008. (ENG., Illus.). 208p. pap. 18.95 *(978-1-59030-612-3(0)*, Trumpeter) Shambhala Pubns., Inc.

—The Open-Focus Brain: Harnessing the Power of Attention to Heal Mind & Body. 2007. (ENG., Illus.). 176p. 22.95 *(978-1-59030-376-4(8)*, Trumpeter) Shambhala Pubns., Inc.

Roda, Claudia, ed. Human Attention in Digital Environments. 2011. (ENG., Illus.). 344p. 104.00 *(978-0-521-76565-7(X))* Cambridge Univ. Pr.

Sears, F. W. Concentration & Will Power. 2007. 220p. per. 15.45 *(978-1-59462-663-0(4)*, Book Jungle) Standard Pubns., Inc.

Seemann, Axel. Joint Attention: New Developments in Psychology, Philosophy of Mind, & Social Neuroscience. 2012. (ENG., Illus.). 488p. (gr. 17). 45.00 ***(978-0-262-01682-7(6))*** MIT Pr.

Steinmetz, Katherine Mickley & Kensinger, Elizabeth, eds. Emotion's Effects on Attention & Memory: Relevance to Posttraumatic Stress Disorder. 2010. (Psychology of Emotions, Motivations & Actions Ser.). pap. 43.00 *(978-1-61668-239-2(6))* Nova Science Pubs., Inc.

Steinmetz, Katherine Mickley & Kensinger, Elizabeth A. How Does Emotion Affect Attention & Memory? Attentional Capture, Tunnel Memory, & the Implications for Posttraumatic Stress Disorder. 2010. (Psychology of Emotions, Motivations & Actions Ser.). 84p. pap. 43.00 *(978-1-61668-848-6(3)*, Nova Novinka) Nova Science Pubs., Inc.

Stiegler, Bernard. Taking Care of Youth & the Generations. 2010. (Meridian: Crossing Aesthetics Ser.). (ENG.). 264p. 75.00 *(978-0-8047-6272-4(4))*; pap. 27.95 *(978-0-8047-6273-1(2))* Stanford Univ. Pr.

Styhre, Alexander. Perception & Organization: Art, Music, Media. 2008. (ENG., Illus.). 272p. (C). 105.00 *(978-0-230-51615-1(7))* Palgrave Macmillan.

Styles, Elizabeth. The Psychology of Attention. 2nd rev. ed. 2006. (ENG., Illus.). 352p. (C). per. 44.95 *(978-1-84169-397-2(9)*, RU3979X, Psychology Press) Taylor & Francis Group GBR. Dist: Taylor & Francis Group.

Titchener, Edward Bradford. Lectures on the Elementary Psychology of Feeling & Attention. 2009. 210p. pap. *(978-0-217-01169-3(1))* Books LLC.

Tsotsos, John K. A Computational Perspective on Visual Attention. 2011. (ENG., Illus.). 328p. (gr. 17). 40.00 *(978-0-262-01541-7(2))* MIT Pr.

Vincent, Nathanael. Attending upon God without Distraction. Kistler, Don, ed. 2010. 224p. *(978-1-60178-093-5(1)*, Soli Deo Gloria Pubns.) Reformation Heritage Bks.

Walford, Gerald A. & Walford, Gerald E. Concentration & Other Mental Control Skills for Sports, Life & the Arts, 1 vol. 2010. 176p. pap. 24.95 *(978-1-4489-7817-5(3))* PublishAmerica, Inc.

Wallace, B. Alan. Stilling the Mind: Shamatha Teachings from Dudjom Lingpa's Vajra Essence. 2011. (ENG.). 224p. pap. 17.95 *(978-0-86171-690-6(6))* Wisdom Pubns.

Weber, Darren. Event-Related Potentials of Attention & Memory in Post-Traumatic Stress. 2008. 276p. pap. *(978-3-639-04833-9(4))* VDM Verlag Dr. Mueller e.K.

White, Benjamin. Mindfulness Within an Organizational Context - a Premise for the Intrasubjective Being. 2008. 172p. pap. *(978-3-639-04291-7(3))* VDM Verlag Dr. Mueller e.K.

Williams, J. Mark G., et al. The Mindful Way Through Depression: Freeing Yourself from Chronic Unhappiness. 2007. (ENG., Illus.). 273p. 45.00 *(978-1-59385-449-2(8))*; pap. 21.95 *(978-1-59385-128-6(6))* Guilford Pubns., Inc.

Williams, Pat & Denney, Jim. Extreme Focus: Harnessing the Life-Changing Power to Achieve Your Dreams. 2011. (ENG.). 288p. pap. 15.95 *(978-0-7573-1562-6(3))* Health Communications, Inc.

Wolff, Jurgen. Focus: Use the Power of Targeted Thinking to Get More Done. 2nd ed. 2010. (ENG., Illus.). 256p. (C). pap. 19.99 *(978-0-273-73461-1(X))* FT Press.

Wolff, Jurgen M. Focus: Your Key to More Productivity at Work. 2010. (ENG., Illus.). 288p. pap. 19.99 *(978-0-13-700256-6(4))* FT Press.

Wright, Richard D. & Ward, Lawrence M. Orienting of Attention. 2008. (ENG., Illus.). 320p. 39.95 *(978-0-19-513049-2(9))* Oxford Univ. Pr., Inc.

Wulf, Gabriele. Attention & Motor Skill Learning. 2007. (ENG., Illus.). 224p. (C). 63.00 *(978-0-7360-6270-1(X))* Human Kinetics Pubs.

Yogananda, Paramhansa. Focusing Power of Attention. 56p. 2.00 *(978-0-87612-402-4(3))* Self-Realization Fellowship Pubs.

Young, Damon. Distraction. 2010. (Art of Living Ser.). 184p. pap. 18.95 *(978-1-84465-254-9(8))* Acumen Publishing, Ltd. GBR. Dist: McGill-Queen's Univ. Pr.

ATTENTION-DEFICIT DISORDER IN ADULTS

Adult ADHD Can Be Sexy! 2010. pap. 19.95 *(978-0-7414-5937-4(X))* Infinity Publishing.

Albrecht, Ava T. Adult ADHD. 2009. (ENG.). 149p. pap. 22.95 *(978-0-7637-5449-5(8))* Jones & Bartlett Learning, LLC.

Barkley, Russell A. Attention Deficit Hyperactivity Disorder in Adults: The Latest Assessment & Treatment Strategies. 2008. *(978-1-887537-30-8(9))* Compact Clinicals.

—Barkley Adult ADHD Rating Scale — IV (BAARS-IV) 2011. (ENG.). 150p. pap. 149.00 *(978-1-60918-203-8(0))* Guilford Pubns., Inc.

Barkley, Russell A. & Benton, Christine M. Taking Charge of Adult ADHD. 2010. (ENG.). 294p. 40.00 *(978-1-60623-710-6(1))*; pap. 16.95 *(978-1-60623-338-2(6))* Guilford Pubns., Inc.

Barkley, Russell A., et al. ADHD in Adults: What the Science Says. 2010. (ENG.). 489p. pap. 30.00 *(978-1-60918-075-1(5))* Guilford Pubns., Inc.

Buitelaar, Jan K., et al, eds. ADHDin Adults: Characterization, Diagnosis, & Treatment. 2011. (ENG., Illus.). 326p. 85.00 *(978-0-521-86431-2(3))* Cambridge Univ. Pr.

Conners, Kevin. Help, My Body Is Killing Me: Solving the Connections of Autoimmune Disease to Thyroid Problems, Fibromyalgia, Infertility, Anxiety, Depression, ADD/ADHD & More. 2010. 116p. 27.49 *(978-1-4520-8509-8(9))* AuthorHouse.

Ford, Ford Madox. The Good Soldier. 2009. 150p. pap. *(978-1-4589-1755-3(X))* Books LLC.

—The Good Soldier. 2009. 140p. pap. *(978-1-4068-8141-7(4))* Echo Library.

—The Good Soldier. 2010. (Vintage Classics Ser.). (ENG.). 252p. pap. 13.95 *(978-0-09-954067-0(3))* Random Hse. GBR. Dist: Independent Pubs. Group.

—The Good Soldier. 2009. 148p. pap. 8.74 *(978-1-60459-699-1(6))* Wilder Pubns., Ltd.

Freed, Jeffrey & Shapiro, Joan. 4 Weeks to an Organized Life with AD/HD. 2007. (ENG.). 216p. per. 16.95 *(978-1-58979-326-2(9))* Taylor Trade Publishing.

Gay, Kim A. Hiding an Elephant: Living with Adult ADHD. 2010. pap. 9.99 *(978-1-61663-433-9(2))* Tate Publishing & Enterprises, LLC.

Gregg, Noel. Adolescents & Adults with Learning Disabilities & ADHD: Assessment & Accommodation. (ENG.). 316p. 2011. pap. 27.00 *(978-1-60623-593-5(1))* 2009. (Illus.). 55.00 *(978-1-60623-034-3(4))* Guilford Pubns., Inc.

Honos-Webb, Lara. The Gift of Adult ADD: How to Transform Your Challenges & Build on Your Strengths. 2008. (ENG.). 248p. pap. 16.95 *(978-1-57224-565-5(4))* New Harbinger Pubns.

Jacobs, Carole & Wendel, Isadore. The Everything Health Guide to Adult ADD/ADHD: Expert advice to find the right diagnosis, evaluation & Treatment. 2010. (ENG.). 304p. pap. 14.95 *(978-1-60550-999-0(X))* Adams Media Corp.

Kerson, Don. Getting Unstuck: Unraveling the Knot of Depression, Attention & Trauma. 2008. (Illus.). 292p. pap. 24.95 *(978-0-9769867-2-0(8))* Greenpoint Psychiatric Pr.

Levrini, Abigail & Prevatt, Frances F. Succeeding with Adult ADHD: Daily Strategies to Help You Achieve Your Goals & Manage Your Life. 2012. pap. 19.95 *(978-1-4338-1125-8(1))* American Psychological Assn.

Mapou, Robert L. Adult Learning Disabilities & ADHD: Research-Informed Assessment. 2008. (AACN Workshop Ser.). (ENG.). 312p. pap. 39.95 *(978-0-19-537178-9(X))* Oxford Univ. Pr., Inc.

Mason, Oren. Reaching for A New Potential. 2009. 189p. pap. 17.98 *(978-0-557-12353-7(4))* Lulu Enterprises Inc.

Orlov, Melissa C. The ADHD Effect on Marriage: Understand & Rebuild Your Relationship in Six Steps. 2010. (ENG.). 225p. pap. 19.95 *(978-1-886941-97-7(1))* Specialty Pr., Inc.

Pera, Gina. Is It You, Me, or Adult A. D. D. ? Stopping the Roller Coaster When Someone You Love Has Attention Deficit Disorder. 2008. (Illus.). 386p. pap. 21.95 *(978-0-9815487-0-8(9))* 1201 Alarm Pr.

—Is It You, Me, or Adult A.D.D.? Stopping the Roller Coaster When Someone You Love Has Attention Deficit Disorder. 2008. xxvii, 369p. *(978-0-9815487-6-0(8))* 1201 Alarm Pr.

Ramsay, J. Russell. Nonmedication Treatments for Adult ADHD: Evaluating Impact on Daily Functioning & Well-Being. 2009. (Illus.). 236p. 59.95 *(978-1-4338-0564-6(2))* American Psychological Assn.

Ramsay, J. Russell & Rostain, Anthony L. Cognitive Behavioral Therapy for Adult ADHD: An Integrative Psychosocial & Medical Approach. 2007. (Practical Clinical Guidebooks). (ENG.). 252p. 125.00 *(978-0-415-95500-3(9))* Routledge.

—Cognitive-Behavioral Therapy for Adult ADHD: An Integrative Psychosocial & Medical Approach. 2007. (Practical Clinical Guidebooks). (ENG.). 252p. per. 32.50 *(978-0-415-95501-0(7))* Routledge.

Ratey, John & Hallowell, Edward M. Driven to Distraction: Recognizing & Coping with Attention Deficit Disorder. rev. ed. 2011. (ENG.). 400p. pap. 15.95 *(978-0-307-74315-2(2)*, Anchor) Knopf Doubleday Publishing Group.

Ratey, Nancy A. Disorganized Mind: Coaching Your ADHD Brain to Take Control of Your Time, Tasks, & Talents. 2008. (ENG.). 304p. pap. 15.99 *(978-0-312-35534-0(3)*, St. Martin's Griffin) St. Martin's Pr.

Retz, W. & Klein, R. G., eds. Attention Deficit Hyperactivity Disorder (ADHD) in Adults. 2009. (Key Issues in Mental Health Ser.). (Illus.). 192p. *(978-3-8055-9237-6(X))* Karger, S. AG.

Sandra Starr Ed.D. Calming the Chaos: A drug-free program to eliminate the symptoms of ADHD. 2009. 124p. 23.95 *(978-1-4401-9104-6(2))* iUniverse, Inc.

Sarkis, Stephanie. 10 Simple Solutions Adult ADD: How to Overcome Chronic Distraction & Accomplish Your Goals. 2nd ed. 2011. (New Harbinger Ten Simple Solutions Ser.). (ENG.). 200p. pap. 15.95 ***(978-1-60882-184-6(6))*** New Harbinger Pubns.

—10 Simple Solutions to Adult Add: How to Overcome Chronic Distraction & Accomplish Your Goals. 2nd ed. 2011. ***(978-1-60882-186-0(2))*** New Harbinger Pubns.

Sarkis, Stephanie Moulton. Adult ADD: A Guide for the Newly Diagnosed. 2011. (New Harbinger Guides for the Newly Diagnosed Ser.). (ENG.). 168p. pap. 16.95 *(978-1-60882-005-4(X))* New Harbinger Pubns.

—Making the Grade with ADD: A Student's Guide to Succeeding in College with Attention Deficit Disorder. 2008. (ENG.). 200p. pap. 16.95 *(978-1-57224-554-9(9))* New Harbinger Pubns.

Schaeffer, Don. Conquering ADD! Sixty Questions for A Clearer Understanding! 2007. (Illus.). 177p. per. 13.95 *(978-0-9774319-3-9(2))* Slight Edge.

Sinfield, Jacqueline. Untapped Brilliance: How to Reach Your Full Potential As an Adult with Attention Deficit Disorder. 2008. 133p. pap. 19.95 *(978-0-9798554-6-7(2))* Love Your Life.

Sleeper-Triplett, Jodi. Empowering Youth with ADHD: A Guide to Coaching Adolescents & Young Adults for Coaches, Parents, & Professionals. 2010. (ENG.). 225p. pap. 24.95 *(978-1-886941-96-0(3))* Specialty Pr., Inc.

Solanto, Mary V. Cognitive-Behavioral Therapy for Adult ADHD: Targeting Executive Dysfunction. 2011. (ENG.). 214p. 35.00 *(978-1-60918-131-4(X))* Guilford Pubns., Inc.

Surman, Craig B., ed. ADHD in Adults: A Practical Guide to Evaluation & Management. 2012. (ENG.). 225p. 189.00 *(978-1-4419-7057-2(6)*, 1441970576) Springer.

Timmerman, John. Real Solutions for Living with ADHD. 156p. pap. 9.99 *(978-0-8307-3485-6(6)*, Regal Bks.) Gospel Light Pubns.

Tuckman, Ari. Integrative Treatment for Adult ADHD: A Practical, Easy-to-Use Guide for Clinicians. 2007. (Professional Ser.). (ENG., Illus.). 272p. per. 49.95 *(978-1-57224-521-1(2))* New Harbinger Pubns.

—More Attention, Less Deficit: Success Strategies for Adults with ADHD. 2009. (ENG.). 380p. pap. 24.95 *(978-1-886941-74-8(2))* Specialty Pr., Inc.

Young, Susan & Bramham, Jessica. ADHD in Adults: A Psychological Guide to Practice. 2006. (ENG., Illus.). 318p. per. 60.95 *(978-0-470-01232-1(3)*, Wiley) Wiley, John & Sons, Inc.

—Cognitive-Behavioural Therapy for ADHD in Adolescents & Adults: A Psychological Guide to Practice. 2nd ed. 2012. (ENG.). 328p. 109.95 ***(978-1-119-96074-4(6)**, Wiley-Blackwell)* Wiley, John & Sons, Inc.

—Cognitive-Behavioural Therapy for Adhd in Adolescents & Adults: A Psychological Guide to Practice. 2nd ed. 2012. (ENG.). 328p. pap. 49.50 ***(978-1-119-96073-7(8)**, Wiley-Blackwell)* Wiley, John & Sons, Inc.

Zylowska, Lidia. The Mindfulness Prescription for Adult ADHD: An 8-Step Program for Strengthening Attention, Managing Emotions, & Achieving Your Goals. 2012. (ENG.). 224p. pap. 18.95 ***(978-1-59030-847-9(6)**, Trumpeter)* Shambhala Pubns., Inc.

ATTENTION-DEFICIT DISORDER IN ADULTS—PATIENTS

see Attention-Deficit-Disordered Adults

ATTENTION DEFICIT DISORDER WITH HYPERACTIVITY

see Attention-Deficit Hyperactivity Disorder

ATTENTION-DEFICIT-DISORDERED ADULTS

Barkley, Russell A., et al. ADHD in Adults: What the Science Says. 2007. (ENG., Illus.). 489p. 60.00 *(978-1-59385-586-4(9))* Guilford Pubns., Inc.

Buitelaar, Jan K., et al, eds. ADHDin Adults: Characterization, Diagnosis, & Treatment. 2011. (ENG., Illus.). 326p. 85.00 *(978-0-521-86431-2(3))* Cambridge Univ. Pr.

Conners, Kevin. Help, My Body Is Killing Me: Solving the Connections of Autoimmune Disease to Thyroid Problems, Fibromyalgia, Infertility, Anxiety, Depression, ADD/ADHD & More. 2010. 116p. pap. 13.99 *(978-1-4520-8510-4(2))* AuthorHouse.

Goldstein, Sam, et al, eds. Learning & Attention Disorders in Adolescence & Adulthood: Assessment & Treatment. 2nd ed. 2011. (ENG., Illus.). 636p. 74.00 *(978-0-470-50518-2(4)*, Wiley) Wiley, John & Sons, Inc.

Hutchinson, Bryan L. One Boy's Struggle: A Memoir: Surviving Life with Undiagnosed ADD. 2008. 179p. pap. 16.95 *(978-0-7414-4440-0(2))* Infinity Publishing.

Lorenc, Cameron. ADD - Is It Me? A Personal Account. 2007. (Illus.). 246p. per. 19.95 *(978-0-9774319-2-2(4))* Slight Edge.

Pinsky, Susan C. Organizing Solutions for People with ADHD, 2nd Edition-Revised & Updated: Tips & Tools to Help You Take Charge of Your Life & Get Organized. 2nd ed. 2012. (ENG., Illus.). 208p. pap. 19.99 ***(978-1-59233-512-1(8)**, 1592335128)* Quayside.

Seiden, Jerry & Halverstadt, Jonathan Scott. ADD, Christianity, & the Church: A Compassionate Healing Resource to Inform, Inspire, & Illuminate. 2008. 208p. pap. 12.95 *(978-1-929753-22-2(5))* Spirit of Hope Publishing.

ATTENTION-DEFICIT-DISORDERED CHILDREN

see also Hyperactive Children

Angelotti, Maren. Of Different Minds: Seeing Your AD/HD Child Through the Eyes of God. 2009. (ENG.). 272p. pap. 14.99 *(978-0-8307-4720-7(6))* Gospel Light Pubns.

Breeding, J. The Wildest Colts Make the Best Horses. 2007. 312p. per. *(978-1-84747-077-5(7))* Chipmunkapublishing.

Brock, Stephen E., et al. Identifying, Assessing, & Treating ADHD at School. 2009. (Developmental Psychopathology at School Ser.). (Illus.). xi, 168p. pap. 49.95 *(978-1-4419-5990-4(4)*, 1441959904) Springer.

Comfort, Randy Lee. Searching to Be Found: Understanding & Helping Adopted & Looked after Children with Attention Difficulties. 2008. 206p. pap. 38.95 *(978-1-85575-464-5(9))* Karnac Bks. GBR. Dist: Stylus Publishing, LLC.

Conners, C. Keith. Attention Deficit Hyperactivity Disorder in Children & Adolescents: The Latest Assessment & Treatment Strategies. 4th ed. 2008. *(978-1-887537-31-5(7))* Compact Clinicals.

Creed, Liam. A Puppy Called Aero: How a Labrador Saved a Boy with Adhd. 2010. (ENG.). 224p. pap. *(978-0-7195-2333-5(8))* Murray, John GBR. Dist: Hachette Bk. Group.

de Ruiter, Dick & Becher, Danny. Healing Sounds for ADHD: New Therapeutic Insights. 2007. (ENG., Illus.). 1p. 23.50 *(978-90-78302-13-1(5))* Binkey Kok NLD. Dist: Red Wheel/Weiser.

DeRuvo, Silvia L., et al. The School Counselor's Guide to ADHD: What to Know & Do to Help Your Students. Rosenthal, David & DeRuvo, Silvia L., eds. Lougy, Richard A., ed. 2009. (Illus.). 184p. 78.95 *(978-1-4129-6652-8(3)*, B66528C); pap. 34.95 *(978-1-4129-6653-5(1)*, B66528P) Corwin Pr.

Dosani, Sabina. Calm Your Hyperactive Child. 2008. (52 brilliant ideas Ser.). (Illus.). 256p. pap. 14.99 *(978-1-905940-48-6(3))* Infinite Ideas GBR. Dist: Sony Electronics.

DuPaul, George J. & Kern, Lee. Young Children with ADHD: Early Identificaiton & Intervention. 2011. (Illus.). 240p. 59.95 *(978-1-4338-0963-7(X))* American Psychological Assn.

DuPaul, George J. & Kern, Lee. Young Children with ADHD: Early Identification & Intervention. 2011. (Illus.). ix, 242p. ***(978-1-4338-0964-4(8))*** American Psychological Assn.

Flick, Grad L., ed. Managing ADHD in the K-8 Classroom: A Teacher's Guide. 2010. (Illus.). 248p. 38.95 *(978-1-4129-6910-9(7)*, B69093P) Corwin Pr.

Giler, Janet Z. Socially ADDept: Teaching Social Skills to Children with ADHD, LD, & Asperger's. rev. ed. 2011. (ENG., Illus.). 224p. pap. 29.95 *(978-0-470-59683-8(X)*, Jossey-Bass) Wiley, John & Sons, Inc.

Grange, Mary Jane. So ... You Are Tired of Being a Lame Duck: A Disaster Manual for Attention Deficit Disorder & Attention Deficit Disorder with Hyperactivity. 2010. 196p. pap. 19.95 *(978-1-4269-3625-8(7))* Trafford Publishing.

Grant, Wilson Wayne. Adhd: Strategies for Success. 2011. 188p. 26.95 ***(978-1-4620-4242-5(2))***; pap. 16.95 ***(978-1-4620-4240-1(6))*** iUniverse, Inc.

Green, Harriet Hope. AD/HD Homework Challenges Transformed! Creative Ways to Achieve Focus & Attention by Building on AD/HD Traits. 2012. (ENG., Illus.). 128p. pap. ***(978-1-84905-880-3(6))*** Kingsley, Jessica Ltd.

Hallowell, Edward M. & Jensen, Peter S. Superparenting for ADD: An Innovative Approach to Raising Your Distracted Child. 2008. (ENG., Illus.). 240p. 25.00 *(978-0-345-49776-5(7)*, Ballantine Bks.) Random House Publishing Group.

Handelman, Kenny. Attention Difference Disorder: How to Turn Your ADHD Child or Teen's Differences into Strengths in 7 Simple Steps. 2011. (ENG.). 230p. pap. 17.95 *(978-1-60037-888-1(9))* Morgan James Publishing.

Healy, Jane M. Different Learners: Identifying, Preventing, & Treating Your Child's Learning Problems. (ENG.). 416p. 2011. pap. 15.00 *(978-1-4165-5642-8(7))* 2010. (Illus.). 26.00 *(978-1-4165-5641-1(9))* Simon & Schuster.

Helie, Renee. No Problem Children...Just Children with Problems: Teaching the Attention Deficit Student An Educators Dilemma. 2008. 72p. pap. *(978-3-639-05388-3(5))* VDM Verlag Dr. Mueller e.K.

Honos-Webb, Lara. The Gift of ADHD: 101 Ways to Turn Your Child's Problems into Strengths. 2008. (Companion Ser.). (ENG., Illus.). 168p. pap., act. bk. ed. 14.95 *(978-1-57224-515-0(8))* New Harbinger Pubns.

Hughes, Lesley A. & Cooper, Paul. Understanding & Supporting Children with ADHD: Strategies for Teachers, Parents & Other Professionals. 2007. (Illus.). 112p. 81.00 *(978-1-4129-1860-2(X)*, B1860XC) SAGE Pubns., Ltd. GBR. Dist: SAGE Pubns., Inc.

Hughes, Lesley A. & Cooper, Paul W. Understanding & Supporting Children with ADHD: Strategies for Teachers, Parents & Other Professionals. 2007. (Illus.). 112p. per. 34.00 *(978-1-4129-1861-9(8)*, B1860XP) SAGE Pubns., Ltd. GBR. Dist: SAGE Pubns., Inc.

Hutchinson, Bryan L. One Boy's Struggle: A Memoir: Surviving Life with Undiagnosed ADD. 2008. 179p. pap. 16.95 *(978-0-7414-4440-0(2))* Infinity Publishing.

Iseman, Jacqueline S., et al. 101 School Success Tools for Students with ADHD. 2010. (ENG., Illus.). 200p. pap. 16.95 *(978-1-59363-403-2(X)*, 1311348) Prufrock Pr.

Jamison, Rita. Parenting Your ADHD Child: Biblical Guidance for Your Child's Diagnosis. 2011. (ENG.). 24p. 3.99 ***(978-1-936768-43-1(7))*** New Growth Pr.

Jensen, Eric P., ed. Different Brains, Different Learners: How to Reach the Hard to Reach. 2nd ed. 2009. (Illus.). 208p. pap. 34.95 *(978-1-4129-6502-6(0)*, B65019P) Corwin Pr.

Kewley, Geoff D., et al. 100 Ideas for Supporting Pupils with ADHD. 2008. (Continuum One Hundreds Ser.). (ENG.). 168p. 19.95 *(978-0-8264-9660-7(1))* Continuum International Publishing Group, Ltd. GBR. Dist: National Bk. Network.

Lamb, Enelle. One Step Forward Two Steps Back - Living with ADHD/ODD, a Mother's Perspective. 2009. 163p. pap. 17.00 *(978-0-557-06391-8(4))* Lulu Enterprises Inc.

McClintock, Laura. The Management of Children with Adhd. 2009. 80p. pap. *(978-3-639-11800-1(6))* VDM Verlag Dr. Mueller e.K.

Miller, Lucy Jane, et al. Sensational Kids: Hope & Help for Children with Sensory Processing Disorder. 2007. (ENG.). 384p. (gr. 12-18). 16.00 *(978-0-399-53307-5(9)*, Perigee Trade) Penguin Group (USA) Inc.

Naparstek, Nathan & Greenwood. Successful Educators. 2009. 204p. pap. 45.99 *(978-1-60752-072-6(9))* Information Age Publishing, Inc.

Nolan, Terry Elizabeth. Michael's Mom: A Road Warrior Without a Map. 2007. 199p. per. 12.99 *(978-1-59886-368-0(1))* Tate Publishing & Enterprises, LLC.

O'Regan, Fintan J. & O'Regan. Adhd. 2nd ed. 2007. (SEN (Continuum) Ser.). (ENG., Illus.). 136p. 29.95 *(978-0-8264-9234-0(7))* Continuum International Publishing Group, Ltd. GBR. Dist: National Bk. Network.

Ottinger, Becky, ed. Tictionary. (Illus.). 260p. pap. 29.95 *(978-1-931282-16-1(1))* Autism Asperger Publishing Co.

Partridge, Lee. Teaching Adolescent AD/HD Boys Through Self-Sufficient Reward Control: A Sociological Investigation. 2010. (Illus.). x, 257p. *(978-0-7734-3808-8(4))* Mellen, Edwin Pr., The.

Pastor, Patricia N. & Reuben, Cynthia A. Diagnosed Attention Deficit Hyperactivity Disorder & Learning Disability, United States, 2004-2006: Data from the National Health Interview Survey. 2008. (DHHS Publication Ser.: Nos. 2008-1565). *(978-0-8406-0623-5(0))* National Ctr. for Health Statistics.

Pfiffner, Linda Jo. All about ADHD: The Complete Practical Guide for Classroom Teachers. 2nd rev. ed. 2011. (ENG.). 176p. (gr. k-8). pap. 21.99 *(978-0-545-10920-8(5)*, Teaching Resources) Scholastic, Inc.

Pierangelo, Roger & Giuliani, George A. Classroom Management Techniques for Students with ADHD: A Step-by-Step Guide for Educators. 2007. (Step-By-Step Guide for Educators Ser.). 120p. 66.95 *(978-1-4129-5427-3(4)*, B17883C); per. 27.95 *(978-1-4129-1788-9(3)*, B17883P) Corwin Pr.

Princeton Review Staff, et al. Colleges for Students with Learning Disabilities. 10th ed. 2010. (College Admissions Guides). (ENG.). 848p. pap. 29.99 *(978-0-375-42961-3(1)*, Princeton Review) Random Hse. Information Group.

Pritchard, Verena. Evidence for Negative Priming in Children. 2010. 92p. pap. *(978-3-8383-1806-6(4))* Lambert Academic Publishing.

Proulx-Schirduan, Victoria, et al. Mindful Education for ADHD Students: Differentiating Curriculum & Instruction Using Multiple Intelligences. 2008. (ENG., Illus.). 176p. 60.00 *(978-0-8077-4927-2(3))*; pap. 27.95 *(978-0-8077-4926-5(5))* Teachers College Pr., Teachers College, Columbia Univ.

—Mindful Education for ADHD Students: Differentiating Curriculum & Instruction using Multiple Intelligences. 2009. (ENG., Illus.). 176p. *(978-1-4411-7993-7(3))* Teachers College Pr., Teachers College, Columbia Univ.

Rapoport, Esta M. Adhd & Social Skills: A Step-by-Step Guide for Teachers & Parents. 2009. (ENG.). 250p. 85.00 *(978-1-60709-280-3(8))*; pap. 34.95 *(978-1-60709-281-0(6))* Rowman & Littlefield Education.

Reid, Robert & Johnson, Joseph. Teacher's Guide to ADHD. 2011. (What Works for Special-Needs Learners Ser.). (ENG., Illus.). 274p. (gr. k-12). 50.00 ***(978-1-60918-980-8(9))***; pap. 28.00 ***(978-1-60918-979-2(5))*** Guilford Pubns., Inc.

Rief, Sandra F. The ADD/ADHD Checklist: A Practical Reference for Parents & Teachers. 2nd ed. 2008. (J-B Ed: Checklist Ser.: 6). (ENG.). 272p. pap. 16.95 *(978-0-470-18970-2(3)*, Jossey-Bass) Wiley, John & Sons, Inc.

Rutledge, Rebecca. ADD/ADHD: Get the Right Diagnosis, Understand Treatment Options, Help Your Child Focus. 2008. (ENG.). 224p. pap. 6.95 *(978-1-59869-666-0(1))* Adams Media Corp.

Sandra Starr Ed.D. Calming the Chaos: A drug-free program to eliminate the symptoms of ADHD. 2009. 124p. pap. 13.95 *(978-1-4401-9106-0(9))* iUniverse, Inc.

Schultz, Jerome J. Nowhere to Hide: Why Kids with ADHD & LD Hate School & What We Can Do about It. 2011. (ENG., Illus.). 336p. 24.95 *(978-0-470-90298-1(1)*, Jossey-Bass) Wiley, John & Sons, Inc.

Seiden, Jerry & Halverstadt, Jonathan Scott. ADD, Christianity, & the Church: A Compassionate Healing Resource to Inform, Inspire, & Illuminate. 2008. 208p. pap. 12.95 *(978-1-929753-22-2(5))* Spirit of Hope Publishing.

Silverman, Stephan M., et al. School Success for Kids with ADHD. 2009. (ENG.). 225p. pap. 16.95 *(978-1-59363-358-5(0))* Prufrock Pr.

Spohrer, Kate E. & Spohrer. Teaching Assistant's Guide to ADHD. 2007. (Teaching Assistant's Ser.). (ENG., Illus.). 160p. 34.95 *(978-0-8264-8375-1(5))* Continuum International Publishing Group, Ltd. GBR. Dist: National Bk. Network.

Taylor, Blake E. S. ADHD & Me: What I Learned from Lighting Fires at the Dinner Table. 2008. (ENG.). 192p. pap. 14.95 *(978-1-57224-522-8(0))* New Harbinger Pubns.

Taylor, John. Learn to Have Fun with Your Senses! The Kids Sensory Survival Guide. 2011. (ENG., Illus.). 110p. (J). (gr. 3-12). pap. 14.95 *(978-1-935567-24-0(1))* Sensory Resources.

Wheeler, Linda. The ADHD Toolkit. 2010. (Illus.). 160p. 71.00 *(978-1-84860-183-3(2)*, B01833C); pap. 32.00 *(978-1-84860-184-0(0)*, B01833P) SAGE Pubns., Ltd. GBR. Dist: SAGE Pubns., Inc.

Wood, Douglas. Miss Little's Gift. 2009. (ENG., Illus.). 32p. (J). (gr. -1-2). 16.99 *(978-0-7636-1686-1(9))* Candlewick Pr.

ATTENTION-DEFICIT-DISORDERED YOUTH

Conners, C. Keith. Attention Deficit Hyperactivity Disorder in Children & Adolescents: The Latest Assessment & Treatment Strategies. 4th ed. 2008. *(978-1-887537-31-5(7))* Compact Clinicals.

Dendy, Chris A. Zeigler & Zeigler, Alex. A Bird's-Eye View of Life with ADD & ADHD: Advice from young survivors, second Edition, 1. 2nd rev. ed. 2007. (ENG & KOR., Illus.). 180p. pap. 19.95 net. *(978-0-9679911-4-6(5))* Dendy, Chris A. Zeigler Consulting LLC.

DeRuvo, Silvia L. Strategies for Teaching Adolescents with Adhd: Effective Classroom Techniques Across the Content Areas, Grades 6-12. 2009. (ENG., Illus.). 176p. pap. 29.95 *(978-0-470-24671-9(5)*, Jossey-Bass) Wiley, John & Sons, Inc.

Goldstein, Sam, et al, eds. Learning & Attention Disorders in Adolescence & Adulthood: Assessment & Treatment. 2nd ed. 2011. (ENG., Illus.). 636p. 74.00 *(978-0-470-50518-2(4),* Wiley) Wiley, John & Sons, Inc.

Gregg, Noel. Adolescents & Adults with Learning Disabilities & ADHD: Assessment & Accommodation. (ENG.). 316p. 2011. pap. 27.00 *(978-1-60623-593-5(1))* 2009. (Illus.). 55.00 *(978-1-60623-034-3(4))* Guilford Pubns., Inc.

Honos-Webb, Lara. ADHD Workbook for Teens: Activities to Help You Gain Motivation & Confidence. 2011. (Instant Help Ser.). (ENG.). 144p. (J). (gr. 6-12). pap. 15.95 *(978-1-57224-865-6(3))* New Harbinger Pubns.

Kyger, Maggie M. & Lovin, LouAnn H. Teaching Mathematics Meaningfully: Solutions for Reaching Struggling Learners. 2007. (Illus.). 299p. per. 31.95 *(978-1-55766-866-0(3))* Brookes, Paul H. Publishing Co.

Monastra, Vincent J. Unlocking the Potential of Patients with ADHD: A Model for Clinical Practice. 2007. 316p. 49.95 *(978-1-4338-0238-6(4))* American Psychological Assn.

Partridge, Lee. Teaching Adolescent AD/HD Boys Through Self-Sufficient Reward Control: A Sociological Investigation. 2010. (Illus.). x, 257p. *(978-0-7734-3808-8(4))* Mellen, Edwin Pr., The.

Quinn, Patricia O. Ad/Hd & the College Student: The Everything Guide to Your Most Urgent Questions. 2012. pap. 14.95 ***(978-1-4338-1131-9(6),*** Magination Pr.) American Psychological Assn.

Sandler, Michael. College Confidence with ADD: The Ultimate Success Manual for ADD Students, from Applying to Academics, Preparation to Social Success, & Everything Else You Need to Know. 2008. (ENG., Illus.). 432p. pap. 14.95 *(978-1-4022-1251-2(8))* Sourcebooks, Inc.

Spodak, Ruth & Stefano, Kenneth. Take Control of ADHD: The Ultimate Guide for Teens with ADHD. 2011. (ENG.). 175p. (gr. 7-12). pap. 16.95 *(978-1-59363-535-0(4))* Prufrock Pr.

Zeigler Dendy, Chris A. Teaching Teens with ADD, ADHD & Executive Function Deficits: A Quick Reference Guide for Teachers & Parents: 2nd Edition. 2nd ed. 2011. 375p. pap. *(978-1-60613-016-2(1))* Woodbine Hse.

ATTENTION DEFICIT DISORDERS
see Attention-Deficit Hyperactivity Disorder

ATTENTION-DEFICIT HYPERACTIVITY DISORDER

Adler, Lenard & Florence, Mari. Scattered Minds: Hope & Help for Adults with Attention Deficit Hyperactivity Disorder. 2007. (ENG.). 208p. (gr. 12-18). 14.95 *(978-0-399-53340-2(0),* Perigee Trade) Penguin Group (USA) Inc.

Alexander-Roberts, Colleen. The AD/HD Parenting Handbook: Practical Advice for Parents from Parents. 2nd rev. ed. 2006. (ENG., Illus.). 320p. per. 15.95 *(978-1-58979-283-8(1))* Taylor Trade Publishing.

American Academy of Child and Adolescent Psychiatry (AACAP). Attention-Deficit / Hyperactivity Disorder GUIDELINES Pocketcard: American Academy of Child & Adolescent Psychiatry (2011) 2011. (ENG.). 6p. 9.95 ***(978-0-9846667-0-6(2))*** International Guidelines Ctr., Inc.

American Academy of Pediatrics. ADHD: A Complete & Authoritative Guide. Reiff, Michael I., ed. 2nd ed. 2011. (ENG.). 350p. pap. 16.95 *(978-1-58110-451-6(0))* American Academy of Pediatrics.

Anderson, Laura. Accidentally Beautiful. 2011. 138p. pap. 14.97 ***(978-0-557-76431-0(9))*** Lulu Enterprises Inc.

Atwood, Robert W., et al. Adhd: Children Who Challenge. 2008. 288p. pap. 20.95 *(978-0-595-47665-7(1),* iUniverse, Inc.) iUniverse, Inc.

Avery, Catherine. Life at Full Throttle: Attention Deficit/Hyperactivity Disorder in Adults. 2010. 132p. 23.95 *(978-1-4401-9461-0(0));* pap. 13.95 *(978-1-4401-9463-4(7))* iUniverse, Inc.

Bailey, Eileen & Haupt, Donald. Adult ADHD - The Complete Idiot's Guide. 2010. (Complete Idiot's Guide Ser.). (ENG.). 336p. (gr. 12). 16.95 *(978-1-61564-006-5(1),* Alpha Bks.) Penguin Group (USA) Inc.

Banaschewski, Tobias, et al. Attention-Deficit Hyperactivity Disorder & Hyperkinetic Disorder. 2010. (Oxford Poetry Library). (ENG., Illus.). 128p. pap. 24.95 *(978-0-19-957765-1(X))* Oxford Univ. Pr., Inc.

Barkley, Russell. ADHD in Adults. 2009. 81p. pap. 41.95 *(978-0-7637-6564-4(3))* Jones & Bartlett Learning, LLC.

—Barkley's Quick Check for Adult ADHD Diagnosis. 2007. 48p. pap. 30.95 *(978-0-7637-6305-3(5))* Jones & Bartlett Learning, LLC.

Barkley, Russell A. Attention Deficit Hyperactivity Disorder in Adults: The Latest Assessment & Treatment Strategies. 2008. *(978-1-887537-30-8(9))* Compact Clinicals.

Barkley, Russell A., et al. ADHD in Adults: What the Science Says. 2010. (ENG.). 489p. pap. 30.00 *(978-1-60918-075-1(5))* Guilford Pubns., Inc.

Bauermeister, Jose J. Hiperactivo, Impulsivo, Distraido - Me Conoces? Guia Acerca del Deficit Atencional para Padres, Maestros y Profesionales. 2nd ed. 2008. (SPA.). 294p. (gr. k-12). pap. 16.95 *(978-1-59385-599-4(0))* Guilford Pubns., Inc.

Beal, Eileen. Ritalin: Its Use & Abuse. 2009. (Drug Abuse Prevention Library). 64p. (gr. 5-5). 58.50 *(978-1-60853-431-9(6))* Rosen Publishing Group, Inc., The.

Bellak-Adams, Kerin. AD/HD Success! Solutions for Boosting Self-Esteem the Diary Method for Ages 7-17. 2010. 146p. pap. *(978-1-61599-024-5(0))* Loving Healing Pr., Inc.

Benavidez, Rolando. Chama Stories: True Confessions of a Ten Year Old Pentecostal Preacher's Kid. 2009. 260p. 24.99 *(978-1-4389-4465-4(9))* AuthorHouse.

Bertin, Mark. The Family ADHD Solution: A Scientific Approach to Maximizing Your Child's Attention & Minimizing Parental Stress. 2011. (ENG.). 240p. pap. 17.00 *(978-0-230-10505-8(X))* Palgrave Macmillan.

Binstock, Melissa. Nourishment: Feeding My Starving Soul When My Mind & Body Betrayed Me. 2011. (ENG.). 288p. pap. 14.95 *(978-0-7573-1542-8(9))* Health Communications, Inc.

Bowes, David B. Trail: A Writing Life Enhanced by Attention Deficit Disorder. 2009. 584p. 33.99 *(978-1-4389-2576-9(X));* pap. 23.49 *(978-1-4389-2575-2(1))* AuthorHouse.

Breeding, J. The Wildest Colts Make the Best Horses. 2007. 312p. per. *(978-1-84747-077-5(7))* Chipmunkapublishing.

Briscoe, William P. Focus on Cognitive Disorder Research. 2006. 240p. 225.00 *(978-1-60021-482-0(7))* Nova Science Pubs., Inc.

Brock, Stephen E., et al. Identifying, Assessing, & Treating ADHD at School. 2009. (Developmental Psychopathology at School Ser.). xi, 168p. (Illus.). pap. 49.95 *(978-1-4419-5990-4(4),* 1441959904); (ENG.). 149.00 *(978-1-4419-0500-0(6),* 1441905006) Springer.

Brown, Richard P. & Gerbarg, Patricia L. Non-Drug Treatments for ADHD: New Options for Kids, Adults, & Clinicians. 2012. (ENG.). 304p. 27.95 *(978-0-393-70622-2(2),* 70622) Norton, W. W. & Co., Inc.

Brown, Thomas. Attention Deficit Disorder: The Unfocused Mind in Children & Adults. 2006. (Yale University Press Health & Wellness Ser.). (ENG., Illus.). 384p. pap. 18.00 *(978-0-300-11989-3(5))* Yale Univ. Pr.

Brown, Thomas E. Attention-Deficit Disorders & Comorbidities in Children, Adolescents, & Adults. 2nd ed. 2009. 99.00 *(978-1-58562-158-3(7))* American Psychiatric Publishing, Inc.

Brynie, Faith Hickman. ADHD: Attention-Deficit/Hyperactivity Disorder. 2008. lib. bdg. *(978-0-8225-7292-3(3))* Twenty First Century Bks.

Buttross, L. Susan. Understanding Attention Deficit Hyperactivity Disorder. 2007. (ENG., Illus.). 126p. 30.00 *(978-1-57806-882-1(7));* per. 14.00 *(978-1-57806-883-8(5))* Univ. Pr. of Mississippi.

Calvert-Phillips, Cynthia. A. D. D. Welcome to Our World: A Positive Perspective on Attention Deficit Disorder. 2006. (ENG., Illus.). 189p. 19.95 *(978-1-930034-98-3(9))* Casscom Media.

Carter, Cheryl R. Organize Your ADD/ADHD Child: A Practical Guide for Parents. 2010. (ENG.). 128p. pap. *(978-1-84905-839-1(3))* Kingsley, Jessica Ltd.

Causse, Celine. Living with a Hyperactive Child, 1 vol. 2010. (ENG.). 96p. pap. 9.99 *(978-2-35934-043-3(3))* Alpen Editions FRA. Dist: Innovative Logistics.

Chandler, Chris. The Science of ADHD: A Guide for Parents & Professionals. 2011. (ENG., Illus.). 352p. 104.95 *(978-1-4051-6234-0(1));* pap. 26.95 *(978-1-4051-6235-7(X))* Wiley, John & Sons, Inc. (Wiley-Blackwell).

Chesner, Jonathan. ADHD in HD: Brains Gone Wild. 2012. (ENG.). 160p. (YA). pap. 14.99 ***(978-1-57542-386-9(3))*** Free Spirit Publishing, Inc.

Compart, Pamela & Laake, Dana. The Kid-Friendly ADHD & Autism Cookbook, Updated & Revised: The Ultimate Guide to the Gluten-Free, Casein-Free Diet. 2012. (ENG., Illus.). 352p. pap. 18.99 *(978-1-59233-472-8(5),* 1592334725) Quayside.

Conners, C. Keith. Attention Deficit Hyperactivity Disorder in Children & Adolescents: The Latest Assessment & Treatment Strategies. 4th ed. 2008. *(978-1-887537-31-5(7))* Compact Clinicals.

Cowan, Stephen Scott. Fire Child, Water Child: How Understanding the Five Types of ADHD Can Help You Improve Your Child's Self-Esteem & Attention. 2012. ***(978-1-60882-092-4(0));*** (ENG.). 216p. pap. 17.95 ***(978-1-60882-090-0(4))*** New Harbinger Pubns.

Cram101 Textbook Reviews & Cram101 Textbook Reviews. Outlines & Highlights for Attention Deficit Hyperactivity Disorder, an Issue of Child & Adolescent Psychiatric Clinics. 2011. 120p. pap. 28.95 ***(978-1-61461-224-7(2))*** Cram101 Inc.

Dance, Vivian L. & Vontress, Linda E. They Called me Slow, but the Light was Hidden in Me. 2011. 56p. pap. 11.49 *(978-1-4520-9184-6(6))* AuthorHouse.

Dendy, Chris A. Zeigler & Zeigler, Alex. A Bird's-Eye View of Life with ADD & ADHD: Advice from young survivors, second Edition, 1. 2nd rev. ed. 2007. (ENG & KOR., Illus.). 180p. pap. 19.95 net. *(978-0-9679911-4-6(5))* Dendy, Chris A. Zeigler Consulting LLC.

DeRuvo, Silvia L., et al. The School Counselor's Guide to ADHD: What to Know & Do to Help Your Students. Rosenthal, David & DeRuvo, Silvia L., eds. Lougy, Richard A., ed. 2009. (Illus.). 184p. 78.95 *(978-1-4129-6652-8(3),* B66528C); pap. 34.95 *(978-1-4129-6653-5(1),* B66528P) Corwin Pr.

Diller, Lawrence H. Remembering Ritalin: A Doctor & Generation Rx Reflect on Life & Psychiatric Drugs. 2011. (ENG.). 272p. (gr. 12). 24.95 *(978-0-399-53664-9(7),* Perigee Trade) Penguin Group (USA) Inc.

Diller, Lawrence H. Remembering Ritalin: A Doctor & Generation Rx Reflect on Life & Psychiatric Drugs. 2012. (ENG.). 304p. (gr. 12). 16.00 ***(978-0-399-53748-6(1),*** Perigee Trade) Penguin Group (USA) Inc.

Dukarm, Carolyn Piver. Pieces of a Puzzle: The Link Between Eating Disorders & Attention Deficit Disorder. 2006. (ENG., Illus.). 136p. per. 16.95 *(978-0-9714609-3-5(0))* Advantage Bks., LLC.

DuPaul, George J. & Kern, Lee. Young Children with ADHD: Early Identificaiton & Intervention. 2011. (Illus.). 240p. 59.95 *(978-1-4338-0963-7(X))* American Psychological Assn.

DuPaul, George J. & Kern, Lee. Young Children with ADHD: Early Identification & Intervention. 2011. (Illus.). ix, 242p. ***(978-1-4338-0964-4(8))*** American Psychological Assn.

Edwards, Jason. Child ADHD - Practical Evidence-Based Treatment. 2007. 320p. 35.00 *(978-0-393-70471-6(8))* Norton, W. W. & Co., Inc.

Elwins, Dannie. Secrets to Overcoming & Winning the Battle Against ADHD Disorder. 2009. 36p. pap. 16.99 *(978-0-557-15402-9(2))* Lulu Enterprises Inc.

Fattig, Michelle. Bully-Be-Gone with Annie: Experience Attention Deficits Through the Eyes of a Child. 2007. (Illus.). 59p. (J). per. *(978-0-9795805-5-0(2))* Flower by the Water Publishing.

—A Prairie Day with Annie: Experience Attention Deficits Through the Eyes of a Child. 2007. (Illus.). 196p. (YA). (gr. 5-18). per. 14.99 *(978-0-9795805-1-2(X))* Flower by the Water Publishing.

—Taming Tommy's Tantrums. 2007. 76p. pap. 10.99 *(978-0-9795805-7-4(9))* Flower by the Water Publishing.

—Viva le Resistance! 2007. (Illus.). 280p. (YA). per. 14.99 *(978-0-9795805-3-6(6))* Flower by the Water Publishing.

—A Windy Day with Annie: Experience Attention Deficits Through the Eyes of a Child. 2007. (Illus.). 74p. (J). per. *(978-0-9795805-0-5(1))* Flower by the Water Publishing.

Fisher, Barbara C., ed. Attention Deficit Disorder: Practical Coping Mechanisms. 2nd rev. ed. 2006. (ENG., Illus.). 408p. 130.00 *(978-0-8493-3099-5(8))* CRC Pr. LLC.

Fitzgerald, Michael. Attention Deficit Hyperactivity Disorder: Creativity, Novelty Seeking & Risk. 2008. 189p. 79.00 *(978-1-60456-855-4(0))* Nova Science Pubs., Inc.

Fitzgerald, Michael, et al, eds. Handbook of Attention Deficit Hyperactivity Disorder. 2007. (ENG., Illus.). 536p. 237.00 *(978-0-470-01444-8(X),* Wiley) Wiley, John & Sons, Inc.

Flick, Grad L., ed. Managing ADHD in the K-8 Classroom: A Teacher's Guide. 2010. (Illus.). 248p. pap. 38.95 *(978-1-4129-6910-9(7),* B69093P) Corwin Pr.

Frank Barnhill. Mistaken for ADHD: How You Can Prevent Mislabeling Your Child as a Failure in Life in the Face of a Looming ADHD Misdiagnosis. 2010. 380p. pap. 24.95 *(978-1-4502-1428-5(2))* iUniverse, Inc.

Freed, Jeffrey & Shapiro, Joan. 4 Weeks to an Organized Life with AD/HD. 2007. (ENG.). 216p. per. 16.95 *(978-1-58979-326-2(9))* Taylor Trade Publishing.

Gnaulati, Enrico. Emotion-regulating Play Therapy with ADHD Children. 2008. (ENG.). 224p. pap. 41.99 *(978-0-7657-0523-5(0),* Aronson, Jason) Rowman & Littlefield Publishers, Inc.

—Emotion-Regulating Play Therapy with ADHD Children: Staying with Playing. 2008. (ENG.). 220p. 73.50 *(978-0-7657-0522-8(2),* Aronson, Jason) Rowman & Littlefield Publishers, Inc.

Goldstein, Sam, et al, eds. Learning & Attention Disorders in Adolescence & Adulthood: Assessment & Treatment. 2nd ed. 2011. (ENG., Illus.). 636p. 74.00 *(978-0-470-50518-2(4),* Wiley) Wiley, John & Sons, Inc.

Goodwin, Tracey Bromley & Oberacker, Holly. Navigating ADHD: Your Guide to the Flip Side of ADHD. 2011. 232p. pap. 15.99 *(978-1-4567-3178-6(5))* AuthorHouse.

Gordon, Jay. The ADD & ADHD Cure: The Natural Way to Treat Hyperactivity & Refocus Your Child. 2008. (ENG.). 240p. 22.95 *(978-0-470-07268-4(7),* Wiley) Wiley, John & Sons, Inc.

Gordon, Michael. ADHD on Trial: Courtroom Clashes over the Meaning of "Disability" 2009. 155p. 44.95 *(978-0-313-36015-2(4),* C36015, Praeger Pubs.) Greenwood Publishing Group, Inc.

Gordon, Stuart M. & Mitchell, Aileen E. Attention Deficit Hyperactivity Disorder (ADHD) 2009. (Psychiatry - Theory, Applications & Treatments Ser.). 129.00 *(978-1-60741-581-7(X),* Nova Biomedical Bks.) Nova Science Pubs., Inc.

Gould, Neil. Close Encounters of the ADHD Kind. 2010. 284p. pap. 15.49 *(978-1-4520-3785-1(X))* AuthorHouse.

Gozal, David & Molfese, Dennis L., eds. Attention Deficit Hyperactivity Disorder: From Genes to Patients. 2010. (Contemporary Clinical Neuroscience Ser.). (Illus.). 576p. pap. 209.00 *(978-1-61737-485-2(7),* 1617374857) Humana Pr.

Grange, Mary Jane. So ... You Are Tired of Being a Lame Duck: A Disaster Manual for Attention Deficit Disorder & Attention Deficit Disorder with Hyperactivity. 2010. 196p. pap. 19.95 *(978-1-4269-3625-8(7))* Trafford Publishing.

Grant, David. That's the Way I Think: Dyslexia, Dyspraxia & ADHD Explained. 2nd rev. ed. 2010. (ENG., Illus.). 176p. pap. 30.95 *(978-0-415-56464-9(5));* 130.00 *(978-0-415-56465-6(4))* Routledge.

Grant, Wilson Wayne. Adhd: Strategies for Success. 2011. 188p. 26.95 ***(978-1-4620-4242-5(2));*** pap. 16.95 ***(978-1-4620-4240-1(6))*** iUniverse, Inc.

Green, Harriet Hope. AD/HD Homework Challenges Transformed! Creative Ways to Achieve Focus & Attention by Building on AD/HD Traits. 2012. (ENG., Illus.). 128p. pap. ***(978-1-84905-880-3(6))*** Kingsley, Jessica Ltd.

Greenman, Jan. Life at the Edge & Beyond: Living with ADHD & Aspergers Syndrome. 2010. 208p. pap. *(978-1-84905-106-4(2))* Kingsley, Jessica Ltd.

Greenspan, Jacob & Greenspan, Stanley I. Overcoming ADHD: Helping Your Child Become Calm, Engaged, & Focused - Without a Pill. 2009. (ENG.). 208p. 25.00 *(978-0-7382-1355-2(1))* Da Capo Pr., Inc.

Grove Deniz, Bethany, et al. Strategies for Success. 2011. 108p. pap. ***(978-3-8443-0159-5(3))*** Lambert Academic Publishing.

Hallowell, Edward M. CrazyBusy: Overstretched, Overbooked, & about to Snap! Strategies for Handling Your Fast-Paced Life. 2007. (ENG.). 256p. per. 14.95 *(978-0-345-48244-0(1),* Ballantine Bks.) Random House Publishing Group.

Hallowell, Edward M. & Jensen, Peter S. Superparenting for ADD: An Innovative Approach to Raising Your Distracted Child. 2008. (ENG., Illus.). 240p. 25.00 *(978-0-345-49776-5(7),* Ballantine Bks.) Random House Publishing Group.

—Superparenting for ADD: An Innovative Approach to Raising Your Distracted Child. 2010. (ENG.). 240p. pap. 15.00 *(978-0-345-49777-2(5),* Ballantine Bks.) Random House Publishing Group.

Hallowell, Edward M. & Ratey, John J. Answers to Distraction. 2010. (ENG.). 368p. pap. 15.00 *(978-0-307-45639-7(0),* Anchor) Knopf Doubleday Publishing Group.

Hammerness, Paul Graves. Adhd. 2008. (Biographies of Disease Ser.). (Illus.). 168p. 45.00 *(978-0-313-34302-5(0),* GR4302, Greenwood Pr.) Greenwood Publishing Group, Inc.

Hawthorne, Woody, Billy: One Family's Insane Journey through the Virginia Mental Health System. 2009. (Illus.). 176p. pap. *(978-1-84747-992-1(8))* Chipmunkapublishing.

Herron MS, NCP, CFCC, Gayle, LPC. Straight Talk about ADD & ADHD. 2008. 169p. pap. 19.95 *(978-0-557-00171-2(4))* Lulu Enterprises Inc.

Hess, Stephan. A Devotional for the Depressed & the Insane. 2011. 376p. pap. 17.72 ***(978-1-4634-3103-7(1))*** AuthorHouse.

Hoffer, Abram. Healing Children's Attention & Behavior Disorders: Complementary Nutritional & Psychological Treatments. 2011. (Professional Edition Ser.). (ENG.). 368p. 49.95 ***(978-1-897025-41-3(6))*** Canadian College of Naturopathic Medicine Pr. CAN. Dist: SCB Distributors.

Honos-Webb, Lara. The Gift of ADHD: How to Transform Your Child's Problems into Strengths. 2nd rev. ed. 2010. (ENG.). 240p. pap. 16.95 *(978-1-57224-850-2(5))* New Harbinger Pubns.

Hosin, Amer A. Autism, ADHD, & Anorexia Nervosa: Essays on Three Childhood Disorders. (Illus.). 120p. 89.95 *(978-0-7734-5163-6(3))* Mellen, Edwin Pr., The.

Hunter, Larry B. Somewhat Odd. 2011. 94p. pap. 19.95 ***(978-1-4512-8137-8(4))*** PublishAmerica, Inc.

Hunter, Scott J. & Sparrow, Elizabeth P. Executive Function & Dysfunction. 2012. (ENG., Illus.). 296p. 99.00 ***(978-0-521-88976-6(6))*** Cambridge Univ. Pr.

Hutchinson, Bryan L. One Boy's Struggle: A Memoir: Surviving Life with Undiagnosed ADD. 2008. 179p. pap. 16.95 *(978-0-7414-4440-0(2))* Infinity Publishing.

Jackson, Brent. Altered Perceptions: A writer's journey through a life with attention deficit disorder, or A. D. D. 2011. 110p. pap. 19.95 ***(978-1-4560-0822-2(6))*** PublishAmerica, Inc.

Jamison, Rita. Parenting Your ADHD Child: Biblical Guidance for Your Child's Diagnosis. 2011. (ENG.). 24p. 3.99 ***(978-1-936768-43-1(7))*** New Growth Pr.

Jaremkiewicz, Anna. Aufmerksamkeit und Sprache. (GER., Illus.). 181p. pap. 46.95 *(978-3-631-56700-5(6))* Lang, Peter GmbH, Europaischer Verlag der Wissenschaften DEU. Dist: Lang, Peter Publishing, Inc.

Jones, Janice. Take Your Pills & Go to Your Room: A Mom's True Story about Life, Children & Adhd. 2011. (ENG.). 122p. pap. 10.95 ***(978-1-4327-7733-3(5))*** Outskirts Pr., Inc.

Kapalka, George. Counseling Boys & Men with ADHD. 2009. (Routledge Series on Counseling & Psychotherapy with Boys & Men Ser.). (ENG., Illus.). 373p. pap. 39.95 *(978-0-415-99344-9(X))* Routledge.

Kelly, Evelyn B. Encyclopedia of Attention Deficit Hyperactivity Disorders, 1 vol. 2009. 295p. 85.00 *(978-0-313-34249-3(0),* GR4249) Greenwood Publishing Group, Inc.

Kerson, Don. Getting Unstuck: Unraveling the Knot of Depression, Attention & Trauma. 2008. (Illus.). 292p. pap. 24.95 *(978-0-9769867-2-0(8))* Greenpoint Psychiatric Pr.

Kewley, Geoff. Attention Deficit Hyperactivity Disorder: What Can Teachers Do? 3rd rev. ed. 2010. (David Fulton / Nasen Ser.). (ENG., Illus.). 120p. pap. 31.95 *(978-0-415-49202-7(5),* Routledge) Taylor & Francis Group GBR. Dist: Taylor & Francis Group.

Kragel, Vicky. They Have ADD/ADHD: So Why Am I the One Taking Pills? 2006. 17.00 *(978-0-8059-8300-5(7))* Dorrance Publishing Co., Inc.

Kropotov, Juri, et al. Neurobiology of ADHD: A New Diagnostic Approach Based on Electrophysiological Endophenotypes. 2013. (Endophenotypes in Neuropsychiatry Ser.). (ENG., Illus.). 300p. 189.00 *(978-3-642-03591-3(4),* 3642035914) Springer.

Kurtz, Lisa A. Understanding Controversial Therapies for Children with Autism, Attention Deficit Disorder, & Other Learning Disabilities: A Guide to Complementary & Alternative Medicine. 2008. (ENG.). 192p. pap. *(978-1-84310-864-1(X))* Kingsley, Jessica Ltd.

Kutscher, Martin L. ADHD: Living Without Brakes. 2009. (ENG., Illus.). 192p. pap. *(978-1-84905-816-2(4))* Kingsley, Jessica Ltd.

—ADHD — Living Without Brakes. 2008. (ENG., Illus.). 144p. pap. *(978-1-84310-873-3(9))* Kingsley, Jessica Ltd.

Lavin, Paul. Clinical Depression: The Overlooked & Insidious Nemesis Plaguing ADHD Children. 2008. (ENG., Illus.). 100p. pap. 26.50 *(978-0-7618-3863-0(5))* Univ. Pr. of America, Inc.

Leedom, Liane J. Just Like His Father? A Guide to Overcoming Your Child's Genetic Connection to Antisocial Behavior, Addiction & ADHD. 2006. per. 14.95 *(978-0-9778013-0-5(6))* Health & Well-Being Pubns., LLC.

Lobb, Tessa. Scary Dairy, Wild Wheat & Coping with E's: A Dietary Approach to Children's Behavioral Problems Through Diet. 2008. (Illus.). 111p. pap. *(978-1-904943-28-0(4))* Grub Street.

Machado, Randy. What's Wrong with U. S. ? 2008. 130p. pap. 24.95 *(978-0-615-22311-7(7))* Machado, Randy J.

Mapou, Robert L. Adult Learning Disabilities & ADHD: Research-Informed Assessment. 2008. (AACN Workshop Ser.). (ENG.). 312p. pap. 39.95 *(978-0-19-537178-9(X))* Oxford Univ. Pr., Inc.

Marsh, Pamela. Impaired Emotion Perception in Adhd & First-Episode Schizophrenia. 2008. 176p. pap. *(978-3-639-04290-0(5))* VDM Verlag Dr. Mueller e.K.

Martin, Jeremy W. Adhd: Beyond the Meds. 2011. 172p. pap. 14.99 ***(978-1-61215-807-5(2))*** Xulon Pr., Inc.

Mason, Oren. Reaching for A New Potential. 2009. 189p. pap. 17.98 *(978-0-557-12353-7(4))* Lulu Enterprises Inc.

Matson, Johnny L., ed. Social Behavior & Skills in Children. 2009. (ENG.). x, 334p. 149.95 *(978-1-4419-0233-7(3),* 1441902333) Springer.

Mayes, Rick, et al. Medicating Children: ADHD & Pediatric Mental Health. 2009. (Illus.). 360p. 44.00 *(978-0-674-03163-0(6))* Harvard Univ. Pr.

McBurnett, Keith & Pfiffner, Linda, eds. Attention Deficit Hyperactivity Disorder: Concepts, Controversies, New Directions. 2007. (Medical Psychiatry Ser.: Vol. 37). (ENG., Illus.). 448p. 230.00 *(978-0-8247-2927-1(7))* Taylor & Francis Group.

McClintock, Laura. The Management of Children with Adhd. 2009. 80p. pap. *(978-3-639-11800-1(6))* VDM Verlag Dr. Mueller e.K.

Menhard, Francha Roffe. The Facts about Ritalin. 2006. (Drugs Ser.). (Illus.). 112p. (YA). (gr. 9-12). lib. bdg. 42.79 *(978-0-7614-2245-7(5))* Marshall Cavendish Corp.

Merlin, Deborah. Victory over ADHD: A Holistic Approach for Helping Children with Attention Deficit Hyper-activity Disorder. 2nd rev. ed. 2009. (ENG., Illus.). 224p. pap. 12.95 *(978-1-57067-234-7(2),* Healthy Living) Book Publishing Co.

Meyers, Karen H. & Golden, Robert N. The Truth about ADHD & Other Neurobiological Disorders. 2010. (Truth about Ser.). (Illus.). 192p. (C). (gr. 9-18). 35.00 *(978-0-8160-7636-9(7))* Facts On File, Inc.

Millichap, J. Gordon. Attention Deficit Hyperactivity Disorder Handbook: A Physician's Guide to ADHD. 2nd ed. (ENG., Illus.). xvii, 182p. 2011. pap. 39.95 ***(978-1-4614-2021-7(0),*** 1461420210) 2009. 189.00 *(978-1-4419-1395-8(3),* 1441913963) Springer.

Monastra, Vincent J. Unlocking the Potential of Patients with ADHD: A Model for Clinical Practice. 2007. 316p. 49.95 *(978-1-4338-0238-6(4))* American Psychological Assn.

Moore, Elaine A. The Amphetamine Debate: The Use of Adderall, Ritalin & Related Drugs for Behavior Modification, Neuroenhancement & Anti-Aging Purposes. 2010. (McFarland Health Topics Ser.). (ENG., Illus.). 248p. pap. 29.95 *(978-0-7864-5873-8(9))* McFarland & Co., Inc. Pubs.

Mullins, Celine. Time to See Adhd in a Whole New Light? 2010. 284p. pap. *(978-3-8383-5100-1(2))* Lambert Academic Publishing.

Murphy, Brenda. LifeTips 101 ADHD-ADD Tips. 2007. 9.99 *(978-1-60275-023-4(8))* LifeTips.

Nambudripad, Devi S. Say Good-Bye to ADD & ADHD. 2nd ed. 2007. (Illus.). xiii, 274p. pap. *(978-0-9759277-1-7(X),* Delta) Random House Publishing Group.

Nass, Ruth D. & Leventhal, Fern. Child's ADHD: Preschool to College. 2nd rev. ed. 2010. 168p. pap. 22.95 *(978-0-7637-8179-8(7))* Jones & Bartlett Learning, LLC.

Neff, Patricia E. ADHD & Maternal Resiliency: A Cross-Cultural Examination of Canadian & American Mothers. 2008. 156p. 94.95 *(978-1-60497-590-1(3))* Cambria Pr.

Newmark, Sanford. ADHD Without Drugs: A Guide to the Natural Care of Children with ADHD. 2010. 237p. pap. *(978-0-9826714-0-5(7),* Nurtured Heart Publications) Ctr. for the Difficult Child.

Nigg, Joel T. What Causes ADHD? Understanding What Goes Wrong & Why. 2009. (ENG., Illus.). 422p. pap. 35.00 *(978-1-60623-352-8(1))* Guilford Pubns., Inc.

O'Regan, Fintan. Adhd: All Your Questions Answered. 2012. (David Fulton / Nasen Ser.). (ENG.). 144p. pap. 35.95 ***(978-0-415-59770-8(6))*** Routledge.

O'Regan, Fintan. Understanding AD/HD: Frequently Asked Questions. 2008. (ENG.) 16p. pap. *(978-1-84310-541-1(1))* Kingsley, Jessica Ltd.

Owens, Clin Guide Attention Deficit (Adhd) A Clinical Guide to Attention Deficit Hyperactivity Disorder (Adhd) in Children & Adolescents. 2011. pap. 54.95 *(978-1-60547-747-3(8))* Lippincott Williams & Wilkins.

Ozdemir, Selda. Attention Deficit Hyperactivity Disorder: An Early Intervention Approach for Preventing Social, Emotional, & Academic Problems. 2008. 180p. pap. *(978-3-8364-7058-2(6))* VDM Verlag Dr. Mueller e.K.

Page, Richard. Analysis of Specific Attentional Functions in Adhd. 2009. 72p. pap. *(978-3-639-13548-0(2))* VDM Verlag Dr. Mueller e.K.

Partridge, Lee. Teaching Adolescent AD/HD Boys Through Self-Sufficient Reward Contro : A Sociological Investigation. 2010. (Illus.). x, 257p. *(978-0-7734-3808-8(4))* Mellen, Edwin Pr., The.

Pastor, Patricia N. & Reuben, Cynthia A. Diagnosed Attention Deficit Hyperactivity Disorder & Learning Disability, United States, 2004-2006: Data from the National Health Interview Survey. 2008. (DHHS Publication Ser.: Nos. 2008-1565). *(978-0-8406-0623-5(0))* National Ctr. for Health Statistics.

Pecherstorfer, Thomas. Neurofeedback & Hrv Biofeedback after Stroke. 2009. 84p. pap. *(978-3-639-20962-4(1))* VDM Verlag Dr. Mueller e.K.

Penguin Books Staff. ADHD: Life & Death. *(978-0-14-774939-0(5)); (978-0-14-774938-3(7))* Penguin Group (USA) Inc.

Peterson, Neil. Embracing the Edge: Stories of Tenacity & Personal Power. 2008. (ENG., Illus.). 195p. pap. 15.95 *(978-1-887542-95-1(7))* Book Pubs. Network.

Phillips-Goodnight, Dee. My Silent Scream: Finding Hope & Grace to Endure: Inside a Mother's Struggle to Raise a Child with OCD, ADHD, & Asperger's Syndrome. 2011. (ENG., Illus.). 148p. pap. 10.99 ***(978-1-936314-54-6(1))*** Word & Spirit Resources, LLC.

Pinsky, Susan C. Organizing Solutions for People with Attention Deficit Disorder: Tips & Tools to Help You Take Charge of Your Life & Get Organized. 2006. (ENG., Illus.). 192p. pap. 19.95 *(978-1-59233-234-2(X),* 159233234X) Quayside.

Pliszka, Steven R. Treating ADHD & Comorbid Disorders: Psychosocial & Psychopharmacological Interventions. (ENG.). 242p. 2011. pap. 27.00 *(978-1-60918-231-1(6))* 2009. (Illus.). 55.00 *(978-1-60623-266-8(5))* Guilford Pubns., Inc.

Potgieter, Marius. I HAVE ADHD/ADD - SO WHAT? A Guide for Teens & Adults. 2010. 160p. pap. 19.40 *(978-1-4457-5666-0(8))* Lulu Enterprises Inc.

Quartier, Vincent. Du développement de la temporalité dans les hyperactivités de L'enfant. 2008. 307p. pap. *(978-3-03911-701-7(7))* Lang, Peter.

Quinn. 100 Q & As about Adhd in Women & Girls. rev. ed. 2010. 242p. pap. 22.95 *(978-0-7637-8452-2(4))* Jones & Bartlett Learning, LLC.

Quinn, Patricia O. Ad/Hd & the College Student: The Everything Guide to Your Most Urgent Questions. 2012. pap. 14.95 ***(978-1-4338-1131-9(6),*** Magination Pr.) American Psychological Assn.

Rafalovich, Adam. Framing ADHD Children: A Critical Examination of the History, Discourse, & Everyday Experience of Attention Deficit/Hyperactivity Disorder. 2007. (ENG.). 208p. per. 29.50 *(978-0-7391-2537-3(0))* Lexington Bks.

Ramsay, J. Russell & Rostain, Anthony L. Cognitive Behavioral Therapy for Adult ADHD: An Integrative Psychosocial & Medical Approach. 2007. (Practical Clinical Guidebooks). (ENG.). 252p. 125.00 *(978-0-415-95500-3(9))* Routledge.

—Cognitive-Behavioral Therapy for Adult ADHD: An Integrative Psychosocial & Medical Approach. 2007. (Practical Clinical Guidebooks). (ENG.). 252p. per. 32.50 *(978-0-415-95501-0(7))* Routledge.

Ratey, John & Hallowell, Edward M. Driven to Distraction: Recognizing & Coping with Attention Deficit Disorder. rev. ed. 2011. (ENG.). 400p. pap. 15.95 *(978-0-307-74315-2(2),* Anchor) Knopf Doubleday Publishing Group.

Ratey, Nancy A. Disorganized Mind: Coaching Your ADHD Brain to Take Control of Your Time, Tasks, & Talents. 2008. (ENG.). 304p. pap. 15.99 *(978-0-312-35534-0(3),* St. Martin's Griffin) St. Martin's Pr.

Reynolds, Cecil R., et al. The Energetic Brain: Understanding & Managing ADHD. 2012. (ENG., Illus.). 448p. pap. 22.95 *(978-0-470-51516-4(8),* Jossey-Bass) Wiley, John & Sons, Inc.

Rickel, Annette U. & Brown, Ronald T. Attention-Deficit/Hyperactivity Disorder in Children & Adults. 2007. (Advances in Psychotherapy — Evidence-Based Practice Ser.: Vol. 7). (Illus.). 96p. pap. 29.80 *(978-0-88937-322-8(1))* Hogrefe Publishing.

Rivers, P. D. Don't Color ME with ADD. 2006. (ENG.). 36p. per. 13.95 *(978-1-59800-580-6(4))* Outskirts Pr., Inc.

Rogers, Dianne. Mothering & Attention Deficit Disorder. 2008. 200p. pap. *(978-3-639-07761-2(X))* VDM Verlag Dr. Mueller e.K.

Root, Elizabeth E. Kids Caught in the Psychiatric Maelstrom: How Pathological Labels & Therapeutic Drugs Hurt Children & Families, 1 vol. 2009. 222p. 44.95 *(978-0-313-38122-5(4),* A2261C, Praeger Pubs.) Greenwood Publishing Group, Inc.

Rosemond, John & Ravenel, M.D., Bose. The Diseasing of America's Children: Exposing the ADHD Fiasco & Empowering Parents to Take Back Control, 0 vols. 2009. 272p. pap. 15.99 *(978-0-7852-9747-5(2))* Nelson, Thomas Inc.

Rothenberger, Aribert & Neumärker, Klaus-Jürgen. Wissenschaftsgeschichte der ADHS: Kramer-Pollnow im Spiegel der Zeit. 2006. (Illus.). VIII, 184p. 44.95 *(978-3-7985-1552-9(2),* 3798515522) Steinkopff, Dietrich DEU. Dist: Springer.

Ryan, Noreen & McDougall, Tim. Nursing Children & Young People. 2009. (Illus.). XVIII, 254p. pap. 51.95 *(978-0-415-45411-7(5));* 160.00 *(978-0-415-45410-0(7))* Routledge.

Rykoff, Allan. In My Brother's Footsteps... the Battle Back. 2009. 132p. pap. 13.45 *(978-1-4389-4301-5(6))* AuthorHouse.

Sandra Starr Ed.D. Calming the Chaos: A drug-free program to eliminate the symptoms of ADHD. 2009. 124p. pap. 13.95 *(978-1-4401-9106-0(9))* iUniverse, Inc.

Sarkis, Stephanie Moulton & Klein, Karl. Add & Your Money: A Guide to Personal Finance for Adults with Attention-Deficit Disorder. 2009. (ENG.). 176p. pap. 18.95 *(978-1-57224-707-9(X))* New Harbinger Pubns.

Schlander, Michael. Health Technology Assessments by the National Institute for Health & Clinical Excellence: A Qualitative Study. (Innovation & Valuation in Health Care Ser.). (Illus.). 2010. xxiv, 245p. pap. 79.95 *(978-1-4419-2459-9(0),* 1441924590) 2008. 245p. 79.95 *(978-0-387-71995-5(4))* Springer.

Schultz, Jerome J. Nowhere to Hide: Why Kids with ADHD & LD Hate School & What We Can Do about It. 2011. (ENG., Illus.). 336p. 24.95 *(978-0-470-90298-1(1),* Jossey-Bass) Wiley, John & Sons, Inc.

Schultz, Jerome J., et al. ADHD in Children. 2nd ed. 2010. (ENG.). 304p. pap., instr.'s gde. ed. 14.95 *(978-1-60550-678-4(8))* Adams Media Corp.

Seiden, Jerry & Halverstadt, Jonathan Scott. ADD, Christianity, & the Church: A Compassionate Healing Resource to Inform, Inspire, & Illuminate. 2008. 208p. pap. 12.95 *(978-1-929753-22-2(5))* Spirit of Hope Publishing.

Selikowitz, Mark. Adhd. 2nd ed. 2009. (Facts Ser.). (ENG., Illus.). 192p. (Orig.). 24.95 *(978-0-19-956503-0(1))* Oxford Univ. Pr., Inc.

Sheen, Brian. Educate, Don't Medicate- the Clear Minded Non-Medication Solution for Children with ADD/ADHD Symptoms. 2008. 216p. pap. 22.14 *(978-1-4357-0167-0(4))* Lulu Enterprises Inc.

—A Voice of Reason: Alternative Medicine for Healing ADD/ADHD Without Medication - Eleven Case Studies. 2007. per. 29.95 *(978-1-928787-20-4(7))* Quan Publishing.

Shriner, Marvin C., ed. Attention Deficit Hyperactivity Disorder. 2006. 190.00 *(978-1-60021-321-2(9))* Nova Science Pubs., Inc.

Silverman, Stephan M., et al. School Success for Kids with ADHD. 2009. (ENG.). 225p. pap. 16.95 *(978-1-59363-358-5(0))* Prufrock Pr.

Sinfield, Jacqueline. Untapped Brilliance: How to Reach Your Full Potential As an Adult with Attention Deficit Disorder. 2008. 133p. pap. 19.95 *(978-0-9798554-6-7(2))* Love Your Life.

Smart, Kimberly. A Christian Perspective on Attention Deficit Disorder. 2007. 61p. pap. 10.95 *(978-1-4303-2617-5(4))* Lulu Enterprises Inc.

Smith, Matthew. An Alternative History of Hyperactivity: Food Additives & the Feingold Diet. 2011. pap. *(978-0-8135-5017-6(3));* (ENG.). 256p. 49.95 *(978-0-8135-5016-9(5))* Rutgers Univ. Pr.

Spohrer, Kate E. & Spohrer. Teaching Assistant's Guide to ADHD. 2007. (Teaching Assistant's Ser.). (ENG., Illus.). 160p. 34.95 *(978-0-8264-8375-1(5))* Continuum International Publishing Group, Ltd. GBR. Dist: National Bk. Network.

Stahl, Stephen M. Attention-Deficit-Hyperactivity Disorder. 2009. (Stahl's Illustrated Ser.). (ENG., Illus.). 166p. pap. 39.99 *(978-0-521-13315-9(7))* Cambridge Univ. Pr.

Stanford, Clare & Tannock, Rosemary, eds. Behavioral Neurobiology of Attention Deficit Hyperactivity Disorder & Its Treatment. 2012. (Current Topics in Behavioral Neurosciences Ser.). (ENG., Illus.). xiv, 433p. 209.00 ***(978-3-642-24611-1(7),*** 3642246117) Springer.

Stauth, Cameron & Bock, Kenneth. Healing the New Childhood Epidemics: Autism, ADHD, Asthma, & Allergies: The Groundbreaking Program for the 4-A Disorders. 2008. (ENG., Illus.). 480p. pap. 16.00 *(978-0-345-49451-1(2),* Ballantine Bks.) Random House Publishing Group.

Steinberg, Mark. The Twenty Hour Solution to Add. Date not set. *(978-0-312-30480-5(3));* mass mkt. *(978-0-312-98495-3(2),* St. Martin's Paperbacks) St. Martin's Pr.

—The Twenty Hour Solution to ADD, ADHD. Date not set. pap. *(978-0-312-31631-0(3),* St. Martin's Paperbacks) St. Martin's Pr.

—The Twenty Hour Solutions to Add. Date not set. pap. *(978-0-312-30481-2(1),* St. Martin's Griffin) St. Martin's Pr.

Stiegler, Bernard. Taking Care of Youth & the Generations. 2010. (Meridian: Crossing Aesthetics Ser.). (ENG.). 264p. 75.00 *(978-0-8047-6272-4(4));* pap. 27.95 *(978-0-8047-6273-1(2))* Stanford Univ. Pr.

Swavely, Terri. Move, Move, Move: Alex's Story! 2009. 24p. pap. 14.95 *(978-1-4389-8070-6(1))* AuthorHouse.

Tamanini, Kara T. Understanding My Attention-Deficit/Hyperactivity Disorder. 2008. 28p. pap. 14.50 *(978-1-60693-170-7(9),* Eloquent Bks.) AEG Literary Publishing Services, Inc.

Target, Mary, et al, eds. Early Development & Its Disturbances: Clinical, Conceptual & Empirical Research on Adhd & Other Psychopathologies & Its Epistemological Reflections. 2010. (Developments in Psychoanalysis Ser.). (Illus.). 320p. pap. 49.95 *(978-1-85575-745-5(1))* Karnac Bks. GBR. Dist: Stylus Publishing, LLC.

Thomas, M. Russell. Turbo Charged Childhood. 2008. 216p. pap. 14.99 *(978-1-60647-380-1(8))* Xulon Pr., Inc.

Timimi, Sami & Leo, Jonathan, eds. Rethinking ADHD: From Brain to Culture. 2009. (ENG., Illus.). 234p. pap. 34.00 *(978-0-230-50712-8(3))* Palgrave Macmillan.

Timmerman, John. Real Solutions for Living with ADHD. 156p. pap. 9.99 *(978-0-8307-3485-6(6),* Regal Bks.) Gospel Light Pubns.

Train, Alan. Adhd: How to Deal with Very Difficult Children. 2nd ed. 2009. (Human Horizons Ser.). (ENG.). 224p. pap. 19.95 *(978-0-285-63835-8(1))* Souvenir Pr. Ltd. GBR. Dist: Independent Pubs. Group.

Travis, Ronald O. Hyperfocus. 2010. 236p. 26.00 *(978-1-4490-9523-9(2));* pap. 17.00 *(978-1-4490-9524-6(0))* AuthorHouse.

Tridas, Eric Q., ed. From ABC to ADHD: What Parents Should Know about Dyslexia & Attention Problems. 2007. per. 18.75 *(978-0-89214-065-7(8))* International Dyslexia Assn., The.

Tubbs, Janet. Creative Therapy for Children with Autism, Add, & Asperger's: Using Artistic Creativity to Reach, Teach, & Touch Our Children. 2008. (ENG.). 224p. pap. 18.95 *(978-0-7570-0300-4(1))* Square One Pubs.

Turecki, Stanley & Tonner, Leslie. El Nino Dificil de Criar.Tr. of Difficult Child. (SPA.). 14.00 *(978-958-04-4140-3(5))* Norma S.A. COL. Dist: Distribuidora Norma, Inc.

Vance, Alasdair, et al, eds. Cognitive Impairment in Children with ADHD. 2010. (Psychiatry - Theory, Applications & Treatments Ser.). pap. 43.00 *(978-1-61668-197-5(7))* Nova Science Pubs., Inc.

Walker, Ida. Recreational Ritalin: The Not-So-Smart Drug. 2012. ***(978-1-4222-2458-8(9)); (978-1-4222-2439-7(2))*** Mason Crest Pubs.

Weathers, Lawrence & Weathers, Mary. Adhd: Drug free & doin' Fine. 2008. (Illus.). 336p. per. 22.95 *(978-0-9659513-2-6(4))* Ponderosa Pr.

Weckerly, Ron. Poems, Pathways & Peace: A Baby Boomer's Journey with ADHD. 2010. 227p. pap. 13.95 *(978-1-59800-544-8(8))* Outskirts Pr., Inc.

Wells, Annie M. A Multi-Modal Approach to Address ADHD: A Non-Drug Emphasis. 2010. 56p. pap. 11.99 *(978-1-4490-6621-5(6))* AuthorHouse.

Weyandt, Lisa L. An ADHD Primer. 2nd rev. ed. 2006. (ENG., Illus.). 232p. 84.95 *(978-0-8058-4969-1(6));* per. 44.95 *(978-0-8058-4970-7(X))* Routledge.

Wheeler, Linda. The ADHD Toolkit. 2010. (Illus.). 160p. 71.00 *(978-1-84860-183-3(2),* B01833C); pap. 32.00 *(978-1-84860-184-0(0),* B01833P) SAGE Pubns., Ltd. GBR. Dist: SAGE Pubns., Inc.

Wiener, Craig. Attention Deficit Hyperactivity Disorder As a Learned Behavioral Pattern: A Less Medicinal More Self-Reliant/Collaborative Intervention. 2007. (ENG.). 300p. per. 47.50 *(978-0-7618-3809-8(0))* Univ. Pr. of America, Inc.

—Attention Deficit Hyperactivity Disorder as a Learned Behavioral Pattern: A Return to Psychology. 2007. (ENG.). 328p. pap. 49.50 *(978-0-7618-3701-5(9))* Univ. Pr. of America, Inc.

Winfrey, Aida McClellan. H. Y. P. E. Healing Young People Thru Empowerment. 2009. (ENG., Illus.). 200p. pap. 14.95 *(978-1-934155-20-2(9))* African American Images.

Wolraich, Mark L. & DuPaul, George J. ADHD Diagnosis & Management: A Practical Guide for the Clinic & the Classroom. 2010. (Illus.). 216p. pap. 34.95 *(978-1-59857-035-9(8))* Brookes, Paul H. Publishing Co.

Wynford, Dore. Dyslexia. 2012. (ENG.). 288p. pap. 14.95 ***(978-1-85782-688-3(4))*** Blake, John Publishing, Ltd. GBR. Dist: Independent Pubs. Group.

Young, Damon. Distraction: A Philosopher's Guide to Being Free. 2008. 184p pap. 19.00 *(978-0-522-85374-2(9))* Melbourne Univ. Publishing AUS. Dist: Independent Pubs. Group.

Young, Joel. ADHD Grown Up: A Guide to Adolescent & Adult ADHD. 2007. (ENG.). 344p. 25.95 *(978-0-393-70468-6(8),* 70468) Norton, W. W. & Co., Inc.

Young, Katharine Anne. Seeing without Seeing: The Dilemma of ADHD. 2010. 36p. 15.49 *(978-1-4490-6940-7(1))* AuthorHouse.

Zaretzky, Ken, et al. Jet Lag for Life. 2007. 19.95 net. *(978-0-9774566-1-1(7))* Very Good Coaching Bks.

Zeigler Dendy, Chris A. Teaching Teens with ADD, ADHD & Executive Function Deficits: A Quick Reference Guide for Teachers & Parents: 2nd Edition. 2nd ed. 2011. 375p. pap. *(978-1-60613-016-2(1))* Woodbine Hse.

Zuniga, Cecilia. Ad/Hd Generation: Holistic Ways to Support Children. 2010. 296p. pap. 22.50 *(978-1-4251-8114-7(7))* Trafford Publishing.

Zylowska, Lidia. The Mindfulness Prescription for Adult ADHD: An 8-Step Program for Strengthening Attention, Managing Emotions, & Achieving Your Goals. 2012. (ENG.). 224p. pap. 18.95 ***(978-1-59030-847-9(6),*** Trumpeter) Shambhala Pubns., Inc.

ATTENTION-DEFICIT HYPERACTIVITY DISORDER—PATIENTS

see Attention-Deficit-Disordered Children; Hyperactive Children

ATTENTION-DEFICIT HYPERACTIVITY DISORDER IN ADULTS

see Attention-Deficit Disorder in Adults

ATTENTION-SEEKING

Mellor, Nigel. Attention Seeking: A Complete Guide for Teachers. 2nd ed. 2008. (Lucky Duck Bks.). 168p. 62.95 *(978-1-4129-4872-2(X),* B28958C); pap 30.00 *(978-1-4129-2895-3(8),* B28958P) SAGE Pubns., Ltd. GBR. Dist: SAGE Pubns., Inc.

Styles, Elizabeth. The Psychology of Attention. 2nd rev. ed. 2006. (ENG., Illus.). 352p. (C). 110.00 *(978-1-84169-396-5(0),* RU3960X, Psychology Press) Taylor & Francis Group GBR. Dist: Taylor & Francis Group.

ATTICA

Robinson, David. New Greek Inscriptions from Attica, Achaia, Lydia. 2009. pap. 19.48 *(978-1-60724-647-3(3))* Gorgias Pr., LLC.

ATTICA CORRECTIONAL FACILITY

Wicker, Tom. A Time to Die: The Attica Prison Revolt. 2011. (ENG.). 356p. pap. 18.00 ***(978-1-60846-215-5(3))*** Haymarket Bks.

ATTICUS, TITUS POMPONIUS

Cicero, Marcus Tullius. Letters to Atticus. 2010. 214p. pap. *(978-1-152-99947-3(8))* Books LLC.

Nepos. Nepos: 3 Lives (Alcibiades, Dion, Atticus) Roebuck, R., ed. 2010. (LAT.). 152p. pap. 17.95 *(978-0-86292-284-9(4))* Bristol Classical Pr. GBR. Dist: International Publishers Marketing.

ATTILA, D. 453

Carolla, Pia, ed. Priscus Panita: Excerpta et Fragmenta. 2008. (Bibliotheca scriptorum Graecorum et Romanorum Teubneriana (BT) Ser.). XLVIII, 140p. (MUS & GEC.). 56.00 *(978-3-11-020138-3(0));* (GEC.). 90.00 ***(978-3-11-184550-0(8))*** De Gruyter, Walter Inc.

Jordanes. The Origin & Deeds of the Goths. 2008. 104p. pap. 18.75 *(978-1-4375-0974-8(6));* (ENG.). 118p. pap. 19.75 *(978-1-4375-0975-5(4))* BiblioBazaar.

Kelly, Christopher. The End of Empire: Attila the Hun & the Fall of Rome. (ENG.). 2010. 350p. pap. 16.95 *(978-0-393-33849-2(5),* 33849) 2009. (Illus.). 368p. 26.95 *(978-0-393-06196-3(5),* 6196) Norton, W. W. & Co., Inc.

Man, John. Attila: The Barbarian King Who Challenged Rome. 2nd ed. 2009. (ENG.). 336p. pap. 18.99 *(978-0-312-53939-9(8),* St. Martin's Griffin) St. Martin's Pr.

ATTIS

Alvar Ezquerra, J. Romanising Oriental Gods: Myth, Salvation & Ethics in the Cults of Cybele, Isis, & Mithras. Gordon, Richard, ed. 2008. (Illus.). 320p. *(978-90-04-13293-1(7))* BRILL.

Nikoloska, Aleksandra. Aspects of the Cult of Cybele & Attis on the Monuments from the Republic of Croatia. 2010. (Bar S Ser.). (ENG., Illus.). 106p. (C). pap. 72.50 *(978-1-4073-0562-2(X))* British Archaeological Reports Ltd. GBR. Dist: Brown, David Bk. Co., The.

ATTITUDE (PSYCHOLOGY)

see also Ageism; Attitude Change; Conformity; Empathy; Ethnic Attitudes; Frustration; Intention; NIMBY Syndrome; Prejudices; Rejection (Psychology); Sexism; Stereotype (Psychology)

Alizade, Alcira M. Psychoanalysis & Positivity. 2010. 176p. pap. 34.95 *(978-1-85575-659-5(5))* Karnac Bks. GBR. Dist: Stylus Publishing, LLC.

Ambrose, Don & Sternberg, Robert. How Dogmatic Beliefs Harm Creativity & Higher-level Thinking. 2011. (Educational Psychology Ser.). (ENG., Illus.). 238p. 125.00 *(978-0-415-89460-9(3))* Routledge.

Avdi, Avdija. Determinants of Public Attitudes Toward the Police: An Exploratory Study. 2011. 148p. pap. ***(978-3-639-33348-0(9))*** VDM Verlag Dr. Mueller e.K.

Bandler, Richard. Get the Life You Want: The Secrets to Quick & Lasting Life Change with Neuro-Linguistic Programming. 2008. (ENG.). 264p. 19.95 *(978-0-7573-0776-8(0))* Health Communications, Inc.

Beattie, Geoffrey. Why Aren't We Saving the Planet? A Psychologist's Perspective. 2010. (ENG., Illus.). 284p. 19.95 *(978-0-415-56197-6(3));* 59.95 *(978-0-415-56196-9(5))* Taylor & Francis Group GBR. (Routledge). Dist: Taylor & Francis Group.

Beattie, Melody. Make Miracles in Forty Days: Turning What You Have into What You Want. 2010. (ENG.). 192p. 23.00 *(978-1-4391-0215-2(5))* Simon & Schuster.

Bennett, Antionette. Introduction to Prayer: A Practical Guide to Bring Understanding. 2009. 92p. pap. 12.95 *(978-1-4327-2994-3(2))* Outskirts Pr., Inc.

Bernal Trujillo, Marta Ines & Gutierrez, Jaime Lopera. La Culpa Es de la Vaca: Anecdotas, Parabolas, Fabulas y Reflexiones Sobre el Liderazgo. 2008. (SPA.). 252p. pap. 12.95 *(978-958-8227-05-4(4))* Circulo de Lectores S.A. COL. Dist: Random Hse., Inc.

Bijou, Jude. Attitude Reconstruction: A Blueprint for Building a Better Life. 2011. 376p. 24.95 *(978-0-9843879-0-8(0))* Synergy Bks.

Blakeley, Karen. Leadership Blind Spots & What to Do about Them. 2007. (ENG., Illus.). 310p. 65.00 *(978-0-470-03193-3(X),* Jossey-Bass) Wiley, John & Sons, Inc.

Boas, Bernadette. Shedding the Corporate Bitch: Shifting Your Bitches to Riches in Life & Business. 2011. (ENG.). 250p. pap. 19.95 *(978-1-60037-940-6(0))* Morgan James Publishing.

Bohner, Gerd. Attitudes & Attitude Change. 2nd ed. 2008. 312p. 71.95 *(978-1-84169-673-7(0));* pap. 31.95 *(978-1-84169-674-4(9))* Taylor & Francis Group GBR. (Psychology Press). Dist: Taylor & Francis Group.

Bowles, Warren. Psychology & Emotion: Understanding How to Deal with Life. 2006. (ENG.). 172p. per. 24.95 *(978-1-4241-3470-0(6))* PublishAmerica, Inc.

Brown, David. Anatomy of Attitudes. 2007. 188p. per. 16.95 *(978-0-595-46109-7(3))* iUniverse, Inc.

Brunskill, Karen. Developing Consideration, Respect & Tolerance: Promoting Children's Resilience & Wellbeing. 2006. (Lucky Duck Bks.). (Illus.). 160p. pap. 36.00 *(978-1-4129-1963-0(0),* B19630P) SAGE Pubns., Ltd. GBR. Dist: SAGE Pubns., Inc.

—Enhancing Courage, Respect & Assertiveness: 9 to 12 Year Olds. 2006. (Lucky Duck Bks.). (Illus.). 200p. pap. 41.00 *(978-1-4129-1964-7(9),* B19649P) SAGE Pubns., Ltd. GBR. Dist: SAGE Pubns., Inc.

—Learning to Be Confident, Determined & Caring for 5 to 7 Year Olds. 2006. (Lucky Duck Bks.). (Illus.). 144p. pap. 34.00 *(978-1-4129-1961-6(4),* B19614P) SAGE Pubns., Ltd. GBR. Dist: SAGE Pubns., Inc.

—Learning to be Honest, Kind & Friendly for 5 to 7 Year Olds. 2006. (Lucky Duck Bks.). (Illus.). 144p. pap. 32.95 *(978-1-4129-1962-3(2),* B19622P) SAGE Pubns., Ltd. GBR. Dist: SAGE Pubns., Inc.

Bytheway, John. How to Be Totally Miserable: A Self-Hinder Book. 2007. (Illus.). 81p. per. 5.95 *(978-1-59038-743-6(0),* Shadow Mountain) Deseret Bk. Co.

Chambers, Wren Andres. The Minority Multimillionaire: Acquire Wealth Through a Positive Mental Attitude, 1 vol. 2010. 64p. pap. 19.95 *(978-1-4512-9268-8(6))* PublishAmerica, Inc.

Clery, Elizabeth, et al, eds. British Social Attitudes: The 26th Report. 2010. (British Social Attitudes Survey Ser.). (Illus.). 320p. (C). 98.00 *(978-1-84920-387-6(3),* B03876C) SAGE Pubns., Ltd. GBR. Dist: SAGE Pubns., Inc.

—British Social Attitudes: The 27th Report. 2010. (British Social Attitudes Survey Ser.). (Illus.). 280p. (C). 94.00 *(978-0-85702-572-2(4),* B25722C) SAGE Pubns., Ltd. GBR. Dist: SAGE Pubns., Inc.

Clery, Elizabeth, et al, eds. British Social Attitudes 28. 2012. (British Social Attitudes Survey Ser.). (Illus.). 232p. 150.00 ***(978-1-4462-5258-1(2),*** B52581C) SAGE Pubns., Ltd. GBR. Dist: SAGE Pubns., Inc.

Cohen, Alan. Enough Already: The Power of Radical Contentment. 2012. (ENG.). xiii, 239p. pap. 15.95 ***(978-1-4019-3520-7(6))*** Hay Hse., Inc.

Cram101 Textbook Reviews & Cram101 Textbook Reviews. Outlines & Highlights for Contemporary Perspectives on the Psychology of Attitudes by G Haddock. 2011. 110p. pap. 28.95 ***(978-1-61830-365-3(1))*** Cram101 Inc.

Cram101 Textbook Reviews Staff. Outlines & Highlights for Attitudes, Personality & Behaviour by Ajzen, Isbn. 2008. 64p. pap. 9.95 *(978-1-4288-5870-1(9))* Cram101 Inc.

Crano, William D. & Prislin, Radmila, eds. Attitudes & Attitude Change. 2008. (Frontiers of Social Psychology Ser.). (ENG., Illus.). 456p. 73.95 *(978-1-84169-481-8(9),* Psychology Press) Taylor & Francis Group GBR. Dist: Taylor & Francis Group.

Curtice, John, et al, eds. British Social Attitudes: The 23rd Report - Perspectives on a Changing Society. 2007. (British Social Attitudes Survey Ser.). (Illus.). 448p. (C). 97.00 *(978-1-4129-3432-9(X),* B3432XC) SAGE Pubns., Ltd. GBR. Dist: SAGE Pubns., Inc.

Damazio, Frank. The Attitude of Faith: Saying Yes to God's Power in Your Life. 2009. 224p. pap. 13.99 *(978-1-60374-114-9(3),* 771149) Whitaker Hse.

David Stegen. Sixty-Six Positive Ways of Being: A Lexicon for the Language of Your Soul. 2009. 112p. pap. 12.95 *(978-1-4401-4750-0(7))* iUniverse, Inc.

Dean, Amy E. Morning Light: A Book of Meditations to Begin Your Day. 2011. (ENG.). 400p. pap. 14.95 *(978-1-61649-108-6(6))* Hazelden Publishing & Educational Services.

Dhoquois, Regine & Zelensky-Tristan, Anne. Chroniques des Petits Abus de Pouvoir. 2010. (FRE.). 182p. *(978-2-296-12877-4(7))* Harmattan Pr.

Dufeal, Ronnie Jerome. It's Your Choice. 2011. 136p. pap. 23.50 ***(978-1-4567-9839-0(1))*** AuthorHouse.

Dyer, Wayne W. Being in Balance: 9 Principles for Creating Habits to Match Your Desires. 2006. xi, 220p. *(978-1-4019-1068-6(8),* 386) Hay Hse. UK, Ltd. GBR. Dist: Grantham Bk. Services.

Eduardos, Charles. Attitude of Gratitude Joy Journal. 2008. 137p. pap. 18.48 *(978-0-557-03494-9(9))* Lulu Enterprises Inc.

Elwins, Dannie. How to Boost Your Self Esteem & Become More Confident Every Time You Look in the Mirror. 2010. 40p. pap. 16.99 *(978-0-557-25883-3(9))* Lulu Enterprises Inc.

Erhman, M. K. Taking a Stand: Being a Leader & Helping Others. 2008. (Essential Health: Strong Beautiful Girls Ser.). 112p. (YA). (gr. 7-12). 34.22 *(978-1-60453-105-3(3))* ABDO Publishing Co.

Eyre, Linda & Eyre, Richard. The Entitlement Trap: How to Rescue Your Child with a New Family System of Choosing, Earning, & Ownership. 2011. (ENG.). 256p. (gr. 12). pap. 18.00 *(978-1-58333-415-7(7),* Avery) Penguin Group (USA) Inc.

Feldman, Richard & Warfield, Ted A. Disagreement. 2010. (ENG.). 256p. pap. 35.00 *(978-0-19-922608-5(3));* 99.00 *(978-0-19-922607-8(5))* Oxford Univ. Pr., Inc.

Fishbein, Martin & Ajzen, Icek. Predicting & Changing Behavior: The Reasoned Action Approach. 2009. (ENG., Illus.). 538p. 80.00 *(978-0-8058-5924-9(1),* Psychology Press) Taylor & Francis Group GBR. Dist: Taylor & Francis Group.

Fletcher, Kingsley. Who Says You Can't? If God Didn't Say It, It's Just an Opinion! 2009. (ENG.). 224p. pap. 14.99 *(978-1-59979-463-1(2),* Charisma Hse.) Charisma Media.

Flowers, Steve & Stahl, Bob. Living with Your Heart Wide Open: How Mindfulness & Compassion Can Free You from Unworthiness, Inadequacy, & Shame. 2011. (ENG.). 200p. pap. 16.95 *(978-1-57224-935-6(8))* New Harbinger Pubns.

Forgas, Joseph P., et al, eds. Psychology of Attitudes & Attitude Change. 2010. (Sydney Symposium in Social Psychology Ser.). (ENG., Illus.). 320p. 79.95 *(978-1-84872-908-7(1),* Psychology Press) Taylor & Francis Group GBR. Dist: Taylor & Francis Group.

Forrest, Jonathan & Hughes-Hallett, Andrew. Keep Calm & Carry on - A handbook to choose your emotions & change your Attitude. 2010. 80p. pap. 12.95 *(978-1-4461-9183-5(4))* Lulu Enterprises Inc.

Frankel, Lois P. Nice Girls Don't Get Rich: 75 Avoidable Mistakes Women Make with Money. 2008. (ENG., Illus.). 288p. pap. 13.99 *(978-0-446-69472-8(X),* Business Plus) Grand Central Publishing.

—Nice Girls Don't Get the Corner Office: 101 Unconscious Mistakes Women Make That Sabotage Their Careers. 2010. (ENG.). 288p. pap. 14.99 *(978-0-446-69331-8(6),* Business Plus) Grand Central Publishing.

Friedman, Jeffrey & Friedman, Shterna, eds. The Nature of Belief Systems. 2012. (ENG.). 416p. (C). 155.00 ***(978-0-415-69618-0(6))*** Routledge.

Gitomer, Jeffrey. Little Gold Book of YES! Attitude: How to Find, Build & Keep a YES! Attitude for a Lifetime of Success. 2006. (Gitomer Ser.). (ENG., Illus.). 208p. 19.99 *(978-0-13-198647-3(3))* FT Press.

Glenn, Sam. A Kick in the Attitude: An Energizing Approach to Recharge Your Team, Work, & Life. 2010. (ENG.). 210p. 21.95 *(978-0-470-52805-1(2),* Wiley) Wiley, John & Sons, Inc.

Grahn, Kimberly. Teachers Attitudes Toward Inclusion. 2008. 156p. pap. *(978-3-639-01719-9(6))* VDM Verlag Dr. Mueller e.K.

Grand, David & Goldberg, Alan. This Is Your Brain on Sports: Beating Blocks, Slumps & Performance Anxiety for Good! 2011. 228p. pap. 24.95 ***(978-1-60844-864-7(9))*** Dog Ear Publishing, LLC.

Graybeal, Bill. It's All in the Attitude: I Am I Can Therefore I Will. 2009. 160p. 25.49 *(978-1-4490-3610-2(4));* pap. 15.49 *(978-1-4490-3609-6(0))* AuthorHouse.

Gross, Mathew Barrett & Gilles, Mel. The Last Myth. 2012. (ENG.). 255p. pap. 18.00 ***(978-1-61614-573-6(0))*** Prometheus Bks., Pubs.

Hall, Lynn K. Counseling Military Families: What Mental Health Professionals Need to Know. 2008. (ENG.). 328p. 34.95 *(978-0-415-95688-8(9));* 95.95 *(978-0-415-95687-1(0))* Routledge.

Hamp, Bob. Think Differently, Live Differently Keys to A Life of Freedom. 2010. (Illus.). 252p. pap. *(978-1-4507-0920-0(6))* Independent Pub.

Harvey, Eric & Sedas, Michelle. The Power Of 10% How Small Changes Can Make A BIG Difference. 2008. (Illus.). 116p. pap. 12.95 *(978-1-885228-71-0(6))* WalkTheTalk.com.

Hayden, Joanna. Introduction to Health Behavior Theory. 2008. 148p. pap. 72.95 *(978-0-7637-4383-3(6))* Jones & Bartlett Learning, LLC.

Hays, Kate F. Performance Psychology in Action: A Casebook for Working with Athletes, Performing Artists, Business Leaders, & Professionals in High-Risk Occupations. 2009. 376p. 49.95 *(978-1-4338-0443-4(3))* American Psychological Assn.

Heath, Sharon. Art@tudes: Mastering the Art of Your Attitude. 24.95 *(978-0-9720678-0-5(9))* Artvations.

Hill, Napoleon. The Think & Grow Rich Workbook: The Practical Steps to Transforming Your Desires into Riches. Fotinos, Joel, ed. 2009. (ENG.). 144p. (gr. 12-18). spiral bd., wbk. ed. 18.95 *(978-1-58542-711-6(X),* Tarcher) Penguin Group (USA) Inc.

Hill, Napoleon, et al. The Secret to Getting Rich Triology: The Ultimate Law of Attraction Classics. 2008. (ENG.). 720p. pap. 14.95 *(978-1-56975-662-1(7))* Ulysses Pr.

Ho, Andrew. Charitable Giving: What Makes a Person Generous? 2011. 56p. pap. ***(978-3-8454-2300-5(5))*** Lambert Academic Publishing.

Holmes, Larry E. How Ordinary Russians Experience Their Lives & World: A Report of a Participant-Observer. 2008. (Illus.). 162p. 99.95 *(978-0-7734-5181-0(1))* Mellen, Edwin Pr., The.

Hunter, Celestine. Dramas of the End Time. 2010. 102p. pap. 15.99 *(978-1-4500-5319-8(X))* Xlibris Corp.

Hunter, Earle Leslie. A Sociological Analysis of Certain Types of Patriotism. 2011. 262p. 47.95 ***(978-1-258-01297-7(9))*** Literary Licensing, LLC.

Isbister, Colin James. All Things in Perspective: Book 2 of the Body of Christ Series A Biblical Perspective of Attitude & Behaviour in the Christian. 2009. pap. 14.99 *(978-1-60791-560-7(X))* Xulon Pr., Inc.

James, Ashia. How Can the Words & Absorbed Attitudes of Others Create Barriers? 2008. 96p. pap. *(978-3-639-05007-3(X))* VDM Verlag Dr. Mueller e.K.

Jenner, Paul. Be More Confident. 2nd ed. 2011. (Teach Yourself: Reference Ser.). (ENG.). 224p. pap. 15.00 *(978-0-07-175479-8(2),* 0071754792) McGraw-Hill Cos., The.

Johnson, Judy J. What's So Wrong with Being Absolutely Right? The Dangerous Nature of Dogmatic Belief. 2008. (ENG.). 430p. 21.98 *(978-1-59102-657-0(1))* Prometheus Bks., Pubs.

Johnson, Tim. Representing Attitudes As Intervals - a Reformulation of Coombs' Theory of Unidimensional Unfolding. 2007. 284p. per. *(978-3-8364-2704-3(4))* VDM Verlag Dr. Mueller e.K.

Jojo. Attitudes of the Heart. 2011. 144p. 29.99 ***(978-1-4628-5433-2(8));*** pap. 19.99 ***(978-1-4628-5432-5(X))*** Xlibris Corp.

Jones, Edwin. Attitude Continuum, 1 vol. 2009. 76p. pap. 16.95 *(978-1-60813-325-3(7))* PublishAmerica, Inc.

Jordan, Brent / Kenton. The Chivalry Code: Discussions on Becoming a Man in a Modern World. 2007. pap. 14.50 *(978-0-9703441-3-7(9))* Satsu Multimedia Pr.

Kakos, Spyridon. Harmonia Philosophica. 2010. 116p. pap. 18.95 *(978-1-4461-1872-6(X))* Lulu Enterprises Inc.

Kalwar, Santosh. Quote Me Everyday. 2010. 400p. pap. 26.50 *(978-1-4461-1863-4(0))* Lulu Enterprises Inc.

Kleinschmidt, Harald. Understanding the Middle Ages: The Transformation of Ideas & Attitudes in the Medieval World. 2008. (Illus.). 424p. pap. 29.95 *(978-0-85115-949-2(4),* Boydell Press) Boydell & Brewer, Ltd. GBR. Dist: Boydell & Brewer, Inc.

Krebs, Dagmar & Schmidt, Peter, eds. New Directions in Attitude Measurement. (ENG.). XIV, 378p. 210.00 ***(978-3-11-185485-4(X))*** De Gruyter, Walter Inc.

Lachs, Mark. Treat Me, Not My Age: A Doctor's Guide to Getting the Best Care As You or a Loved One Gets Older. 2010. (ENG.). 400p. (gr. 12). 27.95 *(978-0-670-02210-6(1),* Viking Adult) Penguin Group (USA) Inc.

Leavy, John Donald & Faucette, Joey. Work Positive in a Negative World: Redefine Your Reality & Achieve Your Business Dreams. 2011. (ENG.). 228p. pap. 19.95 *(978-1-59918-420-3(6),* 1599184206) Entrepreneur Pr. dba Entrepreneur Media, Inc.

Lemuel, Joe. Staying Positive. 2008. 88p. pap. 16.95 *(978-1-60610-575-7(2))* PublishAmerica, Inc.

Lindenfield, Gael. 101 Morale Boosters: Instant Comfort for Difficult Times. 2011. (ENG., Illus.). 288p. pap. 13.95 *(978-0-7499-4293-9(2))* Piatkus Bks. GBR. Dist: Independent Pubs. Group.

Lowe, Ryan C. Get off Your Attitude: Change Your Attitude. Change Your Life. 2011. (ENG.). 148p. pap. 14.99 *(978-0-7684-1302-1(8))* Destiny Image Pubs.

Maio, Gregory & Haddock, Geoff. The Psychology of Attitudes & Attitude Change. 2010. (SAGE Social Psychology Program Ser.). (Illus.). 288p. (C). 116.00 *(978-1-4129-2974-5(1),* B29741C); pap. 48.00 *(978-1-4129-2975-2(X),* B29741P) SAGE Pubns., Ltd. GBR. Dist: SAGE Pubns., Inc.

Maio, Gregory & Haddock, Geoff, eds. Psychology of Attitudes, 4 vols. 2012. (SAGE Library in Social Psychology Ser.). 1968p. 995.00 ***(978-1-4462-0207-4(0),*** B02074C) SAGE Pubns., Ltd. GBR. Dist: SAGE Pubns., Inc.

Matt, Michele. Attitude: The Choice Is Yours. 2nd rev. ed. 2007. 120p. per. 19.95 *(978-0-9790834-8-8(6),* BMS) Book Marketing Solutions, LLC.

Matthews, Robert J. The Measure of Mind: Propositional Attitudes & their Attribution. 2010. (ENG.). 288p. pap. 35.00 *(978-0-19-958553-3(9))* Oxford Univ. Pr., Inc.

—The Measure of Mind: Propositional Attitudes & Their Attribution. 2007. (ENG.). 288p. 75.00 *(978-0-19-921125-8(6))* Oxford Univ. Pr., Inc.

Maxwell, John C. The Difference Maker: Making Your Attitude Your Greatest Asset, 0 vols. 2006. (Illus.). 208p. 19.99 *(978-0-7852-6098-1(6))* Nelson, Thomas Inc.

McGrane, Joshua. Unfolding Ambivalence. 2010. 228p. pap. *(978-3-8383-4786-8(2))* Lambert Academic Publishing.

Meade, Robin. Morning Sunshine! How to Radiate Confidence & Feel It Too. (ENG., Illus.). 2011. 272p. pap. 14.99 *(978-1-59995-165-2(7))* 2009. 256p. 22.99 *(978-1-59995-164-5(9))* Center St.

Munroe, Megan. Bitch, Please: How Nice Girls Can Succeed in a Bitch's World. 2011. (ENG.). 236p. 24.95 *(978-1-59652-806-2(0))* Turner Publishing Co.

Murphy, Shane, ed. The Oxford Handbook of Sport & Performance Psychology. 2012. (Oxford Library of Psychology Ser.). (ENG.). 832p. 175.00 ***(978-0-19-973176-3(4))*** Oxford Univ. Pr., Inc.

Neprash, Jerry A. Brookhart Campaigns in Iowa, 1920-1926. (Columbia University, Studies in the Social Sciences: No. 366). reprint ed. 20.00 *(978-0-404-51366-5(2))* AMS Pr., Inc.

Nicholas, Andrew. Effortless Confidence. 2010. 184p. pap. 33.95 *(978-1-4457-4678-4(6))* Lulu Enterprises Inc.

Nicholas Imoru. How Did I Become Like This? 2010. 120p. pap. *(978-1-907011-06-1(4))* Esteemworld Pubns.

Odukoya, Bimbo. The Single Life. 2008. 192p. per. 13.99 *(978-1-60477-451-1(7))* Xulon Pr., Inc.

Osunsanmi, Lorna Clarke. Becoming Bold: Strategies to Break Out the Bold You! 2011. 176p. 24.23 ***(978-1-4269-4978-4(2));*** pap. 14.23 ***(978-1-4269-4977-7(4))*** Trafford Publishing.

Parkin, Margaret. Tales for Trainers: Using Stories & Metaphors to Facilitate Learning. rev. ed. 2010. (ENG.). 208p. pap. 34.95 *(978-0-7494-6006-8(7))* Kogan Page, Ltd. GBR. Dist: Ingram Pub. Services.

Paulson, Terry L. The Optimism Advantage: 50 Simple Truths to Transform Your Attitudes & Actions into Results. 2010. (ENG.). 224p. 24.95 *(978-0-470-55475-3(4),* Wiley) Wiley, John & Sons, Inc.

Pegues, Deborah Smith. 30 Days to a Great Attitude: Strategies for a Better Outlook on Life. 2009. 176p. pap. 5.99 *(978-0-7369-2641-6(0))* Harvest Hse. Pubs.

Petty, Richard E., et al, eds. Attitudes: Insights from the New Implicit Measures. 2008. (ENG.). 304p. 89.95 *(978-0-8058-5845-7(8),* Psychology Press) Taylor & Francis Group GBR. Dist: Taylor & Francis Group.

Pollick, Kathy L. From Rainshowers to Rainbows: An Inspirational Reminder That Life Is Really What You Make It, 1 vol. 2009. 124p. pap. 19.95 *(978-1-60813-693-3(0))* PublishAmerica, Inc.

Presner, Todd Samuel. Muscular Judaism: The Jewish Body & the Politics of Regeneration. 2007. (Routledge Jewish Studies Ser.). (Illus.). 279p. 160.00 *(978-0-415-77178-8(1))* Routledge.

Pristine, Nancy. The Victory Dance: Placing Yourself in the Winner's Circle in Sports & in Life. 2010. *(978-1-61242-000-4(1))* Arc Manor.

Ramesh, Gopalaswamy & Ramesh, Mahadevan. The ACE of Soft Skills: Attitude, Communication & Etiquette for Success. 2011. (ENG.). 472p. (C). pap. 56.67 *(978-81-317-3285-4(1))* Prentice Hall PTR.

Richo, David. Coming Home to Who You Are: Discovering Your Natural Capacity for Love, Integrity, & Compassion. 2011. (ENG.). 144p. pap. 12.95 *(978-1-59030-684-0(8))* Shambhala Pubns., Inc.

Ro, Pastor. Tenacity: You Are Bigger Than Where You Are. 2009. pap. *(978-1-61623-578-9(0))* Independent Pub.

Sandiford, K. Joy. Debunking Generational Curses. 2010. 88p. pap. 11.95 *(978-1-4327-5335-1(5))* Outskirts Pr., Inc.

Schlappi, Mike. Shot Happens: I got shot what's your Problem? 2009. pap. *(978-1-61584-247-6(0))* Independent Pub.

Schultz, Bob. Practical Happiness: A Young Man's Guide to a Contented Life. 2008. (Illus.). 223p. (YA). (gr. 7). pap. 10.99 *(978-1-883934-13-2(3))* Great Expectations Bk. Co.

Setty, Rajesh. Upbeat: Cultivating the Right Attitude to Thrive in Tough Times. 2009. (ENG.). 96p. pap. 13.95 *(978-1-935073-03-7(6))* Creative Management Partners, LLC.

Sheldon, Kennon M., et al, eds. Designing Positive Psychology: Taking Stock & Moving Forward, 1 vol. 2011. (Series in Positive Psychology Ser.). (ENG., Illus.). 400p. 49.95 *(978-0-19-537358-5(8))* Oxford Univ. Pr., Inc.

Simmons, Russell. Super Rich: A Guide to Having It All. 2011. (ENG.). 208p. (gr. 12). 15.00 *(978-1-59240-618-0(1),* Gotham) Penguin Group (USA) Inc.

Simmons, Russell & Morrow, Chris. Super Rich: A Guide to Having It All. 2011. (ENG.). 192p. (gr. 12). 22.50 *(978-1-59240-587-9(8),* Gotham) Penguin Group (USA) Inc.

Smith, Keith Cameron. The Top 10 Distinctions Between Entrepreneurs & Employees. 2012. (ENG.). 128p. 15.00 ***(978-0-345-53550-4(2),*** Ballantine Bks.) Random House Publishing Group.

Stratton, Kimberly B. Naming the Witch: Magic, Ideology, & Stereotype in the Ancient World. 2007. (Gender, Theory, & Religion Ser.). (ENG., Illus.). 312p. (gr. 17). 55.00 *(978-0-231-13836-9(9))* Columbia Univ. Pr.

Suedfeld, Peter, ed. Attitude Change: The Competing Views. 2007. (ENG.). 259p. (gr. 11). pap. 24.95 *(978-0-202-36172-7(1))* Aldine Transaction.

Szasz, Thomas Stephen. Psychiatry: The Science of Lies. 2009. 176p. 19.95 *(978-0-8156-0910-0(8))* Syracuse Univ. Pr.

Sze, Susan & Cowden, Peter. What about my Child? 2009. 152p. pap. 47.95 *(978-1-4269-0594-0(7))* Trafford Publishing.

Thomson, Katarina, et al, eds. British Social Attitudes: The 24th Report. 2008. (British Social Attitudes Survey Ser.). (Illus.). 408p. (C). 116.00 *(978-1-4129-4774-9(X),* B47749C) SAGE Pubns., Ltd. GBR. Dist: SAGE Pubns., Inc.

—British Social Attitudes: The 25th Report. 2009. (British Social Attitudes Survey Ser.). (Illus.). 280p. (C). 121.00 *(978-1-84860-639-5(7),* B06395C) SAGE Pubns., Ltd. GBR. Dist: SAGE Pubns., Inc.

Tischmann, Peter W. The Challenges of Change. 2007. 260p. (ENG.). 31.99 *(978-1-4257-5920-9(3));* per. 21.99 *(978-1-4257-5912-4(2))* Xlibris Corp.

Tracy, Brian & Stein, Christina Tracy. Kiss That Frog! 12 Great Ways to Turn Negatives into Positives in Your Life & Work. 2012. (ENG.). 192p. 22.95 ***(978-1-60994-280-9(9))*** Berrett-Koehler Pubs., Inc.

Trufant Harvey, Jane. Thank Him: Living Life with an Attitude of Gratitude. 2008. (Illus.). spiral bd. 9.99 *(978-1-58169-279-2(X),* Evergreen Pr.) Genesis Communications, Inc.

VIERO, Alessandra. The happy mussels Method. 2009. 112p. pap. 15.66 *(978-1-4092-7196-3(X))* Lulu Enterprises Inc.

Webb, Catherine M. The Little Book of Perfect Sense. 2010. (Illus.). 48p. pap. *(978-1-84748-740-7(8))* Athena Pr.

When it's you against Them: Keeping A Positive Attitude Despite It All. 2006. 12.95 *(978-0-9785900-1-7(5))* VG Publishing.

White, Benjamin. How You Tell You to Live Life with Words & Attitude. 2011. 104p. 24.99 ***(978-1-4535-9886-3(3));*** pap. 15.99 ***(978-1-4535-9885-6(5))*** Xlibris Corp.

White, Dana. Nail Your Attitude & Win! 2008. 11.97 *(978-0-615-20250-1(0))* White, Dana International.

Wicker, Don. Attitude Is #1: An Interactive Guide to Determine the Correct Attitude in Real-Life Situations. 2010. 108p. 21.99 *(978-1-4520-7112-1(8));* pap. 12.99 *(978-1-4520-7113-8(6))* AuthorHouse.

Williams, Nicole. Girl on Top: Your Guide to Turning Dating Rules into Career Success. 2012. (ENG.). 208p. pap. 15.99 *(978-1-4555-0716-0(4))* Center St.

Wittenbrink, Bernd & Schwarz, Norbert, eds. Implicit Measures of Attitudes. 2007. (ENG., Illus.). 294p. 45.00 *(978-1-59385-402-7(1))* Guilford Pubns., Inc.

Wright, D. Bernard. Squashing Grasshoppers. 2006. (ENG.). 21.99 *(978-1-60034-320-9(1))*; pap. 13.99 *(978-1-60034-315-3(8))* Xulon Pr., Inc.

Yogananda, Paramhansa. How to Have Courage, Calmness, & Confidence. 2010. (ENG.). 158p. pap. 11.95 *(978-1-56589-249-1(6))* Crystal Clarity Pubs.

Young, Stephen. Micromessaging: Why Great Leadership is Beyond Words. 2006. (ENG.). 224p. 24.95 *(978-0-07-146757-5(2), 0071467572)* McGraw-Hill Cos., The.

ATTITUDE (PSYCHOLOGY)—TESTING

Jowell, Roger & Roberts, Caroline, eds. Attitude Measurement, 4 vols. 2008. (SAGE Benchmarks in Social Research Methods Ser.). (Illus.). 1632p. 995.00 *(978-1-4129-2840-3(0)*, B28400C) SAGE Pubns., Ltd. GBR. Dist: SAGE Pubns., Inc.

Khine, Myint Swe. Attitude Research in Science Education Classic & Contemporary Measurements. 2011. *(978-1-61735-325-3(6))*; pap. *(978-1-61735-324-6(8))*; E-Book *(978-1-61735-326-0(4))* Information Age Publishing, Inc.

Steffens, Melanie C. & Jonas, Kai J., eds. Implicit Attitude Measures. 2010. (Illus.). 84p. pap. 89.00 *(978-0-88937-386-0(8))* Hogrefe Publishing.

ATTITUDE AND MOVEMENT OF HUMAN BEINGS

see Human Beings—Attitude and Movement

ATTITUDE CHANGE

Brown, Dennis. Change Your Attitude... Change Your Life. 84p. pap. 15.95 *(978-1-885640-89-5(7))* Insight Publishing.

Brunskill, Karen. Developing Consideration, Respect & Tolerance: Promoting Children's Resilience & Wellbeing. 2006. (Lucky Duck Bks.). (Illus.). 160p. pap. 36.00 *(978-1-4129-1963-0(0)*, B19630P) SAGE Pubns., Ltd. GBR. Dist: SAGE Pubns., Inc.

—Enhancing Courage, Respect & Assertiveness: 9 to 12 Year Olds. 2006. (Lucky Duck Bks.). (Illus.). 200p. pap. 41.00 *(978-1-4129-1964-7(9)*, B19649P) SAGE Pubns., Ltd. GBR. Dist: SAGE Pubns., Inc.

—Learning to Be Confident, Determined & Caring for 5 to 7 Year Olds. 2006. (Lucky Duck Bks.). (Illus.). 144p. pap. 34.00 *(978-1-4129-1961-6(4)*, B19614P) SAGE Pubns., Ltd. GBR. Dist: SAGE Pubns., Inc.

—Learning to be Honest, Kind & Friendly for 5 to 7 Year Olds. 2006. (Lucky Duck Bks.). (Illus.). 144p. pap. 32.95 *(978-1-4129-1962-3(2)*, B19622P) SAGE Pubns., Ltd. GBR. Dist: SAGE Pubns., Inc.

Burke, Barbara A. The Napkin the Melon & the Monkey: How to Be Happy & Successful at Work & in Life by Simply Changing Your Mind. 2010. (ENG.). 144p. 19.95 *(978-1-4019-2573-4(1))* Hay Hse., Inc.

Burke, Barbara A. The Napkin, the Melon & the Monkey: How to Be Happy & Successful by Simply Changing Your Mind. 2012. (ENG.). 144p. pap. 13.95 ***(978-1-4019-2574-1(X))*** Hay Hse., Inc.

Castro-Convers. Contact Experiences Influencing Positive Attitudes Toward Gay Men. 2009. 134p. pap. *(978-3-639-17909-5(9))* VDM Verlag Dr. Mueller e.K.

Clark, Randall. Law Most Beautiful & Best: Medical Argument & Magical Rhetoric in Plato's Laws. 2009. (ENG.). 192p. pap. 28.50 *(978-0-7391-4147-2(3))* Lexington Bks.

Clements, Phil & Clements, Phillip Edward. The Diversity Training Handbook: A Practical Guide to Understanding & Changing Attitudes. 3rd ed. 2008. (ENG., Illus.). 224p. pap., instr.'s hndbk. ed. 44.95 *(978-0-7494-5068-7(1))* Kogan Page, Ltd. GBR. Dist: Ingram Pub. Services.

Cram101 Textbook Reviews. Outlines & Highlights for Persuasive Messages by William Benoit. 2011. 68p. pap. 27.95 ***(978-1-61905-768-5(9))*** Cram101 Inc.

Cram101 Textbook Reviews & Cram101 Textbook Reviews. Outlines & Highlights for the Dynamics of Persuasion: Communication & Attitudes in the 21st Century by Richard Perloff, ISBN. 2011. 220p. pap. 30.95 ***(978-1-61461-849-2(6))*** Cram101 Inc.

Crano, William D. & Prislin, Radmila, eds. Attitudes & Attitude Change. 2008. (Frontiers of Social Psychology Ser.). (ENG., Illus.). 456p. 73.95 *(978-1-84169-481-8(9)*, Psychology Press) Taylor & Francis Group GBR. Dist: Taylor & Francis Group.

Forgas, Joseph P., et al, eds. Psychology of Attitudes & Attitude Change. 2010. (Sydney Symposium in Social Psychology Ser.). (ENG., Illus.). 320p. 79.95 *(978-1-84872-908-7(1)*, Psychology Press) Taylor & Francis Group GBR. Dist: Taylor & Francis Group.

Gibson, Andrew D. Got an Angry Kid? Parenting Spike, a Seriously Difficult Child. 2009. 168p. pap. *(978-1-932690-89-7(1))* Loving Healing Pr., Inc.

Gilligan, Steven, et al. The Hero's Journey: A Voyage of Self Discovery. 2009. (Illus.). 288p. *(978-1-84590-286-5(6))* Crown Hse. Publishing.

Heath, Chip. Switch: How to Change Things When Change Is Hard. l.t. ed. 2011. (ENG.). 486p. 32.99 *(978-1-4104-3313-8(7))* Thorndike Pr.

Heath, Chip & Heath, Dan. Switch: How to Change Things When Change Is Hard. 2010. (ENG.). 320p. 26.00 *(978-0-385-52875-7(2)*, Broadway Business) Knopf Doubleday Publishing Group.

—Switch: How to Change Things When Change Is Hard. 2010. (CHI.). 327p. pap. ***(978-986-213-199-2(3))*** Locus Publishing Co.

Jacobelli, Frank & Watson, Lynn Ann. SmartHelp for Good 'n' Angry Kids: Teaching Children to Manage Anger. 2009. (ENG., Illus.). 222p. pap. 33.95 *(978-0-470-75802-1(3)*, Wiley) Wiley, John & Sons, Inc.

Lamb, Deacon Dick. Heal Your Thought Life: A Re-Minder. 2008. 149p. pap. 24.95 *(978-1-60563-127-1(2))* PublishAmerica, Inc.

MacDonald, James. Lord, Change My Attitude: Before Its Too Late. 2008. (ENG.). 312p. per. 14.99 *(978-0-8024-3439-5(8))* Moody Pubs.

Maio, Gregory & Haddock, Geoff. The Psychology of Attitudes & Attitude Change. 2010. (SAGE Social Psychology Program Ser.). (Illus.). 288p. (C). 116.00 *(978-1-4129-2974-5(1)*, B29741C); pap. 48.00 *(978-1-4129-2975-2(X)*, B29741P) SAGE Pubns., Ltd. GBR. Dist: SAGE Pubns., Inc.

Michaels, Cliff. The 4 Essentials of Entrepreneurial Thinking: What Successful People Didn't Learn in School. 2012. (ENG.). 288p. pap. 19.95 *(978-0-615-45055-1(5))* Michaels, Cliff.

Miller, Matt. The Tyranny of Dead Ideas: Revolutionary Thinking for a New Age of Prosperity. 2010. (ENG.). 288p. pap. 15.00 *(978-0-8050-9150-2(5)*, Holt Paperback) St. Martin's Pr.

Perloff, Richard M. The Dynamics of Persuasion: Communication & Attitudes in the 21st Century. 4th rev. ed. 2010. (Routledge Communication Ser.). (ENG., Illus.). 448p. (C). 150.00 *(978-0-415-80567-4(8))*; pap. 69.95 *(978-0-415-80568-1(6))* Routledge.

Reall, Scott. Your Journey to Freedom, 0 vols. 2008. 256p. pap. 14.99 *(978-1-4185-3571-1(0))* Nelson, Thomas Inc.

Shengold, Leonard. Haunted by Parents. 2007. (ENG., Illus.). 272p. 38.00 *(978-0-300-11610-6(1))* Yale Univ. Pr.

Ursiny, Tim, et al. The Top Performer's Guide to Attitude. 2008. (ENG., Illus.). 128p. 9.95 *(978-1-4022-1036-5(1))* Sourcebooks, Inc.

Willis, Dan. Freedom to Forget: Releasing the Pain from the Past, Embracing Hope for the Future. 2007. 204p. per. 12.99 *(978-0-83368-222-7(2)*, 772227) Whitaker Hse.

ATTITUDE CONTROL SYSTEMS (ASTRONAUTICS)

see Artificial Satellites—Attitude Control Systems

ATTLEE, C. R. (CLEMENT RICHARD), 1883-1967

Attlee, Clement. Twilight of Empire: Memoirs of Clement Attlee. Williams, Francis, ed. 2011. 274p. 47.95 ***(978-1-258-05975-0(4))*** Literary Licensing, LLC.

Crowcroft, Robert. Attlee's War: World War II & the Making of a Labour Leader. 2011. (International Library of Twentieth Centruy History Ser.). (ENG.). 320p. 95.00 *(978-1-84885-286-0(X)*, Tauris Academic Studies) I. B. Tauris & Co., Ltd. GBR. Dist: Macmillan.

Howell, David. Attlee. 2006. (British Prime Ministers of the 20th Century Ser.). (ENG., Illus.). 166p. pap. 16.95 *(978-1-904950-64-6(7))* Haus Publishing GBR. Dist: Consortium Bk. Sales & Distribution.

Thomas-Symonds, Nicklaus. Attlee: A Life in Politics. (ENG., Illus.). 2012. 352p. pap. 24.50 ***(978-1-78076-215-9(1))*** 2010. 344p. 80.00 *(978-1-84511-779-5(4))* I. B. Tauris & Co., Ltd. GBR. Dist: Macmillan.

ATTORNEY AND CLIENT

Aaron, Marjorie Corman. Client Science: Advice for Lawyers on Counseling Clients through Bad News & Other Legal Realities. 2012. (ENG.). 242p. pap. 39.95 ***(978-0-19-989190-0(7))*** Oxford Univ. Pr., Inc.

American Bar Association, Commission on Domestic Violence Staff, contrib. by. Standards of Practice for Lawyers Representing Victims of Domestic Violence, Sexual Assault & Stalking in Civil Protection Order Cases. 2007. x, 59p. *(978-1-59031-946-8(X))* American Bar Assn.

American Immigration Lawyers Association Staff, contrib. by. More Lore Than Law: Advising Clients, Managing Risks, & Practicing Law Without Clear Guidelines: 2007 AILA Midyear Conference Handbook: Advanced Business Immigration Practice. 2007. xiii, 96p. pap. *(978-1-57370-210-2(2))* American Immigration Lawyers Assn.

Anders, Kelly Lynn. Advocacy to Zealousness: Learning Lawyering Skills from Classic Films. 2012. 236p. pap. 28.00 ***(978-1-59460-798-1(2))*** Carolina Academic Pr.

Aspatore Books Staff, compiled by. Addressing a Client's Litigation Issues: Leading Lawyers on Educating Clients, Managing Expectations & Developing a Case Strategy. 2008. (Inside the Minds Ser.). 184p. pap. 110.00 *(978-0-314-98986-4(2))* Aspatore Bks.

—Attracting & Retaining Clients: Leading Lawyers on Marketing a Niche Practice Area, Competing with Larger Firms, & Building a Good Reputation. 2008. 100p. pap. 75.00 *(978-0-314-19473-2(8))* Aspatore Bks.

—Building & Maintaining Client Relationships: Leading Lawyers on Attracting New Clients, Developing Effective Marketing Techniques, & Establishing a Strong Reputation (Inside the Minds) 2010. 100p. pap. 85.00 *(978-0-314-27120-4(1))* Aspatore Bks.

—Client Strategies for Working with Construction Firms: Leading Lawyers on Structuring Agreements, Minimizing Contract Risks, & Understanding the Needs of Clients. 2008. (Inside the Minds Ser.). 428p. pap. 110.00 *(978-0-314-98979-6(X))* Aspatore Bks.

—Elder Law Health Care Strategies: Best Practices from Leading Lawyers Representing Elderly Clients & Long-Term Care Providers (Inside the Minds) 2008. 104p. pap. 75.00 *(978-0-314-19915-7(2))* Aspatore Bks.

—Food, Beverage, & Drug Law Client Strategies: Leading Lawyers on Marketplace Considerations, Regulatory Compliance, & Dispute Resolution (Inside the Minds) 2008. 252p. pap. 135.00 *(978-0-314-99021-1(6))* Aspatore Bks.

—Founding a Law Firm: Leading Lawyers on Establishing Key Client Relationships, Developing a Strategic Plan, & Assessing Growth Opportunities (Inside the Minds) 2008. (Inside the Minds Ser.). 164p. pap. 75.00 *(978-0-314-98671-9(5))* Aspatore Bks.

—Government Contracts Law Client Strategies: Leading Lawyers on Counseling Clients During the Bidding Process, Negotiating Contracts, & Minimizing Litigation Liability. 2008. 344p. pap. 110.00 *(978-0-314-98987-1(0))* Aspatore Bks.

—Government Contracts Settlements & Negotiations: Leading Lawyers on Analyzing & Discussing Contracts, Resolving Disputes, & Addressing the Unique Challenges of Negotiations with the Government. 2008. 312p. pap. 110.00 *(978-0-314-19472-5(X))* Aspatore Bks.

—Immigration Law Client Strategies: Leading Lawyers on Working with Clients to Overcome Challenges in a Rapidly-Changing Field (Inside the Minds) 2008. (Inside the Minds Ser.). 224p. pap. 75.00 *(978-0-314-19558-6(0))* Aspatore Bks.

—Managing Technology Legal Issues: Leading Lawyers on Transactions, Agreements, & Intellectual Property Management. 2008. 344p. pap. 100.00 *(978-0-314-19920-1(9))* Aspatore Bks.

—Strategies for Family Law in Texas: Leading Lawyers on Analyzing Recent Legal Trends, Implementing Creative Strategies, & Overcoming Common Challenges (Inside the Minds) 2010. (Illus.). 308p. pap. 80.00 *(978-0-314-27091-7(4))* Aspatore Bks.

—Strategies for Successful Arbitration: Leading Lawyers on Preparing Your Client, Evaluating Potential Witnesses, & Achieving Success in Dispute Resolution. 2008. 172p. pap. 100.00 *(978-0-314-19509-8(2))* Aspatore Bks.

—Understanding Your Client's IP Needs: Leading Lawyers on Mitigating Financial Risks, Defining IP Standards, & Avoiding Common Mistakes. 2008. 320p. pap. 125.00 *(978-0-314-19506-7(8))* Aspatore Bks.

Binder, et al. Lawyers as Counselors, A Client-Centered Approach. 3rd rev. ed. 2011. (American Casebook Ser.). 592p. pap. 74.00 ***(978-0-314-19491-6(6))*** West Publishing Co., College & Schl. Div.

Blake, Susan. A Practical Approach to Effective Litigation. 7th ed. 2009. (ENG.). 650p. pap. 120.00 *(978-0-19-955030-2(1))* Oxford Univ. Pr., Inc.

Center for Professional Responsibility (American Bar Association) Staff, contrib. by. Compendium of Client Protection Rules. 2007. iii, 108p. pap. *(978-1-59031-874-4(9))* American Bar Assn.

Chinn, Mark A. A Guidebook for Family Lawyers Handling Divorce in a Constructive Manner. 2006. *(978-1-59031-727-3(0))* American Bar Assn.

Colombo, Rose. Fight Back Legal Abuse: How to Protect Yourself from Your Own Attorney. 2010. (ENG.). 296p. pap. 19.95 *(978-1-60037-709-9(2))* Morgan James Publishing.

Cram101 Textbook Reviews. Outlines & Highlights for Interviewing & Investigating: Essential Skills for the Paralegal by Parsons, Stephen P., ISBN. 2011. 138p. pap. 28.95 ***(978-1-4288-5433-8(9))*** Cram101 Inc.

Craver, Charles B. Skills & Values. 2008. xiii, 275p. *(978-1-4224-2197-0(X))* LexisNexis Matthew Bender.

Derrick, John. Boo to Billable Hours: A lawyer's guide to better Billing. 2007. pap. 16.00 *(978-0-9797778-0-6(1))* Podia Pr.

Epstein, Edna Selan. The Attorney-Client Privilege & the Work-Product Doctrine. 5th ed. 2007. (ENG.). 1300p. pap. 195.00 *(978-1-59031-804-1(8))* American Bar Assn.

Ewalt, Henry W. Through the Client's Eyes, Third Edition: New Approaches to Get Clients to Hire You Again & Again. 3rd ed. 2008. (ENG.). 376p. pap. 89.95 *(978-1-60442-027-2(8))* American Bar Assn.

Flannery, William J. & Flannery, William J., Jr. The Lawyer's Field Guide to Effective Business Development. 2007. (ENG., Illus.). 160p. per. 59.95 *(978-1-59031-736-5(X))* American Bar Assn.

Foonberg, Jay. How to Get & Keep Good Clients. 3rd rev. ed. 2007. (ENG., Illus.). 618p. pap. 179.95 *(978-0-9795671-0-0(6))* National Academy of Law Ethics & Management, Inc.

—Lawyer Trust Accounts: Audio CD & CD-ROM with Forms. 2007. cd-rom, audio compact disk 79.95 *(978-0-9795671-4-8(9))* National Academy of Law Ethics & Management, Inc.

Fox, Lawrence J. & Martyn, Susan R. How to Deal with Your Lawyer: Answers to Commonly Asked Questions. 2008. (Legal Almanac Ser.). (ENG., Illus.). 109p. 47.00 *(978-0-19-537077-5(5))* Oxford Univ. Pr., Inc.

Frascogna, Xavier M. & Hetherington, H. Lee. The Lawyer's Guide to Negotiation. 2nd ed. 2011. (ENG.). 239p. pap. 89.95 *(978-1-60442-578-9(4))* American Bar Assn.

Freedman, et al. Understanding Lawyers' Ethics. 4th rev. ed. 2010. (C). pap. 41.00 *(978-1-4224-7022-0(9))* LexisNexis.

Garwin, Arthur. Compendium of Client Protection Rules. 2011. ***(978-1-61632-936-5(X))*** American Bar Assn.

Giesel, Grace M. Mastering Professional Responsibility. 2009. 454p. pap. 34.00 *(978-1-59460-390-7(1))* Carolina Academic Pr.

Gifford, Donald G. Legal Negotiation: Theory & Practice. 2nd ed. 2007. xv, 242p. pap. *(978-0-314-15913-7(4))* West Publishing Co., College & Schl. Div.

Gillers. Regulation Lawyers 8e & Regulation Legal Profession Bundle. 2009. 164.00 *(978-0-7355-9569-9(0)*, Aspen Pubs.) Wolters Kluwer Law & Business.

Glesner Fines, Barbara. Ethical Issues in Family Representation. 2010. 356p. pap. 38.00 *(978-1-59460-517-8(3))* Carolina Academic Pr.

Goodall, Patrick, et al. The Law of Privilege. Thanki QC, Bankim, ed. 2nd ed. 2011. (ENG.). 456p. 350.00 *(978-0-19-959543-3(7))* Oxford Univ. Pr., Inc.

Gordon, Elizabeth Ellen. The Role of Attorneys in Court Ordered Mediations in North Carolina: The Pilot Phase. 2009. 160p. 99.95 *(978-0-7734-4809-4(6))* Mellen, Edwin Pr., The.

Harmon, A. G. The Complete Advocate: A Practice File for Representing Clients from Beginning to End. 2010. *(978-1-4224-2992-1(X))* LexisNexis Matthew Bender.

Haydock, Roger S. & Knapp, Peter B. Lawyering: Practice & Planning. 3rd rev. ed. 2011. (American Casebook Ser.). 449p. 109.00 *(978-0-314-26603-3(8))*, West Legalworks) West.

Herman, G. Nicholas & Cary, Jean M. Legal Counseling, Negotiating, & Mediating: A Practical Approach. 2009. *(978-1-4224-2262-5(3))* LexisNexis Matthew Bender.

—A Practical Approach to Client Interviewing, Counseling, & Decision-Making. 2009. *(978-1-4224-2293-9(3))* LexisNexis Matthew Bender.

Herman, Gregg. 101+ Practical Solutions for the Family Lawyer: Sensible Answers to Common Problems. 3rd ed. 2011. (ENG., Illus.). xvi, 695p. pap. 139.95 incl. cd-rom *(978-1-60442-507-9(5))* American Bar Assn.

Kiser, Randall. Beyond Right & Wrong: The Power of Effective Decision Making for Attorneys & Clients. 2010. (ENG., Illus.). xiii, 444p. 129.00 *(978-3-642-03813-6(1)*, 3642038131) Springer.

Krauss, Geri S. Partner Departures & Lateral Moves: A Legal & Ethical Guide. 2009. (ENG.). 110p. pap. 69.95 *(978-1-60442-523-9(7))* American Bar Assn.

Lande, John. Lawyering with Planned Early Negotiation: How You Can Get Good Results for Clients & Make Money. 2012. (ENG., Illus.). 200p. pap. 74.95 incl. cd-rom *(978-1-61632-101-7(6))* American Bar Assn.

Lyrio, Alexander. IP Client Strategies in Central & South America: Leading Lawyers on Building Client Relationships, Understanding the Impact of Recent Cases & Developments, & Recognizing Regional Influences on Intellectual Property Law. 2009. (Inside the Minds Ser.). (Illus.). 435p. pap. 125.00 *(978-0-314-90777-6(7))* Aspatore Bks.

Macfarlane, Julie. The New Lawyer: How Settlement Is Transforming the Practice of Law. 2008. (ENG.). 304p. pap. 36.95 *(978-0-7748-1436-2(5))* Univ. of British Columbia Pr. CAN. Dist: Univ. of Toronto Pr.

Markovits, D. Modern Legal Ethics: Adversary Advocacy in a Democratic Age. 2010. (ENG.). 376p. (C). pap. 22.95 *(978-0-691-14813-7(9))* Princeton Univ. Pr.

Markovits, Daniel. A Modern Legal Ethics: Adversary Advocacy in a Democratic Age. 2008. (ENG.). 376p. (C). 52.50 *(978-0-691-12162-8(1))* Princeton Univ. Pr.

Martyn. Traversing Ethical Minefield 2e & Regulation Legal Prof Bundle. 2009. 160.00 *(978-0-7355-9571-2(2)*, Aspen Pubs.) Wolters Kluwer Law & Business.

Martyn, Susan R. & Fox, Lawrence J. Traversing the Ethical Minefield: Problems, Law, & Professional Responsibility. 2nd ed. 2008. xxiv, 627p. *(978-0-7355-6963-8(0)*, Aspen Pubs.) Wolters Kluwer Law & Business.

Moliterno, James E. Cases & Materials on the Law Governing Lawyers. 4th ed. 2012. ***(978-1-4224-9866-8(2))*** LexisNexis Matthew Bender.

Müller, Ingo Robert. Spanisches Anwaltshaftungsrecht. 2010. (Schriften der Deutsch-Spanischen Juristenvereinigung Ser.). (GER.). 438p. 108.95 *(978-3-631-60965-1(5))* Lang, Peter GmbH, Europaischer Verlag der Wissenschaften DEU. Dist: Lang, Peter.

Munneke, Gary A. & Davis, Anthony E. Financial Statements & Trust Accounts: Essential Forms for Law Firms. 2011. ***(978-1-61632-959-4(9))*** American Bar Assn.

Nelken, Melissa L. Negotiation: Theory & Practice. 2nd ed. 2007. 516p. pap. 53.00 *(978-1-4224-1162-9(1))* LexisNexis Matthew Bender.

Parry, John. Civil Disability Discrimination Law, Evidence & Testimony. 2010. *(978-1-60442-799-8(X))* American Bar Assn.

—Discrimination Disability Law, Evidence, Testimony. 2009. (ENG.). 684p. pap. 105.00 *(978-1-60442-012-8(X))* American Bar Assn.

Parsons. Interviewing & Investigating: Essential Skills for Paralegal. 4th ed. 2010. pap. 90.95 *(978-0-7355-8735-9(3))* Wolters Kluwer Law & Business.

Parsons, Stephen P. Interviewing & Investigating: Essential Skills for the Legal Professional. 4th ed. 2010. (Illus.). xiii, 575p. *(978-0-7355-8736-6(1)*, Aspen Pubs.) Wolters Kluwer Law & Business.

Pierce, Carl A. & Cornett, Judy M. Professional Responsibility in the Life of the Lawyer. 2010. (American Casebook Ser.). 1137p. 175.00 *(978-0-314-15010-3(2)*, West Legalworks) West.

Pierce, Carl A., et al. Professional Responsibility in the Life of the Lawyer. 2011. xlvi, 1087p. ***(978-0-314-15009-7(9))*** West Publishing Co., College & Schl. Div.

Rodriguez, Oscar Rey. The Attorney-Client Privilege in Civil Litigation. 5th ed. 2011. ***(978-1-61438-156-3(9))*** American Bar Assn.

Rogers, Scott. The Six Minute Solution: A Mindfulness Primer for Lawyers. 2009. (Illus.). pap. 9.95 *(978-0-9773455-2-6(1))* Mindful Living Pr.

Rotunda, Ronald D. & Dzienkowski, John S. Professional Responsibility: A Student's Guide. rev. ed. 2007. (American Casebook Ser.). 1220p. per. 47.00 *(978-0-314-17997-5(6)*, West Legalworks) West.

Rouse, Peter. Every Relationship Matters: Using the Power of Relationships to Transform Your Business, Your Firm & Yourself. 2007. (ENG.). 150p. per. 39.95 *(978-1-59031-781-5(5))* American Bar Assn.

Seide, David Z. & Collins, Gary H. Warning the Witness: A Guide to Internal Investigations & the Attorney-Client Privilege. 2011. (ENG.). 130p. pap. 59.95 *(978-1-60442-916-9(X))* American Bar Assn.

Shdaimah, Corey. Negotiating Justice: Progressive Lawyering, Low-Income Clients, & the Quest for Social Change. 2011. (ENG.). 239p. pap. 24.00 *(978-0-8147-0869-9(2))* New York Univ. Pr.

Shdaimah, Corey S. Negotiating Justice: Progressive Lawyering, Low-Income Clients, & the Quest for Social Change. 2009. (ENG., Illus.). 239p. 55.00 *(978-0-8147-4054-5(5))* New York Univ. Pr.

Silver, Marjorie. The Affective Assistance of Counsel: Practicing Law as a Healing Profession. 2006. 566p. 53.00 *(978-1-59460-111-8(9))* Carolina Academic Pr.

Singer, Gerald M. How to Be a Wealthy Lawyer Through Salesmanship! 2006. pap. 69.95 *(978-1-58477-762-5(1))* Lawbook Exchange, Ltd., The.

Smith, Abbe. Case of a Lifetime: A Criminal Defense Lawyer's Story. (ENG.). 256p. 2009. pap. 18.00 *(978-0-230-61433-8(7))* 2008. 24.95 *(978-0-230-60528-2(1))* Palgrave Macmillan.

Smith, Merete & Precht-Jensen, Øyvind. Advokaters Taushetsplikt under Press? 2010. (NOR.). 166p. *(978-82-15-01731-0(2))* Columbia Univ. Pr.

Steinberg, Marc I. Lawyering & Ethics for the Business Attorney. (American Casebook Ser.). 2nd ed. 2007. ix, 205p. *(978-0-314-16287-8(9))* 3rd ed. 2011. vii, 210p. ***(978-0-314-92751-4(4))*** West Publishing Co., College & Schl. Div.

—Lawyering & Ethics for the Business Attorney, 3d. 3rd rev. ed. 2011. (American Casebook Ser.). 220p. 43.00 *(978-0-314-26484-8(1),* West Legalworks) West.

—Lawyering & Ethics for the Business Lawyer. 2nd rev. ed. 2007. (American Casebook Ser.). 205p. 37.00 *(978-0-314-16288-5(7),* West Legalworks) West.

Talia, M. Sue. How to Avoid the Divorce from Hell: And Dance Together at Your Daughter's Wedding. Talia, M. Sue, ed. 2nd ed. 2006. (ENG.). 339p. (Orig.). pap. 17.95 *(978-0-9651075-0-1(7),* 150-01) Nexus Publishing Co.

Tesler, Pauline H. Collaborative Law: Achieving Effective Resolution in Divorce Without Litigation. 2nd ed. 2009. pap. 129.95 incl. lp *(978-1-59031-974-1(5))* American Bar Assn.

Ware, Attorney Charles Jerome. Understanding the Law: A Primer. 2008. 268p. pap. 21.95 *(978-1-4401-1145-7(6))* iUniverse, Inc.

Webb, Stuart G., et al. The Collaborative Way to Divorce: The Revolutionary Method That Results in Less Stress, Lower Costs, & Happier Kids — Without Going to Court. 2007. (ENG., Illus.). 256p. (gr. 12-18). 15.00 *(978-0-452-28835-5(5),* Plume) Penguin Group (USA) Inc.

Werth, Barry. Damages. 2008. (ENG.). 400p. pap. 25.95 *(978-1-4165-9491-8(4))* Simon & Schuster.

Wright, J. Kim. Lawyers As Peacemakers: Practicing Holistic, Problem-Solving Law. 2011. (ENG.). 528p. pap. 74.95 *(978-1-60442-862-9(7))* American Bar Assn.

Zwier, Paul J., et al. Legal Strategy. 2007. 188p. 50.00 *(978-1-55681-923-0(4))* National Institute for Trial Advocacy.

ATTORNEY-CLIENT PRIVILEGE

see Confidential Communications—Lawyers

ATTORNEYS

see Agency (Law); Lawyers

ATTORNEYS GENERAL

see also Government Litigation; Public Prosecutors

Kyprianou, Despina. The Role of the Cyprus Attorney General's Office in Prosecutions: Rhetoric, Ideology & Practice: Rhetoric, Ideology & Practice. 2009. (ENG., Illus.). xxiv, 249p. 179.00 *(978-3-642-01920-3(X),* 364201920X) Springer.

New Jersey State Attorney General Guidlines. 2007. 800p. 59.95 *(978-1-932777-21-5(0))* Looseleaf Law Pubns., Inc.

Ross, Lynne & Myers, Emily, eds. State Attorneys General Powers & Responsibilities. 2nd ed. 2007. (ENG.). 454p. 50.00 *(978-0-9797381-0-4(5))* National Assn. of Attorneys General.

ATTORNEYS GENERAL—BIOGRAPHY

Brooke, Edward W. Bridging the Divide: My Life. 2006. (ENG., Illus.). 352p. 29.95 *(978-0-8135-3905-8(6))* Rutgers Univ. Pr.

Elkind, Peter. Client 9: The Rise & Fall of Eliot Spitzer. 2010. (ENG.). 320p. (gr. 12). 16.00 *(978-1-59184-392-4(8),* Portfolio Trade) Penguin Group (USA) Inc.

Hill, John L. & Stromberger, Ernie. John Hill for the State of Texas: My Years as Attorney General. 2008. (ENG., Illus.). 280p. 35.00 *(978-1-60344-072-1(0))* Texas A&M Univ. Pr.

Katzenbach, Nicholas D. Some of It Was Fun: Working with RFK & LBJ. 2008. (ENG., Illus.). 320p. 27.95 *(978-0-393-06725-5(4),* 6725) Norton, W. W. & Co., Inc.

Kennedy, John P. Memoirs of the Life of William Wirt V1 A. 2006. pap. 33.95 *(978-1-4286-4976-7(X))* Kessinger Publishing, LLC.

—Memoirs of the Life of William Wirt V2 A. 2006. pap. 34.95 *(978-1-4286-4977-4(8))* Kessinger Publishing, LLC.

Masters, Brooke A. Spoiling for a Fight: The Rise of Eliot Spitzer. 2007. (ENG., Illus.). 384p. pap. 18.00 *(978-0-8050-8302-6(2),* Holt Paperback) Holt, Henry & Co.

Minutaglio, Bill. The President's Counselor: The Rise to Power of Alberto Gonzales. 2006. (SPA., Illus.). 368p. 24.95 *(978-0-06-111920-0(2),* Rayo) HarperCollins Pubs.

O'Brien, Joan & O'Brien, Alyssa. The Quilt of My Life. 2010. 238p. pap. 12.99 *(978-0-557-62696-0(X))* Lulu Enterprises Inc.

Palermo, Joseph A. Robert F. Kennedy: And the Death of American Idealism. Carnes, Mark C., ed. 2007. (Library of American Biography Ser.). (ENG., Illus.). 192p. (C). per. 25.20 *(978-0-321-38610-6(8))* Longman Publishing Group.

Roel, Virgilio G. The Education Revolution: A Salute to the American G I Bill of Rights of 1944 - the Golden Era in Education for Mexican Americans - A Memoir of a Worl. 2009. 544p. pap. 31.95 *(978-1-4401-3968-0(7))* iUniverse, Inc.

Thornburgh, Dick. Where the Evidence Leads: An Autobiography, Revised & Updated. rev. ed. 2010. (ENG., Illus.). 460p. pap. 27.95 *(978-0-8229-6112-3(1))* Univ. of Pittsburgh Pr.

ATTRACTING BIRDS

see Bird Attracting

ATTRACTING WILDLIFE

see Wildlife Attracting

ATTRIBUTES OF GOD

see God—Attributes

ATTRIBUTION (SOCIAL PSYCHOLOGY)

Hutto, Daniel D. Folk Psychological Narratives: The Sociocultural Basis of Understanding Reasons. 2007. (ENG., Illus.). 368p. (gr. 17). 40.00 *(978-0-262-08367-6(1))* MIT Pr.

Malle, Bertram F. How the Mind Explains Behavior: Folk Explanations, Meaning, & Social Interaction. 2006. (ENG., Illus.). 322p. (gr. 17). per. 20.00 *(978-0-262-63339-0(6))* MIT Pr.

Manusov, Valerie & Harvey, John H., eds. Attribution, Communication Behavior, & Close Relationships. 2011. (Advances in Personal Relationships Ser.). (ENG.). 406p. pap. 39.99 *(978-0-521-17727-6(8))* Cambridge Univ. Pr.

Rosen, Lawrence, ed. Other Intentions: Cultural Contexts & the Attribution of Inner States. (Advanced Seminar Ser.). 264p. pap. 24.95 *(978-0-933452-89-3(6))* School for Advanced Research Pr./SAR Pr.

Rosen, Lawrence & Harris, Jennifer. Other Intentions: Cultural Contexts & the Attribution of Inner States. Ziegfeld, Richard, ed. (Advanced Seminar Ser.). 264p. 29.95 *(978-0-933452-88-6(8))* School for Advanced Research Pr./SAR Pr.

Tilly, Charles. Credit & Blame. 2008. (ENG., Illus.). 196p. (C). 24.95 *(978-0-691-13578-6(9))* Princeton Univ. Pr.

—Why? 2008. (ENG., Illus.). 224p. (C). pap. 19.95 *(978-0-691-13648-6(3))* Princeton Univ. Pr.

ATTRITION

see Penitence; Repentance

ATWOOD, MARGARET ELEANOR, 1939-

Atwood, Bert L. My Father Was A Crop Duster: The Story of Atwood Crop Dusters. 2008. (Illus.). 192p. 39.95 *(978-0-9799287-2-7(9))* AAAA Publishing.

Atwood, Margaret. In Other Worlds: SF & the Human Imagination. (ENG.). 272p. 2012. pap. 15.95 ***(978-0-307-74176-9(1),*** Anchor) 2011. 24.95 *(978-0-385-53396-6(9),* Talese, Nan A.) Knopf Doubleday Publishing Group.

Becker, Manuel Benjamin. Forms & Functions of Dystopia in Margaret Atwood's Novels. 2008. 108p. pap. *(978-3-639-00746-6(8))* VDM Verlag Dr. Mueller e.K.

Bloom, Harold, ed. & intro. Margaret Atwood. 2nd rev. ed. 2008. (Bloom's Modern Critical Views Ser.). 216p. (C). (gr. 9-18). 45.00 *(978-1-60413-181-9(0),* Chelsea Hse.) Facts On File, Inc.

Bouson, J. Brooks. Margaret Atwood: The Robber Bride, the Blind Assassin, Oryx & Crake. 2011. (Continuum Studies in Contemporary North American Fiction Ser.). (ENG.). 224p. 29.95 *(978-0-8264-3062-5(7));* 100.00 *(978-0-8264-2437-2(6))* Continuum International Publishing Group, Ltd. GBR. Dist: National Bk. Network.

Dewis, G. M. Cat's Eye. 2011. (Insight Study Guides). 72p. pap. 9.95 ***(978-1-921411-92-2(9))*** Insight Pubns. Pty, Ltd. AUS. Dist: Ingram Pub. Services.

Gault, Cinda. National & Female Identity in Canadian Literature, 1965-1980: The Fiction of Margaret Laurence, margaret Atwood, & Marian Engel. 2012. 320p. 149.95 ***(978-0-7734-2622-1(1))*** Mellen, Edwin Pr., The.

Gorjup, Branko, ed. Margaret Atwood: Essays on Her Works. 2007. (Writers Ser.). (ENG.). 300p. 18.00 *(978-1-55071-267-4(5))* Guernica Editions, Inc. CAN. Dist: Univ. of Toronto Pr.

Gupta, Rama. Margaret Atwood: A Psychoanalytical Study. 2006. 166p. 24.95 *(978-1-932705-63-8(5))* New Dawn Pr., Inc.

Hengen, Shannon & Thomson, Ashley. Margaret Atwood: A Reference Guide, 1988-2005. 2007. (ENG.). 456p. 95.00 *(978-0-8108-5904-3(1))* Scarecrow Pr., Inc.

Kozakewich, Tobi & Moss, John, eds. Margaret Atwood: The Open Eye. 2006. (Reappraisals: Canadian Writers Ser.). (ENG., Illus.). 492p. (gr. 13). pap. *(978-0-7766-0613-2(1))* Univ. of Ottawa Pr./Presses de l'Universite d'Ottawa.

Loudermilk, Kim A. Fictional Feminism: How American Bestsellers Affect the Movement for Women's Equality. 2009. 232p. 39.95 *(978-0-415-80345-8(4))* Routledge.

Macpherson, Heidi Slettedahl. The Cambridge Introduction to Margaret Atwood. 2010. (Cambridge Introductions to Literature Ser.). (ENG.). 156p. (C). 69.00 *(978-0-521-87298-0(7));* pap. 19.99 *(978-0-521-69463-6(9))* Cambridge Univ. Pr.

Mcwilliams, Ellen. Margaret Atwood & the Female Bildungsroman. 2009. 184p. 99.95 *(978-0-7546-6027-9(3))* Ashgate Publishing Co.

Nelson, David, ed. Women's Issues in Margaret Atwood's the Handmaid's Tale. 2011. (Social Issues in Literature Ser.). (Illus.). 224p. (ENG.). pap. 26.50 *(978-0-7377-5800-9(7),* Greenhaven Pr., Inc.); (YA). (gr. 9-12). 38.45 *(978-0-7377-5799-6(X))* Cengage Gale.

Nischik, Reingard M. Engendering Genre: The Works of Margaret Atwood. 2010. (ENG., Illus.). 328p. pap. *(978-0-7766-0724-5(3))* Univ. of Ottawa Pr./Presses de l'Universite d'Ottawa.

Sheckels, Theodore F. The Political in Margaret Atwood's Fiction: The Writing on the Wall of the Tent. 2012. 200p. 99.95 ***(978-1-4094-3379-8(X))*** Ashgate Publishing Co.

Strolz, Andrea. Escaping from the Prison-House of Language & Digging for Meanings in Texts among Texts: Metafiction & Intertextuality in Margaret Atwood's Novels Lady Oracle & the Blind Assassin. 2006. (ENG.). 156p. per. *(978-3-89821-643-2(8))* Ibidem-Verlag.

Thomas, P. L. Reading, Learning, Teaching Margaret Atwood. (Confronting the Text, Confronting the World Ser.: Vol. 6). 160p. (C). pap. 24.95 *(978-0-8204-8671-0(X))* Lang, Peter Publishing, Inc.

TOLAN, Fiona. Margaret Atwood: Feminism & Fiction. 2007. (Costerus New Ser.: 170). 336p. per. 90.00 *(978-90-420-2223-2(X))* Rodopi.

Wilson, Sharon Rose. Myths & Fairy Tales in Contemporary Women's Fiction: From Atwood to Morrison. 2008. (ENG.). 224p. 89.00 *(978-0-230-60554-1(0))* Palgrave Macmillan.

Wisker, Gina. Atwood's the Handmaid's Tale. 2010. (Reader's Guides). (ENG.). 160p. 19.95 *(978-0-8264-2601-7(8));* 90.00 *(978-0-8264-6362-3(2))* Continuum International Publishing Group, Ltd. GBR. Dist: National Bk. Network.

—Margaret Atwood: An Introduction to Critical Views of Her Fiction. Tredell, Nicolas, ed. 2012. (Readers' Guides to Essential Criticism Ser.). (ENG., Illus.). 248p. (C). pap. 22.00 *(978-1-4039-8712-9(2))* Palgrave Macmillan.

Wisker, Gina & Tredell, Nicolas. Margaret Atwood: An Introduction to Critical Views of Her Fiction. 2012. (Readers' Guides to Essential Criticism Ser.). (ENG., Illus.). 248p. (C). 68.00 *(978-1-4039-8711-2(4))* Palgrave Macmillan.

Wynne-Davies, Marion. Margaret Atwood. 2010. (Writers & Their Work Ser.). (ENG.). 119p. (C). pap. 26.00 *(978-0-7463-0943-8(0))* Northcote Hse. Publishers, Ltd. GBR. Dist: Brown, David Bk. Co., The.

ATYPICAL CHILDREN

see Exceptional Children

AUBIGNE, AGRIPPA D', 1552-1630

Bailbe. Agrippa d'Aubigne, Poete des Tragiques. (Publ. Fac. des Lettres et Sc. Hum. Universite de Caen). 38.95 *(978-0-8288-6088-8(2),* F28350) French & European Pubns., Inc.

Junod, Samuel. Agrippa D'Aubigné, Ou, Les Misères du Prophète. 2008. (Cahiers d'humanisme et Renaissance Ser.). (FRE.). 352p. (C). pap. 72.00 *(978-2-600-01083-2(1))* Droz, Librairie CHE. Dist: Brown, David Bk. Co., The.

Osieja, Stefan. Das Literarische Bild des Verfolgten Glaubensgenossen bei den Protestantischen Schriftstellern der Romania zur Zeit der Reformation: Studien zu Agrippa d'Aubigne, Francisco de Enzinas, Juan Perez de Pineda, Raimundo Gonzalez de Montes, Olympia Fulvia Morata, Scipione Lentolo und Taddeo Duno. (Europaische Hochschulschriften Ser.: Vol. 262). (GER.). 358p. 43.95 *(978-3-631-39499-1(3))* Lang, Peter Publishing, Inc.

AUBREY, JOHN, 1626-1697

Burl, Aubrey & Small, Hugh. John Aubrey & Stone Circles. 2010. (Illus.). 320p. 40.00 *(978-1-4456-0157-1(5))* Amberley Publishing GBR. Dist: Casemate Pubs. & Bk. Distributors, LLC.

Jordan, Thomas E. Sir William Petty 1674: Letters to John Aubrey. 2009. (Illus.). i, 133p. *(978-0-7734-3845-3(9))* Mellen, Edwin Pr., The.

Poole, William. John Aubrey & the Advancement of Learning. 2010. (Illus.). 112p. pap. 45.00 *(978-1-85124-319-8(4))* Bodleian Library GBR. Dist: Chicago Distribution Ctr.

AUCHINCLOSS, LOUIS, 1917-2010

Auchincloss, Louis. A Voice from Old New York: A Memoir of My Youth. 2010. (ENG.). 224p. 25.00 *(978-0-547-34153-8(9))* Houghton Mifflin Harcourt Trade & Reference Pubs.

Gelderman, Carol. Louis Auchincloss: A Writers Life. 2007. (Illus.). 267p. per. 24.95 *(978-1-57003-711-5(6))* Univ. of South Carolina Pr.

AUCKLAND (N.Z.)

Allen, Lieut Ss. 2/ Auckland, 1918being a Partial Record of the War Service in France of the 2/ Auckland Regiment During the Great War. 2010. 192p. pap. *(978-1-84574-874-6(3))* Naval & Military Pr., The.

Stone, Russell. Logan Campbell's Auckland: Tales from the Early Years. 2007. (ENG., Illus.). 272p. pap. 32.95 *(978-1-86940-393-5(2))* Auckland Univ. Pr. NZL. Dist: Independent Pubs. Group.

AUCKLAND (N.Z.)—DESCRIPTION AND TRAVEL

Guide, Auckland Pub. Auckland Pub Guide. 2011. 82p. pap. ***(978-0-7552-1362-7(9))*** Authors OnLine, Ltd.

AUCTIONS

see also Art Auctions; Internet Auctions

Anderson, Judy L. Auction Fundraising Simplified. 2010. 356p. pap. 39.95 *(978-1-4520-1240-7(7))* AuthorHouse.

Auction Rate Securities Market: A Review of Problems & Potential Solutions: Hearing Before the Committee on Financial Services, U.S. House of Representatives, One Hundred Tenth Congress, Second Session, September 18, 2008. 2008. (Illus.). iii, 223p. *(978-0-16-082595-8(4),* 552-070-38616-5) United States Government Printing Office.

Baird, Robert. Everything You Need to Know to Raise Money (and Have Fun) with a Charity Auction: An Insider's Guide to the Ins, Outs, Ups & Downs of a Profitable Event. 2009. 141p. pap. 24.95 *(978-1-889102-36-8(9))* Emerson & Church, Pubs.

Baughman, Daren & Baughman, Nancy. Buy It, Sell It, Make Money: Your Guide to Finding & Reselling Luxury Goods Online. 2009. 228p. pap. 19.95 *(978-1-935278-61-0(4),* iUniverse Star) iUniverse, Inc.

Bruno, Guido. Adventures in American Bookshops, Antique Stores & Auction Rooms. 2009. 130p. 24.99 *(978-1-116-77686-7(3))* 2009. 130p. 28.99 *(978-1-116-77685-0(5))* 2009. 130p. pap. 20.75 *(978-1-116-77687-4(1))* 2009. 130p. pap. 19.75 *(978-1-116-77688-1(X))* 2008. 132p. 21.99 *(978-0-559-42179-2(6))* 2008. 132p. pap. 19.75 *(978-0-559-42178-5(8))* BiblioBazaar.

—Adventures in American Bookshops, Antique Stores & Auction Rooms. 2009. 92p. pap. *(978-0-217-67621-2(9))* Books LLC.

—Adventures in American Bookshops, Antique Stores & Auction Rooms. 2008. 132p. 35.95 *(978-1-4368-9403-6(4));* pap. 20.95 *(978-1-4367-6143-7(3))* Kessinger Publishing, LLC.

Busoni, Edward. Making Money with Storage Auctions. 2008. 109p. pap. 18.95 *(978-1-4357-1279-9(X))* Lulu Enterprises Inc.

Cramton, Peter, et al, eds. Combinatorial Auctions. 2010. (ENG., Illus.). 672p. (gr. 17). pap. 28.00 *(978-0-262-51413-2(3))* MIT Pr.

Dalton, James F., et al. Markets in Profile: Profiting from the Auction Process. 2007. (Wiley Trading Ser.: 278). (ENG., Illus.). 224p. 65.00 *(978-0-470-03909-0(4),* Wiley) Wiley, John & Sons, Inc.

Das, Sanmay, et al. Auctions, Market Mechanisms & Their Applications: First International ICST Conference, AMMA 2009, Boston, MA, USA, May 8-9, 2009, Revised Selected Papers. 2009. (Lecture Notes of the Institute for Computer Sciences, Social-Informatics & Telecommunications Engineering Ser.). x, 107p. pap. 72.00 *(978-3-642-03820-4(4),* 3642038204) Springer.

Deb, Saumyanil. The Revelation of Bidder Information in Online Auctions: An Empirical Analysis. 2008. 104p. pap. *(978-3-639-06422-3(4))* VDM Verlag Dr. Mueller e.K.

Defina, Michael. The Mystique of Perfume: Perfume Bottle Auction 17; May 4 2007. 2007. (Illus.). 128p. *(978-1-928655-07-7(6))* Monsen & Baer.

Dramitinos, Manos. Auction Theory for Telecoms. 2012. (Computer Science, Technology & Applications Ser.). 187p. 75.00 *(978-1-61324-646-7(3))* Nova Science Pubs., Inc.

Ferguson, Gary R. Hypnotic Auctions: Discover how to generate massive traffic & tons of bids on your eBay Auctions. 2006. per. 29.97 *(978-0-9788016-2-5(8))* Cherry Creek Publishing.

Fiske, Jay R., et al. The Big Book of Benefit Auctions. 2009. (ENG., Illus.). 270p. pap. 49.95 *(978-0-470-41292-3(5),* Wiley) Wiley, John & Sons, Inc.

Full Committee Hearing on the Impact of the 700 Megahertz Wireless Spectrum Auction on Small Business. 2007. (Illus.). v, 105p. *(978-0-16-080108-2(7),* 552-070-36849-3) United States Government Printing Office.

Green, Tracy & Green, Dwayne. 2008 California Real Estate Tax Auction. 2007. 67p. pap. 34.99 *(978-0-9719445-1-0(2))* Build Leadership Development, Inc.

Hagen, John P. Play Away Please: The Tale of the Sale of Golf's Greatest Icon - The St Andrews Old Course Starter's Box. 2010. (ENG., Illus.). 240p. 24.95 *(978-1-84596-605-8(8))* Mainstream Publishing Co., Ltd. GBR. Dist: Independent Pubs. Group.

Hartzman, Marc. Found on eBay: 100 Genuinely Bizarre Items from the World's Online Yard Sale. *(978-0-7893-0662-3(X))* Universe Publishing.

Hooks, R. Owen. Pine Ridge Horse Farm's Illustrated Guide to the Wild Pony Auction at Chincoteague (2006 Edition), 1. 2nd ed. 2006. (Illus.). 96p. ring bd. 19.95 *(978-0-9771317-1-6(8))* Pine Ridge Horse Farm, Inc.

Joachim, Martin & Alt, Dirk. Amazing Auctions, 1 vol. 2009. (DUT, FRE & ENG., Illus.). 160p. pap. 45.00 *(978-90-79761-10-4(9))* Tectum B.V.B.A. BEL. Dist: Innovative Logistics.

Krishna, Vijay. Auction Theory. 2nd ed. 2009. (ENG., Illus.). 336p. (C). 82.95 *(978-0-12-374507-1(1),* Academic Pr.) Elsevier Science & Technology Bks.

Lebedeva, Ekaterina. Hypertree Decompositions for Combinatorial Auctions - Optimal Winner Determination. 2008. 80p. pap. *(978-3-639-02231-5(9))* VDM Verlag Dr. Mueller e.K.

Lewis, Elen. Ebay: The Story of a Brand That Taught Millions of People to Trust One Another, 1 vol. 2007. (Great Brand Stories Ser.). (ENG., Illus.). 192p. pap. 12.95 *(978-1-905736-10-2(X))* Cyan Communications GBR. Dist: Independent Pubs. Group.

Lusk, Jayson L. & Shogren, Jason F. Experimental Auctions: Methods & Applications in Economic & Marketing Research. 2007. (Quantitative Methods for Applied Economics & Business Research Ser.). (ENG., Illus.). 316p. per. 39.00 *(978-0-521-67124-8(8));* 103.99 *(978-0-521-85516-7(0))* Cambridge Univ. Pr.

Ma, Huiye & Leung, Ho-fung. Bidding Strategies in Agent-Based Continuous Double Auctions. 2008. (Whitestein Series in Software Agent Technologies & Autonomic Computing Ser.). (Illus.). 160p. pap. 59.95 *(978-3-7643-8729-7(7),* 3764387297) Birkhauser Verlag AG CHE. Dist: Springer.

Maurer, Luiz & Barroso, Luiz. Electricity Auctions: An Overview of Efficient Practices. 2011. (World Bank Studies). (ENG.). 176p. pap. 25.00 ***(978-0-8213-8822-8(3),*** 9780821388228) World Bank Pubns.

Maurer, Luiz, et al. Electricity Auctions: An Overview of Efficient Practices. 2011. ***(978-0-8213-8824-2(X))*** World Bank Pubns.

McCampbell, Bryant. Auction Tactics. 2007. (ENG.). 146p. 35.95 *(978-0-548-01371-7(3))* Kessinger Publishing, LLC.

Menezes, Flavio & Monteiro, Paulo K. An Introduction to Auction Theory. 2008. (ENG., Illus.). 208p. (C). 45.00 *(978-0-19-927599-1(8))* Oxford Univ. Pr., Inc.

Murdoch, John. Law of Estate Agency. 5th rev. ed. 2009. (ENG.). 360p. pap. 59.95 *(978-0-7282-0559-8(9))* Estates Gazette, Ltd. GBR. Dist: Taylor & Francis Group.

Parente, Diane H., ed. Best Practices for Online Procurement Auctions. 2007. (Premier Reference Source Ser.). (Illus.). 402p. 180.00 *(978-1-59904-636-5(9))* IGI Global.

Pikovsky, Alexander. Pricing & Bidding Strategies in Iterative Combinatorial Auctions. 2008. 240p. pap. *(978-3-8364-8756-6(X))* VDM Verlag Dr. Mueller e.K.
Shiying, Liu & Avery, Martha. Alibaba: The Inside Story Behind Jack Ma & the Creation of the World's Biggest Online Marketplace. 2009. (ENG., Illus.). 288p. 25.99 *(978-0-06-167219-4(X),* Collins) HarperCollins Pubs.
Subramanian, Guhan. Dealmaking: The New Strategy of Negotiauctions. 2011. (ENG., Illus.). 236p. pap. 16.95 *(978-0-393-33995-6(5),* 33995) Norton, W. W. & Co., Inc.
—Negotiauctions: New Dealmaking Strategies for a Competitive Marketplace. 2010. (ENG., Illus.). 236p. 26.95 *(978-0-393-06946-4(X),* 6946) Norton, W. W. & Co., Inc.
Winning Posters: Pai Xiv. 2007. lib. bdg. 60.00 *(978-1-929530-31-1(5))* Square One Pubs.

AUDEN, W. H. (WYSTAN HUGH), 1907-1973
Acartürk-Höß, Miriam. Making the Mirror Visible ... Deutsche Übersetzungen englischer Lyrik (W. H. Auden) 2010. (Beiträge zur anglo-amerikanischen Literatur Ser.). (GER.). 356p. 86.95 *(978-3-631-61385-6(7))* Lang, Peter GmbH, Europaischer Verlag der Wissenschaften DEU. Dist: Lang, Peter.
Arana, R. Victoria. W. H. Auden's Poetry: Mythos, Theory, & Practice. 2009. 119.99 *(978-1-60497-595-6(4))* Cambria Pr.
Auden, W. H. The Complete Works of W. H Auden,1956-1962, Vol. 4. 2010. (Complete Works of W. H. Auden Ser.). (ENG., Illus.). 1056p. (C). 65.00 *(978-0-691-14755-0(8))* Princeton Univ. Pr.
—Prose Vol .3: Prose - 1949-1955. Mendelson, Edward, ed. 2008. (Complete Works of W. H. Auden: Vol. 3). (ENG., Illus.). 816p. (C). 62.50 *(978-0-691-13326-3(3))* Princeton Univ. Pr.
Beach, Joseph Warren. Making of the Auden Canon. 2009. (ENG.). 323p. pap. 60.00 *(978-0-8166-6022-3(0))* Univ. of Minnesota Pr.
Gwiazda, Piotr K. James Merrill & W. H. Auden: Homosexuality & Poetic Influence. 2007. (American Literature Readings in the Twenty-First Century Ser.). (ENG.). 216p. 89.00 *(978-1-4039-8431-9(X))* Palgrave Macmillan.
Izzo, David Garrett. W. H. Auden Encyclopedia. alt. ed. 2011. (ENG., Illus.). 304p. pap. 55.00 *(978-0-7864-4913-2(6))* McFarland & Co., Inc. Pubs.
Jenkins, Nicholas. The Island - W. H. Auden & the Regeneration of England. 2007. (Illus.). 400p. 35.00 *(978-0-674-02522-6(9))* Harvard Univ. Pr.
Jones, Chris. Strange Likeness: The Use of Old English in Twentieth-Century Poetry. (ENG.). 288p. 2010. pap. 55.00 *(978-0-19-957742-2(0))* 2006. 110.00 *(978-0-19-927832-9(6))* Oxford Univ. Pr., Inc.
Poole, Adrian. Joyce, Eliot, Auden, Beckett: Great Shakespeareans. 2012. (Great Shakespeareans Ser.). (ENG.). 248p. 140.00 *(978-1-4411-8743-7(X))* Continuum International Publishing Group, Ltd. GBR. Dist: National Bk. Network.
Sharpe, Tony. W. H. Auden. 2007. (Routledge Guides to Literature Ser.). (ENG.). 176p. 95.00 *(978-0-415-32735-0(0))*; 162p. per. 28.95 *(978-0-415-32736-7(9))* Routledge.
Wasley, A. The Age of Auden - Postwar Poetry & the American Scene. 2010. (ENG.). 280p. (C). 35.00 *(978-0-691-13679-0(3))* Princeton Univ. Pr.
Wetzsteon, Rachel. Influential Ghosts: A Study of Auden's Sources. 2006. (Studies in Major Literary Authors Ser.). (ENG.). 112p. 125.00 *(978-0-415-97546-9(8))* Routledge.

AUDI AUTOMOBILE
Bentley Publishers. Audi A4 (B6, B7) Service Manual: 1. 8L turbo, 2. 0L turbo, 3. 0L, 3. 2L, including Avant & Cabriolet: 2002, 2003, 2004, 2005, 2006, 2007 2008. 2010. (Illus.). 1430p. 149.95 *(978-0-8376-1574-5(7))* Bentley Pubs.
Fowler, Stan & Morgan, Charlie. The Audi Quattro. 2010. (Little Book Ser.). (ENG., Illus.). 128p. 11.99 *(978-1-906635-53-4(6),* 1906635536) G2 Entertainment Ltd. GBR. Dist: BookMasters Distribution Services (BDS).
Godfrey, Eric, et al. VW Passat & Audi A4: Passat (1998 Thru 2005) & Audi A4 (1996 Thru 2001) 1. 8l 4-Cylinder Turbo & 2. 8l V6 Engines. 2008. (Haynes Manuals Ser.). (ENG., Illus.). 334p. per. 26.95 *(978-1-56392-703-4(9),* 1563927039) Haynes Manuals, Inc.
Haynes, Max. Audi A4: 2002 Thru 2008. 2011. (Haynes Repair Manual Ser.). (ENG., Illus.). 352p. pap. 26.95 *(978-1-56392-837-6(X),* 156392837X) Haynes Manuals, Inc.
Killingsworth, Jeff. Audi A4: 2002 Thru 2008. 2011. (ENG.). 416p. pap. 29.95 *(978-1-56392-846-8(9))* Haynes,Chilton.
Pitt, Colin. Audi Quattro, Volume 1. 2011. (ENG., Illus.). 73p. pap. ***(978-1-84155-863-9(X))*** CP Press.
—Audi Quattro, Volume 2. 2011. (ENG., Illus.). 80p. pap. ***(978-1-84155-864-6(8))*** CP Press.
Robson, Graham. Audi Quattro: Group B, Sport, Sport S1. 2008. (Rally Giants Ser.). (ENG., Illus.). 128p. pap. 29.95 *(978-1-84584-141-6(7),* 1845841417) Veloce Publishing Ltd. GBR. Dist: MBI Distribution Services/Quayside Distribution.
Wagstaff, Ian. Audi R8. 2011. (WSC Giants Ser.). (ENG., Illus.). 128p. pap. 29.95 *(978-1-84584-327-4(4),* 1845843274) Veloce Publishing Ltd. GBR. Dist: MBI Distribution Services/Quayside Distribution.
Walton, Jeremy. Audi Quattro: A Celebration of the World's First Turbocharged 4x4 Coupé. 2007. (Haynes Great Cars Ser.). (ENG., Illus.). 160p. 32.95 *(978-1-84425-330-2(9),* 1844253309) Haynes Publishing PLC GBR. Dist: MBI Distribution Services/Quayside Distribution.

AUDIENCES
see also Motion Picture Audiences; Radio Audiences; Sports Spectators; Television Viewers; Theater Audiences
Beck, Peter J. Presenting History: Past & Present. 2011. (ENG., Illus.). 368p. (C). 85.00 ***(978-0-230-24207-4(3))***; pap. 28.95 ***(978-0-230-24208-1(1))*** Palgrave Macmillan.
Benzecry, Claudio E. The Opera Fanatic: Ethnography of an Obsession. 2011. (ENG., Illus.). 256p. 85.00 *(978-0-226-04340-1(1))*; pap. 29.00 *(978-0-226-04342-5(8))* Univ. of Chicago Pr.
Boczkowski, Pablo J. News at Work: Imitation in an Age of Information Abundance. 2010. (ENG., Illus.). 272p. 75.00 *(978-0-226-06279-2(1))*; pap. 27.50 *(978-0-226-06280-8(5))* Univ. of Chicago Pr.
Buran, Aylin. Fazil Say & the Classical Music Stage as Informal Learning Space. 2010. (Europäische Hochschulschriften. Reihe 36: Musikwissenschaft Ser.). 152p. pap. 43.95 *(978-3-631-61248-4(6))* Lang, Peter GmbH, Europaischer Verlag der Wissenschaften DEU. Dist: Lang, Peter.
Butsch, Richard. The Citizen Audience: Crowds, Publics, & Individuals. 2007. 186p. 125.00 *(978-0-415-97789-0(4))*; per. 34.95 *(978-0-415-97790-6(8),* 0415977908) Routledge.
Griffiths, Alison. Shivers down Your Spine: Cinema, Museums, & the Immersive View. 2008. (Film & Culture Ser.). (Illus.). 320p. pap. 24.50 *(978-0-231-12989-3(0))* Columbia Univ. Pr.
Ivey, Bill & Tepper, Steven J., eds. Engaging Art: The Next Great Transformation of America's Cultural Life. 2007. (ENG., Illus.). 408p. 131.00 *(978-0-415-96041-0(X))* Routledge.
Kennedy, Dennis. The Spectator & the Spectacle: Audiences in Modernity & Postmodernity. (ENG., Illus.). 260p. 2011. pap. 35.99 ***(978-1-107-40360-4(X))*** 2009. 93.00 *(978-0-521-89976-5(1))* Cambridge Univ. Pr.
Kovach, Bill & Rosenstiel, Tom. Blur: How to Know What's True in the Age of Information Overload. 2010. (ENG.). 240p. 26.00 *(978-1-59691-565-7(X))* Bloomsbury Publishing.
Kumaedy, Karen. A Choreographer's Process. 2010. 148p. pap. *(978-3-639-27662-6(0))* VDM Verlag Dr. Mueller e.K.
Malbon, Elizabeth Struthers. Between Author & Audience in Mark: Narration, Characterization, Interpretation. 2009. xii, 196p. *(978-1-906055-50-8(2))* Sheffield Phoenix Pr.
Prendergast, Monica. Teaching Spectatorship: Essays & Poems on Audience in Performance. 2008. (C). 104.95 *(978-1-60497-539-0(3))* Cambria Pr.
Schilb, John. Rhetorical Refusals: Defying Audiences' Expectations. 2007. (ENG.). 224p. per. 35.00 *(978-0-8093-2789-8(9))* Southern Illinois Univ. Pr.
Tepper, Stephen & Ivey, Bill, eds. Engaging Art: The Next Great Transformation of America's Cultural Life. 2007. (ENG., Illus.). 408p. pap. 36.95 *(978-0-415-96042-7(8))* Routledge.
Tracy, Christine M. The Newsphere: Understanding the News & Information Environment. 2012. (C). pap. 129.95 ***(978-1-4331-1042-9(3))***; pap. 34.95 ***(978-1-4331-1043-6(1))*** Lang, Peter Publishing, Inc.
Walwin, Jeni, ed. Searching for Art's New Publics. 2010. (Illus.). 224p. pap. 35.00 *(978-1-84150-311-0(8))* Intellect, Ltd. GBR. Dist: Chicago Distribution Ctr.

AUDIENCES, TELEVISION
see Television Viewers

AUDIENCES, THEATER
see Theater Audiences

AUDIO BOOKS
see Audiobooks

AUDIO EQUIPMENT
see Sound—Equipment and Supplies

AUDIO TAPES
see Audiotapes

AUDIO-VISUAL AIDS
see Audio-Visual Materials

AUDIO-VISUAL EDUCATION
see also Audio-Visual Materials; Instructional Materials Personnel; Motion Pictures in Education; Radio in Education; Video Tapes in Education; Visual Education
also subdivision Audio-Visual Aids, or Study and Teaching under subjects, e.g. Music—Audio-Visual Aids
Bucaria, Chiara. Dark Humour As a Culture-Specific Phenomenon. 2009. 220p. pap. *(978-3-639-19997-0(9))* VDM Verlag Dr. Mueller e.K.
Cram101 Textbook Reviews & Cram101 Textbook Reviews. Outlines & Highlights for Instructional Technology & Media for Learning by Sharon Smaldino, Isbn: 9780138008154. 2011. 158p. pap. 29.95 ***(978-1-4288-4282-3(9))*** Cram101 Inc.
Demir, Onan & Celik, Cari. Multimedia in Education & Special Education. 2009. xiv, 259p. 110.00 *(978-1-60741-073-7(7))* Nova Science Pubs., Inc.
Harteveld, Casper. Triadic Game Design. 2011. (ENG., Illus.). xvii, 316p. 129.00 *(978-1-84996-156-1(5),* 1849961565) Springer.
Kinnaird, Mike. Sounds Like a Good Idea: Using Audio Technology in the Classroom. 2008. (ENG., Illus.). 160p. 60.00 *(978-1-85539-448-3(0),* Network Continuum Education) Continuum International Publishing Group, Ltd. GBR. Dist: National Bk. Network.
Laybourne, Kit. Mediapedia: Creative Tools & Techniques for Camera, Computer, & Beyond. 2008. (ENG., Illus.). 304p. pap. 24.95 *(978-1-59921-401-6(6),* Knack) Globe Pequot Pr., The.
Rodrigues, Eduardo Santos Junqueira. Digital Technologies & Writing in Students ' Communicative Practices: An Ethnographical Study of an Inner-City High School in the Northeast of Brazil. 2008. 252p. pap. *(978-3-8364-7564-8(2))* VDM Verlag Dr. Mueller e.K.
Schmidt-Weigand, Florian. Designing Text & Visualizations in Multimedia Learning - How to Overcome Split Attention Effects? 2007. 132p. per. *(978-3-8364-3288-7(9))* VDM Verlag Dr. Mueller e.K.
Smaldino, Sharon E., et al. Instructional Technology & Media for Learning. 10th ed. 2011. (ENG., 360p. (C). Illus.). pap. 126.40 *(978-0-13-800815-4(9))*; 89.60 *(978-0-13-269407-0(7))* Allyn & Bacon, Inc.

AUDIO-VISUAL EQUIPMENT
Here are entered general works on projectors, screens, sound equipment, pointers, tables, exhibit boards, etc.
see also names of particular equipment, e.g. Motion Picture Projectors
Audiovisual Communication Handbook. Date not set. 4.00 *(978-0-942716-08-5(6))* World Neighbors.
Blevins, Jamie. Nursing Students' Perceptions of Two-Way Interactive Video. 2008. 136p. pap. *(978-3-639-00658-2(5))* VDM Verlag Dr. Mueller e.K.
Faulkner, Michael & D-Fuse. VJ: Audio-Visual Art & VJ Culture. 2006. (ENG., Illus.). 192p. pap. 40.00 *(978-1-85669-490-2(9))* King, Laurence Publishing GBR. Dist: Hachette Bk. Group.
Friedman, Ira. The Bay Audio Guide to Companion Selling. 2007. 120p. 80.00 *(978-0-615-15899-0(4))* Bay Audio, LLC.
Huntington, John. Control Systems for Live Entertainment. 3rd ed. 2007. (ENG., Illus.). 464p. per. 57.95 *(978-0-240-80937-3(8),* Focal Pr.) Elsevier Science & Technology Bks.
ICTS Exam Secrets Test Prep Staff, ed. ICTS LBS II Technology Specialist (161) Exam Secrets Study Guide: ICTS Test Review for the Illinois Certification Testing System. 2011. (C). 62.99 *(978-1-61403-570-1(9))* Mometrix Media LLC.
InfoComm International Staff & Laurik, Sven. CTS Certified Technology Specialist, Set, No. 2. 2011. (ENG., Illus.). 548p. 70.00 incl. cd-rom *(978-0-07-173919-1(X),* 007173919X) McGraw-Hill Osborne.
Javes, Carol. Learn Multimedia Management First North American Edition. 2007. 148p. per. 37.99 *(978-1-59095-807-0(1))* TotalRecall Pubns., Inc.
Mannino, Philip. ABC's of Audio-Visual Equipment & the School Projectionist Manual. 2nd ed. pap. 4.00 *(978-0-911328-01-7(5))* School Projectionist Club of America.
Rennie, Ellie. Community Media: A Global Introduction. 2006. (Critical Media Studies). (ENG.). 224p. 88.00 *(978-0-7425-3924-2(5))*; per. 29.95 *(978-0-7425-3925-9(3))* Rowman & Littlefield Publishers, Inc.

AUDIO-VISUAL LIBRARY SERVICE
see also Vertical Files (Libraries)
Javes, Carol. Learn Multimedia Management First North American Edition. 2007. 148p. per. 37.99 *(978-1-59095-807-0(1))* TotalRecall Pubns., Inc.
Moyer, Jessica E., ed. Integrated Advisory Service: Breaking Through the Book Boundary to Better Serve Library Users, 1 vol. 405p. 58.00 *(978-1-59158-718-7(2),* LU8718) Libraries Unlimited, Inc.

AUDIO-VISUAL MATERIALS
see also Filmstrips; Motion Pictures; Slides (Photography); Sound Recordings; Transparencies; Video Recordings
also subdivision Audio-Visual Aids, or Study and Teaching under subjects, e.g. Music—Audio-Visual Aids
Audiovisual Communication Handbook. Date not set. 4.00 *(978-0-942716-08-5(6))* World Neighbors.
Burnett, Eric. History through Film: Volume I. 2008. 251p. pap. 24.49 *(978-1-4357-1482-3(2))* Lulu Enterprises Inc.
Cornelia, et al. audio • visual: on Visual Music & Related Media. Cornelia, ed. 2009. (GER & ENG., Illus.). 320p. 70.00 incl. DVD *(978-3-89790-293-0(1))* Arnoldsche Art Pubs. DEU. Dist: Antique Collectors' Club.
Cram101 Textbook Reviews & Cram101 Textbook Reviews. Outlines & Highlights for Teaching & Learning with Technology by Judy Lever-Duffy, Isbn: 9780205543250. 2011. 204p. pap. 30.95 ***(978-1-61744-052-6(3))*** Cram101 Inc.
Daniels, Dieter, ed. Audiovisuology - See This Sound No. 1: An Interdisciplinary Survey of Audiovisual Culture. 2010. (ENG., Illus.). 452p. pap. 49.95 *(978-3-86560-686-0(5))* Verlag der Buchhandlung Walther Konig DEU. Dist: D.A.P./Distributed Art Pubs.
Daniels, Dieter, et al. See This Sound. 2011. (ENG., Illus.). 260p. pap. 49.95 ***(978-3-86560-687-7(3))*** Verlag der Buchhandlung Walther Konig DEU. Dist: D.A.P./Distributed Art Pubs.
Deptford.Tv. Deptford TV Diaries II - Pirate Strategies. 2008. (Illus.). 180p. pap. *(978-1-906496-11-1(0))* Nute Publishing, Ltd.
Eshun, Kodwo & Ehmann, Antje, eds. Harun Farocki: Against What Against Whom. 2010. (ENG., Illus.). 256p. pap. 49.95 *(978-3-86560-587-0(7))* Verlag der Buchhandlung Walther Konig DEU. Dist: D.A.P./Distributed Art Pubs.
Gibbons, Thomas & Humphreys, Peter. Audiovisual Regulation under Pressure: Comparative Cases from North America & Europe. 2011. (ENG.). 256p. 125.00 *(978-0-415-59021-1(3))* Routledge.
Grant, Cathy. The BUFVC Handbook. 2009. (ENG., Illus.). 200p. (gr. 17). pap. 40.00 *(978-0-901299-80-2(4))* Wallflower Pr. GBR. Dist: Columbia Univ. Pr.
InfoComm International Staff & Laurik, Sven. CTS Certified Technology Specialist, Set, No. 2. 2011. (ENG., Illus.). 548p. 70.00 incl. cd-rom *(978-0-07-173919-1(X),* 007173919X) McGraw-Hill Osborne.
Information Today Inc, creator. AV Market Place: The Complete Business Directory of Products & Services for the Audio/Video Industry. (AV Market Place Ser.). 2010. (ENG.). 1622p. pap. 273.75 *(978-1-57387-377-2(2))* 2009. (Illus.). 1677p. pap. 277.75 *(978-1-57387-344-4(6))* Information Today, Inc.
Lever-Duffy & McDonald & Mizell & Cram101 Textbook Reviews Staff. Teaching & Learning with Technology. 2007. 60p. per. 9.95 *(978-1-4288-2050-0(7))* Cram101 Inc.
Lever-Duffy, Judy & McDonald, Jean B. Teaching & Learning with Technology (with MyEducationKit) 4th ed. 2010. (ENG.). (C). pap. 130.40 *(978-0-13-707398-6(4))* Allyn & Bacon, Inc.
Macomber, Phyl T. The Power of T. H. E. P. A. C. T. The Solution to Adapting the Curriculum. 2010. (Illus.). 232p. 75.00 *(978-0-9844401-7-7(8))* Make A Differnece, Inc.
Nehmer, Kathleen Suttles, ed. Educators Guide to Free Videos: Secondary Edition. 56th ed. 2009. (Educators Guide to Free Videotapes: Secondary Edition Ser.). 321p. pap. 54.75 *(978-0-87708-486-0(6))* Educators Progress Service, Inc.
—Educators Guide to Free Videotapes: Elementary/Middle School. 8th ed. 2007. (Educators Guide to Free Videotapes: Elementary/Middle School Edition Ser.). 319p. per. 54.25 *(978-0-87708-448-8(3))* Educators Progress Service, Inc.
Oppenheim, Joanne F. & Oppenheim, Stephanie. Oppenheim Toy Portfolio: The Best Toys, Books, & DVDs for Kids. annuals 2006. (Oppenheim Toy Portfolio Ser.: 14). (Illus.). 228p. per. 10.00 *(978-0-9721050-6-4(9))* Oppenheim Toy Portfolio, Inc.
Orey, Michael, et al, eds. Educational Media & Technology Yearbook: Volume 33 2008, 1 vol. 2008. (Education Media Yearbook Ser.). 368p. 80.00 *(978-1-59158-647-0(X),* LU8647) Libraries Unlimited, Inc.
Orey, Michael & Branch, Robert Maribe. Educational Media & Technology Yearbook, 2007, 1 vol., Vol. 32. 2007. (Education Media Yearbook Ser.). (Illus.). 336p. 80.00 *(978-1-59158-442-1(6),* LU4426) Libraries Unlimited, Inc.
Russell, William B., III. Using Film in the Social Studies. 2007. (ENG.). 66p. per. 21.99 *(978-0-7618-3768-8(X))* Univ. Pr. of America, Inc.
Stamatoudi, Irini A. Copyright & Multimedia Products: A Comparative Analysis. 2007. (Cambridge Intellectual Property & Information Law Ser.). (ENG.). 336p. pap. 69.00 *(978-0-521-04948-1(2))* Cambridge Univ. Pr.
Stockinger, P. Introduction to Audiovisual Archives. 2012. (Iste Ser.: 603). (ENG.). 145.00 ***(978-1-84821-337-1(9),*** Wiley-ISTE) Wiley, John & Sons, Inc.
Weiss, Alan. MBA V, 5 vols. 2008. (Illus.). 295.00 incl. audio *(978-1-928611-14-1(1))* Summit Consulting Group, Inc.
Zewide, Tizeta. Modeling Audio Data for Multi-Criteria Query Formulation. 2009. 104p. pap. *(978-3-639-19388-6(1))* VDM Verlag Dr. Mueller e.K.

AUDIO-VISUAL MATERIALS CENTERS
see Instructional Materials Centers

AUDIO-VISUAL MATERIALS PERSONNEL
see Instructional Materials Personnel

AUDIO-VISUAL SPECIALISTS
see Instructional Materials Personnel

AUDIOBOOKS
Audio Renaissance Catalog. pap. *(978-1-58063-217-1(3))* Macmillan Audio.
Bowker Staff, ed. Books Out Loud, 2 vols. 25th rev. ed. 2010. 380.00 *(978-1-59237-615-5(0))* 25th rev. ed. 2010. 380.00 *(978-1-59237-614-8(2))* 26th rev. ed. 2011. 400.00 *(978-1-59237-689-6(4))* 26th rev. ed. 2011. 400.00 *(978-1-59237-687-2(8))* 26th rev. ed. 2011. 400.00 *(978-1-59237-688-9(5))* Grey Hse. Publishing.
—Books Out Loud 2009, 2 vols. 24th ed. 2009. 365.00 *(978-0-6352-4977-5(5))* Bowker LLC, R. R.
—Books Out Loud 2010, 2 vols. 25th rev. ed. 2010. 380.00 *(978-1-59237-613-1(4))* Grey Hse. Publishing.
Cambridge ESOL Staff. Cambridge Certificate in Advanced English Official Examination Papers from University of Cambridge Esol Examinations. 2010. (CAE Practice Tests Ser.). (ENG., Illus.). 184p. pap., stu. ed. 46.80 incl. audio compact disk *(978-0-521-15692-9(0))* Cambridge Univ. Pr.
Esteves, Kelli. Audiobooks & Struggling Readers. 2009. 156p. pap. *(978-3-639-14677-6(8))* VDM Verlag Dr. Mueller e.K.
Kempf, Joe. My Sister Is Annoying! And Other Prayers for Children. 2009. (Illus.). 48p. (J). (gr. k-4). 16.95 *(978-0-7648-1827-1(9),* Liguori) Liguori Pubns.
Living Language Staff. Living Language French. unabr. ed. 2010. (Essential Ser.). (ENG.). 272p. 22.99 *(978-0-307-47842-9(4),* Living Language) Random Hse. Information Group.
Rü, et al. Tondokumente von der Walze zum Hörbuch: Geschichte - Medienspezifik - Rezeption. 2008. (GER., Illus.). 463p. (C). 77.00 *(978-3-89971-473-9(3))* Vandenhoeck & Ruprecht GmbH & Co. KG DEJ. Dist: ISD.
Rubery, Matthew, ed. Audiobooks Sound Studies & Literature. 2011. (Routledge Research in Cultural & Media Studies). (ENG., Illus.). 266p. (C). 125.00 *(978-0-415-88352-8(0))* Routledge.
Saricks, Joyce G. Read On — Audiobooks: Reading Lists for Every Taste. 2011. E-Book *(978-1-59158-807-8(3))* Libraries Unlimited, Inc.
—Read on... Audiobooks: Reading Lists for Every Taste, 1 vol. Trott, Barry, ed. (Read on Ser.). 145p. pap. 30.00 *(978-1-59158-804-7(9),* LU8804) Libraries Unlimited, Inc.

AUDIODISC PLAYERS
see Compact Disc Players

AUDIOLOGY
see also Deafness; Hearing
Atcherson, Samuel & Stoody, Tina, eds. Auditory Electrophysiology: A Clinical Guide. 2012. (ENG., Illus.). 400p. pap. 99.99 *(978-1-60406-363-9(7))* Thieme Medical Pubs., Inc.

Bess, Fred H. & Humes, Larry E. Audiology: The Fundamentals. 4th rev. ed. 2008. (ENG., Illus.). 362p. 83.99 *(978-0-7817-6643-2(5))* Lippincott Williams & Wilkins.

The BEST Guide to Marketing for Audiologists. 2008. 112p. pap. 35.00 *(978-0-9766294-2-9(9))* American Academy of Audiology.

Burkard, Robert, et al, eds. Handbook of Clinical Audiology. 6th rev. ed. 2009. (ENG., Illus.). 1056p. 98.99 *(978-0-7817-8106-0(X))* Lippincott Williams & Wilkins.

Cheng, L. -R. L., ed. Education for Speech & Language Pathology: Emerging Issues. 2010. (ENG., Illus.). 58p. pap. *(978-3-8055-9486-8(0))* Karger, S. AG.

Cram101 Textbook Reviews. Outlines & Highlights for Audiology: Fundamentals by Fred H Bess, ISBN. 2011. 104p. pap. 28.95 ***(978-1-61812-191-2(X))*** Cram101 Inc.

—Outlines & Highlights for Audiology & Communication Disorder by Larry E Humes, Isbn: 9780781775557 0781775558. 2011. 132p. pap. 28.95 ***(978-1-61490-438-0(3))*** Cram101 Inc.

—Outlines & Highlights for Foundations of Aural Rehabilitation by Tye-Murray. 2011. 198p. pap. 30.95 ***(978-1-61490-912-5(1))*** Cram101 Inc.

—Outlines & Highlights for Introduction to Audiology by Frederick N Martin, Isbn: 9780205593118. 2010. 94p. pap. 27.95 *(978-1-61698-100-6(8))* Cram101 Inc.

Cram101 Textbook Reviews. Outlines & Highlights for Survey of Audiology by David a Debonis, Isbn: 9780205531950 0205531954. 2011. 156p. pap. 29.95 ***(978-1-61812-200-1(2))*** Cram101 Inc.

Cram101 Textbook Reviews & Cram101 Textbook Reviews. Outlines & Highlights for Understanding Research & Evidence-Based Practice in Communication Disorders: A Primer for Students & Practitioners by Wi. 2011. 78p. pap. 27.95 ***(978-1-61490-529-5(0))*** Cram101 Inc.

Cranford, Jerry L. Basics of Audiology: Vibrations to Sounds. 2007. (Illus.). 132p. per. 49.95 *(978-1-59756-180-8(0))* Plural Publishing, Inc.

Donohue, Constance L. & Debonis, David A. Survey of Audiology: Fundamentals for Audiologists & Health Professionals. 2nd ed. 2007. (ENG., Illus.). 552p. (C). per. 135.40 *(978-0-205-53195-0(4))* Allyn & Bacon, Inc.

Erlmann, Veit. Reason & Resonance: A History of Modern Aurality. 2010. (ENG., Illus.). 422p. (gr. 17). 32.95 *(978-1-935408-04-8(6))* Zone Bks.

Fraysse, B., ed. Cochlear Implantation: 1st International Electro-Acoustic Workshop, Toulouse, December 2005: Supplement Issue: Audiology & Neurotology 2006, Vol. 11, Suppl. 1. (Illus.). 76p. pap. *(978-3-8055-8212-4(9))* Karger, S. AG.

Ginsberg, Sarah, et al. Scholarship of Teaching & Learning in Speech-Language Pathology & Audiology: Evidence-Based Education. 2011. (Illus.). 192p. pap. 79.95 *(978-1-59756-429-8(X))* Plural Publishing, Inc.

Glattke, Theodore J. & Robinette, Martin S., eds. Otoacoustic Emissions: Clinical Applications. 3rd ed. 2007. (ENG., Illus.). 496p. 89.99 *(978-1-58890-411-9(3))* Thieme Medical Pubs., Inc.

Goldfarb, Robert & Serpanos, Yula Cherpelis. Professional Writing in Speech-Language: Pathology & Audiology Workbook. 2011. 288p. (C). spiral bd. 49.95 *(978-1-59756-418-2(4))* Plural Publishing, Inc.

Hamill, Teri & Price, Lloyd. The Hearing Sciences. 2008. (Illus.). (C). per. 89.00 *(978-1-59756-199-0(1))* Plural Publishing, Inc.

Harris, J. P., ed. Inner Ear Medicine - Targeted Therapies. 2009. (Illus.). 92p. pap. *(978-3-8055-9288-8(4))* Karger, S. AG.

Haynes, William O. & Johnson, Carole E. Understanding Research & Evidence-Based Practice in Communication Disorders: A Primer for Students & Practitioners. 2008. (ENG., Illus.). 528p. (C). 116.00 *(978-0-205-45363-4(5))* Allyn & Bacon, Inc.

Hickson, Louise & Wong, Lena, eds. Evidence-Based Practice in Audiology: Evaluating Interventions for Children & Adults with Hearing Impairment. 2012. (ENG., Illus.). 340p. pap. 69.95 *(978-1-59756-419-9(2))* Plural Publishing, Inc.

Hosford-Dunn, Holly, et al. Audiology. 2nd ed. 2007. 84.95 *(978-3-13-116412-4(3))* Thieme Medical Pubs., Inc.

—Audiology: Practice Management. 2nd ed. 2007. (ENG.). 416p. 89.99 *(978-1-58890-511-6(X))* Thieme Medical Pubs., Inc.

Hull, Ray H., ed. Introduction to Aural Rehabilitation. 2009. (Illus.). 400p. pap. 89.95 *(978-1-59756-281-2(5))* Plural Publishing, Inc.

Humes, Larry & Bess, Fred H. Audiology & Communication Disorders: An Overview. 2008. (ENG., Illus.). 269p. pap. 86.99 *(978-0-7817-7555-7(8))* Lippincott Williams & Wilkins.

Hunter, Lisa & Shahnaz, Navid. Acoustic Immittance Measures: Basic & Advanced Practice. 2012. (Illus.). 175p. pap. 55.00 *(978-1-59756-437-3(0))* Plural Publishing, Inc.

Jerger, James. Audiology: An Editorial Journey. 2008. (Illus.). 142p. pap. 35.00 *(978-0-9766294-1-2(0))* American Academy of Audiology.

—Audiology in the USA. 2009. (Illus.). 128p. 49.95 *(978-1-59756-316-1(1))* Plural Publishing, Inc.

Johnson, Carole E. Introduction to Auditory Rehabilitation: A Contemporary Issues Approach. 2011. (ENG.). 640p. (C). pap. 110.40 *(978-0-205-42417-7(1))* Allyn & Bacon, Inc.

Johnson, Cheryl Deconde & Seaton, Jane. Educational Audiology Handbook (Book Only) 2nd ed. 2011. (ENG.). 720p. (C). pap. 186.95 *(978-1-111-31983-0(9))* Delmar Cengage Learning.

Johnson Seaton Staff, et al. Educational Audiology Handbook. 2nd ed. 2011. (ENG.). 720p. (C). pap. 186.95 *(978-1-4180-4130-4(0))* Delmar Cengage Learning.

Kent-Walsh, Jennifer. What Every Speech-Language Pathologist - Audiologist Should Know about Service Learning. rev. ed. 2011. (ENG.). 64p. (C). pap. 10.40 ***(978-0-13-248595-1(8))*** Allyn & Bacon, Inc.

Kileny, Paul & Ruth, Rober. The Audiologist's Handbook of Neurophysiological Monitoring. 2013. (Illus.). 280p. pap. 55.00 *(978-1-59756-343-7(9))* Plural Publishing, Inc.

Kramer, Steven. Audiology: Science to Practice. 2008. (Illus.). 394p. (C). 79.95 *(978-1-59756-033-7(2))* Plural Publishing, Inc.

Kramer, Steven & Guthrie, Lesli. Audiology Workbook. 2008. (Illus.). 203p. (C). spiral bd. 45.00 *(978-1-59756-299-7(8))* Plural Publishing, Inc.

LaPointe, Leonard L. Journal of Medical Speech: Language Pathology Collective Essays. 2009. (ENG.). 264p. (C). pap. 83.95 *(978-1-4354-9769-6(4))* Delmar Cengage Learning.

Lass, Norman J. & Woodford, Charles M. Hearing Science Fundamentals. 2007. (ENG., Illus.). 256p. (C). per. 60.95 *(978-0-323-04342-7(9)*, Mosby) Elsevier - Health Sciences Div.

Madell, Jane Reger & Flexer, Carol Ann. Pediatric Audiology: Diagnosis, Technology, & Management. 2008. 84.95 *(978-1-60406-002-7(6))* Thieme Medical Pubs., Inc.

Madell, Jane Reger & Flexer, Carol Ann, eds. Pediatric Audiology: Diagnosis, Technology, & Management. 2008. (ENG., Illus.). 352p. 89.99 *(978-1-60406-001-0(8))* Thieme Medical Pubs., Inc.

Martin, Frederick N. & Clark, John Greer. Introduction to Audiology. 11th rev. ed. 2011. (ENG.). 504p. (C). pap. 130.67 *(978-0-13-210821-8(6))* Allyn & Bacon, Inc.

McPherson, Bradley & Brouillette, Ron. Audiology in Developing Countries. 2008. 55.00 *(978-1-60456-945-2(X))* Nova Science Pubs., Inc.

Meline, Timothy. A Research Primer for Communication Sciences & Disorders. 2009. (ENG.). 312p. (C). pap. 77.33 *(978-0-13-701597-9(6)*, Allyn & Bacon) Pearson Education Canada CAN. Dist: Pearson Education.

Montano, Joseph J. & Spitzer, Jaclyn B., eds. Adult Audiologic Rehabilitation. 2009. (Illus.). 491p. 110.00 *(978-1-59756-250-8(5))* Plural Publishing, Inc.

Moser, Paul James. Electronics & Instrumentation for Audiologists. 2008. (ENG.). 416p. 84.95 *(978-0-8058-5555-5(6)*, Psychology Press) Taylor & Francis Group GBR. Dist: Taylor & Francis Group.

National Student Speech Language and Hearing Association Staff. Communication Sciences Student Survival Guide. 2nd ed. 2009. (ENG.). 288p. (C). pap. 41.95 *(978-1-4354-8102-2(X))* Delmar Cengage Learning.

Neumann, K. & Kob, M., eds. Report of the COST Project. 2009. (Illus.). 68p. pap. *(978-3-8055-9181-2(0))* Karger, S. AG.

Newton, Valerie E. & Newton. Paediatric Audiological Medicine. Newton, Valerie E., ed. 2nd ed. 2009. (ENG., Illus.). 536p. 143.99 *(978-0-470-31987-1(9)*, Wiley) Wiley, John & Sons, Inc.

Ohlemiller, Kevin K. & Clark, William W. Anatomy & Physiology of Hearing for Audiologists. 2007. (ENG., Illus.). 480p. (C). 138.95 *(978-1-4018-1444-1(1))* Delmar Cengage Learning.

Peterson, Miles E. & Bell, Theodore S. Foundations of Audiology: A Practical Approach. 2007. (ENG., Illus.). 304p. (C). per. 72.00 *(978-0-13-118568-5(3)*, Prentice Hall) Prentice Hall PTR.

Praxis II Exam Secrets Test Prep Staff, ed. Praxis II Audiology (0341) Exam Flashcard Study System: Praxis II Test Practice Questions & Review for the Praxis II Subject Assessments. 2011. (C). 62.99 *(978-1-61403-699-9(3))* Mometrix Media LLC.

Ramachandran, Virginia & Stach, Brad A. Professional Communication in Audiology. 2012. (Illus.). 200p. pap. 55.00 *(978-1-59756-365-9(X))* Plural Publishing, Inc.

Rhoades, Ellen/A & Duncan, Jill, eds. Auditory-Verbal Practice: Toward a Family-Centered Approach. 2010. *(978-0-398-07925-3(0))*; 420p. pap. *(978-0-398-07926-0(9))* Thomas, Charles C. Pub., Ltd.

Richburg, Cynthia McCormick & Smiley, Donna Fisher. School-Based Audiology. 2011. (Illus.). 300p. pap. 59.95 *(978-1-59756-385-7(4))* Plural Publishing, Inc.

Robb, Michael P. Intro: A Beginner's Guide to Communication Sciences & Disorders. 2010. (Illus.). 410p. (C). pap. 98.95 *(978-1-59756-339-0(0))* Plural Publishing, Inc.

Robinette, Martin S. & Glattke, Theodore J. Otoacoustic Emissions: Clinical Applications. 3rd ed. 2007. (Illus.). xix, 436p. 84.95 *(978-3-13-103713-8(X))* Thieme Medical Pubs., Inc.

Roeser, Ross, ed. Audiology Desk Reference: A Guide to the Practice of Audiology. 2011. (ENG., Illus.). 452p. pap. 89.95 *(978-1-60406-398-1(X))* Thieme Medical Pubs., Inc.

Roseberry-McKibbin, Celeste & Hegde, M. N. An Advanced Review of Speech-Language Pathology: Preparation for the PRAXIS & Comprehensive Examination. 3rd ed. 2010. 115.00 *(978-1-4164-0484-2(8))* PRO-ED, Inc.

Rudman, Jack. Speech Pathology & Audiology. (Undergraduate Program Field Tests Ser.: Vol. 25). (C). 49.95 *(978-0-8373-6075-1(7)*, Passbooks) National Learning Corp.

Ruscello, Dennis M. & Mosby. Mosby's Review Questions for the Speech-Language Pathology PRAXIS Examination. 2009. (ENG., Illus.). 376p. pap. 73.95 *(978-0-323-05904-6(X)*, Mosby) Elsevier - Health Sciences Div.

Sandridge, Sharon, et al. Audiology Preceptor Handbook. 2010. (Illus.). 500p. 98.00 *(978-1-59756-320-8(X))* Plural Publishing, Inc.

Schow, Ronald L. & Nerbonne, Michael A. Introduction to Audiologic Rehabilitation. 5th rev. ed. 2006. (ENG., Illus.). 528p. (C). 136.80 *(978-0-205-48292-4(9))* Allyn & Bacon, Inc.

Schwartz, Howard D. A Primer on Communication & Communicative Disorders. 2011. (ENG.). 336p. (C). pap. 100.00 *(978-0-205-49636-5(9))* Allyn & Bacon, Inc.

Silman, Shlomo & Emmer, Michele B. Instrumentation for Audiology & Hearing Science: Theory & Practice. 2011. (Illus.). 200p. pap. 89.95 *(978-1-59756-381-9(1))* Plural Publishing, Inc.

Stach & Stach, Brad A. Clinical Audiology: An Introduction. 2nd ed. 2008. (ENG., Illus.). 816p. (C). 114.95 *(978-0-7668-6288-3(7))* Delmar Cengage Learning.

Taylor, Brian. Consultative Selling Skills for Audiologists. 2011. (Core Clinical Concepts in Audiology Ser.). (Illus.). 160p. pap. 55.00 *(978-1-59756-424-3(9))* Plural Publishing, Inc.

The Thought Propels the Sound. 2008. 40.95 *(978-1-59756-191-4(6))* Plural Publishing, Inc.

Tye-Murray, Nancy. Foundations of Aural Rehabilitation: Children, Adults, & Their Family Members. 3rd ed. 2008. (ENG., Illus.). 792p. (C). pap. 142.95 *(978-1-4283-1215-9(3))* Delmar Cengage Learning.

Valente, Michael, et al, eds. Audiology Answers for Otolaryngologists: A High-Yield Pocket Guide. 2010. (ENG., Illus.). 120p. pap. 49.99 *(978-1-60406-357-8(2))* Thieme Medical Pubs., Inc.

Valente, Michael, et al. Audiology. 2nd ed. 2007. (Illus.). xiii, 528p. 94.95 *(978-3-13-116422-3(0))* Thieme Medical Pubs., Inc.

—The Audiology Capstone: Research, Presentation, & Publication. 2011. (ENG., Illus.). 424p. pap. 79.99 *(978-1-60406-359-2(9))* Thieme Medical Pubs., Inc.

—Audiology Treatment. 2nd ed. 2007. (ENG., Illus.). 544p. 99.99 *(978-1-58890-520-8(9))* Thieme Medical Pubs., Inc.

von Ilberg, C. A., et al. Electric-Acoustic Stimulation of the Auditory System: A Review of the First Decade. Supplement Issue: 'Audiology & Neurotology 2011, Vol. 16, Suppl. 2' 2011. (Illus.). 30p. pap. ***(978-3-8055-9783-8(5))*** Karger, S. AG.

Weinstein, Barbara. Geriatric Audiology. 2011. (ENG., Illus.). 368p. 79.99 *(978-1-60406-174-1(X))* Thieme Medical Pubs., Inc.

Werner, Lynne, et al, eds. Human Auditory Development. 2011. (Springer Handbook of Auditory Research Ser.). (ENG., Illus.). xiv, 284p. 139.00 ***(978-1-4614-1420-9(2)***, 1461414202) Springer.

Wicklund, Karen. Singing Voice Rehabilitation: A Guide for the Voice Teacher & Speech-Language Pathologist. 2009. (ENG.). 264p. (C). 102.95 *(978-1-4354-3854-5(X))* Delmar Cengage Learning.

AUDIOMETER

see Audiometry

AUDIOMETRY

Brixen, Eddy. Audio Metering: Measurements, Standards & Practice. 2nd ed. 2010. (DAN & ENG., Illus.). 272p. pap. 39.95 *(978-0-240-81467-4(3)*, Focal Pr.) Elsevier Science & Technology Bks.

DeRuiter, Mark & Ramachandran, Virginia. Basic Audiometry Learning Manual. 2010. (Illus.). 150p. pap. 55.00 *(978-1-59756-371-0(4))* Plural Publishing, Inc.

Fatakia, Adil, et al. Physiology of Hearing. 4th ed. 2007. pap. *(978-1-56772-107-2(9))* American Academy of Otolaryngology-Head & Neck Surgery Foundation, Inc.

Galdon Romero, Javier. Temporary Changes in Hearing of Pop-Rock Musicians. 2011. 140p. pap. ***(978-3-8443-0736-8(2))*** Lambert Academic Publishing.

Greenberg, Steven, et al, eds. Speech Processing in the Auditory System. 2010. (Springer Handbook of Auditory Research Ser.). (Illus.). xiv, 496p. pap. 229.00 *(978-1-4419-1831-4(0*, 1441918310) Springer.

Hall, James W., III & Swanepoel, De Wet. Objective Assessment of Hearing. 2009. (Illus.). 175p. pap. 55.00 *(978-1-59756-353-6(6))* Plural Publishing, Inc.

Hunter, Lisa & Shahnaz, Navid. Acoustic Immittance Measures: Basic & Advanced Practice. 2012. (Illus.). 175p. pap. 55.00 *(978-1-59756-437-3(0))* Plural Publishing, Inc.

Lawson, Gary & Peterson, Mary. Speech Audiometry. 2011. (Illus.). viii, 166p. pap. 55.00 *(978-1-59756-370-3(6))* Plural Publishing, Inc.

Martin, Frederick N. & Clark, John Greer. Introduction to Audiology. 11th rev. ed. 2011. (ENG.). 504p. (C). pap. 130.67 *(978-0-13-210821-8(6))* Allyn & Bacon, Inc.

Parks, Thomas N., et al, eds. Plasticity of the Auditory System. 2012. (Springer Handbook of Auditory Research Ser.). (ENG., Illus.). xii, 324p. pap. 219.00 *(978-1-4419-1932-8(5)*, 1441919325) Springer.

Peck, James E. Pseudohypacusis: False & Exaggerated Hearing Loss. 2011. (Illus.). 256p. 79.95 *(978-1-59756-397-0(8))* Plural Publishing, Inc.

Roeser, Ross J., et al. Audiology Diagnosis. 2nd ed. 2007. (Illus.). (ENG.). 616p. 89.99 *(978-1-58890-542-0(X))*; xiii, 602p. 84.95 *(978-3-13-116432-2(8))* Thieme Medical Pubs., Inc.

Valente, Maureen. Pure-Tone Audiometry & Masking. 2009. (Core Clinical Concepts in Audiology Ser.). (Illus.). 196p. 45.00 *(978-1-59756-340-6(4))* Plural Publishing, Inc.

Valente, Michael, et al, eds. Audiology Answers for Otolaryngologists: A High-Yield Pocket Guide. 2010. (ENG., Illus.). 120p. pap. 49.99 *(978-1-60406-357-8(2))* Thieme Medical Pubs., Inc.

AUDIOTAPE RECORDERS AND RECORDING, DIGITAL

see Digital Audiotape Recorders and Recording

AUDIOTAPES

Bitner, Jason. Cassette from My Ex: Stories & Soundtracks of Lost Loves. 2009. (ENG., Illus.). 224p. 22.99 *(978-0-312-56552-7(6)*, St. Martin's Griffin) St. Martin's Pr.

Kim, Casey. Rip Your Own: Digitize Your Records & Tapes. 2010. (ENG., Illus.). 176p. pap. 24.99 *(978-1-59863-583-6(2))* Course Technology.

AUDIOTAPES—BIBLIOGRAPHY

Bowker Staff, ed. Books Out Loud 2009, 2 vols. 24th ed. 2009. 365.00 *(978-0-8352-4977-5(8))* Bowker LLC, R. R.

—Books Out Loud 2010, 2 vols. 25th rev. ed. 2010. 380.00 *(978-1-59237-613-1(4))* Grey Hse. Publishing.

AUDIOTAPES—CATALOGS

Bowker Staff, ed. Books Out Loud, 2 vols. 25th rev. ed. 2010. 380.00 *(978-1-59237-614-8(2))* 25th rev. ed. 2010. 380.00 *(978-1-59237-615-5(0))* 26th rev. ed. 2011. 400.00 *(978-1-59237-688-9(6))* 26th rev. ed. 2011. 400.00 *(978-1-59237-689-6(4))* 26th rev. ed. 2011. 400.00 *(978-1-59237-687-2(8))* Grey Hse. Publishing.

Schwieger, Peter, ed. Tibetische Handschriften und Blockdrucke: Teil 13: (Die mTshur-phu-Ausgabe der Sammlung Rin-chen gter-mdzod chen-mo, nach dem Exemplar der Orientabteilung, Staatsbibliothek zu Berlin Preussischer Kulturbesitz, Hs or 778, Bande 4052) 2009. (Verzeichnis der Orientalischen Handschriften in Deutschland (VOHD) Ser.). (GER & TIB.). 474p. (C). 117.00 *(978-3-515-07347-9(7))* Steiner, Franz Verlag Wiesbaden GmbH DEU. Dist: Brown, David Bk. Co., The.

AUDIT, MANAGEMENT

see Management Audit

AUDITING

see also Accounting; Auditing, Internal; Energy Auditing; Financial Statements; Tax Auditing

also subdivision Accounting under names of industries, trades, etc.

Aamir, Suhaib & Farooq, Umar. Auditor Client Relationship & Audit Quality. 2011. 116p. pap. ***(978-3-8454-1566-6(5))*** Lambert Academic Publishing.

Accounting & Auditing for Nonprofit: Companies-Products-Services. 600p. *(978-0-7605-0650-9(7))* Rector Pr., Ltd.

Accounting & Auditing Standards: Pending Proposals & Emerging Issues: Hearing Before the Subcommittee on Capital Markets, Insurance, & Government Sponsored Enterprises of the Committee on Financial Services, U.S. House of Representatives, One Hundred Eleventh Congress, Second Session, May 21, 2010. 2010. v, 118p. *(978-0-16-086767-5(3)*, 552-070-41688-9) United States Government Printing Office.

Aicpa. AICPA Audit & Accounting Guide: Brokers & Dealers in Securities. 2007. pap. 86.25 *(978-0-87051-685-6(X))* American Institute of Certified Public Accountants.

—AICPA Audit & Accounting Manual 2007. 2007. pap. 148.75 *(978-0-87051-708-2(2))* American Institute of Certified Public Accountants.

—AICPA Government Auditing Standards & Circular A-133 Audits. 2007. pap. 73.75 *(978-0-87051-690-0(6))* American Institute of Certified Public Accountants.

—Audit & Accounting Guide: Health Care Entities, with Conforming Changes as of June 1 2010. 2010. pap. 106.25 *(978-0-87051-915-4(8))* American Institute of Certified Public Accountants.

—Audit Guide Audit Sampling. 2008. pap. 86.25 *(978-0-87051-740-2(6))* American Institute of Certified Public Accountants.

—Audit Risk Alert Bank, Credit Union, & Other Depository & Lending Institution Industry Developments-2007. 2007. pap. 48.75 *(978-0-87051-696-2(5))* American Institute of Certified Public Accountants.

—Audit Risk Alert Compliation an Review Alert 2007/08. 2007. pap. 48.75 *(978-0-87051-706-8(6))* American Institute of Certified Public Accountants.

—Audit Risk Alert Construction Contractors 2007-2008. 2007. pap. 36.25 *(978-0-87051-700-6(7))* American Institute of Certified Public Accountants.

—Audit Risk Alert Government Auditing Standards & Circular A-133 Developments 2007/2008. 2007. pap. 36.25 *(978-0-87051-695-5(7))* American Institute of Certified Public Accountants.

—Establishing & Maintaining a System of Quality Control for a CPA Firm's Accounting & Auditing Practice. 2007. pap. 50.00 *(978-0-87051-704-4(X))* American Institute of Certified Public Accountants.

AICPA Staff. Audit Risk Alert: Government Standards & Circular A-133 Developments. 2009. 45p. pap. 48.95 *(978-0-87051-844-7(5))* American Institute of Certified Public Accountants.

American Institute of Certified Public Accountants, SAS No. 70 Task Force Staff & American Institute of Certified Public Accountants, Auditing Standards Board Staff, contrib. by. Service Organizations: Applying SAS No. 70, As Amended: With Conforming Changes As of May 1, 2007. 2007. (Illus.). xx, 208p. pap. *(978-0-87051-672-6(8))* American Institute of Certified Public Accountants.

American Institute of Certified Public Accountants Staff, contrib. by. Analytical Procedures: With Conforming Changes As of May 1, 2007. 2007. (Illus.). xii, 70p. *(978-0-87051-674-0(4))* American Institute of Certified Public Accountants.

Arens, et al. Auditing & Assurance Services. 14th rev. ed. 2011. (ENG.). 872p. (C). 233.33 *(978-0-13-257595-9(7)*, Prentice Hall) Prentice Hall PTR.

Arens, Alvin A., et al. Auditing & Assurance Services. 10th ed. 2006. (ENG.). pap. 18.95 *(978-1-4288-1044-0(7))* Cram101 Inc.

—Auditing & Assurance Services. 14th ed. 2011. (ENG.). 872p. (C). 133.33 *(978-0-13-280543-8(X)*, Prentice Hall) Prentice Hall PTR.

—Auditing & Assurance Services: An Integrated Approach. 13th ed. 2009. (ENG., Illus.). 872p. (C). 233.33 *(978-0-13-608473-0(7)*, Prentice Hall) Prentice Hall PTR.

—Student Value Edition for Auditing & Assurance Services. 14th ed. 2011. (ENG.). 872p. (C). ring bd. 151.67 *(978-0-13-257596-6(5)*, Prentice Hall) Prentice Hall PTR.

Arens and Elder, Beasley. Essentials of Auditing & Assurance Ser. 2006. pap. 14.95 *(978-1-4288-0772-3(1))* Cram101 Inc.

Arnason, Sigurjon Thor & Willett, Keith D. How to Achieve 27001 Certification: An Example of Applied Compliance Management. 2007. (ENG., Illus.). 352p. 89.95 (978-0-8493-3648-5(1)) Auerbach Pubs., Inc.

Ashton, Robert H. & Ashton, Alison Hubbard, eds. Judgment & Decision-Making Research in Accounting & Auditing. 2007. (Cambridge Series on Judgment & Decision Making). (ENG., Illus.). 312p. pap. 61.00 (978-0-521-66438-7(1)) Cambridge Univ. Pr.

Association of Governing Boards of Universities and Colleges, creator. The Audit Committee. 2011. pap. 15.00 (978-0-926508-06-4(7)) Assn. of Governing Boards of Universities & Colleges.

Attestation & Other Special Engagements: 2007 Edition. 2007. pap. 189.00 (978-0-8080-9088-5(7)) Toolkit Media Group.

Audit Committe Effectiveness Center. The AIPCA Audit Committee Toolkit. 2nd ed. 2007. pap. 25.00 (978-0-87051-679-5(5)) American Institute of Certified Public Accountants.

Audits of Certain Nonprofit Organizations. annuals 2nd ed. 33.00 (978-0-87051-016-8(9)) American Institute of Certified Public Accountants.

AuditWatch & Georgiades, George. Knowledge-Based Audits of Commercial Entities: 2007 Edition. 2007th rev. ed. 2007. pap. 189.00 (978-0-8080-9201-8(4)) Toolkit Media Group.

Baldwin, Carryl L. Audit Process & Mental Workloads. 2012. (ENG., Illus.). 343p. 119.95 (978-0-415-32594-3(3), CRC Press) Taylor & Francis Group GBR. Dist: Taylor & Francis Group.

Beasley, Mark & Carcello, Joseph. GAAS Guide, 2012 eBook (with CD-ROM) 2011. 1600p. E-Book 226.00 (978-0-8080-2793-5(X)) Toolkit Media Group.

Beasley, Mark S., et al. Auditing Cases: An Interactive Learning Approach. 4th ed. 2008. (ENG.). 432p. (C). pap. 60.00 (978-0-13-242350-2(2), Prentice Hall) Prentice Hall PTR.

Beebe, Larry. Knowledge-Based Audits of Employee Benefits Plans. 2008. 150p. cd-rom 189.00 (978-0-8080-9185-1(9)) Toolkit Media Group.

Biegelman, Martin T. & Biegelman, Daniel R. Foreign Corrupt Practices Act Compliance Guidebook: Protecting Your Organization from Bribery & Corruption. 2010. (Wiley Corporate F&a Ser.: 8). (ENG., Illus.). 384p. 68.50 (978-0-470-52793-1(5), Wiley) Wiley, John & Sons, Inc.

Bisk, Nathan M. Bisk Comprehensive CPA Review: Business Environment & Concepts. 39th ed. 2009. (Bisk Comprehensive CPA Review Ser.). 608p. pap. 49.95 (978-1-57961-736-3(0)) Bisk Education, Inc.

—Bisk Comprehensive CPA Review: Regulation. 39th ed. 2009. (Bisk Comprehensive CPA Review Ser.). pap. 49.95 (978-1-57961-735-6(2)) Bisk Education, Inc.

—Bisk Comprehensive Exam Review: Auditing & Attestation. 39th ed. 2009. (Bisk Comprehensive CPA Review Ser.). 912p. pap. 49.95 (978-1-57961-734-9(4)) Bisk Education, Inc.

—Bisk CPA Comprehensive Exam Review: Auditing & Attestation. 38th ed. 2008. (Illus.). 864p. pap. 46.95 (978-1-57961-679-3(8)) Bisk Education, Inc.

Bongiorno, Benedetto. Knowledge-Based Audits of Real Estate Entities. 2008. 150p. pap. 189.00 (978-0-8080-9187-5(5)) Toolkit Media Group.

Boum, John. Public Sector Auditing: Is It Value for Money? 2008. (ENG., Illus.). 426p. 60.00 (978-0-470-05722-3(X), Wiley) Wiley, John & Sons, Inc.

Boynton and Joh, Kell. Modern Auditing. 2006. pap. 17.95 (978-1-4288-0764-8(0)) Cram101 Inc.

Bragg, Steven M. Practitioner's Guide to GAAS 2012: Including all SASs, SSAEs, SSARSs, & Interpretations. 9th ed. 2011. (ENG.). 979p. pap. 95.00 (978-0-470-92395-5(4), Wiley) Wiley, John & Sons, Inc.

Bragg, Steven M. & Roehl-Anderson, Janice M. The Controller's Function: The Work of the Managerial Accountant. 4th ed. 2011. (Wiley Corporate F&a Ser.: 563). (ENG., Illus.). 484p. 95.00 (978-0-470-93742-6(4), Wiley) Wiley, John & Sons, Inc.

Braiotta, Louis, Jr., et al. The Audit Committee Handbook. 5th ed. 2010. (ENG., Illus.). 400p. 99.95 (978-0-470-56048-8(7), Wiley) Wiley, John & Sons, Inc.

Broadus, W A., Jr., et al. Guide to Single Audits, 3 vols. Incl. Vol. 1. ring bd. 168.00 (978-0-7646-0442-3(2)); Vol. 2. ring bd. 168.00 (978-0-7646-0443-0(0)); Vol. 3. ring bd. 168.00 (978-0-7646-0444-7(9)); 1998. 168.00 (978-0-7646-0441-6(4)) Practitioners Publishing Co.

Buckless, Frank A., et al. Assurance Practice Set for Comprehensive Assurance & Systems Tool (CAST)-Integrated Practice Set. 2nd ed. 2010. (ENG.). 128p. (C). pap. 46.67 (978-0-13-214640-1(1), Prentice Hall) Prentice Hall PTR.

—Auditing Cases: An Interactive Learning Approach. 5th rev. ed. 2011. (ENG.). 408p. (C). pap. 60.00 (978-0-13-256723-7(7), Prentice Hall) Prentice Hall PTR.

Buckless, Frank A., et al. Computerized Practice Set for Comprehensive Assurance & Systems Tool (CAST)-Integrated Practice Set. 2nd ed. 2010. (ENG.) 112p. (C). pap. 46.67 (978-0-13-214641-8(X), Prentice Hall) Prentice Hall PTR.

Carcello, Joseph & Beasley, Mark. GAAS Guide, 2007. 2007th rev. ed. 2006. 1136p. pap. 159.00 (978-0-8080-9048-9(8), CCH) Wolters Kluwer Tax & Accounting.

Carmichael, Douglas R., et al. Guide to Audits of Employee Benefit Plans, 3 vols. Incl. Vol. 1. ring bd. 172.00 (978-0-7646-0320-4(5)); Vol. 2. ring bd. 172.00 (978-0-7646-0321-1(3)); Vol. 3. ring bd. 172.00 (978-0-7646-0322-8(1)); 1997. Set ring bd. 172.00 (978-0-7646-0319-8(1)) Practitioners Publishing Co.

—Guide to Audits of Financial Institutions, 4 vols. Incl. Vol. 1. ring bd. 278.00 (978-0-7646-0506-2(2)); Vol. 2. ring bd. (978-0-7646-0507-9(0)); Vol. 3. ring bd. 278.00 (978-0-7646-0508-6(9)); Vol. 4. ring bd. 278.00 (978-0-7646-0509-3(7)); 1998. 278.00 (978-0-7646-0505-5(4)); 265.00 (978-1-56433-997-3(1)) Practitioners Publishing Co.

—Guide to Audits of Nonprofit Organizations, 3 vols. Incl. Vol. 1. Holland, Stephen F. ring bd. 184.00 (978-0-7646-0438-6(4)); Vol. 2. Holland, Stephen E. ring bd. 184.00 (978-0-7646-0439-3(2)); Vol. 3. Holland, Stephen E. ring bd. 184.00 (978-0-7646-0440-9(6)); 1998. 184.00 (978-0-7646-0437-9(6)); Set ring bd. 177.00 (978-0-7646-0171-2(7)) Practitioners Publishing Co.

CCH Editors. TOP Accounting Issues for 2009 CPE Course. 2008. 200p. pap. 31.00 (978-0-8080-1886-5(8)) Toolkit Media Group.

Chapman, Christopher S., et al, eds. Accounting, Organizations, & Institutions: Essays in Honour of Anthony Hopwood. 2009. (ENG., Illus.). 464p. 135.00 (978-0-19-954635-0(5)) Oxford Univ. Pr., Inc.

Collings, Steven. Interpretation & Application of International Standards on Auditing. 2011. (Wiley Regulatory Reporting Ser.). (ENG.). 648p. pap. 105.00 (978-0-470-66112-3(7), Wiley) Wiley, John & Sons, Inc.

Cosserat, Graham & Rodda, Neil. Modern Auditing. 3rd ed. 2009. (ENG., Illus.). 744p. pap. 60.95 (978-0-470-31973-4(9), Wiley) Wiley, John & Sons, Inc.

Cram101 Textbook Reviews. Outlines & Highlights for Auditing & Assurance Services: An Applied Approach by Iris Stuart, ISBN. 2011. 168p. pap. 29.95 (978-1-4288-0420-3(X)) Cram101 Inc.

—Outlines & Highlights for Wiley Cpa Exam Review 2010, Auditing & Attestation by Patrick R Delaney Cp. 2011. 56p. pap. 26.95 (978-1-61905-581-0(3)) Cram101 Inc.

Cram101 Textbook Reviews & Cram101 Textbook Reviews. Outlines & Highlights for Audit Process: Principles, Practice & Cases by Iain Gray & Stuart Manson, ISBN. 2011. 108p. pap. 28.95 (978-1-61461-627-6(2)) Cram101 Inc.

—Outlines & Highlights for Auditing: Assurance & Risk by W. Robert Knechel. 2011. 242p. pap. 31.95 (978-1-61830-409-4(7)) Cram101 Inc.

—Outlines & Highlights for Auditing & Assurance Services by Alvin a Arens. 2011. 226p. pap. 30.95 (978-1-61830-410-0(0)) Cram101 Inc.

—Outlines & Highlights for Auditing It Infrastructures for Compliance by Kim. 2011. 112p. pap. 28.95 (978-1-61830-420-9(8)) Cram101 Inc.

—Outlines & Highlights for the Controllers Function: The Work of the Managerial Accountant by Steven Bragg, ISBN. 2011. 70p. pap. 27.95 (978-1-61461-234-6(X)) Cram101 Inc.

Cram101 Textbook Reviews Staff. Outlines & Highlights for Auditing: A Business Risk Approach by Rittenberg, Johnstone, & Gramling, ISBN. 2009. 228p. pap. 31.95 (978-1-4288-2851-3(6)) Cram101 Inc.

—Outlines & Highlights for Auditing & Assurance Services by Louwers, Isbn: 9780077250331. 2009. 200p. pap. 30.95 (978-1-4288-6825-0(9)) Cram101 Inc.

—Outlines & Highlights for Auditing & Assurance Services by William F Messier, Isbn: 9780077236533. 2009. 196p. pap. 30.95 (978-1-4288-2325-9(5)); 74p. pap. 27.95 (978-1-4288-9852-3(2)) Cram101 Inc.

—Outlines & Highlights for Mp Principles of Auditing & Other Assurance Services by Whittington, Isbn: 9780073291925. 2007. 160p. pap. 12.95 (978-1-4288-5703-2(6)) Cram101 Inc.

Crawford, Michael A. & Loyd, D. Scot. Local Government & Single Audits (2008) 2008. 170p. pap. 218.00 (978-0-8080-9189-9(1)) Toolkit Media Group.

Crawford, Micheal & Loyd, Scot. Knowledge-Based Single Audits. 2008. 150p. cd-rom 189.00 (978-0-8080-9188-2(3)) Toolkit Media Group.

Cutforth, Arthur E. Audits. 2009. 164p. pap. 20.75 (978-1-116-32247-7(1)); (ENG.). 165p. pap. 19.99 (978-1-116-32249-1(8), BiblioLife); (ENG.). 165p. pap. 21.99 (978-1-116-32248-4(X), BiblioLife) BiblioBazaar.

Dauber, Nick A. & Dauber. Wiley the Complete Guide to Auditing Standards, & Other Professional Standards for Accountants 2009. 5th ed. 2009. (ENG.). 549p. pap. 95.00 (978-0-470-41152-0(X), Wiley) Wiley, John & Sons, Inc.

Dauber, Nick A., et al. The Complete Guide to Auditing Standards & Other Professional Standards for Accountants 2008. 4th ed. 2008. (ENG.). 532p. pap. 95.00 (978-0-470-18397-7(7), Wiley) Wiley, John & Sons, Inc.

Defense Contract Audit Agency: Who Is Responsible for Reform?: Hearing Before the Committee on Homeland Security & Governmental Affairs, United States Senate, of the One Hundred Eleventh Congress, First Session, September 23, 2009. 2011. (Illus.). iii, 285p. (978-0-16-088675-1(9), 552-070-42841-1) United States Government Printing Office.

Department of Economic and Social Affairs Division for Social Change Staff, contrib. by. Auditing for Social Change: A Strategy for Citizen Engagement in Public Sector Accountability. 2007. (ENG.). 220p. pap. 24.00 (978-92-1-123164-9(7)) United Nations Pubns.

Dicksee, Lawrence R. Auditing: A Practical Manual for Auditors. 2010. (ENG.). 932p. pap. 61.75 (978-1-174-61124-7(3)) BiblioBazaar.

The ExamMatrix CPA Exam Review - Auditing & Attestation. 2007. per. 995.00 net. (978-1-933366-07-4(9)) ExamMatrix.

Fearnley, Stella, et al. Reaching Key Financial Reporting Decisions: How Directors & Auditors Interact. 2011. (ENG.). 384p. 75.00 (978-0-470-74874-9(5), Wiley) Wiley, John & Sons, Inc.

Foreign Corrupt Practices ACT: Hearing Before the Subcommittee on Crime, Terrorism, & Homeland Security of the Committee on the Judiciary, House of Representatives, One Hundred Twelfth Congress, First Session, June 14, 2011. 2011. iii, 88p. (978-0-16-089497-8(2), 552-070-43456-9) United States Government Printing Office.

Friedfel, Alan & Mintzer, Rich. The Pocket Idiot's Guide to Surviving an Audit. 2010. (Pocket Idiot's Guide Ser.). (ENG.). 208p. (gr. 12-18). 9.95 (978-1-59257-964-8(7), Alpha Bks.) Penguin Group (USA) Inc.

Garczynski, Michael F. & Georgiades, George. Knowledge-Based Audits of Health Care Entities. 2008. 156p. pap. 189.00 incl. audio compact disk (978-0-8080-9186-8(7)) Toolkit Media Group.

Georgiades, George. Audit Procedures. 2007th rev. ed. 2006. 880p. pap. 179.00 (978-0-8080-9044-1(5), CCH) Wolters Kluwer Tax & Accounting.

Georgiades, George B. GAAS Practice Manual, 2007. 2007th rev. ed. 2006. 1536p. pap. 159.00 (978-0-8080-9039-7(9), CCH) Wolters Kluwer Tax & Accounting.

Golden, Thomas W., et al. A Guide to Forensic Accounting Investigation. 2nd ed. 2011. (ENG., Illus.). 648p. 180.00 (978-0-470-59907-5(3), Wiley) Wiley, John & Sons, Inc.

Government Accountability Office (U.S.) Staff, compiled by. Government Auditing Standards 2007. rev. ed. 2007. (ENG.). 228p. pap. 12.50 (978-0-16-078028-6(4), Government Accountability Office) United States Government Printing Office.

Gray, Iain & Manson, Stuart. Audit Process: Priciples Practice & Cases - Isa Edition. 4th ed. 2007. 836p. pap. 74.99 (978-1-84480-678-2(2), Cengage Learning GBR. Dist: CENGAGE Learning.

Gul. Theory & Practice of Australian Auditing. 2nd ed. 616p. pap. (978-0-17-008686-8(0)) CENGAGE Learning.

HCPro, creator. The National Patient Safety Goals: FAQs. 2008. 81p. spiral bd. 79.00 (978-1-60146-311-1(1)) Opus Communications.

Help! I'm Being Audited! (978-0-9645848-1-5(6)) JTH Publishing.

Henderson, Perry M., contrib. by. TOP Auditing Issues for 2009 CPE Course. 2008. 200p. pap. 31.00 (978-0-8080-1887-2(6)) Toolkit Media Group.

Henderson, Perry M. & Ulvog, James. TOP Auditing Issues for 2009 CPE Course. 2008. 250p. pap. 0.00 (978-0-8080-1874-2(4)) Toolkit Media Group.

Hooks, Karen L. Auditing & Assurance Services: Understanding the Integrated Audit. 2010. (ENG., Illus.). 960p. (C). 221.95 (978-0-471-72634-0(6), Wiley) Wiley, John & Sons, Inc.

Hopkins, Leon. Audit Report. ring bd. 440.00 (978-0-406-02014-7(0), U.K., MICHIE) LEXIS Publishing.

Hunt, Max, et al. Guide to HUD Audits, 3 vols. Incl. Vol. 1. ring bd. (978-0-7646-0017-3(6)); Vol. 2. ring bd. (978-0-7646-0018-0(4)); Vol. 3. ring bd. (978-0-7646-0019-7(2)); 1996. 150.00 (978-0-7646-0016-6(8)); Set ring bd. 159.00 (978-0-7646-0240-5(3)) Practitioners Publishing Co.

Information Center Of Registered Accountants Staff, ed. Guidelines to the Auditor in Prospectus Related Engagements. 2009. 151p. 65.00 (978-90-466-0276-8(1)) Maklu Uitgevers N.V. BEL. Dist: International Specialized Bk. Services.

Ingenix, creator. DRG Desk Reference: The Ultimate Resource for Improving the New MS-DRG Assignment Practices. 2011. (ENG.). 930p. pap. 209.95 (978-1-60151-547-6(2)) 2010. (Illus.). 908p. pap. 209.95 (978-1-60151-376-2(3)) OptumInsight, Inc.

Ingraham, Laura R. & Jenkins, J. Gregory. Comprehensive Assurance & Systems Tool (CAST)-Integrated Practice Set. 2nd ed. 2010. (ENG.). 344p. (C). pap. 113.33 (978-0-13-137721-9(3), Prentice Hall) Prentice Hall PTR.

Isaca. Security, Audit & Control Features SAP ERP, 3rd Edition. 2009. pap. (978-1-60420-115-4(0)) Information Systems Audit and Control Assn.

Jack, Lisa, et al, eds. The Routledge Companion to Accounting Communication. 2012. (ENG., Illus.). 480p. (C). 165.00 (978-0-415-61714-7(6)) Routledge.

Kaplan CPA Education Staff. CPA Exam: Quick Review Flash Cards Auditing & Attestation. 2006. n/ap. 98.95 (978-1-4195-9106-8(1)) Dearborn Financial Publishing.

Kaplan CPA Review. CPA Exam Study Manual: Auditing & Attestation 2009/2010. 2009. (ENG.). 576p. pap. 49.95 (978-1-4277-8869-6(3)) Kaplan Publishing.

Khwaja, Munawer Sultan, et al, eds. Risk-Based Tax Audits: Approaches & Country Experiences. 2011. (Directions in Development Ser.). (ENG.). 136p. pap. 20.00 (978-0-8213-8754-2(5), 9780821387542) World Bank Pubns.

Khwaja, Munawer Sultan, et al. Risk-Based Tax Audits: Approaches & Country Experiences. 2011. (978-0-8213-8755-9(3)) World Bank Pubns.

Kim. Auditing It Infrastructures for Compliance. 2010. 384p. pap. 89.95 (978-0-7637-9181-0(4)) Jones & Bartlett Learning, LLC.

Knapp. Knapp Contemporary Audit. Date not set. (Adaptable Courseware Ser.). 12.00 (978-0-314-11198-2(0)) Southwest Educational Development Laboratory.

Knechel, W. Robert, et al. Auditing: Assurance & Risk. 3rd rev. ed. 2006. (ENG., Illus.). 888p. (C). 287.95 (978-0-324-31318-5(7)) Cengage South-Western.

Konrath. Auditing A Risk Analysis Approach. 2006. pap. 15.95 (978-1-4288-0985-7(6)) Cram101 Inc.

Krigger, John & Dorsi, Chris. Saturn Energy Auditor Field Guide. 2009. (ENG.). 306p. (C). pap., instr.'s gde. ed. 61.20 (978-0-13-512543-4(X), Prentice Hall) Prentice Hall PTR.

Kroon, Caroline & Veldboer, Tamara. Mirror on the Wall, What Is Most Optimal Post-Audit Framework of All? 2010. 80p. pap. (978-3-8383-7480-2(0)) Lambert Academic Publishing.

Laurdan Associates. Employment-Labor Law Audit: Ella. 9th rev. ed. 2008. ring bd. 225.00 (978-0-9771406-1-9(X)) Laurdan Assocs., Inc.

Leung, David. The Truth about Accounting Researching Financial Reporting & Auditing. 2011. 158p. 114.95 (978-1-4094-2049-1(3), Gower Publishing Co., Ltd.) Ashgate Publishing, Ltd. GBR. Dist: Ashgate Publishing Co.

Link, Edward P. Un audit du Systeme, et non des Gens: Un guide de poche ISO 9001:2008 pour chaque Employé. Desroches, Martine, tr. 2010.Tr. of Audit of the System, not of the People. (ENG., Illus.). 127p. spiral bd. (978-0-9668699-3-4(1)) Quality Pursuit, Inc.

Linnas, Raivo. New Approach to Audit, Control & Supervision of the Local Government. 2010. 184p. pap. (978-3-8383-5519-1(9)) Lambert Academic Publishing.

Lipman, Frederick D. Audit Committees. 5th ed. 2007. (Corporate Practice Ser.: 49-5th). ring bd. 195.00 (978-1-55871-548-6(7)) Bureau of National Affairs, Inc., (BNA), The.

Lonsdale, Jeremy, et al. Performance Auditing: Contributing to Accountability in Democratic Government. Lonsdale, Jeremy et al, eds. 2011. (Illus.). 368p. 150.00 (978-1-84844-972-5(0)) Elgar, Edward Publishing, Inc.

Louwers, et al. Auditing & Assurance Services. 5th ed. 2013. (978-0-07-802544-0(3)) McGraw-Hill Cos., The.

Louwers, Ramsay. Auditing & Assurances. 2006. pap. 13.95 (978-1-4288-1290-1(3)) Cram101 Inc.

Louwers, Timothy, et al. Auditing & Assurance Services with Acl. 5th ed. 2012. (ENG.). (C). 228.00 incl. cd-rom (978-0-07-752016-8(5), 0077520165, McGraw-Hill/Irwin) McGraw-Hill Higher Education.

—MP LL Auditing & Assurance Services w/ACL CD 5e. 5th ed. 2012. (ENG.). (C). ring bd., ring bd. 159.67 incl. cd-rom (978-0-07-755491-0(4), 0077554914, McGraw-Hill/Irwin) McGraw-Hill Higher Education.

Louwers, Timothy, et al. Study Guide to accompany Auditing & Assurance Services. 4th ed. 2010. (ENG.). 160p. (C). pap. 87.33 (978-0-07-726831-2(8), 0077268318, McGraw-Hill/Irwin) McGraw-Hill Higher Education.

Louwers, Timothy J., et al. Auditing & Assurance Services. 3rd ed. 2007. (Illus.). 865p. 158.44 incl. cd-rom (978-0-07-337936-4(0), 9780073379364) 4th ed. 2010. 864p. 182.50 (978-0-07-813664-1(4)) McGraw-Hill Higher Education. (McGraw-Hill/Irwin).

Marchetti, Anne M. Enterprise Risk Management Best Practices: From Assessment to Ongoing Compliance. 2011. (Wiley Corporate F&a Ser.: 561). (ENG., Illus.). 180p. 60.00 (978-0-470-91740-4(7), Wiley) Wiley, John & Sons, Inc.

Mauch, S. Q. E. Peter. Quality Auditor. 2009. 32p. pap. 16.78 (978-0-557-05897-6(X)) Lulu Enterprises Inc.

McDubus, Onyuka Felix. A Concise Course on Auditing. 2011. 80p. pap. (978-3-8443-9541-9(5)) Lambert Academic Publishing.

Messier, William. Auditing & Assurance Services. 7th ed. 2009. 576p. 177.19 (978-0-07-352708-6(4), McGraw-Hill/Irwin) McGraw-Hill Higher Education.

Messier, William, et al. Auditing & Assurance Services. 8th ed. 2011. (ENG.). (C). 243.67 (978-0-07-759613-2(7), 0077596137, McGraw-Hill/Irwin) McGraw-Hill Higher Education.

—Auditing & Assurance Services: A Systematic Approach. 8th ed. 2011. (ENG.). (C). 228.00 incl. cd-rom (978-0-07-752015-1(7), 0077520157, McGraw-Hill/Irwin) McGraw-Hill Higher Education.

Messier, William F., et al. Auditing & Assurance Services: A Systematic Approach. 5th rev. ed. 2006. (Illus.). 800p. 171.88 incl. cd-rom (978-0-07-333720-3(X), 9780073337203, McGraw-Hill/Irwin) McGraw-Hill Higher Education.

—Auditing & Assurance Services: A Systematic Approach, AS5 Edition. 6th ed. 2008. (Illus.). xxxii, 786p. (978-0-07-352690-4(8), Irwin Professional Publishing) McGraw-Hill Schl. Education Group.

Millichamp, A. H. & Taylor, John. Auditing. 9th ed. 2008. 640p. (C). pap. 69.99 (978-1-84480-940-0(4)) Cengage Learning GBR. Dist: CENGAGE Learning.

Min, Young-Woon. Understanding & Auditing It Systems. 2011. 740p. pap. 95.00 (978-1-257-75883-8(7)); pap. 95.00 (978-1-257-12408-4(0)) Lulu Enterprises Inc.

Mintz, Steven M. & Morris, Roselyn E. Ethical Obligations & Decision Making in Accounting: Text & Cases. 2007. (ENG., Illus.). 304p. (C). per. 79.33 (978-0-07-340399-1(7), 0073403997, McGraw-Hill/Irwin) McGraw-Hill Higher Education.

Montgomery, Robert H. Auditing Theory & Practice. 2010. 574p. 44.99 (978-1-140-18329-7(X)); pap. 43.75 (978-1-140-18330-3(3)) BiblioBazaar.

Mulli, Boniface Kalinda & F.All (Illinois USA), Prof. Hamdi. Review of Internal Control Systems. 2011. 72p. pap. (978-3-8443-0499-2(1)) Lambert Academic Publishing.

Narasimham, R., et al. Diagnostic Study of Accounting & Auditing Arrangements: Mongolia. 2007. (Asian Development Bank Ser.). (ENG., Illus.). 119p. pap. (978-971-561-591-4(0)) Asian Development Bank PHL. Dist: Independent Pubs. Group.

—Diagnostic Study of Accounting & Auditing Arrangements in the People's Republic of China. 2007. (Asian Development Bank Ser.). (ENG., Illus.). 181p. pap. (978-971-561-589-1(9)) Asian Development Bank PHL. Dist: Independent Pubs. Group.

—Republic of Kazakhstan. 2007. (Diagnostic Study of Accounting & Auditing Ser.). (ENG.). 96p. pap. (978-971-561-590-7(2)) Asian Development Bank PHL. Dist: Independent Pubs. Group.

Ojo, Marianne. The Role of the External Auditor in Bank Regulation & Supervision. 2008. 380p. pap. (978-3-639-08746-8(1)) VDM Verlag Dr. Mueller e.K.

Paino, Halil, et al. Impairment of Audit Quality. 2010. 240p. pap. (978-3-8383-7564-9(5)) Lambert Academic Publishing.

Pallais, Don, et al. Guide to Auditor's Reports, 2 vols. Incl. Vol. 1. ring bd. 156.00 (978-0-7646-0339-6(6)); Vol. 2. ring bd. 156.00 (978-0-7646-0340-2(X)); 1997. 150.00 (978-0-7646-0338-9(8)) Practitioners Publishing Co.

Pany, Kurt & Whittington, Ray. Principles of Auditing & Other Assurance Services. 18th ed. 2011. (ENG.). (C). 228.00 incl. cd-rom (978-0-07-748627-3(7), 0077486277, McGraw-Hill/Irwin) McGraw-Hill Higher Education.

Paugh, Jennifer. The National Patient Safety Goals Calculator: Tools to Assess Compliance. 2009. (Illus.). 34p. pap. 149.00 incl. cd-rom (978-1-60146-662-4(5)) Opus Communications.

Permanent Court of Arbitration, The Hague, The Hague, compiled by. The Rhine Chlorides Arbitration Concerning the Auditing of Accounts (Netherlands-France) Award Of 2004. 2008. (Permanent Court of Arbitration Award Ser.). (FRE & ENG.). 196p. 69.95 (978-90-6704-266-6(8)) T.M.C. Asser Pr. NLD. Dist: Springer.

Porbundawalla, Kersi & Tarantino, Anthony. Managing Governance, Risk & Compliance: How to Achieve Compliance through Process Documentation, Controls & Tests. 2010. (ENG.). 224p. 75.00 *(978-0-470-69944-7(2)*, Wiley) Wiley, John & Sons, Inc.

Porter, Brenda, et al. Principles of External Auditing. 3rd ed. 2008. (ENG., Illus.). 816p. pap. 65.95 *(978-0-470-01825-5(9)*, Wiley) Wiley, John & Sons, Inc.

Practitioners Publishing Co. Staff. PPC's Guide to HUD Audits, 3 vols. 2006. 234.00 *(978-0-7646-3618-9(9))*; Vol. 3. *(978-0-7646-3621-9(9))* Practitioners Publishing Co.

—PPC's Guide to Nontraditional Engagements, 3 vols., Vol. 2. 2006. *(978-0-7646-3782-7(7))* Practitioners Publishing Co.

Puncel, Luis. Audit Procedures, 2008 (with CD-ROM) 2008th rev. ed. 2007. 100p. pap. 190.00 incl. audio compact disk *(978-0-8080-9123-3(9))* Toolkit Media Group.

Reid, Tracey L. Unclaimed Property: A Reporting Process & Audit Survival Guide. 2008. (ENG., Illus.). 212p. 63.50 *(978-0-470-27824-6(2)*, Wiley) Wiley, John & Sons, Inc.

Retail Audit. Date not set. *(978-0-88061-083-4(2))* International Loss Control Institute, Inc.

Ricchiute. Auditing: Study Guide. 3rd ed. Date not set. (Accounting Ser.). pap., stu. ed. *(978-0-538-81693-9(7))* CENGAGE Learning.

Ricchiute, David N. Auditing & Assurance Services. 7th ed. 2006. (ENG.). pap. 16.95 *(978-1-4288-1140-9(0))* Cram101 Inc.

Rittenberg, Larry E., et al. Auditing: A Business Risk Approach. 8th ed. 2011. (ENG.). 1056p. (C). 264.95 *(978-0-538-47623-2(0))* Cengage South-Western.

Rufus, Robert. Effects of Decision-Aid Use on Evaluations of Tax Preparer Liability. 2010. 96p. pap. 71.00 *(978-3-8383-1546-1(4))* Lambert Academic Publishing.

Ruppel, Warren. Not-for-Profit Organazation Audits with Single Audits. 2008. 1100p. pap. 230.00 incl. audio compact disk *(978-0-8080-9196-7(4))* Toolkit Media Group.

Russell, J. P. The Process Auditing Techniques Guide. 2nd ed. 2010. 25.00 *(978-0-87389-782-2(X))* ASQ Quality Pr.

Saha, Ashit. Auditing Practice in India & Expectations Differences of the Users. 2011. 212p. pap. ***(978-3-8443-9797-0(3))*** Lambert Academic Publishing.

Schelker, Mark. Making Auditors Effective: Theory, Evidence, Perspectives. 2008. 167p. (C). pap. 36.00 *(978-3-8329-3437-8(5))* Nomos Verlagsgesellschaft DEU. Dist: International Specialized Bk. Services.

Schroeder, Douglas A. Accounting & Causal Effects: Econometric Challenges. 2010. (Springer Series in Accounting Scholarship Ser.). (Illus.). xxv, 459p. 219.00 *(978-1-4419-7224-8(2)*, 1441972242) Springer.

Schweiger, Carsten. Media-Auditing: Eine Betrachtung des deutschen Marktes. 2009. 72p. pap. *(978-3-639-16354-4(0))* VDM Verlag Dr. Mueller e.K.

Senft, Sandra & Gallegos, Frederick. Information Technology Control & Audit, Third Edition. 3rd rev. ed. 2008. (ENG., Illus.). 808p. (C). 89.95 *(978-1-4200-6550-3(5))* Auerbach Pubs., Inc.

Sharma, R. B. Peer Review System in India-Icai. 2010. 208p. pap. *(978-3-639-25045-9(1))* VDM Verlag Dr. Mueller e.K.

Shim, Jae, et al. Corporate Controller's Handbook of Financial Management (2008-2009) 2008. 1900p. pap. 189.00 *(978-0-8080-9172-1(7))* Toolkit Media Group.

Simplifying Regulatory Compliance: A Crosswalk of CMS & TJC Requirements. 2nd ed. 2007. per. 159.00 *(978-0-9752634-5-7(5))* CBRCC, Inc.

Soltani, Bahram. Auditing: An International Approach. 2007. (ENG., Illus.). 688p. pap. 110.00 *(978-0-273-65773-6(9))* Financial Times/Prentice Hall.

Srivastava, Rajendra P. & Mock, Theodore J., eds. Belief Functions in Business Decisions. 2010. (Studies in Fuzziness & Soft Computing Ser.). (ENG., Illus.). x, 345p. pap. 159.00 *(978-3-7908-2503-9(4)*, 3790825034) Physica-Verlag DEU. Dist: Springer.

Steiniger, Hans L. Auditing the Food & Beverage Operation: An Operational Audit Approach. 2007. 487p. pap. 29.95 *(978-1-4241-6769-2(8))* PublishAmerica, Inc.

Stevens, Kevin & Wiley Publishing, Inc. Staff. Wiley Cpa Exam Review Focus Notes: Auditing & Attestation 2012. 7th ed. 2011. (ENG.). 274p. pap. 40.00 ***(978-1-118-12131-3(7)***, Wiley) Wiley, John & Sons, Inc.

Stuart, Iris. Auditing & Assurance Services: An Applied Approach. 2011. (ENG., Illus.). 464p. (C). 175.33 *(978-0-07-340400-4(4)*, 0073404004, McGraw-Hill/Irwin) McGraw-Hill Higher Education.

Tewarie, Wiekram. A Structured Approach to IT Auditing: Model Based Development of Audit Terms of Reference. 2011. (ENG.). 513p. pap. 89.95 *(978-90-8659-535-8(9))* VU Univ. Pr. NLD. Dist: Independent Pubs. Group.

Tidrick, Donald E. Auditing & Attestation. 2007th ed. 2008. (ENG.). 256p. per. *(978-0-9771658-0-3(9))* Efficient Learning Systems, Inc.

Trussel, John M. & Frazer, J. Douglas. The Lakeside Company: Case Studies in Auditing. 11th ed. 2007. (ENG., Illus.). 150p. (C). per. 46.67 *(978-0-13-158851-6(6)*, Prentice Hall) Prentice Hall PTR.

Trussel, John M. & Frazer, J. Douglas. Lakeside Company: Case Studies in Auditing. 12th rev. ed. 2011. (ENG., Illus.). 168p. (C). pap. 46.67 ***(978-0-13-256725-1(3)***, Prentice Hall) Prentice Hall PTR.

United Nations Staff. Voluntary Funds Administered by the United Nations High Commissioner for Refugees: Financial Report & Audited Financial Statements for the Year Ended 31 December 2008 & Report of the Board of Auditors. 2009. (ENG.). 152p. pap. 20.00 *(978-92-1-820114-0(X))* United Nations Pubns.

United States, General Accounting Office Staff, contrib. by. Audits of Public Companies. 2008. (Illus.). 133p. 82.00 *(978-1-60456-503-4(9))* Nova Science Pubs., Inc.

van Esch, Sandy & Puttick, G. The Principles & Practice of Auditing. Kana, Suresh, ed. 9th ed. 2008. (ENG., Illus.). 528p. spiral bd. 64.00 *(978-0-7021-7268-7(5))* Juta Academic ZAF. Dist: Independent Pubs. Group.

Van Peursem, Karen A., et al, eds. Audit Education. 2012. (ENG.). 168p. (C). 125.00 ***(978-0-415-69873-3(1))*** Routledge.

Wallace, Eric. Construction Guide: Accounting & Knowledge-Based Audits 2008. 2008. 998p. pap. 169.00 *(978-0-8080-9169-1(7))* Toolkit Media Group.

—Construction Guide Combo. 2008. 2600p. pap. 211.00 *(978-0-8080-9170-7(0))* Toolkit Media Group.

Weirich, Thomas R., et al. Accounting & Auditing Research: Tools & Strategies. 7th ed. 2009. (ENG., Illus.). 240p. (C). pap. 78.95 *(978-0-470-50697-4(0)*, Wiley) Wiley, John & Sons, Inc.

Weiss, Renee. Audit Committee Characteristics & Monitoring Effectiveness. 2009. 116p. pap. *(978-3-639-05753-9(8))* VDM Verlag Dr. Mueller e.K.

Welton, Ralph E. & Friedlob, George Thomas. Keys to Reading an Annual Report. 4th rev. ed. 2008. (Barron's Business Keys Ser.). (ENG., Illus.). 208p. pap. 8.99 *(978-0-7641-3915-4(0))* Barron's Educational Series, Inc.

Whittington & Pany. Principles of Auditing & Other Assurance Services. 18th ed. 2012. *(978-0-07-811103-7(X)*, Irwin Professional Publishing) McGraw-Hill Schl. Education Group.

Whittington, O. Ray & Pany, Kurt. Principles of Auditing & Other Assurance Services. 16th rev. ed. 2007. 832p. (C). 158.44 *(978-0-07-352686-7(X)*, 9780073526867, McGraw-Hill/Irwin) McGraw-Hill Higher Education.

Whittington, Ray & Pany, Kurt. Principles of Auditing & Assurance Services. 18th ed. 2011. (ENG.). (C). 243.67 *(978-0-07-750400-7(3)*, 0077504003, McGraw-Hill/Irwin) McGraw-Hill Higher Education.

—Principles of Auditing & Other Assurance Services. 17th ed. 2009. (Illus.). 832p. 134.75 *(978-0-07-337965-4(4))* McGraw-Hill Professional Publishing.

—Student Study Guide to accompany Principles of Auditing & Other Assurance Services. 18th ed. 2011. (ENG.). 224p. (C). pap. 82.67 *(978-0-07-732850-4(7)*, 0077328507, McGraw-Hill/Irwin) McGraw-Hill Higher Education.

Wiley. Advantage Audit. 2011. 150.00 ***(978-1-118-11640-1(2)***, Wiley) Wiley, John & Sons, Inc.

Williams, Jan R. & Carcello, Joseph V. GAAP Guide Level A. 2008. 1400p. pap. 185.00 *(978-0-8080-9218-6(9))* Toolkit Media Group.

—GAAP Guide, Level A: Restatement & Analysis of Current FASB Standards. 2007. 1400p. pap. 253.00 incl. cd-rom *(978-0-8080-9128-8(X))* Toolkit Media Group.

Woolf, Emile & Hindson, Moira. Audit & Accountancy Pitfalls: A Casebook for Practising Accountants, Lawyers & Insurers. 2010. (ENG.). 336p. 60.00 *(978-0-470-68667-6(7)*, Wiley) Wiley, John & Sons, Inc.

Young, Jan. Cycle Count & Physical Inventory Design & Execution. 2010. 77p. pap. 19.95 *(978-0-557-36935-5(5))* Lulu Enterprises Inc.

AUDITING—DATA PROCESSING

Biskie, Steve. Surviving an SAP Audit: A Practical Guide to SAP Audits. 2009. 500p. *(978-1-59229-253-0(4))* Galileo Pr.

Coderre, David. Fraud Analysis Techniques Using ACL. 2009. (ENG., Illus.). 176p. pap. 210.50 *(978-0-470-39244-7(4)*, Wiley) Wiley, John & Sons, Inc.

Cram101 Textbook Reviews Staff. Outlines & Highlights for Core Concepts of Information Technology Auditing by James E Hunton, Isbn: 9780471222934. 2009. 94p. pap. 27.95 *(978-1-4288-2291-7(7))* Cram101 Inc.

Dowell, Dwayne K. & Jelen, Bill. Excel for Auditors: Audit Spreadsheets Using Excel 97 through Excel 2007. 2006. (Excel for Professionals Ser.). (ENG., Illus.). 212p. pap. 24.95 *(978-1-932802-16-0(9))* Tickling Keys, Inc.

Earle, Aaron E. The CISA Examination Handbook. 2010. (Illus.). 79.95 *(978-1-4200-4286-3(6))* Auerbach Pubs., Inc.

Goldmann, Peter D., et al. Anti-Fraud Risk & Control. 2009. (ENG., Illus.). 192p. pap., stu. ed., wbk. ed. 52.95 *(978-0-470-49653-4(3)*, Wiley) Wiley, John & Sons, Inc.

Hunton, James E., et al. Core Concepts of Information Technology Auditing. 2nd ed. 2010. (ENG.). 282p. (C). pap. 89.95 *(978-0-470-08739-8(0)*, Wiley) Wiley, John & Sons, Inc.

IDEA & Mueller, John Paul. Mastering IDEEAscript: The Definitive Guide. 2011. (ENG., Illus.). 504p. pap. 195.00 *(978-1-118-00448-7(5)*, Wiley) Wiley, John & Sons, Inc.

Kinney, William, et al, eds. Internal Audit Handbook: Management with the SAP-Audit Roadmap. Keil, Ziggie, tr. from GER. 2007. (Illus.). 608p. 209.00 incl. cd-rom *(978-3-540-70886-5(3))* Springer.

Madray, J. Russell. Compilations & Reviews. 2008. 1100p. pap. 209.00 incl. audio compact disk *(978-0-8080-9168-4(9))* Toolkit Media Group.

Moeller, Robert R. IT Audit, Control, & Security. 2nd ed. 2010. (Wiley Corporate F&a Ser.: 13). (ENG., Illus.). 667p. 90.00 *(978-0-471-40676-1(7)*, Wiley) Wiley, John & Sons, Inc.

Ross, Kenton E., et al. Century 21 Accounting Advanced Course - Electronic Auditor. 6th ed. (BE - Accounting Advanced Ser.). 76.95 *(978-0-538-63212-6(7))* Cengage South-Western.

Weiss, Martin & Solomon, Michael G. Laboratory Manual to accompany Auditing IT Infrastructure for Compliance. 2012. 78p. pap. 29.95 *(978-1-4496-3841-2(4))* Jones & Bartlett Learning, LLC.

AUDITING—INTERNAL CONTROL

see Auditing, Internal

AUDITING—LAW AND LEGISLATION

Adam, Michael. Die Privilegierung des EMAS-Auditierten Unternehmens. 2011. (GER.). 186p. 64.95 *(978-3-631-61455-6(1))* Lang, Peter GmbH, Europaischer Verlag der Wissenschaften DEU. Dist: Lang, Peter.

Arrunada, Benito. The Economics of Audit Quality: Private Incentives & the Regulation of Audit & Non-Audit Services. 2010. (ENG.). 212p. pap. 139.00 *(978-1-4419-5082-6(6)*, 1441950826) Springer.

Backman. Audit Committee Regulation & Practice 3e. 2010. ring bd. 285.00 *(978-0-7355-9493-7(7)*, Aspen Pubs.) Wolters Kluwer Law & Business.

Crilly, William M., et al. The AMA Handbook of Due Diligence, 2 vols. 2nd ed. 2010. (ENG.). 848p. 295.00 *(978-0-8144-1382-1(X))* Amacom.

Hamilton, James & Trautmann, Ted. Sarbanes-Oxley Manual. 2008. 350p. pap. 87.00 *(978-0-8080-1858-2(2))* Toolkit Media Group.

Hopkins, Leon. Audit Report. ring bd. 440.00 *(978-0-406-02014-7(0)*, U.K., MICHIE) LEXIS Publishing.

Knapp, Michael C. Contemporary Auditing: Real Issues & Cases. 8th ed. 2010. (ENG.). 608p. (C). pap. 121.95 *(978-0-538-46679-0(0))* Cengage South-Western.

Lammers, Carsten. Der Prüfungsausschuss des Aufsichtsrats Nach Dem Sarbanes-Oxley Act und Dem Bilmog: Zum Spannungsverhältnis Zwischen Us-Amerikanischem Kapitalmarktrecht, Europäischen Vorgaben und Deutschem Aktienrecht. 2011. (Frankfurter wirtschaftsrechtliche Studien Ser.). (GER.). 434p. 104.95 ***(978-3-631-62077-9(2))*** Lang, Peter GmbH, Europaischer Verlag der Wissenschaften DEU. Dist: Lang, Peter.

Pallais, Don. Audits & Other Accountants' Services. 2011. (ENG.). 240p. pap. 74.95 *(978-1-60442-810-0(4))* American Bar Assn.

Quick. Auditing, Trust & Governance. 2007. (ENG., Illus.). 304p. (C). pap. 59.95 *(978-0-415-44890-1(5))* Routledge.

Quick, Reiner, et al. Auditing, Trust & Governance: Regulation in Europe. Turley, Stuart & Willekens, Marleen, eds. 2008. (ENG., Illus.). 304p. (C). 175.00 *(978-0-415-44889-5(1))* Routledge.

Santiso, Carlos. The Political Economy of Government Auditing: Financial Governance & the Rule of Law in Latin America & Beyond. 2009. (Law, Development & Globalization Ser.). (ENG., Illus.). 182p. 130.00 *(978-0-415-47773-4(5)*, Routledge Cavendish) Taylor & Francis Group GBR. Dist: Taylor & Francis Group.

Shandong Sheng (China), Ren min dai biao da hui Chang wu wei yuan hui Fa zhi gong zuo wei yuan hui Staff, et al, contrib. by. Shandong Sheng Cai Zheng Jian du Tiao Li Shi Yi. 2009. (CHI.). *(978-7-5058-8008-5(X))* Jingji Kexue Chubanshe.

United States, Congress House Committee on Government Reform Subcommittee on Regulatory Affairs Staff, contrib. by. A Balancing ACT: Cost, Compliance, & Competitiveness after Sarbanes-Oxley: Hearing Before the Subcommittee on Regulatory Affairs of the Committee on Government Reform, House of Representatives, One Hundred Ninth Congress, Second Session, June 19, 2006. 2007. iii, 108p. *(978-0-16-078461-3(1)*, 552-070-35747-5) United States Government Printing Office.

AUDITING—PROBLEMS, EXERCISES, ETC.

Delaney, Patrick R. & Whittington, O. Ray. Wiley CPA Exam Review 2012 Test Bank: Auditing & Attestation. 17th ed. 2012. (ENG.). 105.00 ***(978-0-470-92385-6(7)***, Wiley) Wiley, John & Sons, Inc.

Gray, Iain & Manson, Stuart. The Audit Process: Principles, Practice & Cases. 5th ed. 2011. (ENG., Illus.). 864p. pap. 75.99 *(978-1-4080-3049-3(7))* Cengage Learning GBR. Dist: CENGAGE Learning.

Millichamp, Alan & Taylor, John. Auditing. 10th ed. 2012. (ENG., Illus.). 250p. pap. 67.99 ***(978-1-4080-4408-7(0))*** Cengage Learning GBR. Dist: CENGAGE Learning.

Rudman, Jack. Auditing. (ACT Proficiency Examination Program Ser.: Vol. 14). (C). 49.95 *(978-0-8373-5564-1(8))*; (Dantes Subject Standardized Tests Ser.: Vol. 69). 49.95 *(978-0-8373-6569-5(4))* National Learning Corp. (Passbooks).

Smith, C, et al. Wiley CPA Exam Review 2012: Auditing & Attestation. 9th ed. 2011. (ENG.). 676p. pap. 65.00 ***(978-0-470-92390-0(3)***, Wiley) Wiley, John & Sons, Inc.

Tidrick, Donald. Auditing & Attestation - Supplemental Outlines. 2008. (ENG.). 244p. per. *(978-0-9746541-7-1(5))* Efficient Learning Systems, Inc.

Vallabhaneni, S. Rao. Wiley CIA Exam Review Focus Notes Vol. 1: Internal Audit Activity's Role in Governance, Risk & Control. 2008. (ENG.). 152p. pap. 36.95 *(978-0-470-27706-5(8)*, Wiley) Wiley, John & Sons, Inc.

AUDITING, INTERNAL

see also Controllership

Aicpa. The AICPA Audit Committee Toolkit: Government Organizations, 2nd Edition. 2011. pap. 31.25 ***(978-0-87051-962-8(X))*** American Institute of Certified Public Accountants.

Aicpa. Audit Risk Akert SEC & PCAOB Alert 2007/2008. 2007. pap. 48.75 *(978-0-87051-698-6(1))* American Institute of Certified Public Accountants.

Anderson, Urton, et al. Implementing the International Professional Practices Framework. 3rd ed. 2009. (Illus.). xi, 270p. pap. *(978-0-89413-676-4(3))* Institute of Internal Auditors, Inc.

Avellanet, A. Wayne. Internal Control Compliance Deskbook: The 2007 PCAOB Standard & SEC Guidance. 2007. xxi, 853p. pap. *(978-0-7913-6419-2(4))* Warren, Gorham & Lamont, Inc.

Bluestein, Abram I., et al. The Customer Satisfaction Audit. 2008. 112p. pap. *(978-1-902433-98-1(X))* Cambridge Strategy Pubns. Ltd.

Buckless, Frank A., et al. Manual AIS Practice Set for Comprehensive Assurance & Systems Tool (CAST)-Integrated Practice Set. 2nd ed. 2010. (ENG.). 80p. (C). pap. 46.67 *(978-0-13-214657-9(6)*, Prentice Hall) Prentice Hall PTR.

Cangemi, Michael P. & Cangemi, Marc I. Managing the Audit Function: A Corporate Audit Department Procedures Guide with URL. 4th ed. 2014. (Wiley Corporate F&A Ser.). (ENG., Illus.). 384p. pap. 75.00 ***(978-0-470-57527-7(1)***, Wiley) Wiley, John & Sons, Inc.

Chorafas, Dimitris N. IT Auditing & Sarbanes-Oxley Compliance: Key Strategies for Business Improvement. 2008. (ENG., Illus.). 305p. 97.95 *(978-1-4200-8617-1(0))* Auerbach Pubs., Inc.

Coderre, David. Fraud Analysis Techniques Using ACL. 2009. (ENG., Illus.). 176p. pap. 210.50 *(978-0-470-39244-7(4)*, Wiley) Wiley, John & Sons, Inc.

—Internal Audit: Efficiency Through Automation. 2008. (IIA (Institute of Internal Auditors) Ser.: 9). (ENG., Illus.). 250p. 57.95 *(978-0-470-39242-3(8)*, Wiley) Wiley, John & Sons, Inc.

Coderre, David & Coderre. Computer Aided Fraud Prevention & Detection: A Step by Step Guide. 2009. (ENG., Illus.). 304p. 63.50 *(978-0-470-39243-0(6)*, Wiley) Wiley, John & Sons, Inc.

Cohen, Alain-Gérard. Public Internal Financial Control: A New Framework for Public Sector Management. 2007. (Illus.). ix, 174p. *(978-0-89413-605-4(4))* Institute of Internal Auditors, Inc.

Cram101 Textbook Reviews. Outlines & Highlights for Auditing for Managers: The Ultimate Risk Management Tool by Jennifer M. Pickett. 2011. 76p. pap. 27.95 ***(978-1-61905-196-6(6))*** Cram101 Inc.

Cram101 Textbook Reviews & Cram101 Textbook Reviews. Outlines & Highlights for Brinks Modern Internal Auditing: A Common Body of Knowledge by Robert Moeller. 2011. 76p. pap. 27.95 ***(978-1-61830-411-7(9))*** Cram101 Inc.

—Outlines & Highlights for Brinks Modern Internal Auditing by Robert Moeller. 2011. 118p. pap. 28.95 ***(978-1-61830-432-2(1))*** Cram101 Inc.

—Outlines & Highlights for the Essential Handbook of Internal Auditing by K H Spencer Pickett. 2011. 80p. pap. 27.95 ***(978-1-61830-264-9(7))*** Cram101 Inc.

—Outlines & Highlights for the Internal Auditing Handbook by K H Spencer Pickett. 2011. 114p. pap. 28.95 ***(978-1-61830-237-3(X))*** Cram101 Inc.

Davies, Marlene & Aston, John. Auditing Fundamentals. 2011. (ENG., Illus.). 328p. pap. 97.50 *(978-0-273-71173-5(3))* Pearson Education, Ltd. GBR. Dist: Trans-Atlantic Pubns., Inc.

Donaldson, Deborah. Financial Institutions Internal Audit Desk Reference. 2nd ed. 2007. cd-rom 325.00 *(978-0-9799077-5-3(5))* Financial Managers Society, Inc.

Funkhouser, Mark. Honest, Competent Government: The Promise of Performance Auditing. 2008. 84p. *(978-0-89413-634-4(8))* Institute of Internal Auditors, Inc.

Goldmann, Peter D., et al. Anti-Fraud Risk & Control. 2009. (ENG., Illus.). 192p. pap., stu. ed., wbk. ed. 52.95 *(978-0-470-49653-4(3)*, Wiley) Wiley, John & Sons, Inc.

Graham, Lynford. Internal Controls: Guidance for Private, Government, & Nonprofit Entities. 2007. (ENG., Illus.). 256p. 99.95 *(978-0-470-08948-4(2)*, Wiley) Wiley, John & Sons, Inc.

Gupta, Pradeep. Internal Auditing Practices in Indi. 2010. 240p. pap. *(978-3-639-27330-4(3))* VDM Verlag Dr. Mueller e.K.

Harrer, Julie. Internal Control Strategies: A Mid to Small Business Guide. 2008. (ENG., Illus.). 308p. 57.95 *(978-0-470-37619-5(8)*, Wiley) Wiley, John & Sons, Inc.

—SOX 404 from the Trenches: Real World Implementation Strategies. 2007. pap. 61.25 *(978-0-87051-678-8(7))* American Institute of Certified Public Accountants.

Hightower, Rose. Internal Controls Policies & Procedures. 2008. (ENG., Illus.). 272p. pap. 84.50 *(978-0-470-28717-0(9)*, Wiley) Wiley, John & Sons, Inc.

Holland and Knight, LLP Staff. Corporate Compliance Answer Book 2009. Myers, Christopher, ed. 2009. 1145p. pap. 295.00 *(978-1-4024-1126-7(X))* Practising Law Institute.

Institute of Internal Auditors, Research Foundation Staff, contrib. by. Internal Audit Capability Model (IA-CM) for the Public Sector: Overview & Application Guide. 2009. (Illus.). ix, 137p. pap. ***(978-0-89413-675-7(5))*** Institute of Internal Auditors, Inc.

Kinney, William, et al, eds. Internal Audit Handbook: Management with the SAP-Audit Roadmap. Keil, Ziggie, tr. from GER. 2007. (Illus.). 608p. 209.00 incl. cd-rom *(978-3-540-70886-5(3))* Springer.

Leitch, Matthew. A Pocket Guide to Risk Mathematics: Key Concepts Every Auditor Should Know. 2010. (ENG., Illus.). 202p. pap. 50.00 *(978-0-470-71052-4(7)*, Wiley) Wiley, John & Sons, Inc.

Liu, Ming & Lin, Z. Jun. Corporate Governance, Auditor Choice & Auditor Switch - Evidence from Chin. 2009. 108p. pap. *(978-3-639-10868-2(X))* VDM Verlag Dr. Mueller e.K.

Lomas, Paul & Kramer, Daniel, eds. Corporate Internal Investigations: An International Guide. 2008. (ENG.). 728p. 180.00 *(978-0-19-955411-9(0))* Oxford Univ. Pr., Inc.

Mainardi, Robert L. Harnessing the Power of Continuous Auditing: Developing & Implementing a Practical Methodology. 2011. (Wiley Corporate F&a Ser.: 10). (ENG., Illus.). 304p. 78.00 *(978-0-470-63769-2(2)*, Wiley) Wiley, John & Sons, Inc.

Milam, Susan & Maeda, Martha. The Complete Guide to Spotting Accounting Fraud & Cover-Ups: Everything You Need to Know Explained Simply. 2010. (ENG.). 336p. per. 24.95 *(978-1-60138-212-2(X))* Atlantic Publishing Co.

Moeller, Robert & Moeller. Brink's Modern Internal Auditing: A Common Body of Knowledge. 7th ed. 2009. (ENG., Illus.). 792p. 194.50 *(978-0-470-29303-4(9)*, Wiley) Wiley, John & Sons, Inc.

Moeller, Robert R. Sarbanes-Oxley Internal Controls: Effective Auditing with As5, COBIT, & Itil. 2008. (ENG., Illus.). 384p. 78.95 *(978-0-470-17092-2(1)*, Wiley) Wiley, John & Sons, Inc.

Ntsiful, Samuel & Mwenechanya, Makiwa. The Independence & Objectivity of the Internal Auditor. 2011. 68p. pap. ***(978-3-8454-1315-0(8))*** Lambert Academic Publishing.

Palmes, Paul C. Process Driven Comprehensive Auditing: A New Way to Conduct: ISO 9001:2008 Internal Audits. 2nd ed. 2009. 42.00 *(978-0-87389-754-9(4))* ASQ Quality Pr.

Phillips, Ann W. ISO 9001:2008 Internal Audits Made Easy: Tools, Techniques & Step-By-Step Guidelines for Successful Internal Audits. 2008. 42.00 *(978-0-87389-751-8(X))* ASQ Quality Pr.

Pickett, K. H. Spencer. The Essential Guide to Internal Auditing. 2nd ed. 2011. (ENG., Illus.). 384p. pap. 55.00 *(978-0-470-74693-6(9)*, Wiley) Wiley, John & Sons, Inc.

—The Internal Auditing Handbook. 3rd ed. 2010. (ENG., Illus.). 1088p. 225.00 *(978-0-470-51871-7(5)*, Wiley) Wiley, John & Sons, Inc.

Reading, Kurt F. Internal Auditing: Assurance & Consulting Services. 2007. (Illus.). *(978-0-89413-610-8(0))* Institute of Internal Auditors, Inc.

Reider, Rob. Effective Operations & Controls for the Small Privately Held Business. 2008. (ENG., Illus.). 396p. 75.00 *(978-0-470-22276-8(X)*, Wiley) Wiley, John & Sons, Inc.

Ridley, Jeffrey. Cutting Edge Internal Auditing, with CD-ROM. 2008. (ENG., Illus.). 486p. 75.00 *(978-0-470-51039-1(0)*, Wiley) Wiley, John & Sons, Inc.

Rodgers, Waymond. Biometric & Auditing Issues Addressed in a Throughput Model. 2012. 374p. ***(978-1-61735-654-4(9))***; 374p. pap. ***(978-1-61735-653-7(0))***; xi, 361p. E-Book ***(978-1-61735-655-1(7))*** Information Age Publishing, Inc.

Roth, James. Best Practices: Evaluating the Corporate Culture. 2010. (Illus.). xi, 258p. pap. ***(978-0-89413-682-5(8))*** Institute of Internal Auditors, Inc.

Russell, J. P. The Internal Auditing Pocket Guide: Preparing, Performing, Reporting, & Follow-Up. 2nd ed. 2007. (Illus.). 25.00 *(978-0-87389-710-5(2))* ASQ Quality Pr.

Schaeffer, Mary S. Fraud in Accounts Payable: How to Prevent It. 2008. (ENG.). 200p. 57.95 *(978-0-470-26045-6(9)*, Wiley) Wiley, John & Sons, Inc.

Selim, Georges & Woodward, Sally. Internal Auditors as Consultants. 2006. 320p. pap. 60.00 *(978-0-470-85282-8(8))* Wiley, John & Sons, Inc.

Shim, Jae K. Internal Control & Fraud Detection. 2011. (Illus.). 200p. pap. 39.95 *(978-1-906403-62-1(7))* Global Professional Publishing GBR. Dist: Stylus Publishing, LLC.

Sobel, Paul J. Auditor's Risk Management Guide: Integrating Auditing & ERM (2007) 2007th rev. ed. 2007. 586p. pap. 200.00 *(978-0-8080-9089-2(5))* Toolkit Media Group.

Steiniger, Hans L. Auditing the Food & Beverage Operation. 2008. 502p. pap. 34.95 *(978-1-60474-338-8(7))* PublishAmerica, Inc.

Straesser, Anne-Katrin. The 7 Secrets of Highly Profitable Internal Control Systems. 2009. 122p. pap. *(978-3-8391-2698-1(3))* Books on Demand GmbH

Switzer, Susan M. Internal Audit Reports Post Sarbanes-Oxley: A Guide to Process-Driven Reporting. 2007. (IIA (Institute of Internal Auditors) Ser.: 7). (ENG., Illus.). 256p. 68.50 *(978-0-470-05084-2(5)*, Wiley) Wiley, John & Sons, Inc.

Tate, W. The Organisation Shadow Side Audit. 2008. 132p. pap. *(978-1-902433-97-4(1))* Cambridge Strategy Pubns. Ltd.

Taylor, John. Forensic Accounting. 2011. (ENG., Illus.). 504p. pap. 112.50 *(978-0-273-72296-0(4))* Pearson Education, Ltd. GBR. Dist: Trans-Atlantic Pubns., Inc.

Tickner, William & Tickner, Peter. How to Be a Successful Frauditor. 2010. (Wiley Corporate F&a Ser.: 1). (ENG., Illus.). 416p. 55.00 *(978-0-470-68185-5(3)*, Wiley) Wiley, John & Sons, Inc.

United States, Congress House Committee on Government Reform Subcommittee on Regulatory Affairs Staff, contrib. by. A Balancing ACT: Cost, Compliance, & Competitiveness after Sarbanes-Oxley: Hearing Before the Subcommittee on Regulatory Affairs of the Committee on Government Reform, House of Representatives, One Hundred Ninth Congress, Second Session, June 19, 2006. 2007. iii, 108p. *(978-0-16-078461-3(1)*, 552-070-35747-5) United States Government Printing Office.

United States, Congress House Committee on the Judiciary Subcommittee on Commercial and Administrative Law Staff, contrib. by. Legal Services Corporation Improvement ACT: Hearing Before the Subcommittee on Commercial & Administrative Law of the Committee on the Judiciary, House of Representatives, One Hundred Ninth Congress, Second Session, on H.R. 6101, September 26, 2006. 2007. iii, 142p. *(978-0-16-078050-9(0)*, 552-070-35458-1) United States Government Printing Office.

Vallabhaneni, S. Rao. Business Analysis & Information Technology, 4 vols., Vol. 3. 2008. (ENG.). 322p. pap. 36.95 *(978-0-470-27708-9(4)*, Wiley) Wiley, John & Sons, Inc.

—CIA Exam Review Focus Notes, Vols. 1-4, Set. 2008. (ENG.). 960p. pap. 147.50 *(978-0-470-27710-2(6)*, Wiley) Wiley, John & Sons, Inc.

—Conducting the Internal Audit Engagement, 3 vols., Vol. 2. 2008. (ENG.). 166p. pap. 36.95 *(978-0-470-27707-2(6)*, Wiley) Wiley, John & Sons, Inc.

—Focus Notes: Business Management Skills, Vol. 4. 2008. (ENG.). 156p. pap. 36.95 *(978-0-470-27709-6(2)*, Wiley) Wiley, John & Sons, Inc.

—Wiley CIA Exam Review CD. 2006. (ENG.). 103.95 *(978-0-470-05612-7(6)*, Wiley) Wiley, John & Sons, Inc.

—Wiley CIA Exam Review Focus Notes Vol. 1: Internal Audit Activity's Role in Governance, Risk & Control. 2008. (ENG.). 152p. pap. 36.95 *(978-0-470-27706-5(8)*, Wiley) Wiley, John & Sons, Inc.

Various Authors. Best-Practice Approaches to Internal Auditing. 2011. (ENG., Illus.). 240p. 85.00 *(978-1-84930-023-0(2))* Bloomsbury Publishing.

Verschoor, Curtis C. Ethics & Compliance: Challenges for Internal Auditing. 2007. ix, 103p. ***(978-0-89413-612-2(7))*** Institute of Internal Auditors, Inc.

Weightman, Jane. The Employee Motivation Audit. 2008. 100p. pap. *(978-0-9559707-0-2(9))* Cambridge Strategy Pubns. Ltd.

Wells, Joseph T. Principles of Fraud Examination. 3rd ed. 2010. (ENG., Illus.). 500p. (C). 192.95 *(978-0-470-64629-8(2)*, Wiley) Wiley, John & Sons, Inc.

Wich, Holger. Internes Kontrollsystem und Management-Informationssystem: Analyse der Systembedeutung für Unternehmensleitung und Abschlussprüfer. 2008. (Schriften zu Theorie und Praxis der Rechnungslegung und Wirtschaftsprüfung Ser.). 376p. pap. 81.95 *(978-3-631-56776-0(6))* Lang, Peter GmbH, Europaischer Verlag der Wissenschaften DEU. Dist: Lang, Peter.

Young, Michael R. & Nusbaum, Jack H. Accounting Irregularities & Financial Fraud: A Corporate Governance Guide. 3rd rev. ed. 2006. xxx, 387p. 149.00 *(978-0-8080-8968-1(4))* Toolkit Media Group.

AUDITING, TAX

see Tax Auditing

AUDITION (COMPUTER PROGRAM)

see Adobe Audition (Computer Program)

AUDITION (PHYSIOLOGY)

see Hearing

AUDITIONS

see also Acting—Auditions

Alterman, Glenn. Glenn Alterman's Secrets to Successful Cold Readings. 2007. (Career Development Ser.). (ENG.). 224p. pap. 14.95 *(978-1-57525-566-8(9))* Smith & Kraus Pubs., Inc.

Bellantoni, Paul. So You Wanna Sing in Germany? 2008. 156p. pap. 22.95 *(978-1-4357-1882-1(8))* Lulu Enterprises Inc.

Break-A-Leg Books. Actor's audition Log. 6th rev. ed. 2008. spiral bd. 12.95 *(978-0-9668522-4-0(9))* Break-A-Leg Bks.

Hal Leonard Corp., creator. Sing the Classics: Audition Songs for Female Singers. 2011. (ENG.). 56p. pap. 14.99 incl. audio compact disk ***(978-1-4584-1901-9(0)***, 1458419010) Music Sales Corp.

—Sing the Classics: Audition Songs for Male Singers. 2011. (ENG.). 56p. pap. 14.99 incl. audio compact disk ***(978-1-4584-1900-2(2)***, 1458419002) Music Sales Corp.

Hal Leonard Corporation Staff, creator. Classic Soul - Audition Songs for Male Singers: Piano/Vocal/Guitar Arrangements with CD Backing Tracks. 2010. (ENG.). 48p. pap. 14.99 incl. audio compact disk *(978-1-4234-8951-1(9)*, 1423489519) Music Sales Corp.

Wyman, C. S. A. The Organic Actor. 2008. 280p. pap. 27.00 *(978-1-4343-6215-5(9))* AuthorHouse.

Yager, Jan. Getting Booked: The Basics about Appearing on TV & Radio Plus Annotated Contact Information for 350+ Major Shows. 2012. 175p. pap. 49.95 *(978-1-889262-69-7(2))* Hannacroix Creek Bks., Inc.

AUDITORIUMS

see also Music-Halls; Public Buildings; Theaters

Noory Yeganeh, Saba. Developments in Auditorium Design in Last Fifty Years 1960-2009. 2011. 140p. pap. ***(978-3-8443-3325-1(8))*** Lambert Academic Publishing.

Solis, Julia. Stages of Decay. 2012. (ENG., Illus.). 144p. 34.95 ***(978-1-935613-46-6(4))*** Batty, Mark Pub., LLC.

Swallow, Dave. Live Audio: The Art of Mixing a Show. 2010. (ENG., Illus.). 256p. pap. 39.95 *(978-0-240-81604-3(8)*, Focal Pr.) Elsevier Science & Technology Bks.

AUDITORY EVOKED RESPONSE

Don, Manuel, et al. Auditory Evoked Potentials: Basic Principles & Clinical Application. 2006. (Point (Lippincott Williams & Wilkins) Ser.). (ENG., Illus.). 736p. 153.99 *(978-0-7817-5756-0(8))* Lippincott Williams & Wilkins.

Hall, James W., III. New Handbook for Auditory Evoked Responses. 2006. (ENG., Illus.). 736p. 157.40 *(978-0-205-36104-5(8))* Allyn & Bacon, Inc.

Picton, Terence W. Human Auditory Evoked Potentials. 2010. (Illus.). 648p. 159.95 *(978-1-59756-362-8(5))* Plural Publishing, Inc.

Rance, Gary. The Auditory Steady-State Response: Generation, Recording, & Clinical Application. 2008. (Illus.). 335p. 98.00 *(978-1-59756-151-7(4))* Plural Publishing, Inc.

AUDITORY NERVE

see Acoustic Nerve

AUDITORY PATHWAYS

see also Acoustic Nerve; Cerebral Cortex; Ear; Hearing

Grecu, Andrei. Musical Instrument Sound Separation: Extracting Instruments from Musical Performances - Theory & Algorithms. 2008. 176p. pap. *(978-3-8364-5945-7(0))* VDM Verlag Dr. Mueller e.K.

Greenberg, Steven, et al, eds. Speech Processing in the Auditory System. 2010. (Springer Handbook of Auditory Research Ser.). (Illus.). xiv, 496p. pap. 229.00 *(978-1-4419-1831-4(0)*, 1441918310) Springer.

Harris, Jeffrey P. & Zeng, Fan-Gang, eds. Micro- & Nanotechnology for Neurotology, Vol. 11. (Illus.). 74p. pap. *(978-3-8055-8100-4(9))* Karger, S. AG.

Housley, Gary D., et al, eds. Cochlear Transduction & Transmission: A Series of Synopses Arising from the Auditory Function & Dysfunction Satellite Symposium of the 34th IUPS Congress. (Illus.). 70p. *(978-3-8055-7408-2(8))* Karger, S. AG.

Jones, Sherri & Jones, Timothy. Genetics, Embryology, & Development of Auditory & Vestibular Systems. 2011. (Illus.). 530p. pap. 149.95 *(978-1-59756-201-0(7))* Plural Publishing, Inc.

Meddis, Ray, et al, eds. Computational Models of the Auditory System. 2010. (Springer Handbook of Auditory Research Ser.). (ENG., Illus.). xii, 350p. 139.00 *(978-1-4419-1370-8(X)*, 144191370X) Springer.

Oertel, Donata & Fay, Richard R., eds. Integrative Functions in the Mammalian Auditory Pathway. 2010. (Springer Handbook of Auditory Research Ser.). (Illus.). xiv, 431p. pap. 199.00 *(978-1-4419-3183-2(X)*, 144193183X) Springer.

Palmer, Alan & Rees, Adrian. The Oxford Handbook of Auditory Science: The Auditory Brain, 3 vols. 2010. (Oxford Library of Psychology Ser.). (ENG., Illus.). 592p. 125.00 *(978-0-19-923328-1(4))* Oxford Univ. Pr., Inc.

Parks, Thomas N., et al, eds. Plasticity of the Auditory System. 2012. (Springer Handbook of Auditory Research Ser.). (ENG., Illus.). xii, 324p. pap. 219.00 *(978-1-4419-1932-8(5)*, 1441919325) Springer.

Pressnitzer, Daniel, et al, eds. Auditory Signal Processing: Physiology, Psychoacoustics, & Models. 2010. (ENG., Illus.). xiv, 524p. pap. 225.00 *(978-1-4419-1953-3(8)*, 1441919538) Springer.

Riess Jones, Mari, et al, eds. Music Perception: Springer Handbook in Auditory Research (SHAR) 2010. (Springer Handbook of Auditory Research Ser.). (Illus.). 350p. 139.00 *(978-1-4419-6113-6(5)*, 1441961135) Springer.

Ryugo, David K. & Fay, Richard R., eds. Auditory & Vestibular Efferents. 2010. (Springer Handbook of Auditory Research Ser.). (Illus.). xvi, 360p. 139.00 *(978-1-4419-7069-5(X)*, 144197069X) Springer.

Salami, Angelo. Neuroplasticity in the Auditory Brainstem from Physiology to the Drug Therapy. 2011. *(978-1-61761-949-6(3))* Nova Science Pubs., Inc.

Schacht, Jochen, et al, eds. Auditory Trauma, Protection, & Repair. 2008. (Springer Handbook of Auditory Research Ser.). (Illus.). 350p. 149.00 *(978-0-387-72560-4(1))* Springer.

Schacht, Jochen & Fay, Richard R., eds. Auditory Trauma, Protection, & Repair. 2010. (Springer Handbook of Auditory Research Ser.). (Illus.). xvi, 352p. pap. 149.00 *(978-1-4419-4443-6(5)*, 1441944435) Springer.

Sokolowski, Bernd, ed. Auditory & Vestibular Research: Methods & Protocols. 2010. (Methods in Molecular Biology Ser.). (Illus.). xii, 428p. pap. 129.00 *(978-1-61737-939-0(5)*, 1617379395) Humana Pr.

Syka, Josef & Merzenich, Michael M., eds. Plasticity & Signal Representation in the Auditory System. 2010. (Illus.). x, 416p. pap. 279.00 *(978-1-4419-3581-6(9)*, 1441935819) Springer.

Trussell, Laurence O., et al, eds. Synaptic Mechanisms in the Auditory System. 2011. (Springer Handbook of Auditory Research Ser.). (ENG., Illus.). xiv, 231p. 139.00 *(978-1-4419-9516-2(1)*, 1441995161) Springer.

Velluti, Ricardo A. The Auditory System in Sleep. 2007. (ENG., Illus.). 224p. 91.95 *(978-0-12-373890-5(3)*, Academic Pr.) Elsevier Science & Technology Bks.

Werner, Lynne, et al, eds. Human Auditory Development. 2011. (Springer Handbook of Auditory Research Ser.). (ENG., Illus.). xiv, 284p. 139.00 ***(978-1-4614-1420-9(2)***, 1461414202) Springer.

Winer, Jeffery A. & Schreiner, Christoph E., eds. The Auditory Cortex: Fundamental Neuroscience. 2010. (ENG., Illus.). 504p. 279.00 *(978-1-4419-0073-9(X)*, 144190073X) Springer.

AUDUBON, JOHN JAMES, 1785-1851

Arthur, Stanley Clisby. Audubon: An Intimate Life of the American Woodsman. 544p. 2008. 57.95 *(978-1-4366-9625-8(9))* 2007. (ENG.). per. 42.95 *(978-1-4325-9101-4(0))* Kessinger Publishing, LLC.

Audubon, John James. John James Audubon's Journal Of 1826: The Voyage to the Birds of America. Patterson, Daniel, ed. & intro. by. 2011. (ENG., Illus.). 536p. 50.00 *(978-0-8032-2531-2(8))* Univ. of Nebraska Pr.

—The Life of John James Audubon: The Naturalist. 443p. reprint ed. 98.00 *(978-0-7222-8454-4(3))* Library Reprints, Inc.

—The Life of John James Audubon, the Naturalist. 2007. (ENG.). 440p. 51.95 *(978-0-548-18905-4(6))*; pap. 36.95 *(978-1-4304-9329-7(1))* Kessinger Publishing, LLC.

—120 Audubon Bird Prints. 2008. (Dover Electronic Clip Art Ser.). (ENG., Illus.). 64p. pap. 22.95 *(978-0-486-99854-1(1))* Dover Pubns., Inc.

Audubon, John W. Audubon's Western Journal 1849-1850. 2007. 260p. per. 28.95 *(978-1-4067-5336-3(X))* Audubon Pr. & Christian Bk. Service.

Burroughs, John. John James Audubon. 2008. 68p. per. *(978-1-4065-9010-4(X))* Dodo Pr.

—John James Audubon. (Beacon Biographies Ser.). 144p. reprint ed. 88.00 *(978-0-7222-8519-0(1))* Library Reprints, Inc.

—John James Audubon. 2008. (ENG.). 168p. per. *(978-1-4086-3591-9(7))* Read Bks.

Chalmers, John. Audubon in Edinburgh: The Scottish Associates of John James Audubon. 2006. (ENG., Illus.). 240p. pap. 45.00 *(978-1-901663-79-2(5))* NMS Enterprises Ltd. - Publishing GBR. Dist: National Bk. Network.

DeLatte, Carolyn E. Lucy Audubon, a Biography. 2009. (Southern Biography Ser.). (Illus.). xxiii, 248p. pap. *(978-0-8071-3381-1(7))* Louisiana State Univ. Pr.

Flynn, Ron. The Audubon Price Guide Book. 2008. 252p. pap. 59.95 *(978-1-4357-0809-9(1))* Lulu Enterprises Inc.

Heitman, Danny. A Summer of Birds: John James Audubon at Oakley House 2008. (Hill Collection: Holdings of the LSU Libraries Ser.). (Illus.). 152p. 26.95 *(978-0-8071-3330-9(2))* Louisiana State Univ. Pr.

Payne, Raphael Semmes. The Baltimore Oriole & a Biographical Sketch of Audubon. 2011. 60p. 36.95 ***(978-1-258-08630-5(1))*** Literary Licensing, LLC.

St. John, Horace Stebbing Roscoe. Audubon, the Naturalist of the New World His Adventures & Discoveries by Mrs Horace St John Rev & Cor , with Additions, & Illustrated With. 2006. (Illus.). 348p. per. 23.99 *(978-1-4255-3517-9(8))* MPublishing.

Vedder, Lee A. John James Audubon & the Birds of America: A Visionary Achievement in Ornithological Illustration. 2006. (Huntington Library Classics Ser.). (Illus.). 93p. 24.95 *(978-0-87328-217-8(5))* Huntington Library Pr.

AUGER EFFECT

Lohmann, Bernd. Angle & Spin Resolved Auger Emission: Theory & Applications to Atoms & Molecules. (Springer Series on Atomic, Optical, & Plasma Physics Ser.). (Illus.). xvi, 338p. 2010. pap. 199.00 *(978-3-642-09407-1(4)*, 3642094074) 2008. 199.00 *(978-3-540-74629-4(3))* Springer.

Sharma, Ajay & Raj Mittal Singla, Prof. Vacancy Alignment in Atomic Inner Shells. 2010. 124p. pap. *(978-3-8383-7623-3(4))* Lambert Academic Publishing.

VanDendael, Isabelle. Use of Auger Electron Spectroscopy to Study an Industrial Process. 2010. 228p. pap. *(978-3-8383-4676-2(9))* Lambert Academic Publishing.

AUGSBURG (GERMANY)

Häberlein, Mark. The Fuggers of Augsburg: Pursuing Wealth & Honor in Renaissance Germany. 2012. E-Book ***(978-0-8139-3258-3(0))*** Univ. Pr. of Virginia.

Strieder, Jacob. Jacob Fugger the Rich: Merchant & Banker of Augsburg, 1459-1525. Gras, N. S. B., ed. Hartsough, Mildred L., tr. 264p. 2008. 42.95 *(978-1-4366-8793-5(4))* 2007. (ENG.). per. 27.95 *(978-1-4325-8812-0(5))* Kessinger Publishing, LLC.

Van Amberg, Joel. A Real Presence: Religious & Social Dynamics of the Eucharistic Conflicts in Early Modern Augsburg, 1520-1530. 2011. (ENG.). X, 270p. ***(978-90-04-21698-3(7))*** BRILL.

AUGSBURG CONFESSION

The Augsburg Confession. 64p. 1.75 *(978-0-570-09823-2(8))* Concordia Publishing Hse.

Cobb, James G. Lutheran DNA: Testing the Augsburg Confession in the Parish. 2010. 116p. pap. 14.00 *(978-1-60899-357-4(4)*, Resource Pubns.) Wipf & Stock Pubs.

Jacobs, Henry Eyster, ed. The Four Hundred Four Theses of Dr. John Eck, Published in 1530: A Contribution to the History of the Augsburg Confession. reprint ed. 27.50 *(978-0-404-19854-1(6))* AMS Pr., Inc.

Krauth, Charles P. The Conservative Reformation & Its Theology V1. 2007. (ENG.). 472p. 52.95 *(978-0-548-15312-3(4))*; per. 37.95 *(978-1-4304-4695-8(1))* Kessinger Publishing, LLC.

Krauth, Charles Porterfield. Conservative Reformation & Its Theology. 2006. 560p. 39.99 *(978-0-7586-0994-6(9))* Concordia Publishing Hse.

Melanchthon, Philip. The Augsburg Confession. 2009. Orig. Title: Confessio Augustana. 64p. pap. *(978-1-4099-2858-4(6))* Dodo Pr.

Melanchthon, Philipp. The Apology of the Augsburg Confession. 2008. 320p. 28.99 *(978-0-554-33056-3(3))* 2008. 320p. 29.99 *(978-0-554-23753-4(9))* 2007. (ENG.). 290p. pap. 21.99 *(978-1-4264-4986-4(0))* 2006. 318p. pap. 24.99 *(978-1-4264-5287-1(X))* BiblioBazaar.

Reu, Johann M. The Augsburg Confession. reprint ed. 76.50 *(978-0-404-19859-6(7))* AMS Pr., Inc.

AUGURY

see Divination

AUGUSTA (GA.)

Bragg, C. L. Never for Want of Powder: The Confederate Powder Works in Augusta, Georgia. 2007. 344p. (C). 44.95 *(978-1-57003-657-6(8))* Univ. of South Carolina Pr.

Fleming, Berry. Autobiography of a Colony: The First Half-Century of Augusta, Georgia. 2009. (ENG.). 224p. pap. 24.95 *(978-0-8203-3442-4(1))* Univ. of Georgia Pr.

Jones, Charles Colcock & Dutcher, Salem. Memorial History of Augusta, Georgia. (Illus.). 569p. reprint ed. lib. bdg. 98.00 *(978-0-7222-0873-1(1))* Library Reprints, Inc.

Spalding, Phinizy. The History of the Medical College of Georgia. 2011. (ENG., Illus.). 322p. 44.95 *(978-0-8203-4041-8(3))*; pap. 24.95 *(978-0-8203-4040-1(5))* Univ. of Georgia Pr.

Tabagari, Giorgi. European Security Architecture after Russo-Georgian War. 2010. 56p. pap. *(978-3-639-22595-2(3))* VDM Verlag Dr. Mueller e.K.

AUGUSTANA COLLEGE

Blanck, Dag. The Creation of an Ethnic Identity: Being Swedish American in the Augustana Synod, 1860-1917. 2006. (ENG., Illus.). 280p. 55.00 *(978-0-8093-2715-7(5))* Southern Illinois Univ. Pr.

AUGUSTANA EVANGELICAL LUTHERAN CHURCH

Follstad, Virginia P. The Augustana Evangelical Lutheran Church in Print: A Selective Union List with Annotations of Serial Publications Issued by the Augustana Evangelical Lutheran Church & Its Agencies & Associates 1855-1962, with Selected Serial Publications After 1962. 2007. (ATLA Bibliography Ser.: No. 53). (ENG.). 378p. per. 65.00 *(978-0-8108-5831-2(2))* Scarecrow Pr., Inc.

Yale University. Linonian Society. Constitution & Bylaws. 2011. 24p. pap. 11.99 ***(978-1-4181-9242-6(2))*** MPublishing.

AUGUSTINE, SAINT, BISHOP OF HIPPO, 354-430

Alexander, David C. The Emergence of Augustine's Early Ecclesiology (386-391) 2008. (Patristic Studies). (C). 91.95 *(978-1-4331-0103-8(3))* Lang, Peter Publishing, Inc.

Alexopoulos, Theodoros. Der Ausgang des thearchischen Geistes: Eine Untersuchung der Filioque-Frage anhand Photios - »Mystagogie«, Konstantin Melitiniotes - »Zwei Antirrhetici« und Augustins »De Trinitate«. 2009. (GER.). 324p. (C). 64.00 *(978-3-89971-526-2(8))* Vandenhoeck & Ruprecht GmbH & Co. KG DEU. Dist: ISD.

Augustine, Aurelius. Selections from Augustine: Living Selections from the Great Devotional Classics. Cannon, William R. & Potts, J. Manning, eds. 2011. 42p. 35.95 ***(978-1-258-04008-6(5))*** Literary Licensing, LLC.

Augustine, Saint. Confessions. Wills, Garry, tr. 2008. (ENG.). 368p. (gr. 12-18). 16.00 *(978-0-14-310570-1(1)*, Penguin Classics) Penguin Group (USA) Inc.

—The Confessions. 2006. (ENG.). pap. *(978-1-4065-1000-3(9))* Dodo Pr.

—Confessions. Sheed, F. J., tr. from LAT. 2nd rev. ed. 2007. (Hackett Classics Ser.). (Illus.). 384p. (C). 29.95 *(978-0-87220-817-9(6))*; pap. 9.95 *(978-0-87220-816-2(8))* Hackett Publishing Co., Inc.

—The Confessions of Saint Augustine. 2007. 260p. pap. 21.99 *(978-1-4346-0334-0(2))* BiblioBazaar.

—The Confessions of Saint Augustine. 2008. 468p. per. 9.99 *(978-1-59986-572-0(6))* Filiquarian Publishing, LLC.

—The Confessions of Saint Augustine. Blaiklock, E. M., tr. from LAT. 2010. (Hodder Classics Ser.). (ENG.). 304p. pap. 12.95 *(978-0-340-98012-5(5)*, Hodder & Stoughton) Hodder General Publishing Div. GBR. Dist: Independent Pubs. Group.

—The Confessions of Saint Augustine. 2008. 208p. pap. 7.99 *(978-1-60459-407-2(1))* Wilder Pubns., Ltd.

—Confessions of Saint Augustine. 2006. pap. *(978-1-4068-0603-8(X))* Echo Library.

—The Confessions of Saint Augustine. Warner, Rex, tr. 2009. (ENG.). 384p. (gr. 12-18). pap. 6.95 *(978-0-451-53121-6(3)*, Signet Classics) Penguin Group (USA) Inc.

—The Confessions of Saint Augustine. I.t. ed. 2007. (ENG.). 288p. pap. 23.99 *(978-1-4346-0407-1(1))* BiblioBazaar.

—The Confessions of St Augustine. 2009. 244p. pap. *(978-1-150-71714-7(9))* Books LLC.

—Confessions of St Augustine. 2006. 14.95 *(978-1-60206-010-4(X)*, Cosimo Classics) Cosimo, Inc.

—De Civitate Dei. Walsh, P. G., ed. 2009. (Classical Texts). (LAT, ENG & EGY.). 160p. (C). pap. 35.00 *(978-0-85668-793-6(8))* Aris & Phillips GBR. Dist: Brown, David Bk. Co., The.

—De Civitate Dei. Walsh, P. G., ed. & tr. by. from LAT. 2009. (Classical Texts). (LAT, ENG & EGY.). 160p. (C). 85.00 *(978-0-85668-798-3(7))* Aris & Phillips GBR. Dist: Brown, David Bk. Co., The.

—De Civitate Dei. 2007. (Classical Texts). (LAT & ENG.). 200p. (C). 80.00 *(978-0-85668-759-4(6))*; pap. 36.00 *(978-0-85668-758-7(8))* Aris & Phillips GBR. Dist: Brown, David Bk. Co., The.

Augustine, Saint, creator. The Confessions of St Augustine. 2010. (ENG.). 294p. pap. 28.75 *(978-1-145-63627-9(6))*; 392p. pap. 33.75 *(978-1-176-24699-7(2))* BiblioBazaar.

Augustine, Saint, text. Confessions. 2007. (ENG.). 380p. 48.95 *(978-0-548-00423-4(4))* Kessinger Publishing, LLC.

Augustine, Saint & Augustine. The Confessions of St. Augustine: Modern English Version. 2008. 224p. reprint ed. 5.99 *(978-0-8007-8762-2(5))* Revell.

Augustine, Saint, et al. The Confessions of St Augustine. 2010. 392p. pap. 33.75 *(978-1-142-94561-9(8))* BiblioBazaar.

Augustine, St. Augustine, Later Works: Library of Christian Classics, V8. Burnaby, John & Baillie, John, eds. 2011. 360p. 51.95 ***(978-1-258-09926-8(8))*** Literary Licensing, LLC.

Augustine, St. The Confessions of St. Augustine. Helms, Hal M., ed. 2010. (Paraclete Essentials Ser.). (ENG.). 352p. pap. 16.99 *(978-1-55725-695-9(0))* Paraclete Pr., Inc.

Augustine, St & Augustine, St. St Augustine: Against the Academicians. Garvey, Mary Patricia, tr. 2011. 90p. 38.95 ***(978-1-258-04003-1(4))*** Literary Licensing, LLC.

Augustinus, Aurelius. Select Letters. Baxter, James H., tr. reprint ed. 37.50 *(978-0-404-14502-6(7))* AMS Pr., Inc.

Ayres, Lewis. Augustine & the Trinity. 2010. (ENG.). 376p. 80.00 *(978-0-521-83886-3(X))* Cambridge Univ. Pr.

Baker-Brian, Nicholas John. Manichaeism in the Later Roman Empire: A Study of Augustine's Contra Adimantum. 2009. 392p. 119.95 *(978-0-7734-4755-4(5))* Mellen, Edwin Pr., The.

Barua, Ankur. The Divine Body in History: A Comparative Study of the Symbolism of Time & Embodiment in St. Augustine & Ramanuja. 2009. 267p. 51.95 *(978-3-03911-917-2(6))* Lang, Peter AG GBR. Dist: Lang, Peter.

BeDuhn, Jason David. Augustine's Manichaean Dilemma Vol. 1: Conversion & Apostasy, 373-388 C. E. 2009. (Divinations: Rereading Late Ancient Religion Ser.). 408p. (C). 69.95 *(978-0-8122-4210-2(6))* Univ. of Pennsylvania Pr.

Bennett, Jana Marguerite. Water Is Thicker Than Blood: An Augustinian Theology of Marriage & Singlehood. 2008. (ENG.). 288p. 55.00 *(978-0-19-531543-1(X))* Oxford Univ. Pr., Inc.

Berg, Jacob Albert van den. Biblical Argument in Manichaean Missionary Practice: The Case of Adimantus & Augustine. 2009. (Nag Hammadi & Manichaean Studies). *(978-90-04-18034-5(6))* BRILL.

Bertrand, Louis. Saint Augustin. 2008. 320p. 28.99 *(978-0-554-32238-4(2))*; 29.99 *(978-0-554-22935-5(8))* BiblioBazaar.

—Saint Augustin. Vincent O'Sullivan, tr. 2007. (ENG.). 290p. pap. 21.99 *(978-1-4264-3381-8(6))*; 316p. pap. 24.99 *(978-1-4264-3431-0(6))* BiblioBazaar.

—Saint Augustin. 2009. 246p. pap. *(978-1-4589-6784-8(0))* Books LLC.

—Saint Augustin. O'Sullivan, Vincent, tr. 2007. (ENG.). 256p. per. *(978-1-4065-5276-8(3))* Dodo Pr.

Beyenka, Mary Melchior. Consolation in St Augustine. 2011. 142p. 40.95 ***(978-1-258-01406-3(8))*** Literary Licensing, LLC.

Bieberstein, S., et al, eds. Becoming Living Communities - Construyendo comunidades vivas - Lebendige Gemeinschaften Werden. 2008. (Journal of the European Society of Women in Theological Research Ser.). (ENG, GER & SPA.). 241p. (C). pap. 51.00 *(978-90-429-2208-2(7))* Peeters Pubs. & Booksellers BEL. Dist: Brown, David Bk. Co., The.

Birzer, Bradley J. Sanctifying the World: The Augustinian Life & Mind of Christopher Dawson. 2007. 315p. 30.00 *(978-0-931888-86-1(7))* Christendom Pr.

Boeve, L., et al, eds. Augustine & Postmodern Thought: A New Alliance against Modernity? 2009. (Bibliotheca Ephemeridum Theologicarum Lovaniensium Ser.). (ENG., Illus.). 277p. (C). pap. 116.00 *(978-90-429-2120-7(X))* Peeters Pubs. & Booksellers BEL. Dist: Brown, David Bk. Co., The.

Bogan, Mary Inez. The Vocabulary & Style of the Soliloquies & Dialogues of St Augustine. 2011. 242p. 46.95 ***(978-1-258-05753-4(0))*** Literary Licensing, LLC.

Bonner, Gerald. Freedom & Necessity: St. Augustine's Teaching on Divine Power & Human Freedom. 2007. 142p. per. 24.95 *(978-0-8132-1474-0(2))* Catholic Univ. of America Pr.

Brennan, Josephine. A Study of the Clausulae in the Sermons of St Augustine. 2011. 144p. 40.95 ***(978-1-258-01248-9(0))*** Literary Licensing, LLC.

British Library, illus. The Confessions of St. Augustine. 2007. 94p. 19.95 *(978-1-58617-223-7(9))* Ignatius Pr.

Brooks, Richard O. & Murphy, James Bernard, eds. Augustine & Modern Law. 2011. (Philosophers & Law Ser.). 572p. 300.00 *(978-0-7546-2894-1(9))* Ashgate Publishing Co.

Brown, Brian, et al. Augustine & World Religions. 2008. (Augustine in Conversation: Tradition & Innovation Ser.). (ENG.). 310p. pap. 34.99 *(978-0-7391-2580-9(X))* Lexington Bks.

Brown, Montague Brow. Freedom, Philosophy & Faith: The Transformative Role of Judeo-Christian Freedom in Western Thought. 2011. (ENG.). 300p. 75.00 ***(978-0-7391-5090-0(1))*** Lexington Bks.

Brown, Peter. Religion & Society in the Age of St. Augustine. 2007. (Studies in Augustine: Ser.). 352p. pap. 39.00 *(978-1-55635-174-7(7)*, Wipf and Stock) Wipf & Stock Pubs.

Burnaby, John. Amor Dei: A Study of the Religion of St. Augustine - The Hulsean Lectures For 1938. 2007. 352p. pap. 39.00 *(978-1-55635-501-1(7))* Wipf & Stock Pubs.

Burton, Philip. Language in the Confessions of Augustine. (ENG.). 2009. 216p. pap. 39.95 *(978-0-19-955445-4(5))* 2007. 224p. 95.00 *(978-0-19-926622-7(0))* Oxford Univ. Pr., Inc.

Byassee, Jason. Praise Seeking Understanding: Reading the Psalms with Augustine. 2007. (Radical Traditions Ser.). 290p. per. 32.00 *(978-0-8028-4012-7(4))* Eerdmans, William B. Publishing Co.

—Reading Augustine: A Guide to the Confessions. 2006. (Cascade Companions: Ser.). 102p. pap. 14.00 *(978-1-59752-529-9(4)*, Cascade Bks.) Wipf & Stock Pubs.

Cameron, Michael. Christ Meets Me Everywhere: Augustine's Early Figurative Exegesis, 1 vol. 2012. (Oxford Studies in Historical Theology Ser.). (ENG.). 384p. 74.00 ***(978-0-19-975129-7(3))*** Oxford Univ. Pr., Inc.

Cary, Phillip. Inner Grace: Augustine in the Traditions of Plato & Paul. 2008. (ENG.). 208p. 55.00 *(978-0-19-533648-1(8))* Oxford Univ. Pr., Inc.

—Outward Signs: The Powerlessness of External Things in Augustine's Thought. 2008. (ENG.). 352p. 74.00 *(978-0-19-533649-8(6))* Oxford Univ. Pr., Inc.

Chadwick, Henry. Augustine of Hippo: A Life. (ENG.). 2010. 208p. pap. 16.95 *(978-0-19-958806-0(6))* 2009. 160p. 19.95 *(978-0-19-956830-7(8))* Oxford Univ. Pr., Inc.

Chang, Curtis. Engaging Unbelief: A Captivating Strategy from Augustine & Aquinas. 2007. 188p. pap. 22.00 *(978-1-55635-520-2(3))* Wipf & Stock Pubs.

Cho, Dongsun. St. Augustine's Doctrine of Eternal Punishment: His Biblical & Theological Argument. 2010. 109.95 *(978-0-7734-3676-3(6))* Mellen, Edwin Pr., The.

Christian, William A. Augustine on the Creation of the World. 2011. 28p. 35.95 ***(978-1-258-01984-6(1))*** Literary Licensing, LLC.

Clark, Gillian. Augustine: The Confessions. 2009. (Greece & Rome Live Ser.). (Illus.). 100p. (C). 80.00 *(978-1-904675-40-2(9))* Bristol Phoenix Pr. GBR. Dist: Chicago Distribution Ctr.

Clark, Mary T. Augustine, Philosopher of Freedom: A Study in Comparative Philosophy. 2011. 284p. 48.95 ***(978-1-258-01834-4(9))*** Literary Licensing, LLC.

Conybeare, Catherine. The Irrational Augustine. 2006. (Oxford Early Christian Studies). (ENG.). 240p. 110.00 *(978-0-19-926208-3(X))* Oxford Univ. Pr., Inc.

Coyle, J. K. Manichaeism & Its Legacy. 2009. (Nag Hammadi & Manichaean Studies). xxiv, 346p. *(978-90-04-17574-7(1))* BRILL.

Cristaudo, Wayne & Wong, Heung-Wah, eds. Augustine: His Legacy & Relevance. 2010. (University of Hong Kong European Studies in Philosophical Theology Ser.). (ENG.). 330p. (C). pap. 36.00 *(978-1-921511-73-8(7))* ATF Pr. AUS. Dist: Brown, David Bk. Co., The.

Daly, Christopher T., et al. Augustine & History. 2007. (Augustine in Conversation Ser.). (ENG.). 340p. per. 41.99 *(978-0-7391-2271-6(1))* Lexington Bks.

de Kroon, Marijn. We Believe in God & in Christ. Not in the Church: The Influence of Wessel Gansfort on Martin Bucer. 2009. (Princeton Theological Seminary Studies in Reformed Theology & History Ser.). (ENG.). 128p. pap. 30.00 *(978-0-664-23293-1(0))* Westminster John Knox Pr.

De Paulo, Craig J. N. Augustinian Just War Theory & the Wars in Afghanistan & Iraq: Confessions, Contentions, & the Lust for Power. 2011. (C). pap. 34.95 ***(978-1-4331-1232-4(9))*** Lang, Peter Publishing, Inc.

De Rosset, Rosalie, ed. The Confessions of St. Augustine: Books One to Ten. 2007. (Moody Classics Ser.). (ENG.). 304p. per. 8.99 *(978-0-8024-5651-9(0))* Moody Pubs.

Decret, François. Early Christianity in North Africa. 2011. (ENG.). 240p. pap. 38.00 *(978-0-227-17356-5(2))* Clarke, James Co., Ltd. GBR. Dist: Brown, David Bk. Co., The.

—Early Christianity in North Africa. Smither, Edward L., tr. 2009. 240p. pap. 26.00 *(978-1-55635-692-6(7)*, Cascade Bks.) Wipf & Stock Pubs.

Deely, John. Augustine & Poinsot: The Protosemiotic Development. 2009. (ENG., Illus.). 200p. 35.00 *(978-1-58966-173-8(7))* Univ. of Scranton Pr.

Demacopoulos, George & Papanikolaou, Aristotle, eds. Orthodox Readings of Augustine. 2008. 304p. pap. 24.00 *(978-0-88141-327-4(5))* St. Vladimir's Seminary Pr.

Dittrich, Constance. Augustinus, ein Lehrer des Abendlandes: Einführung und Dokumente. Dittrich, Constance et al, eds. 2009. (Schriften der Universitätsbibliothek Eichstätt Ser.). (GER.). 136p. pap. 30.00 *(978-3-447-05923-7(0))* Harrassowitz, Otto Verlag DEU. Dist: ISD.

Dobell, Brian. Augustine's Intellectual Conversion: The Journey from Platonism to Christianity. (ENG.). 2012. 270p. pap. 36.00 ***(978-1-107-40424-3(X))*** 2009. (Illus.). 268p. 86.00 *(978-0-521-51339-5(1))* Cambridge Univ. Pr.

Dodaro, Robert. Christ & the Just Society in the Thought of Augustine. 2008. (ENG.). 264p. pap. 37.99 *(978-0-521-06964-9(5))* Cambridge Univ. Pr.

Doody, John & Paffenroth, Kim, eds. Augustine & History. 2007. (Augustine in Conversation Ser.). (ENG.). 340p. 94.50 *(978-0-7391-2270-9(3))* Lexington Bks.

Doody, John A., et al. Augustine & Philosophy. 2010. (Augustine in Conversation: Tradition & Innovation Ser.). (ENG.). 78.99 *(978-0-7391-4538-8(X))*; pap. 34.99 *(978-0-7391-4539-5(8))* Lexington Bks.

Doueihi, Milad. Augustine & Spinoza. 2011. (ENG.). 128p. 29.95 *(978-0-674-05063-1(0))* Harvard Univ. Pr.

Drobner, Hubertus R. Augustinus von Hippo: Sermones ad Populum. 2010. (Patrologia - Beiträge zum Studium der Kirchenväter Ser.). (GER.). 184p. 50.95 *(978-3-631-61258-3(3))* Lang, Peter GmbH, Europaischer Verlag der Wissenschaften DEU. Dist: Lang, Peter.

Dunham, Scott A. The Trinity & Creation in Augustine: An Ecological Analysis. 2008. (SUNY Series on Religion & the Environment). ix, 198p. (C). 65.00 *(978-0-7914-7523-2(9))* State Univ. of New York Pr.

—Trinity & Creation in Augustine: An Ecological Analysis. 2009. 208p. pap. 23.95 *(978-0-7914-7524-9(7)*, Suny Pr.) State Univ. of New York Pr.

Dyson, Robert W. St Augustine of Hippo: The Christian Transformation of Political Philosophy. 2006. (Continuum Studies in Philosophy). (ENG.). 206p. 155.00 *(978-0-8264-8588-5(X))* Continuum International Publishing Group, Ltd. GBR. Dist: National Bk. Network.

Ebbeler, Jennifer. Disciplining Christians: Correction & Community in Augustine's Letters, 1 vol. 2012. (Oxford Studies in Late Antiquity Ser.). (ENG.). 304p. 74.00 *(978-0-19-537256-4(5))* Oxford Univ. Pr., Inc.

Enos, Richard Leo & Thompson, Roger, eds. The Rhetoric of St. Augustine of Hippo: De Doctrina Christiana & the Search for a Distinctly Christian Rhetoric. 2008. (ENG.). 420p. (C). pap. 49.95 *(978-1-60258-008-4(1))* Baylor Univ. Pr.

Ettenhuber, Katrin. Donne's Augustine: Renaissance Cultures of Interpretation. 2011. (ENG.). 288p. 110.00 *(978-0-19-960910-9(1))* Oxford Univ. Pr., Inc.

Evers, A. Church, Cities, & People: A Study of the Plebs in the Church & Cities of Roman Africa in Late Antiquity. 2010. (Interdisciplinary Studies in Ancient Culture & Religion Ser.). (ENG.). 367p. (C). pap. 85.00 *(978-90-429-2206-8(0))* Peeters Pubs. & Booksellers BEL. Dist: Brown, David Bk. Co., The.

Falbo, Giovanni. St. Monica: The Power of a Mother's Love. 2007. (Illus.). 142p. per. 14.95 *(978-0-8198-7099-5(4))* Pauline Bks. & Media.

Fehrenbach, Paul K. Soul & Self: Parallels Between Spiritual & Psychological Growth. 2006. 107p. per. 14.95 *(978-0-8091-4423-5(9)*, 4423-9) Paulist Pr.

Fitzgerald, Allan D., et al, eds. Augustine Through the Ages: An Encyclopedia. 2009. (Illus.). 902p. pap. 75.00 *(978-0-8028-6479-6(1))* Eerdmans, William B. Publishing Co.

Fladerer, Ludwig. Augustinus als Exeget: Zu seinen Kommentaren des Galaterbriefes und der Genesis. 2010. (Sitzungsberichte der Phil. -Hist. Klasse Ser.). (GER.). 261p. (C). pap. 80.00 *(978-3-7001-6647-4(8))* Austrian Academy of Sciences Press AUT. Dist: Brown, David Bk. Co., The.

Fleteren, Frederick Van. Life of Augustine of Hippo: Child, Convert, Monk, Priest, 354-396, Volume 1. 2010. 410p. (C). 90.95 *(978-1-4331-0284-4(6))* Lang, Peter Publishing, Inc.

Fredriksen, Paula. Augustine & the Jews: A Christian Defense of Jews & Judaism. 2010. 528p. pap. 20.00 *(978-0-300-16628-6(1))* Yale Univ. Pr.

Fürst, Alfons. Von Origenes und Hieronymus Zu Augustinus: Studien Zur Antiken Theologiegeschichte. 2011. (Arbeiten Zur Kirchengeschichte Ser.). (GER.). VIII, 536p. 140.00 ***(978-3-11-025102-9(7))*** De Gruyter, Walter Inc.

Gascoigne, Robert. The Church & Secularity: Two Stories of Liberal Society. 2009. (Moral Traditions Ser.). (ENG.). 192p. pap. 26.95 *(978-1-58901-490-9(1))* Georgetown Univ. Pr.

Gaudoin-Parker, Michael L. Augustine & Francis. 2012. ***(978-0-8189-1342-6(8)***, St. Pauls) St Pauls/Alba Hse. Pubs.

Gerber, Chad Tyler. The Spirit of Augustine's Early Theology: Contextualizing Augustine's Pneumatology. 2012. (Ashgate Studies in Philosophy & Theology in Late Antiquity Ser.). 224p. 89.95 ***(978-1-4094-2437-6(5))*** Ashgate Publishing Co.

Gotte, Johannes. Preliminary Studies for the Interpretation of St Augustine's Concept of Providence: Folia, Supplement 1, June 1953. 2011. 26p. 35.95 ***(978-1-258-03814-4(5))*** Literary Licensing, LLC.

Green, Bradley G. Colin Gunton & the Failure of Augustine: The Theology of Colin Gunton in Light of Augustine. 2012. (ENG.). 226p. pap. 39.00 ***(978-0-227-68005-6(7))*** Clarke, James Co., Ltd. GBR. Dist: Brown, David Bk. Co., The.

—Colin Gunton & the Failure of Augustine: The Theology of Colin Gunton in Light of Augustine. 2011. (Distinguished Dissertations in Christian Theology Ser.). 240p. pap. 26.00 ***(978-1-60899-268-3(3)***, Pickwick Pubns.) Wipf & Stock Pubs.

Green, J. D. Augustinianism: Studies in the Process of Spiritual Tranvaluation. 2007. (Studies in Spirituality Supplements Ser.). (ENG.). 114p. (C). pap. 70.00 *(978-90-429-1976-1(0))* Peeters Pubs. & Booksellers BEL. Dist: Brown, David Bk. Co., The.

Gregory, Eric. Politics & the Order of Love: An Augustinian Ethic of Democratic Citizenship. 2010. (ENG.). 434p. pap. 30.00 *(978-0-226-30752-7(2))* Univ. of Chicago Pr.

Guardini, Romano. The Conversion of Augustine. 2nd ed. 2007. 250p. 55.00 *(978-1-934182-12-3(5)*, 978-1-934182-12-3) Alethes Pr.

Harding & Harding, Brian. Augustine & Roman Virtue. 2008. (Continuum Studies in Philosophy Ser.). (ENG.). 220p. 130.00 *(978-1-84706-285-7(7))* Continuum International Publishing Group, Ltd. GBR. Dist: National Bk. Network.

Harding, Brian. Augustine & Roman Virtue. 2011. (ENG.). 220p. pap. 44.95 ***(978-1-4411-7527-4(X))*** Continuum International Publishing Group, Ltd. GBR. Dist: National Bk. Network.

Harkins, Franklin T. Reading & the Work of Restoration: History & Scripture in the Theology of Hugh of St. Victor. 2009. (Studies & Texts). (LAT & ENG.). xii, 336p. 80.00 *(978-0-88844-167-6(3))* Pontifical Institute of Mediaeval Studies, Dept. of Pubns. CAN. Dist: Univ. of Toronto Pr.

Harnack, Adolf. Monasticism: Its Ideals & History & the Confessions of St. Augustine. Kellett, E. E., tr. 2007. (ENG.). 172p. 37.95 *(978-0-548-08146-4(8))* Kessinger Publishing, LLC.

Harrison, Carol. Rethinking Augustine's Early Theology: An Argument for Continuity. 2008. (ENG.). 318p. 50.00 *(978-0-19-954364-9(X))* Oxford Univ. Pr., Inc.

Harvey, John F. Moral Theology of the Confessions of Saint Augustine. 2009. 194p. pap. 22.00 *(978-1-60608-423-6(2)*, Wipf and Stock) Wipf & Stock Pubs.

Harvey, John F. Moral Theology of the Confessions of St. Augustine. 2011. 194p. 42.95 ***(978-1-258-02235-8(4))*** Literary Licensing, LLC.

Heidl, Gyorgy. The Influence of Origen on the Young Augustine. 2009. 140.00 *(978-1-59333-702-5(7))* Gorgias Pr., LLC.

Hermanowicz, Erika & Hermanowicz, Erika T. Possidius of Calama: A Study of the North African Episcopate at the Time of Augustine. 2008. (Oxford Early Christian Studies). (ENG.). 288p. 125.00 *(978-0-19-923635-0(6))* Oxford Univ. Pr., Inc.

Hochschild, Paige E. Memory in Augustine's Theological Anthropology. 2012. (Oxford Early Christian Studies). (ENG.). 272p. 125.00 ***(978-0-19-964302-8(4))*** Oxford Univ. Pr., Inc.

Hogrefe, Arne. Umstrittene Vergangenheit: Historische Argumente in der Auseinandersetzung Augustins mit den Donatisten. 2009. (Millennium-Studien / Millennium Studies).Tr. of History of the Donatist Schism & the Conflict between Catholics & Donatists at the Time of Augustine. (GER.). XII, 394p. 140.00 *(978-3-11-020363-9(4))*; 210.00 ***(978-3-11-173381-4(5))*** De Gruyter, Walter Inc.

Hollingworth, Miles. Pilgrim City: St. Augustine of Hippo & His Innovation in Political Thought. 2010. (ENG.). 256p. 120.00 *(978-0-567-31002-6(7)*, T&T Clark Int'l) Continuum International Publishing Group, Ltd. GBR. Dist: National Bk. Network.

—Pilgrim City: St Augustine of Hippo & His Innovation in Political Thought. 2010. (ENG.). 256p. 34.95 *(978-0-567-48010-1(0)*, T&T Clark Int'l) Continuum International Publishing Group, Ltd. GBR. Dist: National Bk. Network.

Huppe, Bernard Felix. Doctrine & Poetry: Augustine's Influence on Old English Poetry. 2011. 258p. 47.95 ***(978-1-258-00256-5(6))*** Literary Licensing, LLC.

Ireland, Patricia Sodano. Guardian of a Pure Heart: St. Augustine on the Path to Heaven. 2009. *(978-0-8189-1281-8(2))* St Pauls/Alba Hse. Pubs.

Jenson, Matt & Jenson. Gravity of Sin: Augustine, Luther & Barth on Homo Incurvatus in Se. 2007. (ENG.). 224p. 49.95 *(978-0-567-03138-9(1))*; 155.00 *(978-0-567-03137-2(3))* Continuum International Publishing Group, Ltd. GBR. (T&T Clark Int'l). Dist: National Bk. Network.

Kampowski, Stephan. Arendt, Augustine, & the New Beginning: The Action Theory & Moral Thought of Hannah Arendt in the Light of Her Dissertation on St. Augustine. 2008. 384p. pap. 50.00 *(978-0-8028-2724-1(1))* Eerdmans, William B. Publishing Co.

Kany, Roland. Augustine's Trinitarian Thought: A Critical Reappraisal of Modern Scholarship on de Trinitate. 2013. (ENG.). 352p. 160.00 *(978-0-567-50000-7(4)*, T&T Clark Int'l) Continuum International Publishing Group, Ltd. GBR. Dist: National Bk. Network.

Kaufman, Peter Iver. Incorrectly Political: Augustine & Thomas More. 2007. 304p. pap. 35.00 *(978-0-268-03314-9(5))* Univ. of Notre Dame Pr.

Kelley, Joseph T., anno. Saint Augustine of Hippo: Selections from Confessions & other Essential Writings-Annotated & Explained. 2010. 192p. pap. 16.99 *(978-1-59473-282-9(5))* SkyLight Paths Publishing.

Kim, Jangsaeng. A Comparative Study on Suffering in Augustine & Asvaghosa Through Gate Control Theory, Vol. 835. 2006. (European University Studies 23 Ser.). 241p. pap. *(978-0-8204-9912-3(9))*; pap. *(978-3-631-55279-7(3))* Lang, Peter AG.

Kim, Yoon-Kyung. Augustine's Changing Interpretations of Genesis 1-3: From de Genesi contra Manichaeos to de Genesi ad Litteram. 2006. 208p. 109.95 *(978-0-7734-5670-9(8))* Mellen, Edwin Pr., The.

Kirwan, Christopher. Augustine-arg Philosophers. 2008. (ENG.). 336p. 45.00 *(978-0-415-48759-7(5))* Routledge.

Lam, Joseph & Lam Cong, Joseph Quy. Theologische Verwandtschaft: Augustinus Von Hippo und Joseph Ratzinger/Papst Benedikt XVI. 2009. (GER.). 268p. *(978-3-429-03077-3(3))* Echter Wuerzburg.

Lee, Alexander. Petrarch & St. Augustine: Classical Scholarship, Christian Theology & the Origins of the Renaissance in Italy. 2012. (Brill's Studies in Intellectual History: Vol. 210). (ENG.). x, 382p. ***(978-90-04-22403-2(3))*** BRILL.

Levering, Matthew, ed. Aquinas the Augustinian. 2007. 291p. per. 39.95 *(978-0-8132-1492-4(0))* Catholic Univ. of America Pr.

Lombardi, Elena. The Syntax of Desire: Language & Love in Augustine, the Modistae, Dante. 2007. (ENG.). 360p. *(978-0-8020-9070-6(2))* Univ. of Toronto Pr.

M ller, Christof (Ed) & Mayer, Cornelius. Gnade - Freiheit - Rechtfertigung: Augustin sche Topoi und ihre Wirkungsgeschichte. Internationales Kolloquium zum 1650. Geburtstag Augustins vom 25. bis 27. November 2004 im Erbacher Hof zu Mainz. (Abhandlungen der Geistes- und Sozialwissenschaftlichen Klasse (AM-GS) Ser.). (ENG & GER.). 153p. (C). pap. 34.00 *(978-3-515-09050-6(9))* Steiner, Franz Verlag Wiesbaden GmbH DEU. Dist: Brown, David Bk. Co., The.

MacKendrick, Karmen, et al. Seducing Augustine: Bodies, Desires, Confessions. MacKendrick, Karmen, ed. 3rd ed. 2010. (ENG.). 176p. 75.00 *(978-0-8232-3193-5(3))*; pap. 28.00 *(978-0-8232-3194-2(1))* Fordham Univ. Pr.

Marion, Jean-Luc. In the Self's Place: The Approach of Saint Augustine. 2012. (Cultural Memory in the Present Ser.). (ENG.). 480p. 90.00 ***(978-0-8047-6290-8(2))***; pap. 27.95 ***(978-0-8047-6291-5(0))*** Stanford Univ. Pr.

Markus, R. A. Signs & Meanings: World & Text in Ancient Christianity, 2nd Edition. 2011. 158p. pap. 18.00 ***(978-1-61097-400-4(X))***, Wipf and Stock) Wipf & Stock Pubs.

Martin, Thomas F., et al. St. Augustine. 2010. (Library of World Biography Ser.). (ENG.). 176p. (C). pap. 25.33 *(978-0-205-56831-4(9)*, Prentice Hall) Prentice Hall PTR.

Mason, Arthur James, ed. The Mission of St Augustine to England: According to the Original Documents, Being a Handbook for the Thirteenth Centenary. 2012. (ENG.). 276p. pap. 45.00 ***(978-1-107-61982-1(3))*** Cambridge Univ. Pr.

Mathewes, Charles T. Evil & the Augustinian Tradition. 2007. (ENG.). 284p. pap. 39.99 *(978-0-521-03544-6(9))* Cambridge Univ. Pr.

—The Republic of Grace: Augustinian Thoughts for Dark Times. 2010. 280p. pap. 20.00 *(978-0-8028-6508-3(9))* Eerdmans, William B. Publishing Co.

Mattox, John Mark. St. Augustine & the Theory of Just War. (Continuum Studies in Philosophy Ser.). (ENG.). 208p. 2009. 34.95 *(978-0-8264-4635-0(3))* 2006. 120.00 *(978-0-8264-8779-7(3))* Continuum International Publishing Group, Ltd. GBR. Dist: National Bk. Network.

McCabe, Joseph. Saint Augustine & His Age. 2009. 200p. pap. 18.01 *(978-1-4589-6786-2(7))* General Bks. LLC.

—Saint Augustine & His Age. 2007. (ENG.). 448p. 51.95 *(978-0-548-13591-4(6))* 2006. pap. 36.95 *(978-1-4286-4719-0(8))* Kessinger Publishing, LLC.

Meilaender, Gilbert. The Way That Leads There: Augustinian Reflections on the Christian Life. 2006. 172p. per. 16.00 *(978-0-8028-3213-9(X))* Eerdmans, William B. Publishing Co.

Meissner, Joshua. The Perjured City. 2008. 120p. pap. *(978-3-639-06166-6(7))* VDM Verlag Dr. Mueller e.K.

Miles, Margaret R. Augustine & the FundamentalistÕs Daughter. 2011. 236p. pap. 26.00 ***(978-1-60899-759-6(6)***, Cascade Bks.) Wipf & Stock Pubs.

—Augustine & the Fundamentalist's Daughter. 2012. (ENG.). 234p. pap. 35.00 ***(978-0-7188-9262-3(3))*** Lutherworth Pr., The GBR. Dist: Brown, David Bk. Co., The.

—Desire & Delight: A New Reading of Augustine's Confessions. 2006. 144p. pap. 18.00 *(978-1-59752-751-4(3)*, Wipf and Stock) Wipf & Stock Pubs.

—Rereading Historical Theology: Before, During, & after Augustine. 2007. 326p. pap. 36.00 *(978-1-55635-216-4(6))* Wipf & Stock Pubs.

Moon, Joshua. Jeremiah's New Covenant: An Augustinian Reading. 2011. pap. *(978-1-57506-702-5(1))* Eisenbrauns, Inc.

Morgan, Edward. The Incarnation of the Word: The Theology of Language of Augustine of Hippo. 2011. (ENG.). 208p. pap. 39.95 ***(978-0-567-63571-6(6)***, T&T Clark Int'l) Continuum International Publishing Group, Ltd. GBR. Dist: National Bk. Network.

Morgan, Edward & Morgan. The Incarnation of the Word: The Theology of Language of Augustine of Hippo. 2010. (ENG., Illus.). 208p. 120.00 *(978-0-567-03382-6(1)*, T&T Clark Int'l) Continuum International Publishing Group, Ltd. GBR. Dist: National Bk. Network.

Mullany, Katherine T. Augustine of Hippo: The First Modern Man. 2011. 208p. 44.95 ***(978-1-258-01626-5(5))*** Literary Licensing, LLC.

Nightingale, Andrea. Once Out of Nature: Augustine on Time & the Body. 2011. (ENG.). 264p. 39.00 *(978-0-226-58575-8(1))* Univ. of Chicago Pr.

O'Donnell, James J. Augustine Confessions: Augustine Confessions: Volume 1: Introduction & Text. 2012. (ENG.). 287p. pap. 45.00 ***(978-0-19-966072-8(7))*** Oxford Univ. Pr., Inc.

O'Toole, Christopher J. Philosophy of Creation in the Writings O. 2006. pap. 20.95 *(978-1-4286-5971-1(4))* Kessinger Publishing, LLC.

Pacioni, Virgilio. Augustine of Hippo: His Philosophy in a Historical & Contemporary Perspective. 2010. (Illus.). 344p. pap. *(978-0-85244-737-6(X))* Gracewing, Ltd.

Paffenroth, Kim. Augustine & World Religions. Brown, Brian & Doody, John A., eds. 2008. (Augustine in Conversation: Tradition & Innovation Ser.). (ENG.). 310p. 89.50 *(978-0-7391-2579-3(6))* Lexington Bks.

Paffenroth/Hughes. Augustine & Liberal Education. 2008. (Augustine in Conversation: Tradition & Innovation Ser.). (ENG.). 232p. pap. 31.50 *(978-0-7391-2383-6(1))* Lexington Bks.

Partoens, Gert, et al. Ministerium Sermonis: Philological, Historical, & Theological Studies on Augustine's Sermones Ad Populum. 2010. (Instrumenta Patristica et Mediaevalia Ser.). (FRE, GER & ENG.). 403p. (C). 152.00 *(978-2-503-53192-2(X))* Brepols Pubs. BEL. Dist: ISD.

Peters, James R. The Logic of the Heart: Augustine, Pascal, & the Rationality of Faith, 1 vol. 2009. 304p. (C). pap. 35.00 *(978-0-8010-3599-9(6))* Baker Academic.

Phelan, Gerald B. Some Illustrations of St Thomas' Development of the Wisdom of St Augustine: The Mu Nu Sigma Lecture 1946. 2011. 60p. 36.95 ***(978-1-258-04410-7(2))*** Literary Licensing, LLC.

Piper, John. The Legacy of Sovereign Joy: God's Triumphant Grace in the Lives of Augustine, Luther, & Calvin. 2nd ed. 2006. (Swans Are Not Silent Ser.: Vol. 1). 160p. pap. 15.99 *(978-1-58134-813-2(4))* Crossway.

Podzeit, Utz. Die Freude an der Tora als Weisung des Weges zum Vater: Auslegungen der Rabbinen und des Aurelius Augustinus zu Psalm 1. 2009. (GER.). 98p. pap. 35.95 *(978-3-631-59067-6(9))* Lang, Peter GmbH, Europaischer Verlag der Wissenschaften DEU. Dist: Lang, Peter.

Pope Pius XI. St Augustine: Encyclical Letter, Ad Salutem. 2011. 56p. 36.95 ***(978-1-258-04204-2(5))*** Literary Licensing, LLC.

Possidius. The Life of Saint Augustine. 2008. (LAT & ENG.). *(978-1-889758-90-9(6)*, Evolution Publishing & Manufacturing) Arx Publishing.

Powers, Kevin. Augustine on Natural Theology. 2008. 96p. pap. *(978-3-639-07114-6(X))* VDM Verlag Dr. Mueller e.K.

Pranger, M. B. Eternity's Ennui: Temporality, Perseverance & Voice in Augustine & Western Literature. 2010. (Brill's Studies in Intellectual History). 480p. *(978-90-04-18936-2(X))* BRILL.

Rau, Catherine & Rau, Lucy. St Augustine's Theory of Time. 2011. 48p. pap. 35.95 ***(978-1-258-03933-2(8))*** Literary Licensing, LLC.

Rees, Geoffrey. The Romance of Innocent Sexuality. 2011. 318p. pap. 37.00 *(978-1-60608-661-2(8))* Cascade Bks.

Rickaby, Joseph. St. Augustine's City of God. 2009. 119p. pap. 11.00 *(978-1-60608-383-3(X)*, Wipf and Stock) Wipf & Stock Pubs.

Saak, Eric Leland. Creating Augustine: Interpreting Augustine & Augustinianism in the Later Middle Ages. 2012. (ENG.). 272p. 125.00 ***(978-0-19-964638-8(4))*** Oxford Univ. Pr., Inc.

Schadel, Erwin. Trinität als Archetyp? Erläuterungen zur C. G. Jung, Hegel und Augustinus. 2008. (Schriften zur Triadik und Ontodynamik Ser.). 174p. pap. 49.95 *(978-3-631-57927-5(6))* Lang, Peter GmbH, Europaischer Verlag der Wissenschaften DEU. Dist: Lang, Peter.

Schaff, Philip, ed. Nicene & Post-Nicene Fathers: First Series Volume I - the Confessions & Letters of St. Augustine. 2007. 636p. 37.95 *(978-1-60206-591-8(8))*; (ENG.). per. 26.95 *(978-1-60206-590-1(X))* Cosimo, Inc.

—Nicene & Post-Nicene Fathers: First Series, Volume II St. Augustine. 2007. 640p. (ENG.). 37.95 *(978-1-60206-593-2(4))*; per. 26.95 *(978-1-60206-592-5(6))* Cosimo, Inc.

—Nicene & Post-Nicene Fathers: First Series, Volume III St. Augustine. 2007. 588p. (ENG.). 35.95 *(978-1-60206-595-6(0))*; per. 24.95 *(978-1-60206-594-9(2))* Cosimo, Inc.

—Nicene & Post-Nicene Fathers: First Series, Volume IV St. Augustine. 2007. 684p. (ENG.). 37.95 *(978-1-60206-597-0(7))*; per. 26.95 *(978-1-60206-596-3(9))* Cosimo, Inc.

—Nicene & Post-Nicene Fathers: First Series, Volume V St. Augustine. 2007. 640p. (ENG.). 37.95 *(978-1-60206-599-4(3))*; per. 26.95 *(978-1-60206-598-7(5))* Cosimo, Inc.

—Nicene & Post-Nicene Fathers: First Series, Volume VI St. Augustine. 2007. 592p. (ENG.). 35.95 *(978-1-60206-601-4(9))*; per. 24.95 *(978-1-60206-600-7(0))* Cosimo, Inc.

—Nicene & Post-Nicene Fathers: First Series, Volume VII St. Augustine. 2007. 596p. (ENG.). 35.95 *(978-1-60206-603-8(5))*; per. 24.95 *(978-1-60206-602-1(7))* Cosimo, Inc.

Schaff, Philip & Coxe, Arthur Cleveland, eds. Nicene & Post-Nicene Fathers: First Series, Volume VIII St. Augustine. 2007. 712p. 37.95 *(978-1-60206-605-2(1))*; per. 27.95 *(978-1-60206-604-5(3))* Cosimo, Inc.

Schiller, Isabella. Die handschriftliche Überlieferung der Werke des heiligen Augustinus, Band 10: Ostdeutschland und Berlin. Teil 1: Werkverzeichnis, Teil 2: Verzeichnis nach Bibliotheken, 2 vols. 2009. (Sitzungsberichte der Phil. -Hist. Klasse Ser.). (GER.). 973p. (C). pap. 149.00 *(978-3-7001-6559-0(5))* Austrian Academy of Sciences Press AUT. Dist: Brown, David Bk. Co., The.

Schultheiss, Jochen. Generationenbeziehungen in den Confessiones des Augustinus: Theologie und literarische Form in der Spatantike. 2011. (Hermes - Einzelschrift Ser.). (GER.). 317p. (C). pap. 85.00 ***(978-3-515-09721-5(X))*** Steiner, Franz Verlag Wiesbaden GmbH DEU. Dist: Brown, David Bk. Co., The.

Schumacher, Lydia. Divine Illumination: The History & Future of Augustine's Theory of Knowledge. 2011. (Challenges in Contemporary Theology Ser.: 25). (ENG.). 264p. 125.95 *(978-0-470-65742-3(1)*, Wiley-Blackwell) Wiley, John & Sons, Inc.

Seele, Peter. Philosophie der Epochenschwelle: Augustin zwischen Antike und Mittelalter. 2008. (Quellen und Studien Zur Philosophie Ser.). Tr. of Philosophy of the Epochal Transition. (GER.). XIII, 285p. 119.00 *(978-3-11-019475-3(9))* De Gruyter, Walter Inc.

Six-Means, Horace E. Augustine Catholic Christianization: The Catholicization of Roman Africa, 391-408. 2011. ***(978-1-4331-0804-4(6))*** Lang, Peter GmbH, Europaischer Verlag der Wissenschaften.

Smither, Edward L. & Broadman and Holman Publishers Staff. Augustine As Mentor: A Model for Preparing Spiritual Leaders 2009. (ENG.). 272p. pap. 17.99 *(978-0-8054-4707-1(5)*, B&H Academic) B&H Publishing Group.

Stalnaker, Aaron. Overcoming Our Evil: Human Nature & Spiritual Exercises in Xunzi & Augustine. (Moral Traditions Ser.). (ENG.). 352p. 2009. pap. 29.95 *(978-1-58901-503-6(7))* 2006. 49.95 *(978-1-58901-094-9(9))* Georgetown Univ. Pr.

Stark, Judith, ed. Feminist Interpretations of Augustine. 2007. (Re-Reading the Canon Ser.). (ENG.). 304p. (C). 75.00 *(978-0-271-03257-3(X))* Pennsylvania State Univ. Pr.

Stark, Judith Chelius & Stark, Judith, eds. Feminist Interpretations of Augustine. 2007. (Re-Reading the Canon Ser.). (ENG.). 304p. pap. 35.00 *(978-0-271-03258-0(8))* Pennsylvania State Univ. Pr.

Stock, Brian. Augustine's Inner Dialogue: The Philosophical Soliloquy in Late Antiquity. 2010. (ENG.). 256p. 89.00 *(978-0-521-19031-2(2))* Cambridge Univ. Pr.

Switalski, Bruno. Plotinus & the Ethics of St Augustine V1: Neoplatonism & the Ethics of St. Augustine. 2011. 146p. 40.95 ***(978-1-258-03756-7(4))*** Literary Licensing, LLC.

Taylor, Chloë. The Culture of Confession from Augustine to Foucault: A Genealogy of the 'confessing Animal' 2008. (ENG., Illus.). 312p. 125.00 *(978-0-415-96371-8(0))* Routledge.

Tepaske, Bradley. Sexuality & the Religious Imagination. 2008. 281p. pap. 27.95 *(978-1-882670-51-2(5))* Spring Journal.

Teselle, Eugene. Augustine's Strategy as an Apologist: The Saint Augustine Lecture 1973. 2010. 94p. pap. 12.00 *(978-1-60899-871-5(1)*, Wipf and Stock) Wipf & Stock Pubs.

Teske, Roland J. Augustine of Hippo: Philosopher, Exegete, & Theologian: A Second Collection of Essays. 2009. pap. *(978-0-87462-764-0(8))* Marquette Univ. Pr.

—To Know God & the Soul: Essays on the Thought of Saint Augustine. 2008. 289p. 74.95 *(978-0-8132-1487-0(4))* Catholic Univ. of America Pr.

Teske, Roland J., et al. Tolle Lege: Essays on Augustine & on Medieval Philosophy in Honor of Roland J. Teske, SJ. 2011. *(978-0-87462-807-4(5))* Marquette Univ. Pr.

Thompson, George N., ed. St. Augustine on the End of the World. 55p. (Orig.). reprint ed. pap. 5.95 *(978-0-940564-15-2(7))* Mayflower Pilgrim Pr.

Topping, Ryan. St Augustine. 2010. (Continuum Library of Educational Thought Ser.). (ENG.). 208p. 140.00 *(978-0-8264-2661-1(1))* Continuum International Publishing Group, Ltd. GBR. Dist: National Bk. Network.

Tornau, Christian. Zwischen Rhetorik und Philosophie: Augustins Argumentationstechnik in De civitate Dei und ihr bildungsgeschichtlicher Hintergrund. 2006. (Untersuchungen Zur Antiken Literatur und Geschichte Ser.). (GER.). VIII, 466p. 154.00 *(978-3-11-019130-1(X))* De Gruyter, Walter Inc.

Unterseher, Lisa A. The Mark of Cain & the Jews. 2009. 98.00 *(978-1-59333-896-1(1))* Gorgias Pr., LLC.

Van Geest, P. The Incomprehensibility of God. Augustine as a Negative Theologian. 2011. (Late Antique History & Religion Ser.). (ENG.). 262p. (C). 95.00 *(978-90-429-2473-4(X))* Peeters Pubs. & Booksellers BEL. Dist: Brown, David Bk. Co., The.

Vessey, Mark, ed. A Companion to Augustine. 2012. (Blackwell Companions to the Ancient World Ser.: 88). (ENG.). 640p. 199.95 ***(978-1-4051-5946-3(4)***, Wiley-Blackwell) Wiley, John & Sons, Inc.

Visser, Arnoud. Reading Augustine in the Reformation: The Flexibility of Intellectual Authority in Europe, 1500-1620, 1 vol. 2011. (Oxford Studies in Historical Theology Ser.). (ENG.). 256p. 74.00 *(978-0-19-976593-5(6))* Oxford Univ. Pr., Inc.

von Herrmann, Friedrich-Wilhelm. Augustine & the Phenomenological Question of Time: Augustinus und Die Phänomenologische Frage Nach der Zeit. Van Fleteren, Frederick & Hackett, Jeremiah, trs. from GER. 2008. 216p. *(978-0-7734-5131-5(5))* Mellen, Edwin Pr., The.

Walsh, P. G. Augustine: De Civitate Dei X. 2012. (Classical Texts). (ENG & LAT.). 240p. (C). 80.00 *(978-0-85668-849-2(5))*; pap. 36.00 *(978-0-85668-848-5(7))* Aris & Phillips GBR. Dist: Brown, David Bk. Co., The.

Walsh, P. G., ed. Augustine: De Civitate Dei VIII & IX. (ENG & LAT.). 280p. (C). 2012. pap. 36.00 *(978-0-85668-853-9(3))* 2011. 80.00 *(978-0-85668-854-6(1))* Aris & Phillips GBR. Dist: Brown, David Bk. Co., The.

Walsh, P. G. & intro. Augustine Bks. 6 & 7: De Civitate Dei. 2010. (Classical Texts). (LAT & ENG.). 220p. (C). pap. 35.00 *(978-0-85668-879-9(7))* Aris & Phillips GBR. Dist: Brown, David Bk. Co., The.

Warfield, Benjamin Breckenridge. Calvin & Augustine. Craig, Samuel G., ed. 2011. 518p. 60.95 ***(978-1-258-01604-3(4))*** Literary Licensing, LLC.

Warfield, Benjamin Breckinridge. Studies in Tertullian & Augustine. 420p. 2008 49.95 *(978-1-4366-8545-0(1))* 2007. (ENG.). per. 34.95 *(978-1-4325-7127-6(3))* Kessinger Publishing, LLC.

Watkins, ed. The Confessions of St. Augustine: Spiritual Meditations & Divine Insights. Pusey, E. B., tr. 2006. (Sacred Wisdom Ser.). (ENG., Illus.). 432p. 8.95 *(978-1-84293-206-3(3)*, Watkins Publishing) Duncan Baird Pubs. GBR. Dist: Sterling Publishing Co., Inc.

Watson, John. The Philosophical Basis of Religion. 2007. (ENG.). 512p. 55.95 *(978-0-548-04836-8(3))* Kessinger Publishing, LLC.

Watson, Thomas Ramey. Perversions, Originals, & Redemptions in Paradise Lost: The Typological Scheme & Sign Theory That Unify Milton's Epic. 2007. (ENG.). 200p. 67.50 *(978-0-7618-3781-7(7))*; per. 36.99 *(978-0-7618-3782-4(5))* Univ. Pr. of America, Inc.

Weidmann, Clemens. Die handschriftliche Uberlieferung der Werke des heiligen Augustinus. Band XI: Russland, Slowenien, Ungarn. Teil 1: Werkverzeichnis, Teil 2: Verzeichnis nach Bibliotheken, 2 vols. 2010. (VERoFFENTLICHUNGEN der KOMMISSION ZUR HERAUSGABE des CORPUS der LATEINISCHEN KIRCHENVaTER Ser.). (GER.). 298p. (C). pap. 59.00 *(978-3-7001-6826-3(8))* Austrian Academy of Sciences Press AUT. Dist: Brown, David Bk. Co., The.

Wetzel, James. Augustine. 2010. (Guides for the Perplexed Ser.). (ENG.). 168p. 24.95 *(978-1-84706-196-6(6))*; 80.00 *(978-1-84706-195-9(8))* Continuum International Publishing Group, Ltd. GBR. Dist: National Bk. Network.

—Augustine & the Limits of Virtue. 2008. (ENG.). 264p. pap. 53.00 *(978-0-521-06481-1(3))* Cambridge Univ. Pr.

Williams, Michael. Authorised Lives in Early Christian Biography: Between Eusebius & Augustine. 2008. (Cambridge Classical Studies). (ENG.). 274p. 99.00 *(978-0-521-89490-6(5))* Cambridge Univ. Pr.

Willis, Geoffrey G. St. Augustine & the Donatist Controversy. (Orthodoxies & Heresies in the Early Church Ser.). reprint ed. 39.50 *(978-0-404-62397-5(2))* AMS Pr., Inc.

Wills, Garry. Augustine's Confessions: The Biography of a Book. 2011. (Lives of Great Religious Bks.). (ENG.). 176p. 19.95 *(978-0-691-14357-6(9))* Princeton Univ. Pr.

Wills, Garry. Font of Life: Ambrose, Augustine, & the Mystery of Baptism. 2012. (Emblems of Antiquity Ser.). (ENG., Illus.). 208p. 21.95 ***(978-0-19-976851-6(X))*** Oxford Univ. Pr., Inc.

Wisse, Maarten. Trinitarian Theology beyond Participation: Augustine's de Trinitate & Contemporary Theology. 2011. (T&T Clark Studies in Systematic Theology Ser.). (ENG.). 352p. 120.00 *(978-0-567-11831-8(2)*, T&T Clark Int'l) Continuum International Publishing Group, Ltd. GBR. Dist: National Bk. Network.

Woods, SJ, Henry. Augustine & Evolution: A Study in the Saint's de Genesi ad Litteram & de Trinitate. 2009. 160p. pap. 14.00 *(978-1-60608-688-9(X)*, Wipf and Stock) Wipf & Stock Pubs.

AUGUSTINIANS

Alonso, Carlos & Eyles, Maureen. A History of the Augustinians & the Martyrs of Mombasa (1598-1698) 2007. (Illus.). 112p. *(978-9966-08-268-8(9))* Paulines Pubns., Africa.

Bourdua, Louise & Dunlop, Anne, eds. Art & the Augustinian Order in Early Renaissance Italy. 2007. (Church, Faith & Culture in the Medieval West Ser.). (Illus.). 250p. 124.95 *(978-0-7546-5655-5(1))* Ashgate Publishing Co.

O'Conner, Kim, text. An Augustinian Tradition. 2008. 50.00 *(978-0-9772092-6-2(1))* Booksmith Group, The.

Thomas à Kempis. Chronicle of the Canons Regular of Mount. 2006. pap. *(978-1-84702-494-7(7))*; pap. *(978-1-4068-0600-7(5))* Echo Library.

—The Chronicle of the Canons Regular of Mount St. Agnes. 2007. (ENG.). 148p. per. 18.99 *(978-1-4346-2805-3(1))* BiblioBazaar.

—The Chronicle of the Canons Regular of Mount St Agnes. 2008. 168p. pap. 22.99 *(978-0-554-36549-7(9))*; 25.99 *(978-0-554-27246-7(6))* BiblioBazaar.

—The Chronicle of the Canons Regular of Mount St Agnes. Arthur, J. P., tr. 2007. 160p. per. *(978-1-4065-1890-0(5))* Dodo Pr.

—The Chronicle of the Canons Regular of Mount St. Agnes. Lt. ed. 2007. (ENG.). 168p. per. 21.99 *(978-1-4346-2834-3(5))* BiblioBazaar.

—The Chronicles of the Canons Regular of Mount St Agnes. 2009. 136p. pap. 9.99 *(978-1-60450-612-9(1)*, Serenity Pubs.) Arc Manor.

Tourscher, Francis Edward. Old St Augustine's in Philadelphi: With Some Records of the Work of the Austin Friars in the United States. 2011. 268p. 47.95 ***(978-1-258-03383-5(6))*** Literary Licensing, LLC.

AUGUSTUS, EMPEROR OF ROME, 63 B.C.-14 A.D.

Augustus & Scheid, John. Res Gestae Divi Augusti: Hauts Faits du Divin Auguste. 2007. (Collection des universites de France Serie Latine Ser.). (LAT, FRE & GEC., Illus.). 166p. (C). pap. 74.00 ***(978-2-251-01446-3(2))*** Societe d'edition Les Belles lettres FRA. Dist: ISD.

Bispham, Edward. From Asculum to Actium: The Municipalization of Italy from the Social War to Augustus. 2008. (Oxford Classical Monographs). (Illus.). 600p. 215.00 *(978-0-19-923184-3(2))* Oxford Univ. Pr., Inc.

Capponi, Livia. Roman Egypt. 2011. (Illus.). 128p. pap. 19.95 *(978-1-85399-726-6(9))* Duckworth Publishers GBR. Dist: International Publishers Marketing.

Carter, Jesse Benedict. Religion of Numa & Other Essays on the. 2006. pap. *(978-1-4065-1301-1(6))* Dodo Pr.

Clark, Matthew D. H. Augustus, First Roman Emperor: Power & Propaganda & the Politics of Survivla. 2011. (Bristol Phoenix Press - Greece & Rome Live Ser.). (Illus.). 160p. pap. 25.00 *(978-1-904675-14-3(X))* Bristol Phoenix Pr. GBR. Dist: Chicago Distribution Ctr.

—Augustus, First Roman Emperor: Power, Propaganda & the Politics of Survival. 2010. (Bristol Phoenix Press - Greece & Rome Live Ser.). (Illus.). 149p. 75.00 *(978-1-904675-43-3(3))* Bristol Phoenix Pr. GBR. Dist: Chicago Distribution Ctr.

Davis, P. J. Ovid & Augustus: A Political Reading of Ovid's Erotic Poems. 2006. 240p. 130.00 *(978-0-7156-3559-9(X))* Duckworth Publishers GBR. Dist: International Publishers Marketing.

Eck, Werner. The Age of Augustus. 2nd rev. ed. 2007. (Blackwell Ancient Lives Ser.: 7). (ENG., Illus.). 224p. pap. 33.95 *(978-1-4051-5149-8(8)*, Wiley-Blackwell) Wiley, John & Sons, Inc.

Edmondson, Jonathan. Augustus. 2009. (Edinburgh Readings on the Ancient World Ser.). (ENG., Illus.). 384p. (gr. 17). 115.00 *(978-0-7486-1594-0(6))*; pap. 37.50 *(978-0-7486-1595-7(4))* Edinburgh Univ. Pr. GBR. Dist: Columbia Univ. Pr.

Everitt, Anthony. Augustus: The Life of Rome's First Emperor. 2007. (ENG.). 432p. pap. 18.00 *(978-0-8129-7058-6(6)*, Random Hse. Trade Paperbacks) Random House Publishing Group.

Fantham, Elaine. Julia Augusti: The Emperor's Daughter. 2006. (Women of the Ancient World Ser.). (Illus.). 175p. per. 34.95 *(978-0-415-33146-3(3))*; 115.00 *(978-0-415-33145-6(5))* Routledge.

Fields, Nic. The Roman Army of the Principate 27 BC-AD 117. 2009. (Battle Orders Ser.). (ENG., Illus.). 96p. pap. 25.95 *(978-1-84603-386-5(1))* Osprey Publishing, Ltd. GBR. Dist: Random Hse., Inc.

Galinsky, Karl. Augustus: Introduction to the Life of an Emperor. 2012. (ENG., Illus.). 300p. (C). 90.00 *(978-0-521-76797-2(0))*; pap. 27.99 ***(978-0-521-74442-3(3))*** Cambridge Univ. Pr.

Herklotz, Friederike. Prinzeps und Pharao: Der Kult des Augustus in Ägypten. 2007. (Oikumene. Studien zur antiken Weltgeschichte Ser.). (GER., Illus.). 507p. (C). 105.00 ***(978-3-938032-15-2(4))*** Antike, Verlag, e.K. DEU. Dist: ISD.

Lange, Carsten Hjort. Res Publica Constituta: Actium, Apollo, & the Accomplishment of the Triumviral Assignment. 2009. (Impact of Empire Ser.). (Illus.). 250p. *(978-90-04-17501-3(6))* BRILL.

Levick, Barbara. Augustus: Image & Substance. rev. ed. 2010. (ENG., Illus.). 376p. (C). pap. 43.67 *(978-0-582-89421-1(2))* Longman Publishing Group.

Lintott, Andrew. Romans in the Age of Augustus. 2010. (Peoples of Europe Ser.: 17). (ENG., Illus.). 216p. pap. 33.95 *(978-1-4051-7654-5(7)*, Wiley-Blackwell) Wiley, John & Sons, Inc.

—The Romans in the Age of Augustus. 2010. (Peoples of Europe Ser.: 14). (ENG., Illus.). 216p. 94.95 *(978-1-4051-7655-2(5)*, Wiley-Blackwell) Wiley, John & Sons, Inc.

Miller, John F. Apollo, Augustus, & the Poets. (ENG., Illus.). 2011. 422p. pap. 50.00 ***(978-1-107-40358-1(8))*** 2009. 420p. 113.00 *(978-0-521-51683-9(8))* Cambridge Univ. Pr.

Patey, Douglas Lane. Probability & Literary Form: Philosophic Theory & Literary Practice in the Augustan Age. 2010. (ENG.). 396p. pap. 47.00 *(978-0-521-12872-8(2))* Cambridge Univ. Pr.

Powell, Anton. Virgil the Partisan: A Study in the Re-Integration of Classics. 2008. (ENG.). 280p. (C). 56.00 *(978-1-905125-21-0(6))* Classical Pr. of Wales, The GBR. Dist: Brown, David Bk. Co., The.

Powell, Anton & Smith, Christopher E., eds. The Lost Memoirs of Augustus. 2009. (ENG.). 239p. (C). 100.00 *(978-1-905125-25-8(9))* Classical Pr. of Wales, The GBR. Dist: Brown, David Bk. Co., The.

Putnam, Michael C. J. Horace's Carmen Saeculare: Ritual Magic & the Poet's Art. 2011. 190p. pap. 21.00 ***(978-0-300-18266-8(X))*** Yale Univ. Pr.

Rawson, Claude. Henry Fielding: And the Augustan Ideal under Stress. (British Studies). (ENG.). 1p. pap. 30.98 *(978-1-57392-318-7(4)*, Humanity Bks.) Prometheus Bks., Pubs.

Rehak, Paul. Imperium & Cosmos: Augustus & the Northern Campus Martius. Younger, John G., ed. (Wisconsin Studies in Classics Ser.). (ENG., Illus.). 288p. 2009. pap. 29.95 *(978-0-299-22014-3(1))* 2006. 60.00 *(978-0-299-22010-5(9))* Univ. of Wisconsin Pr.

Richardson, J. S. Augustan Rome 44 BC to AD 14: The Restoration of the Republic & the Establishment of the Empire. 2012. (Edinburgh History of Ancient Rome Ser.). (ENG., Illus.). 320p. (gr. 17). 156.00 ***(978-0-7486-1954-2(2))***; pap. 50.00 ***(978-0-7486-1955-9(0))*** Edinburgh Univ. Pr. GBR. Dist: Columbia Univ. Pr.

Ross, David O. Backgrounds to Augustan Poetry: Gallus Elegy & Rome. 2010. (ENG.). 188p. pap. 27.99 *(978-0-521-13669-3(5))* Cambridge Univ. Pr.

Schuol, Monika. Augustus und Die Juden: Rechtsstellung und Interessenpolitik der Kleinasiatischen Diaspora. 2007. (Studien zur Alten Geschichte Ser.). (GER.). 436p. (C). 83.00 ***(978-3-938032-16-9(2))*** Antike, Verlag, e.K. DEU. Dist: ISD.

Sellar, William Young. The Roman Poets of the Augustan Age: Horace & the Elegiac Poets. Ker, W. P., ed. 2010. (Cambridge Library Collection - Classics Ser.). (Illus.). 418p. pap. 31.99 *(978-1-108-02100-5(X))* Cambridge Univ. Pr.

Shuckburgh, Evelyn S., ed. C. Suetoni Tranquilli: Divus Augustus. 2nd ed. 2011. (ENG & LAT.). 260p. pap. 23.99 *(978-0-521-72015-1(X))* Cambridge Univ. Pr.

Spawforth, A. J. S. Greece & the Augustan Cultural Revolution. 2011. (Greek Culture in the Roman World Ser.). (ENG., Illus.). 328p. 99.00 ***(978-1-107-01211-0(2))*** Cambridge Univ. Pr.

Thomas, Richard F. Virgil & the Augustan Reception. 2006. (ENG.). 348p. (C). pap. 72.00 *(978-0-521-02895-0(7))* Cambridge Univ. Pr.

Thorsten, Opper. The Meroe Head of Augustus. 2012. (Objects in Focus Ser.). (ENG., Illus.). 64p. (C). pap. 10.00 *(978-0-7141-5091-8(6))* British Museum Pr. GBR. Dist: Brown, David Bk. Co., The.

AURA

see also Kirlian Photography

Ambrose, Kala. The Awakened Aura: Experiencing the Evolution of Your Energy Body. 2011. (ENG., Illus.). 240p. pap. 14.95 *(978-0-7387-2759-2(8))* Llewellyn Pubns.

Atkisson, Clyde E. & Anderson, Virginia B. Auric Healing As Taught by Reverend Virginia B. Anderson. 2007. 83p. pap. 9.95 *(978-0-7414-4240-6(X))* Infinity Publishing.

Kett, Kendra. The Pinwheel Girl Takes Flight: Everywoman's Journey Through Seven Stages of Transformation. 2008. (Illus.). 268p. pap. 24.95 *(978-0-9642823-3-9(X))* Key Answer Products, Inc.

Larson, Cynthia Sue. Aura Advantage: How the colors in your Aura can help you attain your desires & attract Success. 2006. pap. 16.95 *(978-1-928806-14-1(7))* Lightworker Pubns.

Levanah Shell Bdolak. Seeing the Incredible Aur: Your Stepping Stone to Enlightenment. 2009. 160p. pap. 11.99 *(978-1-4389-7783-6(2))* AuthorHouse.

Lubeck, Walter. The Aura Healing Handbook. (Illus.). 224p. 15.95 *(978-0-914955-61-0(6))* Lotus Pr.

One Of The Brethren. The Mystery of the Human Aur. 2011. 34p. 35.95 ***(978-1-258-00491-0(7))*** Literary Licensing, LLC.

Panchadasi, Swami. Human Aura. reprint ed. pap. 3.00 *(978-0-911662-37-5(5))* Yoga Publn. Society.

Rosetree, Rose. Read People Deeper: Body Language + Face Reading + Auras. 2008. (Illus.). 277p. pap. 14.95 *(978-0-9752538-3-0(2))* Women's Intuition Worldwide LLC.

Thackray, Rupert. Aural Awakening. 284p. 35.00 *(978-0-86422-268-8(8))* UWA Publishing AUS. Dist: International Specialized Bk. Services.

Van Crump, John. Auric Polarization: A Hands on Guide. 2011. 128p. pap. 17.99 *(978-1-4269-5259-3(7))* Trafford Publishing.

Webster, Richard. The Complete Book of Auras: Learn to See, Read, Strengthen & Heal Auras. 2010. (ENG.). 216p. pap. 16.95 *(978-0-7387-2180-4(8))* Llewellyn Pubns.

AURANGZIB, EMPEROR OF HINDUSTAN, 1619-1707

Elphinstone, Mountstuart. Aurangzeb. Sharma, Sri Ram, ed. 2008. (Oxford in Asia Historical Reprints Ser.). 220p. 29.95 *(978-0-19-547575-3(5))* Oxford Univ. Pr., Inc.

AURELIUS ANTONINUS, MARCUS, EMPEROR OF ROME, 121-180

see Marcus Aurelius, Emperor of Rome, 121-180

AURICULAR CONFESSION

see Confession

AUROBINDO, SRI, 1872-1950

see Ghose, Aurobindo, 1872-1950

AURORAS

Akasofu, Syun-Ichi. Exploring the Secrets of the Aurora. 2nd rev. ed. 2007. (Astrophysics & Space Science Library). (Illus.). 288p. pap. 79.95 *(978-0-387-45094-0(7)*, 0387450947) Springer.

—The Northern Lights: Secrets of the Aurora Borealis. Brown, Tricia, ed. 2009. (ENG., Illus.). 192p. pap. 18.95 *(978-0-88240-755-5(4)*, Alaska Northwest Bks.) Graphic Arts Ctr. Publishing Co.

Awad, Jenny. The Aurora Farmers Fair: 100 Years. 2008. (Images of America Ser.). (ENG., Illus.). 128p. pap. 19.99 *(978-0-7385-5168-5(6))* Arcadia Publishing.

Berry, Janice, et al. Aurora Borealis: A Photo Memory. 2nd ed. 2010. (Illus.). 64p. ***(978-1-57833-458-2(6))*** Todd Communications.

Bortolotti, Dan. Auroras: Fire in the Sky. 2011. (Illus.). 144p. 29.95 *(978-1-55407-681-9(1))* Firefly Bks., Ltd.

Collins, Sherah J. Aurora. 2008. (Images of America Ser.). (ENG., Illus.). 128p. per. 21.99 *(978-0-7385-4824-1(3))* Arcadia Publishing.

Meng, C. I., et al, eds. Auroral Physics. 2010. (ENG.). 518p. pap. 48.00 *(978-0-521-15741-4(2))* Cambridge Univ. Pr.

Robson, Mark. Aurora. 2011. (Dragon Orb Ser.). (ENG., Illus.). 352p. (J). (gr. 4-7). pap. 8.99 *(978-1-84738-448-5(X))* Simon & Schuster, Ltd. GBR. Dist: Independent Pubs. Group.

Stefnisson, Sigurdur H. Aurora Borealis: The Northern Lights. 2007. 12.99 *(978-1-59868-213-7(X)*, 0700641) Avalanche Publishing, Inc.

AUSCHWITZ (CONCENTRATION CAMP)

Adelsberger, Lucie. Auschwitz: A Doctor's Story. Ray, Susan H., tr. 2006. (ENG.). 176p. pap. 19.95 *(978-1-55553-659-6(X)*, Northeastern University Pr.) Univ. Pr. of New England.

Avey, Denis. The Man Who Broke into Auschwitz: A True Story of World War II. 2012. (ENG., Illus.). 288p. pap. 15.00 ***(978-0-306-82149-3(4))*** Da Capo Pr., Inc.

Bezwinska, J. & Czech, Danuta. KL Auschwitz Seen by the SS. 2007. (Classic Holocaust Accounts, Memoirs & Reports). 330p. pap. 29.95 *(978-0-86527-504-1(1))* Fertig, Howard Publisher.

Buergenthal, Thomas. A Lucky Child: A Memoir of Surviving Auschwitz as a Young Boy. 2010. (ENG., Illus.). 272p. pap. 14.99 *(978-0-316-04339-7(7)*, Back Bay Bks.) Little Brown & Co.

Busch, Ty G. A Life Reborn & Renewed: The Story of Alex Gross in His Own Words, Thoughts, Ideas & Lessons. 2011. 232p. pap. 15.86 ***(978-1-4269-6101-4(4))*** Trafford Publishing.

Chare, Nicholas. Auschwitz & Afterimages: Abjection, Witnessing & Representation. 2011. (New Encounters: Arts, Cultures, Concepts Ser.). (ENG., Illus.). 240p. 90.00 *(978-1-84885-590-8(7))*; pap. 30.00 *(978-1-84885-591-5(5))* I. B. Tauris & Co., Ltd. GBR. Dist: Macmillan.

Cherish, Barbara. Auschwitz Kommandant: A Daughter's Search for the Father She Never Knew. 2009. (ENG., Illus.). 256p. 37.95 *(978-0-7524-4900-5(1))* History Pr. Ltd., The GBR. Dist: Independent Pubs. Group.

Cherish, Barbara U. The Auschwitz Kommandant: A Daughter's Search for the Father She Never Knew. 2011. (ENG., Illus.). 264p. pap. 15.95 *(978-0-7524-5755-0(1))* History Pr. Ltd., The GBR. Dist: Independent Pubs. Group.

Ebner, Murray & Ebner, Mark. Chosen for Reasons Unknown: A Survivor's Journey. 2010. 318p. pap. 19.95 *(978-0-9821374-0-6(0))* Lucky Charm Publishing.

Fernández Vítores, Raúl & Fernández Vítores, Raúl. Séneca en Auschwitz: La Escritura Culpable. 2010. (SPA.). 107p. *(978-84-8393-070-0(6))* Paginas de Espuma.

Gilbert, Martin. Auschwitz & the Allies. 2011. (ENG.). 350p. pap. 16.95 *(978-1-59687-416-9(3))* IBks., Inc.

Hamans, Paul. Edith Stein & Companions. 2010. 250p. pap. 17.95 *(978-1-58617-336-4(7))* Ignatius Pr.

Hoess, Rudolf. The Commandant: An Account by the First Commanding Officer of Auschwitz. Amann, Jurg, ed. Pollinger, Andrew, tr. 2012. (ENG.). 112p. (gr. 12). 17.95 *(978-1-59020-677-5(0))* Overlook Pr., The.

International Auschwitz Committee. Nazi Medicine: Doctors, Victims & Medicine in Auschwitz. 2007. 724p. (C). reprint ed. pap. 49.95 *(978-0-86527-491-4(6))* Fertig, Howard Publisher.

Landau, Felix. No Longer Alone: My Intimate Walk with Jesus Christ. 2011. 132p. 28.95 ***(978-1-4497-2378-1(0))***; pap. 11.95 ***(978-1-4497-2377-4(2))*** Author Solutions, Inc. (WestBow Pr.).

Lengyel, Olga. Five Chimneys: The Story of Auschwitz. 2007. 213p. pap. 19.95 *(978-0-86527-502-7(5))* Fertig, Howard Publisher.

—Five Chimneys: The Story of Auschwitz. 2011. 220p. 44.95 ***(978-1-258-00636-5(7))*** Literary Licensing, LLC.

Levi, Primo. Auschwitz Report. Gordon, Robert S. C., ed. Wolf, Judith, tr. from ITA. 2006. (ENG.). 128p. 17.95 *(978-1-84467-092-5(9)*, 844092) Verso Bks. GBR. Dist: Norton, W. W. & Co., Inc.

—Sobreviviendo en Auschwitz - Si Esto Es el Hombre / Survival in Auschwitz - If This Is a Man. 2008. 108p. pap. *(978-1-60796-015-7(X))* Editorial Benei Noaj.

Mantegazza, Raffaele. The Smell of Smoke. Donatelli Noble, Cinzia, tr. 2008. 192p. pap. *(978-88-95145-22-8(4))* Italian Paths of Culture.

Matthäus, Jürgen, ed. Approaching an Auschwitz Survivor: Holocaust Testimony & Its Transformations. 1 vol. 2009. (Oxford Oral History Ser.). (ENG., Illus.). 224p. 74.00 *(978-0-19-538915-9(8))* Oxford Univ. Pr., Inc.

—Approaching an Auschwitz Survivor: Holocaust Testimony & its Transformations. 1 vol. 2010. (Oxford Oral History Ser.). (ENG., Illus.). 224p. pap. 24.95 *(978-0-19-977253-7(3))* Oxford Univ. Pr., Inc.

Mendelsohn, John & Detwiler, Donald S. The Wannsee Protocol: And a 1944 Report on Auschwitz by the Office of Strategic Services. 2009. *(978-1-61619-011-8(6))* Lawbook Exchange, Ltd., The.

Michel, Ernest W. Promises Kept: One Man's Journey Against Incredible Odds. 2008. (ENG., Illus.). 320p. per. 16.95 *(978-1-56980-338-7(2))* Barricade Bks., Inc.

Moorehead, Caroline. A Train in Winter: An Extraordinary Story of Women, Friendship, & Resistance in Occupied France. (P. S. Ser.). 2012. 400p. pap. 15.99 ***(978-0-06-165071-0(4)***, HarperPerennial) 2011. 608p. pap. 27.99 *(978-0-06-206880-2(7)*, HarperLuxe) HarperCollins Pubs.

My Stories of Survival & Beyond. 2010. mass mkt. 15.95 *(978-0-9814686-4-8(0))* Holocaust Survivors' Memoirs Project.

Nyiszli, Miklos. Auschwitz: A Doctor's Eyewitness Account. Kremer, Tibere & Seaver, Richard, trs. 2011. (ENG.). 240p. pap. 14.95 *(978-1-61145-011-8(X)*, 611011, Arcade Publishing) Skyhorse Publishing Co., Inc.

Pogozhev, Andrej. Escape from Auschwitz. Krupnick, Vladimir & Armstrong, John, trs. from RUS. 2007. (Illus.). 174p. 32.95 *(978-1-932033-83-0(1))* Casemate Pubs. & Bk. Distributors, LLC.

Primo Levi. Survival in Auschwitz. 2007. 160p. (ENG.). *(978-956-291-563-2(8))*; *(978-956-291-529-8(8))*; (ENG.). per. *(978-956-291-530-4(1))* Editorial Benei Noaj.

Ragusin, Elsie A. An American in Auschwitz: An Inspirational Biography of Faith, Tenacity & Patriotism. 2006. (Illus.). 118p. per. 15.95 *(978-0-9776777-4-0(5))* Legacy Publishing Services, Inc.

Singer, Edith. March to Freedom: A Memoir of the Holocaust. 2008. (Illus.). 102p. (YA). pap. *(978-0-9817794-0-9(9))* Impact Publishing.

Steinbacher, Sybille. Auschwitz: A History. Whiteside, Shaun, tr. 2006. (ENG.). 176p. pap. 12.99 *(978-0-06-082582-9(0)*, HarperPerennial) HarperCollins Pubs.

Steinkamp, Mary. Maria- A True Story of Faith & Forgiveness. 2008. (Illus.). 64p. per. *(978-1-55452-243-9(9)*, Guardian Bks.) Essence Publishing.

Tenenbaum, Joseph. Auschwitz in Retrospect: The Self-Portrait of Rudolph Hoess, Commander of Auschwitz. 2011. 38p. 35.95 ***(978-1-258-00128-5(4))*** Literary Licensing, LLC.

Venezia, Shlomo. Inside the Gas Chambers: Eight Months in the Sonderkommando of Auschwitz. 2011. (ENG.). 232p. pap. 14.95 *(978-0-7456-4384-7(1))* Polity Pr. GBR. Dist: Wiley, John & Sons, Inc.

Venezia, Shlomo & Prasquier, Béatrice. Inside the Gas Chambers: Eight Months in the Sonderkommando of Auschwitz. 2009. (ENG., Illus.). 232p. 59.95 *(978-0-7456-4383-0(3))* Polity Pr. GBR. Dist: Wiley, John & Sons, Inc.

Wetzler, Alfred, ed. Escape from Hell: The True Story of the Auschwitz Protocol. 2006. (Illus.). 292p. 34.95 *(978-1-84545-183-7(X))* Berghahn Bks., Inc.

Zubrzycki, Genevieve. The Crosses of Auschwitz: Nationalism & Religion in Post-Communist Poland. 2006. (Illus.). 280p. 75.00 *(978-0-226-99303-4(5))*; (ENG., per. 32.50 *(978-0-226-99304-1(3))* Univ. of Chicago Pr.

AUSCHWITZ TRIAL, FRANKFURT AM MAIN, GERMANY, 1963-1965

Rothman, Herman. Hitler's Will: A Memoir of the Holocaust. 2009. (ENG., Illus.). 192p. 34.95 *(978-0-7524-4834-3(X))* History Pr. Ltd., The GBR. Dist: Independent Pubs. Group.

Wittmann, Rebecca. Beyond Justice: The Auschwitz Trial. 2012. (ENG., Illus.). 360p. pap. 19.95 ***(978-0-674-06387-7(2))*** Harvard Univ. Pr.

AUSCULTATION

see also Chest—Diseases—Diagnosis; Heart—Sounds

Brook, Angus. The Early Heidegger & Ethics. 2009. 100p. pap. *(978-3-639-10769-2(1))* VDM Verlag Dr. Mueller e.K.

Brown, Elspeth M., et al. Heart Sounds. 2nd ed. 2008. (Made Easy Ser.). (ENG., Illus.). 160p. (C). pap. 49.95 *(978-0-443-06907-9(7)*, Churchill Livingstone) Elsevier - Health Sciences Div.

Lehrer, Steven. Understanding Lung Sounds with Audio CD. 3rd ed. 2008. (ENG., Illus.). 160p. pap. 61.95 *(978-1-4160-6838-9(4)*, Saunders) Elsevier - Health Sciences Div.

Springhouse Publishing Company Staff. Auscultation Skills: Breath & Heart Sounds. 4th rev. ed. 2009. (ENG., Illus.). 256p. pap. 57.99 *(978-1-60547-454-0(1))* Lippincott Williams & Wilkins.

Springhouse Publishing Company Staff, ed. Nursing Know-How: Evaluating Heart & Breath Sounds. 2008. (ENG., Illus.). 384p. 47.99 *(978-0-7817-9203-5(7))* Lippincott Williams & Wilkins.

AUSTEN, JANE, 1775-1817

Adams, Carol J., et al. The Bedside, Bathtub & Armchair Companion to Jane Austen. 2008. (Bedside, Bathtub & Armchair Companions Ser.). (ENG., Illus.). 228p. pap. 19.95 *(978-0-8264-2933-9(5))* Continuum International Publishing Group, Ltd. GBR. Dist: National Bk. Network.

Adams, Jennifer & Grillone, Jennifer. Remarkably Jane: Notable Quotations on Jane Austen, 1 vol. 2009. (ENG., Illus.). 128p. 14.99 *(978-1-4236-0478-5(4))* Gibbs Smith, Publisher.

Adams, Oscar Fay. The Story of Jane Austen's Life. 2009. 190p. pap. 19.99 *(978-0-217-89784-6(3))* General Bks. LLC.

—The Story of Jane Austen's Life. 2009. 292p. 43.95 *(978-1-104-69366-4(6))*; pap. 28.95 *(978-1-104-66703-0(7))* Kessinger Publishing, LLC.

Austen, Jane. The Annotated Sense & Sensibility. Shapard, David M., ed. 2011. (ENG., Illus.). 784p. pap. 16.95 *(978-0-307-39076-9(4)*, Anchor) Knopf Doubleday Publishing Group.

—Jane Austen's Little Instruction Book. 2008. (Charming Petite Ser.). 5.95 *(978-1-59359-815-0(7))* Peter Pauper Pr. Inc.

—Letters of Jane Austen. Lord Brabourne, Edward Hugessen Knatchbull-Hugessen, ed. 2009. (Cambridge Library Collection - Literary Studies). (ENG.). 396p. pap. 23.99 *(978-1-108-00339-1(7))*; 380p. pap. 23.99 *(978-1-108-00340-7(0))* Cambridge Univ. Pr.

—Letters of Jane Austen V1. Edward, Lord Brabourne, ed. 2007. (ENG.). 396p. 49.95 *(978-0-548-10449-1(2))* Kessinger Publishing, LLC.

—Letters of Jane Austen V2. Edward, Lord Brabourne, ed. 2007. (ENG.). 380p. 48.95 *(978-0-548-10450-7(6))* Kessinger Publishing, LLC.

—Love & Friendship & Other Early Works. 2007. (ENG.). 192p. *(978-1-84702-798-6(9))* Echo Library.

—Persuasion. Blank, Antje, ed. 2006. (Cambridge Edition of the Works of Jane Austen Ser.). (ENG., Illus.). 480p. 75.00 *(978-0-521-82418-7(4))* Cambridge Univ. Pr.

—Pride & Prejudice. Cox, Marian, ed. 2010. 108p. pap. 24.95 *(978-1-4441-1623-6(1))* Hodder Education GBR. Dist: Trans-Atlantic Pubns., Inc.

—Pride & Prejudice. Hubbard, Shelagh, ed. 2010. (Illus.). 96p. pap. 19.95 *(978-1-4441-1027-2(6))* Hodder Education GBR. Dist: Trans-Atlantic Pubns., Inc.

—Pride & Prejudice. Rogers, Pat, ed. 2006. (Cambridge Edition of the Works of Jane Austen Ser.). (ENG., Illus.). 622p. 75.00 *(978-0-521-82514-6(8))* Cambridge Univ. Pr.

—Selected Letters. Jones, Vivien, ed. 2009. (Oxford World's Classics Ser.). (ENG.). 352p. pap. 12.95 *(978-0-19-953843-0(3))* Oxford Univ. Pr., Inc.

—Sense & Sensibility & Persuasion. 2008. 520p. 55.95 *(978-0-548-94320-5(6))* Kessinger Publishing, LLC.

—Sense & Sensibility, & Persuasion. 2007. 524p. per. 40.95 *(978-0-548-59923-5(8))* Kessinger Publishing, LLC.

—The Wit & Wisdom of Jane Austen: Quotes from Her Novels, Letters, & Diaries. 2008. (ENG.). 160p. pap. 12.95 *(978-1-56975-681-2(3))* Ulysses Pr.

Austen, Jane & Shapard, David M. The Annotated Pride & Prejudice. annot. ed. 2007. (ENG., Illus.). 784p. pap. 16.95 *(978-0-307-27810-4(7)*, Anchor) Knopf Doubleday Publishing Group.

Austen, Jane, et al. Later Manuscripts. Todd, Janet & Bree, Linda, eds. 2008. (Cambridge Edition of the Works of Jane Austen Ser.). (ENG., Illus.). 872p. (C). 127.00 *(978-0-521-84348-5(0))* Cambridge Univ. Pr.

Austen-Leigh, James E. A Memoir of Jane Austen: And Other Family Recollections. Sutherland, Kathryn, ed. 2008. (Oxford World's Classics Ser.). (ENG., Illus.). 352p. (Orig.). pap. 12.95 *(978-0-19-954077-8(2))* Oxford Univ. Pr., Inc.

Austen-Leigh, James Edward. A Memoir of Jane Austen. 2008. 172p. 25.99 *(978-0-554-27284-9(9))* 2008. 172p. 22.99 *(978-0-554-36587-9(1))* 2007. (ENG.). 154p. per. 19.99 *(978-1-4346-2872-5(8))* 2007. (ENG.). 170p. per. 21.99 *(978-1-4346-2907-4(4))* BiblioBazaar.

—A Memoir of Jane Austen. 2009. 186p. pap. *(978-0-217-66579-7(9))* Books LLC.

—A Memoir of Jane Austen. 2009. (Cambridge Library Collection - Literary Studies). (ENG.). 260p. pap. 17.99 *(978-1-108-00356-8(7))* Cambridge Univ. Pr.

Austen Leigh, James Edward. A Memoir of Jane Austen: Together with 'Lady Susan': a Novel. 2009. (Cambridge Library Collection - Literary Studies). 384p. pap. 23.99 *(978-1-108-00357-5(5))* Cambridge Univ. Pr.

Austen-Leigh, James Edward & Austen, Jane. A Memoir of Jane Austen. 2008. 384p. 48.95 *(978-1-4369-8784-4(9))*; pap. 33.95 *(978-1-4367-3981-8(0))* Kessinger Publishing, LLC.

Austen-Leigh, William & Austen-Leigh, Richard Arthur. Jane Austen, Her Life & Letters: A Family Record. 2006. (B&N Library of Essential Reading Ser.). (ENG., Illus.). 400p. pap. 9.95 *(978-0-7607-8323-8(3))* Barnes & Noble, Inc.

Austen, Susan Coolidge. Letters of Jane Austen: Selected from the Compilation of Her Great Nephew, Edward, Lord Brabourne. 2009. 344p. 32.99 *(978-1-113-04707-6(0))*; pap. 31.75 *(978-1-113-04705-2(4))* BiblioBazaar.

Axelrad, Arthur M. Jane Austen's Sanditon: A Village by the Sea. 2010. 496p. 38.95 *(978-1-4520-0179-1(0))*; pap. 26.95 *(978-1-4520-0178-4(2))* AuthorHouse.

Baker, William. Critical Companion to Jane Austen: A Literary Reference to Her Life & Work. 2007. (Critical Companion Ser.). (Illus.). 656p. (C). (gr. 9). 75.00 *(978-0-8160-6416-8(4))* Facts On File, Inc.

Barchas, Janine. Matters of Fact in Jane Austen: History, Location, & Celebrity. 2012. ***(978-1-4214-0640-4(3))*** Johns Hopkins Univ. Pr.

Bautz, Annika. Jane Austen - Sense & Sensibility/ Pride & Prejudice/ Emma. Tredell, Nicolas, ed. 2009. (Readers' Guides to Essential Criticism Ser.). (ENG.). 192p. 80.00 *(978-0-230-51712-7(9))*; pap. 25.00 *(978-0-230-51713-4(7))* Palgrave Macmillan.

—The Reception of Jane Austen & Walter Scott: A Comparative Longitudinal Study. 2007. (Continuum Reception Studies). (ENG., Illus.). 208p. 130.00 *(978-0-8264-9546-4(X))* Continuum International Publishing Group, Ltd. GBR. Dist: National Bk. Network.

Bettina, Fischer-Starcke. Corpus Ling Study Literature: Jane Austen & Her Contemporaries. 2010. (Corpus & Discourse Ser.). (ENG., Illus.). 240p. pap. 44.95 *(978-1-84706-438-7(8))* Continuum International Publishing Group, Ltd. GBR. Dist: National Bk. Network.

Blakemore, Erin. The Heroine's Bookshelf: Life Lessons, from Jane Austen to Laura Ingalls Wilder. 2010. (ENG.). 224p. 19.99 *(978-0-06-195876-2(X))* HarperCollins Pubs.

Bloom, Harold. Emma - Jane Austen. 2nd rev. ed. 2010. (Bloom's Modern Critical Interpretations Ser.). 150p. (C). (gr. 9-18). 45.00 *(978-1-60413-816-0(5)*, Chelsea Hse.) Facts On File, Inc.

Bottomer, Phyllis Ferguson. So Odd a Mixture: Along the Autistic Spectrum in 'Pride & Prejudice' 2007. (ENG.). 16p. per. *(978-1-84310-499-5(7))* Kingsley, Jessica Ltd.

Bradbrook, Frank W. Jane Austen & her Predecessors. 2010. (ENG.). 188p. pap. 19.99 *(978-0-521-14825-2(1))* Cambridge Univ. Pr.

Brownstein, Rachel M. Why Jane Austen? 2011. (ENG., Illus.). 320p. (gr. 17). 29.50 *(978-0-231-15390-4(2))* Columbia Univ. Pr.

Butler, Marilyn. Jane Austen. 2007. (Very Interesting People Ser.). (ENG.). 128p. per. 9.99 *(978-0-19-921760-1(2))* Oxford Univ. Pr., Inc.

Byrne, Paula. Jane Austen & the Theatre. 2007. (ENG., Illus.). 256p. per. 32.95 *(978-1-84725-047-6(5)*, Hambledon Continuum) Continuum International Publishing Group, Ltd. GBR. Dist: National Bk. Network.

Carroll, Joseph, et al. Graphing Jane Austen: The Evolutionary Basis of Literary Meaning. 2012. (Cognitive Studies in Literature & Performance Ser.). (ENG., Illus.). 318p. 90.00 ***(978-1-137-00240-2(9))*** Palgrave Macmillan.

Carson, Susannah, ed. A Truth Universally Acknowledged: 33 Great Writers on Why We Read Jane Austen. 2010. (ENG.). 320p. pap. 15.00 *(978-0-8129-8001-1(8)*, Random Hse. Trade Paperbacks) Random House Publishing Group.

Collins, Irene & Collins. Jane Austen: The Parson's Daughter. 2007. (ENG., Illus.). 304p. 24.95 *(978-1-85285-562-8(2)*, Hambledon Continuum) Continuum International Publishing Group, Ltd. GBR. Dist: National Bk. Network.

Copeland, Edward & McMaster, Juliet, eds. The Cambridge Companion to Jane Austen. 2nd ed. 2010. (Cambridge Companions to Literature Ser.). (ENG., Illus.). (C). 300p. 85.00 *(978-0-521-76308-0(8))*; 302p. pap. 24.99 *(978-0-521-74650-2(7))* Cambridge Univ. Pr.

Corbett, Mary Jean. Family Likeness: Sex, Marriage, & Incest from Jane Austen to Virginia Woolf. 2010. 280p. pap. 24.95 *(978-0-8014-7663-1(1))* 2008. 272p. 57.95 *(978-0-8014-4707-5(0))* Cornell Univ. Pr.

Cottom, Daniel. The Civilized Imagination: A Study of Ann Radcliffe, Jane Austen & Sir Walter Scott. 2009. (ENG.). 240p. pap. 28.99 *(978-0-521-11097-6(1))* Cambridge Univ. Pr.

Craik, Wendy. Jane Austen (Rle Jane Austen) 2011. (Routledge Library Editions: Jane Austen Ser.). (ENG.). 220p. 120.00 *(978-0-415-67285-6(6))* Routledge.

Dadlez, E. M. Mirrors to One Another: Emotion & Value in Jane Austen & David Hume. 2009. (New Directions in Aesthetics Ser.: 9). (ENG.). 256p. 104.95 *(978-1-4051-9348-1(4)*, Wiley-Blackwell) Wiley, John & Sons, Inc.

Darwin, Francis. Rustic Sounds & Other Studies in Literature & Natural History. 2010. (ENG.). 246p. pap. 26.75 *(978-1-171-67830-4(4))* BiblioBazaar.

—Rustic Sounds & Other Studies in Literature & Natural History. 2010. 104p. pap. *(978-1-152-77226-7(0))* Books LLC.

—Rustic Sounds & Other Studies in Literature & Natural History. 2010. (Illus.). 104p. pap. 19.85 *(978-1-154-97767-7(6))* General Bks. LLC.

Davidson, Jenny. Hypocrisy & the Politics of Politeness: Manners & Morals from Locke to Austen. 2007. (ENG., Illus.). 256p. pap. 55.00 *(978-0-521-04738-8(2))* Cambridge Univ. Pr.

Deresiewicz, William. A Jane Austen Education: How Six Novels Taught Me about Love, Friendship, & the Things That Really Matter. (ENG.). 272p. (gr. 12). 2012. pap. 15.00 ***(978-0-14-312125-1(1)**,* Penguin (Non-Classics)) 2011. 25.95 *(978-1-59420-288-9(5)*, Penguin Pr. HC, The) Penguin Group (USA) Inc.

—A Jane Austen Education: How Six Novels Taught Me about Love, Friendship, & the Things That Really Matter. lt. ed. 2011. 333p. 31.99 ***(978-1-4104-4026-6(5))*** Thorndike Pr.

Di Paolo, Marc. Emma Adapted: Jane Austen's Heroine from Book to Film. 2007. 202p. (C). 67.95 *(978-1-4331-0000-0(2))* Lang, Peter Publishing, Inc.

Donlon, Eleanor. Study Guide for Mansfield Park by Jane Austen. 2010. 46p. pap. ***(978-1-58617-419-4(3))*** Ignatius Pr.

Dryden, Robert. Jane Austen for Beginners. 2012. (For Beginners Ser.). (ENG., Illus.). 176p. pap. 16.99 ***(978-1-934389-61-4(7)**,* For Beginners) Steerforth Pr.

Edward & Brabourne, Lord. Letters of Jane Austen. 2009. 392p. 33.99 *(978-1-115-92024-7(3))*; pap. 33.75 *(978-1-115-92025-4(1))* BiblioBazaar.

—Letters of Jane Austen. 2009. 392p. 38.99 *(978-1-115-92023-0(5))*; pap. 32.75 *(978-1-115-92026-1(X))* BiblioBazaar.

Evans, Mary. Jane Austen & the State (RLE Jane Austen) 2011. (Routledge Library Editions: Jane Austen Ser.). (ENG.). 112p. 90.00 *(978-0-415-67253-5(8))* Routledge.

Fischer-Starcke, Bettina. Corpus Linguistics in Literary Analysis: Jane Austen & Her Contemporaries. 2010. (Corpus & Discourse Ser.). (ENG., Illus.). 240p. 140.00 *(978-1-84706-437-0(X))* Continuum International Publishing Group, Ltd. GBR. Dist: National Bk. Network.

Fitzpatrick, William J. Monarch Notes on Austen's Emma & Mansfield Park. (C). 3.95 *(978-0-671-00704-1(1)*, Arco) Peterson's.

Foster Stovel, Nora, ed. Jane Austen Sings the Blues. 2009. (ENG., Illus.). 304p. pap. 26.95 *(978-0-88864-510-4(4))* Univ. of Alberta Pr. CAN. Dist: Michigan State Univ. Pr.

Franklin, Caroline. The Female Romantics: Nineteenth-Century Women Novelists & Byronism. 2012. (Routledge Studies in Romanticism Ser.). (ENG., Illus.). 264p. (C). 125.00 *(978-0-415-99541-2(8))* Routledge.

Fullerton, Susannah. A Dance with Jane Austen: How a Novelist & Her Characters Went to the Ball. 2012. (ENG., Illus.). 144p. 24.95 ***(978-0-7112-3245-7(8))*** Lincoln, Frances Ltd. GBR. Dist: Perseus-PGW.

Gale. Dlb 363. 2011. (Dictionary of Literary Biography Ser.). (Illus.). 500p. lib. bdg. 315.00 *(978-0-7876-8181-4(4))* Cengage Gale.

—Dlb 364. 2011. (Dictionary of Literary Biography Ser.). (Illus.). 500p. lib. bdg. 315.00 *(978-0-7876-8182-1(2))* Cengage Gale.

—Dlb 365. 2012. (Dictionary of Literary Biography Ser.). (ENG., Illus.). 512p. lib. bdg. 315.00 *(978-0-7876-8183-8(0))* Cengage Gale.

Graham, Peter W. Jane Austen & Charles Darwin: Naturalists & Novelists. 2008. (Nineteenth Century Ser.). 214p. 99.95 *(978-0-7546-5851-1(1))* Ashgate Publishing Co.

Halsey, Katie. Jane Austen & her Readers, 1786-1945. 2012. (Anthem Nineteenth-Century Ser.). 298p. 99.00 *(978-0-85728-352-8(9))* Anthem Pr. GBR. Dist: Books International, Inc.

Hannon, Patrice. 101 Things You Didn't Know about Jane Austen: The Truth about the World's Most Intriguing Romantic Literary Heroine. 2007. (ENG.). 256p. per. 9.95 *(978-1-59869-284-6(4))* Adams Media Corp.

Hardy, John Philips. Jane Austen's Heroine's: Intimacy in Human Relationships. 2011. (Routledge Library Editions: Jane Austen Ser.). (ENG.). 160p. 110.00 *(978-0-415-67311-2(9))* Routledge.

Harman, Claire. Jane's Fame: How Jane Austen Conquered the World. 2010. (ENG., Illus.). 304p. 26.00 *(978-0-8050-8258-6(1))* Holt, Henry & Co.

—Jane's Fame: How Jane Austen Conquered the World. 2011. (ENG., Illus.). 320p. pap. 16.00 *(978-0-312-68065-7(1))* Picador.

Harris, Jocelyn. A Revolution Almost Beyond Expression: Jane Austen's Persuasion. 2007. (ENG., Illus.). 280p. 54.50 *(978-0-87413-966-2(X))* Univ. of Delaware Pr.

Hecimovich. Austens Emma. 2009. (Reader's Guides). (ENG.). 128p. 19.95 *(978-0-8264-9848-9(5))* Continuum International Publishing Group, Ltd. GBR. Dist: National Bk. Network.

—Austen's Emma. 2009. (Reader's Guides). (ENG.). 128p. 75.00 *(978-0-8264-9847-2(7))* Continuum International Publishing Group, Ltd. GBR. Dist: National Bk. Network.

Heydt-Stevenson, Jill. Austen's Unbecoming Conjunctions: Subversive Laughter, Embodied History. 2008. (ENG., Illus.). 288p. pap. 32.00 *(978-0-230-60248-9(7))* Palgrave Macmillan.

Hill, Constance. Jane Austen: Her Homes & Her Friends. 2008. (Illus.). 200p. pap. *(978-1-4099-2351-0(7))* Dodo Pr.

Honan, Park. Jane Austen Her Life. 2008. (Illus.). 464p. 32.95 *(978-1-904435-81-5(5))* Little Bks., Ltd. GBR. Dist: Independent Pubs. Group.

Hopkins, Lisa. Relocating Shakespeare & Austen on Screen. 2009. (ENG.). 240p. 100.00 *(978-0-230-57955-2(8))* Palgrave Macmillan.

Hubbard, Shelagh. Pride & Prejudice, Pack. 2010. (Illus.). 200p. spiral bd. 210.00 *(978-1-4441-1037-1(3))* Hodder Education GBR. Dist: Trans-Atlantic Pubns., Inc.

Ivins, Holly. The Jane Austen Pocket Bible: Everything You Want to Know about Jane & Her Novels. 2011. (ENG.). 192p. pap. 9.95 *(978-1-907087-18-9(4))* Crimson Publishing, Ltd. GBR. Dist: National Bk. Network.

Jenkyns, Richard. A Fine Brush on Ivory: An Appreciation of Jane Austen. 2007. (ENG.). 232p. per. 15.95 *(978-0-19-921099-2(3))* Oxford Univ. Pr., Inc.

Johnson, Claudia L. Jane Austen's Cults & Cultures. 2012. (ENG., Illus.). 240p. 35.00 ***(978-0-226-40203-1(7))*** Univ. of Chicago Pr.

Johnson, Claudia L. & Tuite, Clara, eds. A Companion to Jane Austen. (Blackwell Companions to Literature & Culture Ser.: 150). (ENG.). 560p. 2012. pap. 44.95 ***(978-0-470-67238-9(2))*** 2009. (Illus.). 219.95 *(978-1-4051-4909-9(4))* Wiley, John & Sons, Inc. (Wiley-Blackwell).

Kantor, Elizabeth. The Jane Austen Guide to Happily Ever After. 2012. ***(978-1-59698-194-2(6))*** Regnery Publishing, Inc., An Eagle Publishing Co.

Kelly, Pauline E. Jane Austen Dictionary. 2009. 148p. pap. 18.95 *(978-0-9768812-3-0(3))* Inkwell Publishing.

Knox-Shaw, Peter. Jane Austen & the Enlightenment. 2009. (ENG.). 290p. pap. 31.00 *(978-0-521-75997-7(8))* Cambridge Univ. Pr.

Kordich, Catherine J. Bloom's How to Write about Jane Austen. Bloom, Harold, ed. 2008. (Bloom's How to Write about Literature Ser.). 240p. (C). (gr. 9-18). 45.00 *(978-0-7910-9743-4(9)*, Chelsea Hse.) Facts On File, Inc.

Kramp, Michael. Disciplining Love: Austen & the Modern Man. 2007. xvi, 202p. cd-rom 14.95 *(978-0-8142-9126-9(0))*; 248p. 49.95 *(978-0-8142-1046-8(5))* Ohio State Univ. Pr.

Le Faye, Deirdre, ed. Jane Austen's Letters. 4th ed. 2011. (ENG., Illus.). 688p. 45.00 *(978-0-19-957607-4(6))* Oxford Univ. Pr., Inc.

Lee, Hermione. Virginia Woolf's Nose: Essays on Biography. annot. ed. 2007. (ENG.). 160p. (C). per. 15.95 *(978-0-691-13044-6(2))* Princeton Univ. Pr.

Leithart, Peter Jane Austen, 0 vols. 2010. (Christian Encounters Ser.). 192p. pap. 12.00 *(978-1-59555-302-7(9))* Nelson, Thomas Inc.

—Writer of Fancy: The Playful Piety of Jane Austen. 2008. 256p. 16.95 *(978-1-58182-645-6(1)*, Cumberland Hse.) Sourcebooks, Inc.

Leithart, Peter J. Jane Austen: Writer of Fancy. 2009. (ENG., Illus.). 292p. 18.95 *(978-1-58182-703-3(2)*, Cumberland Hse.) Sourcebooks, Inc.

Leona, Toker. Towards the Ethics of Form in Fiction: Narratives of Cultural Remission. 2010. (Theory interpretation Narrativ Ser.). (ENG.). 272p. 54.95 *(978-0-8142-1122-9(4))* Ohio State Univ. Pr.

Mandal, Anthony. Jane Austen & the Popular Novel: The Determined Author. 2007. (ENG., Illus.). 256p. 84.00 *(978-0-230-00896-0(8))* Palgrave Macmillan.

—The Reception of Jane Austen in Europe. Southam, Brian, ed. 2007. (Reception of Writers in Europe Ser.). (ENG.). 464p. 300.00 *(978-0-8264-6932-8(9))* Continuum International Publishing Group, Ltd. GBR. Dist: National Bk. Network.

Mazzeno, Laurence W. Jane Austen: Two Centuries of Criticism. 2011. (Literary Criticism in Perspective Ser.). 312p. 75.00 *(978-1-57113-394-6(1))* Camden Hse.

Mazzeno, Laurence W. Pride & Prejudice, by Jane Austen. 2011. ***(978-1-58765-843-3(7))*** Salem Pr., Inc.

Mitton, Geraldine Edith. Jane Austen & Her Times. 2009. 204p. pap. 19.99 *(978-1-150-35237-9(X))* General Bks. LLC.

Monaghan, David, et al. The Cinematic Jane Austen: Essays on the Filmic Sensibility of the Novels. 2009. (ENG.). 204p. pap. 35.00 *(978-0-7864-3506-7(2))* McFarland & Co., Inc. Pubs.

Morini, Massimiliano. Jane Austen's Narrative Techniques: A Stylistic & Pragmatic Analysis. 2009. 172p. 99.95 *(978-0-7546-6607-3(7))* Ashgate Publishing Co.

Nardin, Jane. Those Elegant Decorums: The Concept of Propriety in Jane Austen's Novels. 2011. (ENG.). 178p. pap. 23.95 ***(978-1-4384-4229-7(7)**,* Suny Pr.) State Univ. of New York Pr.

Nazar, Hina. Enlightened Sentiments: Judgment & Autonomy in the Age of Sensibility. 2012. (ENG., Illus.). 600p. 45.00 ***(978-0-8232-4007-4(X))*** Fordham Univ. Pr.

Newgarden, Anne. Becoming Jane: The Wit & Wisdom of Jane Austen. 2007. 208p. per. 12.95 *(978-1-4013-0904-6(6))* Miramax Bks.

Norman, Andrew. Jane Austen: An Unrequited Love. (ENG., Illus.). 2010. 224p. pap. 17.95 *(978-0-7524-5529-7(X))* 2009. 208p. 36.95 *(978-0-7524-4874-9(9))* History Pr. Ltd., The GBR. Dist: Independent Pubs. Group.

Olsen, Kirstin. All Things Austen: A Concise Encyclopedia of Jane Austen's World. 2008. (Illus.). 400p. pap. 29.95 *(978-1-84645-052-5(7)*, GWP052) Greenwood Publishing Group, Inc.

Owen, David. Rethinking Jane Austen's Lady Susan: The Case for Her "Failed" Epistolary Novella. 2010. ix, 186p. 109.95 *(978-0-7734-3646-6(4))* Mellen, Edwin Pr., The.

Page, Norman. The Language of Jane Austen (Routledge Revivals) 2011. (Routledge Revivals Ser.). (ENG.). 218p. 110.00 ***(978-0-415-68787-4(X)**,* Routledge.

Potter Style. Jane Austen Note Cards - Pride & Prejudice. 2010. (ENG.). 16p 12.00 *(978-0-307-58742-8(8)*, Potter Style) Crown Publishing Group.

Puzzle Society Staff. Pocket Posh Jane Austen: 100 Puzzles & Quizzes. 2011. (ENG.). 160p. pap. 7.99 *(978-1-4494-0123-8(6))* Andrews McMeel Publishing.

Ray, Joan Elizabeth Klingel. Jane Austen for Dummies. 2006. (ENG., Illus.). 384p. per. 19.99 *(978-0-470-00829-4(6)*, For Dummies) Wiley, John & Sons, Inc.

Reeve, Katharine. Jane Austen in Bath: Walking Tours of the Writer's City. 2006. (ENG., Illus.). 144p. 19.95 *(978-1-892145-32-1(4))* Little Bookroom.

Ross, Josephine. Jane Austen: A Companion. 2006. (ENG., Illus.). 274p. per. 18.95 *(978-0-8135-3954-6(4))* Rutgers Univ. Pr.

Routledge Library Editions: Jane Austen, 4 vols. 2011. (Routledge Library Editions: Jane Austen Ser.). 752p. 395.00 *(978-0-415-67313-6(5))* Routledge.

Russell, Adam. Isabelle de Montolieu Reads Jane Austen's Fictional Minds: The First French Translations of Free Indirect Discourse from Jane Austen's Persuasion. 2011. (ENG.). 249p. pap. ***(978-3-0343-0677-5(6))*** Lang, Peter.

Scheuermann, Mona. Reading Jane Austen. (ENG., 2012. Illus.). 220p. pap. 27.00 ***(978-0-230-34019-0(9))*** 2009. 224p. 89.00 *(978-0-230-61877-0(4))* Palgrave Macmillan.

Searle, Alison. The Eyes of Your Heart: Literary & Theological Trajectories of Imagining Biblically. 2009. (Paternoster Theological Monographs Ser.). 250p. pap. 29.00 *(978-1-60608-602-5(2)*, Wipf and Stock) Wipf & Stock Pubs.

Selwyn, David. Jane Austen & Children. 2010. (ENG., Illus.). 256p. 39.95 *(978-1-84725-041-4(6))* Continuum International Publishing Group, Ltd. GBR. Dist: National Bk. Network.

Smith, Amy Elizabeth. All Roads Lead to Austen. 2012. (ENG.). 384p. pap. 14.99 ***(978-1-4022-6585-3(9))*** Sourcebooks, Inc.

Smith, Debra White. What Jane Austen Taught Me about Love & Romance. 2007. 192p. per. 11.99 *(978-0-7369-1889-3(2))* Harvest Hse. Pubs.

Smith, Goldwin. Life of Jane Austen. 2009. 112p. pap. 19.99 *(978-1-151-13810-1(X))* General Bks. LLC.

Smith, Lori. A Walk with Jane Austen: A Journey into Adventure, Love, & Faith. 2007. (ENG.). 256p. pap. 13.99 *(978-1-4000-7370-2(7)*, WaterBrook Pr.) Doubleday Religious Publishing Group, The.

Sourcebooks Staff. Jane Austen Companion to Life. 2010. (ENG., Illus.). 64p. 9.99 *(978-1-4022-4015-7(5))* Sourcebooks, Inc.

Southam, B. C. Jane Austen Vol. 1: The Critical Heritage, 1811-1870. 2009. 276p. pap. 45.00 *(978-0-415-56876-0(5))* Routledge.

—Jane Austen Vol. 2: The Critical Heritage, 1870-1940. 2009. 308p. pap. 45.00 *(978-0-415-56877-7(3))* Routledge.

Spence, Jon & Spence. Becoming Jane Austen. movie tie-in ed. 2007. (ENG., Illus.). 312p. 17.95 *(978-1-84725-046-9(7))* Continuum International Publishing Group, Ltd. GBR. Dist: National Bk. Network.

Stafford, Fiona. Jane Austen. 2008. (Brief Lives Ser.). (ENG.). 120p. pap. 13.95 *(978-1-84391-906-3(0))* Hesperus Pr. GBR. Dist: Independent Pubs. Group.

Steiner, Enit K. Jane Austen's Civilized Women: Morality, Gender & the Civilizing Process, 1 vol. 2012. (Gender & Genre Ser.: 9). (ENG.). 240p. 99.00 *(978-1-84893-177-0(8))* Pickering & Chatto Pubs., Ltd. GBR. Dist: Ashgate Publishing Co.

Stovel, Bruce. Jane Austen & Company: Collected Essays. Stovel, Nora Foster, ed. 2011. 296p. pap. 34.95 *(978-0-88864-548-7(1))* Univ. of Alberta Pr. CAN. Dist: Michigan State Univ. Pr.

Sullivan, Margaret. The Jane Austen Handbook. 2011. (ENG., Illus.). 224p. 16.95 *(978-1-59474-505-8(6))* Quirk Bks.

Sutherland, John & Le Faye, Deirdre. So You Think You Know Jane Austen? A Literary Quizbook. 2009. (Oxford World's Classics Ser.). (ENG., Illus.). 240p. 11.95 *(978-0-19-953899-7(9))* Oxford Univ. Pr., Inc.

Sutherland, Kathryn. Jane Austen's Textual Lives: From Aeschylus to Bollywood. 2007. (ENG., Illus.). 408p. pap. 49.95 *(978-0-19-923428-8(0))* Oxford Univ. Pr., Inc.

Tanner, Tony. Jane Austen. 2007. (ENG.). 312p. 120.00 *(978-0-230-00823-6(2))*; pap. 39.00 *(978-0-230-00824-3(0))* Palgrave Macmillan.

Tarpley, Joyce Kerr. Constancy & the Ethics of Jane Austen's Mansfield Park. 2010. (ENG.). xiv, 288p. 69.95 *(978-0-8132-1790-1(3))* Catholic Univ. of America Pr.

The Puzzle Society. Pocket Posh Jane Austen: 100 Puzzles & Quizzes. 2011. (ENG.). 160p. pap. 7.99 *(978-1-4494-0356-0(5))* Andrews McMeel Publishing.

Todd, Janet. The Cambridge Introduction to Jane Austen. 2006. (Cambridge Introductions to Literature Ser.). (ENG., Illus.). 162p. per. 23.99 *(978-0-521-67469-0(7))*; (C). 75.00 *(978-0-521-85806-9(2))* Cambridge Univ. Pr.

Todd, Janet M., ed. Jane Austen in Context. 2006. (Cambridge Edition of the Works of Jane Austen Ser.). (ENG., Illus.). 498p. per. 42.00 *(978-0-521-68853-6(1))* Cambridge Univ. Pr.

Toker, Leona. Towards the Ethics of Form in Fiction: Narratives of Cultural Remission. 2010. (Theory interpretation Narrativ Ser.). (ENG.). 272p. cd-rom 14.95 *(978-0-8142-9220-4(8))* Ohio State Univ. Pr.

Tuite, Clara. Romantic Austen: Sexual Politics & the Literary Canon. 2008. (Cambridge Studies in Romanticism Ser.). (ENG.). 264p. pap. 37.99 *(978-0-521-05439-3(7))* Cambridge Univ. Pr.

Tytler, Sarah. Jane Austen & Her Works. 2007. (ENG.). 408p. 49.95 *(978-0-548-08589-9(7))* Kessinger Publishing, LLC.

Vallhora, Karen. Austen's Oughts: Judgment after Locke & Shaftesbury. 2010. (ENG.). 85.00 *(978-1-61149-137-1(1))*; (Illus.). 368p. 77.50 *(978-0-87413-082-9(4))* Univ. of Delaware Pr.

Villard, Lonie & Brimley Johnson, R. Jane Austen: A French Appreciation. 2011. (Routledge Library Editions: Jane Austen Ser.). (ENG.). 256p. 120.00 *(978-0-415-67289-4(9))* Routledge.

Walker, Eric. Marriage, Writing, & Romanticism: Wordsworth & Austen after War. 2011. (ENG., Illus.). 304p. pap. 23.95 *(978-0-8047-7365-2(3))* Stanford Univ. Pr.

Walker, Eric C. Marriage, Writing, & Romanticism: Wordsworth & Austen after War. 2009. (ENG., Illus.). 304p. 60.00 *(978-0-8047-6092-8(6))* Stanford Univ. Pr.

Wallace, Robert K. Jane Austen & Mozart: Classical Equilibrium in Fiction & Music. 2009. (ENG.). 312p. pap. 24.95 *(978-0-8203-3391-5(3))* Univ. of Georgia Pr.

Wells, Juliette. Everybody's Jane: Austen in the Popular Imagination. 2012. (ENG., Illus.). 256p. 100.00 *(978-1-4411-7654-7(3))*; pap. 29.95 *(978-1-4411-4554-3(0))* Continuum International Publishing Group, Ltd. GBR. Dist: National Bk. Network.

White, Laura Mooneyham. Jane Austen's Anglicanism. 2011. (Illus.). 228p. 89.95 *(978-1-4094-1863-4(4))* Ashgate Publishing Co.

Wilkes, Diane. Jane Austen Tarot Book. 2007. (ENG., Illus.). 174p. pap. 17.95 *(978-0-7387-1025-9(3))* Llewellyn Pubns.

Wilkes, Joanne. Women Reviewing Women in Nineteenth-Century Britain: The Critical Reception of Jane Austen Charlotte Bronte & George Elliot. 2010. (Nineteenth Century Ser.). 194p. 99.95 *(978-0-7546-6336-2(1))* Ashgate Publishing Co.

Wilson, Kim. In the Garden with Jane Austen. 2011. (ENG., Illus.). 128p. 19.95 *(978-0-7112-2594-7(X))* Lincoln, Frances Ltd. GBR. Dist: Perseus-PGW.

—Tea with Jane Austen. 2011. (ENG., Illus.). 112p. 19.95 *(978-0-7112-3189-4(3))* Lincoln, Frances Ltd. GBR. Dist: Perseus-PGW.

Wiltshire, John. Jane Austen: Introductions & Interventions. 2006. (ENG.). 144p. 110.00 *(978-0-230-00749-9(X))*; pap. 39.00 *(978-0-230-00750-5(3))* Palgrave Macmillan.

Wollaston, Emily & Dale, Sue. Little Book of Jane Austen. 2008. (Little Book Ser.). (ENG., Illus.). 128p. 11.99 *(978-1-906229-58-0(9))*, 1906229589) G2 Entertainment Ltd. GBR. Dist: BookMasters Distribution Services (BDS).

Wye, Margaret. Architectural Influences on Jane Austen's Narratives: Structure as an Active Agent of Fictive Knowledge in the Long Eighteenth Century. 2009. (Illus.). 280p. *(978-0-7734-4769-1(5))* Mellen, Edwin Pr., The.

YOUNG, K. A. Y. Imagining Minds: the Neuro-Aesthetics of Austen, Eliot, & Hardy. 2010. (Theory interpretation Narrativ Ser.). pap. 26.95 *(978-0-8142-5174-4(9))* Ohio State Univ. Pr.

Young, Kay. Imagining Minds: The Neuro-Aesthetics of Austen, Eliot & Hardy. 2010. *(978-0-8142-9238-9(0))*; 59.95 *(978-0-8142-1139-7(9))* Ohio State Univ. Pr.

AUSTENITE

see also Steel, Heat Resistant

Brooks, Charlie R. Principles of the Austenitization of Steels. 2007. (Illus.). 232p. 276.00 *(978-1-85166-770-3(9))* Springer.

Niknafs, Salar. Direct Observation of High-Temperature Phase Transformations in Steel. 2009. 120p. pap. *(978-3-639-08515-0(9))* VDM Verlag Dr. Mueller e.K.

Technology Research Editors, ed. Effects of Heat Treatment on Retained Austenite, 2007 Ed. 2007. pap. 128.50 *(978-1-60030-423-1(0)*, Search-In-Print) CSA Journal Division.

AUSTER, PAUL, 1947-

Auster, Paul. The Invention of Solitude. rev. ed. 2007. (ENG., Illus.). 192p. (Orig.). (gr. 12-18). 15.00 *(978-0-14-311222-8(8)*, Penguin (Non-Classics)) Penguin Group (USA) Inc.

Auster, Paul. Winter Journal. 2012. (ENG.). 240p. 26.00 ***(978-0-8050-9553-1(5))*** Holt, Henry & Co.

Auster, Paul, told to. Double Game, 1 vol. 2007. (ENG., Illus.). 296p. 39.95 *(978-1-933045-69-6(8))* D.A.P./Distributed Art Pubs.

Borbála, Bökös. The World is an Illusion: Four Essays on Paul Auster. 2008. 80p. pap. *(978-3-639-09512-8(X))* VDM Verlag Dr. Mueller e.K.

Brown, Mark. Paul Auster. 2008. (Contemporary American & Canadian Novelists Ser.). (ENG.). 224p. 84.00 *(978-0-7190-7396-0(0))*; pap. 26.00 *(978-0-7190-7397-7(9))* Manchester Univ. Pr. GBR. Dist: Macmillan.

de Cortanze, Gerard. Paul Austers New York. (GER.). *(978-3-8067-2826-2(7))* Gerstenberg DEU. Dist: International Bk. Import Service, Inc.

Donovan, Christopher. Postmodern Counternarratives: Irony & Audience in the Novels of Paul Auster, Don Delillo, Charles Johnson, & Tim O'Brien. 2009. 10p. 39.95 *(978-0-415-80344-1(6))* Routledge.

Dupre, Joan. Fighting Fathers/Saving Sons. 2009. 144p. pap. *(978-3-639-13459-9(1))* VDM Verlag Dr. Mueller e.K.

Hotger, Beate. Identitat im Filmischen Werk von Paul Auster. (Europaische Hochschulschriften Ser.). (GER., Illus.). 353p. 43.95 *(978-3-631-38470-1(X))* Lang, Peter Publishing, Inc.

Martin, Brendan. Paul Auster's Postmodernity. 2007. (Studies in Major Literary Authors Ser.). (ENG.). 248p. 125.00 *(978-0-415-96203-2(X))* Routledge.

Peacock, James. Understanding Paul Auster. (Understanding Contemporary American Literature Ser.). 264p. 2011. (ENG.). pap. 21.95 ***(978-1-61117-052-8(4))*** 2010. 39.95 *(978-1-57003-864-8(3))* Univ. of South Carolina Pr.

AUSTERITY COOKING

see Low Budget Cooking

AUSTERLITZ, BATTLE OF, CZECH REPUBLIC, 1805

Burton, R.G. The Road to Austerlitz: Napoleon's Campaign Of 1805. 2008. 140p. pap. 42.00 *(978-1-84677-582-6(5))*; pap. *(978-1-84677-581-9(7))* Leonaur Ltd.

AUSTIN, J. L. (JOHN LANGSHAW), 1911-1960

Fann, K. T. Symposium on J L Austin. 2011. (Routledge Revivals Ser.). (ENG.). 502p. 150.00 *(978-0-415-67922-0(2))* Routledge.

Gustafsson, Martin & Sorli, Richard, eds. The Philosophy of J. L. Austin. 2012. (ENG.). 256p. 75.00 ***(978-0-19-921975-9(3))*** Oxford Univ. Pr., Inc.

Marsen, Sky. Narrative Dimensions of Philosophy: A Semiotic Exploration in the Work of Merleau-Ponty, Kierkegaard & Austin. 2006. (ENG., Illus.). 224p. 110.00 *(978-0-230-00532-7(2))* Palgrave Macmillan.

Warnock. Austin-arg Philosophers. 2008. (ENG.). 176p. 45.00 *(978-0-415-48817-4(6))* Routledge.

AUSTIN, MARY HUNTER, 1868-1934

Austin, Mary Hunter. Earth Horizon: Facsimile of Original 1932 Edition. 2007. (ENG.). 424p. per. 34.95 *(978-0-86534-539-3(2))* Sunstone Pr.

—The Flock. 2010. 286p. pap. 28.75 *(978-1-178-30515-9(5))*; 286p. pap. 28.75 *(978-1-141-02373-8(3))*; 282p. pap. 28.75 *(978-1-141-49107-0(9))* BiblioBazaar.

—The Flock. 2009. 94p. pap. *(978-0-217-29454-6(5))* Books LLC.

—The Land of Journeys' Ending: Facsimile of Original 1924 Edition. 2007. (ENG.). 488p. per. 30.95 *(978-0-86534-571-3(6))* Sunstone Pr.

—The Land of Little Rain: Facsimile of Original 1904 Edition. 2007. (ENG.). 320p. per. 26.95 *(978-0-86534-540-9(6))* Sunstone Pr.

Goodman, Susan & Dawson, Carl. Mary Austin & the American West. 2009. (Illus.). 352p. 35.00 *(978-0-520-24635-5(7))* Univ. of California Pr.

Stout, Janis P. Picturing a Different West: Vision, Illustration, & the Tradition of Cather & Austin. 2007. (Grover E. Murray Studies in the American Southwest Ser.). (Illus.). 352p. 40.00 *(978-0-89672-610-9(X))* Texas Tech Univ. Pr.

AUSTIN, STEPHEN FULLER, 1793-1836

Cummins, Light Townsend. Emily Austin of Texas, 1795-1851. 2009. (Texas Biography Ser.). (ENG., Illus.). 224p. 27.95 *(978-0-87565-351-8(0))* Texas Christian Univ. Pr.

Glasscock, Sallie. Dreams of an Empire: The Story of Stephen Fuller Austin & His Colony in Texas. 2011. 234p. 46.95 ***(978-1-258-02021-7(1))*** Literary Licensing, LLC.

AUSTIN (TEX.)

Baird, David. Frommer's San Antonio & Austin. 9th ed. 2011. (Frommer's Complete Guides: 999). (ENG., Illus.). 352p. pap. 16.99 *(978-1-118-00285-8(7)*, Frommers) Wiley, John & Sons, Inc.

Barnet, Diane. Inside South Austin: A Guide. 2009. (Illus.). 72p. pap. 12.95 *(978-1-893271-50-0(1))* Maverick Publishing Co.

Brown, Amy K. Austin, San Antonio & the Texas Hill Country: A Complete Guide. 2007. (Great Destinations Austin, San Antonio & the Texas Hill Country Ser.). (ENG., Illus.). 248p. per. 18.95 *(978-1-58157-040-3(6)*, 157040) Countryman Pr.

Carmack, Liz. Rodeo Austin: Blue Ribbons, Buckin' Broncs, & Big Dreams - The Story of the Star of Texas Fair & Rodeo. 2012. (Illus.). 128p. 29.95 ***(978-1-60344-568-9(4))*** Texas A&M Univ. Pr.

Finan, Kristin. The Cheap Bastard's Guide to Austin: Secrets of Living the Good Life — for Less! 2011. (Cheap Bastard Ser.). (ENG., Illus.). 240p. pap. 14.95 *(978-0-7627-7300-8(6))* Globe Pequot Pr., The.

Galloway, J. R. The servant girl Murders. 2010. 346p. pap. 17.95 *(978-1-60910-123-7(5))* Booklocker.com, Inc.

Hylton, Hilary & Rossie, Cam. Insiders' Guide to Austin, 7th. 7th ed. 2011. (Insiders' Guide Ser.). (ENG.). 456p. pap. 18.95 *(978-0-7627-6466-2(X)*, Insiders' Guide) Globe Pequot Pr., The.

Isaacson, Rupert. The Horse Boy: A Father's Quest to Heal His Son. l.t. ed. 2009. 541p. 32.95 *(978-1-4104-1589-9(9))* Thorndike Pr.

Johnson, Scott A. & Johnson, Johnson. Haunted Austin, Texas. 2009. (Illus.). 160p. pap. 14.99 *(978-0-7643-3298-2(8))* Schiffer Publishing, Ltd.

Long, Joshua. Weird City: Sense of Place & Creative Resistance in Austin, Texas. 2010. (ENG.). 221p. pap. 25.00 *(978-0-292-72241-5(9))*; (Illus.). 50.00 *(978-0-292-72206-4(0))* Univ. of Texas Pr.

MAPSCO Staff, creator. MAPSCO Austin Street Guide: Austin & 32 Surrounding Communities. 2007. (MAPSCO Street Guide Ser.). (Illus.). 796p. pap. 44.95 *(978-1-56966-412-4(9))* Mapsco, Inc.

Mears, Michelle M. And Grace Will Lead Me Home: African American Freedmen Communities of Austin, Texas, 1865-1928. 2009. (Illus.). 256p. 45.00 *(978-0-89672-654-3(1))* Texas Tech Univ. Pr.

Parent, Laurence. Portrait of Austin. 2008. 120p. 26.95 *(978-1-56037-480-0(2))* Farcountry Pr.

Permenter, Paris & Bigley, John. Day Trips from Austin: Getaway Ideas for the Local Traveler. 6th ed. 2010. (Day Trips Ser.). (ENG., Illus.). 256p. pap. 14.95 *(978-0-7627-6006-0(0))* Globe Pequot Pr., The.

Powell, William Dylan. Austin Then & Now. 2006. (Then & Now Thunder Bay Ser.). (ENG., Illus.). 144p. 19.95 *(978-1-59223-658-9(8)*, Thunder Bay Pr.) Advantage Pubs. Group.

Simons, Jim. Molly Chronicles Serotonin Serenade. 2007. pap. 14.95 *(978-1-891386-75-6(1))* Plain View Pr.

Stelter, Keith. Best Easy Day Hikes Austin. 2009. (Best Easy Day Hikes Ser.). (ENG., Illus.). 104p. pap. 9.95 *(978-0-7627-5291-1(2)*, Falcon Guides) Globe Pequot Pr., The.

Turk, Janis. Frommer's San Antonio & Austin Day by Day. 2010. (Frommer's Day by Day - Pocket Ser.: 254). (ENG., Illus.). 216p. pap. 14.99 *(978-0-470-67780-3(5)*, Frommers) Wiley, John & Sons, Inc.

Universal Map Enterprises Inc., Staff. Austin, TX Greater. 4.95 *(978-0-7625-3562-0(8))* Universal Map Enterprises, Inc.

Wellman, Kaie. Eat. shop Austin: A Curated Guide of Inspired & Unique Locally Owned Eating & Shopping Establishments. 3rd rev. ed. 2010. (Eat. shop Guides). (ENG.). 192p. pap. 14.95 *(978-0-9844253-1-0(4))* Cabazon Bks.

Wellman, Kaie & Malina, Marianne. Eat. Shop. Austin: The Indispensable Guide to Inspired, Locally Owned Eating & Shopping Establishments. 2nd ed. 2007. (Eat. shop guides Ser.). (ENG., Illus.). 192p. pap. 14.95 *(978-0-9789588-5-5(3))* Cabazon Bks.

Zeller-Plumer, Jeanine Marie. Haunted Austin: History & Hauntings in the Capital City. 2010. 112p. pap. 14.99 *(978-1-60949-040-9(1))* History Pr., The.

AUSTIN AUTOMOBILE

see also Austin-Healey Automobile

Clymer, F. Austin-Healey Owner's Handbook for the Maintenance & Repair of the 6-Cylinder Models 1956-1968. 2007. 264p. per. 39.95 *(978-1-58850-074-8(6))* Veloce Enterprises, Inc.

Mills, Rinsey. Original Austin Seven: The Restorer's Guide to All Passenger Car & Sports Models, 1922-39. 2008. (Original Ser.). (ENG.). 128p. 49.95 *(978-1-906133-05-4(0)*, 1906133050) Herridge & Sons Ltd.

Peck, Colin. The Last Real Austins: 1946 To 1959. 2009. (Those Were the Days Ser.). (ENG., Illus.). 96p. pap. 29.95 *(978-1-84584-193-5(X)*, 184584193X) Veloce Publishing Ltd. GBR. Dist: MBI Distribution Services/Quayside Distribution.

Wood, Jonathan. The Austin Seven. 2008. (Album Ser.: Vol. 343). (ENG., Illus.). 32p. pap. 11.95 *(978-0-7478-0416-1(8))* Shire Pubns., Ltd. GBR. Dist: Random Hse., Inc.

AUSTIN FRIARS

see Augustinians

AUSTIN-HEALEY AUTOMOBILE

see also Sprite Automobile

Baggott, John. Big Healeys in Competition: Austin-Healy 100, 3000 & Jensen Healey in Race & Rally. 2006. (Crowood Autoclassics Ser.). (ENG., Illus.). 200p. 34.95 *(978-1-86126-828-0(9)*, 1861268289) Crowood Pr., Ltd. GBR. Dist: MBI Distribution Services/Quayside Distribution.

Barker, John & Horier, Terry. MG Midget & Austin Healey Sprite: All Models. 2011. (Essential Buyer's Guide Ser.). (ENG., Illus.). 64p. pap. 19.95 *(978-1-84584-354-0(1)*, 1845843541) Veloce Publishing Ltd. GBR. Dist: MBI Distribution Services/Quayside Distribution.

Clarke, R. M., ed. Road & Track on Austin-Healey, 1953-1970. (Illus.). 88p. pap. 16.95 *(978-0-946489-10-7(6))* MBI Publishing Co. LLC.

Clausager, Anders Ditlev. Original Austin-Healey: The Restorer's Guide to 100, 100-Six And 3000. 2011. (ENG., Illus.). 96p. 44.95 *(978-1-906133-20-7(4)*, 1906133204) Herridge & Sons, Ltd. GBR. Dist: MBI Distribution Services/Quayside Distribution.

Pressnell, Jon. Austin-Healey: The Bulldog Breed. 2011. (Haynes Classic Makes Ser.). (ENG., Illus.). 192p. 39.95 *(978-1-84425-519-1(0)*, 1844255190) Haynes Publishing PLC GBR. Dist: MBI Distribution Services/Quayside Distribution.

Robson, Graham. Austin-Healey. 2010. (Shire Library). (ENG., Illus.). 64p. pap. 12.95 *(978-0-7478-0769-8(8))* Shire Pubns., Ltd. GBR. Dist: Random Hse., Inc.

—Austin Healey 100-6 & 3000. 2007. (Rally Giants Ser.). (ENG., Illus.). 128p. pap. 29.95 *(978-1-84584-128-7(X)*, 184584128X) Veloce Publishing Ltd. GBR. Dist: MBI Distribution Services/Quayside Distribution.

Trummel, Reid. Big Healeys: All Models 1953 To 1967. 2012. (Essential Buyer's Guide Ser.). (ENG., Illus.). 64p. pap. 19.95 ***(978-1-84584-392-2(4)***, 1845843924) Veloce Publishing Ltd. GBR. Dist: MBI Distribution Services/Quayside Distribution.

AUSTIN MINI AUTOMOBILES

see Mini Automobiles

AUSTRALASIA

Aarde, Rudi van. World & Its Peoples. 2010. *(978-0-7614-7921-5(X))*; *(978-0-7614-7922-2(8))*; *(978-0-7614-7923-9(6))*; *(978-0-7614-7925-3(2))*; *(978-0-7614-7914-7(7))*; *(978-0-7614-7915-4(5))*; *(978-0-7614-7916-1(3))*; *(978-0-7614-7917-8(1))*; *(978-0-7614-7918-5(X))*; *(978-0-7614-7919-2(8))*; *(978-0-7614-7920-8(1))* Marshall Cavendish Corp. (Marshall Cavendish Reference Bks.).

Cameron, Rosalea. The Ecology of Third Culture Kids. 2008. 240p. pap. *(978-3-639-01700-7(5))* VDM Verlag Dr. Mueller e.K.

Coghlan, T.A. & Ewing, T. T. The Progress of Australasia in the Nineteenth Century. 2011. (Cambridge Library Collection - History Ser.). 502p. pap. 35.99 *(978-1-108-03072-4(6))* Cambridge Univ. Pr.

Cope, Gordon. So We Sold Our House & Ran Away to the South Pacific, 1 vol. 2006. (ENG., Illus.). 224p. 12.95 *(978-1-894856-99-7(6))* Fifth Hse. Pubs. CAN. Dist: Ingram Pub. Services.

Europa Publications Staff. The Far East & Australasia 2007. 38th rev. ed. 2006. (Illus.). 1504p. 615.00 *(978-1-85743-381-4(5))* Routledge.

The Far East & Australasia 2011. 42nd rev. ed. 2010. (ENG.). 1608p. 835.00 *(978-1-85743-571-9(0))* Routledge.

Flanagan, Roderick. The History of New South Wales: With an Account of Van Diemen's Land [Tasmania], New Zealand, Port Phillip [Victoria], Moreton Bay, & Other Australian Settlements. 2011. (Cambridge Library Collection - History Ser.). (ENG.). Vol. 1. 566p. pap. 39.99 ***(978-1-108-03892-8(1))*** Vol. 2. 594p. pap. 43.00 ***(978-1-108-03893-5(X))*** Cambridge Univ. Pr.

Routledge Staff, creator. Far East & Australasia 2008. 39th rev. ed. 2008. (Far East & Australasia Ser.). 1507p. 700.00 *(978-1-85743-427-9(7))* Routledge.

Temple, Rita. A Beach for Christmas. 2009. (Illus.). 96p. pap. 31.99 *(978-1-4389-4438-8(1))* AuthorHouse.

AUSTRALASIAN ANTARCTIC EXPEDITION (1911-1914)

Mawson, Douglas & Fiennes, Ranulph. The Home of the Blizzard: A True Story of Antarctic Survival. 2007. (Illus.). 484p. pap. 14.95 *(978-1-60239-144-4(0))* Skyhorse Publishing Co., Inc.

AUSTRALIA

Carr-Lambert, Marsha. Everything (in the World) You Ever Wanted to Know about Australia. 72p. *(978-0-9640940-1-7(0))* Teacher's Little Pal, Co.

Clarke, Marcus. Old Tales of a Young Country. 2008. 218p. 39.95 *(978-1-4372-1046-0(5))*; pap. 24.95 *(978-1-4370-8097-1(9))* Kessinger Publishing, LLC.

Cleland. Learn English Through Topics about Australia. Date not set. 187p. pap. 9.95 *(978-0-582-66569-9(8))* Addison-Wesley Longman, Ltd. GBR. Dist: Trans-Atlantic Pubns., Inc.

Spencer, Baldwin. Across Australia. 2010. 136p. pap. 22.54 *(978-1-151-86268-6(1))* General Bks. LLC.

Spencer, Baldwin & Gillen, F. J. Across Australia. 2010. (Cambridge Library Collection - Linguistics Ser.). (ENG.). 408p. pap. 31.99 *(978-1-108-02041-1(0))*; 482p. pap. 35.99 *(978-1-108-02042-8(9))* Cambridge Univ. Pr.

Spencer, Baldwin & Gillen, Francis James. Across Australia. 2010. 398p. pap. 33.75 *(978-1-145-45021-9(0))* BiblioBazaar.

Trollope, Anthony. Australia & New Zealand. 2009. 250p. pap. *(978-1-4590-3693-2(X))* Books LLC.

—Australia & New Zealand, 2 vols. reprint ed. lib. bdg. 196.00 *(978-0-7426-2469-6(2))* Classic Bks.

AUSTRALIA—ANTIQUITIES

Attenbrow, Val. Sydney's Aboriginal Past: Investigating the Archaeological & Historical Records. 2nd ed. 2010. (ENG., Illus.). 240p. pap. 49.95 *(978-1-74223-116-7(0)*, UNSW Press) NewSouth Publishing AUS. Dist: Independent Pubs. Group.

Brockwell, Sally. Archaeological Settlement Patterns & Mobility Strategies: Lower Adelaide River, Northern Australia. 2009. (Bar S Ser.). (ENG., Illus.). 141p. (C). pap. 95.00 *(978-1-4073-0461-8(5))* British Archaeological Reports Ltd. GBR. Dist: Brown, David Bk. Co., The.

Claughton, Peter, et al. Mining in a Medieval Landscape: The Royal Silver Mines of the Tamar Valley. 2009. (Illus.). 200p. pap. 36.00 *(978-0-85989-828-7(8))* Univ. of Exeter Pr. GBR. Dist: Chicago Distribution Ctr.

Hay, Ashley & Stacey, Robyn. Museum: The Macleays, Their Collections & the Search for Order. 2007. (Illus.). 188p. 85.00 *(978-0-521-87453-3(X))* Cambridge Univ. Pr.

Hiscock, Peter. Archaeology of Ancient Australia. 2007. (ENG., Illus.). 368p. 160.00 *(978-0-415-33810-3(7))*; per. 46.95 *(978-0-415-33811-0(5))* Routledge.

Jewish Museum of Australia. Jewish Museum of Australia. 2008. (Illus.). 200p. (C). pap. 50.00 *(978-1-875670-44-4(0))* Macmillan Art Publishing AUS. Dist: Brown, David Bk. Co., The.

Law, Wallace Boone. Measured on Stone: Stone Artefact Reduction, Residential Mobility, & Aboriginal Land Use in Arid Central Australia. 2009. (Illus.). 154p. (C). pap. 92.50 *(978-1-4073-0445-8(3))* British Archaeological Reports Ltd. GBR. Dist: Brown, David Bk. Co., The.

Lawrence, Susan & Davies, Peter. An Archaeology of Australia Since 1788. 2010. (Contributions to Global Historical Archaeology Ser.). (Illus.). xx, 424p. 129.00 *(978-1-4419-7484-6(9)*, 1441974849) Springer.

Layton, Robert. Australian Rock Art: A New Synthesis. 2010. (ENG., Illus.). 304p. pap. 42.00 *(978-0-521-12578-9(2))* Cambridge Univ. Pr.

Nash, Michael. Shipwreck Archaeology in Australia. 2007. 232p. 40.00 *(978-0-9802964-3-3(9))* UWA Publishing AUS. Dist: International Specialized Bk. Services.

Richards, Nathan. Ships' Graveyards: Abandoned Watercraft & the Archaeological Site Formation Process. 2008. (Co-published with the Society for Historical Archaeology Ser.). (ENG., Illus.). 304p. 65.00 *(978-0-8130-3257-3(1))* Univ. Pr. of Florida.

Rippon, Stephen, et al. Mining in a Medieval Landscape: The Royal Silver Mines of the Tamar Valley. 2009. (Illus.). 200p. 110.00 *(978-0-85989-827-0(X))* Univ. of Exeter Pr. GBR. Dist: Chicago Distribution Ctr.

Smith, Claire & Burke, Heather. Digging it up down Under: A Practical Guide to Doing Archaeology in Australia. 2006. (World Archaeological Congress Cultural Heritage Manual Ser.). (Illus.). XXVI, 326p. (C). 159.00 *(978-0-387-35260-2(0)*, 0387352600) Springer.

—Digging It up down Under: A Practical Guide to Doing Archaeology in Australia. 2007. (World Archaeological Congress Cultural Heritage Manual Ser.). (Illus.). 352p. per. 39.95 *(978-0-387-75700-1(7)*, 0387757007) Springer.

Staniforth, Mark & Nash, Michael, eds. Maritime Archaeology: Australian Approaches. 2008. (Springer Series in Underwater Archaeology Ser.). (Illus.). 222p. pap. 49.95 *(978-0-387-76985-1(4)*, 0387769854) Springer.

Weinberger, Susanne. Warfare in the Austrian Weinviertel during the Early Bronze Age. 2008. (Mitteilungen der Prahistorischen Kommission Ser.). (Illus.). 125p. (C). pap. 59.00 *(978-3-7001-3953-9(5))* Austrian Academy of Sciences Press AUT. Dist: Brown, David Bk. Co., The.

AUSTRALIA—ARMED FORCES

Beeston, Joseph Lievesley. Five Months at Anzac. 2007. (Illus.). 80p. per. *(978-1-4065-3736-9(5))* Dodo Pr.

Blaxland, John C. Strategic Cousins: Australian & Canadian Expeditionary Forces & the British & American Empires. 2006. (ENG., Illus.). 432p. (C). *(978-0-7735-3035-5(5))*; per. *(978-0-7735-3064-5(9))* McGill-Queen's Univ. Pr.

Bradley, Phillip. To Salamaua. 2010. (Australian Army History Ser.). (ENG., Illus.). xvii, 372p. 58.00 *(978-0-521-76390-5(8))* Cambridge Univ. Pr.

Buttsworth, Sara. Body Count - Gender & Soldier Identity in Australia & the United States. 2007. pap. *(978-3-8364-2797-5(4))* VDM Verlag Dr. Mueller e.K.

Cotton. East Timor, Australia & Regional Order. 2006. 208p. 39.95 *(978-0-415-42984-9(6))* Routledge.

De Vries, Susanna. To Hell & Back. Lt. ed. 2009. 320p. 29.99 *(978-0-7531-5690-2(3))* Isis Publishing Ltd. GBR. Dist: Ulverscroft Large Print Bks., Ltd.

Dean, Peter. The Architect of Victory: The Military Career of Lieutenant General Sir Frank Horton Berryman. 2011. (Australian Army History Ser.). (ENG., Illus.). 406p. 55.00 *(978-0-521-76685-2(0))* Cambridge Univ. Pr.

Etcell, Pamela May. Our Daily Bread - the Field Bakery & the Anzac Legend. 2008. 308p. pap. *(978-3-639-01982-7(2))* VDM Verlag Dr. Mueller e.K.

Fleming, Robert. The Australian Army in World War I. 2012. (Men-at-Arms Ser.). (ENG., Illus.). 48p. pap. 17.95 ***(978-1-84908-632-5(X))*** Osprey Publishing, Ltd. GBR. Dist: Random Hse., Inc.

Glenn, Russell W. Counterinsurgency in a Test Tube: Analyzing the Success of the Regional Assistance Mission to Solomon Islands (RAMSI) 2007. (Illus.). 190p. per. 30.00 *(978-0-8330-4027-5(8),* mg551) RAND Corp., The.

Gorman, Eugene. With the Twenty-Second: A History of the Twenty-Second Battalion, 1st Aif. 2009. 206p. pap. *(978-1-84734-929-3(3))* Naval & Military Pr., The.

Grey, Jeffrey. Australian Brass: The Career of Lieutenant General Sir Horace Robertson. 2009. (ENG.). 272p. pap. 38.99 *(978-0-521-12251-1(1))* Cambridge Univ. Pr.

—A Military History of Australia. 3rd rev. ed. 2008. (Illus.). 334p. pap. 42.00 *(978-0-521-69791-0(3))*; 348p. 90.00 *(978-0-521-87523-3(4))* Cambridge Univ. Pr.

Harvey, Norman K. From Anzac to the Hindenburg Line the History of the 9th Battalion Aif. 2009. 352p. pap. *(978-1-84734-927-9(7))* Naval & Military Pr., The.

Horner, David, et al, eds. Australian Peacekeeping: Sixty Years in the Field. 2009. (ENG., Illus.). 352p. pap. 46.00 *(978-0-521-73592-6(2))* Cambridge Univ. Pr.

James, Karl. The Hard Slog: Australians in the Bougainville Campaign, 1944-45. 2012. (Australian Army History Ser.). (ENG., Illus.). 336p. 60.00 ***(978-1-107-01732-0(7))*** Cambridge Univ. Pr.

Johnston, Mark. The Australian Army in World War II. 2007. (Elite Ser.). (ENG., Illus.). 64p. pap. 18.95 *(978-1-84603-123-6(0))* Osprey Publishing, Ltd. GBR. Dist: Random Hse., Inc.

Keown,A.W. Forward with the Fifth the Story of Five Years War Service, Fifth Inf Batt , a I F. 2009. 376p. pap. *(978-1-84574-700-8(3))* Naval & Military Pr., The.

Longmore, C. Old Sixteenth Being a Record of the 16th Battalion a I F , During the Great War. 2009. 298p. pap. *(978-1-84734-928-6(5))* Naval & Military Pr., The.

McPhedran, Ian. Soldiers Without Borders: Beyond the SAS - A Global Network of Brothers-in-Arms. 2008. (Illus.). 400p. *(978-0-7322-8555-5(0))* HarperCollins Pubs. Australia.

Murphy, Lyle Vincent. During the War I Rode A Horse: A Cheeky Story of the 10th Australian Light Horse 1914-1919. 2011. 244p. pap. 20.30 ***(978-1-4567-9672-3(0))*** AuthorHouse.

Olden, A. C. N. Westralian Cavalry in the War the Story of the Tenth Light Horse Regiment, a I F , in the Great War. 2009. 480p. pap. *(978-1-84734-930-9(7))* Naval & Military Pr., The.

Park, William. Australia's World War 2 Nominal Roll: Accurate record or true Record? 2009. 124p. pap. *(978-3-639-18008-4(9))* VDM Verlag Dr. Mueller e.K.

Richardson, J. D. History of the 7th Light Horse Regiment a I F. 2009. (Illus.). 164p. pap. *(978-1-84734-931-6(5))* Naval & Military Pr., The.

AUSTRALIA—BIOGRAPHY

Ager, Karen. Enemy Within: My Journey with Arthritis. 2010. (ENG., Illus.). 240p. 19.95 *(978-1-74110-850-7(0))* New Holland Pubs. Pty, Ltd. AUS. Dist: Tuttle Publishing.

Andre, Peter. Peter Andre: My Story. 2010. (ENG., Illus.). 274p. pap. 14.95 *(978-1-84454-918-4(6))* Blake, John Publishing, Ltd. GBR. Dist: Independent Pubs. Group.

Apter, Jeff. Fortunate Son: The Unlikely Rise of Keith Urban. 2009. (ENG., Illus.). 320p. pap. 19.95 *(978-1-74166-808-7(5))* Random Hse. Australia AUS. Dist: Independent Pubs. Group.

Arnim, Elizabeth Von. Christine. 2007. 92p. per. *(978-1-4068-4559-4(0))* Echo Library.

Aspinall, Julie. Kylie - Queen of the World. 2008. (ENG., Illus.). 262p. pap. 15.95 *(978-1-84454-587-2(3))* Blake, John Publishing, Ltd. GBR. Dist: Independent Pubs. Group.

Australia, Emigration. The Long Road Home. 2010. 245p. pap. 31.50 *(978-1-4452-7651-9(8))* Lulu Enterprises Inc.

Backhouse, Shane. The Master of the Keys. 2011. 304p. 29.99 ***(978-1-4535-9844-3(8))***; pap. 19.99 ***(978-1-4535-9843-6(X))*** Xlibris Corp.

Barnes, J. A. Humping my Drum. 2008. 482p. pap. 30.00 *(978-1-4092-0400-8(6))* Lulu Enterprises Inc.

Bassett, Jennifer. Ned Kelly: A True Story. Oxford University Press Staff, ed. 3rd ed. 2008. (ENG., Illus.). 64p. 9.38 *(978-0-19-478912-7(8))* Oxford Univ. Pr., Inc.

Bell, Gail. Poison: A History & a Family Memoir. Date not set. pap. *(978-0-312-30680-9(6),* St. Martin's Griffin); mass mkt. *(978-0-312-98563-9(0),* St. Martin's Paperbacks) St. Martin's Pr.

Benaud, Richie. Over but Not Out: My Story So Far. 2010. (ENG., Illus.). 404p. 32.95 *(978-1-4447-0592-8(X),* Hodder & Stoughton) Hodder General Publishing Div. GBR. Dist: Independent Pubs. Group.

—Over but Not Out - My Life So Far. 2011. (ENG., Illus.). 432p. pap. 14.95 *(978-1-4447-0593-5(8),* Hodder & Stoughton) Hodder General Publishing Div. GBR. Dist: Independent Pubs. Group.

Benge, Janet & Benge, Geoff. Christian Heroes - Then & Now - David Bussau: Facing the World Head-on. 2008. (ENG.). 206p. per. *(978-1-57658-415-6(1))* YWAM Publishing.

Bic-Calamus. Incomplete Memoirs of a Complete Breakdown. 2010. 134p. 22.50 *(978-1-60860-991-8(X),* Eloquent Bks.) AEG Literary Publishing Services, Inc.

Bijkerk, Pia Jane. My Heart Wanders: A Celebration of Taking Risks, Letting Go & Making a Home Wherever You Are. 2011. (ENG., Illus.). 304p. 55.00 ***(978-1-74196-746-3(5))*** Murdoch Bks. Pty Ltd. AUS. Dist: Independent Pubs. Group.

Bishop, Michael. They Found Our Engineer: The Story of Arthur Goddard. the Land Rover's first Engineer. 2011. 152p. pap. 22.02 ***(978-1-4567-7758-6(0))*** AuthorHouse.

Blackmore, J. T. Ludwig Boltzmann: His Later Life & Philosophy, 1900-1906: Book Two: the Philosopher. 2010. (Boston Studies in the Philosophy of Science Ser.). 340p. pap. 269.00 *(978-90-481-4547-8(3),* 9048145473) Springer.

Blair, Joe. By the Iowa Sea: A Memoir. 2012. (ENG.). 288p. 24.00 ***(978-1-4516-3605-5(9),*** Scribner) Scribner.

Blanch, Ben. Streets to Success. 2010. 397p. pap. 39.50 *(978-1-4461-4625-5(1))* Lulu Enterprises Inc.

Blottner, Gene. Wild Bill Elliott: A Complete Filmography. 2007. (ENG., Illus.). 328p. 55.00 *(978-0-7864-2986-8(0))* McFarland & Co., Inc. Pubs.

Blucher, Peter & Lynch, Alastair. Taking Nothing for Granted: A Sportsman's Fight Against Chronic Fatigue. 2008. 384p. *(978-0-7322-8811-2(8),* HarperSports) HarperCollins Pubs. Australia.

Bowen, Jill. Kidman the Forgotten King. 2007. *(978-0-7322-8610-1(7),* Fourth Estate) HarperCollins Pubs. Australia.

Brittingham, Margaret. Mom from down Under: A Book of Answered Prayer. 2011. pap. 10.99 *(978-1-61739-544-4(7))* Tate Publishing & Enterprises, LLC.

Bruhwiler, Mark A. From Seven Hills to the Seven Seas: A Memoir of A Boy Adrift. 2011. 204p. pap. 20.99 ***(978-1-4525-0238-0(2),*** BalboaPr.AU) Author Solutions, Inc.

Bryant, Louella. While in Darkness There Is Light: Idealism & Tragedy on an Australian Commune. 2008. (ENG.). 226p. pap. 16.00 *(978-0-9768993-9-6(6))* Black Lawrence Pr.

Bryden, Christine. Who Will I Be When I Die? 2012. (ENG., Illus.). 176p. pap. ***(978-1-84905-312-9(X))*** Kingsley, Jessica Ltd.

Burnette, Lisa. Learning to Walk. 2009. 224p. pap. 15.71 *(978-1-4092-7484-1(5))* Lulu Enterprises Inc.

Cadwallader, Alan, ed. In the Land of Larks & Heroes: Australian Reflections on St Mary MacKillop. 2010. (ENG.). 197p. pap. 40.00 *(978-1-921511-99-8(0))* ATF Pr. AUS. Dist: Brown, David Bk. Co., The.

Cambridge, Ada. Thirty Years in Australia. 2009. (ENG.). 313p. pap. 23.99 *(978-1-117-02765-4(1),* BiblioLife) BiblioBazaar.

—Thirty Years in Australia. 2008. 352p. 46.95 *(978-1-4374-3969-4(1))*; pap. 31.95 *(978-1-4373-5041-8(0))* Kessinger Publishing, LLC.

Campling, Christopher R. I Was Glad: The Memoirs of Christopher Campling, Dean Emeritus of Ripon Cathedral. 2007. (ENG., Illus.). 391p. pap. *(978-1-85756-616-1(5))* Janus Publishing Co.

Canton, Richard Todd. Russell Street Memories (A Sentimental Journey Home) This Way Is My Way. 2010. 100p. pap. 11.95 *(978-1-4502-4651-4(6))* iUniverse, Inc.

Chambers, Mason. Mason Chambers Adventures Through Life. 2010. (Illus.). 192p. pap. 14.49 *(978-1-4389-4759-4(3))* AuthorHouse.

Chessell, Gwen. Alexander Collie: Colonial Surgeon, Naturalist & Explorer. 2008. 224p. pap. 35.95 *(978-0-9802965-3-2(6))* UWA Publishing AUS. Dist: International Specialized Bk. Services.

Choules, Claude. The Last of the Last: The Final Survivor of the First World War. 2010. (ENG., Illus.). 224p. *(978-1-84596-631-7(7))* Mainstream Publishing Co., Ltd. GBR. Dist: Independent Pubs. Group.

Clark, Walter James. Poor Little Wally! 2010. 140p. 29.99 *(978-1-4535-3461-8(X))*; pap. 19.99 *(978-1-4535-3460-1(1))* Xlibris Corp.

Clarke, Banjo & Chance, Camilla. Wisdom Man: Biography of Banjo Clarke. 2012. (ENG., Illus.). 304p. pap. 15.95 *(978-0-14-300345-8(3),* Penguin Global) Penguin Group (USA) Inc.

Clode, Danielle. Voyages to the South Seas: In Search of Terres Australes. 2007. (ENG., Illus.). 368p. 25.00 *(978-0-522-85264-6(5))* Melbourne Univ. Publishing AUS. Dist: Independent Pubs. Group.

Coffey, Tabatha. It's Not Really about the Hair: The Honest Truth about Life, Love, & the Business of Beauty. 2012. (ENG.). 224p. pap. 14.99 ***(978-0-06-210395-6(4))*** HarperCollins Pubs.

Coleman, Peter, et al. Arndt's Story: The Life of an Australian Economist. 2007. (Illus.). 338p. pap. *(978-0-7315-3810-2(2))* Asia Pacific Pr. AUS. Dist: International Specialized Bk. Services.

Collins, Bud & Laver, Rod. The Education of a Tennis Player. 2010. (ENG.). 300p. pap. 19.95 *(978-0-942257-62-5(6))* New Chapter Pr., Inc.

Cook, Pam. Baz Luhrmann. 2010. (ENG., Illus.). 208p. pap. 26.00 *(978-1-84457-158-1(0))*; 228p. 85.00 *(978-1-84457-157-4(2))* BFI Publishing GBR. Dist: Macmillan.

Cooke, Cameron William. Symphony. 2010. 308p. pap. 19.99 *(978-1-4500-3411-1(X))* Xlibris Corp.

Cool, Catherine. Each in His Lonely Night. 2007. 226p. pap. 14.95 *(978-0-7414-3973-4(5))* Infinity Publishing.

Cool, Catherine. Vivid Air: Travels to a Further Shore. 2006. 345p. pap. *(978-0-7414-3697-9(3))* Infinity Publishing.

Crisp, David. My Life as an Orphan. 2008. (Illus.). 472p. pap. *(978-1-84748-214-3(7))* Athena Pr.

Cummins, Michael. Afraid of the Light: An Aussie's Journey from the Nightmare of Substance Abuse to the Love of Christ. 2007. 174p. per. 12.99 *(978-1-60247-152-8(5))* Tate Publishing & Enterprises, LLC.

Curran, James. Curtin's Empire. 2011. (ENG., Illus.). 652p. pap. 29.99 *(978-0-521-14622-7(4))* Cambridge Univ. Pr.

Dalton, Robin, contrib. by. An Incidental Memoir. (Illus.). 400p. *(978-0-670-88187-1(2))* Penguin Group (USA) Inc.

Dargavel, John. The Zealous Conservator: A Life of Charles Lane Poole. 2008. 252p. pap. 26.95 *(978-1-921401-14-5(1))* UWA Publishing AUS. Dist: International Specialized Bk. Services.

Dauer, J. C., et al. Australian History 1901 - 2001 As Seen Through Banknotes. 2007. (Illus.). ***(978-0-9728466-1-5(1))*** Dauer, M.D., Edward A.

Davey, Paul. Politics in the Blood: The Anthonys of Richmond. 2008. (ENG., Illus.). 432p. pap. 44.95 *(978-1-921410-23-9(X),* UNSW Press) NewSouth Publishing AUS. Dist: Independent Pubs. Group.

Day, David. Andrew Fisher. 2008. (Illus.). 512p. *(978-0-7322-7610-2(1),* Fourth Estate) HarperCollins Pubs. Australia.

—Chifley: A Life. 2007. *(978-0-7322-7997-4(6),* HarperPerennial) HarperCollins Pubs. Australia.

De Vries, Susanna. Desert Queen: The Many Lives & Loves of Daisy Bates. 2008. (Illus.). 304p. *(978-0-7322-8243-1(8))* HarperCollins Pubs. Australia.

—To Hell & Back. Lt. ed. 2009. 320p. 29.99 *(978-0-7531-5690-2(3))* Isis Publishing Ltd. GBR. Dist: Ulverscroft Large Print Bks., Ltd.

Dean, Peter. The Architect of Victory: The Military Career of Lieutenant General Sir Frank Horton Berryman. 2011. (Australian Army History Ser.). (ENG., Illus.). 406p. 55.00 *(978-0-521-76685-2(0))* Cambridge Univ. Pr.

DeVrye, Catherine. Serendipity Road: A Memoir. 2008. (ENG., Illus.). 356p. pap. 24.95 *(978-1-55278-645-1(5))* McArthur & Co. CAN. Dist: National Bk. Network.

Dewing, Dorothy. Bloody Pommies! 2009. (Illus.). 280p. pap. 15.49 *(978-1-4389-7694-5(1))* AuthorHouse.

Dixon, Robert & Lee, Christopher, eds. The Diaries of Frank Hurley 1912-1944. 2011. (Anthem Studies in Travel Ser.). (ENG., Illus.). 302p. 99.00 *(978-0-85728-774-8(5))*; pap. 40.00 *(978-0-85728-775-5(3))* Anthem Pr. GBR. Dist: Books International, Inc.

Donovan, Jason. Between the Lines: My Story Uncut. 2008. (ENG., Illus.). 336p. 15.95 *(978-0-00-726442-1(9))* HarperCollins Pubs. Ltd. GBR. Dist: Independent Pubs. Group.

Dousset, Ray. Rotor in the Green. 2007. 408p. per. 21.99 *(978-1-60266-316-9(5))* Xulon Pr., Inc.

Drury, Nevill. Homage to Pan: The Life, Art & Sex-Magic of Rosaleen Norton. 2010. (Illus.). 255p. pap. *(978-1-902197-26-5(7))* Oneiros Bks.

Eason, Alan. The A-Z of Bradman: A Comprehensive Companion to the Life & Career of the Don - Extraordinary Cricketer & Legendary Australian. 2009. (ENG.). 448p. pap. 34.95 *(978-1-921372-16-2(8))* Scribe Pubns. AUS. Dist: Independent Pubs. Group.

Easton, Robin. Naked in Eden: My Adventure & Awakening in the Australian Rainforest. 2010. (ENG.). 360p. 24.95 *(978-0-7573-1512-1(7))* Health Communications, Inc.

Eden, Charles Henry. Australian Search Party. Bates, Henry Walter, ed. 2007. (ENG.). 80p. per. *(978-1-4065-1642-5(2))* Dodo Pr.

Edmond, Martin. Luca Antara. 2008. (ENG., Illus.). 288p. pap. 19.95 *(978-1-84243-289-1(3))* Oldcastle Bks., Ltd. GBR. Dist: Independent Pubs. Group.

—Luca Antara: Passages in Search of Australia. (ENG., Illus.). 2010. 272p. pap. 16.95 *(978-1-84243-319-5(9))* 2008. 288p. 32.95 *(978-1-84243-272-3(9))* Oldcastle Bks., Ltd. GBR. Dist: Independent Pubs. Group.

Errington, Wayne & Van Onselen, Peter. John Winston Howard: The Biography. 2007. (ENG., Illus.). 440p. 38.00 *(978-0-522-85334-6(X),* Melbourne University Pr.) Melbourne Univ. Publishing AUS. Dist: Independent Pubs. Group.

Evans, Mark. Dirty Deeds: My Life Inside/Outside of AC/DC. 2011. (ENG.). 288p. pap. 19.95 *(978-1-935950-04-2(5))* Bazillion Points.

Ewbank, Tim. Olivia: The Biography of Olivia Newton-John. 2012. (ENG., Illus.). 320p. pap. 14.95 ***(978-0-7499-0984-0(6))*** Little, Brown Bk. Group Ltd. GBR. Dist: Independent Pubs. Group.

Farram, Steven. Charles 'Moth' Eaton: Pioneer Aviator of the Northern Territory. 2007. (Illus.). 70p. pap. *(978-0-9803846-1-1(3))* Darwin, Charles Univ. Pr.

Faulkner, Samantha. Life B'long Ali Drummond: A Life in the Torres Strait. 2007. (ENG., Illus.). 140p. pap. 22.45 *(978-0-85575-556-0(3))* Aboriginal Studies Pr. AUS. Dist: Independent Pubs. Group.

Fearne, Paul. Diary of a Schizophrenic. 2010. 176p. pap. *(978-1-84991-157-3(6))* Chipmunkapublishing.

Fekadu, Tewodros. No One's Son: The remarkable true story of a defiant African boy & his bold quest for Freedom. 2012. (ENG., Illus.). 560p. pap. 19.95 ***(978-1-935248-26-2(X))*** Leapfrog Pr.

Fertig, Dennis. Rupert Murdoch. 2012. (Titans of Business Ser.). (ENG.). 48p. (gr. 4-6). pap. 8.99 ***(978-1-4329-6438-2(0))***; lib. bdg. 32.00 ***(978-1-4329-6431-3(3))*** Heinemann-Raintree. (NA-h).

Fewster, Kevin, ed. Bean's Gallipoli: The Diaries of Australia's Official War Correspondent. 2009. (ENG.). 292p. pap. 19.95 *(978-1-74175-733-0(9))* Allen & Unwin AUS. Dist: Independent Pubs. Group.

Fitch, Ron J. Australian Railwayman. 2006. (Illus.). 248p. pap. 35.00 *(978-1-877058-48-6(3))* Rosenberg Publishing Pty, Ltd. AUS. Dist: International Specialized Bk. Services.

Foster, Chrissie. Hell on the Way to Heaven: An Australian Mother's Love - The Power of the Catholic Church, & a Fight for Justice over Child Sexual Abuse. 2010. (ENG., Illus.). 391p. 27.95 *(978-1-74166-952-7(9))* Random Hse. Australia AUS. Dist: Independent Pubs. Group.

Fowler, Andrew. The Most Dangerous Man in the World: A Definitive Account of Julian Assange & WikiLeaks. 2011. (ENG.). 288p. 24.95 *(978-1-61608-489-9(8),* 608489) Skyhorse Publishing Co., Inc.

Friend, Kerrie. Image: 52 Weeks to a New You. 2006. 176p. per. *(978-1-921005-20-6(3))* Zeus Pubns.

Gabbrielli, Emilio. Polenta & Goann. McGilvray, Barbara, tr. 2008. 240p. pap. *(978-88-95145-23-5(2))* Italian Paths of Culture.

Gentle Satan: Growing up with Australia's Most Notorious Crime Boss. 2009. (Illus.). pap. 19.95 *(978-0-615-28629-7(1))* Polaris Entertainment.

Gibbons, Alice. Where the Earth Ends. 2009. 284p. pap. 16.99 *(978-1-60791-571-3(5))* Xulon Pr., Inc.

Gibson, Geoffrey. The Taciturn Man: And Other Tales of Australia. 2011. 116p. ***(978-1-61599-121-1(2))***; pap. ***(978-1-61599-120-4(4))*** Loving Healing Pr., Inc. (Modern History Pr.).

Goldsworthy, Anna. Piano Lessons: A Memoir. 2010. (ENG.). 256p. 24.99 *(978-0-312-64628-8(3))* St. Martin's Pr.

Graham, Stanley. An Australian Life. 2010. 390p. pap. 31.50 *(978-1-4457-4826-9(6))* Lulu Enterprises Inc.

Gray, Anne. George W. Lambert Retrospective: Heroes & Icons. 2008. (Illus.). 212p. *(978-0-642-54127-7(2))*; pap. *(978-0-642-54121-5(3))* National Gallery of Australia.

Greenhalgh, Alan. The Glass Half Full. 2007. 264p. 35.50 *(978-1-84753-381-4(7))* Lulu Enterprises Inc.

Grey, Jeffrey. Australian Brass: The Career of Lieutenant General Sir Horace Robertson. 2009. (ENG.). 272p. pap. 38.99 *(978-0-521-12251-1(1))* Cambridge Univ. Pr.

Griffin, James Thomas. John Wren: A Life Reconsidered. 2007. (ENG., Illus.) 448p. per. 24.95 *(978-1-920769-48-2(X))* Scribe Pubns. AUS. Dist: Independent Pubs. Group.

Griffiths, Anthony. Hugh Jackman: The Biography. 2012. (ENG.). 288p. 24.95 *(978-1-84454-904-7(6))* Blake, John Publishing, Ltd. GBR. Dist: Independent Pubs. Group.

Hall, John Vine. Hope for the Hopeless an Autobiography of John Vine Hall Ed by Rev Newman Hall Abridged with the Author's Sanction. 2006. 276p. per. 23.99 *(978-1-4255-2453-1(2))* MPublishing.

Hall, Lincoln. Dead Lucky: Life after Death on Mount Everest. 2009. (ENG.). 336p. (gr. 12-18). pap. 15.95 *(978-1-58542-719-2(5),* Tarcher) Penguin Group (USA) Inc.

Hall, Sandra. Tabloid Man: The Life & Times of Ezra Norton. 2008. (Illus.). 352p. *(978-0-7322-8259-2(4),* Fourth Estate) HarperCollins Pubs. Australia.

Heard, Barry. The View from Connor's Hill: A Memoir. 2008. (ENG.). 267p. pap. 24.95 *(978-1-921215-48-3(8))* Scribe Pubns. AUS. Dist: Independent Pubs. Group.

Heaton, J. H., ed. Australian Dictionary of Dates & Men of the Time: Containing the History of Australasia from 1542 to Date. 2011. (Cambridge Library Collection - History Ser.). (ENG.). 568p. pap. 39.99 ***(978-1-108-03904-8(3))*** Cambridge Univ. Pr.

Herbert, Emily. Katie V Peter - the Inside Story Of. 2010. (ENG., Illus.). 266p. pap. 12.95 *(978-1-84454-927-6(5))* Blake, John Publishing, Ltd. GBR. Dist: Independent Pubs. Group.

Hill, Holly. Sugarbabe: The Controversial Real Story of a Woman in Search of a Sugar Daddy. 2010. (ENG.). 304p. pap. 16.95 *(978-1-61608-034-1(5),* 608034) Skyhorse Publishing Co., Inc.

Hind, Jane. Green Fields & Red Paddocks: The Leaving of England. 2007. (Illus.). 132p. per. *(978-1-84748-052-1(7))* Athena Pr.

Hodge, Shane. The Comeback: The Things That Matter? Are the Things that Matter. 2011. 222p. pap. 21.99 ***(978-1-60746-399-3(7))*** FastPencil, Inc.

Homan, Berni. A Drop of Rain. 2011. 204p. 29.99 ***(978-1-4568-2780-9(4))***; pap. 19.99 ***(978-1-4568-2779-3(0))*** Xlibris Corp.

Horton, Robert. Jim. 2010. 164p. pap. 13.69 *(978-1-4269-2457-6(7))* Trafford Publishing.

Howitt, Bob & Deaker, John. The Converts: Changing Codes. 2008. (Illus.). 271p. *(978-1-86950-636-0(7))* HarperCollins Pubs. Australia.

Hughes, Annette. Art Life Chooks: Learning to Leave the City & Love the Country. 2008. 304p. *(978-0-7322-8689-7(1),* Fourth Estate) HarperCollins Pubs. Australia.

Hughes, Richard. Foreign Devil: Thirty Years of Reporting in the Far East. 2008. (ENG.). 336p. per. 18.95 *(978-1-933698-17-5(9))* 1500 Bks.

Hughes, Robert. Things I Didn't Know. 2007. (Vintage Ser.). (ENG.). 416p. pap. 15.95 *(978-0-307-38598-7(1),* Vintage) Knopf Doubleday Publishing Group.

Hurlston, David. Ron Mueck. 2011. (Illus.). 192p. pap. 30.00 *(978-0-300-17683-4(X))* Yale Univ. Pr.

Huynh, Kim. Where the Sea Takes Us: A Vietnamese-Australian Story. 2008. 368p. *(978-0-7322-8560-9(7),* HarperPerennial) HarperCollins Pubs. Australia.

Hwa, Candy. Dedicated to You. 2010. 214p. 29.99 *(978-1-4535-0095-8(2))*; pap. 19.99 *(978-1-4535-0094-1(4))* Xlibris Corp.

Incognito, R. Bodycage: A transgender Autobiography. 2008. 500p. pap. *(978-1-84747-709-5(7))* Chipmunkapublishing.

Irwin, Terri. Steve & Me. 2008. (ENG.). 288p. pap. 15.95 *(978-1-4169-5474-3(0))* Gallery Pr., The IRL. Dist: Simon & Schuster, Inc.

—Steve & Me: Life with the Crocodile Hunter. l.t. ed. 2008. (Thorndike Biography Ser.). (Illus.). 385p. 30.95 *(978-1-4104-0352-0(1))* Thorndike Pr.

Jacobs, Paul Gordon. Neither-nor: A Young Australian's Experience with Deafness. 2007. (Gallaudet New Deaf Lives Ser.). (ENG., Illus.). 176p. per. 29.95 *(978-1-56368-350-3(4))* Gallaudet Univ. Pr.

James, Clive. North Face of Soho. 3rd ed. 2007. (ENG.). 272p. 19.95 *(978-0-330-48127-4(4)*, Picador) Pan Macmillan GBR. Dist: Trans-Atlantic Pubns., Inc.

Jellay, Val. So You Want to Be in Show Business? 2009. 330p. pap. 35.00 *(978-0-9802836-3-1(9))* JoJo Publishing AUS. Dist: International Publishers Marketing.

Jenkin, John. William & Lawrence Bragg, Father & Son: The Most Extraordinary Collaboration in Science. 2011. (ENG., Illus.). 500p. pap. 45.00 *(978-0-19-960670-2(6))* Oxford Univ. Pr., Inc.

Johns, Andrew & Cadigan, Neil. The Two of Me. 2008. (Illus.). 496p. *(978-0-7322-8654-5(9))* HarperCollins Pubs. Australia.

Johnston, Ian M. Tractors, Kalashnikovs & Green Tea: My Life of Tractors & Travels. 2011. (Illus.). 320p. 39.95 ***(978-1-921719-04-2(4))*** Rosenberg Publishing Pty, Ltd. AUS. Dist: International Specialized Bk. Services.

Jolly, Dick. Wreck Rescue & Salvage. 2006. (Illus.). 176p. pap. *(978-1-904445-42-5(X))* Whittles Publishing.

Kadiba, John. Night Dreams of Passing Memories. 2011. 214p. 29.99 ***(978-1-4628-8740-8(6))***; pap. 19.99 ***(978-1-4628-8739-2(2))*** Xlibris Corp.

Kay, Hanna. Notes from the Shed: A Journal. rev. ed. 2007. (Illus.). 208p. (C). pap. 40.00 *(978-1-876832-58-2(4))* Macmillan Art Publishing AUS. Dist: Brown, David Bk. Co., The.

Keneally, Thomas. A Commonwealth of Thieves: The Improbable Birth of Australia. 2007. (ENG., Illus.). 400p. pap. 16.00 *(978-1-4000-7956-8(X)*, Anchor) Knopf Doubleday Publishing Group.

Kennelly, Tadhg. Tadhg Kennelly: Unfinished Business. 2010. (ENG., Illus.). 286p. pap. 30.95 *(978-1-85635-639-8(6))* Mercier Pr., Ltd., The IRL. Dist: Dufour Editions, Inc.

King, J. E., ed. A Biographical Dictionary of Australian & New Zealand Economists. 2007. (Elgar Original Reference Ser.). 360p. (C). 198.00 *(978-1-84542-869-3(2))* Elgar, Edward Publishing, Inc.

Kirkwood, Ray. Variant Breed: Confessions of a Light-Keeper. 2010. pap. *(978-1-921578-43-4(2))* BookPal.

Krumins-Caldwell, Gunta. On Silver Wings. 2011. 168p. pap. 13.95 ***(978-1-60860-284-1(2)***, Eloquent Bks.) AEG Literary Publishing Services, Inc.

Lance, Kate. Alan Villiers: Voyager of the Winds. 2009. (ENG., Illus.). 320p. 34.95 *(978-0-948065-95-8(8))* National Maritime Museum GBR. Dist: Independent Pubs. Group.

Laney, Don W. Charley's Boys: St. Bernard College in the Sixties. 2010. 112p. 21.49 *(978-1-4520-2464-6(2))*; pap. 16.95 *(978-1-4520-2465-3(0))* AuthorHouse.

Lange, Gerhard H. F. How i became an Australian. 2007. 68p. pap. 6.50 *(978-1-84753-884-0(3))* Lulu Enterprises Inc.

Lee, Francis. Out of Bounds: Journey of a Migrant. 2010. 282p. pap. 19.99 *(978-1-4535-3476-2(8))*; 302p. 29.99 *(978-1-4500-1714-5(2))*; 302p. pap. 19.99 *(978-1-4500-1713-8(4))* Xlibris Corp.

Leonard, Tracey. The Full Catastrophe. 2010. 300p. pap. *(978-1-58768-061-8(0)*, HiddenSpring) Paulist Pr.

Les Thompson. Hello Ego! A Personal Journey through the World of Broadcasting. 2009. 420p. 37.26 *(978-1-4269-1720-2(1))*; pap. 27.26 *(978-1-4269-1719-6(8))* Trafford Publishing.

Linds, T. J. In Focus. 2009. 103p. pap. 17.57 *(978-1-4092-9682-9(2))* Lulu Enterprises Inc.

Livermore, Colette. Hope Endures: Leaving Mother Teresa, Losing Faith, & Searching for Meaning. 2008. (ENG., Illus.). 272p. 25.00 *(978-1-4165-9361-4(6)*, Free Pr.) Free Pr.

Lowe, David Michael. Australian Between Empires: The Life of Percy Spender, 1 vol. 2010. (Empires in Perspective Ser.). (ENG., Illus.). 256p. 99.00 *(978-1-84893-000-1(3))* Pickering & Chatto Pubs., Ltd. GBR. Dist: Ashgate Publishing Co.

Lowman, Margaret D., et al. It's a Jungle up There: More Tales from the Treetops. 2008. (ENG., Illus.). 320p. pap. 18.00 *(978-0-300-12923-6(8))* Yale Univ. Pr.

Marsden, J.B. Memoirs of the Life & Labours of the Rev. Samuel Marsden of Paramatta, Senior Chaplain of New South Wales: And of his Early Connexion with the Missions to New Zealand & Tahiti. 2011. (Cambridge Library Collection - Religion Ser.). (ENG., Illus.). 342p. pap. 28.99 ***(978-1-108-03891-1(3))*** Cambridge Univ. Pr.

Marsh, Nigel. Fat, Forty, & Fired: One Man's Frank, Funny, & Inspiring Account of Losing His Job & Finding His Life. 2007. (ENG.). 288p. 19.95 *(978-0-7407-6433-2(0))* Andrews McMeel Publishing.

Martin, A. W. Robert Menzies: A Life Volume I. 2009. 460p. 68.00 *(978-1-59740-302-3(4))* ACLS Humanities E-Book.

—Robert Menzies: A Life Volume II. 620p. 2009. 92.00 *(978-1-59740-303-0(2))* 2008. pap. 62.00 *(978-1-59740-670-3(8))* ACLS Humanities E-Book.

Martin, Robert Dickson. My Seven Dinner Guests. 2010. 490p. 34.50 *(978-1-60860-336-7(9)*, Eloquent Bks.) AEG Literary Publishing Services, Inc.

Masel, Deborah. Soul to Soul: Writings from Dark Places. 2011. ***(978-965-229-559-0(0))*** Gefen Bks.

Mawer, Allen. Diary of a Spitfire Pilot: Over the English Channel & over Darwin. 2011. (Illus.). 224p. pap. 29.95 *(978-1-921719-18-9(4))* Rosenberg Publishing Pty, Ltd. AUS. Dist: International Specialized Bk. Services.

Maylor, Rob & Macklin, Robert. Sniper Elite: The World of a Top Special Forces Marksman. 2011. (ENG., Illus.). 352p. 25.99 *(978-0-312-64541-0(4))* St. Martin's Pr.

McColl-Jones, Mike. Graham Kennedy Treasures: Friends Remember the King. 2008. (ENG.). 272p. 56.00 *(978-0-522-85545-6(8))* Melbourne Univ. Publishing AUS. Dist: Independent Pubs. Group.

McCormack, Chris. I'm Here to Win: A World Champion's Advice for Peak Performance. 2011. (ENG., Illus.). 288p. 27.99 *(978-1-4555-0267-7(7))* Center St.

McCracken, Robert. Under down Under: A local bloke born in Kalgoorlie. 2007. 556p. per. 32.95 *(978-0-595-44791-6(0))* iUniverse, Inc.

McKay, Gary. Going Back: Australian Veterans Return to Viet Nam. 2008. (ENG.). 228p. pap. 19.95 *(978-1-74114-634-9(8))* Allen & Unwin AUS. Dist: Independent Pubs. Group.

McKeough, Sue. A Destiny to Be Reached. 2009. 268p. 27.50 *(978-1-60693-978-9(5)*, Strategic Bk. Publishing) AEG Literary Publishing Services, Inc.

McMillan, David. Escape: the Past: 'Living Fast' Redefined As Bangkok Hilton Escapee David Mcmillan Opens His Past As A Teenage Drug-Trafficker. 2012. (ENG., Illus.). 264p. pap. 16.95 ***(978-981-4358-27-9(4))*** Monsoon Bks. Pte. Ltd.

McMullin, Ross. Pompey Elliot. 2009. (ENG.). 736p. pap. 34.95 *(978-1-921372-01-8(X))* Scribe Pubns. AUS. Dist: Independent Pubs. Group.

Mellor, Ken. Urban Mystic, Discovering the Transcendent Through Everyday Life. 2009. 472p. pap. 22.25 *(978-1-60693-823-2(1)*, Strategic Bk. Publishing) AEG Literary Publishing Services, Inc.

Merz, Mischa. The Sweetest Thing: A Boxer's Memoir. 2011. (ENG., Illus.). 304p. pap. 18.95 *(978-1-58322-928-6(0))* Seven Stories Pr.

Millar, Ann & Browne, Geoffrey, eds. The Biographical Dictionary of the Australian Senate, 1963-2009, Vol. 3. 2010. (Biographical Dictionary of the Australian Senate Ser.). (ENG., Illus.). 608p. 65.00 *(978-0-86840-996-2(0)*, UNSW Press) NewSouth Publishing AUS. Dist: Independent Pubs. Group.

Mills, Dean. Dollar & A Dream. 2007. pap. 13.00 *(978-0-8059-8563-4(8))* Dorrance Publishing Co., Inc.

Moore, Laurie & Williams, Stephan. True Story of Jimmy Governor: Killing Us Every Day. (Illus.). 256p. 18.95 *(978-1-86508-481-7(6))* Allen & Unwin AUS. Dist: Independent Pubs. Group.

Moorehead, Alan. Cooper's Creek: Tragedy & Adventure in the Australian Outback. 2010. (ENG.). 224p. pap. 14.95 *(978-1-61608-022-8(1)*, 608022) Skyhorse Publishing Co., Inc.

Mumford, Stephen. David Armstrong. 2007. (Philosophy Now Ser.). (ENG.). 216p. (C). *(978-0-7735-3330-1(3))*; (Illus.). per. *(978-0-7735-3331-8(1))* McGill-Queen's Univ. Pr.

Munday, Don. Tin Dog, Damper & Dust: A Shearer's Life. (Illus.). 248p. pap. 16.95 *(978-1-875560-06-6(8))* UWA Publishing AUS. Dist: International Specialized Bk. Services.

Nesling, John. The Long Way Round: An Extended Journey Through the Lands down Under. 2006. (ENG., Illus.). 284p. per. 21.23 *(978-1-4120-8791-9(0))* Trafford Publishing.

Newkey-Burden, Chas. Dannii Minogue: The Biography. 2010. (ENG., Illus.). 256p. pap. 12.95 *(978-1-84454-959-7(3))* Blake, John Publishing, Ltd. GBR. Dist: Independent Pubs. Group.

Nguyen, Pauline & Nguyen, Luke. Secrets of the Red Lantern: Stories & Vietnamese Recipes from the Heart. 2008. (ENG.). 344p. 40.00 *(978-0-7407-7743-1(2))* Andrews McMeel Publishing.

Niall, Brenda. Life Class: The Education of a Biographer. 2007. (ENG., Illus.). 224p. 25.00 *(978-0-522-85343-8(9))* Melbourne Univ. Publishing AUS. Dist: Independent Pubs. Group.

Noever, Peter, et al, eds. Alois Riegl Revisited: Beiträge zu Werk und Rezeption - Contributions to the Opus & its Reception. 2010. (VERoFFENTLICHUNGEN der KOMMISSION FuR KUNSTGESCHICHTE Ser.). 148p. (C). pap. 73.00 *(978-3-7001-6498-2(X))* Austrian Academy of Sciences Press AUT. Dist: Brown, David Bk. Co., The.

Norman, Phillip. Sex, Drugs & Hospitality. 2008. (Illus.). 92p. per. *(978-1-84748-101-6(9))* Athena Pr.

O'Brien, Chris. Never Say Die. 2008. 320p. *(978-0-7322-8809-9(6))* HarperCollins Pubs. Australia.

Obrist, Hans Ulrich, ed. Maria Lassnig: The Pen Is the Sister of the Brush, 1943-1997, 1 vol. 2010. (ENG., Illus.). 192p. 44.00 *(978-3-86521-739-4(7))* Steidl, Gerhard Druckerei und Verlag DEU. Dist: Innovative Logistics.

Page, Charles. Wings of Destiny: Wing Commander Charles Learmonth DFC & Bar, & the Air War in New Guinea. 2008. (Illus.). 416p. pap. 35.00 *(978-1-877058-64-6(5))* Rosenberg Publishing Pty, Ltd. AUS. Dist: International Specialized Bk. Services.

Page, Jack. Swatting Lizards in Bangkok. 2009. 220p. pap. 15.99 *(978-1-60791-852-3(8))* Xulon Pr., Inc.

Pascarl, Jacqueline. Since I Was A Princess. 2008. 384p. *(978-0-7322-8597-5(6))* HarperCollins Pubs. Australia.

Pedley, Derek. The Outlaw's Story. 2007. (ENG., Illus.). 328p. per. 19.95 *(978-1-84454-418-9(4))* Blake, John Publishing, Ltd. GBR. Dist: Independent Pubs. Group.

Petersen, Bob. Peter Jackson: A Biography of the Australian Heavyweight Champion, 1860-1901. 2011. (ENG., Illus.). 260p. pap. 39.95 *(978-0-7864-5881-3(X))* McFarland & Co., Inc. Pubs.

Pickering, Sam. A Tramp's Wallet. 2011. 272p. pap. 25.00 *(978-0-88146-235-7(7))* Mercer Univ. Pr.

Plant, Richard. Life's a Blur. 2011. 192p. 26.95 *(978-1-4502-9357-0(3))*; pap. 16.95 *(978-1-4502-9352-5(2))* iUniverse, Inc.

—Life's A Brew: A Laugh in A Glass. 2011. 176p. 25.95 ***(978-1-4620-2905-1(1))***; pap. 15.95 ***(978-1-4620-2906-8(X))*** iUniverse, Inc.

—Life's A Buzz (2) 2011. 276p. 30.95 ***(978-1-4620-4636-2(3))***; pap. 20.95 ***(978-1-4620-4637-9(1))*** iUniverse, Inc.

Pollack, Adam J. In the Ring with Bob Fitzsimmons. 2007. ***(978-0-9799822-0-0(0))*** Pollack, Adam J.

Price, John. Memoir of George Swan Fowler Christian Merchant. 2009. 120p. pap. 26.45 *(978-1-4446-2276-8(5))* Audubon Pr. & Christian Bk. Service.

Rainbow, K. M. A Dragon Whisperer's Guide to Love. 2009. 196p. pap. 23.99 *(978-1-4452-2008-6(3))* Lulu Enterprises Inc.

Riktam, Barry. The Telling Stones. 2011. 212p. pap. ***(978-0-9566432-5-4(6))*** Non-Duality Bks.

Roberts, Chris. A Tribute to Heath Ledger: The Illustrated Biography. 2009. (ENG., Illus.). 112p. pap. 19.95 *(978-1-84732-169-5(0))* Carlton Bks., Ltd. GBR. Dist: Sterling Publishing Co., Inc.

Robinson, Deborah. Daisy Bates: In Her Own Words. Peyton, Dianne, ed. 2007. 240p. per. 50.00 *(978-0-9709263-2-6(4))* Robinson Omnimedia Publishing & Studios.

Ruston, David. A Life with Roses. 2011. (Illus.). 288p. 49.95 *(978-1-921719-09-7(5))* Rosenberg Publishing Pty, Ltd. AUS. Dist: International Specialized Bk. Services.

Ryan, Christian. Golden Boy: Kim Hughes & the Bad Old Days of Australian Cricket. 2010. (ENG., Illus.). 460p. 24.95 ***(978-1-74237-463-5(8))*** Allen & Unwin AUS. Dist: Independent Pubs. Group.

Sais, George. Living Lies. 2010. 280p. 29.99 *(978-1-4535-2078-9(3))* Xlibris Corp.

Santer, Lynn. Beyond World Safari. 2009. 236p. pap. 25.95 *(978-0-9803547-5-1(7))* JoJo Publishing AUS. Dist: International Publishers Marketing.

Sawers, Brian. The Sawers from Pitcairn. 2010. 258p. 29.99 *(978-1-4500-4786-9(6))* Xlibris Corp.

Scott, Denise. The Tour. 2012. (ENG.). 244p. pap. 26.95 ***(978-1-74066-905-4(3))*** Hardie Grant Bks. AUS. Dist: Independent Pubs. Group.

Sherborne, Craig & Scott, Jeremy. Dancing on Ice: A 1930s Arctic Adventure. 2010. (ENG.). 272p. (gr. 6). pap. 14.95 *(978-1-905847-76-1(9))* Old Street Publishing GBR. Dist: Consortium Bk. Sales & Distribution.

Sheridan, Simon. The Complete Kylie. 25th ed. 2012. (ENG.). 304p. 24.95 ***(978-0-85768-725-8(5)***, Titan Bks.) Titan Bks. Ltd. GBR. Dist: Random Hse., Inc.

Shute, Jason. Henry Ayers: The Man Who Became a Rock. 2011. (ENG., Illus.). 288p. 45.00 *(978-1-84885-563-2(X))* I. B. Tauris & Co., Ltd. GBR. Dist: Macmillan.

Simms, John. Stay Young in Old Age. 2011. 164p. pap. 19.99 ***(978-1-4568-8300-3(3))*** Xlibris Corp.

Simon, Bill, et al. Back on the Block: Bill Simon's Story. 2009. (ENG., Illus.). 224p. pap. 31.95 *(978-0-85575-677-2(2))* Aboriginal Studies Pr. AUS. Dist: Independent Pubs. Group.

Smith, Babette. A Cargo of Women: Susannah Watson & the Convicts of the Princess Royal. 2nd ed. 2008. (ENG., Illus.). 321p. 27.95 *(978-1-74175-551-0(4))* Allen & Unwin AUS. Dist: Independent Pubs. Group.

Smith, Cathy. The Adventures of Henry Dent: Farmer, Poet, Gold Digger, Sawyer. 2010. 92p. pap. 11.49 *(978-1-4520-8102-1(6))* AuthorHouse.

Smith, Charles. Ya Think So! 2011. 432p. pap. 22.95 ***(978-1-4327-6380-0(6))*** Outskirts Pr., Inc.

Spence, Catherine Helen & Spence, Catherine Helen. An Autobiography. 2010. (Illus.). 114p. pap. 20.40 *(978-1-153-58566-8(9))* General Bks. LLC.

—An Autobiography. 2010. 140p. 35.95 *(978-1-161-42124-8(6))* Kessinger Publishing, LLC.

Spence, Catherine Helen. An Autobiography. 2008. 176p. 25.99 *(978-0-554-22035-2(0))* 2008. 204p. 24.99 *(978-0-554-37582-3(6))* 2008. 204p. 27.99 *(978-0-554-28279-4(8))* 2008. 176p. 22.99 *(978-0-554-31338-2(3))* 2006. 184p. pap. 19.99 *(978-1-4264-1503-6(6))* BiblioBazaar.

—An Autobiography. 2008. 164p. pap. *(978-1-4065-9168-2(8))* Dodo Pr.

—An Autobiography. 2010. 140p. pap. 16.76 *(978-1-162-65259-7(4))*; 28.76 ***(978-1-169-25962-1(6))*** Kessinger Publishing, LLC.

—An Autobiography (Spence) 2007. (ENG.). 184p. pap. 19.99 *(978-1-4346-5051-1(0))*; 202p. pap. 22.99 *(978-1-4346-5052-8(9))* BiblioBazaar.

Stoldt, Erling. Wind in My Hair. 2010. 172p. pap. 12.50 *(978-1-60976-204-9(5)*, Eloquent Bks.) AEG Literary Publishing Services, Inc.

Stone, Chris. Coming Clean. 2011. 118p. 29.99 ***(978-1-4628-8252-6(8))***; pap. 19.99 ***(978-1-4628-8251-9(X))*** Xlibris Corp.

Strange, Carolyn, et al. Griffith Taylor: Visionary, Environmentalist, Explorer. 2008. (ENG., Illus.). 287p. pap. *(978-0-8020-9663-0(8))* Univ. of Toronto Pr.

Streidl, Max. Brought down to Be Raised Up. 2011. 84p. 24.99 ***(978-1-4653-0075-1(9))***; pap. 15.99 ***(978-1-4653-0074-4(0))*** Xlibris Corp.

Summers, Ronnie & Gee, Helen. Ronnie: Tasmanian Songman. 2010. (ENG., Illus.). 164p. pap. 21.95 *(978-1-921248-10-8(6))* Magabala Bks. AUS. Dist: Independent Pubs. Group.

Sutherland, Stan. In This Man's Army. 2010. 364p. pap. 23.95 *(978-1-4401-9861-8(6))* iUniverse, Inc.

Swindler, Daris R. New Britain Diary 1954: An Anthropologist's Journal. 2007. (ENG., Illus.). 150p. per. 18.95 *(978-0-9791921-1-1(0))* Ravenna Pr.

Thirring, Walter. The Joy of Discovery: Great Encounters along the Way. 2010. 208p. 48.00 *(978-981-4322-96-6(2))* World Scientific Publishing Co., Inc.

Thomson, David. Nicole Kidman. 2008. (Vintage Ser.). (ENG., Illus.). 304p. pap. 15.95 *(978-1-4000-7781-6(8)*, Vintage) Knopf Doubleday Publishing Group.

Torrevillas, Hermaneli. A Mystical Connection. 2011. 416p. 34.99 ***(978-1-4568-6917-5(5))***; pap. 23.99 ***(978-1-4568-6916-8(7))*** Xlibris Corp.

Upfield, Arthur. Up & down the Real Australia: Autobiographical Articles & the Murchison Murders. 2009. (ENG.). 248p. pap. 22.97 *(978-1-4092-5584-0(0))* Lulu Enterprises Inc.

Varlrynen, Tarja. Culture & International Conflict Resolution: A Critical Analysis of the Work of John Burton. 2010. (New Approaches to Conflict Analysis Ser.). (ENG.). 180p. pap. 32.95 *(978-0-7190-8140-8(8))* Manchester Univ. Pr. GBR. Dist: Macmillan.

Venn-Brown, Anthony. A Life of Unlearning: A Journey to Find the Truth. rev. ed. 2007. (ENG.). 400p. pap. 14.95 *(978-1-74110-546-9(3))* New Holland Pubs. Pty, Ltd. AUS. Dist: Tuttle Publishing.

Vickers-Rich, Patricia, et al. The Artist & the Scientists: Bringing Prehistory to Life, 1 vol. 2010. (ENG., Illus.). 320p. pap. 48.00 *(978-0-521-16299-9(8))* Cambridge Univ. Pr.

Wang, Gungwu & Asad Latif. Wang Gungwu: Junzi: Scholar-Gentleman in Conversation with Asad-Ul Iqbal Latif. 2010. (Illus.). xvii, 261p. ***(978-981-4311-53-3(7))*** Institute of Southeast Asian Studies.

Watkins, Robert. A Face in the Crowd. 2011. 202p. 29.99 ***(978-1-4568-3784-6(2))***; pap. 19.99 ***(978-1-4568-3783-9(4))*** Xlibris Corp.

Watson, Jessica. True Spirit: The True Story of a 16-Year-Old Who Sailed Solo, Nonstop & Unassisted Around the World. 2010. (ENG., Illus.). 368p. pap. 16.00 *(978-1-4516-1631-6(7)*, Beyond Words/Atria Bks.) Atria Bks.

Wickham, Tracey & Meares, Peter. Treading Water: My Life in & Out of the Pool. 2010. (ENG.). 400p. pap. 26.95 *(978-1-74166-951-0(0))* Random Hse. Australia AUS. Dist: Independent Pubs. Group.

Wilde, Simon. Shane Warne: Portrait of a Flawed Genius. (ENG., Illus.). 2008. 288p. pap. 19.95 *(978-0-7195-6941-8(9))* 2007. 228p. 32.95 *(978-0-7195-6869-5(2))* Murray, John GBR. Dist: Independent Pubs. Group.

Witton, George. Bushveldt Carbineers: The War Against the Boers in South Africa & the 'Breaker' Morant Incident. 2007. 228p. *(978-1-84677-336-5(9))*; per. *(978-1-84677-335-8(0))* Leonaur Ltd.

Wolff, Michael. The Man Who Owns the News: Inside the Secret World of Rupert Murdoch. 2010. (ENG.). 480p. pap. 16.00 *(978-0-7679-2952-3(7))* Broadway Bks.

Yacoub, Therese & Quincey, Christian de. Sex, Spirit & the Soul of Therapy. 2011. 328p. pap. 13.99 ***(978-1-61667-214-0(5))*** Raider Publishing International.

AUSTRALIA—CHURCH HISTORY

Clifton & Clifton, Shane. Pentecostal Churches in Transition: Analysing the Developing Ecclesiology of the Assemblies of God in Australia. 2009. (Global Pentecostal & Charismatic Studies). (Illus.). ix, 249p. *(978-90-04-17526-6(1))* BRILL.

Giurgola, Romaldo. Luminous Simplicity: The Architecture & Art of St. Patrick's Cathedral, Parramatta. rev. ed. 2006. (Illus.). 192p. (C). 99.00 *(978-1-876832-83-4(5))* Macmillan Art Publishing AUS. Dist: Brown, David Bk. Co., The.

Hariankis, Stylianos. The Infallibility of the Church in Orthodox Theology. Kariatlis, Philip, tr. from GEC. 2008. (ENG.). 276p. (C). per. 18.00 *(978-1-920691-98-1(7)*, ATF Imprint) ATF Pr. AUS. Dist: Brown, David Bk. Co., The.

Jensz, Felicity. German Moravian Missionaries in the British Colony of Victoria, Australia, 1848-1908: Influential Strangers. 2010. (Studies in Christian Mission Ser.). 264p. *(978-90-04-17921-9(6))* BRILL.

Kelly, Gabrielle & Saunders, Kevin, eds. Towards the Intelligent Use of Liberty. 2011. (Dominican Ser.). (ENG.). 420p. (C). pap. 12.00 *(978-1-920691-74-5(X))* ATF Pr. AUS. Dist: Brown, David Bk. Co., The.

Manley, Ken R. From Woolloomooloo to 'eternity' A History of Australian Baptists, 2 vols. 2006. (Illus.). xxviii, 856p. 44.99 *(978-1-84227-404-0(X)*, Paternoster) Authentic Media.

Porter, Muriel. Sydney Anglicans & the Threat to World Anglicanism: The Sydney Experiment. 2011. (Ashgate Contemporary Ecclesiology Ser.). 190p. 99.95 ***(978-1-4094-2028-6(0))***; pap. 39.95 ***(978-1-4094-2027-9(2))*** Ashgate Publishing Co.

Zander, Viktor. Identity & Marginality among New Australians: Religion & Ethnicity in Victoria's Slavic Baptist Community. (Religion & Society Ser.). (ENG.). XVI, 327p. 225.00 ***(978-3-11-188443-1(0))*** De Gruyter, Walter Inc.

AUSTRALIA—CIVILIZATION

Cain Gray, Lara. Reading Culture: The Transfer & Translation of Australianness in Contemporary Fiction. 2008. 196p. pap. *(978-3-639-04503-1(3))* VDM Verlag Dr. Mueller e.K.

Franzke, Leonora. Aboriginal Australi. 2008. 72p. pap. *(978-3-639-05125-4(4))* VDM Verlag Dr. Mueller e.K.

Garde, Ulrike. Brecht & Co: German-Speaking Playwrights on the Australian Stage. 426p. pap. 76.95 *(978-3-03910-832-9(8))* Lang, Peter Publishing, Inc.

Gregory, J. W. Australia. 2012. (ENG.). 166p. pap. 19.99 ***(978-1-107-63940-9(9))*** Cambridge Univ. Pr.

Jones, Joseph, ed. Image of Australia. 2012. (ENG., Illus.). 238p. 30.00 ***(978-0-292-74424-0(2))*** Univ. of Texas Pr.

Morgan, Kenneth. Australia: A Very Short Introduction. 2012. (Very Short Introductions Ser.). (ENG., Illus.). 152p. pap. 11.95 ***(978-0-19-958993-7(3))*** Oxford Univ. Pr., Inc.

Muller, Theodore. The Swiss Swagman. Garland, Maurie, ed. Pammer, Frank, tr. from GER. 2007. (Illus.). xiv, 330p. pap. *(978-1-921221-02-6(X))* Brolga Publishing.

Sillitoe, Paul & Sillitoe, Jackie. Grass-Clearing Man: A Factional Ethnography of Life in the New Guinea Highlands. 2009. (Illus.). 200p. (C). pap. 18.50 *(978-1-57766-601-1(1))* Waveland Pr., Inc.

Smitz, Paul & Blake, Barry. Australian Language & Culture. 3rd rev. ed. 2007. (Lonely Planet Language & Culture: Australian Ser.). (ENG., Illus.). 256p. pap. 8.99 *(978-1-74059-099-0(6))* Lonely Planet Pubns.

Soutphommasane, Tim. Reclaiming Patriotism: Nation-Building for Australian Progressives. 1 vol. 2009. 166p. pap. 27.99 *(978-0-521-13472-9(2))* Cambridge Univ. Pr.

Warhurst, John. Behind Closed Doors: Politics, Scandals & the Lobbying Industry. 2007. (ENG.). 96p. pap. 15.95 *(978-0-86840-879-8(4))*, UNSW Press) NewSouth Publishing AUS. Dist: Independent Pubs. Group.

AUSTRALIA—COLONIES

Proudfoot, Lindsay & Hall, Dianne. Imperial Spaces: Placing the Irish & Scots in Colonial Australia. 2011. (Studies in Imperialism Ser.) (ENG., Illus.). 288p. 95.00 ***(978-0-7190-7837-8(7))*** Manchester Univ. Pr. GBR. Dist: Macmillan.

Samuels, Charlie. A Timeline of the Colonial World. 2010. (History Highlights: A Gareth Stevens Timeline Ser.). (ENG.). 48p. (J). (gr. 6-8). pap. 14.05 *(978-1-4339-3496-4(5)*, Stevens, Gareth Secondary Library) Stevens, Gareth Publishing LLLP.

Shellam, Tiffany. Shaking Hands on the Fringe: Negotiating the Aboriginal World at King George's Sound. 2009. 267p. pap. 27.95 *(978-1-921401-26-8(5))* UWA Publishing AUS. Dist: International Specialized Bk. Services.

AUSTRALIA—COLONIZATION

Etherington, Norman, ed. Mapping European Conquest: Australia & Southern Africa. 2007. (Illus.). 230p. (C). pap. 31.00 *(978-0-9802964-4-0(7))* UWA Publishing AUS. Dist: International Specialized Bk. Services.

Kerwin, Dale. Aboriginal Dreaming Paths & Trading Routes: The Colonisation of the Australian Economic Landscape. (Illus.). 230p. 2012. pap. 37.95 ***(978-1-84519-529-8(9))*** 2010. (ENG., 89.95 *(978-1-84519-338-6(5))* Sussex Academic Pr. GBR. Dist: International Specialized Bk. Services.

AUSTRALIA—COMMERCE

Australia: Business Financing Handbook. (Illus.). 70p. (Orig.). pap. 295.00 *(978-0-7605-1180-0(2))* Rector Pr., Ltd.

BIA. Essential Australian Manufacturers: Food, Textile, Clothing, & Chemical Companies. 6th rev. ed. 2006. 300p. (J). pap. 249.00 *(978-1-4187-4193-8(0))* Business Information Agency.

Doing Business in Australia. Date not set. (Doing Business in Regions & Countries Around the World Ser.). *(978-1-882390-51-9(2))* Training Management Corp.

Karavdic, Munib. E-Commerce & Export Performance. 2006. (Illus.). 89.95 *(978-1-934043-18-9(4))* Cambria Pr.

Malbon, Justin & Bishop, Bernard. Australian Export: A Guide to Law & Practice. 2006. (Illus.). 318p. pap. 70.00 *(978-0-521-61395-8(7))* Cambridge Univ. Pr.

Marsh. Australia Can Compete. Date not set. xviii, 261p. pap. 9.95 *(978-0-582-71256-0(4))* Addison-Wesley Longman, Ltd. GBR. Dist: Trans-Atlantic Pubns., Inc.

McGaughey, Sara L. Narratives of Internationalisation: Legitimacy, Standards & Portfolio Entrepreneurs. 2008. (New Horizons in International Business Ser.). 424p. (C). 162.00 *(978-1-84542-002-4(0))* Elgar, Edward Publishing, Inc.

Ninan, Abraham. Economic Development of a Queensland Industry. 2008. 328p. pap. *(978-3-639-05523-8(3))* VDM Verlag Dr. Mueller e.K.

Pitinanondha, Thitima. Operational Risk Management Systems. 2010. 128p. pap. *(978-3-639-24312-3(9))* VDM Verlag Dr. Mueller e.K.

Romanowski, Nick. Sustainable Freshwater Aquaculture: The Complete Guide from Backyard to Investor. 2006. (ENG., Illus.). 160p. pap. 40.95 *(978-0-86840-835-4(2)*, UNSW Press) NewSouth Publishing AUS. Dist: Independent Pubs. Group.

AUSTRALIA—CONSTITUTIONAL HISTORY

see Constitutional History—Australia

AUSTRALIA—CONSTITUTIONAL LAW

see Constitutional Law—Australia

AUSTRALIA—DESCRIPTION AND TRAVEL

Adams, Francis William Lauderdale. The Australians: A Social Sketch. 2011. (Cambridge Library Collection - History Ser.). 324p. pap. 24.99 *(978-1-108-03065-6(3))* Cambridge Univ. Pr.

Angas, George French. Savage Life & Scenes in Australia & New Zealand: Being an Artist's Impressions of Countries & People at the Antipodes. 2011. (Cambridge Library Collection - Travel & Exploration Ser.). (ENG., Illus.). Vol. 1. 362p. pap. 29.99 ***(978-1-108-03906-2(5))*** Vol. 2. 306p. pap. 24.99 ***(978-1-108-03907-9(3))*** Cambridge Univ. Pr.

Arthur, Paul Longley. Virtual Voyages: Travel Writing & the Antipodes 1605-1837. (Anthem Studies in Travel Ser.). (Illus.). 216p. 2011. pap. 40.00 *(978-0-85728-408-2(8))* 2010. (ENG., 99.00 *(978-1-84331-800-2(8))* Anthem Pr. GBR. Dist: Books International, Inc.

Aurousseau, M., ed. The Letters of F. W. Ludwig Leichhardt. 2010. (Hakluyt Society, Second Ser.). 440p. 69.95 *(978-1-4094-1499-5(X))*; 360p. 69.95 *(978-1-4094-1501-5(5))*; 400p. 69.95 *(978-1-4094-1500-8(7))*; 1200p. 180.00 *(978-1-4094-2623-3(8))* Hakluyt Society GBR. Dist: Ashgate Publishing Co.

Australia, Emigration. The Long Road Home. 2010. 245p. pap. 31.50 *(978-1-4452-7651-9(8))* Lulu Enterprises Inc.

Australia, National Museum of. Charles Darwin: An Australian Selection. 2008. (ENG.). 144p. pap. 29.95 *(978-1-876944-72-8(2))* National Museum of Australia AUS. Dist: Independent Pubs. Group.

Ayres Helen & Ayres, Helen. Influences on Career Development in Australian Tourism: A Guide for Human Resource Management. 2008. 404p. pap. *(978-3-639-07399-7(1))* VDM Verlag Dr. Mueller e.K.

Barrington, George. A Voyage to Botany Bay with- a Sequel to a Voyage to Botany Bay. 2007. 148p. per. *(978-1-4068-8000-7(0))* Echo Library.

Berner, R. Thomas and Paulette L. Australia: Bits & Pieces. 2008. 75p. pap. 29.95 *(978-1-4357-3372-5(X))* Lulu Enterprises Inc.

Boorman, Charley. Right to the Edge: Sydney to Tokyo by Any Means. 2010. (ENG., Illus.). 336p. pap. 15.95 *(978-0-7515-4345-2(4))*; 352p. 29.95 *(978-1-84744-351-9(6))* Little, Brown Bk. Group Ltd. GBR. Dist: Independent Pubs. Group.

—Right to the Edge No. 2: Sydney to Toyko by Any Means. 2010. (ENG., Illus.). 336p. pap. 19.95 *(978-1-84744-352-6(4))* Little, Brown Bk. Group Ltd. GBR. Dist: Independent Pubs. Group.

Bridgman, Howard, et al. The Australian Physical Environment. 2008. (ENG., Illus.). xxvi, 462p. pap. 11.00 *(978-0-19-554109-0(X))* Oxford Univ. Pr., Inc.

Byerley, Frederick J. Narrative of the Overland Expedition of. 2006. pap. *(978-1-4068-2064-5(4))* Echo Library.

Carnegie, David W. Spinifex & Sand. 2007. (Illus.). pap. *(978-1-4065-1288-5(5))* Dodo Pr.

—Spinifex & Sand: Five Years' Pioneering & Exploration in Western Australia. 2007. (ENG.). 244p. per. *(978-1-4068-4391-0(1))* Echo Library.

Carnegie, David Wynford. Spinifex & Sand. 2008. 336p. 28.99 *(978-0-554-31548-5(3))* 2008. 336p. 29.99 *(978-0-554-22245-5(0))* 2007. (ENG.). 350p. pap. 23.99 *(978-1-4264-1926-3(0))* 2007. (ENG.). 332p. pap. 24.99 *(978-1-4264-2037-5(4))* BiblioBazaar.

Chaffey, Will. Swimming with Crocodiles: The True Story of a Young Man in Search of Meaning & Adventure Who Finds Himself in an Epic Struggle for Survival. 2011. (ENG.). 328p. pap. 14.95 *(978-1-61145-021-7(7)*, 611021, Arcade Publishing) Skyhorse Publishing Co., Inc.

Chatwin, Bruce. The Songlines. rev. ed. 2012. (ENG.). 320p. (gr. 12). pap. 16.00 ***(978-0-14-242257-1(6)***, Penguin Classics) Penguin Group (USA) Inc.

Clacy, Charles (Ellen). A Lady's Visit to the Gold Diggings of Australia in 1852-53. 2007. 108p. per. *(978-1-4068-4606-5(6))* Echo Library.

—A Lady's Visit to the Gold Diggings of Australia in 1852-53. 2007. 144p. per. *(978-1-4065-1374-5(1))* Dodo Pr.

Clacy, Ellen. A Lady's Visit to the Gold Diggings of Australia in 1852-53. 152p. 2008. 21.99 *(978-0-554-31244-6(1))* 2008. 24.99 *(978-0-554-21941-7(7))* 2006. (ENG.). pap. 19.99 *(978-1-4264-1299-8(1))* BiblioBazaar.

—A Lady's Visit to the Gold Diggings of Australia in 1852-53. 2011. (Cambridge Library Collection - Travel & Exploration Ser.). (ENG., Illus.). 316p. pap. 28.99 ***(978-1-108-03980-2(4))*** Cambridge Univ. Pr.

Clacy, Ellen. A Lady's Visit to the Gold Diggings of Australia in 1852-53. l.t. ed. 2006. (ENG.). 148p. pap. 19.99 *(978-1-4264-1323-0(8))* BiblioBazaar.

Clark, Anne. Australian Adventure: Letters from an Ambassador's Wife. 2011. (ENG., Illus.). 240p. pap. 25.00 *(978-0-292-72935-3(9))* Univ. of Texas Pr.

Comthwaite, Dave. BoardFree: The Story of an Incredible Skateboard Journey across Australia. 2008. (ENG., Illus.). 288p. pap. 21.95 *(978-1-906032-19-7(X))* Anova Bks. GBR. Dist: Independent Pubs. Group.

Crawford, James Coutts. Recollections of Travel in New Zealand & Australia. 2011. (Cambridge Library Collection - Travel & Exploration Ser.). (ENG., Illus.) 504p. pap. 37.99 ***(978-1-108-03939-0(1))*** Cambridge Univ. Pr.

Davitt, Michael. Life & Progress in Australasia. 2011. (Cambridge Library Collection - History Ser.). (ENG., Illus.). 504p. pap. 37.99 ***(978-1-108-03940-6(5))*** Cambridge Univ. Pr.

Dennis, Simone. Truncated Travel: Life in the Migration Exclusion Zone on Christmas Island, Indian Ocean, Australia. 2008. xxxii, 213p. 99.95 *(978-1-60497-510-9(5))* Cambria Pr.

Dooley, Sean. The Big Twitch: One Man, One Continent, a Race Against Time - A True Story about Birdwatching. 2006. (ENG., Illus.). 320p. pap. 16.95 *(978-1-74114-528-1(7))* Allen & Unwin AUS. Dist: Independent Pubs. Group.

Duncan, Norman. Australian Byways. 2009. 218p. pap. *(978-0-217-72205-6(9))* Books LLC.

Dunderdale, George. The Book of the Bush. 2008. 340p. 29.99 *(978-0-554-25910-9(9))* 2008. 340p. 28.99 *(978-0-554-35213-3(3))* 2007. (ENG.). 336p. pap. 24.99 *(978-1-4346-0108-7(0))* BiblioBazaar.

—The Book of the Bush. 2008. (Illus.). 332p. pap. *(978-1-4099-3197-3(8))* Dodo Pr.

—The Book of the Bush. 2008. (ENG.). 220p. per. *(978-1-4068-2671-5(5))* Echo Library.

—The Book of the Bush: Illustrated by J. Macfarlane. 2007. (ENG.). 302p. pap. 23.99 *(978-1-4346-0023-3(8))* BiblioBazaar.

Eden, Charles Henry. Australian Search Party. Bates, Henry Walter, ed. 2007. (ENG.). 80p. per. *(978-1-4065-1642-5(2))* Dodo Pr.

Favell Lee Mortimer. Far Off. 2006. (ENG.). 200p. pap. 19.99 *(978-1-4264-6563-5(7))* BiblioBazaar.

Flaherty, Liz. Action Literacy: Surf & Sand. 2008. 32p. pap. 10.95 *(978-0-86431-711-7(5))* ACER Pr. AUS. Dist: International Specialized Bk. Services.

Flint, Layne R. In Search of Mad Billy. 2011. 238p. pap. 12.99 ***(978-1-61667-184-6(X))*** Raider Publishing International.

Flynn, Errol. Beam Ends. Date not set. lib. bdg. 22.95 *(978-0-8488-1975-0(6))* Amereon LTD.

Forrest, John. Explorations in Australia. 2008. 304p. 29.99 *(978-0-554-26897-2(3))* 2007. (ENG.). 274p. pap. 21.99 *(978-1-4346-2104-7(9))* 2007. (ENG.). 302p. pap. 24.99 *(978-1-4346-2132-0(4))* BiblioBazaar.

Forrest, John. Explorations in Australia: I-Explorations in Search of Dr Leichardt & Party. II-from Perth to Adelaide, around the Great Australian Bight. III-from Champion Bay, across the Desert to the Telegraph & to Adelaide. 2011. (Cambridge Library Collection - Travel & Exploration Ser.). (ENG., Illus.). 410p. pap. 31.99 ***(978-1-108-03918-5(9))*** Cambridge Univ. Pr.

Greenwood, Simon & Greenwood, Fiona. Greenwood Guides to Australia & New Zealand, Canada, & South Africa: The Greenwood Guide to Canada-Special Hand-Picked Accommodation. (Illus.). 136p. pap. 15.95 *(978-0-9537980-3-2(8))* Greenwood Guides GBR. Dist: CPG Publishing, Inc.

Grenzhaeuser, Nathalie. Nathalie Grenzhaeuser: Trespassing. 2012. (ENG., Illus.). 116p. 40.00 ***(978-3-86984-238-7(5))*** Verlag fur Moderne Kunst DEU. Dist: D.A.P./Distributed Art Pubs.

Gunn, Jeanie. We of the Never-Never. 2007. (ENG.). 228p. pap. 20.99 *(978-1-4264-1630-9(X))*; 222p. pap. 22.99 *(978-1-4264-1718-4(7))* BiblioBazaar.

—We of the Never-Never. 2007. (ENG.). 172p. per. *(978-1-4068-6267-6(3))* Echo Library.

—We of the Never-Never. 2007. (ENG.). 224p. pap. 13.45 *(978-1-60424-914-9(5)*, Book Jungle) Standard Pubns., Inc.

Hampshire, David & Kidd, Martin. Culture Wise Australia: The Essential Guide to Culture, Customs & Business Etiquette. 2008. (Culture Wise Ser.). (ENG., Illus.). 224p. pap. 17.95 *(978-1-905303-22-9(X))* Survival Bks., Ltd.

Harbaugh, Harold. Alone near Alice: Australia's Outback. 2008. 212p. pap. 17.95 *(978-0-595-53386-2(8))* iUniverse, Inc.

Heinsohn, Robert & Cermak, Michael. Life in the Cape York Rainforest. 2009. (Illus.). 106p. pap. 35.00 *(978-0-643-09501-4(2))* CSIRO Publishing AUS. Dist: Stylus Publishing, LLC.

Herle, Anita & Rouse, Sandra, eds. Cambridge & the Torres Strait: Centenary Essays on the 1898 Anthropological Expedition. 2008. (ENG., Illus.). 272p. pap. 37.99 *(978-0-521-10386-2(X))* Cambridge Univ. Pr.

Hill, Geoff & O'Carroll, Colin. Oz: Around Australia on a Triumph. 2011. (ENG., Illus.). 230p. pap. 21.95 *(978-0-85640-857-1(3))* Blackstaff Pr., Ltd. GBR. Dist: Dufour Editions, Inc.

Hutchison, David. Fremantle Walks. 2006. (Illus.). 208p. (Orig.). pap. 17.95 *(978-1-921064-30-2(7))* Fremantle Pr. AUS. Dist: Independent Pubs. Group.

James, Winifred. The Mulberry Tree. 281p. reprint ed. 98.00 *(978-0-7222-9503-8(0))* Library Reprints, Inc.

Jardine, Frank & Jardine, Alexander. Narrative of the Overland Expedition of the Messrs Jardine, from Rockhampton to Cape York, Northern Queensland. Byerley, Frederick, ed. 2007. (Illus.). 152p. per. *(978-1-4065-2707-0(6))* Dodo Pr.

Jenkyns, C. Carolyn. Hard Life in the Colonies & Other Experiences by Sea & Land. 2007. (ENG.). 396p. 49.95 *(978-0-548-01500-1(7))* Kessinger Publishing, LLC.

Jukes, Joseph Beete. A Sketch of the Physical Structure of Australia: So Far as it Is at Present Known. 2011. (Cambridge Library Collection - Physical Sciences Ser.). (ENG., Illus.). 118p. pap. 19.99 *(978-1-108-03084-7(X))* Cambridge Univ. Pr.

King, Philip Parker. Narrative of a Survey of the Intertropical & Western Coasts of Australia Performed between the years 1818 & 1822, Volume 1. 2006. 314p. pap. 23.99 *(978-1-4264-4620-7(9))* 2007. (ENG.). 354p. pap. 26.99 *(978-1-4264-4671-9(3))* BiblioBazaar.

Landor, Edward Wilson. The Bushman. 2008. 284p. 28.99 *(978-0-554-22382-7(1))*; 25.99 *(978-0-554-31685-7(4))* BiblioBazaar.

—The Bushman. 2007. 192p. per. *(978-1-4068-1503-0(9))* Echo Library.

—The Bushman: Life in a New Country. 2007. (Illus.). 288p. per. *(978-1-4065-2591-5(X))* Dodo Pr.

Landor, Edwin Wilson. The Bushman: Life in a New Country. 2007. (ENG.). 268p. pap. 21.99 *(978-1-4264-2175-4(3))*; 346p. pap. 24.99 *(978-1-4264-2243-0(1))* BiblioBazaar.

Lane, Cyril Grant. Adventures in the Big Bush: In the Haunts of the Aboriginal. 2006. (ENG.). 336p. per. 30.95 *(978-1-4286-5516-4(6))* Kessinger Publishing, LLC.

Lane, James M. Living Abroad in Australia. 2008. (Living Abroad Ser.). (ENG.). 296p. pap. 19.95 *(978-1-59880-139-2(2))* Westview Pr.

Lawrence, Joan. North Shore Walks. (Exploring the Suburbs Ser.). (Illus.). 170p. pap. *(978-0-86806-349-2(5)*, Hale & Iremonger) GHR Pr., The.

Leichhardt, Ludwig. Journal of an Overland Expedition in Australia. 2008. 356p. 31.99 *(978-0-554-21890-8(9))* BiblioBazaar.

—Journal of an Overland Expedition in Australia: From Moreton Bay to Port Essington, a distance of upwards of 3000 miles, during the Years 1844-1345. 2006. (ENG.). 370p. pap. 25.99 *(978-1-4264-1174-8(X))* BiblioBazaar.

—Journal of an Overland Expedition in Australia: From Moreton Bay to Port Essington, a Distance of upwards of 3000 miles, During the Years 1844-1845. l.t. ed. 2006. 352p. pap. 26.99 *(978-1-4264-1196-0(0))* BiblioBazaar.

Leichhardt, Ludwig. Journal of an Overland Expedition in Australia, from Moreton Bay to Port Essington: A Distance of Upwards of 3000 Miles, during the Years 1844-1845. 2011. (Cambridge Library Collection - Travel & Exploration Ser.). (ENG., Illus.). 586p. pap. 43.00 ***(978-1-108-03917-8(0))*** Cambridge Univ. Pr.

Lewis. Australia, Vol. 1. Date not set. 17.95 *(978-0-914629-63-4(8))* St. Martin's Pr.

Lindqvist, Sven. Terra Nullius: A Journey Through No One's Land. Death, Sarah, tr. from SWE. 2007. Orig. Title: Terra Nullius: en Resa Genom Ingens Land. (ENG., Illus.). 248p. 24.95 *(978-1-59558-051-1(4))* New Pr., The.

Locken, E. Travel Journal Australia. 2009. 192p. pap. 20.95 *(978-0-557-08017-5(7))* Lulu Enterprises Inc.

—Travel Journal Canberra. 2010. 192p. pap. 19.99 *(978-0-557-44765-7(8))* Lulu Enterprises Inc.

Lumholtz, Carl. Among Cannibals: An Account of Four Years' Travels in Australia & of Camp Life with the Aborigines of Queensland. 2009. (Cambridge Library Collection - Linguistics Ser.). (ENG., Illus.). 480p. pap. 34.99 *(978-1-108-00633-0(7))* Cambridge Univ. Pr.

—Through Central Borneo. 2010. 292p. pap. 30.45 *(978-1-4446-9277-8(1))* Harrison House Pubs.

Marreiros, Sabina & Bachmann, Markus. Remote Luxury: Top Resorts Down Under. 2007. (ENG., Illus.). 248p. 60.00 *(978-1-86470-198-2(6))* Images Publishing Group AUS. Dist: National Bk. Network.

Martin, Paul. Travels with Bertha: Two Years Travelling Around Australia in a 1978 Ford Falcon. 2012. (ENG.). 256p. pap. 29.95 ***(978-1-907593-42-0(X))*** Liberties Pr. IRL. Dist: Dufour Editions, Inc.

Mears, Ray. Ray Mears Goes Walkabout. 2009. (ENG., Illus.). 288p. pap. 14.95 *(978-0-340-96147-6(3)*, Hodder & Stoughton) Hodder General Publishing Div. GBR. Dist: Independent Pubs. Group.

Meredith, Louisa Anne. Notes & Sketches of New South Wales: During a Residence in that Colony from 1839 To 1844. 2010. (Cambridge Library Collection - Women's Writing Ser.). (ENG., Illus.). 180p. pap. 19.99 *(978-1-108-02417-4(3))* Cambridge Univ. Pr.

Mortimer, Favell Lee. Far Off. 2008. 224p. 27.99 *(978-0-554-24470-9(5))* 2008. 224p. 24.99 *(978-0-554-33773-9(8))* 2006. (ENG.). 222p. pap. 22.99 *(978-1-4264-6622-9(6))* BiblioBazaar.

—Far Off. 2009. 228p. pap. *(978-0-217-83521-3(X))* Books LLC.

Mundy, Godfrey Charles. Our Antipodes. 2009. 246p. pap. 32.19 *(978-1-4588-3747-9(5))* General Bks. LLC.

—Our Antipodes. 2006. (Illus.). 305p. per. *(978-1-74076-185-7(5))* Pandanus Bks.

Nesling, John. The Long Way Round: An Extended Journey Through the Lands down Under. 2006. (ENG., Illus.). 284p. per. 21.23 *(978-1-4120-8791-9(0))* Trafford Publishing.

Palfy, Thomas. Postcards from Melbourne. 2011. 28p. pap. 19.95 ***(978-1-4467-3095-9(6))*** Lulu Enterprises Inc.

—The West of the West. 2008. 44p. pap. 27.50 *(978-1-4092-2091-6(5))* Lulu Enterprises Inc.

—The West of the West (large print Edition) 2008. 56p. pap. 30.95 *(978-1-4092-3557-6(2))* Lulu Enterprises Inc.

Parker, Anne Z. Stories from the Origin. 2007. 186p. pap. 15.50 *(978-0-615-16538-7(9))* Parker, Anne Z.

Pinkerton, John. Early Australian Voyages. 2009. (ENG.). 193p. 30.99 *(978-1-117-40355-7(6))*; pap. 22.75 *(978-1-117-40356-4(4))* BiblioBazaar.

—Early Australian Voyages. 2009. 126p. pap. *(978-1-4099-9019-2(2))* Dodo Pr.

Portman, Carl. A Daintree Diary - Tales from Travels to the Daintree Rainforest in Tropical North Queensland, Australi. 2010. 216p. pap. *(978-1-905723-53-9(9))* CFZ Pr.

Pukstas, Daniel J. Upside-down & Blindfolded. 2009. 120p. pap. 12.95 *(978-1-4401-2819-6(7))* iUniverse, Inc.

Roeder, Hartmut, photos by. Australia: The Red Continent. 2007. (Illus.). 189p. 59.95 *(978-1-877339-61-5(X))* NZVP Bks. & Calendars Ltd. NZL. Dist: Perseus-PGW.

Rougemont, Louis de. The Adventures of Louis de Rougemont. 2010. 420p. pap. 34.75 *(978-1-177-12002-9(X))* BiblioBazaar.

—The Adventures of Louis de Rougemont. 2009. 258p. pap. *(978-1-4099-7442-0(1))* Dodo Pr.

—The Adventures of Louis de Rougemont. 2010. 166p. pap. 25.23 *(978-1-153-69120-8(5))* General Bks. LLC.

—The Adventures of Louis de Rougemont. 2010. 216p. pap. 19.96 *(978-1-162-65151-4(2))*; 31.96 ***(978-1-169-29135-5(X))***; 39.95 *(978-1-161-42016-6(9))* Kessinger Publishing, LLC.

—The adventures of Louis de Rougemont. 2010. 422p. pap. 35.75 *(978-1-176-16987-6(4))* BiblioBazaar.

Schmalegger, Doris. Aboriginal Tourism Development in Central Australia: How to reach the four-wheel-drive market. 2008. 160p. pap. *(978-3-639-10658-9(X))* VDM Verlag Dr. Mueller e.K.

Skippy Productions, des. North Queensland Deserted towns, COOKTOWN-PALMER: Cooktown-Palmer, 9 vols, Vol1. 2007. (Illus.). 56p. *(978-0-9757750-1-1(4))* Hooper, Colin.

Stamer, William. Recollections of a Life of Adventure. 2007. (Travel in America Ser.). (ENG.). 332p. 49.95 *(978-1-4290-0402-2(9))*; 49.95 *(978-1-4290-0400-8(2))*; per. 24.95 *(978-1-4290-0403-9(7))* Applewood Bks.

Stokes, John Lort. Discoveries in Australia: With an Account of the Coasts & Rivers Explored, 1. l.t. ed. 2006. (ENG.). 456p. pap. 30.99 *(978-1-4264-5869-9(X))* BiblioBazaar.

—Discoveries in Australia: With an Account of the Hitherto Unknown Coasts Surveyed During the Voyage of the H. M. S. Beagle, Between the Years 1837 & 1843. 2011. (Cambridge Library Collection - Travel & Exploration Ser.). (ENG., Illus.). 588p. Vol. 1. pap. 43.00 ***(978-1-108-03271-1(0))*** Vol. 2. pap. 43.00 ***(978-1-108-03272-8(9))*** Cambridge Univ. Pr.

—Discoveries in Australia, Volume 1: With an Account of the Coasts & Rivers Explored. 2006. (ENG.). 402p. pap. 26.99 *(978-1-4264-5809-5(6))* BiblioBazaar.

—Discoveries in Australia, Volume 2: Discoveries in Australia; with an Account of the Coasts & Rivers Explored & Surveyed During the Voyage of H. M. S. Beagle, in the Years 1837-38-39-40-41-42-43. by Command of the Lords

Commissioners of the Admiralty. Also a Narrative of Captain Owen Stanley's Visits to the Islands in the Arafura Sea. 2007. (ENG.). 414p. pap. 26.99 *(978-1-4264-5874-3(6))*; 472p. pap. 30.99 *(978-1-4264-5915-3(7))* BiblioBazaar.

Stuart, John McDouall. Explorations in Australia. 2008. 436p. 32.99 *(978-0-554-22905-8(6))* BiblioBazaar.

—Explorations in Australia. Hardman, William, ed. 2007. (ENG.). 384p. pap. 25.99 *(978-1-4264-3293-4(3))*; 434p. pap. 28.99 *(978-1-4264-3348-1(4))* BiblioBazaar.

Sykes, Tom & Sykes, Simon. The Hitchers of Oz: An Anthology of Hitchhiking Stories & Observations from Australasia & Beyond. 2009. (Illus.). 248p. pap. 24.00 *(978-1-921479-19-9(1)*, Glass Hse. Boks.) Interactive Pubns. Pty, Ltd. AUS. Dist: SPD-Small Pr. Distribution.

Thomas Cook Publishing Staff. Australia. 3rd ed. 2010. (Drive Around - Thomas Cook Ser.). (ENG., Illus.). 288p. pap. 26.95 *(978-1-84848-328-6(7))* Cook, Thomas Publishing GBR. Dist: Globe Pequot Pr., The.

Tredinnick, Mark. The Blue Plateau: An Australian Pastoral. 2009. (ENG.). 256p. pap. 16.00 *(978-1-57131-320-1(6))* Milkweed Editions.

Tuckey, James Hingston. An Account of a Voyage to Establish a Colony at Port Philip in Bass's Strait, on the South Coast of New South Wales: In His Majesty's Ship Calcutta, in the Years 1802-3-4. 2011. (Cambridge Library Collection - History Ser.). (ENG.). 260p. pap. 23.99 ***(978-1-108-03903-1(0))*** Cambridge Univ. Pr.

VV., AA., et al. Australia. 2008. (Country Guide Ser.). (SPA.). 1,100p. pap. 45.99 *(978-84-08-07723-7(6))* Lonely Planet Pubns.

Wallace, Alfred Russel. The Malay Archipelago: The Land of the Orang-Utan & the Bird of Paradise. 2nd ed. 2011. (Stanfords Travel Classics Ser.). 552p. pap. 19.95 *(978-1-906780-31-9(5))* Beaufoy, John Publishing GBR. Dist: Midpoint Trade Bks., Inc.

Watters, John. Bonza Voyage. 2008. 291p. pap. 21.50 *(978-1-4092-0630-9(0))* Lulu Enterprises Inc.

Weiner, Hadva & Adler, Yoram. Yom Ehad Gam Atem Tetsu La-Derekh: Sipure Masa Be-Karavan. 2008. (HEB., Illus.). 231p. *(978-965-7187-82-1(6))* Aharoni, Jacob Sicka.

Wheeler, Tony. Badlands: A Tourist on the Axis of Evil. 2nd ed. 2010. (Travel Literature Ser.). (ENG., Illus.). 352p. pap. 14.99 *(978-1-74220-104-7(0))* Lonely Planet Pubns.

Worgan, George B. Journal of a First Fleet Surgeon. 2011. 60p. ***(978-1-84902-460-0(X))*** Benediction Classics.

AUSTRALIA—DESCRIPTION AND TRAVEL—VIEWS

see Australia—Pictorial Works

AUSTRALIA—DIRECTORIES

Cunningham Library & Acer. 2008 Australasian Education Directory. 2008. 262p. pap. 83.95 *(978-0-86431-976-0(2))* ACER Pr. AUS. Dist: International Specialized Bk. Services.

AUSTRALIA—DISCOVERY AND EXPLORATION

Adam, Dawne. Hell's Airport: from Commitment to Incarceration & Back Again. 2009. 56p. pap. 19.02 *(978-0-557-10000-2(3))* Lulu Enterprises Inc.

Becke, Louis. The Naval Pioneers of Australia. 2006. (ENG.). 202p. pap. 20.99 *(978-1-4264-6556-7(4))*; 228p. pap. 22.99 *(978-1-4264-6615-1(3))* BiblioBazaar.

Becke, Louis & Jeffery, Walter. The Naval Pioneers of Australia. 2008. 232p. 27.99 *(978-0-554-24463-1(2))* BiblioBazaar.

—The Naval Pioneers of Australia. 2007. (Illus.). 212p. per. *(978-1-4065-3707-9(1))* Dodo Pr.

Byerley, Frederick J. Narrative of the Overland Expedition of. 2006. pap. *(978-1-4068-2064-5(4))* Echo Library.

Clarke, Philip A. Aboriginal Plant Collectors: Botanists & Australian Aboriginal People in the Nineteenth Century. 2008. (Illus.). 191p. (C). 39.95 *(978-1-877058-68-4(8))* Rosenberg Publishing Pty, Ltd. AUS. Dist: International Specialized Bk. Services.

Clode, Danielle. Voyages to the South Seas: In Search of Terres Australes. 2007. (ENG., Illus.). 368p. 25.00 *(978-0-522-85264-6(5))* Melbourne Univ. Publishing AUS. Dist: Independent Pubs. Group.

Collingridge, George. The First Discovery of Australia & New Guinea. 2008. 140p. 24.99 *(978-0-554-27916-9(9))* BiblioBazaar.

—The First Discovery of Australia & New Guinea. 2009. 162p. 36.95 *(978-1-104-54491-1(1))*; 164p. pap. 21.95 *(978-1-104-49138-3(9))* Kessinger Publishing, LLC.

Day, Alan. The A to Z of the Discovery & Exploration of Australia. 2009. (A to Z Guide Ser.: No. 27). (ENG.). 370p. pap. 34.45 *(978-0-8108-6810-6(5))* Scarecrow Pr., Inc.

Duyker, Edward. FranCois Peron - An Impetuous Life: Naturalist & Voyager. 2007. (ENG., Illus.). 426p. 45.00 *(978-0-522-85260-8(2)*, Miegunyah Pr., The) Melbourne Univ. Publishing AUS. Dist: Independent Pubs. Group.

Early Voyages to Terra Australis, Now Called Australia: A Collection of Documents, & Extracts from Early Manuscript Maps, Illustrative of the History of Discovery on the Coasts of That Vast Island, from the Beginning of the Sixteenth Century to the Time. 2010. (Cambridge Library Collection - Travel & Exploration Ser.). (ENG., Illus.). 372p. pap. 28.99 *(978-1-108-01002-3(4))* Cambridge Univ. Pr.

Edmond, Martin. Luca Antara. 2008. (ENG., Illus.). 288p. pap. 19.95 *(978-1-84243-289-1(3))* Oldcastle Bks., Ltd. GBR. Dist: Independent Pubs. Group.

—Luca Antara: Passages in Search of Australia. (ENG., Illus.). 2010. 272p. pap. 16.95 *(978-1-84243-319-5(9))* 2008. 288p. 32.95 *(978-1-84243-272-3(9))* Oldcastle Bks., Ltd. GBR. Dist: Independent Pubs. Group.

Eyre, Edward John. Journals of Expeditions of Discovery into Central Australia & Overland from Adelaide to King George's Sound in the Years 1840-1, Vol. 1. 2007. (Illus.). 360p. per. *(978-1-4065-3397-2(1))* Dodo Pr.

—Journals of Expeditions of Discovery into Central Australia, & Overland from Adelaide to King George's Sound, in the Years 1840-1, Vol. 1. 2011. (Cambridge Library Collection - Travel & Exploration Ser.). (ENG., Illus.). 492p. pap. 35.99 ***(978-1-108-03897-3(2))*** Cambridge Univ. Pr.

—Journals of Expeditions of Discovery into Central Australia & Overland from Adelaide to King George's Sound in the Years 1840-1, Vol. 2. 2007. (Illus.). 392p. per. *(978-1-4065-3398-9(X))* Dodo Pr.

Eyre, Edward John. Journals of Expeditions of Discovery into Central Australia, & Overland from Adelaide to King George's Sound, in the Years 1840-1, Vol. 2. 2011. (Cambridge Library Collection - Travel & Exploration Ser.). (ENG., Illus.). 546p. pap. 39.99 ***(978-1-108-03898-0(0))*** Cambridge Univ. Pr.

Favenc, Ernest. The Explorers of Australia & Their Life-Work. 2009. 356p. 31.99 *(978-0-559-10075-8(2))*; 29.99 *(978-0-559-10086-4(8))*; pap. 20.99 *(978-0-559-10083-3(3))*; pap. 32.75 *(978-0-559-10079-6(5))* BiblioBazaar.

—The Explorers of Australia & Their Life-Work. 2007. (Illus.). 324p. per. *(978-1-4065-1693-7(7))* Dodo Pr.

—The History of Australian Exploration. 2011. 462p. pap. ***(978-1-84902-520-1(7))*** Benediction Classics.

—History of Australian Exploration from 1. 2006. pap. *(978-1-4068-2067-6(9))* Echo Library.

—The History of Australian Exploration from 1788 To 1888. 2008. 560p. 33.99 *(978-0-554-31673-4(0))* 2008. 560p. 36.99 *(978-0-554-22370-4(8))* 2007. (ENG.). 516p. pap. 30.99 *(978-1-4264-2163-1(X))* BiblioBazaar.

—The History of Australian Exploration from 1788 To 1888. 2007. 464p. per. *(978-1-4065-1694-4(5))* Dodo Pr.

—The History of Australian Exploration from 1788 To 1888. 2009. 494p. 53.95 *(978-1-104-97572-2(6))*; pap. 38.95 *(978-1-104-91418-9(2))* Kessinger Publishing, LLC.

—The History of Australian Exploration from 1788 to 1888. l.t. ed. 2007. (ENG.). 556p. pap. 32.99 *(978-1-4264-2231-7(8))* BiblioBazaar.

Flinders, Matthew. A Voyage to Terra Australis: Undertaken for the Purpose of Completing the Discovery of that Vast Country, & Prosecuted in the Years 1801, 1802, And 1803. 2010. (Cambridge Library Collection - Travel & Exploration Ser.). (Illus.). 630p. pap. 43.00 *(978-1-108-01819-7(X))*; 508p. pap. 37.99 *(978-1-108-01818-0(1))* Cambridge Univ. Pr.

Forrest, John. Explorations in Australia. 2008. 304p. 29.99 *(978-0-554-26897-2(3))* 2007. (ENG.). 274p. pap. 21.99 *(978-1-4346-2104-7(9))* 2007. (ENG.). 302p. pap. 24.99 *(978-1-4346-2132-0(4))* BiblioBazaar.

Forrest, John. Explorations in Australia: I-Explorations in Search of Dr Leichardt & Party. II-from Perth to Adelaide, around the Great Australian Bight. III-from Champion Bay, across the Desert to the Telegraph & to Adelaide. 2011. (Cambridge Library Collection - Travel & Exploration Ser.). (ENG., Illus.). 410p. pap. 31.99 ***(978-1-108-03918-5(9))*** Cambridge Univ. Pr.

Giles, Ernest. Australia Twice Traversed. 2008. 588p. 36.99 *(978-0-554-22244-8(2))* 2008. 588p. 33.99 *(978-0-554-31547-8(5))* 2007. (ENG.). 586p. pap. 32.99 *(978-1-4264-2036-8(6))* 2007. (ENG.). 526p. pap. 30.99 *(978-1-4264-1925-6(2))* BiblioBazaar.

—Australia Twice Traversed. 2009. 202p. pap. *(978-0-217-33739-7(2))*; 232p. pap. *(978-1-4590-3701-4(4))* Books LLC.

—Australia Twice Traversed. 2007. (Illus.). 540p. per. *(978-1-4065-4453-4(1))* Dodo Pr.

—Australia Twice Traversed 2 Volume Set: The Romance of Exploration. 2011. (Cambridge Library Collection - Travel & Exploration Ser.). (ENG., Illus.). 844p. pap., pap. 62.00 ***(978-1-108-03902-4(2))*** Cambridge Univ. Pr.

—Australia Twice Traversed: Volume 1: The Romance of Exploration. 2011. (Cambridge Library Collection - Travel & Exploration Ser.). (ENG., Illus.). 416p. pap. 31.99 ***(978-1-108-03900-0(6))*** Cambridge Univ. Pr.

—Australia Twice Traversed: Volume 2: The Romance of Exploration. 2011. (Cambridge Library Collection - Travel & Exploration Ser.). (ENG., Illus.). 412p. pap. 31.99 ***(978-1-108-03901-7(4))*** Cambridge Univ. Pr.

Grant, James. The Narrative of a Voyage of Discovery, Performed in His Majesty's Vessel the Lady Nelson ... in the Years 1800, 1801, & 1802, to New South Wales. 2011. (Cambridge Library Collection - Travel & Exploration Ser.). (ENG., Illus.). 256p. pap. 42.00 ***(978-1-108-03941-3(3))*** Cambridge Univ. Pr.

Gregory, Augustus Charles. Journals of Australian Explorations. 2008. 468p. 33.99 *(978-0-554-23315-4(0))*; 31.99 *(978-0-554-32618-4(3))* BiblioBazaar.

Gregory, Augustus Charles & Francis Thomas Gregory. Journals of Australian Explorations. 2007. (ENG.). 404p. pap. 26.99 *(978-1-4264-4158-5(4))*; 466p. pap. 30.99 *(978-1-4264-4199-8(1))* BiblioBazaar.

Howitt, William. The History of Discovery in Australia, Tasmania, & New Zealand: From the Earliest Date to the Present Day. 2011. (Cambridge Library Collection - Travel & Exploration Ser.). (ENG.). 456p. pap. 34.99 *(978-1-108-02949-0(3))*; (Illus.). 488p. pap. 35.99 *(978-1-108-02950-6(7))* Cambridge Univ. Pr.

Jardine, Frank & Jardine, Alexander. Narrative of the Overland Expedition of the Messrs Jardine, from Rockhampton to Cape York, Northern Queensland. Byerley, Frederick, ed. 2007. (Illus.). 152p. per. *(978-1-4065-2707-0(6))* Dodo Pr.

King, Phillip P. Narrative of a Survey of the Intertropical & Western Coasts of Australia. 2007. (Illus.). 340p. per. *(978-1-4065-1949-5(9))*; 536p. per. *(978-1-4065-1950-1(2))* Dodo Pr.

Landsborough, William. Journal of Landsborough's Expedition from Carpentaria. 2008. 200p. 25.99 *(978-0-554-27215-3(6))* BiblioBazaar.

—Journal of Landsborough's Expedition from Carpentaria: In Search of Burke & Wills. 2007. (ENG.). 176p. pap. 19.99 *(978-1-4346-2738-4(1))*; 198p. pap. 21.99 *(978-1-4346-2771-1(3))* BiblioBazaar.

—Journal of Landsborough's Expedition from Carpentaria, in Search of Burke & Wills. 2007. 192p. per. *(978-1-4065-2595-3(2))* Dodo Pr.

Lee, Ida. The Logbooks of the Lady Nelson. 2009. 272p. 25.99 *(978-0-559-12184-5(9))*; 28.99 *(978-0-559-12170-8(9))*; pap. 26.75 *(978-0-559-12182-1(2))*; pap. 27.75 *(978-0-559-12174-6(1))* BiblioBazaar.

—The Logbooks of the Lady Nelson. 2007. (ENG.). 256p. per. *(978-1-4065-5153-2(8))* Dodo Pr.

Leed, Ida. The Coming of the British to Australia, 1788-1829. 2007. (Illus.). 370p. reprint ed. pap. 34.95 *(978-1-60105-129-5(8)*, 6D7D) Scholar's Bookshelf.

Leichhardt, Ludwig. Journal of an Overland Expedition in Australia. 2008. 356p. 31.99 *(978-0-554-21890-8(9))* BiblioBazaar.

—Journal of an Overland Expedition in Australia: From Moreton Bay to Port Essington, a distance of upwards of 3000 miles, during the Years 1844-1845. 2006. (ENG.). 370p. pap. 25.99 *(978-1-4264-1174-8(X))* BiblioBazaar.

—Journal of an Overland Expedition in Australia: From Moreton Bay to Port Essington, a Distance of upwards of 3000 miles, During the Years 1844-1845. l.t. ed. 2006. 352p. pap. 26.99 *(978-1-4264-1196-0(0))* BiblioBazaar.

Leichhardt, Ludwig. Journal of an Overland Expedition in Australia, from Moreton Bay to Port Essington: A Distance of Upwards of 3000 Miles, during the Years 1844-1845. 2011. (Cambridge Library Collection - Travel & Exploration Ser.). (ENG., Illus.). 586p. pap. 43.00 ***(978-1-108-03917-8(0))*** Cambridge Univ. Pr.

May, Sally K. Collecting Cultures: Myth, Politics, & Collaboration in the 1948 Arnhem Land Expedition. 2009. (Indigenous Archaeologies Ser.). (ENG.). 250p. 75.00 *(978-0-7591-0598-0(7))* AltaMira Pr.

McKinlay, John. McKinlay's Journal of Exploration in the Interior of Australia. 2008. 216p. 27.99 *(978-0-554-24572-0(8))* 2006. (ENG.). 190p. pap. 19.99 *(978-1-4264-6883-4(0))* 2007. 212p. pap. 22.99 *(978-1-4264-6965-7(9))* BiblioBazaar.

Mitchell, T. L. Three Expeditions into the Interior of Eastern Australia: With Descriptions of the Recently Explored Region of Australia Felix & of the Present Colony of New South Wales, 2 Vols. 2011. (Cambridge Library Collection - Travel & Exploration Ser.). (Illus.). Set. 924p. pap. 67.00 *(978-1-108-03064-9(5))* Vol. 1. 422p. pap. 32.99 *(978-1-108-03062-5(9))* Vol. 2. 490p. pap. 35.99 *(978-1-108-03063-2(7))* Cambridge Univ. Pr.

Mitchell, Thomas. Journal of an Expedition into the Interior of Tropical Australia. 2008. 384p. 31.99 *(978-0-554-23154-9(9))* 2007. (ENG.). 382p. pap. 26.99 *(978-1-4264-3877-6(X))* 2006. 338p. pap. 23.99 *(978-1-4264-3807-3(9))* BiblioBazaar.

Oxley, John. Journals of Two Expeditions into the Interior of New South Wales. 2009. 450p. pap. 36.95 *(978-1-104-87558-9(6))* Kessinger Publishing, LLC.

Pinkerton, John. Early Australian Voyages. 2009. (ENG.). 193p. 30.99 *(978-1-117-40355-7(6))*; pap. 22.75 *(978-1-117-40356-4(4))* BiblioBazaar.

—Early Australian Voyages. 2009. 126p. pap. *(978-1-4099-9019-2(2))* Dodo Pr.

Scott, Ernest. The Life of Captain Matthew Flinders. 2008. (Illus.). 460p. pap. *(978-1-4065-9688-5(4))* Dodo Pr.

—The Life of Captain Matthew Flinders, R. N. 2011. (Cambridge Library Collection - Travel & Exploration Ser.). (ENG., Illus.). 612p. pap. 43.00 ***(978-1-108-04061-7(6))*** Cambridge Univ. Pr.

Scott, Ernest. Terre Napoleon a History of French Exp. 2006. pap. *(978-1-4068-0447-8(9))* Echo Library.

Stevens, Henry N. & Barwick, George F., eds. New Light on the Discovery of Australia, as Revealed by the Journal of Captain Don Diego de Prado y Tovar. 2010. (Hakluyt Society, Second Ser.). 278p. 69.95 *(978-1-4094-1431-5(0))* Hakluyt Society GBR. Dist: Ashgate Publishing Co.

Stokes, John Lort. Discoveries in Australia: With an Account of the Coasts & Rivers Explored, 1. l.t. ed. 2006. (ENG.). 456p. pap. 30.99 *(978-1-4264-5869-9(X))* BiblioBazaar.

—Discoveries in Australia: With an Account of the Hitherto Unknown Coasts Surveyed During the Voyage of the H. M. S. Beagle, Between the Years 1837 & 1843. 2011. (Cambridge Library Collection - Travel & Exploration Ser.). (ENG., Illus.). 588p. Vol. 1. pap. 43.00 ***(978-1-108-03271-1(0))*** Vol. 2. pap. 43.00 ***(978-1-108-03272-8(9))*** Cambridge Univ. Pr.

—Discoveries in Australia, Volume 1: With an Account of the Coasts & Rivers Explored. 2006. (ENG.). 402p. pap. 26.99 *(978-1-4264-5809-5(6))* BiblioBazaar.

—Discoveries in Australia, Volume 2: Discoveries in Australia; with an Account of the Coasts & Rivers Explored & Surveyed During the Voyage of H. M. S. Beagle, in the Years 1837-38-39-40-41-42-43. by Command of the Lords Commissioners of the Admiralty. Also a Narrative of Captain Owen Stanley's Visits to the Islands in the Arafura Sea. 2007. (ENG.). 414p. pap. 26.99 *(978-1-4264-5874-3(6))*; 472p. pap. 30.99 *(978-1-4264-5915-3(7))* BiblioBazaar.

Stuart, John McDouall. Explorations in Australia. 2008. 436p. 32.99 *(978-0-554-22905-8(6))* BiblioBazaar.

—Explorations in Australia. Hardman, William, ed. 2007. (ENG.). 384p. pap. 25.99 *(978-1-4264-3293-4(3))*; 434p. pap. 28.99 *(978-1-4264-3348-1(4))* BiblioBazaar.

Stuart, John, McDouall. Explorations in Australia the Journals. 2006. pap. *(978-1-4068-0794-3(X))* Echo Library.

Stuart, John McDouall. The Journals of John Mcdouall Stuart during the Years 1858 - 1862: When He Fixed the Centre of the Continent & Successfully Crossed It from Sea to Sea. Hardman, William, ed. 2011. (Cambridge Library Collection - Travel & Exploration Ser.). (ENG., Illus.). 568p. pap. 43.00 ***(978-1-108-03916-1(2))*** Cambridge Univ. Pr.

Sturt, Charles. Two Expeditions into the Interior of Southern Australia, during the Years 1828, 1829, 1830, And 1831: With Observations on the Soil, Climate, & General Resources of the Colony of New South Wales. 2011. (Cambridge Library Collection - Travel & Exploration Ser.). (ENG., Illus.). Vol. 1. 318p. pap. 28.99 ***(978-1-108-03885-0(9))*** Vol. 2. 298p. pap. 23.99 ***(978-1-108-03886-7(7))*** Cambridge Univ. Pr.

Tench, Watkin. A Complete Account of the Settlement at Port Jackson. 2009. 196p. pap. *(978-1-4099-0447-2(4))* Dodo Pr.

Walker, David & Tampke, Jurgen, eds. From Berlin to Burdekin. (Illus.). 300p. *(978-0-86840-332-8(6)*, UNSW Press) NewSouth Publishing.

AUSTRALIA—ECONOMIC CONDITIONS

Abeysekera, Indra. Reputation Building, Website Disclosure & the Case of Intellectual Capital. 2011. (Studies in Managerial & Financial Accounting: Vol. 21). (Illus.). 344p. *(978-0-85724-505-2(8))* Emerald Group Publishing Ltd. GBR. Dist: Turpin Distribution, Inc.

Beeson, Mark. Far East & Australasia 2010. Europa Publications Staff, ed. 41st ed. 2009. 1588p. 810.00 *(978-1-85743-533-7(8))* Routledge.

Bertolatti, Dean. Antimicrobial Resistance in Gram-Positive Cocci Isolated from Poultry. 2010. 228p. pap. *(978-3-639-27832-3(1))* VDM Verlag Dr. Mueller e.K.

Betta, Michela, ed. The Moral, Social, & Commercial Imperatives of Genetic Testing & Screening: The Australian Case. 2010. (International Library of Ethics, Law, & the New Medicine Ser.). xv, 268p. pap. 169.00 *(978-90-481-7154-5(7)*, 9048171547) Springer.

BIA. Essential Australian Manufacturers: Food, Textile, Clothing, & Chemical Companies. 6th rev. ed. 2006. 300p. (J). pap. 249.00 *(978-1-4187-4193-8(0))* Business Information Agency.

Bolton, Geoffrey. Land of Vision & Mirage: Western Australia Since 1826. 2008. 270p. pap. 32.00 *(978-0-9802964-0-2(4))* UWA Publishing AUS. Dist: International Specialized Bk. Services.

Cardew, Richard V., et al, eds. Why Cities Change: Urban Development & Economic Change in Sydney. 2007. (ENG., Illus.). 312p. 190.00 *(978-0-415-41802-7(X))* Routledge.

Christen, Kimberly A. Aboriginal Business: Alliances in a Remote Australian Town. 2009. pap. 29.95 *(978-1-930618-98-5(0))* School for Advanced Research Pr./SAR Pr.

Coghlan. Labour & Industry in Australia, from the First Settlement in 1788 to the Establishment of the Commonwealth In 1901. 2010. 322p. pap. 39.81 *(978-1-152-66541-5(3))*; 392p. pap. 46.31 *(978-1-152-66492-0(1))*; 338p. pap. 41.20 *(978-1-152-66545-3(6))*; 342p. pap. 41.66 *(978-1-152-66547-7(2))* General Bks. LLC.

Coghlan, T.A. Labour & Industry in Australia: From the First Settlement in 1788 to the Establishment of the Commonwealth In 1901. 2009. 604p. pap. 31.99 *(978-1-117-37741-4(5)*, BiblioLife) BiblioBazaar.

—Labour & Industry in Australia: From the First Settlement in 1788 to the Establishment of the Commonwealth In 1901. 2011. (Cambridge Library Collection - History Ser.). Vol. 1. 600p. pap. 43.00 *(978-1-108-03067-0(X))* Vol. 2. 608p. pap. 43.00 *(978-1-108-03068-7(8))* Vol. 3. 614p. pap. 43.00 *(978-1-108-03069-4(6))* Vol. 4. 670p. pap. 45.00 *(978-1-108-03070-0(X))* Cambridge Univ. Pr.

—Labour & Industry in Australia, from the First Settlement in 1788 to the Establishment of the Commonwealth In 1901. 2010. 674p. pap. 47.75 *(978-1-178-12332-6(4))* BiblioBazaar.

Coghlan, Timothy Augustine. Labour & Industry in Australia from the First Settlement in 1788 to the Establishment of the Commonwealth In 1901. 2010. 602p. pap. 44.75 *(978-1-178-11914-5(9))* BiblioBazaar.

—Labour & Industry in Australia from the First Settlement in 1788 to the Establishment of the Commonwealth In 1901. 2010. 324p. pap. 35.89 *(978-1-152-66539-2(1))* 2010. 338p. pap. 35.89 *(978-1-152-66543-9(X))* 2009. (Illus.). 368p. pap. 27.83 *(978-1-150-02801-4(7))* General Bks. LLC.

—Labour & Industry in Australia, from the First Settlement in 1788 to the Establishment of the Commonwealth In 1901. 2010. (ENG.). 616p. pap. 45.75 *(978-1-171-70265-8(5))*; 612p. pap. 45.75 *(978-1-176-48775-8(2))*; (ENG.). 600p. pap. 44.75 *(978-1-176-49601-9(8))* BiblioBazaar.

—Labour & Industry in Australia, from the First Settlement in 1788 to the Establishment of the Commonwealth In 1901. 2010. 346p. pap. *(978-1-151-84782-9(8))* Books LLC.

Cowlishaw, Gillian. The City's Outback. 2009. (ENG.). 272p. pap. 25.99 *(978-1-921410-87-1(6)*, UNSW Press) NewSouth Publishing AUS. Dist: Independent Pubs. Group.

Crawford, Robert, et al. Consumer Australia: Historical Perspectives. 2010. (Illus.). 225p. *(978-1-4438-2270-1(1))* Cambridge Scholars Pub.

Denemark, David, et al, eds. Australian Social Attitudes 2: Citizenship, Work, & Aspirations. 2007. (ENG., Illus.). 320p. per. 53.95 *(978-0-86840-861-3(1)*, UNSW Press) NewSouth Publishing AUS. Dist: Independent Pubs. Group.

Esposto, Alexis. Drifting Apart. 2009. 92p. pap. *(978-3-639-19189-9(7))* VDM Verlag Dr. Mueller e.K.

Euromonitor International Staff. Consumer Asia Pacific & Australasia 2011. 18th ed. 2010. 312p. (C). pap. *(978-1-84264-535-2(8))* Euromonitor International PLC.

Gale. Consumer Asia Pacific & Australasia. 19th ed. 2011. (Consumer Asia Pacific & Australasia Ser.). (ENG.). 342p. ***(978-1-84264-552-6(8))*** Euromonitor International PLC.

Griggs, P. D. Global Industry, Local Innovation: The History of Cane Sugar Production in Australia, 1820-1995. 2011. 964p. *(978-3-0343-0431-3(5))* Lang, Peter.

Groenewegen, Peter & McFarlane, Bruce. A History of Australian Economic Thought. 2010. (Routledge Revivals Ser.). (ENG.). 290p. 115.00 *(978-0-415-60913-5(5))* Routledge.

Holland, Peter. Developing Organisational Competitiveness Through New Patterns of Work. 2010. 348p. pap. *(978-3-8383-2119-6(7))* Lambert Academic Publishing.

Hughes, Philip, et al. Building Stronger Communities. 2007. (ENG., Illus.). 256p. per. 35.95 *(978-0-86840-814-9(X)*, UNSW Press) NewSouth Publishing AUS. Dist: Independent Pubs. Group.

Icon Group International, Inc. Staff, compiled by. The 2006 Economic & Product Market Databook for Adelaide, Australia. 2006. 618p. ring bd. 95.00 *(978-0-497-79954-0(5))* Icon Group International, Inc.

—The 2006 Economic & Product Market Databook for Brisbane, Australia. 2006. 618p. ring bd. 95.00 *(978-0-497-80249-3(X))* Icon Group International, Inc.

—The 2006 Economic & Product Market Databook for Canberra, Australia. 2006. 618p. ring bd. 95.00 *(978-0-497-80300-1(3))* Icon Group International, Inc.

—The 2006 Economic & Product Market Databook for Darwin, Australia. 2006. 618p. ring bd. 95.00 *(978-0-497-79980-9(4))* Icon Group International, Inc.

—The 2006 Economic & Product Market Databook for Geelong, Australia. 2006. 618p. ring bd. 95.00 *(978-0-497-80583-8(9))* Icon Group International, Inc.

—The 2006 Economic & Product Market Databook for Gold Coast, Australia. 2006. 618p. ring bd. 95.00 *(978-0-497-80606-4(1))* Icon Group International, Inc.

—The 2006 Economic & Product Market Databook for Hobart, Australia. 2006. 618p. ring bd. 95.00 *(978-0-497-81901-9(5))* Icon Group International, Inc.

—The 2006 Economic & Product Market Databook for Kingston, Norfolk Island. 2006. 618p. ring bd. 95.00 *(978-0-497-80748-1(3))* Icon Group International, Inc.

—The 2006 Economic & Product Market Databook for Melbourne, Australia. 2006. 618p. ring bd. 95.00 *(978-0-497-81006-1(9))* Icon Group International, Inc.

—The 2006 Economic & Product Market Databook for Newcastle, Australia. 2006. 618p. ring bd. 95.00 *(978-0-497-81117-4(0))* Icon Group International, Inc.

—The 2006 Economic & Product Market Databook for Perth, Australia. 2006. 618p. ring bd. 95.00 *(978-0-497-81209-6(6))* Icon Group International, Inc.

—The 2006 Economic & Product Market Databook for Sydney, Australia. 2006. 618p. ring bd. 95.00 *(978-0-497-81595-0(8))* Icon Group International, Inc.

—The 2006 Economic & Product Market Databook for the Settlement, Christmas Island. 2006. 618p. ring bd. 95.00 *(978-0-497-81668-1(7))* Icon Group International, Inc.

—The 2006 Economic & Product Market Databook for Townsville, Australia. 2006. 618p. ring bd. 95.00 *(978-0-497-81708-4(X))* Icon Group International, Inc.

—The 2006 Economic & Product Market Databook for Wollongong, Australia. 2006. 618p. ring bd. 95.00 *(978-0-497-81828-9(0))* Icon Group International, Inc.

Kelly, Simon. Australian Trends in Wealth Inequality. 2008. 212p. pap. *(978-3-639-07256-3(1))* VDM Verlag Dr. Mueller e.K.

Kerwin, Dale. Aboriginal Dreaming Paths & Trading Routes: The Colonisation of the Australian Economic Landscape. 2010. (ENG., Illus.). 230p. 89.95 *(978-1-84519-338-6(5))* Sussex Academic Pr. GBR. Dist: International Specialized Bk. Services.

King, J. E. Readings in Australian Labour. 376p. (Illus.). 64.95 *(978-0-7329-1262-8(8))*; pap. 29.95 *(978-0-7329-1261-1(X))* Macmillan Education Australia AUS. Dist: Paul & Co. Pubs. Consortium, Inc.

Langworthy, A. Human Capital & Regional Development. 2009. 236p. pap. *(978-3-639-13632-6(2))* VDM Verlag Dr. Mueller e.K.

Marginson, Simon, et al. International Student Security. 2010. (ENG., Illus.). 528p. pap. 42.00 *(978-0-521-13805-5(1))* Cambridge Univ. Pr.

Meng, Erika C. H. & Brennan, John P. Economic Analysis of Diversity in Modern Wheat. 2009. (ENG., Illus.). 204p. 99.95 *(978-1-57808-575-0(6))* BIOS Scientific Publishers Ltd. GBR. Dist: Taylor & Francis Group.

Mohsin, Asad. Malaysian Tourists & Marketing of Northern Territory of Australi. 2010. 272p. pap. *(978-3-639-24149-5(5))* VDM Verlag Dr. Mueller e.K.

Murgulov, Zoltan. New Economy Equity Offers in Australia - Initial & Seasoned Equity Offers. 2008. 252p. pap. *(978-3-639-01784-7(6))* VDM Verlag Dr. Mueller e.K.

Ninan, Abraham. Economic Development of a Queensland Industry. 2008. 328p. pap. *(978-3-639-05523-8(3))* VDM Verlag Dr. Mueller e.K.

Northcott, Clarence H. Australian Social Development. (Columbia University, Studies in the Social Sciences: No. 189). reprint ed. 29.50 *(978-0-404-51189-0(9))* AMS Pr., Inc.

—Australian Social Development. 2009. 306p. 36.99 *(978-1-116-67578-8(1))*; 306p. 32.99 *(978-1-116-67579-5(X))*; 306p. pap. 29.75 *(978-1-116-67580-1(3))*; (ENG.). 305p. pap. 23.99 *(978-1-116-67583-2(8)*, BiblioLife); (ENG.). 305p. pap. 24.99 *(978-1-116-67582-5(X)*, BiblioLife) BiblioBazaar.

Organisation for Economic Co-operation and Development. Australia: Towards A Seamless National Economy. 2010. (OECD Reviews of Regulatory Reform Ser.). (Illus.). 204p. pap. 63.00 *(978-92-64-06716-5(7))* Organization for Economic Cooperation & Development.

Organisation for Economic Co-operation and Development Staff. Australia. 2008. 160p. pap. 63.00 *(978-92-64-04822-5(7))* Organization for Economic Cooperation & Development.

—Jobs for Immigrants Vol. 1: Labour Market Integration in Australia, Denmark, Germany & Sweden. 2007. pap. 58.00 *(978-92-64-03359-7(9))* Organization for Economic Cooperation & Development.

—Oecd Economic Surveys: Australia - Volume 2006 Issue 12. 2006. 156p. per. 52.00 *(978-92-64-02635-3(5))* Organization for Economic Cooperation & Development.

Price, Gary. Horticultural Research; Growth of European Olive in the Rangelands. 2010. 244p. pap. *(978-3-639-22411-5(6))* VDM Verlag Dr. Mueller e.K.

Russell-Smith, Jeremy, et al, eds. Culture, Ecology & Economy of Fire Management in North Australian Savannas. 2010. 416p. pap. 68.95 *(978-0-643-09402-4(4))* CSIRO Publishing AUS. Dist: Stylus Publishing, LLC.

Sanchez, Mariela. Agri-Food Restructuring in the Australia Beef Industry. 2010. 220p. pap. *(978-3-8383-7212-9(3))* Lambert Academic Publishing.

Stapelberg, Rudolph Frederick. Research into the Development & Application of Asset Management. 2010. 468p. pap. *(978-3-8383-8866-3(6))* Lambert Academic Publishing.

Stilwell, Frank & Jordan, Kirrily. Who Gets What? Analysing Economic Inequality in Australia. 2007. (Illus.). 276p. pap. 40.00 *(978-0-521-70032-0(9))* Cambridge Univ. Pr.

Tabart, Tim. Reinventing & Renewing Local Community. 2010. 176p. pap. *(978-3-8383-8163-3(7))* Lambert Academic Publishing.

Wadud, Ikm Mokhtarul. Trade Arrangements, Productivity Growth & Firm Level Efficiency. 2010. 340p. pap. *(978-3-639-25997-1(1))* VDM Verlag Dr. Mueller e.K.

White, Neil. Company Towns. 2012. ***(978-1-4426-4327-7(7))*** Univ. of Toronto Pr.

Williams, Lachlan J. & Lee, Ethan N. Australia: Economics, Political & Social Issues. 2008. 89.00 *(978-1-60456-856-1(9))* Nova Science Pubs., Inc.

AUSTRALIA—ECONOMIC POLICY

Edwards, Lindy. How to Argue with an Economist: Reopening Political Debate in Australia. 2nd rev. ed. 2007. (ENG.). 208p. pap. 29.00 *(978-0-521-69943-3(6))* Cambridge Univ. Pr.

Esposto, Alexis. Drifting Apart. 2009. 92p. pap. *(978-3-639-19189-9(7))* VDM Verlag Dr. Mueller e.K.

Mendes, Philip. Australia's Welfare Wars Revisited: The Players, the Politics & the Ideologies. 2008. (ENG.). 320p. pap. 40.95 *(978-0-86840-991-7(X)*, UNSW Press) NewSouth Publishing AUS. Dist: Independent Pubs. Group.

Organisation for Economic Co-operation and Development Staff. Australia. 2008. 160p. pap. 63.00 *(978-92-64-04822-5(7))* Organization for Economic Cooperation & Development.

—Oecd Economic Surveys: Australia - Volume 2006 Issue 12. 2006. 156p. per. 52.00 *(978-92-64-02635-3(5))* Organization for Economic Cooperation & Development.

Painter, Martin. Collaborative Federalism: Economic Reform in Australia in The 1990s. 2009. (Reshaping Australian Institutions Ser.). (ENG.). 220p. pap. 33.99 *(978-0-521-12056-2(X))* Cambridge Univ. Pr.

Poulos, Patricia. 'Payback' & 'The Devil Called' The Sequel: 'Elders' & 'The Real Story' 2009. (Illus.). 211p. pap. *(978-0-9807439-0-6(7))* Poulos, Patricia Books.

Rawsthorne, Margot & Howard, Amanda. Working with Communities: Critical Perspectives. 2011. 176p. pap. ***(978-1-86335-934-4(6))*** Common Ground Publishing Pty, Ltd.

Williams, Lachlan J. & Lee, Ethan N. Australia: Economics, Political & Social Issues. 2008. 89.00 *(978-1-60456-856-1(9))* Nova Science Pubs., Inc.

AUSTRALIA—EMIGRATION AND IMMIGRATION

Alexakis, Effy & Janiszewski, Leonard. In Their Own Image: Greek Australians. (Illus.). 240p. *(978-0-86806-655-4(9)*, Hale & Iremonger) GHR Pr., The.

Australia, Emigration. How to Settle Successfully in Australia. 2010. 156p. pap. 27.50 *(978-1-4452-7653-3(4))* Lulu Enterprises Inc.

—Two Sides to Every Story. 2010. 96p. pap. 20.95 *(978-1-4452-7649-6(6))* Lulu Enterprises Inc.

Baas, Michiel. Imagined Mobility: Migration & Transnationalism among Indian Students in Australia. 2010. (Anthem South Asian Studies). (ENG., Illus.). 276p. 99.00 *(978-1-84331-893-4(8))* Anthem Pr. GBR. Dist: Books International, Inc.

Bagaric, Mirko, et al. Migration & Refugee Law in Australia: Cases & Commentary. 2007. 499p. per. 107.00 *(978-0-521-69137-6(0))* Cambridge Univ. Pr.

Barkley-Jack, Jan. Hawkesbury Settlement Revealed: A New Look at Australia's Third Mainland Settlement, 1793-1802. 2009. (Illus.). 488p. 59.95 *(978-1-877058-88-2(2))* Rosenberg Publishing Pty, Ltd. AUS. Dist: International Specialized Bk. Services.

Bottomley, Gillian. From Another Place: Migration & the Politics of Culture. 2010. (ENG.). 192p. pap. 28.99 *(978-0-521-12574-1(X))* Cambridge Univ. Pr.

Casimiro, Suzy. Settlement Crossroads. 2009. 280p. pap. *(978-3-639-14383-6(3))* VDM Verlag Dr. Mueller e.K.

Chetkovich, Jean. Irish Migration to Australia After 1945. 2009. 284p. pap. *(978-3-639-11278-8(4))* VDM Verlag Dr. Mueller e.K.

Chilton, Lisa. Agents of Empire: British Female Migration to Canada & Australia, 1860s-1930. 2007. (Studies in Gender & History Ser.). (ENG., Illus.). 272p. *(978-0-8020-9274-8(8))*; pap. *(978-0-8020-9474-2(0))* Univ. of Toronto Pr.

Collins, M. Getting into Australia 3e. 3rd ed. 2008. 194p. pap. 20.00 *(978-1-84528-170-0(5))* How To Books GBR. Dist: Parkwest Pubns., Inc.

Connell, John & Mcmanus, Phil. Rural Revival? Place Marketing Tree Change & Regional Migration in Australia. 2011. (Perspectives on Rural Policy & Planning Ser.). (Illus.). 214p. 99.95 *(978-0-7546-7511-2(4))* Ashgate Publishing Co.

Dennis, Simone. Truncated Travel: Life in the Migration Exclusion Zone on Christmas Island, Indian Ocean, Australia. 2008. xxxii, 213p. 99.95 *(978-1-60497-510-9(5))* Cambria Pr.

Fitzpatrick, David. Oceans of Consolation. (Illus.). 626p. pap. *(978-1-85918-036-5(1))* Cork Univ. Pr.

Francesco, Ricatti. Embodying Migrants: Italians in Postwar Australia. 2011. 331p. pap. *(978-3-0343-0466-5(8))* Lang, Peter Publishing, Inc.

Garbutt, Rob. The Locals: Identity, Place & Belonging in Australia & Beyond. 2011. (Cultural Identity Studies). (Illus.). 264p. pap. 60.95 *(978-3-0343-0154-1(5))* Lang, Peter AG GBR. Dist: Lang, Peter.

Geary, Laurence M., et al. Ireland, Australia & New Zealand: History, Politics & Culture. 2008. (Illus.). 270p. 75.00 *(978-0-7165-2861-6(4))*; pap. 32.95 *(978-0-7165-2862-3(2))* Irish Academic Pr. IRL. Dist: International Specialized Bk. Services.

Han, Gil-Soo. Korean Diaspora & Media in Australia: In Search of Identities. 2012. (ENG.). 214p. pap. 29.95 ***(978-0-7618-5455-5(X))*** Univ. Pr. of America, Inc.

Highley, John. Immigration & the Financial Crisis: The United States & Australia Compared. Nieuwenhuysen, J. P. & Neerup, Stine, eds. 2011. (Monash Studies in Global Movements Ser.). (Illus.). 256p. 115.00 ***(978-1-84980-991-7(7))*** Elgar, Edward Publishing, Inc.

Holz, Carl, ed. Immigration to Australi: Step by Step Guide. 2008. 156p. pap. 29.95 *(978-0-9814695-7-7(4))* Rapid Publishing LLC.

Immigration Law Client Strategies in the Asia-Pacific: Leading Lawyers on Navigating Recent Changes, Analyzing Key Laws, & Looking Ahead to Emerging Trends (Inside the Minds) 2009. 376p. pap. 100.00 *(978-0-314-23132-1(3))* Aspatore Bks.

Jacobs, Keith. Experience & Representation: Contemporary Perspectives on Australian Migration. 2010. (Studies in Migration & Diaspora Ser.). (Illus.). 176p. 99.95 *(978-0-7546-7610-2(2))* Ashgate Publishing Co.

Lenhart, Maureen Bettina. Pflegekräftemigration Nach Österreich: Eine empirische Analyse. 2010. (Forschungsergebnisse der Wirtschaftsuniversität Wien Ser.). (GER.). 298p. 79.95 *(978-3-631-59385-1(6))* Lang, Peter GmbH, Europäischer Verlag der Wissenschaften DEU. Dist: Lang, Peter.

Leuner, Beata. Migration, Multiculturalism & Language Maintenance in Australia: Polish Migration to Melbourne in the 1980s. 2008. (Illus.). 320p. pap. *(978-3-03911-513-6(8))* Lang, Peter.

Mansouri, Fethi & Lobo, Michele. Migration Citizenship & Intercultural Relations: Looking Through the Lens of Social Inclusion. 2011. (Studies in Migration & Diaspora Ser.). (Illus.). 268p. 114.95 ***(978-1-4094-2880-0(X))*** Ashgate Publishing Co.

Markus, Andrew & Semyonov, Moshe. Immigration & Nation Building: Australia & Israel Compared. Markus, Andrew & Semyonov, Moshe, eds. 2011. 224p. 110.00 *(978-1-84980-063-1(4))* Elgar, Edward Publishing, Inc.

Mascitelli, Bruno & Battiston, Simone. The Italian expatriate vote in Australia: Democratic right, democratic wrong, or political Opportunism? 2008. 275p. pap. *(978-1-921421-09-9(6))* Connor Court Publishing Pty Ltd.

McIntyre, Perry. Free Passage: The Reunion of Irish Convicts & Their Families in Australia, 1788-1852. 2011. (Illus.). 368p. pap. *(978-0-7165-3101-2(1))* Irish Academic Pr. IRL. Dist: International Specialized Bk. Services.

—Free Passage: The Reunion of Irish Convicts & Their Families in Australia 1788-1852. 2011. (Illus.). 304p. 74.95 *(978-0-7165-3100-5(3))* Irish Academic Pr. IRL. Dist: International Specialized Bk. Services.

Mizukami, Tetsuo. The Sojourner Community: Japanese Migration & Residency in Australia. 2006. (Social Sciences in Asia Ser.: Vol. 10). (Illus.). 202p. pap. *(978-90-04-15479-7(5))* BRILL.

Myers, Janet. Antipodal England: Emigration & Portable Domesticity in the Victorian Imagination. 2011. (Illus.). 185p. pap. 23.95 ***(978-1-4384-2714-0(X)***, Suny Pr.) State Univ. of New York Pr.

Neerup, Stine. Nations of Immigrants: Australia & the USA Compared. Nieuwenhuysen, J. P. & Higley, John, eds. 2009. (Monash Studies in Global Movements Ser.). (Illus.). 224p. 119.00 *(978-1-84844-636-6(5))* Elgar, Edward Publishing, Inc.

O'Connor, Lily. Dreams of Hope: From Dublin to Geelong. 2007. (ENG.). 281p. pap. 24.95 *(978-0-86322-358-7(3))* Brandon/Mount Eagle Pubns., Ltd. IRL. Dist: Dufour Editions, Inc.

Panich, Catherine. Sanctuary (Routledge Revivals) 2012. (Routledge Revivals Ser.). (ENG.). 218p. 120.00 ***(978-0-415-52533-6(0))*** Routledge.

Renzaho, Andre M. N. Migrants Getting Fat in Australia: Acculturation & its Effects on the Nutrition & Physical Activity of African Migrants to Developed Countries. 2007. (Illus.). 163p. 150.00 *(978-1-60021-496-7(7)*, Bibliotheca Pr.) Nova Science Pubs., Inc.

Richards, Eric. Destination Australia: Migration to Australia since 1901. 2009. (ENG., Illus.). 432p. pap. 36.00 *(978-0-7190-8037-1(1))* Manchester Univ. Pr. GBR. Dist: Macmillan.

Schüpbach, Doris. Shared Languages, Shared Identities, Shared Stories: A Qualitative Study of Life Stories by Immigrants from German-speaking Switzerland in Australia. 2008. (Variolingua. Nonstandard - Standard - Substandard Ser.). (Illus.). 352p. pap. 81.95 *(978-3-631-57947-3(0))* Lang, Peter GmbH, Europäischer Verlag der Wissenschaften DEU. Dist: Lang, Peter.

Thomson, Alistair. Moving Stories: Migrant Women's Lives & Letters,Britain & Australia 1930-2005. 2011. (ENG., Illus.). 352p. 36.95 *(978-0-7190-7646-6(3))* Manchester Univ. Pr. GBR. Dist: Macmillan.

Wright, Christine. Wellington's Men in Australia: Peninsular War Veterans & the Making of Empire C. 1820-40. 2011. (War, Culture & Society, 1750-1850 Ser.). (ENG., Illus.). 256p. 85.00 *(978-0-230-25230-1(3))* Palgrave Macmillan.

AUSTRALIA—ETHNIC RELATIONS

Barda, Racheline. Egyptian-Jewish Emigres in Australia. 2011. ***(978-1-60497-763-9(9))*** Cambria Pr.

Colic-Peisker, Val. Migration, Class, & Transnational Identities: Croatians in Australia & America. 2008. (Studies of World Migrations Ser.). (ENG., Illus.). 272p. 47.00 *(978-0-252-03360-5(4))* Univ. of Illinois Pr.

Cowlishaw, Gillian. Blackfellas, Whitefellas, & the Hidden Injuries of Race. 2008. (ENG., Illus.). 288p. pap. 39.95 *(978-1-4051-1404-2(5)*, Wiley-Blackwell) Wiley, John & Sons, Inc.

Demosthenous, Catherine. Social Inclusion & Exclusion in University. 2010. 184p. pap. *(978-3-639-27669-5(8))* VDM Verlag Dr. Mueller e.K.

Douglass, William A. Global Vasconia: Essays on the Basque Diaspora. 2006. (Basque Diaspora & Migration Ser.). 314p. 29.95 *(978-1-877802-67-6(0)*, Center for Basque Studies) Univ. of Nevada Pr.

Fozdar, Farida, et al. Race & Ethnic Relations. 2008. (ENG., Illus.). xii, 324p. pap. 65.00 *(978-0-19-556050-3(7))* Oxford Univ. Pr., Inc.

Gabbrielli, Emilio. Polenta & Goann. McGilvray, Barbara, tr. 2008. 240p. pap. *(978-88-95145-23-5(2))* Italian Paths of Culture.

Gorman, Sean. White Line Black Lives - the Biography of Australian Football's Krakouer Brothers. 2008. 328p. pap. *(978-3-639-01965-0(2))* VDM Verlag Dr. Mueller e.K.

Haque, Ohidul. Gender, Ethnicity & Employment: An Analysis of Migrant Women in Australia. 2008. (Contributions to Economics Ser.). 230p. 129.00 *(978-3-7908-1999-1(9))* Physica-Verlag DEU. Dist: Springer.

Jupp, James. From White Australia to Woomera: The Story of Australian Immigration. 2nd rev. ed. 2007. 243p. per. 42.00 *(978-0-521-69789-7(1))* Cambridge Univ. Pr.

Khoo, Tseen, ed. Locating Asian Australian Cultures. 2007. (ENG.). 256p. 150.00 *(978-0-415-41148-6(3))* Routledge.

Lally, Janice. The Australian Aboriginal Collection in the Museum Fnr Völkerkunde, Berlin. 2008. 488p. pap. *(978-3-639-03491-2(0))* VDM Verlag Dr. Mueller e.K.

Malinkowa, Trudla. Shores of Hope: Wends Go Overseas. 3rd ed. 2009. (Illus.). xix, 302p. ***(978-3-7420-1634-8(2))***; pap. ***(978-1-881848-12-7(4))*** Concordia Univ. Pr.

Mizukami, Tetsuo. The Sojourner Community: Japanese Migration & Residency in Australia. 2006. (Social Sciences in Asia Ser.: Vol. 10). (Illus.). 202p. pap. *(978-90-04-15479-7(5))* BRILL.

Nielsen, George R. In Search of a Home: Nineteenth-Century Wendish Immigration. 2007. (ENG.). 228p. pap. 19.95 *(978-1-58544-638-4(6))* Texas A&M Univ. Pr.

Osborne, Elizabeth. Throwing off the Cloak: Reclaiming Self-Reliance in Torres Strait. 2009. (ENG., Illus.). xvii, 188p. pap. 35.95 *(978-0-85575-662-8(4))* Aboriginal Studies Pr. AUS. Dist: Independent Pubs. Group.

Perkins, Maureen, ed. Visibly Different: Face, Place & Race in Australia. (Illus.). 186p. pap. 41.95 *(978-3-03911-323-1(2))* Lang, Peter Publishing, Inc.

Pfeffer, Jeremy. From One End of the Earth to the Other: The London Bet Din, 1805-1855, & the Jewish Convicts Transported to Australia. 2009. (ENG., Illus.). 355p. pap. 44.95 *(978-1-84519-366-9(0))* Sussex Academic Pr. GBR. Dist: International Specialized Bk. Services.

Rando, Gaetano & Turcotte, Gerry. Literary & Social Diasporas: An Italian Australian Perspective. 2007. 236p. pap. 35.95 *(978-90-5201-383-1(7))* Lang, Peter Publishing, Inc.

Ravenscroft, Alison. The Postcolonial Eye: White Australian Desire & the Visual Field of Race. 2012. (Illus.). 194p. 99.95 ***(978-1-4094-3078-0(2))*** Ashgate Publishing Co.

Rolls, Eric. Sojourners. (Illus.). 542p. pap. *(978-0-7022-2539-0(8))* Univ. of Queensland Pr.

Stavridis, Stavros & Chibo, David, eds. The Assyrians in Australian Archives 2010. 140.00 *(978-1-60724-993-1(6))* Gorgias Pr., LLC.

AUSTRALIA—FOREIGN ECONOMIC RELATIONS

Botterill, Linda Courtenay. Wheat Marketing in Transition: The Transformation of the Australian Wheat Board. 2012. (Environment & Policy Ser.). (ENG., Illus.). xii, 146p. 189.00 ***(978-94-007-2803-5(4)***, 9400728034) Springer.

D'Sylva, Dalton. Jewels in the Australian Crown. 2009. pap. *(978-1-921578-74-8(2))* BookPal.

Esposto, Alexis. Drifting Apart. 2009. 92p. pap. *(978-3-639-19189-9(7))* VDM Verlag Dr. Mueller e.K.

AUSTRALIA—FOREIGN RELATIONS

Arnold, Lorna & Smith, Mark. Britain, Australia & the Bomb: The Nuclear Tests & Their Aftermath. 2nd ed. 2006. (ENG., Illus.). 272p. pap. 44.95 *(978-1-4039-2102-4(4))* Palgrave Macmillan.

Battersby, Paul. To the Islands: White Australia & the Malay Archipelago since 1788. 2010. (ENG.). 266p. pap. 31.50 *(978-0-7391-2052-1(2))* Lexington Bks.

Baxter, Christopher & Stewart, Andrew. Diplomats at War: British & Commonwealth Diplomacy in Wartime. 2008. (History of International Relations, Diplomacy, & Intelligence Ser.: Vol. 3). 298p. *(978-90-04-16897-8(4))* BRILL.

Benvenuti, Andrea. Anglo-Australian Relations & the 'Turn to Europe', 1961-1972. 2008. (Royal Historical Society Studies in History New Ser.: Volume 66).

A

(Illus.). 230p. 90.00 *(978-0-86193-295-5(1))* Royal Historical Society GBR. Dist: Boydell & Brewer, Inc.

Blaxland, John C. Strategic Cousins: Australian & Canadian Expeditionary Forces & the British & American Empires. 2006. (ENG., Illus.). 432p. (C). *(978-0-7735-3035-5(5))* McGill-Queen's Univ. Pr.

Bridge, Carl. William Hughes: Australia: The Paris Peace Conferences of 1919-23 & their Aftermath. 2011. (Makers of the Modern World Ser.). (ENG., Illus.). 220p. 19.95 ***(978-1-905791-90-3(9))*** Haus Publishing GBR. Dist: Consortium Bk. Sales & Distribution.

Burke, Anthony. Fear of Security: Australia's Invasion Anxiety. 2008. (ENG.). 304p. (C). pap. 29.99 *(978-0-521-71427-3(3))* Cambridge Univ. Pr.

Cleary, Paul. Shakedown: Australia's Grab for Timor Oil. 2007. (ENG., Illus.). xxx, 304p. (Orig.). pap. 26.95 *(978-1-74114-926-5(6))* Allen & Unwin AUS. Dist: Independent Pubs. Group.

Cotton. East Timor, Australia & Regional Order. 2006. 208p. 39.95 *(978-0-415-42984-9(6))* Routledge.

Devetak, Richard, et al. An Introduction to International Relations: Australian Perspectives. Devetak, Richard et al, eds. 2007. (ENG., Illus.). 462p. (C). pap. 56.00 *(978-0-521-68276-3(2))* Cambridge Univ. Pr.

Fitzgerald, John. Big White Lie: Chinese Australians in White Australia. 2007. (ENG., Illus.). 312p. per. 40.95 *(978-0-86840-870-5(0)*, UNSW Press) NewSouth Publishing AUS. Dist: Independent Pubs. Group.

Gyngell, Allan & Wesley, Michael. Making Australian Foreign Policy. 2nd rev. ed. 2007. (Illus.). 339p. per. 51.00 *(978-0-521-70031-3(0))* Cambridge Univ. Pr.

Heazle, Michael, et al, eds. Foreign Policy Challenges in the 21st Century. 2009. 256p. 119.00 *(978-1-84720-915-3(7))* Elgar, Edward Publishing, Inc.

Kelton, Maryanne. More Than an Ally: Australia's Contemporary Relations with the Us. 2008. 238p. 114.95 *(978-0-7546-7367-5(7))* Ashgate Publishing Co.

Levi, Werner. American-Australian Relations. 2009. (ENG.). 192p. pap. 40.00 *(978-0-8166-5815-2(3))* Univ. of Minnesota Pr.

Lowe, David Michael. Australian Between Empires: The Life of Percy Spender, 1 vol. 2010. (Empires in Perspective Ser.). (ENG., Illus.). 256p. 99.00 *(978-1-84893-000-1(3))* Pickering & Chatto Pubs., Ltd. GBR. Dist: Ashgate Publishing Co.

Mansouri, Fethi. Australia & the Middle East: A Front-Line Relationship. Mansouri, Fethi, ed. 2006. (Library of International Relations Ser.). (ENG.). 216p. 94.00 *(978-1-84511-209-7(1)*, Tauris Academic Studies) I. B. Tauris & Co., Ltd. GBR. Dist: Macmillan.

Mansouri, Fethi, ed. Australia & the Middle East: A Front-Line Relationship. 2011. (ENG.). 272p. pap. 45.00 ***(978-1-84885-968-5(6))*** I. B. Tauris & Co., Ltd. GBR. Dist: Macmillan.

McCausland, Jeffrey D. The Other Special Relationship: The United States & Australia at the Start of the 21st Century. 2007. xix, 333p. pap. *(978-1-58487-276-4(4))* Strategic Studies Institute, U.S. Army War College Commandant (AWCC-DSI/Pubns.).

Murray, Lt- P. L. Official Records of the Australian Military Contingents to the War in South Africa. 2007. 620p. per. *(978-1-84574-395-6(4))* Naval & Military Pr., The.

Paul, Erik. Little America: Australia, the 51st State. 2006. (ENG.). 272p. per. 36.00 *(978-0-7453-2539-2(4))* Pluto Pr. GBR. Dist: Macmillan.

—The 51st State: Australia in the US Empire. 2006. (ENG.). 272p. 100.00 *(978-0-7453-2540-8(8))* Pluto Pr. GBR. Dist: Macmillan.

Peter Hruby. Dangerous Dreamers: The Australian Anti-Democratic Left & Czechoslovak Agents. 2010. 420p. 36.95 *(978-1-4401-7501-5(2))*; pap. 26.95 *(978-1-4401-7499-5(7))* iUniverse, Inc.

Stavridis, Stavros & Chibo, David, eds. The Assyrians in Australian Archives. 2010. 140.00 *(978-1-60724-993-1(6))* Gorgias Pr., LLC.

Stavridis, Stavros T. The Greek-Turkish War 1919-23. 2008. (Conflict & Trade in the Middle East Ser.: 1). 105.00 *(978-1-59333-967-8(4))* Gorgias Pr., LLC.

Taylor, Brendan, ed. Australia As an Asia Pacific Regional Power: Friendships in Flux? 2007. (Routledge Security in Asia Pacific Ser.). (ENG.). 224p. (C). 158.00 *(978-0-415-40421-1(5))* Routledge.

Taylor, Brendan, ed. Australia as an Asia-Pacific Regional Power: Friendships in Flux? 2012. (Routledge Security in Asia Pacific Ser.). (ENG.). 224p. (C). pap. 42.95 ***(978-0-415-54092-6(5))*** Routledge.

Thomson, Mark, et al, eds. Asia-Pacific Security: US, Australia & Japan & the New Security Triangle. 2007. (Asian Security Studies). (Illus.). 200p. 160.00 *(978-0-415-41710-5(4))* Routledge.

Tow, William T. & Chin, Kin Wah. ASEAN, India, Australia: Towards Closer Engagement in a New Asia. 2009. (Illus.). xxv, 417p. *(978-981-230-963-1(2))* Institute of Southeast Asian Studies.

Ungerer, Carl, ed. Australian Foreign Policy in the Age of Terror. 2007. (ENG.). 320p. pap. 44.95 *(978-0-86840-815-6(8)*, UNSW Press) NewSouth Publishing AUS. Dist: Independent Pubs. Group.

Walton, David. Australia, Japan & Southeast Asia: Early Post-War Initiatives in Regional Diplomacy. 2011. (Asian Political, Economic & Security Issues Ser.). 140.00 ***(978-1-61470-811-7(8))*** Nova Science Pubs., Inc.

Wang, Yi. Australia-China Relations Post 1949: Sixty Years of Trade & Politics. 2012. 266p. 114.95 ***(978-1-4094-3728-4(0))*** Ashgate Publishing Co.

Waters, Christopher. Australia & Appeasement: Imperial Foreign Policy & the Origins of World War II. 2011. (ENG., Illus.). 320p. 99.00 ***(978-1-84885-998-2(8))*** I. B. Tauris & Co., Ltd. GBR. Dist: Macmillan.

Woolcott, Richard & Wollcott, Richard. Undiplomatic Activities. 2009. (ENG.). 208p. pap. 19.95 *(978-1-921372-31-5(1))* Scribe Pubns. AUS. Dist: Independent Pubs. Group.

AUSTRALIA—GENEALOGY

Aldridge, Franklin Rudolph & Aldridge, Daisy. Aldridge Family Genealogy & History: The Descendants of Jesse Aldridge & Rachel Cobb. 2011. 114p. 39.95 ***(978-1-258-07721-1(3))*** Literary Licensing, LLC.

Blaich, Irene & Blaich, Horst. The Wennagel Story: The Fate of the Wennagel Families of Master Builders from the Black Forest, Germany, the Templer Settlements in the Holy Land & on to Australia from 1699-2007. 2007. (ENG., Illus.). 498p. pap. 50.00 *(978-1-4251-2629-2(4))* Trafford Publishing.

Brand, Heather, ed. Red Hot: Asian Art Today from the Chaney Family Collection. 2008. (ENG., Illus.). 208p. pap. 39.95 *(978-0-300-13889-4(X))* Museum of Fine Arts, Houston.

Causland, Gladys E. Five Generations of Life, Strife, Spice. 2011. 248p. 46.95 ***(978-1-258-06996-4(2))*** Literary Licensing, LLC.

Davidson, Iain & McDougall, Russell, eds. The Roth Family, Anthropology, & Colonial Administration. 2008. (Univ Col London Inst Arch Pub Ser.). (ENG., Illus.). 304p. 94.00 *(978-1-59874-228-2(0))* Left Coast Pr., Inc.

Kimber, S. A. Descendants of Richard Kimber: General History of the Descendants of Richard Kimber of Grove, Berks., England. fac. ed. 91p. pap. 17.50 *(978-0-7404-0626-3(4))* Higginson Bk. Co.

AUSTRALIA—GUIDEBOOKS

Adam, Dawne. Hell's Airport: from Commitment to Incarceration & Back Again. 2009. 56p. pap. 19.02 *(978-0-557-10000-2(3))* Lulu Enterprises Inc.

Beletsky, Les. Australia: The East. 2006. (Travellers' Wildlife Guides). (ENG., Illus.). 520p. pap. 29.95 *(978-1-56656-614-8(2))* Interlink Publishing Group, Inc.

Collins, M. Getting into Australia 3e. 3rd ed. 2008. 194p. pap. 20.00 *(978-1-84528-170-0(5))* How To Books GBR. Dist: Parkwest Pubns., Inc.

Cromarty, Jim. Sydney, Australia. 2007. (ENG.). 112p. pap. 7.99 *(978-1-84550-234-8(5))* Christian Focus Pubns. GBR. Dist: STL Distribution North America.

Darroch, Donald. East Coast Australia. 4th ed. 2010. (Footprint - Handbooks Ser.). (ENG., Illus.). 352p. 24.95 *(978-1-907263-09-5(8))* Footprint Handbooks GBR. Dist: Globe Pequot Pr., The.

Donald, Darroch. Brisbane & Queensland Footprint Focus. 2012. (Footprint Focus Ser.). (ENG., Illus.). 144p. pap. 12.95 *(978-1-908206-46-6(2))* Footprint Handbooks GBR. Dist: Globe Pequot Pr., The.

Dorling Kindersley Publishing Staff. DK Eyewitness Travel Guide: Australia: Australia. 2012. (Eyewitness Travel Guides). (ENG.). 616p. pap. 30.00 *(978-0-7566-8414-3(5))* Dorling Kindersley Publishing, Inc.

—Eyewitness Travel Back Roads Australia. 2011. (Eyewitness travel back Roads Ser.). (ENG.). 264p. pap. 25.00 *(978-0-7566-6961-4(8))* Dorling Kindersley Publishing, Inc.

Duman, Roberta. A City by City Guide to Living & Working in Australia. 2006. (Illus.). 274p. per. 26.00 *(978-1-84528-089-5(X))* Parkwest Pubns., Inc.

Egginton, Jane. Working & Living in Australia, 2nd. 2nd ed. 2009. (ENG., Illus.). 296p. pap. *(978-1-86011-406-9(7))* Cadogan Guides GBR. Dist: Globe Pequot Pr., The.

Elder, Bruce. Australia Travel Pack, 9th. 2011. (Globetrotter Travel Packs Ser.). (ENG., Illus.). 128p. 14.95 *(978-1-84773-969-8(5)*, Globetrotter) New Holland Pubs., Ltd. GBR. Dist: Globe Pequot Pr., The.

—Queensland. 2nd ed. 2008. (Globetrotter Travel Packs Ser.). (ENG., Illus.). 128p. pap. 14.95 *(978-1-84773-036-7(1))* New Holland Pubs., Ltd. GBR. Dist: Globe Pequot Pr., The.

Explorer Publishing, creator. Sydney Explorer Residents' Guide. 2007. (Explorer (Explorer Publishing) Ser.). (ENG., Illus.). 418p. pap. 24.95 *(978-976-8182-90-6(3))* Explorer Publishing UAE. Dist: Globe Pequot Pr., The.

Fodor's Travel Publications, Inc. Staff. Fodor's Australia, 21st Edition. 2012. (Full-Color Gold Guides). (ENG.). 752p. pap. 26.99 ***(978-0-307-92844-3(6)***, Fodor's) Fodor's Travel Pubns.

Gibney, James. A bit about Japan, India, New Zealand & Queensland Too. 2010. 130p. pap. 19.00 *(978-0-557-53506-4(9))* Lulu Enterprises Inc.

Gray, Vicky. Didgeridoos & Didgeridon'ts: A Brit's Guide to Moving Your Life down Under. 2009. (Illus.). 208p. pap. *(978-1-905430-53-6(1))* Lean Marketing Pr.

Greenwood, Simon & Greenwood, Fiona. The Greenwood Guides to Australia & New Zealand, Canada, & South Africa: The Greenwood Guide to Australia & New Zealand-Special Hand-Picked Accommodation. (Illus.). 264p. pap. 19.95 *(978-0-9537980-1-8(1))* Greenwood Guides GBR. Dist: CPG Publishing, Inc.

—Greenwood Guides to Australia & New Zealand, Canada, & South Africa: The Greenwood Guide to Canada-Special Hand-Picked Accommodation. (Illus.). 136p. pap. 15.95 *(978-0-9537980-3-2(8))* Greenwood Guides GBR. Dist: CPG Publishing, Inc.

—Greenwood Guides to Australia & New Zealand, Canada, & South Africa: The Greenwood Guide to South Africa-Special Hand-Picked Accommodation. 2nd ed. (Illus.). 224p. pap. 19.95 *(978-0-9537980-2-5(X))* Greenwood Guides GBR. Dist: CPG Publishing, Inc.

Gregg, Emma. The Rough Guide to East Coast Australia. 2011. 568p. 24.99 *(978-1-4053-8265-6(1))* Rough Guides, Ltd. GBR. Dist: Dorling Kindersley Publishing, Inc.

Halliday, James. Wine Atlas of Australia. 2009. (ENG., Illus.). 320p. 50.00 *(978-1-74066-685-5(2))* Hardie Grant Bks. AUS. Dist: Independent Pubs. Group.

Hampshire, David. Living & Working in Australia: A Survival Handbook. 7th ed. 2011. (ENG., Illus.). 400p. pap. 25.95 *(978-1-907339-25-7(6))* Survival Bks., Ltd.

Insight Guides. Australia Insight Guide. rev. ed. 2009. (Insight Guides). (ENG., Illus.). 400p. pap. 24.99 *(978-981-282-056-3(6))* APA Publications Services SGP. Dist: Ingram Pub. Services.

—Australia Insight Guide. 6th ed. 2011. (Insight Guides). (Illus.). 400p. pap. 24.99 *(978-1-78005-010-2(0))* APA Publications Services SGP. Dist: Ingram Pub. Services.

—Melbourne Insight City Guide. 2nd ed. 2011. (City Guide Ser.). (ENG., Illus.). 320p. pap. 19.99 *(978-981-282-369-4(7))* APA Publications Services SGP. Dist: Ingram Pub. Services.

Jack, R. Ian. Exploring the Hawkesbury. 2nd ed. (Illus.). 176p. pap. *(978-0-86417-360-7(1)*, Kangaroo Pr.) Simon & Schuster Australia.

Kunz, Martin & teNeues. Australia/Pacific. 2009. (ENG., Illus.). pap. 12.95 *(978-3-8327-9309-8(7))* teNeues Publishing Co.

Leonard, Gary. Eucalypts of the Sydney Region: A Bushwalker's Guide. 2nd ed. 2007. (ENG.). 96p. pap. 25.95 *(978-0-86840-862-0(X)*, UNSW Press) NewSouth Publishing AUS. Dist: Independent Pubs. Group.

Little Hills Press Staff. Backpackers Guide to Australia. Hormillosa, Dan & Baker, Chris, eds. (Illus.). 480p. 14.95 *(978-1-86315-223-5(7))* Little Hills Pr. AUS. Dist: CPG Publishing, Inc.

Llewellyn, Marc, et al. Frommer's Australia 2012. 18th ed. 2012. (Frommer's Color Complete Ser.). (ENG., Illus.). 832p. pap. 26.99 ***(978-1-118-06506-8(9)***, Frommers) Wiley, John & Sons, Inc.

Lonely Planet Staff, et al. Central Australia: Adelaide to Darwin. 5th rev. ed. 2009. (Regional Guide Ser.). (ENG., Illus.). 336p. pap. 22.99 *(978-1-74104-663-2(7))* Lonely Planet Pubns.

—Cycling Australia. 2nd ed. 2009. (Cycling Ser.). (ENG., Illus.). 372p. pap. 24.99 *(978-1-74104-040-1(X))* Lonely Planet Pubns.

Louis, Regis. East Coast Australia. 4th rev. ed. 2011. (Regional Guide Ser.). (ENG., Illus.). 524p. pap. 24.99 *(978-1-74179-471-7(4))* Lonely Planet Pubns.

Maxwell, Virginia & McClymont, David. Australia Berlitz Handbook. 2011. (Illus.). 304p. pap. 17.99 ***(978-981-268-901-6(X))*** APA Publications Services SGP. Dist: Ingram Pub. Services.

Metusela, Christine & Waitt, Gordon. Tourism & Australian Beach Cultures: Revealing Bodies. 2012. (Tourism & Cultural Change Ser.). (ENG.). 200p. 129.95 ***(978-1-84541-286-9(9))***; pap. 39.95 ***(978-1-84541-285-2(0))*** Channel View Pubns., Ltd. GBR. Dist: Univ. of Toronto Pr.

MONACO BOOKS, compiled by. Dream Routes: Australia & New Zealand, 1 vol. 2010. (ENG., Illus.). 256p. 29.95 *(978-3-89944-534-3(1)*, Monaco Bks.) Verlag Wolfgang Kunth GmbH & Co. KG DEU. Dist: Innovative Logistics.

Moran, Pip & Muir, Jenni. AAA Spiral Australia. 6th ed. 2011. 222p. spiral bd. 17.95 *(978-1-59508-424-8(X))* AAA.

Neilson, Jeff & Collins Publishers Staff. Going to Live in Australia. 2nd ed. 2008. (Illus.). 258p. 22.00 *(978-1-84528-261-5(2))* How To Books GBR. Dist: Parkwest Pubns., Inc.

O'Brien, Katrina & Swaffer, Andrew. West Coast Australia Handbook. 4th ed. 2012. (Footprint - Handbooks Ser.). (ENG., Illus.). 404p. 24.95 *(978-1-907263-24-8(1))* Footprint Handbooks GBR. Dist: Globe Pequot Pr., The.

Parish, Steve. Eccentric Australia. 2008. (Bradt Travel Guide Ser.). (ENG., Illus.). 128p. pap. 19.99 *(978-1-84162-237-8(0))* Bradt Travel Guides GBR. Dist: Globe Pequot Pr., The.

Parry, Tom. Australia: Hitchhiking the Outback. 2006. (ENG.). 256p. per. 18.50 *(978-1-85788-390-9(X))* Ebsco Publishing.

Pascoe, Bruce & AIATSIS. The Little Red Yellow Black Book: An Introduction to Indigenous Australia. 2009. (ENG., Illus.). 156p. pap. 13.95 *(978-0-85575-615-4(2))* Aboriginal Studies Pr. AUS. Dist: Independent Pubs. Group.

Penney, Barry. Australia: The Essential Guide to Customs & Culture. 2006. (Culture Smart! A Quick Guide to Customs & Etiquette Ser.). (ENG., Illus.). 168p. pap. 9.95 *(978-1-85733-310-7(1))* Kuperard Pubs. GBR. Dist: Random Hse., Inc.

Penrith, Deborah. Australia. 5th ed. 2008. (ENG., Illus.). 320p. pap. 24.95 *(978-1-85458-418-2(9))* Crimson Publishing, Ltd. GBR. Dist: National Bk. Network.

Rawlings, Charles & Worby, Meg. Australia. 16th rev. ed. 2011. (Country Travel Guide Ser.). (ENG., Illus.). 1088p. pap. 29.99 *(978-1-74179-807-4(8))* Lonely Planet Pubns.

Rawlings-Way, Charles. Discover Australia, 40 vols. 2nd rev. ed. 2012. (Country Guide Ser.). (ENG., Illus.). 408p. pap. 25.99 *(978-1-74220-111-5(3))* Lonely Planet Pubns.

Rough, Guides. The Rough Guide to Australia. 10th ed. 2011. (ENG., Illus.). 1108p. 26.99 *(978-1-4053-8225-0(2))* Rough Guides, Ltd. GBR. Dist: Dorling Kindersley Publishing, Inc.

Sharp, Ilsa. Australia, 1 vol. 2008. (CultureShock! Ser.). 432p. pap. 15.95 *(978-0-7614-5472-4(1))* Marshall Cavendish Corp.

Smith, Roff. National Geographic Traveler - Australia. 4th rev. ed. 2010. (ENG., Illus.). 400p. pap. 27.95 *(978-1-4262-0596-5(1)*, National Geographic) National Geographic Society.

Southern, Carl, ed. The Australian Bed & Breakfast 2010. 2009. (ENG., Illus.). 276p. pap. 16.95 *(978-1-58980-793-8(6))* Pelican Publishing Co., Inc.

Southern, Carl, ed. The Australian Bed & Breakfast Book 2012. 2012. (Illus.). 288p. pap. 31.95 ***(978-0-9758040-7-0(3))*** Inn Australia AUS. Dist: Trans-Atlantic Pubns., Inc.

Stott, Hermione. Perth Insight City Guide. 2nd ed. 2011. (City Guide Ser.). (Illus.). 272p. pap. 19.99 *(978-981-282-373-1(5))* APA Publications Services SGP. Dist: Ingram Pub. Services.

Swaffer, Andrew & O'Brien, Katrina. Perth Footprint Focus. 2012. (Footprint Focus Ser.). (ENG., Illus.). 112p. pap. 11.95 *(978-1-908206-47-3(0))* Footprint Handbooks GBR. Dist: Globe Pequot Pr., The.

Thomas Cook Publishing Staff. East Coast Australia. 2nd ed. 2010. (Travellers - Thomas Cook Ser.). (ENG., Illus.). 176p. pap. 16.95 *(978-1-84848-236-4(1))* Cook, Thomas Publishing GBR. Dist: Globe Pequot Pr., The.

—Southeast Australia Including Tasmania. 2nd ed. 2010. (Travellers - Thomas Cook Ser.). (ENG., Illus.). 176p. pap. 16.95 *(978-1-84848-237-1(X))* Cook, Thomas Publishing GBR. Dist: Globe Pequot Pr., The.

Time Out Guides Staff. Time Out Sydney. 7th ed. 2011. (Time Out Guides). (ENG., Illus.). 336p. pap. 19.95 *(978-1-84670-206-8(2))* Time Out Guides Ltd. GBR. Dist: Perseus-PGW.

Uden, Tim. BUG Australia (4th Edition) The Backpackers' Ultimate Guide. rev. ed. 2007. (Illus.). 416p. pap. *(978-0-9581796-7-6(0))* BUG Backpackers Guide.

Veltman, Laura. Living & Working in Australia: All You Need to Know for Starting a New Life 'down Under' 9th ed. 2007. 430p. pap. 26.00 *(978-1-84528-183-0(7))* Parkwest Pubns., Inc.

Wallpaper Magazine Editors, ed. Wallpaper* City Guide Perth. 2011. (ENG.). 128p. pap. 9.95 ***(978-0-7148-6263-7(0))*** Phaidon Pr., Inc.

Womersley, Steve, et al. Eyewitness Travel Guides Top Ten Sydney. 2011. (Eyewitness top 10 travel Guide Ser.). (ENG.). 160p. 14.00 *(978-0-7566-7038-2(1))* Dorling Kindersley Publishing, Inc.

AUSTRALIA—HISTORICAL GEOGRAPHY

Dovers, Stephen. Ten Commitments: Reshaping the Lucky Country's Environment. Lindenmayer, David et al, eds. 2009. 264p. pap. 35.00 *(978-0-643-09585-4(3))* CSIRO Publishing AUS. Dist: Stylus Publishing, LLC.

Kleeman, Grant & Peters, Andrew. Skills in Australian Geography. 2nd rev. ed. 2007. 96p. pap. 31.95 *(978-0-521-69265-6(2))* Cambridge Univ. Pr.

AUSTRALIA—HISTORY

Adams, Simon. The Unforgiving Rope: Murder & Hanging on Australia's Western Frontier. 2009. 285p. pap. 32.95 *(978-1-921401-22-0(2))* UWA Publishing AUS. Dist: International Specialized Bk. Services.

Amos, Keith. Fenians in Australia. 330p. *(978-0-86840-170-6(6)*, UNSW Press) NewSouth Publishing.

Attwood, Bain & Markus, Andrew. The 1967 Referendum: Race, Power & the Australian Constitution. 2nd ed. 2007. 196p. pap. 31.45 *(978-0-85575-555-3(5))* Aboriginal Studies Pr. AUS. Dist: Independent Pubs. Group.

Barker, Jason R. & Walters, Rebecca. New Zealand & Australia in Focus: Economics, the Environment & Issues in Health Care. 2012. ***(978-1-62081-208-2(8))*** Nova Science Pubs., Inc.

Barkley-Jack, Jan. Hawkesbury Settlement Revealed: A New Look at Australia's Third Mainland Settlement, 1793-1802. 2009. (Illus.). 488p. 59.95 *(978-1-877058-88-2(2))* Rosenberg Publishing Pty, Ltd. AUS. Dist: International Specialized Bk. Services.

Beard, J. S. Studies in Western Australian History Sheet 3: Great Victoria Desert. (Illus.). 61p. pap. 5.45 *(978-0-85564-085-9(5))* UWA Publishing AUS. Dist: International Specialized Bk. Services.

Beck, Sanderson. South Asia, 1800-1950. 2008. 629p. pap. 25.00 *(978-0-9792532-3-2(3))* World Peace Communications.

Betteridge, Margaret, et al. Red Cedar in Australia. 2008. (ENG., Illus.). 128p. pap. 49.95 *(978-1-876991-19-7(4))* Historic Houses Trust of New South Wales AUS. Dist: National Bk. Network.

Blainey, Geoffrey. A History of Victoria. (Illus.). 2007. 304p. 103.00 *(978-0-521-86977-5(3))* 2006. (ENG., Illus.). 316p. pap. 39.99 *(978-0-521-68987-8(2))* Cambridge Univ. Pr.

—The Shorter History of Australia. rev. ed. 2009. (ENG.). xii, 324p. 22.95 *(978-1-74166-771-4(2))* Random Hse. Australia AUS. Dist: Independent Pubs. Group.

Blaxland, John C. Strategic Cousins: Australian & Canadian Expeditionary Forces & the British & American Empires. 2006. (ENG., Illus.). 432p. (C). *(978-0-7735-3035-5(5))* McGill-Queen's Univ. Pr.

Carboni, Raffaello. The Eureka Stockade. 2007. (ENG.). 124p. per. *(978-1-4068-4198-5(6))* Echo Library.

—The Eureka Stockade. 2010. (Illus.). 102p. pap. 20.00 *(978-1-153-70184-6(7))* General Bks. LLC.

Carter, Paul. The Road to Botany Bay: An Exploration of Landscape & History. 2010. (ENG., Illus.). 416p. pap. 22.50 *(978-0-8166-6997-4(X))* Univ. of Minnesota Pr.

Choules, Claude. The Last of the Last: The Final Survivor of the First World War. 2010. (ENG., Illus.). 224p. *(978-1-84596-631-7(7))* Mainstream Publishing Co., Ltd. GBR. Dist: Independent Pubs. Group.

Christopher, Emma. A Merciless Place: The Lost Story of Britain's Convict Disaster in Africa. 2011. (ENG., Illus.). 448p. ***(978-0-19-969593-5(8))*** Oxford Univ. Pr., Inc.

Clark, Anna. History's Children: History Wars in the Classroom. 2008. (ENG.). 192p. pap. 26.95 *(978-0-86840-863-7(8))* NewSouth Publishing AUS. Dist: Independent Pubs. Group.

Clark, Chris. The Encyclopaedia of Australia's Battles. 2011. (ENG., Illus.). 310p. pap. 26.95 *(978-1-74237-335-5(6))* Allen & Unwin AUS. Dist: Independent Pubs. Group.

Coghlan. Labour & Industry in Australia, from the First Settlement in 1788 to the Establishment of the Commonwealth In 1901. 2010. 342p. pap. 41.66 *(978-1-152-66547-7(2))*; 322p. pap. 39.81 *(978-1-152-66541-5(3))*; 392p.

pap. 46.31 *(978-1-152-66492-0(1))*; 338p. pap. 41.20 *(978-1-152-66545-3(6))* General Bks. LLC.

Coghlan, T.A. Labour & Industry in Australia: From the First Settlement in 1788 to the Establishment of the Commonwealth In 1901. 2009. 604p. pap. 31.99 *(978-1-117-37741-4(5)*, BiblioLife) BiblioBazaar.

—Labour & Industry in Australia: From the First Settlement in 1788 to the Establishment of the Commonwealth In 1901. 2011. (Cambridge Library Collection - History Ser.). Vol. 1. 600p. pap. 43.00 *(978-1-108-03067-0(X))* Vol. 2. 608p. pap. 43.00 *(978-1-108-03068-7(8))* Vol. 3. 614p. pap. 43.00 *(978-1-108-03069-4(6))* Vol. 4. 670p. pap. 45.00 *(978-1-108-03070-0(X))* Cambridge Univ. Pr.

—Labour & Industry in Australia, from the First Settlement in 1788 to the Establishment of the Commonwealth In 1901. 2010. 674p. pap. 47.75 *(978-1-178-12332-6(4))* BiblioBazaar.

Coghlan, Timothy Augustine. Labour & Industry in Australia from the First Settlement in 1788 to the Establishment of the Commonwealth In 1901. 2010. 602p. pap. 44.75 *(978-1-178-11914-5(9))* BiblioBazaar.

—Labour & Industry in Australia from the First Settlement in 1788 to the Establishment of the Commonwealth In 1901. 2010. 324p. pap. 35.89 *(978-1-152-66539-2(1))* 2010. 338p. pap. 35.89 *(978-1-152-66543-9(X))* 2009. (Illus.). 368p. pap. 27.83 *(978-1-150-02801-4(7))* General Bks. LLC.

—Labour & Industry in Australia, from the First Settlement in 1788 to the Establishment of the Commonwealth In 1901. 2010. (ENG.). 616p. pap. 45.75 *(978-1-171-70265-8(5))*; 612p. pap. 45.75 *(978-1-176-48775-8(2))*; (ENG.). 600p. pap. 44.75 *(978-1-176-49601-9(8))* BiblioBazaar.

—Labour & Industry in Australia, from the First Settlement in 1788 to the Establishment of the Commonwealth In 1901. 2010. 346p. pap. *(978-1-151-84782-9(8))* Books LLC.

Crotty, Martin & Roberts, David. Turning Points in Australian History. 2008. (ENG.). 320p. pap. 22.99 *(978-1-921410-56-7(6)*, UNSW Press) NewSouth Publishing AUS. Dist: Independent Pubs. Group.

Crotty, Martin & Roberts, David Andrew, eds. The Great Mistakes of Australian History. 2006. (ENG.). 256p. per. 31.95 *(978-0-86840-995-5(2)*, UNSW Press) NewSouth Publishing AUS. Dist: Independent Pubs. Group.

Dauer, J. C., et al. Australian History 1901 - 2001 As Seen Through Banknotes. 2007. (Illus.). ***(978-0-9728466-1-5(1))*** Dauer, M.D., Edward A.

Dawbin, Annie Baxter. The Journal of Annie Baxter Dawbin, July 1858-May 1868. Frost, Lucy, ed. (Illus.). 724p. *(978-0-7022-2811-7(7))*; *(978-0-7022-3046-2(4))* Univ. of Queensland Pr.

Dawson, Robert. The Present State of Australia. 2008. 491p. 33.99 *(978-0-554-98961-7(1))*; 487p. 33.99 *(978-0-554-99308-9(2))*; 491p. pap. 38.75 *(978-0-554-98962-4(X))*; 487p. pap. 38.75 *(978-0-554-99309-6(0))* BiblioBazaar.

Day, Alan. The A to Z of the Discovery & Exploration of Australia. 2009. (A to Z Guide Ser.: No. 27). (ENG.). 370p. pap. 34.45 *(978-0-8108-6810-6(5))* Scarecrow Pr., Inc.

Dekar, Paul R. Community of the Transfiguration: The Journey of a New Monastic Community. 2008. (New Monastic Library: Resources for Radical Discipleship Ser.). (Illus.). 186p. pap. 23.00 *(978-1-55635-430-4(4)*, Wipf & Stock Pubs.

Dent, Warren. Free Settlers & Convicts in Early Australia: A Short History of the Dents & the Taylors 1633-2010. 2010. pap. 34.95 *(978-0-7414-6108-7(0))* Infinity Publishing.

Docherty, James C. The A to Z of Australia. 2010. (A to Z Guide Ser.). (ENG.). 554p. pap. 34.45 *(978-0-8108-7634-7(5))* Scarecrow Pr., Inc.

—Historical Dictionary of Australia. 3rd ed. 2007. (Historical Dictionaries of Asia, Oceania, & the Middle East Ser.). (ENG., Illus.). 552p. 128.00 *(978-0-8108-5612-7(3))* Scarecrow Pr., Inc.

Drake-Brockman, Henrietta. Voyage to Disaster. 2006. (Illus.). 324p. reprint ed. 49.50 *(978-1-920694-72-2(2))* UWA Publishing AUS. Dist: International Specialized Bk. Services.

Duffield, Ian. Across Many Boundaries. 224p. *(978-0-7185-0096-2(2)*, Burns & Oates) Continuum International Publishing Group, Ltd.

Eslick, C. & Hughes, J. Bibliography of New South Wales. 435p. pap. *(978-0-86840-154-6(4)*, UNSW Press) NewSouth Publishing.

Evans, Raymond. A History of Queensland. 2007. (Illus.). 328p. 88.00 *(978-0-521-87692-6(3))*; (ENG., 350p. pap. 30.00 *(978-0-521-54539-6(0))* Cambridge Univ. Pr.

Eyre, Edward John. Journals of Expeditions of Discovery into Central Australia & Overland from Adelaide to King George's Sound in the Years 1840-1, Vol. 1. 2007. (Illus.). 360p. per. *(978-1-4065-3397-2(1))* Dodo Pr.

—Journals of Expeditions of Discovery into Central Australia, & Overland from Adelaide to King George's Sound, in the Years 1840-1, Vol. 1. 2011. (Cambridge Library Collection - Travel & Exploration Ser.). (ENG., Illus.). 492p. pap. 35.99 ***(978-1-108-03897-3(2))*** Cambridge Univ. Pr.

—Journals of Expeditions of Discovery into Central Australia & Overland from Adelaide to King George's Sound in the Years 1840-1, Vol. 2. 2007. (Illus.). 392p. per. *(978-1-4065-3398-9(X))* Dodo Pr.

Eyre, Edward John. Journals of Expeditions of Discovery into Central Australia, & Overland from Adelaide to King George's Sound, in the Years 1840-1, Vol. 2. 2011. (Cambridge Library Collection - Travel & Exploration Ser.). (ENG., Illus.). 546p. pap. 39.99 ***(978-1-108-03898-0(0))*** Cambridge Univ. Pr.

Garvey, Nathan. The Celebrated George Barrington: A Spurious Author; the Book Trade, & Botany Bay. 2008. 327p. 49.95 *(978-1-875567-54-6(2))* Hordern Hse. AUS. Dist: Oak Knoll Pr.

Geary, Laurence M., et al. Ireland, Australia & New Zealand: History, Politics & Culture. 2008. (Illus.). 270p. 75.00 *(978-0-7165-2861-6(4))*; pap. 32.95 *(978-0-7165-2862-3(2))* Irish Academic Pr. IRL. Dist: International Specialized Bk. Services.

Genever, Geof. Failure of Justice: The Story of the Irvinebank Massacre. 2006. (Illus.). 26p. pap. *(978-0-9803177-0-1(3))* Eacham Historical Society Incorporated.

Gibson, Ross. 26 Views of the Starburst World: William Dawes at Sydney Cove 1788-1791. 2012. (Illus.). 224p. pap. 32.95 ***(978-1-74258-297-9(4))*** UWA Publishing AUS. Dist: International Specialized Bk. Services.

Gregory, J. W. Australia. 2012. (ENG.). 166p. pap. 19.99 ***(978-1-107-63940-9(9))*** Cambridge Univ. Pr.

Heathcote. Australian Experience. Date not set. 322p. pap. 9.95 *(978-0-582-71178-5(9))* Addison-Wesley Longman, Ltd GBR. Dist: Trans-Atlantic Pubns., Inc.

Heaton, J. H., ed. Australian Dictionary of Dates & Men of the Time: Containing the History of Australasia from 1542 to Date. 2011. (Cambridge Library Collection - History Ser.). (ENG.). 568p. pap. 39.99 ***(978-1-108-03904-8(9))*** Cambridge Univ. Pr.

Heeres, J. E. The Part Borne by the Dutch in the Discovery of Australia 1606-1765. 2007. 232p. per. *(978-1-4065-4445-9(0))* Dodo Pr.

Holmes, Katie & Ward, Stuart, eds. Exhuming Passions: The Pressure of the Past in Ireland & Australia. 2011. 320p. 79.95 ***(978-0-7165-3144-9(5))*** Irish Academic Pr. IRL. Dist: International Specialized Bk. Services.

Horner, David. Australia & the New World Order: From Peacekeeping to Peace Enforcement, 1998-1991. 2011. (ENG., Illus.). 696p. 125.00 *(978-0-521-76587-9(0))* Cambridge Univ. Pr.

Howitt, Alfred William. The Native Tribes of South-East Australia, 2 vols. 2010. (Cambridge Library Collection - Linguistics Ser.). (ENG.). 878p. pap. 65.00 *(978-1-108-00632-3(9))* Cambridge Univ. Pr.

Jampoler, Andrew C. A. Horrible Shipwreck: A Full & Particular Account of the Melancholy Loss of the British Convict Ship Amphitrite. 2010. (Illus.). 288p. 34.95 *(978-1-59114-411-3(6))* Naval Institute Pr.

Johnston, Anna. Missionary Writing & Empire, 1800-1860. 2007. (Cambridge Studies in Nineteenth-Century Literature & Culture Ser.). (ENG., Illus.). 280p. pap. 60.00 *(978-0-521-04955-9(5))* Cambridge Univ. Pr.

Jones, Noreen. North to Matsumae: Australian Whalers to Japan. 2008. 238p. (C). pap. 35.95 *(978-0-9802965-1-8(X))* UWA Publishing AUS. Dist: International Specialized Bk. Services.

Kean, Hilda. People & Their Pasts: Public History Today. Kean, Hilda & Ashton, Paul, eds. 2009. (ENG., Illus.). 288p. 89.00 *(978-0-230-54669-1(2))* Palgrave Macmillan.

Keneally, Thomas. A Commonwealth of Thieves: The Improbable Birth of Australia. 2007. (ENG., Illus.). 400p. pap. 16.00 *(978-1-4000-7956-8(X)*, Anchor) Knopf Doubleday Publishing Group.

Kerby, Robert. The Undermerchant's Woman: A Shockingly True Story. 2011. 344p. pap. 29.95 ***(978-1-4626-2479-9(0))*** PublishAmerica, Inc.

Kerwin, Dale. Aboriginal Dreaming Paths & Trading Routes: The Colonisation of the Australian Economic Landscape. 2012. (Illus.). 230p. pap. 37.95 ***(978-1-84519-529-8(9))*** Sussex Academic Pr. GBR. Dist: International Specialized Bk. Services.

Konishi, Shino. The Aboriginal Male in the Enlightenment World, 1 vol. 2012. (Body, Gender & Culture Ser.). (ENG., Illus.). 256p. 99.00 ***(978-1-84893-216-6(2))*** Pickering & Chatto Pubs., Ltd. GBR. Dist: Ashgate Publishing Co.

Krasnoff, Stan. A Claytons Defense. 2008. 128p. 22.50 *(978-1-60693-268-1(3)*, Strategic Bk. Publishing) AEG Literary Publishing Services, Inc.

Krvacska, James J. Reflections from the Jetty: Using Reason to Reform Your Life. 2011. pap. 19.95 ***(978-0-7414-5515-4(3))*** Infinity Publishing.

Lasry, Lex. The Defence of Unpopular Causes. 2009. (ENG.). 256p. pap. 28.95 *(978-0-522-85495-4(8))* Melbourne Univ. Publishing AUS. Dist: Independent Pubs. Group.

Lawrence, Joan. Eastern Suburbs Walks. (Illus.). 128p. pap. *(978-0-86806-389-8(4)*, Hale & Iremonger) GHR Pr., The.

Livingston, William S. & Louis, Wm. Roger, eds. Australia, New Zealand, & the Pacific Islands since the First World War. 2011. (ENG.). 260p. pap. 25.00 *(978-0-292-72934-6(0))* Univ. of Texas Pr.

Love, Peter. Labour & the Money Power: Australian Labour Populism, 1890-1950. 256p. (Orig.). 2009. 38.00 *(978-1-59740-295-8(8))* 2008. pap. 25.00 *(978-1-59740-654-3(6))* ACLS Humanities E-Book.

Lovell, Mike, ed. & compiled by. Arthur Lovell - Aviation Pioneer & Navigator. 2007. *(978-0-9776414-5-1(7))* LifeReloaded.

MacDonald, Helen. Human Remains: Dissection & Its Histories. 2011. (ENG., Illus.). 236p. pap. 26.00 ***(978-0-300-13636-4(6))*** Yale Univ. Pr.

Macdonald, Helen & Ferber, Sarah. The Body Divided: Human Beings & Human 'Materials' in the History of Medical Science. 2012. (History of Medicine in Context Ser.). (Illus.). 223p. 124.95 ***(978-0-7546-6834-3(7))*** Ashgate Publishing Co.

Macintyre, Stuart. A Concise History of Australia. 3rd rev. ed. 2009. (Cambridge Concise Histories Ser.). (ENG., Illus.). 368p. 81.00 *(978-0-521-51608-2(0))*; pap. 28.99 *(978-0-521-73593-3(9))* Cambridge Univ. Pr.

Macintyre, Stuart & Scalmer, Sean, eds. What If? Australian History as It Might Have Been. 2007. (ENG.). 336p. per. 25.95 *(978-0-522-85174-8(6))* Melbourne Univ. Publishing AUS. Dist: Independent Pubs. Group.

Mahbub, Parvez. Stochastic Disaggregation of Daily Rainfall for Fine Timescale. 2010. 140p. pap. *(978-3-639-25923-0(8))* VDM Verlag Dr. Mueller e.K.

McCalman, Iain, et al, eds. Gold: Forgotten Histories & Lost Objects of Australia. 2011. (ENG., Illus.). 394p. pap. 50.00 ***(978-1-107-40353-6(7))*** Cambridge Univ. Pr.

McKay, Gary. Tracy: The Storm That Wiped Out Darwin on Christmas Day 1974. (Illus.). 229p. pap. 19.95 *(978-1-86508-558-6(8))* Allen & Unwin AUS. Dist: Independent Pubs. Group.

Monash, John. Australian Victories in France in 1918. (Great War Ser.: No. 24). (Illus.). 424p. reprint ed. 39.95 *(978-0-89839-181-7(4))* Battery Pr.

Morgan, Kenneth. Australia: A Very Short Introduction. 2012. (Very Short Introductions Ser.). (ENG., Illus.). 152p. pap. 11.95 ***(978-0-19-958993-7(3))*** Oxford Univ. Pr., Inc.

Nicholas, Stephen, ed. Convict Workers: Reinterpreting Australia's Past. 2007. (Studies in Australian History). (ENG., Illus.). 260p. pap. 56.00 *(978-0-521-03598-9(8))* Cambridge Univ. Pr.

Peel, Mark & Twomey, Christina. A History of Australia. 2012. (Palgrave Essential Histories Ser.). (ENG., Illus.). 328p. (C). 90.00 *(978-0-230-00163-3(7))*; pap. 27.95 *(978-0-230-00164-0(5))* Palgrave Macmillan.

Pudasaini, Madhu Sudan. Erosion Modelling under Different Land Use. 2010. 236p. pap. *(978-3-8383-4163-7(5))* Lambert Academic Publishing.

Richards, Nathan. Ships' Graveyards: Abandoned Watercraft & the Archaeological Site Formation Process. 2008. (Co-published with the Society for Historical Archaeology Ser.). (ENG., Illus.). 304p. 65.00 *(978-0-8130-3257-3(1))* Univ. Pr. of Florida.

Roth, Henry Ling. The Discovery & Settlement of Port Mackay, Queensland. 2011. (Cambridge Library Collection - Travel & Exploration Ser.). (ENG., Illus.). 142p. pap. 19.99 ***(978-1-108-03933-8(2))*** Cambridge Univ. Pr.

Rusden, George William. History of Australia. 2011. (Cambridge Library Collection - History Ser.). Vol. 1. (Illus.). 672p. pap. 45.00 *(978-1-108-03055-7(6))* Vol. 2. 760p. pap. 50.00 *(978-1-108-03056-4(4))* Vol. 3. 714p. pap. 48.00 *(978-1-108-03057-1(2))* Cambridge Univ. Pr.

—History of Australia 3 Volume Set. 2011. (Cambridge Library Collection - History Ser.). (Illus.). 2134p. pap., pap., pap. 140.00 *(978-1-108-03058-8(0))* Cambridge Univ. Pr.

Russell, Lynette. Roving Mariners: Australian Aboriginal Whalers & Sealers in the Southern Oceans, 1790-1870. 2012. (Tribal Worlds: Critical Studies in American Indian Nation Building Ser.). (ENG.). 256p. 80.00 ***(978-1-4384-4423-9(0))*** State Univ. of New York Pr.

Savoy, Sharon. Ballroom! Obsession & Passion inside the World of Competitive Dance. 2010. (ENG & ABK., Illus.). 176p. 24.95 *(978-0-8130-3517-8(1))* Univ. Pr. of Florida.

Scott, Anne M., et al. European Perceptions of Terra Australis. 2012. (Illus.). 334p. 124.95 ***(978-1-4094-2605-9(X))*** Ashgate Publishing Co.

Scott, Ernest. Terre Napoléon: A History of French Explorations & Projects in Australia. 2011. (Cambridge Library Collection - Travel & Exploration Ser.). (Illus.). 344p. pap. 28.99 *(978-1-108-03078-6(5))* Cambridge Univ. Pr.

Scott, Ernest, et al, eds. Australia Vol. 7, Pt. 1: Cambridge History of the British Empire. 2010. 788p. pap. 75.00 *(978-0-521-16853-3(8))* Cambridge Univ. Pr.

Shellam, Tiffany. Shaking Hands on the Fringe: Negotiating the Aboriginal World at King George's Sound. 2009. 267p. pap. 27.95 *(978-1-921401-26-8(5))* UWA Publishing AUS. Dist: International Specialized Bk. Services.

Skippy Productions, des. North Queensland Deserted towns, COOKTOWN-PALMER: Cooktown-Palmer, 9 vols, Vol1. 2007. (Illus.). 56p. *(978-0-9757750-1-1(4))* Hooper, Colin.

Smith, Babette. A Cargo of Women: Susannah Watson & the Convicts of the Princess Royal. 2nd ed. 2008. (ENG., Illus.). 321p. 27.95 *(978-1-74175-551-0(4))* Allen & Unwin AUS. Dist: Independent Pubs. Group.

Smith, Keith Vincent. Mari Nawi: Aboriginal Odysseys. 2010. (Illus.). 216p. pap. 35.00 *(978-1-921719-00-4(1))* Rosenberg Publishing Pty, Ltd. AUS. Dist: International Specialized Bk. Services.

South West Aboriginal Land and Sea Council Staff, et al. It's Still in My Heart, This Is My Country: The Single Noongar Claim History. 2009. 327p. pap. 39.95 *(978-1-921401-42-8(7))* UWA Publishing AUS. Dist: International Specialized Bk. Services.

Stevens, Simon. Colonial Life in Greenough. 2010. 356p. pap. *(978-3-639-22291-3(1))* VDM Verlag Dr. Mueller e.K.

Sutherland, Alexander & Sutherland, George. The History of Australia & New Zealand from 1606 To 1890. 2008. (Illus.). 268p. pap. *(978-1-4099-1835-6(1))* Dodo Pr.

Todd, Jan. Colonial Technology: Science & the Transfer of Innovation to Australia. 2009. (Studies in Australian History Ser.). (ENG., Illus.). 316p. pap. 42.00 *(978-0-521-10984-0(1))* Cambridge Univ. Pr.

Torrens, Robert. Colonization of South Australia. 2009. 348p. 46.95 *(978-1-104-10811-3(9))*; pap. 31.95 *(978-1-104-08510-0(0))* Kessinger Publishing, LLC.

Twist, Graham V. From Aston to Aussie: Adventures of a £10;00 Pom. 2010. 68p. pap. 32.99 *(978-1-4520-8202-8(2))* AuthorHouse.

Twomey, Anne. The Chameleon Crown: The Queen & Her Australian Governors. 2006. 256p. *(978-1-86287-629-3(0))* Federation Pr.

Upfield, Arthur. Up & down the Real Australia: Autobiographical Articles & the Murchison Murders. 2009. (ENG.). 248p. pap. 22.97 *(978-1-4092-5584-0(0))* Lulu Enterprises Inc.

Van Wyk, Susan & Curators of the National Gallery Of Victoria Staff. The Paris End: Photography, Fashion & Glamour. 2007. (ENG., Illus.). 128p. 34.95 *(978-0-7241-0273-0(6))* National Gallery of Victoria AUS. Dist: National Bk. Network.

Victoria Advocate, compiled by. Vintage Victoria: A Journey Through Time, Vol. I. 2007. 155p. 39.95 *(978-0-9796544-0-4(8))* Victoria Advocate.

Walsh, Quentin R. The Whaling Expedition of the Ulysses, 1937-38. Capelotti, P. J., ed. 2010. (New Perspectives on Maritime History & Nautical Archaeology Ser.). (ENG., Illus.). 400p. 34.95 *(978-0-8130-3479-9(5))* Univ. Pr. of Florida.

Ward, Stuart, et al, eds. Australia's Empire. 2008. (Oxford History of the British Empire Companion Ser.). (ENG., Illus.). 340p. 75.00 *(978-0-19-927373-7(1))* Oxford Univ. Pr., Inc.

Waterson, Duncan B. Squatter, Selector, & Storekeeper: A History of the Darling Downs, 1859-93. 2009. 332p. 15.00 *(978-1-59740-790-8(9))* ACLS Humanities E-Book.

Weaver, John C. A Sadly Troubled History: The Meanings of Suicide in the Modern Age. 2009. (McGill-Queen's/Associated Medical Services Studies in the History of Medicine, H Ser.). (ENG., Illus.). 464p. (C). *(978-0-7735-3513-8(6))* McGill-Queen's Univ. Pr.

Webb, Ken. History Matrix Stage 5 with Student CD-ROM: A multi-level Approach. 2008. pap., stu. ed. incl. cd-rom *(978-0-521-71246-0(7))* Cambridge Univ. Pr.

Weller, Richard. Boom Town 2050: Scenarios for a Rapidly Growing City. 2009. 453p. 99.95 *(978-1-921401-21-3(4))* UWA Publishing AUS. Dist: International Specialized Bk. Services.

Welsh, Frank. Australia: A New History of the Great Southern Land. 2008. (ENG., Illus.). 768p. (gr. 12). 24.95 *(978-1-58567-861-7(9))* Overlook Pr., The.

West, Barbara A. & Murphy, Frances T. A Brief History of Australia. 2010. (Brief History Ser.). (Illus.). 368p. (C). (gr. 9). pap. 19.95 *(978-0-8160-8251-3(0)*, Checkmark Bks.); 49.50 *(978-0-8160-7885-1(8))* Facts On File, Inc.

White, Charles. The History of Australian Bushranging V2: 1863-1880 Ben Hal To. 2007. (ENG.). 408p. per. 34.95 *(978-1-4304-4376-6(6))* Kessinger Publishing, LLC.

Wiseman, Judith Proctor. Thomson Time: Arnhem Land in the 1930s: a Photographic Essay. 2006. (Illus.). 212p. 24.95 *(978-0-7306-2509-4(5))* Museum Victoria Publishing AUS. Dist: Antique Collectors' Club.

Wood Street Galleries, prod. Workin' down Under. 2007. pap. *(978-0-9760949-2-0(4))* Wood Street Galleries.

AUSTRALIA—HISTORY—ANECDOTES

Parker, Anne Z. Stories from the Origin. 2007. 186p. pap. 15.50 *(978-0-615-16538-7(9))* Parker, Anne Z.

AUSTRALIA—HISTORY—SOURCES

Swinburne, Gwendolen H. A Source Book of Australian History. 2008. 296p. 25.99 *(978-0-554-34574-1(9))* 2008. 296p. 28.99 *(978-0-554-25271-1(6))* 2007. (ENG.). 268p. pap. 21.99 *(978-1-4264-8568-8(9))* 2007. (ENG.). 292p. pap. 23.99 *(978-1-4264-8625-8(1))* BiblioBazaar.

Swinburne, Gwendolen H., ed. A Source Book of Australian History. 2009. 256p. pap. *(978-1-4099-6288-5(1))* Dodo Pr.

AUSTRALIA—HISTORY, MILITARY

Army Staff, Australian. The Australian Army at War. 2008. 102p. pap. 14.95 *(978-1-4357-5834-6(X))* Lulu Enterprises Inc.

Bigwood, Richard "Barney" & Bigwood BA. Arts. (Hons), Andrew. We Were Reos: Australian Infantry Reinforcements in VIETNAM. 2011. 228p. 29.99 ***(978-1-4628-7664-8(1))***; pap. 19.99 ***(978-1-4628-7663-1(3))*** Xlibris Corp.

Bou, Jean. Duty First: A History of the Royal Australian Regiment. Horner, David, ed. 2008. (ENG.). 560p. 29.95 *(978-1-74175-374-5(0))* Allen & Unwin AUS. Dist: Independent Pubs. Group.

—Light Horse: A History of Australia's Mounted Arm. 2009. (Australian Army History Ser.). (ENG., Illus.). 376p. 55.00 *(978-0-521-19708-3(2))* Cambridge Univ. Pr.

Bradley, Phillip. The Battle for Wau: New Guinea's Frontline, 1942-1943. 2008. (Australian Army History Ser.). (ENG., Illus.). 304p. 56.00 *(978-0-521-89681-8(9))* Cambridge Univ. Pr.

Brown, Martin & Osgood, Richard. Digging up Plugstreet: The Western Front Unearthed. 2009. (ENG., Illus.). 224p. 59.95 *(978-1-84425-542-9(5)*, 1844255425) Haynes Publishing PLC GBR. Dist: MBI Distribution Services/Quayside Distribution.

Chataway, Lieut T. P. & Chataway ., Lieut T. P. History of the 15th Battalion Aif 1914-1918. 2010. 364p. pap. *(978-1-84574-868-5(9))* Naval & Military Pr., The.

Collett, Col H. B. & Collett ., H. B. 28th a Record of War Service with the Australian Imperial Force, 1915-1915. 2010. 250p. pap. *(978-1-84574-865-4(4))* Naval & Military Pr., The.

Connor, John. Anzac & Empire: George Foster Pearce & the Foundations of Australian Defence, 1 vol. 2011. (Australian Army History Ser.). (ENG., Illus.). 248p. 55.00 *(978-1-107-00950-9(2))* Cambridge Univ. Pr.

Etcell, Pamela May. Our Daily Bread - the Field Bakery & the Anzac Legend. 2008. 308p. pap. *(978-3-639-01982-7(2))* VDM Verlag Dr. Mueller e.K.

Fewster, Kevin, ed. Bean's Gallipoli: The Diaries of Australia's Official War Correspondent. 2009. (ENG.). 292p. pap. 19.95 *(978-1-74175-733-0(9))* Allen & Unwin AUS. Dist: Independent Pubs. Group.

FitzSimons, Peter. Tobruk. 2008. (Illus.). 608p. *(978-0-7322-8631-6(X))* HarperCollins Pubs. Australia.

Fleming, Robert. The Australian Army in World War I. 2012. (Men-at-Arms Ser.). (ENG., Illus.). 48p. pap. 17.95 ***(978-1-84908-632-5(X))*** Osprey Publishing, Ltd. GBR. Dist: Random Hse., Inc.

Green, F. C. Fortieth: A record of the 40th battalion A. I. F. 2007. 272p. (ENG.). *(978-1-84734-792-3(4))*; per. *(978-1-84734-730-5(4))* Naval & Military Pr., The.

Grey, Jeffrey. A Military History of Australia. 3rd rev. ed. 2008. (Illus.). 334p. pap. 42.00 *(978-0-521-69791-0(3))*; 348p. 90.00 *(978-0-521-87523-3(4))* Cambridge Univ. Pr.

Harvey, Sgt. W. J. Mm. Red & White Diamondauthorised History of the Twenty-Fourth Battalion Aif. 2010. 394p. pap. *(978-1-84574-871-5(9))* Naval & Military Pr., The.

Johnston, Mark. The Proud: An Illustrated History of the 6th Australian Division, 1939-1946. 6th ed. 2008. (Australian Army History Ser.). (Illus.). 288p. 49.99 *(978-0-521-51411-8(8))* Cambridge Univ. Pr.

Kelton, Maryanne. More Than an Ally: Australia's Contemporary Relations with the Us. 2008. 238p. 114.95 *(978-0-7546-7367-5(7))* Ashgate Publishing Co.

Knyvett, R. Hugh & Cuttriss, G. P. Diggers at War: Accounts of Australians During the Great War in the Middle East, at Gallipoli & on the Western Front. 2008. 320p. *(978-1-84677-562-8(0))*; pap. *(978-1-84677-561-1(2))* Leonaur Ltd.

Laird, Malcolm & Mackenzie, Steve. The ANZACs. 2011. (Illus.). 72p. pap. 22.00 ***(978-0-9864653-0-7(5))*** Stratus, Wydawnccitwo, Juszczak, Artur POL. Dist: Casemate Pubs. & Bk. Distributors, LLC.

MacKenzie, Lieut. M. C. Story of the Seventeenth Battalion Aif in the Great War, 1914-1918. 2010. 380p. pap. *(978-1-84574-861-6(1))* Naval & Military Pr., The.

Maylor, Rob & Macklin, Robert. Sniper Elite: The World of a Top Special Forces Marksman. 2011. (ENG., Illus.). 352p. 25.99 *(978-0-312-64541-0(4))* St. Martin's Pr.

Moroney, Jennifer D. P., et al. Lessons from U. S. Allies in Security Cooperation with Third Countries: The Cases of Australia, France, & the United Kingdom, 1 vol. 2011. (ENG.). 154p. pap. 32.95 ***(978-0-8330-5262-9(4))*** RAND Corp., The.

Moulds, Doreen. Faces of Love & War. 2010. 104p. pap. 8.99 *(978-1-61667-030-6(4))* Raider Publishing International.

Murray, Lt- P. L. Official Records of the Australian Military Contingents to the War in South Africa. 2007. 620p. per. *(978-1-84574-395-6(4))* Naval & Military Pr., The.

Newton, L. M. Story of the Twelftha Record of the 12th Battalion Aif During the Great War 1914-18. 2010. 576p. pap. *(978-1-84574-867-8(0))* Naval & Military Pr., The.

Nichol, N. P. Mc Nichol. Thirty-Seventhhistory of the Thirty-Seventh Battalion, Aif. 2010. 422p. pap. *(978-1-84574-860-9(3))* Naval & Military Pr., The.

Pratten, Garth. Australian Battalion Commanders in the Second World War. 2009. (Australian Army History Ser.). (ENG., Illus.). 458p. (C). 57.00 *(978-0-521-76345-5(2))* Cambridge Univ. Pr.

Schreer, Benjamin. The Howard Legacy: Australian Military Strategy, 1996 - 2007. 2008. (Analysen zur Sicherheitspolitik. German Strategic Studies). 304p. pap. 74.95 *(978-3-631-58477-4(6))* Lang, Peter GmbH, Europaischer Verlag der Wissenschaften DEU. Dist: Lang, Peter.

Short History of the 34th Battalion, Aif. 2010. 54p. pap. *(978-1-84574-875-3(1))* Naval & Military Pr., The.

Spirit of the Forty- Secondnarrative of the 42nd Battalion, 11th Infantry Brigade 3rd Division, Aif 1914-18. 2010. 218p. pap. *(978-1-84574-869-2(7))* Naval & Military Pr., The.

Walker & Buckland. Citations of the Distinguished Conduct Medal 1914-1920: Section 1. 2007. 144p. per. *(978-1-84734-787-9(8))* Naval & Military Pr., The.

—Citations of the Distinguished Conduct Medal 1914-1920: Section 2. 2007. 588p. per. *(978-1-84734-786-2(X))*; per. *(978-1-84734-785-5(1))* Naval & Military Pr., The.

—Citations of the Distinguished Conduct Medal 1914-1920: Section 3. 2007. 524p. per. *(978-1-84734-784-8(3))* Naval & Military Pr., The.

Walker, R. W. Recipients of the Distinguished Conduct Medal 1914-1920. 2010. 224p. pap. *(978-1-84574-862-3(X))* Naval & Military Pr., The.

Walter C, Belford. Legs-Elevenbeing the Story of the 11th Battalion Aif in the Great War. 2011. 680p. pap. ***(978-1-84574-873-9(5))*** Naval & Military Pr., The.

AUSTRALIA—HISTORY, NAVAL

Drake-Brockman, Henrietta. Voyage to Disaster. 2006. (Illus.). 324p. reprint ed. 49.50 *(978-1-920694-72-2(2))* UWA Publishing AUS. Dist: International Specialized Bk. Services.

Yule, Peter & Woolner, Derek. The Collins Class Submarine Story: Steel, Spies, & Spin. 2008. (ENG., Illus.). 390p. 57.00 *(978-0-521-86894-5(7))* Cambridge Univ. Pr.

AUSTRALIA—IN LITERATURE

Arnold, John & Hay, John, eds. The Bibliography of Australian Literature, 5 vols., Vol. 3 (K-O) 2008. (Bibliography of Australian Literature Ser.). (ENG.). xxviii, 751p. 142.00 *(978-0-7022-3598-6(9))* Univ. of Queensland Pr. AUS. Dist: Independent Pubs. Group.

Budurlean, Alma. Otherness in the Novels of Patrick White. 2009. (Anglo-amerikanische Studien - Anglo-American Studies). 178p. 57.95 *(978-3-631-58909-0(3))* Lang, Peter GmbH, Europaischer Verlag der Wissenschaften DEU. Dist: Lang, Peter.

Clark, Maureen. Mudrooroo: A Likely Story: Identity & Belonging in Postcolonial Australia. 2007. 261p. pap. *(978-90-5201-356-5(X))* Lang, Peter AG.

Duke, Michael. Detective Inspector Napoleon Bonaparte: His Life & Times. 2010. (Illus.). 275p. *(978-1-4438-2375-3(9))* Cambridge Scholors Pub.

Frank, Helen T. Cultural Encounters in Translated Children's Literature: Images of Australia in French Translation. 2007. (Illus.). 262p. pap. *(978-1-905763-03-0(4))* St. Jerome Publishing.

Huggan, Graham. Australian Literature: Postcolonialism, Racism, Transnationalism. 2007. (Oxford Studies in Postcolonial Literatures Ser.). (ENG.). 192p. 85.00 *(978-0-19-922967-3(8))*; per. 24.95 *(978-0-19-927462-8(2))* Oxford Univ. Pr., Inc.

Lever, Susan. David Foster: The Satirist of Australia. 2007. 94.95 *(978-1-934043-98-1(2))* Cambria Pr.

Mackinnon, Hamilton, ed. The Austral Edition of the Selected Works of Marcus Clarke. 2007. (ENG.). 544p. per. 42.95 *(978-1-4304-4261-5(1))* Kessinger Publishing, LLC.

O'Reilly, Nathanael. Postcolonial Issues in Australian Literature. 2010. *(978-1-60497-711-0(6))* Cambria Pr.

Snodgrass, Mary Ellen. Peter Carey: A Literary Companion. 2010. (McFarland Literary Companions Ser.). (ENG., Illus.). 355p. pap. 39.95 *(978-0-7864-4152-5(6))* McFarland & Co., Inc. Pubs.

AUSTRALIA—INTELLECTUAL LIFE

Heyward, Michael. The Em Malley Affair. (Illus.). 304p. pap. *(978-0-7022-2562-8(2))* Univ. of Queensland Pr.

Huggan, Graham. Australian Literature: Postcolonialism, Racism, Transnationalism. 2007. (Oxford Studies in Postcolonial Literatures Ser.). (ENG.). 192p. 85.00 *(978-0-19-922967-3(8))*; per. 24.95 *(978-0-19-927462-8(2))* Oxford Univ. Pr., Inc.

Rando, Gaetano & Turcotte, Gerry. Literary & Social Diasporas: An Italian Australian Perspective. 2007. 236p. pap. 35.95 *(978-90-5201-383-1(7))* Lang, Peter Publishing, Inc.

Stokes, Geoffrey, et al, eds. Global Citizens: Australian Activists for Change. 2008. (Illus.). 240p. pap. 38.99 *(978-0-521-73187-4(9))* Cambridge Univ. Pr.

Warren, John & Zitzlsperger, Ulrike, eds. Vienna Meets Berlin: Cultural Interaction 1918-1933. 2nd rev. ed. 2008. (Britische und Irische Studien zur deutschen Sprache und Literatur. British & Irish Studies in German Language & Literature Ser.). 340p. pap. 68.95 *(978-3-03911-853-3(6))* Lang, Peter AG GBR. Dist: Lang, Peter.

AUSTRALIA—LANGUAGES

see also Tasmanian Languages

Donaldson, Ngiyambaa. 2009. (Cambridge Studies in Linguistics Ser.). (ENG.). 380p. pap. 51.00 *(978-0-521-10919-2(1))* Cambridge Univ. Pr.

Ellis, E. Earle. The Making of the New Testament Documents. 2009. 544p. pap. 59.95 *(978-1-58983-438-5(0))* Society of Biblical Literature.

Haddon, A. C. & Ray, Sidney H. Reports of the Cambridge Anthropological Expedition to Torres Straits: Volume 3, Linguistics, 6 vols. 2011. (ENG., Illus.). 544p. pap. 60.00 *(978-0-521-17987-4(4))* Cambridge Univ. Pr.

Napaljarri, Peggy Rockman & Cataldi, Lee. Warlpiri Dreamings & Histories: Newly Recorded Stories from the Aboriginal Elders of Central Australia. 2010. (Sacred Literature Trust Ser.). (ENG.). 232p. pap. 30.95 *(978-0-300-16530-2(7))* Yale Univ. Pr.

Tsunoda, Tasaku. A Grammar of Warrongo. (Mouton Grammar Library [MGL] Ser.: 53). (ENG., Illus.). 2012. (gr. 17-17). E-Book 321.00 ***(978-3-11-026182-0(0))*** 2011. XXX, 751p. 210.00 ***(978-3-11-023876-1(4))*** De Gruyter, Mouton DEU. Dist: de Gruyter, Walter GmbH & Co. KG.

AUSTRALIA—MAPS

AA Publishing. Motoring Atlas Australia. 2012. (ENG.). 218p. spiral bd. 22.95 ***(978-0-7495-7262-4(0))*** Automobile Assn. GBR. Dist: Independent Pubs. Group.

Army Staff, Australian. The Australian Army at War. 2008. 102p. pap. 14.95 *(978-1-4357-5834-6(X))* Lulu Enterprises Inc.

Australia - New Zealand. (Cartographia International Road Map Ser.). (Illus.). *(978-963-352-970-6(0)*, 6970) Cartographia Kft.

Australia Handy Atlas. (Illus.). spiral bd. 17.95 *(978-1-86500-255-2(0))* Hema Maps Pty, Ltd. AUS. Dist: Map Link.

Boraas, Tracey & AA Publishing Staff. Australia. 3rd ed. 2010. (ENG., Illus.). 128p. pap. 25.00 *(978-0-7495-6569-5(1))* Automobile Assn. GBR. Dist: Independent Pubs. Group.

Comire, S. Joshua & Porter, Malcolm. Atlas of Australia & the Pacific. 2010. (Illus.). 48p. (YA). pap. 11.75 *(978-1-4358-9113-5(9)*, Rosen Central) Rosen Publishing Group, Inc., The.

de Tessan, Henry, et al. Sydney: 50 Adventures on Foot. 2008. (ENG., Illus.). 50p. 14.95 *(978-0-8118-6283-7(6))* Chronicle Bks. LLC.

Elder, Bruce. Queensland. 2nd ed. 2008. (Globetrotter Travel Packs Ser.). (ENG., Illus.). 128p. pap. 14.95 *(978-1-84773-036-7(1))* New Holland Pubs., Ltd. GBR. Dist: Globe Pequot Pr., The.

Hammond World Atlas Corporation Staff, ed. Australia & New Zealand. Date not set. pap. 29.95 *(978-0-06-008762-3(5))* HarperCollins Pubs.

ITMB Staff. Map Melbourne Aus. 2010. 8.95 *(978-1-55341-715-6(1))* ITMB Publishing, Ltd. CAN. Dist: Rand McNally.

—Map Sydney Aus. 2010. 8.95 *(978-1-55341-710-1(0))* ITMB Publishing, Ltd. CAN. Dist: Rand McNally.

ITMB Staff & Other Publisher Map Staff. Map Australia. 2011. 10.95 *(978-1-55341-121-5(8))* ITMB Publishing, Ltd. CAN. Dist: Rand McNally.

Rough Guides Staff. Melbourne. 4th ed. 2009. (ENG., Illus.). 284p. 18.99 *(978-1-84836-099-0(1))* Rough Guides, Ltd. GBR. Dist: Dorling Kindersley Publishing, Inc.

AUSTRALIA—NATIONAL SECURITY

see National Security—Australia

AUSTRALIA—NATIVE RACES

see Aboriginal Australians—Government Relations

AUSTRALIA—PARLIAMENT

Malor, J., et al, eds. Annotations to the Acts & Regulations of the Australian Parliament. 490.00 *(978-0-409-49007-7(5)*, MICHIE) LEXIS Publishing.

Millar, Ann & Browne, Geoffrey, eds. The Biographical Dictionary of the Australian Senate, 1963-2009, Vol. 3. 2010. (Biographical Dictionary of the Australian Senate Ser.). (ENG., Illus.). 608p. 65.00 *(978-0-86840-996-2(0)*, UNSW Press) NewSouth Publishing AUS. Dist: Independent Pubs. Group.

AUSTRALIA—PICTORIAL WORKS

Francke, Klaus D., photos by. Australia Flying High. 2007. (Flying High Ser.). (ENG., Illus.). 640p. 24.95 *(978-88-544-0224-9(9)*, White Star) Rizzoli International Pubns., Inc.

Hopper, Steve & Brown, Andrew. Orchids of Western Australia. 2008. 421p. (C). 80.00 *(978-0-9802964-5-7(5))* UWA Publishing AUS. Dist: International Specialized Bk. Services.

Howe, Graham, ed. & contrib. by. E. O. Hoppe's Australia. 2008. (ENG., Illus.). 208p. 49.95 *(978-0-393-06611-1(8)*, 6611) Norton, W. W. & Co., Inc.

Hunt, Susan. Sydney Views 1788-1888. 2008. (ENG.). 144p. pap. 49.95 *(978-1-876991-26-5(7))* Historic Houses Trust of New South Wales AUS. Dist: National Bk. Network.

Images Australia Pty Ltd Staff, contrib. by. Water Spaces Vol. 3: A Pictorial Review. 2006. (Water Spaces Ser.). (ENG., Illus.). 224p. 55.00 *(978-1-86470-081-7(5))* Images Publishing Group AUS. Dist: National Bk. Network.

Lewis, Megan. Conversations with the Mob. 2008. 240p. 45.00 *(978-1-921401-03-9(6))* UWA Publishing AUS. Dist: International Specialized Bk. Services.

Marx, Jack. Jason Benjamin: What Binds Us. rev. ed. 2006. (Illus.). 196p. (C). 99.00 *(978-1-876832-65-0(7))* Macmillan Art Publishing AUS. Dist: Brown, David Bk. Co., The.

MONACO BOOKS, compiled by. Dream Routes: Australia & New Zealand, 1 vol. 2010. (ENG., Illus.). 256p. 29.95 *(978-3-89944-534-3(1)*, Monaco Bks.) Verlag Wolfgang Kunth GmbH & Co. KG DEU. Dist: Innovative Logistics.

National Museum of Australia. A Different Time: The Expedition Photopgraphs of Herbert Basedow 1903-1928. 2008. (ENG.). 224p. 44.95 *(978-1-876944-65-0(X))* National Museum of Australia AUS. Dist: Independent Pubs. Group.

Palfy, Thomas. Australia Illustrated: the Eastern States. 2008. 68p. pap. 34.65 *(978-1-4092-2073-2(7))* Lulu Enterprises Inc.

Parish, Steve, photos by. Great Barrier Reef. 2006. (Illus.). 128p. pap. *(978-1-74021-738-5(1))* Parish, Steve Publishing.

Roeder, Hartmut, photos by. Australia: The Red Continent. 2007. (Illus.). 189p. 59.95 *(978-1-877339-61-5(X))* NZVP Bks. & Calendars Ltd. NZL. Dist: Perseus-PGW.

AUSTRALIA—POLITICS AND GOVERNMENT

Adams, Peter J. Gambling, Freedom & Democracy. 2012. (Routledge Studies in Social & Political Thought Ser.). (ENG., Illus.). 236p. pap. 42.95 ***(978-0-415-54130-5(1))*** Routledge.

Arbuckle, Trevor. Reduce, Reuse, Recycle or Regulate. 2008. 212p. pap. *(978-3-639-02087-8(1))* VDM Verlag Dr. Mueller e.K.

Aroney, Nicholas. The Constitution of a Federal Commonwealth: The Making & Meaning of the Australian Constitution. 2009. (ENG.). 446p. 136.00 *(978-0-521-88864-6(6))*; pap. 51.99 *(978-0-521-71689-5(6))* Cambridge Univ. Pr.

Atkinson, Bernardine. Nuking the World: Ecological Sustainability & Nuclear Power: Critical information about arresting climate change & creating energy security. International Edition. 2010. 232p. (ENG.). 32.45 *(978-1-4269-3356-1(8))*; pap. 22.45 *(978-1-4269-3355-4(X))* Trafford Publishing.

Babidge, Sally. Aboriginal Family & the State: The Conditions of History. 2010. (Anthropology & Cultural History in Asia & the Indo-Pacific Ser.). (Illus.). 292p. 114.95 *(978-0-7546-7935-6(7))* Ashgate Publishing Co.

Barraclough, Simon & Gardner, Heather. Analysing Health Policy: A Problem-Oriented Approach. 2007. (ENG.). 288p. (C). pap. 58.95 *(978-0-7295-3843-5(5)*, Churchill Livingstone) Elsevier - Health Sciences Div.

Barrett, Lindsay. The Prime Minister's Christmas Card: Blue Poles & Cultural Politics in the Whitlam Era. 2011. (ENG.). 264p. (C). pap. 26.95 *(978-1-86487-275-0(6))* Power Pubns. AUS. Dist: Univ. of Washington Pr.

Beecher, Eric, ed. The Best Australian Political Writing 2009. 2009. (Best Australian Political Writing Ser.). (ENG.). 416p. pap. 22.95 *(978-0-522-85632-3(2))* Melbourne Univ. Publishing AUS. Dist: Independent Pubs. Group.

Bennister, Mark. Prime Ministers in Power: Political Leadership in Britain & Australia. 2012. (Palgrave Studies in Political Leadership Ser.). (ENG., Illus.). 240p. 85.00 ***(978-0-230-27321-4(1))*** Palgrave Macmillan.

Bolton, Geoffrey. Land of Vision & Mirage: Western Australia Since 1826. 2008. 270p. pap. 32.00 *(978-0-9802964-0-2(4))* UWA Publishing AUS. Dist: International Specialized Bk. Services.

Botterill, Linda C. & Wilhite, Donald A., eds. From Disaster Response to Risk Management: Australia's National Drought Policy. 2010. (Advances in Natural & Technological Hazards Research Ser.). xii, 212p. pap. 149.00 *(978-90-481-6799-9(X)*, 904816799X) Springer.

Botterill, Linda Courtenay. Wheat Marketing in Transition: The Transformation of the Australian Wheat Board. 2012. (Environment & Policy Ser.). (ENG., Illus.). xii, 146p. 189.00 ***(978-94-007-2803-5(4)***, 9400728034) Springer.

Bramble, Tom & Kuhn, Rick. Labor's Conflict: Big Business, Workers & the Politics of Class. 2010. (ENG., Illus.). 234p. pap. 35.00 *(978-0-521-13804-8(3))* Cambridge Univ. Pr.

Breen, Marcus. Rock Dogs: Politics & the Australian Music Industry. 2006. (ENG., Illus.). 284p. per. 45.50 *(978-0-7618-3469-4(9))* Univ. Pr. of America, Inc.

Bretherton, Diane & Balvin, Nikola, eds. Peace Psychology in Australia. 2012. (Peace Psychology Book Ser.). (ENG., Illus.). 384p. 169.00 ***(978-1-4614-1402-5(4)***, 1461414024) Springer.

Briskman, Linda, et al. Human Rights Overboard: Seeking Asylum in Australia. 2009. (ENG.). 448p. pap. 29.95 *(978-1-921372-40-7(0))* Scribe Pubns. AUS. Dist: Independent Pubs. Group.

Buchan, Bruce. Empire of Political Thought: Indigenous Australians & the Lanuage of Colonial Government, 1 vol. 2008. (Empires in Perspective Ser.). (ENG., Illus.). 272p. 99.00 *(978-1-85196-925-8(X))* Pickering & Chatto Pubs., Ltd. GBR. Dist: Ashgate Publishing Co.

Clarke, Michael, et al. Australia's Uranium Trade: The Domestic & Foreign Policy Challenges of a Contentious Export. 2011. (Illus.). 228p. 99.95 ***(978-1-4094-2991-3(1))*** Ashgate Publishing Co.

Connor, John. Anzac & Empire: George Foster Pearce & the Foundations of Australian Defence, 1 vol. 2011. (Australian Army History Ser.). (ENG., Illus.). 248p. 55.00 *(978-1-107-00950-9(2))* Cambridge Univ. Pr.

Cook, Tony, et al. Government & Democracy in Australia. 2nd rev. ed. 2008. (ENG.). xxxiv, 414p. pap. 65.00 *(978-0-19-556171-5(6))* Oxford Univ. Pr., Inc.

Corbett, Jenny. Laggards & Leaders in Labour Market Reform: Comparing Japan & Australia. Corbett, Jenny et al, eds. 2009. (Illus.). 284p. 150.00 *(978-0-415-49594-3(6))* Routledge.

Crase, Lin, ed. Water Policy in Australia: The Impact of Change & Uncertainty. 2008. (Issues in Water Resource Policy Ser.). (ENG., Illus.). 280p. 95.00 *(978-1-933115-58-0(0)*, RFF Pr.) Earthscan LLC.

Curran, James. Curtin's Empire. 2011. (ENG., Illus.). 652p. pap. 29.99 *(978-0-521-14622-7(4))* Cambridge Univ. Pr.

Davey, Paul. Politics in the Blood: The Anthonys of Richmond. 2008. (ENG., Illus.). 432p. pap. 44.95 *(978-1-921410-23-9(X)*, UNSW Press) NewSouth Publishing AUS. Dist: Independent Pubs. Group.

Day, David. Andrew Fisher. 2008. (Illus.). 512p. *(978-0-7322-7610-2(1)*, Fourth Estate) HarperCollins Pubs. Australia.

Denemark, David, et al, eds. Australian Social Attitudes 2: Citizenship, Work, & Aspirations. 2007. (ENG., Illus.). 320p. per. 53.95 *(978-0-86840-861-3(1)*, UNSW Press) NewSouth Publishing AUS. Dist: Independent Pubs. Group.

D'Mello, Zane. Managing the It Relationship. 2010. 172p. pap. *(978-3-8383-5925-0(9))* Lambert Academic Publishing.

Eburn, Michael. Australia's International Disaster Response. 2010. 368p. pap. *(978-3-639-24062-7(6))* VDM Verlag Dr. Mueller e.K.

Eckersley, Richard, et al. Australia: A Work in Progress - the Natural & Built Environment. Poiner, Gretchen, ed. 2008. 128p. pap. *(978-0-9775076-3-4(7))* Independent Scholars Assn. of Australia.

Edwards, Lindy. How to Argue with an Economist: Reopening Political Debate in Australia. 2nd rev. ed. 2007. (ENG.). 208p. pap. 29.00 *(978-0-521-69943-3(6))* Cambridge Univ. Pr.

Frame, Tom. Church & State: Australia's Imaginary Wall. 2006. (ENG.). 96p. (Orig.). pap. 15.95 *(978-0-86840-916-0(2)*, UNSW Press) NewSouth Publishing AUS. Dist: Independent Pubs. Group.

Georgeou, Nichole. Neoliberalism, Development, & Aid Volunteering. 2012. (Routledge Studies in Development & Society Ser.). (ENG., Illus.). 216p. (C). 125.00 ***(978-0-415-80915-3(0))*** Routledge.

Gregory, J. W. Australia. 2012. (ENG.). 166p. pap. 19.99 ***(978-1-107-63940-9(9))*** Cambridge Univ. Pr.

Gyngell, Allan & Wesley, Michael. Making Australian Foreign Policy. 2nd rev. ed. 2007. (Illus.). 339p. per. 51.00 *(978-0-521-70031-3(0))* Cambridge Univ. Pr.

Hudson, Wayne & Carter, David A., eds. The Republicanism Debate. 290p. pap. *(978-0-86840-277-2(X)*, UNSW Press) NewSouth Publishing.

Hunt, Erling M. American Precedents in Australian Federation. (Columbia University, Studies in the Social Sciences: No. 326). reprint ed. 32.50 *(978-0-404-51326-9(3))* AMS Pr., Inc.

Irving, Helen, ed. The Centenary Companion to Australian Federation. 2010. (ENG., Illus.). 504p. pap. 38.99 *(978-0-521-12647-2(9))* Cambridge Univ. Pr.

Jones, Grant. Social Action & Institution Building in the Three Houses of the Australian Parliament: The Work of Parliamentary Committees. 2006. (Illus.). 362p. *(978-0-7734-5740-9(2))* Mellen, Edwin Pr., The.

Kaplan-Myrth, Nili. Hard Yakka: Transforming Indigenous Health Policy & Politics. 2007. (ENG.). 186p. 68.50 *(978-0-7391-1410-0(7))* Lexington Bks.

Khoo, Tseen, ed. Locating Asian Australian Cultures. 2007. (ENG.). 256p. 150.00 *(978-0-415-41148-6(3))* Routledge.

Kirk, Neville. Labour & the Politics of Empire: Britain & Australia, 1900 to the Present. 2011. (Studies in Imperialism Ser.). (ENG., Illus.). 336p. 105.00 *(978-0-7190-8079-1(7))* Manchester Univ. Pr. GBR. Dist: Macmillan.

Kollár, Matúa. Position of Australia in the International Relations. 2010. 68p. pap. *(978-3-8383-6690-6(5))* Lambert Academic Publishing.

Krasnoff, Stan. A Claytons Defense. 2008. 128p. 22.50 *(978-1-60693-268-1(3)*, Strategic Bk. Publishing) AEG Literary Publishing Services, Inc.

Lee, H. P. & Winterton, George, eds. Australian Constitutional Landmarks. 2010. 468p. pap. 45.00 *(978-0-521-15285-3(2))* Cambridge Univ. Pr.

Lee, Michelle. A Fair Go. 2007. 240p. per. *(978-3-8364-3450-8(4))* VDM Verlag Dr. Mueller e.K.

Lobo, Michele. Reimagining Citizenship in Suburban Australia. 2010. 252p. pap. *(978-3-8383-0150-1(1))* Lambert Academic Publishing.

Love, Peter. Labour & the Money Power: Australian Labour Populism, 1890-1950. 256p. (Orig.). 2009. 38.00 *(978-1-59740-295-8(8))* 2008. pap. 25.00 *(978-1-59740-654-3(6))* ACLS Humanities E-Book.

Lowe, David Michael. Australian Between Empires: The Life of Percy Spender, 1 vol. 2010. (Empires in Perspective Ser.). (ENG., Illus.). 256p. 99.00

(978-1-84893-000-1(3)) Pickering & Chatto Pubs., Ltd. GBR. Dist: Ashgate Publishing Co.

Lucy, Niall & Mickler, Steve. The War on Democracy: Conservative Opinion in the Australian Press. 2006. 192p. pap. 26.95 *(978-1-920694-90-6(0))* UWA Publishing AUS. Dist: International Specialized Bk. Services.

Lucy, Richard. Australian Form of Government: Models in Dispute. 2nd rev. ed. (Illus.). 392p. 69.95 *(978-0-7329-1295-6(4))*; pap. 34.95 *(978-0-7329-1294-9(6))* Macmillan Education Australia AUS. Dist: Paul & Co. Pubs. Consortium, Inc.

Macarthur, Karin. Power Elites & the Politics of Spin. 2011. 140p. pap. ***(978-3-8454-0778-4(6))*** Lambert Academic Publishing.

Maddison, Sarah, et al. An Introduction to Australian Public Policy: Theory & Practice. 2009. (ENG., Illus.). 296p. (C). pap. 55.00 *(978-0-521-70571-4(1))* Cambridge Univ. Pr.

Marchant, Sylvia. The Historical Traditions of the Australian Senate. 2011. 280p. pap. ***(978-3-8433-9485-7(7))*** Lambert Academic Publishing.

Martin, A. W. Robert Menzies: A Life Volume I. 460p. 2009. 68.00 *(978-1-59740-302-3(4))* 2008. pap. 46.00 *(978-1-59740-655-0(4))* ACLS Humanities E-Book.

—Robert Menzies: A Life Volume II. 620p. 2009. 92.00 *(978-1-59740-303-0(2))* 2008. pap. 62.00 *(978-1-59740-670-3(8))* ACLS Humanities E-Book.

McClelland, Alison & Smyth, Paul. Social Policy in Australia: Understanding for Action. 2nd rev. ed. 2010. (ENG., Illus.). xvi, 304p. (Orig.). 59.95 *(978-0-19-556286-6(0))* Oxford Univ. Pr., Inc.

Megalogenis, George. The Longest Decade. 2009. (ENG.). 416p. pap. 24.95 *(978-1-921215-94-0(1))* Scribe Pubns. AUS. Dist: Independent Pubs. Group.

Mendes, Philip. Australia's Welfare Wars Revisited: The Players, the Politics & the Ideologies. 2008. (ENG.). 320p. pap. 40.95 *(978-0-86840-991-7(X))*, UNSW Press) NewSouth Publishing AUS. Dist: Independent Pubs. Group.

—Inside the Welfare Lobby - A History of the Australian Council of Social Service: The Role of Interest Groups in Australian Social Policy. 2006. (ENG.). vi, 145p. (C). pap. 29.95 *(978-1-84519-119-1(6))* Sussex Academic Pr. GBR. Dist: International Specialized Bk. Services.

Miragliotta, Narelle, et al. The Australian Political System in Action. 2009. (ENG., Illus.). x, 316p. pap. 55.00 *(978-0-19-556317-7(4))* Oxford Univ. Pr., Inc.

Moreton-Robinson, Aileen, ed. Sovereign Subjects: Indigenous Sovereignty Matters. 2008. (Cultural Studies Ser.). (ENG.). xvi, 240p. pap., pap., mass mkt. 29.95 *(978-1-74114-724-7(7))* Allen & Unwin AUS. Dist: Independent Pubs. Group.

Murphy, Brian. The Other Australia: Experiences of Migration. 2008. (ENG., Illus.). 288p. pap. 38.99 *(978-0-521-10224-7(3))* Cambridge Univ. Pr.

Noffs, David. The Wool Curtain: An Essay on Australia & Its Politics. Date not set. 15p. pap. 2.95 *(978-0-929875-18-7(4))* Noffs Assocs., Inc.

Northcott, Clarence H. Australian Social Development. (Columbia University, Studies in the Social Sciences: No. 189). reprint ed. 29.50 *(978-0-404-51189-0(9))* AMS Pr., Inc.

—Australian Social Development. 2009. 306p. 32.99 *(978-1-116-67579-5(X))*; 306p. 36.99 *(978-1-116-67578-8(1))*; 306p. pap. 29.75 *(978-1-116-67580-1(3))*; (ENG.). 305p. pap. 23.99 *(978-1-116-67583-2(8)*, BiblioLife); (ENG.). 305p. pap. 24.99 *(978-1-116-67582-5(X)*, BiblioLife) BiblioBazaar.

Nugus, Peter. Monarchist. 2009. 308p. pap. *(978-3-639-18898-1(5))* VDM Verlag Dr. Mueller e.K.

Olsson, Amanda. Election Finance in New South Wales. 2008. 392p. pap. *(978-3-639-05084-4(3))* VDM Verlag Dr. Mueller e.K.

Osborne, Elizabeth. Throwing off the Cloak: Reclaiming Self-Reliance in Torres Strait. 2009. (ENG., Illus.). xvii, 188p. pap. 35.95 *(978-0-85575-662-8(4))* Aboriginal Studies Pr. AUS. Dist: Independent Pubs. Group.

Painter, Martin. Collaborative Federalism: Economic Reform in Australia in The 1990s. 2009. (Reshaping Australian Institutions Ser.). (ENG.). 220p. pap. 33.99 *(978-0-521-12056-2(X))* Cambridge Univ. Pr.

Paul, Erik. The 51st State: Australia in the US Empire. 2006. (ENG.). 272p. 100.00 *(978-0-7453-2540-8(8))* Pluto Pr. GBR. Dist: Macmillan.

Perera, Suvendrini. Australia & the Insular Imagination: Beaches, Borders, Boats & Bodies. 2009. (ENG., Illus.). 228p. 89.00 *(978-0-230-61353-9(5))* Palgrave Macmillan.

Quiggin, J. C., et al, eds. Water Policy Reform: Lessons in Sustainability from the Murray Darling Basin. 2012. (Illus.). 264p. 110.00 ***(978-1-78100-031-1(X))*** Elgar, Edward Publishing, Inc.

Radcliffe, Russ, ed. Best Australian Political Cartoons 2007. 2008. (Best Australian Political Cartoons Ser.). (ENG.). 192p. pap. 24.95 *(978-1-921215-56-8(9))* Scribe Pubns. AUS. Dist: Independent Pubs. Group.

—Best Australian Political Cartoons 2008. 2009. (Best Australian Political Cartoons Ser.). (ENG.). 192p. pap. 24.95 *(978-1-921372-32-2(X))* Scribe Pubns. AUS. Dist: Independent Pubs. Group.

Reeves, William Pember. State Experiments in Australia & New Zealand. 2011. (Cambridge Library Collection - History Ser.). (ENG.). 380p. pap. 31.99 *(978-1-108-03060-1(2))*; (Illus.). 420p. pap. 31.99 *(978-1-108-03059-5(9))* Cambridge Univ. Pr.

Reid, Kirsty. Gender, Crime & Empire: Convicts, Settlers & the State in Early Colonial Australia. 2008. (Studies in Imperialism Ser.). (ENG., Illus.). 304p. 89.00 *(978-0-7190-6698-6(0))* Manchester Univ. Pr. GBR. Dist: Macmillan.

Reinfjord, Kristine. Marginalisation of Australian Aborigines. 2009. 116p. pap. *(978-3-639-15035-3(X))* VDM Verlag Dr. Mueller e.K.

Rhodes, R. A. W., ed. The Australian Study of Politics. 2009. (ENG., Illus.). 528p. 179.00 *(978-0-230-20103-3(2))*; pap. *(978-0-230-20104-0(0))* Palgrave Macmillan.

Rhodes, R. A. W., et al. Comparing Westminster. 2011. (ENG.). 288p. pap. 40.00 *(978-0-19-969558-4(X))* Oxford Univ. Pr., Inc.

Richards, Eric. Destination Australia: Migration to Australia since 1901. 2009. (ENG., Illus.). 432p. pap. 36.00 *(978-0-7190-8037-1(1))* Manchester Univ. Pr. GBR. Dist: Macmillan.

Robson, Stephen. The Clash of Conceptual Languages Around Australia's Mabo Decision. 2008. 264p. pap. *(978-3-639-03165-2(2))* VDM Verlag Dr. Mueller e.K.

Rumley, Dennis, et al, eds. Australia's Arc of Instability: The Political & Cultural Dynamics of Regional Security. 2010. (GeoJournal Library). (Illus.). xx, 323p. pap. 269.00 *(978-90-481-6974-0(7))*, 9048169747) Springer.

Sarangi, Prakash & Löfgren, Hans, eds. The Politics & Culture of Globalisation: India & Australia. 2009. 358p. 90.00 ***(978-81-87358-22-0(X))*** Berghahn Bks., Inc.

Saunders, Cheryl. The Constitution of Australia: A Contextual Analysis. 2011. (ENG.). 338p. pap. 34.00 *(978-1-84113-734-6(0))* Hart Publishing Ltd. GBR. Dist: International Specialized Bk. Services.

Schreer, Benjamin. The Howard Legacy: Australian Military Strategy, 1996 - 2007. 2008. (Analysen zur Sicherheitspolitik. German Strategic Studies). 304p. pap. 74.95 *(978-3-631-58477-4(6))* Lang, Peter GmbH, Europaischer Verlag der Wissenschaften DEU. Dist: Lang, Peter.

Schweinsberg, Stephen. Sustainable Tourism Development & Rural Community Values. 2010. 320p. pap. *(978-3-8383-1824-0(2))* Lambert Academic Publishing.

Sharpe, Matthew & Boucher, Geoff. The Times Will Suit Them: Postmodern Conservatism in Australia. 2008. (ENG.). 256p. pap. 27.95 *(978-1-74175-624-1(3))* Allen & Unwin AUS. Dist: Independent Pubs. Group.

Short, Damien. Reconciliation & Colonial Power: Indigenous Rights in Australia. 2008. (Illus.). 222p. 114.95 *(978-0-7546-4938-0(5))* Ashgate Publishing Co.

Smith, Rodney, et al, eds. Contemporary Politics in Australia: Theories, Practices & Issues. 2012. (ENG.). 460p. (C). pap. 99.00 ***(978-0-521-13753-9(5))*** Cambridge Univ. Pr.

Smith, Rodney, et al. Keywords in Australian Politics. 2006. 217p. per. 45.99 *(978-0-521-67283-2(X))* Cambridge Univ. Pr.

Smullen, Amanda. Translating Agency Reform: Rhetoric & Culture in Comparative Perspective. 2010. (Public Sector Organizations Ser.). (ENG., Illus.). 256p. 95.00 *(978-0-230-58072-5(6))* Palgrave Macmillan.

Solomon, David. Pillars of Power: Australia's Institutions. 2007. 255p. pap. 35.00 *(978-1-86287-645-3(2))* Federation Pr. AUS. Dist: Gaunt, Inc.

Stokes, Geoffrey, et al, eds. Global Citizens: Australian Activists for Change. 2008. (Illus.). 240p. pap. 38.99 *(978-0-521-73187-4(9))* Cambridge Univ. Pr.

Strangio, Paul & Walter, James. No, Prime Minister: Reclaiming Politics from Leaders. 2007. (Briefings Ser.). (ENG.). 96p. pap. 15.95 *(978-0-86840-887-3(5)*, UNSW Press) NewSouth Publishing AUS. Dist: Independent Pubs. Group.

Stuart, Nicholas. What Goes Up... ... Behind the 2007 Election. 2008. (ENG.). 288p. pap. 24.95 *(978-1-921215-86-5(0))* Scribe Pubns. AUS. Dist: Independent Pubs. Group.

Tanton, Robert. Predictions of the Australian Federal Grants to the States. 2010. 128p. pap. *(978-3-8383-6554-1(2))* Lambert Academic Publishing.

Triadafilopoulos, Triadafilos, ed. Wanted & Welcome? Policies for Highly Skilled Immigrants in Comparative Perspective. 2012. (Immigrants & Minorities, Politics & Policy Ser.). (ENG.). 10p. 139.00 *(978-1-4614-0081-3(3)*, 1461400813) Springer.

Tucker, Tony. Corporate Governance in the Australian Public Service. 2010. 300p. pap. *(978-3-8383-8126-8(2))* Lambert Academic Publishing.

Ungerer, Carl, ed. Australian Foreign Policy in the Age of Terror. 2007. (ENG.). 320p. pap. 44.95 *(978-0-86840-815-6(8)*, UNSW Press) NewSouth Publishing AUS. Dist: Independent Pubs. Group.

van Onselen, Peter, ed. Liberals & Power: The Road Ahead. 2009. (ENG.). 336p. pap. 24.00 *(978-0-522-85590-6(3))* Melbourne Univ. Publishing AUS. Dist: Independent Pubs. Group.

Watson, Virginia. Mining Australia's Northern Frontier. 2008. 332p. pap. *(978-3-8364-8334-6(3))* VDM Verlag Dr. Mueller e.K.

Weller, Patrick. Cabinet Government in Australia, 1901-2006: Practice, Principles, Performance. 2007. (ENG., Illus.). 304p. per. 44.95 *(978-0-86840-874-3(3)*, UNSW Press) NewSouth Publishing AUS. Dist: Independent Pubs. Group.

Wittwer, Glyn, ed. Economic Modeling of Water: The Australian CGE Experience. 2012. (Global Issues in Water Policy Ser.). (ENG., Illus.). xv, 186p. 129.00 ***(978-94-007-2875-2(1)***, 9400728751) Springer.

Young, Sally. How Australia Decides: Election Reporting & the Media. 2010. (ENG., Illus.). 352p. (C). pap. 35.00 *(978-0-521-14707-1(7))* Cambridge Univ. Pr.

Young, Sally, ed. Government Communication in Australia. 2007. (Illus.). 347p. per. 40.99 *(978-0-521-68171-1(5))* Cambridge Univ. Pr.

AUSTRALIA—POPULATION

Browne, Elspeth. Empty Cradle. 152p. pap. *(978-0-86840-008-2(4)*, UNSW Press) NewSouth Publishing.

Luck, Gary W., et al, eds. Demographic Change in Australia's Rural Landscapes: Implications for Society & the Environment. 2010. (Landscape Ser.). xviii, 388p. 179.00 *(978-90-481-9652-4(3)*, 9048196523) Springer.

Smith, Stephen. Place & People: New Dimensions in Regional Research. 2007. (Illus.). 203p. per. *(978-0-9757519-3-0(X))* Black Swan Pr.

AUSTRALIA—RACE RELATIONS

Anderson, Warwick. The Cultivation of Whiteness: Science, Health, & Racial Destiny in Australia. 2006. (ENG., Illus.). 400p. per. 26.95 *(978-0-8223-3840-6(8))* Duke Univ. Pr.

Austin-Broos, Diane. Arrernte Present, Arrernte Past: Invasion, Violence, & Imagination in Indigenous Central Australia. 2009. (ENG., Illus.). 336p. 70.00 *(978-0-226-03263-4(9))*; pap. 25.00 *(978-0-226-03264-1(7))* Univ. of Chicago Pr.

Babidge, Sally. Aboriginal Family & the State: The Conditions of History. 2010. (Anthropology & Cultural History in Asia & the Indo-Pacific Ser.). (Illus.). 292p. 114.95 *(978-0-7546-7935-6(7))* Ashgate Publishing Co.

Banivanua-Mar, Tracey. Violence & Colonial Dialogue: The Australian-Pacific Indentured Labor Trade. 2007. (Illus.). x, 270p. (C). 51.00 *(978-0-8248-3025-0(3))* Univ. of Hawaii Pr.

Blackmore, Ernie. Speakin' Out Blak - an Exploration of Finding an Urban Indigenous Voice Through Contemporary Australian Theatre. 2008. 188p. pap. *(978-3-639-06884-9(X))* VDM Verlag Dr. Mueller e.K.

Clark, Jennifer. Aborigines & Activism: Race, Aborigines & the Coming of the Sixties to Australia. 2008. 308p. (C). pap. 35.95 *(978-0-9802965-7-0(9))* UWA Publishing AUS. Dist: International Specialized Bk. Services.

Costa, Ravi De. A Higher Authority: Indigenous Transnationalism & Australia. annot. ed. 2006. (ENG.). 254p. per. 40.95 *(978-0-86840-954-2(5)*, UNSW Press) NewSouth Publishing AUS. Dist: Independent Pubs. Group.

Cowlishaw, Gillian. Blackfellas, Whitefellas, & the Hidden Injuries of Race. 2008. (ENG., Illus.). 288p. pap. 39.95 *(978-1-4051-1404-2(5)*, Wiley-Blackwell) Wiley, John & Sons, Inc.

Elder, Catriona. Dreams & Nightmares of White Australia: Representing Aboriginal Assimilation in the Mid-Twentieth Century. 2009. (Illus.). 257p. pap. *(978-3-03911-722-2(X))* Lang, Peter.

Fitzgerald, John. Big White Lie: Chinese Australians in White Australia. 2007. (ENG., Illus.). 312p. per. 40.95 *(978-0-86840-870-5(0)*, UNSW Press) NewSouth Publishing AUS. Dist: Independent Pubs. Group.

Fozdar, Farida, et al. Race & Ethnic Relations. 2008. (ENG., Illus.). xii, 324p. pap. 65.00 *(978-0-19-556050-3(7))* Oxford Univ. Pr., Inc.

Gorman, Sean. White Lines Black Lives - the Biography of Australian Footballs Krakouer Brothers. 2008. 328p. pap. *(978-3-639-01965-0(2))* VDM Verlag Dr. Mueller e.K.

Hallinan, Christopher J. & Judd, Barry, eds. Indigenous People, Race Relations & Australian Sport. 2012. (Sport in the Global Society â€" Contemporary Perspectives Ser.). (ENG., Illus.). 160p. (C). 125.00 *(978-0-415-58269-8(5))* Routledge.

Lee, Michelle. A Fair Go. 2007. 240p. per. *(978-3-8364-3450-8(4))* VDM Verlag Dr. Mueller e.K.

McGregor, Russell. Imagined Destinies: Aboriginal Australians & the Doomed Race Theory, 1880-1939. 2011. 342p. 51.00 ***(978-1-59740-810-3(7))*** ACLS Humanities E-Book.

Moreton-Robinson, Aileen, ed. Sovereign Subjects: Indigenous Sovereignty Matters. 2008. (Cultural Studies Ser.). (ENG.). xvi, 240p. pap., pap., mass mkt. 29.95 *(978-1-74114-724-7(7))* Allen & Unwin AUS. Dist: Independent Pubs. Group.

Paterson, Alistair. The Lost Legions: Culture Contact in Colonial Australia. 2008. (Indigenous Archaeologies Ser.). (ENG., Illus.). 288p. 90.00 *(978-0-7591-0683-3(5))*; per. 37.95 *(978-0-7591-0684-0(3))* AltaMira Pr.

Shellam, Tiffany. Shaking Hands on the Fringe: Negotiating the Aboriginal World at King George's Sound. 2009. 267p. pap. 27.95 *(978-1-921401-26-8(5))* UWA Publishing AUS. Dist: International Specialized Bk. Services.

Stephenson, Peta. The Outsiders Within: Telling Australia's Indigenous-Asian Story. 2007. (ENG., Illus.). 256p. per. 35.95 *(978-0-86840-836-1(0)*, UNSW Press) NewSouth Publishing AUS. Dist: Independent Pubs. Group.

Trigger, David Samuel. Whitefella Comin' Aboriginal Responses to Colonialism in Northern Australia. 2010. (ENG.). 276p. pap. 27.99 *(978-0-521-13178-0(2))* Cambridge Univ. Pr.

Vickers, Jill & Isaac, Annette. The Politics of Race: Canada, the United States & Australia. 2nd ed. 2012. (ENG., Illus.). 304p. pap. ***(978-1-4426-1131-3(6))*** Univ. of Toronto Pr.

AUSTRALIA—RELATIONS

Battersby, Paul. To the Islands: White Australia & the Malay Archipelago Since 1788. 2007. (ENG.). 266p. 78.99 *(978-0-7391-2051-4(4))* Lexington Bks.

Brawley, Sean & Guoth, Nick, eds. Australia's Asian Sporting Context 1920S - 30S. 2012. (ENG.). 160p. (C). 125.00 *(978-0-415-56049-8(7))* Routledge.

Mein Smith, Philippa, et al. Remaking the Tasman World. 2009. (ENG., Illus.). 296p. pap. 24.95 *(978-1-877257-62-9(1))* Canterbury Univ. Pr. NZL. Dist: Independent Pubs. Group.

Newman, Andrew & Williams, Brad, eds. Japan, Australia & Asia-Pacific Security. 2006. (Routledge Security in Asia Pacific Ser.). (ENG.). 224p. (C). 160.00 *(978-0-415-38139-0(8)*, RU398X) Routledge.

Sarangi, Prakash & Löfgren, Hans, eds. The Politics & Culture of Globalisation: India & Australia. 2009. 358p. 90.00 ***(978-81-87358-22-0(X))*** Berghahn Bks., Inc.

Summo-O'Connell, Renata. Imagined Australia: Reflections Around the Reciprocal Construction of Identity Between Australia & Europe. 2009. 408p. *(978-3-0343-0008-7(5))* Lang, Peter.

AUSTRALIA—RELIGION

ATF Press, creator. Rainbow Spirit Theology: Toward an Australian Aboriginal Theology. 2011. (ENG., Illus.). 97p. (C). per. 5.00 *(978-1-920691-80-6(4))* ATF Pr. AUS. Dist: Brown, David Bk. Co., The.

Bouma, Gary. Australian Soul: Religion & Spirituality in the 21st Century. 2006. (ENG.). 248p. pap. 40.99 *(978-0-521-67389-1(5))* Cambridge Univ. Pr.

Budden, Chris. Following Jesus in Invaded Space. 2011. (ENG.). 256p. pap. 37.50 *(978-0-227-17358-9(9))* Clarke, James Co., Ltd. GBR. Dist: Brown, David Bk. Co., The.

Catford, Cheryl. A New Era for Pentecostal Women Leaders? 2010. 408p. pap. *(978-3-8383-8041-4(X))* Lambert Academic Publishing.

Dekar, Paul R. Community of the Transfiguration: The Journey of a New Monastic Community. 2008. (New Monastic Library: Resources for Radical Discipleship Ser.). (Illus.). 186p. pap. 23.00 *(978-1-55635-430-4(4))* Wipf & Stock Pubs.

Eddy, Glenys. Becoming Buddhist: Experiences of Socialization & Self-Transformation in Australian Buddhist Centres. 2012. (ENG.). 288p. 120.00 ***(978-1-4411-1846-2(2))*** Continuum International Publishing Group, Ltd. GBR. Dist: National Bk. Network.

Golightly Marshall, Brian Leonard. 2012 Mayan Calendar Found in the Great Pyramid & Christ Return. 2008. 694p. pap. 28.95 *(978-1-4092-1992-7(5))* Lulu Enterprises Inc.

Haddon, A. C., et al. Reports of the Cambridge Anthropological Expedition to Torres Straits: Volume 5, Sociology, Magic & Religion of the Western Islanders, 6 vols. 2011. (ENG., Illus.). 462p. pap. 60.00 *(978-0-521-17989-8(0))* Cambridge Univ. Pr.

—Reports of the Cambridge Anthropological Expedition to Torres Straits: Volume 6, Sociology, Magic & Religion of the Eastern Islanders, 6 vols. 2011. (ENG., Illus.). 395p. pap. 60.00 *(978-0-521-17990-4(4))* Cambridge Univ. Pr.

Jupp, James, ed. The Encyclopedia of Religion in Australia. 2009. (Illus.). 822p. 155.00 *(978-0-521-86407-7(0))* Cambridge Univ. Pr.

Napaljarri, Peggy Rockman & Cataldi, Lee. Warlpiri Dreamings & Histories: Newly Recorded Stories from the Aboriginal Elders of Central Australia. 2010. (Sacred Literature Trust Ser.). (ENG.). 232p. pap. 30.95 *(978-0-300-16530-2(7))* Yale Univ. Pr.

Rocha, Cristina & Barker, Michelle, eds. Buddhism in Australia: Traditions in Change. 2011. (Routledge Critical Studies in Buddhism Ser.). (ENG., Illus.). 192p. (C). 130.00 *(978-0-415-56818-0(8)*, Routledge) Taylor & Francis Group GBR. Dist: Taylor & Francis Group.

Tacey, David. Edge of the Sacred: Jung, Psyche, Earth. 2009. 207p. pap. 25.00 *(978-3-85630-729-5(X))* Daimon Verlag CHE. Dist: AtlasBooks Distribution.

Yang, Yong-Sun, ed. Korean Methodist Church in Australia & New Zealand. 2009. (ENG & KOR., Illus.). 236p. pap. 30.00 *(978-1-59689-081-7(9)*, Hermit Kingdom Pr., The) Hermit Kingdom Pr., The.

—Korean Methodist Church in Australia & New Zealand (Hardcover) 2009. (ENG & KOR., Illus.). 236p. 60.00 *(978-1-59689-069-5(X)*, Hermit Kingdom Pr., The) Hermit Kingdom Pr., The.

AUSTRALIA—ROYAL AUSTRALIAN AIR FORCE

Listemann, Phil H. No. 453 (RAAF) Squadron, 1941-1945: Buffalo, Spitfire. 2009. (Illus.). 88p. pap. 38.95 *(978-2-9532544-1-9(2))* Listemann, Philippe FRA. Dist: Casemate Pubs. & Bk. Distributors, LLC.

AUSTRALIA—ROYAL AUSTRALIAN NAVY

Birkler, John, et al. Australia's Submarine Design Capabilities & Capacities: Challenges & Options for the Future Submarine, 1 vol. 2012. (ENG.). 310p. pap. 42.00 *(978-0-8330-5057-1(5)*, mg-1033) RAND Corp., The.

Nott, Rodney & Payne, Noel. The Vung Tau Ferry: HMAS Sydney & Escort Ships - Vietnam 1965-1972. 2008. 253p. pap. 29.95 *(978-1-877058-72-1(6))* Rosenberg Publishing Pty, Ltd. AUS. Dist: International Specialized Bk. Services.

Patel, Malti. Lifting the Mists: For elderly immigrants & their families: an Easy Guide to a Complex Welfare System. 2007. 150p. per. *(978-0-9745683-3-1(3))* Majmundar, Harikrishna.

Pfennigwerth, Ian. The Royal Australian Navy & MacArthur. 2009. (Illus.). 208p. pap. 39.95 *(978-1-877058-83-7(1))* Rosenberg Publishing Pty, Ltd. AUS. Dist: International Specialized Bk. Services.

—Tiger Territory: The Untold Story of The Royal Australian Navy in Southeast Asia from 1948 to 1971. 2008. (Illus.). 317p. pap. 29.95 *(978-1-877058-65-3(3))* Rosenberg Publishing Pty, Ltd. AUS. Dist: International Specialized Bk. Services.

Schank, John F., et al. Learning from Experience Vol. IV: Lessons from Australia's Collins Submarine Program. 2012. (ENG.). 86p. pap. 20.00 ***(978-0-8330-5898-0(3))*** RAND Corp., The.

AUSTRALIA—SOCIAL CONDITIONS

Adams, Simon. The Unforgiving Rope: Murder & Hanging on Australia's Western Frontier. 2009. 285p. pap. 32.95 *(978-1-921401-22-0(2))* UWA Publishing AUS. Dist: International Specialized Bk. Services.

AndresWyn. Making of a Generation. 2010. *(978-0-8020-9258-8(6))*; (ENG.). pap. *(978-0-8020-9467-4(8))* Univ. of Toronto Pr.

Attwood, Bain, et al. Possession: Batman's Treaty & the Matter of History. 2009. (ENG., Illus.). 248p. pap. 26.00 *(978-0-522-85114-4(2))* Melbourne Univ. Publishing AUS. Dist: Independent Pubs. Group.

Baas, Michiel. Imagined Mobility: Migration & Transnationalism among Indian Students in Australia. 2010. (Illus.). xiv, 261p. E-Book *(978-0-85728-680-2(3))* Anthem Pr.

Babacan, Alperhan. Seeking Asylum in a Global World. 2009. 316p. pap. *(978-3-639-15814-4(8))* VDM Verlag Dr. Mueller e.K.

Baird, Marian, et al. Women & Workchoices: Impacts on the Low Pay Sector - Summary Report. 2007. *(978-0-9803798-7-7(3))* University of South Australia - Hawke Institute.

Barclay, Elaine, et al, eds. Crime in Rural Australia. 2007. (Illus.). 224p. per. *(978-1-86287-635-4(5))* Federation Pr.

Beeson, Mark. Far East & Australasia 2010. Europa Publications Staff, ed. 41st ed. 2009. 1588p. 810.00 *(978-1-85743-533-7(8))* Routledge.

Beeton, Sue. Community Development Through Tourism. 2006. (Landlinks Press Ser.). (Illus.). 256p. pap. 43.95 *(978-0-643-06962-6(3))* CSIRO Publishing AUS. Dist: Stylus Publishing, LLC.

Begum, Sharmina, et al. Stormwater Management: An Introduction to Green Gully. 2011. (Environmental Science, Engineering & Technology Ser.). pap. 43.00 *(978-1-61209-311-6(6))* Nova Science Pubs., Inc.

Bertone, Santina. From Factory Fodder to Multicultural Mediators. 2008. 316p. pap. *(978-3-639-02877-5(5))* VDM Verlag Dr. Mueller e.K.

Bolton, Geoffrey. Land of Vision & Mirage: Western Australia Since 1826. 2008. 270p. pap. 32.00 *(978-0-9802964-0-2(4))* UWA Publishing AUS. Dist: International Specialized Bk. Services.

Brigg, Morgan & Bleiker, Roland. Mediating Across Differ Cl. 2010. (Illus.). 264p. 52.00 *(978-0-8248-3459-3(3))* Univ. of Hawaii Pr.

—Mediating Across Differ Pa. 2010. 264p. pap. 28.00 *(978-0-8248-3519-4(0))* Univ. of Hawaii Pr.

Bursian, Olga. Migrant Women ACT. 2011. pap. *(978-1-86335-885-9(4))* Common Ground Publishing Pty, Ltd.

Çagatay, Ifakat Tülay. The Glycosylation of Dichelobacter Nodosus Fimbriae. 2010. 136p. pap. *(978-3-8383-5699-0(3))* Lambert Academic Publishing.

Cardinal, Linda & Brown, Nicholas, eds. Managing Diversity: Practices of Citizenship. 2007. (Governance Ser.). (ENG.). 232p. pap. *(978-0-7766-0654-5(9))* Univ. of Ottawa Pr./Presses de l'Universite d'Ottawa.

Christen, Kimberly A. Aboriginal Business: Alliances in a Remote Australian Town. 2009. pap. 29.95 *(978-1-930618-98-5(0))* School for Advanced Research Pr./SAR Pr.

Chua, Wei Ling. Racism in Australia: The Causes, Incidents, Reasoning, & Solutions. 2011. 248p. pap. 17.99 ***(978-1-4525-0265-6(X))*** Balboa Pr.

Clark, Jennifer. Aborigines & Activism: Race, Aborigines & the Coming of the Sixties to Australia. 2008. 308p. (C). pap. 35.95 *(978-0-9802965-7-0(9))* UWA Publishing AUS. Dist: International Specialized Bk. Services.

Cookson, Peter. The Nature of Support. 2010. 152p. pap. *(978-3-8383-4972-5(5))* Lambert Academic Publishing.

Cowlishaw, Gillian. Blackfellas, Whitefellas, & the Hidden Injuries of Race. 2008. (ENG., Illus.). 288p. pap. 39.95 *(978-1-4051-1404-2(5),* Wiley-Blackwell) Wiley, John & Sons, Inc.

—The City's Outback. 2009. (ENG.). 272p. pap. 25.99 *(978-1-921410-87-1(6),* UNSW Press) NewSouth Publishing AUS. Dist: Independent Pubs. Group.

Cvoro, Uros. The Changing Roles of the National Museum of Australia in Creating Australian Identity: How the Politics of a Nation Shaped Its Culture. 2011. ***(978-0-7734-2547-7(0))*** Mellen, Edwin Pr., The.

De Borchgrave, Arnaud, et al. Conflict, Community, & Criminality in Southeast Asia & Australia: Assessments from the Field. 2009. pap. 21.95 *(978-0-89206-583-7(4),* CSIS Pr., The) Ctr. for Strategic & International Studies.

Denemark, David, et al, eds. Australian Social Attitudes 2: Citizenship, Work, & Aspirations. 2007. (ENG., Illus.). 320p. per. 53.95 *(978-0-86840-861-3(1),* UNSW Press) NewSouth Publishing AUS. Dist: Independent Pubs. Group.

Dennis, Simone. Truncated Travel: Life in the Migration Exclusion Zone on Christmas Island, Indian Ocean, Australia. 2008. xxxii, 213p. 99.95 *(978-1-60497-510-9(5))* Cambria Pr.

Durie, Jane. Locating Whiteness in Western Sydney: Theory, Pedagogy, Identity. 2010. 296p. pap. *(978-3-8383-4625-0(4))* Lambert Academic Publishing.

Eckersley, R. M. Measuring Progress: Is Life Getting Better? (Illus.). 382p. (Orig.). pap. 34.95 *(978-0-643-06296-2(3))* CSIRO Publishing AUS. Dist: Accents Pubns. Service, Inc.

Eckersley, Richard, et al. Australia: A Work in Progress - the Natural & Built Environment. Poiner, Gretchen, ed. 2008. 128p. pap. *(978-0-9775076-3-4(7))* Independent Scholars Assn. of Australia.

Eickelkamp, Ute, ed. Growing up in Central Australia: New Anthropological Studies of Aboriginal Childhood & Adolescence. 2011. (Illus.). 310p. 95.00 *(978-0-85745-082-1(4))* Berghahn Bks., Inc.

Elton, Jude, et al. Women & Workchoices: Impacts on the Low Pay Sector - Full Report. 2007. *(978-0-9803798-8-4(1))* University of South Australia - Hawke Institute.

Evans, Geoffrey. A Just Transition to Sustainability in a Climate Change Hot-Spot. 2010. 376p. pap. *(978-3-639-14571-7(2))* VDM Verlag Dr. Mueller e.K.

Fitzgerald, John. Big White Lie: Chinese Australians in White Australia. 2007. (ENG., Illus.). 312p. per. 40.95 *(978-0-86840-870-5(0),* UNSW Press) NewSouth Publishing AUS. Dist: Independent Pubs. Group.

Francesco, Ricatti. Embodying Migrants: Italians in Postwar Australia. 2011. 331p. pap. *(978-3-0343-0466-5(8))* Lang, Peter Publishing, Inc.

Franzke, Leonora. Aboriginal Australi. 2008. 72p. pap. *(978-3-639-05125-4(4))* VDM Verlag Dr. Mueller e.K.

Gillespie, Alexander & Burns, William C. G., eds. Climate Change in the South Pacific: Impacts & Responses in Australia, New Zealand, & Small Island States: Impacts & Responses in Australia, New Zealand, & Small Island States. 2010. (Advances in Global Change Research Ser.). 396p. pap. 239.00 *(978-90-481-5365-7(4),* 9048153654) Springer.

Gothard, Jan, ed. Asian Orientations. (Studies in Western Australian History: Vol. XVI). pap. *(978-0-86422-435-4(4))* UWA Publishing AUS. Dist: International Specialized Bk. Services.

Green, Ed. 'Staying Bush' The Lives of Gay Men in Rural Australia. 2008. 460p. pap. *(978-3-639-01780-9(3))* VDM Verlag Dr. Mueller e.K.

Guggisberg, Manuela & Guggisberg, Marika. Can Children from Minority Backgrounds Be Gifted? 2010. 84p. pap. *(978-3-8383-9266-0(3))* Lambert Academic Publishing.

Habibis, Daphne & Walter, Maggie. Social Inequality in Australia: Discourses, Realities & Futures. Hatton, T. Alan, ed. 2008. (ENG.). xviii, 310p. pap. 75.00 *(978-0-19-555909-5(6))* Oxford Univ. Pr., Inc.

Haddon, A. C., et al. Reports of the Cambridge Anthropological Expedition to Torres Straits: Volume 5, Sociology, Magic & Religion of the Western Islanders, 6 vols. 2011. (ENG., Illus.). 462p. pap. 60.00 *(978-0-521-17989-8(0))* Cambridge Univ. Pr.

—Reports of the Cambridge Anthropological Expedition to Torres Straits: Volume 6, Sociology, Magic & Religion of the Eastern Islanders, 6 vols. 2011. (ENG., Illus.). 395p. pap. 60.00 *(978-0-521-17990-4(4))* Cambridge Univ. Pr.

Haebich, Anna & Offord, Baden, eds. Landscapes of Exile: Once Perilous, Now Safe. 2008. (Illus.). 283p. pap. 69.95 *(978-3-03911-090-2(X))* Lang, Peter Publishing, Inc.

Haigh, Tony. How to Survive a Terrorist Attack in Australia. l.t. ed. 2007. (Illus.). 132p. per. 24.90 *(978-0-9803335-0-3(4))* Andrews, Diane Publishing, Cairns AUS. Dist: Lulu Enterprises Inc.

Herbert-Cheshire, Lynda & Cheshire, Lynda. Governing Rural Development: Discourses & Practices of Self-Help in Australian Rural Policy. 2006. (Perspectives on Rural Policy & Planning Ser.). (Illus.). 184p. 130.00 *(978-0-7546-4024-0(8))* Ashgate Publishing Co.

Hing, Nerilee. Changing Fortunes. 2009. 636p. pap. *(978-3-8364-8317-9(3))* VDM Verlag Dr. Mueller e.K.

Horsfield, Alan. Action Numeracy: The Facts of Living. 2008. 32p. pap. 10.95 *(978-0-86431-824-4(3))* ACER Pr. AUS. Dist: International Specialized Bk. Services.

Hughes, Colin A. & Costar, Brian. Limiting Democracy: The Erosion of Electoral Rights in Australia. 2006. (ENG.). 96p. pap. 15.95 *(978-0-86840-948-1(0),* UNSW Press) NewSouth Publishing AUS. Dist: Independent Pubs. Group.

Ibrani Shahrimin, Mohamad. Children, Computers & Collaborations. 2010. 164p. pap. *(978-3-8383-6394-3(9))* Lambert Academic Publishing.

Ison, Ray, ed. Agricultural Extension & Rural Development: Breaking out of Traditions. 2007. (ENG., Illus.). 252p. pap. 56.00 *(978-0-521-03941-3(X))* Cambridge Univ. Pr.

Jang, Haeyoung, et al. Sex Trafficking or Shadow Tourism? 2010. 228p. pap. *(978-3-8383-1552-2(9))* Lambert Academic Publishing.

Johnson, P. Anna. Australia Years the Life of A Nuclear Mi. 2007. 220p. pap. 16.80 *(978-1-4303-0941-3(5))* Lulu Enterprises Inc.

Jorm, Christine. Reconstructing Medical Practice: Engagement Professionalism & Critical Relationships in Health Care. 2012. 232p. 124.95 ***(978-1-4094-2976-0(8),*** Gower Publishing Co., Ltd.) Ashgate Publishing, Ltd. GBR. Dist: Ashgate Publishing Co.

Karp, Jann. Corruption & Crisis Control: The Nature of the Game. 2008. 176p. pap. *(978-3-639-01231-6(3))* VDM Verlag Dr. Mueller e.K.

Khoo, Tseen, ed. Locating Asian Australian Cultures. 2007. (ENG.). 256p. 150.00 *(978-0-415-41148-6(3))* Routledge.

Kylin, Camilla. Coping with Boundaries. 2008. 68p. pap. *(978-3-8364-9696-4(8))* VDM Verlag Dr. Mueller e.K.

Langmore, John. To Firmer Ground: Restoring Hope in Australia. 2007. (ENG.). 272p. pap. 29.95 *(978-0-86840-847-7(6),* UNSW Press) NewSouth Publishing AUS. Dist: Independent Pubs. Group.

Lee, Iris. Assessment for Contemporary Needs. 2010. 184p. pap. *(978-3-639-18313-9(4))* VDM Verlag Dr. Mueller e.K.

Lennie, June. Troubling Empowerment. 2009. 484p. pap. *(978-3-639-16819-8(4))* VDM Verlag Dr. Mueller e.K.

Levey. Political Theory & Australian Multiculturalism. 2008. 328p. 100.00 *(978-1-84545-492-0(8))* Berghahn Bks., Inc.

Lewis, Sophie. Catching up to Tulsi. 2008. 72p. pap. 14.00 *(978-0-8059-7651-9(5))* Dorrance Publishing Co., Inc.

Lo, Meihan. Quality of Life among Elderly Chinese Immigrants in Australi. 2010. 180p. pap. *(978-3-8383-1342-9(9))* Lambert Academic Publishing.

Lynch, Andrew, et al, eds. Counter-Terrorism & Beyond: The Culture of Law & Justice after 9/11. 2010. (Routledge Research in Terrorism & the Law Ser.). (Illus.). 256p. 125.00 *(978-0-415-57175-3(8),* Routledge) Taylor & Francis Group GBR. Dist: Taylor & Francis Group.

Lynch, Andrew, et al, eds. Counter-Terrorism & Beyond: The Culture of Law & Justice After 9/11. 2012. (ENG.). pap. 44.95 ***(978-0-415-63139-6(4))*** Routledge.

Marginson, Simon, et al. International Student Security. 2010. (ENG., Illus.). 528p. pap. 42.00 *(978-0-521-13805-5(1))* Cambridge Univ. Pr.

Markus, Andrew & Semyonov, Moshe. Immigration & Nation Building: Australia & Israel Compared. Markus, Andrew & Semyonov, Moshe, eds. 2011. 224p. 110.00 *(978-1-84980-063-1(4))* Elgar, Edward Publishing, Inc.

Maushart, Susan. The Winter of Our Disconnect: How Three Totally Wired Teenagers (And a Mother Who Slept with Her iPhone)Pulled the Plug on Their Technology & Lived to Tell the Tale. 2011. (ENG.). 288p. (gr. 12). 16.95 *(978-1-58542-855-7(8),* Tarcher) Penguin Group (USA) Inc.

McClelland, Alison & Smyth, Paul. Social Policy in Australia: Understanding for Action. 2nd rev. ed. 2010. (ENG., Illus.). xvi, 304p. (Orig.). 59.95 *(978-0-19-556286-6(0))* Oxford Univ. Pr., Inc.

McDonald, Paula. Womens Level of Labour Force Participation. 2008. 240p. pap. *(978-3-639-05175-9(0))* VDM Verlag Dr. Mueller e.K.

McQueen, Humphrey. Social Sketches of Australia, 1888-2001. 3rd rev. ed. 2008. (ENG., Illus.). 420p. per. 20.95 *(978-0-7022-3440-8(0))* Univ. of Queensland Pr. AUS. Dist: Independent Pubs. Group.

Measham, Thomas. Learning & Change in Rural Regions - Understanding Influences on Sense of Place. 2008. 280p. pap. *(978-3-639-02076-2(6))* VDM Verlag Dr. Mueller e.K.

Monk, Lee-Ann. Attending Madness: At Work in the Australian Colonial Asylum. 2008. 280p. 82.00 *(978-90-420-2419-9(4))* Rodopi.

Mooney, Shelagh. Career Barriers for Women Hotel Managers. 2009. 112p. pap. *(978-3-639-13350-9(1))* VDM Verlag Dr. Mueller e.K.

Morley, Philip. Incorporating Socio-Economic Criteria into Marine Reserve Planning. 2010. 116p. pap. *(978-3-8383-6783-5(9))* Lambert Academic Publishing.

Mullins, Steve, et al, eds. Community, Environment & History: Keppel Bay case Studies. 2007. pap. *(978-1-876780-97-5(5))* Central Queensland Univ. Pr. AUS. Dist: Central Queensland Univ. Pr.

Mundy, Godfrey Charles. Our Antipodes. 2009. 246p. pap. 32.19 *(978-1-4588-3747-9(5))* General Bks. LLC.

—Our Antipodes. 2006. (Illus.). 305p. per. *(978-1-74076-185-7(5))* Pandanus Bks.

Murphy, Brian. The Other Australia: Experiences of Migration. 2008. (ENG., Illus.). 288p. pap. 38.99 *(978-0-521-10224-7(3))* Cambridge Univ. Pr.

Murphy, John. 'A Decent Provision for the Poor' A History of Australian Social Policy 1870 To 1945. 2011. (Modern Economic & Social History Ser.). (Illus.). 294p. 124.95 *(978-1-4094-0759-1(4))* Ashgate Publishing Co.

Murray, Georgina. Capitalist Networks & Social Power in Australia & New Zealand. 2007. (Corporate Social Responsibility Ser.). (Illus.). 262p. 124.95 *(978-0-7546-4708-9(0))* Ashgate Publishing Co.

Muskett, Philip E. The Art of Living in Australia. 2008. 384p. pap. *(978-1-4099-0343-7(5))* Dodo Pr.

Najman, Jake M. & Western, J. S. A Sociology of Australian Society: Introductory Readings. 2nd rev. ed. (Illus.). 656p. 69.95 *(978-0-7329-2004-3(3))* Macmillan Education Australia AUS. Dist: Paul & Co. Pubs. Consortium, Inc.

Najman, Jake M. & Western, John. A Sociology of Australian Society: Introductory Readings. 2nd rev. ed. (Illus.). 656p. pap. 34.95 *(978-0-7329-2003-6(5))* Macmillan Education Australia AUS. Dist: Paul & Co. Pubs. Consortium, Inc.

Nayton, Gaye. The Archaeology of Market Capitalism: A Western Australian Perspective. 2011. (Contributions to Global Historical Archaeology Ser.). (ENG., Illus.). xii, 280p. 129.00 *(978-1-4419-8317-6(1),* 1441983171) Springer.

Neo, Wei Ren. Development of Data Acquisition System of Ntu Venture II. 2010. 88p. pap. *(978-3-8383-8514-3(4))* Lambert Academic Publishing.

Northcott, Clarence H. Australian Social Development. (Columbia University, Studies in the Social Sciences: No. 189). reprint ed. 29.50 *(978-0-404-51189-0(9))* AMS Pr., Inc.

—Australian Social Development. 2009. 306p. 36.99 *(978-1-116-67578-8(1));* 306p. 32.99 *(978-1-116-67579-5(X));* 306p. pap. 29.75 *(978-1-116-67580-1(3));* (ENG.). 305p. pap. 23.99 *(978-1-116-67583-2(8),* BiblioLife); (ENG.). 305p. pap. 24.99 *(978-1-116-67582-5(X),* BiblioLife) BiblioBazaar.

O'Farrell, Patrick. The Irish in Australia: 1992 Edition. 2nd ed. (Illus.). 333p. pap. *(978-0-86840-181-2(1),* UNSW Press) NewSouth Publishing.

Papadelos, Pam. From Revolution to Deconstruction: Exploring Feminist Theory & Practice in Australia. 2010. 248p. pap. *(978-3-0343-0351-4(3))* Lang, Peter.

Pauwels, Anne, et al, eds. Maintaining Minority Languages in Transnational Contexts. 2007. (Palgrave Studies in Minority Languages & Communities Ser.). (ENG., Illus.). 224p. 100.00 *(978-0-230-01919-5(6))* Palgrave Macmillan.

Pearse, Emma. Sophie: The Incredible True Story of the Castaway Dog. l.t. ed. 2012. (ENG.). 321p. 31.99 ***(978-1-4104-4734-0(0))*** Thorndike Pr.

Pocock, Barbara. The Australian Work & Life Index (AWALI) Concepts, Methodology & Rationale. 2007. *(978-0-9803798-3-9(0))* University of South Australia - Hawke Institute.

—Awali 2007. 2007. *(978-0-9803798-4-6(9))* University of South Australia - Hawke Institute.

—Early Signs - the Impact of WorkChoices on Work & Family. 2006. *(978-0-9803798-5-3(7))* University of South Australia - Hawke Institute.

Pooley, Julie, et al. Indicators of Community Resilience. 2010. 256p. pap. *(978-3-8383-3971-9(1))* Lambert Academic Publishing.

Povinelli, Elizabeth A. Economies of Abandonment: Social Belonging & Endurance in Late Liberalism. 2011. (ENG., Illus.). 256p. 79.95 *(978-0-8223-5066-8(1));* pap. 22.95 *(978-0-8223-5084-2(X))* Duke Univ. Pr.

Price, Gary. Horticultural Research; Growth of European Olive in the Rangelands. 2010. 244p. pap. *(978-3-639-22411-5(6))* VDM Verlag Dr. Mueller e.K.

Proudley, Mae. Fire, Families & Decisions. 2010. 184p. pap. *(978-3-639-23666-8(1))* VDM Verlag Dr. Mueller e.K.

Reid, Kirsty. Gender,Crime & Empire: Convicts, Settlers & the State in Early Colonial Australia. 2008. (Studies in Imperialism Ser.). (ENG., Illus.). 304p. 89.00 *(978-0-7190-6698-6(0))* Manchester Univ. Pr. GBR. Dist: Macmillan.

Riggs, Damien W. Priscilla (White), Queen of the Desert: Race Privilege, Queer Rights, & Postcolonial Location. 2006. 152p. (C). 69.95 *(978-0-8204-8658-1(2));* pap. 25.95 *(978-0-8204-8657-4(4))* Lang, Peter Publishing, Inc.

Robinson, Catherine. Beside One's Self: Homelessness Felt & Lived. 2011. 200p. ***(978-0-8156-3252-8(5))*** Syracuse Univ. Pr.

Sanchez, Mariela. Agri-Food Restructuring in the Australia Beef Industry. 2010. 220p. pap. *(978-3-8383-7212-9(3))* Lambert Academic Publishing.

Sawers-Diggins, Lannah. Bullseye. 2010. 104p. 24.99 *(978-1-4535-2731-3(1));* pap. 15.99 *(978-1-4535-2730-6(3))* Xlibris Corp.

Schwarz, Anja & West-Pavlov, Russel, eds. Polyculturalism & Discourse. 2007. (Illus.). 300p. (C). per. *(978-90-420-2307-9(4))* Rodopi B.V. Editions.

Short, Damien. Reconciliation & Colonial Power: Indigenous Rights in Australia. 2008. (Illus.). 222p. 114.95 *(978-0-7546-4938-0(5))* Ashgate Publishing Co.

Smaal, Yorick & Willett, Graham, eds. Out Here: Gay & Lesbian Perspectives VI. 2011. (Monash Studies in Australian Society Ser.). (ENG.). 230p. pap. 37.95 ***(978-1-921867-00-2(0))*** Monash Univ. Publishing AUS. Dist: International Specialized Bk. Services.

Sorenson, Peter. Signs of Mid-Life: Images from the Contemporary Australian Mid-Life MalePsyche. 2008. 180p. pap. *(978-3-639-10033-4(6))* VDM Verlag Dr. Mueller e.K.

Spence, Catherine Helen & Spence, Catherine Helen. An Autobiography. 2010. (Illus.). 114p. pap. 20.40 *(978-1-153-58566-8(9))* General Bks. LLC.

—An Autobiography. 2010. 140p. 35.95 *(978-1-161-42124-8(6))* Kessinger Publishing, LLC.

Spence, Catherine Helen. An Autobiography. 2008. 176p. 22.99 *(978-0-554-31338-2(3))* 2008. 204p. 27.99 *(978-0-554-28279-4(8))* 2008. 204p. 24.99 *(978-0-554-37582-3(6))* 2008. 176p. 25.99 *(978-0-554-22035-2(0))* 2006. 184p. pap. 19.99 *(978-1-4264-1503-6(6))* BiblioBazaar.

—An Autobiography. 2008. 164p. pap. *(978-1-4065-9168-2(8))* Dodo Pr.

—An Autobiography. 2010. 140p. pap. 16.76 *(978-1-162-65259-7(4));* 28.76 ***(978-1-169-25962-1(6))*** Kessinger Publishing, LLC.

Stehlik, Daniela Anna. Drought & Climate Change: A Rural Australian Perspective, Adaptation, & Social Impact. 2011. 210p. 99.95 *(978-1-4398-4545-5(X),* CRC Press) Taylor & Francis Group GBR. Dist: Taylor & Francis Group.

Stephenson, Peta. The Outsiders Within: Telling Australia's Indigenous-Asian Story. 2007. (ENG., Illus.). 256p. per. 35.95 *(978-0-86840-836-1(0),* UNSW Press) NewSouth Publishing AUS. Dist: Independent Pubs. Group.

Stokes, Geoffrey, et al, eds. Global Citizens: Australian Activists for Change. 2008. (Illus.). 240p. pap. 38.99 *(978-0-521-73187-4(9))* Cambridge Univ. Pr.

Taylor, Kathryn. Far From Home: Trauma & Posttraumatic Stress Disorder among Homeless Adults in Sydney. 2008. 128p. pap. *(978-3-8364-8028-4(X))* VDM Verlag Dr. Mueller e.K.

Tiffen, Rodney & Gittins, Ross. How Australia Compares. 2nd ed. 2009. (ENG., Illus.). 294p. pap. 85.00 *(978-0-521-71245-3(9))* Cambridge Univ. Pr.

Tuck, Robert J. Ethics of Chinese & Australian Business Managers: A Comparative Investigation about Corruption. 2011. (Ethical Issues in the 21st Century Ser.). (Illus.). 690p. 125.00 *(978-1-61668-193-7(4))* Nova Science Pubs., Inc.

Viravong, Sumana, ed. Lao Seri: An Anthology of Lao Australian refugee Writing. 2007. (ENG & LAO.). (J). per. *(978-1-876418-75-5(3))* Casula Powerhouse.

Wakholi, Peter Mbago. African Cultural Education & the African Youth in Western Australia. 2008. 136p. pap. *(978-3-639-02631-3(4))* VDM Verlag Dr. Mueller e.K.

Wark, McKenzie & Schumann, H. Celebrities, Cultures & Cyberspace. 200p. pap. *(978-1-86403-045-7(3))* Pluto Pr. Australia.

West, Margie, ed. Yalangbara: Art of the Djang'kawa. 2008. pap. *(978-0-9803846-7-3(2))* Darwin, Charles Univ. Pr.

Westoby, Peter. The Sociality of Refugee Healing: In Dialogue with Southern Sudanese Refugees Resettling in Australia - Towards A Social Model of Healing. 2009. 220p. pap. 30.00 *(978-1-86335-625-1(8))* Common Ground Publishing Pty, Ltd.

White, Rob, et al. Youth & Society: Exploring the Social Dynamics of Youth Experience. 2nd rev. ed. 2008. (ENG.). 320p. (Orig.). (C). pap. 64.95 *(978-0-19-555133-4(8))* Oxford Univ. Pr., Inc.

Wierenga, Ani. Young People Making a Life. 2009. (ENG., Illus.). 256p. 100.00 *(978-0-230-54928-9(4))* Palgrave Macmillan.

Williams, Lachlan J. & Lee, Ethan N. Australia: Economics, Political & Social Issues. 2008. 89.00 *(978-1-60456-856-1(9))* Nova Science Pubs., Inc.

Williams, Philippa. Fitting it all together - Work, Home & Community in two Australian Master-Planned Communities. 2006. *(978-0-9803798-2-2(2))* University of South Australia - Hawke Institute.

Zangalis, George. Migrant Workers & Ethnic Communities: Their Struggles for Social Justice & Cultural Rights. 2009. 604p. 80.00 *(978-1-86335-619-0(3))* Common Ground Publishing Pty, Ltd.

AUSTRALIA—SOCIAL LIFE AND CUSTOMS

Adams, Francis William Lauderdale. The Australians: A Social Sketch. 2011. (Cambridge Library Collection - History Ser.). 324p. pap. 24.99 *(978-1-108-03065-6(3))* Cambridge Univ. Pr.

Ante, Kristi Nicole. Dwelling in Motion. 2008. 104p. per. *(978-3-8364-5842-9(X))* VDM Verlag Dr. Mueller e.K.

Bates, Daisy. The Passing of the Aborigines: A Lifetime Spent among the Natives of Australia. 2010. 228p. pap. 45.95 *(978-1-4092-2468-6(6))* Lulu Enterprises Inc.

Bursian, Olga. Migrant Women ACT. 2011. pap. *(978-1-86335-885-9(4))* Common Ground Publishing Pty, Ltd.

Chatwin, Bruce. The Songlines. rev. ed. 2012. (ENG.). 320p. (gr. 12). pap. 16.00 ***(978-0-14-242257-1(6),*** Penguin Classics) Penguin Group (USA) Inc.

Club Management Issues in Australia & North America. 2006. (ENG., Illus.). 260p. 125.00 *(978-0-7890-3163-1(9))*; per. 57.95 *(978-0-7890-3164-8(7))* Routledge.

Coronado, Gabriela, et al. Chaos Theory & the Larrikin Principle. 2010. (Illus.). 243p. pap. 32.00 *(978-87-630-0235-6(3))* Copenhagen Business Schl. Pr. DNK. Dist: International Specialized Bk. Services.

Crocombe, Angela. A Lighter Footprint: A Practical Guide to Minimising Your Impact on the Planet. 2009. (ENG.). 236p. pap. 22.95 *(978-1-921215-59-9(3))* Scribe Pubns. AUS. Dist: Independent Pubs. Group.

Deger, Jennifer. Shimmering Screens: Making Media in an Aboriginal Community. 2006. (Illus.). 256p. pap. 22.50 *(978-0-8166-4922-8(7))*; (Visible Evidence Ser.: Vol. 19). 67.50 *(978-0-8166-4921-1(9))* Univ. of Minnesota Pr.

Dux, Monica & Simic, Zora. The Great Feminist Denial. 2008. (ENG.). 240p. pap. 26.95 *(978-0-522-85415-2(X))* Melbourne Univ. Publishing AUS. Dist: Independent Pubs. Group.

Dwyer, Andrew. Outback: Recipes & Stories from the Campfire. 2007. (ENG., Illus.). 240p. 40.00 *(978-0-522-85380-3(3),* Miegunyah Pr., The) Melbourne Univ. Publishing AUS. Dist: Independent Pubs. Group.

Flaherty, Liz. Action Literacy: Surf & Sand. 2008. 32p. pap. 10.95 *(978-0-86431-711-7(5))* ACER Pr. AUS. Dist: International Specialized Bk. Services.

Foster, David. In the New Country. 213p. pap. 13.99 *(978-1-84115-037-6(1))*; 224p. pap. 19.99 *(978-1-84115-036-9(3))* HarperCollins Pubs. Ltd. GBR. (Fourth Estate). Dist: Trafalgar Square Publishing.

Francesco, Ricatti. Embodying Migrants: Italians in Postwar Australia. 2011. 331p. pap. *(978-3-0343-0466-5(8))* Lang, Peter Publishing, Inc.

Fritz, Clemens W. A. From English in Australia to Australian English: 1788-1900. 2007. (English Corpus Linguistics Ser.: Vol. 4). XII, 297p. pap. 62.95 *(978-3-631-56702-9(2))* Lang, Peter GmbH, Europaischer Verlag der Wissenschaften DEU. Dist: Lang, Peter Publishing, Inc.

Funder. Images of Australian Families. Date not set. 166p. pap. 59.50 *(978-0-582-87075-8(5))* Addison-Wesley Longman, Ltd. GBR. Dist: Trans-Atlantic Pubns., Inc.

Gabbrielli, Emilio. Polenta & Goann. McGilvray, Barbara, tr. 2008. 240p. pap. *(978-88-95145-23-5(2))* Italian Paths of Culture.

Gibson, Chris & Connell, John, eds. Festival Places: Revitalising Rural Australia. 2011. (Toursim & Cultural Change Ser.). (ENG., Illus.). 296p. 149.95 *(978-1-84541-157-1(6))*; pap. 54.95 *(978-1-84541-156-4(8))* Channel View Pubns., Ltd. GBR. Dist: Univ. of Toronto Pr.

Gray, Vicky. Didgeridoos & Didgeridon'ts: A Brit's Guide to Moving Your Life down Under. 2009. (Illus.). 208p. pap. *(978-1-905430-53-6(1))* Lean Marketing Pr.

Hampshire, David. Living & Working in Australia: A Survival Handbook. 7th ed. 2011. (ENG., Illus.). 400p. pap. 25.95 *(978-1-907339-25-7(6))* Survival Bks., Ltd.

Hampshire, David & Kidd, Martin. Culture Wise Australia: The Essential Guide to Culture, Customs & Business Etiquette. 2008. (Culture Wise Ser.). (ENG., Illus.). 224p. pap. 17.95 *(978-1-905303-22-9(X))* Survival Bks., Ltd.

Hatherell, William. The Third Metropolis: Imagining Brisbane through Art & Literature 1940 - 1970. 2008. (ENG.). 310p. pap. 36.95 *(978-0-7022-3543-6(1))* Univ. of Queensland Pr. AUS. Dist: Independent Pubs. Group.

Heard, Barry. The View from Connor's Hill: A Memoir. 2008. (ENG.). 267p. pap. 24.95 *(978-1-921215-48-3(8))* Scribe Pubns. AUS. Dist: Independent Pubs. Group.

Herle, Anita & Rouse, Sandra, eds. Cambridge & the Torres Strait: Centenary Essays on the 1898 Anthropological Expedition. 2008. (ENG., Illus.). 272p. pap. 37.99 *(978-0-521-10386-2(X))* Cambridge Univ. Pr.

Hirst, John B. Convict Society & Its Enemies: A History of Early New South Wales. 2009. 248p. 37.00 *(978-1-59740-300-9(8))* ACLS Humanities E-Book.

Howe, Graham, ed. & contrib. by. E. O. Hoppe's Australia. 2008. (ENG., Illus.). 208p. 49.95 *(978-0-393-06611-1(8),* 6611) Norton, W. W. & Co., Inc.

Howitt, Alfred William. The Native Tribes of South-East Australia, 2 vols. 2010. (Cambridge Library Collection - Linguistics Ser.). (ENG.). 878p. pap. 65.00 *(978-1-108-00632-3(9))* Cambridge Univ. Pr.

Joel, Asher & Pringle, Helen. Australian Protocol & Procedures. 3rd rev. ed. 2007. (ENG., Illus.). 528p. pap. 80.95 *(978-0-86840-946-7(4),* UNSW Press) NewSouth Publishing AUS. Dist: Independent Pubs. Group.

Jupp, James, et al. eds. Social Cohesion in Australia. 2007. 240p. pap. 44.00 *(978-0-521-70943-9(1))* Cambridge Univ. Pr.

Kerwin, Dale. Aboriginal Dreaming Paths & Trading Routes: The Colonisation of the Australian Economic Landscape. 2010. (ENG., Illus.). 230p. 89.95 *(978-1-84519-338-6(5))* Sussex Academic Pr. GBR. Dist: International Specialized Bk. Services.

Lally, Janice. The Australian Aboriginal Collection in the Museum Fur Völkerkunde, Berlin. 2008. 488p. pap. *(978-3-639-03491-2(0))* VDM Verlag Dr. Mueller e.K.

Lewis, Megan. Conversations with the Mob. 2008. 240p. 45.00 *(978-1-921401-03-9(6))* UWA Publishing AUS. Dist: International Specialized Bk. Services.

Lowe, Pat & Pike, Jimmy. You Call It Desert: We Used to Live There. 2010. Orig. Title: Jilji - Life in the Great Sandy Desert. (ENG & AUS., Illus.). 168p. pap. 29.95 *(978-1-921248-11-5(4))* Magabala Bks. AUS. Dist: Independent Pubs. Group.

Lydon, Jane. Fantastic Dreaming: The Archaeology of an Aboriginal Mission. 2009. (Worlds of Archaeology Ser.). (ENG.). 330p. pap. 35.00 *(978-0-7591-1105-9(7))*; (Illus.). 85.00 *(978-0-7591-1104-2(9))* AltaMira Pr.

McCoy, Brian F. Holding Men: Kanyirninpa & the Health of Aboriginal Men. 2009. (ENG.). 296p. pap. 31.95 *(978-0-85575-658-1(6))* Aboriginal Studies Pr. AUS. Dist: Independent Pubs. Group.

Mears, Ray. Ray Mears Goes Walkabout. 2009. (ENG., Illus.). 288p. pap. 14.95 *(978-0-340-96147-6(3),* Hodder & Stoughton) Hodder General Publishing Div. GBR. Dist: Independent Pubs. Group.

Milligan, Angela. Customs & Etiquette of Australia. 2010. (Customs & Etiquette Pocket Guides Ser.). (Illus.). 93p. per. 6.95 *(978-1-85733-381-7(0))* Bravo, Ltd. GBR. Dist: Midpoint Trade Bks., Inc.

Morgan, Sally. My Place. 2008. (ENG.). 496p. 25.00 *(978-1-921361-22-7(0))* Fremantle Pr. AUS. Dist: Independent Pubs. Group.

Napaljarri, Peggy Rockman & Cataldi, Lee. Warlpiri Dreamings & Histories: Newly Recorded Stories from the Aboriginal Elders of Central Australia. 2010. (Sacred Literature Trust Ser.). (ENG.). 232p. pap. 30.95 *(978-0-300-16530-2(7))* Yale Univ. Pr.

Neilson, Jeff & Collins Publishers Staff. Going to Live in Australia. 2nd ed. 2008. (Illus.). 258p. 22.00 *(978-1-84528-261-5(2))* How To Books GBR. Dist: Parkwest Pubns., Inc.

O'Connor, Lily. Dreams of Hope: From Dublin to Geelong. 2007. (ENG.). 281p. pap. 24.95 *(978-0-86322-358-7(3))* Brandon/Mount Eagle Pubns., Ltd. IRL. Dist: Dufour Editions, Inc.

O'Keefe, Brendan. Simeon Pearce's Randwick: Dream & Reality. (Illus.). 75p. pap. *(978-0-86840-305-2(9),* UNSW Press) NewSouth Publishing.

Organisation for Economic Co-operation and Development Staff. Australia. 2009. (Jobs for Youth Ser.). (Illus.). 149p. pap. 63.00 *(978-92-64-06019-7(7))* Organization for Economic Cooperation & Development.

Payton & Payton, Philip. Making Moonta: The Invention of Australia's Little Cornwall. 2007. (Illus.). 269p. (C). 89.95 *(978-0-85989-795-2(8))* Univ. of Exeter Pr. GBR. Dist: Chicago Distribution Ctr.

Payton, Philip. Making Moonta: The Invention of Australia's Little Cornwall. 2007. (Illus.). 269p. per. 32.50 *(978-0-85989-796-9(6))* Univ. of Exeter Pr. GBR. Dist: Chicago Distribution Ctr.

Penney, Barry. Australia: The Essential Guide to Customs & Culture. 2006. (Culture Smart! A Quick Guide to Customs & Etiquette Ser.). (ENG., Illus.). 168p. pap. 9.95 *(978-1-85733-310-7(1))* Kuperard Pubs. GBR. Dist: Random Hse., Inc.

Pickering, Sam. A Tramp's Wallet. 2011. 272p. pap. 25.00 *(978-0-88146-235-7(7))* Mercer Univ. Pr.

Pung, Alice. Unpolished Gem: My Mother, My Grandmother, & Me. 2009. (ENG.). 304p. (gr. 12-18). 16.00 *(978-0-452-29000-6(7),* Plume) Penguin Group (USA) Inc.

Reinfjord, Kristine. Marginalisation of Australian Aborigines. 2009. 116p. pap. *(978-3-639-15035-3(X))* VDM Verlag Dr. Mueller e.K.

Rendle-Short, Francesca. Bite Your Tongue. 2012. (Illus.). 246p. pap. 24.95 ***(978-1-876756-96-3(9))*** Spinifex Pr. AUS. Dist: Independent Pubs. Group.

Richardson, Adele. My First Look at - Australia. 24p. (J). 2011. (ENG.). (gr. 1-17). pap. 7.99 *(978-1-926722-33-7(7),* Creative Paperbacks) 2006. (Illus.). (gr. -1-3). lib. bdg. 15.95 *(978-1-58341-443-9(6),* Creative Education) Creative Co., The.

Schüpbach, Doris. Shared Languages, Shared Identities, Shared Stories: A Qualitative Study of Life Stories by Immigrants from German-speaking Switzerland in Australia. 2008. (Variolingua. Nonstandard - Standard - Substandard Ser.). (Illus.). 352p. pap. 81.95 *(978-3-631-57947-3(0))* Lang, Peter GmbH, Europaischer Verlag der Wissenschaften DEU. Dist: Lang, Peter.

Sharp, Ilsa. Australia, 1 vol. 2008. (CultureShock! Ser.). 432p. pap. 15.95 *(978-0-7614-5472-4(1))* Marshall Cavendish Corp.

—CultureShock! Australia. 2007. (Illus.). 432p. pap. 15.95 *(978-981-261-117-8(7))* Marshall Cavendish International (Asia) Private Ltd. SGP. Dist: Marshall Cavendish Corp.

Sharwood, Anthony. You Talkin' to Me? The Diary of an Olympic Cabbie. 216p. 14.95 *(978-1-86508-506-7(5))* Allen & Unwin AUS. Dist: Independent Pubs. Group.

Shea, Peter M. Champagne from Six: A brief social history of entertainments & recreations at Beechworth & the Ovens goldfields, Victoria Australia 1852-18. 2010. 100p. pap. 28.99 *(978-1-60911-243-1(1),* Eloquent Bks.) AEG Literary Publishing Services, Inc.

Sherborne, Craig & Scott, Jeremy. Dancing on Ice: A 1930s Arctic Adventure. 2010. (ENG.). 272p. (gr. 6). pap. 14.95 *(978-1-905847-76-1(9))* Old Street Publishing GBR. Dist: Consortium Bk. Sales & Distribution.

Smith, Stephen. Place & People: New Dimensions in Regional Research. 2007. (Illus.). 203p. per. *(978-0-9757519-3-0(X))* Black Swan Pr.

Spencer, Baldwin & Gillen, F. J. Native Tribes of Central Australia. 2010. (Cambridge Library Collection - Linguistics Ser.). (ENG., Illus.). 740p. pap. 48.00 *(978-1-108-02044-2(5))* Cambridge Univ. Pr.

Thiele, Colin. With Dew on My Boots & Other Footprints. 340p. pap. *(978-0-7344-0405-3(0),* Lothian Children's Bks.) Hachette Australia.

Thomas, Northcote Whitridge. Kinship Organisations & Group Marriage in Australia. 2010. (Cambridge Library Collection - Travel & Exploration Ser.). (ENG., Illus.). 188p. pap. 19.99 *(978-1-108-01051-1(2))* Cambridge Univ. Pr.

Timothy, Lynch. Satan's Empire: The Panic over Ritual Abuse in Australia. 2011. 452p. pap. ***(978-3-639-31742-8(4))*** VDM Verlag Dr. Mueller e.K.

Tonkinson, Myrna, et al. Mortality, Mourning & Mortuary Practices in Indigenous Australia. 2009. (Anthropology & Cultural History in Asia & the Indo-Pacific Ser.). (Illus.). 260p. 114.95 *(978-0-7546-7449-8(5))* Ashgate Publishing Co.

Tredinnick, Mark. The Blue Plateau: An Australian Pastoral. 2009. (ENG.). 256p. pap. 16.00 *(978-1-57131-320-1(6))* Milkweed Editions.

Twopenny, Richard. Town Life in Australia. 2007. (ENG.). 190p. pap. 19.99 *(978-1-4346-0225-1(7))*; 210p. pap. 22.99 *(978-1-4346-0299-2(0))* BiblioBazaar.

Wark, McKenzie & Schumann, H. Celebrities, Cultures & Cyberspace. 200p. pap. *(978-1-86403-045-7(3))* Pluto Pr. Australia.

AUSTRALIA—STATISTICS

United Nations Publications Staff. Yearbook for Asia & the Pacific 2007. 2008. (ENG.). 206p. pap. 90.00 *(978-92-1-019241-5(9))* United Nations Pubns.

AUSTRALIA IN LITERATURE

see Australia—In Literature

AUSTRALIAN ABORIGINES

see Aboriginal Australians

AUSTRALIAN ARCHITECTURE

see Architecture—Australia

AUSTRALIAN ART

see Art, Australian

AUSTRALIAN ARTS

see Arts—Australia

AUSTRALIAN AUTHORS

see Authors, Australian

AUSTRALIAN BADGERS

see Wombats

AUSTRALIAN BALLADS AND SONGS

see Folk Songs, Australian; Songs, Aboriginal Australian; Songs, Australian

AUSTRALIAN CATTLE DOG

Beauchamp, Richard G. Australian Cattle Dogs. 2nd rev. ed. 2007. (Complete Pet Owner's Manual Ser.). (ENG., Illus.). 96p. per. 8.99 *(978-0-7641-3649-8(6))* Barron's Educational Series, Inc.

Linzy, Jan, et al. Australian Cattle Dog Champions, 2003-2006. 2007. (Illus.). 165p. spiral bd. 46.95 *(978-1-55893-231-9(3))* Camino E.E. & Bk. Co.

AUSTRALIAN DRAMA

Blackmore, Ernie. Speakin' Out Blak - an Examination of Finding an Urban Indigenous Voice Through Contemporary Australian Theatre. 2008. 188p. pap. *(978-3-639-06884-9(X))* VDM Verlag Dr. Mueller e.K.

Chowdhury, Khairul. Empowering & Disempowering Indigenes. 2010. 328p. pap. *(978-3-8383-4953-4(9))* Lambert Academic Publishing.

AUSTRALIAN DRAMA—HISTORY AND CRITICISM

Bollen, Jonathan, et al. Men at Play: Masculinities in Australian Theatre since the 1950s. 2008. (Illus.). 264p. per. 75.00 *(978-90-420-2357-4(0))* Rodopi.

Grehan, Helena. Performance, Ethics & Spectatorship in a Global Age. Reinelt, Janelle & Singleton, Brian, eds. 2009. (Studies in International Performance Ser.). (ENG., Illus.). 224p. 89.00 *(978-0-230-51801-8(X))* Palgrave Macmillan.

Hamilton, Margaret. Transfigured Stages: Major Practitioners & Theatre Aesthetics in Australia. 2011. (ENG., Illus.). 244p. pap. 70.00 ***(978-90-420-3356-6(8))*** Rodopi.

AUSTRALIAN ENGLISH

see English Language—Australia

AUSTRALIAN ESSAYS

Beecher, Eric, ed. The Best Australian Political Writing 2009. 2009. (Best Australian Political Writing Ser.). (ENG.). 416p. pap. 22.95 *(978-0-522-85632-3(2))* Melbourne Univ. Publishing AUS. Dist: Independent Pubs. Group.

AUSTRALIAN FICTION

see also Short Stories, Australian

Arthur, Keri. Beneath a Darkening Moon. 2012. (ENG.). 400p. mass mkt. 7.99 ***(978-0-440-24650-3(4),*** Dell) Random House Publishing Group.

AUSTRALIAN FICTION—HISTORY AND CRITICISM

Cain Gray, Lara. Reading Culture: The Transfer & Translation of Australianness in Contemporary Fiction. 2008. 196p. pap. *(978-3-639-04503-1(3))* VDM Verlag Dr. Mueller e.K.

Callahan, David. Rainforest Narratives: The Works of Janette Turner Hospital. 2010. (ENG.). viii, 370p. pap. 31.95 *(978-0-7022-3727-0(2))* Univ. of Queensland Pr. AUS. Dist: Independent Pubs. Group.

Elder, Catriona. Dreams & Nightmares of White Australia: Representing Aboriginal Assimilation in the Mid-Twentieth Century. 2009. (Illus.). 257p. pap. *(978-3-03911-722-2(X))* Lang, Peter.

Jewell, Melinda. The Representation of Dance in Australian Novels: The Darkness Beyond the Stage-Lit Dream. 2010. 402p. pap. 90.95 *(978-3-0343-0417-7(X))* Lang, Peter Publishing, Inc.

Ouyang, Yu. Chinese in Australian Fiction, 1888-1988. 2008. 556p. (C). 139.95 *(978-1-60497-516-1(4))* Cambria Pr.

Rolls, Alistair, ed. Mostly French: French (in) Detective Fiction. 2009. (Modern French Identities Ser.). (Illus.). 211p. pap. 49.95 *(978-3-03911-957-8(5))* Lang, Peter AG GBR. Dist: Lang, Peter.

Snodgrass, Mary Ellen. Peter Carey: A Literary Companion. 2010. (McFarland Literary Companions Ser.). (ENG., Illus.). 355p. pap. 39.95 *(978-0-7864-4152-5(6))* McFarland & Co., Inc. Pubs.

Stone, Claudia, compiled by. The Collected Bony Bulletins: Original & Complete, As Edited & Published by Philip T. Asdell. 2007. spiral bd. *(978-0-9792866-0-5(3))* Corgi Publishing.

Sue Kossew Staff. Writing Woman, Writing Place. 2006. (Routledge Research in Postcolonial Literatures Ser.). 256p. 34.00 *(978-0-415-41859-1(3))* Routledge.

Turcotte, Gerry. Peripheral Fear: Transformations of the Gothic in Canadian & Australian Fiction. 2009. (Nouvelle poétique comparatiste - New Comparative Poetics Ser.). 258p. pap. 49.95 *(978-90-5201-488-3(4))* PIE - Peter Lang BEL. Dist: Lang, Peter.

Vernay, Jean-Francois. Water from the Moon: Illusion & Reality in the Works of Australian Novelist Christopher Koch. 2007. (ENG.). 228p. (C). 99.95 *(978-1-934043-35-6(4))* Cambria Pr.

Weaver, Roslyn. Apocalypse in Australian Fiction & Film: A Critical Study. Palumbo, Donald E. & Sullivan, C. W., III, eds. 2011. (Critical Explorations in Science Fiction & Fantasy Ser.). (ENG., Illus.). 240p. pap. 35.00 *(978-0-7864-6051-9(2))* McFarland & Co., Inc. Pubs.

AUSTRALIAN FOLK SONGS

see Folk Songs, Australian

AUSTRALIAN FOOTBALL

Hindley, Debbie. In the Outer, Not on the Outer - the Importance of Women to Australian Rules Football. 2008. 188p. pap. *(978-3-639-02478-4(8))* VDM Verlag Dr. Mueller e.K.

Main, Jim. Aussie Rules for Dummies. 2nd ed. 2008. (ENG.). 384p. pap. 19.99 ***(978-0-7314-0595-4(1),*** For Dummies) Wiley, John & Sons, Inc.

AUSTRALIAN HEELER

see Australian Cattle Dog

AUSTRALIAN KELPIE

Schwartz, Charlotte. Australian Kelpie. 2007. (Comprehensive Owner's Guide Ser.). (ENG., Illus.). 155p. 24.95 *(978-1-59378-369-3(8))* Kennel Club Bks.

AUSTRALIAN LANGUAGES

Here are entered works on the aboriginal languages of Australia, and those languages of adjacent islands which agree with the continental languages in vocabulary and grammatical structure. Works which also discuss Papuan languages spoken in Australia may also be classified under Papuan Languages.

see also Tasmanian Languages

Dawson, James. Australian Aborigines: The Languages & Customs of Several Tribes of Aborigines in the Western District of Victoria, Australia. 2009. (Cambridge Library Collection - Linguistics Ser.). (ENG., Illus.). 240p. pap. 22.99 *(978-1-108-00655-2(8))* Cambridge Univ. Pr.

Dixon, R. M. W. Australian Languages: Their Nature & Development. 2007. (Cambridge Language Surveys Ser.). (ENG., Illus.). 780p. pap. 105.00 *(978-0-521-04604-6(1))* Cambridge Univ. Pr.

—A Grammar of Yidin. 2010. (Cambridge Studies in Linguistics Ser.). (ENG & PAA.). 592p. pap. 45.00 *(978-0-521-14242-7(3))* Cambridge Univ. Pr.

—The Languages of Australia. 2011. (Cambridge Library Collection - Linguistics Ser.). (Illus.). 572p. pap. 39.99 *(978-1-108-01785-5(1))* Cambridge Univ. Pr.

—Searching for Aboriginal Languages: Memoirs of a Field Worker. 2011. (Cambridge Library Collection - Linguistics Ser.). (ENG.). 350p. pap. 28.99 *(978-1-108-02504-1(8))* Cambridge Univ. Pr.

Green, Jenny, ed. Central & Eastern Anmatyerr to English Dictionary. 2010. (ENG.). 761p. 69.95 *(978-1-86465-080-8(X))* IAD Pr. AUS. Dist: Independent Pubs. Group.

Icon Group International, Inc. Staff, compiled by. Webster's Nhirrpi - English Thesaurus Dictionary. 2008. 50p. ring bd. 28.95 incl. audio compact disk *(978-0-497-83641-2(6))* Icon Group International, Inc.

—Webster's Pakanha - English Thesaurus Dictionary. 2008. 61p. ring bd. 28.95 incl. audio compact disk *(978-0-497-83656-6(4))* Icon Group International, Inc.

—Webster's Wageman - English Thesaurus Dictionary. 2008. 103p. ring bd. 28.95 incl. audio compact disk *(978-0-497-83759-4(5))* Icon Group International, Inc.

—Webster's Yanyuwa - English Thesaurus Dictionary. 2008. 29p. ring bd. 28.95 incl. audio compact disk *(978-0-497-83766-2(8))* Icon Group International, Inc.

Johnston, Trevor & Schembri, Adam. Australian Sign Language (Auslan) An introduction to sign language Linguistics. 2007. (ENG., Illus.). 338p. 95.99 *(978-0-521-83297-7(7))* Cambridge Univ. Pr.

—Australian Sign Language: Auslan: An Introduction to Sign Language Linguistics. 2007. (ENG., Illus.). 338p. per. 44.00 *(978-0-521-54056-8(9))* Cambridge Univ. Pr.

Leitner, Gerhard & Malcolm, Ian G. The Habitat of Australia's Aboriginal Languages: Past, Present, & Future. 2007. (Trends in Linguistics Ser.: Vol. 179). (ENG.). VIII, 389p. 154.00 *(978-3-11-019079-3(6))* De Gruyter, Mouton DEU. Dist: de Gruyter, Walter GmbH & Co. KG.

Leitner, Gerhard & Malcolm, Ian G., eds. The Habitat of Australia's Aboriginal Languages: Past, Present & Future. 2007. (Trends in Linguistics. Studies & Monographs [TiLSM] Ser.). (ENG.). VIII, 389p. 238.00 ***(978-3-11-916532-4(4))*** De Gruyter, Mouton DEU. Dist: de Gruyter, Walter GmbH & Co. KG.

McGregor, William B. Verb Classification in Australian Languages. (Empirical Approaches to Language Typology [EALT] Ser.). (ENG.). XXV, 531p. 270.00 ***(978-3-11-179894-3(1))*** De Gruyter, Mouton DEU. Dist: de Gruyter, Walter GmbH & Co. KG.

Qi, Ruying. The Bilingual Acquisition of English & Mandarin: Chinese Children in Australia. 2011. ***(978-1-60497-774-5(4))*** Cambria Pr.

Schmidt, Annette. Young People's Dyirbal: An Example of Language Death from Australia. 2009. (Cambridge Studies in Linguistics Ser.). (ENG.). 272p. pap. 36.99 *(978-0-521-10639-9(7))* Cambridge Univ. Pr.

AUSTRALIAN LITERATURE

see also Australian Drama; Australian Essays; Australian Fiction; Australian Poetry; Australian Wit and Humor

Blackmore, Ernie. Speakin' Out Blak - an Examination of Finding an Urban Indigenous Voice Through Contemporary Australian Theatre. 2008. 188p. pap. *(978-3-639-06884-9(X))* VDM Verlag Dr. Mueller e.K.

Bode, Katherine. Reading by Numbers: Recalibrating the Literary Field. 2012. (Anthem Scholarship in the Digital Age Ser.). (Illus.). 275p. 99.00 ***(978-0-85728-454-9(1))*** Anthem Pr. GBR. Dist: Books International, Inc.

Christenberry, H. Faye & Courtney, Angela. Literary Research & the Literatures of Australia & New Zealand: Strategies & Sources. 2011. (Illus.). xii, 267p. E-Book ***(978-0-8108-7745-0(7))*** Scarecrow Pr., Inc.

Davies, Kayt. Pomegranate Flesh. 2010. 276p. pap. *(978-3-8383-4171-2(6))* Lambert Academic Publishing.

Grenville, Kate. The Lieutenant. 2010. (ENG.). 320p. pap. 14.95 *(978-0-8021-4503-1(5),* Grove Pr.) Grove/Atlantic, Inc.

Jose, Nicholas. Anthology of Australian Aboriginal Literature. Heiss, Anita & Minter, Peter, eds. 2008. (ENG.). 288p. (C). *(978-0-7735-3459-9(8))* McGill-Queen's Univ. Pr.

Keneally, Thomas, frwd. The Literature of Australia: An Anthology. 2009. (ENG.). 1504p. 49.95 *(978-0-393-07261-7(4),* 7261) Norton, W. W. & Co., Inc.

Ruppe-Senn, Sigrid. Aboriginal Autobiographical Writings. 2008. 92p. pap. *(978-3-639-05626-6(4))* VDM Verlag Dr. Mueller e.K.

Skrzynecki, Peter, ed. Joseph's Coat: An Anthology of Multicultural Writing. 224p. pap. *(978-0-86806-186-3(7),* Hale & Iremonger) GHR Pr., The.

Toorn, Penny Van. Writing Never Arrives Naked: Early Aboriginal Writing in Australia. 2006. (ENG., Illus.). 280p. pap. 35.95 *(978-0-85575-544-7(X))* Aboriginal Studies Pr. AUS. Dist: Independent Pubs. Group.

AUSTRALIAN LITERATURE—BIBLIOGRAPHY

Arnold, John, et al, eds. The Bibliography of Australian Literature, 5 vols., Vol. 4 (P-Z) 2009. (Bibliography of Australian Literature Ser.). (ENG.). xxvi, 994p. 123.00 *(978-0-7022-3669-1(6))* Univ. of Queensland Pr. AUS. Dist: Independent Pubs. Group.

Arnold, John & Hay, John, eds. The Bibliography of Australian Literature, 5 vols., Vol. 3 (K-O) 2008. (Bibliography of Australian Literature Ser.). (ENG.). xxviii, 751p. 142.00 *(978-0-7022-3598-6(9))* Univ. of Queensland Pr. AUS. Dist: Independent Pubs. Group.

AUSTRALIAN LITERATURE—HISTORY AND CRITICISM

Althans, Katrin. Darkness Subverted: Aboriginal Gothic in Black Australian Literature & Film. 2010. (Representations & Reflections Ser.). (GER & ENG.). 219p. (C). 54.00 *(978-3-89971-768-6(6))* Vandenhoeck & Ruprecht GmbH & Co. KG DEU. Dist: ISD.

Brennan, Bernadette. The Play of Language in Brian Castro's Fiction: No Boundaries for Australia's Acclaimed Novelist. 2008. 99.95 *(978-1-60497-564-2(4))* Cambria Pr.

Budurlean, Alma. Otherness in the Novels of Patrick White. 2009. (Anglo-amerikanische Studien - Anglo-American Studies). 178p. 57.95 *(978-3-631-58909-0(3))* Lang, Peter GmbH, Europaischer Verlag der Wissenschaften DEU. Dist: Lang, Peter.

Byrne, Desmond. Australian Writers. 2010. 294p. pap. 30.45 *(978-1-4455-4368-0(0))* Thorndike Pr.

Christenberry, H. Faye & Courtney, Angela. Literary Research & the Literatures of Australia & New Zealand: Strategies & Sources. 2010. (Literary Research: Strategies & Sources Ser.). (ENG., Illus.). 280p. (gr. 17). pap. 49.95 *(978-0-8108-6749-9(4))* Scarecrow Pr., Inc.

Clark, Maureen. Mudrooroo: A Likely Story: Identity & Belonging in Postcolonial Australia. 2007. 261p. pap. *(978-90-5201-356-5(X))* Lang, Peter AG.

CRANSTON, C. A. & ZELLER, Robert, eds. The Littoral Zone: Australian Contexts & their Writers. 2007. (Nature, Culture & Literature Ser.: 4). 324p. per. 86.40 *(978-90-420-2218-8(3))* Rodopi.

Croft, Stephen. Victorian Literature. 2009. (ENG., Illus.). 208p. (YA). pap. 15.95 *(978-0-19-832879-7(6))* Oxford Univ. Pr., Inc.

Damien, Paul. Help! Debunking the Outrageous Claims of Self-Help Gurus. 2008. 176p. pap. 12.95 *(978-1-934454-14-5(1))* Synergy Bks.

D'Arcens, Louise. Old Songs in the Timeless Land: Medievalism in Australian Literature 1840-1910. 2011. (Making the Middle Ages Ser.). (ENG., Illus.). 216p. (C). 80.00 ***(978-2-503-53566-1(6))*** Brepols Pubs. BEL. Dist: ISD.

Duke, Michael. Detective Inspector Napoleon Bonaparte: His Life & Times. 2010. (Illus.). 275p. *(978-1-4438-2375-3(9))* Cambridge Scholars Pub.

Freadman, Richard. Literature, Criticism & the Universities: Interviews with Leonie Kramer, S. L. Goldberg & Howard Felperin. pap. 2.00 *(978-0-909751-81-4(1))* UWA Publishing AUS. Dist: International Specialized Bk. Services.

Hayes, Patrick. J. M. Coetzee & the Novel: Writing & Politics after Beckett. 2010. (Oxford English Monographs). (ENG.). 276p. 99.00 *(978-0-19-958795-7(7))* Oxford Univ. Pr., Inc.

Huggan, Graham. Australian Literature: Postcolonialism, Racism, Transnationalism. 2007. (Oxford Studies in Postcolonial Literatures Ser.). (ENG.). 192p. 85.00 *(978-0-19-922967-3(8));* per. 24.95 *(978-0-19-927462-8(2))* Oxford Univ. Pr., Inc.

Kato, Megumi. Narrating the Other: Australian Literary Perceptions of Japan. 2008. (Japan Studies Centre Monographs Ser.). 234p. pap. 34.95 *(978-1-876924-59-1(4),* Monash Univ. Pr.) Monash Univ. Publishing AUS. Dist: International Specialized Bk. Services.

Konzett, Matthias Piccolruaz & Lamb-Faffelberger, Margarete, eds. Elfriede Jelinek: Writing Woman, Nation, & Identity: A Critical Anthology. 2007. 320p. 57.50 *(978-0-8386-4154-5(7))* Fairleigh Dickinson Univ. Pr.

Leist, Anton & Singer, Peter, eds. J. M. Coetzee & Ethics: Philosophical Perspectives on Literature. 2010. (ENG.). 408p. (gr. 17). 82.50 *(978-0-231-14840-5(2));* pap. 27.50 *(978-0-231-14841-2(0))* Columbia Univ. Pr.

Lynch, Catherine. The Metaphor of an Adopted Body. 2009. 404p. pap. *(978-3-639-14672-1(7))* VDM Verlag Dr. Mueller e.K.

Matthias, Bettina. The Hotel as Setting in Early Twentieth-Century German & Austrian Literature: Checking in to Tell a Story. 2006. (Studies in German Literature Linguistics & Culture Ser.). (Illus.). 231p. 80.00 *(978-1-57113-321-2(6))* Camden Hse.

McCredden, Lyn. Luminous Moments: The Contemporary Sacred. 2010. (ENG.). 171p. (C). pap. 34.00 *(978-1-921511-95-0(8))* ATF Pr. AUS. Dist: Brown, David Bk. Co., The.

McMahon, Elizabeth & Olubas, Brigitta, eds. Remembering Patrick White: Contemporary Critical Essays. 2010. (ENG., Illus.). 235p. 66.00 *(978-90-420-2849-4(1))* Rodopi.

Morton, Peter. Lusting for London: Australian Expatriate Writers at the Hub of the Empire, 1870-1950. 2011. (ENG., Illus.). 304p. 90.00 ***(978-0-230-33888-3(7))*** Palgrave Macmillan.

O'Reilly, Nathanael. Postcolonial Issues in Australian Literature. 2010. *(978-1-60497-711-0(6))* Cambria Pr.

O'Sullivan, Vincent. The Unsparing Scourge: Australian Satirical Texts. pap. 12.95 *(978-0-86422-056-1(1))* UWA Publishing AUS. Dist: International Specialized Bk. Services.

Pabisch, Peter & Greisenegger, Wolfgang, eds. Von Eierschwammerlhöhen zur D. H. Lawrence Ranch: Österreichisches Literaturgeschehen in den Rockys? 2010. (Jahrbuch für Internationale Germanistik. Reihe A: Kongressberichte Ser.). (GER.). 264p. pap. *(978-3-0343-0334-7(3))* Lang, Peter.

Pierce, Peter, ed. The Cambridge History of Australian Literature. 2009. (ENG.). 622p. 185.00 *(978-0-521-88165-4(X))* Cambridge Univ. Pr.

Randall, Don. David Malouf. 2007. (Contemporary World Writers Ser.). (ENG.). 240p. 79.00 *(978-0-7190-6832-4(0));* pap. 26.00 *(978-0-7190-6833-1(9))* Manchester Univ. Pr. GBR. Dist: Macmillan.

Rando, Gaetano & Turcotte, Gerry. Literary & Social Diasporas: An Italian Australian Perspective. 2007. 236p. pap. 35.95 *(978-90-5201-383-1(7))* Lang, Peter Publishing, Inc.

Riegler, Roxane. Das Verborgene Sichtbar Machen: Ethnische Minderheiten in der österreichischen Literatur der Neunziger Jahre. 2010. (Austrian Culture Ser.). (GER.). 178p. (C). 68.95 *(978-1-4331-0831-0(3))* Lang, Peter Publishing, Inc.

Schultze, Regina. Ned Kelly in Fiction. 2011. 40p. pap. ***(978-3-640-38191-3(2))*** Hammer, Patrick, Tanja Hammer, Matthias Knoop, Julius Mittenzwei, Georg Steinbach u. Michael Teltscher. GRIN Verlag GbR.

Slater, Lisa. Telling Stories Different. 2009. 200p. pap. *(978-3-639-20368-4(2))* VDM Verlag Dr. Mueller e.K.

Stewart, Frank, et al, eds. Where the Rivers Meet: New Writing from Australia. 2007. (Illus.). 184p. per. 20.00 *(978-0-8248-3178-3(0))* Univ. of Hawaii Pr.

VanDen Driesen, Cynthia. Writing the Nation: Patrick White & the Indigene. 2009. (Illus.). 243p. 73.00 *(978-90-420-2516-5(6))* Rodopi.

Wendell Capili, Jose, ed. From the Editors: Migrant Communities & emerging Australian Literature. 2007. per. *(978-1-876418-80-9(X))* Casula Powerhouse.

Wilbanks, Ray. Australian Voices: Writers & Their Work. 2010. (ENG., Illus.). 244p. pap. 25.00 *(978-0-292-72378-8(4))* Univ. of Texas Pr.

Yates, W. E. Nestroy: Satire & Parody in Viennese Popular Comedy. 2010. (ENG.). 220p. pap. 22.99 *(978-0-521-16839-7(2))* Cambridge Univ. Pr.

AUSTRALIAN LITERATURE—WOMEN AUTHORS

Bode, Katherine. Damaged Men Desiring Women. 2008. 296p. per. *(978-3-8364-3661-8(2))* VDM Verlag Dr. Mueller e.K.

AUSTRALIAN LOVEBIRD

see Budgerigar

AUSTRALIAN MUSIC

see Music, Australian

AUSTRALIAN MYTHOLOGY

see Mythology, Aboriginal Australian

AUSTRALIAN NATIONAL CHARACTERISTICS

see National Characteristics, Australian

AUSTRALIAN NEWSPAPERS

Hall, Sandra. Tabloid Man: The Life & Times of Ezra Norton. 2008. (Illus.). 352p. *(978-0-7322-8259-2(4),* Fourth Estate) HarperCollins Pubs. Australia.

AUSTRALIAN PAINTERS

see Painters—Australia

AUSTRALIAN PAINTING

see Painting, Australian

AUSTRALIAN POETRY

Brooks, David, et al, eds. The Best Australian Poetry 2008: A Selection of the Best Poems from Australia's Literary Journals. 2009. (Best Australian Poetry Ser.). (ENG.). 156p. pap. 17.95 *(978-0-7022-3654-9(3))* Univ. of Queensland Pr. AUS. Dist: Independent Pubs. Group.

Horton, Helen & Neilsen, Philip, eds. 50 Years of Queensland Poetry. Date not set. pap. *(978-1-875998-28-9(4))* Central Queensland Univ. Pr.

Murray, Les. Taller When Prone: Poems, 1 vol. 2012. (ENG.). 112p. pap. 14.00 ***(978-0-374-53308-3(3))*** Farrar, Straus & Giroux.

Stevens, Bertram. The Golden Treasury of Australian Verse. 2009. 384p. 29.99 *(978-1-116-28916-9(4));* 384p. 31.99 *(978-1-116-28915-2(6));* 384p. pap. 33.75 *(978-1-116-28917-6(2));* 384p. pap. 32.75 *(978-1-116-28918-3(0));* 400p. 34.99 *(978-1-116-28922-0(9));* 400p. 41.99 *(978-1-116-28921-3(0));* 400p. pap. 34.75 *(978-1-116-28923-7(7));* 400p. pap. 33.75 *(978-1-116-28924-4(5))* BiblioBazaar.

AUSTRALIAN POETRY—HISTORY AND CRITICISM

Macartney, Frederick T. Australian Poetry 1947. 2006. 72p. per. *(978-1-4067-3486-7(1),* Hesperides Pr.) Read Bks.

AUSTRALIAN RULES FOOTBALL

see Australian Football

AUSTRALIAN SHEEPDOG

see Australian Kelpie

AUSTRALIAN SHEPHERD DOG

Coile, D. Caroline. Australian Shepherds. (Barron's Dog Bibles Ser.). (Illus.). 2011. (ENG.). 176p. 18.99 *(978-1-4380-7016-2(0))* 2011. v, 168p. ***(978-0-7641-4551-3(7))*** 2nd ed. 2009. (ENG., 112p. pap. 8.99 *(978-0-7641-4137-9(6))* Barron's Educational Series, Inc.

Cox-Evick, Christina. Australian Shepherd Dog. 2011. (Smart Owner's Guide Ser.). (ENG.). 176p. pap. 15.95 *(978-1-59378-792-9(8));* (Illus.). 17.95 *(978-1-59378-783-7(9))* Kennel Club Bks.

Jarrell, Elizabeth M. Australian Shepherd. 2012. 222p. ***(978-0-7938-3615-4(8))*** TFH Pubns., Inc.

Libby, Tracy. The Australian Shepherd. Hunthausen, Wayne, ed. 2007. (Terra-Nova Ser.). (Illus.). 207p. 19.95 *(978-0-7938-3677-2(8))* TFH Pubns., Inc.

AUSTRALIAN SONGS

see Songs, Aboriginal Australian

AUSTRALIAN WIT AND HUMOR

Radcliffe, Russ, ed. Best Australian Political Cartoons 2007. 2008. (Best Australian Political Cartoons Ser.). (ENG.). 192p. pap. 24.95 *(978-1-921215-56-8(9))* Scribe Pubns. AUS. Dist: Independent Pubs. Group.

—Best Australian Political Cartoons 2008. 2009. (Best Australian Political Cartoons Ser.). (ENG.). 192p. pap. 24.95 *(978-1-921372-32-2(X))* Scribe Pubns. AUS. Dist: Independent Pubs. Group.

Ruehl, Peter. Men Are Stupid, Women Are Crazy: The Best of Ruehl. 2012. (ENG.). 320p. pap. 29.95 ***(978-0-522-86112-9(1))*** Melbourne Univ. Publishing AUS. Dist: Independent Pubs. Group.

Thorne, David. The Internet Is a Playground: Irreverent Correspondences of an Evil Online Genius. 2011. (ENG.). 368p. (gr. 12). pap. 14.95 *(978-1-58542-881-6(7),* Tarcher) Penguin Group (USA) Inc.

AUSTRALIANS

Megalogenis, George. The Longest Decade. 2009. (ENG.). 416p. pap. 24.95 *(978-1-921215-94-0(1))* Scribe Pubns. AUS. Dist: Independent Pubs. Group.

Morton, Peter. Lusting for London: Australian Expatriate Writers at the Hub of the Empire, 1870-1950. 2011. (ENG., Illus.). 304p. 90.00 ***(978-0-230-33888-3(7))*** Palgrave Macmillan.

AUSTRALIANS—FOREIGN COUNTRIES

Harris. Head over Heel. 2010. (ENG., Illus.). 320p. pap. 17.95 *(978-1-85788-521-7(X))* Ebsco Publishing.

King, Madonna & Wockner, Cindy. Bali 9: The Untold Story. 2008. (Illus.). 416p. *(978-0-7322-8733-7(2))* HarperCollins Pubs. Australia.

Lancaster, Rosemary. Je Suis Australienne: Remarkable Women in France, 1880-1945. 2008. 234p. (C). pap. 26.95 *(978-1-921401-13-8(3))* UWA Publishing AUS. Dist: International Specialized Bk. Services.

McNeil, Judith L. The Girl with the Cardboard Port. 2010. (ENG.). 245p. (Orig.). pap. 21.00 *(978-0-908988-80-8(X),* Hourglass) Exisle Publishing Ltd. NZL. Dist: BookMasters Distribution Services (BDS).

Nielsen, Ellie. Buying a Piece of Paris: The Home of My Dreams in the City of Lights. 2010. (ENG.). 256p. pap. 14.99 *(978-0-312-60633-6(8),* St. Martin's Griffin) St. Martin's Pr.

Young, J. P. Two Australians in Scotland. 2008. 182p. pap. 20.53 *(978-1-4092-3633-7(1))* Lulu Enterprises Inc.

AUSTRALOPITHECINES

Falk, Dean. The Fossil Chronicles: How Two Controversial Discoveries Changed Our View of Human Evolution. 2011. (ENG., Illus.). 280p. 34.95 *(978-0-520-26670-4(6))* Univ. of California Pr.

Gundling, Tom. First in Line: Tracing Our Ape Ancestry. 2011. (ENG., Illus.). 222p. pap. 24.00 ***(978-0-300-18017-6(9))*** Yale Univ. Pr.

Johanson, Donald & Edgar, Blake. From Lucy to Language: Revised, Updated, & Expanded. 2006. (ENG., Illus.). 288p. 65.00 *(978-0-7432-8064-8(4))* Simon & Schuster.

Wong, Kate & Johanson, Donald. Lucy's Legacy: The Quest for Human Origins. 2010. (ENG., Illus.). 336p. pap. 15.00 *(978-0-307-39640-2(1),* Three Rivers Pr.) Crown Publishing Group.

AUSTRIA

Coil, Spencer Anthony. Uniforms & Equipment of the Central Powers in World War I: Volume One: Austria-Hungary & Bulgaria. 2007. (Illus.). 336p. pap. 69.95 *(978-0-7643-2781-0(X))* Schiffer Publishing, Ltd.

von Trapp, Georg & Trapp, Georg von. To the Last Salute: Memories of an Austrian U-Boat Commander. Campbell, Elizabeth M., tr. from GER. & intro. by. 2009. (ENG., Illus.). 224p. pap. 14.95 *(978-0-8032-1350-0(6),* Bison Bks.) Univ. of Nebraska Pr.

AUSTRIA—BIOGRAPHY

Angetter, Daniela & Angetter, Ewald. Gunther Burstyn (1879-1945) Sein 'Panzer' - eine bahnbrechende Erfindung zur falschen Zeit am falschen Ort. 2008. 127p. (C). pap. 29.00 *(978-3-7001-6530-9(7))* Austrian Academy of Sciences Press AUT. Dist: Brown, David Bk. Co., The.

Angner, Erik. Hayek & Natural Law. 2007. (Routledge Frontiers of Political Economy Ser.). (ENG.). 160p. (C). 150.00 *(978-0-415-39715-5(4))* Routledge.

Ambom, Marie-Theres, ed. Josef Stauffer - Notizen aus meinem Leben: Erlebte Leiden und Freuden. 2008. 136p. pap. 39.95 *(978-3-631-56531-5(3))* Lang, Peter GmbH, Europaischer Verlag der Wissenschaften DEU. Dist: Lang, Peter.

Bachmann, et al. Kriegstagebuch: Mit Briefen von Jack Hamesh an Ingeborg Bachmann. (GER.). 107p. ***(978-3-518-42145-1(X))*** Suhrkamp Verlag.

Bachmann, Ingeborg. War Diary. Holler, Hans, ed. Mitchell, Mike, tr. from GER. 2011. (SB-The German List Ser.). 108p. 15.00 *(978-0-85742-008-4(9))* Seagull Bks. GBR. Dist: Chicago Distribution Ctr.

Barber, Charles. Corresponding with Carlos: A Biography of Carlos Kleiber. 2011. (ENG., Illus.). 404p. 85.00 ***(978-0-8108-8143-3(8))*** Scarecrow Pr., Inc.

Beales, Derek. In the Shadow of Maria Theresa, 1741-1780, Vol. 1. 2008. (ENG., Illus.). 568p. pap. 74.00 *(978-0-521-52588-6(8))* Cambridge Univ. Pr.

Blackmore, J. T., ed. Ludwig Boltzmann: His Later Life & Philosophy, 1900 — 1906: Book One: A Documentary History. 2010. (Boston Studies in the Philosophy of Science Ser.). (Illus.). 292p. pap. 239.00 *(978-90-481-4492-1(2),* 9048144922) Springer.

Blum, Antonie. The Naked Life: From Vienna to the Siberian Forest. 2008. 296p. pap. 21.95 *(978-0-595-44902-6(6))* iUniverse, Inc.

Boer, Reint De. The Engineer & the Scandal: A Piece of Science History. 2010. (ENG.). x, 293p. pap. 109.00 *(978-3-642-06206-3(7),* 3642062067) Springer.

Böhm, Gottfried. Der Maler Max Weiler: Das Geistige in der Natur. 2nd ed. 2008. (Illus.). 481p. 99.95 *(978-3-211-38473-2(1),* 3211384731) Springer.

Bonyhady, Tim. Good Living Street: Portrait of a Patron Family, Vienna 1900. 2011. (ENG., Illus.). 400p. 35.00 *(978-0-307-37880-4(2),* Pantheon) Knopf Doubleday Publishing Group.

Breuer, Miklos. My 20th Century. 2008. 190p. pap. 13.50 *(978-1-4357-3830-0(6))* Lulu Enterprises Inc.

Bright, James Franck. Joseph II. 2008. 236p. 27.99 *(978-0-554-40347-2(1));* 24.99 *(978-0-554-40358-8(7));* pap. 26.75 *(978-0-554-40351-9(X));* pap. 25.75 *(978-0-554-40357-1(9))* BiblioBazaar.

—Joseph II. 2009. 122p. pap. *(978-1-150-67331-3(1))* Books LLC.

—Joseph II. 2008. 236p. 41.95 *(978-1-4372-1609-7(9));* pap. 26.95 *(978-1-4370-8693-5(4))* Kessinger Publishing, LLC.

Brook-Shepherd, Gordon. Uncrowned Emperor: The Life & Times of Otto Von Habsburg. 2007. (ENG., Illus.). 288p. pap. 32.95 *(978-1-85285-549-9(5),* Hambledon Continuum) Continuum International Publishing Group, Ltd. GBR. Dist: National Bk. Network.

Buschek, Alfred. Elisabeth, Empress of Austria. 2010. pap. 16.95 *(978-0-7414-5899-5(3))* Infinity Publishing.

Carter, David. Brief Lives: Sigmund Freud. 2011. (Brief Lives Ser.). (ENG.). 120p. pap. 12.95 *(978-1-84391-922-3(2))* Hesperus Pr. GBR. Dist: Independent Pubs. Group.

Cobbald, Jane. Viktor Schauberger: A Life of Learning from Nature. 2007. (Illus.). 170p. per. *(978-0-86315-569-7(3))* Floris Bks.

Coen, Deborah R. Vienna in the Age of Uncertainty: Science, Liberalism, & Private Life. 2011. (ENG., Illus.). 392p. pap. 35.00 *(978-0-226-11173-5(3))* Univ. of Chicago Pr.

Crankshaw, Edward. Maria Theresa. 2012. 380p. pap. ***(978-1-4482-0518-9(2),*** 146525, Bloomsbury Reader) Bloomsbury Publishing Plc.

Cubitt, C. E. Life of Friedrich August Von Hayek. 2006. iii, 391p. pap. *(978-0-7552-0243-0(0))* Authors OnLine, Ltd.

Dabernig, Josef. Handschriftliche Kopie des Buches Von Dr. Franz Xaver Mayr "Schönheit und Verdauung Oder Die Verjüngung des Menschen Nur Durch Sachgemäe Wartung des Darmes", 5. Auflage - 1975 (Erstausgabe 1920), Verlag Neues Leben Bad Goisern, Oberösterreich 1977, Kugelschreiber Auf Papier, 109 Seiten (54 Seiten 19.7 X 15 Cm, 55 Seiten 21 X 15 Cm); Handschriftliche Kopie des Buches Von Vittorio Gregotti "Il Terr. 2009. (ITA, GER & ENG.). 148p. pap. 28.00 *(978-3-03764-006-7(5))* JRP Ringier Kunstverlag AG CHE. Dist: D.A.P./Distributed Art Pubs.

Dalinger, Brigitte & Ifkovits, Kurt, eds. Gute Unterhaltung: Fritz Grünbaum und die Vergnügungskultur im Wien der 1920er und 1930er Jahre. 2008. (Schriftenreihe des Österreichischen Theatermuseums Ser.). (GER., Illus.). 128p. pap. 39.95 *(978-3-631-58041-7(X))* Lang, Peter GmbH, Europaischer Verlag der Wissenschaften DEU. Dist: Lang, Peter.

Diamant, Ann Redmon & Diamant, Alfred. Worlds Apart, Worlds United: A European-American Story, the Memoirs of Ann & Alfred Diamant. 2010. 560p. 33.99 *(978-1-4490-0375-3(3));* pap. 23.49 *(978-1-4490-0376-0(1))* AuthorHouse.

Enz, Charles P. No Time to be Brief: A scientific biography of Wolfgang Pauli. 2010. (ENG., Illus.). 584p. pap. 55.00 *(978-0-19-958815-2(5))* Oxford Univ. Pr., Inc.

Estermann, Lorenz. Lorenz Estermann: Public Hyperbindings. 2010. (ENG., Illus.). 104p. 55.00 *(978-3-7757-2609-2(8))* Hatje Cantz Verlag GmbH & Co KG DEU. Dist: D.A.P./Distributed Art Pubs.

Fisher, John. Centennial Memoir: A Jewish Man's Life in the 20th Century. 2009. (Illus.). xii, 79p. pap. *(978-0-9791086-2-4(4))* American Life Pubs., LLC.

Freud, Sophie. Living in the Shadow of the Freud Family, 1 vol. Freud, Sophie, ed. 2007. (Illus.). 472p. 34.95 *(978-0-275-99415-0(5),* C9415, Praeger Pubs.) Greenwood Publishing Group, Inc.

Fritsch, Elisabeth. Wie Die Pharmazie ein Frauenberuf Wurde: Materialien Zu Den in Wien Ausgebildeten und Berufstätigen Pharmazeutinnen: Mit Schwerpunkt

Von 1905 Bis 1945. 2007. (GER.). 183p. pap. *(978-3-8325-1703-8(0))* Logos Verlag Berlin.

Gay, José María Pérez. The Unfortunate Passion of Hermann Broch. Jiménez, Eduardo, tr. from SPA. 2008. 148p. pap. 24.95 *(978-0-9796457-3-0(5))* Floricanto Pr.

Gay, Peter. Mozart: A Life. 2006. (ENG.). 192p. (gr. 12-18). 14.00 *(978-0-14-303773-6(0),* Penguin (Non-Classics)) Penguin Group (USA) Inc.

Geese, Stephan. Memoirs of Stephan Geese: In Search of a Homeland. 2010. 200p. pap. 14.49 *(978-1-4520-0918-6(X))* AuthorHouse.

Gelber, Mark H. Stefan Zweig Reconsidered: New Perspectives on His Literary & Biographical Writings. 2007. (Conditio Judaica Ser.). (FRE, GER & ENG.). VI, 225p. pap. *(978-3-484-65162-3(8))* Verlag Max Niemeyer.

Gelber, Mark H., ed. Stefan Zweig Reconsidered: New Perspectives on his Literary & Biographical Writings. (Conditio Judaica Ser.). (ENG.). VI, 225p. 165.00 ***(978-3-11-182225-9(7))*** De Gruyter, Walter Inc.

Godt, Irving. Marianne Martines: A Woman Composer in the Vienna of Mozart & Haydn. Rice, John A., ed. 2010. (Eastman Studies in Music Ser.: Volume 77). (Illus.). 320p. 75.00 *(978-1-58046-351-5(7))* Univ. of Rochester Pr.

Grundmann, Stefan & Riesenhuber, Karl, eds. Deutschsprachige Zivilrechtslehrer des 20. Jahrhunderts in Berichten ihrer Schüler 1: Eine Ideengeschichte in Einzeldarstellungen. 2007. (GER., Illus.). XVI, 398p. 147.00 *(978-3-89949-456-3(3))* De Gruyter, Walter Inc.

Grundmann, Stefan & Riesenhuber, Karl, eds. Zivilrechtslehrer des 20. Jahrhunderts in Berichten ihrer Schüler 2: Eine Ideengeschichte in Einzeldarstellungen.Tr. of Twentieth Century German Civil Law Instructors Described by their Students. (GER.). 2011. XVI, 398p. 224.00 ***(978-3-11-187472-2(9))*** 2011. XVIII, 521p. 210.00 ***(978-3-11-916125-1(X))*** 2010. (Illus.). XVIII, 521p. 140.00 *(978-3-89949-457-0(1))* De Gruyter, Walter Inc.

Hacohen, Mordecai & Hacohen. Homeland: From Clandestine Immigration to Israeli Independence. 2009. 256p. 24.95 *(978-0-8253-0590-0(X))* Beaufort Bks., Inc.

Harrer, Heinrich. Seven Years in Tibet. 2009. (ENG.). 368p. (gr. 12-18). 14.95 *(978-1-58542-743-7(8),* Tarcher) Penguin Group (USA) Inc.

Haslinger, Ingrid. 'Rudolf war immer ein guter Sohn' - Mayerling war ganz anders: Neue Dokumente und Zeitzeugnisse. 2009. (Illus.). 360p. *(978-3-35002-674-1(4))* Cadmo.

Hayek, F. A. Hayek on Hayek: An Autobiological Dialogue. Hayek, F. A. & Kresge, S., eds. 2008. (Collected Works of F. A. Hayek Ser.). (ENG., Illus.). 177p. (C). (gr. 12). pap. 14.50 *(978-0-86597-740-2(2))* Liberty Fund, Inc.

Heller, Francis H. Steel Helmet & Mortarboard: An Academic in Uncle Sam's Army. 2009. (ENG., Illus.). 216p. (gr. 9). 24.95 *(978-0-8262-1838-4(5))* Univ. of Missouri Pr.

Hunt, John, compiled by. Antal Dorati 1906-1988: Discography & Concert Register. 2009. 307p. pap. *(978-1-901395-16-7(2))* John/Hunt.

Hunt, Swanee. Half-Life of a Zealot. 2006. (ENG., Illus.). 424p. 32.95 *(978-0-8223-3875-8(0))* Duke Univ. Pr.

Johnson, Julie M. The Memory Factory: The Forgotten Women Artists of Vienna 1900. 2012. (Central European Studies). (ENG., Illus.). 368p. pap. 35.00 ***(978-1-55753-613-6(9))*** Purdue Univ. Pr.

Kramer, Peter D. Freud: Inventor of the Modern Mind. 2009. (ENG.). 224p. pap. 13.99 *(978-0-06-176889-7(8),* HarperPerennial) HarperCollins Pubs.

Kubizek, August. The Young Hitler I Knew: The Definitive Inside Look at the Artist Who Became a Monster. 2011. (ENG., Illus.). 272p. pap. 14.95 *(978-1-61145-058-3(6),* 611058, Arcade Publishing) Skyhorse Publishing Co., Inc.

Lauterpacht, Elihu. The Life of Hersch Lauterpacht. 2010. (ENG., Illus.). 518p. 140.00 *(978-1-107-00041-4(6))* Cambridge Univ. Pr.

Leake, John. Entering Hades: The Double Life of a Serial Killer. 2009. (ENG.). 432p. (gr. 12-18). 7.99 *(978-0-425-22801-2(0),* Berkley) Penguin Group (USA) Inc.

Lendvai, Paul. Inside Austria: New Challenges, Old Demons. 2010. (Columbia/Hurst Ser.). (ENG.). 320p. (gr. 17). 40.00 *(978-0-231-70162-4(4))* Columbia Univ. Pr.

Lindstrom, Fredrik. Empire & Identity: Biographies of the Austrian State Problem in the Late Habsburg Empire. 2008. (Central European Studies). (Illus.). 311p. (C). pap. 34.95 *(978-1-55753-464-4(0))* Purdue Univ. Pr.

Macho, Eva. Alexander Freiherr von Bach: Stationen einer umstrittenen Karriere. 2008. (Beiträge zur Neueren Geschichte Österreichs Ser.). (GER., Illus.). 252p. pap. 56.95 *(978-3-631-57821-6(0))* Lang, Peter GmbH, Europaischer Verlag der Wissenschaften DEU. Dist: Lang, Peter.

—Karl Friedrich Nowak (1882-1932) Sein Wirken als Kregsberichterstatter, Autor und Verleger aus zeitgenössischer und heutiger Sicht. 2008. (Europäische Hochschulschriften. Reihe 3: Geschichte und ihre Hilfswissenschaften Ser.). 290p. pap. 74.95 *(978-3-631-58168-1(8))* Lang, Peter GmbH, Europaischer Verlag der Wissenschaften DEU. Dist: Lang, Peter.

Magida, Arthur J. The Nazi Séance: The Strange Story of the Jewish Psychic in Hitler's Circle. 2011. (ENG., Illus.). 288p. 26.00 *(978-0-230-62053-7(1))* Palgrave Macmillan.

Melograni, Piero. Wolfgang Amadeus Mozart: A Biography. Cochrane, Lydia G., tr. from ITA. 2008. (Illus.). 316p. pap. 22.50 *(978-0-226-51961-6(9))* Univ. of Chicago Pr.

Merlino, Joseph P. & Jacobs, Marilyn S. Freud At 150: Twenty First Century Essays on a Man of Genius. 2007. (ENG.). 208p. pap. 36.99 *(978-0-7657-0547-1(8))* Rowman & Littlefield Publishers, Inc.

Merlino/Jacobs/Etal. Freud At 150: 21st Century Essays on a Man of Genius. 2007. (ENG.). 208p. 68.50 *(978-0-7657-0548-8(6))* Rowman & Littlefield Publishers, Inc.

Mitchell, Donald. Discovering Mahler: Writings on Mahler, 1955-2005. Fournier-Facio, Gaston, ed. 2010. (Illus.). 730p. 95.00 *(978-1-84383-345-1(X),* Boydell Press) Boydell & Brewer, Ltd. GBR. Dist: Boydell & Brewer, Inc.

Müller-Johnson, Liesl. Rosl's Daughter: Cabaret & Childhood in 1920s Vienna. 2011. (Illus.). 188p. 36.50 ***(978-1-84624-572-5(9))*** Book Guild, Ltd. GBR. Dist: Trans-Atlantic Pubns., Inc.

Neschwara, Christian. Ein österreichischer Jurist im Vormärz: Selbstbiographische Skizzen des Freiherrn Karl Josef Pratobevera (1769-1853) 2009. (Rechtshistorische Reihe Ser.). (GER., Illus.). 300p. pap. 74.95 *(978-3-631-57612-0(9))* Lang, Peter GmbH, Europaischer Verlag der Wissenschaften DEU. Dist: Lang, Peter.

Neugebauer, Wolfgang & Scholz, Kurt, eds. Julius Wagner-Jauregg im Spannungsfeld politischer Ideen und Interessen - eine Bestandsaufnahme: Beiträge des Workshops vom 6. /7. November 2006 im Wiener Rathaus. 2008. (Wiener Vorlesungen: Forschungen Ser.). 94p. pap. 28.95 *(978-3-631-58122-3(X))* Lang, Peter GmbH, Europaischer Verlag der Wissenschaften DEU. Dist: Lang, Peter.

Neurath, Otto. Otto Neurath: the Language of the Global Polis, 1 vol. 2011. (ENG., Illus.). 176p. pap. 35.00 *(978-90-5662-798-0(8))* NAi Uitgevers / Publishers Stichting NLD. Dist: D.A.P./Distributed Art Pubs.

Noever, Peter & Pokorny, Marek, eds. Josef Hoffmann: Architecture Guide. 2011. (ENG., Illus.). 200p. pap. 40.00 *(978-3-7757-2733-4(7))* Hatje Cantz Verlag GmbH & Co KG DEU. Dist: D.A.P./Distributed Art Pubs.

Ortolani, Riz & Sarde, Philippe. Romy Schneider. 2007. (ENG., Illus.). 120p. 60.00 *(978-3-940004-03-1(0),* Earbooks) edel classics GmbH DEU. Dist: AtlasBooks Distribution.

Ottnis, Nurdy. The Show Is Over: A Circus Story. 2009. 108p. pap. 17.99 *(978-1-4490-3433-7(0))* AuthorHouse.

Parry, Eugena. Lisette Model: Shooting off My Mouth - Spitting into the Mirror - A Narrative Autobiography, 1 vol. Heiting, Manfred, ed. 2010. (ENG., Illus.). 128p. 45.00 *(978-3-86521-920-6(9))* Steidl, Gerhard Druckerei und Verlag DEU. Dist: Innovative Logistics.

Paterson, Carrie, ed. Adolf Loos - A Private Portrait. Pontasch, Constance C. & Saunders, Nicholas, trs. from GER. collector's ltd. ed. 2011. (ENG., Illus.). 200p. 24.95 *(978-0-9832540-0-3(1))* DoppelHouse Pr.

Perutz, Vivien, ed. What A Time I Am Having: Selected Letters of Max Perutz. 2009. (ENG., Illus.). 506p. 40.00 *(978-0-87969-864-5(0))* Cold Spring Harbor Laboratory Pr.

Pouvreau, David. The Dialectical Tragedy of the Concept of Wholeness: Ludwig von Bertalanffy's Biography Revisited. Schober, Elisabeth, tr. from FRE. 2009. (Exploring Unity Through Diversity Ser.). 240p. pap. 28.99 *(978-0-9817032-8-2(3))* Emergent Pubns.

Raab, Diana M. Regina's Closet: Finding My Grandmother's Secret Journal. 2007. (Illus.) 192p. 23.00 *(978-0-8253-0575-7(6))* Beaufort Bks., Inc.

Rainer, Arnulf, photos by & text. Arnulf Rainer: Cross 1956-2009. 2010. (ENG., Illus.). 216p. 130.00 ***(978-3-86984-000-0(5))*** Verlag der Buchhandlung Walther Konig DEU. Dist: D.A.P./Distributed Art Pubs.

Redsand, Anna. Viktor Frankl: A Life Worth Living. 2006. (ENG., Illus.). 150p. (J). (gr. 5-9). 19.00 *(978-0-618-72343-0(9),* Clarion Bks.) Houghton Mifflin Harcourt Trade & Reference Pubs.

Robinson, Paul E. Herbert Von Karajan: The Maestro as Superstar. 2007. 288p. per. 20.95 *(978-0-595-46147-9(6))* iUniverse, Inc.

Runciman, John F. Haydn. 2009. 104p. pap. 18.75 *(978-1-113-05881-2(1))* BiblioBazaar.

—Haydn. 2007. (ENG.). 68p. per. *(978-1-4065-8479-0(7))* Dodo Pr.

—Haydn. 2007. (Illus.). 60p. per. *(978-1-4068-2351-6(1))* Echo Library.

Saunders, Dave. Arnold: Schwarzenegger & the Movies. 2009. (ENG., Illus.). 256p. pap. 18.95 *(978-1-84511-948-5(7))* I. B. Tauris & Co., Ltd. GBR. Dist: Macmillan.

Schwarz, Vera. Meine roten Großmütter: Politische Aktivität aus der KPÖ ausgetretener/ausgeschlossener Frauen. 2010. (Politik und Demokratie. Reihe des Wiener Instituts fur Politikwissenschaft Ser.). 154p. 40.95 *(978-3-631-58722-5(8))* Lang, Peter GmbH, Europaischer Verlag der Wissenschaften DEU. Dist: Lang, Peter.

Segev, Tom. Simon Wiesenthal: The Life & Legends. 2012. (ENG., Illus.). 512p. pap. 16.95 ***(978-0-8052-1208-2(6),*** Schocken) Knopf Doubleday Publishing Group.

Sheppard, Ruth. Explorer of the Mind: The Biography of Sigmund Freud. 2012. (ENG., Illus.). 92p. 44.95 *(978-0-233-00330-6(4))* Andre Deutsch GBR. Dist: Sterling Publishing Co., Inc.

Sked, Alan. Radetzky: Imperial Victor & Military Genius. 2011. (ENG., Illus.). 288p. 40.00 *(978-1-84885-677-6(6))* I. B. Tauris & Co., Ltd. GBR. Dist: Macmillan.

Snowden, Ruth. Freud — the Key Ideas: A Teach Yourself Guide. 2nd ed. 2010. (Teach Yourself Ser.). (ENG.). 224p. pap. 14.95 *(978-0-07-174002-9(3),* 0071740023) McGraw-Hill Cos., The.

Snyder, Timothy. The Red Prince: The Secret Lives of a Habsburg Archduke. 2010. (ENG., Illus.). 352p. (gr. 13). pap. 16.95 *(978-0-465-01897-0(1))* Basic Bks.

Spiel, Hilde & Shuttleworth, Christine. Return to Vienna: A Journal. 2011. (Illus.). 128p. pap. ***(978-1-57241-177-7(5))*** Ariadne Pr.

Starke, Heidi. The Special Gift. 2008. 144p. pap. 14.95 *(978-1-4357-0839-6(3))* Lulu Enterprises Inc.

Stock, Karl F., et al. Personal Bibliographies of Austrian Personalities. 2008. (GER.). VI, 493p. pap. *(978-3-598-24881-8(4))* Saur, K. G. Verlag GmbH & Co.

Strohmaier, Brigitte & Rosner, Robert W. Marietta Blau - Stars of Disintegration: Biography of a Pioneer of Particle Physics. Dvorak, Paul F., ed. enl. ed. 2006. (Studies in Austrian Literature, Culture, & Thought). (Illus.). 220p. pap. *(978-1-57241-147-0(3))* Ariadne Pr.

Sturm, Gertraud. Leben für die Forschung: Das Ethnologenehepaar Wilhelm und Marie Hein in Sudarabien (1901/02) 2007. (Denkschriften der Phil-Klasse Ser.). (Illus.). 323p. (C). pap. 87.00 *(978-3-7001-3951-5(9))* Austrian Academy of Sciences Press AUT. Dist: Brown, David Bk. Co., The.

Suárez Coalla, Paquita & Maguire, Emily. So I Won't Forget. 2007. (ENG.). 120p. pap. 12.50 *(978-0-9725611-7-4(X))* Editorial Campana.

Szollosi, Nick. Escape: One Refugee's Journey. 2009. (Illus.). v, 78p. E-Book *(978-1-4389-7359-3(4))* AuthorHouse.

Thaler, Manfred Josef. Das Salzburger Domkapitel in der Frühen Neuzeit (1514 Bis 1806) Verfassung und Zusammensetzung. 2011. (Wissenschaft und Religion Ser.). (GER.). 688p. 115.95 *(978-3-631-60601-8(X))* Lang, Peter GmbH, Europaischer Verlag der Wissenschaften DEU. Dist: Lang, Peter.

Thompson, Kirsten Moana, et al. Peter Tscherkassky. 2007. (Austrian Film Museum Bks.). (ENG & GER., Illus.). 256p. (gr. 17). pap. 27.50 *(978-3-901644-16-0(4))* Synema Gesellschaft fur Film u. Medien AUT. Dist: Columbia Univ. Pr.

Tremayne, David. Jochen Rindt: Champion Lost. 2011. (ENG., Illus.). 256p. 69.95 *(978-1-84425-472-9(0),* 1844254720) Haynes Publishing PLC GBR. Dist: MBI Distribution Services/Quayside Distribution.

Vegvari, Margaret. A Bouquet of Wild Strawberries. 2006. 155p. pap. 15.95 *(978-0-7414-3622-1(1))* Infinity Publishing.

Wald, John P. For My Children: A Memoir. 2008. (Illus.). 104p. pap. 11.95 *(978-1-4327-1142-9(3))* Outskirts Pr., Inc.

Wallner, Alfred. Three Months in A Gestapo Prison. 2011. 132p. pap. 11.95 ***(978-1-4620-4376-7(3))*** iUniverse, Inc.

Watchorn, Peter. Isolde ahlgrimm viena & the early music Revival. 2007. (Illus.). 264p. 124.95 *(978-0-7546-5787-3(6))* Ashgate Publishing Co.

Waugh, Alexander. The House of Wittgenstein: A Family at War. 2010. (ENG., Illus.). 368p. pap. 16.95 *(978-0-307-27872-2(7),* Anchor) Knopf Doubleday Publishing Group.

Weidinger, Alfred, ed. Klimt. 2007. (Illus.). 318p. 165.00 *(978-3-7913-3764-7(5))* Prestel Publishing.

Wittgenstein - Zykan. 2010. XII, 503p. pap. *(978-3-11-023142-7(5))* Saur, K. G. Verlag GmbH & Co.

Zeiler, Linda Martina. Was Bleibt? das Politische Wirken und Vermächtnis Von Dr. Fred Sinowatz. 2011. (Beiträge zur Neueren Geschichte Österreichs Ser.). (GER.). 132p. 35.95 *(978-3-631-60527-1(7))* Lang, Peter GmbH, Europaischer Verlag der Wissenschaften DEU. Dist: Lang, Peter.

Zweig, Stefan. South American Letters: New York, Argentina & Brazil, 1940-42. Marshall, Oliver, ed. 2010. (ENG.). 224p. 80.00 *(978-1-4411-0987-3(0));* pap. 24.95 *(978-1-4411-0712-1(6))* Continuum International Publishing Group, Ltd. GBR. Dist: National Bk. Network.

AUSTRIA—CHURCH HISTORY

Emilsen, Susan. Whiff of Heresy. (Illus.). 351p. *(978-0-86840-220-8(6),* UNSW Press) NewSouth Publishing.

Rinnerthaler, Alfred. Eine Kirche für Salzburgs Altkatholiken: Kontroversen rund um die Errichtung einer altkatholischen Kirchengemeinde in Salzburg. 2008. (Wissenschaft und Religion. Veröffentlichungen des Internationalen Forschungszentrums für Grundfragen der Wissenschaften Salzburg Ser.). 178p. pap. 56.95 *(978-3-631-57083-8(X))* Lang, Peter GmbH, Europaischer Verlag der Wissenschaften DEU. Dist: Lang, Peter.

Rumpler, Helmut & Urbanitsch, Peter, eds. Die Habsburgermonarchie 1848-1918 / Soziale Strukturen, Band 9, 2. Teilband: Die Gesellschaft der Habsburgermonarchie im Kartenbild: Verwaltungs-, Sozial-und Infrastrukturem nach dem Zensus 1910. 2010. 362p. (C). 177.00 *(978-3-7001-6721-1(0))* Austrian Academy of Sciences Press AUT. Dist: Brown, David Bk. Co., The.

AUSTRIA—CIVILIZATION

Axtmann, Roland & Kuzmics, Helmut. Authority, State & National Character: The Civilizing Process in Austria & England 1700-1900. 2007. (Studies in European Cultural Transition: Vol. 36). (Illus.). 376p. 134.95 *(978-0-7546-3560-4(0))* Ashgate Publishing Co.

Beethoven-Haus (Bonn, Germany) Staff & Brandstatter, Christian, eds. Vienna 1900: Art, Life & Culture. 2006. (ENG., Illus.). 400p. 50.00 *(978-0-86565-175-3(2))* Vendome Pr., The.

Gerő, András. The Austro-Hungarian Monarchy Revisited. 2010. (ENG., Illus.). 200p. (gr. 17). 40.00 *(978-0-88033-650-5(1))* Eastern European Monographs.

Gronberg, Tag. Vienna: City of Modernity, 1890-1914. 2007. 226p. pap. 63.95 *(978-0-8204-9334-3(1))* Lang, Peter Publishing, Inc.

James, Louis. Xenophobe's Guide to the Austrians. 2011. (Xenophobe's Guide Ser.). (ENG.). 96p. pap. 7.95 *(978-1-906042-21-9(7))* Oval Bks. GBR. Dist: Independent Pubs. Group.

Reinalter, Helmut. Anno Neun 1809-2009: Kritische Essays. 2009. (Illus.). 506p. *(978-3-7065-4356-9(7))* StudienVerlag GesmbH.

Rumpler, Helmut & Urbanitsch, Peter, eds. Die Habsburgermonarchie 1848-1918 / Soziale Strukturen, Band 9, 2. Teilband: Die Gesellschaft der Habsburgermonarchie im Kartenbild: Verwaltungs-, Sozial-und Infrastrukturem nach dem Zensus 1910. 2010. 362p. (C). 177.00 *(978-3-7001-6721-1(0))* Austrian Academy of Sciences Press AUT. Dist: Brown, David Bk. Co., The.

Stoff, Julia, ed. The Programme: Linz 2009 European Capital of Culture. Binder, Otmar & Sinclair-Jones, David, trs. 2008. (Illus.). 287p. 29.95 *(978-3-211-89276-3(1))* Springer Wien AUT. Dist: Springer.

AUSTRIA—DESCRIPTION AND TRAVEL

Baker, Chris. Germany, Austria & Switzerland. 2nd ed. (Short Stay Guides). (Illus.). 144p. 9.95 *(978-1-86315-198-6(2))* Little Hills Pr. AUS. Dist: CPG Publishing, Inc.

Bingham, Elizabeth R. German Survival Guide: The Language & Culture You Need to Travel with Confidence in Germany & Austria. 2nd rev. ed. 2008 192p. pap. 19.95 *(978-0-9703734-6-5(5))* World Prospect Pr.

Enfield, Edward. Dawdling by the Danube. 2008. (ENG., Illus.). 240p. pap. 12.95 ***(978-1-84024-637-7(5))*** Summersdale Pubs. GBR. Dist: Independent Pubs. Group.

Hechenblaikner, Lois. Off Piste. 2009. (ENG., Illus.). 120p. 35.00 *(978-1-904587-78-1(X))* Lewis, Dewi Publishing GBR. Dist: Consortium Bk. Sales & Distribution.

Ihl, Daniela. Egon Erwin Kischs Reportagebuch Landung in Australien: Eine historisch-literarische Studie. 2010. (GER.). 262p. 67.95 *(978-3-631-60164-8(6))* Lang, Peter GmbH, Europaischer Verlag der Wissenschaften DEU. Dist: Lang, Peter.

Kapfinger, Otto. Krischanitz, Federle: Neue Welt Schule. (Illus.). 68p. *(978-3-7757-0520-2(1))* Hatje Cantz Verlag GmbH & Co KG DEU. Dist: D.A.P./Distributed Art Pubs.

Locken, E. Travel Journal Austria. 2010. 192p. pap. 19.99 *(978-0-557-43260-8(X))* Lulu Enterprises Inc.

Luthardt, Ernst-Otto. Austria. 2011. (Horizon Ser.). (ENG.). 160p. 34.95 *(978-3-8003-1739-4(7))* Verlagshaus Wurzburg GmbH & Co. KG DEU. Dist: Independent Pubs. Group.

Mach, Adrea. Exploring Austria: Vienna & Beyond. 2011. 200p. pap. 16.95 *(978-1-4502-7805-8(1))* iUniverse, Inc.

Metras, Mike. Germany to Rome in 64 Days: Our Pilgrimage. 2008. 330p. pap. 21.95 *(978-0-557-00477-5(2))* Lulu Enterprises Inc.

Roraff, Susan, et al. Cultureshock! Austria, 1 vol. 2007. (Cultureshock Austria: A Survival Guide to Customs & Etiquette Ser.). (ENG., Illus.). 32p. pap. 15.95 *(978-0-7614-5399-4(7))* Marshall Cavendish Corp.

Straßen und Städte Österreich 1: 150 000 / Europa 1: 3 500 000. Autoatlas: Touristische Informationen. Ortsregister mit Postleitzahlen. Landeshauptstädte Österreich. Hauptstädte Europa. Straßenverzeichnis. 128p. *(978-88-8029-674-4(4))* Casa Editrice Bonechi.

Temple, Rita. A Beach for Christmas. 2009. (Illus.). 96p. pap. 31.99 *(978-1-4389-4438-8(1))* AuthorHouse.

Weiss, Walter M. Austria. 2011. (Premium Ser.). (ENG., Illus.). 224p. 69.95 *(978-3-8003-1965-7(9))* Verlagshaus Wurzburg GmbH & Co. KG DEU. Dist: Independent Pubs. Group.

AUSTRIA—ECONOMIC CONDITIONS

BIA. Essential Austrian Manufacturers: Food, Textile, Clothing, & Chemical Companies. 6th rev. ed. 2006. 400p. (J). pap. 249.00 *(978-1-4187-4218-8(X))* Business Information Agency.

—Key Banking, Financial, & Insurance Companies of Austria. 6th rev. ed. 2006. 200p. (J). pap. 249.00 *(978-1-4187-4380-2(1))* Business Information Agency.

—Key Construction Companies of Austria. 6th rev. ed. 2006. 400p. (J). pap. 249.00 *(978-1-4187-4346-8(1))* Business Information Agency.

Bramböck, Stefanie. Die Wiener Jazzszene: Eine Musikszene Zwischen Selbsthilfe und Institution. 2010. (GER.). 194p. 57.95 *(978-3-631-59652-4(9))* Lang, Peter GmbH, Europaischer Verlag der Wissenschaften DEU. Dist: Lang, Peter.

Ceylan, Petra. Rechnungslegung über Restrukturierungs- verpflichtungen: UGB/HGB, US-GAAP und IFRS im Vergleich. 2009. 116p. pap. *(978-3-639-19703-7(8))* VDM Verlag Dr. Mueller e.K.

Dachs, Bernhard. Innovative Activities of Multinational Enterprises in Austria. 2009. (Strukturwandel und Strukturpolitik Ser.). 204p. pap. 56.95 *(978-3-631-59094-2(6))* Lang, Peter GmbH, Europaischer Verlag der Wissenschaften DEU. Dist: Lang, Peter.

Ebeling, Richard M. Political Economy, Public Policy & Monetary Economics: Ludwig Von Mises & the Austrian Tradition. 2010. (Routledge Studies in the History of Economics Ser.). (ENG.). 384p. (C). 150.00 *(978-0-415-77951-7(0))* Routledge.

Höllerschmid, Christian. Signalwirkungen und Bilanzpolitik mithilfe selbst erstellten technologiebezogenen immateriellen Vermögens: Reifeprüfung für bilanzrechtliche Sorgenkinder. 2010. (Betriebswirtschaftliche Studien. Rechnungs- und Finanzwesen, Organisation und Institution Ser.). 218p. 64.95 *(978-3-631-59811-5(4))* Lang, Peter GmbH, Europaischer Verlag der Wissenschaften DEU. Dist: Lang, Peter.

Ibp, Usa. Austria Industrial & Business Director. 2006. (Illus.). pap. 99.95 *(978-0-7397-6797-9(6))* International Business Pubns., USA.

Icon Group International, Inc. Staff, compiled by. The 2006 Economic & Product Market Databook for Bregenz, Austria. 2006. 618p. ring bd. 95.00 *(978-0-497-80242-4(2))* Icon Group International, Inc.

—The 2006 Economic & Product Market Databook for Eisenstadt, Austria. 2006. 618p. ring bd. 95.00 *(978-0-497-80506-7(5))* Icon Group International, Inc.

—The 2006 Economic & Product Market Databook for Graz, Austria. 2006. 618p. ring bd. 95.00 *(978-0-497-80618-7(5))* Icon Group International, Inc.

—The 2006 Economic & Product Market Databook for Innsbruck, Austria. 2006. 618p. ring bd. 95.00 *(978-0-497-81924-8(4))* Icon Group International, Inc.

—The 2006 Economic & Product Market Databook for Klagenfurt, Austria. 2006. 618p. ring bd. 95.00 *(978-0-497-82004-6(8))* Icon Group International, Inc.

—The 2006 Economic & Product Market Databook for Linz, Austria. 2006. 618p. ring bd. 95.00 *(978-0-497-80867-9(6))* Icon Group International, Inc.

—The 2006 Economic & Product Market Databook for Salzburg, Austria. 2006. 618p. ring bd. 95.00 *(978-0-497-81410-6(2))* Icon Group International, Inc.

—The 2006 Economic & Product Market Databook for Sankt Poelten, Austria. 2006. 618p. ring bd. 95.00 *(978-0-497-81438-0(2))* Icon Group International, Inc.

—The 2006 Economic & Product Market Databook for Steyr, Austria. 2006. 618p. ring bd. 95.00 *(978-0-497-81569-1(9))* Icon Group International, Inc.

—The 2006 Economic & Product Market Databook for Vienna, Austria. 2006. 618p. ring bd. 95.00 *(978-0-497-81245-4(2))* Icon Group International, Inc.

—The 2006 Economic & Product Market Databook for Villach, Austria. 2006. 618p. ring bd. 95.00 *(978-0-497-81789-3(6))* Icon Group International, Inc.

—The 2006 Economic & Product Market Databook for Wels, Austria. 2006. 618p. ring bd. 95.00 *(978-0-497-81817-3(5))* Icon Group International, Inc.

John, Michael (Ed) & Pammer, Michael. Erfahrung der Moderne: Festschrift fur Roman Sandgruber zum 60. Geburtstag. (ENG & GER., Illus.). 510p. (C). 112.00 *(978-3-515-09020-9(7))* Steiner, Franz Verlag Wiesbaden GmbH DEU. Dist: Brown, David Bk. Co., The.

Kajander, Petri. Government's Role in Early Stage Growth Companies. 2009. 68p. pap. *(978-3-639-00717-6(4))* VDM Verlag Dr. Mueller e.K.

Liehl, Sebastian J. Directors' & Officers' Liability Insurance: Darstellung und Analyse ihrer Relevanz für Österreich. 2010. 112p. pap. *(978-3-639-23681-1(5))* VDM Verlag Dr. Mueller e.K.

Love, David. Unfinished Business: Paul Keating's Interrupted Revolution. (ENG.). 272p. 2010. pap. 22.95 *(978-1-921640-14-8(6))* 2009. pap. 27.95 *(978-1-921372-19-3(2))* Scribe Pubns. AUS. Dist: Independent Pubs. Group.

Madl-Hammertinger, Clara. Properties of Analysts' Earnings Forecasts. 2010. 80p. pap. *(978-3-639-23782-5(X))* VDM Verlag Dr. Mueller e.K.

Meyer, Jasmin. Subprime Crisis & Its Impacts on the Economies of Chile & Austri. 2009. 72p. pap. *(978-3-639-21920-3(1))* VDM Verlag Dr. Mueller e.K.

Organisation for Economic Co-operation and Development. Austria. 2011. (Illus.). 126p. pap. 81.00 ***(978-92-64-09343-0(5))*** Organization for Economic Cooperation & Development.

Organisation for Economic Co-operation and Development Staff. Oecd Economic Surveys: Austria - Volume 2007 Issue 15. 2007. pap. 66.00 *(978-92-64-03355-9(6))* Organization for Economic Cooperation & Development.

—Oecd Economic Surveys: Austria 2009. 2009. 130p. pap. 63.00 *(978-92-64-05439-4(1))* Organization for Economic Cooperation & Development.

Rudolph, Richard L. Banking & Industrialization in Austria-Hungary: The Role of Banks in the Industrialization of the Czech Crownlands, 1873-1914. 2008. (ENG., Illus.). 304p. pap. 42.00 *(978-0-521-08847-3(X))* Cambridge Univ. Pr.

Sajovitz, Mathias. The African Diaspora in the Austrian Political Economy: A Marxist Analysis. 2008. 71p. pap. 11.99 *(978-1-4357-3534-7(X))* Lulu Enterprises Inc.

Scheiblecker, Marcus. The Austrian Business Cycle in the European Context. 2008. (Forschungsergebnisse der Wirtschaftsuniversität Wien Ser.). 228p. pap. 61.95 *(978-3-631-57607-6(2))* Lang, Peter GmbH, Europaischer Verlag der Wissenschaften DEU. Dist: Lang, Peter.

Strahwald-Just, Michaela. European City of Culture Graz 2003: Effects on Tourism. 2008. 100p. pap. *(978-3-639-10711-1(X))* VDM Verlag Dr. Mueller e.K.

Von Mises, Ludwig. Monetary, Fiscal, & Economic Policy Problems Before, During, & after the Great War. Ebeling, Richard, ed. 2012. (ENG.). 450p. (C). (gr. 13). 23.00 ***(978-0-86597-832-4(8))***; pap. 14.50 ***(978-0-86597-833-1(6))*** Liberty Fund, Inc.

Yagi, Kiichiro. Austrian & German Economic Thought: From Subjectivism to Social Evolution. 2010. (Routledge Studies in the History of Economics Ser.). (ENG., Illus.). 176p. (C). 130.00 *(978-0-415-55404-6(7)*, Routledge) Taylor & Francis Group GBR. Dist: Taylor & Francis Group.

Yuldashev, Javlon. Managerial Compensation & Corporate Governance. 2010. 80p. pap. *(978-3-639-28166-8(7))* VDM Verlag Dr. Mueller e.K.

AUSTRIA—ECONOMIC POLICY

Finnane, Mark, ed. Policing in Australia. 256p. pap. 24.95 *(978-0-86840-330-4(X)*, UNSW Press) NewSouth Publishing AUS. Dist: International Specialized Bk. Services.

Organisation for Economic Co-operation and Development Staff. Oecd Economic Surveys: Austria - Volume 2007 Issue 15. 2007. pap. 66.00 *(978-92-64-03355-9(6))* Organization for Economic Cooperation & Development.

—Oecd Economic Surveys: Austria 2009. 2009. 130p. pap. 63.00 *(978-92-64-05439-4(1))* Organization for Economic Cooperation & Development.

Von Mises, Ludwig. Monetary, Fiscal, & Economic Policy Problems Before, During, & after the Great War. Ebeling, Richard, ed. 2012. (ENG.). 450p. (C). (gr. 13). 23.00 ***(978-0-86597-832-4(8))***; pap. 14.50 ***(978-0-86597-833-1(6))*** Liberty Fund, Inc.

AUSTRIA—FOREIGN RELATIONS

Alecu de Flers, Nicole. EU Foreign Policy & the Europeanization of Neutral States: Comparing Irish & Austrian Foreign Policy. 2011. (Routledge Advances in European Politics Ser.). (ENG., Illus.). 192p. (C). 125.00 *(978-0-415-57846-2(9))* Routledge.

Austrian Foreign Policy Yearbook: Report of the Austrian Federal Ministry for Foreign Affairs for the Year 1993. (Studies in Austrian Literature, Culture & Thought). (Illus.). 171p. pap. 5.00 *(978-3-214-08278-9(7))* Ariadne Pr.

Austrian Foreign Policy Yearbook: Report of the Austrian Federal Ministry for Foreign Affairs for the Year 1994. (Studies in Austrian Literature, Culture & Thought). (Illus.). 151p. pap. 5.00 *(978-3-214-08280-2(9))* Ariadne Pr.

Austrian Foreign Policy Yearbook: Report of the Austrian Federal Ministry for Foreign Affairs for the Year 1995. (Studies in Austrian Literature, Culture & Thought). (Illus.). pap. 5.00 *(978-3-214-08283-3(3))* Ariadne Pr.

Berger, Gunther. Relazioni: Internationales Wien. 2009. (GER.). 496p. pap. 84.95 *(978-3-631-56922-1(X))* Lang, Peter GmbH, Europaischer Verlag der Wissenschaften DEU. Dist: Lang, Peter.

Betz, Susanne Helene. Von Innerösterreich in die Toskana: Erzherzogin Maria Magdalena und ihre Heirat mit Cosimo de Medici. 2008. (Beiträge zur Neueren Geschichte Österreichs Ser.). 330p. pap. 81.95 *(978-3-631-53406-9(X))* Lang, Peter GmbH, Europaischer Verlag der Wissenschaften DEU. Dist: Lang, Peter.

Bischof, Günter & Eisterer, Klaus, eds. Transatlantic Relations: Austria & Latin America in the 19th & 20th Centuries. 2006. (ENG.). 304p. pap. 49.95 *(978-3-7065-4213-5(7))* StudienVerlag GesmbH AUT. Dist: Transaction Pubs.

Breuilly, John. Austria, Prussia & the Making of Germany: 1806-1871. 2nd ed. 2011. (Seminar Studies in History Ser.). (ENG., Illus.). 240p. (C). pap. 30.00 *(978-1-4082-7276-3(8))* Longman Publishing Group.

Egupova Evgeniya & Egupova, Evgeniya. The Malaysian Business Cycle: Forecast Performance of Economic Indices. 2008. 92p. pap. *(978-3-639-09546-3(4))* VDM Verlag Dr. Mueller e.K.

Feigl, Inanc, et al, contrib. by. Auf den Spuren der Osmanen in der Osterreichischen Geschichte. (Wiener Osteuropastudien Ser.: Vol. 14). (ENG & GER.). 179p. 35.95 *(978-3-631-38932-4(9))* Lang, Peter Publishing, Inc.

Ferreira-Pereira, Laura C. Inside the Fence but Outside the Walls: The Militarily Non-Allied States in the Security Architecture of Post-Cold War Europe. 2007. 343p. pap. 83.95 *(978-3-03910-940-1(5))* Lang, Peter Publishing, Inc.

Feuerle, Mark & Büttner, Jan Ulrich. Von Wien nach Konstantinopel: Deutsch-türkische Diplomatie am Beginn des 16. Jahrhunderts. 2010. (GER., Illus.). 278p. *(978-3-7752-5921-7(X))* Hahnsche Buchhandlung, Abt. Verlag.

Fichtner, Paula Sutter. Terror & Toleration: The Habsburg Empire Confronts Islam, 1526-1850. 2008. (ENG., Illus.). 256p. 45.00 *(978-1-86189-340-6(X))* Reaktion Bks., Ltd. GBR. Dist: Chicago Distribution Ctr.

Grufeneder, Mario. Sales Increase Oppurtunities for Austrian Airlines in Russi. 2008. 108p. pap. *(978-3-639-11323-5(3))* VDM Verlag Dr. Mueller e.K.

Gumz, Jonathan & Gumz, Jonathan E. The Resurrection & Collapse of Empire in Habsburg Serbia, 1914-1918. 2009. (Cambridge Military Histories Ser.). (ENG., Illus.). 288p. 80.00 *(978-0-521-89627-6(4))* Cambridge Univ. Pr.

Holaubek, Johanna, et al, eds. Egypt & Austria IV: Crossroads, Ägypten und Osterreich IV - Begegnungen. 2008. (Egypt & Austria Ser.). (ENG., Illus.). 302p. (C). pap. 60.00 *(978-80-86277-61-5(5))* Czech Institute of Egyptology CZE. Dist: Brown, David Bk. Co., The.

Ingrao, Charles, et al, eds. Peace of Passarowitz 1718. 2011. (Central European Studies). (Illus.). 310p. pap. 39.95 *(978-1-55753-594-8(9))* Purdue Univ. Pr.

Jaszi, Oscar. The Dissolution of the Habsburg Monarchy. 2011. 498p. 58.95 ***(978-1-258-04628-6(8))*** Literary Licensing, LLC.

Jaszi, Oszkar. The Dissolution of the Habsburg Monarchy. 2009. 516p. 77.00 *(978-1-59740-728-1(3))*; 514p. pap. 51.00 *(978-1-59740-750-2(X))* ACLS Humanities E-Book.

Koch, Klaus, et al, eds. Aussenpolitische Dokumente der Republik Osterreich 1918-1938 (ADO), Band 8. 2009. (Fontes Rerum Austriacarum Ser.). 348p. (C). pap. 77.00 *(978-3-7001-6649-8(4))* Austrian Academy of Sciences Press AUT. Dist: Brown, David Bk. Co., The.

Kröll, Herbert, ed. Austrian-Greek Encounters over the Centuries: History, Diplomacy, Politics, Arts, Economics. 2007. (ENG., Illus.). 246p. 34.95 *(978-3-7065-4526-6(8))* StudienVerlag GesmbH AUT. Dist: Transaction Pubs.

Liebscher, Claudia. Das kulturelle Netz Mitteleuropas - Österreich und seine Nachbarländer. 2008. (GER & ENG.). 360p. pap. 56.95 *(978-3-631-57508-6(4))* Lang, Peter GmbH, Europaischer Verlag der Wissenschaften DEU. Dist: Lang, Peter.

Pons, A. A. The Holocaust: Italy's Struggle with the Hapsburg. Lloyd, P. R., tr. 2007. (ENG.). 342p. 46.95 *(978-0-548-02374-7(3))* Kessinger Publishing, LLC.

Procházka-Eisl, Gisela & Römer, Claudia. Osmanische Beamtenschreiben und Privatbriefe der Zeit Süleymans des Prächtigen Aus Dem Haus-, Hof- und Staatsarchiv Zu Wien. 2007. (Denkschriften der Phil. -Hist. -Klasse Ser.). (GER.). 227p. (C). 83.00 *(978-3-7001-3883-9(0))* Austrian Academy of Sciences Press AUT. Dist: Brown, David Bk. Co., The.

Riegler, Thomas. Im Fadenkreuz: Österreich und der Nahostterrorismus 1973 bis 1985. 2011. (Zeitgeschichte im Kontext Ser.). (GER.). 520p. (C). 84.00 *(978-3-89971-672-6(8))* Vandenhoeck & Ruprecht GmbH & Co. KG DEU. Dist: ISD.

Rohrlich, Elisabeth. Kreiskys Außenpolitik: Zwischen österreichischer Identität und internationalem Programm. 2009. (Zeitgeschichte im Kontext Ser.). (GER., Illus.). 437p. (C). 78.00 *(978-3-89971-553-8(5))* Vandenhoeck & Ruprecht GmbH & Co. KG DEU. Dist: ISD.

Saburov, Petr Aleksandrovich. The Saburov Memoirs: Or Bismarck & Russia. Simpson, James Young, ed. 2011. 318p. 50.95 ***(978-1-258-05542-4(2))*** Literary Licensing, LLC.

Scheiblecker, Marcus. The Austrian Business Cycle in the European Context. 2008. (Forschungsergebnisse der Wirtschaftsuniversität Wien Ser.). 228p. pap. 61.95 *(978-3-631-57607-6(2))* Lang, Peter GmbH, Europaischer Verlag der Wissenschaften DEU. Dist: Lang, Peter.

Sutherland, Stuart. The Austrian Army in Campaign Of 1866: Organisation, Uniforms, Tactics, Commanders, Unit Histories. 2007. (Illus.). 248p. 69.95 *(978-1-906033-10-1(2))* Helion & Co., Ltd. GBR. Dist: Casemate Pubs. & Bk. Distributors, LLC.

AUSTRIA—GENEALOGY

Cihak, Sabine. In tiefer Trauer: Ein inhaltsanalytischer Zeitvergleich von Todesanzeigen In Österreich. 2008. (Europäische Hochschulschriften. Reihe 22: Soziologie Ser.). (GRE.). 156p. pap. 49.95 *(978-3-631-57886-5(5))* Lang, Peter GmbH, Europaischer Verlag der Wissenschaften DEU. Dist: Lang, Peter.

Staudacher, Anna L. ... meldet den Austritt aus dem mosaischen Glauben: 18000 Austritte aus dem Judentum in Wien, 1868 - 1914: Namen - Quellen - Daten. 2009. (GER.). 826p. pap. 141.95 *(978-3-631-55832-4(5))* Lang, Peter GmbH, Europaischer Verlag der Wissenschaften DEU. Dist: Lang, Peter.

AUSTRIA—GUIDEBOOKS

Arnold, Rosemarie. Austria Baedeker Guide. 2012. (Baedeker Guides Ser.). (ENG., Illus.). 594p. pap. 20.00 ***(978-3-8297-6613-5(0))*** Marco Polo Travel Publishing GBR. Dist: Innovative Logistics.

Berlitz Pocket. Austria. 2008. (Pocket Guide Ser.). (ENG., Illus.). 192p. pap. 10.95 *(978-981-268-319-9(4))* APA Publications Services SGP. Dist: Ingram Pub. Services.

Bina, Andrea, et al. Architecture Linz 1900-2010. 2012. (GER & ENG., Illus.). 352p. pap. 49.95 *(978-3-7091-0831-4(4)*, 3709108314) Springer Wien AUT. Dist: Springer.

Bruderer, Sanami & Sanami, Bruderer. Traverse: An Alternative Guidebook to Vorarlberg & North Eastern Switzerland with Critical Reflections on Cultural Identity. 2011. 124p. pap. ***(978-3-639-31898-2(6))*** VDM Verlag Dr. Mueller e.K.

Cannon, Gwen, ed. Austria. Von Preradovic, Paula, tr. 4th rev. ed. 2007. (Michelin Green Guide Austria Ser.). (Illus.). 446p. 21.95 *(978-2-06-712325-0(4))* Michelin.

Dalton, Nick. Frommer's Salzburg Day by Day. 2010. (Frommer's Day by Day - Pocket Ser.: 83). (ENG., Illus.). 192p. pap. 13.99 *(978-0-470-72119-3(7)*, Frommers) Wiley, John & Sons, Inc.

Dorling Kindersley Publishing Staff. DK Eyewitness Travel Guide: Austria: Austria. 2012. (Eyewitness Travel Guide Ser.). (ENG.). 392p. pap. 25.00 *(978-0-7566-8423-5(4))* Dorling Kindersley Publishing, Inc.

Fodor's Travel Publications, Inc. Staff. Austria. 13th ed. 2009. (Fodor's Gold Guides). (ENG., Illus.). 512p. 21.95 *(978-1-4000-0817-9(4)*, Fodor's) Fodor's Travel Pubns.

Gieler, Peter. Austria. 2007. (Culture Smart! A Quick Guide to Customs & Etiquette Ser.). (ENG., Illus.). 168p. pap. 9.95 *(978-1-85733-347-3(0))* Kuperard Pubs. GBR. Dist: Random Hse., Inc.

Gregston, Brent. Austria. 2nd ed. 2009. (Travellers - Thomas Cook Ser.). (ENG., Illus.). 176p. pap. 16.95 *(978-1-84848-068-1(7))* Cook, Thomas Publishing GBR. Dist: Globe Pequot Pr., The.

—Bavaria & the Austrian Tyrol. 3rd ed. 2009. (Drive Around - Thomas Cook Ser.). (ENG., Illus.). 288p. pap. 26.95 *(978-1-84157-999-3(8))* Cook, Thomas Publishing GBR. Dist: Globe Pequot Pr., The.

Hartley, Allan. Trekking in Austria's Hohe Tauern: Venediger, Glockner & Reichen Groups. 2010. (Illus.). 192p. pap. 22.95 *(978-1-85284-568-1(6))* Cicerone Pr. GBR. Dist: Midpoint Trade Bks., Inc.

—Trekking in the Stubai Alps. 3rd ed. 2011. (Illus.). 160p. pap. 22.95 *(978-1-85284-623-7(2))* Cicerone Pr. GBR. Dist: Midpoint Trade Bks., Inc.

Herdrich, Walter. Journey Through Austria. 2011. (Journey Through Ser.). (ENG., Illus.). 140p. 29.95 *(978-3-8003-4053-8(4))* Verlagshaus Wurzburg GmbH & Co. KG DEU. Dist: Independent Pubs. Group.

Kuhler, Michael. Fascinating Austria. 2011. (Fascinating Ser.). (ENG.). 96p. 14.95 *(978-3-88189-665-8(1))* Verlagshaus Wurzburg GmbH & Co. KG DEU. Dist: Independent Pubs. Group.

Lonely Planet Staff, et al. Austria. 6th rev. ed. 2011. (Country Guide Ser.). (ENG., Illus.). 432p. pap. 22.99 *(978-1-74179-284-3(3))* Lonely Planet Pubns.

McNamee, Dardis. Frommer's Austria. 14th ed. (Frommer's Complete Ser.). (ENG.). 512p. 2012. 25.00 *(978-1-119-99889-1(1))* 2011. (Illus.). pap. 21.99 *(978-0-470-97595-4(4))* Wiley, John & Sons, Inc. (Frommers).

McNamee, Dardis & Childs, Maggie. Frommer's Vienna & the Danube Valley. 8th ed. 2011. (Frommer's Complete Guides: 993). (ENG., Illus.). 256p. pap. 16.99 *(978-0-470-97596-1(2)*, Frommers) Wiley, John & Sons, Inc.

Reynolds, Kev. Walking in Austria: 100 Mountain Walks in Austria. 2010. (Illus.). 384p. pap. 24.95 *(978-1-85284-538-4(4))* Cicerone Pr. GBR. Dist: Midpoint Trade Bks., Inc.

Roraff, Susan. Cultureshock Austria, 1 vol. 2011. (ENG.). 240p. pap. 15.95 *(978-0-7614-6051-0(9))* Marshall Cavendish Corp.

Steves, Rick. Rick Steves' Snapshot Munich, Bavaria & Salzburg. 2012. (Rick Steves Snapshot Ser.). (ENG., Illus.). 232p. pap. 11.99 *(978-1-59880-689-2(0))* Avalon Travel Publishing.

—Rick Steves' Vienna, Salzburg & Tirol. 2011. (Rick Steves Ser.). (ENG., Illus.). 484p. pap. 19.99 *(978-1-59880-770-7(6))* Avalon Travel Publishing.

Tesar, Heinz. Heinz Tesar: Architecture of Layers: Nine Recent Works. 2008. (ENG., Illus.). 128p. 68.00 *(978-3-936681-21-5(X))* Edition Axel Menges GmbH DEU. Dist: National Bk. Network.

Wallpaper Magazine Editors, ed. Wallpaper* City Guide Salzburg. 2011. (ENG.). 128p. pap. 9.95 ***(978-0-7148-6261-3(4))*** Phaidon Pr., Inc.

Wells, Mike. The Adlerweg: The Eagle's Way Across the Austrian Tyrol. 2012. (ENG.). 192p. pap. 24.95 ***(978-1-85284-641-1(0))*** Cicerone Pr. GBR. Dist: Midpoint Trade Bks., Inc.

AUSTRIA—HISTORY

see also Anschluss Movement, 1918-1938; Austro-Prussian War, 1866; Hungary—History; Schleswig-Holstein Question

Abbott, John S. C. The Empire of Austria Its Rise & Present Power. 2008. 492p. 33.99 *(978-0-554-25508-8(1))* 2008. 492p. 31.99 *(978-0-554-34811-7(X))* 2007. (ENG.). 444p. pap. 26.99 *(978-1-4264-9195-5(6))* BiblioBazaar.

—The Empire of Austria; Its Rise & Present Power. 2010. (ENG.). 530p. pap. 40.75 *(978-1-176-58957-5(1))* BiblioBazaar.

—The Empire of Austria; Its Rise & Present Power. 2010. (Illus.). 308p. pap. 38.51 *(978-1-153-70131-0(6))* General Bks. LLC.

—The Empire of Austria Its Rise & Present Power. I.t. ed. 2007. (ENG.). 488p. pap. 30.99 *(978-1-4264-9252-5(9))* BiblioBazaar.

—The Empire of Austria; Its Rise & Present Power by John S C Abbott. 2006. 520p. per. 29.99 *(978-1-4255-5776-8(7))* MPublishing.

Abbott, John S. C., creator. The Empire of Austria; Its Rise & Present Power. 2011. 532p. pap. 40.75 ***(978-1-178-52558-8(9))*** BiblioBazaar.

Androsch, Hannes. Afloat on a Turbulent Ocean: A Reflective View of Austria in the 20th Century. 2007. (ENG.). 104p. 19.95 *(978-3-7065-4494-8(6))* StudienVerlag GesmbH AUT. Dist: Transaction Pubs.

Balthasar, Alexander. Die österreichische bundesverfassungsrechtliche Grundordnung unter besonderer Berücksichtigung des demokratischen Prinzips: Versuch einer Interpretation. 2007. LX, 688p. pap. 119.00 *(978-3-211-35435-3(2)*, 3211354352) Springer.

Beales, Derek. In the Shadow of Maria Theresa, 1741-1780, Vol. 1. 2008. (ENG., Illus.). 568p. pap. 74.00 *(978-0-521-52588-6(8))* Cambridge Univ. Pr.

Beaver, Jan G. Collision Course: Franz Conrad von Hötzendorf, Serbia, & the Politics of Preventive War. 2009. 284p. pap. 25.98 *(978-0-557-09600-8(6))* Lulu Enterprises Inc.

Behr, Hans-Georg. Almost a Childhood: Growing up among the Nazis. Bell, Anthea, tr. from GER. 2006. (ENG., Illus.). 300p. pap. 17.95 *(978-1-86207-866-6(1))* Granta Bks. GBR. Dist: Independent Pubs. Group.

Bendel, Rainer & Spannenberger, Norbert. Kirchen Als Integrationsfaktor Für Die Migranten Im Südosten der Habsburgermonarchie Im 18. Jahrhundert. 2010. (GER & ENG., Illus.). 323p. pap. *(978-3-643-10045-0(0))* Lit Verlag.

Bischof, Gunter, et al, eds. From Empire to Republic: Post-World-War-I Austria. 2010. (ENG.). 450p. pap. 40.00 *(978-1-60801-025-7(2))* Univ Of New Orleans Pr.

Bischof, Gunter, et al, eds. Global Austria: Austria's Place in Europe & the World. 2011. (ENG., Illus.). 352p. pap. 40.00 ***(978-1-60801-062-2(7))*** Univ Of New Orleans Pr.

Blum, Jerome. Noble Landowners & Agriculture in Austria, 1815-1848: A Study in the Origins of the Peasant Emancipation of 1848. (Johns Hopkins University Studies in Historical & Political Science: No. 2 1947). reprint ed. 42.50 *(978-0-404-61310-5(1))* AMS Pr., Inc.

Boue, Gilles. The Battle of Essling: Napoleon's First Defeat? 2008. (Men & Battles 3 Ser.). (Illus.). 83p. pap. 19.95 *(978-2-35250-055-1(9))* Histoire et Collections FRA. Dist: Casemate Pubs. & Bk. Distributors, LLC.

Bright, James Franck. Joseph II. 2008. 236p. 27.99 *(978-0-554-40347-2(1))*; 24.99 *(978-0-554-40358-8(7))*; pap. 25.75 *(978-0-554-40357-1(9))*; pap. 26.75 *(978-0-554-40351-9(X))* BiblioBazaar.

—Joseph II. 2009. 122p. pap. *(978-1-150-67331-3(1))* Books LLC.

—Joseph II. 2008. 236p. 41.95 *(978-1-4372-1609-7(9))*; pap. 26.95 *(978-1-4370-8693-5(4))* Kessinger Publishing, LLC.

Brinson, Charmian, et al, eds. Immortal Austria? Austrians in Exile in Britain. 2007. (Yearbook of the Research Centre for German & Austrian Exile Studies: 8). 228p. pap. 60.00 *(978-90-420-2157-0(8))* Rodopi.

Bulloch, Jamie. Austria: The Peace Conferences of 1919-23 & Their Aftermat. 2011. (Makers of the Modern World Ser.). (ENG., Illus.). 220p. 19.95 *(978-1-905791-89-7(5))* Haus Publishing GBR. Dist: Consortium Bk. Sales & Distribution.

Chvojka, Michal. Josef Graf Sedlnitzky als Präsident der Polizei- und Zensurhofstelle in Wien (1817-1848) Ein Beitrag zur Geschichte der Staatspolizei in der Habsburgermonarchie. 2010. (Schriftenreihe der Internationalen Forschungsstelle Demokratische Bewegungen in Mitteleuropa 1770 - 1850 Ser.). (GER.). 420p. 72.95 *(978-3-631-59584-8(0))* Lang, Peter GmbH, Europaischer Verlag der Wissenschaften DEU. Dist: Lang, Peter.

Clare, George. Last Waltz in Vienna. 2nd rev. ed. 2007. (ENG., Illus.). 336p. pap. 13.95 *(978-0-330-49077-1(X))* Macmillan Pubs., Ltd. GBR. Dist: Independent Pubs. Group.

Crankshaw, Edward. Maria Theresa. 2012. 380p. pap. ***(978-1-4482-0518-9(2)***, 146525, Bloomsbury Reader) Bloomsbury Publishing Plc.

Cunliffe-Owen, Marguerite. The Martyrdom of an Empress. 2009. 172p. pap. *(978-0-217-12435-5(6))* Books LLC.

—The Martyrdom of an Empress. 2007. (ENG.). 294p. 43.95 *(978-0-548-05023-1(6))* Kessinger Publishing, LLC.

Deak, Agnes. From Habsburg Neo-Absolutism to the Compromise, 1849-1867. 2009. (ENG., Illus.). 320p. (gr. 17). 60.00 *(978-0-88033-635-2(8))* Eastern European Monographs.

Evans, R. J. W. Austria, Hungary, & the Habsburgs: Central Europe C. 1683-1867. 2008. (ENG., Illus.). 368p. pap. 55.00 *(978-0-19-954162-1(0))* Oxford Univ. Pr., Inc.

Feuerle, Mark & Büttner, Jan Ulrich. Von Wien nach Konstantinopel: Deutsch-türkische Diplomatie am Beginn des 16. Jahrhunderts. 2010. (GER., Illus.). 278p. *(978-3-7752-5921-7(X))* Hahnsche Buchhandlung, Abt. Verlag.

Fichtner, Paula. Historical Dictionary of Austria. 2nd ed. 2009. (Historical Dictionaries of Europe Ser.). (ENG., Illus.). 504p. 126.00 *(978-0-8108-5592-2(5))* Scarecrow Pr., Inc.

Fichtner, Paula Sutter. The A to Z of Austria. 2010. (A to Z Guide Ser.). (ENG.). 506p. pap. 34.45 *(978-0-8108-7649-1(3))* Scarecrow Pr., Inc.

—Terror & Toleration: The Habsburg Empire Confronts Islam, 1526-1850. 2008. (ENG., Illus.). 256p. 45.00 *(978-1-86189-340-6(X))* Reaktion Bks., Ltd. GBR. Dist: Chicago Distribution Ctr.

Fulop, Mihaly. The Unfinished Peace: The Council of Foreign Ministers & the Hungarian Peace Treaty Of 1947. 2011. (ENG., Illus.). 400p. (gr. 17). 60.00 *(978-0-88033-649-9(8))* Eastern European Monographs.

Gandilhon, Denis. Battle of Fontenoy. 2007. (Men & Battles 4 Ser.). (Illus.). 84p. pap. 19.95 *(978-2-35250-057-5(5))* Histoire et Collections FRA. Dist: Casemate Pubs. & Bk. Distributors, LLC.

Gero, Andras. The Austro-Hungarian Dual Monarchy 1867-1918. 2009. (ENG., Illus.). 240p. 50.00 *(978-1-84773-007-7(8))* New Holland Pubs., Ltd. GBR. Dist: National Bk. Network.

Gerö, András. The Austro-Hungarian Monarchy Revisited. 2010. (ENG., Illus.). 200p. (gr. 17). 40.00 *(978-0-88033-650-5(1))* Eastern European Monographs.

Gill, John H. Thunder on the Danube: Napoleon's Defeat of the Habsburgs, 3 vols. 2008. (Illus.). 512p. 60.00 *(978-1-84415-713-6(X))* Pen & Sword Bks. Ltd. GBR. Dist: Casemate Pubs. & Bk. Distributors, LLC.

Gründorf, Wilhelm Ritter von. The Danish Campaign of 1864: Recollections of an Austrian General Staff Officer. 2010. 64p. pap. 39.95 *(978-1-906033-69-9(2))* Helion & Co., Ltd. GBR. Dist: Casemate Pubs. & Bk. Distributors, LLC.

Harding, Bertita. Imperial Twilight - the Story of Karl & Zita of Hungary. 2007. 388p. per. *(978-1-4067-1135-6(7))* Read Bks.

Haslip, Joan. Sissi: Kaiserin von Oesterreich. Zeller, Alfred P., tr. (GER.). 358p. pap. *(978-3-462-02387-9(X))* Kiepenheuer & Witsch GmbH & Company KG DEU. Dist: International Bk. Import Service, Inc.

Herzog, Hillary Hope. Vienna Is Different: Jewish Writers in Austria from the Fin de Siecle to the Present. 2011. (AHS Ser.). 308p. 95.00 *(978-0-85745-181-1(2))* Berghahn Bks., Inc.

Hödl, Günther. Österreichische Historische Bibliographie fÜNf-Jahres-Register. (GER.). 566p. *(978-3-85376-097-0(X))* Bow Historical Bks.

Holaubek, Johanna, et al, eds. Egypt & Austria III: The Danube Monarchy & the Orient/Aypten und Osterreich III: Die Donaumonarchie und der Orient. 2007. (ENG & GER., Illus.). 280p. (C). pap. 50.00 *(978-80-86277-57-8(7))* Czech Institute of Egyptology CZE. Dist: Brown, David Bk. Co., The.

—Egypt & Austria IV: Crossroads, Agypten und Osterreich IV - Begegnungen. 2008. (Egypt & Austria Ser.). (ENG., Illus.). 302p. (C). pap. 60.00 *(978-80-86277-61-5(5))* Czech Institute of Egyptology CZE. Dist: Brown, David Bk. Co., The.

Huguenin-Bergenat, Yves. Kulturgater bei Staatensukzession: Die internationalen Verträge Österreichs nach dem Zerfall der österreichisch-ungarischen Monarchie im Spiegel des aktuellen Völkerrechts. 2010. (Schriften zum Kulturgaterschutz / Cultural Property Studies).Tr. of Cultural Goods & State Succession. (GER.). XVI, 345p. 182.00 *(978-3-11-175307-2(7))* De Gruyter, Walter Inc.

Huguenin-Bergenat, Yves. Kulturgüter bei Staatensukzession: Die internationalen Verträge Österreichs nach dem Zerfall der österreichisch-ungarischen Monarchie im Spiegel des aktuellen Völkerrechts. 2010. (Schriften zum Kulturgüterschutz / Cultural Property Studies).Tr. of Cultural Goods & State Succession. (GER.). XVI, 345p. 119.00 *(978-3-89949-765-6(1))* De Gruyter, Walter Inc.

Husslein-Arco, Agnes. Prince Eugene: Commander Philosopher. 2010. (ENG.). 360p. 75.00 *(978-3-7774-2551-1(6),* Art Stock Bks. Ltd/Csi) Continental Sales, Inc.

Ingrao, Charles, et al, eds. Peace of Passarowitz 1718. 2011. (Central European Studies). (Illus.). 310p. pap. 39.95 *(978-1-55753-594-8(9))* Purdue Univ. Pr.

Jaeger, Franz. War in the Tyrol: The History of the 11th Austrian Infantry Regiment during the Campaign Of 1866. 2010. 40p. pap. 35.00 *(978-1-906033-63-7(3))* Helion & Co., Ltd. GBR. Dist: Casemate Pubs. & Bk. Distributors, LLC.

Jaszi, Oscar. The Dissolution of the Habsburg Monarchy. 2011. 498p. 58.95 ***(978-1-258-04628-6(8))*** Literary Licensing, LLC.

Jaszi, Oszkar. The Dissolution of the Habsburg Monarchy. 2009. 516p. 77.00 *(978-1-59740-728-1(3));* 514p. pap. 51.00 *(978-1-59740-750-2(X))* ACLS Humanities E-Book.

Jeffreys, Darmuid. The Austro-Hungarian Dual Monarchy. 2008. (ENG.). pap. 12.95 *(978-1-84537-757-1(5))* New Holland Pubs., Ltd. GBR. Dist: National Bk. Network.

John, Michael (Ed) & Pammer, Michael. Erfahrung der Moderne: Festschrift fur Roman Sandgruber zum 60. Geburtstag. (ENG & GER., Illus.). 510p. (C). 112.00 *(978-3-515-09020-9(7))* Steiner, Franz Verlag Wiesbaden GmbH DEU. Dist: Brown, David Bk. Co., The.

Judson, Pieter M. Guardians of the Nation: Activists on the Language Frontiers of Imperial Austria. 2007. (Illus.). 332p. 60.50 *(978-0-674-02325-3(0))* Harvard Univ. Pr.

Kelly, T. M., et al. Without Remorse: Czech National Socialism in the Late Habsburg Austria, EEM #689. 2007. (ENG., Illus.). 250p. (gr. 17). 40.00 *(978-0-88033-586-7(6))* Eastern European Monographs.

Lauridsen, John T. Nazism & the Radical Right in Austria, 1918-1934. Wolfe, Michael, tr. 2007. (Illus.). 548p. (C). 78.00 *(978-87-635-0221-4(6))* Museum Tusculanum Pr. DNK. Dist: Chicago Distribution Ctr.

Lewis, Jill. Workers & Politics in Occupied Austria, 1945-55. 2008. (ENG., Illus.). 272p. 89.00 *(978-0-7190-7350-2(2))* Manchester Univ. Pr. GBR. Dist: Macmillan.

Löcher, Bernhard. Das österreichische Feldkirch und seine Jesuitenkollegien St. Nikolaus und Stella Matutina: Höheres Bildungswesen und Baugeschichte im historischen Kontext 1649 Bis 1979. 2008. (Mainzer Studien zur Neueren Geschichte Ser.). 530p. pap. 115.95 *(978-3-631-57381-5(2))* Lang, Peter GmbH, Europaischer Verlag der Wissenschaften DEU. Dist: Lang, Peter.

Mach, Adrea. Exploring Austria: Vienna & Beyond. 2011. 200p. pap. 16.95 *(978-1-4502-7805-8(1))* iUniverse, Inc.

Macho, Eva. Alexander Freiherr von Bach: Stationen einer umstrittenen Karriere. 2008. (Beiträge zur Neueren Geschichte Österreichs Ser.). (GER., Illus.). 252p. pap. 56.95 *(978-3-631-57821-6(0))* Lang, Peter GmbH, Europaischer Verlag der Wissenschaften DEU. Dist: Lang, Peter.

—Karl Friedrich Nowak (1882-1932) Sein Wirken als Kriegsberichterstatter, Autor und Verleger aus zeitgenössischer und heutiger Sicht. 2008. (Europäische Hochschulschriften. Reihe 3: Geschichte und ihre Hilfswissenschaften Ser.). 290p. pap. 74.95 *(978-3-631-58168-1(8))* Lang, Peter GmbH, Europaischer Verlag der Wissenschaften DEU. Dist: Lang, Peter.

Mahan, J. Alexander. Maria Theresa of Austri. 2008. 396p. 43.45 *(978-1-4437-2507-1(2))* 2007. 392p. per. 31.45 *(978-1-4067-3370-9(9))* Audubon Pr. & Christian Bk. Service.

—Maria Theresa of Austri. 2008. 420p. 49.95 *(978-1-4366-8840-6(X))* Kessinger Publishing, LLC.

Markl, Peter & Kadlec, Erich, eds. Karl Popper's Response To 1938. 2008. 162p. pap. 23.95 *(978-3-631-58134-6(3))* Lang, Peter GmbH, Europaischer Verlag der Wissenschaften DEU. Dist: Lang, Peter.

Millard, Frank. The Palace & the Bunker: Royal Resistance to Hitler. 2012. (ENG., Illus.). 192p. 29.95 ***(978-0-7524-6569-2(4))*** History Pr. Ltd.,The GBR. Dist: Independent Pubs. Group.

Miller, Michael. Rabbis & Revolution: The Jews of Moravia in the Age of Emancipation. 2010. (Stanford Studies in Jewish History & C Ser.). (ENG., Illus.). 480p. 60.00 *(978-0-8047-7056-9(5))* Stanford Univ. Pr.

Peterson Dso Mc, Att. Thirty-Ninththe History of the 39th Battalion Australian Imperial Force. 2011. 468p. pap. ***(978-1-84574-864-7(6))*** Naval & Military Pr., The.

Plasser, Fritz, et al, eds. New Perspectives on Austrians & World War II. 2009. (ENG., Illus.). 375p. pap. 40.00 *(978-1-4128-0883-5(9))* Transaction Pubs.

Rathkolb, Oliver. The Paradoxical Republic: Austria, 1945-2005. 2010. (Illus.). 316p. 110.00 *(978-1-84545-639-9(4))* Berghahn Bks., Inc.

Reinalter, Helmut. Anno Neun 1809-2009: Kritische Essays. 2009. (Illus.). 506p. *(978-3-7065-4356-9(7))* StudienVerlag GesmbH.

Romsics, Gergely. The Memory of the Habsburg Empire in German, Austrian, & Hungarian Right-Wing Historiography & Political Thinking, 1918-1941. 2010. (ENG.). 550p. (gr. 17). 80.00 *(978-0-88033-676-5(5))* Eastern European Monographs.

Rosenstatter, Josef. Dramenstoffe aus Karibik und Fernost im lateinischen Barocktheater der Alma Mater Benedictina zu Salzburg. 2010. (Europäische Hochschulschriften. Reihe 15: Klassische Sprachen und Literaturen Ser.). (GER.). 216p. pap. 57.95 *(978-3-631-59417-9(8))* Lang, Peter GmbH, Europaischer Verlag der Wissenschaften DEU. Dist: Lang, Peter.

Rothenberg, Gunther E. Napoleon's Great Adversary: Archduke Charles & the Austrian Army, 1792-1814. 2008. (ENG., Illus.). 304p. pap. 34.95 *(978-1-86227-383-2(9))* History Pr. Ltd.,The GBR. Dist: Independent Pubs. Group.

Rudolph, Richard L. Banking & Industrialization in Austria-Hungary: The Role of Banks in the Industrialization of the Czech Crownlands, 1873-1914. 2008. (ENG., Illus.). 304p. pap. 42.00 *(978-0-521-08847-3(X))* Cambridge Univ. Pr.

Scheer, Tamara. Zwischen Front und Heimat: Österreich-Ungarns Militärverwaltungen im Ersten Weltkrieg. 2009. (Neue Forschungen zur ostmittel- und südosteuropäischen Geschichte. New Researches on East Central & South East European History. Recherches nouvelles sur l'histoire de l'Europe centrale et orientale Ser.). (GER.). 240p. 61.95 *(978-3-631-58721-8(X))* Lang, Peter GmbH, Europaischer Verlag der Wissenschaften DEU. Dist: Lang, Peter.

Sebald, Andrea Elisabeth. Der Kriminalbiologe Franz Exner (1881-1947) Gratwanderung eines Wissenschaftlers durch die Zeit des Nationalsozialismus. 2008. (Rechtshistorische Reihe Ser.). (GER., Illus.). 424p. pap. 99.95 *(978-3-631-57975-6(6))* Lang, Peter GmbH, Europaischer Verlag der Wissenschaften DEU. Dist: Lang, Peter.

Sked, Alan. Metternich & Austria: An Evaluation. 2007. (ENG., Illus.). 224p. 110.00 *(978-1-4039-9114-0(6));* pap. 39.00 *(978-1-4039-9115-7(4))* Palgrave Macmillan.

—Radetzky: Imperial Victor & Military Genius. 2011. (ENG., Illus.). 288p. 40.00 *(978-1-84885-677-6(6))* I. B. Tauris & Co., Ltd. GBR. Dist: Macmillan.

Stoff, Julia, ed. The Programme: Linz 2009 European Capital of Culture. Binder, Otmar & Sinclair-Jones, David, trs. 2008. (Illus.). 287p. 29.95 *(978-3-211-89276-3(1))* Springer Wien AUT. Dist: Springer.

Sutherland, Stuart. The Austrian Army in Campaign Of 1866: Organisation, Uniforms, Tactics, Commanders, Unit Histories. 2007. (Illus.). 248p. 69.95 *(978-1-906033-10-1(2))* Helion & Co., Ltd. GBR. Dist: Casemate Pubs. & Bk. Distributors, LLC.

Svendsen, Nick. The First Schleswig-Holstein War 1848-50. 2008. (Illus.). 155p. 59.95 *(978-1-906033-08-8(0))* Helion & Co., Ltd. GBR. Dist: Casemate Pubs. & Bk. Distributors, LLC.

Szabo, Franz A. J. Legacy of Empire: Treasures of the University of Alberta's Central European Library Collection. 2009. (ENG., Illus.). 59p. pap. *(978-1-55195-235-2(1))* Univ. of Alberta Pr. CAN. Dist: Michigan State Univ. Pr.

Taylor, A. J. P. The Habsburg Monarchy, 1809-1918: A History of the Austrian Empire & Austria-Hungary. reprint ed. 41.50 *(978-0-404-20250-7(0),* DB80) AMS Pr., Inc.

Treadwell, Terry C. German & Austrian Aircraft of the First World War. 2011. (Illus.). 256p. pap. 29.95 *(978-1-4456-0102-1(8))* Amberley Publishing GBR. Dist: Casemate Pubs. & Bk. Distributors, LLC.

Tremayne, Eleanor E. The First Governess of the Netherlands: Margaret of Austria. 2007. (ENG.). 376p. 48.95 *(978-0-548-24057-1(4));* 380p. per. 33.95 *(978-1-4326-4215-0(4))* Kessinger Publishing, LLC.

Vyleta. Crime, Jews & News: Vienna, 1890-1914. 2007. (Illus.). 266p. 90.00 *(978-1-84545-181-3(3))* Berghahn Bks., Inc.

Welzig, Werner, ed. 'Anschluss' - Marz/April 1938 in Osterreich. 2010. (Kulturforschungen Ser.). (GER.). 180p. (C). pap. 59.00 *(978-3-7001-6768-6(7))* Austrian Academy of Sciences Press AUT. Dist: Brown, David Bk. Co., The.

Winninger, Michael. Okh Toy Factory. 2012. (Illus.). 374p. 79.90 ***(978-3-905944-05-1(7))*** Muller History Facts CHE. Dist: Casemate Pubs. & Bk. Distributors, LLC.

Winter, Richard, et al. Vienna's Conscience: Close-ups & Conversations after Hitler. 2007. 128p. 27.00 *(978-1-933370-08-8(4))* Reedy Pr.

Wright, Tony. Austria Since 1945. 296p. 20.00 *(978-1-57181-373-2(X))* Berghahn Bks., Inc.

Wylly, H. C. The Campaign of Magenta & Solferino 1859. 2008. (ENG.). 109p. pap. *(978-1-58545-206-4(8))* Nafziger Collection, Inc., The.

Wytrzens, Günther. Slawische Literaturen - Österreichische Literatur(en) Herausgegeben von Fedor B. Poljakov und Stefan Simonek. 2008. (Wechselwirkungen. Österreichische Literatur im Internationalen Kontext Ser.). 372p. pap. *(978-3-03911-205-0(8))* Lang, Peter.

Zinsmeister, Marian Carne. Austrian Stamps & Their Background 185. 2006. pap. 15.95 *(978-1-4286-6225-4(1))* Kessinger Publishing, LLC.

AUSTRIA—MAPS

Gregston, Brent. Bavaria & the Austrian Tyrol. 3rd ed. 2009. (Drive Around - Thomas Cook Ser.). (ENG., Illus.). 288p. pap. 26.95 *(978-1-84157-999-3(8))* Cook, Thomas Publishing GBR. Dist: Globe Pequot Pr., The.

Knopf Guides Staff. Knopf MapGuide to Vienna. 2011. (Knopf Mapguides Ser.). (ENG., Illus.). 32p. pap. 10.95 *(978-0-307-26383-4(5),* Knopf) Knopf Doubleday Publishing Group.

Schweizer, Hannah. Historische Karten und Ansichten von Wien, 1 vol. 2011. (ENG.). 56p. 14.99 *(978-3-8331-5967-1(7))* h.f.ullmann DEU. Dist: Innovative Logistics.

Tingay, Paul. Vienna. 2008. (ENG., Illus.). 128p. pap. 14.95 *(978-1-84537-970-4(5))* New Holland Pubs., Ltd. GBR. Dist: Globe Pequot Pr., The.

AUSTRIA—POLITICS AND GOVERNMENT

Aigner, Petra. Migration & Politics: Leadership & Legitimacy in Austria. 2008. (Illus.). 274p. pap. 68.95 *(978-3-03910-921-0(9))* Lang, Peter AG GBR. Dist: Lang, Peter.

Andexinger, Manfred. Opposition im Nationalrat: Die FPÖ 1986 Bis 1999. 2009. (Rechts- und Sozialwissenschaftliche Reihe Ser.). (GER.). 178p. pap. 56.95 *(978-3-631-58419-4(9))* Lang, Peter GmbH, Europaischer Verlag der Wissenschaften DEU. Dist: Lang, Peter.

Axtmann, Roland & Kuzmics, Helmut. Authority, State & National Character: The Civilizing Process in Austria & England 1700-1900. 2007. (Studies in European Cultural Transition: Vol. 36). (Illus.). 376p. 134.95 *(978-0-7546-3560-4(0))* Ashgate Publishing Co.

Boettke, Peter J., ed. Handbook on Contemporary Austrian Economics. 2012. (Elgar Original Reference Ser.). (Illus.). 192p. pap. 39.95 ***(978-1-84980-951-1(8))*** Elgar, Edward Publishing, Inc.

Bulloch, Jamie. Austria: The Peace Conferences of 1919-23 & Their Aftermat. 2011. (Makers of the Modern World Ser.). (ENG., Illus.). 220p. 19.95 *(978-1-905791-89-7(5))* Haus Publishing GBR. Dist: Consortium Bk. Sales & Distribution.

Czernin, Count Ottokar. In the World War. 2008. 392p. 31.99 *(978-0-554-23886-9(1))* 2008. 392p. 29.99 *(978-0-554-33189-8(6))* 2007. (ENG.). 346p. pap. 23.99 *(978-1-4254-5121-8(0))* 2007. (ENG.). 388p. pap. 26.99 *(978-1-4264-5422-6(8))* BiblioBazaar.

—In the World War. 2008. (Illus.). 352p. pap. *(978-1-4099-2633-7(8))* Dodo Pr.

De Frantz, Monika. Capital City Cultures: Reconstructing Contemporary Europe in Vienna & Berlin. 2011. (Europe plurielle - Multiple Europes Ser.). 260p. pap. 57.95 *(978-90-5201-739-6(5))* PIE - Peter Lang BEL. Dist: Lang, Peter.

Fulop, Mihaly. The Unfinished Peace: The Council of Foreign Ministers & the Hungarian Peace Treaty Of 1947. 2011. (ENG., Illus.). 400p. (gr. 17). 60.00 *(978-0-88033-649-9(8))* Eastern European Monographs.

Gabor, Robert & Vass, Vilmos. Genuine Social Democracy - Struggles Against Fascism & Communism in Hungary, 1944 - 1948. Date not set. (Atlantic Studies on Society in Change: Vol. 569). 420p. 42.50 *(978-0-88033-467-9(3))* Eastern European Monographs.

Gumz, Jonathan & Gumz, Jonathan E. The Resurrection & Collapse of Empire in Habsburg Serbia, 1914-1918. 2009. (Cambridge Military Histories Ser.). (ENG., Illus.). 288p. 80.00 *(978-0-521-89627-6(4))* Cambridge Univ. Pr.

Jandl, Michael, et al. Migration & Irregular Work in Austria: A Case Study of the Structure & Dynamics of Irregular Foreign Employment in Europe at the Beginning of the 21st Century. 2009. (IMISCOE Reports). (ENG.). 248p. pap. *(978-90-8964-053-6(3),* Leiden Univ. Pr.) Amsterdam Univ. Pr.

Kelly, T. M., et al. Without Remorse: Czech National Socialism in the Late Habsburg Austria, EEM #689. 2007. (ENG., Illus.). 250p. (gr. 17). 40.00 *(978-0-88033-586-7(6))* Eastern European Monographs.

Koch, Klaus, et al, eds. Aussenpolitische Dokumente der Republik Osterreich 1918-1938 (ADO), Band 8. 2009. (Fontes Rerum Austriacarum Ser.). 343p. (C). pap. 77.00 *(978-3-7001-6649-8(4))* Austrian Academy of Sciences Press AUT. Dist: Brown, David Bk. Co., The.

Koller, Maria H. Tobacco Control Program. 2008. 176p. pap. *(978-3-639-04039-5(2))* VDM Verlag Dr. Mueller e.K.

Kovziridze, Tamara. Hierarchy & Interdependence in Multi-Level Structures: Foreign & European Relations of Belgian, German & Austrian Federated Entities. 2009. (ENG.). 291p. pap. 46.00 *(978-90-5487-536-9(4))* VUB Univ. Pr. BEL. Dist: Independent Pubs. Group.

Lendvai, Paul. Inside Austria: New Challenges, Old Demons. 2010. (Columbia/Hurst Ser.). (ENG.). 320p. (gr. 17). 40.00 *(978-0-231-70162-4(4))* Columbia Univ. Pr.

Lesjak, Heli Annika. Explaining Organic Farming Through Past Policies - Comparing Support Policies of Austria, Finland & the European Union. 2008. (Illus.). 236p. pap. *(978-3-639-03896-5(7))* VDM Verlag Dr. Mueller e.K.

Lewis, Jill. Workers & Politics in Occupied Austria, 1945-55. 2008. (ENG., Illus.). 272p. 89.00 *(978-0-7190-7350-2(2))* Manchester Univ. Pr. GBR. Dist: Macmillan.

Liebscher, Claudia. Das kulturelle Netz Mitteleuropas - Österreich und seine Nachbarländer. 2008. (GER & ENG.). 360p. pap. 56.95 *(978-3-631-57508-6(4))* Lang, Peter GmbH, Europaischer Verlag der Wissenschaften DEU. Dist: Lang, Peter.

Lindstrom, Fredrik. Empire & Identity: Biographies of the Austrian State Problem in the Late Habsburg Empire. 2008. (Central European Studies). (Illus.). 311p. (C). pap. 34.95 *(978-1-55753-464-4(0))* Purdue Univ. Pr.

Mata, Petr. Die Habsburgermonarchie 1620 Bis 1740: Leistungen und Grenzen des Absolutismusparadigmas. Winkelbauer, Thomas, tr. 2006. (Forschungen zur Geschichte und Kultur des Östlichen Mitteleuropa (FGKOM) Ser.). (GER.). 474p. (C). 89.00 *(978-3-515-08766-7(4))* Steiner, Franz Verlag Wiesbaden GmbH DEU. Dist: Brown, David Bk. Co., The.

Mitchison, Naomi. Vienna Diary 1934. 2009. 288p. pap. *(978-1-84921-021-8(7))* Kennedy & Boyd.

Pyrah, Robert. The Burgtheater & Austrian Identity: Theatre & Cultural Politics in Vienna, 1918-38. 2006. (Legenda Main Ser.). 263p. 79.50 *(978-1-904350-67-5(4))* European Humanities Research Ctr. GBR. Dist: Brown, David Bk. Co., The.

Rathkolb, Oliver. The Paradoxical Republic: Austria, 1945-2005. 2010. (Illus.). 316p. 110.00 *(978-1-84545-639-9(4))* Berghahn Bks., Inc.

Richtsteig, Michael. Wiener Übereinkommen über diplomatische und konsularische Beziehungen: Entstehungsgeschichte, Kommentierung, Praxis. 2010. 275p. 74.00 *(978-3-8329-4367-7(6))* Nomos Verlagsgesellschaft DEU. Dist: International Specialized Bk. Services.

Rohrlich, Elisabeth. Kreiskys Außenpolitik: Zwischen österreichischer Identität und internationalem Programm. 2009. (Zeitgeschichte im Kontext Ser.). (GER., Illus.). 437p. (C). 78.00 *(978-3-89971-553-8(5))* Vandenhoeck & Ruprecht GmbH & Co. KG DEU. Dist: ISD.

Rumpler, Helmut & Urbanitsch, Peter, eds. Die Habsburgermonarchie 1848-1918 / Soziale Strukturen, Band 9, 2. Teilband: Die Gesellschaft der Habsburgermonarchie im Kartenbild: Verwaltungs-, Sozial- und Infrastrukturen nach dem Zensus 1910. 2010. 362p. (C). 177.00 *(978-3-7001-6721-1(0))* Austrian Academy of Sciences Press AUT. Dist: Brown, David Bk. Co., The.

Sajovitz, Mathias. The African Diaspora in the Austrian Political Economy: A Marxist Analysis. 2008. 71p. pap. 11.99 *(978-1-4357-3534-7(X))* Lulu Enterprises Inc.

Sandeman, G. A. C. Metternich. 2007. (ENG.). 400p. 49.95 *(978-0-548-09698-7(8))* Kessinger Publishing, LLC.

Schick, Gudrun. The European Cross-Border Funding Programmes in Salzburg. 2010. 96p. pap. *(978-3-639-25567-2(0))* VDM Verlag Dr. Mueller e.K.

Schwarz, Vera. Meine roten Großmütter: Politische Aktivität aus der KPÖ ausgetretener/ausgeschlossener Frauen. 2010. (Politik und Demokratie. Reihe des Wiener Instituts für Politikwissenschaft Ser.). 154p. 40.95 *(978-3-631-58722-5(8))* Lang, Peter GmbH, Europaischer Verlag der Wissenschaften DEU. Dist: Lang, Peter.

Seeleib-Kaiser, Martin, et al. Party Politics & Social Welfare: Comparing Christian & Social Democracy in Austria, Germany & the Netherlands. (Globalization & Welfare Ser.). 232p. 2010. pap. 45.00 *(978-1-84980-028-0(6))* 2008. (Illus.). 119.00 *(978-1-84542-542-5(1))* Elgar, Edward Publishing, Inc.

Segev, Tom. Simon Wiesenthal: The Life & Legends. 2010. (ENG., Illus.). 496p. 35.00 *(978-0-385-51946-5(X),* Doubleday) Knopf Doubleday Publishing Group.

Steininger, Rolf, et al, eds. Austria in the Twentieth Century. 2008. (ENG.). 369p. pap. 34.95 *(978-1-4128-0854-5(5))* Transaction Pubs.

Stelzer, Manfred. The Constitution of the Republic of Austria: A Contextual Analysis. 2011. (ENG.). 294p. pap. 40.00 *(978-1-84113-852-7(5))* Hart Publishing Ltd. GBR. Dist: International Specialized Bk. Services.

Stourzh, Gerald. From Vienna to Chicago & Back: Essays on Intellectual History & Political Thought in Europe & America. 2007. (ENG.). 384p. 47.50 *(978-0-226-77636-1(0))* Univ. of Chicago Pr.

Thorpe, Julie. Pan-Germanism Austrofascist State: Pan-Germanism & the Austrofascist State, 1933-38. 2011. (ENG.). 256p. 95.00 *(978-0-7190-7967-2(5))* Manchester Univ. Pr. GBR. Dist: Macmillan.

TransAct: Transnational Activities in the Cultural FieldInterventionen zur Lage in Österreichmuseum in progress. 2009. 513p. 49.95 *(978-3-211-99800-7(4))* Springer Wien AUT. Dist: Actar Birkhauser Distribution.

Unowsky, et al. The Limits of Loyalty: Imperial Symbolism, Popular Allegiances, & State Patriotism in the Late Habsburg Monarchy. 2007. (Austrian & Habsburg Studies). (Illus.). 258p. 90.00 *(978-1-84545-202-5(X))* Berghahn Bks., Inc.

Wolfgang, Muller. A Good Example of Peaceful Coexistence? The Soviet Union, Austria, & Neutrality, 1955-1991. 2011. (Zentraleuropa-Studien Ser.). (ENG.). 381p. (C). pap. 54.00 ***(978-3-7001-6898-0(5)***, Austrian Academy of Sciences of Pr.) Austrian Academy of Sciences Press AUT. Dist: Brown, David Bk. Co., The.

Zeiler, Linda Martina. Was Bleibt? das Politische Wirken und Vermächtnis Von Dr. Fred Sinowatz. 2011. (Beiträge zur Neueren Geschichte Österreichs Ser.). (GER.). 132p. 35.95 *(978-3-631-60527-1(7))* Lang, Peter GmbH, Europaischer Verlag der Wissenschaften DEU. Dist: Lang, Peter.

AUSTRIA—RELIGION

Endraß, Elke & Endrass, Elke. Wie Halten Sie Es MIT der Religion? Prominente Aus der Politik Beziehen Stellung. 2008. (GER., Illus.). 180p. *(978-3-7831-2820-8(X))* Kreuz Verlag GmbH & Co. KG.

Klieber, Rupert. jüdische - christliche - muslimische Lebenswelten der Donaumonarchie: 1848-1918. 2010. (GER., Illus.). 294p. *(978-3-205-78384-8(0))* Bohlau Verlag Gmbh & Cie.

Potz, Richard. State, Law & Religion in Pluralistic Societies - Austrian & Indonesian Perspectives: Austrian-Indonesian Dialogue Symposium, 27-29 May, 2009, Vienna. Potz, Richard et al, eds. 2010. (ENG., Illus.). 210p. (C). 51.00 *(978-3-89971-607-8(8))* Vandenhoeck & Ruprecht GmbH & Co. KG DEU. Dist: ISD.

AUSTRIA—SOCIAL CONDITIONS

Aichhorn, Ulrike, ed. Frauen & Recht. 2007. XXII, 500p. pap. 94.00 *(978-3-211-82969-1(5)*, 3211829695) Springer.

Bischof, Günter, et al, eds. Sexuality in Austria. 2006. (Contemporary Austrian Studies: Vol. 15). (ENG., Illus.). 264p. (gr. 11). pap. 40.00 *(978-1-4128-0606-0(2))* Transaction Pubs.

Blum, Jerome. Noble Landowners & Agriculture in Austria, 1815-1848: A Study in the Origins of the Peasant Emancipation of 1848. (Johns Hopkins University Studies in Historical & Political Science: No. 2 1947). reprint ed. 42.50 *(978-0-404-61310-5(1))* AMS Pr., Inc.

Bramböck, Stefanie. Die Wiener Jazzszene: Eine Musikszene Zwischen Selbsthilfe und Institution. 2010. (GER.). 194p. 57.95 *(978-3-631-59652-4(9))* Lang, Peter GmbH, Europaischer Verlag der Wissenschaften DEU. Dist: Lang, Peter.

Dall, Anita. Corporate Social Responsibility. 2010. 96p. pap. *(978-3-639-24214-0(9))* VDM Verlag Dr. Mueller e.K.

Fitz, Angelika & Heller, Martin, eds. Linz Texas: A City Relates. 2008. (ENG., Illus.). 200p. pap. 49.95 *(978-3-211-78894-3(8)*, 3211788948) Springer.

Gerö, Andràs. Neither Woman nor Jew: The Confluence of Prejudices in the Austro-Hungarian Monarchy at the Turn of the Century. 2010. (ENG.). 190p. (gr. 17). 40.00 *(978-0-88033-669-7(2))* Eastern European Monographs.

Jaszi, Oscar. The Dissolution of the Habsburg Monarchy. 2011. 498p. 58.95 ***(978-1-258-04628-6(8))*** Literary Licensing, LLC.

Jaszi, Oszkar. The Dissolution of the Habsburg Monarchy. 2009. 516p. 77.00 *(978-1-59740-728-1(3))*; 514p. pap. 51.00 *(978-1-59740-750-2(X))* ACLS Humanities E-Book.

Kilaf, Esra. Turkish Immigrants Women S Health in Austri. 2008. 260p. pap. *(978-3-639-01289-7(5))* VDM Verlag Dr. Mueller e.K.

Knittel, Kay M. Seeing Mahler: Music & the Language of Antisemitism in Fin-de-Siècle Vienna. 2010. (Illus.). 218p. 99.95 *(978-0-7546-6372-0(8))* Ashgate Publishing Co.

Koller, Maria H. Tobacco Control Program. 2008. 176p. pap. *(978-3-639-04039-5(2))* VDM Verlag Dr. Mueller e.K.

Krzyzanowski, Michal & Wodak, Ruth. The Politics of Exclusion: Debating Migration in Austria. 2008. (ENG., Illus.). 236p. pap. 49.95 *(978-1-4128-0836-1(7))* Transaction Pubs.

Maringer, Walter. Berufsbild und Identität des Soldaten im sozialen Wandel. 2008. (Europäische Hochschulschriften. Reihe 22: Soziologie Ser.). 112p. pap. 35.95 *(978-3-631-58058-5(4))* Lang, Peter GmbH, Europaischer Verlag der Wissenschaften DEU. Dist: Lang, Peter.

Musner, Lutz & Maderthaner, Wolfgang. Unruly Massess: The Other Side of Fin-de-Siècle Vienna. 2008. (International Studies in Social History). (Illus.). 184p. (C). 90.00 *(978-1-84545-345-9(X))* Berghahn Bks., Inc.

Pflegerl, Johannes & Geserick, Christine. Kinship & Social Security in Austria: A Social History for the Twentieth Century. 2008. (ENG., Illus.). 200p. (gr. 11). pap. 38.95 *(978-3-7065-4480-1(6))* StudienVerlag GesmbH AUT. Dist: Transaction Pubs.

Rathkolb, Oliver. The Paradoxical Republic: Austria, 1945-2005. 2010. (Illus.). 316p. 110.00 *(978-1-84545-639-9(4))* Berghahn Bks., Inc.

Rose, Alison. Jewish Women in Fin de Siècle Vienna. (ENG., Illus.). 328p. 2010. pap. 30.00 *(978-0-292-72159-3(5))* 2008. (C). 60.00 *(978-0-292-71861-6(6))* Univ. of Texas Pr.

Solms-Laubach, Franz. Nietzsche & Early German & Austrian Sociology. 2007. (Monographien und Texte Zur Nietzsche-Forschung Ser.). (ENG.). XXIV, 328p. 154.00 *(978-3-11-018109-8(6))* De Gruyter, Walter Inc.

Solms-Laubach, Franz Graf Zu. Nietzsche & Early German & Austrian Sociology. (Monographien und Texte zur Nietzsche-Forschung Ser.). (ENG., Illus.). XXIV, 328p. 255.00 ***(978-3-11-180407-1(0))*** De Gruyter, Walter Inc.

Steppeler, Lucia. Wellness Tourism As an Active Method for Individual Health Promotion. 2009. 80p. pap. *(978-3-639-13523-7(7))* VDM Verlag Dr. Mueller e.K.

Sundaresan, Usha. The Generation Gap. 2010. 144p. pap. *(978-3-639-22339-2(X))* VDM Verlag Dr. Mueller e.K.

Vienna Institute of Demography. Vienna Yearbook of Population Research 2006. 2008. 241p. (C). pap. 60.00 *(978-3-7001-3808-2(3))* Austrian Academy of Sciences Press AUT. Dist: Brown, David Bk. Co., The.

Warren, John & Zitzlsperger, Ulrike, eds. Vienna Meets Berlin: Cultural Interaction 1918-1933. 2nd rev. ed. 2008. (Britische und Irische Studien zur deutschen Sprache und Literatur. British & Irish Studies in German Language & Literature Ser.). 300p. pap. 68.95 *(978-3-03911-853-3(6))* Lang, Peter AG GBR. Dist: Lang, Peter.

AUSTRIA—SOCIAL LIFE AND CUSTOMS

Budroni, Paolo. Mozart und Salieri - Partner oder Rivalen? Das Fest in der Orangerie zu Schönbrunn vom 7. Februar 1786. 2008. (GER., Illus.). 135p. (C). pap. 18.00 *(978-3-89971-477-7(6))* Vandenhoeck & Ruprecht GmbH & Co. KG DEU. Dist: ISD.

Clare, George. Last Waltz in Vienna. 2nd rev. ed. 2007. (ENG., Illus.). 336p. pap. 13.95 *(978-0-330-49077-1(X))* Macmillan Pubs., Ltd. GBR. Dist: Independent Pubs. Group.

Csúri, Károly & Orosz, Magdolna, eds. Massenfeste: Ritualisierte Öffentlichkeiten in der mittelosteuropäischen Moderne. 2009. (Budapester Studien zur Literaturwissenschaft Ser.). 288p. 74.95 *(978-3-631-59138-3(1))* Lang, Peter GmbH, Europaischer Verlag der Wissenschaften DEU. Dist: Lang, Peter.

Duman, Roberta. A City by City Guide to Living & Working in Australia. 2006. (Illus.). 274p. per. 26.00 *(978-1-84528-089-5(X))* Parkwest Pubns., Inc.

Gieler, Peter. Austria. 2007. (Culture Smart! A Quick Guide to Customs & Etiquette Ser.). (ENG., Illus.). 168p. pap. 9.95 *(978-1-85733-347-3(0))* Kuperard Pubs. GBR. Dist: Random Hse., Inc.

Hopfner, Johanna & Németh, András, eds. Pädagogische und kulturelle Strömungen in der K. U. K. Monarchie: Lebensreform, Herbartianismus und reformpädagogische Bewegungen. 2008. (Erziehung in Wissenschaft und Praxis Ser.). 200p. pap. 56.95 *(978-3-631-56719-7(7))* Lang, Peter GmbH, Europaischer Verlag der Wissenschaften DEU. Dist: Lang, Peter.

Klieber, Rupert. jüdische - christliche - muslimische Lebenswelten der Donaumonarchie: 1848-1918. 2010. (GER., Illus.). 294p. *(978-3-205-78384-8(0))* Bohlau Verlag Gmbh & Cie.

Lang, Maria-Katharina. Mongolische Ethnographica in Wien: Die Sammlung Hans Leder im Museum fur Volkerkunde Wien. 2010. (VERoFFENTLICHUNGEN ZUR SOZIANLANTHROPOLOGIE Ser.). (GER.). 69p. (C). pap. 35.00 *(978-3-7001-6760-0(1))* Austrian Academy of Sciences Press AUT. Dist: Brown, David Bk. Co., The.

Musner, Lutz & Maderthaner, Wolfgang. Unruly Masses: The Other Side of Fin-de-Siécle Vienna. 2008. (International Studies in Social History). (Illus.). 184p. (C). 27.95 *(978-1-84545-446-3(4))* Berghahn Bks., Inc.

Panin, Tonkao. Architectural Spatiality. 2009. 196p. pap. *(978-3-639-19575-0(2))* VDM Verlag Dr. Mueller e.K.

Raspa, Venanzio, ed. Aesthetics of the Graz School. 2011. 279p. 131.95 *(978-3-86838-076-7(0))* Ontos Verlag DEU. Dist: Transaction Pubs.

Roraff, Susan. Cultureshock Austria, 1 vol. 2011. (ENG.). 240p. pap. 15.95 *(978-0-7614-6051-0(9))* Marshall Cavendish Corp.

Roraff, Susan, et al. Cultureshock! Austria, 1 vol. 2007. (Cultureshock Austria: A Survival Guide to Customs & Etiquette Ser.). (ENG., Illus.). 32p. pap. 15.95 *(978-0-7614-5399-4(7))* Marshall Cavendish Corp.

Rose, Alison. Jewish Women in Fin de Siècle Vienna. 2010. (ENG., Illus.). 328p. pap. 30.00 *(978-0-292-72159-3(5))* Univ. of Texas Pr.

Stoff, Julia, ed. The Programme: Linz 2009 European Capital of Culture. Binder, Otmar & Sinclair-Jones, David, trs. 2008. (Illus.). 287p. 29.95 *(978-3-211-89276-3(1))* Springer Wien AUT. Dist: Springer.

Westermann, Angelika. Die Vorderösterreichischen Montanregionen in der Frühen Neuzeit. 2009. (Vierteljahrschrift fur Sozial- und Wirtschaftsgeschichte - Beihefte (VSWG-B) Ser.). (GER., Illus.). 395p. (C). pap. 97.00 *(978-3-515-09306-4(0))* Steiner, Franz Verlag Wiesbaden GmbH DEU. Dist: Brown, David Bk. Co., The.

World Book, Inc Staff, contrib. by. Christmas in Austria & Its Capital, Vienna. 2007. *(978-0-7166-0810-3(3))* World Bk., Inc.

AUSTRIAN ARCHITECTURE

see Architecture—Austria

AUSTRIAN ART

see Art, Austrian

AUSTRIAN LITERATURE

see also Austrian Poetry

Herzog, Hillary Hope. Vienna Is Different: Jewish Writers in Austria from the Fin de Siecle to the Present. 2011. (AHS Ser.). 308p. 95.00 *(978-0-85745-181-1(2))* Berghahn Bks., Inc.

Jonke, Gert. Blinding Moment: Four Pieces about Composers. 2008. *(978-1-57241-156-2(2))* Ariadne Pr.

Kiesel, Helmuth, ed. Literarische Moderne: Begriff und Phänomen. 2007. (GER.). 550p. 154.00 *(978-3-11-019114-1(8))* De Gruyter, Walter Inc.

Peters, Bergit. LiebesArten: Im Theologischen Gespräch MIT Ingeborg Bachmann. 2009. (GER.). 207p. *(978-3-7867-2762-0(7))* Matthias-Grunewald-Verlag GmbH.

Roth, Joseph. Im Bistro nach Mitternacht: Ein Frankreich-Lesebuch. (GER.). 525p. pap. *(978-3-462-02806-5(5))* Kiepenheuer & Witsch GmbH & Company KG DEU. Dist: International Bk. Import Service, Inc.

Stoehr, Ingo R. Contemporary Austrian Writings, Vol. 74. 2006. (German Library: Vol. 74). (ENG & GER.). 296p. pap. 29.95 *(978-0-8264-1509-7(1))* Continuum International Publishing Group, Ltd. GBR. Dist: National Bk. Network.

Wolf, Klaus. Hof - Universitat - Laien: Literatur- und sprachgeschichtliche Untersuchungen zum deutschen Schrifttum der Wiener Schule des Spatmittelalters. 2006. (Wissenliterature im Mittelalter Ser.). (GER., Illus.). 432p. (C). 83.00 *(978-3-89500-540-4(1))* Reichert, Ludwig Dr. DEU. Dist: Brown, David Bk. Co., The.

Zweig, Stefan. Wondrak & Other Stories. Bell, Anthea, tr. from GER. 2009. (ENG., Illus.). 128p. pap. 15.95 *(978-1-901285-86-4(3))* Pushkin Pr., Ltd. GBR. Dist: Consortium Bk. Sales & Distribution.

AUSTRIAN LITERATURE—HISTORY AND CRITICISM

Atzinger, Hildegard. Gina Kaus: Schriftstellerin Und Öffentlichkeit: Zur Stellung einer Schriftstellerin in der literarischen Öffentlichkeit der Zwischenkriegszeit in Österreich und Deutschland. 2008. (Europäische Hochschulschriften. Reihe 1: Deutsche Sprache und Literatur Ser.). 310p. pap. 74.95 *(978-3-631-57787-5(7))* Lang, Peter GmbH, Europaischer Verlag der Wissenschaften DEU. Dist: Lang, Peter.

Baker, G. P. & Hacker, P. M. S. Wittgenstein Vol. 1, Pt. 2: Understanding & Meaning - An Analytical Commentary on the Philosophical Investigations, 2 vols. 2nd ed. 2009. (ENG., Illus.). 384p. pap. 36.95 *(978-1-4051-9925-4(3)*, Wiley-Blackwell) Wiley, John & Sons, Inc.

—Wittgenstein Understanding & Meaning Vol. 1, Pt. 1: An Analytical Commentary on the Philosophical Investigations, 2 vols. 2nd ed. 2009. (ENG., Illus.). 424p. pap. 36.95 *(978-1-4051-9924-7(5)*, Wiley-Blackwell) Wiley, John & Sons, Inc.

Belletini, Lorenzo & Hutchinson, Peter. Schnitzler's Hidden Manuscripts. 2010. (GER & ENG., Illus.). 225p. pap. 55.95 *(978-3-03911-544-0(8))* Lang, Peter Publishing, Inc.

Berendes, Jochen. Ironie - Komik - Skepsis: Studien zum Werk Adalbert Stifters. 2009. (Hermaea Ser.). (GER.). VII, 410p. pap. *(978-3-484-15119-2(6))* Verlag Max Niemeyer.

Bethman, Brenda. "Obscene Fantasies" Elfriede Jelinek's Generic Perversions. 2011. (Austrian Culture Ser.). 150p. (C). 68.95 *(978-1-4331-1060-3(1))* Lang, Peter Publishing, Inc.

Buján López, Carlos & Domínguez Vázquez, María José, eds. Centros y periferias en España y Austria: Aspectos literarios y Culturales. 2009. (SPA.). 288p. pap. *(978-3-03911-791-8(2))* Lang, Peter.

Bushell, Anthony. Poetry in A Provisional State: The Austrian Lyric 1945-1955. 2007. 160p. 85.00 *(978-0-7083-2080-8(5))* Univ. of Wales Pr. GBR. Dist: Chicago Distribution Ctr.

Chevrel, Eric. Les romans de Heimito von Doderer: L'ordre des choses, du temps et de la Langue. 2008. (Contacts. Série 3: Etudes et Documents Ser.). (FRE & GER.). 449p. pap. *(978-3-03910-082-8(3))* Lang, Peter.

Dätsch, Christiane. Existenzproblematik und Erzählstrategie: Studien zum parabolischen Erzählen in der Kurzprosa von Ernst Weiß. 2009. (Studien zur deutschen Literatur Ser.).Tr. of Problem of Existence & Narrative Strategy. Studies on parabolic narration in Ernst Weissâ¿¿ short prose Works. (GER.). X, 306p. pap. *(978-3-484-18186-1(9))* Verlag Max Niemeyer.

Demel, Julie Anne. Die Kunst: ein Entwurf zur Welt: Ein Vergleich zwischen den Werken Alte Meister von Thomas Bernhard und Schlafes Bruder von Robert Schneider. 2009. (Europäische Hochschulschriften. Reihe 1: Deutsche Sprache und Literatur Ser.). (GER.). 154p. pap. 49.95 *(978-3-631-58374-6(5))* Lang, Peter GmbH, Europaischer Verlag der Wissenschaften DEU. Dist: Lang, Peter.

Doppler, Alfred. Stifter und Stifterforschung im 21. Jahrhundert: Biographie - Wissenschaft - Poetik. 2007. (GER., Illus.). XI, 306p. *(978-3-484-10901-8(7))* Verlag Max Niemeyer.

Durnberger, Silke. Entwicklung und Status Quo Franzosisch-Osterreichischer Kulturtransfers im Literarhistorischen Kontext: Eine Europaische Zweierbeziehung. (Europaische Hochschulschriften Ser.: Vol. 265). (GER., Illus.). 33.95 *(978-3-631-39457-1(8))* Lang, Peter Publishing, Inc.

Eddy, Beverley D. Felix Salten: Man of Many Faces. 2010. (Illus.). 412p. *(978-1-57241-169-2(4))* Ariadne Pr.

Emrich, H. M. Texte Zu Rilke. 2008. (GER., Illus.). 96p. pap. *(978-3-86727-722-8(2))* Cuvillier, Eric.

Freed, Mark M. Robert Musil & the NonModern. 2011. (ENG.). 192p. 110.00 *(978-1-4411-2559-0(0))*; pap. 34.95 *(978-1-4411-2251-3(6))* Continuum International Publishing Group, Ltd. GBR. Dist: National Bk. Network.

Fritz, Barbara. Rainer Maria Rilkes Leser in Schule und Gesellschaft: Rezeption 1904-1936. 2009. (Europäische Hochschulschriften. Reihe 1: Deutsche Sprache und Literatur Ser.). (GER., Illus.). 512p. pap. 115.95 *(978-3-631-59006-5(7))* Lang, Peter GmbH, Europaischer Verlag der Wissenschaften DEU. Dist: Lang, Peter.

Fronius, Helen & Richards, Anna, eds. German Women's Writing of the Eighteenth & Nineteenth Centuries: Future Directions in Feminist Criticism. 2011. (Legenda Main Ser.). (ENG., Illus.). 192p. (C). 89.50 *(978-1-906540-86-9(1))* European Humanities Research Ctr. GBR. Dist: Brown, David Bk. Co., The.

Grange, William. The A to Z of Postwar German Literature. 2010. (A to Z Guide Ser.). (ENG.). 376p. pap. 34.45 *(978-0-8108-7618-7(3))* Scarecrow Pr., Inc.

—Historical Dictionary of Postwar German Literature. 2009. (Historical Dictionaries of Literature & the Arts Ser.). (ENG.). 370p. 90.00 *(978-0-8108-5965-4(3))* Scarecrow Pr., Inc.

Hanlin, Todd C. Beyond Vienna: Contemporary Literature from the Austrian Provinces. 2008. *(978-1-57241-163-0(5))* Ariadne Pr.

Harrison, Russell. Thomas Bernhard's Comic Materialism: Class, Art, & "Socialism" in Post-War Austria. 2012. (German Life & Civilization Ser.). (ENG.). 194p. pap. 53.95 ***(978-3-0343-0286-9(X))*** Lang, Peter AG GBR. Dist: Lang, Peter.

Heidelberger-Leonard, Irene & Lühe, Irmela von der. Seiner Zeit Voraus: Jean Améry — Ein Klassiker der Zukunft? 2009. 174p. pap. *(978-3-8353-0464-2(X))* Wallstein-Verlag GmbH Verlag und Werbung.

Hübener, Andrea & Luck, Rätus, eds. Rilkes Welt: Festschrift für August Stahl zum 75. Geburtstag. 2009. (GER.). 470p. 99.95 *(978-3-631-59533-6(6))* Lang, Peter GmbH, Europaischer Verlag der Wissenschaften DEU. Dist: Lang, Peter.

Huemer, Wolfgang & Schuster, Marc-Oliver. Writing the Austrian Traditions: Relations Between Philosophy & Literature. 214p. *(978-1-55195-097-6(9))* Univ. of Alberta Pr.

Kerekes, Amalia. Pop in Prosa: Erzählte Populärkultur in der Deutsch- und Ungarischsprachigen Moderne. (GER., Illus.). 264p. 54.95 *(978-3-631-56597-1(6))* Lang, Peter GmbH, Europaischer Verlag der Wissenschaften DEU. Dist: Lang, Peter Publishing, Inc.

Kienlechner, Sabina. Negativität der Erkenntnis Im Werk Franz Kafkas: Eine Untersuchung Zu Seinem Denken Anhand Einiger Später Texte. (Studien zur deutschen Literatur Ser.). (GER.). IX, 165p. 210.00 ***(978-3-11-182331-7(8))*** De Gruyter, Walter Inc.

Kindt, Tom. Unzuverlässiges Erzählen und literarische Moderne: Eine Untersuchung der Romane von Ernst Weiß. 2008. (Studien zur deutschen Literatur Ser.). (GER.). VI, 248p. pap. *(978-3-484-18184-7(2))* Verlag Max Niemeyer.

Kindt, Tom, et al. Leo Perutz' Romane: Von der Struktur Zur Bedeutung. 2007. (Untersuchungen zur deutschen Literaturgeschichte Ser.). (GER., Illus.). 204p. pap. *(978-3-484-32132-8(6))* Verlag Max Niemeyer.

King, Martina. Pilger und Prophet: Heilige Autorschaft bei Rainer Maria Rilke. 2009. (Palaestra Ser.). (GER.). 413p. (C). 80.00 *(978-3-525-20603-4(8))* Vandenhoeck & Ruprecht GmbH & Co. KG DEU. Dist: ISD.

Koelb, Clayton. Kafka: A Guide for the Perplexed. 2010. (Guides for the Perplexed Ser.). (ENG.). 192p. 19.95 *(978-0-8264-9580-8(X))*; 90.00 *(978-0-8264-9579-2(6))* Continuum International Publishing Group, Ltd. GBR. Dist: National Bk. Network.

Lartillot, Francoise & Hornig, Dieter, eds. Jelinek, une répétition? Jelinek, eine Wiederholung? Apropos des pièces in den Alpen et das Werk - Zu den Theaterstücken in den Alpen und das Werk. 2008. (Genèses de Textes - Textgenesen Ser.). 240p. pap. *(978-3-03911-762-8(9))* Lang, Peter.

Lemon, Robert. Imperial Messages: Orientalism As Self-Critique in the Habsburg Fin de Si+Cle. 2011. (Studies in German Literature Linguistics & Culture Ser.: Volume 101). (Illus.). 184p. 75.00 *(978-1-57113-500-1(6))* Camden Hse.

Lennox, Sara. Cemetery of the Murdered Daughters: Feminism, History, & Ingeborg Bachmann. 2006. 387p. 80.00 *(978-1-55849-551-7(7))*; per. 27.95 *(978-1-55849-552-4(5))* Univ. of Massachusetts Pr.

Liska, Vivian. When Kafka Says We: Uncommon Communities in German-Jewish Literature. 2009. (Helen & Martin Schwartz Lectures in Jewish Studies). (ENG.). 256p. 29.95 *(978-0-253-35308-5(4)*, 0253353084) Indiana Univ. Pr.

Llop Pérez, V. Javier. Rilke y la Muerte. 2010. (SPA.). 196p. *(978-84-7822-563-7(3))* Institucio Alfons el Magnanim, Valencia.

Martín, Florencia. In der Erzählkolonie: Über die Gewalt des Erzählens bei Thomas Bernhard und Sergio Chejfec. 2009. (Europäische Hochschulschriften. Reihe 18: Vergleichende Literaturwissenschaft Ser.). (GER & SPA.). 276p. pap. 74.95 *(978-3-631-58301-2(X))* Lang, Peter GmbH, Europaischer Verlag der Wissenschaften DEU. Dist: Lang, Peter.

Medin, Daniel. Three Sons: Franz Kafka & the Fiction of J. M. Coetzee, Philip Roth & W. G. Sebald. 2010. (Avant-Garde & Modernism Studies). (ENG.). 280p. pap. 29.95 *(978-0-8101-2568-1(4))* Northwestern Univ. Pr.

Miladinovic Zalaznik, Mira & Lughofer, Johann Georg, eds. Joseph Roth: Europäisch-Jüdischer Schriftsteller und Österreichischer Universalist. 2011. (Conditio Judaica Ser.). (GER.). IX, 357p. 126.00 ***(978-3-11-026504-0(4))*** De Gruyter, Walter Inc.

Milletich, Helmut Stefan, et al. Beiträge Zu Einer Literaturgeschichte des Burgenlandes. 2009. (GER., Illus.). *(978-3-205-78308-4(5))* Bohlau Verlag Gmbh & Cie.

Nannicini Streitberger, Chiara. La revanche de la Discontinuité: Bouleversements du Récit chez Bachmann, Valvino et Perec. 2008. (Nouvelle poétique comparatiste - New Comparative Poetics Ser.). (FRE., Illus.). 322p. pap. 50.95 *(978-90-5201-530-9(9))* PIE - Peter Lang BEL. Dist: Lang, Peter.

Oberger, Birgit. Elfriede Jelinek Als Übersetzerin: Eine Einführung. 2008. (Europäische Hochschulschriften. Reihe 18: Vergleichende Literaturwissenschaft Ser.). 138p. pap. 39.95 *(978-3-631-56457-8(0))* Lang, Peter GmbH, Europaischer Verlag der Wissenschaften DEU. Dist: Lang, Peter.

Pö, et al. Ingeborg Bachmann. Interviews: 'Ich sag' es lieber mit den Worten, die ich geschrieben habe.' 2010. 80p. pap. *(978-3-639-27319-9(2))* VDM Verlag Dr. Mueller e.K.

Prohaska, Dorothy. Raimund & Vienna: A Critical Study of Raimund's Plays in their Viennese Setting. 2010. (Anglica Germanica Series 2 Ser.). (ENG.). 232p. pap. 30.99 *(978-0-521-15554-0(1))* Cambridge Univ. Pr.

Robertson, Ritchie. Kafka. 2010. (Brief Insight Ser.). (ENG., Illus.). 176p. 14.95 *(978-1-4027-7530-7(X))* Sterling Publishing Co., Inc.

Ruthner, Clemens. Contested Passions: Sexuality, Eroticism, & Gender in Modern Austrian Literature & Culture. 2011. (GER & ENG.). (C). 98.95 ***(978-1-4331-1423-6(2))*** Lang, Peter Publishing, Inc.

Salzani, Carlo. Crisi e Possibilità: Robert Musil e il tramonto Dell'Occidente. 2010. (Musiliana Ser.). (ITA.). 274p. pap. *(978-3-0343-0376-7(9))* Lang, Peter.

Santner, Eric L. The Royal Remains: The People's Two Bodies & the Endgames of Sovereignty. 2011. (ENG., Illus.). 288p. 95.00 *(978-0-226-73535-1(4))*; pap. 25.00 *(978-0-226-73536-8(2))* Univ. of Chicago Pr.

Saur, Pamela S. Ernst Weiss: Life,Works & Legacy of a Czech Literary Master & friend of Franz Kafka. 2012. (ENG.). 234p. lib. bdg. *(978-1-933146-72-0(9))* Academica Pr., LLC.

Schlipphacke, Heidi. Nostalgia after Nazism: History, Home, & Affect in German & Austrian Literature & Film. 2010. (ENG., Illus.). 312p. 65.00 *(978-1-61148-345-1(X))* Bucknell Univ. Pr.

Schlipphacke, Heidi M. Nostalgia after Nazism: History, Home, & Affect in German & Austrian Literature & Film. 2010. (Illus.). 312p. 65.00 *(978-0-8387-5757-4(X))* Bucknell Univ. Pr.

Shchyhlevska, Natalia. Alfred Gong: Leben und Werk. 2008. (GER., Illus.). 356p. pap. 84.95 *(978-3-03911-420-7(4))* Lang, Peter AG GBR. Dist: Lang, Peter.

Smerilli, Filippo. Moderne - Sprache - Körper: Analysen zum Verhältnis von Körpererfahrung und Sprachkritik in erzählenden Texten Robert Musils. 2009. (Palaestra Ser.). (GER.). 282p. (C). 60.00 *(978-3-89971-710-5(4))* Vandenhoeck & Ruprecht GmbH & Co. KG DEU. Dist: ISD.

Spencer, Malcolm. In the Shadow of Empire: Austrian Experiences of Modernity in the Writings of Musil, Roth, & Bachmann. 2009. (Studies in German Literature Linguistics & Culture Ser.: Volume 23). (Illus.). 264p. 85.00 *(978-1-57113-387-8(9))* Camden Hse.

Stasková, Alice & Lützeler, Paul Michael, eds. Hermann Broch und die Künste. 2009.Tr. of Hermann Broch & the Arts. (GER.). VI, 233p. 126.00 *(978-3-11-020955-6(1))* De Gruyter, Walter Inc.

Stephens, Anthony. Rainer Maria Rilke's 'Gedichte an Die Nacht' An Essay in Interpretation. 2010. (Anglica Germanica Series 2 Ser.). (ENG.). 264p. pap. 35.99 *(978-0-521-15556-4(8))* Cambridge Univ. Pr.

Swales, Martin & Swales, Erika. Adalbert Stifter: A Critical Study. 2010. (Anglica Germanica Series 2 Ser.). (ENG.). 264p. pap. 35.99 *(978-0-521-15528-1(2))* Cambridge Univ. Pr.

Swiderska, Malgorzata. Die Vereinbarkeit des Unvereinbaren: Ingeborg Bachmann als Essayistin. (Untersuchungen zur deutschen Literaturgeschichte Ser.). (GER.). VIII, 111p. 210.00 ***(978-3-11-184039-0(5))*** De Gruyter, Walter Inc.

Thiher, Allen. Understanding Robert Musil. 2009. (Understanding Modern European & Latin American Literature Ser.). 368p. 59.95 *(978-1-57003-836-5(8))* Univ. of South Carolina Pr.

Thomas Bernhard. 3rd ed. (GER.). 153p. pap. *(978-3-88377-393-3(X))* Edition Text & Kritik GmbH.

Uhrmacher, Anne. Spielarten des Komischen: Ernst Jandl und die Sprache. (Reihe Germanistische Linguistik Ser.).Tr. of Varieties of Humour. (GER.). VI, 244p. 165.00 ***(978-3-11-185743-5(3))*** De Gruyter, Walter Inc.

—Spielarten des Komischen: Ernst Jandl und die Sprache. 2007. (Reihe Germanistische Linguistik Ser.).Tr. of Varieties of Humour. (GER.). VII, 244p. pap. *(978-3-484-31276-0(9))* Verlag Max Niemeyer.

Wallace, Ailsa. Hermynia Zur Mühlen: The Guises of Socialist Fiction. 2009. (Oxford Modern Languages & Literature Monographs). (ENG., Illus.). 240p. 99.00 *(978-0-19-957211-3(9))* Oxford Univ. Pr., Inc.

Weiner, Marc. Undertones of Insurrection: Music & Cultural Politics in the Modern German Narrative. 2009. (ENG., Illus.). 366p. pap. 34.95 *(978-1-4128-0840-8(5))* Transaction Pubs.

Wich-Schwarz, Johannes. Transformation of Language & Religion in Rainer Maria Rilke. 2011. 172p. (C). 73.95 ***(978-1-4331-1481-6(X))*** Lang, Peter Publishing, Inc.

Yates, W. E. Grillparzer: A Critical Introduction. 2010. (ENG.). 290p. pap. 23.99 *(978-0-521-16838-0(4))* Cambridge Univ. Pr.

Zolkos, Magdalena. On Jean Amery: Philosophy of Catastrophe. 2011. (ENG.). 344p. 80.00 ***(978-0-7391-4765-8(X))*** Lexington Bks.

Zweig, Stefan. South American Letters: New York, Argentina & Brazil, 1940-42. Marshall, Oliver, ed. 2010. (ENG.). 224p. 80.00 *(978-1-4411-0987-3(0))*; pap. 24.95 *(978-1-4411-0712-1(6))* Continuum International Publishing Group, Ltd. GBR. Dist: National Bk. Network.

AUSTRIAN MUSIC

see Music, Austrian

AUSTRIAN NATIONAL CHARACTERISTICS

see National Characteristics, Austrian

AUSTRIAN PAINTING

see Painting, Austrian

AUSTRIAN POETRY

Brendel, Alfred. Alfred Brendel: Playing the Human Game: Collected Poems of Alfred Brendel. 2011. (ENG & GER., Illus.). 600p. 39.95 *(978-0-7148-5986-6(9))* Phaidon Pr., Inc.

Jirku, Brigitte E. & Schulz, Marion, eds. Mitten ins Herz: KünstlerInnen lesen Ingeborg Bachmann. 2009. (Inter-lit Ser.). (GER.). 230p. pap. 57.95 *(978-3-631-57529-1(7))* Lang, Peter GmbH, Europäischer Verlag der Wissenschaften DEU. Dist: Lang, Peter.

Luft, David. Hugo von Hofmannsthal & the Austrian Idea: Selected Essays & Addresses, 1906-1927. 2011. (Central European Studies). 201p. pap. 24.95 *(978-1-55753-590-0(6))* Purdue Univ. Pr.

Trakl, Georg & Tapscott, Stephen. Georg Trakl: Poems. 2011. pap. ***(978-0-932440-42-6(8))*** Oberlin College Pr.

AUSTRIAN SCHOOL OF ECONOMICS

see also Marginal Utility

Aimar. The Economics of Ignorance & Coordination Subjectivism & the Austrian School of Economics. 2009. (New Thinking in Political Economy Ser.). (Illus.). 320p. 137.00 *(978-1-84844-104-0(5))* Elgar, Edward Publishing, Inc.

Bianchi, Marina, ed. The Evolution of Consumption: Theories & Practices. 2007. (Illus.). 280p. 111.95 *(978-0-7623-1452-2(4))* Emerald Group Publishing Ltd. GBR. Dist: Turpin Distribution Services Ltd.

Boettke, P. J., ed. Handbook on Contemporary Austrian Economics. 2010. (Elgar Original Reference Ser.). 192p. 165.00 *(978-1-84720-411-0(2))* Elgar, Edward Publishing, Inc.

Bouillon, Hardy. Business Ethics & the Austrian Tradition in Economics. 2011. (Routledge Frontiers of Political Economy Ser.). (ENG.). 192p. (C). 130.00 *(978-0-415-60025-5(1))* Routledge.

Cowen, Tyler. Risk & Business Cycles. 2010. pap. 42.95 *(978-0-415-78129-9(9))* Routledge.

De Soto, Jesús Huerta. The Austrian School: Market Order & Entrepreneurial Creativity. 2008. 144p. (C). 119.00 *(978-1-84720-768-5(5))*; pap. 41.00 *(978-1-84720-769-2(3))* Elgar, Edward Publishing, Inc.

Fu Lai, Tony Yu. New perspectives on economic Development: A human agency Approach. 2010. (ENG.). 200p. 104.00 *(978-90-3686-160-6(1))* Wageningen Academic Publishers NLD. Dist: Enfield Publishing & Distribution Co., Inc.

Gordon, David. The Essential Rothbard. 2007. 184p. pap. 19.00 *(978-1-933550-10-7(4))* von Mises, Ludwig ,Institute.

Grassl, Wolfgang & Smith, Barry, eds. Austrian Economics: Historical & Philosophical Background. 2010. (Routledge Revivals Ser.). (ENG.). 262p. 105.00 *(978-0-415-61190-9(3))* Routledge.

Hagemann, Harald, et al, eds. Austrian Economics in Transition: From Carl Menger to Friedrich Hayek. 2010. (ENG., Illus.). 272p. 116.00 *(978-0-230-22226-7(9))* Palgrave Macmillan.

Horwitz, Steven. Microfoundations & Macroeconomics. 2009. 278p. pap. 39.95 *(978-0-415-56957-6(5))* Routledge.

Kirzner, Israel M. Essays on Capital & Interest: An Austrian Perspective. 2012. ***(978-0-86597-780-8(1))***; pap. ***(978-0-86597-781-5(X))*** Liberty Fund, Inc.

Koppl, Roger, et al, eds. What Is so Austrian about Austrian Economics? 2010. (Advances in Austrian Economics Ser.). (Illus.). 258p. *(978-0-85724-261-7(X))* Emerald Group Publishing Ltd.

Krecke, Elisabeth, et al. Cognition & Economics. 2006. 296p. 155.95 *(978-0-7623-1378-5(1))* Emerald Group Publishing Ltd. GBR. Dist: Turpin Distribution Services Ltd.

Marsh, Leslie, ed. Hayek in Mind: Hayek's Philosophical Psychology. 2011. (Advances in Austrian Economics Ser.). 323p. ***(978-1-78052-398-9(X))*** Emerald Group Publishing Ltd.

Neck, Reinhard, ed. Die Österreichische Schule der Nationalökonomie. 2008. (Schriftenreihe der Karl Popper Foundation Ser.). 224p. pap. 56.95 *(978-3-631-54668-0(8))* Lang, Peter GmbH, Europaischer Verlag der Wissenschaften DEU. Dist: Lang, Peter.

Rizzo, Mario J., ed. Austrian Law & Economics, 2 vols. 2011. (Economic Approaches to Law Ser.). (Illus.). 1488p. 790.00 ***(978-1-84542-753-5(X))*** Elgar, Edward Publishing, Inc.

Steele, Gerry & Steele, G. R. The Economics of Friedrich Hayek, Second Edition. 2nd annot. ed. 2007. (ENG.). 288p. 126.00 *(978-1-4039-4352-1(4))* Palgrave Macmillan.

Stephan, Gunter. Introduction into Capital Theory: A Neo-Austrian Perspective. 2010. (ENG., Illus.). x, 291p. pap. 69.95 *(978-3-642-08216-0(5),* 3642082165) Springer.

Veryser, Harry C. It didn't have to be this Way: How Austrian Economics Leads to Peace & Prosperity. 2012. (ENG.). 28.95 *(978-1-935191-07-0(1))* ISI Bks.

AUSTRIANS

James, Louis. Xenophobe's Guide to the Austrians. 2011. (Xenophobe's Guide Ser.). (ENG.). 96p. pap. 7.95 *(978-1-906042-21-9(7))* Oval Bks. GBR. Dist: Independent Pubs. Group.

Warren, John & Zitzlsperger, Ulrike, eds. Vienna Meets Berlin: Cultural Interaction 1918-1933. 2nd rev. ed. 2008. (Britische und Irische Studien zur deutschen Sprache und Literatur. British & Irish Studies in German Language & Literature Ser.). 300p. pap. 68.95 *(978-3-03911-853-3(6))* Lang, Peter AG GBR. Dist: Lang, Peter.

AUSTRIANS—CANADA

Morrison, Hermine. Tears on the School Desk. 2007. 160p. per. *(978-1-55452-116-5(6))* Essence Publishing.

AUSTRIANS—FOREIGN COUNTRIES

Fry, Helen. The King's Most Loyal Enemy Aliens: Germans Who Fought for Britain in the Second World War. 2007. (ENG., Illus.). 256p. 44.95 *(978-0-7509-4700-8(4))* Sutton Publishing.

Holaubek, Johanna (E, et al. Egypt & Austria II: Proceedings of a Symposium. 2006. (ENG & GER., Illus.). 170p. (C). pap. 30.00 *(978-80-86277-52-3(6))* Czech Institute of Egyptology CZE. Dist: Brown, David Bk. Co., The.

AUSTRIANS—UNITED STATES

Lobl, Frederick. Don't Pay for Water: Vienna & Cape Cod, A Romance of Business, A Story of Love. 2011. 206p. 44.95 ***(978-1-258-07223-0(8))*** Literary Licensing, LLC.

AUSTROASIATIC LANGUAGES

see also Mon-Khmer Languages; Sino-Tibetan Languages; Vietnamese Language

Fox, James J., ed. To Speak in Pairs: Essays on the Ritual Languages of Eastern Indonesia. 2006. (Cambridge Studies in Oral & Literate Culture Ser.). (ENG.). 352p. pap. 69.00 *(978-0-521-02800-4(0))* Cambridge Univ. Pr.

Kruspe, Nicole. A Dictionary of Mah Meri as Spoken at Bukit Bangkong. 2010. (MAY & ENG.). 424p. pap. 40.00 *(978-0-8248-3493-7(3))* Univ. of Hawaii Pr.

AUSTRO-HUNGARIAN MONARCHY

see Austria

AUSTRO-ITALIAN WAR, 1866

Hold, Alexander. History of the Campaign of 1866 in Italy. 2010. (Illus.). 152p. pap. 49.95 *(978-1-906033-62-0(5))* Helion & Co., Ltd. GBR. Dist: Casemate Pubs. & Bk. Distributors, LLC.

AUSTRO-PRUSSIAN WAR, 1866

see also Koniggratz, Battle of, Sadova, Czech Republic, 1866

Barry, Quintin. The Road to Königgrätz: Helmuth von Moltke & the Austro-Prussian War 1866. 2010. (Illus.). 536p. 69.95 *(978-1-906033-37-8(4))* Helion & Co., Ltd. GBR. Dist: Casemate Pubs. & Bk. Distributors, LLC.

Bassett-Powell, Bruce. Armies of Bismarck's Wars. 2012. (Illus.). 248p. 69.95 ***(978-1-935149-23-1(7),*** Casemate) Casemate Pubs. & Bk. Distributors, LLC.

Breuilly, John. Austria, Prussia & the Making of Germany: 1806-1871. 2nd ed. 2011. (Seminar Studies in History Ser.). (ENG., Illus.). 240p. (C). pap. 30.00 *(978-1-4082-7276-3(8))* Longman Publishing Group.

The Contribution of the Royal Bavarian Army to the War Of 1866. 2010. 136p. pap. 49.95 *(978-1-906033-66-8(8))* Helion & Co., Ltd. GBR. Dist: Casemate Pubs. & Bk. Distributors, LLC.

Hold, Alexander. History of the Campaign of 1866 in Italy. 2010. (Illus.). 152p. pap. 49.95 *(978-1-906033-62-0(5))* Helion & Co., Ltd. GBR. Dist: Casemate Pubs. & Bk. Distributors, LLC.

Jaeger, Franz. War in the Tyrol: The History of the 11th Austrian Infantry Regiment during the Campaign Of 1866. 2010. 40p. pap. 35.00 *(978-1-906033-63-7(3))* Helion & Co., Ltd. GBR. Dist: Casemate Pubs. & Bk. Distributors, LLC.

Rottauscher, Maximilian. With Tegetthoff at Lissa: The Memoirs of an Austrian Naval Officer 1861-66. 2010. 96p. pap. 39.95 *(978-1-906033-70-5(6))* Helion & Co., Ltd. GBR. Dist: Casemate Pubs. & Bk. Distributors, LLC.

Sutherland, Stuart. A Bibliography of the Seven Weeks' War Of 1866. 2nd ed. 2010. (Illus.). 128p. pap. 49.95 *(978-1-906033-64-4(1))* Helion & Co., Ltd. GBR. Dist: Casemate Pubs. & Bk. Distributors, LLC.

—The Organization of the German State Forces in 1866. 2010. 112p. pap. 49.95 *(978-1-906033-68-2(4))* Helion & Co., Ltd. GBR. Dist: Casemate Pubs. & Bk. Distributors, LLC.

AUSTRONESIAN LANGUAGES

see also Malayan Languages; Melanesian Languages; Polynesian Languages

Adelaar, K. Alexander & Himmelmann, Nikolaus, eds. The Austronesian Languages of Asia & Madagascar. 2011. (Routledge Language Family Ser.). 864p. (C). pap. 71.95 *(978-0-415-68153-7(7))* Routledge.

Austin, Peter K. & Musgrave, Simon, eds. Voice & Grammatical Functions in Austronesian Languages. 2007. (Center for the Study of Language & Information - Lecture Notes Ser.). (Illus.). 250p. 65.00 *(978-1-57586-499-0(1))*; pap. 27.50 *(978-1-57586-500-3(9))* CSLI Pubns.

Bowern, Claire & Meier, Joseph. Sivisa Titan: Sketch Grammar, Texts, Vocabulary Based on Material Collected by P. Josef Meier & Po Minis. 2011. pap. 40.00 *(978-0-8248-3553-8(0))* Univ. of Hawaii Pr.

Florey, Margaret, ed. Endangered Languages of Austronesia. 2010. (ENG., Illus.). 448p. 165.00 *(978-0-19-954454-7(9))* Oxford Univ. Pr., Inc.

Fox, James J., ed. To Speak in Pairs: Essays on the Ritual Languages of Eastern Indonesia. 2006. (Cambridge Studies in Oral & Literate Culture Ser.). (ENG.). 352p. pap. 69.00 *(978-0-521-02800-4(0))* Cambridge Univ. Pr.

Icon Group International, Inc. Staff, compiled by. Webster's Nauruan - English Thesaurus Dictionary. 2008. 246p. ring bd. 28.95 incl. audio compact disk *(978-0-497-83629-0(7))* Icon Group International, Inc.

—The 2009-2014 World Outlook for Household Refrigerators & Combination Refrigerator-Freezers. 2008. 298p. ring bd. 28.95 incl. audio compact disk *(978-0-497-83636-8(X))* Icon Group International, Inc.

Lemarechal, A. Comparative Grammar & Typology: Essays on the Historical Grammar of the Austronesian Languages. 2010. (Orbis Supplementa Ser.). (ENG.). 368p. (C). pap. 115.00 *(978-90-429-2254-9(0))* Peeters Pubs. & Booksellers BEL. Dist: Brown, David Bk. Co., The.

Mercado, Raphael, et al. Austronesian & Theoretical Linguistics. 2010. (Illus.) vi, 379p. ***(978-90-272-8775-5(9))***; ***(978-90-272-5550-1(4))*** Benjamins, John Publishing Co.

Moyse-Faurie, Claire & Sabel, Joachim, eds. Topics in Oceanic Morphosyntax. 2011. (Trends in Linguistics. Studies & Monographs [TiLSM] Ser.). (ENG., Illus.). E-Book 210.00 ***(978-3-11-025198-1(7))***; VI, 344p. 140.00 ***(978-3-11-025989-6(3))*** De Gruyter Mouton DEU. Dist: de Gruyter, Walter GmbH & Co. KG.

Palmer, Bill. Kokota Grammar. 2008. (C). pap. 36.00 *(978-0-8248-3251-3(5))* Univ. of Hawaii Pr.

Paul, I., et al, eds. Formal Issues in Austronesian Linguistics. 2010. (Studies in Natural Language & Linguistic Theory Ser.). 276p. pap. 159.00 *(978-90-481-5357-2(3),* 9048153573) Springer.

Stolz, Thomas, et al, eds. Hispanisation: The Impact of Spanish on the Lexicon & Grammar of the Indigenous Languages of Austronesia & the Americas. 2008. (Empirical Approaches to Language Typology Ser.: Vol. 39). (ENG.). X, 286p. 147.00 *(978-3-11-019793-8(6))* De Gruyter, Mouton DEU. Dist: de Gruyter, Walter GmbH & Co. KG.

AUTHENTICATION

see also Legal Documents

Clarke, Nathan. Transparent User Authentication: Biometrics, RFID & Behavioural Profiling. 2011. (ENG., Illus.). xviii, 229p. 99.00 ***(978-0-85729-804-1(6),*** 0857298046) Springer.

Information Security & Privacy. 2008. (Lecture Notes in Computer Science / Security & Cryptology Ser.). spiral bd. 99.00 *(978-3-540-69971-2(6))* Springer.

Jonker, Willem & Petkovic, Milan. Secure Data Management: 6th VLDB Workshop, SDM 2009, Lyon, France, August 28, 2009, Proceedings. 2009. (Lecture Notes in Computer Science / Information Systems & Applications, incl. Internet/Web, & HCI Ser.). ix, 173p. pap. 72.00 *(978-3-642-04218-8(X),* 364204218X) Springer.

Judith Beck, M. A. The Ecology of Conversation: Learning to Communicate from Your Core. 2010. 112p. 23.95 *(978-1-4269-2332-6(5))*; pap. 13.95 *(978-1-4269-2331-9(7))* Trafford Publishing.

Kim. Access Control, Authentication & Public Key Infrastructure. 2010. 398p. pap. 89.95 *(978-0-7637-9128-5(8))* Jones & Bartlett Learning, LLC.

Langenbach, C. J. & Ulrich, O., eds. Elektronische Signaturen: Kulturelle Rahmenbedingungen einer technischen Entwicklung. 2010. (Illus.). 212p. *(978-3-540-42659-2(0))* Springer Singapore Pte. Ltd.

Lee, Pil Joong & Cheon, Jung Hee. Information Security & Cryptoloy - ICISC 2008: 11th International Conference, Seoul, Korea, December 3-5, 2008, Revised Selected Papers. 2009. (Lecture Notes in Computer Science / Security & Cryptology Ser.). xiii, 433p. pap. 89.95 *(978-3-642-00729-3(5))* Springer.

Mason, Stephen. Digital Evidence & Electronic Signature Law Review. 2010. (Illus.). 166p. pap. ***(978-0-9563120-0-6(4))*** Pario Communications Ltd.

Nauheimer, Frank. Development of a Lattice Based Blind Signature Scheme: Post-quantum Cryptography. 2008. 68p. pap. *(978-3-639-10101-0(4))* VDM Verlag Dr. Mueller e.K.

Sinnott, John. Legalization of Notarized & Certified Documents 2008. 2008. (Practical Guides to Document Authentication Ser.). (Illus.). 774p. 195.00 *(978-0-19-534046-4(9))* Oxford Univ. Pr., Inc.

Sinnott, John P. Practical Guide to Document Authentication 2007: Legalization of Notarized & Certified Documents. 2006. 784p. 190.00 *(978-0-379-21229-7(3))* Oxford Univ. Pr., Inc.

—A Practical Guide to Document Authentication 2010: Legalization of Notarized & Certified Documents, 1 vol. 2010. (Practical Guides to Document Authentication Ser.). (ENG., Illus.). 838p. 220.00 *(978-0-19-972967-8(0))* Oxford Univ. Pr., Inc.

—A Practical Guide to Document Authentication 2011: Legalization of Notarized & Certified Documents, 1 vol. 2011. (Practical Guides to Document Authentication Ser.). (ENG.). 856p. 200.00 *(978-0-19-975920-0(0))* Oxford Univ. Pr., Inc.

Sinnott, John P., et al. Practical Guide to Document Authentication 2009. 2009. (Practical Guides to Document Authentication Ser.). (ENG.). 778p. 200.00 *(978-0-19-538323-2(0))* Oxford Univ. Pr., Inc.

Traore, Issa & Ahmed, Ahmed Awad E. Continuous Authentication Using Biometrics: Data, Models, & Metrics. 2011. ***(978-1-61350-131-3(5))***; 385p. 195.00 ***(978-1-61350-129-0(3))*** IGI Global.

Yung, Moti, et al. Information Security & Cryptology: 4th International Conference, Inscrypt 2008, Beijing, China, December 14-17, 2008, Revised Selected Papers. 2009. (Lecture Notes in Computer Science / Security & Cryptology Ser.). (ENG.). xiii, 439p. pap. 99.00 *(978-3-642-01439-0(9))* Springer.

AUTHENTICITY (PHILOSOPHY)

Alemi, Minoo, et al. Topic-Based Listening & Speaking. 2011. 64p. pap. ***(978-3-8433-9094-1(0))*** Lambert Academic Publishing.

Braman, Brian J. Meaning & Authenticity: Bernard Lonergan & Charles Taylor on the Drama of Authentic Human Existence. 2008. (Lonergan Studies). (ENG.). 160p. *(978-0-8020-9802-3(9))* Univ. of Toronto Pr.

Brown, Kate. Weimar Radicals: Nazi & Communists Between Authenticity & Performance. 2009. (Illus.). 240p. 90.00 *(978-1-84545-564-4(9))* Berghahn Bks., Inc.

Carpenter, Scott. Aesthetics of Fraudulence in Nineteenth-Century France: Frauds Hoaxes & Counterfeits. 2009. (Illus.). 204p. 99.95 *(978-0-7546-6807-7(X))* Ashgate Publishing Co.

Caust, Lesley. The Irreducible Other: The Second Sex Meets This Sex Which is Not One: Women, subjectivity, & ethics in Beauvoir & Irigaray. 2008. 224p. pap. *(978-3-639-08683-6(X))* VDM Verlag Dr. Mueller e.K.

Dooley, Mark. Roger Scruton: The Philosopher on Dover Beach. 2009. (ENG.). 200p. 29.95 *(978-1-84706-013-6(7))* Continuum International Publishing Group, Ltd. GBR. Dist: National Bk. Network.

Eksteins, Modris. Solar Dance: Van Gogh, Forgery, & the Eclipse of Certainty. 2012. ***(978-0-674-06494-2(1))***; (Illus.). 368p. 27.95 ***(978-0-674-06567-3(0))*** Harvard Univ. Pr.

Erfani, Farhang. The Aesthetics of Autonomy: Ricœur & Sartre on Emancipation, Authenticity, & Selfhood. 2011. (ENG.). 166p. 60.00 *(978-0-7391-1258-8(9))* Lexington Bks.

Fillitz, Thomas & Saris, A. Jamie, eds. Debating Authenticity: Concepts of Modernity in Anthropological Perspective. 2012. (ENG.). 276p. 85.00 ***(978-0-85745-496-6(X))*** Berghahn Bks., Inc.

Goodman, Tobias. Ancient Purple: Relevant Selections of Latin & Greek Poetry & Prose in New Translation with Commentary. 2011. 194p. pap. 14.95 ***(978-1-58754-023-3(1)***, Asphodel Pr.) Moyer Bell.

Haji, Ishtiyaque & Cuypers, Stefaan E. Moral Responsibility, Authenticity, & Education. 2012. (Routledge International Studies in the Philosophy of Education Ser.). (ENG., Illus.). 258p. pap. 42.95 ***(978-0-415-54175-6(1))*** Routledge.

Hermens, Erma & Fiske, Tina. Art, Conservation & Authenticities: Material, Concept, Context. 2010. (ENG., Illus.). 280p. pap. 90.00 *(978-1-904982-51-7(4))* Archetype Pubns. GBR. Dist: National Bk. Network.

Irvine, David. Becoming Real: Journey to Authenticity. 2nd ed. 2008. 290p. pap. 19.95 *(978-1-932021-28-8(0))* DC Pr. LLC.

Kaipan, Joy. Invitation to Wholeness: A Journey with Martin Heidegger. 2009. v, 92p. pap. *(978-81-7086-506-3(9)*, Library of Congress — New Delhi Overseas Office) Asian Trading Corp.

Keith, Chris & Le Donne, Anthony, eds. Jesus, Criteria, & the Demise of Authenticity. 2012. (ENG.). 256p. 120.00 ***(978-0-567-49955-4(3))***; pap. 34.95 ***(978-0-567-37723-4(7))*** Continuum International Publishing Group, Ltd. GBR. (T&T Clark Int'l). Dist: National Bk. Network.

Knudsen, Britta Timm & Waade, Anne Marit, eds. Re-Investing Authenticity: Tourism, Place & Emotions. 2010. (Tourism & Cultural Change Ser.). (ENG., Illus.). 296p. 129.95 *(978-1-84541-128-2(5))*; pap. 54.95 *(978-1-84541-127-5(7))* Channel View Pubns., Ltd. GBR. Dist: Univ. of Toronto Pr.

Morin, Jill J. Better Make It Real: Creating Authenticity in an Increasingly Fake World, 1 vol. 2010. (Illus.). 173p. 32.95 *(978-0-313-37680-1(8)*, C37680, Praeger Pubs.) Greenwood Publishing Group, Inc.

Naso, Ronald. Hypocrisy Unmasked: Dissociation, Shame, & the Ethics of Inauthenticity. 2010. (New Imago Ser.). (ENG.). 236p. 68.50 *(978-0-7657-0677-5(6)*, Aronson, Jason) Rowman & Littlefield Publishers, Inc.

Naso, Ronald C. Hypocrisy Unmasked: Dissociation, Shame, & the Ethics of Inauthenticity. 2010. xiii, 221p. 65.00 *(978-0-7657-0679-9(2)*, Aronson, Jason) Rowman & Littlefield Publishers, Inc.

O'Brien, Mahon. Heidegger & Authenticity: From Resoluteness to Releasement. 2011. (Continuum Studies in Continental Philosophy Ser.). (ENG.). 224p. 120.00 *(978-1-4411-1118-0(2))* Continuum International Publishing Group, Ltd. GBR. Dist: National Bk. Network.

Oliver, Jonathan. Impersonations, 1 vol. 2009. 129p. pap. 19.95 *(978-1-60703-598-5(7))* PublishAmerica, Inc.

Pearce, Nicholas & Steuber, Jason, eds. Original Intentions: Essays on Production, Reproduction, & Interpretation in the Arts of China. 2012. (ENG., Illus.). 320p. 60.00 ***(978-0-8130-3972-5(X))*** Univ. Pr. of Florida.

Potter, Andrew. The Authenticity Hoax: How We Get Lost Finding Ourselves. 304p. 2011. pap. 14.99 *(978-0-06-125135-1(6)*, HarperPerennial) 2010. 25.99 *(978-0-06-125133-7(X))* HarperCollins Pubs.

Roach, Margaret. And I Shall Have Some Peace There: Trading in the Fast Lane for My Own Dirt Road. (ENG.). 272p. 2012. pap. 14.99 *(978-0-446-55610-1(6))* 2011. 25.99 *(978-0-446-55609-5(2))* Grand Central Publishing.

—And I Shall Have Some Peace There: Trading in the Fast Lane for My Own Dirt Road. l.t. ed. 2011. 351p. 31.99 *(978-1-4104-3744-0(2))* Thorndike Pr.

Schweber, Howard. Democracy & Authenticity: Toward a Theory of Public Justification. 2011. (ENG.). 436p. (C). 99.00 ***(978-1-107-01533-3(2))*** Cambridge Univ. Pr.

Sessions, Robert. Becoming Real: Authenticity in an Age of Distractions. 2011. (ENG.). 300p. (YA). pap. 21.95 ***(978-1-888160-57-4(8))*** Ice Cube Pr.

Vannini, Phillip & Williams, Patrick. Authenticity in Culture, Self, & Society. 2009. (Illus.). 292p. 114.95 *(978-0-7546-7516-7(5))* Ashgate Publishing Co.

Zeller, Christoph. A¨sthetik des Authentischen: Literatur und Kunst Um 1970. 2010. (Spectrum Literaturwissenschaft / spectrum Literature Ser.).Tr. of Aesthetics of the Authentic. (GER., Illus.). IX, 333p. 140.00 *(978-3-11-022720-8(7))* De Gruyter, Walter Inc.

AUTHOR AND PUBLISHER

see Authors and Publishers

AUTHOR NOTATION

see Shelflisting

AUTHORITARIANISM

see also Authority; Despotism; Fascism; National Socialism; Totalitarianism

Adams, Jacqueline. A Dictatorship: Visual & Social Representations. 2012. (Contemporary Sociological Perspectives Ser.). (ENG., Illus.). 320p. (C). 140.00 *(978-0-415-99803-1(4))*; pap. 39.95 *(978-0-415-99804-8(2))* Routledge.

Albrecht, Holger, ed. Contentious Politics in the Middle East: Political Opposition under Authoritarianism. 2010. (Governance & International Relations in the Middle East Ser.). (ENG., Illus.). 256p. 69.95 *(978-0-8130-3474-4(4))* Univ. Pr. of Florida.

Aldridge, Bob. America in Peril. 2008. (ENG.). 339p. pap. 16.95 *(978-1-932717-15-0(3))* Hope Publishing Hse.

Ambrosio, Thomas. Authoritarian Backlash: Russian Resistance to Democratization in the Former Soviet Union. 2009. (Post-Soviet Politics Ser.). 256p. 114.95 *(978-0-7546-7350-7(2))* Ashgate Publishing Co.

Angrist, Michele Penner. Party Building in the Modern Middle East. 2006. (ENG., Illus.). 224p. (C). 50.00 *(978-0-295-98646-3(8))* Univ. of Washington Pr.

Awad, Samir. Persistence of Authoritarianism in the Middle East. 2010. 224p. pap. *(978-3-8383-4269-6(0))* Lambert Academic Publishing.

Baier, Thomas, ed. Die Legitimation der Einzelherrschaft im Kontext der Generationenthematik. 2008. (Beiträge Zur Altertumskunde Ser.).Tr. of Legitimation of Sole Rule in the Context of the Generation Discussion. (GER.). 336p. 147.00 *(978-3-11-020362-2(6))*; 224.00 ***(978-3-11-173741-6(1))*** De Gruyter, Walter Inc.

Black, Jane. Absolutism in Renaissance Milan: Plenitude of Power under the Visconti & the Sforza 1329-1535. 2009. (ENG.). 300p. 110.00 *(978-0-19-956529-0(5))* Oxford Univ. Pr., Inc.

Blum, Isa. Chaos in Yemen: Societal Collapse & the New Authoritarianism. 2012. (ENG., Illus.). 208p. (C). pap. 42.95 ***(978-0-415-62575-3(0))*** Routledge.

Blumi, Isa. Chaos in Yemen. 2010. (Routledge Advances in Middle East & Islamic Studies). (ENG., Illus.). 224p. (C). 140.00 *(978-0-415-78077-3(2))* Routledge.

Boukhars, Anouar. Politics in Morocco: Executive Monarchy & Enlightened Authoritarianism. 2010. (Routledge Studies in Middle Eastern Politics Ser.). (ENG.). 216p. (C). 125.00 *(978-0-415-49274-4(2))* Routledge.

Bremmer, Ian. The J Curve: A New Way to Understand Why Nations Rise & Fall. 2007. (ENG., Illus.). 336p. pap. 20.99 *(978-0-7432-7472-2(5))* Simon & Schuster.

Brooker, Paul. Non-Democratic Regimes. 2nd ed. 2009. (Comparative Government & Politics Ser.). (ENG., Illus.). 304p. 115.00 *(978-0-230-20274-0(8))*; pap. 39.00 *(978-0-230-20275-7(6))* Palgrave Macmillan.

Brown, B. J. & Baker, Sally. Responsible Citizens: Individuals, Health & Policy under Neoliberalism. 2012. (Key Issues in Modern Sociology Ser.). 200p. 99.00 ***(978-0-85728-458-7(4))*** Anthem Pr. GBR. Dist: Books International, Inc.

Brownlee, Jason. Authoritarianism in an Age of Democratization. 2007. (ENG.). 278p. (C). 82.99 *(978-0-521-86951-5(X))*; (Illus.). 288p. per. 26.00 *(978-0-521-68966-3(X))* Cambridge Univ. Pr.

Bunce, Valerie, et al, eds. Democracy & Authoritarianism in the Postcommunist World. 2009. (ENG., Illus.). 360p. (C). 88.00 *(978-0-521-11598-8(1))*; pap. 30.99 *(978-0-521-13308-1(4))* Cambridge Univ. Pr.

Bunce, Valerie & Wolchik, Sharon. Defeating Authoritarian Leaders in Postcommunist Countries. 2011. (Cambridge Studies in Contentious Politics Ser.). (ENG., Illus.). 396p. pap. 30.00 ***(978-0-521-18725-1(7))***; 95.00 *(978-1-107-00685-0(6))* Cambridge Univ. Pr.

Burnell, Peter & Schlumberger, Oliver, eds. International Politics & National Political Regimes: Promoting Democracy - Promoting Autocracy. 2011. (ENG., Illus.). 136p. (C). 140.00 ***(978-0-415-69406-3(X))*** Routledge.

Burt, Jo-Marie. Political Violence & the Authoritarian State in Peru: Silencing Civil Society. (ENG.). 2010. 308p. pap. 29.00 *(978-0-230-62117-6(1))* 2007. 304p. 95.00 *(978-0-230-60038-6(7))* Palgrave Macmillan.

Calirman, Claudia. Brazilian Art under Dictatorship: Antonio Manuel, Artur Barrio, & Cildo Meireles. 2012. (ENG., Illus.). 264p. 89.95 ***(978-0-8223-5139-9(0))***; pap. 24.95 ***(978-0-8223-5153-5(6))*** Duke Univ. Pr.

Canfield, Robert L. & Rasuly-Paleczek, Gabriele, eds. Ethnicity & Authority in Central Asia: New Games Great & Small. 2010. (Central Asian Studies). (ENG., Illus.). 272p. (C). 140.00 *(978-0-415-78069-8(1)*, Routledge) Taylor & Francis Group GBR. Dist: Taylor & Francis Group.

Carnegie, Paul J. The Road from Authoritarianism to Democratization in Indonesia. 2010. (ENG., Illus.). 194p. 89.00 *(978-0-230-10242-2(5))* Palgrave Macmillan.

Case, William, ed. Contemporary Authoritarianism in Southeast Asia: Structures, Institutions & Agency. 2010. 184p. 125.00 *(978-0-415-55641-5(4))* Routledge.

Cavatorta, Francesco & Lust, Ellen, eds. Civil Society Activism under Authoritarian Rule: A Comparative Perspective. 2012. (Routledge/ECPR Studies in European Political Science Ser.). (ENG., Illus.). 272p. (C). 135.00 ***(978-0-415-69264-9(4))*** Routledge.

Champion, Jeffrey. The Tyrants of Syracuse: War in Ancient Sicily: Vol 1: 480-367 BC. 2010. (Illus.). 192p. 39.95 *(978-1-84884-063-8(2))* Pen & Sword Bks. Ltd. GBR. Dist: Casemate Pubs. & Bk. Distributors, LLC.

Conason, Joe. It Can Happen Here: Authoritarian Peril in the Age of Bush. 2008. (ENG.). 256p. pap. 16.99 *(978-0-312-37930-8(7)*, St. Martin's Griffin) St. Martin's Pr.

Cook, Steven A. Ruling, but Not Governing: The Military & Political Development in Egypt, Algeria, & Turkey. 2007. 208p. 55.00 *(978-0-8018-8590-7(6))* Johns Hopkins Univ. Pr.

Costa Pinto, Antonio & Morlino, Leonardo, eds. Dealing with the Legacy of Authoritarianism: The Politics of the Past in Southern European Democracies. 2011. (ENG., Illus.). 208p. (C). 140.00 *(978-0-415-58708-2(5))* Routledge.

Davis, Harry. The Palace of Crystal: A World Without War. 2007. (ENG.). 248p. per. 27.20 *(978-0-9556055-0-5(4))* Arena Bks. GBR. Dist: Lightning Source UK, Ltd.

de Meneses, Filipe. Salazar: A Political Biography. 2009. (ENG., Illus.). 544p. pap. 28.00 *(978-1-929631-90-2(1))* Enigma Bks.

Dennis, Mike & LaPorte, Norman. State & Minorities in Communist East Germany, 1945-1990. 2011. (MGH Ser.). 254p. 100.00 *(978-0-85745-195-8(2))* Berghahn Bks., Inc.

Desai, Raj, et al. The Logic of Authoritarian Bargains: A Test of a Structural Model. 2007. *(978-0-9790376-2-7(X))* Brookings Global Economy & Development.

DeVotta, Neil. From Civil War to Soft Authoritarianism: Ethnonationalism & Democratic Regression in Sri Lanka. 2012. (Routledge Contemporary South Asia Ser.). 208p. (C). 140.00 *(978-0-415-66545-2(0))* Routledge.

Diamond, Stephen F. From 'Che' to Chin: Labor & Authoritarianism in the New Global Economy. 2009. 260p. pap. 39.95 *(978-1-60042-090-0(7))* Vandeplas Publishing.

DuBois, Lindsay. The Politics of the Past in an Argentine Working-Class Neighbourhood. 2008. 284p. pap. *(978-0-8020-9635-7(2))* Univ. of Toronto Pr.

Ermakoff, Ivan. Ruling Oneself Out: A Theory of Collective Abdications. 2008. (Politics, History, & Culture Ser.). (ENG., Illus.). 440p. 99.95 *(978-0-8223-4143-7(3))*; pap. 27.95 *(978-0-8223-4164-2(6))* Duke Univ. Pr.

Ezrow, Natasha M. & Frantz, Erica. Dictators & Dictatorships: Understanding Authoritarian Regimes & Their Leaders. 2011. (ENG., Illus.). 336p. 120.00 *(978-1-4411-1468-6(8))*; pap. 39.95 *(978-1-4411-7396-6(X))* Continuum International Publishing Group, Ltd. GBR. Dist: National Bk. Network.

Fernández Jilberto, Alex E. Dictadura militar y oposicion politica en Chile: 1973 - 1981. (Latin America Studies). (SPA.). 455p. 171.00 ***(978-3-11-126461-5(0))*** De Gruyter, Mouton DEU. Dist: de Gruyter, Walter GmbH & Co. KG.

Fernández Jilberto, Alex E. Dictadura militar y oposicion politica en Chile: 1973 - 1981. (Latin America Studies). (SPA.). 455p. 255.00 ***(978-3-11-205053-8(3))*** De Gruyter, Mouton DEU. Dist: de Gruyter, Walter GmbH & Co. KG.

Frantz, Erica & Ezrow, Natasha. The Politics of Dictatorship: Institutions & Outcomes in Authoritarian Regimes. 2011. (Illus.). 130p. 45.00 *(978-1-58826-785-6(7))* Rienner, Lynne Pubs.

Furlong, Paul. Social & Political Thought of Julius Evola. 2011. (Extremism & Democracy Ser.). (ENG.). 192p. (C). 138.00 *(978-0-415-58968-0(1))* Routledge.

Gaidar, Yegor & Gaidar, E. T. Collapse of an Empire: Lessons for Modern Russia. Bouis, Antonina W., tr. from RUS. 2007. (ENG., Illus.). 332p. 29.95 *(978-0-8157-3114-6(0))* Brookings Institution Pr.

Gandhi, Jennifer. Political Institutions under Dictatorship. 2010. (ENG., Illus.). 256p. (C). pap. 27.99 *(978-0-521-15571-7(1))* Cambridge Univ. Pr.

Gel'Man, Vladimir. The Politics of Sub-National Authoritarianism in Russia. Ross, Cameron, ed. 2010. (Post-Soviet Politics Ser.). (Illus.). 248p. 99.95 *(978-0-7546-7888-5(1))* Ashgate Publishing Co.

Ginsburg, Tom & Moustafa, Tamir, eds. The Politics of Courts in Authoritarian Regimes. 2008. (ENG., Illus.). 392p. 90.00 *(978-0-521-89590-3(1))* Cambridge Univ. Pr.

—Rule of Law: The Politics of Courts in Authoritarian Regimes. 2008. (ENG., Illus.). 392p. pap. 36.99 *(978-0-521-72041-0(9))* Cambridge Univ. Pr.

Giroux, Henry A. Against the Terror of Neoliberalism: Politics Beyond the Age of Greed. 2008. (Cultural Politics & the Promise of Democracy Ser.). 240p. 125.00 *(978-1-59451-520-0(4))*; per. 31.95 *(978-1-59451-521-7(2))* Paradigm Pubs.

Haber, Stephen, et al. Mexico Since 1980. 2008. (World Since 1980 Ser.). (ENG., Illus.). 272p. (C). 90.00 *(978-0-521-84641-7(2))*; pap. 24.99 *(978-0-521-60887-9(2))* Cambridge Univ. Pr.

Hagopian, Frances. Traditional Politics & Regime Change in Brazil. 2007. (Cambridge Studies in Comparative Politics). (ENG.). 344p. pap. 69.00 *(978-0-521-03288-9(1))* Cambridge Univ. Pr.

Hashmi, Arshi Saleem. Nexus Between Religious Groups & Authoritarian Regimes in Conflicts. 2011. 80p. pap. ***(978-3-8443-2447-1(X))*** Lambert Academic Publishing.

Hetherington, Marc J. & Weiler, Jonathan. Authoritarianism & Polarization in American Politics. 2009. (ENG., Illus.). 246p. (C). 80.00 *(978-0-521-88433-4(0))*; pap. 26.99 *(978-0-521-71124-1(X))* Cambridge Univ. Pr.

Hewitt, Vernon. Political Mobilisation & Democracy in India: States of Emergency. 2009. 236p. pap. 39.95 *(978-0-415-54479-5(3))* 2007. (ENG., Illus.). 240p. (C). 160.00 *(978-0-415-42375-5(9))* Routledge.

Hobson, Theo. Milton's Vision: The Birth of Christian Liberty. 2008. (ENG.). 192p. 29.95 *(978-1-84706-342-7(X))* Continuum International Publishing Group, Ltd. GBR. Dist: National Bk. Network.

Humphrey, Mathew. Ecological Politics & Democratic Theory: The Challenge to the Deliberative Ideal. annot. ed. 2007. (Extremism & Democracy Ser.). 169p. 150.00 *(978-0-415-31431-2(3))* Routledge.

Jamal, Amaney. Barriers to Democracy: The Other Side of Social Capital in Palestine & the Arab World. 2009. (ENG., Illus.). 192p. (C). pap. 20.95 *(978-0-691-14099-5(5))* Princeton Univ. Pr.

Jamal, Amaney A. Barriers to Democracy: The Other Side of Social Capital in Palestine & the Arab World. 2007. (ENG., Illus.). 192p. (C). 46.95 *(978-0-691-12727-9(1))* Princeton Univ. Pr.

Jugert, Philipp. Collective Security Motivation. 2010. 132p. pap. *(978-3-639-26333-6(2))* VDM Verlag Dr. Mueller e.K.

Kanishka Jayasuriya, 30 Sutcliffe St. Reconstituting the Global Liberal Order: Legitimacy, Regulation & Security. 2009. 170p. pap. 37.50 *(978-0-415-49977-4(1))* Routledge.

Kasahun Woldemariam. The Rise of Elective Dictatorship & the Erosion of Social Capital: Peace, Development, & Democracy in Africa. 2009. *(978-1-59221-668-0(4))*; 338p. pap. *(978-1-59221-669-7(2))* Africa World Pr.

Katema, Washington. How Are Rights Claimed under an Authoritarian Rule? 2011. 76p. pap. ***(978-3-8443-9097-1(9))*** Lambert Academic Publishing.

King, Stephen J. & Cammett, Melani. The New Authoritarianism in the Middle East & North Africa. 2009. (Indiana Series in Middle East Studies). (ENG.). 288p. 65.00 *(978-0-253-35397-9(1)*, 0253353971); pap. 24.95 *(978-0-253-22146-9(3)*, 0253221463) Indiana Univ. Pr.

Klaiber, Jeffrey. The Church, Dictatorships, & Democracy in Latin America. 2009. 336p. pap. 40.00 *(978-1-60608-947-7(1)*, Wipf and Stock) Wipf & Stock Pubs.

Krohn-Hansen, Christian & Krohn-hansen, Christian. Political Authoritarianism in the Dominican Republic. 2008. (ENG., Illus.). 268p. 95.00 *(978-0-230-60953-2(8))* Palgrave Macmillan.

Kuzu, Durukan. The Andijan Uprising & Uzbekistan. 2010. 148p. pap. *(978-3-8383-5376-0(5))* Lambert Academic Publishing.

Landry, Pierre. Decentralized Authoritarianism in China: The Communist Party's Control of Local Elites in the Post-Mao Era. 2008. (ENG., Illus.). 320p. 98.00 *(978-0-521-88235-4(4))* Cambridge Univ. Pr.

Law, Stephen. The War for Children's Minds. 2007. (Illus.). 198p. per. 22.95 *(978-0-415-42768-5(1))* Routledge.

—The War for Children's Minds: Liberal Values & Why We Should Defend Them. 2006. (Illus.). 198p. 31.95 *(978-0-415-37855-0(9)*, RU8559X) Routledge.

Lee, Julian C. H. Islamization & Activism in Malaysia. 2010. 165p. *(978-981-4279-02-4(1))* Institute of Southeast Asian Studies.

Lendvai, Paul. Hungary: Between Democracy & Authoritarianism. 2012. (Columbia/Hurst Ser.). (ENG.). 288p. (gr. 17). 35.00 ***(978-0-231-70322-2(8))*** Columbia Univ. Pr.

Levitsky, Steven & Way, Lucan. Competitive Authoritarianism: Hybrid Regimes after the Cold War. 2010. (Problems of International Politics Ser.). (ENG., Illus.). 520p. (C). 95.00 *(978-0-521-88252-1(4))*; pap. 29.99 *(978-0-521-70915-6(6))* Cambridge Univ. Pr.

Lovell, David W. From Marx to Lenin: An evaluation of Marx's responsibility for Soviet Authoritarianism. 2009. (ENG.). 252p. pap. 38.99 *(978-0-521-12553-6(7))* Cambridge Univ. Pr.

Lunt, Peter. Stanley Milgram: Understanding Obedience & Its Implications. Stevens, Richard, ed. 2009. (Mind Shapers Ser.). (ENG., Illus.). 176p. (C). pap. 22.00 *(978-0-230-57315-4(0))* Palgrave Macmillan.

Luo, Shen. Zhuan Zhi Wen Hua Xia de Zhongguo. 2009. ("Wen Hua Qing Li" Xi Lie Ser.: Vol. 26). (CHI.). 338p. *(978-1-932138-82-5(X))* Mirror Bks. USA.

Maier, Hans, ed. Totalitarianism & Political Religions Volume III: Concepts for the Comparison of Dictatorships - Theory & History of Interpretations. 2012. (Totalitarianism Movements & Political Religions Ser.). (ENG.). 440p. (C). pap. 42.95 ***(978-0-415-54248-7(0))*** Routledge.

Maier, Hans & Schäfer, Michael, eds. Totalitarianism & Political Religions, Volume II: Concepts for the Comparison of Dictatorships. 2012. (Totalitarianism Movements & Political Religions Ser.). (ENG.). 352p. (C). pap. 42.95 ***(978-0-415-54076-6(3))*** Routledge.

McGlinchey, Eric. Chaos, Violence, Dynasty: Politics & Islam in Central Asia. 2011. (Central Eurasia in Context Ser.). (ENG.). 232p. pap. 26.95 ***(978-0-8229-6168-0(7))*** Univ. of Pittsburgh Pr.

Milgram, Stanley & Milgram. Obedience to Authority: An Experimental View. 2009. (ENG., Illus.). 256p. pap. 14.99 *(978-0-06-176521-6(X)*, HarperPerennial) HarperCollins Pubs.

Montaigne, Michel de. Selected Essays: With la Boétie's Discourse on Voluntary Servitude. Atkinson, James B. & Sices, David, trs. from FRE. 2012. (Illus.). 410p. (Orig.). (C). 39.95 ***(978-1-60384-596-0(8))***; pap. 12.95 ***(978-1-60384-595-3(X))*** Hackett Publishing Co., Inc.

Munoz Conde, Francisco & Vormbaum, Thomas, eds. Transformation von Diktaturen in Demokratien und Aufarbeitung der Vergangenheit: Humboldt-Kolleg an der Universidad Pablo de Olavide 7. bis 9. Februar 2008. 2010. (Juristische Zeitgeschichte / Abteilung 2 Ser.).Tr. of Transformation of Dictatorships into Democracies & Coming to Terms with the Past. (GER.). X, 303p. 70.00 *(978-3-11-024796-1(8))* De Gruyter, Walter Inc.

Musil, Pelin Ayan. Authoritarian Party Structures & Democratic Political Setting in Turkey. 2011. (ENG., Illus.). 246p. 85.00 ***(978-0-230-33752-7(X))*** Palgrave Macmillan.

Newman Saul. From Bakunin to Lacan: Anti-Authoritarianism & the Dislocation of Power. 2007. (ENG.). 208p. per. 31.50 *(978-0-7391-2455-0(2))* Lexington Bks.

Nonneman. Democracy, Reform & Authoritarianism in the Arab World V4. 2010. 400p. *(978-0-415-47284-5(9))* Routledge.

Omer, Haim. The New Authority: Family, School, & Community. Herbsman, Michal & Sappir, Shoshana London, trs. from HEB. 2010. (ENG.). 270p. pap. 29.99 *(978-0-521-13776-8(4))*; (Illus.). 296p. 90.00 *(978-0-521-76137-6(9))* Cambridge Univ. Pr.

Owen, Roger. The Rise & Fall of Arab Presidents for Life. 2012. (ENG., Illus.). 220p. 24.95 ***(978-0-674-06583-3(2))*** Harvard Univ. Pr.

Pennock, J. Roland & Chapman, John. Coercion. Chapman, John W., ed. 2006. (ENG., Illus.). 328p. (gr. 11). pap. 32.95 *(978-0-202-30882-1(0))* Aldine Transaction.

Pepinsky, Thomas Blake & Pepinsky, Thomas B. Economic Crises & the Breakdown of Authoritarian Regimes: Indonesia & Malaysia in Comparative Perspective. 2009. (ENG., Illus.). 344p. 98.00 *(978-0-521-76793-4(8))*; pap. 28.99 *(978-0-521-74438-6(5))* Cambridge Univ. Pr.

Pinto, Antonio Costa, ed. Ruling Elites & Decision-Making in Fascist-Era Dictatorships. 2010. (EEM Social Science Monographs). (ENG., Illus.). 240p. (gr. 17). 50.00 *(978-0-88033-656-7(0))* Eastern European Monographs.

Pratt, Nicola. Democracy & Authoritarianism in the Arab World. 2007. 235p. (C). pap. 22.00 *(978-1-58826-486-2(6))*; lib. bdg. 55.00 *(978-1-58826-461-9(0))* Rienner, Lynne Pubs.

Radel, Jeffry L., ed. Political Facts & Perceptions. 2010. (Global Political Studies). (Illus.). 174p. 89.00 *(978-1-60876-636-9(5))* Nova Science Pubs., Inc.

Rajah, Jothie. Authoritarian Rule of Law: Legislation, Discourse & Legitimacy in Singapore. 2012. (Cambridge Studies in Law & Society Ser.). (ENG.). 352p. 99.00 ***(978-1-107-01241-7(4))***; pap. 29.99 ***(978-1-107-63416-9(4))*** Cambridge Univ. Pr.

Rathkolb, Oliver & Ogris, Günther, eds. Authoritarianism, History, & Democratic Dispositions in Austria, Poland, Hungary & the Cech Republic. 2011. (ENG.). 206p. 39.95 *(978-3-7065-4862-5(3))* StudienVerlag GesmbH AUT. Dist: Transaction Pubs.

Retallack, James. German Right, 1860 - 1920: Political Limits of the Authoritarian Imagination. 2006. (German & European Studies). (ENG., Illus.). 416p. (978-0-8020-9145-1(8)) Univ. of Toronto Pr.

Retallack, James N. & Retallack, James. The German Right, 1860-1920: Political Limits of the Authoritarian Imagination. 2006. (German & European Studies). (ENG., Illus.). 416p. pap. (978-0-8020-9419-3(8)) Univ. of Toronto Pr.

Ross, Cameron. Federalism & Local Politics in Russia. 2010. (ENG.). xv, 306p. pap. 39.95 (978-0-415-59018-1(3)) Routledge.

Samuel Nathan. Moravian Mafi: Religious Greed & Dictatorship. 2009. 120p. 22.95 (978-1-4401-5867-4(3)); pap. 12.95 (978-1-4401-5868-1(1)) iUniverse, Inc.

Schaeffer, Robert. Red Inc: Dictatorship & the Development of Capitalism in China, 1949-2009. 2011. (Illus.). 272p. 117.00 (978-1-59451-711-2(8)) Paradigm Pubs.

Schaeffer, Robert K. Red: Dictatorship & the Development of Capitalism in China,1949-2009. 2012. (Illus.). 272p. pap. 29.95 (978-1-59451-712-9(6)) Paradigm Pubs.

Schlumberger. Debating Arab Authoritarianism: Dynamics & Durability in Nondemocratic Regimes. Schlumberger, Oliver, ed. 2008. (ENG.). 360p. pap. 24.95 (978-0-8047-6333-2(X)) Stanford Univ. Pr.

Schmitt, Carl. Dictatorship. 2012. (ENG.). 288p. 69.95 (978-0-7456-4647-3(6)) Polity Pr. GBR. Dist: Wiley, John & Sons, Inc.

—Dictatorship: From the Origin of the Modern Concept of Sovereignty to Proletarian Class Struggle. 2012. (ENG.). 288p. pap. 24.95 (978-0-7456-4648-0(4)) Polity Pr. GBR. Dist: Wiley, John & Sons, Inc.

Schofield, Norman. The Political Economy of Democracy & Tyranny. (Illus.). xii, 338p. pap. (978-3-486-58826-2(5)) Oldenbourg Verlag (GW).

Sciulli, David. Theory of Societal Constitutionalism: Foundations of a Non-Marxist Critical Theory. 2010. (American Sociological Assocation Rose Monographs). (ENG.). 380p. (C). pap. 39.99 (978-0-521-14831-3(6)) Cambridge Univ. Pr.

Shearman, David & Smith, Joseph Wayne. The Climate Change Challenge & the Failure of Democracy, 1 vol. 2007. (Politics & the Environment Ser.). 208p. 49.95 (978-0-313-34504-3(X), C34504, Praeger Pubs.) Greenwood Publishing Group, Inc.

Simpson, Bradley. Economists with Guns: Authoritarian Development & U. S. -Indonesian Relations, 1960-1968. (ENG.). 376p. 2010. pap. 24.95 (978-0-8047-7182-5(0)) 2008. 60.00 (978-0-8047-5634-1(1)) Stanford Univ. Pr.

Slater, Dan. Ordering Power: Contentious Politics & Authoritarian Leviathans in Southeast Asia. 2010. (Cambridge Studies in Comparative Politics Ser.). (ENG., Illus.). 336p. 85.00 (978-0-521-19041-1(X)); pap. 28.99 (978-0-521-16545-7(8)) Cambridge Univ. Pr.

Spechler, Martin C. The Political Economy of Reform in Central Asia: Uzbekistan under Authoritarianism. (Illus.). 192p. 2012. (ENG.). (C). pap. 44.95 (978-0-415-50196-5(2)) 2008. 160.00 (978-0-415-77554-0(X)) Routledge.

Stacher, Joshua. Adaptable Autocrats: Regime Power in Egypt & Syria. 2012. (Stanford Studies in Middle Eastern & I Ser.). (ENG.). 240p. 80.00 (978-0-8047-8062-9(5)); pap. 24.95 (978-0-8047-8063-6(3)) Stanford Univ. Pr.

Todd, Allan & Waller, Sally. History for the IB Diploma: Origins & Development of Authoritarian & Single Party States. 2011. (Ib Ser.). (ENG.). 240p. pap. 32.00 (978-0-521-18934-7(9)) Cambridge Univ. Pr.

Westra, Laura. Faces of State Terrorism. 2012. 248p. (978-90-04-22456-8(4)) BRILL.

White, Stephen, ed. Russia's Authoritarian Elections. 2011. (Routledge Europe-Asia Studies). (ENG., Illus.). 216p. (C). 140.00 (978-0-415-69671-5(2)) Routledge.

Woods, Kevin M., et al, eds. The Saddam Tapes: The Inner Workings of a Tyrant's Regime, 1978-2001. 2011. (ENG., Illus.). 392p. 99.00 (978-1-107-01685-9(1)); pap. 36.99 (978-1-107-69348-7(9)) Cambridge Univ. Pr.

Wright, Teresa. Accepting Authoritarianism: State-Society Relations in China's Reform Era. 2010. (ENG.). 264p. pap. 24.95 (978-0-8047-6904-4(4)); (Illus.). 70.00 (978-0-8047-6903-7(6)) Stanford Univ. Pr.

Zack-Williams, Tunde, ed. When the State Fails: Studies on Intervention in the Sierra Leone Civil War, 1 vol. 2012. (ENG., Illus.). 288p. 99.00 (978-0-7453-3221-5(8)) Pluto Pr. GBR. Dist: Macmillan.

Zafirovski, Milan. The Protestant Ethic & the Spirit of Authoritarianism: Puritanism, Democracy, & Society. (ENG., Illus.). xx, 337p. 2010. pap. 129.00 (978-1-4419-2381-3(0), 1441923810) 2007. 129.00 (978-0-387-49320-6(4), 0387493204) Springer.

AUTHORITARIANISM (PERSONALITY TRAIT)

Norris, Gareth. The Developing Idea of the Authoritarian Personality: An Historical Review of the Scholarly Debate, 1950-2011. 2011. (ENG.). 236p. 119.95 (978-0-7734-2570-5(5)) Mellen, Edwin Pr., The.

Robertson, John M. Tough Guys & True Believers: Managing Authoritarian Men in the Psychotherapy Room. 2012. (Routledge Series on Counseling & Psychotherapy with Boys & Men Ser.). (ENG., Illus.). 326p. 125.00 (978-0-415-89042-7(X)); pap. 34.95 (978-0-415-89043-4(8)) Routledge.

AUTHORITIES, PUBLIC

see Corporations, Government; Special Districts

AUTHORITY

see also Authoritarianism; Consensus (Social Sciences); Despotism; Divine Right of Kings; Power (Philosophy)

Avery, Desmond. Beyond Power: Simone Weil & the Notion of Authority. 2008. (ENG.). 210p. 68.50 (978-0-7391-2386-7(6)) Lexington Bks.

Baehr, Peter. Caesarism, Charisma, & Fate: Historical Sources & Modern Resonances in the Work of Max Weber. 2008. (ENG., Illus.). 254p. 44.95 (978-1-4128-0813-2(8)) Transaction Pubs.

Barnes, Thomas Garden, et al. Law & Authority in Early Modern England: Essays Presented to Thomas Garden Barnes. 2007. 246p. (C). (978-0-87413-959-4(7)) Univ. of Delaware Pr.

Bendix, Reinhard. Nation-Building & Citizenship: Studies of Our Changing Social Order. 2009. 466p. 70.00 (978-1-59740-328-3(8)); 464p. pap. 46.00 (978-1-59740-329-0(6)) ACLS Humanities E-Book.

Bingham, Charles. Authority Is Relational: Rethinking Educational Empowerment. 2008. pap. 24.95 (978-0-7914-7404-4(6)) State Univ. of New York Pr.

—Authority Is Relational: Rethinking Educational Empowerment. 2008. 172p. 55.00 (978-0-7914-7403-7(8)) State Univ. of New York Pr.

Bizer, Marc. Homer & the Politics of Authority in Renaissance France, 1 vol. 2011. (Classical Presences Ser.). (ENG., Illus.). 272p. 85.00 (978-0-19-973156-5(X)) Oxford Univ. Pr., Inc.

Blass, Thomas. The Man Who Shocked the World: The Life & Legacy of Stanley Milgram. 2009. (ENG., Illus.). 384p. pap. 16.95 (978-0-465-00807-0(0)) Basic Bks.

Canning, Joseph. Ideas of Power in the Late Middle Ages, 1296-1417. 2011. (ENG.). 232p. 99.00 (978-1-107-01141-0(8)) Cambridge Univ. Pr.

Carter, April. Authority & Democracy. 2009. (ENG.). 124p. 104.00 (978-0-415-55535-7(3)) Routledge.

Cram101 Textbook Reviews & Cram101 Textbook Reviews. Outlines & Highlights for the New Authority: Family, School, & Community by Haim Omer, ISBN. 2011. 66p. pap. 27.95 (978-1-61461-021-2(5)) Cram101 Inc.

Crease, Robert & Selinger, Evan. The Philosophy of Expertise. 2006. (ENG., Illus.). 432p. (gr. 17). 60.00 (978-0-231-13644-0(7)) Columbia Univ. Pr.

Darwall, Stephen. The Second-Person Standpoint: Morality, Respect, & Accountability. 2009. 362p. pap. 24.50 (978-0-674-03462-4(7)) Harvard Univ. Pr.

Dean, Mitchell M. Governmentality: Power & Rule in Modern Society. 2nd ed. 2009. 304p. (C). 112.00 (978-1-84787-383-5(9), B73835C); pap. 53.00 (978-1-84787-384-2(7), B73835P) SAGE Pubns., Ltd. GBR. Dist: SAGE Pubns., Inc.

Delap, Lucy, et al, eds. The Politics of Domestic Authority in Britain Since 1800. 2009. (ENG., Illus.). 336p. 95.00 (978-0-230-57994-1(9)) Palgrave Macmillan.

Dollimore, Jonathan. Political Shakespeare: Essays in Cultural Materialism. Sinfield, Alan, ed. 2nd ed. 2012. (ENG., Illus.). 295p. pap. (978-0-7190-4352-9(2)) Manchester Univ. Pr.

Edmundson, William A. Three Anarchical Fallacies: An Essay on Political Authority. 2007. (Cambridge Studies in Philosophy & Law Ser.). (ENG.). 208p. pap. 50.00 (978-0-521-03751-8(4)) Cambridge Univ. Pr.

Estlund, David M. Democratic Authority: A Philosophical Framework. 2009. (ENG., Illus.). 312p. (C). pap. 25.95 (978-0-691-14324-8(2)) Princeton Univ. Pr.

Fox-Decent, Evan. Sovereignty's Promise: The State as Fiduciary. 2012. (ENG.). 335p. 99.00 (978-0-19-969831-8(7)) Oxford Univ. Pr., Inc.

Fry, Quentin G. & O'Donnell, Curt. Psychology of Power. 2012. (978-1-61942-486-9(X)) Nova Science Pubs., Inc.

Gordon, Nickel. laquo;We Will Make P Eace with Youraquo; The Christians of Najran in Muqatil's Tafsir. 2011. (SPA.). 102.70 (978-1-61143-991-5(4)) Gorgias Pr., LLC.

Greenaway, James. The Differentiation of Authority: The Medieval Turn Toward Existence. 2012. (ENG.). 320p. 69.95 (978-0-8132-1956-1(6)) Catholic Univ. of America Pr.

Greenblatt, Stephen. Shakespeare's Freedom. (Rice University Campbell Lectures). (Illus.). 2012. 168p. pap. 14.00 (978-0-226-30667-4(4)) 2010. 160p. 24.00 (978-0-226-30666-7(6)) Univ. of Chicago Pr.

Griffin, Lynne Reeves & Whitaker Staff. Negotiation Generation: Take Back Your Parental Authority Without Punishment. 2007. (ENG.). 272p. (gr. 12-18). 14.00 (978-0-425-21701-6(9), Berkley Trade) Penguin Group (USA) Inc.

Guinote, Ana & Vescio, Theresa K., eds. The Social Psychology of Power. 2010. (ENG., Illus.). 469p. 60.00 (978-1-60623-619-2(9)) Guilford Pubns., Inc.

Hajer, Maarten A. Authoritative Governance: Policy Making in the Age of Mediatization. 2009. (ENG., Illus.). 224p. 85.00 (978-0-19-928167-1(X)) Oxford Univ. Pr., Inc.

Hawks, Melanie. Influencing Without Authority. 2009. pap. (978-0-8389-8510-6(6)) Assn. of College & Research Libraries.

Higgins, John. Images of Authority: Working Within the Shadow of the Crown. 2009. (Management, Policy + Education Ser.). (Illus.). 240p. pap. 38.00 (978-1-904750-63-5(X)) Libri Publishing Ltd GBR. Dist: Independent Pubs. Group.

Hollister, William Wallac. Government & the Arts of Obedience. 2006. pap. 20.95 (978-1-4286-5651-2(0)) Kessinger Publishing, LLC.

Kling, Arnold. Unchecked & Unbalanced: How the Discrepancy Between Knowledge & Power Caused the Financial Crisis & Threatens Democracy. 2009. (Hoover Studies in Politics, Economics, & Society Ser.). (ENG.). 136p. 33.00 (978-1-4422-0124-8(X)) Rowman & Littlefield Publishers, Inc.

Kristjánsson, Kristján. Social Freedom: The Responsibility View. 2007. (ENG.). 236p. pap. 51.00 (978-0-521-04413-4(8)) Cambridge Univ. Pr.

Lewis, James R. & Hammer, Olav, eds. Handbook of Religion & the Authority of Science. 2010. (Brill Handbooks on Contemporary Religion). (Illus.). 909p. (978-90-04-18791-7(X)) BRILL.

Marcuse, Herbert. A Study on Authority. De Bres, Joris, tr. from GER. 2008. (Radical Thinkers Ser.). (ENG.). 112p. per. 12.95 (978-1-84467-209-7(3), 844209) Verso Bks. GBR. Dist: Norton, W. W. & Co., Inc.

May, T. Autonomy, Authority & Moral Responsibility. 2010. (Law & Philosophy Library). 204p. pap. 219.00 (978-90-481-4949-0(5), 9048149495) Springer.

Mayer, Susan Jean. Classroom Discourse & Democracy: Making Meanings Together. 2012. xvi, 211p. (978-1-4331-1286-7(8)); pap. (978-1-4331-1285-0(X)) Lang, Peter GmbH, Europaischer Verlag der Wissenschaften.

Milgram, Stanley & Milgram. Obedience to Authority: An Experimental View. 2009. (ENG., Illus.). 256p. pap. 14.99 (978-0-06-176521-6(X), HarperPerennial) HarperCollins Pubs.

Neville, Leonora. Authority in Byzantine Provincial Society, 950-1100. 2009. (ENG., Illus.). 224p. pap. 33.00 (978-0-521-10117-2(4)) Cambridge Univ. Pr.

Newman Saul. From Bakunin to Lacan: Anti-Authoritarianism & the Dislocation of Power. 2007. (ENG.). 208p. per. 31.50 (978-0-7391-2455-0(2)) Lexington Bks.

Omer, Haim. The New Authority: Family, School, & Community. Herbsman, Michal & Sappir, Shoshana London, trs. from HEB. 2010. (ENG.). 270p. pap. 29.99 (978-0-521-13776-8(4)); (Illus.). 296p. 90.00 (978-0-521-76137-6(9)) Cambridge Univ. Pr.

Revault d'Allonnes, Myriam. Le Pouvoir des Commencements: Essai Sur Lautorité. (FRE.). 266p. (978-2-02-067638-0(9)) Editions du Seuil.

Rickaby, Joseph. Civil Authority. 2010. 195p. reprint ed. pap. 14.95 (978-0-9818158-9-3(8)) Workingman's Publishing Hse.

Rittberger, Volker. Authority in the Global Political Economy. Rittberger, Volker & Nettesheim, Martin, eds. 2008. (ENG.). 320p. 105.00 (978-0-230-57389-5(4)) Palgrave Macmillan.

Roberts, Alasdair. The Collapse of Fortress Bush: The Crisis of Authority in American Government. 2008. (ENG., Illus.). 272p. 37.00 (978-0-8147-7606-3(X)) New York Univ. Pr.

Ronell, Avital. Loser Sons: Politics & Authority. 2012. (ENG., Illus.). 208p. 35.00 (978-0-252-03664-4(6)) Univ. of Illinois Pr.

Russell, Bertrand. Authority & the Individual. 2008. 136p. (978-1-4437-2509-5(9)) 2006. (ENG.). 132p. per. (978-1-4067-3379-2(2)) Read Bks. (Hesperides Pr.).

Shaw, Tamsin. Nietzsche's Political Skepticism. (ENG.). 192p. (C). 2010. pap. 22.95 (978-0-691-14653-9(5)) 2007. 29.95 (978-0-691-13322-5(0)) Princeton Univ. Pr.

Smith, Roger. Social Work & Power. 2008. (New Directions in Social Work Ser.). (ENG., Illus.). 224p. pap. 34.00 (978-1-4039-9124-9(3)) Palgrave Macmillan.

AUTHORITY—RELIGIOUS ASPECTS

see also Bible—Evidences, Authority, etc.; Catholic Church—Infallibility; Church—Authority; Church—Teaching Office; Popes—Infallibility; Tradition (Theology)

Amadi-Azuogu, Adolphus. The Politics of Power & the Ordination of Women. 2007. 436p. per. 21.99 (978-1-60266-602-3(4)) Xulon Pr., Inc.

Ande, Titre. Leadership & Authority: Bula Matari & Life-Community Ecclesiology in Congo. 2011. (Regnum Studies in Mission Ser.). 208p. pap. 23.00 (978-1-61097-437-0(9), Wipf and Stock) Wipf & Stock Pubs.

Arthur, Gordon. Law Liberty & Church: Authority & Justice in the Major Churches in England. 2006. (Ashgate New Critical Thinking in Religion, Theology, & Biblical Studies). 222p. 99.95 (978-0-7546-5437-7(0)) Ashgate Publishing Co.

Austin, Victor Lee. Up with Authority: Why We Need Authority to Flourish as Human Beings. 2010. (ENG.). 192p. 90.00 (978-0-567-30809-2(X)); pap. 29.95 (978-0-567-02051-2(7)) Continuum International Publishing Group, Ltd. GBR. (T&T Clark Int'l). Dist: National Bk. Network.

Azra, Azyumardi, et al. Varieties of Religious Authority: Changes & Challenges in 20th Century Indonesian Islam. 2010. xvii, 211p. (978-981-230-940-2(3)) Institute of Southeast Asian Studies.

Bevere, John. Honor's Reward Curriculum. 2007. 198.00 (978-1-933185-35-4(X)) Messenger International.

—Honor's Reward Devotional Workbook. 2007. pap. 15.99 (978-1-933185-34-7(1)) Messenger International.

Black, John Sutherland. The Christian Consciousness: Its Relation to Evolution in Morals And. 2007. (ENG.). 260p. per. 27.95 (978-1-4304-4553-1(X)) Kessinger Publishing, LLC.

Bloomer, George G. Authority Abusers. 2008. (ENG.). 204p. 19.99 (978-1-60374-046-3(5)) Whitaker Hse.

Boustan, Ra'anan S., et al, eds. Jewish Studies at the Crossroads of Anthropology & History: Authority, Diaspora, Tradition. 2011. (Jewish Culture & Contexts Ser.). (Illus.). 448p. (C). 69.95 (978-0-8122-4303-1(X)) Univ. of Pennsylvania Pr.

Brennan, Patrick Mck. Civilizing Authority: Society, State, & Church. 2007. (ENG.). 252p. 68.50 (978-0-7391-1806-1(4)) Lexington Bks.

Cahoy, William John. In the Name of the Church: Vocation & Authorization of Lay Ecclesial Ministry. 2012. (978-0-8146-3423-3(0)) Liturgical Pr.

Campiani, A. & Filoramo, G., eds. Foundations of Power & Conflicts of Authority in Late-Antique Monasticism: Proceedings of the International Seminar Turin, December 2-4 2004. 2007. (Orientalia Lovaniensia Analecta Ser.: 157). (ENG, FRE & GER., Illus.). 364p. (C). 109.00 (978-90-429-1832-0(2)) Peeters Pubs. & Booksellers BEL. Dist: Brown, David Bk. Co., The.

Campolo, Tony. Choose Love Not Power: How to Right the World's Wrongs from a Place of Weakness. 2009. (ENG.). 224p. pap. 14.99 (978-0-8307-5124-2(6)) Gospel Light Pubns.

Carroll, Jackson W. As One with Authority, Second Edition: Reflective Leadership in Ministry. 2011. 234p. pap. 26.00 (978-1-60899-737-4(5), Cascade Bks.) Wipf & Stock Pubs.

Clifford, Catherine E. One Teacher: Doctrinal Authority in the Church. 2010. 186p. pap. 26.00 (978-0-8028-2598-8(2)) Eerdmans, William B. Publishing Co.

Crosby, Michael H. The Dysfunctional Church: Addiction & Codependency in the Family of Catholicism. 2011. 256p. (Orig.). pap. 28.00 (978-1-61097-147-8(7), Wipf and Stock) Wipf & Stock Pubs.

DaillT, Jean. A Treatise on the Right Use of the Fathers in the Decision of the Controversies Existing at This Day in Religion. 2006. 416p. per. 26.99 (978-1-4255-4553-6(X)) MPublishing.

Davies, Rupert E. The Problem of Authority in the Continental Reformers: A Study in Luther, Zwingli, & Calvin. 2009. 158p. pap. 18.00 (978-1-60608-728-2(2), Wipf and Stock) Wipf & Stock Pubs.

Engler, Steven & Grieve, Gregory Price, eds. Historicizing Tradition in the Study of Religion. (Religion & Society Ser.). (ENG.). VI, 395p. 255.00 (978-3-11-181868-9(3)) De Gruyter, Walter Inc.

Geisler, Norman L., et al. Is Rome the True Church A Consideration of the Roman Catholic Claim. 2008. 240p. pap. 17.99 (978-1-4335-0231-6(3)) Crossway.

Geldenhuys, J. Norval. Supreme Authority: The Authority of the Lord, His Apostles & the New Testament. 2008. 126p. pap. 11.00 (978-1-55635-768-8(0)) Wipf & Stock Pubs.

Hanna, Tony. With Respect: Authority in the Catholic Church. 2008. (ENG.) 95p. pap. 19.95 (978-1-85607-609-8(1)) Columba Pr. IRL. Dist: Dufour Editions, Inc.

Hietamäki, Minna. Agreeable Agreement: An Examination of the Quest for Consensus in Ecumenical Dialogue. 2010. (Ecclesiological Investigations Ser.). (ENG., Illus.). 272p. 130.00 (978-0-567-60718-8(6), T&T Clark Int'l) Continuum International Publishing Group, Ltd. GBR. Dist: National Bk. Network.

Hilkert, Mary C. Speaking with Authority: Catherine of Siena & the Voices of Women Today. 2008. 176p. pap. 15.95 (978-0-8091-4586-7(3)) Paulist Pr.

Kramer, Gudrun, ed. Speaking for Islam: Religious Authorities in Muslim Societies. 2006. (Social, Economic & Political Studies of the Middle East Ser.: Vol. 100). 305p. (978-90-04-14949-6(X)) BRILL.

Lacey, Michael J. & Oakley, Francis. The Crisis of Authority in Catholic Modernity, 1 vol. 2011. (ENG., Illus.). 392p. pap. 35.00 (978-0-19-977878-2(7)) Oxford Univ. Pr., Inc.

Land, Darin H. The Diffusion of Ecclesiastical Authority: Sociological Dimensions of Leadership in the Book of Acts. 2008. (Princeton Theological Monographs). 256p. pap. 28.00 (978-1-55635-575-2(0), Pickwick Pubns.) Wipf & Stock Pubs.

Lee, Rastonya. When God Places You in Authority over Others. 2011. pap. 8.99 (978-1-61739-327-3(4)) Tate Publishing & Enterprises, LLC.

MacMillan, John A. The Authority of the Believer. 2007. 174p. pap. 12.99 (978-1-60066-083-2(5)) WingSpread Publishers.

MacMillan, Rev. J. A. The Authority of the Believer: Principles set forth in the Epistle to the Ephesians. 2011. 42p. pap. 6.99 (978-1-61720-271-1(1)) Wilder Pubns., Ltd.

MacMillan, Rev. J. A. & MacMillan, John A. The Authority of the Intercessor. 2011. 28p. pap. 5.99 (978-1-61720-272-8(X)) Wilder Pubns., Ltd.

—Spiritual Authority: The Believer & the Intercessor. 2011. 68p. pap. 9.99 (978-1-61720-273-5(8)) Wilder Pubns., Ltd.

Millet, Robert, ed. By What Authority? The Vital Questions of Religious Authority in Christianity. 2010. 356p. pap. 35.00 (978-0-88146-201-2(2)) Mercer Univ. Pr.

Mills, Martin A. Identity Ritual & State in Tibetan Buddhism. 2010. (ENG.) 426p. pap. 39.95 (978-0-415-59138-6(4)) Routledge.

Neustein, Amy, ed. Tempest in the Temple: Jewish Communities & Child Sex Scandals. 2009. (Brandeis Series in American Jewish History, Culture & Life Ser.). (ENG.). 308p. 35.00 (978-1-58465-671-5(9), Brandeis University Press) Univ. Pr. of New England.

Oden, Thomas C. Doctrinal Standards in the Wesleyan Tradition. 2008. 432p. pap. 32.00 (978-0-687-65111-5(5)) Abingdon Pr.

Oman, John. Honest Religion. 2007. 240p. per. (978-1-4067-8815-0(5), Pomona Pr.) Read Bks.

Osto, Douglas. Power, Wealth & Women in Indian Mahayana Buddhism: The Gandavyuha-Sutra. 2008. (Routledge Critical Studies in Buddhism Ser.). (ENG., Illus.). 200p. (C). 150.00 (978-0-415-48073-4(6)) Routledge.

Patterson, Elaine. You are Rich. 2011. 108p. pap. 12.01 (978-1-4490-8096-9(0)) AuthorHouse.

Perkins, Robert L., ed. Without Authority. 2007. (International Kierkegaard Commentary Ser.: 18). 353p. 50.00 (978-0-88146-048-3(6)) Mercer Univ. Pr.

Petrenko, Vitali. The Development of Authority Within the Russian Orthodox Church: A Theological & Historical Inquiry. 2011. (ENG.). 310p. pap. 65.95 (978-3-03911-372-9(0)) Lang, Peter AG GBR. Dist: Lang, Peter.

Portaro, Sam. Transforming Vocation. 2008. (Transformations Ser.). 160p. pap. 16.00 (978-0-89869-586-1(4)) Church Publishing, Inc.

Porter, Jean. Ministers of the Law: A Natural Law Theory of Legal Authority. 2010. pap. 30.00 (978-0-8028-6563-2(1)) Eerdmans, William B. Publishing Co.

Pridgen, Ronald L. Your Biblical Rights. 2009. 160p. 25.49 (978-1-4389-4537-8(X)); pap. 15.49 (978-1-4389-4536-1(1)) AuthorHouse.

Ramm, Bernard. The Witness of the Spirit: An Essay on the Contemporary Relevance of the Internal Witness of the Holy Spirit. 2011. 140p. pap. 12.00 (978-1-61097-585-8(5), Wipf and Stock) Wipf & Stock Pubs.

Rannie, Rick. The Way of Authority & Power. 2011. 116p. pap. 11.95 (978-1-4627-0643-3(6)) Cross Bks. Publishing.

Riccards, Michael P. Faith & Leadership: The Papacy & the Roman Catholic Church. 2012. (ENG.). 650p. (gr. 17). 110.00 (978-0-7391-7132-5(1)) Lexington Bks.

Rousseau, Philip. Ascetics, Authority, & the Church in the Age of Jerome & Cassian. 2nd ed. 2010. (ENG.). 304p. pap. 30.00 *(978-0-268-04029-1(X))* Univ. of Notre Dame Pr.

Sarma, Deepak. Authority & Its Challenges in Hindu Texts, Translations, & Transnational Communities: Proceedings of Two of the Sessions at the Fourth DANAM Conference, Held on Site at the American Academy of Religion, Washington, DC, 17-19 November 2006. 2009. *(978-0-937194-52-2(2),* Deepak Heritage Bks.) Deepak, A Publishing.

Schutz, John Howard. Paul & the Anatomy of Apostolic Authority. 2007. (New Testament Library). (ENG.). 307p. per. 40.00 *(978-0-664-22812-5(7))* Westminster John Knox Pr.

Smith, Robert. Authority Issues: When It's Hard Being Told What to Do. 2011. (ENG.). 24p. 3.99 ***(978-1-936768-39-4(9))*** New Growth Pr.

St Irenaeus of Lyons. The Third Book of St. Irenaeus Bishop of Lyons Against Heresies. 2008. 120p. pap. 10.00 *(978-1-55635-796-1(6))* Wipf & Stock Pubs.

Stein, Dina. Textual Mirrors: Reflexivity, Midrash, & the Rabbinic Self. 2012. (Divinations: Rereading Late Ancient Religion Ser.). 248p. (C). 79.95 ***(978-0-8122-4436-6(2))*** Univ. of Pennsylvania Pr.

Stevenson, Jeffery S. All People, All Times: Rethinking Biblical Authority in Churches of Christ. 2009. 292p. pap. 16.99 *(978-1-60791-539-3(1))* Xulon Pr., Inc.

Stone, Suzanne Last. Rabbinic & Lay Communal Authority. 2007. (Orthodox Forum Ser.). xxiv, 173p. *(978-0-88125-953-7(5))* Ktav Publishing Hse., Inc.

Takim, Liyakat N. & Takim, Liyakatali. The Heirs of the Prophet: Charisma & Religious Authority in Shi'ite Islam. 2007. 236p. per. 29.95 *(978-0-7914-6738-1(4))* State Univ. of New York Pr.

Under Cover Curriculum. 2007. 198.00 *(978-1-933185-11-8(2))* Messenger International.

Under Cover Workbook. 2007. 14.99 *(978-1-933185-10-1(4))* Messenger International.

Van Den Belt, Henk. The Authority of Scripture in Reformed Theology: Truth & Trust. 2008. (Studies in Reformed Theology Ser.). 384p. *(978-90-04-16307-2(7))* BRILL.

Waschbü, et al. Alter Melanchthon: Muster theologischer Autoritätsstiftung bei Matthias Flacius Illyricus. Forschungen zur Kirchen- und Dogmengeschichte 96. 2008. (Forschungen Zur Kirchen- und Dogmengeschichte Ser.). (GER.). 208p. (C). 63.00 *(978-3-525-55300-8(5))* Vandenhoeck & Ruprecht GmbH & Co. KG DEU. Dist: ISD.

When God Calls Us to Write. 2008. (ENG.). 62p. 5.00 *(978-0-9742432-3-8(X))* Flying Scroll Publishing, LLC.

AUTHORITY FILES (CATALOGING)

see Authority Files (Information Retrieval)

AUTHORITY FILES (INFORMATION RETRIEVAL)

Here are entered authority files that include both name and subject authority records, as well as works about such files.

see also Subject Headings

Dryden. Respect for Authority: Authority Control, Context Control, & Arc. 2007. (Illus.). 183p. 75.00 *(978-0-7890-3589-9(8))* Routledge.

IFLA Cataloguing Section, ed. UNIMARC Manual: Authorities Format. 2009. (IFLA Series on Bibliographic Control Ser.). (ENG.). 309p. *(978-3-598-24286-1(7))* Saur, K. G. Verlag GmbH & Co.

Patton, Glenn E., ed. Functional Requirements for Authority Data: A Conceptual Model. 2009. (IFLA Series on Bibliographic Control Ser.). (ENG.). 100p. *(978-3-598-24282-3(4));* ***(978-3-11-173941-0(4))*** Saur, K. G. Verlag GmbH & Co.

Respect for Authority: Authority Control, Context Control, & Archival Description. 2008. (ENG., Illus.). 192p. pap. 45.00 *(978-0-7890-3590-5(1))* Routledge.

AUTHORITY IN LITERATURE

Bowers, Toni. Force or Fraud: British Seduction Stories & the Problem of Resistance, 1660-1760. 2011. (ENG., Illus.). 384p. 110.00 *(978-0-19-959213-5(6))* Oxford Univ. Pr., Inc.

Brusati, Celeste, et al, eds. The Authority of the Word: Reflecting on Image & Text in Northern Europe, 1400-1700. 2011. (ENG., Illus.). XLII, 710p. ***(978-90-04-21515-3(8))*** BRILL.

Cohen, Daniel A. Pillars of Salt, Monuments of Grace: New England Crime Literature & the Origins of American Popular Culture, 1674-1860. 2006. (Commonwealth Center Studies in American Culture Ser.). (Illus.). 350p. per. 19.95 *(978-1-55849-529-6(0))* Univ. of Massachusetts Pr.

Coovadia, Imraan. Authority & Authorship in V.S. Naipaul. 2009. (ENG., Illus.). 192p. 89.00 *(978-0-230-61535-9(X))* Palgrave Macmillan.

Fallon, Stephen M. Milton's Peculiar Grace: Self-Representation & Authority. 2008. 296p. pap. 29.50 *(978-0-8014-7485-9(X))* Cornell Univ. Pr.

Hanning, Robert W. Serious Play: Desire & Authority in the Poetry of Ovid, Chaucer, & Ariosto. 2010. (Leonard Hastings Schoff Lectures). (ENG.). 312p. (gr. 17). 45.00 *(978-0-231-15210-5(8))* Columbia Univ. Pr.

Howe, Lawrence. Mark Twain & the Novel: The Double-Cross of Authority. 2009. (Cambridge Studies in American Literature & Culture Ser.). (ENG.). 280p. pap. 41.00 *(978-0-521-10762-4(8))* Cambridge Univ. Pr.

Lipton, Emma. Affections of the Mind: The Politics of Sacramental Marriage in Late Medieval English Literature. 2007. (ENG.). 280p. per. 34.00 *(978-0-268-03405-4(2))* Univ. of Notre Dame Pr.

Lundin, Roger. From Nature to Experience: The American Search for Cultural Authority. Lundin, Roger, ed. 2007. (American Intellectual Culture Ser.). (ENG.). 278p. pap. 30.95 *(978-0-7425-4840-4(6))* Rowman & Littlefield Publishers, Inc.

Minnis, Alastair. Translations of Authority in Medieval English Literature: Valuing the Vernacular. (ENG.). 2012. 290p. pap. 36.99 ***(978-1-107-40394-9(4))*** 2009. 288p. 98.00 *(978-0-521-51594-8(7))* Cambridge Univ. Pr.

Morrow, John & Scott, Jonathan, eds. Liberty, Authority, Formality: Political Ideas & Culture, 1600-1900. 2008. (ENG.). 281p. pap. 34.90 *(978-1-84540-135-1(2))* Imprint Academic GBR. Dist: Ingram Pub. Services.

Rickard, Jane. Authorship & Authority: The Writings of James V1 & 1. 2008. (ENG., Illus.). 256p. 79.00 *(978-0-7190-7486-8(X))* Manchester Univ. Pr. GBR. Dist: Macmillan.

Ronell, Avital. Loser Sons: Politics & Authority. 2012. (ENG., Illus.). 208p. 35.00 ***(978-0-252-03664-4(6))*** Univ. of Illinois Pr.

Stevenson, Jane. Women Latin Poets: Language, Gender, & Authority from Antiquity to the Eighteenth Century. 2008. (ENG.). 680p. pap. 55.00 *(978-0-19-922973-4(2))* Oxford Univ. Pr., Inc.

Voigt, Lisa. Writing Captivity in the Early Modern Atlantic: Circulations of Knowledge & Authority in the Iberian & English Imperial Worlds. 2009. (Published for the Omohundro Institute of Early American History & Culture, Williamsburg, VA Ser.). (ENG., Illus.). 352p. 69.95 *(978-0-8078-3199-1(9));* pap. 26.95 *(978-0-8078-5944-5(3))* Univ. of North Carolina Pr.

AUTHORITY, DELEGATION OF

see Delegation of Authority

AUTHORS

see also Anonyms and Pseudonyms; Bio-Bibliography; Blacklisting of Authors; Child Authors; Journalists; Litterateurs; Physicians As Authors; Women Authors

also particular classes of writers, e.g. Dramatists, Historians, Poets; also names of authors, e.g. Shakespeare, William, 1564-1616

Abse, Leo. The Bi-Sexuality of Daniel Defoe: A Psychoanalytic Survey of the Man & His Works. 2007. 308p. per. 58.50 *(978-1-85575-456-0(8))* Karnac Bks. GBR. Dist: Stylus Publishing, LLC.

Bagehot, Walter. Biographical Studies. 2010. 414p. pap. 34.75 *(978-1-148-95197-3(0));* 410p. pap. 34.75 *(978-1-147-21477-2(8));* 404p. pap. 34.75 *(978-1-142-97359-9(X))* BiblioBazaar.

—Biographical Studies. 2009. 274p. pap. *(978-0-217-18153-2(8));* 278p. pap. *(978-1-4588-2444-8(6));* 264p. pap. *(978-1-4590-5114-0(9))* Books LLC.

—Biographical Studies. Hutton, Richard Holt, ed. 408p. 2010. 39.96 *(978-1-163-40907-7(3))* 2007. (ENG.). 49.95 *(978-0-548-10138-4(8))* Kessinger Publishing, LLC.

—Biographical Studies. 2007. (ENG.). 428p. per. *(978-1-4067-2174-4(3))* Read Bks.

Bagehot, Walter & Hutton, Richard Holt. Biographical Studies. 2010. 386p. pap. 33.75 *(978-1-177-13600-6(7));* 438p. pap. 35.75 *(978-1-177-13363-0(6));* (ENG.). 432p. pap. 35.75 *(978-1-177-59109-6(X))* BiblioBazaar.

Bailey, John. Some Political Ideas & Persons. 2008. 264p. 42.95 *(978-1-4365-5842-6(5))* 2007. (ENG.). 268p. per. 27.95 *(978-0-548-75789-5(5))* Kessinger Publishing, LLC.

Baker. The Way We Write: Interviews with Award-Winning Writers. Baker, Barbara, ed. 2007. (ENG.). 256p. 22.95 *(978-0-8264-9505-1(2))* Continuum International Publishing Group, Ltd. GBR. Dist: National Bk. Network.

Ballman, Donna. The Writer's Guide to the Courtroom: Let's Quill All the Lawyers. 2009. (Get It Write Ser.). (ENG.). 288p. pap. 17.95 *(978-1-933016-53-5(1))* Behler Pubns., LLC.

Barrie, J. M. The Little White Bird. 2007. (ENG.). 224p. (gr. 4-7). 27.95 *(978-1-4218-3869-4(9),* 1st World Library - Literary Society) 1st World Publishing, Inc.

—The Little White Bird. 2009. 322p. 36.99 *(978-1-116-05389-0(6))* 2009. 322p. 32.99 *(978-1-116-05390-6(X))* 2009. 322p. pap. 30.75 *(978-1-116-05391-3(8))* 2009. 322p. (gr. 4-7). pap. 29.75 *(978-1-116-05392-0(6))* 2008. 204p. (gr. 4-7). 27.99 *(978-0-554-26046-4(8))* 2008. 204p. (gr. 4-7). 24.99 *(978-0-554-35349-4(0))* BiblioBazaar.

—The Little White Bird. 2008. 180p. pap. 12.95 *(978-1-60597-983-0(X));* (ENG.). pap. 12.95 *(978-1-60597-677-8(6))* Standard Pubns., Inc. (Book Jungle).

Bogousslavsky, J., et al, eds. Neurological Disorders in Famous Artists - Part 3. 2010. (Frontiers of Neurology & Neuroscience Ser.). (Illus.). 242p. *(978-3-8055-9330-4(9))* Karger, S. AG.

Cheshire, Simon. You've Got to Read This: A Beginner's Guide to Great Writers & the History of Books. 2011. 224p. pap. ***(978-0-9565049-6-8(5))*** Cheshire, Simon.

Collins, David J. Reforming Saints: Saints' Lives & Their Authors in Germany, 1470-1530. 2008. (Oxford Studies in Historical Theology Ser.). (ENG., Illus.). 208p. 65.00 *(978-0-19-532953-7(8))* Oxford Univ. Pr., Inc.

Cont Auth. 2010. (Contemporary Authors Ser.). 293.00 *(978-1-4144-4594-6(6))* Cengage Gale.

Dexter, Gary, ed. Poisoned Pens: Literary Invective from Amis to Zola. 2010. (ENG.). 240p. pap. 14.95 *(978-0-7112-3162-7(1))* Lincoln, Frances Ltd. GBR. Dist: Perseus-PGW.

Diamond, Marie Josephine. Encyclopedia of World Writers, 1800 to the Present. 2nd rev. ed. 2011. 640p. (C). (gr. 9). 85.00 *(978-0-8160-8204-9(9))* Facts On File, Inc.

Disraeli, Isaac. Curiosities of Literature. 2009. 474p. 42.99 *(978-1-115-46669-1(0))* 2009. 474p. 35.99 *(978-1-115-46670-7(4))* 2009. 474p. pap. 37.75 *(978-1-115-46671-4(2))* 2009. 474p. pap. 36.75 *(978-1-115-46672-1(0))* 2009. 302p. 30.99 *(978-1-110-81930-0(7))* 2009. 302p. pap. 28.75 *(978-1-110-81929-4(3))* 2009. 380p. 33.99 *(978-1-110-08499-9(4))* 2009. 318p. 32.99 *(978-1-110-12793-1(6))* 2009. 344p. 32.99 *(978-1-110-20724-4(7))* 2009. 344p. 32.99 *(978-1-110-17040-1(8))* 2009. 380p. pap. 32.75 *(978-1-110-08497-5(8))* 2009. 318p. pap. 29.75 *(978-1-110-12791-7(X))* 2009. 344p. pap. 31.75 *(978-1-110-20722-0(0))* 2009. 344p. pap. 31.75 *(978-1-110-17037-1(8))* 2009. 304p. 24.99 *(978-1-103-99319-2(4))* 2009. 304p. pap. 18.99 *(978-1-103-99311-6(9))* 2009. 332p. 25.99 *(978-1-103-26856-6(2))* 2009. 332p. pap. 19.99 *(978-1-103-26853-5(8))* 2009. 400p. 26.99 *(978-0-559-97742-8(5))* 2009. 400p. pap. 20.99 *(978-0-559-97739-8(5))* 2008. 472p. 31.99 *(978-0-559-80762-6(7))* 2008. 472p. pap. 36.75 *(978-0-559-80758-9(9))* 2008. 328p. 28.99 *(978-0-559-61260-2(5))* 2008. 328p. pap. 30.75 *(978-0-559-61258-9(3))* 2008. (ENG.). 672p. per. 47.75 *(978-1-4375-3136-7(9))* 2008. (ENG.). 608p. per. 44.75 *(978-1-4375-3025-4(7))* BiblioBazaar.

—Curiosities of Literature. 2009. (Illus.). 142p. pap. *(978-1-150-20965-9(8));* (Illus.). 124p. pap. *(978-1-150-54748-5(0));* 394p. pap. *(978-0-217-77779-7(1));* 434p. pap. *(978-0-217-77782-7(1));* 256p. pap. *(978-0-217-77797-1(X));* 272p. pap. *(978-0-217-81668-7(1));* 274p. pap. *(978-0-217-82547-4(8));* 480p. pap. *(978-0-217-81682-3(7));* 172p. pap. *(978-0-217-19817-2(1));* 234p. pap. *(978-0-217-19821-9(X));* 372p. pap. *(978-1-4590-6449-2(6));* 162p. pap. *(978-1-4590-6440-9(2));* (Illus.). 346p. pap. *(978-0-217-19805-9(8))* Books LLC.

—Curiosities of Literature. 2009. 408p. pap. 25.23 *(978-0-217-81685-4(1))* General Bks. LLC.

Ditchfield, Peter Hampson. Books Fatal to Their Authors. l.t. ed. 2006. 158p. pap. 21.99 *(978-1-4264-3094-7(9))* BiblioBazaar.

Donskis, Leonidas. Power & Imagination: Studies in Politics & Literature. 2008. (New Studies in Aesthetics Ser.: Vol. 39). (Illus.). 192p. (C). 67.95 *(978-1-4331-0125-0(4))* Lang, Peter Publishing, Inc.

Erichsen, Hugo. Methods of Authors. 2011. 96p. pap. 8.99 ***(978-1-61203-294-8(X))*** Bottom of the Hill Publishing.

Fido, Martin. The World of Charles Dickens: The Life, Times & Works of the Great Victorian Novelist. 2012. (ENG., Illus.). 144p. 24.95 ***(978-1-84732-943-1(8))*** Carlton Bks., Ltd. GBR. Dist: Sterling Publishing Co., Inc.

Fyvie, John. Some Literary Eccentrics. 2009. 160p. pap. 19.99 *(978-0-217-99572-6(1))* General Bks. LLC.

—Some Literary Eccentrics. 2007. (ENG.). 302p. 43.95 *(978-0-548-26133-0(4));* 304p. per. 28.95 *(978-1-4326-6529-6(4))* Kessinger Publishing, LLC.

Gale Editor, ed. The Writers Directory, 2 vols. 29th ed. 2011. 2820p. lib. bdg. 349.00 *(978-1-55862-835-9(5),* St. James Pr.) Cengage Gale.

Glanville, Jo & Index on Censorship (Organization) Staff, eds. Beyond Bars: 50 Years of the PEN Writers in Prison Committee. 2011. (Index on Censorship Ser.). 192p. pap. 13.00 *(978-0-85702-847-1(2),* B28471P) SAGE Pubns., Ltd. GBR. Dist: SAGE Pubns., Inc.

Gore, Catherine G. Cecil, a Peer, 3 vols., 2 bks., Set. reprint ed. 84.50 *(978-0-404-61879-7(0))* AMS Pr., Inc.

Grey, Amelia. Fall in Love Like a Romance Writer: Your Favorite Novelists Share Their Secret Keys to a Long & Lasting Love. 2011. (ENG.). 264p. pap. 14.95 *(978-0-7573-1554-1(2))* Health Communications, Inc.

Gura, Mark & Reissman, Rose Cherie. Teaching with Author Web Sites, K-8. 2009. (Illus.). 152p. pap. 31.95 *(978-1-4129-7386-1(4),* B73861P) Corwin Pr.

Hale, Edward Everett. Lights of Two Centuries. 2007. (ENG.). 610p. 59.95 *(978-0-548-16803-5(2));* 612p. per. 44.95 *(978-1-4304-6523-2(9))* Kessinger Publishing, LLC.

Hallman, J. C., ed. The Story about the Story: Great Writers Explore Great Literature. 2009. (ENG.). 420p. pap. 18.95 *(978-0-9802436-9-7(6))* Tin Hse. Bks., LLC.

Halsey, Francis W. Seeing Europe with Famous Authors. 2009. (Illus.). 224p. 28.99 *(978-1-115-41602-3(2))* 2009. (Illus.). 230p. 28.99 *(978-1-115-41607-8(3))* 2009. (Illus.). 228p. 28.99 *(978-1-115-41589-7(1))* 2009. (Illus.). 222p. 28.99 *(978-1-115-41587-3(5))* 2009. (Illus.). 228p. 32.99 *(978-1-115-41590-3(5))* 2009. (Illus.). 230p. 32.99 *(978-1-115-41598-9(0))* 2009. (Illus.). 222p. 32.99 *(978-1-115-41588-0(3))* 2009. (Illus.). 224p. 32.99 *(978-1-115-41603-0(0))* 2009. (Illus.). 230p. 32.99 *(978-1-115-41609-2(X))* 2009. (Illus.). 222p. pap. 23.75 *(978-1-115-41583-5(2))* 2009. (Illus.). 228p. pap. 24.75 *(978-1-115-41585-9(9))* 2009. (Illus.). 230p. pap. 24.75 *(978-1-115-41593-4(X))* 2009. (Illus.). 224p. pap. 24.75 *(978-1-115-41599-6(9))* 2009. (Illus.). 230p. pap. 24.75 *(978-1-115-41605-4(7))* 2009. (Illus.). 222p. pap. 24.75 *(978-1-115-41584-2(0))* 2009. (Illus.). 228p. pap. 25.75 *(978-1-115-41586-6(7))* 2009. (Illus.). 230p. pap. 25.75 *(978-1-115-41595-8(6))* 2009. (Illus.). 224p. pap. 25.75 *(978-1-115-41600-9(6))* 2009. (Illus.). 230p. pap. 25.75 *(978-1-115-41606-1(5))* 2008. 180p. 25.99 *(978-0-554-26961-0(9))* 2008. 220p. 27.99 *(978-0-554-25826-3(9))* 2008. 220p. 24.99 *(978-0-554-35129-2(3))* 2008. 180p. 22.99 *(978-0-554-36264-9(3))*vol. 7. 2008. 200p. 25.99 *(978-0-554-27330-3(6))* BiblioBazaar.

Halsey, Francis Whiting. Our Literary Deluge & Some of Its Deeper Waters. 2008. 268p. 25.99 *(978-0-559-77998-5(4));* pap. 26.75 *(978-0-559-77994-7(1))* BiblioBazaar.

—Our Literary Deluge & Some of Its Deeper Waters. 2007. (ENG.). 264p. 42.95 *(978-0-548-02139-2(2))* Kessinger Publishing, LLC.

Harland, Marion. Where Ghosts Walk: The Haunts of Familiar Characters in History & Literature. 2009. 388p. pap. 19.95 *(978-1-4344-0792-4(6))* Wildside Pr., LLC.

Harmon, Kristen & Nelson, Jennifer. Deaf American Prose 1980-2010. 2012. E-Book ***(978-1-56368-524-8(8))*** Gallaudet Univ. Pr.

Harmon, Kristen & Nelson, Jennifer, eds. Deaf American Prose: 1980-2010. 2012. (Gallaudet Deaf Literature Ser.). (ENG.). 336p. pap. 60.00 ***(978-1-56368-523-1(X))*** Gallaudet Univ. Pr.

Hitchcock, Thomas. Unhappy Loves of Men of Genius. 2009. 250p. 28.99 *(978-1-110-62727-1(0));* pap. 25.75 *(978-1-110-62724-0(6))* BiblioBazaar.

—Unhappy Loves of Men of Genius. 2010. 82p. pap. *(978-1-152-09277-8(4))* Books LLC.

—Unhappy Loves of Men of Genius. 2009. 252p. 41.95 *(978-1-104-55851-2(3));* pap. 26.95 *(978-1-104-51830-1(9))* Kessinger Publishing, LLC.

Jack, Ian, ed. The Deep End. 2007. (Granta: the Magazine of New Writing Ser.). (ENG., Illus.). 256p. per. 14.95 *(978-1-929001-28-6(2))* Grove/Atlantic, Inc.

Kizziar, John. AS PUNISHMENT: a diary of the time spent inside. 2007. 224p. per. 12.95 *(978-1-4327-0239-7(4))* Outskirts Pr., Inc.

Klaus, Carl H. & Stuckey-French, Ned, eds. Essayists on the Essay: Montaigne to Our Time. 2012. (ENG.). 333p. pap. 25.00 ***(978-1-60938-076-2(2))*** Univ. of Iowa Pr.

Lacombe, Michael A., et al. Osler's Bedside Library: Great Writers Who Inspired a Great Physician. 2010. (Illus.). xiv, 362p. *(978-1-934465-49-3(6))* American College of Physicians.

Lang, Andrew. Letters to Dead Authors. reprint ed. 37.50 *(978-0-404-03819-9(0))* AMS Pr., Inc.

Lettmann, Vicky & Roan, Carol, eds. When Last on the Mountain: The View from Writers Over 50. 2011. (ENG.). 392p. pap. 17.95 *(978-0-9823545-2-0(5))* Holy Cow! Pr.

Lockwood, Helen D. Tools & the Man. reprint ed. 27.50 *(978-0-404-03999-8(5))* AMS Pr., Inc.

Lonely Planet Staff. Lights, Camera... Travel! George, Don & McCarthy, Andrew, eds. 2011. (Anthology Ser.). (ENG.). 320p. pap. 15.99 *(978-1-74220-493-2(7))* Lonely Planet Pubns.

MacLaren, Ian. Books & Bookmen. 2009. (ENG.). 67p. pap. 16.75 *(978-1-117-41232-0(6))* BiblioBazaar.

Maclaren, Ian. Books & Bookmen. 2009. (ENG.). 67p. pap. 16.99 *(978-1-117-41233-7(4),* BiblioLife) BiblioBazaar.

Maclaren, Jan & MacLaren, Jan. Books & Bookmen. 2010. 68p. pap. 17.75 *(978-1-117-96847-6(2))* BiblioBazaar.

Malone, Aubrey. Literary Trivia: Over 300 Curious Lists for Bookworms. 2008. (ENG.). 320p. pap. 15.95 *(978-1-85375-643-6(1))* Prion GBR. Dist: Independent Pubs. Group.

McCarthy, Justin. Portraits of the Sixties. 2009. 214p. pap. *(978-0-217-03312-1(1))* Books LLC.

—Portraits of the Sixties. 2009. 220p. pap. 19.99 *(978-0-217-78745-1(2))* General Bks. LLC.

Metzdorf, Ragna. Stilwandel des Kinderfilms: 1960er Bis 1980er Jahre. 2011. (Kinder- und Jugendkultur, -literatur und -medien. Theorie - Geschichte - Didaktik Ser.). (GER.). 196p. 57.95 *(978-3-631-60988-0(4))* Lang, Peter GmbH, Europaischer Verlag der Wissenschaften DEU. Dist: Lang, Peter.

Monteiro, Adolfo Casais, et al. Cartas Em Familia: Correspondência Entre o Escritor e Seus Pais: 1929-1943. 2008. (POR.). 407p. *(978-972-27-1624-6(7))* Imprensa Nacional Casa da Moeda, INCM.

Overton, Grant M. Why Authors Go Wrong & Other Explanations. 2009. 222p. 28.99 *(978-1-110-90377-1(4));* pap. 24.75 *(978-1-110-90374-0(X))* BiblioBazaar.

Page, Amy & Peters, Amy. The Writer's Devotional: 365 Inspirational Exercises, Ideas, Tips, & Motivations on Writing. 2012. (ENG., Illus.). 384p. 17.95 *(978-1-4027-8183-4(0))* Sterling Publishing Co., Inc.

Pahlow, Mark. Who would by This? The Archie Mcphee Story. Holub, Gibson, ed. & des. by. 2008. 184p. 24.95 *(978-0-9786649-7-8(3))* Accoutrements.

Peschel, Bill. Writers Gone Wild: The Feuds, Frolics, & Follies of Literature's Great Adventurers, Drunkards, Lovers, Iconoclasts, & Misanthropes. 2010. (ENG.). 272p. (gr. 12). 14.95 *(978-0-399-53618-2(3),* Perigee Trade) Penguin Group (USA) Inc.

Picador USA Staff. The Paris Review Interviews, IV. Paris Review Staff, ed. 2009. (ENG.). 496p. pap. 18.00 *(978-0-312-42744-3(1))* Picador.

Prescott, William H. Biographical & Critical Miscellanies. 2009. (ENG.). 740p. pap. 50.75 *(978-1-117-46957-7(3));* 388p. 33.99 *(978-1-116-07274-7(2));* 388p. 38.99 *(978-1-116-07273-0(4));* 388p. pap. 33.75 *(978-1-116-07275-4(0))* BiblioBazaar.

—Biographical & Critical Miscellanies. 2007. pap. *(978-1-4067-5504-6(4))* Read Bks.

Quiller-Couch, Arthur Thomas. Memories & Opinions: An Unfinished Autobiography. 2008. (ENG.). 124p. (C). pap. 31.99 *(978-0-521-73674-9(9))* Cambridge Univ. Pr.

Reichl, Ruth & Gourmet Magazine Editors, eds. History in a Glass: Sixty Years of Wine Writing from Gourmet. 2007. (Modern Library). (ENG., Illus.). 400p. per. 16.95 *(978-0-8129-7194-1(9))* Random House Publishing Group.

Ridley, Anna Cate. Real Cheesy Facts about: Geography: Everything Weird, Dumb, & Unbelievable You Never Learned in School. 2007. (Real Cheesy Facts Ser.). (ENG.). 176p. pap. *(978-1-57587-275-9(7))* Crane Hill Pubs.

Robinson, Marilyn. Writers Workshop Twelfth Literary Annual. 2007. 64p. per. *(978-0-923889-14-2(0))* Inquisitors Publishing Co.

Rodden, John. Performing the Literary Interview: How Writers Craft Their Public Selves. 2007. (ENG.). 276p. pap. 24.95 *(978-0-8032-2236-6(X))* Univ. of Nebraska Pr.

Sainte-Beuve, Charles Augustin. Portraits of Men. 2009. 116p. pap. *(978-0-217-03306-0(7))* Books LLC.

—Portraits of Men. Edeveain, Forsyth, tr. 2009. 232p. 41.95 *(978-1-104-20691-8(9))*; pap. 26.95 *(978-1-4374-9094-7(8))* Kessinger Publishing, LLC.

Scott, Walter, Sr. The Lives of the Novelists. reprint ed. lib. bdg. 79.00 *(978-0-7812-0292-3(2))* Reprint Services Co.

—The Lives of the Novelists. reprint ed. 39.00 *(978-0-403-04158-9(9))* Somerset Pubs., Inc.

Sethi, Sunil. The Big Bookshelf: Sunil Sethi in Conversation with 30 Famous Writers. 2012. (ENG., Illus.). 264p. (gr. 12). pap. 22.00 ***(978-0-14-341629-6(4)***, Penguin Global) Penguin Group (USA) Inc.

Simon, Jules. Victor Cousin. 2009. 188p. 22.99 *(978-1-103-42809-0(8))*; pap. 16.99 *(978-1-103-42807-6(1))* BiblioBazaar.

—Victor Cousin. Anderson, Melville B. & Anderson, Edward P., trs. 2007. 220p. 39.95 *(978-0-548-22364-2(5))*; 224p. per. 24.95 *(978-1-4325-4516-1(7))* Kessinger Publishing, LLC.

—Victor Cousin. 2008. 196p. pap. *(978-1-4086-9893-8(5))* Read Bks.

Speerstra, Karen. Questions Writers Ask: Wise, Whimsical, & Witty Answers from the Pros. 2010. 320p. pap. 16.95 *(978-1-934759-32-5(5))* Reed, Robert D. Pubs.

Sutherland, John. Curiosities of Literature: A Feast for Book Lovers. 2009. (ENG., Illus.). 288p. 22.95 *(978-1-60239-371-4(0)*, 239371) Skyhorse Publishing Co., Inc.

Sutherland, John & Fender, Stephen. Love, Sex, Death & Words: Surprising Tales from a Year in Literature. 2011. (ENG.). 544p. pap. 16.95 ***(978-1-84831-247-0(4))*** Totem Bks. GBR. Dist: Consortium Bk. Sales & Distribution.

Symons, Arthur. Figures of Several Centuries. 2009. 408p. pap. 33.75 *(978-1-115-55008-6(X))* 2008. 240p. 24.99 *(978-0-554-39097-0(3))* 2008. 240p. 27.99 *(978-0-554-29794-1(9))* 2007. (ENG.). 214p. pap. 20.99 *(978-1-4346-8440-0(7))* 2007. (ENG.). 238p. pap. 22.99 *(978-1-4346-8441-7(5))* BiblioBazaar.

—Figures of Several Centuries. 2008. 192p. per. *(978-1-4065-6677-2(2))* Dodo Pr.

—Figures of Several Centuries. 2010. 128p. pap. 7.89 *(978-1-152-46353-0(5))* General Bks. LLC.

Thomson Gale, creator. Something about the Author: Facts & Pictures about Authors & Illustrators of Books for Young People. 2007. (Something about the Author Ser.: Vol. 182). (ENG., Illus.). 224p. 202.00 *(978-0-7876-8806-6(1))* Cengage Gale.

Turck, Hermann. The Man of Genius. 2008. 490p. 53.95 *(978-1-4365-9609-1(2))* 2007. (ENG.). 492p. per. 38.95 *(978-0-548-80586-2(5))* Kessinger Publishing, LLC.

The Writers Directory, 2.0. 28th ed. 2011. 332.00 *(978-1-55862-798-7(7)*, St. James Pr.) Cengage Gale.

AUTHORS—BIOGRAPHY

Abad Faciolince, Héctor Joaquín & Abad Faciolince, Héctor. Traiciones de la Memoria. 2010. (SPA., Illus.). 265p. *(978-84-204-0574-2(4)*, Alfaguara) Santillana USA Publishing Co., Inc.

Abad, Héctor. Oblivion: A Memoir, 1 vol. McLean, Anne & Harvey, Rosalind, trs. from SPA. 2012. (ENG., Illus.). 272p. 26.00 ***(978-0-374-22397-7(1))*** Farrar, Straus & Giroux.

Abbas, Khwaja Ahmad. Udas Divaren. 2010. (URD.). 240p. *(978-969-8455-48-4(5))* Jumhoori Publications.

Abbott, Karen. American Rose: A Nation Laid Bare - The Life & Times of Gypsy Rose Lee. 2010. (ENG., Illus.). 448p. 26.00 *(978-1-4000-6691-9(3)*, Random House) Random House Publishing Group.

Abbott, Karen. American Rose: A Nation Laid Bare: the Life & Times of Gypsy Rose Lee. 2012. (ENG., Illus.). 448p. pap. 17.00 ***(978-0-8129-7851-3(X)***, Random Hse. Trade Paperbacks) Random House Publishing Group.

Abbott, Lawrence. Jane Dolinger: The Adventurous Life of an American Travel Writer. 2010. (ENG.). 288p. 89.00 *(978-0-230-62208-1(9))* Palgrave Macmillan.

Aberjhani. The American Poet Who Went Home Again. 2008. 309p. pap. 16.95 *(978-1-4357-1769-5(4))* Lulu Enterprises Inc.

Abrams, Dennis. Gail Carson Levine. 2007. (Who Wrote That? Ser.). (Illus.). 120p. (gr. 6-12). lib. bdg. 35.00 *(978-0-7910-8970-5(3)*, Chelsea Hse.) Facts On File, Inc.

Achebe, Chinua. The Education of a British-Protected Child: Essays. 2010. (ENG.). 192p. pap. 14.95 *(978-0-307-47367-7(8)*, Anchor) Knopf Doubleday Publishing Group.

Ackerley, J. R. My Dog Tulip. movie tie-in ed. 2010. (ENG., Illus.). 208p. pap. 14.00 *(978-1-59017-414-2(3)*, NYRB Classics) New York Review of Bks., Inc., The.

Ackerman, Diane. One Hundred Names for Love: A Stroke, A Marriage, & the Language of Healing. 2011. (ENG.). 322p. 26.95 *(978-0-393-07241-9(X)*, 7241) Norton, W. W. & Co., Inc.

—One Hundred Names for Love: A Stroke, A Marriage, & the Language of Healing. l.t. ed. 2011. 515p. 32.99 *(978-1-4104-3648-1(9))* Thorndike Pr.

Ackroyd, Peter. Poe: A Life Cut Short. 2009. (ENG., Illus.). 224p. 22.95 *(978-0-385-50800-1(X)*, Talese, Nan A.) Knopf Doubleday Publishing Group.

Ada, Alma Flor. Alma Flor Ada & YOU, 1 vol., Vol. 2. 2nd ed. 2008. (Author & YOU Ser.). (Illus.). 128p. pap. 35.00 *(978-1-59158-228-1(8)*, LU2288) Libraries Unlimited, Inc.

Adams, Agatha Boyd. Thomas Wolfe, Carolina Student: A Brief Biography. 2011. 92p. 38.95 ***(978-1-258-07349-7(8))*** Literary Licensing, LLC.

Adams, Elbridge L. & Zelie, John Sheridan. Joseph Conrad, the Man: And A Burial in Kent. 2011. 84p. 37.95 ***(978-1-258-09072-2(4))*** Literary Licensing, LLC.

Adams, Hazard. Academic Child: A Memoir. 2008. (ENG., Illus.). 278p. pap. 39.95 *(978-0-7864-4011-5(2))* McFarland & Co., Inc. Pubs.

Adams, Jad. Kipling. 2013. (ENG.). 240p. pap. 19.95 ***(978-1-908323-06-4(X))*** Haus Publishing GBR. Dist: Consortium Bk. Sales & Distribution.

Adams, Katherine. Owning Up: Privacy, Property, & Belonging in U. S. Women's Life Writing, 1840-1890. 2009. (ENG., Illus.). 304p. 65.00 *(978-0-19-533680-1(1))* Oxford Univ. Pr., Inc.

Adams, Maureen. Shaggy Muses: The Dogs Who Inspired Virginia Woolf, Emily Dickenson, Elizabeth Barrett Browning, Edith Wharton, & Emily Bronte. 2011. (Illus.). 320p. pap. 16.00 *(978-0-226-00536-2(4))* Univ. of Chicago Pr.

—Shaggy Muses: The Dogs Who Inspired Virginia Woolf, Emily Dickinson, Elizabeth Barrett Browning, Edith Wharton, & Emily Bront. 2007. (ENG., Illus.). 320p. 24.95 *(978-0-345-48406-2(1)*, Ballantine Bks.) Random House Publishing Group.

Adams, Oscar Fay. A Brief Handbook of American Authors. 2009. 222p. 28.99 *(978-1-110-41659-2(8))* 2009. 222p. pap. 23.75 *(978-1-110-41655-4(5))* 2008. 204p. 24.99 *(978-0-559-26988-2(9))* 2008. 204p. pap. 23.75 *(978-0-559-26987-5(0))* BiblioBazaar.

—A Dictionary of American Authors. 2007. (ENG.). 598p. 59.95 *(978-0-548-26352-5(3))*; 600p. per. 44.95 *(978-1-4326-6764-1(5))* Kessinger Publishing, LLC.

—The Story of Jane Austen's Life. 2009. 190p. pap. 19.99 *(978-0-217-89784-6(3))* General Bks. LLC.

—The Story of Jane Austen's Life. 2009. 292p. 43.95 *(978-1-104-69366-4(6))*; pap. 28.95 *(978-1-104-66703-0(7))* Kessinger Publishing, LLC.

Adams, Timothy Dow. Telling Lies in Modern American Autobiography. 2011. (ENG.). 224p. pap. 40.00 *(978-0-8078-5995-7(8))* Univ. of North Carolina Pr.

Agulló y Cobo, Mercedes. A Vueltas con el Autor de Lazarillo: Con el Testamento e Inventario de Bienes de Don Diego Hurtado de Mendoza. 2010. (Illus.). 140p. *(978-84-8359-175-8(8))* Calambur Editorial, S.L.

Aimée, Rose. A Road Without A Map. 2011. 120p. 22.95 ***(978-1-4620-5611-8(3))***; pap. 12.95 ***(978-1-4620-5610-1(5))*** iUniverse, Inc.

Ainger, Alfred. The Letters of Charles Lamb. 2009. 394p. 38.99 *(978-1-115-28329-8(4))*; 33.99 *(978-1-115-28328-1(6))*; pap. 33.75 *(978-1-115-28327-4(8))* BiblioBazaar.

Aksakov, Sergei. A Russian Schoolboy. Duff, J. D., tr. from RUS. 2009. (ENG.). 200p. pap. 11.95 *(978-1-58988-051-1(X))* Dry, Paul Bks., Inc.

Aksenov, Vitalii. Kto Byl Shekspirom? Intellektualnyi Detektiv Dlia Vsekh, Kto Liubit Razgadyvat Tainy. 2010. (RUS., Illus.). 272p. *(978-5-9676-0236-8(4))* Petropolis, telekommunikacionnyj kompleks.

Al-Mallah, Majd Yaser & Fitzpatrick, Coeli. 20th Century Arabic Writers, Vol. 346. 2008. (Dictionary of Literary Biography Ser.). (ENG.). 372p. 315.00 *(978-0-7876-8164-7(4))* Cengage Gale.

Al-Mustafa, Madihah. Still Standing. 2009. 516p. 34.99 *(978-1-4389-5690-9(8))*; pap. 24.49 *(978-1-4389-5689-3(4))* AuthorHouse.

Alain-Fournier. Le Grand Meaulnes. 2007. (FRE.). 220p. pap. 20.99 *(978-1-4264-2005-4(6))* 2006. 238p. pap. 22.99 *(978-1-4264-2116-7(8))* BiblioBazaar.

—Le Grand Meaulnes. pap. 21.95 incl. audio compact disk *(978-88-7754-838-2(X))* Cideb ITA. Dist: Distribooks, Inc.

Albani, Emma. Forty Years of Song. 2011. 178p. ***(978-1-84902-532-4(0))*** Benediction Classics.

Albert, Susan Wittig. An Extraordinary Year of Ordinary Days. 2010. (ENG.). 240p. 24.95 *(978-0-292-72306-1(7))* Univ. of Texas Pr.

—Together, Alone: A Memoir of Marriage & Place. (ENG., Illus.). 2011. 195p. pap. 19.95 *(978-0-292-72646-8(5))* 2009. 196p. 24.95 *(978-0-292-71970-5(1))* Univ. of Texas Pr.

Albrecht, Friedrich. Klaus Mann der Mittler: Studien aus vier Jahrzehnten. 2009. (Convergences Ser.). (GER.). 350p. pap. *(978-3-03911-744-4(0))* Lang, Peter.

Alcala, Kathleen. The Desert Remembers My Name: On Family & Writing. 2007. (Camino Del Sol Ser.). (ENG.). 192p. 32.00 *(978-0-8165-2626-0(5))*; pap. 14.95 *(978-0-8165-2627-7(3))* Univ. of Arizona Pr.

Aldiss, Brian W. An Exile on Planet Earth: Articles & Reflections. 2012. (ENG.). 192p. 35.00 ***(978-1-85124-373-0(9))*** Bodleian Library GBR. Dist: Chicago Distribution Ctr.

Aldrich, Nelson W., ed. George, Being George: George Plimpton's Life as Told, Admired, Deplored, & Envied by 200 Friends, Relatives, Lovers, Acquaintances, Rivals — and a Few Unappreciative Observers. 2009. (ENG., Illus.). 432p. pap. 18.00 *(978-0-8129-7418-8(2)*, Random Hse. Trade Paperbacks) Random House Publishing Group.

Alexander, Darmonica. Hold on, Someone Is on the Other Line! 2011. 280p. 29.99 ***(978-1-4568-0014-7(0))***; pap. 19.99 ***(978-1-4568-0013-0(2))*** Xlibris Corp.

Alexander, James W. Forty Years' Familiar Letters of James W Alexander, D D, Constituting, with the Notes, a Memoir of His Life Edited by the Surviving Correspondent. 2006. 388p. per. 26.99 *(978-1-4255-4169-9(0))*; (ENG.). 428p. per. 26.99 *(978-1-4255-4680-9(3))* MPublishing.

Alexander, Paul. Salinger: A Biography. 2010. (ENG.). 363p. pap. 17.99 *(978-0-312-67334-5(5)*, Renaissance Bks.) St. Martin's Pr.

Ali, Sara Mansour. A Woman under Threat: Memoirs of a Sudanese Feminist & Militant writer on Sudanese women's problem under Threat. 2011. 124p. 29.99 ***(978-1-4628-7331-9(6))***; pap. 19.99 ***(978-1-4628-7330-2(8))*** Xlibris Corp.

Alikhail, Mohammed B. Goal: My Journey from Afghanistan. 2008. 216p. pap. 17.95 *(978-0-595-47048-8(3))* iUniverse, Inc.

Alison, Jane. The Sisters Antipodes. 2010. (ENG.). 288p. pap. 14.95 *(978-0-547-24773-1(7)*, Mariner Bks.) Houghton Mifflin Harcourt Trade & Reference Pubs.

—The Sisters Antipodes: A Memoir. 2009. (ENG., Illus.). 288p. 23.00 *(978-0-15-101280-0(6))* Houghton Mifflin Harcourt Trade & Reference Pubs.

Allen, Charles. Kipling Sahib: India & the Making of Rudyard Kipling. 2009. (ENG., Illus.). 448p. 28.00 *(978-1-60598-031-7(5)*, 605031) Pegasus Bks.

—Kipling Sahib: India & the Making of Rudyard Kipling, 1865-1900. 2010. (ENG.). 448p. pap. 16.95 *(978-1-60598-090-4(0)*, 605090) Pegasus Bks.

Allen, Eddie B., Jr. & Allen, Eddie B. Low Road: The Life & Legacy of Donald Goines. 2008. (ENG., Illus.). 224p. pap. 16.99 *(978-0-312-38351-0(7)*, St. Martin's Griffin) St. Martin's Pr.

Allen, Glenn. It Sucks to Know Me. 2011. 296p. 25.74 *(978-1-4567-3403-9(2))*; pap. 15.95 *(978-1-4567-3401-5(6))* AuthorHouse.

Allen, John B. Struggles & Good Outcomes. 2011. 42p. pap. 16.95 ***(978-1-4626-0028-1(X))*** PublishAmerica, Inc.

Allen, Keith. Grow Up. 2008. (ENG., Illus.). 384p. pap. 15.95 *(978-0-09-191071-6(4))* Ebury Publishing GBR. Dist: Independent Pubs. Group.

Allen, Richard. Mud Running. 2011. 176p. pap. 10.95 ***(978-1-257-05514-2(3))*** Lulu Enterprises Inc.

Allen, Roger, ed. Essays in Arabic Literary Biography, 1850-1950, No. III. 2010. (Essays in Arabic Literary Biography Ser.). (ENG.). 395p. (C). 102.00 *(978-3-447-06141-4(3))* Harrassowitz, Otto Verlag DEU. Dist: ISD.

Allende, Isabel. The Sum of Our Days: A Memoir. 2009. (P. S. Ser.). Tr. of Suma de los Dias. 336p. pap. 14.99 *(978-0-06-155184-0(8)*, HarperPerennial) HarperCollins Pubs.

—The Sum of Our Days: A Memoir. Peden, Margaret Sayers, tr. from SPA. 2008. Tr. of Suma de los Dias. (ENG.). 320p. 26.95 *(978-0-06-155183-3(X))*; 528p. pap. 26.95 *(978-0-06-156310-2(2)*, HarperLuxe) HarperCollins Pubs.

—La Suma de los Dias. (SPA & ENG.). 2009. 352p. pap. 14.99 *(978-0-06-155188-8(0))* 2007. 368p. 26.95 *(978-0-06-155187-1(2))* HarperCollins Pubs. (Rayo).

Allibone, S. Austin. A Critical Dictionary of English Literature & British & American Authors Living & Deceased Vol. 1: From the Earliest Accounts to the Latter Half of the Nineteenth Century Abb to Duf Part Two. 2006. pap. 42.95 *(978-1-4286-4586-8(1))* Kessinger Publishing, LLC.

—A Critical Dictionary of English Literature & British & American Authors Living & Deceased Vol. 2: From the Earliest Accounts to the Latter Half of the Nineteenth Century Mab to Rad. 2006. pap. 43.95 *(978-1-4286-4582-0(9))* Kessinger Publishing, LLC.

—A Critical Dictionary of English Literature & British & American Authors Living & Deceased Vol. 2: From the Earliest Accounts to the Latter Half of the Nineteenth Century Rad to Szy Part Two. 2006. pap. 44.95 *(978-1-4286-4583-7(7))* Kessinger Publishing, LLC.

—A Critical Dictionary of English Literature & British & American Authors Living & Deceased Vol. 3: From the Earliest Accounts to the Latter Half of the Nineteenth Century Taa to Wil Part One. 2006. pap. 36.95 *(978-1-4286-4588-2(8))* Kessinger Publishing, LLC.

—A Critical Dictionary of English Literature & British & American Authors Living & Deceased Vol. 3: From the Earliest Accounts to the Latter Half of the Nineteenth Century Wil to Zwe Part Two. 2006. pap. 33.95 *(978-1-4286-4589-9(6))* Kessinger Publishing, LLC.

Allison, Dorothy. Conversations with Dorothy Allison. Claxton, Mae Miller, ed. 2012. (Literary Conversations Ser.). (ENG.). 208p. 40.00 ***(978-1-61703-286-8(7))*** Univ. Pr. of Mississippi.

Allsopp, Fred W. Albert Pike's Reply to Pope Leo XIII. 2006. pap. 12.95 *(978-1-4286-6583-5(8))* Kessinger Publishing, LLC.

Almond, Steve. (Not That You Asked) Rants, Exploits, & Obsessions. 2008. (ENG.). 304p. 15.00 *(978-0-8129-7759-2(9)*, Random Hse. Trade Paperbacks) Random House Publishing Group.

Alther, Lisa. Kinfolks: Falling off the Family Tree. 2012. (ENG.). 288p. pap. 14.95 ***(978-1-61145-176-4(0)***, 611176, Arcade Publishing) Skyhorse Publishing Co., Inc.

Altschuld, James W. Needs Assessment Phase II Bk. 3: Collecting Data, 5 vols. 2009. (Illus.). 152p. (C). pap. 48.00 *(978-1-4129-7513-1(1)*, B75131P) SAGE Pubns., Inc.

Aluko, T. M. The Story of My Life. 2006. 372p. pap. *(978-978-129-464-8(7))* Heinemann Educational Bks. (Nigeria), Ltd. NGA. Dist: Michigan State Univ. Pr.

Alvarado, Beth. Anthropologies: A Family Memoir. 2011. (Sightline Bks.). (Illus.). 202p. pap. 19.95 *(978-1-60938-037-3(1))* Univ. of Iowa Pr.

Amado, Jorge. A Menino Grapiuna. (POR.). pap. 10.75 *(978-85-01-02053-6(2))* Distribuidora Record de Servicos de Imprensa SA BRA. Dist: Distribooks, Inc.

Amani, Alexander. A Nomad's Journey: Lessons learned from an eclectic Soul. 2010. 108p. (ENG.). 23.99 *(978-1-4490-8567-4(9))*; pap. 17.95 *(978-1-4490-8566-7(0))* AuthorHouse.

Ambrose, Tom. Heroes & Exiles Gay Icons Through the Ages. 2010. (ENG., Illus.). 224p. pap. 15.95 *(978-1-84773-468-6(5))* New Holland Pubs., Ltd. GBR. Dist: National Bk. Network.

Ambrosek, Renee. E. L. Konigsburg. 2009. (Library of Author Biographies Ser.). 112p. (gr. 5-8). 63.90 *(978-1-60853-532-3(0)*, Rosen Central) Rosen Publishing Group, Inc., The.

Amiel, Henri-Frederic. Amiel's Journal. 2008. 428p. 30.99 *(978-0-554-32095-3(9))*; 32.99 *(978-0-554-22792-4(4))* BiblioBazaar.

Amthor, Wiebke & Lühe, Irmela von der, eds. Auf der Suche nach einem Weg: Neuer Forschungen zu Leben und Werk Klaus Manns. 2008. (Berliner Beiträge zur Literatur- und Kulturgeschichte Ser.). (GER., Illus.). 200p. pap. 57.95 *(978-3-631-56758-6(8))* Lang, Peter GmbH, Europaischer Verlag der Wissenschaften DEU. Dist: Lang, Peter.

Andersen, Hans Christian. A Boy's Life. Little, Anastazia, tr. 2011. (Green Integer Ser.). (ENG.). 136p. pap. 12.95 *(978-1-933382-46-3(5))* Green Integer.

—The True Story of My Life. 2007. (ENG.). 192p. 26.95 *(978-1-4218-4173-1(3))*; per. 11.95 *(978-1-4218-4271-4(8))* 1st World Publishing, Inc. (1st World Library - Literary Society).

—The True Story of My Life. 2008. 184p. 25.99 *(978-0-554-22470-1(4))* 2008. 184p. 22.99 *(978-0-554-31773-1(7))* 2007. (ENG.). 162p. pap. 19.99 *(978-1-4264-2371-0(3))* 2007. (ENG.). 182p. pap. 21.99 *(978-1-4264-2419-9(1))* BiblioBazaar.

—The True Story of My Life - A Sketch. A Story Teller's Autobiography. 2008. 148p. pap. 9.99 *(978-1-60450-175-9(8))* Arc Manor.

Andersen, Hans Christian & Michael, Maurice. The Mermaid Man: The Autobiography of Hans Christian Andersen. 2011. 242p. 46.95 ***(978-1-258-01184-0(0))*** Literary Licensing, LLC.

Anderson, Chuck. Midlife Meditations. 2011. 138p. pap. 24.95 ***(978-1-4626-3041-7(3))*** PublishAmerica, Inc.

Anderson, Donald. Gathering Noise from My Life: A Camouflaged Memoir. 2012. pap. ***(978-1-60938-111-0(4))*** Univ. of Iowa Pr.

Anderson, Rasmus B. Life Story of Rasmus B. Anderson. 678p. reprint ed. lib. bdg. 128.00 *(978-0-7222-0361-3(6))* Library Reprints, Inc.

André, María Claudia, et al. Latin American Women Writers: An Encyclopedia. 2007. 560p. 235.00 *(978-0-415-97971-9(4))* Routledge.

Andreevski, Cane. Koneski: Kazuvanja Za Zivotot I Literaturata. 2008. (MAC.). 148p. *(978-9989-103-70-4(4))* Slovo.

Andres, Patricia Ann. Erzählen heißt, der Wahrheit verschworen Sein: Kommentierte Edition der deutsch- und englischsprachigen Fassung des bisher unveröffentlichten KZ-Berichts Die Zeit im Lager - Through Work to Freedom von Raoul Auernheimer. 2009. (Europäische Hochschulschriften. Reihe 1: Deutsche Sprache und Literatur Ser.). (GER.). 378p. pap. 81.95 *(978-3-631-58824-6(0))* Lang, Peter GmbH, Europaischer Verlag der Wissenschaften DEU. Dist: Lang, Peter.

Andrews, James T. Red Cosmos: K. E. Tsiolkovskii, Grandfather of Soviet Rocketry. 2009. (Centennial of Flight Ser.). (ENG.). 168p. 49.00 *(978-1-60344-117-9(4))* Texas A&M Univ. Pr.

Anesko, Michael. Monopolizing the Master: Henry James & the Politics of Modern Literary Scholarship. 2012. (ENG., Illus.). 272p. 35.00 ***(978-0-8047-6932-7(X))*** Stanford Univ. Pr.

Angela, Miss. My Life Experiences. 2007. pap. 8.00 *(978-0-8059-7436-2(9))* Dorrance Publishing Co., Inc.

Angell, Roger. Let Me Finish. 2007. (ENG.). 320p. pap. 15.00 *(978-0-15-603218-6(X)*, Mariner Bks.) Houghton Mifflin Harcourt Trade & Reference Pubs.

—Let Me Finish. l.t. ed. 2006. (Thorndike Biography Ser.). 411p. 29.95 *(978-0-7862-8870-0(1))* Thorndike Pr.

Angelou, Maya. Letter to My Daughter. (ENG.). 192p. 2009. pap. 15.00 *(978-0-8129-8003-5(4)*, Random Hse. Trade Paperbacks) 2008. 25.00 *(978-1-4000-6612-4(3)*, Random House) Random House Publishing Group.

Anna Mae Queen Holmes. Treasured Reflections of Time: Memoirs of Anna Mae Queen Holmes. 2009. 76p. pap. 27.49 *(978-1-4389-8481-0(2))* AuthorHouse.

Annan, Noel Gilroy & Stephen, Leslie. Leslie Stephen: His Thought & Character in Relation to His Time. 2011. 354p. 51.95 ***(978-1-258-09927-5(6))*** Literary Licensing, LLC.

Anonymous. The Life & Letters of Washington Irving. 2009. 240p. pap. *(978-1-151-11947-6(4))* Books LLC.

Anthony Hope. Father Stafford. l.t. ed. 2007. (ENG.). 166p. pap. 21.99 *(978-1-4264-8239-7(6))* BiblioBazaar.

Antrim, Donald. The Afterlife: A Memoir. 2007. (ENG.). 208p. pap. 13.00 *(978-0-312-42635-4(6))* Picador.

Aplin, John. The Inheritance of Genius: A Thackeray Family Biography, 1798-1875. 2010. 324p. pap. 53.00 *(978-0-7188-9224-1(0))* Lutherworth Pr., The GBR. Dist: Brown, David Bk. Co., The.

Appelfeld, Aharon. A Table for One: Under the Light of Jerusalem. 2007. 150p. per. 12.95 *(978-1-59264-197-0(0))* Toby Pr. LLC, The.

Arbuckle, Marsialle. I Have a Story to Tell. 2010. 248p. (ENG.). 24.99 *(978-1-4520-1271-1(7))*; pap. 14.49 *(978-1-4520-1270-4(9))* AuthorHouse.

Arenas, Reinaldo. Antes Que Anochezca. 2011. Tr. of Before Night Falls. (SPA., Illus.). 343p. pap. *(978-84-8383-571-5(1))* Tusquets Editores.

Argersinger, Jana L. & Person, Leland S., eds. Hawthorne & Melville: Writing a Relationship. 2008. (ENG., Illus.). 392p. pap. 26.95 *(978-0-8203-3096-5(5))*; lib. bdg. 69.95 *(978-0-8203-2751-8(4))* Univ. of Georgia Pr.

Arndt, Christiane. It Used to Be Such a Certain Thing, Just Being Myself. 2009. 94p. pap. *(978-3-639-18214-9(6))* VDM Verlag Dr. Mueller e.K.

Arnim, Elizabeth Von. Christine. 2007. 92p. per. *(978-1-4068-4559-4(0))* Echo Library.

Arslan, Antonia. Ishtar 2: Cronache Del Mio Risveglio. 2010. (ITA.). 111p. *(978-88-17-04369-4(9))* Rizzoli International Pubns., Inc.

Athas, Daphne. Chapel Hill in Plain Sight: Notes from the Other Side of the Tracks. 2010. (Illus.). 256p. pap. 16.95 *(978-0-9820771-3-9(0))* Eno Pubs.

Athill, Diana. Instead of a Letter: A Memoir. 2010. (ENG.). 237p. pap. 14.95 *(978-0-393-33857-7(6)*, 33857) Norton, W. W. & Co., Inc.

—Letters to a Friend. 2012. (ENG.). 352p. 24.95 (978-0-393-06295-3(3), 6295) Norton, W. W. & Co., Inc.

—Somewhere Towards the End. l.t. ed. 2009. 232p. 31.50 (978-1-4104-1911-8(9)) Thorndike Pr.

—Somewhere Towards the End: A Memoir. 2009. (ENG.). 208p. pap. 13.95 (978-0-393-33800-3(2), 33800); 192p. 24.95 (978-0-393-06770-5(X), 6770) Norton, W. W. & Co., Inc.

Athill, Diana. Yesterday Morning. 2012. (ENG., Illus.). 176p. pap. 13.95 (978-1-84708-426-2(5)) Granta Bks. GBR. Dist: Ingram Pub. Services.

Atiyaman, Pala. Cennaikku Vanten. 2008. (TAM.). 136p. (978-81-89945-47-3(5)) Kalachchuvadu Pathippagam.

Atkins, G. Douglas. E. B. White: The Essayist as First-Class Writer. 2012. (ENG., Illus.). 192p. 80.00 (978-0-230-34066-4(0)) Palgrave Macmillan.

Attwood, Martin. Hidden Debts: A memoir of Italy. 2009. 296p. pap. 21.95 (978-1-4401-3833-1(8)) iUniverse, Inc.

Auchincloss, Louis. Edith Warton: University of Minnesota Pamphlets on American Writers. 2009. (ENG.). 48p. pap. 25.00 (978-0-8166-0250-6(6)) Univ. of Minnesota Pr.

—A Voice from Old New York: A Memoir of My Youth. 2010. (ENG.). 224p. 25.00 (978-0-547-34153-8(9)) Houghton Mifflin Harcourt Trade & Reference Pubs.

Augustyn, Adam, ed. American Literature from 1600 Through the 1850s. 2010. (Britannica Guide to World Literature Ser.). (ENG.). 240p. (YA). lib. bdg. 45.00 (978-1-61530-124-9(0)) Rosen Publishing Group, Inc., The.

—American Literature from 1600 Through The 1850S. 2010. (Britannica Guide to World Literature Ser.). (Illus.). 240p. (YA). 90.00 (978-1-61530-236-9(0)) Rosen Publishing Group, Inc., The.

—American Literature from 1945 Through Today. 2010. (Britannica Guide to World Literature Ser.). 240p. (YA). (ENG.). lib. bdg. 45.00 (978-1-61530-133-1(X)); (Illus.). 90.00 (978-1-61530-237-6(9)) Rosen Publishing Group, Inc., The.

Auslander, Shalom. Foreskin's Lament: A Memoir. 2008. (ENG.). 320p. (gr. 12-18). 15.00 (978-1-59448-333-2(7), Riverhead Trade (Paperbacks)) Penguin Group (USA) Inc.

Austen-Leigh, James E. A Memoir of Jane Austen: And Other Family Recollections. Sutherland, Kathryn, ed. 2008. (Oxford World's Classics Ser.). (ENG., Illus.). 352p. (Orig.). pap. 12.95 (978-0-19-954077-8(2)) Oxford Univ. Pr., Inc.

Austen-Leigh, James Edward. A Memoir of Jane Austen. 2008. 172p. 22.99 (978-0-554-36587-9(1)) 2008. 172p. 25.99 (978-0-554-27284-9(9)) 2007. (ENG.). 154p. per. 19.99 (978-1-4346-2872-5(8)) 2007. (ENG.). 170p. per. 21.99 (978-1-4346-2907-4(4)) BiblioBazaar.

—A Memoir of Jane Austen. 2009. 186p. pap. (978-0-217-66579-7(9)) Books LLC.

—A Memoir of Jane Austen. 2009. (Cambridge Library Collection - Literary Studies). (ENG.). 260p. pap. 17.99 (978-1-108-00356-8(7)) Cambridge Univ. Pr.

Austen Leigh, James Edward. A Memoir of Jane Austen: Together with 'Lady Susan': a Novel. 2009. (Cambridge Library Collection - Literary Studies). 384p. pap. 23.99 (978-1-108-00357-5(5)) Cambridge Univ. Pr.

Austen-Leigh, James Edward & Austen, Jane. A Memoir of Jane Austen. 2008. 384p. 48.95 (978-1-4369-8784-4(9)); pap. 33.95 (978-1-4367-3981-8(0)) Kessinger Publishing, LLC.

Auster, Paul. Collected Prose: Autobiographical Writings, True Stories, Critical Essays, Prefaces, & Collaborations with Artists, & Interviews. 2010. (ENG., Illus.). 608p. pap. 22.00 (978-0-312-42992-8(4)) Picador.

Auster, Paul. Winter Journal. 2012. (ENG.). 240p. 26.00 (978-0-8050-9553-1(5)) Holt, Henry & Co.

Austin, B. K. The Tin Shack. 2011. 48p. pap. 9.95 (978-1-4620-4311-8(9)) iUniverse, Inc.

Austin, Mary S. Philip Freneau the Poet of the Revolutio. 2006. pap. 28.95 (978-1-4286-4320-8(6)) Kessinger Publishing, LLC.

Authors & Artists for Young Adults, Vol. 82. 2010. (Authors & Artists for Young Adults Ser.). (ENG.). 168.00 (978-0-7876-7801-2(5)) Cengage Gale.

Authors & Artists for Young Adults: A Biographical Guide to Novelists, Poets, Playwrights Screenwriters, Lyricists, Illustrators, Cartoonists, Animators, & Other Creative Artists. 2011. 168.00 (978-0-7876-9478-4(9)) Cengage Gale.

Avison, Margaret. I Am Here & Not Not-There. 2009. (ENG., Illus.). 352p. pap. 27.95 (978-0-88984-315-8(5)) Porcupine's Quill, Inc. CAN. Dist: Univ. of Toronto Pr.

Ayres, Brenda. The Life & Works of Augusta Jane Evans Wilson, 1835-1909. 2012. (Illus.). 250p. 104.95 (978-1-4094-4073-4(7)) Ashgate Publishing Co.

Azuela, Arturo. Prisma de Mariano Azuela. 2009. (SPA., Illus.). 346p. 27.00 (978-970-722-013-3(9)) Plaza y Valdes, S.A. de C.V. MEX. Dist: Sony Electronics.

Babii, Valentyna. "Z Bratamy Shche Ia Slovom Podilliusia" Biobibliohrafichnyi Pokazhchyk. 2009. (UKR., Illus.). 111p. (978-611-517-015-9(X)) Tverdynja.

Badt-Strauss, Bertha. White Fire: The Life & Works of Jessie Sampter. 2011. 218p. 44.95 (978-1-258-06256-9(9)) Literary Licensing, LLC.

Bailey, Alice Sparks. Tile Patchwork: A Quilt in Story Form. (Illus.). 256p. (Orig.). pap. (978-0-9638163-8-2(1)) Hisel Bk. Ends Co.

Bailey, Blake. Cheever: A Life. 2010. (Vintage Ser.). (ENG.). 816p. pap. 16.95 (978-1-4000-7968-1(3), Vintage) Knopf Doubleday Publishing Group.

Bain, Donald & Bain, Donald. Murder, He Wrote: A Successful Writer's Life. 2006. (ENG.). 256p. per. 19.95 (978-1-55753-421-7(7)) Purdue Univ. Pr.

Baines, Paul, ed. The Wiley-Blackwell Encyclopedia of Eighteenth-Century Writers & Writing, 1660-1789. 2011. (ENG.). 432p. 199.95 (978-1-4051-5669-1(4), Wiley-Blackwell) Wiley, John & Sons, Inc.

Baker, Barbara, ed. The Way We Write: Interviews with Award-Winning Writers. 2006. (ENG.). 256p. 80.00 (978-0-8264-9122-0(7)) Continuum International Publishing Group, Ltd. GBR. Dist: National Bk. Network.

Baker, Bill. Michael Avon Oeming on His Work & Career. 2007. (Talking with Graphic Novelists Ser.). 164p. (YA). (gr. 7-12). lib. bdg. 30.50 (978-1-4042-1075-2(X)) Rosen Publishing Group, Inc., The.

Baker, Phil. The Devil Is a Gentleman: The Life & Times of Dennis Wheatley. 2010. (Dark Masters Ser.). (ENG., Illus.). 699p. 40.00 (978-1-903517-75-8(3)) Dedalus, Ltd.

—William S. Burroughs. 2010. (Reaktion Books - Critical Lives Ser.). (ENG., Illus.). 192p. pap. 16.95 (978-1-86189-663-6(8)) Reaktion Bks., Ltd. GBR. Dist: Chicago Distribution Ctr.

Baker, William. Harold Pinter. 2008. (Writers Lives Ser.). (ENG.). 176p. 24.95 (978-0-8264-9971-4(6)) Continuum International Publishing Group, Ltd. GBR. Dist: National Bk. Network.

Bakewell, Sarah. How to Live: Or a Life of Montaigne in One Question & Twenty Attempts at an Answer. (ENG.). 2011. 416p. pap. 16.95 (978-1-59051-483-2(1)) 2010. (Illus.). 400p. 25.00 (978-1-59051-425-2(4)) Other Pr., LLC.

Baksi, Kurdo. Stieg Larsson: Our Days in Stockholm. Thompson, Laurie, tr. from SWE. 2010. (ENG.). 144p. 22.00 (978-1-60598-174-1(5), 605174) Pegasus Bks.

—Stieg Larsson: The Man Behind the Girl with the Dragon Tattoo. 2011. (ENG.). 192p. pap. 12.99 (978-1-4516-4709-9(3)) Gallery Pr., The IRL. Dist: Simon & Schuster, Inc.

—Stieg Larsson, My Friend. Thompson, Laurie, tr. from SWE. 2010. (SWE & ENG.). 224p. (978-0-85705-021-2(4)) Quercus.

Bald, Margaret. From the Sahara to Samarkand: The Remarkabke Journeys of Rosita Forbes. 2010. (ENG.). 369p. pap. 15.00 (978-1-60419-030-4(2)) Axios Pr.

Balderstone, Gregory. Where Words Are Unspoken: The Autobiography of Gregory Balderstone (Goyo B.) 2011. 96p. pap. 19.95 (978-1-4512-8267-2(2)) PublishAmerica, Inc.

Bales, Jack. Willie Morris: An Exhaustive Annotated Bibliography & a Biography. alt. ed. 2010. (ENG., Illus.). 403p. pap. 49.95 (978-0-7864-4574-5(2)) McFarland & Co., Inc. Pubs.

Bambara, Toni Cade. Conversations with Toni Cade Bambara. Lewis, Thabiti, ed. 2012. (Literary Conversations Ser.). (ENG.). 176p. 40.00 (978-1-60473-432-4(9)) Univ. Pr. of Mississippi.

Banks, Brian R. Muse & Messiah: The Life, Imagination & Legacy of Bruno Schulz (1892-1942) 2nd ed. 2009. (Illus.). pap. (978-0-9556259-7-8(1)) Inkermen Pr.

Banks, Russell & Roche, David. Conversations with Russell Banks. 2010. xv, 193p. pap. (978-1-60473-746-2(8)) Univ. Pr. of Mississippi.

Bann, Stephen. Paul Delaroche: History Painted. 2008. (ENG., Illus.). 304p. 95.00 (978-1-86189-007-8(9)) Reaktion Bks., Ltd. GBR. Dist: Chicago Distribution Ctr.

Banta, Grace. Graciela, No One's Child. 2010. 240p. pap. 28.95 (978-1-4502-2522-9(5)) iUniverse, Inc.

Bänziger, Hans. Frisch und Dürrenmatt: Materialien und Kommentare. (Untersuchungen zur deutschen Literaturgeschichte Ser.). (GER., Illus.). VIII, 184p. 210.00 (978-3-11-184957-7(0)) De Gruyter, Walter Inc.

Barker, Christopher. The Arms of the Infinite: Elizabeth Smart & George Barker. 2010. (Illus.). 258p. (C). pap. 29.95 (978-1-55458-270-9(9)) Wilfrid Laurier Univ. Pr. CAN. Dist: Univ. of Toronto Pr.

Barnard, Louise & Barnard, Robert. A Bronte Encyclopedia. 2007. (ENG., Illus.). 416p. 128.95 (978-1-4051-5119-1(6), Wiley-Blackwell) Wiley, John & Sons, Inc.

Barnard, Teresa. Anna Seward: A Constructed Life - A Critical Biography. 2009. (Illus.). 208p. 99.95 (978-0-7546-6616-5(6)) Ashgate Publishing Co.

Barnes, Julian. Nothing to Be Frightened Of. 2011. 19.95 (978-1-60998-242-3(8)) AudioGO.

—Nothing to Be Frightened Of. 2009. (Vintage Ser.). (ENG.). 256p. pap. 15.00 (978-0-307-38998-5(7), Vintage) Knopf Doubleday Publishing Group.

Barnes, Nigel. A Dream Within a Dream: The Life of Edgar Allan Poe. 2009. (ENG.). 360p. pap. 23.95 (978-0-7206-1322-3(1)) Owen, Peter Ltd. GBR. Dist: Independent Pubs. Group.

Barnum, Jill, et al. Whole Oceans Away: Melville & the Pacific. 2008. (Illus.). 350p. (978-0-87338-893-1(3)) Kent State Univ. Pr.

Baron, Carl, ed. A Memoir of D. H. Lawrence: 'the Betrayal' G. H. Neville. 2010. (ENG.). 224p. pap. 27.99 (978-0-521-13543-6(5)) Cambridge Univ. Pr.

Barral, Carlos. Cuando las Horas Veloces. (SPA.). 294p. (978-84-7223-280-8(8), 6020) Tusquets Editores.

Barré, Jean-Luc. François Mauriac: Biographie Intime. 2009. (FRE., Illus.). (978-2-213-62636-9(7)); (978-2-213-65577-2(4)) Fayard, Artheme, Librairie.

Barrett, Charlotte. Diary & Letters of Madame Darblay Vol. 2006. (ENG.). 608p. per. (978-1-4067-3520-8(5), Hesperides Pr.) Read Bks.

Barris, Chuck. Della: A Memoir of My Daughter. 2010. (ENG., Illus.). 224p. 25.00 (978-1-4391-6799-1(0)) Simon & Schuster.

Barrowcliffe, Mark. The Elfish Gene: Dungeons, Dragons & Growing up Strange. 2009. (ENG.). 288p. pap. 14.00 (978-1-56947-601-7(2)) Soho Pr., Inc.

Barrows, W. (William). The General; or, Twelve Nights in the Hunters' Camp: A Narrative of Real Life / [William] Barrows; Illustrated by G. G. White. 2006. 284p. per. 23.99 (978-1-4255-2538-5(5)) MPublishing.

Barstow, Phyllida. My Animals (And Other Family) 2009. (ENG., Illus.). 224p. 24.95 (978-1-906122-13-3(X)) Unwin, Merlin Bks. GBR. Dist: SCB Distributors.

Bartlett, Rosamund. Tolstoy: A Russian Life. 2011. (ENG., Illus.). 560p. 35.00 (978-0-15-101438-5(8)) Houghton Mifflin Harcourt Trade & Reference Pubs.

Basbanes, Nicholas A. About the Author: Inside the Creative Process. 2010. 27.95 (978-0-9799491-3-5(0)) Fine Books Press.

Baskervill, William Malone. Southern Writers: Biographical & Critical Studies. 2009. (ENG.). 415p. 41.99 (978-1-117-13656-1(6)) 2009. (ENG.). 415p. pap. 33.75 (978-1-117-13657-8(4)) 2008. 416p. 30.99 (978-0-559-32703-2(X)) 2008. 416p. pap. 33.75 (978-0-559-32702-5(1)) BiblioBazaar.

—Southern Writers: Biographical & Critical Studies. 2009. 98p. pap. (978-0-217-55675-0(2)) Books LLC.

Bass, Rick. Why I Came West: A Memoir. (ENG.). 256p. 2009. pap. 14.95 (978-0-547-23771-8(5), Mariner Bks.) 2008. 24.00 (978-0-618-59675-1(5)) Houghton Mifflin Harcourt Trade & Reference Pubs.

Bataille, Georges. Guilty. 2011. (SUNY series in Contemporary French Thought Ser.). 256p. 85.00 (978-1-4384-3461-2(8)); pap. 29.95 (978-1-4384-3462-9(6)) State Univ. of New York Pr.

Bate, W. Jackson. Samuel Johnson: A Biography. 2009. (ENG.). 668p. pap. 24.95 (978-1-58243-524-4(3), Counterpoint Pr.) Basic Bks. GBR. Dist: Perseus-PGW.

Batt, Matthew. Sugarhouse: Turning the Neighborhood Crack House into Our Home Sweet Home. 2012. (ENG.). 272p. pap. 14.95 (978-0-547-63453-1(6), Mariner Bks.) Houghton Mifflin Harcourt Trade & Reference Pubs.

Batten, Robert J. The G Street Chronicles: Our Amazing Journey. 2011. pap. 20.99 (978-1-61739-153-8(0)) Tate Publishing & Enterprises, LLC.

Battersby, Eileen. Second Readings: From Beckett to Black Beauty. 2010. (ENG.). 301p. pap. 27.95 (978-1-905483-81-5(3)) Liberties Pr. IRL. Dist: Dufour Editions, Inc.

Batty, Nancy Ellen. The Ring of Recollection: Transgenerational Haunting in the Novels of Shashi Deshpande. 2010. (Illus.). 347p. 91.00 (978-90-420-3100-5(X)) Rodopi.

Bauer, Paul J. & Dawidziak, Mark. Jim Tully: American Writer, Irish Rover, Hollywood Brawler. 2011. (Illus.). 384p. 55.00 (978-1-60635-076-8(5)) Kent State Univ. Pr.

Baumlin, James S. & Knickerbocker, Eric, eds. Jim W. Corder on Living & Dying in West Texas: A Postmodern Scrapbook. 2007. 15.00 (978-0-913785-06-5(7), Moon City Pr.) Department of English.

Baumlin, James S. & Miller, Keith D., eds. The Heroes Have Gone: Personal Essays on the American West, Sport, & Popular Culture by Jim W. Corder. 2008. pap. (978-0-913785-11-9(3), Moon City Pr.) Department of English.

Baxter III, E. R. Niagara Digressions. 2012. (ENG., Illus.). 250p. pap. 20.00 (978-0-9837405-2-0(6)) Starcherone Bks.

Beahm, George. Bedazzled: A Book about Stephenie Meyer & the Twilight Phenomenon. 2009. (ENG., Illus.). 256p. pap. 11.95 (978-1-59929-041-6(3)) Underwood Books.

—Discovering the Golden Compass: A Guide to Philip Pullman's Dark Materials. 2007. (ENG., Illus.). 248p. (YA). (gr. 7-12). per. 16.95 (978-1-57174-506-4(8)) Hampton Roads Publishing Co., Inc.

Beauman, Nicola. The Other Elizabeth Taylor. 2009. (ENG., Illus.). 464p. pap. 25.00 (978-1-906462-10-9(0)) Persephone Bks. Ltd. GBR. Dist: Consortium Bk. Sales & Distribution.

Beauvoir, Simone de. Memoires D'une Jeune Fille Rangee. 2008. (Collection Folio Ser.). (FRE.). 472p. per. (978-2-07-035552-5(7)) Gallimard, Editions.

Bechard, Deni Y. Cures for Hunger. 2012. (ENG.). 320p. 24.00 (978-1-57131-331-7(1)) Milkweed Editions.

Béchard, Deni Y. Cures for Hunger. 2012. (ENG.). 366p. 29.95 (978-0-86492-671-5(5)) Goose Lane Editions CAN. Dist: Univ. of Toronto Pr.

Bechdel, Alison. Are You My Mother? 2012. (ENG., Illus.). 304p. 22.00 (978-0-618-98250-9(7)) Houghton Mifflin Harcourt Trade & Reference Pubs.

Becker, Jillian. Giving Up: The Last Days of Sylvia Plath. mass mkt. (978-0-312-99041-1(3), St. Martin's Paperbacks) St. Martin's Pr.

Becker, Lucille Frackman. George Simenon: Maigret & the 'Romans Durs' 2006. (Illus.). 224p. 24.95 (978-1-904950-86-8(8)) Haus Publishing GBR. Dist: Consortium Bk. Sales & Distribution.

Beckford, William. Recollections of an Excursion to the Monasteries of Alcobaça & Batalha. 2009. 86p. pap. 14.14 (978-0-217-74830-8(9)) General Bks. LLC.

Beckmon, Jon. Codename: Lehi. 2011. 360p. 29.99 (978-1-4535-2373-5(1)); pap. 19.99 (978-1-4535-2372-8(3)) Xlibris Corp.

Beer, Janet, ed. The Cambridge Companion to Kate Chopin. 2008. (Cambridge Companions to Literature Ser.). (ENG.). 208p. (C). 81.00 (978-0-521-88344-3(X)); pap. 29.99 (978-0-521-70982-8(2)) Cambridge Univ. Pr.

Begley, Louis, ed. Franz Kafka: The Tremendous World Inside My Head. 2009. (ENG.). 208p. pap. 14.00 (978-1-934633-23-6(2), 934623) Atlas & Co.

Beier, Ulli & Omodele, Remi. Weighing the Cost of Pin-Making: Ulli Beier in Conversations. 2011. (978-1-59221-859-2(8)); 276p. pap. (978-1-59221-860-8(1)) Africa World Pr.

Bell-Villada, Gene H. Garcia Marquez: The Man & His Work, Second Edition. 2nd ed. 2010. (ENG., Illus.). 360p. 65.00 (978-0-8078-3351-3(7)); pap. 22.95 (978-0-8078-6525-5(7)) Univ. of North Carolina Pr.

Bellanca, Mary Ellen. Daybooks of Discovery: Nature Diaries in Britain, 1770-1870. 2007. (Under the Sign of Nature Ser.). (ENG.). 248p. (gr. 17). 59.50 (978-0-8139-2612-4(2)); (C). (gr. 13-17). per. 22.50 (978-0-8139-2613-1(0)) Univ. Pr. of Virginia.

Bellow, Saul. To Jerusalem & Back. 2010. (ENG.). 234p. pap. 19.95 (978-1-4128-1184-2(8)) Transaction Pubs.

Belmonte, Kevin & Stokes, Mitch. John Bunyan, 0 vols. 2010. (Christian Encounters Ser.). 192p. pap. 12.00 (978-1-59555-304-1(5)) Nelson, Thomas Inc.

Below, Ida Comstock. Eugene Field in His Home. 2009. 166p. 26.99 (978-1-110-44992-7(5)); 164p. 26.99 (978-1-110-44994-1(1)); 166p. pap. 20.75 (978-1-110-44989-7(5)); 164p. pap. 20.75 (978-1-110-44990-3(9)); 168p. 22.99 (978-0-559-93807-8(1)); 168p. pap. 16.99 (978-0-559-93804-7(7)) BiblioBazaar.

—Eugene Field in His Home. 2009. 48p. pap. (978-0-217-47429-0(2)) Books LLC.

—Eugene Field in His Home. 2007. 164p. 36.95 (978-0-548-41665-5(6)); (ENG.). per. 21.95 (978-0-548-39328-4(1)) Kessinger Publishing, LLC.

—Eugene Field in His Home. 2009. 124p. pap. 26.45 (978-1-4446-4031-1(3)) Research Pr.

Benedict, Elizabeth. Mentors Muses & Monsters. 2012. pap. (978-1-4384-4350-8(1)) State Univ. of New York Pr.

Benedict, Elizabeth. Mentors, Muses & Monsters: 30 Writers on the People Who Changed Their Lives. 2009. (ENG., Illus.). 288p. pap. 24.99 (978-1-4391-0861-1(7), Free Pr.) Free Pr.

Benford, M. Sue. Strong Woman, Unshrouding the Secrets of the Soul. 2011. 268p. pap. 17.95 (978-0-9789499-5-2(1)) Cradle Pr.

Bennett, Joan. Sir Thomas Browne: 'A Man of Achievement in Literature' 2010. (ENG.). 264p. pap. 23.99 (978-0-521-14823-8(5)) Cambridge Univ. Pr.

Benson, Arthur Christopher. The Altar Fire. 2009. 412p. 34.99 (978-1-115-21730-9(5)); 336p. 36.99 (978-1-115-21721-7(6)); 336p. 32.99 (978-1-115-21720-0(8)); 412p. 41.99 (978-1-115-21732-3(1)); 336p. pap. 31.75 (978-1-115-21718-7(6)) BiblioBazaar.

—The Altar Fire. 2009. 288p. pap. (978-0-217-37749-2(1)) Books LLC.

—The Altar Fire. 2007. 232p. per. (978-1-4065-4813-6(8)) Dodo Pr.

—The Altar Fire. 2008. 408p. pap. (978-1-4097-7754-0(5)) Read Bks.

—Edward Fitzgerald. 2009. 122p. pap. (978-1-150-43876-9(2)) Books LLC.

Benson, Jackson J. The Ox-Bow Man: A Biography of Walter Van Tilburg Clark. 2006. (Western Literature Ser.). (ENG., Illus.). 448p. per. 21.95 (978-0-87417-691-9(3)) Univ. of Nevada Pr.

Benton, Michael J. Literary Biography: An Introduction. 2009. (ENG., Illus.). 280p. 110.95 (978-1-4051-9446-4(4), Wiley-Blackwell) Wiley, John & Sons, Inc.

Berg, Elizabeth. Escaping into the Open: The Art of Writing True. 2012. (P. S. Ser.). (ENG.). 272p. pap. 14.99 (978-0-06-220044-0(5), HarperPerennial) HarperCollins Pubs.

Bergé, Carol, intro. Light Years: An Anthology on Sociocultural Happenings (Multimedia in the East Village, 1960-1966) 2010. (ENG., Illus.). 632p. pap. 40.00 (978-1-933132-46-4(9)) Spuyten Duyvil.

Bergman, David. Gay American Autobiography: Writings from Whitman to Sedaris. Bergman, David, ed. 2009. (Living Out: Gay & Lesbian Autobiog Ser.). (ENG.). 426p. pap. 29.95 (978-0-299-23044-9(9)) Univ. of Wisconsin Pr.

Bergmann, Ulrike. Die Mesalliance: Georg Forster: Weltumsegler - Therese Forster: Schriftstellerin. 2008. (GER.). 300p. (978-3-940111-54-8(6)) Buchergilde, Edition, GmbH.

Berkow, Ira. Full Swing: Hits, Runs & Errors in a Writer's Life. 2007. (ENG., Illus.). 304p. per. 16.95 (978-1-56663-755-8(4)) Dee, Ivan R. Pub.

Bernhard, John. America's Call: The rocky road of the American Dream... a travelogue of one man's Discovery. 2011. 272p. 29.95 (978-1-4575-0001-5(9)) Dog Ear Publishing, LLC.

Bernhard, Thomas. Gathering Evidence & My Prizes: A Memoir. 2011. (Vintage International Ser.). (ENG.). 416p. pap. 16.95 (978-1-4000-7762-5(1), Vintage) Knopf Doubleday Publishing Group.

—My Prizes: An Accounting. Janeway, Carol, tr. from GER. 2010. (ENG.). 144p. 22.00 (978-0-307-27287-4(7), Knopf) Knopf Doubleday Publishing Group.

Bernier, Rosamond. Some of My Lives: A Scrapbook Memoir, 1 vol. 2011. (ENG., Illus.). 304p. 30.00 (978-0-374-26661-5(1)) Farrar, Straus & Giroux.

Bernstein, Harry. The Dream: A Memoir. 2009. (ENG.). 288p. pap. 16.00 (978-0-345-50389-3(9), Ballantine Bks.) Random House Publishing Group.

Berry, Chris J. Sixty Psychic Years: Autobiography. 2010. 248p. 24.99 (978-1-4520-1039-7(0)); pap. 14.49 (978-1-4520-1038-0(2)) AuthorHouse.

Berry, Wendell. Conversations with Wendell Berry. Grubbs, Morris Allen, ed. 2007. (ENG., Illus.). 218p. 50.00 (978-1-57806-991-0(2)); per. 22.00 (978-1-57806-992-7(0)) Univ. Pr. of Mississippi.

Bg, Gabrielle. Many Voices. 2011. 186p. pap. 11.00 (978-1-257-88086-7(1)) Lulu Enterprises Inc.

Bickley, R. Bruce, Jr. Joel Chandler Harris: A Biography & Critical Study. 2008. (ENG.). 184p. per. 22.95 (978-0-8203-3185-0(6)) Univ. of Georgia Pr.

Bidinger, Elizabeth. The Ethics of Working Class Autobiography: Representation of Family by Four American Authors. 2006. (ENG.). 212p. per. 45.00 (978-0-7864-2576-1(8)) McFarland & Co., Inc. Pubs.

Bild Buch Staff. Mein Leben mit Ruby: Von Herrchen. (GER.). 128p. pap. (978-3-548-42001-1(X)) Ullstein-Taschenbuch-Verlag DEU. Dist: International Bk. Import Service, Inc.

Bill. I'D Rather Kiss Your Ass! 2011. 350p. pap. 29.95 (978-1-4626-4051-5(6)) PublishAmerica, Inc.

A Biographical Guide to Novelists, Poets, Playwrights Screenwriters, Lyricists, Illustrators, Cartoonists, Animators, & Other Creative Artists, 79. 2009. (Authors & Artists for Young Adults Ser.). (ENG.). 224p. 168.00 (978-0-7876-7798-5(1)) Cengage Gale.

Biographiq. D H Lawrence - Prolific English Writer. 2008. 68p. pap. 9.99 (978-1-59986-364-1(2), Biographiq) Filiquarian Publishing, LLC.

—Gertrude Stein - a Catalyst of Modern Art. 2008. 68p. pap. 9.99 *(978-1-59986-042-8(2),* Biographiq) Filiquarian Publishing, LLC.

—Leonard Cohen - Artist of Influence (Biography) 2008. 64p. pap. 9.99 *(978-1-59986-079-4(1),* Biographiq) Filiquarian Publishing, LLC.

—Mary Wollstonecraft Shelley - Gothic Novelist (Biography) 2008. 100p. pap. 9.99 *(978-1-59986-379-5(0),* Biographiq) Filiquarian Publishing, LLC.

—Rabindranath Tagore - Life & Times of a Bengali Poet (Biography) 2008. 60p. pap. 9.99 *(978-1-59986-386-3(3),* Biographiq) Filiquarian Publishing, LLC.

—Rachel Carson - Environmental Pioneer (Biography) 2008. 68p. pap. 9.99 *(978-1-59986-384-9(7),* Biographiq) Filiquarian Publishing, LLC.

—William F Buckley, Jr - an American Conservative. 2008. 52p. pap. 9.99 *(978-1-59986-067-1(8),* Biographiq) Filiquarian Publishing, LLC.

Bioy Casares, Adolfo. Memorias: Infancia, Adolescencia y Cómo Se Hace un Escritor. 3rd ed. (SPA., Illus.). 216p. *(978-84-7223-420-8(7),* 6020) Tusquets Editores.

Bird, Robert. Fyodor Dostoevsky. 2012. (Reaktion Books - Critical Lives Ser.). (Illus.). 224p. pap. 16.95 ***(978-1-86189-900-2(9))*** Reaktion Bks., Ltd. GBR. Dist: Chicago Distribution Ctr.

Birge, June Rossbach Bingham. Braided Lives: A 20th Century Pursuit of Happiness. 2008. 480p. pap. 24.95 *(978-0-9801250-2-3(2))* Straus Historical Society, Inc.

Birkerts, Sven. The Other Walk: Essays, 1 vol. 2011. (ENG.). 192p. pap. 15.00 *(978-1-55597-593-7(3))* Graywolf Pr.

Birkett, Jennifer. Margaret Storm Jameson: A Life. 2009. (ENG., Illus.). 400p. 55.00 *(978-0-19-955820-9(5))* Oxford Univ. Pr., Inc.

Birns, Nicholas. Willa Cather. 2011. ***(978-1-58765-826-6(7))*** Salem Pr., Inc.

Biro, Adam. One Must Also Be Hungarian. Tihanyi, Catherine, tr. from ENG. 2007. (Illus.). 168p. 20.00 *(978-0-226-05212-0(5))* Univ. of Chicago Pr.

Bishop-Malamou, Deborah. Been There, Done That. 2011. 200p. 29.99 ***(978-1-4568-7910-5(3))***; pap. 19.99 ***(978-1-4568-7909-9(X))*** Xlibris Corp.

Bishop, Rosemarie E. A Brother's Love. 2008. 328p. pap. 19.99 *(978-1-4363-9134-4(2))* Xlibris Corp.

Bita, Lili & Zaller, Robert. The Storm Rider: A Memoir. 2012. ***(978-1-935244-10-3(8))*** Somerset Hall Pr.

Black, Baxter. Lessons from a Desperado Poet: How to Find Your Way When You Don't Have a Map, How to Win the Game When You Don't Know the Rules, & When Someone Says It Can't Be Done, What They Mean Is They Can't Do It. 2011. (ENG., Illus.). 232p. 22.95 *(978-0-7627-6997-1(1),* TwoDot) Globe Pequot Pr., The.

Black, Margaret Moyes. Robert Louis Stevenson. 2008. 136p. 24.99 *(978-0-554-30017-7(6))*; 21.99 *(978-0-554-39320-9(4))* BiblioBazaar.

Black, William. Goldsmith. 2011. (Cambridge Library Collection - English Men of Letters Ser.). (ENG.). 174p. pap. 19.99 ***(978-1-108-03470-8(5))*** Cambridge Univ. Pr.

Blackwell, T. An Enquiry into the Life & Writings of Homer. 2007. (ENG.). 424p. 51.95 *(978-0-548-00733-4(0))* Kessinger Publishing, LLC.

Blakemore, Erin. The Heroine's Bookshelf: Life Lessons, from Jane Austen to Laura Ingalls Wilder. 2010. (ENG.). 224p. 19.99 *(978-0-06-195876-2(X))* HarperCollins Pubs.

Bleecker, Ronald & Kaylor, Deb. Faith & Fortitude: My WWII Memoirs. 2011. 164p. pap. 14.95 ***(978-1-936780-49-5(6))*** Mill City Pr., Inc.

Blew, Mary Clearman. This Is Not the Ivy League: A Memoir. 2011. (American Lives Ser.). (ENG.). 224p. 24.95 *(978-0-8032-3011-8(7))* Univ. of Nebraska Pr.

Blind, Mathilde. George Eliot. 2010. (Cambridge Library Collection - Literary Studies). 232p. pap. 22.99 *(978-1-108-01960-6(9))* Cambridge Univ. Pr.

Bloch-Dano, Evelyne. Le Dernier Amour de George Sand. 2010. 314p. pap. *(978-2-246-73201-3(8))* Grasset et Fasquelle.

—Madame Proust: A Biography. Kaplan, Alice, tr. from FRE. 2007. (ENG., Illus.). 272p. 27.50 *(978-0-226-05642-5(2))* Univ. of Chicago Pr.

Bloch, Michael. James Lees-Milne: The Life. 2009. (ENG., Illus.). 416p. 39.95 *(978-0-7195-6034-7(9))* Murray, John GBR. Dist: Independent Pubs. Group.

Block, Matthew, ed. The Sherman Diaries: Volume Five: Moving On. 2008. 466p. pap. 19.95 *(978-0-9768896-1-8(7))* Square Circles Publishing.

Blockside, Martin. 'A Life Lived Quickly' Tennyson's Friend Arthur Hallam & His Legend. 2011. (Illus.). 323p. 79.95 *(978-1-84519-418-5(7))* Sussex Academic Pr. GBR. Dist: International Specialized Bk. Services.

Bloom, Harold. Night - Elie Wiesel. 2nd rev. ed. 2010. (Bloom's Modern Critical Interpretations Ser.). 206p. (C). (gr. 9). 45.00 *(978-1-60413-867-2(X),* Chelsea Hse.) Facts On File, Inc.

Bloom, Harold, ed. Khaled Hosseini's the Kite Runner. 2009. (Bloom's Guides). 96p. (C). (gr. 9-18). 30.00 *(978-1-60413-199-4(3),* Chelsea Hse.) Facts On File, Inc.

Bloom, Susan P. & Mercier, Cathryn M. Russell Freedman. 2009. (Scarecrow Studies in Young Adult Literature Ser.). (ENG., Illus.). 182p. 45.00 *(978-0-8108-5772-8(3))* Scarecrow Pr., Inc.

Bloomfield, Lori Ann. The Last River Child. 2009. 280p. pap. 17.95 ***(978-1-897187-66-1(1))*** Second Story Pr. CAN. Dist: Univ. of Toronto Pr.

Blowers, Tonya & Bazin, Claire. Janet Frame. 2011. (Writers & Their Work Ser.). (ENG.). 140p. (C). 80.00 *(978-0-7463-1056-4(0))*; pap. 26.00 *(978-0-7463-1011-3(0))* Northcote Hse. Publishers, Ltd. GBR. Dist: Brown, David Bk. Co., The.

Blundell, John. Female Force: Ayn Rand. 2011. (ENG., Illus.). 32p. (YA). pap. 3.99 *(978-1-4507-4924-4(0))* Bluewater Productions, Inc.

Blythe, Ronald. At the Yeoman's House. 2012. (ENG., Illus.). 128p. 34.95 ***(978-1-904634-88-1(5))*** Enitharmon Pr. GBR. Dist: Dufour Editions, Inc.

Boccaccio, Giovanni. Life of Dante. Wicksteed, Philip, tr. from ITA. 2009. (Oneworld Classics Ser.). (ENG., Illus.). 128p. pap. 12.95 *(978-1-84749-091-9(3))* Alma Classics GBR. Dist: Independent Pubs. Group.

Bociurkiw, Marusya. Comfort Food for Breakups: The Memoir of a Hungry Girl. 2007. (ENG., Illus.). 176p. pap. 16.95 *(978-1-55152-219-7(5))* Arsenal Pulp Pr. CAN. Dist: Consortium Bk. Sales & Distribution.

Bodanis, David. Passionate Minds: Emilie du Chatelet, Voltaire, & the Great Love Affair of the Enlightenment. 2007. (ENG., Illus.). 384p. pap. 15.00 *(978-0-307-23721-7(4),* Three Rivers Pr.) Crown Publishing Group.

Bogner, Ralf Georg. Der Autor Im Nachruf: Formen und Funktionen der Literarischen Memorialkultur Von der Reformation Bis Zum Vormärz. (Studien und Texte zur Sozialgeschichte der Literatur Ser.). (GER.). XII, 460p. 255.00 ***(978-3-11-185913-2(4))*** De Gruyter, Walter Inc.

Boissier, Gaston. Cicero & His Friends A Study of Roman. 2006. pap. 34.95 *(978-1-4286-4099-3(1))* Kessinger Publishing, LLC.

Bok, Edward. Why I Believe in Poverty Including, Two Persons. 2006. 60p. per. 11.95 *(978-1-59605-560-5(X))* Cosimo, Inc.

Bolaño, Roberto. Roberto Bolano: the Last Interview: And Other Conversations. Perez, Sybil, tr. 2011. (ENG.). 128p. pap. 15.95 ***(978-1-61219-095-2(2))*** Melville Hse. Publishing.

Boll, Heinrich. What's to Become of the Boy? Or, Something to Do with Books. Vennewitz, Leila, tr. from GER. 2011. (ENG.). 96p. pap. 14.95 *(978-1-61219-001-3(4))* Melville Hse. Publishing.

Bollinger, Andrea & et al. Briefe von und an Friedrich Nietzsche Mai 1872 - Dezember 1874. Pieper, Annemarie, ed. (GER.). VI, 835p. 418.00 ***(978-3-11-174497-1(3))*** De Gruyter, Walter Inc.

Bolton, Clyde. Hadacol Days: A Southern Boyhood: A Memoir. 2010. (ENG.). 24.95 *(978-1-58838-200-9(1),* NewSouth Bks.) NewSouth, Inc.

Boman, Steve. Film School: The True Story of a Midwestern Family Man Who Went to the World's Most Famous Film School, Fell Flat on His Face, Had a Stroke, & Sold a Television Series to CBS. 2011. (ENG.). 352p. pap. 16.95 *(978-1-936661-05-3(5))* BenBella Bks.

Bompas, George C. The Problem of the Shakespeare Plays. 2009. 96p. pap. 14.14 *(978-1-4589-3377-5(6))* General Bks. LLC.

Bond, Jenny & Sheedy, Chris. Who the Hell Is Pansy O'Hara? The Fascinating Stories Behind 50 of the World's Best-Loved Books. 2008. (ENG.). 336p. (gr. 12-18). 13.00 *(978-0-14-311364-5(X),* Penguin (Non-Classics)) Penguin Group (USA) Inc.

Bone. Richard Wright, Vol. 74. 2009. (ENG.). 48p. pap. 25.00 *(978-0-8166-0524-8(6))* Univ. of Minnesota Pr.

Bonwick, James. An Octogenarian's Reminiscences. 2011. (Cambridge Library Collection - History Ser.). (ENG., Illus.). 402p. pap. 31.99 ***(978-1-108-03896-6(4))*** Cambridge Univ. Pr.

Boreham, F. W. Lover of Life: F. W. Boreham's Tribute to His Mentor (Revised & Expanded) rev. ed. 2007. 44p. pap. 9.00 *(978-0-9790334-0-7(3))* Broadbanks, John Publishing.

Borges, Jorge Luis. Textos Cautivos: Ensayos Reseñas en "El Hogar" [de Buenos Ayres]. Sacerio-Garí, Enrique & Rodríguez Monegal, Emir, eds. (SPA., Illus.). 248p. *(978-84-7223-092-7(9),* 6030) Tusquets Editores.

Bosco, Ronald A. & Myerson, Joel. Dlb 351 Moby-Dick Doc. 2009. (Dictionary of Literary Biography Ser.). (ENG., Illus.). 480p. 315.00 *(978-0-7876-8169-2(5))* Cengage Gale.

Boston, Anne. Lesley Blanch: Inner Landscapes, Wilder Shores. 2010. (ENG., Illus.). 384p. 40.00 *(978-0-7195-6037-8(3))* Murray, John GBR. Dist: Independent Pubs. Group.

Boswell, James. Boswell's Life of Johnson. 2008. 604p. 33.99 *(978-0-554-35711-9(9))* 2008. 604p. 36.99 *(978-0-554-26408-0(0))* 2007. (ENG.). 532p. pap. 30.99 *(978-1-4346-1018-8(7))* 2007. (ENG.). 600p. pap. 32.99 *(978-1-4346-1117-8(5))* BiblioBazaar.

—Boswell's Life of Johnson. 2010. 162p. pap. *(978-1-151-92686-9(8))* 2010. 158p. pap. *(978-1-151-92689-0(2))* 2009. 76p. pap. *(978-0-217-44806-2(2))* 2009. 626p. pap. *(978-1-4590-5783-8(X))* 2009. 264p. pap. *(978-1-4590-5786-9(4))* 2009. 110p. pap. *(978-0-217-72732-7(8))* Books LLC.

—Boswell's Life of Johnson. Osgood, Charles Grosvenor, ed. 2008. 580p. pap. *(978-1-4099-0610-0(8))* Dodo Pr.

—Boswell's Life of Johnson. 2010. 166p. pap. 14.31 *(978-1-151-92683-8(3))* General Bks. LLC.

—James Boswell: As His Contemporaries Saw Him. Larson, Lyle, ed. 2008. (Illus.). 256p. (C). 52.50 *(978-0-8386-4171-2(7))* Fairleigh Dickinson Univ. Pr.

—The Journal of a Tour to the Hebrides with Samuel Johnson, LI D. 2009. 332p. pap. *(978-1-4099-0611-7(6))* Dodo Pr.

—Life of Johnson. 2008. 144p. 21.99 *(978-0-554-35398-2(9))*; 24.99 *(978-0-554-26095-2(6))* BiblioBazaar.

—Life of Johnson. Chapman, R. W. & Fleeman, J. D., eds. 2008. (Oxford World's Classics Ser.). (ENG.). 1536p. pap. 19.95 *(978-0-19-954021-1(7))* Oxford Univ. Pr., Inc.

—Life of Johnson. 2006. (ENG.). 384p. per. *(978-1-4067-3122-4(6),* Hesperides Pr.) Read Bks.

Boswell, James & Osgood, Charles Grosvenor. Boswell's Life of Johnson. 2010. 602p. pap. 44.75 *(978-1-143-69866-8(5))*; 600p. pap. 44.75 *(978-1-143-53652-6(5))* BiblioBazaar.

Boucquey, Thierry & Diamond, Marie Josephine. Encyclopedia of World Writers, Beginnings to the Twentieth Century. 2007. (Facts on File Library of World Literature). *(978-0-8160-5191-5(7))*; *(978-0-8160-5190-8(9))* Facts On File, Inc.

Bouillier, Grégoire & Huisman, Violaine. Report on Myself. Benderson, Bruce, tr. from FRE. 2009. (ENG.). 160p. pap. 13.95 *(978-0-618-96861-9(X))* Houghton Mifflin Harcourt Publishing Co.

Bouvier, Pierre. Aimé Césaire, Frantz Fanon: Portraits de Décolonisés. 2010. (FRE., Illus.). 288p. (C). pap. 41.00 ***(978-2-251-90003-2(9))*** Societe d'edition Les Belles lettres FRA. Dist: ISD.

Bowden, Charles. Some of the Dead Are Still Breathing: Living in the Future. 2009. (ENG.). 256p. 24.00 *(978-0-15-101395-1(0))* Houghton Mifflin Harcourt Trade & Reference Pubs.

Bowering, George. Pinboy: A Memoir. 2011. (ENG.). 320p. 32.00 *(978-1-897151-93-8(4))* Cormorant Bks. Inc. CAN. Dist: Univ. of Toronto Pr.

Bowker, Gordon. James Joyce: A Biography. 2012. (ENG., Illus.). 656p. 35.00 ***(978-0-374-17872-7(0))*** Farrar, Straus & Giroux.

Boylan, Jennifer Finney. I'M Looking Through You: Growing up Haunted - A Memoir. 2008. (ENG.). 288p. pap. 14.95 *(978-0-7679-2175-6(5))* Broadway Bks.

Boyt, Susie. My Judy Garland Life: A Memoir. 2010. (ENG., Illus.). 320p. pap. 15.00 *(978-1-60819-208-3(3))* Bloomsbury Publishing.

Bradby, D. Jean Genet. (Routledge Modern & Contemporary Dramatists Ser.). (ENG., Illus.). 224p. 2012. 99.95 *(978-0-415-37504-7(5))* 2011. pap. 27.95 *(978-0-415-37506-1(1))* Routledge.

Bradford, Richard. The Life of a Long Distance Writer: The Biography of Alan Sillitoe. 2008. (ENG., Illus.). 400p. 38.95 *(978-0-7206-1317-9(5))* Owen, Peter Ltd. GBR. Dist: Independent Pubs. Group.

Bradley, Tom. Fission among the Fanatics. 2007. (ENG.). 322p. per. 16.00 *(978-1-933132-33-4(7))* Spuyten Duyvil.

Braestrup, Kate. Here If You Need Me: A Memoir. 2008. (ENG.). 224p. pap. 13.99 *(978-0-316-06631-0(1),* Back Bay Bks.) Little Brown & Co.

—Marriage & Other Acts of Charity: A Memoir. (ENG.). 2011. 240p. pap. 14.99 *(978-0-316-03190-5(9),* Back Bay Bks.) 2010. 320p. pap. 24.99 *(978-0-316-05383-9(X))* Little Brown & Co.

Bramall, Mary. Why Me? 2010. 48p. pap. 10.49 *(978-1-4389-8995-2(4))* AuthorHouse.

Branch, Crystal. Everybody Has A Story to Tell, This Is Mine. 2010. 104p. pap. 24.00 *(978-1-4520-6193-1(9))* AuthorHouse.

Branch, Edgar Marquess & Twain, Mark. The Literary Apprenticeship of Mark Twain. 2011. 356p. 51.95 ***(978-1-258-04881-5(7))*** Literary Licensing, LLC.

Branson, Susan. Dangerous to Know: Women, Crime, & Notoriety in the Early Republic. 2011. (Illus.). 200p. (C). pap. 19.95 ***(978-0-8122-2187-9(7))*** Univ. of Pennsylvania Pr.

Brassaï. Henry Miller: The Paris Years. Bent, Timothy, tr. from FRE. 2011. (ENG., Illus.). 240p. pap. 14.95 *(978-1-61145-028-6(4),* 611028, Arcade Publishing) Skyhorse Publishing Co., Inc.

Brassard, George J. The Interview: Life struggles from a bipolar Pastor. 2011. pap. 11.99 *(978-1-61739-289-4(8))* Tate Publishing & Enterprises, LLC.

Brasset, Edmund A. A Doctor's Pilgrimage: An Autobiography. 2011. 256p. 47.95 ***(978-1-258-07373-2(0))*** Literary Licensing, LLC.

Braun, Werner & Coakley, David. Is the War Over? The Memoir of Werner Kurt Braun. 2010. (Illus.). 236p. pap. 15.99 *(978-1-4520-2946-7(6))* AuthorHouse.

Brecht, Martin & Brecht, Christoph. Johann Valentin Andreae 1586-1654: Eine Biographie. 2008. (GER., Illus.). 389p. (C). 68.00 *(978-3-525-55334-3(X))* Vandenhoeck & Ruprecht GmbH & Co. KG DEU. Dist: ISD.

Bredhold, Luella & Bredhold, Clarence. Our Global Adventures. 2011. 302p. pap. 22.95 ***(978-1-61493-004-4(X))*** Peppertree Pr., The.

Breger, Louis. Dostoevsky: The Author as Psychoanalyst. 2008. (ENG.). 315p. pap. 34.95 *(978-1-4128-0843-9(X))* Transaction Pubs.

Breit, Harvey. The Writer Observed. 2011. 286p. 48.95 ***(978-1-258-09963-3(2))*** Literary Licensing, LLC.

Brenner, Anita. Avant-Garde Art & Artists in Mexico: Anita Brenner's Journals of the Roaring Twenties. Glusker, Susannah Joel, ed. 2010. (ENG., Illus.). 901p. 125.00 *(978-0-292-72184-5(6))* Univ. of Texas Pr.

Brenner, Marie. Apples & Oranges: My Brother & Me, Lost & Found. 2009. (ENG., Illus.). 304p. pap. 15.00 *(978-0-312-42880-8(4))* Picador.

Brenson, Michael. Table of Isotopes. Date not set. *(978-0-374-28146-5(7))* Farrar, Straus & Giroux.

Brett, Brian. Trauma Farm: A Rebel History of Rural Life, 1 vol. 2011. (ENG.). 384p. pap. 16.95 *(978-1-55365-803-0(5),* Greystone Bks.) D&M Pubs. Inc. CAN. Dist: Perseus-PGW.

Brewer, Danny & Shahin, Sumar. Calling: How a Man's Dream Revealed His Mission & Led Him to Truth. 2010. (ENG.). 102p. pap. 11.99 *(978-1-59932-204-9(8))* Advantage Media Group.

Brewer, Sonny, ed. Don't Quit Your Day Job: Acclaimed Authors & the Day Jobs they Quit. 2011. (ENG.). 432p. pap. 15.95 *(978-1-84982-136-0(4))* MP Publishing Ltd. GBR. Dist: Perseus-PGW.

Brewster, Thomas A. The Great American Novel. 2008. 128p. pap. 13.95 *(978-0-595-46795-2(4))* iUniverse, Inc.

Breytenbach, Breyten. A Veil of Footsteps: (Memoir of a Nomadic Fictional Character) 2010. (Illus.). 302p. 23.00 *(978-0-7981-4927-3(2))* International Publishers Marketing.

Bridgwater, Tess. Finding My Footprints in Sarum. 2012. (Illus.). ***(978-0-9697003-4-0(2))*** Complete Business Services.

Briggs, Anthony. Brief Lives: Fyodor Dostoevsky. 2012. (Brief Lives Ser.). (ENG.). 128p. pap. 12.95 ***(978-1-84391-925-4(7))*** Hesperus Pr. GBR. Dist: Independent Pubs. Group.

Briggs, Anthony. Leo Tolstoy. 2010. (Brief Lives Ser.). (ENG.). 119p. pap. 15.95 *(978-1-84391-911-7(7))* Hesperus Pr. GBR. Dist: Independent Pubs. Group.

Brightwell, C. L. (Cecilia Lucy). Memorials of the Life of Amelia Opie, Selected & Arranged from Her Letters, Diaries, & Other Manuscripts, by Cecilia Lucy Brightwell. 2006. 460p. per. 29.99 *(978-1-4255-5073-8(8))* MPublishing.

Brinkley, Douglas. Jack Kerouac Biography. 2007. 496p. 34.95 *(978-0-670-06354-3(1),* Viking Adult) Penguin Group (USA) Inc.

Brodsky, Louis Daniel. William Faulkner, Life Glimpses. 2011. (ENG.). 238p. pap. 25.00 ***(978-0-292-73991-8(5))*** Univ. of Texas Pr.

Bromfield, Ellen G. Heritage. Date not set. lib. bdg. 21.95 *(978-0-8488-1760-2(5))* Amereon LTD.

Bronson, Bertrand H. Johnson & Boswell: Three Essays. 2011. 118p. 39.95 ***(978-1-258-02667-7(8))*** Literary Licensing, LLC.

Brontë, Charlotte. The Life & Works of Charlotte Bronte & Her Sisters, 7. reprint ed. lib. bdg. 686.00 *(978-0-7426-2194-7(4))* Classic Bks.

Brooker, Peter. Bohemia in London: The Social Scene of Early Modernism. 2007. (ENG., Illus.). 224p. pap. 31.00 *(978-0-230-54692-9(7))* Palgrave Macmillan.

Brooks, Larry. Happy As Larry: My Life & Legacy. 2010. (Illus.). 192p. 24.99 *(978-1-4490-9113-2(X))*; pap. 14.49 *(978-1-4490-9114-9(8))* AuthorHouse.

Brooks, Peter. Henry James Goes to Paris. 2007. (ENG., Illus.). 288p. 24.95 *(978-0-691-12954-9(1))* Princeton Univ. Pr.

Brookshire, Lajoyce. Faith under Fire: Betrayed by a Thing Called Love. 2009. (ENG.). 272p. pap. 15.00 *(978-1-4165-9601-1(1),* Gallery Books/Karen Hunter Publishing) Gallery Books/Karen Hunter Publishing.

Brotchie, Alastair. Alfred Jarry: A Pataphysical Life. 2011. (ENG., Illus.). 424p. (gr. 17). 34.95 *(978-0-262-01619-3(2))* MIT Pr.

Brown, Andrew. Stendhal. 2010. (Brief Lives Ser.). (ENG.). 207p. pap. 17.95 *(978-1-84391-913-1(3))* Hesperus Pr. GBR. Dist: Independent Pubs. Group.

Brown, Carolyn J. A Daring Life: A Biography of Eudora Welty. 2012. (ENG.). 144p. 20.00 ***(978-1-61703-295-0(6))*** Univ. Pr. of Mississippi.

Brown, Dale. The Book of Buechner: A Journey Through His Writings. 2007. (ENG., Illus.). 394p. 25.00 *(978-0-664-23113-2(6))* Westminster John Knox Pr.

Brown, Eleanor Gertrude. Milton's Blindness. 2011. 178p. 42.95 ***(978-1-258-03796-3(3))*** Literary Licensing, LLC.

Brown, Horatio F., ed. Letters & Papers of John Addington Symonds. 296p. 2008. 43.95 *(978-1-4366-7412-6(3))* 2007. (ENG.). per. 28.95 *(978-1-4325-9958-4(5))* Kessinger Publishing, LLC.

Brown, Hume Peter. The Youth of Goethe. 2007. 188p. (ENG.). 96.99 *(978-1-4280-7652-5(2))*; per. 89.99 *(978-1-4280-7636-5(0))* IndyPublish.com.

Brown, James. The Los Angeles Diaries: A Memoir. 2011. (ENG.). 224p. pap. 14.95 *(978-1-58243-720-0(3),* Counterpoint) Counterpoint LLC.

—This River. 2010. 225p. 23.95 *(978-1-50747-722-8(X))* Phoenix Bks., Inc.

—This River: A Memoir. 2011. (ENG.). 224p. pap. 14.95 ***(978-1-58243-721-7(1),*** Counterpoint) Counterpoint LLC.

Brown, John. John Bunyan: His Life Times & Work. 3rd ed. 2007. (Illus.). 522p. pap. 45.00 *(978-1-55635-219-5(0),* Wipf and Stock) Wipf & Stock Pubs.

—John Bunyan His Life Times & Work. 2006. (Illus.). pap. 40.95 *(978-1-4286-5050-3(4))* Kessinger Publishing, LLC.

Brown, Julie. Writers on the Spectrum: How Autism & Asperger Syndrome Have Influenced Literary Writing. 2009. (ENG.). 256p. pap. *(978-1-84310-913-6(1))* Kingsley, Jessica Ltd.

Brown, Lois. Pauline Elizabeth Hopkins: Black Daughter of the Revolution. 2008. (ENG., Illus.). 704p. 49.95 *(978-0-8078-3166-3(2))* Univ. of North Carolina Pr.

Brown, Peter D. G. Oskar Panizza & the Love Council: A History of the Scandalous Play on Stage & in Court, with the Complete Text in English & a Biography of the Author. 2010. (ENG., Illus.). 292p. pap. 49.95 *(978-0-7864-4273-7(5))* McFarland & Co., Inc. Pubs.

Brown, Rita Mae. Animal Magnetism: My Life with Creatures Great & Small. 2010. (ENG., Illus.). 256p. pap. 16.00 *(978-0-345-51180-5(8),* Ballantine Bks.) Random House Publishing Group.

—Animal Magnetism: My Life with Creatures Great & Small. Lt. ed. 2010. (ENG.). 353p. 31.95 *(978-1-4104-2520-1(7))* Thorndike Pr.

Brown, Roi. I Am, Roi. 2007. (Illus.). 412p. 33.99 *(978-1-4251-6719-6(5))* Trafford Publishing.

Brown, Roi Joseph. I Am, Roi. 2007. (Illus.). 412p. per. 25.80 *(978-1-4251-0650-8(1))* Trafford Publishing.

Brown, William Wells & Greenspan, Ezra. William Wells Brown: A Reader. Greenspan, Ezra, ed. 2008. (ENG., Illus.). 488p. pap. 24.95 *(978-0-8203-3224-6(0))*; lib. bdg. 64.95 *(978-0-8203-3223-9(2))* Univ. of Georgia Pr.

Browning, Oscar. Life of George Eliot. 2011. (Cambridge Library Collection - Literary Studies). (ENG.). 194p. pap. 19.99 ***(978-1-108-04049-5(7))*** Cambridge Univ. Pr.

Broyard, Bliss. One Drop: My Father's Hidden Life — A Story of Race & Family Secrets. 2008. (ENG., Illus.). 544p. pap. 15.99 *(978-0-316-00806-8(0),* Back Bay Bks.) Little Brown & Co.

Bruce, Harry. Page Fright: Foibles & Fetishes of Famous Writers. 2010. 360p. pap. 18.95 *(978-0-7710-1713-1(8),* Emblem Edns) McClelland & Stewart CAN. Dist: Random Hse., Inc.

Bruck, Edith. Lettera Alla Madre. 2007. (Texts & Translations Ser.: Vol. 18). (ITA & ENG.). 250p. per. 10.95 *(978-0-87352-935-8(9))* Modern Language Assn. of America.

Brulotte & Brulotte, Gaetan. La Chambre des Lucidités. (FRE., Illus.). 175p. *(978-2-89583-073-3(8))* Editions Trois-Pistoles.

Brun, Friederike. Friederike Brun Reader: Supplement to an Encyclopedia of German Women Writers. Keith-Smith, Brian, ed. 2006. 256p. *(978-0-7734-5531-3(0))* Mellen, Edwin Pr., The.

Bryant, William Cullen. A Discourse on the Life, Character & Genius of Washington Irving, Delivered Before the New York Historical Society, at the Academy of Music in New Y. 2006. 492p. per. 29.99 (978-1-4255-5527-6(6)) MPublishing.

Bryce-Echenique, Alfredo. Una Vida de Novela. 2010. 240p. pap. 21.99 (978-9972-848-36-0(1)) Alfaguara-Santillana PER. Dist: Santillana USA Publishing Co., Inc.

Bryher & Bryher. The Heart to Artemis: A Writer's Memoirs. 2006. (ENG.). 336p. per. 19.95 (978-1-930464-08-7(8)) Consortium Bk. Sales & Distribution.

Bryher & Ellerman, Annie Winifred. The Heart to Artemis: A Writer's Memoirs. 2011. 320p. 50.95 (978-1-258-09656-4(0)) Literary Licensing, LLC.

Bryson, Bill. The Life & Times of the Thunderbolt Kid: A Memoir. (ENG., Illus.). 288p. 2007. pap. 15.99 (978-0-7679-1937-1(8)) 2006. 25.00 (978-0-7679-1936-4(X)) Broadway Bks. (Broadway).

—The Life & Times of the Thunderbolt Kid: A Memoir. 2006. cd-rom 34.99 (978-1-59895-390-9(7)) Findaway World, LLC.

Buchan, John. John Macnab. 22.95 (978-0-8488-0434-3(1)) Amereon LTD.

Buckley, Christopher. Losing Mum & Pup: A Memoir. (ENG.). 2010. 272p. pap. 13.99 (978-0-446-54095-7(1)) 2009. (Illus.). 272p. 24.99 (978-0-446-54094-0(3)) 2009. 400p. 29.99 (978-0-446-55239-4(9)) Grand Central Publishing. (Twelve).

Buckley-Ott, Cara L. & Leverette, Marc, eds. It's Not TV: Watching HBO in the Post-Television ERA. 2007. XII, 260p. 105.00 (978-0-415-96037-3(1)) Routledge.

Buechner, Frederick. The Yellow Leaves: A Miscellany. 2008. (ENG.). 152p. 17.00 (978-0-664-23276-4(0)) Westminster John Knox Pr.

Bullock, Philip Ross, ed. The Correspondence of Jean Sibelius & Rosa Newmarch, 1906-1939. 2011. (Illus.). 312p. 90.00 (978-1-84383-683-4(1), Boydell Press) Boydell & Brewer, Ltd. GBR. Dist: Boydell & Brewer, Inc.

Bunyan, John. Grace Abounding to the Chief of Sinners. 2007. (Hendrickson Christian Classics Ser.). 165p. 9.95 (978-1-59856-142-5(1)) Hendrickson Pubs. Marketing, LLC.

—Grace Abounding to the Chief of Sinners: In a Faithful Account of the Life & Death of John Bunyan. 2007. 244p. (ENG.). 24.95 (978-1-60206-458-4(X)); per. 10.95 (978-1-60206-457-7(1)) Cosimo, Inc.

—Memoir of John Bunyan. 2007. 168p. per. (978-1-4068-2293-9(0)) Echo Library.

Bunzel, Wolfgang. "Die Welt Umwälzen" Bettine Von Arnim Geb. Brentano (1785-1859) 2009. (Illus.). 126p. (978-3-9811109-7-5(8)) Freies Deutsches Hochstift, Frankfurter Goethe-Museum.

Burana, Lily. I Love a Man in Uniform: A Memoir of Love, War, & Other Battles. 2010. (ENG.). 368p. pap. 14.95 (978-1-60286-125-1(0), Weinstein Bks.) Perseus Bks. Group.

Burdett, Osbert. William Blake's Apprenticeship & Marriage. 2006. pap. 15.95 (978-1-4286-7597-1(3)) Kessinger Publishing, LLC.

Burge, James. Dante's Invention. 2011. (ENG., Illus.). 252p. 29.95 (978-0-7524-5586-0(9)) History Pr. Ltd., The GBR. Dist: Independent Pubs. Group.

Burgess, Glenda. The Geography of Love. 2008. 304p. (978-0-7322-8739-9(1)) HarperCollins Pubs. Australia.

—The Geography of Love: A Memoir. 2009. (ENG.). 320p. pap. 14.00 (978-0-7679-2870-0(9)) Broadway Bks.

Burman, Ben Lucien. Ben Lucien Burman: A Critical Appreciation & A Biographical Sketch. 2011. 16p. pap. 35.95 (978-1-258-06834-9(6)) Literary Licensing, LLC.

Burn, Stephen J. David Foster Wallace's Infinite Jest: A Reader's Guide. 2nd ed. 2012. (ENG.). 144p. pap. 19.95 (978-1-4411-5707-2(7)) Continuum International Publishing Group, Ltd. GBR. Dist: National Bk. Network.

Burn, Stephen J., ed. Conversations with David Foster Wallace. 2012. (Literary Conversations Ser.). (ENG.). 208p. 65.00 (978-1-61703-226-4(3)) Univ. Pr. of Mississippi.

—Conversations with David Foster Wallace. 2012. (Literary Conversations Ser.). (ENG.). 208p. pap. 25.00 (978-1-61703-227-1(1)) Univ. Pr. of Mississippi.

Burney, Fanny. The Diary & Letters of Madame D'Arblay. 2009. 532p. 35.99 (978-0-559-08286-3(X)); 32.99 (978-0-559-08302-0(5)); pap. 23.99 (978-0-559-08297-9(5)); pap. 30.99 (978-0-559-08290-0(8)) BiblioBazaar.

—Diary & Letters of Madame d'Arblay (1778-1840), Vol. 1. Dobson, Austin, ed. 2007. 564p. per. 43.95 (978-0-548-76857-0(9)) Kessinger Publishing, LLC.

—Diary & Letters of Madame d'Arblay (1778-1840) Barrett, Charlotte, ed. 2007. Vol. 3. 556p. per. 42.95 (978-0-548-77302-4(5)) Vol. 5. 564p. per. 43.95 (978-0-548-74776-6(8)) Vol. 6. 560p. per. 42.95 (978-0-548-76510-4(3)) Kessinger Publishing, LLC.

—The Early Diary of Frances Burney, 1768-1778. 2009. 392p. 26.99 (978-1-103-83634-5(X)); pap. 20.99 (978-1-103-83630-7(7)) BiblioBazaar.

—The Early Diary of Frances Burney, 1768-1778. 2009. 396p. pap. (978-0-217-38368-4(8)) Books LLC.

—The Early Diary of Frances Burney, 1768-1778. 2009. 396p. pap. 24.30 (978-1-4589-1582-5(4)) General Bks. LLC.

—Fanny Burney & Her Friends: Select Passages from Her Diary & Other Writings. 2008. (ENG.). 356p. per. (978-1-4086-6406-3(2)) Read Bks.

Burney, Fanny & Seeley, Leonard Benton. Fanny Burney & Her Friends: Select Passages from Her Diary & Other Writings. 2010. 386p. pap. 33.75 (978-1-143-43465-5(X)); 370p. pap. 32.75 (978-1-142-55157-5(1)); 374p. pap. 32.75 (978-1-142-43190-7(8)) BiblioBazaar.

Burns, Jennifer. Goddess of the Market: Ayn Rand & the American Right, 1 vol. 2011. (ENG., Illus.). 384p. pap. 18.95 (978-0-19-983248-4(X)) Oxford Univ. Pr., Inc.

Burnside, John. A Lie about My Father. 2007. (ENG.). 336p. pap. 15.00 (978-1-55597-467-1(6)) Graywolf Pr.

Burroughs, Augusten. Dry: A Memoir. Date not set. pap. (978-0-312-31819-2(7)); mass mkt. (978-0-312-99095-4(2)) St. Martin's Pr. (St. Martin's Paperbacks).

—Magical Thinking: True Stories. mass mkt. (978-0-312-99042-8(1), St. Martin's Paperbacks) St. Martin's Pr.

—Possible Side Effects. 2007. (ENG.). 304p. pap. 14.00 (978-0-312-42681-1(X)) Picador.

—Running with Scissors: A Memoir. 2006. (ENG.). 352p. mass mkt. 7.99 (978-0-312-93885-7(3), St. Martin's Paperbacks) St. Martin's Pr.

—Running with Scissors: A Memoir. 2006. lib. bdg. 18.40 (978-1-4176-8418-2(6), Turtleback) Turtleback Bks.

—A Wolf at the Table: A Memoir of My Father. 2009. (ENG.). 272p. pap. 14.00 (978-0-312-42827-3(8)) Picador.

—You Better Not Cry: Stories. 2010. (ENG.). 224p. pap. 14.00 (978-0-312-43006-1(X)) Picador.

Burstein, Andrew. The Original Knickerbocker: The Life of Washington Irving. (ENG., Illus.). 2008. 432p. per. 17.50 (978-0-465-00854-4(2)) 2007. 440p. 27.50 (978-0-465-00853-7(4)) Basic Bks.

Burt, Daniel S. The Literary 100: A Ranking of the Most Influential Novelists, Playwrights, & Poets of All Time. 2nd rev. ed. 2008. (Literature 100 Ser.). 560p. (C). (gr. 9-18). 50.00 (978-0-8160-6267-6(6)); (Illus.). pap. 19.95 (978-0-8160-6268-3(4), Checkmark Bks.) Facts On File, Inc.

Burt, E. S. Regard for the Other: Autothanatography in Rousseau, de Quincey, Baudelaire, & Wilde. 2009. (ENG.). 288p. 80.00 (978-0-8232-3090-7(2)); pap. 30.00 (978-0-8232-3091-4(0)) Fordham Univ. Pr.

Burton, Alan. From a Window Or: Memoirs of a Distant Mind. 2008. 496p. 30.99 (978-1-4389-3084-8(4)); pap. 20.49 (978-1-4389-3083-1(6)) AuthorHouse.

Burton, Antoinette. The Postcolonial Careers of Santha Rama Rau. 2007. (Next Wave Ser.). (ENG., Illus.). 216p. (C). 79.95 (978-0-8223-4050-8(X)); per. 22.95 (978-0-8223-4071-3(2)) Duke Univ. Pr.

Burton, Ryan & Davis, Darren G. Twilight Unbound. 2010. (Illus.). 40p. 12.99 (978-1-4507-0015-3(2)) Bluewater Productions, Inc.

Burton, Thomas. Diary of Thomas Burton. 2009. 438p. pap. 29.50 (978-1-150-77071-5(6)) General Bks. LLC.

Busby, Brian John. A Gentleman of Pleasure: One Life of John Glassco - Poet, Memoirist, Translator, & Pornographer. 2011. (ENG., Illus.). 400p. (978-0-7735-3818-4(6)) McGill-Queen's Univ. Pr.

Bush, Jonathan. Untitled Biography of Telford Taylor. Date not set. (978-0-374-28164-9(5)) Farrar, Straus & Giroux.

Bushman, Richard L. On the Road with Joseph Smith: An Author's Diary. 2007. 14.95 (978-1-58958-102-9(4)) Kofford, Greg Books, Inc.

Butler, Blake. Nothing: A Portrait of Insomnia. 2011. (ENG.). 288p. pap. 14.99 (978-0-06-199738-9(2), HarperPerennial) HarperCollins Pubs.

Butler, Marilyn. Jane Austen. 2007. (Very Interesting People Ser.). (ENG.). 128p. per. 9.99 (978-0-19-921760-1(2)) Oxford Univ. Pr., Inc.

Butler, Samuel. The Correspondence of Samuel Butler with His Sister May. Howard, Daniel Francis, ed. 2011. 284p. 48.95 (978-1-258-04522-7(2)) Literary Licensing, LLC.

Buxton, Thomas Fowell. Memoirs of Sir Thomas Fowell Buxton. 260p. reprint ed. 98.00 (978-0-7222-9837-4(4)) Library Reprints, Inc.

Byers, Lloyd & Byers, Mary. Keep Moving Forward: My Son's Last Words. 2011. 144p. 28.95 (978-1-4497-1630-1(X)); pap. 11.95 (978-1-4497-1629-5(6)) Author Solutions, Inc. (WestBow Pr.).

Byrd, Richard E. Alone. 2011. 306p. pap. 29.95 (978-1-4474-2410-9(7)) Palmer Pr., The.

Byrne, Paula. Mad World: Evelyn Waugh & the Secrets of Brideshead. 2011. (ENG.). 384p. pap. 16.99 (978-0-06-088131-3(3), HarperPerennial) HarperCollins Pubs.

Cabassa, Sarah. The Death of Me: A New Creation. 2009. (Illus.). 112p. 21.49 (978-1-4389-7256-5(3)); pap. 10.99 (978-1-4389-7255-8(5)) AuthorHouse.

Cabell, Craig. Ian Rankin & Inspector Rebus: The Official Story of the Bestselling Author & His Ruthless Detective. 2010. (ENG., Illus.). 268p. 26.95 (978-1-84454-866-8(X)) Blake, John Publishing, Ltd. GBR. Dist: Independent Pubs. Group.

—Ian Rankin & Inspector Rebus: The Story of the Best-Selling Author & His Complex Detective. 2011. (ENG., Illus.). 266p. pap. 12.95 (978-1-84358-292-2(9)) Blake, John Publishing, Ltd. GBR. Dist: Independent Pubs. Group.

Cabell, Craig. Terry Pratchett: The Spirit of Fantasy. 2012. (ENG., Illus.). 246p. 27.95 (978-1-84358-507-7(3)) Blake, John Publishing, Ltd. GBR. Dist: Independent Pubs. Group.

Cade, Jared. Agatha Christie & the Eleven Missing Days. (ENG., Illus.). 3rd ed. 2006. 256p. per. 19.95 (978-0-7206-1280-6(2)) 4th rev. ed. 2011. 300p. pap. 19.95 (978-0-7206-1390-2(6)) Owen, Peter Ltd. GBR. Dist: Independent Pubs. Group.

Cady, Edwin Harrison. The Road to Realism: The Early Years of William Dean Howells, 1837-1885. 2011. 294p. 48.95 (978-1-258-05807-4(3)) Literary Licensing, LLC.

Calabi, Silvio & Helsley, Steve. Hemingway's Guns: The Sporting Arms of Ernest Hemingway. 2010. (ENG.). 156p. 40.00 (978-0-89272-720-9(9)) Down East Bks.

Caldecott, Moyra. Multidimensional Life: A writer on the process of Writing. 2007. per. 16.95 (978-1-84319-549-8(6), Bladud Bks.) Mushroom Publishing GBR. Dist: Lightning Source, Inc.

Callcott, Maria. Journal of a Residence in Chile, during the Year 1822. 2011. (Cambridge Library Collection - Women's Writing Ser.). (ENG., Illus.). 552p. pap. 39.99 (978-1-108-03378-7(4)) Cambridge Univ. Pr.

Callinicos, Luli. Oliver Tambo: His Life & Legacy, 1917-1993. 2011. (ENG.). 36p. pap. 8.95 (978-1-919855-85-1(8)) STE Pubs. ZAF. Dist: Independent Pubs. Group.

Callow, Simon. Charles Dickens & the Great Theatre of the World. 2012. (Vintage Ser.). (ENG.). 384p. pap. 16.00 (978-0-345-80323-8(X), Vintage) Knopf Doubleday Publishing Group.

Cameron, Julia. The Creative Life: True Tales of Inspiration. (ENG., 256p. (gr. 12). 2012. Illus.). pap. 15.95 (978-0-399-16052-3(3)) 2010. 23.95 (978-1-58542-824-3(8)) Penguin Group (USA) Inc. (Tarcher).

Cameron, Julia. Floor Sample: A Creative Memoir. 2007. (ENG.). 416p. (gr. 12-18). 14.95 (978-1-58542-557-0(5), Tarcher) Penguin Group (USA) Inc.

Campbell, Gordon & Corns, Thomas N. John Milton: Life, Work, & Thought. (ENG., Illus.). 2010. 512p. pap. 24.95 (978-0-19-959103-9(2)) 2008. 476p. 39.95 (978-0-19-928984-4(0)) Oxford Univ. Pr., Inc.

Campbell, Ian. Thomas Carlyle. 2011. 192p. pap. (978-1-84921-089-8(6)) Kennedy & Boyd.

Campbell, James. Syncopations: Beats, New Yorkers, & Writers in the Dark. 2008. 251p. pap. 24.95 (978-0-520-25237-0(3)) Univ. of California Pr.

Camus, Albert. Notebooks, 1935-1942. 2010. (ENG.). 236p. pap. 16.95 (978-1-56663-872-2(0)) Dee, Ivan R. Pub.

—Notebooks 1942-1951, Vol. 2. 2010. (ENG.). 288p. pap. 18.95 (978-1-56663-873-9(9)) Dee, Ivan R. Pub.

—Notebooks 1951-1959, Vol. 3. 2010. (ENG.). 288p. pap. 18.95 (978-1-56663-850-0(X)) Dee, Ivan R. Pub.

—Notebooks 1951-1959, Vol. 3. Bloom, Ryan, tr. from FRE. 2008. (ENG.). 288p. 27.50 (978-1-56663-775-6(9)) Dee, Ivan R. Pub.

Candelaria, Nash. Second Communion. 2009. pap. 18.00 (978-1-931010-56-6(0)) Bilingual Pr./Editorial Bilingue.

Canetti, Elias. Party in the Blitz. Hofmann, Michael, tr. 2010. (ENG.). 256p. pap. 13.95 (978-0-8112-1830-6(9), 21830) New Directions Publishing Corp.

Canning, Richard. E. M. Forster. 2010. (Brief Lives Ser.). (ENG.). 120p. pap. 15.95 (978-1-84391-916-2(8)) Hesperus Pr. GBR. Dist: Independent Pubs. Group.

Cannon, John. The Brontes: A Family History. 2008. (ENG., Illus.). 160p. per. (978-0-7509-4808-1(6)) History Pr. Ltd., The.

Cantrill, G. Dennis. Gray Roads to Grass Roots: Journey Through Life. 2011. pap. 17.99 (978-1-61346-012-2(0)) Tate Publishing & Enterprises, LLC.

Capper, Charles. Margaret Fuller: An American Romantic Life Volume II: the Public Years. 2010. (ENG., Illus.). 672p. pap. 35.00 (978-0-19-539632-4(4)) Oxford Univ. Pr., Inc.

Caputo, Philip. Means of Escape: A War Correspondent's Memoir of Life & Death in Afghanistan, the Middle East, & Vietnam. 2009. (ENG.). 400p. pap. 17.00 (978-0-8050-8963-9(2), Holt Paperback) Holt, Henry & Co.

Carabine, Hubbard. Lives of Victorian Literary Figures: Conrad, Haggard & Kipling by Their Contemporaries, 3 vols., Pt. VII. 2009. (Lives of Victorian Literary Figures Ser.). (ENG., Illus.). 1376p. 495.00 (978-1-85196-963-0(2)) Pickering & Chatto Pubs., Ltd. GBR. Dist: Ashgate Publishing Co.

Carberry, Juanita. Letzte Tage in Kenia. (GER.). (978-3-612-65000-9(9)) Econ-Verlag GmbH DEU. Dist: International Bk. Import Service, Inc.

Carey, John. William Golding: The Man Who Wrote Lord of the Flies. 2010. (ENG., Illus.). 592p. 32.50 (978-1-4391-8732-6(0), Free Pr.) Free Pr.

Carkeet, David. Campus Sexpot: A Memoir. 2007. (Association of Writers & Writing Programs Award for Creative Nonfiction Ser.). (ENG.). 152p. per. 17.95 (978-0-8203-3013-6(2)) Univ. of Georgia Pr.

Carl Van Doren. Contemporary American Novelists. 2007. 124p. pap. 18.99 (978-1-4346-0017-2(3)); (ENG.). 138p. pap. 19.99 (978-1-4346-0020-2(3)) BiblioBazaar.

Carleton, William. The Poor Scholar. 2008. 152p. 21.99 (978-0-554-34798-1(9)); 24.99 (978-0-554-25495-1(6)) BiblioBazaar.

—The Poor Scholar. 2009. 148p. pap. (978-1-4099-3035-8(1)) Dodo Pr.

—The Poor Scholar: The Works of William Carleton, Vol. 3. l.t. ed. 2007. (ENG.). 148p. pap. 19.99 (978-1-4264-9184-9(0)) BiblioBazaar.

—The Poor Scholar: The Works of William Carleton Volume Three. 2007. 134p. pap. 18.99 (978-1-4264-9130-6(1)) BiblioBazaar.

—The Station; the Party Fight & Funeral; the Lough Derg Pilgrim: The Works of William Carleton. 2007. (ENG.). 182p. pap. 19.99 (978-1-4264-9126-9(3)); Vol. 3. 204p. pap. 22.99 (978-1-4264-9180-1(8)) BiblioBazaar.

Carlson, Rick. Some Funny Things Happened to Me on the Way to My Life: A Biography of a Regular Guy. 2011. 88p. pap. 19.95 (978-1-4560-0369-2(0)) PublishAmerica, Inc.

Carlyle, Thomas. Life of Friedrich Schiller. 2009. 384p. pap. (978-0-217-50340-2(3)); 386p. pap. (978-0-217-01255-3(8)) Books LLC.

—Reminiscences. 2009. 352p. 25.99 (978-1-103-80204-3(6)); pap. 19.99 (978-1-103-80196-1(1)) BiblioBazaar.

—Reminiscences. 2009. 66p. pap. (978-0-217-85249-4(1)) Books LLC.

—Reminiscences. Campbell, Ian & Fielding, K. J., eds. 2009. 488p. pap. (978-1-84921-000-3(4)) Kennedy & Boyd.

Carlyle, Thomas & Norton, Charles Eliot. Reminiscences. 2009. 618p. 38.99 (978-1-115-49199-0(7)); 45.99 (978-1-115-49198-3(9)); pap. 45.75 (978-1-115-49200-3(4)); pap. 44.75 (978-1-115-49201-0(2)) BiblioBazaar.

Carnell, Rachel & King, Kathryn. Political Biography of Eliza Haywood, 1 vol. 2012. (Eighteenth-Century Political Biographies Ser.). (ENG.). 288p. 99.00 (978-1-85196-917-3(9)) Pickering & Chatto Pubs., Ltd. GBR. Dist: Ashgate Publishing Co.

Caro, Elme. George Sand. 2008. 148p. 21.99 (978-0-554-36689-0(4)) 2008. 148p. 24.99 (978-0-554-27386-0(1)) 2007. (FRE.). 130p. pap. 18.99 (978-1-4346-3114-5(1)) 2007. 144p. pap. 19.99 (978-1-4346-3115-2(X)) BiblioBazaar.

Carolina Mundo & Becky Bedolla. My Family, My Story: Alisal Union School District Project. 2009. 104p. pap. 10.99 (978-1-4389-5500-1(6)) AuthorHouse.

Carpenter, Mary Fern. Have I Told You about the Time ? A Legacy of Stories & Memories. 2008. 156p. pap. 16.95 (978-1-4327-3227-1(7)) Outskirts Pr., Inc.

Carr, John F. H. Beam Piper: A Biography. Palumbo, Donald & Sullivan, C. W., III, eds. 2008. (Critical Explorations in Science Fiction & Fantasy Ser.: Vol. 8). (ENG., Illus.). 262p. 45.00 (978-0-7864-3375-9(2)) McFarland & Co., Inc. Pubs.

Carr, Pat. One Page at a Time: On a Writing Life. 2010. (Illus.). 288p. 25.95 (978-0-89672-716-8(5)) Texas Tech Univ. Pr.

Carradice, Phil. Herbert Williams. 2010. (University of Wales Press - Writers of Wales Ser.). (Illus.). 117p. pap. 25.00 (978-0-7083-2192-8(5)) Univ. of Wales Pr. GBR. Dist: Chicago Distribution Ctr.

Carrera, Margarita. Sumario Del Recuerdo: Memorias (1929-1981) 2006. (Colección Escritores Centroamericanos Ser.). (SPA., Illus.). 244p. pap. (978-99922-48-51-5(3)) Fondo de Cultura Economica.

Cart, Michael. Talking Animals & Others. 2009. (ENG.). 272p. (gr. 12). 29.95 (978-1-59020-170-1(1)) Overlook Pr., The.

Carter, David. Honore de Balzac. 2008. (Brief Lives Ser.). (ENG.). 96p. pap. 13.95 (978-1-84391-908-7(7)) Hesperus Pr. GBR. Dist: Independent Pubs. Group.

—Marquis de Sade. 2011. (Brief Lives Ser.). (ENG.). 120p. pap. 15.95 (978-1-84391-917-9(6)) Hesperus Pr. GBR. Dist: Independent Pubs. Group.

Carter, Elizabeth. Memoirs of the Life of Mrs Elizabeth Carter: With a New Edition of her Poems, Some of Which Have Never Appeared Before. Pennington, Montagu, ed. 2011. (Cambridge Library Collection - Women's Writing Ser.). (ENG., Illus.). 658p. pap. 45.00 (978-1-108-03386-2(5)) Cambridge Univ. Pr.

Carter, Marie. The Trapeze Diaries. 2008. 95p. 26.00 (978-1-931236-85-0(2)); 95p. pap. 16.00 (978-1-931236-84-3(4)); 96p. per. 16.00 net. (978-1-934909-84-3(X)) Hanging Loose Pr.

Carter, Robert Ayres. I'll Go No More A-Roving: More Memories of A Writer's Life; 1976-1983. 2011. 580p. pap. 23.28 (978-1-4634-4714-4(0)) AuthorHouse.

Carter, Robert Ayres. Somewhere I Have Never Traveled: Memories of A Writer's Life 1969-1976. 2010. 464p. pap. 20.49 (978-1-4520-3543-7(1)) AuthorHouse.

Carter, Zoe FitzGerald. Imperfect Endings: A Daughter's Story of Love, Loss, & Letting Go. 2011. (ENG.). 288p. pap. 15.00 (978-1-4391-4831-0(7)) Simon & Schuster.

Cartmell, J. W., ed. Goethe's Boyhood: Taken from the First Three Books of Autobiography. 2011. (GER & ENG.). 176p. pap. 24.99 (978-0-521-16952-3(6)) Cambridge Univ. Pr.

Caruso, Donna. Journey Without A Map: Stories of an Immigrant Daughter of Immigrants. 2008. (ENG.). 223p. pap. 19.95 (978-1-897235-36-2(4)) Thistledown Pr., Ltd. CAN. Dist: Univ. of Toronto Pr.

Cary, Elisabeth Luther. Emerson, Poet & Thinker. 2009. 172p. pap. 19.99 (978-1-4588-2565-0(5)) General Bks. LLC.

—William Morris, Poet, Craftsman, Socialist. 2010. 144p. pap. (978-1-152-11827-0(7)) Books LLC.

Casares, Adolfo Bioy. Borges. 2007. (SPA., Illus.). 1663p. (978-950-732-085-9(7)) Ediciones Destino.

Casares, Adolfo Bioy & Bioy Casares, Adolfo. Borges. 2006. 1664p. 58.95 (978-84-233-3873-3(8)) Ediciones Destino ESP. Dist: Planeta Publishing Corp.

Case, Henry Jay. Guy Hamilton Scull, Soldier, Writer, Explorer & War Correspondent. 2009. 324p. pap. 29.75 (978-1-115-58200-1(3)) BiblioBazaar.

Case, Keshia A., et al. Edgar Allan Poe in Richmond. 2009. (Images of America Ser.). (ENG., Illus.). 128p. pap. 21.99 (978-0-7385-6714-3(0)) Arcadia Publishing.

Cash, Jean W. Larry Brown: A Writer's Life. 2011. (Willie Morris Books in Memoir & Biography Ser.). (ENG., Illus.). 400p. 35.00 (978-1-60473-980-0(0)) Univ. Pr. of Mississippi.

Casil, Amy Sterling. Lois Duncan. 2009. (Library of Author Biographies Ser.). 112p. (gr. 5-8). 63.90 (978-1-60853-543-9(6), Rosen Central) Rosen Publishing Group, Inc., The.

Castillo, Celia. Against the Odds: Memoirs of A Migrant Worker. 2011. 94p. pap. 15.99 (978-1-4628-8634-0(5)) Xlibris Corp.

Castronovo, David & Groth, Janet. Critic in Love: A Romantic Biography of Edmund Wilson. 2007. (ENG., Illus.). 240p. per. 16.95 (978-1-59376-153-0(8)) Counterpoint LLC.

Catling, Patrick Skene. Better Than Working. 2006. (ENG., Illus.). 302p. pap. 27.95 (978-1-905483-06-8(6)) Liberties Pr. IRL. Dist: Dufour Editions, Inc.

Cave, Nick. Nick Cave: Sinner Saint - The True Confessions, Thirty Years of Essential Interviews. Snow, Mat, ed. 2011. (ENG., Illus.). 224p. pap. 19.95 (978-0-85965-448-7(6)) Plexus Publishing, Ltd. GBR. Dist: Perseus-PGW.

Chacel, Rosa. Memorias de Leticia Valle. Morán Rodriguez, Carmen, tr. 2010. (SPA.). 328p. pap. 16.80 (978-84-8489-458-2(4)) Iberoamericana Vervuert Publishing Corp.

Chaddock, Katherine Elise. The Multi-Talented Mr. Erskine: Shaping Mass Culture through Great Books & Fine Music. 2012. (ENG., Illus.). 270p. 90.00 (978-0-230-11775-4(9)) Palgrave Macmillan.

Chadwick, Ellis H. In the Footsteps of the Bront#235;s. 2011. (Cambridge Library Collection - Literary Studies). (ENG., Illus.). 604p. pap. 43.00 ***(978-1-108-03416-6(0))*** Cambridge Univ. Pr.

Chambers, Claire. British Muslim Fictions: Interviews with Contemporary Writers. 2011. (ENG., Illus.). 288p. 90.00 *(978-0-230-25233-2(8))* Palgrave Macmillan.

Chambers, Claire, ed. British Muslim Fictions: Interviews with Contemporary Writers. 2011. (ENG., Illus.). 288p. pap. 28.00 *(978-0-230-30878-7(3))* Palgrave Macmillan.

Chambers, Douglas B., ed. Personal Souths: Interviews from the Southern Quarterly. 2012. (ENG.). 352p. 65.00 ***(978-1-61703-290-5(5))***; 312p. pap. 30.00 ***(978-1-61703-291-2(3))*** Univ. Pr. of Mississippi.

Chambers, Roland. The Last Englishman: The Double Life of Arthur Ransome. 2012. (ENG., Illus.). 400p. 29.95 *(978-1-56792-417-6(4))* Godine, David R. Pub.

Chamoun, Tracy. In the Name of the Father. 2009. 123p. pap. 17.97 *(978-0-557-09473-8(9))* Lulu Enterprises Inc.

Chang, Ying-Ying. The Woman Who Could Not Forget: Iris Chang Before & Beyond the Rape of Nanking - A Memoir. 2011. (ENG., Illus.). 400p. 29.95 *(978-1-60598-172-7(9)*, 605172) Pegasus Bks.

Chaos, I. B. Trauma: The Story of My Life. 2011. 136p. pap. 10.68 ***(978-1-4634-2845-7(6))*** AuthorHouse.

Charters, Ann & Charters, Samuel Barclay. Brother-Souls: John Clellon Holmes, Jack Kerouac, & the Beat Generation. 2010. (ENG., Illus.). 464p. 35.00 *(978-1-60473-579-6(1))* Univ. Pr. of Mississippi.

Chase, Lewis Nathaniel. Poe & His Poetry. 2008. 132p. 35.95 *(978-1-4366-2320-9(0))*; pap. 20.95 *(978-0-548-86643-1(1))* Kessinger Publishing, LLC.

Cheche, Tom. Exit: A Sporting Life Just off the Jersey Turnpike. 2009. 252p. pap. 15.95 *(978-1-934937-90-7(8))* Mill City Pr., Inc.

Cheever, Susan. Louisa May Alcott. l.t. ed. 2011. 443p. 31.99 *(978-1-4104-3552-1(0))* Thorndike Pr.

—Louisa May Alcott: A Personal Biography. (ENG., Illus.). 320p. 2011. pap. 16.00 *(978-1-4165-6992-3(8))* 2010. 26.00 *(978-1-4165-6991-6(X))* Simon & Schuster.

Chekhov, Mikhail Pavlovich. Anton Chekhov: A Brother's Memoir. Alper, Eugene, tr. from RUS. 2009. (ENG., Illus.). 256p. 25.00 *(978-0-230-61883-1(9))* Palgrave Macmillan.

Chen, Peter Min-Liang. A Scholar's Path: An Anthology of Classical Chinese Poems & Prose of Chen Qing Shan - A Pioneer Writer of Malayan-Singapore Literature. 2010. (Illus.). 636p. pap. 45.00 *(978-981-4317-48-1(9))* World Scientific Publishing Co., Inc.

Chen, William Y. Yi Wang San Ji. 2008. (CHI & ENG.). 185p. pap. ***(978-0-939083-82-4(5))*** Kan sasana Printer.

Cheney, Ednah, ed. Louisa May Alcott: Her Life, Letters, & Journals. 2010. (ENG., Illus.). 428p. pap. 19.95 *(978-1-4290-4460-8(8))* Applewood Bks.

Cheng, Shirley. The Adventures of a Blind & Disabled Award-Winning Author: Inspiration & Motivation to Empower You to Go for Your Own Gold Medals. 2009. 210p. pap. 15.97 *(978-0-615-17515-7(5))* Dance With Your Heart! Publishing.

Cherry, Kelly. Girl in a Library: On Women Writers & the Writing Life. 2009. 234p. pap. 16.95 *(978-1-886157-66-8(9))* BkMk Pr. of the Univ. of Missouri-Kansas City.

Chessell, Antony. The LIFE & TIMES of ABRAHAM HAYWARD, Q. C. VICTORIAN ESSAYIST 'One of the two best read men in England' 2008. (Illus.). 407p. 47.50 *(978-1-4092-2467-9(8))* Lulu Enterprises Inc.

Chesterton, Cecil & Perry, Michael W. G.K. Chesterton, a Criticism. 2007. (Illus.). 179p. *(978-1-58742-060-3(0))* Inkling Bks.

Chetanananda. Girish Chandra Ghosh: A Bohemian Devotee of Sri Ramakrishna. 2009. *(978-0-916356-92-7(2))*; pap. *(978-0-916356-93-4(0))* Vedanta Society of Saint Louis.

Chilton, John. Hot Jazz, Warm Feet. 2007. (Illus.). 268p. pap. 24.00 *(978-0-9550908-3-7(0))* Northway Pubns. GBR. Dist: Parkwest Pubns., Inc.

Chin, Staceyann. The Other Side of Paradise: A Memoir. 2010. (ENG.). 304p. pap. 16.00 *(978-0-7432-9291-7(X)*, Scribner) Scribner.

Chipperfield, Faith. In Quest of Love the Life & Death of M. 2006. pap. 30.95 *(978-1-4286-5595-9(6))* Kessinger Publishing, LLC.

Chisholm, Anne. Frances Partridge: The Biography. 2010. (ENG., Illus.). 404p. pap. 16.95 *(978-0-7538-2699-7(2)*, Phoenix) Orion Publishing Group, Ltd. GBR. Dist: Independent Pubs. Group.

Chitham, Edward. A Life of Emily Bronte. 2010. (ENG., Illus.). 224p. pap. 29.95 *(978-1-84868-406-5(1))* Amberley Publishing GBR. Dist: Casemate Pubs. & Bk. Distributors, LLC.

Chittick, Kathryn. Dickens & The 1830s. 2010. (ENG.). 224p. pap. 32.99 *(978-0-521-12939-8(7))* Cambridge Univ. Pr.

Chong, Kevin. My Year of the Racehorse: Falling in Love with the Sport of Kings, 1 vol. 2012. (ENG.). 232p. pap. 18.95 ***(978-1-55365-520-6(6)***, Greystone Bks.) D&M Pubs. Inc. CAN. Dist: Perseus-PGW.

Chong, Kil-Su. Kuunmong Tasi Ilki. 2010. 272p. *(978-89-7199-397-2(9))* Dolbegae Publishing Co.

Chorley, Henry Fothergill. Personal Reminiscences by Chorley, Plancht, & Young Ed by Richard Henry Stoddard. 2006. 320p. per. 23.99 *(978-1-4255-3161-4(X))* MPublishing.

Chou, E. Shan. Memory Violence, Queues: Lu Xun Interprets China. 2011. pap. ***(978-0-924304-68-2(5))*** Assn. for Asian Studies, Inc.

Choyce, Lesley. Seven Ravens: Two Summers in a Life by the Sea. 2009. 200p. pap. 19.00 *(978-1-894987-39-4(X))* Wolsak & Wynn Pubs., Ltd. CAN. Dist: Univ. of Toronto Pr.

Christensen, Mark. Acid Christ: Ken Kesey, LSD, & the Politics of Ecstasy. 2010. (ENG., Illus.). 440p. 26.95 *(978-1-936182-00-8(9))* Schaffner Pr., Inc.

Christensen, Mark. Acid Christ: Ken Kesey, LSD & the Politics of Ecstasy. 2011. (ENG.). 440p. pap. 16.95 ***(978-1-936182-27-5(0))*** Schaffner Pr., Inc.

Christian, William. Parkin: Canada's Most Famous Forgotten Man. 2008. (ENG., Illus.). 349p. pap. 26.95 *(978-0-9781600-3-6(7))* Dundurn CAN. Dist: Ingram Pub. Services.

Christie, Agatha. An Autobiography. 2012. (ENG.). 560p. pap. 16.99 ***(978-0-06-220457-8(2)***, William Morrow Paperbacks) HarperCollins Pubs.

Christie, Agatha. Autobiography. 2011. (ENG., Illus.). 544p. 29.99 *(978-0-06-207359-4(1))* HarperCollins Pubs.

Chura, Patrick. Thoreau the Land Surveyor. (ENG., Illus.). 2011. 224p. pap. 19.95 ***(978-0-8130-4147-6(3))*** 2010. 192p. 34.95 *(978-0-8130-3493-5(0))* Univ. Pr. of Florida.

Ciampi, Paolo. I due Viaggiatori: Alla scoperta del mondo con Odoardo Beccari ed Emilio Salgari. 2010. (non Guide Ser.). (ITA., Illus.). 192p. (C). pap. 20.00 *(978-88-564-0129-5(0))* Polistampa ITA. Dist: Brown, David Bk. Co., The.

Cixous, Hélène. Hélène Cixous. 2011. (ENG.). 224p. pap. 19.95 *(978-0-7456-4868-2(1))* Polity Pr. GBR. Dist: Wiley, John & Sons, Inc.

Cixous, Héléne. Hemlock. 2011. (ENG.). 224p. 64.95 *(978-0-7456-4867-5(3))* Polity Pr. GBR. Dist: Wiley, John & Sons, Inc.

Cixous, Hélène & Calle-Gruber, Mireille. Hélène Cixous, Photos de Racines. (FRE., Illus.). 212p. *(978-2-7210-0454-3(9))* Des Femmes.

Clabough, Casey. The Art of the Magic Striptease: The Literary Layers of George Garrett. 2008. (ENG.). 224p. 39.95 *(978-0-8130-3176-7(1))* Univ. Pr. of Florida.

Clara Barrus. Our Friend John Burroughs. 2007. (ENG.). 168p. pap. 19.99 *(978-1-4264-4944-4(5))* 2006. 188p. pap. 21.99 *(978-1-4264-5245-1(4))* BiblioBazaar.

Claridge, Laura. Emily Post: Daughter of the Gilded Age, Mistress of American Manners. 2009. (ENG., Illus.). 560p. pap. 18.00 *(978-0-8129-6741-8(0)*, Random Hse. Trade Paperbacks) Random House Publishing Group.

Clarke, Edwin Leavitt. American Men of Letters, Their Nature & Nurture. 2009. 172p. 26.99 *(978-1-115-21975-4(8))*; 30.99 *(978-1-115-21977-8(4))*; pap. 21.75 *(978-1-115-21973-0(1))* BiblioBazaar.

Clarke, Gerald. Capote: A Biography. 2010. (ENG., Illus.). 656p. pap. 17.99 *(978-1-4391-8750-0(9))* Simon & Schuster.

Clarke, Jaime, ed. Conversations with Jonathan Lethem. 2011. (Literary Conversations Ser.). (ENG.). 224p. pap. 25.00 ***(978-1-60473-972-5(X))***; 65.00 *(978-1-60473-963-3(0))* Univ. Pr. of Mississippi.

Clarkson, Wensley. Car Trouble: A Childhood on Four Wheels. 2011. (ENG., Illus.). 224p. pap. 16.95 *(978-1-84596-612-6(0))* Mainstream Publishing Co., Ltd. GBR. Dist: Independent Pubs. Group.

Claude Cl, Smith. Ohio Outback. 2011. 160p. 24.95 *(978-1-60635-054-6(4))* Kent State Univ. Pr.

Clayton, John. The Cowboy Girl: The Life of Caroline Lockhart. 2007. (Women in the West Ser.). (ENG., Illus.). 338p. pap. 21.95 *(978-0-8032-5990-4(5)*, Bison Bks.) Univ. of Nebraska Pr.

Cleverly, Michael & Braudis, Bob. The Kitchen Readings: Untold Stories of Hunter S. Thompson. 2008. (Illus.). 304p. pap. 13.99 *(978-0-06-115928-2(X)*, HarperPerennial) HarperCollins Pubs.

Clews, Hetty. The Shining Places: From the End to the Beginning. 2011. 84p. 20.95 ***(978-1-4620-0076-0(2))*** iUniverse, Inc.

Cliff, Michelle. If I Could Write This in Fire. 2008. 104p. 21.95 *(978-0-8166-5474-1(3))*; xi, 89p. pap. *(978-0-8166-5475-8(1))* Univ. of Minnesota Pr.

Clifford, Catherine Mae. The Journey Begins. 2008. 152p. pap. 13.99 *(978-1-60477-845-8(8))* Xulon Pr., Inc.

Clinton, Craig. Cora Urquhart Potter: The Victorian Actress as Provocateur. 2010. (ENG., Illus.). 262p. pap. 55.00 *(978-0-7864-4957-6(8))* McFarland & Co., Inc. Pubs.

Cobbe, Frances P. Life of Frances Power Cobbe. reprint ed. 250.00 *(978-0-7222-1554-8(1))* Library Reprints, Inc.

Coelho, Paulo. Palabros Esenciales. 2008.Tr. of Essential Words. (SPA.). 78p. 16.95 *(978-987-612-146-0(4))* V & R Editorial ARG. Dist: Baker & Taylor Bks.

Coffey, B. R., ed. Summer Days: Stories from Childhood. 2007. 248p. pap. 22.50 *(978-1-921361-03-6(4))* Fremantle Pr. AUS. Dist: Independent Pubs. Group.

Cohen, Amy. The Late Bloomer's Revolution. 2008. (ENG.). 304p. pap. 12.95 *(978-0-7868-8817-7(2))* Hyperion Pr.

Cohn. Edward Albee-Aw V77. 2009. pap. 25.00 *(978-0-8166-0527-9(0))* Univ. of Minnesota Pr.

Cole, G. D. H. Samuel Butler. 2007. (ENG.). 116p. 34.95 *(978-0-548-06642-3(6))* Kessinger Publishing, LLC.

Cole, Tuna Shards a Life in Pieces. 2011. 250p. pap. 15.95 ***(978-0-557-56131-5(0))*** Lulu Enterprises Inc.

Coleman, Finnie D. Sutton E. Griggs & the Struggle Against White Supremacy. 2007. 232p. 35.00 *(978-1-57233-480-9(0))* Univ. of Tennessee Pr.

Coleridge, Samuel Taylor. Biographia Epistolaris, Volume 1. 2007. (ENG.). 328p. pap. 24.99 *(978-1-4264-2962-0(2))*; 290p. pap. 21.99 *(978-1-4264-3015-2(9))* BiblioBazaar.

—Letters of Samuel Taylor Coleridge. 2009. 358p. pap. *(978-0-217-85646-1(2))* Books LLC.

Coles, Don A Dropped Glove in Regent Street: An Autobiography by Other Means. 2007. (ENG., Illus.). 144p. per. 14.95 *(978-1-55065-222-2(2))* Vehicule Pr. CAN. Dist: Independent Pubs. Group.

Collier, J. Payne. Memoirs of the Principal Actors in the Plays of Shakespeare. 2008. 320p. 45.95 *(978-1-4365-6194-5(9))* 2007. (ENG.). 324p. per. 30.95 *(978-0-548-76621-7(5))* Kessinger Publishing, LLC.

—Memoirs of the Principal Actors in the Plays of Shakespeare. 2007. (ENG.). 320p. per. *(978-1-4067-3566-6(3))* Read Bks.

Colquhoun, Archibald. Manzoni & His Times: A Biography. 2011. 322p. 50.95 ***(978-1-258-02898-5(0))*** Literary Licensing, LLC.

Coltelli, Laura, ed. Reading Leslie Marmon Silko: Critical Perspectives Through Gardens in the Dunes. 2008. (Essays & Studies). (ENG.). 240p. pap. 24.95 *(978-88-8492-432-2(4))* Plus/Pisa University Pr. ITA. Dist: Univ. of Nebraska Pr.

Colton, Elaine. The Newport Girls: A Memoir. 2010. 124p. 23.95 *(978-1-4502-3108-4(X))*; (ENG.). pap. 13.95 *(978-1-4502-3106-0(3))* iUniverse, Inc.

Cornillas José. Vidas y muertes de Luis Martín-Santos. 2009. (Tiempo de Memoria Ser.: Vol. 74). (SPA., Illus.). 456p. pap. 25.95 *(978-84-8383-123-6(6))* Tusquets Editores ESP. Dist: Ediciones Urano S. A.

Corners, Peter. Growing up Dead: The Hallucinated Confessions of a Teenage Deadhead. 2009. (ENG.). 288p. pap. 14.95 *(978-0-306-81733-5(0))* Da Capo Pr., Inc.

Conniff, Richard. Swimming with Piranhas at Feeding Time: My Life Doing Dumb Stuff with Animals. 2009. (ENG.). 320p. 25.95 *(978-0-393-06893-1(5)*, 6893) Norton, W. W. & Co., Inc.

Connon, Bryan. Beverley Nichols: A Life. 2009. (ENG.). 344p. pap. 29.95 *(978-1-60469-044-6(5)*, 1604690445) Timber Pr., Inc.

Conrad, John. Joseph Conrad: Times Remembered: 'Ojciec Jest Tutaj' 2008. (ENG.). 236p. pap. 31.99 *(978-0-521-07128-4(3))* Cambridge Univ. Pr.

Conrad, Joseph. Joseph Conrad's Letters to R. B. Cunninghame Graham. 2011. (ENG.). 238p. pap. 34.99 *(978-0-521-12941-1(9))* Cambridge Univ. Pr.

—A Personal Record. Date not set. lib. bdg. 17.95 *(978-0-8488-1670-4(6))* Amereon LTD.

—A Personal Record. 116p. 2008. 24.99 *(978-0-554-21533-4(0))* 2008. 21.99 *(978-0-554-30836-4(3))* 2007. (ENG.). pap. 19.99 *(978-1-4264-0370-5(4))* 2007. (ENG.). pap. 18.99 *(978-1-4264-0319-4(4))* BiblioBazaar.

—A Personal Record. 2009. 92p. pap. *(978-0-217-67454-6(2))* Books LLC.

—A Personal Record. Najder, Zdzislaw & Stape, J. H., eds. 2008. (Cambridge Edition of the Works of Joseph Conrad Ser.). (ENG., Illus.). 284p. 162.99 *(978-0-521-86176-2(4))* Cambridge Univ. Pr.

—A Personal Record. 2007. (ENG.). 112p. per. *(978-1-4065-8533-9(5))* Dodo Pr.

—A Personal Record. 2008. 272p. 42.95 *(978-1-4365-2066-3(5))* 2007. (ENG.). 276p. per. 27.95 *(978-0-548-74082-8(8))* Kessinger Publishing, LLC.

—A Personal Record. 2008. 162p. 29.95 *(978-1-4344-7455-1(0))*; 164p. pap. 14.95 *(978-1-4344-7419-3(4))* Wildside Pr., LLC.

Conroy, Pat. My Reading Life. 2010. (ENG., Illus.). 352p. 25.00 *(978-0-385-53357-7(8)*, Talese, Nan A.) Knopf Doubleday Publishing Group.

—My Reading Life. l.t. ed. 2010. (ENG.). 352p. pap. 25.00 *(978-0-7393-7784-0(1))* Random Hse. Large Print.

Constant, Benjamin. The Red Book. 2011. (Oneworld Classics Ser.). (ENG.). 76p. pap. 12.95 *(978-1-84749-164-0(2))* Alma Classics GBR. Dist: Independent Pubs. Group.

Contemporary Authors. (Contemporary Authors Ser.). (ENG.). 2008. 480p. 293.00 *(978-0-7876-9528-6(9))* 2008. 480p. 293.00 *(978-0-7876-9525-5(4))* 2008. 480p. 293.00 *(978-0-7876-9527-9(0))* 2008. 480p. 293.00 *(978-0-7876-9526-2(2))* 2008. 480p. 293.00 *(978-0-7876-9524-8(6))* 2008. 464p. 293.00 *(978-0-7876-9523-1(8))* 2008. 480p. 293.00 *(978-0-7876-9522-4(X))* 2008. 464p. 293.00 *(978-0-7876-9521-7(1))* 2007. 464p. 293.00 *(978-0-7876-7886-9(4))*274. 2008. 480p. 293.00 *(978-1-4144-1917-6(1))*275. 2009. 464p. 293.00 *(978-1-4144-1918-3(X))*276. 2009. 464p. 293.00 *(978-1-4144-1919-0(8))*277. 2009. 464p. 293.00 *(978-1-4144-1920-6(1))*278. 2009. 480p. 293.00 *(978-1-4144-3430-8(8))* Vol. 287. 2010. 480p. 293.00 *(978-1-4144-3952-5(0))* Vol. 288. 2010. 293.00 *(978-1-4144-3953-2(9))* Vol. 289. 2010. 293.00 *(978-1-4144-3954-9(7))* Vol. 290. 2010. 293.00 *(978-1-4144-3955-6(5))* Vol. 291. 2010. 293.00 *(978-1-4144-3956-3(3))* Vol. 292. 2010. 293.00 *(978-1-4144-3957-0(1))* Cengage Gale.

Contemporary Authors: A Bio-Bibliographical Guide to Current Writers in Fiction, General Nonfiction, Poetry, Journalism, Drama, Motion Pictures, Television. 2011. (ENG.). 293.00 *(978-1-4144-6087-1(2))*; 293.00 *(978-1-4144-6086-4(4))*; (ENG.). 293.00 *(978-1-4144-6085-7(6))*; (ENG.). 293.00 *(978-1-4144-6084-0(8))* Cengage Gale.

Contemporary Authors New Revision. 2010. (Contemporary Authors New Revision Ser.). (ENG.). Vol. 193. 193rd rev. ed. 464p. 293.00 *(978-1-4144-3963-1(6))* Vol. 194. 194th rev. ed. 464p. 293.00 *(978-1-4144-3964-8(4))* Vol. 195. 195th rev. ed. 464p. 293.00 *(978-1-4144-3965-5(2))* Vol. 196. 196th rev. ed. 293.00 *(978-1-4144-3966-2(0))* Vol. 197. 197th rev. ed. 293.00 *(978-1-4144-3967-9(9))* Vol. 198. 198th rev. ed. 293.00 *(978-1-4144-3968-6(7))* Vol. 199. 199th rev. ed. 293.00 *(978-1-4144-3969-3(5))* Cengage Gale.

Contemporary Authors New Revision Series. (Contemporary Authors New Revision Ser.). 179. 2008. 448p. 293.00 *(978-1-4144-1923-7(6))*180. 2008. 480p. 293.00 *(978-1-4144-1924-4(4))*181. rev. ed. 2009. 464p. 293.00 *(978-1-4144-1925-1(2))*182. rev. ed. 2009. 464p. 293.00 *(978-1-4144-1926-8(0))*183. rev. ed. 2009. 448p. 293.00 *(978-1-4144-1927-5(9))*184. 184th rev. ed. 2009. 464p. 293.00 *(978-1-4144-3435-3(9))* Vol. 200. 200th rev. ed. 2010. 293.00 *(978-1-4144-4595-3(4))* Cengage Gale.

Contemporary Authors New Revision Series, Vol. 201. 201st rev. ed. 2010. (Contemporary Authors New Revision Ser.). 293.00 *(978-1-4144-4596-0(2))* Cengage Gale.

Contemporary Authors New Revision Series: A Bio-Bibliographical Guide to Current Writers in Fiction, General Non-Fiction, Poetry, Journalism, Drama, Motion Pictures, Television, & Other Fields. 2011. (ENG.). 293.00 *(978-1-4144-6111-3(9))*; (ENG.). 293.00 *(978-1-4144-6110-6(0))*; (ENG.). 293.00 *(978-1-4144-6109-0(7))*; (ENG.). 293.00 *(978-1-4144-6108-3(9))*; 293.00 *(978-1-4144-6107-6(0))*; (ENG.). 293.00 *(978-1-4144-6106-9(2))* Cengage Gale.

Conway, Megan, ed. Sixteenth-Century French Writers, Vol. 327. 2006. (Dictionary of Literary Biography Ser.: Vol. 327). (ENG., Illus.). 560p. 315.00 *(978-0-7876-8145-6(8))* Cengage Gale.

Conway, Steven. Know Hope: The Baydan Huxley Story. 2009. 228p. pap. 15.00 *(978-1-4389-5299-4(6))* AuthorHouse.

Cook, Daniel. Cook: The Lives of Jonathan Swift, 3 vols. 2011. *(978-0-415-59137-9(6))*; *(978-0-415-59136-2(8))*; *(978-0-415-59135-5(X))* Routledge.

Cook, Daniel, ed. Cook Set: The Lives of Jonathan Swift, 3 vols. 2011. (ENG.). 1669p. (C). 795.00 *(978-0-415-59134-8(1))* Routledge.

Cook, Edward Tyas. The Life of John Ruskin, 1819-1860. 2010. (Cambridge Library Collection - Literary Studies). (ENG., Illus.). 580p. pap. 43.00 *(978-1-108-00971-3(9))* Cambridge Univ. Pr.

—The Life of John Ruskin, 1860-1900, 2. 2010. (Cambridge Library Collection - Literary Studies). (ENG., Illus.). 640p. pap. 43.00 *(978-1-108-00972-0(7))* Cambridge Univ. Pr.

Cook, Paul. American Literature from the Colonies to the Civil War. rev. ed. 2008. (ENG.). 448p. pap. 77.96 *(978-0-7575-5848-1(8))* Kendall Hunt Publishing Co.

Cook, Richard M. Alfred Kazin: A Biography. 2008. (ENG., Illus.). 464p. 35.00 *(978-0-300-11505-5(9))* Yale Univ. Pr.

Cooke, George Willis. George Eliot: A Critical Study of Her Life, Writings & Philosophy. 2007. 388p. per. *(978-1-4065-1499-5(3))* Dodo Pr.

—George Eliot: A Critical Study of her Life, Writings & Philosophy. 2010. (Cambridge Library Collection - Literary Studies). 450p. pap. 32.99 *(978-1-108-01961-3(7))* Cambridge Univ. Pr.

—George Eliot; a Critical Study of Her Life, Writings & Philosophy. 2007. (ENG.). 428p. pap. 26.99 *(978-1-4264-5572-8(0))*; 484p. pap. 30.99 *(978-1-4264-5620-6(4))* BiblioBazaar.

Cooke, Harriet B. Memories of My Life Work the Autobiography of Mrs Harriet B Cooke. 2006. 360p. per. 26.99 *(978-1-4255-3659-6(X))* MPublishing.

Cooke, Stewart. The Court Journals & Letters of Frances Burney: Volume II: 1787. 2011. (Illus.). 416p. 185.00 *(978-0-19-926280-9(2))* Oxford Univ. Pr., Inc.

Cooper, Suzanne Fagence. Effie: The Passionate Lives of Effie Gray, John Ruskin & John Everett Millais. (ENG.). 288p. 2012. pap. 15.99 ***(978-1-250-01625-6(8)***, St. Martin's Griffin) 2011. (Illus.). 26.99 *(978-0-312-58173-2(4))* St. Martin's Pr.

Copland, James L. Life's Observations by an Everyday Nobody. 2010. 220p. pap. 14.95 *(978-1-60911-341-4(1)*, Eloquent Bks.) AEG Literary Publishing Services, Inc.

Corby Jr., Elmer S. 1897-2007: 110 Years of Memories, More Smiles Than Tears, 1 vol. 2010. 188p. pap. 24.95 *(978-1-4489-8269-1(3))* PublishAmerica, Inc.

Corder, Jim W. Yonder: Life on the Far Side of Change. 2011. (ENG.). 248p. 24.95 ***(978-0-8203-3803-3(6))*** Univ. of Georgia Pr.

Corfe, Robert. This Was My England: The Story of a Childhood. 2011. (ENG., Illus.). 357p. pap. 30.18 ***(978-1-906791-73-5(2))*** Arena Bks. GBR. Dist: Lightning Source UK, Ltd.

Corke, Helen. In Our Infancy, 1882-1912 Pt. 1: An Autobiography. 2008. (ENG.). 260p. pap. 37.99 *(978-0-521-08166-5(1))* Cambridge Univ. Pr.

Cornwall, Harry. Back to California. 2010. 271p. pap. 22.95 *(978-1-4327-4296-6(5))* Outskirts Pr., Inc.

Cornwell, Gareth, et al. The Columbia Guide to South African Literature in English Since 1945. 2010. (Columbia Guides to Literature Since 1945 Ser.). (ENG., Illus.). 288p. (gr. 17). 80.00 *(978-0-231-13046-2(5))* Columbia Univ. Pr.

Corpet, Olivier & White, Garrett, eds. Woman of Letters: Irne Nmirovsky & Suite Franaise. 2008. (ENG.). 128p. 29.95 *(978-0-9794727-5-6(X))* Five Ties Publishing.

Coulanges, Danielle. Cads, Princes & Best Friends: A Tale of Lust, Love & Redemption. 2008. (ENG.). 292p. 30.95 *(978-0-595-70171-1(X))*; per. 20.95 *(978-0-595-46224-7(3))* iUniverse, Inc.

Courthope, William. Addison. 2011. (Cambridge Library Collection - English Men of Letters Ser.). (ENG.). 204p. pap. 22.99 ***(978-1-108-03442-5(X))*** Cambridge Univ. Pr.

Cousins, A. D. Companion to Thomas More. Grace, Damian, ed. 2009. (ENG.). 253p. 58.00 *(978-1-61147-420-6(5))* Fairleigh Dickinson Univ. Pr.

Cousins, A. D. & Grace, Damian. A Companion to Thomas More. 2009. 58.00 *(978-0-8386-4215-3(2))* Fairleigh Dickinson Univ. Pr.

Coustillas, Pierre. The Heroic Life of George Gissing, 1857-1888 Part I, Pt. 1. 2011. (ENG., Illus.). 384p. 99.00 *(978-1-84893-171-8(9))* Pickering & Chatto Pubs., Ltd. GBR. Dist: Ashgate Publishing Co.

—The Heroic Life of George Gissing, 1888-1897 Part II. 2012. (ENG.). 384p. 99.00 *(978-1-84893-173-2(5))* Pickering & Chatto Pubs., Ltd. GBR. Dist: Ashgate Publishing Co.

A

—The Heroic Life of George Gissing, 1897-1903 Part III, 1 vol. 2012. (ENG.). 500p. 99.00 *(978-1-84893-175-6(1))* Pickering & Chatto Pubs., Ltd. GBR. Dist: Ashgate Publishing Co.

Cox, Juanita, ed. In the Eye of the Storm: Edgar Mittelholzer, 1909-2009 - Critical Perspectives. 2012. 352p. pap. 35.95 *(978-1-84523-128-6(7))* Peepal Tree Pr., Ltd. GBR. Dist: Independent Pubs. Group.

Coyne, Patrick. A Bio-Bibliography of Alice Duer Miller, American Writer, 1874-1942. 2010. (Illus.). 340p. 119.95 *(978-0-7734-3756-2(8))* Mellen, Edwin Pr., The.

Cozean, Jesse. My Grandfather's War: A Young Man's Lessons from the Greatest Generation. 2011. (ENG., Illus.). 256p. 19.95 *(978-0-7627-7383-1(9)*, Lyons Pr.) Globe Pequot Pr., The.

Craciun, Adriana, et al. The Works of Charlotte Smith, 4 vols., Pt. III. Curran, Stuart, ed. 2007. (Pickering Masters Ser.). (ENG.). 1712p. 675.00 *(978-1-85196-795-7(8))* Pickering & Chatto Pubs., Ltd. GBR. Dist: Ashgate Publishing Co.

Crain, Doreen A. My Son & an Alien! 2006. 17.00 *(978-0-8059-8830-7(0))* Dorrance Publishing Co., Inc.

Crampton, Nancy. Writers. 2007. (ENG.). 224p. pap. 25.00 *(978-1-59372-028-5(9))* Quantuck Lane Pr. & The Mill Road Collaborative, The.

Cranfill, Thomas Mabry & Bruce, Dorothy Hart. Barnaby Rich. 2011. (ENG.). 146p. pap. 19.95 *(978-0-292-72933-9(2))* Univ. of Texas Pr.

Crankshaw, Edward. Tolstoy: The Making of a Novelist. 2012. 278p. pap. ***(978-1-4482-0521-9(2)***, 146527, Bloomsbury Reader) Bloomsbury Publishing Plc.

Crawford, Charlotte. Sterling. 2011. 144p. pap. 13.14 ***(978-1-4269-6506-7(0))*** Trafford Publishing.

Cremony, John Carey. Life among the Apaches. 2008. (ENG.). 325p. 36.99 *(978-1-4264-1071-0(9))*; 32.99 *(978-1-4264-1153-3(7))*; pap. 31.75 *(978-1-4264-1087-1(5))*; pap. 30.75 *(978-1-4264-1137-3(5))* BiblioBazaar.

—Life among the Apaches. 2009. 196p. pap. *(978-1-150-11268-3(9))* Books LLC.

Crews, Daniel A. Twilight of the Renaissance: The Life of Juan de Valdés. 2008. (SPA & ENG., Illus.). 320p. *(978-0-8020-9867-2(3))* Univ. of Toronto Pr.

Crisler, Jesse & McElrath, Joseph. Frank Norris: A Life. 2010. (ENG., Illus.). 520p. pap. 25.00 *(978-0-252-07729-6(6))* Univ. of Illinois Pr.

Crisler, Jesse S. & Crowe, Chris. "How I Came to Write" LDS Authors for Young Adults. 2007. 292p. pap. 15.00 *(978-0-939555-09-3(3))* Ctr. for the Study of Christian Values in Literature.

Croft-Cooke, Rupert. The Purple Streak. 2012. 190p. pap. ***(978-1-4482-0497-7(6)***, 146506, Bloomsbury Reader) Bloomsbury Publishing Plc.

—The Wild Hills. 2012. 218p. pap. ***(978-1-4482-0522-6(0)***, 146528, Bloomsbury Reader) Bloomsbury Publishing Plc.

Cronin, John. Gerald Griffin, 1803-1840: A Critical Biography. 2010. (ENG.). 188p. pap. 28.99 *(978-0-521-12943-5(5))* Cambridge Univ. Pr.

Crosby, Howard. George Henry Moore, L L D: A memoir / by Rev. Howard Crosby, D. D. 2011. 26p. pap. 11.99 ***(978-1-4181-9295-2(3))*** MPublishing.

Crosland, Camilla. Landmarks of a Literary Life 1820-1892. 2010. (Cambridge Library Collection - Women's Writing Ser.). (Illus.). 316p. pap. 24.99 *(978-1-108-02194-4(8))* Cambridge Univ. Pr.

Crossley-Holland, Kevin. Hidden Roads: A Memoir of Childhood. 2010. (ENG., Illus.). 288p. pap. 13.95 *(978-1-84916-211-1(5))* Quercus GBR. Dist: Independent Pubs. Group.

Crowe, Eyre. With Thackeray in Americ. 2010. 190p. pap. 28.45 *(978-1-4455-5827-1(0)*, Kent Pr.) Kent Communications, Ltd.

—With Thackeray in America. 2010. (Cambridge Library Collection - History Ser.). 204p. pap. 22.99 *(978-1-108-00299-8(4))* Cambridge Univ. Pr.

Crowley, John W. The Black Heart's Truth: The Early Career of W. D. Howells. 2011. (ENG.). 208p. pap. 40.00 *(978-0-8078-6527-9(3))* Univ. of North Carolina Pr.

Crozier, Lorna. Addicted: Notes from the Belly of the Beast, 1 vol. Lane, Patrick, ed. 2nd ed. 2006. (ENG.). 240p. pap. 18.95 *(978-1-55365-115-4(4)*, Greystone Bks.) D&M Pubs. Inc. CAN. Dist: Perseus-PGW.

—Small Beneath the Sky: A Prairie Memoir, 1 vol. 2010. (ENG., Illus.). 208p. 23.95 *(978-1-55365-343-1(2)*, Greystone Bks.) D&M Pubs. Inc. CAN. Dist: Perseus-PGW.

Cudjoe, Selwyn & Cudjoe, Selwyn R. Caribbean Visionary: A. R. F. Webber & the Making of the Guyanese Nation. 2008. (Caribbean Studies Ser.). (ENG.). 304p. 50.00 *(978-1-60473-106-4(0))* Univ. Pr. of Mississippi.

Cudjoe, Selwyn R. Caribbean Visionary: A. R. F. Webber & the Making of the Guyanese Nation. 2011. (Caribbean Studies Ser.). (ENG.). 304p. pap. 30.00 ***(978-1-61703-197-7(6))*** Univ. Pr. of Mississippi.

Cullinane, James G. Arses & Elbows: A Memoir. 2007. 244p. (ENG.). 28.95 *(978-0-595-69889-9(1))*; per. 18.95 *(978-0-595-46046-5(1))* iUniverse, Inc.

Cumberland, Gerald. Set down in Malice a Book of Reminiscences. 2007. (ENG.). 284p. 43.95 *(978-0-548-02895-7(8))* Kessinger Publishing, LLC.

Cummings, Carolyn "Kiki". On Being: A Rock & Roll Fan. 2010. 172p. 23.50 *(978-1-60860-608-5(2)*, Eloquent Bks.) AEG Literary Publishing Services, Inc.

Curran, John. Agatha Christie's Secret Notebooks: Fifty Years of Mysteries in the Making. 2010. (Illus.). 496p. 25.99 *(978-0-06-198836-3(7))* HarperCollins Pubs.

Curry, Jennifer, et al, eds. World Authors 2000-2005. 2007. (Wilson Authors Ser.). 800p. 170.00 *(978-0-8242-1077-9(8))* Wilson, H.W.

Curti, Merle & Burritt, Elihu. The Learned Blacksmith: The Letters & Journals of Elihu Burritt. 2011. 254p. 47.95 ***(978-1-258-04904-1(X))*** Literary Licensing, LLC.

Curtis, Anthony. Virginia Woolf. 2008. (Illus.). 256p. 24.95 *(978-1-905791-47-7(X))* Haus Publishing GBR. Dist: Consortium Bk. Sales & Distribution.

Curtis, Sky. Doctored: A True Story. 2010. (ENG., Illus.). 264p. pap. 22.95 ***(978-1-926708-18-8(0))*** Inanna Pubns. & Education, Inc. CAN. Dist: SPD-Small Pr. Distribution.

Curtright, Travis. The One Thomas More. 2012. ***(978-0-8132-1995-0(7))*** Catholic Univ. of America Pr.

Cusk, Rachel. Aftermath: Life after Marriage, 1 vol. 2012. (ENG.). 160p. 23.00 ***(978-0-374-10213-5(9))*** Farrar, Straus & Giroux.

Cypert, Rick. The Virtue of Suspense: The Life & Works of Charlotte Armstrong. 2008. (ENG., Illus.). 180p. 48.50 *(978-1-57591-122-9(1))* Susquehanna Univ. Pr.

Cyr, Jim. The Cracked Pot: Finding Grace in the Cracks of Childhood Abuse. 2007. 124p. per. 11.50 *(978-1-59330-497-3(8))* Aventine Pr.

Dü, et al. Wovon ich schreibe: Eine kleine Poetik des Lebens. 2009. (GER.). 188p. *(978-3-8321-8088-1(5))* DuMont.

Dahl, Roald. Going Solo. 2009. (ENG.). 224p. (YA). (gr. 7-18). 6.99 *(978-0-14-241383-8(6)*, Puffin) Penguin Group (USA) Inc.

D'Allemand, Patricia. José María Samper: Nación y Cultura en el Siglo XIX Colombiano. 2012. (Hispanic Studies: Culture & Ideas Ser.). (SPA.). 169p. pap. 53.95 ***(978-3-0343-0288-3(6))*** Lang, Peter AG GBR. Dist: Lang, Peter.

Dalton, Eric C. A Road Most Bumpy. 2011. 30p. pap. 16.95 ***(978-1-4512-7754-8(7))*** PublishAmerica, Inc.

Daniels, Susana. Lois Lowry. 2009. (Library of Author Biographies Ser.). 112p. (gr. 5-8). 63.90 *(978-1-60853-544-6(4)*, Rosen Central) Rosen Publishing Group, Inc., The.

Danticat, Edwidge. Brother, I'm Dying. l.t. ed. 2008. 288p. lib. bdg. 31.95 *(978-1-60285-133-7(6))* Ctr. Point Large Print.

—Brother, I'm Dying. 2008. (Vintage Contemporaries Ser.). (ENG.). 288p. pap. 15.00 *(978-1-4000-3430-7(2)*, Vintage) Knopf Doubleday Publishing Group.

—Create Dangerously: The Immigrant Artist at Work. 2011. (Vintage Contemporaries Ser.). (ENG.). 208p. pap. 14.95 *(978-0-307-94643-0(6)*, Vintage) Knopf Doubleday Publishing Group.

—Create Dangerously: The Immigrant Artist at Work. 2010. (Toni Morrison Lecture Ser.). (ENG.). 208p. 19.95 *(978-0-691-14018-6(9))* Princeton Univ. Pr.

Darnton, John. Almost a Family. 2012. (ENG., Illus.). 384p. pap. 16.95 ***(978-0-307-27880-7(8)***, Anchor) Knopf Doubleday Publishing Group.

Darnton, John. Almost a Family: A Memoir. 2011. (ENG., Illus.). 368p. 27.95 *(978-0-307-26617-0(6))* Knopf, Alfred A. Inc.

Darst, Jeanne. Fiction Ruined My Family. 2011. (ENG.). 320p. (gr. 12). 25.95 *(978-1-59448-814-6(2)*, Riverhead Bks. (Hardcover)) Penguin Group (USA) Inc.

Daugherty, Tracy. Hiding Man. 2010. (ENG., Illus.). 592p. pap. 20.00 *(978-0-312-42930-0(4))* Picador.

—Just One Catch: A Biography of Joseph Heller. 2011. (ENG., Illus.). 560p. 35.00 *(978-0-312-59685-9(5))* St. Martin's Pr.

Dault, Nancy. My Experiences with Animals. 2008. 188p. pap. 24.95 *(978-1-60672-303-6(0))* PublishAmerica, Inc.

David, Anna. Falling for Me: How I Hung Curtains, Learned to Cook, Traveled to Seville, & Fell in Love. 2011. (ENG.). 252p. pap. 14.99 *(978-0-06-199604-7(1)*, William Morrow Paperbacks) HarperCollins Pubs.

Davidson, Ian. Voltaire: A Life. 2010. (ENG., Illus.). 560p. 35.00 *(978-1-60598-119-2(2)*, 605119) Pegasus Bks.

Davidson, Margaret Miller. Biography & Poetical Remains of the Late Margaret Miller Davidson / by Washington Irving. 2006. 244p. per. 20.99 *(978-1-4255-2043-4(X))* MPublishing.

Davies, Hunter. The Beatles, Football & Me. 2007. (ENG., Illus.). 352p. pap. 15.95 *(978-0-7553-1403-4(4))* Headline Bk. Publishing GBR. Dist: Independent Pubs. Group.

Davis, Bertram H. & Johnson, Samuel. Johnson Before Boswell: A Study of John Hawkins' Life of Samuel Johnson. 2011. 234p. 46.95 ***(978-1-258-08966-5(1))*** Literary Licensing, LLC.

Davis, Deborah. Party of the Century: The Fabulous Story of Truman Capote & His Black & White Ball. 2007. (ENG., Illus.). 320p. per. 17.95 *(978-0-470-09821-9(X)*, Wiley) Wiley, John & Sons, Inc.

Davis, Donald. Tales from a Free-Range Childhood. 2011. E-Book *(978-0-89587-508-2(X))*; 224p. 19.95 *(978-0-89587-507-5(1))*; 224p. pap. 12.95 *(978-0-89587-509-9(8))* Blair, John F. Pub.

Davis, Hollis. Rungs of the Ladder, 1 vol. 2010. 196p. pap. 24.95 *(978-1-4489-6010-1(X))* PublishAmerica, Inc.

Davis, Jack E. An Everglades Providence: Marjory Stoneman Douglas & the American Environmental Century. (Environmental History & the American South Ser.). (ENG., Illus.). 764p. 2011. pap. 26.95 *(978-0-8203-3779-1(X))* 2009. 34.95 *(978-0-8203-3071-6(X))* Univ. of Georgia Pr.

Davis, Paul D. Family, Friends & Follies. 2009. 316p. pap. 15.95 *(978-1-4389-9767-4(1))* AuthorHouse.

Davis, Philip. Bernard Malamud: A Writer's Life. 2010. (ENG., Illus.). 400p. pap. 18.95 *(978-0-19-957147-5(3))* Oxford Univ. Pr., Inc.

Davis, Richard Harding. Adventures & Letters of Richard Harding Davis. 2008. 304p. 28.99 *(978-0-554-30853-1(3))* 2008. 304p. 29.99 *(978-0-554-21550-1(0))* 2006. (ENG.). pap. 17.99 *(978-1-4264-0392-7(5))* BiblioBazaar.

—Adventures & Letters of Richard Harding Davis. 2006. pap. *(978-1-4065-1135-2(8))* Dodo Pr.

Davis, Steven L. J. Frank Dobie: A Liberated Mind. 2009. (ENG., Illus.). 296p. 24.95 *(978-0-292-72114-2(5))* Univ. of Texas Pr.

Davison, Colin. Through the Magic Door: Ursula Moray Williams, Gobbolino & the Little Wooden Horse. 2011. (ENG., Illus.). 260p. 29.95 ***(978-0-85716-006-5(0))*** Northumbria University Press GBR. Dist: Independent Pubs. Group.

Dawidoff, Nicholas. The Crowd Sounds Happy: A Story of Love, Madness, & Baseball. 2009. (Vintage Ser.). (ENG.). 288p. pap. 15.00 *(978-0-375-70007-1(2)*, Vintage) Knopf Doubleday Publishing Group.

de Beauvoir, Simone. Wartime Diary. Simons, Margaret A. et al, eds. Cordero, Anne Deing, tr. from FRE. 2008. (Beauvoir Ser.). (ENG.). 368p. 42.00 *(978-0-252-03377-3(9))* Univ. of Illinois Pr.

de la L Oulton, Carolyn W. Let the Flowers Go: A Life of Mary Cholmondeley, 1 vol. 2009. (Gender & Genre Ser.). (ENG., Illus.). 272p. 99.00 *(978-1-85196-649-3(8))* Pickering & Chatto Pubs., Ltd. GBR. Dist: Ashgate Publishing Co.

de la Mothe, John. C. P. Snow & the Struggle of Modernity. 2011. (ENG., Illus.). 264p. pap. 25.00 *(978-0-292-72916-2(2))* Univ. of Texas Pr.

De Lope, Manuel. Jardines de Africa. (SPA.). 92p. pap. 5.95 *(978-84-204-8041-1(X))* Alfaguara, Ediciones, S.A.- Grupo Santillana ESP. Dist: Santillana USA Publishing Co., Inc.

de Maistre, Xavier. Journey Around My Room. 2011. (Green Integer Ser.). (ENG.). 200p. pap. 12.95 *(978-1-933382-78-4(3))* Green Integer.

de Quincey, Thomas. Autobiographic Sketches. 2008. 360p. 29.99 *(978-0-559-85832-1(9))*; pap. 31.75 *(978-0-559-85830-7(2))* BiblioBazaar.

—Autobiographic Sketches. 2006. 608p. per. 34.99 *(978-1-4255-6469-8(0))* MPublishing.

—Confessions of an English Opium-Eater. 2008. 292p. *(978-1-4437-3367-0(9)*, Pomona Pr.) Read Bks.

—Confessions of an English Opium-Eater & Suspiria de Profundis. 2006. 288p. per. 23.99 *(978-1-4255-2659-7(4))* MPublishing.

—Confessions of an English Opium-Eater & Suspiria de Profundis. 2007. 292p. per. *(978-1-4067-6002-6(1))* Read Bks.

De Roche, Linda. Mary Higgins Clark: Life & Letters, 1 vol. 2011. (Illus.). 172p. 44.95 *(978-0-313-36637-6(3)*, C36637); E-Book *(978-0-313-36638-3(1))* Greenwood Publishing Group, Inc. (Praeger Pubs.).

Deakin, Mary H. The Early Life of George Eliot. 2008. 230p. 41.95 *(978-1-4365-1481-1(9))* 2007. (ENG.). 232p. per. 26.95 *(978-0-548-70138-6(5))* Kessinger Publishing, LLC.

Dear, Pamela. Contemporary Authors New Revision Series. 2008. (Contemporary Authors New Revision Ser.). 166th rev. ed. 464p. 293.00 *(978-0-7876-7920-0(8))* 168th rev. ed. 464p. 293.00 *(978-0-7876-9532-3(7))* 169th rev. ed. 464p. 293.00 *(978-0-7876-9533-0(5))* 171st rev. ed. 480p. 293.00 *(978-0-7876-9535-4(1))* 172nd rev. ed. 464p. 293.00 *(978-0-7876-9536-1(X))* 173rd rev. ed. 480p. 293.00 *(978-0-7876-9537-8(8))* 174th rev. ed. 480p. 293.00 *(978-0-7876-9538-5(6))* 175th rev. ed. 464p. 293.00 *(978-0-7876-9539-2(4))* 176th rev. ed. 480p. 293.00 *(978-0-7876-9540-8(8))* 177th rev. ed. 464p. 293.00 *(978-1-4144-1921-3(X))* Cengage Gale.

Dear, Pamela, ed. Contemporary Authors New Revision Series, Vol. 153. 2006. (Contemporary Authors New Revision Ser.). 464p. 293.00 *(978-0-7876-7907-1(0))* Cengage Gale.

Dearden, James S. John Ruskin: An Illustrated Life of John Ruskin, 1819-1900. 2nd ed. 2008. (Shire Library). (ENG., Illus.). 64p. pap. 12.95 *(978-0-7478-0599-1(7))* Shire Pubns., Ltd. GBR. Dist: Random Hse., Inc.

Deathridge, John. Pegasus Pocket Guide to Beethoven. 2010. 352p. pap. 15.75 *(978-1-933648-75-0(9))* Pegasus Bks.

DeCaires Narain, Denise. Olive Senior. 2011. (Writers & Their Work Ser.). (ENG.). 154p. (C). 80.00 *(978-0-7463-1094-6(3))* Northcote Hse. Publishers, Ltd. GBR. Dist: Brown, David Bk. Co., The.

Delany, Paul. George Gissing: A Life. 2009. (ENG., Illus.). 472p. pap. 28.95 *(978-0-7538-2573-0(2)*, Phoenix) Orion Publishing Group, Ltd. GBR. Dist: Independent Pubs. Group.

Delany, Samuel R. Conversations with Samuel R. Delany. Freedman, Carl, ed. 2009. (Literary Conversations Ser.). (ENG.). 256p. 50.00 *(978-1-60473-277-1(6))*; pap. 22.00 *(978-1-60473-278-8(4))* Univ. Pr. of Mississippi.

Delbanco, Andrew. Melville: His World & Work. 2006. (Vintage Ser.). (ENG., Illus.). 448p. per. 17.00 *(978-0-375-70297-6(0)*, Vintage) Knopf Doubleday Publishing Group.

Delibes, Miguel. Diario de un Emigrante. (Classicos Contemporaneos Comentados Ser.). (SPA., Illus.). 226p. 19.95 *(978-84-233-2866-6(X)*, DE866X) Ediciones Destino ESP. Dist: Continental Bk. Co., Inc.

DeLuca, Vito & Deluca, Vito. Hero Unaware. 2009. 222p. pap. 14.99 *(978-0-557-11203-6(6))* Lulu Enterprises Inc.

DeMaria, Robert, Jr. Samuel Johnson & the Life of Reading. 2009. (ENG.). 288p. (gr. 17). pap. 30.00 *(978-0-8018-9242-4(2))* Johns Hopkins Univ. Pr.

Dennison, Charles George. Zulu Frontiersman. Lock, Ron, ed. 2008. 228p. 49.95 *(978-1-59114-988-0(6))* Naval Institute Pr.

dePaola, Tomie. Christmas Remembered. 2009. (ENG.). 96p. (J). (gr. -1-18). pap. 9.99 *(978-0-14-241481-1(6)*, Puffin) Penguin Group (USA) Inc.

Derleth, August. Concord Rebel: A Life of Henry D. Thoreau. 2011. 230p. 46.95 ***(978-1-258-00228-2(0))*** Literary Licensing, LLC.

Derleth, August. In the Course of My Walks. Quinney, Richard, ed. 2009. (ENG., Illus.). 88p. 25.00 *(978-0-9815620-2-5(7))* Borderland Bks.

Deschapelles, Jorge. Cuban Summers. 2010. 157p. 27.00 *(978-0-557-47848-4(0))* Lulu Enterprises Inc.

Desclos, Marie-Laurence & Fortenbaugh, William, eds. Strato of Lampsacus: Text, Translation, & Discussion. 2010. (LAT, FRE, GER & ENG.). 486p. 69.95 *(978-1-4128-1127-9(9))* Transaction Pubs.

Deufert, Diane. Matthias Bergius (1536-1592) Antike Dichtungstradition im konfessionellen Zeitalter. 2011. (Hypomnemata Ser.). (GER., Illus.). 448p. (C). 134.00 ***(978-3-525-25295-6(1))*** Vandenhoeck & Ruprecht GmbH & Co. KG DEU. Dist: ISD.

Devine, Luke. From Anglo-First-Wave towards American Second-Wave Jewish Feminism: Negotiating with Jewish Feminist Theology & its Communities in the Writing of Amy Levy. 2010. 110.00 *(978-1-61719-915-8(X))* Gorgias Pr., LLC.

DeYoung, Terri, ed. Essays in Arabic Literary Biography 925-1350: Edited by Terri Deyoung & Mary St. Germain. 2011. (Mizan Ser.). (ENG.). 371p. (C). 105.00 ***(978-3-447-06598-6(2))*** Harrassowitz, Otto Verlag DEU. Dist: ISD.

Dhingra, Lavina & Cheung, Floyd. Naming Jhumpa Lahiri: Canons & Controversies. 2012. ***(978-0-7391-6998-8(X))*** Lexington Bks.

Diamond, Morris I. The Name Dropper or People I Schlepped With. 2011. 350p. pap. 21.95 ***(978-1-59393-653-2(2))*** BearManor Media.

Diamond, Ron. The Legacy of a Baby Boomer: A Diminishing Breed, 1 vol. 2010. 48p. pap. 16.95 *(978-1-4489-4077-6(X))* PublishAmerica, Inc.

DiBattista, Maria. Imagining Virginia Woolf: An Experiment in Critical Biography. 2008. (ENG.). 208p. (C). 21.95 *(978-0-691-13812-1(5))* Princeton Univ. Pr.

Dibble, Brian. Doing Life: A Biography of Elizabeth Jolley. 2008. 334p. pap. 32.00 *(978-1-921401-06-0(0))* UWA Publishing AUS. Dist: International Specialized Bk. Services.

Dick, Anne R. The Search for Philip K. Dick, 1928-1982. 2010. (ENG.). 288p. pap. 14.95 *(978-1-61696-000-1(0))* Tachyon Pubns.

Dick, Philip K. The Exegesis of Philip K. Dick. Jackson, Pamela & Lethem, Jonathan, eds. 2011. (ENG., Illus.). 976p. 40.00 *(978-0-547-54925-5(3))* Houghton Mifflin Harcourt Trade & Reference Pubs.

Dickens, Charles. The Letters of Charles Dickens - Volume I - 1833 To 1856. Mamie Dickens & Georgina Hogarth, eds. 2009. (Illus.). 344p. pap. 9.95 *(978-1-60386-218-9(8)*, Merchant Bks.) Rough Draft Printing.

Dickens, Charles. Pictures from Italy. 2011. (Cambridge Library Collection - Travel & Exploration Ser.). (ENG., Illus.). 284p. pap. 23.99 ***(978-1-108-03384-8(9))*** Cambridge Univ. Pr.

Dickerson, Cw 2. Floyd F. More Choices to Guide the Journey. 2011. 100p. pap. 19.95 ***(978-1-4626-2075-3(2))*** PublishAmerica, Inc.

Dickinson, Rachel, ed. John Ruskin's Correspondence with Joan Severn: Sense & Nonsense Letters. 2009. (Legenda Main Ser.). (ENG.). 312p. (C). 89.50 *(978-1-905981-90-8(2))* European Humanities Research Ctr. GBR. Dist: Brown, David Bk. Co., The.

Dickison, Stephanie. The 30-Second Commute: A Non-Fiction Comedy about Writing & Working from Home. 2009. (ENG.). 200p. pap. 19.95 *(978-1-55022-837-3(4))* ECW Pr. CAN. Dist: Independent Pubs. Group.

Didion, Joan. Blue Nights. 2011. (Playaway Adult Nonfiction Ser.). (ENG.). 44.99 ***(978-1-61657-045-3(8))*** Findaway World, LLC.

—Blue Nights. 2011. (ENG.). 208p. 25.00 *(978-0-307-26767-2(9)*, Knopf) Knopf Doubleday Publishing Group.

—Blue Nights. 2012. (ENG.). 208p. pap. 15.00 ***(978-0-307-38738-7(0)***, Vintage) Knopf Doubleday Publishing Group.

—Blue Nights. l.t. ed. 2011. (ENG.). 192p. pap. 25.00 *(978-0-7393-7843-4(0))* Random Hse. Large Print.

—The Year of Magical Thinking. 2011. 14.72 *(978-0-7848-3506-7(3)*, Everbind) Marco Bk. Co.

DiDonato, Tiffanie & Dyball, Rennie. Dwarf: A Memoir. 2012. (ENG.). 272p. (gr. 12). pap. 15.00 ***(978-0-452-29811-8(3)***, Plume) Penguin Group (USA) Inc.

Dil, Anwar S. Bangladesh, an Intercultural Panorama. 2011. (Illus.). 407p. ***(978-984-20-0167-3(9))*** Intercultural Forum.

Dillingham, William B. Melville & His Circle: The Last Years. 2008. (ENG.). 232p. pap. 22.95 *(978-0-8203-3272-7(0))* Univ. of Georgia Pr.

Dimatteo, Maria-Josephine. Letters: The Ones I Should Have Written & A Few I Wish I Hadn't. 2009. 180p. 26.99 *(978-1-4389-9964-7(X))*; pap. 17.99 *(978-1-4389-9966-1(6))* AuthorHouse.

Dittman, Michael J. Masterpieces of Beat Literature, 1 vol. 2006. (Greenwood Introduces Literary Masterpieces Ser.). 136p. 49.95 *(978-0-313-33283-8(5)*, GR3283, Greenwood Pr.) Greenwood Publishing Group, Inc.

Dixon, Sergine. Germaine de Stael, Daughter of the Enlightenment: The Writer & Her Turbulent Era. 2007. (Gateway Bookshelf Ser.). (ENG., Illus.). 340p. per. 39.98 *(978-1-59102-560-3(5)*, Humanity Bks.) Prometheus Bks., Pubs.

Dmitrii Venevitinov: Usadby Venevitinovykh: Tvorcheskoe Nasledie Poeta. 2010. (RUS., Illus.). 214p. *(978-5-91338-021-0(5))* Centr Duhovnogo Vozrozdenija Cernozemnogo kraja, Fond.

Dobson, Austin. Fielding. 2011. (Cambridge Library Collection - English Men of Letters Ser.). (ENG.). 214p. pap. 22.99 ***(978-1-108-03454-8(3))*** Cambridge Univ. Pr.

Dobson, Kathy. With a Closed Fist: Growing up in Canada's Toughest Nighbourhood. 2012. (ENG., Illus.). 224p. pap. 19.95 ***(978-1-55065-323-6(7))*** Vehicule Pr. CAN. Dist: Independent Pubs. Group.

Doerr, Anthony. Four Seasons in Rome: On Twins, Insomnia, & the Biggest Funeral in the History of the World. 2008. (ENG., Illus.). 224p. pap. 14.00 *(978-1-4165-7316-6(X)*, Scribner) Scribner.

Dolby, George. Charles Dickens as I Knew Him: The Story of the Reading Tours in Great Britain & America 1866-1870. 2011. (Cambridge Library Collection -

Literary Studies). (ENG., Illus.). 486p. pap. 35.99 ***(978-1-108-03979-6(0))*** Cambridge Univ. Pr.

Dolin, Tim. T Hardy. 2008. (Life & Times Ser.). (Illus.). 192p. 15.95 *(978-1-904950-77-6(9))* Haus Publishing GBR. Dist: Consortium Bk. Sales & Distribution.

Dollarhide, Louis & Abadie, Ann J., eds. Eudora Welty: A Form of Thanks. 2011. (ENG.). 138p. pap. 30.00 ***(978-1-61703-212-7(3))*** Univ. Pr. of Mississippi.

Domínguez, Frank & Greenia, George D. Castilian Writers, 1200-1400. 2007. (Dictionary of Literary Biography Ser.: Vol. 337). (ENG.). 528p. 315.00 *(978-0-7876-8155-5(5))* Cengage Gale.

Domínguez Michael, Christopher. Diccionario Crítico de la Literatura Mexicana, 1955-2005. 2007. (Letras Mexicanas Ser.). (SPA.). 588p. 30.95 *(978-968-16-8478-5(8))* Fondo de Cultura Economica USA.

Domoslawski, Artur. Ryszard Kapuscinski: The Biography. Lloyd-Jones, Antonia, tr. from POL. 2012. (ENG.). 464p. 34.95 ***(978-1-84467-858-7(X)***, 844858) Verso Bks. GBR. Dist: Norton, W. W. & Co., Inc.

Donaghy, Michael. The Shape of the Dance: Essays, Interviews & Digressions. 2009. (ENG., Illus.). 224p. 29.95 *(978-0-330-45628-9(8)*, Picador) Pan Macmillan GBR. Dist: Trans-Atlantic Pubns., Inc.

Donaldson, Frances. Evelyn Waugh: Portrait of a Country Neighbour. 2012. 158p. pap. ***(978-1-4482-0307-9(4)***, 143314, Bloomsbury Reader) Bloomsbury Publishing Plc.

Donaldson, Ian. Ben Jonson: A Life. 2012. (ENG., Illus.). 512p. 39.95 *(978-0-19-812976-9(9))* Oxford Univ. Pr., Inc.

Donaldson, Scott. Death of a Rebel: The Charlie Fenton Story. 2011. (ENG.). 198p. 65.00 ***(978-1-61147-493-0(0))*** Fairleigh Dickinson Univ. Pr.

Donaubauer, Yvonne E. Dolf's Hospital Days. 2011. 176p. pap. 12.95 ***(978-1-4626-3856-7(2))*** PublishAmerica, Inc.

Donnelly, Mary. Alice Walker: The Color Purple & Other Works. 2009. (Writers & Their Works 4 Ser.). 144p. (gr. 7). 42.79 *(978-0-7614-4281-3(2))* Marshall Cavendish Corp.

Donnelly, Wendy. The Black Hole. 2009. 288p. pap. 21.50 *(978-1-4452-4111-1(0))* Lulu Enterprises Inc.

Doody, Margaret Anne. Frances Burney: The Life in the Works. 2010. (ENG.). 462p. pap. 34.99 *(978-0-521-15892-3(3))* Cambridge Univ. Pr.

Doppler, Alfred. Stifter und Stifterforschung im 21. Jahrhundert: Biographie - Wissenschaft - Poetik. 2007. (GER., Illus.). XI, 306p. *(978-3-484-10901-8(7))* Verlag Max Niemeyer.

Dorfman, Ariel. Feeding on Dreams: Confessions of an Unrepentant Exile. (ENG.). 352p. 2012. pap. 14.95 ***(978-0-547-84418-3(2)***, Mariner Bks.) 2011. 27.00 *(978-0-547-54946-0(6))* Houghton Mifflin Harcourt Trade & Reference Pubs.

Döring, Jörg & Joch, Markus, eds. Alfred Andersch 'revisited' Werkbiographische Studien im Zeichen der Sebald-Debatte. 2011. (GER., VI, 384p. Illus.). 210.00 ***(978-3-11-026827-0(2))***; 140.00 ***(978-3-11-026809-6(4))*** De Gruyter, Walter Inc.

Dorion, Helene. Days of Sand. Kaplansky, Jonathan, tr. from FRE. 2008. (ENG.). 120p. per. 18.00 *(978-1-897151-07-5(1))* Cormorant Bks. Inc. CAN. Dist: Univ. of Toronto Pr.

Dossick, Philip. Transplant: 35th Anniversary Edition. 2011. 224p. 28.95 *(978-1-4502-9713-4(7))*; pap. 18.95 *(978-1-4502-9714-1(5))* iUniverse, Inc.

Dostoyevsky, Fyodor. Winter Notes on Summer Impressions. FitzLyon, Kyril, tr. from RUS. 2009. (Oneworld Classics Ser.). (ENG., Illus.). 160p. pap. 14.95 *(978-1-84749-064-3(6))* Alma Classics GBR. Dist: Independent Pubs. Group.

—A Writer's Diary. Morson, Gary Saul, ed. Lantz, Kenneth, tr. from RUS. 2009. (ENG.). 648p. pap. 27.95 *(978-0-8101-2521-6(8))* Northwestern Univ. Pr.

Doty, Kathryn Adams. Becoming the Mother of Me: A Memoir. 2009. (ENG.). 144p. pap. 16.95 *(978-1-889020-27-3(3))* Edinborough Pr.

Dougherty, David C. Shouting down the Silence: A Biography of Stanley Elkin. 2010. (ENG., Illus.). 296p. 40.00 *(978-0-252-03508-1(9))* Univ. of Illinois Pr.

Douglas-Fairhurst, Robert. Becoming Dickens: The Invention of a Novelist. 2011. (Illus.). 400p. 29.95 *(978-0-674-05003-7(7)*, Belknap Pr.) Harvard Univ. Pr.

Douglas, George Brisbane. James Hogg. 2008. 155p. 22.99 *(978-0-554-59760-7(8))*; 156p. 25.99 *(978-0-554-59749-2(7))*; 156p. pap. 20.75 *(978-0-554-59756-0(X))*; 155p. pap. 21.75 *(978-0-554-59750-8(0))* BiblioBazaar.

—James Hogg. 2009. 90p. pap. *(978-1-4590-8837-5(9))* Books LLC.

—James Hogg. 2008. 164p. 36.95 *(978-1-4369-0670-8(9))*; pap. 21.95 *(978-1-4368-8315-3(6))* Kessinger Publishing, LLC.

Dowden, Edward. Correspondence of Henry Taylor. 2009. 444p. pap. 36.75 *(978-1-115-85166-4(7))*; pap. 35.75 *(978-1-115-85167-1(5))* BiblioBazaar.

Downie, J. A. Political Biography of Henry Fielding, 1 vol. 2009. (Eighteenth-Century Political Biographies Ser.). (ENG.). 272p. 99.00 *(978-1-85196-915-9(2))* Pickering & Chatto Pubs., Ltd. GBR. Dist: Ashgate Publishing Co.

Downing, Frederick L. Elie Wiesel: A Religious Biography. 2008. 282p. 29.00 *(978-0-88146-099-5(0))* Mercer Univ. Pr.

Downing, Michael. Life with Sudden Death: A Tale of Moral Hazard & Medical Misadventure. 2010. (ENG.). 256p. pap. 15.95 *(978-1-58243-615-9(0)*, Counterpoint) Counterpoint LLC.

Drabble, Margaret. The Pattern in the Carpet: A Personal History with Jigsaws. 2009. (ENG., Illus.). 368p. 25.00 *(978-0-547-24144-9(5))* Houghton Mifflin Harcourt Trade & Reference Pubs.

Dreiser, Theodore. Letters to Women Vol. 2: New Letters. Riggio, Thomas P., ed. 2009. (Dreiser Edition Ser.). (ENG., Illus.). 432p. 62.00 *(978-0-252-03376-6(0))* Univ. of Illinois Pr.

Drew, Bernard A. 100 Most Popular African American Authors: Biographical Sketches & Bibliographies, 1 vol. 2006. (Popular Authors Ser.). (Illus.). 372p. 55.00 *(978-1-59158-322-6(5)*, LU3225) Libraries Unlimited, Inc.

—100 Most Popular Contemporary Mystery Authors: Biographical Sketches & Bibliographies, 1 vol. 2011. (Popular Authors Ser.). (Illus.). 439p. 65.00 *(978-1-59884-445-0(8)*, A2900C) Libraries Unlimited, Inc.

—The 100 Most Popular Contemporary Mystery Authors: Biographical Sketches & Bibliographies. 2011. E-Book *(978-1-59884-446-7(6))* Libraries Unlimited, Inc.

—100 Most Popular Thriller & Suspense Authors: Biographical Sketches & Bibliographies, 1 vol. 2009. (Popular Authors Ser.). 468p. 65.00 *(978-1-59158-699-9(2)*, LU8699) Libraries Unlimited, Inc.

Drichel, Simone. Frameworks: Contemporary Criticism on Janet Frame. Cronin, Jan, ed. 2009. (Illus.). 256p. 70.00 *(978-90-420-2676-6(6))* Rodopi.

Duberman, Martin. A Saving Remnant: The Radical Lives of Barbara Deming & David McReynolds. 2011. (ENG.). 336p. 27.95 *(978-1-59558-323-9(8))* New Pr., The.

Duberman, Martin B. The Worlds of Lincoln Kirstein. 2008. (ENG.). 736p. pap. 22.95 *(978-0-8101-2518-6(8))* Northwestern Univ. Pr.

Dubner, Stephen J. Choosing My Religion: A Memoir of a Family Beyond Belief. 2006. (P. S. Ser.). (Illus.). 368p. per. 14.99 *(978-0-06-113299-5(3)*, HarperPerennial) HarperCollins Pubs.

DuBois, Allison. Secrets of the Monarch: What the Dead Can Teach Us about Living a Better Life. lt. ed. 2008. (Thorndike Core Ser.). 255p. 31.95 *(978-1-4104-0357-5(2))* Thorndike Pr.

DuBow, Wendy, ed. Conversations with Anaïs Nin. 2011. (ENG.). pap. 30.00 *(978-1-61703-059-8(7))* Univ. Pr. of Mississippi.

Dubus, Andre, III. Townie: A Memoir. (ENG.). 400p. 2012. pap. 15.95 ***(978-0-393-34067-9(8)***, 34067) 2011. 25.95 *(978-0-393-06466-7(2)*, 6466) Norton, W. W. & Co., Inc.

Dudgeon, Piers. The Girl from Leam Lane: The Life & Writing of Catherine Cookson. rev. ed. 2007. (ENG., Illus.). 320p. per. 13.95 *(978-0-7553-1498-0(0))* Headline Bk. Publishing GBR. Dist: Independent Pubs. Group.

—Neverland: J. M. Barrie, the du Mauriers, & the Dark Side of Peter Pan. 2011. (ENG., Illus.). 352p. pap. 15.95 *(978-1-60598-191-8(5)*, 605191) Pegasus Bks.

Duff, Gerald. Home Truths: A Deep East Texas Memory. 2011. (ENG.). 160p. pap. 21.95 *(978-0-87565-435-5(5))* Texas Christian Univ. Pr.

Dugan, Eleanor Knowles. The Precious Lies of Madeleine de Scudéry: Her Admirable & Infuriating Life. Book 1, 4 books, Book 1. 2009. pap. 12.50 *(978-0-9790994-0-3(4))* Grand Cyrus Pr.

—The Precious Lies of Madeleine de Scudéry: Her Admirable & Infuriating Life. Book 2, 4 books, Book 2. 2009. pap. 12.50 *(978-0-9790994-1-0(2))* Grand Cyrus Pr.

—The Precious Lies of Madeleine de Scudéry: Her Admirable & Infuriating Life. Book 3, 4 books, Book 3. 2009. pap. 12.50 *(978-0-9790994-2-7(0))* Grand Cyrus Pr.

—The Precious Lies of Madeleine de Scudéry: Her Admirable & Infuriating Life. Book 4, 4 books, Book 4. 2009. pap. 12.50 *(978-0-9790994-3-4(9))* Grand Cyrus Pr.

Dugan, Sally. Baroness Orczy's the Scarlet Pimpernel: A Publishing History. 2012. (Illus.). 285p. ***(978-1-4094-2717-9(X))*** Ashgate Publishing, Ltd.

Dukes, David. A Journey Back Home: The Story of the Johnson-Brinson Project & Break Away. 2010. 160p. (ENG.). 22.49 *(978-1-4490-4893-8(5))*; pap. 11.99 *(978-1-4490-4892-1(7))* AuthorHouse.

Duncklee, John. Good Years for the Buzzards. 2008. 180p. pap. 15.95 *(978-0-595-53244-5(6))* iUniverse, Inc.

Dunlop, Eileen. Robert Louis Stevenson: The Travelling Mind. 2009. (ENG., Illus.). 160p. pap. 15.95 *(978-1-905267-21-7(5))* NMS Enterprises Ltd. - Publishing GBR. Dist: National Bk. Network.

Durrell, Lawrence. Sicilian Carousel. 2009. (ENG.). 295p. pap. 12.00 *(978-1-60419-015-1(9))* Axios Pr.

Dusinberre, Aaron. It's What Makes Me, Me. 2011. 90p. pap. 9.95 ***(978-1-4560-1645-6(8))*** PublishAmerica, Inc.

Dworkin, Andrea. Heartbreak: The Political Memoir of a Feminist Militant. 2007. 184p. 29.95 *(978-0-8264-9442-9(0))* Continuum International Publishing Group, Ltd. GBR. Dist: National Bk. Network.

Dyer, Geoff. Out of Sheer Rage: Wrestling with D. H. Lawrence. 2009. (ENG.). 256p. pap. 15.00 *(978-0-312-42946-1(0))* Picador.

Eades, Scottie. Road to Normal. 2007. 176p. pap. 16.00 *(978-0-9798776-0-5(1))* Great American Pr., The.

Earp, James. The Governor's Four Hearts: The True Inspirational Story of One Family's Journey from Death to Really Living. 2011. pap. 21.99 *(978-1-61739-258-0(8))* Tate Publishing & Enterprises, LLC.

Eaude, Michael. Triumph at Midnight in the Century: A Critical Biography of Arturo Barea: Explaining the Roots of the Spanish Civil War. 2009. (ENG., Illus.). 243p. 74.95 *(978-1-84519-288-4(5))* Sussex Academic Pr. GBR. Dist: International Specialized Bk. Services.

—Triumph at Midnight of the Century: A Critical Biography of Arturo Barea - Explaining the Roots of the Spanish Civil War. 2011. (ENG., Illus.). 244p. pap. 34.95 *(978-1-84519-469-7(1))* Sussex Academic Pr. GBR. Dist: International Specialized Bk. Services.

Ebers, Georg. The Story of My Life: From Childhood to Manhood. 2007. (ENG.). 278p. pap. 21.99 *(978-1-4264-1672-9(5))*; 270p. pap. 23.99 *(978-1-4264-1760-3(8))* BiblioBazaar.

—Story of My Life from Childhood to Manho. 2006. pap. 34.95 *(978-1-4286-5285-9(X))* Kessinger Publishing, LLC.

Edel, Henry James, Vol. 4. 2009. pap. 25.00 *(978-0-8166-0206-3(9))* Univ. of Minnesota Pr.

Edgerton, Clyde & Edgerton, Clyde. Solo: My Adventures in the Air. 2006. (ENG., Illus.). 283p. pap. 12.95 *(978-1-56512-546-9(0)*, 1565125460, Shannon Ravenel Bks.) Algonquin Bks. of Chapel Hill.

Edgeworth, Maria. The Life & Letters. 2008. 284p. 25.99 *(978-0-554-32153-0(X))*; 296p. 25.99 *(978-0-554-32154-7(8))*; 296p. 28.99 *(978-0-554-22851-8(3))*; 284p. 28.99 *(978-0-554-22850-1(5))* BiblioBazaar.

—The Life & Letters. AUGUSTUS J.C. HARE, ed. 2007. (ENG.). Vol. 1. 248p. pap. 20.99 *(978-1-4264-3202-6(X))* Vol. 1. 282p. pap. 23.99 *(978-1-4264-3237-8(2))* Vol. 2. 260p. pap. 21.99 *(978-1-4264-3203-3(8))* Vol. 2. 294p. pap. 23.99 *(978-1-4264-3238-5(0))* BiblioBazaar.

—The Life & Letters of Maria Edgeworth. 2008. 300p. 28.99 *(978-0-554-22942-3(0))*; 25.99 *(978-0-554-32245-2(5))* BiblioBazaar.

—The Life & Letters of Maria Edgeworth. Augustus J.C. Hare, ed. 2007. (ENG.). Vol. 2. 266p. pap. 21.99 *(978-1-4264-3389-4(1))*Vol 2. 298p. pap. 23.99 *(978-1-4264-3439-6(1))* BiblioBazaar.

—The Life & Letters of Maria Edgeworth. Hare, Augustus J. C., ed. 2007. (ENG.). 632p. per. *(978-1-4065-1647-0(3))* Dodo Pr.

—The Life & Letters of Maria Edgeworth. 2007. (ENG.). 192p. per. *(978-1-4068-5007-9(1))*; 184p. per. *(978-1-4068-5006-2(3))* Echo Library.

Edib, Halidé. House with Wisteria: Memoirs of Turkey Old & New. 2009. (ENG.). 442p. pap. 34.95 *(978-1-4128-1002-9(7))* Transaction Pubs.

Edmond-Paul, Mary, ed. Lighted Windows: Critical Essays on Robin Hyde. 2008. (Illus.). 226p. pap. 40.00 *(978-1-877372-58-2(7))* Otago University Pr. NZL. Dist: International Specialized Bk. Services.

Edmondson, John, ed. Dickens on France: Fiction, Journalism, & Travel. 2007. (ENG., Illus.). 464p. per. 20.00 *(978-1-56656-688-9(6)*, Interlink Bks.) Interlink Publishing Group, Inc.

Edwards, Anne. Leaving Home: A Hollywood Blacklisted Writer's Years Abroad. 2012. (ENG., Illus.). 248p. 29.95 ***(978-0-8108-8199-0(3))***; E-Book ***(978-0-8108-8200-3(0))*** Scarecrow Pr., Inc.

Edwards, Anne K. & Quillen, Lida E., eds. How I Wrote My First Book: The Story Behind the Story. 2011. pap. 15.95 *(978-1-60619-149-1(7))* Twilight Times Bks.

Edwards, Caterina. Finding Rosa: A Mother with Alzheimer's, a Daughter in Search of the Past, 1 vol. 2009. (ENG.). 304p. 24.95 *(978-1-55365-389-9(0)*, Greystone Bks.) D&M Pubs. Inc. CAN. Dist: Perseus-PGW.

Edwards, Natalie, et al, eds. Textual & Visual Selves: Photography, Film, & Comic Art in French Autobiography. 2011. (ENG., Illus.). 288p. pap. 25.00 *(978-0-8032-3631-8(X))* Univ. of Nebraska Pr.

Edwards, Steve. Breaking into the Backcountry. 2010. (ENG.). 192p. pap. 16.95 *(978-0-8032-2653-1(5)*, Bison Bks.) Univ. of Nebraska Pr.

Efron, Georgii. The Diaries of Georgy Efron, August 1942-August 1943 (The Tashkent Period) 2010. vii, 152p. 99.95 *(978-0-7734-3645-9(5))* Mellen, Edwin Pr., The.

Eggers, Dave. A Heartbreaking Work of Staggering Genius: A Memoir Based on a True Story. *(978-0-676-80884-1(0)*, Vintage) Knopf Doubleday Publishing Group.

Eisner, Will. Life, in Pictures: Autobiographical Stories. 2007. (ENG., Illus.). 496p. 29.95 *(978-0-393-06107-9(8)*, 6107) Norton, W. W. & Co., Inc.

Ekardt, Dennis E. Every Life Is A Story & This Is Mine: A Memoir & Recollections. 2010. 332p. pap. 17.72 *(978-1-4520-9851-7(4))* AuthorHouse.

El Saadawi, Nawal. A Daughter of Isis: The Autobiography of Nawal el Saadawi. 2nd ed. 2009. (ENG., Illus.). 400p. 120.95 *(978-1-84813-231-3(X))* Zed Bks., Ltd. GBR. Dist: Macmillan.

—Walking Through Fire: A Life of Nawal el Saadawi. 2nd ed. 2009. (ENG.). 352p. 120.95 *(978-1-84813-228-3(X))*; pap. 22.95 *(978-1-84813-229-0(8))* Zed Bks., Ltd. GBR. Dist: Macmillan.

El Saadawi, Nawal & Malti-Douglas, Fedwa. Daughter of Isis: The Autobiography of Nawal el Saadawi. 2nd ed. 2009. (ENG.). 400p. pap. 22.95 *(978-1-84813-232-0(8))* Zed Bks., Ltd. GBR. Dist: Macmillan.

Eliot, George. George Eliot's Life: As Related in Her Letters & Journals. Cross, John Walter, ed. 2010. (Cambridge Library Collection - Literary Studies). (ENG., Illus.). 518p. pap. 37.99 *(978-1-108-02006-0(2))* Cambridge Univ. Pr.

—George Eliot's Life, as Related in her Letters & Journals. Cross, John Walter, ed. 2010. (Cambridge Library Collection - Literary Studies). (Illus.). 470p. pap. 35.99 *(978-1-108-02007-7(0))*; 492p. pap. 35.99 *(978-1-108-02008-4(9))* Cambridge Univ. Pr.

Elizabeth, Charlotte. Personal Recollections. 2008. 360p. 31.99 *(978-0-554-43107-9(6))*; 29.99 *(978-0-554-43115-4(7))*; pap. 32.75 *(978-0-554-43109-3(2))*; pap. 31.75 *(978-0-554-43113-0(0))* BiblioBazaar.

—Personal Recollections. 2006. pap. *(978-1-4065-1408-7(X))* Dodo Pr.

Ellement, Connie & Davidson, Ron. The Divided Kingdom. 152p. pap. 13.95 *(978-0-949206-48-0(2))* Fremantle Pr. AUS. Dist: Independent Pubs. Group.

Eller, Jonathan R. Becoming Ray Bradbury. 2011. (ENG., Illus.). 360p. 34.95 ***(978-0-252-03629-3(8))*** Univ. of Illinois Pr.

Ellinghausen, Laurie. Labor & Writing in Early Modern England, 1567-1667. 2008. (Illus.). 166p. 99.95 *(978-0-7546-5730-4(9))* Ashgate Publishing Co.

Elliott, Graham. Babylon Behind the Wire: A collection of true day-to-day short stories of a chef's life working in Iraq. 2011. 178p. pap. 29.95 ***(978-1-4626-0777-8(2))*** PublishAmerica, Inc.

Elliott, Stephen. The Adderall Diaries: A Memoir of Moods, Masochism, & Murder. (ENG.). 2010. 192p. pap. 14.00 *(978-1-55597-570-8(4))* 2009. 224p. 23.00 *(978-1-55597-538-8(0))* Graywolf Pr.

Ellis, David. D. H. Lawrence: Dying Game 1922-1930: Volume 3: The Cambridge Biography of D. H. Lawrence. 2011. (ENG.). 850p. pap. 51.99 ***(978-1-107-40299-7(9))*** Cambridge Univ. Pr.

Ellis, Derrick. From Vodka to Coffee: I Had to Get Sober or Stay Broke. 2010. 132p. pap. 132.00 *(978-1-4520-2382-0(2))* AuthorHouse.

Ellis, Sherry, ed. Illuminating Fiction. 2009. (ENG.). 224p. pap. 19.95 *(978-1-59709-068-1(9))* Red Hen Pr.

Ellroy, James. The Hilliker Curse: My Pursuit of Women. 2010. (ENG.). 224p. 24.95 *(978-0-307-59350-4(9)*, Knopf) Knopf Doubleday Publishing Group.

Ellwood, Thomas. The History of Thomas Ellwood Written by Himself. 2008. 208p. 27.99 *(978-0-554-23818-0(7))*; 24.99 *(978-0-554-33121-8(7))* BiblioBazaar.

—The History of Thomas Ellwood Written by Himself. 2007. 180p. per. *(978-1-4065-2496-3(4))* Dodo Pr.

—Life of Thomas Ellwood. 2007. (ENG.). 292p. 43.95 *(978-0-548-13417-7(0))* 2006. pap. 28.95 *(978-1-4286-4520-2(9))* Kessinger Publishing, LLC.

Elworthy, Terence. Spindrift. 2011. 264p. pap. 17.08 ***(978-1-4269-0106-5(2))*** Trafford Publishing.

Emerson, R. W. & Emerson, Clarke. Memoirs of Margaret Fuller Ossoli, 2 vols., Set. reprint ed. 200.00 *(978-0-7950-1719-3(7))* New Library Press LLC.

Emerson, Ralph Waldo. Ralph Waldo Emerson No. 202: Selected Journals, 1841-1877. Rosenwald, Lawrence, ed. 2010. (ENG.). 992p. (gr. 12-18). 40.00 *(978-1-59853-068-1(2))* Library of America, The.

—Ralph Waldo Emerson's: Selected Journals, 1820-1842. Rosenwald, Lawrence, ed. 2010. (ENG.). 992p. (gr. 12-18). 40.00 *(978-1-59853-067-4(4))* Library of America, The.

Endless Mountains Writing Project Staff. Voices of the Twin Tiers: A Celebration of Writing Contest Winners 2007-2008. 2008. 176p. pap. 15.95 *(978-0-9800429-6-2(8))* Pen & Publish Inc.

Engdahl. Nobel Lectures in Literature 2001 - 2005. 2008. 61.00 *(978-981-279-435-2(2))*; pap. 43.00 *(978-981-279-436-9(0))* World Scientific Publishing Co., Inc.

Enowitch, Bennett I. Eros & Thanatos: A Psycho-Literary Investigation of Walter Vogt's Life & Works. (Studies in Modern German Literature: Vol. 103). (Illus.). xii,142p. pap. 40.95 *(978-3-03910-320-1(2))* Lang, Peter Publishing, Inc.

Ephron, Nora. I Remember Nothing: And Other Reflections. (Vintage Ser.). (ENG.). 160p. 2011. pap. 14.00 *(978-0-307-74280-3(6)*, Vintage) 2010. 22.95 *(978-0-307-59560-7(9)*, Knopf) Knopf Doubleday Publishing Group.

—I Remember Nothing: And Other Reflections. lt. ed. 2010. (ENG.). 160p. pap. 23.00 *(978-0-7393-7804-5(X))* Random Hse. Large Print.

Eppridge, Bill, photos by. Roaring in the Blood: Remembering Robert F. Jones. 2009. (ENG., Illus.). 208p. 35.00 *(978-0-9660212-9-5(0)*, 966029) Skyhorse Publishing Co., Inc.

Epstein, Barbara. The Company They Kept: Writers on Unforgettable Friendships. 2006. 298p. pap. *(978-1-59017-204-9(3))* New York Review of Bks., Inc., The.

Epstein, Barbara & Silvers, Robert B., eds. The Company They Kept: Writers on Unforgettable Friendships. 2006. (ENG.). 316p. 24.95 *(978-1-59017-203-2(5))* New York Review of Bks., Inc., The.

Epstein, Joseph, ed. Literary Genius: 25 Classic Writers Who Define English & American Literature. 2007. (ENG., Illus.). 256p. pap. 18.95 *(978-1-58988-035-1(8))* Dry, Paul Bks., Inc.

Epstein, Joseph & Moser, Barry. Literary Genius: 25 Classic Writers Who Define English & American Literature. 2007. *(978-1-58988-039-9(0))* Dry, Paul Bks., Inc.

Ergun, Leyla. The Reason. 2009. 108p. 27.49 *(978-1-4389-9311-9(0))*; pap. 16.49 *(978-1-4389-9312-6(9))* AuthorHouse.

Erickson, John R. Story Craft: Reflections on Faith, Culture, & Writing from the Author of Hank the Cowdog. 2009. 168p. pap. 12.99 *(978-1-59188-891-8(3))* Maverick Bks., Inc.

Ernaux, Annie. Things Seen. Kaplansky, Jonathan, tr. from FRE. 2010. (ENG.). 106p. 30.00 *(978-0-8032-1077-6(9))*; pap. 16.95 *(978-0-8032-2815-3(5)*, Bison Bks.) Univ. of Nebraska Pr.

Eskenazi, Gerald. A Sportswriter's Life: From the Desk of a New York Times Reporter. 2011. (SPORTS & AMERICAN CULTURE Ser.). (ENG., Illus.). 224p. (gr. 9). pap. 19.95 *(978-0-8262-1958-9(6))* Univ. of Missouri Pr.

Eskin, Stanley G. Simenon: A Critical Biography. alt. ed. 2011. (ENG., Illus.). 318p. pap. 25.00 ***(978-0-7864-6728-0(2))*** McFarland & Co., Inc. Pubs.

Essmann, Jeffrey. Life on the List: Assorted Sordid Tales & Unsavory Revelations. 2009. 96p. pap. 13.95 *(978-1-60381-421-8(3)*, Fanny Pr.) Coffeetown Enterprises, Inc.

Eubanks, W. Ralph. The House at the End of the Road: The Story of Three Generations of an Interracial Family in the American South. 2009. (Illus.). 224p. 26.99 *(978-0-06-137573-6(X))* Smithsonian Institution Pr.

Eugster, Sandra. Notes from Nethers: Growing up in a Sixties Commune. 2007. (ENG., Illus.). 320p. per. 18.95 *(978-0-89733-561-4(9))* Academy Chicago Pubs., Ltd.

Europa Publications. International Who's Who of Authors & Writers 2010. 25th rev. ed. 2009. (ENG.). 864p. 460.00 *(978-1-85743-528-3(1))* Routledge.

Europa Publications, ed. International Who's Who of Authors & Writers 2011. 26th rev. ed. 2010. 880p. 470.00 *(978-1-85743-565-8(6)*, Routledge) Taylor & Francis Group GBR. Dist: Taylor & Francis Group.

Falack, Rochelle Lynn. Finding My Breath: My Journey from OCD to Yoga. 2010. 196p. 24.99 *(978-1-4520-7918-9(8))* AuthorHouse.

Farber, Thomas. A Lover's Quarrel: On Writing & the Writing Life. 2007. 268p. pap. 19.95 *(978-0-9788699-2-2(3))* Ellsberg Bks.

Fargnoli, Nicholas. William Faulkner: A Literary Companion. Fargnoli, Nicholas, ed. 2007. (ENG., Illus.). 592p. pap. 17.95 *(978-1-933648-58-3(9))* Pegasus Bks.

Farr, Sidney Saylor. My Appalachia: A Memoir. 2007. (ENG., Illus.). 272p. 35.00 *(978-0-8131-2450-6(6))* Univ. Pr. of Kentucky.

Farrant, M. A. C. The Secret Lives of Litterbugs. 2009. (ENG.). 256p. pap. 16.95 *(978-1-55470-159-9(7))* Key Porter Bks. CAN. Dist: Perseus-PGW.

Farrar, John. Recollections of Seventy Years by Mrs John Farrar. 2006. 340p. per. 23.99 *(978-1-4255-3464-6(3))* MPublishing.

Faught, C. Brad. Into Africa: The Imperial Life of Margery Perham. 2012. (ENG., Illus.). 288p. 75.00 ***(978-1-84885-490-1(0))*** I. B. Tauris & Co., Ltd. GBR. Dist: Macmillan.

Fears, David, compiled by. Mark Twain Day-by-Day: An Annotated Chronology of the Life of Samuel L. Clemens, Vol. 1 (1835-1885), 3 vols., Vol. 1. 2008. 1148p. 125.00 *(978-0-9714868-2-9(4))* Horizon Micro Publishing, LLC.

Febos, Melissa. Whip Smart: The True Story of a Secret Life. 2011. (ENG.). 288p. pap. 14.99 *(978-0-312-58378-1(8),* St. Martin's Griffin) St. Martin's Pr.

Federal Bureau Of Investigation & Ernest Hemingway. Ernest Hemingway: The FBI Files. 2007. 128p. per. 22.99 *(978-1-59986-244-6(1),* Filibust) Filiquarian Publishing, LLC.

Federman, Raymond. Shhh: The Story of a Childhood. 2010. 264p. pap. 18.00 *(978-0-9842133-0-6(9))* Starcherone Bks.

Feiffer, Jules. Backing into Forward: A Memoir. 2010. (ENG., Illus.). 464p. 30.00 *(978-0-385-53158-0(3),* Talese, Nan A.) Knopf Doubleday Publishing Group.

—Backing into Forward: A Memoir. 2012. (ENG.). 456p. pap. 19.00 ***(978-0-226-24035-0(5))*** Univ. of Chicago Pr.

Felber, Ron. Searchers: A True Story. Date not set. lib. bdg. 21.95 *(978-0-8488-1650-6(1))* Amereon LTD.

Felix, Emma. My Hands. 2008. 9p. pap. 24.95 *(978-1-60672-406-4(1))* PublishAmerica, Inc.

Fellner, Steve. All Screwed Up. 2009. 181p. 24.95 *(978-0-9815163-4-9(3))* Benu Pr.

Fenn, George. By Conduct & Courage: The Life of George Alfred Henty. 2011. 336p. pap. 19.95 ***(978-1-61179-137-2(5))*** Fireship Pr.

Fenton, Robert W. Edgar Rice Burroughs & Tarzan: A Biography of the Author & His Creation. alt. ed. 2010. (ENG., Illus.). 254p. pap. 38.00 *(978-0-7864-4908-8(X))* McFarland & Co., Inc. Pubs.

Ferguson, Dana. Authors & Artists for Young Adults. 2008. (Authors & Artists for Young Adults Ser.: No. 78). (ENG.). 217p. 168.00 *(978-0-7876-7797-8(3))* Cengage Gale.

Fergusson, Maggie. George Mackay Brown: The Life. 2007. (ENG., Illus.). 384p. per. 18.95 *(978-0-7195-6605-9(3))* Murray, John GBR. Dist: Independent Pubs. Group.

Ferrell, Dewitt T. My Heroes. Burns, Megan F., ed. 2011. (Illus.). 432p. 19.95 ***(978-1-935186-19-9(1))*** Waldenhouse Pubs., Inc.

Ferrer, Lerin Francisco. Familias Como la Mía. 2011. 336p. *(978-84-8383-291-2(7))* Tusquets Editores.

Ferrero, Jesus. Belver Yin. (SPA.). 14.95 *(978-84-01-38080-8(4))* Plaza & Janes Editories, S.A. ESP. Dist: AIMS International Bks., Inc.

Ferris, Kathleen. James Joyce & the Burden of Disease. 2010. (ENG.). 184p. pap. 30.00 *(978-0-8131-2664-7(9))* Univ. Pr. of Kentucky.

Fershleiser, Rachel & Smith, Larry. Not Quite What I Was Planning: Six-Word Memoirs by Writers Famous & Obscure. 2008. (ENG., Illus.). 240p. pap. 12.99 *(978-0-06-137405-0(9),* HarperPerennial) HarperCollins Pubs.

Fidler, William Perry & Wilson, Augusta Evans. Augusta Evans Wilson, 1835-1909: A Biography. 2011. 272p. 47.95 ***(978-1-258-06773-1(0))*** Literary Licensing, LLC.

Fielding, Henry. Henry Fielding: The Journal of a Voyage to Lisbon, Shamela, & Occasional Writings. Battestin, Martin C., ed. 2008. (Wesleyan Edition of the Works of Henry Fielding Ser.). (ENG., Illus.). 800p. 299.00 *(978-0-19-926675-3(1))* Oxford Univ. Pr., Inc.

Fields, Annie. A Shelf of Old Books. 2010. 242p. pap. 26.75 *(978-1-177-91560-1(X))*; (ENG.). 236p. pap. 26.75 *(978-1-176-28843-0(1))*; 242p. pap. 26.75 *(978-1-175-81265-0(X))*; 246p. pap. 26.75 *(978-1-147-66657-1(1))*; 240p. pap. 26.75 *(978-1-145-75153-8(9))* BiblioBazaar.

—A Shelf of Old Books. 2009. 62p. pap. *(978-1-151-58259-1(X))* Books LLC.

Fields, Dorothy C. Whispers, Daydreams & Twilight Memories. 96p. pap. 10.00 *(978-0-87012-689-5(X))* McClain Printing Co.

Fields, James Thomas. Yesterdays with Authors, by James T Fields. 2006. 356p. per. 26.99 *(978-1-4255-3869-9(X))* MPublishing.

Finch, David. R. M. Patterson: A Life of Great Adventure, 1 vol. 2010. (ENG., Illus.). 312p. pap. *(978-1-894898-95-9(8))* TouchWood Editions.

Fincke, Gary. The Canals of Mars: A Memoir. 2010. (ENG.). 232p. pap. 29.95 *(978-0-87013-880-5(4))* Michigan State Univ. Pr.

Findley, John M. Just Lucky. 2010. 640p. 36.49 *(978-1-4490-9074-6(5))*; pap. 25.99 *(978-1-4490-9073-9(7))* AuthorHouse.

Finke, Don & Finke, Nikki. Imagine That: Over 45 Years of Auto Racing Experiences. 2010. 432p. 33.95 *(978-1-4490-8750-0(7))*; pap. 24.95 *(978-1-4490-8752-4(3))* AuthorHouse.

Finn, Rose. A Finn Life by No Means: The Early Memoirs of Patrick Joseph Finn. 2010. (Illus.). 152p. 22.49 *(978-1-4490-7185-1(6))*; pap. 11.99 *(978-1-4490-7184-4(8))* AuthorHouse.

Fintoni, Monica, et al, eds. The World of the Aztecs: In the Florentine Codex. Paoletti, Andrea & Carden, Jeremy, trs. 2008. (ENG., Illus.). 64p. pap. 19.95 *(978-88-7461-102-7(1))* Mandragora ITA. Dist: Antique Collectors' Club.

Firkins, Oscar W. Ralph Waldo Emerson. 2009. 210p. pap. *(978-0-217-27038-0(7))* Books LLC.

—Ralph Waldo Emerson. 2008. 386p. 48.95 *(978-0-548-96371-5(1))* 2007. (ENG.). 388p. per. 33.95 *(978-0-548-63915-3(9))* Kessinger Publishing, LLC.

—Ralph Waldo Emerson. 379p. reprint ed. 58.00 *(978-0-7950-1534-2(8))* New Library Press LLC.

Firner, Nadja. Theodore Dreiser's Dawn - the Formation of a Mind. 2008. 128p. pap. *(978-3-639-03065-5(6))* VDM Verlag Dr. Mueller e.K.

Fisher, Benjamin F., ed. Poe in His Own Time: A Biographical Chronicle of His Life, Drawn from Recollections, Interviews, & Memoirs by Family, Friends, & Associates. 2010. (Writers in Their Own Time Ser.). (ENG., Illus.). 276p. pap. 27.95 *(978-1-58729-863-9(5))* Univ. of Iowa Pr.

Fisher, Carrie. Shockaholic. (ENG., Illus.). 176p. 2012. pap. 13.99 ***(978-0-7432-6483-9(5))*** 2011. 22.00 *(978-0-7432-6482-2(7))* Simon & Schuster.

Fisher, M. F. K. A Stew or a Story: An Assortment of Short Works. 2nd ed. 2007. (ENG.). 400p. per. 15.95 *(978-1-59376-165-3(1))* Counterpoint LLC.

Fisher, Rudolph. The City of Refuge: The Collected Stories of Rudolph Fisher. McCluskey, John, Jr., ed. & intro. by. 2nd exp. ed. 2008. (ENG.). 352p. (C). pap. 24.95 *(978-0-8262-1812-4(1))* Univ. of Missouri Pr.

Fisher, Vardis. Love & Death. 21.95 *(978-0-88411-558-8(5))* Amereon LTD.

Fitzgerald, Edward. Letters & Literary Remains of Edward FitzGerald, 7 vols. Wright, William A., ed. reprint ed. 535.00 *(978-0-404-02440-6(8))* AMS Pr., Inc.

—Letters of Edward FitzGerald. Wright, William Aldis, ed. 2007. (ENG.). 220p. per. *(978-1-4065-5968-2(7))* Dodo Pr.

—Letters of Edward FitzGerald. 2007. (ENG.). 376p. 48.95 *(978-0-548-14139-7(8))*; Vol. 1. 372p. 48.95 *(978-0-548-14138-0(X))* Kessinger Publishing, LLC.

Fitzgerald, Edward & Wright, William Aldis. Letters of Edward FitzGerald. 2008. (ENG.). 284p. pap. 28.75 *(978-1-4375-0627-3(5))*; Vol. 2. 244p. pap. 25.75 *(978-1-4375-0626-6(7))* BiblioBazaar.

Fitzgerald, F. Scott. A Short Autobiography. West, James L. W., III, ed. 2011. (ENG.). 224p. pap. 15.00 *(978-1-4391-9906-0(X),* Scribner) Scribner.

Fitzgerald, F. Scott & West, James L. W., III. A Short Autobiography. 2011. (ENG.). 224p. lib. bdg. 25.00 *(978-1-4516-2116-7(7),* Scribner) Scribner.

Fitzgerald, Stephanie. Alice Walker: Author & Social Activist. 2008. (Signature Lives Ser.). (ENG., Illus.). 112p. (gr. 6-7). lib. bdg. 35.32 *(978-0-7565-3474-5(7),* Signature Lives) Compass Point Bks.

Fleishman, Avrom. George Eliot's Intellectual Life. 2011. (ENG.). 310p. pap. 39.99 *(978-1-107-40266-9(2))* Cambridge Univ. Pr.

Fleming, John. Romulus Linney: Maverick of the Theater. 2009. (ENG.). 352p. pap. 19.95 *(978-1-57525-598-9(7))* Smith & Kraus Pubs., Inc.

Fletcher, Harrison Candelaria. Descanso for My Father: Fragments of a Life. 2012. (American Lives Ser.). (ENG., Illus.). 168p. pap. 14.95 ***(978-0-8032-3839-8(8),*** Bison Bks.) Univ. of Nebraska Pr.

Flynn, Robert. Burying the Farm: A Memoir of Chillicothe, Texas. 2008. *(978-0-916727-30-7(0))* Wings Pr.

Foglio, Frank. Face to Face with the Heart of Grace. 2011. 276p. pap. 17.99 ***(978-1-4343-1099-6(X))*** AuthorHouse.

Foran, Charles. Mordecai: The Life & Times. (ENG., Illus.). 800p. 2011. pap. 21.95 *(978-0-676-97965-7(3),* Vintage Canada) 2010. 34.00 *(978-0-676-97963-3(7))* Knopf Canada CAN. Dist: Random Hse., Inc.

Ford, Ford Madox. Memories & Impressions: A Study in Atmospheres. reprint ed. lib. bdg. 98.00 *(978-0-7426-3085-7(4))* Classic Bks.

—Memories & Impressions: A Study in Atmospheres. 2007. (ENG.). 390p. 48.95 *(978-0-548-03744-7(2))* Kessinger Publishing, LLC.

—Provence. Coyle, John, ed. 2009. (ENG., Illus.). 400p. pap. 28.95 *(978-1-85754-989-8(9))* Carcanet Pr., Ltd. GBR. Dist: Independent Pubs. Group.

Ford, Gary. My Gift: ...A Few Pages of Inspiration & Love. 2009. 216p. pap. 50.49 *(978-1-4389-0508-2(4))* AuthorHouse.

Forrest, Emma. Your Voice in My Head. 2011. (ENG.). 224p. 22.95 *(978-1-59051-446-7(7))* Other Pr., LLC.

Forrest, Leon. Conversations with Leon Forrest. Williams, Dana A., ed. 2007. (ENG., Illus.). 141p. per. 22.00 *(978-1-57806-990-3(4))* Univ. Pr. of Mississippi.

—Conversations with Leon Forrest. Williams, Dana A., ed. 2007. (ENG., Illus.). 141p. 50.00 *(978-1-57806-989-7(0))* Univ. Pr. of Mississippi.

Forsberg, Tor. North of Iskut: Grizzlies, Bannock & Adventure. unabr. ed. 2010. (ENG., Illus.). 224p. pap. 24.95 *(978-1-894759-42-7(7))* Caitlin Pr., Inc. CAN. Dist: Partners Pubs. Group, Inc.

Forshaw, Barry. The Man Who Left to Soon: The Life & Works of Stieg Larsson. 2011. (ENG., Illus.). 310p. pap. 12.95 *(978-1-84358-370-7(4))* Blake, John Publishing, Ltd. GBR. Dist: Independent Pubs. Group.

—Stieg Larsson Biography. 2010. (ENG., Illus.). 294p. 27.95 *(978-1-84454-940-5(2))* Blake, John Publishing, Ltd. GBR. Dist: Independent Pubs. Group.

Forster, John. The Life of Charles Dickens. 2011. 944p. pap. ***(978-1-84902-285-9(2))*** Benediction Classics.

—The Life of Charles Dickens. 2011. (Cambridge Library Collection - Literary Studies). (ENG., Illus.). 492p. pap. 35.99 ***(978-1-108-03936-9(7))***; 576p. pap. 43.00 ***(978-1-108-03937-6(5))***; 426p. pap. 32.99 ***(978-1-108-03935-2(9))*** Cambridge Univ. Pr.

Fortenberry, Dick. No ETA: The Pioneering Days of Skydiving. 2011. 292p. 28.95 ***(978-1-4620-2644-9(3))*** iUniverse, Inc.

Fortner, Michael. Greetings from Jungleland. 2009. 220p. pap. 19.30 *(978-0-557-19540-4(3))* Lulu Enterprises Inc.

Fosberg, Michael A. Incognito: An American Odyssey of Race & Self-Discovery. 2011. 317p. pap. ***(978-0-615-41396-9(X))*** Incognito, Inc.

Foster, Stephen. Walking Ollie: Or, Winning the Love of a Difficult Dog. 2008. (ENG.). 192p. (gr. 12-18). 12.00 *(978-0-399-53429-4(6),* Perigee Trade) Penguin Group (USA) Inc.

Fournier, Jean-Louis. Where We Going, Daddy? Life with Two Sons Unlike Any Other. Hunter, Adriana, tr. from FRE. 2010. (ENG.). 128p. pap. 12.00 *(978-1-59051-338-5(X))* Other Pr., LLC.

Fowles, John. The Journals: Volume 1: 1949-1965. Drazin, Charles, ed. & intro. by. 2009. (ENG.). 668p. pap. 24.95 *(978-0-8101-2514-8(5))* Northwestern Univ. Pr.

—The Journals: Volume 2: 1966-1990. Drazin, Charles, ed. & intro. by. 2009. (ENG.). 464p. pap. 24.95 *(978-0-8101-2515-5(3))* Northwestern Univ. Pr.

Fox, Caroline. Memories of Old Friends. 2009. 130p. pap. *(978-0-217-23583-9(2))*; 122p. pap. *(978-0-217-02164-7(6))*; 308p. pap. *(978-0-217-51389-0(1))* Books LLC.

—Memories of Old Friends. 440p. reprint ed. 98.00 *(978-0-7222-1741-2(2))* Library Reprints, Inc.

Foxworthy, Bruce L. Making Do & Hanging On: Growing up in Apple Country Through the Great Depression. 2008. 352p. pap. 17.99 *(978-1-4343-9917-5(6))* AuthorHouse.

Francavilla, Joseph. Harlan Ellison. 2011. ***(978-1-58765-828-0(3))*** Salem Pr., Inc.

Frank, Tenney. Vergil: A Biography. 2007. 130p. pap. 18.99 *(978-1-4346-2186-3(3))* BiblioBazaar.

Frankel, Valerie. It's Hard Not to Hate You. (ENG.). 256p. 2012. pap. 14.99 ***(978-1-250-01388-0(7),*** St. Martin's Griffin) 2011. 24.99 *(978-0-312-60978-8(7))* St. Martin's Pr.

Frankel, Valerie. Thin Is the New Happy. 2009. (ENG.). 272p. pap. 14.99 *(978-0-312-37393-1(7),* St. Martin's Griffin) St. Martin's Pr.

Franks, Lucinda. My Father's Secret War: A Memoir. 2007. 320p. 24.95 *(978-1-4013-5226-4(X))* Miramax Bks.

Franzen, Jonathan. The Discomfort Zone: A Personal History. 2006. (ENG.). 208p. 22.00 *(978-0-374-29919-4(6))* Farrar, Straus & Giroux.

—The Discomfort Zone: A Personal History. 2007. (ENG.). 208p. per. 14.00 *(978-0-312-42640-8(2))* Picador.

Fraser, Antonia. Must You Go? My Life with Harold Pinter. 2010. (ENG., Illus.). 336p. 28.95 *(978-0-385-53250-1(4),* Talese, Nan A.) Knopf Doubleday Publishing Group.

—Must You Go? My LIfe with Harold Pinter. 2011. (ENG., Illus.). 384p. pap. 16.00 *(978-0-307-47557-2(3),* Anchor) Knopf Doubleday Publishing Group.

Fraser, Laura. All over the Map. 2011. (ENG.). 288p. pap. 14.00 *(978-0-307-45064-7(3))* Broadway Bks.

Fraser, Raymond. When the Earth Was Flat. 2007. (ENG., Illus.). 160p. pap. 17.00 *(978-0-88753-439-3(2))* Black Moss Pr. CAN. Dist: LitDistCo.

Fraser, Russell. A Mingled Yarn: The Life of R. P. Blackmur. 2010. (ENG., Illus.). 390p. pap. 39.95 *(978-1-4128-1447-8(2))* Transaction Pubs.

Frayn, Michael. My Father's Fortune: A Life. 2011. 25.95 *(978-1-60998-221-8(5))*; 49.95 *(978-0-7927-7576-8(7),* Sound Library) AudioGO.

—My Father's Fortune: A Life. 2011. (ENG., Illus.). 288p. 25.00 *(978-0-8050-9377-3(X),* Metropolitan Bks.) Holt, Henry & Co.

Freeman, Judith. The Long Embrace: Raymond Chandler & the Woman He Loved. 2008. (Vintage Ser.). (ENG., Illus.). 368p. pap. 14.95 *(978-1-4000-9517-9(4),* Vintage) Knopf Doubleday Publishing Group.

Freidin, Gregory, ed. The Enigma of Isaac Babel: Biography, History, Context. 2009. (ENG., Illus.). 288p. 60.00 *(978-0-8047-5903-8(0))* Stanford Univ. Pr.

French, Patrick. The World Is What It Is: The Authorized Biography of V. S. Naipaul. 2009. (Vintage Ser.). (ENG., Illus.). 592p. pap. 17.00 *(978-1-4000-7980-3(2),* Vintage) Knopf Doubleday Publishing Group.

Friedman, Bruce Jay. Lucky Bruce: A Literary Memoir. 2011. (ENG., Illus.). 275p. 26.95 ***(978-1-926845-31-9(5))*** Biblioasis CAN. Dist: Consortium Bk. Sales & Distribution.

Friedman, Donald. The Writer's Brush: Paintings, Drawings, & Sculpture by Writers. 2007. (ENG., Illus.). 480p. 50.00 *(978-0-922811-76-2(8))* Mid-List Pr.

Friedman, Steve. Lost on Treasure Island: A Memoir of Longing, Love, & Lousy Choices in New York City. 2011. (ENG.). 320p. 24.95 *(978-1-61145-020-0(9),* 611020, Arcade Publishing) Skyhorse Publishing Co., Inc.

Friend, Lonn. Life on Planet Rock. 2006. (ENG., Illus.). 320p. pap. 14.95 *(978-0-7679-2208-1(5),* Morgan Road Bks.) Broadway Bks.

Fries, Kenny. The History of My Shoes & the Evolution of Darwin's Theory. 2007. (ENG., Illus.). 224p. per. 14.95 *(978-0-7867-2007-1(7))* Da Capo Pr., Inc.

Froude, James. Bunyan. 2007. (ENG.). 188p. 37.95 *(978-0-548-05027-9(9))* Kessinger Publishing, LLC.

Froude, James Anthony. Bunyan. 2011. (Cambridge Library Collection - English Men of Letters Ser.). (ENG.). 194p. pap. 19.99 ***(978-1-108-03466-1(7))*** Cambridge Univ. Pr.

—Thomas Carlyle: A History of his Life in London, 1834-1881. 2011. (Cambridge Library Collection - Literary Studies). (ENG.). 500p. pap. 35.99 *(978-1-108-02933-9(7))*; (Illus.). 476p. pap. 34.99 *(978-1-108-02932-2(9))* Cambridge Univ. Pr.

—Thomas Carlyle: A History of the First Forty Years of his Life, 1795-1835. 2011. (Cambridge Library Collection - Literary Studies). (ENG.). 508p. pap. 37.99 *(978-1-108-02930-8(2))*; (Illus.). 462p. pap. 34.99 *(978-1-108-02929-2(9))* Cambridge Univ. Pr.

—Thomas Carlyle V1 A History of His Life. 2006. pap. 37.95 *(978-1-4286-3587-6(4))* Kessinger Publishing, LLC.

—Thomas Carlyle V2 A History of His Life. 2006. pap. 38.95 *(978-1-4286-3589-0(0))* Kessinger Publishing, LLC.

Fu, Shen. Chapters from a Floating Life. Black, Shirley, tr. 2007. 112p. per. 11.95 *(978-1-59654-382-9(5))* Disruptive Publishing.

—Six Records of a Floating Life. 2011. 13.77 *(978-0-7848-3461-9(X),* Everbind) Marco Bk. Co.

Fuguet, Alberto. Mi Cuerpo es una Celda. 2008. 300p. pap. 19.95 *(978-958-45-1533-9(0))* Norma S.A. COL. Dist: Grupo Editorial Norma.

Fuller, Amy Elisabeth, ed. Contemporary Authors. (Contemporary Authors Ser.). (ENG.). 2008. 464p. 293.00 *(978-0-7876-7890-6(2))* 2007. 448p. 293.00 *(978-0-7876-7887-6(2))* Cengage Gale.

—Contemporary Authors: A Bio-Bibliographical Guide to Current Writers in Fiction, General Nonfiction, Poetry, Journalism, Drama, Motion Pictures, Television, & Other Fields, Vol. 252. 2007. (Contemporary Authors Ser.). (ENG.). 464p. 293.00 *(978-0-7876-7881-4(3))* Cengage Gale.

—Contemporary Authors, Volume 254, Vol. 254. 2007. (Contemporary Authors Ser.). (ENG., Illus.). 470p. 293.00 *(978-0-7876-7883-8(X))* Cengage Gale.

—Contemporary Authors, Volume 259: A Bio-Bibliographical Guide to Current Writers in Fiction, General Nonfiction, Poetry, Journalism, Drama, Motion Pictures, Television, & Other Fields. 2007. (Contemporary Authors Ser.: Vol. 259). (ENG.). 464p. 293.00 *(978-0-7876-7888-3(0))* Cengage Gale.

Fuller, Margaret. Memoirs of Margaret Fuller Ossoli. 2009. 360p. 26.99 *(978-1-103-33798-9(X))*; pap. 20.99 *(978-1-103-33793-4(9))* BiblioBazaar.

—Memoirs of Margaret Fuller Ossoli. 2009. 160p. pap. *(978-0-217-86489-3(9))* Books LLC.

—Memoirs of Margaret Fuller Ossoli. 2006. 372p. per. 26.99 *(978-1-4255-3872-9(X))*; (ENG.). 352p. per. 26.99 *(978-1-4255-3584-1(4))* MPublishing.

Fullerton, Susannah. A Dance with Jane Austen: How a Novelist & Her Characters Went to the Ball. 2012. (ENG., Illus.). 144p. 24.95 ***(978-0-7112-3245-7(8))*** Lincoln, Frances Ltd. GBR. Dist: Perseus-PGW.

Furey, Hester Lee. American Radical & Reform Writers. 2008. (Dictionary of Literary Biography Ser.: Vol. 345). (ENG.). 426p. 315.00 *(978-0-7876-8163-0(6))* Cengage Gale.

Furiya, Linda. How to Cook a Dragon: Living, Loving, & Eating in China. 2008. (ENG.). 256p. pap. 16.95 *(978-1-58005-255-9(X))* Seal Pr.

Furlani, Andre. Guy Davenport: Postmodern & After. 2007. (Avant-Garde & Modernism Studies Ser.). (ENG.). 296p. 59.95 *(978-0-8101-2385-4(1))* Northwestern Univ. Pr.

—Guy Davenport: Postmodernism & After. 2007. (Avant-Garde & Modernism Studies). (ENG.). 296p. per. 27.95 *(978-0-8101-2389-2(4))* Northwestern Univ. Pr.

Gabbin, Joanne Veal, ed. Shaping Memories: Reflections of African American Women Writers. 2009. (ENG.). 240p. 30.00 *(978-1-60473-274-0(1))* Univ. Pr. of Mississippi.

Gabrial, Jan. Inside the Volcano: My Life with Malcolm Lowry. 2010. (ENG., Illus.). 224p. pap. 31.00 *(978-0-230-61978-4(9))* Palgrave Macmillan.

Gabrielsson, Eva. There Are Things I Want You to Know about Stieg Larsson & Me. Coverdale, Linda, tr. from FRE.Tr. of Millénium, Stieg et Moi. (ENG., Illus.). 224p. 2012. pap. 14.95 ***(978-1-60980-410-7(4))*** 2011. 23.95 *(978-1-60980-363-6(9))* Seven Stories Pr.

Gac-Artigas, Alejandro. Yo, Alejandro. (Memorias Coleccion). (SPA., Illus.). 120p. pap. 18.95 *(978-84-207-4798-9(X),* ANY798) Grupo Anaya, S.A. ESP. Dist: Continental Bk. Co., Inc.

Gaer, Joseph, ed. Ambrose Gwinett Bierce: Bibliography & Biographical Data. 2007. (ENG.). 108p. per. 19.95 *(978-1-4325-7111-5(7))* Kessinger Publishing, LLC.

Gaiman, Neil. Don't Panic: Douglas Adams & the Hitchhiker's Guide to the Galaxy 2009. 5th ed. 2009. (ENG., Illus.). 288p. pap. 14.95 *(978-1-84856-496-1(1),* Titan Bks.) Titan Bks. Ltd. GBR. Dist: Random Hse., Inc.

Gale. CourseReader 0-30: Chaucer Instant Access Code. 2011. (C). 40.95 *(978-1-111-35434-3(0))* Wadsworth.

Gale, ed. A Biographical Guide to Novelists, Poets, Playwrights Screenwriters, Lyricists, Illustrators, Cartoonists, Animators, & Other Creative Artists. (Authors & Artists for Young Adults Ser.). 2012. (ENG.). 264p. lib. bdg. 168.00 *(978-0-7876-9480-7(0))* 2011. 212p. lib. bdg. 168.00 *(978-0-7876-9479-1(7))* Cengage Gale.

Gale Cengage Publishing, creator. Contemporary Authors, Volume 262: A Bio-Bibliographical Guide to Current Writers in Fiction, General Nonfiction, Poetry, Journalism, Drama, Motion Pictures, Television, & Other Fields. 2008. (Contemporary Authors Ser.). (ENG., Illus.). 464p. 293.00 *(978-0-7876-9520-0(3))* Cengage Gale.

—Something about the Author: Facts & Pictures about Authors & Illustrators of Books for Young People. 2008. (Something about the Author Ser.: Vol. 186). (ENG., Illus.). 240p. (J). 202.00 *(978-0-7876-9935-2(7))* Cengage Gale.

—Something about the Author: Facts & Pictures about Authors & Illustrators of Books of Young People. 2008. (Something about the Author Ser.). (ENG., Illus.). 384p. 202.00 *(978-0-7876-9934-5(9))* Cengage Gale.

—Something about the Author Volume 184: Facts & Pictures about Authors & Illustrators of Books for Young People. 2008. (Something about the Author Ser.: Vol. 184). (ENG., Illus.). 240p. 202.00 *(978-0-7876-9933-8(0))* Cengage Gale.

Gale Editor, ed. American Writers: Supplement XXII. 22nd ed. 2011. lib. bdg. 218.00 (978-1-4144-8024-4(5), Charles Scribner's Sons) Cengage Gale.

—Contemporary Authors: A Bio-Bibliographical Guide to Current Writers in Fiction, General Nonfiction, Poetry, Journalism, Drama, Motion Pictures, Television. 2011. 500p. (ENG.). lib. bdg. 293.00 (978-1-4144-6096-3(1)); (ENG.). lib. bdg. 293.00 (978-1-4144-6095-6(3)); (ENG.). lib. bdg. 293.00 (978-1-4144-6094-9(5)); (ENG.). lib. bdg. 293.00 (978-1-4144-6093-2(7)); (ENG.). lib. bdg. 293.00 (978-1-4144-6092-5(9)); (ENG.). lib. bdg. 293.00 (978-1-4144-6091-8(0)); (ENG.). 293.00 (978-1-4144-6089-5(9)); 293.00 (978-1-4144-6088-8(0)); (ENG.). lib. bdg. 293.00 (978-1-4144-6090-1(2)) Cengage Gale.

—Contemporary Authors New Revision Series: A Bio-Bibliographical Guide to Current Writers in Fiction, General Non-Fiction, Poetry, Journalism, Drama, Motion Pictures, Television, & Other Fields. 2011. 500p. (ENG.). lib. bdg. 293.00 (978-1-4144-6843-3(1)); (ENG.). lib. bdg. 293.00 (978-1-4144-6120-5(8)); (ENG.). lib. bdg. 293.00 (978-1-4144-6119-9(4)); (ENG.). lib. bdg. 293.00 (978-1-4144-6117-5(8)); (ENG.). lib. bdg. 293.00 (978-1-4144-6118-2(6)); (ENG.). lib. bdg. 293.00 (978-1-4144-6116-8(X)); lib. bdg. 293.00 (978-1-4144-6115-1(1)); (ENG.). 293.00 (978-1-4144-6112-0(7)); (ENG.). 293.00 (978-1-4144-6113-7(5)); (ENG.). lib. bdg. 293.00 (978-1-4144-6114-4(3)) Cengage Gale.

Gale Editors, ed. Nobel Prize Laureates in Literature Pt. 2: Faulkner-Kipling. 2006. (Dictionary of Literary Biography Ser.: Vol. 330). (ENG., Illus.). 640p. 315.00 (978-0-7876-8148-7(2)) Cengage Gale.

—Something about the Author, Vol. 171. 2006. (Something about the Author Ser.). (ENG.). 352p. 202.00 (978-0-7876-8795-3(2)) Cengage Gale.

Gale Group, creator. Contemporary Authors: Volume 260. 2007. (Contemporary Authors Ser.). (ENG., Illus.). 464p. 293.00 (978-0-7876-7889-0(9)) Cengage Gale.

Gale, Maggie B. J. B. Priestley. 2008. (Routledge Modern & Contemporary Dramatists Ser.). (Illus.). CCXIV, 10p. pap. 29.95 (978-0-415-40243-9(3)) Routledge.

—J.B. Priestley. 2008. (Routledge Modern & Contemporary Dramatists Ser.). (Illus.). CCXIV, 10p. 110.00 (978-0-415-40242-2(5)) Routledge.

Galeano, Eduardo. Voices of Time: A Life in Stories. Fried, Mark, tr. 2007. (ENG., Illus.). 368p. pap. 18.00 (978-0-312-42682-8(8)) Picador.

Galling, Ines. Balanceakte am Fjord: Ästhetische Tradition, Variation und Innovation in Jon Fosses Dramen. 2010. (Imaginatio borealis. Bilder des Nordens Ser.). (GER.). 260p. 67.95 (978-3-631-59452-0(6)) Lang, Peter GmbH, Europäischer Verlag der Wissenschaften DEU. Dist: Lang, Peter.

Galloway, Janice. This Is Not about Me. (ENG.). 2010. 352p. pap. 16.95 (978-1-84708-059-8(5)) 2008. 320p. 32.95 (978-1-84708-061-5(8)) Granta Bks. GBR. Dist: Independent Pubs. Group.

Gamble, Sarah. Angela Carter: A Literary Life. 2009. (Literary Lives Ser.). (ENG.). 240p. pap. 36.00 (978-0-230-58098-5(X)) Palgrave Macmillan.

Garner, Paul A. Dewdrops & Rainfall: An Autobiography. 2011. 190p. pap. 24.95 **(978-1-4626-0825-6(6))** PublishAmerica, Inc.

Gammel, Irene. Looking for Anne of Green Gables: The Story of L. M. Montgomery & Her Literary Classic. 2009. (ENG., Illus.). 320p. pap. 18.99 (978-0-312-38238-4(3), St. Martin's Griffin) St. Martin's Pr.

Gann, Ernest K. Song of the Sirens. 2007. (ENG., Illus.). 336p. per. 19.95 (978-1-57409-254-7(5)) Sheridan Hse., Inc.

García Márquez, Gabriel. Living to Tell the Tale. (978-1-4000-8869-0(0)) Knopf Doubleday Publishing Group.

Garfield, Simon. The Error World: An Affair with Stamps. 2009. (ENG.). 256p. 24.00 (978-0-15-101396-8(9)) Houghton Mifflin Harcourt Trade & Reference Pubs.

Garland, Hamlin. A Daughter of the Middle Border. 2008. 400p. 31.99 (978-0-554-30035-1(4)); 29.99 (978-0-554-39338-4(7)) BiblioBazaar.

—A Daughter of the Middle Border. 2008. (Illus.). 364p. pap. (978-1-4065-8900-9(4)) Dodo Pr.

—A Daughter of the Middle Border. 2007. (ENG.). 410p. 49.95 (978-0-548-01436-3(1)) Kessinger Publishing, LLC.

—A Daughter of the Middle Border. 2007. 327p. per. 19.95 (978-0-87351-566-5(8), Borealis Bk.) Minnesota Historical Society Pr.

—A Son of the Middle Border. 2007. 384p. per. 19.95 (978-0-87351-565-8(X), Borealis Bk.) Minnesota Historical Society Pr.

—A Son of the Middle Border. 2007. (ENG.). 504p. per. (978-1-4067-7081-0(7)) Read Bks.

Gaskell, E. C. The Life of Charlotte Bronte. 2010. 738p. pap. 41.56 (978-1-166-34050-6(3)); 53.56 **(978-1-166-39200-0(7))** Kessinger Publishing, LLC.

Gaskell, Elizabeth. The Life of Charlotte Bronte. 2010. 374p. pap. 32.75 (978-1-146-89625-9(3)) BiblioBazaar.

—The Life of Charlotte Bronte. 2011. 580p. 58.95 **(978-1-169-84143-7(0))** 2010. 580p. 47.16 (978-1-163-21029-1(3)) 2010. 448p. pap. 29.56 (978-1-163-17769-3(5)) 2010. 580p. pap. 35.16 (978-1-162-64556-8(3)) 2010. 450p. 41.56 **(978-1-166-13819-6(4))** Kessinger Publishing, LLC.

—The Life of Charlotte Brontë. 2011. 462p. pap. 36.75 **(978-1-173-36958-3(9))** 2010. 320p. pap. 30.75 (978-1-178-28250-4(3)) 2010. 304p. pap. 29.75 (978-1-177-72707-5(2)) 2010. 302p. pap. 29.75 (978-1-149-01816-3(X)) 2010. 638p. pap. 45.75 (978-1-148-78885-2(9)) 2010. 454p. pap. 36.75 (978-1-143-39838-4(6)) 2010. 752p. pap. 52.75 (978-1-143-61817-8(3)) 2010. 308p. pap. 29.75 (978-1-143-79646-3(2)) 2010. 588p. pap. 44.75 (978-1-145-92539-7(1)) 2010. 304p. pap. 29.75 (978-1-142-08432-5(9)) 2008. 268p. 28.99 (978-0-554-28540-5(1)) 2008. 268p. pap. 25.99 (978-0-554-37843-5(4)) BiblioBazaar.

—The Life of Charlotte Brontë. 2009. 316p. pap. (978-1-151-10401-4(9)) Books LLC.

—The Life of Charlotte Brontë. 2010. (Cambridge Library Collection - Literary Studies). (Illus.). 340p. pap. 28.99 (978-1-108-02051-0(8)); 368p. pap. 29.99 (978-1-108-02050-3(X)) Cambridge Univ. Pr.

—The Life of Charlotte Brontë. 2010. (Illus.). 158p. pap. 7.84 (978-1-150-93975-4(3)); 298p. pap. 12.03 (978-1-154-13743-9(0)); 290p. pap. 36.84 (978-1-151-52705-9(X)) General Bks. LLC.

—The Life of Charlotte Brontë. 2009. 738p. 66.95 (978-1-120-10739-8(3)); pap. 51.95 (978-1-104-99472-3(0)) Kessinger Publishing, LLC.

—Life of Charlotte Bronte. 2010. 176p. pap. (978-1-4076-1803-6(2)) HardPr.

—The Life of Charlotte Brontë. 2010. 594p. pap. 44.75 (978-1-142-41244-9(X)) BiblioBazaar.

—The Life of Charlotte Brontë. 2008. Vol. 1. pap. 9.99 (978-1-60450-500-9(1)) Vol. 2. pap. 9.99 (978-1-60450-501-6(X)) Arc Manor. (Serenity Pubs.).

—The Life of Charlotte Brontë. 2007. 1. (ENG.). 248p. pap. 20.99 (978-1-4346-1639-5(8))1. (ENG.). 276p. pap. 23.99 (978-1-4346-1808-5(0)) Vol. 2. (ENG.). 236p. pap. 20.99 (978-1-4346-5669-8(1)) Vol. 2. 266p. pap. 23.99 (978-1-4346-5670-4(5)) BiblioBazaar.

Gaskell, Elizabeth & Shorter, Clement King. The Life of Charlotte Brontë. 2010. 758p. pap. 52.75 (978-1-175-97356-6(4)) BiblioBazaar.

Gaskell, Elizabeth, et al. The Life of Charlotte Brontë. 2010. 584p. pap. 43.75 (978-1-148-17896-7(1)) BiblioBazaar.

Gaskell, Elizabeth Cleghorn & Gaskell, Elizabeth. The Life of Charlotte Brontë. 2010. 418p. pap. 34.75 (978-1-178-17496-0(4)); 300p. pap. 28.75 (978-1-147-02057-1(4)); 590p. pap. 44.75 (978-1-147-13566-4(5)); 590p. pap. 44.75 (978-1-147-03078-5(2)); 320p. pap. 30.75 (978-1-147-01820-2(0)); 368p. pap. 32.75 (978-1-146-91675-2(2)); 332p. pap. 31.75 (978-1-144-61655-5(7)) BiblioBazaar.

—The Life of Charlotte Brontë. 2010. (Illus.). 164p. pap. 8.04 (978-1-150-81579-9(5)) General Bks. LLC.

—Life of Charlotte Brontë - 2010. (Illus.). 156p. pap. 24.39 (978-1-153-74409-6(0)) General Bks. LLC.

—Life of Charlotte Bronte - 2010. (Illus.). 140p. pap. 22.91 (978-1-153-74563-5(1)) General Bks. LLC.

Gaudern, Sally. Ted, Bert & Ernest: Three Sons of the Empire. 2011. 200p. pap. **(978-1-908447-55-5(9))** Grosvenor Hse. Publishing Ltd.

Gavin, William F. Speechwright: An Insider's Take on Political Rhetoric. 2011. (ENG.). 172p. 24.95 **(978-1-61186-017-7(2))** Michigan State Univ. Pr.

Gay, John & Summers, Jennifer Gay. Any Way I Can - Fifty Years in Show Business. 2008. 240p. pap. 19.95 (978-1-59393-318-0(5)) BearManor Media.

Gay, José María Pérez. The Unfortunate Passion of Hermann Broch. Jiménez, Eduardo, tr. from SPA. 2008. 148p. pap. 24.95 (978-0-9796457-3-0(5)) Floricanto Pr.

Gayle, Mike. The To-Do List. 2010. (ENG.). 352p. 13.95 (978-0-340-93675-7(4), Hodder & Stoughton) Hodder General Publishing Div. GBR. Dist: Independent Pubs. Group.

Gayton, Don. Man Facing West, 1 vol. 2011. (Illus.). 170p. pap. 18.95 (978-1-897235-79-9(8)) Thistledown Pr., Ltd. CAN. Dist: Univ. of Toronto Pr.

Gebauer, Phyllis. Hot Widow: A Memoir. 2008. 294p. pap. 16.95 (978-1-56474-471-5(X), Fithian Pr) Daniel & Daniel, Pubs., Inc.

Gee, Maggie. My Animal Life. 2011. (ENG., Illus.). 232p. 21.95 (978-1-84659-987-3(3), Telegram Bks.) Saqi Bks. GBR. Dist: Consortium Bk. Sales & Distribution.

Gelber, Mark H. Stefan Zweig Reconsidered: New Perspectives on His Literary & Biographical Writings. 2007. (Conditio Judaica Ser.). (FRE, GER & ENG.). VI, 225p. pap. (978-3-484-65162-3(8)) Verlag Max Niemeyer.

Gelber, Mark H., ed. Stefan Zweig Reconsidered: New Perspectives on his Literary & Biographical Writings. (Conditio Judaica Ser.). (ENG.). VI, 225p. 165.00 **(978-3-11-182225-9(7))** De Gruyter, Walter Inc.

Gelderman, Carol. Louis Auchincloss: A Writers Life. 2007. (Illus.). 267p. per. 24.95 (978-1-57003-711-5(6)) Univ. of South Carolina Pr.

Gelderman, Carol, ed. Conversations with Mary Mccarthy. 2011. (ENG.). pap. 30.00 (978-1-61703-014-7(7)) Univ. Pr. of Mississippi.

Geng, Steve. Thick As Thieves: A Brother, a Sister - A True Story of Two Turbulent Lives. 2008. (ENG.). 304p. pap. 15.00 (978-0-8050-8767-3(2), Holt Paperback) Holt, Henry & Co.

George Edward, Woodberry. Nathaniel Hawthorne. 2007. (ENG.). 212p. pap. 20.99 (978-1-4264-9236-5(7)) BiblioBazaar.

George, Nelson. City Kid: A Writer's Memoir of Ghetto Life & Post-Soul Success. 2010. (ENG.). 288p. (gr. 12-18). 14.00 (978-0-452-29604-6(8), Plume) Penguin Group (USA) Inc.

George, William. Mark Twain. 2007. 192p. pap. 11.95 (978-0-935174-53-3(2)) Tree by the River Publishing/Music Business Bks.

Gerassi, John, ed. Talking with Sartre: Conversations & Debates. 2009. (ENG.). 336p. pap. 20.00 (978-0-300-15901-1(3)) Yale Univ. Pr.

Gershon, Karen. A Tempered Wind: An Autobiography. 2009. (Jewish Lives Ser.). (ENG.). 216p. 69.95 (978-0-8101-2612-1(5)); pap. 21.95 (978-0-8101-2613-8(3)) Northwestern Univ. Pr.

Gewirtz, Isaac. Beatific Soul: Jack Kerouac on the Road. 2007. (ENG., Illus.). 208p. 35.00 (978-1-85759-497-3(5)) Scala, Editions FRA. Dist: National Bk. Network.

Ghibellino, Ettore. Goethe & Anna Amalia: A Forbidden Love? Farrelly, Dan, tr. from GER. 2007. (ENG., Illus.). 360p. pap. 49.95 (978-1-904505-24-2(4)) Carysfort Pr. IRL. Dist: Dufour Editions, Inc.

Ghosh, Amitav. Incendiary Circumstances: A Chronicle of the Turmoil of Our Times. 2007. (ENG.). 320p. per. 18.95 (978-0-618-87221-3(3)) Houghton Mifflin Harcourt Trade & Reference Pubs.

Gibson, Evelyn Stevens. Winds of My Yesteryears Blow Warm. 2008. 172p. 25.49 (978-1-4389-2223-2(X)); pap. 15.49 (978-1-4389-2222-5(1)) AuthorHouse.

Gibson, Ian. Lorca - Dali, el Amor Que No Pudo Ser (Dali, the Love That Couldn't Be) (SPA., Illus.). 380p. 19.50 (978-84-01-01217-4(1)) Plaza & Janes Editores, S.A. ESP. Dist: Astran, Inc.

Gibson, John. Reminiscences of Sir Walter Scott. 2008. 48p. pap. 15.95 (978-1-4370-2481-4(5)) Kessinger Publishing, LLC.

Gidding, Joshua. Failure: An Autobiography a Story of How the Truth Can Set You Free. 2009. 232p. pap. 14.95 (978-1-905736-35-5(5)) Marshall Cavendish GBR. Dist: Midpoint Trade Bks., Inc.

Gide, André & La Jeunesse, Ernest. Recollections of Oscar Wilde. 2007. 104p. per. 13.85 (978-1-59569-081-4(6)) Mondial.

Giesbert, Franz-Olivier. The American. 2007. (Vintage Ser.). (ENG.). 160p. pap. 13.95 (978-1-4000-9585-8(9), Vintage) Knopf Doubleday Publishing Group.

Gifford, Barry & Lee, Lawrence. Jack's Book: An Oral Biography of Jack Kerouac. 2012. (ENG.). 368p. (gr. 12). pap. 16.00 **(978-0-14-312186-6(X)**, Penguin (Non-Classics)) Penguin Group (USA) Inc.

Gilbar, Steven. Not Forgotten: American Writers Remember the Lives of Literary Mentors, Friends, & Rivals. 2006. (ENG.). 227p. pap. 17.95 (978-1-56792-294-3(5)) Godine, David R. Pub.

Gilbert, Elizabeth. Committed: A Love Story. 2011. (ENG.). 304p. (gr. 12). 16.00 (978-0-14-311870-1(6), Penguin (Non-Classics)) Penguin Group (USA) Inc.

—Committed: A Skeptic Makes Peace with Marriage. 2010. (ENG.). 304p. (gr. 12). 26.95 (978-0-670-02165-9(2), Viking Adult) Penguin Group (USA) Inc.

—Committed: A Skeptic Makes Peace with Marriage. Lt. ed. 471p. 2011. (ENG.). pap. 17.99 (978-1-59413-453-1(7), Large Print Pr.) 2010. 34.95 (978-1-4104-2276-7(3)) Thorndike Pr.

Gildner, Gary. Warsaw Sparks: A Memoir. 2008. (ENG., Illus.). 256p. pap. 15.95 (978-0-8032-1756-0(0), Bison Bks.) Univ. of Nebraska Pr.

Giles, Wanda H. & Giles, James Richard. Dlb 350 21St Cen Am Nvlsts. 2009. (Dictionary of Literary Biography Ser.). (ENG., Illus.). 512p. 315.00 (978-0-7876-8168-5(7)) Cengage Gale.

Gill-Schoen, Juanita. 18 Wheels & Bill. 2011. 116p. 21.23 **(978-1-4567-4608-7(1))**; pap. 12.95 **(978-1-4567-4607-0(3))** AuthorHouse.

Gill, Stephen, ed. 21st-Century Oxford Authors: William Wordsworth 2010. (ENG., Illus.). 800p. 160.00 (978-0-19-923861-3(8)) Oxford Univ. Pr., Inc.

Gillespie, Marcia, et al. Maya Angelou: A Glorious Celebration. Lt. ed. 2008. 250p. 31.95 (978-1-4104-0983-6(X)) Thorndike Pr.

Gilman, Susan Jane. Undress Me in the Temple of Heaven. 2010. (ENG.). 320p. pap. 13.99 (978-0-446-69693-7(5)) Grand Central Publishing.

Gilmour, David. The Last Leopard: A Life of Giuseppe Tomasi Di Lampedusa. 2007. (ENG., Illus.). 277p. pap. 33.95 (978-0-9550105-1-4(9)) Eland Bks. GBR. Dist: Dufour Editions, Inc.

Gingher, Marianne. Adventures in Pen Land: One Writer's Journey from Inklings to Ink. 2008. (ENG., Illus.). 200p. (gr. 9). pap. 19.95 (978-0-8262-1817-9(2)) Univ. of Missouri Pr.

Glancy, Diane. The Dream of a Broken Field. 2011. (ENG.). 220p. pap. 30.00 (978-0-8032-3481-9(3)) Univ. of Nebraska Pr.

Glassco, John. Memoirs of Montparnasse. 2007. (New York Review Books Classics). (ENG., Illus.). 296p. pap. 15.95 (978-1-59017-184-4(5), NYRB Classics) New York Review of Bks., Inc., The.

Glassman, Steve, ed. Florida Crime Writers: 24 Interviews. 2007. (ENG.). 250p. per. 35.00 (978-0-7864-3083-3(4)) McFarland & Co., Inc. Pubs.

Gleiman, Lubomir. From the Maelstrom: A Pilgrim's Story of Dissent & Survival in the Twentieth Century. 2011. 712p. 30.00 **(978-1-4520-2017-4(5))**; pap. 27.50 **(978-1-4520-2018-1(3))** AuthorHouse.

Glenn, Charles. American Abroad: The Struggles of Youth. 2011. 72p. pap. 12.84 (978-1-4520-8890-7(X)) AuthorHouse.

Glenn, Wendy J. Laurie Halse Anderson: Speaking in Tongues. 36th ed. 2009. (Scarecrow Studies in Young Adult Literature Ser.). (ENG.). 184p. 45.00 (978-0-8108-7281-3(1)) Scarecrow Pr., Inc.

Glenny, Misha. DarkMarket: Cyberthieves, Cybercops & You. 2012. (Vintage Ser.). (ENG.). 304p. pap. 16.00 **(978-0-307-47644-9(8)**, Vintage) Knopf Doubleday Publishing Group.

Glori, Cesaremaria. La Tragica Morte Di Ippolito Nievo: Il Naufragio Doloso Del Piroscafo Ercole: Coinvolgimento e Responsabilità Della Massoneria Nella Caduta Del Regno Delle Due Sicilie. 2010. (ITA., Illus.). 167p. (978-88-89756-82-9(9)) Solfanelli.

Glyde, John. The Life of Edward Fitzgerald. 2007. 376p. 48.95 (978-0-548-04351-6(5)) Kessinger Publishing, LLC.

Glyer, Diana Pavlac. The Company They Keep: C. S. Lewis & J. R. R. Tolkien as Writers in Community. 2008. xix, 293p. pap. 30.00 (978-0-87338-991-4(3)) 2006. (Illus.). 293p. 45.00 (978-0-87338-890-0(9)) Kent State Univ. Pr.

Godwin, Gail. The Making of a Writer: Journals, 1961-1963. Neufeld, Rob, ed. 2007. 352p. per. 16.95 (978-0-8129-7469-0(7), Random Hse. Trade Paperbacks) Random House Publishing Group.

—The Making of a Writer Vol. 2: Journals, 1963-1969. Neufeld, Rob, ed. 2011. (ENG.). 336p. 26.00 (978-1-4000-6433-5(3), Random House) Random House Publishing Group.

Gold, Charles H. Hatching Ruin , or Mark Twain's Road to Bankruptcy. 2011. (MARK TWAIN & HIS CIRCLE Ser.). (ENG., Illus.). 184p. (C). (gr. 13). pap. 25.00 (978-0-8262-1959-6(4)) Univ. of Missouri Pr.

Gold, Herbert. Still Alive! A Feisty Bohemian Explores the Art of Growing Old. 2011. (ENG.). 264p. pap. 12.95 (978-1-61145-029-3(2), 611029, Arcade Publishing) Skyhorse Publishing Co., Inc.

Goldhaft, Arthur d. The Golden Egg: An Autobiography. Levin, Meyer, ed. 2011. 320p. 50.95 **(978-1-258-09492-8(4))** Literary Licensing, LLC.

Golla, Robert, ed. Conversations with Michael Crichton. 2011. (Literary Conversations Ser.). (ENG.). 224p. 55.00 (978-1-61703-012-3(0)); pap. 25.00 (978-1-61703-013-0(9)) Univ. Pr. of Mississippi.

Gollnick, Albert F. The Autobiography of Albert F Gollnick. 2011. 170p. 42.95 **(978-1-258-08629-9(8))** Literary Licensing, LLC.

Gombrowicz, Witold. Diary. Vallee, Lillian, tr. from POL. 2012. (Margellos World Republic of Letters Ser.). (ENG.). 800p. pap. 20.00 **(978-0-300-11806-3(6))** Yale Univ. Pr.

Gonzalez, Rigoberto. Butterfly Boy: Memories of a Chicano Mariposa. 2011. (Writing in Latinidad Ser.). (ENG.). 224p. pap. 19.95 **(978-0-299-21904-8(6))** Univ. of Wisconsin Pr.

Gonzßlez, Pedro Blas. Unamuno: A Lyrical Essay. 2007. 140p. per. 22.95 (978-0-915745-75-3(5)) Floricanto Pr.

Gooch, Brad. Flannery: A Life of Flannery O'Connor. (ENG., Illus.). 464p. 2010. pap. 16.99 (978-0-316-01899-9(6), Back Bay Bks.) 2009. 30.00 (978-0-316-00066-6(3)) Little Brown & Co.

Gooch, Debbie E. Will to Live. 2009. 40p. pap. 16.99 (978-1-4389-7502-3(3)) AuthorHouse.

Goodman, Charlotte Margolis. Jean Stafford: The Savage Heart. 2011. (ENG., Illus.). 416p. pap. 35.00 **(978-0-292-73574-3(X))** Univ. of Texas Pr.

Goodman, Susan. Edith Wharton's Inner Circle. 2011. (ENG., Illus.). 187p. pap. 19.95 (978-0-292-72915-5(4)) Univ. of Texas Pr.

Goodrich, Austin. Hot War, Cold War & Beyond, Tales from the Trenches of the 20th Century: The Memoirs of Austin Goodrich. 2011. 132p. pap. 13.95 (978-1-4502-9578-9(9)) iUniverse, Inc.

Gopnik, Adam. Through the Children's Gate: A Home in New York. 2007. (Vintage Ser.). (ENG.). 336p. pap. 14.95 (978-1-4000-7575-1(0), Vintage) Knopf Doubleday Publishing Group.

Gordon, Lois. Nancy Cunard: Heiress, Muse, Political Idealist. (ENG., Illus.). 504p. 2009. pap. 22.95 (978-0-231-13939-7(X)) 2007. (gr. 17). 34.95 (978-0-231-13938-0(1)) Columbia Univ. Pr.

Gordon, Mary. Circling My Mother. 2008. (Illus.). 272p. pap. 14.95 (978-0-307-27761-9(5), Anchor) Knopf Doubleday Publishing Group.

Gorky, Maksim & Hettlinger, Graham. Childhood. 2010. (978-1-56663-906-4(9)) Dee, Ivan R. Pub.

Gosse, Edmund. Father & Son. 2006. (Orig.). pap. (978-1-4068-2140-6(3)) Echo Library.

—The Life of Swinburne. 2011. (Cambridge Library Collection - Literary Studies). (ENG.). 58p. pap. 12.99 **(978-1-108-03414-2(4))** Cambridge Univ. Pr.

Gosse, Edmund. Sir Thomas Browne. 2009. 228p. 23.99 (978-1-103-82707-7(3)); 228p. pap. 17.99 (978-1-103-82702-2(2)); 224p. 23.99 (978-1-103-56070-7(0)); 224p. pap. 17.99 (978-1-103-56068-4(9)) BiblioBazaar.

—Sir Thomas Browne. 2009. 142p. pap. (978-0-217-99135-3(1)); 136p. pap. (978-0-217-99133-9(5)) Books LLC.

—Sir Thomas Browne. 2007. (ENG.). 228p. 41.95 (978-0-548-12774-2(3)) 2006. pap. 26.95 (978-1-4286-3772-6(9)) Kessinger Publishing, LLC.

Gottzmann, Carola L. & Hörner, Petra. Lexikon der deutschsprachigen Literatur des Baltikums und St. Petersburgs: Vom Mittelalter bis zur Gegenwart. 2007.Tr. of Lexicon of German-language literature of the Baltic States & St. Petersburg. (GER., Illus.). XII, 1476p. 503.00 (978-3-11-019338-1(8)) De Gruyter, Walter Inc.

Gottzmann, Carola L. & Hörner, Petra. Lexikon der deutschsprachigen Literatur des Baltikums und St. Petersburgs: Vom Mittelalter bis zur Gegenwart. 2012.Tr. of Lexicon of German-language literature of the Baltic States & St. Petersburg. (GER., Illus.). XII, 1476p. E-Book 755.00 **(978-3-11-182206-8(0))** De Gruyter, Walter Inc.

Gougeon, Len. Emerson & Eros: The Making of a Cultural Hero. 2011. 272p. pap. 24.95 **(978-0-7914-7078-7(4)**, Suny Pr.) State Univ. of New York Pr.

Gould, Emily. And the Heart Says Whatever. 2010. (ENG.). 224p. pap. 16.00 (978-1-4391-2389-8(6), Free Pr.) Free Pr.

Graham, Masako Nakagawa. The Autobiographical Narrative in Modern Japan: A Study of Kasai Zenzo, a Shi-Shosetsu Writer. 2007. 188p. (978-0-7734-5396-8(2)) Mellen, Edwin Pr., The.

Graham, Ysenda Maxtone. The Real Mrs. Miniver: Jane Struther's Story. mass mkt. (978-0-312-98686-5(6), St. Martin's Paperbacks) St. Martin's Pr.

Grahame, Kenneth. Dream Days. 2011. (Hesperus Classics Ser.). (ENG.). 136p. pap. 14.95 (978-1-84391-195-1(7)) Hesperus Pr. GBR. Dist: Independent Pubs. Group.

Gralak, Iwona & Pacawski, Jan. Pisarze Regionu Swietokrzyskiego. (978-83-86006-92-2(7)) Kieleckie Towarzystwo Naukowe.

Grandbois, Peter. The Arsenic Lobster: A Hybrid Memoir. 2009. 128p. pap. 16.00 (978-1-933132-72-3(8)) Spuyten Duyvil.

Grange, William. The A to Z of Postwar German Literature. 2010. (A to Z Guide Ser.). (ENG.). 376p. pap. 34.45 (978-0-8108-7618-7(3)) Scarecrow Pr., Inc.

—Historical Dictionary of Postwar German Literature. 2009. (Historical Dictionaries of Literature & the Arts Ser.). (ENG.). 370p. 90.00 (978-0-8108-5965-4(3)) Scarecrow Pr., Inc.

Grant, Joan Marshall. Far Memory: The Autobiography of Joan Grant. 2009. (978-1-59731-362-9(9)); pap. (978-1-59731-361-2(0)) Perennis, Sophia.

Grass, Günter. Peeling the Onion: A Memoir. Heim, Michael Henry, tr. 2008. (ENG., Illus.). 448p. pap. 15.00 *(978-0-15-603534-7(0)*, Mariner Bks.) Houghton Mifflin Harcourt Trade & Reference Pubs.

Grass, Günter & nter. Unterwegs Von Deutschland Nach Deutschland: Tagebuch 1990. 2009. (GER., Illus.). 255p. *(978-3-86521-881-0(4))* Steidl, Gerhard Druckerei und Verlag.

Graves, John. My Dogs & Guns. 2007. (ENG.). 96p. 19.95 *(978-1-60239-029-4(0)*, 239029) Skyhorse Publishing Co., Inc.

Gray, Alasdair. A Life in Pictures. 2011. (ENG., Illus.). 303p. 39.95 *(978-1-84195-640-6(0))* Canongate Bks. GBR. Dist: Independent Pubs. Group.

Gray, Francine du Plessix. Madame de Stael: The First Modern Woman. 2008. (ENG.). 1p. 24.00 *(978-1-934633-17-5(8))* Atlas & Co.

Gray, Ralph D. Meredith Nicholson: A Writing Life. 2007. (Indiana Biography Ser.). (Illus.). 281p. *(978-0-87195-257-8(2))* Indiana Historical Society.

Gray, William. Robert Louis Stevenson. (Illus.). 208p. *(978-0-333-98401-7(3))* Palgrave Macmillan.

Grayson, David, pseud. Adventures in Friendship. 2010. 248p. pap. 26.75 *(978-1-177-90119-2(6))* 2010. 254p. pap. 26.75 *(978-1-141-05020-8(X))* 2010. 244p. pap. 26.75 *(978-1-141-33080-5(6))* 2009. 244p. 23.99 *(978-0-559-95736-9(X))* 2009. 244p. pap. 17.99 *(978-0-559-95733-8(5))* 2008. 128p. 24.99 *(978-0-554-23355-0(X))* 2008. 128p. 21.99 *(978-0-554-32658-0(2))* 2007. (ENG.). 116p. pap. 18.99 *(978-1-4264-4240-7(8))* 2007. (ENG.). 126p. pap. 19.99 *(978-1-4264-4304-6(8))* BiblioBazaar.

—Adventures in Friendship. 2009. 80p. pap. *(978-1-151-55998-2(9))* Books LLC.

—Adventures in Friendship. 2008. (ENG.). 132p. per. *(978-1-4065-8829-3(6))* Dodo Pr.

—Adventures in Friendship. 2006. (ENG.). pap. *(978-1-4068-1146-9(7))* Echo Library.

—Adventures in Friendship. 2010. (Illus.). 66p. pap. 19.82 *(978-1-4432-1553-4(8))* General Bks. LLC.

—Adventures in Friendship. 2010. 96p. pap. *(978-1-4076-0883-9(5))* HardPr.

—Adventures in Friendship. 2010. 240p. 33.56 *(978-1-163-34024-0(3))* 2010. 240p. pap. 21.56 *(978-1-162-78344-4(3))* 2007. (ENG.). 238p. 41.95 *(978-0-548-02867-4(2))* Kessinger Publishing, LLC.

Grayson, David, pseud & Baker, Ray Stannard. Adventures in Friendship. 2010. 250p. pap. 26.75 *(978-1-147-95283-4(3))* BiblioBazaar.

Grayson, David, pseud & Fogarty, Thomas. Adventures in Friendship. 2010. 240p. 32.99 *(978-1-140-16493-7(7))*; pap. 26.75 *(978-1-140-16494-4(5))* BiblioBazaar.

Grayson, Richard. Autumn in Brooklyn. 2009. 267p. pap. 15.00 *(978-0-578-03208-5(2))* Suoerstition Mountain Pr.

—A Year in Rockaway. 2010. 192p. pap. 12.99 *(978-0-557-56444-6(1))* Lulu Enterprises Inc.

Green, F. C. Stendhal. 2011. (ENG.). 346p. pap. 28.99 *(978-1-107-60072-0(3))* Cambridge Univ. Pr.

Green, Ken. Children of the Sun. 2008. (Illus.). 552p. *(978-0-09-461430-7(X))* Axios Pr.

Green, Michelle Y. Oscar Invincible: The Life of Film Pioneer Oscar Micheaux. 2007. *(978-0-8037-3003-8(9)*, Dial) Penguin Group (USA) Inc.

Greenberg, Michael. Beg, Borrow, Steal: A Writer's Life. 2009. (ENG., Illus.). 232p. 19.95 *(978-1-59051-341-5(X))* Other Pr., LLC.

Greene, Bob. And You Know You Should Be Glad: A True Story of Lifelong Friendship. 2007. 336p. pap. 13.95 *(978-0-06-088194-8(1)*, William Morrow Paperbacks) HarperCollins Pubs.

Greene, Gael. Insatiable: Tales from a Life of Delicious Excess. 2007. (ENG., Illus.). 400p. per. 13.99 *(978-0-446-69510-7(6))* Grand Central Publishing.

Greene, Gina. The Happy Side of Life. 2011. 166p. pap. 24.95 ***(978-1-4626-1179-9(6))*** PublishAmerica, Inc.

Greene, Graham. Graham Greene: A Life in Letters. Greene, Richard, ed. 2008. (ENG., Illus.). 480p. 35.00 *(978-0-393-06642-5(8)*, 6642) Norton, W. W. & Co., Inc.

Greene, Harlan. Mr. Skylark: John Bennett & the Charleston Renaissance. 2010. (ENG.). 408p. pap. 24.95 *(978-0-8203-3624-4(6))* Univ. of Georgia Pr.

Greene, Oscar H. From Homecoming to Twilight: Stories from the Emotional Journey of a Ninety-Year Old Colored Man (1939-1981) 2009. 128p. 23.99 *(978-1-4389-4254-4(0))*; pap. 13.99 *(978-1-4389-4255-1(9))* AuthorHouse.

Greene, Robert. Greene's Groatsworth of Wit: Bought with a Million of Repentance. 2010. 63p. pap. 38.50 *(978-1-4092-1161-7(4))* Lulu Enterprises Inc.

Greenfield, Robert. A Day in the Life: One Family, the Beautiful People, & the End of the Sixties. 2009. (ENG., Illus.). 368p. 24.95 *(978-0-306-81622-2(9))* Perseus Bks. Group.

Greenhill, Joseph. Susan: A Memoir. 2007. 208p. pap. 13.95 *(978-1-59858-172-0(4))* Dog Ear Publishing, LLC.

Greenlaw, Lavinia. The Importance of Music to Girls. 2009. (ENG.). 224p. pap. 15.00 *(978-0-312-42837-2(5))* Picador.

Gregoire, Lucien. Let's All Get Behind the Pope: End of Faith = End of Prejudice. 2009. 316p. 27.99 *(978-1-4389-5074-7(8))*; pap. 17.49 *(978-1-4389-5073-0(X))* AuthorHouse.

Grene, David. Of Farming & Classics: A Memoir. 2006. (Illus.). 184p. 32.50 *(978-0-226-30801-2(4))* Univ. of Chicago Pr.

Grenier, Edouard. Literary Reminiscences. Ram, Abel, tr. 2007. (ENG.). 308p. 43.95 *(978-0-548-02179-8(1))* Kessinger Publishing, LLC.

Grenville, Kate. Searching for the Secret River: The Story Behind the Bestselling Novel. 2007. (Illus.). 221p. pap. *(978-1-84767-002-1(4))* Canongate Bks.

Grey, Zane. Zane Grey, the Man & His Work: An Autobiographical Sketch, Critical Appreciations & Bibliography. 2011. 80p. 37.95 ***(978-1-258-00927-4(7))*** Literary Licensing, LLC.

Griffith, George. Around the World in 65 Days with George Griffith: The Story of the Real Phileas Fogg. Godwin, Robert, ed. 2010. (ENG., Illus.). 238p. pap. 12.95 *(978-1-897350-27-0(9))* Collector's Guide Publishing, Inc. CAN. Dist: Independent Pubs. Group.

Griffiths, Gavin. Joseph Conrad. 2008. (Brief Lives Ser.). (ENG.). 120p. pap. 13.95 *(978-1-84391-907-0(9))* Hesperus Pr. GBR. Dist: Independent Pubs. Group.

Grigsby, Harry 'Mick'. 'Mick' Back When. 2011. 688p. pap. 33.95 ***(978-1-4620-2886-3(1))*** iUniverse, Inc.

Grimassi, Raven. The Cauldron of Memory: Retrieving Ancestral Knowledge & Wisdom. 2009. (ENG., Illus.). 264p. pap. 17.95 *(978-0-7387-1575-9(1))* Llewellyn Pubns.

Grimes, Tom. Mentor: A Memoir. 2010. (ENG.). 200p. 24.95 *(978-0-9825048-8-8(8))*; pap. 16.95 *(978-0-9825048-9-5(6))* Tin Hse. Bks., LLC.

Gronicka, Andre Von. Henry Von Heiseler A RussoGerman Writer. 2006. pap. 26.95 *(978-1-4286-6138-7(7))* Kessinger Publishing, LLC.

Gross, John, ed. The New Oxford Book of Literary Anecdotes. 2008. (Oxford Books of Prose & Verse Ser.). (ENG.). 400p. pap. 16.95 *(978-0-19-954341-0(0))* Oxford Univ. Pr., Inc.

Grossi, Paolo. Pierre-Louis Ginguené, Historien de la Littérature Italienne. (FRE.). xiii, 397p. 69.95 *(978-3-03911-150-3(7))* Lang, Peter CHE. Dist: Lang, Peter Publishing, Inc.

Grunwald, Henry Anatole. Salinger: The Classic Critical & Personal Portrait. 2009. 320p. pap. 14.99 *(978-0-06-185250-3(3)*, HarperPerennial) HarperCollins Pubs.

Guene & Satrapi, Marjane. Persepolis: Eine Kindheit im Iran & Jugendjahre. (FRE., Illus.). 400p. pap. *(978-2-84414-240-5(0)*, Debolsillo) L'Assn.

Guerra, Elizabeth. Stewart Farrar: Writer on A Broomstick, the Biography of Stewart Farrar. 2008. 232p. per. 17.99 *(978-0-9791402-7-3(7))* Stewart, R. J. Bks.

Guess, Carol. My Father in Water. 2011. 88p. pap. 15.00 ***(978-1-84861-185-6(4))*** Shearsman Bks. GBR. Dist: SPD-Small Pr. Distribution.

Guignery, Vanessa, ed. Novelists in the New Millennium: Conversations with Writers. 2012. (ENG., Illus.). 240p. (C). 80.00 ***(978-0-230-23823-7(8))***; pap. 27.00 ***(978-0-230-23824-4(6))*** Palgrave Macmillan.

Gulley, Philip. I Love You, Miss Huddleston: And Other Inappropriate Longings of My Indiana Childhood. (ENG.). 2010. 208p. pap. 12.99 *(978-0-06-180955-2(1)*, HarperOne) 2009. 208p. 21.99 *(978-0-06-073659-0(3)*, HarperOne) 2009. 272p. pap. 21.99 *(978-0-06-172020-8(8)*, HarperLuxe) HarperCollins Pubs.

Gunton, Paul. Travels in a Teacup. 2009. (Illus.). 220p. 24.99 *(978-1-4343-6376-3(7))*; pap. 14.49 *(978-1-4343-6375-6(9))* AuthorHouse.

Guomundsson, Halldor. The Islander: A Biography of Halldor Laxness. Roughton, Phil, tr. from ICE. 2008. (ENG., Illus.). 400p. 44.95 *(978-1-84724-284-6(7))* Quercus GBR. Dist: Independent Pubs. Group.

Gupta, Uma Das. Rabindranath Tagore: An Illustrated Life. 2012. (ENG., Illus.). 144p. pap. 14.95 ***(978-0-19-807600-1(2))*** Oxford Univ. Pr., Inc.

Gurdjieff, G. Meetings with Remarkable Men. 2010. 318p. pap. 10.50 *(978-1-57898-893-8(4))* Martino Publishing.

Gutiérrez, José Ismael. Reinaldo Arenas: Entre el placer y el Infierno. 2007. (SPA.). per. 13.95 *(978-1-933439-12-9(2))* Cursack Bks.

Guyotat, Pierre. Coma. Wedell, Noura, tr. from FRE. 2010. (Semiotext(e) / Native Agents Ser.). (ENG., Illus.). 232p. (gr. 17). pap. 17.95 *(978-1-58435-089-7(X))* Semiotexte/Smart Art.

Gwyn, Richard. The Vagabond's Breakfast. 2011. (ENG.). 192p. pap. 17.95 *(978-0-9560125-5-5(8))* Alcemi GBR. Dist: Dufour Editions, Inc.

Habich, Robert D. Building Their Own Waldos: Emerson's First Biographers & the Politics of Life-Writing in the Gilded Age. 2011. (ENG.). 248p. pap. 29.95 *(978-1-58729-962-9(3))* Univ. of Iowa Pr.

Hacht, Anne Marie & Hayes, Dwayne D. Gale Contextual Encyclopedia of American Literature. 2009. *(978-1-4144-3134-5(1))*; *(978-1-4144-3133-8(3))*; *(978-1-4144-3132-1(5))*; (Illus.). 1819p. 495.00 *(978-1-4144-3131-4(7))* Cengage Gale.

Haddad-Wotling, Karen & Ferré, Vincent. Proust, L'étranger. 2010. (FRE.). 167p. E-Book *(978-90-420-3038-1(0))* Rodopi.

Haggard, H. Rider. Days of My Life an Autobiography Comp. 2006. pap. *(978-1-4068-2054-6(7))* Echo Library.

Hagins, Bill. It's All Good. 2011. 380p. pap. 29.95 ***(978-1-4512-8295-5(8))*** PublishAmerica, Inc.

Hale, Edward Everett. James Russell Lowell & His Friends. (ENG.). 388p. 2007. 48.95 *(978-0-548-13730-7(7))* 2006. per. 33.95 *(978-1-4286-4897-5(6))* Kessinger Publishing, LLC.

Hale, Veda. Swell Suffering: A Biography of Maurine Whipple. 2011. 471p. pap. 31.95 *(978-1-58958-124-1(5))* 2009. *(978-1-58958-122-7(9))* Kofford, Greg Books, Inc.

Haley, James L. Wolf: The Lives of Jack London. 2011. (ENG., Illus.). 400p. (gr. 9). pap. 17.99 *(978-0-465-02503-9(X))* Basic Bks.

Hall, Calvin L. & Hall, Clavin L. African American Journalists: Autobiography as Memoir & Manifesto. 2009. (ENG.). 146p. pap. 40.00 *(978-0-8108-6930-1(6))* Scarecrow Pr., Inc.

Hall, Douglas John. The Messenger: Friendship, Faith, & Finding OneÕs Way. 2011. 192p. pap. 22.00 ***(978-1-61097-317-5(8)***, Cascade Bks.) Wipf & Stock Pubs.

Hall, James C. & Hathaway, Heather, eds. Conversations with Paule Marshall. 2010. (Literary Conversations Ser.). (ENG.). 240p. 40.00 *(978-1-60473-741-3(3))* Univ. Pr. of Mississippi.

Hall, Lesley A. Naomi Mitchison: Volume 15 in the Conversation Pieces Series. 2007. 146p. per. 12.00 *(978-1-933500-10-2(7))* Aqueduct Pr.

Hall, Meredith. Without a Map: A Memoir. (ENG.). 2008. 256p. per. 14.00 *(978-0-8070-7274-5(5))* 2007. 248p. 24.95 *(978-0-8070-7273-8(7))* Beacon Pr.

Hallett, George, ed. Portraits of African Writers. 2007. (ENG., Illus.). 160p. (gr. 11). 44.95 *(978-1-86814-386-3(4))* Witwatersrand Univ. Pr. Pubns. ZAF. Dist: Transaction Pubs.

Hamilton, Ed. Legends of the Chelsea Hotel: Living with the Artists & Outlaws in New York's Rebel Mecca. 2007. (ENG., Illus.). 368p. per. 16.95 *(978-1-56858-379-2(6))* Da Capo Pr., Inc.

Hamilton, Geoff & Jones, Brian. Encyclopedia of Contemporary Writers & Their Work. 2010. (Literary Movements Ser.). 432p. (C). (gr. 9-18). 75.00 *(978-0-8160-7578-2(6))* Facts On File, Inc.

Hamilton, Hugo. The Harbor Boys: A Memoir. 2007. 272p. per. 13.95 *(978-0-06-078469-0(5)*, HarperPerennial) HarperCollins Pubs.

Hamilton, Rosemary. Only When I'm High: The Runways of A Southern Belle. 2008. 336p. pap. 17.99 *(978-1-4259-0146-2(8))* AuthorHouse.

Hamsun, Marie. The Nobel Novelist Knur Hamsun During the Nazi Occupation of Norway: The Final Chapter that Was Omitted from Marie Hamsun's Autobiography of Their Life Together. Magnuson, Elmer T., tr. from NOR. 2011. (Illus.). 164p. 109.95 ***(978-0-7734-3944-3(7))*** Mellen, Edwin Pr., The.

Handke, Peter. A Sorrow Beyond Dreams: A Life Story, 1 vol. Manheim, Ralph, tr. 2012. (ENG.). 96p. pap. 14.00 ***(978-0-374-53364-9(4))*** Farrar, Straus & Giroux.

Hannay, Margaret. Mary Sidney, Lady Wroth. 2010. (Illus.). 430p. 99.95 *(978-0-7546-6053-8(2))* Ashgate Publishing Co.

Hannon, Patrice. 101 Things You Didn't Know about Jane Austen: The Truth about the World's Most Intriguing Romantic Literary Heroine. 2007. (ENG.). 256p. per. 9.95 *(978-1-59869-284-6(4))* Adams Media Corp.

Hans, Birgit, ed. D'Arcy Mcnickle's the Hungry Generations: The Evolution of a Novel. 2007. (ENG., Illus.). 341p. (C). 34.95 *(978-0-8263-3862-4(3))* Univ. of New Mexico Pr.

Hanson, Peter. Dalton Trumbo, Hollywood Rebel: A Critical Survey & Filmography. alt. ed. 2007. (ENG., Illus.). 255p. per. 35.00 *(978-0-7864-3246-2(2))* McFarland & Co., Inc. Pubs.

Hanson, Peter & Herman, Paul Robert. Tales from the Script: 50 Hollywood Screenwriters Share Their Stories. 2010. (ENG.). 368p. pap. 15.99 *(978-0-06-185592-4(8))* HarperCollins Pubs.

Hargis Sr, John W. Before It's Too Late, Solutions & Issues in Politics. 2011. 106p. pap. 19.95 ***(978-1-4626-0716-7(0))*** PublishAmerica, Inc.

Harjo, Joy & Winder, Tanaya. Soul Talk, Song Language: Conversations with Joy Harjo. 2011. (ENG., Illus.). 164p. 24.95 *(978-0-8195-7150-2(4))* Wesleyan Univ. Pr.

Harkleroad, Lyle. Honeycomb Meadow: A Humbling Journey for Today's Generation. 2011. 112p. pap. 19.95 ***(978-1-4626-0344-2(0))*** PublishAmerica, Inc.

Harlow, Virginia. Thomas Sergeant Perry: A Biography & Letters to Perry from William, Henry, & Garth Wilkinson James. 2011. 410p. 54.95 ***(978-1-258-08843-9(6))*** Literary Licensing, LLC.

Harman, Claire. Jane's Fame: How Jane Austen Conquered the World. 2010. (ENG., Illus.). 304p. 26.00 *(978-0-8050-8258-6(1))* Holt, Henry & Co.

—Jane's Fame: How Jane Austen Conquered the World. 2011. (ENG., Illus.). 320p. pap. 16.00 *(978-0-312-68065-7(1))* Picador.

—Myself & the Other Fellow: A Life of Robert Lewis Stevenson. 2006. (Illus.). 544p. per. 16.95 *(978-0-06-093525-2(1)*, HarperPerennial) HarperCollins Pubs.

Harnack, Curtis. We Have All Gone Away. 2011. (Bur Oak Book Ser.). (ENG.). 188p. pap. 19.95 *(978-1-58729-969-8(0))* Univ. of Iowa Pr.

Harper, Graeme, ed. Inside Creative Writing: Interviews with Contemporary Writers. 2012. (ENG., Illus.). 224p. (C). pap. 20.00 ***(978-0-230-21217-6(4))*** Palgrave Macmillan.

Harriman, Margaret Case. The Vicious Circle: The Story of the Algonquin Round Table. 2011. 320p. 50.95 ***(978-1-258-10551-8(9))*** Literary Licensing, LLC.

Harris, Alexander. Breaking Borders: One man's journey to erase the lines that Divide. 2008. 288p. 30.95 *(978-0-595-69446-4(2))*; pap. 20.95 *(978-0-595-45415-0(1))* iUniverse, Inc.

Harris, Alexandra, et al. Virginia Woolf. 2011. (Brief Lives Ser.). (ENG.). 120p. pap. 14.95 *(978-1-84391-909-4(5))* Hesperus Pr. GBR. Dist: Independent Pubs. Group.

Harris, Edward A. I Found the Love of My Life on the Internet! There can be no Distance Between Two Loving Hearts! 2010. 132p. 23.99 *(978-1-4520-8638-5(9))*; pap. 13.99 *(978-1-4520-8637-8(0))* AuthorHouse.

Harris, Frank. My Life & Loves, V1. 2006. pap. 19.95 *(978-1-59654-383-6(3)*, olympiapress.com) Disruptive Publishing.

—My Life & Loves, V2. 2006. pap. 23.95 *(978-1-59654-384-3(1)*, olympiapress.com) Disruptive Publishing.

—My Life & Loves, V3. 2006. pap. 17.95 *(978-1-59654-385-0(X)*, olympiapress.com) Disruptive Publishing.

—My Life & Loves, V4. 2006. pap. 17.95 *(978-1-59654-386-7(8)*, olympiapress.com) Disruptive Publishing.

—Oscar Wilde: His Life & Confessions. 2007. (Illus.). 456p. per. *(978-1-4065-3269-2(X))* Dodo Pr.

—Oscar Wilde, His Life & Confessions. 2007. (ENG.). 284p. 28.95 *(978-1-4218-9741-7(5)*, 1st World Library - Literary Society) 1st World Publishing, Inc.

—Oscar Wilde His Life & Confessions Vol. 2006. pap. *(978-1-4068-1113-1(0))* Echo Library.

Harris, Frederick Morgan & Harbison, Helen Harris. Frederick Morgan Harris: A Little of His Life & Some of His Letters. 2011. 122p. 39.95 ***(978-1-258-01972-3(8))*** Literary Licensing, LLC.

Harrison, Frederic. Autobiographic Memoirs. 2009. 430p. 34.99 *(978-1-116-35225-2(7))*; 430p. pap. 35.75 *(978-1-116-35226-9(5))*; 372p. 33.99 *(978-1-115-80429-5(4))*; 430p. 41.99 *(978-1-116-35224-5(9))*; 372p. 38.99 *(978-1-115-80428-8(6))*; 430p. pap. 34.75 *(978-1-116-35227-6(3))*; (ENG.). 431p. pap. 28.99 *(978-1-116-35228-3(1)*, BiblioLife); (ENG.). 431p. pap. 26.99 *(978-1-116-35229-0(X)*, BiblioLife); 372p. pap. 31.75 *(978-1-115-80431-8(6))*; (ENG.). 371p. pap. 26.99 *(978-1-115-80432-5(4)*, BiblioLife); (ENG.). 371p. pap. 25.99 *(978-1-115-80433-2(2)*, BiblioLife) BiblioBazaar.

—Autobiographic Memoirs. 2010. 244p. pap. 32.47 *(978-1-152-62626-3(4))*; 208p. pap. 29.13 *(978-1-152-62630-0(2))* General Bks. LLC.

Harrison, Kathryn. The Kiss: A Memoir. 2011. 256p. pap. 15.00 *(978-0-8129-7971-8(0)*, Random Hse. Trade Paperbacks) Random House Publishing Group.

Harrison, Shirley. The Life & Times of the Real Winnie-the-Pooh: The Teddy Bear Who Inspired A. A. Milne, 1 vol. 2011. (ENG.). 192p. 24.95 *(978-1-4556-1482-0(3))* Pelican Publishing Co., Inc.

Harrison, Stephen, ed. A Companion to Latin Literature. 2007. (Blackwell Companions to the Ancient World Ser.: 13). (ENG., Illus.). 472p. per. 49.95 *(978-1-4051-6131-2(0)*, Wiley-Blackwell) Wiley, John & Sons, Inc.

Hart, John S. (John Seely). The Female Prose Writers of America: With Portraits, Biographical Notices, & Specimens of their Writings. 2006. 552p. per. 32.99 *(978-1-4255-6099-7(7))* MPublishing.

Hart, Stephen M. Gabriel Garcia Marquez. 2010. (Reaktion Books - Critical Lives Ser.). (ENG., Illus.). 208p. pap. 16.95 *(978-1-86189-763-3(4))* Reaktion Bks., Ltd. GBR. Dist: Chicago Distribution Ctr.

Harte, Liam. The Literature of the Irish in Britain: Autobiography & Memoir, 1725-2001. 2011. (ENG., Illus.). 344p. (C). pap. 28.95 *(978-0-230-29636-7(X))* Palgrave Macmillan.

Harwell, David Horace. Walker Percy Remembered: A Portrait in the Words of Those Who Knew Him. (ENG.). 200p. 2010. pap. 18.00 *(978-0-8078-7153-9(2))* 2006. 27.95 *(978-0-8078-3039-0(9))* Univ. of North Carolina Pr.

Harwood, Laurence. C. S. Lewis, My Godfather: Letters, Photos & Recollections. 2007. (ENG., Illus.). 148p. 16.00 *(978-0-8308-3498-3(2))* InterVarsity Pr.

Hasan, Mushirul. Between Modernity & Nationalism: Halide Edip's Encounter with Gandhi's India. 2010. (ENG., Illus.). 304p. 49.95 *(978-0-19-806332-2(6))* Oxford Univ. Pr., Inc.

Hastings, Selina. Nancy Mitford. 2012. (Vintage Ser.). (ENG., Illus.), 304p. pap. 16.00 ***(978-0-307-94946-2(X)***, Vintage) Knopf Doubleday Publishing Group.

Hastings, Selina. The Secret Lives of Somerset Maugham: A Biography. 2010. (ENG., Illus.). 640p. 35.00 *(978-1-4000-6141-9(5))* Random Hse., Inc.

Haven, Cynthia L., ed. An Invisible Rope: Portraits of Czesław Milosz. 2011. (ENG., Illus.). 304p. 59.95 *(978-0-8040-1132-7(X))*; pap. 26.95 *(978-0-8040-1133-4(8))* Swallow Pr.

Havergal, Maria Vernon G. Memorials of Frances Ridley Havergal. 2006. pap. 34.95 *(978-1-4286-5283-5(3))* Kessinger Publishing, LLC.

Havrilesky, Heather. Disaster Preparedness: A Memoir. 2011. (ENG.). 256p. (gr. 12). 15.00 *(978-1-59448-546-6(1)*, Riverhead Trade (Paperbacks)) Penguin Group (USA) Inc.

Hawes, Donald & Hawes. Charles Dickens. 2007. (Writers Live Ser.). (ENG.). 176p. 24.95 *(978-0-8264-8964-7(8))*; 110.00 *(978-0-8264-8963-0(X))* Continuum International Publishing Group, Ltd. GBR. Dist: National Bk. Network.

Hawes, Elizabeth. Camus, a Romance. 2010. (ENG.). 336p. pap. 14.00 *(978-0-8021-4488-1(8)*, Grove Pr.) Grove/Atlantic, Inc.

Hawkins, John. The Life of Samuel Johnson, LL.D. Brack, O. M., ed. 2009. (ENG., Illus.). 528p. lib. bdg. 59.95 *(978-0-8203-2995-6(9))* Univ. of Georgia Pr.

Hawkins, Peter S. Dante: A Brief History. 2006. (Blackwell Brief Histories of Religion Ser.). (ENG., Illus.). 200p. per. 28.95 *(978-1-4051-3052-3(0))*; 99.95 *(978-1-4051-3051-6(2))* Wiley, John & Sons, Inc. (Wiley-Blackwell).

Hawkins, Ruth A. Unbelievable Happiness & Final Sorrow: The Hemingway-Pfeiffer Marriage. 2012. (ENG., Illus.). 391p. 34.95 ***(978-1-55728-974-2(3))*** Univ. of Arkansas Pr.

Hawthorne, Julian. Nathaniel Hawthorne & His Wife: A Biography, 2 vols., Set. reprint ed. 200.00 *(978-0-7950-2136-7(4))* New Library Press LLC.

—Nathaniel Hawthorne & His Wife: A Biography, Vol. 2. 2008. 476p. pap. *(978-1-4086-8884-7(0))* Read Bks.

Haydock, James. Beacon's River. 2009. 320p. pap. 21.99 *(978-1-4389-8239-7(9))* AuthorHouse.

Hayes, Kevin J. Edgar Allan Poe. 2nd rev. ed. 2009. (Reaktion Books - Critical Lives Ser.). (ENG., Illus.). 192p. pap. 16.95 *(978-1-86189-515-8(1))* Reaktion Bks., Ltd. GBR. Dist: Chicago Distribution Ctr.

Hayes, Richard Baxter. Memoirs of Richard Baxter Hayes. Hayes, W. M., ed. 2011. 234p. 46.95 ***(978-1-258-09765-3(6))*** Literary Licensing, LLC.

Haynall, Carolyn. I Was Once Like You: Before I Got Alzheimer's. 2011. 308p. 24.95 ***(978-1-4678-4952-4(9))***; pap. 16.95 ***(978-1-4678-4953-1(7))*** AuthorHouse.

Hayslett, Duane. The Fixer. 2011. 214p. pap. 24.95 **(978-1-4560-1939-6(2))** PublishAmerica, Inc.
Hayworth, Eugene. Fever Vision: The Life & Works of Coleman Dowell. 2007. (Dalkey Archive Scholarly Ser.). (ENG., Illus.). 234p. per. 24.95 *(978-1-56478-457-5(6))* Dalkey Archive Pr.
Head, Bessie & MacKenzie, Craig. A Woman Alone: Autobiographical Writings. 2008. (AWS African Writers Ser.). (ENG., Illus.). 137p. pap. 15.95 *(978-0-435-90603-0(8))* Longman Publishing.
Heaphy, Maura. Science Fiction Authors: A Research Guide, 1 vol. 2008. (Author Research Ser.). 352p. (gr. 9-18). pap. 40.00 *(978-1-59158-515-2(5)*, LU5155) Libraries Unlimited, Inc.
Hearn, Lafcadio & Bisland, Elizabeth. The Life & Letters of Lafcadio Hearn V2. 2007. (ENG.). 562p. 58.95 *(978-0-548-15649-0(2))*; pap. 43.95 *(978-1-4304-5114-3(9))* Kessinger Publishing, LLC.
Heath Ph. D., Samuel D. G. The American Poet: Weedpatch Gazette 1993-1994. 2009. 376p. pap. 24.95 *(978-1-4401-5791-2(X))* iUniverse, Inc.
—The American Poet: Weedpatch Gazette 1995-1996. 2009. 320p. pap. 22.95 *(978-1-4401-5656-4(5))* iUniverse, Inc.
—The American Poet: Weedpatch Gazette For 1990-1991. 2009. 252p. pap. 19.95 *(978-1-4401-6017-2(1))* iUniverse, Inc.
—The American Poet: Weedpatch Gazette For 1992. 2009. 416p. pap. 26.95 *(978-1-4401-6015-8(5))* iUniverse, Inc.
—The American Poet: Weedpatch Gazette For 1997. 2009. 436p. pap. 27.95 *(978-1-4401-5396-9(5))* iUniverse, Inc.
Hedrick, Joan. Solitary Comrade: Jack London & His Work. 2011. (ENG.). 284p. pap. 40.00 *(978-0-8078-9682-2(9))* Univ. of North Carolina Pr.
Hegarty, Paul & Kennedy, Danny. Dennis Cooper: Writing at the Edge. 2008. (ENG., Illus.). 217p. (C). 74.50 *(978-1-84519-187-0(0))* Sussex Academic Pr. GBR. Dist: International Specialized Bk. Services.
Heidelberger-Leonard, Irene. The Philosopher of Auschwitz: Jean Amery & Living with the Holocaust. Bell, Anthea, tr. 2010. (ENG., Illus.). 304p. 35.00 *(978-1-84885-150-4(2))* I. B. Tauris & Co., Ltd. GBR. Dist: Macmillan.
Heidler, Harold. The lucky Son. 2008. 155p. pap. 15.54 *(978-1-4357-4153-9(6))* Lulu Enterprises Inc.
Heller, Anne Conover. Ayn Rand & the World She Made. 2010. (ENG., Illus.). 608p. pap. 18.00 *(978-1-4000-7893-6(8)*, Anchor) Knopf Doubleday Publishing Group.
Heller, Erica. Yossarian Slept Here: When Joseph Heller Was Dad, the Apthorp Was Home, & Life Was a Catch-22. (ENG., Illus.). 288p. 2012. pap. 16.00 **(978-1-4391-9769-1(5))** 2011. 25.00 *(978-1-4391-9768-4(7))* Simon & Schuster.
Heller, Marvin J. The Seventeenth Century Hebrew Book: An Abridged Thesaurus, 2 vols. (Illus.). 2011. lxxi, 1524p. *(978-90-04-18639-2(5))* 2011. lxxi, 1524p. *(978-90-04-15758-3(1))* 2010. 516p. *(978-90-04-18638-5(7))* BRILL.
Helmes-Hayes, Rick. Measuring the Mosaic: An Intellectual Biography of John Porter. 2010. 592p. *(978-0-8020-9703-3(0))* Univ. of Toronto Pr.
Hemingway, Ernest. A Moveable Feast: The Restored Edition. (ENG.). 256p. 2010. pap. 15.00 *(978-1-4391-8271-0(X))* 2009. (Illus.). 25.00 *(978-1-4165-9131-3(1))* Scribner. (Scribner).
Hemingway, Patrick. Hemingway at Home. 2008. 160p. 40.00 *(978-0-8109-9518-5(2))* Abrams.
Hemingway, Valerie. Running with the Bulls: My Years with the Hemingways. 29.45 *(978-0-7862-7528-1(6))* Thorndike Pr.
Hemley, Robin. Do-Over! In Which a Forty-Eight-Year-Old Father of Three Returns to Kindergarten, Summer Camp, the Prom, & Other Embarrassments. 2009. (ENG., Illus.). 336p. 23.99 *(978-0-316-02060-2(5))* Little Brown & Co.
Hemmings, F. W. J. Alexandre Dumas: The King of Romance. 2012. 249p. pap. **(978-1-4482-0527-1(1)**, 146218, Bloomsbury Reader) Bloomsbury Publishing Plc.
—The Life & Times of Emile Zola. 2012. 192p. pap. **(978-1-4482-0520-2(4)**, 146526, Bloomsbury Reader) Bloomsbury Publishing Plc.
Hemmingson, Michael. Gordon Lish & His Influence on Twentieth-Century American Liter. 2009. (Studies in Major Literary Authors Ser.). (ENG.). 256p. (C). 125.00 *(978-0-415-99177-3(3))* Routledge.
Henderson, Paula Laureen. Lost Angels: Encounters with First Nations. 2011. (ENG & FRE.). 223p. pap. *(978-0-9783141-1-8(5))* Gumdrop Enterprise.
Hendrickson, Paul. Hemingway's Boat: Everything He Loved in Life, & Lost, 1934-1961. 2011. (ENG., Illus.). 544p. 30.00 *(978-1-4000-4162-6(7)*, Knopf) Knopf Doubleday Publishing Group.
Hendrickx, Marc. Yesterday's Tomorrow: Leonard Cohen. 2008. 0144p. pap. 21.95 *(978-1-876040-77-2(7))* Brandl & Schlesinger AUS. Dist: Independent Pubs. Group.
Henry, Nancy. The Life of George Eliot. 2012. (Blackwell Critical Biographies Ser.). (ENG.). 314p. 89.95 **(978-1-4051-3705-8(3)**, Wiley-Blackwell) Wiley, John & Sons, Inc.
Herman, Jan, et al, eds. Le Chevalier de Mouhy: Bagarre et Bigarrure. 2010. (Illus.). 242p. pap. 62.00 *(978-90-420-3094-7(1))* Rodopi.
Herman, Ottó. Ungarns Spinnen-Fauna. 2010. 162p. pap. 21.75 *(978-1-149-00843-0(1))* BiblioBazaar.
Heron, Gil Scott. The Last Holiday: A Memoir. 2012. (ENG.). 384p. 25.00 **(978-0-8021-2901-7(3)**, Grove Pr.) Grove/Atlantic, Inc.
Herrin, Lamar. Romancing Spain. 2006. (ENG.). 272p. 23.95 *(978-1-932961-22-5(4))* Unbridled Bks.
Herzen, Alexander. The Memoirs of Alexander Herzen, Part 1-2. Duff, J. D., tr. 2011. 400p. 54.95 **(978-1-258-09826-9(2))** Literary Licensing, LLC.
Herzog, Tobey C. Writing Vietnam, Writing Life: Caputo, Heinemann, O'Brien, Butler. 2008. (ENG.). 240p. 39.95 *(978-1-58729-631-4(4))* Univ. of Iowa Pr.
Hester, Elliott. Adventures of a Continental Drifter: An Around-the-World Excursion into Weirdness, Danger, Lust, & the Perils of Street Food. 2006. (ENG.). 320p. pap. 15.95 *(978-0-312-31242-8(3)*, St. Martin's Paperbacks) St. Martin's Pr.
—Adventures of Continental Drifter. Date not set. mass mkt. *(978-0-312-98878-4(8)*, St. Martin's Paperbacks) St. Martin's Pr.
Hewison, Robert. John Byrne: Art & Life. 2011. (Illus.). 144p. 70.00 *(978-1-84822-047-8(2)*, Lund Humphries Pubs.) Ashgate Publishing, Ltd. GBR. Dist: Ashgate Publishing Co.
—Ruskin on Venice: The Paradise of Cities. 2010. (ENG., Illus.). 500p. 85.00 *(978-0-300-12178-0(4))* Yale Univ. Pr.
Hiaasen, Carl. The Downhill Lie: A Hacker's Return to a Ruinous Sport. 2008. (ENG.). 224p. 22.00 *(978-0-307-26653-8(2)*, Knopf) Knopf Doubleday Publishing Group.
—The Downhill Lie: A Hacker's Return to a Ruinous Sport. l.t. ed. 2008. (ENG.). 368p. pap. 22.00 *(978-0-7393-2787-6(9))* Random Hse. Large Print.
Hibbert, Christopher. Charles Dickens: The Making of a Literary Giant. 2009. (ENG., Illus.). 336p. pap. 19.95 *(978-0-230-61426-0(4))* Palgrave Macmillan.
Hichens, Mark. Inimitable P G Wodehouse: The Story of His Life & a Treasury of His Wit. 2009. (Illus.). 240p. 28.50 *(978-1-84624-334-9(3))* Book Guild, Ltd. GBR. Dist: Trans-Atlantic Pubns., Inc.
Hickman, Lisa C. William Faulkner & Joan Williams: The Romance of Two Writers. 2006. (ENG., Illus.). 228p. per. 35.00 *(978-0-7864-2599-0(7))* McFarland & Co., Inc. Pubs.
Higgins, D. S. Private Diaries of Sir H. Rider Haggard, 1914-1925. 320p. 24.95 *(978-0-8488-2586-7(1))* Amereon LTD.
Higham, Charles. In & Out of Hollywood: A Biographer's Memoir. 2009. (ENG., Illus.). 300p. 29.95 *(978-0-299-23340-2(5))* Univ. of Wisconsin Pr.
Hijuelos, Oscar. Thoughts Without Cigarettes: A Memoir. 2011. (ENG.). 384p. (gr. 12). 27.50 *(978-1-59240-629-6(7)*, Gotham) Penguin Group (USA) Inc.
Hill, David T. Journalism & Politics in Indonesia. 2010. (Illus.). 288p. pap. 42.95 **(978-0-415-66684-8(8))** Routledge.
Hill, Judith. Lady Gregory: An Irish Life. 2011. (ENG.). 616p. pap. 26.95 *(978-1-84889-110-4(5))* Collins Pr., The IRL. Dist: Dufour Editions, Inc.
Hillman, Robert. The Boy in the Green Suit: A Memoir. 2009. (ENG.). 240p. pap. 19.95 *(978-1-921372-51-3(6))* Scribe Pubns. AUS. Dist: Independent Pubs. Group.
Hindus, Milton. The Crippled Giant: A Bizarre Adventure in Contemporary Letters. 2011. 158p. 41.95 **(978-1-258-09427-0(4))** Literary Licensing, LLC.
Hinton, James. Life & Letters of James Hinton. 2008. 388p. 29.99 *(978-0-559-62453-7(0))*; pap. 32.75 *(978-0-559-62451-3(4))* BiblioBazaar.
—Life & Letters of James Hinton. 2009. 228p. pap. *(978-0-217-50287-0(3))* Books LLC.
—Life & Letters of James Hinton. 2009. 266p. pap. 21.33 *(978-0-217-50469-0(8))* General Bks. LLC.
—Life & Letters of James Hinton. Hopkins, Ellice, ed. 2007. (ENG.). 384p. 48.95 *(978-0-548-08108-2(5))* Kessinger Publishing, LLC.
Hinton, KaaVonia. Sharon M. Draper: Embracing Literacy. 2008. (Scarecrow Studies in Young Adult Literature Ser.). (ENG.). 148p. 45.00 *(978-0-8108-5985-2(8))* Scarecrow Pr., Inc.
Hiranandani, Popati & Panjwani, Jyoti. The Pages of My Life: Autobiography & Selected Stories. 2011. (ENG.). 304p. 35.00 *(978-0-19-806694-1(5))* Oxford Univ. Pr., Inc.
Hirsch, Stanley. Memoirs of a Geriatric Ski Bum. 2011. 160p. 29.99 **(978-1-4653-5256-9(2))**; pap. 19.99 **(978-1-4653-5255-2(4))** Xlibris Corp.
Hitchens, Christopher. Hitch-22: A Memoir. (ENG., Illus.). 2011. 448p. pap. 14.99 *(978-0-446-54034-6(X))* 2010. 448p. 26.99 *(978-0-446-54033-9(1))* 2010. 768p. 28.99 *(978-0-446-56698-8(5))* Grand Central Publishing. (Twelve).
Hively, Evelyn Helmick. Darling Ro & the Benet Women. 2011. 160p. 34.95 *(978-1-60635-096-6(X))* Kent State Univ. Pr.
Hoagland, Edward. Sex & the River Styx. 2011. (ENG.). 272p. 27.50 *(978-1-60358-336-7(X))*; pap. 17.95 *(978-1-60358-337-4(8))* Chelsea Green Publishing.
Hobart, Alice Tisdale. Portrait of a Novelist. 2011. 28p. 35.95 **(978-1-258-08396-0(5))** Literary Licensing, LLC.
Hobi, Caroline. Willibald Alexis: Rube Ist Die Erste Bürgerpflicht. (GER.). 365p. pap. 75.95 *(978-3-03911-230-2(9))* Lang, Peter Publishing, Inc.
Hodge, Jane Aiken. The Private World of Georgette Heyer. 2011. 256p. pap. 14.99 *(978-1-4022-5192-4(0))* Sourcebooks, Inc.
Hodson, Leighton. Marcel Proust. 2009. 422p. pap. 45.00 *(978-0-415-56898-2(6))* Routledge.
Hofmann, Robert A. One Brain Cell Away from Retarded. 2011. 186p. pap. 24.95 **(978-1-4560-3829-8(X))** PublishAmerica, Inc.
Hogan, Rose. Mrs Craik: Author of John Halifax, Gentleman. 2009. (Illus.). 72p. pap. *(978-1-84748-405-5(0))* Athena Pr.
Hogg, David. The Life of Allan Cunningham. 2007. (ENG.). 386p. 48.95 *(978-0-548-15131-0(8))*; 388p. per. 33.95 *(978-1-4304-4477-0(0))* Kessinger Publishing, LLC.
Holden Ronning, Anne. For Was I Not Born Here? Identity & Culture in the Work of Yvonne du Fresne. 2010. (Illus.). 200p. 56.00 *(978-90-420-2957-6(9))* Rodopi.
Holliday, Cherryl. Dreams Really Do Come True. 2011. 272p. pap. **(978-1-908447-87-6(7))** Grosvenor Hse. Publishing Ltd.
Holloway, Jean & Garland, Hamlin. Hamlin Garland: A Biography. 2011. 380p. 53.95 **(978-1-258-02483-3(7))** Literary Licensing, LLC.
Holman. Thomas Wolfe, Vol. 6. 2009. pap. 25.00 *(978-0-8166-0208-7(5))* Univ. of Minnesota Pr.
Holmström, Lakshmi & Bama, Karukku. 2nd ed. 2012. (ENG., Illus.). 168p. 19.95 **(978-0-19-807830-2(7))** Oxford Univ. Pr., Inc.
Honan, Park. Jane Austen Her Life. 2008. (Illus.). 464p. 32.95 *(978-1-904435-81-5(5))* Little Bks., Ltd. GBR. Dist: Independent Pubs. Group.
Hopkins, Ellen & Wilson, Leah. A New Dawn: Your Favorite Authors on Stephenie Meyer's Twilight Series. 2008. x, 174p. *(978-0-9792331-5-9(1))* BenBella Bks.
Hopkins, John. The South American Diaries (1972-1973) 2008. (Illus.). 235p. *(978-0-932274-69-4(2))* Cadmus Editions.
Hopkinson, Deborah. Deborah Hopkinson & YOU, 1 vol. 2007. (Author & YOU Ser.). (Illus.). 112p. pap. 35.00 *(978-1-59158-278-6(4)*, LU2784) Libraries Unlimited, Inc.
Horbacz, Sophia. Sophia, My Life's Journey. 2008. 164p. pap. 12.95 *(978-0-9822540-8-0(3))* Peppertree Pr., The.
Hornby, Nick. Fever Pitch: Ballfieber - Die Geschichte eines Fans. Geiss, Marcus & Stegelmann, Henning, trs. from ENG. (GER.). 409p. pap. *(978-3-462-02586-6(4))* Kiepenheuer & Witsch GmbH & Company KG DEU. Dist: International Bk. Import Service, Inc.
Horowitz, Helen Lefkowitz. Wild Unrest: Charlotte Perkins Gilman & the Making of the Yellow Wall-Paper. (ENG.). 272p. 2012. pap. 18.95 **(978-0-19-989193-1(1))** 2010. (Illus.). 24.95 *(978-0-19-973980-6(3))* Oxford Univ. Pr., Inc.
Hotchner, A. E. The Boyhood Memoirs of A. E. Hotchner: King of the Hill & Looking for Miracles. 2007. (ENG.). 432p. (gr. 9). per. 19.95 *(978-1-883982-60-7(X))* Missouri Historical Society Pr.
—Paul & Me: 53 Years of Adventures & Misadventures with My Pal Paul Newman. 2011. (Illus.). 256p. pap. 15.95 *(978-0-307-47491-0(X)*, Anchor) Knopf Doubleday Publishing Group.
Houellebecq, Mi. Piattaforma Nel Centro Del. pap. 21.95 *(978-88-452-5407-9(0))* Fabbri Editori - RCS Libri ITA. Dist: Distribooks, Inc.
Howard, Patrick. Releasing the Torment Within: An Autobiography on Patrick Howard. 2011. 132p. pap. 24.95 **(978-1-4512-8414-0(4))** PublishAmerica, Inc.
Howat, Irene. Patricia St. John: The Story Behind the Stories. 2008. (Trail Blazers Ser.). (ENG.). 160p. pap. 8.99 *(978-1-84550-328-4(7))* Christian Focus Pubns. GBR. Dist: STL Distribution North America.
Howe, Ben Ryder. My Korean Deli: Risking It All for a Convenience Store. 2009. 304p. 25.99 *(978-0-06-171033-9(4))* HarperCollins Pubs.
—My Korean Deli: Risking It All for a Convenience Store. 2011. (ENG.). 320p. 25.00 *(978-0-8050-9343-8(5))* Holt, Henry & Co.
Howe, Will David. Charles Lamb & His Friends. 2011. 398p. 54.95 **(978-1-258-06901-8(6))** Literary Licensing, LLC.
Howell, Peter. Martial. 2009. (Ancients in Action Ser.). 128p. pap. 24.95 *(978-1-85399-702-0(1))* Duckworth Publishers GBR. Dist: International Publishers Marketing.
Howells, William Dean. Literary Friends & Acquaintances: A Personal Retrospect of American Authorship. 2008. 448p. 30.99 *(978-0-559-26972-1(2))* 2008. 448p. pap. 35.75 *(978-0-559-26970-7(6))* 2007. (ENG.). 298p. pap. 21.99 *(978-1-4264-1355-1(6))* 2006. 296p. pap. 23.99 *(978-1-4264-1366-7(1))* BiblioBazaar.
—Literary Friends & Acquaintances: A Personal Retrospect of American Authorship. 2007. (ENG.). 296p. 43.95 *(978-0-548-18629-9(4))*; 300p. per. 28.95 *(978-1-4304-8960-3(X))* Kessinger Publishing, LLC.
—My Mark Twain: Reminiscences & Criticisms. 2007. (ENG.). 72p. per. *(978-1-4065-3130-5(8))* Dodo Pr.
—My Mark Twain: Reminiscences & Criticisms. 2008. 60p. pap. 10.99 *(978-1-59547-688-3(1))* NuVision Pubns., LLC.
Howington, Helen. All in A Lifetime. 2010. 160p. 24.95 *(978-1-4520-6766-7(X))*; pap. 14.95 *(978-1-4520-6764-3(3))* AuthorHouse.
Howitt, Mary Botham. Mary Howitt: Volume 1: An Autobiography. Howitt, Margaret, ed. 2011. (Cambridge Library Collection - Literary Studies). (Illus.). 352p. pap. 29.99 *(978-1-108-02573-7(0))* Cambridge Univ. Pr.
—Mary Howitt: Volume 2: An Autobiography. Howitt, Margaret, ed. 2011. (Cambridge Library Collection - Literary Studies). (Illus.). 388p. pap. 31.99 *(978-1-108-02574-4(9))* Cambridge Univ. Pr.
Hrabal, Bohumil. Vita Nuova: A Novel. Liman, Tony, tr. from CZE. 2010. (Writings from an Unbound Europe Ser.). (ENG.). 248p. pap. 19.95 *(978-0-8101-2546-9(3))* Northwestern Univ. Pr.
Hubbard, Elbert. Little Journeys to the Homes of Famous Women. 2009. 128p. pap. *(978-1-150-15076-0(9))* Books LLC.
—Little Journeys to the Homes of Famous Women. 2009. 148p. pap. 19.99 *(978-1-151-18233-3(8))* General Bks. LLC.
—Little Journeys to the Homes of Famous Women. 429p. reprint ed. 98.00 *(978-0-7222-8419-3(5))* Library Reprints, Inc.
—Little Journeys to the Homes of the Great, 5. l.t. ed. 2006. (ENG.). 226p. pap. 22.99 *(978-1-4264-7357-9(5))* BiblioBazaar.
—Little Journeys to the Homes of the Great, Volume 5: Little Journeys to the Homes of English Authors. 2007. 202p. pap. 20.99 *(978-1-4264-7284-8(6))* BiblioBazaar.
Hubbard, Frederick. A Yankee Engineer Abroad: Part I: Europe. 2010. 408p. 28.49 *(978-1-4520-6436-9(9))*; pap. 17.99 *(978-1-4520-6437-6(7))* AuthorHouse.
Hucke, Karl-Heinz. Jene Scheu vor allem Mercantilischen: Schillers Arbeits- und Finanzplan. (Studien und Texte zur Sozialgeschichte der Literatur Ser.). (GER.). VIII, 93p. 210.00 **(978-3-11-186295-8(X))** De Gruyter, Walter Inc.
Hudson, W. H. Far Away & Long Ago: A Childhood in Argentina. 2007. 356p. 32.95 *(978-1-4344-9351-4(2))*; per. 19.95 *(978-1-4344-9350-7(4))* Wildside Pr., LLC.
Hughes, Barbara. Between Literature & History: The Diaries & Memoires of Mary Leadbeater & Dorothea Herbert. 2010. (Reimagining Ireland Ser.). 255p. pap. 53.95 *(978-3-03911-889-2(7))* Lang, Peter AG GBR. Dist: Lang, Peter.
Hughes, Thomas. Memoir of a Brother. 196p. 2009. 22.99 *(978-1-103-17669-4(2))* 2009. pap. 16.99 *(978-1-103-17666-3(8))* 2008. 22.99 *(978-0-559-26671-3(5))* 2008. pap. 22.75 *(978-0-559-26668-3(5))* BiblioBazaar.
Hugo, Victor. The Memoirs of Victor Hugo. 2008. 272p. 25.99 *(978-0-554-38530-3(9))* 2008. 272p. 28.99 *(978-0-554-29227-4(0))* 2007. (ENG.). 238p. per. 20.99 *(978-1-4346-7182-0(8))* 2007. (ENG.). 268p. per. 23.99 *(978-1-4346-7183-7(6))* BiblioBazaar.
—The Memoirs of Victor Hugo. 2008. 260p. per. *(978-1-4065-6896-7(1))* Dodo Pr.
—The Memoirs of Victor Hugo. 2007. 188p. per. *(978-1-4068-1408-8(3))* Echo Library.
—The Memoirs of Victor Hugo. 2008. (Large Print Ser.). lib. bdg. 26.00 *(978-1-58287-963-5(X))*; lib. bdg. 25.00 *(978-1-58287-480-7(8))* North Bks.
—The Memoirs of Victor Hugo. 2009. (ENG.). 224p. pap. 15.45 *(978-1-4385-1792-6(0)*, Book Jungle) Standard Pubns., Inc.
—The Memoirs of Victor Hugo. 2008. 408p. 39.95 *(978-1-4344-7072-0(5))*; pap. 24.95 *(978-1-4344-7071-3(7))* Wildside Pr., LLC.
Huizinga, Johan. Erasmus & the Age of Reformation. 2010. 208p. pap. 18.00 *(978-1-60899-950-7(5)*, Wipf and Stock) Wipf & Stock Pubs.
Hummel, Thomas R. A Journey Through Literary America. 2009. (Illus.). 277p. 45.00 *(978-0-9817425-1-9(3))* Val de Grace Bks. & Film, Inc.
Humphries, Jefferson, ed. Conversations with Reynolds Price. 2008. (ENG.). 316p. pap. 25.00 *(978-0-87805-483-1(9))* Univ. Pr. of Mississippi.
Hungerford, T. A. G. Stories from Suburban Road. 232p. 18.26 *(978-0-909144-71-5(0))* Fremantle Pr. AUS. Dist: Independent Pubs. Group.
Hunt, Leigh. Leigh Hunt's Autobiography: The Earliest Sketches. Fogle, Stephen Francis, ed. 2011. 72p. 36.95 **(978-1-258-09075-3(9))** Literary Licensing, LLC.
—Lord Byron & Some of His Contemporaries. reprint ed. 59.50 *(978-0-404-03419-1(5))* AMS Pr., Inc.
—Stories from the Italian Poets with Lives of the Writers. 2009. 438p. 41.99 *(978-1-113-90473-7(9))* BiblioBazaar.
Hunt, Leigh & Thomas George Thrum. Stories from the Italian Poets: With Lives of the Writers, Vol. 1. l.t. ed. 2007. 290p. pap. 23.99 *(978-1-4264-4515-6(6))* BiblioBazaar.
Hurston, Zora Neale. Dust Tracks on a Road: An Autobiography. 2010. (P. S. Ser.). (ENG.). 336p. pap. 16.99 *(978-0-06-200483-3(2)*, HarperPerennial) HarperCollins Pubs.
Husain, Ed. The Islamist: Why I Became an Islamic Fundamentalist, What I Saw Inside, & Why I Left. 2009. (ENG.). 320p. (gr. 12-18). 16.00 *(978-0-14-311598-4(7)*, Penguin (Non-Classics)) Penguin Group (USA) Inc.
Hustvedt, Siri. The Shaking Woman or a History of My Nerves. 2010. (ENG.). 224p. 23.00 *(978-0-8050-9169-4(6))* Holt, Henry & Co.
Hutchinson, A. S. M. The Book of Simon. 2007. (ENG.). 108p. 34.95 *(978-0-548-01049-5(8))* Kessinger Publishing, LLC.
Hutchison, Hazel. Brief Lives: Henry James. 2012. (Brief Lives Ser.). (ENG.). 112p. pap. 13.95 *(978-1-84391-923-0(0))* Hesperus Pr. GBR. Dist: Independent Pubs. Group.
Hutton, Holt Richard. Sir Walter Scott: (English Men of Letters Series) 2007. (ENG.). 150p. pap. 18.99 *(978-1-4346-2925-8(2))*; 170p. pap. 21.99 *(978-1-4346-2949-4(X))* BiblioBazaar.
Hutton, Richard Holt. Sir Walter Scott. 2011. (Cambridge Library Collection - English Men of Letters Ser.). (ENG.). 190p. pap. 19.99 **(978-1-108-03467-8(5))** Cambridge Univ. Pr.
Huxman, Norman. The, Home Kid: Saga of A Runaway Orphan. 2011. (ENG.). 160p. pap. 16.95 **(978-1-4327-7814-9(5))** Outskirts Pr., Inc.
Hyman. Flannery Oconnor-Aw V54. 2009. pap. 25.00 *(978-0-8166-0384-8(7))* Univ. of Minnesota Pr.
Iglesias, Karl. The 101 Habits of Highly Successful Screenwriters: Insider Secrets from Hollywood's Top Writers. 2nd ed. 2011. (ENG.). 272p. pap. 14.95 **(978-1-4405-2789-0(X))** Adams Media Corp.
Ilan, Stavans & Stavans, Ilan. Gabriel Garcia Marquez: The Early Years. 2010. (ENG., Illus.). 256p. 25.00 *(978-0-312-24033-2(3))* Palgrave Macmillan.
Inderwies, Stefan. Agneta Horns Leverne: Eine apologetische Autobiographie? 2009. (Europäische Hochschulschriften. Reihe 18: Vergleichende Literaturwissenschaft Ser.). (GER.). 144p. pap. 38.95 *(978-3-631-59149-9(7))* Lang, Peter GmbH, Europaischer Verlag der Wissenschaften DEU. Dist: Lang, Peter.
Instituto de Investigaciones Literarias Gonzalo Picón Febres Staff, contrib. by. Diccionario General de la Literatura Venezolana, 2 Vols. 2nd ed. (SPA.). *(978-980-221-120-3(6))* Bow Historical Bks.
International Who's Who of Authors & Writers 2009. 24th rev. ed. 2008. 856p. 430.00 *(978-1-85743-470-5(6))* Europa Pubns.
International Who's Who of Authors & Writers 2012. 27th rev. ed. 2011. (ENG.). 912p. 490.00 *(978-1-85743-516-7(4))* Routledge.
Introspection Writers Group. Windows of Life. 2008. 96p. pap. 15.00 *(978-0-9792132-8-1(2))* Reflections Publishing, Inc.
Irmscher, Christoph. Public Poet, Private Man: Henry Wadsworth Longfellow At 200. 2009. (Illus.). 236p. pap. 24.95 net. *(978-1-55849-584-5(3))* Univ. of Massachusetts Pr.

Irvine, Alexander. From the Bottom Up. 2008. 232p. 24.99 *(978-0-554-35838-3(7))*; 27.99 *(978-0-554-26535-3(4))* BiblioBazaar.

—From the Bottom Up. 2007. (Illus.). 216p. per. *(978-1-4065-3423-8(4))* Dodo Pr.

—From the Bottom Up. 2007. 144p. per. *(978-1-4068-3802-2(0))* Echo Library.

Irving, Clifford. The Hoax. 2007. 400p. pap. 14.95 *(978-1-4013-0854-4(6))* Miramax Bks.

Irving, Pierre Munroe. The Life & Letters of Washington Irving. 2009. 452p. 33.99 *(978-1-113-79650-9(2))* 2009. 452p. pap. 22.99 *(978-1-113-79645-5(6))* 2009. 496p. 35.99 *(978-1-113-44313-7(8))* 2009. 496p. pap. 37.75 *(978-1-113-44310-6(3))* 2009. 464p. 35.99 *(978-1-110-73367-5(4))* 2009. 464p. pap. 36.75 *(978-1-110-73365-1(8))* 2008. 460p. 31.99 *(978-0-559-38255-0(3))* 2008. 452p. 30.99 *(978-0-559-31914-3(2))* 2008. 452p. pap. 35.75 *(978-0-559-31912-9(6))* 2008. 460p. pap. 35.75 *(978-0-559-38254-3(5))* BiblioBazaar.

—The Life & Letters of Washington Irving. 2009. 236p. pap. *(978-1-151-10874-6(X))*; 270p. pap. *(978-0-217-35417-2(3))* Books LLC.

—The Life & Letters of Washington Irving. 2009. 232p. pap. 20.03 *(978-1-151-07206-1(0))*; 324p. pap. 22.72 *(978-1-150-72675-0(X))*; 244p. pap. 20.59 *(978-1-4589-2391-2(6))*; 276p. pap. 21.51 *(978-0-217-94177-8(X))*; 230p. pap. 19.99 *(978-0-217-94174-7(5))* General Bks. LLC.

—The Life & Letters of Washington Irving. 1. 2007. pap. 36.95 *(978-1-4304-5091-7(6))* Vol. 1. 2007. 448p. 51.95 *(978-0-548-15628-5(X))* Vol. 3. 2008. 460p. 52.95 *(978-1-4366-6519-3(1))* Vol. 3. 2008. 460p. pap. 37.95 *(978-0-548-86547-7(7))* Kessinger Publishing, LLC.

—The Life & Letters of Washington Irving, 4 vols., Set. reprint ed. 400.00 *(978-0-7950-2344-6(8))* New Library Press LLC.

—The Life & Letters of Washington Irving. 2008. 456p. pap. *(978-1-4437-0728-2(7))* 2008. 404p. pap. *(978-1-4437-0722-0(8))* 2008. 396p. pap. *(978-1-4437-0724-4(4))* 2007. 428p. per. *(978-1-4086-2650-4(0))* Read Bks.

—The Life & Letters of Washington Irving by His Nephew, Pierre M. Irving. 2006. (ENG.). 496p. per. 29.99 *(978-1-4255-5538-2(1))*; 408p. per. 26.99 *(978-1-4255-4406-5(1))*; (ENG.). 472p. per. 29.99 *(978-1-4255-5238-1(2))*; (ENG.). 496p. per. 29.99 *(978-1-4255-5539-9(X))*; 456p. per. 29.99 *(978-1-4255-5037-0(1))* MPublishing.

Irving, Pierre Munroe, ed. The Life & Letters of Washington Irving, Vol. 2. 2010. 420p. pap. 34.95 *(978-1-120-89676-6(2))* Kessinger Publishing, LLC.

Irving, Washington. The Crayon Miscellany. 2008. 381p. 31.99 *(978-0-559-00049-2(9))*; 29.99 *(978-0-559-00059-1(6))*; pap. 33.75 *(978-0-559-00050-8(2))*; pap. 32.75 *(978-0-559-00055-3(3))* BiblioBazaar.

—Oliver Goldsmith: A Biography. l.t. ed. 2007. (ENG.). 322p. pap. 24.99 *(978-1-4264-2757-2(3))* BiblioBazaar.

—Oliver Goldsmith: A Biography. 2007. 280p. per. *(978-1-4065-3434-4(X))* Dodo Pr.

Isaacson, Lanae H. Dlb 354 Norwgn Wrtrs. 2009. (Dictionary of Literary Biography Ser.). (ENG., Illus.). 446p. 315.00 *(978-0-7876-8172-2(5))* Cengage Gale.

Isaacson, Walter. American Sketches: Great Leaders, Creative Thinkers, & Heroes of a Hurricane. 2010. (ENG.). 304p. pap. 15.00 *(978-1-4391-8344-1(9))* Simon & Schuster.

Isbell, Mary. Writing Through Literature: An Anthology of Literary Texts for Academic Inquiry. rev. ed. 2011. (ENG.). 370p. pap. 59.99 ***(978-0-7575-9068-9(3))*** Kendall Hunt Publishing Co.

Isherwood, Christopher. Diaries, 1960-1969, Vol. 2. 2010. 800p. *(978-0-7011-6940-4(0)*, Chatto & Windus) Random Hse.

Isherwood, Christopher. Liberation: Diaries:1970-1983. 2012. (ENG.). 768p. 39.99 ***(978-0-06-208474-3(7))*** HarperCollins Pubs.

Israel, Lee. Can You Ever Forgive Me? Memoirs of a Literary Forger. 2008. (ENG., Illus.). 144p. 19.95 *(978-1-4165-8867-2(1))* Simon & Schuster.

Ivins, Holly. The Jane Austen Pocket Bible: Everything You Want to Know about Jane & Her Novels. 2011. (ENG.). 192p. pap. 9.95 *(978-1-907087-18-9(4))* Crimson Publishing, Ltd. GBR. Dist: National Bk. Network.

Iyer, Pico. The Man Within My Head. 2012. (ENG.). 256p. 25.95 ***(978-0-307-26761-0(X)***, Knopf) Knopf Doubleday Publishing Group.

Izzo, David Garrett. Christopher Isherwood Encyclopedia. alt. ed. 2010. (ENG., Illus.). 198p. pap. 45.00 *(978-0-7864-4687-2(0))* McFarland & Co., Inc. Pubs.

Jack London. John Barleycorn. l.t. ed. 2007. (ENG.). 200p. pap. 21.99 *(978-1-4264-7146-9(7))* BiblioBazaar.

Jack, Zachary M., ed. Homer Croy: Corn Country. 2010. (ENG.). 264p. pap. 24.50 *(978-1-888160-74-1(8)*, Tall Corn Bks.) Ice Cube Pr.

Jackson, H. Joaquin. One Ranger Limited Edition. 2009. (ENG., Illus.). 253p. 150.00 *(978-0-292-72112-8(9))* Univ. of Texas Pr.

Jackson, Lawrence. Ralph Ellison: Emergence of Genius. 2007. (ENG.). 520p. pap. 24.95 *(978-0-8203-2993-2(2))* Univ. of Georgia Pr.

Jacobs, Alan. The Narnian: The Life & Imagination of C. S. Lewis. 2006. (ENG., Illus.). 368p. per. 14.95 *(978-0-06-087269-4(1)*, Harper San Francisco) HarperCollins Pubs.

Jagoe, Armiger. Southern Boy: Growing up on the MIssissippi Gulf Coast in The 1920-30s. 2009. 180p. pap. 16.95 *(978-1-4401-4454-7(0))* iUniverse, Inc.

Jahanbegloo, Ramin & Kakar, Sudhir. India Analysed: Sudhir Kakar in Conversation with Ramin Jahanbegloo. 2009. (ENG.). 128p. 29.95 *(978-0-19-569893-0(2))* Oxford Univ. Pr., Inc.

James Brunner Publisher. Thoreau & Children. 2010. pap. 20.00 *(978-0-9749689-1-9(9))* Brunner, James.

James, E. Mary Phillip. James Fenimore Cooper. 2006. 392p. per. *(978-1-4067-2844-6(6)*, Hesperides Pr.) Read Bks.

James, Eloisa. Paris in Love: A Memoir. 2012. (ENG., Illus.). 272p. 26.00 ***(978-1-4000-6956-9(4)***, Random House) Random House Publishing Group.

James, Henry. Hawthorne. 2011. (Cambridge Library Collection - English Men of Letters Ser.). (ENG.). 198p. pap. 19.99 ***(978-1-108-03462-3(4))*** Cambridge Univ. Pr.

James, Henry. A Small Boy & Others. 2008. 248p. pap. *(978-1-4099-5455-2(2))* Dodo Pr.

—A Small Boy & Others. 424p. 2008. 51.95 *(978-1-4365-3962-3(5))* 2007. (ENG.). per. 36.95 *(978-0-548-69227-1(0))* Kessinger Publishing, LLC.

—A Small Boy & Others. 2007. (ENG.). 424p. per. *(978-1-4067-7027-8(2))* Read Bks.

Jameson, W. C., ed. Hot Coffee & Cold Truth: Living & Writing the West. 2006. (ENG., Illus.). 218p. pap. 14.95 *(978-0-8263-4061-0(X))* Univ. of New Mexico Pr.

Japp, Alexander H. Robert Louis Stevenson: A Record, an Estimate & a Memorial. 2007. (Illus.). 172p. per. *(978-1-4065-2706-3(8))* Dodo Pr.

Jarrett-Macauley, Delia. The Life of una Marson, 1905-1965. 2010. (ENG., Illus.). 256p. pap. 24.95 *(978-0-7190-8256-6(0))* Manchester Univ. Pr. GBR. Dist: Macmillan.

Jay, Harriett. Robert Buchanan Some Account of His Life. 2006. pap. 26.95 *(978-1-4286-5926-1(9))* Kessinger Publishing, LLC.

Jean Paul. Hesperus; or, Forty-Five Dog-Post-Days / a Biography from the German of Jean Paul Friedrich Richter; Tr by Charles T Brooks. 2006. (ENG.). 532p. per. 29.99 *(978-1-4255-5952-6(2))*; 488p. per. 29.99 *(978-1-4255-5486-6(5))* MPublishing.

Jeffares, Norman A. W. B. Yeats. 2010. 498p. pap. 45.00 *(978-0-415-56893-7(5))* Routledge.

Jefferies, Richard. The Story of My Heart: An Autobiography. 2007. (ENG.). 86p. pap. 16.99 *(978-1-4346-4403-9(0))* BiblioBazaar.

Jefferies, Zay. Paul Dyer Merica, 1889-1957: A Biographical Memoir. 2011. 20p. 35.95 ***(978-1-258-03194-7(9))*** Literary Licensing, LLC.

Jeffers, Thomas L. Norman Podhoretz: A Biography. 2010. (Illus.). 408p. 35.00 *(978-0-521-19814-1(3))* Cambridge Univ. Pr.

Jelen, Sheila E. Intimations of Difference: Dvora Baron in the Modern Hebrew Renaissance. 2007. (Judaic Traditions in Literature, Music & Art Ser.). (Illus.). 240p. 24.95 *(978-0-8156-3130-9(8))* Syracuse Univ. Pr.

Jenkins, Ellen J. Eighteenth-Century British Historians. 2007. (Dictionary of Literary Biography Ser.). (ENG., Illus.). 512p. 315.00 *(978-0-7876-8154-8(7))* Cengage Gale.

JENKINS, Phil. Without Prejudice. 2009. 166p. pap. 21.50 *(978-1-4092-8674-5(6))* Lulu Enterprises Inc.

Jennings, Luke. Blood Knots. 2010. (Illus.). 320p. *(978-1-84887-132-8(5))* Down The Shore Publishing.

Jensen, Carsten Selch, et al. Crusading & Chronicle Writing in the Medieval Baltic Frontier: A Companion to the Chronicle of Henry of Livonia. 2011. (Illus.). 522p. 134.95 ***(978-0-7546-6627-1(1))*** Ashgate Publishing Co.

Jerome, Jerome K. Diary of a Pilgrimage. 2007. (ENG.). 148p. 25.96 *(978-1-4218-3874-8(5)*, 1st World Library - Literary Society) 1st World Publishing, Inc.

—Diary of a Pilgrimage. 2009. 136p. pap. 7.99 *(978-1-60450-631-0(8)*, Serenity Pubs.) Arc Manor.

—Diary of a Pilgrimage. 2008. 116p. 24.99 *(978-0-554-21478-8(4))* 2008. 116p. 21.99 *(978-0-554-30781-7(2))* 2006. pap. 13.99 *(978-1-4264-0219-7(8))* 2006. (ENG.). 118p. pap. 18.99 *(978-1-4264-0090-2(X))* BiblioBazaar.

—Diary of a Pilgrimage. 2007. (ENG.). 116p. per. *(978-1-4065-2743-8(2))* Dodo Pr.

—Diary of a Pilgrimage. 2010. (Illus.). 76p. pap. 20.00 *(978-1-153-60055-2(2))* General Bks. LLC.

Jin, Ba. The Autobiography of Ba Jin. 2008. 87p. pap. 16.95 *(978-0-88093-869-3(2))* Univ. of Indianapolis Pr.

Jodidio, Philip. Richard Meier. Jodidio, Philip, ed. 2008. (FRE, GER & ENG., Illus.). 528p. 150.00 *(978-3-8228-3683-5(4))* TASCHEN DEU. Dist: Ingram Pub. Services.

Jodorowsky, Alejandro. The Spiritual Journey of Alejandro Jodorowsky: The Creator of El Topo. 2008. (ENG.). 1p. pap. 21.95 *(978-1-59477-173-6(1)*, Park Street Pr.) Inner Traditions International, Ltd.

Johanson, Paula. Will Hobbs. 2009. (Library of Author Biographies Ser.). 112p. (gr. 5-8). 63.90 *(978-1-60853-560-6(6)*, Rosen Central) Rosen Publishing Group, Inc., The.

John, Angela V. Evelyn Sharp: Rebel Woman, 1869-1955. 2009. (ENG., Illus.). 304p. 95.00 *(978-0-7190-8014-2(2))*; mass mkt. 33.00 *(978-0-7190-8015-9(0))* Manchester Univ. Pr. GBR. Dist: Macmillan.

John Bunyan. Grace Abounding to the Chief of Sinners. 2007. (ENG.). 136p. pap. 18.99 *(978-1-4346-3844-1(8))*; 150p. pap. 19.99 *(978-1-4346-3845-8(6))* BiblioBazaar.

Johnson, David. What Makes Me Happy Is Family & Good Friends, 1 vol. 2009. 64p. pap. 16.95 *(978-1-60813-395-6(8))* PublishAmerica, Inc.

Johnson, David R. Conrad Richter. 2008. pap. 24.95 *(978-0-271-02788-3(6))* Pennsylvania State Univ. Pr.

Johnson, Don Hanlon. Everyday Hopes, Utopian Dreams: Reflections on American Ideals. 2006. (ENG.). 176p. pap. 14.95 *(978-1-55643-599-7(1))* North Atlantic Bks.

Johnson, Gerald. I Just Want to Tell You the Truth. 2010. 76p. pap. 15.00 *(978-1-4520-5442-1(8))* AuthorHouse.

Johnson, Joyce. The Voice Is All: The Lonely Victory of Jack Kerouac. 2012. (ENG.). 512p. 32.95 ***(978-0-670-02510-7(0)***, Viking Adult) Penguin Group (USA) Inc.

Johnson, Kenny. The Last Hustle. 2011. 296p. pap. ***(978-0-9566432-8-5(0))*** Non-Duality Bks.

Johnson, Samuel. A Journey to the Western Isles of Scotland. 2009. 146p. pap. 5.99 *(978-1-60450-370-8(X))* Arc Manor.

Johnson, Steve & Ruhl. Slender Threads. pap. 15.00 *(978-0-06-251507-0(1))* HarperCollins Pubs.

Jones, B. Lorraine. Intertwining Moments. 2009. 128p. pap. 10.99 *(978-1-4389-9744-5(2))* AuthorHouse.

Jones, Brett. Ghosts of a Dreamer. 2011. 66p. pap. 19.95 ***(978-1-4512-7708-1(3))*** PublishAmerica, Inc.

Jones, Brian Jay. Washington Irving: The Definitive New Biography of One of America's Greatest Writers. 2011. (ENG., Illus.). 480p. pap. 17.95 *(978-1-61145-354-6(2)*, 611354, Arcade Publishing) Skyhorse Publishing Co., Inc.

Jones, Diana Wynne. Reflections. 2012. (ENG.). 272p. (gr. 8). 24.99 ***(978-0-06-221989-3(8)***, Greenwillow Bks.) HarperCollins Pubs.

Jones, Henry Festing. Samuel Butler: A Sketch. 2007. 56p. per. *(978-1-4065-3542-6(7))* Dodo Pr.

Jones, Kaylie. Lies My Mother Never Told Me: A Memoir. 2009. 352p. 25.99 *(978-0-06-177870-4(2)*, Morrow, William & Co.); 560p. pap. 25.99 *(978-0-06-188371-2(9)*, HarperLuxe) HarperCollins Pubs.

Jones, Teddy & Muth, Marcia. Left Early, Arrived Late: Scenes from the Life of Marcia Muth, Memory Painter. 2008. 160p. pap. 19.95 *(978-0-86534-665-9(8))* Sunstone Pr.

Jong, Erica. Fear of Fifty: A Midlife Memoir. 2006. (ENG.). 352p. (gr. 12-18). 14.95 *(978-1-58542-524-2(9)*, Tarcher) Penguin Group (USA) Inc.

—Seducing the Demon: Writing for My Life. 2007. (ENG., Illus.). 304p. (gr. 12-18). 14.95 *(978-1-58542-514-3(1)*, Tarcher) Penguin Group (USA) Inc.

Joseph, Diana. I'M Sorry You Feel That Way: The Astonishing but True Story of a Daughter, Sister, Slut, Wife, Mother, & Friend to Man & Dog. 2010. (ENG.). 224p. (gr. 12-18). 15.00 *(978-0-425-23221-7(2)*, Berkley Trade) Penguin Group (USA) Inc.

Joshi, S. T. I Am Providence: The Life & Times of H. P. Lovecraft, 2 vols. 2010. 100.00 *(978-0-9824296-7-9(3))* Hippocampus Pr.

Judd, Denis. Alison Uttley: Spinner of Tales - The Authorised Biography of the Creator of Little Grey Rabbit. 3rd ed. 2010. (ENG., Illus.). 308p. 24.95 *(978-0-7190-8456-0(3))* Manchester Univ. Pr. GBR. Dist: Macmillan.

Judd, Denis. The Private Diaries of Alison Uttley: Author of Little Grey Rabbit, Foreword by Ronald Blythe. 2011. (Illus.). 336p. pap. 29.95 ***(978-1-84468-128-0(9))*** Pen & Sword Bks. Ltd. GBR. Dist: Casemate Pubs. & Bk. Distributors, LLC.

Judt, Tony. The Memory Chalet. 2011. (ENG., Illus.). 240p. (gr. 12). 15.00 *(978-0-14-311997-5(4)*, Penguin (Non-Classics)) Penguin Group (USA) Inc.

Juers, Evelyn. House of Exile: The Lives & Times of Heinrich Mann & Nelly Kroeger-Mann, 1 vol. (ENG., Illus.). 400p. 2012. pap. 18.00 ***(978-0-374-53341-0(5))*** 2011. 30.00 *(978-0-374-17316-6(8))* Farrar, Straus & Giroux.

Juliet, Charles. Conversations with Samuel Beckett & Bram van Velde. Nesme, Axel & Tucker, Janey, trs. from FRE. 2009. (French Literature Ser.). (ENG.). 192p. pap. 13.95 *(978-1-56478-531-2(9)*, 478531) Dalkey Archive Pr.

Julsen, Sue. Bitter Memories: A Memoir of Heartache & Survival. 2010. 317p. pap. 18.95 *(978-1-4327-5048-0(8))* Outskirts Pr., Inc.

Jung, Sandro. David Mallet, Anglo-Scot: Poetry, Patronage, & Politics, in the Age of Union. 2008. (Illus.). 216p. 48.50 *(978-0-87413-005-8(0))* Univ. of Delaware Pr.

Jun'ichiro, Tanizaki. Memoir of Forgetting the Capital. 2011. (ENG.). (gr. 17). 50.00 *(978-4-8419-0547-2(2))* Columbia Univ. Pr.

Kaag, John. Idealism, Pragmatism, & Feminism: The Philosophy of Ella Lyman Cabot. 2011. (ENG.). 242p. 70.00 ***(978-0-7391-6780-9(4))*** Lexington Bks.

Kaag, John J. Idealism, Pragmatism, & Feminism: The Philosophy of Ella Lyman Cabot. 2011. ***(978-0-7391-6781-6(2))*** Lexington Bks.

Kach A Fanas, Nick. Spirit of the Daisy. 2009. 268p. pap. 18.49 *(978-1-4389-8610-4(6))* AuthorHouse.

Kaczor, Christopher, ed. O Rare Ralph Mcinerny: Stories & Reflections on a Legendary Notre Dame Professor. 2011. (ENG., Illus.). 155p. pap. 18.00 *(978-1-58731-585-5(8))* St. Augustine's Pr., Inc.

Kaczynski, Richard. Aleister Crowley. Wasserman, James, ed. 2009. (ENG.). 1p. pap. 12.95 *(978-1-57863-456-9(3)*, Weiser Bks.) Red Wheel/Weiser.

—Perdurabo: The Life of Aleister Crowley. rev. exp. ed. 2010. (ENG., Illus.). 720p. 29.95 *(978-1-55643-899-8(0))* North Atlantic Bks.

Kafka, Franz. Brief an den Vater: Fassung der Handschrift. (GER.). pap. 14.95 *(978-3-596-14674-1(7))* Fischer Taschenbuch Verlag DEU. Dist: Distribooks, Inc.

—Dearest Father. Stokes, Hannah & Stokes, Richard, trs. from GER. 2009. (Oneworld Modern Classics Ser.). (ENG.). 128p. pap. 14.95 *(978-1-84749-025-4(5))* Alma Classics GBR. Dist: Independent Pubs. Group.

Kafka, Franz. Kafka Selected Letters. Winston, Richard & Winston, Clara, trs. 2012. (Oneworld Classics Ser.). (ENG.). 528p. 19.95 ***(978-1-84749-194-7(4))*** Alma Classics GBR. Dist: Independent Pubs. Group.

Kahan, Gerald. George Alexander Stevens & the Lecture on Heads. 2008. (ENG.). 232p. pap. 22.95 *(978-0-8203-3264-2(X))* Univ. of Georgia Pr.

Kaiserová, Kristina & Röhrborn, Gert, eds. Present Tensions: European Writers on Overcoming Dictatorships. 2008. (ENG & MUL.). 316p. 44.95 *(978-963-9776-21-0(1))* Central European Univ. Pr.

Kamen, Paula. Finding Iris: Friendship, Ambition, & an Extraordinary Mind. 2007. (ENG.). 304p. 26.00 *(978-0-306-81466-2(8))* Da Capo Pr., Inc.

Kang, Zhengguo. Confessions: An Innocent Life in Communist China. Wilf, Susan, tr. from CHI. 2008. (ENG., Illus.). 480p. pap. 15.95 *(978-0-393-33200-1(4)*, 33200) Norton, W. W. & Co., Inc.

Kaniuk, Yoram. Life on Sandpaper. Berris, Anthony, tr. from HEB. 2011. (Hebrew Literature Ser.). (ENG.). 400p. pap. 15.95 *(978-1-56478-613-5(7)*, 478613) Dalkey Archive Pr.

Kannan, R. Anna: The Life & Times of C.N. Annadurai. 2010. (Illus.). xi, 423p. *(978-0-670-08328-2(3)*, Library of Congress — New Delhi Overseas Office) Penguin Group India.

Kantner, Seth. Shopping for Porcupine: A Life in Arctic Alaska. (ENG., Illus.). 256p. 2009. pap. 19.95 *(978-1-57131-311-9(7))* 2008. 28.00 *(978-1-57131-301-0(X))* Milkweed Editions.

Kapitan, Rudolph F. Seasons of My Life. 314p. pap. 15.99 *(978-0-9701515-2-0(7))* Rumsclad Publishing.

Kari, Martin. Lifetime Journeys: Volume One. 2011. 316p. 21.99 ***(978-1-61667-173-0(4))*** Raider Publishing International.

Karinthy, Frigyes. A Journey Round My Skull. Barker, Vernon Duckworth, tr. from HUN. 2008. (New York Review Books Classics). (ENG.). 312p. pap. 17.95 *(978-1-59017-258-2(2)*, NYRB Classics) New York Review of Bks., Inc., The.

Kaser, James. The Chicago of Fiction: A Resource Guide. 2011. (ENG.). 672p. 100.00 *(978-0-8108-7724-5(4))* Scarecrow Pr., Inc.

Kasties, Bert. Walter Hasenclever: Eine Biographie der deutschen Moderne. (Studien und Texte zur Sozialgeschichte der Literatur Ser.). (GER.). 420p. 210.00 ***(978-3-11-186667-3(X))*** De Gruyter, Walter Inc.

Kate Sanborn. Memories & Anecdotes. l.t. ed. 2006. 178p. pap. 21.99 *(978-1-4264-8519-0(0))* BiblioBazaar.

Katz, Steve. Time's Wallet. 2010. 184p. pap. 15.95 *(978-1-933996-22-6(6))* Counterpath Pr.

Kauffmann, Stanley. Albums of a Life: A Memoir. 2007. 350p. 30.00 *(978-1-931357-53-1(6))*; per. 18.95 *(978-1-931357-48-7(X))* Sheep Meadow Pr., The.

Kay, Jackie. Red Dust Road: An Autobiographical Journey. 2011. (ENG.). 304p. 24.00 *(978-1-935633-34-1(1)*, 935634) Atlas & Co.

Kay, Peter. Saturday Night Peter: Memoirs of a Stand-Up Comedian. 2009. (ENG., Illus.). 258p. 36.95 ***(978-1-84605-363-4(3))*** Random Hse. GBR. Dist: Independent Pubs. Group.

Keane, Angela. Revolutionary Women Writers: Charlotte Smith & Helen M. Williams. 2011. (Writers & Their Work Ser.). (ENG.). 128p. (C). 80.00 *(978-0-7463-1096-0(X))* Northcote Hse. Publishers, Ltd. GBR. Dist: Brown, David Bk. Co., The.

—Revolutionary Women Writers: Charlotte Smith & Helen Maria Williams. 2012. (Writers & Their Work Ser.). (ENG.). 128p. (C). pap. 26.00 *(978-0-7463-0971-1(6))* Northcote Hse. Publishers, Ltd. GBR. Dist: Brown, David Bk. Co., The.

Kearns, Michael. Lasting Connections: Two Plays That Survived the Plague. 2009. 128p. pap. 18.69 *(978-0-325-02159-1(7)*, E02159) Heinemann.

Keates, Jonathan. Stendhal. Date not set. pap. 10.99 *(978-0-7493-2475-9(9))* Heinemann.

Keeler, Greg. Trash Fish: A Life. 2008. (ENG.). 176p. pap. 14.95 *(978-1-58243-402-5(6)*, Counterpoint Pr.) Basic Bks. GBR. Dist: Perseus-PGW.

Keene, Donald. So Lovely a Country Will Never Perish: Wartime Diaries of Japanese Writers. 2010. (Asia Perspectives: History, Society, & Culture Ser.). (ENG.). 192p. (gr. 17). 24.95 *(978-0-231-15146-7(2))* Columbia Univ. Pr.

Keller, Christoph. The Best Dancer. Gallup, Alison, tr. from GER. 2009.Tr. of beste Tanzer. (ENG., Illus.). 303p. pap. 16.95 *(978-1-932010-22-0(X))* Ooligan Pr.

Keller, Elizabeth Leavitt. Walt Whitman in Mickle Street. 2011. 246p. pap. 29.45 ***(978-1-4460-7409-1(9))*** Aslan Pr.

Kellman, Steven G., ed. Magill's Survey of American Literature Vol. 2: Sandra Cisneros — John Guare, 6 vols. rev. ed. 2006. (Illus.). 2600p. lib. bdg. 83.00 *(978-1-58765-287-5(0))* Salem Pr., Inc.

—Magill's Survey of American Literature Vol. 3: H. D. — Nella Larsen, 6 vols. rev. ed. 2006. (Illus.). 2600p. lib. bdg. 83.00 *(978-1-58765-288-2(9))* Salem Pr., Inc.

—Magill's Survey of American Literature Vol. 4: Stephen Leacock — Flannery O'Connor, 6 vols. rev. ed. 2006. (Illus.). 2600p. lib. bdg. 83.00 *(978-1-58765-289-9(7))* Salem Pr., Inc.

—Magill's Survey of American Literature Vol. 5: Clifford Odets — Gertrude Stein, 6 vols. rev. ed. 2006. (Illus.). 2600p. lib. bdg. 83.00 *(978-1-58765-290-5(0))* Salem Pr., Inc.

—Magill's Survey of American Literature, Revised Edition, Volume 1 Vol. 1: Edward Abbey — Kate Chopin, 6 vols. rev. ed. 2006. (Illus.). 2600p. lib. bdg. 83.00 *(978-1-58765-286-8(2))* Salem Pr., Inc.

—Magill's Survey of American Literature, Volume 6: Steinbeck-Zindel, 6 vols. rev. ed. 2006. (Magill's Survey of American Literature Ser.). (Illus.). 500p. 83.00 *(978-1-58765-291-2(9))* Salem Pr., Inc.

Kellman, Steven G. & Magill, Frank N. Magill's Survey of World Literature. 2009. 84.00 *(978-1-58765-435-0(0))*; 84.00 *(978-1-58765-434-3(2))*; 83.00 *(978-1-58765-433-6(4))*; 83.00 *(978-1-58765-432-9(6))*; 83.00 *(978-1-58765-436-7(9))*; 83.00 *(978-1-58765-437-4(7))*; 3000p. 499.00 *(978-1-58765-431-2(8))* Salem Pr., Inc.

Kellogg, Thelma Louise. The Life & Works of John Davis, 1774-1853. Ellis, H. M., ed. 2011. 140p. 40.95 ***(978-1-258-04931-7(7))*** Literary Licensing, LLC.

Kelly, Frank King. Kissing Joy as it Flies - Living in Eternity's Sunrise. 2009. 574p. 45.95 *(978-0-615-25915-4(4))*; (ENG.). 579p. pap. 29.95 *(978-0-615-26002-0(0))* Kelly, Frank K.

Kelly, Ian. Casanova: Actor, Lover, Priest, Spy. (ENG.). 416p. (gr. 12). 2011. 15.95 (978-1-58542-844-1(2)) 2008. 28.95 (978-1-58542-658-4(X)) Penguin Group (USA) Inc. (Tarcher).

Kelly, Nigel. Quentin Crisp: The Profession of Being. A Biography. 2011. (ENG., Illus.). 227p. pap. 45.00 (978-0-7864-6475-3(5)) McFarland & Co., Inc. Pubs.

Kelton, Elmer. Sandhills Boy: The Winding Trail of a Texas Writer. 2010. (ENG., Illus.). 304p. 7.99 (978-0-7653-5428-0(4), Forge Bks.) Doherty, Tom Assocs., LLC.

Kenan, Randall. The Fire This Time. 2007. (ENG.). 149p. 20.00 (978-1-933633-24-4(7)) Melville Hse. Publishing.

Kendall, Elizabeth. Autobiography of a Wardrobe. 2009. (ENG.). 240p. pap. 15.00 (978-0-307-38609-0(0), Anchor) Knopf Doubleday Publishing Group.

Kendon, Frank. The Small Years. 2010. (ENG.). 232p. pap. 22.99 (978-0-521-15547-2(9)) Cambridge Univ. Pr.

Keneally, Thomas. Searching for Schindler. 2008. (ENG., Illus.). 288p. 25.00 (978-0-385-52617-3(2), Talese, Nan A.) Knopf Doubleday Publishing Group.

Kennaway, Guy. Sunbathing Naked & Other Miracle Cures. 2008. (ENG.). 256p. pap. (978-1-84767-045-8(8)) Canongate Bks.

Kennedy, Des. The Way of a Gardener: A Life's Journey, 1 vol. 2010. (ENG.). 272p. pap. 17.95 (978-1-55365-417-9(X), Greystone Bks.) D&M Pubs. Inc. CAN. Dist: Perseus-PGW.

Kennedy, John P. Memoirs of the Life of William Wirt V1 A. 2006. pap. 33.95 (978-1-4286-4976-7(X)) Kessinger Publishing, LLC.

—Memoirs of the Life of William Wirt V2 A. 2006. pap. 34.95 (978-1-4286-4977-4(8)) Kessinger Publishing, LLC.

Kenneth G. Redden. My Song: Comatose yet Aware. 2009. 112p. pap. 10.99 (978-1-4389-6188-0(X)) AuthorHouse.

Kenney, Gerard I. Lake of the Old Uncles. 2008. (ENG., Illus.). 200p. pap. 22.99 (978-1-55002-802-7(2), Dundurn Pr.) Dundurn CAN. Dist: Ingram Pub. Services.

Kent, Adaline. The Autobiography from the Notebooks & Sculpture of Adaline Kent. 2011. 86p. 38.95 (978-1-258-09523-9(8)) Literary Licensing, LLC.

Kenyon, Frederic G. The Letters of Elizabeth Barrett Browning. 2009. 496p. 35.99 (978-1-116-89319-9(3)) 2009. 496p. 42.99 (978-1-116-89318-2(5)) 2009. 496p. pap. 38.75 (978-1-116-89320-5(7)) 2009. 496p. pap. 37.75 (978-1-116-89321-2(5)) 2008. 484p. 33.99 (978-0-554-24473-0(X)) 2008. 484p. 31.99 (978-0-554-33776-0(2)) BiblioBazaar.

—The Letters of Elizabeth Barrett Browning. 2010. 266p. pap. (978-1-152-99765-3(3)); 258p. pap. (978-1-152-99767-7(X)) Books LLC.

Ker, Ian. G. K. Chesterton: A Biography. 2012. (ENG., Illus.). 784p. pap. 35.00 (978-0-19-965576-2(6)) Oxford Univ. Pr., Inc.

Kern, Alice. Tapestry of Hope. (Illus.). 165p. (Orig.). (C). reprint ed. pap. 13.00 (978-0-9644994-0-9(1)) Kern, Alice L.

Kertscher, Hans-Joachim, ed. G. A. Bürger und J. W. L. Gleim. (Hallesche Beiträge zur Europäischen Aufklärung Ser.). (GER.). XXVI, 264p. 210.00 (978-3-11-187587-3(3)) De Gruyter, Walter Inc.

Kessinger, Judy A. Do Your Best, Be Your Best. 2011. 40p. pap. 16.95 (978-1-4626-0815-7(9)) PublishAmerica, Inc.

Kessler, Deirdre. Green Gables: Lucy Maud Montgomery's Favourite Places. 2nd rev. ed. 2010. (ENG., Illus.). 72p. pap. 16.95 (978-0-88780-909-5(X)) Formac Publishing Co., Ltd. CAN. Dist: Casemate Pubs. & Bk. Distributors, LLC.

Ketchie, Cotton. A Country Boy's Education. 2007. 345p. pap. 17.95 (978-0-7414-4338-0(4)) Infinity Publishing.

Khan, Farheen. Behind the Veil: A Hijabi's Journey to Happiness. 2010. (ENG.). 153p. pap. 15.95 (978-1-897404-23-2(9)) Burman Books, Inc. CAN. Dist: Innovative Logistics.

Khazin, Mikhail. [Evreiskoe Schaste: Zapisi Dlia Druzei. 2007. (RUS.). (978-1-55779-164-1(3)) Hermitage Pubs.

Khorana, Meena G. & Greenwood. The Life & Works of Ruskin Bond. 2009. 188p. pap. 45.99 (978-1-60752-075-7(3)) Information Age Publishing, Inc.

Kidd, Sue Monk & Taylor, Ann Kidd. Traveling with Pomegranates: A Mother & Daughter Journey to the Sacred Places of Greece, Turkey, & France. 2010. (ENG.). 304p. (gr. 12). 15.00 (978-0-14-311797-1(1), Penguin (Non-Classics)) Penguin Group (USA) Inc.

—Traveling with Pomegranates: A Mother-Daughter Story. l.t. ed. 2010. (ENG.). 420p. pap. 17.99 (978-1-59413-419-7(7), Large Print Pr.) 2009. 403p. 32.95 (978-1-4104-1937-8(1)) Thorndike Pr.

Kiely, Kevin. Francis Stuart: Artist & Outcast. 2008. (ENG., Illus.). 376p. pap. 42.95 (978-1-905785-25-4(9)) Liffey Pr., The IRL. Dist: Dufour Editions, Inc.

Killam, Douglas & Kerfoot, Alicia L. Student Encyclopedia of African Literature, 1 vol. 2007. 368p. 85.00 (978-0-313-33580-8(X), GR3580, Greenwood Pr.) Greenwood Publishing Group, Inc.

Kim, Richard E. Lost Names: Scenes from a Korean Boyhood. 2nd anniv. ed. 2011. (ENG.). 224p. pap. 18.95 (978-0-520-26812-8(1)) Univ. of California Pr.

King, Bruce. Robert Graves: A Biography. 2009. (ENG.). 200p. 26.95 (978-1-905791-94-1(1)) Haus Publishing GBR. Dist: Consortium Bk. Sales & Distribution.

King, Don W. Hunting the Unicorn: A Critical Biography of Ruth Pitter. 2008. (Illus.). 342p. 55.00 (978-0-87338-947-1(6)) Kent State Univ. Pr.

King, Francis & Crowley, Aleister. Megatherion: The Magickal World of Aleister Crowley. 2012. (ENG., Illus.). 200p. pap. 19.95 (978-1-84068-180-2(2)) Creation Bks. GBR. Dist: SCB Distributors.

King, Roger. Love & Fatigue in America. 2012. (ENG.). 254p. 26.95 (978-0-299-28720-7(3)) Univ. of Wisconsin Pr.

King, Stephen. On Writing: A Memoir of the Craft. 10th anniv. ed. 2010. (ENG.). 288p. 27.00 (978-1-4391-9363-1(0)); pap. 16.00 (978-1-4391-5681-0(6)) Scribner. (Scribner).

—Stephen King Goes to the Movies. 2009. (ENG.). 640p. mass mkt. 7.99 (978-1-4165-9236-5(9)) Pocket Books.

King, White Goldfish. Final Series Book of World Famous Television Executive Billionaire Star Celebrity. 2008. 648p. 34.99 (978-1-4257-7232-1(3)); pap. 23.99 (978-1-4257-7226-0(9)) Xlibris Corp.

Kingsolver, Barbara & Kingsolver, Camille. Animal, Vegetable, Miracle: A Year of Food Life. l.t. ed. 2007. pap. 26.95 (978-0-06-128529-5(3), HarperLuxe) HarperCollins Pubs.

Kingsolver, Barbara, et al. Animal, Vegetable, Miracle: A Year of Food Life. (P. S. Ser.). 2008. (ENG., Illus.). 400p. pap. 15.99 (978-0-06-085256-6(9), HarperPerennial) 2007. 384p. 26.95 (978-0-06-085255-9(0)) HarperCollins Pubs.

Kingston, Maxine Hong. I Love a Broad Margin to My Life. (Vintage International Ser.). (ENG.). 240p. 2012. pap. 15.00 (978-0-307-45459-1(2), Vintage) 2011. 24.95 (978-0-307-27019-1(X), Knopf) Knopf Doubleday Publishing Group.

Kinkead-Weekes, Mark. D. H. Lawrence: Triumph to Exile 1912-1922: Volume 2: The Cambridge Biography of D. H. Lawrence. 2011. (ENG.). 1022p. pap. 61.99 (978-1-107-40300-0(6)) Cambridge Univ. Pr.

Kipling, Rudyard. The Bridge-Builders. 2008. 48p. pap. 9.99 (978-1-59547-611-1(3)) NuVision Pubns., LLC.

—The Bridge-Builders. 2009. (ENG.). 48p. pap. 6.45 (978-1-4385-2373-6(4), Book Jungle) Standard Pubns., Inc.

Kirksey, Joyce. My Trials Came to Make Me Strong: The Untold Story of Joyce Kirksey. 2007. 9.00 (978-0-8059-8712-6(6)) Dorrance Publishing Co., Inc.

Kirn, Walter. Lost in the Meritocracy: The Undereducation of an Overachiever. 2010. (ENG.). 224p. pap. 14.95 (978-0-307-27945-3(6), Anchor) Knopf Doubleday Publishing Group.

Kishkan, Theresa. Mnemonic: A Book of Trees. 2011. (ENG.). 248p. pap. 19.95 (978-0-86492-651-7(0)) Goose Lane Editions CAN. Dist: Univ. of Toronto Pr.

Kitchen, Judith. Half in Shade: Family, Photography, & Fate. 2012. (ENG.). 214p. pap. 16.00 (978-1-56689-296-4(1)) Coffee Hse. Pr.

Klam, Julie. Please Excuse My Daughter. 2009. (ENG.). 272p. (gr. 12-18). 15.00 (978-1-59448-357-8(4), Riverhead Trade (Paperbacks)) Penguin Group (USA) Inc.

Klein, Nancy I. A Life of Joy: The Sidney Klein Story. 2010. 148p. pap. 11.99 (978-1-4520-2974-0(1)) AuthorHouse.

Klein, Stephanie. Moose: A Memoir. 2009. (Illus.). 320p. pap. 14.99 (978-0-06-167286-6(6), Harper Paperbacks) HarperCollins Pubs.

Klimaszewski, Melisa. Wilkie Collins. 2011. (Brief Lives Ser.). (ENG.). 152p. pap. 15.95 (978-1-84391-915-5(X)) Hesperus Pr. GBR. Dist: Independent Pubs. Group.

Knechtges, David R. & Chang, Taiping, eds. Ancient & Early Medieval Chinese Literature: A Reference Guide. 2010. (Handbook of Oriental Studies. Section 4 China Ser.). 792p. (978-90-04-19127-3(5)) BRILL.

Knight, George R. A.T. Jones: Point Man on Adventism's Charismatic Frontier. 2011. (978-0-8280-2562-1(2)) Review & Herald Publishing Assn.

Knight, Jesse F. & Darley, Stephen. The Last of the Great Swashbucklers: Rafael Sabatini: A Bio-Bibliography. 2010. 65.00 (978-1-58456-279-5(X)) Oak Knoll Pr.

Knight, Michael Muhammad. Impossible Man: Or, F. Scott Fitzgerald & the Rise of Islam. 2009. (ENG.). 272p. pap. 15.95 (978-1-59376-226-1(7), Soft Skull Pr.) Counterpoint LLC.

—Why I Am a Five Percenter. 2011. (ENG.). 304p. (gr. 12). 14.95 (978-1-58542-868-7(X), Tarcher) Penguin Group (USA) Inc.

Knight, William, ed. Journals of Dorothy Wordsworth V1. 2007. (ENG.). 272p. 42.95 (978-0-548-12179-5(6)) Kessinger Publishing, LLC.

—Journals of Dorothy Wordsworth V2. 2007. (ENG.). 304p. 43.95 (978-0-548-12178-8(8)) Kessinger Publishing, LLC.

Knopf, Sabine. Katharina Kippenberg: Herrin der Insel. 2010. (GER., Illus.). 184p. pap. (978-3-86729-051-7(2)) Heydick, Erika Sax-Verlag Beucha.

Knopp, Lisa. Interior Places. 2008. (ENG.). 299p. pap. 21.95 (978-0-8032-1143-8(0), Bison Bks.) Univ. of Nebraska Pr.

Knutsen, Chris & Steiker, Valerie. Brooklyn Was Mine. 2008. (ENG.). 240p. (gr. 12-18). 15.00 (978-1-59448-282-3(9), Riverhead Trade (Paperbacks)) Penguin Group (USA) Inc.

Koch, Karl H. Life's a Trampoline, Learn to Bounce. 2008. 389p. pap. 29.95 (978-1-60610-399-9(7)) PublishAmerica, Inc.

Koelb, Clayton. Kafka: A Guide for the Perplexed. 2010. (Guides for the Perplexed Ser.). (ENG.). 192p. 19.95 (978-0-8264-9580-8(X)); 90.00 (978-0-8264-9579-2(6)) Continuum International Publishing Group, Ltd. GBR. Dist: National Bk. Network.

Kohner, Frederick. Early Pleasures: Memoirs of a Sensual Youth. 2011. 200p. 23.95 (978-0-930773-96-0(9)) Black Heron Pr.

Kohnstamm, Thomas. Do Travel Writers Go to Hell? A Swashbuckling Tale of High Adventures, Questionable Ethics, & Professional Hedonism. 2008. (ENG., Illus.). 288p. pap. 13.95 (978-0-307-39465-1(4), Three Rivers Pr.) Crown Publishing Group.

Koizumi, Setsuko. Reminiscences of Lafcadio Hearn. 2009. 100p. pap. 18.75 (978-1-110-86319-8(5)) BiblioBazaar.

—Reminiscences of Lafcadio Hearn. Hisada, Paul Kiyoshi & Johnson, Frederick, trs. 2008. 98p. pap. 18.95 (978-1-4370-3839-2(5)) Kessinger Publishing, LLC.

Kolloen, Ingar Sletten. Knut Hamsun: Dreamer & Dissenter. Skuggevik, Erik & Dawkin, Deborah, trs. from NOR. 2009. (ENG., Illus.). 384p. 40.00 (978-0-300-12356-2(6)) Yale Univ. Pr.

Konrad, George. A Guest in My Own Country: A Hungarian Life. Heim, Michael Henry, ed. Tucker, Jim, tr. from HUN. 2007. (ENG.). 312p. pap. 17.95 (978-1-59051-139-8(5)) Other Pr., LLC.

Koranda, Margareta. So War Es Wirklich. 2011. 134p. pap. 14.90 (978-0-557-70262-6(3)) Lulu Enterprises Inc.

Kramer, Reinhold. Mordecai Richler: Leaving St. Urbain. 2008. (ENG., Illus.). 528p. (C). (978-0-7735-3355-4(9)) McGill-Queen's Univ. Pr.

—Mordecai Richler: Leaving St Urbain. 2010. (Art of Living Ser.). (ENG., Illus.). 498p. (C). pap. (978-0-7735-3742-2(2)) McGill-Queen's Univ. Pr.

Krasny, Michael. Off Mike: A Memoir of Talk Radio & Literary Life. 2007. (ENG., Illus.). 344p. 24.95 (978-0-8047-5671-6(6), Stanford General Bks.) Stanford Univ. Pr.

Krass, Peter. Ignorance, Confidence, & Filthy Rich Friends: The Business Adventures of Mark Twain, Chronic Speculator & Entrepreneur. 2007. (ENG., Illus.). 278p. 22.95 (978-0-471-93337-3(6), Wiley) Wiley, John & Sons, Inc.

Krause, Pat. Acts of Love: A Memoir. 2008. (ENG.). 256p. per. (978-1-55050-368-5(5)) Coteau Bks.

Kremer, Charles Edward. Memoirs of Charles Edward Kremer. 2011. 314p. 50.95 (978-1-258-09001-2(5)) Literary Licensing, LLC.

Krissdottir, Morine. Descents of Memory: The Life of John Cowper Powys. 2009. (ENG.). 464p. (gr. 12-18). pap. 16.95 (978-1-59020-265-4(1)) Overlook Pr., The.

Kühlmann, Wilhelm, et al. Killy Literaturlexikon 1. A - Blu: Autoren und Werke des deutschsprachigen Kulturraums, Band 1. 2nd ed. 2008. (GER.). XLIV, 605p. 277.00 (978-3-11-018962-9(3)) De Gruyter, Walter Inc.

Kumar, Lisa. Something about the Author. 2008. (Something about the Author Ser.). (ENG.). 384p. 202.00 (978-0-7876-9938-3(1)); 224p. 202.00 (978-0-7876-9937-6(3)); 368p. 202.00 (978-0-7876-9936-9(5)) Cengage Gale.

Kumar, Lisa, ed. Something about the Author. 2008. (Something about the Author Ser.). (ENG.). 368p. 202.00 (978-0-7876-8807-3(X)) Cengage Gale

—Something about the Author: Facts & Pictures about Authors & Illustrators of Books for Young People. 2007. (Something about the Author Ser.). (ENG., Illus.). 352p. 202.00 (978-0-7876-8799-1(5)); Vol. 173. 336p. 202.00 (978-0-7876-8797-7(9)) Cengage Gale.

Kunzel, Bonnie & Fichtelberg, Susan. Tamora Pierce, 1 vol. 2007. (Teen Reads: Student Companions to Young Adult Literature Ser.). 296p. 45.00 (978-0-313-33660-7(1), GR3660, Greenwood Pr.) Greenwood Publishing Group, Inc.

Kureishi, Hanif. My Ear at His Heart: Reading My Father. 2010. (ENG., Illus.). 208p. 24.00 (978-1-4165-7212-1(0), Scribner) Scribner.

Kuriyama, Constance Brown. Christopher Marlowe: A Renaissance Life. 2010. (Illus.). 280p. pap. 24.95 (978-0-8014-7688-4(7)) Cornell Univ. Pr.

Kuryluk, Ewa. Frascati: Apoteoza Topografii. 2009. (POL., Illus.). 338p. (978-83-08-04377-6(1)) Wydawnictwo Literackie.

Kyle, John Edward. Going Against the Grain. 2011. 292p. 29.99 (978-1-4568-8503-8(0)); pap. 19.99 (978-1-4568-8502-1(2)) Xlibris Corp.

La Blanc, Michael & Greve, Jennifer, eds. Authors & Artists for Young Adults, Vol. 73. 2007. (Authors & Artists for Young Adults Ser.). (ENG., Illus.). 224p. 168.00 (978-0-7876-7792-3(2)) Cengage Gale.

La Farge, Oliver, frwd. Raw Material: The Autobiographical Examination of an Artist's Journey into Maturity. 2009. 260p. pap. 24.95 (978-0-86534-673-4(9)) Sunstone Pr.

Labuschagne, Gerry. Impact & Change. 2010. (Illus.). 96p. pap. 11.49 (978-1-4490-9156-9(3)) AuthorHouse.

Lady, L. To Lisa with Love: Best Friends Forever. 2011. 56p. pap. 10.16 (978-1-4269-4495-6(0)) Trafford Publishing.

Lady, Teresa. Michael Talbot: Story of a Writer, 1 vol. 2009. 124p. pap. 19.95 (978-1-4489-9525-7(6)) PublishAmerica, Inc.

Laffont, Bompiani. Dictionnaire des Personnages Litteraires et Dramatiques de Tous les Tempes et de Tous les Pays. (FRE.). 83.95 (978-0-8288-9900-0(2), F12885) French & European Pubns., Inc.

Laguerre, Enrique A. Infiernos Privados. 195p. pap. 10.95 (978-1-56758-014-3(9)) Editorial Cultural, Inc.

Laird, Susan & Laird. Mary Wollstonecraft: Philosophical Mother of Coeducation. 2008. (Continuum Library of Educational Thought). (ENG.). 272p. 140.00 (978-0-8264-8414-7(X)) Continuum International Publishing Group, Ltd. GBR. Dist: National Bk. Network.

Lamb, Charles. The Works of Charles Lamb, with a Sketch of His Life & Final Memorials by Sir Thomas Noon Talfourd. 2006. 564p. per. 32.99 (978-1-4255-6182-6(9)); 620p. per. 34.99 (978-1-4255-6539-8(5)) MPublishing.

Lamb, Matt. Unforeseen Life, 1 vol. 2010. 108p. pap. 19.95 (978-1-4489-5500-8(9)) PublishAmerica, Inc.

Lamott, Anne. Grace (Eventually) Thoughts on Faith. 2008. (ENG.). 272p. (gr. 12-18). 14.00 (978-1-59448-287-8(X), Riverhead Trade (Paperbacks)) Penguin Group (USA) Inc.

—Grace (Eventually) Thoughts on Faith. l.t. ed. 2007. (Thorndike Core Ser.). 287p. 32.95 (978-0-7862-9622-4(4)) Thorndike Pr.

—Plan B: Further Thoughts on Faith. l.t. ed. 32.95 (978-0-7862-7814-5(5), Large Print Pr.) Thorndike Pr.

Lamott, Anne. Some Assembly Required: A Journal of My Son's First Son. l.t. ed. 2012. (ENG.). 33.99 (978-1-4104-4719-7(7)) Thorndike Pr.

Lamott, Anne & Lamott, Sam. Some Assembly Required: A Journal of My Son's First Son. 2012. (ENG.). 288p. (gr. 12). 26.95 (978-1-59448-841-2(X), Riverhead Bks. (Hardcover)) Penguin Group (USA) Inc.

Lancaster, Jen. My Fair Lazy: One Reality Television Addict's Attempt to Discover If Not Being a Dumb Ass Is the New Black, Or, a Culture-Up Manifesto. 2010. (ENG.). 384p. (gr. 12). 24.95 (978-0-451-22986-1(X), N A L Hardcover) Penguin Group (USA) Inc.

—My Fair Lazy: One Reality Television Addict's Attempt to Discover If Not Being a Dumb Ass Is the New Black; Or, a Culture-Up Manifesto. 2011. (ENG.). 400p. (gr. 12). 15.00 (978-0-451-23186-4(4), N A L Trade) Penguin Group (USA) Inc.

—Pretty in Plaid: A Life, a Witch, & a Wardrobe, Or, the Wonder Years Before the Condescending, Egomaniacal, Self-Centered Smart Ass Phase. 2010. (ENG.). 384p. (gr. 12). 15.00 (978-0-451-22853-6(7), N A L Trade) Penguin Group (USA) Inc.

Lanchester, John. Family Romance: A Love Story. 2008. (ENG., Illus.). 384p. (gr. 12-18). 16.00 (978-0-14-311295-2(3), Penguin (Non-Classics)) Penguin Group (USA) Inc.

Lane, Leeann. Rosamond Jacob, 1888-1960: Third Pesron Singular. 2011. (ENG., Illus.). 334p. pap. 52.95 (978-1-906359-54-6(7)) Univ. College Dublin Pr. IRL. Dist: Dufour Editions, Inc.

Lang, Andrew. The Life & Letters of John Gibson Lockhart. 2009. 448p. 27.99 (978-1-103-07761-8(9)); pap. 21.99 (978-1-103-07754-0(6)) BiblioBazaar.

Langdon, Roger & Langdon, Ellen. The Life of Roger Langdon: Told by Himself, with Additions by his Daughter. 2010. (Cambridge Library Collection - Physical Sciences Ser.). (ENG.). 110p. pap. 19.99 (978-1-108-02164-7(6)) Cambridge Univ. Pr.

Lankeit, William C. A Dozen Lives to Live. 2011. 174p. pap. 24.95 (978-1-4560-1661-6(X)) PublishAmerica, Inc.

Lansac, Philippe & London, Jack. Jack London's Grand North. 2007. (ENG., Illus.). 112p. pap. 19.95 (978-0-7627-4363-6(8)) Globe Pequot Pr., The.

Laor, Dan. Life of Agnon. 2009. (978-0-8419-1446-9(X)) Holmes & Meier Pubs., Inc.

Lappin, Elena. What Language Do You Dream In? A Memoir. 2012. (ENG., Illus.). 304p. 26.00 (978-0-374-28885-3(2)) Farrar, Straus & Giroux.

Larsen, Lyle. Stein & Hemingway: The Story of a Turbulent Friendship. 2011. (ENG., Illus.). 220p. pap. 45.00 (978-0-7864-6056-4(3)) McFarland & Co., Inc. Pubs.

Larson, Hanne. Nine Charles Street: Remembering the Power of the Lord. 2006. (Illus.). 51p. 14.99 (978-0-9754305-5-2(6), 2500) Praxis Pr., Inc.

LaRue, Monique. Between Books: The Writer's Time. 2010. (FRE & ENG.). 104p. 14.95 (978-0-86492-534-3(4)) Goose Lane Editions CAN. Dist: Univ. of Toronto Pr.

Lathrop, George Parsons. A Study of Hawthorne. 2008. 328p. 28.99 (978-0-554-32085-4(1)) 2008. 328p. 29.99 (978-0-554-22782-5(7)) 2007. (ENG.). 292p. pap. 21.99 (978-1-4264-3046-6(9)) 2006. 326p. pap. 24.99 (978-1-4264-3111-1(2)) BiblioBazaar.

—A Study of Hawthorne. 2007. (ENG.). 252p. per. (978-1-4065-3573-0(7)) Dodo Pr.

—A Study of Hawthorne. 2007. (ENG.). 200p. per. (978-1-4068-1737-9(6)) Echo Library.

Lathrop, Rose Hawthorne. Memories of Hawthorne. 2009. (ENG.). 497p. 42.99 (978-1-117-56364-0(2)) 2009. (ENG.). 497p. pap. 37.75 (978-1-117-56365-7(0)) 2008. 364p. 31.99 (978-0-554-23819-7(5)) 2008. 364p. 29.99 (978-0-554-33122-5(5)) 2007. (ENG.). 326p. pap. 23.99 (978-1-4264-5052-5(4)) 2006. 362p. pap. 26.99 (978-1-4264-5353-3(1)) BiblioBazaar.

—Memories of Hawthorne. 2009. 208p. pap. (978-1-150-46148-4(9)) Books LLC.

—Memories of Hawthorne. 2007. (ENG.). 300p. per. (978-1-4065-3575-4(3)) Dodo Pr.

—Memories of Hawthorne. 2007. (ENG.). 224p. per. (978-1-4068-1734-8(1)) Echo Library.

—Memories of Hawthorne. 2007. (ENG.). 494p. 53.95 (978-0-548-20548-8(5)); 496p. per. 38.95 (978-1-4325-2288-9(4)) Kessinger Publishing, LLC.

Latimer, Matthew. Speech-less: Tales of a White House Survivor. 2010. (ENG.). 304p. pap. 15.00 (978-0-307-46429-3(6), Three Rivers Pr.) Crown Publishing Group.

Laurichesse, Jean-Yves. Richard Millet: L'Invention du Pays. 2007. (Faux Titre: 293). 277p. pap. 74.25 (978-90-420-2185-3(3)) Rodopi.

Lawrence, Frederick. The Life of Henry Fielding: With Notices of His Writings, His Times, & His Contemporaries. 2007. (ENG.). 396p. 49.95 (978-0-548-14415-2(X)) Kessinger Publishing, LLC.

—Life of Henry Fielding with Notices of H. 2006. pap. 34.95 (978-1-4286-5675-8(8)) Kessinger Publishing, LLC.

Lawson, Valerie. Mary Poppins, She Wrote: The Life of P. L. Travers. 2008. (ENG., Illus.). 416p. pap. 27.95 (978-0-7432-9950-3(7)) Simon & Schuster.

Le Gallienne, Richard. The Romantic '90s. 2011. 284p. 48.95 (978-1-258-05679-7(8)) Literary Licensing, LLC.

Leach, Karoline. In the Shadow of the Dreamchild: The Myth & Reality of Lewis Carroll. 2nd rev. ed. 2009. (ENG.). 256p. pap. 23.95 (978-0-7206-1318-6(3)) Owen, Peter Ltd. GBR. Dist: Independent Pubs. Group.

Leacock, Stephen. Boy I Left Behind Me. 2006. 228p. per. (978-1-4067-1912-3(9), Hesperides Pr.) Read Bks.

Leader, Zachary. The Life of Kingsley Amis. 2007. (ENG., Illus.). 1008p. 39.95 (978-0-375-42498-4(9), Pantheon) Knopf Doubleday Publishing Group.

—The Life of Kingsley Amis. 2011. (ENG.). 1012p. pap. 25.95 (978-0-8101-2759-3(8)) Northwestern Univ. Pr.

Lear, Linda. Beatrix Potter: A Life in Nature. 2008. (ENG., Illus.). 608p. per. 21.99 (978-0-312-37796-0(7), St. Martin's Griffin) St. Martin's Pr.

A

Lease, Benjamin. Anglo-American Encounters: England & the Rise of American Literature. 2009. (ENG.). 316p. pap. 42.00 *(978-0-521-10852-2(7))* Cambridge Univ. Pr.

Leask, William Keith. James Boswell. 2009. 164p. pap. 21.95 *(978-1-120-30307-3(9))* Kessinger Publishing, LLC.

—James Boswell. 2007. (ENG.). 164p. per. *(978-1-4086-2699-3(3))* Read Bks.

Lebedoff, David. The Same Man: George Orwell & Evelyn Waugh in Love & War. 2008. (ENG., Illus.). 288p. 26.00 *(978-1-4000-6634-6(4),* Random House) Random House Publishing Group.

Leckie, Shirley Anne & Parezo, Nancy J., eds. Their Own Frontier: Women Intellectuals Re-Visioning the American West. 2008. (Women in the West Ser.). (ENG., Illus.). 414p. (C). pap. 27.95 *(978-0-8032-2958-7(5))* Univ. of Nebraska Pr.

Leclaire, Anne D. Listening below the Noise: The Transformative Power of Silence. 2010. 256p. pap. 13.99 *(978-0-06-135336-9(1),* HarperPerennial) HarperCollins Pubs.

Lee, Anthony W. Mentoring in Eighteenth-Century British Literature & Culture. 2009. 264p. 114.95 *(978-0-7546-6977-7(7))* Ashgate Publishing Co.

Lee, Hermione. Edith Wharton. 2008. (Vintage Ser.). (ENG., Illus.). 912p. pap. 24.00 *(978-0-375-70287-7(3),* Vintage) Knopf Doubleday Publishing Group.

—Virginia Woolf's Nose: Essays on Biography. annot. ed. 2007. (ENG.). 160p. (C). per. 15.95 *(978-0-691-13044-6(2))* Princeton Univ. Pr.

—Willa Cather: A Life Saved Up. 2008. (ENG., Illus.). 416p. pap. 16.95 *(978-1-84408-492-0(2))* Little, Brown Bk. Group Ltd. GBR. Dist: Independent Pubs. Group.

Lee, Laurie. As I Walked Out One Midsummer Morning. 2011. 192p. pap. 15.95 *(978-1-56792-392-6(5),* Non Pareil Bks.) Godine, David R. Pub.

—Cider with Rosie. Date not set. (Illus.). 256p. pap. 41.00 *(978-0-582-23359-1(3))* Addison-Wesley Longman, Ltd. GBR. Dist: Trans-Atlantic Pubns., Inc.

—Cider with Rosie. 2008. (Nonpareil Book Ser.). (ENG.). 212p. pap. 15.95 *(978-1-56792-355-1(0),* Non Pareil Bks.) Godine, David R. Pub.

Lee, Simon Richard. The Fourth Helen of the Apocalypse! 2009. 278p. pap. 27.50 *(978-1-4092-9483-2(8))* Lulu Enterprises Inc.

Lefkowitz, Frances. To Have Not. 2010. 296p. pap. 14.50 *(978-1-59692-354-6(7))* MacAdam/Cage Publishing, Inc.

Leick, Karen. Gertrude Stein & the Making of an American Celebrity. 2009. (Studies in Major Literary Authors Ser.). (ENG., Illus.). 256p. (C). 125.00 *(978-0-415-99472-9(1))* Routledge.

Leifer, Carol. When You Lie about Your Age, the Terrorists Win: Reflections on Looking in the Mirror. 2010. (ENG.). 208p. pap. 14.00 *(978-0-345-50297-1(3),* Villard Bks.) Random House Publishing Group.

Leith, Linda. Marrying Hungary. 2008. (ENG.). 160p. pap. 15.95 *(978-1-897109-29-8(6))* Signature Editions CAN. Dist: Univ. of Toronto Pr.

—Writing in the Time of Nationalism: From Two Solitudes to Blue Metropolis. 2010. 176p. pap. 15.95 *(978-1-897109-48-9(2))* Signature Editions CAN. Dist: Univ. of Toronto Pr.

Leithart, Peter. Jane Austen. 0 vols. 2010. (Christian Encounters Ser.). 192p. pap. 12.00 *(978-1-59555-302-7(9))* Nelson, Thomas Inc.

—Writer of Fancy: The Playful Piety of Jane Austen. 2008. 256p. 16.95 *(978-1-58182-645-6(1),* Cumberland Hse.) Sourcebooks, Inc.

Lekas, Stephanie. Behind the Red Door. 2009. 48p. pap. 14.92 *(978-0-557-15611-5(4))* Lulu Enterprises Inc.

Leland, Charles G. Memoirs by Charles Godfrey Leland. 2006. pap. 37.95 *(978-1-4286-5552-2(2))* Kessinger Publishing, LLC.

Leleux, Robert. The Memoirs of a Beautiful Boy. 2009. (ENG.). 304p. pap. 15.99 *(978-0-312-36169-3(6),* St. Martin's Griffin) St. Martin's Pr.

Lent, Michael & McCarthy, Brian. Stephen King. 2012. (ENG., Illus.). 40p. (YA). pap. 7.99 ***(978-1-4507-7567-0(5))*** Bluewater Productions, Inc.

Leon, Rhadames De. Memories of a Swing Maker: Story of a Corrections Officer in USA. 2011. 354p. pap. 19.99 ***(978-1-4653-4368-0(7))*** Xlibris Corp.

Leonin, Mia. Havana & Other Missing Fathers. 2009. (Camino del Sol Ser.). (ENG.). 192p. pap. 16.95 *(978-0-8165-2815-8(2))* Univ. of Arizona Pr.

Leskovar, Christy. Finding the Bad Inn: Discovering My Family's. 2010. 25.00 *(978-1-57510-150-7(5))* Pictorial Histories Publishing Co., Inc.

Lesley, Craig. Burning Fence. Date not set. mass mkt. *(978-0-312-99185-2(1),* St. Martin's Paperbacks) St. Martin's Pr.

—Burning Fence: A Memoir of Fathers & Sons. Date not set. pap. *(978-0-312-31847-5(2),* St. Martin's Paperbacks) St. Martin's Pr.

—Burning Fence: A Western Memoir of Fatherhood. 2006. (ENG., Illus.). 384p. pap. 16.00 *(978-0-312-42625-5(9))* Picador.

Lesser, Wendy. Room for Doubt. 2008. (Vintage Ser.). (ENG.). 224p. pap. 13.95 *(978-0-307-27496-0(9),* Vintage) Knopf Doubleday Publishing Group.

Lever, Susan. David Foster: The Satirist of Australia. 2007. 94.95 *(978-1-934043-98-1(2))* Cambria Pr.

Levin Becker, Daniel. Many Subtle Channels: In Praise of Potential Literature. 2012. (ENG.). 296p. 27.95 ***(978-0-674-06577-2(8))*** Harvard Univ. Pr.

Levy, David W. Mark Twain: The Divided Mind of America's Best-Loved Writer. 2010. (Library of American Biography Ser.). (ENG.). 240p. (C). pap. 25.20 *(978-0-205-55375-4(3),* Prentice Hall) Prentice Hall PTR.

Lewes, George Henry. The Life & Works of Goethe: With Sketches of His Age & Contemporaries, Vol. 1. 2006. 456p. per. 29.99 *(978-1-4255-5042-4(8))* MPublishing.

Lewington, Ken. To Be a Pilgrim. 2009. 216p. pap. 15.99 *(978-1-4389-3695-6(8))* AuthorHouse.

Lewis, C. S. Surprised by Joy: The Shape of My Early Life. 22.95 *(978-0-8488-1078-8(3))* Amereon LTD.

—Surprised by Joy / the Four Loves. 2011. (ENG.). 336p. 22.00 *(978-0-547-59939-7(0))* Houghton Mifflin Harcourt Trade & Reference Pubs.

Lewis, Greg. I Refuse to Quit! The Autobiography of a Dreamer. 2009. 306p. pap. 17.95 *(978-1-4327-3428-2(8))* Outskirts Pr., Inc.

Lewis, Jason. Behold the Reckoning. 2011. 318p. pap. 15.95 ***(978-1-4626-0967-3(8))*** PublishAmerica, Inc.

Lewis, Jeremy. Grub Street Irregular: Scenes from Literary Life. 2008. (ENG.). 352p. 38.95 *(978-0-00-255906-5(4))* HarperCollins Pubs. Ltd. GBR. Dist: Independent Pubs. Group.

Lewis, John L. Heywood Broun: As He Seemed to Us. 2006. pap. 16.95 *(978-1-4286-5933-9(1))* Kessinger Publishing, LLC.

Lewis, Michael. Home Game: An Accidental Guide to Fatherhood. (ENG., Illus.). 2010. 190p. pap. 13.95 *(978-0-393-33809-6(6),* 33809) 2009. 192p. 23.95 *(978-0-393-06901-3(X),* 6901) Norton, W. W. & Co., Inc.

Lewis, Monica. Dancing My Way to Sanity. 2011. 136p. 29.99 ***(978-1-4568-8625-7(8))***; pap. 19.99 ***(978-1-4568-8624-0(X))*** Xlibris Corp.

Lewis, Peter. Charles Dickens & the Staplehurst Train Crash. 2010. (ENG.). 192p. pap. 24.95 *(978-1-84868-793-6(1))* Amberley Publishing GBR. Dist: Casemate Pubs. & Bk. Distributors, LLC.

Lewis, Roger. Anthony Burgess. Date not set. pap. *(978-0-312-32252-6(6))*; mass mkt. *(978-0-312-99390-0(0))* St. Martin's Pr. (St. Martin's Paperbacks).

Lewis, Susan. One Day at a Time: A Memoir. 2012. (ENG.). 440p. pap. 12.95 ***(978-0-09-956007-4(0))*** Random Hse. GBR. Dist: Independent Pubs. Group.

L'Heureux, John & Karagueuzian, Dikran. Conversations with John L'Heureux. 2011. (ENG.). 184p. pap. 17.00 *(978-1-57586-600-0(5))* CSLI Pubns.

Li, Shuxue. Lewis Mumford: Critic of Culture & Civilization. 2009. 241p. pap. 49.95 *(978-3-03911-557-0(X))* Lang, Peter AG GBR. Dist: Lang, Peter.

Li, Stephanie. Toni Morrison: A Biography. 2010. (Greenwood Biographies Ser.). (Illus.). 184p. 35.00 *(978-0-313-37839-3(8),* GR7839) Greenwood Publishing Group, Inc.

Liberman, Sherri. Lynne Reid Banks. 2009. (Library of Author Biographies Ser.). 112p. (gr. 5-8). 63.90 *(978-1-60853-545-3(2),* Rosen Central) Rosen Publishing Group, Inc., The.

Liddy, James. The Full Shilling. 2009. (ENG., Illus.). 149p. pap. 26.95 *(978-1-903392-91-1(8))* Salmon Publishing IRL. Dist: Dufour Editions, Inc.

Liederbach, Nate & Harris, James, eds. Of a Monstrous Child: An Anthology of Creative Writing Relationships. 2011. (ENG.). 414p. pap. 24.00 *(978-0-9844510-4-3(8))* Lost Horse Pr.

Lili, Anamika Haka. Alokera Jhamadhara. (BEN.). 128p. *(978-7-01-000001-5(8))* People's Publishing Hse., The.

Lillios, Anna. Crossing the Creek: The Literary Friendship of Zora Neale Hurston & Marjorie Kinnan Rawlings. (ENG., Illus.). 2011. 216p. pap. 19.95 *(978-0-8130-3809-4(X))* 2010. 208p. 29.95 *(978-0-8130-3500-0(7))* Univ. Pr. of Florida.

Liman, Antonin Vaclav. Ibuse Masuji: A Century Remembered. 2008. (Illus.). 430p. 25.00 *(978-80-246-1452-6(9))*; 25.00 *(978-80-246-1448-9(0))* Karolinum, nakladatelstvi Univerzity Karlovy CZE. Dist: Chicago Distribution Ctr.

Lindberg, Richard C. Whiskey Breakfast: My Swedish Family, My American Life. 2011. (ENG., Illus.). 328p. pap. 22.95 ***(978-0-8166-4684-5(8))*** Univ. of Minnesota Pr.

Lindbergh, Reeve. Under a Wing. 2009. (ENG., Illus.). 224p. pap. 14.00 *(978-1-4391-4883-9(X))* Simon & Schuster.

Lindfors, Bernth. Early Black South African Writing in English. 2011. ***(978-1-59221-840-0(7))***; (Illus.). 236p. pap. ***(978-1-59221-841-7(5))*** Africa World Pr.

Lipsky, David. Although of Course You End up Becoming Yourself: A Road Trip with David Foster Wallace. 2010. (ENG.). 352p. pap. 16.99 *(978-0-307-59243-9(X))* Broadway Bks.

Litot, Monsignor Ed. Police Chaplain's Diary: A Happy Life Despite 80 Years of Fibromyalgia. 2009. 280p. pap. 15.95 *(978-1-4490-3258-6(3))* AuthorHouse.

Little, Charlene Pillow. The Song of Sarah: Poverty & Plenty, Grit & Grace, Wit & Wisdom. 2011. 432p. 36.95 ***(978-1-4620-1401-9(1))***; pap. 26.95 ***(978-1-4620-1399-9(6))*** iUniverse, Inc.

Littleton, Betty. A Family Portrait. 2010. 316p. pap. 75.99 *(978-1-4520-4355-5(8))* AuthorHouse.

Lobe, Kirsten. Paris, Baby! 2011. (ENG.). 352p. pap. 14.99 *(978-0-312-60532-2(3),* St. Martin's Griffin) St. Martin's Pr.

Lobo Antunes, António. The Fat Man & Infinity: And Other Writings. Costa, Margaret Jull, tr. from SPA. 2009. (ENG.). 320p. 26.95 *(978-0-393-06198-7(1),* 6198) Norton, W. W. & Co., Inc.

Lockhart, J. G. Memoirs of the Life of Sir Walter Scott, Bart , by John Gibson Lockhart. 2006. (ENG.). 336p. per. 23.99 *(978-1-4255-3403-5(1))*; (ENG.). 336p. per. 23.99 *(978-1-4255-3371-7(X))*; (ENG.). 324p. per. 23.99 *(978-1-4255-3205-5(5))*; 320p. per. 23.99 *(978-1-4255-3144-7(X))*; (ENG.). 320p. per. 23.99 *(978-1-4255-3143-0(1))* MPublishing.

Lockhart, John Gibson. Memoirs of the Life of Sir Walter Scott V1. 2007. 526p. 55.95 *(978-0-548-06384-2(2))* Kessinger Publishing, LLC.

Lockington, Laura. Cupboard Love: A Food Romance. 2008. 191p. 21.95 *(978-1-84624-280-9(0))* Book Guild, Ltd. GBR. Dist: Trans-Atlantic Pubns., Inc.

Lockridge, Laurence S., et al, eds. Nineteenth-Century Lives. 2008. (ENG., Illus.). 240p. pap. 36.00 *(978-0-521-09050-6(4))* Cambridge Univ. Pr.

Loncraine, Rebecca. The Real Wizard of Oz: The Life & Times of L. Frank Baum. 2010. (ENG.). 352p. (gr. 12). 18.00 *(978-1-59240-558-9(4),* Gotham) Penguin Group (USA) Inc.

London, Jack. The Cruise of the Snark. 2008. 232p. 27.99 *(978-0-554-28675-4(0))*; 24.99 *(978-0-554-37978-4(3))* BiblioBazaar.

—The Cruise of the Snark. 2008. 228p. pap. 13.95 *(978-1-60096-748-1(5))*; 240p. pap. 14.95 *(978-1-4341-0056-6(1))*; 228p. pap. 13.95 *(978-1-60096-131-1(2))* Editorium, The.

—The Cruise of the Snark. 2008. 176p. pap. 12.99 *(978-1-59547-590-9(7))* NuVision Pubns., LLC.

—John Barleycorn. 2008. 204p. 22.99 *(978-0-554-33980-1(3))*; 25.99 *(978-0-554-24677-2(5))* BiblioBazaar.

—John Barleycorn. 2009. 132p. pap. *(978-1-4068-7735-9(2))* Echo Library.

—John Barleycorn. 2010. 356p. pap. 22.95 *(978-0-557-50352-0(3))* Lulu Enterprises Inc.

—John Barleycorn. 2008. (Large Print Ser.). lib. bdg. 26.00 *(978-1-58287-969-7(9))*; lib. bdg. *(978-1-58287-486-9(7))* North Bks.

—John Barleycorn. 2008. 184p. pap. 13.99 *(978-1-59547-600-5(8))* NuVision Pubns., LLC.

—John Barleycorn: Alcoholic Memoirs. Sutherland, John, ed. 2009. (Oxford World's Classics Ser.). (ENG.). 288p. pap. 13.95 *(978-0-19-955557-4(5))* Oxford Univ. Pr., Inc.

—John Barleycorn: Alcoholic Memoirs. 2009. 316p. pap. 30.75 ***(978-1-113-78205-2(6))*** BiblioBazaar.

London, Jack. John Barleycorn: Alcoholic Memoirs. 2009. (ENG.). 313p. pap. 24.99 *(978-1-113-78201-4(3))*; pap. 23.99 *(978-1-113-78199-4(8))* BiblioBazaar. (BiblioLife).

Long, Robert Emmet & Long. Truman Capote, Enfant Terrible. 2008. (ENG.). 144p. 24.95 *(978-0-8264-2763-2(4))* Continuum International Publishing Group, Ltd. GBR. Dist: National Bk. Network.

Lopes, Maria Angélica Guimarães. The Brazilian Short Story in the Late Twentieth Century: A Selection from Nineteen Authors. 2009. 176p. 99.95 *(978-0-7734-4904-6(3))* Mellen, Edwin Pr., The.

Lopez, Lorraine, ed. An Angle of Vision: Women Writers on Their Poor & Working-Class Roots. 2009. (Class: Culture Ser.). (ENG.). 216p. pap. 23.95 *(978-0-472-05078-9(8))*; 65.00 *(978-0-472-07078-7(9))* Univ. of Michigan Pr.

Lord, Elton. Among Others. 2006. 288p. per. *(978-1-4067-3209-2(5),* Hesperides Pr.) Read Bks.

Lord, Isabel Garland. A Summer to Be: A Memoir by the Daughter of Hamlin Garland. Newlin, Keith, ed. & intro. by. 2010. (ENG., Illus.). 424p. pap. 23.95 *(978-0-8032-3243-3(8),* Bison Bks.) Univ. of Nebraska Pr.

Lorence, James J. A Hard Journey: The Life of Don West. (Illus.). 344p. 2010. (ENG.). pap. 25.00 *(978-0-252-07733-3(4))* 2007. 39.95 *(978-0-252-03231-8(4))* Univ. of Illinois Pr.

Lounsbury, Thomas RaynesFord. James Fenimore Cooper: American Men of Letters. 2007. (ENG.). 224p. pap. 20.99 *(978-1-4346-3364-4(0))*; 250p. pap. 22.99 *(978-1-4346-3365-1(9))* BiblioBazaar.

Loving, Jerome. Emerson, Whitman, & the American Muse. 2011. (ENG.). 232p. pap. 40.00 *(978-0-8078-9714-0(0))* Univ. of North Carolina Pr.

—Mark Twain: The Adventures of Samuel L. Clemens. (Illus.). 520p. 2011. (ENG.). pap. 21.95 *(978-0-520-26985-9(3))* 2010. 50.00 *(978-0-520-25257-8(8))* Univ. of California Pr.

Lowndes, Emma. Turning Victorian Ladies into Women: The Life of Bessie Rayner Parkes,1829 - 1925. 2011. (ENG., Illus.). 264p. *(978-1-936320-28-8(2))* Academica Pr., LLC.

Lowry, Joseph E. & Stewart, Devin J., eds. Essays in Arabic Literary Biography II: 1350-1850. 2009. (Essays in Arabic Literary Biography Ser.). (ENG.). 440p. (C). pap. 102.00 *(978-3-447-05933-6(8))* Harrassowitz, Otto Verlag DEU. Dist: ISD.

Loye, David. 3,000 Years of Love: The Life of Riane Eisler & David Loye. 2007. 256p. pap. 18.95 *(978-0-9789827-5-1(4))* Franklin, Benjamin Pr.

Lubbe, Fredericka van der. Martin Aedler & the High Dutch Minerva: The First German Grammar for the English. 2007. (Duisburg Papers on Research in Language & Culture Ser.). (HEB, LAT, MUL, GER & ENG., Illus.). 312p. pap. 59.95 *(978-3-631-56287-1(X))* Lang, Peter Publishing, Inc.

Luhan, Mabel. Lorenzo in Taos. 2007. 396p. per. 32.95 *(978-0-86534-594-2(5))* Sunstone Pr.

Lusted, Marilyn. A Very Strange Childhood. 2010. (Illus.). 68p. pap. 10.49 *(978-1-4520-3125-5(8))* AuthorHouse.

Lutz, Wilfrid. Ludwig Röder Im Strudel der Zeit: Biographie. 2009. (GER.). 140p. *(978-3-89754-310-2(9))* Roll, J.H., Verlag, GmbH.

Lycett, Andrew. The Man Who Created Sherlock Holmes: The Life & Times of Sir Arthur Conan Doyle. 2008. (ENG., Illus.). 576p. pap. 32.99 *(978-0-7432-7525-5(X),* Free Pr.) Free Pr.

Lynch, Audry. The Rebel Figure in American Literature & Film: The Interconnected Lives of John Steinbeck & James Dean. 2009. 124p. 89.95 *(978-0-7734-4662-5(1))* Mellen, Edwin Pr., The.

Lynch, Claire. Irish Autobiography: Stories of Self in the Narrative of a Nation. 2009. (Reimagining Ireland Ser.). (ENG.). 234p. pap. 49.95 *(978-3-03911-856-4(0))* Lang, Peter AG GBR. Dist: Lang, Peter.

Lynch, James A. A Boy Named Jim. 2011. 144p. pap. 11.95 ***(978-1-4582-0021-1(3)),*** Abbott Pr.) Author Solutions, Inc.

Lystra, Karen. Dangerous Intimacy: The Untold Story of Mark Twain's Final Years. 2006. (Illus.). 342p. per. 19.95 *(978-0-520-25000-0(1))* Univ. of California Pr.

Macaskill, Hilary. Agatha Christie at Home. 2009. (ENG., Illus.). 144p. 40.00 *(978-0-7112-3029-3(3))* Lincoln, Frances Ltd. GBR. Dist: Perseus-PGW.

Macaulay, James. Doctor Johnson: His Life, Works & Table Talk. 2008. 215p. 22.99 *(978-0-554-79559-1(0))*; 290p. pap. 20.75 *(978-0-554-79556-0(6))*; 203p. 25.99 *(978-0-554-79549-2(3))*; 215p. pap. 21.75 *(978-0-554-79552-2(3))* BiblioBazaar.

Macdonogh, Giles. Brillat Savarin: The Judge & His Stomach. 2008. (ENG.). 256p. pap. 25.00 *(978-1-56663-717-6(1))* Dee, Ivan R. Pub.

MacFarland, Anne & MacDonald, Susanne Rike. Three Score Years & Then: Memoirs of Anne MacFarland. 2011. 104p. 39.95 ***(978-1-258-08384-7(1))*** Literary Licensing, LLC.

Macken, Ultan. Walter Macken: Dreams on Paper. 2010. (ENG., Illus.). 448p. 47.95 *(978-1-85635-630-5(2))* Mercier Pr., Ltd., The IRL. Dist: Dufour Editions, Inc.

Mackenzie, R. Shelton (Robert Shelton). Life of Charles Dickens by R Shelton MacKenzie with Personal Recollections & Anecdotes; — Letters by 'Boz', Never Before Published; — and Uncollect. 2006. 504p. per. 29.99 *(978-1-4255-5680-8(9))* MPublishing.

Mackin, Randy. George Scarbrough, Appalachian Poet: A Biographical & Literary Study with Unpublished Writings. 2011. (Contributions to Southern Appalachian Studies). (ENG., Illus.). 220p. pap. 45.00 *(978-0-7864-6371-8(6))* McFarland & Co., Inc. Pubs.

MacKinnon, Douglas. Rolling Pennies in the Dark: A Memoir with a Message. 2012. (ENG.). 240p. lib. bdg. 24.00 *(978-1-4516-0788-8(1),* Howard Bks.) Howard Books.

MacLauchlin, Cory. Butterfly in the Typewriter: The Tragic Life of John Kennedy Toole & the Remarkable Story of a Confederacy of Dunces. 2012. (ENG., Illus.). 352p. 26.00 ***(978-0-306-82040-3(4))*** Da Capo Pr., Inc.

MacMillan, Margaret. Stephen Leacock. 2011. (ENG.). 204p. (gr. 12). 19.95 ***(978-0-670-06681-0(8),*** Penguin Global) Penguin Group (USA) Inc.

MacRi, Frank J. The Voyage: An Autobiography. 2008. 48p. pap. 10.95 *(978-1-4327-0982-2(8))* Outskirts Pr., Inc.

Macy, John Albert. Edgar Allan Poe. 2008. 134p. 35.95 *(978-1-4366-2343-8(X))*; 136p. pap. 20.95 *(978-0-548-89065-3(X))* Kessinger Publishing, LLC.

—Edgar Allan Poe. 112p. reprint ed. 88.00 *(978-0-7222-8534-3(5))* Library Reprints, Inc.

—Edgar Allan Poe. 2008. 136p. pap. *(978-1-4097-1794-2(1))* Read Bks.

Madden, David & Mecholsky, Kristopher. James M. Cain: Hard-Boiled Mythmaker. 2011. (ENG.). 240p. 49.00 *(978-0-8108-8118-1(7))* Scarecrow Pr., Inc.

Madden, R. R. The Literary Life & Correspondence of the Countess of Blessington V1. 2008. 558p. 57.95 *(978-1-4365-4784-0(9))* 2007. 560p. per. 42.95 *(978-0-548-68945-5(8))* Kessinger Publishing, LLC.

Madden, Richard Robert. The Literary Life & Correspondence of the Countess of Blessington R R Madden. 2006. 608p. per. 34.99 *(978-1-4255-6483-4(6))*; 564p. per. 32.99 *(978-1-4255-6174-1(8))* MPublishing.

—The Literary Life & Correspondence of the Countess of Blessington V3. 2007. (ENG.). 522p. 55.95 *(978-0-548-17257-5(9))*; 524p. per. 40.95 *(978-1-4304-7084-7(4))* Kessinger Publishing, LLC.

Maddox, Brenda. George Eliot in Love. 2010. (ENG., Illus.). 256p. 25.00 *(978-0-230-10518-8(1))* Palgrave Macmillan.

Madhopuri, Balbir. Changiya Rukh: Against the Night. Jain, Tripti, tr. from PAN. 2010. (ENG.). 224p. 29.95 *(978-0-19-806550-0(7))* Oxford Univ. Pr., Inc.

Mae Stephenson Abernathy. We Wanted to Live. 2009. 140p. pap. 14.99 *(978-1-4389-4650-4(3))* AuthorHouse.

Maes, Nicholas. Robertson Davies: Magician of Words. 2009. (Quest Biography Ser.). (ENG., Illus.). 192p. pap. 19.99 *(978-1-55002-872-0(3))* Dundurn CAN. Dist: Ingram Pub. Services.

Maguire, Toni. When Daddy Comes Home. 2007. (ENG.). 348p. pap. 12.95 *(978-0-00-724400-3(2))* HarperCollins Pubs. Ltd. GBR. Dist: Independent Pubs. Group.

Mailer, Norris Church. A Ticket to the Circus: A Memoir. 2011. (Illus.). 448p. pap. 15.00 *(978-0-8129-7987-9(7),* Random Hse. Trade Paperbacks) Random House Publishing Group.

Mairowitz, David Zane & Crumb, Robert. Kafka. Appignanesi, Richard, ed. 2007. (ENG., Illus.). 176p. pap. 14.95 *(978-1-56097-806-0(6),* 56806) Fantagraphics Bks.

Mairowitz, David Zane & Korkos, Alain. Introducing Camus. 2012. (Introducing Ser.). (ENG., Illus.). 126p. 9.95 ***(978-1-84831-345-3(4))*** Totem Bks. GBR. Dist: Consortium Bk. Sales & Distribution.

Maitland, Sara. A Book of Silence. 2009. (ENG.). 320p. 25.00 *(978-1-58243-517-6(0),* Counterpoint Pr.) Basic Bks. GBR. Dist: Perseus-PGW.

Makower, F. Elizabeth Longford. (Illus.). xi, 212p. pap. 15.99 *(978-0-340-69472-5(6),* Hodder & Stoughton) Hodder General Publishing Div. GBR. Dist: Trafalgar Square Publishing.

Malamud Smith, Janna. My Father Is a Book: A Memoir of Bernard Malamud. 2007. (ENG.). 304p. pap. 14.95 *(978-0-618-87263-3(9))* Houghton Mifflin Harcourt Trade & Reference Pubs.

Malcolm, Janet. Two Lives: Gertrude & Alice. (Illus.). 240p. 2008. (ENG.). pap. 13.00 *(978-0-300-14310-2(9))* 2007. 25.00 *(978-0-300-12551-1(8))* Yale Univ. Pr.

Malik, Abdurrauf. Sayyid Sajjad Zahir: Marksi Danishvar Aur Kamyunist Rahnuma. 2010. (URD., Illus.). 216p. *(978-969-8548-02-5(5))* Jumhoori Publications.

Malina, Judith. The Piscator Notebook. 2012. (ENG., Illus.). 256p. 115.00 *(978-0-415-60073-6(1))*; pap. 31.95 *(978-0-415-60074-3(X))* Routledge.

Mallory, Carole. Loving Mailer. 2010. (ENG.). 203p. 22.95 *(978-1-60747-715-0(7))* Phoenix Bks., Inc.

Malmsteen, Patrick. If You Were Sober, Would You? A mind boggling tale of a family's 4 year emigration to Spain, their highs & lows, the low down on the Property-buyin. 2010. 96p. pap. 11.49 *(978-1-4490-7302-2(6))* AuthorHouse.

Maloney, Stuart. 26: A Behind-the-Scenes Tour of Life with Cerebral Palsy. 2011. 236p. pap. 17.09 ***(978-1-4670-0788-7(9))*** AuthorHouse.

Mancini, Albert N. & Pierce, Glenn Palen, eds. Seventeenth-Century Italian Poets & Dramatists. 2008. (Dictionary of Literary Biography Ser.). (ENG., Illus.). 448p. 315.00 *(978-0-7876-8157-9(1))* Cengage Gale.

Manderino, John. Crying at Movies: A Memoir. 2008. (ENG.). 200p. pap. 15.95 *(978-0-89733-580-5(5))* Academy Chicago Pubs., Ltd.

Manguso, Sarah. The Two Kinds of Decay: A Memoir. 2009. (ENG.). 192p. pap. 14.00 *(978-0-312-42844-0(8))* Picador.

Mankiewicz, Tom & Crane, Robert. My Life as a Mankiewicz: An Insider's Journey through Hollywood. 2012. (Screen Classics Ser.). (ENG., Illus.). 368p. 39.95 ***(978-0-8131-3605-9(9))*** Univ. Pr. of Kentucky.

Mann, Susan. The Talented Women of the Zhang Family. 2007. (Illus.). 352p. 60.00 *(978-0-520-25089-5(3))*; 322p. per. 26.95 *(978-0-520-25090-1(7))* Univ. of California Pr.

Manseau, Peter. Vows: The Story of a Priest, a Nun, & Their Son. 2006. (ENG., Illus.). 416p. pap. 15.00 *(978-0-7432-4908-9(9)*, Free Pr.) Free Pr.

Mantz, Ruth Elvish. The Life of Katherine Mansfield. 2008. 388p. *(978-1-4437-2527-9(7)*, Hesperides Pr.) Read Bks.

—Life of Katherine Mansfield. 2006. 384p. per. *(978-1-4067-3435-5(7)*, Hesperides Pr.) Read Bks.

Maradas, Tadaram. A Pictorial Memoir: 23 Years in the Making. 2010. 244p. pap. 78.49 *(978-1-4520-0167-8(7))* AuthorHouse.

Marcus, Leonard S. Listening for Madeleine: A Portrait of Madeleine L'Engle in Many Voices, 1 vol. 2012. (ENG., Illus.). 336p. 27.00 ***(978-0-374-29897-5(1))*** Farrar, Straus & Giroux.

Margaret Fuller Ossoli. Memoirs of Margaret Fuller Ossoli. I.t. ed. 2007. 178p. pap. 24.99 *(978-1-4264-6825-4(3))*; (ENG.). 312p. pap. 24.99 *(978-1-4264-6824-7(5))* BiblioBazaar.

Margolis, Nadia. An Introduction to Christine de Pizan. 2011. (New Perspectives on Medieval Literature: Authors & Traditions Ser.). (ENG., Illus.). 272p. 69.95 *(978-0-8130-3650-2(X))* Univ. Pr. of Florida.

Mariani, Paul. Gerard Manley Hopkins: A Life. 2008. (ENG.). 496p. (gr. 12-18). 34.95 *(978-0-670-02031-7(1)*, Viking Adult) Penguin Group (USA) Inc.

Marias, Javier. Written Lives. 2007. (Illus.). 208p. pap. *(978-1-84195-886-6(7))* Canongate Bks.

—Written Lives. Costa, Margaret Jull, tr. 2007. (ENG., Illus.). 208p. per. 14.95 *(978-0-8112-1689-0(6)*, 21689) New Directions Publishing Corp.

Maricourt, Thierry. Dictionnaire du Roman Policier Nordique. 2010. (FRE., Illus.). 240p. (C). pap. 35.00 ***(978-2-251-74245-8(X))*** Societe d'edition Les Belles lettres FRA. Dist: ISD.

Marie, Tia. The Disregarded Child: My Life with Autism. 2011. pap. 10.99 *(978-1-61739-338-9(X))* Tate Publishing & Enterprises, LLC.

Marini, Francesca. Francis Bacon. 2009. (Skira MINI Artbooks Ser.). (ENG., Illus.). 96p. pap. 8.99 *(978-88-6130-709-4(4))* Skira Editore ITA. Dist: Random Hse., Inc.

Marion, Joyce. Grab the Holy Spirit & Run On. 2010. 434p. 34.99 *(978-1-61579-739-4(4))* Xulon Pr., Inc.

Maristain, Monica & Bolaño, Roberto, eds. The Last Interview: And Other Conversations. Perez, Sybil, tr. from ENG. 2009. (ENG.). 128p. pap. 14.95 *(978-1-933633-83-1(2))* Melville Hse. Publishing.

Markham, Ian S. Against Atheism: Why Dawkins, Hitchens, & Harris Are Fundamentally Wrong. 2010. (ENG., Illus.). 176p. 94.95 *(978-1-4051-8964-4(9))*; pap. 27.95 *(978-1-4051-8963-7(0))* Wiley, John & Sons, Inc. (Wiley-Blackwell).

Markoe, Merrill. Cool, Calm & Contentious. 2011. (ENG.). 288p. 24.00 *(978-0-345-51891-0(8)*, Villard Bks.) Random House Publishing Group.

Markoe, Merrill. Cool, Calm & Contentious: Essays. 2012. (ENG.). 304p. pap. 15.00 ***(978-0-345-51892-7(6)***, Villard Bks.) Random House Publishing Group.

Marks, Jeffrey. Anthony Boucher: A Biobibliography. 2008. (ENG & AFR., Illus.). 223p. per. 35.00 *(978-0-7864-3320-9(5))* McFarland & Co., Inc. Pubs.

Markus, Julia. J. Anthony Froude: The Last Undiscovered Great Victorian. 2007. (ENG., Illus.). 352p. pap. 23.95 *(978-1-4165-8921-1(X)*, Scribner) Scribner.

Marlowe, Arthur. Shakespeare's Dark Secrets. 2008. 116p. pap. *(978-1-84426-507-7(2))* Upfront Publishing Ltd.

Marrocu, Luciano. Orwell: La solitudine di uno Scrittore. 2009. (Vite Ser.). (ITA., Illus.). 240p. (C). pap. 27.00 *(978-88-96209-00-4(5))* Vandenhoeck & Ruprecht GmbH & Co. KG DEU. Dist: Brown, David Bk. Co., The.

Marshall, Paule. Triangular Road: A Memoir. (ENG., 2010. Illus.). 176p. (gr. 9). pap. 14.00 *(978-0-465-01922-9(6))* 2009. 192p. 23.00 *(978-0-465-01359-3(7)*, Basic Civitas Bks.) Basic Bks.

Martin, David Lozell. Losing Everything. 2011. (ENG.). 208p. pap. 14.99 ***(978-0-7432-9434-8(3))*** Simon & Schuster.

Martin, David Lozell. Losing Everything: A Memoir. 2008. (ENG.). 208p. 24.00 *(978-0-7432-9433-1(5))* Simon & Schuster.

Martin, Edward A. A Biographical Encyclopedia of Medical Travel Authors: Continental Europe, 6 Vols., Vol.3. 2010. *(978-0-7734-3685-5(5))* Mellen, Edwin Pr., The.

—A Biographical Encyclopedia of Medical Travel Authors: England & Wales, 6 Vols., Vol.4. 2010. *(978-0-7734-3687-9(1))* Mellen, Edwin Pr., The.

—A Biographical Encyclopedia of Medical Travel Authors: Ireland, 6 vols., Vol.5. 2010. *(978-0-7734-3689-3(8))* Mellen, Edwin Pr., The.

—A Biographical Encyclopedia of Medical Travel Authors: Scotland, 6 vols., Vol.6. 2010. *(978-0-7734-3691-6(X))* Mellen, Edwin Pr., The.

—A Biographical Encyclopedia of Medical Travel Authors: The Americas & Canada, 6 Vols., Vol.1. 2010. *(978-0-7734-3681-7(2))* Mellen, Edwin Pr., The.

—A Biograpical Encyclopedia of Medical Travel Authors: Australia, New Zealand, South Africa, the Pacific & the Antarctic, 6 Vols., Vol.2. 2010. *(978-0-7734-3683-1(9))* Mellen, Edwin Pr., The.

Martin, Gerald. Gabriel Garcia Marquez: A Life. 2010. (Vintage Ser.). (ENG., Illus.). 688p. pap. 18.95 *(978-0-307-47286-1(8)*, Vintage) Knopf Doubleday Publishing Group.

—Gabriel Garcia Márquez: Una Vida. 2009. (Vintage Espanol Ser.). (SPA., Illus.). 784p. pap. 19.95 *(978-0-307-47228-1(0)*, Vintage) Knopf Doubleday Publishing Group.

Martin, John. Beyond Belief: The Real Life of Daniel Defoe. 2007. (Illus.). 318p. *(978-1-905170-56-2(4))* Accent Pr. Ltd.

Martin, Peter. Samuel Johnson: A Biography. (Illus.). 640p. 2010. pap. 19.95 *(978-0-674-05737-1(6))* 2008. 35.00 *(978-0-674-03160-9(1))* Harvard Univ. Pr. (Belknap Pr.).

—Samuel Johnson: A Biography. 2010. (ENG., Illus.). 568p. pap. 24.99 *(978-0-7538-2592-1(9)*, Phoenix) Orion Publishing Group, Ltd. GBR. Dist: Hachette Bk. Group.

Martineau, Harriet. Harriet Martineau's Autobiography V2. Chapman, Maria Weston, ed. 2007. (ENG.). 612p. 59.95 *(978-0-548-12335-5(7))* Kessinger Publishing, LLC.

Martineau, Harriet & Chapman, Maria Weston. Harriet Martineau's Autobiography. 2010. (Cambridge Library Collection - Women's Writing Ser.). (ENG.). 506p. pap. 37.99 *(978-1-108-02258-3(8))*; 530p. pap. 39.99 *(978-1-108-02257-6(X))*; (Illus.). 460p. pap. 34.99 *(978-1-108-02256-9(1))* Cambridge Univ. Pr.

Martinez, Elizabeth Coonrod. Josefina Niggli, Mexican American Writer: A Critical Biography. 2007. (ENG., Illus.). 327p. (C). pap. 30.00 *(978-0-8263-4272-0(8))* Univ. of New Mexico Pr.

Marty, Sid. Leaning on the Wind: Under the Spell of the Great Chinook, 1 vol. 2009. (ENG.). 352p. pap. *(978-1-894974-62-2(X))* Heritage Hse.

Mary Lou, Sanelli. Among Friends. 2009. 160p. pap. 15.00 *(978-1-929355-52-5(1)*, Aequitas Bks.) Pleasure Boat Studio: A Literary Pr.

Marzials, Frank. Life of Charles Dickens. 2010. (Illus.). 118p. pap. 14.83 *(978-1-77045-340-1(7))* General Bks. LLC.

Marzials, Frank T. Life of Charles Dickens. 2010. (ENG.). 282p. pap. 28.75 *(978-1-174-90115-7(2))* BiblioBazaar.

—The Life of Charles Dickens. 2011. 200p. 39.95 ***(978-1-169-86143-5(1))*** 2010. 200p. 31.96 *(978-1-163-33180-4(5))* 2010. 200p. pap. 19.96 ***(978-1-162-74182-6(1))*** 2007. (ENG.). 198p. 39.95 *(978-0-548-01994-8(0))* Kessinger Publishing, LLC.

Marzials, Frank T. (Frank Thomas) & Anderson, John Parker, creators. Life of Charles Dickens. 2011. 220p. pap. 24.75 ***(978-1-178-93167-9(6))*** BiblioBazaar.

Marzials, Frank Thomas. Life of Charles Dickens. 2009. 204p. 22.99 *(978-1-103-42906-6(X))*; pap. 16.99 *(978-1-103-42902-8(7))* BiblioBazaar.

—Life of Charles Dickens. 2009. 126p. pap. *(978-1-150-67841-7(0))* Books LLC.

—The Life of Charles Dickens. 2010. 568p. pap. 43.75 *(978-1-146-72306-0(7))* BiblioBazaar.

Marzials, Frank Thomas & Anderson, John Parker. Life of Charles Dickens. 2010. (ENG.). 212p. pap. 24.75 *(978-1-177-57893-6(X))* BiblioBazaar.

Maschietto, Francesco Ludovico, et al. Elena Lucrezia Cornaro Piscopia (1646-1684) The First Woman in the World to Earn a University Degree. 2006. (ENG & LAT.). 40.00 *(978-0-916101-57-2(6))* St. Joseph's Univ. Pr.

Masefield, John. John M. Synge: A Few Personal Recollections, with Biographical Notes. reprint ed. lib. bdg. 98.00 *(978-0-7426-3157-1(5))* Classic Bks.

Masefield, Muriel. The Story of Fanny Burney: Being an Introduction to the Diary & Letters of Madame D'Arblay. 2011. (ENG.). 190p. pap. 35.00 ***(978-1-107-60496-4(6))*** Cambridge Univ. Pr.

Masel, Deborah. Soul to Soul: Writings from Dark Places. 2011. ***(978-965-229-559-0(0))*** Gefen Bks.

Masilela, Johnny. Deliver Us from Evil: Scenes from a Rural Transvaal Upbringing. (Illus.). 79p. pap. *(978-0-7957-0046-0(6))* Kwela Bks.

Massett, Stephen C. Drifting about or What Jeems Pipes of Pi. 2006. pap. 26.99 *(978-1-4255-4027-2(9))* MPublishing.

Masson, David. De Quincey. 2011. (Cambridge Library Collection - English Men of Letters Ser.). (ENG.). 214p. pap. 22.99 ***(978-1-108-03459-3(4))*** Cambridge Univ. Pr.

Masters, Jarvis Jay. That Bird Has My Wings: The Autobiography of an Innocent Man on Death Row. 2010. (ENG.). 304p. pap. 14.99 *(978-0-06-173048-1(3)*, HarperOne) HarperCollins Pubs.

Masterson, Sherry. The Silent Struggle. 2011. 96p. pap. 19.95 ***(978-1-4560-0176-6(0))*** PublishAmerica, Inc.

Máté, Ferenc. A Real Life: Restoring What Matters Family, Good Friends & a True Community. 3rd ed. 2011. (ENG.). 285p. 24.95 *(978-0-920256-69-5(4)*, 25669) Albatross Publishing CAN. Dist: Norton, W. W. & Co., Inc.

Mathews, John Joseph. Twenty Thousand Mornings: An Autobiography. Kalter, Susan, ed. 2012. (American Indian Literature & Critical Studies Ser.). (ENG., Illus.). 352p. 29.95 ***(978-0-8061-4253-1(7))*** Univ. of Oklahoma Pr.

Match, Ben. The Pinnacle of my Life. 2011. 64p. pap. 9.99 *(978-1-4567-4715-2(0))* AuthorHouse.

Matoff, Susan. Conflicted Life. 2011. (ENG., Illus.). 677p. 99.50 *(978-1-84519-417-8(9))* Sussex Academic Pr. GBR. Dist: International Specialized Bk. Services.

Matteson, John. Eden's Outcasts: The Story of Louisa May Alcott & Her Father. 2008. (ENG., Illus.). 512p. pap. 17.95 *(978-0-393-33359-6(0)*, 33359) Norton, W. W. & Co., Inc.

Matteson, John. The Lives of Margaret Fuller: A Biography. 2012. (ENG., Illus.). 528p. 32.95 ***(978-0-393-06805-4(6)***, 6805) Norton, W. W. & Co., Inc.

Matthews, Thomas Stanley. Name & Address: An Autobiography. 2011. 318p. 50.95 ***(978-1-258-08296-3(9))*** Literary Licensing, LLC.

Matthiessen, Peter. The Snow Leopard. rev. ed. 2008. (ENG., Illus.). 368p. (gr. 12-18). 16.00 *(978-0-14-310551-0(5)*, Penguin Classics) Penguin Group (USA) Inc.

Matuschek, Oliver. Three Lives: A Biography of Stefan Zweig. 2012. (ENG.). 512p. 32.00 ***(978-1-906548-29-2(3))*** Pushkin Pr., Ltd. GBR. Dist: Consortium Bk. Sales & Distribution.

Maugham, W. Somerset. The Skeptical Romancer: Selected Travel Writing. Iyer, Pico, ed. 2009. (ENG.). 248p. 24.00 *(978-0-307-27212-6(5)*, Everyman's Library) Knopf Doubleday Publishing Group.

—The Skeptical Romancer: Selected Travel Writing. Iyer, Pico, ed. 2012. (Vintage International Ser.). (ENG.). 224p. pap. 15.00 ***(978-0-307-47318-9(X)***, Vintage) Knopf Doubleday Publishing Group.

Maugham, W. Somerset. A Writer's Notebook. 2009. (Vintage International Ser.). (ENG.). 384p. pap. 16.95 *(978-0-307-47319-6(8)*, Vintage) Knopf Doubleday Publishing Group.

Maunder, Andrew & Law, Graham. Wilkie Collins: A Literary Life. 2008. (Literary Lives Ser.). (ENG.). 240p. 89.00 *(978-1-4039-4896-0(8))* Palgrave Macmillan.

Maupassant, Guy de. Sicily. 2007. (Italica Historical Travel Guides Ser.). (ENG., Illus.). 102p. pap. 15.00 *(978-1-59910-008-1(8))* Italica Pr.

Max, D. T. Every Love Story Is a Ghost Story: A Life of David Foster Wallace. 2012. (ENG.). 368p. 26.95 ***(978-0-670-02592-3(5)***, Viking Adult) Penguin Group (USA) Inc.

Maxwell, William. Conversations with William Maxwell. Burkhardt, Barbara, ed. 2012. (Literary Conversations Ser.). (ENG.). 256p. 40.00 ***(978-1-61703-254-7(9))*** Univ. Pr. of Mississippi.

May, Charles E. Short Story Writers. 2007. (Magill's Choice Ser.). 73.00 *(978-1-58765-391-9(5))*; 73.00 *(978-1-58765-392-6(3))*; 73.00 *(978-1-58765-390-2(7))*;Set. 1344p. 217.00 *(978-1-58765-339-6(3))* Salem Pr., Inc.

May, Jill P., et al. Howard Pyle: Imagining an American School of Art. 2011. (ENG., Illus.). 296p. 45.00 *(978-0-252-03626-2(3))* Univ. of Illinois Pr.

May, Joseph. Samuel Longfellow: Memoir & Letters. 2009. (ENG.). 316p. 36.99 *(978-1-117-73458-3(7))* BiblioBazaar.

May, Stephen J. Michener: A Writer's Journey. 2009. (ENG.). 306p. pap. 19.95 *(978-0-8061-4042-1(9))* Univ. of Oklahoma Pr.

Maynard, Frank & Maynard, Frank. Cowboy's Lament: A Life on the Open Range. Hoy, Jim, ed. 2010. (Voice in the American West Ser.). (Illus.). 248p. 29.95 *(978-0-89672-705-2(X))* Texas Tech Univ. Pr.

Mayzel, Nachman, ed. Dos Mendele Buch: Letters & Autobiographical Sketches, Photos, Drawings, Facsimiles of Mendele Meycher Sforim. 2011. 514p. 60.95 ***(978-1-258-01912-9(4))*** Literary Licensing, LLC.

Mc Kay, Betty. I Only Came for the Music. 2009. 152p. pap. *(978-1-84748-448-2(4))* Athena Pr.

McAteer, Joan. What Was I to Do? 2008. 139p. pap. 9.95 *(978-1-4357-1252-2(8))* Lulu Enterprises Inc.

McBurney, Margaret, ed. It's All about Kindness: Remembering June Callwood. 2010. (ENG.). 256p. 20.00 *(978-1-897151-79-2(9))* Cormorant Bks. Inc. CAN. Dist: Univ. of Toronto Pr.

McCaig, Donald. Eminent Dogs, Dangerous Men: Searching Through Scotland for a Border Collie. 2007. (ENG., Illus.). 240p. per. 15.95 *(978-1-59921-059-9(2)*, Lyons Pr.) Globe Pequot Pr., The.

McCann, Debbie. Life in The '50's: Memoirs of a Baby Boomer. 2009. 432p. pap. 20.49 *(978-1-4389-9103-0(7))* AuthorHouse.

McCarthy, Justin. Reminiscences. 2009. 462p. 35.99 *(978-1-115-99654-9(1))*; 42.99 *(978-1-115-99653-2(3))*; pap. 35.75 *(978-1-115-99656-3(8))*; pap. 36.75 *(978-1-115-99655-6(X))* BiblioBazaar.

—Reminiscences. 2009. 254p. pap. *(978-0-217-85258-6(0))*; 220p. pap. *(978-0-217-85252-4(1))*; 296p. pap. *(978-0-217-85246-3(7))* Books LLC.

McCarthy, William. Anna Letitia Barbauld: Voice of the Enlightenment. 2008. (ENG., Illus.). 792p. (gr. 17). 62.00 *(978-0-8018-9016-1(0))* Johns Hopkins Univ. Pr.

McCauley, Lisa. Du Crow's Nest par Pascal Fuselier. 2008. 276p. pap. 24.95 *(978-0-557-00349-5(0))* Lulu Enterprises Inc.

McClane, Kenneth A. Color: Essays on Race, Family, & History. 2009. (ND Afro/Amer Intellectual Heritage Ser.). (ENG.). 120p. pap. 19.00 *(978-0-268-03515-0(6))* Univ. of Notre Dame Pr.

McCracken, Elizabeth. An Exact Replica of a Figment of My Imagination: A Memoir. 2010. (ENG.). 208p. pap. 12.99 *(978-0-316-02766-3(9)*, Back Bay Bks.) Little Brown & Co.

McCracken, Ellen. The Life & Writing of Fray Angelico Chavez: A New Mexico Renaissance Man. 2009. (Paso Por Aqui Ser. in the Nuevomexicano Literary Heritage Ser.). (ENG., Illus.). 472p. (C). 45.00 *(978-0-8263-4760-2(6))* Univ. of New Mexico Pr.

McCulloch, John. The Dilemma of Modernity: Ramón Gómez de la Serna & the Spanish Modernist Novel. 2007. 206p. (C). 68.95 *(978-0-8204-8183-8(1))* Lang, Peter Publishing, Inc.

McDonald, Lynn. Florence Nightingale at First Hand. 2010. (ENG.). 216p. (C). pap. 24.95 *(978-1-55458-191-7(5)*, Wilfrid Laurier Univ. Pr. CAN. Dist: Univ. of Toronto Pr.

McDowell, Lesley. Between the Sheets: Nine 20th Century Women Writers & Their Famous Literary Partnerships. 2010. (ENG.). 352p. (gr. 12). 30.00 *(978-1-59020-238-8(4))* Overlook Pr., The.

McEwan, Ian. Conversations with Ian McEwan. Roberts, Ryan, ed. 2010. (Literary Conversations Ser.). (ENG.). 224p. 50.00 *(978-1-60473-419-5(1))*; pap. 22.00 *(978-1-60473-420-1(5))* Univ. Pr. of Mississippi.

McFarland, Philip. Loves of Harriet Beecher Stowe. 2008. (ENG.). 336p. pap. 17.00 *(978-0-8021-4390-7(3)*, Grove Pr.) Grove/Atlantic, Inc.

McFarland, Ron. The Rockies in First Person: A Critical Study of Recent American Memoirs from the Region. 2008. (ENG., Illus.). 219p. pap. 39.95 *(978-0-7864-3717-7(0))* McFarland & Co., Inc. Pubs.

McGahern, John. All Will Be Well. 2007. (Vintage International Ser.). (ENG.). 304p. pap. 14.95 *(978-1-4000-7986-5(1)*, Vintage) Knopf Doubleday Publishing Group.

McGowan, Matthew M. Ovid in Exile: Power & Poetic Redress in the Tristia & Epistulae Ex Ponto. 2009. *(978-90-04-17076-6(6))* BRILL.

McGrigor, Mary & Watson, Norman. Poet McGonagall: The Biography of William McGonagall. 2010. (ENG., Illus.). 320p. 16.95 *(978-1-84158-884-1(9))* Birlinn, Ltd. GBR. Dist: Interlink Publishing Group, Inc.

McInerny, Ralph. I Alone Have Escaped to Tell You: My Life & Pastimes. 2011. (ENG., Illus.). 192p. pap. 22.00 ***(978-0-268-03523-5(7))*** Univ. of Notre Dame Pr.

McInerny, Ralph. Some Catholic Writers. 2007. 166p. 23.00 *(978-1-58731-777-4(X))* St. Augustine's Pr., Inc.

McKay, Claude. A Long Way from Home. Jarrett, Gene Andrew, ed. 2007. (Multi-Ethnic Literatures of the Americas Ser.). (ENG.). 312p. per. 23.95 *(978-0-8135-3968-3(4))* Rutgers Univ. Pr.

McKay, Claude, ed. A Long Way from Home. 2007. (Multi-Ethnic Literatures of the Americas (MELA) Ser.). (ENG.). 302p. 68.00 *(978-0-8135-3967-6(6))* Rutgers Univ. Pr.

McLaren, Duncan. Looking for Enid: The Mysterious & Inventive Life of Enid Blyton. Jones, Philip Gwyn, ed. 2008. (ENG., Illus.). 336p. pap. 16.95 *(978-1-84627-116-8(9))* Granta Bks. GBR. Dist: Independent Pubs. Group.

—Looking for Enid: The Mysterious & Inventive Life of Enid Blyton. 2007. (ENG., Illus.). 336p. 29.95 *(978-1-84708-115-5(0))* Granta Bks. GBR. Dist: Independent Pubs. Group.

McLean, James "Doc". Articles of Love. 2011. 40p. pap. 21.99 ***(978-1-4568-4342-7(7))*** Xlibris Corp.

McMinn, Joseph. Jonathan Swift & the Arts. 2010. (Illus.). 187p. 46.00 *(978-0-87413-068-3(9))*; (ENG.). 46.00 *(978-1-61149-125-8(8))* Univ. of Delaware Pr.

McMonagle, Michael Francis. Seven Lives of the Devil's Spawn: From Destruction to Salvation A True Wild Cat Story. 2011. 144p. 23.50 ***(978-1-60976-292-6(4)***, Eloquent Bks.) AEG Literary Publishing Services, Inc.

McMurtry, Larry. Books: A Memoir. 2009. (ENG.). 272p. pap. 14.00 *(978-1-4165-8335-6(1))* Simon & Schuster.

—Literary Life: A Second Memoir. 2011. (ENG.). 192p. pap. 14.00 *(978-1-4391-5994-1(7))* Simon & Schuster.

McNamee, Thomas. The Man Who Changed the Way We Eat: Craig Claiborne & the American Food Renaissance. 2012. (ENG.). 352p. 27.00 ***(978-1-4391-9150-7(6)***, Free Pr.) Free Pr.

McPhee, John. Silk Parachute, 1 vol. (ENG.). 240p. 2011. pap. 15.00 *(978-0-374-53262-8(1))* 2010. 25.00 *(978-0-374-26373-7(6))* Farrar, Straus & Giroux.

McRae, William. Faith that Kept Me: How You Stay Committed to Your Purpose. 2010. 116p. pap. 15.00 *(978-1-4520-4485-9(6))* AuthorHouse.

McSherry, James. A Clean Street's A Happy Street: A Bronx Memoir. 2007. 164p. (YA). 19.95 *(978-0-595-68484-7(X))*; (ENG.). per. 9.95 *(978-1-58348-863-8(4))* iUniverse, Inc. (iUniverse Star).

McWilliam, Candia. What to Look for in Winter: A Memoir in Blindness. 2012. (ENG.). 464p. 27.99 ***(978-0-06-209450-6(5))*** HarperCollins Pubs.

Mcwilliams, Carey. Ambrose Bierce: A Biography. 2011. 374p. 53.95 ***(978-1-258-06821-9(4))*** Literary Licensing, LLC.

Mda, Zakes. Sometimes There Is a Void: Memoirs of an Outsider. 2012. (ENG., Illus.). 576p. 35.00 ***(978-0-374-28094-9(0))*** Farrar, Straus & Giroux.

Meade, Marion. Lonelyhearts: The Screwball World of Nathanael West & Eileen Mckenney. (ENG., Illus.). 2011. 432p. pap. 15.95 *(978-0-547-38638-6(9)*, Mariner Bks.) 2010. 416p. 28.00 *(978-0-15-101149-0(4))* Houghton Mifflin Harcourt Trade & Reference Pubs.

Meanor, Patrick & Lee, Richard E. American Short-Story Writers since World War II: Fifth Series, Vol 335. 2007. (Dictionary of Literary Biography Ser.). (ENG., Illus.). 480p. 315.00 *(978-0-7876-8153-1(9))* Cengage Gale.

Meddeb, Abdelwahab. Tombeau of Ibn Arabi & White Traverses. Nancy, Jean-Luc & Mandell, Charlotte, trs. from FRE. 3rd ed. 2010. (ENG.). 88p. 70.00 *(978-0-8232-3114-0(3))* Fordham Univ. Pr.

Medrano, Manuel & Paredes, Américo. Américo Paredes: In His Own Words, an Authorized Biography. 2010. (Al Filo: Mexican American Studies Ser.). (ENG., Illus.). 224p. 22.95 *(978-1-57441-287-1(6))* Univ. of North Texas Pr.

Meehan, J. P. The Lady of the Limberlost: A Biography. 24.95 *(978-0-8488-0094-9(X))* Amereon LTD.

Meehan, Sean Ross. Mediating American Autobiography: Photography in Emerson, Thoreau, Douglass, & Whitman. 2008. (ENG., Illus.). 264p. (C). 39.95 *(978-0-8262-1792-9(3))* Univ. of Missouri Pr.

Meinecke, Bill. True Friends: Life with Five Seeing Eye Dogs. 2009. 112p. 22.00 *(978-1-4389-8051-5(5))*; pap. 12.00 *(978-1-4389-8050-8(7))* AuthorHouse.

Meinecke, Tom. Arms of God: From Prussia to Texas to Death in the Brazos River. 2010. 208p. pap. 16.00 *(978-1-4520-1596-5(1))* AuthorHouse.

Meisami, Julie Scott & Starkey, Paul, eds. Encyclopedia of Arabic Literature. 2010. (ENG.). 862p. pap. 90.00 *(978-0-415-57113-5(8))* Routledge.

Meltzer, Milton. Nathaniel Hawthorne: A Biography. 2006. (American Literary Greats Ser.). (Illus.). 160p. (gr. 6-18). lib. bdg. 31.93 (978-0-7613-3459-0(9), Millbrook Pr.) Lerner Publishing Group.

Melville, Lewis. Lady Mary Wortley Montague: Her Life & Letters (1689-1762) 2007. (ENG.). 276p. pap. 21.99 (978-1-4264-4239-1(4)); 308p. pap. 24.99 (978-1-4264-4303-9(X)) BiblioBazaar.

—Life & Letters of John Gay: (1685-1732) 2006. (ENG.). 172p. pap. 19.99 (978-1-4264-7421-7(0)); 194p. pap. 21.99 (978-1-4264-7498-9(9)) BiblioBazaar.

—The Life of William Makepeace Thackeray V2. 2007. (ENG.). 348p. 46.95 (978-0-548-15137-2(7)); 352p. per. 31.95 (978-1-4304-4483-1(5)) Kessinger Publishing, LLC.

Mencken, H. L. Mencken on Mencken: A New Collection of Autobiographical Writings. Joshi, S. T., ed. 2010. (Illus.). 296p. pap. 24.95 (978-0-8071-3592-1(5)) Louisiana State Univ. Pr.

Menzies, Heather. Enter Mourning: A Memoire on Death, Dementia, & Coming Home. 2009. (ENG., Illus.). 240p. pap. 19.95 (978-1-55470-155-1(4)) Key Porter Bks. CAN. Dist: Perseus-PGW.

Méras, Phyllis. Country Editor: Henry Beetle Hough & the Vineyard Gazette. 2006. (Illus.). pap. 21.95 (978-1-884592-42-3(2)) Images from the Past, Inc.

Mercer, Jeremy. Time Was Soft There: A Paris Sojourn at Shakespeare & Co. 2006. (ENG.). 272p. pap. 15.00 (978-0-312-34740-6(5)) Picador.

Mercer, Wendy S. The Life & Travels of Xavier Marmier (1808-1892) Bringing World Literature to France. 2007. (British Academy Postdoctoral Fellowship Monographs). (Illus.). 320p. 135.00 (978-0-19-726388-4(7)) Oxford Univ. Pr., Inc.

Merrifield, Andy. John Berger. 2012. (Reaktion Books - Critical Lives Ser.). (Illus.). 224p. pap. 16.95 (978-1-86189-904-0(1)) Reaktion Bks., Ltd. GBR. Dist: Chicago Distribution Ctr.

Messent, Peter. Mark Twain & Male Friendship: The Twichell, Howells, & Rogers Friendships. 2009. (ENG., Illus.). 272p. 49.95 (978-0-19-539116-9(0)) Oxford Univ. Pr., Inc.

Messerli, Douglas. My Year 2005: Terrifying Times - Readings, Events, Memories. 2006. (Green Integer Ser.). (ENG., Illus.). 430p. per. 15.95 (978-1-933382-65-4(1)) Green Integer.

Messner, T. L. Three Women & the Men They Dance With, 1 vol. 2009. 131p. pap. 24.95 (978-1-60703-953-2(2)) PublishAmerica, Inc.

Meyer, Nicholas. The View from the Bridge: Memories of Star Trek & a Life in Hollywood. 2010. (ENG.). 272p. (gr. 12). 16.00 (978-0-452-29653-4(6), Plume) Penguin Group (USA) Inc.

Meyers, Jeffrey. The Genius & the Goddess: Arthur Miller & Marilyn Monroe. 2012. (ENG., Illus.). 384p. pap. 19.95 (978-0-252-07854-5(3)) Univ. of Illinois Pr.

—Orwell: Life & Art. 2010. (ENG., Illus.). 272p. pap. 25.00 (978-0-252-07746-3(6)) Univ. of Illinois Pr.

—Samuel Johnson: The Struggle. 2008. (ENG.). 552p. 35.00 (978-0-465-04571-6(5)) Perseus Bks. Group.

Meysenbug, Malwida von. Memoiren einer Idealistin. 2009. 308p. 25.99 (978-1-103-30566-7(2)); pap. 19.99 (978-1-103-30561-2(1)) BiblioBazaar.

Meysenbug, Malwida von & Wiggershaus, Renate. Memoiren einer Idealistin. (GER., Illus.). 278p. (978-3-89741-007-7(9)) Helmer, Ulrike.

Michener, James A. The World Is My Home: A Memoir. 2007. (ENG.). 528p. pap. 15.95 (978-0-8129-7813-1(7), Random Hse. Trade Paperbacks) Random House Publishing Group.

Miederhoff, Thorsten. Man erspare es mir, mein Juristenherz Auszuschütten: Dr. iur. Kurt Tucholsky (1890-1935) 2008. (Rechtshistorische Reihe Ser.). (GER., Illus.). 302p. pap. 74.95 (978-3-631-57581-9(5)) Lang, Peter GmbH, Europaischer Verlag der Wissenschaften DEU. Dist: Lang, Peter.

Miele, Leonard. Voice of the Tide: The Cape Cod Heritage of Katharine Lee Bates. 2009. (Illus.). 112p. pap. 20.00 (978-0-932027-13-9(X)) Spinner Pubns., Inc.

Mielziner, Ella McKenna Friend & Mielziner, Moses. Moses Mielziner, 1828-1903: A Biography with A Bibliography of His Writings. Bloch, Joshua, ed. 2011. 298p. 48.95 (978-1-258-09334-1(0)) Literary Licensing, LLC.

Miguel, Bobby. Every Good Boy Does Fine. 2010. 188p. pap. 14.99 (978-1-4490-2545-8(5)) AuthorHouse.

Miles, Barry. Charles Bukowski. 2006. (ENG.). 320p. pap. 14.95 (978-0-7535-1142-8(8)) Virgin Bks. Ltd. GBR. Dist: Independent Pubs. Group.

Millar, Paul. No Fretful Sleeper: A Life of Bill Pearson. 2010. (ENG., Illus.). 400p. pap. 34.95 (978-1-86940-419-2(X)) Auckland Univ. Pr. NZL. Dist: Independent Pubs. Group.

Miller. A Life of Goodwill: Three Leaders & Their Impact on an Organization. 2009. 236p. pap. 14.49 (978-1-4389-9695-0(0)) AuthorHouse.

Miller, Fred J. Fred J Miller: A Biography of A Man Who Hoped Never to Grow So Old That A New Idea Would Shock Him. 2011. 40p. 35.95 (978-1-258-07405-0(2)) Literary Licensing, LLC.

Miller, Karen E. Quinones. Angry Ass Black Woman. 2012. (ENG.). 288p. pap. 15.00 (978-1-4516-0782-6(2), Gallery Books/Karen Hunter Publishing) Gallery Books/Karen Hunter Publishing.

Miller, Leo S. Leo S. Miller Campus Penny-Pincher. 2007. 136p. pap. 12.00 (978-0-9789908-3-1(8)) Ketch Publishing.

Miller, Meredith. The A to Z of Lesbian Literature. 2010. (A to Z Guide Ser.). (ENG.). 300p. pap. 34.45 (978-0-8108-7609-5(4)) Scarecrow Pr., Inc.

Miller, Teresa. Means of Transit: A Slightly Embellished Memoir. 2008. (ENG., Illus.). 200p. 24.95 (978-0-8061-3971-5(4)) Univ. of Oklahoma Pr.

Millet, Catherine. Jealousy: The Other Life of Catherine M. Stevenson, Helen, tr. (ENG.). 192p. 2011. pap. 14.00 (978-0-8021-4519-2(1)) 2010. 23.00 (978-0-8021-1915-5(8)) Grove/Atlantic, Inc. (Grove Pr.).

Mills, Howard. Peacock: His Circle & His Age. 2010. (ENG.). 276p. pap. 23.99 (978-0-521-14830-6(8)) Cambridge Univ. Pr.

Milne, Lesley. Mikhail Bulgakov: A Critical Biography. 2009. (Major European Authors Ser.). (Illus.). 340p. pap. 36.99 (978-0-521-12246-7(5)) Cambridge Univ. Pr.

Minick, Jim. The Blueberry Years: A Memoir of Farm & Family. (ENG.). 352p. 2012. pap. 16.99 (978-1-250-01158-9(2), St. Martin's Griffin) 2010. (Illus.). 27.99 (978-0-312-57142-9(9), Dunne, Thomas Bks.) St. Martin's Pr.

Mitchell, Allan. The Devil's Captain: Ernst Jünger in Nazi Paris, 1941-1944. 2011. (Illus.). 140p. 49.95 (978-0-85745-114-9(6)) Berghahn Bks., Inc.

Mitchell, David & Mitchell, Mike. Vivo: The Life of Gustav Meyrink. 2008. (ENG.). 196p. pap. 15.99 (978-1-903517-69-7(9)) Dedalus, Ltd.

Mitchell, Donald G. My Farm of Edgewood. 2009. 340p. 36.99 (978-1-115-34673-3(3)); 32.99 (978-1-115-34672-6(5)); pap. 31.75 (978-1-115-34670-2(9)) BiblioBazaar.

Mitchell, Malinda. It Was Easier to Write. 2011. 72p. pap. 19.95 (978-1-4512-7655-8(9)) PublishAmerica, Inc.

Mitchell, Verner D. Western Echoes of the Harlem Renaissance: The Life & Writings of Anita Scott Coleman. Davis, Cynthia J., ed. 2008. (ENG., Illus.). 240p. (C). 45.00 (978-0-8061-3956-2(0)); pap. 19.95 (978-0-8061-3975-3(7)) Univ. of Oklahoma Pr.

Mitchell, Xavier R. Behaving Wisely. 2011. 120p. pap. 19.95 (978-1-4626-0719-8(5)) PublishAmerica, Inc.

Mitchison, Naomi & Smith, Ali. Small Talk: Memories of an Edwardian Childhood. 2009. 158p. pap. (978-1-84921-020-1(9)) Kennedy & Boyd.

Mittelman, Jennifer K., told to. Our Cherry Tree Still Stands: The Story of Michael Herskovitz. 2009. 104p. pap. 11.95 (978-1-4401-3607-8(6)) iUniverse, Inc.

Moe, Jens. My America: The Culture of Giving. 2011. 336p. 32.95 (978-1-4620-3129-0(3)); pap. 22.95 (978-1-4620-3128-3(5)) iUniverse, Inc.

Moffat, Wendy. A Great Unrecorded History: A New Life of E. M. Forster. 2010. (ENG., Illus.). 416p. 32.50 (978-0-374-16678-6(1)) Farrar, Straus & Giroux.

—A Great Unrecorded History: A New Life of E. M. Forster. 2011. (ENG., Illus.). 432p. pap. 20.00 (978-0-312-57289-1(1)) Picador.

Mohamed, Adam & Mohamed, Noorjehan. Journey into the Unknown. 2011. (ENG.). 152p. pap. 17.95 (978-1-920222-47-5(2)) STE Pubs. ZAF. Dist: Independent Pubs. Group.

Monroe, Debra. On the Outskirts of Normal: Forging a Family Against the Grain. 2010. 248p. 22.50 (978-0-87074-560-7(3)) Southern Methodist Univ. Pr.

Monroy, Armando. I Have to Live with Myself, & So, A Personal Narrative. 2011. 300p. 31.95 (978-1-4502-8217-8(2)); pap. 21.95 (978-1-4502-8218-5(0)) iUniverse, Inc.

Montaldi-Seelhorst, Gabriele. Francesco Biamonti (1928-2001) Das Romanwerk. 2009. (Grundlagen der Italianistik Ser.). (GER.). 194p. 57.95 (978-3-631-59784-2(3)) Lang, Peter GmbH, Europaischer Verlag der Wissenschaften DEU. Dist: Lang, Peter.

Montana Historical Society. Blackfeet Man: James Willard Schultz. 2011. 36p. 35.95 (978-1-258-06494-5(4)) Literary Licensing, LLC.

Montgomery, Lee. The Things Between Us: A Memoir. 2007. (ENG.). 256p. pap. 14.00 (978-1-4165-4310-7(4), Free Pr.) Free Pr.

Montiel, Dito. A Guide to Recognizing Your Saints: A Memoir. movie tie-in ed. 2006. (ENG., Illus.). 208p. per. 13.95 (978-1-56025-960-2(4)) Da Capo Pr., Inc.

Moon, Brenda. More Usefully Employed. 2006. (Occasional Publications). (ENG., Illus.). 319p. (C). 70.00 (978-0-85698-169-2(9)) Egypt Exploration Society GBR. Dist: Brown, David Bk. Co., The.

Moon, Mistique. What the Hell Was That?, 1 vol. 2009. 132p. pap. 19.95 (978-1-60703-496-4(4)) PublishAmerica, Inc.

Mooney, Brian. Frank Baines: A Life Beyond the Sea. 2011. (Illus.). 316p. pap. 16.95 (978-1-85418-741-3(4)) Thorogood GBR. Dist: Stylus Publishing, LLC.

Moore, D. Stanley. Grandpa's Bedtime Stories. 2009. 69p. pap. 23.70 (978-0-557-21619-2(2)) Lulu Enterprises Inc.

—Grandpa's Bedtime Stories in Black & White. 2009. 69p. pap. 5.88 (978-0-557-21656-7(7)) Lulu Enterprises Inc.

Moore, David. Dying Is Not on My Day Planner for Tomorrow. 2011. 116p. 23.95 (978-1-4634-2707-8(7)); pap. 14.95 (978-1-4634-2706-1(9)) AuthorHouse.

Moore, George. Memoirs of My Dead Life. 2008. 272p. 25.99 (978-0-554-31991-9(8)) 2008. 272p. 28.99 (978-0-554-22688-0(X)) 2007. (ENG.). 242p. pap. 20.99 (978-1-4264-2861-6(8)) 2007. (ENG.). 270p. pap. 23.99 (978-1-4264-2898-2(7)) BiblioBazaar.

—Memoirs of My Dead Life. 2007. (ENG.). 236p. per. (978-1-4065-4586-9(4)) Dodo Pr.

—Memoirs of My Dead Life. 2009. (ENG.). 236p. pap. 14.95 (978-1-4385-1344-7(5), Book Jungle) Standard Pubns., Inc.

—Memoirs of My Dead Life. 2008. 360p. 32.95 (978-1-4344-6397-5(4)); pap. 19.95 (978-1-4344-6396-8(6)) Wildside Pr., LLC.

Moore, J. S. Rooting Branches: Understanding Apples Book Three. 2010. 194p. 19.95 (978-1-4327-5624-6(9)); pap. 12.95 (978-1-4327-5346-7(0)) Outskirts Pr., Inc.

Moore, Lady Tina. Shattered but Not Destroyed. 2010. 96p. pap. 9.99 (978-1-60911-943-0(6), Eloquent Bks.) AEG Literary Publishing Services, Inc.

Moore, Michael. Here Comes Trouble: Stories from My Life. 2012. (ENG.). 500p. pap. 15.99 (978-1-4555-1307-9(5)) 2011. (ENG.). 448p. 26.99 (978-0-446-53224-2(X)) 2011. (Illus.). ix, 427p. (978-0-446-54075-9(7)) 2011. (ENG.). 592p. 28.99 (978-0-446-54121-3(4)) Grand Central Publishing.

Moore, Susanna. Light Years: A Girlhood in Hawai'i. 2009. (ENG.). 208p. pap. 13.00 (978-0-8021-4406-5(3), Grove Pr.) Grove/Atlantic, Inc.

Moorehead, Caroline. Gellhorn: A Twentieth-Century Life. pap. 16.00 (978-0-8050-6554-1(7), Owl Bks.) Holt, Henry & Co.

Morace, Robert A. John Cheever. 2011. (978-1-58765-827-3(5)) Salem Pr., Inc.

Morais, Fernando. El Mago: La Extraordinaria Historia de Paulo Coelho. 2008. (SPA.). 704p. pap. 18.99 (978-0-06-137508-8(X), Rayo) HarperCollins Pubs.

—Paulo Coelho: A Warrior's Life - The Authorized Biography. (ENG.). 2010. 464p. pap. 15.99 (978-0-06-177429-4(4), HarperOne) 2009. 608p. 26.99 (978-0-06-171888-5(2), HarperOne) 2009. 784p. pap. 26.99 (978-0-06-188588-4(6), HarperLuxe) HarperCollins Pubs.

Moran, Thomas, ed. Chinese Fiction Writers, 1900-1949, Vol. 328. 2006. (Dictionary of Literary Biography Ser.: Vol. 328). (ENG., Illus.). 512p. 315.00 (978-0-7876-8146-3(6)) Cengage Gale.

Morgan, Charles. Epitaph on George Moore. 2007. (ENG.). 68p. per. (978-1-4067-0323-8(0)) Read Bks.

Morgan, Phyllis S. N. Scott Momaday: Remembering Ancestors, Earth, & Traditions - An Annotated Bio-Bibliography. annot. ed. 2010. (American Indian Literature & Critical Studies Ser.). (ENG.). 400p. (C). 60.00 (978-0-8061-4054-4(2)) Univ. of Oklahoma Pr.

Morgan, Rebecca. Under the Magnolia Trees: My Childhood Memories. 2010. 72p. pap. (978-1-84991-223-5(8)) Chipmunkapublishing.

Morgan, Susan. Bombay Anna: The Real Story & Remarkable Adventures of the King & I Governess. 2008. (Illus.). 272p. 40.00 (978-0-520-25226-4(8)) Univ. of California Pr.

Morgan, Ted. Literary Outlaw: The Life & Times of William S. Burroughs. 2012. (ENG.). 768p. pap. 24.95 (978-0-393-34260-4(3), 34260) Norton, W. W. & Co., Inc.

Morgan, Vanessa. I Go Hard. 2010. 132p. pap. 13.95 (978-1-4520-7597-6(2)) AuthorHouse.

Mori, Kyoko. Yarn: Remembering the Way Home. 2009. (ENG.). 240p. pap. 15.95 (978-1-934848-63-0(8)) GemmaMedia.

Morín, José R. Lopez. The Legacy of Américo Paredes. 2006. (Rio Grande/Rio Bravo Ser.: No. 10). (ENG., Illus.). 192p. per. 19.95 (978-1-58544-536-3(3)) Texas A&M Univ. Pr.

Morris, Mary. The River Queen: A Memoir. 2008. (ENG., Illus.). 288p. pap. 17.00 (978-0-312-42789-4(1)) Picador.

Morrison, Robert. The English Opium-Eater: A Biography of Thomas de Quincey. 2010. (ENG., Illus.). 488p. 37.99 (978-0-297-85279-7(5), Weidenfeld & Nicolson) Orion Publishing Group, Ltd. GBR. Dist: Hachette Bk. Group.

—The English Opium Eater: A Biography of Thomas de Quincey. 2010. (ENG.). 480p. 35.00 (978-1-60598-132-1(X), 605132) Pegasus Bks.

Morrow, Barbara Olenyik. Nature's Storyteller: The Life of Gene Stratton-Porter. 2010. (978-0-87195-284-4(X)) Indiana Historical Society.

Morse, John T., Jr. Thomas Sergeant Perry A Memoir. 2006. pap. 24.95 (978-1-4286-5755-7(X)) Kessinger Publishing, LLC.

Mort, Terry. The Hemingway Patrols: Ernest Hemingway & His Hunt for U-Boats. 2011. (ENG.). 272p. pap. 17.99 (978-1-4165-9787-2(5), Scribner) Scribner.

Morton, Brian. Edgar Allan Poe. 2010. (Life&Times Ser.). (ENG., Illus.). 192p. 14.95 (978-1-905791-52-1(6)) Haus Publishing GBR. Dist: Consortium Bk. Sales & Distribution.

Moseley, Merritt, ed. Booker Prize Novels, 1969-2005, Vol. 326. 2006. (Dictionary of Literary Biography Ser.: Vol. 326). (ENG., Illus.). 392p. 315.00 (978-0-7876-8144-9(X)) Cengage Gale.

Moser, Benjamin. Why This World: A Biography of Clarice Lispector, 1 vol. (ENG., Illus.). 496p. 2012. pap. 19.95 (978-0-19-989582-3(1)) 2009. 99.00 (978-0-19-538556-4(X)) Oxford Univ. Pr., Inc.

Moses, Kate. Cakewalk: A Memoir. 2010. (ENG.). 368p. 26.00 (978-0-385-34298-8(5), Dial Pr.) Random House Publishing Group.

Moses, Sibyl E. African American Women Writers in New Jersey, 1836-2000: A Biographical Dictionary & Bibliographic Guide. 2006. (ENG., Illus.). 256p. per. 29.95 (978-0-8135-4019-1(4)) Rutgers Univ. Pr.

Mosher, Howard Frank. The Great Northern Express: A Writer's Journey Home. 2012. 246p. (978-0-307-45070-8(8)); (ENG.). 256p. E-Book (978-0-307-45095-1(3)); (ENG.). 256p. 25.00 (978-0-307-45069-2(4)) Crown Publishing Group.

Mosley, Nicholas. Paradoxes of Peace: or The Presence of Infinity. 2009. (British Literature Ser.). (ENG.). 190p. pap. 13.95 (978-1-56478-539-8(4)) Dalkey Archive Pr.

Mosley, Walter. Conversations with Walter Mosley. Brady, Owen E., ed. 2011. (Literary Conversations Ser.). (ENG.). 256p. 55.00 (978-1-60473-942-8(8)); pap. 25.00 (978-1-60473-943-5(6)) Univ. Pr. of Mississippi.

Mossé, Claude. Démosthène, Ou, Les Ambiguïtés de la Politique. (FRE., Illus.). 159p. (978-2-200-21169-1(4)) Armand, Colin.

Mossman, Carol A. Writing with a Vengeance: The Countess de Chabrillan's Rise from Prostitution. 2009. (ENG., Illus.). 224p. (978-0-8020-9691-3(3)) Univ. of Toronto Pr.

Motier, Donald. Gerard: The Influence of Jack Kerouac's Brother on His Life & Writing, 1 vol. 2010. 66p. pap. 19.95 (978-1-4489-5519-0(X)) PublishAmerica, Inc.

Motley, John Lothrop. Correspondence. Curtis, George W., ed. 16. 67.50 (978-0-404-04536-4(7))17. 67.50 (978-0-404-04537-1(5)) AMS Pr., Inc.

Mott, Eric L. We Met at Starbucks: A Love Story. 2008. 73p. pap. 16.95 (978-1-60563-163-9(9)) PublishAmerica, Inc.

Moutoux, David T. A Journal: 2009. 2010. 300p. pap. 21.95 (978-1-4327-6070-0(X)) Outskirts Pr., Inc.

Mowat, Farley. Bay of Spirits: A Love Story. 2009. (ENG., Illus.). 432p. pap. 16.95 (978-0-7710-6467-8(5), McClelland & Stewart) McClelland & Stewart CAN. Dist: Random Hse., Inc.

—Eastern Passage. (ENG.). 224p. 2011. pap. 19.95 (978-0-7710-6492-0(6), Emblem Edns) 2010. 27.95 (978-0-7710-6491-3(8), McClelland & Stewart) McClelland & Stewart CAN. Dist: Random Hse., Inc.

—Otherwise. 2009. (ENG.). 368p. pap. 16.95 (978-0-7710-6490-6(X), Emblem Edns) McClelland & Stewart CAN. Dist: Random Hse., Inc.

Moylan, Virginia Lynn. Zora Neale Hurston's Final Decade. 2011. (ENG., Illus.). 144p. 24.95 (978-0-8130-3578-9(3)) Univ. Pr. of Florida.

MP. Such Is Life. 2011. 124p. pap. 12.33 (978-1-4269-8942-1(3)) Trafford Publishing.

Mqhayi, S. E. K. Abantu Besizwe: Historical & Biographical Writings, 1902 - 1944. Opland, Jeff, ed. & tr. by. 2010. (ENG.). 640p. pap. 39.95 (978-1-86814-501-0(8)) Witwatersrand Univ. Pr. Pubns. ZAF. Dist: Transaction Pubs.

Muggeridge, Malcolm. Chronicles of Wasted Time: An Autobiography. 2006. (ENG.). 576p. per. (978-1-57383-376-9(2), Regent College Publishing) Regent College Publishing.

Muka, Carolyn Kennedy. An Uncommon Everyday Woman. 2008. 164p. pap. 12.95 (978-0-9821654-3-0(9)) Peppertree Pr., The.

Mukhopadhyay, Parimal. You Only Have One Address, 1 vol. 2010. 238p. pap. 24.95 (978-1-61582-598-1(3)) PublishAmerica, Inc.

Muller, Connie. Hello-Goodbye My Precious Child: A Mother's True Story of Her Special Child's Journey from Heaven to Earth & Back to Heaven. 2011. (Illus.). 272p. pap. 15.95 (978-1-4327-7498-1(0)) Outskirts Pr., Inc.

Muller, Gilbert H. William Cullen Bryant: Author of America. 2008. (Illus.). 410p. 30.00 (978-0-7914-7467-9(4)) State Univ. of New York Pr.

Mumford, Lewis. Thomas Beer, Aristocrat of Letters: The Saturday Review of Literature, May 4 1940. 2011. 20p. pap. 35.95 (978-1-258-05425-0(6)) Literary Licensing, LLC.

Muradi, Michael F. Memoirs of a Legend in Infancy: Volume 1. 2008. 108p. pap. 16.95 (978-1-60813-160-0(2)) PublishAmerica, Inc.

Murphy, Dervla. Wheels within Wheels: The Makings of a Traveller. 2010. (ENG., Illus.). 240p. pap. 29.95 (978-1-906011-40-6(0)) Eland Bks. GBR. Dist: Dufour Editions, Inc.

Murra, Jason. To Hell & Back the Life Account of Jason Murr. 2009. 96p. pap. 11.95 (978-1-4401-5981-7(5)) iUniverse, Inc.

Murray, Andy. Into the Unknown: The Fantastic Life of Nigel Kneale. 2006. (Illus.). 191p. per. 17.95 (978-1-900486-50-7(4)) Headpress GBR. Dist: SCB Distributors.

Murray, Iain H. Life of Lloyd-Jones, 2 vols. Incl. Life of D. Martyn Lloyd-Jones Vol. 1: The First Forty Years, 1899-1939. 412p. 1983. 35.99 (978-0-85151-353-9(0)); Vol. 2. Life of D. Martyn Lloyd-Jones Vol. 2: The Fight of Faith, 1939-1981. 862p. 1990. 39.99 (978-0-85151-564-9(9)); (Illus.). (David Martin Lloyd-Jones Collection). 69.99 (978-0-85151-729-2(3)) Banner of Truth, The.

Murray, Isobel. Jessie Kesson: Writing Her Life. 2011. 322p. pap. (978-1-84921-080-5(2)) Kennedy & Boyd.

Murray, Meg McGavran. Margaret Fuller, Wandering Pilgrim. (ENG.). 552p. 2012. pap. 26.95 (978-0-8203-4335-8(8)) 2008. (Illus.). 49.95 (978-0-8203-2894-2(4)) Univ. of Georgia Pr.

Mustafa, Sophia. The Tanganyika Way. 2009. 240p. pap. 28.95 (978-1-894770-51-4(X)) TSAR Pubns. CAN. Dist: Univ. of Toronto Pr.

Mutter, Helen. Opening the Door. 2010. 120p. 21.95 (978-1-60911-224-0(5), Eloquent Bks.) AEG Literary Publishing Services, Inc.

Myers, Albert J. Mankind Man Unkind. 2011. 192p. 29.99 (978-1-4628-7155-1(0)); pap. 19.99 (978-1-4628-7154-4(2)) Xlibris Corp.

Myers, Ron. The Wholly Liable. 2011. 216p. pap. 9.99 (978-1-61667-255-3(2)) Raider Publishing International.

Nadel, Ira B. Leon Uris: Life of a Best Seller. 2010. (ENG., Illus.). 366p. 27.95 (978-0-292-70935-5(8)) Univ. of Texas Pr.

Naimy, Mikhail & Gibran, Kahlil. Kahlil Gibran: A Biography. 2011. 294p. 48.95 (978-1-258-03100-8(0)) Literary Licensing, LLC.

Naipaul, V. S. A Writer's People: Ways of Looking & Feeling. 2009. (Vintage International Ser.). (ENG.). 208p. pap. 15.00 (978-0-375-70729-2(8), Vintage) Knopf Doubleday Publishing Group.

Najjar, Alexandre. Kahlil Gibran: A Biography. 2008. (ENG., Illus.). 192p. pap. 14.95 (978-0-86356-668-4(5)) Saqi Bks. GBR. Dist: Consortium Bk. Sales & Distribution.

Nancy, Jean-Luc & Meddeb, Abdelwahab. Tombeau of Ibn Arabi & White Traverses. Mandell, Charlotte, tr. from FRE. 2010. (ENG.). 88p. pap. 18.00 (978-0-8232-3115-7(1)) Fordham Univ. Pr.

Naqishbendi, Rauf. The Garden of the Poets, 1 vol. 2009. 392p. pap. 29.95 (978-1-60703-704-0(1)) PublishAmerica, Inc.

Narain, Denise deCaires. Olive Senior. 2011. (Writers & Their Work Ser.). (ENG.). 154p. (C). pap. 26.00 (978-0-7463-1099-1(4)) Northcote Hse. Publishers, Ltd. GBR. Dist: Brown, David Bk. Co., The.

Nelson, Lee. Hoofbeats of the Heart: A Personal History. 2011. pap. 17.99 (978-1-59955-909-4(9), Council Pr.) Cedar Fort, Inc./CFI Distribution.

Nestor, Tom. Talking to Kate. 2009. (ENG.). 254p. pap. 23.95 (978-1-905172-91-7(5)) Collins Pr., The IRL. Dist: Dufour Editions, Inc.

Newell, Stephanie. The Forger's Tale: The Search for Odeziaku. 2006. (New African Histories Ser.). (ENG., Illus.). 272p. per. 24.95 (978-0-8214-1710-2(X)) Ohio Univ. Pr.

Newlin, Keith. Hamlin Garland: A Life. 2008. (ENG., Illus.). 536p. 40.00 *(978-0-8032-3347-8(7))* Univ. of Nebraska Pr.

Newman, Irv. Living on House Money. 2008. 140p. pap. 13.95 *(978-0-9818683-1-8(2))* Peppertree Pr., The.

Newton-Smith, William. Dr. Muhlenberg. (American Religious Leaders Ser.). 272p. reprint ed. 98.00 *(978-0-7222-8474-2(8))* Library Reprints, Inc.

Ngugi wa Thiong'o. Dreams in a Time of War: A Childhood Memoir. 2010. (ENG.). 272p. 24.95 *(978-0-307-37883-5(7),* Pantheon) Knopf Doubleday Publishing Group.

Niall, Brenda. Life Class: The Education of a Biographer. 2007. (ENG., Illus.). 224p. 25.00 *(978-0-522-85343-8(9))* Melbourne Univ. Publishing AUS. Dist: Independent Pubs. Group.

Nichol, John. Thomas Carlyle. 2007. 214p. pap. 20.99 *(978-1-4346-2037-8(9))* BiblioBazaar.

—Thomas Carlyle. 2011. (Cambridge Library Collection - English Men of Letters Ser.). (ENG.). 264p. pap. 23.99 ***(978-1-108-03447-0(0))*** Cambridge Univ. Pr.

Nicol, Eric. Anything for a Laugh: Memoirs. unabr. ed. (ENG., Illus.). 264p. *(978-1-55017-187-7(9))* Harbour Publishing Co., Ltd.

Nicosia, Gerald & Santos, Anne Marie. One & Only: The Untold Story of on the Road. 2011. (ENG., Illus.). 242p. 22.95 *(978-1-936740-04-8(4),* Viva Editions) Cleis Pr.

Nizankiewicz, Michael J. I Did it My Way: ... & it Wasn't Always the Right Way. 2010. 100p. pap. 17.99 *(978-1-4520-3060-9(X))* AuthorHouse.

Nock, Albert J. The Memoirs of a Superfluous Man. reprint ed. 30.00 *(978-0-404-20192-0(X))* AMS Pr., Inc.

Nolville, Florence. Isaac B. Singer: A Life. Temerson, Catherine, tr. from FRE. 2008. (ENG., Illus.). 192p. pap. 14.95 *(978-0-8101-2482-0(3))* Northwestern Univ. Pr.

Nolan, Tom. Ross MacDonald: A Biography. 2008. (ENG., Illus.). 496p. pap. 30.95 *(978-1-4391-0205-3(8),* Scribner) Scribner.

Norburn, Roger. A Katherine Mansfield Chronology. 2008. (Author Chronologies Ser.). (ENG., Illus.). 240p. 105.00 *(978-0-230-52559-7(8))* Palgrave Macmillan.

Norman, Andrew. Arthur Conan Doyle: The Man Behind Sherlock Holmes. 2010. (ENG., Illus.). 192p. pap. 16.95 *(978-0-7524-5275-3(4))* History Pr. Ltd.,The GBR. Dist: Independent Pubs. Group.

—Jane Austen: An Unrequited Love. (ENG., Illus.). 2010. 224p. pap. 17.95 *(978-0-7524-5529-7(X))* 2009. 208p. 36.95 *(978-0-7524-4874-9(9))* History Pr. Ltd.,The GBR. Dist: Independent Pubs. Group.

—Thomas Hardy: Behind the Mask. 2011. (ENG., Illus.). 224p. 26.95 *(978-0-7524-5630-0(X))* History Pr. Ltd.,The GBR. Dist: Independent Pubs. Group.

Norris, Kathleen. Acedia & Me: A Marriage, Monks, & a Writer's Life. (ENG.). 352p. (gr. 12). 2010. pap. 16.00 ***(978-1-59448-438-4(4),*** Riverhead Trade (Paperbacks)) 2008. 25.95 ***(978-1-59448-996-9(3),*** Riverhead Bks. (Hardcover)) Penguin Group (USA) Inc.

Nova, Craig & Beattie, Ann. Brook Trout & the Writing Life. 2011. (ENG.). 176p. pap. 15.95 *(978-0-9820771-4-6(9))* Eno Pubs.

Novalis, et al. The Birth of Novalis: Friedrich Von Hardenberg's Journal of 1797, with Selected Letters & Documents. 2007. (Suny Series, Intersections: Philosophy & Critical Theory Ser.). 159p. 26.00 *(978-0-7914-6969-9(7))* State Univ. of New York Pr.

Nunez, Sigrid. Sempre Susan: A Memoir of Susan Sontag. 2011. (ENG.). 144p. 20.00 *(978-1-935633-22-8(8),* 935622) Atlas & Co.

O. Se, Maidhc Dainin. House, Don't Fall on Me. Fitzmaurice, Gabriel, tr. 2008. (ENG.). 224p. pap. 22.95 *(978-1-85635-550-6(0))* Mercier Pr., Ltd., The IRL. Dist: Dufour Editions, Inc.

Oates, Joyce Carol. A Widow's Story: A Memoir. (ENG.). 2012. 320p. pap. 14.99 ***(978-0-06-202050-5(1))*** 2011. 432p. 27.99 *(978-0-06-201553-2(2))* HarperCollins Pubs. (Ecco).

—A Widow's Story: A Memoir. l.t. ed. 2011. 676p. 32.99 *(978-1-4104-3692-4(6))* Thorndike Pr.

O'Brien, Edna. James Joyce: A Life. 2011. (ENG.). 192p. (gr. 12). 14.00 *(978-0-14-311993-7(1),* Penguin (Non-Classics)) Penguin Group (USA) Inc.

O'Brien, Louis. Hasta la Flip-Flops! - My Reign in Spain - Mallorca 1967-92. 2011. 404p. pap. ***(978-1-908447-97-5(4))*** Grosvenor Hse. Publishing Ltd.

Ocampo, Victoria. La Viajera y Sus Sombras: Crónica de un Aprendizaje. 2010. (Tierra Firme Ser.). (SPA.). 289p. pap. 29.99 *(978-950-557-845-0(8))* Fondo de Cultura Económica.

Oddie, William. Chesterton & the Romance of Orthodoxy: The Making of GKC, 1874-1908. 2010. (ENG.). 416p. pap. 29.95 *(978-0-19-958201-3(7))* Oxford Univ. Pr., Inc.

Oglesby, Carl. Ravens in the Storm: A Personal History of the 1960s Anti-War Movement. 2010. (ENG., Illus.). 352p. pap. 21.99 *(978-1-4165-4748-8(7),* Scribner) Scribner.

Oglesby, Catherine. Corra Harris & the Divided Mind of the New South. 2008. (ENG., Illus.). 272p. 59.95 *(978-0-8130-3247-4(4))* Univ. Pr. of Florida.

O'Grady, Chris. Love Song to A Long Gone Time. 2007. pap. 22.00 *(978-0-8059-8526-9(3))* Dorrance Publishing Co., Inc.

Oh, Seiwoong. Encyclopedia of Asian American Literature. 2007. (Encyclopedia of American Ethnic Literature Ser.). 400p. (C). (gr. 9). 75.00 *(978-0-8160-6086-3(X))* Facts On File, Inc.

Okunev, Yuri. Detstvo, kotorogo ne Bylo... 2010.Tr. of Missing Childhood. (RUS., Illus.). 244p. *(978-1-934881-28-6(7),* M-Graphics) M-Graphics Publishing.

Oliphant, Dave. Harbingers of Books to Come: A Texan's Literary Life. 2009. (ENG.). 548p. 24.95 *(978-0-916727-60-4(2))* Wings Pr.

Oliphant, Laurence. When a Stone Begins to Roll: Notes of an Adventurer, Diplomat & Mystic: Extracts from Episodes in a Life of Adventure. Meyer, T. H., ed. 2011. (ENG., Illus.). 160p. pap. 15.00 *(978-0-58420-091-8(X),* Lindisfarne Bks.) SteinerBooks, Inc.

Oliphant, Margaret O. The Autobiography & Letters of Mrs M. O. W. Oliphant. Walker, Annie L., ed. 2011. (Cambridge Library Collection - Women's Writing Ser.). (ENG., Illus.). 386p. pap. 31.99 ***(978-1-108-03385-5(7))*** Cambridge Univ. Pr.

—Sheridan. 2011. (Cambridge Library Collection - English Men of Letters Ser.). (ENG.). 224p. pap. 22.99 ***(978-1-108-03441-8(1))*** Cambridge Univ. Pr.

Olivares, Julian, ed. Tomas Rivera: The Complete Works. 2008. 363p. pap. 19.95 *(978-1-55885-509-0(2))* Arte Publico Pr.

Olivia, Lungu. Biography & Fiction in Virginia Woolf's Novels. 2011. 88p. pap. ***(978-3-639-32433-4(1))*** VDM Verlag Dr. Mueller e.K.

Olsen, Kirstin. All Things Austen: A Concise Encyclopedia of Jane Austen's World. 2008. (Illus.). 400p. pap. 29.95 *(978-1-84645-052-5(7),* GWP052) Greenwood Publishing Group, Inc.

Olson, Brent. Papa: Figuring Out What Matters. 2009. (ENG.). 132p. pap. 13.50 *(978-1-933794-21-1(6))* Kirk Hse. Pubs.

Ontiveros, R. C. Grandes Aventuras de un Pequeño Viajero. 2011. 110p. 29.99 ***(978-1-4568-5951-0(X))*** Xlibris Corp.

Oomen, Anne-Marie. An American Map. 2010. xii, 205p. pap. 18.95 *(978-0-8143-3420-1(2))* Wayne State Univ. Pr.

Oppeln-Bronikowski, Friedrich-Wilhelm von. Friedrich Von Oppeln-Bronikowski (1873-1936) Offizier, Übersetzer, Schriftsteller, Journalist und Streiter Gegen Den Antisemitismus in der Weimarer Republik: Sein Leben und Wirken. 2009. (GER., Illus.). 219p. *(978-3-7980-0581-5(8))* Starke & Dormi Publications.

Oppenheim, E. Phillips. Pool of Memory. 2006. 320p. per. *(978-1-4067-0222-4(6),* Hesperides Pr.) Read Bks.

Orfalea, Gregory. Angeleno Days: An Arab American Writer on Family, Place, & Politics. 2009. (ENG.). 232p. pap. 17.95 *(978-0-8165-2773-1(3))* Univ. of Arizona Pr.

Orguillés, David Mayor. Julio Verne. 2007. (Grandes biografías Ser.). (SPA & ENG., Illus.). 192p. 8.95 *(978-84-9764-560-7(X))* Edimat Libros, S. A. ESP. Dist: Independent Pubs. Group.

Orwell, George. Homage to Catalonia - Down & Out in Paris & London. 2010. (ENG.). 448p. 22.00 *(978-0-547-44733-9(7))* Houghton Mifflin Harcourt Trade & Reference Pubs.

Osborn, Louise Brown. The Life, Letters & Writings of John Hoskyns, 1566-1638. 2011. 338p. 51.95 ***(978-1-258-05820-3(0))*** Literary Licensing, LLC.

Osborne, Huw. Rhys Davies. 2nd rev. ed. 2009. (University of Wales Press - Writers of Wales Ser.). (ENG., Illus.). 144p. pap. 25.00 *(978-0-7083-2167-6(4))* Univ. of Wales Pr. GBR. Dist: Chicago Distribution Ctr.

Oskison, John Milton. Tales of the Old Indian Territory & Essays on the Indian Condition. Larre, Lionel, ed. 2012. (American Indian Lives Ser.). (ENG., Illus.). 680p. pap. 60.00 ***(978-0-8032-3792-6(8))*** Univ. of Nebraska Pr.

Ossoli, Margaret F. Memoirs of Margaret Fuller Ossoli. 2008. 308p. 28.99 *(978-0-554-33816-3(5));* 316p. 29.99 *(978-0-554-24512-6(4));* 316p. 28.99 *(978-0-554-33815-6(7));* 308p. 29.99 *(978-0-554-24513-3(2))* BiblioBazaar.

—Memoirs of Margaret Fuller Ossoli. 2009. 350p. pap. 21.95 *(978-1-4385-1877-0(3));* (ENG.). 348p. pap. *(978-1-4385-1460-4(3))* Standard Pubns., Inc. (Book Jungle).

—Memoirs of Margaret Fuller Ossoli V1. 2007. 348p. (ENG.). 46.95 *(978-0-548-16346-7(4));* per. 31.95 *(978-1-4304-5965-1(4))* Kessinger Publishing, LLC.

Ovejero, Jose. Escritores Delincuentes. 2012. (SPA., Illus.). 326p. pap. 24.99 ***(978-84-204-7508-0(4),*** Alfaguara) Santillana USA Publishing Co., Inc.

Overton, Grant. Authors of the Day. 2007. (ENG.). 426p. 51.95 *(978-0-548-05811-4(3))* Kessinger Publishing, LLC.

Oxford, Kelly. Everything Is Perfect When You're a Liar. 2012. 288p. 25.99 ***(978-0-06-210222-5(2))*** HarperCollins Pubs.

Oxford University Press Staff, ed. Bronte Story. 3rd ed. 2008. (ENG.). 80p. 9.38 *(978-0-19-479109-0(2))* Oxford Univ. Pr., Inc.

Pö, et al. Ingeborg Bachmann. Interviews: 'Ich sag' es lieber mit den Worten, die ich geschrieben habe.' 2010. 80p. pap. *(978-3-639-27319-9(2))* VDM Verlag Dr. Mueller e.K.

Pacitti, Tony. My Best Friend Is a Wookiee: A Memoir. 2010. xix, 234p. *(978-1-4405-0860-6(7))* Adams Media Corp.

Padgett, Davenport. Padgett's My Name. 2008. 547p. pap. 35.00 *(978-0-557-02101-7(4))* Lulu Enterprises Inc.

Pagdi, Gayatri. Walking with Chris. 2008. 228p. pap. *(978-1-84747-772-9(0))* Chipmunkapublishing.

Pagnol, Marcel. La Gloire de Mon Pere.Tr. of My Father's Glory. (FRE.). 13.95 *(978-0-8288-9896-6(0),* F117480);Tome I. 14.95 French & European Pubns., Inc.

—La Gloire de Mon Pere. Lathrop, Tom & Lathrop, Connie, eds. 2007. (Moliere & Co. Ser.: 8).Tr. of My Father's Glory. (FRE.). 244p. (C). per. 13.95 *(978-1-58977-046-1(3),* European Masterpieces) LinguaText, Ltd.

Painter, Deborah. Forry: The Life of Forrest J Ackerman. 2010. (ENG., Illus.). 224p. 45.00 *(978-0-7864-4884-5(9))* McFarland & Co., Inc. Pubs.

Pajak, Robert. The Sight Unseen: Chronicles of Lemia. 2011. pap. 20.99 ***(978-1-61346-459-5(2))*** Tate Publishing & Enterprises, LLC.

Palescandolo, Frank. The Last Beatnik. 2009. 96p. pap. 9.95 *(978-1-4401-7554-1(3))* iUniverse, Inc.

Palin, Michael. Halfway to Hollywood: Diaries, 1980-1988. 2011. (ENG., Illus.). 680p. 32.50 *(978-0-312-68202-6(6),* Dunne, Thomas Bks.) St. Martin's Pr.

Palin, Michael, frwd. Traveller: Observations from an American in Exile. 2009. (Illus.). viii, 143p. pap. 17.00 *(978-0-9820007-0-0(7))* Burton & Park Pubs.

Palmier, Jean-Michel & Perrier, Florent. Walter Benjamin: Le Chiffonnier, L'ange et le Petit Bossu: Esthétique et Politique Chez Walter Benjamin. 2006. (FRE., Illus.). 916p. (C). pap. 59.00 ***(978-2-252-03591-7(9))*** Klincksieck, Editions FRA. Dist: ISD.

Pamuk, Orhan. Istanbul: Memories & the City. Freely, Maureen, tr. from TUR. 2006. (Vintage International Ser.). (ENG., Illus.). 400p. pap. 16.95 *(978-1-4000-3388-1(6),* Vintage) Knopf Doubleday Publishing Group.

—The Naive & the Sentimental Novelist. 2010. (Charles Eliot Norton Lectures). 208p. 22.95 *(978-0-674-05076-1(2))* Harvard Univ. Pr.

—The Naive & the Sentimental Novelist. 2011. (Vintage International Ser.). (ENG.). 208p. pap. 14.95 *(978-0-307-74524-8(4),* Vintage) Knopf Doubleday Publishing Group.

Pang, Yang. Ye Shengtao He Ta de Jia Ren. 2010. (CHI., Illus.). *(978-7-5047-3251-4(6))* China Logistics Publishing Hse.

Papanikolas, Zeese. American Silence. 2007. (ENG., Illus.). 222p. 29.95 *(978-0-8032-3756-8(1))* Univ. of Nebraska Pr.

Papleka, Feride. Dhimitër S. Shuteriqi. 2010. (ALB., Illus.). 701p. *(978-99956-10-36-4(1))* Akademia e Shkencave.

Paradis, James G. Samuel Butler, Victorian Against the Grain: A Critical Overview. 2007. (Illus.). 416p. *(978-0-8020-9745-3(6))* Univ. of Toronto Pr.

Paretsky, Sara. Writing in an Age of Silence. 2nd ed. 2009. (ENG.). 160p. pap. 12.95 *(978-1-84467-377-3(4),* 844377) Verso Bks. GBR. Dist: Norton, W. W. & Co., Inc.

Parini, Jay. American Writers Supplement. 18th rev. ed. 2008. (American Writers Ser.). (ENG.). 592p. 218.00 *(978-0-684-31552-2(1),* Charles Scribner's Sons) Cengage Gale.

—Brit Wrtr Sup 15. 15th ed. 2009. (British Writers Ser.). 544p. 218.00 *(978-0-684-31555-3(6))* Cengage Gale.

—British Writers. (British Writers Ser.). (ENG.). 3rd ed. 2009. 608p. 218.00 *(978-0-684-31599-7(8),* Charles Scribner's Sons) 14th rev. ed. 2008. 465p. 218.00 *(978-0-684-31553-9(X))* Cengage Gale.

—British Writers Supplement. 13th rev. ed. 2007. (British Writers Ser.). (ENG.). 570p. 218.00 *(978-0-684-31518-8(1),* Charles Scribner's Sons) Cengage Gale.

Parini, Jay, ed. American Writers Supplement: Max Apple to Franz Wright. 17th rev. ed. 2007. (American Writers Ser.). (ENG.). 592p. 218.00 *(978-0-684-31517-1(3),* Charles Scribner's Sons) Cengage Gale.

Paris Review Staff. The Paris Review Interviews. 2nd rev. ed. 2007. (ENG.). 528p. pap. 18.00 *(978-0-312-36314-7(1))* Picador.

Paris Review Staff & Gourevitch, Philip, eds. The Paris Review Interviews, Vol. 3. 3rd rev. ed. 2008. (ENG.). 464p. pap. 18.00 *(978-0-312-36315-4(X))* Picador.

Parker, Cornelia Stratton. An American Idyll. reprint ed. lib. bdg. 48.00 *(978-0-7426-1356-0(9))* Classic Bks.

—An American Idyll. 2007. (ENG.). 212p. per. *(978-1-4067-5104-8(9))* Read Bks.

Parker, Gabrielle. Aimé Césaire. 2010. (Inspirations Ser.). (ENG.). 100p. pap. 10.95 *(978-1-906413-24-8(X))* Arcadia Bks. Ltd. GBR. Dist: Independent Pubs. Group.

Parker, William Belmont. Edward Rowland Sill His Life & Work. 2007. (ENG.). 334p. 45.95 *(978-0-548-01194-2(X))* Kessinger Publishing, LLC.

Parkinson, George Ellis. I Just Had to Get on with It. 2011. 172p. pap. 16.77 ***(978-1-4567-7273-4(2))*** AuthorHouse.

Parks, Tim. Teach Us to Sit Still: A Skeptic's Search for Health & Healing. 2011. (ENG.). 336p. 25.99 *(978-1-60961-158-3(6))* Rodale Pr., Inc.

Parmelee, Mario Donato. Awkward Bitch: My Life with MS. 2009. 316p. pap. 15.49 *(978-1-4389-9048-4(0))* AuthorHouse.

Parsons, Bob. A Journey of Hope. 2010. 208p. pap. 14.49 *(978-1-4520-7189-3(6))* AuthorHouse.

Pasi, Marco. Aleister Crowley & the Temptation of Politics. 2012. (ENG.). 256p. (C). 85.00 *(978-1-84553-367-0(4))* Equinox Publishing Ltd. GBR. Dist: ISD.

Paston, George. Lady Mary Wortley Montagu & Her Times. 2009. 468p. pap. *(978-0-217-01010-8(5))* Books LLC.

Pat Upton Stamm. Twelve Kids, One Bathroom, & a Milk Bottle. 2009. 208p. pap. 17.95 *(978-1-4401-8874-9(2))* iUniverse, Inc.

Pato, Almendro: Under the Almond Tree. 2010. 256p. 24.99 *(978-1-4520-7877-9(7));* pap. 10.99 *(978-1-4520-7878-6(5))* AuthorHouse.

Pato, Chus. Hordes of Writing. Moure, Erin, tr. 2011. 90p. pap. ***(978-1-84861-167-2(6))*** Shearsman Bks.

Patout, Paulette. Alfonso Reyes y Francia. 2009. (Otras Publicaciones Ser.). (SPA.). 761p. pap. 38.99 *(978-968-12-0464-8(6))* El Colegio de México, A.C., Biblioteca Miguel Cosio Villegas MEX. Dist: Fondo de Cultura Economica USA.

Patterson, William H., Jr. Robert A. Heinlein Vol. 1: In Dialogue with His Century. 2010. (ENG.). 624p. 29.99 *(978-0-7653-1960-9(8),* Tor Bks.) Doherty, Tom Assocs., LLC.

—Robert A. Heinlein Vol. 1: Learning Curve, 1907-1949. 2011. (ENG., Illus.). 640p. pap. 19.99 *(978-0-7653-1962-3(4),* Tor Bks.) Doherty, Tom Assocs., LLC.

Paul, C. Kegan. Memories. 2009. 400p. 33.99 *(978-1-116-73856-8(2));* 38.99 *(978-1-116-73855-1(4));* pap. 33.75 *(978-1-116-73858-2(9));* pap. 34.75 *(978-1-116-73857-5(0));* 33.99 *(978-1-116-05228-2(8));* 38.99 *(978-1-116-05227-5(X));* pap. 34.75 *(978-1-116-05229-9(6))* BiblioBazaar.

Pauly, Thomas H. Zane Grey: His Life, His Adventures, His Women. 2007. (Illus.). 408p. per. 24.95 *(978-0-252-07492-9(0))* Univ. of Illinois Pr.

Pavolini, Lorenzo. Accanto Alla Tigre. 2010. (ITA., Illus.). 243p. *(978-88-6044-145-4(5))* Fandango.

Pawar, Urmila. The Weave of My Life: A Dalit Woman's Memoirs. Pandit, Maya, tr. from MAR. 2009. (ENG., Illus.). 320p. (gr. 17). 35.00 *(978-0-231-14900-6(X))* Columbia Univ. Pr.

Payment, Simone. Scott O'Dell. (Library of Author Biographies Ser.). 112p. (gr. 5-8). 2009. 63.90 *(978-1-60853-554-5(1),* Rosen Central) 2006. (Illus.). pap. 12.95 *(978-1-4042-0651-9(5))* Rosen Publishing Group, Inc., The.

Payne, Darwin. Owen Wister: Chronicler of the West, Gentleman of the East. 2011. (ENG., Illus.). 416p. pap. 24.95 *(978-0-8032-3769-8(3),* Bison Bks.) Univ. of Nebraska Pr.

Payton, Philip. John Betjeman & Cornwall: The Celebrated Cornish Nationalist. 2010. (Illus.). 258p. 95.00 *(978-0-85989-847-8(4));* 288p. pap. 30.00 *(978-0-85989-848-5(2))* Univ. of Exeter Pr. GBR. Dist: Chicago Distribution Ctr.

Pearce, Joseph. Solzhenitsyn: A Soul in Exile. 2011. (Illus.). 392p. pap. 19.95 ***(978-1-58617-496-5(7))*** Ignatius Pr.

Pearson, Carol Lynn. Goodbye, I Love You. 2006. 199p. per. 13.99 *(978-1-55517-984-7(3))* Cedar Fort, Inc./CFI Distribution.

Pearson, Tom B. Exceptional Fortitude: The Life of Tom B. Pearson. 2010. 520p. pap. 29.99 *(978-1-4520-2533-9(9))* AuthorHouse.

Pease, Donald E. Theodor Seuss Geisel. 2010. (Lives & Legacies Ser.). (ENG., Illus.). 160p. 19.95 *(978-0-19-532302-3(5))* Oxford Univ. Pr., Inc.

Pelayo, Ruben. Gabriel García Márquez: A Biography. 1 vol. 2008. (Greenwood Biographies Ser.). (Illus.). 188p. 35.00 *(978-0-313-34630-9(5),* GR4630, Greenwood Pr.) Greenwood Publishing Group, Inc.

Pellek, Dick. Afghanistan to Zambia: Chronicles of a Footloose Forester. 2010. 328p. 28.49 *(978-1-4520-3152-1(5));* pap. 17.99 *(978-1-4520-3151-4(7))* AuthorHouse.

Pellico, Silvio. My Ten Years' Imprisonment. 2008. 240p. 24.99 *(978-0-554-36452-0(2))* 2008. 240p. 27.99 *(978-0-554-27149-1(4))* 2007 226p. pap. 20.99 *(978-1-4346-2590-8(7))* 2007. (ENG.). 238p. pap. 22.99 *(978-1-4346-2668-4(7))* BiblioBazaar.

—My Ten Years' Imprisonment. 2009. 216p. pap. *(978-1-4099-5640-2(7))* Dodo Pr.

—My Ten Years' Imprisonment. 2010. (Illus.). 112p. pap. 20.31 *(978-1-153-64371-9(5))* 2009. 134p. pap. 19.48 *(978-1-150-68889-8(0))* General Bks. LLC.

—My Ten Years' Imprisonment. Roscoe, Thomas, tr. 2008. 2010. 31.96 ***(978-1-166-35465-7(2))*** 2010. pap. 19.96 ***(978-1-166-29963-7(5))*** 2009. 39.95 *(978-1-120-07004-3(X))* 2009. pap. 24.95 *(978-1-120-00991-3(X))* Kessinger Publishing, LLC.

Pellico, Silvio & Roscoe, Thomas. My Ten Years' Imprisonment. 2010. (ENG.). 208p. pap. 24.75 *(978-1-177-45374-5(6))* BiblioBazaar.

Pemberton, T. Edgar. Life of Bret Harte. 2007. (ENG.). 400p. 49.95 *(978-0-548-08522-6(6))* Kessinger Publishing, LLC.

Pennell, Elizabeth Robins. Mary Wollstonecraft Godwin. 2008. 216p. 39.95 *(978-1-4372-0962-4(9));* pap. 24.95 *(978-1-4370-8010-0(3))* Kessinger Publishing, LLC.

Penney, Alexandra. The Bag Lady Papers: The Priceless Experience of Losing It All. 2010. 240p. 23.99 *(978-1-4013-4118-3(7))* Hyperion Pr.

Penzler, Otto, ed. The Lineup: The World's Greatest Crime Writers Tell the Inside Story of Their Greatest Detectives. 2010. (ENG.). 416p. pap. 15.99 *(978-0-316-03194-3(1),* Back Bay Bks.) Little Brown & Co.

Perec, Georges. Thoughts of Sorts. Bellos, David, tr. from FRE. & intro. by. 2009. (ENG.). 176p. pap. 16.95 *(978-1-56792-362-9(3),* Verba Mundi) Godine, David R. Pub.

Pereira, Malin, ed. Into a Light Both Brilliant & Unseen: Conversations with Contemporary Black Poets. 2010. (ENG.). 260p. 59.95 *(978-0-8203-3107-2(4));* pap. 19.95 *(978-0-8203-3713-5(7))* Univ. of Georgia Pr.

Pérez Herrero, Pedro. Ruben Darío: Nicaraguan Poet. (SPA.). 160p. 4.95 *(978-84-7679-082-3(1))* Informacion y Revistas ESP. Dist: AIMS International Bks., Inc.

Perkins, Eleanor Ellis & Perkins, Lucy Fitch. Eve among the Puritans: A Biography of Lucy Fitch Perkins. 2011. 264p. 47.95 ***(978-1-258-07388-6(9))*** Literary Licensing, LLC.

Perkins, Tom. Valley Boy: The Education of Tom Perkins. 2008. (ENG.). 240p. (gr. 12-18). 15.00 *(978-1-59240-403-2(0),* Gotham) Penguin Group (USA) Inc.

Perret, Gene. Tales from the Script - the Behind-the-Camera Adventures of a TV Comedy Writer. 2010. 286p. pap. 21.95 *(978-1-59393-529-0(3))* BearManor Media.

Perry, Bliss. Life & Letters of Henry Lee Higginson. 2009. (ENG.). 582p. 44.99 *(978-1-117-11245-9(4));* 584p. pap. 43.75 *(978-1-117-11246-6(2))* BiblioBazaar.

—Life & Letters of Henry Lee Higginson. 557p. reprint ed. 88.00 *(978-0-7950-2198-5(4))* New Library Press LLC.

—Life & Letters of Henry Lee Higginson. 2007. (ENG., Illus.). 584p. per. *(978-1-4067-3024-1(6))* Read Bks.

Perry Sr., A. J. Little Red Wagons to the Moon: The Life of Audie James Perry Sr. 2011. 142p. pap. 24.95 ***(978-1-4512-8059-3(9))*** PublishAmerica, Inc.

Petelin, Viktor. Moi XX Vek: Schaste Byt Samim Soboi, Zhizneopisanie V Vospominaniiakh o Protivoborstve Ofitsialnoi Ideologii: Dokumenty, Pisma, Stati, Razmyshleniia. 2009. (RUS., Illus.). 638p. ***(978-5-9524-4505-5(5))*** Centrooligraf, AO zakrytogo tipa, torgovo-izdatel'skoe obedinenie.

A

Peters, Jason. Wendell Berry: Life & Work. Peters, Jason, ed. 2010. (Culture of the Land Ser.). (ENG.). 368p. pap. 21.95 (978-0-8131-9257-4(9)) Univ. Pr. of Kentucky.

Peters, Jason, ed. Wendell Berry: Life & Work. 2007. (Culture of the Land Ser.). (ENG., Illus.). 368p. 50.00 (978-0-8131-2442-1(5)) Univ. Pr. of Kentucky.

Peterson, Brenda. I Want to Be Left Behind: Finding Rapture Here on Earth. 2010. (ENG.). 288p. 25.00 (978-0-306-81804-2(3)) Da Capo Pr., Inc.

Peterson, Nancy J., ed. Conversations with Sherman Alexie. 2009. (Literary Conversations Ser.). (ENG.). 224p. 50.00 (978-1-60473-279-5(2)); pap. 22.00 (978-1-60473-280-1(6)) Univ. Pr. of Mississippi.

Petrov, Vladimir. M.A. Sholokhov: Zhizn I Iskusstvo: Khudozhestvenno-Dokumentalnaia Biograficheskaia Letopis. 2009. (RUS., Illus.). 414p. (978-5-87259-519-9(0)) Kniga.

Petrulionis, Sandra Harbert. Thoreau in His Own Time: A Biographical Chronicle of His Life, Drawn from Recollections, Interviews, & Memoirs by Family, Friends, & Associates. 2012. (Writers in Their Own Time Ser.). (ENG.). 268p. pap. 27.50 (978-1-60938-087-8(8)) Univ. of Iowa Pr.

Petry, Elisabeth. At Home Inside: A Daughter's Tribute to Ann Petry. 2008. (ENG., Illus.). 208p. 30.00 (978-1-60473-100-2(1)) Univ. Pr. of Mississippi.

Pettersson, Jan-Erik. Stieg Larsson: The Real Story of the Man Who Played with Fire. 2011. (ENG., Illus.). 288p. 22.95 (978-1-4027-8940-3(8)) Sterling Publishing Co., Inc.

Peyer, Bernd C. The Thinking Indian: Native American Writers, 1850S-1920S. 2007. 384p. pap. 65.95 (978-0-8204-8766-3(X)) Lang, Peter Publishing, Inc.

Pharies, David A. The University of Chicago Spanish-English Dictionary, Sixth Edition: Diccionario Universidad de Chicago Inglés-Español, Sexta Edición. 6th ed. 2012. 626p. 40.00 (978-0-226-66695-2(6)) Univ. of Chicago Pr.

Philipponnat, Olivier & Lienhardt, Patrick. The Life of Irène Némirovsky, 1903-1942. Cameron, Euan, tr. from FRE. 2010. (ENG., Illus.). 464p. 35.00 (978-0-307-27021-4(1)) Knopf, Alfred A. Inc.

Phillips, Caryl. Color Me English: Migration & Belonging Before & after 9/11. 2011. (ENG.). 352p. 25.95 (978-1-59558-650-6(4)) New Pr., The.

Phillips, Julie. James Tiptree, Jr: The Double Life of Alice B. Sheldon. 2007. (ENG., Illus.). 560p. pap. 21.00 (978-0-312-42694-1(1)) Picador.

Phillips, Mary Shepard & Devine, Susan Hatch. Lovingly, Mother: The Letters of Louise Sahol Hatch 1871-1968. 2010. 176p. pap. 13.49 (978-1-4490-6680-2(1)) AuthorHouse.

Piatka, Naava. No Goodbyes: A Father-Daughter Memoir of Love, War & Resurrection. 2009. 332p. 32.95 (978-0-595-49603-7(2)); pap. 22.95 (978-0-595-49815-4(9)) iUniverse, Inc.

Pickard, Samuel T. Life & Letters of John Greenleaf Whitt. 2006. (ENG.). pap. 36.95 (978-1-4286-4203-4(X)) Kessinger Publishing, LLC.

Pickering, Sam. A Comfortable Boy: A Memoir. 2010. 192p. 26.00 (978-0-88146-182-4(2)) Mercer Univ. Pr.

Pierce, Susan & Johnston, Joan. A Stranger's Game. 2009. (ENG.). 448p. mass mkt. 7.99 (978-0-7434-5439-1(1)) Pocket Books.

Pimentel, Cpa. My Last Stop. 2010. 206p. pap. 13.50 (978-1-60911-533-3(3), Eloquent Bks.) AEG Literary Publishing Services, Inc.

Pines, Paul. My Brother's Madness: A Memoir. 2007. (ENG.). 318p. per. 15.95 (978-1-931896-34-4(8)) Curbstone Pr.

Pinkwater, Daniel M. Uncle Boris in the Yukon & Other Shaggy Dog Stor. 2011. (ENG.). 208p. pap. 14.99 (978-1-4516-4660-3(7)) Simon & Schuster.

Pinocchio. 2008.Tr. of Avventure di Pinocchio. (Illus.). pap. (978-1-84830-918-0(X), Wildhern Pr.) Echo Library.

Piozzi, Hester Lynch. Anecdotes of Samuel Johnson. 2012. (ENG.). 228p. pap. 24.00 (978-1-107-69915-1(0)) Cambridge Univ. Pr.

Piper, Andrew. Johann Wolfgang Von Goethe. 2010. (Brief Lives Ser.). (ENG.). 112p. pap. 15.95 (978-1-84391-910-0(9)) Hesperus Pr. GBR. Dist: Independent Pubs. Group.

Piper, Leonard. Tragedy of Erskine Childers: Dangerous Waters. 2006. (ENG., Illus.). 264p. pap. 29.95 (978-1-84725-020-9(3), Hambledon Continuum) Continuum International Publishing Group, Ltd. GBR. Dist: National Bk. Network.

Pipher, Mary. Seeking Peace: Chronicles of the Worst Buddhist in the World. 2010. (ENG.). 272p. (gr. 12-18). 16.00 (978-1-59448-440-7(6), Riverhead Trade (Paperbacks)) Penguin Group (USA) Inc.

Pipher, Mary, et al. Grace of Grass & Water: Writing in Honor of Paul Gruchow. 2007. per. (978-1-888160-28-4(4)) Ice Cube Pr.

Pite, Ralph. Thomas Hardy: The Guarded Life. 2007. (ENG., Illus.). 544p. 37.00 (978-0-300-12337-1(X)) Yale Univ. Pr.

Pitol, Sergio. Autobiografía Soterrada. 2010. (SPA., Illus.). 144p. pap. 20.95 (978-607-411-038-8(7)) Editorial Almadia MEX. Dist: Latin American Book Source, Inc.

Pittman, Patsy. Pocket Change. 2010. (Illus.). 80p. pap. 19.95 (978-0-929915-56-2(9)) Headline Bks.

Pizzichini, Lilian. The Blue Hour: A Life of Jean Rhys. 2009. (ENG., Illus.). 336p. 29.95 (978-0-393-05803-1(4), 5803) Norton, W. W. & Co., Inc.

Plant, Deborah G. Zora Neale Hurston: A Biography of the Spirit, 1 vol. 2007. (Women Writers of Color Ser.). (Illus.). 264p. 49.95 (978-0-275-98751-0(5), C8751, Praeger Pubs.) Greenwood Publishing Group, Inc.

—Zora Neale Hurston: A Biography of the Spirit. 2011. (ENG.). 264p. pap. 15.95 (978-1-4422-0612-0(8)) Rowman & Littlefield Publishers, Inc.

Plante, David. The Pure Lover: A Memoir of Grief, 1 vol. 2010. (ENG.). 128p. pap. 16.00 (978-0-8070-0620-7(3)) Beacon Pr.

Plath, James. Historic Photos of Ernest Hemingway. 2009. (Historic Photos Ser.). (ENG.). 206p. 39.95 (978-1-59652-516-0(9)) Turner Publishing Co.

Platt, Camille Smith. Real Cheesy Facts about: Famous Authors: Everything Weird, Dumb, & Unbelievable You Never Learned in School. 2006. (Real Cheesy Facts Ser.). (ENG., Illus.). 176p. per. (978-1-57587-250-6(1)) Crane Hill Pubs.

Plautus, Titus Maccius. The Captivi of Plautus. 2010. 104p. pap. 18.75 (978-1-146-55575-3(X)) BiblioBazaar.

—The Captivi of Plautus. 2009. 330p. pap. (978-1-151-74036-6(5)) Books LLC.

Plautus, Titus Maccius & Henson, J. The Captivi of Plautus. 2010. 168p. pap. 21.75 (978-1-144-81982-6(2)) BiblioBazaar.

Plautus, Titus Maccius & Lindsay, W. m. 1858-1937. The Captivi of Plautus. 2010. 430p. pap. 35.75 (978-1-177-80422-6(0)) BiblioBazaar.

Ploetz, Dagmar. Ignazio Silone: Rebell & Romancier: Ein Schriftstellerleben im 20. Jahrhundert. (GER.). 574p. pap. (978-3-462-02910-9(X)) Kiepenheuer & Witsch GmbH & Company KG DEU. Dist: International Bk. Import Service, Inc.

Plut, Joseph. Conversations with Jon Hassler. 2010. (Illus.). xiv, 264p. 19.95 (978-1-932472-97-4(5)) Nodin Pr.

Pocock, Geoffrey A. Outrider of Empire: The Life & Adventures of Roger Pocock. 2008. (ENG., Illus.). 400p. pap. 34.95 (978-0-88864-448-0(5)) Univ. of Alberta Pr. CAN. Dist: Michigan State Univ. Pr.

Pocock, Gordon. Boileau & the Nature of Neoclassicism. 2010. (Major European Authors Ser.). (ENG.). 224p. pap. 27.99 (978-0-521-13675-4(X)) Cambridge Univ. Pr.

Poli, Annarosa & Kanceff, Emanuele. Alla Riscoperta Di George Sand, Viaggiatrice in Italia. 2010. (FRE & ITA., Illus.). 254p. (978-88-7760-092-9(6)) CIRVI.

Polizzotti, Mark. Revolution of the Mind, Revised Edition: The Life of Andre Breton. 2009. (ENG.). 680p. pap. 29.95 (978-0-9795137-8-7(2)) Commonwealth Bks.,Black Widow.

Pollack, Neal. Stretch: The Unlikely Making of a Yoga Dude. 2010. (ENG.). 336p. pap. 14.99 (978-0-06-172769-6(5), HarperPerennial) HarperCollins Pubs.

Pollock, Ida. Starlight - a Memoir by Ida Pollock. 2009. (Illus.). 220p. pap. (978-0-7552-0491-5(3)) Authors OnLine, Ltd.

Poolos, J. Ralph Waldo Emerson: The Father of the American Renaissance. 2009. (Library of American Thinkers Ser.). 112p. (gr. 6-6). 66.50 (978-1-60853-516-3(9), Rosen Central) Rosen Publishing Group, Inc., The.

Porter, Cathy. The Diaries of Sofia Tolstoy. 2010. (P. S. Ser.). (ENG.). 640p. pap. 16.99 (978-0-06-199741-9(2), HarperPerennial) HarperCollins Pubs.

Porter, David. On the Divide: The Many Lives of Willa Cather. 2010. (ENG., Illus.). 416p. pap. 29.95 (978-0-8032-3279-2(9)) Univ. of Nebraska Pr.

Porter, David H. On the Divide: The Many Lives of Willa Cather. 2008. (ENG., Illus.). 416p. 29.95 (978-0-8032-3755-1(3)) Univ. of Nebraska Pr.

Porter, David H. & Marks, Lucy. Seeking Life Whole: Willa Cather & the Brewsters. 2009. 45.00 (978-0-8386-4199-6(7)) Fairleigh Dickinson Univ. Pr.

Porter, J. S. Lightness & Soul: Musings on Eight Jewish Writers. 2011. 128p. pap. 18.95 (978-1-927079-02-7(0)) Seraphim Editions CAN. Dist: Univ. of Toronto Pr.

Posey, Alexander. Lost Creeks: Collected Journals. Sivils, Matthew Wynn, ed. & intro. by. 2009. (ENG., Illus.). 200p. 45.00 (978-0-8032-1628-0(9)) Univ. of Nebraska Pr.

Potter, Charles Francis. The Preacher & I: An Autobiography. 2011. 448p. 56.95 (978-1-258-09704-2(4)) Literary Licensing, LLC.

Potter, Dawn. Tracing Paradise: Two Years in Harmony with John Milton. 2009. (Illus.). 144p. pap. 22.95 net. (978-1-55849-701-6(3)) Univ. of Massachusetts Pr.

Potter, Rockwell Harmon. The Harvest of the Years: Rockwell Harmon Potter Autobiography. Strong, Kendrick, ed. 2011. 110p. 39.95 (978-1-258-09770-7(2)) Literary Licensing, LLC.

Potts, Rolf. Marco Polo Didn't Go There: Stories & Revelations from One Decade as a Postmodern Travel Writer. 2008. (ENG.). 344p. pap. 19.95 (978-1-932361-61-2(8)) Travelers' Tales, Inc.

Powell, Steven, ed. Conversations with James Ellroy. 2012. (Literary Conversations Ser.). (ENG.). 224p. 65.00 (978-1-61703-103-8(8)); pap. 25.00 (978-1-61703-104-5(6)) Univ. Pr. of Mississippi.

Power, Nani. Feed the Hungry: A Memoir with Recipes. 2008. (ENG.). 224p. 23.00 (978-1-4165-5606-0(0), Free Pr.) Free Pr.

Powers, Paul S. Pulp Writer: Twenty Years in the American Grub Street. Powers, Laurie, ed. 2007. (ENG., Illus.). 276p. pap. 19.95 (978-0-8032-5984-3(0), Bison Bks.) Univ. of Nebraska Pr.

Price, Reynolds. Ardent Spirits: Leaving Home, Coming Back. (ENG.). 416p. 2012. pap. 17.00 (978-0-7432-9190-3(5)) 2009. (Illus.). 35.00 (978-0-7432-9189-7(1)) Scribner. (Scribner).

Price, Reynolds. Clear Pictures: First Loves, First Guides. 2009. (ENG., Illus.). 320p. pap. 20.00 (978-1-4391-0933-5(8), Scribner) Scribner.

Price, S. L. Far Afield: A Sportswriting Odyssey. 2009. 272p. pap. 13.99 (978-0-06-170872-5(0), HarperPerennial) HarperCollins Pubs.

Prideaux, Sue. Strindberg: A Life. 2012. (ENG., Illus.). 352p. 40.00 (978-0-300-13693-7(5)) Yale Univ. Pr.

Priestley, J.B. George Meredith. 2007. (ENG.). 220p. 39.95 (978-0-548-14531-9(8)) 2006. pap. 24.95 (978-1-4286-5838-7(6)) Kessinger Publishing, LLC.

—Thomas Love Peacock. 2007. (ENG.). 228p. 41.95 (978-0-548-14506-7(7)) 2006. pap. 26.95 (978-1-4286-5809-7(2)) Kessinger Publishing, LLC.

Prieto, Julio. De la Sombrología: Seis Comienzos en Busca de Macedonio Fernández. 2010. (Ediciones de Iberoamericana Ser.). pap. 29.80 (978-84-8489-534-3(3)) Iberoamericana Vervuert Publishing Corp.

Pritchett, V. S. At Home & Abroad. 2012. 344p. pap. (978-1-4482-0087-0(3), 142605, Bloomsbury Reader) Bloomsbury Publishing Plc.

—Chekhov: A Biography. 2012. 256p. pap. (978-1-4482-0092-4(X), 143052, Bloomsbury Reader) Bloomsbury Publishing Plc.

Prosser, David. Pumps with Holes In. 2011. 258p. pap. (978-1-78003-178-1(5)) Pen Pr. Pubs., Ltd.

Proulx, Annie. Bird Cloud. 2011. (ENG.). 256p. pap. 16.00 (978-0-7432-8881-1(5), Scribner) Scribner.

—Bird Cloud: A Memoir. 2011. (ENG., Illus.). 256p. 26.00 (978-0-7432-8880-4(7), Scribner) Scribner.

Proulx, E. Annie. Bird Cloud: A Memoir. l.t. ed. 2011. 365p. 32.99 (978-1-4104-3493-7(1)) Thorndike Pr.

Pugliese, Stanislao G. Bitter Spring: A Life of Ignazio Silone. 2009. (ENG., Illus.). 448p. 35.00 (978-0-374-11348-3(3)) Farrar, Straus & Giroux.

Purdon, Liam O. & Torrey, Beef, eds. Conversations with Tom Robbins. 2010. (Literary Conversations Ser.). (ENG.). 240p. 50.00 (978-1-60473-826-1(X)); pap. 22.00 (978-1-60473-827-8(8)) Univ. Pr. of Mississippi.

Putnam, Marian C., et al. Letters & Diaries of Margaret Cabot Lee. 2011. 422p. 56.95 (978-1-258-02732-2(1)) Literary Licensing, LLC.

Pykett, Lyn. Wilkie Collins (Authors in Context) 2009. (Oxford World's Classics Ser.). (ENG., Illus.). 272p. pap. 14.95 (978-0-19-955611-3(3)) Oxford Univ. Pr., Inc.

Pym, Barbara. A Very Private Eye: An Autobiography in Diaries & Letters. 2007. (Illus.). 380p. (C). reprint ed. pap. 18.95 (978-1-55921-331-8(0)) Moyer Bell.

Qiu, Shi. Wo Wei Lu Xun Mao Dun Bian Hu. 2009. (CHI.). 7p. pap. (978-7-80741-515-2(0)) Wenhui Chubanshe.

Quanjer, Johan Henri. The Luminous Journey: The Reflection of Pneumatocracy, the Rule of the Soul, in my Extraordinary Life. 2009. (Illus.). 428p. pap. 28.95 (978-0-9800817-7-0(7)) Eremitical Pr.

Quarrington, Paul. Cigar Box Banjo: Notes on Music & Life, 1 vol. 2010. (ENG.). 256p. 26.95 (978-1-55365-438-4(2), Greystone Bks.) D&M Pubs. Inc. CAN. Dist: Perseus-PGW.

Quindlen, Anna. Good Dog. Stay. 2007. (ENG., Illus.). 96p. 14.95 (978-1-4000-6713-8(8), Random House) Random House Publishing Group.

—Good Dog. Stay. l.t. ed. 2008. (Thorndike Nonfiction Ser.). (Illus.). 105p. 30.95 (978-1-4104-0689-7(X)) Thorndike Pr.

Quindlen, Anna. Lots of Candles, Plenty of Cake. 2012. (ENG.). 208p. 26.00 (978-1-4000-6934-7(3), Random House) Random House Publishing Group.

—Lots of Candles, Plenty of Cake. l.t. ed. 2012. (ENG.). 272p. pap. 26.00 (978-0-7393-7855-7(4)) Random Hse. Large Print.

Quinn, Erin. Walking on Eggshells. 2008. 53p. pap. 16.95 (978-1-60563-043-4(8)) PublishAmerica, Inc.

Quint, Jacquie. Falcon Cove Stories: A Look at it's Beginnings. 2010. 160p. pap. 12.99 (978-1-4490-8915-3(1)) AuthorHouse.

Quirós Fernández, María Teresa. Stereophonie der Autobiographie: Autobiographisches Schreiben von Paaren am Beispiel von María Teresa León und Rafael Alberti. 2009. (Mimesis Ser.).Tr. of Stereophonic Autobiography. Concept & Model of Autobiographies Written by Couples using the example of María Teresa león & Rafael Alberti. (GER.). VII, 213p. pap. (978-3-484-55048-3(1)) Verlag Max Niemeyer.

Raab, Diana & Brown, James. Writers on the Edge: 22 Writers Speak about Addiction & Dependency. 2012. (978-1-61599-109-9(3)); 204p. pap. (978-1-61599-108-2(5)) Loving Healing Pr., Inc. (Modern History Pr.).

Raab, Diana M., ed. Writers & Their Notebooks. 2010. 208p. 49.95 (978-1-57003-865-5(1)); pap. 24.95 (978-1-57003-866-2(X)) Univ. of South Carolina Pr.

Rabassa, Gregory. If This Be Treason: Translation & Its Dyscontents. 2006. (ENG.). 208p. per. 14.95 (978-0-8112-1665-4(9)) New Directions Publishing Corp.

Rackstraw, Loree. Love as Always, Kurt: Vonnegut as I Knew Him. 2009. (ENG., Illus.). 304p. 25.00 (978-0-306-81803-5(5)) Da Capo Pr., Inc.

—Love as Always, Kurt: Vonnegut As I Knew Him. 2013. (ENG.). 304p. pap. 15.00 (978-0-306-81863-9(9)) Da Capo Pr., Inc.

Rahbaran, Shiva. Nicholas Mosley's Life & Art: A Biography in Six Interviews. 2009. (Dalkey Archive Scholarly Ser.). (ENG.). 160p. pap. 25.95 (978-1-56478-564-0(5), 478564) Dalkey Archive Pr.

—The Paradox of Freedom: A Study of Nicholas Mosley's Intellectual Development in His Novels & Other Writings. 2007. (Dalkey Archive Scholarly Ser.). (ENG.). 316p. per. 29.95 (978-1-56478-488-9(6), 478488) Dalkey Archive Pr.

Rahn, B. J. Ngaio Marsh: The Woman & Her Work. 2007. (ENG.). 272p. per. 40.00 (978-0-8108-5939-5(4)) Scarecrow Pr., Inc.

Raine. And Raindrops Fall down My Cheeks. 2010. 108p. 21.50 (978-1-60911-228-8(8), Eloquent Bks.) AEG Literary Publishing Services, Inc.

Raipuri, Akhtar Husain. The Dust of the Road: A Translation of Gard-e-Raah. 2008. (ENG., Illus.). 302p. 29.95 (978-0-19-547215-8(2)) Oxford Univ. Pr., Inc.

Rajewska-Perzynska, Agnieszka. Rolf Bongs: Dissoziation eines Schriftstellers im Spannungsfeld zwischen Selbststilisierung und Anpassung. 2009. (Studien zur deutschen und europäischen Literatur des 19. und 20. Jahrhunderts Ser.). (GER.). 304p. 72.95 (978-3-631-59375-2(9)) Lang, Peter GmbH, Europaischer Verlag der Wissenschaften DEU. Dist: Lang, Peter.

Rambin, R. Lavelle. How Am I Doing? 2011. 76p. pap. 19.95 (978-1-4512-7955-9(8)) PublishAmerica, Inc.

Ramesh, Kotti Sree & Kandula, Nirupa Rani. Claude Mckay: The Literary Identity from Jamaica to Harlem & Beyond. 2006. (ENG., Illus.). 216p. per. 35.00 (978-0-7864-2582-2(2)) McFarland & Co., Inc. Pubs.

Rampersad, Arnold. Ralph Ellison: A Biography. 2008. (Vintage Ser.). (ENG., Illus.). 704p. pap. 17.95 (978-0-375-70798-8(0), Vintage) Knopf Doubleday Publishing Group.

Ramsey, Bruce. Unsanctioned Voice: Garet Garrett, Journalist of the Old Right. 2009. (ENG.). 290p. pap. 17.95 (978-0-87004-465-6(6)) Caxton Pr.

Ramsey, Leon. To Tell the Truth. 2010. 108p. pap. 10.99 (978-1-4520-4369-2(8)) AuthorHouse.

Randolph, Jody Allen. Close to the Next Moment: Interviews from a Changing Ireland. 2010. (ENG.). 302p. pap. 29.95 (978-1-84777-048-6(7)) Carcanet Pr., Ltd. GBR. Dist: Independent Pubs. Group.

Raphael, Frederic. Ifs & Buts: Personal Terms V. 2011. (ENG.). 200p. pap. 32.95 (978-1-84777-122-3(X)) Carcanet Pr., Ltd. GBR. Dist: Independent Pubs. Group.

—Ticks & Crosses No. 4: Personal Terms. 2009. (ENG.). 224p. pap. 37.95 (978-1-85754-930-0(9)) Carcanet Pr., Ltd. GBR. Dist: Independent Pubs. Group.

Rascoe, Burton. Prometheans: Ancient & Modern. 2007. (ENG.). 294p. 43.95 (978-0-548-06562-4(4)) Kessinger Publishing, LLC.

Rasmussen, R. Kent, ed. Mark Twain. 2010. (Critical Insights Ser.). 350p. 85.00 (978-1-58765-689-7(2)) Salem Pr., Inc.

Rathwell, Richard. Quicker & Deader. 2011. 173p. pap. 16.50 (978-1-889960-23-4(3)) First Intensity Pr.

Raworth, Tom. Earn Your Milk. 2009. (ENG.). 184p. pap. (978-1-84471-508-4(6)) Salt Publishing.

Ray, Georgia. Grace Flandrau: Voice Interrupted. 2007. (ENG., Illus.). 304p. 34.95 (978-1-889020-22-8(2)) Edinborough Pr.

Ray, Martin. Thomas Hardy Remembered. 2007. (Nineteenth Century Ser.). 358p. 124.95 (978-0-7546-3973-2(8)) Ashgate Publishing Co.

Raya, Bijaya. Amadera Katha. 2008. (BEN., Illus.). 574p. (978-81-7756-687-1(3)) Ananda Publishers Pvt Ltd, Publishers & Booksellers.

Raymond, Dwayne. Mornings with Mailer: A Recollection of Friendship. 2010. (ENG.). 256p. pap. 13.99 (978-0-06-173359-8(8), HarperPerennial) HarperCollins Pubs.

Raymond, Ida. Southland Writers Biographical & Critical Sketches of the Living Female Writers of the South with Extracts from Their Writings by Ida Raymond Vo. 2006. (ENG.). 524p. per. 29.99 (978-1-4255-5804-8(6)); 464p. per. 29.99 (978-1-4255-5136-0(X)) MPublishing.

Raymond, Jean-Francois. Diplomates Ecrivains Du Canada: Des Voix Nouvelles. (FRE.). 164p. pap. 29.95 (978-90-5201-346-6(2)) Lang, Peter Publishing, Inc.

Raynard, Sophie, ed. The Teller's Tale: Lives of the Classic Fairy Tale Writers. 2012. (ENG.). 160p. 75.00 (978-1-4384-4355-3(2)) State Univ. of New York Pr.

Reardon, Joan & Reardon, J. M. F. K. Fisher among the Pots & Pans: Celebrating Her Kitchens. 2009. (California Studies in Food & Culture Ser.). (ENG., Illus.). 184p. pap. 19.95 (978-0-520-26168-6(2)) Univ. of California Pr.

Rechy, John. About My Life & the Kept Woman: A Memoir. 2009. (ENG., Illus.). 384p. pap. 14.00 (978-0-8021-4404-1(7), Grove Pr.) Grove/Atlantic, Inc.

Redworth, Glyn & British Hispanic Foundation Staff. The She-Apostle: The Extraordinary Life & Death of Luisa de Carvajal. 2008. (ENG., Illus.). 288p. 39.95 (978-0-19-953353-4(9)) Oxford Univ. Pr., Inc.

Reed, Jennifer. Paula Danziger: Voice of Teen Troubles. 2006. (Authors Teens Love Ser.). (Illus.). 104p. (YA). (gr. 7-12). lib. bdg. 31.93 (978-0-7660-2444-1(X)) Enslow Pubs., Inc.

Reesman, Jeanne Campbell. Jack London's Racial Lives: A Critical Biography. (ENG., Illus.). 2011. 440p. pap. 26.95 (978-0-8203-3781-4(1)) 2009. 448p. 34.95 (978-0-8203-2789-1(1)) Univ. of Georgia Pr.

Reesman, Jeanne Campbell, et al. Jack London, Photographer. 2010. (ENG., Illus.). 288p. 49.95 (978-0-8203-2967-3(3)) Univ. of Georgia Pr.

Reeve, Katharine. Jane Austen in Bath: Walking Tours of the Writer's City. 2006. (ENG., Illus.). 144p. 19.95 (978-1-892145-32-1(4)) Little Bookroom.

Reichard, Susan E. Philip Pullman: Master of Fantasy. 2006. (Authors Teens Love Ser.). (Illus.). 104p. (YA). (gr. 7-12). lib. bdg. 31.93 (978-0-7660-2447-2(4)) Enslow Pubs., Inc.

Reid, Panthea. Tillie Olsen: One Woman, Many Riddles. (ENG., Illus.). 2011. 484p. pap. 26.95 (978-0-8135-5187-6(0)) 2009. 464p. 34.95 (978-0-8135-4637-7(0)) Rutgers Univ. Pr.

Reid, T. Wemyss. Richard Monckton Milnes V1 the Life Lett. 2006. pap. 42.95 (978-1-4286-4172-3(6)) Kessinger Publishing, LLC.

Reisen, Harriet. Louisa May Alcott: The Woman Behind Little Women. 2009. (ENG.). 384p. 26.00 (978-0-8050-8299-9(9)) Holt, Henry & Co.

—Louisa May Alcott: The Woman Behind Little Women. 2010. (ENG.). 464p. pap. 16.00 (978-0-312-65887-8(7)) Picador.

Reitz, Richard. Internal Landscape, External Reality: Hunting, Fishing, Life, in Essay & Story. 2007. 224p. per. 17.95 (978-0-595-44696-4(5)) iUniverse, Inc.

Renard, Jules. The Journal of Jules Renard. Bogan, Louise & Roget, Elizabeth, eds. & trs. by. from FRE. 2008. (ENG.). 264p. pap. 16.95 (978-0-9794198-7-4(5)) Tin Hse. Bks., LLC.

Renehan Jr., Edward J. Legend & Legacy: The Life of Seymour St. John. 2008. 304p. 30.00 (978-1-4389-1565-4(9)); pap. 15.95 (978-1-4389-1564-7(0)) AuthorHouse.

Renton, Richard. John Forster & His Friendships. 2007. (ENG.). 354p. 46.95 (978-0-548-04708-8(1)) Kessinger Publishing, LLC.

Resnick, Rachel. Love Junkie: A Memoir. 2009. (ENG.). 256p. pap. 14.00 (978-1-59691-646-3(X)) Bloomsbury Publishing.

Restif de La Bretonne & Testud, Pierre. Journal. 2010. (FRE.). 442p. (978-2-84578-117-7(2)) Manucius.

Reyes, Alfonso, et al. Cronica Parcial: Cartas de Alfonso Reyes y Amado Alonso, 1927-1952. 2008. (Estudios Lingüísticos y Literarios Ser.). (SPA., Illus.). 266p. pap. 29.99 (978-968-12-1370-1(X)) El Colegio de México, A.C., Biblioteca Miguel Cosio Villegas MEX. Dist: Fondo de Cultura Economica USA.

Reynolds, Abigail Elizabeth. An (Extra)Ordinary Journey A Life in Two Genders. 2009. 120p. pap. 19.95 (978-0-557-15639-9(4)) Lulu Enterprises Inc.

Reynolds, Frederick. The Life & Times of Frederick Reynolds. 2009. 154p. pap. (978-1-150-31229-8(7)); (Illus.). 168p. pap. (978-1-150-51640-5(2)); 320p. pap. (978-0-217-12437-9(2)); 202p. pap. (978-0-217-12434-8(8)) Books LLC.

—The Life & Times of Frederick Reynolds. 2009. 172p. pap. 19.99 (978-1-151-29311-4(3)) General Bks. LLC.

Reynolds, Stephen. A Poor Man's House. 2009. 236p. pap. (978-1-4099-3249-9(4)) Dodo Pr.

Rhode, Michael G., ed. Harvey Pekar: Conversations. 2008. (ENG., Illus.). 240p. 50.00 (978-1-60473-085-2(4)) Univ. Pr. of Mississippi.

Rhynes, Martha. Jack London: Writer of Adventure. 2011. 122p. pap. 9.95 **(978-1-4327-7282-6(1))** Outskirts Pr., Inc.

Ricchiuti, Paul B. Arthur S. Maxwell: Remembering an Adventist Legend. 2009. 12.99 (978-0-8163-2336-4(4)) Pacific Pr. Publishing Assn.

Rice, Anne. Called Out of Darkness: A Spiritual Confession. 2010. (ENG.). 256p. pap. 15.95 (978-0-307-38848-3(4), Anchor) Knopf Doubleday Publishing Group.

Rice, Pum. Child Abuse, My Story. 2011. 58p. pap. 21.49 **(978-1-4583-4688-9(9))** Lulu Enterprises Inc.

Rich, Mark. C. M. Kornbluth: The Life & Works of a Science Fiction Visionary. 2009. (ENG., Illus.). 451p. pap. 39.95 (978-0-7864-4393-2(6)) McFarland & Co., Inc. Pubs.

Richard, Mark. House of Prayer No. 2: A Writer's Journey Home. 2011. (ENG.). 224p. 23.95 (978-0-385-51302-9(X), Talese, Nan A.) Knopf Doubleday Publishing Group.

Richards, David Adams. God Is: My Search for Faith in a Secular World. 2010. (ENG.). 176p. pap. 19.95 **(978-0-385-66652-7(7)**, Anchor Can) Doubleday Canada, Ltd. CAN. Dist: Random Hse., Inc.

Richards, Penny. My Breast Cancer Sally. 2009. 192p. pap. 15.95 (978-0-557-11316-3(4)) Lulu Enterprises Inc.

Richards, Sal. Behind the Laughter, Hidden Tears. 2010. 170p. 26.95 (978-1-60911-240-0(7)); pap. 12.50 (978-1-60911-255-4(5)) AEG Literary Publishing Services, Inc. (Strategic Bk. Publishing).

Richards, Susan. Chosen Forever: A Memoir. 2009. (ENG.). 256p. pap. 13.95 (978-0-15-603302-2(X), Mariner Bks.) Houghton Mifflin Harcourt Trade & Reference Pubs.

—Chosen Forever: A Memoir. 2008. (ENG., Illus.). 288p. 23.00 (978-1-56947-492-1(3)) Soho Pr., Inc.

Richardson, Robert D. First We Read, Then We Write: Emerson on the Creative Process. 2009. (ENG.). 112p. 19.95 (978-1-58729-793-9(0)) Univ. of Iowa Pr.

Richardson, T. C. The Autobiography of the Rambling Longhorn. 2011. 98p. 38.95 **(978-1-258-09652-6(8))** Literary Licensing, LLC.

Rieder, Bernadette. Unter Beweis: Das Leben: Sechs Autobiographien Deutschsprachiger SchriftstellerInnen Aus Israel. 2008. (GER., Illus.). 395p. (C). 68.00 (978-3-89971-460-9(1)) Vandenhoeck & Ruprecht GmbH & Co. KG DEU. Dist: ISD.

Ritchie, Alan. Ruark Remembered: By the Man Who Knew Him Best. Casada, Jim, ed. 2009. (ENG., Illus.). 288p. 40.00 (978-0-9778551-3-1(9), 977853) Skyhorse Publishing Co., Inc.

—Ruark Remembered - Deluxe Edition. Casada, James, ed. 2007. 350p. lthr. 90.00 (978-0-9778551-4-8(7)) Sporting Classics.

Rivera, Armanco Chávez. Cuba per Se: Cartas de la Diaspora. 2009. (Coleccion Polymita Ser.). (SPA.). 574p. pap. 39.95 (978-1-59388-138-2(X), 8-138-X) Ediciones Universal.

Rivera, Carmen. Border Crossings & Beyond: The Life & Works of Sandra Cisneros, 1 vol. 2009. (Women Writers of Color Ser.) 127p. 34.95 (978-0-313-34518-0(X), C34518, Praeger Pubs.) Greenwood Publishing Group, Inc.

Rivero Taravillo, Antonio & Rivero, Antonio. Luis Cernuda Los Años Del Exilio (1938-1963) años de exilio, 1938-1963. 2011. (SPA., Illus.). 408p. pap. 26.95 **(978-84-8383-321-6(2))** Tusquets Editores ESP. Dist: Ediciones Urano S. A.

Robb, David. Auld Campaigner: A Life of Alexander Scott. 2007. (Illus.). 220p. (C). 70.00 (978-1-903765-38-8(2)) Dunedin Academic Pr. GBR. Dist: International Specialized Bk. Services.

Robbins, Jann. Harold & Me: My Life, Love, & Hard Times with Harold Robbins. 2010. (ENG.). 304p. pap. 19.99 (978-0-7653-2087-2(8), Forge Bks.) Doherty, Tom Assocs., LLC.

Robbins, Mary Susann. Earth, Air, Fire, & Water: A Memoir of the Sixties & Beyond. 2008. (ENG.). 170p. pap. 28.50 (978-0-7391-2792-6(6)) Lexington Bks.

Roberts, Neil. Ted Hughes: A Literary Life. 2007. (Literary Lives Ser.). (ENG.). 256p. 95.00 (978-1-4039-3605-9(6)) Palgrave Macmillan.

Roberts, Robin & Gayles, Gloria Wade. Anne Mccaffrey: A Life with Dragons. 2007. (ENG., Illus.). 243p. 28.00 (978-1-57806-998-9(X)) Univ. Pr. of Mississippi.

Roberts, Ronald. Biography of Nadine Gordimer. (978-0-374-21890-4(0)) Farrar, Straus & Giroux.

Roberts, S. C. Doctor Johnson & Others. 2012. (ENG.). 136p. pap. 34.99 **(978-1-107-68567-3(2))** Cambridge Univ. Pr.

Robertson, Ian Ross & Robertson, Ian. Sir Andrew Macphail: The Life & Legacy of a Canadian Man of Letters. 2008. (ENG., Illus.). 448p. (C). (978-0-7735-3419-3(9)) McGill-Queen's Univ. Pr.

Robertson, Mary. Watch the Right Lock: A Car & His Family in the Fifties. 2008. 216p. pap. 14.49 (978-1-4389-1902-7(6)) AuthorHouse.

Robertson, Ray. Why Not? Fifteen Reasons to Live. 2011. (ENG.). 175p. pap. 16.95 **(978-1-926845-27-2(7))** Biblioasis CAN. Dist: Consortium Bk. Sales & Distribution.

Robertson, Ritchie. Kafka. 2010. (Brief Insight Ser.). (ENG., Illus.). 176p. 14.95 (978-1-4027-7530-7(X)) Sterling Publishing Co., Inc.

Robins, Ashley. Oscar Wilde - The Great Drama of His Life: How His Tragedy Reflected His Personality. 2011. (ENG., Illus.). 276p. 55.00 (978-1-84519-434-5(9)) Sussex Academic Pr. GBR. Dist: International Specialized Bk. Services.

Robins, Ashley H. Oscar Wilde — The Great Drama of His Life: How His Tragedy Reflected His Personality. 2012. (Illus.). 272p. pap. 34.95 **(978-1-84519-541-0(8))** Sussex Academic Pr. GBR. Dist: International Specialized Bk. Services.

Robinson, Eden. The Sasquatch at Home: Traditional Protocols & Modern Storytelling. 2011. (Henry Kreisel Memorial Lecture Ser.). (ENG.). 64p. pap. 10.95 (978-0-88864-559-3(7)) Univ. of Alberta Pr. CAN. Dist: Michigan State Univ. Pr., Chicago Distribution Ctr.

Robinson, Gwen. At Home in Tokyo. 2007. 400p. pap. (978-0-7552-0264-5(3)) Authors OnLine, Ltd.

Robinson, Henry Crabb. Diary, Reminiscences & Correspondence. Sadler, Thomas, ed. 2011. (Cambridge Library Collection - Literary Studies). (ENG.). 610p. pap. 43.00 (978-1-108-02490-7(4)); (ENG.). 538p. pap. 39.99 (978-1-108-02489-1(0)); (Illus.). 542p. pap. 39.99 (978-1-108-02488-4(2)) Cambridge Univ. Pr.

Robinson, Kenneth Allen. Thoreau & the Wild Appetite. 2011. 28p. 35.95 **(978-1-258-01112-3(3))** Literary Licensing, LLC.

Roche, David, ed. Conversations with Russell Banks. 2010. (Literary Conversations Ser.). (ENG.). 240p. 40.00 (978-1-60473-745-5(X)) Univ. Pr. of Mississippi.

Rochelson, Meri-Jane. A Jew in the Public Arena: The Career of Israel Zangwill. 2010. pap. 24.95 (978-0-8143-3493-5(8)) 2008. (Illus.). 368p. 34.95 (978-0-8143-3344-0(3)) Wayne State Univ. Pr.

Rodríguez, Luis J. It Calls You Back: An Odyssey Through Love, Addictions, Revolutions, & Healing. 2011. (ENG.). 336p. 24.99 (978-1-4165-8416-2(1), Touchstone) Touchstone.

Roe, Jill. Her Brilliant Career: The Life of Stella Miles Franklin. 2009. Orig. Title: Stella Miles Franklin: A Biography. (Illus.). 752p. 39.95 (978-0-674-03609-3(3), Belknap Pr.) Harvard Univ. Pr.

Rogak, Lisa. Boy Named Shel: The Life & Times of Shel Silverstein. 2nd ed. 2009. (ENG., Illus.). 256p. pap. 16.99 (978-0-312-53931-3(2), St. Martin's Griffin) St. Martin's Pr.

—Haunted Heart: The Life & Times of Stephen King. (ENG., Illus.). 2010. 336p. pap. 15.99 (978-0-312-60350-2(9), St. Martin's Griffin) 2009. 320p. 25.95 (978-0-312-37732-8(0), Dunne, Thomas Bks.) St. Martin's Pr.

Rogers, B. The Last Englishman. (Illus.). 256p. 32.50 (978-1-85410-838-8(7)) Aurum Pr., Ltd. GBR. Dist: Trafalgar Square Publishing.

Rogers, Byron. The Last Englishman: The Life of J. L. Carr. (Illus.). 288p. pap. 14.99 (978-1-85410-984-2(7)) Aurum Pr., Ltd. GBR. Dist: Trafalgar Square Publishing.

Rogers, John. With Elia & His Friends in Books & Dreams. 2009. 112p. 21.99 (978-1-103-53943-7(4)); pap. 15.99 (978-1-103-53939-0(6)) BiblioBazaar.

Rogers, Steve. Lost in Love Grass: The Fragmented Tale of an Alzheimer's Afflicted Lifetime Duffer. 2010. 150p. 22.50 (978-1-934925-67-6(5), Strategic Bk. Publishing) AEG Literary Publishing Services, Inc.

Röhnelt, Tobias. Timm Kröger: Leben und Werk. 2009. (Rechtshistorische Reihe Ser.). (GRE & GER.). 196p. pap. 56.95 (978-3-631-58112-4(2)) Lang, Peter GmbH, Europaischer Verlag der Wissenschaften DEU. Dist: Lang, Peter.

Roig, Denise. Butter Cream: A Year in a Montreal Pastry School. 2008. (ENG.). 176p. pap. 15.95 (978-1-897109-30-4(X)) Signature Editions CAN. Dist: Univ. of Toronto Pr.

Roiphe, Anne. Art & Madness: A Memoir of Lust Without Reason. (ENG.). 240p. 2012. pap. 15.95 **(978-0-307-47396-7(1)**, Anchor) 2011. 24.95 (978-0-385-53164-1(8), Talese, Nan A.) Knopf Doubleday Publishing Group.

Roiphe, Anne. Epilogue: A Memoir. (ENG.). 2009. 256p. pap. 14.99 (978-0-06-125463-5(0), HarperPerennial) 2008. 288p. pap. 24.95 (978-0-06-166857-9(5), HarperLuxe) HarperCollins Pubs.

Roiphe, Katie. Uncommon Arrangements: Seven Marriages. 2008. 352p. pap. 15.00 (978-0-385-33938-4(0), Dial Pr.) Random House Publishing Group.

Rolls, Albert. Stephen King: A Biography, 1 vol. 2008. (Greenwood Biographies Ser.). (Illus.). 216p. 35.00 (978-0-313-34572-2(4), GR4572, Greenwood Pr.) Greenwood Publishing Group, Inc.

Rollyson, Carl. Norman Mailer: The Last Romantic. 2008. 420p. pap. 26.95 (978-0-595-50448-0(5)) iUniverse, Inc.

—Rebecca West. 2008. pap. 29.95 (978-0-595-48868-1(4)) iUniverse, Inc.

Rollyson, Carl, ed. Notable American Novelists, 3 vols., Set. 2007. (Magill's Choice Ser.). (Illus.). 1536p. lib. bdg. 217.00 (978-1-58765-393-3(1), Magill's Choice) Salem Pr., Inc.

Rollyson, Carl E. Notable American Novelists. 2007. (Magill's Choice Ser.). 73.00 (978-1-58765-394-0(X)); 73.00 (978-1-58765-395-7(8)); 73.00 (978-1-58765-396-4(6)) Salem Pr., Inc.

Rorato, Lara & Spunta, Marina, eds. Letteratura come Fantasticazione: In Conversazione con Gianni Celati. 2009. (ITA.). x, 379p. (978-0-7734-3900-9(5)) Mellen, Edwin Pr., The.

Rosenberg, Aaron. Colleen Doran. 2009. (Library of Graphic Novelists Ser.). 112p. (gr. 7-12). 63.90 (978-1-60853-654-2(8)) Rosen Publishing Group, Inc., The.

—Madeleine L'Engle. 2009. (Library of Author Biographies Ser.). 112p. (gr. 5-8). 63.90 (978-1-60853-547-7(9), Rosen Central) Rosen Publishing Group, Inc., The.

Rosenblatt, Helena, ed. The Cambridge Companion to Constant. 2009. (Cambridge Companions to Philosophy Ser.). (ENG.). 448p. 99.00 (978-0-521-85646-1(9)); pap. 30.99 (978-0-521-67243-6(0)) Cambridge Univ. Pr.

Rosenblatt, Roger. Making Toast: A Family Story. 2011. (ENG.). 128p. pap. 12.99 (978-0-06-182595-8(6)) 2010. 176p. 21.99 (978-0-06-182593-4(X)) HarperCollins Pubs. (Ecco).

—Making Toast: A Family Story. Lt. ed. 2010. 236p. 31.99 (978-1-4104-2861-5(3)) Thorndike Pr.

Rosenkranz, Moses. Childhood: An Autobiographical Fragment. 2007. (Judaic Traditions in Literature, Music & Art Ser.). 227p. 24.95 (978-0-8156-3178-1(2)) Syracuse Univ. Pr.

Ross, John J. Shakespeare's Tremor & Orwell's Cough: The Medical Lives of Great Writers. 2012. (ENG., Illus.). 304p. 24.99 **(978-0-312-60076-1(3))** St. Martin's Pr.

Ross, La'camii Victoria Renee Ann. A Life Lived: My Faith, My Life, My Purpose. #8482; 2010. 136p. pap. 13.99 (978-1-4520-6395-9(8)) AuthorHouse.

Ross-Stroud, Catherine. Janet McDonald: The Original Project Girl. 2008. (Scarecrow Studies in Young Adult Literature Ser.). (ENG., Illus.). 160p. 45.00 (978-0-8108-5802-2(9)) Scarecrow Pr., Inc.

Ross, Val. Robertson Davies: A Portrait in Mosaic. 2009. 400p. pap. 19.95 (978-0-7710-7776-0(9), Emblem Edns) McClelland & Stewart CAN. Dist: Random Hse., Inc.

Rossetti, Lucy M. Mrs Shelley. 2010. 148p. 28.76 (978-1-169-26331-4(3)); pap. 16.76 (978-1-162-67521-3(7)) Kessinger Publishing, LLC.

Rossetti, Lucy M. & Rossetti, Lucy M. Mrs Shelley. 2010. 148p. 35.95 (978-1-161-44386-8(X)) Kessinger Publishing, LLC.

Rossetti, Lucy Madox. Mrs Shelley. 2009. 250p. 28.99 (978-1-110-87750-8(1)) 2009. 250p. pap. 25.75 (978-1-110-87749-2(8)) 2008. 248p. 24.99 (978-0-559-21595-7(9)) 2008. 248p. pap. 25.75 (978-0-559-21592-6(4)) BiblioBazaar.

—Mrs Shelley. 2008. 172p. pap. (978-1-4099-3236-9(2)) Dodo Pr.

—Mrs. Shelley. 2009. (ENG.). 249p. pap. 22.99 (978-1-110-87746-1(3)); pap. 20.99 (978-1-110-87744-7(7)) BiblioBazaar. (BiblioLife).

—Mrs Shelley. 2010. 248p. 32.99 (978-1-140-28183-2(6)) BiblioBazaar.

Rossetti, Lucy Madox Brown. Mrs Shelley. 2010. (ENG.). 260p. pap. 26.75 (978-1-176-86124-4(7)) BiblioBazaar.

—Mrs Shelley. 2010. (Illus.). 116p. pap. 20.59 (978-1-153-64309-2(X)) General Bks. LLC.

Roth, Joseph & Hofmann, Michael. Joseph Roth: A Life in Letters. 2012. (ENG.). 512p. 39.95 **(978-0-393-06064-5(0)**, 6064) Norton, W. W. & Co., Inc.

Roth, Philip. Notes for My Biographer. 2012. (ENG.). 288p. 26.00 **(978-0-547-89684-7(0))** Houghton Mifflin Harcourt Trade & Reference Pubs.

Rouse, Wade. At Least in the City Someone Would Hear Me Scream: Misadventures in Search of the Simple Life. 2010. (ENG.). 320p. pap. 14.00 (978-0-307-45191-0(7), Three Rivers Pr.) Crown Publishing Group.

Rousseau, George S. Notorious Sir John Hill: The Man Destroyed by Ambition in the Era of Celebrity. 2012. (ENG.). 424p. (gr. 17). 90.00 **(978-1-61146-120-6(0))** Lehigh Univ. Pr.

Rousseau, Jean-Jacques. The Confessions of J J Rousseau, Complete. 2007. 472p. per. (978-1-4068-4056-8(4)) Echo Library.

Routledge Staff, creator. International Who's Who of Authors & Writers. 22nd rev. ed. 2006. (International Who's Who of Authors & Writers Ser.). 800p. (978-1-85743-385-2(8)) Routledge, Chapman & Hall, Inc.

Rowbotham, Sheila. Edward Carpenter: A Life of Liberty & Love. 2008. (ENG., Illus.). 548p. 39.95 (978-1-84467-295-0(6), 844295) Verso Bks. GBR. Dist: Norton, W. W. & Co., Inc.

Rowland, Peter. Dickensian Digressions: The Hunter, the Haunter & the Haunted. 2010. (Illus.). 324p. lib. bdg. (978-1-936320-07-3(X)) Academica Pr., LLC.

—The Unobtrusive Miss Hawker: The Life & Works of 'Lanoe Falconer', Vate Victorian Novelist & Short story Writer, 1848-1908. 2009. (978-1-933146-63-8(X)) Academica Pr., LLC.

Rowlandson, Maurice L. Maurice's Deuteronomy. 2007. 192p. pap. 18.95 (978-1-84799-240-6(4)) Lulu Enterprises Inc.

Rowley, Hazel. Richard Wright: The Life & Times. 2008. (Illus.). 638p. pap. 22.50 (978-0-226-73038-7(7)) Univ. of Chicago Pr.

—Tête-à-Tête: The Tumultuous Lives & Loves of Simone de Beauvoir & Jean-Paul Sartre. 2008. (ENG.). 416p. pap. 16.00 (978-1-4223-9557-8(X)) DIANE Publishing Co.

—Tête-à-Tête: The Tumultuous Lives & Loves of Simone de Beauvoir & Jean-Paul Sartre. 2006. (P. S. Ser.). (ENG., Illus.). 480p. per. 15.95 (978-0-06-052060-1(4), HarperPerennial) HarperCollins Pubs.

Rubens, Bernice. When I Grow Up: A Memoir. 2006. (ENG., Illus.). 256p. per. 14.95 (978-0-349-12017-1(X), Warner Books) Little, Brown Bk. Group Ltd. GBR. Dist: Independent Pubs. Group.

Rubin, C M & Rubin, Gabriela. The Real Alice in Wonderland: A Role Model for the Ages. 2010. 144p. 29.95 (978-1-4490-8131-7(2)) AuthorHouse.

Rubio, Mary Henley. Lucy Maud Montgomery: The Gift of Wings. 2010. (ENG.). 720p. pap. 21.95 (978-0-385-66760-9(4), Anchor Can) Doubleday Canada, Ltd. CAN. Dist: Random Hse., Inc.

Ruggier, Joe & John Paul. Pope Caesar's Wake- Letters to Pope Woytyla. 3rd ed. 2012. **(978-1-897303-17-7(3))** Multicultural Bks.

Ruiz Arzálluz, Iñigo, et al. La Vita Terrentii de Petrarca. 2010. (LAT & SPA.). xix, 159p. (978-88-8455-647-9(3)) Antenore.

Rule, Jane. Loving the Difficult. 2008. (Illus.). 205p. (978-0-9736882-6-9(2)) Hedgerow Pr.

Rule, Jane. Taking My Life. 2011. (ENG.). 278p. pap. 19.95 **(978-0-88922-673-9(3))** Talonbooks, Ltd. CAN. Dist: Consortium Bk. Sales & Distribution.

Ruppel, Richard. Homosexuality in the Life & Work of Joseph Conrad: Love Between the Lines. 2009. 114p. pap. 39.95 (978-0-415-87669-8(9)) Routledge.

Ruskin, John & O'Gorman, Francis. Praeterita. 2012. (Oxford World's Classics Ser.). (ENG.). 512p. pap. 16.95 **(978-0-19-280241-5(0))** Oxford Univ. Pr., Inc.

Russell, Allen. Heroes of My Transplant. 2007. (ENG.). 108p. 14.99 (978-1-932496-63-5(7)) Penman Publishing, Inc.

Russell, Renny. Rock Me on the Water: A Life on the Loose. 2007. (ENG., Illus.). 254p. per. 29.95 (978-0-9760539-1-0(8)) Animist Pr.

—Rock Me on the Water: A Life on the Loose. 2007. (ENG., Illus.). 254p. 39.95 (978-0-9760539-0-3(X)) Animist Pr.

—Rock Me on the Water: A Life on the Loose. ltd. ed. 2007. 256p. 149.00 (978-0-9760539-2-7(6)) Animist Pr.

Russell, Robert James, et al, eds. Authors & Artists for Young Adults, Volume 76. 2008. (Authors & Artists for Young Adults Ser.: Vol. 76). (ENG., Illus.). 224p. (J). 168.00 (978-0-7876-7795-4(7)) Cengage Gale.

Rutkoff, Peter. Across the Green Line: Cyprus Portraits. 2007. (Illus.). 136p. pap. 14.95 (978-1-880977-22-4(2)) XOXOX Pr.

Rybczynski, Witold. My Two Polish Grandfathers: And Other Essays on the Imaginative Life. 2009. (ENG., Illus.). 240p. 25.00 (978-0-7432-3598-3(3), Scribner) Scribner.

Rybolt, William. Stonewalled. 2006. (ENG., Illus.). 308p. per. 24.99 (978-1-4120-9394-1(5)) Trafford Publishing.

Sabbag, Robert. Down Around Midnight: A Memoir of Crash & Survival. 2010. (ENG.). 224p. (gr. 12). 15.00 (978-0-14-311760-5(2), Penguin (Non-Classics)) Penguin Group (USA) Inc.

Sabor, Peter. The Court Journals & Letters of Frances Burney: Volume I: 1786. 2011. (ENG., Illus.). 400p. 185.00 (978-0-19-926160-4(1)) Oxford Univ. Pr., Inc.

Safran, Gabriella. Wandering Soul: The Dybbuk's Creator, S. An-Sky. 2010. (Illus.). 392p. 29.95 (978-0-674-05570-4(5)) Harvard Univ. Pr.

Saint-Exupéry, Antoine de. Flight to Arras. 2007. 260p. per. (978-1-4067-0579-9(9)) Read Bks.

—Wind, Sand & Stars. Date not set. 250p. 22.95 (978-0-8488-2596-6(9)) Amereon LTD.

Saintsbury, George. Dryden. 2009. 208p. 23.99 (978-1-103-61888-0(1)); pap. 17.99 (978-1-103-61885-9(7)) BiblioBazaar.

—Dryden. 2009. 120p. pap. (978-0-217-20515-3(1)) Books LLC.

—Dryden. 2011. (Cambridge Library Collection - English Men of Letters Ser.). (ENG.). 206p. pap. 22.99 **(978-1-108-03461-6(6))** Cambridge Univ. Pr.

Sajben, Miklos. Dancing boots & pigs' Feet. 2009. 195p. pap. 14.00 (978-0-557-05914-0(3)) Lulu Enterprises Inc.

Salick, Roydon. Ismith Khan: The Man & His Works. 2012. (ENG., Illus.). 128p. pap. 22.95 (978-1-84523-174-3(0)) Peepal Tree Pr., Ltd. GBR. Dist: Independent Pubs. Group.

Sallie, Rose C. Tanzie. A Budding Rose. 2011. 108p. pap. 10.95 **(978-1-4670-2626-0(3))** AuthorHouse.

Salt, Henry Stephens. De Quincey. 2008. 128p. 35.95 (978-1-4365-0294-8(2)) 2007. (ENG.). 132p. per. 20.95 (978-0-548-74319-5(3)) Kessinger Publishing, LLC.

Sams, Amanda. Authors & Artists for Young Adults. 2008. (Authors & Artists for Young Adults Ser.: Vol. 77). (ENG.). 224p. 168.00 (978-0-7876-7796-1(5)) Cengage Gale.

Sams, Amanda D., ed. Contemporary Authors New Revision Series, Volume 160. 2007. (New Revision Ser.: Vol. 160). (ENG.). 432p. 293.00 (978-0-7876-7914-9(3)) Cengage Gale.

—Contemporary Authors, Volume 163: A Bio-Bibliographical Guide to Current Writers in Fiction, General Nonfiction, Poetry, Journalism, Drama, Motion Pictures, Television, & Other Fields. 163rd rev. ed. 2007. (New Revision Ser.: Vol. 163). (ENG.). 448p. 293.00 (978-0-7876-7917-0(8)) Cengage Gale.

Samuels. John Updike, Vol. 79. 2009. pap. 25.00 (978-0-8166-0529-3(7)) Univ. of Minnesota Pr.

Samuels, Selina, ed. Australian Writers, 1975-2000, Vol. 325. 2006. (Dictionary of Literary Biography Ser.: Vol. 325). (ENG., Illus.). 392p. 315.00 (978-0-7876-8143-2(1)) Cengage Gale.

Samway, Patrick. Educating Darfur Refugees: A Jesuit's Efforts in Chad. 2007 (Illus.). 300p. 35.00 (978-1-58966-157-8(5)); pap. 25.00 (978-1-58966-164-6(8)) Univ. of Scranton Pr.

Sanborn, Kate. Memories & Anecdotes. 2009. 268p. 24.99 (978-1-103-10076-7(9)) 2009. 268p. pap. 18.99 (978-1-103-10074-3(2)) 2008. 180p. 25.99 (978-0-554-25223-0(6)) 2008. 180p. 22.99 (978-0-554-34526-0(9)) 2007. (ENG.). 160p. pap. 19.99 (978-1-4264-8461-2(5)) BiblioBazaar.

—Memories & Anecdotes. 2009. 126p. pap. (978-0-217-51376-0(X)) Books LLC.

—Memories & Anecdotes. 2007. (ENG., Illus.). 168p. per. (978-1-4065-4299-8(7)) Dodo Pr.
—Memories & Anecdotes. 2007. 264p. 42.95 (978-0-548-53630-8(9)); (ENG.). per. 27.95 (978-0-548-47069-5(3)) Kessinger Publishing, LLC.
Sandars, Mary F. Honore de Balzac His Life & Writings. 2007. 254p. pap. 21.99 (978-1-4346-2030-9(1)) BiblioBazaar.
Sander, Gordon F. Serling: The Rise & Twilight of TV's Last Angry Man. 2011. 320p. pap. 18.95 (978-0-8014-7730-0(1)) Cornell Univ. Pr.
Sanders, Ed. Fug You: An Informal History of the Peace Eye Bookstore, the Fuck You Press, the Fugs, & Counterculture in the Lower East Side. 2011. (ENG., Illus.). 448p. 26.99 (978-0-306-81888-2(4)) Da Capo Pr., Inc.
Sandford, Christopher. Masters of Mystery: The Strange Friendship of Arthur Conan Doyle & Harry Houdini. 2011. (ENG., Illus.). 304p. 27.00 (978-0-230-61950-0(9)) Palgrave Macmillan.
Sandor, Marjorie. The Late Interiors: A Life under Construction. 2011. (ENG.). 208p. 22.95 (978-1-61145-005-7(5), 611005, Arcade Publishing) Skyhorse Publishing Co., Inc.
Saramago, José. The Notebook. Hopkinson, Amanda & Hahn, Daniel, trs. from POR. 2nd ed. 2011. (ENG.). 304p. pap. 16.95 (978-1-84467-701-6(X), 844701) Verso Bks. GBR. Dist: Norton, W. W. & Co., Inc.
—O Caderno. 2nd ed. 2010. (POR.). (978-972-21-2092-0(1)) Caminho, Editorial.
Saramago, José. Small Memories. Costa, Margaret Jull, tr. 2012. (ENG.). 176p. pap. 13.95 (978-0-547-75263-1(6), Mariner Bks.) Houghton Mifflin Harcourt Trade & Reference Pubs.
Sarraute, Nathalie. Childhood. 2007. 256p. pap. 16.00 (978-0-226-73492-7(7)) Univ. of Chicago Pr.
Sasson, Victor. Memoirs of A Baghdad Childhood. 2011. 116p. pap. 12.95 (978-1-4620-1733-1(9)) iUniverse, Inc.
Sassoon, Elias. 13 Months of Sassoon: A Diary of Time. 2010. 209p. pap. 13.27 (978-0-557-31839-1(4)) Lulu Enterprises Inc.
Satiat, Nadine. Gertrude Stein. 2010. (FRE., Illus.). 1288p. (978-2-08-121992-2(1)) Flammarion et Cie.
Sauerwein, Stan. Lucy Maud Montgomery (Junior Edition) 2007. (Amazing Stories Junior Ser.). (Illus.). 96p. pap. (978-1-55439-724-2(3)) Altitude Publishing Canada Ltd.
Saunders, Richard. Never Been Rich: The Life & Work of a Southern Ruralist Writer, Harry Harrison Kroll. 2011. (ENG.). 264p. 42.00 (978-1-57233-825-8(3)) Univ. of Tennessee Pr.
Saunders, Robert. What Few Will Think & None Will Say. 2011. 182p. pap. 24.95 (978-1-4560-1237-3(1)) PublishAmerica, Inc.
Savage, Michael. Train Tracks: Holiday Stories. 2012. (ENG.). 208p. 23.99 (978-0-06-221084-5(X), Morrow, William & Co.) HarperCollins Pubs.
Savage, Richie. Alive & Kicking. 2010. 296p. pap. 15.49 (978-1-4520-3120-0(7)) AuthorHouse.
SAYNER, Joanne. Women without a Past? German Autobiographical Writings & Fascism. 2007. (Genus Ser.: 8). 392p. per. 105.00 (978-90-420-2228-7(0)) Rodopi.
Sayre, Robert F., et al. Emerson & Thoreau: Figures of Friendship. Lysaker, John T. & Rossi, William, eds. 2010. (American Philosophy Ser.). (ENG.). 222p. pap. 22.95 (978-0-253-22143-8(9), 0253221439) Indiana Univ. Pr.
Scammell, Michael. Koestler: The Literary & Political Odyssey of a Twentieth-Century Skeptic. 2009. (Illus.). 720p. 35.00 (978-0-394-57630-5(6)) Random Hse., Inc.
Scharnhorst, Gary. Kate Field: The Many Lives of a Nineteenth-Century American Journalist. (Writing American Women Ser.). (Illus.). 2009. 306p. 27.95 (978-0-8156-0874-5(8)) 2008. xiv, 306p. (978-0-8456-0874-6(6)) Syracuse Univ. Pr.
Scharnhorst, Gary, ed. Twain in His Own Time: A Biographical Chronicle of His Life, Drawn from Recollections, Interviews, & Memoirs by Family, Friends, & Associates. 2010. (Writers in Their Own Time Ser.). 290p. pap. 27.95 (978-1-58729-914-8(3)) Univ. of Iowa Pr.
Schaub, Danielle, ed. & photos by. Reading Writers Reading: Canadian Authors' Reflections. 2006. (Currents, a Canadian Literature Ser.). (FRE & ENG., Illus.). 368p. 60.00 (978-0-88864-459-6(0)) Univ. of Alberta Pr. CAN. Dist: Michigan State Univ. Pr.
Schellin, Peter Friedrich. The Wrong Ocean. 2011. 108p. 21.95 (978-1-4634-3005-4(1)); pap. 17.95 (978-1-4634-3006-1(X)) AuthorHouse.
Schenck, Theresa M. William W. Warren: The Life, Letters, & Times of an Ojibwe Leader. 2009. (American Indian Lives Ser.). (ENG.). 232p. pap. 19.95 (978-0-8032-2498-8(2)) Univ. of Nebraska Pr.
Schenkar, Joan. The Talented Miss Highsmith: The Secret Life & Serious Art of Patricia Highsmith. 2011. (ENG., Illus.). 704p. pap. 24.00 (978-0-312-36381-9(8)) Picador.
Scherer, Silvester Nicholas. House Bites Man. 2011. 180p. 29.99 (978-1-4653-5067-1(5)); pap. 19.99 (978-1-4653-5066-4(7)) Xlibris Corp.
Schmidt, Austin Guildford. Optimus Magister, Bonus Liber. 2011. 28p. 35.95 (978-1-258-08032-7(X)) Literary Licensing, LLC.
Schnakenberg, Robert. Secret Lives of Great Authors: What Your Teachers Never Told You about Famous Novelists, Poets, & Playwrights. 2008. (ENG., Illus.). 304p. per. 16.95 (978-1-59474-211-8(1)) Quirk Bks.
Schuessler, Michael Karl & Schuessler, Michael K. Elena Poniatowska: An Intimate Biography. 2007. (ENG., Illus.). 272p. pap. 19.95 (978-0-8165-2501-0(3)) Univ. of Arizona Pr.
Schultz, David E. & Joshi, S. T., eds. An Epicure in the Terrible: A Centennial Anthology of Essays in Honor of H. P. Lovecraft. rev. exp. ed. 2011. (ENG.). pap. 20.00 (978-0-9846386-1-1(X)) Hippocampus Pr.
Schultz, William Todd. Tiny Terror: Why Truman Capote (Almost) Wrote Answered Prayers. 2011. (Inner Lives Ser.). (ENG.). 190p. 17.95 (978-0-19-975204-1(4)) Oxford Univ. Pr., Inc.
Schulz, Karlheinz. Goethe: Eine Biographie in 16 Kapiteln. (GER., Illus.). 603p. (978-3-15-009745-8(2)) Reclam, Philip jun., Verlag GmbH.
Schwartz, Sheila. F Scott Fitzgerald. 2012. (Life&Times Ser.). (ENG.). 220p. pap. 14.95 (978-1-907822-00-1(3)) Haus Publishing GBR. Dist: Consortium Bk. Sales & Distribution.
Scotchie, Joseph. Thomas Wolfe Revisited. 158p. 22.99 (978-1-56664-163-0(2), Land of the Sky Bks.) WorldComm.
Scott, Walter, Sr. The Journal of Sir Walter Scott, Vol. 1. 2008. (Illus.). pap. (978-1-4065-7398-5(1)) Dodo Pr.
Scott, Walter, Sr. Memoirs of Jonathan Swift: Dean of St. Patrick's, Dublin (1834) 2011. (Cambridge Library Collection - Literary Studies). (ENG.). 326p. pap. 28.99 (978-1-108-03418-0(7)); 268p. pap. 23.99 (978-1-108-03419-7(5)); 594p. pap., pap. 51.00 (978-1-108-03420-3(9)) Cambridge Univ. Pr.
Seaton, Maureen. Sex Talks to Girls: A Memoir. 2008. (Living Out: Gay & Lesbian Autobiog Ser.). (ENG.). 212p. 26.95 (978-0-299-22880-4(0)) Univ. of Wisconsin Pr.
Seats, Michael Robert. Murakami Haruki: The Simulacrum In Contemporary Japanese Culture. 2009. (Studies of Modern Japan Ser.). (ENG.). 384p. pap. 41.99 (978-0-7391-2725-4(X)) Lexington Bks.
Sebald, W. G. The Emergence of Memory: Conversations with W. G. Sebald. Schwartz, Lynne Sharon, ed. 2010. (ENG.). 176p. pap. 15.95 (978-1-58322-915-6(9)) Seven Stories Pr.
Sebula, Nicole. My Crazy Life. 2008. 164p. pap. 24.95 (978-1-60610-990-8(1)) PublishAmerica, Inc.
See, Lisa. On Gold Mountain. 2012. (Vintage Ser.). (ENG., Illus.). 464p. pap. 15.95 (978-0-307-95039-0(5), Vintage) Knopf Doubleday Publishing Group.
Selgin, Peter. Confessions of a Left-Handed Man: An Artist's Memoir. 2011. (Sightline Bks.). (ENG.). 248p. pap. 19.95 (978-1-60938-056-4(8)) Univ. of Iowa Pr.
Sellers, Heather. You Don't Look Like Anyone I Know. 2010. (ENG.). 368p. (gr. 12). 25.95 (978-1-59448-773-6(1), Riverhead Bks. (Hardcover)) Penguin Group (USA) Inc.
—You Don't Look Like Anyone I Know: A True Story of Family, Face Blindness, & Forgiveness. 2011. (ENG.). 368p. (gr. 12). 16.00 (978-1-59448-540-4(2), Riverhead Trade (Paperbacks)) Penguin Group (USA) Inc.
Sellers, Susan, ed. White Ink: Interviews on Sex, Text, & Politics. 2008. (European Perspectives: a Series in Social Thought & Cultural Criticism Ser.). (ENG.). 256p. (gr. 17). 79.50 (978-0-231-14776-7(7)); pap. 26.50 (978-0-231-14777-4(5)) Columbia Univ. Pr.
Sellin, Bernard. The Life & Works of David Lindsay. Gunnell, Kenneth, tr. from FRE. annot. ed. 2007. (ENG.). 284p. per. 58.00 (978-0-521-03401-2(9)) Cambridge Univ. Pr.
Selzer, Richard. Diary. 2011. (ENG.). 256p. 28.00 (978-0-300-12461-3(9)) Yale Univ. Pr.
Senior, Nassau William. Biographical Sketches. 2010. 540p. pap. 40.75 (978-1-148-80287-9(8)) 2010. 542p. pap. 40.75 (978-1-146-72664-1(3)) 2010. 526p. pap. 40.75 (978-1-142-99133-3(4)) 2009. 534p. 43.99 (978-1-116-80217-7(1)) 2009. 534p. 36.99 (978-1-116-80218-4(X)) 2009. 534p. pap. 39.75 (978-1-116-80220-7(1)) 2009. (ENG.). 532p. pap. 30.99 (978-1-116-80222-1(8), BiblioLife) 2009. (ENG.). 532p. pap. 31.99 (978-1-116-80221-4(X), BiblioLife) 2009. 534p. pap. 40.75 (978-1-116-80219-1(8)) BiblioBazaar.
—Biographical Sketches. 2009. 260p. pap. (978-0-217-44646-4(9)) Books LLC.
Senna, Danzy. Where Did You Sleep Last Night? A Personal History. 2010. (ENG.). 208p. pap. 14.00 (978-0-312-42939-3(8)) Picador.
Sensibar, Judith L. Faulkner & Love: The Women Who Shaped His Art, a Biography. (ENG., Illus.). 616p. 2010. pap. 28.00 (978-0-300-16568-5(4)) 2009. 40.00 (978-0-300-11503-1(2)) Yale Univ. Pr.
Serafin, Steven & Mihailovich, Vasa D. Dlb 353 Cen & E Eur Writers. 2009. (Dictionary of Literary Biography Ser.). (ENG., Illus.). 480p. 315.00 (978-0-7876-8171-5(7)) Cengage Gale.
Serra, Renato & Menetti, Andrea. Mio Carissimo. 2009. (ITA.). 269p. (978-88-7847-262-4(X)) Monte Universita Parma.
Sesniak, Dorothy Hudson-Mary Harrell. The, Miesse Family Their Westward Trek Volume I: Johann Daniel & the Descendants of Sons Jacob, Joseph, & Abraham. 2011. (ENG.). 686p. pap. 35.95 (978-1-4327-5825-7(X)) Outskirts Pr., Inc.
Seton, George. Gossip about Letters & Letter-Writers. 2008. 272p. 25.99 (978-0-559-48049-2(0)); pap. 26.75 (978-0-559-48046-1(6)) BiblioBazaar.
—Gossip about Letters & Letter-Writers. 2009. (Illus.). 180p. pap. (978-0-217-21669-2(2)); 180p. pap. (978-1-4590-9728-5(9)); 178p. pap. (978-1-4590-9729-2(7)) Books LLC.
Settle, Mary Lee. Learning to Fly: A Writer's Memoir. Hobson Freeman, Anne, ed. 2007. (ENG., Illus.). 240p. 24.95 (978-0-393-05732-4(1), 5732) Norton, W. W. & Co., Inc.
Sexton, Linda Gray. Half in Love: Surviving the Legacy of Suicide. 2011. (ENG.). 336p. 25.00 (978-1-58243-718-7(1), Counterpoint) Counterpoint LLC.
—Half in Love: Surviving the Legacy of Suicide. 2010. 300p. 26.95 (978-1-60747-761-7(0)) Phoenix Bks., Inc.
Seymour, Miranda. Thrumpton Hall: A Memoir of Life in My Father's House. 2009. 304p. pap. 14.99 (978-0-06-146658-8(1), HarperPerennial) HarperCollins Pubs.
Shackelford, Otis M. Seeking the Best. 2009. 84p. pap. 16.95 (978-1-151-40377-3(6)) General Bks. LLC.
Shafak, Elif. Black Milk: On the Conflicting Demands of Writing, Creativity, & Motherhood. 2012. (ENG.). 288p. (gr. 12). pap. 16.00 (978-0-14-312108-4(1), Penguin (Non-Classics)) Penguin Group (USA) Inc.
Shafak, Elif. Black Milk: On Writing, Motherhood, & the Harem Within. Zapsu, Hande, tr. from TUR. 2011. (ENG.). 288p. (gr. 12). 25.95 (978-0-670-02264-9(0), Viking Adult) Penguin Group (USA) Inc.
Shaffer, Brian W. The Encyclopedia of Twentieth-Century Fiction, 3 vols. 2011. (Wiley-Blackwell Encyclopedia of Literature Ser.: 1). (ENG.). 1584p. 595.00 (978-1-4051-9244-6(5), Wiley-Blackwell) Wiley, John & Sons, Inc.
Shah, Tahir. The Caliph's House: A Year in Casablanca. 2006. (ENG., Illus.). 368p. pap. 16.00 (978-0-553-38310-2(8), Bantam) Random House Publishing Group.
—In Arabian Nights: A Caravan of Moroccan Dreams. 2009. (ENG.). 400p. pap. 16.00 (978-0-553-38443-7(0)) Random House Publishing Group.
Shalev, Meir. My Russian Grandmother & Her American Vacuum Cleaner: A Family Memoir. Fallenberg, Evan, tr. from HEB. 2011. (ENG., Illus.). 224p. 25.95 (978-0-8052-4287-4(2), Schocken) Knopf Doubleday Publishing Group.
Shapiro, Dani. Devotion: A Memoir. 2010. 256p. 24.99 (978-0-06-162834-4(4)) HarperCollins Pubs.
—Slow Motion: A Memoir of a Life Rescued by Tragedy. 2010. (P. S. Ser.). (ENG.). 272p. pap. 14.99 (978-0-06-182669-6(3), HarperPerennial) HarperCollins Pubs.
Sharpe, Ernest Jack. One Life, Memoirs: Tall Tales of Newaygo Newt, Backwoods Philosophy. 2011. 114p. 39.95 (978-1-258-10402-3(4)) Literary Licensing, LLC.
Sharpe, Tony. W. H. Auden. 2007. (Routledge Guides to Literature Ser.). (ENG.). 176p. 95.00 (978-0-415-32735-0(0)); 162p. per. 28.95 (978-0-415-32736-7(9)) Routledge.
Sharps, John Geoffrey & Chapple, J. A. V., eds. Elizabeth Gaskell: Portrait in Letters. 2nd rev. ed. 2008. (ENG., Illus.). 192p. pap. 26.00 (978-0-7190-7789-0(3)) Manchester Univ. Pr. GBR. Dist: Macmillan.
Shavelson, Melville. HT Succeed in Hollywood. 2007. pap. (978-1-59393-066-0(6)) BearManor Media.
Shaw, Hugh. Our Last November. 2011. 156p. pap. 24.95 (978-1-4560-5744-2(8)) PublishAmerica, Inc.
Shaw, LeRoy R. & Shaw, Leroy R. Witness of Deceit: Gerhart Hauptmann As Critic of Society. 2011. 138p. 40.95 (978-1-258-06004-6(3)) Literary Licensing, LLC.
Shaw, Margaret Dinzler. Memoirs in the Light of Day: An Essay Collection. 2008. vii, 210p. pap. (978-0-9676130-5-5(1)) Lamberson Corona Pr.
Shayne, Vic & Small, Martin. Remember Us: My Journey from the Shtetl Through the Holocaust. 2009. (ENG., Illus.). 336p. 24.95 (978-1-60239-723-1(6), 239723) Skyhorse Publishing Co., Inc.
Shchyhlevska, Natalia. Alfred Gong: Leben und Werk. 2008. (GER., Illus.). 356p. pap. 84.95 (978-3-03911-420-7(4)) Lang, Peter AG GBR. Dist: Lang, Peter.
Sheba-Bassett. Eye of the Dream. 2010. 140p. pap. 13.45 (978-1-4520-3425-6(7)) AuthorHouse.
Sheikh, Nazneen. Moon over Marrakech: A Memoir of Loving Too Deeply in a Foreign Land. 2010. (ENG.). 288p. 22.00 (978-1-897151-71-6(3)) Cormorant Bks. Inc. CAN. Dist: Univ. of Toronto Pr.
Shelden, Michael. Mark Twain: Man in White - The Grand Adventure of His Final Years. 2010. (ENG., Illus.). 528p. 30.00 (978-0-679-44800-6(4)) Random Hse., Inc.
Shelley, Alan. Not So Private Lives. 2009. 164p. pap. 11.99 (978-1-4389-8415-5(4)) AuthorHouse.
Shelley, Mary Wollstonecraft. Lives of the Most Eminent Literary & Scientific Men of Italy, Spain & Portugal, 2 Vols. reprint ed. lib. bdg. 196.00 (978-0-7426-2105-3(7)) Classic Bks.
Shen Fu. Six Records of a Life Adrift. Sanders, Graham, tr. from CHI. 2011. (Illus.). 148p. (C). pap. 13.95 (978-1-60384-198-6(9)); lib. bdg. 44.00 (978-1-60384-199-3(7)) Hackett Publishing Co., Inc.
Shengold, Nina. River of Words: Portraits of Hudson Valley Writers. 2010. (Illus.). 240p. 29.95 (978-1-4384-3425-4(1), Suny Pr.) State Univ. of New York Pr.
Shephard, Sue. The Surprising Life of Constance Spry: From Social Reformer to Society Florist. 2010. (ENG., Illus.). 368p. 38.95 (978-0-230-74181-2(9), Macmillan) Pan Macmillan GBR. Dist: Trans-Atlantic Pubns., Inc.
Sherard, Robert H. Twenty Years in Paris: Being Some Recollections of a Literary Life. 2nd ed. (Illus.). reprint ed. 44.50 (978-0-404-18386-8(7)) AMS Pr., Inc.
Sherard, Robert Harborough. The Life of Oscar Wilde. 2009. 198p. pap. 19.99 (978-1-150-72673-6(3)) General Bks. LLC.
—The Life of Oscar Wilde. 2009. 538p. 57.95 (978-1-104-83465-4(0)) 2007. (ENG.). 484p. 53.95 (978-0-548-15135-8(0)) 2007. (ENG.). 536p. per. 42.95 (978-1-4325-9971-3(2)) 2007. (ENG.). 488p. per. 38.95 (978-1-4304-4481-7(9)) Kessinger Publishing, LLC.
Sherborne, Michael. H G Wells: Another Kind of Life. 2012. (ENG.). 400p. pap. 22.95 (978-0-7206-1391-9(4)) Owen, Peter Ltd. GBR. Dist: Independent Pubs. Group.
Sherman, Joseph, ed. Writers in Yiddish, 333. 2007. (Dictionary of Literary Biography Ser.). (ENG., Illus.). 480p. 315.00 (978-0-7876-8151-7(2)) Cengage Gale.
Sherman, Joseph & Estraikh, G. David Bergelson: From Modernism to Socialist Realism. 2007. (Legenda Studies in Yiddish Ser.). (ENG., Illus.). 250p. (C). 89.50 (978-1-905981-12-0(0)) European Humanities Research Ctr. GBR. Dist: Brown, David Bk. Co., The.
Sherrard-Johnson, Cherene. Dorothy West's Paradise: A Biography of Class & Color. 2012. (ENG., Illus.). 256p. (C). pap. 24.95 (978-0-8135-5167-8(6)); 264p. 72.00 (978-0-8135-5166-1(8)) Rutgers Univ. Pr.
Sherwood, Mary Martha. The Life & Times of Mrs Sherwood (1775-1851) From the Diaries of Captain & Mrs Sherwood. Darton, F. J. Harvey, ed. 2011. (Cambridge Library Collection - Literary Studies). (ENG., Illus.). 562p. pap. 39.99 (978-1-108-03380-0(6)) Cambridge Univ. Pr.
Shields, A. Randolph. The Inevitable: Contemporary Writers Confront Death. Morrow, Bradford, ed. 2011. (ENG.). 336p. pap. 17.95 (978-0-393-33936-9(X), 33936) Norton, W. W. & Co., Inc.
Shields, Charles J. And So It Goes: Kurt Vonnegut: A Life. 2011. (ENG., Illus.). 528p. 30.00 (978-0-8050-8693-5(5)) Holt, Henry & Co.
—Mockingbird: A Portrait of Harper Lee. 2009. (ENG.). 339p. pap. 15.00 (978-1-4379-6591-9(1)) DIANE Publishing Co.
—Mockingbird: A Portrait of Harper Lee. 2007. (ENG., Illus.). 368p. pap. 16.99 (978-0-8050-8319-4(7), Holt Paperback) Holt, Henry & Co.
Shields, David. Enough about You: Notes Toward the New Autobiography. 2009. (ENG.). 192p. pap. 14.95 (978-1-59376-219-3(4), Soft Skull Pr.) Counterpoint LLC.
—The Thing about Life Is That One Day You'll Be Dead. 2009. (Vintage Ser.). (ENG.). 256p. pap. 14.95 (978-0-307-38796-7(8), Vintage) Knopf Doubleday Publishing Group.
Shihab, Aziz. Does the Land Remember Me? A Memoir of Palestine. 2011. (Arab American Writing Ser.). (ENG., Illus.). 149p. pap. 17.95 (978-0-8156-0968-1(X)) Syracuse Univ. Pr.
Shillinglaw, Susan. A Journey into Steinbeck's California. 2nd ed. 2011. (ArtPlace Ser.). (ENG.). 230p. pap. 24.95 (978-0-9846239-1-4(4)); (978-0-9846254-7-5(X)) Roaring Forties Pr.
Shorter, Clement K. Charlotte Bronte & Her Circle. 2009. 538p. pap. 40.75 (978-1-113-64875-4(9)); pap. 39.75 (978-1-113-64873-0(2)) BiblioBazaar.
—Charlotte Bronte & Her Circle. 2007. (ENG.). 544p. 57.95 (978-0-548-08175-4(1)) Kessinger Publishing, LLC.
Shpiller, Katerina. Mama, Ne Chitai! Ispoved "Neblagodarnoi" Docheri. 2010. (RUS., Illus.). 415p. (978-5-17-069900-1(X)) AST, Tvorceskoe kooperativnoe ob'edinenie.
Shrubsall, Dennis. The Private Reflections & Opinions of W. H. Hudson (1841-1922), the First Literary Environmentalist. 2008. (Illus.). 180p. 99.95 (978-0-7734-5021-9(1)) Mellen, Edwin Pr., The.
Shukert, Rachel. Everything Is Going to Be Great: An Underfunded & Overexposed European Grand Tour. 2010. (ENG.). 336p. pap. 13.99 (978-0-06-178235-0(1), HarperPerennial) HarperCollins Pubs.
Shull, Jodie A. Pablo Neruda: Passion, Poetry, Politics. 2009. (Latino Biography Library). (Illus.). 128p. (J). (gr. 6). lib. bdg. 31.93 (978-0-7660-2966-8(2)) Enslow Pubs., Inc.
Shurin, Aaron. King of Shadows. 2008. (ENG.). 184p. pap. 16.95 (978-0-87286-490-0(1)) City Lights Bks.
Sikes, Anne. My Book of Memoirs. 2007. 156p. pap. 16.95 (978-1-4303-2487-4(2)) Lulu Enterprises Inc.
Sil, Narashingha P. The Life of Sharatchandra Chattopadhyay: Drifter & Dreamer. 2011. (ENG.). 180p. (gr. 17). 65.00 (978-1-61147-507-4(4)) Fairleigh Dickinson Univ. Pr.
Silko, Leslie Marmon. The Turquoise Ledge: A Memoir. (ENG.). 336p. (gr. 12). 2011. 16.00 (978-0-14-312010-0(7), Penguin (Non-Classics)) 2010. 25.95 (978-0-670-02211-3(X), Viking Adult) Penguin Group (USA) Inc.
Silverberg, Robert A. & Silverberg, Robert. Other Spaces, Other Times: A Life Spent in the Future. 2009. (ENG., Illus.). 200p. 29.95 (978-1-933065-12-0(5)) Nonstop Pr.
Silvers, Robert B., ed. The Company They Kept Vol. 2: Writers on Unforgettable Friendships. 2011. (ENG.). 232p. 22.95 (978-1-59017-487-6(9)) New York Review of Bks., Inc., The.
Silvers, Robert B. & Epstein, Barbara, eds. The Company They Kept: Writers on Unforgettable Friendships. 2009. (ENG.). 316p. pap. 19.95 (978-1-59017-334-3(1)) New York Review of Bks., Inc., The.
Simmons, Marc. Charles F. Lummis: Author & Adventurer: A Gathering. 2008. 120p. 22.95 (978-0-86534-639-0(9)); pap. 16.95 (978-0-86534-636-9(4)) Sunstone Pr.
Simon, Roger L. Blacklisting Myself: Memoir of a Hollywood Apostate in the Age of Terror. 2009. (ENG.). 250p. 25.95 (978-1-59403-247-9(5)) Encounter Bks.
Simoson, Andrew. Voltaire's Riddle: Micromégas & the Measure of All Things. 2009. 396p. 58.95 net. (978-0-88385-345-0(0)) Mathematical Assn. of America.
Sims, Michael. The Story of Charlotte's Web: E. B. White's Eccentric Life in Nature & the Birth of an American Classic. 2011. (ENG., Illus.). 320p. 25.00 (978-0-8027-7754-6(6)) Walker & Co.
Sinclair, Upton. My Lifetime in Letters. 2011. 440p. 56.95 (978-1-258-09460-7(6)) Literary Licensing, LLC.
Singer, Isaac Bashevis. More Stories from My Father's Court. 2009. 216p. 22.00 (978-1-4379-6490-5(7)) DIANE Publishing Co.
Singer, Wayne. Medical Fraternity the Brothers Grim or. 2007. 85p. 16.95 (978-1-4241-6559-9(8)) PublishAmerica, Inc.
Sitnik, Richard W. Some Times in My Life: A Memoir. 2007. 260p. per. 14.95 (978-1-4327-0545-9(8)) Outskirts Pr., Inc.
Sjåvik, Jan. The A to Z of Scandinavian Literature & Theater. 2009. (A to Z Guide Ser.: No. 60). (ENG.). 404p. pap. 34.45 (978-0-8108-6843-4(1)) Scarecrow Pr., Inc.

Skemp, Sheila L. First Lady of Letters: Judith Sargent Murray & the Struggle for Female Independence. 2009. (Early American Studies). 512p. 42.50 *(978-0-8122-4140-2(1))* Univ. of Pennsylvania Pr.

Skene, James. Memories of Sir Walter Scott. Thomson, Basil, ed. 2008. 258p. 42.95 *(978-1-4365-1868-0(7))* 2007. (ENG.). 260p. per. 27.95 *(978-0-548-73695-1(2))* Kessinger Publishing, LLC.

Sklenicka, Carol. Raymond Carver: A Writer's Life. (ENG., Illus.). 592p. 2010. pap. 20.00 *(978-0-7432-6246-0(8))* 2009. 35.00 *(978-0-7432-6245-3(X))* Scribner. (Scribner).

Skloot, Floyd. The Wink of the Zenith: The Shaping of a Writer's Life. (ENG.). 2011. 256p. pap. 16.95 *(978-0-8032-3845-9(2)*, Bison Bks.) 2008. 252p. 24.95 *(978-0-8032-1119-3(8))* Univ. of Nebraska Pr.

—A World of Light. 2011. (ENG.). 216p. pap. 16.95 *(978-0-8032-3847-3(9)*, Bison Bks.) Univ. of Nebraska Pr.

Skura, Meredith Anne. Tudor Autobiography: Listening for Inwardness. 2008. (ENG., Illus.). 272p. 45.00 *(978-0-226-76187-9(8))* Univ. of Chicago Pr.

Slater, Lauren. The $60,000 Dog: My Life with Animals. 2012. (ENG.). 256p. 25.95 ***(978-0-393-08111-4(7)**, 8111)* Norton, W. W. & Co., Inc.

Slater, Michael. Charles Dickens. 2011. (Illus.). 720p. pap. 23.00 *(978-0-300-17093-1(9))* Yale Univ. Pr.

Slawenski, Kenneth. J. D. Salinger: A Life. 2011. (Illus.). 464p. 27.00 *(978-1-4000-6951-4(3))* Random Hse., Inc.

Slide, Anthony. A Man Named Smith: The Novels & Screen Legacy of Thorne Smith. 2010. 210p. pap. 19.95 *(978-1-59393-528-3(5))* BearManor Media.

Slim, Iceberg. The Naked Soul of Iceberg Slim. 2013. (ENG.). 336p. pap. 14.99 *(978-1-936399-13-0(X)*, Cash Money Content) Cash Money Content LLC.

Small, David. Stitches: A Memoir. 2010. (ENG., Illus.). 329p. pap. 16.95 *(978-0-393-33896-6(7)*, 33896) Norton, W. W. & Co., Inc.

Smarandache, Florentin. Frate cu meridianele si paralelele, Vol. 4. 2008. (RUM.). pap. 33.50 *(978-973-7743-74-9(1))* Multimedia Larga.

Smiles, Samuel. The Autobiography of Samuel Smiles. Mackay, Thomas, ed. 2007. (ENG.). 464p. 52.95 *(978-0-548-15501-1(1))*; pap. 37.95 *(978-1-4304-4932-4(2))* Kessinger Publishing, LLC.

Smiley, Jane. Charles Dickens: A Life. 2011. (ENG.). 224p. (gr. 12). 14.00 *(978-0-14-311992-0(3)*, Penguin (Non-Classics)) Penguin Group (USA) Inc.

Smith, Artemis (Anselm L. N. V. Morpurgo). ArtemisSmith's 'ODD GIRL' Revisited: An Autobiographical Correlate. 2010. (ENG., Illus.). 310p. pap. 100.00 net. *(978-1-878998-30-9(7)*, Monograph of THE SAVANT GARDE INSTITUTE, A) Savant Garde Workshop.

Smith, Artemis (Baroness Anselm L. N. V. Morpurgo). ArtemisSmith's 'ODD GIRL' Revisited An autobiographical Correlate. 2010. (Illus.). 310p. *(978-1-878998-00-2(5)*, Authors Limited Manuscript Editions Series) Savant Garde Workshop.

Smith, Dai. Raymond Williams: A Warrior's Tale. Donahaye, Jasmine, ed. 2008. (ENG., Illus.). 450p. pap. 20.95 *(978-1-905762-99-6(2))*; 39.95 *(978-1-905762-56-9(9))* Parthian Bks. GBR. Dist: Independent Pubs. Group.

Smith, Dustin Beall. Key Grip: A Memoir of Endless Consequences. 2008. (ENG.). 176p. pap. 12.95 *(978-0-547-05369-1(X)*, Mariner Bks.) Houghton Mifflin Harcourt Trade & Reference Pubs.

Smith, Emma. The Great Western Beach: A Memoir of a Cornish Childhood Between the Wars. 2008. (ENG., Illus.). 384p. 29.95 *(978-0-7475-9591-5(7))* Bloomsbury Publishing Plc GBR. Dist: Independent Pubs. Group.

Smith, Huston & Paine, Jeffery. Tales of Wonder: Adventures Chasing the Divine, an Autobiography. 2009. (ENG., Illus.). 240p. 25.99 *(978-0-06-115426-3(1)*, HarperOne); 288p. pap. 25.99 *(978-0-06-166904-0(0)*, HarperLuxe) HarperCollins Pubs.

Smith, Jacquelyn. My Struggle My Battle My Victories. 2008. 116p. pap. 12.49 *(978-1-4343-8240-5(0))* AuthorHouse.

Smith, Janie. Hope Beyond Trauma a Mother's Journey. 2011. 190p. pap. 14.95 ***(978-1-60746-188-5(4))*** FastPencil, Inc.

Smith, Larry. The Moment: Wild, Poignant, Life-Changing Stories from 125 Writers & Artists Famous & Obscure. 2012. (ENG.). 192p. pap. 14.99 *(978-0-06-171955-3(X)*, HarperPerennial) HarperCollins Pubs.

Smith, Larry. The Moment: Wild, Poignant, Life-Changing Stories from 125 Wrtiers & Artists. 2012. E-Book ***(978-0-06-209921-1(3)**, HarperPerennial)* HarperCollins Pubs.

Smith, Larry & Fershleiser, Rachel. Not Quite What I Was Planning: Six-Word Memoirs by Writers Famous & Obscure. rev. exp. deluxe ed. 2008. (ENG.). 256p. 16.99 *(978-0-06-171371-2(6))* HarperCollins Pubs.

Smith, Lawrence G. Cesare Pavese & America: Life, Love, & Literature. 2008. (Illus.). 352p. 39.95 *(978-1-55849-673-6(4))* Univ. of Massachusetts Pr.

Smith, Lori. A Walk with Jane Austen: A Journey into Adventure, Love, & Faith. 2007. (ENG.). 256p. pap. 13.99 *(978-1-4000-7370-2(7)*, WaterBrook Pr.) Doubleday Religious Publishing Group, The.

Smith, Norman. Resisting Manchukuo: Chinese Women Writers & the Japanese Occupation. 2007. (ENG., Illus.). 216p. 85.00 *(978-0-7748-1335-8(0))* UBC Pr. CAN. Dist: Univ. of Washington Pr.

Smith, Robert Paul. Where Did You Go? Out. What Did You Do? Nothing. 2010. (ENG., Illus.). 144p. pap. 13.95 *(978-0-393-33941-3(6)*, 33941) Norton, W. W. & Co., Inc.

Smith, Samuel & Smith, Thelma. Experiences in the Southwest: The Sharecropper's Son, Part II. 2010. 120p. pap. 16.49 *(978-1-4490-3906-6(5))* AuthorHouse.

Smith, Sophie Shilleto. Dean Swift. 380p. 2008. 48.95 *(978-0-548-99106-0(5))* 2007. (ENG.). per. 33.95 *(978-0-548-65635-8(5))* Kessinger Publishing, LLC.

Smith, Thomas R. & Lenfestey, James, eds. Robert Bly in This World. 2011. (ENG.). 308p. 34.95 ***(978-0-8166-7770-2(0))*** Univ. of Minnesota Pr.

Smthng about Auth. 2008. (Something about the Author Ser.). (ENG.). 272p. 202.00 *(978-1-4144-2164-3(8))* Cengage Gale.

Snell, Susan. Phil Stone of Oxford: A Vicarious Life. 2008. (ENG.). 432p. pap. 26.95 *(978-0-8203-3366-3(2))* Univ. of Georgia Pr.

Snyder, Gary & Harrison, Jim. The Etiquette of Freedom: Gary Snyder, Jim Harrison, andThe Practice of the Wild. Ebenkamp, Paul, ed. 2010. (ENG., Illus.). 160p. 28.00 *(978-1-58243-629-6(0)*, Counterpoint) Counterpoint LLC.

Snyder, Gary & Harrison, Jim. The Etiquette of Freedom: Gary Snyder, Jim Harrison andThe Practice of the Wild. Ebenkamp, Paul, ed. 2012. (ENG.). 160p. pap. 19.95 ***(978-1-61902-056-6(4)**, Counterpoint)* Counterpoint LLC.

Sojourner, Mary. Solace: Rituals of Loss & Desire. 2007. (ENG.). 176p. pap. 14.95 *(978-0-7432-2959-2(X)*, Scribner) Scribner.

Soloway, Jill. Tiny Ladies in Shiny Pants: Based on a True Story. 2006. (ENG.). 272p. pap. 17.99 *(978-0-7432-7218-6(8)*, Free Pr.) Free Pr.

Something about the Author. (ENG.). 2011. 202.00 *(978-1-4144-6127-4(5))* 2011. 202.00 *(978-1-4144-6126-7(7))* 2011. 202.00 *(978-1-4144-6125-0(9))* 2011. 202.00 *(978-1-4144-6124-3(0))* 2011. 202.00 *(978-1-4144-6123-6(2))* 2008. 240p. 202.00 *(978-1-4144-2162-9(1))* 2008. 368p. 202.00 *(978-1-4144-2163-6(X))*193. 2008. 400p. 202.00 *(978-1-4144-2165-0(6))*194. 2009. 240p. 202.00 *(978-1-4144-2166-7(4))*195. 2009. 400p. 202.00 *(978-1-4144-2167-4(2))*196. 2009. 240p. 202.00 *(978-1-4144-2168-1(0))*197. 2009. 368p. 202.00 *(978-1-4144-2169-8(9))* Vol. 205. 2010. 202.00 *(978-1-4144-4218-1(1))* Vol. 206. 2010. 202.00 *(978-1-4144-4219-8(X))* Vol. 207. 2010. 202.00 *(978-1-4144-4220-4(3))* Vol. 208. 2010. 202.00 *(978-1-4144-4221-1(1))* Vol. 210. 2010. 202.00 *(978-1-4144-4223-5(8))* Vol. 211. 2010. 202.00 *(978-1-4144-4224-2(6))* Vol. 212. 2010. 202.00 *(978-1-4144-4225-9(4))* Cengage Gale.

Something about the Author Something about the Author. Vol. 209. 2010. (Something about the Author Ser.). (ENG.). 202.00 *(978-1-4144-4222-8(X))* Cengage Gale.

Sommers, Michael A. Chris Crutcher. 2009. (Library of Author Biographies Ser.). 112p. (gr. 5-8). 63.90 *(978-1-60853-528-6(2)*, Rosen Central) Rosen Publishing Group, Inc., The.

—J. D. Salinger. 2009. (Library of Author Biographies Ser.). 112p. (gr. 5-8). 63.90 *(978-1-60853-535-4(5)*, Rosen Central) Rosen Publishing Group, Inc., The.

Sontag, Susan. Reborn: Journals & Notebooks, 1947-1963. Rieff, David, ed. 2008. (ENG., Illus.). 336p. 25.00 *(978-0-374-10074-2(8))* Farrar, Straus & Giroux.

Sontag, Susan & Rieff, David. Reborn: Journals & Notebooks, 1947 — 1963. 2009. (ENG.). 336p. pap. 15.00 *(978-0-312-42850-1(2))* Picador.

Sorensen, Lita. Bryan Talbot. 2009. (Library of Graphic Novelists Ser.). 112p. (gr. 7-12). 63.90 *(978-1-60853-653-5(X))* Rosen Publishing Group, Inc., The.

Sorensen, Ted. Counselor: A Life at the Edge of History. 2009. (ENG.). 592p. pap. 17.99 *(978-0-06-079872-7(6)*, HarperPerennial) HarperCollins Pubs.

Sorin, Gerald. Howard Fast: Life & Literature in the Left Lane. 2012. (Modern Jewish Experience Ser.). (ENG., Illus.). 472p. 40.00 ***(978-0-253-00727-8(5)**, 0253007275)* Indiana Univ. Pr.

Sortino, David P. The Promised Cookie: No Longer Angry Children. 2011. 208p. 24.95 ***(978-1-4567-4274-4(4))***; pap. 14.95 ***(978-1-4567-4272-0(8))*** AuthorHouse.

Southam. 19th Century Novelists. 2007. 1725.00 *(978-0-415-44420-0(9))* Routledge.

Southern, Antonia. Player, Playwright & Preacher's Kid: The Story of Nathan Field 1587-1620. 2009. (Illus.). 252p. pap. *(978-1-84748-527-4(8))* Athena Pr.

—The Queen's Godson: Sir John Harington of Kelston,1560-1612. 2010. (Illus.). 344p. lib. bdg. *(978-1-936320-03-5(7))* Academica Pr., LLC.

Sova, Dawn B. Critical Companion to Edgar Allan Poe: A Literary Reference to His Life & Work. 2007. (Critical Companion Ser.). (Illus.). 464p. (C). (gr. 9). 75.00 *(978-0-8160-6408-3(3))* Facts On File, Inc.

Spark, Muriel. Curriculum Vitae: A Volume of Autobiography. 2011. (ENG., Illus.). 224p. pap. 14.95 *(978-0-8112-1923-5(2)*, 21923) New Directions Publishing Corp.

Spence, Jon & Spence. Becoming Jane Austen. movie tie-in ed. 2007. (ENG., Illus.). 312p. 17.95 *(978-1-84725-046-9(7))* Continuum International Publishing Group, Ltd. GBR. Dist: National Bk. Network.

Spence, Jonathan D. Return to Dragon Mountain: Memories of a Late Ming Man. 2008. (ENG.). 352p. (gr. 12-18). 16.00 *(978-0-14-311445-1(X)* Penguin (Non-Classics)) Penguin Group (USA) Inc.

Spiel, Hilde. The Dark & the Bright: Memoirs 1911-1989. 2007. (Studies in Austrian Literature, Culture, & Thought). 476p. *(978-1-57241-154-8(6))* Ariadne Pr.

Spitz, Bob. Dearie: The Remarkable Life of Julia Child. 2012. (ENG., Illus.). 560p. 28.95 ***(978-0-307-27222-5(2)**, Knopf)* Knopf Doubleday Publishing Group.

Spring, Albert. M. E. Kerr. 2009. (Library of Author Biographies Ser.). 112p. (gr. 5-8). 63.90 *(978-1-60853-546-0(0)*, Rosen Central) Rosen Publishing Group, Inc., The.

Spring, Justin. Secret Historian: The Life & Times of Samuel Steward, Professor, Tattoo Artist, & Sexual Renegade. (ENG., Illus.). 496p. 2011. pap. 18.00 *(978-0-374-53302-1(4))* 2010. 32.50 *(978-0-374-28134-2(3))* Farrar, Straus & Giroux.

Spurling, Hilary. Pearl Buck in China: Journey to the Good Earth. (ENG.). 320p. 2011. pap. 15.00 *(978-1-4165-4043-4(1))* 2010. (Illus.). 27.00 *(978-1-4165-4042-7(3))* Simon & Schuster.

Squires, Michael. D. H. Lawrence & Frieda: A Portrait of Love & Loyalty. 2008. (ENG., Illus.). 200p. 29.95 *(978-0-233-00232-3(4))* Andre Deutsch GBR. Dist: Independent Pubs. Group.

Srikantsarma, Indragant. Paripari Paricayalu. 2009. (TEL.). 135p. *(978-1-892408-29-7(5))* Vanguri Foundation of America, Inc.

Stackelberg, Roderick. Out of Hitler's Shadow: Childhood & Youth in Germany & the United States, 1935-1967. 2010. 180p. 26.95 *(978-1-4502-6034-3(9))*; pap. 16.95 *(978-1-4502-6033-6(0))* iUniverse, Inc.

Stafford, Fiona. Jane Austen. 2008. (Brief Lives Ser.). (ENG.). 120p. pap. 13.95 *(978-1-84391-906-3(0))* Hesperus Pr. GBR. Dist: Independent Pubs. Group.

Stair, James D. An Apology for Sir James Dalrymple of Stair. (Bannatyne Club, Edinburgh Publications: No. 12). reprint ed. 37.50 *(978-0-404-52712-9(4))* AMS Pr., Inc.

Stallings, Billee J. & Evans, Jo-an J. Murray Leinster: The Life & Works. 2011. (ENG., Illus.). 227p. pap. 40.00 *(978-0-7864-6504-0(2))* McFarland & Co., Inc. Pubs.

Stancliff, Michael. Frances Ellen Watkins Harper: African American Reform Rhetoric & the Rise of a Modern Nation State. 2010. (Studies in American Popular History & Culture Ser.). (ENG., Illus.). 220p. 125.00 *(978-0-415-99763-8(1))* Routledge.

Stannard, Martin. Muriel Spark: The Biography. 2011. (ENG.). 670p. pap. 24.95 ***(978-0-8101-2791-3(1))*** Northwestern Univ. Pr.

—Muriel Spark: The Biography. 2010. (ENG., Illus.). 627p. 35.00 *(978-0-393-05174-2(9)*, 5174) Norton, W. W. & Co., Inc.

Stanway, Eric. From Brickbats to Bouquets. 2007. 236p. per. *(978-1-905179-03-9(0)*, Lonely Scribe) Armadillo Design Ltd.

Starova, Luan. My Father's Books. Kramer, Christina E., tr. from MAC. 2012. (ENG.). 136p. pap. 24.95 ***(978-0-299-28794-8(7))*** Univ. of Wisconsin Pr.

Starova, Luan & Kramer, Christina Elizabeth. My Father's Books. 2012. E-Book ***(978-0-299-28793-1(9))*** Univ. of Wisconsin Pr.

Stead, C. K. South-West of Eden: A Memoir, 1932-1956. 2010. (ENG., Illus.). 360p. 27.95 *(978-1-86940-454-3(8))* Auckland Univ. Pr. NZL. Dist: Independent Pubs. Group.

Stearne, Evangelist Lottie. Treasure in the Midst of Ruins: Birth Out of Bondage. 2009. 84p. pap. 14.00 *(978-1-4343-9484-2(0))* AuthorHouse.

Stearns, Frank Preston. The Life & Genius of Nathaniel Hawthorne. 2008. 336p. 29.99 *(978-0-554-22374-2(0))* 2008. 336p. 28.99 *(978-0-554-31677-2(3))* 2007. (ENG.). 312p. pap. 23.99 *(978-1-4264-2167-9(2))* BiblioBazaar.

—The Life & Genius of Nathaniel Hawthorne. 2008. pap. *(978-1-4065-7521-7(6))* Dodo Pr.

—Life & Genius of Nathaniel Hawthorne. 2006. pap. *(978-1-4068-3014-9(3))* Echo Library.

—The Life & Genius of Nathaniel Hawthorne. lt. ed. 2006. 334p. pap. 24.99 *(978-1-4264-2235-5(0))* BiblioBazaar.

Stedman, Edmund Clarence. Edgar Allan Poe. 2009. 100p. pap. 13.75 *(978-1-110-44237-9(8))* BiblioBazaar.

—Edgar Allan Poe. 2007. (ENG.). 108p. 34.95 *(978-0-548-20722-2(4))*; per. 19.95 *(978-1-4325-2530-9(1))* Kessinger Publishing, LLC.

—Edgar Allan Poe. 2008. 100p. pap. *(978-1-4097-1213-8(3))*; (ENG.). 96p. per. *(978-1-4086-4506-2(8))* Read Bks.

Stein, Harry. I Can't Believe I'm Sitting Next to a Republican: A Survival Guide for Conservatives Marooned among the Angry, Smug, & Terminally Self-Righteous. (ENG.). 2010. 224p. pap. 15.95 *(978-1-59403-480-0(X))* 2009. (Illus.). 250p. 25.95 *(978-1-59403-253-0(X))* Encounter Bks.

Steinbeck, John. Travels with Charley in Search of America: (Penguin Classics Deluxe Edition) 2012. (Penguin Classics Deluxe Edition Ser.). (ENG.). 240p. (gr. 12). pap. 16.00 ***(978-0-14-310700-2(3)**, Penguin Classics)* Penguin Group (USA) Inc.

Steinbeck, John & Demott, Robert. Steinbeck: Travels with Charley & Later Novels, 1947-1962. Railsback, Brian, ed. 2007. (ENG.). 1125p. (gr. 12). 40.00 *(978-1-59853-004-9(6))* Library of America, The.

Steinbeck, John & Ricketts, Edward F. Sea of Cortez: A Leisurely Journal of Travel & Research. 2009. (ENG.). 656p. (gr. 12-18). 25.00 *(978-0-14-311721-6(1)*, Penguin (Non-Classics)) Penguin Group (USA) Inc.

Steinberg, David. Book of David. 2013. (ENG.). 208p. pap. 15.99 *(978-0-7432-7233-9(1))* Simon & Schuster.

Stelzig, Eugene L. Romantic Autobiography in England. 2009. (Nineteenth Century Ser.). (Illus.). 232p. 99.95 *(978-0-7546-6366-9(3))* Ashgate Publishing Co.

Stelzig, Eugene L. Henry Crabb Robinson in Germany: A Study in Nineteenth-Century Life Writing. 2010. 137p. 36.00 *(978-0-8387-5763-5(4))*; (ENG.). 36.00 *(978-1-61148-350-5(6))* Bucknell Univ. Pr.

Stephen, Leslie. George Eliot. 2010. (Cambridge Library Collection - Literary Studies). 224p. pap. 22.99 *(978-1-108-01962-0(5))* Cambridge Univ. Pr.

—Samuel Johnson. 2011. (Cambridge Library Collection - English Men of Letters Ser.). (ENG.). 208p. pap. 22.99 ***(978-1-108-03478-4(0))*** Cambridge Univ. Pr.

—Swift. 2011. (Cambridge Library Collection - English Men of Letters Ser.). (ENG.). 228p. pap. 22.99 ***(978-1-108-03449-4(7))*** Cambridge Univ. Pr.

Stephenson, Barry. Veneration & Revolt: Hermann Hesse & Swabian Pietism. 2009. (Editions SR Ser.). (ENG.). 330p. 85.00 *(978-1-55458-149-8(4))* Wilfrid Laurier Univ. Pr. CAN. Dist: Univ. of Toronto Pr.

Sterling, Kristin. Jane Goodall. 2008. pap. 26.95 *(978-0-8225-9471-0(4))* Lerner Publishing Group.

Sterne, Laurence. The Works of Laurence Sterne with a Life of the Author. 2006. (Illus.). 444p. per. 26.99 *(978-1-4255-4919-0(5))* MPublishing.

Stevens, Janice. William Saroyan: Places in Time. 2008. (ENG.). 88p. 26.95 *(978-1-933502-24-3(X)*, Craven Street Bks.) Linden Publishing Co., Inc.

Stevens, Jen & Salo, Dorothea. Fantasy Authors: A Research Guide, 1 vol. 2008. (Author Research Ser.). (Illus.). 268p. pap. 45.00 *(978-1-59158-497-1(3)*, LU4973) Libraries Unlimited, Inc.

Stevens, Mark. Luisa's Nature. 2008. 252p. per. 15.00 *(978-1-932279-71-9(7))* Wyatt-MacKenzie Publishing.

Stieler, Hilde. Monika Molander: Supplement to an Encyclopedia of German Women Writers. Keith-Smith, Brian, ed. 2006. 224p. *(978-0-7734-5529-0(9))* Mellen, Edwin Pr., The.

Stier, Wayne. Stars When the Sun Shines: A Memoir. 2010. (ENG.). 1p. pap. 18.95 *(978-1-57863-473-6(3)*, Weiser Bks.) Red Wheel/Weiser.

Still, James & Olson, Ted. James Still in Interviews, Oral Histories & Memoirs. Olson, Ted, ed. 2009. (Contributions to Southern Appalachian Studies). (ENG., Illus.). 320p. pap. 39.95 *(978-0-7864-3698-9(0))* McFarland & Co., Inc. Pubs.

Stimson, F. J. My Story. reprint ed. 150.00 *(978-0-7222-9270-9(8))* Library Reprints, Inc.

Stites, Alfred. Forget the Goal, the Journey Counts — 71 Jobs Later. 2010. (Illus.). viii, 216p. pap. ***(978-1-933455-26-6(8))*** M S I Pr.

Stoddard, Richard Henry. Anecdote Biographies of Thackeray & Dickens / Edited by Richard Henry Stoddard. 2006. 332p. per. 23.99 *(978-1-4255-3375-5(2))* MPublishing.

Stoney, Barbara. Enid Blyton: The Biography. 2007. (ENG., Illus.). 240p. per. 16.95 *(978-0-7524-4030-9(6))* History Pr. Ltd.,The GBR. Dist: Independent Pubs. Group.

Stowe, Harriet Beecher. Stowe in Her Own Time: A Biographical Chronicle of Her Life, Drawn from Recollections, Interviews, & Memoirs by Family, Friends, & Associates. Belasco, Susan, ed. 2009. (Writers in Their Own Time Ser.). (ENG., Illus.). 332p. pap. 27.95 *(978-1-58729-782-3(5))* Univ. of Iowa Pr.

Strachey, G. Lytton. Books & Characters. 2006. pap. *(978-1-4068-3119-1(0))* Echo Library.

Strachey, Giles Lytton. Books & Characters: French & English. 2007. 214p. pap. 20.99 *(978-1-4264-6075-3(9))*; (ENG.). 242p. pap. 22.99 *(978-1-4264-6146-0(1))* BiblioBazaar.

Strathern, Paul. Tolstoy in 90 Minutes. 2006. (Philosophers in 90 Minutes Ser.). (ENG.). 128p. 16.95 *(978-1-56663-693-3(0))*; per. 8.95 *(978-1-56663-692-6(2))* Dee, Ivan R. Pub.

Stratton-Porter, Gene. Gene Stratton-Porter: A Little Story of the Life & Work & Ideals of the Bird Woman. Egerton, Sarah Fyge, ed. 2011. 58p. 36.95 ***(978-1-258-02464-2(0))*** Literary Licensing, LLC.

Strauss, Darin. Half a Life: A Memoir. 2010. (ENG.). 204p. 22.00 *(978-1-934781-70-8(3))* McSweeney's Publishing.

—Half a Life: A Memoir. 2011. (ENG.). 224p. pap. 13.00 *(978-0-8129-8253-4(3)*, Random Hse. Trade Paperbacks) Random House Publishing Group.

Strayed, Cheryl. Wild: From Lost to Found on the Pacific Crest Trail. 2012. (ENG., Illus.). 336p. 25.95 ***(978-0-307-59273-6(1)**, Knopf)* Knopf Doubleday Publishing Group.

Strom, Robert. Lady of Burlesque: The Career of Gypsy Rose Lee. 2011. (ENG., Illus.). 243p. pap. 39.95 *(978-0-7864-3826-6(6))* McFarland & Co., Inc. Pubs.

Stuart, Jesse. The Thread That Runs So True. 24.95 *(978-0-8488-0638-5(7)*, Amereon LTD.

—The Thread That Runs So True. 2006. (Illus.). 331p. *(978-1-931672-42-9(3))* Stuart, Jesse Foundation, The.

Sturrock, Donald. Storyteller: The Authorized Biography of Roald Dahl. (ENG., Illus.). 672p. 2011. pap. 18.99 *(978-1-4391-8976-4(5))* 2010. 30.00 *(978-1-4165-5082-2(8))* Simon & Schuster.

Sturt, George. A Small Boy in the Sixties. 2012. (ENG.). 258p. pap. 36.99 ***(978-1-107-63302-5(8))*** Cambridge Univ. Pr.

Styron, Alexandra. Reading My Father: A Memoir. (ENG., Illus.). 2012. 320p. pap. 15.00 *(978-1-4165-9181-8(8))* 2011. 304p. 25.00 *(978-1-4165-9179-5(6))* Scribner. (Scribner).

Styron, William. Darkness Visible: A Memoir of Madness. 2007. (Modern Library). (ENG.). 96p. 15.95 *(978-0-679-64352-4(4)*, Modern Library) Random House Publishing Group.

Sueyoshi, Amy Haruko. Queer Compulsions: Race, Nation, & Sexuality in the Affairs of Yone Noguchi. 2012. 45.00 ***(978-0-8248-3497-5(6))*** Univ. of Hawaii Pr.

Sukys, Julija. Silence Is Death: The Life & Work of Tahar Djaout. 2007. (France Overseas: Studies in Empire & D Ser.). (ENG., Illus.). 202p. 26.95 *(978-0-8032-4320-0(0))* Univ. of Nebraska Pr.

Sullivan, Ceri & Harper, Graeme, eds. Authors at Work: The Creative Environment. 2009. (Essays & Studies: Volume 62). (Illus.). 192p. 50.00 *(978-1-84384-195-1(9)*, D. S. Brewer) Boydell & Brewer, Ltd. GBR. Dist: Boydell & Brewer, Inc.

Sullivan, Kevin. Joyce among the Jesuits. 2011. 268p. 47.95 ***(978-1-258-03891-5(9))*** Literary Licensing, LLC.

Sullivan, Robert. The Thoreau You Don't Know: What the Prophet of Environmentalism Really Meant. 368p. 2011. (ENG.). pap. 14.99 *(978-0-06-171032-2(6)*, HarperPerennial) 2009. 25.99 *(978-0-06-171031-5(8))* HarperCollins Pubs.

Sullivan, Robert E. Macaulay: The Tragedy of Power. 2009. (Illus.). 624p. 42.00 *(978-0-674-03624-6(7)*, Belknap Pr.) Harvard Univ. Pr.

Sumner, Gregory D. Unstuck in Time: A Journey Through Kurt Vonnegut's Life & Novels. 2011. (ENG., Illus.). 368p. 24.95 *(978-1-60980-349-0(3))* Seven Stories Pr.

Sussman, Henry. The Poet, the Philosopher, the Reader, & the Critic. *(978-0-8047-3855-2(6))* Stanford Univ. Pr.

Sutcliffe, Benjamin M. The Prose of Life: Russian Women Writers from Khrushchev to Putin. 2009. (ENG.). 224p. pap. 26.95 *(978-0-299-23204-7(2))* Univ. of Wisconsin Pr.

Sutherland, John. Lives of the Novelists: A History of Fiction in 294 Lives. 2012. (ENG.). 832p. 39.95 ***(978-0-300-17947-7(2))*** Yale Univ. Pr.

Swados, Elizabeth. Waiting: Selected Nonfiction. 2011. 200p. pap. 19.00 *(978-1-934909-21-8(1))* Hanging Loose Pr.

Swift, Graham. Making an Elephant: Writing from Within. 2010. (Vintage International Ser.). (ENG., Illus.). 416p. pap. 16.95 *(978-0-307-45575-8(0),* Vintage) Knopf Doubleday Publishing Group.

Swofford, Anthony. Hotels, Hospitals, & Jails: A Memoir. 2012. (ENG.). 300p. 26.99 ***(978-1-4555-0673-6(7))***; 384p. 28.99 ***(978-1-4555-1351-2(2))*** Grand Central Publishing. (Twelve).

Syme, S. Leonard. Memoir of a Useless Boy. 2011. 212p. 29.99 ***(978-1-4653-3957-7(4))***; pap. 19.99 ***(978-1-4653-3956-0(6))*** Xlibris Corp.

Symonds, Emily. Lady Mary Wortley Montagu & Her Times. 2007. 616p. 59.95 *(978-0-548-05055-2(4))* Kessinger Publishing, LLC.

Symons, A.J.A. The Quest for Corvo: An Experiment in Biography. 2011. 306p. 48.95 ***(978-1-258-08238-3(1))*** Literary Licensing, LLC.

Symons, John. Stranger on the Shore. 2009. (ENG., Illus.). 160p. pap. 24.95 *(978-0-85683-264-2(2))* Shepheard-Walwyn Pubs., Ltd. GBR. Dist: Independent Pubs. Group.

Sze, Arthur, ed. Chinese Writers on Writing. 2010. (Writer's World Ser.). (ENG.). 320p. 60.00 *(978-1-59534-062-7(9))*; pap. 18.95 *(978-1-59534-063-4(7))* Trinity Univ. Pr.

Taber, Gladys. Especially Father. 22.95 *(978-0-89190-590-5(1))* Amereon LTD.

Taddeo, Julie Anne. Catherine Cookson Country: On the Borders of Legitimacy Fiction & History. 2012. (Illus.). 240p. 99.95 ***(978-1-4094-0580-1(X))*** Ashgate Publishing Co.

Tagore, Rabindranath. Boyhood Days. Chakravarty, Radha, tr. from BEN. 2011. (Hesperus Worldwide Ser.). (ENG.). 86p. pap. 15.95 *(978-1-84391-850-9(1))* Hesperus Pr. GBR. Dist: Independent Pubs. Group.

—Boyhood Days. Chakravarty, Radha, tr. from BEN. 2008. (ENG., Illus.). 144p. (gr. 12-18). 9.00 *(978-0-14-333021-9(7),* Penguin Global) Penguin Group (USA) Inc.

Talese, Gay. A Writer's Life. 2007. (ENG.). 448p. per. 17.00 *(978-0-8129-7728-8(9),* Random Hse. Trade Paperbacks) Random House Publishing Group.

Tame, Peter D. Andre Chamson, 1900-1983 Book 1: The Life of a French Novelist, 2 vols. 2006. 332p. *(978-0-7734-5681-5(3))* Mellen, Edwin Pr., The.

—Andre Chamson, 1900-1983 Book 2: The Life of a French Novelist, 2 vols. 2006. 392p. *(978-0-7734-5683-9(X))* Mellen, Edwin Pr., The.

Tames, Richard. William Morris: An Illustrated Life of William Morris, 1834-1896. 2nd ed. 2008. (Shire Library). (ENG., Illus.). 64p. pap. 12.95 *(978-0-7478-0435-2(4))* Shire Pubns., Ltd. GBR. Dist: Random Hse., Inc.

Tarrant, Ernest. Within the Shadows. 2009. 428p. pap. 22.99 *(978-1-4389-5716-6(5))* AuthorHouse.

Tarte, Bob. Fowl Weather. 2007. (ENG.). 306p. 23.95 *(978-1-56512-502-5(9),* 1565125029) Algonquin Bks. of Chapel Hill.

Tate, Andrew & Tate, Andrew. Douglas Coupland. 2008. (Contemporary American & Canadian Novelists Ser.). (ENG.). 192p. 79.00 *(978-0-7190-7488-2(6))*; pap. 26.00 *(978-0-7190-7661-9(7))* Manchester Univ. Pr. GBR. Dist: Macmillan.

Taylor, Bayard. The Unpublished Letters of Bayard Taylor in the Huntington Library. Schultz, John Richie, ed. 2011. 256p. 47.95 ***(978-1-258-05893-7(6))*** Literary Licensing, LLC.

Taylor, Michael. Hugh Miller: Stonemason, Geologist, Writer. 2007. (ENG., Illus.). 144p. per. 19.95 *(978-1-905267-05-7(3))* NMS Enterprises Ltd. - Publishing GBR. Dist: National Bk. Network.

Taylor, Philip Meadows. The Story of My Life, by M Taylor Ed by His Daughter [A M Taylor]. 2010. 430p. pap. 35.75 *(978-1-147-03180-5(0))* BiblioBazaar.

Taylor, Susan B., ed. The Brontes: A Documentary Volume. 2008. (Dictionary of Literary Biography Ser.). (ENG., Illus.). 464p. 315.00 *(978-0-7876-8158-6(X))* Cengage Gale.

Taylor, William (Bill) Jefferson. Growing up on a One Mule Farm. 2009. 116p. pap. 12.99 *(978-1-4490-5337-6(8))* AuthorHouse.

Tea, Michelle. The Chelsea Whistle: A Memoir. 2nd ed. 2008. (ENG.). 384p. pap. 18.00 *(978-1-58005-239-9(8))* Seal Pr.

Tebben, Karin. Tannhauser: Biographie einer Legende. 2010. (GER., Illus.). 247p. (C). 68.00 *(978-3-525-20867-0(7))* Vandenhoeck & Ruprecht GmbH & Co. KG DEU. Dist: ISD.

Tedesco, William. A True Family. 2010. 52p. pap. 11.49 *(978-1-4520-1156-1(7))* AuthorHouse.

Terkel, Studs. P. S. Further Thoughts from a Lifetime of Listening. 2008. (ENG.). 230p. pap. 16.95 *(978-1-59558-423-6(4))* New Pr., The.

—Touch & Go: A Memoir. (ENG., 269p. 2008. Illus.). pap. 17.95 *(978-1-59558-411-3(0))* 2007. 24.95 *(978-1-59558-043-6(3))* New Pr., The.

Tetro, Joe. Lost in Americ: Memoirs of a Maverick. 2008. 704p. pap. 25.99 *(978-1-4389-2454-0(2))* AuthorHouse.

Tew, Marcus & Tew. Writers Talk: Conversations with Contemporary British Novelists. Tolan, Fiona & Wilson, Leigh, eds. 2008. (ENG.). 210p. 115.00 *(978-0-8264-9058-2(1))* Continuum International Publishing Group, Ltd. GBR. Dist: National Bk. Network.

Thacker, Robert. Alice Munro: Writing Her Lives. 2011. (Illus.). 664p. pap. 22.99 *(978-0-7710-8510-9(9),* Emblem Edns) McClelland & Stewart CAN. Dist: Random Hse., Inc.

Thackeray, William Makepeace. The Irish Sketch Book. 2009. 356p. 26.99 *(978-1-103-41881-7(5))*; pap. 20.99 *(978-1-103-41879-4(3))* BiblioBazaar.

—The Irish Sketch Book. 2009. 278p. pap. *(978-0-217-33173-9(4))*; 174p. pap. *(978-0-217-08480-2(X))* Books LLC.

—The Irish Sketch Book. 2009. 294p. pap. 21.70 *(978-1-4588-8149-6(0))* General Bks. LLC.

—Thackeray, the Humourist & the Man of Letters: The Story of His Life, Including a Selection from His Characteristic Speeches, Now for the First Time Gathered Together. Taylor, Theodore, ed. 2007. 256p. 42.95 *(978-0-548-11225-0(8))* Kessinger Publishing, LLC.

Thapar, Trisha. The Angel. 2008. 156p. pap. 11.99 *(978-1-4389-3464-8(5))* AuthorHouse.

Tharoor, Shashi. Bookless in Baghdad: Reflections on Writing & Writers. 2012. (ENG.). 288p. pap. 14.95 ***(978-1-61145-408-6(5),*** 611408, Arcade Publishing) Skyhorse Publishing Co., Inc.

The Jenna Fox. The Curious Case of the Jenna Fox: It's Jenna from your Block, (Poor, but RICH Inside) 2011. 144p. pap. 24.95 ***(978-1-4560-9596-3(X))*** PublishAmerica, Inc.

The-Lou. The Lies by Ni: How A Player Got Played (Based on My Life Story) 2011. 128p. pap. 12.00 ***(978-1-4634-2158-8(3))*** AuthorHouse.

The Writers' Trust of Canada. A Writer's Life: The Margaret Laurence Lectures. 2011. (ENG., Illus.). 416p. pap. 22.95 *(978-0-7710-8928-2(7),* Emblem Edns) McClelland & Stewart CAN. Dist: Random Hse., Inc.

Theroux, Phyllis. The Journal Keeper: A Memoir. (ENG.). 2011. 304p. pap. 14.95 *(978-0-8021-4528-4(0),* Grove Pr.) 2010. 305p. 24.00 *(978-0-8021-1897-4(6),* Atlantic Monthly Pr.) Grove/Atlantic, Inc.

Thick, Malcolm. Sir Hugh Plat: The Search for Useful Knowledge in Early-Modern London. 2010. (ENG., Illus.). 432p. (C). 60.00 *(978-1-903018-65-1(X))* Prospect Bks. GBR. Dist: Brown, David Bk. Co., The.

Thie, Jennifer. And Then Came Arthur: Hope Comes in Many Forms. 2007. per. 14.25 *(978-1-932279-57-3(1))* Wyatt-MacKenzie Publishing.

Thiebaud, Twinka. What Doncha Know? about Henry Miller. 2nd ed. 2011. (Illus.). 103p. pap. 12.95 *(978-0-9759255-2-0(0))* Eio Bks.

Thiruchelvam, Vinesh. Eventually. 2010. 224p. pap. 14.49 *(978-1-4490-8541-4(5))* AuthorHouse.

Thomas, Abigail. A Three Dog Life. rev. l.t. ed. 2007. (Thorndike Biography Ser.). 203p. 30.95 *(978-0-7862-9369-8(1))* Thorndike Pr.

Thomas, Dylan. A Child's Christmas in Wales. 2009. (ENG., Illus.). 64p. pap. 9.95 *(978-0-8112-1731-6(0),* 21731) New Directions Publishing Corp.

Thomas, Edward. Lafcadio Hearn. 2009. 94p. pap. 18.75 *(978-1-110-68250-8(6))* 2008. 96p. pap. 18.75 *(978-0-559-21056-3(6))* BiblioBazaar.

—Lafcadio Hearn. 2009. 48p. pap. *(978-0-217-01022-1(9))* Books LLC.

—Lafcadio Hearn. 2007. (ENG.). 108p. 33.95 *(978-0-548-42568-8(X))*; 96p. per. 18.95 *(978-0-548-40258-0(2))* Kessinger Publishing, LLC.

—Lafcadio Hearn. 2008. 92p. pap. *(978-1-4097-1687-7(2))* Read Bks.

Thomas, Graham A. The Dan Brown Enigma (Nt) 2011. (ENG., Illus.). 304p. 24.95 *(978-1-84358-302-8(X))* Blake, John Publishing, Ltd. GBR. Dist: Independent Pubs. Group.

Thomas, Jennifer. A Different Light. 2010. 346p. 29.99 *(978-1-4535-0526-7(1))*; pap. 19.99 *(978-1-4535-0525-0(3))* Xlibris Corp.

Thomas, Lowell. So Far ... So Good ... so There! 2011. 196p. pap. 14.95 ***(978-1-4620-3611-0(2))*** iUniverse, Inc.

Thomas Paine. The Age of Reason - Thomas Paine. Moncure Daniel Conway, ed. 2010. 180p. pap. 4.95 *(978-1-60386-341-4(9),* Merchant Bks.) Rough Draft Printing.

Thompson, Bobbie Jo. Alex's Tragedy. 2008. 192p. pap. 24.95 *(978-1-60563-420-3(4))* PublishAmerica, Inc.

Thompson, Elizabeth. Day by Day: The Chronicles of a Hard of Hearing Reporter. 2008. *(978-1-56368-391-6(1))* Gallaudet Univ. Pr.

Thomson Gale, creator. Authors & Artists for Young Adults. (Authors & Artists for Young Adults Ser.). (ENG., Illus.). 224p. Vol. 71. 2006. 168.00 *(978-0-7876-7790-9(6))* Vol. 75. 2007. 168.00 *(978-0-7876-7794-7(9))* Cengage Gale.

—Authors & Artists for Young Adults: Volume 70, Vol. 70. 2006. (Authors & Artists for Young Adults Ser.). (ENG., Illus.). 250p. 168.00 *(978-0-7876-7789-3(2))* Cengage Gale.

—Authors & Artists for Young Adults, Volume 72, Vol. 72. 2006. (Authors & Artists for Young Adults Ser.). (ENG., Illus.). 250p. 168.00 *(978-0-7876-7791-6(4))* Cengage Gale.

—Authors & Artists for Young Adults Volume 74, Vol. 74. 2007. (Authors & Artists fro Young Adults Ser.). (ENG., Illus.). 240p. 168.00 *(978-0-7876-7793-0(0))* Cengage Gale.

—Contemporary Authors. (Contemporary Authors New Revision Ser.). (ENG.). Vol. 155. 2007. 464p. 293.00 *(978-0-7876-7909-5(7))* Vol. 249. 2006. (Illus.). 480p. 293.00 *(978-0-7876-7878-4(3))* Vol. 253. 2007. 470p. 293.00 *(978-0-7876-7882-1(1))* Vol. 256. 2007. 464p. 293.00 *(978-0-7876-7885-2(6))* Cengage Gale.

—Contemporary Authors: A Bio-Bibliographical Guide to Current Writers in Fiction, General Nonfiction, Poetry, Journalism, Drama, Motion Pictures, Television, & Other Fields. 2007. (Contemporary Authors Ser.). (ENG.). Vol. 251. 464p. 293.00 *(978-0-7876-7880-7(5))* Vol. 255. 470p. 293.00 *(978-0-7876-7884-5(8))* Cengage Gale.

—Contemporary Authors New Revision. 2007. (ENG.). (New Revision Ser.: Vol. 159). 448p. 293.00 *(978-0-7876-7913-2(5))*; Vol. 154. (Contemporary Authors New Revision Ser.). 480p. 293.00 *(978-0-7876-7908-8(9))* Cengage Gale.

—Contemporary Authors New Revision: Volume 156. 2007. (New Revision Ser.: Vol. 156). (ENG.). 448p. 293.00 *(978-0-7876-7910-1(0))* Cengage Gale.

—Contemporary Authors New Revision: Volume 161. 2007. (New Revision Ser.: Vol. 161). (ENG., Illus.). 470p. 293.00 *(978-0-7876-7915-6(1))* Cengage Gale.

—Contemporary Authors New Revision Series: A Bio-Bibliographical Guide to Current Writers in Fiction, General Nonfiction, Poetry, Journalism, Drama, Motion Pictures, Television, & Other Fields. 2007. (Contemporary Authors New Revision Ser.: Vol. 164). 464p. 164th rev. ed. 293.00 *(978-0-7876-7918-7(6))* 165th rev. ed. 293.00 *(978-0-7876-7919-4(4))* Cengage Gale.

—Contemporary Authors New Revision Series: Volume 162. 2007. (New Revision Ser.: Vol. 162). (ENG., Illus.). 464p. 293.00 *(978-0-7876-7916-3(X))* Cengage Gale.

—Contemporary Authors, Volume 158: A Bio-Bibliographical Guide to Current Writers in Fiction, General Nonfiction, Poetry, Journalism, Drama, Motion Pictures, Television, & Other Fields. 2007. (New Revision Ser.: Vol. 158). (ENG.). 464p. 293.00 *(978-0-7876-7912-5(7))* Cengage Gale.

—Contemporary Authors, Volume 250: A Bio-Bibliographical Guide to Current Writers in Fiction, General Nonfiction, Poetry, Journalism, Drama, Motion Pictures, Television, & Other Fields, Vol. 250. 2007. (Contemporary Authors Ser.). (ENG., Illus.). 480p. 293.00 *(978-0-7876-7879-1(1))* Cengage Gale.

—Dictionary of Literary Biography, Volume 331: Nobel Prize Laureates in Literature, Part 3: Lagerkvist-Pontoppidan. 2007. (Dictionary of Literary Biography Ser.: Vol. 331). (ENG., Illus.). 544p. 315.00 *(978-0-7876-8149-4(0))* Cengage Gale.

—Nobel Prize Laureates in Literature: Part 4: Quasimodo-Yeats. 2007. (Dictionary of Literary Biography Ser.: Vol. 332). (ENG., Illus.). 560p. 315.00 *(978-0-7876-8150-0(4))* Cengage Gale.

—Nobel Prize Laureates in Literature, Part 1: Agnon-Eucken. 2006. (Dictionary of Literary Biography Ser.: Vol. 329). (ENG., Illus.). 592p. 315.00 *(978-0-7876-8147-0(4))* Cengage Gale.

—Something about the Author. (Something about the Author Ser.). (ENG., Illus.). 2007. 256p. 202.00 *(978-0-7876-8802-8(9))* Vol. 172. 2006. 224p. 202.00 *(978-0-7876-8796-0(0))* Cengage Gale.

—Something about the Author: Facts & Pictures about Authors & Illustrators of Books for Young People. (Something about the Author Ser.: Vol. 181). (ENG., Illus.). 2007. 368p. 202.00 *(978-0-7876-8805-9(3))* Vol. 170. 2006. 224p. 202.00 *(978-0-7876-8794-6(4))* Cengage Gale.

—Something about the Author: Volume 169, Vol. 169. 2006. (Something about the Author Ser.). (ENG., Illus.). 336p. 202.00 *(978-0-7876-8793-9(6))* Cengage Gale.

—Something about the Author: Volume 176. 2007. (Something about the Author Ser.). (ENG., Illus.). 240p. 202.00 *(978-0-7876-8800-4(2))* Cengage Gale.

—Something about the Author: Volume 177. 2007. (Something about the Author Ser.). (ENG., Illus.). 368p. 202.00 *(978-0-7876-8801-1(0))* Cengage Gale.

—Something about the Author: Volume 179. 2007. (Something about the Author Ser.: Vol. 179). (ENG., Illus.). 368p. 202.00 *(978-0-7876-8803-5(7))* Cengage Gale.

—Something about the Author: Volume 180. 2007. (Something about the Author Ser.: Vol. 180). (ENG., Illus.). 272p. 202.00 *(978-0-7876-8804-2(5))* Cengage Gale.

Thomson Gale Staff. Contemporary Authors. (ENG.). 2007. (New Revision Ser.: Vol. 157). 464p. 293.00 *(978-0-7876-7911-8(9))* Vol. 248. 2006. (Contemporary Authors Ser.). 480p. 293.00 *(978-0-7876-7877-7(5))* Cengage Gale.

—Something about the Author Vol 174. 2007. (Something about the Author Ser.). (ENG.). 224p. 202.00 *(978-0-7876-8798-4(7))* Cengage Gale.

Thoreau, Henry David. Letters to Various Persons. 2009. 108p. pap. *(978-1-150-35644-5(8))* Books LLC.

—Letters to Various Persons. 236p. 2008. 41.95 *(978-0-548-92105-0(9))* 2007. (ENG.). per. 26.95 *(978-0-548-57059-3(0))* Kessinger Publishing, LLC.

—Letters to Various Persons. 2008. 240p. pap. *(978-1-4437-1185-2(3))* Read Bks.

—Of Woodland Pools, Spring-Holes & Ditches: Excerpts from the Journal of Henry David Thoreau. 2010. (ENG.). 112p. 25.00 *(978-1-58243-575-6(8),* Counterpoint Pr.) Basic Bks. GBR. Dist: Perseus-PGW.

—Walden: oder Leben in den Wäldern, 2 vols., Set. Sanborn, Franklin B., ed. reprint ed. 58.50 *(978-0-404-19080-4(4))* AMS Pr., Inc.

—Walden & Civil Disobedience. 2012. (ENG.). 336p. (gr. 12). 5.95 ***(978-0-451-53216-9(3),*** Signet Classics) Penguin Group (USA) Inc.

Thoreau, Henry David. Walden & on the Duty of Civil Disobedience. 21.95 *(978-0-8488-0644-6(1))* Amereon LTD.

Thoreau, Henry David & Tobyne, Dan. Thoreau's Maine Woods. 2010. (ENG.). 128p. 35.00 *(978-0-89272-814-5(0))* Down East Bks.

Thorndike, John. The Last of His Mind: A Year in the Shadow of Alzheimer's. (ENG., 2011. Illus.). 256p. pap. 14.95 *(978-0-8040-1136-5(2))* 2009. 248p. 24.95 *(978-0-8040-1122-8(2))* Swallow Pr.

Thornton Sr., Gary M. Getting Closer. 2008. 129p. pap. 19.95 *(978-1-4241-3102-0(2))* PublishAmerica, Inc.

Thurman, Chris. Guy Butler: Reassessing a South African Literary Life. 2010. 382p. pap. 48.95 *(978-1-86914-183-7(0))* University of Kwazulu-Natal Press ZAF. Dist: International Specialized Bk. Services.

Tiernan, Martin Farnun. Memoirs of Martin F Tiernan. 2011. 188p. 42.95 ***(978-1-258-08906-1(8))*** Literary Licensing, LLC.

Tiernan, Sonja. Eva Gore-Booth: An Image of Such Politics. 2012. (ENG., Illus.). 256p. 100.00 ***(978-0-7190-8231-3(5))*** Manchester Univ. Pr. GBR. Dist: Macmillan.

Tischler, Nancy M. Encyclopedia of Contemporary Christian Fiction: From C. S. Lewis to Left Behind, 1 vol. 2009. 400p. 95.00 *(978-0-313-34568-5(6),* GR4568, Greenwood Pr.) Greenwood Publishing Group, Inc.

Titchmarsh, Alan. Knave of Spades: Growing Pains of a Gardener. 2009. (ENG., Illus.). 384p. 32.95 *(978-0-340-95304-4(7),* Hodder & Stoughton) Hodder General Publishing Div. GBR. Dist: Independent Pubs. Group.

—Knave of Spades: The Growing Pains of a Gardener. 2009. (ENG., Illus.). 320p. 22.95 *(978-0-340-95305-1(5),* Hodder & Stoughton) Hodder General Publishing Div. GBR. Dist: Independent Pubs. Group.

Titchmarsh, Alan & Alexander, Jenny. Knave of Spades. 2010. (ENG., Illus.). 384p. pap. 13.95 *(978-0-340-95306-8(3),* Hodder & Stoughton) Hodder General Publishing Div. GBR. Dist: Independent Pubs. Group.

Todorov, Tzvetan. Duties & Delights: The Life of a Go-Between. Portevin, Catherine, ed. Walker, Gila, tr. from FRE. 2008. (SB-the French List Ser.). (ENG.). 424p. 39.95 *(978-1-905422-89-0(X))* Seagull Bks. GBR. Dist: Chicago Distribution Ctr.

Tokarev, D. "Mezhdu Indiei I Gegelem" Tvorchestvo Borisa Poplavskogo V Komparativnoi Perspektive. 2011. 347p. *(978-5-86793-828-4(X))* Novoe literaturnoe obozrenie.

Tolan, Sandy. The Lemon Tree: An Arab, a Jew, & the Heart of the Middle East. annot. ed. 2007. (ENG., Illus.). 384p. pap. 17.00 *(978-1-59691-343-1(6))* Bloomsbury Publishing.

Tolstoi, Ilia Lvovich. Reminiscences of Tolstoy. Calderon, George, tr. from RUS. 2009. 120p. *(978-1-907230-07-3(6))* Sparkling Bks.

Tolstoy, Leo. Last Steps: The Late Writings of Leo Tolstoy. Parini, Jay, ed. & tr. by. from RUS. 2009. (ENG.). 256p. (gr. 12-18). pap. 14.00 *(978-0-14-119119-5(8),* Penguin Classics) Penguin Group (USA) Inc.

Tolstoy, Leo & Tolstoy, Leo. Boyhood. Hogarth, C. J., tr. 2011. 92p. pap. 9.99 ***(978-1-59547-473-5(0))*** NuVision Pubns., LLC.

Tomalin, Claire. Charles Dickens: A Life. (ENG., 576p. (gr. 12). 2012. Illus.). pap. 18.00 ***(978-0-14-312205-0(3),*** Penguin (Non-Classics)) 2011. 36.00 *(978-1-59420-309-1(1),* Penguin Pr. HC, The) Penguin Group (USA) Inc.

Tomalin, Claire. Thomas Hardy: The Time-Torn Man. 2008. (ENG., Illus.). 512p. (gr. 12-18). 17.00 *(978-0-14-311287-7(2),* Penguin (Non-Classics)) Penguin Group (USA) Inc.

Toruno, et al. Cita con la Memoria: Elena Garro Cuenta Su Vida a Rhina Toruño. (SPA.). 118p. *(978-987-20648-6-0(5))* Prueba de Galera, Ediciones.

Toruño-Haensly, Rhina. Crossing Cultures: Hispanic Authors & the Challenges They Overcame in the United States = Cruzando Culturas: Autores Hispanos y Sus Desafíos Superados en Los Estados Unidos. 2011. (Currents in Comparative Romance Languages & Literatures Ser.). (SPA & ENG., Illus.). 214p. (C). 76.95 *(978-1-4331-1253-9(1))* Lang, Peter Publishing, Inc.

Totaro, John. Till Then Is Now. 2011. 162p. pap. 19.99 ***(978-1-4568-7385-1(7))*** Xlibris Corp.

Toussaint, Jean-Philippe. Self-Portrait Abroad. Lambert, John, tr. from FRE. 2010. (Netherlandic & Belgian Literature Ser.). (ENG.). 80p. pap. 12.95 *(978-1-56478-586-2(6),* 478586) Dalkey Archive Pr.

Tovey, Doreen. A Comfort of Cats. 2008. (ENG.). 192p. pap. 12.95 ***(978-1-84024-655-1(3))*** Summerdale Pubs. GBR. Dist: Independent Pubs. Group.

—The Coming of Saska. 2007. (ENG.). 160p. pap. 12.95 ***(978-1-84024-595-0(6))*** Summerdale Pubs. GBR. Dist: Independent Pubs. Group.

Tracy, Kathleen. Judy Blume: A Biography, 1 vol. 2007. (Greenwood Biographies Ser.). (Illus.). 152p. (gr. 4-8). 35.00 *(978-0-313-34272-1(5),* GR4272, Greenwood Pr.) Greenwood Publishing Group, Inc.

Traill, Henry Duff. Sterne. 2011. (Cambridge Library Collection - English Men of Letters Ser.). (ENG.). 190p. pap. 19.99 ***(978-1-108-03452-4(7))*** Cambridge Univ. Pr.

Tran, Christy & Dobbe, Patti. My Determined Spirit: A Story of Survival. 2011. 144p. pap. 11.95 ***(978-1-4620-3993-7(6))*** iUniverse, Inc.

Tranströmer, Tomas. Memories Look at Me: A Memoir. Fulton, Robin, tr. from SWE. 2011. (ENG.). 64p. (gr. 9-17). pap. 11.95 ***(978-0-8112-2018-7(4),*** 22018) New Directions Publishing Corp.

Tremblay, M. Anthony. David Adams Richards of the Miramichi: A Biographical Introduction to His Work. 2010. (Illus.). 384p. *(978-1-4426-4162-4(2))*; pap. *(978-1-4426-1077-4(8))* Univ. of Toronto Pr.

Tremblay, Michel & Gaboriau, Linda. Bonbons Assortis: Assorted Candies. Gaboriau, Linda, tr. from FRE. 2006. (ENG.). 160p. per. 17.95 *(978-0-88922-541-1(9))* Talonbooks, Ltd. CAN. Dist: Consortium Bk. Sales & Distribution.

Tre'butien, G. S. Journal of Eugenie de Guerin. 2007. (ENG.). 464p. 52.95 *(978-0-548-03862-8(7))* Kessinger Publishing, LLC.

Trillin, Calvin. About Alice. 2008. (ENG.). 78p. 15.00 *(978-1-4223-9340-6(2))* DIANE Publishing Co.

—About Alice. 2006. (ENG.). 96p. 14.95 *(978-1-4000-6615-5(8),* Random House) Random House Publishing Group.

—Quite Enough of Calvin Trillin: Forty Years of Funny Stuff. 2011. (ENG.). 368p. 27.00 *(978-1-4000-6982-8(3),* Random House) Random House Publishing Group.

Triplet, Christopher. Fear of Rejection. 2011. 32p. pap. 16.95 ***(978-1-4560-0777-5(7))*** PublishAmerica, Inc.

Trollope, Anthony. Autobiography of Anthony Trollope. 2007. (ENG.). 224p. per. *(978-1-4065-2106-1(X))* Dodo Pr.

—Autobiography of Anthony Trollope. 2007. 280p. per. 9.99 *(978-1-59986-618-5(8))* Filiquarian Publishing, LLC.

Trollope, Anthony. Thackeray. 2011. (Cambridge Library Collection - English Men of Letters Ser.). (ENG.). 224p. pap. 22.99 ***(978-1-108-03476-0(4))*** Cambridge Univ. Pr.

Trollope, Thomas Adolphus. What I Remember, vol. 2. l.t. ed. 2008. 296p. 28.99 *(978-0-554-30437-3(6))* BiblioBazaar.
—What I Remember. 2009. 314p. pap. *(978-0-217-65511-8(4))*; 292p. pap. *(978-0-217-14566-4(3))*; 482p. pap. *(978-0-217-65522-4(X))* Books LLC.
—What I Remember. 2010. (Cambridge Library Collection - Literary Studies). (ENG.). 418p. pap. 31.99 *(978-1-108-02293-4(6))*; (Illus.). 420p. pap. 31.99 *(978-1-108-02292-7(8))*; (Illus.). 434p. pap. 32.99 *(978-1-108-02294-1(4))* Cambridge Univ. Pr.
—What I Remember, Vol. 2. 2008. 248p. pap. *(978-1-4065-3935-6(X))* Dodo Pr.
—What I Remember. 2009. 448p. pap. 28.20 *(978-0-217-65517-0(3))* General Bks. LLC.
—What I Remember. 2007. (ENG.). 554p. 57.95 *(978-0-548-04807-8(X))* Kessinger Publishing, LLC.
—What I Remember. 2006. 416p. per. *(978-1-4067-3136-1(6)*, Hesperides Pr.) Read Bks.
—What I Remember 3 Volume Set. 2010. (Cambridge Library Collection - Literary Studies). (ENG., Illus.). 1272p. pap. 95.00 *(978-1-108-02295-8(2))* Cambridge Univ. Pr.
Trombley, Laura Skandera. Mark Twain's Other Woman: The Hidden Story of His Final Years. 2011. (Vintage Ser.). 352p. pap. 16.95 *(978-0-307-47494-0(1)*, Vintage) Knopf Doubleday Publishing Group.
Troncoso, Sergio. Crossing Borders: Personal Essays. 2011. pap. 16.95 *(978-1-55885-710-0(9))* Arte Publico Pr.
Trowbridge, John Townsend. The Drummer Boy. 2008. 240p. 27.99 *(978-0-554-27541-3(4))* 2008. 240p. 24.99 *(978-0-554-36844-3(7))* 2007. (ENG.). 216p. pap. 20.99 *(978-1-4346-3440-5(X))* 2007. (ENG.). 236p. pap. 22.99 *(978-1-4346-3441-2(8))* BiblioBazaar.
—My Own Story with Recollections of Noted Persons. 2007. (ENG.). 560p. 57.95 *(978-0-548-03703-4(5))* Kessinger Publishing, LLC.
Trubiano, Marisa S. Ennio Flaiano & His Italy: Postcards from a Changing World. 2010. 59.50 *(978-0-8386-4213-9(6))* Fairleigh Dickinson Univ. Pr.
Tshibanda Wamuela Bujitu. André Baillon: Le Belge de Marly. 2009. (Illus.). 124p. *(978-2-507-00170-4(4))* Pire, Luc Editions.
TSykalov, V. K. & TSykalov, Vladimir Konstantinovich. "I Gliadia Vdal, Podniav Zabralo, Bylye Vizhu Vremenna —" Avtobiograficheskie Epizody. 2010. (Illus.). 580p. *(978-5-7493-1501-1(0))* Magyar ISBN Iroda, Orszagos Szechenyi Konyvtar.
Tuck, Harley H. & Cizer, Ann I. Angel on My Shoulder: I've Joined the Lucky Bastard Club. 2010. 216p. 24.99 *(978-1-4520-4685-3(9))*; pap. 16.00 *(978-1-4520-4684-6(0))* AuthorHouse.
Tuck, Lily. Woman of Rome: A Life of Elsa Morante. 2009. (ENG., Illus.). 288p. pap. 13.99 *(978-0-06-147259-6(X)*, HarperPerennial) HarperCollins Pubs.
Tucker, Kenneth. The Old Lit Professor's Book of Favorite Readings. 2010. 756p. pap. 36.49 *(978-1-4490-5963-7(5))* AuthorHouse.
Tupper, Martin Farquhar. My Life as an Author. 2007. 368p. pap. 25.99 *(978-1-4346-1161-1(2))*; (ENG.). 416p. pap. 28.99 *(978-1-4346-1232-8(5))* BiblioBazaar.
Turco, Lewis. La Famigli: The Family. 2009. 200p. pap. 12.00 *(978-1-59954-006-1(1))* Bordighera Incorporated.
Turley, Richard Marggraf. Bright Stars: John Keats, Barry Cornwall & Romantic Literary Culture. 2010. (Liverpool University Press - Liverpool English Texts & Studies). (ENG., Illus.). 195p. 95.00 *(978-1-84631-211-3(6))* Liverpool Univ. Pr. GBR. Dist: Chicago Distribution Ctr.
Tusquets, Esther. Private Correspondence. 2008. *(978-0-8387-5686-7(7))* Bucknell Univ. Pr.
Tusquets, Esther & Ichiishi, Barbara F. We Had Won the War. 2012. **(978-1-4331-1626-1(X))**; E-Book **(978-1-4539-0234-9(1))** Lang, Peter Publishing, Inc.
Twain, Mark, pseud. Autobiographical Writings. Rasmussen, R. Kent, ed. & intro. by. 2012. (ENG.). 544p. (gr. 12). pap. 16.00 **(978-0-14-310667-8(8)**, Penguin Classics) Penguin Group (USA) Inc.
—Autobiography of Mark Twain, Vol. 1. Smith, Harriet E., ed. 2012. (ENG.). 440p. pap. 26.95 **(978-0-520-27225-5(0))** Univ. of California Pr.
—Chapters from My Autobiography. 2011. 274p. **(978-1-84902-343-6(3))** Benediction Classics.
—Chapters from My Autobiography. 2009. 332p. 25.99 *(978-0-559-09789-8(1))*; 29.99 *(978-0-559-09773-7(5))*; pap. 30.75 *(978-0-559-09782-9(4))*; pap. 31.75 *(978-0-559-09777-5(8))* BiblioBazaar.
—Chapters from My Autobiography. 2009. 280p. pap. *(978-1-4065-6793-9(0))* Dodo Pr.
—Chapters from My Autobiography. 2010. (Illus.). 184p. pap. 26.90 *(978-1-153-75056-1(2))* General Bks. LLC.
—Life on the Mississippi 1983. 26.95 *(978-0-8488-0654-4(4))* Amereon LTD.
—Life on the Mississippi 1983. 2007. (ENG.). 232p. per. 8.99 *(978-1-4209-3026-9(5))* Digireads.com.
—Life on the Mississippi 1983. 2008. (Illus.). 644p. pap. *(978-1-4065-7129-5(6))* Dodo Pr.
—Life on the Mississippi 1983. 2008. 492p. 53.95 *(978-0-548-99669-0(5))* 2007. (ENG.). 496p. per. 38.95 *(978-0-548-65009-7(8))* Kessinger Publishing, LLC.
—Life on the Mississippi 1983. 624p. reprint ed. lib. bdg. 128.00 *(978-0-7222-0314-9(4))*; lib. bdg. 128.00 *(978-0-7222-0697-3(6))* Library Reprints, Inc.
—Life on the Mississippi 1983. 2009. (ENG.). 400p. (gr. 12-18). pap. 4.95 *(978-0-451-53120-9(5)*, Signet Classics) Penguin Group (USA) Inc.
—Life on the Mississippi 1983. 2007. (Paperback Classics Ser.). (ENG., Illus.). 416p. pap. 9.95 *(978-0-375-75937-6(9)*, Modern Library) Random House Publishing Group.
—Life on the Mississippi 1983. 2008. 592p. *(978-1-4437-2342-8(8))* 2006. (ENG., Illus.). 588p. per. *(978-1-4067-2182-9(4))* Read Bks. (Hesperides Pr.).
Twain, Mark, pseud, et al. Autobiography of Mark Twain, Vol. 1. Fischer, Victor et al, eds. 2010. (Mark Twain Papers). (Illus.). 743p. 34.95 *(978-0-520-26719-0(2))* Univ. of California Pr.
Tytler, Sarah. The Songstresses of Scotland, 2 Vols. reprint ed. 125.00 *(978-0-7222-1497-8(9))* Library Reprints, Inc.
Umrigar, Thrity. First Darling of the Morning: Selected Memories of an Indian Childhood. 2008. (P. S. Ser.). (ENG.). 320p. pap. 14.95 *(978-0-06-145161-4(4)*, HarperPerennial) HarperCollins Pubs.
Una, Lady Troubridg. Life & Death of Radclyffe Hall. 2006. 200p. per. *(978-1-4067-3506-2(X)*, Hesperides Pr.) Read Bks.
Unferth, Deb Olin. Revolution: The Year I Fell in Love & Went to Join the War. 2011. (ENG.). 224p. 24.00 *(978-0-8050-9323-0(0))* Holt, Henry & Co.
Unger, Rudolph M. One Man's Journey: Faith-Family-Freedom. (Illus.). 520p. pap. 25.00 *(978-0-9710761-2-9(X))* Unger, Rudolph M.
Unrue, Darlene Harbour. Katherine Anne Porter Remembered. 2010. (American Writers Remembered Ser.). (ENG., Illus.). 336p. 45.00 *(978-0-8173-1667-9(1))*; *(978-0-8173-8458-6(8))* Univ. of Alabama Pr.
Updike, John. Self-Consciousness: Memoirs. 2012. (ENG.). 272p. pap. 16.00 **(978-0-8129-8296-1(7)**, Random Hse. Trade Paperbacks) Random House Publishing Group.
Urey, Winston M. Visiting Spirits! 2008. 212p. pap. 24.95 *(978-1-60672-874-1(1))* PublishAmerica, Inc.
Usera, Abe. God's Work. 2010. 112p. (ENG.). 21.49 *(978-1-4520-1037-3(4))*; pap. 10.99 *(978-1-4520-1035-9(8))* AuthorHouse.
Utley, Crystal. All about Me My Second Chance: My Life Story. 2011. 36p. pap. 17.99 **(978-1-4520-3491-1(5))** AuthorHouse.
Uttley, Alison & Judd, Denis. The Private Diaries of Alison Uttley. 2011. (Illus.). 256p. 39.95 **(978-1-84468-124-2(6))** Pen & Sword Bks. Ltd. GBR. Dist: Casemate Pubs. & Bk. Distributors, LLC.
Valcarcel, Emilio Diaz, ed. En el Mejor de los Mundos. 235p. pap. 12.95 *(978-1-56758-004-4(1))* Editorial Cultural, Inc.
Valentine, Mark. Time, a Falconer: A Study of Sarban. 2011. (Illus.). 140p. **(978-1-905784-26-4(0))** Tartarus Pr.
Valentino, Rudolph. My Private Diary. 2011. 340p. 51.95 **(978-1-258-09930-5(6))** Literary Licensing, LLC.
Valerio, Anthony. Toni Cade Bambara's On Sicilian Night. 2007. 87p. pap. 10.00 *(978-1-884419-84-3(4))* Bordighera Incorporated.
Van Dyke, Henry. Out-of-Doors in the Holy Land. 2007. (ENG.). 312p. 35.00 *(978-1-4344-8995-1(7))*; pap. 19.95 *(978-1-4344-8994-4(9))* Wildside Pr., LLC.
Van Gerpen, Harlan W. I said Yes. 2011. 156p. 22.23 **(978-1-4634-4825-7(2))**; pap. 12.99 **(978-1-4634-4826-4(0))** AuthorHouse.
Van Ghent. Willa Cather-Aw V36. 2009. (ENG.). 48p. pap. 25.00 *(978-0-8166-0321-3(9))* Univ. of Minnesota Pr.
Van, Hoang. Hoang Van Family,Commitment, Hope & Love from Dismay to Happiness. 2009. 80p. pap. 9.95 *(978-0-9823002-0-6(4))* Peppertree Pr., The.
Van Meter, Ryan. If You Knew Then What I Know Now. 2011. (ENG.). 176p. pap. 15.95 *(978-1-932511-94-9(6))* Sarabande Bks., Inc.
Van Wyk, Chris. Shirley, Goodness & Mercy: A Childhood in Africa. 2006. (ENG.). 320p. per. 13.95 *(978-0-330-44483-5(2))* Macmillan Pubs., Ltd. GBR. Dist: Independent Pubs. Group.
Vance, John A., ed. Boswell's Life of Johnson: New Questions, New Answers. 2009. (ENG.). 288p. pap. 24.95 *(978-0-8203-3376-2(X))* Univ. of Georgia Pr.
Vaneman, Garry. Cruisin' 'n' Losin' 2008. 251p. pap. 14.99 *(978-0-557-00269-6(9))* Lulu Enterprises Inc.
VanLiere, Donna. Finding Grace: A True Story about Losing Your Way in Life... & Finding It Again. 2009. (ENG.). 224p. 21.95 *(978-0-312-38051-9(8))* St. Martin's Pr.
Vanzant, Iyanla. Gestern habe ich Geweint. (GER.). *(978-3-612-18016-2(9))* Econ-Verlag GmbH DEU. Dist: International Bk. Import Service, Inc.
Vargas Llosa, Mario. A Fish in the Water: A Memoir. Lane, Helen, tr. 2011. (ENG.). 544p. pap. 22.00 **(978-1-250-00577-9(9))** Picador.
Vasconcelos, José. Primeros Recuerdos. 2007. (Centzontle Ser.). (SPA.). 82p. pap. 6.99 *(978-968-16-8472-3(9))* Fondo de Cultura Económica.
Vassanji, M. G. Mordecai Richler. 2011. (ENG.). 204p. (gr. 12). 19.95 **(978-0-670-06672-3(9)**, Penguin Global) Penguin Group (USA) Inc.
Vassanji, M. G. A Place Within: Rediscovering India. 2009. (ENG.). 464p. pap. 18.00 *(978-0-385-66179-9(7)*, Anchor Can) Doubleday Canada, Ltd. CAN. Dist: Random Hse., Inc.
Vathrakogianni, Aikaterini. Women on Kazantzakis: Biography & Fiction. 2011. 92p. pap. **(978-3-8433-9357-7(5))** Lambert Academic Publishing.
Vaus, Will. The Professor of Narnia: The C. S. Lewis Story. 2008. (ENG.). 160p. pap. 15.99 *(978-0-9817061-0-8(X))* Believe Bks., LLC.
Veevers-Carter, Wendy. Clarence Day: An American Writer. 2007. 460p. per. 28.95 *(978-0-595-43165-6(8))* iUniverse, Inc.
Vejdovsky, Boris & Hemingway, Mariel. Hemingway: A Life in Pictures. 2011. (ENG., Illus.). 208p. pap. 29.95 *(978-1-55407-946-9(2))* Firefly Bks., Ltd.
Velicka, Domas. Domas Velicka: Kurybinis Palikimas Kovojanciai Tautai. Rinktiniai Rastai, Dokumentai, Literatura. Velickaite (Velicka), Asta Komelija, ed. 2007. (LIT., Illus.). 520p. pap. *(978-0-9771413-2-6(2))* Velicka, Asta Komelija.
—Domas Velicka: Kurybinis Palikimas Kovojanciai Tautai. Rinktiniai Rastai, Dokumentai, Literatura. Asta Komelija Velickaite (Velicka) Staff, ed. 2006. (LIT., Illus.). 512p. pap. *(978-0-9771413-1-9(4))* Velicka, Asta Komelija.
Velicka, Domas & Velicka, Domas. Domas Velicka: Kurybinis Palikimas Kovojanciai Tautai. Rinktiniai Rastai, Dokumentai, Literatura. Velickaite (Velicka), Asta Komelija, ed. (LIT., Illus.). 2010. 512p. pap. *(978-0-9771413-4-0(9))* 2009. 510p. pap. *(978-0-9771413-3-3(0))* Velicka, Asta Komelija.
Veljko Bojic. 2008. pap. *(978-1-59712-255-9(6))* Catawba Publishing Co.
Venables, Edmund. Life of John Bunyan. 2008. 236p. 24.99 *(978-0-559-66603-2(9))*; 236p. pap. 24.75 *(978-0-559-66601-8(2))*; 128p. 24.99 *(978-0-554-21672-0(8))*; 128p. 21.99 *(978-0-554-30975-0(0))* BiblioBazaar.
—Life of John Bunyan. 2009. 176p. pap. *(978-0-217-01296-6(5))* Books LLC.
Venema, Janny. Kiliaen Van Rensselaer, 1586-1643: Designing a New World. 2011. 352p. pap. 34.95 *(978-90-8704-196-0(9))* State Univ. of New York Pr.
Ventura de Molina, Jacinto. Jacinto Ventura de Molina: Los Caminos de la Escritura Negra en el Río de Plata. Acree, William G. & Borucki, Alex, eds. 2010. (SPA., Illus.). 285p. pap. 29.80 *(978-84-8489-492-6(4))* Iberoamericana Vervuert Publishing Corp.
Vickers, Julia. Lou Von Salomé: A Biography of the Woman Who Inspired Freud, Nietzsche & Rilke. 2008. (ENG., Illus.). 217p. pap. 39.95 *(978-0-7864-3606-4(9))* McFarland & Co., Inc. Pubs.
Vidal, Gore. Gore Vidal: Snapshots in History's Glare. 2009. (ENG., Illus.). 272p. 40.00 *(978-0-8109-5049-8(9))* Abrams.
—Point to Point Navigation: A Memoir 1964 to 2006. 2007. (Vintage Ser.). (ENG., Illus.). 288p. pap. 16.00 *(978-0-307-27501-1(9)*, Vintage) Knopf Doubleday Publishing Group.
Villarreal, Rene & Martinez, Raúl. Hemingway's Cuban Son: Reflections on the Writer by His Longtime Majordomo. 2009. (Illus.). x, 157p. *(978-0-87333-897-4(9))* Kent State Univ. Pr.
Villarreal, Rene & Villarreal, Raul. Hemingway's Cuban Son: Reflections on the Writer by His Longtime Majordomo. 2009. (Illus.). 224p. 24.95 *(978-0-87338-977-8(8))* Kent State Univ. Pr.
Villasenor, Victor. Beyond Rain of Gold. (ENG.). 2012. 416p. pap. 17.95 **(978-1-4019-3123-0(5))** 2011. 256p. 27.95 *(978-1-4019-3122-3(7))* Hay Hse., Inc.
Villaseñor, Victor. Beyond Rain of Gold. 2011. *(978-1-4019-3124-7(3))* Hay Hse., Inc.
Villasenor, Victor. Burro Genio. 2006. (SPA & ENG., Illus.). 336p. per. 13.95 *(978-0-06-055683-8(3)*, Rayo) HarperCollins Pubs.
—Crazy Loco Love: A Memoir. 2010. (ENG., Illus.). 416p. pap. 16.00 *(978-1-58270-272-8(1)*, Beyond Words/Atria Bks.) Atria Bks.
Villaseñor, Victor. Crazy Loco Love: A Memoir. 2010. E-Book *(978-1-4391-9382-2(7))* Beyond Words Publishing, Inc.
Virtanen, Beth L. Finnish-North American Literature in English: A Concise Anthology. 2009. viii, 578p. *(978-0-7734-3818-7(1))* Mellen, Edwin Pr., The.
Vivian, Robert. The Least Cricket of Evening. 2011. (ENG.). 208p. pap. 14.95 *(978-0-8032-3431-4(7)*, Bison Bks.) Univ. of Nebraska Pr.
Vizenor, Gerald. Interior Landscapes: Autobiographical Myths & Metaphors. 2nd ed. 2009. (Illus.). 292p. pap. 29.95 *(978-1-4384-2982-3(7)*, Suny Pr.) State Univ. of New York Pr.
Völker, Martin A., ed. "Gebunden Sind Die Flugel Der Gedanken" Louise Brachmann (1777-1822) Supplement to an Encyclopedia of German Women Writers. 2006. 180p. *(978-0-7734-5533-7(1))* Mellen, Edwin Pr., The.
Volkov, Solomon. Romanov Riches: Russian Writers & Artists under the Tsars. 2011. (ENG., Illus.). 304p. 30.00 *(978-0-307-27063-4(7)*, Knopf) Knopf Doubleday Publishing Group.
Von Hornstein, Erika. Adieu Potsdam. (GER.). 252p. pap. *(978-3-462-02145-5(1))* Kiepenheuer & Witsch GmbH & Company KG DEU. Dist: International Bk. Import Service, Inc.
von Rezzori, Gregor. The Snows of Yesteryear. Broch De Rothermann, H. F., tr. from GER. 2008. (ENG., Illus.). 304p. pap. 15.95 *(978-1-59017-281-0(7)*, NYRB Classics) New York Review of Bks., Inc., The.
Vonnegut, Kurt. Kurt Vonnegut: the Last Interview: And Other Conversations. 2011. (ENG.). 176p. pap. 15.95 **(978-1-61219-090-7(1))** Melville Hse. Publishing.
Vonnegut, Kurt & Stringer, Lee. Like Shaking Hands with God: A Conversation about Writing. 2010. (ENG., Illus.). 80p. pap. 9.95 *(978-1-60980-074-1(5))* Seven Stories Pr.
Vosbikian, Irene. Bedros. pap. 16.00 *(978-0-7388-4760-3(7))* Xlibris Corp.
W. Ambrose Bebb. A Welsh Hundred: Glimpses of Life in Wales drawn from a pair of family diaries for 1841 And 1940. Marc K. Stengel, tr. 2009. 232p. pap. 14.49 *(978-1-4343-5991-9(3))* AuthorHouse.
Wü, et al. Ich war immer verärgert, wenn ich ein Mädchen bekam: Thomas und Katia Mann als Eltern. 2010. (GER., Illus.). 378p. *(978-3-492-05283-2(5))* Piper Verlag GmbH.
Wagamese, Richard. One Native Life, 1 vol. (ENG.). 272p. 2009. pap. 17.95 *(978-1-55365-312-7(2))* 2008. 29.95 *(978-1-55365-364-6(5))* D&M Pubs. Inc. CAN. Dist: Perseus-PGW.
—One Story, One Song, 1 vol. 2011. (ENG.). 216p. 25.95 *(978-1-55365-506-0(0))* D&M Pubs. Inc. CAN. Dist: Perseus-PGW.
Wagenbach, Klaus. Kafka: A Life in Prague. 2nd ed. 2011. (Red Bks.). (ENG., Illus.). 171p. 19.95 **(978-1-906598-38-4(6))** Haus Publishing GBR. Dist: Consortium Bk. Sales & Distribution.
Wagner-Martin, Linda. Ernest Hemingway: A Literary Life. 2010. (Literary Lives Ser.). (ENG., Illus.). 216p. pap. 30.00 *(978-0-230-27696-3(2))* Palgrave Macmillan.
Wagner, Rob & Politi, Paul Leo. Leo Politi: Capturing the Heart of Los Angeles. Calistro, Paddy, ed. 2008. (Illus.). 238p. 45.00 *(978-1-883318-76-5(9))* Angel City Pr.
Wainaina, Binyavanga. One Day I Will Write about This Place: A Memoir. 2011. (ENG.). 272p. 24.00 *(978-1-55597-591-3(7))* Graywolf Pr.
Walden. 2008. 29.90 *(978-1-60591-103-8(8))* Title Player, Inc.
Waldman, Ayelet. Bad Mother: A Chronicle of Maternal Crimes, Minor Calamities, & Occasional Moments of Grace. 2009. (ENG.). 224p. 24.95 *(978-0-385-52793-4(4))* Broadway Bks.
—Bad Mother: A Chronicle of Maternal Crimes, Minor Calamities, & Occasional Moments of Grace. 2010. (ENG.). 224p. pap. 14.95 *(978-0-7679-3069-7(X)*, Anchor) Knopf Doubleday Publishing Group.
Walker, Alice. World Has Changed: Conversations with Alice Walker. 2010. (ENG.). 368p. 25.95 *(978-1-59558-496-0(X))* New Pr., The.
—The World Has Changed: Conversations with Alice Walker. Byrd, Rudolph P., ed. 2011. (ENG., Illus.). 368p. pap. 18.95 *(978-1-59558-705-3(5))* New Pr., The.
Walker, Andrew. Guvnor Droog's Ramblings. 2009. 100p. pap. 17.95 *(978-1-4092-9767-3(5))* Lulu Enterprises Inc.
Walker, Gina Luria & Fitzer, Anna M., eds. Memoirs of Women Writers, 4 vols., Pt. 1, Vols. 1-4. 2011. (Chawton House Library: Women's Memoirs Ser.). (ENG.). 1808p. 625.00 *(978-1-84893-051-3(8))* Pickering & Chatto Pubs., Ltd. GBR. Dist: Ashgate Publishing Co.
Walker, Ronald. Rekindling Through the Past: Memoirs Through the Acknowledgments of Plights. 2011. 46p. pap. 16.95 **(978-1-4560-3018-5(3))** PublishAmerica, Inc.
Wallach, Jennifer Jensen. Closer to the Truth Than Any Fact: Memoir, Memory, & Jim Crow. (ENG.). 192p. 2010. pap. 22.95 *(978-0-8203-3502-5(9))* 2008. 34.95 *(978-0-8203-3069-3(8))* Univ. of Georgia Pr.
—Richard Wright: From Black Boy to World Citizen. 2010. (ENG.). 224p. 26.00 *(978-1-56663-824-1(0))* Dee, Ivan R. Pub.
Walles, Jim. I Laugh to Keep from Crying. 2011. 40p. pap. 19.57 **(978-1-4269-7177-8(X))** Trafford Publishing.
Walsh, Courtney A. Lipstick & Thongs in the Loony Bin. 2007. 196p. pap. 14.95 *(978-0-615-15953-9(2))* Walsh, Courtney A.
Walton, Eileen. A Fine Line: In Pursuit of a Normal Life. 2010. 192p. pap. 14.95 *(978-1-4520-6843-5(7))* AuthorHouse.
Ward, Adolphus William. Dickens. 2011. (Cambridge Library Collection - English Men of Letters Ser.). (ENG.). 240p. pap. 22.99 **(978-1-108-03450-0(0))** Cambridge Univ. Pr.
Ward, Charles E. The Life of John Dryden. 2011. 390p. 53.95 **(978-1-258-05675-9(5))** Literary Licensing, LLC.
Wardale, Roger. Arthur Ransome under Sail. 2010. (ENG., Illus.). 256p. pap. 20.00 *(978-1-85058-855-9(4)*, Sigma Pr.) Stobart Davies, Ltd. GBR. Dist: Brown, David Bk. Co., The.
Warren, Mercy Otis. Mercy Otis Warren: Selected Letters. Richards, Jeffrey H. & Harris, Sharon M., eds. 2009. (ENG., Illus.). 320p. lib. bdg. 44.95 *(978-0-8203-2680-1(1))* Univ. of Georgia Pr.
wa'Thiong'o, Ngugi. Dreams in a Time of War: A Childhood Memoir. 2011. (Illus.). 272p. pap. 15.00 *(978-0-307-47621-0(9)*, Anchor) Knopf Doubleday Publishing Group.
wa'Thiong'o, Ngugi. In the House of the Interpreter: A Memoir. 2012. (ENG.). 256p. 25.95 **(978-0-307-90769-1(4)**, Pantheon) Knopf Doubleday Publishing Group.
Watmough, David. Myself Through Others: Memoirs. 2008. (ENG., Illus.). 208p. pap. 24.99 *(978-1-55002-799-0(9)*, Dundurn Pr.) Dundurn CAN. Dist: Ingram Pub. Services.
Watt, Julie. Poisoned Lives: The Regency Poet Letitia Elizabeth Landon (L. E. L.) & British Gold Coast Administrator George Maclean. 2010. (ENG., Illus.). 300p. 74.95 *(978-1-84519-420-6(9))* Sussex Academic Pr. GBR. Dist: International Specialized Bk. Services.
Waugh, Alec. A Year to Remember: A Reminiscence Of 1931. 2012. 201p. pap. **(978-1-4482-0127-3(6)**, 142580, Bloomsbury Reader) Bloomsbury Publishing Plc.
Waugh, Alexander. Fathers & Sons: The Autobiography of a Family. 2008. (ENG., Illus.). 480p. pap. 16.00 *(978-0-7679-2748-2(6))* Broadway Bks.
Waxman, Laura Hamilton. Jane Goodall. 2008. pap. 52.95 *(978-0-8225-9391-1(2))* Lerner Publishing Group.
Wayne, Tiffany K. Critical Companion to Ralph Waldo Emerson. 2010. (Critical Companion to Ser.). (Illus.). 456p. (C). (gr. 9-18). 75.00 *(978-0-8160-7358-0(9))* Facts On File, Inc.
Weaver, Helen. The Awakener: A Memoir of Jack Kerouac & the Fifties. 2009. (ENG.). 180p. pap. 16.95 *(978-0-87286-505-1(3))* City Lights Bks.
Weber, Katharine. The Memory of All That: George Gershwin, Kay Swift, & My Family's Legacy of Infidelities. 2012. (ENG.). 288p. pap. 14.00 **(978-0-307-39589-4(8))** Broadway Bks.
—The Memory of All That: George Gershwin, Kay Swift, & My Family's Legacy of Infidelities. 2011. (Illus.). 288p. 24.00 *(978-0-307-39588-7(X)*, Crown) Crown Publishing Group.
Weeks, Edward. The Open Heart. 2009. 250p. 41.95 *(978-1-104-84861-3(9))* 2007. (ENG.). 248p. per. 26.95 *(978-0-548-44598-3(2))* Kessinger Publishing, LLC.
Weil, Sylvie. At Home with André & Simone Weil. Ivry, Benjamin, tr. from FRE. 2010. (ENG.). 192p. 24.95 *(978-0-8101-2704-3(0))* Northwestern Univ. Pr.

Weinstein, Philip. Becoming Faulkner: The Art & Life of William Faulkner, 1 vol. 2012. (ENG., Illus.). 272p. pap. 19.95 ***(978-0-19-989835-0(9))*** Oxford Univ. Pr., Inc.

Weir, Theresa. The Orchard. 2011. (Memoir Ser.). 54.99 ***(978-1-61113-799-6(3)***, Sound Library) AudioGO.

—The Orchard: A Memoir. (ENG.). 2012. 256p. pap. 12.99 ***(978-0-446-58468-5(1))*** 2011. 240p. 24.99 *(978-0-446-58469-2(X))* Grand Central Publishing.

—Orchard: A Memoir. l.t. ed. 2011. lib. bdg. 34.95 ***(978-1-61173-204-7(2))*** Ctr. Point Large Print.

The Weird World of HP Lovecraft. 2008. 29.90 *(978-1-60591-225-7(5))* Title Player, Inc.

Weis, Margaret & Hickman, Tracy. Realms of Dragons: The Universes of Margaret Weis & Tracy Hickman. Date not set. 320p. pap. 16.00 *(978-0-06-105326-9(0))* HarperCollins Pubs.

Weisbecker, Allan C. Can't You Get along with Anyone? A Writer's Memoir & a Tale of a Lost Surfer's Paradise. 2007. (Illus.). 500p. spiral bd. 29.95 *(978-0-9797117-0-1(3))* Bandito Bks.

Weisbord, Merrily. The Love Queen of Malabar: Memoir of a Friendship with Kamala Das. 2010. (ENG., Illus.). 288p. (C). *(978-0-7735-3791-0(0))* McGill-Queen's Univ. Pr.

Weiss, Andrea. In the Shadow of the Magic Mountain: The Erika & Klaus Mann Story. 2008. (Illus.). 310p. 27.50 *(978-0-226-88672-5(7))* Univ. of Chicago Pr.

Weiss, Jonathan M. Irene Nemirovsky: Her Life & Works. 2006. (Stanford Studies in Jewish History & C Ser.). (ENG., Illus.). 224p. 28.95 *(978-0-8047-5481-1(0))* Stanford Univ. Pr.

Weiss, Miranda. Tide, Feather, Snow: A Life in Alaska. 2009. 288p. 24.99 *(978-0-06-171025-4(3))* HarperCollins Pubs.

Weiss, Peter. Holderlin: A Play in Two Acts. 2010. (SB-the German List Ser.). (ENG.). 219p. 14.95 *(978-1-906497-72-9(9))* Seagull Bks. GBR. Dist: Chicago Distribution Ctr.

Welch, Diana, et al. The Kids Are All Right: A Memoir. 2010. (ENG.). 368p. pap. 15.00 *(978-0-307-39605-1(3)*, Three Rivers Pr.) Crown Publishing Group.

Welland, Sasha Su-Ling. A Thousand Miles of Dreams: The Journeys of Two Chinese Sisters. 2007. (Asian Voices Ser.). (ENG., Illus.). 392p. per. 19.95 *(978-0-7425-5314-9(0))* Rowman & Littlefield Publishers, Inc.

Weller, Sam & Bradbury, Ray. Listen to the Echoes: The Ray Bradbury Interviews. 2010. (ENG., Illus.). 336p. pap. 18.95 *(978-1-935554-03-5(4))* Melville Hse. Publishing.

West, Helen B. Blackfoot Country: Blackfeet Man, James Willard Schultz. 2011. 16p. pap. 35.95 ***(978-1-258-06517-1(7))*** Literary Licensing, LLC.

West, Paul. The Shadow Factory. 2008. (ENG.). 115p. 23.00 *(978-0-930829-65-0(4))* Lumen, Inc.

West, Virginia. Mommie's Gone. 2011. 158p. pap. 24.95 ***(978-1-4626-0685-6(7))*** PublishAmerica, Inc.

Wheatley, Christopher J. Thornton Wilder & Amos Wilder: Writing Religion in Twentieth-Century America. 2011. (ENG.). 232p. pap. 29.00 ***(978-0-268-04424-4(4))*** Univ. of Notre Dame Pr.

Wheatley, Vera & Martineau, Harriet. The Life & Work of Harriet Martineau. 2011. 436p. 56.95 ***(978-1-258-00837-6(8))*** Literary Licensing, LLC.

Wheeler, Richard S. An Accidental Novelist: A Literary Memoir. 2007. (ENG.). 240p. 28.95 *(978-0-86534-562-1(7))*; per. 22.95 *(978-0-86534-563-8(5))* Sunstone Pr.

Wherry, George Edward. Cambridge & Charles Lamb. 2009. (Cambridge Library Collection - Cambridge Ser.). (ENG.). 120p. pap. 19.99 *(978-1-108-00254-7(4))* Cambridge Univ. Pr.

Whibley, Charles. The Letters of an Englishman. 2008. 260p. 42.95 *(978-1-4365-1889-5(X))* 2007. (ENG.). 264p. per. 27.95 *(978-0-548-73585-5(9))* Kessinger Publishing, LLC.

Whicher, George Frisbie. The Life & Romances of Mrs. Eliza Haywood. 2007. (ENG.). 202p. pap. 20.99 *(978-1-4264-4450-0(8))*; 228p. pap. 22.99 *(978-1-4264-4518-7(0))* BiblioBazaar.

White, Edmund. City Boy: My Life in New York During the 1960s & '70s. 2009. (ENG.). 304p. 26.00 *(978-1-59691-402-5(5))* Bloomsbury Publishing.

—City Boy: My Life in New York During the 1960s & '70s. 2010. (ENG.). 304p. pap. 16.00 *(978-1-60819-234-2(2))* Bloomsbury Publishing.

—Marcel Proust: A Life. 2009. (Penguin Lives Ser.). (ENG.). 176p. (gr. 12-18). 14.00 *(978-0-14-311498-7(0)*, Penguin (Non-Classics)) Penguin Group (USA) Inc.

—Rimbaud: The Double Life of a Rebel. 2009. (ENG.). 256p. pap. 14.00 *(978-1-934633-20-5(8)*, 934620) Atlas & Co.

White Smith, Debra. Marriage Revolution: Rethinking Your Relationship in Light of God's Design. 2008. 201p. per. 12.99 *(978-0-7369-1767-4(5))* Harvest Hse. Pubs.

Whitehouse, J. Howard. To the Memory of Ruskin. 2006. pap. 16.95 *(978-1-4286-5519-5(0))* Kessinger Publishing, LLC.

Whorry, Charles Lee. Silent Cry: A Masterpiece by Charles Lee. 2nd ed. Date not set. 225p. reprint ed. pap. 19.95 *(978-0-9707415-0-9(2))* Whorry, Charles Lee.

Whyte, Jack. Forty Years in Canada: A Memoir, 1 vol. 2007. (ENG., Illus.). 192p. *(978-1-894974-22-6(0))* Heritage Hse.

Wiater, Stanley, et al. The Twilight & Other Zones: The Dark Worlds of Richard Matheson. 2009. (ENG.). 352p. 19.95 *(978-0-8065-3113-7(4)*, Citadel Pr.) Kensington Publishing Corp.

Wiebe, Rudy. Of This Earth: A Mennonite Boyhood in the Boreal Forest, 1 vol. 2007. (ENG., Illus.). 393p. pap. 15.95 *(978-1-56148-602-1(7))* Good Bks.

Wien, Harlan. From Nowhere I Came. 2007. 0.00 *(978-0-9799705-0-4(4))* Wien's.

Wiesel, Elie. Night Trilogy: Night - Dawn - Day. 2008. (ENG.). 352p. pap. 17.95 *(978-0-8090-7364-1(1)*, Hill & Wang) Farrar, Straus & Giroux.

Wilber, Ken. The Pocket Ken Wilber. 2008. (Shambhala Pocket Classics Ser.). (ENG.). 192p. pap. 6.95 *(978-1-59030-637-6(6))* Shambhala Pubns., Inc.

Wilde, Jane Francesca. Social Studies. 2010. (Cambridge Library Collection - Women's Writing Ser.). 354p. pap. 29.99 *(978-1-108-02195-1(6))* Cambridge Univ. Pr.

Wilde, Oscar. Intentions. 2006. (ENG.). 132p. per. 10.95 *(978-1-59818-853-0(4))* Aegypan.

—Intentions. 2009. 160p. 25.99 *(978-1-60512-395-0(1))*; pap. 12.99 *(978-1-60512-495-7(8))* Akasha Publishing, LLC. (Akasha Classics).

—Intentions. 2008. 148p. 21.99 *(978-0-554-30761-9(8))*; 24.99 *(978-0-554-21458-0(X))* BiblioBazaar.

—Intentions. 2007. (ENG.). 192p. per. 9.99 *(978-1-59986-651-2(X))* Filiquarian Publishing, LLC.

—Intentions. 2008. 272p. pap. *(978-1-4097-2557-2(X))* Read Bks.

—Oscar Wilde in America: The Interviews. Hofer, Matthew & Scharnhorst, Gary, eds. 2010. (ENG., Illus.). 208p. 40.00 *(978-0-252-03472-5(4))* Univ. of Illinois Pr.

Wilkinson, Clement J. James John, Garth Wilkinson. 303p. reprint ed. 98.00 *(978-0-7222-9966-1(4))* Library Reprints, Inc.

Willeford, Charles. I Was Looking for a Street. 2010. (ENG., Illus.). 154p. pap. 15.95 *(978-0-9820947-7-8(9))* PictureBox, Inc.

Williams, Alfonsine. The Dreamer's Disease. 2011. 132p. pap. 24.95 ***(978-1-4626-1137-9(0))*** PublishAmerica, Inc.

Williams, Hermine Weigel. Therese Von Jakob Robinson: A Biographical Portrait. 2007. 277p. *(978-0-595-90010-7(0))* iUniverse, Inc.

Williams, James S. Jean Cocteau. 2010. (French Film Directors Ser.). (ENG., Illus.). 240p. pap. 24.95 *(978-0-7190-5884-4(8))* Manchester Univ. Pr. GBR. Dist: Macmillan.

—Jean Cocteau. 2008. (Reaktion Books - Critical Lives Ser.). (ENG., Illus.). 192p. per. 16.95 *(978-1-86189-354-3(X))* Reaktion Bks., Ltd. GBR. Dist: Chicago Distribution Ctr.

Williams, Penry & Nicholls, Mark. Sir Walter Raleigh: In Life & Legend. 2011. (ENG., Illus.). 400p. 34.95 *(978-1-4411-1209-5(X))* Continuum International Publishing Group, Ltd. GBR. Dist: National Bk. Network.

Williams, Peter. Whistlng in the Soup: Not So-Tall Tales of Growing up in Troubled Times. 2007. 248p. per. 11.95 *(978-1-4327-0355-4(2))* Outskirts Pr., Inc.

Williams, Susan Millar. A Devil & a Good Woman, Too: The Lives of Julia Peterkin. 2008. (ENG., Illus.). 392p. pap. 19.95 *(978-0-8203-3250-5(X))* Univ. of Georgia Pr.

Williamson, Eric Miles. Oakland, Jack London, & Me. 2007. (ENG.). 224p. per. 24.95 *(978-1-933896-11-3(6))* Texas Review Pr.

Willis, Irene Cooper. Brontes. 2006. 148p. per. *(978-1-4067-2557-5(9)*, Hesperides Pr.) Read Bks.

Willis, Jay Thomas. Born to Be Destroyed: How My Upbringing Almost Destroyed Me. 2010. pap. *(978-0-7414-6236-7(2))* Infinity Publishing.

Wills, Maralys. A Circus Without Elephants: A Memoir. 2010. 288p. pap. 16.95 *(978-1-57197-449-5(0)*, Ivy House Publishing Group) Pentland Pr., Inc.

Wilson, Edmund. Israel & the Dead Sea Scrolls. 2011. (ENG.). 440p. pap. 34.95 ***(978-1-4128-4248-8(4))*** Transaction Pubs.

Wilson, Frances. The Ballad of Dorothy Wordsworth: A Life. 2009. (ENG., Illus.). 336p. 30.00 *(978-0-374-10867-0(6))* Farrar, Straus & Giroux.

Wilson, Kim. Tea with Jane Austen. 2011. (ENG., Illus.). 112p. 19.95 *(978-0-7112-3189-4(3))* Lincoln, Frances Ltd. GBR. Dist: Perseus-PGW.

Wilson, Mike. Young Jack London. ltd. ed. 2006. per. *(978-0-9672491-5-5(5))* WORDSWORTH Publishing Co.

Wilson, Richard L. The Journal of A Modern Mad Man. 2011. 128p. pap. 12.95 ***(978-1-4670-3485-2(1))*** AuthorHouse.

Wilson, Todd. Aleister Crowley - Nature of the Beast. 2007. 176p. pap. 19.95 *(978-1-904658-27-6(X))* Aeon Bks. Ltd. GBR. Dist: Stylus Publishing, LLC.

Winchester, Simon. The Alice Behind Wonderland. 2011. (ENG., Illus.). 192p. 16.95 *(978-0-19-539619-5(7))* Oxford Univ. Pr., Inc.

Winegarten, Renee. Germaine de Stael & Benjamin Constant: A Dual Biography. 2008. (ENG., Illus.). 352p. 35.00 *(978-0-300-11925-1(9))* Yale Univ. Pr.

Wingate, Ashmore Kyle Paterson. Life & Writings of John Ruskin. 2009. 154p. pap. *(978-0-217-50392-1(6))* Books LLC.

Winkler, Anthony C. Trust the Darkness: My Life as a Writer. 2008. (Illus.). 462p. *(978-0-230-02604-9(4))* Macmillan Caribbean.

Winnington, G. Peter. Vast Alchemies: The Definitive Illustrated Biography. 2009. (ENG., Illus.). 300p. pap. 23.95 *(978-0-7206-1341-4(8))* Owen, Peter Ltd. GBR. Dist: Independent Pubs. Group.

Winstead, Karen A. John Capgrave's Fifteenth Century. 2006. (Middle Ages Ser.). (Illus.). 248p. (C). 59.95 *(978-0-8122-3977-5(6))* Univ. of Pennsylvania Pr.

Winter, William. The Life & Writings of William Law Symonds. 2009. 670p. 46.99 *(978-1-116-69457-4(3))*; 39.99 *(978-1-116-69458-1(1))*; pap. 46.75 *(978-1-116-69460-4(3))*; pap. 47.75 *(978-1-116-69459-8(X))* BiblioBazaar.

Winters, Kathleen C. & Winters, Kathleen. Anne Morrow Lindbergh: First Lady of the Air. 2008. (ENG., Illus.). 256p. pap. 14.95 *(978-0-230-60411-7(0))* Palgrave Macmillan.

Winterson, Jeanette. Why Be Happy When You Could Be Normal? 2012. (ENG.). 224p. 25.00 ***(978-0-8021-2010-6(5)***, Grove Pr.) Grove/Atlantic, Inc.

Wodehouse, P. g. P. G. Wodehouse: A Life in Letters. Ratcliffe, Sophie, ed. 2012. (ENG., Illus.). 624p. 35.00 ***(978-0-393-08899-1(5)***, 8899) Norton, W. W. & Co., Inc.

Wohl, Burton. Wolves, Whales & November Gales. 2006. 206p. pap. 24.95 *(978-1-4137-9984-2(1))* PublishAmerica, Inc.

Woiwode, Larry. A Step from Death: A Memoir. 2008. (ENG.). 288p. 24.00 *(978-1-58243-373-8(9))* Counterpoint LLC.

—A Step from Death: A Memoir. 2009. (ENG.). 288p. pap. 15.95 *(978-1-58243-469-8(7)*, Counterpoint Pr.) Basic Bks. GBR. Dist: Perseus-PGW.

Wolcott, James. Lucking Out: My Life Getting down & Semi-Dirty in Seventies New York. 2011. (ENG.). 272p. 25.95 *(978-0-385-52778-1(0)*, Doubleday) Knopf Doubleday Publishing Group.

Wolf, Mark J. P. J. R. R. Tolkien: Of Words & Worlds. 2009. (ENG., Illus.). 228p. 18.95 *(978-1-58182-702-6(4)*, Cumberland Hse.) Sourcebooks, Inc.

Wollaston, Emily. Little Book of Thomas Hardy. 2008. (Little Book Ser.). (ENG., Illus.). 128p. 11.99 *(978-1-906229-60-3(0)*, 1906229600) G2 Entertainment Ltd. GBR. Dist: BookMasters Distribution Services (BDS).

Wollaston, Emily & Dale, Sue. Little Book of Jane Austen. 2008. (Little Book Ser.). (ENG., Illus.). 128p. 11.99 *(978-1-906229-58-0(9)*, 1906229589) G2 Entertainment Ltd. GBR. Dist: BookMasters Distribution Services (BDS).

Wood, Monica. When We Were the Kennedys: A Memoir from Mexico, Maine. 2012. (ENG.). 256p. 24.00 ***(978-0-547-63014-4(X))*** Houghton Mifflin Harcourt Trade & Reference Pubs.

Wood, Pamela. Charles Bukowski's Scarlet. 2010. (Illus.). 234p. pap. 15.95 *(978-0-941543-58-3(7))* Sun Dog Pr.

Woodberry, George Edward. Nathaniel Hawthorne. 2008. 240p. 24.99 *(978-0-554-34851-3(9))* 2008. 240p. 27.99 *(978-0-554-25548-4(0))* 2007. (ENG.). 238p. pap. 22.99 *(978-1-4264-9293-8(6))* BiblioBazaar.

—Nathaniel Hawthorne. 2009. 112p. pap. *(978-0-217-51662-4(9))* Books LLC.

—Nathaniel Hawthorne. 2008. 172p. pap. *(978-1-4099-3690-9(2))* Dodo Pr.

Woodcock, George. Letter to the Past: An Autobiography. 2010. (ENG.). 331p. pap. 30.00 *(978-1-55005-192-6(X))* Fitzhenry & Whiteside, Ltd. CAN. Dist: Ingram Pub. Services.

Woolf, Jenny. The Mystery of Lewis Carroll: Discovering the Whimsical, Thoughtful, & Sometimes Lonely Man Who Created Alice in Wonderland. 2011. (ENG., Illus.). 336p. pap. 16.99 *(978-0-312-67371-0(X)*, St. Martin's Griffin) St. Martin's Pr.

Woolf, Virginia. The Platform of Time: Memoirs of Family & Friends. Rosenbaum, S. P., ed. 2008. (ENG., Illus.). 232p. pap. 16.95 *(978-1-84391-711-3(4))* Hesperus Pr. GBR. Dist: Independent Pubs. Group.

Worboyes, Sally. East End Girl: Growing up the Hard Way. 2006. (ENG., Illus.). 304p. per. 14.95 *(978-0-340-83732-0(2)*, Hodder & Stoughton) Hodder General Publishing Div. GBR. Dist: Independent Pubs. Group.

Wordsworth, Dorothy. Grasmere & Alfoxden Journals. Woof, Pamela, ed. 2008. (Oxford World's Classics Ser.). (ENG., Illus.). 368p. pap. 12.95 *(978-0-19-953687-0(2))* Oxford Univ. Pr., Inc.

Worster, W. W. Wanderers. 24.95 *(978-0-8488-0686-6(7))* Amereon LTD.

Wozonig, Karin S. Die Literatin Betty Paoli: Weibliche Mobilität Im 19. Jahrhundert. (GER.). 221p. *(978-3-85409-306-0(3))* Locker, Erhard, Ges.mbH Verlag.

Wriggins, Sally Hovey. Asia on My Mind: From Ceylon to the Silk Road. 2008. (Illus.). 284p. pap. 22.95 *(978-1-4327-2180-0(1))* Outskirts Pr., Inc.

Wright, Richard & Wright, Richard. Black Boy. 2008. (P. S. Ser.). (ENG.). 464p. pap. 16.99 *(978-0-06-144308-4(5)*, HarperPerennial) HarperCollins Pubs.

Wright, Thomas. Biographia Britannica Literaria. 2009. (LAT.). 571p. pap. 30.99 *(978-1-117-70043-4(7)*, BiblioLife) BiblioBazaar.

—Biographia Britannica Literaria. 2009. 362p. pap. *(978-0-217-95726-7(9))*; 440p. pap. *(978-0-217-44609-9(4))* Books LLC.

—Built of Books: How Reading Defined the Life of Oscar Wilde. 2010. (ENG.). 384p. pap. 18.00 *(978-0-8050-9246-2(3)*, Holt Paperback) St. Martin's Pr.

—The Life of John Payne. 2007. (ENG.). 324p. 45.95 *(978-0-548-04855-9(X))* Kessinger Publishing, LLC.

Wu, Duncan. William Hazlitt: The First Modern Man. (ENG., Illus.). 2010. 592p. pap. 24.95 *(978-0-19-958884-8(8))* 2008. 400p. 49.95 *(978-0-19-954958-0(3))* Oxford Univ. Pr., Inc.

Wulu, Sr. The Miracles & Riches of God: Autobiography of John Nimley Wulu, Sr. of Monrovia, Liberia, West Africa (Founder & Builder of Schools) 2008. 136p. pap. 10.99 *(978-1-4389-1800-6(3))* AuthorHouse.

Wyllie, Barbara. Vladimir Nabokov. 2010. (Reaktion Books - Critical Lives Ser.). (ENG., Illus.). 192p. pap. 16.95 *(978-1-86189-660-5(3))* Reaktion Bks., Ltd. GBR. Dist: Chicago Distribution Ctr.

Xie, Bingying. Autobiography of a Chinese Girl: A Genuine Autobiography. Crome, Keith & Williams, James, eds. 2007. (Kegan Paul Travellers Ser.). (Illus.). 216p. 110.00 *(978-0-7103-1041-5(2))* Kegan Paul International, Ltd. GBR. Dist: Columbia Univ. Pr.

Yang, Belle. Forget Sorrow: An Ancestral Tale. 2010. (ENG., Illus.). 250p. 23.95 *(978-0-393-06834-4(X)*, 6834) Norton, W. W. & Co., Inc.

Ying, Li-Hua. The A to Z of Modern Chinese Literature. 2010. (A to Z Guide Ser.). (ENG.). 500p. pap. 34.45 *(978-0-8108-7614-9(0))* Scarecrow Pr., Inc.

Ying, Li-Hua & Woronoff, Jon. Historical Dictionary of Modern Chinese Literature. 2009. (Historical Dictionaries of Literature & the Arts Ser.). (ENG.). 494p. 105.00 *(978-0-8108-5516-8(X))* Scarecrow Pr., Inc.

Yoseloff, Martin. Remember Me to Marcie. 6.95 *(978-0-8453-7696-6(9)*, Cornwall Bks.) Associated Univ. Presses.

—A Time to Be Young. 4.50 *(978-0-8453-6445-1(6)*, Cornwall Bks.) Associated Univ. Presses.

Young, Augustus. The Nicotine Cat & Other People. 2009. 300p. pap. 22.00 *(978-1-84840-041-2(1))* New Island Books IRL. Dist: International Specialized Bk. Services.

Young, James. A Waterfallcutoff. 2011. 54p. 24.99 ***(978-1-4653-3773-3(3))***; pap. 15.99 ***(978-1-4628-9157-3(8))*** Xlibris Corp.

Young, Karl. A Memoir of Karl Young. 2011. 66p. 36.95 ***(978-1-258-01290-8(1))*** Literary Licensing, LLC.

Young, Phillip. 2 Much 2 Young. 2008. 144p. 26.50 *(978-1-4251-8476-6(6))* Trafford Publishing.

Young, Reggie Scott, et al. This Louisiana Thing That Drives Me: The Legacy of Ernest J. Gaines. 2009. (Illus.). 96p. 40.00 *(978-1-887366-83-0(0))* Univ. of Louisiana at Lafayette Pr.

Young, Richard A. & Cisneros, Odile. Historical Dictionary of Latin American Literature & Theater. 2011. xxvii, 719p. E-Book *(978-0-8108-7498-5(9))* Scarecrow Pr., Inc.

Yutang, Lin. Gay Genius. 2006. 396p. per. *(978-1-4067-1251-3(5)*, Hesperides Pr.) Read Bks.

Zaborowska, Magdalena J. James Baldwin's Turkish Decade: Erotics of Exile. 2009. (ENG., Illus.). 416p. 94.95 *(978-0-8223-4144-4(1))* Duke Univ. Pr.

Zaborowska, Magdalena J. & Zaborowska, Magdalena. James Baldwin's Turkish Decade: Erotics of Exile. 2009. (ENG., Illus.). 416p. pap. 26.95 *(978-0-8223-4167-3(0))* Duke Univ. Pr.

Zackheim, Victoria. The Face in the Mirror: Writers Reflect on Their Dreams of Youth & the Reality of Age. Zacheim, Victoria, ed. 2009. (ENG., Illus.). 300p. 25.00 *(978-1-59102-752-2(7))* Prometheus Bks., Pubs.

Zara, Christopher. Tortured Artists: From Picasso & Monroe to Warhol & Winehouse, the Twisted Secrets of the World's Most Creative Minds. 2012. (ENG., Illus.). 272p. pap. 15.95 ***(978-1-4405-3003-6(3))*** Adams Media Corp.

Zhao, Chuanren, et al. Zhongguo Shu Ming Shi Yi Da Ci Dian. 2007. (CHI.). *(978-7-80737-206-6(0))* Shandong Friendship Publishing Hse.

Zheng, Da. Chiang Yee: The Silent Traveller from the East — A Cultural Biography. 2010. (ENG., Illus.). 358p. (C). 49.95 *(978-0-8135-4693-3(1))* Rutgers Univ. Pr.

Zhengguo, Kang. Confessions. 2007. 27.95 *(978-0-7930-6467-0(8))* Norton, W. W. & Co., Inc.

—Confessions: An Innocent Life in Communist China. Wilf, Susan, tr. from CHI. 2007. (ENG., Illus.). 544p. 27.95 *(978-0-393-06467-4(0)*, 6467) Norton, W. W. & Co., Inc.

Zhou, Yangzhi. Wo de Zu Fu Zhou Libo: Ren Jian Shi Dou Fu Yu Liu Feng. 2010. (CHI., Illus.). *(978-7-80214-658-7(5))* Unitp Publishing Hse.

Ziedenberg, Gerald. Inspiration through Adversity. 2010. 288p. (ENG.). 29.95 *(978-1-4520-3130-9(4))*; pap. 24.95 *(978-1-4520-3129-3(0))* AuthorHouse.

Ziener, Heather A. Torn Sneakers. 2009. 156p. pap. 11.99 *(978-1-4389-9832-9(5))* AuthorHouse.

Zimmerman, Anne. An Extravagant Hunger: The Passionate Years of M. F. K. Fisher. (ENG.). 352p. 2012. pap. 16.95 ***(978-1-58243-804-7(8))*** 2011. (Illus.). 26.00 *(978-1-58243-546-6(4))* Counterpoint LLC. (Counterpoint).

Zschokke, Heinrich. Autobiography of Heinrich Zschokke. 2009. 234p. pap. *(978-0-217-68644-0(3))* Books LLC.

—Autobiography of Heinrich Zschokke. 2007. (ENG.). 230p. 41.95 *(978-0-548-15485-4(6))*; pap. 26.95 *(978-1-4304-4913-3(6))* Kessinger Publishing, LLC.

Zuckerman, Millie. A Second Chance at Life. 2011. 118p. 39.95 ***(978-1-936343-88-1(6))*** Peppertree Pr., The.

Zuiker, Anthony & Gold, Todd. Mr. Csi: How a Vegas Dreamer Made a Killing in Hollywood, One Body at a Time. 2011. (ENG.). 304p. 26.99 *(978-0-06-172549-4(8))* HarperCollins Pubs.

Zweig, Stefan. Balzac, Dickens, Dostoevsky: Master Builders of the Spirit. 2009. (ENG.). 291p. pap. 34.95 *(978-1-4128-1047-0(7))* Transaction Pubs.

AUTHORS—CORRESPONDENCE

Abbey, Edward. Postcards from Ed: Dispatches & Salvos from an American Iconoclast. Petersen, David, ed. (ENG.). 2007. 336p. pap. 16.00 *(978-1-57131-285-3(4))* 2006. (Illus.). 304p. 24.95 *(978-1-57131-284-6(6))* Milkweed Editions.

Adams, Henry. Letters to a Niece & Prayer to the Virgin of Chartres. 2007. (ENG.). 140p. 35.95 *(978-0-548-01948-1(7))* Kessinger Publishing, LLC.

—Letters to a Niece & Prayer to the Virgin of Chartres. 2007. 144p. per. *(978-1-4067-2971-9(X))* Read Bks.

Akkach. Letters of a Sufi Scholar: The Correspondence of 'Abd al-Ghan? Al-N?bulus? (1641-1731) 2009. (Islamic History & Civilization Ser.). (ARA & ENG., Illus.). 292p. *(978-90-04-17102-2(9))* BRILL.

Altholz, Josef L., et al, eds. The Correspondence of Lord Acton & Richard Simpson: Volume 2, 3 vols. 2008. (ENG.). 356p. pap. 46.00 *(978-0-521-08369-0(9))* Cambridge Univ. Pr.

—The Correspondence of Lord Acton & Richard Simpson: Volume 3, 3 vols. 2008. (ENG.). 384p. pap. 53.00 *(978-0-521-08380-5(X))* Cambridge Univ. Pr.

Altholz, Josef L. & McElrath, Damian, eds. The Correspondence of Lord Acton & Richard Simpson: Volume 1, 3 vols. 2008. (ENG.). 260p. pap. 37.99 *(978-0-521-08355-3(9))* Cambridge Univ. Pr.

Anderson, G. A. The Letters of Thomas Manning to Charles. 2006. pap. 21.95 *(978-1-4286-4763-3(5))* Kessinger Publishing, LLC.

Anonymous. The Life & Letters of Washington Irving. 2009. 240p. pap. *(978-1-151-11947-6(4))* Books LLC.

Archer, William. Real Conversations Conversation Vii with. 2006. pap. 15.95 *(978-1-4286-4326-0(5))* Kessinger Publishing, LLC.

Arfanotti, Elisabetta, et al. Corpus epistolare e documentario di Leon Battista Alberti. Benigni, Paola, ed. 2007. (Edizione nazionale opere di leon battista

Alberti Ser.). (Illus.). 668p. (C). 99.00 *(978-88-596-0402-0(8))* Edizioni Polistampa ITA. Dist: Brown, David Bk. Co., The.

Arnim, Ludwig Achim & Burwick, Roswitha. Werke und Briefwechsel: Historisch-Kritische Ausgabe. 2007. (GER., Illus.). XIV, 1161p. *(978-3-484-15602-9(3))* Verlag Max Niemeyer.

Arnim, Ludwig Achim von. Schaubahne I. Pietsch, Yvonne, ed. 2010. (GER., Illus.). VIII, 905p. *(978-3-484-15613-5(9))* Verlag Max Niemeyer.

Atkinson, Caroline P., ed. Letters of Susan Hale. 2008. 516p. 32.99 *(978-0-559-60822-3(5))*; pap. 38.75 *(978-0-559-60819-6(7))* BiblioBazaar.

—Letters of Susan Hale. 2007. (ENG.). 498p. 53.95 *(978-0-548-02065-4(5))* Kessinger Publishing, LLC.

Austen, Jane. Letters of Jane Austen. Lord Brabourne, Edward Hugessen Knatchbull-Hugessen, ed. 2009. (Cambridge Library Collection - Literary Studies). (ENG.). 396p. pap. 23.99 *(978-1-108-00339-1(7))*; 380p. pap. 23.99 *(978-1-108-00340-7(0))* Cambridge Univ. Pr.

—Letters of Jane Austen V1. Edward, Lord Brabourne, ed. 2007. (ENG.). 396p. 49.95 *(978-0-548-10449-1(2))* Kessinger Publishing, LLC.

—Letters of Jane Austen V2. Edward, Lord Brabourne, ed. 2007. (ENG.). 380p. 48.95 *(978-0-548-10450-7(6))* Kessinger Publishing, LLC.

—Selected Letters. Jones, Vivien, ed. 2009. (Oxford World's Classics Ser.). (ENG.). 352p. pap. 12.95 *(978-0-19-953843-0(3))* Oxford Univ. Pr., Inc.

Austen, Susan Coolidge. Letters of Jane Austen: Selected from the Compilation of Her Great Nephew, Edward, Lord Brabourne. 2009. 344p. 32.99 *(978-1-113-04707-6(0))*; pap. 31.75 *(978-1-113-04705-2(4))* BiblioBazaar.

Austin, James C. Fields of the Atlantic Monthly: Letters to an Editor, 1861-1870. 2011. 456p. 57.95 ***(978-1-258-07494-4(X))*** Literary Licensing, LLC.

Barbauld, Barbauld. The Correspondence of Samuel Richardson: Selected from the Original Manuscripts, Bequeathed by Him to His Family, to Which Are Prefixed, a Biograp. 2010. 356p. pap. 32.75 *(978-1-149-08172-3(4))*; 366p. pap. 32.75 *(978-1-149-04468-1(3))* BiblioBazaar.

Barrett, Charlotte. Diary & Letters of Madame Darblay Vol. 2006. (ENG.). 608p. per. *(978-1-4067-3520-8(5))*, Hesperides Pr.) Read Bks.

Bataille, Georges & Leiris, Michel. Correspondence: Georges Bataille & Michel Leiris. Heron, Liz, tr. from FRE. 2008. (SB-The French List Ser.). (ENG.). 312p. 29.95 *(978-1-905422-67-8(9))* Seagull Bks. GBR. Dist: Chicago Distribution Ctr.

Becker, Jurek. Jurek Beckers Neuigkeiten. (GER.). *(978-3-612-26646-0(2))* Econ-Verlag GmbH DEU. Dist: International Bk. Import Service, Inc.

Beckett, Samuel. The Letters of Samuel Beckett, Vol. 1. Fehsenfeld, Martha Dow & Overbeck, Lois More, eds. 2009. (Letters of Samuel Beckett Ser.). (FRE, GER & ENG., Illus.). 882p. 55.00 *(978-0-521-86793-1(2))* Cambridge Univ. Pr.

Beckett, Samuel. The Letters of Samuel Beckett, 1941-1956, Vol. 2. Craig, George et al, eds. 2011. (Letters of Samuel Beckett Ser.). (ENG & FRE., Illus.). 886p. 50.00 ***(978-0-521-86794-8(0))*** Cambridge Univ. Pr.

Bellow, Saul. Saul Bellow: Letters. Taylor, Benjamin F., ed. 2010. (ENG., Illus.). 608p. (gr. 12). 35.00 *(978-0-670-02221-2(7)*, Viking Adult) Penguin Group (USA) Inc.

Bellow, Saul. Saul Bellow: Letters. Taylor, Benjamin F., ed. 2012. (ENG., Illus.). 622p. (gr. 12). 20.00 ***(978-0-14-312046-9(8)***, Penguin (Non-Classics)) Penguin Group (USA) Inc.

Benjamin, Walter & Adorno, Gretel. Correspondence 1930-1940. Lonitz, Henri & Godde, Christoph, eds. Honban, Weiland, tr. from GER. 2008. (ENG., Illus.). 336p. 19.95 *(978-0-7456-3669-6(1))* Polity Pr. GBR. Dist: Wiley, John & Sons, Inc.

Bennett, Arnold. Arnold Bennett's Letters to His Nephew. 2007. (ENG.). 376p. 48.95 *(978-0-548-11732-3(2))* Kessinger Publishing, LLC.

Bèze, Théodore de, et al. Correspondance de Théodore de Bèze. 2009. (Travaux d'Humanisme et Renaissance Ser.). (LAT & FRE., Illus.). 272p. (C). 164.00 *(978-2-600-01330-7(X))* Droz, Librairie CHE. Dist: Brown, David Bk. Co., The.

Bigongiari, Piero, et al. La Certezza Della Poesia: Lettere (1942-1970) 2008. (Diaspro Ser.). (ITA., Illus.). 366p. (C). 39.50 *(978-88-596-0430-3(3))* Edizioni Polistampa ITA. Dist: Brown, David Bk. Co., The.

Birkhoff, Barbara. As Between Friends: Criticism of Themselves & One Another in the Letters of Coleridge, Wordsworth & Lamb. 2011. 58p. 36.95 ***(978-1-258-01369-1(X))*** Literary Licensing, LLC.

Birley, Anthony R. Onomasticon to the Younger Pliny: Letters & Panegyric. XI, 111p. 180.00 ***(978-3-11-184387-2(4))*** De Gruyter, Walter Inc.

Bogarde, Dirk. Ever, Dirk: The Bogarde Letters. Coldstream, John, ed. 2009. (ENG., Illus.). 664p. 23.95 *(978-0-7538-2589-1(9)*, Phoenix) Orion Publishing Group, Ltd. GBR. Dist: Independent Pubs. Group.

Borrow, George. Letters of George Borrow to the British & Foreign Bible Society. Darlow, T. H., ed. 2008. 376p. pap. *(978-1-4099-3270-3(2))* Dodo Pr.

Borrow, George Henry. Letters of George Borrow to the British & Foreign Bible Society. 2008. 428p. 32.99 *(978-0-554-29571-8(7))* 2008. 428p. 30.99 *(978-0-554-38874-8(X))* 2007. (ENG.). 384p. pap. 25.99 *(978-1-4346-7924-6(1))* 2007. (ENG.). 426p. pap. 28.99 *(978-1-4346-7925-3(X))* BiblioBazaar.

—Letters of George Borrow to the British & Foreign Bible Society. 2009. 278p. pap. *(978-1-150-67704-5(X))* Books LLC.

—Letters of George Borrow to the British & Foreign Bible Society, Published by Direction of the Committee. 2010. 268p. pap. 30.44 *(978-1-152-17287-6(5))* General Bks. LLC.

—Letters of George Borrow to the British & Foreign Bible Society, Published by the Direction of the Committee. 2009. 260p. pap. 29.71 *(978-1-151-50451-7(3))* General Bks. LLC.

Boswell, James. The General Correspondence of James Boswell, 1757-1763. Hankins, David & Caudle, James, eds. 2006. (Private Papers of James Boswell). (ENG.). 568p. 85.00 *(978-0-300-08306-4(8))* Yale Univ. Pr.

—Letters, 2 vols. reprint ed. 59.00 *(978-0-403-04137-4(6))* Somerset Pubs., Inc.

Boswell, James, et al, contrib. by. The Correspondence of James Boswell & William Johnson Temple, 1756-1795. 528p. 95.00 *(978-0-7486-0758-7(7))* Edinburgh Univ. Pr. GBR. Dist: Columbia Univ. Pr.

Bradu, Fabienne. Artaud, Todavía. 2009. (Vida y Pensamiento de México Ser.). (SPA.). 196p. pap. 14.95 *(978-968-16-8458-7(3))* Fondo de Cultura Economica USA.

Braley, Berton. Pegasus Pulls a Hack: Memoirs of A Modern Minstrel. 2011. 328p. 50.95 ***(978-1-258-09754-7(0))*** Literary Licensing, LLC.

Breton, André. Entretiens avec André Parinaud (1913-1952) (Coll. Le Point du Jour). (FRE.). 8.95 *(978-0-7859-0636-0(3)*, M3136) French & European Pubns., Inc.

Brontë, Charlotte. Selected Letters. Smith, Margaret, ed. 2010. (Oxford World's Classics Ser.). (ENG.). 320p. pap. 12.95 *(978-0-19-957696-8(3))* Oxford Univ. Pr., Inc.

—Selected Letters of Charlotte Brontë. Smith, Margaret, ed. 2007. (ENG., Illus.). 344p. 55.00 *(978-0-19-920587-5(6))* Oxford Univ. Pr., Inc.

Browder, N. C. Anthem of an Ordinary American. 2007. pap. 14.95 *(978-0-7414-3871-3(2))* Infinity Publishing.

Brown, Edward. Letters of Thomas Edward Brown V1. 2007. (ENG.). 240p. 41.95 *(978-0-548-10141-4(8))* Kessinger Publishing, LLC.

—Letters of Thomas Edward Brown V2. 2007. (ENG.). 252p. 41.95 *(978-0-548-10142-1(6))* Kessinger Publishing, LLC.

Bulwer-Lytton, Edward. Life Letters & Literary Remains of Edw. 2006. pap. 34.95 *(978-1-4286-4895-1(X))* Kessinger Publishing, LLC.

—The Life Letters & Literary Remains of Edward Bulwer, Lord Lytton V1. (ENG.). 400p. 2007. 49.95 *(978-0-548-13724-6(2))* 2006. per. 34.95 *(978-1-4286-4891-3(7))* Kessinger Publishing, LLC.

Burney, Fanny. The Diary & Letters of Madame D'Arblay. 2009. 532p. 35.99 *(978-0-559-08286-3(X))*; 32.99 *(978-0-559-08302-0(5))*; pap. 30.99 *(978-0-559-08290-0(8))*; pap. 23.99 *(978-0-559-08297-9(5))* BiblioBazaar.

—Diary & Letters of Madame d'Arblay (1778-1840), Vol. 1. Dobson, Austin, ed. 2007. 564p. per. 43.95 *(978-0-548-76857-0(9))* Kessinger Publishing, LLC.

—Diary & Letters of Madame d'Arblay (1778-1840) Barrett, Charlotte, ed. 2007. Vol. 3. 556p. per. 42.95 *(978-0-548-77302-4(5))* Vol. 5. 564p. per. 43.95 *(978-0-548-74776-6(8))* Vol. 6. 560p. per. 42.95 *(978-0-548-76510-4(3))* Kessinger Publishing, LLC.

Burroughs, William S. Rub Out the Words: The Letters of William S. Burroughs, 1959-1974. 2012. (ENG.). 448p. 35.00 *(978-0-06-171142-8(X)*, Ecco); 624p. pap. 35.00 *(978-0-06-208886-4(6)*, HarperLuxe) HarperCollins Pubs.

Butler, Samuel. The Correspondence of Samuel Butler with His Sister May. Howard, Daniel Francis, ed. 2011. 284p. 48.95 ***(978-1-258-04522-7(2))*** Literary Licensing, LLC.

Cadalso, Jose. Cartas Marruecas. 2010. 240p. pap. 26.75 *(978-1-148-46774-0(2))* BiblioBazaar.

—Cartas Marruecas. 19th ed. (SPA., Illus.). 352p. 14.95 *(978-84-376-0145-8(2)*, CT1078) Ediciones Cátedra ESP. Dist: Continental Bk. Co., Inc.

—Cartas Marruecas. (SPA.). 164p. 12.95 *(978-84-239-1078-6(4)*, ECS107) Espasa Calpe, S.A. ESP. Dist: Continental Bk. Co., Inc.

—Cartas Marruecas. 2010. (SPA.). 168p. 16.00 *(978-84-9897-301-3(5))* Linkgua Ediciones, S.L. ESP. Dist: AtlasBooks Distribution.

—Cartas Marruecas. (SPA.). 312p. *(978-84-01-90523-0(0))* Plaza & Janes Editories, S.A. ESP. Dist: AIMS International Bks., Inc.

Cadalso, Jose, et al. Cartas Marruecas. 2nd annot. ed. (SPA., Illus.). 280p. 11.95 *(978-84-7039-442-3(8)*, CCD505) Castalia, Editorial S.A. ESP. Dist: Continental Bk. Co. Inc.

Canetti, Vesa & Canetti, Elias. Dearest Georg - Love, Literature, & Power in Dark Times: The Letters of Elias, Veza, & Georges Canetti, 1933-1948. Lauer, Karen & Wachinger, Kristian, eds. Dollenmayer, David, tr. from GER. 2010. (ENG., Illus.). 448p. 24.95 *(978-1-59051-297-5(9))* Other Pr., LLC.

Carlyle, Thomas. Correspondence of Thomas Carlyle & Ral. 2007. pap. *(978-1-4065-1272-4(9))* Dodo Pr.

—The Correspondence of Thomas Carlyle & Ralph Waldo Emerson, 1834-1872. 2009. 384p. 26.99 *(978-1-103-16530-8(5))*; pap. 20.99 *(978-1-103-16529-2(1))* BiblioBazaar.

—The Correspondence of Thomas Carlyle & Ralph Waldo Emerson, 1834-1872. 2009. 272p. pap. *(978-0-217-75195-7(4))*; 222p. pap. *(978-0-217-75194-0(6))*; 204p. pap. *(978-0-217-07535-0(5))* Books LLC.

—Early Letters of Thomas Carlyle. 2008. 392p. pap. 32.75 *(978-0-559-52299-4(1))* BiblioBazaar.

—Early Letters of Thomas Carlyle. 2009. 288p. pap. *(978-0-217-83149-9(4))* Books LLC.

—Early Letters of Thomas Carlyle: 1814-1826. Norton, Charles Eliot, ed. 2007. pap. 33.95 *(978-1-4304-5097-9(5))* Kessinger Publishing, LLC.

—Letters of Thomas Carlyle to His Youngest. 2006. pap. 28.95 *(978-1-4286-5341-2(4))* Kessinger Publishing, LLC.

—New Letters of Thomas Carlyle V1. Carlyle, Alexander, ed. 2007. (ENG.). 356p. 46.95 *(978-0-548-10698-3(3))* Kessinger Publishing, LLC.

—New Letters of Thomas Carlyle V2. Carlyle, Alexander, ed. 2007. (ENG.). 376p. 48.95 *(978-0-548-10699-0(1))* Kessinger Publishing, LLC.

Carlyle, Thomas. Thomas Carlyle: Letters to His Wife. Bliss, Trudy, ed. 2011. 418p. 54.95 ***(978-1-258-08732-6(4))*** Literary Licensing, LLC.

Carlyle, Thomas & Emerson, Ralph Waldo. The Correspondence of Thomas Carlyle & Ralph Waldo Emerson, 1834-1872. 2008. 300p. 25.99 *(978-0-554-34034-0(8))*; 328p. 28.99 *(978-0-554-34035-7(6))*; 300p. 28.99 *(978-0-554-24731-1(3))*; 328p. 29.99 *(978-0-554-24732-8(1))* BiblioBazaar.

Caron, James E. Mark Twain, Unsanctified Newspaper Reporter. 2008. (Mark Twain & His Circle Ser.). (ENG., Illus.). 464p. (C). 49.95 *(978-0-8262-1802-5(4))* Univ. of Missouri Pr.

Carroll, Lewis, pseud. Lewis Carroll & the House of Macmillan. Cohen, Morton N. & Gandolfo, Anita, eds. 2007. (Cambridge Studies in Publishing & Printing History Ser.). (ENG., Illus.). 396p. pap. 79.00 *(978-0-521-04471-4(5))* Cambridge Univ. Pr.

Celan, Paul & Shmuel, Ilana. The Correspondence of Paul Celan & Ilana Shmueli. Gillespie, Susan H., tr. from GER. 2011. (Illus.). 280p. pap. 19.95 *(978-1-931357-89-0(7))* Sheep Meadow Pr., The.

Chatwin, Bruce. Under the Sun: The Letters of Bruce Chatwin. Shakespeare, Nicholas & Chatwin, Elizabeth, eds. (ENG., Illus.). 560p. (gr. 12). 2012. 20.00 ***(978-0-14-312038-4(7)***, Penguin (Non-Classics)) 2011. 35.00 *(978-0-670-02246-5(2)*, Viking Adult) Penguin Group (USA) Inc.

Chekhov, Anton. Letters of Anton Chekhov. 2008. 356p. 31.99 *(978-0-554-29498-8(2))*; 29.99 *(978-0-554-38801-4(4))* BiblioBazaar.

Chesterfield, Earl of. Chesterfield's Letters to His Son 1746 - 1771. 2007. 656p. per. *(978-1-4068-4539-6(6))* Echo Library.

Child, Lydia Maria. Letters of Lydia Maria Child, with a Biographical Introduction by John G Whittier & an Appendix by Wendell Phillips. 2006. 328p. per. 23.99 *(978-1-4255-3287-1(X))* MPublishing.

Christie, William, ed. The Letters of Francis Jeffrey to Thomas & Jane Welsh Carlyle, 1 vol. 2008. (Pickering Masters Ser.). (ENG.). 240p. 195.00 *(978-1-85196-982-1(9))* Pickering & Chatto Pubs., Ltd. GBR. Dist: Ashgate Publishing Co.

Cicero, Marcus Tullius. Letters of Cicero. 2007. (ENG.). 76p. per. *(978-1-4068-4601-0(5))* Echo Library.

—Letters of Cicero. Muirhead, J. H., ed. 2009. 336p. 45.95 *(978-1-104-16589-5(9))*; pap. 30.95 *(978-1-104-14133-2(7))* Kessinger Publishing, LLC.

—Selected Letters. Walsh, P. G., tr. from LAT. 2008. (Oxford World's Classics Ser.). (LAT & ENG., Illus.). 384p. pap. 17.95 *(978-0-19-921420-4(4))* Oxford Univ. Pr., Inc.

Clapp, Susannah. A Card from Angela Carter. 2012. (ENG., Illus.). 112p. 19.99 ***(978-1-4088-2690-4(9))*** Bloomsbury Publishing.

Clark, Lydia Jane. Letters of Lydia Jane Clark, 1858-1936. 2011. 206p. 44.95 ***(978-1-258-03307-1(0))*** Literary Licensing, LLC.

Clemens, Samuel Langhorne. Mark Twain's Aquarium: The Samuel Clemens-Angelfish Correspondence, 1905-1910. Cooley, John, ed. 2009. (ENG.). 328p. pap. 24.95 *(978-0-8203-3498-1(7))* Univ. of Georgia Pr.

Cole, Cyrenus. I Remember, I Remember. 543p. reprint ed. lib. bdg. 98.00 *(978-0-7222-0396-5(9))* Library Reprints, Inc.

Collins, Wilkie. Six Letters of Wilkie Collins. 2011. 34p. 35.95 ***(978-1-258-07751-8(5))*** Literary Licensing, LLC.

Conrad, Joseph. The Collected Letters of Joseph Conrad Vol. 8: 1923-1924. Davies, Laurence & Moore, Gene M., eds. 2008. (Cambridge Edition of the Letters of Joseph Conrad Ser.). (ENG., Illus.). 498p. 165.00 *(978-0-521-56197-6(3))* Cambridge Univ. Pr.

—The Collected Letters of Joseph Conrad Vol. 9: Uncollected Letters & Indexes. Davies, Laurence et al, eds. 2008. (Cambridge Edition of the Letters of Joseph Conrad Ser.). (ENG., Illus.). 432p. 150.00 *(978-0-521-88189-0(7))* Cambridge Univ. Pr.

—Notes on Life & Letters. 2008. 208p. 27.99 *(978-0-554-21660-7(4))* 2008. 208p. 24.99 *(978-0-554-30963-7(7))* 2006. 216p. pap. 20.99 *(978-1-4264-0609-6(6))* 2006. (ENG.). 204p. pap. 22.99 *(978-1-4264-0651-5(7))* BiblioBazaar.

—Notes on Life & Letters. reprint ed. lib. bdg. 98.00 *(978-0-7426-2674-4(1))* Classic Bks.

—Notes on Life & Letters. 2007. (ENG.). 196p. per. *(978-1-4065-8520-9(3))* Dodo Pr.

—Notes on Life & Letters. 2008. 148p. pap. *(978-1-4068-9033-4(2))* Echo Library.

—Notes on Life & Letters. 2007. (ENG.). 276p. 39.95 *(978-1-4344-9504-4(3))*; per. 24.95 *(978-1-4344-9503-7(5))* Wildside Pr., LLC.

Cook, Raymond & Jackson, Alan, eds. Faithfully Yours: The Letters of Byron Herbert Reece. 2007. 140p. pap. 17.00 *(978-0-87797-374-4(1))* Cherokee Publishing Co.

Cosgrove, Bryony, ed. Portrait of a Friendship: The Letters of Barbara Blackman & Judith Wright, 1950-2000. 2007. (ENG., Illus.). 752p. 46.00 *(978-0-522-85355-1(2))* Melbourne Univ. Publishing AUS. Dist: Independent Pubs. Group.

Crane-Gartz, Kate. Letters of Protest. Sinclair, Mary Craig, ed. 2011. 154p. 41.95 ***(978-1-258-03112-1(4))*** Literary Licensing, LLC.

Curti, Merle & Burritt, Elihu. The Learned Blacksmith: The Letters & Journals of Elihu Burritt. 2011. 254p. 47.95 ***(978-1-258-04904-1(X))*** Literary Licensing, LLC.

Davies, Russell T. & Cook, Benjamin. The Writer's Tale. 2010. (Illus.). 768p. (YA). 24.99 *(978-1-84607-861-3(X))* Random Hse. GBR. Dist: Diamond Bk. Distributors.

Davis, Richard Harding. Adventures & Letters of Richard Harding Davis. 2008. 304p. 28.99 *(978-0-554-30853-1(3))* 2008. 304p. 29.99 *(978-0-554-21550-1(0))* 2006. (ENG.). pap. 17.99 *(978-1-4264-0392-7(5))* 2006. (ENG.). 314p. pap. 23.99 *(978-1-4264-0341-5(0))* BiblioBazaar.

—Adventures & Letters of Richard Harding Davis. reprint ed. lib. bdg. 48.00 *(978-0-7426-1305-8(4))* Classic Bks.

—Adventures & Letters of Richard Harding Davis. 2006. pap. *(978-1-4065-1135-2(8))* Dodo Pr.

Döring, Detlef, et al, eds. 1731-1733: Unter Einschluss des Briefwechsels von Luise Adelgunde Victorie Gottsched. 2008. (GER.). XLVI, 685p. 335.00 *(978-3-11-020306-6(5))* De Gruyter, Walter Inc.

—1734-1735: Unter Einschluß des Briefwechsels von Luise Adelgunde Victorie Gottsched. 2009. (GER.). XLVIII, 550p. 321.00 *(978-3-11-021561-8(6))* De Gruyter, Walter Inc.

—1736-1737: Unter Einschluß des Briefwechsels von Luise Adelgunde Victorie Gottsched. 2010. (GER.). XLVIII, 674p. 321.00 ***(978-3-11-023292-9(8))*** De Gruyter, Walter Inc.

—1738- Juni 1739: Unter Einschluß des Briefwechsels von Luise Adelgunde Victorie Gottsched. 2011. (GER.). LII, 580p. 321.00 ***(978-3-11-025864-6(1))*** De Gruyter, Walter Inc.

Debord, Guy. Correspondence: The Foundation of the Situationist International (June 1957 - August 1960) Kendall, Stuart & McHale, John, trs. from FRE. 2008. (Semiotext(e) / Foreign Agents Ser.). (ENG.). 400p. (gr. 17). 55.00 *(978-1-58435-063-7(6))*; pap. 19.95 *(978-1-58435-055-2(5))* Semiotexte/Smart Art.

Dick, Philip K. The Selected Letters of Philip K. Dick, 1980-1982. 2010. (ENG.). 288p. 49.95 *(978-1-887424-26-4(1))* Underwood Books.

Dickens, Charles. Charles Dickens's Letters to Charles Lever. Livingston, Flora Virginia, ed. 2011. 82p. 37.95 ***(978-1-258-06870-7(2))*** Literary Licensing, LLC.

—Letters of Charles Dickens: 1833-1870. Hogarth, Georgina & Dickens, Mary, eds. 2011. (Cambridge Library Collection - Literary Studies). (ENG., Illus.). 778p. pap. 50.00 ***(978-1-108-04004-4(7))*** Cambridge Univ. Pr.

—The Selected Letters of Charles Dickens. Hartley, Jenny, ed. 2012. (ENG.). 584p. 34.95 ***(978-0-19-959141-1(5))*** Oxford Univ. Pr., Inc.

Dostoyevsky, Fyodor. Dostoevsky Letters & Reminiscences. 2006. pap. 28.95 *(978-1-4286-5486-0(0))* Kessinger Publishing, LLC.

Draga domnule Rotaru (antiscrisori) 2011. (RUM.). pap. 19.95 *(978-973-7782-88-5(7))* Multimedia Larga.

Dryden, John. The Letters of John Dryden: With Letters Addressed to Him. Ward, Charles E., ed. 2011. 218p. 44.95 ***(978-1-258-04874-7(4))*** Literary Licensing, LLC.

Dufour, A., et al. Theodore de Beze: Correspondance. Tome XXXI 1590. 2009. (Travaux d'Humanisme et Renaissance Ser.). (FRE & LAT., Illus.). 305p. (C). 217.00 *(978-2-600-01277-5(X))* Droz, Librairie CHE. Dist: Brown, David Bk. Co., The.

Durylin, S. N. & Genieva, E. V. "IA Nikomu Tak Ne Pishu, Kak Vam — " Perepiska Sergeia Nikolaevicha Durylina I Eleny Vasilevny Genievoi. 2010. (Illus.). 525p. *(978-5-7380-0283-0(0))* Rudomino, Izdatel'stvo.

Dwight, Marianne & Orvis, Helen Dwight. Letters from Brook Farm, 1844-1847. Reed, Amy Louise, ed. 2011. 220p. 44.95 ***(978-1-258-09496-6(7))*** Literary Licensing, LLC.

Eberwein, Jane Donahue & MacKenzie, Cindy, eds. Reading Emily Dickinson's Letters: Critical Essays. 2009. (Illus.). 304p. 39.95 net. *(978-1-55849-741-2(2))* Univ. of Massachusetts Pr.

Edel, Leon. The Selected Letters of Henry James. 22.95 *(978-0-89190-316-1(X))* Amereon LTD.

Edelman, Marian Wright & Edelman, Marian W. The Sea Is So Wide & My Boat Is So Small: Charting a Course for the Next Generation. 2008. 176p. 19.95 *(978-1-4013-2333-2(2))* Hyperion Pr.

Edward & Brabourne, Lord. Letters of Jane Austen. 2009. 392p. 33.99 *(978-1-115-92024-7(3))*; pap. 33.75 *(978-1-115-92025-4(1))* BiblioBazaar.

—Letters of Jane Austen. 2009. 392p. 38.99 *(978-1-115-92023-0(5))*; pap. 32.75 *(978-1-115-92026-1(X))* BiblioBazaar.

Emerson, Ralph Waldo. Correspondence Between John Sterling and. 2006. pap. 19.95 *(978-1-4286-3641-5(2))* Kessinger Publishing, LLC.

Erasmus, Desiderius. Correspondence of Erasmus. 2011. (Collected Works of Erasmus Ser.). (ENG.). ***(978-1-4426-4203-4(3))*** Univ. of Toronto Pr.

Erasmus, Desiderius, et al. Correspondence of Erasmus, Letters 1802. 2010. (Collected Works of Erasmus Ser.). (Illus.). 624p. *(978-0-8020-9059-1(1))* Univ. of Toronto Pr.

Fages, Pedro & Serra, Junipero. Letters of Captain Don Pedro Fages & President Junipero Serra at San Diego, California in October 1772. 2011. 16p. pap. 35.95 ***(978-1-258-02669-1(4))*** Literary Licensing, LLC.

Fénelon, François & Helms, Hal McElwaine. The Complete Fenelon. Edmonson, Robert, ed. 2008. (Paraclete Giants Ser.). (ENG.). 310p. (gr. 13). pap. 24.95 *(978-1-55725-607-2(1))* Paraclete Pr., Inc.

Fermor, Patrick Leigh, et al. In Tearing Haste: The Letters Between Deborah Devonshire & Patrick Leigh Fermor. Mosley, Charlotte, ed. 2010. (ENG., Illus.). 416p. 30.00 *(978-1-59017-358-9(9))* New York Review of Bks., Inc., The.

Feuchtersleben, Ernst, et al. Sämtliche Werke und Briefe: Kritische Ausgabe. 2006. (Veröffentlichungen zur Literaturwissenschaft Ser.). (GER., Illus.). (C). 114.00 *(978-3-7001-3801-3(6))* Austrian Academy of Sciences Press AUT. Dist: Brown, David Bk. Co., The.

Field, Michael. The Fowl & the Pussycat: Love Letters of Michael Field, 1876-1909. Bickle, Sharon, ed. 2008. (Victorian Literature & Culture Ser.). (ENG., Illus.). 336p. (gr. 17). 49.50 *(978-0-8139-2751-0(X))* Univ. Pr. of Virginia.

Fitzgerald, Edward. Letters of Edward FitzGerald. 2006. pap. 33.95 *(978-1-4286-5337-5(6))*; Vol. 2. pap. 33.95 *(978-1-4286-5338-2(4))* Kessinger Publishing, LLC.

—Letters of Edward FitzGerald, Vol. 1. 2006. 368p. per. (978-1-4067-3540-6(X), Hesperides Pr.) Read Bks.

—More Letters of Edward FitzGerald. 2007. 300p. 43.95 (978-0-548-15627-8(1)); pap. 28.95 (978-1-4304-5090-0(8)) Kessinger Publishing, LLC.

Fitzgerald, F. Scott. The Crack-Up. Wilson, Edmund, ed. 2009. (ENG.). 352p. pap. 15.95 (978-0-8112-1820-7(1), 21820) New Directions Publishing Corp.

Fitzgerald, Penelope. So I Have Thought of You: The Letters of Penelope Fitzgerald. Dooley, Terence, ed. 2010. (ENG., Illus.). 336p. pap. 17.95 (978-0-00-713641-4(2), Fourth Estate) HarperCollins Pubs. Ltd. GBR. Dist: Independent Pubs. Group.

Flammer, Charles. Letters of a Businessman. 2011. 116p. 39.95 (978-1-258-03009-4(8)) Literary Licensing, LLC.

Fonzio, Bartolomeo. Letters to Friends. Daneloni, Alessandro, ed. Davies, Martin, tr. from LAT. 2011. (I Tatti Renaissance Library: 47). (ENG & LAT., Illus.). 256p. 29.95 (978-0-674-05836-1(4)) Harvard Univ. Pr.

Ford, Ronald. Letters of Bernard Shaw to the Times. 2007. 316p. 75.00 (978-0-7165-2918-7(1)); pap. 32.00 (978-0-7165-2919-4(X)) Irish Academic Pr. IRL. Dist: International Specialized Bk. Services.

France, Anatole. On Life & Letters, vols. 4, Set. Date not set. 86.95 (978-0-8369-4977-3(3)) Ayer Co. Pubs., Inc.

Francke, Gotthilf August. Hertzliebe Mama: Briefe aus Jenaer Studientagen 1719-1720. Maller, Thomas et al, eds. (GER.). XIX, 170p. 210.00 (978-3-11-183551-8(0)) De Gruyter, Walter Inc.

Franco, Niccolò & Falardo, Domenica. Epistolario (1540-1548) Ms Vat. Lat. 5642. 2007. (Filibrary: No. 26). (ITA.). 654p. (978-1-893127-26-5(5)) Forum Italicum, Inc.

Franklin, Benjamin. The Papers of Benjamin Franklin Vol. 39: January 21 Through May 15, 1783. Cohn, Ellen R., ed. 2009. (Papers of Benjamin Franklin Ser.). (ENG., Illus.). 752p. 95.00 (978-0-300-13448-3(7)) Yale Univ. Pr.

Frisch, Max & Durrenmatt, Friedrich. Correspondence. 2012. (Seagull Books - the Swiss List Ser.). (ENG., Illus.). 290p. 20.00 (978-1-906497-91-0(5)) Seagull Bks. GBR. Dist: Chicago Distribution Ctr.

Gates, Norman T. Richard Aldington. 2008. pap. 31.95 (978-0-271-02844-6(0)) Pennsylvania State Univ. Pr.

George Sand And Gustave Flaubert. The George Sand-Gustave Flaubert Letters. McKenzie, A. L., tr. 2009. 578p. 26.95 (978-1-60762-049-5(9)); pap. 15.95 (978-1-60762-050-1(2)) Norilana Bks.

Georges Simenon: Itinerary of a Belgian Writer. 2012. (ENG., Illus.). 144p. pap. 38.00 (978-2-87386-768-3(X)) Lannoo Pubs./Racine.

Gibran, Khalil. Love Letters: The Love Letters of Kahlil Gibran to May Ziadah. Bushrui, Suheil & Al-Kuzbari, Salma H., eds. & trs. by. 2008. (ENG., Illus.). 216p. pap. 14.95 (978-1-85168-557-8(X)) Oneworld Pubns. GBR. Dist: National Bk. Network.

Gide, André. Correspondance avec Francis Jammes, 1893-1938. (FRE.). 6.95 (978-0-8288-9776-1(X), F10253) French & European Pubns., Inc.

Gide, Andre, et al. The Correspondence of Andre Gide & Edmund Gosse, 1904-1928. Brugmans, Linette F., ed. 2011. 238p. 46.95 (978-1-258-04391-9(2)) Literary Licensing, LLC.

Glendinning, Victoria, ed. Love's Civil War: Elizabeth Bowen & Charles Ritchie. 2009. (ENG., Illus.). 496p. pap. 19.95 (978-0-7710-3568-5(3), Emblem Edns) McClelland & Stewart CAN. Dist: Random Hse., Inc.

Godwin, William & Clemit, Pamela. Letters of William Goodwin, Vol. 1. 2011. (ENG., Illus.). 368p. 185.00 (978-0-19-956261-9(X)) Oxford Univ. Pr., Inc.

Goldman-Price, Irene, ed. My Dear Governess: The Letters of Edith Wharton to Anna Bahlmann. 2012. (ENG., Illus.). 336p. 30.00 (978-0-300-16989-8(2)) Yale Univ. Pr.

Gottsched, Johann Christoph. Briefwechsel: Unter Einschluss des Briefwechsels Von Luise Adelgunde Victorie Gottsched. 2007. (GER.). LXVIII, 568p. 279.00 (978-3-11-018381-8(1)) De Gruyter, Walter Inc.

Goyen, William. William Goyen: Selected Letters from a Writer's Life. Phillips, Robert, ed. 2011. (ENG., Illus.). 471p. pap. 40.00 (978-0-292-72964-3(2)) Univ. of Texas Pr.

Greacen, Lavinia. J. G. Farrell in His Own Words: Selected Letters & Diaries. 2010. 464p. pap. 24.95 (978-1-85918-476-9(6)) Cork Univ. Pr. IRL. Dist: Stylus Publishing, LLC.

Greene, Graham. Graham Greene: A Life in Letters. Greene, Richard, ed. 2008. (ENG., Illus.). 480p. 35.00 (978-0-393-06642-5(8), 6642) Norton, W. W. & Co., Inc.

Grey, Zane & Grey, Lina Elise. Dolly & Zane Grey: Letters from a Marriage. Kant, Candace C., ed. 2008. (Western Literature Ser.). (ENG., Illus.). 472p. 34.95 (978-0-87417-749-7(9)) Univ. of Nevada Pr.

Gubsky, Nikolai. Angry Dust: An Autobiography. 2011. 426p. 56.95 (978-1-258-01806-1(3)) Literary Licensing, LLC.

Haffenden, John, ed. Selected Letters of William Empson. 2009. (ENG., Illus.). 800p. pap. 55.00 (978-0-19-953986-4(3)) Oxford Univ. Pr., Inc.

Haggerty, George E. Horace Walpole's Letters: Masculinity & Friendship in the Eighteenth Century. 2011. (Transit Series (bucknell Ser.). (ENG.). 186p. 60.00 (978-1-61148-010-8(8)); (978-0-8387-5817-5(7)) Bucknell Univ. Pr.

Harmon, George D. Letters of Luther Rice Mills, a Confederate Soldier: The North Carolina Historical Review, V4, No. 3, July 1927. 2011. 30p. 35.95 (978-1-258-03619-5(3)) Literary Licensing, LLC.

Hamet, Thomas B. Letters of Anne Gilchrist & Walt Whitm. 2006. pap. 28.95 (978-1-4286-5452-5(6)) Kessinger Publishing, LLC.

Harper, Henry Howard. Letters from an Outsider to an Insider. 2011. 128p. 40.95 (978-1-258-03107-7(8)) Literary Licensing, LLC.

Harrison, James Albert. The Last Letters of Edgar Allan Poe to Sarah Helen Whitman. 2008. 68p. pap. 26.45 (978-1-4437-1424-2(0), Kent Pr.) Kent Communications, Ltd.

Härtl, Heinz, ed. Briefwechsel III (1805-1806) 2011. (GER.). 1104p. 308.00 (978-3-11-025069-5(1)) De Gruyter, Walter Inc.

Harwood, Laurence. C. S. Lewis, My Godfather: Letters, Photos & Recollections. 2007. (ENG., Illus.). 148p. 16.00 (978-0-8308-3498-3(2)) InterVarsity Pr.

Hearn, Lafcadio. The Japanese Letters of Lafcadio Hearn. 2009. 78p. pap. (978-0-217-33203-3(X)) Books LLC.

—The Japanese Letters of Lafcadio Hearn. Bisland, Elizabeth, ed. 2007. (ENG.). 522p. 55.95 (978-0-548-15641-4(7)); pap. 40.95 (978-1-4304-5106-8(8)) Kessinger Publishing, LLC.

—Lafcadio Hearn: American Writings. Benfey, Christopher, ed. 2009. (ENG.). 900p. (gr. 12-18). 40.00 (978-1-59853-039-1(9)) Library of America, The.

—Letters from the Raven: Being the Correspondence of Lafcadio Hearn with Henry Watkin. 2009. 216p. 23.99 (978-0-559-93650-0(8)); pap. 17.99 (978-0-559-93646-3(X)) BiblioBazaar.

—Letters from the Raven: Being the Correspondence of Lafcadio Hearn with Henry Watkin. 216p. 2008. 39.95 (978-1-4366-8491-0(9)) 2007. (ENG.). per. 24.95 (978-1-4325-5651-8(7)) Kessinger Publishing, LLC.

—Letters from the Raven: Being the Correspondence of Lafcadio Hearn with Henry Watkin. 2008. 212p. pap. (978-1-4437-1143-2(8)) Read Bks.

—Letters from the Raven: Being the Correspondence of Lafcadio Hearn with Henry Watkin. 2007. 212p. 29.95 (978-1-4344-9560-0(4)); per. 19.95 (978-1-4344-9559-4(0)) Wildside Pr., LLC.

Hemingway, Ernest. The Letters of Ernest Hemingway, 1907-1922, Vol. 1. Spanier, Sandra & Trogdon, Robert W., eds. 2011. (Cambridge Edition of the Letters of Ernest Hemingway Ser.). (ENG., Illus.). 516p. 40.00 (978-0-521-89733-4(5)) Cambridge Univ. Pr.

Hogg, James & Hogg, James. The Collected Letters of James Hogg, 1820-1831, 2 vols., Vol. 2. Hughes, Gillian, ed. 2006. (Collected Works of James Hogg Ser.). (ENG., Illus.). 450p. (gr. 17). 98.00 (978-0-7486-1673-2(X)) Edinburgh Univ. Pr. GBR. Dist: Columbia Univ. Pr.

—The Collected Letters of James Hogg, 1832-1835, vol. 3. Hughes, Gillian, ed. 2008. (Collected Works of James Hogg Ser.). (ENG., Illus.). 450p. (gr. 17). 75.00 (978-0-7486-1675-6(6)) Edinburgh Univ. Pr. GBR. Dist: Columbia Univ. Pr.

Housman, Laurence. The Unexpected Years. 2011. 350p. 51.95 (978-1-258-08316-8(7)) Literary Licensing, LLC.

Howell, James. Certain Letters of James Howell: Selected from the Familiar Letters As First Published Between 1645 And 1655. Walsh, Richard John, ed. 2011. 102p. 39.95 (978-1-258-01951-8(5)) Literary Licensing, LLC.

Humboldt, Wilhelm von. Briefe an Friedrich August Wolf. Mattson, Philip, ed. (GER.). X, 635p. 374.00 (978-3-11-177624-8(7)) De Gruyter, Walter Inc.

Huneker, James. Intimate Letters of James Gibbons Huneker. Huneker, Josephine, ed. 2007. (ENG.). 330p. 45.95 (978-0-548-02502-4(9)) Kessinger Publishing, LLC.

Huxley, Aldous. Aldous Huxley: Selected Letters. Sexton, James, ed. & intro. by. 2007. (ENG., Illus.). 512p. 35.00 (978-1-56663-629-2(9)) Dee, Ivan R. Pub.

Irving, Pierre Munroe. The Life & Letters of Washington Irving. 2009. 452p. 33.99 (978-1-113-79650-9(2)) 2009. 452p. pap. 22.99 (978-1-113-79645-5(6)) 2009. 496p. 35.99 (978-1-113-44313-7(8)) 2009. 496p. pap. 37.75 (978-1-113-44310-6(3)) 2009. 464p. 35.99 (978-1-110-73367-5(4)) 2009. 464p. pap. 36.75 (978-1-110-73365-1(8)) 2008. 452p. 30.99 (978-0-559-31914-3(2)) 2008. 460p. 31.99 (978-0-559-38255-0(3)) 2008. 452p. pap. 35.75 (978-0-559-31912-9(6)) 2008. 460p. pap. 35.75 (978-0-559-38254-3(5)) BiblioBazaar.

—The Life & Letters of Washington Irving. 2009. 236p. pap. (978-1-151-10874-6(X)); 270p. pap. (978-0-217-35417-2(3)) Books LLC.

—The Life & Letters of Washington Irving. 2009. 324p. pap. 22.72 (978-1-150-72675-0(X)); 232p. pap. 20.03 (978-1-151-07206-1(0)); 230p. pap. 19.99 (978-0-217-94174-7(5)); 276p. pap. 21.51 (978-0-217-94177-8(X)); 244p. pap. 20.59 (978-1-4589-2391-2(6)) General Bks. LLC.

—The Life & Letters of Washington Irving. 1. 2007. pap. 36.95 (978-1-4304-5091-7(6)) Vol. 1. 2007. 448p. 51.95 (978-0-548-15628-5(X)) Vol. 3. 2008. 460p. 52.95 (978-1-4366-6519-3(1)) Vol. 3. 2008. 460p. pap. 37.95 (978-0-548-86547-7(7)) Kessinger Publishing, LLC.

—The Life & Letters of Washington Irving, 4 vols., Set. reprint ed. 400.00 (978-0-7950-2344-6(8)) New Library Press LLC.

—The Life & Letters of Washington Irving. 2008. 404p. pap. (978-1-4437-0722-0(8)) 2008. 396p. pap. (978-1-4437-0724-4(4)) 2008. 456p. pap. (978-1-4437-0728-2(7)) 2007. 428p. per. (978-1-4086-2650-4(0)) Read Bks.

—The Life & Letters of Washington Irving by His Nephew, Pierre M. Irving. 2006. 408p. per. 26.99 (978-1-4255-4406-5(1)); 456p. per. 29.99 (978-1-4255-5037-0(1)); (ENG.). 472p. per. 29.99 (978-1-4255-5238-1(2)); (ENG.). 496p. per. 29.99 (978-1-4255-5538-2(1)); (ENG.). 496p. per. 29.99 (978-1-4255-5539-9(X)) MPublishing.

Irving, Pierre Munroe, ed. The Life & Letters of Washington Irving, Vol. 2. 2010. 420p. pap. 34.95 (978-1-120-89676-6(2)) Kessinger Publishing, LLC.

Irving, Washington. Letters of Washington Irving to Henry Brevoort. Hellman, George S., ed. 2006. pap. 42.95 (978-1-4286-5106-7(3)) Kessinger Publishing, LLC.

James, Henry. The Complete Letters of Henry James, 1872-1876, 2 vols. Walker, Pierre A. & Zacharias, Greg W., eds. 2009. (Complete Letters of Henry James Ser.). (ENG., Illus.). Vol. 1. 486p. 125.00 (978-0-8032-2225-0(4)) Vol. 2. 342p. 130.00 (978-0-8032-2297-7(1)) Univ. of Nebraska Pr.

—The Complete Letters of Henry James, 1872-1876: Volume 3. Zacharias, Greg W. & Walker, Pierre A., eds. 2011. (Complete Letters of Henry James Ser.). (ENG., Illus.). 328p. 95.00 (978-0-8032-3457-4(0)) Univ. of Nebraska Pr.

—The Letters of Henry James. 2009. 472p. 35.99 (978-1-110-36321-6(4)); pap. 36.75 (978-1-110-36317-9(6)) BiblioBazaar.

—The Letters of Henry James. Lubbock, Percy, ed. 2008. 544p. 57.95 (978-0-548-99829-8(9)) 2007. (ENG.). 548p. per. 42.95 (978-0-548-64838-4(7)) Kessinger Publishing, LLC.

—The Middle Years. 2008. 128p. 21.99 (978-0-559-73138-9(8)); pap. 19.75 (978-0-559-73135-8(3)) BiblioBazaar.

James, Henry. A Most Unholy Trade: Being Letters on the Drama. 2011. 18p. 35.95 (978-1-258-07286-5(6)) Literary Licensing, LLC.

James, Henry & Mamoli Zorzi, Rosella. Letters to Isabella Stewart Gardner. 2009. (ENG., Illus.). 336p. pap. 17.95 (978-1-901285-83-3(9)) Pushkin Pr., Ltd. GBR. Dist: Consortium Bk. Sales & Distribution.

JEUNE, Pline Le. Lettres - Tome II - Livres IV-VI. Methy, Nicole & Zehnacker, Hubert, eds. 2011. (Collection des universites de France Serie Latine Ser.). (FRE.). 359p. (C). pap. 68.00 (978-2-251-01459-3(4)) Societe d'edition Les Belles lettres FRA. Dist: ISD.

—Lettres, T. 1, livres I a III. Zehnacker, Hubert, ed. 2009. (Collection des universites de France Serie Latine Ser.). (FRE.). 193p. (C). pap. 53.00 (978-2-251-01451-7(9)) Societe d'edition Les Belles lettres FRA. Dist: ISD.

Johnson, Samuel. Letters of Samuel Johnson V1: Oct 30, 1731-Dec 21 1776. Hill, George Birkbeck, ed. 2007. pap. 37.95 (978-1-4304-5101-3(7)) Kessinger Publishing, LLC.

—Selected Letters of Samuel Johnson. 2008. 296p. 43.95 (978-1-4365-2371-4(0)) 2007. (ENG.). 300p. per. 28.95 (978-0-548-73959-4(5)) Kessinger Publishing, LLC.

Johnston, Carolyn. Harmattan, a Wind of Change: Life & Letters from Northern Nigeria at the End of Empire. 2010. (ENG., Illus.). 304p. 55.00 (978-1-84885-143-6(X), Radcliffe Pr., The) I. B. Tauris & Co., Ltd. GBR. Dist: Macmillan.

Joseph, Franklin H. Letters Home from Britain at War 1941. 2011. 106p. 39.95 (978-1-258-02948-7(0)) Literary Licensing, LLC.

Juana Inés de la Cruz, et al. Carta de Sor Juana Inés de la Cruz a Su Confesor: Autodefensa Espiritual. (SPA., Illus.). 253p. (978-968-499-210-8(6)) Autores-Editores.

Kafka, Franz. Dearest Father. Stokes, Hannah & Stokes, Richard, trs. from GER. 2009. (Oneworld Modern Classics Ser.). (ENG.). 128p. pap. 14.95 (978-1-84749-025-4(5)) Alma Classics GBR. Dist: Independent Pubs. Group.

Kant, Candace C., ed. Dolly & Zane Grey: Letters from a Marriage. 2011. (Western Literature Ser.). (ENG., Illus.). 472p. pap. 24.95 (978-0-87417-862-3(2)) Univ. of Nevada Pr.

Kaywell, Joan F. & Kaywell, Joan, eds. Dear Author: Letters of HopeTop Young Adult Authors Respond to Kids' Toughest Issues. 2007. (ENG.). 272p. (YA). (gr. 8-18). 15.99 (978-0-399-23705-8(4), Philomel) Penguin Group (USA) Inc.

Kazantzakis, Nikos. The Selected Letters of Nikos Kazantzakis. 2011. (Princeton Modern Greek Studies). (ENG.). 960p. (C). 99.50 (978-0-691-14702-4(7)) Princeton Univ. Pr.

Keats, John & Mee, Jon. Selected Letters. Gittings, Robert, ed. 2009. (Oxford World's Classics Ser.). (ENG.). 480p. (Orig.). pap. 11.95 (978-0-19-955573-4(7)) Oxford Univ. Pr., Inc.

Kenner, Hugh & Glasheen, Adaline. A Passion for Joyce: The Letters of Hugh Kenner & Adaline Glasheen. Burns, Edward, ed. 2008. (ENG.). 471p. 159.95 (978-1-904558-96-5(8)) Univ. College Dublin Pr. IRL. Dist: Dufour Editions, Inc.

Kerouac, Jack & Ginsberg, Allen S. Jack Kerouac & Allen Ginsberg: The Letters. Morgan, Bill & Stanford, David, eds. (ENG.). 528p. (gr. 12). 2011. 20.00 (978-0-14-311954-8(0), Penguin (Non-Classics)) 2010. 35.00 (978-0-670-02194-9(6), Viking Adult) Penguin Group (USA) Inc.

King, Don W., ed. Out of My Bone: The Letters of Joy Davidman. 2009. (Illus.). 426p. 28.00 (978-0-8028-6399-7(X)) Eerdmans, William B. Publishing Co.

Kingsley, Charles. Charles Kingsley, His Letters, & Memories of His Life. 2007. (ENG.). 444p. 35.00 (978-1-4344-9182-4(X)); (ENG.). 432p. 35.00 (978-1-4344-9181-7(1)); 432p. per. 19.95 (978-1-4344-9087-2(4)); (ENG.). 444p. per. 19.95 (978-1-4344-9088-9(2)) Wildside Pr., LLC.

Kingsley, Charles. Charles Kingsley, his Letters & Memories of his Life. Kingsley, Frances Eliza, ed. 2011. (Cambridge Library Collection - Literary Studies). (ENG.). 518p. pap. 37.99 (978-1-108-03485-2(3)); (Illus.). 522p. pap. 37.99 (978-1-108-03484-5(5)) Cambridge Univ. Pr.

Kipling, Rudyard. Letters of Travel. 2008. 200p. 25.99 (978-0-554-24130-2(7)); 22.99 (978-0-554-33433-2(X)) BiblioBazaar.

—Letters of Travel. 2007. (ENG.). 180p. per. (978-1-4065-2900-5(1)) Dodo Pr.

—Letters of Travel. 2007. (ENG.). 140p. per. (978-1-4068-1910-6(7)) Echo Library.

—Letters of Travel the Dominions Edition Letters of Travel. 2008. 176p. pap. 12.99 (978-1-59547-614-2(8)) NuVision Pubns., LLC.

—O Beloved Kids: Rudyard Kipling's Letters to His Children. Gilbert, Elliot L., ed. 2008. (ENG., Illus.). 240p. 18.95 (978-1-904435-80-8(7)) Little Bks., Ltd. GBR. Dist: Independent Pubs. Group.

Klippert, Zoë, ed. An Englishwoman in California: The Letters of Catherine Hubback, 1871-76. 2010. (Illus.). 240p. 40.00 (978-1-85124-344-0(5)) Bodleian Library GBR. Dist: Chicago Distribution Ctr.

Knowles, Owen, ed. My Dear Friend . Further Letters to & about Joseph Conrad. 2008. 248p. 77.00 (978-90-420-2464-9(X)) Rodopi.

Kurtz, Benjamin P. & Autrey, Carrie C., eds. Four New Letters of Mary Wollstonecraft & Helen M Williams. 2011. 96p. 38.95 (978-1-258-02854-1(9)) Literary Licensing, LLC.

Lamb, Charles. The Best Letters of Charles Lamb. 2008. 328p. 29.99 (978-0-554-23201-0(4)) 2008. 328p. 28.99 (978-0-554-32504-0(7)) 2007. (ENG.). 346p. pap. 24.99 (978-1-4264-3982-7(2)) 2007. (ENG.). 304p. pap. 23.99 (978-1-4264-3952-0(0)) BiblioBazaar.

—The Best Letters of Charles Lamb. Johnson, Edward Gilpin, ed. 2007. 276p. per. (978-1-4065-2577-9(4)) Dodo Pr.

—The Best Letters of Charles Lamb. Johnson, Edward Gilpin, ed. 2007. (ENG.). 336p. 45.95 (978-0-548-15632-2(8)); 340p. per. 30.95 (978-1-4304-5095-5(9)) Kessinger Publishing, LLC.

—Letters of Charles Lamb V1. MacDonald, William, ed. 2007. (ENG.). 476p. 52.95 (978-0-548-14644-6(6)) Kessinger Publishing, LLC.

—Letters of Charles Lamb V1. 2006. (Illus.). pap. 37.95 (978-1-4286-5996-4(X)) Kessinger Publishing, LLC.

—Letters of Charles Lamb V2. MacDonald, William, ed. 2007. (ENG.). 480p. 53.95 (978-0-548-14643-9(8)) Kessinger Publishing, LLC.

—Letters of Charles Lamb V2. 2006. (Illus.). pap. 38.95 (978-1-4286-5995-7(1)) Kessinger Publishing, LLC.

—Miscellaneous Essays. 2009. (ENG.). 280p. pap. 38.99 (978-0-521-10088-5(7)) Cambridge Univ. Pr.

Lamb, Charles & Lamb, Mary. The Letters of Charles & Mary Anne Lamb, 3 vols. Lucas, E. V., ed. reprint ed. (978-0-404-03840-3(9)) AMS Pr., Inc.

Lathrop, Joseph & Pomeroy, Abigail Alexander. The Letters of Joseph Stoddard Lathrop & Abigail Alexander Pomeroy, 1837-1838. 2011. 72p. 36.95 (978-1-258-05017-7(X)) Literary Licensing, LLC.

Le Faye, Deirdre, ed. Jane Austen's Letters. 4th ed. 2011. (ENG., Illus.). 688p. 45.00 (978-0-19-957607-4(6)) Oxford Univ. Pr., Inc.

Levy, Bernard-Henri & Houellebecq, Michel. Public Enemies: Dueling Writers Take on Each Other & the World. Frendo, Miriam & Wyne, Frank, trs. from FRE. 2011. 320p. pap. 17.00 (978-0-8129-8078-3(6), Random Hse. Trade Paperbacks) Random House Publishing Group.

Lewis, C. S. & Calabria, Giovanni. The Latin Letters of C. S. Lewis. Moynihan, Martin, tr. from LAT. 2009. Orig. Title: Letters: A Study in Friendship. 126p. pap. 12.00 (978-1-58731-455-1(X)) St. Augustine's Pr., Inc.

Lindsay, Elizabeth Sherman. Letters of Elizabeth Sherman Lindsay, 1911-1954. James, Olivia, ed. 2011. 276p. 47.95 (978-1-258-02836-7(0)) Literary Licensing, LLC.

Liszt, Franz, et al. The Liszt/D'Agoult Correspondence: English Translations & Commentaries. 2011. (978-1-57647-165-4(9)) Pendragon Pr.

Logan, Deborah A. Harriet Martineau: Further Letters. 2011. (ENG.). 626p. 120.00 (978-1-61146-087-2(5)) Lexington Bks.

Lovecraft, H. P. & Howard, Robert E. A Means to Freedom: The Letters of H. P. Lovecraft & Robert E. Howard. Joshi, S. T. et al, eds. 2011. pap. 55.00 (978-0-9844802-9-6(3)) Hippocampus Pr.

Lowry, Malcolm. The Voyage That Never Ends: Fictions, Poems, Fragments, Letters. Hofmann, Michael, ed. 2007. (ENG., Illus.). 536p. 27.95 (978-1-59017-235-3(3), NYRB Classics) New York Review of Bks., Inc., The.

MacDonald, Edgar E. The Education of the Heart: The Correspondence of Rachel Mordecai Lazarus & Maria Edgeworth. 2011. (ENG.). 364p. pap. 50.00 (978-0-8078-9717-1(5)) Univ. of North Carolina Pr.

Machado, Antonio. Antonio Machado's Cartas de Amor a Pilar de Valderrama/Love Letters to Pilar de Valderrama: A Facing Page Translation from Spanish to English. Aldaz, Anna-Marie, tr. from SPA. 2008. (SPA & ENG.). 280p. 109.95 (978-0-7734-4878-0(0)) Mellen, Edwin Pr., The.

Madden, R. R. The Literary Life & Correspondence of the Countess of Blessington V1. 2008. 558p. 57.95 (978-1-4365-4784-0(9)) 2007. 560p. per. 42.95 (978-0-548-68945-5(8)) Kessinger Publishing, LLC.

Madden, Richard Robert. The Literary Life & Correspondence of the Countess of Blessington R R Madden. 2006. 564p. per. 32.99 (978-1-4255-6174-1(8)); 608p. per. 34.99 (978-1-4255-6483-4(6)) MPublishing.

—The Literary Life & Correspondence of the Countess of Blessington V3. 2007. (ENG.). 522p. 55.95 (978-0-548-17257-5(9)); 524p. per. 40.95 (978-1-4304-7084-7(4)) Kessinger Publishing, LLC.

Manganyi, N. & Attwell, David, eds. Bury Me at the Marketplace: Es¿kia Mphahlele & Company. Letters 1943¿2006. 2010. (ENG.). 496p. pap. 39.95 (978-1-86814-489-1(5)) Witwatersrand Univ. Pr. Pubns. ZAF. Dist: Transaction Pubs.

Mayzel, Nachman, ed. Dos Mendele Buch: Letters & Autobiographical Sketches, Photos, Drawings, Facsimiles of Mendele Meycher Sforim. 2011. 514p. 60.95 (978-1-258-01912-9(4)) Literary Licensing, LLC.

McLoughlin, Kate. Martha Gellhorn: The War Writer in the Field & in the Text. 2007. (ENG., Illus.). 288p. 79.00 (978-0-7190-7636-7(6)) Manchester Univ. Pr. GBR. Dist: Macmillan.

McQueen, Lee. Writer in the Library! 41 Writers Reveal How They Use Libraries to Develop Their Skill, Craft & Careers. McQueen, Lee, ed. 2008. (Illus.). 171p. pap. 9.99 (978-0-9798515-4-4(8)) McQueen Pr.

Melville, Lewis. Lady Mary Wortley Montague: Her Life & Letters (1689-1762) 2007. (ENG.). 276p. pap. 21.99 (978-1-4264-4239-1(4)); 308p. pap. 24.99 (978-1-4264-4303-9(X)) BiblioBazaar.

Meredith, George. The Works of George Meredith: the Egoist V2: a Comedy in Narrative. 2007. pap. 31.95 (978-1-4304-9281-8(3)) Kessinger Publishing, LLC.

Milosz, Czeslaw. Legends of Modernity: Essays & Letters from Occupied Poland, 1942-1943. Levine, Madeline, tr. from POL. 2006. (ENG., Illus.). 288p. per. 14.00 (978-0-374-53046-4(7)) Farrar, Straus & Giroux.

Minnigerode, Meade. Some Personal Letters of Herman Melville. 2006. pap. 24.95 (978-1-4286-3937-9(3)) Kessinger Publishing, LLC.

Mitford, Mary Russell. Recollections of a Literary Life: Or, Books, Places, & People. 2010. (Cambridge Library Collection - Women's Writing Ser.). (ENG.). 314p. pap. 24.99 (978-1-108-02058-9(5)); 340p. pap. 28.99 (978-1-108-02057-2(7)); (ENG.). 308p. pap. 24.99 (978-1-108-02059-6(3)) Cambridge Univ. Pr.

Monroe, Harriet. A Poet's Life: Seventy Years in A Changing World. 2011. 534p. 60.95 (978-1-258-06438-9(3)) Literary Licensing, LLC.

Montagu, Mary Wortley. The Letters & Works of Lady Mary Wortley Montagu. Wharncliffe, James Archibald Stuart-Wortley-Mackenzie & Thomas, William Moy, eds. 2011. (Cambridge Library Collection - Women's Writing Ser.). (ENG.). 552p. pap. 39.99 (978-1-108-07316-5(6)); (Illus.). 544p. pap. 39.99 (978-1-108-07315-8(8)) Cambridge Univ. Pr.

Montague, A. P. Selected Letters of Pliny. 2011. 324p. 50.95 (978-1-258-03942-4(7)) Literary Licensing, LLC.

Moorehead, Caroline. The Collected Letters of Martha Gellhorn. pap. 16.00 (978-0-8050-6556-5(3), Owl Bks.) Holt, Henry & Co.

Morra, Linda M., ed. Corresponding Influence: Selected Letters of Emily Carr & Ira Dilworth. 2008. (ENG., Illus.). 350p. pap. (978-0-8020-9575-6(5)) Univ. of Toronto Pr.

Morris, William. Letters from the Right Honourable Lady Mary Wortley Montagu. 2007. 564p. 32.95 (978-1-4344-8761-2(X)); per. 19.95 (978-1-4344-8760-5(1)) Wildside Pr., LLC.

Mosley, Charlotte. The Mitfords: Letters Between Six Sisters. 2008. (ENG.). 896p. pap. 19.95 (978-0-06-137540-8(3), HarperPerennial) HarperCollins Pubs.

Motley, John Lothrop. The Correspondence of John Lothrop Motley. 2008. 440p. 30.99 (978-0-559-32079-8(5)); pap. 34.75 (978-0-559-32078-1(7)) BiblioBazaar.

—The Correspondence of John Lothrop Motley. 2009. 278p. pap. (978-0-217-75188-9(1)) Books LLC.

Motyer, Arthur, et al. The Staircase Letters: An Extraordinary Friendship at the End of Life. 2008. (ENG.). 160p. pap. 13.95 (978-0-307-35641-3(8), Vintage Canada) Random Hse. of Canada, Ltd. CAN. Dist: Random Hse., Inc.

Murdoch, Iris. Iris Murdoch: A Writer at War - Letters & Diaries, 1939-1945, 1 vol. Conradi, Peter, ed. 2011. (ENG., Illus.). 304p. 35.00 (978-0-19-975603-2(1)) Oxford Univ. Pr., Inc.

Naipaul, V. S. Letters Between a Father & Son. 2011. (Illus.). 480p. pap. (978-0-330-52296-0(5)) Picador.

New, Melvyn & De Voogd, Peter, eds. The Letters of Laurence Sterne, 1739-1764, 8 vols. 2009. (Florida Edition of the Works of Laurence Sterne: Vol. 8, Pt. 1). (ENG., Illus.). 400p. 75.00 (978-0-8130-3236-8(9)) Univ. Pr. of Florida.

New, Melvyn & de Voogd, Peter, eds. The Letters of Laurence Sterne, 1765-1768, 8 vols. 2009. (Florida Edition of the Works of Laurence Sterne: Vol. 8, Pt. 2). (ENG., Illus.). 352p. 75.00 (978-0-8130-3237-5(7)) Univ. Pr. of Florida.

Nicolas, Pasternak, tr. from RUS. Boris Pasternak. 2010. (Hoover Inst press Publication). (ENG.). 419p. 39.00 (978-0-8179-1024-2(7)) Hoover Institution Pr.

Novalis, et al. The Birth of Novalis: Friedrich Von Hardenberg's Journal of 1797, with Selected Letters & Documents. 2007. (Suny Series, Intersections: Philosophy & Critical Theory Ser.). 159p. 26.00 (978-0-7914-6969-9(7)) State Univ. of New York Pr.

Ocampo, Victoria. La Viajera y Sus Sombras: Crónica de un Aprendizaje. 2010. (Tierra Firme Ser.). (SPA.). 289p. pap. 29.99 (978-950-557-845-0(8)) Fondo de Cultura Económica.

O'Connor, Flannery. The Presence of Grace & Other Book Reviews. Martin, Carter W., ed. 2008. (ENG.). 192p. per. 22.95 (978-0-8203-3139-3(2)) Univ. of Georgia Pr.

Oliphant, Mary C. Simms, et al, eds. The Letters of William Gilmore Simms: Volume II, 1845-1849. 2011. (Project of the Simms Initiatives Ser.). (ENG.). 640p. pap. 29.95 (978-1-61117-028-3(1)) Univ. of South Carolina Pr.

—The Letters of William Gilmore Simms: Volume III, 1850-1857. 2011. (Project of the Simms Initiatives Ser.). (ENG.). 592p. pap. 29.95 (978-1-61117-029-0(X)) Univ. of South Carolina Pr.

—The Letters of William Gilmore Simms: Volume IV, 1858-1866. 2011. (Project of the Simms Initiatives Ser.). (ENG.). 672p. pap. 29.95 (978-1-61117-030-6(3)) Univ. of South Carolina Pr.

—The Letters of William Gilmore Simms, 1830-1844, Vol. 5. 2011. (Project of the Simms Initiatives Ser.). (ENG.). 608p. pap. 29.95 (978-1-61117-031-3(1)) Univ. of South Carolina Pr.

—The Letters of William Gilmore Simms, 1867-1870, Vol. I. 2011. (Project of the Simms Initiatives Ser.). (ENG.). 600p. pap. 29.95 (978-1-61117-027-6(3)) Univ. of South Carolina Pr.

Oliphant, Mary C. Simms & Eaves, T. C. Duncan, eds. The Letters of William Gilmore Simms, 1834-1870, Vol. VI. 2011. (Project of the Simms Initiatives Ser.). (ENG.). 458p. pap. 29.95 (978-1-61117-032-0(X)) Univ. of South Carolina Pr.

Oppermann, Irene. Zur Funktion historischer Beispiele in Ciceros Briefen. (Beiträge zur Altertumskunde Ser.). (GER.). 338p. 180.00 (978-3-11-184277-6(0)) De Gruyter, Walter Inc.

Origo, Iris. The Last Attachment: The Story of Byron & Teresa Guiccioli. 560p. 2008. 57.95 (978-1-4367-1608-6(X)) 2007. (ENG.). per. 42.95 (978-1-4325-9479-4(6)) Kessinger Publishing, LLC.

O'Sullivan, Vincent & Scott, Margaret, eds. The Collected Letters of Katherine Mansfield: Volume 5: 1922, 5 vols. 2008. (ENG., Illus.). 400p. 125.00 (978-0-19-818399-0(2)) Oxford Univ. Pr., Inc.

Pasternak, Boris Leonidovich. Boris Pasternak: Family Correspondence, 1921-1960. Slater, Maya, ed. Nicolas, Pasternak, tr. from RUS. 2010. (Hoover Inst press Publication). (ENG.). 419p. pap. 25.00 (978-0-8179-1025-9(5)) Hoover Institution Pr.

Pasternak, Evgenij & Pasternak, Elena, eds. Boris Pasternak - Kurt Wolff - Im Meer der Hingabe. Briefwechsel 1958-1960: unter Mitarbeit von Fedor Poljakov. Mit einem Vorwort von Gerd Ruge. 2010. (Russian Culture in Europe Ser.). (GER.). 208p. pap. 35.95 (978-3-631-58152-0(1)) Lang, Peter GmbH, Europaischer Verlag der Wissenschaften DEU. Dist: Lang, Peter.

Paz Lozano, Octavio. Cartas a Tomás Segovia, 1957-1985. 2008. (Tezontle Ser.). (SPA.). 200p. pap. 14.99 (978-968-16-8576-8(8)) Fondo de Cultura Economica USA.

Paz Lozano, Octavio & Segovia, Tomas. Cartas a Tomas Segovia, 1957-1985. 2008. (Tezontle Ser.). (SPA.). 200p. 21.99 (978-968-16-8575-1(X)) Fondo de Cultura Economica USA.

Petrarca, Francesco. Familiaria: Bucher der Vertraulichkeiten Band 2. Widmer, Berthe, ed. 2009. (GER.). L, 915p. 277.00 (978-3-11-019159-2(8)) De Gruyter, Walter Inc.

Pfeiffer, Kathleen, ed. Brother Mine: The Correspondence of Jean Toomer & Waldo Frank. 2010. (ENG., Illus.). 208p. 45.00 (978-0-252-03540-1(2)) Univ. of Illinois Pr.

Phelps, William L. Autobiography, with Letters. reprint ed. 57.50 (978-0-404-15320-5(8)) AMS Pr., Inc.

Pietralunga, Mark. Cesare Pavese & Antonio Chiuminatto: Their Correspondence. 2007. (Toronto Italian Studies). (ITA & ENG.). 320p. (978-0-8020-9294-6(2)) Univ. of Toronto Pr.

Poe, Edgar Allan, et al. The Letters of Edgar Allan Poe. 3rd ed. 2008. (978-0-87752-247-8(2)); (978-0-87752-246-1(4)); (978-0-87752-248-5(0)) Gordian Pr., The.

Porter, Katherine Anne & Unrue, Darlene Harbour. Selected Letters of Katherine Anne Porter: Chronicles of a Modern Woman. 2012. (ENG., Illus.). 420p. 55.00 (978-1-61703-620-0(X)) Univ. Pr. of Mississippi.

Poteat, Hubert McNeill. Selected Letters of Pliny. 2011. 238p. 46.95 (978-1-258-03943-1(5)) Literary Licensing, LLC.

Puchkoff, Pincus, et al. My Four Homes or Ktayim: Fragments 3, Memoirs. 2011. 236p. 46.95 (978-1-258-09165-1(8)) Literary Licensing, LLC.

Pym, Barbara. A Very Private Eye: An Autobiography in Diaries & Letters. 2007. (Illus.). 380p. (C). reprint ed. pap. 18.95 (978-1-55921-331-8(0)) Moyer Bell.

Richardson, Samuel. The Correspondence of Samuel Richardson. 2009. 106p. pap. 14.14 (978-1-150-09776-8(0)) General Bks. LLC.

—The Correspondence of Samuel Richardson, 6 vols. Barbauld, Anna L., ed. reprint ed. (978-0-404-05300-0(9)) AMS Pr., Inc.

—The Correspondence of Samuel Richardson: Author of Pamela, Clarissa, & Sir Charles Grandison. Barbauld, Anna Laetitia, ed. 2011. (Cambridge Library Collection - Literary Studies). (ENG.). 348p. pap. 28.99 (978-1-108-03412-8(8)); 414p. pap. 31.99 (978-1-108-03407-4(1)); 356p. pap. 29.99 (978-1-108-03408-1(X)); 348p. pap. 28.99 (978-1-108-03409-8(8)); 362p. pap. 29.99 (978-1-108-03411-1(X)); (Illus.). 390p. pap. 31.99 (978-1-108-03410-4(1)) Cambridge Univ. Pr.

—The Correspondence of Samuel Richardson: Selected from the Original Manuscripts, Bequeathed by Him to His Family, to Which Are Prefixed, a Biograp. 2010. 356p. pap. 32.75 (978-1-148-91247-9(9)) BiblioBazaar.

—The Correspondence of Samuel Richardson, Author of Pamela, Clarissa, & Sir Charles Grandison: Selected from the Original Manuscripts, Bequeathed By. 2010. 350p. pap. 32.75 (978-1-143-91271-9(3)); 392p. pap. 33.75 (978-1-142-85205-4(9)) BiblioBazaar.

—The Correspondence of Samuel Richardson, Author of Pamela, Clarissa, & Sir Charles Grandison; Selected from the Original. 2010. 96p. pap. 19.99 (978-1-154-27492-9(6)); pap. 19.99 (978-1-153-98651-9(5)); (Illus.). pap. 19.99 (978-1-154-09080-2(9)) General Bks. LLC.

—The Correspondence of Samuel Richardson; Selected from the Original Manuscripts, Bequeathed by Him to His Family, to Which Are. 2010. (Illus.). 96p. pap. 19.99 (978-1-154-26131-8(X)); 106p. pap. 14.14 (978-1-154-28528-4(6)); 96p. pap. 14.14 (978-1-154-06705-7(X)) General Bks. LLC.

—The Correspondence of Samuel Richardson Selected from the Original Manuscripts, Bequeathed by Him to His Family, to Which Are Prefixed. 2010. 112p. pap. (978-1-152-00628-7(2)) Books LLC.

—The Correspondence of Samuel Richardson Selected from the Original Manuscripts, Bequeathed by Him to His Family, to Which Are Prefixed. 2010. 94p. pap. 20.00 (978-1-155-06203-7(5)); 98p. pap. 20.00 (978-1-152-00711-6(4)) General Bks. LLC.

Richardson, Samuel & Barbauld, (Anna Letitia). The Correspondence of Samuel Richardson Selected from the Original Manuscripts, Bequeathed by Him To. 2009. 342p. 32.99 (978-1-115-26137-1(1)); 36.99 (978-1-115-26138-8(X)); pap. 32.75 (978-1-115-26136-4(3)); pap. 31.75 (978-1-115-26135-7(5)) BiblioBazaar.

Richardson, Samuel & Barbauld, Anna Loetitia. The Correspondence of Samuel Richardson V5: Author of Pamela, Clarissa, & Sir Charles Grandison (1804) 2010. 354p. 37.56 (978-1-165-22285-8(X)); pap. 25.56 (978-1-165-11802-1(5)) Kessinger Publishing, LLC.

Richardson, Samuel & Phillips, Richard. The Correspondence of Samuel Richardson, Author of Pamela, Clarissa, & Sir Charles Grandison: Selected from the Original Manuscripts, Bequeathed By. 2010. 358p. pap. 32.75 (978-1-147-05387-6(1)); 360p. pap. 32.75 (978-1-145-55752-9(X)); 340p. pap. 31.75 (978-1-144-46038-7(7)) BiblioBazaar.

Richter, Ludwig. Der Briefwechsel zwischen Bohuslav Balbín und Christian Weise 1678-1688: Lateinisch-deutsche Ausgabe. Richter, Ludwig, ed. Rautenstrauch, Gunther, tr. from LAT. 2010. (Forschungen zur Geschichte und Kultur des ostlichen Mitteleuropa Ser.). (GER & LAT., Illus.). 339p. (C). 74.00 (978-3-515-09688-1(4)) Steiner, Franz Verlag Wiesbaden GmbH DEU. Dist: Brown, David Bk. Co., The.

Rilke, Rainer Maria. Letters on God & Letters to a Young Woman. Kidder, Annemarie S., tr. from GER. 2012. (ENG.). 88p. pap. 14.95 (978-0-8101-2740-1(7)) Northwestern Univ. Pr.

—Letters to a Young Poet. Snell, Reginald, tr. 2011. Orig. Title: Briefe an Einen Jungen Dichter. 78p. pap. 4.85 (978-1-61427-017-1(1)) Martino Publishing.

Roberts, Arthur W. Cicero Selected Orations & Letters. 2006. pap. 48.95 (978-1-4286-4765-7(1)) Kessinger Publishing, LLC.

Roberts, Michael John. The Letters of Symmachus. 2012. (978-90-04-21163-6(2)) BRILL.

Roberts, S. C. Adventures with Authors. 2010. 288p. pap. 30.99 (978-0-521-13641-9(5)) Cambridge Univ. Pr.

Robinson, Henry C. Diary, Reminiscences, & Correspondence of Henry Crabb Robinson, 2 vols. Sadler, Thomas, ed. reprint ed. 115.00 (978-0-404-05365-9(3)) AMS Pr., Inc.

Roth, Joseph & Hofmann, Michael. Joseph Roth: A Life in Letters. 2012. (ENG.). 512p. 39.95 (978-0-393-06064-5(0), 6064) Norton, W. W. & Co., Inc.

Ruskin, John. John Ruskin's Letters to William Ward: With a Short Biography of William Ward. 2009. 220p. 23.99 (978-1-103-46426-5(4)); pap. 17.99 (978-1-103-46423-4(X)) BiblioBazaar.

Saint-Exupéry, Antoine de. Oeuvres Completes: Lettres a Sa Mere. (Gallimard Ser.). (FRE.). pap. 27.95 (978-2-07-022726-6(X)) Schoenhof's Foreign Bks., Inc.

Salinas, Pedro & Guillén, Jorge. Correspondencia (1923-1951) Soria Olmedo, Andrés, tr. (SPA., Illus.). 638p. (978-84-7223-481-9(9), 6030) Tusquets Editores.

Salter, James & Phelps, Robert. Memorable Days: The Selected Letters of James Salter & Robert Phelps. McIntyre, John, ed. 2010. (ENG.). 224p. 25.00 (978-1-58243-605-0(3), Counterpoint Pr.) Basic Bks. GBR. Dist: Perseus-PGW.

Salzman, Michele Renee, comment. The Letters of Symmachus. 2011. (978-1-58983-597-9(2)); (978-1-58983-598-6(0)) Society of Biblical Literature.

Sand, George & Flaubert, Gustave. The George Sand-Gustave Flaubert Letters. McKenzie, A. L., tr. 2007. 480p. per. (978-1-4065-3854-0(X)) Dodo Pr.

Selzer, Richard. Letters to a Best Friend. Josyph, Peter, ed. 2009. (Excelsior Editions Ser.). (Illus.). 256p. 14.95 (978-1-4384-2721-8(2), Suny Pr.) State Univ. of New York Pr.

Seton, Elizabeth Ann & Code, Joseph B. Letters of Mother Seton to Mrs Julianna Scott. 2011. 490p. 58.95 (978-1-258-03349-1(6)) Literary Licensing, LLC.

Sevigne, Mme De. Correspondance: Juillet 1675 - Septembre 1680, Vol. II. deluxe ed. (Pleiade Ser.). (FRE.). 75.95 (978-2-07-010525-0(3)) Gallimard, Editions FRA. Dist: Schoenhof's Foreign Bks., Inc.

—Correspondance: Mars 1646 - Juillet 1675, Vol. I. (Pleiade Ser.). (FRE.). 73.95 (978-2-07-010524-3(5)) Gallimard, Editions FRA. Dist: Schoenhof's Foreign Bks., Inc.

—Lettres Choisies. (Folio Ser.: No. 1935). (FRE.). 380p. pap. 12.95 (978-2-07-037935-4(3)) Schoenhof's Foreign Bks., Inc.

Shackford, Martha Hale. Letters from Elizabeth Barrett to B R Ha. 2006. pap. 21.95 (978-1-4286-5815-8(7)) Kessinger Publishing, LLC.

Shakespeare, Nicholas, et al. Under the Sun: The Letters of Bruce Chatwin. 2010. (Illus.). 560p. (978-0-224-08989-0(7), Jonathan Cape) Random Hse.

Sharpe, Charles Kirkpatrick. Letters from & to Charles Kirkpatrick Sharpe Esq. Allardyce, Alexander, ed. 2011. (Illus.). 618p. pap. (978-1-84921-065-2(9)); 648p. pap. (978-1-84921-066-9(7)) Kennedy & Boyd.

Sharps, John Geoffrey & Chapple, J. A. V., eds. Elizabeth Gaskell: Portrait in Letters. 2nd rev. ed. 2008. (ENG., Illus.). 192p. pap. 26.00 (978-0-7190-7789-0(3)) Manchester Univ. Pr. GBR. Dist: Macmillan.

Sheldon, Julie, ed. The Letters of Elizabeth Rigby, Lady Eastlake. 2009. (ENG.). 608p. 99.95 (978-1-84631-194-9(2)) Liverpool Univ. Pr. GBR. Dist: Chicago Distribution Ctr.

Shelford, April G. Transforming the Republic of Letters: Pierre-Daniel Huet & European Intellectual Life, 1650-1720. 2007. (Changing Perspectives on Early Modern Europe Ser.: Volume 7). (Illus.). 275p. 75.00 (978-1-58046-243-3(X)) Univ. of Rochester Pr.

Shelley, Mary Wollstonecraft. History of a Six Weeks' Tour Through a Part of France, Switzerland, Germany & Holland: With Letter. 2009. 196p. pap. 16.99 (978-1-103-20109-9(3)) BiblioBazaar.

Shrubsall, Dennis, ed. The Unpublished Letters of W. H. Hudson, the First Literary Environmentalist 1841-1922, 2 vols., Vol. 1. 2006. 384p. (978-0-7734-5573-3(6)) Mellen, Edwin Pr., The.

Shrubsall, Dennis, ed. & compiled by. The Unpublished Letters of W. H. Hudson, the First Literary Environmentalist 1841-1922, 2 vols., Vol. 2. 2006. 492p. (978-0-7734-5575-7(2)) Mellen, Edwin Pr., The.

Siddiqi, Naim & Elahi, Maqbool. Pacpan Salah Murasalat Ke Cand Nuqush. 2010. (URD.). 160p. (978-969-503-797-3(6)) Al-Faisal Nashran Tajran.

Slivon, Fred P., Jr. & Albert, Frants. The Next Will Be Better: A Correspondence. 2008. (Illus.). 248p. pap. 14.00 (978-0-9815269-0-4(X)) Paper Mill Pr.

Sliwa, Krzysztof. Cartas, documentos y escrituras del Dr. Frey Lope Félix de Vega Carpio(1562-1635), 2 vols., Vol. 12. 2007. (SPA., Illus.). 890p. pap. 49.95 (978-1-58871-116-8(1), SLIWA, Juan de la Cuesta-Hispanic Monographs) LinguaText, Ltd.

Smith, Constance Babington & Macaulay, Rose. Letters to a Friend. 2012. 336p. pap. (978-1-4482-0422-9(4), 145950, Bloomsbury Reader) Bloomsbury Publishing Plc.

Smith, Harry B., ed. The Dickens-Kolle Letters. 2007. (ENG.). 114p. 34.95 (978-0-548-00750-1(0)) Kessinger Publishing, LLC.

Smith, Martin Ferguson. Dearest Jean: Rose Macaulay's Letters to a Cousin. 2011. (ENG., Illus.). 400p. 90.00 (978-0-7190-8521-5(7)) Manchester Univ. Pr. GBR. Dist: Macmillan.

Smith, Morton & Scholem, Gershom Gerhard. Morton Smith & Gershom Scholem, Correspondence, 1945-1982. 2008. (Jerusalem Studies in Religion & Culture Ser.: Vol. 9). 204p. (978-90-04-16839-8(7)) BRILL.

Smith, Nicholas D. The Literary Manuscripts & Letters of Hannah More. 2008. (Illus.). 230p. 114.95 (978-0-7546-6270-9(5)) Ashgate Publishing Co.

Smollett, Tobias George. The Letters of Tobias Smollett. Noyes, Edward S., ed. 2011. 282p. 47.95 (978-1-258-04533-3(8)) Literary Licensing, LLC.

St. Helier, Susan M. Memories of Fifty Years. 358p. reprint ed. 98.00 (978-0-7222-1746-7(3)) Library Reprints, Inc.

Stadler. Gunta Stolzl Bauhaus Master. 2009. (978-3-7757-2417-3(6)) Museum of Modern Art.

Stael, Madame de. 1788-1791, Tome I, Pt. 2. Jasinski, ed. 20.95 (978-0-8288-9661-0(5), F73291) French & European Pubns., Inc.

—Lettres de Jeunesse de 1777 a Aout, 1788, Tome I, Pt. 1. Jasinski, ed. 20.95 (978-0-8288-9660-3(7), F73290) French & European Pubns., Inc.

—Lettres de Mezery et de Coppet (16 Mai 1794-16 Mai 1795), Tome III, Pt. 1. Jasinski, ed. 27.95 (978-0-8288-9664-1(X), F73294) French & European Pubns., Inc.

—Lettres Diverses de 1792 a Mai 1794, Tome II, Pt. 2. Jasinski, ed. 31.95 (978-0-8288-9663-4(1), F73293) French & European Pubns., Inc.

—Lettres d'une Nouvelle Republicaine, Tome III, Pt. 2. Jasinski, ed. 39.95 (978-0-8288-9665-8(8), F73295) French & European Pubns., Inc.

—Lettres Inedites a Louis de Norbonne, Tome II, Pt. 1. Jasinski, ed. 26.95 (978-0-8288-9662-7(3), F73292) French & European Pubns., Inc.

Stanhope, Philip Dormer. The Letters of Philip Dormer Stanhope, Earl of Chesterfield V2. Mahon, Lord, ed. 2007. (ENG.). 490p. 53.95 (978-0-548-15631-5(X)); 492p. per. 38.95 (978-1-4304-5094-8(0)) Kessinger Publishing, LLC.

Stashower, Daniel, et al. Arthur Conan Doyle: A Life in Letters. 2008. (ENG.). 720p. (gr. 12-18). 18.00 (978-0-14-311433-8(6), Penguin (Non-Classics)) Penguin Group (USA) Inc.

Stegner, Page, ed. The Selected Letters of Wallace Stegner. 2007. (ENG.). 480p. 30.00 (978-1-59376-168-4(6)) Counterpoint LLC.

Stegner, Wallace. The Selected Letters of Wallace Stegner. Stegner, Page, ed. 2008. (ENG.). 480p. pap. 16.95 (978-1-58243-446-9(8), Counterpoint Pr.) Basic Bks. GBR. Dist: Perseus-PGW.

Stein, Gertrude & Picasso, Pablo. Correspondence: Pablo Picasso & Gertrude Stein. Madeline, Laurence, ed. Fox, Lorna Scott, tr. from FRE. 2008. (S3-the French List Ser.). (ENG., Illus.). 390p. 29.95 (978-1-905422-91-3(1)) Seagull Bks. GBR. Dist: Chicago Distribution Ctr.

Stendhal. Letters to Pauline. Brown, Andrew & Lewis, Sophie, trs. from FRE. 2011. (Hesperus Classics Ser.). (ENG.). 166p. pap. 15.95 (978-1-84391-167-8(1)) Hesperus Pr. GBR. Dist: Independent Pubs. Group.

Stevenson, Robert Louis. Vailima Letters. 2008. 224p. 27.99 (978-0-554-21808-3(9)) 2008. 224p. 24.99 (978-0-554-31111-1(9)) 2006. (ENG.). 224p. pap. 20.99 (978-1-4264-0953-0(2)) 2006. (ENG.). 220p. pap. 22.99 (978-1-4264-1004-8(2)) BiblioBazaar.

—Vailima Letters. 2007. (ENG.). 208p. per. (978-1-4065-8229-1(8)) Dodo Pr.

Stölzl, Gunta, et al. Gunta Stölzl: Bauhaus-Meister. 2009. (Illus.). 123p. (978-3-7757-2371-8(4)) Museum of Modern Art.

Stouck, Jordan, et al, eds. Collecting Stamps Would Have Been More Fun: Canadian Publishing & the Correspondence of Sinclair Ross, 1933-1986. 2010. (ENG., Illus.). 344p. pap. 34.95 (978-0-88864-521-0(X)) Univ. of Alberta Pr. CAN. Dist: Michigan State Univ. Pr.

Tolstoy, Leo. Last Steps: The Late Writings of Leo Tolstoy. Parini, Jay, ed. & tr. by. from RUS. 2009. (ENG.). 256p. (gr. 12-18). pap. 14.00 (978-0-14-119119-5(8), Penguin Classics) Penguin Group (USA) Inc.

—Tolstois Love Letters with A Study on Th. 2006. pap. 20.95 (978-1-4286-5963-6(3)) Kessinger Publishing, LLC.

Tooze, George H. The Life & Letters of Emily Chubbic Judson: Volume 1. 2009. 304p. 60.00 (978-0-88146-131-2(8)) Mercer Univ. Pr.

—The Life & Letters of Emily Chubbic Judson: Volume 2. 2009. (Illus.). 304p. 60.00 (978-0-88146-149-7(0)) Mercer Univ. Pr.

Töpffer, Rodolphe, et al. Correspondance Complète. 2009. (HISTOIRE des IDeES et CRITIQUE LITTeRAIRE Ser.). (FRE., Illus.). 528p. (C). pap. 96.00 (978-2-600-01296-6(6)) Droz, Librairie CHE. Dist: Brown, David Bk. Co., The.

Traubel, Horace. With Walt Whitman in Camden. 2009. 132p. pap. (978-1-4539-5059-8(X)) Books LLC.

Twain, Mark, pseud. Complete Letters of Mark Twain. 2009. 424p. 27.99 (978-0-559-12053-4(2)); 512p. 32.99 (978-0-559-12020-6(6)); 512p. 35.99 (978-0-559-12002-2(8)); 424p. 32.99 (978-0-559-12040-4(0)); 424p. pap. 34.75 (978-0-559-12045-9(1)); 424p. pap. 33.75 (978-0-559-12050-3(8)); 512p. pap. 38.75 (978-0-559-12014-5(1)); 512p. pap. 30.99 (978-0-559-12009-1(5)) BiblioBazaar.

—The Complete Letters of Mark Twain. 2007. 548p. per. *(978-1-4068-2314-1(7))* Echo Library.

—Complete Letters of Mark Twain. 2008. Vol. 1. 332p. pap. *(978-1-4065-7116-5(4))* Vol. 2. 440p. pap. *(978-1-4065-7117-2(2))* Dodo Pr.

Tyrrell, Robert Yelvert. Cicero in His Letters. 2006. pap. 37.95 *(978-1-4286-3991-1(8))* Kessinger Publishing, LLC.

Volponi, Paolo, et al. Scrivo a Te Come Guardandomi Allo Specchio: Lettere a Pasolini (1954-1975) 2009. (Diaspro Ser.). (ITA.). 214p. (C). 29.50 *(978-88-596-0510-2(5))* Edizioni Polistampa ITA. Dist: Brown, David Bk. Co., The.

Voltaire, Francois, pseud. Correspondance: 1704-1738. Besterman, ed. (Pleiade Ser.). 65.95 *(978-2-07-010928-9(3))* Schoenhof's Foreign Bks., Inc.

—Correspondance: 1739-1748. Besterman, ed. (Pleiade Ser.). 65.95 *(978-2-07-010929-6(1))* Schoenhof's Foreign Bks., Inc.

—Correspondance: 1749-1753, Vol. 3. Besterman, ed. (Pleiade Ser.). 61.95 *(978-2-07-010807-7(4))* Schoenhof's Foreign Bks., Inc.

—Correspondance: 1754-1757, Vol. 4. Besterman, ed. (Pleiade Ser.). 65.05 *(978-2-07-010819-0(8))* Schoenhof's Foreign Bks., Inc.

Wachtel, Eleanor. Random Illuminations: Conversations with Carol Shields. 2007. (ENG.). 184p. pap. 19.95 *(978-0-86492-501-5(8))* Goose Lane Editions CAN. Dist: Univ. of Toronto Pr.

Wakefield, Eva I. The Letters of Robert G. Ingersoll. *(978-0-8022-1792-9(3))* Philosophical Library, Inc.

Walpole, Horace. The Letters of Horace Walpole. 2009. 218p. pap. *(978-0-217-95659-8(9))*; 218p. pap. *(978-0-217-12144-6(6))*; 496p. pap. *(978-0-217-08931-9(3))*; 56p. pap. *(978-1-4589-2270-0(7))*; 132p. pap. *(978-1-4589-2271-7(5))*; 58p. pap. *(978-1-4589-2273-1(1))*; 66p. pap. *(978-1-4589-7947-6(4))*; 554p. pap. *(978-1-4589-7950-6(4))*; 60p. pap. *(978-0-217-39245-7(8))*; 120p. pap. *(978-0-217-94105-1(2))*; 60p. pap. *(978-0-217-94107-5(9))*; 60p. pap. *(978-0-217-94108-2(7))* Books LLC.

—The Letters of Horace Walpole. 2009. 504p. pap. 29.13 *(978-0-217-39244-0(X))* General Bks. LLC.

Warren, Robert Penn. Selected Letters of Robert Penn Warren; Volume Four: New Beginnings & New Directions, 1953-1968. Hendricks, Randy & Perkins, James A., eds. 2008. (Southern Literary Studies). 589p. 65.00 *(978-0-8071-3300-2(0))* Louisiana State Univ. Pr.

Waugh, Evelyn, et al. A Bitter Trial: Evelyn Waugh & John Carmel Cardinal Heenan on the Liturgical Changes. 2011. 123p. ***(978-1-58617-522-1(X))*** Ignatius Pr.

Wharncliffe, Lord. Letters & Works of Lady Mary Wortley M. 2006. pap. 36.95 *(978-1-4286-4229-4(3))*; pap. 33.95 *(978-1-4286-4230-0(7))* Kessinger Publishing, LLC.

White, E. B. Letters of E. B. White. Guth, Dorothy Lobrano, ed. 2007. (ENG.). 768p. pap. 19.95 *(978-0-06-137459-3(8)*, HarperPerennial) HarperCollins Pubs.

Wilcox, Amanda. The Gift of Correspondence in Classical Rome: Friendship in Cicero's Ad Familiares & Seneca's Moral Epistles. 2012. E-Book ***(978-0-299-28833-4(1))***; (ENG.). 216p. pap. 34.95 ***(978-0-299-28834-1(X))*** Univ. of Wisconsin Pr.

Wilde, Oscar. Cartas a Lord Alfred Douglas. (SPA.). *(978-84-7223-096-5(1)*, 6030) Tusquets Editores.

—De Profundis. 2006. 108p. per. 9.95 *(978-1-59818-905-6(0))*; 22.95 *(978-1-59818-273-6(0))* Aegypan.

—De Profundis. 2009. 136p. 24.99 *(978-1-110-83953-7(7))*; 136p. pap. 19.75 *(978-1-110-83950-6(2))*; 176p. 22.99 *(978-1-103-76890-5(5))*; 176p. pap. 16.99 *(978-1-103-76883-7(2))* BiblioBazaar.

—De Profundis. reprint ed. lib. bdg. 98.00 *(978-0-7812-7903-1(8))* Classic Bks.

—De Profundis. 2008. (Clasicos de la literatura Ser.). (SPA.). 203p. pap. 5.95 *(978-84-9764-363-4(1))* Edimat Libros, S. A. ESP. Dist: Independent Pubs. Group.

—De Profundis. 2007. pap. 4.99 *(978-1-59986-662-8(5))* Filiquarian Publishing, LLC.

—De Profundis. 2008. 164p. pap. *(978-1-4097-1199-5(4))* Read Bks.

—De Profundis. 2007. 72p. per. *(978-1-59462-821-4(1)*, Book Jungle) Standard Pubns., Inc.

—De Profundis - Oscar Wilde. 2007. (ENG.). 72p. pap. 9.45 *(978-1-60424-462-5(3))*; per. 8.95 *(978-1-60424-128-0(4))* Standard Pubns., Inc. (Book Jungle).

Wilder, Thornton, et al. The Selected Letters of Thornton Wilder. 2009. (ENG.). 768p. pap. 19.99 *(978-0-06-076508-8(9)*, HarperPerennial) HarperCollins Pubs.

Williams, John, ed. Dear Chester, Dear John: Letters Between Chester Hines & John A. Williams. 2008. 256p. 24.95 *(978-0-8143-3359-4(1))* Wayne State Univ. Pr.

Williams, John A., ed. Dear Chester, Dear John: Letters Between Chester Hines & John A. Williams. 2008. (African American Life Ser.). (Illus.). 241p. 24.95 *(978-0-8143-3355-6(9))* Wayne State Univ. Pr.

Williams, William Carlos & Krivak, Andrew. The Letters of William Carlos Williams to Edgar Irving Williams, 1902-1912. 2009. (Illus.). 400p. 65.00 *(978-0-8386-4148-4(2))* Fairleigh Dickinson Univ. Pr.

Wolfe, Thomas. Windows of the Heart: The Correspondence of Thomas Wolfe & Margaret Roberts. 2007. (Illus.). 201p. 34.95 *(978-1-57003-674-3(8))* Univ. of South Carolina Pr.

Wollstonecraft, Mary. Letters Written During a Short Residence in Sweden, Norway & Denmark. 2010. 88p. pap. 20.00 *(978-1-152-37474-4(5))* General Bks. LLC.

—Letters Written During a Short Residence in Sweden, Norway, & Denmark. 2010. 284p. pap. 28.75 *(978-1-144-26869-3(9))* BiblioBazaar.

—Letters Written During a Short Residence in Sweden, Norway, & Denmark. 2009. 102p. pap. *(978-1-151-44237-6(2))* Books LLC.

—Letters Written during a Short Residence in Sweden, Norway, & Denmark. 2010. (Cambridge Library Collection - Women's Writing Ser.). (ENG.). 276p. pap. 23.99 *(978-1-108-01889-0(0))* Cambridge Univ. Pr.

—Letters Written During a Short Residence in Sweden, Norway, & Denmark. 2010. (ENG.). 196p. pap. 23.75 *(978-1-177-64555-3(6))* BiblioBazaar.

—Letters Written During a Short Residence in Sweden, Norway & Denmark. 2011. 276p. pap. 27.75 ***(978-1-178-88885-0(1))*** BiblioBazaar.

—Letters Written During a Short Residence in Sweden, Norway & Denmark. 2010. 196p. 30.36 ***(978-1-164-25960-2(1))***; pap. 18.36 ***(978-1-164-06069-7(4))*** Kessinger Publishing, LLC.

Wollstonecraft, Mary. Letters Written During a Short Residence in Sweden, Norway & Denmark. reprint ed. lib. bdg. 98.00 *(978-0-7426-2148-0(0))* Classic Bks.

Wollstonecraft, Mary, et al. Letters written in Sweden, Norway, & Denmark. 2009. (Oxford World's Classics Ser.). (ENG., Illus.). 256p. pap. 16.95 *(978-0-19-923063-1(3))* Oxford Univ. Pr., Inc.

Woodberry, George Edward. Selected Letters of George Edward Woodberry. 2011. 310p. 48.95 ***(978-1-258-04339-1(4))*** Literary Licensing, LLC.

Woodsford, Frances. Dear Mr Bigelow: A Transatlantic Friendship. 2009. (ENG., Illus.). 400p. 29.95 *(978-0-7011-8480-3(9))* Random Hse. GBR. Dist: Independent Pubs. Group.

Woolley, David, ed. The Correspondence of Jonathan Swift, D. D. Nos. 1101-1508: Letters 1734-1745,, 4 vols., Vol. 3. 2007. (Illus.). 674p. 86.95 *(978-0-8204-3548-0(1))* Lang, Peter Publishing, Inc.

Wright, William Aldis. Letters & Literary Remains of Edward F. 2006. pap. 38.95 *(978-1-4286-3903-4(9))*; pap. 38.95 *(978-1-4286-3904-1(7))*; pap. 40.95 *(978-1-4286-3905-8(5))* Kessinger Publishing, LLC.

Xavier, M. Woman's Whims; or, the Female Barometer Tr from the French of X B Saintine by Fayette Robinson. 2006. 100p. per. 16.99 *(978-1-4255-0706-0(9))* MPublishing.

Xu, Xueji & Zhong, Shumin. Yang Yunping Wen Shu Zi Liao Hui Bian Mu Lu. 2008. (CHI., Illus.). viii, 317p. *(978-986-01-4879-4(1))* Hualien County Hacc.

Zeikowitz, Richard E. Letters Between Forster & Isherwood on Homosexuality & Literature. 2008. (ENG., Illus.). 208p. 89.00 *(978-0-230-60675-3(X))* Palgrave Macmillan.

AUTHORS—HOMES AND HAUNTS

see Literary Landmarks

AUTHORS—JUVENILE LITERATURE

Herron, Carolivia. Always an Olivia: A Remarkable Family History. 2012. (Jewish Identity Ser.). (Illus.). 32p. (J). (gr. 2-4). pap. 9.95 ***(978-0-7613-9100-5(2)**, Kar-Ben Publishing)* Lerner Publishing Group.

Johnson, Claudia Durst. Social & Psychological Disorder in the Works of Edgar Allan Poe. 2010. (Social Issues in Literature Ser.). (ENG., Illus.). 168p. 38.45 *(978-0-7377-5016-4(2)*, Greenhaven Pr., Inc.) Cengage Gale.

AUTHORS—LEGAL STATUS, LAWS, ETC.

Adeney, Elizabeth. The Moral Rights of Authors. 2nd rev. ed. 2006. (ENG.). 968p. 493.75 *(978-0-19-928474-0(1))* Oxford Univ. Pr., Inc.

Kwall, Roberta. The Soul of Creativity: Forging a Moral Rights Law for the United States. 2009. (ENG.). 272p. 70.00 *(978-0-8047-5643-3(0))*; pap. 24.95 *(978-0-8047-6367-7(4))* Stanford Univ. Pr.

Speth, Maria Crimi. Protect Your Writings: A Legal Guide for Authors. 2010. 112p. 22.95 *(978-1-4502-4365-0(7))*; pap. 12.95 *(978-1-4502-4364-3(9))* iUniverse, Inc.

AUTHORS—PSYCHOLOGY

Bridge, Marie, ed. On the Way Home: Conversations Between Writers & Psychoanalysts. 2007. 156p. 28.95 *(978-1-85575-472-0(X))* Karnac Bks. GBR. Dist: Stylus Publishing, LLC.

Carpenter, Edward & Barnefield, George. The Psychology of the Poet Shelley. 128p. 2008. 35.95 *(978-1-4366-7628-1(2))* 2007. (ENG.). per. 20.95 *(978-1-4325-6862-7(0))* Kessinger Publishing, LLC.

Davis, Jeff. Journey from the Center to the Page. 2nd ed. 2008. (ENG., Illus.). 320p. pap. 16.00 *(978-0-9766843-8-1(1))* Monkfish Bk. Publishing Co.

DiBattista, Maria. Imagining Virginia Woolf: An Experiment in Critical Biography. 2008. (ENG.). 208p. (C). 21.95 *(978-0-691-13812-1(5))* Princeton Univ. Pr.

Djos, Matts G. Writing under the Influence: Alcoholism & the Alcoholic Perception from Hemingway to Berryman. 2010. (ENG.). 188p. 79.00 *(978-0-230-10260-6(3))* Palgrave Macmillan.

Harley, Thomas. Matthew Poole: His Life, His Times, His Contributions along with His Argument against the Infallibility of the Roman Catholic Church. 2009. 232p. 28.95 *(978-1-4401-1607-0(5))* iUniverse, Inc.

Kleefeld, Gunther. Das Gedicht Als Sühne: Georg Trakls Dichtung und Krankheit eine Psychoanalytische Studie. (Studien zur deutschen Literatur Ser.). (GER.). VII, 408p. 195.00 ***(978-3-11-184971-3(6))*** De Gruyter, Walter Inc.

Miller, Alice. The Body Never Lies: The Lingering Effects of Hurtful Parenting. Jenkins, Andrew, tr. from GER. 2006. (ENG.). 224p. per. 15.95 *(978-0-393-32863-9(5)*, 32863) Norton, W. W. & Co., Inc.

Millier, Brett Candlish. Flawed Light: American Women Poets & Alcohol. 2009. (ENG.). 168p. 40.00 *(978-0-252-03461-9(9))* Univ. of Illinois Pr.

Milner, Marion. Bothered by Alligators. 2012. (ENG., Illus.). 296p. 90.00 *(978-0-415-68455-2(2))*; pap. 26.99 *(978-0-415-68456-9(0))* Routledge.

Morrison, Delmont & Morrison, Shirley Linden. Memories of Loss & Dreams of Perfection: Unsuccessful Childhood Grieving & Adult Creativity. Sheikh, Anees A., ed. (Imagery & Human Development Ser.). 156p. 35.95 *(978-0-89503-309-3(7))* Baywood Publishing Co., Inc.

Nemeth, Alexander J. Voltaire's Tormented Soul: A Psychobiographic Inquiry. 2008. 359p. 60.00 *(978-0-934223-92-8(0))* Lehigh Univ. Pr.

Sanborn, Frank B. Personality of Thoreau. 2006. pap. 18.95 *(978-1-4286-4774-9(0))* Kessinger Publishing, LLC.

Underwood, Doug. Chronicling Trauma: Journalists & Writers on Violence & Loss. 2011. (History of Communication Ser.). (ENG., Illus.). 264p. 50.00 ***(978-0-252-03640-8(9))*** Univ. of Illinois Pr.

AUTHORS—RELATIONS WITH WOMEN

Bullen, Daniel. The Love Lives of the Artists: Five Stories of Creative Intimacy. 2011. (ENG., Illus.). 336p. 28.00 *(978-1-58243-775-0(0)*, Counterpoint) Counterpoint LLC.

Ellroy, James. The Hilliker Curse: My Pursuit of Women. 2010. (ENG.). 224p. 24.95 *(978-0-307-59350-4(9)*, Knopf) Knopf Doubleday Publishing Group.

Freeman, Judith. The Long Embrace: Raymond Chandler & the Woman He Loved. 2008. (Vintage Ser.). (ENG., Illus.). 368p. pap. 14.95 *(978-1-4000-9517-9(4)*, Vintage) Knopf Doubleday Publishing Group.

Meyers, Jeffrey. The Genius & the Goddess: Arthur Miller & Marilyn Monroe. 2010. (ENG., Illus.). 384p. 29.95 *(978-0-252-03544-9(5))* Univ. of Illinois Pr.

Roiphe, Katie. Uncommon Arrangements: Seven Marriages. 2008. 352p. pap. 15.00 *(978-0-385-33938-4(0)*, Dial Pr.) Random House Publishing Group.

Rumbold, Valerie. Women's Place in Pope's World. 2006. (Cambridge Studies in Eighteenth-Century English Literature & Thought Ser.). (ENG.). 336p. (C). pap. 69.00 *(978-0-521-02672-7(5))* Cambridge Univ. Pr.

Sensibar, Judith L. Faulkner & Love: The Women Who Shaped His Art, a Biography. (ENG., Illus.). 616p. 2010. pap. 28.00 *(978-0-300-16568-5(4))* 2009. 40.00 *(978-0-300-11503-1(2))* Yale Univ. Pr.

Spoto, Donald. Spellbound by Beauty: Alfred Hitchcock & His Leading Ladies. 2009. (ENG., Illus.). 352p. pap. 16.00 *(978-0-307-35131-9(9)*, Three Rivers Pr.) Crown Publishing Group.

Szalczer, Eszter. Sunflowers: Wall Calendar 2001. 2009. (ENG., Illus.). 254p. pap. 41.95 *(978-1-870041-70-6(4))* Norvik Pr. GBR. Dist: Dufour Editions, Inc.

AUTHORS—WIVES

see Authors' Spouses

AUTHORS, AFRICAN

Aluko, T. M. The Story of My Life. 2006. 372p. pap. *(978-978-129-464-8(7))* Heinemann Educational Bks. (Nigeria), Ltd. NGA. Dist: Michigan State Univ. Pr.

Azodo, Ada Uzoamaka. Emerging Perspectives on Aminata Sow Fall: The Real & the Imaginary in Her Novels. 2007. *(978-1-59221-556-0(4))* Africa World Pr.

Carter, David. Marquis de Sade. 2011. (Brief Lives Ser.). (ENG.). 120p. pap. 15.95 *(978-1-84391-917-9(6))* Hesperus Pr. GBR. Dist: Independent Pubs. Group.

Chewe, Derrick. My Life. 2010. (Illus.). 180p. pap. 14.49 *(978-1-4520-0357-3(2))* AuthorHouse.

Choukri, Mohamed. In Tangier: Paul Bowles, Jean Genet, Tennessee Williams. Bowles, Paul et al, trs. from ARA. 2010. (ENG.). 320p. pap. 15.95 *(978-1-84659-061-0(2))* Telegram Bks. GBR. Dist: Consortium Bk. Sales & Distribution.

Djebar, Assia. Blanc de l Algerie. pap. 16.95 *(978-2-253-15340-5(0))* Librairie Generale Francaise, LGF FRA. Dist: Distribooks, Inc.

—Le Blanc de L'Algérie: Récit. (FRE.). 279p. *(978-2-226-08457-6(6)*, Branch Line Video) Albin-Michel, Editions.

El Saadawi, Nawal. A Daughter of Isis: The Autobiography of Nawal el Saadawi. 2nd ed. 2009. (ENG., Illus.). 400p. 120.95 *(978-1-84813-231-3(X))* Zed Bks., Ltd. GBR. Dist: Macmillan.

—Walking Through Fire: A Life of Nawal el Saadawi. 2nd ed. 2009. (ENG.). 352p. 120.95 *(978-1-84813-228-3(X))* Zed Bks., Ltd. GBR. Dist: Macmillan.

Elder, Arlene A. Narrative Shape-Shifting: Myth, Humor & History in the Fiction of Ben Okri, B. Kojo Laing & Yvonne Vera. 2009. 174p. 80.00 *(978-1-84701-012-4(1)*, Currey, James) Boydell & Brewer, Ltd. GBR. Dist: Boydell & Brewer, Inc.

Elliott, Graham. Babylon Behind the Wire: A collection of true day-to-day short stories of a chef's life working in Iraq. 2011. 378p. pap. 29.95 ***(978-1-4626-0777-8(2))*** PublishAmerica, Inc.

Enrick, Nathan. A True South African Story. 2011. 210p. 29.99 ***(978-1-4628-7429-3(0))*** Xlibris Corp.

Gikandi, Simon. Encyclopedia of African Literature. 2009. (ENG., Illus.). 648p. (C). 62.95 *(978-0-415-54962-2(0))* Routledge.

Giovannucci, Perri. Literature & Development in North Africa: The Modernizing Mission. 2008. (Literary Criticism & Cultural Theory Ser.). (ENG.). 254p. 125.00 *(978-0-415-95818-9(0))* Routledge.

Guluma, Endalkachew. The Predicament of the Diaspor. 2010. 108p. pap. *(978-3-8383-6763-7(4))* Lambert Academic Publishing.

Hallett, George, ed. Portraits of African Writers. 2007. (ENG., Illus.). 160p. (gr. 11). 44.95 *(978-1-86814-386-3(4))* Witwatersrand Univ. Pr. Pubns. ZAF. Dist: Transaction Pubs.

Killam, Douglas & Kerfoot, Alicia L. Student Encyclopedia of African Literature, 1 vol. 2007. 368p. 85.00 *(978-0-313-33580-8(X)*, GR3580, Greenwood Pr.) Greenwood Publishing Group, Inc.

Lindfors, Bernth. Early Black South African Writing in English. 2011. ***(978-1-59221-840-0(7))***; (Illus.). 236p. pap. ***(978-1-59221-841-7(5))*** Africa World Pr.

Marques, Irene. Critical Approaches, Vol. 1. Irene, Marques, ed. 2008. 208p. *(978-978-35035-4-0(5))* Michigan State Univ. Pr.

Meddeb, Abdelwahab. Tombeau of Ibn Arabi & White Traverses. Nancy, Jean-Luc & Mandell, Charlotte, trs. from FRE. 3rd ed. 2010. (ENG.). 88p. 70.00 *(978-0-8232-3114-0(3))* Fordham Univ. Pr.

Nancy, Jean-Luc & Meddeb, Abdelwahab. Tombeau of Ibn Arabi & White Traverses. Mandell, Charlotte, tr. from FRE. 2010. (ENG.). 88p. pap. 18.00 *(978-0-8232-3115-7(1))* Fordham Univ. Pr.

Nwakanma, Obi. Christopher Okigbo 1930-67: Thirsting for Sunlight. 2010. (Illus.). 304p. 95.00 *(978-1-84701-013-1(X)*, Currey, James) Boydell & Brewer, Ltd. GBR. Dist: Boydell & Brewer, Inc.

Odamtten, Vincent O. Broadening the Horizon: Critical Introductions to Amma Darko. 2007. 160p. pap. 23.50 *(978-0-9547023-8-0(7))* Clarke, Ayebia Publishing, Ltd. GBR. Dist: Rienner, Lynne Pubs.

Ojaide, Tanure. Dictionary of Literary Biography: Twentieth-Century African Writers. 2011. (Illus.). 432p. 315.00 *(978-0-7876-8178-4(4))* Cengage Gale.

Okolo, M. S. C. African Literature As Political Philosophy. 2007. (Africa in the New Millennium Ser.). (ENG.). 218p. 123.95 *(978-1-84277-894-4(3))*; per. 36.95 *(978-1-84277-895-1(1))* Zed Bks., Ltd. GBR. Dist: Macmillan.

Shihab, Aziz. Does the Land Remember Me? A Memoir of Palestine. 2011. (Arab American Writing Ser.). (ENG., Illus.). 149p. pap. 17.95 ***(978-0-8156-0968-1(X))*** Syracuse Univ. Pr.

Ventura de Molina, Jacinto. Jacinto Ventura de Molina: Los Caminos de la Escritura Negra en el Río de Plata. Acree, William G. & Borucki, Alex, eds. 2010. (SPA., Illus.). 285p. pap. 29.80 *(978-84-8489-492-6(4))* Iberoamericana Vervuert Publishing Corp.

wa'Thiong'o, Ngugi. Dreams in a Time of War: A Childhood Memoir. 2011. (Illus.). 272p. pap. 15.00 *(978-0-307-47621-0(9)*, Anchor) Knopf Doubleday Publishing Group.

wa'Thiong'o, Ngugi. In the House of the Interpreter: A Memoir. 2012. (ENG.). 256p. 25.95 ***(978-0-307-90769-1(4)**, Pantheon)* Knopf Doubleday Publishing Group.

AUTHORS, AFRICAN AMERICAN

see African American Authors

AUTHORS, AMERICAN

Abbott, Craig S. Forging Fame: The Strange Career of Scharmel Iris. 2007. (Illus.). 204p. 34.00 *(978-0-87580-376-0(8))* Northern Illinois Univ. Pr.

Abbott, Karen. American Rose: A Nation Laid Bare - The Life & Times of Gypsy Rose Lee. 2010. (ENG., Illus.). 448p. 26.00 *(978-1-4000-6691-9(3)*, Random House) Random House Publishing Group.

Abbott, Karen. American Rose: A Nation Laid Bare: the Life & Times of Gypsy Rose Lee. 2012. (ENG., Illus.). 448p. pap. 17.00 ***(978-0-8129-7851-3(X)**,* Random Hse. Trade Paperbacks) Random House Publishing Group.

Aberjhani. The American Poet Who Went Home Again. 2008. 309p. pap. 16.95 *(978-1-4357-1769-5(4))* Lulu Enterprises Inc.

Abingdon. Faces on Faith - Frederick Beuchner, Marion Wright Edelman, Gustavo Gutierrez: Classic Interviews with 20th-Century Leaders. 2008. cd-rom 25.00 *(978-0-687-65333-1(9))* Abingdon Pr.

Ackroyd, Peter. Poe: A Life Cut Short. 2009. (ENG., Illus.). 224p. 22.95 *(978-0-385-50800-1(X)*, Talese, Nan A.) Knopf Doubleday Publishing Group.

Acuña, Dorothy Chapman. Short Stories from el Barrio Libre, 1 vol. 2009. 78p. pap. 14.95 *(978-1-61546-297-1(2))* PublishAmerica, Inc.

Ada, Alma Flor. Alma Flor Ada & YOU, 1 vol., Vol. 2. 2nd ed. 2008. (Author & YOU Ser.). (Illus.). 128p. pap. 35.00 *(978-1-59158-228-1(8)*, LU2288) Libraries Unlimited, Inc.

Adams, Agatha Boyd. Thomas Wolfe, Carolina Student: A Brief Biography. 2011. 92p. 38.95 ***(978-1-258-07349-7(8))*** Literary Licensing, LLC.

Adams, Hazard. Academic Child: A Memoir. 2008. (ENG., Illus.). 278p. pap. 39.95 *(978-0-7864-4011-5(2))* McFarland & Co., Inc. Pubs.

Adams, Henry. The Life of George Cabot Lodge. 2009. 216p. 23.99 *(978-1-103-52336-8(8))* 2009. 216p. pap. 17.99 *(978-1-103-52334-4(1))* 2008. 212p. 23.99 *(978-0-559-20450-0(7))* 2008. 212p. pap. 17.99 *(978-0-559-20448-7(5))* BiblioBazaar.

—The Life of George Cabot Lodge. 2008. 212p. 39.95 *(978-0-548-91886-9(4))* 2007. (ENG.). 216p. per. 24.95 *(978-0-548-57011-1(6))* Kessinger Publishing, LLC.

Adams, Katherine. Owning Up: Privacy, Property, & Belonging in U. S. Women's Life Writing, 1840-1890. 2009. (ENG., Illus.). 304p. 65.00 *(978-0-19-533680-1(1))* Oxford Univ. Pr., Inc.

Adams, Maureen. Shaggy Muses: The Dogs Who Inspired Virginia Woolf, Emily Dickenson, Elizabeth Barrett Browining, Edith Wharton, & Emily Bronte. 2011. (Illus.). 320p. pap. 16.00 *(978-0-226-00536-2(4))* Univ. of Chicago Pr.

—Shaggy Muses: The Dogs Who Inspired Virginia Woolf, Emily Dickinson, Elizabeth Barrett Browning, Edith Wharton, & Emily Bront. 2007. (ENG., Illus.). 320p. 24.95 *(978-0-345-48406-2(1)*, Ballantine Bks.) Random House Publishing Group.

Adams, Oscar Fay. A Brief Handbook of American Authors. 2009. 222p. 28.99 *(978-1-110-41659-2(8))* 2009. 222p. pap. 23.75 *(978-1-110-41655-4(5))* 2008. 204p. 24.99 *(978-0-559-26988-2(9))* 2008. 204p. pap. 23.75 *(978-0-559-26987-5(0))* BiblioBazaar.

—A Dictionary of American Authors. 2007. (ENG.). 598p. 59.95 *(978-0-548-26352-5(3))*; 600p. per. 44.95 *(978-1-4326-6764-1(5))* Kessinger Publishing, LLC.

Adams, Timothy Dow. Telling Lies in Modern American Autobiography. 2011. (ENG.). 224p. pap. 40.00 *(978-0-8078-5995-7(8))* Univ. of North Carolina Pr.
Agee, Jonis. Riding Shotgun: Women Write about Their Mothers. 2008. (ENG., Illus.). 248p. 24.95 *(978-0-87351-614-3(1),* Borealis Bk.) Minnesota Historical Society Pr.
Ahmad, Dohra. Landscapes of Hope: Anti-Colonial Utopianism in America. 2009. (ENG.). 272p. 65.00 *(978-0-19-533276-6(8))* Oxford Univ. Pr., Inc.
Alarcón, Norma, et al. El Mundo Zurdo: Selected Works from the Meetings of the Society for the Study of Gloria Anzaldúa, 2007 & 2009. 2010. *(978-1-879960-83-1(4))* Aunt Lute Bks.
Albert, Elisa. Freud's Blind Spot: 23 Original Essays on Cherished, Estranged, Lost, Hurtful, Hopeful, Complicated Siblings. 2010. (ENG.). 288p. pap. 15.00 *(978-1-4391-5472-4(4),* Free Pr.) Free Pr.
Albert, Susan Wittig. An Extraordinary Year of Ordinary Days. 2010. (ENG.). 240p. 24.95 *(978-0-292-72306-1(7))* Univ. of Texas Pr.
—Together, Alone: A Memoir of Marriage & Place. (ENG., Illus.). 2011. 195p. pap. 19.95 *(978-0-292-72646-8(5))* 2009. 196p. 24.95 *(978-0-292-71970-5(1))* Univ. of Texas Pr.
Alcala, Kathleen. The Desert Remembers My Name: On Family & Writing. 2007. (Camino Del Sol Ser.). (ENG.). 192p. 32.00 *(978-0-8165-2626-0(5));* pap. 14.95 *(978-0-8165-2627-7(3))* Univ. of Arizona Pr.
Alcott, Amos Bronson. Concord Days by a Bronson Alcott. 2011. 292p. pap. 23.99 ***(978-1-4255-8968-4(5))*** MPublishing.
Alcott, Amos Bronson. Notes of Conversations, 1848-1875: Amos Bronson Alcott. English, Karen, ed. 2007. 288p. (C). 55.00 *(978-0-8386-4118-7(0))* Fairleigh Dickinson Univ. Pr.
Alcott, Louisa May. Little Women Abroad: The Alcott Sisters' Letters from Europe, 1870-1871. Shealy, Daniel, ed. 2008. (ENG., Illus.). 376p. 34.95 *(978-0-8203-3009-9(4))* Univ. of Georgia Pr.
Aldrich, Nelson W., ed. George, Being George: George Plimpton's Life as Told, Admired, Deplored, & Envied by 200 Friends, Relatives, Lovers, Acquaintances, Rivals — and a Few Unappreciative Observers. 2009. (ENG., Illus.). 432p. pap. 18.00 *(978-0-8129-7418-8(2),* Random Hse. Trade Paperbacks) Random House Publishing Group.
Alexander, Edward. Lionel Trilling & Irving Howe: And Other Stories of Literary Friendship. 2009. (ENG.). 134p. 34.95 *(978-1-4128-1014-2(0))* Transaction Pubs.
Alexander, James W. Forty Years' Familiar Letters of James W Alexander, D D, Constituting, with the Notes, a Memoir of His Life Edited by the Surviving Correspondent. 2006. (ENG.). 428p. per. 26.99 *(978-1-4255-4680-9(3));* 388p. per. 26.99 *(978-1-4255-4169-9(0))* MPublishing.
Alison, Jane. The Sisters Antipodes. 2010. (ENG.). 288p. pap. 14.95 *(978-0-547-24773-1(7),* Mariner Bks.) Houghton Mifflin Harcourt Trade & Reference Pubs.
—The Sisters Antipodes: A Memoir. 2009. (ENG., Illus.). 288p. 23.00 *(978-0-15-101280-0(6))* Houghton Mifflin Harcourt Trade & Reference Pubs.
Allen, Eddie B., Jr. & Allen, Eddie B. Low Road: The Life & Legacy of Donald Goines. 2008. (ENG., Illus.). 224p. pap. 16.99 *(978-0-312-38351-0(7),* St. Martin's Griffin) St. Martin's Pr.
Allison, Dorothy. Conversations with Dorothy Allison. Claxton, Mae Miller, ed. 2012. (Literary Conversations Ser.). (ENG.). 208p. 40.00 ***(978-1-61703-286-8(7))*** Univ. Pr. of Mississippi.
Allsopp, Fred W. Albert Pike's Reply to Pope Leo XIII. 2006. pap. 12.95 *(978-1-4286-6583-5(8))* Kessinger Publishing, LLC.
Alonso, Harriet Hyman. Robert E. Sherwood: The Playwright in Peace & War. 2007. (Illus.). 398p. lib. bdg. 80.00 *(978-1-55849-618-7(1));* 394p. per. 28.95 *(978-1-55849-619-4(X))* Univ. of Massachusetts Pr.
Alther, Lisa. Kinfolks: Falling off the Family Tree. 2012. (ENG.). 288p. pap. 14.95 ***(978-1-61145-176-4(0),*** 611176, Arcade Publishing) Skyhorse Publishing Co., Inc.
Alvarado, Beth. Anthropologies: A Family Memoir. 2011. (Sightline Bks.). (Illus.). 202p. pap. 19.95 *(978-1-60938-037-3(1))* Univ. of Iowa Pr.
Amani, Alexander. A Nomad's Journey: Lessons learned from an eclectic Soul. 2010. 108p. (ENG.). 23.99 *(978-1-4490-8567-4(9));* pap. 17.95 *(978-1-4490-8566-7(0))* AuthorHouse.
Ambrosek, Renee. E. L. Konigsburg. 2009. (Library of Author Biographies Ser.). 112p. (gr. 5-8). 63.90 *(978-1-60853-532-3(0),* Rosen Central) Rosen Publishing Group, Inc., The.
—E.L. Konigsburg. 2006. (Library of Author Biographies). (ENG., Illus.). 112p. (gr. 5-8). pap. 12.95 *(978-1-4042-0648-9(5))* Rosen Publishing Group, Inc., The.
Anatol, Giselle Liza. Bringing Light to Twilight: Perspectives on a Pop Culture Phenomenon. Anatol, Giselle Liza, ed. 2011. (ENG., Illus.). 258p. pap. 26.00 *(978-0-230-11068-7(1))* Palgrave Macmillan.
Anderson, John Dennis. Student Companion to William Faulkner, 1 vol. 2007. (Student Companions to Classic Writers Ser.). 160p. 65.00 *(978-0-313-33439-9(0),* GR3439, Greenwood Pr.) Greenwood Publishing Group, Inc.
Anesko, Michael. Monopolizing the Master: Henry James & the Politics of Modern Literary Scholarship. 2012. (ENG., Illus.). 272p. 35.00 ***(978-0-8047-6932-7(X))*** Stanford Univ. Pr.
Angela, Miss. My Life Experiences. 2007. pap. 8.00 *(978-0-8059-7436-2(9))* Dorrance Publishing Co., Inc.
Angelou, Maya. The Heart of a Woman. 2009. (ENG.). 352p. pap. 15.00 *(978-0-8129-8032-5(8),* Random Hse. Trade Paperbacks) Random House Publishing Group.
Anzaldúa, Gloria. The Gloria Anzaldúa Reader. Keating, AnaLouise, ed. 2009. (Latin America Otherwise Ser.). (ENG., Illus.). 376p. 89.95 *(978-0-8223-4555-8(2));* pap. 24.95 *(978-0-8223-4564-0(1))* Duke Univ. Pr.
Argersinger, Jana L. & Person, Leland S., eds. Hawthorne & Melville: Writing a Relationship. 2008. (ENG., Illus.). 392p. pap. 26.95 *(978-0-8203-3096-9(5));* lib. bdg. 69.95 *(978-0-8203-2751-8(4))* Univ. of Georgia Pr.
Armbrester, Margaret. Samuel Ullman & Youth: The Life, the Legacy. 2009. (ENG., Illus.). 166p. pap. 22.50 *(978-0-8173-5583-0(8))* Univ. of Alabama Pr.
Armbruster, Elif S. Domestic Biographies: Stowe, Howells, James, & Wharton at Home. 2011. (Studies on Themes & Motifs in Literature Ser.). (C). pap. 39.95 *(978-1-4331-1224-9(8)); (978-1-4331-1249-2(3))* Lang, Peter Publishing, Inc.
Aronson, Judith. Likenesses: With the Sitters Writing about One Another. 2010. (ENG., Illus.). 152p. pap. 29.95 *(978-1-85754-994-2(5))* Carcanet Pr., Ltd. GBR. Dist: Independent Pubs. Group.
Atkins, G. Douglas. E. B. White: The Essayist as First-Class Writer. 2012. (ENG., Illus.). 192p. 80.00 ***(978-0-230-34066-4(0))*** Palgrave Macmillan.
Auchincloss, Louis. Edith Wharton: University of Minnesota Pamphlets on American Writers. 2009. (ENG.). 48p. pap. 25.00 *(978-0-8166-0250-6(6))* Univ. of Minnesota Pr.
Augustyn, Adam, ed. American Literature from 1600 Through the 1850s. 2010. (Britannica Guide to World Literature Ser.). (ENG.). 240p. (YA). lib. bdg. 45.00 *(978-1-61530-124-9(0))* Rosen Publishing Group, Inc., The.
—American Literature from 1600 Through The 1850S. 2010. (Britannica Guide to World Literature Ser.). (Illus.). 240p. (YA). 90.00 *(978-1-61530-236-9(0))* Rosen Publishing Group, Inc., The.
—American Literature from 1945 Through Today. 2010. (Britannica Guide to World Literature Ser.). 240p. (YA). (ENG.). lib. bdg. 45.00 *(978-1-61530-133-1(X));* (Illus.). 90.00 *(978-1-61530-237-6(9))* Rosen Publishing Group, Inc., The.
Auslander, Shalom. Foreskin's Lament: A Memoir. 2008. (ENG.). 320p. (gr. 12-18). 15.00 *(978-1-59448-333-2(7),* Riverhead Trade (Paperbacks)) Penguin Group (USA) Inc.
Auster, Paul. Collected Prose: Autobiographical Writings, True Stories, Critical Essays, Prefaces, & Collaborations with Artists, & Interviews. 2010. (ENG., Illus.). 608p. pap. 22.00 *(978-0-312-42992-8(4))* Picador.
—The Invention of Solitude. rev. ed. 2007. (ENG., Illus.). 192p. (Orig.). (gr. 12-18). 15.00 *(978-0-14-311222-8(8),* Penguin (Non-Classics)) Penguin Group (USA) Inc.
Auster, Paul. Winter Journal. 2012. (ENG.). 240p. 26.00 ***(978-0-8050-9553-1(5))*** Holt, Henry & Co.
Austin, Mary Hunter. Earth Horizon: Facsimile of Original 1932 Edition. 2007. (ENG.). 424p. per. 34.95 *(978-0-86534-539-3(2))* Sunstone Pr.
Austin, Mary S. Philip Freneau the Poet of the Revolutio. 2006. pap. 28.95 *(978-1-4286-4320-8(6))* Kessinger Publishing, LLC.
Ayres, Brenda. The Life & Works of Augusta Jane Evans Wilson, 1835-1909. 2012. (Illus.). 250p. 104.95 ***(978-1-4094-4073-4(7))*** Ashgate Publishing Co.
Azuela, Arturo. Prisma de Mariano Azuela. 2009. (SPA., Illus.). 346p. 27.00 *(978-970-722-013-3(9))* Plaza y Valdes, S.A. de C.V. MEX. Dist: Sony Electronics.
Bach, Richard. The Bridge Across Forever: A True Love Story. 2006. (ENG.). 320p. pap. 14.99 *(978-0-06-114848-4(2),* William Morrow Paperbacks) HarperCollins Pubs.
Badt-Strauss, Bertha. White Fire: The Life & Works of Jessie Sampter. 2011. 218p. 44.95 ***(978-1-258-06256-9(9))*** Literary Licensing, LLC.
Baker, Phil. William S. Burroughs. 2010. (Reaktion Books - Critical Lives Ser.). (ENG., Illus.). 192p. pap. 16.95 *(978-1-86189-663-6(8))* Reaktion Bks., Ltd. GBR. Dist: Chicago Distribution Ctr.
Baker, Richard. Letters from Across the Big Divide: The Ghost Writings of Charles M. Russell. 2008. 240p. pap. 15.95 *(978-0-595-50111-3(7))* iUniverse, Inc.
Bales, Jack. Willie Morris: An Exhaustive Annotated Bibliography & a Biography. alt. ed. 2010. (ENG., Illus.). 403p. pap. 49.95 *(978-0-7864-4574-5(2))* McFarland & Co., Inc. Pubs.
Bambara, Toni Cade. Conversations with Toni Cade Bambara. Lewis, Thabiti, ed. 2012. (Literary Conversations Ser.). (ENG.). 176p. 40.00 ***(978-1-60473-432-4(9))*** Univ. Pr. of Mississippi.
Banks, Russell & Roche, David. Conversations with Russell Banks. 2010. xv, 193p. pap. ***(978-1-60473-746-2(8))*** Univ. Pr. of Mississippi.
Barnes, Nigel. A Dream Within a Dream: The Life of Edgar Allan Poe. 2009. (ENG.). 360p. pap. 23.95 *(978-0-7206-1322-3(1))* Owen, Peter Ltd. GBR. Dist: Independent Pubs. Group.
Barnum, Jill, et al. Whole Oceans Away: Melville & the Pacific. 2008. (Illus.). 350p. *(978-0-87338-893-1(3))* Kent State Univ. Pr.
Barris, Chuck. Della: A Memoir of My Daughter. 2010. (ENG., Illus.). 224p. 25.00 *(978-1-4391-6799-1(0))* Simon & Schuster.
Barrows, W. (William). The General; or, Twelve Nights in the Hunters' Camp: A Narrative of Real Life / [William] Barrows; Illustrated by G. G. White. 2006. 284p. per. 23.99 *(978-1-4255-2538-5(5))* MPublishing.
Barry, Sandra. Elizabeth Bishop: Nova Scotia's "Home-Made" Poet, 1 vol. 2011. (ENG., Illus.). 122p. pap. 15.95 ***(978-1-55109-823-4(7))*** Down East Bks.
Baskervill, William Malone. Southern Writers: Biographical & Critical Studies. 2009. (ENG.). 415p. 41.99 *(978-1-117-13656-1(6))* 2009. (ENG.). 415p. pap. 33.75 *(978-1-117-13657-8(4))* 2008. 416p. 30.99 *(978-0-559-32703-2(X))* 2008. 416p. pap. 33.75 *(978-0-559-32702-5(1))* BiblioBazaar.
—Southern Writers: Biographical & Critical Studies. 2009. 98p. pap. *(978-0-217-55675-0(2))* Books LLC.
—Southern Writers Set, 2 vols. reprint ed. lib. bdg. 250.00 *(978-0-7222-4845-4(8))* Library Reprints, Inc.
Bass, Rick. Why I Came West: A Memoir. (ENG.). 256p. 2009. pap. 14.95 *(978-0-547-23771-8(5),* Mariner Bks.) 2008. 24.00 *(978-0-618-59675-1(5))* Houghton Mifflin Harcourt Trade & Reference Pubs.
Batt, Matthew. Sugarhouse: Turning the Neighborhood Crack House into Our Home Sweet Home. 2012. (ENG.). 272p. pap. 14.95 ***(978-0-547-63453-1(6),*** Mariner Bks.) Houghton Mifflin Harcourt Trade & Reference Pubs.
Bauer, Paul J. & Dawidziak, Mark. Jim Tully: American Writer, Irish Rover, Hollywood Brawler. 2011. (Illus.). 384p. 55.00 *(978-1-60635-076-8(5))* Kent State Univ. Pr.
Baxter III, E. R. Niagara Digressions. 2012. (ENG., Illus.). 250p. pap. 20.00 ***(978-0-9837405-2-0(6))*** Starcherone Bks.
Beagle, Donald Robert. Poet of the Lost Cause: A Life of Father Ryan. 2008. (ENG., Illus.). 48.95 *(978-1-57233-606-3(4))* Univ. of Tennessee Pr.
Beahm, George. Discovering the Golden Compass: A Guide to Philip Pullman's Dark Materials. 2007. (ENG., Illus.). 248p. (YA). (gr. 7-12). per. 16.95 *(978-1-57174-505-4(8))* Hampton Roads Publishing Co., Inc.
Beath, Mary. Hiking Alone: Trails Out, Trails Home. 2008. (ENG., Illus.). 368p. pap. 14.95 *(978-0-8263-4329-1(5))* Univ. of New Mexico Pr.
Bechdel, Alison. Are You My Mother? 2012. (ENG., Illus.). 304p. 22.00 *(978-0-618-98250-9(7))* Houghton Mifflin Harcourt Trade & Reference Pubs.
Beckmon, Jon. Codename: Lehi. 2011. 360p. 29.99 ***(978-1-4535-2373-5(1));*** pap. 19.99 ***(978-1-4535-2372-8(3))*** Xlibris Corp.
Beer, Janet, ed. The Cambridge Companion to Kate Chopin. 2008. (Cambridge Companions to Literature Ser.). (ENG.). 208p. (C). 81.00 *(978-0-521-88344-3(X));* pap. 29.99 *(978-0-521-70982-8(2))* Cambridge Univ. Pr.
Bell-Villada, Gene H. Garcia Marquez: The Man & His Work, Second Edition. 2nd ed. 2010. (ENG., Illus.). 360p. 65.00 *(978-0-8078-3351-3(7));* pap. 22.95 *(978-0-8078-6525-5(7))* Univ. of North Carolina Pr.
Bellow, Saul. Saul Bellow: Letters. Taylor, Benjamin F., ed. 2012. (ENG., Illus.). 622p. (gr. 12). 20.00 ***(978-0-14-312046-9(8),*** Penguin (Non-Classics)) Penguin Group (USA) Inc.
Bellow, Saul. To Jerusalem & Back. 2010. (ENG.). 234p. pap. 19.95 *(978-1-4128-1184-2(8))* Transaction Pubs.
Below, Ida Comstock. Eugene Field in His Home. 2009. 164p. 26.99 *(978-1-110-44994-1(1));* 166p. 26.99 *(978-1-110-44992-7(5));* 166p. pap. 23.75 *(978-1-110-44989-7(5));* 168p. pap. 20.75 *(978-1-110-44990-3(9));* 158p. 22.99 *(978-0-559-93807-8(1));* 168p. pap. 16.99 *(978-0-559-93804-7(7))* BiblioBazaar.
—Eugene Field in His Home. 2009. 48p. pap. *(978-0-217-47429-0(2))* Books LLC.
—Eugene Field in His Home. 2007. 164p. 36.95 *(978-0-548-41665-5(6));* (ENG.). per. 21.95 *(978-0-548-39328-4(1))* Kessinger Publishing, LLC.
—Eugene Field in His Home. 2009. 124p. pap. 26.45 *(978-1-4446-4031-1(3))* Research Pr.
Belpré, Pura & Sánchez González, Lisa. The Stories I Read to the Children: The Life & Writing of Pura Belpré. 2011. pap. 28.00 *(978-1-936117-15-4(0),* Library Juice Pr.) Litwin Bks., LLC.
Benedict, Elizabeth. Mentors Muses & Monsters. 2012. pap. ***(978-1-4384-4350-8(1))*** State Univ. of New York Pr.
Benedict, Elizabeth. Mentors, Muses & Monsters: 30 Writers on the People Who Changed Their Lives. 2009. (ENG., Illus.). 288p. 24.99 *(978-1-4391-0561-7(7),* Free Pr.) Free Pr.
Benet, Laura. Caleb's Luck. 2011. 32p. pap. 35.95 ***(978-1-258-06405-1(7))*** Literary Licensing, LLC.
Benson, Jackson J. Under the Big Sky: A Biography of A. B. Guthrie Jr. 2009. (ENG., Illus.). 336p. 29.95 *(978-0-8032-2286-1(6))* Univ. of Nebraska Pr.
Berg, Elizabeth. Escaping into the Open: The Art of Writing True. 2012. (P. S. Ser.). (ENG.). 272p. pap. 14.99 ***(978-0-06-220044-0(5),*** HarperPerennial) HarperCollins Pubs.
Bergé, Carol, intro. Light Years: An Anthology on Sociocultural Happenings (Multimedia in the East Village, 1960-1966) 2010. (ENG., Illus.). 632p. pap. 40.00 *(978-1-933132-46-4(9))* Spuyten Duyvil.
Berkow, Ira. Full Swing: Hits, Runs & Errors in a Writer's Life. 2007. (ENG., Illus.). 304p. per. 16.95 *(978-1-56663-755-8(4))* Dee, Ivan R. Pub.
Bernheimer, Kate, ed. Brothers & Beasts: An Anthology of Men on Fairy Tales. 2007. (Series in Fairy-Tale Studies). 208p. pap. 15.95 *(978-0-8143-3267-2(6))* Wayne State Univ. Pr.
Bernstein, Harry. The Dream: A Memoir. 2009. (ENG.). 288p. pap. 16.00 *(978-0-345-50389-3(9),* Ballantine Bks.) Random House Publishing Group.
—The Invisible Wall: A Love Story That Broke Barriers. 2008. (ENG.). 352p. pap. 15.00 *(978-0-345-49610-2(8),* Ballantine Bks.) Random House Publishing Group.
Berrigan, Ted. Dear Sandy, Hello: Letters from Ted to Sandy Berrigan. Berrigan, Sandy & Padgett, Ron, eds. 2010. (ENG., Illus.). 368p. pap. 19.95 *(978-1-56689-249-0(X))* Coffee Hse. Pr.
Berruti, Massimo. Dim-Remembered Stories: A Critical Study of R. H. Barlow. 2011. pap. 20.00 ***(978-0-9846386-3-5(6))*** Hippocampus Pr.
Berry, Wendell. Conversations with Wendell Berry. Grubbs, Morris Allen, ed. 2007. (ENG., Illus.). 218p. 50.00 *(978-1-57806-991-0(2));* per. 22.00 *(978-1-57806-992-7(0))* Univ. Pr. of Mississippi.
Bickley, R. Bruce, Jr. Joel Chandler Harris: A Biography & Critical Study. 2008. (ENG.). 184p. per. 22.95 *(978-0-8203-3185-0(6))* Univ. of Georgia Pr.
Bidinger, Elizabeth. The Ethics of Working Class Autobiography: Representation of Family by Four American Authors. 2006. (ENG.). 212p. per. 45.00 *(978-0-7864-2576-1(8))* McFarland & Co., Inc. Pubs.
Bierfelt, Kristin. The North Shore Literary Trail: From Bradstreet's Andover to Hawthorne's Salem. 2008. 19.99 *(978-1-59629-520-9(1))* History Pr., The.
Bigelow, Christopher Kimball, ed. & compiled by. Conversations with Mormon Authors. 2007. (ENG.). 284p. 39.95 *(978-0-85051-111-6(9));* 272p. pap. 17.95 *(978-0-85051-108-6(9))* Luso-Brazilian Bks. (Mormon Arts & Letters).
Bigsby, Christopher. Arthur Miller: 1962-2005. 2011. (ENG., Illus.). 616p. 65.00 ***(978-0-472-11817-5(X))*** Univ. of Michigan Pr.
Biographiq. Edgar Allan Poe - Poet of the Macabre. 2008. 64p. pap. 9.99 *(978-1-59986-365-8(0),* Biographiq) Filiquarian Publishing, LLC.
—Ezra Pound - Modernist Man. 2008. 60p. pap. 9.99 *(978-1-59986-040-4(6),* Biographiq) Filiquarian Publishing, LLC.
—Gertrude Stein - a Catalyst of Modern Art. 2008. 68p. pap. 9.99 *(978-1-59986-042-8(2),* Biographiq) Filiquarian Publishing, LLC.
—Rachel Carson - Environmental Pioneer (Biography) 2008. 68p. pap. 9.99 *(978-1-59986-384-9(7),* Biographiq) Filiquarian Publishing, LLC.
—William F Buckley, Jr - an American Conservative. 2008. 52p. pap. 9.99 *(978-1-59986-067-1(8),* Biographiq) Filiquarian Publishing, LLC.
Bird, Robert Montgomery. Sheppard Lee. 2009. 132p. pap. *(978-1-150-00590-9(4))* Books LLC.
Birge, June Rossbach Bingham. Braided Lives: A 20th Century Pursuit of Happiness. 2008. 480p. pap. 24.95 *(978-0-9801250-2-3(2))* Straus Historical Society, Inc.
Birkerts, Sven. The Other Walk: Essays, 1 vol. 2011. (ENG.). 192p. pap. 15.00 *(978-1-55597-593-7(3))* Graywolf Pr.
Bims, Nicholas. Willa Cather. 2011. ***(978-1-58765-826-6(7))*** Salem Pr., Inc.
Bishop, Rosemarie E. A Brother's Love. 2008. 328p. pap. 19.99 *(978-1-4363-9134-4(2))* Xlibris Corp.
Black, Baxter. Lessons from a Desperado Poet: How to Find Your Way When You Don't Have a Map, How to Win the Game When You Don't Know the Rules, & When Someone Says It Can't Be Done, What They Mean Is They Can't Do It. 2011. (ENG., Illus.). 232p. 22.95 *(978-0-7627-6997-1(1),* TwoDot) Globe Pequot Pr., The.
Blackshear, Helen. Mother Was a Rebel: In Praise of Gentle People. 2007. 212p. pap. 19.95 *(978-1-60306-037-0(5))* NewSouth, Inc.
Blewett, Mary H. The Yankee Yorkshireman: Migration Lived & Imagined. 2009. (Studies of World Migrations Ser.). (ENG., Illus.). 232p. 62.00 *(978-0-252-03405-3(8));* pap. 21.00 *(978-0-252-07613-8(3))* Univ. of Illinois Pr.
Block, Matthew, ed. The Sherman Diaries: Volume Five: Moving On. 2008. 466p. pap. 19.95 *(978-0-9768896-1-8(7))* Square Circles Publishing.
Bloom, Harold. The House on Mango Street. 2nd rev. ed. 2010. (Bloom's Guides). 122p. (C). (gr. 9-18). 30.00 *(978-1-60413-812-2(2),* Chelsea Hse.) Facts On File, Inc.
Bloom, Harold, ed. Truman Capote, New Edition. 2nd rev. ed. 2009. (Bloom's Modern Critical Views Ser.). 216p. (C). (gr. 9-18). 45.00 *(978-1-60413-398-1(8),* Chelsea Hse.) Facts On File, Inc.
Blundell, John. Female Force: Ayn Rand. 2011. (ENG., Illus.). 32p. (YA). pap. 3.99 *(978-1-4507-4924-4(0))* Bluewater Productions, Inc.
Bob, Dolgan. Sportswriter who punched Sam M. 2011. 352p. pap. 28.95 *(978-1-60635-044-7(7))* Kent State Univ. Pr.
Bode, Elroy. In a Special Light. 2006. (ENG.). 160p. 24.95 *(978-1-59534-026-9(2))* Trinity Univ. Pr.
Bok, Edward. Why I Believe in Poverty Including, Two Persons. 2006. 60p. per. 11.95 *(978-1-59605-560-5(X))* Cosimo, Inc.
Bolton, Charles Knowles. Gamaliel Bradford: A Memoir. 2011. 18p. 35.95 ***(978-1-258-06448-8(0))*** Literary Licensing, LLC.
Bolton, Clyde. Hadacol Days: A Southern Boyhood: A Memoir. 2010. (ENG.). 24.95 *(978-1-58838-200-9(1),* NewSouth Bks.) NewSouth, Inc.
Bond, Jenny & Sheedy, Chris. Who the Hell Is Pansy O'Hara? The Fascinating Stories Behind 50 of the World's Best-Loved Books. 2008. (ENG.). 336p. (gr. 12-18). 13.00 *(978-0-14-311364-5(X),* Penguin (Non-Classics)) Penguin Group (USA) Inc.
Bone, Richard Wright, Vol. 74. 2009. (ENG.). 48p. pap. 25.00 *(978-0-8166-0524-8(6))* Univ. of Minnesota Pr.
Boorman, Neil. Bonfire of the Brands: How I Learned to Live Without Labels. 2007. (Illus.). 256p. pap. *(978-1-84195-987-0(1))* Canongate Bks.
Bosco, Ronald A. & Myerson, Joel. Dlb 351 Moby-Dick Doc. 2009. (Dictionary of Literary Biography Ser.). (ENG., Illus.). 480p. 315.00 *(978-0-7876-8169-2(5))* Cengage Gale.
Botta, Anne C. Lynch (Anne Charlotte Lyn. Memoirs of Anne C L Botta, Written by Her Friends with Selections from Her Correspondence & from Her Writings in Prose & Poetry. 2006. 484p. per. 29.99 *(978-1-4255-5313-5(3))* MPublishing.
Bottoms, David. The Onion's Dark Core: A Little Book of Poetry Talk. 2010. pap. 15.95 *(978-1-935708-02-5(3))* Press 53, LLC.
Bowden, Charles. Some of the Dead Are Still Breathing: Living in the Future. 2009. (ENG.). 256p. 24.00 *(978-0-15-101395-1(0))* Houghton Mifflin Harcourt Trade & Reference Pubs.
Bower, Lynn. Silent Workplace: Shops, stores, businesses, & factories where Hoosiers once earned a Living. 2008. (Illus.). 144p. pap. 22.00 *(978-0-9745186-4-0(6),* 877-547-5073) Studio Indiana.
Boyd, Herb. Baldwin's Harlem: A Biography of James Baldwin. 2008. (ENG.). 272p. pap. 17.99 *(978-0-7432-9308-2(8),* Beyond Words/Atria Bks.) Atria Bks.
Boylan, Jennifer Finney. I'M Looking Through You: Growing up Haunted - A Memoir. 2008. (ENG.). 288p. pap. 14.95 *(978-0-7679-2175-6(5))* Broadway Bks.

Bradley, Tom. Fission among the Fanatics. 2007. (ENG.). 322p. per. 16.00 *(978-1-933132-33-4(7))* Spuyten Duyvil.

Bradley, William Aspenwall. William Cullen Bryant. 2009. 240p. 23.99 *(978-1-103-54889-7(1))*; pap. 17.99 *(978-1-103-54886-6(7))* BiblioBazaar.

—William Cullen Bryant: English Men of Letters. 2007. pap. 26.95 *(978-1-4304-8326-7(1))* Kessinger Publishing, LLC.

Bradu, Fabienne. Artaud, Todavía. 2009. (Vida y Pensamiento de México Ser.). (SPA.). 196p. pap. 14.95 *(978-968-16-8458-7(3))* Fondo de Cultura Economica USA.

Brady, Sally Ryder. A Box of Darkness: The Story of a Marriage. 2011. (Playaway Adult Nonfiction Ser.). 74.99 ***(978-1-61707-444-8(6))*** Findaway World, LLC.

—A Box of Darkness: The Story of a Marriage. 2011. (ENG., Illus.). 256p. 23.99 *(978-0-312-65416-0(2))* St. Martin's Pr.

Braestrup, Kate. Here If You Need Me: A Memoir. 2008. (ENG.). 224p. pap. 13.99 *(978-0-316-06631-0(1),* Back Bay Bks.) Little Brown & Co.

—Marriage & Other Acts of Charity: A Memoir. 2011. (ENG.). 240p. pap. 14.99 *(978-0-316-03190-5(9),* Back Bay Bks.) Little Brown & Co.

Bram, Christopher. Eminent Outlaws: The Gay Writers Who Changed America. 2012. (ENG., Illus.). 384p. 27.99 *(978-0-446-56313-0(7),* Twelve) Grand Central Publishing.

Branch, Edgar Marquess & Twain, Mark. The Literary Apprenticeship of Mark Twain. 2011. 356p. 51.95 ***(978-1-258-04881-5(7))*** Literary Licensing, LLC.

Branson, Susan. Dangerous to Know: Women, Crime, & Notoriety in the Early Republic. 2011. (Illus.). 200p. (C). pap. 19.95 ***(978-0-8122-2187-9(7))*** Univ. of Pennsylvania Pr.

Brashear, Minnie M. Mark Twain, Son of Missouri. (ENG.). 332p. 2007. 45.95 *(978-0-548-14387-2(0))* 2006. per. 30.95 *(978-1-4286-5640-6(5))* Kessinger Publishing, LLC.

Brassaï. Henry Miller: The Paris Years. Bent, Timothy, tr. from FRE. 2011. (ENG., Illus.). 240p. pap. 14.95 *(978-1-61145-028-6(4),* 611028, Arcade Publishing) Skyhorse Publishing Co., Inc.

Brecher, Irving. The Wicked Wit of the West! The Last Great Golden-Age Screenwriter Shares the Hilarity & Heartaches of Working with Groucho, Garland, Gleason, Burns, Berle, Benny & Many More. 2009. 360p. pap. 25.00 *(978-1-934730-23-2(8))* Yehuda, Ben Pr.

Bredahl, A. Carl, Jr., ACarl. New Ground: Western American Narrative & the Literary Canon. 2011. (ENG.). 208p. pap. 40.00 ***(978-0-8078-5641-3(X))*** Univ. of North Carolina Pr.

Breit, Harvey. The Writer Observed. 2011. 286p. 48.95 ***(978-1-258-09963-3(2))*** Literary Licensing, LLC.

Brennen, Carlene. Hemingway's Cats. 2nd ed. 2011. (Illus.). 200p. pap. 14.95 *(978-1-56164-489-6(7))* Pineapple Pr., Inc.

Brenner, Marie. Apples & Oranges: My Brother & Me, Lost & Found. 2009. (ENG., Illus.). 304p. pap. 15.00 *(978-0-312-42880-8(4))* Picador.

Brewer, Sonny, ed. Don't Quit Your Day Job: Acclaimed Authors & the Day Jobs They Quit. 2010. (ENG.). 272p. 24.95 *(978-1-84982-108-7(9))* MP Publishing Ltd. GBR. Dist: Perseus-PGW.

—Don't Quit Your Day Job: Acclaimed Authors & the Day Jobs they Quit. 2011. (ENG.). 432p. pap. 15.95 *(978-1-84982-136-0(4))* MP Publishing Ltd. GBR. Dist: Perseus-PGW.

Brewster, Thomas A. The Great American Novel. 2008. 128p. pap. 13.95 *(978-0-595-46795-2(4))* iUniverse, Inc.

Brinkley, Douglas. Jack Kerouac Biography. 2007. 496p. 34.95 *(978-0-670-06354-3(1),* Viking Adult) Penguin Group (USA) Inc.

Brinkmeyer, Robert H. The Fourth Ghost: White Southern Writers & European Fascism, 1930-1950. 2009. *(978-0-8071-3383-5(3))* Louisiana State Univ. Pr.

Brodsky, Louis Daniel. William Faulkner, Life Glimpses. 2011. (ENG.). 238p. pap. 25.00 ***(978-0-292-73991-8(5))*** Univ. of Texas Pr.

Bromfield, Louis. From My Experience. 355p. reprint ed. lib. bdg. 26.95 *(978-0-88411-540-3(2))* Amereon LTD.

Brookshire, Lajoyce. Faith under Fire: Betrayed by a Thing Called Love. 2009. (ENG.). 272p. pap. 15.00 *(978-1-4165-9601-1(1),* Gallery Books/Karen Hunter Publishing) Gallery Books/Karen Hunter Publishing.

Brown, Carolyn J. A Daring Life: A Biography of Eudora Welty. 2012. (ENG.). 144p. 20.00 ***(978-1-61703-295-0(6))*** Univ. Pr. of Mississippi.

Brown, Dale. The Book of Buechner: A Journey Through His Writings. 2007. (ENG., Illus.). 394p. 25.00 *(978-0-664-23113-2(6))* Westminster John Knox Pr.

—Conversations with American Writers: The Doubt, the Faith, the In-Between. 2008. (Illus.). 318p. pap. 18.00 *(978-0-8028-6228-0(4))* Eerdmans, William B. Publishing Co.

Brown, Fleda. Driving with Dvorák: Essays on Memory & Identity. 2010. (American Lives Ser.). (ENG.). 284p. 24.95 *(978-0-8032-2476-6(1))* Univ. of Nebraska Pr.

Brown, James. The Los Angeles Diaries: A Memoir. 2011. (ENG.). 224p. pap. 14.95 *(978-1-58243-720-0(3),* Counterpoint) Counterpoint LLC.

—This River. 2010. 225p. 23.95 *(978-1-60747-722-8(X))* Phoenix Bks., Inc.

—This River: A Memoir. 2011. (ENG.). 224p. pap. 14.95 *(978-1-58243-721-7(1),* Counterpoint) Counterpoint LLC.

Brown, Lois. Pauline Elizabeth Hopkins: Black Daughter of the Revolution. 2008. (ENG., Illus.). 704p. 49.95 *(978-0-8078-3166-3(2))* Univ. of North Carolina Pr.

Brown, Mary Ward. Fanning the Spark: A Memoir. 2009. (ENG., Illus.). 160p. 24.95 *(978-0-8173-1645-7(0))* Univ. of Alabama Pr.

Brown, Rita Mae. Animal Magnetism: My Life with Creatures Great & Small. 2010. (ENG., Illus.). 256p. pap. 16.00 *(978-0-345-51180-5(8),* Ballantine Bks.) Random House Publishing Group.

—Animal Magnetism: My Life with Creatures Great & Small. l.t. ed. 2010. (ENG.). 353p. 31.95 *(978-1-4104-2520-1(7))* Thorndike Pr.

Brown, Robert V. N. Reflections from Chapel Hill, V1, No 1, June 1961. Brown, Robert V. N. et al, eds. 2011. 26p. 35.95 ***(978-1-258-07337-4(4))*** Literary Licensing, LLC.

Broyard, Bliss. One Drop: My Father's Hidden Life — A Story of Race & Family Secrets. 2008. (ENG., Illus.). 544p. pap. 15.99 *(978-0-316-00806-8(0),* Back Bay Bks.) Little Brown & Co.

Bruni, Frank. Born Round: A Story of Family, Food, & a Ferocious Appetite. 2010. (ENG.). 368p. (gr. 12). 16.00 *(978-0-14-311767-4(X),* Penguin (Non-Classics)) Penguin Group (USA) Inc.

Bryant, William Cullen. A Discourse on the Life, Character & Genius of Washington Irving, Delivered Before the New York Historical Society, at the Academy of Music in New Y. 2006. 492p. per. 29.99 *(978-1-4255-5527-6(6))* MPublishing.

Bryer, Jackson R. & Hartig, Mary C. The Facts on File Companion to American Drama. 2nd rev. ed. 2010. (Companion to Literature Ser.). 656p. (C). (gr. 9-18). 85.00 *(978-0-8160-7748-9(7))* Facts On File, Inc.

Buckley, Theresa M. Zuba. American Born: A Biography of Joseph John Brozena. 2007. 14.00 *(978-0-8059-8892-5(0))* Dorrance Publishing Co., Inc.

Buechner, Frederick. The Yellow Leaves: A Miscellany. 2008. (ENG.). 152p. 17.00 *(978-0-664-23276-4(0))* Westminster John Knox Pr.

Bufill, José Ángel & Reyes, Alfonso. Los Amigos Cubanos de Alfonso Reyes: Correspondencia. 2010. (SPA.). xi, 944p. *(978-93-480-4827-1(9))* Alexandria Library, Inc.

Burana, Lily. I Love a Man in Uniform: A Memoir of Love, War, & Other Battles. 2010. (ENG.). 368p. pap. 14.95 *(978-1-60286-125-1(0),* Weinstein Bks.) Perseus Bks. Group.

Burgess, Glenda. The Geography of Love. 2008. 304p. *(978-0-7322-8739-9(1))* HarperCollins Pubs. Australia.

—The Geography of Love: A Memoir. 2009. (ENG.). 320p. pap. 14.00 *(978-0-7679-2870-0(9))* Broadway Bks.

Burkhardt, Barbara A. William Maxwell: A Literary Life. 2008. (ENG., Illus.). 336p. pap. 25.95 *(978-0-252-07583-4(8))* Univ. of Illinois Pr.

Burman, Ben Lucien. Ben Lucien Burman: A Critical Appreciation & A Biographical Sketch. 2011. 16p. pap. 35.95 ***(978-1-258-06834-9(6))*** Literary Licensing, LLC.

Burn, Stephen J. David Foster Wallace's Infinite Jest: A Reader's Guide. 2nd ed. 2012. (ENG.). 144p. pap. 19.95 *(978-1-4411-5707-2(7))* Continuum International Publishing Group, Ltd. GBR. Dist: National Bk. Network.

Burn, Stephen J., ed. Conversations with David Foster Wallace. 2012. (Literary Conversations Ser.). (ENG.). 208p. 65.00 ***(978-1-61703-226-4(3))*** Univ. Pr. of Mississippi.

—Conversations with David Foster Wallace. 2012. (Literary Conversations Ser.). (ENG.). 208p. pap. 25.00 ***(978-1-61703-227-1(1))*** Univ. Pr. of Mississippi.

Burns, Carole. Off the Page: Writers Talk about Beginnings, Endings, & Everything in Between. 2007. (ENG.). 240p. per. 14.95 *(978-0-393-33088-5(5),* 33088) Norton, W. W. & Co., Inc.

Burns, Jennifer. Goddess of the Market: Ayn Rand & the American Right, 1 vol. (ENG., Illus.). 384p. 2011. pap. 18.95 *(978-0-19-983248-4(X))* 2009. 27.95 *(978-0-19-532487-7(0))* Oxford Univ. Pr., Inc.

Burroughs, Augusten. You Better Not Cry: Stories. 2010. (ENG.). 224p. pap. 14.00 *(978-0-312-43006-1(X))* Picador.

Burroughs, John. Pepacton. 2009. 252p. 23.99 *(978-1-103-01518-4(4))*; pap. 17.99 *(978-1-103-01516-0(8))* BiblioBazaar.

—Pepacton. 2007. (ENG.). 136p. per. *(978-1-4068-2367-7(8))* Echo Library.

—Pepacton. 2008. (ENG.). 300p. 32.95 *(978-1-4344-9786-4(0))*; per. 19.95 *(978-1-4344-9785-7(2))* Wildside Pr., LLC.

Burstein, Andrew. The Original Knickerbocker: The Life of Washington Irving. (ENG., Illus.). 2008. 432p. per. 17.50 *(978-0-465-00854-4(2))* 2007. 440p. 27.50 *(978-0-465-00853-7(4))* Basic Bks.

Burton, Alan. From a Window Or: Memoirs of a Distant Mind. 2008. 496p. 30.99 *(978-1-4389-3084-8(4))*; pap. 20.49 *(978-1-4389-3083-1(6))* AuthorHouse.

Burton, Ryan & Davis, Darren G. Twilight Unbound. 2010. (Illus.). 40p. 12.99 *(978-1-4507-0015-3(2))* Bluewater Productions, Inc.

Busby, Mark & Dixon, Terrell, eds. John Graves, Writer. 2007. (ENG., Illus.). 286p. 34.95 *(978-0-292-71494-6(7))* Univ. of Texas Pr.

Cady, Edwin Harrison. The Road to Realism: The Early Years of William Dean Howells, 1837-1885. 2011. 294p. 48.95 ***(978-1-258-05807-4(3))*** Literary Licensing, LLC.

Calabi, Silvio & Helsley, Steve. Hemingway's Guns: The Sporting Arms of Ernest Hemingway. 2010. (ENG.). 156p. 40.00 *(978-0-89272-720-9(9))* Down East Bks.

Callaghan, Morley. That Summer in Paris. 2007. (Exile Classics Ser.). (ENG., Illus.). 232p. pap. 16.95 *(978-1-55096-688-6(X))* Exile Editions, Ltd. CAN. Dist: Independent Pubs. Group.

Cameron, Julia. The Creative Life: True Tales of Inspiration. (ENG., 256p. (gr. 12). 2012. Illus.). pap. 15.95 ***(978-0-399-16052-3(3))*** 2010. 23.95 *(978-1-58542-824-3(8))* Penguin Group (USA) Inc. (Tarcher).

Cameron, Julia. Floor Sample: A Creative Memoir. 2007. (ENG.). 416p. (gr. 12-18). 14.95 *(978-1-58542-557-0(5),* Tarcher) Penguin Group (USA) Inc.

Cameron, Kenneth Walter. Emerson & Thoreau As Readers: Selected Chapters from the Transcendentalists & Minerva. 2011. 122p. 40.95 ***(978-1-258-02339-3(3))*** Literary Licensing, LLC.

Campion, Christopher John. Escape from Bellevue: A Memoir of Rock 'n' Roll, Recovery, & Redemption. 2009. (ENG.). 384p. (gr. 12-18). 18.00 *(978-1-59240-530-5(4),* Gotham) Penguin Group (USA) Inc.

Canning, Richard. Whitman. 2012. (Poetic Lives Ser.). (ENG.). 112p. pap. 12.95 *(978-1-84391-305-4(4))* Hesperus Pr. GBR. Dist: Independent Pubs. Group.

Capper, Charles. Margaret Fuller: An American Romantic Life Volume II: the Public Years. 2010. (ENG., Illus.). 672p. pap. 35.00 *(978-0-19-539632-4(4))* Oxford Univ. Pr., Inc.

Caputo, Philip. Means of Escape: A War Correspondent's Memoir of Life & Death in Afghanistan, the Middle East, & Vietnam. 2009. (ENG.). 400p. pap. 17.00 *(978-0-8050-8963-9(2),* Holt Paperback) Holt, Henry & Co.

Carkeet, David. Campus Sexpot: A Memoir. 2007. (Association of Writers & Writing Programs Award for Creative Nonfiction Ser.). (ENG.). 152p. per. 17.95 *(978-0-8203-3013-6(2))* Univ. of Georgia Pr.

Carl Van Doren. Contemporary American Novelists. 2007. 124p. pap. 18.99 *(978-1-4346-0017-2(3))*; (ENG.). 138p. pap. 19.99 *(978-1-4346-0020-2(3))* BiblioBazaar.

Carlyle, Thomas. The Correspondence of Thomas Carlyle & Ralph Waldo Emerson, 1834-1872. l.t. ed. 2006. (ENG.). 1. 298p. pap. 23.99 *(978-1-4264-7372-2(9))*2. 324p. pap. 24.99 *(978-1-4264-7373-9(7))* BiblioBazaar.

Caron, James E. Mark Twain, Unsanctified Newspaper Reporter. (MARK TWAIN & HIS CIRCLE Ser.). (ENG., Illus.). 464p. (C). 2011. (gr. 13). pap. 35.00 *(978-0-8262-1955-8(1))* 2008. 49.95 *(978-0-8262-1802-5(4))* Univ. of Missouri Pr.

Carr. Riverine: An Anthology of Hudson Valley Writers. Carr, Laurence, ed. 2010. (Codhill Press Ser.). 314p. pap. 20.00 *(978-1-930337-32-9(9),* Suny Pr.) State Univ. of New York Pr.

Carr, John F. H. Beam Piper: A Biography. Palumbo, Donald & Sullivan, C. W., III, eds. 2008. (Critical Explorations in Science Fiction & Fantasy Ser.: Vol. 8). (ENG., Illus.). 262p. 45.00 *(978-0-7864-3375-9(2))* McFarland & Co., Inc. Pubs.

Carr, Pat. One Page at a Time: On a Writing Life. 2010. (Illus.). 288p. 25.95 *(978-0-89672-716-8(5))* Texas Tech Univ. Pr.

Carr, Virginia Spencer. Paul Bowles: A Life. 2009. (ENG.). 428p. pap. 21.95 *(978-0-8101-2525-4(0))* Northwestern Univ. Pr.

Carroll, Lucy E. The Hymn Writers of Early Pennsylvani. 2008. 132p. pap. 14.99 *(978-1-60647-520-1(7))* Xulon Pr., Inc.

Carroll, Pamela Sissi. Sharon Creech, 1 vol. 2007. (Teen Reads: Student Companions to Young Adult Literature Ser.). 216p. 45.00 *(978-0-313-33598-3(2),* GR3598, Greenwood Pr.) Greenwood Publishing Group, Inc.

Cart, Michael. Talking Animals & Others. 2009. (ENG.). 272p. (gr. 12). 29.95 *(978-1-59020-170-1(1))* Overlook Pr., The.

Carter, Forrest. The Education of Little Tree. 20.95 *(978-0-8488-0955-3(6))* Amereon LTD.

Carter, Robert Ayres. Somewhere I Have Never Traveled: Memories of A Writer's Life 1969-1976. 2010. 464p. pap. 20.49 *(978-1-4520-3543-7(1))* AuthorHouse.

Carter, Zoe FitzGerald. Imperfect Endings: A Daughter's Story of Love, Loss, & Letting Go. 2011. (ENG.). 288p. pap. 15.00 *(978-1-4391-4831-0(7))* Simon & Schuster.

Cary, Elisabeth Luther. Emerson, Poet & Thinker. 2009. 172p. pap. 19.99 *(978-1-4588-2565-0(5))* General Bks. LLC.

Cash, Jean W. Larry Brown: A Writer's Life. 2011. (Willie Morris Books in Memoir & Biography Ser.). (ENG., Illus.). 400p. 35.00 *(978-1-60473-980-0(0))* Univ. Pr. of Mississippi.

Casil, Amy Sterling. Lois Duncan. 2009. (Library of Author Biographies Ser.). 112p. (gr. 5-8). 63.90 *(978-1-60853-543-9(6),* Rosen Central) Rosen Publishing Group, Inc., The.

Castrodale, Mary L. The Water's Edge: A Walk Through My Life. 2009. 304p. pap. 25.66 *(978-0-615-18624-5(6))* Marylou Pubns.

Castronovo, David & Groth, Janet. Critic in Love: A Romantic Biography of Edmund Wilson. 2007. (ENG., Illus.). 240p. per. 16.95 *(978-1-59376-153-0(8))* Counterpoint LLC.

Catling, Patrick Skene. Better Than Working. 2006. (ENG., Illus.). 302p. pap. 27.95 *(978-1-905483-06-8(6))* Liberties Pr. IRL. Dist: Dufour Editions, Inc.

Chaddock, Katherine Elise. The Multi-Talented Mr. Erskine: Shaping Mass Culture through Great Books & Fine Music. 2012. (ENG., Illus.). 270p. 90.00 ***(978-0-230-11775-4(9))*** Palgrave Macmillan.

Chambers, Douglas B., ed. Personal Souths: Interviews from the Southern Quarterly. 2012. (ENG.). 352p. 65.00 ***(978-1-61703-290-5(5))***; 312p. pap. 30.00 ***(978-1-61703-291-2(3))*** Univ. Pr. of Mississippi.

Charters, Ann & Charters, Samuel Barclay. Brother-Souls: John Clellon Holmes, Jack Kerouac, & the Beat Generation. 2010. (ENG., Illus.). 464p. 35.00 *(978-1-60473-579-6(1))* Univ. Pr. of Mississippi.

Chase, Lewis Nathaniel. Poe & His Poetry. 2008. 132p. 35.95 *(978-1-4366-2320-9(0))*; pap. 20.95 *(978-0-548-86648-1(1))* Kessinger Publishing, LLC.

Cheche, Tom. Exit: A Sporting Life Just off the Jersey Turnpike. 2009. 252p. pap. 15.95 *(978-1-934937-90-7(8))* Mill City Pr., Inc.

Cheever, Susan. Louisa May Alcott. l.t. ed. 2011. 443p. 31.99 *(978-1-4104-3552-1(0))* Thorndike Pr.

—Louisa May Alcott: A Personal Biography. 2011. (ENG., Illus.). 320p. pap. 16.00 *(978-1-4165-6992-3(8))* Simon & Schuster.

Cheney, Ednah, ed. Louisa May Alcott: Her Life, Letters, & Journals. 2010. (ENG., Illus.). 428p. pap. 19.95 *(978-1-4290-4460-8(8))* Applewood Bks.

Cherry, Kelly. Girl in a Library: On Women Writers & the Writing Life. 2009. 234p. pap. 16.95 *(978-1-886157-66-8(9))* BkMk Pr. of the Univ. of Missouri-Kansas City.

Child, Lydia Maria. Letters of Lydia Maria Child, with a Biographical Introduction by John G Whittier & an Appendix by Wendell Phillips. 2006. 328p. per. 23.99 *(978-1-4255-3287-1(X))* MPublishing.

Childs, John Brown, ed. Hurricane Katrina: Response & Responsibilities. 2nd ed. 2008. (ENG.). 224p. pap. 10.00 *(978-1-55643-792-2(7))* North Atlantic Bks.

Childs, Peter. Ian Mcewan's Enduring Love. 2007. (Routledge Guides to Literature Ser.). (ENG.). 160p. per. 28.95 *(978-0-415-34559-0(6))* Routledge.

—Rout Guid End Love Cont & Crit. 2007. (Routledge Guides to Literature Ser.). (ENG.). 160p. 95.00 *(978-0-415-34558-3(8))* Routledge.

Chipperfield, Faith. In Quest of Love the Life & Death of M. 2006. pap. 30.95 *(978-1-4286-5595-9(6))* Kessinger Publishing, LLC.

Christensen, Mark. Acid Christ: Ken Kesey, LSD, & the Politics of Ecstasy. 2010. (ENG., Illus.). 440p. 26.95 *(978-1-936182-00-8(9))* Schaffner Pr., Inc.

Christensen, Mark. Acid Christ: Ken Kesey, LSD & the Politics of Ecstasy. 2011. (ENG.). 440p. pap. 16.95 ***(978-1-936182-27-5(0))*** Schaffner Pr., Inc.

Chubb, Edwin Watts. Stories of Authors: British & American. 2008. (Illus.). 288p. pap. *(978-1-4099-5064-6(6))* Dodo Pr.

—Stories of Authors: British & American. 2007. (ENG.). 414p. 49.95 *(978-0-548-06735-2(X))* Kessinger Publishing, LLC.

Chura, Patrick. Thoreau the Land Surveyor. (ENG., Illus.). 2011. 224p. pap. 19.95 ***(978-0-8130-4147-6(3))*** 2010. 192p. 34.95 *(978-0-8130-3493-5(0))* Univ. Pr. of Florida.

Clabough, Casey. The Art of the Magic Striptease: The Literary Layers of George Garrett. 2008. (ENG.). 224p. 39.95 *(978-0-8130-3176-7(1))* Univ. Pr. of Florida.

Clara Barrus. Our Friend John Burroughs. 2007. (ENG.). 168p. pap. 19.99 *(978-1-4264-4944-4(5))* 2006. 188p. pap. 21.99 *(978-1-4264-5245-1(4))* BiblioBazaar.

Claridge, Laura. Emily Post: Daughter of the Gilded Age, Mistress of American Manners. 2009. (ENG., Illus.). 560p. pap. 18.00 *(978-0-8129-6741-8(0),* Random Hse. Trade Paperbacks) Random House Publishing Group.

Clark, Heather. The Grief of Influence: Sylvia Plath & Ted Hughes. 2011. (ENG.). 272p. 99.00 *(978-0-19-955819-3(1))* Oxford Univ. Pr., Inc.

Clark, Helen Archibal. Longfellows Country. 2006. pap. 30.95 *(978-1-4286-3456-5(8))* Kessinger Publishing, LLC.

Clark, Lewis Gaylord. Knick-Knacks from an Editor's Table by L Gaylord Clark. 2006. 352p. per. 23.99 *(978-1-4255-3556-8(9))* MPublishing.

Clarke, Edwin L. American Men of Letters: Their Nature & Nurture. (Columbia University, Studies in the Social Sciences: No. 168). reprint ed. 32.50 *(978-0-404-51168-5(6))* AMS Pr., Inc.

Clarke, Edwin Leavitt. American Men of Letters, Their Nature & Nurture. 2009. 172p. 30.99 *(978-1-115-21977-8(4))*; 26.99 *(978-1-115-21975-4(8))*; pap. 21.75 *(978-1-115-21973-0(1))* BiblioBazaar.

Clarke, Gerald. Capote: A Biography. 2010. (ENG., Illus.). 656p. pap. 17.99 *(978-1-4391-8750-0(9))* Simon & Schuster.

Clarke, Harry, illus. Nightmares in Decay: The Edgar Allan Poe Illustrations of Harry Clarke. 2010. 88p. pap. 19.95 *(978-1-902197-30-2(5))* Oneiros Bks. GBR. Dist: SCB Distributors.

Clarke, Jaime, ed. Conversations with Jonathan Lethem. 2011. (Literary Conversations Ser.). (ENG.). 224p. pap. 25.00 ***(978-1-60473-972-5(X))***; 65.00 *(978-1-60473-963-3(0))* Univ. Pr. of Mississippi.

Claude Cl, Smith. Ohio Outback. 2011. 160p. 24.95 *(978-1-60635-054-6(4))* Kent State Univ. Pr.

Clayton, John. The Cowboy Girl: The Life of Caroline Lockhart. 2007. (Women in the West Ser.). (ENG., Illus.). 338p. pap. 21.95 *(978-0-8032-5990-4(5),* Bison Bks.) Univ. of Nebraska Pr.

Clemens, Cyril. Young Sam Clemens. 292p. 2008. 43.95 *(978-1-4367-0393-2(X))* 2007. (ENG.). per. 28.95 *(978-1-4325-7262-4(8))* Kessinger Publishing, LLC.

Clemens, Samuel Langhorne. Mark Twain's Aquarium: The Samuel Clemens-Angelfish Correspondence, 1905-1910. Cooley, John, ed. 2009. (ENG.). 328p. pap. 24.95 *(978-0-8203-3498-1(7))* Univ. of Georgia Pr.

Cleverly, Michael & Braudis, Bob. The Kitchen Readings: Untold Stories of Hunter S. Thompson. 2008. (Illus.). 304p. pap. 13.99 *(978-0-06-115928-2(X),* HarperPerennial) HarperCollins Pubs.

Cliff, Michelle. If I Could Write This in Fire. 2008. 104p. 21.95 *(978-0-8166-5474-1(3))*; xi, 89p. pap. *(978-0-8166-5475-8(1))* Univ. of Minnesota Pr.

Cline, Lynn. Literary Pilgrims: The Santa Fe & Taos Writers' Colonies, 1917-1950. 2007. (ENG., Illus.). 184p. pap. 19.95 *(978-0-8263-3851-8(8))* Univ. of New Mexico Pr.

Clinton, Craig. Cora Urquhart Potter: The Victorian Actress as Provocateur. 2010. (ENG., Illus.). 262p. pap. 55.00 *(978-0-7864-4957-6(8))* McFarland & Co., Inc. Pubs.

Coady, Roxanne J. & Johannessen, Joy. The Book That Changed My Life: 71 Remarkable Writers Celebrate the Books That Matter Most to Them. Coady, Roxanne J., ed. 2007. (ENG.). 224p. (gr. 12-18). 13.00 *(978-1-59240-317-2(4),* Gotham) Penguin Group (USA) Inc.

Cody, Sherwin. Four Famous American Writers: Washington Irving Edgar Allan Poe James Russell Lowell Bayard Taylo: A Book for Young Americans. 2007. (ENG.). 166p. pap. 19.99 *(978-1-4264-3873-8(7))*; 186p. pap. 21.99 *(978-1-4264-5225-3(X))* BiblioBazaar.

Cohen, Daniel A. Pillars of Salt, Monuments of Grace: New England Crime Literature & the Origins of American Popular Culture, 1674-1860. 2006. (Commonwealth Center Studies in American Culture Ser.). (Illus.). 350p. per. 19.95 *(978-1-55849-529-6(0))* Univ. of Massachusetts Pr.

Cohen, Kerry. Seeing Ezra: A Mother's Story of Autism, Unconditional Love, & the Meaning of Normal. (ENG.). 2012. 256p. pap. 16.00 ***(978-1-58005-433-1(1))*** 2011. 288p. 25.00 *(978-1-58005-369-3(6))* Seal Pr.

Cohen, Rich. Israel Is Real: An Obsessive Quest to Understand the Jewish Nation & Its History. 2010. (ENG., Illus.). 400p. pap. 16.00 *(978-0-312-42976-8(2))* Picador.

Cohen, Samuel S. & Konstantinou, Lee. The Legacy of David Foster Wallace. 2012. (New American Canon Ser.). (ENG.). 244p. pap. 19.95 ***(978-1-60938-082-3(7))*** Univ. of Iowa Pr.

Cohn. Edward Albee-Aw V77. 2009. pap. 25.00 *(978-0-8166-0527-9(0))* Univ. of Minnesota Pr.

Coltelli, Laura, ed. Reading Leslie Marmon Silko: Critical Perspectives Through Gardens in the Dunes. 2008. (Essays & Studies). (ENG.). 240p. pap. 24.95 *(978-88-8492-432-2(4))* Plus/Pisa University Pr. ITA. Dist: Univ. of Nebraska Pr.

Colton, Elaine. The Newport Girls: A Memoir. 2010. 124p. 23.95 *(978-1-4502-3108-4(X))*; (ENG.). pap. 13.95 *(978-1-4502-3106-0(3))* iUniverse, Inc.

Comfort, Philip Wesley. Spirit Journey. 2nd ed. 2007. 144p. pap. 18.00 *(978-1-59244-654-4(X)*, Wipf and Stock) Wipf & Stock Pubs.

Connelly, Bonnie & Stern, Susan. Let's Link Literature & Social Studies. 2007. 300p. per. 24.95 *(978-0-89334-433-7(8)*, Humanics Learning) Humanics Publishing Group.

Conniff, Richard. Swimming with Piranhas at Feeding Time: My Life Doing Dumb Stuff with Animals. (ENG.). 2010. 304p. pap. 15.95 *(978-0-393-30457-2(4)*, 30457) 2009. 320p. 25.95 *(978-0-393-06893-1(5)*, 6893) Norton, W. W. & Co., Inc.

Conway, Steven. Know Hope: The Baydan Huxley Story. 2009. 228p. pap. 15.00 *(978-1-4389-5299-4(6))* AuthorHouse.

Cook-Lynn, Elizabeth. Notebooks of Elizabeth Cook-Lynn. 2007. (Sun Tracks Ser.: Vol. 59). (ENG.). 208p. pap. 16.95 *(978-0-8165-2583-6(8))* Univ. of Arizona Pr.

Cook, Raymond & Jackson, Alan, eds. Faithfully Yours: The Letters of Byron Herbert Reece. 2007. 140p. pap. 17.00 *(978-0-87797-374-4(1))* Cherokee Publishing Co.

Cooke, Harriet B. Memories of My Life Work the Autobiography of Mrs Harriet B Cooke. 2006. 360p. per. 26.99 *(978-1-4255-3659-6(X))* MPublishing.

Cooper, William Fredrick. One Season (in Pinstripes) A Memoir. 2011. (ENG.). 448p. pap. 15.00 *(978-1-59309-354-9(3)*, Strebor Bks.) Strebor Bks.

Corder, Jim W. Yonder: Life on the Far Side of Change. 2011. (ENG.). 248p. 24.95 ***(978-0-8203-3803-3(6))*** Univ. of Georgia Pr.

Cormier, Robert. Heroes. Slee, Marian, ed. 2011. (York Notes Ser.). (ENG., Illus.). 72p. (gr. 7-9). pap. 18.95 ***(978-1-4082-7003-5(X)***, Longman) Pearson Education, Ltd. GBR. Dist: Trans-Atlantic Pubns., Inc.

Coyne, Patrick. A Bio-Bibliography of Alice Duer Miller, American Writer, 1874-1942. 2010. (Illus.). 340p. 119.95 *(978-0-7734-3756-2(8))* Mellen, Edwin Pr., The.

Crain, Doreen A. My Son & an Alien! 2006. 17.00 *(978-0-8059-8830-7(0))* Dorrance Publishing Co., Inc.

Crampton, Nancy. Writers. 2007. (ENG.). 224p. pap. 25.00 *(978-1-59372-028-5(9))* Quantuck Lane Pr. & The Mill Road Collaborative, The.

Crandell, Doug. The All-American Industrial Motel: A Memoir. 2007. (ENG.). 256p. 22.95 *(978-1-55652-616-9(4))* Chicago Review Pr., Inc.

Cremony, John Carey. Life among the Apaches. 2008. (ENG.). 325p. 36.99 *(978-1-4264-1071-0(9))*; 32.99 *(978-1-4264-1153-3(7))*; pap. 31.75 *(978-1-4264-1087-1(5))*; pap. 30.75 *(978-1-4264-1137-3(5))* BiblioBazaar.

—Life among the Apaches. 2009. 196p. pap. *(978-1-150-11268-3(9))* Books LLC.

Crew, Hilary S. Donna Jo Napoli. 2010. (Scarecrow Studies in Young Adult Literature Ser.). (ENG.). 200p. 50.00 *(978-0-8108-7446-6(6))* Scarecrow Pr., Inc.

Crisler, Jesse & McElrath, Joseph. Frank Norris: A Life. 2010. (ENG., Illus.). 520p. pap. 25.00 *(978-0-252-07729-6(6))* Univ. of Illinois Pr.

Crisler, Jesse S. & Crowe, Chris. "How I Came to Write" LDS Authors for Young Adults. 2007. 292p. pap. 15.00 *(978-0-939555-09-3(3))* Ctr. for the Study of Christian Values in Literature.

Crosby, Fanny J. Fanny J Crosby: An Autobiography. 2008. 240p. 14.95 *(978-1-59856-281-1(9))* Hendrickson Pubs. Marketing, LLC.

Crosby, Howard. George Henry Moore, L L D: A memoir / by Rev. Howard Crosby, D. D. 2011. 26p. pap. 11.99 ***(978-1-4181-9295-2(3))*** MPublishing.

Crowe, Thomas Rain. Zoro's Field: My Life in the Appalachian Woods. 2006. (ENG.). 240p. per. 18.95 *(978-0-8203-2862-1(6))* Univ. of Georgia Pr.

Crowley, John W. The Black Heart's Truth: The Early Career of W. D. Howells. 2011. (ENG.). 208p. pap. 40.00 *(978-0-8078-6527-9(3))* Univ. of North Carolina Pr.

Crumbley, Paul & Gantt, Patricia M., eds. Body My House: May Swenson's Work & Life. 2006. (Illus.). 254p. 34.95 *(978-0-87421-635-6(4)*, Utah State Univ. Pr.) Univ. Pr. of Colorado.

Cudjoe, Selwyn & Cudjoe, Selwyn R. Caribbean Visionary: A. R. F. Webber & the Making of the Guyanese Nation. 2008. (Caribbean Studies Ser.). (ENG.). 304p. 50.00 *(978-1-60473-106-4(0))* Univ. Pr. of Mississippi.

Cunningham, Sarah. Picking Dandelions: A Search for Eden among Life's Weeds, 1 vol. 2010. (ENG.). 224p. pap. 14.99 *(978-0-310-29247-0(6))* Zondervan.

Cunningham, Scott. Cunningham's Book of Shadows: The Path of an American Traditionalist. 2009. (ENG., Illus.). 288p. 19.95 *(978-0-7387-1914-6(5))* Llewellyn Pubns.

Curti, Merle & Burritt, Elihu. The Learned Blacksmith: The Letters & Journals of Elihu Burritt. 2011. 254p. 47.95 ***(978-1-258-04904-1(X))*** Literary Licensing, LLC.

Curtis, George William. Early Letters of George Wm. Curtis. 2007. (ENG.). 184p. per. 19.99 *(978-1-4346-7352-7(9))*; 206p. per. 22.99 *(978-1-4346-7353-4(7))* BiblioBazaar.

—Early Letters of George Wm. Curtis. 2007. 172p. per. *(978-1-4065-1502-2(7))* Dodo Pr.

Cypert, Rick. The Virtue of Suspense: The Life & Works of Charlotte Armstrong. 2008. (ENG., Illus.). 180p. 48.50 *(978-1-57591-122-9(1))* Susquehanna Univ. Pr.

Dana, Robert. Paris on the Flats: Versions of a Literary Life. 2010. *(978-1-59732-072-6(2))*; pap. *(978-1-59732-073-3(0))* Univ. of Tampa Pr.

Daniel, Grady. A Love That Changes Lives. 2011. 166p. pap. 14.99 *(978-1-61215-598-2(7))* Xulon Pr., Inc.

Daniels, Susana. Lois Lowry. 2009. (Library of Author Biographies Ser.). 112p. (gr. 5-8). 63.90 *(978-1-60853-544-6(4)*, Rosen Central) Rosen Publishing Group, Inc., The.

Dann, Patty. The Goldfish Went on Vacation: A Memoir of Loss (and Learning to Tell the Truth about It) 2007. (ENG.). 176p. per. 11.95 *(978-1-59030-564-5(7)*, Trumpeter) Shambhala Pubns., Inc.

Danticat, Edwidge. Create Dangerously: The Immigrant Artist at Work. 2011. (Vintage Contemporaries Ser.). (ENG.). 208p. pap. 14.95 *(978-0-307-94643-0(6)*, Vintage) Knopf Doubleday Publishing Group.

Darnton, John. Almost a Family. 2012. (ENG., Illus.). 384p. pap. 16.95 ***(978-0-307-27880-7(8)***, Anchor) Knopf Doubleday Publishing Group.

Darst, Jeanne. Fiction Ruined My Family. 2011. (ENG.). 320p. (gr. 12). 25.95 *(978-1-59448-814-6(2)*, Riverhead Bks. (Hardcover)) Penguin Group (USA) Inc.

Daugherty, Tracy. Hiding Man. 2010. (ENG., Illus.). 592p. pap. 20.00 *(978-0-312-42930-0(4))* Picador.

David, Anna. Falling for Me: How I Hung Curtains, Learned to Cook, Traveled to Seville, & Fell in Love. 2011. (ENG.). 252p. pap. 14.99 *(978-0-06-199604-7(1)*, William Morrow Paperbacks) HarperCollins Pubs.

Davis, Ann. No More Indians. 2007. (ENG.). 22.95 *(978-1-60037-064-9(0))* Morgan James Publishing.

—No More Indians: Or No Book on Earth Has Lied More Sincerely Than My Ol' Virginia Text. 2007. (ENG., Illus.). 139p. per. 12.95 *(978-1-60037-063-2(2))* Morgan James Publishing.

Davis, Donald. Tales from a Free-Range Childhood. 2011. E-Book *(978-0-89587-508-2(X))*; 224p. 19.95 *(978-0-89587-507-5(1))*; 224p. pap. 12.95 *(978-0-89587-509-9(8))* Blair, John F. Pub.

Davis, Jack E. An Everglades Providence: Marjory Stoneman Douglas & the American Environmental Century. (Environmental History & the American South Ser.). (ENG., Illus.). 764p. 2011. pap. 26.95 *(978-0-8203-3779-1(X))* 2009. 34.95 *(978-0-8203-3071-6(X))* Univ. of Georgia Pr.

Davis, Judith March. Pagoda Dreamer. 2010. 274p. pap. 15.95 *(978-1-934938-90-4(4)*, Langdon Street Pr.) Hillcrest Publishing Group, Inc.

Davis, Philip. Bernard Malamud: A Writer's Life. (ENG., Illus.). 400p. 2010. pap. 18.95 *(978-0-19-957147-5(3))* 2007. 45.00 *(978-0-19-927009-5(0))* Oxford Univ. Pr., Inc.

Davis, Richard Harding. Adventures & Letters of Richard Harding Davis. 2008. 304p. 28.99 *(978-0-554-30853-1(3))* 2008. 304p. 29.99 *(978-0-554-21550-1(0))* 2006. (ENG.). pap. 17.99 *(978-1-4264-0392-7(5))* 2006. (ENG.). 314p. pap. 23.99 *(978-1-4264-0341-5(0))* BiblioBazaar.

—Adventures & Letters of Richard Harding Davis. 2006. pap. *(978-1-4065-1135-2(8))* Dodo Pr.

Davis, Steven L. J. Frank Dobie: A Liberated Mind. 2009. (ENG., Illus.). 296p. 24.95 *(978-0-292-72114-2(5))* Univ. of Texas Pr.

de Cortanze, Gerard. Hemingways Kuba. (GER.). *(978-3-8067-2848-4(8))* Gerstenberg DEU. Dist: International Bk. Import Service, Inc.

de Maistre, Xavier. Journey Around My Room. 2011. (Green Integer Ser.). (ENG.). 200p. pap. 12.95 *(978-1-933382-78-4(3))* Green Integer.

de Rachewiltz, Mary, et al. Ezra Pound to His Parents: Letters 1895-1929. 2011. (ENG., Illus.). 768p. 65.00 *(978-0-19-958439-0(7))* Oxford Univ. Pr., Inc.

De Roche, Linda. Mary Higgins Clark: Life & Letters, 1 vol. 2011. (Illus.). 172p. 44.95 *(978-0-313-36637-6(3)*, C36637); E-Book *(978-0-313-36638-3(1))* Greenwood Publishing Group, Inc. (Praeger Pubs.)

Delbanco, Andrew. Melville: His World & Work. 2006. (Vintage Ser.). (ENG., Illus.). 448p. per. 17.00 *(978-0-375-70297-6(0)*, Vintage) Knopf Doubleday Publishing Group.

Denard, Carolyn C., ed. Toni Morrison: Conversations. 2008. (ENG.). 224p. 50.00 *(978-1-60473-018-0(8))*; pap. 22.00 *(978-1-60473-019-7(6))* Univ. Pr. of Mississippi.

Denham, Robert D. & Wright, Charles. Charles Wright in Conversation: Interviews, 1979-2006. 2008. (ENG.). 183p. pap. 39.95 *(978-0-7864-3965-2(3))* McFarland & Co., Inc. Pubs.

dePaola, Tomie. Christmas Remembered. 2009. (ENG.). 96p. (J). (gr. -1-18). pap. 9.99 *(978-0-14-241481-1(6)*, Puffin) Penguin Group (USA) Inc.

Deppman, Jed. Trying to Think with Emily Dickinson. 2008. (Illus.). 272p. (ENG.). pap. 26.95 *(978-1-55849-684-2(X))*; lib. bdg. 80.00 net. *(978-1-55849-683-5(1))* Univ. of Massachusetts Pr.

Derleth, August. Concord Rebel: A Life of Henry D. Thoreau. 2011. 230p. 46.95 ***(978-1-258-00228-2(0))*** Literary Licensing, LLC.

—In the Course of My Walks. Quinney, Richard, ed. 2009. (ENG., Illus.). 88p. 25.00 *(978-0-9815620-2-5(7))* Borderland Bks.

—Wisconsin Writers & Writing. pap. 16.00 *(978-1-896648-98-9(3))* Battered Silicon Dispatch Box, The.

DeSalvo, Louise A. On Moving: A Writer's Meditation on New Houses, Old Haunts, & Finding Home Again. 2009. (ENG., Illus.). 240p. 22.00 *(978-1-58234-581-9(3))* Bloomsbury Publishing.

Dewey, Anne Day. Beyond Maximus: The Construction of Public Voice in Black Mountain Poetry. 2007. (ENG.). 304p. 60.00 *(978-0-8047-5647-1(3))* Stanford Univ. Pr.

Diamond, Morris I. The Name Dropper or People I Schlepped With. 2011. 350p. pap. 21.95 ***(978-1-59393-653-2(2))*** BearManor Media.

Dick, Anne R. The Search for Philip K. Dick, 1928-1982. 2010. (ENG.). 288p. pap. 14.95 *(978-1-61696-000-1(0))* Tachyon Pubns.

Dickens, Charles. The Letters of Charles Dickens - Volume I - 1833 To 1856. Mamie Dickens & Georgina Hogarth, eds. 2009. (Illus.). 344p. pap. 9.95 *(978-1-60386-218-9(8)*, Merchant Bks.) Rough Draft Printing.

Dickson, Foster. The Life & Poetry of John Beecher (1904-1980) Advocate of Poetry as a Spoken Art. 2009. 152p. *(978-0-7734-4654-0(0))* Mellen, Edwin Pr., The.

Didion, Joan. The Year of Magical Thinking. 2007. (Vintage International Ser.). (ENG., Illus.). 240p. pap. 14.95 *(978-1-4000-7843-1(1)*, Vintage) Knopf Doubleday Publishing Group.

DiDonato, Tiffanie & Dyball, Rennie. Dwarf: A Memoir. 2012. (ENG.). 272p. (gr. 12). pap. 15.00 ***(978-0-452-29811-8(3)***, Plume) Penguin Group (USA) Inc.

Dittman, Michael J. Masterpieces of Beat Literature, 1 vol. 2006. (Greenwood Introduces Literary Masterpieces Ser.). 136p. 49.95 *(978-0-313-33283-8(5)*, GR3283, Greenwood Pr.) Greenwood Publishing Group, Inc.

Djos, Matts G. Writing under the Influence: Alcoholism & the Alcoholic Perception from Hemingway to Berryman. 2010. (ENG.). 188p. 79.00 *(978-0-230-10260-6(3))* Palgrave Macmillan.

Doane, George Washington. The Sacred Sympathy of Sorrow the Discourse Commemorative of the Rev William Croswell Preached in the Church of the Advent, Boston on Sunday, De. 2011. 32p. pap. 11.99 ***(978-1-4181-9453-6(0))*** MPublishing.

Dodson, Kenneth. The Poet & the Sailor: The Story of My Friendship with Carl Sandburg. Dodson, Richard, ed. 2007. (Illus.). 224p. 37.00 *(978-0-252-03127-4(X))* Univ. of Illinois Pr.

Doerr, Anthony. Four Seasons in Rome: On Twins, Insomnia, & the Biggest Funeral in the History of the World. 2008. (ENG., Illus.). 224p. pap. 14.00 *(978-1-4165-7316-6(X)*, Scribner) Scribner.

Dollarhide, Louis & Abadie, Ann J., eds. Eudora Welty: A Form of Thanks. 2011. (ENG.). 138p. pap. 30.00 ***(978-1-61703-212-7(3))*** Univ. Pr. of Mississippi.

Domínguez Michael, Christopher. Diccionario Crítico de la Literatura Mexicana, 1955-2005. 2007. (Letras Mexicanas Ser.). (SPA.). 588p. 30.95 *(978-968-16-8478-5(8))* Fondo de Cultura Economica USA.

Donaldson, Scott. Death of a Rebel: The Charlie Fenton Story. 2011. (ENG.). 198p. 65.00 ***(978-1-61147-493-0(0))*** Fairleigh Dickinson Univ. Pr.

Dorfman, Ariel. Feeding on Dreams: Confessions of an Unrepentant Exile. (ENG.). 352p. 2012. pap. 14.95 ***(978-0-547-84418-3(2)***, Mariner Bks.) 2011. 27.00 *(978-0-547-54946-0(6))* Houghton Mifflin Harcourt Trade & Reference Pubs.

Dorman, Dave. The Art of Dave Dorman. 2008. 256p. 49.99 *(978-1-935002-07-9(4))* Desperado Publishing.

Dossick, Philip. Transplant: 35th Anniversary Edition. 2011. 224p. 28.95 *(978-1-4502-9713-4(7))*; pap. 18.95 *(978-1-4502-9714-1(5))* iUniverse, Inc.

Doty, Kathryn Adams. Becoming the Mother of Me: A Memoir. 2009. (ENG.). 144p. pap. 16.95 *(978-1-889020-27-3(3))* Edinborough Pr.

Dougherty, David C. Shouting down the Silence: A Biography of Stanley Elkin. 2010. (ENG., Illus.). 296p. 40.00 *(978-0-252-03508-1(9))* Univ. of Illinois Pr.

Dowling, David. The Business of Literary Circles in Nineteenth-Century America. 2011. (Nineteenth-Century Major Lives & Letters Ser.). (ENG.). 304p. 89.00 *(978-0-230-11046-5(0))* Palgrave Macmillan.

—Capital Letters: Authorship in the Antebellum Literary Market. 2009. (ENG., Illus.). 226p. 39.95 *(978-1-58729-784-7(1))* Univ. of Iowa Pr.

Dowling, Linda. Charles Eliot Norton: The Art of Reform in Nineteenth-Century America. 2008. (Becoming Modern: New Nineteenth-Century Studies). (ENG.). 248p. pap. 26.00 *(978-1-58465-678-4(6)*, University of New Hampshire Press) Univ. Pr. of New England.

Downing, Michael. Life with Sudden Death: A Tale of Moral Hazard & Medical Misadventure. 2010. (ENG.). 256p. pap. 15.95 *(978-1-58243-615-9(0)*, Counterpoint) Counterpoint LLC.

Dreiser, Theodore. Letters to Women Vol. 2: New Letters. Riggio, Thomas P. ed. 2009. (Dreiser Edition Ser.). (ENG., Illus.). 432p. 62.00 *(978-0-252-03376-6(0))* Univ. of Illinois Pr.

—Newspaper Days: An Autobiography. 2009. 388p. pap. *(978-1-150-04638-4(4))* Books LLC.

—Newspaper Days: An Autobiography. 2009. 512p. 55.95 *(978-1-120-84509-2(2))*; pap. 40.95 *(978-1-120-65516-5(1))* Kessinger Publishing, LLC.

Drew, Bernard A. 100 Most Popular Contemporary Mystery Authors: Biographical Sketches & Bibliographies, 1 vol. 2011. (Popular Authors Ser.). (Illus.). 439p. 65.00 *(978-1-59884-445-0(8)*, A2900C) Libraries Unlimited, Inc.

—The 100 Most Popular Contemporary Mystery Authors: Biographical Sketches & Bibliographies. 2011. E-Book *(978-1-59884-446-7(6))* Libraries Unlimited, Inc.

—100 Most Popular Thriller & Suspense Authors: Biographical Sketches & Bibliographies, 1 vol. 2009. (Popular Authors Ser.). 468p. 65.00 *(978-1-59158-699-9(2)*, LU8699) Libraries Unlimited, Inc.

Driscoll, Charles B. Kansas Irish. 2011. (ENG., Illus.). 320p. pap. 16.50 *(978-1-929731-09-1(4))* Rowfant Pr.

Duberman, Martin B. The Worlds of Lincoln Kirstein. 2008. (ENG.). 736p. pap. 22.95 *(978-0-8101-2518-6(8))* Northwestern Univ. Pr.

Dubner, Stephen J. Choosing My Religion: A Memoir of a Family Beyond Belief. 2006. (P. S. Ser.). (Illus.). 368p. per. 14.99 *(978-0-06-113299-5(3)*, HarperPerennial) HarperCollins Pubs.

DuBow, Wendy, ed. Conversations with Anaïs Nin. 2011. (ENG.). pap. 30.00 *(978-1-61703-059-8(7))* Univ. Pr. of Mississippi.

Dueñas, Alcira. Indians & Mestizos in the Lettered City: Reshaping Justice, Social Hierarchy, & Political Cuture in Colonial Peru. 2010. (ENG., Illus.). 320p. 70.00 *(978-1-60732-018-0(5))* Univ. Pr. of Colorado.

Duff, Gerald. Home Truths: A Deep East Texas Memory. 2011. (ENG.). 160p. pap. 21.95 *(978-0-87565-435-5(5))* Texas Christian Univ. Pr.

Duffey, Bernard I. The Chicago Renaissance in American Letters: A Critical History. 2011. 294p. 48.95 ***(978-1-258-04728-3(4))*** Literary Licensing, LLC.

Dukes, David. A Journey Back Home: The Story of the Johnson-Brinson Project & Break Away. 2010. 160p. (ENG.). 22.49 *(978-1-4490-4893-8(5))*; pap. 11.99 *(978-1-4490-4892-1(7))* AuthorHouse.

Duncan, Robert Edward & Mottram, Eric. The Unruly Garden: Robert Duncan & Eric Mottram Letters & Essays. Evans, Amy & Zamir, Shamoon, eds. 2007. 225p. pap. 73.95 *(978-3-03911-394-1(1))* Lang, Peter Publishing, Inc.

Eberwein, Jane Donahue & MacKenzie, Cindy, eds. Reading Emily Dickinson's Letters: Critical Essays. 2009. (Illus.). 304p. 39.95 net. *(978-1-55849-741-2(2))* Univ. of Massachusetts Pr.

Edel. Henry James, Vol. 4. 2009. pap. 25.00 *(978-0-8166-0206-3(9))* Univ. of Minnesota Pr.

Edgerton, Clyde & Edgerton, Clyde. Solo: My Adventures in the Air. 2006. (ENG., Illus.). 288p. pap. 12.95 *(978-1-56512-546-9(0)*, 1565125460, Shannon Ravenel Bks.) Algonquin Bks. of Chapel Hill.

Edwards, Anne. Leaving Home: A Hollywood Blacklisted Writer's Years Abroad. 2012. (ENG., Illus.). 248p. 29.95 ***(978-0-8108-8199-0(3))***; E-Book ***(978-0-8108-8200-3(0))*** Scarecrow Pr., Inc.

Edwards, Anne K. & Quillen, Lida E., eds. How I Wrote My First Book: The Story Behind the Story. 2011. pap. 15.95 *(978-1-60619-149-1(7))* Twilight Times Bks.

Edwards, Justin D. Understanding Jamaica Kincaid. 2007. (Understanding Contemporary American Literature Ser.). 159p. 39.95 *(978-1-57003-688-0(8))* Univ. of South Carolina Pr.

Edwards, Steve. Breaking into the Backcountry. 2010. (ENG.). 192p. pap. 16.95 *(978-0-8032-2653-1(5)*, Bison Bks.) Univ. of Nebraska Pr.

Eisner, Will. Life, in Pictures: Autobiographical Stories. 2007. (ENG., Illus.). 496p. 29.95 *(978-0-393-06107-9(8)*, 6107) Norton, W. W. & Co., Inc.

Elbert, Monika M., et al, eds. Reinventing the Peabody Sisters. annot. ed. 2006. 294p. (C). 39.95 *(978-1-58729-504-1(0))* Univ. of Iowa Pr.

Eldred, Greg. The Anti-Aesthetics of Jean Genet. 2009. 100p. pap. *(978-3-639-16467-1(9))* VDM Verlag Dr. Mueller e.K.

Eller, Jonathan R. Becoming Ray Bradbury. 2011. (ENG., Illus.). 360p. 34.95 ***(978-0-252-03629-3(8))*** Univ. of Illinois Pr.

Elliott, Jane. Popular Feminist Fiction As American Allegory: Representing National Time. 2008. (ENG.). 240p. 89.00 *(978-0-230-60542-8(7))* Palgrave Macmillan.

Elliott, Stephen. The Adderall Diaries: A Memoir of Moods, Masochism, & Murder. 2010. (ENG.). 192p. pap. 14.00 *(978-1-55597-570-8(4))* Graywolf Pr.

Ellis, Sherry, ed. Illuminating Fiction. 2009. (ENG.). 224p. pap. 19.95 *(978-1-59709-068-1(9))* Red Hen Pr.

Ellroy, James. The Hilliker Curse. 2011. (Vintage Ser.). (ENG.). 224p. pap. 14.95 *(978-0-307-47739-2(8)*, Vintage) Knopf Doubleday Publishing Group.

Elmer, Emma. If You're Going Through Hell, Keep Going. 2007. 143p. pap. 13.95 *(978-0-7414-4322-9(8))* Infinity Publishing.

Emerson, Ralph Waldo. Correspondence Between John Sterling and. 2006. pap. 19.95 *(978-1-4286-3641-5(2))* Kessinger Publishing, LLC.

—Emerson in Concord: A Memoir Written for the Social Circle in Concord Massachusetts. 2007. (ENG.). 272p. 42.95 *(978-0-548-03085-1(5))* Kessinger Publishing, LLC.

—Emerson in Concord: A Memoir Written for the Social Circle in Concord Massachusetts. 266p. reprint ed. 48.00 *(978-0-7950-1533-5(X))* New Library Press LLC.

—Mr Emerson Writes a Letter about Walden. West, Herbert Faulkner, ed. 2011. 18p. 35.95 ***(978-1-258-00329-6(5))*** Literary Licensing, LLC.

—Ralph Waldo Emerson No. 202: Selected Journals, 1841-1877. Rosenwald, Lawrence, ed. 2010. (ENG.). 992p. (gr. 12-18). 40.00 *(978-1-59853-068-1(2))* Library of America, The.

—Ralph Waldo Emerson's: Selected Journals, 1820-1842. Rosenwald, Lawrence, ed. 2010. (ENG.). 992p. (gr. 12-18). 40.00 *(978-1-59853-067-4(4))* Library of America, The.

Endless Mountains Writing Project Staff. Voices of the Twin Tiers; A Celebration of Writing Contest Winners 2007-2008. 2008. 176p. pap. 15.95 *(978-0-9800429-6-2(8))* Pen & Publish Inc.

Ephron, Amy. Loose Diamonds: And Other Things I've Lost (And Found) along the Way. 2012. (ENG.). 176p. pap. 13.99 (978-0-06-195878-6(6), William Morrow Paperbacks) HarperCollins Pubs.

—Loose Diamonds: ...And Other Things I've Lost (And Found) along the Way. 2011. (ENG.). 224p. 19.99 (978-0-06-195874-8(3), Morrow, William & Co.) HarperCollins Pubs.

Eppridge, Bill, photos by. Roaring in the Blood: Remembering Robert F. Jones. 2009. (ENG., Illus.). 208p. 35.00 (978-0-9660212-9-5(0), 966029) Skyhorse Publishing Co., Inc.

Epstein, Joseph, ed. Literary Genius: 25 Classic Writers Who Define English & American Literature. 2007. (ENG., Illus.). 256p. pap. 18.95 (978-1-58988-035-1(8)) Dry, Paul Bks., Inc.

Epstein, Joseph & Moser, Barry. Literary Genius: 25 Classic Writers Who Define English & American Literature. 2007. (978-1-58988-039-9(0)) Dry, Paul Bks., Inc.

Erickson, John R. Story Craft: Reflections on Faith, Culture, & Writing from the Author of Hank the Cowdog. 2009. 168p. pap. 12.99 (978-1-59188-891-8(3)) Maverick Bks., Inc.

Erskine, John. Leading American Novelists. 2009. 228p. pap. 21.24 (978-1-150-67522-5(5)) General Bks. LLC.

—Leading American Novelists. 2008. 402p. 49.95 (978-0-548-99242-5(8)) 2007. (ENG.). 404p. per. 34.95 (978-0-548-65460-6(3)) Kessinger Publishing, LLC.

Essmann, Jeffrey. Life on the List: Assorted Sordid Tales & Unsavory Revelations. 96p. 2010. 23.95 (978-1-60381-464-5(7)) 2009. pap. 13.95 (978-1-60381-421-8(3)) Coffeetown Enterprises, Inc. (Fanny Pr.).

Eubanks, Georgann. Literary Trails of the North Carolina Mountains: A Guidebook. 2007. (ENG., Illus.). 440p. pap. 20.95 (978-0-8078-5833-2(1)) Univ. of North Carolina Pr.

—Literary Trails of the North Carolina Piedmont: A Guidebook. 2010. (ENG., Illus.). 464p. 37.50 (978-0-8078-3333-9(9)); pap. 19.95 (978-0-8078-5979-7(6)) Univ. of North Carolina Pr.

Eubanks, W. Ralph. The House at the End of the Road: The Story of Three Generations of an Interracial Family in the American South. 2009. (Illus.). 224p. 26.99 (978-0-06-137573-6(X)) Smithsonian Institution Pr.

Everson, Ida Gertrude. George Henry Calvert: American Literary Pioneer. 2011. 346p. 51.95 (**978-1-258-06367-2(0)**) Literary Licensing, LLC.

Fadiman, Anne, ed. Rereadings: Seventeen Writers Revisit Books They Love. 2006. (ENG.). 272p. per. 14.00 (978-0-374-53054-9(8)) Farrar, Straus & Giroux.

Farber, Thomas. Brief Nudity. 2009. 176p. pap. 20.00 (978-0-9795285-2-1(6)) El Leon Literary Arts.

—A Lover's Quarrel: On Writing & the Writing Life. 2007. 268p. pap. 19.95 (978-0-9788699-2-2(3)) Ellsberg Bks.

Fargnoli, Nicholas. William Faulkner: A Literary Companion. Fargnoli, Nicholas, ed. 2007. (ENG., Illus.). 592p. pap. 17.95 (978-1-933648-58-3(9)) Pegasus Bks.

Farr, Sidney Saylor. My Appalachia: A Memoir. 2007. (ENG., Illus.). 272p. 35.00 (978-0-8131-2450-6(6)) Univ. Pr. of Kentucky.

Farrar, John. Recollections of Seventy Years by Mrs John Farrar. 2006. 340p. per. 23.99 (978-1-4255-3464-6(3)) MPublishing.

Faulkner, D. W. William Kennedy: Conversations & Interpretations. 2008. 180p. (C). 25.00 (978-0-7914-7003-9(2)) State Univ. of New York Pr.

Faulkner, Jimmy. Byways of Baldwin: Its People, History, Scenic Attractions & Growth From 1936. 2007. 496p. 35.00 (978-1-60306-019-6(7)) NewSouth, Inc.

Faulkner, John. My Brother Bill. 2010. pap. 22.50 (978-1-57003-933-1(X)) Univ. of South Carolina Pr.

Febos, Melissa. Whip Smart: The True Story of a Secret Life. 2011. (ENG.). 288p. pap. 14.99 (978-0-312-58378-1(8), St. Martin's Griffin) St. Martin's Pr.

Federal Bureau Of Investigation & Ernest Hemingway. Ernest Hemingway: The FBI Files. 2007. 128p. per. 22.99 (978-1-59986-244-6(1), Filibust) Filiquarian Publishing, LLC.

Federspiel, Michael R. Picturing Hemingway's Michigan. 2010. (Illus.). 224p. 39.95 (978-0-8143-3447-8(4)) Wayne State Univ. Pr.

Feiffer, Jules. Backing into Forward: A Memoir. 2012. (ENG.). 456p. pap. 19.00 (**978-0-226-24035-0(5)**) Univ. of Chicago Pr.

Fellner, Steve. All Screwed Up. 2009. 181p. 24.95 (978-0-9815163-4-9(3)) Benu Pr.

Felver, Christopher. Beat. 2007. (Illus.). 208p. 29.95 (978-0-86719-671-9(8)) Last Gasp of San Francisco.

Fenton, Robert W. Edgar Rice Burroughs & Tarzan: A Biography of the Author & His Creation. alt. ed. 2010. (ENG., Illus.). 254p. pap. 38.00 (978-0-7864-4908-8(X)) McFarland & Co., Inc. Pubs.

Fidler, William Perry & Wilson, Augusta Evans. Augusta Evans Wilson, 1835-1909: A Biography. 2011. 272p. 47.95 (**978-1-258-06773-1(0)**) Literary Licensing, LLC.

Field, Edward. The Man Who Would Marry Susan Sontag: And Other Intimate Literary Portraits of the Bohemian Era. 2007. (Living Out: Gay & Lesbian Autobiog Ser.). (ENG., Illus.). 302p. per. 21.95 (978-0-299-21324-4(2)) Univ. of Wisconsin Pr.

Fields, Annie. Authors & Friends. 2010. (ENG.). 374p. pap. 33.75 (978-1-171-73261-7(9)) 2010. (ENG.). 370p. pap. 32.75 (978-1-171-73477-2(8)) 2010. (ENG.). 370p. pap. 32.75 (978-1-145-62504-4(5)) 2010. 374p. pap. 33.75 (978-1-149-09459-4(1)) 2010. 370p. pap. 32.75 (978-1-146-23894-6(0)) 2010. 370p. pap. 32.75 (978-1-146-23181-7(4)) 2010. 372p. pap. 32.75 (978-1-146-10496-8(0)) 2010. 372p. pap. 32.75 (978-1-143-02763-5(9)) 2008. 369p. 31.99 (978-0-559-02954-7(3)) 2008. 369p. 29.99 (978-0-559-02964-6(0)) 2008. 240p. 24.99 (978-0-554-32146-2(7)) 2008. 240p. 27.99 (978-0-554-22843-3(2)) 2008. 369p. pap. 32.75 (978-0-559-02956-1(X)) 2008. 369p. pap. 31.75 (978-0-559-02961-5(6)) 2007. (ENG.). 210p. pap. 20.99 (978-1-4264-3195-1(3)) 2006. 236p. pap. 22.99 (978-1-4264-3230-9(5)) BiblioBazaar.

—Authors & Friends. 2007. (ENG.). 204p. per. (978-1-4065-2399-7(2)) Dodo Pr.

—Authors & Friends. 2010. (Illus.). 138p. pap. 22.72 (978-1-153-58971-0(0)) General Bks. LLC.

—Authors & Friends. 2010. 172p. pap. (978-1-4076-5041-8(6)) HardPr.

—Authors & Friends. 2010. 190p. pap. 18.36 (978-1-162-65415-7(5)); 37.95 (978-1-161-42280-1(3)) Kessinger Publishing, LLC.

—Charles Dudley Warner. 2010. 228p. pap. 25.75 (978-1-177-93315-5(2)); 230p. pap. 25.75 (978-1-147-37152-9(0)); 226p. pap. 25.75 (978-1-141-07577-5(6)) BiblioBazaar.

—Charles Dudley Warner. 2009. 82p. pap. 14.14 (978-0-217-45756-9(8)) General Bks. LLC.

Fields, Annie & Fields, James T. Charles Dudley Warner. 2009. 216p. 32.99 (978-1-116-14374-4(7)); 216p. 28.99 (978-1-116-14375-1(5)); 216p. pap. 24.75 (978-1-116-14376-8(3)); 216p. pap. 23.75 (978-1-116-14377-5(1)); (ENG.). 214p. pap. 22.99 (978-1-116-14378-2(X), BiblioLife); (ENG.). 214p. pap. 20.99 (978-1-116-14379-9(8), BiblioLife) BiblioBazaar.

Fields, James T. Charles Dudley Warner. 2007. (ENG.). 212p. 39.95 (978-0-548-04278-6(0)) Kessinger Publishing, LLC.

Fincke, Gary. The Canals of Mars: A Memoir. 2010. (ENG.). 232p. pap. 29.95 (978-0-87013-880-5(4)) Michigan State Univ. Pr.

Fiore, Kyle. Santa Fe & Taos: The Writer's ERA, 1916-1941. 2008. 264p. per. 28.95 (978-0-86534-650-5(X)) Sunstone Pr.

Firestone, Jennifer & Lomax, Dana Teen, eds. Letters to Poets: Conversations about Poetics, Politics, & Community. 2008. 200p. pap. 24.00 (978-0-9754990-8-5(4)) Saturnalia Bks.

Firkins, Oscar W. Ralph Waldo Emerson. 2009. 210p. pap. (978-0-217-27038-0(7)) Books LLC.

—Ralph Waldo Emerson. 2008. 386p. 48.95 (978-0-548-96371-5(1)) 2007. (ENG.). 388p. per. 33.95 (978-0-548-63915-3(9)) Kessinger Publishing, LLC.

—Ralph Waldo Emerson. 379p. reprint ed. 58.00 (978-0-7950-1534-2(8)) New Library Press LLC.

Firner, Nadja. Theodore Dreiser's Dawn - the Formation of a Mind. 2008. 128p. pap. (978-3-639-03065-5(6)) VDM Verlag Dr. Mueller e.K.

Fisher, Benjamin F., ed. Poe in His Own Time: A Biographical Chronicle of His Life, Drawn from Recollections, Interviews, & Memoirs by Family, Friends, & Associates. 2010. (Writers in Their Own Time Ser.). (ENG., Illus.). 276p. pap. 27.95 (978-1-58729-863-9(5)) Univ. of Iowa Pr.

Fisher, Carrie. Shockaholic. (ENG., Illus.). 176p. 2012. pap. 13.99 (**978-0-7432-6483-9(5)**) 2011. 22.00 (978-0-7432-6482-2(7)) Simon & Schuster.

Fisher, James L. Understanding Tony Kushner. 2008. (Understanding Contemporary American Literature Ser.). 208p. 39.95 (978-1-57003-749-8(3)) Univ. of South Carolina Pr.

Fisher, Rudolph. The City of Refuge: The Collected Stories of Rudolph Fisher. McCluskey, John, Jr., ed. & intro. by. 2nd exp. ed. 2008. (ENG.). 352p. (C). pap. 24.95 (978-0-8262-1812-4(1)) Univ. of Missouri Pr.

Fitzgerald, Stephanie. Alice Walker: Author & Social Activist. 2008. (Signature Lives Ser.). (ENG., Illus.). 112p. (gr. 6-7). lib. bdg. 35.32 (978-0-7565-3474-5(7), Signature Lives) Compass Point Bks.

Fleming, John. Romulus Linney: Maverick of the Theater. 2009. (ENG.). 352p. pap. 19.95 (978-1-57525-598-9(7)) Smith & Kraus Pubs., Inc.

Fletcher, Harrison Candelaria. Descanso for My Father: Fragments of a Life. 2012. (American Lives Ser.). (ENG., Illus.). 168p. pap. 14.95 (**978-0-8032-3839-8(8)**, Bison Bks.) Univ. of Nebraska Pr.

Flitcroft, John E. & Thompson, Daniel P. The Novelist of Vermont: A Biographical & Critical Study of Daniel Pierce Thompson. 2011. 362p. 51.95 (**978-1-258-10013-1(4)**) Literary Licensing, LLC.

Flynn, Nick. The Ticking Is the Bomb: A Memoir. 2011. (ENG.). 283p. pap. 14.95 (978-0-393-33886-7(X), 33886) Norton, W. W. & Co., Inc.

Flynn, Robert. Burying the Farm: A Memoir of Chillicothe, Texas. 2008. (978-0-916727-30-7(0)) Wings Pr.

Fogle, Sarah D. Martha Grimes Walks into a Pub: Essays on the Ensuing Fiction. Fogle, Sarah D., ed. 2010. (ENG., Illus.). 206p. pap. 40.00 (978-0-7864-4286-7(7)) McFarland & Co., Inc. Pubs.

Foley, Jack. Visions & Affiliations: A California Literary Time Line Part Two. 2011. 716p. pap. 50.00 (**978-1-61364-068-5(4)**) Pantograph Pr.

Ford, James L. Forty Odd Years in the Literary Shop. 2007. (ENG.). 434p. 51.95 (978-0-548-02019-7(1)) Kessinger Publishing, LLC.

Forrest, Leon. Conversations with Leon Forrest. Williams, Dana A., ed. 2007. (ENG., Illus.). 141p. per. 22.00 (978-1-57806-990-3(4)) Univ. Pr. of Mississippi.

—Conversations with Leon Forrest. Williams, Dana A., ed. 2007. (ENG., Illus.). 141p. 50.00 (978-1-57806-989-7(0)) Univ. Pr. of Mississippi.

Fortner, Michael. Greetings from Jungleland. 2009. 220p. pap. 19.30 (978-0-557-19540-4(3)) Lulu Enterprises Inc.

Fosberg, Michael A. Incognito: An American Odyssey of Race & Self-Discovery. 2011. 317p. pap. (**978-0-615-41396-9(X)**) Incognito, Inc.

Foster, Russell J. Daughter of Boston: The Extraordinary Diary of a Nineteenth-century Woman, Caroline Healey Dall. Deese, Helen R., ed. 2006. (ENG.). 488p. pap. 20.00 (978-0-8070-5035-4(0)) Beacon Pr.

Fradkin, Philip L. Wallace Stegner & the American West. 2009. (ENG.). 392p. pap. 19.95 (978-0-520-25957-7(2)) Univ. of California Pr.

Francavilla, Joseph. Harlan Ellison. 2011. (**978-1-58765-828-0(3)**) Salem Pr., Inc.

Francis, Conseula, ed. Conversations with Octavia Butler. (Literary Conversations Ser.). (ENG.). 288p. 2010. 50.00 (978-1-60473-275-7(X)) 2009. pap. 22.00 (978-1-60473-276-4(8)) Univ. Pr. of Mississippi.

Frankel, Valerie. It's Hard Not to Hate You. (ENG.). 256p. 2012. pap. 14.99 (**978-1-250-01388-0(7)**, St. Martin's Griffin) 2011. 24.99 (978-0-312-60978-8(7)) St. Martin's Pr.

Frankel, Valerie. Thin Is the New Happy. 2009. (ENG.). 272p. pap. 14.99 (978-0-312-37393-1(7), St. Martin's Griffin) St. Martin's Pr.

Fraser, Russell. A Mingled Yarn: The Life of R. P. Blackmur. 2010. (ENG., Illus.). 390p. pap. 39.95 (978-1-4128-1447-8(2)) Transaction Pubs.

Freed, Lynn. Reading, Writing, & Leaving Home: Life on the Page. 2006. (ENG., Illus.). 256p. pap. 14.95 (978-0-15-603034-2(9), Mariner Bks.) Houghton Mifflin Harcourt Trade & Reference Pubs.

Freedman, Carl, ed. Conversations with Ursula K. le Guin. 2008. (ENG.). 224p. 50.00 (978-1-60473-093-7(5)); pap. 22.00 (978-1-60473-094-4(3)) Univ. Pr. of Mississippi.

Freeman, James A. Clarence Hawkes: America's Blind Naturalist & the World He Lived In. 2009. pap. (978-1-935052-21-0(7)) White River Pr.

Friedman, Steve. Lost on Treasure Island: A Memoir of Longing, Love, & Lousy Choices in New York City. 2011. (ENG.). 320p. 24.95 (978-1-61145-020-0(9), 611020, Arcade Publishing) Skyhorse Publishing Co., Inc.

Fries, Kenny. The History of My Shoes & the Evolution of Darwin's Theory. 2007. (ENG., Illus.). 224p. per. 14.95 (978-0-7867-2007-1(7)) Da Capo Pr., Inc.

Frith, Margaret & Rock, Victoria, eds. Once upon a Time: Celebrating the Magic of Children's Books in Honor of the Twentieth Anniversary of Reading Is Fundamental. 2006. (Illus.). 64p. (J). (gr. 4-8). reprint ed. pap. 7.00 (978-1-4223-5726-2(0)) DIANE Publishing Co.

Fuguet, Alberto. Mi Cuerpo es una Celda. 2008. 300p. pap. 19.95 (978-958-45-1533-9(0)) Norma S.A. COL. Dist: Grupo Editorial Norma.

Furey, Hester Lee. American Radical & Reform Writers. 2008. (Dictionary of Literary Biography Ser.: Vol. 345). (ENG.). 426p. 315.00 (978-0-7876-8163-0(6)) Cengage Gale.

Furlani, Andre. Guy Davenport: Postmodern & After. 2007. (Avant-Garde & Modernism Studies Ser.). (ENG.). 296p. 59.95 (978-0-8101-2385-4(1)) Northwestern Univ. Pr.

—Guy Davenport: Postmodern & After. 2007. (Avant-Garde & Modernism Studies). (ENG.). 296p. per. 27.95 (978-0-8101-2389-2(4)) Northwestern Univ. Pr.

Gaer, Joseph, ed. Ambrose Gwinett Bierce: Bibliography & Biographical Data. 2007. (ENG.). 108p. per. 19.95 (978-1-4325-7111-5(7)) Kessinger Publishing, LLC.

Gale Editor, ed. American Writers: Supplement XXII. 22nd ed. 2011. lib. bdg. 218.00 (978-1-4144-8024-4(5), Charles Scribner's Sons) Cengage Gale.

Gale Editors, ed. Contemporary Authors, Vol. 247. 2006. (Contemporary Authors Ser.). (ENG.). 480p. 293.00 (978-0-7876-7876-0(7)) Cengage Gale.

Gale, Robert L. An Edwin Arlington Robinson Encyclopedia. alt. ed. 2011. (ENG.). 279p. pap. 55.00 (978-0-7864-4909-5(8)) McFarland & Co., Inc. Pubs.

Garebian, Keith. The Making of Cabaret. 2nd ed. 2011. (ENG., Illus.). 256p. 99.00 (978-0-19-973249-4(3)); pap. 19.95 (978-0-19-973250-0(7)) Oxford Univ. Pr., Inc.

Garland, Hamlin. A Daughter of the Middle Border. 2008. 400p. 31.99 (978-0-554-30035-1(4)); 29.99 (978-0-554-39338-4(7)) BiblioBazaar.

—A Daughter of the Middle Border. 2008. (Illus.). 364p. pap. (978-1-4065-8900-9(4)) Dodo Pr.

—A Daughter of the Middle Border. 2007. (ENG.). 410p. 49.95 (978-0-548-01436-3(1)) Kessinger Publishing, LLC.

—A Daughter of the Middle Border. 2007. 327p. per. 19.95 (978-0-87351-566-5(8), Borealis Bk.) Minnesota Historical Society Pr.

—A Son of the Middle Border. 2007. 384p. per. 19.95 (978-0-87351-565-8(X), Borealis Bk.) Minnesota Historical Society Pr.

—A Son of the Middle Border. 2007. (ENG.). 504p. per. (978-1-4067-7081-0(7)) Read Bks.

Gastil, Raymond D. & Singer, Barnett. The Pacific Northwest: Growth of a Regional Identity. 2010. (ENG., Illus.). 227p. pap. 38.00 (978-0-7864-4540-0(8)) McFarland & Co., Inc. Pubs.

Gebauer, Phyllis. Hot Widow: A Memoir. 2008. 294p. pap. 16.95 (978-1-56474-471-5(X), Fithian Pr) Daniel & Daniel, Pubs., Inc.

Gelderman, Carol, ed. Conversations with Mary Mccarthy. 2011. (ENG.). pap. 30.00 (978-1-61703-014-7(7)) Univ. Pr. of Mississippi.

George Edward, Woodberry. Nathaniel Hawthorne. 2007. (ENG.). 212p. pap. 20.99 (978-1-4264-9236-5(7)) BiblioBazaar.

Gewirtz, Isaac. Beatific Soul: Jack Kerouac on the Road. 2007. (ENG., Illus.). 208p. 35.00 (978-1-85759-497-3(5)) Scala, Editions FRA. Dist: National Bk. Network.

Gibson, Margaret. The Prodigal Daughter: Reclaiming an Unfinished Childhood. 2008. (ENG., Illus.). 216p. (gr. 9). per. 19.95 (978-0-8262-1783-7(4)) Univ. of Missouri Pr.

Gidding, Joshua. Failure: An Autobiography a Story of How the Truth Can Set You Free. 2009. 232p. pap. 14.95 (978-1-905736-35-5(5)) Marshall Cavendish GBR. Dist: Midpoint Trade Bks., Inc.

Gifford, Barry & Lee, Lawrence. Jack's Book: An Oral Biography of Jack Kerouac. 2012. (ENG.). 368p. (gr. 12). pap. 16.00 (**978-0-14-312188-6(X)**, Penguin (Non-Classics)) Penguin Group (USA) Inc.

Gilbar, Steven. Not Forgotten: American Writers Remember the Lives of Literary Mentors, Friends, & Rivals. 2006. (ENG.). 227p. pap. 17.95 (978-1-56792-294-3(5)) Godine, David R. Pub.

Giles, Janice Holt. 40 Acres & No Mule. 30.95 (978-0-8488-1010-8(4)) Amereon LTD.

Giles, Paul. American Catholic Arts & Fictions: Culture, Ideology, Aesthetics. 2008. (Cambridge Studies in American Literature & Culture Ser.). (ENG.). 564p. pap. 74.00 (978-0-521-05773-8(6)) Cambridge Univ. Pr.

Giles, Wanda H. & Giles, James Richard. Dlb 350 21St Cen Am Nvlsts. 2009. (Dictionary of Literary Biography Ser.). (ENG., Illus.). 512p. 315.00 (978-0-7876-8168-5(7)) Cengage Gale.

Gillespie, Marcia, et al. Maya Angelou: A Glorious Celebration. l.t. ed. 2008. 250p. 31.95 (978-1-4104-0983-6(X)) Thorndike Pr.

Gilman, Charlotte Perkins. The Selected Letters of Charlotte Perkins Gilman. Knight, Denise D. & Tuttle, Jennifer S., eds. 2009. (Amer Lit Realism & Naturalism Ser.). (ENG., Illus.). 504p. 60.00 (978-0-8173-1648-8(5)) Univ. of Alabama Pr.

Gilmore, Paul. Aesthetic Materialism: Electricity & American Romanticism. 2008. (ENG.). 256p. 60.00 (978-0-8047-6123-9(X)) Stanford Univ. Pr.

Gingher, Marianne. Adventures in Pen Land: One Writer's Journey from Inklings to Ink. 2008. (ENG., Illus.). 200p. (gr. 9). pap. 19.95 (978-0-8262-1817-9(2)) Univ. of Missouri Pr.

Ginsberg, Allen S., et al. The Book of Martyrdom & Artifice: First Journals & Poems, 1937-1952. 2008. (ENG., Illus.). 544p. per. 17.50 (978-0-306-81562-1(1)) Da Capo Pr., Inc.

Glancy, Diane. The Dream of a Broken Field. 2011. (ENG.). 220p. pap. 30.00 (978-0-8032-3481-9(3)) Univ. of Nebraska Pr.

Glassman, Steve, ed. Florida Crime Writers: 24 Interviews. 2007. (ENG.). 250p. per. 35.00 (978-0-7864-3083-3(4)) McFarland & Co., Inc. Pubs.

Glenday, Michael K., ed. F. Scott Fitzgerald. 2012. (ENG.). 208p. 75.00 (978-0-333-66899-3(5)); pap. 24.95 (978-0-333-66900-6(2)) Palgrave Macmillan.

Glenn, Wendy J. Laurie Halse Anderson: Speaking in Tongues. 36th ed. 2009. (Scarecrow Studies in Young Adult Literature Ser.). (ENG.). 184p. 45.00 (978-0-8108-7281-3(1)) Scarecrow Pr., Inc.

Godwin, Parke. Biography of William Cullen Bryant with. 2006. pap. 37.95 (978-1-4286-3461-9(4)); pap. 36.95 (978-1-4286-3462-6(2)) Kessinger Publishing, LLC.

Gold, Charles H. Hatching Ruin , or Mark Twain's Road to Bankruptcy. 2011. (MARK TWAIN & HIS CIRCLE Ser.). (ENG., Illus.). 184p. (C). (gr. 13). pap. 25.00 (978-0-8262-1959-6(4)) Univ. of Missouri Pr.

Gold, Herbert. Bohemia: Where Art, Angst, Love, & Strong Coffee Meet. 2007. (ENG.). 250p. per. 12.00 (978-0-9753662-4-0(6)) Axios Pr.

—Still Alive! A Feisty Bohemian Explores the Art of Growing Old. 2011. (ENG.). 264p. pap. 12.95 (978-1-61145-029-3(2), 611029, Arcade Publishing) Skyhorse Publishing Co., Inc.

Goldman, David. A Father's Love: One Man's Unrelenting Battle to Bring His Abducted Son Home. 2012. (ENG., Illus.). 288p. (gr. 12). pap. 16.00 (**978-0-452-29791-3(5)**, Plume) Penguin Group (USA) Inc.

Goldman-Price, Irene, ed. My Dear Governess: The Letters of Edith Wharton to Anna Bahlmann. 2012. (ENG., Illus.). 336p. 30.00 (**978-0-300-16989-8(2)**) Yale Univ. Pr.

Goldsmith, Kenneth. Kenneth Goldsmith: Brief an Bettina Funcke. 2011. (ENG., Illus.). 32p. pap. 10.00 (**978-3-7757-2866-9(X)**) Hatje Cantz Verlag GmbH & Co KG DEU. Dist: D.A.P./Distributed Art Pubs.

Golla, Robert, ed. Conversations with Michael Crichton. 2011. (Literary Conversations Ser.). (ENG.). 224p. 55.00 (978-1-61703-012-3(0)); pap. 25.00 (978-1-61703-013-0(9)) Univ. Pr. of Mississippi.

Gonzalez, Rigoberto. Butterfly Boy: Memories of a Chicano Mariposa. 2011. (Writing in Latinidad Ser.). (ENG.). 224p. pap. 19.95 (**978-0-299-21904-8(6)**) Univ. of Wisconsin Pr.

Gooch, Brad. Flannery: A Life of Flannery O'Connor. 2010. (ENG., Illus.). 464p. pap. 16.99 (978-0-316-01899-6(9), Back Bay Bks.) Little Brown & Co.

Goodman, Charlotte Margolis. Jean Stafford: The Savage Heart. 2011. (ENG., Illus.). 416p. pap. 35.00 (**978-0-292-73574-3(X)**) Univ. of Texas Pr.

Goodman, Susan. Edith Wharton's Inner Circle. 2011. (ENG., Illus.). 187p. pap. 19.95 (978-0-292-72915-5(4)) Univ. of Texas Pr.

Gordon, Lyndall. Lives Like Loaded Guns: Emily Dickinson & Her Family's Feuds. 2011. (ENG.). 512p. (gr. 12). 18.00 (978-0-14-311914-2(1), Penguin (Non-Classics)) Penguin Group (USA) Inc.

Gordon, Mary. Circling My Mother. 2008. (Illus.). 272p. pap. 14.95 (978-0-307-27761-9(5), Anchor) Knopf Doubleday Publishing Group.

Gottfried, Martin. Arthur Miller: His Life & Work. 2008. (ENG.). 484p. pap. 18.00 (978-1-4379-5234-6(8)) DIANE Publishing Co.

Gottlieb, Michael. Memoir & Essay. 2010. 170p. pap. 16.00 (978-0-9825495-0-6(4)) Faux Pr.

Gougeon, Len. Emerson & Eros: The Making of a Cultural Hero. 2011. 272p. pap. 24.95 (**978-0-7914-7078-7(4)**, Suny Pr.) 2007. 268p. 40.00 (978-0-7914-7077-0(6)) State Univ. of New York Pr.

Gougeon, Len. Virtue's Hero: Emerson, Antislavery, & Reform. 2010. (ENG.). 424p. pap. 29.95 (978-0-8203-3469-1(3)) Univ. of Georgia Pr.

Gourevitch, Philip. The Paris Review Interviews. 2007. (Illus.). 528p. pap. (978-1-84195-925-2(1)) Canongate Bks.

Gourevitch, Philip, ed. The Paris Review Interviews. 2007. Vol. 2. (Illus.). 448p. (978-1-84767-033-5(4)) Vol. 181. 184p. pap. (978-1-84767-077-9(6)) Canongate Bks.

Goyen, William. Goyen: Autobiographical Essays, Notebooks, Evocations, Interviews. Gibbons, Reginald, ed. & intro. by. 2009. (ENG.). 220p. pap. 25.00 *(978-0-292-72225-5(7))* Univ. of Texas Pr.
—William Goyen: Selected Letters from a Writer's Life. Phillips, Robert, ed. 2011. (ENG., Illus.). 471p. pap. 40.00 *(978-0-292-72964-3(2))* Univ. of Texas Pr.
Grandbois, Peter. The Arsenic Lobster: A Hybrid Memoir. 2009. 128p. pap. 16.00 *(978-1-933132-72-3(8))* Spuyten Duyvil.
Graves, John. My Dogs & Guns. 2007. (ENG.). 96p. 19.95 *(978-1-60239-029-4(0),* 239029) Skyhorse Publishing Co., Inc.
Gray, Ralph D. Meredith Nicholson: A Writing Life. 2007. (Indiana Biography Ser.). (Illus.). 281p. *(978-0-87195-257-8(2))* Indiana Historical Society.
Gray, Richard & Robinson, Owen. A Companion to the Literature & Culture of the American South. 2007. (Blackwell Companions to Literature & Culture Ser.: 58). (ENG., Illus.). 672p. per. 55.95 *(978-1-4051-6369-9(0),* Wiley-Blackwell) Wiley, John & Sons, Inc.
Grayson, David, pseud. Adventures in Contentment. 2010. (ENG.). 266p. pap. 27.75 *(978-1-177-39106-1(6))* 2010. (ENG.). 272p. pap. 27.75 *(978-1-175-45338-9(2))* 2010. 292p. pap. 28.75 *(978-1-175-90283-2(7))* 2008. 156p. 25.99 *(978-0-554-23362-8(2))* 2008. 156p. 22.99 *(978-0-554-32665-8(5))* 2006. 136p. pap. 18.99 *(978-1-4264-4248-3(3))* 2007. (ENG.). 152p. pap. 21.99 *(978-1-4264-4312-1(9))* BiblioBazaar.
—Adventures in Contentment. 2008. (ENG.). 164p. per. *(978-1-4065-8828-6(8))* Dodo Pr.
—Adventures in Contentment. 2006. (ENG.). pap. *(978-1-4068-1145-2(9))* Echo Library.
—Adventures in Contentment. 2010. (Illus.). 84p. pap. 20.00 *(978-1-4432-1552-7(X))* General Bks. LLC.
—Adventures in Contentment. 2010. 118p. pap. *(978-1-4076-0891-4(6))* HardPr.
—Adventures in Contentment. 2010. 260p. 34.36 *(978-1-163-21284-4(9))* Kessinger Publishing, LLC.
—Adventures in Contentment. 2009. (ENG.). 128p. pap. 10.45 *(978-1-4385-2667-6(9),* Book Jungle) Standard Pubns., Inc.
Grayson, Richard. Autumn in Brooklyn. 2009. 267p. pap. 15.00 *(978-0-578-03208-5(2))* Suoerstition Mountain Pr.
Green, Mary. Diamela Eltit: Reading the Mother. 2007. (Monografíías A Ser.: Volume 249). 180p. 90.00 *(978-1-85566-155-4(1),* Tamesis Bks.) Boydell & Brewer, Ltd. GBR. Dist: Boydell & Brewer, Inc.
Green, Michelle Y. Oscar Invincible: The Life of Film Pioneer Oscar Micheaux. 2007. *(978-0-8037-3003-8(9),* Dial) Penguin Group (USA) Inc.
Greene, Anthony C. & McAuley, Kathleen A. Edgar Allan Poe at Fordham: An Educator's Guide. 2007. (Illus.). 28p. pap. *(978-0-941980-61-6(8))* Bronx County Historical Society, The.
Greene, Bob. And You Know You Should Be Glad: A True Story of Lifelong Friendship. l.t. ed. 2006. 408p. per. 15.95 *(978-0-06-112685-7(3),* Morrow, William & Co.) HarperCollins Pubs.
Greene, Harlan. Mr. Skylark: John Bennett & the Charleston Renaissance. 2010. (ENG.). 408p. pap. 24.95 *(978-0-8203-3624-4(6))* Univ. of Georgia Pr.
Greenfield, Robert. A Day in the Life: One Family, the Beautiful People, & the End of the Sixties. 2009. (ENG., Illus.). 368p. 24.95 *(978-0-306-81622-2(9))* Perseus Bks. Group.
Greenhill, Joseph. Susan: A Memoir. 2007. 208p. pap. 13.95 *(978-1-59858-172-0(4))* Dog Ear Publishing, LLC.
Greenough, Sarah. Beat Memories: The Photographs of Allen Ginsberg. 2010. (Illus.). 144p. 49.95 *(978-3-7913-5052-3(8))* Prestel Publishing.
Greer, Bonnie. Langston Hughes: The Value of Contradiction. 2011. (BlackAmber Inspirations Ser.). (ENG., Illus.). 190p. pap. 14.95 *(978-1-906413-76-7(2),* Black Amber) Arcadia Bks. Ltd. GBR. Dist: Dufour Editions, Inc.
Grey, Zane. Zane Grey, the Man & His Work: An Autobiographical Sketch, Critical Appreciations & Bibliography. 2011. 80p. 37.95 ***(978-1-258-00927-4(7))*** Literary Licensing, LLC.
Grey, Zane & Grey, Lina Elise. Dolly & Zane Grey: Letters from a Marriage. Kant, Candace C., ed. 2008. (Western Literature Ser.). (ENG., Illus.). 472p. 34.95 *(978-0-87417-749-7(9))* Univ. of Nevada Pr.
Grimes, Nikki. Out of the Dark. 2009. (ENG., Illus.). 56p. (J). pap. 8.00 *(978-1-57274-977-1(6),* Author at Work) Owen, Richard C. Pubs., Inc.
Grimes, Tom. Mentor: A Memoir. 2010. (ENG.). 200p. 24.95 *(978-0-9825048-8-8(8))*; pap. 16.95 *(978-0-9825048-9-5(6))* Tin Hse. Bks., LLC.
Guess, Carol. My Father in Water. 2011. 88p. pap. 15.00 ***(978-1-84861-185-6(4))*** Shearsman Bks. GBR. Dist: SPD-Small Pr. Distribution.
Gulick, Bill. Sixty-Four Years as a Writer. 2006. (ENG., Illus.). 344p. per. 16.95 *(978-0-87004-453-3(2))* Caxton Pr.
Gulley, Philip. I Love You, Miss Huddleston: And Other Inappropriate Longings of My Indiana Childhood. 2010. (ENG.). 208p. pap. 12.99 *(978-0-06-180955-2(1),* HarperOne) HarperCollins Pubs.
Gutierrez, Gabriella. Communal Feminisms: Chicanas, Chilenas, & Cultural Exile. 2009. (ENG.). 354p. pap. 34.99 *(978-0-7391-4459-6(6))* Lexington Bks.
Gwin, Minrose. Wishing for Snow: A Memoir. 2011. (ENG.). 240p. pap. 14.99 *(978-0-06-204634-5(9),* William Morrow Paperbacks) HarperCollins Pubs.
Gyopár, László. Thoreau's Ideas for Modern Times: An Analysis of Walden & 'Civil Disobedience' 2008. 80p. pap. *(978-3-639-10508-7(7),* VDM Verlag Dr. Mueller e.K.
Habich, Robert D. Building Their Own Waldos: Emerson's First Biographers & the Politics of Life-Writing in the Gilded Age. 2011. (ENG.). 248p. pap. 29.95 *(978-1-58729-962-9(3))* Univ. of Iowa Pr.
Hacht, Anne Marie & Hayes, Dwayne D. Gale Contextual Encyclopedia of American Literature. 2009. *(978-1-4144-3132-1(5))*; *(978-1-4144-3134-5(1))*; *(978-1-4144-3133-8(3))*; (Illus.). 1819p. 495.00 *(978-1-4144-3131-4(7))* Cengage Gale.
Hadas, Rachel. Strange Relation. 2011. (ENG.). 204p. pap. 16.95 *(978-1-58988-061-0(7))* Dry, Paul Bks., Inc.
Hagstrom, Jack W. C. & Morgan, Bill. James Ingram Merrill: A Descriptive Bibliography. 2009. 95.00 *(978-1-58456-264-1(1))* Oak Knoll Pr.
Hahn, Emily. No Hurry to Get Home. 2010. 324p. pap. 19.95 *(978-0-7592-4327-9(1))* E-Reads.
Hahn, Emily & Cuthbertson, Ken. Congo Solo: Misadventures Two Degrees North. 2011. (Illus.). 304p. (C). pap. ***(978-0-7735-3904-4(2))*** McGill-Queen's Univ. Pr.
Haines, Colin. "Frightened by a Word" Shirley Jackson & Lesbian Gothic. 2007. (Acta Universitatis Upsaliensis Ser.: Vol. 133). 234p. pap. *(978-91-554-6844-6(6))* Uppsala Universitet/Acta Universitatis Uppsaliensis.
Haines, John. Descent. 2010. (Notable Voices Ser.). 212p. pap. 24.00 *(978-1-933880-18-1(X))* Cavankerry Pr., Ltd.
Hale, Edward Everett. James Russell Lowell & His Friends. (ENG.). 388p. 2007. 48.95 *(978-0-548-13730-7(7))* 2006. per. 33.95 *(978-1-4286-4897-5(6))* Kessinger Publishing, LLC.
Hale, Veda. Swell Suffering: A Biography of Maurine Whipple. 2011. 471p. pap. 31.95 *(978-1-58958-124-1(5))* 2009. *(978-1-58958-122-7(9))* Kofford, Greg Books, Inc.
Haley, James L. Wolf: The Lives of Jack London. 2011. (ENG., Illus.). 400p. (gr. 9). pap. 17.99 *(978-0-465-02503-9(X))* Basic Bks.
Hall, Donald. Unpacking the Boxes: A Memoir of a Life in Poetry. 2009. (ENG.). 208p. pap. 14.95 *(978-0-547-24794-6(X),* Mariner Bks.) Houghton Mifflin Harcourt Trade & Reference Pubs.
Hall, James C. & Hathaway, Heather, eds. Conversations with Paule Marshall. 2010. (Literary Conversations Ser.). (ENG.). 240p. 40.00 *(978-1-60473-743-1(3))* Univ. Pr. of Mississippi.
Hall, Meredith. Without a Map: A Memoir. (ENG.). 2008. 256p. per. 14.00 *(978-0-8070-7274-5(5))* 2007. 248p. 24.95 *(978-0-8070-7273-8(7))* Beacon Pr.
Haltom, Susan & Brown, Jane Roy. One Writer's Garden: Eudora Welty's Home Place. 2011. (ENG.). 304p. 35.00 *(978-1-61703-119-9(4))* Univ. Pr. of Mississippi.
Hamalian, Linda. The Cramoisy Queen: A Life of Caresse Crosby. 2nd ed. 2009. (Illus.). 296p. pap. 17.95 *(978-0-8093-2901-4(8))* Southern Illinois Univ. Pr.
Hamilton, Caroline. One Man Zeitgeist: Dave Eggers, Publishing & Publicity. 2010. (ENG.). 144p. 110.00 *(978-1-4411-6696-8(3))* Continuum International Publishing Group, Ltd. GBR. Dist: National Bk. Network.
Hamilton, Caroline D. One Man Zeitgeist: Dave Eggers, Publishing & Publicity. 2012. (ENG.). 144p. pap. 34.95 ***(978-1-4411-1737-3(7))*** Continuum International Publishing Group, Ltd. GBR. Dist: National Bk. Network.
Hamilton, Geoff & Jones, Brian. Encyclopedia of Contemporary Writers & Their Work. 2010. (Literary Movements Ser.). 432p. (C). (gr. 9-18). 75.00 *(978-0-8160-7578-2(6))* Facts On File, Inc.
Hampl, Patricia. The Florist's Daughter. 2009. (ENG.). 240p. pap. 13.95 *(978-0-15-603403-6(4),* Mariner Bks.) Houghton Mifflin Harcourt Trade & Reference Pubs.
Haralson, Eric, ed. Encyclopedia of American Poetry: The Nineteenth Century. 2011. 549p. pap. 59.95 *(978-0-415-89076-2(4))* Routledge.
—Encyclopedia of American Poetry: The Twentieth Century. 2013. (ENG.). 866p. pap. 59.95 *(978-0-415-89077-9(2))* Routledge.
Harford, James & Harford. Merton & Friends: A Joint Biography of Thomas Merton, Robert Lax, & Edward Rice. 2007. (ENG., Illus.). 320p. 36.95 *(978-0-8264-1869-2(4))* Continuum International Publishing Group, Ltd. GBR. Dist: National Bk. Network.
Hargrove, Nancy Duvall. T. S. Eliot's Parisian Year. 2010. (ENG., Illus.). 336p. pap. 29.95 *(978-0-8130-3553-6(8))* Univ. Pr. of Florida.
Harlow, Virginia. Thomas Sergeant Perry: A Biography & Letters to Perry from William, Henry, & Garth Wilkinson James. 2011. 410p. 54.95 ***(978-1-258-08843-9(6))*** Literary Licensing, LLC.
Harnack, Curtis. We Have All Gone Away. 2011. (Bur Oak Book Ser.). (ENG.). 188p. pap. 19.95 *(978-1-58729-969-8(0))* Univ. of Iowa Pr.
Harriman, Margaret Case. The Vicious Circle: The Story of the Algonquin Round Table. 2011. 320p. 50.95 ***(978-1-258-10551-8(9))*** Literary Licensing, LLC.
Harrison, Brady, ed. All Our Stories Are Here: Critical Perspectives on Montana Literature. 2009. (ENG.). 296p. 50.00 *(978-0-8032-1390-6(5))* Univ. of Nebraska Pr.
Harrison, James Albert. The Last Letters of Edgar Allan Poe to Sarah Helen Whitman. 2008. 68p. pap. 26.45 *(978-1-4437-1424-2(0),* Kent Pr.) Kent Communications, Ltd.
Harrison, Jim. The Palmetto & Its South Carolina Home. 2012. (ENG.). 96p. 29.95 ***(978-1-61117-049-8(4))*** Univ. of South Carolina Pr.
Harrison, Kathryn. The Kiss: A Memoir. 2011. 256p. pap. 15.00 *(978-0-8129-7971-8(3),* Random Hse. Trade Paperbacks) Random House Publishing Group.
Harsham, Richard. For Crying Out Loud. 2011. 176p. 29.99 ***(978-1-4568-5171-2(3))***; pap. 19.99 ***(978-1-4568-5170-5(5))*** Xlibris Corp.
Hart, Stephen M. Gabriel Garcia Marquez. 2010. (Reaktion Books - Critical Lives Ser.). (ENG., Illus.). 208p. pap. 16.95 *(978-1-86189-763-3(4))* Reaktion Bks., Ltd. GBR. Dist: Chicago Distribution Ctr.
Harter, Christopher. An Author Index to Little Magazines of the Mimeograph Revolution, 1958-1980. 2008. (ENG.). 752p. 150.00 *(978-0-8108-6113-8(5))* Scarecrow Pr., Inc.
Harwell, David Horace. Walker Percy Remembered: A Portrait in the Words of Those Who Knew Him. (ENG.). 200p. 2010. pap. 18.00 *(978-0-8078-7153-9(2))* 2006. 27.95 *(978-0-8078-3039-0(9))* Univ. of North Carolina Pr.
Hassell, Susan Whitcomb. A Hundred & Sixty Books by Washington Authors. 2009. 44p. pap. 15.95 *(978-1-120-11998-8(7))* Kessinger Publishing, LLC.
—A Hundred & Sixty Books by Washington Authors. 40p. reprint ed. lib. bdg. 88.00 *(978-0-7222-4721-1(4))* Library Reprints, Inc.
Havrilesky, Heather. Disaster Preparedness: A Memoir. 2011. (ENG.). 256p. (gr. 12). 15.00 *(978-1-59448-546-6(1),* Riverhead Trade (Paperbacks)) Penguin Group (USA) Inc.
Hawkins, Ruth A. Unbelievable Happiness & Final Sorrow: The Hemingway-Pfeiffer Marriage. 2012. (ENG., Illus.). 391p. 34.95 ***(978-1-55728-974-2(3))*** Univ. of Arkansas Pr.
Hawthorne, Nathaniel. Passages from the American Notebooks. 2008. 176p. 25.99 *(978-0-554-22540-1(9))* 2008. 168p. 25.99 *(978-0-554-22539-5(5))* 2008. 176p. 22.99 *(978-0-554-31843-1(1))* 2008. 168p. 22.99 *(978-0-554-31842-4(3))* Vol. 1. 2007. (ENG.). 154p. pap. 19.99 *(978-1-4264-2569-1(4))* Vol. 1. 2007. (ENG.). 164p. pap. 21.99 *(978-1-4264-2610-0(0))* Vol. 2. 2007. (ENG.). 162p. pap. 19.99 *(978-1-4264-2570-7(8))* Vol. 2. 2007. (ENG.). 174p. pap. 21.99 *(978-1-4264-2611-7(9))* BiblioBazaar.
Hayes, Kevin J. The Cambridge Introduction to Herman Melville. 2007. (Cambridge Introductions to Literature Ser.). (ENG.). 152p. (C). 78.99 *(978-0-521-85480-1(6))*; 150p. per. 25.00 *(978-0-521-67104-0(3))* Cambridge Univ. Pr.
—Edgar Allan Poe. 2nd rev. ed. 2009. (Reaktion Books - Critical Lives Ser.). (ENG., Illus.). 192p. pap. 16.95 *(978-1-86189-515-8(1))* Reaktion Bks., Ltd. GBR. Dist: Chicago Distribution Ctr.
Hayworth, Eugene. Fever Vision: The Life & Works of Coleman Dowell. 2007. (Dalkey Archive Scholarly Ser.). (ENG., Illus.). 234p. per. 24.95 *(978-1-56478-457-5(6),* Dalkey Archive Pr.
Heaphy, Maura. Science Fiction Authors: A Research Guide. 1 vol. 2008. (Author Research Ser.). 352p. (gr. 9-18). pap. 40.00 *(978-1-59158-515-2(5),* LU5155) Libraries Unlimited, Inc.
—100 Most Popular Science Fiction Authors: Biographical Sketches & Bibliographies. 1 vol. (Popular Authors Ser.). 565p. 65.00 *(978-1-59158-746-0(8),* LU7468) Libraries Unlimited, Inc.
Hearn, Lafcadio. The Japanese Letters of Lafcadio Hearn. 2009. 78p. pap. *(978-0-217-33203-3(X),* Books LLC.
—The Japanese Letters of Lafcadio Hearn. Bisland, Elizabeth, ed. 2007. (ENG.). 522p. 55.95 *(978-0-548-15641-4(7))*; pap. 40.95 *(978-1-4304-5106-8(8))* Kessinger Publishing, LLC.
—Lafcadio Hearn: American Writings. Benfey, Christopher, ed. 2009. (ENG.). 900p. (gr. 12-18). 40.00 *(978-1-59853-039-1(9))* Library of America, The.
—Letters from the Raven: Being the Correspondence of Lafcadio Hearn with Henry Watkin. 2009. 216p. 23.99 *(978-0-559-93650-0(8))*; pap. 17.99 *(978-0-559-93646-3(X))* BiblioBazaar.
—Letters from the Raven: Being the Correspondence of Lafcadio Hearn with Henry Watkin. 216p. 2008. 39.95 *(978-1-4366-8491-0(9))* 2007. (ENG.). per. 24.95 *(978-1-4325-5651-8(7))* Kessinger Publishing, LLC.
—Letters from the Raven: Being the Correspondence of Lafcadio Hearn with Henry Watkin. 2008. 212p. pap. *(978-1-4437-1143-2(8))* Read Bks.
—Letters from the Raven: Being the Correspondence of Lafcadio Hearn with Henry Watkin. 2007. 212p. 29.95 *(978-1-4344-9560-0(4))*; per. 19.95 *(978-1-4344-9559-4(0))* Wildside Pr., LLC.
Hearn, Lafcadio & Bisland, Elizabeth. The Life & Letters of Lafcadio Hearn V2. 2007. (ENG.). 562p. 58.95 *(978-0-548-15649-0(2))*; pap. 43.95 *(978-1-4304-5114-3(9))* Kessinger Publishing, LLC.
Hedley, Jane. I Made You to Find Me: The Coming of Age of the Woman Poet & the Politics of Poetic Address. 2009. (ENG.). 199p. cd-rom 14.95 *(978-0-8142-9199-3(6))* Ohio State Univ. Pr.
Hedrick, Joan. Solitary Comrade: Jack London & His Work. 2011. (ENG.). 264p. pap. 40.00 *(978-0-8078-9682-2(9))* Univ. of North Carolina Pr.
Hegarty, Paul & Kennedy, Danny. Dennis Cooper: Writing at the Edge. 2008. (ENG., Illus.). 217p. (C). 74.50 *(978-1-84519-187-0(0))* Sussex Academic Pr. GBR. Dist: International Specialized Bk. Services.
Heilman, Robert Bechtold. Robert B. Heilman: His Life in Letters. Alexander, Edward et al, eds. 2009. (ENG., Illus.). 808p. 64.00 *(978-0-295-98866-5(5))* Univ. of Washington Pr.
Heller, Anne Conover. Ayn Rand & the World She Made. 2010. (ENG., Illus.). 608p. pap. 18.00 *(978-1-4000-7893-6(8),* Anchor) Knopf Doubleday Publishing Group.
Heller, Michael. Speaking the Estranged: Essays on the Work of George Oppen. 2008. (ENG.). 152p. pap. *(978-1-84471-440-7(3))* Salt Publishing.
Hemingway, Edward, illus. Hemingway & Bailey's Bartending Guide to Great American Writers. 2006. (ENG.). 100p. 15.95 *(978-1-56512-482-0(0),* 1565124820) Algonquin Bks. of Chapel Hill.
Hemingway, Patrick. Hemingway at Home. 2008. 160p. 40.00 *(978-0-8109-9518-5(2))* Abrams.
Hemley, Robin. Do-Over! In Which a Forty-Eight-Year-Old Father of Three Returns to Kindergarten, Summer Camp, the Prom, & Other Embarrassments. 2009. (ENG., Illus.). 336p. 23.99 *(978-0-316-02060-2(5))* Little Brown & Co.
Hemmingson, Michael. Gordon Lish & His Influence on Twentieth-Century American Liter. 2009. (Studies in Major Literary Authors Ser.). (ENG.). 256p. (C). 125.00 *(978-0-415-99177-3(3))* Routledge.
Henderson, Cathy & Oram, Richard W. Dlb 355. 2010. (Dictionary of Literary Biography Ser.). (ENG., Illus.). xlii, 589p. 315.00 *(978-0-7876-8173-9(3))* Cengage Gale.
Hendin, Josephine. The World of Flannery O'Connor. 2009. (Flannery O'Connor Studies). 194p. pap. 20.00 *(978-1-60608-465-6(8),* Wipf and Stock) Wipf & Stock Pubs.
Henry, Arthur. The House in the Woods. 2009. 130p. pap. 19.99 *(978-1-151-10324-6(1))* General Bks. LLC.
—The House in the Woods. 2009. 358p. 46.95 *(978-1-120-85919-8(0))*; pap. 31.95 *(978-1-120-76298-6(7))* Kessinger Publishing, LLC.
Herralde, Jorge. Para Roberto Bolano. 2006. (Coleccion Dorada Ser.). (SPA & ENG., Illus.). 110p. pap. 9.95 *(978-958-8160-95-5(2))* Villegas Editores S.A. COL. Dist: Independent Pubs. Group.
Herrero Brasas, Juan A. Walt Whitman's Mystical Ethics: Homosexuality & the Marginality of Friendship at the Crossroads of Modernity. 2011. 216p. pap 23.95 *(978-1-4384-3010-2(8),* Suny Pr.) State Univ. of New York Pr.
Herrin, Lamar. Romancing Spain. 2006. (ENG.). 272p. 23.95 *(978-1-932961-22-5(4))* Unbridled Bks.
Herron, Rachael. A Life in Stitches: Knitting My Way Through Love, Loss, & Laughter. 2011. (ENG.). 144p. pap. 14.95 *(978-1-4521-0053-1(5))* Chronicle Bks. LLC.
Herzog, Tobey C. Writing Vietnam, Writing Life: Caputo, Heinemann, O'Brien, Butler. 2008. (ENG.). 240p. 39.95 *(978-1-58729-631-4(4))* Univ. of Iowa Pr.
Hester, Elliott. Adventures of a Continental Drifter: An Around-the-World Excursion into Weirdness, Danger, Lust, & the Perils of Street Food. 2006. (ENG.). 320p. pap. 15.95 *(978-0-312-31242-8(3),* St. Martin's Paperbacks) St. Martin's Pr.
—Adventures of Continental Drifter. Date not set. mass mkt. *(978-0-312-98878-4(8),* St. Martin's Paperbacks) St. Martin's Pr.
Hickman, Lisa C. William Faulkner & Joan Williams: The Romance of Two Writers. 2006. (ENG., Illus.). 228p. per. 35.00 *(978-0-7864-2599-0(7))* McFarland & Co., Inc. Pubs.
Hickman, Miranda B. & Feenstra, Robin E. One Must Not Go Altogether with the Tide: The Letters of Ezra Pound & Stanley Nott. 2011. (Illus.). 432p. (C). *(978-0-7735-3816-0(X))* McGill-Queen's Univ. Pr.
Higginson, Thomas Wentworth. Short Studies of American Authors. 2009. 66p. pap. 17.75 *(978-1-116-86693-3(5))*; pap. 16.75 *(978-1-116-86694-0(3))* BiblioBazaar.
—Short Studies of American Authors. 2007. (ENG.). 68p. per. 16.95 *(978-0-548-61695-6(7))* Kessinger Publishing, LLC.
—Short Studies of American Authors. 2008. 100p. pap. *(978-1-4086-9232-5(5))* Read Bks.
Hijuelos, Oscar. Thoughts Without Cigarettes: A Memoir. 2011. (ENG.). 384p. (gr. 12). 27.50 *(978-1-59240-629-6(7),* Gotham) Penguin Group (USA) Inc.
Hinojosa, Rolando. A Voice of My Own: Essays & Stories. 2011. pap. 19.95 *(978-1-55885-712-4(5))* Arte Publico Pr.
Hirsh-Dickinson, Sally. Dirty Whites & Dark Secrets: Sex & Race in Peyton Place. 2011. (Revisiting New England Ser.). 240p. (C). 85.00 *(978-1-61168-041-6(7))*; (ENG.). pap. 39.95 *(978-1-61168-042-3(5))* Univ. Pr. of New England. (University of New Hampshire Press).
Hobart, Alice Tisdale. Portrait of a Novelist. 2011. 28p. 35.95 ***(978-1-258-08396-0(5))*** Literary Licensing, LLC.
Holloway, Jean & Garland, Hamlin. Hamlin Garland: A Biography. 2011. 380p. 53.95 ***(978-1-258-02483-3(7))*** Literary Licensing, LLC.
Holm, Bill. Music of Failure. 25th ed. 2010. (Fesler-Lampert Minnesota Heritage Ser.). (Illus.). 160p. pap. 16.95 *(978-0-8166-7008-6(0))* Univ. of Minnesota Pr.
Holman, John P Marquand, Vol. 46. 2009. (ENG.). 48p. pap. 25.00 *(978-0-8166-0350-3(2))* Univ. of Minnesota Pr.
—Thomas Wolfe, Vol. 6. 2009. pap. 25.00 *(978-0-8166-0208-7(5))* Univ. of Minnesota Pr.
Holmes, Oliver Wendell. Ralph Waldo Emerson. 2009. 456p. 31.99 *(978-1-113-87677-5(8))* 2009. 456p. pap. 22.99 *(978-1-113-87672-0(7))* 2008. 328p. 29.99 *(978-0-554-24371-9(7))* 2008. 328p. 28.99 *(978-0-554-33674-9(X))* 2006. (ENG.). 288p. pap. 21.99 *(978-1-4264-6388-4(X))* 2006. (ENG.). 326p. pap. 24.99 *(978-1-4264-6462-1(2))* BiblioBazaar.
—Ralph Waldo Emerson. 2009. 260p. pap. *(978-0-217-98091-3(0))* Books LLC.
—Ralph Waldo Emerson. Warner, Charles Dudley, ed. 2008. 264p. pap. *(978-1-4065-6111-1(8))* Dodo Pr.
Hopkins, Ellen & Wilson, Leah. A New Dawn: Your Favorite Authors on Stephenie Meyer's Twilight Series. 2008. x, 174p. *(978-0-9792331-5-9(1))* BenBella Bks.
Hopkins, John. The South American Diaries (1972-1973) 2008. (Illus.). 235p. *(978-0-932274-69-4(2))* Cadmus Editions.
Hopkinson, Deborah. Deborah Hopkinson & YOU, 1 vol. 2007. (Author & YOU Ser.). (Illus.). 112p. pap. 35.00 *(978-1-59158-278-6(4),* LU2784) Libraries Unlimited, Inc.
Horne, Gerald C. W. E. B. du Bois: A Biography, 1 vol. 2009. (Greenwood Biographies Ser.). (Illus.). 211p. 35.00 *(978-0-313-34979-9(7),* GR4979) Greenwood Publishing Group, Inc.
Horowitz, Helen Lefkowitz. Wild Unrest: Charlotte Perkins Gilman & the Making of the Yellow Wall-Paper. (ENG.). 272p. 2012. pap. 18.95 ***(978-0-19-989193-1(1))*** 2010. (Illus.). 24.95 *(978-0-19-973980-6(3))* Oxford Univ. Pr., Inc.

Hotchner, A. E. The Boyhood Memoirs of A. E. Hotchner: King of the Hill & Looking for Miracles. 2007. (ENG.). 432p. (gr. 9). per. 19.95 (978-1-883982-60-7(X)) Missouri Historical Society Pr.

—Paul & Me: 53 Years of Adventures & Misadventures with My Pal Paul Newman. 2011. (Illus.). 256p. pap. 15.95 (978-0-307-47481-0(X), Anchor) Knopf Doubleday Publishing Group.

Howard, Hugh. Writers of the American South: Their Literary Landscapes. 2011. (ENG.). 9.98 (978-0-7893-2414-6(8), Rizzoli Universe Promotional Bks.) Rizzoli International Pubns., Inc.

Howells, William Dean. Literary Friends & Acquaintances: A Personal Retrospect of American Authorship. 2008. 448p. 30.99 (978-0-559-26972-1(2)) 2008. 448p. pap. 35.75 (978-0-559-26970-7(6)) 2008. 288p. 25.99 (978-0-554-31261-3(1)) 2008. 288p. 28.99 (978-0-554-21958-5(1)) 2007. (ENG.). 298p. pap. 21.99 (978-1-4264-1355-1(6)) 2006. 296p. pap. 23.99 (978-1-4264-1366-7(1)) BiblioBazaar.

—Literary Friends & Acquaintances: A Personal Retrospect of American Authorship. 2006. (ENG.). pap. (978-1-4068-1444-6(X)) Echo Library.

—Literary Friends & Acquaintances: A Personal Retrospect of American Authorship. 2007. (ENG.). 296p. 43.95 (978-0-548-18629-9(4)); 300p. per. 28.95 (978-1-4304-8960-3(X)) Kessinger Publishing, LLC.

—My Mark Twain: Reminiscences & Criticisms. 2007. (ENG.). 72p. per. (978-1-4065-3130-5(8)) Dodo Pr.

—My Mark Twain: Reminiscences & Criticisms. 2008. 60p. pap. 10.99 (978-1-59547-688-3(1)) NuVision Pubns., LLC.

Howington, Helen. All in A Lifetime. 2010. 160p. 24.95 (978-1-4520-6766-7(X)); pap. 14.95 (978-1-4520-6764-3(3)) AuthorHouse.

Huffer, Mary Lee Stephenson. Emily Dickinson's Experiential Poetics & Rev. Dr. Charles Wadsworth's Rhetoric of Sensation: The Intellectual Friendship between the Poet & a Pastor. 2007. 180p. 99.95 (978-0-7734-5282-4(6)) Mellen, Edwin Pr., The.

Hughes, Evan. Literary Brooklyn: The Writers of Brooklyn & the Story of American City Life. 2011. (ENG., Illus.). 352p. pap. 17.00 (978-0-8050-8986-8(1), Holt Paperback) Holt, Henry & Co.

Hummel, Thomas R. A Journey Through Literary America. 2009. (Illus.). 277p. 45.00 (978-0-9817425-1-9(3)) Val de Grace Bks. & Film, Inc.

Hurston, Zora Neale. Dust Tracks on a Road: An Autobiography. 2010. (P. S. Ser.). (ENG.). 336p. pap. 16.99 (978-0-06-200483-3(2), HarperPerennial) HarperCollins Pubs.

Hutchison, Hazel. Brief Lives: Henry James. 2012. (Brief Lives Ser.). (ENG.). 112p. pap. 13.95 (978-1-84391-923-0(0)) Hesperus Pr. GBR. Dist: Independent Pubs. Group.

Hyman, Flannery Oconnor-Aw V54. 2009. pap. 25.00 (978-0-8166-0384-8(7)) Univ. of Minnesota Pr.

Iglesias, Karl. The 101 Habits of Highly Successful Screenwriters: Insider Secrets from Hollywood's Top Writers. 2nd ed. 2011. (ENG.). 272p. pap. 14.95 **(978-1-4405-2789-0(X))** Adams Media Corp.

Inscoe, John C. & Ruppersburg, Hugh, eds. The New Georgia Encyclopedia Companion to Georgia Literature. 2007. (ENG.). 472p. per. 24.95 (978-0-8203-2876-8(6)) Univ. of Georgia Pr.

Introspection Writers Group. Windows of Life. 2008. 96p. pap. 15.00 (978-0-9792132-8-1(2)) Reflections Publishing, Inc.

Irmscher, Christoph. Longfellow Redux. 2008. (ENG., Illus.). 376p. pap. 25.95 (978-0-252-07586-5(2)) Univ. of Illinois Pr.

—Public Poet, Private Man: Henry Wadsworth Longfellow At 200. 2009. (Illus.). 236p. pap. 24.95 net. (978-1-55849-584-5(3)) Univ. of Massachusetts Pr.

Irvine, Alexander. From the Bottom Up: The Life Story of Alexander Irvine. 2007. (ENG.). 208p. pap. 20.99 (978-1-4346-1317-2(8)); 230p. pap. 22.99 (978-1-4346-1369-1(0)) BiblioBazaar.

Irving, Clifford. The Hoax. 2007. 400p. pap. 14.95 (978-1-4013-0854-4(6)) Miramax Bks.

Irving, Washington. The Crayon Miscellany. 2008. 381p. 31.99 (978-0-559-00049-2(9)); 29.99 (978-0-559-00059-1(6)); pap. 33.75 (978-0-559-00050-8(2)); pap. 32.75 (978-0-559-00055-3(3)) BiblioBazaar.

—Letters of Washington Irving to Henry Brevoort. Hellman, George S., ed. 2006. pap. 42.95 (978-1-4286-5106-7(3)) Kessinger Publishing, LLC.

Irving, Washington. Washington Irving Diary: Spain, 1828-1829. Penney, Clara Louisa, ed. 2011. 176p. 42.95 **(978-1-258-01189-5(1))** Literary Licensing, LLC.

Isaacson, Walter. American Sketches: Great Leaders, Creative Thinkers, & Heroes of a Hurricane. 2010. (ENG.). 304p. pap. 15.00 (978-1-4391-8344-1(9)) Simon & Schuster.

Jack London. John Barleycorn. l.t. ed. 2007. (ENG.). 200p. pap. 21.99 (978-1-4264-7146-9(7)) BiblioBazaar.

Jack, Zachary. Participatory Sportswriting: An Anthology, 1870-1937. Jack, Zachary Michael, ed. 2008. (ENG.). 254p. pap. 45.00 (978-0-7864-3953-9(X)) McFarland & Co., Inc. Pubs.

Jack, Zachary M., ed. Homer Croy: Corn Country. 2010. (ENG.). 264p. pap. 24.50 (978-1-888160-74-1(8), Tall Corn Bks.) Ice Cube Pr.

Jack, Zachary Michael, ed. Iowa, the Definitive Collection: Classic & contemporary readings by Iowans, for Iowans. 2009. 532p. pap. 26.95 (978-1-888160-38-3(1), Tall Corn Bks.) Ice Cube Pr.

Jackson, H. Joaquin. One Ranger Limited Edition. 2009. (ENG., Illus.). 253p. 150.00 (978-0-292-72112-8(9)) Univ. of Texas Pr.

Jackson, Lawrence. Ralph Ellison: Emergence of Genius. 2007. (ENG.). 520p. pap. 24.95 (978-0-8203-2993-2(2)) Univ. of Georgia Pr.

Jackson, Leon. The Business of Letters: Authorial Economies in Antebellum America. 2007. (ENG.). 344p. 35.00 (978-0-8047-5705-8(4)) Stanford Univ. Pr.

Jackson, Shirley. Life among the Savages. 22.95 (978-0-89190-624-7(X)) Amereon LTD.

Jackson, Spoon & Tannenbaum, Judith. By Heart: Poetry, Prison, & Two Lives. 2010. (ENG., Illus.). 224p. pap. 20.00 (978-0-9815593-5-3(2)) New Village Pr.

Jacob, Kathryn Allamong. King of the Lobby: The Life & Times of Sam Ward, Man-about-Washington in the Gilded Age. 2009. (ENG., Illus.). 240p. (gr. 17). 40.00 (978-0-8018-9397-1(6)) Johns Hopkins Univ. Pr.

Jacobson, James R. Hope for Tomorrow's Families/A Model That Values Variety. 2009. 160p. 23.25 (978-1-60860-490-6(X), Eloquent Bks.) AEG Literary Publishing Services, Inc.

Jagoe, Armiger. Southern Boy: Growing up on the Mississippi Gulf Coast in The 1920-30s. 2009. 180p. pap. 16.95 (978-1-4401-4454-7(0)) iUniverse, Inc.

Jahner, Elaine A. Spaces of the Mind: Narrative & Community in the American West. 2008. (Frontiers of Narrative Ser.). (ENG.). 212p. pap. 19.95 (978-0-8032-1833-8(8)) Univ. of Nebraska Pr.

Jaksic, Iván. The Hispanic World & American Intellectual Life, 1820-1880. 2007. (Studies of the Americas Ser.). (ENG.). 272p. 95.00 (978-1-4039-8079-3(9)) Palgrave Macmillan.

James, E. Mary Phillip. James Fenimore Cooper. 2006. 392p. per. (978-1-4067-2844-6(6), Hesperides Pr.) Read Bks.

James, Henry. The Complete Letters of Henry James, 1876-1878. Walker, Pierre A. & Zacharias, Greg W., eds. 2012. (Complete Letters of Henry James Ser.). (ENG.). 392p. 95.00 **(978-0-8032-4063-6(5))** Univ. of Nebraska Pr.

—Hawthorne. 2011. (Cambridge Library Collection - English Men of Letters Ser.). (ENG.). 198p. pap. 19.99 **(978-1-108-03462-3(4))** Cambridge Univ. Pr.

—A Most Unholy Trade: Being Letters on the Drama. 2011. 18p. 35.95 **(978-1-258-07286-5(6))** Literary Licensing, LLC.

James, Henry & Mamoli Zorzi, Rosella. Letters to Isabella Stewart Gardner. 2009. (ENG., Illus.). 336p. pap. 17.95 (978-1-901285-83-3(9)) Pushkin Pr., Ltd. GBR. Dist: Consortium Bk. Sales & Distribution.

Jameson, W. C., ed. Hot Coffee & Cold Truth: Living & Writing the West. 2006. (ENG., Illus.). 218p. pap. 14.95 (978-0-8263-4061-0(X)) Univ. of New Mexico Pr.

—Notes from Texas: On Writing in the Lone Star State. 2008. (ENG., Illus.). 250p. 27.95 (978-0-87565-358-7(8)) Texas Christian Univ. Pr.

Jeffares, Norman A. W. B. Yeats. 2010. 498p. pap. 45.00 (978-0-415-56893-7(5)) Routledge.

Jeffers, Robinson & Jeffers, Una. The Collected Letters of Robinson Jeffers Vol. 1: With Selected Letters of Una Jeffers, 1890-1930. Karman, James, ed. 2009. (ENG., Illus.). 1016p. 95.00 (978-0-8047-6251-9(1)) Stanford Univ. Pr.

Jiménez de Báez, Yvette & Guiterrez de Velasco, Luzelena. Pedro Páramo: Diálogos en Contrapunto (1955-2005) 2008. (Estudios Lingüísticos y Literarios Ser.). (SPA.). 410p. pap. 38.99 (978-968-12-1377-0(7)) El Colegio de México, A.C., Biblioteca Miguel Cosio Villegas MEX. Dist: Fondo de Cultura Economica USA.

Johanson, Paula. Will Hobbs. 2009. (Library of Author Biographies Ser.). 112p. (gr. 5-8). 63.90 (978-1-60853-560-6(6), Rosen Central) Rosen Publishing Group, Inc., The.

John Jerningham's Journal. 2006. 144p. per. 16.99 (978-1-4255-1043-5(4)) MPublishing.

Johnson, Claudia Durst. War in Kurt Vonnegut's Slaughterhouse-Five. Greenhaven Editor, ed. 2011. (Social Issues in Literature Ser.). (ENG., Illus.). 224p. pap. 26.50 (978-0-7377-5818-4(X), Greenhaven Pr., Inc.); (YA). (gr. 9-12). 38.45 (978-0-7377-5817-7(1)) Cengage Gale.

Johnson, David R. Conrad Richter. 2008. pap. 24.95 (978-0-271-02788-3(6)) Pennsylvania State Univ. Pr.

Johnson, Joyce. The Voice Is All: The Lonely Victory of Jack Kerouac. 2012. (ENG.). 512p. 32.95 **(978-0-670-02510-7(0)**, Viking Adult) Penguin Group (USA) Inc.

Johnson, Nora. Coast to Coast: A Family Romance. 2007. (ENG., Illus.). 288p. pap. 19.95 (978-1-4165-6809-4(3)) Simon & Schuster.

Johnson, William. A River Without Banks. 2010. 160p. pap. 18.95 (978-0-87071-582-2(8)) Oregon State Univ. Pr.

Jones, Arlene Swift. God, Put Out One of My Eyes. 2010. 262p. pap. 24.00 (978-0-9843418-0-1(3)) Antrim Hse.

Jones, Brian Jay. Washington Irving: The Definitive New Biography of One of America's Greatest Writers. 2011. (ENG., Illus.). 480p. pap. 17.95 (978-1-61145-354-6(2), 611354, Arcade Publishing) Skyhorse Publishing Co., Inc.

Jones, Teddy & Muth, Marcia. Left Early, Arrived Late: Scenes from the Life of Marcia Muth, Memory Painter. 2008. 160p. pap. 19.95 (978-0-86534-665-9(8)) Sunstone Pr.

Jong, Erica. Fear of Fifty: A Midlife Memoir. 2006. (ENG.). 352p. (gr. 12-18). 14.95 (978-1-58542-524-2(9), Tarcher) Penguin Group (USA) Inc.

—Seducing the Demon: Writing for My Life. 2007. (ENG., Illus.). 304p. (gr. 12-18). 14.95 (978-1-58542-514-3(1), Tarcher) Penguin Group (USA) Inc.

Jonza, Nancylee Novell. The Underground Stream: The Life & Art of Caroline Gordon. 2010. (ENG.). 502p. pap. 26.95 (978-0-8203-3626-8(2)) Univ. of Georgia Pr.

Joseph, Diana. I'M Sorry You Feel That Way: The Astonishing but True Story of a Daughter, Sister, Slut, Wife, Mother, & Friend to Man & Dog. 2010. (ENG.). 224p. (gr. 12-18). 15.00 (978-0-425-23221-7(2), Berkley Trade) Penguin Group (USA) Inc.

Joshi, S. T. I Am Providence: The Life & Times of H. P. Lovecraft, 2 vols. 2010. 100.00 (978-0-9824296-7-9(3)) Hippocampus Pr.

Kaag, John J. Idealism, Pragmatism, & Feminism: The Philosophy of Ella Lyman Cabot. 2011. **(978-0-7391-6781-6(2))** Lexington Bks.

Kaczor, Christopher, ed. O Rare Ralph Mcinerny: Stories & Reflections on a Legendary Notre Dame Professor. 2011. (ENG., Illus.). 155p. pap. 18.00 (978-1-58731-585-5(8)) St. Augustine's Pr., Inc.

Kaluta, Michael Wm. The Art of Michael Wm. Kaluta. 2008. 256p. 49.99 (978-0-9801479-7-1(2)); 79.99 (978-0-9801479-8-8(0)) Desperado Publishing.

Kant, Candace C., ed. Dolly & Zane Grey: Letters from a Marriage. 2011. (Western Literature Ser.). (ENG., Illus.). 472p. pap. 24.95 **(978-0-87417-862-3(2))** Univ. of Nevada Pr.

Kantner, Seth. Shopping for Porcupine: A Life in Arctic Alaska. (ENG., Illus.). 256p. 2009. pap. 19.95 (978-1-57131-311-9(7)) 2008. 28.00 (978-1-57131-301-0(X)) Milkweed Editions.

Karell, Linda. Writing Together - Writing Apart: Collaboration in Western American Literature. 2008. (ENG.). 219p. pap. 19.95 (978-0-8032-1834-5(6)) Univ. of Nebraska Pr.

Kasdorf, Julia Spicher. The Body & the Book: Writing from a Mennonite Life. 2009. (Keystone Bks.). (ENG.). 208p. pap. 24.95 (978-0-271-03544-4(7)) Pennsylvania State Univ. Pr.

Kaser, James. The Chicago of Fiction: A Resource Guide. 2011. (ENG.). 672p. 100.00 (978-0-8108-7724-5(4)) Scarecrow Pr., Inc.

Kate Sanborn. Memories & Anecdotes. l.t. ed. 2006. 178p. pap. 21.99 (978-1-4264-8519-0(0)) BiblioBazaar.

Katrovas, Richard. The Years of Smashing Bricks: An Anecdotal Memoir. 2007. 134p. per. 16.95 (978-0-88748-468-1(9)) Carnegie-Mellon Univ. Pr.

Katz, Steve. Time's Wallet. 2010. 184p. pap. 15.95 (978-1-933996-22-6(6)) Counterpath Pr.

Kauffmann, Stanley. Albums of a Life: A Memoir. 2007. 350p. 30.00 (978-1-931357-53-1(6)); per. 18.95 (978-1-931357-48-7(X)) Sheep Meadow Pr., The.

Kaywell, Joan F. & Kaywell, Joan, eds. Dear Author: Letters of HopeTop Young Adult Authors Respond to Kids' Toughest Issues. 2007. (ENG.). 272p. (YA). (gr. 8-18). 15.99 (978-0-399-23705-8(4), Philomel) Penguin Group (USA) Inc.

Kearns, Michael. Lasting Connections: Two Plays That Survived the Plague. 2009. 128p. pap. 18.69 (978-0-325-02159-1(7), E02159) Heinemann.

Keeler, Greg. Trash Fish: A Life. 2008. (ENG.). 176p. pap. 14.95 (978-1-58243-402-5(6), Counterpoint Pr.) Basic Bks. GBR. Dist: Perseus-PGW.

Keillor, Garrison. Homegrown Democrat: A Few Plain Thoughts from the Heart of America. 2006. (ENG.). 272p. (gr. 12-18). 15.00 (978-0-14-303768-2(4), Penguin (Non-Classics)) Penguin Group (USA) Inc.

Keller, Elizabeth Leavitt. Walt Whitman in Mickle Street. 2011. 246p. pap. 29.45 **(978-1-4460-7409-1(9))** Aslan Pr.

Kellogg, Elijah. Arthur Brown, the Young Captain by Rev Elijah Kellogg. 2006. 296p. per. 23.99 (978-1-4255-2950-5(X)) MPublishing.

Kelly, Frank King. Kissing Joy as it Flies - Living in Eternity's Sunrise. 2009. 574p. 45.95 (978-0-615-25915-4(4)); (ENG.). 579p. pap. 29.95 (978-0-615-26002-0(0)) Kelly, Frank K.

Kelton, Elmer. Sandhills Boy: The Winding Trail of a Texas Writer. 2010. (ENG., Illus.). 304p. 7.99 (978-0-7653-5428-0(4), Forge Bks.) Doherty, Tom Assocs., LLC.

Kendall, Elizabeth. Autobiography of a Wardrobe. 2009. (ENG.). 240p. pap. 15.00 (978-0-307-38609-0(0), Anchor) Knopf Doubleday Publishing Group.

Kennedy, John P. Memoirs of the Life of William Wirt V1 A. 2006. pap. 33.95 (978-1-4286-4976-7(X)) Kessinger Publishing, LLC.

—Memoirs of the Life of William Wirt V2 A. 2006. pap. 34.95 (978-1-4286-4977-4(8)) Kessinger Publishing, LLC.

Kent, Adaline. The Autobiography from the Notebooks & Sculpture of Adaline Kent. 2011. 86p. 38.95 **(978-1-258-09523-9(8))** Literary Licensing, LLC.

Ketchie, Cotton. A Country Boy's Education. 2007. 345p. pap. 17.95 (978-0-7414-4338-0(4)) Infinity Publishing.

Kilmer, Joyce. Literature in the Making, by Some of Its Makers. 2009. 98p. pap. (978-1-151-32016-2(1)) Books LLC.

—Literature in the Making, by Some of Its Makers. 336p. 2008. 45.95 (978-0-548-93168-4(2)) 2007. per. 30.95 (978-0-548-59569-5(0)) Kessinger Publishing, LLC.

Kim, Richard E. Lost Names: Scenes from a Korean Boyhood. 2nd anniv. ed. 2011. (ENG.). 224p. pap. 18.95 (978-0-520-26812-8(1)) Univ. of California Pr.

King, Don W., ed. Out of My Bone: The Letters of Joy Davidman. 2009. (Illus.). 426p. 28.00 (978-0-8028-6399-7(X)) Eerdmans, William B. Publishing Co.

King, Grace. Memories of a Southern Woman of Letters. 408p. 2008. 49.95 (978-1-4366-8865-9(5)) 2007. (ENG.). per. 34.95 (978-1-4325-1774-8(0)) Kessinger Publishing, LLC.

King, Stephen. On Writing: A Memoir of the Craft. 10th anniv. ed. 2010. (ENG.). 288p. 27.00 (978-1-4391-9363-1(0), Scribner) Scribner.

King, William Davies. Another Part of a Long Story: Literary Traces of Eugene O'Neill & Agnes Boulton. 2010. (ENG., Illus.). 328p. 60.00 (978-0-472-11717-8(3)) Univ. of Michigan Pr.

Kirk, Lydia Chapin. Distinguished Service: Lydia Chapin Kirk, Partner in Diplomacy, 1896-1984. 2007. (ADST-DACOR Diplomats & Diplomacy Ser.). (Illus.). 273p. (978-0-8156-0891-2(8)) Syracuse Univ. Pr.

Kirksey, Joyce. My Trials Came to Make Me Strong: The Untold Story of Joyce Kirksey. 2007. 9.00 (978-0-8059-8712-6(6)) Dorrance Publishing Co., Inc.

Kirn, Walter. Lost in the Meritocracy: The Undereducation of an Overachiever. 2010. (ENG.). 224p. pap. 14.95 (978-0-307-27945-3(6), Anchor) Knopf Doubleday Publishing Group.

Kitchen, Judith. Half in Shade: Family, Photography, & Fate. 2012. (ENG.). 214p. pap. 16.00 **(978-1-56689-296-4(1))** Coffee Hse. Pr.

Klam, Julie. Please Excuse My Daughter. 2009. (ENG.). 272p. (gr. 12-18). 15.00 (978-1-59448-357-8(4), Riverhead Trade (Paperbacks)) Penguin Group (USA) Inc.

Klein, Stacey Jean. Margaret Junkin Preston, Poet of the Confederacy: A Literary Life. 2007. (Illus.). 137p. (978-1-57003-704-7(3)) Univ. of South Carolina Pr.

Klein, Stephanie. Moose: A Memoir. 2009. (Illus.). 320p. pap. 14.99 (978-0-06-167286-6(6), Harper Paperbacks) HarperCollins Pubs.

Kling, Kevin. The Dog Says How. 2007. (ENG.). 224p. 22.95 (978-0-87351-599-3(4), Borealis Bk.) Minnesota Historical Society Pr.

Kloefkorn, William. Breathing in the Fullness of Time. 2009. (ENG.). 244p. 22.95 (978-0-8032-1932-8(6)) Univ. of Nebraska Pr.

Knight, George R. A.T. Jones: Point Man on Adventism's Charismatic Frontier. 2011. (978-0-8280-2562-1(2)) Review & Herald Publishing Assn.

Knight, Michael Muhammad. Impossible Man: Or, F. Scott Fitzgerald & the Rise of Islam. 2009. (ENG.). 272p. pap. 15.95 (978-1-59376-226-1(7), Soft Skull Pr.) Counterpoint LLC.

—Why I Am a Five Percenter. 2011. (ENG.). 304p. (gr. 12). 14.95 (978-1-58542-868-7(X), Tarcher) Penguin Group (USA) Inc.

Knights, Pamela. The Cambridge Introduction to Edith Wharton. 2009. (Cambridge Introductions to Literature Ser.). (ENG., Illus.). 170p. (C). 65.99 (978-0-521-86765-8(7)); pap. 20.99 (978-0-521-68719-5(5)) Cambridge Univ. Pr.

Koch, Karl H. Life's a Trampoline, Learn to Bounce. 2008. 389p. pap. 29.95 (978-1-60610-399-9(7)) PublishAmerica, Inc.

Kolin, Philip C., ed. Shakespeare & Southern Writers: A Study in Influence. 2011. (ENG.). 177p. pap. 30.00 **(978-1-61703-206-6(9))** Univ. Pr. of Mississippi.

Komunyakaa, Yusef. Conversations with Yusef Komunyakaa. Hanshaw, Shirley A. James, ed. 2010. (Literary Conversations Ser.). (ENG.). 224p. 65.00 (978-1-60473-421-8(3)); pap. 22.00 (978-1-60473-422-5(1)) Univ. Pr. of Mississippi.

Konkel, Mary Hugolina. Rene Fernandat Poet & Critic. 2006. pap. 27.95 (978-1-4286-6142-4(5)) Kessinger Publishing, LLC.

Kooser, Ted. Lights on a Ground of Darkness: An Evocation of a Place & Time. 2009. (ENG., Illus.). 72p. pap. 10.95 (978-0-8032-2642-5(X), Bison Bks.) Univ. of Nebraska Pr.

Kopley, Richard. Edgar Allan Poe & the Dupin Mysteries. 2008. (ENG.). 272p. 85.00 (978-0-230-60470-4(6)) Palgrave Macmillan.

Kopp, Achim, ed. Francis Lieber's Brief & Practical German Grammar. 2008. (Sprachgeschichte des Deutschen in Nordamerika: Quellen und Studien. History of the German Language in America: Sources & Studies). 226p. pap. 61.95 (978-3-631-57699-1(4)) Lang, Peter GmbH, Europäischer Verlag der Wissenschaften DEU. Dist: Lang, Peter.

Kotynek, Roy & Cohassey, John. American Cultural Rebels: Avant-Garde & Bohemian Artists, Writers & Musicians from the 1850s Through the 1960s. 2008. (ENG.). 262p. per. 39.95 (978-0-7864-3709-2(X)) McFarland & Co., Inc. Pubs.

Krapf, Norbert. The Ripest Moments: A Southern Indiana Childhood. 2008. (Illus.). xiii, 262p. (978-0-87195-262-2(9)) Indiana Historical Society.

Krass, Peter. Ignorance, Confidence, & Filthy Rich Friends: The Business Adventures of Mark Twain, Chronic Speculator & Entrepreneur. 2007. (ENG., Illus.). 278p. 22.95 (978-0-471-93337-3(6), Wiley) Wiley, John & Sons, Inc.

Kunzel, Bonnie & Fichtelberg, Susan. Tamora Pierce, 1 vol. 2007. (Teen Reads: Student Companions to Young Adult Literature Ser.). 296p. 45.00 (978-0-313-33660-7(1), GR3660, Greenwood Pr.) Greenwood Publishing Group, Inc.

Kuttner, Paul. An endless Struggle. 2009. 702p. pap. 26.95 (978-0-533-15498-2(7)) Vantage Pr., Inc.

Kwall, Roberta. The Soul of Creativity: Forging a Moral Rights Law for the United States. 2009. (ENG.). 272p. 70.00 (978-0-8047-5643-3(0)); pap. 24.95 (978-0-8047-6367-7(4)) Stanford Univ. Pr.

La Farge, Oliver, frwd. Raw Material: The Autobiographical Examination of an Artist's Journey into Maturity. 2009. 260p. pap. 24.95 (978-0-86534-673-4(9)) Sunstone Pr.

Lady, Teresa. Michael Talbot: Story of a Writer, 1 vol. 2009. 124p. pap. 19.95 (978-1-4489-9525-7(6)) PublishAmerica, Inc.

Lamb, Deacon Dick. Heal Your Thought Life: A Re-Minder. 2008. 149p. pap. 24.95 (978-1-60563-127-1(2)) PublishAmerica, Inc.

Lancaster, Jen. My Fair Lazy: One Reality Television Addict's Attempt to Discover If Not Being a Dumb Ass Is the New Black; Or, a Culture-Up Manifesto. 2011. (ENG.). 400p. (gr. 12). 15.00 (978-0-451-23186-4(4), N A L Trade) Penguin Group (USA) Inc.

Lang, Harry G. Teaching from the Heart & Soul: The Robert F. Panara Story. 2007. (Gallaudet New Deaf Lives Ser.). (ENG., Illus.). 232p. (C). per. 29.95 (978-1-56368-358-9(X)) Gallaudet Univ. Pr.

Lang, John, ed. Appalachia & Beyond: Conversations with Writers from the Mountain South. 2006. (Illus.). 352p. per. 24.95 (978-1-57233-535-6(1)) Univ. of Tennessee Pr.

Lange, Charlotte. Modos de Parodia: Guillermo Cabrera Infante, Reinaldo Arenas, Jorge Ibargüengoitia y José Augustin. 2008. (Hispanic Studies: Culture & Ideas Ser.). (SPA.). 252p. pap. 66.95 (978-3-03911-554-9(5)) Lang, Peter AG GBR. Dist: Lang, Peter.

Langevin, Roger G. The Langevin Legacy. 2008. 272p. (ENG.). 29.99 *(978-1-4363-0630-0(2))*; per. 19.99 *(978-1-4363-0629-4(9))* Xlibris Corp.

Lanier, Sidney. Letters of Sidney Lanier: Selections from His Correspondence 1866- 2007. pap. 27.95 *(978-1-4304-5082-5(7))* Kessinger Publishing, LLC.

Lansac, Philippe & London, Jack. Jack London's Grand North. 2007. (ENG., Illus.). 112p. pap. 19.95 *(978-0-7627-4363-6(8))* Globe Pequot Pr., The.

Larcom, Lucy. A New England Girlhood outlined from memory (Beverly MA) l.t. ed. 2007. (ENG.). 176p. pap. 19.99 *(978-1-4346-1745-3(9))* BiblioBazaar.

Larsen, Deborah. The Tulip & the Pope: A Nun's Story. annot. ed. 2006. (Vintage Ser.). (ENG.). 288p. pap. 14.00 *(978-0-375-71290-6(9)*, Vintage) Knopf Doubleday Publishing Group.

Larsen, Lyle. Stein & Hemingway: The Story of a Turbulent Friendship. 2011. (ENG., Illus.). 220p. pap. 45.00 *(978-0-7864-6056-4(3))* McFarland & Co., Inc. Pubs.

Larsen, Wally. Selected Utah Poets of the Year: 1965-1982, 1984-1987, 1989-1992, 1994-1997. 2007. *(978-0-8425-2674-6(9))* Brigham Young Univ.

Laskin, David. A Common Life: Four Generations of American Literary Friendships & Influence. 2007. (ENG., Illus.). 464p. pap. 29.95 *(978-1-4165-7606-8(1))* Simon & Schuster.

Lathrop, George Parsons. A Study of Hawthorne. 2008. 328p. 29.99 *(978-0-554-22782-5(7))* 2008. 328p. 28.99 *(978-0-554-32085-4(1))* 2007. (ENG.). 292p. pap. 21.99 *(978-1-4264-3046-6(9))* 2006. 326p. pap. 24.99 *(978-1-4264-3111-1(2))* BiblioBazaar.

—A Study of Hawthorne. 2007. (ENG.). 252p. per. *(978-1-4065-3573-0(7))* Dodo Pr.

—A Study of Hawthorne. 2007. (ENG.). 200p. per. *(978-1-4068-1737-9(6))* Echo Library.

Lathrop, Rose Hawthorne. Memories of Hawthorne. 2009. (ENG.). 497p. 42.99 *(978-1-117-56364-0(2))* 2009. (ENG.). 497p. pap. 37.75 *(978-1-117-56365-7(0))* 2008. 364p. 31.99 *(978-0-554-23819-7(5))* 2008. 364p. 29.99 *(978-0-554-33122-5(5))* 2007. (ENG.). 326p. pap. 23.99 *(978-1-4264-5052-5(4))* 2006. 362p. pap. 26.99 *(978-1-4264-5353-3(1))* BiblioBazaar.

—Memories of Hawthorne. 2009. 208p. pap. *(978-1-150-46148-4(9))* Books LLC.

—Memories of Hawthorne. 2007. (ENG.). 300p. per. *(978-1-4065-3575-4(3))* Dodo Pr.

—Memories of Hawthorne. 2007. (ENG.). 224p. per. *(978-1-4068-1734-8(1))* Echo Library.

—Memories of Hawthorne. 2007. (ENG.). 494p. 53.95 *(978-0-548-20548-8(5))*; 496p. per. 38.95 *(978-1-4325-2288-9(4))* Kessinger Publishing, LLC.

Latimer, Matthew. Speech-less: Tales of a White House Survivor. 2010. (ENG.). 304p. pap. 15.00 *(978-0-307-46429-3(6)*, Three Rivers Pr.) Crown Publishing Group.

Le Clair, Robert C. Young Henry James 18431870. 2006. pap. 37.95 *(978-1-4286-5923-0(4))* Kessinger Publishing, LLC.

Lease, Benjamin. Anglo-American Encounters: England & the Rise of American Literature. 2009. (ENG.). 316p. pap. 42.00 *(978-0-521-10852-2(7))* Cambridge Univ. Pr.

Leclaire, Anne D. Listening below the Noise: The Transformative Power of Silence. 2010. 256p. pap. 13.99 *(978-0-06-135336-9(1)*, HarperPerennial) HarperCollins Pubs.

Lee, Hermione. Willa Cather: A Life Saved Up. 2008. (ENG., Illus.). 416p. pap. 16.95 *(978-1-84408-492-0(2))* Little, Brown Bk. Group Ltd. GBR. Dist: Independent Pubs. Group.

Lee, Jae, illus. The Long Road Home. ltd. ed. 2008. 240p. 69.95 *(978-1-892950-92-5(8))* Overlook Connection Pr., The.

Lee, John Thomas. New Found Letters of Josiah Gregg, Santa Fe Trader Historian: Proceedings of the American Antiquarian Society, V40, Part 1, April 16 1930. 2011. 26p. 35.95 ***(978-1-258-03630-0(4))*** Literary Licensing, LLC.

Lefkowitz, Frances. To Have Not. 2010. 296p. pap. 14.50 *(978-1-59692-354-6(7))* MacAdam/Cage Publishing, Inc.

Leick, Karen. Gertrude Stein & the Making of an American Celebrity. 2009. (Studies in Major Literary Authors Ser.). (ENG., Illus.). 256p. (C). 125.00 *(978-0-415-99472-9(1))* Routledge.

Leifer, Carol. When You Lie about Your Age, the Terrorists Win: Reflections on Looking in the Mirror. 2010. (ENG.). 208p. pap. 14.00 *(978-0-345-50297-1(3)*, Villard Bks.) Random House Publishing Group.

Leland, Charles G. Memoirs by Charles Godfrey Leland. 2006. pap. 37.95 *(978-1-4286-5552-2(2))* Kessinger Publishing, LLC.

Leleux, Robert. The Memoirs of a Beautiful Boy. 2009. (ENG.). 304p. pap. 15.99 *(978-0-312-36169-3(6)*, St. Martin's Griffin) St. Martin's Pr.

LeMaster, J. R. & Wilson, James D., eds. The Mark Twain Encyclopedia. 2nd ed. 2011. (ENG.). 896p. pap. 65.00 *(978-0-415-89053-8(6))* Routledge.

Lent, Michael & McCarthy, Brian. Stephen King. 2012. (ENG., Illus.). 40p. (YA). pap. 7.99 ***(978-1-4507-7567-0(5))*** Bluewater Productions, Inc.

Leonin, Mia. Havana & Other Missing Fathers. 2009. (Camino del Sol Ser.). (ENG.). 192p. pap. 16.95 *(978-0-8165-2815-8(2)*, Univ. of Arizona Pr.

Lesley, Craig. Burning Fence. Date not set. mass mkt. *(978-0-312-99185-2(1)*, St. Martin's Paperbacks) St. Martin's Pr.

—Burning Fence: A Memoir of Fathers & Sons. Date not set. pap. *(978-0-312-31847-5(2)*, St. Martin's Paperbacks) St. Martin's Pr.

Leslie, Eliza. Selections from Eliza Leslie. Madden, Etta M., ed. & intro. by. 2011. (Legacies of Nineteenth-Century American Women Writers Ser.). (ENG., Illus.). 368p. pap. 40.00 *(978-0-8032-3295-2(0))* Univ. of Nebraska Pr.

Levin Becker, Daniel. Many Subtle Channels: In Praise of Potential Literature. 2012. (ENG.). 296p. 27.95 ***(978-0-674-06577-2(8))*** Harvard Univ. Pr.

Levy, David W. Mark Twain: The Divided Mind of America's Best-Loved Writer. 2010. (Library of American Biography Ser.). (ENG.). 240p. (C). pap. 25.20 *(978-0-205-55375-4(3)*, Prentice Hall) Prentice Hall PTR.

Lewis, Greg. I Refuse to Quit! The Autobiography of a Dreamer. 2009. 306p. pap. 17.95 *(978-1-4327-3428-2(8))* Outskirts Pr., Inc.

Lewis, John L. Heywood Broun: As He Seemed to Us. 2006. pap. 16.95 *(978-1-4286-5933-9(1))* Kessinger Publishing, LLC.

L'Heureux, John & Karagueuzian, Dikran. Conversations with John L'Heureux. (ENG.). 2011. 184p. pap. 17.00 *(978-1-57586-600-0(5))* 2010. (Illus.). 200p. 27.00 *(978-1-57586-601-7(3))* CSLI Pubns.

Li, Shuxue. Lewis Mumford: Critic of Culture & Civilization. 2009. 241p. pap. 49.95 *(978-3-03911-557-0(X))* Lang, Peter AG GBR. Dist: Lang, Peter.

Liederbach, Nate & Harris, James, eds. Of a Monstrous Child: An Anthology of Creative Writing Relationships. 2011. (ENG.). 414p. pap. 24.00 *(978-0-9844510-4-3(8))* Lost Horse Pr.

Lillios, Anna. Crossing the Creek: The Literary Friendship of Zora Neale Hurston & Marjorie Kinnan Rawlings. (ENG., Illus.). 2011. 216p. pap. 19.95 *(978-0-8130-3809-4(X))* 2010. 208p. 29.95 *(978-0-8130-3500-0(7))* Univ. Pr. of Florida.

Lindsay, Nicholas Vachel. Letters of Nicholas Vachel Lindsay to a Joseph Armstrong: The Baylor Bulletin, V43, No. 3, September 1940. Armstrong, A. Joseph, ed. 2011. 138p. 40.95 ***(978-1-258-03543-3(X))*** Literary Licensing, LLC.

Lobe, Kirsten. Paris, Baby! 2011. (ENG.). 352p. pap. 14.99 *(978-0-312-60532-2(3)*, St. Martin's Griffin) St. Martin's Pr.

Lofaro, Michael A., ed. Agee Agonistes: Essays on the Life, Legend, & Works of James Agee. 2007. (Illus.). 334p. 48.00 *(978-1-57233-574-5(2))* Univ. of Tennessee Pr.

Loh, Sandra Tsing. Mother on Fire: A True Motherf%#$@ Story about Parenting! 2009. (ENG.). 320p. pap. 15.00 *(978-0-307-45041-8(4)*, Three Rivers Pr.) Crown Publishing Group.

Loncraine, Rebecca. The Real Wizard of Oz: The Life & Times of L. Frank Baum. 2010. (ENG.). 352p. (gr. 12). 18.00 *(978-1-59240-558-9(4)*, Gotham) Penguin Group (USA) Inc.

London, Jack. The Cruise of the Snark. 2008. 232p. 24.99 *(978-0-554-37978-4(3))*; 27.99 *(978-0-554-28675-4(0))* BiblioBazaar.

—The Cruise of the Snark. 2008. 228p. pap. 13.95 *(978-1-60096-748-1(5))*; 228p. pap. 13.95 *(978-1-60096-131-1(2))*; 240p. pap. 14.95 *(978-1-4341-0056-6(1))* Editorium, The.

—The Cruise of the Snark. 2008. 176p. pap. 12.99 *(978-1-59547-590-9(7))* NuVision Pubns., LLC.

—John Barleycorn. 2007. (ENG.). 216p. 27.95 *(978-1-4218-3258-6(5))*; per. 12.95 *(978-1-4218-3358-3(1))* 1st World Publishing, Inc. (1st World Library - Literary Society).

—John Barleycorn. 2008. 204p. 25.99 *(978-0-554-24677-2(5))* 2008. 204p. 22.99 *(978-0-554-33980-1(3))* 2007. (ENG.). 182p. pap. 19.99 *(978-1-4264-7070-7(3))* BiblioBazaar.

—John Barleycorn. 2008. (ENG.). 100p. pap. 8.99 *(978-1-4209-3093-1(1))* Digireads.com.

—John Barleycorn. 2007. (ENG.). 176p. per. *(978-1-4065-5221-8(6))* Dodo Pr.

—John Barleycorn. 132p. 2009. pap. *(978-1-4068-7735-9(2))* 2007. (ENG.). per. *(978-1-4068-1491-0(1))* Echo Library.

—John Barleycorn. 2007. (ENG.). 220p. 34.75 *(978-1-934568-09-5(0))* Ellis, Frederick.

—John Barleycorn. 2010. 356p. pap. 22.95 *(978-0-557-50352-0(3))* Lulu Enterprises Inc.

—John Barleycorn. 2008. (Twelve-Point Ser.). lib. bdg. *(978-1-58287-486-9(7))*; lib. bdg. 26.00 *(978-1-58287-969-7(9))* North Bks.

—John Barleycorn. 2008. 184p. pap. 13.99 *(978-1-59547-600-5(8))* NuVision Pubns., LLC.

—The Road. 2008. 116p. pap. 10.99 *(978-1-59547-585-5(0))* NuVision Pubns., LLC.

Long, Robert Emmet & Long. Truman Capote, Enfant Terrible. 2008. (ENG.). 144p. 24.95 *(978-0-8264-2763-2(4))* Continuum International Publishing Group, Ltd. GBR. Dist: National Bk. Network.

Longstreet, Stephen. The Boy in the Model-T: A Journey in the Just Gone Past. 2011. 322p. 50.95 ***(978-1-258-08131-7(8))*** Literary Licensing, LLC.

Lopez, Lorraine, ed. An Angle of Vision: Women Writers on Their Poor & Working-Class Roots. 2009. (Class: Culture Ser.). (ENG.). 216p. pap. 23.95 *(978-0-472-05078-9(8))*; 65.00 *(978-0-472-07078-7(9))* Univ. of Michigan Pr.

Lord, Isabel Garland. A Summer to Be: A Memoir by the Daughter of Hamlin Garland. Newlin, Keith, ed. & intro. by. 2010. (ENG., Illus.). 424p. pap. 23.95 *(978-0-8032-3243-3(8)*, Bison Bks.) Univ. of Nebraska Pr.

Lorence, James J. A Hard Journey: The Life of Don West. (Illus.). 344p. 2010. (ENG.). pap. 25.00 *(978-0-252-07733-3(4))* 2007. 39.95 *(978-0-252-03231-8(4))* Univ. of Illinois Pr.

Lounsbury, Thomas RaynesFord. James Fenimore Cooper: American Men of Letters. 2007. (ENG.). 224p. pap. 20.99 *(978-1-4346-3364-4(0))*; 250p. pap. 22.99 *(978-1-4346-3365-1(9))* BiblioBazaar.

Lovecraft, H. P., et al. O Fortunate Floridian: H. P. Lovecraft's Letters to R. H. Barlow. 2007. 506p. 40.00 *(978-1-59732-034-4(X))* Univ. of Tampa Pr.

Loving, Jerome. Emerson, Whitman, & the American Muse. 2011. (ENG.). 232p. pap. 40.00 *(978-0-8078-9714-0(0))* Univ. of North Carolina Pr.

—Emily Dickinson: The Poet on the Second Story. 2009. (Cambridge Studies in American Literature & Culture Ser.). (ENG.). 148p. pap. 33.00 *(978-0-521-10907-9(8))* Cambridge Univ. Pr.

—Mark Twain: The Adventures of Samuel L. Clemens. (Illus.). 520p. 2011. (ENG.). pap. 21.95 *(978-0-520-26985-9(3))* 2010. 50.00 *(978-0-520-25257-8(8))* Univ. of California Pr.

Loye, David. 3,000 Years of Love: The Life of Riane Eisler & David Loye. 2007. 256p. pap. 18.95 *(978-0-9789827-5-1(4))* Franklin, Benjamin Pr.

Lucey, Donna M. Archie & Amelie: Love & Madness in the Gilded Age. 2007. (ENG., Illus.). 352p. per. 14.95 *(978-0-307-35145-6(9)*, Three Rivers Pr.) Crown Publishing Group.

Lynch, Audry. The Rebel Figure in American Literature & Film: The Interconnected Lives of John Steinbeck & James Dean. 2009. 124p. 89.95 *(978-0-7734-4662-5(1))* Mellen, Edwin Pr., The.

Lystra, Karen. Dangerous Intimacy: The Untold Story of Mark Twain's Final Years. 2006. (Illus.). 342p. per. 19.95 *(978-0-520-25000-0(1))* Univ. of California Pr.

Mabie, Hamilton Wright. Backgrounds of Literature. 2007. (ENG.). 340p. 46.95 *(978-0-548-05083-5(X))* Kessinger Publishing, LLC.

MacEnulty, Pat. Wait until Tomorrow: A Daughter's Memoir. 2011. (ENG.). 256p. pap. 16.95 *(978-1-55861-701-8(9))* Feminist Pr. at The City Univ. of New York.

Mackin, Randy. George Scarbrough, Appalachian Poet: A Biographical & Literary Study with Unpublished Writings. 2011. (Contributions to Southern Appalachian Studies). (ENG., Illus.). 220p. pap. 45.00 *(978-0-7864-6371-8(6))* McFarland & Co., Inc. Pubs.

MacKinnon, Douglas. Rolling Pennies in the Dark: A Memoir with a Message. 2012. (ENG.). 240p. lib. bdg. 24.00 *(978-1-4516-0788-8(1)*, Howard Bks.) Howard Books.

MacLauchlin, Cory. Butterfly in the Typewriter: The Tragic Life of John Kennedy Toole & the Remarkable Story of a Confederacy of Dunces. 2012. (ENG., Illus.). 352p. 26.00 ***(978-0-306-82040-3(4))*** Da Capo Pr., Inc.

Maclean, Norman. The Norman Maclean Reader. Weltzien, O. Alan, ed. & intro. by. 2012. (ENG., Illus.). 320p. pap. 17.50 ***(978-0-226-50027-0(6))*** Univ. of Chicago Pr.

Macy, John Albert. Edgar Allan Poe. 2008. 134p. 35.95 *(978-1-4366-2343-8(X))*; 136p. pap. 20.95 *(978-0-548-89065-3(X))* Kessinger Publishing, LLC.

—Edgar Allan Poe. 112p. reprint ed. 88.00 *(978-0-7222-8534-3(5))* Library Reprints, Inc.

—Edgar Allan Poe. 2008. 136p. pap. *(978-1-4097-1794-2(1))* Read Bks.

Madden, David & Mecholsky, Kristopher. James M. Cain: Hard-Boiled Mythmaker. 2011. (ENG.). 240p. 49.00 *(978-0-8108-8118-1(7))* Scarecrow Pr., Inc.

Maddrey, Joseph. The Making of T. S. Eliot: A Study of the Literary Influences. 2009. (ENG.). 190p. pap. 45.00 *(978-0-7864-4271-3(9))* McFarland & Co., Inc. Pubs.

Maher, Paul. Kerouac: His Life & Work. 2007. (ENG., Illus.). 584p. per. 18.95 *(978-1-58979-366-8(8))* Taylor Trade Publishing.

Mailer, Norris Church. A Ticket to the Circus: A Memoir. 2011. (Illus.). 448p. pap. 15.00 *(978-0-8129-7987-9(7)*, Random Hse. Trade Paperbacks) Random House Publishing Group.

Malcolm, Janet. Two Lives: Gertrude & Alice. (Illus.). 240p. 2008. (ENG.). pap. 13.00 *(978-0-300-14310-2(9))* 2007. 25.00 *(978-0-300-12551-1(8))* Yale Univ. Pr.

Malina, Judith. The Piscator Notebook. 2012. (ENG., Illus.). 256p. 115.00 *(978-0-415-60073-6(1))*; pap. 31.95 *(978-0-415-60074-3(X))* Routledge.

Mallory, Carole. Loving Mailer. 2010. (ENG.). 203p. 22.95 *(978-1-60747-715-0(7))* Phoenix Bks., Inc.

Mandel, Naomi. Bret Easton Ellis: American Psycho, Glamorama, Lunar Park. 2011. (Continuum Studies in Contemporary North American Fiction Ser.). (ENG.). 192p. 100.00 *(978-0-8264-4648-0(5))* Continuum International Publishing Group, Ltd. GBR. Dist: National Bk. Network.

Manderino, John. Crying at Movies: A Memoir. 2008. (ENG.). 200p. pap. 15.95 *(978-0-89733-580-5(5))* Academy Chicago Pubs., Ltd.

Manguso, Sarah. The Two Kinds of Decay: A Memoir. 2009. (ENG.). 192p. pap. 14.00 *(978-0-312-42844-0(8))* Picador.

Maradas, Tadaram. A Pictorial Memoir: 23 Years in the Making. 2010. 244p. pap. 78.49 *(978-1-4520-0167-8(7))* AuthorHouse.

Marcus, Leonard S. Listening for Madeleine: A Portrait of Madeleine L'Engle in Many Voices, 1 vol. 2012. (ENG., Illus.). 336p. 27.00 ***(978-0-374-29897-5(1))*** Farrar, Straus & Giroux.

Marcus, Leonard S. Pass It Down: Five Picture Book Families Make Their Mark. 2006. (ENG., Illus.). 64p. (J). (gr. 2-7). 19.95 *(978-0-8027-9600-4(1))*; lib. bdg. 20.85 *(978-0-8027-9601-1(X))* Walker & Co.

Marcus, Morton. Striking Through the Masks: A Literary Memoir. 2008. (Illus.). 590p. pap. 18.95 *(978-0-932319-09-8(2))* Capitola Bk. Co.

Markoe, Merrill. Cool, Calm & Contentious: Essays. 2012. (ENG.). 304p. pap. 15.00 ***(978-0-345-51892-7(6)***, Villard Bks.) Random House Publishing Group.

Marquart, Debra. The Horizontal World: Growing up Wild in the Middle of Nowhere. 2007. (ENG.). 304p. per. 15.95 *(978-1-58243-363-9(1))* Counterpoint LLC.

Marrs, Suzanne. Eudora Welty: A Biography. 2006. (ENG., Illus.). 672p. pap. 16.95 *(978-0-15-603063-2(2)*, Mariner Bks.) Houghton Mifflin Harcourt Trade & Reference Pubs.

—What There Is to Say We Have Said: The Correspondence of Eudora Welty & William Maxwell. (ENG.). 2012. 523p. pap. 16.95 ***(978-0-547-75032-3(3)***, Mariner Bks.) 2011. (Illus.). 512p. 35.00 *(978-0-547-37649-3(9))* Houghton Mifflin Harcourt Trade & Reference Pubs.

Marsh, Alec. Ezra Pound. 2011. (Reaktion Books - Critical Lives Ser.). (Illus.). 247p. pap. 16.95 *(978-1-86189-862-3(2))* Reaktion Bks., Ltd. GBR. Dist: Chicago Distribution Ctr.

Martin, David Lozell. Losing Everything. 2011. (ENG.). 208p. pap. 14.99 ***(978-0-7432-9434-8(3))*** Simon & Schuster.

Martin, David Lozell. Losing Everything: A Memoir. 2008. (ENG.). 208p. 24.00 *(978-0-7432-9433-1(5))* Simon & Schuster.

Martin, Lee. Such a Life. 2012. (American Lives Ser.). (ENG.). 232p. pap. 16.95 ***(978-0-8032-3647-9(6))*** Univ. of Nebraska Pr.

Martin, NaVada. Spirit of Art & Words. 10.00 *(978-0-9636530-0-0(8))* NIM Pr.

Mary Lou, Sanelli. Among Friends. 2009. 160p. pap. 15.00 *(978-1-929355-52-5(1)*, Aequitas Bks.) Pleasure Boat Studio: A Literary Pr.

Mason, Martha. Breath: A Lifetime in the Rhythm of an Iron Lung - A Memoir. 2010. (ENG., Illus.). 368p. pap. 16.00 *(978-1-60819-119-2(2))* Bloomsbury Publishing.

Masters, Jarvis Jay. That Bird Has My Wings: The Autobiography of an Innocent Man on Death Row. 2010. (ENG.). 304p. pap. 14.99 *(978-0-06-173048-1(3)*, HarperOne) HarperCollins Pubs.

Mathieu, Bertrand. Orpheus in Brooklyn. 2006. pap. 18.95 *(978-1-933993-16-4(2))* Apocryphile Pr.

Matteson, John. Eden's Outcasts: The Story of Louisa May Alcott & Her Father. 2008. (ENG., Illus.). 512p. pap. 17.95 *(978-0-393-33359-6(0)*, 33359) 2007. 29.95 *(978-0-7930-5964-5(X))* Norton, W. W. & Co., Inc.

Matthews, Brander. An Introduction to the Study of American Literature. 2008. 227p. 28.99 *(978-0-554-73250-3(5))*; 184p. 25.99 *(978-0-554-73262-6(9))*; 227p. pap. 26.75 *(978-0-554-73254-1(8))*; 184p. pap. 25.75 *(978-0-554-73260-2(2))* BiblioBazaar.

—An Introduction to the Study of American Literature. 2009. 174p. pap. *(978-0-217-77534-2(9))* Books LLC.

—An Introduction to the Study of American Literature. 2007. (ENG.). 256p. 42.95 *(978-0-548-02046-3(9))* Kessinger Publishing, LLC.

Matthews, Sebastian. In My Father's Footsteps. 2009. 280p. pap. 19.95 *(978-0-393-33813-3(4))* Norton, W. W. & Co., Inc.

Matthews, Thomas Stanley. Name & Address: An Autobiography. 2011. 318p. 50.95 ***(978-1-258-08296-3(9))*** Literary Licensing, LLC.

Matthias, John. Who Was Cousin Alice? & Other Questions. 2011. 370p. pap. ***(978-1-84861-168-9(4))*** Shearsman Bks.

Maud, Ralph. Charles Olson at the Harbor. Olson, Charles, ed. 2008. (ENG., Illus.). 224p. pap. 19.95 *(978-0-88922-576-3(1))* Talonbooks, Ltd. CAN. Dist: Consortium Bk. Sales & Distribution.

Max, D. T. Every Love Story Is a Ghost Story: A Life of David Foster Wallace. 2012. (ENG.). 368p. 26.95 ***(978-0-670-02592-3(5)***, Viking Adult) Penguin Group (USA) Inc.

Maxwell, William. Conversations with William Maxwell. Burkhardt, Barbara, ed. 2012. (Literary Conversations Ser.). (ENG.). 256p. 40.00 ***(978-1-61703-254-7(9))*** Univ. Pr. of Mississippi.

May, Stephen J. Michener: A Writer's Journey. 2009. (ENG.). 306p. pap. 19.95 *(978-0-8061-4042-1(9))* Univ. of Oklahoma Pr.

Maynard, Frank & Maynard, Frank. Cowboy's Lament: A Life on the Open Range. Hoy, Jim, ed. 2010. (Voice in the American West Ser.). (Illus.). 248p. 29.95 *(978-0-89672-705-2(X))* Texas Tech Univ. Pr.

Maynard, Lee. The Pale Light of Sunset: Scattershots & Hallucinations in an Imagined Life. 2009. xvii, 329p. pap. *(978-1-933202-43-3(2))*; (ENG.) 348p. 23.95 *(978-1-933202-42-6(4)*, Vandalia Pr.) West Virginia Univ. Pr.

McAteer, Joan. What Was I to Do? 2008. 139p. pap. 9.95 *(978-1-4357-1252-2(8))* Lulu Enterprises Inc.

McBride, Elizabeth. Last of the Nice Girls: How a Nice Girl from the British Empire Ends up a Witch in the New Mexico Desert. Miller Allen, Michelle, ed. 2007. (Illus.). per. 28.95 *(978-0-938513-38-4(9)*, Green Phoenix Productions) Amador Publishers, LLC.

McCann, Debbie. Life in The '50's: Memoirs of a Baby Boomer. 2009. 432p. pap. 20.49 *(978-1-4389-9103-0(7))* AuthorHouse.

McCann, Sean. A Pinnacle of Feeling: American Literature & Presidential Government. 2008. (20/21 Ser.). (ENG.). 248p. (C). 39.95 *(978-0-691-13695-0(5))* Princeton Univ. Pr.

McCauley, Lisa. Du Crow's Nest par Pascal Fuselier. 2008. 276p. pap. 24.95 *(978-0-557-00349-5(0))* Lulu Enterprises Inc.

McClennen, Sophia A. Ariel Dorfman: An Aesthetics of Hope. 2010. (ENG., Illus.). 408p. 94.95 *(978-0-8223-4586-2(2))*; pap. 26.95 *(978-0-8223-4604-3(4))* Duke Univ. Pr.

McCracken, Ellen. The Life & Writing of Fray Angelico Chavez: A New Mexico Renaissance Man. 2009. (Paso Por Aqui Ser. in the Nuevomexicano Literary Heritage Ser.). (ENG., Illus.). 472p. (C). 45.00 *(978-0-8263-4760-2(6))* Univ. of New Mexico Pr.

McCullough, David. The Greater Journey: Americans in Paris. (ENG., Illus.). 576p. 2012. pap. 20.00 ***(978-1-4165-7177-3(9))*** 2011. 37.50 *(978-1-4165-7176-6(0))* Simon & Schuster.

—The Greater Journey: Americans in Paris. l.t. ed. 2011. (Illus.). 861p. 35.99 *(978-1-4104-3820-1(1))* Thorndike Pr.

McDonald, Craig, ed. Rogue Males: Conversations & Confrontations about the Writing Life. 2009. 320p. pap. 14.95 *(978-1-932557-45-9(8))* Bleak Hse. Bks., Inc.

McFarland, Philip. Loves of Harriet Beecher Stowe. 2008. (ENG.). 336p. pap. 17.00 *(978-0-8021-4390-7(3)*, Grove Pr.) Grove/Atlantic, Inc.

McFarland, Ron. The Rockies in First Person: A Critical Study of Recent American Memoirs from the Region. 2008. (ENG., Illus.). 219p. pap. 39.95 *(978-0-7864-3717-7(0))* McFarland & Co., Inc. Pubs.

McInerny, Ralph. I Alone Have Escaped to Tell You: My Life & Pastimes. 2011. (ENG., Illus.). 192p. pap. 22.00 ***(978-0-268-03523-5(7))*** Univ. of Notre Dame Pr.

McInerny, Ralph. Some Catholic Writers. 2007. 166p. 23.00 *(978-1-58731-777-4(X))* St. Augustine's Pr., Inc.

McKay, Claude. A Long Way from Home. Jarrett, Gene Andrew, ed. 2007. (Multi-Ethnic Literatures of the Americas Ser.). (ENG.). 312p. per. 23.95 *(978-0-8135-3968-3(4))* Rutgers Univ. Pr.

McKay, Claude, ed. A Long Way from Home. 2007. (Multi-Ethnic Literatures of the Americas (MELA) Ser.). (ENG.). 302p. 68.00 *(978-0-8135-3967-6(6))* Rutgers Univ. Pr.

McKeen, William. Mile Marker Zero: The Moveable Feast of Key West. 2011. (ENG., Illus.). 320p. 25.00 *(978-0-307-59200-2(6)*, Crown) Crown Publishing Group.

McLoughlin, Kate. Martha Gellhorn: The War Writer in the Field & in the Text. 2007. (ENG., Illus.). 288p. 79.00 *(978-0-7190-7636-7(6))* Manchester Univ. Pr. GBR. Dist: Macmillan.

McMaster, John Bach. Benjamin Franklin As a Man of Letters. 2008. 309p. 29.99 *(978-0-559-03355-1(9))*; 28.99 *(978-0-559-03359-9(1))*; pap. 29.75 *(978-0-559-03356-8(7))*; pap. 28.75 *(978-0-559-03358-2(3))* BiblioBazaar.

—Benjamin Franklin As a Man of Letters. 2007. (ENG.). 304p. 43.95 *(978-0-548-03546-7(6))* Kessinger Publishing, LLC.

McMurtry, Larry. Literary Life: A Second Memoir. 2011. (ENG.). 192p. pap. 14.00 *(978-1-4391-5994-1(7))* Simon & Schuster.

McNair, Wesley. A Place Called Maine: 24 Authors on the Maine Experience. 2008. (ENG.). 320p. 25.00 *(978-0-89272-760-5(8))* Down East Bks.

McNamee, Thomas. The Man Who Changed the Way We Eat: Craig Claiborne & the American Food Renaissance. 2012. (ENG.). 352p. 27.00 ***(978-1-4391-9150-7(6)***, Free Pr.) Free Pr.

Mcwilliams, Carey. Ambrose Bierce: A Biography. 2011. 374p. 53.95 ***(978-1-258-06821-9(4))*** Literary Licensing, LLC.

Mead, Alice & Neptume, Arnold, eds. Giants of the Dawnland: Ancient Wabanaki Tales. Date not set. 76p. (YA). pap. 8.00 *(978-1-888034-01-1(7))* Loose Cannon Pr.

Meadow Brook Writing Project. In the Company of Writers 2007. 2009. 156p. pap. 14.95 *(978-1-4401-5916-9(5))* iUniverse, Inc.

Medrano, Manuel & Paredes, Américo. Américo Paredes: In His Own Words, an Authorized Biography. 2010. (Al Filo: Mexican American Studies Ser.). (ENG., Illus.). 224p. 22.95 *(978-1-57441-287-1(6))* Univ. of North Texas Pr.

Meehan, J. P. The Lady of the Limberlost: A Biography. 24.95 *(978-0-8488-0094-9(X))* Amereon LTD.

Meehan, Sean Ross. Mediating American Autobiography: Photography in Emerson, Thoreau, Douglass, & Whitman. 2008. (ENG., Illus.). 264p. (C). 39.95 *(978-0-8262-1792-9(3))* Univ. of Missouri Pr.

Meehan, William F., III, ed. Conversations with William F. Buckley Jr. 2009. (Literary Conversations Ser.). (ENG.). 208p. pap. 22.00 *(978-1-60473-225-2(3))* Univ. Pr. of Mississippi.

—Conversations with William F. Buckley Jr. 2009. (Literary Conversations Ser.). (ENG.). 208p. 50.00 *(978-1-60473-224-5(5))* Univ. Pr. of Mississippi.

Mellors, Julie, ed. Contemporary Authors, Vol. 245. 2006. (Contemporary Authors Ser.). (ENG.). 464p. 293.00 *(978-0-7876-7874-6(0))* Cengage Gale.

—Contemporary Authors, Volume 246: A Bio-Bibliographical Guide to Current Writers in Fiction, General Nonfiction, Poetry, Journalism, Drama, Motion Pictures, Television, & Other Fields, Vol. 246. 2006. (Contemporary Authors Ser.). (ENG., Illus.). 464p. 293.00 *(978-0-7876-7875-3(9))* Cengage Gale.

Meltzer, Milton. Nathaniel Hawthorne: A Biography. 2006. (American Literary Greats Ser.). (Illus.). 160p. (gr. 6-18). lib. bdg. 31.93 *(978-0-7613-3459-0(9)*, Millbrook Pr.) Lerner Publishing Group.

Mencken, H. L. Happy Days: Mencken's Autobiography, 1880-1892, Volume 1. 2006. (ENG.). 336p. pap. 27.00 *(978-0-8018-8531-0(0))* Johns Hopkins Univ. Pr.

—Heathen Days: Mencken's Autobiography, 1890-1936, Volume 3. 2006. (ENG.). 320p. pap. 27.00 *(978-0-8018-8532-7(9))* Johns Hopkins Univ. Pr.

—Mencken on Mencken: A New Collection of Autobiographical Writings. Joshi, S. T., ed. 2010. (Illus.). 296p. pap. 24.95 *(978-0-8071-3592-1(5))* Louisiana State Univ. Pr.

—Newspaper Days: Mencken's Autobiography: 1899-1906, Volume 2. 2006. (ENG.). 336p. pap. 27.00 *(978-0-8018-8534-1(5))* Johns Hopkins Univ. Pr.

—Thirty-Five Years of Newspaper Work: A Memoir. Hobson, Fred et al, eds. 2006. (ENG., Illus.). 432p. pap. 28.00 *(978-0-8018-8556-3(6))* Johns Hopkins Univ. Pr.

Meneshian, Murad A. Raffi: The Prophet from Payajuk. 2010. (Illus.). 360p. (YA). *(978-1-931834-33-9(4)*, Mayreni) Mayreni Publishing.

Mengert, Christina & Wilkinson, Joshua Marie, eds. 12 X 12: Conversations in 21st-Century Poetry & Poetics. 2009. (ENG.). 284p. pap. 29.95 *(978-1-58729-791-5(4))* Univ. of Iowa Pr.

Méras, Phyllis. Country Editor: Henry Beetle Hough & the Vineyard Gazette. 2006. (Illus.). pap. 21.95 *(978-1-884592-42-3(2))* Images from the Past, Inc.

Mermann-Jozwiak, Elisabeth & Sullivan, Nancy. Conversations with Mexican American Writers: Languages & Literatures in the Borderlands. 2009. (ENG.). 192p. 50.00 *(978-1-60473-214-6(8))*; pap. 22.00 *(978-1-60473-215-3(6))* Univ. Pr. of Mississippi.

Messent, Peter. The Cambridge Introduction to Mark Twain. 2007. (Cambridge Introductions to Literature Ser.). (ENG.). 150p. per. 23.99 *(978-0-521-67075-3(6))* Cambridge Univ. Pr.

—Mark Twain & Male Friendship: The Twichell, Howells, & Rogers Friendships. 2009. (ENG., Illus.). 272p. 49.95 *(978-0-19-539116-9(0))* Oxford Univ. Pr., Inc.

Messent, Peter B. The Cambridge Introduction to Mark Twain. annot. ed. 2007. (Cambridge Introductions to Literature Ser.). (ENG.). 150p. 75.00 *(978-0-521-85445-0(8))* Cambridge Univ. Pr.

Meyer, Hershel D. History & Conscience: The Case of Howard Fast. 2011. 60p. 36.95 ***(978-1-258-07669-6(1))*** Literary Licensing, LLC.

Meyer, Michael J. Harper Lee's To Kill a Mockingbird: New Essays. 2010. (Illus.). xxiii, 265p. E-Book 49.95 *(978-0-8108-7723-8(6))* Scarecrow Pr., Inc.

Meyers, Jeffrey. Ernest Hemingway. 2009. 610p. pap. 45.00 *(978-0-415-56892-0(7))* Routledge.

—The Genius & the Goddess: Arthur Miller & Marilyn Monroe. (ENG., Illus.). 384p. 2012. pap. 19.95 ***(978-0-252-07854-5(3))*** 2010. 29.95 *(978-0-252-03544-9(5))* Univ. of Illinois Pr.

Michael, Christopher Domínguez. Critical Dictionary of Mexican Literature, 1955-2010. Dillman, Lisa, tr. from POR. 2012. (Scholarly Ser.). (ENG.). 672p. pap. 29.00 ***(978-1-56478-606-7(4)***, 478606) Dalkey Archive Pr.

Michaud, Nicolas & Dunn, George A., eds. The Hunger Games & Philosophy: A Critique of Pure Treason. 2012. (Blackwell Philosophy & Pop Culture Ser.: 42). (ENG.). 320p. pap. 17.95 ***(978-1-118-06507-5(7)***, Wiley) Wiley, John & Sons, Inc.

Michener, James A. The World Is My Home: A Memoir. 2007. (ENG.). 528p. pap. 15.95 *(978-0-8129-7813-1(7)*, Random Hse. Trade Paperbacks) Random House Publishing Group.

Miele, Leonard. Voice of the Tide: The Cape Cod Heritage of Katharine Lee Bates. 2009. (Illus.). 112p. pap. 20.00 *(978-0-932027-13-9(X))* Spinner Pubns., Inc.

Mielziner, Ella McKenna Friend & Mielziner, Moses. Moses Mielziner, 1828-1903: A Biography with A Bibliography of His Writings. Bloch, Joshua, ed. 2011. 298p. 48.95 ***(978-1-258-09334-1(0))*** Literary Licensing, LLC.

Milder, Robert & Fuller, Randall, eds. The Business of Reflection: Hawthorne in His Notebooks. 2009. (ENG.). 352p. 104.95 *(978-0-8142-0476-4(7))*; pap. 48.95 *(978-0-8142-5170-6(6))*; cd-rom 14.95 *(978-0-8142-9185-6(6))* Ohio State Univ. Pr.

Miles, Barry. Charles Bukowski. (ENG.). 2006. 320p. per. 14.95 *(978-0-7535-1102-2(9))* 2011. 352p. 16.95 *(978-0-7535-1818-2(X))* Virgin Bks. Ltd. GBR. Dist: Independent Pubs. Group.

Miller, Adam David. Ticket to Exile. 2007. 237p. per. *(978-1-59714-065-2(1))* Heyday.

Miller, E. Ethelbert. The 5th Inning. 2012. (Busboys & Poets Ser.). (ENG., Illus.). 176p. pap. 15.95 ***(978-1-60486-521-9(0))*** PM Pr.

Miller, James E., Jr. T. S. Eliot: The Making of an American Poet, 1888-1922. 2007. (Penn State Press Ser.). (ENG.). 488p. pap. 25.00 *(978-0-271-02762-3(2))* Pennsylvania State Univ. Pr.

Miller, Joaquin. Joaquin Miller, His California Diary: Beginning in 1855, Ending In 1857. Richards, John Stewart, ed. 2011. 104p. 39.95 ***(978-1-258-08788-3(X))*** Literary Licensing, LLC.

Miller, Leo S. Leo S. Miller Campus Penny-Pincher. 2007. 136p. pap. 12.00 *(978-0-9789908-3-1(8))* Ketch Publishing.

Miller, Teresa. Means of Transit: A Slightly Embellished Memoir. 2008. (ENG., Illus.). 200p. 24.95 *(978-0-8061-3971-5(4))* Univ. of Oklahoma Pr.

Miller, Toby. Jd Salinger-Aw V51. 2009. pap. 25.00 *(978-0-8166-0366-4(9))* Univ. of Minnesota Pr.

Millier, Brett Candlish. Flawed Light: American Women Poets & Alcohol. 2009. (ENG.). 168p. 40.00 *(978-0-252-03461-9(9))* Univ. of Illinois Pr.

Mills, Robert L. The Laugh Makers. 2009. 368p. pap. 24.95 *(978-1-59393-323-4(1))* BearManor Media.

Minick, Jim. The Blueberry Years: A Memoir of Farm & Family. (ENG.). 352p. 2012. pap. 16.99 ***(978-1-250-01158-9(2)***, St. Martin's Griffin) 2010. (Illus.). 27.99 *(978-0-312-57142-9(9)*, Dunne, Thomas Bks.) St. Martin's Pr.

Minnigerode, Meade. Some Personal Letters of Herman Melville. 2006. pap. 24.95 *(978-1-4286-3937-9(3))* Kessinger Publishing, LLC.

Mitchell, Douglas L. A Disturbing & Alien Memory: Southern Novelists Writing History. 2009. *(978-0-8071-3373-6(6))* Louisiana State Univ. Pr.

Mitchell, Janet. The Creepy Girl, & Other Stories. 2009. 152p. pap. 18.00 *(978-0-9788811-7-7(6))* Starcherone Bks.

Mitchell, Ted, ed. Thomas Wolfe: An Illustrated Biography. 2007. (ENG., Illus.). 352p. per. 22.00 *(978-1-933648-10-1(4))* Pegasus Bks.

Mitchell, Verner D. Western Echoes of the Harlem Renaissance: The Life & Writings of Anita Scott Coleman. Davis, Cynthia J., ed. 2008. (ENG., Illus.). 240p. (C). 45.00 *(978-0-8061-3956-2(0))*; pap. 19.95 *(978-0-8061-3975-3(7))* Univ. of Oklahoma Pr.

Mittelman, Jennifer K., told to. Our Cherry Tree Still Stands: The Story of Michael Herskovitz. 2009. 104p. pap. 11.95 *(978-1-4401-3607-8(6))* iUniverse, Inc.

Moates, Marianne. Truman Capote's Southern Years: Stories from a Monroeville Cousin. 2008. (ENG., Illus.). 256p. pap. 19.95 *(978-0-8173-5527-2(8))* Univ. of Alabama Pr.

Moglen, Helene & Chen, Nancy N., eds. Bodies in the Making: Transgressions & Transformations. 2007. (ENG., Illus.). 216p. pap. 12.00 *(978-0-9712546-3-3(X))* North Atlantic Bks.

Monroe, Debra. On the Outskirts of Normal: Forging a Family Against the Grain. 2010. 248p. 22.50 *(978-0-87074-560-7(3))* Southern Methodist Univ. Pr.

Montesi, Al. Italians in Memphis: A Memoir. 2006. 205p. per. 14.00 net. *(978-0-918476-31-9(3))* Cornerstone Pr.

Moody, A. David. Ezra Pound Vol. 1: The Young Genius, 1885-1920. 2009. (ENG., Illus.). 528p. pap. 24.95 *(978-0-19-957146-8(5))* Oxford Univ. Pr., Inc.

Moore, Susanna. Light Years: A Girlhood in Hawai'i. 2009. (ENG.). 208p. pap. 13.00 *(978-0-8021-4406-5(3)*, Grove Pr.) Grove/Atlantic, Inc.

Moorehead, Caroline. Selected Letters of Martha Gellhorn. 2007. (ENG.). 544p. per. 20.00 *(978-0-8050-8322-4(7)*, Holt Paperback) Holt, Henry & Co.

Morace, Robert A. John Cheever. 2011. ***(978-1-58765-827-3(5))*** Salem Pr., Inc.

Morais, Fernando. Paulo Coelho: A Warrior's Life - The Authorized Biography. 2010. (ENG.). 464p. pap. 15.99 *(978-0-06-177429-4(4)*, HarperOne) HarperCollins Pubs.

Moran, Dominic. Pablo Neruda. 2009. (Reaktion Books - Critical Lives Ser.). (ENG., Illus.). 192p. pap. 16.95 *(978-1-86189-514-1(3))* Reaktion Bks., Ltd. GBR. Dist: Chicago Distribution Ctr.

Morell, Paula M. Tales from the South: Volume III. Morell, Paula M. & Branton, Suzanne, eds. 2010. 182p. pap. 14.00 *(978-0-9846199-0-0(9))* Temenos Publishing.

Morgan, Bill. Beat Atlas: A State by State Guide to the Beat Generation. 2011. (ENG., Illus.). 225p. pap. 15.95 *(978-0-87286-512-9(6))* City Lights Bks.

Morgan, Phyllis S. N. Scott Momaday: Remembering Ancestors, Earth, & Traditions - An Annotated Bio-Bibliography. annot. ed. 2010. (American Indian Literature & Critical Studies Ser.). (ENG.). 400p. (C). 60.00 *(978-0-8061-4054-4(2))* Univ. of Oklahoma Pr.

Mori, Kyoko. Yarn: Remembering the Way Home. 2009. (ENG.). 240p. pap. 15.95 *(978-1-934848-63-0(8))* GemmaMedia.

Morín, José R. Lopez. The Legacy of Américo Paredes. 2006. (Rio Grande/Río Bravo Ser.: 10). (ENG., Illus.). 192p. 40.00 *(978-1-58544-509-7(6))*; per. 19.95 *(978-1-58544-536-3(3))* Texas A&M Univ. Pr.

Morris, Catherine. The Six Years Project: Lucy R. Lippard & the Emergence of Conceptual Art. 2012. ***(978-0-262-01816-6(0))*** MIT Pr.

Morris, Mary. The River Queen: A Memoir. 2008. (ENG., Illus.). 288p. pap. 17.00 *(978-0-312-42789-4(1))* Picador.

Morris, Roy, Jr. Lighting Out for the Territory: How Samuel Clemens Headed West & Became Mark Twain. (ENG., Illus.). 304p. 2011. pap. 16.00 *(978-1-4165-9867-1(7))* 2010. 26.00 *(978-1-4165-9866-4(9))* Simon & Schuster.

Morrow, Barbara Olenyik. Nature's Storyteller: The Life of Gene Stratton-Porter. 2010. *(978-0-87195-284-4(X))* Indiana Historical Society.

Morrow, Laurie. Cold Noses & Warm Hearts. 2006. (ENG., Illus.). 232p. per. 19.95 *(978-1-59543-441-8(0)*, 4418) Willow Creek Pr., Inc.

Morse, John T., Jr. Thomas Sergeant Perry A Memoir. 2006. pap. 24.95 *(978-1-4286-5755-7(X))* Kessinger Publishing, LLC.

Mort, Terry. The Hemingway Patrols: Ernest Hemingway & His Hunt for U-Boats. 2011. (ENG.). 272p. pap. 17.99 ***(978-1-4165-9787-2(5)***, Scribner) Scribner.

Morton, Brian. Edgar Allan Poe. 2010. (Life&Times Ser.). (ENG., Illus.). 192p. 14.95 *(978-1-905791-52-1(6))* Haus Publishing GBR. Dist: Consortium Bk. Sales & Distribution.

Moser, Benjamin. Why This World: A Biography of Clarice Lispector, 1 vol. 2012. (ENG., Illus.). 496p. pap. 19.95 ***(978-0-19-989582-3(1))*** Oxford Univ. Pr., Inc.

Moses, Kate. Cakewalk: A Memoir. 2010. (ENG.). 368p. 26.00 *(978-0-385-34298-8(5)*, Dial Pr.) Random House Publishing Group.

Mosher, Howard Frank. The Great Northern Express: A Writer's Journey Home. 2012. 246p. ***(978-0-307-45070-8(8))***; (ENG.). 256p. E-Book ***(978-0-307-45095-1(3))***; (ENG.). 256p. 25.00 ***(978-0-307-45069-2(4))*** Crown Publishing Group.

Mosley, Shelley, et al, eds. Romance Today: An A-to-Z Guide to Contemporary American Romance Writers, 1 vol. 2006. (Illus.). 424p. 85.00 *(978-0-313-32841-1(2)*, GR2841, Greenwood Pr.) Greenwood Publishing Group, Inc.

Mosley, Walter. Conversations with Walter Mosley. Brady, Owen E., ed. 2011. (Literary Conversations Ser.). (ENG.). 256p. 55.00 *(978-1-60473-942-8(8))*; pap. 25.00 *(978-1-60473-943-5(6))* Univ. Pr. of Mississippi.

Motier, Donald. Gerard: The Influence of Jack Kerouac's Brother on His Life & Writing, 1 vol. 2010. 66p. pap. 19.95 *(978-1-4489-5519-0(X))* PublishAmerica, Inc.

Motley, John Lothrop. The Correspondence of John Lothrop Motley. 2008. 440p. 30.99 *(978-0-559-32079-8(5))*; pap. 34.75 *(978-0-559-32078-1(7))* BiblioBazaar.

—The Correspondence of John Lothrop Motley. 2009. 278p. pap. *(978-0-217-75188-9(1))* Books LLC.

Mott, Eric L. We Met at Starbucks: A Love Story. 2008. 73p. pap. 16.95 *(978-1-60563-163-9(9))* PublishAmerica, Inc.

Moxley, Jennifer. The Middle Room. 2007. 633p. pap. 25.00 *(978-1-930068-36-0(0))* 'A 'A Arts.

Moylan, Virginia Lynn. Zora Neale Hurston's Final Decade. 2011. (ENG., Illus.). 144p. 24.95 *(978-0-8130-3578-9(3))* Univ. Pr. of Florida.

Muller, Gilbert H. William Cullen Bryant: Author of America. 2008. (Illus.). 410p. 30.00 *(978-0-7914-7467-9(4))* State Univ. of New York Pr.

Mulvey, Christopher. Transatlantic Manners: Social Patterns in Nineteenth-Century Anglo-American Travel Literature. 2008. (ENG., Illus.). 256p. pap. 37.99 *(978-0-521-05561-1(X))* Cambridge Univ. Pr.

Mumford, Lewis. In Old Friendship: The Correspondence of Lewis Mumford & Henry A. Murray, 1928-1981. 2007. 447p. 29.95 *(978-0-8156-3113-2(8))* Syracuse Univ. Pr.

Munn, Charles Clark. Rockhaven. 2011. 226p. 26.95 ***(978-1-4638-9855-7(X))***; pap. 15.95 ***(978-1-4638-0126-7(2))*** Rodgers, Alan Bks.

Muradi, Michael F. Memoirs of a Legend in Infancy: Volume 1. 2008. 108p. pap. 16.95 *(978-1-60813-160-0(2))* PublishAmerica, Inc.

Murphy, Russell Elliott. Critical Companion to T. S. Eliot: A Literary Reference to His Life & Work. 2007. (Critical Companion Ser.). (Illus.). 624p. (C). (gr. 9). 75.00 *(978-0-8160-6183-9(1))* Facts On File, Inc.

Murray, Meg McGavran. Margaret Fuller, Wandering Pilgrim. (ENG.). 552p. 2012. pap. 26.95 ***(978-0-8203-4335-8(8))*** 2008. (Illus.). 49.95 *(978-0-8203-2894-2(4))* Univ. of Georgia Pr.

Myles, Eileen & Cooper, Dennis. Up Is up, but So Is Down: New York's Downtown Literary Scene, 1974-1992. Stosuy, Brandon, ed. 2006. (ENG., Illus.). 500p. pap. 30.00 *(978-0-8147-4011-8(1))* New York Univ. Pr.

Nadel, Ira B. Leon Uris: Life of a Best Seller. 2010. (ENG., Illus.). 366p. 27.95 *(978-0-292-70935-5(8))* Univ. of Texas Pr.

Nel, Philip. Crockett Johnson & Ruth Krauss: How an Unlikely Couple Found Love, Dodged the FBI, & Transformed Children's Literature. 2012. (Children's Literature Association Ser.). (ENG., Illus.). 368p. 70.00 ***(978-1-61703-624-8(2))***; pap. 40.00 ***(978-1-61703-636-1(6))*** Univ. Pr. of Mississippi.

Nelson, Lee. Hoofbeats of the Heart: A Personal History. 2011. pap. 17.99 *(978-1-59955-909-4(9)*, Council Pr.) Cedar Fort, Inc./CFI Distribution.

Nelson, Michael. Americans & the Making of the Riviera. 2007. (ENG., Illus.). 232p. per. 35.00 *(978-0-7864-3160-1(1))* McFarland & Co., Inc. Pubs.

—Presidents Words. Russell, Riley, ed. 2010. 320p. pap. 24.95 *(978-0-7006-1739-5(6))* Univ. of Kansas Pubns.

Nelson, Michael & Riley, Russell L. The President's Words: Speeches & Speechwriting in the Modern White House. 2010. ix, 310p. 39.95 *(978-0-7006-1738-8(8))* Univ. Pr. of Kansas.

Nelson, W. Dale. Gin Before Breakfast: The Dilemma of the Poet in the Newsroom. 2007. (Illus.). 242p. 14.95 *(978-0-8156-0888-2(8))* Syracuse Univ. Pr.

Neumeyer, Peter F., ed. Floating Worlds: The Letters of Edward Gorey & Peter F. Neumeyer. 2011. (Illus.). 256p. 35.00 *(978-0-7649-5947-9(6))* Pomegranate Communications, Inc.

Neville, Susan & Neville, Susan S. Sailing the Inland Sea: On Writing, Literature, & Land. 2007. (ENG.). 240p. pap. 19.95 *(978-0-253-21902-2(7)*, 0253219027, Quarry Bks.) Indiana Univ. Pr.

Newcomb, John Timberman. How Did Poetry Survive? The Making of Modern American Verse. 2012. E-Book ***(978-0-252-09390-6(9))***; (ENG., Illus.). 352p. 75.00 ***(978-0-252-03679-8(4))*** Univ. of Illinois Pr.

Newell, Mike. No Bottom: In Conversation with Barry Lopez. 2008. 152p. pap. 22.00 *(978-1-880977-07-1(9))* XOXOX Pr.

Newkey-Burden, Chas. Stephanie Meyer Queen of Twilight: The Biography. 2010. (ENG., Illus.). 240p. pap. 12.95 *(978-1-84454-936-8(4))* Blake, John Publishing, Ltd. GBR. Dist: Independent Pubs. Group.

Newlin, Keith. Hamlin Garland: A Life. 2008. (ENG., Illus.). 536p. 40.00 *(978-0-8032-3347-8(7))* Univ. of Nebraska Pr.

Newton-Smith, William. Dr. Muhlenberg. (American Religious Leaders Ser.). 272p. reprint ed. 98.00 *(978-0-7222-8474-2(8))* Library Reprints, Inc.

Nisly, L. Lamar. Conversations with Tim Gautreaux. 2012. (Literary Conversations Ser.). (ENG., Illus.). 224p. 40.00 ***(978-1-61703-607-1(2))*** Univ. Pr. of Mississippi.

Niven, Larry. Stars & Gods. 2011. (ENG.). 368p. pap. 15.99 *(978-0-7653-3005-5(9)*, Tor Bks.) Doherty, Tom Assocs., LLC.

Nolan, Tom. Ross MacDonald: A Biography. 2008. (ENG., Illus.). 496p. pap. 30.95 *(978-1-4391-0205-3(8)*, Scribner) Scribner.

Norton, Charles Eliot & Ruskin, John. The Correspondence of John Ruskin & Charles Eliot Norton. Bradley, John Lewis & Ousby, Ian, eds. 2011. (ENG.). 552p. pap. 70.00 *(978-0-521-18771-8(0))* Cambridge Univ. Pr.

Oates, Joyce Carol. The Journal of Joyce Carol Oates, 1973-1982. 2008. (Illus.). 544p. pap. 16.95 *(978-0-06-122799-8(4)*, HarperPerennial) HarperCollins Pubs.

O'Connor, Flannery. The Presence of Grace & Other Book Reviews. Martin, Carter W., ed. 2008. (ENG.). 192p. per. 22.95 *(978-0-8203-3139-3(2))* Univ. of Georgia Pr.

Ogilvie, Elizabeth. My World Is an Island. reprint ed. lib. bdg. 23.95 *(978-0-88411-334-8(5))* Amereon LTD.

Oglesby, Carl. Ravens in the Storm: A Personal History of the 1960s Anti-War Movement. 2010. (ENG., Illus.). 352p. pap. 21.99 *(978-1-4165-4748-8(7)*, Scribner) Scribner.

O'Grady, Chris. Love Song to A Long Gone Time. 2007. pap. 22.00 *(978-0-8059-8526-9(3))* Dorrance Publishing Co., Inc.

Ohmart, Ben. Tim Kelly. 2009. 172p. pap. 19.95 *(978-1-59393-317-3(7))* BearManor Media.

Oliphant, Dave. Harbingers of Books to Come: A Texan's Literary Life. 2009. (ENG.). 548p. 24.95 *(978-0-916727-60-4(2))* Wings Pr.

Oliphant, Mary C. Simms, et al, eds. The Letters of William Gilmore Simms: Volume II, 1845-1849. 2011. (Project of the Simms Initiatives Ser.). (ENG.). 640p. pap. 29.95 *(978-1-61117-028-3(1))* Univ. of South Carolina Pr.

—The Letters of William Gilmore Simms: Volume III, 1850-1857. 2011. (Project of the Simms Initiatives Ser.). (ENG.). 592p. pap. 29.95 *(978-1-61117-029-0(X))* Univ. of South Carolina Pr.

—The Letters of William Gilmore Simms: Volume IV, 1858-1866. 2011. (Project of the Simms Initiatives Ser.). (ENG.). 672p. pap. 29.95 *(978-1-61117-030-6(3))* Univ. of South Carolina Pr.

—The Letters of William Gilmore Simms, 1830-1844, Vol. 5. 2011. (Project of the Simms Initiatives Ser.). (ENG.). 608p. pap. 29.95 *(978-1-61117-031-3(1))* Univ. of South Carolina Pr.

—The Letters of William Gilmore Simms, 1867-1870, Vol. I. 2011. (Project of the Simms Initiatives Ser.). (ENG.). 600p. pap. 29.95 *(978-1-61117-027-6(3))* Univ. of South Carolina Pr.

Oliphant, Mary C. Simms & Eaves, T. C. Duncan, eds. The Letters of William Gilmore Simms, 1834-1870, Vol. VI. 2011. (Project of the Simms Initiatives Ser.). (ENG.). 458p. pap. 29.95 *(978-1-61117-032-0(X))* Univ. of South Carolina Pr.

Olivares, Julian, ed. Tomas Rivera: The Complete Works. 2008. 363p. pap. 19.95 *(978-1-55885-509-0(2))* Arte Publico Pr.

Olson, Brent. Papa: Figuring Out What Matters. 2009. (ENG.). 132p. pap. 13.50 *(978-1-933794-21-1(6))* Kirk Hse. Pubs.

Olson, Charles. Muthologos: Lectures & Interviews. Maud, Ralph, ed. 2nd rev. ed. 2010. (ENG., Illus.). 496p. pap. 39.95 *(978-0-88922-639-5(3))* Talonbooks, Ltd. CAN. Dist: Consortium Bk. Sales & Distribution.

Olson, Ted, ed. CrossRoads: A Southern Culture Annual 2009. 2009. (Illus.). 300p. pap. 30.00 *(978-0-88146-095-7(8))* Mercer Univ. Pr.

O'Neill, Molly. Mostly True: A Memoir of Family, Food, & Baseball. 2008. (ENG.). 288p. pap. 20.95 *(978-0-7432-3269-2(0)*, Scribner) Scribner.

Oomen, Anne-Marie. An American Map. 2010. xii, 205p. pap. 18.95 *(978-0-8143-3420-1(2))* Wayne State Univ. Pr.

Oreggioni, Alberto F. Nuevo Diccionario de Literatura Uruguaya, 2001, 2 vols. (SPA., Illus.). *(978-9974-1-0217-0(0))* Bow Historical Bks.

O'Reilley, Mary Rose. The Love of Impermanent Things: A Threshold Ecology. 2008. (ENG.). 320p. pap. 16.00 *(978-1-57131-312-6(5))* Milkweed Editions.

Orfalea, Gregory. Angeleno Days: An Arab American Writer on Family, Place, & Politics. 2009. (ENG.). 232p. pap. 17.95 *(978-0-8165-2773-1(3))* Univ. of Arizona Pr.

Osmers, Henry. They Were All Strangers: The Wreck of the John Milton at Montauk, New York. 2010. 110p. pap. 17.95 *(978-1-4327-5122-7(0))* Outskirts Pr., Inc.

Overton, Grant. Authors of the Day. 2007. (ENG.). 426p. 51.95 *(978-0-548-05811-4(3))* Kessinger Publishing, LLC.

Overton, Grant M. The Women Who Make Our Novels. 2009. (ENG.). 408p. 41.99 *(978-1-117-38198-5(6))*; pap. 26.99 *(978-1-117-38200-5(1)*, BiblioLife); pap. 33.75 *(978-1-117-38199-2(4))* BiblioBazaar.

—The Women Who Make Our Novels. 408p. 2008. 49.95 *(978-0-548-96461-3(0))* 2007. (ENG.). per. 34.95 *(978-0-548-64009-8(2))* Kessinger Publishing, LLC.

Packer, George. Interesting Times: Writings from a Turbulent Decade. 2010. (ENG.). 432p. pap. 16.00 *(978-0-374-53252-9(4))* Farrar, Straus & Giroux.

Padgett, Ron. Joe: A Memoir of Joe Brainard. 2008. (ENG., Illus.). 357p. 30.00 *(978-1-56689-150-8(4))* Coffee Hse. Pr.

Paine, Albert. Mark Twains Notebook. 2006. 420p. per. *(978-1-4067-3689-2(9)*, Hesperides Pr.) Read Bks.

Paine, Albert Bigelow. The Boys' Life of Mark Twain. 2007. (ENG.). 256p. per. *(978-1-4065-4165-6(6))* Dodo Pr.

Painter, Deborah. Forry: The Life of Forrest J Ackerman. 2010. (ENG., Illus.). 224p. 45.00 *(978-0-7864-4884-5(9))* McFarland & Co., Inc. Pubs.

Painter, F. V. N. Poets of Virginia. (Illus.). 336p. reprint ed. lib. bdg. 98.00 *(978-0-7222-4617-7(X))* Library Reprints, Inc.

Papanikolas, Zeese. American Silence. 2007. (ENG., Illus.). 222p. 29.95 *(978-0-8032-3756-8(1))* Univ. of Nebraska Pr.

Paretsky, Sara. Writing in an Age of Silence. 2nd ed. 2009. (ENG.). 160p. pap. 12.95 *(978-1-84467-377-3(4)*, 844377) Verso Bks. GBR. Dist: Norton, W. W. & Co., Inc.

Parini, Jay. American Writers Supplement. 18th rev. ed. 2008. (American Writers Ser.). (ENG.). 592p. 218.00 *(978-0-684-31552-2(1)*, Charles Scribner's Sons) Cengage Gale.

Parini, Jay, ed. American Writers Supplement: Max Apple to Franz Wright. 17th rev. ed. 2007. (American Writers Ser.). (ENG.). 592p. 218.00 *(978-0-684-31517-1(3)*, Charles Scribner's Sons) Cengage Gale.

Parker, William Belmont. Edward Rowland Sill His Life & Work. 2007. (ENG.). 334p. 45.95 *(978-0-548-01194-2(X))* Kessinger Publishing, LLC.

Parks, Gordon & Hule, Wing Young. A Choice of Weapons. 2010. (ENG.). 192p. pap. 17.95 *(978-0-87351-769-0(5))* Minnesota Historical Society Pr.

Parry, Albert. Garrets & Pretenders: Bohemian Life in America from Poe to Kerouac. 2012. (New York City Ser.). (ENG.). 480p. pap. 16.95 ***(978-0-486-48605-5(2))*** Dover Pubns., Inc.

Parsons, Bob. A Journey of Hope. 2010. 208p. pap. 14.49 *(978-1-4520-7189-3(6))* AuthorHouse.

Pat Upton Stamm. Twelve Kids, One Bathroom, & a Milk Bottle. 2009. 208p. pap. 17.95 *(978-1-4401-8874-9(2))* iUniverse, Inc.

Patel, Shailja. Migritude. 2010. (ENG., Illus.). 140p. pap. 15.95 *(978-1-885030-05-4(3))* Muae Publishing, Inc.

Patell, Cyrus R. K. & Waterman, Bryan, eds. The Cambridge Companion to the Literature of New York. 2010. (Cambridge Companions to Literature Ser.). (ENG., Illus.). 232p. (C). 78.00 *(978-0-521-51471-2(1))*; pap. 24.99 *(978-0-521-73555-1(6))* Cambridge Univ. Pr.

Patterson, Daniel. Early American Nature Writers: A Biographical Encyclopedia, 1 vol. Thompson, Roger & Bryson, Scott, eds. 2007. 448p. 125.00 *(978-0-313-34680-4(1)*, GR4680, Greenwood Pr.) Greenwood Publishing Group, Inc.

Patterson, William H., Jr. Robert A. Heinlein Vol. 1: In Dialogue with His Century. 2010. (ENG.). 624p. 29.99 *(978-0-7653-1960-9(8)*, Tor Bks.) Doherty, Tom Assocs., LLC.

—Robert A. Heinlein Vol. 1: Learning Curve, 1907-1949. 2011. (ENG., Illus.). 640p. pap. 19.99 *(978-0-7653-1962-3(4)*, Tor Bks.) Doherty, Tom Assocs., LLC.

Pauly, Thomas H. Zane Grey: His Life, His Adventures, His Women. 2007. (Illus.). 408p. per. 24.95 *(978-0-252-07492-9(0))* Univ. of Illinois Pr.

Payment, Simone. Scott O'Dell. (Library of Author Biographies Ser.). 112p. (gr. 5-8). 2009. 63.90 *(978-1-60853-554-5(1)*, Rosen Central) 2006. (Illus.). pap. 12.95 *(978-1-4042-0651-9(5))* Rosen Publishing Group, Inc., The.

Payne, Darwin. Owen Wister: Chronicler of the West, Gentleman of the East. 2011. (ENG., Illus.). 416p. pap. 24.95 *(978-0-8032-3769-8(3)*, Bison Bks.) Univ. of Nebraska Pr.

Paz Lozano, Octavio & Segovia, Tomás. Cartas a Tomás Segovia, 1957-1985. 2008. (Tezontle Ser.). (SPA.). 200p. 21.99 *(978-968-16-8575-1(X))* Fondo de Cultura Economica USA.

Peale, Norman Vincent. New Style Hypocrites. 2011. 16p. pap. 35.95 ***(978-1-258-00979-3(X))*** Literary Licensing, LLC.

Pearson, Carol Lynn. Goodbye, I Love You. 2006. 199p. per. 13.99 *(978-1-55517-984-7(3))* Cedar Fort, Inc./CFI Distribution.

Pelayo, Ruben. Gabriel García Márquez: A Biography, 1 vol. 2008. (Greenwood Biographies Ser.). (Illus.). 188p. 35.00 *(978-0-313-34630-9(5)*, GR4630, Greenwood Pr.) Greenwood Publishing Group, Inc.

Pemberton, T. Edgar. Life of Bret Harte. 2007. (ENG.). 400p. 49.95 *(978-0-548-08522-6(6))* Kessinger Publishing, LLC.

Pendexter, Hugh. Bird of Freedom. 2011. 348p. 51.95 ***(978-1-258-06853-0(2))*** Literary Licensing, LLC.

Penzler, Otto, ed. The Lineup: The World's Greatest Crime Writers Tell the Inside Story of Their Greatest Detectives. 2010. (ENG.). 416p. pap. 15.99 *(978-0-316-03194-3(1)*, Back Bay Bks.) Little Brown & Co.

Perkins, Eleanor Ellis & Perkins, Lucy Fitch. Eve among the Puritans: A Biography of Lucy Fitch Perkins. 2011. 264p. 47.95 ***(978-1-258-07388-6(9))*** Literary Licensing, LLC.

Perkins, Tom. Valley Boy: The Education of Tom Perkins. 2008. (ENG.). 240p. (gr. 12-18). 15.00 *(978-1-59240-403-2(0)*, Gotham) Penguin Group (USA) Inc.

Perrin, Robert Keith. Rabid Wolf. pap. 13.95 *(978-0-9664200-0-5(4))* Perrin, Robert Keith.

Perry, Evelyn. Robin Mckinley: Girl Reader, Woman Writer. 2010. (Scarecrow Studies in Young Adult Literature Ser.). (ENG.). 154p. 39.95 *(978-0-8108-5819-0(3))* Scarecrow Pr., Inc.

Perry, Evelyn M. Robin McKinley: Girl Reader, Woman Writer. 2011. xvii, 135p. E-Book *(978-0-8108-7744-3(9))* Scarecrow Pr., Inc.

Persky, Stan. Topic Sentence: A Writer's Education. 2007. (ENG., Illus.). 368p. pap. 21.00 *(978-1-55420-028-3(8))* New Star Bks., Ltd. CAN. Dist: SPD-Small Pr. Distribution.

Peters, Jason. Wendell Berry: Life & Work. Peters, Jason, ed. 2010. (Culture of the Land Ser.). (ENG.). 368p. pap. 21.95 *(978-0-8131-9257-4(9))* Univ. Pr. of Kentucky.

Peters, Jason, ed. Wendell Berry: Life & Work. 2007. (Culture of the Land Ser.). (ENG., Illus.). 368p. 50.00 *(978-0-8131-2442-1(5))* Univ. Pr. of Kentucky.

Peters, Margot. Lorine Niedecker: A Poet's Life. 2011. (ENG., Illus.). 334p. 34.95 ***(978-0-299-28500-5(6))*** Univ. of Wisconsin Pr.

Peterson, Brenda. I Want to Be Left Behind: Finding Rapture Here on Earth. 2010. (ENG.). 288p. 25.00 *(978-0-306-81804-2(3))* Da Capo Pr., Inc.

Peterson, Nancy J., ed. Conversations with Sherman Alexie. 2009. (Literary Conversations Ser.). (ENG.). 224p. 50.00 *(978-1-60473-279-5(2))*; pap. 22.00 *(978-1-60473-280-1(6))* Univ. Pr. of Mississippi.

Petrulionis, Sandra Harbert. Thoreau in His Own Time: A Biographical Chronicle of His Life, Drawn from Recollections, Interviews, & Memoirs by Family, Friends, & Associates. 2012. (Writers in Their Own Time Ser.). (ENG.). 268p. pap. 27.50 ***(978-1-60938-087-8(8))*** Univ. of Iowa Pr.

Petry, Alice Hall, ed. On Harper Lee: Essays & Reflections. 2008. (ENG.). 224p. pap. 21.95 *(978-1-57233-642-1(0))* Univ. of Tennessee Pr.

Petry, Elisabeth. At Home Inside: A Daughter's Tribute to Ann Petry. 2008. (ENG., Illus.). 208p. 30.00 *(978-1-60473-100-2(1))* Univ. Pr. of Mississippi.

Pfeiffer, Kathleen, ed. Brother Mine: The Correspondence of Jean Toomer & Waldo Frank. 2010. (ENG., Illus.). 208p. 45.00 *(978-0-252-03540-1(2))* Univ. of Illinois Pr.

Phillip Bell, Lee & Maloney, Michael. The Young & Restless Life of William J. Bell: Creator of the Young & the Restless & the Bold & the Beautiful, & former head writer of Days of our Lives. 2012. (ENG.). 288p. 24.99 ***(978-1-4022-7211-0(1))*** Sourcebooks, Inc.

Phillips, Glasgow. The Royal Nonesuch: Or, What Will I Do When I Grow Up? 2007. (ENG.). 384p. per. 14.00 *(978-0-8021-7028-6(5)*, Black Cat) Grove/Atlantic, Inc.

Piatka, Naava. No Goodbyes: A Father-Daughter Memoir of Love, War & Resurrection. 2009. 332p. 32.95 *(978-0-595-49603-7(2))*; pap. 22.95 *(978-0-595-49815-4(9))* iUniverse, Inc.

Pickering, Sam. A Comfortable Boy: A Memoir. 2010. 192p. 26.00 *(978-0-88146-182-4(2))* Mercer Univ. Pr.

Pierce, Susan & Johnston, Joan. A Stranger's Game. 2009. (ENG.). 448p. mass mkt. 7.99 *(978-0-7434-5439-1(1))* Pocket Books.

Pine, M. S. John Bannister Tabb the PriestPoet. 2006. pap. 21.95 *(978-1-4286-4665-0(5))* Kessinger Publishing, LLC.

Pineda, Jon. Sleep in Me. (American Lives Ser.). (ENG.). 168p. 2012. pap. 14.95 ***(978-0-8032-4341-5(3))*** 2010. 21.95 *(978-0-8032-2535-0(0))* Univ. of Nebraska Pr.

Piñero, Miguel. Outlaw: The Collected Works of Miguel Piñero. 2010. pap. 19.95 *(978-1-55885-606-6(4))* Arte Publico Pr.

Pines, Paul. My Brother's Madness: A Memoir. 2007. (ENG.). 318p. per. 15.95 *(978-1-931896-34-4(8))* Curbstone Pr.

Pinkwater, Daniel M. Uncle Boris in the Yukon & Other Shaggy Dog Stor. 2011. (ENG.). 208p. pap. 14.99 *(978-1-4516-4660-3(7))* Simon & Schuster.

Pipher, Mary. Seeking Peace: Chronicles of the Worst Buddhist in the World. 2010. (ENG.). 272p. (gr. 12-18). 16.00 *(978-1-59448-440-7(6)*, Riverhead Trade (Paperbacks)) Penguin Group (USA) Inc.

Pipher, Mary, et al. Grace of Grass & Water: Writing in Honor of Paul Gruchow. 2007. per. *(978-1-888160-28-4(4))* Ice Cube Pr.

Pittman, Patsy. Pocket Change. 2010. (Illus.). 80p. pap. 19.95 *(978-0-929915-56-2(9))* Headline Bks.

Plant, Deborah G. Zora Neale Hurston: A Biography of the Spirit, 1 vol. 2007. (Women Writers of Color Ser.). (Illus.). 264p. 49.95 *(978-0-275-98751-0(5)*, C8751, Praeger Pubs.) Greenwood Publishing Group, Inc.

—Zora Neale Hurston: A Biography of the Spirit. 2011. (ENG.). 264p. pap. 15.95 *(978-1-4422-0612-0(8))* Rowman & Littlefield Publishers, Inc.

Plante, David. The Pure Lover: A Memoir of Grief, 1 vol. 2010. (ENG.). 128p. pap. 16.00 *(978-0-8070-0620-7(3))* Beacon Pr.

Plath, James. Historic Photos of Ernest Hemingway. 2009. (Historic Photos Ser.). (ENG.). 206p. 39.95 *(978-1-59652-516-0(9))* Turner Publishing Co.

Plut, Joseph. Conversations with Jon Hassler. 2010. (Illus.). xiv, 264p. 19.95 *(978-1-932472-97-4(5))* Nodin Pr.

Podnieks, Elizabeth. Rough Draft: The Modernist Diaries of Emily Holmes Coleman, 1929-1937. 2012. (ENG.). 430p. (gr. 17). 90.00 ***(978-1-61149-376-4(5))*** Univ. of Delaware Pr.

The Poets & Poetry of Cecil County, Maryland. 2007. (ENG.). 328p. pap. 23.99 *(978-1-4264-6042-5(2))*; 384p. pap. 26.99 *(978-1-4264-6113-2(5))* BiblioBazaar.

Poolos, J. Ralph Waldo Emerson: The Father of the American Renaissance. 2009. (Library of American Thinkers Ser.). 112p. (gr. 6-6). 66.50 *(978-1-60853-516-3(9)*, Rosen Central) Rosen Publishing Group, Inc., The.

Porter, David. On the Divide: The Many Lives of Willa Cather. 2010. (ENG., Illus.). 416p. pap. 29.95 *(978-0-8032-3279-2(9))* Univ. of Nebraska Pr.

Porter, David H. On the Divide: The Many Lives of Willa Cather. 2008. (ENG., Illus.). 416p. 29.95 *(978-0-8032-3755-1(3))* Univ. of Nebraska Pr.

Porter, David H. & Marks, Lucy. Seeking Life Whole: Willa Cather & the Brewsters. 2009. 45.00 *(978-0-8386-4199-6(7))* Fairleigh Dickinson Univ. Pr.

Porter, Katherine Anne & Unrue, Darlene Harbour. Selected Letters of Katherine Anne Porter: Chronicles of a Modern Woman. 2012. (ENG., Illus.). 420p. 55.00 ***(978-1-61703-620-0(X))*** Univ. Pr. of Mississippi.

Potter, Charles Francis. The Preacher & I: An Autobiography. 2011. 448p. 56.95 ***(978-1-258-09704-2(4))*** Literary Licensing, LLC.

Potter, Dawn. Tracing Paradise: Two Years in Harmony with John Milton. 2009. (Illus.). 144p. pap. 22.95 net. *(978-1-55849-701-6(3))* Univ. of Massachusetts Pr.

Potter, Rockwell Harmon. The Harvest of the Years: Rockwell Harmon Potter Autobiography. Strong, Kendrick, ed. 2011. 110p. 39.95 ***(978-1-258-09770-7(2))*** Literary Licensing, LLC.

Potts, Rolf. Marco Polo Didn't Go There: Stories & Revelations from One Decade as a Postmodern Travel Writer. 2008. (ENG.). 344p. pap. 19.95 *(978-1-932361-61-2(8))* Travelers' Tales, Inc.

Pound, Ezra & Preda, Roxana. Ezra Pound's Economic Correspondence, 1933-1940. 2007. (ENG., Illus.). 320p. 59.95 *(978-0-8130-3088-3(9))* Univ. Pr. of Florida.

Powell, Steven, ed. Conversations with James Ellroy. 2012. (Literary Conversations Ser.). (ENG.). 224p. 65.00 ***(978-1-61703-103-8(8))***; pap. 25.00 ***(978-1-61703-104-5(6))*** Univ. Pr. of Mississippi.

Powell, Thomas. The Living Authors of America. 2008. 370p. 48.95 *(978-0-548-93480-7(0))* 2007. (ENG.). 372p. per. 33.95 *(978-0-548-57155-2(4))* Kessinger Publishing, LLC.

Power, Nani. Feed the Hungry: A Memoir with Recipes. 2008. (ENG.). 224p. 23.00 *(978-1-4165-5606-0(0)*, Free Pr.) Free Pr.

Powers, Paul S. Pulp Writer: Twenty Years in the American Grub Street. Powers, Laurie, ed. 2007. (ENG., Illus.). 276p. pap. 19.95 *(978-0-8032-5984-3(0)*, Bison Bks.) Univ. of Nebraska Pr.

Pozza, David M. Paradox: The Literary Landscape of Edward Abbey. 2006. 108p. (C). 52.95 *(978-0-8204-6330-8(2))* Lang, Peter Publishing, Inc.

Prenshaw, Peggy Whitman. Conversations with Greil Marcus. 2012. (Literary Conversations Ser.). (ENG., Illus.). 240p. 40.00 ***(978-1-61703-622-4(6))*** Univ. Pr. of Mississippi.

Price, John. Not Just Any Land: A Personal & Literary Journey into the American Grasslands. 2007. (ENG.). 240p. pap. 14.95 *(978-0-8032-6026-9(1)*, Bison Bks.) Univ. of Nebraska Pr.

Price, Leah, ed. Unpacking My Library: Writers & Their Books. 2011. (ENG., Illus.). 208p. 20.00 *(978-0-300-17092-4(0))* Yale Univ. Pr.

Price, S. L. Far Afield: A Sportswriting Odyssey. 2009. 272p. pap. 13.99 *(978-0-06-170872-5(0)*, HarperPerennial) HarperCollins Pubs.

Proctor, Bob & Hill, Napoleon. Think & Grow Rich: Collector's Edition, 1 vol. 2011. (ENG.). 152p. 21.95 ***(978-1-927005-05-7(1))*** Burman Books, Inc. CAN. Dist: Innovative Logistics.

Proulx, Annie. Bird Cloud. 2011. (ENG.). 256p. pap. 16.00 *(978-0-7432-8881-1(5)*, Scribner) Scribner.

Pulsifer, Susan Farley Nichols. Letters 1948: To the Memory of Harold Trowbridge Pulsifer. 2011. 42p. 35.95 ***(978-1-258-02945-6(6))*** Literary Licensing, LLC.

Purdon, Liam O. & Torrey, Beef, eds. Conversations with Tom Robbins. 2010. (Literary Conversations Ser.). (ENG.). 240p. 50.00 *(978-1-60473-826-1(X))*; pap. 22.00 *(978-1-60473-827-8(8))* Univ. Pr. of Mississippi.

Quindlen, Anna. Good Dog. Stay. l.t. ed. 2008. (Thorndike Nonfiction Ser.). (Illus.). 105p. 30.95 *(978-1-4104-0689-7(X))* Thorndike Pr.

Quindlen, Anna. Lots of Candles, Plenty of Cake. l.t. ed. 2012. (ENG.). 272p. pap. 26.00 ***(978-0-7393-7855-7(4))*** Random Hse. Large Print.

Quinn, Erin. Walking on Eggshells. 2008. 53p. pap. 16.95 *(978-1-60563-043-4(8))* PublishAmerica, Inc.

Raab, Diana & Brown, James. Writers on the Edge: 22 Writers Speak about Addiction & Dependency. 2012. ***(978-1-61599-109-9(3))***; 204p. pap. ***(978-1-61599-108-2(5))*** Loving Healing Pr., Inc. (Modern History Pr.).

Raab, Diana M., ed. Writers & Their Notebooks. 2010. 208p. 49.95 *(978-1-57003-865-5(1))*; pap. 24.95 *(978-1-57003-866-2(X))* Univ. of South Carolina Pr.

Rackstraw, Loree. Love as Always, Kurt: Vonnegut as I Knew Him. 2009. (ENG., Illus.). 304p. 25.00 *(978-0-306-81803-5(5))* Da Capo Pr., Inc.

—Love as Always, Kurt: Vonnegut As I Knew Him. 2013. (ENG.). 304p. pap. 15.00 *(978-0-306-81863-9(9))* Da Capo Pr., Inc.

Ramesh, Kotti Sree & Kandula, Nirupa Rani. Claude Mckay: The Literary Identity from Jamaica to Harlem & Beyond. 2006. (ENG., Illus.). 216p. per. 35.00 *(978-0-7864-2582-2(2))* McFarland & Co., Inc. Pubs.

Ramsey, Bruce. Unsanctioned Voice: Garet Garrett, Journalist of the Old Right. 2009. (ENG.). 290p. pap. 17.95 *(978-0-87004-465-6(6))* Caxton Pr.

Raskin, Andy. The Ramen King & I: How the Inventor of Instant Noodles Fixed My Love Life. 2010. (ENG.). 304p. (gr. 12). 16.00 *(978-1-59240-554-1(1)*, Gotham) Penguin Group (USA) Inc.

Rasmussen, R. Kent, ed. Mark Twain. 2010. (Critical Insights Ser.). 350p. 85.00 *(978-1-58765-689-7(2))* Salem Pr., Inc.

Rathmell, George. Realms of Gold: The Colorful Writers of San Francisco 1850-1950. 2008. 223p. pap. 17.95 *(978-0-7414-4537-7(9))* Infinity Publishing.

Rausch, Andrew J. The Wit & Wisdom of Stephen King. Rausch, Andrew J., ed. 2011. 146p. pap. 14.95 ***(978-1-59393-648-8(6))*** BearManor Media.

Ray, Georgia. Grace Flandrau: Voice Interrupted. 2007. (ENG., Illus.). 304p. 34.95 *(978-1-889020-22-8(2))* Edinborough Pr.

Raymond, Dwayne. Mornings with Mailer: A Recollection of Friendship. 2010. (ENG.). 256p. pap. 13.99 *(978-0-06-173359-8(8)*, HarperPerennial) HarperCollins Pubs.

Raymond, Ida. Southland Writers Biographical & Critical Sketches of the Living Female Writers of the South with Extracts from Their Writings by Ida Raymond Vo. 2006. 464p. per. 29.99 *(978-1-4255-5136-0(X))*; (ENG.). 524p. per. 29.99 *(978-1-4255-5804-8(6))* MPublishing.

Raynolds, Robert. Thomas Wolfe: Memoir of a Friendship. 2012. 174p. pap. 19.95 ***(978-0-292-74155-3(3))*** Univ. of Texas Pr.

Reardon, Joan & Reardon, J. M. F. K. Fisher among the Pots & Pans: Celebrating Her Kitchens. 2009. (California Studies in Food & Culture Ser.). (ENG., Illus.). 184p. pap. 19.95 *(978-0-520-26168-6(2))* Univ. of California Pr.

Reed, Jennifer. Paula Danziger: Voice of Teen Troubles. 2006. (Authors Teens Love Ser.). (Illus.). 104p. (YA). (gr. 7-12). lib. bdg. 31.93 *(978-0-7660-2444-1(X))* Enslow Pubs., Inc.

Reese, Taylor. A Picture of the Past. 2007. per. 16.95 *(978-1-59712-095-1(2))* Catawba Publishing Co.

Reesman, Jeanne Campbell. Jack London's Racial Lives: A Critical Biography. (ENG., Illus.). 2011. 440p. pap. 26.95 *(978-0-8203-3781-4(1))* 2009. 448p. 34.95 *(978-0-8203-2789-1(1))* Univ. of Georgia Pr.

Reid, Panthea. Tillie Olsen: One Woman, Many Riddles. (ENG., Illus.). 2011. 484p. pap. 26.95 ***(978-0-8135-5187-6(0))*** 2009. 464p. 34.95 *(978-0-8135-4637-7(0))* Rutgers Univ. Pr.

Reidel, James. Vanished Act: The Life & Art of Weldon Kees. 2007. (ENG., Illus.). 448p. pap. 19.95 *(978-0-8032-5977-5(8))* Univ. of Nebraska Pr.

Reisen, Harriet. Louisa May Alcott: The Woman Behind Little Women. 2009. (ENG.). 384p. 26.00 *(978-0-8050-8299-9(9))* Holt, Henry & Co.

—Louisa May Alcott: The Woman Behind Little Women. 2010. (ENG.). 464p. pap. 16.00 *(978-0-312-65887-8(7))* Picador.

Renehan Jr., Edward J. Legend & Legacy: The Life of Seymour St. John. 2008. 304p. 30.00 *(978-1-4389-1565-4(9))*; pap. 15.95 *(978-1-4389-1564-7(0))* AuthorHouse.

Research International Staff, ed. Freelancers of North America. 2nd ed. pap. 37.95 *(978-0-911085-05-1(X))* Author Aid/Research Assocs. International.

Resnick, Rachel. Love Junkie: A Memoir. 2009. (ENG.). 256p. pap. 14.00 *(978-1-59691-646-3(X))* Bloomsbury Publishing.

Reynolds, Abigail Elizabeth. An (Extra)Ordinary Journey:A Life in Two Genders. 2009. 120p. pap. 19.95 *(978-0-557-15639-9(4))* Lulu Enterprises Inc.

Reynolds, Larry J. Righteous Violence: Revolution, Slavery, & the American Renaissance. 2011. (ENG., Illus.). 264p. 59.95 ***(978-0-8203-2825-6(1))***; pap. 24.95 ***(978-0-8203-4140-8(1))*** Univ. of Georgia Pr.

Reynolds, Michael S. Hemingway: The 1930s through the Final Years. 2012. (Movie Tie-in Editions Ser.). (ENG., Illus.). 800p. pap. 24.95 ***(978-0-393-34320-5(0)***, 34320) Norton, W. W. & Co., Inc.

Rhode, Michael G., ed. Harvey Pekar: Conversations. 2008. (ENG., Illus.). 240p. 50.00 *(978-1-60473-085-2(4))* Univ. Pr. of Mississippi.

Rhynes, Martha. Jack London: Writer of Adventure. 2011. 122p. pap. 9.95 ***(978-1-4327-7282-6(1))*** Outskirts Pr., Inc.

Rice, Anne. Called Out of Darkness: A Spiritual Confession. 2010. (ENG.). 256p. pap. 15.95 *(978-0-307-38848-3(4)*, Anchor) Knopf Doubleday Publishing Group.

Rich, Mark. C. M. Kornbluth: The Life & Works of a Science Fiction Visionary. 2009. (ENG., Illus.). 451p. pap. 39.95 *(978-0-7864-4393-2(6))* McFarland & Co., Inc. Pubs.

A

Richards, Susan. Chosen Forever: A Memoir. 2009. (ENG.). 256p. pap. 13.95 (*978-0-15-603302-2(X)*, Mariner Bks.) Houghton Mifflin Harcourt Trade & Reference Pubs.

—Chosen Forever: A Memoir. 2008. (ENG., Illus.). 288p. 23.00 (*978-1-56947-492-1(3)*) Soho Pr., Inc.

Richardson, Robert D. First We Read, Then We Write: Emerson on the Creative Process. 2009. (ENG.). 112p. 19.95 (*978-1-58729-793-9(0)*) Univ. of Iowa Pr.

Richardson, T. C. The Autobiography of the Rambling Longhorn. 2011. 98p. 38.95 (***978-1-258-09652-6(8)***) Literary Licensing, LLC.

Richmond, Tim. Fingerprints on the Sky the Authorized Harlan Ellison Bibliography: The Fully Illustrated Reader's Guide. 2007. (Illus.). 59.95 (*978-1-892950-68-0(5)*) Overlook Connection Pr., The.

Rideout, Walter B. Sherwood Anderson Vol. 2: A Writer in America, 2 vols. 2006. (ENG., Illus.). 520p. 60.00 (*978-0-299-22020-4(6)*) Univ. of Wisconsin Pr.

Rieff, David. Swimming in a Sea of Death: A Son's Memoir. 2008. (ENG.). 192p. pap. 14.00 (*978-0-7432-9947-3(7)*) Simon & Schuster.

Rio Raigadas, David. Robert Laxalt: The Voice of Basques! in North American Literature. 2007. 230p. (C). pap. 24.95 (*978-1-877802-71-3(9)*) Ctr. for Basque Studies.

Ritchie, Alan. Ruark Remembered: By the Man Who Knew Him Best. Casada, Jim, ed. 2009. (ENG., Illus.). 288p. 40.00 (*978-0-9778551-3-1(9)*, 977853) Skyhorse Publishing Co., Inc.

—Ruark Remembered - Deluxe Edition. Casada, James, ed. 2007. 350p. lthr. 90.00 (*978-0-9778551-4-8(7)*) Sporting Classics.

Rivera, Carmen. Border Crossings & Beyond: The Life & Works of Sandra Cisneros, 1 vol. 2009. (Women Writers of Color Ser.). 127p. 34.95 (*978-0-313-34518-0(X)*, C34518, Praeger Pubs.) Greenwood Publishing Group, Inc.

Robbins, Jann. Harold & Me: My Life, Love, & Hard Times with Harold Robbins. 2010. (ENG.). 304p. pap. 19.99 (*978-0-7653-2087-2(8)*, Forge Bks.) Doherty, Tom Assocs., LLC.

Robbins, Mary Susann. Earth, Air, Fire, & Water: A Memoir of the Sixties & Beyond. 2008. (ENG.). 170p. 73.50 (*978-0-7391-2791-9(8)*); pap. 28.50 (*978-0-7391-2792-6(6)*) Lexington Bks.

Roberson, William H. Walter M. Miller, Jr. A Reference Guide to His Fiction & His Life. 2011. (ENG.). 218p. pap. 40.00 (*978-0-7864-6361-9(9)*) McFarland & Co., Inc. Pubs.

Robinson, Kenneth Allen. Thoreau & the Wild Appetite. 2011. 28p. 35.95 (***978-1-258-01112-3(3)***) Literary Licensing, LLC.

Robinson, Owen. William Faulkner's "Light in August" 2009. 95.00 (*978-0-415-34450-0(6)*); pap. 26.95 (*978-0-415-34451-7(4)*) Routledge.

Roche, David, ed. Conversations with Russell Banks. 2010. (Literary Conversations Ser.). (ENG.). 240p. 40.00 (*978-1-60473-745-5(X)*) Univ. Pr. of Mississippi.

Rodgers, Marion Elizabeth. Mencken: The American Iconoclast - The Life & Times of the Bad Boys of Baltimore. 2007. (ENG., Illus.). 672p. per. 30.00 (*978-0-19-533129-5(X)*) Oxford Univ. Pr., Inc.

Rodriguez, Luis J. It Calls You Back: An Odyssey Through Love, Addictions, Revolutions, & Healing. 2011. (ENG.). 336p. 24.99 (*978-1-4165-8416-2(1)*, Touchstone) Touchstone.

Roffman, Karin. From the Modernist Annex: American Women Writers in Museums & Libraries. 2nd ed. 2010. (ENG., Illus.). 272p. 44.50 (*978-0-8173-1698-3(1)*) Univ. of Alabama Pr.

Rogak, Lisa. Boy Named Shel: The Life & Times of Shel Silverstein. 2nd ed. 2009. (ENG., Illus.). 256p. pap. 16.99 (*978-0-312-53931-3(2)*, St. Martin's Griffin) St. Martin's Pr.

—Haunted Heart: The Life & Times of Stephen King. (ENG., Illus.). 2010. 336p. pap. 15.99 (*978-0-312-60350-2(9)*, St. Martin's Griffin) 2009. 320p. 25.95 (*978-0-312-37732-8(0)*, Dunne, Thomas Bks.) St. Martin's Pr.

Roiphe, Anne. Art & Madness: A Memoir of Lust Without Reason. 2012. (ENG.). 240p. pap. 15.95 (***978-0-307-47396-7(1)***, Anchor) Knopf Doubleday Publishing Group.

Rolls, Albert. Stephen King: A Biography, 1 vol. 2008. (Greenwood Biographies Ser.). (Illus.). 216p. 35.00 (*978-0-313-34572-2(4)*, GR4572, Greenwood Pr.) Greenwood Publishing Group, Inc.

Rollyson, Carl. Norman Mailer: The Last Romantic. 2008. 420p. pap. 26.95 (*978-0-595-50448-0(5)*) iUniverse, Inc.

Rollyson, Carl, ed. Notable American Novelists, 3 vols., Set. 2007. (Magill's Choice Ser.). (Illus.). 1536p. lib. bdg. 217.00 (*978-1-58765-393-1(1)*, Magill's Choice) Salem Pr., Inc.

Rollyson, Carl E. Notable American Novelists. 2007. (Magill's Choice Ser.). 73.00 (*978-1-58765-395-7(8)*); 73.00 (*978-1-58765-396-4(6)*); 73.00 (*978-1-58765-394-0(X)*) Salem Pr., Inc.

Rooney, Kathleen. For You, for You I Am Trilling These Songs. 2009. (ENG.). 224p. pap. 14.95 (*978-1-58243-545-9(6)*, Counterpoint Pr.) Basic Bks. GBR. Dist: Perseus-PGW.

Rosco, Jerry. Glenway Wescott Personally: A Biography. 2010. (ENG., Illus.). 328p. pap. 19.95 (*978-0-299-17734-8(3)*) Univ. of Wisconsin Pr.

Rose, Daniel Asa. Larry's Kidney: Being the True Story of How I Found Myself in China with My Black Sheep Cousin & His Mail-Order Bride, Skirting the Law to Get Him a Transplant - And Save His Life. 2010. 320p. pap. 14.99 (*978-0-06-170871-8(2)*, Harper Paperbacks) HarperCollins Pubs.

Rosen, Michael J., ed. Dogs We Love: With Jane Smiley, Edward Albee, Ann Beattie, Armistead Maupin, & Fourteen Other Dog People. 2008. (ENG., Illus.). 176p. 15.95 (*978-1-57965-358-3(8)*, 1579653588) Artisan.

Rosenberg, Aaron. Colleen Doran. 2009. (Library of Graphic Novelists Ser.). 112p. (gr. 7-12). 63.90 (*978-1-60853-654-2(8)*) Rosen Publishing Group, Inc., The.

—Madeleine L'Engle. 2009. (Library of Author Biographies Ser.). 112p. (gr. 5-8). 63.90 (*978-1-60853-547-7(9)*, Rosen Central) Rosen Publishing Group, Inc., The.

Rosenberger, Francis C. Virginia Reader: A Treasury of Writings. lib. bdg. 33.95 (*978-0-8488-2108-1(4)*) Amereon LTD.

Rosenthal, Sarah, ed. A Community Writing Itself: Conversations with Vanguard Writers of the Bay Area. 2010. (Dalkey Archive Scholarly Ser.). (ENG.). 420p. pap. 29.95 (*978-1-56478-584-8(X)*, 478584) Dalkey Archive Pr.

Ross-Stroud, Catherine. Janet McDonald: The Original Project Girl. 2008. (Scarecrow Studies in Young Adult Literature Ser.). (ENG., Illus.). 160p. 45.00 (*978-0-8108-5802-2(9)*) Scarecrow Pr., Inc.

Roth, Philip. Notes for My Biographer. 2012. (ENG.). 288p. 26.00 (***978-0-547-89684-7(0)***) Houghton Mifflin Harcourt Trade & Reference Pubs.

Rounds, Charles R. Wisconsin Authors & Their Works. 400p. reprint ed. lib. bdg. 98.00 (*978-0-7222-0324-8(1)*) Library Reprints, Inc.

Rountree, Helen C. Life in an Eastern Woodland Indian Village. 2007. (Illus.). 45p. pap. 19.95 (*978-0-9648727-3-8(0)*) Rountree, Helen C.

Rouse, Wade. At Least in the City Someone Would Hear Me Scream: Misadventures in Search of the Simple Life. 2010. (ENG.). 320p. pap. 14.00 (*978-0-307-45191-0(7)*, Three Rivers Pr.) Crown Publishing Group.

Rowbotham, Sheila. Edward Carpenter: A Life of Liberty & Love. 2008. (ENG., Illus.). 548p. 39.95 (*978-1-84467-295-0(6)*, 844295) Verso Bks. GBR. Dist: Norton, W. W. & Co., Inc.

Roza, Mathilde Helene. Following Strangers: The Life & Literary Works of Robert M. Coates. 2011. 344p. 49.95 (*978-1-57003-981-2(X)*) Univ. of South Carolina Pr.

Rubin, Louis Decimus Jr., et al. Southern Literary Study: Problems & Possibilities. 2011. (ENG.). 248p. pap. 40.00 (***978-0-8078-9767-6(1)***) Univ. of North Carolina Pr.

Rucker, Rudy. Nested Scrolls: The Autobiography of Rudolf von Bitter Rucker. (ENG.). 336p. 2012. pap. 15.99 (***978-0-7653-2753-6(8)***) 2011. (Illus.). 25.99 (*978-0-7653-2752-9(X)*) Doherty, Tom Assocs., LLC. (Tor Bks.).

Rusho, W. L., ed. The Mystery of Everett Ruess, 1 vol. 2010. (ENG.). 272p. pap. 16.99 (*978-1-4236-1711-2(8)*) Gibbs Smith, Publisher.

Rutkoff, Peter. Across the Green Line: Cyprus Portraits. 2007. (Illus.). 136p. pap. 14.95 (*978-1-880977-22-4(2)*) XOXOX Pr.

Sabbag, Robert. Down Around Midnight: A Memoir of Crash & Survival. 2010. (ENG.). 224p. (gr. 12). 15.00 (*978-0-14-311760-5(2)*, Penguin (Non-Classics)) Penguin Group (USA) Inc.

Salter, James & Phelps, Robert. Memorable Days: The Selected Letters of James Salter & Robert Phelps. McIntyre, John, ed. 2010. (ENG.). 224p. 25.00 (*978-1-58243-605-0(3)*, Counterpoint Pr.) Basic Bks. GBR. Dist: Perseus-PGW.

Salwak, Dale, ed. AfterWord: Conjuring the Literary Dead. 2011. (ENG.). 240p. pap. 19.95 (*978-1-58729-989-6(5)*) Univ. of Iowa Pr.

Sams, Amanda D., ed. Contemporary Authors. 167th rev. ed. 2008. (Contemporary Authors New Revision Ser.). (ENG.). 480p. 293.00 (*978-0-7876-9531-6(9)*) Cengage Gale.

Sams, Amanda D., et al, eds. Contemporary Authors New Revision, Volume 170: A Bio-Bibliographical Guide to Current Writers in Fiction, General Nonfiction, Poetry, Journalism, Drama, Motion Pictures, Television, & Other Fields. 170th rev. ed. 2008. (Contemporary Authors New Revision Ser.). (ENG., Illus.). 448p. 293.00 (*978-0-7876-9534-7(3)*) Cengage Gale.

Samson, Lisa & Samson, Ty. Love Mercy: A Mother & Daughter's Journey from the American Dream to the Kingdom of God, 1 vol. 2010. (ENG.). 176p. pap. 14.99 (*978-0-310-28477-2(5)*) Zondervan.

Sanborn, Frank B. Personality of Thoreau. 2006. pap. 18.95 (*978-1-4286-4774-9(0)*) Kessinger Publishing, LLC.

Sanborn, Kate. Memories & Anecdotes. rev. ed. 2007. (ENG.). 160p. pap. 19.99 (*978-1-4264-8461-2(5)*) BiblioBazaar.

Sander, Gordon F. Serling: The Rise & Twilight of TV's Last Angry Man. 2011. 320p. pap. 18.95 (***978-0-8014-7730-0(1)***) Cornell Univ. Pr.

Sanders, Ed. Fug You: An Informal History of the Peace Eye Bookstore, the Fuck You Press, the Fugs, & Counterculture in the Lower East Side. 2011. (ENG., Illus.). 448p. 26.99 (*978-0-306-81888-2(4)*) Da Capo Pr., Inc.

Saroyan, William & Justice, William E. He Flies Through the Air with the Greatest of Ease: A William Saroyan Reader. 2008. (*978-1-59714-089-8(9)*, Great Valley Bks.) Heyday.

Sassoon, Elias. 13 Months of Sassoon: A Diary of Time. 2010. 209p. pap. 13.27 (*978-0-557-31839-1(4)*) Lulu Enterprises Inc.

Satiat, Nadine. Gertrude Stein. 2010. (FRE., Illus.). 1288p. (*978-2-08-121992-2(1)*) Flammarion et Cie.

Saunders, Richard. Never Been Rich: The Life & Work of a Southern Ruralist Writer, Harry Harrison Kroll. 2011. (ENG.). 264p. 42.00 (***978-1-57233-825-8(3)***) Univ. of Tennessee Pr.

Savage, Michael. Train Tracks: Holiday Stories. 2012. (ENG.). 208p. 23.99 (***978-0-06-221084-5(X)***, Morrow, William & Co.) HarperCollins Pubs.

Sayre, Robert F., et al. Emerson & Thoreau: Figures of Friendship. Lysaker, John T. & Rossi, William, eds. 2010. (American Philosophy Ser.). (ENG.). 222p. pap. 22.95 (*978-0-253-22143-8(9)*, 0253221439) Indiana Univ. Pr.

Schafer, Edith Nalle. Literary Circles of Washington. 2008. (ENG., Illus.). 79p. pap. 12.95 (*978-1-55709-081-2(5)*) Applewood Bks.

Scharnhorst, Gary. Kate Field: The Many Lives of a Nineteenth-Century American Journalist. 2008. (Writing American Women Ser.). (Illus.). xiv, 306p. (*978-0-8456-0874-6(6)*) Syracuse Univ. Pr.

Scharnhorst, Gary, ed. Twain in His Own Time: A Biographical Chronicle of His Life, Drawn from Recollections, Interviews, & Memoirs by Family, Friends, & Associates. 2010. (Writers in Their Own Time Ser.). 290p. pap. 27.95 (*978-1-58729-914-8(3)*) Univ. of Iowa Pr.

Schenck, Theresa M. William W. Warren: The Life, Letters, & Times of an Ojibwe Leader. 2009. (American Indian Lives Ser.). (ENG.). 232p. pap. 19.95 (*978-0-8032-2498-8(2)*) Univ. of Nebraska Pr.

Schenkar, Joan. The Talented Miss Highsmith: The Secret Life & Serious Art of Patricia Highsmith. 2011. (ENG., Illus.). 704p. pap. 24.00 (*978-0-312-36381-9(8)*) Picador.

Schmidt, Michael, ed. The Great Modern Poets. 2009. (ENG., Illus.). 208p. 12.99 (*978-1-905204-32-8(9)*, 1905204329) Quercus GBR. Dist: Book Sales, Inc.

Schmidt, Shannon McKenna & Rendon, Joni. Novel Destinations: Literary Landmarks from Jane Austen's Bath to Ernest Hemingway's Key West. 2008. (ENG., Illus.). 368p. 25.00 (*978-1-4262-0277-3(6)*, National Geographic) National Geographic Society.

Schreiner, Samuel Agnew, Jr., et al. The Concord Quartet: Alcott, Emerson, Hawthorne, Thoreau, & the Friendship That Freed the American Mind. 2006. (ENG., Illus.). 256p. 24.95 (*978-0-471-64663-1(6)*, Wiley) Wiley, John & Sons, Inc.

Schuchardt, Read Mercer, ed. You Do Not Talk about Fight Club: I Am Jack's Completely Unauthorized Essay Collection. 2008. (Smart Pop Ser.). (ENG.). 216p. pap. 14.95 (*978-1-933771-52-6(6)*) BenBella Bks.

Schultz, David E. & Joshi, S. T., eds. An Epicure in the Terrible: A Centennial Anthology of Essays in Honor of H. P. Lovecraft. rev. exp. ed. 2011. (ENG.). pap. 20.00 (***978-0-9846386-1-1(X)***) Hippocampus Pr.

Schultz, William Todd. Tiny Terror: Why Truman Capote (Almost) Wrote Answered Prayers. 2011. (Inner Lives Ser.). (ENG.). 190p. 17.95 (*978-0-19-975204-1(4)*) Oxford Univ. Pr., Inc.

Schuyler, James. The Letters of James Schuyler to Frank O'Hara. Corbett, William, ed. 2006. (ENG.). 96p. per. 11.95 (*978-1-885586-48-3(5)*) Turtle Point Pr.

Schwartz, Lynne Sharon. Not Now, Voyager: A Memoir. 2010. (ENG.). 192p. pap. 14.95 (*978-1-58243-588-6(X)*, Counterpoint Pr.) Basic Bks. GBR. Dist: Perseus-PGW.

Schwartz, Sheila. F Scott Fitzgerald. 2012. (Life&Times Ser.). (ENG.). 220p. pap. 14.95 (***978-1-907822-00-1(3)***) Haus Publishing GBR. Dist: Consortium Bk. Sales & Distribution.

Scotchie, Joseph. Thomas Wolfe Revisited. 158p. 22.99 (*978-1-56664-163-0(2)*, Land of the Sky Bks.) WorldComm.

Selgin, Peter. Confessions of a Left-Handed Man: An Artist's Memoir. 2011. (Sightline Bks.). (ENG.). 248p. pap. 19.95 (*978-1-60938-056-4(8)*) Univ. of Iowa Pr.

Sellers, Heather. You Don't Look Like Anyone I Know: A True Story of Family, Face Blindness, & Forgiveness. 2011. (ENG.). 368p. (gr. 12). 16.00 (*978-1-59448-540-4(2)*, Riverhead Trade (Paperbacks)) Penguin Group (USA) Inc.

Selzer, Richard. Letters to a Best Friend. Josyph, Peter, ed. 2009. (Excelsior Editions Ser.). (Illus.). 256p. 14.95 (*978-1-4384-2721-8(2)*, Suny Pr.) State Univ. of New York Pr.

Senna, Danzy. Where Did You Sleep Last Night? A Personal History. 2010. (ENG.). 208p. pap. 14.00 (*978-0-312-42939-3(8)*) Picador.

Shackelford, Otis M. Seeking the Best. 2009. 84p. pap. 16.95 (*978-1-151-40377-3(6)*) General Bks. LLC.

Shaffer, Brian W. The Encyclopedia of Twentieth-Century Fiction, 3 vols. 2011. (Wiley-Blackwell Encyclopedia of Literature Ser.: 1). (ENG.). 1584p. 595.00 (*978-1-4051-9244-6(5)*, Wiley-Blackwell) Wiley, John & Sons, Inc.

Shaffer, David W. Footprints on Broadway: My Journey to the Feet of the Stars. 2009. 484p. 30.99 (*978-1-4389-8463-6(4)*); pap. 20.49 (*978-1-4389-8462-9(6)*) AuthorHouse.

Shapiro, Dani. Devotion: A Memoir. 2011. (P. S. Ser.). (ENG.). 272p. pap. 14.99 (*978-0-06-162835-1(2)*, HarperPerennial) HarperCollins Pubs.

Shapiro, Myra. Four Sublets: Becoming a Poet in New York. 2007. 189p. pap. 18.00 (*978-1-887344-12-8(8)*) Chicory Blue Pr., Inc.

Shaw, Margaret Dinzler. Memoirs in the Light of Day: An Essay Collection. 2008. vii, 210p. pap. (*978-0-9676130-5-5(1)*) Lamberson Corona Pr.

Shelden, Michael. Mark Twain: Man in White - The Grand Adventure of His Final Years. 2010. (ENG., Illus.). 528p. 30.00 (*978-0-679-44800-6(4)*) Random Hse., Inc.

Shengold, Nina. River of Words: Portraits of Hudson Valley Writers. 2010. (Illus.). 240p. 29.95 (*978-1-4384-3425-4(1)*, Suny Pr.) State Univ. of New York Pr.

Sherrard-Johnson, Cherene. Dorothy West's Paradise: A Biography of Class & Color. 2012. (ENG., Illus.). 256p. (C). pap. 24.95 (*978-0-8135-5167-8(6)*); 264p. 72.00 (*978-0-8135-5166-1(8)*) Rutgers Univ. Pr.

Shields, A. Randolph. The Inevitable: Contemporary Writers Confront Death. Morrow, Bradford, ed. 2011. (ENG.). 336p. pap. 17.95 (*978-0-393-33936-9(X)*, 33936) Norton, W. W. & Co., Inc.

Shields, David. Enough about You: Notes Toward the New Autobiography. 2009. (ENG.). 192p. pap. 14.95 (*978-1-59376-219-3(4)*, Soft Skull Pr.) Counterpoint LLC.

Shillinglaw, Susan. A Journey into Steinbeck's California. 2nd ed. 2011. (ArtPlace Ser.). (ENG.). 230p. pap. 24.95 (***978-0-9846239-1-4(4)***; ***978-0-9846254-7-5(X)***) Roaring Forties Pr.

Shoup, Barbara & Denman, Margaret-Love, eds. Novel Ideas: Contemporary Authors Share the Creative Process. 2nd rev. ed. 2009. (ENG.). 344p. pap. 22.95 (*978-0-8203-3279-6(8)*) Univ. of Georgia Pr.

Shrake, Bud, pseud. Land of the Permanent Wave: An Edwin Bud Shrake Reader. Davis, Steven L., ed. & intro. by. 2009. (ENG., Illus.). 343p. pap. 29.95 (*978-0-292-71996-5(5)*) Univ. of Texas Pr.

Shurin, Aaron. King of Shadows. 2008. (ENG.). 184p. pap. 16.95 (*978-0-87286-490-0(1)*) City Lights Bks.

Sienkiewicz, Henryk. Life & Death & Other Legends & Stories. Curtin, Jeremiah, tr. 2011. 34p. 12.95 (***978-1-4638-9925-7(4)***) Rodgers, Alan Bks.

Sigal, Clancy. A Woman of Uncertain Character: The Amorous & Radical Adventures of My Mother Jennie (Who Always Wanted to Be a Respectable Jewish Mom) by Her Bastard Son. 2007. (ENG.). 304p. pap. 15.95 (*978-0-7867-1995-2(8)*) Da Capo Pr., Inc.

Sigourney, L. H. Letters of Life. 2007. (ENG.). 416p. 49.95 (*978-0-548-15619-3(0)*); pap. 34.95 (*978-1-4304-5080-1(0)*) Kessinger Publishing, LLC.

Silko, Leslie Marmon. The Turquoise Ledge: A Memoir. (ENG.). 336p. (gr. 12). 2011. 16.00 (*978-0-14-312010-0(7)*, Penguin (Non-Classics)) 2010. 25.95 (*978-0-670-02211-3(X)*, Viking Adult) Penguin Group (USA) Inc.

Silverberg, Robert A. & Silverberg, Robert. Other Spaces, Other Times: A Life Spent in the Future. 2009. (ENG., Illus.). 200p. 29.95 (*978-1-933065-12-0(5)*) Nonstop Pr.

Simmonds, Roy S. The Two Worlds of William March. 3rd ed. 2011. (Library Alabama Classics Ser.). (ENG.). 388p. pap. 45.00 (*978-0-8173-5687-3(8)*) Univ. of Alabama Pr.

Simmons, Marc. Charles F. Lummis: Author & Adventurer: A Gathering. 2008. 120p. 22.95 (*978-0-86534-639-0(9)*); pap. 16.95 (*978-0-86534-636-9(4)*) Sunstone Pr.

Simon, Roger L. Blacklisting Myself: Memoir of a Hollywood Apostate in the Age of Terror. 2009. (ENG.). 250p. 25.95 (*978-1-59403-247-9(5)*) Encounter Bks.

—Turning Right at Hollywood & Vine: The Perils of Coming Out Conservative in Tinseltown. 2011. (ENG.). 232p. pap. 15.95 (*978-1-59403-481-7(8)*) Encounter Bks.

Sims, Michael. The Story of Charlotte's Web: E. B. White's Eccentric Life in Nature & the Birth of an American Classic. 2011. (ENG., Illus.). 320p. 25.00 (*978-0-8027-7754-6(6)*) Walker & Co.

Sine Cera: 95 Pennies & a Nickel, Seven. 2006. 7.50 (*978-0-9789581-6-9(0)*) SLCC Community Writing Ctr.

Sine Cera: So They Said. 2007. per. 7.50 (*978-0-9789581-7-6(9)*) SLCC Community Writing Ctr.

Sjoholm, Barbara. Incognito Street: How Travel Made Me a Writer. 2006. (ENG., Illus.). 256p. per. 15.95 (*978-1-58005-172-9(3)*) Seal Pr.

Skemp, Sheila L. First Lady of Letters: Judith Sargent Murray & the Struggle for Female Independence. 2009. (Early American Studies). 512p. 42.50 (*978-0-8122-4140-2(1)*) Univ. of Pennsylvania Pr.

Skinner, Knute. Help Me to a Getaway: A Memoir. 2010. (ENG., Illus.). 248p. pap. 26.95 (*978-1-907056-29-1(7)*) Salmon Publishing IRL. Dist: Dufour Editions, Inc.

Skloot, Floyd. The Wink of the Zenith: The Shaping of a Writer's Life. (ENG.). 2011. 256p. pap. 16.95 (*978-0-8032-3845-9(2)*, Bison Bks.) 2008. 252p. 24.95 (*978-0-8032-1119-3(8)*) Univ. of Nebraska Pr.

—A World of Light. 2011. (ENG.). 216p. pap. 16.95 (*978-0-8032-3847-3(9)*, Bison Bks.) Univ. of Nebraska Pr.

Slater, Lauren. The $60,000 Dog: My Life with Animals. 2012. (ENG.). 256p. 25.95 (***978-0-393-08111-4(7)***, 8111) Norton, W. W. & Co., Inc.

Small, David. Stitches: A Memoir. 2010. (ENG., Illus.). 329p. pap. 16.95 (*978-0-393-33896-6(7)*, 33896) Norton, W. W. & Co., Inc.

Smeaton, William Henry Oliphant. Longfellow & His Poetry. 2008. 144p. pap. (*978-1-4086-8499-3(3)*) Read Bks.

Smiley, Jane. 13 Ways of Looking at the Novel. 2006. (ENG.). 608p. pap. 16.95 (*978-1-4000-3318-8(7)*, Anchor) Knopf Doubleday Publishing Group.

Smiley, Tavis. Fail Up: 20 Lessons on Building Success from Failure. 2011. (ENG.). 288p. 19.95 (*978-1-4019-3390-6(4)*) Hay Hse., Inc.

Smith, Dustin Beall. Key Grip: A Memoir of Endless Consequences. 2008. (ENG.). 176p. pap. 12.95 (*978-0-547-05369-1(X)*, Mariner Bks.) Houghton Mifflin Harcourt Trade & Reference Pubs.

Smith, Huston & Paine, Jeffery. Tales of Wonder: Adventures Chasing the Divine, an Autobiography. 2009. (ENG., Illus.). 240p. 25.99 (*978-0-06-115426-3(1)*, HarperOne); 288p. pap. 25.99 (*978-0-06-166904-0(0)*, HarperLuxe) HarperCollins Pubs.

Smith, Larry. The Moment: Wild, Poignant, Life-Changing Stories from 125 Writers & Artists Famous & Obscure. 2012. (ENG.). 192p. pap. 14.99 (*978-0-06-171965-3(X)*, HarperPerennial) HarperCollins Pubs.

Smith, Larry. The Moment: Wild, Poignant, Life-Changing Stories from 125 Wrtiers & Artists. 2012. E-Book (***978-0-06-209921-1(3)***, HarperPerennial) HarperCollins Pubs.

Smith, Martha Nell & Loeffelholz, Mary, eds. A Companion to Emily Dickinson. 2008. (Blackwell Companions to Literature & Culture Ser.: 51). (ENG., Illus.). 544p. 219.95 (*978-1-4051-2280-1(3)*, Wiley-Blackwell) Wiley, John & Sons, Inc.

Smith, Mary L. P. & Rexford, Eben E. Eben E Rexford, a Biographical Sketch: A Memorial Containing Silver Threads among the Gold & His Last Poem. 2011. 76p. 37.95 (***978-1-258-07212-4(2)***) Literary Licensing, LLC.

Smith, Robert Paul. Where Did You Go? Out. What Did You Do? Nothing. 2010. (ENG., Illus.). 144p. pap. 13.95 (978-0-393-33941-3(6), 33941) Norton, W. W. & Co., Inc.

Smith, Samuel & Smith, Thelma. Experiences in the Southwest: The Sharecropper's Son, Part II. 2010. 120p. pap. 16.49 (978-1-4490-3906-6(5)) AuthorHouse.

Smith, Thomas R. & Lenfestey, James, eds. Robert Bly in This World. 2011. (ENG.). 308p. 34.95 (978-0-8166-7770-2(0)) Univ. of Minnesota Pr.

Snell, Susan. Phil Stone of Oxford: A Vicarious Life. 2008. (ENG.). 432p. pap. 26.95 (978-0-8203-3366-3(2)) Univ. of Georgia Pr.

Snodgrass, Mary Ellen. Leslie Marmon Silko: A Literary Companion. 2011. (McFarland Literary Companions Ser.). (ENG., Illus.). 411p. pap. 39.95 (978-0-7864-4853-1(9)) McFarland & Co., Inc. Pubs.

Snyder, Gary & Harrison, Jim. The Etiquette of Freedom: Gary Snyder, Jim Harrison, andThe Practice of the Wild. Ebenkamp, Paul, ed. 2010. (ENG., Illus.). 160p. 28.00 (978-1-58243-629-6(0), Counterpoint) Counterpoint LLC.

Snyder, Gary & Harrison, Jim. The Etiquette of Freedom: Gary Snyder, Jim Harrison andThe Practice of the Wild. Ebenkamp, Paul, ed. 2012. (ENG.). 160p. pap. 19.95 (978-1-61902-056-6(4), Counterpoint) Counterpoint LLC.

Sojourner, Mary. Solace: Rituals of Loss & Desire. 2007. (ENG.). 176p. pap. 14.95 (978-0-7432-2969-2(X), Scribner) Scribner.

Solomon, Rakesh H. Albee in Performance. 2010. (ENG., Illus.). 320p. pap. 26.00 (978-0-253-22205-3(2), 0253222052) Indiana Univ. Pr.

Soloway, Jill. Tiny Ladies in Shiny Pants: Based on a True Story. 2006. (ENG.). 272p. pap. 17.99 (978-0-7432-7218-6(8), Free Pr.) Free Pr.

Sommers, Michael A. Chris Crutcher. 2009. (Library of Author Biographies Ser.). 112p. (gr. 5-8). 63.90 (978-1-60853-528-6(2), Rosen Central) Rosen Publishing Group, Inc., The.

—J. D. Salinger. 2009. (Library of Author Biographies Ser.). 112p. (gr. 5-8). 63.90 (978-1-60853-535-4(5), Rosen Central) Rosen Publishing Group, Inc., The.

Sontag, Susan. As Consciousness Is Harnessed to Flesh: Journals & Notebooks, 1963-1980, 1 vol. Rieff, David, ed. 2012. (ENG.). 544p. 30.00 (978-0-374-10076-6(4)) Farrar, Straus & Giroux.

Sontag, Susan & Rieff, David. Reborn: Journals & Notebooks, 1947 — 1963. 2009. (ENG.). 336p. pap. 15.00 (978-0-312-42850-1(2)) Picador.

Souhami, Diana. Gertrude & Alice. 2009. (ENG., Illus.). 304p. pap. 20.00 (978-1-84885-148-1(0)) I. B. Tauris & Co., Ltd. GBR. Dist: Macmillan.

Spelman, Cornelia Maude. Missing: A Memoir. 2010. (ENG., Illus.). 176p. 22.95 (978-0-8101-2712-8(1)) Northwestern Univ. Pr.

Spence, James R. Watering the Sahara: Recollections of Paul Green from 1894 To 1937. Bauer, Margaret D., ed. 2008. (Illus.). 260p. pap. 15.00 (978-0-86526-333-8(7)) North Carolina Office of Archives & History.

Spitz, Bob. Dearie: The Remarkable Life of Julia Child. 2012. (ENG., Illus.). 560p. 28.95 (978-0-307-27222-5(2), Knopf) Knopf Doubleday Publishing Group.

Spring, Albert. M. E. Kerr. 2009. (Library of Author Biographies Ser.). 112p. (gr. 5-8). 63.90 (978-1-60853-546-0(0), Rosen Central) Rosen Publishing Group, Inc., The.

Spring, Justin. Secret Historian: The Life & Times of Samuel Steward, Professor, Tattoo Artist, & Sexual Renegade. 2011. (ENG., Illus.). 496p. pap. 18.00 (978-0-374-53302-1(4)) Farrar, Straus & Giroux.

Spurling, Hilary. Pearl Buck in China: Journey to the Good Earth. 2011. (ENG.). 320p. pap. 15.00 (978-1-4165-4043-4(1)) Simon & Schuster.

Squier, Susan Merrill. Virginia Woolf & London: The Sexual Politics of the City. 2011. (ENG.). 232p. pap. 40.00 (978-0-8078-6596-5(6)) Univ. of North Carolina Pr.

Stallings, Billee J. & Evans, Jo-an J. Murray Leinster: The Life & Works. 2011. (ENG., Illus.). 227p. pap. 40.00 (978-0-7864-6504-0(2)) McFarland & Co., Inc. Pubs.

Stambuk, Andrew. The Man Who Is & Is Not There: The Poetry & Prose of Robert Francis. 2011. 184p. lib. bdg. 80.00 (978-1-55849-897-6(4)) Univ. of Massachusetts Pr.

—The Man Who Is & Is Not There: The Poetry & Prose of Robert Francis. 2011. 184p. pap. 24.95 (978-1-55849-898-3(2)) Univ. of Massachusetts Pr.

Stancliff, Michael. Frances Ellen Watkins Harper: African American Reform Rhetoric & the Rise of a Modern Nation State. 2010. (Studies in American Popular History & Culture Ser.). (ENG., Illus.). 220p. 125.00 (978-0-415-99763-8(1)) Routledge.

Stanish, Marjorie. Cooking down East, 2nd Edition: Favorite Maine Recipes, with New Recipe Notes by Top Maine Chefs. 2nd ed. 2010. (ENG.). 254p. 27.95 (978-0-89272-913-5(9)) Down East Bks.

Stavans, Ilan & Albin, Verónica. Knowledge & Censorship. 2008. (ENG.). 192p. 53.00 (978-1-4039-8410-4(7)) Palgrave Macmillan.

Stearns, Frank Preston. The Life & Genius of Nathaniel Hawthorne. 2008. 336p. 29.99 (978-0-554-22374-2(0)) 2008. 336p. 28.99 (978-0-554-31677-2(3)) 2007. (ENG.). 312p. pap. 23.99 (978-1-4264-2167-9(2)) BiblioBazaar.

—The Life & Genius of Nathaniel Hawthorne. 2008. pap. (978-1-4065-7521-7(6)) Dodo Pr.

—Life & Genius of Nathaniel Hawthorne. 2006. pap. (978-1-4068-3014-9(3)) Echo Library.

—The Life & Genius of Nathaniel Hawthorne. Lt. ed. 2006. 334p. pap. 24.99 (978-1-4264-2235-5(0)) BiblioBazaar.

Stedman, Edmund Clarence. Edgar Allan Poe. 2009. 100p. pap. 18.75 (978-1-110-44237-9(8)) BiblioBazaar.

—Edgar Allan Poe. 2007. (ENG.). 108p. 34.95 (978-0-548-20722-2(4)); per. 19.95 (978-1-4325-2530-9(1)) Kessinger Publishing, LLC.

—Edgar Allan Poe. 2008. 100p. pap. (978-1-4097-1213-8(3)); (ENG.). 96p. per. (978-1-4086-4506-2(8)) Read Bks.

Stegner, Wallace. The Selected Letters of Wallace Stegner. Stegner, Page, ed. 2008. (ENG.). 480p. pap. 16.95 (978-1-58243-446-9(8), Counterpoint Pr.) Basic Bks. GBR. Dist: Perseus-PGW.

Stein, Gertrude & Picasso, Pablo. Correspondence: Pablo Picasso & Gertrude Stein. Madeline, Laurence, ed. Fox, Lorna Scott, tr. from FRE. 2008. (SB-the French List Ser.). (ENG., Illus.). 390p. 29.95 (978-1-905422-91-3(1)) Seagull Bks. GBR. Dist: Chicago Distribution Ctr.

Stein, Harry. I Can't Believe I'm Sitting Next to a Republican: A Survival Guide for Conservatives Marooned among the Angry, Smug, & Terminally Self-Righteous. (ENG.). 2010. 224p. pap. 15.95 (978-1-59403-480-0(X)) 2009. (Illus.). 250p. 25.95 (978-1-59403-253-0(X)) Encounter Bks.

Steinbeck, John. Travels with Charley in Search of America: (Penguin Classics Deluxe Edition) 2012. (Penguin Classics Deluxe Edition Ser.). (ENG.). 240p. (gr. 12). pap. 16.00 (978-0-14-310700-2(3), Penguin Classics) Penguin Group (USA) Inc.

Stern, Gerald. Stealing History. 2012. (ENG.). 224p. 24.95 (978-1-59534-114-3(5)) Trinity Univ. Pr.

Stern, Gerald. What I Can't Bear Losing. 2009. (ENG.). 350p. pap. 17.95 (978-1-59534-054-2(8)) Trinity Univ. Pr.

Stevens, Janice. William Saroyan: Places in Time. 2008. (ENG.). 86p. 26.95 (978-1-933502-24-3(X), Craven Street Bks.) Linden Publishing Co., Inc.

Stevens, Jen & Salo, Dorothea. Fantasy Authors: A Research Guide, 1 vol. 2008. (Author Research Ser.). (Illus.). 268p. pap. 45.00 (978-1-59158-497-1(3), LU4973) Libraries Unlimited, Inc.

Stier, Wayne. Stars When the Sun Shines: A Memoir. 2010. (ENG.). 1p. pap. 18.95 (978-1-57863-473-6(3), Weiser Bks.) Red Wheel/Weiser.

Still, James & Olson, Ted. James Still in Interviews, Oral Histories & Memoirs. Olson, Ted, ed. 2009. (Contributions to Southern Appalachian Studies). (ENG., Illus.). 320p. pap. 39.95 (978-0-7864-3698-9(0)) McFarland & Co., Inc. Pubs.

Stites, Alfred. Forget the Goal, the Journey Counts — 71 Jobs Later. 2010. (Illus.). viii, 216p. pap. (978-1-933455-26-6(8)) M S I Pr.

Stoneham, Michael. John Brown & the Era of Literary Confrontation. 2009. (Studies in American Popular History & Culture Ser.). (ENG.). 240p. 125.00 (978-0-415-99682-2(1)) Routledge.

Stouffer, Tere & CliffsNotes Staff. CliffsNotes on Sparks' A Walk to Remember. 2009. (ENG.). 72p. pap. 5.99 (978-0-470-46022-1(9), Cliff Notes) Wiley, John & Sons, Inc.

Stouffer, Tere & Wasowski, Richard P. On Nicholas Sparks the Notebook. 2009. (ENG.). 72p. pap. 5.99 (978-0-470-46009-2(1), Cliff Notes) Wiley, John & Sons, Inc.

Stover, Arthur Douglas. Eminent Mainers: Succint Biographies of Thousands of Amazing Mainers, Mostly Dead, & a Few People from Away Who Have Done Something Useful Within the State of Maine. 2010. (Illus.). 531p. per. 20.00 (978-0-88448-285-7(5)) Tilbury Hse. Pubs.

Stowe, Harriet Beecher. Palmetto Leaves. 2009. (ENG., Illus.). 352p. pap. 19.95 (978-0-8130-3491-1(4)) Univ. Pr. of Florida.

—Stowe in Her Own Time: A Biographical Chronicle of Her Life, Drawn from Recollections, Interviews, & Memoirs by Family, Friends, & Associates. Belasco, Susan, ed. 2009. (Writers in Their Own Time Ser.). (ENG., Illus.). 332p. pap. 27.95 (978-1-58729-782-3(5)) Univ. of Iowa Pr.

Stratton-Porter, Gene. Gene Stratton-Porter: A Little Story of the Life & Work & Ideals of the Bird Woman. Egerton, Sarah Fyge, ed. 2011. 58p. 36.95 (978-1-258-02464-2(0)) Literary Licensing, LLC.

Strauss, Darin. Half a Life: A Memoir. 2011. (ENG.). 224p. pap. 13.00 (978-0-8129-8253-4(3), Random Hse. Trade Paperbacks) Random House Publishing Group.

Strom, Robert. Lady of Burlesque: The Career of Gypsy Rose Lee. 2011. (ENG., Illus.). 243p. pap. 39.95 (978-0-7864-3826-6(6)) McFarland & Co., Inc. Pubs.

Stuart, Jesse. The Thread That Runs So True. 24.95 (978-0-8488-0638-5(7)) Amereon LTD.

—The Thread That Runs So True. 2006. (Illus.). 331p. (978-1-931672-42-9(3)) Stuart, Jesse Foundation, The.

Stuhr, Rebecca. Reading Khaled Hosseini, 1 vol. 2009. (Pop Lit Book Club Ser.). 160p. 35.00 (978-0-313-35511-0(8), GR5511) Greenwood Publishing Group, Inc.

Styron, William. Letters to My Father. West, James L. W., III, ed. 2009. (Southern Literary Studies). (Illus.). 256p. 28.00 (978-0-8071-3400-9(7)) Louisiana State Univ. Pr.

Sumner, Gregory D. Unstuck in Time: A Journey Through Kurt Vonnegut's Life & Novels. 2011. (ENG., Illus.). 368p. 24.95 (978-1-60980-349-0(3)) Seven Stories Pr.

Suter, John Wallace. Life & Letters of William Reed Huntington: A Champion of Unity. 2011. 590p. 64.95 (978-1-258-03620-1(7)) Literary Licensing, LLC.

Swados, Elizabeth. Waiting: Selected Nonfiction. 2011. 200p. pap. 19.00 (978-1-934909-21-8(1)) Hanging Loose Pr.

Swan, Alison, ed. Fresh Water: Women Writing on the Great Lakes. 2006. (ENG.). 256p. per. 26.95 (978-0-87013-789-1(1)) Michigan State Univ. Pr.

Swaney, Alexandra & Newby, Rick, eds. Notes for a Novel: The Selected Poems of Frieda Fligelman. 2008. (Illus.). 240p. pap. 15.95 (978-0-9769684-1-2(X)) Drumlummon Institute.

Swift, Rebecca. Poetic Lives: Dickinson. 2011. (Poetic Lives Ser.). (ENG.). 160p. pap. 12.95 (978-1-84391-306-1(2)) Hesperus Pr. GBR. Dist: Independent Pubs. Group.

Swirski, Peter. Ars Americana, Ars Politica: Partisan Expression in Contemporary American Literature & Culture. 2010. (ENG.). 221p. (C). (978-0-7735-3765-1(1)); pap. (978-0-7735-3766-8(X)) McGill-Queen's Univ. Pr.

Swist, Wally. The Friendship of Two New England Poets: Robert Frost & Robert Francis. 2009. (Illus.). viii, 65p. (978-0-7734-3899-6(8)) Mellen, Edwin Pr., The.

Swofford, Anthony. Hotels, Hospitals, & Jails: A Memoir. 2012. (ENG.). 300p. 26.99 (978-1-4555-0673-6(7)); 384p. 28.99 (978-1-4555-1351-2(2)) Grand Central Publishing. (Twelve).

Taber, Gladys. The Book of Stillmeadow. reprint ed. lib. bdg. 23.95 (978-0-89190-593-6(6), Rivercity Pr.) Amereon LTD.

Taber, Gladys Bagg. Harvest of Yesterdays. 21.95 (978-0-8488-1190-7(9)) Amereon LTD.

Tarte, Bob. Fowl Weather. 2007. (ENG.). 306p. 23.95 (978-1-56512-502-5(9), 1565125029) Algonquin Bks. of Chapel Hill.

Taylor, Andrew. Thinking America: New England Intellectuals & the Varieties of American Identity. (Becoming Modern: New Nineteenth-Century Studies). 244p. 2011. pap. 29.95 (978-1-58465-863-4(0)) 2010. (ENG.). 55.00 (978-1-58465-862-7(2), University of New Hampshire Press) Univ. Pr. of New England.

Tea, Michelle. The Chelsea Whistle: A Memoir. 2nd ed. 2008. (ENG.). 384p. pap. 18.00 (978-1-58005-239-9(3)) Seal Pr.

Terkel, Studs. P. S. Further Thoughts from a Lifetime of Listening. 2008. (ENG.). 230p. pap. 16.95 (978-1-59558-423-6(4)) New Pr., The.

—Touch & Go: A Memoir. 2008. (ENG., Illus.). 269p. pap. 17.95 (978-1-59558-411-3(0)) New Pr., The.

Terry, Amos Moses. Scuttlebutts & Notions. 2007. 204p. 25.95 (978-1-59824-429-8(9)); per. 12.95 (978-1-59824-430-4(2)) E-BookTime LLC.

Thaxter, Celia. Among the Isles of Shoals by Celia Thaxter. 2006. 196p. per. 18.99 (978-1-4255-1591-1(6)) MPublishing.

—Letters of Celia Thaxter. 2009. 276p. 24.99 (978-1-103-31949-7(3)) 2009. 268p. 24.99 (978-1-103-32684-6(8)) 2009. 276p. pap. 18.99 (978-1-103-31947-3(7)) 2009. 268p. pap. 18.99 (978-1-103-32679-2(1)) 2008. 272p. 25.99 (978-0-559-27779-5(2)) 2008. 272p. pap. 26.75 (978-0-559-27776-4(8)) BiblioBazaar.

—Letters of Celia Thaxter. 2007. (ENG.). 264p. 42.95 (978-0-548-15623-0(9)); pap. 27.95 (978-1-4304-5086-3(X)) Kessinger Publishing, LLC.

—Letters of Celia Thaxter. 2008. 272p. pap. (978-1-4097-3055-2(7)) Read Bks.

The Jenna Fox. The Curious Case of the Jenna Fox: It's Jenna from your Block, (Poor, but RICH Inside) 2011. 144p. pap. 24.95 (978-1-4560-9596-3(X)) PublishAmerica, Inc.

Theroux, Phyllis. The Journal Keeper: A Memoir. (ENG.). 2011. 304p. pap. 14.95 (978-0-8021-4528-4(0), Grove Pr.) 2010. 305p. 24.00 (978-0-8021-1897-4(6), Atlantic Monthly Pr.) Grove/Atlantic, Inc.

Thesing, William B. Reading, Learning, Teaching James Dickey. 2008. (Confronting the Text, Confronting the World Ser.). 176p. (C). 32.95 (978-0-8204-8177-7(7)) Lang, Peter Publishing, Inc.

Thiebaud, Twinka. What Doncha Know? about Henry Miller. 2nd ed. 2011. (Illus.). 103p. pap. 12.95 (978-0-9759255-2-0(0)) Eio Bks.

Thomas, Abigail. A Three Dog Life. 2006. (ENG.). 192p. 22.00 (978-0-15-101211-4(3)) Houghton Mifflin Harcourt Trade & Reference Pubs.

—A Three Dog Life. rev. Lt. ed. 2007. (Thorndike Biography Ser.). 203p. 30.95 (978-0-7862-9369-8(1)) Thorndike Pr.

—A Three Dog Life: A Memoir. 2007. (ENG.). 208p. pap. 13.00 (978-0-15-603323-7(2), Mariner Bks.) Houghton Mifflin Harcourt Trade & Reference Pubs.

Thomas Fensch. Behind Islands in the Stream: Hemingway, Cuba, the FBI & the crook Factory. 2010. 148p. 22.95 (978-1-4502-0601-3(8)); pap. 12.95 (978-1-4502-0170-4(9)) iUniverse, Inc.

Thomas, Graham A. The Dan Brown Enigma (Nt) 2011. (ENG., Illus.). 304p. 24.95 (978-1-84358-302-8(X)) Blake, John Publishing, Ltd. GBR. Dist: Independent Pubs. Group.

Thomas, Josephine Lehman. Fisherman's Wife. 2008. (Illus.). 54p. pap. 15.95 (978-1-59322-040-2(5)) Down The Shore Publishing.

Thomas Paine. The Age of Reason - Thomas Paine. Moncure Daniel Conway, ed. 2010. 180p. pap. 4.95 (978-1-60386-341-4(9), Merchant Bks.) Rough Draft Printing.

Thompson, Anita, ed. Ancient Gonzo Wisdom: Interviews with Hunter S. Thompson. 2009. (ENG.). 432p. pap. 18.00 (978-0-306-81651-2(2)) Perseus Bks. Group.

Thompson, Elizabeth. Day by Day: The Chronicles of a Hard of Hearing Reporter. 2008. (978-1-56368-391-6(1)) Gallaudet Univ. Pr.

Thompson, Hunter S. Gonzo. Crist, Steve, ed. 2009. (ENG., Illus.). 240p. 19.95 (978-1-934429-44-0(9)) AMMO Bks., LLC.

Thomson Gale, creator. Contemporary Authors, Vol. 151. 2006. (Contemporary Authors New Revision Ser.). (ENG.). 448p. 293.00 (978-0-7876-7905-7(4)) Cengage Gale.

—Contemporary Authors New Revision: Volume 152, Vol. 152. 2006. (Contemporary Authors New Revision Ser.). (ENG.). 464p. 293.00 (978-0-7876-7906-4(2)) Cengage Gale.

Thoreau, Henry David. The Journal, 1837-1861. Searls, Damion, ed. 2009. (ENG., Illus.). 704p. pap. 22.95 (978-1-59017-321-3(X), NYRB Classics) New York Review of Bks., Inc., The.

—Letters to Various Persons. 2009. 108p. pap. (978-1-150-35644-5(8)) Books LLC.

—Letters to Various Persons. 236p. 2008. 41.95 (978-0-548-92105-0(9)) 2007. (ENG.). per. 26.95 (978-0-548-57059-3(0)) Kessinger Publishing, LLC.

—Letters to Various Persons. 2008. 240p. pap. (978-1-4437-1185-2(3)) Read Bks.

—Of Woodland Pools, Spring-Holes & Ditches: Excerpts from the Journal of Henry David Thoreau. 2010. (ENG.). 112p. 25.00 (978-1-58243-575-6(8), Counterpoint Pr.) Basic Bks. GBR. Dist: Perseus-PGW.

—Walden. 2011. (ENG.). 304p. pap. 18.00 (978-0-88146-231-9(4)) Mercer Univ. Pr.

—Walden & Civil Disobedience. 2012. (ENG.). 336p. (gr. 12). 5.95 (978-0-451-53216-9(3), Signet Classics) Penguin Group (USA) Inc.

—Walden, Civil Disobedience, & Other Writings. Rossi, William, ed. 3rd ed. 2008. (Norton Critical Editions Ser.). (ENG., Illus.). 688p. (C). per. 13.00 (978-0-393-93090-0(4), 93090) Norton, W. W. & Co., Inc.

—Walden or, Life in the Woods. 2007. (Illus.). 522p. 9.99 (978-0-7858-2222-6(4), Castle Bks., Inc.) Book Sales, Inc.

—Walden; or, Life in the Woods: Bold-faced Ideas for Living a Truly Transcendent Life. Ross, Laura, ed. 2009. (ENG., Illus.). 448p. 12.95 (978-1-4027-6667-1(X), Sterling Innovation) Sterling Publishing Co., Inc.

Thoreau, Henry David & Tobyne, Dan. Thoreau's Maine Woods. 2010. (ENG.). 128p. 35.00 (978-0-89272-814-5(0)) Down East Bks.

Thorndike, John. The Last of His Mind: A Year in the Shadow of Alzheimer's. (ENG., 2011. Illus.). 256p. pap. 14.95 (978-0-8040-1136-5(2)) 2009. 248p. 24.95 (978-0-8040-1122-8(2)) Swallow Pr.

Ticknor, Caroline. Glimpses of Authors. 2009. (ENG.). 380p. 38.99 (978-1-117-34277-1(8)); pap. 32.75 (978-1-117-34278-8(6)) BiblioBazaar.

—Glimpses of Authors. 2009. 212p. pap. 19.99 (978-0-217-48504-3(9)) General Bks. LLC.

—Glimpses of Authors. 2008. 380p. 48.95 (978-1-4369-8726-4(1)); pap. 33.95 (978-1-4368-5947-9(6)) Kessinger Publishing, LLC.

Tidwell, John Edgar & Ragar, Cheryl R., eds. Montage of a Dream: The Art & Life of Langston Hughes. 2007. (ENG.). 376p. (C). 44.95 (978-0-8262-1716-5(8)) Univ. of Missouri Pr.

Tietchen, Todd F. The Cubalogues. 2010. (ENG., Illus.). 192p. 29.95 (978-0-8130-3520-8(1)) Univ. Pr. of Florida.

Timrod, Henry. The Essays of Henry Timrod. Parks, Edd Winfield, ed. 2007. (ENG.). 192p. per. 22.95 (978-0-8203-3146-1(5)) Univ. of Georgia Pr.

Tindall. Wallace Stevens-Aw V11. 2009. pap. 25.00 (978-0-8166-0243-8(3)) Univ. of Minnesota Pr.

Tirone Smith, Mary-Ann. Girls of Tender Age: A Memoir. 2007. (ENG., Illus.). 320p. pap. 19.99 (978-0-7432-7978-9(6), Free Pr.) Free Pr.

Tolstoy, Leo. Last Steps: The Late Writings of Leo Tolstoy. Parini, Jay, ed. & tr. by. from RUS. 2009. (ENG.). 256p. (gr. 12-18). pap. 14.00 (978-0-14-119119-5(8), Penguin Classics) Penguin Group (USA) Inc.

Tooze, George, ed. The Life & Letters of Emily Chubbuck Judson: January 1848 - September 1851. 2010. (Baptists Ser.). 700p. 60.00 (978-0-88146-189-3(X)) Mercer Univ. Pr.

Tooze, George H. The Life & Letters of Emily Chubbic Judson: Volume 1. 2009. 304p. 60.00 (978-0-88146-131-2(8)) Mercer Univ. Pr.

—The Life & Letters of Emily Chubbic Judson: Volume 2. 2009. (Illus.). 304p. 60.00 (978-0-88146-149-7(0)) Mercer Univ. Pr.

Torres, Hector A. Conversations with Contemporary Chicana & Chicano Writers. 2007. (ENG.). 367p. pap. 29.95 (978-0-8263-4088-7(1)) Univ. of New Mexico Pr.

Torrey, Beef, ed. Conversations with Thomas Mcguane. 2006. (ENG.). 214p. 50.00 (978-1-57806-886-9(X)); per. 22.00 (978-1-57806-887-6(8)) Univ. Pr. of Mississippi.

Torrey, Beef & Simonson, Kevin, eds. Conversations with Hunter S. Thompson. 2008. (ENG.). 240p. 50.00 (978-1-934110-76-8(0)) Univ. Pr. of Mississippi.

Torrey, Beef, et al. Conversations with Hunter S. Thompson. Torrey, Beef & Simonson, Kevin, eds. 2008. (ENG.). 240p. pap. 22.00 (978-1-934110-77-5(9)) Univ. Pr. of Mississippi.

Toruno, et al. Cita con la Memoria: Elena Garro Cuenta Su Vida a Rhina Toruño. (SPA.). 118p. (978-987-20648-6-0(5)) Prueba de Galera, Ediciones.

Toruño-Haensly, Rhina. Crossing Cultures: Hispanic Authors & the Challenges They Overcame in the United States = Cruzando Culturas: Autores Hispanos y Sus Desafíos Superados en Los Estados Unidos. 2011. (Currents in Comparative Romance Languages & Literatures Ser.). (SPA & ENG., Illus.). 214p. (C). 76.95 (978-1-4331-1253-9(1)) Lang, Peter Publishing, Inc.

Townsend, J. W. Kentucky in American Letters Set, 2 vols. reprint ed. lib. bdg. 250.00 (978-0-7222-4941-3(1)) Library Reprints, Inc.

Tracy, Kathleen. Judy Blume: A Biography, 1 vol. 2007. (Greenwood Biographies Ser.). (Illus.). 152p. (gr. 4-8). 35.00 (978-0-313-34272-1(5), GR4272, Greenwood Pr.) Greenwood Publishing Group, Inc.

Trigiani, Adriana. Don't Sing at the Table: Life Lessons from My Grandmothers. 2011. (ENG.). 224p. pap. 13.99 (978-0-06-195895-3(6), Harper Paperbacks) HarperCollins Pubs.

Trollope, Anthony. An Autobiography. 2009. 236p. 28.99 (978-1-110-54577-3(0)); pap. 25.75 (978-1-110-54574-2(6)); 23.99 (978-1-103-50382-7(0)); pap. 17.99 (978-1-103-50380-3(4)); 23.99 (978-1-103-41222-8(1)); pap. 17.99 (978-1-103-41219-8(1)) BiblioBazaar.

—An Autobiography. 2009. 104p. pap. (978-0-217-16556-3(7)); 98p. pap. (978-0-217-81006-7(3)) Books LLC.

—An Autobiography. 2009. (Oxford World's Classics Ser.). (ENG.). 448p. 11.95 (978-0-19-953764-8(X), Oxford Univ. Pr., Inc.

Trollope, Anthony & Trollope, Henry Merivale. An Autobiography. 2009. 276p. 30.99 (978-1-115-80423-3(5)); 34.99 (978-1-115-80422-6(7)); pap. 27.75 (978-1-115-80424-0(3)); pap. 26.75 (978-1-115-80425-7(1)) BiblioBazaar.

Trombley, Laura Skandera. Mark Twain's Other Woman: The Hidden Story of His Final Years. 2011. (Vintage Ser.). 352p. pap. 16.95 (978-0-307-47494-0(1), Vintage) Knopf Doubleday Publishing Group.

Troncoso, Sergio. Crossing Borders: Personal Essays. 2011. pap. 16.95 (978-1-55885-710-0(9)) Arte Publico Pr.

Trouard, Dawn, ed. Conversations with Ann Beattie. 2006. (ENG., Illus.). 190p. 50.00 (978-1-57806-922-4(X)); per. 22.00 (978-1-57806-923-1(8)) Univ. Pr. of Mississippi.

Trubek, Anne. A Skeptic's Guide to Writers' Houses. 2010. (Illus.). 176p. 24.95 (978-0-8122-4292-8(0)) Univ. of Pennsylvania Pr.

Turco, Lewis. La Famigli: The Family. 2009. 200p. pap. 12.00 (978-1-59954-006-1(1)) Bordighera Incorporated.

Twain, Mark, pseud. Autobiographical Writings. Rasmussen, R. Kent, ed. & intro. by. 2012. (ENG.). 544p. (gr. 12). pap. 16.00 (978-0-14-310667-8(8), Penguin Classics) Penguin Group (USA) Inc.

—Autobiography of Mark Twain, Vol. 1. Smith, Harriet E., ed. 2012. (ENG.). 440p. pap. 26.95 (978-0-520-27225-5(0)) Univ. of California Pr.

—Chapters from My Autobiography. 2011. 274p. (978-1-84902-343-6(3)) Benediction Classics.

—Chapters from My Autobiography. 2010. (Illus.). 184p. pap. 26.90 (978-1-153-75056-1(2)) General Bks. LLC.

—Life on the Mississippi. 2012. (ENG., Illus.). 576p. 19.95 (978-0-486-48917-9(5)) Dover Pubns., Inc.

Twain, Mark, pseud. Mark Twain: The Complete Interviews. Scharnhorst, Gary, ed. 2006. (Studies in American Literary Realism & Naturalism). (Illus.). 768p. 75.00 (978-0-8173-1522-1(5)) Univ. of Alabama Pr.

Twain, Mark, pseud & Scharnhorst, Gary. Mainly the Truth: Interviews with Mark Twain. 2009. (Amer Lit Realism & Naturalism Ser.). (ENG., Illus.). 344p. pap. 24.95 (978-0-8173-5539-5(1)) Univ. of Alabama Pr.

Tyler, Moses Coit. Three Men of Letters. 2009. 210p. 32.99 (978-1-117-02741-8(4)) 2008. 212p. 24.99 (978-0-559-80415-1(6)) 2008. 212p. pap. 23.75 (978-0-559-80412-0(1)) BiblioBazaar.

—Three Men of Letters. 2009. 190p. pap. (978-0-217-30638-6(1)) Books LLC.

—Three Men of Letters. (ENG.). 2007. 212p. 39.95 (978-0-548-12621-9(6)) 2006. pap. 24.95 (978-1-4286-3603-3(X)) Kessinger Publishing, LLC.

Underwood, Doug. Chronicling Trauma: Journalists & Writers on Violence & Loss. 2011. (History of Communication Ser.). (ENG., Illus.). 264p. 50.00 (978-0-252-03640-8(9)) Univ. of Illinois Pr.

Unrue, Darlene Harbour. Katherine Anne Porter Remembered. 2010. (American Writers Remembered Ser.). (ENG., Illus.). 336p. 45.00 (978-0-8173-1667-9(1)); (978-0-8173-8458-6(8)) Univ. of Alabama Pr.

Updike, John. Self-Consciousness: Memoirs. 2012. (ENG.). 272p. pap. 16.00 (978-0-8129-8296-1(7), Random Hse. Trade Paperbacks) Random House Publishing Group.

Valcarcel, Emilio Diaz, ed. En el Mejor de los Mundos. 235p. pap. 12.95 (978-1-56758-004-4(1)) Editorial Cultural, Inc.

Valerio, Anthony. Toni Cade Bambarra's On Sicilian Night. 2007. 87p. pap. 10.00 (978-1-884419-84-3(4)) Bordighera Incorporated.

Van Doren, Carl. Contemporary American Novelists. 2008. 140p. 21.99 (978-0-554-35184-1(6)); 24.99 (978-0-554-25881-2(1)) BiblioBazaar.

—Contemporary American Novelists. 2007. (ENG.). 88p. per. (978-1-4068-2593-0(X)) Echo Library.

—Contemporary American Novelists, 1900-1920. 2009. 126p. pap. (978-1-4099-8753-6(1)) Dodo Pr.

—Contemporary American Novelists, 1900-1920. 2008. (ENG.). 192p. per. (978-1-4086-4419-5(3)) Read Bks.

Van Dyke, Henry. Out-of-Doors in the Holy Land. 2007. (ENG.). 312p. 35.00 (978-1-4344-8995-1(7)); pap. 19.95 (978-1-4344-8994-4(9)) Wildside Pr., LLC.

Van Ghent. Willa Cather-Aw V36. 2009. (ENG.). 48p. pap. 25.00 (978-0-8166-0321-3(9)) Univ. of Minnesota Pr.

Van Meter, Ryan. If You Knew Then What I Know Now. 2011. (ENG.). 176p. pap. 15.95 (978-1-932511-94-9(6)) Sarabande Bks., Inc.

Van Vechten, Carl. The Splendid Drunken Twenties: Selections from the Daybooks, 1922-1930. Kellner, Bruce, ed. 2007. (Illus.). 384p. per. 21.00 (978-0-252-07462-2(9)) Univ. of Illinois Pr.

VanLiere, Donna. Finding Grace: A True Story about Losing Your Way in Life... & Finding It Again. 2009. (ENG.). 224p. 21.95 (978-0-312-38051-9(8)) St. Martin's Pr.

Varner, Paul. Historical Dictionary of the Beat Movement. 2012. (Historical Dictionaries of Literature & the Arts Ser.). (ENG.). 400p. 95.00 (978-0-8108-7189-2(0)) Scarecrow Pr., Inc.

Vaughan, David K. Words to Measure a War: Nine American Poets of World War II. 2009. (ENG.). 204p. pap. 35.00 (978-0-7864-4306-2(5)) McFarland & Co., Inc. Pubs.

Veevers-Carter, Wendy. Clarence Day: An American Writer. 2007. 460p. per. 28.95 (978-0-595-43165-6(8)) iUniverse, Inc.

Venable, W. H. CD: Beginnings of Literary Culture in the Ohio Valley, Historical & Biographical Sketches. 2007. cd-rom 19.95 (978-0-7884-2658-2(3)) Heritage Bks.

Vernon, Alex. Hemingway's Second War: Bearing Witness to the Spanish Civil War. 2011. (ENG.). 264p. pap. 29.95 (978-1-58729-981-0(X)) Univ. of Iowa Pr.

Vidal, Gore. Gore Vidal: Snapshots in History's Glare. 2009. (ENG., Illus.). 272p. 40.00 (978-0-8109-5049-8(9)) Abrams.

Villarreal, Rene & Martínez, Raúl. Hemingway's Cuban Son: Reflections on the Writer by His Longtime Majordomo. 2009. (Illus.). x, 157p. (978-0-87333-897-4(9)) Kent State Univ. Pr.

Villarreal, Rene & Villarreal, Raul. Hemingway's Cuban Son: Reflections on the Writer by His Longtime Majordomo. 2009. (Illus.). 224p. 24.95 (978-0-87338-977-8(8)) Kent State Univ. Pr.

Villasenor, Victor. Burro Genio. 2006. (SPA & ENG., Illus.). 336p. per. 13.95 (978-0-06-056683-8(3), Rayo) HarperCollins Pubs.

—Crazy Loco Love: A Memoir. 2010. (ENG., Illus.). 416p. pap. 16.00 (978-1-58270-272-8(1), Beyond Words/Atria Bks.) Atria Bks.

Villaseñor, Victor. Crazy Loco Love: A Memoir. 2010. E-Book (978-1-4391-9382-2(7)) Beyond Words Publishing, Inc.

—Wild Steps of Heaven: A Memoir. 2006. 304p. pap. 13.95 (978-0-06-113903-1(3), Rayo) HarperCollins Pubs.

Virtanen, Beth L. Finnish-North American Literature in English: A Concise Anthology. 2009. viii, 578p. (978-0-7734-3818-7(1)) Mellen, Edwin Pr., The.

Vivian, Robert. The Least Cricket of Evening. 2011. (ENG.). 208p. pap. 14.95 (978-0-8032-3431-4(7), Bison Bks.) Univ. of Nebraska Pr.

Vizenor, Gerald. Interior Landscapes: Autobiographical Myths & Metaphors. 2nd ed. 2009. (Illus.). 292p. pap. 29.95 (978-1-4384-2982-3(7), Suny Pr.) State Univ. of New York Pr.

Vonnegut, Kurt. A Man Without a Country. 2007. (KOR., Illus.). 143p. (978-89-546-0347-8(5)) Munhak Dongne Publishing Corp.

—A Man Without a Country. Simon, Daniel, ed. 2007. (ENG., Illus.). 160p. pap. 13.95 (978-0-8129-7736-3(X), Random Hse. Trade Paperbacks) Random House Publishing Group.

—A Man Without a Country. 2007. (CHI., Illus.). 153p. pap. (978-986-173-236-7(5)) Rye Field Publishing, Co.

Vonnegut, Kurt & Stringer, Lee. Like Shaking Hands with God: A Conversation about Writing. 2010. (ENG., Illus.). 80p. pap. 9.95 (978-1-60980-074-1(5)) Seven Stories Pr.

Wagner Buyer, Laurie & Buyer, Laurie Wagner. Spring's Edge: A Ranch Wife's Chronicles. 2008. (ENG., Illus.). 229p. pap. 19.95 (978-0-8263-4391-8(0)) Univ. of New Mexico Pr.

Wagner-Martin, Linda. Ernest Hemingway: A Literary Life. 2010. (Literary Lives Ser.). (ENG., Illus.). 216p. pap. 30.00 (978-0-230-27696-3(2)) Palgrave Macmillan.

Wagner, Rob & Politi, Paul Leo. Leo Politi: Capturing the Heart of Los Angeles. Calistro, Paddy, ed. 2008. (Illus.). 208p. 45.00 (978-1-883318-76-5(9)) Angel City Pr.

Wakefield, Dan. How Do We Know When It's God? A Spiritual Memoir. 2010. 270p. pap. 21.95 (978-0-9825214-5-8(6)) Beech River Bks.

Wald, Alan M. The Revolutionary Imagination: The Poetry & Politics of John Wheelwright & Sherry Mangan. 2011. (ENG.). 312p. pap. 40.00 (978-0-8078-6632-0(6)) Univ. of North Carolina Pr.

—Trinity of Passion: The Literary Left & the Antifascist Crusade. 2007. (ENG., Illus.). 344p. 38.95 (978-0-8078-3075-8(5)) Univ. of North Carolina Pr.

Walker, Alice. The Chicken Chronicles: Sitting with the Angels Who Have Returned with My Memories - Glorious, Rufus, Gertrude Stein, Splendor, Hortensia, Agnes of God, the Gladyses, & Babe - A Memoir. 2011. (ENG.). 208p. 21.95 (978-1-59558-645-2(8)) New Pr., The.

—World Has Changed: Conversations with Alice Walker. 2010. (ENG.). 368p. 25.95 (978-1-59558-496-0(X)) New Pr., The.

—The World Has Changed: Conversations with Alice Walker. Byrd, Rudolph P., ed. 2011. (ENG., Illus.). 368p. pap. 18.95 (978-1-59558-705-3(5)) New Pr., The.

Wallace, Rob. Improvisation & the Making of American Literary Modernism. (ENG.). 216p. 2012. pap. 44.95 (978-1-4411-1375-7(4)) 2010. 110.00 (978-1-4411-6946-4(6)) Continuum International Publishing Group, Ltd. GBR. Dist: National Bk. Network.

Wallach, Jennifer Jensen. Richard Wright: From Black Boy to World Citizen. 2010. (ENG.). 224p. 26.00 (978-1-56663-824-1(0)) Dee, Ivan R. Pub.

Walonen, Michael K. Writing Tangier in the Postcolonial Transition: Space & Power in Expatriate & North African Literature. 2011. (Illus.). 176p. 99.95 (978-1-4094-3381-1(1)) Ashgate Publishing Co.

Walsh, John Evangelist. Emily Dickinson in Love: The Case for Otis Lord. 2012. (ENG.). 216p. 25.00 (978-0-8135-5275-0(3)) Rutgers Univ. Pr.

Walsh, William J. Speak So I Shall Know Thee: Interviews with Southern Writers. alt. ed. 2012. (ENG.). 328p. pap. 25.00 (978-0-7864-6749-5(5)) McFarland & Co., Inc. Pubs.

Ward, Julius H. The Life & Letters of James Gates Percival. 2008. 598p. 59.95 (978-1-4365-4914-1(0)) 2007. (ENG.). 600p. per. 44.95 (978-0-548-69266-0(1)) Kessinger Publishing, LLC.

Ward, Robert. Understanding James Leo Herlihy. 2012. (Understanding Contemporary American Literature Ser.). (ENG.). 128p. 39.95 (978-1-61117-074-0(5)) Univ. of South Carolina Pr.

Warren, Colleen. Annie Dillard & the Word Made Flesh: An Incarnational Theory of Language. 2010. 39.50 (978-0-9823720-1-2(9)); (ENG.). 39.50 (978-1-61146-065-0(4)) Lehigh Univ. Pr.

Warren, Mercy Otis. Mercy Otis Warren: Selected Letters. Richards, Jeffrey H. & Harris, Sharon M., eds. 2009. (ENG., Illus.). 320p. lib. bdg. 44.95 (978-0-8203-2680-1(1)) Univ. of Georgia Pr.

Warren, Robert Penn. Sel Letters of Robt P Warren Vol 5: Backward Glances & New Visions, 1969-1979. Perkins, James A. & Hendricks, Randy, eds. 2011. (Southern Literary Studies). (Illus.). 632p. 90.00 (978-0-8071-3827-4(4)) Louisiana State Univ. Pr.

—Selected Letters of Robert Penn Warren; Volume Four: New Beginnings & New Directions, 1953-1968. Hendricks, Randy & Perkins, James A., eds. 2008. (Southern Literary Studies). 589p. 65.00 (978-0-8071-3300-2(0)) Louisiana State Univ. Pr.

Wasowski, Richard P. Cliffsnotes on Nicholas Sparks & Micah Sparts' Three Weeks with My Brother. 2011. (ENG., Illus.). 72p. pap. 5.99 (978-0-470-94573-5(7), Cliff Notes) Wiley, John & Sons, Inc.

—CliffsNotes on Nicholas Sparks' the Last Song. 2011. (ENG., Illus.). 96p. pap. 5.99 (978-0-470-94574-2(5), Cliff Notes) Wiley, John & Sons, Inc.

Watson, Jay, ed. Conversations with Larry Brown. 2007. (ENG.). 202p. 50.00 (978-1-57806-949-1(1)); (Illus.). per. 22.00 (978-1-57806-950-7(5)) Univ. Pr. of Mississippi.

Watson, Nicola J. Literary Tourism & Nineteenth-Century Culture. Watson, Nicola J., ed. 2009. (ENG.). 240p. 89.00 (978-0-230-22281-6(1)) Palgrave Macmillan.

Wayne, Tiffany K. Critical Companion to Ralph Waldo Emerson. 2010. (Critical Companion to Ser.). (Illus.). 456p. (C). (gr. 9-18). 75.00 (978-0-8160-7358-0(9)) Facts On File, Inc.

Webb, Jack, ed. The Best of Border Voices: Poet Laureates, Pulitzer Prize Winners & the Wisdom of Kids. 2007. (Illus.). 328p. 24.95 (978-1-933769-24-0(6)) Level 4 Press, Inc.

Weber, Katharine. The Memory of All That: George Gershwin, Kay Swift, & My Family's Legacy of Infidelities. 2012. (ENG.). 288p. pap. 14.00 (978-0-307-39589-4(8)) Broadway Bks.

—The Memory of All That: George Gershwin, Kay Swift, & My Family's Legacy of Infidelities. 2011. (Illus.). 288p. 24.00 (978-0-307-39588-7(X), Crown) Crown Publishing Group.

Weinstein, Philip. Becoming Faulkner: The Art & Life of William Faulkner, 1 vol. 2012. (ENG., Illus.). 272p. pap. 19.95 (978-0-19-989835-0(9)) Oxford Univ. Pr., Inc.

Weir, Theresa. The Orchard. 2011. (Memoir Ser.). 54.99 (978-1-61113-799-6(3), Sound Library) AudioGO.

—The Orchard: A Memoir. 2012. (ENG.). 256p. pap. 12.99 (978-0-446-58468-5(1)) Grand Central Publishing.

The Weird World of HP Lovecraft. 2008. 29.90 (978-1-60591-225-7(5)) Title Player, Inc.

Weller, Sam & Bradbury, Ray. Listen to the Echoes: The Ray Bradbury Interviews. 2010. (ENG., Illus.). 336p. pap. 18.95 (978-1-935554-03-5(4)) Melville Hse. Publishing.

Wetmore Jr, Kevin J. & Smith-Howard, Alycia, eds. Suzan-Lori Parks: A Casebook. 2012. (Casebooks on Modern Dramatists Ser.). (ENG.). 176p. pap. 42.95 (978-0-415-54226-5(X)) Routledge.

Wheatley, Christopher J. Thornton Wilder & Amos Wilder: Writing Religion in Twentieth-Century America. 2011. (ENG.). 232p. pap. 29.00 (978-0-268-04424-4(4)) Univ. of Notre Dame Pr.

Wheeler, Richard S. An Accidental Novelist: A Literary Memoir. 2007. (ENG.). 240p. 28.95 (978-0-86534-562-1(7)); per. 22.95 (978-0-86534-563-8(5)) Sunstone Pr.

White, Andrew Dickson. Autobiography of Andrew Dickson White. 2007. Vol. 1. 548p. pap. 30.99 (978-1-4346-1503-9(0)) Vol. 2. 564p. 30.99 (978-1-4346-1510-7(3)) BiblioBazaar.

—Autobiography of Andrew Dickson White Volume 2. l.t. ed. 2007. 622p. 33.99 (978-1-4346-1604-3(5)) BiblioBazaar.

White, E. B. Letters of E. B. White. Guth, Dorothy Lobrano, ed. 2007. (ENG.). 768p. pap. 19.95 (978-0-06-137459-3(8), HarperPerennial) HarperCollins Pubs.

White, Edmund. City Boy: My Life in New York During the 1960s & '70s. 2009. (ENG.). 304p. 26.00 (978-1-59691-402-5(5)) Bloomsbury Publishing.

—City Boy: My Life in New York During the 1960s & '70s. 2010. (ENG.). 304p. pap. 16.00 (978-1-60819-234-2(2)) Bloomsbury Publishing.

Whitley, Edward. American Bards: Walt Whitman & Other Unlikely Candidates for National Poet. 2010. (ENG., Illus.). 256p. 49.95 (978-0-8078-3421-3(1)) Univ. of North Carolina Pr.

Whitman, Walt. Letters Written by Walt Whitman to His Mother, 1866-1872. 2011. 78p. 37.95 (978-1-258-09499-7(1)) Literary Licensing, LLC.

—Memoranda During the War. 2009. (ENG.). 176p. pap. 13.00 (978-1-4379-6708-1(6)) DIANE Publishing Co.

—Memoranda During the War: Civil War Journals, 1863 — 1865. 2010. (ENG.). 112p. pap. 6.95 (978-0-486-47641-4(3)) Dover Pubns., Inc.

Whittemore, Reed. Against the Grain: The Literary Life of a Poet - A Memoir. 2007. (Illus.). 336p. 26.95 (978-1-928755-09-8(7)) Dryad Pr.

Wiater, Stanley, et al. The Twilight & Other Zones: The Dark Worlds of Richard Matheson. 2009. (ENG.). 352p. 19.95 (978-0-8065-3113-7(4), Citadel Pr.) Kensington Publishing Corp.

Wieczorek, Bryant. This Is Me! the True Spirit of American Youth. 2009. 92p. pap. 19.95 (978-0-615-14734-5(8)) Wieczorek, Bryant.

Wien, Harlan. From Nowhere I Came. 2007. 0.00 (978-0-9799705-0-4(4)) Wien's.

Wilber, Ken. The Pocket Ken Wilber. 2008. (Shambhala Pocket Classics Ser.). (ENG.). 192p. pap. 6.95 (978-1-59030-637-6(6)) Shambhala Pubns., Inc.

Willeford, Charles. I Was Looking for a Street. 2010. (ENG., Illus.). 154p. pap. 15.95 (978-0-9820947-7-8(9)) PictureBox, Inc.

Williams, Alfonsine. The Dreamer's Disease. 2011. 132p. pap. 24.95 (978-1-4626-1137-9(0)) PublishAmerica, Inc.

Williams, Hermine Weigel. Therese Von Jakob Robinson: A Biographical Portrait. 2007. 277p. (978-0-595-90010-7(0)) iUniverse, Inc.

Williams, John, ed. Dear Chester, Dear John: Letters Between Chester Hines & John A. Williams. 2008. 256p. 24.95 (978-0-8143-3359-4(1)) Wayne State Univ. Pr.

Williams, John A., ed. Dear Chester, Dear John: Letters Between Chester Hines & John A. Williams. 2008. (African American Life Ser.). (Illus.). 241p. 24.95 (978-0-8143-3355-6(9)) Wayne State Univ. Pr.

Williams, Susan Millar. A Devil & a Good Woman, Too: The Lives of Julia Peterkin. 2008. (ENG., Illus.). 392p. pap. 19.95 (978-0-8203-3250-5(X)) Univ. of Georgia Pr.

Williams, Terry Tempest. A Voice in the Wilderness: Conversations with Terry Tempest Williams. Austin, Michael, ed. 2006. (ENG., Illus.). 208p. per. 19.95 (978-0-87421-634-9(6), Utah State Univ. Pr.) Univ. Pr. of Colorado.

Williams, Terry Tempest & Thoreau, Henry David. Walden. 2008. (Shambhala Library). (ENG., Illus.). 496p. 18.95 (978-1-59030-638-3(4)) Shambhala Pubns., Inc.

Williamson, Eric. Say It Hot: Essays on American Writers Living, Dying, & Dead. 2011. (Illus.). 224p. pap. 24.95 (978-1-933896-38-0(8)) Texas Review Pr.

Williamson, Eric Miles. Oakland, Jack London, & Me. 2007. (ENG.). 224p. per. 24.95 (978-1-933896-11-3(6)) Texas Review Pr.

Wills, Maralys. A Circus Without Elephants: A Memoir. 2010. 288p. pap. 16.95 (978-1-57197-449-5(0), Ivy House Publishing Group) Pentland Pr., Inc.

Wilson, Edmund. Israel & the Dead Sea Scrolls. 2011. (ENG.). 440p. pap. 34.95 (978-1-4128-4248-8(4)) Transaction Pubs.

Wilson, James Grant. The Life & Letters of Fitz Greene Halleck. 2007. (ENG.). 610p. 59.95 (978-0-548-04847-4(9)) Kessinger Publishing, LLC.

—Life & Letters of FitzGreene Halleck. 2006. pap. 44.95 (978-1-4286-5311-5(2)) Kessinger Publishing, LLC.

Wilson, Reuel K. To the Life of the Silver Harbor: Edmund Wilson & Mary McCarthy on Cape Cod. 2008. (ENG., Illus.). 192p. 26.95 (978-1-58465-713-2(8)) Univ. Pr. of New England.

Wineapple, Brenda. White Heat: The Friendship of Emily Dickinson & Thomas Wentworth Higginson. 2009. (ENG., Illus.). 432p. pap. 18.00 (978-0-307-45630-4(7), Anchor) Knopf Doubleday Publishing Group.

Winter, William. The Life & Writings of William Law Symonds. 2009. 670p. 46.99 (978-1-116-69457-4(3)); 39.99 (978-1-116-69458-1(1)); pap. 46.75 (978-1-116-69460-4(3)); pap. 47.75 (978-1-116-69459-8(X)) BiblioBazaar.

Winters, Kathleen C. & Winters, Kathleen. Anne Morrow Lindbergh: First Lady of the Air. 2008. (ENG., Illus.). 256p. pap. 14.95 (978-0-230-60411-7(0)) Palgrave Macmillan.

Wise, Benjamin E. William Alexander Percy: The Curious Life of a Mississippi Planter & Sexual Freethinker. 2012. (ENG., Illus.). 368p. 35.00 (978-0-8078-3535-7(8)) Univ. of North Carolina Pr.

Witschi, Nicolas S. Alonzo "Old Block" Delano. 2006. 52p. (978-0-88430-169-1(9)) Boise State Univ. Western Writers Series.

Witschi, Nicolas S., ed. A Companion to the Literature & Culture of the American West. 2011. (Blackwell Companions to Literature & Culture Ser.: 129). (ENG., Illus.). 576p. 199.95 (978-1-4051-8733-6(6), Wiley-Blackwell) Wiley, John & Sons, Inc.

Woiwode, Larry. A Step from Death: A Memoir. 2009. (ENG.). 288p. pap. 15.95 (978-1-58243-469-8(7), Counterpoint Pr.) Basic Bks. GBR. Dist: Perseus-PGW.

Wolfe, Thomas. Windows of the Heart: The Correspondence of Thomas Wolfe & Margaret Roberts. 2007. (Illus.). 201p. 34.95 (978-1-57003-674-3(8)) Univ. of South Carolina Pr.

Wood, Monica. When We Were the Kennedys: A Memoir from Mexico, Maine. 2012. (ENG.). 256p. 24.00 (978-0-547-63014-4(X)) Houghton Mifflin Harcourt Trade & Reference Pubs.

Wood, Pamela. Charles Bukowski's Scarlet. 2010. (Illus.). 234p. pap. 15.95 (978-0-941543-58-3(7)) Sun Dog Pr.

Woodberry, George Edward. Selected Letters of George Edward Woodberry. 2011. 310p. 48.95 (978-1-258-04339-1(4)) Literary Licensing, LLC.

Wormser, Baron. The Road Washes Out in Spring: A Poet's Memoir of Living off the Grid. 2008. (ENG.). 212p. pap. 19.95 (978-1-58465-704-0(9)) Univ. Pr. of New England.

Worthen, John. T. S. Eliot. 2010. (ENG., Illus.). 240p. 25.00 (978-1-906598-35-8(5)) Haus Publishing GBR. Dist: Consortium Bk. Sales & Distribution.

Wriggins, Sally Hovey. Asia on My Mind: From Ceylon to the Silk Road. 2008. (Illus.). 284p. pap. 22.95 (978-1-4327-2180-0(1)) Outskirts Pr., Inc.

Wright, John Hardy. Hawthorne's Haunts in New England. 2008. pap. 19.99 (978-1-59629-425-7(6)) History Pr., The.

Writers of Modern America, Vol. 18. Date not set. 32.95 (978-0-8369-4809-7(2)) Ayer Co. Pubs., Inc.

Writers of the American Midwest: Anthology. 8.97 (978-0-13-050125-7(5)) Prentice Hall PTR.

Writers of the American Midwest Guide: Special Anthologies. 16.47 (978-0-13-050126-4(3)) Prentice Hall PTR.

Wyllie, Barbara. Vladimir Nabokov. 2010. (Reaktion Books - Critical Lives Ser.). (ENG., Illus.). 192p. pap. 16.95 (978-1-86189-660-5(3)) Reaktion Bks., Ltd. GBR. Dist: Chicago Distribution Ctr.

Yang, Belle. Forget Sorrow: An Ancestral Tale. 2010. (ENG., Illus.). 250p. 23.95 (978-0-393-06834-4(X), 6834) Norton, W. W. & Co., Inc.

Yoseloff, Martin. Remember Me to Marcie. 6.95 *(978-0-8453-7696-6(9)*, Cornwall Bks.) Associated Univ. Presses.
—A Time to Be Young. 4.50 *(978-0-8453-6445-1(6)*, Cornwall Bks.) Associated Univ. Presses.
Young, Phillip. 2 Much 2 Young. 2008. 144p. 26.50 *(978-1-4251-8476-6(6))* Trafford Publishing.
Young, Reggie Scott, et al. This Louisiana Thing That Drives Me: The Legacy of Ernest J. Gaines. 2009. (Illus.). 96p. 40.00 *(978-1-887366-83-0(0))* Univ. of Louisiana at Lafayette Pr.
Young, Thomas Daniel. Waking Their Neighbors Up: The Nashville Agrarians Rediscovered. 2010. (Mercer University Lamar Memorial Lectures). (ENG.). 106p. pap. 19.95 *(978-0-8203-3475-2(8))* Univ. of Georgia Pr.
Zackheim, Victoria. The Face in the Mirror: Writers Reflect on Their Dreams of Youth & the Reality of Age. Zackheim, Victoria, ed. 2009. (ENG., Illus.). 300p. 25.00 *(978-1-59102-752-2(7))* Prometheus Bks., Pubs.
Zimmerman, Anne. An Extravagant Hunger: The Passionate Years of M. F. K. Fisher. (ENG.). 352p. 2012. pap. 16.95 ***(978-1-58243-804-7(8))*** 2011. (Illus.). 26.00 *(978-1-58243-546-6(4))* Counterpoint LLC. (Counterpoint).
Zinsser, William. Writing Places: The Life Journey of a Writer & Teacher. 2010. (ENG.). 208p. pap. 14.99 *(978-0-06-172903-4(5)*, Harper Paperbacks) HarperCollins Pubs.
Zinsser, William K. Writing Places: The Life Journey of a Writer & Teacher. 2009. 208p. 22.99 *(978-0-06-172902-7(7))* HarperCollins Pubs.
Zlosnik, Sue. Patrick McGrath. 2011. (University of Wales Press - Gothic Authors: Critical Revisions Ser.). (ENG.). 154p. 85.00 *(978-0-7083-2375-5(8))*; pap. 25.00 *(978-0-7083-2374-8(X))* Univ. of Wales Pr. GBR. Dist: Chicago Distribution Ctr.
Zuiker, Anthony & Gold, Todd. Mr. Csi: How a Vegas Dreamer Made a Killing in Hollywood, One Body at a Time. 2011. (ENG.). 304p. 26.99 *(978-0-06-172549-4(8))* HarperCollins Pubs.
Zweig, Robert. Return to Naples. 2007. pap. 18.00 *(978-0-9763565-6-1(2))* Dusty Spark Publishing.

AUTHORS, AMERICAN—BIBLIOGRAPHY

Bloom, Harold, ed. Bloom's Modern Critical Interpretations. 2011. (Bloom's Modern Critical Interpretations Ser.). (C). (gr. 9). 4320.00 ***(978-0-7910-9982-7(2)***, Chelsea Hse.) Facts On File, Inc.
—Bloom's Modern Critical Views. 2011. (Bloom's Modern Critical Views Ser.). (C). (gr. 9). 4725.00 ***(978-0-7910-9990-2(3)***, Chelsea Hse.) Facts On File, Inc.
Bonner, John W., Jr. Bibliography of Georgia Authors, 1949-1965. 2010. (ENG.). 276p. pap. 24.95 *(978-0-8203-3526-1(6))* Univ. of Georgia Pr.
Burton, Patricia A. More Than Silence: A Bibliography of Thomas Merton. 2008. (ATLA Bibliography Ser.). (ENG.). 234p. 75.00 *(978-0-8108-6095-7(3))* Scarecrow Pr., Inc.
Coyne, Patrick. A Bio-Bibliography of Alice Duer Miller, American Writer, 1874-1942. 2010. (Illus.). 340p. 119.95 *(978-0-7734-3756-2(8))* Mellen, Edwin Pr., The.
Dominguez, Frank & Greenia, George D. Castilian Writers, 1200-1400. 2007. (Dictionary of Literary Biography Ser.: Vol. 337). (ENG.). 528p. 315.00 *(978-0-7876-8155-5(5))* Cengage Gale.
Gallup, Donald. Ts Eliot A Bibliography. 2006. 192p. per. *(978-1-4067-3211-5(7)*, Hesperides Pr.) Read Bks.
Joshi, S. T. H. L. Mencken: An Annotated Bibliography. annot. ed. 2009. (ENG.). 398p. 85.00 *(978-0-8108-6934-9(9))* Scarecrow Pr., Inc.
Kellman, Steven G., ed. Magill's Survey of American Literature, 6 vols., Set. rev. ed. 2006. (Illus.). 2866p. (YA). (gr. 9-18). lib. bdg. 499.00 *(978-1-58765-285-1(4))* Salem Pr., Inc.
Marks, Jeffrey. Anthony Boucher: A Biobibliography. 2008. (ENG & AFR., Illus.). 223p. per. 35.00 *(978-0-7864-3320-9(5))* McFarland & Co., Inc. Pubs.
Mearns, Jack. John Sanford: An Annotated Bibliography. 2008. 168p. 95.00 *(978-1-58456-211-5(0))* Oak Knoll Pr.
Meyer, Michael J. The John Steinbeck Bibliography, 1996-2006. 2008. (ENG.). 446p. 125.00 *(978-0-8108-6200-5(X))* Scarecrow Pr., Inc.
O'Brien, Philip M. Supplement to T.E. Lawrence — A Bibliography. 2008. *(978-1-58456-221-4(8))* Oak Knoll Pr.
Orr, Gregg & Torrey, Beef. Jim Harrison: A Comprehensive Bibliography, 1964-2008. 2009. (Illus.). 376p. (ENG.). 65.00 *(978-0-8032-1614-3(9))*; 120.00 *(978-0-8032-2624-1(1))* Univ. of Nebraska Pr.
Pastore, Stephen R. Sinclair Lewis: A Descriptive Bibliography. 2nd ed. 2009. (Illus.). 350p. 50.00 *(978-1-58966-156-1(7))* Univ. of Scranton Pr.
Roberson, William H. Walter M. Miller, Jr: A Reference Guide to His Fiction & His Life. 2011. (ENG.). 218p. pap. 40.00 *(978-0-7864-6361-9(9))* McFarland & Co., Inc. Pubs.
Robins, William & Robins, William M. Stanley Elkin: A Comprehensive Bibliography. 2009. (ENG.). 506p. 125.00 *(978-0-8108-6956-1(X))* Scarecrow Pr., Inc.
Sounes, Howard. Locked in the Arms of a Crazy Life. 2007. (Illus.). 202p. pap. *(978-1-84195-897-2(2))* Canongate Bks.
Tischler, Nancy M. Encyclopedia of Contemporary Christian Fiction: From C. S. Lewis to Left Behind, 1 vol. 2009. 400p. 95.00 *(978-0-313-34568-5(6)*, GR4568, Greenwood Pr.) Greenwood Publishing Group, Inc.

AUTHORS, ARAB

Al-Mallah, Majd Yaser & Fitzpatrick, Coeli. 20th Century Arabic Writers, Vol. 346. 2008. (Dictionary of Literary Biography Ser.). (ENG.). 312p. 315.00 *(978-0-7876-8164-7(4))* Cengage Gale.
Alam Al-Adab Al-°Arab I Al-Mu° aoSir: Siyar Wa-Siyar Dh at Iyah, 2 Vols. *(978-3-515-06770-6(1))* Bow Historical Bks.
Allen, Roger, ed. Essays in Arabic Literary Biography, 1850-1950, No. III. 2010. (Essays in Arabic Literary Biography Ser.). (ENG.). 395p. (C). 102.00 *(978-3-447-06141-4(3))* Harrassowitz, Otto Verlag DEU. Dist: ISD.
Altoma, Salih. Iraq's Modern Arabic Literature: A Guide to English Translations since 1950. 2010. (ENG.). 184p. (gr. 17). 65.00 *(978-0-8108-7705-4(8))* Scarecrow Pr., Inc.
Altoma, Salih J. Iraq's Modern Arabic Literature: A Guide to English Translations since 1950. 2010. E-Book *(978-0-8108-7706-1(6))* Scarecrow Pr., Inc.
Cheikho, Louis. Arabic Christian Poets Before & after Islam. 2006. (Christianity in the Islamic World Ser.: 1). 1445p. 312.00 *(978-1-59333-536-6(9))* Gorgias Pr., LLC.
Choukri, Mohamed. For Bread Alone. Bowles, Paul, tr. from ARA. 2007. (ENG.). 169p. per. 14.95 *(978-1-84659-010-8(8)*, Telegram Bks.) Saqi Bks. GBR. Dist: Consortium Bk. Sales & Distribution.
Clark, Peter, ed. Emerging Arab Voices: Nadwa 1: A Bilingual Reader. 2011. (ENG.). 320p. pap. 21.95 ***(978-0-86356-414-7(3))*** Saqi Bks. GBR. Dist: Consortium Bk. Sales & Distribution.
DeYoung, Terri, ed. Essays in Arabic Literary Biography 925-1350: Edited by Terri Deyoung & Mary St. Germain. 2011. (Mizan Ser.). (ENG.). 371p. (C). 105.00 ***(978-3-447-06598-6(2))*** Harrassowitz, Otto Verlag DEU. Dist: ISD.
Esber, Ninar. Conversations with My Father, Adonis. Fox, Lorna Scott, tr. from FRE. 2008. (SB-the French List Ser.). (ENG.). 232p. 24.95 *(978-1-905422-90-6(3))* Seagull Bks. GBR. Dist: Chicago Distribution Ctr.
Gibran, Khalil. Love Letters: The Love Letters of Kahlil Gibran to May Ziadah. Bushrui, Suheil & Al-Kuzbari, Salma H., eds. & trs. by. 2008. (ENG., Illus.). 216p. pap. 14.95 *(978-1-85168-557-8(X))* Oneworld Pubns. GBR. Dist: National Bk. Network.
Herman, Ottó. Ungarns Spinnen-Fauna. 2010. 162p. pap. 21.75 *(978-1-149-00843-0(1))* BiblioBazaar.
Hoffman, Adina. My Happiness Bears No Relation to Happiness: A Poet's Life in the Palestinian Century. (ENG., Illus.). 464p. 2010. pap. 20.00 *(978-0-300-16427-5(0))* 2009. 27.50 *(978-0-300-14150-4(5))* Yale Univ. Pr.
Khaldi, Boutheina. Egypt Awakening in the Early Twentieth Century: May Ziada's Intellectual Circles. 2012. (Middle East Today Ser.). (ENG., Illus.). 240p. 85.00 ***(978-0-230-34086-2(5))*** Palgrave Macmillan.
Lowry, Joseph E. & Stewart, Devin J., eds. Essays in Arabic Literary Biography II: 1350-1850. 2009. (Essays in Arabic Literary Biography Ser.). (ENG.). 440p. (C). pap. 102.00 *(978-3-447-05933-6(8))* Harrassowitz, Otto Verlag DEU. Dist: ISD.
Manasirah, Izz al-Din. Jamrat Al-Nass Al-Shiri: Muqarabat Fi Al-Shir Wa-Al-Shuara Wa-Al-Hadathah Wa-Al-Faliyah. 2007. 574p. *(978-0-00-702260-1(3))* Dar Mijdalawi lil-Nashr wa-al-Tawzi.
Meisami, Julie Scott & Starkey, Paul, eds. Encyclopedia of Arabic Literature. 2010. (ENG.). 862p. pap. 90.00 *(978-0-415-57113-5(8))* Routledge.
Moore, Lindsey. Arab, Muslim, Woman: Voice & Vision in Postcolonial Literature & Film. 2008. (Transformations Ser.). (ENG., Illus.). 208p. (C). 170.00 *(978-0-415-40416-7(9))* Routledge.
Naimy, Mikhail & Gibran, Kahlil. Kahlil Gibran: A Biography. 2011. 294p. 48.95 ***(978-1-258-03100-8(0))*** Literary Licensing, LLC.
Najjar, Alexandre. Kahlil Gibran: A Biography. 2008. (ENG., Illus.). 192p. pap. 14.95 *(978-0-86356-568-4(5))* Saqi Bks. GBR. Dist: Consortium Bk. Sales & Distribution.
Nash, Geoffrey. The Anglo-Arab Encounter: Fiction & Autobiography by Arab Writers in English. 2007. 215p. pap. *(978-3-03911-026-1(8))* Lang, Peter AG.
Orfalea, Gregory. Angeleno Days: An Arab American Writer on Family, Place, & Politics. 2009. (ENG.). 232p. pap. 17.95 *(978-0-8165-2773-1(3))* Univ. of Arizona Pr.
Suba'i, Ahmad. My Days in Mecca. 2009. 120p. 29.95 *(978-1-935049-11-1(9))* FirstForumPress.
Sukys, Julija. Silence Is Death: The Life & Work of Tahar Djaout. 2007. (France Overseas: Studies in Empire & D Ser.). (ENG., Illus.). 202p. 26.95 *(978-0-8032-4320-0(0))* Univ. of Nebraska Pr.

AUTHORS, ASIAN

Aftab, Tahira. Biti Kahani: Autobiography of Princess Shahr Bano Begam of Pataudi. 2012. (ENG.). 350p. 29.95 *(978-0-19-906012-2(6))* Oxford Univ. Pr., Inc.
Akkach. Letters of a Sufi Scholar: The Correspondence of 'Abd al-Ghan? Al-N?bulus? (1641-1731) 2009. (Islamic History & Civilization Ser.). (ARA & ENG., Illus.). 292p. *(978-90-04-17102-2(9))* BRILL.
Chong, Kil-Su. Kuunmong Tasi Ilki. 2010. 272p. *(978-89-7199-397-2(9))* Dolbegae Publishing Co.
Gabroussenko, Tatiana. Soldiers on the Cultural Front: Developments in the Early History of North Korean Literature & Literary Policy. 2010. 246p. (C). 49.00 *(978-0-8248-3396-1(1))* Univ. of Hawaii Pr.
Hill, David T. Journalism & Politics in Indonesia. 2010. (Illus.). 288p. pap. 42.95 ***(978-0-415-66684-8(6))*** Routledge.
Ho, Hung-Sik. Koryo Ui Tong Asia Si Munhak: Paekkaujip. 2009. (KOR.). 343p. *(978-89-7009-522-6(5))* Min-jogsa.
Kohn, Michael. Lama of the Gobi: How Mongolia's mystic monk spread Tibetan Buddhism in the world's harshest Desert. 2010. (ENG.). 248p. pap. 14.95 *(978-988-17742-6-2(8))* Blacksmith Bks. HKG. Dist: National Bk. Network.
Mannur, Anita. Culinary Fictions: Food in South Asian Diasporic Culture. 2009. (ENG., Illus.). 272p. 72.50 *(978-1-4399-0077-2(9))*; pap. 27.95 *(978-1-4399-0078-9(7))* Temple Univ. Pr.
Najjar, Alexandre. The Silence of My Father. Wilson, Laurie, tr. from FRE. 2010. (ENG.). 120p. pap. 12.95 *(978-1-84659-065-8(5)*, Telegram Bks.) Saqi Bks. GBR. Dist: Consortium Bk. Sales & Distribution.
Quayum, Mohammad A., ed. Peninsular Muse: Interviews with Modern Malaysian & Singaporean Poets, Novelists & Dramatists. 2007. (Modern Poetry Ser.: Vol. 2). 305p. pap. *(978-3-03911-061-2(6))* Lang, Peter AG.
Rahbaran, Shiva. The Paradox of Freedom: A Study of Nicholas Mosley's Intellectual Development in His Novels & Other Writings. annot. ed. 2007. (Dalkey Archive Scholarly Ser.). (ENG.). 316p. 39.95 *(978-1-56478-386-8(3)*, 478386) Dalkey Archive Pr.
Rahbaran, Shiva & Mobasser, Nilou. Iranian Writers Uncensored: Freedom, Democracy, & the Word in Contemporary Iran. 2012. (ENG., Illus.). 312p. pap. 17.95 ***(978-1-56478-688-3(9)***, 478688) Dalkey Archive Pr.
Robinson, H. R. A Modern de Quincey: An Autobiography. 2nd ed. 2006. (ENG., Illus.). pap. 23.00 *(978-974-524-038-4(9))* Orchid Pr. THA. Dist: National Bk. Network.
Sa'di, Muslih-uddin, et al. The Bustan or Orchard of Sa'di. 2009. 132p. pap. 12.90 *(978-0-557-20275-1(2)*, Lulu Enterprises Inc.
Sharlet, Jocelyn. Patronage & Poetry in the Islamic World: Social Mobility & Status in the Medieval Middle East & Central Asia. 2011. (Library of Middle East History Ser.). (ENG.). 336p. 99.00 *(978-1-84885-369-0(6)*, Tauris Academic Studies) I. B. Tauris & Co., Ltd. GBR. Dist: Macmillan.
Sil, Narashingha P. The Life of Sharatchandra Chattopadhyay: Drifter & Dreamer. 2011. (ENG.). 180p. (gr 17). 65.00 ***(978-1-61147-507-4(4))*** Fairleigh Dickinson Univ. Pr.
Yi, Ki-Dae. 19-Segi Choson Ui Sosolga Wa Hanmun Changp'yon Sosol. 2010. (KOR.). 306p. *(978-89-303-1466-4(X))* Jibmundang.
Yongun, Han. Selected Writings of Han Yongun: From Social Darwinism to Socialism with a Buddhist Face. Miller, Owen & Tikhonov, Vladimir, trs. from KOR. 2007. (Illus.). 263p. *(978-1-905246-47-2(1))* BRILL.

AUTHORS, ARGENTINE

Bioy Casares, Adolfo. Memorias: Infancia, Adolescencia y Cómo Se Hace un Escritor. 3rd ed. (SPA., Illus.). 216p. *(978-84-7223-420-8(7)*, 6020) Tusquets Editores.
Casares, Adolfo Bioy. Borges. 2007. (SPA., Illus.). 1663p. *(978-950-732-085-9(7))* Ediciones Destino.
Casares, Adolfo Bioy & Bioy Casares, Adolfo. Borges. 2006. 1664p. 58.95 *(978-84-233-3873-3(8))* Ediciones Destino ESP. Dist: Planeta Publishing Corp.
Díaz, Gwendolyn Josie & Díaz, Gwendolyn. Women & Power in Argentine Literature: Stories, Interviews, & Critical Essays. 2007. (Texas Pan American Literature in Translation Ser.). (ENG., Illus.). 392p. pap. 24.95 *(978-0-292-71649-0(4))* Univ. of Texas Pr.
Mackintosh, Fiona J. & Posso, Karl. Árbol de Alejandra: Pizarnik Reassessed. Mackintosh, Fiona J., ed. 2007. (Monografías A Ser.: Volume 248). 182p. 90.00 *(978-1-85566-153-0(5)*, Tamesis Bks.) Boydell & Brewer, Ltd. GBR. Dist: Boydell & Brewer, Inc.
McNeese, Tim. Jorge Luis Borges. 2008. (Great Hispanic Heritage Ser.). (Illus.). 120p. (gr. 6-12). lib. bdg. 35.00 *(978-0-7910-9665-9(3)*, Chelsea Hse.) Facts On File, Inc.
Ocampo, Victoria. La Viajera y Sus Sombras: Crónica de un Aprendizaje. 2010. (Tierra Firme Ser.). (SPA.). 289p. pap. 29.99 *(978-950-557-845-0(8))* Fondo de Cultura Económica.
Prieto, Julio. De la Sombrología: Seis Comienzos en Busca de Macedonio Fernández. 2010. (Ediciones de Iberoamericana Ser.). pap. 29.80 *(978-84-8489-534-3(3))* Iberoamericana Vervuert Publishing Corp.
Sorrentino, Fernando. Seven Conversations with Jorge Luis Borges. Zlotchew, Clark M., tr. from SPA. 2010. (ENG.). 220p. pap. 16.95 *(978-1-58968-060-3(9))* Dry, Paul Bks., Inc.

AUTHORS, AUSTRALIAN

Bonwick, James. An Octogenarian's Reminiscences. 2011. (Cambridge Library Collection - History Ser.). (ENG., Illus.). 402p. pap. 31.99 ***(978-1-108-03896-6(4))*** Cambridge Univ. Pr.
Cave, Nick. Nick Cave: Sinner Saint - The True Confessions, Thirty Years of Essential Interviews. Snow, Mat, ed. 2011. (ENG., Illus.). 224p. pap. 19.95 *(978-0-85965-448-7(6))* Plexus Publishing, Ltd. GBR. Dist: Perseus-PGW.
Cole, Catherine. The Poet Who Forgot. 2008. 216p. pap. 19.50 *(978-1-921401-04-6(4))* UWA Publishing AUS. Dist: International Specialized Bk. Services.
Dibble, Brian. Doing Life: A Biography of Elizabeth Jolley. 2008. 334p. pap. 32.00 *(978-1-921401-06-0(0))* UWA Publishing AUS. Dist: International Specialized Bk. Services.
Farmer, Beverley. Body of Water. 256p. *(978-0-7022-2254-2(2))*; 298p. pap. *(978-0-7022-2283-2(6))* Univ. of Queensland Pr.
Grenville, Kate. Searching for the Secret River: The Story Behind the Bestselling Novel. 2007. (Illus.). 221p. pap. *(978-1-84767-002-1(4))* Canongate Bks.
Head, Dominic. The Cambridge Introduction to J. M. Coetzee. 2009. (Cambridge Introductions to Literature Ser.). (ENG.). 130p. (C). 65.99 *(978-0-521-86747-4(9))*; pap. 22.99 *(978-0-521-68709-6(8))* Cambridge Univ. Pr.
Hillman, Robert. The Boy in the Green Suit: A Memoir. 2009. (ENG.). 240p. pap. 19.95 *(978-1-921372-51-3(6))* Scribe Pubns. AUS. Dist: Independent Pubs. Group.
James, Clive & James, C. Unreliable Memoirs. 2009. (ENG.). 224p. pap. 13.95 *(978-0-393-33608-5(5)*, 33608) Norton, W. W. & Co., Inc.
Lever, Susan. David Foster: The Satirist of Australia. 2007. 94.95 *(978-1-934043-98-1(2))* Cambria Pr.
Matuschek, Oliver. Three Lives: A Biography of Stefan Zweig. 2012. (ENG.). 512p. 32.00 ***(978-1-906548-29-2(3))*** Pushkin Pr., Ltd. GBR. Dist: Consortium Bk. Sales & Distribution.
Moore, John Noel. John Marsden: Darkness, Shadow, & Light. (Illus.). 2011. xi, 186p. E-Book *(978-0-8108-7743-6(0))* 2010. (ENG., Illus.). 198p. 49.95 *(978-0-8108-5478-9(3))* Scarecrow Pr., Inc.
Nettlebeck, Amanda, ed. Provisional Maps: Critical Essays on David Malouf. 248p. pap. 18.00 *(978-0-86422-300-5(5))* UWA Publishing AUS. Dist: International Specialized Bk. Services.
Nielsen, Ellie. Buying a Piece of Paris: The Home of My Dreams in the City of Lights. 2010. (ENG.). 256p. pap. 14.99 *(978-0-312-60633-6(8)*, St. Martin's Griffin) St. Martin's Pr.
Randall, Don. David Malouf. 2007. (Contemporary World Writers Ser.). (ENG.). 240p. 79.00 *(978-0-7190-6832-4(0))*; pap. 26.00 *(978-0-7190-6833-1(9))* Manchester Univ. Pr. GBR. Dist: Macmillan.
Roe, Jill. Her Brilliant Career: The Life of Stella Miles Franklin. 2009. Orig. Title: Stella Miles Franklin: A Biography. (Illus.). 752p. 39.95 *(978-0-674-03609-3(3)*, Belknap Pr.) Harvard Univ. Pr.
Stewart, Frank, et al, eds. Where the Rivers Meet: New Writing from Australia. 2007. (Illus.). 184p. per. 20.00 *(978-0-8248-3178-3(0))* Univ. of Hawaii Pr.
Thiele, Colin. With Dew on My Boots & Other Footprints. 340p. pap. *(978-0-7344-0405-3(0)*, Lothian Children's Bks.) Hachette Australia.
Vuaille-Barcan, Marie-Laure. Transfert de Langue, Transfert de Culture: La Traduction en Français du Roman Southern Steel de L'australienne Dymphna Cusack. 2011. (FRE.). 173p. pap. 58.95 ***(978-3-0343-0722-2(5))*** Lang, Peter AG GBR. Dist: Lang, Peter.

AUTHORS, AUSTRIAN

Adam, Gottfried & Schelander, Robert, eds. Jakob Glatz: Theologe - Pädagoge - Schriftsteller. 2010. (GER.). 123p. (C). 44.00 *(978-3-89971-709-9(0))* Vandenhoeck & Ruprecht GmbH & Co. KG DEU. Dist: ISD.
Andres, Patricia Ann. Erzählen heißt, der Wahrheit verschworen Sein: Kommentierte Edition der deutsch- und englischsprachigen Fassung des bisher unveröffentlichten KZ-Berichts Die Zeit im Lager - Through Work to Freedom von Raoul Auernheimer. 2009. (Europäische Hochschulschriften. Reihe 1: Deutsche Sprache und Literatur Ser.). (GER.). 378p. pap. 81.95 *(978-3-631-58824-6(0))* Lang, Peter GmbH, Europaischer Verlag der Wissenschaften DEU. Dist: Lang, Peter.
Begley, Louis. The Tremendous World I Have Inside My Head: Franz Kafka: A Biographical Essay. 2008. (ENG., Illus.). 208p. 22.00 *(978-1-934633-06-9(2)*, Atlas & Co.
Begley, Louis, ed. Franz Kafka: The Tremendous World Inside My Head. 2009. (ENG.). 208p. pap. 14.00 *(978-1-934633-23-6(2)*, 934623) Atlas & Co.
Bernhard, Thomas. Gathering Evidence & My Prizes: A Memoir. 2011. (Vintage International Ser.). (ENG.). 416p. pap. 16.95 *(978-1-4000-7762-5(1)*, Vintage) Knopf Doubleday Publishing Group.
—My Prizes: An Accounting. Janeway, Carol, tr. from GER. 2010. (ENG.). 144p. 22.00 *(978-0-307-27287-4(7)*, Knopf) Knopf Doubleday Publishing Group.
Broch, Hermann. Briefe an Erich von Kahler (1940-1951) Latzeler, Paul Michael, ed. 2011. (Quellen und Forschungen zur Literatur- und Kulturgeschichte Ser.).Tr. of Letters to Erich von Kahler (1940-1951). (GER., Illus.). XX, 198p. 154.00 ***(978-3-11-174995-2(9))*** De Gruyter, Walter Inc.
—Briefe an Erich von Kahler (1940-1951) Lützeler, Paul Michael, ed. 2010. (Quellen und Forschungen zur Literatur- und Kulturgeschichte Ser.).Tr. of Letters to Erich von Kahler (1940-1951). (GER.). XX, 198p. 98.00 *(978-3-11-022744-4(4))* De Gruyter, Walter Inc.
Canetti, Elias. Party in the Blitz. Hofmann, Michael, tr. 2010. (ENG.). 256p. pap. 13.95 *(978-0-8112-1830-6(9)*, 21830) New Directions Publishing Corp.
Canetti, Vesa & Canetti, Elias. Dearest Georg - Love, Literature, & Power in Dark Times: The Letters of Elias, Veza, & Georges Canetti, 1933-1948. Lauer, Karen & Wachinger, Kristian, eds. Dollenmayer, David, tr. from GER. 2010. (ENG., Illus.). 448p. 24.95 *(978-1-59051-297-5(9))* Other Pr., LLC.
Celan, Paul & Bachmann, Ingeborg. Correspondence. Hoban, Wieland, tr. from GER. 2010. (SB-the German List Ser.). (Illus.). 373p. 24.95 *(978-1-906497-44-6(3))* Seagull Bks. GBR. Dist: Chicago Distribution Ctr.
Doppler, Alfred. Stifter und Stifterforschung im 21. Jahrhundert: Biographie - Wissenschaft - Poetik. 2007. (GER., Illus.). XI, 306p. *(978-3-484-10901-8(7))* Verlag Max Niemeyer.
Feuchtersleben, Ernst, et al. Sämtliche Werke und Briefe: Kritische Ausgabe. 2006. (Veröffentlichungen zur Literaturwissenschaft Ser.). (GER., Illus.). (C). 114.00 *(978-3-7001-3801-3(6))* Austrian Academy of Sciences Press AUT. Dist: Brown, David Bk. Co., The.
Gay, José María Pérez. The Unfortunate Passion of Hermann Broch. Jiménez, Eduardo, tr. from SPA. 2008. 148p. pap. 24.95 *(978-0-9796457-3-0(5))* Floricanto Pr.
Gelber, Mark H. Stefan Zweig Reconsidered: New Perspectives on His Literary & Biographical Writings. 2007. (Conditio Judaica Ser.). (FRE, GER & ENG.). VI, 225p. pap. *(978-3-484-65162-3(8))* Verlag Max Niemeyer.
Gelber, Mark H., ed. Stefan Zweig Reconsidered: New Perspectives on his Literary & Biographical Writings. (Conditio Judaica Ser.). (ENG.). VI, 225p. 165.00 ***(978-3-11-182225-9(7))*** De Gruyter, Walter Inc.
Grange, William. The A to Z of Postwar German Literature. 2010. (A to Z Guide Ser.). (ENG.). 376p. pap. 34.45 *(978-0-8108-7618-7(3))* Scarecrow Pr., Inc.

—Historical Dictionary of Postwar German Literature. 2009. (Historical Dictionaries of Literature & the Arts Ser.). (ENG.). 370p. 90.00 (978-0-8108-5965-4(3)) Scarecrow Pr., Inc.

Handke, Peter. A Sorrow Beyond Dreams: A Life Story, 1 vol. Manheim, Ralph, tr. 2012. (ENG.). 96p. pap. 14.00 **(978-0-374-53364-9(4))** Farrar, Straus & Giroux.

Herzog, Todd, et al. Rebirth of a Culture: Jewish Identity & Jewish Writing in Germany & Austria Today. 2008. 198p. (C). 75.00 (978-1-84545-511-8(8)) Berghahn Bks., Inc.

Hochradl, Karin. Olga Neuwirths und Elfriede Jelineks gemeinsames Musiktheaterschaffen: Ästhetik, Libretto, Analyse, Rezeption. 2010. (Salzburger Beiträge zur Musik- und Tanzforschung Ser.). (GER & ENG., Illus.). 852p. pap. (978-3-03911-691-1(6)) Lang, Peter.

Janouch, Gustav, et al. Conversations with Kafka. 2nd ed. 2012. (ENG.). 228p. pap. 14.95 **(978-0-8112-1950-1(X)**, 21950) New Directions Publishing Corp.

Kafka, Franz. Brief an den Vater: Fassung der Handschrift. (GER.). pap. 14.95 (978-3-596-14674-1(7)) Fischer Taschenbuch Verlag DEU. Dist: Distribooks, Inc.

—Dearest Father. Stokes, Hannah & Stokes, Richard, trs. from GER. 2009. (Oneworld Modern Classics Ser.). (ENG.). 128p. pap. 14.95 (978-1-84749-025-4(5)) Alma Classics GBR. Dist: Independent Pubs. Group.

—Diarios 1910-1923. (SPA.). 446p. (978-84-7223-863-3(6), 6130) Tusquets Editores.

Kafka, Franz. Kafka Selected Letters. Winston, Richard & Winston, Clara, trs. 2012. (Oneworld Classics Ser.). (ENG.). 528p. 19.95 **(978-1-84749-194-7(4))** Alma Classics GBR. Dist: Independent Pubs. Group.

Kleefeld, Gunther. Das Gedicht Als Sühne: Georg Trakls Dichtung und Krankheit eine Psychoanalytische Studie. (Studien zur deutschen Literatur Ser.). (GER.). VII, 408p. 195.00 **(978-3-11-184971-3(6))** De Gruyter, Walter Inc.

Koelb, Clayton. Kafka: A Guide for the Perplexed. 2010. (Guides for the Perplexed Ser.). (ENG.). 192p. 19.95 (978-0-8264-9580-8(X)); 90.00 (978-0-8264-9579-2(6)) Continuum International Publishing Group, Ltd. GBR. Dist: National Bk. Network.

Mitchell, David & Mitchell, Mike. Vivo: The Life of Gustav Meyrink. 2008. (ENG.). 196p. pap. 15.99 (978-1-903517-69-7(X)) Dedalus, Ltd.

Robertson, Ritchie. Kafka. 2010. (Brief Insight Ser.). (ENG., Illus.). 176p. 14.95 (978-1-4027-7530-7(X)) Sterling Publishing Co., Inc.

Roth, Joseph & Hofmann, Michael. Joseph Roth: A Life in Letters. 2012. (ENG.). 512p. 39.95 **(978-0-393-06064-5(0)**, 6064) Norton, W. W. & Co., Inc.

Shchyhlevska, Natalia. Alfred Gong: Leben und Werk. 2008. (GER., Illus.). 356p. pap. 84.95 (978-3-03911-420-7(4)) Lang, Peter AG GBR. Dist: Lang, Peter.

Sonvilla-Weiss, Stefan. Synthesis & Nullification: Works, 1991-2011. 2012. (ENG.). 224p. pap. 49.95 **(978-3-7091-1028-7(9)**, 3709110289) Springer Wien AUT. Dist: Springer.

Spiel, Hilde. The Dark & the Bright: Memoirs 1911-1989. 2007. (Studies in Austrian Literature, Culture, & Thought). (978-1-57241-154-8(6)) Ariadne Pr.

Tuta, Anita. Thomas Bernhard: Ein Theatermacher inmitten medialer Konfusion und Konstruktion. 2010. 120p. pap. (978-3-639-25086-2(9)) VDM Verlag Dr. Mueller e.K.

von Rezzori, Gregor. The Snows of Yesteryear. Broch De Rothermann, H. F., tr. from GER. 2008. (ENG., Illus.). 304p. pap. 15.95 (978-1-59017-281-0(7), NYRB Classics) New York Review of Bks., Inc., The.

Wagenbach, Klaus. Kafka: A Life in Prague. 2nd ed. 2011. (Red Bks.). (ENG., Illus.). 171p. 19.95 **(978-1-906598-88-4(6))** Haus Publishing GBR. Dist: Consortium Bk. Sales & Distribution.

Wheatley, Catherine. Cache. 2012. (BFI Film Classics Ser.). (ENG., Illus.). 96p. (C). pap. 15.00 **(978-1-84457-349-3(4))** Palgrave Macmillan.

Zolkos, Magdalena. On Jean Amery: Philosophy of Catastrophe. 2011. (ENG.). 344p. 80.00 **(978-0-7391-4765-8(X))** Lexington Bks.

AUTHORS, BLACKLISTING OF

see Blacklisting of Authors

AUTHORS, CANADIAN

Aimée, Rose. A Road Without A Map. 2011. 120p. 22.95 **(978-1-4620-5611-8(3))**; pap. 12.95 **(978-1-4620-5610-1(5))** iUniverse, Inc.

Arcan, Nelly. Putain: Récit. (FRE.). 186p. (978-2-02-050041-8(8)) Editions du Seuil.

Avison, Margaret. I Am Here & Not Not-There. 2009. (ENG., Illus.). 352p. pap. 27.95 (978-0-88984-315-8(5)) Porcupine's Quill, Inc. CAN. Dist: Univ. of Toronto Pr.

—A Kind of Perseverance. 2010. (ENG., Illus.). 56p. pap. 12.95 (978-0-88984-326-4(0)) Porcupine's Quill, Inc. CAN. Dist: Univ. of Toronto Pr.

Barker, Christopher. The Arms of the Infinite: Elizabeth Smart & George Barker. 2010. (Illus.). 258p. (C). pap. 29.95 (978-1-55458-270-9(9)) Wilfrid Laurier Univ. Pr. CAN. Dist: Univ. of Toronto Pr.

Bechard, Deni Y. Cures for Hunger. 2012. (ENG.). 320p. 24.00 **(978-1-57131-331-7(1))** Milkweed Editions.

Béchard, Deni Y. Cures for Hunger. 2012. (ENG.). 366p. 29.95 **(978-0-86492-671-5(5))** Goose Lane Editions CAN. Dist: Univ. of Toronto Pr.

Bhautoo-Dewnarain, Nandini. Rohinton Mistry: An Introduction. 2006. viii, 126p. pap. (978-81-7596-311-5(5)) Cambridge Univ. Pr. India Pvt. Ltd.

Biographiq. Leonard Cohen - Artist of Influence (Biography) 2008. 64p. pap. 9.99 (978-1-59986-079-4(1), Biographiq) Filiquarian Publishing, LLC.

Bloom, Harold, ed. Alice Munro. 2009. (Bloom's Modern Critical Views Ser.). 218p. (C). (gr. 9-18). 45.00 (978-1-60413-587-9(5), Chelsea Hse.) Facts On File, Inc.

Bloomfield, Lori Ann. The Last River Child. 2009. 280p. pap. 17.95 **(978-1-897187-66-1(1))** Second Story Pr. CAN. Dist: Univ. of Toronto Pr.

Bociurkiw, Marusya. Comfort Food for Breakups: The Memoir of a Hungry Girl. 2007. (ENG., Illus.). 176p. pap. 16.95 (978-1-55152-219-7(5)) Arsenal Pulp Pr. CAN. Dist: Consortium Bk. Sales & Distribution.

Bowering, George. Pinboy: A Memoir. 2011. (ENG.). 320p. 32.00 (978-1-897151-93-8(4)) Cormorant Bks. Inc. CAN. Dist: Univ. of Toronto Pr.

Bowling, Tim. In the Suicide's Library: A Booklover's Journey. 2010. (ENG.). 320p. pap. (978-1-55447-089-1(7)) Gaspereau Pr.

—The Lost Coast: Salmon, Memory & the Death of Wild Culture. unabr. ed. 2007. (ENG., Illus.). 255p. 29.95 (978-0-88971-211-9(5)) Harbour Publishing Co., Ltd. CAN. Dist: Ingram Pub. Services.

Brassard, George J. The Interview: Life struggles from a bipolar Pastor. 2011. pap. 11.99 (978-1-61739-289-4(8)) Tate Publishing & Enterprises, LLC.

Brennan, Brian. How the West Was Written: The Life & Times of James H. Gray, 1 vol. 2006. (ENG., Illus.). 224p. 19.95 (978-1-894856-62-1(7)) Fifth Hse. Pubs. CAN. Dist: Ingram Pub. Services.

Brett, Brian. Trauma Farm: A Rebel History of Rural Life, 1 vol. 2011. (ENG.). 384p. pap. 16.95 (978-1-55365-803-0(5), Greystone Bks.) D&M Pubs. Inc. CAN. Dist: Perseus-PGW.

Brulotte & Brulotte, Gaetan. La Chambre des Lucidités. (FRE., Illus.). 175p. (978-2-89583-073-3(8)) Editions Trois-Pistoles.

Busby, Brian John. A Gentleman of Pleasure: One Life of John Glassco - Poet, Memoirist, Translator, & Pornographer. 2011. (ENG., Illus.). 400p. (978-0-7735-3818-4(6)) McGill-Queen's Univ. Pr.

Byrnes, Terence, photos by & text. Closer to Home: The Author & the Author Portrait. 2009. (ENG., Illus.). 180p. pap. 29.95 (978-1-55065-248-2(6)) Vehicule Pr. CAN. Dist: Independent Pubs. Group.

Callaghan, Morley. That Summer in Paris. 2007. (Exile Classics Ser.). (ENG., Illus.). 232p. pap. 16.95 (978-1-55096-688-6(X)) Exile Editions, Ltd. CAN. Dist: Independent Pubs. Group.

Carpenter, Cari M. Seeing Red: Anger, Sentimentality, & American Indians. 2008. (ENG., Illus.). 208p. 49.95 (978-0-8142-1079-6(1)) Ohio State Univ. Pr.

Caruso, Donna. Journey Without A Map: Stories of an Immigrant Daughter of Immigrants. 2008. (ENG.). 223p. pap. 19.95 (978-1-897235-36-2(4)) Thistledown Pr., Ltd. CAN. Dist: Univ. of Toronto Pr.

Chong, Kevin. My Year of the Racehorse: Falling in Love with the Sport of Kings, 1 vol. 2012. (ENG.). 232p. pap. 18.95 **(978-1-55365-520-6(6)**, Greystone Bks.) D&M Pubs. Inc. CAN. Dist: Perseus-PGW.

Chown, Alice A. The Stairway. 2007. (ENG.). 336p. 45.95 (978-0-548-37284-5(5)); per. 30.95 (978-0-548-31600-9(7)) Kessinger Publishing, LLC.

Choyce, Lesley. Seven Ravens: Two Summers in a Life by the Sea. 2009. 200p. pap. 19.00 (978-1-894987-39-4(X)) Wolsak & Wynn Pubs., Ltd. CAN. Dist: Univ. of Toronto Pr.

Christian, William. Parkin: Canada's Most Famous Forgotten Man. 2008. (ENG., Illus.). 349p. pap. 26.95 (978-0-9781600-3-6(7)) Dundurn CAN. Dist: Ingram Pub. Services.

Clarke, Arthur C. Amongst Thistles & Thorns. 2011. (Caribbean Modern Classics Ser.). (ENG.). 208p. pap. 17.95 (978-1-84523-147-7(3)) Peepal Tree Pr., Ltd. GBR. Dist: Independent Pubs. Group.

Coles, Don. A Dropped Glove in Regent Street: An Autobiography by Other Means. 2007. (ENG., Illus.). 144p. per. 14.95 (978-1-55065-222-2(2)) Vehicule Pr. CAN. Dist: Independent Pubs. Group.

Cowan, Shannon, et al. Double Lives: Writing & Motherhood. 2008. (ENG.). 280p. (C). pap. (978-0-7735-3377-6(X)) McGill-Queen's Univ. Pr.

Crozier, Lorna. Addicted: Notes from the Belly of the Beast, 1 vol. Lane, Patrick, ed. 2nd ed. 2006. (ENG.). 240p. pap. 18.95 (978-1-55365-115-4(4), Greystone Bks.) D&M Pubs. Inc. CAN. Dist: Perseus-PGW.

—Small Beneath the Sky: A Prairie Memoir, 1 vol. 2010. (ENG., Illus.). 208p. 23.95 (978-1-55365-343-1(2), Greystone Bks.) D&M Pubs. Inc. CAN. Dist: Perseus-PGW.

Curtis, Sky. Doctored: A True Story. 2010. (ENG., Illus.). 264p. pap. 22.95 **(978-1-926708-18-8(0))** Inanna Pubns. & Education, Inc. CAN. Dist: SPD-Small Pr. Distribution.

Dorion, Helene. Days of Sand. Kaplansky, Jonathan, tr. from FRE. 2008. (ENG.). 120p. per. 18.00 (978-1-897151-07-5(1)) Cormorant Bks. Inc. CAN. Dist: Univ. of Toronto Pr.

Dorward, Nate. Antiphonies: Essays on Women's Experimental Poetries in Canada. 2008. 256p. pap. 20.00 (978-0-9735875-4-8(7)) Gig, The CAN. Dist: SPD-Small Pr. Distribution.

Doubleday Publisher. Ernest Thompson Seton: A Biographical Sketch. 2011. 50p. 36.95 **(978-1-258-02176-4(5))** Literary Licensing, LLC.

Dvorak, Marta & Jones, Manina, eds. Carol Shields & the Extra-Ordinary. 2007. (ENG., Illus.). 288p. (C). (978-0-7735-3220-5(X)) McGill-Queen's Univ. Pr.

Edwards, Caterina. Finding Rosa: A Mother with Alzheimer's, a Daughter in Search of the Past, 1 vol. 2009. (ENG.). 304p. 24.95 (978-1-55365-389-9(0), Greystone Bks.) D&M Pubs. Inc. CAN. Dist: Perseus-PGW.

Farrant, M. A. C. The Secret Lives of Litterbugs. 2009. (ENG.). 256p. pap. 16.95 (978-1-55470-159-9(7)) Key Porter Bks. CAN. Dist: Perseus-PGW.

Fields, Dorothy C. Whispers, Daydreams & Twilight Memories. 96p. pap. 10.00 (978-0-87012-689-5(X)) McClain Printing Co.

Finch, David. R. M. Patterson: A Life of Great Adventure, 1 vol. 2010. (ENG., Illus.). 312p. pap. (978-1-894898-95-9(8)) TouchWood Editions.

Footman, Tim. Leonard Cohen: Hallelujah: A New Biography. 2009. (ENG., Illus.). 300p. pap. 19.95 (978-1-84240-472-0(5)) Chrome Dreams GBR. Dist: Independent Pubs. Group.

Foran, Charles. Mordecai: The Life & Times. (ENG., Illus.). 800p. 2011. pap. 21.95 (978-0-676-97965-7(3), Vintage Canada) 2010. 34.00 (978-0-676-97963-3(7)) Knopf Canada CAN. Dist: Random Hse., Inc.

Forsberg, Tor. North of Iskut: Grizzlies, Bannock & Adventure. unabr. ed. 2010. (ENG., Illus.). 224p. pap. 24.95 (978-1-894759-42-7(7)) Caitlin Pr., Inc. CAN. Dist: Partners Pubs. Group, Inc.

Foschini, Lorenza & Karpeles, Eric. Proust's Overcoat: The True Story of One Man's Passion for All Things Proust. 2010. (ENG., Illus.). 144p. 19.99 (978-0-06-196567-8(7), Ecco) HarperCollins Pubs.

Fraser, Raymond. When the Earth Was Flat. 2007. (ENG., Illus.). 160p. pap. 17.00 (978-0-88753-439-3(2)) Black Moss Pr. CAN. Dist: LitDistCo.

Friesen, Gerald & Owram, Doug. Thinkers & Dreamers. 2010. (978-1-4426-4195-2(9)) Univ. of Toronto Pr.

Gammel, Irene. Looking for Anne of Green Gables: The Story of L. M. Montgomery & Her Literary Classic. 2009. (ENG., Illus.). 320p. pap. 18.99 (978-0-312-38238-4(3), St. Martin's Griffin) St. Martin's Pr.

Gayton, Don. Man Facing West, 1 vol. 2011. (Illus.). 170p. pap. 18.95 (978-1-897235-79-9(8)) Thistledown Pr., Ltd. CAN. Dist: Univ. of Toronto Pr.

Glassco, John. Memoirs of Montparnasse. 2007. (New York Review Books Classics). (ENG., Illus.). 296p. pap. 15.95 (978-1-59017-184-4(5), NYRB Classics) New York Review of Bks., Inc., The.

Gray, Charlotte. Nellie McClung. Saul, John Ralston, ed. 2011. (ENG.). 204p. (gr. 12). 19.95 **(978-0-670-06674-2(5)**, Penguin Global) Penguin Group (USA) Inc.

Hall, Douglas John. The Messenger: Friendship, Faith, & Finding OneÕs Way. 2011. 192p. pap. 22.00 **(978-1-61097-317-5(8)**, Cascade Bks.) Wipf & Stock Pubs.

Hebert, Anne L. Anne Hébert: Essays on Her Works. Skallerup, Lee, ed. 2010. (Writers Ser.). (ENG.). 184p. 18.00 (978-1-55071-278-0(0)) Guernica Editions, Inc. CAN. Dist: Univ. of Toronto Pr.

Heighton, Steven. Memos & Dispatches on Writing. 2011. (ENG.). 72p. pap., wbk. ed. 16.95 (978-1-55022-937-0(0)) ECW Pr. CAN. Dist: Independent Pubs. Group.

Helmes-Hayes, Rick. Measuring the Mosaic: An Intellectual Biography of John Porter. 2010. 592p. (978-0-8020-9703-3(0)) Univ. of Toronto Pr.

Henderson, Paula Laureen. Lost Angels: Encounters with First Nations. 2011. (ENG & FRE.). 223p. pap. (978-0-9783141-1-8(5)) Gumdrop Enterprise.

Hendrickx, Marc. Yesterday's Tomorrow: Leonard Cohen. 2008. 0144p. pap. 21.95 (978-1-876040-77-2(7)) Brandl & Schlesinger AUS. Dist: Independent Pubs. Group.

Hodgins, Jack. Jack Hodgins: Essays on His Works. Hannan, Annika, ed. 2009. (Writers Ser.). (ENG.). 250p. 18.00 (978-1-55071-300-8(0)) Guernica Editions, Inc. CAN. Dist: Univ. of Toronto Pr.

Hooper, Brad. The Fiction of Alice Munro: An Appreciation, 1 vol. 2008. (Illus.). 184p. 44.95 (978-0-275-99121-0(0), C9121, Praeger Pubs.) Greenwood Publishing Group, Inc.

Huck, Sybille. Frauenrollen in Margaret Laurences Romanen: Weibliche Identitätsentwicklung in The Stone Angel, A Bird in the House und The Diviners. 2008. (GER & ENG.). 106p. **(978-3-8366-6144-7(6))** Diplomica GmbH.

Hunter, Martin. Young Hunting: A Memoir. 2008. (ENG.). 208p. pap. 19.95 (978-1-55022-852-6(8)) ECW Pr. CAN. Dist: Independent Pubs. Group.

Jones, Nick. All the Days of His Life: A Biography of Archdeacon H. A. Cody. (Illus.). 432p. pap. 11.95 (978-0-919326-07-1(2)) New Brunswick Museum CAN. Dist: Goose Lane Editions.

Kennedy, Des. The Way of a Gardener: A Life's Journey, 1 vol. 2010. (ENG.). 272p. pap. 17.95 (978-1-55365-417-9(X), Greystone Bks.) D&M Pubs. Inc. CAN. Dist: Perseus-PGW.

King, Thomas. The Truth about Stories: A Native Narrative. 2008. (ENG.). 184p. pap. 19.95 (978-0-8166-4627-2(9)) Univ. of Minnesota Pr.

Kishkan, Theresa. Mnemonic: A Book of Trees. 2011. (ENG.). 248p. pap. 19.95 **(978-0-86492-651-7(0))** Goose Lane Editions CAN. Dist: Univ. of Toronto Pr.

Koch, Eric. I Remember the Location Exactly. 2010. (ENG., Illus.). 208p. pap. 15.00 (978-0-88962-861-8(0)) Mosaic Pr.

Kramer, Reinhold. Mordecai Richler: Leaving St. Urbain. 2008. (ENG., Illus.). 528p. (C). (978-0-7735-3355-4(9)) McGill-Queen's Univ. Pr.

—Mordecai Richler: Leaving St Urbain. 2010. (Art of Living Ser.). (ENG., Illus.). 498p. (C). pap. (978-0-7735-3742-2(2)) McGill-Queen's Univ. Pr.

Krause, Pat. Acts of Love: A Memoir. 2008. (ENG.). 256p. per. (978-1-55050-368-5(5)) Coteau Bks.

LaRue, Monique. Between Books: The Writer's Time. 2010. (FRE & ENG.). 104p. 14.95 **(978-0-86492-534-3(4))** Goose Lane Editions CAN. Dist: Univ. of Toronto Pr.

Leacock, Stephen. Boy I Left Behind Me. 2006. 228p. per. (978-1-4067-1912-3(9), Hesperides Pr.) Read Bks.

Leith, Linda. Marrying Hungary. 2008. (ENG.). 160p. pap. 15.95 (978-1-897109-29-8(6)) Signature Editions CAN. Dist: Univ. of Toronto Pr.

—Writing in the Time of Nationalism: From Two Solitudes to Blue Metropolis. 2010. 176p. pap. 15.95 (978-1-897109-48-9(2)) Signature Editions CAN. Dist: Univ. of Toronto Pr.

Lentz, Francois. Présence de Gabrielle Roy: Résonances Actuelles et Propositions Pédagogiques. 2009. (FRE., Illus.). 99p. (978-1-895407-43-3(5)) Presses Universitaires de Saint-Boniface.

Lindquist, N. J. & Nelles, Wendy Elaine, eds. Hot Apple Cider: Words to Stir the Heart & Warm the Soul. 2008. (ENG., Illus.). 296p. 15.99 (978-0-9784963-0-2(2)) That's Life! Communications CAN. Dist: STL Distribution North America.

MacMillan, Margaret. Stephen Leacock. 2011. (ENG.). 204p. (gr. 12). 19.95 **(978-0-670-06681-0(8)**, Penguin Global) Penguin Group (USA) Inc.

Maes, Nicholas. Robertson Davies: Magician of Words. 2009. (Quest Biography Ser.). (ENG., Illus.). 192p. pap. 19.99 (978-1-55002-872-0(3)) Dundurn CAN. Dist: Ingram Pub. Services.

Maillet, Antonine. Fais Confiance à la Mer, Elle Te Portera: Essai. 2010. (FRE.). 229p. (978-2-7609-6071-8(4)) Lemeac Editeur, Inc.

Mallory, Enid. Robert Service: Under the Spell of the Yukon, 1 vol. (ENG., Illus.). 2010. 256p. (978-1-894384-95-7(4)) 2nd rev. ed. 2009. 288p. pap. (978-1-894974-26-4(3)) Heritage Hse.

Manguel, Alberto. A Reader on Reading. 2011. (ENG., Illus.). 320p. pap. 18.00 (978-0-300-17208-9(7)) Yale Univ. Pr.

Marty, Sid. Leaning on the Wind: Under the Spell of the Great Chinook, 1 vol. 2009. (ENG.). 352p. pap. (978-1-894974-62-2(X)) Heritage Hse.

McBurney, Margaret, ed. It's All about Kindness: Remembering June Callwood. 2010. (ENG.). 256p. 20.00 (978-1-897151-79-2(9)) Cormorant Bks. Inc. CAN. Dist: Univ. of Toronto Pr.

Mckillop, Brian. Pierre Berton: A Biography. 2010. (ENG., Illus.). 808p. pap. 21.00 (978-0-7710-5756-4(3), Emblem Edns) McClelland & Stewart CAN. Dist: Random Hse., Inc.

Menzies, Heather. Enter Mourning: A Memoire on Death, Dementia, & Coming Home. 2009. (ENG., Illus.). 240p. pap. 19.95 (978-1-55470-155-1(4)) Key Porter Bks. CAN. Dist: Perseus-PGW.

Morra, Linda M., ed. Corresponding Influence: Selected Letters of Emily Carr & Ira Dilworth. 2008. (ENG., Illus.). 350p. pap. (978-0-8020-9575-6(5)) Univ. of Toronto Pr.

Mowat, Farley. Bay of Spirits: A Love Story. 2009. (ENG., Illus.). 432p. pap. 16.95 (978-0-7710-6467-8(5), McClelland & Stewart) McClelland & Stewart CAN. Dist: Random Hse., Inc.

—Otherwise. 2009. (ENG.). 368p. pap. 16.95 (978-0-7710-6490-6(X), Emblem Edns) McClelland & Stewart CAN. Dist: Random Hse., Inc.

Munro, Sheila. Lives of Mothers & Daughters: Growing up with Alice Munro. 2008. (ENG., Illus.). 288p. per. 12.95 (978-1-4027-5763-1(8)) Union Square Pr.

Mustafa, Sophia. The Tanganyika Way. 2009. 240p. pap. 28.95 (978-1-894770-51-4(X)) TSAR Pubns. CAN. Dist: Univ. of Toronto Pr.

Nicol, Eric. Anything for a Laugh: Memoirs. unabr. ed. (ENG., Illus.). 264p. (978-1-55017-187-7(9)) Harbour Publishing Co., Ltd.

Oxford, Kelly. Everything Is Perfect When You're a Liar. 2012. 288p. 25.99 **(978-0-06-210222-5(2))** HarperCollins Pubs.

Page, P. K. Brazilian Journal. 2nd ed. 2011. (Collected Works). (ENG., Illus.). 304p. pap. 27.95 (978-0-88984-347-9(3)) Porcupine's Quill, Inc. CAN. Dist: Univ. of Toronto Pr.

Popham, Elizabeth A. A. M. Klein: Letters. 2009. (ENG.). (978-1-4426-4107-5(X)) Univ. of Toronto Pr.

Purdy, Al. The Al Purdy A Frame Anthology. Vermeersch, Paul, ed. 2009. (ENG., Illus.). 160p. pap. 26.95 (978-1-55017-502-8(5)) Harbour Publishing Co., Ltd. CAN. Dist: Ingram Pub. Services.

—Reaching for the Beaufort Sea: An Autobiography. unabr. ed. (ENG., Illus.). 296p. (978-1-55017-088-7(0)) Harbour Publishing Co., Ltd.

Quarrington, Paul. Cigar Box Banjo: Notes on Music & Life, 1 vol. 2010. (ENG.). 256p. 26.95 (978-1-55365-438-4(2), Greystone Bks.) D&M Pubs. Inc. CAN. Dist: Perseus-PGW.

Raymond, Jean-Francois. Diplomates Ecrivains Du Canada: Des Voix Nouvelles. (FRE.). 164p. pap. 29.95 (978-90-5201-346-6(2)) Lang, Peter Publishing, Inc.

Research International Staff, ed. Freelancers of North America. 2nd ed. pap. 37.95 (978-0-911085-05-1(X)) Author Aid/Research Assocs. International.

Richards, David Adams. God Is: My Search for Faith in a Secular World. 2010. (ENG.). 176p. pap. 19.95 **(978-0-385-66652-7(7)**, Anchor Can) Doubleday Canada, Ltd. CAN. Dist: Random Hse., Inc.

Rifkind, Candida. Comrades & Critics: Women, Literature, & the Left in 1930s Canada. 2009. (ENG.). 256p. (978-0-8020-9267-0(5)) Univ. of Toronto Pr.

Robertson, Ian Ross & Robertson, Ian. Sir Andrew Macphail: The Life & Legacy of a Canadian Man of Letters. 2008. (ENG., Illus.). 448p. (C). (978-0-7735-3419-3(9)) McGill-Queen's Univ. Pr.

Robertson, Ray. Why Not? Fifteen Reasons to Live. 2011. (ENG.). 175p. pap. 16.95 **(978-1-926845-27-2(7))** Biblioasis CAN. Dist: Consortium Bk. Sales & Distribution.

Robinson, Eden. The Sasquatch at Home: Traditional Protocols & Modern Storytelling. 2011. (Henry Kreisel Memorial Lecture Ser.). (ENG.). 64p. pap. 10.95 (978-0-88864-559-3(7)) Univ. of Alberta Pr. CAN. Dist: Michigan State Univ. Pr., Chicago Distribution Ctr.

Roig, Denise. Butter Cream: A Year in a Montreal Pastry School. 2008. (ENG.). 176p. pap. 15.95 (978-1-897109-30-4(X)) Signature Editions CAN. Dist: Univ. of Toronto Pr.

Ross, Val. Robertson Davies: A Portrait in Mosaic. 2009. 400p. pap. 19.95 (978-0-7710-7776-0(9), Emblem Edns) McClelland & Stewart CAN. Dist: Random Hse., Inc.

Rubio, Mary Henley. Lucy Maud Montgomery: The Gift of Wings. 2010. (ENG.). 720p. pap. 21.95 (978-0-385-66760-9(4), Anchor Can) Doubleday Canada, Ltd. CAN. Dist: Random Hse., Inc.

Rule, Jane. Loving the Difficult. 2008. (Illus.). 205p. (978-0-9736882-6-9(2)) Hedgerow Pr.

Rule, Jane. Taking My Life. 2011. (ENG.). 278p. pap. 19.95 (978-0-88922-673-9(3)) Talonbooks, Ltd. CAN. Dist: Consortium Bk. Sales & Distribution.

Rybczynski, Witold. My Two Polish Grandfathers: And Other Essays on the Imaginative Life. 2009. (ENG., Illus.). 240p. 25.00 (978-0-7432-3598-3(3), Scribner) Scribner.

Sanger, Peter. Through Darkling Air: The Poetry of Richard Outram. 2010. (ENG.). 512p. (978-1-55447-061-7(7)) Gaspereau Pr.

Sauerwein, Stan. Lucy Maud Montgomery (Junior Edition) 2007. (Amazing Stories Junior Ser.). (Illus.). 96p. pap. (978-1-55439-724-2(3)) Altitude Publishing Canada Ltd.

Schaub, Danielle, ed. & photos by. Reading Writers Reading: Canadian Authors' Reflections. 2006. (Currents, a Canadian Literature Ser.). (FRE & ENG., Illus.). 368p. 60.00 (978-0-88864-459-6(0)) Univ. of Alberta Pr. CAN. Dist: Michigan State Univ. Pr.

Sheikh, Nazneen. Moon over Marrakech: A Memoir of Loving Too Deeply in a Foreign Land. 2010. (ENG.). 288p. 22.00 (978-1-897151-71-6(3)) Cormorant Bks. Inc. CAN. Dist: Univ. of Toronto Pr.

Stouck, Jordan, et al, eds. Collecting Stamps Would Have Been More Fun: Canadian Publishing & the Correspondence of Sinclair Ross, 1933-1986. 2010. (ENG., Illus.). 344p. pap. 34.95 (978-0-88864-521-0(X)) Univ. of Alberta Pr. CAN. Dist: Michigan State Univ. Pr.

Swan, Alison, ed. Fresh Water: Women Writing on the Great Lakes. 2006. (ENG.). 256p. per. 26.95 (978-0-87013-789-1(1)) Michigan State Univ. Pr.

Tate, Andrew & Tate, Andrew. Douglas Coupland. 2008. (Contemporary American & Canadian Novelists Ser.). (ENG.). 192p. 79.00 (978-0-7190-7488-2(6)); pap. 26.00 (978-0-7190-7661-9(7)) Manchester Univ. Pr. GBR. Dist: Macmillan.

Thacker, Robert. Alice Munro: Writing Her Lives. 2011. (Illus.). 664p. pap. 22.99 (978-0-7710-8510-9(9), Emblem Edns) McClelland & Stewart CAN. Dist: Random Hse., Inc.

The Writers' Trust of Canada. A Writer's Life: The Margaret Laurence Lectures. 2011. (ENG., Illus.). 416p. pap. 22.95 (978-0-7710-8528-2(7), Emblem Edns) McClelland & Stewart CAN. Dist: Random Hse., Inc.

Tremblay, M. Anthony. David Adams Richards of the Miramichi: A Biographical Introduction to His Work. 2010. (Illus.). 384p. (978-1-4426-4162-4(2)); pap. (978-1-4426-1077-4(8)) Univ. of Toronto Pr.

Tremblay, Michel & Gaboriau, Linda. Bonbons Assortis: Assorted Candies. Gaboriau, Linda, tr. from FRE. 2006. (ENG.). 160p. per. 17.95 (978-0-88922-541-1(9)) Talonbooks, Ltd. CAN. Dist: Consortium Bk. Sales & Distribution.

Vassanji, M. G. Mordecai Richler. 2011. (ENG.). 204p. (gr. 12). 19.95 (978-0-670-06672-8(9), Penguin Global) Penguin Group (USA) Inc.

Vassanji, M. G. A Place Within: Rediscovering India. 2009. (ENG.). 464p. pap. 18.00 (978-0-385-66179-9(7), Anchor Can) Doubleday Canada, Ltd. CAN. Dist: Random Hse., Inc.

Wachtel, Eleanor. Random Illuminations: Conversations with Carol Shields. 2007. (ENG.). 184p. pap. 19.95 (978-0-86492-501-5(8)) Goose Lane Editions CAN. Dist: Univ. of Toronto Pr.

Wagamese, Richard. One Native Life, 1 vol. (ENG.). 272p. 2009. pap. 17.95 (978-1-55365-312-7(2)) 2008. 29.95 (978-1-55365-364-6(5)) D&M Pubs. Inc. CAN. Dist: Perseus-PGW.

—One Story, One Song, 1 vol. 2011. (ENG.). 216p. 25.95 (978-1-55365-506-0(0)) D&M Pubs. Inc. CAN. Dist: Perseus-PGW.

Watmough, David. Myself Through Others: Memoirs. 2008. (ENG., Illus.). 208p. pap. 24.99 (978-1-55002-799-0(9), Dundurn Pr.) Dundurn CAN. Dist: Ingram Pub. Services.

White, Howard. Writing in the Rain. unabr. ed. (ENG.). 256p. pap. 16.95 (978-1-55017-010-8(4)) Harbour Publishing Co., Ltd. CAN. Dist: Ingram Pub. Services.

Whyte, Jack. Forty Years in Canada: A Memoir, 1 vol. 2007. (ENG., Illus.). 192p. (978-1-894974-22-6(0)) Heritage Hse.

Wiesenthal, Christine. The Half-Lives of Pat Lowther. 2005. (Illus.). 530p. pap. (978-0-8020-9480-3(5)) Univ. of Toronto Pr.

Woodcock, George. Beyond the Blue Mountain: An Autobiography. 2010. (ENG.). 300p. pap. 25.00 (978-1-55005-184-1(9)) Fitzhenry & Whiteside, Ltd. CAN. Dist: Ingram Pub. Services.

—Letter to the Past: An Autobiography. 2010. (ENG.). 331p. pap. 30.00 (978-1-55005-192-6(X)) Fitzhenry & Whiteside, Ltd. CAN. Dist: Ingram Pub. Services.

York, Lorraine. Literary Celebrity in Canada. 2007. (ENG.). 192p. (978-0-8020-9282-3(9)) Univ. of Toronto Pr.

Young, Allab R. Time & Place: The Life & Times of Thomas H. Raddall. 200p. pap. 14.95 (978-0-919107-31-1(1)) Acadiensis Pr. CAN. Dist: Goose Lane Editions.

AUTHORS, CARIBBEAN

Chin, Staceyann. The Other Side of Paradise: A Memoir. 2010. (ENG.). 304p. pap. 16.00 (978-0-7432-9291-7(X), Scribner) Scribner

Cliff, Michelle. If I Could Write This in Fire. 2008. 104p. 21.95 (978-0-8166-5474-1(3)); xi, 89p. pap. (978-0-8166-5475-8(1)) Univ. of Minnesota Pr.

Cox, Juanita, ed. In the Eye of the Storm: Edgar Mittelholzer, 1909-2009 - Critical Perspectives. 2012. 352p. pap. 35.95 (978-1-84523-128-6(7)) Peepal Tree Pr., Ltd. GBR. Dist: Independent Pubs. Group.

Dance, Daryl C. New World Adams: Interviews with West Indian Writers. 2nd ed. 2008. (ENG., Illus.). 366p. pap. 29.95 (978-1-900715-04-1(X)) Peepal Tree Pr., Ltd. GBR. Dist: Independent Pubs. Group.

French, Patrick. The World Is What It Is: The Authorized Biography of V. S. Naipaul. 2009. (Vintage Ser.). (ENG., Illus.). 592p. pap. 17.00 (978-1-4000-7980-3(2), Vintage) Knopf Doubleday Publishing Group.

Gadsby, Meredith M. Sucking Salt: Caribbean Women Writers, Migration, & Survival. 2006. (ENG.). 240p. (C). 44.95 (978-0-8262-1665-6(X)) Univ. of Missouri Pr.

Naipaul, V. S. Letters Between a Father & Son. 2011. (Illus.). 480p. pap. (978-0-330-52296-0(5)) Picador.

Naipaul, V. S. A Writer's People: Ways of Looking & Feeling. 2009. (Vintage International Ser.). (ENG.). 208p. pap. 15.00 (978-0-375-70729-2(8), Vintage) Knopf Doubleday Publishing Group.

Parker, Gabrielle. Aimé Césaire. 2010. (Inspirations Ser.). (ENG.). 100p. pap. 10.95 (978-1-906413-24-8(X)) Arcadia Bks. Ltd. GBR. Dist: Independent Pubs. Group.

Renton, David. C L R James: Cricket's Philosopher King. 2007. (ENG., Illus.). 202p. 24.95 (978-1-905791-01-9(1)) Haus Publishing GBR. Dist: Consortium Bk. Sales & Distribution.

Salick, Roydon. Ismith Khan: The Man & His Works. 2012. (ENG., Illus.). 128p. pap. 22.95 (978-1-84523-174-3(0)) Peepal Tree Pr., Ltd. GBR. Dist: Independent Pubs. Group.

Schatteman, Renee T., ed. Conversations with Caryl Phillips. 2009. (Literary Conversations Ser.). (ENG.). 240p. 50.00 (978-1-60473-209-2(1)); pap. 22.00 (978-1-60473-210-8(5)) Univ. Pr. of Mississippi.

Thompson, Ralph, et al. Writers Who Paint Painters Who Write: 3 Jamaican Artists. 2008. (ENG.). 64p. pap. 19.95 (978-1-84523-064-7(7)) Peepal Tree Pr., Ltd. GBR. Dist: Independent Pubs. Group.

AUTHORS, CATHOLIC

see Catholic Authors

AUTHORS, CHINESE

Achard, Jean-Luc. Enlightened Rainbows: The Life & Works of Shardza Tashi Gyeltsen. 2008. (Brill's Tibetan Studies Library Ser.). 500p. (978-90-04-16823-7(0)) BRILL.

Besio, Kimberly & Tung, Constantine, eds. Three Kingdoms & Chinese Culture. 2008. (SUNY Series in Chinese Philosophy & Culture). (Illus.). 193p. per. 29.95 (978-0-7914-7012-1(1)) State Univ. of New York Pr.

Chen, Peter Min-Liang. A Scholar's Path: An Anthology of Classical Chinese Poems & Prose of Chen Qing Shan - A Pioneer Writer of Malayan-Singapore Literature. 2010. (Illus.). 636p. pap. 45.00 (978-981-4317-48-1(9)) World Scientific Publishing Co., Inc.

Chen, William Y. Yi Wang San Ji. 2008. (CHI & ENG.). 185p. pap. (978-0-939083-82-4(5)) Kan sasana Printer.

Chou, E. Shan. Memory Violence, Queues: Lu Xun Interprets China. 2011. pap. (978-0-924304-68-2(5)) Assn. for Asian Studies, Inc.

Fu, Shen. Chapters from a Floating Life. Black, Shirley, tr. 2007. 112p. per. 11.95 (978-1-59654-382-9(5)) Disruptive Publishing.

—Six Records of a Floating Life. 2011. 13.77 (978-0-7848-3461-9(X), Everbind) Marco Bk. Co.

Furiya, Linda. How to Cook a Dragon: Living, Loving, & Eating in China. 2008. (ENG.). 256p. pap. 16.95 (978-1-58005-255-9(X)) Seal Pr.

Ha, Jingjun. Remapping Chinese Literature. 2008. 84p. pap. (978-3-639-08329-3(6)) VDM Verlag Dr. Mueller e.K.

Jin, Ba. The Autobiography of Ba Jin. 2008. 87p. pap. 16.95 (978-0-88093-869-3(2)) Univ. of Indianapolis Pr.

Kang, Zhengguo. Confessions: An Innocent Life in Communist China. Wilf, Susan, tr. from CHI. 2008. (ENG., Illus.). 480p. pap. 15.95 (978-0-393-33200-1(4), 33200) Norton, W. W. & Co., Inc.

Kingston, Maxine Hong. I Love a Broad Margin to My Life. 2012. (Vintage International Ser.). (ENG.). 240p. pap. 15.00 (978-0-307-45459-1(2), Vintage) Knopf Doubleday Publishing Group.

Knechtges, David R. & Chang, Taiping, eds. Ancient & Early Medieval Chinese Literature: A Reference Guide. 2010. (Handbook of Oriental Studies. Section 4 China Ser.). 792p. (978-90-04-19127-3(5)) BRILL.

Kong, Belinda. Tiananmen Fictions outside the Square: The Chinese Literary Diaspora & the Politics of Global Culture. 2012. (Asian American History & Culture Ser.). (ENG., Illus.). 278p. pap. 26.95 (978-1-4399-0759-7(5)) Temple Univ. Pr.

—Tiananmen Fictions Outside the Square: The Chinese Literary Diaspora & the Politics of Global Culture. 2012. E-Book (978-1-4399-0760-3(9)) Temple Univ. Pr.

Mann, Susan. The Talented Women of the Zhang Family. 2007. (Illus.). 352p. 60.00 (978-0-520-25089-5(3)); 322p. per. 26.95 (978-0-520-25090-1(7)) Univ. of California Pr.

Nylan, Michael. Yang Xiong & the Pleasures of Reading & Classical Learning in China. 2011. (978-0-940490-32-1(3)) American Oriental Society.

Pang, Yang. Ye Shengtao He Ta de Jia Ren. 2010. (CHI., Illus.). (978-7-5047-3251-4(5)) China Logistics Publishing Hse.

Qiu, Shi. Wo Wei Lu Xun Mao Dun Bian Hu. 2009. (CHI.). 7p. pap. (978-7-80741-515-2(0)) Wenhui Chubanshe.

Salmon, Claudine. Sastra Indonesia Awal: Kontribusi Orang Tionghoa. 2010. (IND., Illus.). 562p. (978-979-9102-94-2(4)) Kepustakaan Populer Gramedia, KPG.

Shen Fu. Six Records of a Life Adrift. Sanders, Graham, tr. from CHI. 2011. (Illus.). 148p. (C). pap. 13.95 (978-1-60384-198-6(9)); lib. bdg. 44.00 (978-1-60384-199-3(7)) Hackett Publishing Co., Inc.

Smith, Norman. Resisting Manchukuo: Chinese Women Writers & the Japanese Occupation. 2007. (ENG., Illus.). 216p. 85.00 (978-0-7748-1335-8(0)) UBC Pr. CAN. Dist: Univ. of Washington Pr.

Spence, Jonathan D. Return to Dragon Mountain: Memories of a Late Ming Man. 2008. (ENG.). 352p. (gr. 12-18). 16.00 (978-0-14-311445-1(X), Penguin (Non-Classics)) Penguin Group (USA) Inc.

Sze, Arthur, ed. Chinese Writers on Writing. 2010. (Writer's World Ser.). (ENG.). 320p. 60.00 (978-1-59534-062-7(9)); pap. 18.95 (978-1-59534-063-4(7)) Trinity Univ. Pr.

Wang, Jing M. When I Was Born: Women's Autobiography in Modern China. 2008. (Wisconsin Studies in Autobiography Ser.). (ENG.). 276p. 65.00 (978-0-299-22510-0(0)) Univ. of Wisconsin Pr.

Wang, Weiling. Sui Yue Chuan Zhen: Wo He Dang Dai Zuo Jia. 2009. (CHI., Illus.). (978-7-81119-534-7(8)) Capital Normal Univ. Pr.

Wanlong Gao. Recasting Lin Shu. 2009. 264p. pap. 20.21 (978-1-4251-9221-1(1)) Trafford Publishing.

Ward, Jean Elizabeth. Li ch'ing-chao: Remembered. 2008. 150p. pap. 23.50 (978-1-4357-3278-0(2)) Lulu Enterprises Inc.

—Yu hsuan-chi: Remembered. 2008. 180p. pap. 23.50 (978-1-4357-3274-2(X)) Lulu Enterprises Inc.

Welland, Sasha Su-Ling. A Thousand Miles of Dreams: The Journeys of Two Chinese Sisters. (Asian Voices Ser.). (ENG., Illus.). 392p. 2007. per. 19.95 (978-0-7425-5314-9(0)) 2006. 26.95 (978-0-7425-5313-2(2)) Rowman & Littlefield Publishers, Inc.

Williams, Philip. Prisoners in Contemporary Chinese Literary & Social Sciences Re. Wu, Yenna, ed. 2006. (Routledge Studies in Asia's Transformations). (Illus.). XIV, 186p. 160.00 (978-0-415-77020-0(3)) Routledge.

Xie, Bingying. Autobiography of a Chinese Girl: A Genuine Autobiography. Crome, Keith & Williams, James, eds. 2007. (Kegan Paul Travellers Ser.). (Illus.). 216p. 110.00 (978-0-7103-1041-5(2)) Kegan Paul International, Ltd. GBR. Dist: Columbia Univ. Pr.

Xu, Xueji & Zhong, Shumin. Yang Yunping Wen Shu Zi Liao Hui Bian Mu Lu. 2008. (CHI., Illus.). viii, 317p. (978-986-01-4879-4(1)) Hualien County Hacc.

Ying, Li-Hua. The A to Z of Modern Chinese Literature. 2010. (A to Z Guide Ser.). (ENG.). 500p. pap. 34.45 (978-0-8108-7614-9(0)) Scarecrow Pr., Inc.

Ying, Li-Hua & Woronoff, Jon. Historical Dictionary of Modern Chinese Literature. 2009. (Historical Dictionaries of Literature & the Arts Ser.). (ENG.). 494p. 105.00 (978-0-8108-5516-8(X)) Scarecrow Pr., Inc.

Yutang, Lin. Gay Genius. 2006. 396p. per. (978-1-4067-1251-3(5), Hesperides Pr.) Read Bks.

Zhao, Chuanren, et al. Zhongguo Shu Ming Shi Yi Da Ci Dian. 2007. (CHI.). (978-7-80737-206-6(0)) Shandong Friendship Publishing Hse.

Zhengguo, Kang. Confessions. 2007. 27.95 (978-0-7930-6467-0(8)) Norton, W. W. & Co., Inc.

—Confessions: An Innocent Life in Communist China. Wilf, Susan, tr. from CHI. 2007. (ENG., Illus.). 544p. 27.95 (978-0-393-06467-4(0), 6467) Norton, W. W. & Co., Inc.

Zhou, Yangzhi. Wo de Zu Fu Zhou Libo: Ren Jian Shi Dou Fu Yu Liu Feng. 2010. (CHI., Illus.). (978-7-80214-658-7(5)) Unitp Publishing Hse.

AUTHORS, CUBAN

Ada, Alma Flor. Alma Flor Ada & YOU, 1 vol., Vol. 2. 2nd ed. 2008. (Author & YOU Ser.). (Illus.). 126p. pap. 35.00 (978-1-59158-228-1(8), LU2288) Libraries Unlimited, Inc.

Arenas, Reinaldo. Antes Que Anochezca. 2011.Tr. of Before Night Falls. (SPA., Illus.). 343p. pap. (978-84-8383-571-5(1)) Tusquets Editores.

Bufill, José Ángel & Reyes, Alfonso. Los Amigos Cubanos de Alfonso Reyes: Correspondencia. 2010. (SPA.). xi, 944p. (978-93-480-4827-1(9)) Alexandria Library, Inc.

Campuzano, Luisa. Alejo Carpentier: Acá y Allá. 2007. (Serie Antonio Cornejo Polar Ser.: Vol. 5). (SPA., Illus.). 374p. (978-1-930744-31-8(5)) Instituto Internacional de Literatura Iberoamericana (IILI).

Gutiérrez, José Ismael. Reinaldo Arenas: Entre el placer y el Infierno. 2007. (SPA.). per. 13.95 (978-1-933439-12-9(2)) Cursack Bks.

Lange, Charlotte. Modos de Parodia: Guillermo Cabrera Infante, Reinaldo Arenas, Jorge Ibargüengoitia y José Augustín. 2008. (Hispanic Studies: Culture & Ideas Ser.). (SPA.). 252p. pap. 66.95 (978-3-03911-554-9(5)) Lang, Peter AG GBR. Dist: Lang, Peter.

Miaja, Maria Teresa. Del Alba Al Anochecer: La Escritura en Reinaldo Arenas. 2008. (SPA.). 179p. pap. 24.80 (978-84-8489-409-4(6)) Iberoamericana Vervuert Publishing Corp.

Rivera, Armanco Chávez. Cuba per Se: Cartas de la Diaspora. 2009. (Coleccion Polymita Ser.). (SPA.). 574p. pap. 39.95 (978-1-59388-138-2(X), 8-138-X) Ediciones Universal.

AUTHORS, CZECH

Hrabal, Bohumil. Vita Nuova: A Novel. Liman, Tony, tr. from CZE. 2010. (Writings from an Unbound Europe Ser.). (ENG.). 248p. pap. 19.95 (978-0-8101-2546-9(3)) Northwestern Univ. Pr.

AUTHORS, ENGLISH

Adams, Elbridge L. & Zelie, John Sheridan. Joseph Conrad, the Man: And A Burial in Kent. 2011. 84p. 37.95 (978-1-258-09072-2(4)) Literary Licensing, LLC.

Adams, Jad. Kipling. 2013. (ENG.). 240p. pap. 19.95 (978-1-908323-06-4(X)) Haus Publishing GBR. Dist: Consortium Bk. Sales & Distribution.

Adams, Maureen. Shaggy Muses: The Dogs Who Inspired Virginia Woolf, Emily Dickenson, Elizabeth Barrett Browning, Edith Wharton, & Emily Bronte. 2011. (Illus.). 320p. pap. 16.00 (978-0-226-00536-2(4)) Univ. of Chicago Pr.

Adams, Oscar Fay. The Story of Jane Austen's Life. 2009. 190p. pap. 19.99 (978-0-217-89784-6(3)) General Bks. LLC.

—The Story of Jane Austen's Life. 2009. 292p. 43.95 (978-1-104-69366-4(6)); pap. 28.95 (978-1-104-66703-0(7)) Kessinger Publishing, LLC.

Aksenov, Vitalii. Kto Byl Shekspirom? Intellektualnyi Detektiv Dlia Vsekh, Kto Liubit Razgadyvat Tainy. 2010. (RUS., Illus.). 272p. (978-5-9676-0236-8(4)) Petropolis, telekommunikacionnyj kompleks.

Aldiss, Brian W. An Exile on Planet Earth: Articles & Reflections. 2012. (ENG.). 192p. 35.00 (978-1-85124-373-0(9)) Bodleian Library GBR. Dist: Chicago Distribution Ctr.

Alexander, Michael. Geoffrey Chaucer. 2012. (ENG., Illus.). 40p. pap. 9.99 (978-1-85759-748-6(6)) Scala, Editions FRA. Dist: National Bk. Network.

Allen, Charles. Kipling Sahib: India & the Making of Rudyard Kipling. 2009. (ENG., Illus.). 448p. 28.00 (978-1-60598-031-7(5), 605031) Pegasus Bks.

Allen, Keith. Grow Up. 2008. (ENG., Illus.). 384p. pap. 15.95 (978-0-09-191071-6(4)) Ebury Publishing GBR. Dist: Independent Pubs. Group.

Altholz, Josef L., et al, eds. The Correspondence of Lord Acton & Richard Simpson: Volume 2, 3 vols. 2008. (ENG.). 356p. pap. 46.00 (978-0-521-08369-0(9)) Cambridge Univ. Pr.

—The Correspondence of Lord Acton & Richard Simpson: Volume 3, 3 vols. 2008. (ENG.). 384p. pap. 53.00 (978-0-521-08380-5(X)) Cambridge Univ. Pr.

Altholz, Josef L. & McElrath, Damian, eds. The Correspondence of Lord Acton & Richard Simpson: Volume 1, 3 vols. 2008. (ENG.). 260p. pap. 37.99 (978-0-521-08355-3(9)) Cambridge Univ. Pr.

Andermahr, Sonya. Jeanette Winterson. 2008. (New British Fiction Ser.). (ENG.). 176p. 80.00 (978-0-230-50760-9(3)); pap. 18.00 (978-0-230-50761-6(1)) Palgrave Macmillan.

Andrew, Malcolm. The Palgrave Literary Dictionary of Chaucer. 2009. (Palgrave Literary Dictionaries Ser.). (ENG.). 288p. pap. 35.00 (978-0-230-23148-1(9)) Palgrave Macmillan.

Angeli, Helen Rosetti. Shelley & His Friends in Italy. 2007. (ENG.). 380p. 48.95 (978-0-548-10980-9(X)) Kessinger Publishing, LLC.

Annan, Noel Gilroy & Stephen, Leslie. Leslie Stephen: His Thought & Character in Relation to His Time. 2011. 354p. 51.95 (978-1-258-09927-5(6)) Literary Licensing, LLC.

Anstey, Sandra & Lee, Victor, eds. William Wordsworth: Selected Poems. 2nd rev. ed. 2008. (Oxford Student Texts). (ENG., Illus.). 192p. (YA). 15.95 (978-0-19-832550-5(9)) Oxford Univ. Pr., Inc.

Anthony Hope. Father Stafford. Lt. ed. 2007. (ENG.). 166p. pap. 21.99 (978-1-4264-8239-7(6)) BiblioBazaar.

Aplin, John. The Inheritance of Genius: A Thackeray Family Biography, 1798-1875. 2010. 324p. pap. 53.00 (978-0-7188-9224-1(0)) Lutherworth Pr., The GBR. Dist: Brown, David Bk. Co., The.

Aplin, John, ed. The Correspondence & Journals of the Thackeray Family, 5 vols. 2011. (Pickering Masters Ser.). (ENG., Illus.). 1808p. 795.00 (978-1-85196-640-0(4)) Pickering & Chatto Pubs., Ltd. GBR. Dist: Ashgate Publishing Co.

Archer, Jeffrey. Prison Diary. 2006. (Prison Diary Ser.: Vol. 3). (ENG.). 480p. pap. 16.95 (978-0-312-35479-4(7), St. Martin's Griffin) St. Martin's Pr.

Archer, William. Real Conversations. 2009. 144p. pap. 19.99 (978-0-217-97915-3(7)) General Bks. LLC.

—Real Conversations Conversation VII with. 2006. pap. 15.95 (978-1-4286-4326-0(5)) Kessinger Publishing, LLC.

Aronson, Judith. Likenesses: With the Sitters Writing about One Another. 2010 (ENG., Illus.). 152p. pap. 29.95 (978-1-85754-994-2(5)) Carcanet Pr., Ltd. GBR. Dist: Independent Pubs. Group.

Ashton, Gail. Geoffrey Chaucer. 2011. (Brief Lives Ser.). (ENG., Illus.). 120p. pap. 12.95 (978-1-84391-918-6(4)) Hesperus Pr. GBR. Dist: Independent Pubs. Group.

Athill, Diana. Instead of a Letter: A Memoir. 2010. (ENG.). 237p. pap. 14.95 (978-0-393-33857-7(6), 33857) Norton, W. W. & Co., Inc.

—Letters to a Friend. 2012. (ENG.). 352p. 24.95 (978-0-393-06295-3(3), 6295) Norton, W. W. & Co., Inc.

—Somewhere Towards the End. Lt. ed. 2009. 232p. 31.50 (978-1-4104-1911-8(8)) Thorndike Pr.

—Somewhere Towards the End: A Memoir. 2009. (ENG.). 208p. pap. 13.95 (978-0-393-33800-3(2), 33800) Norton, W. W. & Co., Inc.

Athill, Diana. Yesterday Morning. 2012. (ENG., Illus.). 176p. pap. 13.95 (978-1-84708-426-2(5)) Granta Bks. GBR. Dist: Ingram Pub. Services.

Austen-Leigh, James E. A Memoir of Jane Austen: And Other Family Recollections. Sutherland, Kathryn, ed. 2008. (Oxford World's Classics Ser.). (ENG., Illus.). 352p. (Orig.). pap. 12.95 (978-0-19-954077-8(2)) Oxford Univ. Pr., Inc.

Austen-Leigh, James Edward. A Memoir of Jane Austen. 2008. 172p. 22.99 (978-0-554-36587-9(1)) 2008. 172p. 25.99 (978-0-554-27284-9(9)) 2007. (ENG.). 154p. per. 19.99 (978-1-4346-2872-5(8)) 2007. (ENG.). 170p. per. 21.99 (978-1-4346-2907-4(4)) BiblioBazaar.

—A Memoir of Jane Austen. 2009. 186p. pap. (978-0-217-66579-7(9)) Books LLC.

—A Memoir of Jane Austen. 2009. (Cambridge Library Collection - Literary Studies). (ENG.). 260p. pap. 17.99 (978-1-108-00356-8(7)) Cambridge Univ. Pr.

Austen Leigh, James Edward. A Memoir of Jane Austen: Together with 'Lady Susan': a Novel. 2009. (Cambridge Library Collection - Literary Studies). 384p. pap. 23.99 (978-1-108-00357-5(5)) Cambridge Univ. Pr.

Austen-Leigh, James Edward & Austen, Jane. A Memoir of Jane Austen. 2008. 384p. 48.95 (978-1-4369-8784-4(9)); pap. 33.95 (978-1-4367-3981-8(0)) Kessinger Publishing, LLC.

Austen-Leigh, William & Austen-Leigh, Richard Arthur. Jane Austen, Her Life & Letters: A Family Record. 2006. (B&N Library of Essential Reading Ser.). (ENG., Illus.). 400p. pap. 9.95 (978-0-7607-8323-8(3)) Barnes & Noble, Inc.

Bachrach, Arthur J. D. H. Lawrence in New Mexico: The Time Is Different There. 2006. (ENG., Illus.). 136p. pap. 17.95 (978-0-8263-3496-1(2)) Univ. of New Mexico Pr.

Bagehot, Walter. Shakespeare, the Man: An Essay. 2009. 54p. pap. 16.75 (978-1-113-34787-9(2)) BiblioBazaar.

Baines, Paul, ed. The Wiley-Blackwell Encyclopedia of Eighteenth-Century Writers & Writing, 1660-1789. 2011. (ENG.). 432p. 199.95 (978-1-4051-5669-1(4), Wiley-Blackwell) Wiley, John & Sons, Inc.

Baker, Brian. Iain Sinclair. 2008. (Contemporary British Novelists Ser.). (ENG.). 192p. pap. 26.00 (978-0-7190-6905-5(X)) Manchester Univ. Pr. GBR. Dist: Macmillan.

Baker, Phil. The Devil Is a Gentleman: The Life & Times of Dennis Wheatley. 2010. (Dark Masters Ser.). (ENG., Illus.). 699p. 40.00 (978-1-903517-75-8(3)) Dedalus, Ltd.

Baker, William. Harold Pinter. 2008. (Writers Lives Ser.). (ENG.). 176p. 24.95 (978-0-8264-9971-4(6)); 90.00 (978-0-8264-9970-7(8)) Continuum International Publishing Group, Ltd. GBR. Dist: National Bk. Network.

—A Wilkie Collins Chronology. Page, Norman, ed. 2007. (Author Chronologies Ser.). (ENG.). 240p. 105.00 (978-1-4039-9481-3(1)) Palgrave Macmillan.

Barker, Christopher. The Arms of the Infinite: Elizabeth Smart & George Barker. 2010. (Illus.). 258p. (C). pap. 29.95 (978-1-55458-270-9(9)) Wilfrid Laurier Univ. Pr. CAN. Dist: Univ. of Toronto Pr.

Barnard, Louise & Barnard, Robert. A Bronte Encyclopedia. 2007. (ENG., Illus.). 416p. 128.95 (978-1-4051-5119-1(6), Wiley-Blackwell) Wiley, John & Sons, Inc.

Barnard, Teresa. Anna Seward: A Constructed Life - A Critical Biography. 2009. (Illus.). 208p. 99.95 (978-0-7546-6616-5(6)) Ashgate Publishing Co.

Baron, Carl, ed. A Memoir of D. H. Lawrence: 'the Betrayal' G. H. Neville. 2010. (ENG.). 224p. pap. 27.99 (978-0-521-13543-6(5)) Cambridge Univ. Pr.

Barrowcliffe, Mark. The Elfish Gene: Dungeons, Dragons & Growing up Strange. 2009. (ENG.). 288p. pap. 14.00 (978-1-56947-601-7(2)) Soho Pr., Inc.

Bastide, Judith & Rich, Michael. Follow these Writers... in Sussex: A Handbook for Literary Detectives. 2011. (Illus.). 148p. pap. 15.66 (978-1-4567-7220-8(1)) AuthorHouse.

Bate, Jonathan. Soul of the Age: A Biography of the Mind of William Shakespeare. 2009. (ENG., Illus.). 496p. 35.00 (978-1-4000-6206-5(3)) Random Hse., Inc.

Bate, W. Jackson. Samuel Johnson: A Biography. 2009. (ENG.). 668p. pap. 24.95 (978-1-58243-524-4(3), Counterpoint Pr.) Basic Bks. GBR. Dist: Perseus-PGW.

Beckford, William. Recollections of an Excursion to the Monasteries of Alcobaça & Batalha. 2009. 86p. pap. 14.14 (978-0-217-74830-8(9)) General Bks. LLC.

Beddoes, Thomas Lovell. The Letters of Thomas Lovell Beddoes. Gosse, Edmund, ed. 2007. (ENG.). 282p. 43.95 (978-0-548-15650-6(6)); pap. 28.95 (978-1-4304-5115-0(7)) Kessinger Publishing, LLC.

Beer, John. Coleridge's Play of Mind. 2010. (ENG.). 288p. 99.00 (978-0-19-957401-8(4)) Oxford Univ. Pr., Inc.

Beilin, Elaine V., ed. Early Tudor Women Writers Vol. 1. 2009. (Ashgate Critical Essays on Women Writers in England, 1550-1700 Ser.). 510p. 275.00 (978-0-7546-6165-8(2)) Ashgate Publishing Co.

Bell, Fergus Hanna, ed. A Salute from the Banderol: The Selected Writings of Sam Hanna Bell. 2010. (ENG., Illus.). 240p. 42.95 (978-0-85640-839-7(5)) Blackstaff Pr., Ltd. GBR. Dist: Dufour Editions, Inc.

Bellanca, Mary Ellen. Daybooks of Discovery: Nature Diaries in Britain, 1770-1870. 2007. (Under the Sign of Nature Ser.). (ENG.). 248p. (gr. 17). 59.50 (978-0-8139-2612-4(2)); (C). (gr. 13-17). per. 22.50 (978-0-8139-2613-1(0)) Univ. Pr. of Virginia.

Bennett, Alan. A Life Like Other People's. 2010. (ENG., Illus.). 256p. 22.00 (978-0-374-19192-4(1)) Farrar, Straus & Giroux.

Bennett, Arnold. Arnold Bennett's Letters to His Nephew. 2007. (ENG.). 376p. 48.95 (978-0-548-11732-3(2)) Kessinger Publishing, LLC.

Bennett, Joan. Sir Thomas Browne: 'A Man of Achievement in Literature' 2010. (ENG.). 264p. pap. 23.99 (978-0-521-14823-8(5)) Cambridge Univ. Pr.

Benson, Arthur Christopher. The Altar Fire. 2009. 336p. 32.99 (978-1-115-21720-0(8)); 336p. 36.99 (978-1-115-21721-7(6)); 412p. 34.99 (978-1-115-21730-9(5)); 412p. 41.99 (978-1-115-21732-3(1)); 336p. pap. 31.75 (978-1-115-21718-7(6)) BiblioBazaar.

—The Altar Fire. 2009. 288p. pap. (978-0-217-37749-2(1)) Books LLC.

—The Altar Fire. 2007. 232p. per. (978-1-4065-4813-6(8)) Dodo Pr.

—The Altar Fire. 2008. 408p. pap. (978-1-4097-7754-0(5)) Read Bks.

Bentley, Phyllis Eleano. Bronte Sisters. 2006. 52p. per. (978-1-4067-0992-6(1), Hesperides Pr.) Read Bks.

Benton, Michael J. Literary Biography: An Introduction. 2009. (ENG., Illus.). 280p. 110.95 (978-1-4051-9446-4(4), Wiley-Blackwell) Wiley, John & Sons, Inc.

Bergmann, Helena. A Revised Reading of Mary Hays' Philosophical Novel 'Memoirs of Emma Courtney' (1796) Enlarging the Canon of the Mary Wollstonecraft Literary-Philosophical Circle. 2011. 192p. 109.95 (978-0-7734-3948-1(X)) Mellen, Edwin Pr., The.

Bevington, David. George Peel. 2011. (University Wits Ser.). 502p. 240.00 (978-0-7546-2856-9(6)) Ashgate Publishing Co.

—Shakespeare & Biography. 2010. (Oxford Shakespeare Topics Ser.). (ENG.). 192p. 45.00 (978-0-19-958648-6(9)) Oxford Univ. Pr., Inc.

Bieri, James. Percy Bysshe Shelley: A Biography. 2008. (ENG., Illus.). 888p. (gr. 17). 92.00 (978-0-8018-8860-1(3)); pap. 47.00 (978-0-8018-8861-8(1)) Johns Hopkins Univ. Pr.

Biographiq. D H Lawrence - Prolific English Writer. 2008. 68p. pap. 9.99 (978-1-59986-364-1(2), Biographiq) Filiquarian Publishing, LLC.

—Mary Wollstonecraft Shelley - Gothic Novelist (Biography) 2008. 100p. pap. 9.99 (978-1-59986-379-5(0), Biographiq) Filiquarian Publishing, LLC.

Birkhoff, Barbara. As Between Friends: Criticism of Themselves & One Another in the Letters of Coleridge, Wordsworth & Lamb. 2011. 58p. 36.95 (978-1-258-01369-1(X)) Literary Licensing, LLC.

Blackburn, Julia. The Three of Us: A Family Story. 2009. (Vintage Ser.). (ENG., Illus.). 320p. pap. 16.00 (978-0-307-27893-7(X), Vintage) Knopf Doubleday Publishing Group.

Bloch, Michael. James Lees-Milne: The Life. 2009. (ENG., Illus.). 416p. 39.95 (978-0-7195-6034-7(9)) Murray, John GBR. Dist: Independent Pubs. Group.

Blocksidge, Martin. 'A Life Lived Quickly' Tennyson's Friend Arthur Hallam & His Legend. 2011. (Illus.). 323p. 79.95 (978-1-84519-418-5(7)) Sussex Academic Pr. GBR. Dist: International Specialized Bk. Services.

Blythe, Ronald. At the Yeoman's House. 2012. (ENG., Illus.). 128p. 34.95 (978-1-904634-88-1(5)) Enitharmon Pr. GBR. Dist: Dufour Editions, Inc.

Blythe, Ronald. A Writer's Day-Book. 2007. 158p. per. (978-1-84233-124-8(8)) Trent Polytechnic.

Bogarde, Dirk. Ever, Dirk: The Bogarde Letters. Coldstream, John, ed. 2009. (ENG., Illus.). 664p. 23.95 (978-0-7538-2589-1(9), Phoenix) Orion Publishing Group, Ltd. GBR. Dist: Independent Pubs. Group.

Bolton, Sarah K. Famous English Authors of the Nineteenth Century. 2007. (ENG.). 468p. 52.95 (978-0-548-27000-4(7)); per. 37.95 (978-1-4326-7450-2(1)) Kessinger Publishing, LLC.

Bompas, George C. The Problem of the Shakespeare Plays. 2009. 96p. pap. 14.14 (978-1-4589-3377-5(6)) General Bks. LLC.

Bond, Jenny & Sheedy, Chris. Who the Hell Is Pansy O'Hara? The Fascinating Stories Behind 50 of the World's Best-Loved Books. 2008. (ENG.). 336p. (gr. 12-18). 13.00 (978-0-14-311364-5(X), Penguin (Non-Classics)) Penguin Group (USA) Inc.

Booth, George. Master Why. 2009. 548p. pap. 28.95 (978-1-4092-5463-8(1)) Lulu Enterprises Inc.

Boston, Anne. Lesley Blanch: Inner Landscapes Wilder Shores. 2011. (ENG., Illus.). 384p. pap. 15.95 (978-0-7195-6547-2(2)) Murray, John GBR. Dist: Independent Pubs. Group.

—Lesley Blanch: Inner Landscapes, Wilder Shores. 2010. (ENG., Illus.). 384p. 40.00 (978-0-7195-6037-8(3)) Murray, John GBR. Dist: Independent Pubs. Group.

Boswell, James. The Journal of a Tour to the Hebrides with Samuel Johnson, Ll D. 2009. 332p. pap. (978-1-4099-0611-7(6)) Dodo Pr.

—The Life of Johnson. 2008. 620p. 34.99 (978-0-554-32577-4(2)); 620p. 38.99 (978-0-554-23274-4(X)); 656p. 39.99 (978-0-554-22968-3(4)); 656p. 35.99 (978-0-554-32271-1(4)) BiblioBazaar.

—Life of Johnson. 2008. 144p. 24.99 (978-0-554-26095-2(6)); 21.99 (978-0-554-35398-2(9)) BiblioBazaar.

—Life of Johnson. Chapman, R. W. & Fleeman, J. D., eds. 2008. (Oxford World's Classics Ser.). (ENG.). 1536p. pap. 19.95 (978-0-19-954021-1(7)) Oxford Univ. Pr., Inc.

—Life of Johnson. 2006. (ENG.). 384p. per. (978-1-4067-3122-4(6), Hesperides Pr.) Read Bks.

Boyt, Susie. My Judy Garland Life: A Memoir. 2010. (ENG., Illus.). 320p. pap. 15.00 (978-1-60819-208-3(3)) Bloomsbury Publishing.

Bradford, Richard. First Boredom, Then Fear: The Life of Philip Larkin. 2009. (ENG., Illus.). 220p. pap. 19.95 (978-0-7206-1325-4(6)) Owen, Peter Ltd. GBR. Dist: Independent Pubs. Group.

—The Life of a Long Distance Writer: The Biography of Alan Sillitoe. 2008. (ENG., Illus.). 400p. 38.95 (978-0-7206-1317-9(5)) Owen, Peter Ltd. GBR. Dist: Independent Pubs. Group.

Breit, Harvey. The Writer Observed. 2011. 286p. 48.95 (978-1-258-09963-3(2)) Literary Licensing, LLC.

Brennecke Jr, Ernest & Brennecke Jr., Ernest. John Milton, the Elder & His Music. 2011. 270p. 47.95 (978-1-258-03003-2(9)) Literary Licensing, LLC.

Bridge, Marie, ed. On the Way Home: Conversations Between Writers & Psychoanalysts. 2007. 156p. 28.95 (978-1-85575-472-0(X)) Karnac Bks. GBR. Dist: Stylus Publishing, LLC.

Brightwell, C. L. (Cecilia Lucy). Memorials of the Life of Amelia Opie, Selected & Arranged from Her Letters, Diaries, & Other Manuscripts, by Cecilia Lucy Brightwell. 2006. 460p. per. 29.99 (978-1-4255-5073-8(8)) MPublishing.

Bronson, Bertrand H. Johnson & Boswell: Three Essays. 2011. 118p. 39.95 (978-1-258-02667-7(8)) Literary Licensing, LLC.

Brontë, Charlotte. Selected Letters. Smith, Margaret, ed. 2010. (Oxford World's Classics Ser.). (ENG.). 320p. pap. 12.95 (978-0-19-957696-8(3)) Oxford Univ. Pr., Inc.

Brooke, Stopford Augustus. Milton. 2009. 158p. pap. (978-0-217-25703-9(8)) Books LLC.

Brooker, Peter. Bohemia in London: The Social Scene of Early Modernism. 2007. (ENG., Illus.). 224p. pap. 31.00 (978-0-230-54692-9(7)) Palgrave Macmillan.

Brown, Edward. Letters of Thomas Edward Brown V1. 2007. (ENG.). 240p. 41.95 (978-0-548-10141-4(8)) Kessinger Publishing, LLC.

—Letters of Thomas Edward Brown V2. 2007. (ENG.). 252p. 41.95 (978-0-548-10142-1(6)) Kessinger Publishing, LLC.

Brown, Eleanor Gertrude. Milton's Blindness. 2011. 178p. 42.95 (978-1-258-03796-3(3)) Literary Licensing, LLC.

Brown, John. John Bunyan: His Life Times & Work. 3rd ed. 2007. (Illus.). 522p. pap. 45.00 (978-1-55635-219-5(0), Wipf and Stock) Wipf & Stock Pubs.

—John Bunyan His Life Times & Work. 2006. (Illus.). pap. 40.95 (978-1-4286-5050-3(4)) Kessinger Publishing, LLC.

Brown, Mark, ed. Howard Barker Interviews, 1980-2010: Conversations in Catastrophe. 2011. (Illus.). 214p. pap. 30.00 (978-1-84150-398-1(3)) Intellect, Ltd. GBR. Dist: Chicago Distribution Ctr.

Brown, Peter. Chaucer & the Making of Optical Space. 2007. (Illus.). 378p. pap. 85.95 (978-3-03911-340-8(2)) Lang, Peter Publishing, Inc.

Brown, Wallace Cable & Churchill, Charles. Charles Churchill: Poet, Rake & Rebel. 2011. 254p. 46.95 (978-1-258-01589-3(7)) Literary Licensing, LLC.

Browning, Elizabeth Barrett & Browning, Robert. The Brownings' Correspondence, 1849-1851: Vol. 16: Letters 2813-2900, Vol. 16. Kelley, Philip et al, eds. 2007. (Illus.). 110.00 (978-0-911459-32-6(4)) Wedgestone Pr.

—The Brownings' Correspondence, 1851-1852: Vol. 17; Letters 2901-3000. Kelley, Philip et al, eds. 2010. (Illus.). 432p. 110.00 (978-0-911459-34-0(0)) Wedgestone Pr.

—The Brownings' Correspondence, 1852-1853: Letters 3001-3173, Vol. 18. Kelley, Philip et al, eds. 2010. (Illus.). 432p. 110.00 (978-0-911459-35-7(9)) Wedgestone Pr.

Browning, Oscar. Life of George Eliot. 2011. (Cambridge Library Collection - Literary Studies). (ENG.). 194p. pap. 19.99 (978-1-108-04049-5(7)) Cambridge Univ. Pr.

Bryher & Ellerman, Annie Winifred. The Heart to Artemis: A Writer's Memoirs. 2011. 320p. 50.95 (978-1-258-09656-4(0)) Literary Licensing, LLC.

Bryson, Bill. Shakespeare: The World as Stage. 2008. (ENG.). 208p. pap. 13.99 (978-0-06-167369-6(2), HarperPerennial) HarperCollins Pubs.

Buckell, Gareth. Rayner Heppenstall: A Critical Study. 2007. (Dalkey Archive Scholarly Ser.). (ENG.). 91p. pap. 29.95 (978-1-56478-471-1(1)) Dalkey Archive Pr.

Buckley-Ott, Cara L. & Leverette, Marc, eds. It's Not TV: Watching HBO in the Post-Television ERA. 2007. XII, 260p. 105.00 (978-0-415-96037-3(1)) Routledge.

Buel, Richard. Joel Barlow: American Citizen in a Revolutionary World. 2011. (ENG., Illus.). 448p. (gr. 17). 34.95 (978-0-8018-9769-6(6)) Johns Hopkins Univ. Pr.

Bullock, Philip Ross, ed. The Correspondence of Jean Sibelius & Rosa Newmarch, 1906-1939. 2011. (Illus.). 312p. 90.00 (978-1-84383-683-4(1), Boydell Press) Boydell & Brewer, Ltd. GBR. Dist: Boydell & Brewer, Inc.

Bunyan, John. Grace Abounding: With Other Spiritual Autobiographies. Stachniewski, John & Pacheco, Anita, eds. 2008. (Oxford World's Classics Ser.). (ENG.). 336p. pap. 11.95 (978-0-19-955498-0(6)) Oxford Univ. Pr., Inc.

—Grace Abounding to the Chief of Sinners. 2008. 148p. 21.99 (978-0-559-79474-2(6)); 148p. pap. 20.75 (978-0-559-79472-8(X)); 152p. 21.99 (978-0-554-37023-1(9)); 152p. 24.99 (978-0-554-27720-2(4)) BiblioBazaar.

—Grace Abounding to the Chief of Sinners. 2007. (Authentic Original Classic Ser.). 173p. per. 13.99 (978-0-7684-2457-7(7)) Destiny Image Pubs.

—Grace Abounding to the Chief of Sinners. 2007. (ENG.). 88p. per. (978-1-4068-2294-6(9)) Echo Library.

—Grace Abounding to the Chief of Sinners. 2007. (Hendrickson Christian Classics Ser.). 165p. 6.97 (978-1-59856-206-4(1)); 9.95 (978-1-59856-142-5(1)) Hendrickson Pubs. Marketing, LLC.

—Grace Abounding to the Chief of Sinners. 2007. per. 9.99 (978-1-4245-0793-1(6)) Treasures Media Inc.

—Grace Abounding to the Chief of Sinners: In a Faithful Account of the Life & Death of John Bunyan. 2007. 244p. (ENG.). 24.95 (978-1-60206-458-4(X)); per. 10.95 (978-1-60206-457-7(1)) Cosimo, Inc.

Burdett, Osbert. William Blake's Apprenticeship & Marriage. 2006. pap. 15.95 (978-1-4286-7597-1(3)) Kessinger Publishing, LLC.

Burns, Carole. Off the Page: Writers Talk about Beginnings, Endings, & Everything in Between. 2007. (ENG.). 240p. per. 14.95 (978-0-393-33088-5(5), 33088) Norton, W. W. & Co., Inc.

Burnside, John. A Lie about My Father. 2007. (ENG.). 336p. pap. 15.00 (978-1-55597-467-1(8)) Graywolf Pr.

Butler, Andrew M., ed. An Unofficial Companion to the Novels of Terry Pratchett. 2008. (Illus.). 472p. (C). 49.95 (978-1-84645-001-3(2), GWP001) Greenwood Publishing Group, Inc.

Butler, Marilyn. Jane Austen. 2007. (Very Interesting People Ser.). (ENG.). 128p. per. 9.99 (978-0-19-921760-1(2)) Oxford Univ. Pr., Inc.

Butler, Samuel. The Correspondence of Samuel Butler with His Sister May. Howard, Daniel Francis, ed. 2011. 284p. 48.95 (978-1-258-04522-7(2)) Literary Licensing, LLC.

Butterfield, David & Stray, Christopher, eds. A. E. Housman: Classical Scholar. 2009. (Illus.). 224p. 120.00 (978-0-7156-3808-8(4)) Duckworth Publishers GBR. Dist: International Publishers Marketing.

Byrne, Paula. Mad World: Evelyn Waugh & the Secrets of Brideshead. 2011. (ENG.). 384p. pap. 16.99 (978-0-06-088131-3(3), HarperPerennial) HarperCollins Pubs.

Byron, George Gordon. The Letters & Journals of Lord Byron. 2007. (ENG.). 272p. per. (978-1-4068-2424-7(0)); 360p. per. (978-1-4068-1229-9(3)) Echo Library.

Cabell, Craig. Terry Pratchett: The Spirit of Fantasy. 2012. (ENG., Illus.). 246p. 27.95 (978-1-84358-507-7(3)) Blake, John Publishing, Ltd. GBR. Dist: Independent Pubs. Group.

Cade, Jared. Agatha Christie & the Eleven Missing Days. 4th rev. ed. 2011. (ENG., Illus.). 300p. pap. 19.95 (978-0-7206-1390-2(6)) Owen, Peter Ltd. GBR. Dist: Independent Pubs. Group.

Caine, T. Hall. Recollection of Dante Gabriel Rossetti. 2007. (ENG.). 320p. 45.95 (978-0-548-09817-2(4)) Kessinger Publishing, LLC.

Caldecott, Moyra. Multidimensional Life: A writer on the process of Writing. 2007. per. 16.95 (978-1-84319-549-8(6), Bladud Bks.) Mushroom Publishing GBR. Dist: Lightning Source, Inc.

Callcott, Maria. Journal of a Residence in Chile, during the Year 1822. 2011. (Cambridge Library Collection - Women's Writing Ser.). (ENG., Illus.). 552p. pap. 39.99 (978-1-108-03378-7(4)) Cambridge Univ. Pr.

Callow, Simon. Charles Dickens & the Great Theatre of the World. 2012. (Vintage Ser.). (ENG.). 384p. pap. 16.00 (978-0-345-80323-8(X), Vintage) Knopf Doubleday Publishing Group.

Campbell, Gordon & Corns, Thomas N. John Milton: Life, Work, & Thought. 2010. (ENG., Illus.). 512p. pap. 24.95 (978-0-19-959103-9(2)) Oxford Univ. Pr., Inc.

Campbell, James Dykes. Samuel Taylor Coleridge: A Narrative of the Events of His Life. 2007. (ENG.). 332p. 45.95 (978-0-548-08779-4(2)) Kessinger Publishing, LLC.

Canning, Richard. E. M. Forster. 2010. (Brief Lives Ser.). (ENG.). 120p. pap. 15.95 (978-1-84391-916-2(8)) Hesperus Pr. GBR. Dist: Independent Pubs. Group.

Cannon, John. The Brontes: A Family History. 2008. (ENG., Illus.). 160p. per. (978-0-7509-4808-1(6)) History Pr. Ltd.,The.

Carabine, Hubbard. Lives of Victorian Literary Figures: Conrad, Haggard & Kipling by Their Contemporaries, 3 vols., Pt. VII. 2009. (Lives of Victorian Literary Figures Ser.). (ENG., Illus.). 1376p. 495.00 (978-1-85196-963-0(2)) Pickering & Chatto Pubs., Ltd. GBR. Dist: Ashgate Publishing Co.

Carlson, David R. Chaucer's Jobs. 2008. (New Middle Ages Ser.). (ENG.). 180p. pap. 30.00 (978-0-230-60243-4(6)) Palgrave Macmillan.

Carlson, Julie Ann. England's First Family of Writers: Mary Wollstonecraft, William Godwin, Mary Shelley. 2007. (ENG.). 344p. (gr. 17). 54.00 (978-0-8018-8618-8(X)) Johns Hopkins Univ. Pr.

Carlyle, Thomas. Life of John Sterling. 2008. 284p. 25.99 (978-0-554-38015-5(3)) 2008. 284p. 28.99 (978-0-554-28712-6(9)) 2007. (ENG.). 252p. pap. 21.99 (978-1-4346-6112-8(1)) 2007. (ENG.). 282p. pap. 23.99 (978-1-4346-6113-5(X)) BiblioBazaar.

—Life of John Sterling. 2007. pap. (978-1-4065-1276-2(1)) Dodo Pr.

Carnell, Rachel. Political Biography of Delarivier Manley, 1 vol. 2008. (Eighteenth-Century Political Biographies Ser.). (ENG., Illus.). 320p. 99.00 (978-1-85196-857-2(1)) Pickering & Chatto Pubs., Ltd. GBR. Dist: Ashgate Publishing Co.

Carnell, Rachel & King, Kathryn. Political Biography of Eliza Haywood, 1 vol. 2012. (Eighteenth-Century Political Biographies Ser.). (ENG.). 288p. 99.00 (978-1-85196-917-3(9)) Pickering & Chatto Pubs., Ltd. GBR. Dist: Ashgate Publishing Co.

Carpenter, Edward & Barnefield, George. The Psychology of the Poet Shelley. 128p. 2008. 35.95 (978-1-4366-7628-1(2)) 2007. (ENG.). per. 20.95 (978-1-4325-6862-7(0)) Kessinger Publishing, LLC.

Carroll, Lewis, pseud. Lewis Carroll & the House of Macmillan. Cohen, Morton N. & Gandolfo, Anita, eds. 2007. (Cambridge Studies in Publishing & Printing History Ser.). (ENG., Illus.). 396p. pap. 79.00 (978-0-521-04471-4(5)) Cambridge Univ. Pr.

Carter, Elizabeth. Memoirs of the Life of Mrs Elizabeth Carter: With a New Edition of her Poems, Some of Which Have Never Appeared Before. Pennington, Montagu, ed. 2011. (Cambridge Library Collection - Women's Writing Ser.). (ENG., Illus.). 658p. pap. 45.00 (978-1-108-03386-2(5)) Cambridge Univ. Pr.

Cary, Elisabeth Luther. William Morris, Poet, Craftsman, Socialist. 2010. 144p. pap. (978-1-152-11827-0(7)) Books LLC.

Cary, Henry Francis. Lives of English Poets. 2009. 208p. pap. (978-0-217-93954-6(6)) Books LLC.

—Lives of English Poets. 2007. pap. (978-1-4065-1321-9(0)) Dodo Pr.

—Lives of the English Poets: From Johnson to Kirke White, Designed as a Continuation of Johnson's Lives. 2007. (ENG.). 276p. pap. 21.99 (978-1-4264-4268-1(8)); 310p. pap. 24.99 (978-1-4264-4332-9(3)) BiblioBazaar.

Cathcart & Vaughn. Real Conversations 1 & 2. pap. 37.95 (978-0-8384-9607-7(5)) Cengage Heinle.

Çelikkol, Ayse. Romances of Free Trade: British Literature, Laissez-Faire, & the Global Nineteenth Century, 1 vol. 2011. (ENG.). 208p. 74.00 (978-0-19-976900-1(1)) Oxford Univ. Pr., Inc.

Chadwick, Ellis H. In the Footsteps of the Bront#235;s. 2011. (Cambridge Library Collection - Literary Studies). (ENG., Illus.). 604p. pap. 43.00 (978-1-108-03416-6(0)) Cambridge Univ. Pr.

Chambers, Roland. The Last Englishman: The Double Life of Arthur Ransome. 2012. (ENG., Illus.). 400p. 29.95 (978-1-56792-417-6(4)) Godine, David R. Pub.

Chatwin, Bruce. Under the Sun: The Letters of Bruce Chatwin. Shakespeare, Nicholas & Chatwin, Elizabeth, eds. 2012. (ENG., Illus.). 560p. (gr. 12). 20.00 (978-0-14-312038-4(7), Penguin (Non-Classics)) Penguin Group (USA) Inc.

Chesterton, Cecil & Perry, Michael W. G.K. Chesterton, a Criticism. 2007. (Illus.). 179p. (978-1-58742-060-3(0)) Inkling Bks.

Chisholm, Anne. Frances Partridge: The Biography. 2010. (ENG., Illus.). 404p. pap. 16.95 (978-0-7538-2699-7(2), Phoenix) Orion Publishing Group, Ltd. GBR. Dist: Independent Pubs. Group.

Chitham, Edward. A Life of Emily Bronte. 2010. (ENG., Illus.). 224p. pap. 29.95 (978-1-84868-406-5(1)) Amberley Publishing GBR. Dist: Casemate Pubs. & Bk. Distributors, LLC.

Chittick, Kathryn. Dickens & The 1830s. 2010. (ENG.). 224p. pap. 32.99 (978-0-521-12939-8(7)) Cambridge Univ. Pr.

Chorley, Henry Fothergill. Personal Reminiscences by Chorley, Planchit, & Young Ed by Richard Henry Stoddard. 2006. 320p. per. 23.99 (978-1-4255-3161-4(X)) MPublishing.

Christie, Agatha. An Autobiography. 2012. (ENG.). 560p. pap. 16.99 **(978-0-06-220457-8(2)**, William Morrow Paperbacks) HarperCollins Pubs.

Christie, Agatha. Autobiography. 2011. (ENG., Illus.). 544p. 29.99 (978-0-06-207359-4(1)) HarperCollins Pubs.

Chubb, Edwin Watts. Stories of Authors: British & American. 2008. (Illus.). 288p. pap. (978-1-4099-5064-6(6)) Dodo Pr.

—Stories of Authors: British & American. 2007. (ENG.). 414p. 49.95 (978-0-548-06735-2(X)) Kessinger Publishing, LLC.

Cibber, Theophilus. The Lives of the Poets of Great Britain & Ireland. 2008. 364p. 31.99 (978-0-554-23358-1(4)) 2008. 332p. 29.99 (978-0-554-24096-1(3)) 2008. 336p. 29.99 (978-0-554-24131-9(6)) 2008. 344p. 29.99 (978-0-554-25951-2(6)) 2008. 332p. 28.99 (978-0-554-33399-1(6)) 2008. 336p. 28.99 (978-0-554-33434-9(8)) 2008. 364p. 29.99 (978-0-554-32661-0(2)) 2008. 344p. 28.99 (978-0-554-35254-1(0)) Vol. 2. 2007. (ENG.). 340p. pap. 24.99 (978-1-4346-0156-8(0)) BiblioBazaar.

—The Lives of the Poets of Great Britain & Ireland. 2007. (ENG.). 248p. per. (978-1-4068-4592-1(2)); 220p. per. (978-1-4068-4594-5(9)); 224p. per. (978-1-4068-4595-2(7)); 228p. per. (978-1-4068-4593-8(0)); 236p. per. (978-1-4068-4596-9(5)) Echo Library.

—The Lives of the Poets of Great Britain & Ireland: (1753) Volume V. 2007. (ENG.). 298p. pap. 21.99 (978-1-4264-5798-2(7)); 354p. pap. 24.99 (978-1-4264-5858-3(4)) BiblioBazaar.

—The Lives of the Poets of Great Britain & Ireland (1753) Volume I. 2007. (ENG.). 318p. pap. 23.99 (978-1-4264-4243-8(2)); 362p. pap. 26.99 (978-1-4264-4307-7(2)) BiblioBazaar.

—The Lives of the Poets of Great Britain & Ireland (1753) Volume IV. 2007. (ENG.). 292p. pap. 21.99 (978-1-4264-5762-3(6)); 328p. pap. 24.99 (978-1-4264-5822-4(3)) BiblioBazaar.

—The Lives of the Poets of Great Britain & Ireland Volume II. 2007. (ENG.). 292p. pap. 21.99 (978-1-4346-0071-4(8)) BiblioBazaar.

Claeys, Gregory. French Revolution Debate in Britain: The Origins of Modern Politics. annot. ed. 2007. (British History in Perspective Ser.). (ENG.). 192p. pap. 39.00 (978-0-333-62647-4(8)) Palgrave Macmillan.

—The French Revolution Debate in Britain: The Origins of Modern Politics. annot. ed. 2007. (British History in Perspective Ser.). (ENG.). 192p. 110.00 (978-0-333-62646-7(X)) Palgrave Macmillan.

Clapp, Susannah. A Card from Angela Carter. 2012. (ENG., Illus.). 112p. 19.99 **(978-1-4088-2690-4(9))** Bloomsbury Publishing.

Clarkson, Wensley. Car Trouble: A Childhood on Four Wheels. 2011. (ENG., Illus.). 224p. pap. 16.95 (978-1-84596-612-6(0)) Mainstream Publishing Co., Ltd. GBR. Dist: Independent Pubs. Group.

Cobbe, Frances P. Life of Frances Power Cobbe. reprint ed. 250.00 (978-0-7222-1554-8(1)) Library Reprints, Inc.

Cole, G. D. H. Samuel Butler. 2007. (ENG.). 116p. 34.95 (978-0-548-06642-3(6)) Kessinger Publishing, LLC.

Coleridge, Samuel Taylor. Biographia Epistolaris, Volume 1. 2007. (ENG.). 328p. pap. 24.99 (978-1-4264-2962-0(2)); 290p. pap. 21.99 (978-1-4264-3015-2(9)) BiblioBazaar.

Colledge, Gary. Dickens, Christianity & 'the Life of Our Lord' Humble Veneration, Profound Conviction. 2009. (Continuum Literary Studies). (ENG.). 196p. 120.00 (978-0-8264-2353-5(1)) Continuum International Publishing Group, Ltd. GBR. Dist: National Bk. Network.

Colley, Ann C. Victorians in the Mountains: Sinking the Sublime. 2010. (Illus.). 266p. 99.95 (978-1-4094-0633-4(4)) Ashgate Publishing Co.

Collins, K. K. George Eliot: Interviews & Recollections. 2010. (Interviews & Recollections Ser.). (ENG.). 304p. 89.00 (978-0-333-99363-7(2)) Palgrave Macmillan.

Collins, Wilkie. Six Letters of Wilkie Collins. 2011. 34p. 35.95 **(978-1-258-07751-8(5))** Literary Licensing, LLC.

Connon, Bryan. Beverley Nichols: A Life. 2009. (ENG.). 344p. pap. 29.95 (978-1-60469-044-6(5), 1604690445) Timber Pr., Inc.

Conrad, Joseph. The Collected Letters of Joseph Conrad Vol. 9: Uncollected Letters & Indexes. Davies, Laurence et al, eds. 2008. (Cambridge Edition of the Letters of Joseph Conrad Ser.). (ENG., Illus.). 432p. 150.00 (978-0-521-88189-0(7)) Cambridge Univ. Pr.

Considine, John, ed. The Ashgate Series on Early English Lexicographers Vol. 3: Seventeenth Century. 2012. (Ashgate Critical Essays on Early English Lexicographers Ser.). 532p. 275.00 **(978-0-7546-5693-7(4))** Ashgate Publishing Co.

Cook, Edward Tyas. The Life of John Ruskin, 1819-1860. 2010. (Cambridge Library Collection - Literary Studies). (ENG., Illus.). 580p. pap. 43.00 (978-1-108-00971-3(9)) Cambridge Univ. Pr.

—The Life of John Ruskin, 1860-1900, 2. 2010. (Cambridge Library Collection - Literary Studies). (ENG., Illus.). 640p. pap. 43.00 (978-1-108-00972-0(7)) Cambridge Univ. Pr.

Cooke, George Willis. George Eliot: A Critical Study of Her Life, Writings & Philosophy. 2007. 388p. per. (978-1-4065-1499-5(3)) Dodo Pr.

—George Eliot; a Critical Study of Her Life, Writings & Philosophy. 2007. (ENG.). 428p. pap. 26.99 (978-1-4264-5572-8(0)); 484p. pap. 30.99 (978-1-4264-5620-6(4)) BiblioBazaar.

Cooke, Stewart. The Court Journals & Letters of Frances Burney: Volume II: 1787. 2011. (Illus.). 416p. 185.00 (978-0-19-926280-9(2)) Oxford Univ. Pr., Inc.

Cooper, Suzanne Fagence. Effie: The Passionate Lives of Effie Gray, John Ruskin & John Everett Millais. (ENG.). 288p. 2012. pap. 15.99 **(978-1-250-01625-6(8)**, St. Martin's Griffin) 2011. (Illus.). 26.99 (978-0-312-58173-2(4)) St. Martin's Pr.

Corfe, Robert. This Was My England: The Story of a Childhood. 2011. (ENG., Illus.). 357p. pap. 30.18 **(978-1-906791-73-5(2))** Arena Bks. GBR. Dist: Lightning Source UK, Ltd.

Corke, Helen. In Our Infancy, 1882-1912 Pt. 1: An Autobiography. 2008. (ENG.). 260p. pap. 37.99 (978-0-521-08166-5(1)) Cambridge Univ. Pr.

Corman, Brian. Women Novelists Before Jane Austen: The Critics & Their Canons. 2008. (ENG.). 320p. (978-0-8020-9770-5(7)) Univ. of Toronto Pr.

Cottle, Joseph. Reminiscences of Samuel Taylor Coleridge & Robert Southey. 2008. 408p. 30.99 (978-0-559-52503-2(6)); pap. 33.75 (978-0-559-52500-1(1)) BiblioBazaar.

—Reminiscences of Samuel Taylor Coleridge & Robert Southey. 2009. 332p. pap. (978-1-4589-6382-6(9)); 348p. pap. (978-1-4589-6386-4(1)) Books LLC.

Courthope, William. Addison. 2011. (Cambridge Library Collection - English Men of Letters Ser.). (ENG.). 204p. pap. 22.99 **(978-1-108-03442-5(X))** Cambridge Univ. Pr.

Cousins, A. D. Companion to Thomas More. Grace, Damian, ed. 2009. (ENG.). 253p. 58.00 (978-1-61147-420-6(5)) Fairleigh Dickinson Univ. Pr.

Cousins, A. D. & Grace, Damian. A Companion to Thomas More. 2009. 58.00 (978-0-8386-4215-3(2)) Fairleigh Dickinson Univ. Pr.

Coustillas, Pierre. The Heroic Life of George Gissing, 1857-1888 Part I, Pt. 1. 2011. (ENG., Illus.). 384p. 99.00 (978-1-84893-171-8(9)) Pickering & Chatto Pubs., Ltd. GBR. Dist: Ashgate Publishing Co.

—The Heroic Life of George Gissing, 1888-1897 Part II. 2012. (ENG.). 384p. 99.00 (978-1-84893-173-2(5)) Pickering & Chatto Pubs., Ltd. GBR. Dist: Ashgate Publishing Co.

—The Heroic Life of George Gissing, 1897-1903 Part III, 1 vol. 2012. (ENG.). 500p. 99.00 (978-1-84893-175-6(1)) Pickering & Chatto Pubs., Ltd. GBR. Dist: Ashgate Publishing Co.

Cox, Jessica. Charlotte Bronte. 2011. (Brief Lives Ser.). (ENG.). 112p. pap. 12.95 (978-1-84391-920-9(6)) Hesperus Pr. GBR. Dist: Independent Pubs. Group.

Craciun, Adriana, et al. The Works of Charlotte Smith, 4 vols., Pt. III. Curran, Stuart, ed. 2007. (Pickering Masters Ser.). (ENG.). 1712p. 675.00 (978-1-85196-795-7(8)) Pickering & Chatto Pubs., Ltd. GBR. Dist: Ashgate Publishing Co.

Craddock, Thomas. Charles Lamb. 2009. 228p. 23.99 (978-1-103-17114-9(3)); pap. 17.99 (978-1-103-17112-5(7)) BiblioBazaar.

Craik, Wendy. Jane Austen (Rle Jane Austen) 2011. (Routledge Library Editions: Jane Austen Ser.). (ENG.). 220p. 120.00 (978-0-415-57285-6(6)) Routledge.

Cranfill, Thomas Mabry & Bruce, Dorothy Hart. Barnaby Rich. 2011. (ENG.). 146p. pap. 19.95 (978-0-292-72933-9(2)) Univ. of Texas Pr.

Croft-Cooke, Rupert. The Purple Streak. 2012. 190p. pap. **(978-1-4482-0497-7(6)**, 146506, Bloomsbury Reader) Bloomsbury Publishing Plc.

—The Wild Hills. 2012. 218p. pap. **(978-1-4482-0522-6(0)**, 146528, Bloomsbury Reader) Bloomsbury Publishing Plc.

—The Wintry Sea. 2012. 200p. pap. **(978-1-4482-0514-1(X)**, 146522, Bloomsbury Reader) Bloomsbury Publishing Plc.

Cronin, John. Gerald Griffin, 1803-1840: A Critical Biography. 2010. (ENG.). 188p. pap. 28.99 (978-0-521-12943-5(5)) Cambridge Univ. Pr.

Crosland, Camilla. Landmarks of a Literary Life 1820-1892. 2010. (Cambridge Library Collection - Women's Writing Ser.). (Illus.). 316p. pap. 24.99 (978-1-108-02194-4(8)) Cambridge Univ. Pr.

Cross, John Walter. George Eliots Life V1 As Related in Her. 2006. pap. 34.95 (978-1-4286-3860-0(1)) Kessinger Publishing, LLC.

—George Eliots Life V3 As Related in Her. 2006. pap. 36.95 (978-1-4286-3861-7(X)) Kessinger Publishing, LLC.

Crossley-Holland, Kevin. Hidden Roads: A Memoir of Childhood. 2010. (ENG., Illus.). 288p. pap. 13.95 (978-1-84916-211-1(5)) Quercus GBR. Dist: Independent Pubs. Group.

Crow, Anne. AS/A-Level English Literature, Pack. 2010. (Illus.). 200p. tchr. ed. 225.00 (978-0-340-96785-8(5)) Hodder Education GBR. Dist: Trans-Atlantic Pubns., Inc.

Crowe, Eyre. With Thackeray in Americ. 2010. 190p. pap. 28.45 (978-1-4455-5827-1(0), Kent Pr.) Kent Communications, Ltd.

—With Thackeray in America. 2010. (Cambridge Library Collection - History Ser.). 204p. pap. 22.99 (978-1-108-00299-8(4)) Cambridge Univ. Pr.

Cruse, Amy. The Elizabethan Lyrists & Their Poetry. 2009. 104p. pap. (978-0-217-07573-2(8)) Books LLC.

—The Elizabethan Lyrists & Their Poetry. 2008. 148p. 35.95 (978-1-4365-0499-7(6)) 2007. (ENG.). 152p. per. 20.95 (978-0-548-72180-3(7)) Kessinger Publishing, LLC.

Cumberland, Gerald. Set down in Malice a Book of Reminiscences. 2007. (ENG.). 284p. 43.95 (978-0-548-02895-7(8)) Kessinger Publishing, LLC.

Curran, John. Agatha Christie's Secret Notebooks: Fifty Years of Mysteries in the Making. 2010. (Illus.). 496p. 25.99 (978-0-06-198836-3(7)) HarperCollins Pubs.

Curtis, Anthony. Virginia Woolf. 2008. (Illus.). 256p. 24.95 (978-1-905791-47-7(X)) Haus Publishing GBR. Dist: Consortium Bk. Sales & Distribution.

Curtright, Travis. The One Thomas More. 2012. **(978-0-8132-1995-0(7))** Catholic Univ. of America Pr.

Cusk, Rachel. Aftermath: Life after Marriage, 1 vol. 2012. (ENG.). 160p. 23.00 **(978-0-374-10213-5(3))** Farrar, Straus & Giroux.

Cusk, Rachel. The Last Supper: A Summer in Italy. 2010. (ENG., Illus.). 256p. pap. 15.00 (978-0-312-42965-2(7)) Picador.

Cuthbertson, Guy & Newlyn, Lucy. Edward Thomas: Prose Writings: A Selected Edition: Volume II: England & Wales. 2011. (Edward thomas prose writing selected Edition Ser.) (ENG., Illus.). 512p. 160.00 (978-0-19-955826-1(4)) Oxford Univ. Pr., Inc.

Dailey, Donna & Tomedi, John. Bloom's Literary Guide to London. 2007. (Bloom's Literary Guide Ser.). (Illus.). 256p. per. 14.95 (978-0-7910-9377-1(8), Chelsea Hse.) Facts On File, Inc.

Darlington, Beth. Love Letters of William & Mary Wordsworth. 2009. (Illus.). 272p. pap. 26.95 (978-0-8014-7533-7(3)) Cornell Univ. Pr.

Davies, Hunter. The Beatles, Football & Me. 2007. (ENG., Illus.). 352p. pap. 15.95 (978-0-7553-1403-4(4)) Headline Bk. Publishing GBR. Dist: Independent Pubs. Group.

—William Wordsworth. rev. ed. 2009. (ENG., Illus.). 400p. pap. 22.95 (978-0-7112-3045-3(5)) Lincoln, Frances Ltd. GBR. Dist: Perseus-PGW.

Davies, W. H. Later Days. 2008. 224p. (978-1-4437-3466-0(7), Pomona Pr.) Read Bks.

Davis, Bertram H. & Johnson, Samuel. Johnson Before Boswell: A Study of John Hawkins' Life of Samuel Johnson. 2011. 234p. 46.95 **(978-1-258-08966-5(1))** Literary Licensing, LLC.

Davis, Paul. Translation & the Poet's Life: The Ethics of Translating in English Culture, 1646-1726. 2009. (ENG., Illus.). 336p. 125.00 (978-0-19-929783-2(5)) Oxford Univ. Pr., Inc.

Davison, Colin. Through the Magic Door: Ursula Moray Williams, Gobbolino & the Little Wooden Horse. 2011. (ENG., Illus.). 260p. 29.95 **(978-0-85716-006-5(0))** Northumbria University Press GBR. Dist: Independent Pubs. Group.

De Grazia, Margreta & Wells, Stanley, eds. The New Cambridge Companion to Shakespeare. 2nd ed. 2010. (Cambridge Companions to Literature Ser.). (ENG., Illus.). 380p. (C). 90.00 (978-0-521-88632-1(5)); pap. 30.00 (978-0-521-71393-1(5)) Cambridge Univ. Pr.

de la L Oulton, Carolyn W. Let the Flowers Go: A Life of Mary Cholmondeley, 1 vol. 2009. (Gender & Genre Ser.). (ENG., Illus.). 272p. 99.00 (978-1-85196-649-3(8)) Pickering & Chatto Pubs., Ltd. GBR. Dist: Ashgate Publishing Co.

de la Mothe, John. C. P. Snow & the Struggle of Modernity. 2011. (ENG., Illus.). 264p. pap. 25.00 (978-0-292-72916-2(2)) Univ. of Texas Pr.

de Quincey, Thomas. Autobiographic Sketches. 2008. 360p. 29.99 (978-0-559-85832-1(9)); pap. 31.75 (978-0-559-85830-7(2)) BiblioBazaar.

—Autobiographic Sketches. 2006. 608p. per. 34.99 (978-1-4255-6469-8(0)) MPublishing.

—The Confessions of an English Opium-Eater. Carey, John A. & Lindop, Grevel, eds. 2009. (Oxford World's Classics Ser.). (ENG.). 304p. pap. 12.95 (978-0-19-953793-8(3)) Oxford Univ. Pr., Inc.

—Confessions of an English Opium-Eater & Suspiria de Profundis. 2006. 288p. per. 23.99 (978-1-4255-2659-7(4)) MPublishing.

—Confessions of an English Opium-Eater & Suspiria de Profundis. 2007. 292p. per. (978-1-4067-6002-6(1)) Read Bks.

Deakin, Mary H. The Early Life of George Eliot. 2008. 230p. 41.95 (978-1-4365-1481-1(9)) 2007. (ENG.). 232p. per. 26.95 (978-0-548-70138-6(5)) Kessinger Publishing, LLC.

Dearden, James S. John Ruskin: An Illustrated Life of John Ruskin, 1819-1900. 2nd ed. 2008. (Shire Library). (ENG., Illus.). 64p. pap. 12.95 (978-0-7478-0599-1(7)) Shire Pubns., Ltd. GBR. Dist: Random Hse., Inc.

Deathridge, John. Pegasus Pocket Guide to Beethoven. 2010. 352p. pap. 15.75 (978-1-933648-75-0(9)) Pegasus Bks.

Deeney, John F. Mark Ravenhill. 2008. (Routledge Modern & Contemporary Dramatists Ser.). (Illus.). 192p. pap. 27.95 (978-0-415-37511-5(8)); 99.00 (978-0-415-37510-8(X)) Routledge.

Delany, Paul. George Gissing: A Life. 2009. (ENG., Illus.). 472p. pap. 28.95 (978-0-7538-2573-0(2), Phoenix) Orion Publishing Group, Ltd. GBR. Dist: Independent Pubs. Group.

DeMaria, Robert, Jr. Samuel Johnson & the Life of Reading. 2009. (ENG.). 288p. (gr. 17). pap. 30.00 (978-0-8018-9242-4(2)) Johns Hopkins Univ. Pr.

DePietro, Thomas, ed. Conversations with Kingsley Amis. (Literary Conversations Ser.). (ENG.). 224p. 2010. 50.00 (978-1-60473-290-0(3)) 2009. pap. 22.00 (978-1-60473-291-7(1)) Univ. Pr. of Mississippi.

DeSalvo, Louise A. On Moving: A Writer's Meditation on New Houses, Old Haunts, & Finding Home Again. 2009. (ENG., Illus.). 240p. 22.00 (978-1-58234-581-9(3)) Bloomsbury Publishing.

Devine, Luke. From Anglo-First-Wave towards American Second-Wave Jewish Feminism: Negotiating with Jewish Feminist Theology & its Communities in the Writing of Amy Levy. 2010. 110.00 (978-1-61719-915-8(X)) Gorgias Pr., LLC.

Di Liddo, Annalisa. Alan Moore: Comics as Performance, Fiction as Scalpel. 2009. (Illus.). 192p. 50.00 (978-1-60473-212-2(1)); (ENG., pap. 22.00 (978-1-60473-213-9(X)) Univ. Pr. of Mississippi.

DiBattista, Maria. Imagining Virginia Woolf: An Experiment in Critical Biography. 2008. (ENG.). 208p. (C). 21.95 (978-0-691-13812-1(5)) Princeton Univ. Pr.

Dickens, Charles. Charles Dickens's Letters to Charles Lever. Livingston, Flora Virginia, ed. 2011. 82p. 37.95 **(978-1-258-06870-7(2))** Literary Licensing, LLC.

—Letters of Charles Dickens: 1833-1870. Hogarth, Georgina & Dickens, Mary, eds. 2011. (Cambridge Library Collection - Literary Studies). (ENG., Illus.). 778p. pap. 50.00 **(978-1-108-04004-4(7))** Cambridge Univ. Pr.

—Pictures from Italy. 2011. (Cambridge Library Collection - Travel & Exploration Ser.). (ENG., Illus.). 284p. pap. 23.99 **(978-1-108-03384-8(9))** Cambridge Univ. Pr.

—The Selected Letters of Charles Dickens. Hartley, Jenny, ed. 2012. (ENG.). 584p. 34.95 **(978-0-19-959141-1(5))** Oxford Univ. Pr., Inc.

Dickens, Monica. One Pair of Hands. Date not set. 310p. 24.95 (978-0-8488-2667-3(1)) Amereon LTD.

Dinsdale, Ann. The Brontes at Haworth. 2006. (ENG., Illus.). 160p. 35.00 (978-0-7112-2572-5(9)) Lincoln, Frances Ltd. GBR. Dist: Perseus-PGW.

Disraeli, Isaac. The Literary Character. 2009. 218p. pap. (978-1-4589-2798-9(3)) Books LLC.

—The Literary Character. 108p. pap. (978-0-217-12151-4(9), Adlard Coles) Greystoke Pr.

—Literary Character of Men of Genius. 2008. 560p. 36.99 (978-0-554-25472-2(7)); 33.99 (978-0-554-34775-2(X)) BiblioBazaar.

—Literary Character of Men of Genius. 2008. 396p. pap. (978-1-4068-7007-7(2)) Echo Library.

—Literary Character of Men of Genius: Drawn from Their Own Feelings & Confessions. 2007. (ENG.). 488p. pap. 28.99 (978-1-4264-9108-5(5)); 556p. pap. 32.99 (978-1-4264-9162-7(X)) BiblioBazaar.

Dobson, Austin. Fanny Burney. 2007. (ENG.). 222p. 39.95 (978-0-548-04225-0(X)) Kessinger Publishing, LLC.

—Fanny Burney. 2006. 216p. per. (978-1-4067-3414-0(4), Hesperides Pr.) Read Bks.

—Fielding. 2011. (Cambridge Library Collection - English Men of Letters Ser.). (ENG.). 214p. pap. 22.99 **(978-1-108-03454-8(3))** Cambridge Univ. Pr.

Dobson, Austin. Horace Walpole A Memoir with an Appendix. 2006. pap. 31.95 (978-1-4286-5212-5(4)) Kessinger Publishing, LLC.

Dolby, George. Charles Dickens as I Knew Him: The Story of the Reading Tours in Great Britain & America 1866-1870. 2011. (Cambridge Library Collection - Literary Studies). (ENG., Illus.). 486p. pap. 35.99 **(978-1-108-03979-6(0))** Cambridge Univ. Pr.

Dolin, Tim. T Hardy. 2008. (Life & Times Ser.). (Illus.). 192p. 15.95 (978-1-904950-77-6(9)) Haus Publishing GBR. Dist: Consortium Bk. Sales & Distribution.

Donaghy, Michael. The Shape of the Dance: Essays, Interviews & Digressions 2009. (ENG., Illus.). 224p. 29.95 (978-0-330-45628-9(8), Picador) Pan Macmillan GBR. Dist: Trans-Atlantic Pubns., Inc.

Donaldson, Frances. Evelyn Waugh: Portrait of a Country Neighbour. 2012. 158p. pap. **(978-1-4482-0307-9(4)**, 143314, Bloomsbury Reader) Bloomsbury Publishing Plc.

Donnelly, Wendy. The Black Hole. 2009. 288p. pap. 21.50 (978-1-4452-4111-1(0)) Lulu Enterprises Inc.

Doody, Margaret Anne. Frances Burney: The Life in the Works. 2010. (ENG.). 462p. pap. 34.99 (978-0-521-15892-3(3)) Cambridge Univ. Pr.

Downie, J. A. Political Biography of Henry Fielding, 1 vol. 2009. (Eighteenth-Century Political Biographies Ser.). (ENG.). 272p. 99.00 (978-1-85196-915-9(2)) Pickering & Chatto Pubs., Ltd. GBR. Dist: Ashgate Publishing Co.

Drabble, Margaret. A Writer's Britain. 2nd ed. 2009. (ENG.). 296p. 24.95 (978-0-500-51493-1(3), 551493) Thames & Hudson.

Dromgoole, Dominic. The Mirror Behind the Curtain: Perspectives on Leading Playwrights Writing for the Proscenium Stage. 2011. (Diaries, Letters & Essays Ser.). (ENG.). 224p. pap. 22.95 (978-1-4081-0584-9(5), Methuen Drama) A & C Black GBR. Dist: Macmillan.

Drummond, Maldwin. After You, Mr. Lear: In the Wake of Edward Lear in Italy. 2007. (ENG.). 240p. pap. 24.95 (978-1-57409-255-4(3)) Sheridan Hse., Inc.

Dryden, John. The Letters of John Dryden: With Letters Addressed to Him. Ward, Charles E., ed. 2011. 218p. 44.95 **(978-1-258-04874-7(4))** Literary Licensing, LLC.

Dudgeon, Piers. The Girl from Leam Lane: The Life & Writing of Catherine Cookson. rev. ed. 2007. (ENG., Illus.). 320p. per. 13.95 (978-0-7553-1498-0(0)) Headline Bk. Publishing GBR. Dist: Independent Pubs. Group.

—Neverland: J. M. Barrie, the du Mauriers, & the Dark Side of Peter Pan. 2009. (ENG., Illus.). 352p. 26.95 (978-1-60598-063-8(3), 605063) Pegasus Bks.

Dugan, Sally. Baroness Orczy's the Scarlet Pimpernel: A Publishing History. 2012. (Illus.). 285p. **(978-1-4094-2717-9(X))** Ashgate Publishing, Ltd.

Duncan, Robert Edward & Mottram, Eric. The Unruly Garden: Robert Duncan & Eric Mottram Letters & Essays. Evans, Amy & Zamir, Shamoon, eds. 2007. 225p. pap. 73.95 (978-3-03911-394-1(1)) Lang, Peter Publishing, Inc.

Durrell, Lawrence. Sicilian Carousel. 2009. (ENG.). 295p. pap. 12.00 (978-1-60419-015-1(9)) Axios Pr.

—Spirit of Place: Letters & Essays on Travel. Thomas, Alan, ed. 2011. (ENG.). 642p. pap. 12.00 (978-1-60419-035-9(3)) Axios Pr.

Dyer, Geoff. Out of Sheer Rage: Wrestling with D. H. Lawrence. 2009. (ENG.). 256p. pap. 15.00 (978-0-312-42946-1(0)) Picador.

Easley, Alexis. Literary Celebrity, Gender, & Victorian Authorship, 1850-1914. 2011. (Illus.). 273p. (978-1-936249-01-5(4)); (ENG., 280p. 75.00 (978-1-61149-016-9(2)) Univ. of Delaware Pr.
Edmonds, Cyrus R. John Milton: a Biography. 2007. (ENG.). 260p. per. 27.95 (978-1-4304-4267-7(0)) Kessinger Publishing, LLC.
Edmondson, John, ed. Dickens on France: Fiction, Journalism, & Travel. 2007. (ENG., Illus.). 464p. per. 20.00 (978-1-56656-688-9(6), Interlink Bks.) Interlink Publishing Group, Inc.
Edmunds, Edward William. Chaucer & His Poetry. 2009. 224p. 24.99 (978-0-554-40020-4(0)); pap. 24.75 (978-0-554-40019-8(7)) BiblioBazaar.
Eliot, George. George Eliot's Life: As Related in Her Letters & Journals. Cross, John Walter, ed. 2010. (Cambridge Library Collection - Literary Studies). (ENG., Illus.). 518p. pap. 37.99 (978-1-108-02006-0(2)) Cambridge Univ. Pr.
—George Eliot's Life, as Related in her Letters & Journals. Cross, John Walter, ed. 2010. (Cambridge Library Collection - Literary Studies). (Illus.). 470p. pap. 35.99 (978-1-108-02007-7(0)); 492p. pap. 35.99 (978-1-108-02008-4(9)) Cambridge Univ. Pr.
Elizabeth, Charlotte. Personal Recollections. 2008. 360p. 31.99 (978-0-554-43107-9(6)); 29.99 (978-0-554-43115-4(7)); pap. 31.75 (978-0-554-43113-0(0)); pap. 32.75 (978-0-554-43109-3(2)) BiblioBazaar.
—Personal Recollections. 2006. pap. (978-1-4065-1408-7(X)) Dodo Pr.
Ellinghausen, Laurie. Labor & Writing in Early Modern England, 1567-1667. 2008. (Illus.). 166p. 99.95 (978-0-7546-5780-4(9)) Ashgate Publishing Co.
Ellis, David. D. H. Lawrence: Dying Game 1922-1930: Volume 3: The Cambridge Biography of D. H. Lawrence. 2011. (ENG.). 850p. pap. 51.99 **(978-1-107-40299-7(9))** Cambridge Univ. Pr.
Ellis, Edwin J. The Real Blake: A Portrait Biography. 2007. (ENG.). 480p. 53.95 (978-0-548-09660-4(0)) Kessinger Publishing, LLC.
Ellwood, Thomas. The History of Thomas Ellwood Written by Himself. 2008. 208p. 27.99 (978-0-554-23818-0(7)); 24.99 (978-0-554-33121-8(7)) BiblioBazaar.
—The History of Thomas Ellwood Written by Himself. 2007. 180p. per. (978-1-4065-2496-3(4)) Dodo Pr.
Elton, Oliver. An Introduction to Michael Drayton. 2007. (ENG.). 224p. 39.95 (978-0-548-35367-7(0)); per. 24.95 (978-0-548-29620-2(0)) Kessinger Publishing, LLC.
Emerson, Ralph Waldo. Correspondence Between John Sterling and. 2006. pap. 19.95 (978-1-4286-3641-5(2)) Kessinger Publishing, LLC.
Encyclopedia Britannica. A Brief Guide to William Shakespeare. 2010. (ENG.). 448p. pap. 13.95 (978-0-7624-3854-9(1)) Running Pr. Bk. Pubs.
Epstein, Joseph, ed. Literary Genius: 25 Classic Writers Who Define English & American Literature. 2007. (ENG., Illus.). 256p. pap. 18.95 (978-1-58988-035-1(8)) Dry, Paul Bks., Inc.
Epstein, Joseph & Moser, Barry. Literary Genius: 25 Classic Writers Who Define English & American Literature. 2007. (978-1-58988-039-9(0)) Dry, Paul Bks., Inc.
Ergun, Leyla. The Reason. 2009. 108p. 27.49 (978-1-4389-9311-9(0)); pap. 16.49 (978-1-4389-9312-6(9)) AuthorHouse.
Ewing, Lucy Elizabeth Lee. George Frederick Watts, Sandro Botticelli, Matthew Arnold. 2009. 84p. pap. 17.95 (978-1-104-05814-2(6)) Kessinger Publishing, LLC.
Faught, C. Brad. Into Africa: The Imperial Life of Margery Perham. 2012. (ENG., Illus.). 288p. 75.00 **(978-1-84885-490-1(0))** I. B. Tauris & Co., Ltd. GBR. Dist: Macmillan.
Fenn, George. By Conduct & Courage: The Life of George Alfred Henty. 2011. 336p. pap. 19.95 **(978-1-61179-137-2(5))** Fireship Pr.
Fermor, Una Mary Ellis. Christopher Marlowe (Routledge Revivals) 2012. (ENG.). 186p. (C). 120.00 **(978-0-415-63043-6(6))** Routledge.
Field, Michael. The Fowl & the Pussycat: Love Letters of Michael Field, 1876-1909. Bickle, Sharon, ed. 2008. (Victorian Literature & Culture Ser.). (ENG., Illus.). 336p. (gr. 17). 49.50 (978-0-8139-2751-0(X)) Univ. Pr. of Virginia.
Fielding, Henry. Works of Henry Fielding, Pt. 2. 2006. (Illus.). pap. 42.95 (978-1-4286-6176-9(X)) Kessinger Publishing, LLC.
Fields, James T. Yesterdays with Authors. 2010. 368p. pap. 32.75 (978-1-142-38669-6(4)) 2008. 480p. 33.99 (978-0-554-24333-7(4)) 2008. 480p. 31.99 (978-0-554-33636-7(7)) 2006. (ENG.). 426p. pap. 26.99 (978-1-4264-6199-6(2)) 2006. (ENG.). 476p. pap. 30.99 (978-1-4264-6254-2(9)) BiblioBazaar.
—Yesterdays with Authors. 2007. (ENG.). 428p. per. (978-1-4065-2400-0(X)) Dodo Pr.
—Yesterdays with Authors. 2007. 364p. 46.95 (978-0-548-54968-1(0)); (ENG.). per. 31.95 (978-0-548-49129-4(1)) Kessinger Publishing, LLC.
—Yesterdays with Authors. 2007. (ENG.). 428p. per. (978-1-4067-7742-0(0)) Read Bks.
Fields, James Thomas. Yesterdays with Authors, by James T Fields. 2006. 356p. per. 26.99 (978-1-4255-3869-9(X)) MPublishing.
Figgis, Darrell. Shakespeare: A Study. 2007. pap. (978-1-59731-310-0(6)) Perennis, Sophia.
Finney, Brian. Martin Amis. 2008. XII, 180p. 28.95 (978-0-415-40292-7(1)); 95.00 (978-0-415-40291-0(3)) Routledge.
Fleishman, Avrom. George Eliot's Intellectual Life. (ENG.). 2011. 310p. pap. 39.99 (978-1-107-40266-9(2)) 2010. 308p. 90.00 (978-0-521-11736-4(4)) Cambridge Univ. Pr.
Fleming, Anne. Byron the Maker & 2, Vol. 1. 2009. (Illus.). 520p. 42.50 (978-1-84624-339-4(4)) Book Guild, Ltd. GBR. Dist: Trans-Atlantic Pubns., Inc.
Ford, Ford Madox. Provence. Coyle, John, ed. 2009. (ENG., Illus.). 400p. pap. 28.95 (978-1-85754-989-8(9)) Carcanet Pr., Ltd. GBR. Dist: Independent Pubs. Group.
Forster, John. The Life of Charles Dickens. 2011. 944p. pap. **(978-1-84902-285-9(2))** Benediction Classics.
—The Life of Charles Dickens. 2011. (Cambridge Library Collection - Literary Studies). (ENG., Illus.). 492p. pap. 35.99 **(978-1-108-03936-9(7))**; 576p. pap. 43.00 **(978-1-108-03937-6(5))**; 426p. pap. 32.99 **(978-1-108-03935-2(9))** Cambridge Univ. Pr.
—The Life of Charles Dickens V1: 1812-184. 2006. pap. 36.95 (978-1-4286-4784-8(8)) Kessinger Publishing, LLC.
—The Life of Charles Dickens V2: 1842-185. 2006. pap. 40.95 (978-1-4286-4785-5(6)) Kessinger Publishing, LLC.
Foster, Allan. Sherlock Holmes & Conan Doyle Locations: A Visitor's Guide. 2011. (ENG., Illus.). 166p. pap. 35.00 (978-0-7864-4617-9(X)) McFarland & Co., Inc. Pubs.
Foster, Stephen. Walking Ollie: Or, Winning the Love of a Difficult Dog. 2008. (ENG.). 192p. (gr. 12-18). 12.00 (978-0-399-53429-4(6), Perigee Trade) Penguin Group (USA) Inc.
Fowler, Peter. English Countryside Explored. 2009. (ENG., Illus.). 160p. pap. 29.95 (978-0-7524-5020-9(4)) History Pr. Ltd.,The GBR. Dist: Independent Pubs. Group.
Fowles, John. The Journals: Volume 1: 1949-1965. Drazin, Charles, ed. & intro. by. 2009. (ENG.). 668p. pap. 24.95 (978-0-8101-2514-8(5)) Northwestern Univ. Pr.
—The Journals: Volume 2: 1966-1990. Drazin, Charles, ed. & intro. by. 2009. (ENG.). 464p. pap. 24.95 (978-0-8101-2515-5(3)) Northwestern Univ. Pr.
Francis, Samuel. Psychological Fictions of J. G. Ballard. 2012. (ENG.). 210p. 110.00 (978-1-4411-6195-6(3)) Continuum International Publishing Group, Ltd. GBR. Dist: National Bk. Network.
Franzen, Christine. The Ashgate Series on Early English Lexicographers: The Old & Middle English. 2012. (Ashgate Critical Essays on Early English Lexicographers Ser.). 718p. 275.00 **(978-0-7546-5691-3(8))** Ashgate Publishing Co.
Fraser, Antonia. Must You Go? My Life with Harold Pinter. 2011. (ENG., Illus.). 384p. pap. 16.00 (978-0-307-47557-2(3), Anchor) Knopf Doubleday Publishing Group.
Fraser, Robert. Night Thoughts: The Surreal Life of the Poet David Gascoyne. 2012. (ENG., Illus.). 480p. 55.00 **(978-0-19-955814-8(0))** Oxford Univ. Pr., Inc.
Fredeman, William E., ed. The Correspondence of Dante Gabriel Rossetti: The Last Decadek, 1873-1882 - Kelmscott to Birchington, 1875-1877, 9 vols. 2008. (Illus.). 516p. 220.00 (978-1-84384-134-0(7), D. S. Brewer) Boydell & Brewer, Ltd. GBR. Dist: Boydell & Brewer, Inc.
—The Correspondence of Dante Gabriel Rossetti 9: The Last Decade, 1873-1882: Kelmscott to Birchington IV. 1880-1882, 9 vols. 2010. (Illus.). 768p. 220.00 (978-1-84384-227-9(0), D. S. Brewer) Boydell & Brewer, Ltd. GBR. Dist: Boydell & Brewer, Inc.
From Jane Austen to Virgina Woolf. (GER.). pap. 19.95 (978-3-423-09332-3(3)) Deutscher Taschenbuch Verlag GmbH & Co KG DEU. Dist: Distribooks, Inc.
Froude, James. Bunyan. 2007. (ENG.). 188p. 37.95 (978-0-548-05027-9(9)) Kessinger Publishing, LLC.
Froude, James Anthony. Bunyan. 2011. (Cambridge Library Collection - English Men of Letters Ser.). (ENG.). 194p. pap. 19.99 **(978-1-108-03466-1(7))** Cambridge Univ. Pr.
Fullerton, Susannah. A Dance with Jane Austen: How a Novelist & Her Characters Went to the Ball. 2012. (ENG., Illus.). 144p. 24.95 **(978-0-7112-3245-7(8))** Lincoln, Frances Ltd. GBR. Dist: Perseus-PGW.
Gabrial, Jan. Inside the Volcano: My Life with Malcolm Lowry. 2010. (ENG., Illus.). 224p. pap. 31.00 (978-0-230-61978-4(9)) Palgrave Macmillan.
Gaiman, Neil. Don't Panic: Douglas Adams & the Hitchhiker's Guide to the Galaxy 2009. 5th ed. 2009. (ENG., Illus.). 288p. pap. 14.95 (978-1-84856-496-1(1), Titan Bks.) Titan Bks. Ltd. GBR. Dist: Random Hse., Inc.
Gale Editor, ed. British Writers: Supplement XVIII. 18th ed. 2011. lib. bdg. 218.00 (978-1-4144-8026-8(1), Charles Scribner's Sons) Cengage Gale.
Gale Editors, ed. British Writers Supplement. 12th ed. 2006. (British Writers Ser.). (ENG.). 528p. 218.00 (978-0-684-31511-9(4), Charles Scribner's Sons) Cengage Gale.
Gale, Maggie B. J. B. Priestley. 2008. (Routledge Modern & Contemporary Dramatists Ser.). (Illus.). CCXIV, 10p. pap. 29.95 (978-0-415-40243-9(3)) Routledge.
—J.B. Priestley. 2008. (Routledge Modern & Contemporary Dramatists Ser.). (Illus.). CCXIV, 10p. 110.00 (978-0-415-40242-2(5)) Routledge.
Galt, John. The Autobiography of John Galt V1. 2007. (ENG.). 398p. 49.95 (978-0-548-15497-7(X)); 400p. per. 34.95 (978-1-4304-4928-7(4)) Kessinger Publishing, LLC.
Gardner, Philip, ed. The Journals & Diaries of E. M. Forster, 3 vols. 2011. (Pickering Masters Ser.). (ENG., Illus.). 880p. 495.00 (978-1-84893-114-5(X)) Pickering & Chatto Pubs., Ltd. GBR. Dist: Ashgate Publishing Co.
Garebian, Keith. The Making of Cabaret. 2nd ed. 2011. (ENG., Illus.). 256p. 99.00 (978-0-19-973249-4(3)); pap. 19.95 (978-0-19-973250-0(7)) Oxford Univ. Pr., Inc.
Garfield, Simon. The Error World: An Affair with Stamps. 2009. (ENG.). 256p. 24.00 (978-0-15-101396-8(9)) Houghton Mifflin Harcourt Trade & Reference Pubs.
Gary Spencer, Millidge. Alan Moore: Storyteller. 2011. (ENG., Illus.). 320p. 45.00 (978-0-7893-2229-6(3)) Universe Publishing.
Gaskell, Elizabeth. The Life of Charlotte Brontë. 2009. 368p. pap. (978-0-217-09266-1(7)); 346p. pap. (978-0-217-12575-8(1)) Books LLC.
—The Life of Charlotte Brontë. 2010. (Cambridge Library Collection - Literary Studies). (Illus.). 340p. pap. 28.99 (978-1-108-02051-0(8)) Cambridge Univ. Pr.
—The Life of Charlotte Brontë. Easson, Angus, ed. 2009. (Oxford World's Classics Ser.). (ENG.). 624p. pap. 14.95 (978-0-19-955476-8(5)) Oxford Univ. Pr., Inc.
Gates, Norman T. Richard Aldington. 2008. pap. 31.95 (978-0-271-02844-6(0)) Pennsylvania State Univ. Pr.
Gayle, Mike. The To-Do List. 2010. (ENG.). 352p. 13.95 (978-0-340-93675-7(4), Hodder & Stoughton) Hodder General Publishing Div. GBR. Dist: Independent Pubs. Group.
Gee, Maggie. My Animal Life. 2011. (ENG., Illus.). 232p. 21.95 (978-1-84659-987-3(3), Telegram Bks.) Saqi Bks. GBR. Dist: Consortium Bk. Sales & Distribution.
Gershon, Karen. A Tempered Wind: An Autobiography. 2009. (Jewish Lives Ser.). (ENG.). 216p. 69.95 (978-0-8101-2612-1(5)); pap. 21.95 (978-0-8101-2613-8(3)) Northwestern Univ. Pr.
Gide, Andre, et al. The Correspondence of Andre Gide & Edmund Gosse, 1904-1928. Brugmans, Linette F., ed. 2011. 238p. 46.95 **(978-1-258-04391-9(2))** Literary Licensing, LLC.
Gilfillan, George. Modern Literature & Literary Men; Being a Second Gallery of Literary Portraits, by George Gilfillan. 2006. 384p. per. 26.99 (978-1-4255-4100-2(3)) MPublishing.
Gill, Peter. Apprenticeship. 2009. (ENG.). 128p. 18.95 (978-1-84002-871-3(8)) Oberon Bks., Ltd. GBR. Dist: Consortium Bk. Sales & Distribution.
Gill, Stephen, ed. 21st-Century Oxford Authors: William Wordsworth. 2010. (ENG., Illus.). 600p. 160.00 (978-0-19-923861-3(8)) Oxford Univ. Pr., Inc.
Glendinning, Victoria. Leonard Woolf: A Biography. 2008. (ENG., Illus.). 512p. pap. 16.95 (978-1-58243-411-7(5), Counterpoint Pr.) Basic Bks. GBR. Dist: Perseus-PGW.
—Leonard Woolf: A Biography. 2006. (ENG., Illus.). 512p. 30.00 (978-0-7432-4653-8(5), Free Pr.) Free Pr.
Glendinning, Victoria, ed. Love's Civil War: Elizabeth Bowen & Charles Ritchie. 2009. (ENG., Illus.). 496p. pap. 19.95 (978-0-7710-3568-5(3), Emblem Edns) McClelland & Stewart CAN. Dist: Random Hse., Inc.
Glyer, Diana Pavlac. The Company They Keep: C. S. Lewis & J. R. R. Tolkien as Writers in Community. 2008. xix, 293p. pap. 30.00 (978-0-87338-991-4(3)) 2006. (Illus.). 293p. 45.00 (978-0-87338-890-0(9)) Kent State Univ. Pr.
Godwin, William. Memoirs of the Author of 'A Vindication of the Rights of Woman' 2008. (ENG.). 76p. per. (978-1-4065-8797-5(4)) Dodo Pr.
Godwin, William & Clemit, Pamela. Letters of William Goodwin, Vol. 1. 2011. (ENG., Illus.). 368p. 185.00 (978-0-19-956261-9(X)) Oxford Univ. Pr., Inc.
Gordon, Lois. Nancy Cunard: Heiress, Muse, Political Idealist. 2009. (ENG., Illus.). 504p. pap. 22.95 (978-0-231-13939-7(X)) Columbia Univ. Pr.
Gosse, Edmund. Father & Son. 2006. (Orig.). pap. (978-1-4068-2140-6(3)) Echo Library.
—The Life of Swinburne. 2011. (Cambridge Library Collection - Literary Studies). (ENG.). 58p. pap. 12.99 **(978-1-108-03414-2(4))** Cambridge Univ. Pr.
Gosse, Edmund. Sir Thomas Browne. 2009. 228p. 23.99 (978-1-103-82707-7(3)); 228p. pap. 17.99 (978-1-103-82702-2(2)); 224p. 23.99 (978-1-103-56070-7(0)); 224p. pap. 17.99 (978-1-103-56068-4(9)) BiblioBazaar.
—Sir Thomas Browne. 2009. 142p. pap. (978-0-217-99135-3(1)); 136p. pap. (978-0-217-99133-9(5)) Books LLC.
—Sir Thomas Browne. 2007. (ENG.). 228p. 41.95 (978-0-548-12774-2(3)) 2006. pap. 26.95 (978-1-4286-3772-6(9)) Kessinger Publishing, LLC.
Gotlieb, Howard. William Beckford of Fonthill: Writer, Traveler, Collector, Caliph, 1760-1844. 2011. 120p. 39.95 **(978-1-258-08573-5(9))** Literary Licensing, LLC.
Gourevitch, Philip. The Paris Review Interviews. 2007. (Illus.). 528p. pap. (978-1-84195-925-2(1)) Canongate Bks.
Gourevitch, Philip, ed. The Paris Review Interviews. 2007. Vol. 2. (Illus.). 448p. (978-1-84767-033-5(4)) Vol. 181. 184p. pap. (978-1-84767-077-9(6)) Canongate Bks.
Graham, William. Last Links with Byron, Shelley, & Keats. 2008. 152p. pap. (978-1-4097-2994-5(X)) Read Bks.
Graham, Ysenda Maxtone. The Real Mrs. Miniver: Jane Struther's Story. mass mkt. (978-0-312-98686-5(6), St. Martin's Paperbacks) St. Martin's Pr.
Grahame, Kenneth. Dream Days. 2011. (Hesperus Classics Ser.). (ENG.). 136p. pap. 14.95 (978-1-84391-195-1(7)) Hesperus Pr. GBR. Dist: Independent Pubs. Group.
Grant, Joan Marshall. Far Memory: The Autobiography of Joan Grant. 2009. (978-1-59731-362-9(9)); pap. (978-1-59731-361-2(0)) Perennis, Sophia.
Gray, Austin K. Teresa or Her Demon Lover. 2007. (ENG.). 422p. 51.95 (978-0-548-06768-0(6)) Kessinger Publishing, LLC.
Gray, Simon. Coda. 2008. (ENG.). 272p. pap. 15.95 (978-1-84708-100-1(2)) Granta Bks. GBR. Dist: Independent Pubs. Group.
—The Smoking Diaries Vol. 2: The Year of the Jouncer. 2008. (ENG.). 288p. pap. 17.95 (978-1-84708-055-4(3)) Granta Bks. GBR. Dist: Independent Pubs. Group.
Green, Dudley. Patrick Bronte: Father of Genius. 2009. (ENG., Illus.). 284p. 34.95 (978-1-84588-625-7(9)) History Pr. Ltd.,The GBR. Dist: Independent Pubs. Group.
—Patrick Brontë: Father of Genius. 2010. (ENG., Illus.). 384p. pap. 24.95 (978-0-7524-5445-0(5)) History Pr. Ltd.,The GBR. Dist: Independent Pubs. Group.
Green, Ken. Children of the Sun. 2008. (Illus.). 552p. (978-0-09-461430-7(X)) Axios Pr.
Greene, Robert. Greene's Groatsworth of Wit: Bought with a Million of Repentance. 2010. 63p. pap. 38.50 (978-1-4092-1161-7(4)) Lulu Enterprises Inc.
Greenlaw, Lavinia. The Importance of Music to Girls. 2009. (ENG.). 224p. pap. 15.00 (978-0-312-42837-2(5)) Picador.
Griffin, William, Jr. C. S. Lewis: Spirituality for Mere Christians. 2007. (C. S. Lewis Secondary Studies Ser.). 220p. pap. 24.00 (978-1-59752-649-4(5)) Wipf & Stock Pubs.
Griffith, George. Around the World in 65 Days with George Griffith: The Story of the Real Phileas Fogg. Godwin, Robert, ed. 2010. (ENG., Illus.). 238p. pap. 12.95 (978-1-897350-27-0(9)) Collector's Guide Publishing, Inc. CAN. Dist: Independent Pubs. Group.
Griffiths, Gavin. Joseph Conrad. 2008. (Brief Lives Ser.). (ENG.). 120p. pap. 13.95 (978-1-84391-907-0(9)) Hesperus Pr. GBR. Dist: Independent Pubs. Group.
Grigson, Caroline, ed. The Life & Poems of Anne Hunter: Haydn's Tuneful Voice. 2009. (Liverpool University Press - Liverpool English Texts & Studies). (ENG., Illus.). 256p. 95.00 (978-1-84631-191-8(8)) Liverpool Univ. Pr. GBR. Dist: Chicago Distribution Ctr.
Gristwood, Sarah. Poetic Lives: Byron. 2012. (Poetic Lives Ser.). (ENG.). 112p. pap. 12.95 (978-1-84391-307-8(0)) Hesperus Pr. GBR. Dist: Independent Pubs. Group.
Groes. Ian McEwan. Groes, Sebastian, ed. 2009. (Contemporary Critical Perspectives Ser.). (ENG.). 176p. 29.95 (978-0-8264-9722-2(5)) Continuum International Publishing Group, Ltd. GBR. Dist: National Bk. Network.
Groes, Sebastian. Ian McEwan. 2009. (Contemporary Critical Perspectives Ser.). (ENG.). 176p. 75.00 (978-0-8264-9721-5(7)) Continuum International Publishing Group, Ltd. GBR. Dist: National Bk. Network.
Gross, John, ed. The New Oxford Book of Literary Anecdotes. 2008. (Oxford Books of Prose & Verse Ser.). (ENG.). 400p. pap. 16.95 (978-0-19-954341-0(0)) Oxford Univ. Pr., Inc.
Guerra, Elizabeth. Stewart Farrar: Writer on A Broomstick, the Biography of Stewart Farrar. 2008. 232p. per. 17.99 (978-0-9791402-7-3(7)) Stewart, R. J. Bks.
Guiccioli, Teresa. Lord Byron Jugt Par les Ttmoins de Sa Vie My Recollections of Lord Byron; & Those of Eye-Witnesses of His Life. 2006. 676p. per. 36.99 (978-1-4255-6798-9(3)) MPublishing.
Guignery, Vanessa, et al. Conversations with Julian Barnes. Guignery, Vanessa & Roberts, Ryan, eds. 2009. (Literary Conversations Ser.). (ENG.). 212p. 50.00 (978-1-60473-203-0(2)); pap. 22.00 (978-1-60473-204-7(0)) Univ. Pr. of Mississippi.
Hadfield, Andrew. Edmund Spenser: A Life. 2012. (ENG., Illus.). 640p. 45.00 **(978-0-19-959102-2(4))** Oxford Univ. Pr., Inc.
Haffenden, John, ed. Selected Letters of William Empson. 2009. (ENG., Illus.). 800p. pap. 55.00 (978-0-19-953986-4(3)) Oxford Univ. Pr., Inc.
Haggerty, George E. Horace Walpole's Letters: Masculinity & Friendship in the Eighteenth Century. 2011. (Transit Series (bucknell Ser.). (ENG.). 186p. 60.00 (978-1-61148-010-8(8)); (978-0-8387-5817-5(7)) Bucknell Univ. Pr.
Hahn, Daniel. Shelley. 2009. (Poetic Lives Ser.). (ENG.). 152p. pap. 16.95 (978-1-84391-300-9(3)) Hesperus Pr. GBR. Dist: Independent Pubs. Group.
Hahn, Daniel & Robins, Nicholas, eds. The Oxford Guide to Literary Britain & Ireland. 3rd ed. 2008. (ENG., Illus.). 384p. 60.00 (978-0-19-861460-9(8)) Oxford Univ. Pr., Inc.
Hamilton, A. C. Sir Philip Sidney: A Study of His Life & Works. 2010. (ENG.). 228p. pap. 23.99 (978-0-521-15890-9(7)) Cambridge Univ. Pr.
Hamilton, Geoff & Jones, Brian. Encyclopedia of Contemporary Writers & Their Work. 2010. (Literary Movements Ser.). 432p. (C). (gr. 9-18). 75.00 (978-0-8160-7578-2(6)) Facts On File, Inc.
Hammill, Faye, et al, eds. Encyclopedia of British Women's Writing, 1900-1950. 2008. (ENG.). 360p. pap. 41.00 (978-0-230-22177-2(7)) Palgrave Macmillan.
Hannay, Margaret. Mary Sidney, Lady Wroth. 2010. (Illus.). 430p. 99.95 (978-0-7546-6053-8(2)) Ashgate Publishing Co.
Hannay, Margaret P. Ashgate Critical Essays on Women Writers in England 1550-1700: Volume 2:Mary Sidney. 2009. (Ashgate Critical Essays on Women Writers in England, 1550-1700 Ser.). (Illus.). 482p. 275.00 (978-0-7546-6083-5(4)) Ashgate Publishing Co.
Harman, Claire. Jane's Fame: How Jane Austen Conquered the World. 2011. (ENG., Illus.). 320p. pap. 16.00 (978-0-312-68065-7(1)) Picador.
Harnet, Thomas B. Letters of Anne Gilchrist & Walt Whitm. 2006. pap. 28.95 (978-1-4286-5452-5(6)) Kessinger Publishing, LLC.
Harris, Alexandra. Romantic Moderns: English Writers, Artists & the Imagination from Virginia Woolf to John Piper. 2010. (ENG., Illus.). 320p. 40.00 (978-0-500-25171-3(1), 525171) Thames & Hudson.
Harris, Alexandra, et al. Virginia Woolf. 2011. (Brief Lives Ser.). (ENG.). 120p. pap. 14.95 (978-1-84391-909-4(5)) Hesperus Pr. GBR. Dist: Independent Pubs. Group.
Harris, Frank. The Man Shakespeare. 2008. 428p. 32.99 (978-0-554-22940-9(4)); 30.99 (978-0-554-32243-8(9)) BiblioBazaar.
—The Man Shakespeare. 2007. 336p. per. (978-1-4065-3268-5(1)) Dodo Pr.
—My Life & Loves. 2010. 180p. pap. (978-1-151-74773-0(4)) Books LLC.
—My Life & Loves, V1. 2006. pap. 19.95 (978-1-59654-383-6(3), olympiapress.com) Disruptive Publishing.

—My Life & Loves, V2. 2006. pap. 23.95 *(978-1-59654-384-3(1),* olympiapress.com) Disruptive Publishing.

—My Life & Loves, V3. 2006. pap. 17.95 *(978-1-59654-385-0(X),* olympiapress.com) Disruptive Publishing.

—My Life & Loves, V4. 2006. pap. 17.95 *(978-1-59654-386-7(8),* olympiapress.com) Disruptive Publishing.

Harris, John F. Samuel Butler, Author of Erewhon: The Ma. 2006. pap. 28.95 *(978-1-4286-6032-8(1))* Kessinger Publishing, LLC.

Harrison, Shirley. The Life & Times of the Real Winnie-the-Pooh: The Teddy Bear Who Inspired A. A. Milne, 1 vol. 2011. (ENG.). 192p. 24.95 *(978-1-4556-1482-0(3))* Pelican Publishing Co., Inc.

Harwood, Laurence. C. S. Lewis, My Godfather: Letters, Photos & Recollections. 2007. (ENG., Illus.). 148p. 16.00 *(978-0-8308-3498-3(2))* InterVarsity Pr.

Harwood, Lee. Not the Full Story - Six Interviews with Lee Harwood. Corcoran, Kelvin, ed. 2008. (Illus.). 116p. pap. *(978-1-84861-001-9(7))* Shearsman Bks.

Hastings, Selina. Nancy Mitford. 2012. (Vintage Ser.). (ENG., Illus.). 304p. pap. 16.00 ***(978-0-307-94946-2(X)***, Vintage) Knopf Doubleday Publishing Group.

Havergal, Maria Vernon G. Memorials of Frances Ridley Havergal. 2006. pap. 34.95 *(978-1-4286-5283-5(3))* Kessinger Publishing, LLC.

Hawes, Donald & Hawes. Charles Dickens. 2007. (Writers Lives Ser.). (ENG.). 176p. 24.95 *(978-0-8264-8964-7(8))*; 110.00 *(978-0-8264-8963-0(X))* Continuum International Publishing Group, Ltd. GBR. Dist: National Bk. Network.

Hawkes, David. John Milton: A Hero of Our Time. 2010. (ENG.). 356p. 28.00 *(978-1-58243-437-7(9),* Counterpoint Pr.) Basic Bks. GBR. Dist: Perseus-PGW.

Hawkins, John. The Life of Samuel Johnson, LL.D. Brack, O. M., ed. 2009. (ENG., Illus.). 528p. lib. bdg. 59.95 *(978-0-8203-2995-6(9))* Univ. of Georgia Pr.

Hayes, M. Hunter. Understanding Will Self. annot. ed. 2007. (Understanding Modern British Literature Ser.). 221p. 39.95 *(978-1-57003-675-0(6))* Univ. of South Carolina Pr.

Haynes, Jim. In Praise of Joy: White-Washing Fences with Jim Haynes - A Celebration. Aster, Howard, ed. 2010. (ENG., Illus.). 160p. per. 15.00 *(978-0-88962-846-5(7))* Mosaic Pr.

Head, Dominic. Ian Mcewan. 2008. (Contemporary British Novelists Ser.). (ENG.). 232p. 79.00 *(978-0-7190-6656-6(5))*; 240p. pap. 26.00 *(978-0-7190-6657-3(3))* Manchester Univ. Pr. GBR. Dist: Macmillan.

Healey, Nicola. Dorothy Wordsworth & Hartley Coleridge: The Poetics of Relationship. 2012. (ENG., Illus.). 288p. 85.00 ***(978-0-230-27772-4(1))*** Palgrave Macmillan.

Heaphy, Maura. Science Fiction Authors: A Research Guide, 1 vol. 2008. (Author Research Ser.). 352p. (gr. 9-18). pap. 40.00 *(978-1-59158-515-2(5),* LU5155) Libraries Unlimited, Inc.

—100 Most Popular Science Fiction Authors: Biographical Sketches & Bibliographies, 1 vol. (Popular Authors Ser.). 565p. 65.00 *(978-1-59158-746-0(8),* LU7468) Libraries Unlimited, Inc.

Henry, Nancy. The Life of George Eliot. 2012. (Blackwell Critical Biographies Ser.). (ENG.). 314p. 89.95 ***(978-1-4051-3705-8(3)***, Wiley-Blackwell) Wiley, John & Sons, Inc.

Henstra, Sarah. The Counter-Memorial Impulse in Twentieth-Century English Fiction. 2009. (ENG.). 216p. 84.00 *(978-0-230-57714-5(8))* Palgrave Macmillan.

Herford, C. H. Robert Browning. 2007. (ENG.). 320p. 45.95 *(978-0-548-03393-7(5))* Kessinger Publishing, LLC.

Hester Lynch, Piozzi. Anecdotes of the Late Samuel Johnson. 2007. (ENG.). 132p. pap. 18.99 *(978-1-4346-1739-2(4))* BiblioBazaar.

Hewison, Robert. Ruskin on Venice: The Paradise of Cities. 2010. (ENG., Illus.). 500p. 85.00 *(978-0-300-12178-0(4))* Yale Univ. Pr.

Hibbert, Christopher. Charles Dickens: The Making of a Literary Giant. 2009. (ENG., Illus.). 336p. pap. 19.95 *(978-0-230-61426-0(4))* Palgrave Macmillan.

Hibbert, Christopher & Hitchings, Henry. Samuel Johnson: A Personal History. 2009. (ENG., Illus.). 384p. pap. 19.95 *(978-0-230-61427-7(2))* Palgrave Macmillan.

Hichens, Mark. Inimitable P G Wodehouse: The Story of His Life & a Treasury of His Wit. 2009. (Illus.). 240p. 28.50 *(978-1-84624-334-9(3))* Book Guild, Ltd. GBR. Dist: Trans-Atlantic Pubns., Inc.

Hill, Susan. Howards End Is on the Landing: A Year of Reading from Home. 2010. (ENG.). 240p. pap. 15.95 ***(978-1-84668-266-7(5))*** Profile Bks. Ltd. GBR. Dist: Consortium Bk. Sales & Distribution.

Himmelfarb, Gertrude, ed. The Spirit of the Age: Victorian Essays. 2009. (ENG., Illus.). 336p. pap. 23.00 *(978-0-300-15138-1(1))* Yale Univ. Pr.

Hinchman, Walter S. Lives of Great English Writers from Chaucer to Browning. 2008. 600p. 33.99 *(978-0-559-81810-3(6))*; pap. 43.75 *(978-0-559-81807-3(6))* BiblioBazaar.

Hines, Jessica. Looking for the Big B: Bollywood, Bachchan & Me. 2008. (ENG.). 1p. pap. 19.95 *(978-0-7475-6862-9(6))* Bloomsbury Publishing Plc GBR. Dist: Independent Pubs. Group.

Hinton, James. Life & Letters of James Hinton. 2008. 388p. 29.99 *(978-0-559-62453-7(0))*; pap. 32.75 *(978-0-559-62451-3(4))* BiblioBazaar.

—Life & Letters of James Hinton. 2009. 228p. pap. *(978-0-217-50287-0(3))* Books LLC.

—Life & Letters of James Hinton. 2009. 266p. pap. 21.33 *(978-0-217-50469-0(8))* General Bks. LLC.

—Life & Letters of James Hinton. Hopkins, Ellice, ed. 2007. (ENG.). 384p. 48.95 *(978-0-548-08108-2(5))* Kessinger Publishing, LLC.

Hird, June & Hird, Laura. Dear Laura. 2007. pap. *(978-1-84195-899-6(9))* Canongate Bks.

Hodge, Jane Aiken. The Private World of Georgette Heyer. 2011. 256p. pap. 14.99 *(978-1-4022-5192-4(0))* Sourcebooks, Inc.

Hogan, Rose. Mrs Craik: Author of John Halifax, Gentleman. 2009. (Illus.). 72p. pap. *(978-1-84748-405-5(0))* Athena Pr.

Hogg, Thomas Jefferson. Shelley at Oxford. 2009. 208p. pap. 14.14 *(978-0-217-55193-9(9))*; pap. 14.14 *(978-1-4589-7256-9(9))* General Bks. LLC.

Holdridge, Jefferson. The Poetry of Paul Muldoon. 2009. (ENG.). 232p. pap. 33.95 *(978-1-905785-30-8(5))* Liffey Pr., The IRL. Dist: Dufour Editions, Inc.

Hopkins, Lisa. Bram Stoker: A Literary Life. annot. ed. 2007. (Literary Lives Ser.). (ENG.). 208p. 84.00 *(978-1-4039-4647-8(7))* Palgrave Macmillan.

Howe, Will David. Charles Lamb & His Friends. 2011. 398p. 54.95 ***(978-1-258-06901-8(6))*** Literary Licensing, LLC.

Howitt, Mary Botham. Mary Howitt: Volume 1: An Autobiography. Howitt, Margaret, ed. 2011. (Cambridge Library Collection - Literary Studies). (Illus.). 352p. pap. 29.99 *(978-1-108-02573-7(0))* Cambridge Univ. Pr.

—Mary Howitt: Volume 2: An Autobiography. Howitt, Margaret, ed. 2011. (Cambridge Library Collection - Literary Studies). (Illus.). 388p. pap. 31.99 *(978-1-108-02574-4(9))* Cambridge Univ. Pr.

Hubbard, Elbert. Little Journeys to the Homes of the Great, 5. l.t. ed. 2006. (ENG.). 226p. pap. 22.99 *(978-1-4264-7357-9(5))* BiblioBazaar.

—Little Journeys to the Homes of the Great, Volume 5: Little Journeys to the Homes of English Authors. 2007. 202p. pap. 20.99 *(978-1-4264-7284-8(6))* BiblioBazaar.

Hudson, Nicholas. Samuel Johnson & the Making of Modern England. 2007. (ENG.). 304p. pap. 60.00 *(978-0-521-04574-2(6))* Cambridge Univ. Pr.

Hudson, W. H. Far Away & Long Ago: A Childhood in Argentina. 2007. 356p. 32.95 *(978-1-4344-9351-4(2))*; per. 19.95 *(978-1-4344-9350-7(4))* Wildside Pr., LLC.

Hulme, Peter & McDougall, Russell, eds. Writing, Travel & Empire: Colonial Narratives of Other Cultures. 2007. (International Library of Colonial History Ser.). (ENG., Illus.). 256p. 79.00 *(978-1-84511-304-9(7))* I. B. Tauris & Co., Ltd. GBR. Dist: Macmillan.

Humphreys, A. R. William Shenstone. 2009. (ENG.). 152p. pap. 27.99 *(978-0-521-12527-7(8))* Cambridge Univ. Pr.

Hunt, Leigh. The Autobiography of Leigh Hunt. 2009. 138p. pap. 19.99 *(978-0-217-57180-7(8))*; 214p. pap. 19.99 *(978-0-217-28093-8(5))* General Bks. LLC.

—The Autobiography of Leigh Hunt. 2007. (ENG.). 436p. 51.95 *(978-0-548-11004-1(2))* Kessinger Publishing, LLC.

—Leigh Hunt's Autobiography: The Earliest Sketches. Fogle, Stephen Francis, ed. 2011. 72p. 36.95 ***(978-1-258-09075-3(9))*** Literary Licensing, LLC.

Hunt, Leigh. Lord Byron & Some of His Contemporaries. 2008. 460p. 31.99 *(978-0-554-56536-1(6))*; 459p. 33.99 *(978-0-554-56527-9(7))*; 460p. pap. 35.75 *(978-0-554-56534-7(X))*; 459p. pap. 36.75 *(978-0-554-56530-9(7))* BiblioBazaar.

—Lord Byron & Some of His Contemporaries. 2009. 350p. pap. *(978-0-217-84812-1(5))* Books LLC.

Hunt, Leigh & Hunt, Thornton Leigh. The Autobiography of Leigh Hunt. 2009. 472p. pap. 37.75 *(978-1-116-35220-7(6))*; 42.99 *(978-1-116-35218-4(4))*; 35.99 *(978-1-116-35219-1(2))*; pap. 36.75 *(978-1-116-35221-4(4))* BiblioBazaar.

Hurley, Michael D. G. K. Chesterton. 2012. (Writers & Their Work Ser.). (ENG.). 128p. (C). 80.00 *(978-0-7463-1210-0(5))*; pap. 26.00 *(978-0-7463-1211-7(3))* Northcote Hse. Publishers, Ltd. GBR. Dist: Brown, David Bk. Co., The.

Husain, Ed. The Islamist: Why I Became an Islamic Fundamentalist, What I Saw Inside, & Why I Left. 2009. (ENG.). 320p. (gr. 12-18). 16.00 *(978-0-14-311598-4(7),* Penguin (Non-Classics)) Penguin Group (USA) Inc.

Ingersoll, Earl G. & Ingersoll, Mary C., eds. Conversations with Anthony Burgess. 2008. (ENG.). 224p. 50.00 *(978-1-60473-095-1(1))* Univ. Pr. of Mississippi.

—Conversations with Anthony Burgess. 2008. (ENG.). 224p. pap. 22.00 *(978-1-60473-096-8(X))* Univ. Pr. of Mississippi.

Ingram, Jill Phillips. Idioms of Self-Interest: Credit, Identity, & Propetry in English Renaissance Literature. annot. ed. 2006. (Literary Criticism & Cultural Theory Ser.). (ENG.). 128p. 125.00 *(978-0-415-97842-2(4))* Routledge.

Ingram, John Henry. Marlowe & His Poetry. 2008. 302p. 43.95 *(978-1-4365-2439-1(3))* 2007. (ENG.). 304p. per. 28.95 *(978-0-548-72589-4(6))* Kessinger Publishing, LLC.

Irvine, Alexander. From the Bottom Up. 2008. 232p. 24.99 *(978-0-554-35838-3(7))*; 27.99 *(978-0-554-26535-3(4))* BiblioBazaar.

—From the Bottom Up. 2007. (Illus.). 216p. per. *(978-1-4065-3423-8(4))* Dodo Pr.

Isherwood, Christopher. Isherwood on Writing. Berg, James J., ed. 2007. (Illus.). 208p. 25.95 *(978-0-8166-4693-7(7))* Univ. of Minnesota Pr.

Isherwood, Christopher. Liberation: Diaries:1970-1983. 2012. (ENG.). 768p. 39.99 ***(978-0-06-208474-3(7))*** HarperCollins Pubs.

Ivins, Holly. The Jane Austen Pocket Bible: Everything You Want to Know about Jane & Her Novels. 2011. (ENG.). 192p. pap. 9.95 *(978-1-907087-18-9(4))* Crimson Publishing, Ltd. GBR. Dist: National Bk. Network.

Izzo, David Garrett. W. H. Auden Encyclopedia. alt. ed. 2011. (ENG., Illus.). 304p. pap. 55.00 *(978-0-7864-4913-2(6))* McFarland & Co., Inc. Pubs.

Já, et al. Life in the Work of Virginia Woolf. 2010. 60p. pap. *(978-3-8383-8330-9(3))* Lambert Academic Publishing.

Jacobs, Alan. The Narnian: The Life & Imagination of C. S. Lewis. 2006. (ENG., Illus.). 368p. per. 14.95 *(978-0-06-087269-4(1),* Harper San Francisco) HarperCollins Pubs.

James, Felicity. Charles Lamb, Coleridge & Wordsworth: Reading Friendship in the 1790s. 2008. (ENG.). 256p. 84.00 *(978-0-230-54524-3(6))* Palgrave Macmillan.

Jarrett-Macauley, Delia. The Life of una Marson, 1905-1965. 2010. (ENG., Illus.). 256p. pap. 24.95 *(978-0-7190-8256-6(0))* Manchester Univ. Pr. GBR. Dist: Macmillan.

Jefferies, Richard. The Story of My Heart: An Autobiography. 2007. (ENG.). 86p. pap. 16.99 *(978-1-4346-4403-9(0))* BiblioBazaar.

—The Story of My Heart: An Autobiography. 2007. 76p. per. *(978-1-4065-2720-9(3))* Dodo Pr.

—The Story of My Heart: My Autobiography. 2009. 196p. 22.99 *(978-1-103-11434-4(4))*; pap. 16.99 *(978-1-103-11431-3(X))* BiblioBazaar.

Jennings, Luke. Blood Knots. 2010. (Illus.). 320p. *(978-1-84887-132-8(5))* Down The Shore Publishing.

Jerrold, Walter. Charles Lamb. 2009. 72p. pap. *(978-0-217-19084-8(7))*; pap. *(978-0-217-45768-2(1))* Books LLC.

—Charles Lamb. 2007. (ENG., Illus.). 88p. per. *(978-1-4065-3466-5(8))* Dodo Pr.

—Charles Lamb. 2007. (ENG.). 118p. 34.95 *(978-0-548-02460-7(X))* Kessinger Publishing, LLC.

Jeslyn Medoff Staff & Evans, Robert. Jane Barker Pt. 4,Vol. 6: Rinted Writings 1641-1700. 2009. (Early Modern Englishwoman: A Facsimile Library of Essential Works - Printed Writings, 1641-1700: Ser. II, Part Four Ser.). 448p. 170.00 *(978-0-7546-3145-3(1))* Ashgate Publishing Co.

John, Angela V. Evelyn Sharp: Rebel Woman, 1869-1955. 2009. (ENG., Illus.). 304p. 95.00 *(978-0-7190-8014-2(2))*; mass mkt. 33.00 *(978-0-7190-8015-9(0))* Manchester Univ. Pr. GBR. Dist: Macmillan.

John Bunyan. Grace Abounding to the Chief of Sinners. 2007. (ENG.). 136p. pap. 18.99 *(978-1-4346-3844-1(8))* BiblioBazaar.

—Grace Abounding to the Chief of Sinners. 2010. 132p. pap. 4.49 *(978-1-60386-289-9(7),* Merchant Bks.) Rough Draft Printing.

Johnson, Claudia Durst. Women's Search for Independence in Charlotte Bronte's Jane Eyre. 2011. (Social Issues in Literature Ser.). 224p. (J). (ENG.). pap. 26.50 *(978-0-7377-5451-3(6))*; lib. bdg. 38.45 *(978-0-7377-5450-6(8))* Cengage Gale. (Greenhaven Pr., Inc.).

Johnson, Claudia L. Jane Austen's Cults & Cultures. 2012. (ENG., Illus.). 240p. 35.00 ***(978-0-226-40203-1(7))*** Univ. of Chicago Pr.

Johnson, Samuel. Letters of Samuel Johnson V1: Oct 30, 1731-Dec 21 1776. Hill, George Birkbeck, ed. 2007. pap. 37.95 *(978-1-4304-5101-3(7))* Kessinger Publishing, LLC.

—Lives of the English Poets: Waller, Milton, Cowley. 2006. (ENG.). 164p. pap. 19.99 *(978-1-4264-1213-4(4))*; 162p. pap. 21.99 *(978-1-4264-1256-1(8))* BiblioBazaar.

—Lives of the Poets. 2008. (ENG.). 144p. per. 7.99 *(978-1-60450-091-2(3))* Arc Manor.

—Lives of the Poets. 2008. 528p. 35.99 *(978-0-554-23101-3(8))*; 32.99 *(978-0-554-32404-3(0))* BiblioBazaar.

—Lives of the Poets. 2009. 152p. pap. 11.45 *(978-1-4385-1986-9(9),* Book Jungle) Standard Pubns., Inc.

—Lives of the Poets: Prior, Congreve, Blackmore & Pope. 2007. 152p. per. *(978-1-4065-3505-1(2))* Dodo Pr.

—Selected Letters of Samuel Johnson. 2008. 296p. 43.95 *(978-1-4365-2371-4(0))* 2007. (ENG.). 300p. per. 28.95 *(978-0-548-73959-4(5))* Kessinger Publishing, LLC.

Johnston, Georgia. The Formation of 20th-Century Queer Autobiography: Reading Vita Sackville-West, Virginia Woolf, Hilda Doolittle, & Gertrude Stein. 2007. (ENG.). 216p. 84.00 *(978-1-4039-7618-5(X))* Palgrave Macmillan.

Joll, Nicholas, ed. Philosophy & the Hitchhiker's Guide to the Galaxy. 2012. (ENG., Illus.). 272p. (C). pap. 21.00 ***(978-0-230-29112-6(0))*** Palgrave Macmillan.

Jones, Diana Wynne. Reflections. 2012. (ENG.). 272p. (gr. 8). 24.99 ***(978-0-06-221989-3(8)***, Greenwillow Bks.) HarperCollins Pubs.

Jordan, Bob & Jordan, R. R. Writers & Their Other Work: Twentieth-Century British Writers & English Teaching Abroad. 2006. (ENG., Illus.). 304p. 58.00 *(978-0-7188-3033-5(4))* Lutherworth Pr., The GBR. Dist: Brown, David Bk. Co., The.

Jordan, R. R. Writers & Their Other Work: Twentieth-Century British Writers & English Teaching Abroad. 2006. (ENG., Illus.). 299p. per. 40.00 *(978-0-7188-3066-3(0))* Lutherworth Pr., The GBR. Dist: Brown, David Bk. Co., The.

Joshi, S. T. & Pardoe, Rosemary, eds. Warnings to the Curious: A Sheaf of Criticism on M. R. James. 2007. 338p. per. 20.00 *(978-0-9771734-8-8(8))* Hippocampus Pr.

Judd, Denis. Alison Uttley: Spinner of Tales - The Authorised Biography of the Creator of Little Grey Rabbit. 3rd ed. 2010. (ENG., Illus.). 308p. 24.95 *(978-0-7190-8456-0(3))* Manchester Univ. Pr. GBR. Dist: Macmillan.

—Private Diaries of Alison Uttley: Author of Little Grey Rabbit. 2009. (Illus.). 336p. 50.00 *(978-1-84468-040-5(1))* Pen & Sword Bks. Ltd. GBR. Dist: Casemate Pubs. & Bk. Distributors, LLC.

Judd, Denis. The Private Diaries of Alison Uttley: Author of Little Grey Rabbit, Foreword by Ronald Blythe. 2011. (Illus.). 336p. pap. 29.95 ***(978-1-84468-128-0(9))*** Pen & Sword Bks. Ltd. GBR. Dist: Casemate Pubs. & Bk. Distributors, LLC.

Judt, Tony. The Memory Chalet. 2011. (ENG., Illus.). 240p. (gr. 12). 15.00 *(978-0-14-311997-5(4),* Penguin (Non-Classics)) Penguin Group (USA) Inc.

Kaczynski, Richard. Aleister Crowley. Wasserman, James, ed. 2009. (ENG.). 1p. pap. 12.95 *(978-1-57863-456-9(3),* Weiser Bks.) Red Wheel/Weiser.

—Perdurabo: The Life of Aleister Crowley. rev. exp. ed. 2010. (ENG., Illus.). 720p. 29.95 *(978-1-55643-899-8(0))* North Atlantic Bks.

Kahan, Gerald. George Alexander Stevens & the Lecture on Heads. 2008. (ENG.). 232p. pap. 22.95 *(978-0-8203-3264-2(X))* Univ. of Georgia Pr.

Kaplan, Cora. Victoriana: Histories, Fictions, Criticism. 2007. (ENG., Illus.). 264p. (gr. 17). 85.00 *(978-0-231-14216-8(1))*; pap. 27.50 *(978-0-231-14217-5(X))* Columbia Univ. Pr.

Kavanagh, Julia. English Women of Letters. 2009. 136p. pap. *(978-0-217-46927-2(2))*; 258p. pap. *(978-1-4590-7035-6(6))* Books LLC.

—English Women of Letters, 2 Vols. reprint ed. 250.00 *(978-0-7222-1922-5(9))* Library Reprints, Inc.

Kay, Peter. Saturday Night Peter: Memoirs of a Stand-Up Comedian. 2009. (ENG., Illus.). 258p. 36.95 ***(978-1-84605-363-4(3))*** Random Hse. GBR. Dist: Independent Pubs. Group.

Keane, Angela. Revolutionary Women Writers: Charlotte Smith & Helen M. Williams. 2011. (Writers & Their Work Ser.). (ENG.). 128p. (C). 80.00 *(978-0-7463-1096-0(X))* Northcote Hse. Publishers, Ltd. GBR. Dist: Brown, David Bk. Co., The.

—Revolutionary Women Writers: Charlotte Smith & Helen Maria Williams. 2012. (Writers & Their Work Ser.). (ENG.). 128p. (C). pap. 26.00 *(978-0-7463-0971-1(6))* Northcote Hse. Publishers, Ltd. GBR. Dist: Brown, David Bk. Co., The.

Keats, John. Bright Star: Love Letters & Poems of John Keats to Fanny Brawne. 2009. (ENG.). 144p. (gr. 12). 14.00 *(978-0-14-311774-2(2),* Penguin (Non-Classics)) Penguin Group (USA) Inc.

Keats, John. The Letters of John Keats. Forman, H. Buxton, ed. 2011. (Cambridge Library Collection - Literary Studies). (ENG., Illus.). 598p. pap. 43.00 ***(978-1-108-03421-0(7))*** Cambridge Univ. Pr.

Keegan, Bridget. British Labouring-Class Nature Poetry, 1730-1837. 2008. (ENG.). 224p. 89.00 *(978-0-230-53696-8(4))* Palgrave Macmillan.

Kelly, Nigel. Quentin Crisp: The Profession of Being. A Biography. 2011. (ENG., Illus.). 227p. pap. 45.00 ***(978-0-7864-6475-3(5))*** McFarland & Co., Inc. Pubs.

Kelly, Pauline E. Jane Austen Dictionary. 2009. 148p. pap. 18.95 *(978-0-9768812-3-0(3))* Inkwell Publishing.

Kemp, Harry, ed. The Bronze Treasury: An Anthology of Eighty-One Obscure English Poets Together with Their Biographical Portraits. 2011. 472p. 57.95 ***(978-1-258-09446-1(0))*** Literary Licensing, LLC.

Kendon, Frank. The Small Years. 2010. (ENG.). 232p. pap. 22.99 *(978-0-521-15547-2(9))* Cambridge Univ. Pr.

Kenny, Anthony & Kenny. Arthur Hugh Clough: A Poet's Life. 2007. (ENG., Illus.). 288p. 29.95 *(978-0-8264-8269-3(4))* Continuum International Publishing Group, Ltd. GBR. Dist: National Bk. Network.

Kent, Charles. Charles Dickens As a Reader by Charles Kent. 2006. 288p. per. 23.99 *(978-1-4255-2655-9(1))* MPublishing.

Ker, Ian. G. K. Chesterton: A Biography. (ENG., Illus.). 2012. 784p. pap. 35.00 ***(978-0-19-965576-2(6))*** 2011. 688p. 65.00 *(978-0-19-960128-8(3))* Oxford Univ. Pr., Inc.

Ketraro, Einav. The Organism of the Letter. 2009. 128p. pap. *(978-3-8364-6535-9(3))* VDM Verlag Dr. Mueller e.K.

Ketton-Cremer. Thomas Gray. 2011. (ENG.). 340p. pap. 28.99 *(978-0-521-14146-8(X))* Cambridge Univ. Pr.

Khorana, Meena G. & Greenwood. The Life & Works of Ruskin Bond. 2009. 188p. pap. 45.99 *(978-1-60752-075-7(3))* Information Age Publishing, Inc.

Kiely, Kevin. Francis Stuart: Outcast Witness. (Illus.). 336p. *(978-0-7165-2785-5(5))* Irish Academic Pr. IRL. Dist: International Specialized Bk. Services.

King, Bruce. Robert Graves: A Biography. 2009. (ENG.). 200p. 26.95 *(978-1-905791-94-1(1))* Haus Publishing GBR. Dist: Consortium Bk. Sales & Distribution.

King, Francis & Crowley, Aleister. Megatherion: The Magickal World of Aleister Crowley. 2012. (ENG., Illus.). 200p. pap. 19.95 ***(978-1-84068-180-2(2))*** Creation Bks. GBR. Dist: SCB Distributors.

King, R. W. Parson Primrose: The Life, Work & Friendships of Henry Francis Cary, 1772-1842. 2011. 384p. 53.95 ***(978-1-258-03470-2(0))*** Literary Licensing, LLC.

King, Roger. Love & Fatigue in America. 2012. (ENG.). 254p. 26.95 ***(978-0-299-28720-7(3))*** Univ. of Wisconsin Pr.

Kingsley, Charles. Charles Kingsley, His Letters, & Memories of His Life. 2007. (ENG.). 444p. 35.00 *(978-1-4344-9182-4(X))*; (ENG.). 432p. 35.00 *(978-1-4344-9181-7(1))*; (ENG.). 444p. per. 19.95 *(978-1-4344-9088-9(2))*; 432p. per. 19.95 *(978-1-4344-9087-2(4))* Wildside Pr., LLC.

Kingsley, Charles. Charles Kingsley, his Letters & Memories of his Life. Kingsley, Frances Eliza, ed. 2011. (Cambridge Library Collection - Literary Studies). (ENG.). 518p. pap. 37.99 ***(978-1-108-03485-2(3))***; (Illus.). 522p. pap. 37.99 ***(978-1-108-03484-5(5))*** Cambridge Univ. Pr.

Kingsley, Henry. Austin Elliot. 2010. (ENG.). 364p. pap. 32.75 *(978-1-177-36368-6(2))* 2010. 350p. pap. 32.75 *(978-1-177-82926-7(6))* 2010. 366p. pap. 32.75 *(978-1-148-33460-8(2))* 2010. 366p. pap. 32.75 *(978-1-146-60970-8(1))* 2010. 356p. pap. 32.75 *(978-1-144-93600-4(4))* 2009. 298p. 30.99 *(978-1-116-27523-0(6))* 2009. (ENG.). 296p. pap. 23.99 *(978-1-116-27526-1(0),* BiblioLife) 2009. (ENG.). 296p. pap. 21.99 *(978-1-116-27527-8(9),* BiblioLife) 2009. 340p. 25.99 *(978-1-103-01432-3(3))* 2009. 340p. pap. 19.99 *(978-1-103-01428-6(5))* BiblioBazaar.

—Austin Elliot. 2010. 104p. pap. *(978-1-151-90453-9(8))* 2009. 226p. pap. *(978-0-217-33422-8(9))* 2009. 334p. pap. *(978-0-217-17908-9(8))* 2009. 246p. pap. *(978-1-4590-3681-9(6))* Books LLC.

—Austin Elliot. 2010. 98p. pap. 19.99 *(978-1-154-12134-6(8))* General Bks. LLC.
—Austin Elliot. 2008. 356p. 46.95 *(978-1-4365-3217-4(5))* 2007. (ENG.). 360p. per. 31.95 *(978-0-548-69329-2(3))* Kessinger Publishing, LLC.
Kinkead-Weekes, Mark. D. H. Lawrence: Triumph to Exile 1912-1922: Volume 2: The Cambridge Biography of D. H. Lawrence. 2011. (ENG.). 1022p. pap. 61.99 ***(978-1-107-40300-0(6))*** Cambridge Univ. Pr.
Kinney, Clare R. Ashgate Critical Essays on Women Writers in England. 1550-1700: Volume 4:Mary Wroth. 2009. (Ashgate Critical Essays on Women Writers in England, 1550-1700 Ser.). (Illus.). 556p. 300.00 *(978-0-7546-6082-8(6))* Ashgate Publishing Co.
Kipling, Rudyard. O Beloved Kids: Rudyard Kipling's Letters to His Children. Gilbert, Elliot L., ed. 2008. (ENG., Illus.). 240p. 18.95 *(978-1-904435-80-8(7))* Little Bks., Ltd. GBR. Dist: Independent Pubs. Group.
Kitch, Aaron W. Political Economy & the State of Literature in Early Modern England: From Spenser to Jonson. 2009. (Illus.). 228p. 99.95 *(978-0-7546-6756-8(1))* Ashgate Publishing Co.
Klimaszewski, Melisa. Wilkie Collins. 2011. (Brief Lives Ser.). (ENG.). 152p. pap. 15.95 *(978-1-84391-915-5(X))* Hesperus Pr. GBR. Dist: Independent Pubs. Group.
Knight, Jesse F. & Darley, Stephen. The Last of the Great Swashbucklers: Rafael Sabatini: A Bio-Bibliography. 2010. 65.00 *(978-1-58456-279-5(X))* Oak Knoll Pr.
Knight, William, ed. Journals of Dorothy Wordsworth V1. 2007. (ENG.). 272p. 42.95 *(978-0-548-12179-5(6))* Kessinger Publishing, LLC.
—Journals of Dorothy Wordsworth V2. 2007. (ENG.). 304p. 43.95 *(978-0-548-12178-8(8))* Kessinger Publishing, LLC.
Knowles, Owen, ed. My Dear Friend . Further Letters to & about Joseph Conrad. 2008. 248p. 77.00 *(978-90-420-2464-9(X))* Rodopi.
Krawczyk, Scott. Romantic Literary Families. 2009. (Nineteenth-Century Major Lives & Letters Ser.). (ENG.). 244p. 95.00 *(978-0-230-60475-9(7))* Palgrave Macmillan.
Krissdottir, Morine. Descents of Memory: The Life of John Cowper Powys. 2009. (ENG.). 464p. (gr. 12-18). pap. 16.95 *(978-1-59020-265-4(1))* Overlook Pr., The.
Kureishi, Hanif. My Ear at His Heart: Reading My Father. 2010. (ENG., Illus.). 208p. 24.00 *(978-1-4165-7212-1(0)*, Scribner) Scribner.
Kuriyama, Constance Brown. Christopher Marlowe: A Renaissance Life. 2010. (Illus.). 280p. pap. 24.95 *(978-0-8014-7688-4(7))* Cornell Univ. Pr.
Kurtz, Benjamin P. & Autrey, Carrie C., eds. Four New Letters of Mary Wollstonecraft & Helen M Williams. 2011. 96p. 38.95 ***(978-1-258-02854-1(9))*** Literary Licensing, LLC.
Laird, Susan & Laird. Mary Wollstonecraft: Philosophical Mother of Coeducation. 2008. (Continuum Library of Educational Thought). (ENG.). 272p. 140.00 *(978-0-8264-8414-7(X))* Continuum International Publishing Group, Ltd. GBR. Dist: National Bk. Network.
Lamb, Charles. The Best Letters of Charles Lamb. 2008. 328p. 29.99 *(978-0-554-23201-0(4))* 2008. 328p. 28.99 *(978-0-554-32504-0(7))* 2007. (ENG.). 304p. pap. 23.99 *(978-1-4264-3952-0(0))* 2007. (ENG.). 346p. pap. 24.99 *(978-1-4264-3982-7(2))* BiblioBazaar.
—The Best Letters of Charles Lamb. Johnson, Edward Gilpin, ed. 2007. 276p. per. *(978-1-4065-2577-9(4))* Dodo Pr.
—The Best Letters of Charles Lamb. Johnson, Edward Gilpin, ed. 2007. (ENG.). 336p. 45.95 *(978-0-548-15632-2(8))*; 340p. per. 30.95 *(978-1-4304-5095-5(9))* Kessinger Publishing, LLC.
—Lamb & Hazlitt. reprint ed. 30.00 *(978-0-404-07359-6(X))* AMS Pr., Inc.
—Miscellaneous Essays. 2009. (ENG.). 280p. pap. 38.99 *(978-0-521-10088-5(7))* Cambridge Univ. Pr.
—The Works of Charles Lamb, with a Sketch of His Life & Final Memorials by Sir Thomas Noon Talfourd. 2006. 620p. per. 34.99 *(978-1-4255-6539-8(5))*; 564p. per. 32.99 *(978-1-4255-6182-6(9))* MPublishing.
Landry, Peter. The English Romantics. 2007. pap. 21.74 *(978-1-4251-2859-3(9))* Trafford Publishing.
Lane, Carla. Someday I'll Find Me - Carla Lane: Her Frank & Captivating Autobiography. 2006. (ENG., Illus.). 260p. 29.95 *(978-1-86105-973-4(6))* Anova Bks. GBR. Dist: Independent Pubs. Group.
Lang, Andrew. Letters to Dead Authors. reprint ed. 37.50 *(978-0-404-03819-9(0))* AMS Pr., Inc.
—Letters to Dead Authors. 2009. 248p. 23.99 *(978-1-103-21038-1(6))* 2009. 248p. pap. 17.99 *(978-1-103-21033-6(5))* 2008. 248p. 23.99 *(978-0-559-88448-1(6))* 2008. 248p. pap. 17.99 *(978-0-559-88447-4(8))* 2008. 132p. 21.99 *(978-0-554-37839-8(6))* 2008. 132p. 24.99 *(978-0-554-28536-8(3))* 2007. (ENG.). 116p. pap. 18.99 *(978-1-4346-5657-5(8))* 2007. 128p. pap. 19.99 *(978-1-4346-5658-2(6))* BiblioBazaar.
—Letters to Dead Authors. 2007. (ENG.). 104p. per. *(978-1-4065-2626-4(6))* Dodo Pr.
Langley, R. & Langley, R. F. Journals. 2006. (ENG., Illus.). 144p. per. *(978-1-905700-00-4(8))* Shearsman Bks.
Lawrence, Frederick. The Life of Henry Fielding: With Notices of His Writings, His Times, & His Contemporaries. 2007. (ENG.). 396p. 49.95 *(978-0-548-14415-2(X))* Kessinger Publishing, LLC.
—Life of Henry Fielding with Notices of H. 2006. pap. 34.95 *(978-1-4286-5675-8(8))* Kessinger Publishing, LLC.
Lawson, Valerie. Mary Poppins, She Wrote: The Life of P. L. Travers. 2008. (ENG., Illus.). 416p. pap. 27.95 *(978-0-7432-9950-3(7))* Simon & Schuster.
Le Gallienne, Richard. The Romantic '90s. 2011. 284p. 48.95 ***(978-1-258-05679-7(8))*** Literary Licensing, LLC.
Leach, Karoline. In the Shadow of the Dreamchild: The Myth & Reality of Lewis Carroll. 2nd rev. ed. 2009. (ENG.). 256p. pap. 23.95 *(978-0-7206-1318-6(3))* Owen, Peter Ltd. GBR. Dist: Independent Pubs. Group.
Leader, Zachary. The Life of Kingsley Amis. 2007. (ENG., Illus.). 1008p. 39.95 *(978-0-375-42498-4(9)*, Pantheon) Knopf Doubleday Publishing Group.
—The Life of Kingsley Amis. 2011. (ENG.). 1012p. pap. 25.95 *(978-0-8101-2759-3(8))* Northwestern Univ. Pr.
Lear, Linda. Beatrix Potter: A Life in Nature. 2007. (ENG., Illus.). 608p. 30.00 *(978-0-312-36934-7(4))* St. Martin's Pr.
Leask, William Keith. James Boswell. 2009. 164p. pap. 21.95 *(978-1-120-30307-3(9))* Kessinger Publishing, LLC.
—James Boswell. 2007. (ENG.). 164p. per. *(978-1-4086-2699-3(3))* Read Bks.
Lebedoff, David. The Same Man: George Orwell & Evelyn Waugh in Love & War. 2008. (ENG., Illus.). 288p. 26.00 *(978-1-4000-6634-6(4)*, Random House) Random House Publishing Group.
Lee, Anthony W. Mentoring in Eighteenth-Century British Literature & Culture. 2009. 264p. 114.95 *(978-0-7546-6977-7(7))* Ashgate Publishing Co.
Lee, Laurie. As I Walked Out One Midsummer Morning. 2011. 192p. pap. 15.95 *(978-1-56792-392-6(5)*, Non Pareil Bks.) Godine, David R. Pub.
Lee, Ying S. Masculinity & the English Working Class: Studies in Victorian Autobiography & Fiction. 2007. (Literary Criticism & Cultural Theory Ser.). (ENG., Illus.). 264p. (C). 131.00 *(978-0-415-98146-0(8))* Routledge.
Lees, Edwin. Stratford As Connected with Shakespeare. 2009. 48p. pap. *(978-0-217-56375-8(9))* Books LLC.
—Stratford As Connected with Shakespeare. 2006. pap. 17.95 *(978-1-4286-6338-1(X))* Kessinger Publishing, LLC.
Leighton, Angela, ed. Voyages over Voices: Critical Essays on Anne Stevenson. 2011. (Liverpool University Press - Liverpool English Texts & Studies). (ENG.). 257p. 95.00 *(978-1-84631-484-1(4))* Liverpool Univ. Pr. GBR. Dist: Chicago Distribution Ctr.
Leithart, Peter. Writer of Fancy: The Playful Piety of Jane Austen. 2008. 256p. 16.95 *(978-1-58182-645-6(1)*, Cumberland Hse.) Sourcebooks, Inc.
Lesjak, Carolyn. Working Fictions: A Genealogy of the Victorian Novel. 2007. (Post-Contemporary Interventions Ser.). (ENG.). 288p. (C). 84.95 *(978-0-8223-3835-2(1))* Duke Univ. Pr.
Lesjak, Carolyn & Armstrong, Nancy. Working Fictions: A Genealogy of the Victorian Novel. annot. ed. 2007. (Post-Contemporary Interventions Ser.). (ENG.). 288p. per. 23.95 *(978-0-8223-3888-8(2))* Duke Univ. Pr.
Levy-Navarro, Elena & Levy-navarro, Elena. The Culture of Obesity in Early & Late Modernity: Body Image in Shakespeare, Jonson, Middleton, & Skelton. 2008. (ENG.). 252p. 89.00 *(978-0-230-60123-9(5))* Palgrave Macmillan.
Lewes, Darby. Double Vision: Literary Palimpsests of the Eighteenth & Nineteenth Centuries. 2008. (ENG., Illus.). 296p. 78.99 *(978-0-7391-2569-4(9))* Lexington Bks.
Lewington, Ken. To Be a Pilgrim. 2009. 216p. pap. 15.99 *(978-1-4389-3695-6(8))* AuthorHouse.
Lewis, Linda M. Dickens, His Parables, & His Reader. 2012. (ENG.). 312p. (C). (gr. 13). 60.00 *(978-0-8262-1947-3(0))* Univ. of Missouri Pr.
Lewis, Peter. Charles Dickens & the Staplehurst Train Crash. 2010. (ENG.). 192p. pap. 24.95 *(978-1-84868-793-6(1))* Amberley Publishing GBR. Dist: Casemate Pubs. & Bk. Distributors, LLC.
Lewis, Roger. What Am I Still Doing Here? My Years as Me. (ENG.). 2012. 384p. pap. 12.95 ***(978-1-4447-0869-1(4))*** 2011. (Illus.). 368p. 32.95 ***(978-1-4447-0868-4(6))*** Hodder General Publishing Div. GBR. (Hodder & Stoughton). Dist: Independent Pubs. Group.
Lewis, Susan. One Day at a Time: A Memoir. 2012. (ENG.). 440p. pap. 12.95 ***(978-0-09-956007-4(0))*** Random Hse. GBR. Dist: Independent Pubs. Group.
Liberman, Sherri. Lynne Reid Banks. 2009. (Library of Author Biographies Ser.). 112p. (gr. 5-8). 63.90 *(978-1-60853-545-3(2)*, Rosen Central) Rosen Publishing Group, Inc., The.
Light, Alison. Mrs. Woolf & the Servants: An Intimate History of Domestic Life in Bloomsbury. 2009. (ENG., Illus.). 400p. pap. 20.00 *(978-1-59691-694-4(X))* Bloomsbury Publishing.
Liu, Yu. Seeds of a Different Eden: Chinese Gardening Ideas & a New English Aesthetic Ideal. 2008. (Illus.). 224p. 39.95 *(978-1-57003-769-6(8))* Univ. of South Carolina Pr.
LLC, D. W. J. Books. British Writers, 1800 to the Present, 2 vols., Set. 2nd rev. ed. 2009. 1072p. (C). (gr. 9-18). 170.00 *(978-0-8160-7385-6(6))* Facts On File, Inc.
Lockington, Laura. Cupboard Love: A Food Romance. 2008. 191p. 21.95 *(978-1-84624-280-9(0))* Book Guild, Ltd. GBR. Dist: Trans-Atlantic Pubns., Inc.
Lockridge, Laurence S., et al, eds. Nineteenth-Century Lives. 2008. (ENG., Illus.). 240p. pap. 36.00 *(978-0-521-09050-6(4))* Cambridge Univ. Pr.
Lodico, Cheryl. Robert Browning: Idealism & Disillusionment in his Life & Work. 2007. pap. 11.00 *(978-0-8059-8461-3(5))* Dorrance Publishing Co., Inc.
Logan, Deborah A. Harriet Martineau: Further Letters. 2011. (ENG.). 626p. 120.00 ***(978-1-61146-087-2(5))*** Lexington Bks.
Lord, Elton. Among Others. 2006. 288p. per. *(978-1-4067-3209-2(5)*, Hesperides Pr.) Read Bks.
Lounsbury, Thomas R. Studies in Chaucer V1 His Life & Writi. 2006. pap. 42.95 *(978-1-4286-3958-4(6))* Kessinger Publishing, LLC.
—Studies in Chaucer V2 His Life & Writi. 2006. pap. 42.95 *(978-1-4286-3959-1(4))* Kessinger Publishing, LLC.
—Studies in Chaucer V3 His Life & Writi. 2006. pap. 40.95 *(978-1-4286-3960-7(8))* Kessinger Publishing, LLC.
Lowndes, Emma. Turning Victorian Ladies into Women: The Life of Bessie Rayner Parkes,1829 - 1925. 2011. (ENG., Illus.). 264p. *(978-1-936320-28-8(2))* Academica Pr., LLC.
Lowry, Malcolm. The Voyage That Never Ends: Fictions, Poems, Fragments, Letters. Hofmann, Michael, ed. 2007. (ENG., Illus.). 536p. 27.95 *(978-1-59017-235-3(3)*, NYRB Classics) New York Review of Bks., Inc., The.
Lucas, E. V. The Life of Charles Lamb V1: 2007. (ENG.). 572p. per. 43.95 *(978-1-4304-4462-6(2))* Kessinger Publishing, LLC.
Luhan, Mabel. Lorenzo in Taos. 2007. 396p. per. 32.95 *(978-0-86534-594-2(5))* Sunstone Pr.
Mabie, Hamilton Wright. Backgrounds of Literature. 2007. (ENG.). 340p. 46.95 *(978-0-548-05083-5(X))* Kessinger Publishing, LLC.
Macaskill, Hilary. Agatha Christie at Home. 2009. (ENG., Illus.). 144p. 40.00 *(978-0-7112-3029-3(3))* Lincoln, Frances Ltd. GBR. Dist: Perseus-PGW.
Macaulay, James. Doctor Johnson: His Life, Works & Table Talk. 2008. 215p. 22.99 *(978-0-554-79559-1(0))*; 290p. pap. 20.75 *(978-0-554-79556-0(6))*; 203p. 25.99 *(978-0-554-79549-2(3))*; 215p. pap. 21.75 *(978-0-554-79552-2(3))* BiblioBazaar.
Macaulay, Thomas Babington. The Selected Letters of Thomas Babington Macaulay. Pinney, Thomas, ed. 2008. (ENG.). 336p. pap. 46.00 *(978-0-521-08903-6(4))* Cambridge Univ. Pr.
MacHen, Arthur. A Few Letters from Arthur MacHen. 2011. 52p. 36.95 ***(978-1-258-06148-7(1))*** Literary Licensing, LLC.
Mackenzie, R. Shelton (Robert Shelton). Life of Charles Dickens by R Shelton MacKenzie with Personal Recollections & Anecdotes; — Letters by 'Boz', Never Before Published; — and Uncollect. 2006. 504p. per. 29.99 *(978-1-4255-5680-8(9))* MPublishing.
MacSwain, Robert & Ward, Michael, eds. The Cambridge Companion to C.S. Lewis. 2010. (Cambridge Companions to Religion Ser.). (ENG.). 348p. (C). 95.00 *(978-0-521-88413-6(6))*; pap. 29.99 *(978-0-521-71114-2(2))* Cambridge Univ. Pr.
Maitland, Samuel Roffey. Chatterton: An Essay. 2008. 263p. 21.99 *(978-0-554-88200-0(0))*; 119p. pap. 19.75 *(978-0-554-88199-7(3))*; 152p. 24.99 *(978-0-554-88193-5(4))*; 119p. pap. 19.75 *(978-0-554-88194-2(2))* BiblioBazaar.
Makower, F. Elizabeth Longford. (Illus.). xi, 212p. pap. 15.99 *(978-0-340-69472-5(6)*, Hodder & Stoughton) Hodder General Publishing Div. GBR. Dist: Trafalgar Square Publishing.
Malim, Richard. The Earl of Oxford & the Making of Shakespeare: The Literary Life of Edward de Vere in Context. 2011. (ENG., Illus.). 322p. pap. 45.00 *(978-0-7864-6313-8(9))* McFarland & Co., Inc. Pubs.
Maltby, Arthur. Shakespeare as a Challenge for Literary Biography: A History of Biographies of Shakespeare Since 1898. 2009. 324p. 119.95 *(978-0-7734-4732-5(6))* Mellen, Edwin Pr., The.
Mardock, James. Our Scene Is London. 2009. 164p. pap. 39.95 *(978-0-415-87554-7(4))* Routledge.
Marini, Francesca. Francis Bacon. 2009. (Skira MINI Artbooks Ser.). (ENG., Illus.). 96p. pap. 8.99 *(978-88-6130-709-4(4))* Skira Editore ITA. Dist: Random Hse., Inc.
Marlowe, Arthur. Shakespeare's Dark Secrets. 2008. 116p. pap. *(978-1-84426-507-7(2))* Upfront Publishing Ltd.
Marrocu, Luciano. Orwell: La solitudine di uno Scrittore. 2009. (Vite Ser.). (ITA., Illus.). 240p. (C). pap. 27.00 *(978-88-96209-00-4(5))* Vandenhoeck & Ruprecht GmbH & Co. KG DEU. Dist: Brown, David Bk. Co., The.
Martin, John. Beyond Belief: The Real Life of Daniel Defoe. 2007. (Illus.). 318p. *(978-1-905170-56-2(4))* Accent Pr. Ltd.
—Beyond Belief - the Real Life of Daniel Defoe. 2009. (Illus.). 344p. pap. *(978-0-7552-0473-1(5))* Authors OnLine, Ltd.
Martin, Peter. Samuel Johnson: A Biography. (Illus.). 640p. 2010. pap. 19.95 *(978-0-674-05737-1(6))* 2008. 35.00 *(978-0-674-03160-9(1))* Harvard Univ. Pr. (Belknap Pr.).
Martineau, Harriet. Harriet Martineau's Autobiography V2. Chapman, Maria Weston, ed. 2007. (ENG.). 612p. 59.95 *(978-0-548-12335-5(7))* Kessinger Publishing, LLC.
Martineau, Harriet & Chapman, Maria Weston. Harriet Martineau's Autobiography. 2010. (Cambridge Library Collection - Women's Writing Ser.). (ENG.). 506p. pap. 37.99 *(978-1-108-02258-3(8))*; 530p. pap. 39.99 *(978-1-108-02257-6(X))*; (Illus.). 460p. pap. 34.99 *(978-1-108-02256-9(1))* Cambridge Univ. Pr.
Marzials, Frank. Life of Charles Dickens. 2010. (Illus.). 118p. pap. 14.83 *(978-1-77045-340-1(7))* General Bks. LLC.
Marzials, Frank T. Life of Charles Dickens. 2010. (ENG.). 282p. pap. 28.75 *(978-1-174-90115-7(2))* BiblioBazaar.
Marzials, Frank T. The Life of Charles Dickens. 2011. 200p. 39.95 ***(978-1-169-86143-5(1))*** 2010. 200p. 31.96 *(978-1-163-33180-4(5))* 2010. 200p. pap. 19.96 ***(978-1-162-74182-6(1))*** 2007. (ENG.). 198p. 39.95 *(978-0-548-01994-8(0))* Kessinger Publishing, LLC.
Marzials, Frank T. (Frank Thomas) & Anderson, John Parker, creators. Life of Charles Dickens. 2011. 220p. pap. 24.75 ***(978-1-178-93167-9(6))*** BiblioBazaar.
Marzials, Frank Thomas. Life of Charles Dickens. 2009. 204p. 22.99 *(978-1-103-42906-6(X))*; pap. 16.99 *(978-1-103-42902-8(7))* BiblioBazaar.
—Life of Charles Dickens. 2009. 126p. pap. *(978-1-150-67841-7(0))* Books LLC.
—The Life of Charles Dickens. 2010. 568p. pap. 43.75 *(978-1-146-72306-0(7))* BiblioBazaar.
Marzials, Frank Thomas & Anderson, John Parker. Life of Charles Dickens. 2010. (ENG.). 212p. pap. 24.75 *(978-1-177-57893-6(X))* BiblioBazaar.
Masefield, John. John M. Synge: A Few Personal Recollections, with Biographical Notes. reprint ed. lib. bdg. 98.00 *(978-0-7426-3157-1(5))* Classic Bks.
Mason, Edward Tuckerm. Samuel Johnson His Words & His Ways Wh. 2006. pap. 30.95 *(978-1-4286-5481-5(X))* Kessinger Publishing, LLC.
Mason, Emma. The Cambridge Introduction to William Wordsworth. 2010. (Cambridge Introductions to Literature Ser.). (ENG.). 150p. (C). 69.00 *(978-0-521-89668-9(1))*; pap. 19.99 *(978-0-521-72147-9(4))* Cambridge Univ. Pr.
Masson, David. De Quincey. 2011. (Cambridge Library Collection - English Men of Letters Ser.). (ENG.). 214p. pap. 22.99 ***(978-1-108-03459-3(4))*** Cambridge Univ. Pr.
Matoff, Susan. Conflicted Life. 2011. (ENG., Illus.). 677p. 99.50 *(978-1-84519-417-8(9))* Sussex Academic Pr. GBR. Dist: International Specialized Bk. Services.
Maugham, W. Somerset. The Skeptical Romancer: Selected Travel Writing. Iyer, Pico, ed. 2012. (Vintage International Ser.). (ENG.). 224p. pap. 15.00 ***(978-0-307-47318-9(X)***, Vintage) Knopf Doubleday Publishing Group.
Maugham, W. Somerset. A Writer's Notebook. 2009. (Vintage International Ser.). (ENG.). 384p. pap. 16.95 *(978-0-307-47319-6(8)*, Vintage) Knopf Doubleday Publishing Group.
Maunder, Andrew & Law, Graham. Wilkie Collins: A Literary Life. 2008. (Literary Lives Ser.). (ENG.). 240p. 89.00 *(978-1-4039-4896-0(8))* Palgrave Macmillan.
Mc Kay, Betty. I Only Came for the Music. 2009. 152p. pap. *(978-1-84748-448-2(4))* Athena Pr.
McCarthy, William. Anna Letitia Barbauld: Voice of the Enlightenment. 2008. (ENG., Illus.). 792p. (gr. 17). 62.00 *(978-0-8018-9016-1(0))* Johns Hopkins Univ. Pr.
Mcconchie, Roderick, ed. The Ashgate Critical Essays on Early English Lexicographers Vol. 3: Sixteenth Century. 2012. (Ashgate Critical Essays on Early English Lexicographers Ser.). 470p. 275.00 ***(978-0-7546-5692-0(6))*** Ashgate Publishing Co.
Mcdermott, Anne C., ed. The Ashgate Series on Early English Lexicographers Vol. 4: Eighteenth Century. 2012. (Ashgate Critical Essays on Early English Lexicographers Ser.). 600p. 275.00 ***(978-0-7546-5694-4(2))*** Ashgate Publishing Co.
McDonald, Lynn. Florence Nightingale at First Hand. 2010. (ENG.). 216p. (C). pap. 24.95 *(978-1-55458-191-7(5))* Wilfrid Laurier Univ. Pr. CAN. Dist: Univ. of Toronto Pr.
McEwan, Ian. Conversations with Ian McEwan. Roberts, Ryan, ed. 2010. (Literary Conversations Ser.). (ENG.). 224p. 50.00 *(978-1-60473-419-5(1))*; pap. 22.00 *(978-1-60473-420-1(5))* Univ. Pr. of Mississippi.
McInerny, Ralph. Some Catholic Writers. 2007. 166p. 23.00 *(978-1-58731-777-4(X))* St. Augustine's Pr., Inc.
Mckillop, Brian. Pierre Berton: A Biography. 2010. (ENG., Illus.). 808p. pap. 21.00 *(978-0-7710-5756-4(3)*, Emblem Edns) McClelland & Stewart CAN. Dist: Random Hse., Inc.
McLaren, Duncan. Looking for Enid: The Mysterious & Inventive Life of Enid Blyton. Jones, Philip Gwyn, ed. 2008. (ENG., Illus.). 336p. pap. 16.95 *(978-1-84627-116-8(9))* Granta Bks. GBR. Dist: Independent Pubs. Group.
—Looking for Enid: The Mysterious & Inventive Life of Enid Blyton. 2007. (ENG., Illus.). 336p. 29.95 *(978-1-84708-115-5(0))* Granta Bks. GBR. Dist: Independent Pubs. Group.
McLeod, John. J. G. Farrell. 2007. (Writers & Their Work Ser.). (ENG., Illus.). 128p. (C). pap. 26.00 *(978-0-7463-0986-5(4))* Northcote Hse. Publishers, Ltd. GBR. Dist: Brown, David Bk. Co., The.
Melnikoff, Kirk. Robert Greene. 2011. (University Wits Ser.). 608p. 325.00 *(978-0-7546-2858-3(2))* Ashgate Publishing Co.
Melnikoff, Kirk & Gieskes, Edward. Writing Robert Greene: Essays on England's First Notorious Professional Writer. 2008. (Illus.). 258p. 114.95 *(978-0-7546-5701-9(9))* Ashgate Publishing Co.
Melville, Lewis. Life & Letters of John Gay. 2008. 196p. 25.99 *(978-0-554-24781-6(X))*; 22.99 *(978-0-554-34084-5(4))* BiblioBazaar.
—Life & Letters of John Gay: (1685-1732) 2006. (ENG.). 172p. pap. 19.99 *(978-1-4264-7421-7(0))*; 194p. pap. 21.99 *(978-1-4264-7498-9(9))* BiblioBazaar.
—The Life of William Makepeace Thackeray V2. 2007. (ENG.). 348p. 46.95 *(978-0-548-15137-2(7))*; 352p. per. 31.95 *(978-1-4304-4483-1(5))* Kessinger Publishing, LLC.
Mendelson, Sara H. Margaret Cavendish. 2009. (Ashgate Critical Essays on Women Writers in England, 1550-1700 Ser.). (Illus.). 432p. 225.00 *(978-0-7546-6081-1(8))* Ashgate Publishing Co.
Meredith, George. The Works of George Meredith: the Egoist V2: a Comedy in Narrative. 2007. pap. 31.95 *(978-1-4304-9281-8(3))* Kessinger Publishing, LLC.
Merrifield, Andy. John Berger. 2012. (Reaktion Books - Critical Lives Ser.). (Illus.). 224p. pap. 16.95 ***(978-1-86189-904-0(1))*** Reaktion Bks., Ltd. GBR. Dist: Chicago Distribution Ctr.
Merrill, L. R. The Life & Poems of Nicholas Grimald. 476p. 2008. 52.95 *(978-1-4366-7594-9(4))* 2007. (ENG.). per. 37.95 *(978-1-4325-1626-0(4))* Kessinger Publishing, LLC.
Miléadha, Pádraig Ó & Denvir, Gearóid. Duanta Aneas. 2006. (ENG.). 91p. pap. 16.95 *(978-1-905560-02-8(8))* Clo Iar-Chonnachta Teo IRL. Dist: Dufour Editions, Inc.

Mills, Howard. Peacock: His Circle & His Age. 2010. (ENG.). 276p. pap. 23.99 *(978-0-521-14830-6(8))* Cambridge Univ. Pr.

Milton, Anthony. Laudian & Royalist Polemic in Seventeenth-Century England: The Career & Writings of Peter Heylyn. 2008. (Politics, Culture & Society in Early Modern Britain Ser.). (ENG.). 288p. 89.00 *(978-0-7190-6444-9(9))* Manchester Univ. Pr. GBR. Dist: Macmillan.

Minai, Masahiro, ed. William Gilpin 8 Vols. 2006. 1660.00 *(978-4-902454-00-0(9))* Synapse, Edition JPN. Dist: Taylor & Francis Group.

Moffat, Wendy. A Great Unrecorded History: A New Life of E. M. Forster. 2011. (ENG., Illus.). 432p. pap. 20.00 *(978-0-312-57289-1(1))* Picador.

Montagu, Mary Wortley. The Letters & Works of Lady Mary Wortley Montagu. Wharncliffe, James Archibald Stuart-Wortley-Mackenzie & Thomas, William Moy, eds. 2011. (Cambridge Library Collection - Women's Writing Ser.). (ENG.). 552p. pap. 39.99 *(978-1-108-07316-5(6))*; (Illus.). 544p. pap. 39.99 *(978-1-108-07315-8(8))* Cambridge Univ. Pr.

Mooney, Brian. Frank Baines: A Life Beyond the Sea. 2011. (Illus.). 316p. pap. 16.95 ***(978-1-85418-741-3(4))*** Thorogood GBR. Dist: Stylus Publishing, LLC.

Moore, Alan. Alan Moore: Conversations. Berlatsky, Eric L., ed. 2011. (Conversations with Comic Artists Ser.). (ENG.). 240p. 65.00 *(978-1-61703-158-8(5))*; (Illus.). pap. 25.00 *(978-1-61703-159-5(3))* Univ. Pr. of Mississippi.

Moore, Thomas. Letters & Journals of Lord Byron V1 Wi. 2006. pap. 38.95 *(978-1-4286-4542-4(X))* Kessinger Publishing, LLC.

—Letters & Journals of Lord Byron V2 Wi. 2006. pap. 43.95 *(978-1-4286-4543-1(8))* Kessinger Publishing, LLC.

Morley, Henry. English Writers: An Attempt Towards a History of English Literature. 2009. 372p. 26.99 *(978-1-103-85060-0(1))* 2009. 372p. pap. 20.99 *(978-1-103-85053-2(9))* 2008. 384p. 29.99 *(978-0-559-77550-5(4))* 2008. 384p. pap. 32.75 *(978-0-559-77548-2(2))* 2008. 488p. 31.99 *(978-0-559-58759-7(7))* 2008. 488p. pap. 37.75 *(978-0-559-58755-9(4))* BiblioBazaar.

Morley, John M., ed. English Men of Letters, 41 vols. reprint ed. lib. bdg. *(978-0-404-51700-7(5))* AMS Pr., Inc.

Morrison, Robert. The English Opium-Eater: A Biography of Thomas de Quincey. 2010. (ENG., Illus.). 488p. 37.99 *(978-0-297-85279-7(5)*, Weidenfeld & Nicolson) Orion Publishing Group, Ltd. GBR. Dist: Hachette Bk. Group.

—The English Opium Eater: A Biography of Thomas de Quincey. 2010. (ENG.). 480p. 35.00 *(978-1-60598-132-1(X)*, 605132) Pegasus Bks.

Morse, Greg. John Betjeman. 2011. (Shire Library). (ENG., Illus.). 56p. pap. 12.95 *(978-0-7478-1051-3(6))* Shire Pubns., Ltd. GBR. Dist: Random Hse., Inc.

Morton, Karen. A Life Marketed As Fiction: An Analysis of the Work of Eliza Parsons. 2010. *(978-1-934555-22-4(3))* Valancourt Bks.

Mosley, Nicholas. Paradoxes of Peace: or The Presence of Infinity. 2009. (British Literature Ser.). (ENG.). 190p. pap. 13.95 *(978-1-56478-539-8(4))* Dalkey Archive Pr.

Muggeridge, Malcolm. Chronicles of Wasted Time: An Autobiography. 2006. (ENG.). 576p. per. *(978-1-57383-376-9(2)*, Regent College Publishing) Regent College Publishing.

Muir, Pearson M'Adam. Religious Writers of England. 2007. 224p. per. *(978-1-4067-8883-9(X)*, Pomona Pr.) Read Bks.

Mullan, John. Anonymity: A Secret History of English Literature. 2008. (ENG.). 384p. (C). 24.95 *(978-0-691-13941-8(5))* Princeton Univ. Pr.

Mulvey, Christopher. Transatlantic Manners: Social Patterns in Nineteenth-Century Anglo-American Travel Literature. 2008. (ENG., Illus.). 256p. pap. 37.99 *(978-0-521-05561-1(X))* Cambridge Univ. Pr.

Murdoch, Iris. Iris Murdoch: A Writer at War - Letters & Diaries, 1939-1945, 1 vol. Conradi, Peter, ed. 2011. (ENG., Illus.). 304p. 35.00 *(978-0-19-975603-2(1))* Oxford Univ. Pr., Inc.

Murray, Andy. Into the Unknown: The Fantastic Life of Nigel Kneale. 2006. (Illus.). 191p. per. 17.95 *(978-1-900486-50-7(4))* Headpress GBR. Dist: SCB Distributors.

Myers, F W H. Wordsworth. 2008. 180p. 25.99 *(978-0-554-22839-6(4))* 2008. 180p. 22.99 *(978-0-554-32142-4(4))* 2007. (ENG.). 160p. pap. 19.99 *(978-1-4264-3191-3(0))* 2007. (ENG.). 178p. pap. 21.99 *(978-1-4264-3226-2(7))* BiblioBazaar.

—Wordsworth. 2009. 144p. pap. *(978-1-4099-6413-1(2))* Dodo Pr.

Nayar, Pramod K. English Travel Writing & India, 1600-1859: Colonial Aesthetics. 2007. (Routledge Research in Postcolonial Literatures Ser.). (ENG., Illus.). 224p. 120.00 *(978-0-415-40919-3(5))* Routledge.

Nelson, W. Dale. Gin Before Breakfast: The Dilemma of the Poet in the Newsroom. 2007. (Illus.). 242p. 14.95 *(978-0-8156-0888-2(8))* Syracuse Univ. Pr.

Newell, Stephanie. The Forger's Tale: The Search for Odeziaku. 2006. (New African Histories Ser.). (ENG., Illus.). 272p. per. 24.95 *(978-0-8214-1710-2(X))* Ohio Univ. Pr.

Newey, Katherine & Richards, Jeffrey. John Ruskin & the Victorian Theatre. 2010. (ENG., Illus.). 256p. 95.00 *(978-0-230-52499-6(0))* Palgrave Macmillan.

Nichols, Beverley. Garden Open Tomorrow. 2009. (ENG.). 236p. pap. 19.95 *(978-1-60469-097-2(6)*, 1604690976) Timber Pr., Inc.

Nichols, John. Illustrations of the Manners & Expenses of Ancient Times in England in the 15th, 16th & 17th Centuries. reprint ed. 45.00 *(978-0-404-04688-0(6))* AMS Pr., Inc.

—Literary Anecdotes of the Eighteenth Century, 9 vols. reprint ed. 425.00 *(978-0-404-04720-7(3))* AMS Pr., Inc.

—Literary Anecdotes of the Eighteenth Century. 2009. 670p. pap. *(978-1-150-67883-7(6))*; 346p. pap. *(978-0-217-01542-4(5))*; 332p. pap. *(978-0-217-50699-1(2))* Books LLC.

—Literary Anecdotes of the Eighteenth Century. 2009. 562p. pap. 36.09 *(978-1-150-07515-5(5))* General Bks. LLC.

Noakes, Vivien, ed. Isaac Rosenberg: 21st-Century Oxford Authors. 2009. (Illus.). 472p. 125.00 *(978-0-19-955340-2(8))* Oxford Univ. Pr., Inc.

Noel, Roden. Essays on Poetry & Poets. (ENG.). 2007. 376p. 48.95 *(978-0-548-12874-9(X))* 2006. pap. 33.95 *(978-1-4286-3893-8(8))* Kessinger Publishing, LLC.

Norman, Andrew. Agatha Christie: The Finished Portrait. 2007. (ENG., Illus.). 224p. 29.95 *(978-0-7524-3990-7(1))* History Pr. Ltd.,The GBR. Dist: Independent Pubs. Group.

—Jane Austen: An Unrequited Love. (ENG., Illus.). 2010. 224p. pap. 17.95 *(978-0-7524-5529-7(X))* 2009. 208p. 36.95 *(978-0-7524-4874-9(9))* History Pr. Ltd.,The GBR. Dist: Independent Pubs. Group.

—Thomas Hardy: Behind the Mask. 2011. (ENG., Illus.). 224p. 26.95 *(978-0-7524-5630-0(X))* History Pr. Ltd.,The GBR. Dist: Independent Pubs. Group.

Norton, Charles Eliot & Ruskin, John. The Correspondence of John Ruskin & Charles Eliot Norton. Bradley, John Lewis & Ousby, Ian, eds. 2011. (ENG.). 552p. pap. 70.00 *(978-0-521-18771-8(0))* Cambridge Univ. Pr.

Norwich, John Julius. Trying to Please. 2010. (ENG.). 425p. 20.00 *(978-1-60419-031-1(0))* Axios Pr.

O'Brien, Ellen L. Crime in Verse: The Poetics of Murder in the Victorian ERA. 2008. (Illus.). xii, 288p. *(978-88-14-21085-3(3))* Ohio State Univ. Pr.

O'Callaghan, Michelle. The English Wits: Literature & Sociability in Early Modern England. 2010. (ENG.). 244p. 33.00 *(978-0-521-15276-8(X))* Cambridge Univ. Pr.

O'Connell, Jeffrey & O'Connell, Thomas E. Friendships Across Ages: Johnson & Boswell; Holmes & Laski. 2007. (ENG.). 202p. 62.99 *(978-0-7391-2034-7(4))* Lexington Bks.

Oddie, William. Chesterton & the Romance of Orthodoxy: The Making of GKC, 1874-1908. 2010. (ENG.). 416p. pap. 29.95 *(978-0-19-958201-3(7))*, Oxford Univ. Pr., Inc.

Oh, Eunyoung. D. H. Lawrence's Border Crossing: Colonialism in His Travel Writings & Leadership Novels. 2006. (Studies in Major Literary Authors Ser.). (ENG.). 160p. 125.00 *(978-0-415-97644-2(8))* Routledge.

Oliphant, Laurence. When a Stone Begins to Roll: Notes of an Adventurer, Diplomat & Mystic: Extracts from Episodes in a Life of Adventure. Meyer, T. H., ed. 2011. (ENG., Illus.). 160p. pap. 15.00 *(978-1-58420-091-8(X)*, Lindisfarne Bks.) SteinerBooks, Inc.

Oliver, Clementine. Parliament & Political Pamphleteering in Fourteenth-Century England. 2010. (Illus.). 248p. 99.00 *(978-1-903153-31-4(X))* York Medieval Pr. GBR. Dist: Boydell & Brewer, Inc.

Olivia, Lungu. Biography & Fiction in Virginia Woolf's Novels. 2011. 88p. pap. ***(978-3-639-32433-4(1))*** VDM Verlag Dr. Mueller e.K.

Olsen, Kirstin. All Things Austen: A Concise Encyclopedia of Jane Austen's World. 2008. (Illus.). 400p. pap. 29.95 *(978-1-84645-052-5(7)*, GWP052) Greenwood Publishing Group, Inc.

Oppennheim, E. Phillips. Pool of Memory. 2006. 320p. per. *(978-1-4067-0222-4(6)*, Hesperides Pr.) Read Bks.

Orr, Sutherland. Life & Letters of Robert Browning V1. 2007. (ENG.). 336p. 45.95 *(978-0-548-15645-2(X))*; pap. 30.95 *(978-1-4304-5110-5(6))* Kessinger Publishing, LLC.

Orwell, George. Homage to Catalonia - Down & Out in Paris & London. 2010. (ENG.). 448p. 22.00 *(978-0-547-44733-9(7))* Houghton Mifflin Harcourt Trade & Reference Pubs.

Osborn, Louise Brown. The Life, Letters & Writings of John Hoskyns, 1566-1638. 2011. 338p. 51.95 ***(978-1-258-05820-3(0))*** Literary Licensing, LLC.

Osborne, James Insley. Arthur Hugh Clough. 2008. 196p. 37.95 *(978-1-4365-1081-3(3))* 2007. (ENG.). 200p. per. 22.95 *(978-0-548-72780-5(5))* Kessinger Publishing, LLC.

Overton, Grant. Authors of the Day. 2007. (ENG.). 426p. 51.95 *(978-0-548-05811-4(3))* Kessinger Publishing, LLC.

Oxford University Press Staff, ed. Bronte Story. 3rd ed. 2008. (ENG.). 80p 9.38 *(978-0-19-479109-0(2))* Oxford Univ. Pr., Inc.

Page, Norman & Purton, Valerie. The Palgrave Literary Dictionary of Tennyson. Andrew, Malcolm, ed 2010. (Palgrave Literary Dictionaries Ser.). (ENG.). 320p. 116.00 *(978-1-4039-4317-0(6))* Palgrave Macmillan.

Paradis, James G. Samuel Butler, Victorian Against the Grain: A Critical Overview. 2007. (Illus.). 416p. *(978-0-8020-9745-3(6))* Univ. of Toronto Pr.

Parini, Jay. Brit Wrtr Sup 15. 15th ed. 2009. (British Writers Ser.). 544p. 218.00 *(978-0-684-31555-3(6))* Cengage Gale.

—British Writers. (British Writers Ser.). (ENG.). 3rd ed. 2009. 608p. 218.00 *(978-0-684-31599-7(8)*, Charles Scribner's Sons) 14th rev. ed. 2008. 465p. 218.00 *(978-0-684-31553-9(X))* 16th rev. ed. 2010. 218.00 *(978-1-4144-3903-7(2))* Cengage Gale.

—British Writers Supplement. 13th rev. ed. 2007. (British Writers Ser.). (ENG.). 570p. 218.00 *(978-0-684-31518-8(1)*, Charles Scribner's Sons) Cengage Gale.

Parker, Hershel. The Powell Papers: A Confidence Man Amok among the Anglo-American Literati. 2011. (ENG.). 360p. 69.95 *(978-0-8101-2703-6(2))* Northwestern Univ. Pr

Parry, William. The Last Days of Lord Byron: With His Lordship's Opinions on Various Subjects, Particularly on the State & Prospects of Greece. 2007. (ENG.). 272p. 42.95 *(978-0-548-23002-2(1))*; 276p. per. 27.95 *(978-1-4325-5314-2(3))* Kessinger Publishing, LLC.

Pasi, Marco. Aleister Crowley & the Temptation of Politics. 2012. (ENG.). 256p. (C). 85.00 *(978-1-84553-367-0(4))* Equinox Publishing Ltd. GBR. Dist: ISD.

Paterson, Gary H. At the Heart of the 1890s: Essays on Lionel Johnson. 2007. (AMS Studies in the Nineteenth Century). (C). *(978-0-404-64469-7(4))* AMS Pr., Inc.

Pattison, Mark, BD. Milton. 2006. 182p. pap. 19.99 *(978-1-4264-3192-0(9))* 202p. pap. 22.99 *(978-1-4264-3227-9(5))* BiblioBazaar.

Payton, Philip. John Betjeman & Cornwall: The Celebrated Cornish Nationalist. 2010. (Illus.). 258p. 95.00 *(978-0-85989-847-8(4))*; 288p. pap. 30.00 *(978-0-85989-848-5(2))* Univ. of Exeter Pr. GBR. Dist: Chicago Distribution Ctr.

Pearson, Hesketh. Modern Men & Mummers. 2008. 224p. 24.99 *(978-0-559-52361-8(0))*; pap. 24.75 *(978-0-559-52360-1(2))* BiblioBazaar.

—Modern Men & Mummers. 2009. 112p. pap. *(978-1-150-08174-3(0))* Books LLC.

—Modern Men & Mummers. 2008. 220p. 39.95 *(978-1-4365-1360-9(X))* 2007. (ENG.). 224p. per. 24.95 *(978-0-548-74386-7(X))* Kessinger Publishing, LLC.

—Modern Men & Mummers. 2008. 220p. pap. *(978-1-4086-8806-9(9))* Read Bks.

Pennell, Elizabeth Robins. Mary Wollstonecraft Godwin. 2008. 216p. 39.95 *(978-1-4372-0962-4(9))*; pap. 24.95 *(978-1-4370-8010-0(3))* Kessinger Publishing, LLC.

Penzler, Otto, ed. The Lineup: The World's Greatest Crime Writers Tell the Inside Story of Their Greatest Detectives. 2010. (ENG.). 416p. pap. 15.99 *(978-0-316-03194-3(1)*, Back Bay Bks.) Little Brown & Co.

Pepys, Samuel. The Diary of Samuel Pepys. 2008. 216p. 24.99 *(978-0-559-57938-7(1))*; 216p. pap. 23.75 *(978-0-559-57934-9(9))*; 196p. 25.99 *(978-0-554-54977-4(8))*; 196p. 22.99 *(978-0-554-54981-1(6))*; 196p. pap. 23.75 *(978-0-554-54978-1(6))*; 196p. pap. 22.75 *(978-0-554-54980-4(8))* BiblioBazaar.

—The Diary of Samuel Pepys. 2009. 552p. pap. *(978-0-217-32969-9(1))*; 118p. pap. *(978-0-217-32971-2(3))*; 148p. pap. *(978-0-217-34561-3(1))*; 290p. pap. *(978-0-217-38277-9(0))*; 338p. pap. *(978-0-217-38278-6(9))*; 440p. pap. *(978-0-217-57907-0(8))*; 154p. pap. *(978-0-217-57911-7(6))*; 232p. pap. *(978-0-217-57898-1(5))*; 120p. pap. *(978-0-217-57903-2(5))*; 178p. pap. *(978-0-217-75530-6(5))*; 382p. pap. *(978-0-217-75527-6(5))*; 264p. pap. *(978-0-217-11617-6(5))*; 400p. pap. *(978-1-4589-1401-9(1))*; 238p. pap. *(978-1-4588-7064-3(2))* 66p. pap. *(978-1-4588-7066-7(9))* Books LLC.

—The Diary of Samuel Pepys. Braybrooke, Lord, ed. 2009. 706p. pap. *(978-1-4099-8651-5(9))* Dodo Pr.

—The Diary of Samuel Pepys. 2010. 204p. pap. 60.70 *(978-1-153-34359-6(2))* General Bks. LLC.

Peters, Sislyn. Shades of a Colonial Coloured: An Autobiography. 2009. 272p. 38.99 *(978-1-4389-9271-6(8))*; pap. 22.99 *(978-1-4389-9270-9(X))* AuthorHouse.

Phillips, Caryl. Color Me English: Migration & Belonging Before & after 9/11. 2011. (ENG.). 352p. 25.95 *(978-1-59558-650-6(4))* New Pr., The.

Phillips Ingram, Jill. Idioms of Self Interest. 2009. 182p. 34.00 *(978-0-415-87939-2(6))* Routledge.

Phinn, Gervase. Out of the Woods but Not over the Hill. 2011. (ENG., Illus.). 288p. pap. 13.95 *(978-1-4447-0540-9(7)*, Hodder & Stoughton) Hodder General Publishing Div. GBR. Dist: Independent Pubs. Group.

Piozzi, Hester Lynch. Anecdotes of the Late Samuel Johnson. 2008. 152p. 21.99 *(978-0-554-36094-2(2))* 2008. 152p. 24.99 *(978-0-554-26791-3(8))* 2007. (ENG.). 150p. pap. 19.99 *(978-1-4346-1908-2(7))* BiblioBazaar.

—Anecdotes of the Late Samuel Johnson. 2010. 90p. (Illus.). pap. 20.00 *(978-1-153-58585-9(5))*; pap. 20.00 *(978-0-217-11359-5(1))* General Bks. LLC.

Piozzi, Hesther Lynch. Anecdotes of Samuel Johnson. 2012. (ENG.). 228p. pap. 24.00 ***(978-1-107-69915-1(0))*** Cambridge Univ. Pr.

Piozzi, Hesther Lynch. Anecdotes of the late Samuel Johnson. 2009. (ENG.) 154p. pap. 11.95 *(978-1-4385-1932-6(X)*, Book Jungle) Standard Pubns., Inc.

Pite, Raloh, et al, eds. Lives of Victorian Literary Figures V: Mary Elilzabeth Braddon, Wilkie Collins, William Thackeray by Their Contemporaries, 3 vols. 3rd ed. 2007. (Lives of Victorian Literary Figures Ser.). (ENG., Illus.). 1072p. 495.00 *(978-1-85196-819-0(9))* Pickering & Chatto Pubs., Ltd. GBR. Dist: Ashgate Publishing Co.

Pite, Ralph. Thomas Hardy: The Guarded Life. 2007. (ENG., Illus.). 544p. 37.00 *(978-0-300-12337-1(X))* Yale Univ. Pr.

Plumly, Stanley. Posthumous Keats: A Personal Biography. (ENG., Illus.). 2009. 392p. pap. 17.95 *(978-0-393-33772-3(3)*, 33772) 2008. 288p. 27.95 *(978-0-393-06573-2(1)*, 6573) Norton, W. W. & Co., Inc.

Pocock, Geoffrey A. Outrider of Empire: The Life & Adventures of Roger Pocock. 2008. (ENG., Illus.). 400p. pap. 34.95 *(978-0-88864-448-0(5))* Univ. of Alberta Pr. CAN. Dist: Michigan State Univ. Pr.

Poe, Harry Lee. The Inklings of Oxford, 1 vol. 2009. (ENG.). 176p. pap. 24.99 *(978-0-310-28503-8(8))* Zondervan.

Pollock, Ida. Starlight - a Memoir by Ida Pollock. 2009. (Illus.). 220p. pap. *(978-0-7552-0491-5(3))* Authors OnLine, Ltd.

Polsgrove, Carol. Ending British Rule in Africa: Writers in a Common Cause. 2009. (Studies in Imperialism Ser.). (ENG.). 240p. 89.95 *(978-0-7190-7767-8(2))* Manchester Univ. Pr. GBR. Dist: Macmillan.

Poole, Adrian. The Cambridge Companion to English Novelists. 2009. (Cambridge Companions to Literature Ser.). (ENG.). 480p. (C). pap. 29.99 *(978-0-521-69157-4(5))* Cambridge Univ. Pr.

Potts, Gina & Shahriari, Lisa, eds. Virginia Woolf's Bloomsbury Vol. 1: Aesthetic Theory & Literary Practice, 2 vols. 2010. (ENG.). 256p. 84.00 *(978-0-230-51766-0(8))* Palgrave Macmillan.

—Virginia Woolf's Bloomsbury Vol. 2: International Influence & Politics, 2 vols. 2010. (ENG.). 256p. 84.00 *(978-0-230-51767-7(6))* Palgrave Macmillan.

Powys, John Cowper. Autobiography. 2006. 704p. pap. 24.95 *(978-1-58567-821-1(X))* Overlook Pr., The.

—Petrushka & the Dancer: The Diaries of John Cowper Powys, 1929-1939. (Illus.). xxvii, 340p. 50.00 *(978-1-85754-096-3(4))* Carcanet Pr., Ltd. GBR. Dist: Paul & Co. Pubs. Consortium, Inc.

Prandi, Julie. The Poetry of the Self-Taught: An Eighteenth-Century Phenomenon. 2008. 212p. (C). 68.95 *(978-1-4331-0251-6(X))* Lang, Peter Publishing, Inc.

Pratt, Willis Winslow. Byron at Southwell: The Making of A Poet. 2011. 158p. 41.95 ***(978-1-258-01988-4(4))*** Literary Licensing, LLC.

Priestley, J.B. George Meredith. 2007. (ENG.). 220p. 39.95 *(978-0-548-14531-9(8))* 2006. pap. 24.95 *(978-1-4286-5838-7(6))* Kessinger Publishing, LLC.

—Thomas Love Peacock. 2007. (ENG.). 228p. 41.95 *(978-0-548-14506-7(7))* 2006. pap. 26.95 *(978-1-4286-5809-7(2))* Kessinger Publishing, LLC.

Priestley, John. Upward Road. 2009. 287p. pap. 21.50 *(978-1-4092-8397-3(6))* Lulu Enterprises Inc.

Pugh, Syrithe. Classical Intertextuality & Politics in Herrick Fanshawe & Milton. 2010. (Illus.). 206p. 99.95 *(978-0-7546-5614-2(4))* Ashgate Publishing Co.

Pykett, Lyn. Wilkie Collins (Authors in Context) 2009. (Oxford World's Classics Ser.). (ENG., Illus.). 272p. pap. 14.95 *(978-0-19-955611-3(3))* Oxford Univ. Pr., Inc.

Raber, Karen. Ashgate Critical Essays on Women Writers in England 1550-1700: Volume 7:Elizabeth Cary. 2009. (Ashgate Critical Essays on Women Writers in England, 1550-1700 Ser.). 596p. 325.00 *(978-0-7546-6100-9(8))* Ashgate Publishing Co.

Rabey, David I., et al. Howard Barker: Ecstasy & Death - An Expository Study of His Plays & Production Work, 1988-2008. 2009. (ENG.). 320p. 100.00 *(978-1-4039-9473-8(0))* Palgrave Macmillan.

Rahbaran, Shiva. Nicholas Mosley's Life & Art: A Biography in Six Interviews. 2009. (Dalkey Archive Scholarly Ser.). (ENG.). 160p. pap. 25.95 *(978-1-56478-564-0(5)*, 478564) Dalkey Archive Pr.

—The Paradox of Freedom: A Study of Nicholas Mosley's Intellectual Development in His Novels & Other Writings. 2007. (Dalkey Archive Scholarly Ser.). (ENG.). 316p. per. 29.95 *(978-1-56478-488-9(6)*, 478488) Dalkey Archive Pr.

Raine, Kathleen. Autobiographies. 2008. pap. *(978-1-59731-332-2(7))* Perennis Sophia.

Raphael, Frederic. Ifs & Buts: Personal Terms V. 2011. (ENG.). 200p. pap. 32.95 *(978-1-84777-122-3(X))* Carcanet Pr., Ltd. GBR. Dist: Independent Pubs. Group.

—Ticks & Crosses No. 4: Personal Terms. 2009. (ENG.). 224p. pap. 37.95 *(978-1-85754-930-0(9))* Carcanet Pr., Ltd. GBR. Dist: Independent Pubs. Group.

Rauschenbusch-Clough, Emma. A Study of Mary Wollstonecraft & the Rights of Woman. 2007. (ENG.). 244p. 41.95 *(978-0-548-33731-8(4))*; per. 26.95 *(978-1-4326-9648-1(3))* Kessinger Publishing, LLC.

Raworth, Tom. Earn Your Milk. 2009. (ENG.). 184p. pap. *(978-1-84471-508-4(6))*, Salt Publishing.

Ray, Martin. Thomas Hardy Remembered. 2007. (Nineteenth Century Ser.). 358p. 124.95 *(978-0-7546-3973-2(8))* Ashgate Publishing Co.

Redworth, Glyn & British Hispanic Foundation Staff. The She-Apostle: The Extraordinary Life & Death of Luisa de Carvajal. 2008. (ENG., Illus.). 288p. 39.95 *(978-0-19-953353-4(9))* Oxford Univ. Pr., Inc.

Reed, Henry & Wordsworth, William. Wordsworth & Reed: The Poet's Correspondence with His American Editor, 1836-1850. Broughton, Leslie Nathan, ed. 2011. 322p. 50.95 ***(978-1-258-06092-3(2))*** Literary Licensing, LLC.

Reed, Myrtle. Love Affairs of Literary Men. 2007. (ENG.). 226p. 41.95 *(978-0-548-02081-4(7))* Kessinger Publishing, LLC.

Rees, Thomas. Reminiscences of Literary London from 1779 To 1853: With Interesting Anecdotes of Publishers, Authors & Book Auctioneers of that Period. Britton, John, ed. 2010. (Cambridge Library Collection - Printing & Publishing History Ser.). (ENG., Illus.). 180p. pap. 19.99 *(978-1-108-00917-1(4))* Cambridge Univ. Pr.

Reeve, Katharine. Jane Austen in Bath: Walking Tours of the Writer's City. 2006. (ENG., Illus.). 144p. 19.95 *(978-1-892145-32-1(4))* Little Bookroom.

Reichard, Susan E. Philip Pullman: Master of Fantasy. 2006. (Authors Teens Love Ser.). (Illus.). 104p. (YA). (gr. 7-12). lib. bdg. 31.93 *(978-0-7660-2447-2(4))* Enslow Pubs., Inc.

Reid, T. Wemyss. Richard Monckton Milnes V2 the Life Lett. 2006. pap. 42.95 *(978-1-4286-4173-0(4))* Kessinger Publishing, LLC.

Renton, Richard. John Forster & His Friendships. 2007. (ENG.). 354p. 46.95 *(978-0-548-04708-8(1))* Kessinger Publishing, LLC.

Reynolds, Stephen. A Poor Man's House. 2009. 236p. pap. *(978-1-4099-3249-9(4))* Dodo Pr.

Ricchiuti, Paul B. Arthur S. Maxwell: Remembering an Adventist Legend. 2009. 12.99 *(978-0-8163-2336-4(4))* Pacific Pr. Publishing Assn.

Richards, Grant. Memories of a Misspent Youth, 1872-1896. reprint ed. 35.00 *(978-0-404-18383-7(2))* AMS Pr., Inc.

Robbins, Harold. The Last of the Realists: A Distributist Biography of G. K. Chesterton. 2010. (Illus.). 160p. pap. 22.95 *(978-1-932528-01-5(6))* IHS Pr.

Roberts, Lynette. Diaries, Letters & Recollections. McGuinness, Patrick, ed. & intro. by. 2008. (ENG., Illus.). 184p. pap. 27.95 *(978-1-85754-856-3(6))* Carcanet Pr., Ltd. GBR. Dist: Independent Pubs. Group.

Roberts, Neil. Ted Hughes: A Literary Life. (Literary Lives Ser.). (ENG.). 256p. 2009. pap. 35.00 *(978-0-230-58097-8(1))* 2007. 95.00 *(978-1-4039-3605-9(6))* Palgrave Macmillan.

Roberts, S. C. Doctor Johnson & Others. 2012. (ENG.). 186p. pap. 34.99 ***(978-1-107-68567-3(2))*** Cambridge Univ. Pr.

Robertson, Ben P., ed. Diaries of Elizabeth Inchbald, 3 vols., Set. 2007. (Pickering Masters Ser.). (ENG.). 1296p. 247.50 *(978-1-85196-868-8(7))* Pickering & Chatto Pubs., Ltd. GBR. Dist: Ashgate Publishing Co.

Robinson, Henry C. Henry Crabb Robinson on Books & Their Writers, 3 vols. Morley, Edith J., ed. reprint ed. 155.00 *(978-0-404-05410-6(2))* AMS Pr., Inc.

Robinson, Henry Crabb. Diary, Reminiscences & Correspondence. Sadler, Thomas, ed. 2011. (Cambridge Library Collection - Literary Studies). (ENG.). 610p. pap. 43.00 *(978-1-108-02490-7(4))*; (ENG.). 538p. pap. 39.99 *(978-1-108-02489-1(0))*; (Illus.). 542p. pap. 39.99 *(978-1-108-02488-4(2))* Cambridge Univ. Pr.

Robinson, Peter. Talk about Poetry - Conversations on the. 2006. (ENG.). 148p. per. *(978-1-905700-04-2(0))* Shearsman Bks.

Rochelson, Meri-Jane. A Jew in the Public Arena: The Career of Israel Zangwill. 2010. pap. 24.95 *(978-0-8143-3493-5(8))* 2008. (Illus.). 368p. 34.95 *(978-0-8143-3344-0(3))* Wayne State Univ. Pr.

Roe, Nicholas, ed. English Romantic Writers & the West Country. 2010. (ENG., Illus.). 256p. 89.00 *(978-0-230-22374-5(5))* Palgrave Macmillan.

Rogers, Byron. The Last Englishman: The Life of J. L. Carr. (Illus.). 288p. pap. 14.99 *(978-1-85410-984-2(7))* Aurum Pr., Ltd. GBR. Dist: Trafalgar Square Publishing.

Rogers, John. With Elia & His Friends in Books & Dreams. 2009. 112p. 21.99 *(978-1-103-53943-7(4))*; pap. 15.99 *(978-1-103-53939-0(6))* BiblioBazaar.

Rogers, Pat. A Political Biography of Alexander Pope, 1 vol. 2010. (Eighteenth-Century Political Biographies Ser.). (ENG.). 288p. 99.00 *(978-1-85196-846-6(6))* Pickering & Chatto Pubs., Ltd. GBR. Dist: Ashgate Publishing Co.

Rogers, Samuel. Recollections of the Table-Talk of Samuel Rogers to Which Is Added Porsoniana. 2006. 364p. per. 26.99 *(978-1-4255-3771-5(5))* MPublishing.

Roiphe, Katie. Uncommon Arrangements: Seven Marriages. 2008. 352p. pap. 15.00 *(978-0-385-33938-4(0)*, Dial Pr.) Random House Publishing Group.

Rollins, Hyder Edward, ed. The Letters of John Keats: Volume 1, 1814-1818: 1814-1821. 2012. (ENG.). 480p. pap. 39.99 ***(978-1-107-60820-7(1))*** Cambridge Univ. Pr.

—The Letters of John Keats: Volume 2, 1819-1821: 1814-1821. 2012. (ENG.). 464p. pap. 39.99 ***(978-1-107-69204-6(0))*** Cambridge Univ. Pr.

Rollyson, Carl. Rebecca West. 2008. pap. 29.95 *(978-0-595-48868-1(4))* iUniverse, Inc.

Ross, John J. Shakespeare's Tremor & Orwell's Cough: The Medical Lives of Great Writers. 2012. (ENG., Illus.). 304p. 24.99 ***(978-0-312-60076-1(3))*** St. Martin's Pr.

Ross, Margery, ed. Robert Ross, Friend of Friends: Letters to Robert Ross, Art Critic & Writer. reprint ed. 34.50 *(978-0-404-18384-4(0))* AMS Pr., Inc.

Rossetti, Lucy M. Mrs Shelley. 2010. 148p. 28.76 *(978-1-169-26331-4(3))*; pap. 16.76 *(978-1-162-67521-3(7))* Kessinger Publishing, LLC.

Rossetti, Lucy M. & Rossetti, Lucy M. Mrs Shelley. 2010. 148p. 35.95 *(978-1-161-44386-8(X))* Kessinger Publishing, LLC.

Rossetti, Lucy Madox. Mrs Shelley. 2009. 250p. 28.99 *(978-1-110-87750-8(1))* 2009. 250p. pap. 25.75 *(978-1-110-87749-2(8))* 2008. 248p. 24.99 *(978-0-559-21595-7(9))* 2008. 248p. pap. 25.75 *(978-0-559-21592-6(4))* BiblioBazaar.

—Mrs Shelley. 2008. 172p. pap. *(978-1-4099-3236-9(2))* Dodo Pr.

—Mrs. Shelley. 2009. (ENG.). 249p. pap. 22.99 *(978-1-110-87746-1(3))*; pap. 20.99 *(978-1-110-87744-7(7))* BiblioBazaar. (BiblioLife).

—Mrs Shelley. 2010. 248p. 32.99 *(978-1-140-28183-2(6))* BiblioBazaar.

Rossetti, Lucy Madox Brown. Mrs Shelley. 2010. (ENG.). 260p. pap. 26.75 *(978-1-176-86124-4(7))* BiblioBazaar.

—Mrs Shelley. 2010. (Illus.). 116p. pap. 20.59 *(978-1-153-64309-2(X))* General Bks. LLC.

Rossetti, William Michael. Life of John Keats. 2011. 118p. pap. 9.99 ***(978-1-61203-289-4(3))*** Bottom of the Hill Publishing.

Rossetti, William Michael. Lives of Famous Poets. 2009. 260p. pap. *(978-0-217-84200-6(3))* Books LLC.

—Lives of Famous Poets. 2008. 420p. 49.95 *(978-1-4365-3934-0(X))* 2007. (ENG.). 424p. per. 34.95 *(978-0-548-72522-1(5))* Kessinger Publishing, LLC.

Rousseau, George S. Notorious Sir John Hill: The Man Destroyed by Ambition in the Era of Celebrity. 2012. (ENG.). 424p. (gr. 17). 90.00 ***(978-1-61146-120-6(0))*** Lehigh Univ. Pr.

Rowland, Peter. Dickensian Digressions: The Hunter, the Haunter & the Haunted. 2010. (Illus.). 324p. lib. bdg. *(978-1-936320-07-3(X))* Academica Pr., LLC.

—The Unobtrusive Miss Hawker: The Life & Works of 'Lanoe Falconer',Vate Victorian Novelist & Short story Writer,1848-1908. 2009. *(978-1-933146-63-8(X))* Academica Pr., LLC.

Rowlandson, Maurice L. Maurice's Deuteronomy. 2007. 192p. pap. 18.95 *(978-1-84799-240-6(4))* Lulu Enterprises Inc.

Roy, James Alexander. Cowper & His Poetry. 2008. 180p. pap. *(978-1-4086-7992-0(2))* Read Bks.

Rubens, Bernice. When I Grow Up: A Memoir. 2006. (ENG., Illus.). 256p. per. 14.95 *(978-0-349-12017-1(X)*, Warner Books) Little, Brown Bk. Group Ltd. GBR. Dist: Independent Pubs. Group.

Rubin, C M & Rubin, Gabriela. The Real Alice in Wonderland: A Role Model for the Ages. 2010. 144p. 29.95 *(978-1-4490-8131-7(2))* AuthorHouse.

Rumbold, Valerie. Women's Place in Pope's World. 2006. (Cambridge Studies in Eighteenth-Century English Literature & Thought Ser.). (ENG.). 336p. (C). pap. 69.00 *(978-0-521-02672-7(5))* Cambridge Univ. Pr.

Ruppel, Richard. Homosexuality in the Life & Work of Joseph Conrad: Love Between the Lines. 2009. 114p. pap. 39.95 *(978-0-415-87669-8(9))* Routledge.

Ruskin, John. John Ruskin's Letters to William Ward: With a Short Biography of William Ward. 2009. 220p. 23.99 *(978-1-103-46426-5(4))*; pap. 17.99 *(978-1-103-46423-4(X))* BiblioBazaar.

Ruskin, John & O'Gorman, Francis. Praeterita. 2012. (Oxford World's Classics Ser.). (ENG.). 512p. pap. 16.95 ***(978-0-19-280241-5(0))*** Oxford Univ. Pr., Inc.

Russell, G. W. E. Matthew Arnold. 2007. 116p. per. *(978-1-4068-4101-5(3))* Echo Library.

Russell, G. W. E., ed. Matthew Arnold. 2007. (ENG.). 318p. 45.95 *(978-0-548-07576-0(X))* Kessinger Publishing, LLC.

Ryskamp, Charles. William Cowper of the Inner Temple, Esq: A Study of His Life & Works to the Year 1768. 2011. (ENG.). 300p. pap. 24.99 *(978-0-521-16948-6(8))* Cambridge Univ. Pr.

Sabor, Peter. The Court Journals & Letters of Frances Burney: Volume I: 1786. 2011. (ENG., Illus.). 400p. 185.00 *(978-0-19-926160-4(1))* Oxford Univ. Pr., Inc.

Sagar, Keith, ed. Poet & Critic: The Letters of Ted Hughes & Keith Sagar. 2012. (Illus.). 328p. 40.00 ***(978-0-7123-5862-0(5))*** British Library, The GBR. Dist: Chicago Distribution Ctr.

Saintsbury, George. Dryden. 2009. 208p. 23.99 *(978-1-103-61888-0(1))*; pap. 17.99 *(978-1-103-61885-9(7))* BiblioBazaar.

—Dryden. 2009. 120p. pap. *(978-0-217-20515-3(1))* Books LLC.

—Dryden. 2011. (Cambridge Library Collection - English Men of Letters Ser.). (ENG.). 206p. pap. 22.99 ***(978-1-108-03461-6(6))*** Cambridge Univ. Pr.

Salt, Henry Stephens. De Quincey. 2008. 128p. 35.95 *(978-1-4365-0294-8(2))* 2007. (ENG.). 132p. per. 20.95 *(978-0-548-74319-5(3))* Kessinger Publishing, LLC.

Salwak, Dale, ed. AfterWord: Conjuring the Literary Dead. 2011. (ENG.). 240p. pap. 19.95 *(978-1-58729-989-6(5))* Univ. of Iowa Pr.

Samway, Patrick. Educating Darfur Refugees: A Jesuit's Efforts in Chad. 2007. (Illus.). 300p. 35.00 *(978-1-58966-157-8(5))*; pap. 25.00 *(978-1-58966-164-6(8))* Univ. of Scranton Pr.

Scheuerle, William H. Henry Kingsley Revisited: Studies in a Nineteenth-Century Popilar British Novelist. 2010. 88p. 89.95 *(978-0-7734-1436-5(3))* Mellen, Edwin Pr., The.

Schmidt, Michael, ed. The Great Modern Poets. 2009. (ENG., Illus.). 208p. 12.99 *(978-1-905204-32-8(9)*, 1905204329) Quercus GBR. Dist: Book Sales, Inc.

Schmidt, Shannon McKenna & Rendon, Joni. Novel Destinations: Literary Landmarks from Jane Austen's Bath to Ernest Hemingway's Key West. 2008. (ENG., Illus.). 368p. 25.00 *(978-1-4262-0277-3(6)*, National Geographic) National Geographic Society.

Schneider, Matthew. The Long & Winding Road from Blake to the Beatles. 2008. (Nineteenth-Century Major Lives & Letters Ser.). (ENG.). 240p. 89.00 *(978-1-4039-8489-0(1))* Palgrave Macmillan.

Schuchard, Marsha Keith. William Blake's Sexual Path to Spiritual Vision. 2nd ed. 2008. (Illus.). 398p. pap. 19.95 *(978-1-59477-211-5(8))* Inner Traditions International, Ltd.

Scott, Paul. Behind Paul Scott's Raj Quartet: A Life in Letters. Haswell, Janis Tedesco, ed. 2011. Vol. 1. *(978-1-60497-749-3(3))* Vol. 2. *(978-1-60497-750-9(7))* Cambria Pr.

Scott, Walter, Sr. The Works of John Dryden. 2006. pap. 42.95 *(978-1-4286-4771-8(6))* Kessinger Publishing, LLC.

Sellin, Bernard. The Life & Works of David Lindsay. Gunnell, Kenneth, tr. from FRE. annot. ed. 2007. (ENG.). 284p. per. 58.00 *(978-0-521-03401-2(9))* Cambridge Univ. Pr.

Seymour, Miranda. Thrumpton Hall: A Memoir of Life in My Father's House. 2009. 304p. pap. 14.99 *(978-0-06-146658-8(1)*, HarperPerennial) HarperCollins Pubs.

Shaffer, Brian W. The Encyclopedia of Twentieth-Century Fiction, 3 vols. 2011. (Wiley-Blackwell Encyclopedia of Literature Ser.: 1). (ENG.). 1584p. 595.00 *(978-1-4051-9244-6(5)*, Wiley-Blackwell) Wiley, John & Sons, Inc.

Shakespeare, Nicholas, et al. Under the Sun: The Letters of Bruce Chatwin. 2010. (Illus.). 560p. *(978-0-224-08989-0(7)*, Jonathan Cape) Random Hse.

Sharpe, Tony. W. H. Auden. 2007. (Routledge Guides to Literature Ser.). (ENG.). 176p. 95.00 *(978-0-415-32735-0(0))*; 162p. per. 28.95 *(978-0-415-32736-7(9))* Routledge.

Sharps, John Geoffrey & Chapple, J. A. V., eds. Elizabeth Gaskell: Portrait in Letters. 2nd rev. ed. 2008. (ENG., Illus.). 192p. pap. 26.00 *(978-0-7190-7789-0(3))* Manchester Univ. Pr. GBR. Dist: Macmillan.

Sheavyn, Phoebe. The Literary Profession in the Elizabethan Age. 2007. (ENG.). 236p. 41.95 *(978-0-548-09846-2(8))* Kessinger Publishing, LLC.

Shelley, Mary Wollstonecraft. History of a Six Weeks' Tour Through a Part of France, Switzerland, Germany & Holland: With Letter. 2009. 196p. pap. 16.99 *(978-1-103-20109-9(3))* BiblioBazaar.

—History of a Six Weeks' Tour Through a Part of France, Switzerland, Germany & Holland, with Letters Descriptive of a Sail Round the Lake of Geneva, & of the Glaciers of Chamouni. reprint ed. lib. bdg. 98.00 *(978-0-7426-2099-5(9))* Classic Bks.

Shelley, Mary Wollstonecraft. My Best Mary: The Selected Letters of Mary Wollstonecraft Shelley. Spark, Muriel & Stanford, Derek, eds. 2011. 242p. 46.95 ***(978-1-258-03373-6(9))*** Literary Licensing, LLC.

Shelston, Alan. Elizabeth Gaskell. 2011. (Brief Lives Ser.). (ENG.). 104p. pap. 12.95 *(978-1-84391-921-6(4))* Hesperus Pr. GBR. Dist: Independent Pubs. Group.

Shephard, Sue. The Surprising Life of Constance Spry: From Social Reformer to Society Florist. 2010. (ENG., Illus.). 368p. 38.95 *(978-0-230-74181-2(9)*, Macmillan) Pan Macmillan GBR. Dist: Trans-Atlantic Pubns., Inc.

Sherborne, Michael. H G Wells: Another Kind of Life. 2012. (ENG.). 400p. pap. 22.95 ***(978-0-7206-1391-9(4))*** Owen, Peter Ltd. GBR. Dist: Independent Pubs. Group.

Sherwood, Mary Martha. The Life & Times of Mrs Sherwood (1775-1851) From the Diaries of Captain & Mrs Sherwood. Darton, F. J. Harvey, ed. 2011. (Cambridge Library Collection - Literary Studies). (ENG., Illus.). 562p. pap. 39.99 ***(978-1-108-03380-0(6))*** Cambridge Univ. Pr.

Shorter, Clement K. Charlotte Bronte & Her Circle. 2009. 538p. pap. 40.75 *(978-1-113-64875-4(9))*; pap. 39.75 *(978-1-113-64873-0(2))* BiblioBazaar.

—Charlotte Bronte & Her Circle. 2007. (ENG.). 544p. 57.95 *(978-0-548-08175-4(1))* Kessinger Publishing, LLC.

—Charlotte Bronte & Her Sisters. 2007. (ENG.). 280p. 42.95 *(978-0-548-12155-9(9))* Kessinger Publishing, LLC.

Shrubsall, Dennis, ed. The Unpublished Letters of W. H. Hudson, the First Literary Environmentalist 1841-1922, 2 vols., Vol. 1. 2006. 384p. *(978-0-7734-5573-3(6))* Mellen, Edwin Pr., The.

Shrubsall, Dennis, ed. & compiled by. The Unpublished Letters of W. H. Hudson, the First Literary Environmentalist 1841-1922, 2 vols., Vol. 2. 2006. 492p. *(978-0-7734-5575-7(2))* Mellen, Edwin Pr., The.

Sidney, Philip. The Defence of Poesie, Political Discourses, Correspondence & Translation: Volume 3. 2010. (ENG.). 376p. pap. 36.99 *(978-0-521-15833-6(8))* Cambridge Univ. Pr.

Simmons, Clare A. Popular Medievalism in Romantic-Era Britain. 2011. (Nineteenth-Century Major Lives & Letters Ser.). (ENG., Illus.). 246p. 89.00 *(978-0-230-10374-0(X))* Palgrave Macmillan.

Simpson, A. R. B. Another Life: Lawrence after Arabia. 2012. (ENG., Illus.). 384p. pap. 24.95 ***(978-0-7524-6358-2(6))*** History Pr. Ltd.,The GBR. Dist: Independent Pubs. Group.

Simpson, Andrew R. B. Another Life: Lawrence after Arabia. 2009. (ENG., Illus.). 384p. 39.95 *(978-1-86227-464-8(9))* History Pr. Ltd.,The GBR. Dist: Independent Pubs. Group.

Skura, Meredith Anne. Tudor Autobiography: Listening for Inwardness. 2008. (ENG., Illus.). 272p. 45.00 *(978-0-226-76187-9(8))* Univ. of Chicago Pr.

Slater, Michael. Charles Dickens. 2011. (Illus.). 720p. pap. 23.00 *(978-0-300-17093-1(9))* Yale Univ. Pr.

Smiles, Samuel. The Autobiography of Samuel Smiles. Mackay, Thomas, ed. 2007. (ENG.). 464p. 52.95 *(978-0-548-15501-1(1))*; pap. 37.95 *(978-1-4304-4932-4(2))* Kessinger Publishing, LLC.

Smiley, Jane. Charles Dickens: A Life. 2011. (ENG.). 224p. (gr. 12). 14.00 *(978-0-14-311992-0(3)*, Penguin (Non-Classics)) Penguin Group (USA) Inc.

Smith, Constance Babington. John Masefield: A Life. 2008. (ENG., Illus.). 256p. pap. 25.95 *(978-0-7509-3702-3(5))* History Pr. Ltd.,The GBR. Dist: Independent Pubs. Group.

Smith, Constance Babington & Macaulay, Rose. Letters to a Friend. 2012. 386p. pap. ***(978-1-4482-0422-9(4)***, 145950, Bloomsbury Reader) Bloomsbury Publishing Plc.

Smith, Emma. The Great Western Beach: A Memoir of a Cornish Childhood Between the Wars. 2008. (ENG., Illus.). 384p. 29.95 *(978-0-7475-9591-5(7))* Bloomsbury Publishing Plc GBR. Dist: Independent Pubs. Group.

Smith, Gavin D. Lakeland Poets. 2010. (ENG.). 128p. pap. 24.95 *(978-1-84868-536-9(X))* Amberley Publishing GBR. Dist: Casemate Pubs. & Bk. Distributors, LLC.

Smith, Harry B., ed. The Dickens-Kolle Letters. 2007. (ENG.). 114p. 34.95 *(978-0-548-00750-1(0))* Kessinger Publishing, LLC.

Smith, John & Faulkner, Peter. Against the Age: An Introduction to William Morris. 2011. (Routledge Revivals Ser.). (ENG.). 208p. 110.00 *(978-0-415-67601-4(0))* Routledge.

Smith, Lori. A Walk with Jane Austen: A Journey into Adventure, Love, & Faith. 2007. (ENG.). 256p. pap. 13.99 *(978-1-4000-7370-2(7)*, WaterBrook Pr.) Doubleday Religious Publishing Group, The.

Smith, Martin Ferguson. Dearest Jean: Rose Macaulay's Letters to a Cousin. 2011. (ENG., Illus.). 400p. 90.00 *(978-0-7190-8521-5(7))* Manchester Univ. Pr. GBR. Dist: Macmillan.

Smith, Nicholas D. The Literary Manuscripts & Letters of Hannah More. 2008. (Illus.). 230p. 114.95 *(978-0-7546-6270-9(5))* Ashgate Publishing Co.

Smith, Nigel. Andrew Marvell: The Chameleon. 2012. (ENG., Illus.). 416p. pap. 30.00 ***(978-0-300-18196-8(5))*** Yale Univ. Pr.

Somerville, Thomas. My Own Life & Times, 1741-1814. Lee, William, ed. reprint ed. 44.50 *(978-0-404-17206-0(7))* AMS Pr., Inc.

Sorensen, Lita. Bryan Talbot. 2009. (Library of Graphic Novelists Ser.). 112p. (gr. 7-12). 63.90 *(978-1-60853-653-5(X))* Rosen Publishing Group, Inc., The.

Southam. Later 19th Century Novelists. 2007. 1250.00 *(978-0-415-44424-8(1))* Routledge.

—Victorian Poets. 2007. 1450.00 *(978-0-415-44418-7(7))* Routledge.

Southern, Antonia. Player, Playwright & Preacher's Kid: The Story of Nathan Field 1587-1620. 2009. (Illus.). 252p. pap. *(978-1-84748-527-4(8))* Athena Pr.

—The Queen's Godson: Sir John Harington of Kelston,1560-1612. 2010. (Illus.). 344p. lib. bdg. *(978-1-936320-03-5(7))* Academica Pr., LLC.

Speck, William Allen. Robert Southey: Entire Man of Letters. 2006. (ENG., Illus.). 336p. 50.00 *(978-0-300-11681-6(0))* Yale Univ. Pr.

Spence, Jon & Spence. Becoming Jane Austen. movie tie-in ed. 2007. (ENG., Illus.). 312p. 17.95 *(978-1-84725-046-9(7))* Continuum International Publishing Group, Ltd. GBR. Dist: National Bk. Network.

Spicer-Simpson, Theodore & Sherman, Stuart P. Men of Letters of the British Isles: Portrait Medallions from the Life. 2011. 134p. 40.95 ***(978-1-258-03138-1(8))*** Literary Licensing, LLC.

Squier, Susan Merrill. Virginia Woolf & London: The Sexual Politics of the City. 2011. (ENG.). 232p. pap. 40.00 *(978-0-8078-6596-5(6))* Univ. of North Carolina Pr.

Squires, Michael. D. H. Lawrence & Frieda: A Portrait of Love & Loyalty. 2008. (ENG., Illus.). 200p. 29.95 *(978-0-233-00232-3(4))* Andre Deutsch GBR. Dist: Independent Pubs. Group.

Stafford, Fiona. Jane Austen. 2008. (Brief Lives Ser.). (ENG.). 120p. pap. 13.95 *(978-1-84391-906-3(0))* Hesperus Pr. GBR. Dist: Independent Pubs. Group.

Stanford, Donald E. A Critical Study of the Works of Four British Writers. Crump, R. W., ed. 2006. (ACE.). 356p. 119.95 *(978-0-7734-5546-7(9))* Mellen, Edwin Pr., The.

Stanhope, Philip Dormer. The Letters of Philip Dormer Stanhope, Earl of Chesterfield V2. Mahon, Lord, ed. 2007. (ENG.). 490p. 53.95 *(978-0-548-15631-5(X))*; 492p. per. 38.95 *(978-1-4304-5094-8(0))* Kessinger Publishing, LLC.

Stanway, Eric. From Brickbats to Bouquets. 2007. 236p. per. *(978-1-905179-03-9(0)*, Lonely Scribe) Armadillo Design Ltd.

Starecz, Zsuzsanna. The Role of Music in Burgess's Novels. 2008. 68p. pap. *(978-3-639-10685-5(7))* VDM Verlag Dr. Mueller e.K.

Steizig, Eugene L. Romantic Autobiography in England. 2009. (Nineteenth Century Ser.). (Illus.). 232p. 99.95 *(978-0-7546-6366-9(3))* Ashgate Publishing Co.

Stelzig, Eugene L. Henry Crabb Robinson in Germany: A Study in Nineteenth-Century Life Writing. 2010. 137p. 36.00 *(978-0-8387-5763-5(4))*; (ENG.). 36.00 *(978-1-61148-350-5(6))* Bucknell Univ. Pr.

Stephen, Leslie. Samuel Johnson. 2011. (Cambridge Library Collection - English Men of Letters Ser.). (ENG.). 208p. pap. 22.99 ***(978-1-108-03478-4(0))*** Cambridge Univ. Pr.

Sterne, Laurence. The Works of Laurence Sterne with a Life of the Author. 2006. (Illus.). 444p. per. 26.99 *(978-1-4255-4919-0(5))* MPublishing.

Stetz, Margaret D. Facing the Late Victorians: Portraits of Writers & Artists from the Mark Samuels Lasner Collection. 2007. (Illus.). 158p. pap. 49.00 *(978-0-87413-992-1(9))* Univ. of Delaware Pr.

Stewart, William. British & Irish Poets: A Biographical Dictionary, 449-2006. 2007. (ENG.). 503p. 125.00 *(978-0-7864-2891-5(0))* McFarland & Co., Inc. Pubs.

Stoddard, Richard Henry. Anecdote Biographies of Thackeray & Dickens / Edited by Richard Henry Stoddard. 2006. 332p. per. 23.99 *(978-1-4255-3375-5(2))* MPublishing.

Stoddard, Richard Henry, ed. Personal Reminiscences by Barham, Harness & Hodder. 2007. (ENG.). 334p. 45.95 *(978-0-548-02701-1(3))* Kessinger Publishing, LLC.

—Personal Reminiscences by Chorley, Planche & Young. 320p. 2008. 45.95 *(978-1-4366-4783-0(5))* 2008. pap. 30.95 *(978-0-548-89371-5(3))* 2007. (ENG.). 45.95 *(978-0-548-02510-9(X))* Kessinger Publishing, LLC.

—Personal Reminiscences by Constable & Gillies. 2007. (ENG.). 342p. 46.95 *(978-0-548-06519-8(5))* Kessinger Publishing, LLC.

Stoney, Barbara. Enid Blyton: The Biography. 2007. (ENG., Illus.). 240p. per. 16.95 *(978-0-7524-4030-9(6))* History Pr. Ltd.,The GBR. Dist: Independent Pubs. Group.

Stovel, Bruce. Jane Austen & Company: Collected Essays. Stovel, Nora Foster, ed. 2011. 296p. pap. 34.95 *(978-0-88864-548-7(1))* Univ. of Alberta Pr. CAN. Dist: Michigan State Univ. Pr.

Strachey, G. Lytton. Books & Characters. 2006. pap. *(978-1-4068-3119-1(0))* Echo Library.

Strachey, Giles Lytton. Books & Characters: French & English. 2007. 214p. pap. 20.99 *(978-1-4264-6075-3(9))*; (ENG.). 242p. pap. 22.99 *(978-1-4264-6146-0(1))* BiblioBazaar.

Strachey, Lytton. Books & Characters: French & English. 2010. 306p. pap. 29.75 *(978-1-144-00142-9(0))*; 378p. pap. 33.75 *(978-1-144-75308-3(2))* BiblioBazaar.

—Books & Characters: French & English. 2008. 216p. pap. *(978-1-4065-7559-0(3))* Dodo Pr.

Strathcarron, Ian. Joy Unconfined! Lord Byron's Grand Tour Re-Toured. 2011. (ENG., Illus.). 288p. *(978-1-904955-74-0(6))* Signal Bks.

Stroud, Jon & Groome, Clive. Little Book of Betjamin. 2011. (Little Book Of Ser.). (ENG., Illus.). 128p. 11.99 *(978-1-907803-39-0(4))* G2 Entertainment Ltd. GBR. Dist: BookMasters Distribution Services (BDS).

Stubbs, Charles. Charles Kingsley & the Christian Social Movement. 2007. (ENG.). 198p. 39.95 *(978-0-548-05091-0(0))* Kessinger Publishing, LLC.

Stubbs, John. John Donne: The Reformed Soul. 2007. 35.00 *(978-0-7930-6260-7(8))* Norton, W. W. & Co., Inc.

Sturrock, Donald. Storyteller: The Authorized Biography of Roald Dahl. 2011. (ENG., Illus.). 672p. pap. 18.99 *(978-1-4391-8976-4(5))* Simon & Schuster.

Sturt, George. A Small Boy in the Sixties. 2012. (ENG.). 258p. pap. 36.99 ***(978-1-107-63302-5(8))*** Cambridge Univ. Pr.

Suh, Judy. Fascism & Anti-Fascism in Twentieth-Century British Fiction. 2009. (ENG.). 224p. 89.00 *(978-0-230-61368-3(3))* Palgrave Macmillan.

Sullivan, Robert E. Macaulay: The Tragedy of Power. 2009. (Illus.). 624p. 42.00 *(978-0-674-03624-6(7)*, Belknap Pr.) Harvard Univ. Pr.

Sutherland, John. Lives of the Novelists: A History of Fiction in 294 Lives. 2012. (ENG.). 832p. 39.95 ***(978-0-300-17947-7(2))*** Yale Univ. Pr.

Suzuki, Mihoko. Ashgate Critical Essays on Women Writers in England 1550-1700: Volume 5:Anne Clifford & Lucy Hutchinson. 2009. (Ashgate Critical Essays on Women Writers in England, 1550-1700 Ser.). (Illus.). 538p. 300.00 *(978-0-7546-6110-8(5))* Ashgate Publishing Co.

Suzuki, Mihoko, intro. & selected by. Elizabeth Cellier Pt. 3, Vol. 6: Printed Writings 1641-1700. 2006. (Early Modern Englishwoman Ser.: Vol. 5). (Illus.). 264p. 120.00 *(978-0-7546-3102-6(8))* Ashgate Publishing Co.

Suzuki, Mihoko, et al. Mary Carleton Part 3, Vol. 6 &7: Printed Writings 1641-1700. 2006. (Early Modern Englishwoman Ser.: Vol. 6). (Illus.). 448p. 170.00 *(978-0-7546-3104-0(4))* Ashgate Publishing Co.

Swift, Graham. Making an Elephant: Writing from Within. 2010. (Vintage International Ser.). (ENG., Illus.). 416p. pap. 16.95 *(978-0-307-45575-8(0)*, Vintage) Knopf Doubleday Publishing Group.

Sykes Davies, Hugh & Watson, George. The English Mind: Studies in the English Moralists Presented to Basil Willey. 2010. (ENG.). 312p. pap. 33.99 *(978-0-521-13707-2(1))* Cambridge Univ. Pr.

Symonds, John Addington. Percy Bysshe Shelley. l.t. ed. 2007. (ENG.). 156p. pap. 21.99 *(978-1-4264-1697-2(0))* BiblioBazaar.

Symons, A.J.A. The Quest for Corvo: An Experiment in Biography. 2011. 306p. 48.95 ***(978-1-258-08238-3(1))*** Literary Licensing, LLC.

Taylor, Philip Meadows. The Story of My Life, by M Taylor Ed by His Daughter [A M Taylor]. 2010. 430p. pap. 35.75 *(978-1-147-03180-5(0))* BiblioBazaar.

Taylor, Susan B., ed. The Brontes: A Documentary Volume. 2008. (Dictionary of Literary Biography Ser.). (ENG., Illus.). 464p. 315.00 *(978-0-7876-8158-6(X))* Cengage Gale.

Tew, Marcus & Tew. Writers Talk: Conversations with Contemporary British Novelists. Tolan, Fiona & Wilson, Leigh, eds. 2008. (ENG.). 210p. 115.00 *(978-0-8264-9058-2(1))* Continuum International Publishing Group, Ltd. GBR. Dist: National Bk. Network.

Tew, Philip. Jim Crace. 2007. (Contemporary British Novelists Ser.). (ENG.). 240p. 84.00 *(978-0-7190-6912-3(2))*; pap. 26.00 *(978-0-7190-6913-0(0))* Manchester Univ. Pr. GBR. Dist: Macmillan.

—Writers Talk: Conversations with Contemporary British Novelists. Tolan, Fiona & Wilson, Leigh, eds. 2008. (ENG.). 210p. 27.95 *(978-1-84714-024-1(6))* Continuum International Publishing Group, Ltd. GBR. Dist: National Bk. Network.

Thackeray, William Makepeace. The Irish Sketch Book. 2009. 356p. 26.99 *(978-1-103-41881-7(5))*; pap. 20.99 *(978-1-103-41879-4(3))* BiblioBazaar.

—The Irish Sketch Book. 2009. 278p. pap. *(978-0-217-33173-9(4))*; 174p. pap. *(978-0-217-08480-2(X))* Books LLC.

—The Irish Sketch Book. 2009. 294p. pap. 21.70 *(978-1-4588-8149-6(0))* General Bks. LLC.

Thick, Malcolm. Sir Hugh Plat: The Search for Useful Knowledge in Early-Modern London. 2010. (ENG., Illus.). 432p. (C). 60.00 *(978-1-903018-65-1(X))* Prospect Bks. GBR. Dist: Brown, David Bk. Co., The.

Thirkell, Angela. Three Houses: A Victorian Childhood. 2007. (Illus.). 160p. pap. 12.95 *(978-1-55921-389-9(2))* Moyer Bell.

Thomas, Edward. Edward Thomas's Poets. Kendall, Judy, ed. 2008. (Poet's Poets Ser.). (ENG.). 224p. pap. 29.95 *(978-1-85754-908-9(2))* Carcanet Pr., Ltd. GBR. Dist: Independent Pubs. Group.

—A Literary Pilgrim in England. 2009. 230p. pap. *(978-1-4432-8893-4(4))* Books LLC.

Thomas Moore. Life of Lord Byron. l.t. ed. 2007. (ENG.). 366p. pap. 26.99 *(978-1-4264-8291-5(4))* BiblioBazaar.

Ticknor, Caroline. Glimpses of Authors. 2009. (ENG.). 380p. 38.99 *(978-1-117-34277-1(8))*; pap. 32.75 *(978-1-117-34278-8(6))* BiblioBazaar.

—Glimpses of Authors. 2009. 212p. pap. 19.99 *(978-0-217-48504-3(9))* General Bks. LLC.

—Glimpses of Authors. 2008. 380p. 48.95 *(978-1-4369-8726-4(1))*; pap. 33.95 *(978-1-4368-5947-9(6))* Kessinger Publishing, LLC.

Tidwell, Joanne. Politics & Aesthetics in the Diary of Virginia Woolf. 2012. (Studies in Major Literary Authors Ser.). (ENG.). 130p. pap. 42.95 ***(978-0-415-54194-7(8))*** Routledge.

Tidwell, Joanne Campbell. Politics & Aesthetics in the Diary of Virginia Woolf. 2007. (Studies in Major Literary Authors Ser.). (ENG.). 130p. 133.00 *(978-0-415-95817-2(2)*, 0415958172) Routledge.

Todd, Janet. Death & the Maidens: The Death of Fanny Wollstonecraft. 2007. (ENG., Illus.). 336p. 26.00 *(978-1-58243-339-4(9))* Counterpoint LLC.

Tomalin, Claire. Charles Dickens: A Life. 2012. (ENG., Illus.). 576p. (gr. 12). pap. 18.00 ***(978-0-14-312205-0(3)***, Penguin (Non-Classics)) Penguin Group (USA) Inc.

Tomalin, Claire. Thomas Hardy: The Time-Torn Man. 2008. (ENG., Illus.). 512p. (gr. 12-18). 17.00 *(978-0-14-311287-7(2)*, Penguin (Non-Classics)) Penguin Group (USA) Inc.

Tovey, Doreen. A Comfort of Cats. 2008. (ENG.). 192p. pap. 12.95 ***(978-1-84024-655-1(3))*** Summerdale Pubs. GBR. Dist: Independent Pubs. Group.

—The Coming of Saska. 2007. (ENG.). 160p. pap. 12.95 ***(978-1-84024-595-0(6))*** Summerdale Pubs. GBR. Dist: Independent Pubs. Group.

Traill, H. Sterne. 2007. (ENG.). 182p. 37.95 *(978-0-548-04985-3(8))* Kessinger Publishing, LLC.

Traill, H. D. Sterne. 2008. 132p. pap. *(978-1-4099-0715-2(5))* Dodo Pr.

—Sterne. 2006. (ENG.). pap. *(978-1-4068-1070-7(3))* Echo Library.

Traill, Henry Duff. Sterne. 2011. (Cambridge Library Collection - English Men of Letters Ser.). (ENG.). 190p. pap. 19.99 ***(978-1-108-03452-4(7))*** Cambridge Univ. Pr.

Trevelyan, George Otto. The Life & Letters of Lord Macaulay, by His Nephew G Otto Trevelyan. 2006. 436p. per. 26.99 *(978-1-4255-4759-2(1))* MPublishing.

Trollope, Anthony. Autobiography of Anthony Trollope. 2007. (ENG.). 224p. per. *(978-1-4065-2106-1(X))* Dodo Pr.

—Autobiography of Anthony Trollope. 2007. 280p. per. 9.99 *(978-1-59986-618-5(8))* Filiquarian Publishing, LLC.

Trollope, Anthony. Thackeray. 2011. (Cambridge Library Collection - English Men of Letters Ser.). (ENG.). 224p. pap. 22.99 ***(978-1-108-03476-0(4))*** Cambridge Univ. Pr.

Trollope, Fanny. Domestic Manners of the Americans. 2007. (Nonsuch Classics Ser.). (ENG., Illus.). 320p. per. 9.95 *(978-1-84588-213-6(X)*, Nonsuch Publishing, Ltd.) History Pr. Ltd.,The GBR. Dist: Independent Pubs. Group.

Trollope, Thomas Adolphus. What I Remember, vol. 2. l.t. ed. 2008. 296p. 28.99 *(978-0-554-30437-3(6))* BiblioBazaar.

—What I Remember. 2009. 482p. pap. *(978-0-217-65522-4(X))*; 314p. pap. *(978-0-217-65511-8(4))*; 292p. pap. *(978-0-217-14566-4(3))* Books LLC.

—What I Remember. 2010. (Cambridge Library Collection - Literary Studies). (ENG.). 418p. pap. 31.99 *(978-1-108-02293-4(6))*; (Illus.). 420p. pap. 31.99 *(978-1-108-02292-7(8))*; (Illus.). 434p. pap. 32.99 *(978-1-108-02294-1(4))* Cambridge Univ. Pr.

—What I Remember, Vol. 2. 2008. 248p. pap. *(978-1-4065-3935-6(X))* Dodo Pr.

—What I Remember. 2009. 448p. pap. 28.20 *(978-0-217-65517-0(3))* General Bks. LLC.

—What I Remember. 2007. (ENG.). 554p. 57.95 *(978-0-548-04807-8(X))* Kessinger Publishing, LLC.

—What I Remember. 2006. 416p. per. *(978-1-4067-3136-1(6)*, Hesperides Pr.) Read Bks.

—What I Remember 3 Volume Set. 2010. (Cambridge Library Collection - Literary Studies). (ENG., Illus.). 1272p. pap. 95.00 *(978-1-108-02295-8(2))* Cambridge Univ. Pr.

Trussler, Simon. Will's Will: The Last Wishes of William Shakespeare. 2008. (Illus.). 112p. 10.00 *(978-1-905615-24-7(8))* National Archives (PRO), The GBR. Dist: International Publishers Marketing.

Tuckwell, William. Spenser. 2008. 104p. pap. 18.75 *(978-0-559-64919-6(3))* BiblioBazaar.

Tupper, Martin Farquhar. My Life as an Author. 2007. 366p. pap. 25.99 *(978-1-4346-1161-1(2))*; (ENG.). 416p. pap. 28.99 *(978-1-4346-1232-8(5))* BiblioBazaar.

Una, Lady Troubridg. Life & Death of Radclyffe Hall. 2006. 200p. per. *(978-1-4067-3506-2(X)*, Hesperides Pr.) Read Bks.

Uttley, Alison & Judd, Denis. The Private Diaries of Alison Uttley. 2011. (Illus.). 256p. 39.95 ***(978-1-84468-124-2(6))*** Pen & Sword Bks. Ltd. GBR. Dist: Casemate Pubs. & Bk. Distributors, LLC.

Valentine, Mark. Time, a Falconer: A Study of Sarban. 2011. (Illus.). 140p. ***(978-1-905784-26-4(0))*** Tartarus Pr.

Vaus, Will. The Professor of Narnia: The C. S. Lewis Story. 2008. (ENG.). 160p. pap. 15.99 *(978-0-9817061-0-8(X))* Believe Bks., LLC.

Venables, Edmund. Life of John Bunyan. 2008. 236p. 24.99 *(978-0-559-66603-2(9))*; 236p. pap. 24.75 *(978-0-559-66601-8(2))*; 128p. 21.99 *(978-0-554-30975-0(0))*; 128p. 24.99 *(978-0-554-21672-0(8))* BiblioBazaar.

—Life of John Bunyan. 2009. 176p. pap. *(978-0-217-01296-6(5))* Books LLC.

Wainwright, Martin. Wainwright: The Man Who Loved the Lakes. 2007. (ENG., Illus.). 192p. pap. 32.95 *(978-1-84607-294-9(8))* BBC Worldwide GBR. Dist: Independent Pubs. Group.

Walford, Lucy B. Twelve English Authoresses. 200p. reprint ed. 98.00 *(978-0-7222-1495-4(2))* Library Reprints, Inc.

Walker, Gina Luria & Fitzer, Anna M., eds. Memoirs of Women Writers, 4 vols., Pt. 1, Vols. 1-4. 2011. (Chawton House Library: Women's Memoirs Ser.). (ENG.). 1808p. 625.00 *(978-1-84893-051-3(8))* Pickering & Chatto Pubs., Ltd. GBR. Dist: Ashgate Publishing Co.

Wallace, Malcolm William. The Life of Sir Philip Sidney. 2010. (ENG.). 440p. pap. 26.99 *(978-0-521-16622-5(5))* Cambridge Univ. Pr.

Wallhead, Celia M., ed. Writers of the Spanish Civil War: The Testimony of Their Auto/Biographies. 2011. (Spanish Perspectives on English & American Literature, Communication & Culture Ser.). 331p. pap. ***(978-3-0343-0696-6(2))*** Lang, Peter.

Walpole, Horace. The Letters of Horace Walpole. 2009. 132p. pap. *(978-1-4589-2271-7(5))*; 56p. pap. *(978-1-4589-2270-0(7))*; 120p. pap. *(978-0-217-94105-1(2))*; 58p. pap. *(978-1-4589-2273-1(1))*; 66p. pap. *(978-1-4589-7947-6(4))*; 554p. pap. *(978-1-4589-7950-6(4))*; 60p. pap. *(978-0-217-39245-7(8))*; 60p. pap. *(978-0-217-94108-2(7))*; 218p. pap. *(978-0-217-95659-8(9))*; 218p. pap. *(978-0-217-12144-6(6))*; 60p. pap. *(978-0-217-94107-5(9))*; 496p. pap. *(978-0-217-08931-9(3))* Books LLC.

—The Letters of Horace Walpole. 2009. 504p. pap. 29.13 *(978-0-217-39244-0(X))* General Bks. LLC.

Wansell, Geoffrey. Terence Rattigan. 2010. (ENG., Illus.). 436p. pap. 26.95 ***(978-1-84002-838-6(6))*** Oberon Bks., Ltd. GBR. Dist: Consortium Bk. Sales & Distribution.

Ward, Adolphus William. Dickens. 2011. (Cambridge Library Collection - English Men of Letters Ser.). (ENG.). 240p. pap. 22.99 ***(978-1-108-03450-0(0))*** Cambridge Univ. Pr.

Ward, Charles E. The Life of John Dryden. 2011. 390p. 53.95 ***(978-1-258-05675-9(5))*** Literary Licensing, LLC.

Wardale, Roger. Arthur Ransome under Sail. 2010. (ENG., Illus.). 256p. pap. 20.00 *(978-1-85058-855-9(4)*, Sigma Pr.) Stobart Davies, Ltd. GBR. Dist: Brown, David Bk. Co., The.

Warren, Nancy. Embodied Word: Female Spiritualities, Contested Orthodoxies, & English Religious Cultures, 1350-1700. 2010. (ND Reformations: Medieval & Early Modern Ser.). (ENG., Illus.). 352p. pap. 36.00 *(978-0-268-04420-6(1))* Univ. of Notre Dame Pr.

Watson, Dr, Nicola J. The Literary Tourist. 2008. (ENG., Illus.). 256p. pap. 31.00 *(978-0-230-21092-9(9))* Palgrave Macmillan.

Watson, Aaron. Tennyson. 2007. (ENG.). 96p. per. 18.95 *(978-0-548-60645-2(5))* Kessinger Publishing, LLC.

Watson, Alex. Romantic Marginality: Nation & Empire on the Borders of the Page, 1 vol. 2012. (History of the Book Ser.: 9). (ENG., Illus.). 208p. 99.00 *(978-1-84893-192-3(1))* Pickering & Chatto Pubs., Ltd. GBR. Dist: Ashgate Publishing Co.

Watson, Nicola J. Literary Tourism & Nineteenth-Century Culture. Watson, Nicola J., ed. 2009. (ENG.). 240p. 89.00 *(978-0-230-22281-6(1))* Palgrave Macmillan.

—The Literary Tourist: Readers & Places in Romantic & Victorian Britain. 2006. (ENG.). 256p. 84.00 *(978-1-4039-9992-4(9))* Palgrave Macmillan.

Watt, Julie. Poisoned Lives: The Regency Poet Letitia Elizabeth Landon (L. E. L.) & British Gold Coast Administrator George Maclean. 2010. (ENG., Illus.). 300p. 74.95 *(978-1-84519-420-8(9))* Sussex Academic Pr. GBR. Dist: International Specialized Bk. Services.

Watts-Dunton, Theodore. Old Familiar Faces. 2009. 326p. 45.95 *(978-1-120-08436-1(9))*; pap. 30.95 *(978-1-120-01452-8(2))* Kessinger Publishing, LLC.

—Old Familiar Faces. 2007. (ENG.). 320p. per. *(978-1-4086-1058-9(2))* Read Bks.

Waugh, Alec. My Brother Evelyn & Other Profiles. 2012. 348p. pap. ***(978-1-4482-0118-1(7)***, 144302, Bloomsbury Reader) Bloomsbury Publishing Plc.

—A Year to Remember: A Reminiscence Of 1931. 2012. 201p. pap. ***(978-1-4482-0127-3(6)***, 142580, Bloomsbury Reader) Bloomsbury Publishing Plc.

Waugh, Evelyn. Waugh in Abyssinia. 2007. (From Our Own Correpondent Ser.). 253p. per. 18.95 *(978-0-8071-3251-7(9))* Louisiana State Univ. Pr.

Waugh, Evelyn, et al. A Bitter Trial: Evelyn Waugh & John Carmel Cardinal Heenan on the Liturgical Changes. 2011. 123p. ***(978-1-58617-522-1(X))*** Ignatius Pr.

Wells, Lynn. Ian Mcewan. 2010. (New British Fiction Ser.). (ENG.). 176p. 59.50 *(978-1-4039-8781-5(5))*; pap. 14.95 *(978-1-4039-8782-2(3))* Palgrave Macmillan.

West, Paul. The Shadow Factory. 2008. (ENG.). 115p. 23.00 *(978-0-930829-65-0(4))* Lumen, Inc.

Wheatley, Henry Benjamin. Samuel Pepys & the World He Lived In. 2010. (Cambridge Library Collection - Printing & Publishing History Ser.). 328p. pap. 24.99 *(978-1-108-02152-4(2))* Cambridge Univ. Pr.

Wheatley, Vera & Martineau, Harriet. The Life & Work of Harriet Martineau. 2011. 436p. 56.95 ***(978-1-258-00837-6(3))*** Literary Licensing, LLC.

Wherry, George Edward. Cambridge & Charles Lamb. 2009. (Cambridge Library Collection - Cambridge Ser.). (ENG.). 120p. pap. 19.99 *(978-1-108-00254-7(4))* Cambridge Univ. Pr.

Whibley, Charles. Literary Portraits. 2009. 326p. 36.99 *(978-1-116-99105-5(5))* BiblioBazaar.

—Literary Portraits. 2009. 148p. pap. 19.99 *(978-1-151-21235-1(0))* General Bks. LLC.

White, Micheline. Ashgate Critical Essays on Women Writers in England 1550-1700 Vol. 3: Isabella Whitney Aemilia Lanyer & Anne Lock. 2009. (Ashgate Critical Essays on Women Writers in England, 1550-1700 Ser.). 506p. 275.00 *(978-0-7546-6086-6(9))* Ashgate Publishing Co.

White, R. S. John Keats: A Literary Life. Dutton, Richard, ed. 2010. (Literary Lives Ser.). (ENG.). 240p. 84.00 *(978-0-230-57263-8(4))* Palgrave Macmillan.

Whitehouse, J. Howard. To the Memory of Ruskin. 2006. pap. 16.95 *(978-1-4286-5519-5(0))* Kessinger Publishing, LLC.

Whittle, David. Bruce Montgomery/Edmund Crispin: A Life in Music & Books. 2007. (Illus.). 336p. 124.95 *(978-0-7546-3443-0(4))* Ashgate Publishing Co.

Wilde, Oscar. Intentions. 2006. (ENG.). 132p. per. 10.95 *(978-1-59818-853-0(4))* Aegypan.

—Intentions. 2009. 160p. 25.99 *(978-1-60512-395-0(1))*; pap. 12.99 *(978-1-60512-495-7(8))* Akasha Publishing, LLC. (Akasha Classics).

—Intentions. 2008. 148p. 24.99 *(978-0-554-21458-0(X))* 2008. 148p. 21.99 *(978-0-554-30761-9(8))* 2006. (ENG.). 150p. pap. 19.99 *(978-1-4264-0192-3(2))* BiblioBazaar.

—Intentions. reprint ed. lib. bdg. 98.00 *(978-0-7426-2930-1(9))* Classic Bks.

—Intentions. 2007. (ENG.). 192p. per. 9.99 *(978-1-59986-651-2(X))* Filiquarian Publishing, LLC.

—Intentions. 2008. 272p. pap. *(978-1-4097-2557-2(X))* Read Bks.

Williams, C. K. In Time: Poets, Poems, & the Rest. 2012. 240p. 27.50 ***(978-0-226-89951-0(9))*** Univ. of Chicago Pr.

Williams, Paul. Travel with William Cowper: The Evangelical Poet. 2007. (Travel With... Ser.). (Illus.). 128p. per. 15.00 *(978-1-84625-075-0(7))* DayOne Pubns. GBR. Dist: STL Distribution North America.

Williams, Penry & Nicholls, Mark. Sir Walter Raleigh: In Life & Legend. 2011. (ENG., Illus.). 400p. 34.95 *(978-1-4411-1209-5(X))* Continuum International Publishing Group, Ltd. GBR. Dist: National Bk. Network.

Williamson, George Charles. Milton. 2008. 132p. 21.99 *(978-0-559-15578-9(6))*; pap. 19.75 *(978-0-559-15576-5(X))* BiblioBazaar.

—Milton. 2009. 70p. pap. *(978-0-217-23773-4(8))* Books LLC.

Willis, Irene Cooper. Brontes. 2006. 148p. per. *(978-1-4067-2557-5(9)*, Hesperides Pr.) Read Bks.

Wilson, Colin. The Angry Years. 2007. (ENG., Illus.). 256p. 24.95 *(978-1-86105-972-7(8))* Anova Bks. GBR. Dist: Independent Pubs. Group.

Wilson, Frances. The Ballad of Dorothy Wordsworth: A Life. 2009. (ENG., Illus.). 336p. 30.00 *(978-0-374-10867-0(6))* Farrar, Straus & Giroux.

Wilson, Janet. Fleur Adcock. 2007. (Writers & Their Work Ser.). (ENG.). 154p. (C). pap. 26.00 *(978-0-7463-1040-3(4))* Northcote Hse. Publishers, Ltd. GBR. Dist: Brown, David Bk. Co., The.

Wilson, Jean Moorcroft. Isaac Rosenberg. 2008. (ENG., Illus.). 512p. 39.95 *(978-0-297-85145-5(4))* Orion Publishing Group, Ltd. GBR. Dist: Independent Pubs. Group.

—Isaac Rosenberg: The Making of a Great War Poet. 2009. (ENG., Illus.). 504p. 35.00 *(978-0-8101-2604-6(4))* Northwestern Univ. Pr.

Wilson, Kim. Tea with Jane Austen. 2011. (ENG., Illus.). 112p. 19.95 *(978-0-7112-3189-4(3))* Lincoln, Frances Ltd. GBR. Dist: Perseus-PGW.

Wilson, Todd. Aleister Crowley - Nature of the Beast. 2007. 176p. pap. 19.95 *(978-1-904658-27-6(X))* Aeon Bks. Ltd. GBR. Dist: Stylus Publishing, LLC.

Winchester, Simon. The Alice Behind Wonderland. 2011. (ENG., Illus.). 192p. 16.95 *(978-0-19-539619-5(7))* Oxford Univ. Pr., Inc.

Windle, Bertram Coghill Alan. The Wessex of Thomas Hardy. 2009. 360p. 46.95 *(978-1-120-24937-1(6))*; pap. 31.95 *(978-1-120-20729-6(0))* Kessinger Publishing, LLC.

Wingate, Ashmore Kyle Paterson. Life & Writings of John Ruskin. 2009. 154p. pap. *(978-0-217-50392-1(6))* Books LLC.

Winnington, G. Peter. Vast Alchemies: The Definitive Illustrated Biography. 2009. (ENG., Illus.). 300p. pap. 23.95 *(978-0-7206-1341-4(8))* Owen, Peter Ltd. GBR. Dist: Independent Pubs. Group.

Winnington, G. Peter, ed. Mervyn Peake: The Man & His Art. 2007. (Illus.). 216p. *(978-0-7206-1284-4(5))* Owen, Peter Ltd.

Winstead, Karen A. John Capgrave's Fifteenth Century. 2006. (Middle Ages Ser.). (Illus.). 248p. (C). 59.95 *(978-0-8122-3977-5(6))* Univ. of Pennsylvania Pr.

Wintermanns, Caspar & Wintermans, Caspar. Alfred Douglas: A Poet's Life & His Finest Work. 2007. (ENG., Illus.). 300p. 29.95 *(978-0-7206-1270-7(5))* Owen, Peter Ltd. GBR. Dist: Independent Pubs. Group.

Wodehouse, P. g. P. G. Wodehouse: A Life in Letters. Ratcliffe, Sophie, ed. 2012. (ENG., Illus.). 624p. 35.00 ***(978-0-393-08899-1(5)***, 8899) Norton, W. W. & Co., Inc.

Wohlgemut, Esther. Romantic Cosmopolitanism. 2009. (Palgrave Studies in the Enlightenment, Romanticism & the Cultures of Print Ser.). (ENG.). 224p. 89.00 *(978-0-230-23204-4(3))* Palgrave Macmillan.

Wolf, Mark J. Of Words & Worlds: The Imagination & Subcreation of J. R. R. Tolkien. 2008. 256p. 16.95 *(978-1-58182-642-5(7)*, Cumberland Hse.) Sourcebooks, Inc.

Wolf, Mark J. P. J. R. R. Tolkien: Of Words & Worlds. 2009. (ENG., Illus.). 228p. 18.95 *(978-1-58182-702-6(4)*, Cumberland Hse.) Sourcebooks, Inc.

Wolfson, Susan J., ed. Felicia Hemans: Selected Poems, Letters, Reception Materials. 2010. (ENG., Illus.). 552p. (C). pap. 52.50 *(978-0-691-14665-2(9))* Princeton Univ. Pr.

Wollaston, Emily. Little Book of Thomas Hardy. 2008. (Little Book Ser.). (ENG., Illus.). 128p. 11.99 *(978-1-906229-60-3(0)*, 1906229600) G2 Entertainment Ltd. GBR. Dist: BookMasters Distribution Services (BDS).

Wollaston, Emily & Dale, Sue. The Little Book of Brontë Sisters. 2008. (Little Book Ser.). (ENG., Illus.). 128p. 11.99 *(978-1-906229-59-7(7)*, 1906229597) G2 Entertainment Ltd. GBR. Dist: BookMasters Distribution Services (BDS).

—Little Book of Jane Austen. 2008. (Little Book Ser.). (ENG., Illus.). 128p. 11.99 *(978-1-906229-58-0(9)*, 1906229589) G2 Entertainment Ltd. GBR. Dist: BookMasters Distribution Services (BDS).

Wollstonecraft, Mary. Letters Written During a Short Residence in Sweden, Norway & Denmark. 2010. 88p. pap. 20.00 *(978-1-152-37474-4(5))* General Bks. LLC.

—Letters Written During a Short Residence in Sweden, Norway, & Denmark. 2010. 284p. pap. 28.75 *(978-1-144-26869-3(9))* BiblioBazaar.

—Letters Written During a Short Residence in Sweden, Norway, & Denmark. 2009. 102p. pap. *(978-1-151-44237-6(2))* Books LLC.

—Letters Written during a Short Residence in Sweden, Norway, & Denmark. 2010. (Cambridge Library Collection - Women's Writing Ser.). (ENG.). 276p. pap. 23.99 *(978-1-108-01889-0(0))* Cambridge Univ. Pr.

—Letters Written During a Short Residence in Sweden, Norway, & Denmark. 2010. (ENG.). 196p. pap. 23.75 *(978-1-177-64555-3(6))* BiblioBazaar.

Wollstonecraft, Mary. Letters Written During a Short Residence in Sweden, Norway & Denmark. 2011. 276p. pap. 27.75 ***(978-1-178-88885-0(1))*** BiblioBazaar.

—Letters Written During a Short Residence in Sweden, Norway & Denmark. 2010. 196p. 30.36 ***(978-1-164-25960-2(1))***; pap. 18.36 ***(978-1-164-06069-7(4))*** Kessinger Publishing, LLC.

Wood, Clement. Byron & the Women He Loved. 2011. 66p. 36.95 ***(978-1-258-01948-8(5))*** Literary Licensing, LLC.

Woolf, Jenny. The Mystery of Lewis Carroll: Discovering the Whimsical, Thoughtful, & Sometimes Lonely Man Who Created Alice in Wonderland. (ENG., Illus.). 336p. 2011. pap. 16.99 *(978-0-312-67371-0(X)*, St. Martin's Griffin) 2010. 27.99 *(978-0-312-61298-6(2))* St. Martin's Pr.

Woolf, Virginia. The Platform of Time: Memoirs of Family & Friends. Rosenbaum, S. P., ed. 2008. (ENG., Illus.). 232p. pap. 16.95 *(978-1-84391-711-3(4))* Hesperus Pr. GBR. Dist: Independent Pubs. Group.

Worboyes, Sally. East End Girl: Growing up the Hard Way. 2006. (ENG., Illus.). 304p. per. 14.95 *(978-0-340-83732-0(2)*, Hodder & Stoughton) Hodder General Publishing Div. GBR. Dist: Independent Pubs. Group.

Wortham, H. E. Oscar Browning. 2008. 344p. *(978-1-4437-4024-1(1)*, Obscure Pr.) Read Bks.

Wright, Thomas. Biographia Britannica Literaria. 2009. (LAT.). 571p. pap. 30.99 *(978-1-117-70043-4(7)*, BiblioLife) BiblioBazaar.

—Biographia Britannica Literaria. 2009. 362p. pap. *(978-0-217-95726-7(9))*; 440p. pap. *(978-0-217-44609-9(4))* Books LLC.

—The Life of William Cowper. 2009. 594p. pap. *(978-0-217-12035-7(0))*; 576p. pap. *(978-0-217-12039-5(3))* Books LLC.

—The Life of William Cowper. 2008. 734p. 66.95 *(978-1-4365-9933-7(4))* 2007. (ENG.). 736p. per. 51.95 *(978-0-548-80062-1(6))* Kessinger Publishing, LLC.

Wroe, Ann. Being Shelley: The Poet's Search for Himself. 2008. (Vintage Ser.). (ENG., Illus.). 464p. pap. 16.95 *(978-0-307-28052-7(7)*, Vintage) Knopf Doubleday Publishing Group.

Wu, Duncan. William Hazlitt: The First Modern Man. (ENG., Illus.). 2010. 592p. pap. 24.95 *(978-0-19-958884-8(8))* 2008. 400p. 49.95 *(978-0-19-954958-0(3))* Oxford Univ. Pr., Inc.

—Wordsworth's Reading 1800-1815. 2007. (ENG.). 340p. pap. 50.00 *(978-0-521-03741-9(7))* Cambridge Univ. Pr.

Yarnall, Ellis. Wordsworth & the Coleridges. 2009. 344p. 36.99 *(978-1-117-38186-2(2))*; pap. 31.75 *(978-1-117-38187-9(0))*; 36.99 *(978-1-115-41634-4(0))*; 32.99 *(978-1-115-41632-0(4))*; pap. 31.75 *(978-1-115-41629-0(4))*; pap. 32.75 *(978-1-115-41630-6(8))* BiblioBazaar.

—Wordsworth & the Coleridges. 2009. 144p. pap. 19.99 *(978-0-217-90985-3(X))* General Bks. LLC.

Yoseloff, Thomas. A Fellow of Infinite Jest. 2007. (ENG.). 242p. 41.95 *(978-0-548-05710-0(9))* Kessinger Publishing, LLC.

Young, Augustus. The Nicotine Cat & Other People. 2009. 300p. pap. 22.00 *(978-1-84840-041-2(1))* New Island Books IRL. Dist: International Specialized Bk. Services.

Zeikowitz, Richard E. Letters Between Forster & Isherwood on Homosexuality & Literature. 2008. (ENG., Illus.). 208p. 89.00 *(978-0-230-60675-3(X))* Palgrave Macmillan.

Zeitler, Michael. Representations of Culture: Thomas Hardy's Wessex & Victorian Anthropology. 2007. (C). 63.95 *(978-0-8204-8814-1(3))* Lang, Peter Publishing, Inc.

Zimmerman, Virginia. Excavating Victorians. (SUNY Series, Studies in the Long Nineteenth Century). (Illus.). 2009. 241p. pap. 29.95 *(978-0-7914-7280-4(9))* 2007. 231p. 65.00 *(978-0-7914-7279-8(5))* State Univ. of New York Pr.

Zweig, Stefan. Balzac, Dickens, Dostoevsky: Master Builders of the Spirit. 2009. (ENG.). 291p. pap. 34.95 *(978-1-4128-1047-0(7))* Transaction Pubs.

AUTHORS, ENGLISH—BIBLIOGRAPHY

Conrad, Joseph. Memoirs & Impressions - an Annotated Bibliography. 2007. (Illus.). 198p. 56.00 *(978-90-420-2298-0(1))* Rodopi.

Meredith, George. George Meredith - Various Readings & Bibliography. 2009. 380p. pap. 30.95 *(978-1-4446-5040-2(8))* Harrison House Pubs.

AUTHORS, ENGLISH—FIRST EDITIONS

see English Literature—First Editions

AUTHORS, EUROPEAN

Adeney, Elizabeth. The Moral Rights of Authors. 2nd rev. ed. 2006. (ENG.). 968p. 493.75 *(978-0-19-928474-0(1))* Oxford Univ. Pr., Inc.

Amiel, Henri-Frederic. Amiel's Journal. 2008. 428p. 30.99 *(978-0-554-32095-3(9))*; 32.99 *(978-0-554-22792-4(4))* BiblioBazaar.

—Amiel's Journal: The Journal Intime of Henri-Frédéric Amiel. Ward, Humphrey, tr. 2007. (ENG.). 380p. pap. 25.99 *(978-1-4264-3056-5(6))* BiblioBazaar.

—Amiel's Journal: The Journal Intime of Henri-Frédéric Amiel. HUMPHREY WARD, tr. l.t. ed. 2007. (ENG.). 426p. pap. 28.99 *(978-1-4264-3121-0(X))* BiblioBazaar.

Andersen, Hans Christian. The True Story of My Life - A Sketch. A Story Teller's Autobiography. 2008. 148p. pap. 9.99 *(978-1-60450-175-9(8))* Arc Manor.

Andersen, Hans Christian & Michael, Maurice. The Mermaid Man: The Autobiography of Hans Christian Andersen. 2011. 242p. 46.95 ***(978-1-258-01184-0(0))*** Literary Licensing, LLC.

Babii, Valentyna. "Z Bratamy Shche la Slovom Podiliusia" Biobibliohrafichnyi Pokazhchyk. 2009. (UKR., Illus.). 111p. *(978-611-517-015-9(X))* Tverdynja.

Baksi, Kurdo. Stieg Larsson: Our Days in Stockholm. Thompson, Laurie, tr. from SWE. 2010. (ENG.). 144p. 22.00 *(978-1-60598-174-1(5)*, 605174) Pegasus Bks.

Broderick, Colin. Orangutan: A Memoir. 2009. (ENG.). 352p. pap. 14.00 *(978-0-307-45340-2(5))* Crown Publishing Group.

Buszewicz, Maciej. Bruno Schulz. 2008. 80p. 29.95 *(978-83-87730-83-3(1))* Bosz, Szymanik i wspolnicy POL. Dist: Independent Pubs. Group.

Cotârlea, Delia. Schreiben unter der Diktatur: Die Lyrik von Anemone Latzina: Ein monographischer Versuch. 2008. (Schriften zur Europa- und Deutschlandforschung Ser.). 306p. pap. 74.95 *(978-3-631-57022-7(8))* Lang, Peter GmbH, Europaischer Verlag der Wissenschaften DEU. Dist: Lang, Peter.

Danto, Arthur C., et al. The Terror of Illusion: A Dialogue with Crisula Stefanescu, EEM #713. 2007. (ENG.). 200p. (gr. 17). 40.00 *(978-0-88033-611-6(0))* Eastern European Monographs.

Draga domnule Rotaru (antiscrisori) 2011. (RUM.). pap. 19.95 *(978-973-7782-88-5(7))* Multimedia Larga.

Dürrenmatt, Friedrich, et al. Die Schweiz, ein Gefängnis: Rede Auf Václav Havel. (GER.). 73p. *(978-3-257-22952-3(6))* Diogenes Verlag AG.

Eskin, Stanley G. Simenon: A Critical Biography. alt. ed. 2011. (ENG., Illus.). 318p. pap. 25.00 ***(978-0-7864-6728-0(2))*** McFarland & Co., Inc. Pubs.

Fitch, Noel Riley. The Grand Literary Cafes of Europe. 2007. (ENG., Illus.). 160p. 39.95 *(978-1-84537-114-2(3))* New Holland Pubs., Ltd. GBR. Dist: National Bk. Network.

Forshaw, Barry. The Man Who Left to Soon: The Life & Works of Stieg Larsson. 2011. (ENG., Illus.). 310p. pap. 12.95 *(978-1-84358-370-7(4))* Blake, John Publishing, Ltd. GBR. Dist: Independent Pubs. Group.

—Stieg Larsson Biography. 2010. (ENG., Illus.). 294p. 27.95 *(978-1-84454-940-5(2))* Blake, John Publishing, Ltd. GBR. Dist: Independent Pubs. Group.

Friel, Howard. The Lomborg Deception: Setting the Record Straight about Global Warming. 2011. (ENG.). 272p. pap. 18.00 *(978-0-300-17128-0(5))* Yale Univ. Pr.

Georges Simenon: Itinerary of a Belgian Writer. 2012. (ENG., Illus.). 144p. pap. 38.00 ***(978-2-87386-768-3(X))*** Lannoo Pubs./Racine.

Glaser, Chris. Henri's Mantle. 2010. 224p. pap. 25.00 *(978-1-60899-576-9(3)*, Wipf and Stock) Wipf & Stock Pubs.

Grennan, Conor. Little Princes: One Man's Promise to Bring Home the Lost Children of Nepal. 2011. (ENG.). 304p. pap. 14.99 ***(978-0-06-193006-5(7)***, William Morrow Paperbacks) HarperCollins Pubs.

Ivanovic, Radomir V. Umece Pripovedanja. 2010. (Illus.). 311p. *(978-86-7792-227-6(X))* Pegaz d.d.

Kaiserová, Kristina & Röhrborn, Gert, eds. Present Tensions: European Writers on Overcoming Dictatorships. 2008. (ENG & MUL.). 316p. 44.95 *(978-963-9776-21-0(1))* Central European Univ. Pr.

Kyber, Manfred. Grotesque & Humorous Tales. 2010. (ENG., Illus.). 102p. pap. *(978-1-84748-748-3(3))* Athena Pr.

Maricourt, Thierry. Dictionnaire du Roman Policier Nordique. 2010. (FRE., Illus.). 240p. (C). pap. 35.00 ***(978-2-251-74245-8(X))*** Societe d'edition Les Belles lettres FRA. Dist: ISD.

Medieval Manuscripts, Their Makers & Users: A Special Issue of Viator in Honor of Richard & Mary Rouse. 2011. (ENG & FRE., Illus.). 321p. (C). 131.00 ***(978-2-503-53894-5(0))*** Brepols Pubs. BEL. Dist: ISD.

Obradovic, Dimitrije Dositej. The Life & Adventures of Dimitrije Obradovic: Who As A Monk Was Given the Name Dositej. Noyes, George Rapall, ed. 2011. 366p. 53.95 ***(978-1-258-05019-1(6))*** Literary Licensing, LLC.

Papleka, Feride. Dhimitër S. Shuteriqi. 2010. (ALB., Illus.). 701p. *(978-99956-10-36-4(1))* Akademia e Shkencave.

Prideaux, Sue. Strindberg: A Life. 2012. (ENG., Illus.). 352p. 40.00 ***(978-0-300-13693-7(5))*** Yale Univ. Pr.

Quanjer, Johan Henri. The Luminous Journey: The Reflection of Pneumatocracy, the Rule of the Soul, in my Extraordinary Life. 2009. (Illus.). 428p. pap. 28.95 *(978-0-9800817-7-0(7))* Eremitical Pr.

Rosenblatt, Helena, ed. The Cambridge Companion to Constant. 2009. (Cambridge Companions to Philosophy Ser.). (ENG.). 448p. 99.00 *(978-0-521-85646-1(9))*; pap. 30.99 *(978-0-521-67243-6(0))* Cambridge Univ. Pr.

Ruggier, Joe & John Paul. Pope Caesar's Wake- Letters to Pope Woytyla. 3rd ed. 2012. ***(978-1-897303-17-7(3))*** Multicultural Bks.

Schuon, Frithjof. Spiritual Perspectives & Human Facts: A New Translation with Selected Letters. 2007. (Library of Perennial Philosophy). (ENG., Illus.). 296p. per. 21.95 *(978-1-933316-42-0(X))* World Wisdom, Inc.

Serafin, Steven & Mihailovich, Vasa D. Dlb 353 Cen & E Eur Writers. 2009. (Dictionary of Literary Biography Ser.). (ENG., Illus.). 480p. 315.00 *(978-0-7876-8171-5(7))* Cengage Gale.

Smarandache, Florentin. Frate cu meridianele si paralelele, Vol. 4. 2008. (RUM.). pap. 33.50 *(978-973-7743-74-9(1))* Multimedia Larga.

Starova, Luan. My Father's Books. Kramer, Christina E., tr. from MAC. 2012. (ENG.). 136p. pap. 24.95 ***(978-0-299-28794-8(7))*** Univ. of Wisconsin Pr.

Starova, Luan & Kramer, Christina Elizabeth. My Father's Books. 2012. E-Book ***(978-0-299-28793-1(9))*** Univ. of Wisconsin Pr.

Todorov, Tzvetan. Duties & Delights: The Life of a Go-Between. Portevin, Catherine, ed. Walker, Gila, tr. from FRE. 2008. (SB-the French List Ser.). (ENG.). 424p. 39.95 *(978-1-905422-89-0(X))* Seagull Bks. GBR. Dist: Chicago Distribution Ctr.

Töpffer, Rodolphe, et al. Correspondance Complète. 2009. (HISTOIRE des IDeES et CRITIQUE LITTeRAIRE Ser.). (FRE., Illus.). 528p. (C). pap. 96.00 *(978-2-600-01296-6(6))* Droz, Librairie CHE. Dist: Brown, David Bk. Co., The.

Tranströmer, Tomas. Memories Look at Me: A Memoires Fulton, Robin, tr. from SWE. 2011. (ENG.). 64p. (gr. 9-17). pap. 11.95 ***(978-0-8112-2018-7(4)***, 22018) New Directions Publishing Corp.

Tshibanda Wamuela Bujitu. André Baillon: Le Belge de Marly. 2009. (Illus.). 124p. *(978-2-507-00170-4(4))* Pire, Luc Editions.

Venema, Janny. Kiliaen Van Rensselaer, 1586-1643: Designing a New World. 2011. 352p. pap. 34.95 *(978-90-8704-196-0(9))* State Univ. of New York Pr.

AUTHORS, FILIPINO

Joaquin, Sarah K. Of Laughter & Tears. 2007. (Illus.). 209p. per. *(978-0-9712066-5-6(1))* Carayan Pr.

AUTHORS, FRENCH

Alain-Fournier. Le Grand Meaulnes. 2007. (FRE.). 220p. pap. 20.99 *(978-1-4264-2005-4(6))* 2006. 238p. pap. 22.99 *(978-1-4264-2116-7(8))* BiblioBazaar.

—Le Grand Meaulnes. pap. 21.95 incl. audio compact disk *(978-88-7754-838-2(X))* Cideb ITA. Dist: Distribooks, Inc.

Apollinaire, Guillaume & Frisch, Max. An Answer from the Silence: A Story from the Mountains. 2011. (SB-the German List Ser.). 118p. 19.00 *(978-1-906497-92-7(3))* Seagull Bks. London Ltd. GBR. Dist: Chicago Distribution Ctr.

Baldick, Robert. The Life of J. -K. Huysmans. 2006. (Illus.). 592p. per. 23.00 *(978-1-903517-43-7(5))* Dedalus, Ltd.

Banier, Francois-Marie. Beckett, 1 vol. 2009. (ENG., Illus.). 88p. 25.00 *(978-3-86521-983-1(7))* Steidl, Gerhard Druckerei und Verlag DEU. Dist: Innovative Logistics.

Barnett, Marva A., ed. Victor Hugo on Things That Matter: A Reader. 2009. (FRE & ENG., Illus.). 528p. pap. 54.00 *(978-0-300-12245-9(4))* Yale Univ. Pr.

Barré, Jean-Luc. François Mauriac: Biographie Intime. 2009. (FRE., Illus.). *(978-2-213-62636-9(7))*; *(978-2-213-65577-2(4))* Fayard, Artheme, Librairie.

Barrès, Maurice, et al. Mes Cahiers. 2010. (FRE.). *(978-2-84990-146-5(6))* Editions des Equateurs.

Bataille, Georges. Guilty. 2011. (SUNY series in Contemporary French Thought Ser.). 256p. 85.00 *(978-1-4384-3461-2(8))*; pap. 29.95 *(978-1-4384-3462-9(6))* State Univ. of New York Pr.

Bataille, Georges & Leiris, Michel. Correspondence: Georges Bataille & Michel Leiris. Heron, Liz, tr. from FRE. 2008. (SB-The French List Ser.). (ENG.). 312p. 29.95 *(978-1-905422-67-8(9))* Seagull Bks. GBR. Dist: Chicago Distribution Ctr.

Beauvoir, Simone de. Memoires D'une Jeune Fille Rangee. 2008. (Collection Folio Ser.). (FRE.). 472p. per. *(978-2-07-035552-5(7))* Gallimard, Editions.

Becker, Lucille Frackman. George Simenon: Maigret & the 'Romans Durs' 2006. (Illus.). 224p. 24.95 *(978-1-904950-86-8(3))* Haus Publishing GBR. Dist: Consortium Bk. Sales & Distribution.

Biro, Adam. One Must Also Be Hungarian. Tihanyi, Catherine, tr. from ENG. 2007. (Illus.). 168p. 20.00 *(978-0-226-05212-0(5))* Univ. of Chicago Pr.

Bloch-Dano, Evelyne. Le Dernier Amour de George Sand. 2010. 314p. pap. *(978-2-246-73201-3(8))* Grasset et Fasquelle.

—Madame Proust: A Biography. Kaplan, Alice, tr. from FRE. 2007. (ENG., Illus.). 272p. 27.50 *(978-0-226-05642-5(2))* Univ. of Chicago Pr.

Bloom, Harold. Night - Elie Wiesel. 2nd rev. ed. 2010. (Bloom's Modern Critical Interpretations Ser.). 206p. (C). (gr. 9). 45.00 *(978-1-60413-867-2(X)*, Chelsea Hse.) Facts On File, Inc.

Bonnefoy, Yves. L'inachevable: Entretiens Sur la Poésie, 1990-2010. 2010. (FRE.). 531p. *(978-2-226-21511-6(5))* Albin-Michel, Editions.

Bouillier, Grégoire & Huisman, Violaine. Report on Myself. Benderson, Bruce, tr. from FRE. 2009. (ENG.). 160p. pap. 13.95 *(978-0-618-96861-9(X))* Houghton Mifflin Harcourt Publishing Co.

Bradby, D. Jean Genet. (Routledge Modern & Contemporary Dramatists Ser.). (ENG., Illus.). 224p. 2012. 99.95 *(978-0-415-37504-7(5))* 2011. pap. 27.95 *(978-0-415-37506-1(1))* Routledge.

Breton, André. Entretiens avec Andre Parinaud (1913-1952) (Coll. Le Point du Jour). (FRE.). 8.95 *(978-0-7859-0636-0(3)*, M3136) French & European Pubns., Inc.

Brotchie, Alastair. Alfred Jarry: A Pataphysical Life. 2011. (ENG., Illus.). 424p. (gr. 17). 34.95 *(978-0-262-01619-3(2))* MIT Pr.

Brown, Andrew. Stendhal. 2010. (Brief Lives Ser.). (ENG.). 207p. pap. 17.95 *(978-1-84391-913-1(3))* Hesperus Pr. GBR. Dist: Independent Pubs. Group.

Brown, Frederick. Flaubert: A Biography. 2007. (Illus.). 640p. per. 22.50 *(978-0-674-02537-0(7))* Harvard Univ. Pr.

Bulgakov, Mikhail Afanasevich. Life of Monsieur de Moliere. Ginsburg, Mirra, tr. from RUS. 2010. (Oneworld Classics Ser.). 208p. pap. 14.95 *(978-1-84749-127-5(8))* Alma Classics GBR. Dist: Independent Pubs. Group.

Byles, A. T. P., ed. Christine de Pisan: The Book of Fayttes of Armes & of Chyualrye. 2010. (Early English Text Society Original Ser.: Volume 189). 384p. reprint ed. pap. 80.00 *(978-0-85991-690-5(1))* Early English Text Society (EETS) GBR. Dist: Boydell & Brewer, Inc.

Camus, Renaud. Demeures de L'esprit. 2008. (FRE., Illus.). *(978-2-213-64300-7(8))*; *(978-2-213-65441-6(7))* Fayard, Artheme, Librairie.

—Demeures de L'esprit: France I Sud-Ouest. 2008. (FRE., Illus.). *(978-2-213-63584-2(6))* Fayard, Artheme, Librairie.

Caro, Elme. George Sand. 2008. 148p. 21.99 *(978-0-554-36689-0(4))* 2008. 148p. 24.99 *(978-0-554-27386-0(1))* 2007. (FRE.). 130p. pap. 18.99 *(978-1-4346-3114-5(1))* 2007. 144p. pap. 19.99 *(978-1-4346-3115-2(X))* BiblioBazaar.

Carpenter, Kirsty. The Novels of Madame de Souza in Social & Political Perspective. (Illus.). 280p. pap. 63.95 *(978-3-03910-898-5(0))*; 2007. (French Studies of the Eighteenth & Nineteenth Centuries Ser.: Vol. 24). pap. 63.95 *(978-0-8204-8018-3(5))* Lang, Peter Publishing, Inc.

Carter, David. Honore de Balzac. 2008. (Brief Lives Ser.). (ENG.). 96p. pap. 13.95 *(978-1-84391-908-7(7))* Hesperus Pr. GBR. Dist: Independent Pubs. Group.

Chaigne, Louis. Paul Claudel: The Man & the Mystic. De Fontenouvelle, Pierre, tr. 2011. 288p. 48.95 ***(978-1-258-04072-7(7))*** Literary Licensing, LLC.

Chevandier, Christian. La Fabrique D'une Génération: Georges Valero, Postier, Militant et écrivain. 2009. (FRE., Illus.). 448p. (C). pap. 47.00 ***(978-2-251-90002-5(0))*** Societe d'edition Les Belles lettres FRA. Dist: ISD.

Cixous, Hélène. Hélène Cixous. 2011. (ENG.). 224p. pap. 19.95 *(978-0-7456-4868-2(1))* Polity Pr. GBR. Dist: Wiley, John & Sons, Inc.

Cixous, Héléne. Hemlock. 2011. (ENG.). 224p. 64.95 *(978-0-7456-4867-5(3))* Polity Pr. GBR. Dist: Wiley, John & Sons, Inc.

Cixous, Hélène & Calle-Gruber, Mireille. Hélène Cixous, Photos de Racines. (FRE., Illus.). 212p. *(978-2-7210-0454-3(9))* Des Femmes.

Cocteau, Jean. My Contemporaries. 2008. (Peter Owen Modern Classics Ser.). (ENG.). 188p. pap. 15.95 *(978-0-7206-1258-5(6))* Owen, Peter Ltd. GBR. Dist: Independent Pubs. Group.

Cohen, Albert. Book of My Mother. Cohen, Bella, tr. from FRE. 2012. (ENG.). 180p. pap. 15.00 ***(978-1-935744-33-7(X))*** Archipelago Bks.

Collin, William Edwin. Clockmaker of Souls: A Study of Paul Jean Toulet. 2011. 212p. 44.95 ***(978-1-258-01929-7(9))*** Literary Licensing, LLC.

Conley, Katharine. Robert Desnos, Surrealism, & the Marvelous in Everyday Life. 2008. (ENG., Illus.). 282p. pap. 24.95 *(978-0-8032-1841-3(9))* Univ. of Nebraska Pr.

Constant, Benjamin. The Red Book. 2011. (Oneworld Classics Ser.). (ENG.). 76p. pap. 12.95 *(978-1-84749-164-0(2))* Alma Classics GBR. Dist: Independent Pubs. Group.

Curtis, Jerry L. Lucette Desvignes: The Artist in the Arena. 2007. (Illus.). 400p. pap. *(978-1-890357-20-7(0))* Florida Academic Pr.

Davidson, Ian. Voltaire: A Life. 2010. (ENG., Illus.). 560p. 35.00 *(978-1-60598-119-2(2)*, 605119) Pegasus Bks.

de Beauvoir, Simone. Wartime Diary. Simons, Margaret A. et al, eds. Cordero, Anne Deing, tr. from FRE. 2008. (Beauvoir Ser.). (ENG.). 368p. 42.00 *(978-0-252-03377-3(9))* Univ. of Illinois Pr.

De Goncourt, Edmond & De Goncourt, Jules. Pages from the Goncourt Journals. 2006. (New York Review Books Classics). (ENG., Illus.). 472p. pap. 16.95 *(978-1-59017-190-5(X)*, NYRB Classics) New York Review of Bks., Inc., The.

De Riencourt, Amaury. Child of the Century. (Illus.). 242p. *(978-0-907855-10-1(5))* Honeyglen Publishing, Ltd. GBR. Dist: Vine Hse. Distribution.

Debord, Guy. Correspondence: The Foundation of the Situationist International (June 1957 - August 1960) Kendall, Stuart & McHale, John, trs. from FRE. 2008. (Semiotext(e) / Foreign Agents Ser.). (ENG.). 400p. (gr. 17). 55.00 *(978-1-58435-063-7(6))*; pap. 19.95 *(978-1-58435-055-2(5))* Semiotexte/Smart Art.

Dixon, Sergine. Germaine de Stael, Daughter of the Enlightenment: The Writer & Her Turbulent Era. 2007. (Gateway Bookshelf Ser.). (ENG., Illus.). 340p. per. 39.98 *(978-1-59102-560-3(5)*, Humanity Bks.) Prometheus Bks., Pubs.

Doumic, Rene. George Sand Some Aspects of Her Life and. 2006. pap. *(978-1-84702-525-8(0))* Echo Library.

Downing, Frederick L. Elie Wiesel: A Religious Biography. 2008. 282p. 29.00 *(978-0-88146-099-5(0))* Mercer Univ. Pr.

Dumas, Alexandre. My Memoirs by Alexandre Dumas. Bell, A. Craig, ed. 2011. 268p. 47.95 ***(978-1-258-00838-3(6))*** Literary Licensing, LLC.

Duras, Marguerite. Wartime Writings: 1943-1949. Coverdale, Linda, tr. from FRE. 2008. (ENG.). 296p. 26.95 *(978-1-59558-200-3(2))* New Pr., The.

—Wartime Writings: 1943-1949. Bogaert, Sophie & Corpet, Oliver, eds. Coverdale, Linda, tr. 2009. (ENG.). 320p. pap. 17.95 *(978-1-59558-452-6(8)*, 955452) New Pr., The.

Edwards, Natalie, et al, eds. Textual & Visual Selves: Photography, Film, & Comic Art in French Autobiography. 2011. (ENG., Illus.). 288p. pap. 25.00 *(978-0-8032-3631-8(X))* Univ. of Nebraska Pr.

Eisler, Benita. Naked in the Marketplace: The Lives of George Sand. 2007. (ENG.). 304p. per. 16.95 *(978-1-58243-381-3(X))* Counterpoint LLC.

Emery, Elizabeth. Photojournalism & the Origins of the French Writer House Museum (1881-1914) Privacy Publicity & Personality. 2012. (Histories of Material Culture & Collecting, 17001950 Ser.). (Illus.). 262p. 119.95 ***(978-1-4094-0877-2(9))*** Ashgate Publishing Co.

Ernaux, Annie. Things Seen. Kaplansky, Jonathan, tr. from FRE. 2010. (ENG.). 106p. 30.00 *(978-0-8032-1077-6(9))*; pap. 16.95 *(978-0-8032-2815-3(5)*, Bison Bks.) Univ. of Nebraska Pr.

Federman, Raymond. Shhh: The Story of a Childhood. 2010. 264p. pap. 18.00 *(978-0-9842133-0-6(9))* Starcherone Bks.

Fournier, Jean-Louis. Where We Going, Daddy? Life with Two Sons Unlike Any Other. Hunter, Adriana, tr. from FRE. 2010. (ENG.). 128p. pap. 12.00 *(978-1-59051-338-5(X))* Other Pr., LLC.

France, Anatole. On Life & Letters, vols. 4, Set. Date not set. 86.95 *(978-0-8369-4977-3(3))* Ayer Co. Pubs., Inc.

Gely, Raphael. Roles, Action Sociale et Vie Subjective: Recherches a Partir De la Phenomenologie De Michel Henry. (FRE.). 205p. pap. 35.95 *(978-90-5201-347-3(0))* Lang, Peter Publishing, Inc.

George Sand And Gustave Flaubert. The George Sand-Gustave Flaubert Letters. McKenzie, A. L., tr. 2009. 578p. 26.95 *(978-1-60762-049-5(9))*; pap. 15.95 *(978-1-60762-050-1(2))* Norilana Bks.

Gerassi, John, ed. Talking with Sartre: Conversations & Debates. 2009. (ENG.). 336p. pap. 20.00 *(978-0-300-15901-1(3))* Yale Univ. Pr.

Gerrard, Mike. Bloom's Literary Guide to Paris. 2007. (Bloom's Literary Guide Ser.). 176p. per. 14.95 *(978-0-7910-9379-5(4)*, Chelsea Hse.) Facts On File, Inc.

Gide, Andre, et al. The Correspondence of Andre Gide & Edmund Gosse, 1904-1928. Brugmans, Linette F., ed. 2011. 238p. 46.95 ***(978-1-258-04391-9(2))*** Literary Licensing, LLC.

Giesbert, Franz-Olivier. The American. 2007. (Vintage Ser.). (ENG.). 160p. pap. 13.95 *(978-1-4000-9585-8(9)*, Vintage) Knopf Doubleday Publishing Group.

Gille, Elisabeth. The Mirador: Dreamed Memories of Irene Nemirovsky by Her Daughter. Harss, Marina, tr. from FRE. 2011. 256p. pap. 14.95 *(978-1-59017-444-9(5)*, NYRB Classics) New York Review of Bks., Inc., The.

Gray, Francine du Plessix. Madame de Stael: The First Modern Woman. 2008. (ENG.). 1p. 24.00 *(978-1-934633-17-5(8))* Atlas & Co.

Green, F. C. Stendhal. 2011. (ENG.). 346p. pap. 28.99 *(978-1-107-60072-0(3))* Cambridge Univ. Pr.

Gribble, Francis. George Sand & Her Lovers. 2007. (ENG.). 404p. 49.95 *(978-0-548-04378-3(7))* Kessinger Publishing, LLC.

Griggs, Arthur Kingsla. Memoirs of Leon Daudet. 2006. pap. 30.95 *(978-1-4286-5904-9(8))* Kessinger Publishing, LLC.

Grossi, Paolo. Pierre-Louis Ginguené, Historien de la Littérature Italienne. (FRE.). xiii, 397p. 69.95 *(978-3-03911-150-3(7))* Lang, Peter CHE. Dist: Lang, Peter Publishing, Inc.

Guyotat, Pierre. Coma. Wedell, Noura, tr. from FRE. 2010. (Semiotext(e) / Native Agents Ser.). (ENG., Illus.). 232p. (gr. 17). pap. 17.95 *(978-1-58435-089-7(X))* Semiotexte/Smart Art.

Haddad-Wotling, Karen & Ferré, Vincent. Proust, L'étranger. 2010. (FRE.). 167p. E-Book *(978-90-420-3038-1(0))* Rodopi.

Hawes, Elizabeth. Camus, a Romance. 2010. (ENG.). 336p. pap. 14.00 *(978-0-8021-4488-1(8)*, Grove Pr.) Grove/Atlantic, Inc.

Hemmings, F. W. J. Alexandre Dumas: The King of Romance. 2012. 249p. pap. ***(978-1-4482-0527-1(1)***, 146218, Bloomsbury Reader) Bloomsbury Publishing Plc.

—Baudelaire the Damned: A Biography. 2012. 271p. pap. ***(978-1-4482-0515-8(8)***, 146214, Bloomsbury Reader) Bloomsbury Publishing Plc.

—The Life & Times of Emile Zola. 2012. 192p. pap. ***(978-1-4482-0520-2(4)***, 146526, Bloomsbury Reader) Bloomsbury Publishing Plc.

Herman, Jan, et al, eds. Le Chevalier de Mouhy: Bagarre et Bigarrure. 2010. (Illus.). 242p. pap. 62.00 *(978-90-420-3094-7(1))* Rodopi.

Hindus, Milton. The Crippled Giant: A Bizarre Adventure in Contemporary Letters. 2011. 158p. 41.95 ***(978-1-258-09427-0(4))*** Literary Licensing, LLC.

Hugo, Victor. The Memoirs of Victor Hugo. 2008. 272p. 25.99 *(978-0-554-38530-3(9))* 2008. 272p. 28.99 *(978-0-554-29227-4(0))* 2007. (ENG.). 238p. per. 20.99 *(978-1-4346-7182-0(8))* 2007. (ENG.). 268p. per. 23.99 *(978-1-4346-7183-7(6))* BiblioBazaar.

—The Memoirs of Victor Hugo. 2008. 260p. per. *(978-1-4065-6896-7(1))* Dodo Pr.

—The Memoirs of Victor Hugo. 2007. 188p. per. *(978-1-4068-1408-8(3))* Echo Library.

—The Memoirs of Victor Hugo. 2008. (Large Print Ser.). lib. bdg. 26.00 *(978-1-58287-963-5(X))*; lib. bdg. 25.00 *(978-1-58287-480-7(8))* North Bks.

—The Memoirs of Victor Hugo. 2009. (ENG.). 224p. pap. 15.45 *(978-1-4385-1792-6(0)*, Book Jungle) Standard Pubns., Inc.

—The Memoirs of Victor Hugo. 2008. 408p. 39.95 *(978-1-4344-7072-0(5))*; pap. 24.95 *(978-1-4344-7071-3(7))* Wildside Pr., LLC.

—The Memoirs of Victor Hugos. 2006. 164p. 59.00 *(978-1-60021-252-9(2))* Nova Science Pubs., Inc.

Hutcheon, Linda. Formalism & the Freudian Aesthetic: The Example of Charles Mauron. 2006. (ENG.). 268p. pap. 55.00 *(978-0-521-02795-3(0))* Cambridge Univ. Pr.

Huysmans, J-.K. The Road from Decadence. Beaumont, Barbara, ed. 320p. *(978-0-485-11331-0(7))* Continuum International Publishing Group, Ltd.

James, Henry. French Poets & Novelists. 2007. (ENG.). 348p. 46.95 *(978-0-548-03621-1(7))* Kessinger Publishing, LLC.

—French Poets & Novelists. 2008. 448p. pap. *(978-1-4097-6408-3(7))*; pap. *(978-1-4097-1922-9(7))* Read Bks.

Juliet, Charles. Conversations with Samuel Beckett & Bram van Velde. Nesme, Axel & Tucker, Janey, trs. from FRE. 2009. (French Literature Ser.). (ENG.). 192p. pap. 13.95 *(978-1-56478-531-2(9)*, 478531) Dalkey Archive Pr.

Keates, Jonathan. Stendhal. Date not set. pap. 10.99 *(978-0-7493-2475-9(9))* Heinemann.

Keim, Albert. Honore de Balzac. 2007. (Illus.). 140p. per. *(978-1-4065-1868-9(9))* Dodo Pr.

—Honore de Balzac. 2010. (Illus.). 80p. pap. 20.00 *(978-1-153-62917-1(8))* General Bks. LLC.

Keim, Albert & Lumet, Louis. Honoré de Balzac. 2010. 284p. pap. 28.75 *(978-1-147-55341-3(6))* BiblioBazaar.

—Honoré de Balzac. 2010. 104p. pap. 15.96 *(978-1-162-66663-1(3))*; 34.95 *(978-1-161-43528-3(X))* Kessinger Publishing, LLC.

Keim, Albert, et al. Honoré de Balzac. 2010. 284p. (ENG.). pap. 28.75 *(978-1-171-63911-4(2))*; pap. 28.75 *(978-1-176-71091-7(5))* BiblioBazaar.

Kennedy, Seán & Weiss, Katherine, eds. Samuel Beckett: History, Memory, Archive. 2009. (New Interpertations of Beckett in the Twenty-first Century Ser.). (ENG.). 236p. 89.00 *(978-0-230-61944-9(4))* Palgrave Macmillan.

Lejeune, Philippe. On Diary. 2009. 336p. 44.00 *(978-0-8248-3388-6(0))*; (Illus.). (C). pap. 22.00 *(978-0-8248-3389-3(9))* Univ. of Hawaii Pr.

Lerner, Michael G. Edouard Rod (1857-1910) A portrait of the novelist & his Times. (Studies in French Literature Ser.). (GER.). 272p. 210.00 ***(978-3-11-196065-4(X))***; 135.00 ***(978-3-11-102541-4(1)***, De Gruyter, Mouton DEU. Dist: de Gruyter, Walter GmbH & Co. KG.

Liszt, Franz, et al. The Liszt/D'Agoult Correspondence: English Translations & Commentaries. 2011. ***(978-1-57647-165-4(9))*** Pendragon Pr.

Lloyd, Rosemary. Charles Baudelaire. 2008. (Reaktion Books - Critical Lives Ser.). (ENG., Illus.). 192p. per. 16.95 *(978-1-86189-363-5(9))* Reaktion Bks., Ltd. GBR. Dist: Chicago Distribution Ctr.

Lottman, Herbert. Gustave Flaubert. (SPA.). *(978-84-7223-383-6(9)*, 6020) Tusquets Editores.

Mairowitz, David Zane & Korkos, Alain. Introducing Camus. 2012. (Introducing Ser.). (ENG., Illus.). 126p. 9.95 ***(978-1-84831-345-3(4))*** Totem Bks. GBR. Dist: Consortium Bk. Sales & Distribution.

Maison de Victor Hugo Staff, et al, contrib. by. Portraits D'écrivains de 1850 à Nos Jours: Du 5 Novembre 2010 Au 20 Février 2011 à la Maison de Victor Hugo. 2010. (FRE., Illus.). 157p. *(978-2-7596-0143-1(9))* Paris-Musées, Association.

Mallarmé, Stéphane. Correspondance II 1871-1885, Vol. II. Mondor, Henri & Austin, Lloyd James, eds. (FRE.). 340p. 15.95 *(978-0-7859-0023-8(3)*, F67221) French & European Pubns., Inc.

—Correspondence: Vol.1, 1862-1871, Vol. I. Mondor, Henri & Richard, Jean-Pierre, eds. 8th ed. 15.95 *(978-0-7859-0022-1(5)*, F67220) French & European Pubns., Inc.

—1886 1889 Tome III, Tome III. Mondor, ed. 19.95 *(978-0-7859-0024-5(1)*, F67222) French & European Pubns., Inc.

Maupassant, Guy de. Sicily. 2007. (Italica Historical Travel Guides Ser.). (ENG., Illus.). 102p. pap. 15.00 *(978-1-59910-008-1(8))* Italica Pr

Mercer, Wendy S. The Life & Travels of Xavier Marmier (1808-1892) Bringing World Literature to France. 2007. (British Academy Postdoctoral Fellowship Monographs). (Illus.). 320p. 135.00 *(978-0-19-726388-4(7))* Oxford Univ. Pr., Inc.

Mossman, Carol A. Writing with a Vengeance: The Countess de Chabrillan's Rise from Prostitution. 2009. (ENG., Illus.). 224p. *(978-0-8020-9691-3(3))* Univ. of Toronto Pr.

MTrimTe, Prosper. Prosper Mtrimte's Letters to an Incognita; with Recollections by Lamartine & George Sand Edited by Richard Henry Stoddard. 2006. 356p. per. 26.99 *(978-1-4255-3637-4(9))* MPublishing.

Nemeth, Alexander J. Voltaire's Tormented Soul: A Psychobiographic Inquiry. 2008. 359p. 60.00 *(978-0-934223-92-8(0))* Lehigh Univ. Pr.

Norton, James R. Jean-Jacques Rousseau: Advocate of Government by Consent. 2009. (Philosophers of the Enlightenment Ser.). 112p. (gr. 5-8). 66.50 *(978-1-60851-164-8(2)*, Rosen Central) Rosen Publishing Group, Inc., The.

Orguillés, David Mayor. Julio Verne. 2007. (Grandes biografias Ser.). (SPA & ENG., Illus.). 192p. 8.95 *(978-84-9764-560-7(X))* Edimat Libros, S. A. ESP. Dist: Independent Pubs. Group.

Pagnol, Marcel. Le Chateau de Ma Mere.Tr. of My Mother's House. (FRE.). pap. 16.95 *(978-2-87706-051-6(9))* Editions de Fallois FRA. Dist: Distribooks, Inc.

—Le Chateau de Ma Mere.Tr. of My Mother's House. (FRE.). 280p. 13.95 *(978-0-8288-9897-3(9)*, F117481);Tome II. 15.50 French & European Pubns., Inc.

—La Gloire de Mon Pere.Tr. of My Father's Glory. (FRE.). 13.95 *(978-0-8288-9896-6(0)*, F117480);Tome I. 14.95 French & European Pubns., Inc.

—La Gloire de Mon Pere. Lathrop, Tom & Lathrop, Connie, eds. 2007. (Moliere & Co. Ser.: 8).Tr. of My Father's Glory. (FRE.). 244p. (C). per. 13.95 *(978-1-58977-046-1(3)*, European Masterpieces) LinguaText, Ltd.

Pearson, Roger. Stephane Mallarme. 2010. (Reaktion Books - Critical Lives Ser.). (ENG., Illus.). 192p. pap. 16.95 *(978-1-86189-659-9(X))* Reaktion Bks., Ltd. GBR. Dist: Chicago Distribution Ctr.

Perec, Georges. Thoughts of Sorts. Bellos, David, tr. from FRE. & intro. by. 2009. (ENG.). 176p. pap. 16.95 *(978-1-56792-362-9(3)*, Verba Mundi) Godine, David R. Pub.

Philipponnat, Olivier & Lienhardt, Patrick. The Life of Irène Némirovsky, 1903-1942. Cameron, Euan, tr. from FRE. 2010. (ENG., Illus.). 464p. 35.00 *(978-0-307-27021-4(1))* Knopf, Alfred A. Inc.

Pie Books Staff, et al. Herve Moran: The Genius of French Poster Art. 2010. (ENG, JPN & FRE., Illus.). 268p. pap. 35.00 *(978-4-89444-840-7(8)*, PIE Bks.) Rizzoli International Pubns., Inc.

Pocock, Gordon. Boileau & the Nature of Neoclassicism. 2010. (Major European Authors Ser.). (ENG.). 224p. pap. 27.99 *(978-0-521-13675-4(X))* Cambridge Univ. Pr.

Poli, Annarosa & Kanceff, Emanuele. Alla Riscoperta Di George Sand, Viaggiatrice in Italia. 2010. (FRE & ITA., Illus.). 254p. *(978-88-7760-092-9(6))* CIRVI.

Polizzotti, Mark. Revolution of the Mind, Revised Edition: The Life of Andre Breton. 2009. (ENG.). 680p. pap. 29.95 *(978-0-9795137-8-7(2))* Commonwealth Bks.,Black Widow.

Powell, Jessica. Literary Paris: A Guide. 2006. (ENG., Illus.). 220p. 19.95 *(978-1-892145-38-3(3))* Little Bookroom.

Racine, Jean. The Complete Plays of Jean Racine: Volume II: Bajazet. Argent, Geoffrey Alan, tr. from FRE. 2011. 49.95 *(978-0-271-03744-8(X))* Pennsylvania State Univ. Pr.

Reda, Jacques. Europes. Prevots, Aaron, tr. from FRE. 2009. (FRE & ENG.). 153p. pap. 12.00 *(978-0-924047-70-1(4))* Host Pubns., Inc.

Renard, Jules. Journal, 1887-1910, 4 vols. Guichard, Leon & Sigaux, Gilbert, eds. (Bibliotheque de la Pleiade Ser.). Vol. 1: 1887-1895. pap. 18.95 *(978-0-7859-3185-0(6)*, 2264006102) Vol. 2: 1897-1901. pap. 16.95 *(978-0-7859-3186-7(4)*, 2264006110) Vol. 4: 1906-1910. pap. 16.95 *(978-0-7859-3187-4(2)*, 2264006358) French & European Pubns., Inc.

—The Journal of Jules Renard. Bogan, Louise & Roget, Elizabeth, eds. & trs. by. from FRE. 2008. (ENG.). 264p. pap. 16.95 *(978-0-9794198-7-4(5))* Tin Hse. Bks., LLC.

Restif de La Bretonne & Testud, Pierre. Journal. 2010. (FRE.). 442p. *(978-2-84578-117-7(2))* Manucius.

Rooth, Graham. Prophet for a Dark Age: A Companion to the Works of René Guénon. 2008. (ENG., Illus.). 348p. (C). pap. 59.95 *(978-1-84519-251-8(6))* Sussex Academic Pr. GBR. Dist: International Specialized Bk. Services.

Rousseau, Jean-Jacques. The Confessions of J J Rousseau, Complete. 2007. 472p. per. *(978-1-4068-4056-8(4))* Echo Library.

Rowley, Hazel. Tête-à-Tête: The Tumultuous Lives & Loves of Simone de Beauvoir & Jean-Paul Sartre. 2008. (ENG.). 416p. pap. 16.00 *(978-1-4223-9557-8(X))* DIANE Publishing Co.

—Tête-à-Tête: The Tumultuous Lives & Loves of Simone de Beauvoir & Jean-Paul Sartre. 2006. (P. S. Ser.). (ENG., Illus.). 480p. per. 15.95 *(978-0-06-052060-1(4)*, HarperPerennial) HarperCollins Pubs.

Sandars, Mary F. Honore de Balzac His Life & Writings. 2008. 284p. 28.99 *(978-0-554-26864-4(7))* 2008. 284p. 25.99 *(978-0-554-36167-3(1))* 2007. 254p. pap. 21.99 *(978-1-4346-2030-9(1))* 2007. (ENG.). 282p. pap. 23.99 *(978-1-4346-2059-0(X))* BiblioBazaar.

Sarraute, Nathalie. Childhood. 2007. 256p. pap. 16.00 *(978-0-226-73492-7(7))* Univ. of Chicago Pr.

Sartre, Jean-Paul. Saint Genet: Actor & Martyr. Frechtman, Bernard, tr. from FRE. 2012. 640p. pap. 24.95 ***(978-0-8166-7760-3(3))*** Univ. of Minnesota Pr.

Schlehlein, Melinda. Hugues Rebell, a Nietzschean Writer in Fin-de-Siecle France: His Literary & Political Achievement. 2011. 332p. 129.95 ***(978-0-7734-1522-5(X))*** Mellen, Edwin Pr., The.

Sellers, Susan, ed. White Ink: Interviews on Sex, Text, & Politics. 2008. (European Perspectives: a Series in Social Thought & Cultural Criticism Ser.). (ENG.). 256p. (gr. 17). 79.50 *(978-0-231-14776-7(7))*; pap. 26.50 *(978-0-231-14777-4(5))* Columbia Univ. Pr.

Shelford, April G. Transforming the Republic of Letters: Pierre-Daniel Huet & European Intellectual Life, 1650-1720. 2007. (Changing Perspectives on Early Modern Europe Ser.: Volume 7). (Illus.). 275p. 75.00 *(978-1-58046-243-3(X))* Univ. of Rochester Pr.

Simoson, Andrew. Voltaire's Riddle: Micromégas & the Measure of All Things. 2009. 396p. 58.95 net. *(978-0-88385-345-0(0))* Mathematical Assn. of America.

Smiles, Samuel. Jasmin Barber Poet Philanthropist. 2006. pap. *(978-1-4068-0581-9(5))* Echo Library.

Smock, Ann. What Is There to Say? 2007. (ENG.). 208p. pap. 19.95 *(978-0-8032-2238-0(6))* Univ. of Nebraska Pr.

Stael, Madame de. 1788-1791, Tome I, Pt. 2. Jasinski, ed. 20.95 *(978-0-8288-9661-0(5)*, F73291) French & European Pubns., Inc.

—Lettres de Jeunesse de 1777 a Aout, 1788, Tome I, Pt. 1. Jasinski, ed. 20.95 *(978-0-8288-9660-3(7)*, F73290) French & European Pubns., Inc.

—Lettres de Mezery et de Coppet (16 Mai 1794-16 Mai 1795). Tome III, Pt. 1. Jasinski, ed. 27.95 *(978-0-8288-9664-1(X)*, F73294) French & European Pubns., Inc.

—Lettres Diverses de 1792 a Mai 1794, Tome II, Pt. 2. Jasinski, ed. 31.95 *(978-0-8288-9663-4(1)*, F73293) French & European Pubns., Inc.

—Lettres d'une Nouvelle Republicaine, Tome III, Pt. 2. Jasinski, ed. 39.95 *(978-0-8288-9665-8(8)*, F73295) French & European Pubns., Inc.

—Lettres Inedites a Louis de Norbonne, Tome II, Pt. 1. Jasinski, ed. 26.95 *(978-0-8288-9662-7(3)*, F73292) French & European Pubns., Inc.

Stendhal. Letters to Pauline. Brown, Andrew & Lewis, Sophie, trs. from FRE. 2011. (Hesperus Classics Ser.). (ENG.). 166p. pap. 15.95 *(978-1-84391-167-8(1))* Hesperus Pr. GBR. Dist: Independent Pubs. Group.

Strachey, G. Lytton. Books & Characters. 2006. pap. *(978-1-4068-3119-1(0))* Echo Library.

Strachey, Giles Lytton. Books & Characters: French & English. 2007. 214p. pap. 20.99 *(978-1-4264-6075-3(9))*; (ENG.). 242p. pap. 22.99 *(978-1-4264-6146-0(1))* BiblioBazaar.

Strachey, Lytton. Books & Characters: French & English. 2010. 306p. pap. 29.75 *(978-1-144-00142-9(0))*; 378p. pap. 33.75 *(978-1-144-75308-3(2))* BiblioBazaar.

—Books & Characters: French & English. 2008. 216p. pap. *(978-1-4065-7559-0(3))* Dodo Pr.

Tame, Peter D. Andre Chamson, 1900-1983 Book 1: The Life of a French Novelist, 2 vols. 2006. 332p. *(978-0-7734-5681-5(3))* Mellen, Edwin Pr., The.

—Andre Chamson, 1900-1983 Book 2: The Life of a French Novelist, 2 vols. 2006. 392p. *(978-0-7734-5683-9(X))* Mellen, Edwin Pr., The.

Terestchenko, Ivan, photos by. The Private World of Yves Saint Laurent & Pierre Bergé. 2009. (ENG., Illus.). 280p. 95.00 *(978-0-86565-251-4(1))* Vendome Pr., The.

Thomas, Hugh. Beaumarchais in Seville: An Intermezzo. 2009. (ENG., Illus.) 192p. pap. 15.00 *(978-0-300-13633-3(1))* Yale Univ. Pr.

Thompson, Vance. French Portraits: Being Appreciations of the Writers of Young France. 2007. (ENG.). 272p. 42.95 *(978-0-548-37636-2(0))*; per. 27.95 *(978-0-548-31964-2(2))* Kessinger Publishing, LLC.

Todd, Oliver. Albert Camus une Vie. pap. 31.95 *(978-2-07-041062-0(5))* Gallimard, Editions FRA. Dist: Distribooks, Inc.

Toussaint, Jean-Philippe. Self-Portrait Abroad. Lambert, John, tr. from FRE. 2010. (Netherlandic & Belgian Literature Ser.). (ENG.). 80p. pap. 12.95 *(978-1-56478-586-2(6)*, 478586) Dalkey Archive Pr.

Tre'butien, G. S. Journal of Eugenie de Guerin. 2007. (ENG.). 464p. 52.95 *(978-0-548-03862-8(7))* Kessinger Publishing, LLC.

Vassallo, Helen & Wardle, Cathy. Dialogues avec Jeanne Hyvrard. 2006. (Chiasma Ser.: 19). 183p. pap. 37.00 *(978-90-420-2074-0(1))* Rodopi.

Viaud, Samuel. Pierre Loti: Notes of My Youth. Stein, Rose Ellen, tr. 2007. (ENG.). 190p. 37.95 *(978-0-548-01482-0(5))* Kessinger Publishing, LLC.

Voltaire, Francois, pseud. Correspondance: 1704-1738. Besterman, ed. (Pleiade Ser.). 65.95 *(978-2-07-010928-9(3))* Schoenhof's Foreign Bks., Inc.

—Correspondance: 1739-1748. Besterman, ed. (Pleiade Ser.). 65.95 *(978-2-07-010929-6(1))* Schoenhof's Foreign Bks., Inc.

—Correspondance: 1749-1753, Vol. 3. Besterman, ed. (Pleiade Ser.). 61.95 *(978-2-07-010807-7(4))* Schoenhof's Foreign Bks., Inc.

—Correspondance: 1754-1757, Vol. 4. Besterman, ed. (Pleiade Ser.). 65.05 *(978-2-07-010819-0(8))* Schoenhof's Foreign Bks., Inc.

—Memoirs of the Life of Monsieur de Voltaire. Brown, Andrew & Lewis, Sophie, trs. from FRE. 2007. (Hesperus Classics Ser.). (ENG.). 124p. pap. 15.95 *(978-1-84391-152-4(3))* Hesperus Pr. GBR. Dist: Independent Pubs. Group.

Weil, Sylvie. At Home with André & Simone Weil. Ivry, Benjamin, tr. from FRE. 2010. (ENG.). 192p. 24.95 *(978-0-8101-2704-3(0))* Northwestern Univ. Pr.

Wettlaufer, Alexandra. Portraits of the Artist as a Young Woman: Painting & the Novel in France & Britain, 1800-1860. 2011. cd-rom 14.95 *(978-0-8142-9244-0(5))* Ohio State Univ. Pr.

—Portraits of the Artist as a Young Woman: Painting & the Novel in France & Britain, 1800-1860. 2011. 368p. 59.95 *(978-0-8142-1145-8(3))* Ohio State Univ. Pr.

Whibley, Charles. Literary Portraits. 2009. 326p. 36.99 *(978-1-116-99105-5(5))* BiblioBazaar.

—Literary Portraits. 2009. 148p. pap. 19.99 *(978-1-151-21235-1(0))* General Bks. LLC.

White, Edmund. Marcel Proust: A Life. 2009. (Penguin Lives Ser.). (ENG.). 176p. (gr. 12-18). 14.00 *(978-0-14-311498-7(0)*, Penguin (Non-Classics)) Penguin Group (USA) Inc.

—Rimbaud: The Double Life of a Rebel. 2009. (ENG.). 256p. pap. 14.00 *(978-1-934633-20-5(8)*, 934620) Atlas & Co.

Wiesel, Elie. Night Trilogy: Night - Dawn - Day. 2008. (ENG.). 352p. pap. 17.95 *(978-0-8090-7364-1(1)*, Hill & Wang) Farrar, Straus & Giroux.

Williams, James S. Jean Cocteau. 2010. (French Film Directors Ser.). (ENG., Illus.). 240p. pap. 24.95 *(978-0-7190-5884-4(8))* Manchester Univ. Pr. GBR Dist: Macmillan.

—Jean Cocteau. 2008. (Reaktion Books - Critical Lives Ser.). (ENG., Illus.). 192p. per. 16.95 *(978-1-86189-354-3(X))* Reaktion Bks., Ltd. GBR. Dist: Chicago Distribution Ctr.

Wittmeier, Melissa. Delphine Gay, Mme de Girardin, le Vicomte de Launay. 2010. 340p. pap. *(978-3-8383-7178-8(X))* Lambert Academic Publishing.

Zweig, Stefan. Balzac, Dickens, Dostoevsky: Master Builders of the Spirit. 2009. (ENG.). 291p. pap. 34.95 *(978-1-4128-1047-0(7))* Transaction Pubs.

AUTHORS, GERMAN

Albrecht, Friedrich. Klaus Mann der Mittler: Studien aus vier Jahrzehnten. 2009. (Convergences Ser.). (GER.). 350p. pap. *(978-3-03911-744-4(0))* Lang, Peter.

Amthor, Wiebke & Lühe, Irmela von der, eds. Auf der Suche nach einem Weg: Neuer Forschungen zu Leben und Werk Klaus Manns. 2008. (Berliner Beiträge zur Literatur- und Kulturgeschichte Ser.). (GER., Illus.). 200p. pap. 57.95 *(978-3-631-56758-6(8))* Lang, Peter GmbH, Europaischer Verlag der Wissenschaften DEU. Dist: Lang, Peter.

Arnim, Ludwig Achim & Burwick, Roswitha. Werke und Briefwechsel: Historisch-Kritische Ausgabe. 2007. (GER., Illus.). XIV, 1161p. *(978-3-484-15602-9(3))* Verlag Max Niemeyer.

Arnim, Ludwig Achim von. Schaubahne I. Pietsch, Yvonne, ed. 2010. (GER., Illus.). VIII, 905p. *(978-3-484-15613-5(9))* Verlag Max Niemeyer.

Bartel, Heike & Boa, Elizabeth, eds. Pushing at Boundaries: Approaches to Contemporary German Women Writers from Karen Duve to Jenny Erpenbeck. 2006. (German Monitor Ser.: 64). (ENG & GER.). 183p. pap. 49.00 *(978-90-420-2051-1(2))* Rodopi.

Becker, Jurek. Jurek Beckers Neuigkeiten. (GER.). *(978-3-612-26646-0(2))* Econ-Verlag GmbH DEU. Dist: International Bk. Import Service, Inc.

Beier, Ulli & Omodele, Remi. Weighing the Cost of Pin-Making: Ulli Beier in Conversations. 2011. ***(978-1-59221-859-2(8))***; 276p. pap. ***(978-1-59221-860-8(1))*** Africa World Pr.

Benjamin, Walter & Adorno, Gretel. Correspondence 1930-1940. Lonitz, Henri & Godde, Christoph, eds. Honban, Weiland, tr. from GER. 2008. (ENG., Illus.). 336p. 19.95 *(978-0-7456-3669-6(1))* Polity Pr. GBR. Dist: Wiley, John & Sons, Inc.

Bergmann, Ulrike. Die Mesalliance: Georg Forster: Weltumsegler - Therese Forster: Schriftstellerin. 2008. (GER.). 300p. *(978-3-940111-54-8(6))* Buchergilde, Edition, GmbH.

Beutin, Heidi & Beutin, Wolfgang, eds. Ernst Barlach (1870-1938) Sein Leben, sein Schaffen, seine Verfolgung in der NS-Diktatur. 2009. (Bremer Beiträge zur Literatur- und Ideengeschichte Ser.). (GER.). 298p. pap. 64.95 *(978-3-631-58817-8(8))* Lang, Peter GmbH, Europaischer Verlag der Wissenschaften DEU. Dist: Lang, Peter.

Biographiq. Richard Wagner - Total Artwork & Beyond (Biography) 2008. 64p. pap. 9.99 *(978-1-59986-383-2(9)*, Biographiq) Filiquarian Publishing, LLC.

Boll, Heinrich. What's to Become of the Boy? Or, Something to Do with Books. Vennewitz, Leila, tr. from GER. 2011. (ENG.). 96p. pap. 14.95 *(978-1-61219-001-3(4))* Melville Hse. Publishing.

Brecht, Martin & Brecht, Christoph. Johann Valentin Andreae 1586-1654: Eine Biographie. 2008. (GER., Illus.). 389p. (C). 68.00 *(978-3-525-55334-3(X))* Vandenhoeck & Ruprecht GmbH & Co. KG DEU. Dist: ISD.

Brown, Hume Peter. The Youth of Goethe. 2007. 188p. (ENG.). 96.99 *(978-1-4280-7652-5(2))*; per. 89.99 *(978-1-4280-7636-5(0))* IndyPublish.com.

Brown, Peter D. G. Oskar Panizza & the Love Council: A History of the Scandalous Play on Stage & in Court, with the Complete Text in English & a Biography of the Author. 2010. (ENG., Illus.). 292p. pap. 49.95 *(978-0-7864-4273-7(5))* McFarland & Co., Inc. Pubs.

Brun, Friederike. Friederike Brun Reader: Supplement to an Encyclopedia of German Women Writers. Keith-Smith, Brian, ed. 2006. 256p. *(978-0-7734-5531-3(0))* Mellen, Edwin Pr., The.

Bunners, Christian. Paul Gerhardt: Weg - Werk - Wirkung. 2007. (GER.). 320p. (C). 41.00 *(978-3-525-55781-5(7))* Vandenhoeck & Ruprecht GmbH & Co. KG DEU. Dist: ISD.

Bunzel, Wolfgang. "Die Welt Umwälzen" Bettine Von Arnim Geb. Brentano (1785-1859) 2009. (Illus.). 126p. *(978-3-9811109-7-5(8))* Freies Deutsches Hochstift, Frankfurter Goethe-Museum.

Carl, Johanna. The Younger German Novelists: A Critique of Works Written During the First Postwar Decade, 1945-1955. 2011. 306p. 48.95 ***(978-1-258-10313-2(3))*** Literary Licensing, LLC.

Carlyle, Thomas. Life of Friedrich Schiller. 2009. 384p. pap. *(978-0-217-50340-2(3))*; 386p. pap. *(978-0-217-01255-3(8))* Books LLC.

Cartmell, J. W., ed. Goethe's Boyhood: Taken from the First Three Books of Autobiography. 2011. (GER & ENG.). 176p. pap. 24.99 *(978-0-521-16952-3(6))* Cambridge Univ. Pr.

Celan, Paul & Bachmann, Ingeborg. Correspondence. Hoban, Wieland, tr. from GER. 2010. (SB-the German List Ser.). (Illus.). 373p. 24.95 *(978-1-906497-44-6(3))* Seagull Bks. GBR. Dist: Chicago Distribution Ctr.

Celan, Paul & Shmueli, Ilana. The Correspondence of Paul Celan & Ilana Shmueli. Gillespie, Susan H., tr. from GER. 2011. (Illus.). 280p. pap. 19.95 *(978-1-931357-89-0(7))* Sheep Meadow Pr., The.

Clarke, David & De Winde, Arne, eds. Reinhard Jirgl: Perspektiven, Lesarten, Kontexte. 2007. (German Monitor Ser.: 65). (GER.). 282p. 75.00 *(978-90-420-2137-2(3))* Rodopi.

Conterno, Chiara. Metamorfosi Della Fuga: La Ricerca Dell'assoluto Nella Lirica Di Nelly Sachs. 2010. (ITA.). 351p. *(978-88-8098-282-1(6))* Unipress.

Dü, et al. Wovon ich schreibe: Eine kleine Poetik des Lebens. 2009. (GER.). 188p. *(978-3-8321-8088-1(5))* DuMont.

Döring, Detlef, et al, eds. 1731-1733: Unter Einschluss des Briefwechsels von Luise Adelgunde Victorie Gottsched. 2008. (GER.). XLVI, 685p. 335.00 *(978-3-11-020306-6(5))* De Gruyter, Walter Inc.

—1734-1735: Unter Einschluß des Briefwechsels von Luise Adelgunde Victorie Gottsched. 2009. (GER.). XLVIII, 550p. 321.00 *(978-3-11-021561-8(6))* De Gruyter, Walter Inc.

—1736-1737: Unter Einschluß des Briefwechsels von Luise Adelgunde Victorie Gottsched. 2010. (GER.). XLVIII, 674p. 321.00 ***(978-3-11-023292-9(8))*** De Gruyter, Walter Inc.

—1738- Juni 1739: Unter Einschluß des Briefwechsels von Luise Adelgunde Victorie Gottsched. 2011. (GER.). LII, 580p. 321.00 ***(978-3-11-025864-6(1))*** De Gruyter, Walter Inc.

Dobat, Klaus-Dieter. Musik Als Romantische Illusion: Eine Untersuchung Zur Bedeutung der Musikvorstellung E. T. A. Hoffmanns Für Sein Literarisches Werk. (Studien zur deutschen Literatur Ser.). (GER.). VII, 309p. 150.00 ***(978-3-11-184658-3(X))*** De Gruyter, Walter Inc.

Döring, Jörg & Joch, Markus, eds. Alfred Andersch 'revisited' Werkbiographische Studien im Zeichen der Sebald-Debatte. 2011. (GER., VI, 384p. Illus.). 210.00 ***(978-3-11-026827-0(2))***; 140.00 ***(978-3-11-026809-6(4))*** De Gruyter, Walter Inc.

Döscher, Hans-Jürgen. „Kampf gegen das Judenthum": Gustav Stille (1845-1920) Antisemit im deutschen Kaiserreich. 2008. (Illus.). 173p. pap. *(978-3-938690-90-1(9))* Veitl, Friedrich Metropol Friedrich Veitl-Verlag.

Ebers, Georg. The Story of My Life: From Childhood to Manhood. 2007. (ENG.). 278p. pap. 21.99 *(978-1-4264-1672-9(5))*; 270p. pap. 23.99 *(978-1-4264-1760-3(8))* BiblioBazaar.

Eckermann, Johann Peter. Conversations of Goethe with Eckermann & Soret. Oxenford, John, tr. 2011. (Cambridge Library Collection - Philosophy Ser.). (ENG.). 454p. pap. 34.99 ***(978-1-108-04091-4(8))***; 452p. pap. 32.99 ***(978-1-108-04092-1(6))*** Cambridge Univ. Pr.

Emmerich, Wolfgang & Leistner, Bernd. Literarisches Chemnitz: Autoren, Werke, Tendenzen. 2008. (GER., Illus.). 159p. *(978-3-910186-68-2(8))* Heimatland Sachsen, Verlag, GmbH Chemnitz.

Fontane, Theodor & Lepel, Bernhard von. Der Briefwechsel: Kritische Ausgabe Band 1 und 2. Radecke, Gabriele, ed. (Schriften der Theodor Fontane Gesellschaft Ser.).Tr. of Theodor Fontane & Bernhard von Lepel: the Correspondence. (GER.). XXVIII, 1430p. 734.00 ***(978-3-11-179487-7(3))*** De Gruyter, Walter Inc.

Fontane, Theodor, et al. Der Briefwechsel: Kritische Ausgabe Band 1 und 2. 2006. (Schriften der Theodor Fontane Gesellschaft Ser.: Vol. 5).Tr. of Theodor Fontane & Bernhard von Lepel: the Correspondence. (GER., Illus.). XXVIII, 1430p. 461.00 *(978-3-11-016354-4(3))* De Gruyter, Walter Inc.

Francke, Gotthilf August. Hertzliebe Mama: Briefe aus Jenaer Studientagen 1719-1720. Maller, Thomas et al, eds. (GER.). XIX, 170p. 210.00 ***(978-3-11-183551-8(0))*** De Gruyter, Walter Inc.

Gallas, Helga & Heuser, Magdalene, eds. Untersuchungen zum Roman von Frauen Um 1800. (Untersuchungen zur deutschen Literaturgeschichte Ser.). (GER.). VI, 219p. 210.00 ***(978-3-11-186211-8(9))*** De Gruyter, Walter Inc.

Gansel, Carsten & Walenski, Tanja. Erinnerung als Aufgabe? Dokumentation des II. und III. Schriftstellerkongresses in der DDR 1950 und 1952. Formen der Erinnerung 31. 2008. (Formen der Erinnerung Ser.). (GER., Illus.). 684p. (C). 104.00 *(978-3-89971-406-7(7))* Vandenhoeck & Ruprecht GmbH & Co. KG DEU. Dist: ISD.

Das geistliche Schrifttum des Spätmittelalters. 2011.Tr. of Religious Literature of the Late Middle Ages. (GER.). XXVIII, 880p. ***(978-3-11-174163-5(X))***; 352p. *(978-3-598-24994-5(2))* Saur, K. G. Verlag GmbH & Co.

Ghibellino, Ettore. Goethe & Anna Amalia: A Forbidden Love? Farrelly, Dan, tr. from GER. 2007. (ENG., Illus.). 360p. pap. 49.95 *(978-1-904505-24-2(4))* Carysfort Pr. IRL. Dist: Dufour Editions, Inc.

Gilleir, A. & Philipsen, B., eds. Duitstalige literatuur Na 1945: Deel 1: Duitsland 1945-1989. 2006. (ENG.). 254p. (C). pap. 30.00 *(978-90-429-1763-7(6))* Peeters Pubs. & Booksellers BEL. Dist: Brown, David Bk. Co., The.

—Duitstalige literatuur Na 1945: Deel 2: Duitsland na 1989, Oostenrijk en Zwitserland. 2006. (ENG.). 261p. (C). pap. 33.00 *(978-90-429-1764-4(4))* Peeters Pubs. & Booksellers BEL. Dist: Brown, David Bk. Co., The.

Gillett, Robert. Hubert Fichte: Eine kritische Auswahlbibliographie. 2007. (GER.). 256p. 109.95 *(978-0-7734-5165-0(X))* Mellen, Edwin Pr., The.

Goethe, Catharine Eliz. Goethes Mother Correspondence of Cathari. 2006. pap. 28.95 *(978-1-4286-5697-0(9))* Kessinger Publishing, LLC.

Gottsched, Johann Christoph. Briefwechsel: Unter Einschluss des Briefwechsels Von Luise Adelgunde Victorie Gottsched. 2007. (GER.). LXVIII, 568p. 279.00 *(978-3-11-018381-8(1))* De Gruyter, Walter Inc.

Gottzmann, Carola L. & Hörner, Petra. Lexikon der deutschsprachigen Literatur des Baltikums und St. Petersburgs: Vom Mittelalter bis zur Gegenwart. 2007.Tr. of Lexicon of German-language literature of the Baltic States & St. Petersburg. (GER., Illus.). XII, 1476p. 503.00 *(978-3-11-019338-1(8))* De Gruyter, Walter Inc.

Gottzmann, Carola L. & Hörner, Petra. Lexikon der deutschsprachigen Literatur des Baltikums und St. Petersburgs: Vom Mittelalter bis zur Gegenwart. 2012.Tr. of Lexicon of German-language literature of the Baltic States & St. Petersburg. (GER., Illus.). XII, 1476p. E-Book 755.00 ***(978-3-11-182206-8(0))*** De Gruyter, Walter Inc.

Grange, William. The A to Z of Postwar German Literature. 2010. (A to Z Guide Ser.). (ENG.). 376p. pap. 34.45 *(978-0-8108-7618-7(3))* Scarecrow Pr., Inc.

—Historical Dictionary of German Literature To 1945. 2010. (Historical Dictionaries of Literature & the Arts Ser.). (ENG.). 388p. 80.00 *(978-0-8108-6771-0(0))* Scarecrow Pr., Inc.

—Historical Dictionary of Postwar German Literature. 2009. (Historical Dictionaries of Literature & the Arts Ser.). (ENG.). 370p. 90.00 *(978-0-8108-5965-4(3))* Scarecrow Pr., Inc.

Grass, Günter & nter. Unterwegs Von Deutschland Nach Deutschland: Tagebuch 1990. 2009. (GER., Illus.). 255p. *(978-3-86521-881-0(4))* Steidl, Gerhard Druckerei und Verlag.

Gronicka, Andre Von. Henry Von Heiseler A RussoGerman Writer. 2006. pap. 26.95 *(978-1-4286-6138-7(7))* Kessinger Publishing, LLC.

Haarmann, Hermann. Berlin Im Kopf - Arbeit Am Berlin-Mythos: Exil und Innere Emigration 1933 Bis 1945. 2008. (GER.). 157p. pap. *(978-3-936962-69-7(3))* Bostelmann, Jurgen u. Prof. Dr. Klaus Siebenhaar.

Hagen, Eva Maria. Eva und der Wolf. (GER.). *(978-3-612-26643-9(8))* Econ-Verlag GmbH DEU. Dist: International Bk. Import Service, Inc.

Härtl, Heinz, ed. Briefwechsel III (1805-1806) 2011. (GER.). 1104p. 308.00 *(978-3-11-025069-5(1))* De Gruyter, Walter Inc.

Heidelberger-Leonard, Irene. The Philosopher of Auschwitz: Jean Amery & Living with the Holocaust. Bell, Anthea, tr. 2010. (ENG., Illus.). 304p. 35.00 *(978-1-84885-150-4(2))* I. B. Tauris & Co., Ltd. GBR. Dist: Macmillan.

Heine, Heinrich. Ludwig Börne: A Memorial. Sammons, Jeffrey L., tr. from GER. & intro. by. 2006. (Studies in German Literature Linguistics & Culture Ser.). 179p. 65.00 *(978-1-57113-342-7(9))* Camden Hse.

Helmridge-Marsillian, Veronique. The Heroism of Love in Hoffmannswaldau's Heldenbriefe. (Studien zur deutschen Literatur Ser.). (ENG.). VII, 269p. 210.00 ***(978-3-11-185903-3(7))*** De Gruyter, Walter Inc.

Herzog, Todd, et al. Rebirth of a Culture: Jewish Identity & Jewish Writing in Germany & Austria Today. 2008. 198p. (C). 75.00 *(978-1-84545-511-8(8))* Berghahn Bks., Inc.

Heuer, Renate & Boelke-Fabian, Andrea. Lexikon Deutsch-Jüdischer Autoren. 2009. (GER.). XXV, 427p. ***(978-3-598-22696-0(9))*** Saur, K. G. Verlag GmbH & Co.

Hobi, Caroline. Willibald Alexis: Rube Ist Die Erste Biirgerpflicht. (GER.). 365p. pap. 75.95 *(978-3-03911-230-2(9))* Lang, Peter Publishing, Inc.

Hucke, Karl-Heinz. Jene Scheu vor allem Mercantilischen: Schillers Arbeits- und Finanzplan. (Studien und Texte zur Sozialgeschichte der Literatur Ser.). (GER.). VIII, 93p. 210.00 ***(978-3-11-186295-8(X))*** De Gruyter, Walter Inc.

Jean Paul. Hesperus; or, Forty-Five Dog-Post-Days / a Biography from the German of Jean Paul Friedrich Richter; Tr by Charles T Brooks. 2006. 488p. per. 29.99 *(978-1-4255-5486-6(5))*; (ENG.). 532p. per. 29.99 *(978-1-4255-5952-6(2))* MPublishing.

Juers, Evelyn. House of Exile: The Lives & Times of Heinrich Mann & Nelly Kroeger-Mann, 1 vol. (ENG., Illus.). 400p. 2012. pap. 18.00 ***(978-0-374-53341-0(5))*** 2011. 30.00 *(978-0-374-17316-6(8))* Farrar, Straus & Giroux.

Kasties, Bert. Walter Hasenclever: Eine Biographie der deutschen Moderne. (Studien und Texte zur Sozialgeschichte der Literatur Ser.). (GER.). 420p. 210.00 ***(978-3-11-186667-3(X))*** De Gruyter, Walter Inc.

Keller, Christoph. The Best Dancer. Gallup, Alison, tr. from GER. 2009.Tr. of beste Tanzer. (ENG., Illus.). 303p. pap. 16.95 *(978-1-932010-22-0(X))* Ooligan Pr.

Kertscher, Hans-Joachim, ed. G. A. Bürger und J. W. L. Gleim. (Hallesche Beiträge zur Europäischen Aufklärung Ser.). (GER.). XXVI, 264p. 210.00 ***(978-3-11-187587-3(3))*** De Gruyter, Walter Inc.

Killy. Literaturlexikon. Band 7. Kräm - Marp. 2nd ed. 2010. (GER.). IX, 705p. 347.00 *(978-3-11-022048-3(2))* De Gruyter, Walter Inc.

Killy. Literaturlexikon. Band 8. Marq - Or: Autoren und Werke des deutschsprachigen Kulturraumes. 2nd ed. 2010. (GER.). IX, 739p. 347.00 *(978-3-11-022046-9(6))* De Gruyter, Walter Inc.

Killy. Literaturlexikon. Band 9. Os - Roq: Autoren und Werke des deutschsprachigen Kulturraumes. 2nd ed. 2010. (GER.). IX, 714p. 347.00 *(978-3-11-022044-5(X))* De Gruyter, Walter Inc.

King, Alasdair. Hans Magnus Enzensberger: Writing, Media, Democracy. 2007. (Cultural History & Literary Imagination Ser.: Vol. 10). 357p. pap. 81.95 *(978-3-03910-902-9(2))* Lang, Peter Publishing, Inc.

Kirchhoff, Bodo. Legenden Um Den Eigenen Körper: Frankfurter Vorlesungen. (GER., Illus.). 182p. *(978-3-518-11944-0(3))* Suhrkamp Verlag.

Knopf, Sabine. Katharina Kippenberg: Herrin der Insel. 2010. (GER., Illus.). 184p. pap. *(978-3-86729-051-7(2))* Heydick, Erika Sax-Verlag Beucha.

Köhler, Astrid. Brückenschläge: DDR-Autoren vor und nach der Wiedervereinigung. 2007. (GER.). 255p. (C). 41.00 *(978-3-525-20853-3(7))* Vandenhoeck & Ruprecht GmbH & Co. KG DEU. Dist: ISD.

Kosch, Wilhelm, et al. Deutsches Literatur-Lexikon: Das 20. Jahrhundert: Biographisches-Bibliographisches Handbuch. (GER., Illus.). 2008. XV, 304p. *(978-3-908255-11-6(2))* 2007. XIVp. *(978-3-908255-10-9(4))* Saur, K. G. Verlag GmbH & Co.

—Deutsches Literatur-Lexikon. Achtundzwanzigster Band: Biographisches und bibliographisches Handbuch / Walsh - Wedekind. 3rd ed. (GER.). 2008. XVI, 341p. *(978-3-908255-43-7(0))* 2007. XVI, 345p. *(978-3-908255-27-7(9))* Saur, K. G. Verlag GmbH & Co.

Kühlmann, Wilhelm, et al, eds. Die Literatur der Frühen Neuzeit in Deutschland 1520-1620. Verfasserlexikon: Aal, Johannes-Castellio, Sebastian, Band 1. 2011. (GER.). 320p. 224.00 *(978-3-11-022391-0(0))* De Gruyter, Walter Inc.

Kühlmann, Wilhelm, et al. Fri - Hap. 2nd ed. 2009. (GER.). XXII, 655p. 347.00 *(978-3-11-021389-8(3))* De Gruyter, Walter Inc.

—Killy Literaturlexikon 1. A - Blu: Autoren und Werke des deutschsprachigen Kulturraums, Band 1. 2nd ed. 2008. (GER.). XLIV, 605p. 277.00 *(978-3-11-018962-9(3))* De Gruyter, Walter Inc.

—Killy Literaturlexikon 3. Dep - Fre: Autoren und Werke des deutschsprachigen Kulturraums. 2nd ed. 2008. (GER.). VIII, 585p. 347.00 *(978-3-11-020376-9(6))*; VIII, 596p. 347.00 *(978-3-11-020375-2(8))* De Gruyter, Walter Inc.

—Killy Literaturlexikon Bd.5. 2nd ed. 2009. (GER.). VIII, 652p. 347.00 *(978-3-11-021391-1(5))* De Gruyter, Walter Inc.

—Killy Literaturlexikon Bd.6. 2nd ed. 2009. (GER.). IX, 670p. 347.00 *(978-3-11-021393-5(1))* De Gruyter, Walter Inc.

Lanchester, John. Family Romance: A Love Story. 2008. (ENG., Illus.). 384p. (gr. 12-18). 16.00 *(978-0-14-311295-2(3)*, Penguin (Non-Classics)) Penguin Group (USA) Inc.

Lewes, George Henry. The Life & Works of Goethe: With Sketches of His Age & Contemporaries, Vol. 1. 2006. 456p. per. 29.99 *(978-1-4255-5042-4(8))* MPublishing.

—The Life & Works of Goethe: With Sketches of His Age & Contemporaries, Vol. 2. 2006. 504p. per. 29.99 *(978-1-4255-5642-6(6))* MPublishing.

Lewinsky, Tamar. Displaced Poets: Jiddische Schriftsteller im Nachkriegsdeutschland, 1945-1951. Jüdische Religion, Geschichte und Kultur (JRGK) 2008. (Judische Religion, Geschichte und Kultur (JRGK) Ser.). (ENG & GER., Illus.). 288p. (C). 84.00 *(978-3-525-56997-9(1))* Vandenhoeck & Ruprecht GmbH & Co. KG DEU. Dist: ISD.

Lubbe, Fredericka van der. Martin Aedler & the High Dutch Minerva: The First German Grammar for the English. 2007. (Duisburg Papers on Research in Language & Culture Ser.). (HEB, LAT, MUL, GER & ENG., Illus.). 312p. pap. 59.95 *(978-3-631-56287-1(X))* Lang, Peter Publishing, Inc.

Ludwig, Janine. Heiner Müller, Ikone West: Das dramatische Werk Heiner Müllers in der Bundesrepublik - Rezeption und Wirkung. 2009. (GRE & GER., Illus.). 374p. 86.95 *(978-3-631-58854-3(2))* Lang, Peter GmbH, Europaischer Verlag der Wissenschaften DEU. Dist: Lang, Peter.

Lutz, Wilfrid. Ludwig Röder Im Strudel der Zeit: Biographie. 2009. (GER.). 140p. *(978-3-89754-310-2(9))* Roll, J.H., Verlag, GmbH.

Maldonado Alemán, Manuel, ed. Literatura e identidad Cultural: Representaciones del pasado en la narrative alemana a partir De 1945. 2009. (SPA.). 473p. pap. *(978-3-0343-0094-0(8))* Lang, Peter.

Mason, Eudo Colecestra. Rilke, Europe, & the English-Speaking World. 2010. (ENG.). 281p. pap. 23.99 *(978-0-521-16837-3(6))* Cambridge Univ. Pr.

Mauthner, Martin. German Writers in French Exile 1933-1940. 2007. (Illus.). 260p. 75.00 *(978-0-85303-540-4(7))*; pap. 32.95 *(978-0-85303-541-1(5))* Vallentine Mitchell Pubs. GBR. Dist: International Specialized Bk. Services.

Meysenbug, Malwida von. Memoiren einer Idealistin. 2009. 308p. 25.99 *(978-1-103-30566-7(2))*; pap. 19.99 *(978-1-103-30561-2(1))* BiblioBazaar.

Meysenbug, Malwida von & Wiggershaus, Renate. Memoiren einer Idealistin. (GER., Illus.). 278p. *(978-3-89741-007-7(9))* Helmer, Ulrike.

Miederhoff, Thorsten. Man erspare es mir, mein Juristenherz Auszuschütten: Dr. iur. Kurt Tucholsky (1890-1935) 2008. (Rechtshistorische Reihe Ser.). (GER., Illus.). 302p. pap. 74.95 *(978-3-631-57581-9(5))* Lang, Peter GmbH, Europaischer Verlag der Wissenschaften DEU. Dist: Lang, Peter.

Misselwitz, Charlotte & Siebeck, Cornelia, eds. Dissonant Memories Fragmented Present: Exchanging Young Discourses between Israel & Germany. 2011. (ENG.). 232p. pap. 39.95 *(978-3-8376-1273-8(2))* Transcript Verlag DEU. Dist: Transaction Pubs.

Mitchell, Allan. The Devil's Captain: Ernst Jünger in Nazi Paris, 1941-1944. 2011. (Illus.). 140p. 49.95 *(978-0-85745-114-9(6))* Berghahn Bks., Inc.

Das Mittelalter: Autoren und Werke Nach Themenkreisen und Gattungen. 2010.Tr. of Man & God. (GER.). XXXI, 545p. *(978-3-598-24991-4(8))* Saur, K. G. Verlag GmbH & Co.

Mood, John. A New Reading of Rilke's Elegies: Affirming the Unity of Life-and-death. 2009. 136p. 99.95 *(978-0-7734-3864-4(5))* Mellen, Edwin Pr., The.

Niemann, Arnold. Paul Gerhardt ohne Legende: Untersuchungen zum gesellschaftlichen Umfeld Paul Gerhardts. 2009. (GER., Illus.). 360p. (C). 68.00 *(978-3-89971-541-5(1))* Vandenhoeck & Ruprecht GmbH & Co. KG DEU. Dist: ISD.

Nieradka, Magali Laure. Die Hauptstadt der deutschen Literatur: Sanary-sur-Mer als Ort des Exils deutschsprachiger Schriftsteller. 2010. (Formen der Erinnerung Ser.). (GER., Illus.). 300p. (C). 63.00 *(978-3-89971-792-1(9))* Vandenhoeck & Ruprecht GmbH & Co. KG DEU. Dist: ISD.

Nolte, Andreas, ed. Ich stimme fuer Minetta Street. Festschrift aus Anlass des 100. Geburtstags von Mascha Kaleko. 2007. (Illus.). 210p. per. 10.00 *(978-0-9770731-8-4(1))* Proverbium.

Oppeln-Bronikowski, Friedrich-Wilhelm von. Friedrich Von Oppeln-Bronikowski (1873-1936) Offizier, Übersetzer, Schriftsteller, Journalist und Streiter Gegen Den Antisemitismus in der Weimarer Republik: Sein Leben und Wirken. 2009. (GER., Illus.). 219p. *(978-3-7980-0581-5(8))* Starke & Dormi Publications.

Palmier, Jean-Michel & Perrier, Florent. Walter Benjamin: Le Chiffonnier, L'ange et le Petit Bossu: Esthétique et Politique Chez Walter Benjamin. 2006. (FRE., Illus.). 916p. (C). pap. 59.00 ***(978-2-252-03591-7(9))*** Klincksieck, Editions FRA. Dist: ISD.

Peitsch, Helmut. Nachkriegsliteratur 1945 - 1989. 2009. (Schriften des Erich Maria Remarque-Archivs Ser.). (GER.). 404p. (C). 74.00 *(978-3-89971-730-3(9))* Vandenhoeck & Ruprecht GmbH & Co. KG DEU. Dist: ISD.

Piper, Andrew. Johann Wolfgang Von Goethe. 2010. (Brief Lives Ser.). (ENG.). 112p. pap. 15.95 *(978-1-84391-910-0(9))* Hesperus Pr. GBR. Dist: Independent Pubs. Group.

Plachta, Bodo, ed. Literarische Zusammenarbeit.Tr. of Literary Collaboration. (GER.). IX, 316p. 210.00 ***(978-3-11-179573-7(X))*** De Gruyter, Walter Inc.

Prandi, Julie. The Poetry of the Self-Taught: An Eighteenth-Century Phenomenon. 2008. 212p. (C). 68.95 *(978-1-4331-0251-6(X))* Lang, Peter Publishing, Inc.

Rajewska-Perzynska, Agnieszka. Rolf Bongs: Dissoziation eines Schriftstellers im Spannungsfeld zwischen Selbststilisierung und Anpassung. 2009. (Studien zur deutschen und europäischen Literatur des 19. und 20. Jahrhunderts Ser.). (GER.). 304p. 72.95 *(978-3-631-59375-2(9))* Lang, Peter GmbH, Europaischer Verlag der Wissenschaften DEU. Dist: Lang, Peter.

Rasch, Wolfgang. Karl Gutzkow: Erinnerungen, Berichte und Urteile seiner Zeitgenossen. Eine Dokumentation. 2011. (GER.). 210.00 ***(978-3-11-020252-6(2))*** De Gruyter, Walter Inc.

Reich, Wilhelm. Der Einbruch der Sexuellen Zwangsmoral. (GER.). 390p. pap. *(978-3-462-02471-5(X))* Kiepenheuer & Witsch GmbH & Company KG DEU. Dist: International Bk. Import Service, Inc.

Remarque, Erich-Maria. Ein Militanter Pazifist: Texte & Interviews, 1929-1966. (GER.). 495p. pap. *(978-3-462-02732-7(8))* Kiepenheuer & Witsch GmbH & Company KG DEU. Dist: International Bk. Import Service, Inc.

Richter, Ludwig. Der Briefwechsel zwischen Bohuslav Balbín und Christian Weise 1678-1688: Lateinisch-deutsche Ausgabe. Richter, Ludwig, ed. Rautenstrauch, Gunther, tr. from LAT. 2010. (Forschungen zur Geschichte und Kultur des ostlichen Mitteleuropa Ser.). (GER & LAT., Illus.). 339p. (C). 74.00 *(978-3-515-09688-1(4))* Steiner, Franz Verlag Wiesbaden GmbH DEU. Dist: Brown, David Bk. Co., The.

Rickels, Laurence A. Aberrations of Mourning. 2011. 304p. pap. 25.00 *(978-0-8166-7595-1(3))* Univ. of Minnesota Pr.

Rieder, Bernadette. Unter Beweis: Das Leben: Sechs Autobiographien Deutschsprachiger SchriftstellerInnen Aus Israel. 2008. (GER., Illus.). 395p. (C). 68.00 *(978-3-89971-460-9(1))* Vandenhoeck & Ruprecht GmbH & Co. KG DEU. Dist: ISD.

Riegel, Christian. Twenty-First Century Canadian Writers, 334. 2007. (Dictionary of Literary Biography Ser.: Vol. 334). (ENG., Illus.). 352p. 315.00 *(978-0-7876-8152-4(0))* Cengage Gale.

Rilke, Rainer Maria. Letters on God & Letters to a Young Woman. Kidder, Annemarie S., tr. from GER. 2012. (ENG.). 88p. pap. 14.95 ***(978-0-8101-2740-1(7))*** Northwestern Univ. Pr.

—Letters to a Young Poet. Harman, Mark, tr. from GER. 2011. Orig. Title: Briefe an Einen Jungen Dichter. (ENG.). 112p. 15.95 *(978-0-674-05245-1(5))* Harvard Univ. Pr.

—Letters to a Young Poet. Snell, Reginald, tr. 2011. Orig. Title: Briefe an Einen Jungen Dichter. 78p. pap. 4.85 ***(978-1-61427-017-1(1))*** Martino Publishing.

Roback, A. A. Story of Yiddish Literature. 2006. pap. 37.95 *(978-1-4286-3627-9(7))* Kessinger Publishing, LLC.

Ronell, Avital. Dictations: On Haunted Writing. 2006. 240p. per. 26.00 *(978-0-252-07349-6(5))* Univ. of Illinois Pr.

Rosenkranz, Moses. Childhood: An Autobiographical Fragment. 2007. (Judaic Traditions in Literature, Music & Art Ser.). 227p. 24.95 *(978-0-8156-3178-1(2))* Syracuse Univ. Pr.

Russell, Peter. Johannes Brahms & Klaus Groth: The Biography of a Friendship. 2006. (Illus.). 206p. 110.00 *(978-0-7546-5544-2(X))* Ashgate Publishing Co.
SAYNER, Joanne. Women without a Past? German Autobiographical Writings & Fascism. 2007. (Genus Ser.: 8). 392p. per. 105.00 *(978-90-420-2228-7(0))* Rodopi.
Schö, et al. Ernst Jünger - Albert Renger Patzsch. 2010. (GER., Illus.). 216p. pap. *(978-3-7705-4872-9(8))* Wilhelm/Fink#GmbH & Co. Verlags-KG.
Schade, Richard E. & Sevin, Dieter, eds. Practicing Progress: The Promise & Limitations of Enlightenment. Festschrift for John A. Mccarthy. 2007. (Internationale Forschungen Zur Allgemeinen und Vergleichenden Literaturwissenschaft Ser.: 106). 236p. per. 62.00 *(978-90-420-2146-4(2))* Rodopi.
Schmidt, Arno. Two Novels: The Stony Heart & B/Moondocks. Woods, John E., tr. 2011. (German & Austrian Literature Ser.).Tr. of Steinerne Herz & Kauff Auch Mare Crisium. (ENG.). 432p. pap. 16.95 *(978-1-56478-662-3(5)*, 478662) Dalkey Archive Pr.
Schulz, Karlheinz. Goethe: Eine Biographie in 16 Kapiteln. (GER., Illus.). 603p. *(978-3-15-009745-8(2))* Reclam, Philip jun., Verlag GmbH.
Sebald. Die Ringe des Saturn: Eine englische Wallfahrt. (GER., Illus.). 349p. pap. 29.95 *(978-3-596-13655-1(5))* Fischer Taschenbuch Verlag DEU. Dist: Distribooks, Inc.
Sebald, W. G. The Emergence of Memory: Conversations with W. G. Sebald. Schwartz, Lynne Sharon, ed. 2010. (ENG.). 176p. pap. 15.95 *(978-1-58322-915-6(9))* Seven Stories Pr.
Sebald, W.G. History - Memory - Trauma. Denham, Scott & McCulloh, Mark, eds. 2006. (Interdisciplinary German Cultural Studies: Vol. 1). (ENG.). VII, 382p. 133.00 *(978-3-11-018274-3(2))* De Gruyter, Walter Inc.
Sebald, Winfried Georg. The Emergence of Memory: Conversations with W. G. Sebald. Schwartz, Lynne Sharon, ed. 2007. 176p. 23.95 *(978-1-58322-785-5(7))* Seven Stories Pr.
Selwyn, Pamela E. Everyday Life in the German Book Trade. 2008. (Illus.). xvi, 419p. pap. 31.95 *(978-0-271-02797-5(5))* Pennsylvania State Univ. Pr.
Sem - Var. 2nd ed. 2011. (GER.). IX, 793p. 347.00 *(978-3-11-022040-7(7))* De Gruyter, Walter Inc.
Shaw, LeRoy R. & Shaw, Leroy R. Witness of Deceit: Gerhart Hauptmann As Critic of Society. 2011. 138p. 40.95 ***(978-1-258-06004-6(3))*** Literary Licensing, LLC.
Shayne, Vic & Small, Martin. Remember Us: My Journey from the Shtetl Through the Holocaust. 2009. (ENG., Illus.). 336p. 24.95 *(978-1-60239-723-1(6)*, 239723) Skyhorse Publishing Co., Inc.
Sherman, Joseph, ed. Writers in Yiddish, 333. 2007. (Dictionary of Literary Biography Ser.). (ENG., Illus.). 480p. 315.00 *(978-0-7876-8151-7(2))* Cengage Gale.
Sherman, Joseph & Estraikh, G. David Bergelson: From Modernism to Socialist Realism. 2007. (Legenda Studies in Yiddish Ser.). (ENG., Illus.). 250p. (C). 89.50 *(978-1-905981-12-0(0))* European Humanities Research Ctr. GBR. Dist: Brown, David Bk. Co., The.
Steiger, Johann Anselm. Geh' Aus, Mein Herz, und Suche Freud' Paul Gerhardts Sommerlied und die Gelehrsamkeit der Barockzeit (Naturkunde, Emblematik, Theologie) 2007. (GER., Illus.). X, 146p. 35.00 *(978-3-11-019440-1(6))* De Gruyter, Walter Inc.
Stephenson, Barry. Veneration & Revolt: Hermann Hesse & Swabian Pietism. 2009. (Editions SR Ser.). (ENG.). 300p. 85.00 *(978-1-55458-149-8(4))* Wilfrid Laurier Univ. Pr. CAN. Dist: Univ. of Toronto Pr.
Stern, Frank, ed. Feuchtwanger und Exil: Glaube und Kultur, 1933-1945: "Der Tag Wird Kommen" 2011. (Feuchtwanger Studies). (GER.). 509p. pap. 86.95 ***(978-3-0343-0188-6(X))*** Lang, Peter AG GBR. Dist: Lang, Peter.
Stieler, Hilde. Monika Molander: Supplement to an Encyclopedia of German Women Writers. Keith-Smith, Brian, ed. 2006. 224p. *(978-0-7734-5529-0(9))* Mellen, Edwin Pr., The.
Tebben, Karin. Tannhauser: Biographie einer Legende. 2010. (GER., Illus.). 247p. (C). 68.00 *(978-3-525-20867-0(7))* Vandenhoeck & Ruprecht GmbH & Co. KG DEU. Dist: ISD.
Trunk, Yehiel Yeshaia. Poyln: My Life Within Jewish Life in Poland, Sketches & Images. Wróbel, Piotr & Shapiro, Robert M., eds. Clarke, Anna, tr. from YID. 2007. (ENG., Illus.). 152p. *(978-0-8020-9330-1(2))* Univ. of Toronto Pr.
Uther, Hans-Jö & rg. Handbuch zu den 'Kinder- und Hausmärchen' der Brüder Grimm: Entstehung - Wirkung - Interpretation. 2008. (GER., Illus.). XVI, 644p. 81.00 *(978-3-11-019441-8(4))* De Gruyter, Walter Inc.
Vaupel, Angela. Zur Rezeption von Exilliteratur nd Lion Feuchtwangers Werk in Deutschland. (GER.). 280p. 67.95 *(978-3-03911-077-3(2))* Lang, Peter CHE. Dist: Lang, Peter Publishing, Inc.
Vickers, Julia. Lou Von Salomé: A Biography of the Woman Who Inspired Freud, Nietzsche & Rilke. 2008. (ENG., Illus.). 217p. pap. 39.95 *(978-0-7864-3606-4(9))* McFarland & Co., Inc. Pubs.
Völker, Martin A., ed. "Gebunden Sind Die Flugel Der Gedanken" Louise Brachmann (1777-1822) Supplement to an Encyclopedia of German Women Writers. 2006. 180p. *(978-0-7734-5533-7(7))* Mellen, Edwin Pr., The.
Wü, et al. Ich war immer verärgert, wenn ich ein Mädchen bekam: Thomas und Katia Mann als Eltern. 2010. (GER., Illus.). 378p. *(978-3-492-05283-2(5))* Piper Verlag GmbH.
Walkowiak, Maciej. Ernst Von Salomons Autobiographische Romane Als Literarische Selbstgestaltungsstrategien Im Kontext der Historisch-Politischen Semantik. (GER.). 379p. pap. 68.95 *(978-3-631-56863-7(0))* Lang, Peter GmbH, Europaischer Verlag der Wissenschaften DEU. Dist: Lang, Peter Publishing, Inc.
Weber, Christian. Max Kommerell: Eine intellektuelle Biographie. 2011.Tr. of Max Kommerell. Biography of an Intellectual. (GER., Illus.). X, 598p. 210.00 ***(978-3-11-214251-6(9))*** De Gruyter, Walter Inc.
Weidauer, Friedemann J. Gestus-Musik-Text Vol. 33: Gestus — Musik — Text (Gestus — Music — Text) Weidauer, Freidmann & Intl Brecht Society Staff, eds. 2008. (Brecht Yearbook Ser.). (GER & ENG., Illus.). 300p. pap. 40.00 *(978-0-9718963-6-9(4))* Univ. of Wisconsin Pr.
Weiss, Andrea. In the Shadow of the Magic Mountain: The Erika & Klaus Mann Story. 2008. (Illus.). 310p. 27.50 *(978-0-226-88672-5(7))* Univ. of Chicago Pr.
Weiss, Peter. Holderlin: A Play in Two Acts. 2010. (SB-the German List Ser.). (ENG.). 219p. 14.95 *(978-1-906497-72-9(9))* Seagull Bks. GBR. Dist: Chicago Distribution Ctr.
Wildencamp, Adriane. Seasons of Love: In Australia & Germany. (Illus.). 328p. pap. *(978-0-86806-665-3(6)*, Hale & Iremonger) GHR Pr., The.
Williams, Hermine Weigel. Therese Von Jakob Robinson: A Biographical Portrait. 2007. 277p. *(978-0-595-90010-7(0))* iUniverse, Inc.
Wolf, Yvonne, ed. Internationales Alfred-Doblin-Kolloquium Mainz 2005: Alfred Doblin Zwischen Institution und Provokation. (GER.). 338p. pap. 76.95 *(978-3-03911-148-0(5))* Lang, Peter Publishing, Inc.
Wozonig, Karin S. Die Literatin Betty Paoli: Weibliche Mobilität Im 19. Jahrhundert. (GER.). 221p. *(978-3-85409-306-0(3))* Locker, Erhard, Ges.mbH Verlag.
Zocco, Gianna. Sag an, mein Freund, die Ordnung der Unterwelt: Das Gilgamesch-Epos in Hans Henny Jahnns Fluß ohne Ufer. 2010. (Wiener Beiträge zu Komparatistik und Romanistik Ser.). 174p. 53.95 *(978-3-631-60265-2(0))* Lang, Peter GmbH, Europaischer Verlag der Wissenschaften DEU. Dist: Lang, Peter.
Zschokke, Heinrich. Autobiography of Heinrich Zschokke. 2009. 234p. pap. *(978-0-217-68644-0(3))* Books LLC.
—Autobiography of Heinrich Zschokke. 2007. (ENG.). 230p. 41.95 *(978-0-548-15485-4(6))*; pap. 26.95 *(978-1-4304-4913-3(6))* Kessinger Publishing, LLC.
2010/2011. 2010. (GER., Illus.). IX, 227p. pap. *(978-3-484-60568-8(5))* Verlag Max Niemeyer.
2010/2011: Band I: A - O. Band II: P - Z. 2010.Tr. of Karschner's Almanac of German Literature. (GER., Illus.). 1980p. 559.00 *(978-3-11-023029-1(1))* De Gruyter, Walter Inc.

AUTHORS, GREEK

Aristotle. Aristotle II: Posterior Analytics, Topica. Tredennick, Hugh & Forster, E. S., trs. 2011. 762p. 72.95 ***(978-1-258-03196-1(5))*** Literary Licensing, LLC.
Bita, Lili & Zaller, Robert. The Storm Rider: A Memoir. 2012. ***(978-1-935244-10-3(8))*** Somerset Hall Pr.
Blackwell, T. An Enquiry into the Life & Writings of Homer. 2007. (ENG.). 424p. 51.95 *(978-0-548-00733-4(0))* Kessinger Publishing, LLC.
Calotychos, Vangelis, ed. Manolis Anagnostakis: Poetry & Politics, Silence & Agency in Post-War Greece. 2012. (ENG., Illus.). 258p. (gr. 17). 70.00 ***(978-1-61147-465-7(5))*** Fairleigh Dickinson Univ. Pr.
Claudon, C. David. Homer's the Liad: A Study Guide. 2009. pap. *(978-1-61623-178-1(5))* Independent Pub.
Hornblower, Simon. Thucydides & Pindar: Historical Narrative & the World of Epinikian Poetry. 2006. (ENG., Illus.). 480p. pap. 55.00 *(978-0-19-929828-0(9))* Oxford Univ. Pr., Inc.
Kazantzakis, Nikos. The Selected Letters of Nikos Kazantzakis. 2011. (Princeton Modern Greek Studies). (ENG.). 960p. (C). 99.50 *(978-0-691-14702-4(7))* Princeton Univ. Pr.
Kivilo, Maarit. Early Greek Poets' Lives: The Shaping of the Tradition. 2010. xii, 270p. *(978-90-04-18615-6(8))* BRILL.
Landfester, M., ed. Dictionary of Greek & Latin Authors & Texts. 2009. (Brill's New Pauly - Supplements Ser.). *(978-90-04-16783-4(8))* BRILL.
Laurin, Joseph. Poets of Tragedy in Classical Athens. 2008. 304p. 35.00 *(978-1-4251-7653-2(4))* Trafford Publishing.
Martini, Clem. The Greek Playwright: What the First Dramatists Have to Say to Contemporary Playwrights. 2010. (ENG., Illus.). 136p. pap. 19.95 *(978-0-88754-875-8(X))* Playwrights Canada Pr. CAN. Dist: Consortium Bk. Sales & Distribution.
Mary, Lefkowitz. The Lives of the Greek Poets. 2012. 256p. pap. 32.95 ***(978-1-78093-089-3(5))*** Duckworth Publishers GBR. Dist: International Publishers Marketing.
Mike, Maire, et al. Allelographia Nikou Kavvadia - M. Karagatse. 2010. (GRE., Illus.). 142p. *(978-960-325-927-5(6))* Agra, Ekdoseis, Stavros Petsopoulos.
Mossé, Claude. Démosthène, Ou, Les Ambiguïtés de la Politique. (FRE., Illus.). 159p. *(978-2-200-21169-1(4))* Armand, Colin.
Myrsiades, Kostas. Reading Homer: Film & Text. 2009. 258p. 39.99 *(978-0-8386-4219-1(5))*; (ENG.). 56.50 *(978-1-61147-423-7(X))* Fairleigh Dickinson Univ. Pr.
Owens, Ron. Solon of Athens: Poet, Philosopher, Soldier, Statesman. 2010. (ENG.). 399p. 89.95 *(978-1-84519-403-1(9))* Sussex Academic Pr. GBR. Dist: International Specialized Bk. Services.
Reydams-Schils, Gretchen. Thinking Through Excerpts: Studies on Stobaeus. 2011. (Monotheismes et Philosophie Ser.). (ENG, FRE & ITA.). 730p. (C). pap. 160.00 ***(978-2-503-52976-9(3))*** Brepols Pubs. BEL. Dist: ISD.
Vathrakogianni, Aikaterini. Women on Kazantzakis: Biography & Fiction. 2011. 92p. pap. ***(978-3-8433-9357-7(5))*** Lambert Academic Publishing.

AUTHORS, HEBREW

Abramson, Glenda. Hebrew Writing of the First World War. 2008. (Illus.). 405p. 75.00 *(978-0-85303-770-5(1))* Vallentine Mitchell Pubs. GBR. Dist: International Specialized Bk. Services.
Jelen, Sheila E., et al. Hebrew, Gender, & Modernity: Critical Responses to Dvora Baron's Fiction. 2007. (Studies & Texts in Jewish History & Culture). (C). *(978-1-883053-95-6(1))* Univ. Pr. of Maryland.

AUTHORS, HUNGARIAN

Konrad, George. A Guest in My Own Country: A Hungarian Life. Heim, Michael Henry, ed. Tucker, Jim, tr. from HUN. 2007. (ENG.). 312p. pap. 17.95 *(978-1-59051-139-8(5))* Other Pr., LLC.
Markó, Béla. Egy Irredenta Hétköznapjai: (Lehallgatásijegyzokönyvek, 1986. április-1989. December) 2009. (HUN.). 472p. *(978-973-665-257-8(2))* Pallas-Akademia.
Sajben, Miklos. Dancing boots & pigs' Feet. 2009. 195p. pap. 14.00 *(978-0-557-05914-0(3))* Lulu Enterprises Inc.
Szentmártoni Szabó, Géza & Janus. Parthenope Veszedelme: újdonságok a Janus Pannonius-Filológia Köréból. 2010. (HUN & LAT., Illus.). 167p. *(978-963-263-133-2(1))* Napkut Kiado Kft.

AUTHORS, ICELANDIC

Fix, Hans, ed. Snorri Sturluson: Beiträge Zu Werk und Rezeption. (Reallexikon der Germanischen Altertumskunde - Ergänzungsbände Ser.). (GER.). VIII, 294p. 300.00 ***(978-3-11-174566-4(X))*** De Gruyter, Walter Inc.
Guomundsson, Halldor. The Islander: A Biography of Halldor Laxness. Roughton, Phil, tr. from ICE. 2008. (ENG., Illus.). 400p. 44.95 *(978-1-84724-284-6(7))* Quercus GBR. Dist: Independent Pubs. Group.
Schaer, Karin. ... Dette Hidindtil Saa Lidet, Dog Mangesteds Urigtig Bekiendte Land. (GER.). 216p. pap. 46.95 *(978-3-631-56899-6(1))* Lang, Peter GmbH, Europaischer Verlag der Wissenschaften DEU. Dist: Lang, Peter Publishing, Inc.

AUTHORS, INDIC

Abbott, Justin E. Eknath: The Poet-Saints of Maharashtra No. 2. 2011. 304p. 48.95 ***(978-1-258-05075-7(7))*** Literary Licensing, LLC.
Batty, Nancy Ellen. The Ring of Recollection: Transgenerational Haunting in the Novels of Shashi Deshpande. 2010. (Illus.). 347p. 91.00 *(978-90-420-3100-5(X))* Rodopi.
Biographiq. Rabindranath Tagore - Life & Times of a Bengali Poet (Biography) 2008. 60p. pap. 9.99 *(978-1-59986-386-3(3)*, Biographiq) Filiquarian Publishing, LLC.
Burton, Antoinette. The Postcolonial Careers of Santha Rama Rau. 2007. (Next Wave Ser.). (ENG., Illus.). 216p. (C). 79.95 *(978-0-8223-4050-8(X))*; per. 22.95 *(978-0-8223-4071-3(2))* Duke Univ. Pr.
Chew & Grene, Nicolas. R. K. Narayan. 2012. (Writers & Their Work Ser.). (ENG.). 144p. (C). 80.00 *(978-0-7463-1078-6(1))* Northcote Hse Publishers, Ltd. GBR. Dist: Brown, David Bk. Co., The.
Das, Manoj. Chasing the Rainbow: Growing up in an India Village. 2010. (ENG.). 180p. 22.95 *(978-0-19-806521-0(3))* Oxford Univ. Pr., Inc.
Deen, Hanifa. The Crescent & the Pen: The Strange Journey of Taslima Nasreen, 1 vol. 2006. (Illus.). 292p. 49.95 *(978-0-275-99167-8(9)*, C9167, Praeger Pubs.) Greenwood Publishing Group, Inc.
Dwivedi, A. N. Arundhati Roy's Fictional World: A Collection of Critical Essays. 2nd ed. 2010. viii, 147p. *(978-81-7646-730-8(8)*, Library of Congress — New Delhi Overseas Office) B.R. Publishing Corp.
Ghosh, Ranjan & Navarro-Tejero, Antonia, eds. Globalizing Dissent: Essays on Arundhati Roy. 2012. (Routledge Studies in Social & Political Thought Ser.). (ENG.). 230p. pap. 42.95 ***(978-0-415-54136-7(0))*** Routledge.
Gupta, Uma Das. Rabindranath Tagore: An Illustrated Life. 2012. (ENG., Illus.). 144p. pap. 14.95 ***(978-0-19-807600-1(2))*** Oxford Univ. Pr., Inc.
Hunter, Jeffrey W. Contemporary Literary Criticism: Excerpts from Criticism of the Works of Today's Novelists, Poets, Playwrights, Short Story Writers, Scriptwriters, & Other Creative Writers. 2011. 497p. 328.00 *(978-1-4144-5853-3(3))* Cengage Gale.
Jackson, Elizabeth. Feminism & Contemporary Indian Women's Writing. 2010. (ENG.). 216p. 89.00 *(978-0-230-23627-1(8))* Palgrave Macmillan.
Kannan, R. Anna: The Life & Times of C.N. Annadurai. 2010. (Illus.). xi, 423p. *(978-0-670-08328-2(3)*, Library of Congress — New Delhi Overseas Office) Penguin Group India.
Karamanski, Theodore J. Blackbird's Song: Andrew J. Blackbird & the Odawa People. 2012. (ENG.). 39.95 ***(978-1-61186-050-4(4))*** Michigan State Univ. Pr.
King, Thomas. The Truth about Stories: A Native Narrative. 2008. (ENG.). 184p. pap. 19.95 *(978-0-8166-4627-2(9))* Univ. of Minnesota Pr.
Krishna Rao, A. V. & Madhavi Menon, K., contrib. by. Kamala Markandaya: A Critical Study of Her Novels, 1954-1982. 210p. *(978-81-7018-941-1(1))* B.R. Publishing Corp. IND. Dist: Asia Bk. Corp. of America.
Lili, Anamika Heka. Alokera Jharnadhara. (BEN.). 128p. *(978-7-01-000001-5(8))* People's Publishing Hse., The.
Madhopuri, Balbir. Changiya Rukh: Against the Night. Jain, Tripti, tr. from PAN. 2010. (ENG.). 224p. 29.95 *(978-0-19-806550-0(7))* Oxford Univ. Pr., Inc.
Merchant, Hoshang. Forbidden Sex, Forbidden Texts: New India's Gay Poets. 2008. xxi, 270p. 100.00 *(978-0-415-48451-0(0)*, Routledge India) Taylor & Francis Group GBR. Dist: Taylor & Francis Group.
Naheed, Kishwer. A Bad Woman's Story. Soomro, Durdana, tr. from URD. 2010. (ENG., Illus.). 350p. 45.00 *(978-0-19-547737-5(5))* Oxford Univ. Pr., Inc.
Pawar, Urmila. The Weave of My Life: A Dalit Woman's Memoirs. Pandit, Maya, tr. from MAR. 2009. (ENG., Illus.). 320p. (gr. 17). 35.00 *(978-0-231-14900-6(X))* Columbia Univ. Pr.
Raya, Bijaya. Amadera Katha. 2008. (BEN., Illus.). 574p. *(978-81-7756-687-1(3))* Ananda Publishers Pvt Ltd, Publishers & Booksellers.
Raza Umar. Ali Sardar Jafri. 2008. (URD.). 647p. *(978-81-89461-67-6(2))* Kitabi Duniya.
Sankaran, Chitra. Myth Connections: The Use of Hindu Myths & Philosophies in R.K. Narayan & Raja Rao. 2nd ed. 326p. pap. 69.95 *(978-3-03911-322-4(4))* Lang, Peter Publishing, Inc.
Sethi, Sunil. The Big Bookshelf: Sunil Sethi in Conversation with 30 Famous Writers. 2012. (ENG., Illus.). 264p. (gr. 12). pap. 22.00 ***(978-0-14-341629-6(4)***, Penguin Global) Penguin Group (USA) Inc.
Shulman, David Dean & Rao, Velcheru Narayana. Srinatha: The Poet Who Made Gods & Kings. 2012. (ENG.). 224p. pap. 29.95 ***(978-0-19-986304-4(0))*** Oxford Univ. Pr., Inc.
Shyamdas & Vallabhdas, trs. from HIN. Krishna's Inner Circle: The Ashta Chaap Poets. 2009. (BRA.). 403p. 39.95 *(978-0-9825383-0-2(8))* Sacred Woods.
Srikantsarma, Indraganti. Paripari Paricayalu. 2009. (TEL.). 135p. *(978-1-892408-29-7(5))* Vanguri Foundation of America, Inc.
Tagore, Rabindranath. Boyhood Days. Chakravarty, Radha, tr. from BEN. 2011. (Hesperus Worldwide Ser.). (ENG.). 86p. pap. 15.95 *(978-1-84391-850-9(1))* Hesperus Pr. GBR. Dist: Independent Pubs. Group.
—Boyhood Days. Chakravarty, Radha, tr. from BEN. 2008. (ENG., Illus.). 144p. (gr. 12-18). 9.00 *(978-0-14-333021-9(7)*, Penguin Global) Penguin Group (USA) Inc.
Tharoor, Shashi. Bookless in Baghdad: Reflections on Writing & Writers. 2012. (ENG.). 288p. pap. 14.95 ***(978-1-61145-408-6(5)***, 611408, Arcade Publishing) Skyhorse Publishing Co., Inc.
Tickell, Alex. Arundhati Roy's the God of Small Things. 2007. (Routledge Guides to Literature Ser.). 183p. 95.00 *(978-0-415-35842-2(6))*; (ENG.). 200p. per. 28.95 *(978-0-415-35843-9(4))* Routledge.
Toorawa, Shawkat M., ed. & intro. Shifa Al-'Alil: Ghulam 'Ali Azad Bilgrami. 2007. (ARA & ENG.). 123p. (C). pap. 9.95 *(978-0-9774094-3-3(0))* Brown, David Bk. Co., The.
Tulsiram. Murdahiya: [atmakatha]. 2010. (HIN.). *(978-81-267-1963-1(X)*, Library of Congress — New Delhi Overseas Office) Rajkamal Prakashan Pvte Ltd.
Wagamese, Richard. One Story, One Song, 1 vol. 2011. (ENG.). 216p. 25.95 *(978-1-55365-506-0(0))* D&M Pubs. Inc. CAN. Dist: Perseus-PGW.
Weisbord, Merrily. The Love Queen of Malabar: Memoir of a Friendship with Kamala Das. 2010. (ENG., Illus.). 283p. (C). *(978-0-7735-3791-0(0))* McGill-Queen's Univ. Pr.
Womack, Craig S. Art as Performance, Story as Criticism: Reflections on Native Literary Aesthetics. 2009. (ENG.). 376p. (C). 39.95 *(978-0-8061-4064-3(X))* Univ. of Oklahoma Pr.

AUTHORS, IRISH

Behan, Brendan. Borstal Boy. Meyer-Clason, Curt, tr. (GER.). 422p. pap. *(978-3-462-02544-6(9))* Kiepenheuer & Witsch GmbH & Company KG DEU. Dist: International Bk. Import Service, Inc.
Black, William. Goldsmith. Morley, John, ed. (English Men of Letters Ser.). reprint ed. lib. bdg. 27.50 *(978-0-404-51702-1(1))* AMS Pr., Inc.
—Goldsmith. 2009. 120p. pap. 7.99 *(978-1-60450-674-7(1)*, Serenity Pubs.) Arc Manor.
—Goldsmith. 2009. 162p. 26.99 *(978-1-110-46379-4(0))*; pap. 20.75 *(978-1-110-46378-7(2))* BiblioBazaar.
—Goldsmith. 2011. (Cambridge Library Collection - English Men of Letters Ser.). (ENG.). 174p. pap. 19.99 ***(978-1-108-03470-8(5))*** Cambridge Univ. Pr.
—Goldsmith. Morley, John, ed. 2008. (ENG.). 116p. per. *(978-1-4065-9182-8(3))* Dodo Pr.
—Goldsmith. 2008. 158p. 36.95 *(978-1-4365-7696-3(2))* 2007. (ENG.). 160p. per. 21.95 *(978-0-548-79013-7(2))* Kessinger Publishing, LLC.
Bowker, Gordon. James Joyce: A Biography. 2012. (ENG., Illus.). 656p. 35.00 ***(978-0-374-17872-7(0))*** Farrar, Straus & Giroux.
Bracken, Claire & Cahill, Susan, eds. Anne Enright. 2011. 256p. 74.95 *(978-0-7165-3080-0(5))*; pap. 32.95 *(978-0-7165-3081-7(3))* Irish Academic Pr. IRL. Dist: International Specialized Bk. Services.
Brand, Gordon, ed. William Carleton: The Authentic Voice. 2006. (Irish Literary Studies). (Illus.). 455p. 99.00 *(978-0-86140-462-9(9))* Oxford Univ. Pr., Inc.
Carleton, William. The Poor Scholar. 2008. 152p. 24.99 *(978-0-554-25495-1(6))*; 21.99 *(978-0-554-34798-1(9))* BiblioBazaar.
—The Poor Scholar. 2009. 148p. pap. *(978-1-4099-3035-8(1))* Dodo Pr.
—The Poor Scholar: The Works of William Carleton, Vol. 3. l.t. ed. 2007. (ENG.). 148p. pap. 19.99 *(978-1-4264-9184-9(0))* BiblioBazaar.
—The Poor Scholar: The Works of William Carleton Volume Three. 2007. 134p. pap. 18.99 *(978-1-4264-9130-6(1))* BiblioBazaar.
—The Station; the Party Fight & Funeral; the Lough Derg Pilgrim: The Works of William Carleton. 2007. (ENG.). 182p. pap. 19.99 *(978-1-4264-9126-9(3))*; Vol. 3. 204p. pap. 22.99 *(978-1-4264-9180-1(8))* BiblioBazaar.
Cibber, Theophilus. The Lives of the Poets of Great Britain & Ireland. 2008. 336p. 29.99 *(978-0-554-24131-9(5))* 2008. 344p. 28.99 *(978-0-554-35254-1(0))* 2008. 364p. 29.99 *(978-0-554-32661-3(2))* 2008. 336p. 28.99 *(978-0-554-33434-9(8))* 2008. 332p. 29.99 *(978-0-554-33399-1(6))* 2008. 344p. 29.99 *(978-0-554-25951-2(6))* 2008. 332p. 29.99 *(978-0-554-24096-1(3))* 2008. 364p. 31.99 *(978-0-554-23358-1(4))* Vol. 2. 2007. (ENG.). 340p. pap. 24.99 *(978-1-4346-0156-8(0))* BiblioBazaar.
—The Lives of the Poets of Great Britain & Ireland. 2007. (ENG.). 248p. per. *(978-1-4068-4592-1(2))*; 224p. per. *(978-1-4068-4595-2(7))*; 220p. per. *(978-1-4068-4594-5(9))*; 228p. per. *(978-1-4068-4593-8(0))*; 236p. per. *(978-1-4068-4596-9(5))* Echo Library.

—The Lives of the Poets of Great Britain & Ireland: (1753) Volume V. 2007. (ENG.). 298p. pap. 21.99 *(978-1-4264-5798-2(7))*; 334p. pap. 24.99 *(978-1-4264-5858-3(4))* BiblioBazaar.

—The Lives of the Poets of Great Britain & Ireland (1753), Volume I. 2007. (ENG.). 318p. pap. 23.99 *(978-1-4264-4243-8(2))*; 362p. pap. 26.99 *(978-1-4264-4307-7(2))* BiblioBazaar.

—The Lives of the Poets of Great Britain & Ireland (1753), Volume IV. 2007. (ENG.). 292p. pap. 21.99 *(978-1-4264-5762-3(6))*; 328p. pap. 24.99 *(978-1-4264-5822-4(3))* BiblioBazaar.

—The Lives of the Poets of Great Britain & Ireland Volume II. 2007. (ENG.). 292p. pap. 21.99 *(978-1-4346-0071-4(8))* BiblioBazaar.

Coleman, Philip & Johnston, Maria, eds. Reading Pearse Hutchinson: From Findrum to Fisterra. 2011. 302p. 74.95 *(978-0-7165-3083-1(X))* Irish Academic Pr. IRL. Dist: International Specialized Bk. Services.

Cook, Daniel. Cook: The Lives of Jonathan Swift, 3 vols. 2011. *(978-0-415-59135-5(X))*; *(978-0-415-59136-2(8))*; *(978-0-415-59137-9(6))* Routledge.

Cook, Daniel, ed. Cook Set: The Lives of Jonathan Swift, 3 vols. 2011. (ENG.). 1669p. (C). 795.00 *(978-0-415-59134-8(1))* Routledge.

Cormack, Alistair. Yeats & Joyce: Cyclical History & the Reprobate Tradition. 2008. 228p. 99.95 *(978-0-7546-6028-6(1))* Ashgate Publishing Co.

Coughlan, Patricia & O'Toole, Tina, eds. Irish Literature: Feminist Perspectives. 2009. (ENG.). 312p. pap. 46.95 *(978-1-904505-35-8(X))* Carysfort Pr. IRL. Dist: Dufour Editions, Inc.

Craik, Henry. The Life of Jonathan Swift V1. 2007. (ENG.). 416p. 49.95 *(978-0-548-12922-7(3))* 2006. pap. 34.95 *(978-1-4286-3948-5(9))* Kessinger Publishing, LLC.

Crotty, Patrick, et al, eds. Brian Merriman & His World: Merriman ar an Mbinse. 2011. 240p. 75.00 *(978-1-84682-196-7(7))* Four Courts Pr. IRL. Dist: International Specialized Bk. Services.

Edgeworth, Maria. The Life & Letters. 2008. 284p. 28.99 *(978-0-554-22850-1(5))*; 284p. 25.99 *(978-0-554-32153-0(X))*; 296p. 25.99 *(978-0-554-32154-7(8))*; 296p. 28.99 *(978-0-554-22851-8(3))* BiblioBazaar.

—The Life & Letters. AUGUSTUS J.C. HARE, ed. 2007. (ENG.). Vol. 1. 248p. pap. 20.99 *(978-1-4264-3202-6(X))* Vol. 1. 282p. pap. 23.99 *(978-1-4264-3237-8(2))* Vol. 2. 260p. pap. 21.99 *(978-1-4264-3203-3(8))* Vol. 2. 294p. pap. 23.99 *(978-1-4264-3238-5(0))* BiblioBazaar.

—The Life & Letters of Maria Edgeworth. 2008. 300p. 28.99 *(978-0-554-22942-3(0))*; 25.99 *(978-0-554-32245-2(5))* BiblioBazaar.

—The Life & Letters of Maria Edgeworth. Augustus J.C. Hare, ed. 2007. (ENG.). Vol. 2. 266p. pap. 21.99 *(978-1-4264-3389-4(1))*Vol 2. 298p. pap. 23.99 *(978-1-4264-3439-6(1))* BiblioBazaar.

—The Life & Letters of Maria Edgeworth. Hare, Augustus J. C., ed. 2007. (ENG.). 632p. per. *(978-1-4065-1647-0(3))* Dodo Pr.

—The Life & Letters of Maria Edgeworth. 2007. (ENG.). 184p. per. *(978-1-4068-5006-2(3))*; 192p. per. *(978-1-4068-5007-9(1))* Echo Library.

Felter, Maryanne. Crossing Borders: A Critical Introduction to the Works of Mary Rose Callaghan. 2010. 43.00 *(978-0-87413-092-8(1))* Univ. of Delaware Pr.

Felton, R. Todd. A Journey into Ireland's Literary Revival. 2007. (ArtPlace Ser.). (ENG., Illus.). 192p. pap. 21.95 *(978-0-9766706-7-4(4))* Roaring Forties Pr.

Ferris, Kathleen. James Joyce & the Burden of Disease. 2010. (ENG.). 184p. pap. 30.00 *(978-0-8131-2664-7(9))* Univ. Pr. of Kentucky.

Figgis, Darrell. A.E. George W. Russell, A Study of a Man & a Nation. 2007. 172p. per. 17.50 *(978-1-59731-325-4(4))*; (ENG.). 24.95 *(978-1-59731-326-1(2))* Perennis, Sophia.

Finger, Charles J. The Tragic Story of Oscar Wilde's Life. Haldeman-Julius, E., ed. 2011. 66p. 36.95 ***(978-1-258-05415-1(9))*** Literary Licensing, LLC.

Fitzmaurice, Gabriel. Beat the Goatskin till the Goat Cries: Notes from a Kerry Village. 2006. (ENG.). 191p. pap. 21.95 *(978-1-85635-500-1(4))* Mercier Pr., Ltd., The IRL. Dist: Dufour Editions, Inc.

Flannery, Eóin. Colum Mccann & the Aesthetics of Redemption. 2011. 256p. 69.95 *(978-0-7165-3049-7(X))* Irish Academic Pr. IRL. Dist: International Specialized Bk. Services.

Forster, John. The Life & Times of Oliver Goldsmith. 2009. 504p. 43.99 *(978-1-115-30159-6(4))*; 36.99 *(978-1-115-30158-9(6))*; pap. 39.75 *(978-1-115-30155-8(1))* BiblioBazaar.

—The Life & Times of Oliver Goldsmith. 2009. 326p. pap. *(978-1-150-60901-5(X))*; 344p. pap. *(978-0-217-35436-3(X))*; 426p. pap. *(978-0-217-59361-8(5))* Books LLC.

—The Life & Times of Oliver Goldsmith. 2009. 414p. pap. 28.94 *(978-0-217-59364-9(X))* General Bks. LLC.

—The Life & Times of Oliver Goldsmith. 2009. 514p. 55.95 *(978-1-104-58587-7(1))*; 516p. pap. 40.95 *(978-1-104-49632-6(1))* Kessinger Publishing, LLC.

—The Life & Times of Oliver Goldsmith. 2009. 562p. 39.95 *(978-1-4344-5141-5(0))*; pap. 24.95 *(978-1-4344-5042-5(2))* Wildside Pr., LLC.

Gibson, Andrew. Samuel Beckett. 2009. (Reaktion Books - Critical Lives Ser.). (ENG., Illus.). 192p. pap. 16.95 *(978-1-86189-517-2(8))* Reaktion Bks., Ltd. GBR. Dist: Chicago Distribution Ctr.

Gide, André & La Jeunesse, Ernest. Recollections of Oscar Wilde. 2007. 104p. per. 13.85 *(978-1-59569-081-4(6))* Mondial.

Goldsmith, O. Goldsmith: Selected Essays. Lobban, J. H., ed. 2010. (ENG.). 164p. pap. 27.99 *(978-0-521-12670-0(3))* Cambridge Univ. Pr.

Gray, Frank. The Crazy Life of Brendan Behan: The Rise & Fall of Dublin's Laughing Boy. 2010. 276p. pap. 15.49 *(978-1-4490-6895-0(2))* AuthorHouse.

Greacen, Lavinia. J. G. Farrell in His Own Words: Selected Letters & Diaries. 2010. 464p. pap. 24.95 *(978-1-85918-476-9(6))* Cork Univ. Pr. IRL. Dist: Stylus Publishing, LLC.

Griffin, Gerald. Life & Works of Gerald Griffin, 8 vols. reprint ed. 135.00 *(978-0-404-08860-6(0))* AMS Pr., Inc.

Grimshaw, Beatrice. In the Strange South Seas: Travel & adventures of an Irish woman in the South Pacific in 1907. 2007. (Illus.). 388p. pap. *(978-1-906393-01-4(X))* Trotamundas Pr., Ltd. GBR. Dist: Lightning Source, Inc.

Gwynn, Stephen Lucius. Thomas Moore. 2009. 208p. 23.99 *(978-1-103-86074-6(7))* 2009. 208p. pap. 17.99 *(978-1-103-86071-5(2))* 2009. 212p. 23.99 *(978-1-103-65051-4(3))* 2009. 212p. pap. 17.99 *(978-1-103-65047-7(5))* 2008. 212p. 24.99 *(978-0-559-44435-7(4))* 2008. 212p. pap. 23.75 *(978-0-559-44433-3(8))* BiblioBazaar.

Hahn, Daniel & Robins, Nicholas, eds. The Oxford Guide to Literary Britain & Ireland. 3rd ed. 2008. (ENG., Illus.). 384p. 60.00 *(978-0-19-861460-9(8))* Oxford Univ. Pr., Inc.

Hamilton, Hugo. The Harbor Boys: A Memoir. 2007. 272p. per. 13.95 *(978-0-06-078469-0(5)*, HarperPerennial) HarperCollins Pubs.

Hanberry, Gerard. More Lives Than One: The Remarkable Wilde Family Through the Generations. 2012. (ENG.). 360p. 44.95 ***(978-1-84889-120-3(2))*** Collins Pr., The IRL. Dist: Dufour Editions, Inc.

Harris, Frank. Oscar Wilde: His Life & Confessions. 2007. (Illus.). 456p. per. *(978-1-4065-3269-2(X))* Dodo Pr.

—Oscar Wilde, His Life & Confessions. 2007. (ENG.). 284p. 28.95 *(978-1-4218-9741-7(5)*, 1st World Library - Literary Society) 1st World Publishing, Inc.

—Oscar Wilde His Life & Confessions Vol. 2006. pap. *(978-1-4068-1113-1(0))* Echo Library.

Harte, Liam. The Literature of the Irish in Britain: Autobiography & Memoir, 1725-2001. 2011. (ENG., Illus.). 344p. (C). pap. 28.95 *(978-0-230-29636-7(X))* Palgrave Macmillan.

Hepburn, Allan, ed. Listening In: Broadcasts, Speeches, & Interviews by Elizabeth Bowen. 2010. (ENG.). 352p. (gr. 17). 135.00 *(978-0-7486-4041-6(X))*; pap. 45.00 *(978-0-7486-4042-3(8))* Edinburgh Univ. Pr. GBR. Dist: Columbia Univ. Pr.

Hill, Judith. Lady Gregory: An Irish Life. 2011. (ENG.). 616p. pap. 26.95 *(978-1-84889-110-4(5))* Collins Pr., The IRL. Dist: Dufour Editions, Inc.

Houston, Nainsi J. How Irish Women Writers Portray Masculinity: Exposing the Presumptions of Patriarchy. 2006. (Illus.). 216p. 109.95 *(978-0-7734-5558-0(2))* Mellen, Edwin Pr., The.

Hughes, Barbara. Between Literature & History: The Diaries & Memoires of Mary Leadbeater & Dorothea Herbert. 2010. (Reimagining Ireland Ser.). 255p. pap. 53.95 *(978-3-03911-889-2(7))* Lang, Peter AG GBR. Dist: Lang, Peter.

Igoe, Vivien, ed. James Joyce's Dublin Houses & Nora Barnacle's Galway. 2008. (ENG.). 206p. pap. 28.95 *(978-1-84351-082-6(0))* Lilliput Pr., Ltd., The IRL. Dist: Dufour Editions, Inc.

Irving, Washington. Oliver Goldsmith: A Biography. l.t. ed. 2007. (ENG.). 322p. pap. 24.99 *(978-1-4264-2757-2(3))* BiblioBazaar.

—Oliver Goldsmith: A Biography. 2007. 280p. per. *(978-1-4065-3434-4(X))* Dodo Pr.

—Oliver Goldsmith; a Biography by Washington Irving. 2006. 392p. per. 26.99 *(978-1-4255-4222-1(0))* MPublishing.

Irving, Washington & Gaston, Charles Robert. Irving's Oliver Goldsmith: A Biography. 2007. (ENG.). 402p. 49.95 *(978-0-548-06251-7(X))* Kessinger Publishing, LLC.

Jeffares, Norman. The Irish Literary Revival. (Character Sketches Ser.). (Illus.). 64p. 11.95 *(978-1-85514-233-6(3))* National Portrait Gallery Pubns. GBR. Dist: Antique Collectors' Club.

Johnston, Philip, et al. The Lost Tribe in the Mirror: Four Playwrights of Northern Ireland. 2009. (Illus.). 209p. *(978-1-904652-64-9(6))* Lagan Pr.

Juliet, Charles. Conversations with Samuel Beckett & Bram van Velde. Nesme, Axel & Tucker, Janey, trs. from FRE. 2009. (French Literature Ser.). (ENG.). 192p. pap. 13.95 *(978-1-56478-531-2(9)*, 478531) Dalkey Archive Pr.

Katouzian, Homa, ed. Sadeq Hedayat: His Work & His Wondrous World. 2007. (Iranian Studies). (ENG.). 208p. (C). 160.00 *(978-0-415-43403-4(3))* Routledge.

Kelly, Ann Cline. Jonathan Swift & Popular Culture: Myth, Media, & the Man. 2008. (ENG., Illus.). 256p. pap. 32.00 *(978-0-230-60234-2(7))* Palgrave Macmillan.

Kelly, James. Sir Richard Musgrave, 1746-1818: Ultra-Protestant Idealogue. 2009. 266p. 70.00 *(978-1-84682-148-6(7))* Four Courts Pr. IRL. Dist: International Specialized Bk. Services.

Kennedy-Andrews, Elmer, ed. Ciaran Carson: Critical Essays. 2009. 284p. 60.00 *(978-1-84682-156-1(8))*; pap. 30.00 *(978-1-84682-162-2(2))* Four Courts Pr. IRL. Dist: International Specialized Bk. Services.

Kiely, Kevin. Francis Stuart: Artist & Outcast. 2008. (ENG., Illus.). 376p. pap. 42.95 *(978-1-905785-25-4(9))* Liffey Pr., The IRL. Dist: Dufour Editions, Inc.

Lane, Leeann. Rosamond Jacob, 1888-1960: Third Peson Singular. 2011. (ENG., Illus.). 334p. pap. 52.95 *(978-1-906359-54-6(7))* Univ. College Dublin Pr. IRL. Dist: Dufour Editions, Inc.

Liddy, James. The Full Shilling. 2009. (ENG., Illus.). 149p. pap. 26.95 *(978-1-903392-91-1(8))* Salmon Publishing IRL. Dist: Dufour Editions, Inc.

Lucchitti, Irene. The Islandman: The Hidden Life of Tomás O'Crohan. 2008. (Reimagining Ireland Ser.). (ENG.). 232p. pap. 64.95 *(978-3-03911-837-3(4))* Lang, Peter AG GBR. Dist: Lang, Peter.

Lynch, Brendan. Parsons Bookshop: At the Heart of Bohemian Dublin, 1949-1989. 2007. (ENG., Illus.). 264p. per. 27.95 *(978-1-905785-11-7(9))* Liffey Pr., The IRL. Dist: Dufour Editions, Inc.

Lynch, Claire. Irish Autobiography: Stories of Self in the Narrative of a Nation. 2009. (Reimagining Ireland Ser.). (ENG.). 234p. pap. 49.95 *(978-3-03911-856-4(0))* Lang, Peter AG GBR. Dist: Lang, Peter.

MacDonald, Edgar E. The Education of the Heart: The Correspondence of Rachel Mordecai Lazarus & Maria Edgeworth. 2011. (ENG.). 364p. pap. 50.00 ***(978-0-8078-9717-1(5))*** Univ. of North Carolina Pr.

Macgee, Thomas D. Gallery of Irish Writers: The Irish Writers of the Seventeenth Century. reprint ed. 39.50 *(978-0-404-13815-8(2))* AMS Pr., Inc.

Macken, Ultan. Walter Macken: Dreams on Paper. 2010. (ENG., Illus.). 448p. 47.95 *(978-1-85635-630-5(2))* Mercier Pr., Ltd., The IRL. Dist: Dufour Editions, Inc.

Malcolm, David. Understanding John Mcgahern. 2007. (Understanding Modern European & Latin American Literature Ser.). 163p. 39.95 *(978-1-57003-673-6(X))* Univ. of South Carolina Pr.

McGahern, John. All Will Be Well. 2007. (Vintage International Ser.). (ENG.). 304p. pap. 14.95 *(978-1-4000-7986-5(1)*, Vintage) Knopf Doubleday Publishing Group.

McGee, Thomas D'Arcy. The Irish Writers of the Seventeenth Century. 2009. 130p. pap. 19.99 *(978-1-150-72405-3(6))* General Bks. LLC.

McKenna, Neil. The Secret Life of Oscar Wilde: An Intimate Biography. 2006. (ENG.). 576p. per. 18.95 *(978-0-465-04439-9(5))* Basic Bks.

McMinn, Joseph. Jonathan Swift & the Arts. 2010. (Illus.). 187p. 46.00 *(978-0-87413-068-3(9))*; (ENG.). 46.00 *(978-1-61149-125-8(8))* Univ. of Delaware Pr.

Montague, John. The Pear Is Ripe: A Memoir. 2008. (ENG., Illus.). 240p. 45.95 *(978-1-905483-25-9(2))* Liberties Pr. IRL. Dist: Dufour Editions, Inc.

Moore, George. Memoirs of My Dead Life. 2008. 272p. 28.99 *(978-0-554-22688-0(X))* 2008. 272p. 25.99 *(978-0-554-31991-9(8))* 2007. (ENG.). 242p. pap. 20.99 *(978-1-4264-2861-6(8))* 2007. (ENG.). 270p. pap. 23.99 *(978-1-4264-2898-2(7))* BiblioBazaar.

—Memoirs of My Dead Life. 2007. (ENG.). 236p. per. *(978-1-4065-4586-9(4))* Dodo Pr.

—Memoirs of My Dead Life. 2009. (ENG.). 236p. pap. 14.95 *(978-1-4385-1344-7(5)*, Book Jungle) Standard Pubns., Inc.

—Memoirs of My Dead Life. 2008. 360p. 32.95 *(978-1-4344-6397-5(4))*; pap. 19.95 *(978-1-4344-6396-8(6))* Wildside Pr., LLC.

Morgan, Charles. Epitaph on George Moore. 2007. (ENG.). 68p. per. *(978-1-4067-0323-8(0))* Read Bks.

Morin, Emilie. Samuel Beckett & the Problem of Irishness. 2009. (ENG.). 256p. 84.00 *(978-0-230-21986-1(1))* Palgrave Macmillan.

Murphy, Dervla. Wheels within Wheels: The Makings of a Traveller. 2010. (ENG., Illus.). 240p. pap. 29.95 *(978-1-906011-40-6(0))* Eland Bks. GBR. Dist: Dufour Editions, Inc.

Murphy, Rose. Ella Young, Irish Mystic & Rebel - From Literary Dublin to the American West. 2008. (ENG., Illus.). 165p. pap. 26.95 *(978-1-905785-31-5(3))* Liffey Pr., The IRL. Dist: Dufour Editions, Inc.

Nestor, Tom. Talking to Kate. 2009. (ENG.). 254p. pap. 23.95 *(978-1-905172-91-7(5))* Collins Pr., The IRL. Dist: Dufour Editions, Inc.

Nordin, Irene Gilsenan. Reading Eilean Ni Chuilleanain, a Contemporary Irish Poet: The Element of the Spiritual. 2009. 156p. 99.95 *(978-0-7734-4831-5(4))* Mellen, Edwin Pr., The.

O. Se, Maidhc Dainin. House, Don't Fall on Me. Fitzmaurice, Gabriel, tr. 2008. (ENG.). 224p. pap. 22.95 *(978-1-85635-550-6(0))* Mercier Pr., Ltd., The IRL. Dist: Dufour Editions, Inc.

O'Brien, Edna. James Joyce: A Life. 2011. (ENG.). 192p. (gr. 12). 14.00 *(978-0-14-311993-7(1)*, Penguin (Non-Classics)) Penguin Group (USA) Inc.

O'Connor, Maureen. The Female & the Species: The Animal in Irish Women's Writing. 2010. (ENG.). 193p. pap. 48.95 *(978-3-03911-959-2(1))* Lang, Peter AG GBR. Dist: Lang, Peter.

O'Driscoll, Dennis. Stepping Stones: Interviews with Seamus Heaney. 2008. (ENG., Illus.). 560p. 32.00 *(978-0-374-26983-8(1))* Farrar, Straus & Giroux.

Parker, Todd C. Swift As Priest & Satirist. 2009. (Illus.). 231p. 51.50 *(978-0-87413-044-7(1))* Univ. of Delaware Pr.

Perrick, Penny. Something to Hide: The Life of Sheila Wingfield, Viscountess Powerscourt. 2008. (ENG., Illus.). 256p. pap. 34.95 *(978-1-84351-093-2(6))* Lilliput Pr., Ltd., The IRL. Dist: Dufour Editions, Inc.

Pharand, Michel W. & Sparks, Julie, eds. Shaw Vol. 29: The Annual of Bernard Shaw Studies. 2009. 58.00 *(978-0-271-03635-9(4))* Pennsylvania State Univ. Pr.

Piper, Leonard. Tragedy of Erskine Childers: Dangerous Waters. 2006. (ENG., Illus.). 264p. pap. 29.95 *(978-1-84725-020-9(3)*, Hambledon Continuum) Continuum International Publishing Group, Ltd. GBR. Dist: National Bk. Network.

Randolph, Jody Allen. Close to the Next Moment: Interviews from a Changing Ireland. 2010. (ENG.). 302p. pap. 29.95 *(978-1-84777-048-6(7))* Carcanet Pr., Ltd. GBR. Dist: Independent Pubs. Group.

Richtarik, Marilynn. Stewart Parker: A Life. 2012. (ENG., Illus.). 408p. 55.00 ***(978-0-19-969503-4(2))*** Oxford Univ. Pr., Inc.

Robins, Ashley. Oscar Wilde - The Great Drama of His Life: How His Tragedy Reflected His Personality. 2011. (ENG., Illus.). 276p. 55.00 *(978-1-84519-434-5(9))* Sussex Academic Pr. GBR. Dist: International Specialized Bk. Services.

Robins, Ashley H. Oscar Wilde — The Great Drama of His Life: How His Tragedy Reflected His Personality. 2012. (Illus.). 272p. pap. 34.95 ***(978-1-84519-541-0(8))*** Sussex Academic Pr. GBR. Dist: International Specialized Bk. Services.

Russell, George & Russell, George William. Ae's Letters to Minanlabain. 2007. 112p. (ENG.). 24.95 *(978-1-59731-323-0(8))*; per. 16.95 *(978-1-59731-306-3(8))* Perennis, Sophia.

Russell, George W. The Candle of Vision. 2007. 188p. per. 17.50 *(978-1-60206-251-1(X))* Cosimo, Inc.

Ryan, John. Remembering How We Stood: Bohemian Dublin at the Mid-Century. 2009. (ENG.). 168p. pap. 21.95 *(978-1-84351-142-7(8))* Lilliput Pr., Ltd., The IRL. Dist: Dufour Editions, Inc.

Saddlemyer, Ann, ed. W. B. Yeats & George Yeats: The Letters. 2011. (ENG., Illus.). 560p. 49.95 *(978-0-19-818438-6(7))* Oxford Univ. Pr., Inc.

Sampson, Denis. Young John Mcgahern: Becoming a Novelist. 2012. (ENG., Illus.). 208p. 45.00 ***(978-0-19-964177-2(3))*** Oxford Univ. Pr., Inc.

Scott, Walter, Sr. Memoirs of Jonathan Swift: Dean of St. Patrick's, Dublin (1834) 2011. (Cambridge Library Collection - Literary Studies). (ENG.). 268p. pap. 23.99 ***(978-1-108-03419-7(5))***; 326p. pap. 28.99 ***(978-1-108-03418-0(7))***; 594p. pap., pap. 51.00 ***(978-1-108-03420-3(9))*** Cambridge Univ. Pr.

Sherard, Robert Harborough. The Life of Oscar Wilde. 2009. 198p. pap. 19.99 *(978-1-150-72673-6(3))* General Bks. LLC.

—The Life of Oscar Wilde. 2009. 538p. 57.95 *(978-1-104-83465-4(0))* 2007. (ENG.). 484p. 53.95 *(978-0-548-15135-8(0))* 2007. (ENG.). 536p. per. 42.95 *(978-1-4325-9971-3(2))* 2007. (ENG.). 488p. per. 38.95 *(978-1-4304-4481-7(9))* Kessinger Publishing, LLC.

Sloan, John. Oscar Wilde. 2009. (Oxford World's Classics Ser.). (ENG., Illus.). 240p. pap. 14.95 *(978-0-19-955521-5(4))* Oxford Univ. Pr., Inc.

Smith, Sophie Shilleto. Dean Swift. 380p. 2008. 48.95 *(978-0-548-99106-0(5))* 2007. (ENG.). per. 33.95 *(978-0-548-65635-8(5))* Kessinger Publishing, LLC.

Stephen, Leslie. Swift. 2011. (Cambridge Library Collection - English Men of Letters Ser.). (ENG.). 228p. pap. 22.99 ***(978-1-108-03449-4(7))*** Cambridge Univ. Pr.

Stewart, William. British & Irish Poets: A Biographical Dictionary, 449-2006. 2007. (ENG.). 503p. 125.00 *(978-0-7864-2891-5(0))* McFarland & Co., Inc. Pubs.

Stubblefield, R. Jay & Degategno, Paul J. Critical Companion to Jonathan Swift: A Literary Reference to His Life & Work. 2006. (Critical Companion Ser.). (Illus.). 480p. (C). (gr. 9). 75.00 *(978-0-8160-5093-2(7))* Facts On File, Inc.

Sullivan, Kevin. Joyce among the Jesuits. 2011. 268p. 47.95 ***(978-1-258-03891-5(9))*** Literary Licensing, LLC.

Tipper, Karen Sasha Anthony, ed. Lady Jane Wilde's Letters to Mr. John Hilson, 1847-1876: A Critical Edition. 2010. (Illus.). viii, 86p. *(978-0-7734-3763-0(0))* Mellen, Edwin Pr., The.

Tipper, Karen Sasha Anthony, ed. Lady Jane Wilde's Letters to Oscar Wilde, 1875-1895: A Critical Edition. 2011. (ENG.). 204p. 119.95 ***(978-0-7734-2543-9(8))*** Mellen, Edwin Pr., The.

Tomedi, John. Bloom's Literary Guide to Dublin. 2007. (Bloom's Literary Guide Ser.). (Illus.). 224p. per. 14.95 *(978-0-7910-9376-4(X)*, Chelsea Hse.) Facts On File, Inc.

Walsh, Pat. Patrick Kavanagh. 2010. (ENG., Illus.). 288p. pap. 21.95 *(978-1-85635-664-0(7))* Mercier Pr., Ltd., The IRL. Dist: Dufour Editions, Inc.

Wilde, Jane Francesca. Social Studies. 2010. (Cambridge Library Collection - Women's Writing Ser.). 354p. pap. 29.99 *(978-1-108-02195-1(6))* Cambridge Univ. Pr.

Wilde, Oscar. Oscar Wilde in America: The Interviews. Hofer, Matthew & Scharnhorst, Gary, eds. 2010. (ENG., Illus.). 208p. 40.00 *(978-0-252-03472-5(4))* Univ. of Illinois Pr.

Winsten, Stephen. G b S 90: Aspects of Bernard Shaw's Life & Work. Winsten, Stephen, ed. 2011. 286p. 48.95 ***(978-1-258-02677-6(5))*** Literary Licensing, LLC.

Yeats, W. B. Four Years. 2008. (ENG.). 60p. per. *(978-1-4065-9321-1(4))* Dodo Pr.

AUTHORS, ISRAELI

Appelfeld, Aharon. The Story of a Life. 2006. (ENG.). 208p. pap. 13.00 *(978-0-8052-1126-9(8)*, Schocken) Knopf Doubleday Publishing Group.

—A Table for One: Under the Light of Jerusalem. 2007. 150p. per. 12.95 *(978-1-59264-197-0(0))* Toby Pr. LLC, The.

Cole, Peter, ed. Hebrew Writers on Writing. 2008. (Writer's World Ser.). (ENG.). 320p. 45.00 *(978-1-59534-051-1(3))*; pap. 24.95 *(978-1-59534-052-8(1))* Trinity Univ. Pr.

Ghanayim, Mahmud. The Quest for a Lost Identity: Palestinian Fiction in Israel. 2008. (Studies in Arabic Language & Literature). (ENG.). 164p. (C). pap. 57.00 *(978-3-447-05768-4(8))* Harrassowitz, Otto Verlag DEU. Dist: ISD.

Isaksen, Runo. Literature & War: Conversations with Israeli & Palestinian Writers. Dickson, Kari, tr. from NOR. 2008. (ENG.). 256p. pap. 18.00 *(978-1-56656-730-5(0))* Interlink Publishing Group, Inc.

Jelen, Sheila E. Intimations of Difference: Dvora Baron in the Modern Hebrew Renaissance. 2007. (Judaic Traditions in Literature, Music & Art Ser.). (Illus.). 240p. 24.95 *(978-0-8156-3130-9(8))* Syracuse Univ. Pr.

Kaniuk, Yoram. Life on Sandpaper. Berris, Anthony, tr. from HEB. 2011. (Hebrew Literature Ser.). (ENG.). 400p. pap. 15.95 *(978-1-56478-613-5(7)*, 478613) Dalkey Archive Pr.

Laor, Dan. Life of Agnon. 2009. *(978-0-8419-1446-9(X))* Holmes & Meier Pubs., Inc.

Misselwitz, Charlotte & Siebeck, Cornelia, eds. Dissonant Memories Fragmented Present: Exchanging Young Discourses between Israel & Germany. 2011. (ENG.). 232p. pap. 39.95 *(978-3-8376-1273-8(2))* Transcript Verlag DEU. Dist: Transaction Pubs.

Porat, Dina. The Fall of a Sparrow: The Life & Times of Abba Kovner. Yuval, Elizabeth, tr. from HEB. 2009. (Stanford Studies in Jewish History & C Ser.). (ENG., Illus.). 440p. 65.00 (978-0-8047-6248-9(1)) Stanford Univ. Pr.

Shalev, Meir. My Russian Grandmother & Her American Vacuum Cleaner: A Family Memoir. Fallenberg, Evan, tr. from HEB. 2011. (ENG., Illus.). 224p. 25.95 (978-0-8052-4287-4(2), Schocken) Knopf Doubleday Publishing Group.

AUTHORS, ITALIAN

Abate, Nicolò dell', et al. Nicolò Dell'Abate Alla Corte Dei Boiardo: Il Paradiso Ritrovato. 2009. (ITA., Illus.). 334p. (978-88-366-1383-0(7)) Silvana.

Arslan, Antonia. Ishtar 2: Cronache Del Mio Risveglio. 2010. (ITA.). 111p. (978-88-17-04369-4(9)) Rizzoli International Pubns., Inc.

Ascoli, Albert Russell. Favola Fui: Petrarch Writes His Readers. 2010. (Bernardo Lecture Ser.). (ENG.). 47p. pap. 10.00 (978-1-4384-3806-1(0)) State Univ. of New York Pr.

Attwood, Martin. Hidden Debts: A memoir of Italy. 2009. 296p. pap. 21.95 (978-1-4401-3833-1(8)) iUniverse, Inc.

Barnes, John C. & Petrie, Jennifer, eds. Dante & His Literary Precursors: Twelve Essays. 2007. 308p. (C). 65.00 (978-1-85182-652-0(1)) Four Courts Pr. IRL. Dist: International Specialized Bk. Services.

Bemrose, Stephen. A New Life of Dante. rev. ed. 2010. (ENG.). 272p. pap. 32.50 (978-0-85989-845-4(8)) Univ. of Exeter Pr. GBR. Dist: Chicago Distribution Ctr.

Benso, Silvia & Schroeder, Brian, eds. Between Nihilism & Politics: The Hermeneutics of Gianni Vattimo. 2010. (SUNY series in Contemporary Italian Philosophy Ser.). 256p. 80.00 (978-1-4384-3285-4(2)) State Univ. of New York Pr.

Bigongiari, Piero, et al. La Certezza Della Poesia: Lettere (1942-1970) 2008. (Diaspro Ser.). (ITA., Illus.). 366p. (C). 39.50 (978-88-596-0430-3(3)) Edizioni Polistampa ITA. Dist: Brown, David Bk. Co., The.

Blow, Douglas. In Your Face: Professional Improprieties & the Art of Being Conspicuous in Sixteenth-Century Italy. 2009. (ENG., Illus.). 272p. 70.00 (978-0-8047-6215-1(5)); pap. 24.95 (978-0-8047-6215-8(3)) Stanford Univ. Pr.

Bloom, Harold & Foster, Brett. Bloom's Literary Guide to Rome. 2007. (Bloom's Literary Guide Ser.). 224p. pap. 14.95 (978-0-7910-9380-1(8), Chelsea Hse.) Facts On File, Inc.

Boccaccio, Giovanni. Life of Dante. Wicksteed, Philip, tr. from ITA. 2009. (Oneworld Classics Ser.). (ENG., Illus.). 128p. pap. 12.95 (978-1-84749-091-9(3)) Alma Classics GBR. Dist: Independent Pubs. Group.

Boitani, Piero. Dante's Poetry of the Donati: The Barlow Lectures on Dante Delivered at University College London, 17-18 March 2005. 2007. (Society for Italian Studies Occasional Papers Ser.). 55p. pap. 20.00 (978-0-9525901-7-0(4)) Northern Universities Pr. GBR. Dist: Brown, David Bk. Co., The.

Bondanella, Peter, et al, eds. Cassell Dictionary of Italian Literature. 2nd ed. (ITA., Illus.). 727p. pap. (978-0-304-33841-2(9), Burns & Oates) Continuum International Publishing Group, Ltd.

Bruck, Edith. Letter to My Mother. Webster, Brenda, tr. from ITA. 2007. (Texts & Translations Ser.: Vol. 18).Tr. of Lettera Alla Madre. 250p. per. 10.95 (978-0-87352-936-5(7)) Modern Language Assn. of America.

—Lettera Alla Madre. 2007. (Texts & Translations Ser.: Vol. 18). (ITA & ENG.). 250p. per. 10.95 (978-0-87352-935-8(9)) Modern Language Assn. of America.

Burge, James. Dante's Invention. 2011. (ENG., Illus.). 252p. 29.95 (978-0-7524-5586-0(9)) History Pr. Ltd.,The GBR. Dist: Independent Pubs. Group.

Ciampi, Paolo. I due Viaggiatori: Alla scoperta del mondo con Odoardo Beccari ed Emilio Salgari. 2010. (non Guide Ser.). (ITA., Illus.). 192p. (C). pap. 20.00 (978-88-564-0129-5(0)) Polistampa ITA. Dist: Brown, David Bk. Co., The.

Cirigliano, Marc A., tr. from ITA. Melancolia Poetica: A Dual Language Anthology of Italian Poetry, 1160-1560. 2007. (ITA & ENG.). 408p. (978-1-905886-82-1(9)) Troubadour Publishing Ltd.

Claire, Horatio & Clare, Horatio. Sicily: Through Writers' Eyes. 2006. (ENG., Illus.). 320p. per. 33.95 (978-0-907871-94-1(1)) Local Ireland IRL. Dist: Dufour Editions, Inc.

Colquhoun, Archibald. Manzoni & His Times: A Biography. 2011. 322p. 50.95 **(978-1-258-02898-5(0))** Literary Licensing, LLC.

Daniels, Rhiannon. Boccaccio & the Book: Production & Reading in Italy 1340-1520. 2009. (Legenda Italian Perspectives Ser.). (ENG., Illus.). 240p. (C). 89.50 (978-1-906540-49-4(7)) European Humanities Research Ctr. GBR. Dist: Brown, David Bk. Co., The.

Dashwood, J. R. & Ganeri, Margherita. The Risorgimento of Federico de Roberto. 2008. (Italian Modernities Ser.). (ITA & ENG.). 339p. 61.95 (978-3-03911-858-8(7)) Lang, Peter AG GBR. Dist: Lang, Peter.

Franco, Niccolò & Falardo, Domenica. Epistolario (1540-1543) Ms Vat. Lat. 5642. 2007. (Filibrary: No. 26). (ITA.). 654p. (978-1-893127-26-5(5)) Forum Italicum, Inc.

Gilmour, David. The Last Leopard: A Life of Giuseppe Tomasi Di Lampedusa. 2007. (ENG., Illus.). 277p. pap. 33.95 (978-0-9550105-1-4(9)) Eland Bks. GBR. Dist: Dufour Editions, Inc.

Glori, Cesaremaria. La Tragica Morte Di Ippolito Nievo: Il Naufragio Doloso Del Piroscafo Ercole: Coinvolgimento e Responsabilità Della Massoneria Nella Caduta Del Regno Delle Due Sicilie. 2010. (ITA., Illus.). 167p. (978-88-89756-82-9(9)) Solfanelli.

Hawkins, Peter S. Dante: A Brief History. 2006. (Blackwell Brief Histories of Religion Ser.). (ENG., Illus.). 200p. per. 28.95 (978-1-4051-3052-3(0)); 99.95 (978-1-4051-3051-6(2)) Wiley, John & Sons, Inc. (Wiley-Blackwell).

Hunt, Leigh & Thomas George Thrum. Stories from the Italian Poets Volume 1: With Lives of the Writers. 2007. (ENG.). 248p. pap. 20.99 (978-1-4264-4447-0(8)) BiblioBazaar.

Kelly, Ian. Casanova: Actor, Lover, Priest, Spy. (ENG.). 416p. (gr. 12). 2011. 15.95 (978-1-58542-844-1(2)) 2008. 28.95 (978-1-58542-658-4(X)) Penguin Group (USA) Inc. (Tarcher).

Lerner, Giovanna Faleschini. Carlo Levi's Visual Poetics: The Painter as Writer. 2012. (Italian & Italian American Studies). (ENG.). 256p. 85.00 **(978-0-230-39064-5(1))** Palgrave Macmillan.

Lewis, R. W. B. Dante: A Life. 2009. (Penguin Lives Ser.). (ENG.). 224p. (gr. 12-18). 14.00 (978-0-14-311641-7(X), Penguin (Non-Classics)) Penguin Group (USA) Inc.

Long, Joanna O. Then Came Michelangelo. 2010. 188p. pap. 14.95 (978-1-935271-31-4(8)) Published by Westview, Inc.

Mancini, Albert N. & Pierce, Glenn Palen, eds. Seventeenth-Century Italian Poets & Dramatists. 2008. (Dictionary of Literary Biography Ser.). (ENG., Illus.). 448p. 315.00 (978-0-7876-8157-9(1)) Cengage Gale.

Marchesi, Ilaria. The Art of Pliny's Letters: A Poetics of Allusion in the Private Correspondence. 2008. (ENG.). 290p. 99.00 (978-0-521-88227-9(3)) Cambridge Univ. Pr.

Maschietto, Francesco Ludovico, et al. Elena Lucrezia Cornaro Piscopia (1646-1684) The First Woman in the World to Earn a University Degree. 2006. (ENG & LAT.). 40.00 (978-0-916101-57-2(6)) St. Joseph's Univ. Pr.

Máté, Ferenc. A Real Life: Restoring What Matters Family, Good Friends & a True Community. 3rd ed. 2011. (ENG.). 285p. 24.95 (978-0-920256-69-5(4), 25669) Albatross Publishing CAN. Dist: Norton, W. W. & Co., Inc.

Montaldi-Seelhorst, Gabriele. Francesco Biamonti (1928-2001) Das Romanwerk. 2009. (Grundlagen der Italianistik Ser.). (GER.). 194p. 57.95 (978-3-631-59784-2(3)) Lang, Peter GmbH, Europaischer Verlag der Wissenschaften DEU. Dist: Lang, Peter.

Parussa, Sergio. Writing As Freedom, Writing As Testimony: Four Italian Writers & Judaism. 2008. 232p. 24.95 (978-0-8156-3198-9(7)) Syracuse Univ. Pr.

Pavolini, Lorenzo. Accanto Alla Tigre. 2010. (ITA., Illus.). 243p. (978-88-6044-145-4(5)) Fandango.

Pellico, Silvio. My Ten Years' Imprisonment. 2008. 240p. 27.99 (978-0-554-27149-1(4)) 2008. 240p. 24.99 (978-0-554-36452-0(2)) 2007. 226p. pap. 20.99 (978-1-4346-2590-8(7)) 2007. (ENG.). 238p. pap. 22.99 (978-1-4346-2668-4(7)) BiblioBazaar.

—My Ten Years' Imprisonment. 2009. 216p. pap. (978-1-4099-5640-2(7)) Dodo Pr.

—My Ten Years' Imprisonment. 2010. (Illus.). 112p. pap. 20.31 (978-1-153-64371-9(5)) 2009. 134p. pap. 19.48 (978-1-150-68889-8(0)) General Bks. LLC.

—My Ten Years' Imprisonment. Roscoe, Thomas, tr. 208p. 2010. 31.96 **(978-1-166-35465-7(2))** 2010. pap. 19.96 **(978-1-166-29963-7(5))** 2009. 39.95 (978-1-120-07004-3(X)) 2009. pap. 24.95 (978-1-120-00991-3(X)) Kessinger Publishing, LLC.

Pellico, Silvio & Roscoe, Thomas. My Ten Years' Imprisonment. 2010. (ENG.). 208p. pap. 24.75 (978-1-177-45374-5(6)) BiblioBazaar.

Petrarca, Francesco. Familiaria: Bucher der Vertraulichkeiten Band 2. Widmer, Berthe, ed. 2009. (GER.). L, 915p. 277.00 (978-3-11-019159-2(8)) De Gruyter, Walter Inc.

Pietralunga, Mark. Cesare Pavese & Antonio Chiuminatto: Their Correspondence. 2007. (Toronto Italian Studies). (ITA & ENG.). 320p. (978-0-8020-9294-6(2)) Univ. of Toronto Pr.

Pinocchio. 2008.Tr. of Avventure di Pinocchio. (Illus.). pap. (978-1-84830-918-0(X), Wildhern Pr.) Echo Library.

Pirandello, Luigi, et al. Nel Tempo Della Lontananza, 1919-1936. 2008. (ITA.). 485p. (978-88-8241-269-2(5), Spotlight Poets) Sciascia.

Pironti, Tullio. Books & Rough Business. 2009. (ENG.). 232p. pap. 20.95 (978-1-59709-129-9(4)) Red Hen Pr.

Pugliese, Stanislao G. Bitter Spring: A Life of Ignazio Silone. 2009. (ENG., Illus.). 448p. 35.00 (978-0-374-11348-3(3)) Farrar, Straus & Giroux.

Rorato, Lara & Spunta, Marina, eds. Letteratura come Fantasticazione: In Conversazione con Gianni Celati. 2009. (ITA.). x, 379p. (978-0-7734-3900-9(5)) Mellen, Edwin Pr., The.

Ryder, Judith R. The Career & Writings of Demetrius Kydones: A Study of Fourteenth-Century Byzantine Politics, Religion & Society. 296p. (978-90-04-18565-4(8)) BRILL.

Salzani, Carlo. Crisi e Possibilità: Robert Musil e il tramonto Dell'Occidente. 2010. (Musiliana Ser.). (ITA.). 274p. pap. (978-3-0343-0376-7(9)) Lang, Peter.

Serra, Renato & Menetti, Andrea. Mio Carissimo. 2009. (ITA.). 269p. (978-88-7847-262-4(X)) Monte Universita Parma.

Smith, Lawrence G. Cesare Pavese & America: Life, Love, & Literature. 2008. (Illus.). 352p. 39.95 (978-1-55849-673-6(4)) Univ. of Massachusetts Pr.

Soldateschi, Jole. Il tragico Quotidiano: Papini, Palazzeschi, Cassola, Bianciardi. 2010. (Cronaca e Storia Ser.). (ITA.). 280p. pap. 34.00 (978-88-564-0141-7(X)) Polistampa ITA. Dist: Brown, David Bk. Co., The.

Stebbing, Henry. Lives of the Italian Poets V2. 2007. (ENG.). 366p. 48.95 (978-0-548-18899-6(8)); pap. 33.95 (978-1-4304-9322-8(4)) Kessinger Publishing, LLC.

Sulam, Sarra Copia. Jewish Poet & Intellectual in Seventeenth-Century Venice: The Works of Sarra Copia Sulam in Verse & Prose along with Writings of Her Contemporaries in Her Praise, Condemnation, or Defense. Harran, Don, tr. 2009. (Other Voice in Early Modern Europe Ser.). (ENG & ITA., Illus.). 632p. 95.00 (978-0-226-77988-1(2)); pap. 35.00 (978-0-226-77989-8(0)) Univ. of Chicago Pr.

Trubiano, Marisa S. Ennio Flaiano & His Italy: Postcards from a Changing World. 2010. 59.50 (978-0-8386-4213-9(6)) Fairleigh Dickinson Univ. Pr.

Tuck, Lily. Woman of Rome: A Life of Elsa Morante. 2009. (ENG., Illus.). 288p. pap. 13.99 (978-0-06-147259-6(X), HarperPerennial) HarperCollins Pubs.

Unger, Miles J. Machiavelli: A Biography. 2012. (ENG., Illus.). 416p. pap. 16.00 **(978-1-4165-5630-5(3))** Simon & Schuster.

Valentino, Rudolph. My Private Diary. 2011. 340p. 51.95 **(978-1-258-09930-5(6))** Literary Licensing, LLC.

Volponi, Paolo, et al. Scrivo a Te Come Guardandomi Allo Specchio: Lettere a Pasolini (1954-1975) 2009. (Diaspro Ser.). (ITA.). 214p. (C). 29.50 (978-88-596-0510-2(5), Edizioni Polistampa ITA. Dist: Brown, David Bk. Co., The.

Williams, Orlo. Giosue Carducci. 2009. (ENG.). 124p. 28.99 (978-1-117-34295-5(6)); 126p. pap. 19.75 (978-1-117-34296-2(4)); 126p. 21.99 (978-0-554-40247-5(5)); 126p. pap. 19.75 (978-0-554-40244-4(0)); 124p. 21.99 (978-1-103-85823-1(8)); 124p. pap. 15.99 (978-1-103-85814-9(9)) BiblioBazaar.

—Giosue Carducci. 2009. 56p. pap. 14.14 (978-1-151-66785-4(4)) General Bks. LLC.

—Giosue Carducci. 2008. 122p. 35.95 (978-1-4366-2200-4(X)); 124p. pap. 20.95 (978-0-548-86804-1(2)) Kessinger Publishing, LLC.

Wink, Joachim. Paladine Auf Abwegen: Formen und Ausdrucke Religioser Indifferenz in Luigi Pulcis Morgante. (GER.). 343p. 68.95 (978-3-631-57122-4(4)) Lang, Peter GmbH, Europaischer Verlag der Wissenschaften DEU. Dist: Lang, Peter Publishing, Inc.

Zak, Gur. Petrarch's Humanism & the Care of the Self. 2010. (ENG.). 200p. 80.00 (978-0-521-11467-7(5)) Cambridge Univ. Pr.

AUTHORS, JAPANESE

Cornyetz, Nina. The Ethics of Aesthetics in Japanese Cinema & Literature: Polygraphic Desire. 2008. X, 230p. 39.95 (978-0-415-47450-3(4)) Routledge.

Cornyetz, Nina & Holcombe, Randall. The Ethics of Aesthetics in Japanese Cinema & Literature. 2007. (Routledge Contemporary Japan Ser.: Vol. 10). X, 230p. 170.00 (978-0-415-77087-3(4)) Routledge.

Graham, Masako Nakagawa. The Autobiographical Narrative in Modern Japan: A Study of Kasai Zenzo, a Shi-Shosetsu Writer. 2007. 188p. (978-0-7734-5396-8(2)) Mellen, Edwin Pr., The.

Japan Foundation Staff, ed. A Wild Haruki Chase: Reading Murakami Around the World. 2008. (ENG., Illus.). 152p. pap. 16.95 (978-1-933330-66-2(X)) Stone Bridge Pr.

Jun'ichiro, Tanizaki. Memoir of Forgetting the Capital. 2011. (ENG.). (gr. 17). 50.00 (978-4-8419-0547-2(2)) Columbia Univ. Pr.

Keene, Donald. So Lovely a Country Will Never Perish: Wartime Diaries of Japanese Writers. 2010. (Asia Perspectives: History, Society, & Culture Ser.). (ENG.). 192p. (gr. 17). 24.95 (978-0-231-15146-7(2)) Columbia Univ. Pr.

Kimbrough, R. Keller. Preachers, Poets, Women, & the Way: Izumi Shikibu & the Buddhist Literature of Medieval Japan. 2008. (Illus.). 374p. 75.00 (978-1-929280-47-6(5)); (ENG., pap. 29.00 (978-1-929280-48-3(3)) Univ. of Michigan, Ctr. for Japanese Studies.

Liman, Antonin Vaclav. Ibuse Masuji: A Century Remembered. 2008. (Illus.). 430p. 25.00 (978-80-246-1448-9(0)) Karolinum, nakladatelstvi Univerzity Karlovy CZE. Dist: Chicago Distribution Ctr.

MacFarlane, Alan. Secrets of the Modern World: Yukichi Fukuzawa. 2011. 98p. pap. 22.84 **(978-1-60888-112-3(1))** Nimble Bks. LLC.

Ross, Christopher. Mishima's Sword: Travels in Search of a Samurai Legend. 2007. (ENG., Illus.). 272p. per. 15.95 (978-0-306-81568-3(0)) Da Capo Pr., Inc.

Seats, Michael. Murakami Haruki: The Simulacrum in Contemporary Japanese Culture. 2006. (Studies of Modern Japan Ser.). (ENG., Illus.). 384p. 73.50 (978-0-7391-0785-0(2)) Lexington Bks.

Seats, Michael Robert. Murakami Haruki: The Simulacrum in Contemporary Japanese Culture. 2009. (Studies of Modern Japan Ser.). (ENG.). 384p. pap. 41.99 (978-0-7391-2725-4(X)) Lexington Bks.

Slaymaker, Douglas. Yoko Tawada: Voices from Everywhere. 2007. (AsiaWorld Ser.). (ENG.). 186p. 62.99 (978-0-7391-2272-3(X)) Lexington Bks.

Van Compernolle, Timothy J. The Uses of Memory: The Critique of Modernity in the Fiction of Higuchi Ichiyō 2006. (Harvard East Asian Monographs: 275). (Illus.). 215p. 39.95 (978-0-674-02272-0(6)) Harvard Univ., Asia Ctr.

AUTHORS, JEWISH

see Jewish Authors

AUTHORS, LATIN

Agricola, Rodolphus. Letters. (LAT & ENG., Illus.). ix, 435 p. (978-90-232-3808-9(7)) Bow Historical Bks.

Antoninus, Marcus. Meditations. 2006. 164p. per. 14.99 (978-1-59547-954-9(5)) NuVision Pubns., LLC.

Boissier, Gaston. Cicero & His Friends A Study of Roman. 2006. pap. 34.95 (978-1-4286-4099-3(1)) Kessinger Publishing, LLC.

Carter, John M., Sr. Suetonius: Divus Augustus. 2009. (Latin Texts Ser.). (LAT & ENG., Illus.). 240p. pap. 19.95 (978-0-906515-55-6(6)) Bristol Classical Pr. GBR. Dist: International Publishers Marketing.

Cicero. Cicero, XVa, Orations: Philippics 1-6, 2 vols., Volume XVa. 2010. (Loeb Classical Library: 189). (LAT & ENG., Illus.). 400p. 24.00 (978-0-674-99634-2(8)) Harvard Univ. Pr.

Cicero. Letters of a Roman Gentleman: Selected from the Correspondence of Cicero. McKinlay, Arthur Patch, ed. 2011. 284p. 48.95 **(978-1-258-02874-9(3))** Literary Licensing, LLC.

Cicero, Marcus Tullius. Letters of Cicero. 2007. (ENG.). 76p. per. (978-1-4068-4601-0(5)) Echo Library.

—Letters of Cicero. Muirhead, J. H., ed. 2009. 336p. 45.95 (978-1-104-15589-5(9)); pap. 30.95 (978-1-104-14133-2(7)) Kessinger Publishing, LLC.

—Letters to Atticus. 2010. 214p. pap. (978-1-152-99947-3(8)) Books LLC.

—Select Orations & Letters of Cicero: With an Introduction, Notes, & Vocabulary. Kelsey, Francis W., ed. 9th ed. 2007. (Illus.). 526p. pap. 45.00 (978-1-55635-422-9(3), Wipf and Stock) Wipf & Stock Pubs.

—Selected Letters. Walsh, P. G., tr. from LAT. 2008. (Oxford World's Classics Ser.). (LAT & ENG., Illus.). 384p. pap. 17.95 (978-0-19-921420-4(4)) Oxford Univ. Pr., Inc.

Davis, Gregson. A Companion to Horace. 2010. (Blackwell Companions to the Ancient World Ser.: 46). (ENG., Illus.). 488p. 209.95 (978-1-4051-5540-3(X), Wiley-Blackwell) Wiley, John & Sons, Inc.

Erasmus, Desiderius. Correspondence of Erasmus. 2011. (Collected Works of Erasmus Ser.). (ENG.). **(978-1-4426-4203-4(3))** Univ. of Toronto Pr.

Erasmus, Desiderius, et al. Correspondence of Erasmus, Letters 1802. 2010. (Collected Works of Erasmus Ser.). (Illus.). 624p. (978-0-8020-9059-1(1)) Univ. of Toronto Pr.

Fonzio, Bartolomeo. Letters to Friends. Daneloni, Alessandro, ed. Davies, Martin, tr. from LAT. 2011. (I Tatti Renaissance Library: 47). (ENG & LAT., Illus.). 256p. 29.95 (978-0-674-05836-1(4)) Harvard Univ. Pr.

Harrison, Stephen, ed. A Companion to Latin Literature. 2007. (Blackwell Companions to the Ancient World Ser.: 13). (ENG., Illus.). 472p. per. 49.95 (978-1-4051-6131-2(0), Wiley-Blackwell) Wiley, John & Sons, Inc.

Huizinga, Johan. Erasmus & the Age of Reformation. 2009. 312p. 29.99 (978-0-559-07093-8(4)); 28.99 (978-0-559-07108-9(6)); pap. 25.99 (978-0-559-07098-3(5)); pap. 28.75 (978-0-559-07104-1(3)) BiblioBazaar.

—Erasmus & the Age of Reformation. 2008. (ENG.). 240p. 43.99 (978-1-4353-9449-0(6)); per. 36.99 (978-1-4353-9453-7(4)) IndyPublish.com.

—Erasmus & the Age of Reformation. 2010. 208p. pap. 18.00 (978-1-60899-950-7(5), Wipf and Stock) Wipf & Stock Pubs.

Jeans, G. E. & Watson, J. S., trs. Select Letters of Cicero. 2007. (ENG.). 192p. 37.95 (978-0-548-12299-0(7)) Kessinger Publishing, LLC.

Jebb, Richard Claverhouse. Erasmus. 2009. 62p. pap. 16.75 (978-1-113-04056-5(4)) BiblioBazaar.

—Erasmus. 2007. (ENG.). 60p. per. 16.95 (978-1-4326-6810-5(2)) Kessinger Publishing, LLC.

JEUNE, Pline Le. Lettres - Tome II - Livres IV-VI. Methy, Nicole & Zehnacker, Hubert, eds. 2011. (Collection des universites de France Serie Latine Ser.). (FRE.). 359p. (C). pap. 68.00 **(978-2-251-01459-3(4))** Societe d'edition Les Belles lettres FRA. Dist: ISD.

—Lettres, T. 1, livres I a III. Zehnacker, Hubert, ed. 2009. (Collection des universites de France Serie Latine Ser.). (FRE.). 193p. (C). pap. 53.00 **(978-2-251-01451-7(9))** Societe d'edition Les Belles lettres FRA. Dist: ISD.

Jones, Brian. Suetonius Vespasian. 2007. (Latin Texts Ser.). (LAT.). 192p. pap. 19.95 (978-1-85399-584-2(3)) Bristol Classical Pr. GBR. Dist: International Publishers Marketing.

Keene, Charles Haines, ed. Selections Illustrative of Roman Life from the Letters of Pliny. 2011. 144p. 40.95 **(978-1-258-03600-3(2))** Literary Licensing, LLC.

Landfester, M., ed. Dictionary of Greek & Latin Authors & Texts. 2009. (Brill's New Pauly - Supplements Ser.). (978-90-04-16783-4(8)) BRILL.

Levi, Peter. Horace: A Life. 2012. (ENG.). 288p. pap. 18.00 **(978-1-78076-139-8(2)**, Tauris Parke Paperbacks) I. B. Tauris & Co., Ltd. GBR. Dist: Macmillan.

—Virgil: A Life. 2012. (ENG.). 288p. pap. 18.00 **(978-1-84885-904-3(X)**, Tauris Parke Paperbacks) I. B. Tauris & Co., Ltd. GBR. Dist: Macmillan.

Maclennan, Keith. Horace: A Poet for a New Age. 2010. (Greece & Rome: Texts & Contexts Ser.). (ENG., Illus.). 200p. pap. 26.00 (978-0-521-75746-1(0)) Cambridge Univ. Pr.

Maddison, Carol. Marcantonio Flaminio: Poet, Humanist, & Reformer. 2011. (ENG.). 224p. pap. 40.00 **(978-0-8078-6881-2(7))** Univ. of North Carolina Pr.

McGowan, Matthew M. Ovid in Exile: Power & Poetic Redress in the Tristia & Epistulae Ex Ponto. 2009. (978-90-04-17076-6(6)) BRILL.

Morello, Ruth & Morrison, A. D., eds. Ancient Letters: Classical & Late Antique Epistolography. 2007. (ENG., Illus.). 392p. 140.00 (978-0-19-920395-6(4)) Oxford Univ. Pr., Inc.

Oppermann, Irene. Zur Funktion historischer Beispiele in Ciceros Briefen. (Beiträge zur Altertumskunde Ser.). (GER.). 338p. 180.00 **(978-3-11-184277-6(0))** De Gruyter, Walter Inc.

Petrarca, Francesco. Familiaria: Bucher der Vertraulichkeiten Band 2. Widmer, Berthe, ed. 2009. (GER.). L, 915p. 277.00 (978-3-11-019159-2(8)) De Gruyter, Walter Inc.

Roberts, Arthur W. Cicero Selected Orations & Letters. 2006. pap. 48.95 (978-1-4286-4765-7(1)) Kessinger Publishing, LLC.

Roberts, Michael John. The Letters of Symmachus. 2012. **(978-90-04-21163-6(2))** BRILL.

Ruiz Arzálluz, Iñigo, et al. La Vita Terrentii de Petrarca. 2010. (LAT & SPA.). xix, 159p. (978-88-8455-647-9(3)) Antenore.

Salzman, Michele Renee, comment. The Letters of Symmachus. 2011. **(978-1-58983-597-9(2))**; **(978-1-58983-598-6(0))** Society of Biblical Literature.

Schnur, Harry C., et al. Pegasus Devocatus. (LAT, GER & ENG.). x, 272p. pap. 32.50 *(978-90-6186-474-5(7))* Leuven Univ. Pr. BEL. Dist: Cornell Univ. Pr.

Shackleton Bailey, David R. Onomasticon to Cicero's Letters. XII, 161p. 120.00 ***(978-3-11-186697-0(1))*** De Gruyter, Walter Inc.

Stavans, Ilan. Latina Writers. 2008. (Ilan Stavans Library of Latino Civilization Ser.). 148p. 55.00 *(978-0-313-34806-8(5)*, GR4806, Greenwood Pr.) Greenwood Publishing Group, Inc.

Stewart, Jon. Kierkegaard & the Roman World, Vol. 3. 2009. (Kierkegaard Research: Sources, Reception & Resources Ser.). 242p. 99.95 *(978-0-7546-6554-0(2))* Ashgate Publishing Co.

Tyrrell, Robert Yelvert. Cicero in His Letters. 2006. pap. 37.95 *(978-1-4286-3991-1(8))* Kessinger Publishing, LLC.

Wilcox, Amanda. The Gift of Correspondence in Classical Rome: Friendship in Cicero's Ad Familiares & Seneca's Moral Epistles. 2012. E-Book ***(978-0-299-28833-4(1))***; (ENG.). 216p. pap. 34.95 ***(978-0-299-28834-1(X))*** Univ. of Wisconsin Pr.

AUTHORS, LATIN AMERICAN

Cabral, Astrid. Cage. Levitin, Alexis, tr. from POR. 2008. (ENG & POR.). 91p. pap. 12.00 *(978-0-924047-44-2(5))* Host Pubns., Inc.

Cisneros, Odile & Young, Richard. Historical Dictionary of Latin American Literature & Theater. 2010. (Historical Dictionaries of Literature & the Arts Ser.). (ENG.). 748p. 99.00 *(978-0-8108-5099-6(0))* Scarecrow Pr., Inc.

Galeano, Eduardo. Voices of Time: A Life in Stories. Fried, Mark, tr. 2007. (ENG., Illus.). 368p. pap. 18.00 *(978-0-312-42682-8(8))* Picador.

Ilan, Stavans & Stavans, Ilan. Gabriel Garcia Marquez: The Early Years. 2010. (ENG., Illus.). 256p. 25.00 *(978-0-312-24033-2(3))* Palgrave Macmillan.

Kumaraswami, Par & Thornton, Niamh, eds. Revolucionarias: Conflict & Gender in Latin American Narratives by Women. (Illus.). 237p. pap. 63.95 *(978-3-03910-894-7(8))* Lang, Peter Publishing, Inc.

Lopes, Maria Angélica Guimarães. The Brazilian Short Story in the Late Twentieth Century: A Selection from Nineteen Authors. 2009. 176p. 99.95 *(978-0-7734-4904-6(3))* Mellen, Edwin Pr., The.

Maristain, Monica & Bolaño, Roberto, eds. The Last Interview: And Other Conversations. Perez, Sybil, tr. from ENG. 2009. (ENG.). 128p. pap. 14.95 *(978-1-933633-83-1(2))* Melville Hse. Publishing.

Martínez, Juana. Exilios y Residencias: Escrituras de España y América. 2007. (SPA.). 254p. pap. 44.00 *(978-84-8489-184-0(4))* Iberoamericana Vervuert Publishing Corp.

Morais, Fernando. El Mago: La Extraordinaria Historia de Paulo Coelho. 2008. (SPA.). 704p. pap. 18.99 *(978-0-06-137508-8(X)*, Rayo) HarperCollins Pubs.

Ocampo de Gomez, Aurora & Prado Velazquez, Ernesto. Diccionario de Escritores Mexicanos. (SPA.). 69.95 *(978-0-7859-0713-8(0)*, S-6745) French & European Pubns., Inc.

Scott, Renee Sum. What Is Eating Latin American Women Writers: Food, Weight, & Eating Disorders. 2009. 99.99 *(978-1-60497-640-3(3))* Cambria Pr.

Young, Richard A. & Cisneros, Odile. Historical Dictionary of Latin American Literature & Theater. 2011. xxvii, 719p. E-Book *(978-0-8108-7498-5(9))* Scarecrow Pr., Inc.

24 Poetas Latinoamericanos. (SPA.). pap. 16.95 *(978-968-494-079-6(3)*, CI7850) Centro de Informacion y Desarrollo de la Comunicacion y la Literatura MEX. Dist: AIMS International Bks., Inc.

AUTHORS, LITHUANIAN

Goldberg, Leah. With This Night. Kantar, Annie, tr. from HEB. 2011. (ENG.). 120p. pap. 16.00 *(978-0-292-72647-5(3))* Univ. of Texas Pr.

Velicka, Domas. Domas Velicka: Kurybinis Palikimas Kovojanciai Tautai. Rinktiniai Rastai, Dokumentai, Literatura. Velickaite (Velicka), Asta Kornelija, ed. 2007. (LIT., Illus.). 520p. pap. *(978-0-9771413-2-6(2))* Velicka, Asta Kornelija.

—Domas Velicka: Kurybinis Palikimas Kovojanciai Tautai. Rinktiniai Rastai. Dokumentai, Literatura. Asta Kornelija Velickaite (Velicka) Staff, ed. 2006. (LIT., Illus.). 512p. pap. *(978-0-9771413-1-9(4))* Velicka, Asta Kornelija.

Velicka, Domas & Velicka, Domas. Domas Velicka: Kurybinis Palikimas Kovojanciai Tautai. Rinktiniai Rastai, Dokumentai, Literatura. Velickaite (Velicka), Asta Kornelija, ed. (LIT., Illus.). 2010. 512p. pap. *(978-0-9771413-4-0(9))* 2009. 510p. pap. *(978-0-9771413-3-3(0))* Velicka, Asta Kornelija.

AUTHORS, NEW ZEALAND

Drichel, Simone. Frameworks: Contemporary Criticism on Janet Frame. Cronin, Jan, ed. 2009. (Illus.). 256p. 70.00 *(978-90-420-2676-6(6))* Rodopi.

Edmond-Paul, Mary, ed. Lighted Windows: Critical Essays on Robin Hyde. 2008. (Illus.). 226p. pap. 40.00 *(978-1-877372-58-2(7))* Otago University Pr. NZL. Dist: International Specialized Bk. Services.

Gwynne, Joel. The Secular Visionaries: Aestheticism & New Zealand Short Fiction in the Twentieth Century. 2010. (Illus.). 289p. pap. 78.00 *(978-90-420-3184-5(0))* Rodopi.

Holden Ronning, Anne. For Was I Not Born Here? Identity & Culture in the Work of Yvonne du Fresne. 2010. (Illus.). 200p. 56.00 *(978-90-420-2957-6(9))* Rodopi.

Jones, Alison & Middleton, Sue, eds. The Kiss & the Ghost: Sylvia Ashton-Warner & New Zealand. 2009. 148p. *(978-90-8790-785-3(0))* Sense Pubs.

Mantz, Ruth Elvish. The Life of Katherine Mansfield. 2008. 388p. *(978-1-4437-2527-9(7)*, Hesperides Pr.) Read Bks.

—Life of Katherine Mansfield. 2006. 384p. per. *(978-1-4067-3435-5(7)*, Hesperides Pr.) Read Bks.

McMonagle, Michael Francis. Seven Lives of the Devil's Spawn: From Destruction to Salvation A True Wild Cat Story. 2011. 144p. 23.50 ***(978-1-60976-292-6(4)***, Eloquent Bks.) AEG Literary Publishing Services, Inc.

Millar, Paul. No Fretful Sleeper: A Life of Bill Pearson. 2010. (ENG., Illus.). 400p. pap. 34.95 *(978-1-86940-419-2(X))* Auckland Univ. Pr. NZL. Dist: Independent Pubs. Group.

O'Sullivan, Vincent & Scott, Margaret, eds. The Collected Letters of Katherine Mansfield: Volume 5: 1922, 5 vols. 2008. (ENG., Illus.). 400p. 125.00 *(978-0-19-818399-0(2))* Oxford Univ. Pr., Inc.

Rahn, B. J. Ngaio Marsh: The Woman & Her Work. 2007. (ENG.). 272p. per. 40.00 *(978-0-8108-5939-5(4))* Scarecrow Pr., Inc.

Stead, C. K. South-West of Eden: A Memoir, 1932-1956. 2010. (ENG., Illus.). 360p. 27.95 *(978-1-86940-454-3(8))* Auckland Univ. Pr. NZL. Dist: Independent Pubs. Group.

AUTHORS, NORWEGIAN

Camus, Renaud. Demeures de L'esprit: Danemark, Norvège. 2010. (FRE., Illus.). 453p. *(978-2-213-64389-2(X))* Fayard, Artheme, Librairie.

Galling, Ines. Balanceakte am Fjord: Ästhetische Tradition, Variation und Innovation in Jon Fosses Dramen. 2010. (Imaginatio borealis. Bilder des Nordens Ser.). (GER.). 260p. 67.95 *(978-3-631-59452-0(6))* Lang, Peter GmbH, Europaischer Verlag der Wissenschaften DEU. Dist: Lang, Peter.

Hamsun, Marie. The Nobel Novelist Knur Hamsun During the Nazi Occupation of Norway: The Final Chapter that Was Omitted from Marie Hamsun's Autobiography of Their Life Together. Magnuson, Elmer T., tr. from NOR. 2011. (Illus.). 164p. 109.95 ***(978-0-7734-3944-3(7))*** Mellen, Edwin Pr., The.

Isaacson, Lanae H. Dlb 354 Norwgn Wrtrs. 2009. (Dictionary of Literary Biography Ser.). (ENG., Illus.). 446p. 315.00 *(978-0-7876-8172-2(5))* Cengage Gale.

Kolloen, Ingar Sletten. Knut Hamsun: Dreamer & Dissenter. Skuggevik, Erik & Dawkin, Deborah, trs. from NOR. 2009. (ENG., Illus.). 384p. 40.00 *(978-0-300-12356-2(6))* Yale Univ. Pr.

Worster, W. W. Wanderers. 24.95 *(978-0-8488-0686-6(7))* Amereon LTD.

AUTHORS, PHILIPPINE

see Authors, Filipino

AUTHORS, POLISH

Banks, Brian R. Muse & Messiah: The Life, Imagination & Legacy of Bruno Schulz (1892-1942) 2nd ed. 2009. (Illus.). pap. *(978-0-9556259-7-8(1))* Inkermen Pr.

Bujnicki, Tadeusz, et al. Zagary: Srodowisko Kulturowe Grupy Literackiej. 2009. (POL.). 412p. *(978-83-242-0915-6(8))* Universitas, Towarzystwo Autorow i Wydawcow Prac Naukowych.

Cwiklinski, Krzysztof. Znani I Nieobecni: Studia Z Problematyki Polskiej Literatury Emigracyjnej I Zycia Literackiego Na Uchodzstwie. 2008. (POL.). 269p. *(978-83-231-2261-6(X))* Uniwersytet Mikolaja Kopernika, Dzial Wydawnictw.

Domoslawski, Artur. Ryszard Kapuscinski: The Biography. Lloyd-Jones, Antonia, tr. from POL. 2012. (ENG.). 464p. 34.95 ***(978-1-84467-858-7(X)***, 844858) Verso Bks. GBR. Dist: Norton, W. W. & Co., Inc.

Giroud, Vincent. The World of Witold Gombrowicz 1904-1969: Catalog of a Centenary Exhibition at the Beinecke Rare Book & Manuscript Library. 2007. (Illus.). 74p. pap. 20.00 *(978-0-300-13400-1(2))* Yale Univ. Pr.

Gombrowicz, Witold. Diary. Vallee, Lillian, tr. from POL. 2012. (Margellos World Republic of Letters Ser.). (ENG.). 800p. pap. 20.00 ***(978-0-300-11806-3(6))*** Yale Univ. Pr.

Gombrowicz, Witold. A Kind of Testament. De Roux, Dominique, ed. Hamilton, Alastair, tr. from FRE. 2007. (Eastern European Literature Ser.). (ENG.). 160p. per. 12.95 *(978-1-56478-476-6(2)*, 478476) Dalkey Archive Pr.

Gralak, Iwona & Pacawski, Jan. Pisarze Regionu Swietokrzyskiego. *(978-83-86006-92-2(7))* Kieleckie Towarzystwo Naukowe.

Herbert, Zbigniew & Citko, Henryk. Nike, Która Sie Waha. 2008. (POL., Illus.). 68p. *(978-83-89945-32-7(0))*; *(978-83-7009-713-4(8))* Biblioteka Narodowa.

Kuryluk, Ewa. Frascati: Apoteoza Topografii. 2009. (POL., Illus.). 338p. *(978-83-08-04377-6(1))* Wydawnictwo Literackie.

Lekarczyk-Cisek, Barbara. Twarze Pana Cogito. 2008. (POL., Illus.). 68p. *(978-83-61056-06-5(8))* Ossolinneum, Zaklad Narodowy im. Ossolinskich, Wydawnictwo.

Milosz, Czeslaw. Beginning with My Streets: Essays & Recollections. Levine, Madeline, tr. 2010. (ENG., Illus.). 304p. pap. 18.00 *(978-0-374-53272-7(9))* Farrar, Straus & Giroux.

—Legends of Modernity: Essays & Letters from Occupied Poland, 1942-1943. Levine, Madeline, tr. from POL. 2006. (ENG., Illus.). 288p. per. 14.00 *(978-0-374-53046-4(7))* Farrar, Straus & Giroux.

AUTHORS, PORTUGUESE

Lobo Antunes, António. The Fat Man & Infinity: And Other Writings. Costa, Margaret Jull, tr. from SPA. 2009. (ENG.). 320p. 26.95 *(978-0-393-06198-7(1)*, 6198) Norton, W. W. & Co., Inc.

Saramago, José. Cadernos de Lanzarote Vol. 1: 1993-1995. 2nd ed. (POR.). 180p. 31.95 *(978-972-21-0901-7(4))* Caminho, Editorial PRT. Dist: Distribooks, Inc.

—The Notebook. Hahn, Daniel & Hopkinson, Amanda, trs. from POR. 2010. (ENG.). 288p. 23.95 *(978-1-84467-614-9(5)*, 844614) Verso Bks. GBR. Dist: Norton, W. W. & Co., Inc.

—The Notebook. Hopkinson, Amanda & Hahn, Daniel, trs. from POR. 2nd ed. 2011. (ENG.). 304p. pap. 16.95 *(978-1-84467-701-6(X)*, 844701) Verso Bks. GBR. Dist: Norton, W. W. & Co., Inc.

—O Caderno. 2nd ed. 2010. (POR.). *(978-972-21-2092-0(1))* Caminho, Editorial.

Saramago, José. Small Memories. Costa, Margaret Jull, tr. 2012. (ENG.). 176p. pap. 13.95 ***(978-0-547-75263-1(6)***, Mariner Bks.) Houghton Mifflin Harcourt Trade & Reference Pubs.

Seixas, Maria João. República das Mulheres. 2010. (POR., Illus.). 245p. *(978-972-25-2211-3(6))* Bertrand, Livraria.

AUTHORS, RUSSIAN

Aksakov, Sergei. A Russian Schoolboy. Duff, J. D., tr. from RUS. 2009. (ENG.). 200p. pap. 11.95 *(978-1-58988-051-1(X))* Dry, Paul Bks., Inc.

Andrews, James T. Red Cosmos: K. E. Tsiolkovskii, Grandfather of Soviet Rocketry. 2009. (Centennial of Flight Ser.). (ENG., 168p. Illus.). pap. 23.00 *(978-1-60344-168-1(9))*; 49.00 *(978-1-60344-117-9(4))* Texas A&M Univ. Pr.

Asher, Oksana. My Diary: And, Dray-Khmara As a Poet. 2010. 57p. pap. 14.00 *(978-1-933132-75-4(2))* Spuyten Duyvil.

Bartlett, Rosamund. Tolstoy: A Russian Life. 2011. (ENG., Illus.). 560p. 35.00 *(978-0-15-101438-5(8))* Houghton Mifflin Harcourt Trade & Reference Pubs.

Bashirtseff, Marie. Marie Bashkirtseff the Journal of A Youn. 2006. pap. 37.95 *(978-1-4286-3607-1(2))* Kessinger Publishing, LLC.

Benn, Anna & Bartlett, Rosamund. Literary Russia. 2007. (ENG., Illus.). 528p. (gr. 12). 37.50 *(978-1-58567-444-2(3))* Overlook Pr., The.

Bird, Robert. Fyodor Dostoevsky. 2012. (Reaktion Books - Critical Lives Ser.). (Illus.). 224p. pap. 16.95 ***(978-1-86189-900-2(9))*** Reaktion Bks., Ltd. GBR. Dist: Chicago Distribution Ctr.

Blair, Elaine. Literary St. Petersburg: A Guide to the City & Its Writers. 2007. (ENG., Illus.). 140p. pap. 16.95 *(978-1-892145-37-6(5))* Little Bookroom.

Breger, Louis. Dostoevsky: The Author as Psychoanalyst. 2008. (ENG.). 315p. pap. 34.95 *(978-1-4128-0843-9(X))* Transaction Pubs.

Briggs, Anthony. Brief Lives: Fyodor Dostoevsky. 2012. (Brief Lives Ser.). (ENG.). 128p. pap. 12.95 ***(978-1-84391-925-4(7))*** Hesperus Pr. GBR. Dist: Independent Pubs. Group.

Briggs, Anthony. Leo Tolstoy. 2010. (Brief Lives Ser.). (ENG.). 119p. pap. 15.95 *(978-1-84391-911-7(7))* Hesperus Pr. GBR. Dist: Independent Pubs. Group.

Buchinskaya, V. S. Pavel Zaltsman. (Illus.). *(978-0-934393-13-3(3))* Rector Pr., Ltd.

Chandler, Robert. Alexander Pushkin. 2009. (Brief Lives Ser.). (ENG.). 112p. pap. 15.95 *(978-1-84391-912-4(5))* Hesperus Pr. GBR. Dist: Independent Pubs. Group.

Chekhov, Anton. Letters of Anton Chekhov. 2008. 356p. 31.99 *(978-0-554-29498-8(2))*; 29.99 *(978-0-554-38801-4(4))* BiblioBazaar.

Chekhov, Mikhail Pavlovich. Anton Chekhov: A Brother's Memoir. Alper, Eugene, tr. from RUS. 2009. (ENG., Illus.). 256p. 25.00 *(978-0-230-61883-1(9))* Palgrave Macmillan.

Cowley, Joseph. Crime & Punishment by Fyodor Dostoevsky: Adapted by Joseph Cowley. 2011. 144p. pap. 11.95 ***(978-1-4620-3810-7(7))*** iUniverse, Inc.

Crankshaw, Edward. Tolstoy: The Making of a Novelist. 2012. 278p. pap. ***(978-1-4482-0521-9(2)***, 146527, Bloomsbury Reader) Bloomsbury Publishing Plc.

Crosby, Ernest Howard. Tolstoy & His Message. 2007. (ENG.). 108p. 33.95 *(978-0-548-02328-0(X))* Kessinger Publishing, LLC.

Dostoyevsky, Fyodor. Dostoevsky Letters & Reminiscences. 2006. pap. 28.95 *(978-1-4286-5486-0(0))* Kessinger Publishing, LLC.

—Winter Notes on Summer Impressions. FitzLyon, Kyril, tr. from RUS. 2009. (Oneworld Classics Ser.). (ENG., Illus.). 160p. pap. 14.95 *(978-1-84749-064-3(6))* Alma Classics GBR. Dist: Independent Pubs. Group.

Durylin, S. N. & Genieva, E. V. "IA Nikomu Tak Ne Pishu, Kak Vam — " Perepiska Sergeia Nikolaevicha Durylina I Eleny Vasilevny Genievoi. 2010. (Illus.). 525p. *(978-5-7380-0283-0(0))* Rudomino, Izdatel'stvo.

Efron, Georgii. The Diaries of Georgy Efron, August 1942-August 1943 (The Tashkent Period) 2010. vii, 152p. 99.95 *(978-0-7734-3645-9(6))* Mellen, Edwin Pr., The.

Euy: A Zaumist Biography of Alexei Kruchenykh. 2006. 102p. per. 10.00 *(978-0-9770049-4-2(5))* Xexoxial Editions.

Frank, J. Between Religion & Rationality: Essays in Russian Literature & Culture. 2010. (ENG.). 312p. (C). 60.00 *(978-0-691-14256-2(4))* Princeton Univ. Pr.

Frank, Joseph. Between Religion & Rationality: Essays in Russian Literature & Culture. 2010. (ENG.). 312p. (C). pap. 29.95 *(978-0-691-14566-2(0))* Princeton Univ. Pr.

—Dostoievski Vol. 1: Las Semillas de la Rebelion. 2010. (Lengua y Estudios Literarios Ser.). (SPA.). 508p. pap. 10.99 *(978-968-16-1732-5(0))* Fondo de Cultura Economica USA.

—Dostoievski Vol. 2: Los Años de Prueba, 1850-1859. 2010. (Lengua y Estudios Literarios Ser.). (SPA.). 444p. pap. 15.99 *(978-968-16-2448-4(3))* Fondo de Cultura Economica USA.

—Dostoievski Vol. 3: La Secuela de la Liberacion. 2010. (Lengua y Estudios Literarios Ser.). (SPA.). 480p. pap. 21.99 *(978-968-16-3531-2(0))* Fondo de Cultura Economica USA.

Frankel, Edith Rogovin. Novy Mir: A Case Study in the Politics of Literature 1952-1958. 2009. (Cambridge Studies in Russian Literature Ser.). (ENG.). 228p. pap. 31.99 *(978-0-521-10986-4(8))* Cambridge Univ. Pr.

Freidin, Gregory, ed. The Enigma of Isaac Babel: Biography, History, Context. 2009. (ENG., Illus.). 288p. 60.00 *(978-0-8047-5903-8(0))* Stanford Univ. Pr.

Ginzburg, Lidiia. Prokhodiashchie Kharaktery: Proza Voennykh Let: Zapiski Blokadnogo Cheloveka. 2011. (RUS.). 598p. *(978-5-98379-143-5(5))* Novoe isdatel'stvo.

Grossman, Joan Delaney. Ivan Konevskoi: Wise Child of Russian Symbolism. 2010. (Studies in Russian & Slavic Literatures, Cultures, & History Ser.). (ENG.). 276p. 59.00 *(978-1-934843-89-5(X))* Academic Studies Pr.

Herzen, Alexander. The Memoirs of Alexander Herzen, Part 1-2. Duff, J. D., tr. 2011. 400p. 54.95 ***(978-1-258-08926-9(2))*** Literary Licensing, LLC.

Johnson, Wes. Balkan Inferno: Betrayal, War, & Intervention 1990-2005. 2006. (ENG., Illus.). 600p. per. 26.00 *(978-1-929631-63-6(4))* Enigma Bks.

Jones, W. Gareth. Nikolay Novikov: Enlightener of Russia. 2009. (Cambridge Studies in Russian Literature Ser.). (ENG.). 284p. pap. 42.00 *(978-0-521-11144-7(7))* Cambridge Univ. Pr.

Kelly, Laurence. Diplomacy & Murder in Tehran: Alexander Griboyedov & Imperial Russia's Mission to the Shah of Persia. 2006. (ENG., Illus.). 336p. pap. 23.00 *(978-1-84511-196-0(6)*, Tauris Parke Paperbacks) I. B. Tauris & Co., Ltd. GBR. Dist: Macmillan.

Khazin, Mikhail. [Evreiskoe Schaste: Zapisi Dlia Druzei. 2007. (RUS.). *(978-1-55779-164-1(3))* Hermitage Pubs.

Khodasevich, Vladislav. Derzhavin: A Biography. 2007. (Publications of the Wisconsin Center for Pushkin Studies). (Illus.). 344p. 60.00 *(978-0-299-22420-2(1))* Univ. of Wisconsin Pr.

Lappin, Elena. What Language Do You Dream In? A Memoir. 2012. (ENG., Illus.). 304p. 26.00 *(978-0-374-28885-3(2))* Farrar, Straus & Giroux.

Lekmanov, Oleg. Mandelstam. Retivov, Tatiana, tr. from RUS. 2010. (Studies in Russian & Slavic Literatures, Cultures, & History Ser.). (ENG., Illus.). 200p. 32.00 *(978-1-934843-28-4(8))* Academic Studies Pr.

Ljunggren, Anna & Rotkirch, Kristina. Contemporary Russian Fiction: A Short List. 2008. (Glas Ser.). (ENG.). 192p. pap. 12.00 *(978-5-7172-0084-4(6))* GLAS New Russian Writing RUS. Dist: Consortium Bk. Sales & Distribution.

Loseff, Lev. Joseph Brodsky: A Literary Life. Miller, Jane Ann, tr. from RUS. 2012. (ENG.). 352p. pap. 22.00 ***(978-0-300-18160-9(4))*** Yale Univ. Pr.

Lygo, Emily. The Leningrad Thaw: Poetry 1953-1975. 2010. (Russian Transformations: Literature, Culture & Ideas Ser.). 374p. pap. 68.95 *(978-3-03911-370-5(4))* Lang, Peter AG GBR. Dist: Lang, Peter.

Matich, Olga. Erotic Utopia: The Decadent Imagination in Russia's Fin de Siecle. 2007. (ENG., Illus.). 354p. per. 29.95 *(978-0-299-20884-4(2))* Univ. of Wisconsin Pr.

Milne, Lesley. Mikhail Bulgakov: A Critical Biography. 2009. (Major European Authors Ser.). (Illus.). 340p. pap. 36.99 *(978-0-521-12246-7(5))* Cambridge Univ. Pr.

Nicolas, Pasternak, tr. from RUS. Boris Pasternak. 2010. (Hoover inst press Publication). (ENG.). 419p. 39.00 *(978-0-8179-1024-2(7))* Hoover Institution Pr.

Norman, Will & White, Duncan. Transitional Nabokov. 2009. (Illus.). 325p. 58.95 *(978-3-03911-525-9(1))* Lang, Peter AG GBR. Dist: Lang, Peter.

Offord, Derek. Journeys to a Graveyard: Perceptions of Europe in Classical Russian Travel Writing. 2010. (International Archives of the History of Ideas Archives Internationales d'histoire des Idées Ser.). xxvi, 287p. pap. 169.00 *(978-90-481-6994-8(1)*, 9048169941) Springer.

Okunev, Yuri. Detstvo, kotorogo ne Bylo... 2010.Tr. of Missing Childhood. (RUS., Illus.). 244p. *(978-1-934881-28-6(7)*, M-Graphics) M-Graphics Publishing.

Orwin, Donna Tussing. Consequences of Consciousness: Turgenev, Dostoevsky, & Tolstoy. 2007. (ENG.). 256p. 55.00 *(978-0-8047-5703-4(8))* Stanford Univ. Pr.

Pasternak, Boris Leonidovich. Boris Pasternak: Family Correspondence, 1921-1960. Slater, Maya, ed. Nicolas, Pasternak, tr. from RUS. 2010. (Hoover inst press Publication). (ENG.). 419p. pap. 25.00 *(978-0-8179-1025-9(5))* Hoover Institution Pr.

Pearce, Joseph. Solzhenitsyn: A Soul in Exile. 2011. (Illus.). 392p. pap. 19.95 ***(978-1-58617-496-5(7))*** Ignatius Pr.

Persky, Serge M. Contemporary Russian Novelists. 2009. 138p. pap. *(978-1-151-65772-5(7))* Books LLC.

—Contemporary Russian Novelists. Eisemann, Frederick, tr. 330p. 2010. 36.76 *(978-1-166-66105-2(9))* 2010. pap. 24.76 *(978-1-166-60893-4(X))* 2009. 45.95 *(978-1-120-37645-9(9))* 2009. pap. 30.95 *(978-1-120-27336-9(6))* Kessinger Publishing, LLC.

Petelin, Viktor. Moi XX Vek: Schaste Byt Samim Soboi, Zhizneopisanie V Vospominaniiakh o Protivoborstve Ofitsialnoi Ideologii: Dokumenty, Pisma, Stati, Razmyshleniia. 2009. (RUS., Illus.). 638p. *(978-5-9524-4505-5(5))* Centrooligraf, AO zakrytogo tipa, torgovo-izdatel'skoe obedinenie.

Petrov, Vladimir. M.A. Sholokhov: Zhizn I Iskusstvo: Khudozhestvenno-Dokumentalnaia Biograficheskaia Letopis. 2009. (RUS., Illus.). 414p. *(978-5-87259-519-9(0))* Kniga.

Polonsky, Rachel. Molotov's Magic Lantern: Travels in Russian History, 1 vol. (ENG., Illus.). 416p. 2012. pap. 17.00 ***(978-0-374-53320-5(2))*** 2011. 28.00 *(978-0-374-21197-4(3))* Farrar, Straus & Giroux.

Porter, Cathy. The Diaries of Sofia Tolstoy. 2010. (P. S. Ser.). (ENG.). 640p. pap. 16.99 *(978-0-06-199741-9(2)*, HarperPerennial) HarperCollins Pubs.

Pratt, Sarah. The Many Facets of Mikhail Kuzmin: A Miscellany. 2011. (RUS & ENG.). xvii, 318p. *(978-0-89357-382-9(5))* Slavica Pubs.

Pritchett, V. S. Chekhov: A Biography. 2012. 256p. pap. ***(978-1-4482-0092-4(X)***, 143052, Bloomsbury Reader) Bloomsbury Publishing Plc.

Safran, Gabriella. Wandering Soul: The Dybbuk's Creator, S. An-Sky. 2010. (Illus.). 392p. 29.95 *(978-0-674-05570-4(5))* Harvard Univ. Pr.

Schonle, Andreas, ed. Lotman & Cultural Studies: Encounters & Extensions. 2006. (Illus.). 394p. 50.00 *(978-0-299-22040-2(0))* Univ. of Wisconsin Pr.

Seifrid, Thomas. Companion to Andrei Platonov's the Foundation Pit. 2009. (Studies in Russian & Slavic Literatures, Cultures, & History Ser.). (ENG., Illus.). 204p. 40.00 *(978-1-934843-08-6(3))* Academic Studies Pr.

Sekirin, Peter, ed. Americans in Conversation with Tolstoy: Selected Accounts, 1887-1923. 2006. (ENG., Illus.). 228p. per. 39.95 *(978-0-7864-2253-1(X))* McFarland & Co., Inc. Pubs.

Shpiller, Katerina. Mama, Ne Chitai! Ispoved "Neblagodarnoi" Docheri. 2010. (RUS., Illus.). 415p. *(978-5-17-069900-1(X))* AST, Tvorceskoe kooperativnoe ob'edinenie.

Sokolov, B. V. Tainy Bulgakova. 2010. (RUS.). 317p. *(978-5-699-45589-8(2))* Dksmo-Press, Izdatel'skaja firma.
Strathern, Paul. Tolstoy in 90 Minutes. 2006. (Philosophers in 90 Minutes Ser.). (ENG.). 128p. 16.95 *(978-1-56663-693-3(0))*; per. 8.95 *(978-1-56663-692-6(2))* Dee, Ivan R. Pub.
Sutcliffe, Benjamin M. The Prose of Life: Russian Women Writers from Khrushchev to Putin. 2009. (ENG.). 224p. pap. 26.95 *(978-0-299-23204-7(2))* Univ. of Wisconsin Pr.
Tokarev, D. "Mezhdu Indiei I Gegelem" Tvorchestvo Borisa Poplavskogo V Komparativnoi Perspektive. 2011. 347p. *(978-5-86793-828-4(X))* Novoe literaturnoe obozrenie.
Tolstaya, Sofia Andreevna. My Life. Donskov, Andrew, ed. Woodsworth, John & Klioutchanski, Arkadi, trs. from RUS. 2010. (ENG., Ilus.). 1188p. *(978-0-7766-3042-7(3))* Univ. of Ottawa Pr./Presses de l'Universite d'Ottawa.
Tolstoi, Ilia Lvovich. Reminiscences of Tolstoy. Calderon, George, tr. from RUS. 2009. 120p. *(978-1-907230-07-3(6))* Sparkling Bks.
Tolstoy, Leo. A Confession. 2009. 78p. pap. *(978-1-4099-8227-2(0))* Dodo Pr.
—A Confession. 2010. (Hesperus Classics Ser.). (ENG.). 146p. pap. 15.95 *(978-1-84391-190-6(6))* Hesperus Pr. GBR. Dist: Independent Pubs. Group.
—A Confession. 2009. (Penguin Great Ideas Ser.). (ENG.). 112p. (gr. 12-18). 10.00 *(978-0-14-104255-8(9)*, Penguin (Non-Classics)) Penguin Group (USA) Inc.
—Tolstois Love Letters with A Study on Th. 2006. pap. 20.95 *(978-1-4286-5963-6(3))* Kessinger Publishing, LLC.
Tolstoy, Leo & Tolstoy, Leo. Boyhood. Hogarth, C. J., tr. 2011. 92p. pap. 9.99 ***(978-1-59547-473-5(0))*** NuVision Pubns., LLC.
TSykalov, V. K. & TSykalov, Vladimir Konstantinovich. "I Gliadia Vdal, Podniav Zabralo, Bylye Vizhu Vremenna —" Avtobiograficheskie Epizody. 2010. (Illus.). 580p. *(978-5-7493-1501-1(0))* Magyar ISBN iroda, Orszagos Szechenyi Konyvtar.
Vaksberg, Arkadi. The Murder of Maxim Gorky: A Secret Execution. Bludeau, Todd, tr. from RUS. 2006. (ENG., Illus.). 425p. per. 23.00 *(978-1-929631-62-9(6))* Enigma Bks.
Westerman, Frank. Engineers of the Soul: The Grandiose Propaganda of Stalin's Russia. Garrett, Sam, tr. 2011. (ENG.). 320p. (gr. 12) 27.95 *(978-1-59020-087-2(X))* Overlook Pr., The.
Wyllie, Barbara. Vladimir Nabokov. 2010. (Reaktion Books - Critical Lives Ser.). (ENG., Illus.). 192p. pap. 16.95 *(978-1-86189-660-5(3))* Reaktion Bks., Ltd. GBR. Dist: Chicago Distribution Ctr.

AUTHORS, SCANDINAVIAN

Boyesen, Hjalmar Hjorth. Essays on Scandinavian Literature. 2008. 208p. 27.99 *(978-0-554-27513-0(9))* 2008. 208p. 24.99 *(978-0-554-36816-0(1))* 2007. 182p. pap. 19.99 *(978-1-4346-3384-2(5))* 2007. (ENG.). 204p. pap. 22.99 *(978-1-4346-3385-9(3))* BiblioBazaar.
—Essays on Scandinavian Literature. 2009. 192p. pap. *(978-1-4099-0457-1(1))* Dodo Pr.
—Essays on Scandinavian Literature. 2008. 300p. 43.95 *(978-1-4369-5832-5(6))*; pap. 28.95 *(978-1-4368-3827-6(4))* Kessinger Publishing, LLC.
Pettersson, Jan-Erik. Stieg Larsson: The Real Story of the Man Who Played with Fire. 2011. (ENG., Illus.). 288p. 22.95 *(978-1-4027-8940-3(8))* Sterling Publishing Co., Inc.
Sjåvik, Jan. The A to Z of Scandinavian Literature & Theater. 2009. (A to Z Guide Ser.: No. 60). (ENG.). 404p. pap. 34.45 *(978-0-8108-6843-4(1))* Scarecrow Pr., Inc.

AUTHORS, SCOTTISH

Black, Margaret Moyes. Robert Louis Stevenson. 2008. 136p. 21.99 *(978-0-554-39320-9(4))*; 24.99 *(978-0-554-30017-7(6))* BiblioBazaar.
Boswell, James. James Boswell: As His Contemporaries Saw Him. Larson, Lyle, ed. 2008. (Illus.). 256p. (C). 52.50 *(978-0-8386-4171-2(7))* Fairleigh Dickinson Univ. Pr.
—James Boswell: The Journal of His German & Swiss Travels 1764. Danziger, Marlies K., ed. 2008. (Yale Editions of the Private Papers Jame Ser.). (ENG & FRE., Illus.). 490p. 110.00 *(978-0-300-12360-9(4))* Yale Univ. Pr.
—London Journal 1762-1763. 2010. (ENG.). 656p. (gr. 12) pap. 17.00 *(978-0-14-043650-1(2)*, Penguin Classics) Penguin Group (USA) Inc.
Boswell, James, et al, contrib. by. The Correspondence of James Boswell & William Johnson Temple, 1756-1795. 528p. 95.00 *(978-0-7486-0758-7(7))* Edinburgh Univ. Pr. GBR. Dist: Columbia Univ. Pr.
Burns, Robert. The Complete Poetical Works of Robert Burns: With Explanatory & Glossarial Notes; & A Life of the Author, by James Currie, M. D. 2006. (Illus.). 288p. per. 23.99 *(978-1-4255-2569-9(5))* MPublishing.
—Letters Addressed to Clarinda, &c. 2009. (AccessAble Bks.). 76p. pap. 12.95 *(978-1-57003-880-8(5))* Univ. of South Carolina Pr.
—Robert Burns in Your Pocket. 2009. (Illus.). 288p. 12.95 *(978-1-902407-81-4(4))* Waverley Bks. Ltd. GBR. Dist: Interlink Publishing Group, Inc.
Cabell, Craig. Ian Rankin & Inspector Rebus: The Official Story of the Bestselling Author & His Ruthless Detective. 2010. (ENG., Illus.). 268p. 26.95 *(978-1-84454-866-8(X))* Blake, John Publishing, Ltd. GBR. Dist: Independent Pubs. Group.
—Ian Rankin & Inspector Rebus: The Story of the Best-Selling Author & His Complex Detective. 2011. (ENG., Illus.). 266p. pap. 12.95 *(978-1-84358-292-2(9))* Blake, John Publishing, Ltd. GBR. Dist: Independent Pubs. Group.
Cairney, John. The Quest for Robert Louis Stevenson. 2008. (ENG., Illus.). 205p. pap. 16.95 *(978-1-84282-085-8(0))* Luath Pr. Ltd. GBR. Dist: Ingram Pub. Services.
Campbell, Ian. Thomas Carlyle. 2011. 192p. pap. ***(978-1-84921-089-8(6))*** Kennedy & Boyd.
Campbell, James. Syncopations: Beats, New Yorkers, & Writers in the Dark. 2008. 251p. pap. 24.95 *(978-0-520-25237-0(3))* Univ. of California Pr.
Carlyle, Thomas. Correspondence of Thomas Carlyle & Ral. 2007. pap. *(978-1-4065-1272-4(9))* Dodo Pr.
—The Correspondence of Thomas Carlyle & Ralph Waldo Emerson, 1834-1872. 2009. 384p. 26.99 *(978-1-103-16530-8(5))* 2009. 384p. pap. 20.99 *(978-1-103-16529-2(1))*1. 2006. (ENG.). 298p. pap. 23.99 *(978-1-4264-7372-2(9))*2. 2006. (ENG.). 324p. pap. 24.99 *(978-1-4264-7373-9(7))* BiblioBazaar.
—The Correspondence of Thomas Carlyle & Ralph Waldo Emerson, 1834-1872. 2009. 204p. pap. *(978-0-217-07535-0(5))*; 222p. pap. *(978-0-217-75194-0(6))*; 272p. pap. *(978-0-217-75195-7(4))* Books LLC.
—Early Letters of Thomas Carlyle. 2008. 392p. pap. 32.75 *(978-0-559-52299-4(1))* BiblioBazaar.
—Early Letters of Thomas Carlyle. 2009. 288p. pap. *(978-0-217-83149-9(4))* Books LLC.
—Early Letters of Thomas Carlyle: 1814-1826. Norton, Charles Eliot, ed. 2007. pap. 33.95 *(978-1-4304-5097-9(5))* Kessinger Publishing LLC.
—Letters of Thomas Carlyle to His Younges. 2006. pap. 28.95 *(978-1-4286-5341-2(4))* Kessinger Publishing, LLC.
—The Love Letters of Thomas Carlyle & Jane Welsh. 2009. 296p. pap. 20.12 *(978-1-4589-2890-0(X))*; pap. 20.03 *(978-1-4589-2888-7(8))* General Bks. LLC.
—New Letters of Thomas Carlyle V1. Carlyle, Alexander, ed. 2007. (ENG.). 356p. 46.95 *(978-0-548-10698-3(3))* Kessinger Publishing, LLC.
—New Letters of Thomas Carlyle V2. Carlyle, Alexander, ed. 2007. (ENG.). 376p. 48.95 *(978-0-548-10699-0(1))* Kessinger Publishing, LLC.
Carlyle, Thomas. Thomas Carlyle: Letters to His Wife. Bliss, Trudy, ed. 2011. 418p. 54.95 ***(978-1-258-08732-6(4))*** Literary Licensing, LLC.
Carlyle, Thomas & Emerson, Ralph Waldo. The Correspondence of Thomas Carlyle & Ralph Waldo Emerson, 1834-1872. 2008. 300p. 25.99 *(978-0-554-34034-0(8))*; 300p. 28.99 *(978-0-554-24731-1(3))*; 328p. 29.99 *(978-0-554-24732-8(1))*; 328p. 28.99 *(978-0-554-34035-7(6))* BiblioBazaar.
Carroll, David. Edinburgh: Literary Lives & Landscapes. 2012. (ENG., Illus.). 160p. pap. 22.95 ***(978-0-7524-6214-1(8))*** History Pr. Ltd., The GBR. Dist: Independent Pubs. Group.
Carter, Marie. The Trapeze Diaries. 2008. 95p. 26.00 *(978-1-931236-85-0(2))*; 95p. pap. 16.00 *(978-1-931236-84-3(4))*; 96p. per. 16.00 net. *(978-1-934909-84-3(X))* Hanging Loose Pr.
Chesterton, G. K. & Hodder-Williams, J. E. Thomas Carlyle. 2010. 54p. 31.95 *(978-1-161-72643-5(8))* 2007. (ENG.). 52p. per. 16.95 *(978-0-548-78604-3(6))* Kessinger Publishing, LLC.
Chesterton, G. K. & Hodder-Williams, J. E. Thomas Carlyle. 2010. 50p. pap. 16.75 *(978-1-146-38726-2(1))* BiblioBazaar.
Christie, William, ed. The Letters of Francis Jeffrey to Thomas & Jane Welsh Carlyle, 1 vol. 2008. (Pickering Masters Ser.). (ENG.). 240p. 195.00 *(978-1-85196-982-1(9))* Pickering & Chatto Pubs., Ltd. GBR. Dist: Ashgate Publishing Co.
Coren, Michael. R. L. Stevenson. 2007. (ENG.). 162p. pap. 16.95 *(978-1-55005-081-3(8))* Fitzhenry & Whiteside, Ltd. CAN. Dist: Ingram Pub. Services.
Douglas, George Brisbane. James Hogg. 2008. 156p. 25.99 *(978-0-554-59749-2(7))*; 155p. 22.99 *(978-0-554-59760-7(8))*; 155p. pap. 21.75 *(978-0-554-59750-8(0))*; 156p. pap. 20.75 *(978-0-554-59756-0(X))* BiblioBazaar.
—James Hogg. 2009. 90p. pap. *(978-1-4590-8837-5(9))* Books LLC.
—James Hogg. 2008. 164p. 36.95 *(978-1-4369-0670-8(9))*; pap. 21.95 *(978-1-4368-8315-3(6))* Kessinger Publishing, LLC.
Dudgeon, Piers. Neverland: J. M. Barrie, the du Mauriers, & the Dark Side of Peter Pan. 2011. (ENG., Illus.). 352p. pap. 15.95 *(978-1-60598-191-8(5)*, 605191) Pegasus Bks.
Dunlop, Eileen. Robert Louis Stevenson: The Travelling Mind. 2009. (ENG., Illus.). 160p. pap. 15.95 *(978-1-905267-21-7(5))* NMS Enterprises Ltd. - Publishing GBR. Dist: National Bk. Network.
Ferguson, John. The Letters of John Ferguson, Early Resident of Western Washington County: The Kansas Historical Quarterly, V12, No. 4, November 1943. 2011. 16p. pap. 35.95 ***(978-1-258-04875-4(2))*** Literary Licensing, LLC.
Fergusson, Maggie. George Mackay Brown: The Life. 2007. (ENG., Illus.). 384p. per. 18.95 *(978-0-7195-6605-9(3))* Murray, John GBR. Dist: Independent Pubs. Group.
Froude, James Anthony. Thomas Carlyle: A History of his Life in London, 1834-1881. 2011. (Cambridge Library Collection - Literary Studies). (ENG.). 500p. pap. 35.99 *(978-1-108-02933-9(7))*; (Illus.). 476p. pap. 34.99 *(978-1-108-02932-2(9))* Cambridge Univ. Pr.
—Thomas Carlyle: A History of the First Forty Years of his Life, 1795-1835. 2011. (Cambridge Library Collection - Literary Studies). (ENG.). 508p. pap. 37.99 *(978-1-108-02930-8(2))*; (Illus.). 462p. pap. 34.99 *(978-1-108-02929-2(9))* Cambridge Univ. Pr.
—Thomas Carlyle V1 A History of His Life. 2006. pap. 37.95 *(978-1-4286-3587-6(4))* Kessinger Publishing, LLC.
—Thomas Carlyle V2 A History of His Life. 2006. pap. 38.95 *(978-1-4286-3589-0(0))* Kessinger Publishing, LLC.
Galloway, Janice. This Is Not about Me. (ENG.). 2010. 352p. pap. 16.95 *(978-1-84708-099-8(5))* 2008. 320p. 32.95 *(978-1-84708-061-5(8))* Granta Bks. GBR. Dist: Independent Pubs. Group.
Gordon, Mary (Wilson). Christopher North,' a Memoir of John Wilson, Late Professor of Moral Philosophy in the University of Edinburgh, Comp from Family Papers & Other Sou. 2006. 500p. per. 29.99 *(978-1-4255-5561-0(6))* MPublishing.
Gray, William. Robert Louis Stevenson. (Illus.). 208p. *(978-0-333-98401-7(3))* Palgrave Macmillan.
Hall, Lesley A. Naomi Mitchison: Volume 15 in the Conversation Pieces Series. 2007. 146p. per. 12.00 *(978-1-933500-10-2(7))* Aqueduct Pr.
Harman, Claire. Myself & the Other Fellow: A Life of Robert Lewis Stevenson. 2006. (ENG.). 544p. per. 16.95 *(978-0-06-093525-2(1)*, HarperPerennial) HarperCollins Pubs.
Hewison, Robert. John Byrne: Art & Life. 2011. (Illus.). 144p. 70.00 *(978-1-84822-047-8(2)*, Lund Humphries Pubs.) Ashgate Publishing, Ltd. GBR. Dist: Ashgate Publishing Co.
Hogg, David. The Life of Allan Cunningham. 2007. (ENG.). 386p. 48.95 *(978-0-548-15131-0(8))*; 388p. per. 33.95 *(978-1-4304-4477-0(0))* Kessinger Publishing, LLC.
Hogg, James. Memoir of Burns. Roy, G. Ross et al, eds. 2013. (Collected Works of James Hogg Ser.). (ENG., Illus.). 400p. (gr. 17). 75.00 *(978-0-7486-3416-3(9))* Edinburgh Univ. Pr. GBR. Dist: Columbia Univ. Pr.
Hogg, James & Hogg, James. The Collected Letters of James Hogg, 1820-1831, 2 vols., Vol. 2. Hughes, Gillian, ed. 2006. (Collected Works of James Hogg Ser.). (ENG., Illus.). 450p. (gr. 17). 98.00 *(978-0-7486-1673-2(X))* Edinburgh Univ. Pr. GBR. Dist: Columbia Univ. Pr.
—The Collected Letters of James Hogg, 1832-1835, vol. 3. Hughes, Gillian, ed. 2008. (Collected Works of James Hogg Ser.). (ENG., Illus.). 450p. (gr. 17). 75.00 *(978-0-7486-1675-6(6))* Edinburgh Univ. Pr. GBR. Dist: Columbia Univ. Pr.
Hutton, Holt Richard. Sir Walter Scott: (English Men of Letters Series) 2007. (ENG.). 150p. pap. 18.99 *(978-1-4346-2925-8(2))*; 170p. pap. 21.99 *(978-1-4346-2949-4(X))* BiblioBazaar.
Hutton, Richard Holt. Sir Walter Scott. 2011. (Cambridge Library Collection - English Men of Letters Ser.). (ENG.). 190p. pap. 19.99 ***(978-1-108-03467-8(5))*** Cambridge Univ. Pr.
Jenkins, Ellen J. Eighteenth-Century British Historians. 2007. (Dictionary of Literary Biography Ser.). (ENG., Illus.). 512p. 315.00 *(978-0-7876-8154-8(7))* Cengage Gale.
Jung, Sandro. David Mallet, Anglo-Scot: Poetry, Patronage, & Politics, in the Age of Union. 2008. (Illus.). 216p. 48.50 *(978-0-87413-005-8(0))* Univ. of Delaware Pr.
Kay, Jackie. Red Dust Road: An Autobiographical Journey. 2011. (ENG.). 304p. 24.00 *(978-1-935633-34-1(1)*, 935634) Atlas & Co.
Lacy, Della Zill, compiled by. A Brief Look Back at the Twentieth Century. 2007. (Illus.). 406p. pap. 22.95 *(978-0-615-17342-9(X))* Lacy, Della Zill.
Lang, Andrew. The Life & Letters of John Gibson Lockhart. 2009. 448p. 27.99 *(978-1-103-07761-8(9))*; pap. 21.99 *(978-1-103-07754-0(6))* BiblioBazaar.
Leask, William Keith. James Boswell. 2009. 164p. pap. 21.95 *(978-1-120-30307-3(9))* Kessinger Publishing, LLC.
—James Boswell. 2007. (ENG.). 164p. per. *(978-1-4086-2699-3(3))* Read Bks.
Lycett, Andrew. The Man Who Created Sherlock Holmes: The Life & Times of Sir Arthur Conan Doyle. 2008. (ENG., Illus.). 576p. pap. 32.99 *(978-0-7432-7525-5(X)*, Free Pr.) Free Pr.
Manson, John, selected by. Dear Grieve: Letters to Hugh MacDiarmid (C.M. Grieve) 2011. 260p. pap. ***(978-1-84921-078-2(0))*** Kennedy & Boyd.
McGonigal, James. Beyond the Last Dragon: A Life of Edwin Morgan. 2010. (Non-Fiction Ser.). (Illus.). 420p. *(978-1-905207-23-7(9))* Silvermine International Bks., LLC.
McGrigor, Mary & Watson, Norman. Poet McGonagall: The Biography of William McGonagall. 2010. (ENG., Illus.). 320p. 16.95 *(978-1-84158-884-1(9))* Birlinn, Ltd. GBR. Dist: Interlink Publishing Group, Inc.
McGuire, Matt, et al. Contemporary Scottish Literature. Tredell, Nicolas, ed. 2008. (Readers' Guides to Essential Criticism Ser.). (ENG.). 224p. 85.00 *(978-0-230-50669-5(0))*; pap. 25.00 *(978-0-230-50670-1(4))* Palgrave Macmillan.
McKay, George L. Some Notes on Robert Louis Stevenson: His Finances & His Agents & Publishers. 2011. 44p. 35.95 ***(978-1-258-04341-4(6))*** Literary Licensing, LLC.
Mclean, Thomas, ed. Further Letters of Joanna Baillie. 2010. 296p. *(978-0-8386-4149-1(0))* Fairleigh Dickinson Univ. Pr.
Mitchison, Naomi & Smith, Ali. Small Talk: Memories of an Edwardian Childhood. 2009. 158p. pap. *(978-1-84921-020-1(9))* Kennedy & Boyd.
Muir, Willa. Belonging. 2008. (Illus.). 340p. pap. *(978-1-904999-70-6(0))* Kennedy & Boyd.
Murray, Isobel. Jessie Kesson: Writing Her Life. 2011. 322p. pap. ***(978-1-84921-080-5(2))*** Kennedy & Boyd.
Murray, Isobel. Scottish Writers Talking 4. 2008. (Illus.). xv, 298p. pap. *(978-1-904999-88-1(3))* Kennedy & Boyd.
Murray, Isobel, ed. Scottish Writers Talking. 210p. pap. *(978-1-898410-78-2(X)*, Donald, John) Birlinn, Ltd.
Murray, Isobel, ed. & told to. Scottish Writers Talking: George Mackay Brown, Jessie Kesson, Norman Mccaig, William Mcilvanney, David Toulmin. 2008. 196p. pap. *(978-1-904999-89-8(1))* Kennedy & Boyd.
Neat, Timothy. Hamish Henderson: Poetry Becomes People Vol II (1954-2002), 2 vols. 2010. (Illus.). 416p. 40.00 *(978-1-84697-063-4(6))* BirlinnPolygon GBR. Dist: Interlink Publishing Group, Inc.
Nichol, John. Thomas Carlyle. 2007. 214p. pap. 20.99 *(978-1-4346-2037-8(9))* BiblioBazaar.
—Thomas Carlyle. 2011. (Cambridge Library Collection - English Men of Letters Ser.). (ENG.). 264p. pap. 23.99 ***(978-1-108-03447-0(0))*** Cambridge Univ. Pr.
Norman, Andrew. Arthur Conan Doyle: The Man Behind Sherlock Holmes. 2010. (ENG., Illus.). 192p. pap. 16.95 *(978-0-7524-5275-3(4))* History Pr. Ltd., The GBR. Dist: Independent Pubs. Group.
Oliphant, Margaret O. The Autobiography & Letters of Mrs M. O. W. Oliphant. Walker, Annie L., ed. 2011. (Cambridge Library Collection - Women's Writing Ser.). (ENG., Illus.). 386p. pap. 31.99 ***(978-1-108-03385-5(7))*** Cambridge Univ. Pr.
Pollok, David. The Life of Robert Pollok. 2007. (ENG.). 462p. 52.95 *(978-0-548-15102-0(4))*; 464p. per. 37.95 *(978-1-4304-4446-6(0))* Kessinger Publishing, LLC.
Robb, David. Auld Campaigner: A Life of Alexander Scott. 2007. (Illus.). 220p. (C). 70.00 *(978-1-903765-38-8(2))* Dunedin Academic Pr. GBR. Dist: International Specialized Bk. Services.
Russell, Bernard MacClaverty. 2009. 175p. 44.50 *(978-0-8387-5703-1(0))* Bucknell Univ. Pr.
Sandford, Christopher. Masters of Mystery: The Strange Friendship of Arthur Conan Doyle & Harry Houdini. 2011. (ENG., Illus.). 304p. 27.00 *(978-0-230-61950-0(9))* Palgrave Macmillan.
Scott, Walter, Sr. The Journal of Sir Walter Scott, Vol. 1. 2008. (Illus.). pap. *(978-1-4065-7398-5(1))* Dodo Pr.
Smith, George Adam. The Life of Henry Drummond. 2009. 298p. pap. *(978-0-217-55667-5(1))* Books LLC.
—The Life of Henry Drummond. 2007. (ENG.). 556p. 57.95 *(978-0-548-01946-7(0))* Kessinger Publishing, LLC.
Smollett, Tobias George. The Letters of Tobias Smollett. Noyes, Edward S., ed. 2011. 282p. 47.95 ***(978-1-258-04533-3(8))*** Literary Licensing, LLC.
Spark, Muriel. Curriculum Vitae: A Volume of Autobiography. 2011. (ENG., Illus.). 224p. pap. 14.95 *(978-0-8112-1923-5(2)*, 21923) New Directions Publishing Corp.
Stannard, Martin. Muriel Spark: The Biography. 2011. (ENG.). 670p. pap. 24.95 ***(978-0-8101-2791-3(1))*** Northwestern Univ. Pr.
Stevenson, Robert. The Amateur Emigrant: From the Clyde to Sandy Hook. 2007. (Travel in America Ser.). (ENG.). 104p. 49.95 *(978-1-4290-0508-1(4))*; per. 24.95 *(978-1-4290-0509-8(2))* Applewood Bks.
Stevenson, Robert Louis. Lay Morals & Other Papers. 2007. (ENG.). 208p. per. *(978-1-4065-8213-0(1))* Dodo Pr.
—The Silverado Squatters: A Sojourn in Napa County, California, in the Summer Of 1880. 2010. (ENG.). 184p. pap. 16.95 *(978-1-84511-990-4(8)*, Tauris Parke Paperbacks) I. B. Tauris & Co., Ltd. GBR. Dist: Macmillan.
Taylor, Michael. Hugh Miller: Stonemason, Geologist, Writer. 2007. (ENG., Illus.). 144p. per. 19.95 *(978-1-905267-05-7(3))* NMS Enterprises Ltd. - Publishing GBR. Dist: National Bk. Network.
Tytler, Sarah. The Songstresses of Scotland. 2009. 136p. pap. *(978-1-151-12828-7(7))* Books LLC.
—The Songstresses of Scotland, 2 Vols. reprint ed. 125.00 *(978-0-7222-1497-8(9))* Library Reprints, Inc.
Tytler, Sarah & Watson, Jean L. The Songstresses of Scotland. 2009. 680p. 39.99 *(978-1-115-87964-4(2))*; 46.99 *(978-1-115-87963-7(4))*; pap. 46.75 *(978-1-115-87966-8(9))*; pap. 47.75 *(978-1-115-87965-1(0))* BiblioBazaar.
Watts, Cedric & Davies, Laurence. Cunninghame Graham: A Critical Biography. 2008. (ENG., Illus.). 348p. pap. 46.00 *(978-0-521-09009-4(1))* Cambridge Univ. Pr.
Wilson, David Alec. Carlyle till Marriage 1795 To 1826. 2007. (ENG.). 464p. 52.95 *(978-0-548-01657-2(7))* Kessinger Publishing, LLC.
Wilson, Susan, ed. The Correspondence Between Hugh Macdiarmid & Sorley Maclean. annot. ed. 2010. (ENG., Illus.). 288p. (gr. 17). 105.00 *(978-0-7486-3980-9(2))* Edinburgh Univ. Pr. GBR. Dist: Columbia Univ. Pr.
Wylie, William Howie. Thomas Carlyle: The Man & His Books. 2007. (ENG.). 464p. 52.95 *(978-0-548-03876-5(7))* Kessinger Publishing, LLC.

AUTHORS, SOUTH AFRICAN

Breytenbach, Breyten. A Veil of Footsteps: (Memoir of a Nomadic Fictional Character) 2010. (Illus.). 302p. 23.00 *(978-0-7981-4927-3(2))* International Publishers Marketing.
Callinicos, Luli. Oliver Tambo: His Life & Legacy, 1917-1993. 2011. (ENG.). 36p. pap. 8.95 *(978-1-919855-85-1(8))* STE Pubs. ZAF. Dist: Independent Pubs. Group.
Cornwell, Gareth, et al. The Columbia Guide to South African Literature in English Since 1945. 2010. (Columbia Guides to Literature Since 1945 Ser.). (ENG., Illus.). 288p. (gr. 17). 80.00 *(978-0-231-13046-2(5))* Columbia Univ. Pr.
Freed, Lynn. Reading, Writing, & Leaving Home: Life on the Page. 2006. (ENG., Illus.). 256p. pap. 14.95 *(978-0-15-603034-2(9)*, Mariner Bks.) Houghton Mifflin Harcourt Trade & Reference Pubs.
Hallett, George, ed. Portraits of African Writers. 2007. (ENG., Illus.). 160p. (gr. 11). 44.95 *(978-1-86814-386-3(4))* Witwatersrand Univ. Pr. Pubns. ZAF. Dist: Transaction Pubs.
Head, Bessie & MacKenzie, Craig. A Woman Alone: Autobiographical Writings. 2008. (AWS African Writers Ser.). (ENG., Illus.). 137p. pap. 15.95 *(978-0-435-90603-0(8))* Longman Publishing.

Hirson, Denis. We Walk Straight So You Better Get Out the Way. 2007. (ENG.). 168p. per. 19.95 *(978-1-77009-144-3(0))* Jacana Media ZAF. Dist: Independent Pubs. Group.

Labuschagne, Gerry. Impact & Change. 2010. (Illus.). 96p. pap. 11.49 *(978-1-4490-9156-9(3))* AuthorHouse.

Lindfors, Bernth, ed. The Dennis Brutus Tapes: Essays at Autobiography. 2011. (Illus.). 224p. 70.00 *(978-1-84701-034-6(2)*, Currey, James) Boydell & Brewer, Ltd. GBR. Dist: Boydell & Brewer, Inc.

Manganyi, N. & Attwell, David, eds. Bury Me at the Marketplace: Es¿kia Mphahlele & Company. Letters 1943¿2006. 2010. (ENG.). 496p. pap. 39.95 *(978-1-86814-489-1(5))* Witwatersrand Univ. Pr. Pubns. ZAF. Dist: Transaction Pubs.

Masilela, Johnny. Deliver Us from Evil: Scenes from a Rural Transvaal Upbringing. (Illus.). 79p. pap. *(978-0-7957-0046-0(6))* Kwela Bks.

Mda, Zakes. Sometimes There Is a Void: Memoirs of an Outsider. 2012. (ENG., Illus.). 576p. 35.00 ***(978-0-374-28094-9(0))*** Farrar, Straus & Giroux.

Mengel, Ewald, et al, eds. Trauma, Memory, & Narrative in South Africa. 2010. (Illus.). 269p. 70.00 *(978-90-420-3102-9(6))* Rodopi.

Mohamed, Adam & Mohamed, Noorjehan. Journey into the Unknown. 2011. (ENG.). 152p. pap. 17.95 *(978-1-920222-47-5(2))* STE Pubs. ZAF. Dist: Independent Pubs. Group.

Morais, Fernando. Paulo Coelho: A Warrior's Life - The Authorized Biography. 2009. (ENG.). 608p. 26.99 *(978-0-06-171888-5(2)*, HarperOne); 784p. pap. 26.99 *(978-0-06-188588-4(6)*, HarperLuxe) HarperCollins Pubs.

Mqhayi, S. E. K. Abantu Besizwe: Historical & Biographical Writings, 1902 - 1944. Opland, Jeff, ed. & tr. by. 2010. (ENG.). 640p. pap. 39.95 *(978-1-86814-501-0(8))* Witwatersrand Univ. Pr. Pubns. ZAF. Dist: Transaction Pubs.

Neser, Ashlee. Stranger at Home: The Praise Poet in Apartheid South Africa. 2011. (ENG.). 280p. pap. 34.95 ***(978-1-86814-537-9(9))*** Witwatersrand Univ. Pr. Pubns. ZAF. Dist: Transaction Pubs.

Roos, Zuretha. The Saffron Pear Tree: And Other Kitchen Memories. 2006. (Illus.). 391p. per. 14.95 *(978-1-77007-038-7(9))* Struik Pubs. ZAF. Dist: International Publishers Marketing.

Thurman, Chris. Guy Butler: Reassessing a South African Literary Life. 2010. 382p. pap. 48.95 *(978-1-86914-183-7(0))* University of Kwazulu-Natal Press ZAF. Dist: International Specialized Bk. Services.

Van Wyk, Chris. Shirley, Goodness & Mercy: A Childhood in Africa. 2006. (ENG.). 320p. per. 13.95 *(978-0-330-44483-5(2))* Macmillan Pubs., Ltd. GBR. Dist: Independent Pubs. Group.

Watson, Stephen. A City Imagined. 2009. (ENG.). 224p. (gr. 12-18). 15.00 *(978-0-14-302473-6(6)*, Penguin Global) Penguin Group (USA) Inc.

AUTHORS, SPANISH

Aguilar Piñal, Francisco. Bibliografía de Autores Españoles Del Siglo Xviii Obra Completa10, 10 vols. (SPA.). *(978-84-00-05317-8(6))* Bow Historical Bks.

Agulló y Cobo, Mercedes. A Vueltas con el Autor de Lazarillo: Con el Testamento e Inventario de Bienes de Don Diego Hurtado de Mendoza. 2010. (Illus.). 140p. *(978-84-8359-175-8(8))* Calambur Editorial, S.L.

Aisa, Ferran, et al. Joan Salvat-Papasseit (1894-1924) 2010. (CAT., Illus.). 499p. *(978-84-92437-76-4(6))* Base, Editorial.

Alas, Leopoldo & «Clarín», Leopoldo Alas. Narrativa Completa, 2 vols. Caudet, Francisco, tr. 2010. (SPA.). *(978-84-376-2716-8(8))*; *(978-84-376-2704-5(4))*; *(978-84-376-2705-2(2))* Ediciones Cátedra.

Alberti, Rafael, et al. Rafael Alberti: Obras Completas. Marrast, Robert, ed. 2009. (SPA., Illus.). lii, 1273p. pap. *(978-84-322-4057-7(5))* Editorial Seix Barral.

Arellano, Ignacio. Editar a Calderón: Hacia una Edición Crítica de Las Comedias Completas. 2007. (SPA., Illus.). 114p. pap. 16.80 *(978-84-8489-316-5(2))* Iberoamericana Vervuert Publishing Corp.

Armendáriz, Ana & Calderón de la Barca, Pedro. Edición Crítica de "El Médico de Su Honra" de Calderón de la Barca y Recepción Crítica Del Drama. 2007. (SPA.). 636p. pap. 75.00 *(978-84-8489-079-9(1))* Iberoamericana Vervuert Publishing Corp.

Barral, Carlos. Cuando las Horas Veloces. (SPA.). 294p. *(978-84-7223-280-8(8)*, 6020) Tusquets Editores.

Berg, Karen. Javier Marßas's Postmodern Praxis. 2008. 244p. per. *(978-3-8364-3853-7(4))* VDM Verlag Dr. Mueller e.K.

Cadalso, Jose. Cartas Marruecas. 2010. 240p. pap. 26.75 *(978-1-148-46774-0(2))* BiblioBazaar.

—Cartas Marruecas. 19th ed. (SPA., Illus.). 352p. 14.95 *(978-84-376-0145-8(2)*, CT1078) Ediciones Cátedra ESP. Dist: Continental Bk. Co., Inc.

—Cartas Marruecas. (SPA.). 164p. 12.95 *(978-84-239-1078-6(4)*, ECS107) Espasa Calpe, S.A. ESP. Dist: Continental Bk. Co., Inc.

—Cartas Marruecas. 2010. (SPA.). 168p. 16.00 *(978-84-9897-301-3(5))* Linkgua Ediciones, S.L. ESP. Dist: AtlasBooks Distribution.

—Cartas Marruecas. (SPA.). 312p. *(978-84-01-90523-0(0))* Plaza & Janes Editores, S.A. ESP. Dist: AIMS International Bks., Inc.

Cadalso, Jose, et al. Cartas Marruecas. 2nd annot. ed. (SPA., Illus.). 280p. 11.95 *(978-84-7039-442-3(8)*, CCD505) Castalia, Editorial S.A. ESP. Dist: Continental Bk. Co., Inc.

Chacel, Rosa. Memorias de Leticia Valle. Morán Rodríguez, Carmen, tr. 2010. (SPA.). 328p. pap. 16.80 ***(978-84-8489-458-2(4))*** Iberoamericana Vervuert Publishing Corp.

Cocozzella, Peter. Fra Francesc Moner's Bilingual Poetics of Love & Reason: The 'Wisdom Text' by a Catalan Writer of the Early Renaissance. 2010. (Currents in Comparative Romance Languages & Literatures Ser.). 248p. (C). 75.95 *(978-1-4331-0805-1(4))* Lang, Peter Publishing, Inc.

Comillas José. Vidas y muertes de Luis Martín-Santos. 2009. (Tiempo de Memoria Ser.: Vol. 74). (SPA., Illus.). 456p. pap. 25.95 *(978-84-8383-123-6(6))* Tusquets Editores ESP. Dist: Ediciones Urano S. A.

Crews, Daniel A. Twilight of the Renaissance: The Life of Juan de Valdés. 2008. (SPA & ENG., Illus.). 320p. *(978-0-8020-9867-2(3))* Univ. of Toronto Pr.

Cunqueiro, Álvaro. El Pasajero en Galicia. Molina, César Antonio, ed. & prologue by by. (SPA., Illus.). 396p. *(978-84-7223-118-4(6)*, 6030) Tusquets Editores.

De Lope, Manuel. Jardines de Africa. (SPA.). 92p. pap. 5.95 *(978-84-204-8041-1(X))* Alfaguara, Ediciones, S.A.- Grupo Santillana ESP. Dist: Santillana USA Publishing Co., Inc.

Delibes & Delibes, Miguel. Viejas Historias de Castilla la Vieja; La Mortaja; La Partida. Candau, Antonio, tr. 2007. (SPA.). 276p. pap. *(978-84-8489-354-7(5))* Iberoamericana Vervuert Publishing Corp.

Díez Canedo, Aurora & Jiménez, Juan Ramón. Juan Ramón Jiménez en Su Obra. Díez-Canedo, Enrique, ed. 2nd ed. 2007. (Estudios Lingüísticos y Literarios Ser.). (SPA.). 234p. pap. 30.99 *(978-968-12-1330-5(0))* El Colegio de México, A.C., Biblioteca Miguel Cosío Villegas MEX. Dist: Fondo de Cultura Economica USA.

Eaude, Michael. Triumph at Midnight in the Century: A Critical Biography of Arturo Barea: Explaining the Roots of the Spanish Civil War. 2009. (ENG., Illus.). 243p. 74.95 *(978-1-84519-288-4(5))* Sussex Academic Pr. GBR. Dist: International Specialized Bk. Services.

—Triumph at Midnight of the Century: A Critical Biography of Arturo Barea - Explaining the Roots of the Spanish Civil War. 2011. (ENG., Illus.). 244p. pap. 34.95 *(978-1-84519-469-7(1))* Sussex Academic Pr. GBR. Dist: International Specialized Bk. Services.

Ferrer, Lerin Francisco. Familias Como la Mía. 2011. 336p. *(978-84-8383-291-2(7))* Tusquets Editores.

Fintoni, Monica, et al, eds. The World of the Aztecs: In the Florentine Codex. Paoletti, Andrea & Carden, Jeremy, trs. 2008. (ENG., Illus.). 64p. pap. 19.95 *(978-88-7461-102-7(1))* Mandragora ITA. Dist: Antique Collectors' Club.

Forner, Climent. Paraules Sobre Paraules: Pròlegs I Discursos. 2010. (L'Oreneta Ser.: Vol. 19). (CAT.). 382p. *(978-84-89751-89-7(7))* L'Albí, Ediciones.

García Lorca, Federico, et al. Correspondencia y Amistad. 2009. (SPA.). 574p. pap. 29.80 *(978-84-8489-435-3(5))* Iberoamericana Vervuert Publishing Corp.

Gibson, Ian. Lorca - Dali, el Amor Que No Pudo Ser (Dali, the Love That Couldn't Be) (SPA., Illus.). 380p. 19.50 *(978-84-01-01217-4(1))* Plaza & Janes Editores, S.A. ESP. Dist: Astran, Inc.

Giménez Frontín, J. L. Los Días Que Hemos Visto. 2009. (SPA.). 125p. *(978-84-89707-29-0(4))* Fundación Jorge Guillén.

Gómez de la Serna, Ramón, et al. Escribidores y Náufragos: Correspondencia, Ramón Gómez de la Serna — Guillermo de Torre, 1916-1963. 2007. (SPA.). 457p. pap. 29.80 *(978-84-8489-301-1(4))* Iberoamericana Vervuert Publishing Corp.

Gonzßlez, Pedro Blas. Unamuno: A Lyrical Essay. 2007. 140p. per. 22.95 *(978-0-915745-75-3(5))* Floricanto Pr.

Hooper, Kirsty. A Stranger in My Own Land: Sofia Casanova, a Spanish Writer in the European Fin de Siècle. 2008. (ENG.). 264p. (C). pap. 34.95 *(978-0-8265-1614-5(9))*; lib. bdg. 69.95 *(978-0-8265-1613-8(0))* Vanderbilt Univ. Pr.

Howell, Peter. Martial. 2009. (Ancients in Action Ser.). 128p. pap. 24.95 *(978-1-85399-702-0(1))* Duckworth Publishers GBR. Dist: International Publishers Marketing.

Hunter, Jeffrey W. Contemporary Literary Criticism: Excerpts from Criticism of the Works of Today's Novelists, Poets, Playwrights, Short Story Writers, Scriptwriters, & Other Creative Writers. 2011. 497p. 328.00 *(978-1-4144-5853-3(3))* Cengage Gale.

Juttner, Siegfried. Diario de Los Literatos de Espana (1737-1742) Indices (Onomastico, Toponimico y de Obras) 2007. (SPA.). 307p. pap. 59.95 *(978-3-631-57567-3(X))* Lang, Peter Publishing, Inc.

Machado, Antonio. Antonio Machado's Cartas de Amor a Pilar de Valderrama/Love Letters to Pilar de Valderrama: A Facing Page Translation from Spanish to English. Aldaz, Anna-Marie, tr. from SPA. 2008. (SPA & ENG.). 280p. 109.95 *(978-0-7734-4878-0(0))* Mellen, Edwin Pr., The.

Marrugat, Jordi. El Saltamartí de Joan Brossa: Les Mil Cares Del Poeta. 2009. (CAT.). 296p. *(978-84-92408-54-2(5))* Arola Editors, S.L.

Martínez, Juana. Exilios y Residencias: Escrituras de España y América. 2007. (SPA.). 254p. pap. 44.00 *(978-84-8489-184-0(4))* Iberoamericana Vervuert Publishing Corp.

McCulloch, John. The Dilemma of Modernity: Ramón Gómez de la Serna & the Spanish Modernist Novel. 2007. 206p. (C). 68.95 *(978-0-8204-8183-8(1))* Lang, Peter Publishing, Inc.

Meanor, Patrick & Lee, Richard E. American Short-Story Writers since World War II: Fifth Series, Vol 335. 2007. (Dictionary of Literary Biography Ser.). (ENG., Illus.). 480p. 315.00 *(978-0-7876-8153-1(9))* Cengage Gale.

Monzó, Quim. Guadalajara. Bush, Peter, tr. from CAT. 2011. (ENG.). 135p. pap. 12.95 *(978-1-934824-19-1(4))* Open Letter.

Mordzinsky, Daniel. El País de las Palabras. 2006. (SPA.). 180p. pap. 22.99 *(978-958-04-8460-8(0))* Norma S.A. COL. Dist: Distribuidora Norma, Inc.

Nieva de la Paz, Pilar, et al. Mujer, Literatura y Esfera Publica: Espana, 1900-1940. 2009. 232p. pap. *(978-0-89295-127-7(3))* Society of Spanish & Spanish-American Studies.

Nunley, Gayle R. Scripted Geographies: Travel Writings by Nineteenth-Century Spanish Authors. 2006. (ENG & SPA.). 272p. 52.50 *(978-0-8387-5633-1(6))* Bucknell Univ. Pr.

Pato, Chus. Hordes of Writing. Moure, Erin, tr. 2011. 90p. pap. ***(978-1-84861-167-2(6))*** Shearsman Bks.

Pattison, Walter T. Benito Perez Galdos & the Creative Process. 2009. (ENG.). 156p. pap. 40.00 *(978-0-8166-5846-6(3))* Univ. of Minnesota Pr.

Pennington, Eric Wayne. Approaching the Theater of Antonio Buero Vallejo: Contemporary Literary Analyses from Structuralism to Postmodernism. 2010. 390p. (C). 88.95 *(978-0-8204-8840-0(2))* Lang, Peter Publishing, Inc.

Pessarrodona, Marta. El Exilio Violeta: Escritoras y Artistas Catalanas Exiliadas en 1939. 2010. (SPA.). 279p. *(978-84-92874-28-6(7))* Meteora, S.L., Editorial.

Piña-Rosales, Gerardo. Escritores Españoles en los Estados Unidos. 2007. 384p. pap. 25.00 *(978-0-86515-034-8(6))* Santillana USA Publishing Co., Inc.

Quirós Fernández, Maria Teresa. Stereophonie der Autobiographie: Autobiographisches Schreiben von Paaren am Beispiel von María Teresa León und Rafael Alberti. 2009. (Mimesis Ser.).Tr. of Stereophonic Autobiography. Concept & Model of Autobiographies Written by Couples using the example of María Teresa león & Rafael Alberti. (GER.). VII, 213p. pap. *(978-3-484-55048-3(1))* Verlag Max Niemeyer.

Rivero Taravillo, Antonio & Rivero, Antonio. Luis Cernuda. Los Años Del Exilio (1938-1963) años de exilio, 1938-1963. 2011. (SPA., Illus.). 408p. pap. 26.95 ***(978-84-8383-321-6(2))*** Tusquets Editores ESP. Dist: Ediciones Urano S. A.

Ruiz Casanova, José Francisco & Aganzo, Carlos. Singularidad en la Poesía de Manuel Ruiz Amezcua. Ruiz Casanova, José Francisco, ed. 4th ed. 2010. (SPA.). 442p. *(978-84-8439-528-7(6))* Universidad de Jaen Servicio de Publicaciones e Intercambio Científico.

Sabina, Joaquin & Menendez Flores, Javier. Sabina en Carne Viva: Yo Tambien Se Jugarme la Boca. 10th ed. 2007. (ENG., Illus.). 448p. pap. 17.95 *(978-84-666-2872-3(X))* Ediciones B ESP. Dist: Independent Pubs. Group.

Salinas, Pedro & Guillén, Jorge. Correspondencia (1923-1951) Soria Olmedo, Andrés, tr. (SPA., Illus.). 638p. *(978-84-7223-481-9(9)*, 6030) Tusquets Editores.

Samson, Alexander & Thacker, Jonathan. A Companion to Lope de Vega. Samson, Alexander & Thacker, Jonathan, eds. 2010. (Monografías A Ser.: Volume 260). (Illus.). 404p. 90.00 *(978-1-85566-168-4(3)*, Tamesis Bks.) Boydell & Brewer, Ltd. GBR. Dist: Boydell & Brewer, Inc.

Sánchez Conejero, Cristina. Novela y Cine de Ciencia Ficcion Espanola Contemporanea: Una Reflexion Sobre la Humanidad. 2009. 316p. 119.95 *(978-0-7734-5104-9(8))* Mellen, Edwin Pr., The.

Sliwa, Krzysztof. Cartas, documentos y escrituras del Dr. Frey Lope Félix de Vega Carpio(1562-1635), 2 vols., Vol. 12. 2007. (SPA., Illus.). 890p. pap. 49.95 *(978-1-58871-116-8(1)*, SLIWA, Juan de la Cuesta-Hispanic Monographs) LinguaText, Ltd.

Suero, Pablo. España Levanta el Puño: Palabras Al Borde Del Abismo. Soria Olmedo, Andres, tr. 2009. (Papel de Liar Ser.). (SPA.). 304p. pap. 20.00 ***(978-84-936679-5-5(1))*** Global Rhythm Pr. ESP. Dist: Independent Pubs. Group.

Tully, Carol. Johann Nikolas Bohl Von Faber (1770-1836) A German Romantic in Spain. 2008. (GER & ENG.). 544p. 99.00 *(978-0-7083-2001-3(5))* Univ. of Wales Pr. GBR. Dist: Chicago Distribution Ctr.

Tusquets, Esther. Private Correspondence. 2008. *(978-0-8387-5686-7(7))* Bucknell Univ. Pr.

Tusquets, Esther & Ichiishi, Barbara F. We Had Won the War. 2012. ***(978-1-4331-1626-1(X))***; E-Book ***(978-1-4539-0234-9(1))*** Lang, Peter Publishing, Inc.

Villarroel, Torres, et al. Vida, Ascendencia, Nacimiento, Crianza y Aventuras. (Clasicos Castalia). (SPA., Illus.). 308p. 16.95 *(978-84-7039-041-8(4)*, CC522) Castalia, Editorial S.A. ESP. Dist: Continental Bk. Co., Inc.

AUTHORS, TURKISH

Anadolu-Okur, Nilgün, ed. Essays Interpreting the Writings of Novelist Orhan Pamuk: The Turkish Winner of the Nobel Prize in Literature. 2009. 160p. 99.95 *(978-0-7734-4754-7(7))* Mellen, Edwin Pr., The.

Edib, Halidé. House with Wisteria: Memoirs of Turkey Old & New. 2009. (ENG.). 442p. pap. 34.95 *(978-1-4128-1002-9(7))* Transaction Pubs.

Hasan, Mushirul. Between Modernity & Nationalism: Halide Edip's Encounter with Gandhi's India. 2010. (ENG., Illus.). 304p. 49.95 *(978-0-19-806332-2(6))* Oxford Univ. Pr., Inc.

Kemal, Orhan. In Jail with Nazim Hikmet. Rona, Bengisu, tr. from TUR. 2010. (ENG.). 215p. pap. 15.95 ***(978-0-86356-411-6(9))*** Saqi Bks. GBR. Dist: Consortium Bk. Sales & Distribution.

McGaha, Michael. Autobiographies of Orhan Pamuk: The Writer in His Novels. 2008. (Utah Series in Turkish & Islamic Stud Ser.). (ENG.). 213p. (gr. 12). 24.95 *(978-0-87480-930-5(4))* Univ. of Utah Pr.

Pamuk, Orhan. The Naive & the Sentimental Novelist. 2010. (Charles Eliot Norton Lectures). 208p. 22.95 *(978-0-674-05076-1(2))* Harvard Univ. Pr.

—The Naive & the Sentimental Novelist. 2011. (Vintage International Ser.). (ENG.). 208p. pap. 14.95 *(978-0-307-74524-8(4)*, Vintage) Knopf Doubleday Publishing Group.

Shafak, Elif. Black Milk: On the Conflicting Demands of Writing, Creativity, & Motherhood. 2012. (ENG.). 288p. (gr. 12). pap. 16.00 ***(978-0-14-312108-4(1)***, Penguin (Non-Classics)) Penguin Group (USA) Inc.

Shafak, Elif. Black Milk: On Writing, Motherhood, & the Harem Within. Zapsu, Hande, tr. from TUR. 2011. (ENG.). 288p. (gr. 12). 25.95 *(978-0-670-02264-9(0)*, Viking Adult) Penguin Group (USA) Inc.

Willoughby, Jay, ed. Fethullah Gulen: Ensayos, perspectivas y Opiniones. 2009. (SPA.). 216p. pap. 6.95 *(978-1-932099-78-2(6))* Tughra Bks.

Yilmaz Bastug, Melike. A Translational Journey. 2009. 220p. pap. *(978-3-639-16189-2(0))* VDM Verlag Dr. Mueller e.K.

Zaborowska, Magdalena J. James Baldwin's Turkish Decade: Erotics of Exile. 2009. (ENG., Illus.). 416p. 94.95 *(978-0-8223-4144-4(1))* Duke Univ. Pr.

Zaborowska, Magdalena J. & Zaborowska, Magdalena. James Baldwin's Turkish Decade: Erotics of Exile. 2009. (ENG., Illus.). 416p. pap. 26.95 *(978-0-8223-4167-3(0))* Duke Univ. Pr.

AUTHORS, WELSH

Barstow, Phyllida. My Animals (And Other Family) 2009. (ENG., Illus.). 224p. 24.95 ***(978-1-906122-13-3(X))*** Unwin, Merlin Bks. GBR. Dist: SCB Distributors.

Carradice, Phil. Herbert Williams. 2010. (University of Wales Press - Writers of Wales Ser.). (Illus.). 117p. pap. 25.00 *(978-0-7083-2192-8(5))* Univ. of Wales Pr. GBR. Dist: Chicago Distribution Ctr.

Dahl, Roald. Going Solo. 2009. (ENG.). 224p. (YA). (gr. 7-18). 6.99 *(978-0-14-241383-8(6)*, Puffin) Penguin Group (USA) Inc.

Davies, W. H. & Brandon, David. Autobiography of a Supertramp. 2010. (ENG.). 192p. pap. 24.95 *(978-1-84868-980-0(2))* Amberley Publishing GBR. Dist: Casemate Pubs. & Bk. Distributors, LLC.

Emery, Clark. The World of Dylan Thomas. 2011. 332p. 50.95 ***(978-1-258-01110-9(7))*** Literary Licensing, LLC.

Green, Diane. Emyr Humphreys: A Postcolonial Novelist. 2009. (University of Wales Press - Writing Wales in English Ser.). 224p. pap. 25.00 *(978-0-7083-2217-8(4))* Univ. of Wales Pr. GBR. Dist: Chicago Distribution Ctr.

Gwyn, Richard. The Vagabond's Breakfast. 2011. (ENG.). 192p. pap. 17.95 *(978-0-9560125-5-8(8))* Alcemi GBR. Dist: Dufour Editions, Inc.

Horak, Roman, et al, eds. About Raymond Williams. 2010. (ENG.). 208p. (C). pap. 42.95 *(978-0-415-54580-8(3))* Routledge.

Horak, Roman & Seidl, Monika, eds. About Raymond Williams. 2010. (ENG.). 208p. (C). 125.00 *(978-0-415-54579-2(X))* Routledge.

Lewis, Alun. A Cypress Walk. 2007. (ENG., Illus.). 224p. 59.95 *(978-1-904634-30-0(3))* Enitharmon Pr. GBR. Dist: Dufour Editions, Inc.

Matthews, Sean. Raymond Williams. 2007. 200p. 21.95 *(978-0-415-25613-1(5))*; 95.00 *(978-0-415-25612-4(7))* Routledge.

Murray, Iain H. Life of Lloyd-Jones, 2 vols. Incl. Life of D. Martyn Lloyd-Jones Vol. 1: The First Forty Years, 1899-1939. 412p. 1983. 35.99 *(978-0-85151-353-9(0))*; Vol. 2. Life of D. Martyn Lloyd-Jones Vol. 2: The Fight of Faith, 1939-1981. 862p. 1990. 39.99 *(978-0-85151-564-9(9))*; (Illus.). (David Martin Lloyd-Jones Collection). 69.99 *(978-0-85151-729-2(3))* Banner of Truth, The.

Osborne, Huw. Rhys Davies. 2nd rev. ed. 2009. (University of Wales Press - Writers of Wales Ser.). (ENG., Illus.). 144p. pap. 25.00 *(978-0-7083-2167-6(4))* Univ. of Wales Pr. GBR. Dist: Chicago Distribution Ctr.

Smith, Dai. Raymond Williams: A Warrior's Tale. Donahaye, Jasmine, ed. 2008. (ENG., Illus.). 450p. pap. 20.95 *(978-1-905762-99-6(2))*; 39.95 *(978-1-905762-56-9(9))* Parthian Bks. GBR. Dist: Independent Pubs. Group.

Thomas, Aeronwy. My Father's Places: A Memoir by Dylan Thomas's Daughter. 2010. (ENG., Illus.). 224p. 19.95 *(978-1-61608-101-0(5)*, 608101) Skyhorse Publishing Co., Inc.

Thomas, David, III. Dylan Thomas Trail. 3rd ed. 2011. (ENG., Illus.). 144p. pap. 15.95 ***(978-0-86243-609-4(5))*** Y Lolfa GBR. Dist: Dufour Editions, Inc.

Thomas, Dylan. A Child's Christmas in Wales. 2009. (ENG., Illus.). 64p. pap. 9.95 *(978-0-8112-1731-6(0)*, 21731) New Directions Publishing Corp.

W. Ambrose Bebb. A Welsh Hundred: Glimpses of Life in Wales drawn from a pair of family diaries for 1841 And 1940. Marc K. Stengel, tr. 2009. 232p. pap. 14.49 *(978-1-4343-5991-9(3))* AuthorHouse.

Westover, Daniel. R. S. Thomas: A Stylistic Biography. 2011. (University of Wales Press - Writing Wales in English Ser.). (ENG.). 215p. 140.00 *(978-0-7083-2413-4(4))*; 224p. pap. 40.00 *(978-0-7083-2411-0(8))* Univ. of Wales Pr. GBR. Dist: Chicago Distribution Ctr.

AUTHORS, WOMEN

see Women Authors

AUTHORS AND PATRONS

see also Literature and State

Aghacy, Samira. Masculine Identity in Fiction. 2009. 232p. 34.95 *(978-0-8156-3237-5(1))* Syracuse Univ. Pr.

Ferrante, Joan M. To the Glory of Her Sex: Women's Roles in the Composition of Medieval Texts. 2008. 316p. pap. 31.00 *(978-1-59740-580-5(9))* ACLS Humanities E-Book.

Glomski, Jacqueline. Patronage & Humanist Literature in the Age of the Jagiellons: Court & Career in the Writings of Rudolf Agricola Junior, Valentin Eck, & Leonard Cox. 2007. (Erasmus Studies). (ENG., Illus.). 320p. *(978-0-8020-9300-4(0))* Univ. of Toronto Pr.

Gold, Barbara K. Literary Patronage in Greece & Rome. 2011. (ENG.). 288p. pap. 40.00 ***(978-0-8078-6541-5(9))*** Univ. of North Carolina Pr.

Medieval Manuscripts, Their Makers & Users: A Special Issue of Viator in Honor of Richard & Mary Rouse. 2011. (ENG & FRE., Illus.). 321p. (C). 131.00 ***(978-2-503-53894-5(0))*** Brepols Pubs. BEL. Dist: ISD.

Meek, Richard, et al, eds. Shakespeare's Book: Essays in Reading, Writing, & Reception. 2011. (ENG., Illus.). 277p. pap. 25.95 *(978-0-7190-8561-1(6))* Manchester Univ. Pr. GBR. Dist: Macmillan.

Salter, Elizabeth. English & International: Studies in the Literature, Art & Patronage of Medieval England. Pearsall, Derek & Zeeman, Nicolette, eds. 2010. (ENG.). 408p. pap. 42.00 *(978-0-521-13161-2(8))* Cambridge Univ. Pr.

Sharlet, Jocelyn. Patronage & Poetry in the Islamic World: Social Mobility & Status in the Medieval Middle East & Central Asia. 2011. (Library of Middle East History Ser.). (ENG.). 336p. 99.00 *(978-1-84885-369-0(6)*, Tauris Academic Studies) I. B. Tauris & Co., Ltd. GBR. Dist: Macmillan.
Shoemaker, Peter W. Powerful Connections: The Poetics of Patronage in the Age of Louis XIII. 2007. 296p. (C). 60.00 *(978-0-87413-993-8(7))* Univ. of Delaware Pr.
Walker, Greg. Plays of Persuasion: Drama & Politics at the Court of Henry VIII. 2008. 260p. pap. 37.99 *(978-0-521-09072-8(5))* Cambridge Univ. Pr.
White, Paul Whitfield & Westfall, Suzanne R., eds. Shakespeare & Theatrical Patronage in Early Modern England. 2006. (ENG.). 336p. pap. 72.00 *(978-0-521-03430-2(2))* Cambridge Univ. Pr.

AUTHORS AND PRINTERS

see Authorship—Handbooks, Manuals, etc.; Printing—Style Manuals

AUTHORS AND PUBLISHERS

see also Copyright; Literary Agents

Arnold, Danny R. 147 Publishing Tips for Professors. 2008. *(978-1-891859-72-4(2))* Atwood Publishing.
Benson, Christopher & Jones, Hugh. Publishing Law. 4th rev. ed. 2011. (ENG.). 384p. pap. 59.95 *(978-0-415-57517-1(6))* Routledge.
Benson, Philippa J. & Silver, Susan C. What Editors Want: An Author's Guide to Scientific Journal Publishing. 2012. (Chicago Guides to Writing, Editing, & Publishing Ser.). 176p. pap. 20.00 ***(978-0-226-04314-2(2))***; (Illus.). 55.00 ***(978-0-226-04313-5(4))*** Univ. of Chicago Pr.
Bird, Tom. You Were Born to Be Published: Eleven Laws for Getting Your Writing into print Now! 2007. (Illus.). 260p. pap. 18.95 *(978-0-9789216-2-0(3))* Sojourn, Inc.
Brier, Evan. A Novel Marketplace: Mass Culture, the Book Trade, & Postwar American Fiction. 2009. (Illus.). 224p. (C). 49.95 *(978-0-8122-4207-2(6))* Univ. of Pennsylvania Pr.
Briles, Judith, et al. Show Me about Book Publishing: Survive & Thrive in Today's Literary Jungle. 2011. (ENG.). 230p. pap. 18.95 *(978-1-60037-855-3(2))* Morgan James Publishing.
Brito, Manuel. Market Fructification of Innovative American Poetry in the Late 20th Century. 2010. 182p. pap. 50.95 *(978-3-0343-0444-3(7))* Lang, Peter Publishing, Inc.
Bruccoli, Matthew J. On Books & Writers: Selected Essays. Unrue, John C., ed. 2010. 320p. 39.95 *(978-1-57003-902-7(X))* Univ. of South Carolina Pr.
Buinicki, Martin T. Walt Whitman's Reconstruction: Poetry & Publishing between Memory & History. 2011. (Iowa Whitman Ser.). (ENG.). 174p. pap. 29.95 *(978-1-60938-069-4(X))* Univ. of Iowa Pr.
Chang, Leah L. Into Print: The Production of Female Authorship in Early Modern France. 2009. (ENG.). 58.50 *(978-1-61149-113-5(4))*; 58.50 *(978-0-87413-053-9(0))* Univ. of Delaware Pr.
Cloud, Gerald W. John Rodker's Ovid Press: A Bibliographical History. 2010. *(978-1-58456-286-3(2))* Oak Knoll Pr.
Cohen, Lara Langer & Stein, Jordan Alexander, eds. Early African American Print Culture. 2012. (Material Texts). (Illus.). 432p. (C). 55.00 ***(978-0-8122-4425-0(7))*** Univ. of Pennsylvania Pr.
Colton, Jo Ann M. So, You Want to Be A Writer: Jo Ann M. Colton's Little Red Writer Book Series, Book 1. 2010. 80p. pap. 10.49 *(978-1-4490-1328-8(7))* AuthorHouse.
Cross, Laura. The Complete Guide to Hiring a Literary Agent: Everything You Need to Know to Become Successfully Published. 2010. (ENG.). 288p. pap. 24.95 *(978-1-60138-403-4(3))* Atlantic Publishing Co.
Darnton, Robert. The Devil in the Holy Water, or the Art of Slander from Louis XIV to Napoleon. (Material Texts). (Illus.). 552p. (C). 2011. pap. 29.95 ***(978-0-8122-2171-8(0))*** 2009. 65.00 *(978-0-8122-4183-9(5))* Univ. of Pennsylvania Pr.
Dilks, Stephen. Samuel Beckett in the Literary Marketplace. 2011. (Illus.). 400p. *(978-0-8156-3254-2(1))* Syracuse Univ. Pr.
Dowling, David. The Business of Literary Circles in Nineteenth-Century America. 2011. (Nineteenth-Century Major Lives & Letters Ser.). (ENG.). 304p. 89.00 *(978-0-230-11046-5(0))* Palgrave Macmillan.
—Capital Letters: Authorship in the Antebellum Literary Market. 2009. (ENG., Illus.). 226p. 39.95 *(978-1-58729-784-7(1))* Univ. of Iowa Pr.
Dowling, David. Literary Partnerships & the Marketplace: Writers & Mentors in Nineteenth-Century America. 2012. 248p. 39.95 ***(978-0-8071-3847-2(9))*** Louisiana State Univ. Pr.
Dubino, Jeanne. Virginia Woolf & the Literary Marketplace. Dubino, Jeanne, ed. 2010. (ENG., Illus.). 282p. 84.00 *(978-0-230-10706-9(0))* Palgrave Macmillan.
Eckstut, Arielle & Sterry, David Henry. Getting Your Book Published: How to Write It, Sell It, & Market It... Successfully! 2010. (ENG.). 480p. pap. 15.95 *(978-0-7611-6085-4(X)*, 076116085X) Workman Publishing Co., Inc.
Erickson, Beth Ann. Filbert's Fast Guide to Getting Published: Without Falling for Scams, Hooks, Lines, & Sinkers. 2006. per. 19.95 *(978-1-932794-13-7(1))* Filbert Publishing.
Everton, Michael J. The Grand Chorus of Complaint: Authors & the Business Ethics of American Publishing, 1 vol. 2011. (ENG., Illus.). 256p. 65.00 *(978-0-19-975178-5(1))* Oxford Univ. Pr., Inc.
Fang, Karen Y. Romantic Writing & the Empire of Signs: Periodical Culture & Post-Napoleonic Authorship. 2010. (ENG.). 248p. (gr. 17). 35.00 *(978-0-8139-2874-6(5))* Univ. Pr. of Virginia.
Faust, Jessica, et al. The Complete Idiot's Guide to Book Proposals & Query Letters. 2011. (Complete Idiot's Guide Ser.). (ENG.). 320p. (gr. 12). 16.95 *(978-1-61564-045-4(2)*, Alpha Bks.) Penguin Group (USA) Inc.
Feather. Book Publishing 4-Vol. Set, 4 vols. 2011. (Critical Concepts in Media & Cultural Studies). 1616p. (C). 1140.00 *(978-0-415-49005-2(X))* Routledge.
Field, Corey & Slotnick, Barry I. Entertainment Law: Forms & Analysis. 2011. ***(978-1-58852-176-7(1)**,* Law Journal Pr.) Incisive Media.
Flint, Christopher. Print & the Page in Eighteenth-Century Fiction. 2011. (ENG., Illus.). 294p. 95.00 *(978-1-107-00839-7(5))* Cambridge Univ. Pr.
Franta, Andrew. Romanticism & the Rise of the Mass Public. 2009. (Cambridge Studies in Romanticism Ser.). (ENG.). 260p. pap. 38.99 *(978-0-521-11710-4(0))* Cambridge Univ. Pr.
Fry, Patricia. Publish Your Book: Proven Strategies & Resources for the Enterprising Authors. 2012. (ENG.). 256p. pap. 19.95 ***(978-1-58115-884-7(X)**,* 115884, Allworth Pr.) Skyhorse Publishing Co., Inc.
Gardner, Jared. The Rise & Fall of Early American Magazine Culture. 2012. (History of Communication Ser.). (ENG., Illus.). 224p. 50.00 ***(978-0-252-03670-5(0))*** Univ. of Illinois Pr.
Graf, Klaus. Urheberrechtsfibel - nicht nur für Piraten: Der Text des deutschen Urheberrechtsgesetzes, erklärt und kritisch kommentiert. 2009. 284p. pap. *(978-3-86199-002-4(4))* Books on Demand GmbH.
Hamilton, Gail. A Battle of the Books / Recorded by an Unknown Writer for the Use of Authors & Publishers; Edited & Published by Gail Hamilton [I E M a Dod. 2006. 292p. per. 23.99 *(978-1-4255-2774-7(4))* MPublishing.
Hawkes, John D. How to Get Your Book Published. (Illus.). 40p. pap. 1.50 *(978-0-89036-060-6(X))* Liahona Publishing Trust.
Henderson, Cathy & Oram, Richard W. Dlb 355. 2010. (Dictionary of Literary Biography Ser.). (ENG., Illus.). xlii, 589p. 315.00 *(978-0-7876-8173-9(3))* Cengage Gale.
Hinks, John & Day, Matthew, eds. From Compositors to Collectors: Essays on Book-Trade History. 2012. 75.00 ***(978-1-58456-301-3(X))*** Oak Knoll Pr.
Jackson, Leon. The Business of Letters: Authorial Economies in Antebellum America. 2007. (ENG.). 344p. 35.00 *(978-0-8047-5705-8(4))* Stanford Univ. Pr.
Jacobs, Charles. The Writer Within You: A Step-by-Step Guide to Writing & Publishing in Your Retirement Years. 2007. 321p. per. 19.95 *(978-0-9793636-0-3(8))* Caros Bks.
Jones, Hugh & Benson, Christopher. Publishing Law. 4th rev. ed. 2011. (ENG.). 384p. 130.00 *(978-0-415-57513-3(3))* Routledge.
Kahan, Jeffrey. Getting Published in the Humanities: What to Know, Where to Aim, How to Succeed. 2011. (ENG.). 206p. pap. 40.00 *(978-0-7864-5923-0(9))* McFarland & Co., Inc. Pubs.
Karian, Stephen. Jonathan Swift in Print & Manuscript. 2010. (ENG., Illus.). 284p. 89.00 *(978-0-521-19804-2(6))* Cambridge Univ. Pr.
Kaufman, Roy S. Publishing Forms & Contracts. 2008. (ENG., Illus.). 474p. pap. 170.50 *(978-0-19-536734-8(0))* Oxford Univ. Pr., Inc.
Kuhbandner, Birgit. Unternehmer Zwischen Markt und Moderne: Verleger und Die Zeitgenössische Deutschsprachige Literatur an der Schwelle Zum 20. Jahrhundert. 2008. 378p. *(978-3-447-05658-8(4))* Harrassowitz, Otto Verlag.
Landenheim-Gil, Randy. The Everything Guide to Getting Published: Expert advice for building a successful writing Career. 3rd ed. 2012. (ENG.) 304p. pap. 16.95 ***(978-1-4405-2844-6(6))*** Adams Media Corp.
Ledbetter, Kathryn. Tennyson & Victorian Periodicals: Commodities in Context. 2007. (Nineteenth Century Ser.). (Illus.). 244p. 99.95 *(978-0-7546-5719-4(1))* Ashgate Publishing Co.
Legat, Michael. An Author's Guide to Literary Agents. 123p. pap. 19.99 *(978-0-7090-5572-3(2))* Hale, Robert Ltd. GBR. Dist: Trafalgar Square Publishing.
Lerner, Betsy. The Forest for the Trees: An Editor's Advice to Writers. 21st rev. ed. 2010. (ENG.). 304p. (gr. 12). 16.00 *(978-1-59448-483-4(X)*, Riverhead Trade (Paperbacks)) Penguin Group (USA) Inc.
Levine, Mark. Negotiating a Book Contract: A Guide for Authors, Agents & Lawyers. 2nd rev. ed. 2009. 160p. pap. 23.95 *(978-1-55921-383-7(3)*, Asphodel Pr.) Moyer Bell.
Liddle, Dallas. The Dynamics of Genre: Journalism & the Practice of Literature in Mid-Victorian Britain. 2009. (Victorian Literature & Culture Ser.). (ENG.). 248p. (gr. 17). 39.50 *(978-0-8139-2783-1(8))* Univ. Pr. of Virginia.
Luey, Beth. Handbook for Academic Authors. 5th rev. ed. 2009. (ENG., Illus.). 296p. 80.00 *(978-0-521-19498-3(9))*; pap. 23.99 *(978-0-521-14409-4(4))* Cambridge Univ. Pr.
Maeda, Martha & Chesanek, Carissa. Book Publishing 101: Inside Information to Getting Your First Book or Novel Published. 2012. (ENG.). 288p. pap. 24.95 *(978-1-60138-564-2(1))* Atlantic Publishing Co.
Martin, Gail. Launching Your Books Without Losing Your Mind. 2010. 124p. pap. 13.99 *(978-1-935361-06-0(6))* Comfort Publishing Services, LLC.
Maruca, Lisa. The Work of Print: Authorship & the English Text Trades, 1660-1760. 2007. (Literary Conjugations Ser.). (ENG., Illus.). 240p. 80.00 *(978-0-295-98744-6(8))* Univ. of Washington Pr.
Maruca, Lisa M. The Work of Print: Authorship & the English Text Trades, 1660-1760. 2007. (Literary Conjugations, a Robert B. Heilman Book Ser.). (ENG., Illus.). 240p. per. 24.95 *(978-0-295-98757-6(X))* Univ. of Washington Pr.
Meek, Richard, et al, eds. Shakespeare's Book: Essays in Reading, Writing, & Reception. 2011. (ENG., Illus.). 277p. pap. 25.95 *(978-0-7190-8561-1(6))* Manchester Univ. Pr. GBR. Dist: Macmillan.
Mettee, Stephen Blake, ed. The Portable Writer's Conference: Your Guide to Getting Published. 2007. (ENG.). 464p. pap. 19.95 *(978-1-884956-57-7(2))* Quill Driver Bks.
Michelson, Bruce. Printer's Devil - Mark Twain & the American Publishing Revolution. 2006. (Illus.). 320p. 40.00 *(978-0-520-24759-8(0))* Univ. of California Pr.
Miller, Anita. Uncollecting Cheever. 2009. (ENG.). 363p. pap. 18.95 *(978-0-89733-593-5(7))* Academy Chicago Pubs., Ltd.
Mirabal-Garza, Rosie. El Progreso, 1939-1940: The Work of Rodolfo Zepeda Mirabal & Dora Cervera Mirabal. 2006. im. lthr. *(978-0-9789604-0-7(8))* Printers Unlimited, Inc.
Murphy, Priscilla Coit. What a Book Can Do: The Publication & Reception of Silent Spring. 2007. (Studies in Print Culture & the History of the Book). (Illus.). 254p. per. 22.95 *(978-1-55849-582-1(7))* Univ. of Massachusetts Pr.
Nappa, Mike. 77 Reasons Why Your Book Was Rejected. 2011. (ENG.). 384p. pap. 14.99 *(978-1-4022-5412-3(1))* Sourcebooks, Inc.
Nogueira, Maria Xesus. Creation, Publishing, & Criticism: The Advance of Women's Writing. 2010. (Galician Studies). 256p. (C). 76.95 *(978-1-4331-0954-6(9))* Lang, Peter Publishing, Inc.
O'Cinneide, Muireann, et al. Aristocratic Women & the Literary Nation, 1832-1867. Bristow, Joseph, ed. 2008. (Palgrave Studies in Nineteenth-Century Writing & Culture Ser.). (ENG.). 240p. 89.00 *(978-0-230-54670-7(6))* Palgrave Macmillan.
Oliver, Marina. The Beginner's Guide to Writing a Novel: How to Prepare Your First Book for Publication. 4th rev. ed. 2006. (Illus.). 191p. per. 20.00 *(978-1-84528-091-8(1))* Parkwest Pubns., Inc.
Owen, Lynette. Clark's Publishing Agreements: Eighth Edition. 8th ed. 2010. 749p. 215.00 incl. cd-rom *(978-1-84766-544-7(6)*, Bloomsbury Professional) Bloomsbury Publishing Plc GBR. Dist: International Specialized Bk. Services.
—Selling Rights. 5th rev. ed. 2006. 367p. per. 69.95 *(978-0-415-38652-4(7))* 6th rev. ed. 2010. (ENG.). 448p. (C). pap. 69.95 *(978-0-415-49692-6(6))* Routledge.
Parfait, Claire. The Publishing History of Uncle Tom's Cabin 1852-2002. 2007. (Illus.). 280p. 114.95 *(978-0-7546-5514-5(8))* Ashgate Publishing Co.
Parker, Mark. Literary Magazines & British Romanticism. 2006. (Cambridge Studies in Romanticism Ser.). (ENG.). 232p. pap. 50.00 *(978-0-521-03202-5(4))* Cambridge Univ. Pr.
Peterson, Linda H. Becoming a Woman of Letters: Myths of Authorship & Facts of the Victorian Market. 2009. (ENG., Illus.). 308p. (C). 37.50 *(978-0-691-14017-9(0))* Princeton Univ. Pr.
Plachta, Bodo, ed. Literarische Zusammenarbeit.Tr. of Literary Collaboration. (GER.). IX, 316p. 210.00 ***(978-3-11-179573-7(X))*** De Gruyter, Walter Inc.
Price, Lynn. The Writer's Essential Tackle Box: Getting a Hook on the Publishing Industry. 2009. (Get It Write Ser.). (ENG.). 380p. pap. 19.95 *(978-1-933016-34-4(5))* Behler Pubns., LLC.
Pykett, Lyn. Wilkie Collins (Authors in Context) 2009. (Oxford World's Classics Ser.). (ENG., Illus.). 272p. pap. 14.95 *(978-0-19-955611-3(3))* Oxford Univ. Pr., Inc.
Roberts, Ryan. John Fuller & the Sycamore Press: A Bibliographic History. 2010. (Illus.). xi, 148p. 49.95 *(978-1-58456-281-8(1))* Oak Knoll Pr.
Runge, Laura L. Producing the Eighteenth-Century Book: Writers & Publishers in England, 1650-1800. 2009. (ENG.). 65.00 *(978-1-61149-126-5(6))* Univ. of Delaware Pr.
Runge, Laura L. & Rogers, Pat. Producing the Eighteenth-Century Book: Writers & Publishers in England, 1650-1800. 2009. (Illus.). 298p. 65.00 *(978-0-87413-069-0(7))* Univ. of Delaware Pr.
Shay, Helen. Writer's Guide to Copyright, Contract & Law. 4th ed. 2009. 144p. pap. 22.00 *(978-1-84528-321-6(X))* How To Books GBR. Dist: Parkwest Pubns., Inc.
Sher, Richard B. The Enlightenment & the Book: Scottish Authors & Their Publishers in Eighteenth-Century Britain, Ireland, & America. 2007. (ENG., Illus.). 842p. 40.00 *(978-0-226-75252-5(6))* Univ. of Chicago Pr.
Spiers, John, ed. Authors, Publishers & the Shaping of Taste, 2 vols., Vol. 1. 2011. (ENG., Illus.). 264p. 80.00 *(978-0-230-28402-9(7))* Palgrave Macmillan.
Sprigge, Samuel Squire. The Methods of Publishing. 2010. (Cambridge Library Collection - Printing & Publishing History Ser.). (ENG.). 124p. pap. 19.99 *(978-1-108-00918-8(2))* Cambridge Univ. Pr.
Sutherland, John. The Longman Companion to Victorian Fiction. 2nd ed. 2009. (ENG., Illus.). 736p. pap. 45.00 *(978-1-4082-0390-3(1))* Longman Publishing Group.
Swaim, Barton. Scottish Men of Letters & the New Public Sphere, 1802-1834. 2009. 224p. 51.00 *(978-0-8387-5716-1(2))* Bucknell Univ. Pr.
Tatlock, Lynne, ed. Publishing Culture & the Reading Nation: German Book History in the Long Nineteenth Century. 2010. (Studies in German Literature Linguistics & Culture Ser.: Volume 76). (GER & ENG., Illus.). 356p. 75.00 *(978-1-57113-402-8(6))* Camden Hse.
Terrell, P. M. Take the Mystery Out of Promoting Your Book. 2006. 213p. per. 15.00 *(978-1-928662-43-3(9))* Palari Publishing LLP.
Ticknor, Caroline. Hawthorne & His Publisher. 2009. 382p. 33.99 *(978-1-116-63923-0(8))*; 38.99 *(978-1-116-63922-3(X))*; pap. 32.75 *(978-1-116-63925-4(4))*; pap. 33.75 *(978-1-116-63924-7(6))* BiblioBazaar.
—Hawthorne & His Publisher. 2007. 372p. 48.95 *(978-0-548-55053-3(0))*; per. 33.95 *(978-0-548-46963-7(6))* Kessinger Publishing, LLC.
Trogdon, Robert W. The Lousy Racket: Hemingway, Scribners, & the Business of Literature. 2007. 307p. 39.95 *(978-0-87338-904-4(2))* Kent State Univ. Pr.
Turner, Frederick. Renegade: Henry Miller & the Making of Tropic of Cancer. 2012. (Icons of America Ser.). (ENG.). 256p. 24.95 *(978-0-300-14949-4(2))* Yale Univ. Pr.
Underdown, Harold D. Publishing Children's Books - Complete Idiot's Guide. 3rd ed. 2008. (Complete Idiot's Guide Ser.). (ENG., Illus.). 384p. (gr. 12-18). 18.95 *(978-1-59257-750-7(4)*, Alpha Bks.) Penguin Group (USA) Inc.
Whalin, W. Terry. Jumpstart Your Publishing Dreams: Insider Secrets to Skyrocket Your Success. 2009. (ENG.). pap. 19.95 *(978-1-935085-50-8(6))* WTW Pr.
Williams, Miller. Making a Poem: Some Thoughts about Poetry & the People Who Write It. 2006. 127p. per. 18.95 *(978-0-8071-3132-9(6))* Louisiana State Univ. Pr.
Wills, Maralys. Damn the Rejections Full Speed Ahead: The Bumpy Road to Getting Published. 2008. 256p. 24.95 *(978-1-932173-92-5(7))* Stephens Pr. LLC.
Writer's Digest Books Editors. Writer's Digest University: Everything You Need to Write & Sell Your Work. 2010. (ENG.). 528p. pap. 39.99 *(978-1-59963-137-0(7)*, Writer's Digest Bks.) F&W Media, Inc.
Yager, Jan. The Complete Help Book for Authors & Publishers. 2012. pap. 29.95 *(978-1-889262-16-1(1))* Hannacroix Creek Bks., Inc.
Young, John K. Black Writers, White Publishers: Marketplace Politics in Twentieth-Century African American Literature. 2010. (ENG., Illus.). 242p. pap. 25.00 *(978-1-60473-548-2(1))* Univ. Pr. of Mississippi.

AUTHORS AND READERS

see also Books and Reading

Ainsworth, David. Milton & the Spiritual Reader. 2010. 244p. pap. 39.95 *(978-0-415-88390-0(3))* Routledge.
Ascoli, Albert Russell. Favola Fui: Petrarch Writes His Readers. 2010. (Bernardo Lecture Ser.). (ENG.). 47p. pap. 10.00 *(978-1-4384-3806-1(0))* State Univ. of New York Pr.
Bates, Brian R. Wordsworth's Poetic Collections, Supplementary Writing & Parodic Reception, 1 vol. 2012. (History of the Book Ser.). (ENG.). 256p. 99.00 *(978-1-84893-196-1(4))* Pickering & Chatto Pubs., Ltd. GBR. Dist: Ashgate Publishing Co.
Bietenholz, Peter G. Encounters with a Radical Erasmus: Erasmus' Work as a Source of Radical Thought in Early Modern Europe. 2008. (Erasmus Studies). (ENG.). 336p. *(978-0-8020-9905-1(X))* Univ. of Toronto Pr.
Birkerts, Sven. The Gutenberg Elegies: The Fate of Reading in an Electronic Age. 2006. (ENG., Illus.). 272p. per. 16.00 *(978-0-86547-957-9(7))* Faber & Faber, Inc.
Black, Scott. Of Essays & Reading in Early Modern Britain. 2006. (Palgrave Studies in the Enlightenment, Romanticism & the Cultures of Print Ser.). (ENG.). 208p. 84.00 *(978-1-4039-9905-4(8))* Palgrave Macmillan.
Bloom, Harold. The Anatomy of Influence: Literature as a Way of Life. 368p. 2012. (ENG.). pap. 20.00 ***(978-0-300-18144-9(2))*** 2011. 32.50 *(978-0-300-16760-3(1))* Yale Univ. Pr.
Bloomer, W. Martin. Valerius Maximus & the Rhetoric of the New Nobility. 2011. (ENG.). 296p. pap. 40.00 ***(978-0-8078-6509-5(5))*** Univ. of North Carolina Pr.
Bohman-Kalaja, Kimberly. Reading Games: An Aesthetics of Play in Flann O'Brien, Samuel Beckett, & Georges Perec. 2007. (Dalkey Archive Scholarly Ser.). 238p. pap. 34.95 *(978-1-56478-473-5(8))* Dalkey Archive Pr.
Bond, Ernest L. Literature & the Young Adult Reader. 2010. (ENG.). 456p. (C). pap. 98.20 *(978-0-13-111695-5(9)*, Prentice Hall) Prentice Hall PTR.
Brannon, Julie Sloan. Who Reads Ulysses? The Common Reader & the Rhetoric of the Joyce Wars. 2009. 206p. 39.95 *(978-0-415-80347-2(0))* Routledge.
Brayman Hackel, Heidi. Reading Material in Early Modern England: Print, Gender, & Literacy. 2009. (ENG., Illus.). 336p. pap. 36.99 *(978-0-521-10415-9(7))* Cambridge Univ. Pr.
Bueler, Lois E. Clarissa: The Eighteenth-Century Response, 1747-1804. 2008. xx, 341p. *(978-0-404-64860-2(6))* AMS Pr., Inc.
Bueler, Lois E., intro. Clarissa: The Eighteenth-Century Response, 1747-1804. 2009. *(978-0-404-63810-8(4))* AMS Pr., Inc.
Burke, Seán. The Ethics of Writing: Authorship & Legacy in Plato & Nietzsche. 2011. (ENG.). 256p. (gr. 17). pap. 32.00 *(978-0-7486-4179-6(3))* Edinburgh Univ. Pr. GBR. Dist: Columbia Univ. Pr.
Casanova, Mary. Mary Casanova & You, 1 vol. 2006. (Author & YOU Ser.). (Illus.). 156p. per. 35.00 *(978-1-59158-405-6(1)*, LU4051) Libraries Unlimited, Inc.
Chirico, Paul. John Clare & the Imagination of the Reader. 2007. (ENG.). 232p. 95.00 *(978-0-230-51763-9(3))* Palgrave Macmillan.
Colman, George, et al. Clarissa: The Eighteenth-Century Response, 1747-1804. 2009. xx, 341p. *(978-0-404-63811-5(2))* AMS Pr., Inc.
Cook, Paul. American Literature from the Colonies to the Civil War. rev. ed. 2008. (ENG.). 448p. pap. 77.96 *(978-0-7575-5848-1(8))* Kendall Hunt Publishing Co.
DiBattista, Maria. Imagining Virginia Woolf: An Experiment in Critical Biography. 2008. (ENG.). 208p. (C). 21.95 *(978-0-691-13812-1(5))* Princeton Univ. Pr.
Dillon, Sarah & Dillon. Palimpsest: Literature, Criticism, Theory. 2007. (Continuum Literary Studies). (ENG., Illus.). 176p. 130.00 *(978-0-8264-9545-7(1))* Continuum International Publishing Group, Ltd. GBR. Dist: National Bk. Network.
Easley, Alexis. Literary Celebrity, Gender, & Victorian Authorship, 1850-1914. 2011. (Illus.). 273p. *(978-1-936249-01-5(4))*; (ENG., 280p. 75.00 *(978-1-61149-016-9(2))* Univ. of Delaware Pr.
Eisner, Eric. Nineteenth-Century Poetry & Literary Celebrity. 2009. (ENG.). 232p. 95.00 *(978-0-230-22815-3(1))* Palgrave Macmillan.
Erne, Lukas. Shakespeare as Literary Dramatist. 2007. (ENG., Illus.). 300p. pap. 60.00 *(978-0-521-04566-7(5))* Cambridge Univ. Pr.

A

Franta, Andrew. Romanticism & the Rise of the Mass Public. 2009. (Cambridge Studies in Romanticism Ser.). (ENG.). 260p. pap. 38.99 *(978-0-521-11710-4(0))* Cambridge Univ. Pr.

Frost, Simon R. The Business of the Novel: Economics, Aesthetics & the Case of Middlemarch, 1 vol. 2012. (Literary Texts & the Popular Marketplace Ser.). (ENG., Illus.). 256p. 99.00 *(978-1-84893-194-7(8))* Pickering & Chatto Pubs., Ltd. GBR. Dist: Ashgate Publishing Co.

Goldberg, Sander M. Constructing Literature in the Roman Republic. 2010. (ENG.). 262p. (C). pap. 35.99 *(978-0-521-17419-0(8))* Cambridge Univ. Pr.

Grogan, Jane. Exemplary Spenser: Visual & Poetic Pedagogy in the Faerie Queene. 2009. (Illus.). 226p. 99.95 *(978-0-7546-6698-1(0))* Ashgate Publishing Co.

Hammond, Mary. Reading, Publishing & the Formation of Literary Taste in England, 1880-1914. 2006. (Nineteenth Century Ser.). (Illus.). 222p. 110.00 *(978-0-7546-5668-5(3))* Ashgate Publishing Co.

Hartmann, Jonathan. The Marketing of Edgar Allan Poe. (Studies in American Popular History & Culture Ser.). (ENG.). 142p. 2012. pap. 42.95 ***(978-0-415-54319-4(3))*** 2008. 125.00 *(978-0-415-96354-1(0))* Routledge.

Hawkins, Ann R. & Ives, Maura. Women Writers & the Artifacts of Celebrity in the Long Nineteenth Century. 2012. (Illus.). 225p. 99.95 ***(978-0-7546-6702-5(2))*** Ashgate Publishing Co.

Hinnov, Emily M. Encountering Choran Community: Literary Modernism, Visual Culture, & Political Aesthetics in the Interwar Years. 2009. (ENG., Illus.). 246p. 54.00 *(978-1-57591-130-4(2))* Susquehanna Univ. Pr.

Hoche, Dominique T. & Matheson, Lister M. The Reception of Christine De Pizan's Fais D'Armes in Fifteenth-Century England: Chivalric Self-Fashioning. 2008. 220p. 109.95 *(978-0-7734-5158-2(7))* Mellen, Edwin Pr., The.

Huot, Sylvia. The Romance of the Rose & Its Medieval Readers: Interpretation, Reception, Manuscript Transmission. 2007. (Cambridge Studies in Medieval Literature Ser.). (ENG., Illus.). 424p. per. 79.00 *(978-0-521-03931-4(2))* Cambridge Univ. Pr.

Ioppolo, Grace. Dramatists & their Manuscripts in the Age of Shakespeare, Jonson, Middleton & Heywood: Authorship, Authority & the Playhouse. 2008. (Illus.). Xp. pap. 39.95 *(978-0-415-47031-5(5))* Routledge.

Kallendorf, Craig. The Virgilian Tradition: Book history & the history of Reading. 2007. (Variorum Collected Studies). (Illus.). 320p. 154.95 *(978-0-7546-5923-5(2))* Ashgate Publishing Co.

Kameen, Paul. Rereading Poets. 2010. (Pitt Comp Literacy Culture Ser.). (ENG.). 192p. pap. 24.95 *(978-0-8229-6107-9(5))* Univ. of Pittsburgh Pr.

Karian, Stephen. Jonathan Swift in Print & Manuscript. 2010. (ENG., Illus.). 284p. 89.00 *(978-0-521-19804-2(6))* Cambridge Univ. Pr.

Kaywell, Joan F. & Kaywell, Joan, eds. Dear Author: Letters of HopeTop Young Adult Authors Respond to Kids' Toughest Issues. 2007. (ENG.). 272p. (YA). (gr. 8-18). 15.99 *(978-0-399-23705-8(4),* Philomel) Penguin Group (USA) Inc.

Kershner, R. Brandon. Culture of Joyce's Ulysses. 2010. (New Directions in Irish & Irish American Literature Ser.). (ENG.). 272p. 89.00 *(978-0-230-10868-4(7))* Palgrave Macmillan.

Langemack, Chapple. The Author Event Primer: How to Plan, Execute & Enjoy Author Events, 1 vol. 2007. (Illus.). 204p. per. 35.00 *(978-1-59158-302-8(0),* LU3020) Libraries Unlimited, Inc.

Loveman, Kate. Reading Fictions, 1660-1740: Deception in English Literary & Political Culture. 2008. (Illus.). 232p. 99.95 *(978-0-7546-6237-2(3))* Ashgate Publishing Co.

Luey, Beth. Expanding the American Mind: Books & the Popularization of Knowledge. 2010. 224p. pap. 24.95 *(978-1-55849-817-4(6));* lib. bdg. 80.00 *(978-1-55849-816-7(8))* Univ. of Massachusetts Pr.

Machor, James L. Reading Fiction in Antebellum America: Informed Response & Reception Histories, 1820-1865. 2011. (ENG.). 424p. (gr. 17). 75.00 *(978-0-8018-9874-7(9))* Johns Hopkins Univ. Pr.

Mitrano, G. F. & Jarosinski, Eric, eds. The Hand of the Interpreter: Essays on Meaning after Theory. 2008. (Cultural Interactions: Studies in the Relationship between the Arts Ser.). (ENG., Illus.). 370p. pap. 92.95 *(978-3-03911-118-3(3))* Lang, Peter AG GBR. Dist: Lang, Peter.

Myers, Robin, et al. Owners, Annotators & the Signs of Reading. (Publishing Pathways Ser.). (Illus.). xv, 231p. (C). *(978-1-58456-171-2(8))* Oak Knoll Pr.

Oliensis, Ellen. Horace & the Rhetoric of Authority. 2007. (ENG.). 256p. pap. 56.00 *(978-0-521-03088-5(9))* Cambridge Univ. Pr.

Palmer, Beth & Buckland, Adelene. A Return to the Common Reader: Print Culture & the Novel 1850-1900. 2011. (Illus.). 204p. 99.95 *(978-1-4094-0027-1(1))* Ashgate Publishing Co.

Partridge, Stephen. Author, Reader, Book. 2012. ***(978-0-8020-9934-1(3))*** Univ. of Toronto Pr.

Paschalis, Michael, et al, eds. Readers & Writers in the Ancient Novel. 2009. (Ancient Narrative Supplementum Ser.). (ENG., Illus.). 286p. (C). 127.00 ***(978-90-77922-54-5(7))*** Barkhuis Publishing NLD. Dist: Brown, David Bk. Co., The.

Patten, Robert L. Dickens & Victorian Print Cultures. 2012. (Library of Essays on Charles Dickens Ser.). 650p. 275.00 ***(978-1-4094-3093-3(6))*** Ashgate Publishing Co.

Potter, Franz J., ed. Literary Mushrooms: Tales from the Gothic Chapbooks, 1800-1830. 2007. 240p. *(978-0-9795871-2-2(3));* Vol.2. *(978-0-9795871-4-6(X))* Zittaw Pr.

Propertius & Camps. Propertius: Elegies Book 4. Camps, W. A., ed. 2009. (ENG.). 180p. pap. 31.99 *(978-0-521-12599-4(5))* Cambridge Univ. Pr.

Propertius & Propertius, Sextus. Elegies, Bk. 2. 2009. (ENG.). 248p. pap. 34.99 *(978-0-521-10947-5(7))* Cambridge Univ. Pr.

Reid, Hugh. The Nature & Uses of Eighteenth-Century Book Subscription Lists. 2010. iv, 67p. *(978-0-7734-3757-9(6))* Mellen, Edwin Pr., The.

Rickard, Jane. Authorship & Authority: The Writings of James V1 & 1. 2008. (ENG., Illus.). 256p. 79.00 *(978-0-7190-7486-8(X))* Manchester Univ. Pr. GBR. Dist: Macmillan.

Robinson, Owen. Creating Yoknapatawpha: Readers & Writers in Faulkner's Fiction. 2009. 254p. 39.95 *(978-0-415-80295-6(4))* Routledge.

Rosenbaum, Susan B. Professing Sincerity: Modern Lyric Poetry, Commercial Culture, & the Crisis in Reading. 2007. (ENG.). 320p. (gr. 17). 39.50 *(978-0-8139-2610-0(6))* Univ. Pr. of Virginia.

Rothstein, Eric. Gleaning Modernity: Earlier Eighteenth-Century Literature & the Modernizing Process. 2008. 269p. per. 55.00 *(978-0-87413-984-6(8))* Univ. of Delaware Pr.

Schiff, James, ed. Updike in Cincinnati: A Literary Performance. 2007. (Illus.). 176p. 19.95 *(978-0-8214-1748-5(7))* Ohio Univ. Pr.

Silverman, Gillian. Bodies & Books: Reading & the Fantasy of Communion in Nineteenth-Century America. 2012. (Illus.). 256p. (C). 55.00 ***(978-0-8122-4415-1(X))*** Univ. of Pennsylvania Pr.

Steinberg, Gillian D. & Steinberg, Gillian. Philip Larkin & his Audiences. 2010. (ENG.). 232p. 84.00 *(978-0-230-23778-0(9))* Palgrave Macmillan.

Stroup, Sarah Culpepper. Catullus, Cicero, & a Society of Patrons: The Generation of the Text. 2010. (ENG.). 322p. 104.00 *(978-0-521-51390-6(1))* Cambridge Univ. Pr.

Sutherland, John. The Longman Companion to Victorian Fiction. 2nd ed. 2009. (ENG., Illus.). 736p. pap. 45.00 *(978-1-4082-0390-3(1))* Longman Publishing Group.

Takseva, Tatjana. Seventeenth-Century Poetic Genres As Social Categories: A New Reading of the Poetry of John Donne. 2010. (Illus.). vi, 321p. 119.95 *(978-0-7734-3606-0(5))* Mellen, Edwin Pr., The.

Trubek, Anne. A Skeptic's Guide to Writers' Houses. 2010. (Illus.). 176p. 24.95 *(978-0-8122-4292-8(0))* Univ. of Pennsylvania Pr.

Vassena, Raffaella. reawakening National Identity: Dostoevskii's Diary of a Writer & its Impact on Russian Society. 2007. 229p. (C). pap. 46.95 *(978-0-8204-8946-9(8))* Lang, Peter Publishing, Inc.

Vendler, Helen. Invisible Listeners: Lyric Intimacy in Herbert, Whitman, & Ashbery. 2007. (ENG.). 112p. per. 15.95 *(978-0-691-13474-1(X))* Princeton Univ. Pr.

Vlock, Deborah. Dickens, Novel Reading, & the Victorian Popular Theatre. 2006. (Cambridge Studies in Nineteenth-Century Literature & Culture Ser.). (ENG., Illus.). 244p. pap. 45.00 *(978-0-521-02688-8(1))* Cambridge Univ. Pr.

Wang, Yugen. Ten Thousand Scrolls: Reading & Writing in the Poetics of Huang Tingjian & the Late Northern Song. 2011. (Harvard-Yenching Institute Monograph Ser.: 76). (ENG.). 300p. 39.95 *(978-0-674-06255-9(8))* Harvard Univ., Asia Ctr.

Webb, Igor. Rereading the Nineteenth Century: Studies in the Old Criticism from Austen to Lawrence. 2010. (ENG.). 202p. 79.00 *(978-0-230-10027-5(9))* Palgrave Macmillan.

Widiss, Benjamin Leigh. Obscure Invitations: The Persistence of the Author in Twentieth-Century American Literature. 2011. (ENG.). 224p. 65.00 *(978-0-8047-7322-5(X));* pap. 21.95 *(978-0-8047-7323-2(8))* Stanford Univ. Pr.

Wilson-Okamura, David Scott. Virgil in the Renaissance. 2010. (ENG., Illus.). 314p. 100.00 *(978-0-521-19812-7(7))* Cambridge Univ. Pr.

Woodman, Tony & Powell, Jonathan, eds. Author & Audience in Latin Literature. 2007. (ENG.). 292p. pap. 58.00 *(978-0-521-03578-1(3))* Cambridge Univ. Pr.

AUTHORS AND THE THEATER

see also Playwriting

Cunningham, Vanessa. Shakespeare & Garrick. 2011. (ENG., Illus.). 240p. pap. 48.00 *(978-0-521-28642-8(5))* Cambridge Univ. Pr.

Dubost, Thierry. Drama Reinvented: Theatre Adaptation in Ireland, 1970-2007. 2012. (Dramaturgies. Textes, Cultures et Représentations. Texts, Cultures & Performances Ser.). 302p. pap. 48.95 ***(978-90-5201-800-3(6))*** PIE - Peter Lang BEL. Dist: Lang, Peter.

Turner, Henry S. The English Renaissance Stage: Geometry, Poetics, & the Practical Spatial Arts 1580-1630. 2011. (ENG., Illus.). 344p. pap. 50.00 *(978-0-19-959545-7(3))* Oxford Univ. Pr., Inc.

AUTHORS' SPOUSES

Adamson, Alan H. Mr. Charlotte Brontë: The Life of Arthur Bell Nicholls. 2008. (ENG., Illus.). 216p. (C). *(978-0-7735-3365-3(6))* McGill-Queen's Univ. Pr.

Carlyle, Jane Welsh. Letters & Memorials of Jane Welsh Carlyle. Carlyle, Thomas & Froude, James Anthony, eds. 2011. (Cambridge Library Collection - Literary Studies). (ENG.). 410p. pap. 31.99 *(978-1-108-02926-1(4));* 352p. pap. 28.99 *(978-1-108-02927-8(2));* 410p. pap. 31.99 *(978-1-108-02925-4(6))* Cambridge Univ. Pr.

Darlington, Beth. Love Letters of William & Mary Wordsworth. 2009. (Illus.). 272p. pap. 26.95 *(978-0-8014-7533-7(3))* Cornell Univ. Pr.

Dorsett, Lyle W. And God Came In: The Extraordinary Story of Joy Davidman. 2009. (Illus.). xviii, 189p. 17.95 *(978-1-59856-356-6(4))* Hendrickson Pubs. Marketing, LLC.

Eckhardt, Nadine. Duchess of Palms: A Memoir. 2009. (ENG., Illus.). 152p. 29.95 *(978-0-292-71912-5(4))* Univ. of Texas Pr.

Fraser, Antonia. Must You Go? My Life with Harold Pinter. 2010. (ENG., Illus.). 336p. 28.95 *(978-0-385-53250-1(4),* Talese, Nan A.) Knopf Doubleday Publishing Group.

Greer, Germaine. Shakespeare's Wife. (P. S. Ser.). 2009. 432p. pap. 14.99 *(978-0-06-153716-5(0),* HarperPerennial) 2008. 416p. 26.95 *(978-0-06-153715-8(2))* HarperCollins Pubs.

Hawkins, Ruth A. Unbelievable Happiness & Final Sorrow: The Hemingway-Pfeiffer Marriage. 2012. (ENG., Illus.). 391p. 34.95 ***(978-1-55728-974-2(3))*** Univ. of Arkansas Pr.

Hawthorne, Julian. Nathaniel Hawthorne & His Wife: A Biography, 2 vols., Set. reprint ed. 200.00 *(978-0-7950-2136-7(4))* New Library Press LLC.

—Nathaniel Hawthorne & His Wife: A Biography, Vol. 2. 2008. 476p. pap. *(978-1-4086-8884-7(0))* Read Bks.

Igoe, Vivien, ed. James Joyce's Dublin Houses & Nora Barnacle's Galway. 2008. (ENG.). 206p. pap. 28.95 *(978-1-84351-082-6(0))* Lilliput Pr., Ltd., The IRL. Dist: Dufour Editions, Inc.

Juers, Evelyn. House of Exile: The Lives & Times of Heinrich Mann & Nelly Kroeger-Mann, 1 vol. 2011. (ENG., Illus.). 400p. 30.00 *(978-0-374-17316-6(8))* Farrar, Straus & Giroux.

Koizumi, Setsuko. Reminiscences of Lafcadio Hearn. 2009. 100p. pap. 18.75 *(978-1-110-86319-8(5))* BiblioBazaar.

—Reminiscences of Lafcadio Hearn. Hisada, Paul Kiyoshi & Johnson, Frederick, trs. 2008. 98p. pap. 18.95 *(978-1-4370-3839-2(5))* Kessinger Publishing, LLC.

Nayder, Lillian. The Other Dickens: A Life of Catherine Hogarth. 2010. (Illus.). 360p. 35.00 *(978-0-8014-4787-7(9))* Cornell Univ. Pr.

Popoff, Alexandra. Sophia Tolstoy: A Biography. 2011. (ENG.). 368p. pap. 22.99 ***(978-1-4165-9760-5(3),*** Free Pr.) Free Pr.

Robbins, Jann. Harold & Me: My Life, Love, & Hard Times with Harold Robbins. 2010. (ENG.). 304p. pap. 19.99 *(978-0-7653-2087-2(8),* Forge Bks.) Doherty, Tom Assocs., LLC.

Sanchez, Nellie Van de Grift. The Life of Mrs Robert Louis Stevenson. 2008. 272p. pap. *(978-1-4099-1642-0(1))* Dodo Pr.

—The Life of Mrs Robert Louis Stevenson. 2008. (Illus.). 184p. pap. *(978-1-84830-941-8(4),* Wildhern Pr.); 176p. pap. *(978-1-4068-9162-1(2))* Echo Library.

—The Life of Mrs Robert Louis Stevenson. 2007. (ENG.). 376p. 48.95 *(978-0-548-02248-1(8))* Kessinger Publishing, LLC.

Simpson, Alan & McQueen Simpson, Mary, intros. I Too am Here: Selections from the Letters of Jane Welsh Carlyle. 2010. (ENG.). 336p. pap. 29.99 *(978-0-521-13498-9(6))* Cambridge Univ. Pr.

Squires, Michael. D. H. Lawrence & Frieda: A Portrait of Love & Loyalty. 2008. (ENG., Illus.). 200p. 29.95 *(978-0-233-00232-3(4))* Andre Deutsch GBR. Dist: Independent Pubs. Group.

Stowe, Harriet Beecher. Lady Byron Vindicated. 2008. 336p. 28.99 *(978-0-554-36372-1(0))* 2008. 336p. 29.99 *(978-0-554-27069-2(2))* 2007. (ENG.). 294p. pap. 21.99 *(978-1-4346-2422-2(6))* 2007. (ENG.). 332p. pap. 24.99 *(978-1-4346-2468-0(4))* BiblioBazaar.

Tolstaya, Sofia Andreevna. My Life. Donskov, Andrew, ed. Woodsworth, John & Kloutchanski, Arkadi, trs. from RUS. 2010. (ENG., Illus.). 1188p. *(978-0-7766-3042-7(3))* Univ. of Ottawa Pr./Presses de l'Universite d'Ottawa.

Trillin, Calvin. About Alice. 2008. (ENG.). 78p. 15.00 *(978-1-4223-9340-6(2))* DIANE Publishing Co.

—About Alice. 2006. (ENG.). 96p. 14.95 *(978-1-4000-6615-5(8),* Random House) Random House Publishing Group.

Watt, Julie. Poisoned Lives: The Regency Poet Letitia Elizabeth Landon (L. E. L.) & British Gold Coast Administrator George Maclean. 2010. (ENG., Illus.). 300p. 74.95 *(978-1-84519-420-8(9))* Sussex Academic Pr. GBR. Dist: International Specialized Bk. Services.

AUTHORSHIP

see also Academic Writing; Advertising Copy; Authors and Publishers; Authors and Readers; Bill Drafting; Biography As a Literary Form; Business Writing; Children's Literature—Technique; Creative Writing; Dedications; Drama—Technique; Editing; Feature Writing; Fiction—Authorship; Fiction—Technique; Historiography; Journalism—Authorship; Letter Writing; Literary Forgeries and Mystifications; Literature; Mimesis in Literature; Motion Picture Authorship; New Literates, Writing for; Plagiarism; Playwriting; Plots (Drama, Novel, etc.); Poetry—Authorship; Popular Music—Writing and Publishing; Proposal Writing for Grants; Proposal Writing in Education; Proposal Writing in Research; Radio Authorship; Radio Plays—Technique; Report Writing; Rhetoric; Short Story; Technical Writing; Television Authorship; Travel Writing; Versification; Women Authors

also subdivision Authorship under names of individual persons and individual works entered under title, and under disciplines and literary forms; e.g. Shakespeare, William, 1564-1616—Authorship; Bible—Authorship; Poetry—Authorship

Adams, Jennifer & Grillone, Jennifer. Remarkably Jane: Notable Quotations on Jane Austen, 1 vol. 2009. (ENG., Illus.). 128p. 14.99 *(978-1-4236-0478-5(4))* Gibbs Smith, Publisher.

Adler, Carol. Do You REally Need to Write A Book? Tips & Techniques for Writing, Publishing, Marketing & Promoting YOUR BOOK! 2010. pap. 20.00 *(978-1-934280-78-2(X))* Dandelion Bks.

Ahonen, Laura. Constructing Authorship in Popular Music: Artists, Media & Stardom. 2008. 228p. pap. *(978-3-639-09038-3(1))* VDM Verlag Dr. Mueller e.K.

Albert, Susan Wittig. Starting Points: Weekly Writing Prompts for Women with Stories to Tell. 2007. 54p. spiral bd. 8.00 *(978-0-9795329-1-7(4))* Story Circle Network, Inc.

Alderson, Martha. The Plot Whisperer: Secrets of Story Structure Any Writer Can Master. 2011. (ENG.). 256p. pap. 14.95 ***(978-1-4405-2588-9(9))*** Adams Media Corp.

Allen, Moira. Starting Your Career as a Freelance Writer (Second Edition) 2nd ed. 2011. (ENG.). 304p. pap. 24.95 *(978-1-58115-760-4(6),* 115760, Allworth Pr.) Skyhorse Publishing Co., Inc.

Amato, Joseph Anthony. Jacob's Well: A Case for Rethinking Family History. 2008. (ENG., Illus.). 268p. 32.95 *(978-0-87351-613-6(3))* Minnesota Historical Society Pr.

Anderson, Daniel. Write Now. rev. ed. 2011. (ENG.). 496p. (C). pap. 73.33 *(978-0-13-241547-7(X))* Longman Publishing Group.

Andrews, Graham. Writing Winning Essays. 2009. 46p. pap. 14.84 *(978-1-4092-8938-8(9))* Lulu Enterprises Inc.

Appalachian Writers Guide. 16.47 *(978-0-13-050131-8(X))* Prentice Hall PTR.

Aravamudan, Srinivas. Enlightenment Orientalism: Resisting the Rise of the Novel. 2011. (ENG., Illus.). 352p. 85.00 *(978-0-226-02448-6(2));* 360p. pap. 29.00 *(978-0-226-02449-3(0))* Univ. of Chicago Pr.

Ariail, Jane Candler. Affect & the Writing Process. pap. 135.00 *(978-0-8058-5041-3(4))* Erlbaum, Lawrence Assocs., Inc.

Association, Florida Writers. Writing Our History-One Writer at a Time, Florida Writers Association, First 10 Years 2001 - 2011. 2011. 138p. pap. 14.95 ***(978-1-61493-018-1(X))*** Peppertree Pr., The.

Babic, Gregory Victor, ed. Words to Inspire Writers: A Perpetual Calendar of Classic Writing-Related Quotations - on Writers, Writing, Words, Books, Literature, & Publishing - Specifically Selected to Illustrate the Writing Process & to Motivate Authors Every Day. 2008. (ENG.). 200p. pap. *(978-0-9803722-0-5(8))* Sach, F. C. & Sons, Pub.

Baehr, Craig & Schaller, Robert C., Jr. Writing for the Internet: A Guide to Real Communication in Virtual Space, 1 vol. 2009. 219p. 55.00 *(978-0-313-37694-8(8),* GR7694) Greenwood Publishing Group, Inc.

Baig, Barbara. How to Be a Writer: Building Your Creative Skills Through Practice & Play. 2010. (ENG., Illus.). 272p. pap. 16.99 *(978-1-58297-805-5(0),* Writer's Digest Bks.) F&W Media, Inc.

Bailey, Stephen. Academic Writing for International Students of Business. 2010. (ENG., Illus.). 336p. (C). pap. 39.95 *(978-0-415-56471-7(9));* 130.00 *(978-0-415-56470-0(0))* Routledge.

Bainton, George. The Art of Authorship. 2009. (ENG.). 366p. 38.99 *(978-1-117-09357-4(3));* pap. 31.75 *(978-1-117-09358-1(1))* BiblioBazaar.

Baker. The Way We Write: Interviews with Award-Winning Writers. Baker, Barbara, ed. 2007. (ENG.). 256p. 22.95 *(978-0-8264-9505-1(2))* Continuum International Publishing Group, Ltd. GBR. Dist: National Bk. Network.

Baldwin, Carol. Teaching the Story: Fiction Writing in Middle School. 2007. (Illus.). 138p. per. 23.95 *(978-0-929895-95-6(9))* Maupin Hse. Publishing.

Balfour, Janet G. A Basic Study of Writing. 2009. 76p. pap. 10.99 *(978-1-60791-791-5(2))* Xulon Pr., Inc.

Ball, Cheryl E. & Kalmbach, James Robert. RAW: (Reading & Writing) New Media. 2010. (Illus.). 384p. *(978-1-57273-897-3(9)); (978-1-57273-896-6(0))* Hampton Pr., Inc.

Baltimore, Charlene Elizabeth. A Writer's Bible. 2007. 304p. per. 29.95 *(978-1-60441-310-6(7))* PublishAmerica, Inc.

Bank, Richard D. The Everything Guide to Writing Nonfiction: All You Need to Write & Sell Great Nonfiction Books, Articles, Essays, Reviews, & Memoirs. 2009. (ENG.). 304p. pap. 15.95 *(978-1-60550-630-2(3))* Adams Media Corp.

Barton, Bruce. Collective Creation, Collaboration & Devising. 2009. (Critical Perspectives on Canadian Theatre in English Ser.). (ENG.). 312p. pap. 30.00 *(978-0-88754-755-3(9))* Playwrights Canada Pr. CAN. Dist: Consortium Bk. Sales & Distribution.

Bass, Rick. Why I Came West: A Memoir. (ENG.). 256p. 2009. pap. 14.95 *(978-0-547-23771-8(5),* Mariner Bks.) 2008. 24.00 *(978-0-618-59675-1(5))* Houghton Mifflin Harcourt Trade & Reference Pubs.

Baxter, Charles. The Art of Subtext: Beyond Plot. 2007. (Art Of... Ser.). (ENG., Illus.). 120p. pap. 12.00 *(978-1-55597-473-2(2))* Graywolf Pr.

Bean, Joe Patrick. Voices & Techniques of OP-ED Writing. 110.00 *(978-0-8058-1563-4(5))* Erlbaum, Lawrence Assocs., Inc.

Becnel, Kim E. Bloom's How to Write about Ernest Hemingway. Bloom, Harold, ed. 2008. (Bloom's How to Write about Literature Ser.). 288p. (C). (gr. 9). 45.00 *(978-0-7910-9746-5(3),* Chelsea Hse.) Facts On File, Inc.

Beecroft, Alexander. Authorship & Cultural Identity in Early Greece & China: Patterns of Literary Circulation. 2010. (ENG.). 338p. 89.00 *(978-0-521-19431-0(8))* Cambridge Univ. Pr.

Beins, Bernard C. & Beins, Agatha M. Effective Writing in Psychology: Papers, Posters, & Presentations. 2008. (ENG., Illus.). 288p. pap. 41.95 *(978-1-4051-5879-4(4),* Wiley-Blackwell) Wiley, John & Sons, Inc.

Beins, Bernard C., et al. Effective Writing in Psychology: Papers, Posters, & Presentations. 2008. (ENG., Illus.). 288p. 99.95 *(978-1-4051-5878-7(6),* Wiley-Blackwell) Wiley, John & Sons, Inc.

Belmonte, Kevin. The Quotable Chesterton: The Wit & Wisdom of G. K. Chesterton. 2011. 336p. pap. 15.99 *(978-1-59555-205-1(7))* Nelson, Thomas Inc.

Bennett, Arnold. The Author's Craft. reprint ed. lib. bdg. 98.00 *(978-0-7426-2586-0(9))* Classic Bks.

—The Author's Craft. 2007. (ENG.). 52p. per. *(978-1-4065-4778-8(6))* Dodo Pr.

—The Author's Craft. 2010. 38p. pap. 14.14 *(978-1-4432-1923-5(1))* General Bks. LLC.

—The Author's Craft. 2010. 48p. pap. *(978-1-4076-1306-2(5))* HardPr.

—The Author's Craft. 2010. 124p. 28.76 *(978-1-163-33110-1(4))* 2010. 124p. pap. 16.76 *(978-1-162-79268-2(X))* 2008. 126p. pap. 20.95 *(978-1-4370-4800-1(5))* 2007. (ENG.). 122p. 35.95 *(978-0-548-01919-1(3))* Kessinger Publishing, LLC.

—How to Become an Author: A Practical Guide. reprint ed. lib. bdg. 98.00 *(978-0-7426-2536-5(2))* Classic Bks.

Bennett, Hal Zina. Write Starts: Prompts, Quotes, & Exercises to Jumpstart Your Creativity. 2010. (ENG.). 176p. pap. 15.00 *(978-1-57731-689-3(4))* New World Library.

Bent, Mike. The Everything Guide to Comedy Writing: From stand-up to sketch - all you need to succeed in the world of Comedy. 2009. (ENG.). 304p. pap. 15.95 *(978-1-60550-168-0(9))* Adams Media Corp.

Berberian, Martha. Como Ser Escritor: How to Be a Writer. (SPA.). *(978-84-7645-394-0(9)*, 223504) Clie, Editorial.

Berman, Jeffrey. Companionship of Grief: Love & Loss in the Memoirs of C. S. Lewis, John Bayley, Donald Hall, & Calvin Trillin. 2010. 288p. pap. 26.95 *(978-1-55849-804-4(4))*; lib. bdg. 80.00 *(978-1-55849-803-7(6))* Univ. of Massachusetts Pr.

Bernhardt, William. The Fundamentals of Fiction: How to Write with Style, Edit with Grace, & Publish with Pride. 2008. (ENG.). 1p. pap. 29.95 *(978-968-7305-65-3(7))* HAWK Publishing Group.

Bernheimer, Kate, ed. Brothers & Beasts: An Anthology of Men on Fairy Tales. 2007. (Series in Fairy-Tale Studies). 208p. pap. 15.95 *(978-0-8143-3267-2(6))* Wayne State Univ. Pr.

Berry, Nicole. Trois textes: le récit, le paysage, les Sonorités: Essais sur P. B. Shelley, Henry James, Joseph Conrad, John Milton. 2008. (FRE.). 230p. pap. *(978-3-03911-633-1(9))* Lang, Peter.

Bessler, John D. Writing for Life: The Craft of Writing for Everyday Living. 2007. xvi, 329p. 24.95 *(978-0-9792718-0-9(0))* Bottlecap Bks.

Bethany Ee Wei, Ang. Genre Literacy: Where's the Why & Who? 2011. 72p. pap. ***(978-3-8383-5561-0(X))*** Lambert Academic Publishing.

Bigelow, Christopher Kimball, ed. & compiled by. Conversations with Mormon Authors. 2007. (ENG.). 284p. 39.95 *(978-0-85051-111-6(9))*; 272p. pap. 17.95 *(978-0-85051-108-6(9))* Luso-Brazilian Bks. (Mormon Arts & Letters).

Bird, Tom. The Call of the Writer's Craft: Writing & Selling the Book Within. 2009. (ENG.). 256p. pap. 12.95 *(978-1-59869-854-1(0))* Adams Media Corp.

—You Were Born to Write: Complete Your Book in 30 Days or Less by Mastering the Inner Game of Writing. 2007. (Illus.). 112p. pap. 14.95 *(978-0-9789216-1-3(5))* Sojourn, Inc.

Birkerts, Sven. Art of Time in Memoir: Then, Again. 2007. (Art Of... Ser.). (ENG.). 120p. pap. 12.00 *(978-1-55597-489-3(9))* Graywolf Pr.

Bishop, Claire, ed. Participation. 2006. (Documents of Contemporary Art Ser.). (ENG., Illus.). 208p. (gr. 17). pap. 24.95 *(978-0-262-52464-3(3))* MIT Pr.

Blendinger, Jack G. Write Like A Pro! rev. ed. 2008. (ENG.). 98p. spiral bd. 54.81 *(978-0-7575-4404-0(5))* Kendall Hunt Publishing Co.

Bloom, Lynne Z. The Seven Deadly Virtues & Other Lively Essays: Coming of Age as a Writer, Teacher, Risk Taker. 2008. (Illus.). 212p. 29.95 *(978-1-57003-730-6(2))* Univ. of South Carolina Pr.

Blumenfeld, Samuel L. The Marlowe-Shakespeare Connection: A New Study of the Authorship Question. 2008. (ENG., Illus.). 368p. pap. 45.00 *(978-0-7864-3902-7(5))* McFarland & Co., Inc. Pubs.

Bly, Robert W. Getting Started As a Freelance Writer. 2008. (Culture Tools Ser.). (ENG.). 255p. per. 19.95 *(978-1-59181-069-8(8))* Sentient Pubns.

—Secrets of a Freelance Writer: How to Make $100,000 a Year or More. 3rd rev. ed. 2006. (ENG., Illus.). 416p. pap. 18.00 *(978-0-8050-7803-9(7)*, Holt Paperback) Holt, Henry & Co.

Blythe, Ronald. A Writer's Day-Book. 2007. 158p. per. *(978-1-84233-124-8(8))* Trent Polytechnic.

Bond, Jenny & Sheedy, Chris. Who the Hell Is Pansy O'Hara? The Fascinating Stories Behind 50 of the World's Best-Loved Books. 2008. (ENG.). 336p. (gr. 12-18). 13.00 *(978-0-14-311364-5(X)*, Penguin (Non-Classics)) Penguin Group (USA) Inc.

Bourdeau, Debra Taylor & Kraft, Elizabeth. On Second Thought: Updating the Eighteenth-Century Text. 2007. (Illus.). (C). *(978-0-87413-975-4(9))* Univ. of Delaware Pr.

Boyd, Anne E., ed. Wielding the Pen: Writings on Authorship by American Women of the Nineteenth Century. 2009. (ENG.). 488p. (C). (gr. 13-17). 77.00 *(978-0-8018-9274-5(0))*; pap. 36.00 *(978-0-8018-9275-2(9))* Johns Hopkins Univ. Pr.

Brackett, Virginia. Bloom's How to Write about the Brontes. Bloom, Harold, ed. 2008. (Bloom's How to Write about Literature Ser.). 288p. (C). (gr. 9-18). 45.00 *(978-0-7910-9794-6(3)*, Chelsea Hse.) Facts On File, Inc.

Bradbury, Malcolm. Liar's Landscape: Collected Writing from a Storyteller's Life. 2007. (ENG.). 448p. per. 15.95 *(978-0-330-43533-8(7))* Macmillan Pubs., Ltd. GBR. Dist: Independent Pubs. Group.

Bradford, Richard, ed. Life Writing: Essays on Autobiography, Biography & Literature. 2009. (ENG.). 256p. 95.00 *(978-0-230-20252-8(7))* Palgrave Macmillan.

Bradway, Becky & Hesse, Douglas. Creating Nonfiction. 2009. (ENG.). 832p. (C). pap. 62.95 *(978-0-312-44706-9(X))* Bedford/Saint Martin's.

Brandon, Lee. At a Glance: Essays. 5th ed. 2011. (Basic Writing Ser.). (ENG.). 304p. (C). pap. 32.95 *(978-0-495-90630-8(1))* Wadsworth.

Brayfield, Celia. Arts Reviews: And How to Write Them. 2008. (ENG., Illus.). 160p. pap. 16.95 *(978-1-904048-91-6(9))* Oldcastle Bks., Ltd. GBR. Dist: Independent Pubs. Group.

Brockett, Oscar G. & Ball, Robert J. Plays for the Theatre. 10th ed. 2010. (ENG.). 624p. (C). pap. 118.95 *(978-1-4390-8268-3(5))* Wadsworth.

Brohaugh, William. Write Tight: Say Exactly What You Mean with Precision & Power. 2007. 221p. per. 14.95 *(978-1-4022-1051-8(5))* Sourcebooks, Inc.

Bromley, Karen D'Angelo. Writing for Educators: Personal Essays & Practical Advice (HC) Bromley, Karen, ed. 2009. 256p. *(978-1-60752-104-4(0))* Information Age Publishing, Inc.

—Writing for Educators: Personal Essays & Practical Advice (PB) Bromley, Karen, ed. 2009. 256p. pap. *(978-1-60752-103-7(2))* Information Age Publishing, Inc.

Brouillette, Sarah. Postcolonial Writers in the Global Literary Marketplace. (ENG., 2011. Illus.). 216p. pap. 28.00 *(978-0-230-34643-7(X))* 2007. 240p. 95.00 *(978-0-230-50784-5(0))* Palgrave Macmillan.

Brown, Dale. Conversations with American Writers: The Doubt, the Faith, the In-Between. 2008. (Illus.). 318p. pap. 18.00 *(978-0-8028-6228-0(4))* Eerdmans, William B. Publishing Co.

Brown, Earma. Write Your Best Book Now. 2007. 128p. pap. 14.95 *(978-0-9797701-0-4(6))* Butterfly Pr.

Bruce, Harry. Page Fright: Foibles & Fetishes of Famous Writers. 2010. 360p. pap. 18.95 *(978-0-7710-1713-1(8)*, Emblem Edns) McClelland & Stewart CAN. Dist: Random Hse., Inc.

Brulotte & Brulotte, Gaetan. La Chambre des Lucidités. (FRE., Illus.). 175p. *(978-2-89583-073-3(8))* Editions Trois-Pistoles.

Buckridan, Rakib. The Bible & Christianity: Their impending Demise & a Forward-Looking Plea. 2010. 592p. pap. 38.95 *(978-1-60860-305-3(9)*, Eloquent Bks.) AEG Literary Publishing Services, Inc.

Budal, Ingvil Brügger. Modes of Authorship in the Middle Ages. Rankovic, Slavica, ed. 2012. (Papers in Mediaeval Studies). (ENG., Illus.). 436p. 90.00 ***(978-0-88844-822-4(8))*** Pontifical Institute of Mediaeval Studies, Dept. of Pubns. CAN. Dist: Univ. of Toronto Pr.

Buhner, Stephen Harrod. Ensouling Language. 2010. (ENG.). 1p. pap. 24.95 *(978-1-59477-382-2(3))* Inner Traditions International, Ltd.

Burke, Ruth. How to Live on Almost Nothing While Writing the Great American Novel. 2007. 60p. per. 16.95 *(978-1-4241-5096-0(5))* PublishAmerica, Inc.

Burke, Seán. The Ethics of Writing: Authorship & Legacy in Plato & Nietzsche. 2011. (ENG.). 256p. (gr. 17). pap. 32.00 *(978-0-7486-4179-6(3))* Edinburgh Univ. Pr. GBR. Dist: Columbia Univ. Pr.

Burnham, Sophy. For Writers Only: Inspiring Thoughts on the Exquisite Pain & Heady Joy of the Writing Life from Its Great Practitioners. 2011. (ENG.). 224p. (gr. 12). 15.95 ***(978-1-58542-912-7(0)***, Tarcher) Penguin Group (USA) Inc.

Butler, Shane. The Matter of the Page: Essays in Search of Ancient & Medieval Authors. 2011. (Wisconsin Studies in Classics Ser.). (ENG.). 168p. pap. 29.95 *(978-0-299-24824-5(0))* Univ. of Wisconsin Pr.

Cabral, Louise. Islands of Recall: Write Your Life Story. 2007. 168p. per. 15.95 *(978-0-595-43580-7(7))* iUniverse, Inc.

Cameron, Angus & Gregory, Burke, texts. Goldin & Senneby: Headless. 2010. (ENG., Illus.). 80p. pap. 19.00 *(978-1-894212-26-7(6))* Power Plant, The CAN. Dist: D.A.P./Distributed Art Pubs.

Canavor, Natalie. Business Writing in the Digital Age. 2011. (Illus.). 320p. (C). pap., stu. ed. 30.00 ***(978-1-4129-9250-3(8)***, B92503P) SAGE Pubns., Inc.

Carlo, Philip. The Killer Within: In the Company of Monsters. 2011. (ENG.). 256p. (gr. 12). 25.95 *(978-1-59020-431-3(X))* Overlook Pr., The.

Case, Dan & Fielding, Peggy. The Complete Guide to Writing & Selling Magazine Articles. 2nd ed. 2006. 195p. pap. 19.95 *(978-0-937660-25-6(6))* AWOC.COM.

Cash, Alana. Writer's Kit. ring bd. 35.00 *(978-0-9703922-1-3(4))* Vibegirl Productions.

Catholic Church, United States Conference of Catholic Bishops Staff, contrib. by. Style Guide. 2008. v, 108p. *(978-1-60137-021-1(0))* United States Conference of Catholic Bishops.

Cavanaugh, Mary Patricia. Teaching the Art of Writing. rev. ed. 2010. (ENG.). 62p. spiral bd. 44.35 *(978-0-7575-8225-7(7))* Kendall Hunt Publishing Co.

Chartier, Roger. Culture écrite et Société: L'ordre des Livres, XIVe-XVIIIe Siècle. (FRE.). 240p. *(978-2-226-08701-0(X))* Albin-Michel, Editions.

Chesterton, G. K. Defiant Joy: The Remarkable Life & Impact of G. K. Chesterton. 2011. 336p. pap. 16.99 *(978-1-59555-201-3(4))* Nelson, Thomas Inc

Chitty, Antonia. Commercial Writing: How to Earn a Living As a Business Writer. 2009. (ENG.). 256p. 24.95 *(978-0-7090-8594-2(X))* Hale, Robert Ltd. GBR. Dist: Independent Pubs. Group.

Chris, Cynthia & Gerstner, David A., eds. Media Authorship. 2012. (AFI Film Readers Ser.). (ENG.). 256p. (C). 150.00 ***(978-0-415-69942-6(8))*** Routledge.

Coady, Roxanne J. & Johannessen, Joy. The Book That Changed My Life: 71 Remarkable Writers Celebrate the Books That Matter Most to Them. Coady, Roxanne J., ed. 2007. (ENG.). 224p. (gr. 12-18). 13.00 *(978-1-59240-317-2(4)*, Gotham) Penguin Group (USA) Inc.

Cofer, Judith Ortiz. Lessons from a Writer's Life: Readings & Resources for Teachers & Students. 2011. 128p. pap. 18.75 *(978-0-325-03146-0(0)* E03146) Heinemann.

Cole, Joni B. & Cole, Joni. Toxic Feedback: Helping Writers Survive & Thrive. 2006. (ENG.). 168p. pap. 16.95 *(978-1-58465-544-2(5))* Univ. Pr. of New England.

Cole, Peter, ed. Hebrew Writers on Writing. 2008. (Writer's World Ser.). (ENG.). 320p. 45.00 *(978-1-59534-051-1(3))*; pap. 24.95 *(978-1-59534-052-8(1))* Trinity Univ. Pr.

Collins, David J. Reforming Saints: Saints' Lives & Their Authors in Germany, 1470-1530. 2008. (Oxford Studies in Historical Theology Ser.). (ENG., Illus.). 208p. 65.00 *(978-0-19-532953-7(8))* Oxford Univ. Pr., Inc.

Colton, Jo Ann M. So, You Want to Be A Writer: Jo Ann M. Colton's Little Red Writer Book Series, Book 1. 2010. 80p. pap. 10.49 *(978-1-4490-1328-8(7))* AuthorHouse.

Conner, Janet. Writing down Your Soul: How to Activate & Listen to the Extraordinary Voice Within. 2009. (ENG.). 256p. pap. 16.95 *(978-1-57324-356-8(6)*, Conari Pr.) Red Wheel/Weiser.

Coovadia, Imraan. Authority & Authorship in V.S. Naipaul. 2009. (ENG., Illus.). 192p. 89.00 *(978-0-230-61535-9(X))* Palgrave Macmillan.

Cordero, Chelle. Living, Breathing, Writing: A Lesson A Day. 2011. 104p. pap. 9.95 ***(978-1-937227-43-2(X))*** Vanilla Heart Publishing.

—Living, Breathing, Writing: A Lesson A Day, Volume 2. 2011. 104p. pap. 9.95 ***(978-1-937227-70-8(7))*** Vanilla Heart Publishing.

Corradini, Richard, et al, eds. Ego Trouble: Authors & their Identities in the Early Middle Ages. 2010. (Denkschriften der Phil. -Hist. Klasse Ser.). (ENG.). 322p. (C). pap. 81.00 *(978-3-7001-6490-6(4))* Austrian Academy of Sciences Press AUT. Dist: Brown, David Bk. Co., The.

Cottrell, Randy & McKenzie, James F. Health Promotion & Education Research Methods: Using the Five Chapter Thesis/Dissertation Model. 2nd rev. ed. 2010. 345p. 119.95 *(978-0-7637-7507-0(X))* Jones & Bartlett Learning, LLC.

Couser, G. Thomas. Memoir: An Introduction, 1 vol. 2011. (ENG.). 208p. 99.00 *(978-0-19-982690-2(0))*; pap. 18.95 *(978-0-19-982692-6(7))* Oxford Univ. Pr., Inc.

Craig, Randy. Reclaiming Your Readers: Proven Methods for Reader-Focused Writing. 2012. 164p. pap. 19.95 *(978-1-933338-37-8(7)*, Marion Street Pr.) Acorn Guild Pr., LLC.

Crofts, Andrew. The Freelance Writer's Handbook: How to Make Money & Enjoy Your Life. AC, ed. 3rd ed. 2007. (ENG.). 224p. pap. 22.95 *(978-0-7499-2763-9(1)*, Piatkus Bks. GBR. Dist: Independent Pubs. Group.

Curtis, Kathy. Invisible Ink: The Journey Beyond Words. 2007. 63p. per. 14.95 *(978-0-9799645-0-3(4))*, Curtis, Kathy.

D'Agata, John & Fingal, Jim. The Lifespan of a Fact. 2012. (ENG., Illus.). 160p. pap. 17.95 ***(978-0-393-34073-0(2)***, 34073) Norton, W. W. & Co., Inc.

Danziger, Maia. Relax & Write. 2010. 120p. pap. 16.95 *(978-0-557-56330-2(5))* Lulu Enterprises Inc.

Davies, Jane. Adventures in Mixed Media: Collage, Stitch, Fuse, & Journal Your Way to a More Creative Life. 2011. (ENG., Illus.). 144p. pap. 19.99 *(978-0-8230-0081-4(8))* Watson-Guptill Pubns., Inc.

Davis, Carolyn. How to Write Persuasively Today, 1 vol. 2010. (Greenwood Guides to Writing Ser.). 143p. 35.00 *(978-0-313-37837-9(1)*, GR7837) Greenwood Publishing Group, Inc.

Davis, Jane, ed. The Reader. 2007. (Liverpool University Press - Reader Ser.). (ENG., Illus.). 128p. per. 9.95 *(978-0-9551168-4-1(8))* Liverpool Univ. Pr. GBR. Dist: Chicago Distribution Ctr.

Davis, Jeff. Journey from the Center to the Page. 2nd ed. 2008. (ENG., Illus.) 320p. pap. 16.00 *(978-0-9766843-8-1(1))* Monkfish Bk. Publishing Co.

Davis, Juliet. Exploring Writing for Interactive Media: Concepts for Web & Multimedia Content. 2011. (Applied English Ser.). (ENG.). 352p. pap. 57.95 *(978-1-4180-4219-6(6))* Delmar Cengage Learning.

Davis, Peter & Koontz, Tom. Poet's Bookshelf 2: Contemporary Poets on Books That Shaped Their Art. 2008. *(978-0-935306-53-8(6))* Barnwood Pr. Cooperative.

Dearman, Jill. Bang the Keys. 2009. (ENG.). 256p. (gr. 12-18). pap. 16.95 *(978-1-59257-914-3(0)*, Alpha Bks.) Penguin Group (USA) Inc.

Delbanco, Nicholas, ed. The Hopwood Lectures. 2009. (ENG., Illus.). 160p. 60.00 *(978-0-472-11688-1(6))*; pap. 19.95 *(978-0-472-03354-6(9))* Univ. of Michigan Pr.

Denison, Edward. Letters & Other Writings. 2009. 126p. pap. 19.99 *(978-1-150-35549-3(2))* General Bks. LLC.

Dennis, J. K. A Practical Introduction to Writing Studies: A Workbook for Student Writers (Second Edition) 2011. 146p. pap. 39.99 *(978-0-615-41953-4(4))* Three Hse. Publishing.

Derrida, Jacques. Ecriture et la Difference. (FRE.). pap. 17.95 *(978-2-02-005182-8(6))* Editions du Seuil FRA. Dist: Distribooks, Inc.

Dettenrieder, Marc & Hlawati, Adam. Incipio - the essential handbook of 2,000 sentence starters for every Writer. 2008. 214p. pap. 17.95 *(978-1-4357-1866-1(6))* Lulu Enterprises Inc.

DeVries Sokol, Dawn. 500 Artist Journal Pages: Personal Pages & Inspirations. 2013. (1000 Ser.). (ENG., Illus.). 160p. pap. 15.99 *(978-1-59253-709-9(X)*, 159253709X) Quayside.

Diedwardo, Maryann. Pennsylvania Voices Book X: Writing Based on History. 2009. 104p. pap. 10.99 *(978-1-4389-2132-7(2))* AuthorHouse.

Diehn, Gwen. The Complete Decorated Journal: A Compendium of Journaling Techniques. 2012. (ENG., Illus.). 240p. pap. 21.95 ***(978-1-4547-0203-0(6))*** Lark Bks.

Dillard, Annie. Give It All, Give It Now: One of the Few Things I Know about Writing. 2009. (ENG., Illus.). 50p. 19.95 *(978-1-59962-060-2(X)*, Welcome Bks.) Welcome Enterprises, Inc.

DiTiberio, John, et al. Writing & Personality: Finding Your Voice, Your Style, Your Way. 2008. 248p. pap. 38.95 *(978-1-85575-507-9(6))* Karnac Bks. GBR. Dist: Stylus Publishing, LLC.

Dodd, Nancy Ellen. The Writer's Compass: From Story Map to Finished Draft in 7 Stages. 2011. (ENG., Illus.). 224p. pap. 19.99 *(978-1-59963-197-4(0)*, Writer's Digest Bks.) F&W Media, Inc.

Donatone, Frank, et al. Audience, Relevance, & Search: Targeting Web Audiences with Relevant Content. 2010. (ENG., Illus.). 208p. pap. 39.99 *(978-0-13-700420-1(6))* Pearson Education.

Donna Bevans. So You Want to Write a Book: A Manual for the Beginning Writer. 2009. 112p. pap. 11.99 *(978-1-4389-1754-2(6))* AuthorHouse.

Dorleijn, G. J., et al, eds. Authorship Revisited: Conceptions of Authorship around 1900 And 2000. 2010. (Groningen Studies in Cultural Change Ser.). (ENG.). 253p. (C). 70.00 *(978-90-429-2377-5(6))* Peeters Pubs. & Booksellers BEL. Dist: Brown, David Bk. Co., The.

Douglas, Jay. Everything You Need to Write Great Essays: You Can Learn from Watching Movies. 2011. (ENG.). 240p. (gr. 12). 13.95 *(978-1-61564-107-9(6)*, Alpha Bks.) Penguin Group (USA) Inc.

Dowling, David. The Business of Literary Circles in Nineteenth-Century America. 2011. (Nineteenth-Century Major Lives & Letters Ser.). (ENG.). 304p. 89.00 *(978-0-230-11046-5(0))* Palgrave Macmillan.

—Capital Letters: Authorship in the Antebellum Literary Market. 2009. (ENG., Illus.). 226p. 39.95 *(978-1-58729-784-7(1))* Univ. of Iowa Pr.

Dowling, David. Literary Partnerships & the Marketplace: Writers & Mentors in Nineteenth-Century America. 2012. 248p. 39.95 ***(978-0-8071-3847-2(9))*** Louisiana State Univ. Pr.

Dunlap, Louise. Undoing the Silence: Six Tools for Social Change Writing. 2007. (ENG., Illus.). 240p. pap. 21.95 *(978-0-9766054-9-2(X))* New Village Pr.

Duong, Lan P. Treacherous Subjects: Gender, Culture, & Trans-Vietnamese Feminism. 2012. (Asian American History & Cultu Ser.). (ENG., Illus.). 264p. pap. 26.95 ***(978-1-4399-0178-6(3))*** Temple Univ. Pr.

Easley, Alexis. Literary Celebrity, Gender, & Victorian Authorship, 1850-1914. 2011. (Illus.). 273p. *(978-1-936249-01-5(4))*; (ENG., 280p. 75.00 *(978-1-61149-016-9(2))* Univ. of Delaware Pr.

Eckstut, Arielle & Sterry, David Henry. Getting Your Book Published: How to Write It, Sell It, & Market It... Successfully! 2010. (ENG.). 480p. pap. 15.95 *(978-0-7611-6085-4(X)*, 076116085X) Workman Publishing Co., Inc.

Eco, Umberto. Confessions of a Young Novelist. 2011. (Richard Ellmann Lectures in Modern Literature Ser.). (Illus.). 240p. 18.95 *(978-0-674-05869-9(0))* Harvard Univ. Pr.

Edwards, Anne K. & Quillen, Lida E., eds. How I Wrote My First Book: The Story Behind the Story. 2011. pap. 15.95 *(978-1-60619-149-1(7))* Twilight Times Bks.

Edwards, Jim & Vitale, Joe. How to Write & Publish Your Own eBook in as Little as 7 Days: How to Write & Publish Your Own Outrageously Profitable eBook in as Little 7 Days Even If You Can't Write, Can't Type & Failed High School English Class! 2007. (ENG.). per. 19.95 *(978-1-60037-152-3(3))* Morgan James Publishing.

Edwards, Judson. Blissful Affliction: The Ministry & Misery of Writing. 2011. pap. ***(978-1-57312-594-9(6))*** Smyth & Helwys Publishing, Inc.

Eger, Elizabeth. Bluestockings: Women of Reason from Enlightenment to Romanticism. (Palgrave Studies in the Enlightenment, Romanticism & the Cultures of Print Ser.). (ENG., Illus.). 2012. 296p. pap. 29.00 ***(978-1-137-01847-2(X))*** 2010. 256p. 79.00 *(978-0-230-20533-8(X))* Palgrave Macmillan.

Ehnenn, Jill R. Women's Literary Collaboration Queerness & Late-Victorian Culture. 2008. (Nineteenth Century Ser.). (Illus.). 236p. 99.95 *(978-0-7546-5294-6(7))* Ashgate Publishing Co.

Eisner, Eric. Nineteenth-Century Poetry & Literary Celebrity. 2009. (ENG.). 232p 95.00 *(978-0-230-22815-3(1))* Palgrave Macmillan.

Elizabeth Ayres. Writing the Wave: Inspired Rides for Aspiring Writers. 2009. 288p. pap. 19.95 *(978-1-4401-8252-5(3))* iUniverse, Inc.

Ellinghausen, Laurie. Labor & Writing in Early Modern England, 1567-1667. 2008. (Illus.). 166p. 99.95 *(978-0-7546-5780-4(9))* Ashgate Publishing Co.

Ellis, Sherry. Now Write! Nonfiction: Memoir, Journalism, & Creative Nonfiction Exercises from Today's Best Writers & Teachers. 2009. (ENG.). 352p. (gr. 12-18). 14.95 *(978-1-58542-758-1(6)*, Tarcher) Penguin Group (USA) Inc.

Ellis, Sherry & Lamson, Laurie. Now Write! Mysteries: Suspense, Crime, Thriller, & Other Mystery Fiction Exercises from Today's Best Writers & Teachers. 2011. (ENG.). 384p. (gr. 12). 14.95 ***(978-1-58542-903-5(1)***, Tarcher) Penguin Group (USA) Inc.

Erdal, Jennie. Ghosting: A Double Life. 2006. (ENG.). 288p. pap. 13.95 *(978-1-4000-7955-1(1)*, Anchor) Knopf Doubleday Publishing Group.

Erichsen, Hugo. Methods of Authors. 2011. 96p. pap. 8.99 ***(978-1-61203-294-8(X))*** Bottom of the Hill Publishing.

Erickson, Beth Ann. 101 No Cost (and Low Cost) Techniques to Turbo Charge Your Freelance Income. 2006. per. 29.95 *(978-1-932794-08-3(5))* Filbert Publishing.

Erickson, John R. Story Craft: Reflections on Faith, Culture, & Writing from the Author of Hank the Cowdog. 2009. 168p. pap. 12.99 *(978-1-59188-891-8(3))* Maverick Bks., Inc.

Etuk, Emma S. A Splendid Ecstasy: The Trials, Thrills & Joys of Authorship. 2010 112p. 31.99 *(978-1-4490-8633-6(0))*; pap. 15.70 *(978-1-4490-8632-9(2))* AuthorHouse.

Everett, Judith C. & Swanson, Kristen K. Writing for the Fashion Business. 2008. (Illus.). 624p. pap. 88.00 *(978-1-56367-439-6(4))* Fairchild Bks.

Fabian, Johannes. Ethnography As Commentary: Writing from the Virtual Archive. 2008. (ENG.). 152p. 74.95 *(978-0-8223-4261-8(8))*; pap. 21.95 *(978-0-8223-4283-0(9))* Duke Univ. Pr.

Facklam, Margery & Thomas, Peggy. Anatomy of Nonfiction: Writing True Stories for Children. 2011. 236p. pap. 23.95 ***(978-1-889715-59-9(X))*** Writer's Institute Pubns.

Farber, Thomas. A Lover's Quarrel: On Writing & the Writing Life. 2007. 268p. pap. 19.95 *(978-0-9788699-2-2(3))* Ellsberg Bks.

Fawcett, Shaun. Instant Home Writing Kit: How to Save Money, Time & Effort & Simplify Everyday Writing Tasks. 2007. 268p. per. *(978-0-9781700-2-8(4))* Final Draft Pubns.

Fensch, Thomas. Writing Solutions: Beginnings, Middles & Endings. 280p. 30.00 *(978-0-930751-19-7(1))*; pap. 20.00 *(978-0-930751-20-3(5))* New Century Bks.

Fingeroth, Danny. Best of Write Now. 2008. 160p. pap. 19.95 *(978-1-893905-92-4(6))* TwoMorrows Publishing.

Finkelstein, David & McCleery, Alistair. The Book History Reader. Finkelstein, David & McCleery, Alistair, eds. 2nd rev. ed. 2006. (ENG., Illus.). 576p. 157.00 *(978-0-415-35947-4(3))* Routledge.

—The Book History Reader. 2nd rev. ed. 2006. (ENG., Illus.). 576p. per. 49.95 *(978-0-415-35948-1(1))* Routledge.

Finkelstein, David & McCleery, Alistair. An Introduction to Book History. 2nd rev. ed. 2012. (ENG.). 168p. (C). 130.00 ***(978-0-415-68805-5(1))***; pap. 44.95 ***(978-0-415-68806-2(X))*** Routledge.

Foodista, Inc. Staff, et al. The Foodista Best of Food Blogs Cookbook: 100 Great Recipes, Photographs, & Voices. 2010. (ENG., Illus.). 216p. pap. 19.99 *(978-0-7407-9767-5(0))* Andrews McMeel Publishing.

Foster, Jack. How to Get Ideas. 2nd rev. ed. 2007. (BK Life Ser.). (ENG., Illus.). 214p. pap. 20.95 *(978-1-57675-430-6(8))* Berrett-Koehler Pubs., Inc.

Foster, Richard & Yancey, Philip. A Syllable of Water: Twenty Writers of Faith Reflect upon Their Art. Griffin, Emilie, ed. 2008. 240p. pap. 20.00 *(978-1-55725-566-2(0))* Paraclete Pr., Inc.

Friedman, Lauri, ed. Racism. 2006. (OPPOSING VIEWPOINTS VISUALS Ser.). (ENG., Illus.). 108p. (YA). (gr. 7-12). lib. bdg. 35.75 *(978-0-7377-3224-5(5))* Cengage Gale.

Friedman, Lauri S. Climate Change. 2009. (Writing the Critical Essay Ser.). (ENG., Illus.). 128p. (YA). (gr. 7-12). lib. bdg. 31.80 *(978-0-7377-4402-6(2)*, LML02109-222718, Greenhaven Pr., Inc.) Cengage Gale.

Friedman, Rosemary. Life Is a Joke: A Writer's Memoir. 2011. (ENG.). 238p. pap. 24.95 *(978-1-906413-81-1(9))* Arcadia Bks. Ltd. GBR. Dist: Dufour Editions, Inc.

Friedmann, Anthony. Writing for Visual Media. 3rd ed. 2010. (ENG., Illus.). 432p. pap. 46.95 *(978-0-240-81235-9(2)*, Focal Pr.) Elsevier Science & Technology Bks.

Frost, Jan Holmes. Eight Things You Need to Know to Write a Novel. 2011. 104p. pap. 14.95 ***(978-1-61179-132-7(4))*** Fireship Pr.

Fry, Patricia L. The Right Way to Write, Publish & Sell Your Book: Your Guide to Successful Authorship. 2007. 362p. pap. 19.95 *(978-0-9773576-2-8(7))* Matilija Pr.

Fuchs, Miriam & Howes, Craig, eds. Teaching Life Writing Texts. 2008. (ENG.). 400p. 40.00 *(978-0-87352-819-1(0))* Modern Language Assn. of America.

Furman, Dan. Do the Web Write: Writing for & Marketing Your Website. 2009. (ENG.). 180p. pap. 19.95 *(978-1-55180-832-1(3))* Self-Counsel Pr., Inc. CAN. Dist: Midpoint Trade Bks., Inc.

Furman, Rich. Practical Tips for Publishing Scholarly Articles: Writing & Publishing in the Helping Professions. 2007. (ENG.). 128p. (C). 19.95 *(978-1-933478-07-4(1))* Lyceum Bks., Inc.

Furman, Rich & Kinn, Julie. Practical Tips for Publishing Scholarly Articles: Writing & Publishing in the Helping Professions. 2nd ed. 2012. (ENG.). xix, 127p. pap. 23.95 ***(978-1-935871-10-1(2))*** Lyceum Bks., Inc.

Gabbin, Joanne Veal, ed. Shaping Memories: Reflections of African American Women Writers. 2009. (ENG.). 240p. 30.00 *(978-1-60473-274-0(1))* Univ. Pr. of Mississippi.

Gaillet, Lynée Lewis. A Writer's Journal. 2006. *(978-0-07-326031-0(2))* McGraw-Hill Cos., The.

Gallop, Jane. The Deaths of the Author: Reading & Writing in Time. 2011. (ENG.). 184p. 74.95 *(978-0-8223-5063-7(7))*; pap. 21.95 *(978-0-8223-5081-1(5))* Duke Univ. Pr.

Garson, Lorrin R. & Coghill, Anne M., eds. The ACS Style Guide: Effective Communication of Scientific Information. 3rd rev. ed. 2006. (ENG., Illus.). 448p. 59.50 *(978-0-8412-3999-9(1))* American Chemical Society.

Garvey, Mark. Stylized: A Slightly Obsessive History of Strunk & White's the Elements of Style. 2009. (ENG., Illus.). 240p. 22.99 *(978-1-4165-9092-7(7)*, Touchstone) Touchstone.

Gass, William H. A Temple of Texts. 2007. (Dalkey Archive Scholarly Ser.). (ENG.). 418p. per. 14.95 *(978-1-56478-468-1(1)*, 478468) Dalkey Archive Pr.

Gawthorpe, Ann. Teach Yourself How to Write Your Life Story. 2009. (Teach Yourself: Writing Ser.). (ENG.). 192p. pap. 14.95 *(978-0-07-162585-2(2)*, 0071625852) McGraw-Hill Cos., The.

Gebhardt, Richard C. & Smith Gebhardt, Barbara Genelle, eds. Academic Advancement in Composition Studies. 2011. (ENG.). 224p. pap. 42.95 ***(978-0-415-51563-4(7))*** Routledge.

Gershon, Walter S., ed. The Collaborative Turn Working Together in Qualitative Research. 2009. 272p. *(978-90-8790-959-8(4))*; pap. *(978-90-8790-958-1(6))* Sense Pubs.

Gerson, Mark David. The Voice of the Muse: Answering the Call to Write. 2008. pap. 17.00 *(978-0-9795475-5-3(5))* LightLines Media.

Gerwitz, Felice. Writing & Publishing: SERIES NAME: Information in a Nutshell TM. 2007. 128p. per. 8.95 *(978-1-931941-18-1(1))* Media Angels, Inc.

Ghosh, Rishab Aiyer, ed. Code: Collaborative Ownership & the Digital Economy. 2006. (Leonardo Bks.). (ENG., Illus.). 384p. (gr. 17). per. 21.95 *(978-0-262-57236-1(2))* MIT Pr.

Gibbs Kamath, Stephanie A. Viereck. Authorship & First-Person Allegory in Late Medieval France & England. 2012. (Gallica Ser.: Volume 26). 226p. 90.00 ***(978-1-84384-313-9(7)***, D. S. Brewer) Boydell & Brewer, Ltd. GBR. Dist: Boydell & Brewer, Inc.

Gilles, D. B. You're Funny! Turn Your Sense of Humor into a Lucrative New Career. 2011. (ENG.). 200p. pap. 19.95 *(978-1-932907-95-7(5))* Wiese, Michael Productions.

Gillman, Claire. Write Fantastic Non-Fiction - And Get It Published. 2011. (Teach Yourself Ser.). (ENG., Illus.). 196p. pap. 16.95 *(978-1-4441-2402-6(1)*, Hodder & Stoughton) Hodder General Publishing Div. GBR. Dist: Independent Pubs. Group.

Gingher, Marianne. Adventures in Pen Land: One Writer's Journey from Inklings to Ink. 2008. (ENG., Illus.). 200p. (gr. 9). pap. 19.95 *(978-0-8262-1817-9(2))* Univ. of Missouri Pr.

Girard, Dara. The Writer's Guide to Resilience: How to Bounce When You Want to Shatter. 2007. pap. 12.95 *(978-0-9770191-4-4(4))* ILORI Pr. Bks. LLC.

Glicken, Morley D. A Guide to Writing for Human Service Professionals. 2007. (ENG.). 288p. 71.50 *(978-0-7425-5947-9(5))*; per. 31.50 *(978-0-7425-5948-6(3))* Rowman & Littlefield Publishers, Inc.

Glover, Douglas. The Attack of the Copula Spiders: And Other Essays on Writing. 2012. (ENG.). 224p. pap. 17.95 ***(978-1-926845-46-3(3))*** Biblioasis CAN. Dist: Consortium Bk. Sales & Distribution.

González, Aníbal. Killer Books: Writing, Violence, & Ethics in Modern Spanish American Narrative. 2009. (ENG.). 188p. pap. 24.95 *(978-0-292-71808-1(X))* Univ. of Texas Pr.

Goodman, Michelle. My So-Called Freelance Life: How to Survive & Thrive as a Creative Professional for Hire. 2008. (ENG.). 240p. pap. 15.95 *(978-1-58005-259-7(2))* Seal Pr.

Grace, Claudia. Write for Life. 2008. 69p. pap. 19.95 *(978-0-615-18427-2(8))* Access Art Corp., International.

Grace, William J. How to Be Creative with Words. 2011. 362p. 51.95 ***(978-1-258-03407-8(7))*** Literary Licensing, LLC.

Gray-Javid, Carol. Writing about Literature. 2007. pap. 25.00 *(978-0-8059-8622-8(7))* Dorrance Publishing Co., Inc.

Greaney, Aine. Writer with a Day Job: Inspiration & Exercises to Help You Craft a Writing Life Alongside Your Career. 2011. (ENG., Illus.). 240p. pap. 17.99 *(978-1-58297-996-0(0)*, Writer's Digest Bks.) F&W Media, Inc.

Greenberg, Arielle & Zucker, Rachel, eds. Women Poets on Mentorship: Efforts & Affections. 2008. (ENG.). 330p. pap. 24.95 *(978-1-58729-639-0(X))* Univ. of Iowa Pr.

Greene, Brenda M. & Beauford, Fred, eds. Meditations & Ascensions: Black Writers on Writing. 2008. 204p. pap. 18.95 *(978-0-88378-296-5(0))* Third World Press.

Greer, Michael. What Every Student Should Know about Citing Sources with MLA Documentation, Update Edition. 2009. (What Every Student Should Know about... (WESSKA Series) Ser.). (ENG.). (C). pap. 9.80 *(978-0-205-71511-4(7))* Longman Publishing Group.

Greetham, David. The Pleasures of Contamination: Evidence, Text, & Voice in Textual Studies. 2010. (Textual Cultures: Theory & Praxis Ser.). (ENG., Illus.). 402p. 75.00 *(978-0-253-35506-5(0)*, 0253355060); pap. 27.95 *(978-0-253-22216-9(8)*, 0253222168) Indiana Univ. Pr.

Grillner, Katja & Hughes, Rolf. Architecture & Authorship. Anstey, Tim & Grillner, Katja, eds. Hughes, Rolf, ed. 2007. (ENG., Illus.). 205p. pap. 39.95 *(978-1-904772-74-3(9))* Black Dog Publishing Ltd. GBR. Dist: Perseus Distribution.

Grimes, Tom. Mentor: A Memoir. 2010. (ENG.). 200p. 24.95 *(978-0-9825048-8-8(8))*; pap. 16.95 *(978-0-9825048-9-5(6))* Tin Hse. Bks., LLC.

Gristanti, Jennifer. Story Line: Finding Gold in Your Life Story. 2011. (ENG.). 300p. pap. 26.95 *(978-1-932907-89-6(0))* Wiese, Michael Productions.

Groff, Kent I. Writing Tides: Finding Grace & Growth Through Writing. 2007. (Illus.). 187p. per. 19.00 *(978-0-687-64265-6(5))* Abingdon Pr.

Grossman, Mahesh. Write a Book Without Lifting a Finger: How to Hire a Ghostwriter Even if You're on a Shoestring Budget. 2nd ed. 2010. (Customs & Etiquette Pocket Guides Ser.). 242p. pap. 17.95 *(978-1-933174-98-3(6))* 10 Finger Pr.

Gubernatis, Loretto. The Twelve Step Program to Writing Your Own Book. 2009. 272p. pap. 19.99 *(978-1-4415-4508-4(5))* Xlibris Corp.

Gurd, Sean Alexander. Work in Progress: Literary Revision as Social Performance in Ancient Rome, 1 vol. 2011. (American Philological Association American Classical Studies Ser.). (ENG.). 192p. 74.00 *(978-0-19-983751-9(1))* Oxford Univ. Pr., Inc.

Gutkind, Lee. Keep It Real: Everything You Need to Know about Researching & Writing Creative Nonfiction. Fletcher, Hattie, ed. 2008. (ENG.). 176p. 22.95 *(978-0-393-06561-9(8)*, 6561) Norton, W. W. & Co., Inc.

Hackles, Lynne. Writing from Life. 2008. 176p. 18.00 *(978-1-84528-241-7(8))* How To Books GBR. Dist: Parkwest Pubns., Inc.

—Writing from Life: How to Turn Your Personal Experience into Profitable Prose. 2nd ed. 2010. (ENG.). 186p. pap. 20.00 *(978-1-84528-419-0(4))* How To Books GBR. Dist: Parkwest Pubns., Inc.

Hadas, Rachel. Strange Relation. 2011. (ENG.). 204p. pap. 16.95 *(978-1-58988-061-0(7))* Dry, Paul Bks., Inc.

Hafertepe, Kenneth, ed. American Architects & Their Books, 1840-1915. 2007. (Studies in Print Culture & the History of the Book). (Illus.). 303p. 39.95 *(978-1-55849-602-6(5))* Univ. of Massachusetts Pr.

Haga, Enoch John. Write & Publish Your Family History on Your PC. 2007. pap. 34.95 *(978-1-885794-26-0(6))* Haga, Enoch Pub.

Hall, David D. Ways of Writing: The Practice & Politics of Text-Making in Seventeenth-Century New England. (Material Texts). 248p. (C). 2012. pap. 22.50 **(978-0-8122-2208-1(3))** 2008. (Illus.). 49.95 *(978-0-8122-4102-0(9))* Univ. of Pennsylvania Pr.

Hall, Donald. Unpacking the Boxes: A Memoir of a Life in Poetry. 2008. (ENG.). 208p. 24.00 *(978-0-618-99065-8(8))* Houghton Mifflin Harcourt Publishing Co.

—Unpacking the Boxes: A Memoir of a Life in Poetry. 2009. (ENG.). 208p. pap. 14.95 *(978-0-547-24794-6(X)*, Mariner Bks.) Houghton Mifflin Harcourt Trade & Reference Pubs.

Halpern, Dan. Who's Writing This? Fifty-Five Writers on Humor, Courage, Self-Loathing, & the Creative Process. 2009. 208p. pap. 14.99 *(978-0-06-178222-0(X)*, HarperPerennial) HarperCollins Pubs.

Halsey, Francis Whiting. Our Literary Deluge & Some of Its Deeper Waters. 2008. 268p. 25.99 *(978-0-559-77998-5(4))*; pap. 26.75 *(978-0-559-77994-7(1))* BiblioBazaar.

—Our Literary Deluge & Some of Its Deeper Waters. 2007. (ENG.). 264p. 42.95 *(978-0-548-02139-2(2))* Kessinger Publishing, LLC.

Hamilton, Nancy M. Magazine Writing: A Step-by-Step Guide for Success. 2007. 240p. per. 14.95 *(978-0-205-57125-3(5))* Longman Publishing Group.

Harper, Graeme. On Creative Writing. 2010. 152p. E-Book *(978-1-84769-258-0(3))* Multilingual Matters.

—On Creative Writing. 2010. (New Writing Viewpoints Ser.). (ENG.). 152p. 34.95 *(978-1-84769-256-6(7))*; 109.95 *(978-1-84769-257-3(5))* Multilingual Matters GBR. Dist: Univ. of Toronto Pr.

Harper, Timothy. Untitled Asja Guide To Freelance Writing. Date not set. *(978-0-312-31851-2(0))* St. Martin's Pr.

—Untitled ASJA Guide to Freelance Writing. Date not set. mass mkt. *(978-0-312-99187-6(8)*, St. Martin's Paperbacks) St. Martin's Pr.

Harrell, Jack. The Adult Creative Writer. 2008. 164p. pap. *(978-3-639-03609-1(3))* VDM Verlag Dr. Mueller e.K.

Hart, Jack. Storycraft: The Complete Guide to Writing Narrative Nonfiction. (Chicago Guides to Writing, Editing, & Publishing Ser.). (Illus.). 280p. 2012. pap. 15.00 *(978-0-226-31816-5(8))* 2011. 25.00 *(978-0-226-31814-1(1))* Univ. of Chicago Pr.

—A Writer's Coach: The Complete Guide to Writing Strategies That Work. 2007. (ENG., Illus.). 304p. pap. 14.95 *(978-1-4000-7869-1(5)*, Anchor) Knopf Doubleday Publishing Group.

Hartmann, Jonathan. The Marketing of Edgar Allan Poe. 2008. (Studies in American Popular History & Culture Ser.). (ENG.). 142p. 125.00 *(978-0-415-96354-1(0))* Routledge.

Haug, Walter & Wachinger, Burghart, eds. Autorentypen. (Fortuna Vitrea Ser.). (GER.). VII, 176p. 105.00 ***(978-3-11-180201-5(9))*** De Gruyter, Walter Inc.

Hauptman, Robert. Authorial Ethics: How Writers Abuse Their Calling. 2011. (ENG.). 214p. 60.00 *(978-0-7391-3444-3(2))* Lexington Bks.

Hawkins, Ann R. & Ives, Maura. Women Writers & the Artifacts of Celebrity in the Long Nineteenth Century. 2012. (Illus.). 225p. 99.95 ***(978-0-7546-6702-5(2))*** Ashgate Publishing Co.

Haworth, Kevin & Moore, Dinty W., eds. Lit from Within: Contemporary Masters on the Art & Craft of Writing. 2011. (ENG.). 200p. pap. 19.95 *(978-0-8214-1948-9(X))* Ohio Univ. Pr.

Hayes, Levia DiNardo & Waltman, Bradley. Words on Paper: Essays on American Culture for College Writers. 2008. (Pearson English Value Textbook Ser.). (ENG.). 336p. (C). pap. 49.20 *(978-0-205-55873-5(9))* Longman Publishing Group.

Haynes, Anthony. Writing Successful Academic Books. 2010. (ENG., Illus.). 192p. 60.00 *(978-0-521-51498-9(3))* Cambridge Univ. Pr.

Heenan. Writing Process & Product. Date not set. 136p. pap. 22.59 *(978-0-582-87724-5(5))* Addison-Wesley Longman, Ltd. GBR. Dist: Trans-Atlantic Pubns., Inc.

Heffron, Jack. The Writer's Idea Book: How to Develop Great Ideas for Fiction, Nonfiction, Poetry, & Screenplays. 10th anniv. ed. 2012. (ENG.). 352p. pap. 19.99 *(978-1-59963-386-2(8)*, Writer's Digest Bks.) F&W Media, Inc.

Heighton, Steven. Memos & Dispatches on Writing. 2011. (ENG.). 72p. pap., wbk. ed. 16.95 *(978-1-55022-937-0(0))* ECW Pr. CAN. Dist: Independent Pubs. Group.

Hennessy, Brendan. Writing an Essay: Simple Techniques to Transform Your Coursework & Examinations. 5th ed. 2008. (Illus.). 254p. pap. *(978-1-84528-249-3(3))* How To Books.

Herbert, Jo. Writers' & Artists' Yearbook 2011. 2011. (Writers' & Artists' Ser.). (ENG., Illus.). 832p. pap. 24.95 *(978-1-4081-2493-2(9))* A & C Black GBR. Dist: Macmillan.

Herman, Jeff & Herman, Jeff. Jeff Herman's Guide to Book Publishers, Editors, & Literary Agents 2012: Who They Are! What They Want! How to Win Them Over! 22nd ed. 2011. (ENG.). 1104p. pap. 29.99 *(978-1-4022-6061-2(X))* Sourcebooks, Inc.

Herring, Laraine. The Writing Warrior: Discovering the Courage to Free Your True Voice. 2010. (ENG.). 208p. pap. 14.95 *(978-1-59030-796-0(8))* Shambhala Pubns., Inc.

Hesson, Carolyn/J, ed. Christian Writer's Compass: From Ideas to Publication & Marketing. 2010. (ENG.). pap. *(978-0-9708451-9-1(7))* Opine Publishing.

Hidi, Suzanne & Boscolo, Pietro, eds. Writing & Motivation. 2006. (Studies in Writing Ser.). (Illus.). 334p. 140.95 *(978-0-08-045325-5(2))* Emerald Group Publishing Ltd. GBR. Dist: Turpin Distribution Services Ltd.

Hill, Bekki. Coach Yourself to Writing Success. 2011. (Teach Yourself Ser.). (ENG., Illus.). 212p. pap. 15.95 *(978-1-4441-4571-7(1)*, Hodder & Stoughton) Hodder General Publishing Div. GBR. Dist: Independent Pubs. Group.

Hillenbrand, Rainer. Erzählperspektive und Autorintention in Grimmelshausens Simplicissimus: Ein poetologischer Kommentar. 2008. (GER.). 262p. pap. 55.95 *(978-3-631-57655-7(2))* Lang, Peter GmbH, Europaischer Verlag der Wissenschaften DEU. Dist: Lang, Peter.

Hobbins, Daniel. Authorship & Publicity Before Print: Jean Gerson & the Transformation of Late Medieval Learning. 2009. (Middle Ages Ser.). (Illus.). 352p. (C). 55.00 *(978-0-8122-4155-6(X))* Univ. of Pennsylvania Pr.

Hoffman, Gary & Hoffman, Glynis. Adios, Strunk & White, 4th Edition: A Handbook for the New Academic Essay. 2007. (ENG., Illus.). 256p. per. 18.95 *(978-0-937363-40-9(5))* Verve Pr.

Holoman, D. Kern. Writing about Music: A Style Sheet. 2nd ed. 2008. (Illus.). 120p. pap. 19.95 *(978-0-520-25618-7(2))* Univ. of California Pr.

Hoople, Robin P. Inexorable Yankeehood: Henry James Rediscovers America, 1904-1905. 2009. (ENG.). 319p. 69.50 *(978-1-61148-332-1(8))* Bucknell Univ. Pr.

Hoople, Robin P. & Waters, Isobel. Inexorable Yankeehood: Henry James Rediscovers America, 1904-1905. 2009. 69.50 *(978-0-8387-5737-6(5))* Bucknell Univ. Pr.

Houghton, Peggy M. & Houghton, Timothy J. Chicago Manual of Style (CMS) The Easy Way! 2008. *(978-0-923568-89-4(1))* Baker College Publishing Co.

Houston, Velina Hasu. Writer's Block Busters: 101 Exercises to Clear the Deadwood & Make Room for Flights of Fancy. 2008. 128p. pap. 17.95 *(978-1-57525-597-2(9))* Smith & Kraus Pubs., Inc.

Howes, Craig. Teaching Life Writing Texts. Fuchs, Miriam, ed. 2008. (ENG.). 400p. per. 25.00 *(978-0-87352-820-7(4))* Modern Language Assn. of America.

Hoyt, Linda. Crafting Nonfiction: Lessons on Writing Process, Traits, & Craft (Grades K-2) 2011. 288p. pap. 60.00 *(978-0-325-03147-7(9)*, E03147, Firsthand) Heinemann.

Hoyt, Linda. Crafting Nonfiction Intermediate: Lessons on Writing Process, Traits, & Craft (grades 3-5) 2012. 376p. pap. 60.00 ***(978-0-325-03722-6(1)***, E03722, Firsthand) Heinemann.

Hugo, Richard. The Triggering Town: Lectures & Essays on Poetry & Writing. 2010. (ENG.). 109p. pap. 13.95 *(978-0-393-33872-0(X)*, 33872) Norton, W. W. & Co., Inc.

Hunley, Tom C. The Poetry Gymnasium: 95 Proven Exercises to Shape Your Best Verse. 2011. (ENG.). 266p. pap. 35.00 ***(978-0-7864-6514-9(X))*** McFarland & Co., Inc. Pubs.

Ironside, Fabian. Bloom's How to Write about Ralph Waldo Emerson. Bloom, Harold, ed. 2008. (Bloom's How to Write about Literature Ser.). 288p. (C). (gr. 9). 45.00 *(978-0-7910-9833-2(8)*, Chelsea Hse.) Facts On File, Inc.

Isherwood, Christopher & Berg, James J. Isherwood on Writing. 2007. pap. *(978-0-8166-4694-4(5))* Univ. of Minnesota Pr.

Jackson, Leon. The Business of Letters: Authorial Economies in Antebellum America. 2007. (ENG.). 344p. 35.00 *(978-0-8047-5705-8(4))* Stanford Univ. Pr.

Jacob, Dianne. Will Write for Food: The Complete Guide to Writing Cookbooks, Blogs, Reviews, Memoir, & More. 2nd ed. 2010. (ENG.). 360p. pap. 15.95 *(978-0-7382-1404-7(3))* Da Capo Pr., Inc.

Jacobs, Charles. The Writer Within You: A Step-by-Step Guide to Writing & Publishing in Your Retirement Years. 2007. 321p. per. 19.95 *(978-0-9793636-0-3(8))* Caros Bks.

James-Enger, Kelly. Ready, Aim, Specialize! Create Your Own Writing Specialty & Make More Money! 2nd ed. 2007. (ENG.). 256p. per. 16.95 *(978-1-933338-24-8(5)*, Marion Street Pr.) Acorn Guild Pr., LLC.

Jameson, W. C., ed. Hot Coffee & Cold Truth: Living & Writing the West. 2006. (ENG., Illus.). 218p. pap. 14.95 *(978-0-8263-4061-0(X))* Univ. of New Mexico Pr.

—Notes from Texas: On Writing in the Lone Star State. 2008. (ENG., Illus.). 250p. 27.95 *(978-0-87565-358-7(8))* Texas Christian Univ. Pr.

Jason, Philip K. & Lefcowitz, Allan B. Creative Writer's Handbook. 5th ed. 2009. (ENG., Illus.). 432p. (C). pap. 70.60 *(978-0-13-605052-0(2)*, Prentice Hall) Prentice Hall PTR.

Jauss, David. Alone with All That Could Happen: Rethinking Conventional Wisdom about the Craft of Fiction Writing. 2008. (ENG.). 256p. 19.99 *(978-1-58297-538-2(8)*, Writer's Digest Bks.) F&W Media, Inc.

John-Steiner, Vera. Creative Collaboration. 2006. (ENG., Illus.). 288p. per. 26.99 *(978-0-19-530770-2(4))* Oxford Univ. Pr., Inc.

Johnson, Charles. Turning the Wheel: Essays on Buddhism & Writing. 2007. (ENG.). 208p. pap. 15.95 *(978-1-4165-7243-5(0)*, Scribner) Scribner.

Johnston, Bret Anthony, ed. Naming the World: And Other Exercises for the Creative Writer. 2008. (ENG., Illus.). 400p. pap. 16.00 *(978-0-8129-7548-2(0))* Random Hse., Inc.

Jones, Diana Wynne. Reflections. 2012. (ENG.). 272p. (gr. 8). 24.99 ***(978-0-06-221989-3(8)***, Greenwillow Bks.) HarperCollins Pubs.

Kakonge, Donna Kay. How to Write Creative Non-fiction. 2008. 129p. pap. 25.95 *(978-1-4357-2176-0(4))* Lulu Enterprises Inc.

Karell, Linda. Writing Together - Writing Apart: Collaboration in Western American Literature. 2008. (ENG.). 219p. pap. 19.95 *(978-0-8032-1834-5(6))* Univ. of Nebraska Pr.

Karshner, Edward. Writing the Self. 2008. 240p. pap. *(978-3-639-06394-3(5))* VDM Verlag Dr. Mueller e.K.

Katz, Christina. Writer Mama: How to Raise a Writing Career Alongside Your Kids. 2007. (ENG., Illus.). 320p. per. 14.99 *(978-1-58297-441-5(1)*, Writer's Digest Bks.) F&W Media, Inc.

Kearns, Michael S. Writing for the Street, Writing in the Garret: Melville, Dickinson, & Private Publication. 2010. 45.95 (978-0-8142-1140-3(2)); cd-rom 14.95 (978-0-8142-9239-6(9)) Ohio State Univ. Pr.

Keith, Chris. The Pericope Adulterae, the Gospel of John, & the Literacy of Jesus. 2009. (New Testament Tools, Studies & Documents Ser.). (Illus.). 366p. (978-90-04-17394-1(3)) BRILL.

Kenner, Corrine. Tarot & Astrology: Enhance Your Readings with the Wisdom of the Zodiac. 2011. (ENG., Illus.). 312p. pap. 17.95 (978-0-7387-2964-0(7)) Llewellyn Pubns.

Kerr, Christine. Bloom's How to Write about Alice Walker. Bloom, Harold, ed. 2008. (Bloom's How to Write about Literature Ser.). 304p. (C). (gr. 9-18). 45.00 (978-0-7910-9745-8(5), Chelsea Hse.) Facts On File, Inc.

King, Stephen. On Writing: A Memoir of the Craft. 10th anniv. ed. 2010. (ENG.). 288p. pap. 16.00 (978-1-4391-5681-0(6), Scribner) Scribner.

Kirchhoff, Bodo. Legenden Um Den Eigenen Körper: Frankfurter Vorlesungen. (GER., Illus.). 182p. (978-3-518-11944-0(3)) Suhrkamp Verlag.

Kirkpatrick, Katherine, editor. A Circle of Friends: Remembering Madeleine L'Engle (second Edition) 2010. 224p. pap. 20.00 (978-0-557-22788-4(7)) Lulu Enterprises Inc.

—A Circle of Friends: Remembering Madeleine L'Engle. 2010. 224p. pap. 74.00 (978-0-557-18532-0(7)) Lulu Enterprises Inc.

Klaus, Carl H. The Made-Up Self: Impersonation in the Personal Essay. 2010. 174p. pap. 19.95 (978-1-58729-913-1(5)) Univ. of Iowa Pr.

Klinkenborg, Verlyn. Several Short Sentences about Writing. 2012. (ENG.). 224p. 22.00 **(978-0-307-26634-7(6)**, Knopf) Knopf Doubleday Publishing Group.

Knight, Robert M. Writing Public Prose: How to Write Clearly, Crisply, & Concisely. 2012. (ENG.). 108p. pap. 9.95 **(978-1-936863-01-3(4)**, Marion Street Pr.) Acorn Guild Pr., LLC.

Knisely, Karin. A Student Handbook for Writing in Biology. 3rd ed. 2009. (ENG., Illus.). 224p. (C). pap. 21.95 (978-1-4292-3491-7(1)) Freeman, W. H. & Co.

Knoop, Christine Angela. Kundera & the Ambiguity of Authorship. 2011. (MHRA Texts & Dissertations Ser.). 200p. (C). 82.00 (978-1-907322-11-2(6)) Maney Publishing GBR. Dist: Brown, David Bk. Co., The.

Kopec, David A., et al. Evidence Based Design: A Process for Research & Writing. rev. ed. 2011. (ENG.). 224p. (C). pap. 72.20 (978-0-13-217406-0(5), Prentice Hall) Prentice Hall PTR.

Kordich, Catherine J. Bloom's How to Write about Jane Austen. Bloom, Harold, ed. 2008. (Bloom's How to Write about Literature Ser.). 240p. (C). (gr. 9-18). 45.00 (978-0-7910-9743-4(9), Chelsea Hse.) Facts On File, Inc.

Krawczyk, Scott. Romantic Literary Families. 2009. (Nineteenth-Century Major Lives & Letters Ser.). (ENG.). 244p. 95.00 (978-0-230-60475-9(7)) Palgrave Macmillan.

Kremer, Belinda & McNabb, Richard. Collide: Styles, Structures, & Ideas in Disciplinary Writing. 2007. (ENG.). (C). pap. 36.33 incl. cd-rom (978-0-536-46327-2(1)) Pearson Learning Solutions.

Ladd, Karol. The Power of a Positive Wife: Devotional & Journal - 52 Monday Morning Motivations. 2008. (ENG.). 224p. 12.99 (978-1-4165-7902-1(8), Howard Bks.) Howard Books.

Lane, Barry. The Healing Pen: Writing Your Way to Inner Peace & Outer Transformation. 2008. Orig. Title: Writing as a Road to Self-Discovery. per. 18.00 (978-1-931492-10-2(7)) Discover Writing Pr.

Lane, Barry & Ballenger, Bruce. Discovering the Writer Within: The 40 Day Writer's Workshop. 2007. per. 18.00 (978-1-931492-16-4(6)) Discover Writing Pr.

Lane, Barry & Young, Robert. Non-Fiction Writers/Readers Toolbox. 2008. per. (978-1-931492-20-1(4), Discover Writing Pr.

Lang, Andrew. How to Fail in Literature. reprint ed. 37.50 (978-0-404-03837-3(9)) AMS Pr., Inc.

Lanson, Jerry. Writing for Others, Writing for Ourselves: Telling Stories in an Age of Blogging. 2011. (ENG.). 224p. 37.95 (978-0-7425-5534-1(8)) Rowman & Littlefield Publishers, Inc.

—Writing for Ourselves, Writing for Others: How to Craft Stories in the Age of Blogging. 2010. (978-1-4422-0869-8(4)) Rowman & Littlefield Publishers, Inc.

Lara, Adair. You Know You're a Writer When ... 2007. (ENG.). 96p. 9.95 (978-0-8118-6079-6(5)) Chronicle Bks. LLC.

Lavi, Nadine. Facing the Blank Page: Making Writing Easy. 2009. spiral bd. 18.00 (978-1-61623-423-2(7)) Independent Pub.

Leftridge, Alan. Interpretive Writing. 2006. pap. 21.00 (978-1-879931-21-3(4)) National Assn. for Interpretation.

Leonard, Elmore. 10 Rules of Writing. 2007. (ENG., Illus.). 96p. 14.99 (978-0-06-145146-1(0), Morrow, William & Co.) HarperCollins Pubs.

Lepionka, Mary Ellen. Writing & Developing Your College Textbook, Second Edition: A Comprehensive Guide to Textbook Authorship & Higher Education Publishing. 2008. 320p. pap. 37.95 (978-0-9728164-7-2(X)) Atlantic Path Publishing.

Lerner, Betsy. The Forest for the Trees: An Editor's Advice to Writers. 21st rev. ed. 2010. (ENG.). 304p. (gr. 12). 16.00 (978-1-59448-483-4(X), Riverhead Trade (Paperbacks)) Penguin Group (USA) Inc.

Levesque, Richard. ENG060 A Practical Guide for Student Writers (Fullerton Coll - CPS7) 2011. (ENG.). 230p. (C). pap. 29.00 **(978-0-07-303984-3(3)**, 0078039843) McGraw-Hill Cos., The.

Levy, Michelle. Family Authorship & Romantic Print Culture. 2007. (Palgrave Studies in the Enlightenment, Romanticism & the Cultures of Print Ser.). (ENG., Illus.). 256p. 95.00 (978-0-230-54512-0(2)) Palgrave Macmillan.

Lewes, George Henry. The Principles of Success in Literature. 2009. 216p. 23.99 (978-1-103-29890-7(9)) 2009. 216p. pap. 17.99 (978-1-103-29887-7(9)) 2008. 132p. 21.99 (978-0-554-36218-2(X)) 2008. 132p. 24.99 (978-0-554-26915-3(5)) 2007. (ENG.). 114p. pap. 18.99 (978-1-4346-2123-8(5)) 2007. (ENG.). 128p. pap. 19.99 (978-1-4346-2151-1(0)) BiblioBazaar.

—The Principles of Success in Literature. 2007. (ENG.). 276p. 42.95 (978-0-548-12217-4(2)) Kessinger Publishing, LLC.

Liddell, M. J. Sizzling Stories & Successful Submissions. 2010. 34p. pap. 16.95 (978-1-4457-9282-8(6)) Lulu Enterprises Inc.

Liederbach, Nate & Harris, James, eds. Of a Monstrous Child: An Anthology of Creative Writing Relationships. 2011. (ENG.). 414p. pap. 24.00 (978-0-9844510-4-3(8)) Lost Horse Pr.

Loewenstein, Joseph. Ben Jonson & Possessive Authorship. 2007. (Cambridge Studies in Renaissance Literature & Culture Ser.). (ENG., Illus.). 236p. pap. 53.00 (978-0-521-03818-8(9)) Cambridge Univ. Pr.

Lomuscio, James. Writing with Your Head & Your Heart: Balancing Logic & Emotion to Create Powerful Nonfiction. 2008. (ENG.). 144p. (C). pap. 53.33 (978-0-07-353840-2(X), 007353840X) McGraw-Hill Cos., The.

London, Jack. The Radical Jack London: Writings on War & Revolution. Raskin, Jonah, ed. 2008. (Illus.). 304p. 65.00 (978-0-520-25545-6(3)); 285p. pap. 27.95 (978-0-520-25546-3(1)) Univ. of California Pr.

Longstreth, Alec. Transition: Phase 7 #010 And #011. 2008. 116p. pap. 11.00 (978-0-615-25359-6(9)) Longstreth, Alec.

Lord, Udis. Writing Books. Fiction & Non-Fiction. (978-0-937571-04-0(0)) Philippine-American Educational Pr.

Lucas, F. L. Style: The art of writing Well. 2012. (ENG.). 300p. pap. 24.99 **(978-0-85719-187-8(X))** Harriman Hse. Publishing GBR. Dist: Ingram Pub. Services.

Luey, Beth. Handbook for Academic Authors. 5th rev. ed. 2009. (ENG., Illus.). 296p. 80.00 (978-0-521-19498-3(9)); pap. 23.99 (978-0-521-14409-4(4)) Cambridge Univ. Pr.

Lussier, Robert N. Publish Don't Perish: 100 Tips That Improve Your Ability to Get Published. 2010. (978-1-61735-114-3(8)); pap. (978-1-61735-113-6(X)); E-Book (978-1-61735-115-0(6)) Information Age Publishing, Inc.

Luyckx, Kim. Scalability Issues in Authorship Attribution. 2011. (ENG.). 196p. pap. 39.95 **(978-90-5487-823-0(1))** VUB Univ. Pr. BEL. Dist: Independent Pubs. Group.

MacDonald, Susan Peck. Professional Academic Writing in the Humanities & Social Sciences. 2010. (ENG.). 250p. pap. 35.00 (978-0-8093-3007-2(5)) Southern Illinois Univ. Pr.

MacKay, Polina & Hadjiafxendi, Kyriaki, eds. Authorship in Context: From the Theoretical to the Material. 2007. (ENG.). 256p. 84.00 (978-1-4039-4901-1(8)) Palgrave Macmillan.

Magson, Adrian. Write On! The Writer's Help Book. 2011. (ENG.). 256p. pap. 15.95 **(978-1-908006-77-6(3))** Accent Pr. Ltd. GBR. Dist: SCB Distributors.

Maisel, Eric. A Writer's Space: Make Room to Dream, to Work, to Write. 2008. (ENG., Illus.). 256p. pap. 12.95 (978-1-59869-460-4(X)) Adams Media Corp.

Major, James S. Writing Classified & Unclassified Papers in the Intelligence Community. 2008. (Scarecrow Professional Intelligence Education Ser.). (ENG.). 248p. pap. 45.00 (978-0-8108-6192-3(5)) Scarecrow Pr., Inc.

Malouf, David. On Experience. 2008. (Little Books on Big Themes Ser.). (ENG.). 96p. 17.00 (978-0-522-85536-4(9)) Melbourne Univ. Publishing AUS. Dist: Independent Pubs. Group.

Mangelsdorf, Kate & Posey, Evelyn. Choices: A Basic Writing Guide with Readings. 5th ed. 2012. (ENG.). 688p. (C). pap. 47.95 **(978-0-312-61140-8(4))** Bedford/Saint Martin's.

Manser, Martin. Writers & Editors. 2006. (ENG.). 480p. pap. 22.95 (978-0-00-720350-5(0)) HarperCollins Pubs. Ltd. GBR. Dist: Independent Pubs. Group.

Margoliouth, D. S. The Homer of Aristotle. 2009. 258p. 30.99 (978-1-110-47513-1(6)); pap. 25.75 (978-1-110-47509-4(8)) BiblioBazaar.

—The Homer of Aristotle. 2006. (978-1-57898-590-6(0)) Martino Publishing.

Marshall, Justin. Sparknotes Ultimate Style: How to Write an Essay. 2006. (978-1-4114-9976-8(X)) Spark Publishing Group.

Marshall, Simone Celine. The Anonymous Text: The 500-Year History of the Assembly of Ladies. 2010. 219p. 55.95 (978-3-03911-953-0(2)) Lang, Peter Publishing, Inc.

Martin, Jeff & Magee, C. Max, eds. The Late American Novel: Writers on the Future of Books. 2011. (ENG.). 192p. pap. 14.95 (978-1-59376-404-3(9), Soft Skull Pr.) Counterpoint LLC.

Maruca, Lisa. The Work of Print: Authorship & the English Text Trades, 1660-1760. 2007. (Literary Conjugations Ser.). (ENG., Illus.). 240p. 80.00 (978-0-295-98744-6(8)) Univ. of Washington Pr.

Maruca, Lisa M. The Work of Print: Authorship & the English Text Trades, 1660-1760. 2007. (Literary Conjugations, a Robert B. Heilman Book Ser.). (ENG., Illus.). 240p. per. 24.95 (978-0-295-98757-6(X)) Univ. of Washington Pr.

Marx, Christy. Writing for Animation, Comics, & Games. 2006. (ENG., Illus.). 248p. per. 34.95 (978-0-240-80582-5(8), Focal Pr.) Elsevier Science & Technology Bks.

Mason, Lisa. How to Earn a Living as an Internet Writer. 2009. 120p. pap. 25.30 (978-0-557-07420-4(7)) Lulu Enterprises Inc.

Mastrangelo, Lisa. Writing a Progressive Past: Women Teaching & Writing in the Progressive ERA. 2012. pap. **(978-1-60235-258-2(5))** Parlor Pr.

Mathewson, James. Audience, Relevance, & Search LiveLessons Bundle. 2010. (ENG.). pap. 69.99 (978-0-13-260377-5(2), IBM Pr.) Pearson Higher Education & Professional Group.

Matthews, Brander. Recreations of an Anthologist. 2009. 236p. 23.99 (978-1-103-59732-1(9)); pap. 17.99 (978-1-103-59728-4(0)) BiblioBazaar.

—Recreations of an Anthologist. 2008. 234p. 41.95 (978-0-548-92095-4(8)) 2007. 236p. per. 26.95 (978-0-548-59680-7(8)) Kessinger Publishing, LLC.

—Recreations of an Anthologist. 2008. 236p. pap. (978-1-4097-8779-2(6)) Read Bks.

Matthews, Paul. Words in Place: Reconnecting to Nature Through Creative Writing. 2007. (Illus.). 255p. per. (978-1-903458-69-3(2)) Hawthorn Pr.

Mazur, Grace Dane. Hinges: Meditations on the Portals of the Imagination. 2010. (ENG., Illus.). 150p. pap. 29.95 (978-1-56881-715-6(0)) AK Peters, Ltd.

McAleer, Andrew. 101 Habits of Highly Successful Novelists: Insider Secrets from Top Writers. 2008. (ENG.). 240p. pap. 12.95 (978-1-59869-589-2(4)) Adams Media Corp.

McCarthy, Tara. 100 Writing Lessons: Narrative - Descriptive - Expository - Persuasive - Ready-to-Use Lessons to Help Students Become Strong Writers & Succeed on the Tests. 2009. (ENG.). 240p. pap. 25.99 (978-0-545-11002-0(5), Teaching Resources) Scholastic, Inc.

McCarty, Diane Bischoff. Step into Writing: A Beginning Writing & Grammar Primer for the really reluctant Writer. 2008. 46p. (J). spiral bd. (978-0-9712124-3-5(0)) Angel Heart Children's Pr.

McCuen, Jo Ray. Reading for Writers. pap. 78.95 (978-0-8384-8768-6(8)) Cengage Heinle.

McGinnis, Reginald, ed. Originality & Intellectual Property in the French & English Enlightenment. 2012. (Routledge Studies in Eighteenth-Century Literature Ser.). (ENG., Illus.). 250p. pap. 42.95 **(978-0-415-54298-2(7))** Routledge.

McKay, George L. Some Notes on Robert Louis Stevenson: His Finances & His Agents & Publishers. 2011. 44p. 35.95 **(978-1-258-04341-4(6))** Literary Licensing, LLC.

McLean, Gavin. How to Do Local History: Research, Write, Publish - A Guide for Historians & Clients. 2007. (Illus.). 96p. pap. 24.95 (978-1-877372-41-4(2)) Otago University Pr. NZL. Dist: International Specialized Bk. Services.

McMullan, Gordon. Shakespeare & the Idea of Late Writing: Authorship in the Proximity of Death. 2010. (ENG.). 416p. pap. 39.99 (978-0-521-15800-8(1)) Cambridge Univ. Pr.

McQueen, Lee. Writer in the Library! 41 Writers Reveal How They Use Libraries to Develop Their Skill, Craft & Careers. McQueen, Lee, ed. 2008. (Illus.). 171p. pap. 9.99 (978-0-97985*5-4-4(8)) McQueen Pr.

McWilliam, Candia. What to Look for in Winter: A Memoir in Blindness. 2012. (ENG.). 464p. 27.99 **(978-0-06-209450-6(5))** HarperCollins Pubs.

Melander, Rochelle. Write-a-Thon: Write Your Book in 26 Days (And Live to Tell about It) 2011. (ENG.). 240p. pap. 16.99 **(978-1-59963-391-6(4))** F&W Media, Inc.

Menon, Sreelata. Freelance Writing for the 'Newbie' Writer. 2009. 132p. pap. 6.00 (978-81-7806-158-0(9)) Unicorn Bks. Pvt Ltd. IND. Dist: Mahal, Pustak Pubs., Booksellers & Order Suppliers.

Miller, Brenda & Hughes, Holly J. The Pen & the Bell: Mindful Writing in a Busy World. 2012. (ENG.). 256p. pap. 15.00 **(978-1-55896-653-6(6))**; E-Book **(978-1-55896-654-3(4))** Unitarian Universalist Assn. (Skinner Hse. Bks.).

Miller, Cheie K. Writing Conversations: Spend 365 Days With Your Favorite Authors, Learning the Craft of Writing. 2011. E-Book 9.99 **(978-0-9818756-1-3(0))** Wisdom Creek Pr., LLC.

Miller, John E. Laura Ingalls Wilder & Rose Wilder Lane: Authorship, Place, Time, & Culture. 2008. (ENG., Illus.). 280p. (C). 39.95 (978-0-8262-1823-0(7)) Univ. of Missouri Pr.

Milligan, Frank. Time to Write: Discovering the Writer Within After 50. 2008. (Best Half of Life Ser.). (ENG.). 300p. pap. 16.95 (978-1-884956-76-8(9)) Quill Driver Bks.

Mills, Gerald W. Magic for Your Writing: Help for the Aspiring Writer. 2011. 150p. pap. 15.95 (978-1-60619-147-7(0)) Twilight Times Bks.

Miner, Earl & Brady, Jennifer, eds. Literary Transmission & Authority: Dryden & Other Writers. 2006. (Cambridge Studies in Eighteenth-Century English Literature & Thought Ser.). (ENG.). 176p. pap. 41.00 (978-0-521-03201-8(6)) Cambridge Univ. Pr.

Miner, Jeremy T., et al. Collaborative Grantseeking: A Guide to Designing Projects, Leading Partners, & Persuading Sponsors, 1 vol. 2011. (Illus.). 215p. 65.00 (978-0-313-39185-9(8), A3219C); E-Book (978-0-313-39186-6(6), Greenwood Pr.) Greenwood Publishing Group, Inc.

Minot, Stephen. Three Genres: The Writing of Fiction/Literary Nonfiction, Poetry, & Drama. 8th rev. ed. 2006. (ENG.). 496p. (C). per. 100.00 (978-0-13-219738-0(3), Prentice Hall) Prentice Hall PTR.

Modern Language Association of America Staff, creator. MLA Style Manual & Guide to Scholarly Publishing. 3rd ed. 2008. (ENG., Illus.). 336p. 32.50 (978-0-87352-297-7(4)) Modern Language Assn. of America.

Modern Language Association of America Staff, ed. MLA Style Manual & Guide to Scholarly Publishing. 3rd lt. ed. 2008. (ENG.). 400p. pap. 37.50 (978-0-87352-298-4(2)) Modern Language Assn. of America.

Moore, Dinty W. The Mindful Writer: Noble Truths of the Writing Life. 2012. (ENG.). 152p. 12.95 **(978-1-61429-007-0(5))** Wisdom Pubns.

Moore, Roberta, et al. Pearson Business Reference & Writer's Handbook. 2009. (ENG., Illus.). 512p. (C). spiral bd. 57.00 (978-0-13-514053-6(6), Prentice Hall) Prentice Hall PTR.

Morley, David & Neilsen, Philip, eds. The Cambridge Companion to Creative Writing. 2012. (Cambridge Companions to Literature Ser.). (ENG., Illus.). 244p. 90.00 **(978-0-521-76849-8(7))**; pap. 27.99 **(978-0-521-14536-7(8))** Cambridge Univ. Pr.

Morrell, Jessica Page. Thanks, but This Isn't for Us: A (Sort Of) Compassionate Guide to Why Your Writing Is Being Rejected. 2009. (ENG.). 320p. (gr. 12-18). pap. 16.95 (978-1-58542-721-5(7), Tarcher) Penguin Group (USA) Inc.

Morris, Marty. Where Did You Find That? - 2007. 184p. pap. 17.95 (978-0-9788843-8-3(8)) Authors' Publishing Hse.

Morrison, Toni. Burn This Book: PEN Writers on the Power of Language. 2012. (ENG.). 208p. pap. 12.99 **(978-0-06-177401-0(4)**, Harper Paperbacks) HarperCollins Pubs.

Mossin, Andrew. Male Subjectivity & Poetic Form in New American Poetry. 2010. (Modern & Contemporary Poetry & Poetics Ser.). (ENG., Illus.). 246p. 84.00 (978-0-230-61732-2(8)) Palgrave Macmillan.

Munson, Gorham Bert. The Written Word: How to Write for Readers. 2011. 258p. 47.95 **(978-1-258-05397-0(7))** Literary Licensing, LLC.

Nash, Robert J. Me-Search & Re-Search: A Guide for Writing Scholarly Personal Narrative Manuscripts. 2011. **(978-1-61735-394-9(9))**; pap. **(978-1-61735-393-2(0))**; E-Book **(978-1-61735-395-6(7))** Information Age Publishing, Inc.

Nasso, Christine & Des Chenes, Elizabeth, contrib. by. Military Draft. 2007. (Writing the Critical Essay Ser.). (ENG., Illus.). 120p. (J). (gr. 4-7). lib. bdg. 31.80 (978-0-7377-3858-2(8), Greenhaven Pr., Inc.) Cengage Gale.

Neubauer, Bonnie. Take Ten for Writers: 1000 Writing Exercises to Build Momentum in Just 10 Minutes a Day. 2009. (ENG., Illus.). 224p. pap. 17.99 (978-1-58297-533-7(7), Writer's Digest Bks.) F&W Media, Inc.

Neville, Susan & Neville, Susan S. Sailing the Inland Sea: On Writing, Literature, & Land. 2007. (ENG.). 240p. 50.00 (978-0-253-34867-8(6), 0253348676); pap. 19.95 (978-0-253-21902-2(7), 0253219027) Indiana Univ. Pr. (Quarry Bks.).

Newman, Lesléa. Write from the Heart: Inspiration & Exercises for Women Who Want to Write. rev. ed. 2006. 241p. reprint ed. pap. 15.00 (978-1-4223-5236-6(6)) DIANE Publishing Co.

Nicol, Eric. Script Tease: A Wordsmith's Waxings on Life & Writing. 2011. (ENG., Illus.). 208p. pap. 19.99 (978-1-55488-707-1(0)) Dundurn CAN. Dist: Ingram Pub. Services.

Niebuhr, Gary Warren. Caught up in Crime: A Reader's Guide to Crime Fiction & Nonfiction, 1 vol. 2009. (Genreflecting Advisory Ser.). (Illus.). 304p. 60.00 (978-1-59158-428-5(0), LU4280) Libraries Unlimited, Inc.

Oberlander, Judy. 101 Ways (more or less) to Tell Your Life Story: The Unconventional Autobiography. 2008. (Illus.). 54p. spiral bd. (978-0-9743770-1-8(5)) Bad Cat Pr.

O'Collins, Gerald. A Short Guide to Writing a Thesis. 2011. (ENG.). 75p. (C). pap. 29.95 (978-1-921511-01-1(X)) ATF Pr. AUS. Dist: Brown, David Bk. Co., The.

Ogunyemi, Christopher Babatunde. Male Autobiographical Narratives & Gender Imperatives in Nigeri. 2010. 104p. pap. (978-3-639-25820-2(7)) VDM Verlag Dr. Mueller e.K.

Oke, Michael. Write Your Life Story: How to Record & Present Your Memories for Family & Friends to Enjoy. 2nd ed. 2006. (Daily Telegraph Ser.). (Illus.). 318p. per. 30.00 (978-1-84528-133-5(0)) How To Books GBR. Dist: Parkwest Pubns., Inc.

—Write Your Life Story 3e. 3rd ed. 2009. (Illus.). 336p. 26.00 (978-1-84528-305-6(8)) How To Books GBR. Dist: Parkwest Pubns., Inc.

Oliver, Laura, MFA. The Story Within: New Insights & Inspiration for Writers. 2011. (ENG.). 256p. (gr. 12). 13.95 (978-1-61564-114-7(9), Alpha Bks.) Penguin Group (USA) Inc.

Olsen, Eric & Schaeffer, Glenn, eds. We Wanted to Be Writers: Life, Love, & Literature at the Iowa Writers' Workshop. 2011. (ENG., Illus.). 320p. pap. 16.95 (978-1-60239-735-4(X), 239735) Skyhorse Publishing Co., Inc.

Oltermann, Philip. How to Write. 2009. (ENG.). 352p. pap. 16.95 (978-0-85265-138-4(4)) Random Hse. GBR. Dist: Independent Pubs. Group.

O'Reilly, John & Linkson, Tony. Recharge Your Design Batteries. 2009. (ENG., Illus.). 176p. pap. 30.00 (978-1-60061-335-7(7), HOW Bks.) F&W Media, Inc.

O'Roark, Mary Ann, compiled by. Now You Tell Me: 12 Writers Give the Best Advice They Never Got. 2007. 19.99 (978-1-933608-23-5(4)) Arundel Publishing.

Orr, Joel. Joel's BookProgram#8482;: the Simple Secret to Writing A Non-Fiction Book! 2009. 102p. pap. 14.97 (978-0-557-04588-4(6)) Lulu Enterprises Inc.

Overton, Grant. Why Authors Go Wrong & Other Explanations. 2007. (ENG.). 216p. 39.95 (978-0-548-05085-9(6)) Kessinger Publishing, LLC.

Owen, Hilary & Alonso, Claudia Pazos. Antigone's Daughters: Gender, Genealogy, & the Politics of Authorship in 20th-Century Portuguese Women's Writing. 2011. (978-0-8387-5780-2(4)) Bucknell Univ. Pr.

Owens, Hilary & Alonso, A. Antigone's Daughters? Gender, Genealogy & the Politics of Authorship in 20th-Century Portuguese Women's Writing. 2011. (ENG.). 250p. 70.00 (978-1-61148-002-3(7)) Bucknell Univ. Pr.

Pabst, Stephan. Anonymität und Autorschaft: Zur Literatur- und Rechtsgeschichte der Namenlosigkeit. 2011. (Studien und Texte zur Sozialgeschichte der Literatur Ser.). (GER., Illus.). 383p. 168.00 **(978-3-11-023771-9(7))** De Gruyter, Walter Inc.

Page, Amy & Peters, Amy. The Writer's Devotional: 365 Inspirational Exercises, Ideas, Tips, & Motivations on Writing. 2012. (ENG., Illus.). 384p. 17.95 (978-1-4027-8183-4(0)) Sterling Publishing Co., Inc.

Page, Ruth & Thomas, Bronwen, eds. New Narratives: Stories & Storytelling in the Digital Age. 2011. (Frontiers of Narrative Ser.). (ENG., Illus.). 296p. pap. 40.00 (978-0-8032-1786-7(2)) Univ. of Nebraska Pr.

Palazzari, Ronda. Art of Layers: Simple Techniques, Inventive Scrapbook Pages, Imaginative Papercrafts. 2012. (ENG., Illus.). 128p. pap. 24.99 ***(978-1-59963-284-1(5)***, Memory Makers Bks.) F&W Media, Inc.

Paretsky, Sara. Writing in an Age of Silence. 2nd ed. 2009. (ENG.). 160p. pap. 12.95 *(978-1-84467-377-3(4)*, 844377) Verso Bks. GBR. Dist: Norton, W. W. & Co., Inc.

Parfitt, Jo. Expat Writer: Release the Book Within. Jenkins, Debbie, ed. 2007. (ENG.). 188p. per. *(978-1-905430-26-0(4))* Lean Marketing Pr.

Parker, Lucy V. How to Start a Home-Based Writing Business. 5th ed. 2008. (How to Start a Home-Based Business Ser.). (ENG., Illus.). 320p. per. 18.95 *(978-0-7627-4401-5(4))* Globe Pequot Pr., The.

Partridge, Stephen. Author, Reader, Book. 2012. ***(978-0-8020-9934-1(3))*** Univ. of Toronto Pr.

Patrick, Shelby. Dark Recesses of the Mind: Exercises for Writers. 2009. 58p. pap. 12.97 *(978-0-557-05099-4(5))* Lulu Enterprises Inc.

Paul, Ann Whitford. Writing Picture Books: A Hands-on Guide from Story Creation to Publication. 2009. (ENG., Illus.). 256p. pap. 16.99 *(978-1-58297-556-6(6)*, Writer's Digest Bks.) F&W Media, Inc.

Perret, Gene. The New Comedy Writing Step by Step. rev. ed. 2007. (ENG.). 288p. pap. 14.95 *(978-1-884956-66-9(1))* Quill Driver Bks.

—Write Your Book Now! A Proven System to Start & FINISH the Book You've Always Wanted to Write. 2011. (Great Books for Writers Ser.). (ENG.). 144p. pap. 15.95 *(978-1-61035-006-8(5))* Linden Publishing Co., Inc.

Perrin, Robert. The Chicago Manual of Style. 2006. (ENG.). 176p. (C). spiral bd. 34.95 *(978-0-618-76723-6(1)*, 344570) CENGAGE Learning.

Persky, Stan. Topic Sentence: A Writer's Education. 2007. (ENG., Illus.). 368p. pap. 21.00 *(978-1-55420-028-3(8))* New Star Bks., Ltd. CAN. Dist: SPD-Small Pr. Distribution.

Peters, Ben. Birthing the Book Within You: Inspiration & Practical Help to Produce Your Own Book. 2007. 96p. per. 10.97 *(978-0-9789884-2-5(6))* Open Heart Ministries, International.

Peterson, Karen E. The Write Type: Discover Your True Writer's Identity & Create a Customized Writing Plan. 2008. (ENG., Illus.). 256p. per. 12.95 *(978-1-59869-470-3(7))* Adams Media Corp.

Picador USA Staff. The Paris Review Interviews, IV. Paris Review Staff, ed. 2009. (ENG.). 496p. pap. 18.00 *(978-0-312-42744-3(1))* Picador.

Pierce Brosmer, Mary. Women Writing for a Change. 2009. (Illus.). 288p. pap. 18.95 *(978-1-933495-18-7(9))* Ave Maria Pr.

Pipher, Mary. Writing to Change the World. 2007. (ENG.). 272p. (gr. 12-18). 15.00 *(978-1-59448-253-3(5)*, Riverhead Trade (Paperbacks)) Penguin Group (USA) Inc.

Plotnik, Arthur. Spunk & Bite: A Writer's Guide to Bold, Contemporary Style. l.t. ed. 2007. (ENG.). 288p. per. 13.95 *(978-0-375-72227-1(0)*, Random House Reference) Random Hse. Information Group.

Pottle, Robert. Robert Pottle's Matrix Writing Quick Reference Guide. 2008. 32p. 11.95 *(978-0-9709569-5-8(9))* Blue Lobster Pr.

Potucek, Rachel. Book by Authors - North Long Beach Anthology. 2009. 116p. pap. 12.00 *(978-0-557-13647-6(4))* Lulu Enterprises Inc.

Powell, Barry B. Writing & the Origins of Greek Literature. 2007. (ENG., Illus.). 228p. pap. 53.00 *(978-0-521-03631-3(3))* Cambridge Univ. Pr.

Powell, G A, Jr. Daily Conversations with My Interloper: Healthy Exercises in Ennui & Malaise. 2007. (ENG., Illus.). 84p. pap. 23.00 *(978-0-7618-3887-6(2))* Hamilton Bks.

Poynter, Dan. Writing Nonfiction: Turning Thoughts into Books. 5th ed. 2007. (ENG., Illus.). 144p. pap. 14.95 *(978-1-56860-110-6(7))* Para Publishing.

Priddy, Anna. Bloom's How to Write about William Faulkner. Bloom, Harold, ed. 2009. (Bloom's How to Write about Literature Ser.). 240p. (C). (gr. 9). 45.00 *(978-0-7910-9742-7(0)*, Chelsea Hse.) Facts On File, Inc.

The Profession of English Letters. 2006. 266p. 180.00 *(978-0-415-41299-5(4))* Routledge.

Pyne, Stephen J., et al. Voice & Vision: A Guide to Writing History & Other Serious Nonfiction. 2011. (ENG., Illus.). 336p. pap. 19.95 *(978-0-674-06042-5(3))* Harvard Univ. Pr.

Quiller-Couch, Arthur Thomas. On the Art of Writing. 2008. 216p. 24.99 *(978-0-554-37602-8(4))*; 27.99 *(978-0-554-28299-2(2))* BiblioBazaar.

—On the Art of Writing. 2009. 152p. pap. *(978-0-217-26666-6(5))* Books LLC.

—On the Art of Writing. 2008. (ENG.). 228p. (C). pap. 34.99 *(978-0-521-73682-4(X))* Cambridge Univ. Pr.

—On the Art of Writing. 2008. 312p. 45.95 *(978-1-4372-4027-6(5))*; pap. 30.95 *(978-1-4371-1231-3(5))* Kessinger Publishing, LLC.

Quiller-Couch, Arthur. On the Art of Writing. 2008. 232p. *(978-1-4437-3574-2(4))* 2007. 228p. per. *(978-1-4067-9683-4(2))* Read Bks. (Home Farm Bks.).

Raab, Diana M., ed. Writers & Their Notebooks. 2010. 208p. 49.95 *(978-1-57003-865-5(1))*; pap. 24.95 *(978-1-57003-866-2(X))* Univ. of South Carolina Pr.

Ramet, Adele. Creative Writing. 7th ed. 2008. 180p. 20.00 *(978-1-84528-228-8(0))* How To Books GBR. Dist: Parkwest Pubns., Inc.

Ramet, Adèle. Creative Writing: How to Unlock Your Imagination & Develop Your Writing Skills. 8th ed. 2010. (ENG.). 180p. pap. 22.00 *(978-1-84528-402-2(X))* How To Books GBR. Dist: Parkwest Pubns., Inc.

Ranee, Dannelle. Critter Tales: You are Valuable. 2012. (Illus.). 48p. per. 9.95 *(978-1-932344-65-3(9)*, Books To Believe In) Thornton Publishing, Inc.

Ratekin, Tom. Final Acts: Traversing the Fantasy in the Modern Memoir. 2010. 175p. pap. 23.95 *(978-1-4384-2730-0(1))*, Suny Pr.) 2009. 160p. 60.00 *(978-1-4384-2729-4(8))* State Univ. of New York Pr.

Rawlins, Jack & Metzger, Stephen. The Writer's Way. 8th ed. 2011. (ENG.). 448p. (C). pap. 84.95 *(978-0-495-91144-9(5))* Wadsworth.

Reagle, Joseph Michael. Good Faith Collaboration: The Culture of Wikipedia. 2010. (History & Foundation of Information Science Ser.). (ENG.). 264p. (gr. 17). 27.95 *(978-0-262-01447-2(5))* MIT Pr.

Reed, Dale Volberg, et al, eds. Cornbread Nation 4: The Best of Southern Food Writing. 2008. (Cornbread Nation Ser.). (ENG., Illus.). 320p. pap. 19.95 *(978-0-8203-3089-1(2))* Univ. of Georgia Pr.

Reid, John Howard. Write Ways to WIN WRITING CONTESTS: How to Join the Winners' Circle for Prose & Poetry Awards, NEW EXPANDED EDITION. 2008. 139p. pap. 12.50 *(978-0-557-02325-7(4))* Lulu Enterprises Inc.

Reid, Stephen. The Writer's Purposes: A Reader for Composition. 2010. (ENG., Illus.). 408p. (C). pap. 41.60 *(978-0-205-78712-8(6))* Longman Publishing Group.

Reinardy, Jeff, et al. Sports Writing. 2008. (ENG., Illus.). 274p. pap. 44.95 *(978-0-8058-6448-9(2))* Routledge.

Research International Staff, ed. Freelancers of North America. 2nd ed. pap. 37.95 *(978-0-911085-05-1(X))* Author Aid/Research Assocs. International.

Reuter, Christina. Autorschaft Als Kondeszendenz: Johann Georg Hamanns Erlesene Dialogizität. (Theologische Bibliothek Töpelmann Ser.). (GER.). VIII, 311p. 255.00 ***(978-3-11-182457-4(8))*** De Gruyter, Walter Inc.

Revell, Donald. The Art of Attention: A Poet's Eye. 2007. (Art Of... Ser.). (ENG.). 120p. pap. 12.00 *(978-1-55597-474-9(0))* Graywolf Pr.

Rickard, Jane. Authorship & Authority: The Writings of James V1 & 1. 2008. (ENG., Illus.). 256p. 79.00 *(978-0-7190-7486-8(X))* Manchester Univ. Pr. GBR. Dist: Macmillan.

Rickels, Laurence A. Aberrations of Mourning. 2011. 304p. pap. 25.00 *(978-0-8166-7595-1(3))* Univ. of Minnesota Pr.

Ritter, Kelly. Who Owns School? Authority, Students, & Online Discourse. 2010. 212p. *(978-1-57273-952-9(5))*; *(978-1-57273-953-6(3))* Hampton Pr., Inc.

Robbins, Sarah. Teachers' Writing Groups: Collaborative Inquiry & Reflection for Professional Growth. 2006. (ENG.). 201p. pap. 18.95 *(978-1-933483-10-8(5))* Kennesaw State Univ. Pr.

Robinson, Marilyn. Writers Workshop Twelfth Literary Annual. 2007. 64p. per. *(978-0-923889-14-2(0))* Inquisitors Publishing Co.

Rocco, Tonette S. & Hatcher, Timothy G. The Handbook of Scholarly Writing & Publishing. 2011. (ENG., Illus.). 368p. pap. 35.00 *(978-0-470-39335-2(1)*, Jossey-Bass) Wiley, John & Sons, Inc.

Roitfeld, Carine. Carine Roitfeld: Irreverent Limited Edition. Zahm, Olivier & Wiederin, Alex, eds. 2011. (ENG., Illus.). 400p. 250.00 ***(978-0-8478-3780-9(7))*** Rizzoli International Pubns., Inc.

Roman, Harry T. For the Aspiring Writer. 2007. 76p. per. 16.95 *(978-1-4241-8506-1(8))* PublishAmerica, Inc.

Root, Robert. The Nonfictionist's Guide: On Reading & Writing Creative Nonfiction. 2007. (ENG.). 240p. 42.95 *(978-0-7425-5617-1(4))* Rowman & Littlefield Publishers, Inc.

Rosen, Neil M. Open Your Heart with Writing: Mastering Life Through Love of Words. 2007. (Open Your Heart Ser.). (Illus.). 178p. per. 14.95 *(978-1-60166-008-4(1)*, Open Your Heart) Transformation Publishing.

Rosenblatt, Roger. Unless It Moves the Human Heart: The Craft & Art of Writing. 2011. (ENG.). 176p. pap. 13.99 *(978-0-06-196561-6(8)*, Ecco) HarperCollins Pubs.

Rosinsky, Natalie M. Write Your Own Autobiography. 2008. (Write Your Own Ser.). (ENG., Illus.). 64p. (gr. 6-7). lib. bdg. 33.99 *(978-0-7565-3525-4(5)*, Write Your Own) Compass Point Bks.

Rounds, Mike. Executive Authorship: Write Your Way to Career Advancement. 2009. (Illus.). vi, 114p. pap. *(978-1-891440-57-1(8))* CPM Systems.

Roza, Greg. Cool Careers Without College for People who Love to Write. 2009. (Cool Careers Without College Ser.). 144p. (gr. 6-6). 66.50 *(978-1-61511-981-3(7))* Rosen Publishing Group, Inc., The.

Ruberg, Michelle, ed. Writer's Digest Writers Encyclopedia: More Than 1,500 Entries about the Art & Business of Writing. 2007. 544p. 22.99 *(978-1-58297-366-1(0)*, Writer's Digest Bks.) F&W Media, Inc.

Runciman, James. Side Lights. 2008. 212p. 24.99 *(978-0-554-37518-2(4))* 2008. 212p. 27.99 *(978-0-554-28215-2(1))* 2007. (ENG.). 182p. pap. 19.99 *(978-1-4346-4921-8(0))* 2007. (ENG.). 208p. pap. 22.99 *(978-1-4346-4922-5(9))* BiblioBazaar.

—Side Lights. 2007. (ENG.). 136p. per. *(978-1-4068-4076-6(9))* Echo Library.

Russett, Margaret. De Quincey's Romanticism: Canonical Minority & the Forms of Transmission. 2006. (Cambridge Studies in Romanticism Ser.). (ENG.). 312p. pap. 66.00 *(978-0-521-03050-2(1))* Cambridge Univ. Pr.

Ruszkiewicz, John J. How to Write Anything with 2009 MLA & 2010 APA Updates. 2010. (ENG.). 608p. (C). pap. 49.95 *(978-0-312-66831-0(7))* Bedford/Saint Martin's.

Ruszkiewicz, John J. & Dolmage, Jay T. How to Write Anything: A Guide & Reference with Readings with 2009 MLA & 2010 APA Updates. rev. ed. 2010. (ENG.). 910p. (C). pap. 65.95 *(978-0-312-66830-3(9))* Bedford/Saint Martin's.

Sabrio, David & Burchfield, Mitchel. Insightful Writing: A Process Rhetoric with Readings. 2008. (ENG., Illus.). 336p. (C). pap. 83.95 *(978-0-618-87026-4(1)*, 351085) CENGAGE Learning.

Sabrio, David & Burchfield, Mitchell. Insightful Writing: A Process Rhetoric with Readings. 2009. (Illus.). xvii, 302p. *(978-0-618-95840-5(1))* Houghton Mifflin Harcourt Publishing Co.

Sacks, Mike. And Here's the Kicker: Conversations with 21 Top Humor Writers on Their Craft. 2009. (ENG., Illus.). 350p. pap. 17.99 *(978-1-58297-505-4(1)*, Writer's Digest Bks.) F&W Media, Inc.

Salas, Charles G., ed. The Life & the Work: Art & Biography. 2007. (Illus.). 200p. 45.00 *(978-0-89236-823-5(3))* Oxford Univ. Pr., Inc.

Salmon, Richard. Henry James & the Culture of Publicity. 2009. (ENG.). 252p. pap. 36.00 *(978-0-521-10033-5(X))* Cambridge Univ. Pr.

Sanborn, F. B. The Personality of Emerson. 2008. 154p. 36.95 *(978-0-548-97277-9(X))* 2007. (ENG.). 156p. per. 21.95 *(978-0-548-67527-4(9))* Kessinger Publishing, LLC.

Sark. Juicy Pens, Thirsty Paper: Gifting the World with Your Words & Stories, & Creating the Time & Energy to Actually Do It. 2008. (ENG., Illus.). 192p. pap. 18.95 *(978-0-307-34170-9(4)*, Three Rivers Pr.) Crown Publishing Group.

Sauceman, Fred William & Edge, John T., eds. Cornbread Nation 5: The Best of Southern Food Writing. 2010. (ENG., Illus.). 328p. pap. 19.95 *(978-0-8203-3507-0(X))* Univ. of Georgia Pr.

Sayles, Ginie. Writer's Block Is a Crock: Write A Book in 3 Weeks - or Less! 2009. 428p. pap. 26.95 *(978-1-4401-2881-3(2))* iUniverse, Inc.

Sayre, Henry M. Writing about Art. 6th ed. 2008. (ENG., Illus.). 160p. (C). pap. 40.20 *(978-0-205-64578-7(X)*, Prentice Hall) Prentice Hall PTR.

Schecter, I. J. 102 Ways to Earn Money Writing 1,500 Words or Less: The Ultimate Freelancer's Guide. 2010. (ENG.). 224p. pap. 14.99 *(978-1-58297-795-9(X)*, Writer's Digest Bks.) F&W Media, Inc.

Schilb, John & Clifford, John. Making Literature Matter with 2009 MLA Update: An Anthology for Readers & Writers. 4th ed. 2010. (ENG.). 1600p. (C). pap. 82.95 *(978-0-312-67730-5(8))* Bedford/Saint Martin's.

Schmidt, Diane E. Writing in Political Science: A Practical Guide. 4th ed. 2009. (ENG.). 400p. (C). pap. 61.20 *(978-0-205-61736-4(0))* Longman Publishing Group.

Schneider, Meg & Doyen, Barbara. Get Published. 2008. (ENG.). 192p. pap. 9.95 *(978-1-59869-687-5(4))* Adams Media Corp.

Schopenhauer, Arthur. The Art of Literature & the Art of Controversy. 2008. pap. 8.99 *(978-1-4209-3111-2(3))* Digireads.com.

Schubert, Edmund R., ed. How to Write Magical Words: A Writer's Companion. 2011. (ENG.). 324p. pap. 17.95 *(978-1-933523-80-4(8))* Bella Rosa Bks.

Schultz, John, ed. The Story Workshop Reader. 2nd rev. ed. (Illus.). 498p. (C). pap. 10.95 *(978-0-932026-26-2(5))* Columbia College Chicago.

Schwartz, Linda Smoak. The Wadsworth Guide to MLA Documentation. 2nd ed. 2010. (ENG.). 336p. (C). spiral bd. 26.95 *(978-1-111-34737-6(9))* Wadsworth.

Scott, Eric M. & Modler, David R. The Journal Junkies Workshop: Visual Ammunition for the Art Addict. 2010. (ENG.). 160p. pap. 24.99 *(978-1-60061-456-9(6)*, North Light Bks.) F&W Media, Inc.

Segal, Judy Z. Health & the Rhetoric of Medicine. 2008. (ENG.). 232p. pap. 35.00 *(978-0-8093-2866-6(6))* Southern Illinois Univ. Pr.

Seltz Norris, Karen. The Thought of Me: Journal once a year. Shape the story of your Life. 2010. 130p. 25.95 *(978-1-4327-5497-6(1))* Outskirts Pr., Inc.

Sellers, Heather. Chapter after Chapter. 2009. (ENG.). 256p. pap. 12.99 *(978-1-58297-617-4(1)*, Writer's Digest Bks.) F&W Media, Inc.

—Chapter after Chapter: Discover the Dedication & Focus You Need to Write the Book of Your Dreams. 2006. (ENG., Illus.). 300p. 19.99 *(978-1-58297-425-5(X)*, Writer's Digest Bks.) F&W Media, Inc.

—Page after Page. 2009. (ENG.). 240p. pap. 12.99 *(978-1-58297-618-1(X)*, Writer's Digest Bks.) F&W Media, Inc.

Sexton, Phil & Bateman, Tricia. A Picture Is Worth 1,000 Words: Image - Driven Story Prompts & Exercises for Writers. 2006. (ENG., Illus.). 256p. 19.99 *(978-1-58297-472-9(1)*, Writer's Digest Bks.) F&W Media, Inc.

Sexton, Phillip. Legends of Literature: The Best Articles, Interviews, & Essays from the Archives of Writer's Digest Magazine. 2007. (ENG., Illus.). 320p. 19.99 *(978-1-58297-473-6(X)*, Writer's Digest Bks.) F&W Media, Inc.

Shapiro, Susan. Only as Good as Your Word: Writing Lessons from My Favorite Literary Gurus. 2007. (ENG.). 250p. per. 15.95 *(978-1-58005-220-7(7))* Seal Pr.

Shawn, Wallace. Essays. 2010. (ENG.). 164p. pap. 13.95 ***(978-1-60846-096-0(7))*** Haymarket Bks.

Sheavyn, Phoebe. The Literary Profession in the Elizabethan Age. 2007. (ENG.). 236p. 41.95 *(978-0-548-09846-2(8))* Kessinger Publishing, LLC.

Sheehan, Jason. Cooking Dirty: A Story of Life, Sex, Love & Death in the Kitchen. 2010. (ENG.). 368p. pap. 15.00 *(978-0-374-53227-7(3))* Farrar, Straus & Giroux.

Shiach, Don. How to Write Essays: A Step-by-Step Guide for All Levels, with Sample Essays. 2006. (Illus.). 163p. per. 20.00 *(978-1-84528-164-9(0))* How To Books GBR. Dist: Parkwest Pubns., Inc.

Singleton, George. Pep Talks, Warnings, & Screeds: Indispensable Wisdom & Cautionary Advice for Writers. 2008. (ENG., Illus.). 224p. 17.99 *(978-1-58297-565-8(5)*, Writer's Digest Bks.) F&W Media, Inc.

Sjoholm, Barbara. Incognito Street: How Travel Made Me a Writer. 2006. (ENG., Illus.). 256p. per. 15.95 *(978-1-58005-172-9(3))* Seal Pr.

Skarles, Dorothy Ann. Learning to Write the Easy Way for Fun, Posterity & Money. 2007. 178p. pap. 16.95 *(978-1-931201-98-8(6))* Twilight Times Bks.

Slager, Daniel, ed. Views from the Loft: A Portable Writer's Workshop. 2010. (ENG.). 352p. pap. 20.00 *(978-1-57131-323-2(0))* Milkweed Editions.

Smallwood, Carol. Educators As Writers: Publishing for Personal & Professional Development. 2006. 288p. (C). pap. 29.95 *(978-0-8204-8601-7(9))* Lang, Peter Publishing, Inc.

Smallwood, Carol, et al, eds. Women on Poetry: Writing, Revising, Publishing & Teaching. 2012. (ENG., Illus.). 286p. pap. 45.00 ***(978-0-7864-6392-3(9))*** McFarland & Co., Inc. Pubs.

Smallwood, Carol & Holland, Suzann. Women Writing on Family: Tips on Writing, Teaching & Publishing. 2012. 250p. pap. 27.99 *(978-1-926780-13-9(2))* Key Publishing Hse., Inc., The CAN. Dist: AtlasBooks Distribution.

Smith, Helen. 'Grossly Material Things' Women & Book Production in Early Modern England. 2012. (ENG., Illus.). 272p. 110.00 ***(978-0-19-965158-0(2))*** Oxford Univ. Pr., Inc.

Smith, Ronald D. Becoming a Public Relations Writer: A Writing Process Workbook for the Profession. 3rd rev. ed. 2007. (Illus.). 440p. per. 69.95 *(978-0-8058-6301-7(X)*, 080586301X) Routledge.

Spector, Tom & Damron, Rebecca. How Architects Write. 2012. (ENG., Illus.). 192p. (C). 165.00 *(978-0-415-89106-6(X))*; pap. 34.95 *(978-0-415-89107-3(8))* Routledge.

Speerstra, Karen. Questions Writers Ask: Wise, Whimsical, & Witty Answers from the Pros. 2010. 320p. pap. 16.95 *(978-1-934759-32-5(5))* Reed, Robert D. Pubs.

Speth, Maria Crimi. Protect Your Writings: A Legal Guide for Authors. 2010. 112p. 22.95 *(978-1-4502-4365-0(7))*; pap. 12.95 *(978-1-4502-4364-3(9))* iUniverse, Inc.

Spoerhase, Carlos. Autorschaft und Interpretation: Methodische Grundlagen Einer Philologischen Hermeneutik. 2007. (Historia Hermeneutica. Series Studia Ser.). (GER.). VII, 556p. 154.00 *(978-3-11-019272-8(1))* De Gruyter, Walter Inc.

Staines, Gail M. Go Get That Grant! A Practical Guide for Libraries & Nonprofit Organizations. 2010. (ENG.). 124p. (gr. 17). pap. 40.00 *(978-0-8108-7419-0(9))* Scarecrow Pr., Inc.

Stamou, Constantina. Dating Victorians. 2009. 536p. pap. *(978-3-639-15314-9(6))* VDM Verlag Dr. Mueller e.K.

Stanbrough, Harvey. Writing Realistic Dialogue & Flash Fiction: A Thorough Primer for Writers of Fiction & Essays. 2007. 148p. pap. 12.95 *(978-0-9715344-5-2(4))* Central Ave. Pr.

Starke-Meyerring, Doreen. Writing in Knowledge Societies. 2011. ***(978-1-60235-271-1(2))***; 452p. ***(978-1-60235-269-8(0))***; 452p. pap. ***(978-1-60235-268-1(2))*** Parlor Pr.

Starner, Janet Wright & Traister, Barbara. Anonymity in Early Modern England: What's in a Name? 2011. 198p. 99.95 *(978-0-7546-6949-4(1))* Ashgate Publishing Co.

Stavans, Ilan. A Critic's Journey. 2009. (Writers on Writing Ser.). (ENG.). 208p. 65.00 *(978-0-472-11706-2(8))* Univ. of Michigan Pr.

Steiner, Felix. Dargestellte Autorschaft: Autorkonzept und Autorsubjekt in wissenschaftlichen Texten. 2009. (Reihe Germanistische Linguistik Ser.).Tr. of Representations of Authorship. the concept & subject of the author in academic Texts. (GER.). VIII, 279p. 182.00 ***(978-3-11-173796-6(9))*** De Gruyter, Walter Inc.

—Dargestellte Autorschaft: Autorkonzept und Autorsubjekt in wissenschaftlichen Texten. 2009. (Reihe Germanistische Linguistik Ser.).Tr. of Representations of Authorship. the concept & subject of the author in academic Texts. (GER.). VIII, 279p. pap. *(978-3-484-31282-1(3))* Verlag Max Niemeyer.

Steiner, George. My Unwritten Books. 2008. (ENG.). 192p. 23.95 *(978-0-8112-1703-3(5))* New Directions Publishing Corp.

Stelzner, Michael A. Writing White Papers: How to Capture Readers & Keep Them Engaged. 2006. (Illus.). 216p. kivar 34.95 *(978-0-9777169-3-7(7))* WhitePaperSource Publishing.

Sterling, Laurie A. Bloom's How to Write about Herman Melville. Bloom, Harold, ed. 2008. (Bloom's How to Write about Literature Ser.). 304p. (C). (gr. 9). 45.00 *(978-0-7910-9744-1(7)*, Chelsea Hse.) Facts On File, Inc.

Stern, Richard. Still on Call. 2010. (Writers on Writing Ser.). (ENG.). 256p. pap. 26.95 *(978-0-472-05090-1(7))* Univ. of Michigan Pr.

Stevens, Janice. William Saroyan: Places in Time. 2008. (ENG.). 88p. 26.95 *(978-1-933502-24-3(X)*, Craven Street Bks.) Linden Publishing Co., Inc.

Stevenson, Robert Louis. Essays in the Art of Writing. 2010. (ENG.). 172p. pap. 22.75 *(978-1-177-40208-8(4))*; (ENG.). 194p. pap. 23.75 *(978-1-176-28896-6(2))*; 178p. pap. 22.75 *(978-1-149-35686-9(3))* BiblioBazaar.

—Essays in the Art of Writing. 2007. (ENG.). 56p. per. *(978-1-4065-8205-5(0))* Dodo Pr.

—Essays in the Art of Writing. 2010. 40p. pap. 14.14 *(978-1-4432-5301-7(4))* General Bks. LLC.

—Essays in the Art of Writing. 2008. 152p. *(978-1-4437-4050-0(0)*, Obscure Pr.) Read Bks.

Stone, Kelly L. Living Write. 2010. (Illus.). xiii, 207p. *(978-1-4405-0866-0(6))* Adams Media Corp.

Stone Kelly L. Living Write: The Secret to Inviting Your Craft into Your Daily Life. 2010. (ENG., Illus.). 224p. pap. 16.95 *(978-1-4405-0624-6(8))* Adams Media Corp.

Stone, Marjorie & Thompson, Judith, eds. Literary Couplings: Writing Couples, Collaborators, & the Construction of Authorship. (Illus.). 2007. 392p. per. 29.95 *(978-0-299-21764-8(7))* 2006. 388p. 60.00 *(978-0-299-21760-0(4))* Univ. of Wisconsin Pr.

Styne, Marlys Marshall. Seniorwriting: A Brief Guide for Seniors Who Want to Write. 2007. 81p. pap. 9.95 *(978-0-7414-4296-3(5))* Infinity Publishing.

Suerbaum, Almut & Gragnolati, Manuele, eds. Aspects of the Performative in Medieval Culture. 2010. (Trends in Medieval Philology Ser.). (ENG.). VIII, 319p. 140.00 *(978-3-11-022246-3(9))* De Gruyter, Walter Inc.

Sullivan, Ceri & Harper, Graeme, eds. Authors at Work: The Creative Environment. 2009. (Essays & Studies: Volume 62). (Illus.). 192p. 50.00 *(978-1-84384-195-1(9)*, D. S. Brewer) Boydell & Brewer, Ltd. GBR. Dist: Boydell & Brewer, Inc.

Szafraniec, Asja. Beckett, Derrida, & the Event of Literature. 2007. (Cultural Memory in the Present Ser.). (ENG.). 264p. per. 24.95 *(978-0-8047-5457-6(8))* Stanford Univ. Pr.

Szafraniec, Asja & De la Torre, Augusto. Beckett, Derrica, & the Event of Literature. 2007. (Cultural Memory in the Present Ser.). (ENG.). 264p. 65.00 *(978-0-8047-5456-9(X))* Stanford Univ. Pr.

Szyborska, Wisla. Poczta Literacka. (POL., Illus.). 143p. pap. 19.95 *(978-83-08-03077-6(7))* Wydawnictwo Literackie POL. Dist: Distribooks, Inc.

Takahashi, Janet. Artful Journals: Making & Embellishing Memory Books, Garden Diaries & Travel Albums. 2009. (ENG., Illus.). 128p. pap. 15.95 *(978-1-60059-542-4(1))* Lark Bks.

Talbot, Jill, ed. Metawritings: Toward a Theory of Nonfiction. 2012. (ENG.). 242p. pap. 39.95 ***(978-1-60938-089-2(4))*** Univ. of Iowa Pr.

Taromi, Kurosh. Authorship Attribution in Modern Persian Prose. 2010. 164p. pap. *(978-3-639-26307-7(3))* VDM Verlag Dr. Mueller e.K.

Taylor, B. J. The Complete Guide to Writers Groups That Work. 2007. 155p. pap. 14.95 *(978-0-7414-4099-0(7))* Infinity Publishing.

Taylor, Gordon. A Student's Writing Guide: How to Plan & Write Successful Essays. 2009. (ENG., Illus.). 282p. (C). pap. 20.00 *(978-0-521-72979-6(3))* Cambridge Univ. Pr.

Taylor Huff, Lisa. The Writing Coach's Guide to Finally Writing Your Book! How to Stop Making Excuses & Write That Book (even if you aren't a real Writer) 2007. 156p. per. 19.95 *(978-0-595-46279-7(0))* iUniverse, Inc.

Tessmer, Martin. Writing Online Tutorials Book. 2009. 150p. pap. 59.80 *(978-0-557-06196-9(2))* Lulu Enterprises Inc.

Tharoor, Shashi. Bookless in Baghdad: Reflections on Writing & Writers. 2012. (ENG.). 288p. pap. 14.95 ***(978-1-61145-408-6(5)***, 611408, Arcade Publishing) Skyhorse Publishing Co., Inc.

The Writers' Trust of Canada. A Writer's Life: The Margaret Laurence Lectures. 2011. (ENG., Illus.). 416p. pap. 22.95 *(978-0-7710-8928-2(7)*, Emblem Edns) McClelland & Stewart CAN. Dist: Random Hse., Inc.

Thirkell, Robert. C. O. N. F. L. I. C. T: An Insiders' Guide to Storytelling in Factual/Reality TV & Film. movie tie-in ed. 2010. (Professional Media Practice Ser.). (ENG.). 256p. pap. 29.95 *(978-1-4081-2909-8(4)*, Methuen Drama) A & C Black GBR. Dist: Macmillan.

Thomas, Abigail. Thinking about Memoir. 2008. (AARP Ser.). (ENG., Illus.). 128p. 14.95 *(978-1-4027-5235-3(0))* Sterling Publishing Co., Inc.

Tiberghien, Susan M. One Year to a Writing Life: Twelve Lessons to Deepen Every Writer's Art & Craft. 2007. (ENG.). 288p. per. 15.95 *(978-1-60094-058-3(7))* Da Capo Pr., Inc.

Toward Imagery & Form: A Writer's Notebook. 44p. spiral bd. 10.00 *(978-1-884289-29-3(0))* Grandmother Earth.

Trail. Reading Writing: Argument Rhetoric & Reader. pap. 41.95 *(978-0-8384-9640-4(7))* Cengage Heinle.

Trudeau, Smoky. Front-Word, Back-Word, Insight-Out: Lessons on Writing the Novel Lurking Inside You from Start to Finish. 2008. 180p. pap. 15.95 *(978-0-9796545-8-9(0))* Vanilla Heart Publishing.

Turner, Barry, ed. The Writer's Handbook 2010. 2009. (ENG.). 784p. pap. 30.00 *(978-0-230-57324-6(X))* Palgrave Macmillan.

Turnovsky, Geoffrey. The Literary Market: Authorship & Modernity in the Old Regime. 2009. (Material Texts). (Illus.). 280p. (C). 59.95 *(978-0-8122-4195-2(9))* Univ. of Pennsylvania Pr.

Ueland, Brenda. If You Want to Write. 2011. 188p. pap. 7.95 ***(978-1-61427-135-2(6))*** Martino Publishing.

—If You Want to Write: A Book about Art, Independence & Spirit. 2010. 164p. *(978-1-60796-260-1(8))* Editorial Benei Noaj.

—Si Quieres Escribir / If You Want to Write. 2010. 158p. pap. *(978-1-60796-261-8(6))* Editorial Benei Noaj.

Uman, Deborah. Women As Translators in Early Modern England. 2012. (ENG.). 174p. (gr. 17). 65.00 ***(978-1-61149-385-6(4))*** Univ. of Delaware Pr.

UNC Wilmington Department of Creative Writing, ed. Show & Tell: Writers on Writing, Revisited & Expanded. 6th rev. ed. 2009. 432p. pap. 19.95 *(978-0-9823382-0-9(1))* Publishing Laboratory at UNC Wilmington, The.

United States Government Printing Office, compiled by. U. S. Government Printing Office Style Manual: An Official Guide to the Form & Style of Federal Government Printing 2008. 2009. (ENG.). 467p. 41.00 *(978-0-16-081811-0(7))*; 475p. pap., instr.'s gde. ed. 36.00 *(978-0-16-081812-7(5))* United States Government Printing Office.

University of Chicago Press Staff, ed. The Chicago Manual of Style, 15th Edition: CD-ROM for Windows. 2007. (ENG., Illus.). cd-rom 60.00 *(978-0-226-10417-1(6))* Univ. of Chicago Pr.

University of Chicago Staff, ed. The Chicago Manual of Style. 16th ed. 2010. (Illus.). 1026p. 65.00 *(978-0-226-10420-1(6))* Univ. of Chicago Pr.

Unknown. The Writers' & Artists' Yearbook 2012. 2011. (ENG., Illus.). 832p. pap. 35.76 ***(978-1-4081-3580-8(9))*** Bloomsbury Publishing.

Urbansky, Edward. Writing It Right in Chemistry - a Little Blue Book. 2008. 192p. pap. 24.98 *(978-1-4357-1347-5(8))* Lulu Enterprises Inc.

Vander Lei, Elizabeth & Ward, Dean. Real Texts: Reading & Writing Across the Disciplines. 2007. (ENG., Illus.). 528p. (C). per. 58.80 *(978-0-321-31743-8(2))* Longman Publishing.

VanderMeer, Jeff. Booklife: Strategies & Survival Tips for the 21st Century Writer. 2009. (ENG.). 240p. pap. 14.95 *(978-1-892391-90-2(2))* Tachyon Pubns.

VanYoos, N. B. Why Can't I Get Anything Done? 2009. 80p. pap. 10.95 *(978-0-557-03726-1(3))* Lulu Enterprises Inc.

Vassallo, Philip. How to Write Fast under Pressure, 1 vol. 2009. (ENG.). 224p. pap. 18.95 *(978-0-8144-1485-9(0))* Amacom.

Vendera, Jaime J., et al. The 11 Secret Steps to Writing, Designing, Creating & Self-Publishing Your Very Own How-to Book, Ebook or Manual. 2008. 136p. pap. 19.95 *(978-0-9749411-8-9(2))* Vendera Publishing.

Villa Gillet/ Le Monde, ed. The Novelist's Lexicon: Writers on the Words That Define Their Work. 2010. (ENG.). 168p. (gr. 17). 16.95 *(978-0-231-15080-4(6))* Columbia Univ. Pr.

Vinegar, Aron. I Am a Monument: On Learning from Las Vegas. (ENG., Illus.). 248p. (gr. 17). 2012. pap. 16.95 ***(978-0-262-51752-2(3))*** 2008. 29.95 *(978-0-262-22082-8(2))* MIT Pr.

Wakan, Naomi Beth. Compositions: Notes on the Written Word. 2008. (Illus.). 226p. pap. 19.00 *(978-1-894987-25-7(X))* Wolsak & Wynn Pubs., Ltd. CAN. Dist: Univ. of Toronto Pr.

—Late Bloomer: On Writing Later in Life. 2006. (Illus.). 182p. per. 19.00 *(978-1-894987-11-0(X))* Wolsak & Wynn Pubs., Ltd. CAN. Dist: Univ. of Toronto Pr.

Walch Publishing Staff. Daily Writing Fundamentals. 2007. (gr. 5-6). pap., tchr. ed. 21.00 *(978-0-8251-6266-4(1))*; (gr. 7-8). pap., tchr. ed. 21.00 *(978-0-8251-6267-1(X))* Walch Education.

Warland, Betsy. Breathing the Page: Reading the Act of Writing. 2010. (ENG.). 160p. 20.00 *(978-1-897151-78-5(0))* Cormorant Bks. Inc CAN. Dist: Univ. of Toronto Pr.

Watson, Irene, et al, eds. Authors Access: 30 Success Secrets for Authors & Publishers. 2008. 232p. pap. 21.95 *(978-1-932690-98-9(0)*, Modern History Pr.) Loving Healing Pr., Inc.

Weis, Margaret & Hickman, Tracy. Realms of Dragons: The Universes of Margaret Weis & Tracy Hickman. Date not set. 320p. pap. 16.00 *(978-0-06-105326-9(0))* HarperCollins Pubs.

Whaley, Simon. The Positively Productive Writer. 2012. (ENG.). 198p. pap. 19.95 ***(978-1-84694-851-0(7))*** Hunt, John Publishing Ltd. GBR. Dist: National Bk. Network.

Whidden, Seth. Models of Collaboration in Nineteenth-Century French Literature: Several Authors One Pen. 2009. 208p. 99.95 *(978-0-7546-6643-1(3))* Ashgate Publishing Co.

White, Pamela M. Make Money as a Food Writer: In Six Lessons. 2006. spiral bd. 21.95 *(978-0-9767050-0-0(1))* White, Pamela.

Whittaker, Jason. Producing for Web 2. 0: A Student Guide. 3rd ed. 2009. (ENG., Illus.). 272p. (C). stu. ed. 39.95 *(978-0-415-48622-4(X))*; 140.00 *(978-0-415-48621-7(1))* Routledge.

Widiss, Benjamin Leigh. Obscure Invitations: The Persistence of the Author in Twentieth-Century American Literature. 2011. (ENG.). 224p. 65.00 *(978-0-8047-7322-5(X))*; pap. 21.95 *(978-0-8047-7323-2(8))* Stanford Univ. Pr.

Wiedemann, Julius, ed. Web Design: Interactive & Games. 2008. (Icons Ser.). (FRE, GER & ENG., Illus.). 191p. pap. 9.99 *(978-3-8228-4053-5(X))* TASCHEN DEU. Dist: Ingram Pub. Services.

Wiesner, Karen S. & Wiesner, Karen. From First Draft to Finished Novel: A Writer's Guide to Cohesive Story Building. 2008. (ENG., Illus.). 272p. pap. 19.99 *(978-1-58297-551-1(5)*, Writer's Digest Bks.) F&W Media, Inc.

Wilbur, L. Perry. Writing & Selling Articles for Profit. 2011. (ENG.). 174p. pap. 15.95 ***(978-0-941599-91-7(4))*** Piccadilly Bks., Ltd.

Wilbur, L. Perry. Writing Your Bestseller: Everything You Need to Know to Become A Successful Author. 2010. (ENG.). 162p. pap. 14.95 *(978-0-941599-81-8(7))* Piccadilly Bks., Ltd.

Wilde, Oscar. Intentions. 1st ed. 2006. (ENG.). 150p. pap. 19.99 *(978-1-4264-0192-3(2))* BiblioBazaar.

Willard, Nancy. The Left-Handed Story: Writing & the Writer's Life. 2008. (Writers on Writing Ser.). 160p. 64.50 *(978-0-472-09999-3(X))*; pap. 19.95 *(978-0-472-06999-6(3))* Univ. of Michigan Pr.

Williams, Jim. A Message to the Children. 2007. 204p. per. *(978-0-7552-1065-7(4))* Authors OnLine, Ltd.

Williams, Precious. Write What You Know. 2007. 240p. pap. 16.99 *(978-1-58297-444-6(6)*, Writer's Digest Bks.) F&W Media, Inc.

Williams, Thomas A. How to Write a Book. 2008. 184p. per. 14.95 *(978-1-878853-76-9(7)*, Venture Pr.) Williams & Co., Publishers.

Willobee, Sondra B. The Write Stuff: Crafting Sermons That Capture & Convince. 2009. (ENG.). 128p. pap. 17.00 *(978-0-664-23281-8(7))* Westminster John Knox Pr.

Wills, Maralys. Damn the Rejections Full Speed Ahead: The Bumpy Road to Getting Published. 2008. 256p. 24.95 *(978-1-932173-92-5(7))* Stephens Pr. LLC.

Wilson, Douglas. Wordsmithy: Read until Your Brain Creaks & Other Encouragements for the Aspiring Writer. 2011. ***(978-1-59128-099-6(0))*** Canon Pr.

Wilson, Eric G. My Business Is to Create: Blake's Infinite Writing. 2011. (Muse Bks.). (ENG.). 112p. 19.95 *(978-1-58729-990-2(9))* Univ. of Iowa Pr.

Winkley, Cheryl. AUTHORSHIP AS A PEDAGOGICAL TOOL: TEACHERS' PERSPECTIVES ON AUTHORSHIP TO DEVELOP VOICE. 2008. 288p. pap. *(978-3-639-00105-1(2))* VDM Verlag Dr. Mueller e.K.

Wissner-Gross, Elizabeth. Write Your College Essay in Less Than a Day. 2009. (ENG.). 224p. pap. 15.00 *(978-0-345-51727-2(X)*, Ballantine Bks.) Random House Publishing Group.

Wittmann, Reinhard. Buchmarkt und Lektüre Im 18. und 19. Jahrhundert: Beiträge Zum Literarischen Leben, 1750-1880. (Studien und Texte zur Sozialgeschichte der Literatur Ser.). (GER., Illus.). XII, 252p. 105.00 ***(978-3-11-183418-4(2))*** De Gruyter, Walter Inc.

Wolbers, Marian Frances. Uncovering Fashion: Fashion Communications Across the Media. 2009. (Illus.). 320p. pap. 88.00 *(978-1-56367-615-4(X))* Fairchild Bks.

Wolf, Mark J. Of Words & Worlds: The Imagination & Subcreation of J. R. R. Tolkien. 2008. 256p. 16.95 *(978-1-58182-642-5(7)*, Cumberland Hse.) Sourcebooks, Inc.

Wood, Monica. Pocket Muse 2: Endless Inspiration for Writers. 2009. (ENG.). 224p. pap. 12.99 *(978-1-58297-599-3(X)*, Writer's Digest Bks.) F&W Media, Inc.

Wood, Sharon & Bigliazzi, Silvia, eds. Collaboration in the Arts from the Middle Ages to the Present. 2006. (Studies in European Cultural Transition). (Illus.). 234p. 110.00 *(978-0-7546-5512-1(1))* Ashgate Publishing Co.

Woods, Linda & Dinino, Karen. Journal Revolution: Rise up & Create! - Art Journals, Personal Manifestos & Other Artistic Insurrections. 2007. (ENG., Illus.). 128p. pap. 22.99 *(978-1-58180-995-4(6)*, North Light Bks.) F&W Media, Inc.

Woolfe, Sue. The Mystery of the Cleaning Lady: A Writer Looks at Creativity & Neuroscience. 2007. (New Writing Ser.). x, 145p. (Orig.). pap. 19.50 *(978-1-920694-96-8(X))* UWA Publishing AUS. Dist: International Specialized Bk. Services.

Wright, Sylvia. A Writer on Writing - the Building Blocks of Nonfiction. 2009. 96p. pap. 17.95 *(978-0-557-03963-0(0))* Lulu Enterprises Inc.

Writer's Digest Books Editors, ed. Writer's Digest Writing Kit. 2007. (ENG.). 144p. 24.99 *(978-1-58297-442-2(X)*, Writer's Digest Bks.) F&W Media, Inc.

Writer's Digest Books Editors & Brewer, Robert, eds. The Craft & Business of Writing: Essential Tools for Writing Success. 2008. (ENG.). 400p. 24.99 *(978-1-58297-487-3(X)*, Writer's Digest Bks.) F&W Media, Inc.

Wyatt, Jonathan, et al. Deleuze & Collaborative Writing: An Immanent Plane of Composition. 2011. (Complicated Conversation: A Book Ser. of Curriculum Studies). 146p. (C). 129.95 *(978-1-4331-1319-2(8))*; pap. 32.95 *(978-1-4331-1318-5(X)*, Lang, Peter Publishing, Inc.

Wyldeck, Kathi. How to Write an Essay. 2008. 84p. pap. 14.50 *(978-1-84799-429-5(6))* Lulu Enterprises Inc.

Yager, Fred & Yager, Jan. Career Opportunities in the Publishing Industry, Second Edition. 2nd rev. ed. 2009. (Career Opportunities Ser.). 336p. (C). (gr. 9-18). 49.50 *(978-0-8160-7542-3(5)*, Ferguson Publishing Co.) Facts On File, Inc.

Yolanda. Writing Seminar Counsel Guide: Words & Writers. 2011. 28p. pap. 16.95 ***(978-1-4560-5011-5(7))*** PublishAmerica, Inc.

Yopp, Jan Johnson, et al. Student Workbook for Reaching Audiences: A Guide to Media Writing. 5th ed. 2009. (ENG.). 96p. (C). pap. 22.40 *(978-0-205-69324-5(5))* Allyn & Bacon, Inc.

Zousmer, Steve. You Don't Have to Be Famous: How to Write Your Life Story. 2007. (ENG.). 256p. per. 16.99 *(978-1-58297-438-5(1)*, Writer's Digest Bks.) F&W Media, Inc.

AUTHORSHIP—DATA PROCESSING

Grabill, Jeffrey T. Writing Community Change: Designing Technologies for Citizen Action. 2007. (New Dimensions in Computers & Composition Ser.). (C). *(978-1-57273-762-4(X))*; pap. *(978-1-57273-763-1(8))* Hampton Pr., Inc.

Hutchings, William G. Promote Your Book in the Media. 2007. (Illus.). 80p. 129.00 net. *(978-0-9794886-1-0(3))* Mission Bay Publishing.

Kohl, John. The Global English Style Guide: Writing Clear, Translatable Documentation for a Global Market. 2008. 332p. pap. 39.95 *(978-1-59994-657-3(2)*, SAS Pr.) SAS Publishing.

Peng, Chi Yuan. Online Journal Writing. 2008. 112p. pap. *(978-3-8364-8924-9(4))* VDM Verlag Dr. Mueller e.K.

Siegel, Kevin A. Essentials of Adobe RoboHelp 6 HTML: Skills & Drills Workbook. 2007. 248p. spiral bd. 39.00 *(978-1-932733-14-3(0))* IconLogic, Inc.

Stephens, Liz & Ballast, Kerry H. Using Technology to Improve Adolescent Writing: Digital Make-Overs for Writing Lessons. 2010. (ENG.). 160p. (C) pap. 32.99 *(978-0-13-158735-9(6)*, Allyn & Bacon) Pearson Education Canada CAN. Dist: Pearson Education.

Swarts, Jason. Together with Technology: Writing Review, Enculturation, & Technological Mediation. Sides, Charles H., ed. 2007. (Technical Communication Ser.). 175p. 44.95 *(978-0-89503-362-8(3))* Baywood Publishing Co., Inc.

Walker, Janice R. & Taylor, Todd. The Columbia Guide to Online Style. 2nd ed. 2006. (ENG., Illus.). 312p. (gr. 17). 65.00 *(978-0-231-13210-7(7))*; pap. 24.00 *(978-0-231-13211-4(5))* Columbia Univ. Pr.

AUTHORSHIP—HANDBOOKS, MANUALS, ETC.

see also Manuscript Preparation (Authorship); Printing—Style Manuals

Alberts, Laurie. Showing & Telling: Learn How to Show & When to Tell for Powerful & Balanced Writing. 2010. (ENG.). 256p. pap. 16.99 *(978-1-58297-705-8(4)*, Writer's Digest Bks.) F&W Media, Inc.

Alderson, Martha. Blockbuster Plots Scene Tracker Kit: Seven Ways to Build Better Scenes Today! 2007. 45.00 *(978-0-9790596-0-5(7))* Illusion Pr.

Allison, Libby & Williams, Miriam F. Writing for the Government. 2007. (Technical Communication Ser.). (ENG., Illus.). 320p. (C). pap. 76.00 *(978-0-321-42701-4(7))* Longman Publishing Group.

Amberg, Jay. The Creative Writing Handbook. 2008. (Orig.). pap. 13.50 *(978-1-59647-276-1(6))* Good Year Bks.

American Writers. 20th rev. ed. 2010. (American Writers Ser.). (ENG.). suppl. ed. 218.00 *(978-1-4144-3892-4(3))* Cengage Gale.

Anker, Susan. Real Writing Learning Journal. Date not set. pap. *(978-0-312-18005-8(5))* St. Martin's Pr.

Ballon, Rachel. The Writer's Portable Therapist: 25 Sessions to a Creativity Cure. 2006. (ENG.). 304p. per. 12.95 *(978-1-59337-544-7(1))* Adams Media Corp.

Bingham, Harry. The Writers & Artists Guide to How to Write. 2012. (ENG.). 288p. (C). pap. 22.95 ***(978-1-4081-5717-6(9)***, Methuen Drama) A & C Black GBR. Dist: Macmillan.

Bockman, Jeffrey/A. Give Your Family A Gift That Money Can't Buy: Record & Preserve Your Family's History. 4th ed. 2007. (Illus.). 64p. per. 7.95 *(978-0-9796173-0-0(8))* Alenjes Publishing.

Bournis, John, et al. Style Manual for Communication Studies. 3rd ed. 2008. (ENG.). 168p. (C). pap. 40.33 *(978-0-07-338505-1(0)*, 0073385050) McGraw-Hill Cos., The.

Budewitz, Leslie. Books, Crooks & Counselors: How to Write Accurately about Criminal Law & Courtroom Procedure. 2011. (ENG.). 200p. pap. 14.95 *(978-1-61035-019-8(7))* Linden Publishing Co., Inc.

Caliguire, Jeff & Caliguire, Mindy. Write for Your Soul: The Whys & Hows of Journaling. 2006. 24p. 4.99 *(978-1-929794-56-0(8))* Soul Care.

Camenson, Blythe. Careers in Writing. 2nd ed. 2007. (ENG.). 192p. per. 16.95 *(978-0-07-148212-7(1)*, 0071482121) McGraw-Hill Cos., The.

Cameron, Julia. The Writing Diet: Write Yourself Right-Size. 2007. (ENG.). 256p. (gr. 12-18). 19.95 *(978-1-58542-571-6(0)*, Tarcher) Penguin Group (USA) Inc.

Chisholm, Alison, et al. How to Write about Yourself. rev. ed. 2007. 208p. pap. 15.95 *(978-0-7490-0367-8(7))* Allison & Busby, Ltd. GBR. Dist: International Publishers Marketing.

Clement, Shirley. The Writer's Organizer: Plans, Procedures & Forms for Productivity & Profitability. Date not set. 176p. pap. 14.95 *(978-0-9637498-8-8(9))* Toad Hall, Inc.

Coleman-Grider, Angelee. This Is My Will: How to Write Your Own Obiographical Sketches (Your Own Obituaries) 2007. (ENG.). 96p. per. 9.95 *(978-0-9801647-7-0(X))* M.O.R.E. Pubs.

Cross, Laura. The Complete Guide to Hiring a Literary Agent: Everything You Need to Know to Become Successfully Published. 2010. (ENG.). 288p. pap. 24.95 *(978-1-60138-403-4(3))* Atlantic Publishing Co.

Davis, Joe, et al. Research for Writers: Advanced English Composition. rev. ed. 2010. (ENG.). 226p. pap. 75.86 *(978-0-7575-0987-2(8))* Kendall Hunt Publishing Co.

Doland, Michelle, et al, eds. American Directory of Writer's Guidelines: More Than 1,700 Magazine Editors & Book Publishers Explain What They Are Looking for from Freelancers. 6th ed. 2006. (American Directory of Writer's Guidelines Ser.). (ENG., Illus.). 816p. pap. 29.95 *(978-1-884956-58-4(0))* Quill Driver Bks.

Dunne, Will. The Dramatic Writer's Companion: Tools to Develop Characters, Cause Scenes, & Build Stories. 2009. (Chicago Guides to Writing, Editing, & Publishing Ser.). (ENG.). 346p. 45.00 *(978-0-226-17253-8(8))*; 352p. pap. 19.00 *(978-0-226-17254-5(6))* Univ. of Chicago Pr.

Elicksen, Debbie. Book Publishing 101: Workbook. 2nd ed. 2010. 20.00 *(978-0-9865956-1-5(6))* Booklocker.com, Inc.

Fisher, Jim, ed. The Writer's Quotebook: 500 Authors on Creativity, Craft, & the Writing Life. 2006. (ENG.). 256p. 22.95 *(978-0-8135-3882-2(3))* Rutgers Univ. Pr.

Gibaldi, Joseph. MLA Handbook for Writers of Research Papers. 6th Lt. ed. 2006. (Illus.). 361p. pap. 20.00 *(978-0-87352-987-7(1)*, S178L) Modern Language Assn. of America.

Gibaldi, Joseph & Modern Language Association of America Staff. MLA Handbook for Writers of Research Papers. 7th ed. 2009. (ENG., Illus.). xxi, 292p. pap. 22.00 *(978-1-60329-024-1(9))*; pap. 30.00 *(978-1-60329-025-8(7))* Modern Language Assn. of America.

Goldberg, Natalie. Writing down the Bones: Freeing the Writer Within. 2010. (Shambhala Library). (ENG.). 288p. 18.95 *(978-1-59030-794-6(1))* Shambhala Pubns., Inc.

Gregory, Joe & Jenkins, Debbie. The Wealthy Author. 2009. (Illus.). 212p. *(978-1-905430-69-7(8)*, Publishing Academy) Lean Marketing Pr.

Hairston, et al. The Scott, Foresman Handbook for Writers. 5th ed. 18.00 *(978-0-321-02718-4(3))* Addison-Wesley Educational Pubs., Inc.

A Handbook for Authors. pap. 4.95 *(978-0-8078-4573-8(6))* Univ. of North Carolina Pr.

Iverson, Cheryl, et al, eds. AMA Manual of Style: A Guide for Authors & Editors. 10th rev. ed. 2007. (ENG., Illus.). 1032p. 59.95 *(978-0-19-517633-9(2))* Oxford Univ. Pr., Inc.

Jagoe, Armiger. You Are Next in Line: Everyone's Guide for Writing Your Autobiography. 2007. (Capital Careers & Personal Development Ser.). 132p. per. 12.95 *(978-1-933102-60-3(8))* Capital Bks., Inc.

JAMA and Archives Journals. AMA Manual of Style: A Guide for Authors & Editors: Special Online Bundle Package. 10th ed. 2009. (ENG.). 1032p. 99.00 *(978-0-19-539203-6(5))* Oxford Univ. Pr., Inc.

Jordan, Louise. How to Write for Children & Get Published. 2010. (ENG., Illus.). 192p. pap. 15.95 *(978-0-7499-4061-4(1))* Piatkus Bks. GBR. Dist: Independent Pubs. Group.

Jua, Roselyne M. & Besong, Bate. To the Budding Creative Writer: A Handbook. 2009. 140p. pap. *(978-9956-558-93-3(1))* Langaa Research & Publishing Common Initiative Group CMR. Dist: Michigan State Univ. Pr.

Katz, Christina. The Writer's Workout: 366 Tips, Tasks, & Techniques from Your Writing Career Coach. 2011. (ENG.). 384p. pap. 19.99 *(978-1-59963-179-0(2)*, Writer's Digest Bks.) F&W Media, Inc.

Kennedy, Dorothy M., et al. The Bedford Guide for College Writers: With Reader & Research Manual. 8th ed. 2007. (ENG., Illus.). 784p. (C). per. 74.95 *(978-0-312-46930-6(6))* Bedford/Saint Martin's.

Kerr, Cherie. Build to Laugh: How to Construct Sketch Comedy with the Fast & Funny Formula. Date not set. 158p. pap. 14.95 *(978-0-9648882-2-7(X))* ExecuProv.

Kessler, Lauren & McDonald, Duncan. Cengage Advantage Books: When Words Collide (with Student Workbook) 8th ed. 2011. (ENG.). 456p. (C). spiral bd. 119.95 (978-0-495-90144-0(X)) Wadsworth.

Kilian, Crawford. Writing Science Fiction & Fantasy. 2nd rev. ed. 2007. (Writing Ser.). (ENG., Illus.). 192p. pap. 16.95 incl. cd-rom (978-1-55180-785-0(8)) Self-Counsel Pr., Inc. CAN. Dist: National Bk. Network.

Klickmann, Flora. The Lure of the Pen. 2009. 186p. pap. (978-0-217-80206-2(0)) Books LLC.

Kohl, John. The Global English Style Guide: Writing Clear, Translatable Documentation for a Global Market. 2008. 332p. pap. 39.95 (978-1-59994-657-3(2), SAS Pr.) SAS Publishing.

Lamagna, Joseph. Write Right: Not Almost Right. (Illus.). 48p. (Orig.). pap. 10.00 (978-0-9610464-3-9(0)) Lamagna, Joseph.

Ledoux, Denis. The Photo Scribe: A Writing Guide: How to Write the Stories Behind Your Photographs. 3rd ed. 2008. (Illus.). 127p. pap. 19.95 (978-0-9742773-1-8(2)) Soleil Pr.

Leggett, Glenn H., et al. Prentice-Hall Handbook for Writers. 10th ed. Date not set. (978-0-13-695728-7(5)) Prentice Hall PTR.

Lobato, et al. Saber Escribir. (SPA., Illus.). 513p. (978-84-03-09723-0(9)) Aguilar, S. A. de Ediciones-Grupo Santillana.

Long, Priscilla. The Writer's Portable Mentor: A Guide to Art, Craft, & the Writing Life. 2010. 349p. pap. 17.95 (978-0-9842421-0-8(4)) Wallingford Pr.

Lord, Udis. Self-Publishing. (978-0-937571-03-3(2)) Philippine-American Educational Pr.

Lunsford, Andrea A. The Everyday Writer. 4th ed. 2008. (ENG.). 592p. (C). spiral bd. 64.95 (978-0-312-48859-8(9)) Bedford/Saint Martin's.

—Exercise Central to Go for Handbooks by Andrea A. Lunsford. 6th ed. 2007. (ENG.). (C). cd-rom 9.95 (978-0-312-43114-3(7)) Bedford/Saint Martin's.

Lunsford, Ronald F. & Bridges, Bill. The Longwood Guide to Writing. 4th ed. 2007. (Pearson English Value Textbook Ser.). (ENG.). 736p. (C). per. 63.60 (978-0-205-55376-1(1)) Longman Publishing Group.

Mace, Lorraine & Vincent-Northam, Maureen. The Writer's ABC Checklist. 2010. (ENG.). 242p. pap. 14.95 **(978-1-907016-19-6(8))** Accent Pr. Ltd. GBR. Dist: SCB Distributors.

Manual of Style. 670p. 41.95 (978-0-89970-434-0(4), OP290098BHT) American Medical Assn.

Martin, Philip, ed. The New Writer's Handbook Vol. 2: A Practical Anthology of Best Advice for Your Craft & Career. 2008. (ENG.). 280p. pap. 16.95 (978-0-9798249-2-0(3)) Scarletta Pr.

—The New Writer's Handbook 2007: A Practical Anthology of Best Advice for Your Craft & Career. 2007. (ENG.). 288p. per. 16.95 (978-0-9765201-6-0(8)) Scarletta Pr.

McIndoo, Ann. So, You Want to Write! How to Get Your Book Out of Your Head & onto the Paper in 7 Days. 2007. (ENG., Illus.). 143p. per. 13.99 (978-1-60194-003-2(3), Elevate) Advantage Media Group.

McNally, John. The Creative Writer's Survival Guide: Advice from an Unrepentant Novelist. 2010. 272p. pap. 19.95 (978-1-58729-920-9(8)) Univ. of Iowa Pr.

Mendelsohn. Real Writing: Intermediate/Advanced. pap. 18.95 (978-1-56270-008-9(1)) Globe Fearon Educational Publishing.

Miller, Robert. The Writer's Harbrace Handbook. pap. 51.95 (978-0-8384-7309-2(1)) Cengage Heinle.

Miller, Robert Keith. The Writer's Harbrace Handbook. pap. 62.95 (978-0-8384-8047-2(0)); pap. 55.95 (978-0-8384-9901-6(5)); pap. 75.95 (978-0-8384-9584-1(2)); pap. 60.95 (978-0-8384-9249-9(5)); pap. 83.95 (978-0-8384-9196-6(0)); pap. 78.95 (978-0-8384-8927-7(3)); pap. 50.95 (978-0-8384-8909-3(5)); pap. 56.95 (978-0-8384-7906-3(5)); pap. 48.95 (978-0-8384-7588-1(4)); pap. 50.95 (978-0-8384-7587-4(6)); 4th ed. pap. 47.95 (978-0-8384-7487-7(X)) Cengage Heinle.

Myers, Judith Gillespie. Plain Language in Government Writing: A Step-By-Step Guide. 2008. (Illus.). xxiv, 430p. (978-1-56726-224-7(4)) Management Concepts, Inc.

Novakovich, Josip. Fiction Writer's Workshop: The Key Elements of a Writing Workshop - Clear Instruction, Illustrated by Contemporary & Classic Works,Innovative Exercises & Methods to Guage Your Progress. 2nd rev. ed. 2008. (ENG.). 368p. pap. 16.99 (978-1-58297-536-8(1), Writer's Digest Bks.) F&W Media, Inc.

Page, David W. Body Trauma: A Writer's Guide to Wounds & Injuries. 2nd rev. ed. 2006. (Get It Write Ser.). (ENG., Illus.). 254p. per. 17.95 (978-1-933016-41-2(8)) Behler Pubns., LLC.

Perrin, Robert. Pocket Guide to APA Style. 3rd ed. 2008. (ENG.). 176p. (C). pap. 34.95 (978-0-547-20193-1(1)) Wadsworth.

Polti, Georges. The Thirty-Six Dramatic Situations. 2010. 202p. pap. 24.75 (978-1-141-56543-6(9)); 204p. pap. 24.75 (978-1-141-42950-9(0)) BiblioBazaar.

—The Thirty-Six Dramatic Situations. 2007. pap. 12.99 (978-1-59986-806-6(7), FQ Classics) Filiquarian Publishing, LLC.

—The Thirty-Six Dramatic Situations. 2009. 90p. pap. 13.90 (978-1-151-45190-3(8)) General Bks. LLC.

Polti, Georges & Ray, Lucile. The Thirty-Six Dramatic Situations. 2010. (ENG.). 186p. pap. 22.75 (978-1-177-03387-9(9)) BiblioBazaar.

Polti, Georges & Ray, Lucille. The Thirty-Six Dramatic Situations. 2010. 204p. pap. 24.75 (978-1-177-69729-3(7)) BiblioBazaar.

Pringle, Mike & Gonzales, John. The MLA Style of Documentation. 2009. (English MLA Updated Books Ser.). (ENG.). 72p. (C). pap. 15.20 (978-0-13-604973-9(7), Prentice Hall) Prentice Hall PTR.

Reid, Stephen. The Prentice Hall Guide for College Writers. 9th ed. 2010. (ENG.). 768p. (C). 99.33 (978-0-205-75116-7(4)) Longman Publishing Group.

Reinking. Strategies for Successful Writing. 7th ed. 752p. tchr. ed. 18.97 (978-0-13-189570-6(2)); tchr. ed. 51.97 (978-0-13-189532-4(X)) Prentice Hall (Schl. Div.).

Resnick, Laura. Rejection, Romance & Royalties: The Wacky World of a Working Writer. 2007. (ENG.). 306p. per. 16.95 (978-0-9778086-4-9(5)) Jefferson Pr.

Riley, Christopher. The Hollywood Standard: The Complete & Authoritative Guide to Script Format & Style. 2nd ed. 2009. (Hollywood Standard: the Complete & Authoritative Guide To Ser.). (ENG.). 208p. pap. 24.95 (978-1-932907-63-6(7)) Wiese, Michael Productions.

Roach Smith, Marion. The Memoir Project: A Thoroughly Non-Standardized Text for Writing & Life. 2011. (ENG.). 128p. pap., pap. 12.00 (978-0-446-58484-5(3)) Grand Central Publishing.

Rosenwasse. Writing Analytically. 3rd ed. pap. 18.95 (978-0-8384-7971-1(5)) Cengage Heinle.

Rutledge, Patrice-Anne. The Web-Savvy Writer: Book Promotion with a High-Tech Twist. 2006. 248p. per. 19.95 (978-0-9778304-0-4(3)) Pacific Ridge.

Schwartz, Linda Smoak. The Wadsworth Guide to MLA Documentation. 3rd ed. 2012. (ENG.). (C). spiral bd. 25.95 (978-1-4282-6344-4(6)) CENGAGE Learning.

A Set of Writer Helps. (Writer Helps Ser.). 5.35 (978-0-7399-0245-5(8), 2515) Rod & Staff Pubs., Inc.

Silk, Bobbie B., ed. The Writing Center Resource Manual. 2nd rev. ed. Date not set. 264p. ring bd. 15.00 (978-0-9648067-2-6(X)) IWCA Pr.

Stevenson, Robert Louis. The Art of Writing. 2008. 100p. pap. 9.95 (978-1-60096-408-4(7)); pap. 9.95 (978-1-60096-718-4(3)) Editorium, The.

Thompson, Roy, et al. Grammar of the Edit. 2nd ed. 2009. (ENG., Illus.). 224p. pap. 22.95 (978-0-240-52120-6(X), Focal Pr.) Elsevier Science & Technology Bks.

Turner, Barry. The Screenwriter's Handbook 2010. 3rd rev. ed. 2009. (ENG.). 352p. pap. 30.00 (978-0-230-57327-7(4)) Palgrave Macmillan.

Uddin, Moyna. Write Publish Sell Your Book. 2010. 104p. pap. 12.00 (978-0-9774647-9-1(2)) 3-QUEENS Pubns.

Underdown, Harold D. Publishing Children's Books - Complete Idiot's Guide. 3rd ed. 2008. (Complete Idiot's Guide Ser.). (ENG., Illus.). 384p. (gr. 12-18). 18.95 (978-1-59257-750-7(4), Alpha Bks.) Penguin Group (USA) Inc.

Vizetelly, Frank H. The Preparation of Manuscripts for the Printer. 2008. 160p. 22.99 (978-0-559-17458-2(6)); pap. 20.75 (978-0-559-17456-8(X)) BiblioBazaar.

—The Preparation of Manuscripts for the Printer. 2009. 108p. pap. (978-1-4589-0252-8(8)) Books LLC.

Wiebe, Katie Funk. How to Write Your Personal or Family History: If You Don't Do It, Who Will?, 1 vol. 2009. (ENG.). 165p. pap. 11.95 (978-1-56148-665-6(5)) Good Bks.

Winkle, Suellyn & Kress, Anne. NextText: Making Connections Across & Beyond the Disciplines. 2007. (ENG.). 624p. (C). pap. 62.95 (978-0-312-40106-1(X)) Bedford/Saint Martin's.

Wyrick, Jean. Steps to Writing Well. 8th ed. pap. 71.95 (978-0-8384-8523-1(5)); pap. 47.95 (978-0-8384-7484-6(5)); pap. 49.95 (978-0-8384-7826-4(3)); pap. 70.95 (978-0-8384-8230-8(9)); pap. 55.95 (978-0-8384-7361-0(X)); pap. 71.95 (978-0-8384-8015-1(2)) Cengage Heinle.

AUTHORSHIP—MARKETING

Adriel, Jessica. Forgiving Sean. 2009. 208p. pap. 12.95 (978-0-9707262-9-2(5)) ESH Media Group.

Alexander, Kwame. Do the Write Thing: Seven Steps to Publishing Success. 2nd ed. 2011. (ENG.). 208p. pap. 16.95 (978-0-9748142-5-4(3)) Nunes Productions,Ny Words Pr.

Allen, Moira. The Writer's Guide to Queries, Pitches & Proposals, Second Edition. 2nd ed. 2010. (ENG.). 288p. pap. 19.95 (978-1-58115-743-7(6), 115743, Allworth Pr.) Skyhorse Publishing Co., Inc.

Arend, Marsha Haigh. From Brainstorm to Best Seller: A Step-by-Step Guide to Writing & Publishing Your First Book. 2008. (ENG.). 84p. per. 9.95 (978-0-9743176-2-5(4)) Rollaway Bay Pubns., Inc.

Atlantic Publishing Group. How to Make a Living Writing Articles for Newspapers, Magazines, & Online Sources: Everything Your Need to Know to Become a Successful Freelance Writer in 30 Days. 2012. (ENG.). 288p. pap. 24.95 (978-1-60138-567-3(6)) Atlantic Publishing Co.

Balzer, Paula. Writing & Selling Your Memoir: How to Craft Your Life Story So That Somebody Else Will Actually Want to Read It. 2011. (ENG., Illus.). 240p. pap. 17.99 (978-1-59963-135-6(0), Writer's Digest Bks.) F&W Media, Inc.

Barry, Sam & Goldmark, Kathi Kamen. The Write That Book Already! The Tough Love You Need to Get Published Now. 2010. (ENG.). 240p. pap. 14.95 (978-1-60550-147-5(6)) Adams Media Corp.

Baverstock, Alison. Marketing Your Book: an Author's Guide: How to Target Agents, Publishers & Readers. 2nd ed. 2007. (ENG., Illus.). 256p. per. 18.95 (978-0-7136-7383-8(4), Methuen Drama) A & C Black GBR. Dist: Macmillan.

Bird, Tom. You Were Born to Be... Published: The Eleven Laws Sure to Lead to Your Success. 2006. 260p. 29.00 (978-0-9707258-6-8(8)) Sojourn, Inc.

Blizzard, Kristin. SecretsTo Publishing & Marketing Your Book. 2008. 94p. pap. 10.99 (978-0-557-01203-9(1)) Lulu Enterprises Inc.

Bly, Robert. 88 Money-Making Writing Jobs. 2009. (ENG.). 336p. pap. 20.99 (978-1-4022-1507-0(X)) Sourcebooks, Inc.

Bly, Robert W. How to Write & Sell Simple Information for Fun & Profit: Your Guide to Writing & Publishing Books, E-Books, Articles, Special Reports, Audio Programs, DVDs, & Other How-to Content. 2010. (ENG.). 252p. pap. 15.95 (978-1-884995-60-6(8)) Linden Publishing Co., Inc.

Bowerman, Peter. The Well-Fed Self-Publisher: How to Turn One Book into a Full-Time Living. 2006. 294p. per. 19.95 (978-0-9670598-6-0(0)) Fanove Publishing.

Brewer, Robert Lee. 2010 Writer's Market Deluxe. 9th ed. 2009. (ENG.). 1176p. pap. 49.99 (978-1-58297-580-1(9), Writer's Digest Bks.) F&W Media, Inc.

Bromley, Karen D'Angelo. Writing for Educators: Personal Essays & Practical Advice (HC) Bromley, Karen, ed. 2009. 256p. (978-1-60752-104-4(0)) Information Age Publishing, Inc.

—Writing for Educators: Personal Essays & Practical Advice (PB) Bromley, Karen, ed. 2009. 256p. pap. (978-1-60752-103-7(2)) Information Age Publishing, Inc.

Burt, Wendy & Burt-Thomas, Wendy. The Writer's Digest Guide to Query Letters. 2009. (ENG.). 240p. pap. 14.99 (978-1-58297-566-5(3), Writer's Digest Bks.) F&W Media, Inc.

Bykofsky, Sheree & Sander, Jennifer Basye. The Complete Idiot's Guide to Getting Published, 5E. 2011. (Complete Idiot's Guide Ser.). (ENG.). 400p. (gr. 12). 19.95 (978-1-61564-127-7(0), Alpha Bks.) Penguin Group (USA) Inc.

Camenson, Blythe. Careers in Writing. 2nd ed. 2007. (ENG.). 192p. per. 16.95 (978-0-07-148212-7(1), 0071482121) McGraw-Hill Cos., The.

Carter, Susan M., ed. Writer Profits: 15 Writers Tell How They Get Paying Gigs — & How You Can, Too! 2007. per. 14.95 (978-0-9670291-7-7(1)) Nasus Publishing.

Chandler, eng & Chandler, Stephanie. The Author's Guide to Building an Online Platform: Leveraging the Internet to Sell More Books. 2008. (ENG.). 160p. pap. 14.95 (978-1-884956-82-9(3)) Quill Driver Bks.

Chillemi, Stacey. Learn How to Become Wealthy Selling Ebooks. 2010. 271p. pap. 25.95 (978-0-557-37491-5(X)) Lulu Enterprises Inc.

Christensen, Bobbie. Writing, Publishing & Marketing Your 1st Book (or 7th) 2007. 80p. pap. 15.95 (978-0-9729173-4-6(9)) Effective Living Publishing.

Craig, Christie & Hughes, Faye. The Everything Guide to Writing a Romance Novel: From Writing the Perfect Love Scene to Finding the Right Publisher - All You Need to Fulfill Your Dreams. 2008. (ENG., Illus.). 320p. pap. 15.95 (978-1-59869-537-3(1)) Adams Media Corp.

Crook, Marion. Writing Books for Children & Young Adults. 2nd ed. 2007. (ENG., Illus.). 208p. pap. 18.95 (978-1-55180-813-0(7)) Self-Counsel Pr., Inc. CAN. Dist: Midpoint Trade Bks., Inc.

Cross, Laura. The Complete Guide to Hiring a Literary Agent: Everything You Need to Know to Become Successfully Published. 2010. (ENG.). 288p. pap. 24.95 (978-1-60138-403-4(3)) Atlantic Publishing Co.

Day, Abby. How to Get Research Published in Journals: Second Edition. 2nd rev. ed. 2008. (Illus.). 154p. pap. 49.95 (978-0-566-08815-5(0), Gower Publishing Co., Ltd.) Ashgate Publishing, Ltd. GBR. Dist: Ashgate Publishing Co.

Deahl, James, ed. Poetry Markets for Canadians. 6th ed. 240p. pap. 15.95 (978-1-55128-030-1(2)) Mercury Bks. CAN. Dist: LPC/InBook.

Dean, Irvine & Irvine, Dean. Editing Modernity: Women & Little Magazine Cultures in Canada, 1916-1956. 2008. (Studies in Book & Print Culture Ser.). (ENG.). 304p. (978-0-8020-9271-7(3)) Univ. of Toronto Pr.

Denbow, Carol. A Book Inside: How to Write, Publish, & Sell Your Story. 2008. 104p. pap. 18.95 (978-0-615-19924-5(0)) Plain & Simple Bks.

Deval, Jacqueline. Publicize Your Book: An Insider's Guide to Getting Your Book the Attention It Deserves. rev. ed. 2008. (ENG.). 320p. (gr. 12-18). 18.00 (978-0-399-53431-7(8), Perigee Trade) Penguin Group (USA) Inc.

Dietzel, Glenn. Author & Grow Rich: How to Author a Book in 12 Hours of Actual Writing Time. 2007. (ENG.). 26.95 (978-1-60037-294-0(5)) Morgan James Publishing.

—Author & Grow Rich: How to Write a Money-Making Book in Only 12 Hours! 2007. (ENG., Illus.). 264p. per. 16.95 (978-1-60037-293-3(7)) Morgan James Publishing.

Dilks, Stephen. Samuel Beckett in the Literary Marketplace. 2011. (Illus.). 400p. (978-0-8156-3254-2(1)) Syracuse Univ. Pr.

Dubino, Jeanne. Virginia Woolf & the Literary Marketplace. Dubino, Jeanne, ed. 2010. (ENG., Illus.). 282p. 84.00 (978-0-230-10706-9(0)) Palgrave Macmillan.

Edwards, Jim & Vitale, Joe. How to Write & Publish Your Own eBook in as Little as 7 Days: How to Write & Publish Your Own Outrageously Profitable eBook in as Little 7 Days Even If You Can't Write, Can't Type & Failed High School English Class! 2007. (ENG.). per. 19.95 (978-1-60037-152-3(3)) Morgan James Publishing.

Embree, Mary. The Author's Toolkit, Third Edition. 3rd ed. 2010. (ENG.). 224p. pap. 19.95 (978-1-58115-747-5(9), 115747, Allworth Pr.) Skyhorse Publishing Co., Inc.

Erickson, Beth Ann. Filbert's Fast Guide to Getting Published: Without Falling for Scams, Hooks, Lines, & Sinkers. 2006. per. 19.95 (978-1-932794-13-7(1)) Filbert Publishing.

Faust, Jessica, et al. The Complete Idiot's Guide to Book Proposals & Query Letters. 2011. (Complete Idiot's Guide Ser.). (ENG.). 320p. (gr. 12). 16.95 (978-1-61564-045-4(2), Alpha Bks.) Penguin Group (USA) Inc.

Fawcett, Shaun. Instant Book Writing Kit: How to Write, Publish & Market Your Own Money-Making Book (or EBook) Online. 2008. (978-0-9781700-8-0(3)) Final Draft Pubns.

Fry, Patricia. Promote Your Book: Over 250 Proven, Low-Cost Tips & Techniques for the Enterprising Author. 2011. (ENG.). 224p. pap. 19.95 (978-1-58115-857-1(2), 115857, Allworth Pr.) Skyhorse Publishing Co., Inc.

Fry, Patricia. Publish Your Book: Proven Strategies & Resources for the Enterprising Authors. 2012. (ENG.). 256p. pap. 19.95 **(978-1-58115-884-7(X)**, 115884, Allworth Pr.) Skyhorse Publishing Co., Inc.

Fry, Patricia L. The Right Way to Write, Publish & Sell Your Book: Your Guide to Successful Authorship. 2007. 362p. pap. 19.95 (978-0-9773576-2-8(7)) Matilija Pr.

Germano, William P. Getting It Published: A Guide for Scholars & Anyone Else Serious about Serious Books. 2nd ed. 2008. (Chicago Guides to Writing, Editing, & Publishing Ser.). 232p. 48.00 (978-0-226-28852-9(8)); 224p. pap. 19.00 (978-0-226-28853-6(6)) Univ. of Chicago Pr.

Gillies, Mary Ann. The Professional Literary Agent in Britain, 1880-1920: Women & Little Magazine Cultures in Canada, 1916-1956. 2007. (Studies in Book & Print Culture Ser.). (ENG.). 304p. (978-0-8020-9147-5(4)) Univ. of Toronto Pr.

Gladon, Richard J., et al. Getting Published in the Life Sciences. 2011. (ENG.). 368p. pap. 29.95 (978-1-118-01716-6(1), Wiley-Blackwell) Wiley, John & Sons, Inc.

Glynn, Sal. The Dog Walked down the Street: An Outspoken Guide for Writers Who Want to Publish. 2006. 81p. per. 13.95 (978-1-879384-66-8(3)) Cypress Hse.

Gore, Ariel. How to Become a Famous Writer Before You're Dead: Your Words in Print & Your Name in Lights. 2007. (ENG.). 288p. per. 14.99 (978-0-307-34648-3(X), Three Rivers Pr.) Crown Publishing Group.

Graham Scott, Gini. Sell Your Book, Script or Column: How to Write a Winning Query & Make a Winning Pitch. 2007. 92p. per. 9.95 (978-0-595-45009-1(1), ASJA Pr.) iUniverse, Inc.

Green, George & Kremer, Lizzy. Writing a Novel & Getting Published for Dummies(r). 2007. (ENG., Illus.). 314p. pap. 27.99 **(978-0-470-05910-4(9)**, For Dummies) Wiley, John & Sons, Inc.

Haley, Adria, ed. 2012 Novel & Short Story Writer's Market. 31st ed. 2011. (ENG.). 656p. pap. 29.99 (978-1-59963-228-5(4), Writer's Digest Bks.) F&W Media, Inc.

Hammett, Kelly. Glass Marbles for Aspiring Authors: How to Become an Author for Non-Fiction & Poetry. 2007. 150p. 19.99 (978-0-9790539-0-0(0), 1000) Hammett, Kelly Publishing.

—Kelly Hammett in Motion with Her Poetry. 2007. (Illus.). 127p. 19.99 (978-0-9790539-3-1(5)) Hammett, Kelly Publishing.

—Kelly Hammett in Motion with Her Poetry - Limited Edition, 2. 2007. (Illus.). 129p. 24.99 (978-0-9790539-1-7(9), 500) Hammett, Kelly Publishing.

Handel, Sherry S. Teens Get Published. 2008. (YA). per. 14.95 (978-0-9706609-2-3(8)) Blue Jean Pr.

Hartmann, Jonathan. The Marketing of Edgar Allan Poe. 2012. (Studies in American Popular History & Culture Ser.). (ENG.). 142p. pap. 42.95 **(978-0-415-54319-4(3))** Routledge.

Herman, Jeff. Jeff Herman's Guide to Book Publishers, Editors, & Literary Agents 2011, 21E: Who They Are! What They Want! How to Win Them Over! 21st ed. 2010. (ENG.). 1104p. pap. 29.99 (978-1-4022-4337-0(5)) Sourcebooks, Inc.

Hochman, Joel & Leichman, Larry. Bestseller Marketing: A 'Soup to Nuts' Guide to Book Promotion (2007 Edition) 2007. pap. 9.95 (978-0-9790469-5-7(5)) Arbor Bks.

—Ghostwriting: The Ultimate Guide to Creating a Bestseller (2007 Edition) 2007. pap. 9.95 (978-0-9790469-4-0(7)) Arbor Bks.

—Self-Publishing: A 'Soup to Nuts' Guide to Producing a Bestseller (2007 Edition) 2007. pap. 9.95 (978-0-9790469-3-3(9)) Arbor Bks.

Hollars, B. J. You Must Be This Tall to Ride: Contemporary Writers Take You Inside the Story. 2009. (ENG.). 304p. pap. 17.99 (978-1-58297-574-0(4), Writer's Digest Bks.) F&W Media, Inc.

Horowitz, Shel. Grassroots Marketing for Authors & Publishers. 2007. 290p. pap. 24.95 (978-0-9614666-3-3(4), AWM) Accurate Writing & More.

—Grassroots Marketing for Authors & Publishers. 2007. 290p. pap. 24.95 (978-0-7414-3469-2(5)) Infinity Publishing.

Howick, E. Keith, Jr. Blow Us Away! Publishers' Secrets for Successful Manuscripts. 2010. (ENG.). 173p. pap. 16.95 (978-1-886249-39-4(3)) WindRiver Publishing, Inc.

Hutchings, William G. Promote Your Book in the Media. 2007. (Illus.). 80p. 129.00 net. (978-0-9794886-1-0(3)) Mission Bay Publishing.

Jaffe, Aaron. Modernism & the Culture of Celebrity. 2009. (ENG., Illus.). 264p. pap. 38.99 (978-0-521-12379-2(8)) Cambridge Univ. Pr.

James Enger, Kelly. Writer for Hire: 101 Secrets to Freelance Success. 2012. (ENG.). 224p. pap. 16.99 **(978-1-59963-549-1(6)**, Writer's Digest Bks.) F&W Media, Inc.

Jewell, Darin. How to Sell & Market Your Book: A Step-by-Step Guide, 1 vol. 2011. (ENG.). 132p. pap. 12.99 (978-1-907756-39-9(6)) Legend Pr. GBR. Dist: Innovative Logistics.

Jordan, Louise. How to Write for Children & Get Published. 2010. (ENG., Illus.). 192p. pap. 15.95 (978-0-7499-4061-4(1)) Piatkus Bks. GBR. Dist: Independent Pubs. Group.

Kahan, Jeffrey. Getting Published in the Humanities: What to Know, Where to Aim, How to Succeed. 2011. (ENG.). 206p. pap. 40.00 (978-0-7864-5923-0(9)) McFarland & Co., Inc. Pubs.

Karaplis, Joanna, ed. The Canadian Writer's Market, 18th Edition. 2010. (ENG.). 464p. pap. 23.95 (978-0-7710-9585-6(6), McClelland & Stewart) McClelland & Stewart CAN. Dist: Random Hse., Inc.

Katz, Christina. Get Known Before the Book Deal: Use Your Personal Strengths to Grow an Author Platform. 2008. (ENG.). 272p. pap. 16.99 (978-1-58297-554-2(X), Writer's Digest Bks.) F&W Media, Inc.

Kaye, Thomas. Learn How to Write Books That You Will Be Proud to Sell. 2008. 180p. pap. 33.95 (978-1-4092-3491-3(6)) Lulu Enterprises Inc.

Kelby, N. M. The Constant Art of Being a Writer: The Life, Art & Business of Fiction. 2009. (ENG.). 256p. pap. 17.99 (978-1-58297-575-7(2), Writer's Digest Bks.) F&W Media, Inc.

The check digit for ISBN-10 appears in parentheses after the full ISBN-13

Kendall-Tackett, Kathleen A. How to Write for a Genera Audience: A Guide for Academics Who Want to Share Their Knowledge with the World & Have Fun Doing It. 2007. 286p. per. 19.95 *(978-0-9792125-3-6(7))* American Psychological Assn.
Kilian, Crawford. Sell Your Nonfiction Book. 2010. (Writing Ser.). (ENG.). 184p. pap. 17.95 *(978-1-55180-853-6(6))* Self-Counsel Pr., Inc. CAN. Dist: Midpoint Trade Bks., Inc.
King, Sophie. How to Write Short Stories Magazi. 2009. x, 197p. 20.00 *(978-1-84528-280-6(9))* How To Books GBR. Dist: Parkwest Pubns., Inc.
Landenheim-Gil, Randy. The Everything Guide to Getting Published: Expert advice for building a successful writing Career. 3rd ed. 2012. (ENG.). 304p. pap. 16.95 ***(978-1-4405-2844-6(6))*** Adams Media Corp.
Lapworth, Katherine. Get Your Book Published: A Teach Yourself Guide. 2010. (Teach Yourself: Reference Ser.). (ENG.). 224p. pap. 15.00 *(978-0-07-174853-7(9),* 0071748539) McGraw-Hill Cos., The.
Larsen, Michael. How to Write a Book Proposal. 4th ed. 2011. (ENG.). 336p. pap. 19.99 *(978-1-58297-702-7(X),* Writer's Digest Bks.) F&W Media, Inc.
Lavid, Linda. Composition: A fiction writer's guide for the 21st Century. 2007. 108p. per. 10.95 *(978-1-59330-476-8(5))* Aventine Pr.
Law, David A. & Park, Darin, eds. The Complete Guide to Writing Science Fiction, Volume 1: First Contact. 2007. (Complete Guide to Writing Science Fiction Ser.). (ENG.). 311p. per. *(978-1-896944-39-5(6))* Dragon Moon Pr. CAN. Dist: Ingram Pub. Services.
Leacock, Dina. Elements of the Short Story: How to Write a Selling Story. 2007. 67p. per. 10.95 *(978-0-9725614-2-6(0))* Tricorner Publishing.
Levinson, Jay Conrad, et al. Guerrilla Marketing for Writers: 100 No-Cost, Low-Cost Weapons for Selling Your Work. 2010. (Guerilla Marketing Press Ser.). (ENG.). 300p. pap. 19.95 *(978-1-60037-660-3(6))* Morgan James Publishing.
Lindblom, H. Christine & Shofner, Virgie. Book Business. 2011. pap. 24.95 ***(978-1-934603-10-9(4))*** Broken Glass Publishing.
Mace, Lorraine & Vincent-Northam, Maureen. The ABC Checklist for New Writers: How to Open Doors & Get Noticed the First Time Around. 2007. 180p. pap. *(978-0-9550751-7-9(3))* Orana Publishing, Ltd.
Maeda, Martha & Chesanek, Carissa. Book Publishing 101: Inside Information to Getting Your First Book or Novel Published. 2012. (ENG.). 288p. pap. 24.95 *(978-1-60138-564-2(1))* Atlantic Publishing Co.
Martin, Gail. Selling & Promoting Your Book Online. 2011. (Thrifty Author's Guide Ser.). 138p. pap. 12.99 ***(978-1-936695-40-9(5))*** Comfort Publishing Services, LLC.
Martin, Sharlene & Flacco, Anthony. Publish Your Nonfiction Book: Strategies for Learning the Industry, Selling Your Book, & Building a Successful Career. 2009. (ENG.). 304p. pap. 17.99 *(978-1-58297-578-8(7),* Writer's Digest Bks.) F&W Media, Inc.
McAdams, Robert. Beginner¿s Guide to Home Based Publishing: How to Write, Publish, & Sell ¿How to¿ Books: Share Your Knowledge with Others Who Need It. 2006. per. *(978-0-9796990-5-4(3))* McAdams, Robert.
McCallum, Chris. Beginner's Guide to Getting Publi. 6th ed. 2009. (Illus.). 192p. 22.00 *(978-1-84528-217-2(5))* How To Books GBR. Dist: Parkwest Pubns., Inc.
McCutcheon, Marc. Damn! Why Didn't I Write That? How Ordinary People Are Raking in $100,000. 00... or More Writing Nonfiction Books & How You Can Too! 2nd ed. 2006. (ENG.). 256p. pap. 14.95 *(978-1-884956-55-3(6))* Quill Driver Bks.
McNally, John. The Creative Writer's Survival Guide: Advice from an Unrepentant Novelist. 2010. 272p. pap. 19.95 *(978-1-58729-920-9(8))* Univ. of Iowa Pr.
Megarrity, David. Together Alone. 2008. 112p. pap. *(978-3-639-05248-0(X))* VDM Verlag Dr. Mueller e.K.
Meier, Marcia. Navigating the Rough Waters of Today's Publishing World: Critical Advice for Writers from Industry Insiders. 2010. (ENG., Illus.). 130p. pap. 14.95 *(978-1-884995-58-3(6))* Linden Publishing Co., Inc.
Mettee, Stephen Blake. The Fast-Track Course on How to Write a Nonfiction Book Proposal. 2012. (Great Books for Writers Ser.). (ENG.). 140p. pap. 14.95 ***(978-1-61035-050-1(2))*** Linden Publishing Co., Inc.
Mettee, Stephen Blake, ed. The Portable Writer's Conference: Your Guide to Getting Published. 2007. (ENG.). 464p. pap. 19.95 *(978-1-884956-57-7(2))* Quill Driver Bks.
Moniz, Larry. Self-Promotion for Authors. 2007. (Illus.). cd-rom 45.00 *(978-0-9797007-0-5(1))* Midland Assocs. Publishing.
Morrell, David. The Successful Novelist: A Lifetime of Lessons about Writing & Publishing. 2008. (ENG.). 240p. per. 19.99 *(978-1-4022-1055-6(8))* Sourcebooks, Inc.
Nappa, Mike. 77 Reasons Why Your Book Was Rejected. 2011. (ENG.). 384p. pap. 14.99 *(978-1-4022-5412-3(1))* Sourcebooks, Inc.
Obey, Anthony & Obey, Crystal. Start Small Finish Big in Self Publishing. 2007. 120p. per. 25.00 *(978-1-59268-077-1(1))* G M A Publishing & Inspiration Pr.
Pope, Alice. 2010 Children's Writer's & Illustrator's Market. 21st ed. 2009. (ENG.). 448p. pap. 29.99 *(978-1-58297-587-0(6),* Writer's Digest Bks.) F&W Media, Inc.
Pope, Alice, ed. 2011 Children's Writer's & Illustrator's Market. 23rd ed. 2010. (ENG., Illus.). 440p. pap. 29.99 *(978-1-58297-952-6(9),* Writer's Digest Bks.) F&W Media, Inc.
—2011 Novel & Short Story Writer's Market. 30th ed. 2010. (ENG., Illus.). 656p. pap. 29.99 *(978-1-58297-951-9(0),* Writer's Digest Bks.) F&W Media, Inc.
Poynter, Dan. Writing Nonfiction: Turning Thoughts into Books. 5th ed. 2007. (ENG., Illus.). 144p. pap. 14.95 *(978-1-56860-110-6(7))* Para Publishing.
Poynter, Dan & Snow, Danny. U-Publish Com 4 0: A 'Living Book' to Help You Compete with the Giants of Publishing. 2007. 76p. per. 14.99 *(978-1-58832-175-6(4))* Unlimited Publishing LLC.
Poynter, Dan & Snow, Danny O. U-Publish Com 5 0. 2010. 104p. pap. 14.99 *(978-1-58832-200-5(9))* Unlimited Publishing LLC.
Price, Lynn. The Writer's Essential Tackle Box: Getting a Hook on the Publishing Industry. 2009. (Get It Write Ser.). (ENG.). 380p. pap. 19.95 *(978-1-933016-34-4(5))* Behler Pubns., LLC.
Quarton, Marjorie. Part-Time Writer: Notes & Reflections. 2010. (ENG.). 240p. pap. 24.95 ***(978-1-84351-166-3(5))*** Lilliput Pr., Ltd., The IRL. Dist: Dufour Editions, Inc.
Rice, Brenda / Lee. Here's What You Should Know about Creating Your Own Book. 2007. 96p. per. 9.95 *(978-0-9787490-2-6(2))* Bertillion Bks.
Rittenberg, Ann & Whitcomb, Laura. Your First Novel: A Published Author & a Top Agent Share the Keys to Achieving Your Dream. 2006. (Illus.). 298p. *(978-1-58297-386-9(5));* (ENG., 300p. per. 16.99 *(978-1-58297-388-3(1))* F&W Media, Inc. (Writer's Digest Bks.).
Sattersten, Todd. Every Book Is a Startup. 2012. (ENG.). 56p. pap. 24.99 ***(978-1-4493-0901-5(1))*** O'Reilly Media, Inc.
Schecter, I. J. 102 Ways to Earn Money Writing 1,500 Words or Less: The Ultimate Freelancer's Guide. 2010. (ENG.). 224p. pap. 14.99 *(978-1-58297-795-9(X),* Writer's Digest Bks.) F&W Media, Inc.
Scott Meyers, Ashley. Selling Your Screenplay. 2007. 116p. pap. 19.99 *(978-1-60145-148-4(2))* Booklocker.com, Inc.
Shulman, Neil. Get Between the Covers: Leave a Legacy by Writing a Book. 2008. (ENG.). 356p. 27.95 *(978-1-60037-314-5(3));* (Illus.). pap. 17.95 *(978-1-60037-315-2(1))* Morgan James Publishing.
Simmons, Celeste & Compton, Jeff. Are You a Writer: Here's Everything You Need to Know about Publishing! 2007. per. 8.95 *(978-0-9777041-3-2(0))* Third Dimension Publishing.
Smith Jr, James V. The Writer's Little Helper: Everything You Need to Know to Write Better & Get Published. 2012. (ENG.). 208p. pap. 14.99 ***(978-1-59963-409-8(0),*** Writer's Digest Bks.) F&W Media, Inc.
Spencer, Si. 100 Writing Tips for TV & Film. 2010. 54p. pap. 13.50 *(978-1-4452-7777-6(8))* Lulu Enterprises Inc.
Stein, Sol. A -Z Guide to Writing Success & Publishing Know-How: Quick Solutions, Smart Techniques for Fiction & Nonfiction Professionals & Beginners. 2010. (ENG.). 288p. pap. 16.99 *(978-0-312-55095-0(2),* St. Martin's Griffin) St. Martin's Pr.
Stuart, Sally E. Christian Writers' Market Guide 2008: The Essential Reference Tool for the Christian Writer. 2008. (Christian Writer's Market Guide Ser.). (ENG.). 640p. pap. 34.99 *(978-1-4000-7461-7(4))* Doubleday Religious Publishing Group, The.
Terrell, P. M. Take the Mystery Out of Promoting Your Book. 2006. 213p. per. 15.00 *(978-1-928662-43-3(9))* Palari Publishing LLP.
Tooze, Sandra. The Canadian Writer's Market. 17th ed. 2007. (ENG.). 472p. pap. 21.00 *(978-0-7710-3528-4(1),* McClelland & Stewart) McClelland & Stewart CAN. Dist: Random Hse., Inc.
Uddin, Moyna. Write Publish Sell Your Book. 2010. 104p. pap. 12.00 *(978-0-9774647-9-1(2))* 3-QUEENS Pubns.
Ward, Tim. The Author's Guide to Publishing & Marketing. 2009. (ENG.). 224p. pap. 19.95 *(978-1-84694-166-5(0))* Hunt, John Publishing Ltd. GBR. Dist: National Bk. Network.
Weber, Steve. Plug Your Book! Online Book Marketing for Authors, Book Publicity Through Social Networking. Bird, Julie, ed. 2007. 208p. per. 18.95 *(978-0-9772406-1-6(4))* Weber Bks.
Wepner, Shelley B. & Gambrell, Linda B. Beating the Odds: Getting Published in the Field of Literacy. 2006. (Illus.). 100p. 25.95 *(978-0-87207-589-4(3))* International Reading Assn.
Whalin, W. Terry. Jumpstart Your Publishing Dreams: Insider Secrets to Skyrocket Your Success. 2009. (ENG.). 192p. pap. 19.95 *(978-1-935085-50-8(6))* WTW Pr.
Whelchel, Sandy. The National Writers Association Guide to Writing for Beginners: A How-to Reference for Plot, Dialogue, Nonfiction, Internet Publishing, & More. 2007. (ENG.). 132p. 30.00 *(978-1-57886-685-4(5))* Rowman & Littlefield Education.
Whitcomb, Laura. Novel Shortcuts: Ten Techniques That Ensure a Great First Draft. 2009. (ENG., Illus.). 272p. pap. 16.99 *(978-1-58297-567-2(1),* Writer's Digest Bks.) F&W Media, Inc.
Wolff, Jurgen. Your Creative Writing Masterclass: Let Austin, Dickens, Chekhov, Hemingway, Nebokov, Vonnegut & More Than 100 Modern & Classic Authors Teach You the Craft of Writing Successful Novels, Screenplays, & Short Stories. 2012. (ENG.). 256p. pap. 19.95 ***(978-1-85788-578-1(3))*** Ebsco Publishing.
—Your Writing Coach: From Concept to Character, from Pitch to Publication- Everything You Need to Know about Writing Novels, Nonfiction, New Media, Scripts, & Short Stories. 2nd ed. 2012. (ENG.). 256p. pap. 19.95 ***(978-1-85788-577-4(5))*** Ebsco Publishing.
Writer's Digest Books Editors. Writer's Digest University: Everything You Need to Write & Sell Your Work. 2010. (ENG.). 528p. pap. 39.99 *(978-1-59963-137-0(7),* Writer's Digest Bks.) F&W Media, Inc.
—Writer's Market Guide to Getting Published. 3rd ed. 2010. (ENG., Illus.). 368p. pap. 19.99 *(978-1-58297-608-2(2),* Writer's Digest Bks.) F&W Media, Inc.
Writer's Digest Books Editors & Sambuchino, Chuck. Formatting & Submitting Your Manuscript. 3rd ed. 2009. (ENG., Illus.). 324p. pap. 22.99 *(978-1-58297-571-9(X),* Writer's Digest Bks.) F&W Media, Inc.
Yager, Jan. The Complete Help Book for Authors & Publishers. 2012. pap. 29.95 *(978-1-889262-16-1(1))* Hannacroix Creek Bks., Inc.
Young, Maryanna. Blank to Book: From Idea to Amazon in 150 Days! 2007. ring bd. 99.95 *(978-0-9762642-7-9(7))* Aloha Publishing.

AUTHORSHIP—SEX DIFFERENCES

Backscheider, Paula R. Eighteenth-Century Women Poets & Their Poetry: Inventing Agency, Inventing Genre. 2007. (ENG.). 544p. (gr. 17). per. 37.00 *(978-0-8018-8746-8(1))* Johns Hopkins Univ. Pr.
Ballesteros, Isolina. Escritura Femenina y Discurso Autobiografico en la Nueva Novela Espanola. 2nd ed. (American University Studies: Vol. 207). (SPA.). 202p. 29.95 *(978-0-8204-6205-9(5))* Lang, Peter Publishing, Inc.
Ford, Karen Jackson. Gender & the Poetics of Excess: Moments of Brocade. 2009. (ENG.). 272p. pap. 25.00 *(978-1-60473-255-9(5))* Univ. Pr. of Mississippi.
Gornick, Vivian. The Men in My Life. 2008. (Boston Review Bks.). (ENG.). 216p. (gr. 17). 14.95 *(978-0-262-07303-5(X))* MIT Pr.
Lucky, Christina. A Moving Rhetoricke: Gender & Silence in Early Modern England. 2011. (ENG.). 192p. pap. 24.95 *(978-0-7190-8325-9(7))* Manchester Univ. Pr. GBR. Dist: Macmillan.
Reesman, Jeanne Campbell, ed. Speaking the Other Self: American Women Writers. 2011. (ENG.). 352p. pap. 24.95 ***(978-0-8203-3796-2(6))*** Univ. of Georgia Pr.

AUTHORSHIP—STUDY AND TEACHING

Alexander, Jonathan. Literacy, Sexuality, Pedagogy: Theory & Practice for Composition Studies. 2008. (ENG.). 232p. (gr. 13). pap. 24.95 *(978-0-87421-701-8(6),* Utah State Univ. Pr.) Univ. Pr. of Colorado.
Beidler, Peter G. A Reader's Companion to J. D. Salinger's the Catcher in the Rye. 2nd rev. ed. 2011. 290p. 25.95 *(978-1-60381-037-1(4),* Coffeetown Pr.) Coffeetown Enterprises, Inc.
—A Reader's Companion to J. D. Salinger's the Catcher in the Rye: Second Edition. 2nd rev. ed. 2011. 292p. pap. 17.95 *(978-1-60381-013-5(7),* Coffeetown Pr.) Coffeetown Enterprises, Inc.
Donnelly, Dianne, ed. Does the Writing Workshop Still Work? 2010. (New Writing Viewpoints Ser.). (ENG.). 256p. 139.95 *(978-1-84769-269-6(9));* pap. 39.95 *(978-1-84769-268-9(0))* Multilingual Matters GBR. Dist: Univ. of Toronto Pr.
Ebbissa, Dhaba. Addressing Learner Diversity Through Multiple Intelligences Theory: In Efl Classes Higher Institution In Focus. 2011. 152p. pap. ***(978-3-639-32282-8(7))*** VDM Verlag Dr. Mueller e.K.
Eisner, Caroline & Vicinus, Martha, eds. Originality, Imitation, & Plagiarism: Teaching Writing in the Digital Age. 2008. (ENG., Illus.). 280p. (C). pap. 29.95 *(978-0-472-05034-5(6))* Univ. of Michigan Pr.
Ellis, Linda & Marsh, Jamie. Getting Started: The Reading-Writing Workshop, Grades 4-8. 2007. (Illus.). 192p. pap. 30.00 *(978-0-325-00998-8(8),* E00998) Heinemann.
Finkle, David Lee. Writing Extraordinary Essays: Every Middle Schooler Can! - Strategies, Lessons, & Rubrics - Plus Proven Tips for Succeeding on Tests. 2008. (ENG.). 160p. pap. 20.99 *(978-0-545-05898-8(8),* Teaching Resources) Scholastic, Inc.
Goodburn, Amy M., et al. Rewriting Success in Rhetoric & Composition. 2012. ***(978-1-60235-293-3(3));*** pap. ***(978-1-60235-292-6(5))*** Parlor Pr.
Gust, John. Adventures in Fantasy: Lessons & Activities in Narrative & Descriptive Writing, Grades 5-9. 2007. (ENG., Illus.). 272p. per. 24.95 *(978-0-7879-9290-3(9),* Jossey-Bass) Wiley, John & Sons, Inc.
Knights, Ben & Thurgar-Dawson, Chris. Active Reading: Transformative Writing in Literary Studies. 2008. (Continuum Literary Studies). (ENG.). 208p. 49.95 *(978-1-84706-263-5(6))* Continuum International Publishing Group, Ltd. GBR. Dist: National Bk. Network.
Koshy, Anne Susan. The Short Fiction of Angela Carter, Margaret Atwood & Suniti Namjoshi. 2010. 332p. pap. *(978-3-639-26008-3(2))* VDM Verlag Dr. Mueller e.K.
Mermelstein, Leah. Don't Forget to Share: The Crucial Last Step in the Writing Workshop. 2007. (Illus.). 128p. pap. 21.25 *(978-0-325-00951-3(1),* E00951) Heinemann.
Moore, Susan. Exploring Writing: A Life, a Story, a Gift. rev. ed. 2010. (ENG.). 176p. spiral bd. 76.12 *(978-0-7575-3909-1(2))* Kendall Hunt Publishing Co.
Morris, Lisa. Awakening Brilliance in the Writer's Workshop: Using Notebooks, Mentor Texts, & the Writing Process. 2011. ***(978-1-59667-195-9(5))*** Eye On Education, Inc.
Murphy, Christina & Sherwood, Steve. The St. Martin's Sourcebook for Writing Tutors. (ENG.). (C). 3rd ed. 2007. 288p. pap. 12.95 *(978-0-312-44226-2(2))* 4th ed. 2011. 352p. pap. 12.95 *(978-0-312-66191-5(6))* Bedford/Saint Martin's.
Murphy, James J., ed. A Short History of Writing Instruction: From Ancient Greece to Contemporary America. 3rd rev. ed. 2012. (ENG., Illus.). 320p. (C). 130.00 ***(978-0-415-89746-4(7));*** pap. 49.95 ***(978-0-415-89745-7(9))*** Routledge.
Murphy, Robin M. How Social Trauma Affects How We Write: Post 9/11 Rhetorical Theory & Composition Pedagogy. 2010. vii, 159p. 99.95 *(978-0-7734-3695-4(2))* Mellen, Edwin Pr., The.
Nielsen, Roger W. Writing Content: Mastering Magazine & Online Writing. 2009. (ENG.). 202p. pap. 19.95 *(978-0-9820355-4-2(3))* R. W. Nielsen Co.
Pryle, Marilyn & Pryle, Marilyn Bogusch. Teaching Students to Write Effective Essays: Meaningful, Step-by-Step Lessons That Get Students Ready for Writing Assessments. 2007. (ENG.). 96p. (gr. 5). pap. 16.99 *(978-0-439-74658-8(2),* Teaching Resources) Scholastic, Inc.
Rodgers, Johannah. The Social Construction of Authorship. 2009. 164p. pap. *(978-3-639-13997-6(6))* VDM Verlag Dr. Mueller e.K.
Scholastic Teaching Resources Staff. Writing Frames for the Interactive Whiteboard: Quick & Easy Lessons, Models, & Writing Frames That Guide Students to Write Narrative, Descriptive, Expository, & Persuasive Paragraphs & Essays. 2011. (ENG., Illus.). 96p. (gr. 3-6). pap. 21.99 *(978-0-545-30583-9(7),* Teaching Resources) Scholastic, Inc.
Speck, Bruce W., et al, eds. Collaborative Writing: An Annotated Bibliography. 2008. 408p. pap. 45.95 *(978-1-59311-285-1(8))* Information Age Publishing, Inc.
Zeigler, Linda, et al. Enhancing Writing Through Visualization. rev. ed. 2007. (ENG.). 210p. pap. 31.95 *(978-0-7575-4090-5(2))* Kendall Hunt Publishing Co.

AUTHORSHIP, DISPUTED

Craig, Hugh & Kinney, Arthur F., eds. Shakespeare, Computers, & the Mystery of Authorship. 2009. (ENG., Illus.). 254p. 107.00 *(978-0-521-51623-5(4))* Cambridge Univ. Pr.

AUTISM

see also Autistic Children

Abowd, Gregory, et al. Innovative Technologies for Autism. 2011. (Synthesis Lectures on Assistive, Rehabilitative, & Life-Preserving Technologies Ser.). 100p. pap. 35.00 *(978-1-60845-640-6(4))* Morgan & Claypool Pubs.
Acquarone, Stella, ed. Signs of Autism in Infants: Recognition & Early Intervention. 2007. (Illus.). 298p. per. 43.95 *(978-1-85575-486-7(X))* Karnac Bks. GBR. Dist: Stylus Publishing, LLC.
Adams, Lynn. Autism & Asperger Syndrome: Busting the Myths. 2007. (Illus.). 117p. per. 24.95 *(978-1-59756-083-2(9))* Plural Publishing, Inc.
Adreon, Diane, et al. Simple Strategies That Work! Helpful Hints for All Educators of Students with Asperger Syndrome, High-Functioning Autism, & Related Disabilities. 2006. (Illus.). 40p. pap. 19.95 *(978-1-931282-99-4(4))* Autism Asperger Publishing Co.
Aitken, Kenneth J. Dietary Interventions in Autism Spectrum Disorders: Why They Work When They Do, Why They Don't When They Don't. 2008. (ENG., Illus.). 144p. *(978-1-84310-939-6(5))* Kingsley, Jessica Ltd.
Akanda, Zahir Uddin. Teaching Challenges at Autism Schools. 2011. 88p. pap. ***(978-3-8443-9534-1(2))*** Lambert Academic Publishing.
Akshoomoff, Nat, ed. Autism Spectrum Disorders: A Special Issue of Child Neuropsychology. 2006. (Special Issues of Child Neuropsychology Ser.). (ENG., Illus.). 140p. 64.50 *(978-1-84169-818-2(0),* Psychology Press) Taylor & Francis Group GBR. Dist: Taylor & Francis Group.
Alan, Michael. I Wish My Kids Had Cancer: A Family Surviving the Autism Epidemic. 2008. 120p. pap. 19.95 *(978-1-60672-070-7(8))* PublishAmerica, Inc.
American Academy of Pediatrics, creator. Autism: Caring for Children with Autism Spectrum Disorders: A Resource Toolkit for Clinicians. 2007. cd-rom 79.95 *(978-1-58110-276-5(3))* American Academy of Pediatrics.
Anan, Ruth & Turnkington, Carol. The Encyclopedia of Autism Spectrum Disorders. 2006. (Facts on File Library of Health & Living). 336p. (C). (gr. 9). 75.00 *(978-0-8160-6002-3(9))* Facts On File, Inc.
Angell, Kathe Downer. Little Kids in Big Bodies: Autism. My friend Philip. 2011. 28p. (J). pap. 16.95 *(978-1-4327-6116-5(1))* Outskirts Pr., Inc.
Anstadt, Sera. All My Friends Are Crazy. Lawson, Sarah, tr. 2007. 204p. per. *(978-1-84747-386-8(5))* Chipmunkapublishing.
Arnwine, Bonnie. Starting Sensory Integration Therapy: Fun Activities for the Classroom or Home! 2011. (ENG., Illus.). 120p. pap. 19.95 *(978-1-935567-26-4(8))* Sensory Resources.
Arnwine, Timothy M. I Love U: Our Journey Through Autism. 2008. 84p. pap. 12.00 *(978-1-4389-0717-8(6))* AuthorHouse.
Ashcroft, Wendy. Success Strategies for Teaching Kids with Autism. 2009. (ENG.) 225p. pap. 19.95 *(978-1-59363-382-0(3))* Prufrock Pr.
Aspy, Ruth & Grossman, Barry. " Designing Comprehensive Interventions for High-Functioning Individuals with Autism Spectrum Disorders: The Ziggurat Model-Release 2. 0. 2011. 246p. pap. 59.00 ***(978-1-934575-96-3(8))*** Autism Asperger Publishing Co.
—UCC-CL Assessment Booklets (contains 1 manual & 20 Forms) 2007. pap. 24.95 *(978-1-931282-46-8(3))* Autism Asperger Publishing Co.
—UCC-HF Assessment Forms (contains 1 manual & 20 Forms) 2007. pap. 24.95 *(978-1-931282-39-0(0))* Autism Asperger Publishing Co.
—Underlying Characteristics Checklists (UCC) User Manual. 2011. 19.00 ***(978-1-934575-98-7(4))*** Autism Asperger Publishing Co.
—The Ziggurat Model: A Framework for Designing Comprehensive Interventions for Individuals with High-Functioning Autism & Asperger Syndrome. 390p. 49.95 *(978-1-934575-43-7(7))* Autism Asperger Publishing Co.
Aspy, Ruth & Grossman, Barry. The Ziggurat Model ¿ A Framework for Designing Comprehensive Interventions for Individuals with High-Functioning Autism & Asperger Syndrome Updated & Expanded Edition. 2011. 340p. pap. 49.95 ***(978-1-934575-94-9(1))*** Autism Asperger Publishing Co.
Aspy, Ruth, et al. " Underlying Characteristics Checklist — Early Intervention (UCC-EI) 2011. 24.95 ***(978-1-934575-95-6(X))*** Autism Asperger Publishing Co.
Autismo, Curando El. Revista Curando el Autismo. 2010. pap. 3.75 *(978-0-578-05453-7(1))* Curando el Autisom.
Badcock, Christopher R. The Imprinted Brain: How Genes Set the Balance Between Autism & Psychosis. 2009. 240p. *(978-1-84905-023-4(6))* Kingsley, Jessica Ltd.

A

Baker, Angela R. & Bell, Christina. Autism Ot to the Rescue. 2007. 84p. per. 20.00 *(978-1-59858-358-8(1))* Dog Ear Publishing, LLC.

Barbera, Mary & Rasmussen, Tracy. The Verbal Behavior Approach: How to Teach Children with Autism & Related Disorders. 2007. (ENG., Illus.). 176p. pap. *(978-1-84310-852-8(6))* Kingsley, Jessica Ltd.

Barnbaum, Deborah R. The Ethics of Autism: Among Them, but Not of Them. 2008. (Bioethics & the Humanities Ser.). (ENG., Illus.). 248p. pap. 21.95 *(978-0-253-22013-4(0)*, 0253220130) Indiana Univ. Pr.

Barnhill, Ann Clinard. At Home in the Land of Oz: Autism, My Sister, & Me. 2007. (ENG., Illus.). 256p. per. *(978-1-84310-859-7(3))* Kingsley, Jessica Ltd.

Baron-Cohen, Simon. Autism & Asperger Syndrome. 2nd ed. 2008. (Facts Ser.). (ENG., Illus.). 160p. 19.95 *(978-0-19-850490-0(X))* Oxford Univ. Pr., Inc.

Barrows & Barrows, Kate. Autism in Childhood & Autistic Features in Adults: A Psychoanalytic Perspective. 2008. (Psychoanalytic Ideas Ser.). 310p. pap. 38.95 *(978-1-85575-424-9(X))* Karnac Bks. GBR. Dist: Stylus Publishing, LLC.

Bartlett, Suzanne B. A Friend Like John: Understanding Autism. 2011. 28p. pap. 14.75 ***(978-1-4520-3709-7(4))*** AuthorHouse.

Bell, Christina & Baker, Angela. Autism, Therapy, & Fun: OT to the Rescue. 2010. (Illus.). 82p. pap. 19.95 *(978-1-4327-5107-4(7))* Outskirts Pr., Inc.

Belli, Brita. The Autism Puzzle: Connecting the Dots Between Environmental Toxins & Rising Autism Rates. 2012. (ENG., Illus.). 224p. 23.95 ***(978-1-60980-391-9(4))*** Seven Stories Pr.

Bellini, Scott. Building Social Relationships: A Systematic Approach to Teaching Social Interaction Skills to Children & Adolescents with Autism Spectrum Disorders & Other Social Difficulties. 2006. (Illus.). 270p. per. 39.95 *(978-1-931282-94-9(3))* Autism Asperger Publishing Co.

Benaron, Lisa D. Autism, 1 vol. 2008. (Biographies of Disease Ser.). 272p. 45.00 *(978-0-313-34763-4(8)*, GR4763, Greenwood Pr.) Greenwood Publishing Group, Inc.

Benoliel, Jennifer. Autism & PDD Photo Cards Verb Tense Questions. 2008. (J). 89.95 *(978-0-7606-9956-0(9))* LinguiSystems, Inc.

Bernard-Opitz, Vera. Children with Autism Spectrum Disorders: A Structured Teaching & Experience-Based Program for Therapists, Teachers, & Parents. 2007. 54.00 *(978-1-4164-0232-9(2))* PRO-ED, Inc.

Blastland, Michael. The Only Boy in the World: A Father Explores the Mysteries of Autism. 2006. (ENG.). 224p. per. 14.95 *(978-1-56924-291-9(7))* Da Capo Pr., Inc.

Blatt, Gene J., ed. The Neurochemical Basis of Autism: From Molecules to Minicolumns. 2010. (ENG., Illus.). xv, 295p. 179.00 *(978-1-4419-1271-8(1)*, 1441912711) Springer.

Boldt, Alana. Autism: One Family's Journey. 2007. 152p. pap. 9.95 *(978-0-615-16317-8(3))* Boldt, Alana Lynn.

Bondy, Andy & Frost, Lori. Autism 24/7: A Family Guide to Learning at Home & in the Community. 2008. (Illus.). 177p. pap. 19.95 *(978-1-890627-53-9(4))* Woodbine Hse.

Boucher, Jill. Autistic Spectrum: Characteristics, Causes & Practical Issues. 2008. (Illus.). 424p. (C). pap. 57.00 *(978-0-7619-6212-0(3)*, 84602) SAGE Pubns., Ltd. GBR. Dist: SAGE Pubns., Inc.

Boucher, Jill & Bowler, Dermot, eds. Memory in Autism: Theory & Evidence. (ENG.). 384p. 2010. pap. 45.00 *(978-0-521-18401-4(0))* 2008. (Illus.). 104.00 *(978-0-521-86288-2(4))* Cambridge Univ. Pr.

Boushey, Ann. Talking Teenagers: Information & Inspiration for Parents of Teenagers with Autism or Asperger's Syndrome. 2007. (ENG.). 192p. per. *(978-1-84310-844-3(5))* Kingsley, Jessica Ltd.

Bowen, Maggie, et al. Social Skills & Autistic Spectrum Disorders. Bowen, Maggie et al, eds. 2007. (Autistic Spectrum Disorder Support Kit Ser.). (Illus.). 96p. 55.95 *(978-1-4129-2312-5(3)*, B23123C) SAGE Pubns., Ltd. GBR. Dist: SAGE Pubns., Inc.

Boyce, Tammy & Boyce, Tammy. Health, Risk & News: The MMR Vaccine & the Media. 2007. (Media & Culture Ser.). 240p. (C). pap. 32.95 *(978-0-8204-8838-7(0))* Lang, Peter Publishing, Inc.

Brady, Lois Jean. Apps for Autism: More than 200 Effective Apps for Language, Behavioral, Social, Creative, & Cognitive Development. 2011. (ENG., Illus.). 396p. pap. 29.95 *(978-1-935274-49-0(X))* Future Horizons, Inc.

Bråten, Stein, ed. Intersubjective Communication & Emotion in Early Ontogeny. 2006. (Studies in Emotion & Social Interaction Ser.). (ENG., Illus.). 472p. pap. 87.00 *(978-0-521-02989-6(9))* Cambridge Univ. Pr.

Breakey, Christine. The Autism Spectrum & Further Education. 2006. (ENG., Illus.). 28p. per., instr.'s gde. ed. *(978-1-84310-382-0(6))* Kingsley, Jessica Ltd.

Brennan, Lynn Cohen. Teaching Perspective-Taking Skills to Children with Autism Spectrum Disorders. 2010. 42.00 *(978-1-4164-0482-8(1))* PRO-ED, Inc.

Brosen, Sophie Koborg. Do You Understand Me? My Life, My Thoughts, My Autism Spectrum Disorder. 2006. (ENG., Illus.). 128p. (J). (gr. 3-7). per. *(978-1-84310-464-3(4))* Kingsley, Jessica Ltd.

Buckendorf, G. Robert & Liedel, John. Autism: A Guide for Educators, Clinicians, & Parents. 2007. *(978-1-58650-854-8(7))* Super Duper Pubns.

Buckley, Julie A. Healing Our Autistic Children: A Medical Plan for Restoring Your Child's Health. 2010. (ENG.). 256p. pap. 18.00 *(978-0-230-61639-4(9))* Palgrave Macmillan.

Burnett, Anne. Step Ahead of Autism: What You Can Do to Ensure the Best Possible Outcome for Your Child. 2011. pap. 12.95 *(978-1-934716-25-0(1))* Sunrise River Pr.

Burns, Linda. Beating the Odds at Autism: One Family's Winning Hand. 2012. pap. 11.95 ***(978-0-7414-7472-8(7))*** Infinity Publishing.

Burns, Linda, creator. Beating the Odds at Autism: One Family's Winning Hand. 2012. pap. 20.95 ***(978-0-7414-7088-1(8))*** Infinity Publishing.

Burns, Michele Pierce & Wambua, Danson Mandela. Danson: The Extraordinary Discovery of an Autistic Child's Innermost Thoughts & Feelings. 2009. (ENG., Illus.). 124p. pap. 19.95 *(978-0-9800288-4-3(1))* St. Lynn's Pr.

Buron, Kari Dunn. A 5 Could Make Me Lose Control! An Activity-Based Method for Evaluating & Supporting Highly Anxious Students. 2007. 48p. per. 22.95 *(978-1-931282-31-4(5))* Autism Asperger Publishing Co.

—A 5 Is Against the Law! Social Boundaries - Straight Up! - An Honest Guide to Teens & Young Adults. 2007. (Illus.). 48p. (YA). (gr. 7-14). per. 20.95 *(978-1-931282-35-2(8))* Autism Asperger Publishing Co.

Caldwell, Phoebe. From Isolation to Intimacy: Making Friends Without Words. 2007. (ENG., Illus.). 16p. per. *(978-1-84310-500-8(4))* Kingsley, Jessica Ltd.

Caldwell, Phoebe & Horwood, Jane. Using Intensive Interaction & Sensory Integration: A Handbook for Those Who Support People with Severe Autistic Spectrum Disorder. 2008. (ENG., Illus.). 140p. pap. *(978-1-84310-626-5(4))* Kingsley, Jessica Ltd.

Campbell, Jonathan M. Psychological Assessment & Treatment of Children with Autism Spectrum Disorders: An Integrated Action Guide to Diagnosis, Treatment, & Educational Planning. 2009. (ENG.). 336p. 60.00 *(978-0-470-17568-2(0)*, Wiley) Wiley, John & Sons, Inc.

Cardon, Teresa A. Initiations & Interactions: Early Intervention Techniques for Parents of Children with Autism Spectrum Disorders. 2007. (Illus.). 81p. per. 19.95 *(978-1-931282-32-1(3))* Autism Asperger Publishing Co.

Carlisle, Mary Alyce. Up from Autism the Cause & the Cure. 2008. 284p. pap. 19.99 *(978-1-4363-0794-9(5))* Xlibris Corp.

Carlisle, Paul C. Progress in Autism Research. 2007. 269p. 129.00 *(978-1-60021-630-5(7))* Nova Science Pubs., Inc.

Cartwright, Ann & Morgan, Jill. The Teaching Assistant's Guide to Autistic Spectrum Disorders. 2008. (Teaching Assistant's Ser.). (ENG., Illus.). 154p. 24.95 *(978-0-8264-9812-0(4))* Continuum International Publishing Group, Ltd. GBR. Dist: National Bk. Network.

Charman, Tony & Stone, Wendy, eds. Social & Communication Development in Autism Spectrum Disorders: Early Identification, Diagnosis, & Intervention. 2008. (ENG., Illus.). 348p. pap. 35.00 *(978-1-59385-713-4(6))* Guilford Pubns., Inc.

Chauhan, Abha, et al. Autism: Oxidative Stress, Inflammation, & Immune Abnormalities. 2009. (ENG., Illus.). 452p. 164.95 *(978-1-4200-6881-8(4)*, CRC Press) Taylor & Francis Group GBR. Dist: Taylor & Francis Group.

Chawarska, Katarzyna, et al, eds. Autism Spectrum Disorders in Infants & Toddlers: Diagnosis, Assessment, & Treatment. 2010. (ENG.). 348p. pap. 30.00 *(978-1-60623-970-4(8))* Guilford Pubns., Inc.

Chez, Michael G. Autism & Its Medical Management: A Guide for Parents & Professionals. 2009. (ENG., Illus.). 224p. pap. *(978-1-84905-817-9(2))* Kingsley, Jessica Ltd.

Christie, Philip, et al. First Steps in Intervention with Your Child with Autism: Frameworks for Communication. 2009. (ENG., Illus.). 238p. pap. *(978-1-84905-011-1(2))* Kingsley, Jessica Ltd.

Cimera, Robert Evert. Making Autism a Gift: Inspiring Children to Believe in Themselves & Lead Happy, Fulfilling Lives. 2007. (ENG.). 304p. per. 18.95 *(978-0-7425-5288-3(8))* Rowman & Littlefield Publishers, Inc.

Cipani, Ennio. Children & Autism: Stories of Triumph & Hope. 2010. (ENG.). 224p. pap. 15.95 *(978-1-936303-01-4(9))* Demos Medical Publishing, LLC.

—Triumphs in Early Autism Treatment: The Stories of Seven Best Outcome Cases. 2008. 252p. 35.00 *(978-0-8261-5995-3(8))* Springer Publishing Co., Inc.

Cohen, Donald J. Life Is with Others: Selected Writings on Child Psychiatry. Martin, Andres & King, Robert A., eds. 2006. (ENG.). 304p. 37.00 *(978-0-300-11466-9(4))* Yale Univ. Pr.

Cohen, Shirley. Targeting Autism: What We Know, Don't Know, & Can Do to Help Young Children with Autism Spectrum Disorders. 3rd exp. ed. 2006. 241p. per. 21.95 *(978-0-520-24838-0(4))* Univ. of California Pr.

Coleman, Mary, ed. The Neurology of Autism. 2009. (ENG., Illus.). 272p. pap. 29.95 *(978-0-19-538776-6(7))* Oxford Univ. Pr., Inc.

Compart, Pamela & Laake, Dana. The Kid-Friendly ADHD & Autism Cookbook, Updated & Revised: The Ultimate Guide to the Gluten-Free, Casein-Free Diet. 2012. (ENG., Illus.). 352p. pap. 18.99 *(978-1-59233-472-8(5)*, 1592334725) Quayside.

Concept Media. Unlocking the World of Autism: Seven Keys to Becoming Miracle Minded. 2009. (Concept Media: Educational Videos Ser.). (ENG.). (C). 1500.00 *(978-1-4354-8835-9(0)*, Concept Media) Delmar Cengage Learning.

Condict-Cochran, Chelley, EdD. The Positive Positive Negative Positive Principle. 2007. 57p. pap. 11.95 *(978-0-615-17523-2(6))* Cochran, Chelley Condict.

Coplan, James. Making Sense of Autistic Spectrum Disorders: Create the Brightest Future for Your Child with the Best Treatment Options. 2010. (Illus.). 448p. 25.00 *(978-0-553-80681-6(5))* Random House Publishing Group.

Cotugno, Albert J. Group Interventions for Children with Autism Spectrum Disorders: A Focus on Social Competency & Social Skills. 2009. (ENG.). 160p. pap. *(978-1-84310-910-5(7))* Kingsley, Jessica Ltd.

Cowhey, Sharon. Going Through the Motions: Coping with Autism 2. 2006. (ENG.). 80p. per. 16.95 *(978-1-4137-5339-4(6))* PublishAmerica, Inc.

Crawford, Brad & Crawford, Alisha. The First Steps: A Parent's Guide to Fighting Autism. 2010. 256p. pap. 16.99 *(978-1-61579-784-4(X))* Xulon Pr., Inc.

Cresswell, Paul. Childhood Autism & Asperger's Syndrome. 2009. 94p. pap. 20.95 *(978-1-4092-6408-8(4))* Lulu Enterprises Inc.

Crucil, Leslie. You Don't Need to Know That: The Saga of Sammy. 2011. pap. 14.99 ***(978-1-61777-217-7(8))*** Tate Publishing & Enterprises, LLC.

Cumine, Val, et al. Autism in the Early Years. 2nd rev. ed. 2009. (Resource Materials for Teachers Ser.). (ENG., Illus.). 110p. pap., instr.'s gde. ed. 37.95 *(978-0-415-48373-5(5))* Routledge.

Cunningham, Karen Mayer. Defying Austism: A Miraculous Story of Hope. 2009. (ENG.). 128p. 14.99 *(978-1-59979-628-4(7)*, Creation Hse.) Charisma Media.

Daria, T. O. Dasha's Journal: A Cat Reflects on Life, Catness & Autism. 2008. (ENG., Illus.). 160p. pap. *(978-1-84310-586-2(1))* Kingsley, Jessica Ltd.

Davenport, Randi. The Boy Who Loved Tornadoes. 2010. (ENG.). 384p. 23.95 *(978-1-56512-611-4(4)*, 1565126114) Algonquin Bks. of Chapel Hill.

de Boer, Sonja R. Successful Inclusion for Students with Autism: Creating a Complete, Effective ASD Inclusion Program. 2009. (ENG., Illus.). 320p. pap. 32.95 *(978-0-470-23080-0(0)*, Jossey-Bass) Wiley, John & Sons, Inc.

Decker, Jeni. I Wish I Were Engulfed in Flames: My Insane Life Raising Two Boys with Autism. 2012. (ENG., Illus.). 288p. 24.95 *(978-1-61608-485-1(5)*, 608485) Skyhorse Publishing Co., Inc.

DeLong, Janet. Think: ... & into my Life. 2011. 348p. pap. 19.95 *(978-1-4520-9057-3(2))* AuthorHouse.

Densmore, Ann E. Helping Children with Autism Become More Social: 76 Ways to Use Narrative Play, 1 vol. 2007. (Illus.). 272p. 49.95 *(978-0-275-99702-1(2)*, C9702, Praeger Pubs.) Greenwood Publishing Group, Inc.

Desorgher, Sandra & Desorgher, Max. The Power of Exile, Autism: A Journey to Recovery. 400p. *(978-0-620-29365-5(9))* World Community Autism Program.

Dillon, Kathleen. Living with Autism. 2007. per. 0.00 *(978-1-59712-074-6(X))* Catawba Publishing Co.

Dishion, Thomas J., et al. Everyday Parenting: A Professional's Guide to Building Family Management Skills. 2011. pap. 18.95 ***(978-0-87822-658-0(3))*** Research Pr.

Dochniak, Michael J. & Dunn, Denise H. Allergies & Autism. 2010. (Allergies & Infectious Diseases Ser.). 147p. pap. 43.00 *(978-1-60876-352-8(8))* Nova Science Pubs., Inc.

Duncan, David. From Object to Life: An Extraordinary Journey Through Austistic Worlds. 2010. (ENG.). 294p. pap. 16.95 *(978-88-95604-08-4(3))* Pari Publishing ITA. Dist: AtlasBooks Distribution.

Duncan, Tami & Rosner, Bryan. The Lyme-Autism Connection: Unveiling the Shocking Link Between Lyme Disease & Childhood Developmental Disorders. 2008. 288p. pap. 25.95 *(978-0-9763797-5-1(9))* BioMed Publishing Group.

Dwivedi, Parul. My Cure for Autism: A Real Answer. 2008. (Illus.). 52p. per. 20.95 *(978-0-615-18793-8(5))* Magnum Group Co.

Edna, Maithya. Use of Physical Exercise in the Management of Autism Behaviour: Efficacy of a Physical Exercise Programme on the Stereotypic Behaviour & Response Amongst Autistic Children at the Nairobi Autism Unit, Kenya. 2011. 124p. pap. ***(978-3-639-30815-0(8))*** VDM Verlag Dr. Mueller e.K.

Edwards, Denise. Providing Practical Support for People with Autism Spectrum Disorder: Supported Living in the Community. 2008. (ENG., Illus.). 192p. pap. *(978-1-84310-577-0(2))* Kingsley, Jessica Ltd.

Egel, Andrew, et al. School Success for Kids with Autism. 2011. (ENG.). 250p. pap. 16.95 *(978-1-59363-746-0(2))* Prufrock Pr.

Elwins, Dannie. The Guide to Overcoming & Beating Autism. 2009. 40p. pap. 16.99 *(978-0-557-15428-9(6))* Lulu Enterprises Inc.

Eveleigh, Elaine. Notes from a Literal Life. 2009. 96p. pap. *(978-1-84747-661-6(9))* Chipmunkapublishing.

Exkorn, Karen Siff & Exkorn, Karen S. The Autism Sourcebook: Everything You Need to Know about Diagnosis, Treatment, Coping, & Healing — From a Mother Whose Child Recovered. 2006. (ENG.). 432p. pap. 19.99 *(978-0-06-085975-6(X)*, William Morrow Paperbacks) HarperCollins Pubs.

Eyal, Gil. The Autism Matrix: The Social Origins of the Autism Epidemic. 2010. (ENG., Illus.). 240p. 69.95 *(978-0-7456-4399-1(X))*; pap. 24.95 *(978-0-7456-4400-4(7))* Polity Pr. GBR. Dist: Wiley, John & Sons, Inc.

Faherty, Catherine. Understanding Death & Illness & What They Teach about Life: A Practical Guidebook for People with Autism or Aspergers, & Their Loved Ones. 2008. (ENG., Illus.). 341p. pap. 24.95 *(978-1-932565-56-0(6))* Future Horizons, Inc.

Farrell, Michael. The Effective Teacher's Guide to Autism & Communication Difficulties: Practical Strategies. 2nd rev. ed. 2012. (Effective Teacher's Guides). (ENG., Illus.). 104p. 120.00 ***(978-0-415-69382-0(9))***; pap. 35.95 ***(978-0-415-69383-7(7))*** Routledge.

—The Effective Teachers Guide to Moderate Severe & Profound Learning Difficulties (Cognitive Impairments) 2nd rev. ed. 2012. (Effective Teacher's Guides). (ENG., Illus.). 104p. 130.00 ***(978-0-415-69386-8(1))***; pap. 40.95 ***(978-0-415-69387-5(X))*** Routledge.

Fein, Deborah. The Neuropsychology of Autism, 1 vol. 2011. (ENG., Illus.). 528p. 79.95 *(978-0-19-537831-3(8))* Oxford Univ. Pr., Inc.

Fein, Deborah & Dunn, Michelle A. Autism in Your Classroom: A General Educator's Guide to Students with Autism Spectrum Disorders. 2007. (Topics in Autism Ser.). 319p. per. 19.95 *(978-1-890627-61-4(5))* Woodbine Hse.

Feinstein, Adam. A History of Autism: Conversations with the Pioneers. 2010. (ENG., Illus.). 400p. 125.95 *(978-1-4051-8654-4(2))*; pap. 49.95 *(978-1-4051-8653-7(4))* Wiley, John & Sons, Inc. (Wiley-Blackwell).

Fields-Meyer, Tom. Following Ezra: What One Father Learned about Gumby, Otters, Autism, & Love from His Extraordinary Son. 2011. (ENG.). 256p. (gr. 12). 15.00 *(978-0-451-23463-6(4)*, N A L Trade) Penguin Group (USA) Inc.

Fitzgerald, Michael, ed. Young, Violent, & Dangerous to Know. 2010. (Psychiatry - Theory, Applications & Treatments Ser.). 89.00 *(978-1-60876-952-0(6))* Nova Science Pubs., Inc.

Fitzpatrick, Michael. Defeating Autism: A Damaging Delusion. 2008. (Illus.). XVIII, 166p. pap. 39.95 *(978-0-415-44981-6(2))* Routledge.

Forrester, Rachel & Broadhurst, Sarah, eds. Autism & Loss. 2007. (ENG., Illus.). 208p. per. *(978-1-84310-433-9(4))* Kingsley, Jessica Ltd.

Forum on Neuroscience and Nervous System Disorders & Institute of Medicine. Autism & the Environment: Challenges & Opportunities for Research, Workshop Proceedings. 2008. (ENG.). 358p. pap. 71.50 *(978-0-309-10881-2(0))* National Academies Pr.

Freedman, Jeri. Autism. 2008. lib. bdg. 29.25 *(978-1-4042-1852-9(1))* Rosen Publishing Group, Inc., The.

Freeman, Sabrina Karen. The Complete Guide to Autism Treatments: A Parent's Handbook: Make Sure Your Child Gets What Works! 2007. viii, 509p. pap. 29.95 *(978-0-9657565-6-3(4))* SKF Bks., Inc.

Frith, Uta. Autism. Oxford University Press Staff, ed. 2008. (Very Short Introductions Ser.). (ENG., Illus.). 144p. pap. 11.95 *(978-0-19-920756-5(9))* Oxford Univ. Pr., Inc.

Fuentes, Carolyn. Autism. 2007. 187p. pap. 62.60 *(978-0-615-15559-3(6))* Fuentes, Carolyn.

Fuentes, Teacher Carolyn. Autism. 2008. 187p. 32.53 *(978-0-615-20797-1(9))* Fuentes, Carolyn.

Gabriels, Robin L. & Hill, Dina E., eds. Growing up with Autism: Working with School-Age Children & Adolescents. 2010. (ENG.). 302p. (gr. 1-13). pap. 28.00 *(978-1-60918-147-5(6))* Guilford Pubns., Inc.

Gallegos, Elena M. & Shallenberger, Jill M. Autism Methodology Cases to Live By: Legal Guidance for Practical Program Strategies. 2008. *(978-1-57834-100-9(0))* LRP Pubns.

Gallo, Donald P. Diagnosing Autism Spectrum Disorders: A Lifespan Perspective. 2010. (ENG.). 198p. 120.95 *(978-0-470-74924-1(5)*, Wiley) Wiley, John & Sons, Inc.

Gallo-Lopez, Loretta & Rubin, Lawrence C., eds. Play-Based Interventions for Children & Adolescents on the Autism Spectrum. 2012. (ENG., Illus.). 397p. 47.95 *(978-0-415-89075-5(6))* Routledge.

Garvin, Eileen. How to Be a Sister: A Love Story with a Twist of Autism. 2010. (ENG.). 272p. pap. 14.95 *(978-1-61519-016-4(3)*, 1615190163) Experiment LLC, The.

Gasberg, Beth A. Stop That (Seemingly) Senseless Behavior! FBA-based Interventions for People with Autism. 2008. 150p. pap. 19.95 *(978-1-890627-76-8(3))* Woodbine Hse.

George, Jack E. The Autism Handbook: Easy to Understand Information, Insight, Perspectives & Case Studies from a Special Education Teacher. 2009. 178p. pap. *(978-1-926585-50-5(X)*, No.1 Bk. Pubs.) CCB Publishing.

George, Jack E. Zi Bi Zheng Shou Che: Yi Ming Te Chu Jiao Yu Dao Shi ... Liu, Weitong, tr. from ENG. 2012.Tr. of Autism Handbook: Easy to Understand Information, Insight, Perspectives & Case Studies from a Special Education Teacher (Chinese Simplified Edition). (CHI.). 222p. pap. ***(978-1-927360-16-3(1)***, No.1 Bk. Pubs.) CCB Publishing.

George, Lynne. Brandon's Window. 2009. 186p. pap. 39.95 *(978-0-578-00383-2(X))* George, Lynne M.

Gerstle, Val & Walsh, Lynda. Autism Spectrum Disorders in the College Composition Classroom: Making Writing Instruction More Accessible for All Students. 2011. (ENG.). 150p. pap. 20.00 ***(978-0-87462-072-6(4))*** Marquette Univ. Pr.

Ginsberg, Blaze. Episodes: Scenes from Life, Love, & Autism. 2012. (ENG.). 304p. (YA). pap. 9.99 ***(978-0-312-65943-1(1))*** Square Fish.

Giordano, Alessia C. & Lombardi, Viola A. Causes & Risks for Autism. 2008. 69.00 *(978-1-60456-861-5(5))* Nova Science Pubs., Inc.

Goggins, Barbra Monroe. Lessons from Joshu: God Whispers Through Autism. 2010. 224p. pap. 14.95 *(978-1-4490-7639-9(4))* AuthorHouse.

Goldberg, Michael. The Myth of Autism: How a Misunderstood Epidemic Is Destroying Our Children. 2011. (ENG., Illus.). 288p. 24.95 *(978-1-61608-171-3(6)*, 608171) Skyhorse Publishing Co., Inc.

Goldstein, Sam, et al, eds. Assessment of Autism Spectrum Disorders. 2008. (ENG., Illus.). 384p. 50.00 *(978-1-59385-983-1(X))* Guilford Pubns., Inc.

Gottlieb, Daniel. Letters to Sam: A Grandfather's Lessons on Love, Loss, & the Gifts of Life. 2008. (ENG.). 176p. per. 12.95 *(978-1-4027-5345-9(4))* Sterling Publishing Co., Inc.

Graham, James. Autism, Discrimination & the Law: A Quick Guide for Parents, Educators & Employers. 2nd ed. 2008. (ENG.). 144p. per. *(978-1-84310-627-2(2))* Kingsley, Jessica Ltd.

Grandin, Temple. Thinking in Pictures: My Life with Autism. exp. movie tie-in ed. 2010. (Vintage Ser.). (ENG.). 304p. pap. 15.00 *(978-0-307-73958-2(9)*, Vintage) Knopf Doubleday Publishing Group.

—The Way I See It: A Personal Look at Autism & Asperger's. 2nd rev. exp. ed. 2011. (ENG., Illus.). 339p. pap. 19.95 *(978-1-935274-21-6(X))* Future Horizons, Inc.

Grandin, Temple & Duffy, Kate. Developing Talents: Careers for Individuals with Asperger Syndrome & High-Functioning Autism. 2008. 153p. pap. 21.95 *(978-1-934575-28-4(3))* Autism Asperger Publishing Co.

Grandin, Temple & Johnson, Catherine. Animals in Translation: Using the Mysteries of Autism to Decode Animal Behavior. 2010. (ENG.). 368p. 28.00 *(978-1-4391-8710-4(X)*, Scribner) Scribner.

Greene. Member of the Club. (ENG.). 224p. pap. 18.99 *(978-1-84310-705-7(8))* Kingsley, Jessica Ltd. GBR. Dist: Books International, Inc.

Greenspan, Stanley I. & Tippy, Gil. Respecting Autism: The Rebecca School DIR Casebook for Parents & Professionals. 2011. pap. 19.95 ***(978-0-533-16454-7(0))*** Vantage Pr., Inc.

Griffin, Simone Wyn & Sandler, Dianne. Motivate to Communicate! 300 Games & Activities for Your Child with Autism. 2009. (ENG.). 240p. pap. (978-1-84905-041-8(4)) Kingsley, Jessica Ltd.

Grinker, Roy Richard. Unstrange Minds: Remapping the World of Autism. 2008. (ENG.). 352p. per. 16.95 (978-0-465-02764-4(4)) Basic Bks.

Griswold, Alan. Autistic Songs. 2011. 172p. pap. 15.95 (978-1-4502-9994-7(6)) iUniverse, Inc.

Grossberg, Blythe. Asperger's Rules! How to Make Sense of School & Friends. 2012. 14.95 **(978-1-4338-1128-9(6))**; pap. 9.95 **(978-1-4338-1127-2(8))** American Psychological Assn. (Magination Pr.).

Grossman, Barry & Aspy, Ruth. The Ziggurat Model: A Framework for Designing Comprehensive Interventions for Individuals with High-Functioning Autism & Asperger Syndrome. 2007. pap. 49.95 (978-1-931282-36-9(6)) Autism Asperger Publishing Co.

Guli, Laura A., et al. Social Competence Intervention Program (SCIP) (Book & CD) A Drama-Based Intervention for Youth on the Autism Spectrum. 2008. pap. 32.95 (978-0-87822-548-4(X)) Research Pr.

Gyori, Miklos. Autism & Cognitive Architecture. (Illus.). 236p. (C). (978-963-05-8337-4(2)) Akademiai Kiado.

Hall, Elaine. Now I See the Moon: A Mother, a Son, & the Miracle of Autism. 2010. 256p. 19.99 (978-0-06-174380-1(1)) HarperCollins Pubs.

Hall, Laura J. Autism Spectrum Disorders: From Theory to Practice. (ENG., (C). 2008. Illus.). 256p. pap. 34.67 (978-0-13-227534-7(1)) 2nd rev. ed. 2012. 312p. pap. 34.67 **(978-0-13-265809-6(7))** Prentice Hall PTR. (Prentice Hall).

Hanska, Kascia. Hamburger Syndrome. 2009. pap. 14.95 (978-1-59712-361-7(7)) Catawba Publishing Co.

Happe, Francesca & Frith, Uta, eds. Autism & Talent. 2010. (ENG., Illus.). 248p. 69.95 (978-0-19-956014-1(5)) Oxford Univ. Pr., Inc.

Harris, Deborah L. Trapped in A World of Silence. 2010. pap. 14.99 (978-0-578-05568-8(6)) Brand N Stone Publishing Co.

Hart, Megan & Lutz, Kim. The Everything Guide to Cooking for Children with Autism: From Everyday Meals to Holiday Treats - 200 Tasty Recipes Your Child Will Love to Eat. 2010. (ENG., Illus.). 304p. pap. 15.95 (978-1-4405-0021-3(5)) Adams Media Corp.

Healing Project Staff, ed. Voices of Autism: The Healing Companion: Stories for Courage, Comfort & Strength. 2008. (Voices of Ser.). (ENG., Illus.). 300p. pap. 16.95 (978-1-934184-05-9(5)) Lachance Publishing LLC.

Heinks, Julie K. Andrew's Story: One Boy's Journey Back from Autism. 2008. 134p. pap. 24.95 (978-1-60610-943-4(X)) PublishAmerica, Inc.

Hendrickson, Laura, et al. Finding Your Child's Way on the Autism Spectrum: Discovering Unique Strengths, Mastering Behavior Challenges, 1 vol. 2009. (ENG.). 144p. pap. 14.99 (978-0-8024-4505-6(5)) Moody Pubs.

Herskowitz, Valerie. Autism & Computers: Maximizing Independence Through Technology. 2009. 164p. 25.49 (978-1-4389-8115-4(5)); pap. 13.49 (978-1-4389-8114-7(7)) AuthorHouse.

Hewett, Dave, et al. The Intensive Interaction Handbook. 2011. (Illus.). 168p. 120.00 **(978-0-85702-490-9(6)**, B24909C) SAGE Pubns., Ltd. GBR. Dist: SAGE Pubns., Inc.

Hickmott, Olive. Bridges to Success: Keys to Transforming Learning Difficulties; Simple skills for families & teachers to bring success to those with Dyslexia, Dysca. 2011. 250p. pap. **(978-1-908218-78-0(9))** MX Publishing, Ltd.

Hillman, Jennifer & Snyder, Stephen. Childhood Autism: A Clinician's Guide to Early Diagnosis & Integrated Treatment. 2007. (ENG., Illus.). 176p. (C). per. 37.50 (978-0-415-37260-2(7)) Routledge.

Hillman, Jennifer L., et al. Childhood Autism. 2007. (ENG., Illus.). 176p. (C). 95.00 (978-0-415-37259-6(3)) Routledge.

Hobson. Theories of Autism. 2010. (C). pap. 24.95 (978-0-415-43318-1(5), Routledge) Taylor & Francis Group GBR. Dist: Taylor & Francis Group.

Hobson, Peter. Autism & the Development of Mind. 2008. 104.00 (978-0-415-43335-8(5)) Routledge.

—Autism & the Development of Mind. 2nd ed. 2010. (C). pap. 36.95 (978-0-415-43336-5(3), Routledge) Taylor & Francis Group GBR. Dist: Taylor & Francis Group.

—Theories of Autism. 2010. (C). 104.00 (978-0-415-43317-4(7), Routledge) Taylor & Francis Group GBR. Dist: Taylor & Francis Group.

Hobson, Peter N., et al, eds. Foundations for Self-Awareness: An Exploration Through Autism. 2006. (Monographs of the Society for Research in Child Development Ser.). (ENG., Illus.). 200p. pap. 38.95 (978-1-4051-6722-2(X), Wiley-Blackwell) Wiley, John & Sons, Inc.

Hollander, Eric & Anagnostou, Evdokia. Clinical Manual for the Treatment of Autism. 2007. (Illus.). 314p. per. 64.00 (978-1-58562-222-1(2)) American Psychiatric Publishing, Inc.

Hosin, Amer A. Autism, ADHD, & Anorexia Nervosa: Essays on Three Childhood Disorders. (Illus.). 120p. 89.95 (978-0-7734-5163-6(3)) Mellen, Edwin Pr., The.

Howarth, Sandy. No Matter What: Autism. 2009. (Illus.). 284p. pap. (978-1-84747-749-1(6)) Chipmunkapublishing.

Hudson, Jill & Coffin, Amy Bixler. Out & About: Preparing Children with Autism Spectrum Disorders to Participate in Their Communities. 2007. (Illus.). 78p. per. 19.95 (978-1-931282-48-2(X)) Autism Asperger Publishing Co.

Hughes-Lynch, Claire. Teaching Children with High-Functioning Autism: Strategies for the Inclusive Classroom. 2011. (ENG.). 250p. pap. 24.95 (978-1-59363-747-7(0)) Prufrock Pr.

Isaacson, Rupert. The Horse Boy: A Memoir of Healing. 2010. (ENG., Illus.). 400p. pap. 15.99 (978-0-316-00824-2(9), Back Bay Bks.) Little Brown & Co.

Jackson, Claudreen. Jackson Claudre. 2010. 142p. pap. 16.95 (978-1-934363-59-1(6)) Zoe Life Publishing.

Jacobs, Debra S. & Betts, Dion E. Everyday Activities to Help Your Young Child with Autism Live Life to the Full: Simple Exercises to Boost Functional Skills, Sensory Processing, Coordination & Self-Care. 2012. (ENG.). 144p. pap. **(978-1-84905-238-2(7))** Kingsley, Jessica Ltd.

Jameson Tilton, Adele, et al. When Your Child Has... Autism. 2009. (ENG.). 224p. pap. 6.95 (978-1-59869-676-9(9)) Adams Media Corp.

Janzen, Janice, et al. Autism Encyclopedia: The Complete Guide to Autism Spectrum Disorders. 2009. (ENG.). 300p. pap. 22.95 (978-1-59363-360-8(2)) Prufrock Pr.

Janzen, Janice E. Autism Handbook for Parents: Facts & Strategies for Parenting Success. 2009. (ENG.). 175p. pap. 16.95 (978-1-59363-361-5(0)) Prufrock Pr.

Jayson, Leonard & Comm, Maria. Severe Autism, Denied Support: Struggling to Survive in the Mainstream. 2007. 284p. 29.95 (978-1-4251-3600-0(1)); per. 21.95 (978-1-4251-1621-7(3)) Trafford Publishing.

Johnson, Jane & Van Rensselaer, Anne, eds. Families of Adults with Autism: Stories & Advice for the Next Generation. 2008. (ENG.). 176p. pap. (978-1-84310-885-6(2)) Kingsley, Jessica Ltd.

Joshi, Suman, et al. Courage, Heart & Wisdom: Essays on Autism. 2009. 365p. pap. 18.95 (978-1-4327-1107-8(5)) Outskirts Pr., Inc.

Judd, Sandra J., ed. Autism & Pervasive Developmental Disorders Sourcebook: Basic Consumer Health Information about Autism Spectrum & Pervasive Development Disorders, Such as Classical Autism, Asperger Syndrome, Rett Syndrome, & Childhood Disintegrative Disorder, Including Information about Related Genetic Disorders & Medica. 2007. (Health Reference Ser.). 631p. 87.00 (978-0-7808-0953-6(X)) Omnigraphics, Inc.

Julie Jurgens-Shimek. Autism Is a Four Letter Word: Love. 2009. 124p. 21.99 (978-1-4389-6540-6(0)); pap. 15.99 (978-1-4389-6539-0(7)) AuthorHouse.

Karem-Gramig, Pat. Don't Look Now, but Your Kid Is Showing: A Memoir. 2011. pap. 10.99 **(978-1-61777-339-6(5))** Tate Publishing & Enterprises, LLC.

Kaskel, Psy. D. Social Skills Training for Adolescents with Autism. 2009 108p. pap. (978-3-639-20908-2(7)) VDM Verlag Dr. Mueller e.K.

Kessick, Rosemary. Autism & Diet: What You Need to Know. 2009. (ENG., Illus.). 96p. pap. (978-1-84310-983-9(2)) Kingsley, Jessica Ltd.

—Autism & Gastrointestinal Complaints: What You Need to Know. 2009. (ENG., Illus.). 80p. pap. (978-1-84310-984-6(0)) Kingsley, Jessica Ltd.

King, Brian R. Let's Relate on the Autism Spectrum: Strategies for Building Meaningful Relationships. 2011. (ENG.). 272p. pap. **(978-1-84905-856-8(3))** Kingsley, Jessica Ltd.

Kinney, James A. Autism: Hope, Healing & Understanding, 1 vol. 2009. 148p. pap. 24.95 (978-1-60703-595-4(2)) PublishAmerica, Inc.

Kirby, David. Evidence of Harm: Mercury in Vaccines & the Autism Epidemic: A Medical Controversy. Date not set. mass mkt. (978-0-312-99598-0(9), St. Martin's Paperbacks) St. Martin's Pr.

Kluth, Paula & Schwarz, Patrick. Just Give Him the Whale! 20 Ways to Use Fascinations, Areas of Expertise, & Strengths to Support Students with Autism. 2008. 120p. per. 19.95 (978-1-55766-960-5(0)) Brookes, Paul H. Publishing Co.

Koegel, Robert L. & Koegel, Lynn Kern. The PRT Pocket Guide: Pivotal Response Treatment for Autism Spectrum Disorders. 2012. 216p. pap. 19.95 **(978-1-59857-105-9(2))** Brookes, Paul H. Publishing Co.

Kupperman, Phyllis. The Source for Intervention in Autism Spectrum Disorders. 2008. (Illus.). 166p. (978-0-7606-0834-0(2)) LinguiSystems, Inc.

Kutscher, Martin L. & Kutscher, Martin. Kids with A Syndrome Mix of Adhd, Ld, As. 2nd ed. 2007. (ENG., Illus.). 24p. pap. (978-1-84310-811-5(9)) Kingsley, Jessica Ltd.

Lane, Sharon E. Green Is the Cure: Everything You Wanted to Know about 504 Plans, IEPs, Learning Disabilities & What the Hell Is in the Food. 2007. 136p. per. 13.95 (978-0-595-44775-6(9)) iUniverse, Inc.

Langston, Kelly. Autism's Hidden Blessings: Discovering God's Promises for Autistic Children & Their Families, 1 vol. 2009. 208p. pap. 13.99 (978-0-8254-2977-4(3)) Kregel Pubns.

Larkey, Sue. Practical Sensory Programmes for Students with Autism Spectrum Disorder & Other Special Needs. 2006. (ENG., Illus.). 12p. per. (978-1-84310-479-7(2)) Kingsley, Jessica Ltd.

Laugeson, Elizabeth A. & Frankel, Fred. Social Skills for Teenagers with Developmental & Autism Spectrum Disorders. 2010. (ENG., Illus.). 448p. pap. 49.95 (978-0-415-87203-4(0)) Routledge.

Lawson, John. The Role of Autism in Shaping Society. 2009. 112p. 40.00 (978-0-415-41336-7(2), Psychology Press) Taylor & Francis Group GBR. Dist: Taylor & Francis Group.

Lawson, Wendy. The Passionate Mind: How People with Autism Learn. 2010. (ENG., Illus.). 224p. pap. (978-1-84905-121-7(6)) Kingsley, Jessica Ltd.

Le Breton, Dean A. Talk, Talk, Sweet Charlotte. 2009. 192p. 24.99 (978-1-4389-7272-5(5)); pap. 15.95 (978-1-4389-7271-8(7)) AuthorHouse.

Leaf, Ronald, et al. Sense & Nonsense in the Behavioral Treatment of Autism: It Has to Be Said. Eng, John, ed. 2008. 370p. per. 42.95 (978-0-9755859-2-4(4)) DRL Bk., Inc.

LeComer, Laurie. The Socially Included Child: A Parent's Guide to Successful Playdates, Recreation, & Family Events for Children with Autism. 2009. (ENG.). 256p. (gr. 12-18). pap. 14.00 (978-0-425-22965-1(3), Berkley Trade) Penguin Group (USA) Inc.

Lee, Patricia A. In His Glory, I Learned to Lean on God. 2011. 162p. pap. 15.99 **(978-1-934769-47-8(9))** McDougal & Assocs.

Lehmann, Annie Lubliner. The Accidental Teacher: Life Lessons from My Silent Son. 2009. (ENG.). 184p. 45.00 (978-0-472-07074-9(6)); pap. 17.95 (978-0-472-05074-1(5)) Univ. of Michigan Pr.

Lerner, Patricia S. Envisioning a Bright Future: Interventions That Work for Children & Adults with Autism Spectrum Disorders. Lerner, Patricia S., ed. 2008. (ENG.). 414p. pap. 35.00 (978-0-929780-17-7(5)) Optometric Extension Program Fndtn.

Levine, Karen & Chedd, Naomi. Replays: Using Play to Enhance Emotional & Behavioral Development for Children with Autism Spectrum Disorders. 2006. (ENG., Illus.). 16p. per. (978-1-84310-832-0(1)) Kingsley, Jessica Ltd.

Levy, Jonathan. What You Can Do Right Now to Help Your Child with Autism. 2007. (ENG.). 256p. per. 14.95 (978-1-4022-0918-5(5)) Sourcebooks, Inc.

Lewis, Cathleen. Rex: A Mother, Her Autistic Child, & the Music that Transformed Their Lives, 0 vols. 2008. (Illus.). 256p. 24.99 (978-1-59555-150-4(6)) Nelson, Thomas Inc.

Lipsky, Deborah & Richards, Will. Managing Meltdowns: Using the S. C. A. R. E. D Calming Technique with Children & Adults with Autism. 2009. (ENG.). 80p. pap. (978-1-84310-908-2(5)) Kingsley, Jessica Ltd.

Liske, Julie C. In the Eye of the Hurricane: Finding peace within the storm of Autism. 2006. per. 19.95 (978-0-9774754-1-4(7)) Spiritbuilding.

Louise, Stephanie. Autism, the Way Forward: A Self-Help Guide to Teaching Children on the Autistic Spectrum. 2008. 146p. pap. 22.95 (978-1-85575-598-7(X)) Karnac Bks. GBR. Dist: Stylus Publishing, LLC.

Lovaas, O. Ivar, et al. Problems of Autistic Behavior Vol. 1: Experimental Analysis of Autism. 300p. (978-0-8290-0740-4(7)) Irvington Pubs.

Lubetsky, Martin J., et al. Autism Spectrum Disorder, 1 vol. 2011. (Pittsburgh Pocket Psychiatry Ser.). (ENG., Illus.). 360p. pap. 49.95 (978-0-19-975385-7(7)) Oxford Univ. Pr., Inc.

Lucan, Dawn. Practical Autism Manual. 2011. 100p. pap. 21.95 **(978-1-4583-4489-2(4))** 2010. 112p. pap. 14.95 (978-0-557-47586-5(4)) 2010. 80p. pap. 16.95 (978-0-557-44062-7(9)) 2010. (ENG.). 80p. pap. 12.95 (978-0-557-47457-8(4)) Lulu Enterprises Inc.

—Practical Teacher's Autism Manual. 2010. (ENG.). 56p. pap. 24.95 (978-0-557-47438-7(8)); 52p. pap. 24.95 (978-0-557-46483-8(8)) Lulu Enterprises Inc.

—Quick & Easy Autism Cookbook. 2010. 56p. pap. 14.95 (978-0-557-55133-0(1)) Lulu Enterprises Inc.

MacKenzie, Heather. Reaching & Teaching the Child with Autism Spectrum Disorder: Using Learning Preferences & Strengths. 2008. (ENG., Illus.). 240p. pap. (978-1-84310-623-4(X)) Kingsley, Jessica Ltd.

Martos Perez, Juan, et al, eds. New Developments in Autism: The Furture Is Today. 2006. (ENG., Illus.). 352p. per. (978-1-84310-449-0(0)) Kingsley, Jessica Ltd.

Marwick, Trudy. The 'Q' Factor. 2008. 264p. pap. (978-1-84747-779-8(8)) Chipmunkapublishing.

Mather, Nancy & Jaffe, Lynne E. Comprehensive Evaluations: Case Reports for Psychologists, Diagnosticians, & Special Educators. 2010. (ENG., Illus.). 672p. pap. 78.00 (978-0-470-61791-5(8), Wiley) Wiley, John & Sons, Inc.

Matson, Johnny L., ed. Clinical Assessment & Intervention for Autism Spectrum Disorders. 2008. (Practical Resources for the Mental Health Professional Ser.). (ENG., Illus.). 446p. 80.95 (978-0-12-373606-2(4), Academic Pr.) Elsevier Science & Technology Bks.

Mayville, Erik A. & Mulick, James A. Behavioral Foundations of Effective Autism Treatment. 2010. (978-1-59738-031-7(8)) Sloan Publishing.

McCandless, Jaquelyn. Children with Starving Brains: A Medical Treatment Guide for Authism Spectrum Disorder. 4th ed. 2009. 407p. pap. 29.95 (978-1-883647-17-9(7), Bramble Bks.) Bramble Co.

McCarthy, Jenny. Louder Than Words: A Mother's Journey in Healing Autism. 2009. (ENG.). 39.99 (978-1-60775-510-4(6)) Findaway World, LLC.

—Louder Than Words: A Mother's Journey in Healing Autism. 2008. (ENG.). 224p. (gr. 12-18). 14.00 (978-0-452-28980-2(7), Plume) Penguin Group (USA) Inc.

McCarthy, Jenny & Kartzinel, Jerry. Healing & Preventing Autism: A Complete Guide. 2010. (ENG., Illus.). 416p. (gr. 12-18). 16.00 (978-0-452-29592-5(0), Plume) Penguin Group (USA) Inc

McConnell, Kathleen & Ryser, Gail. Practical Ideas That Really Work for Students with Autism Spectrum Disorders. 2nd ed. 2007. (Illus.). 181p. 42.00 (978-1-4164-0227-5(6)) PRO-ED, Inc.

McGregor, Evelyn, et al, eds. Autism: An Integrated View from Neurocognitive, Clinical, & Intervention Research. 2007. (ENG., Illus.). 352p. 120.95 (978-1-4051-5695-0(3), Wiley-Blackwell) Wiley, John & Sons, Inc.

Medina, Kathy. Finding God in Autism: A Forty Day Devotional for Parents of Autistic Children. 2006. 99p. per. 9.99 (978-1-59886-563-9(3)) Tate Publishing & Enterprises, LLC.

Meltzer, Donald. Explorations of Autism: A Psychoanalytic Study. 2008. (Harris Meltzer Trust Ser.). (Illus.). 254p. (C). pap. 39.95 (978-1-85575-664-9(1)) Karnac Bks. GBR. Dist: Stylus Publishing, LLC.

Mesmere, Barbara S., ed. New Autism Research Developments. 2008. (Illus.). 129.00 (978-1-60021-936-8(5), Nova Biomedical Bks.) Nova Science Pubs., Inc.

Messenger, Kristine. Somewhere Between Here & Autism: Laughing with Angels, Dancing with Butterflies. 2009. 212p. 25.00 (978-1-4389-3771-7(7)); pap. 15.95 (978-1-4389-3772-4(5)) AuthorHouse.

Millan, Ann. Autism-Believe in the Future: From Infancy to Independence. 2010. 188p. 26.95 (978-1-4502-2186-3(6)); pap. 16.95 (978-1-4502-2184-9(X)) iUniverse, Inc.

Miller, L. D. Changing the Autistic Brain. 2009. 264p. pap. 16.95 (978-1-934937-74-7(6)) Mill City Pr., Inc.

Miller, Suzy. Awesomism! A New Way to Understand the Diagnosis of Autism. 2008. 116p. pap. 15.95 (978-1-4401-0285-1(6)) iUniverse, Inc.

Mills, Bruce & Cumberland, Debra, eds. Siblings & Autism: Stories Spanning Generations & Cultures. 2010. (ENG., Illus.). 240p. pap. (978-1-84905-831-5(8)) Kingsley, Jessica Ltd.

Millwood, Calvin. Beating Autism. 2008. 96p. pap. 16.95 (978-1-60474-357-9(3)) PublishAmerica, Inc.

Mitnik, G. Donald. Death of a Trillion Dreams. 2009. 178p. pap. 20.12 (978-0-557-15601-6(7)) Lulu Enterprises Inc.

Moor, Julia & Moore, Julia. Playing, Laughing & Learning with Children on the Autism Spectrum 2008: A Practical Resource of Play Ideas for Parents & Carers. 2nd ed. 2008. (ENG., Illus.). 304p. (C). pap. (978-1-84310-608-1(6)) Kingsley, Jessica Ltd.

Moore, Charlotte. George & Sam: Two Boys, One Family, & Autism. 2007. (ENG., Illus.). 320p. pap. 13.95 (978-0-312-37424-2(0), St. Martin's Griffin) St. Martin's Pr.

Mor, Caiseal. A Blessing & a Curse: Autism & Me. 2007. (ENG.). 28p. per. (978-1-84310-573-2(X)) Kingsley, Jessica Ltd.

Moustafa. You Are Not Alone — -A Message to Parents of Children with Autism. 2009. 238p. pap. 15.95 (978-1-935118-71-8(4)) Bellissima Publishing, LLC.

Moustafa, Deena. The Mystery Puzzle — Autism. 2010. 240p. pap. 19.95 (978-1-935118-92-3(7)) Bellissima Publishing, LLC.

Mueller, Kathleen. Facing Autism: A Parent's Guide to a Difficult Journey. 2008. 96p. pap. 11.95 (978-0-595-48698-4(3)) iUniverse, Inc.

Mukhopadhyay, Soma. Curriculum Guide for Autism Using Rapid Prompting Method: With Lesson Plan Suggestions. 2011. (ENG.). 395p. pap. 46.95 **(978-1-4327-7461-5(1))** Outskirts Pr., Inc.

Mukhopadhyay, Soma. Understanding Autism Through Rapid Prompting Method. 2008. 296p. pap. 39.95 (978-1-4327-2928-8(4)) Outskirts Pr., Inc.

Mukhopadhyay, Tito Rajarshi. How Can I Talk If My Lips Don't Move? Inside My Autistic Mind. 2011. (ENG.). 240p. pap. 14.95 (978-1-61145-022-4(5), 611022, Arcade Publishing) Skyhorse Publishing Co., Inc.

Murray, Stuart. Autism. 2011. (ENG., Illus.). 136p. 110.00 (978-0-415-88498-3(5)); pap. 25.95 (978-0-415-88499-0(3)) Routledge.

Myers, Jennifer McIlwee. How to Teach Life Skills to Kids with Autism or Asperger's. 2010. (ENG.). 322p. pap. 19.95 (978-1-935274-13-1(9)) Future Horizons, Inc.

Myles, Brenda Smith, et al. Autism Spectrum Disorders: A Handbook for Parents & Professionals, 2 vols. 2007. 544p. 200.00 (978-0-313-33632-4(6), GR3632, Praeger Pubs.) Greenwood Publishing Group, Inc.

Nambudripad, Devi S. Say Good-Bye to Allergy-Related Autism. 2nd ed. 2007. (Illus.). 286p. per. 18.00 (978-0-9743915-6-4(5)) Delta Publishing Co.

Nambudripad, Devi S. Say Good-Bye to Allergy-Related Autism NAET. 3rd ed. 2011. (ENG., Illus.). 280p. pap. 18.00 **(978-1-934523-17-9(8))** Delta Publishing Co.

Nazeer, Kamran. Send in the Idiots: Stories from the Other Side of Autism. 2007. (ENG., Illus.). 240p. per. 13.95 (978-1-58234-620-5(8)) Bloomsbury Publishing.

Newell, Trauma Fountaine. Alanis's Daily Routine. 2011. 28p. pap. 1.95 **(978-1-935268-82-6(1))** Halo Publishing International.

Nitsick, Janet Syas. Seasons of the Soul. 2006. (Illus.). 86p. per. 9.95 (978-1-59886-392-5(4)) Tate Publishing & Enterprises, LLC.

Notbohm, Ellen. The Autism Trail Guide: Postcards from the Road Less Traveled. 2007. (ENG.). 148p. per. 19.95 (978-1-932565-50-8(7)) Future Horizons, Inc.

Notbohm, Ellen & Zysk, Veronica. 1001 Great Ideas for Teaching & Raising Children with Autism Spectrum Disorders, 2nd Edition. 2nd rev. ed. 2010. (ENG.). 320p. pap. 24.95 (978-1-935274-06-3(6)) Future Horizons, Inc.

Núñez, María & Williams, Katie. Autism: An Integrated View from Neurocognitive, Clinical & Intervention Research. McGregor, Evelyn et al, eds. 2007. (ENG., Illus.). 352p. pap. 49.95 (978-1-4051-5696-7(1), Wiley-Blackwell) Wiley, John & Sons, Inc.

Ockelford, Adam. In the Key of Genius: The Extraordinary Life of Derek Paravicini. 2010. (ENG., Illus.). 288p. pap. 15.95 (978-0-09-951358-2(7)) Random Hse. GBR. Dist: Independent Pubs. Group.

Offit, Paul A. Autism's False Prophets: Bad Science, Risky Medicine, & the Search for a Cure. (ENG., Illus.). 328p. (gr. 17) 2010. pap. 16.95 (978-0-231-14637-1(X)) 2008. 24.95 (978-0-231-14636-4(1)) Columbia Univ. Pr.

—Autisms False Prophets: Bad Science, Risky Medicine, & the Search for a Cure. 2013. (Religion, Culture, & Public Life Ser.). (ENG.). 320p. (gr. 17). 89.50 (978-0-231-16262-3(6)) Columbia Univ. Pr.

Oller, John W. & Oller, Stephen D. Autism: The Diagnosis, Treatment, & Etiology of the Undeniable Epidemic. 2009. 456p. pap. 67.95 (978-0-7637-5280-4(0)) Jones & Bartlett Learning, LLC.

Olmsted, Dan & Blaxill, Mark. The Age of Autism: Mercury, Medicine, & a Man-Made Epidemic. (ENG., 448p. 2011. Illus.). pap. 16.99 (978-0-312-54709-7(9), St. Martin's Griffin) 2010. 27.99 (978-0-312-54562-8(2), Dunne, Thomas Bks.) St. Martin's Pr.

Osteen, Mark. Autism & Representation. 322p. 2009. 39.95 (978-0-415-80627-5(5)) 2007. (ENG., Illus.). 125.00 (978-0-415-95644-4(7)) Routledge.

—One of Us: A Family's Life with Autism. 2010. (ENG., Illus.). 280p. 29.95 (978-0-8262-1902-2(0)) Univ. of Missouri Pr.

Paisner, Daniel & McElwain, Jason J-Mac. The Game of My Life: A True Story of Challenge, Triumph, & Growing up Autistic. 2009. (ENG.). 256p. (gr. 12-18). 14.00 (978-0-451-22619-8(4), N A L Trade) Penguin Group (USA) Inc.

Pavlides, Merope. Animal-Assisted Interventions for Individuals with Autism. 2008. (ENG., Illus.). 192p. per. *(978-1-84310-867-2(4))* Kingsley, Jessica Ltd.
Paxton, Katherine & Estay, Irene A. Counseling People on the Autism Spectrum: A Practical Approach. 2007. (ENG., Illus.). 176p. per. *(978-1-84310-552-7(7))* Kingsley, Jessica Ltd.
Peacock, Tammy. God's Promise: A Family's Journey with Autism. 2006. (ENG., Illus.). 248p. per. 11.95 *(978-1-59800-800-5(5))* Outskirts Pr., Inc.
—Gods Promise A Familys Journey with Aut. 2006. 21.95 *(978-1-4327-0033-1(2))* Outskirts Pr., Inc.
Peete, Rodney & Morton, Danelle. Not My Boy! A Father, a Son, & One Family's Journey with Autism. 2010. (ENG.). 256p. 24.99 *(978-1-4013-2361-5(8))* Hyperion Pr.
Perry, Nancy. Adults on the Autism Spectrum Leave the Nest: Achieving Supported Independence. 2008. (ENG.). 288p. pap. *(978-1-84310-904-4(2))* Kingsley, Jessica Ltd.
Perry, Susan Lynn. Mother Cub. 2007. 112p. per. 12.95 *(978-0-595-47918-4(9))* iUniverse, Inc.
Pfalzgraf, Heidi. Just Another Autistic Kid, but This One's Mine: A Journey Through Autism. 2009. 84p. pap. 12.95 *(978-1-4389-3743-4(1))* AuthorHouse.
Pillay, Sarosha. Sensory Compatibility of Children with Autism & Their Mothers. 2011. 172p. pap. ***(978-3-8443-0811-2(3))*** Lambert Academic Publishing.
Plimley, Lynn & Bowen, Maggie. Social Skills & Autistic Spectrum Disorders. 2007. (Autistic Spectrum Disorder Support Kit Ser.). (Illus.). 96p. per. 24.00 *(978-1-4129-2313-2(1)*, B23123P) SAGE Pubns., Ltd. GBR. Dist: SAGE Pubns., Inc.
Porter, Constance. Break on Through. 2009. 236p. 28.95 *(978-0-595-71397-4(1))*; pap. 18.95 *(978-0-595-47902-3(2))* iUniverse, Inc.
Porter, Joseph. Autism & Reading Comprehension: Ready-to-use Lessons for Teachers. 2011. (ENG., Illus.). 394p. pap. 19.95 *(978-1-935274-15-5(5))* Future Horizons, Inc.
Porter, Melanie. Cognitive & Social Skills in Neurodevelopmental Disorders. 2008. 172p. pap. *(978-3-639-08931-8(6))* VDM Verlag Dr. Mueller e.K.
Potiomkina, Anna. Ella, Me & Disability. 2010. (Illus.). 52p. pap. 22.49 *(978-1-4520-0295-8(9))* AuthorHouse.
Powell, Stuart & Jordan, Rita, eds. Autism & Learning. 2011. (ENG., Illus.). 168p. (C). pap. 40.95 *(978-0-415-68749-2(7))*; 155.00 *(978-0-415-68748-5(9))* Routledge.
Prasher, V. P., ed. Contemporary Issues in Intellectual Disabilities. 2010. (Mental Illnesses & Treatment Ser.). 89.00 *(978-1-61668-023-7(7))* Nova Science Pubs., Inc.
Price, Marean J. Lord, Why Not Me? A Mother's Story of an Autistic Child. (Illus.). 104p. (Orig.). pap. 14.95 *(978-1-883372-00-2(3))* Rondelle Publishing Co.
Ramaswamy, Sudha & Greer, R. Douglas. An Establishing Operation for Academic ResponseAcquisition: Testing the Effects of an Establishing Operation onResponse Acquisition & its Differential Effect onPerformance Tasks of Children with Autism. 2008. 88p. pap. *(978-3-639-09942-3(7))* VDM Verlag Dr. Mueller e.K.
Ramey, Emilia Murry & Ramey, Jody John. Autistics' Guide to Dating: A Book by Autistics, for Autistics & Those Who Love Them or Who Are in Love with Them. 2008. (ENG., Illus.). 112p. per. *(978-1-84310-881-8(X))* Kingsley, Jessica Ltd.
Reed, Phil, ed. Behavioral Theories & Interventions for Autism. 2009. (Illus.). x, 351p. 79.00 *(978-1-60741-165-9(2))* Nova Science Pubs., Inc.
Renyolds, Tammi. LifeTips 101 Autism Tips. 2007. 9.99 *(978-1-60275-002-9(5))* LifeTips.
Rey-Flaud, Henri. Les Enfants de L'indicible Peur: Nouveau Regard Sur L'autisme. 2010. (FRE., Illus.). 519p. *(978-2-7007-0402-0(9))* Montaigne, Editions.
—L'enfant Qui S'est Arrêté Au Seuil du Langage: Comprendre L'autisme. 2008. (FRE.). 425p. *(978-2-7007-0052-7(X))* Montaigne, Editions.
Reynolds, Ab: A Brief Introduction to Teaching Children with Autism. 2011. 102p. pap. 12.95 ***(978-0-557-84591-0(2))*** Lulu Enterprises Inc.
Reynolds, Mishawn K. A Complete Guide to Teaching Art to Those with Autism: Utilizing the Elements & Principles of Design & Life Skills. 2011. 432p. pap. 44.95 ***(978-1-4670-3593-4(9))*** AuthorHouse.
Richardson, Denise. A Kinder Way of Dying. 2011. 210p. 29.99 ***(978-1-4535-6015-0(7))***; pap. 19.99 ***(978-1-4535-6014-3(9))*** Xlibris Corp.
Riegel, Courtney. Through a Mother's Eyes: A Spiral down the Autism Spectrum. 2006. 94p. per. 9.99 *(978-1-59886-590-5(0))* Tate Publishing & Enterprises, LLC.
Robinson, Ricki G. Autism Solutions: How to Create a Healthy & Meaningful Life for Your Child. 2011. 448p. pap. *(978-0-373-89209-9(8))* Harlequin Enterprises, Ltd.
Robinson, Robin, creator. Answers for Autism: Famly Journeys Through Hope & Recovery. 2006. (Illus.). 260p. per. 19.95 *(978-0-9765756-2-7(0))* Sora Publishing.
Rodgers, Howard L. Raising Superman! Autism 101. 2010. 116p. 23.95 *(978-1-4490-8490-5(7))*; pap. 14.95 *(978-1-4490-8489-9(3))* AuthorHouse.
Rogers, Sally J., et al. An Early Start for Your Child with Autism: Using Everyday Activities to Help Kids Connect, Communicate, & Learn. 2012. (ENG.). 326p. 45.00 ***(978-1-4625-0389-6(6))***; pap. 16.95 ***(978-1-60918-470-4(X))*** Guilford Pubns., Inc.
Ron, Mayra. Diary of a Crazy Woman: One Woman's Fight to Help Her Son with Autism Find a Place in the World. 2009. (Illus.). 163p. pap. 14.99 *(978-1-60696-430-9(5))* Tate Publishing & Enterprises, LLC.
Rongey, Harold. Resolving the Mystery That Is... Autism. (Hayes) Burger, Cheryl, ed. & illus. by. 2008. 136p. pap. 16.95 *(978-0-9786301-2-6(2))* R/B Pubs., LLC.
Ruben, Sharon. Awakening Ashley: Mozart Knocks Autism on Its Ear. 2010. 240p. pap. 15.95 *(978-1-936236-24-4(9))* iUniverse, Inc.
Saleem-Muhammad, Rasheedah. Pedro's Visit to the Aquarium: A short story about Autism. 2010. 28p. pap. 14.95 *(978-1-60844-426-7(0))* Dog Ear Publishing, LLC.
Sanders, Roy Q. How to Talk to Parents about Autism. 2008. (ENG.). 256p. pap. 21.95 *(978-0-393-70529-4(3)*, 70529) Norton, W. W. & Co., Inc.
Santiago, Aida. My Angel Gabriel: My Autistic Angel. 2009. 128p. pap. 10.99 *(978-1-4389-4046-5(7))* AuthorHouse.
Saperstein, Jesse A. Atypical: Life with Asperger's in 20 1/3 Chapters. 2010. (ENG.). 240p. (gr. 12-18). 14.00 *(978-0-399-53572-7(1)*, Perigee Trade) Penguin Group (USA) Inc.
Sass, Keith. Too Bad: An autobiography, of Sorts. 2007. 197p. pap. 19.99 *(978-0-9799776-0-2(6))* Zabel Bks.
Sasson, Noah. Face Processing & the Own-Race Bias - a Study of Typical Development & Autism. 2007. 84p. per. *(978-3-8364-2669-5(2))* VDM Verlag Dr. Mueller e.K.
Schopler, Eric & Mesibov, Gary B., eds. Communication Problems in Autism. 2010. (Current Issues in Autism Ser.). 350p. pap. 109.00 *(978-1-4419-3203-7(8)*, 1441932038) Springer.
Schopler, Eric, et al. Adolescent & Adult Psychoeducational Profile: A Comprehensive Evaluation of the Autistic & Developmentally Disabled. pap. *(978-0-8290-1792-2(5))* Irvington Pubs.
Schreibman, Laura. The Science & Fiction of Autism. 2007. (Illus.). 304p. per. 19.00 *(978-0-674-02569-1(5))* Harvard Univ. Pr.
Schroeder, Ruth Knott. Coach Yourself Through the Autism Spectrum. 2009. (ENG., Illus.). 240p. pap. *(978-1-84905-801-8(6))* Kingsley, Jessica Ltd.
Schultz, Stephen. Autism Risk. 2008. 132p. pap. *(978-3-639-06790-3(8))* VDM Verlag Dr. Mueller e.K.
Seach, Diana. Interactive Play for Children with Autism. 2007. (Illus.). 223p. per. 39.95 *(978-0-415-33326-9(1))*; 160.00 *(978-0-415-35373-1(4))* Routledge.
Sears, Robert. The Autism Book: What Every Parent Needs to Know about Early Detection, Treatment, Recovery, & Prevention. 2010. (ENG.). 416p. pap. 14.99 *(978-0-316-04280-2(3))* Little Brown & Co.
Selfe, Lorna. Nadia Revisited. 2011. (ENG., Illus.). 272p. (C). 54.95 *(978-1-84872-038-1(6)*, Psychology Press) Taylor & Francis Group GBR. Dist: Taylor & Francis Group.
Sell, Colleen, ed. A Cup of Comfort for Parents of Children with Special Needs: Stories that celebrate the differences in our extraordinary Kids. 2009. (ENG.). 336p. pap. 9.95 *(978-1-60550-088-1(7))* Adams Media Corp.
Shane, Howard C. & Weiss-Kapp, Sharon. Visual Language in Autism. 2007. pap. 65.00 incl. cd-rom *(978-1-59756-063-4(4))* Plural Publishing, Inc.
Shannon, Joyce Brennfleck, ed. Autism & Pervasive Developmental Disorders Sourcebook. 2nd rev. ed. 2011. (Health Reference Ser.). 600p. 95.00 *(978-0-7808-1146-1(1))* Omnigraphics, Inc.
Shapiro, Bruce K. & Accardo, Pasquale J., eds. Autism Frontiers: Clinical Issues & Innovations. 2008. (Illus.). 256p. 49.95 *(978-1-55766-957-5(0))* Brookes, Paul H. Publishing Co.
Shawn, Allen. Twin: A Memoir. 2010. (ENG.). 240p. (gr. 12). 25.95 *(978-0-670-02237-3(3)*, Viking Adult) Penguin Group (USA) Inc.
—Twin: A Memoir. l.t. ed. 2011. 315p. 31.99 *(978-1-4104-3616-0(0))* Thorndike Pr.
Shlanger, Rhonda Ellen. For the Love of Meliss. 2010. 148p. 29.99 *(978-1-4490-5997-2(X))*; pap. 16.95 *(978-1-4490-5996-5(1))* AuthorHouse.
Shore, Stephen M. & Rastelli, Linda G. Understanding Autism for Dummies. 2006. (ENG., Illus.). 384p. pap. 19.99 *(978-0-7645-2547-6(6)*, For Dummies) Wiley, John & Sons, Inc.
Shumaker, Laura. A Regular Guy: Growing up with Autism. 2008. 225p. pap. 14.95 *(978-0-9801836-0-3(X))* Landscape Pr.
Shumway, Rebekah J. The Gift of Autism. 2010. 175p. pap. 14.95 *(978-0-557-39806-5(1))* Lulu Enterprises Inc.
Sicile-Kira, Chantal. What Is Autism? Understanding Life with Autism or Asperger's. rev. ed. 2012. (ENG.). 174p. pap. 14.95 ***(978-1-59652-842-0(7))*** Turner Publishing Co.
Sicile-Kira, Chantal. 41 Things to Know about Autism. 2010. (Good Things to Know Ser.). (ENG.). 211p. pap. 9.99 *(978-1-59652-583-2(5))* Turner Publishing Co.
Sicile-Kira, Chantal & Sicile-Kira, Jeremy. A Full Life with Autism: From Learning to Forming Relationships to Achieving Independence. 2012. (ENG., Illus.). 256p. pap. 18.00 ***(978-0-230-11246-9(3))*** Palgrave Macmillan.
Siegel, Bryna. Getting the Best for Your Child with Autism: An Expert's Guide to Treatment. 2008. (ENG.). 280p. (gr. -1-7). 40.00 *(978-1-59385-601-4(6))*; per. 16.95 *(978-1-59385-317-4(3))* Guilford Pubns., Inc.
Silberberg, Barrie. The Autism & ADHD Diet: A Step-by-Step Guide to Hope & Healing by Living Gluten Free & Casein Free (GFCF) & Other Interventions. 2009. (ENG.). 256p. pap. 14.99 *(978-1-4022-1845-3(1))* Sourcebooks, Inc.
Silverman, Chloe. Understanding Autism: Parents, Doctors, & the History of a Disorder. 2011. (ENG.). 360p. (C). 35.00 ***(978-0-691-15046-8(X))*** Princeton Univ. Pr.
Simpson, Wallis A. My Andrew: Day-to-Day Living with a Child with an Autism Spectrum Disorder. 2007. 163p. per. 19.95 *(978-1-931282-30-7(7))* Autism Asperger Publishing Co.
Sinclair, Leslie V. Autism Spectrum Disorder: A Supplemental Curriculum for Life's Lessons. 2008. (ENG.). 300p. pap. 34.95 *(978-1-59624-085-8(7))* Cleveland Clinic Pr.
Stillman, William. The Autism Prophecies: How an Evolution of Healers & Intuitives Is Influencing Our Spiritual Future. 2010. (ENG.). 1p. pap. 14.99 *(978-1-60163-116-9(2)*, New Page Bks.) Career Pr., Inc.
—Empowered Autism Parenting: Celebrating (And Defending) Your Child's Place in the World. 2009. (ENG.). 224p. pap. 16.95 *(978-0-470-47587-4(0)*, Jossey-Bass) Wiley, John & Sons, Inc.
—The Soul of Autism: Looking Beyond Labels to Unveil Spiritual Secrets of the Heart Savants. 2008. (ENG.). 1p. pap. 14.99 *(978-1-60163-005-6(0)*, New Page Bks.) Career Pr., Inc.
Striano, Tricia & Reid, Vincent, eds. Social Cognition: Development, Neuroscience & Autism. 2008. (ENG., Illus.). 376p. 116.95 *(978-1-4051-6217-3(1)*, Wiley-Blackwell) Wiley, John & Sons, Inc.
Strickland, Elizabeth. Eating for Autism: The 10-Step Nutrition Plan to Help Treat Your Child's Autism, Asperger's, or ADHD. 2009. (ENG.). 304p. pap. 17.95 *(978-0-7382-1243-2(1))* Da Capo Pr., Inc.
Stup, Sarah. Are Your Eyes Listening? Sarah Stup Collected Works. 2007. (ENG.). 108p. per. 18.00 *(978-0-9788408-0-8(1))* SarahStup.com.
Sullivan, Lori. Overcoming Autism: A Parent's Guide. 2009. 148p. 28.95 *(978-1-4490-2993-7(0))*; pap. 19.95 *(978-1-4490-2992-0(2))* AuthorHouse.
Swavely, Terri. Move, Move, Move: Alex's Story! 2009. 24p. pap. 14.95 *(978-1-4389-8070-6(1))* AuthorHouse.
Sykes, Lisa K. Sacred Spark. 2009. (Illus.). x, 314p. pap. ***(978-0-9717806-4-4(1))*** Fourth Lloyd Productions, LLC.
Tager-Flusberg, Helen. Autism & William's Syndrome. 2007. (Essays in Developmental Psychology Ser.). (ENG.). 192p. 44.95 *(978-1-84169-008-7(2)*, Psychology Press) Taylor & Francis Group GBR. Dist: Taylor & Francis Group.
Tammet, Daniel. Born on a Blue Day: Inside the Extraordinary Mind of an Autistic Savant. 2007. (ENG.). 256p. pap. 15.00 *(978-1-4165-4901-7(3)*, Free Pr.) Free Pr.
Tantam, Digby. Can the World Afford Autistic Spectrum Disorder? Nonverbal Communication, Asperger Syndrome & the Interbrain. 2009. (ENG., Illus.). 256p. *(978-1-84310-694-4(9))* Kingsley, Jessica Ltd.
Teitelbaum, Philip & Teitelbaum, Osnat. Does Your Baby Have Autism? Detecting the Earliest Signs of Autism. 2007. (ENG.). 192p. pap. 17.95 *(978-0-7570-0240-3(4))* Square One Pubs.
Telfer, J. Christopher's Story. 2007. 184p. per. *(978-1-84747-309-7(1))* Chipmunkapublishing.
—Christopher's Story Part Ii. 2008. 156p. pap. *(978-1-84747-378-3(4))* Chipmunkapublishing.
The Health Experts of The Doctors' Prescription for Healthy Living, ed. New Hope for Autism. 2008. 96p. pap. 12.95 *(978-1-893910-53-9(9))* Freedom Pr., Inc., The.
Thompson, Charlotte & Tilton, Adelle Jameson. The Everything Parent's Guide to Children with Autism: Expert, reassuring advice to help your child at home, at school, & at Play. 2nd ed. 2010. (ENG.). 304p. pap. 14.95 *(978-1-4405-0392-4(3))* Adams Media Corp.
Thompson, Travis. Dr. Thompson's Straight Talk on Autism. 2008. (Illus.). 304p. per. 24.95 *(978-1-55766-945-2(7))* Brookes, Paul H. Publishing Co.
—Freedom from Meltdowns: Dr. Thompson's Solutions for Children with Autism. 2008. 304p. *(978-1-55766-986-5(4))* Brookes, Paul H. Publishing Co.
—Individualized Autism Intervention for Young Children: Blending Discrete Trial & Naturalistic Strategies. 2011. (Illus.). 208p. pap. 29.95 *(978-1-59857-173-8(7))* Brookes, Paul H. Publishing Co.
—Making Sense of Autism. 2007. (Illus.). 266p. per. 29.95 *(978-1-55766-915-5(5))* Brookes, Paul H. Publishing Co.
Tickle, Anna & Stott, Bettina. Exploring Bullying with Adults with Autism & Asperger Syndrome: A Photocopiable Workbook. 2010. (ENG., Illus.). 320p. pap. *(978-1-84905-035-7(X))* Kingsley, Jessica Ltd.
Timimi, Sami, et al. Myth of Autism: Medicalising Men's & Boys' Social & Emotional Competence. 2010. (ENG., Illus.). 180p. pap. 32.95 *(978-0-230-54526-7(2))* Palgrave Macmillan.
Tubbs, Janet. Creative Therapy for Children with Autism, Add, & Asperger's: Using Artistic Creativity to Reach, Teach, & Touch Our Children. 2008. (ENG.). 224p. pap. 18.95 *(978-0-7570-0300-4(1))* Square One Pubs.
Tucker, George. Teachers' Views on the Spiritual Development of Children with Autism. 2011. 112p. pap. ***(978-3-8443-1487-8(3))*** Lambert Academic Publishing.
Turkington, Carol & Anan, Ruth. The A to Z of Autism Spectrum Disorders. 2007. (Library of Health & Living). 336p. pap. 19.95 *(978-0-8160-7122-7(5)*, Checkmark Bks.) Facts On File, Inc.
Tyrell, Terrylynn. Community Screening for ASD in Early Intervention Settings: Training Pediatric Medical Practitioners to use Autism Screening Tools to Improve the Early Detection of Autism Spectrum Disorders. 2008. 156p. pap. *(978-3-639-10558-2(3))* VDM Verlag Dr. Mueller e.K.
Ulker, Riza. Human Gaze & Autism. 2010. 88p. pap. *(978-3-639-26339-8(1))* VDM Verlag Dr. Mueller e.K.
Unumb, Lorri Shealy & Unumb, Daniel R. Autism & the Law: Cases, Statutes, & Materials. 2011. 680p. 80.00 *(978-1-59460-875-9(X))* Carolina Academic Pr.
Vandegrift, Berthajane. A Few Impertinent Questions: About Autism, Freudianism & Materialism. 2011. 228p. pap. 18.95 *(978-1-4567-1970-8(X))* AuthorHouse.
Varughese, Tarin. Social Communication Cues for Young Children with Autism Spectrum Disorders & Related Conditions: How to Give Great Greetings, Pay Cool Compliments & Have Fun with Friends. 2011. (ENG.). 160p. pap. *(978-1-84905-870-4(9))* Kingsley, Jessica Ltd.
Verbout, Scott. An Asperger Journey: My Lifelong Battle with Autism. 2011. 76p. pap. 10.95 *(978-1-4502-9535-2(5))* iUniverse, Inc.
Volkmar, Fred R., ed. Autism & Pervasive Development Disorders. 2nd rev. ed. 2007. (Cambridge Child & Adolescent Psychiatry Ser.). (ENG., Illus.). 356p. 106.00 *(978-0-521-54957-8(4))* Cambridge Univ. Pr.
Volkmar, Fred R., et al. A Practical Guide to Autism: What Every Parent, Family Member, & Teacher Needs to Know. 2009. (ENG., Illus.). 628p. pap. 24.95 *(978-0-470-39473-1(0)*, Wiley) Wiley, John & Sons, Inc.
Vrana, Diane. A Love That Matters: One Family's Journey Through Autism ... from Heartache to Healing. 2009. 124p. pap. 13.69 *(978-1-4389-6071-5(9))* AuthorHouse.
Wakefield, Andrew. Callous Disregard: Autism & Vaccines - The Truth Behind a Tragedy. 2010. pap. *(978-1-4507-1187-6(1))* Independent Pub.
—Callous Disregard: Autism & Vaccines - The Truth Behind a Tragedy. 2010. (ENG.). 288p. 26.95 *(978-1-61608-169-0(4)*, 608169) Skyhorse Publishing Co., Inc.
Wakefield, Andrew J. Callous Disregard: Austims & Vaccines - The Truth Behind a Tragedy. 2011. (ENG.). 288p. pap. 17.95 *(978-1-61608-323-6(9)*, 608323) Skyhorse Publishing Co., Inc.
Wall, Kate. Education & Care for Adolescents & Adults with Autism: A Guide for Professionals & Carers. 2007. (Illus.). 168p. (C). 64.00 *(978-1-4129-2381-1(6)*, B23816C); per. 29.00 *(978-1-4129-2382-8(4)*, B23816P) SAGE Pubns., Ltd. GBR. Dist: SAGE Pubns., Inc.
Waltz, Mitzi. Autism: A Social & Medical History. 2012. (ENG.). 256p. 74.95 *(978-0-230-52750-8(7))* Palgrave Macmillan.
Way, Rhonda. Autism: Rebuilding with Builder Dan. 2008. (J). cd-rom 20.00 net. *(978-0-9740360-7-6(2))* Autism Research Institute.
Wehman, Paul, et al. Autism & the Transition to Adulthood: Success Beyond the Classroom. 2008. 304p. 37.95 *(978-1-55766-958-2(9))* Brookes, Paul H. Publishing Co.
West, Bryan. Aspergers, God & Me. 2008. 136p. pap. 18.49 *(978-1-4092-4394-6(X))* Lulu Enterprises Inc.
—Asperger's, God & Me (Australian Edition) 2008. 136p. pap. 18.44 *(978-1-4092-4709-8(0))* Lulu Enterprises Inc.
White, Susan Williams. Social Skills Training for Children with Asperger Syndrome & High-Functioning Autism. 2011. (Practitioner Guides in Child Psychotherapy Ser.). (ENG., Illus.). 182p. 30.00 *(978-1-60918-209-0(X))* Guilford Pubns., Inc.
Williams, Reno. Reno's World, Presenting Autism & Related Disabilities to Youth. 2009. 20p. pap. 10.95 *(978-1-936051-67-0(2))* Peppertree Pr., The.
Willis, Clarissa. My Child Has Autism: What Parents Need to Know. 2009. (ENG.). 160p. pap. 12.95 *(978-0-87659-093-5(8))* Gryphon Hse., Inc.
Winner, Michelle Garcia. Thinking About You Thinking About Me. 2nd rev. ed. 2007. *(978-0-9701320-1-7(8)*, Social Cognitive Deficits) Think Social Publishing, Inc.
Wiseman, Nancy. Could It Be Autism? A Parent's Guide to the First Signs & Next Steps. 2007. (ENG.). 272p. pap. 14.99 *(978-0-7679-1973-9(4)*, Broadway) Broadway Bks.
Wiseman, Nancy D. The First Year: Autism Spectrum Disorders - An Essential Guide for the Newly Diagnosed Child. 2009. (ENG.). 368p. pap. 16.95 *(978-1-60094-065-1(X))* Da Capo Pr., Inc.
Woodward, Bob & Hogenboom, Marga. Autism: A Holistic Approach. 2nd rev. ed. 288p. pap. 45.00 *(978-0-86315-378-5(X))* Floris Bks. GBR. Dist: SteinerBooks, Inc.
Yasmin, Nilofer Farooqi. Mental Retardation, Autism & Stuttering: Effectiveness of Token Economy Technique for Children with Mental Retardation, Autism & Stuttering. 2011. 84p. pap. ***(978-3-639-32947-6(3))*** VDM Verlag Dr. Mueller e.K.
Zager, Dianne, et al, eds. Educating Students with Autism. 2011. (ENG., Illus.). 352p. 150.00 *(978-0-415-87756-5(3))*; pap. 59.95 *(978-0-415-87757-2(1))* Routledge.
Zaks, Zosia. Life & Love: Positive Strategies for Autistic Adults. 2006. (Illus.). 367p. per. 24.95 *(978-1-931282-93-2(5))* Autism Asperger Publishing Co.
Zelan, Karen. Between Their World & Ours: Breakthroughs with Autistc Children. Date not set. mass mkt. *(978-0-312-98923-1(7)*, St. Martin's Paperbacks) St. Martin's Pr.
Zhao, L. B., ed. Autism Research Advances. 2007. 198p. (C). 129.00 *(978-1-60021-523-0(8))* Nova Science Pubs., Inc.
Zimmerman, Andrew W. Autism: Current Theories & Evidence. 2008. (Illus.). 572p. 159.00 *(978-1-60327-488-3(X))* Springer.
Zimmerman, Andrew W., ed. Autism: Current Theories & Evidence. 2010. (Current Clinical Neurology Ser.). (Illus.). xix, 474p. pap. 159.00 *(978-1-61737-901-7(8)*, 1617379018) Humana Pr.

AUTISM—JUVENILE LITERATURE

Rustad, Martha E. H. Some Kids Have Autism. 2008. (Understanding Differences Ser.). (ENG.). 24p. (gr. k-1). pap. 35.70 *(978-1-4296-2075-8(7)*, Pebble Bks.) Capstone Pr., Inc.

AUTISM SPECTRUM DISORDERS

see also Asperger's Syndrome; Autism; Rett Syndrome

Al-Ghani, K.I. & Kenward, Lynda. From Home to School with Autism: How to Make Inclusion a Success. 2011. (ENG., Illus.). 112p. pap. ***(978-1-84905-169-9(0))*** Kingsley, Jessica Ltd.
Amaral, David, et al, eds. Autism Spectrum Disorders, 1 vol. 2011. (ENG., Illus.). 1520p. 250.00 *(978-0-19-537182-6(8))* Oxford Univ. Pr., Inc.

Asp, Elissa D. & de de Villiers, Jessica. When Language Breaks Down: Analysing Discourse in Clinical Contexts. 2010. (ENG., Illus.). 270p. 110.00 (978-0-521-88978-0(2)) Cambridge Univ. Pr.

Aspy, Ruth & Grossman, Barry. * Designing Comprehensive Interventions for High-Functioning Individuals with Autism Spectrum Disorders: The Ziggurat Model-Release 2. 0. 2011. 246p. pap. 59.00 **(978-1-934575-96-3(8))** Autism Asperger Publishing Co.

ATIA, Seat Center. Assistive Technology & Autism Spectrum Disorders: Research-Based Practice & Innovation in the Field. 2010. 92p. pap. 49.95 (978-0-557-23400-4(X)) Lulu Enterprises Inc.

Barry, Tammy D. Enhancing Communication in Children with Autism Spectrum Disorders. 2010. (ENG.). 72p. pap. 12.95 (978-1-59363-409-4(9)) Prufrock Pr.

Barton, Michael. It's Raining Cats & Dogs: An Autism Spectrum Guide to the Confusing World of Idioms, Metaphors & Everyday Expressions. 2012. (ENG., Illus.). 96p. **(978-1-84905-283-2(2))** Kingsley, Jessica Ltd.

Bernard-Opitz, Vera & Häußler, Anne. Visual Support for Children with Autism Spectrum Disorders. 2011. 228p. pap. 34.95 (978-1-934575-82-6(8)) Autism Asperger Publishing Co.

Bernier, Raphael & Gerdts, Jennifer. Autism Spectrum Disorders: A Reference Handbook. 1 vol. 2010. (Contemporary World Issues Ser.). (Illus.). 324p. 55.00 (978-1-59884-334-7(6), A2264C) ABC-CLIO, LLC.

Beytien, Alyson. Raising the Entire Autism Spectrum: Candid Advice & Creative Strategies from a Mom of 3 Boys on the Autism Spectrum. 2011. (ENG.). 286p. pap. 14.95 (978-1-935274-50-6(3)) Future Horizons, Inc.

Bierens, Francesca. A Spectrum of Light: Inspirational Interviews with Families Affected by Autism. 2009. (ENG.). 192p. pap. (978-1-84905-013-5(9)) Kingsley, Jessica Ltd.

Boelte, Sven & Hallmayer, Joachim, eds. Autism Spectrum Conditions: FAQs on Autism, Asperger Syndrome, & Atypical Autism Answered by International Experts. 2011. 283p. pap. 49.00 (978-0-88937-393-8(0)) Hogrefe Publishing.

Brooke, Stephanie L., ed. The Use of the Creative Therapies with Autism Spectrum Disorders. 2009. 396p. 83.95 (978-0-398-07891-1(2)); pap. 59.95 (978-0-398-07892-8(0)) Thomas, Charles C. Pub., Ltd.

Burns, Dan E. Saving Ben: A Father's Story of Autism. 2009. (Mayborn Literary Nonfiction Ser.). (ENG., Illus.). 192p. 22.95 (978-1-57441-269-7(8)) Univ. of North Texas Pr.

Cannon, Lynn, et al. Unstuck & on Target! An Executive Function Curriculum to Improve Flexibility for Children with Autism Spectrum Disorders, Research Edition. 2011. (Illus.). 256p. pap. 44.95 **(978-1-59857-203-2(2))** Brookes, Paul H. Publishing Co.

Carnahan, Christina & Williamson, Pamela, eds. Quality Literacy Instruction for Students with Autism Spectrum Disorders. 2010. (Illus.). 466p. (C). pap. 59.00 (978-1-934575-66-6(6)) Autism Asperger Publishing Co.

Chevallier, Coralie. Communication in Autism Spectrum Disorders. 2010. 244p. pap. (978-3-8383-6254-0(3)) Lambert Academic Publishing.

Clements, John, et al. Transition or Transformation? Helping Young People with Autistic Spectrum Disorder Set Out on a Hopeful Road Towards Their Adult Lives. 2010. (Illus.). 177p. pap. (978-1-84310-964-8(6)) Kingsley, Jessica Ltd.

Cowden, Jo E. The Cowden Preautism Observation Inventory: With Effective Intervention Activities for Sensory Motor Stimulation & Joint Attention. 2011. (Illus.). 226p. pap. 43.95 (978-0-398-08643-5(5)) Thomas, Charles C. Pub., Ltd.

Culp, Susan. A Buffet of Sensory Interventions: Solutions for Middle & High School Students with Autism Spectrum Disorders. 2011. (ENG., Illus.). 150p. pap. 19.95 **(978-1-934575-83-3(6))** Autism Asperger Publishing Co.

David, Preece. Autism, Family Life & Short Breaks: An Investigation into the Experience of Family Life & Short Breaks of Families That Have Children on the Autism Spectrum in an English County. 2011. 332p. pap. **(978-3-639-32987-2(2))** VDM Verlag Dr. Mueller e.K.

Etherington, Natasha. Gardening for Children with Autism Spectrum Disorders & Special Educational Needs: Engaging with Nature to Combat Anxiety, Promote Sensory Integration & Build Social Skills. 2012. (ENG., Illus.). 160p. pap. **(978-1-84905-278-8(6))** Kingsley, Jessica Ltd.

Faherty, Catherine. Communication: What Does It Mean to Me? A Contract for Communication that will promote understanding between individuals with autism or Asperger's & their families, teachers, therapists, co-workers, & many More! 2010. (ENG., Illus.). 118p. pap. 19.95 (978-1-935274-17-9(1)) Future Horizons, Inc.

Franke, Lauren & Durbin, Christine. * coaching comprehension ¿ creating Conversation: Story-based language intervention for children with language impairments that are complicated by other developmental disabilities such as autism spectrum disorders: Nurturing Narratives ¿ Story-based language intervention for children with language impairments that are complicated by other developmental disabilities such as autism spectrum Disorders. 2011. (ENG., Illus.). 162p. pap. 34.95 (978-1-934575-69-7(0)) Autism Asperger Publishing Co.

Gallo, Donald P. Diagnosing Autism Spectrum Disorders: A Lifespan Perspective. 2010. (ENG.). 198p. pap. 47.95 (978-0-470-74923-4(7) Wiley) Wiley, John & Sons, Inc.

Goldberg, Michael. The Myth of Autism: How a Misunderstood Epidemic Is Destroying Our Children. 2011. (ENG., Illus.). 288p. 24.95 (978-1-61608-171-3(6), 608171) Skyhorse Publishing Co., Inc.

Gonzalez, America X., et al. Speech in Action: Interactive Activities Combining Speech Language Pathology & Adaptive Physical Education. 2011. (ENG., Illus.). 144p. pap. (978-1-84905-846-9(6)) Kingsley, Jessica Ltd.

Hatton, Sue. An Introduction to Supporting People with Autistic Spectrum Condition. 2011. (ENG., Illus.). 80p. pap. **(978-0-85725-701-7(3))** Learning Matters Ltd.

Hedgcock, Ron. Confessions of an Unashamed Asperger. 2011. 276p. pap. **(978-1-84991-394-2(3))** Chipmunkapublishing.

Hollander, Eric, et al, eds. Textbook of Autism Spectrum Disorders. 2010. (ENG., Illus.). pap. 89.00 (978-1-58562-341-9(5)) American Psychiatric Publishing, Inc.

Holloway, Monica. Cowboy & Wills: A Love Story. 2010. (ENG.). 304p. pap. 15.00 (978-1-4165-9504-5(X)) Gallery Pr., The IRL. Dist: Simon & Schuster, Inc.

Hope-West, Allison. Securing Appropriate Education Provision for Children with Autism Spectrum Disorders: A Guide for Parents & Professionals. 2011. (ENG.). 144p. pap. (978-1-84905-153-8(4)) Kingsley, Jessica Ltd.

Iland, Emily. Drawing a Blank: Improving Comprehension for Readers on the Autism Spectrum. 2011. (Illus.). 266p. pap. 34.95 (978-1-934575-77-2(1)) Autism Asperger Publishing Co.

Ivey, Julie. Educational Strategies for Children with Autism Spectrum Disorders. 2009. (ENG.). pap. 12.95 (978-1-59363-371-4(8)) Prufrock Pr.

Kabot, Susan & Reeve, Christine. Setting up Classroom Spaces That Support Students with Autis Spectrum Disorders. 2010. (Illus.). 84p. pap. 23.95 (978-1-934575-68-0(2)) Autism Asperger Publishing Co.

Kalyva, Efrosini. Autism: Educational & Therapeutic Approaches. 2011. (Illus.). 200p. (C). 120.00 (978-0-85702-488-6(4), B24888C); pap. 46.00 (978-0-85702-489-3(2), B24886P) SAGE Pubns., Ltd. GBR. Dist: SAGE Pubns., Inc.

Keen, Deb & Rodger, Sylvia. Working with Parents of a Newly Diagnosed Child with Autism Spectrum Disorder: A Guide for Professionals. 2012. (ENG., Illus.). 288p. pap. **(978-1-84905-120-0(8))** Kingsley, Jessica Ltd.

Kliman, Gilbert. Reflective Network Therapy in the Preschool Classroom. 2011. (ENG.). 390p. pap. 38.95 **(978-0-7618-5470-8(3))** Univ. Pr. of America, Inc.

Lim, Hayoung A. Developmental Speech-Language Training Through Music for Children with Autism Spectrum Disorders: Theoretical Orientation & Clinical Application. 2011. (ENG., Illus.). 208p. pap. (978-1-84905-849-0(0)) Kingsley, Jessica Ltd.

Loeppky, Angela. Living with Rain Girl: And other under the weather Conditions. 2010. 152p. pap. (978-1-926676-94-4(7)) Word Alive Pr.

Lubetsky, Martin J., et al. Autism Spectrum Disorder, 1 vol. 2011. (Pittsburgh Pocket Psychiatry Ser.). (ENG., Illus.). 360p. pap. 49.95 (978-0-19-975385-7(7)) Oxford Univ. Pr., Inc.

Luiselli, James K., ed. Teaching & Behavior Support for Children & Adults with Autism Spectrum Disorder: A Practitioner's Guide. 2011. (ENG., Illus.). 272p. pap. 39.95 (978-0-19-973640-9(5)) Oxford Univ. Pr., Inc.

Matson, Johnny L., ed. Applied Behavior Analysis for Children with Autism Spectrum Disorders. 2011. (ENG.). vii, 262p. pap. 49.95 (978-1-4419-8132-5(2), 1441981322) Springer.

Matson, Johnny L. & Sturmey, Peter, eds. International Handbook of Autism & Pervasive Developmental Disorders, 2 vols. 2011. (Autism & Child Psychopathology Ser.). (ENG., Illus.). xxv, 555p. 559.00 (978-1-4419-8064-9(4), 1441980644) Springer.

Morris, Mary Ann & Evans, Patricia. A Clinical Guide to Autistic Spectrum Disorders. 2011. (ENG., Illus.). 128p. pap. 67.95 (978-1-60831-269-6(0)) Lippincott Williams & Wilkins.

Moyer, Sherry. The ECLIPSE Model: Teaching Self-Regulation, Executive Function, Attribution & Sensory Awareness to Students with Asperger Syndrome, High Functioning Autism, & Related Disorders. 2009. (Illus.). 290p. (C). pap. 24.95 (978-1-934575-37-6(2)) Autism Asperger Publishing Co.

MTTC Exam Secrets Test Prep Staff, ed. MTTC Autism Spectrum Disorder (64) Test Flashcard Study System: MTTC Exam Practice Questions & Review for the Michigan Test for Teacher Certification. 2011. (C). 62.99 (978-1-61403-589-3(X)) Mometrix Media LLC.

Neihart, Maureen & Poon, Kenneth. Gifted Children with Autism Spectrum Disorders. 2009. (ENG.). pap. 12.95 (978-1-59363-373-8(4)) Prufrock Pr.

Nelson, Andrew. Foundation Role Plays for Autism: Role Plays for Working with Individuals with Autism Spectrum Disorders, Parents, Peers, Teachers, & Other Professionals. 2010. 160p. pap. 60.95 (978-1-84905-063-0(5)) Kingsley, Jessica Ltd. GBR. Dist: Books International, Inc.

O'Kelley, Sarah, et al. Diagnosis & Treatment of Children with Autism Spectrum Disorders. 2009. (ENG.). pap. 12.95 (978-1-59363-372-1(6)) Prufrock Pr.

Paradiz, Valerie, et al. * Lesson Plan a la Carte¿: Integrated Planning for Students with Special Needs. 2011. 91p. pap. 21.95 **(978-1-934575-92-5(5))** Autism Asperger Publishing Co.

Patel, Dilip R. & Greydanus, Donald E. Autism Spectrum Disorders: Practical Overview for Pediatricians, an Issue of Pediatric Clinics. 2012. (Clinics: Internal Medicine Ser.: 59-1). (ENG., Illus.). xvii, 224p. 92.00 **(978-1-4557-3908-0(1)**, Saunders) Elsevier - Health Sciences Div.

Pearson, Nina, et al. Autism Spectrum Disorder. 2010. (ENG.). (C). 41.40 (978-0-13-705112-0(3), Prentice Hall) Prentice Hall PTR.

Pelletier-Milet, Claudine. Riding on the Autism Spectrum: The Miracle of Equine-Assisted Therapy. 2012. (ENG.). 208p. pap. 19.95 **(978-1-57076-499-8(9))** Trafalgar Square Bks.

Reed, Phil, ed. Behavioral Theories & Interventions for Autism. 2009. (Illus.). x, 351p. 79.00 (978-1-60741-165-9(2)) Nova Science Pubs., Inc.

Reichow, Brian, et al, eds. Evidence-Based Practices & Treatments for Children with Autism. 2011. xvii, 408p. pap. 49.95 **(978-1-4419-6974-3(8)**, 1441969748) Springer.

Roth, Ilona & Rezaie, Payam, eds. Researching the Autism Spectrum: Contemporary Perspectives. 2011. (Illus.). 418p. (ENG.). 125.00 (978-0-521-51896-3(2)); pap. 59.00 (978-0-521-73686-2(2)) Cambridge Univ. Pr.

Ruble, Lisa A., et al. Collaborative Model for Promoting Competence & Success for Students with ASD. 2012. (ENG., Illus.). xxvii, 273p. pap. 44.95 **(978-1-4614-2331-7(7)**, 1461423317) Springer.

Saulnier, Celine A., et al. Essentials of Autism Spectrum Disorders Evaluation & Assessment. 2012. (Essentials of Psychological Assessment Ser.: 83). (ENG.). 222p. pap. 38.95 **(978-0-470-62194-3(X)**, Wiley) Wiley, John & Sons, Inc.

Scott, Robbyn Val. Scott Scott, 1 vol. 2010. 98p. pap. 16.95 (978-1-61546-041-0(1)) PublishAmerica, Inc.

Sheehan, Martin R., et al. Managing the Cycle of Meltdowns for Students with Autism Spectrum Disorder. 2012. 240p. pap. 27.16 **(978-1-4129-9403-3(9)**, B94033P) Corwin Pr.

Shumway, Rebekah J. The Gift of Autism. 2010. 175p. pap. 14.95 (978-0-557-39806-5(1)) Lulu Enterprises Inc.

Simpson, Richard L. & Myles, Brenda Smith. Asperger Syndrome & Higher Functioning Autism Spectrum Disorders: A Guide for Effective Practice. 3rd ed. 2010. (Illus.). viii, 279p. 38.00 (978-1-4164-0489-7(9)) PRO-ED, Inc.

Siri, Ken & Lyons, Tony. Cutting-Edge Therapies for Autism 2011-2012. 2011. (ENG., Illus.). 528p. pap. 17.95 (978-1-61608-252-9(6), 608252) Skyhorse Publishing Co., Inc.

Smith, John, et al. Helping Children with Autism Spectrum Conditions through Everyday Transitions: Small Changes - Big Challenges. 2012. (ENG., Illus.). 192p. pap. **(978-1-84905-275-7(1))** Kingsley, Jessica Ltd.

Tantam, Digby. Autism Spectrum Disorders Through the LifeSpan. 2011. (Illus.). 576p. **(978-1-84310-993-8(X))** Kingsley, Jessica Ltd.

Taylor, Paul G. A Beginner's Guide to Autism Spectrum Disorders: Essential Information for Parents & Professionals. 2011. (ENG.). 112p. pap. (978-1-84905-233-7(6)) Kingsley, Jessica Ltd.

Wahlberg, Timothy. Finding the Gray: The Black & White World of Asperger's & Autism. 2010. pap. 19.55 (978-0-615-35704-1(0)) Wahlberg & Assocs.

Wayman, Lydia. Interview with Autism. 2010. 101p. pap. 16.52 (978-0-557-53417-3(8)) Lulu Enterprises Inc.

Williams, Randy & Williams, Betty. Effective Programs for the Treatment of Autism: Applied Behavior Analysis Models. 2010. (ENG.). 304p. 160.00 (978-0-415-99931-1(6)) Routledge.

—Effective Programs for Treating Autism Spectrum Disorder: Applied Behavior Analysis Models. 2010. (ENG.). 304p. pap. 59.95 (978-0-415-99932-8(4)) Routledge.

Wong, Y. H., ed. Autism Spectrum Disorder: Special Issue: Neurosignals 2010, Vol. 18, No. 2. 2011. (Illus.). 84p. pap. (978-3-8055-9712-8(6)) Karger, S. AG.

Young, Linda. Hope for Families of Children on the Autism Spectrum. 2011. (ENG.). pap. 14.99 (978-0-89112-297-5(4), Leafwood Pubs.) Abilene Christian Univ. Pr.

Zager, Dianne, et al. Educating College Students with Autism Spectrum Disorders: The OASIS Model. 2012. (ENG.). 160p. 130.00 **(978-0-415-52437-7(7))**; pap. 39.95 **(978-0-415-52438-4(5))** Routledge.

AUTISTIC CHILDREN

Abeles, Jennifer. The Heart of Autism: Motivational Intervention Strategies for Caregivers & Professionals. 2006. (ENG.). 162p. per. 19.95 (978-1-932565-34-8(5)) Future Horizons, Inc.

Adams, Lynn. Parenting on the Autism Spectrum: A Survival Guide. 2009. (Illus.). 136p. pap. 24.95 (978-1-59756-289-8(0)) Plural Publishing, Inc.

Akanda, Zahir Uddin. Teaching Challenges at Autism Schools. 2011. 88p. pap. **(978-3-8443-9534-1(2))** Lambert Academic Publishing.

Al-Ghani, K.I. & Kenward, Lynda. From Home to School with Autism: How to Make Inclusion a Success. 2011. (ENG., Illus.). 112p. pap. **(978-1-84905-169-9(0))** Kingsley, Jessica Ltd.

Alan, Michael. I Wish My Kids Had Cancer: A Family Surviving the Autism Epidemic. 2008. 120p. pap. 19.95 (978-1-60672-070-7(8)) PublishAmerica, Inc.

American Academy of Pediatrics, creator. Autism: Caring for Children with Autism Spectrum Disorders: A Resource Toolkit for Clinicians. 2007. cd-rom 79.95 (978-1-58110-276-5(3)) American Academy of Pediatrics.

Anderson, Kyra & Forman, Vicki. Gravity Pulls You In: Perspectives on Parenting Children on the Autism Spectrum. 2010. 174p. 19.95 (978-1-60613-002-5(1)) Woodbine Hse.

Anderson, Laura. Accidentally Beautiful. 2011. 138p. pap. 14.97 **(978-0-557-76431-0(9))** Lulu Enterprises Inc.

Anderson, Margaret. Tales from the Table: Lovaas - ABA Intervention with Children on the Autistic Spectrum. 2007. (ENG., Illus.). 16p. per. (978-1-84310-306-6(0)) Kingsley, Jessica Ltd.

Anderson, Stephen R., et al. Self-Help Skills for People with Autism: A Systematic Teaching Approach. 2007. (Topics in Autism Ser.). (Illus.). 187p. per. 21.95 (978-1-890627-41-6(0)) Woodbine Hse.

Arnwine, Timothy M. I Love U: Our Journey Through Autism. 2008. 84p. pap. 12.00 (978-1-4389-0717-8(6)) AuthorHouse.

Arwood, Ellyn Lucas & Kaulitz, Carole. Learning with a Visual Brain in an Auditory World: Visual Language Strategies for Individuals with Autism Spectrum Disorders. 2007. pap. 29.95 (978-1-931282-38-3(2)) Autism Asperger Publishing Co.

Arwood, Ellyn Lucas, et al. Visual Thinking Strategies for Individuals with Autism Spectrum Disorders - the Language of Pictures. 2009. (Illus.). 199p. pap. 24.95 (978-1-934575-50-5(X)) Autism Asperger Publishing Co.

Aspy, Ruth & Grossman, Barry. The Ziggurat Model ¿ A Framework for Designing Comprehensive Interventions for Individuals with High-Functioning Autism & Asperger Syndrome Updated & Expanded Edition. 2011. 340p. pap. 49.95 **(978-1-934575-94-9(1))** Autism Asperger Publishing Co.

Aune, Beth, et al. More Behavior Solutions In & Beyond the Inclusive Classroom. 2011. (ENG.). 110p. pap. 14.95 (978-1-935274-48-3(1)) Future Horizons, Inc.

Austin, Jo. Walking with Love & Autism. 2010. (ENG., Illus.). 112p. pap. **(978-1-84748-714-8(9))** Athena Pr.

Baker, Jed. No More Meltdowns: Positive Strategies for Dealing with & Preventing Out-of-Control Behavior. 2008. (ENG.). 150p. pap. 14.95 (978-1-932565-62-1(0)) Future Horizons, Inc.

Ball, James. Early Intervention & Autism: Real-Life Questions, Real-Life Answers. 2008. (ENG., Illus.). 424p. per. 24.95 (978-1-932565-55-3(8)) Future Horizons, Inc.

Barbera, Mary & Rasmussen, Tracy. The Verbal Behavior Approach: How to Teach Children with Autism & Related Disorders. 2007. (ENG., Illus.). 176p. pap. (978-1-84310-852-8(6)) Kingsley, Jessica Ltd.

Barrows & Barrows, Kate. Autism in Childhood & Autistic Features in Adults: A Psychoanalytic Perspective. 2008. (Psychoanalytic Ideas Ser.). 310p. pap 38.95 (978-1-85575-424-9(X)) Karnac Bks. GBR. Dist: Stylus Publishing, LLC.

Barry, Tammy. An Introduction to Children with Autism. 2009. (ENG.). pap. 12.95 (978-1-59363-370-7(X)) Prufrock Pr.

Barry, Tammy D. Enhancing Communication in Children with Autism Spectrum Disorders. 2010. (ENG.). 72p. pap. 12.95 (978-1-59363-409-4(9)) Prufrock Pr.

Batts, Brenda. Ready, Set, Potty! Toilet Training for Children with Autism & Other Developmental Disorders. 2010. (ENG., Illus.). 144p. pap. (978-1-84905-833-9(4)) Kingsley, Jessica Ltd.

Benoliel, Jennifer. Autism & PDD Photo Cards Wh Questions. 2007. (J). 89.95 (978-0-7606-9994-2(1)) LinguiSystems, Inc.

Bernard-Opitz, Vera. Children with Autism Spectrum Disorders: A Structured Teaching & Experience-Based Program for Therapists, Teachers, & Parents. 2007. 54.00 (978-1-4164-0232-9(2)) PRO-ED, Inc.

Bernard-Opitz, Vera & Häußler, Anne. Visual Support for Children with Autism Spectrum Disorders. 2011. 228p. pap. 34.95 (978-1-934575-82-6(8)) Autism Asperger Publishing Co.

Betts, Dion E., et al. Hints & Tips for Helping Children with Autism Spectrum Disorders: Useful Strategies for Home, School, & the Community. 2008. (ENG.). 192p. pap. (978-1-84310-896-2(8)) Kingsley, Jessica Ltd.

Betts, Stacey W. Asperger Syndrome in the Inclusive Classroom: Advice & Strategies for Teachers. 2007. (ENG.). 16p. per. (978-1-84310-840-5(2)) Kingsley, Jessica Ltd.

Beytien, Alyson. Raising the Entire Autism Spectrum: Candid Advice & Creative Strategies from a Mom of 3 Boys on the Autism Spectrum. 2011. (ENG.). 286p. pap. 14.95 (978-1-935274-50-6(3)) Future Horizons, Inc.

Bierens, Francesca. A Spectrum of Light: Inspirational Interviews with Families Affected by Autism. 2009. (ENG.). 192p. pap. (978-1-84905-013-5(9)) Kingsley, Jessica Ltd.

Blastland, Michael. The Only Boy in the World: A Father Explores the Mysteries of Autism. 2006. (ENG.). 224p. per. 14.95 (978-1-56924-291-9(7)) Da Capo Pr., Inc.

Bolduc, Kathleen Deyer. Autism & Alleluias. 2010. 144p. pap. 14.00 (978-0-8170-1568-8(X)) Judson Pr.

Bolzoni, Lucia. Communication difficile: le cas de L'autisme: Une étude comparative des déficits pragmatiques chez des enfants francais et allemands atteints d'autisme ou du Syndrome D'Asperger. 2008. (Europäische Hochschulschriften. Reihe 13: Französische Sprache und Literatur Ser.). 194p. pap. 56.95 (978-3-631-56502-5(X)) Lang, Peter GmbH, Europaischer Verlag der Wissenschaften DEU. Dist: Lang, Peter.

Bondy, Andy & Frost, Lori. Autism 24/7: A Family Guide to Learning at Home & in the Community. 2008. (Illus.). 177p. pap. 19.95 (978-1-890627-53-9(4)) Woodbine Hse.

Bondy, Andy & Frost, Lori. A Picture's Worth: PECS & Other Visual Communication Strategies in Autism. 2nd ed. 2011. (Topics in Autism Ser.). 160p. pap. 19.95 **(978-1-60613-015-5(3))** Woodbine Hse.

Boroson, Barbara. Autism Spectrum Disorders in the Mainstream Classroom: How to Reach & Teach Students with ASDs. 2011. (ENG.). 224p. pap. 24.99 (978-0-545-16876-2(7), Teaching Resources) Scholastic, Inc.

Boutot, E. Amanda & Myles, Brenda Smith. Autism Spectrum Disorders: Foundations, Characteristics, & Effective Strategies. 2010. (ENG.). 320p. (C). pap. 52.60 (978-0-205-54575-9(0), Prentice Hall) Prentice Hall PTR.

Bowen, Maggie & Plimley, Lynn. The Autism Inclusion Toolkit: Traing Materials & Facilitator Notes. 2008. 128p. pap. 50.95 (978-1-4129-4757-2(X), B47565P) SAGE Pubns., Ltd. GBR. Dist: SAGE Pubns., Inc.

—The Autism Inclusion Toolkit: Training Materials & Facilitator Notes. 2008. 128p. 153.00 (978-1-4129-4756-5(1), B47565C) SAGE Pubns., Ltd. GBR. Dist: SAGE Pubns., Inc.

Bowler, Dermot. Autism Spectrum Disorders: Psychological Theory & Research. 2006. (ENG., Illus.). 318p. per. 62.95 (978-0-470-02686-1(3), Wiley) Wiley, John & Sons, Inc.

Brady, Lois Jean, et al. Speak, Move, Play, & Learn with Children on the Autism Spectrum: Activities to Boost Communication Skills, Sensory Integration & Coordination Using Simple Ideas from Speech & Language Pathology & Occupational Therapy. 2012. (ENG., Illus.). 160p. pap. **(978-1-84905-872-8(5))** Kingsley, Jessica Ltd.

Braten, Stein, contrib. by. Intersubjective Communication & Emotion in Early Ontogeny. (Illus.). xvi, 454p. *(978-2-7351-0772-8(8))* Editions de la Maison des sciences de l'homme.

Breakey, Christine. The Autism Spectrum & Further Education. 2006. (ENG., Illus.). 28p. per., instr.'s gde. ed. *(978-1-84310-382-0(6))* Kingsley, Jessica Ltd.

Brennan, Lynn Cohen. Teaching Perspective-Taking Skills to Children with Autism Spectrum Disorders. 2010. 42.00 *(978-1-4164-0482-8(1))* PRO-ED, Inc.

Brenneman, Simone. Effervescence: A True-Life Tale of Autism & of Courage. 2009. 196p. 25.50 *(978-1-4389-7753-9(0))*; pap. 15.99 *(978-1-4389-7754-6(9))* AuthorHouse.

Brosen, Sophie Koborg. Do You Understand Me? My Life, My Thoughts, My Autism Spectrum Disorder. 2006. (ENG., Illus.). 128p. (J). (gr. 3-7). per. *(978-1-84310-464-3(4))* Kingsley, Jessica Ltd.

Brower, Francine. 100 Ideas for Supporting Pupils on the Autistic Spectrum. 2007. (Continuum One Hundreds Ser.). (ENG., Illus.). 128p. 20.95 *(978-0-8264-9421-4(8))* Continuum International Publishing Group, Ltd. GBR. Dist: National Bk. Network.

Browning, Robert & Stover, Donald. Behavior Modification in Child Treatment: An Experimental & Clinical Approach. 2009. (ENG., Illus.). 428p. pap. 45.95 *(978-0-202-36293-9(0))* Aldine Transaction.

Bruey, Carolyn Thorwarth & Urban, Mary Beth. The Autism Transition Guide: Planning the Journey from School to Adult Life. 2009. *(978-1-890627-81-2(X))* Woodbine Hse.

Buckendorf, G. Robert & Liedel, John. Autism: A Guide for Educators, Clinicians, & Parents. 2007. *(978-1-58650-854-8(7))* Super Duper Pubns.

Buggey, Tom. Seeing Is Believing: Video Self-Modeling for People with Autism & Other Developmental Disabilities. 2008. 125p. pap. 19.95 *(978-1-890627-88-1(7))* Woodbine Hse.

Burnett, Anne. Step Ahead of Autism: What You Can Do to Ensure the Best Possible Outcome for Your Child. 2011. pap. 12.95 *(978-1-934716-25-0(1))* Sunrise River Pr.

Burns, Dan E. Saving Ben: A Father's Story of Autism. 2009. (Mayborn Literary Nonfiction Ser.). (ENG., Illus.). 192p. 22.95 *(978-1-57441-269-7(8))* Univ. of North Texas Pr.

Burns, Michele Pierce & Wambua, Danson Mandela. Danson: The Extraordinary Discovery of an Autistic Child's Innermost Thoughts & Feelings. 2009. (ENG., Illus.). 124p. pap. 12.95 *(978-0-9800288-4-3(1))* St. Lynn's Pr.

Buron, Kari Dunn. A 5 Could Make Me Lose Control! An Activity-Based Method for Evaluating & Supporting Highly Anxious Students. 2007. 48p. per. 22.95 *(978-1-931282-31-4(5))* Autism Asperger Publishing Co.

—A 5 Is Against the Law! Social Boundaries - Straight Up! - An Honest Guide to Teens & Young Adults. 2007. (Illus.). 48p. (YA). (gr. 7-14). per. 20.95 *(978-1-931282-35-2(8))* Autism Asperger Publishing Co.

Calinescu, Matei. Matthew's Enigma: A Father's Portrait of His Autistic Son. Jianu, Angela, tr. from ROM. 2009. (ENG., Illus.). 224p. 50.00 *(978-0-253-35297-2(5)*, 0253352975); pap. 19.95 *(978-0-253-22066-0(1)*, 0253220661) Indiana Univ. Pr.

Cannon, Lynn, et al. Unstuck & on Target! An Executive Function Curriculum to Improve Flexibility for Children with Autism Spectrum Disorders, Research Edition. 2011. (Illus.). 256p. pap. 44.95 ***(978-1-59857-203-2(2))*** Brookes, Paul H. Publishing Co.

Cardon, Teresa A. Initiations & Interactions: Early Intervention Techniques for Parents of Children with Autism Spectrum Disorders. 2007. (Illus.). 81p. per. 19.95 *(978-1-931282-32-1(3))* Autism Asperger Publishing Co.

Carrion, Christine. Animals Can Demonstrate Values Too. 2010. 30p. pap. 13.95 *(978-1-60844-382-6(5))* Dog Ear Publishing, LLC.

Carter, Margaret Ann. Pirates: An Early-Years Group Program for Developing Social Understanding & Social Competence for Children with Autism Spectrum Disorders & Related Challenges. 2007. pap. 29.95 *(978-1-931282-34-5(X))* Autism Asperger Publishing Co.

Chalfant, Anne M. Managing Anxiety in People with Autism: A Treatment Guide for Parents, Teachers, & Mental Health Professionals. 2011. 283p. pap. 19.95 *(978-1-60613-004-9(8))* Woodbine Hse.

Charlop-Christy, Marjorie H. How to Do Incidental Teaching. 2007. 14.00 *(978-1-4164-0146-9(6))* PRO-ED, Inc.

Chestone, Tom. Dad, I'm Sorry I'm Autistic. 2010. 100p. pap. 11.95 *(978-0-557-14345-0(4))* Lulu Enterprises Inc.

Chez, Michael G. Autism & Its Medical Management: A Guide for Parents & Professionals. 2008. (ENG., Illus.). 240p. *(978-1-84310-834-4(8))* Kingsley, Jessica Ltd.

Chilvers, Rebecca. The Hidden World of Autism: Writing & Art by Children with High-Functioning Autism. 2007. (ENG., Illus.). 128p. pap. *(978-1-84310-451-3(2))* Kingsley, Jessica Ltd.

Chwast, Debra. An Unexpected Life: Speaking Through Art. 2011. (ENG., Illus.). 224p. 27.95 *(978-1-4027-7403-4(6))* Sterling Publishing Co., Inc.

Cimera, Robert Evert. Making Autism a Gift: Inspiring Children to Believe in Themselves & Lead Happy, Fulfilling Lives. 2007. (ENG.). 304p. per. 18.95 *(978-0-7425-5288-3(8))* Rowman & Littlefield Publishers, Inc.

Clark Brack, Jenny. Learn to Move, Moving up! Sensorimotor Elementary-School Activity Themes. 2009. pap. 34.95 *(978-1-934575-38-3(0))* Autism Asperger Publishing Co.

Clements, John, et al. Transition or Transformation? Helping Young People with Autistic Spectrum Disorder Set Out on a Hopeful Road Towards Their Adult Lives. 2010. (Illus.). 177p. pap. *(978-1-84310-964-8(6))* Kingsley, Jessica Ltd.

Clemons, Brenda. Jordan: Living with Autism & Multiple Complex Developmental Disorder, A Guide for the Rest of Us. 2007. 108p. per. 19.95 *(978-1-4241-8328-9(6))* PublishAmerica, Inc.

Cohen, Kerry. Seeing Ezra: A Mother's Story of Autism, Unconditional Love, & the Meaning of Normal. (ENG.). 2012. 256p. pap. 16.00 ***(978-1-58005-433-1(1))*** 2011. 288p. 25.00 *(978-1-58005-369-3(6))* Seal Pr.

Cohen, Marlene J. & Sloan, Donna L. Visual Supports for People with Autism: A Guide for Parents & Professionals. 2007. (Topics in Autism Ser.). (Illus.). 168p. per. 21.95 *(978-1-890627-47-8(X))* Woodbine Hse.

Concept Media. Unlocking the World of Autism: Seven Keys to Becoming Miracle Minded. 2009. (Concept Media: Educational Videos Ser.). (ENG.). (C). 1500.00 *(978-1-4354-8835-9(0)*, Concept Media) Delmar Cengage Learning.

Condict-Cochran, Chelley, EdD. The Positive Positive Negative Positive Principle. 2007. 57p. pap. 11.95 *(978-0-615-17523-2(6))* Cochran, Chelley Condict.

Conner, Julie. Just Be His Mommy: One Case History of Love, Faith, & Autism. 2009. pap. 21.99 *(978-1-61566-075-9(5))* Tate Publishing & Enterprises, LLC.

Converse, Judy. Special-Needs Kids Eat Right: Strategies to Help Kids on the Autism Spectrum Focus, Learn, & Thrive. 2009. (ENG.). 304p. (gr. 12-18). pap. 15.95 *(978-0-399-53488-1(1)*, Perigee Trade) Penguin Group (USA) Inc.

Costley, Debra, et al. A Practical Guide for Teachers of Students with an Autism Spectrum. 2012. (ENG.). 160p. pap. ***(978-1-84905-310-5(3))*** Kingsley, Jessica Ltd.

Coyne, Phyllis, et al. Developing Leisure Time Skills for Persons with Autism: Structured Playtime Activities with Valuable Support Strategies for Adults. 2011. (ENG., Illus.). 228p. pap. 29.95 ***(978-1-935274-55-1(4))*** Future Horizons, Inc.

Crawford, Brad & Crawford, Alisha. The First Steps: A Parent's Guide to Fighting Autism. 2010. 256p. pap. 16.99 *(978-1-61579-784-4(X))* Xulon Pr., Inc.

Cumine, Val, et al. Asperger Syndrome: A Practical Guide for Teachers. 2nd ed. 2009. (Illus.). (ENG.). 116p. 37.95 *(978-0-415-48371-1(9))*; xi, 112p. 37.95 ***(978-0-203-86486-9(7))*** Routledge.

—Autism in the Early Years. 2nd rev. ed. 2009. (Resource Materials for Teachers Ser.). (ENG., Illus.). 110p. pap., instr.'s gde. ed. 37.95 *(978-0-415-48373-5(5))* Routledge.

Cumpata, JoEllen & Fell, Susan. A Quest for Social Skills for Students with Autism or Asperger's: Ready-to-use lessons with games, role-play activities, & More! 2010. (Illus.). 300p. pap. 24.95 *(978-1-935274-11-7(2))* Future Horizons, Inc.

Cunningham, Karen Mayer. Defying Austism: A Miraculous Story of Hope. 2009. (ENG.). 128p. 14.99 *(978-1-59979-628-4(7)*, Creation Hse.) Charisma Media.

Davenport, Randi. The Boy Who Loved Tornadoes. 2010. (ENG.). 384p. 23.95 *(978-1-56512-611-4(4)*, 1565126114) Algonquin Bks. of Chapel Hill.

Delaine, Susan K. The Autism Cookbook: 101 Gluten-Free & Dairy-Free Recipes. 2010. (ENG., Illus.). 256p. 17.95 *(978-1-61608-019-8(1)*, 608019) Skyhorse Publishing Co., Inc.

Delaney, Tara. 101 Games & Activities for Children with Autism, Asperger's & Sensory Processing Disorders. 2009. (ENG., Illus.). 240p. pap. 16.95 *(978-0-07-162336-0(1)*, 0071623361) McGraw-Hill Cos., The.

Derbyshire, Georgina J. Stand up for Autism: A Boy, a Dog, & a Prescription for Laughter. 2010. (ENG., Illus.). 144p. pap. *(978-1-84905-099-9(6))* Kingsley, Jessica Ltd.

A Different Kind of Kin: For Relatives of Persons with Autism. 2007. pap. 16.99 *(978-0-9795106-0-1(0))* Kansas Windmill Pr.

Dixon, Janet. ISPEEK at Home: Over 1300 Visual Communication Images. 2007. (Ispeek Ser.). (ENG.). cd-rom *(978-1-84310-510-7(1))* Kingsley, Jessica Ltd.

—ISPEEK at School: Over 1300 Visual Communication Images. 2007. (Ispeek Ser.). (ENG., Illus.). cd-rom *(978-1-84310-511-4(X))* Kingsley, Jessica Ltd.

Dyrbjerg, Pernille & Vedel, Maria. Everyday Education: Visual Support for Children with a Autism. 2006. (ENG., Illus.). 128p. *(978-1-84310-457-5(1))* Kingsley, Jessica Ltd.

Elwins, Dannie. The Guide to Overcoming & Beating Autism. 2009. 40p. pap. 16.99 *(978-0-557-15428-9(6))* Lulu Enterprises Inc.

Endow, Judy. Paper Words. 2009. viii, 180p. pap. 18.95 *(978-1-934575-49-9(6))* Autism Asperger Publishing Co.

—Practical Strategies for Stabilizing Students with Classic Autism: Getting to Go! 2010. (Illus.). 96p. pap. 21.95 *(978-1-934575-75-8(5))* Autism Asperger Publishing Co.

Eyal, Gil. The Autism Matrix: The Social Origins of the Autism Epidemic. 2010. (ENG., Illus.). 240p. 69.95 *(978-0-7456-4399-1(X))*; pap. 24.95 *(978-0-7456-4400-4(7))* Polity Pr. GBR. Dist: Wiley, John & Sons, Inc.

Faherty, Catherine. Communication: What Does It Mean to Me? A Contract for Communication that will promote understanding between individuals with autism or Asperger's & their families, teachers, therapists, co-workers, & many More! 2010. (ENG., Illus.). 118p. pap. 19.95 *(978-1-935274-17-9(1))* Future Horizons, Inc.

Farrell, Michael. The Effective Teacher's Guide to Autism & Communication Difficulties: Practical Strategies. 2nd rev. ed. 2012. (Effective Teacher's Guides). (ENG., Illus.). 104p. 120.00 ***(978-0-415-69382-0(9))***; pap. 35.95 ***(978-0-415-69383-7(7))*** Routledge.

—The Effective Teachers Guide to Moderate Severe & Profound Learning Difficulties (Cognitive Impairments) 2nd rev. ed. 2012. (Effective Teacher's Guides). (ENG., Illus.). 104p. 130.00 ***(978-0-415-69386-8(1))***; pap. 40.95 ***(978-0-415-69387-5(X))*** Routledge.

Fein, Deborah & Dunn, Michelle A. Autism in Your Classroom: A General Educator's Guide to Students with Autism Spectrum Disorders. 2007. (Topics in Autism Ser.). 319p. per. 19.95 *(978-1-890627-61-4(5))* Woodbine Hse.

Finland, Glen. Next Stop: A Memoir. 2012. (ENG.). 304p. (gr. 12). 25.95 ***(978-0-399-15860-5(X)***, Putnam Adult) Penguin Group (USA) Inc.

Firestone, Barbara. Autism Heroes: Portraits of Families Meeting the Challenge. 2007. (ENG., Illus.). 24p. *(978-1-84310-837-5(2))* Kingsley, Jessica Ltd.

Fitzer, Adrienne & Sturmey, Peter. Language & Autism: Applied Behavior Analysis, Evidence, & Practice. 2008. 40.00 *(978-1-4164-0376-0(0))* PRO-ED, Inc.

Flanagan, Maureen A. Improving Speech & Eating Skills in Children with Autism Spectrum Disorders - an Oral Motor Program for Home & School. 2008. pap. 21.95 *(978-1-934575-23-9(2))* Autism Asperger Publishing Co.

Fleischmann, Arthur. Carly's Voice: Breaking Through Autism. 2012. (ENG.). 400p. 24.00 ***(978-1-4391-9414-0(9)***, Touchstone) Touchstone.

Fleischmann, Arthur & Fleischmann, Carly. Carly's Voice: Breaking Through Autism. 2012. pap. ***(978-1-4391-9415-7(7))*** Simon & Schuster.

Forum on Neuroscience and Nervous System Disorders & Institute of Medicine. Autism & the Environment: Challenges & Opportunities for Research, Workshop Proceedings. 2008. (ENG.). 358p. pap. 71.50 *(978-0-309-10881-2(0))* National Academies Pr.

Franke, Lauren & Durbin, Christine. * coaching comprehension ¿ creating Conversation: Story-based language intervention for children with language impairments that are complicated by other developmental disabilities such as autism spectrum disorders: Nurturing Narratives ¿ Story-based language intervention for children with language impairments that are complicated by other developmental disabilities such as autism spectrum Disorders. 2011. (ENG., Illus.). 162p. pap. 34.95 *(978-1-934575-69-7(0))* Autism Asperger Publishing Co.

Frankel, Fred & Wood, Jeffrey J. Social Skills Success for Students with Autism/Asperger's: How to Teach Conversation Skills, Prevent Meltdowns, & Help Kids Fit In. 2011. (ENG., Illus.). 256p. pap. 29.95 ***(978-0-470-95238-2(5)***, Jossey-Bass) Wiley, John & Sons, Inc.

Freihow, Halfdan W. Dear Gabriel. Ferguson, Robert, tr. from NOR. 2007. (ENG.). 226p. *(978-1-59692-249-5(4))* MacAdam/Cage Publishing, Inc.

Freihow, Halfdan W. Somewhere over the Sea: A Father's Letter to His Autistic Son, 1 vol. Ferguson, Robert, tr. from NOR. 2012. (ENG.). 208p. pap. 14.95 ***(978-1-77089-100-5(5))*** House of Anansi Pr. CAN. Dist: Perseus-PGW.

Gabriels, Robin L. & Hill, Dina E., eds. Growing up with Autism: Working with School-Age Children & Adolescents. 2007. (ENG., Illus.). 302p. (gr. 1-13). 55.00 *(978-1-59385-459-1(5))* Guilford Pubns., Inc.

Gallegos, Elena M. & Shallenberger, Jill M. Autism Methodology Cases to Live By: Legal Guidance for Practical Program Strategies. 2008. *(978-1-57834-100-9(0))* LRP Pubns.

Gammeltoft, Lone & Nordenhof, Marianne Sollok. Autism, Play & Social Interaction. Van Acker, Erik, tr. from DAN. 2007. (ENG., Illus.). 64p. *(978-1-84310-520-6(9))* Kingsley, Jessica Ltd.

Gardner, Nuala. A Friend Like Henry: The Remarkable True Story of an Autistic Boy & the Dog That Unlocked His World. 2008. (ENG.). 280p. pap. 14.99 *(978-1-4022-1406-6(5))* Sourcebooks, Inc.

Garvin, Eileen. How to Be a Sister: A Love Story with a Twist of Autism. 2010. (ENG.). 272p. pap. 14.95 *(978-1-61519-016-4(3)*, 1615190163) Experiment LLC, The.

Gaston, Lynn & Gaston, Randy. Three Times the Love: Finding Answers & Hope for Our Triplets with Autism. 2010. (ENG.). 240p. (gr. 12-18). 15.00 *(978-1-58333-379-2(7)*, Avery) Penguin Group (USA) Inc.

George, Jack E. The Autism Handbook: Easy to Understand Information, Insight, Perspectives & Case Studies from a Special Education Teacher. 2009. 178p. pap. *(978-1-926585-50-5(X)*, No.1 Bk. Pubs.) CCB Publishing.

George, Jack E. Zi Bi Zheng Shou Che: Yi Ming Te Chu Jiao Yu Dao Shi ... Liu, Weitong, tr. from ENG. 2012.Tr. of Autism Handbook: Easy to Understand Information, Insight, Perspectives & Case Studies from a Special Education Teacher (Chinese Simplified Edition). (CHI.). 222p. pap. ***(978-1-927360-16-3(1)***, No.1 Bk. Pubs.) CCB Publishing.

Goldman, Helena, et al. Augmentative Communication Assessment Profile (Acap) (Illus.). 56p. spiral bd. *(978-0-86388-286-9(2)*, 002-4766) Speechmark Publishing Ltd.

Goldstein, Sam, et al, eds. Assessment of Autism Spectrum Disorders. 2008. (ENG., Illus.). 384p. 50.00 *(978-1-59385-983-1(X))* Guilford Pubns., Inc.

Gonzalez, Zack. Saving Deets! 2009. 220p. pap. 18.50 *(978-1-4269-1762-2(7))* Trafford Publishing.

Gosney, Sheila. Acquainted with Autism: Ministering to Families Affected by Autism. 2009. 144p. pap. 14.95 *(978-1-59317-494-1(2))* Warner Pr. Pubs.

Gottlieb, Daniel. The Wisdom of Sam: Observation on Life from an Uncommon Child. 2011. (ENG.). 200p. pap. 12.95 *(978-1-4019-2388-4(7))* Hay Hse., Inc.

—The Wisdom of Sam: Observations on Life from an Uncommon Child. 2010. (ENG.). 168p. 19.95 *(978-1-4019-2385-3(2))* Hay Hse., Inc.

Gray, Bvm, Carol. The New Social Story Book: Over 150 Social Stories That Teach Everyday Social Skills to Children with Autism or Asperger's Syndrome, & Their Peers. 2nd rev. anniv. exp. ed. 2010. (ENG., Illus.). 254p. pap. 34.95 *(978-1-935274-05-6(8))* Future Horizons, Inc.

Greenfeld, Karl Taro. Boy Alone: A Brother's Memoir. 2010. (ENG.). 352p. pap. 14.99 *(978-0-06-113667-2(0)*, HarperPerennial) 2009. 552p. pap. 25.99 *(978-0-06-177489-8(8)*, HarperLuxe) HarperCollins Pubs.

Greenman, Jan. Life at the Edge & Beyond: Living with ADHD & Aspergers Syndrome. 2010. 208p. pap. *(978-1-84905-106-4(2))* Kingsley, Jessica Ltd.

Greenspan, Stanley I. & Wieder, Serena. Engaging Autism: Using the Floortime Approach to Help Children Relate, Communicate & Think. 2009. (Merloyd Lawrence Book Ser.). (ENG.). 448p. pap. 18.00 *(978-0-7382-1094-0(3))* Perseus Bks. Group.

Gregory, Marilyn. Warming Trends: A chilling disappearance... A journey from fear to Faith. 2010. 344p. pap. 19.99 *(978-1-61507-099-2(0))* Cross Bks. Publishing.

Grossberg, Blythe. Asperger's Rules! How to Make Sense of School & Friends. 2012. 14.95 ***(978-1-4338-1128-9(6))***; pap. 9.95 ***(978-1-4338-1127-2(8))*** American Psychological Assn. (Magination Pr.).

Gutstein, Steven, ed. The Relationship Development Intervention Program & Education. 2007. 259p. per. 22.50 *(978-0-9777186-1-0(1))* Connections Center.

Hagood, Linda. Better Together: Building Relationships with People Who Have Visual Impairment & Autism Spectrum Disorder (or Atypical Social Development) 2008. (Illus.). vi, 418p. *(978-1-880366-40-0(1))* Texas Schl. for the Blind & Visually Impaired.

Haldane, Carol. Dannie's Dilemma. 2008. 68p. pap. *(978-1-84747-676-0(7))* Chipmunkapublishing.

Hall, Elaine. Now I See the Moon: A Mother, a Son, & the Miracle of Autism. 2010. 256p. 19.99 *(978-0-06-174380-1(1))* HarperCollins Pubs.

Hall, Elaine & Hall, Neal. Now I See the Moon: A Mother, a Son, & the Miracle of Autism. 2011. (ENG.). 304p. pap. 14.99 *(978-0-06-174381-8(X)*, Harper Paperbacks) HarperCollins Pubs.

Hall, Elaine & Isaacs, Diane. Seven Keys to Unlock Autism: Making Miracles in the Classroom. 2011. (ENG.). 224p. 24.95 ***(978-0-470-64409-6(5)***, Jossey-Bass) Wiley, John & Sons, Inc.

Hall, Laura J. Autism Spectrum Disorders: From Theory to Practice. (ENG., (C). 2008. Illus.). 256p. pap. 34.67 *(978-0-13-227534-7(1))* 2nd rev. ed. 2012. 312p. pap. 34.67 ***(978-0-13-265809-6(7))*** Prentice Hall PTR. (Prentice Hall).

Hallett, Sandy & Wisor, Nikki. How Our Children with Autism Raised Us As Parents: The Ninety-Nine Jobs Needed to Raise Kids with Autism. 2009. 240p. pap. 22.00 *(978-1-4349-9514-8(3)*, RoseDog Bks.) Dorrance Publishing Co., Inc.

Hanbury, Martin. Educating Students on the Autistic Spectrum: A Practical Guide. 2nd ed. 2012. (Illus.). 144p. 100.00 ***(978-0-85702-893-8(6)***, B28938C); pap. 40.00 ***(978-0-85702-894-5(4)***, B28938P) SAGE Pubns., Ltd. GBR. Dist: SAGE Pubns., Inc.

Hanbury, Martin. Positive Behaviour Strategies to Support Children & Young People with Autism. 2007. (Illus.). 120p. 65.00 *(978-1-4129-2910-3(5)*, B29105C); per. 30.00 *(978-1-4129-2911-0(3)*, B29105P) SAGE Pubns., Ltd. GBR. Dist: SAGE Pubns., Inc.

Handleman, Jan S. & Harris, Sandra L. Preschool Education Programs for Children with Autism. 3rd ed. 2007. 46.00 *(978-1-4164-0257-2(8))* PRO-ED, Inc.

Harland. A Will of His Own Reflections on Parenting a Child with Autism - Revised Edition. 2007. (ENG.). 176p. pap. *(978-1-84310-869-6(0))* Kingsley, Jessica Ltd.

Harper-Hill, Keely & Lord, Stephanie. Planning to Learn: Creating & Using a Personal Planner with Young People on the Autism Spectrum. 2007. (ENG., Illus.). 224p. pap. *(978-1-84310-561-9(6))* Kingsley, Jessica Ltd.

Harris, Sandra L. & Weiss, Mary Jane. Right from the Start: Behavioral Intervention for Young Children with Autism. 2nd ed. 2007. (Topics in Autism Ser.). (Illus.). 175p. per. 18.95 *(978-1-890627-80-5(1))* Woodbine Hse.

Hart, Megan & Lutz, Kim. The Everything Guide to Cooking for Children with Autism: From Everyday Meals to Holiday Treats - 200 Tasty Recipes Your Child Will Love to Eat. 2010. (ENG., Illus.). 304p. pap. 15.95 *(978-1-4405-0021-3(5))* Adams Media Corp.

Heinkel-Wolfe, Peggy. See Sam Run: A Mother's Story of Autism. 2008. (Mayborn Literary Nonfiction Ser.). (Illus.). 192p. 22.95 *(978-1-57441-244-4(2))* Univ. of North Texas Pr.

Hendrickson, Laura, et al. Finding Your Child's Way on the Autism Spectrum: Discovering Unique Strengths, Mastering Behavior Challenges, 1 vol. 2009. (ENG.). 144p. pap. 14.99 *(978-0-8024-4505-6(5))* Moody Pubs.

Henry, Kimberly A. & Henry, M.D., Kimberly A. How Do I Teach This Kid to Read? Teaching Literacy Skills to Young Children with Autism, from Phonics to Fluency. 2010. (ENG., Illus.). 200p. pap. 19.95 *(978-1-935274-14-8(7))* Future Horizons, Inc.

Herbert, Martha & Weintraub, Karen. The Autism Revolution: Whole-Body Strategies for Making Life All It Can Be. 2012. (ENG.). 320p. 26.00 ***(978-0-345-52719-6(4)***, Ballantine Bks.) Random House Publishing Group.

Herskowitz, Valerie. Autism & Computers: Maximizing Independence Through Technology. 2009. 164p. 25.49 *(978-1-4389-8115-4(5))*; pap. 13.49 *(978-1-4389-8114-7(7))* AuthorHouse.

Hilsen, Lindsay. A Step-by-Step Curriculum for Early Learners with Autism Spectrum Disorders. 2011. (ENG.). 384p. pap. ***(978-1-84905-874-2(1))*** Kingsley, Jessica Ltd.

Hobson, Peter. Autism & the Development of Mind. 2nd ed. 2010. (C). pap. 36.95 *(978-0-415-43336-5(3)*, Routledge) Taylor & Francis Group GBR. Dist: Taylor & Francis Group.

Hoffman, Anne, et al. Discrimination Training Alternatives: Module 1. 2007. DVD 35.00 *(978-1-928598-12-1(9))* Pyramid Educational Products, Inc.

Hollander, Eric & Anagnostou, Evdokia. Clinical Manual for the Treatment of Autism. 2007. (Illus.). 314p. per. 64.00 *(978-1-58562-222-1(2))* American Psychiatric Publishing, Inc.

Hope-West, Allison. Securing Appropriate Education Provision for Children with Autism Spectrum Disorders: A Guide for Parents & Professionals. 2011. (ENG.). 144p. pap. *(978-1-84905-153-8(4))* Kingsley, Jessica Ltd.

Hosin, Amer A. Autism, ADHD, & Anorexia Nervosa: Essays on Three Childhood Disorders. (Illus.). 120p. 89.95 *(978-0-7734-5163-6(3))* Mellen, Edwin Pr., The.

Howlin, Patricia, et al. Teaching Children with Autism to Mind-Read. 2nd ed. 2013. (ENG.). 160p. pap., wbk. ed. 34.95 *(978-0-470-09324-5(2)*, Wiley) Wiley, John & Sons, Inc.

Hughes-Lynch, Claire. Teaching Children with High-Functioning Autism: Strategies for the Inclusive Classroom. 2011. (ENG.). 250p. pap. 24.95 *(978-1-59363-747-7(0))* Prufrock Pr.

Hughes-Lynch, Claire E. Children with High-Functioning Autism: A Parent's Guide. 2010. (ENG.). 225p. pap. 17.95 *(978-1-59363-402-5(1))* Prufrock Pr.

Hulse, Brett. In the Land of Hickamadoola. 2010. 16p. 10.99 *(978-1-4520-9120-4(X))* AuthorHouse.

Hundert, Joel. Inclusion of Students with Autism: Using ABA-Based Supports in General Education. 2009. 51.00 *(978-1-4164-0390-6(6))* PRO-ED, Inc.

Ingersoll, Brooke & Dvortcsak, Anna. Teaching Social Communication to Children with Autism: A Manual for Parents. 2010. (ENG., Illus.). 144p. pap. 25.00 *(978-1-60623-440-2(4))* Guilford Pubns., Inc.

—Teaching Social Communication to Children with Autism: A Practitioner's Guide to Parent Training. 2009. (Illus.). 390p. *(978-1-60623-441-9(2))* Guilford Pubns., Inc.

—Teaching Social Communication to Children with Autism Set: A Practitioner's Guide to Parent Training & A Manual for Parents, 2 bks. 2010. (ENG.). pap. 85.00 *(978-1-60623-442-6(0))* Guilford Pubns., Inc.

Isaacson, Rupert. The Horse Boy: A Father's Quest to Heal His Son. l.t. ed. 2009. 541p. 32.95 *(978-1-4104-1589-9(9))* Thorndike Pr.

—The Horse Boy: A Memoir of Healing. 2010. (ENG., Illus.). 400p. pap. 15.99 *(978-0-316-00824-2(9)*, Back Bay Bks.) Little Brown & Co.

Ivey, Julie. Educational Strategies for Children with Autism Spectrum Disorders. 2009. (ENG.). pap. 12.95 *(978-1-59363-371-4(8))* Prufrock Pr.

Jackson, Claudreen. Jackson Claudre. 2010. 142p. pap. 16.95 *(978-1-934363-59-1(6))* Zoe Life Publishing.

Jameson Tilton, Adele, et al. When Your Child Has... Autism. 2009. (ENG.). 224p. pap. 6.95 *(978-1-59869-676-9(9))* Adams Media Corp.

Jeanette D. Harmon. The Other Normal: Understanding Asperger's. 2011. 216p. pap. 24.95 ***(978-1-4560-6048-0(1))*** PublishAmerica, Inc.

Jepson, Bryan. Changing the Course of Autism: A Scientific Approach for Parents & Physicians. 2007. (ENG., Illus.). 345p. per. 18.95 *(978-1-59181-061-2(2))* Sentient Pubns.

Johnson, Paul & St Thomas, Bruce. Empowering Children Through Art & Expression: Culturally Sensitive Ways of Healing Trauma & Grief. 2007. (ENG., Illus.). 224p. per. *(978-1-84310-789-7(9))* Kingsley, Jessica Ltd.

Johnston-Tyler, Jan. Mom's Guide to Asperger Syndrome & Related Disorders. 2007. pap. 21.95 *(978-1-931282-42-0(0))* Autism Asperger Publishing Co.

Jones, Darlene. To See the World Through Cody's Eyes. 2006. (ENG.). 76p. per. 16.95 *(978-1-4241-5804-1(4))* PublishAmerica, Inc.

Joshi, Suman S. Children with Autism & Their Allies in Action: Who Are They? What Do They Think?How Do They Help? 2007. 140p. per. 14.95 *(978-1-4327-1306-5(X))* Outskirts Pr., Inc.

Julie Jurgens-Shimek. Autism Is a Four Letter Word: Love. 2009. 124p. 21.99 *(978-1-4389-6540-6(0))*; pap. 15.99 *(978-1-4389-6539-0(7))* AuthorHouse.

Kathy, Cohen. Mom, Are You Listening? A Story of Unconditional Love. 2006. pap. 16.99 *(978-1-933994-06-2(1))* Troy Book Makers, The.

Kaweski, Walter G., Jr. Teaching Adolescents with Autism: Practical Strategies for the Inclusive Classroom. 2011. (Illus.). 248p. pap. 34.95 *(978-1-4129-9529-0(9)*, B95290P) Corwin Pr.

Kennedy, Anna. Not Stupid. (ENG., Illus.). 2009. 288p. pap. 14.95 *(978-1-84454-784-5(1))* 2008. 302p. 29.95 *(978-1-84454-507-0(5))* Blake, John Publishing, Ltd. GBR. Dist: Independent Pubs. Group.

Kidd, Susan Larson. My Child Has Autism, Now What? 10 Steps to Get You Started. 2010. (ENG., Illus.). 128p. pap. *(978-1-84905-841-4(5))* Kingsley, Jessica Ltd.

Kirk, Sally. Hope for the Autism Spectrum: A Mother & Son Journey of Insight & Biomedical Intervention. 2008. (ENG., Illus.). 320p. *(978-1-84310-894-8(1))* Kingsley, Jessica Ltd.

Kluth, Paula. You're Going to Love This Kid! Teaching Students with Autism in the Inclusive Classroom, Second Edition. 2nd ed. 2010. (Illus.). 368p. pap. 34.95 *(978-1-59857-079-3(X))* Brookes, Paul H. Publishing Co.

Kluth, Paula & Chandler-Olcott, Kelly. A Land We Can Share: Teaching Literacy to Students with Autism. 2007. (Illus.). 220p. per. 26.95 *(978-1-55766-855-4(8))* Brookes, Paul H. Publishing Co.

Kluth, Paula & Schwarz, Patrick. Just Give Him the Whale! 20 Ways to Use Fascinations, Areas of Expertise, & Strengths to Support Students with Autism. 2008. 120p. per. 19.95 *(978-1-55766-960-5(0))* Brookes, Paul H. Publishing Co.

Koenig, Kathleen. Practical Social Skills for Autism Spectrum Disorders: Designing Child-Specific Interventions. 2012. (ENG., Illus.). 304p. 32.95 *(978-0-393-70698-7(2)*, 70698) Norton, W. W. & Co., Inc.

Kupperman, Phyllis. The Source for Intervention in Autism Spectrum Disorders. 2008. (Illus.). 166p. *(978-0-7606-0834-0(2))* LinguiSystems, Inc.

Kurtz, Lisa A. Understanding Controversial Therapies for Children with Autism, Attention Deficit Disorder, & Other Learning Disabilities: A Guide to Complementary & Alternative Medicine. 2008. (ENG.). 192p. pap. *(978-1-84310-864-1(X))* Kingsley, Jessica Ltd.

Labosh, Kathy. The Child with Autism Goes to Florida: Hundreds of practical tips, with reviews of theme parks, rides, resorts, & More! 2011. (ENG.). 125p. pap. 14.95 *(978-1-935274-24-7(4))* Future Horizons, Inc.

—The Child with Autism Learns about Faith: 15 Ready-to-Use Scripture Lessons, from the Garden of Eden to the Parting of the Red Sea. 2011. (ENG.). 97p. pap. 14.95 *(978-1-935274-19-3(8))* Future Horizons, Inc.

Labosh, Kathy & Miller, LaNita. The Child with Autism at Home & in the Community: Over 600 must-have tips for making home life & outings easier for Everyone! 2011. (ENG.). 100p. pap. 14.95 *(978-1-935274-20-9(1))* Future Horizons, Inc.

Larkey, Sue. Practical Sensory Programmes for Students with Autism Spectrum Disorder & Other Special Needs. 2006. (ENG., Illus.). 12p. per. *(978-1-84310-479-7(2))* Kingsley, Jessica Ltd.

Laugeson, Elizabeth A. & Frankel, Fred. Social Skills for Teenagers with Developmental & Autism Spectrum Disorders. 2010. (ENG., Illus.). 448p. pap. 49.95 *(978-0-415-87203-4(0))* Routledge.

Lawrence, Clare. Autism & Flexischooling: A Shared Classroom & Homeschooling Approach. 2012. (ENG.). 160p. pap. ***(978-1-84905-279-5(4))*** Kingsley, Jessica Ltd.

—How to Make School Make Sense: A Parents' Guide to Helping the Child with Asperger Syndrome. 2008. (ENG.). 128p. pap. *(978-1-84310-664-7(7))* Kingsley, Jessica Ltd.

—Successful School Change & Transition for the Child with Asperger Syndrome: A Parents' Guide to Smooth School Transition for the Child with Asperger Syndrome. 2010. (ENG.). 160p. pap. *(978-1-84905-052-4(X))* Kingsley, Jessica Ltd.

Le Breton, Dean A. Talk, Talk, Sweet Charlotte. 2009. 192p. 24.99 *(978-1-4389-7272-5(5))*; pap. 15.95 *(978-1-4389-7271-8(7))* AuthorHouse.

Leach, Debra. Bringing ABA into Your Inclusive Classroom: A Guide to Improving Outcomes for Students with Autism Spectrum Disorders. 2010. (Illus.). 224p. pap. 29.95 net. *(978-1-59857-077-9(3))* Brookes, Paul H. Publishing Co.

Leaf, Ronald, et al. It's Time for School! Building Quality ABA Educational Programs for Students with Autism Spectrum Disorders. Eng, John, ed. 2008. 286p. per. 39.95 *(978-0-9755859-3-1(2))* DRL Bk., Inc.

Lehmann, Annie Lubliner. The Accidental Teacher: Life Lessons from My Silent Son. 2009. (ENG.). 184p. 45.00 *(978-0-472-07074-9(6))*; pap. 17.95 *(978-0-472-05074-1(5))* Univ. of Michigan Pr.

Levine, Karen & Chedd, Naomi. Replays: Using Play to Enhance Emotional & Behavioral Development for Children with Autism Spectrum Disorders. 2006. (ENG., Illus.). 16p. per. *(978-1-84310-832-0(1))* Kingsley, Jessica Ltd.

Lewis, Cathleen. Rex: A Mother, Her Autistic Child, & the Music that Transformed Their Lives, 0 vols. 2008. (Illus.). 256p. 24.99 *(978-1-59555-150-4(6))* Nelson, Thomas Inc.

Ling, John. I Can't Do That! My Social Stories to Help with Communication, Self-Care & Personal Skills. 2nd ed. 2010. (Lucky Duck Bks.). (Illus.). 120p. pap. 38.00 *(978-0-85702-044-4(7)*, B20444P) SAGE Pubns., Ltd. GBR. Dist: SAGE Pubns., Inc.

Lloyd, Pat. Let's All Listen: Songs for Group Work in Settings That Include Students with Learning Difficulties & Autism. 2007. (ENG., Illus.). 160p. pap. *(978-1-84310-583-1(7))* Kingsley, Jessica Ltd.

Lucan, Dawn. Quick & Easy Autism Cookbook. 2010. 56p. pap. 14.95 *(978-0-557-55133-0(1))* Lulu Enterprises Inc.

Luiselli, James K., et al, eds. Effective Practices for Children with Autism: Educational & Behavior Support Interventions that Work. 2008. (ENG., Illus.). 496p. (C). 67.95 *(978-0-19-531704-6(1))* Oxford Univ. Pr., Inc.

Lynn, George T. The Asperger Plus Child: How to Identify & Help Children with Asperger Syndrome & Seven Common Co-Existing Conditions. 2007. 280p. per. 29.95 *(978-1-931282-33-8(1))* Autism Asperger Publishing Co.

Lyons, Tony. 1,001 Tips for the Parents of Autistic Girls: Everything You Need to Know about Diagnosis, Doctors, Schools, Taxes, Vacations, Babysitters, Treatments. 2010. (ENG.). 480p. pap. 17.95 *(978-1-61608-104-1(X)*, 608104) Skyhorse Publishing Co., Inc.

Lytel, Jayne. Act Early Against Autism: Give Your Child a Fighting Chance from the Start. 2008. (ENG.). 272p. (gr. 12-18). 14.95 *(978-0-399-53394-5(X)*, Perigee Trade) Penguin Group (USA) Inc.

Mahoney, Gerald & MacDonald, James D. Autism & Developmental Delays in Young Children: The Responsive Teaching Curriculum for Parents & Professionals: Curriculum Guide. 2007. (Illus.). xiii, 337p. 87.00 *(978-1-4164-0236-7(5))* PRO-ED, Inc.

Malian, Freda. How We Survived Our 'Difficult' Child & Learned to Thrive. 2009. 244p. pap. *(978-1-84747-941-9(3))* Chipmunkapublishing.

Marcus, Lee M., et al. Families of Children with Autism: What Educational Professionals Should Know. 2010. (ENG.). 72p. pap. 12.95 *(978-1-59363-408-7(0))* Prufrock Pr.

Marie, Tia. The Disregarded Child: My Life with Autism. 2011. pap. 10.99 *(978-1-61739-338-9(X))* Tate Publishing & Enterprises, LLC.

Marlin, Brigid. A Meaning for Danny. 2012. 286p. pap. 15.95 ***(978-0-7414-6692-1(9))*** Infinity Publishing.

Martin, Areva. The Everyday Advocate: Standing up for Your Child with Autism or Other Special Needs. 2011. (ENG.). 336p. (gr. 12). 15.00 *(978-0-451-23229-8(1)*, N A L Trade) Penguin Group (USA) Inc.

Martin, Earle. The Boy Who Saved My Life: Walking into the Light with My Autistic Grandson. 2011. (ENG.). 136p. 19.95 *(978-1-936474-01-1(8))* Bright Sky Pr.

Martin, Nicole. Art as an Early Intervention Tool for Children with Autism. 2009. (ENG., Illus.). 160p. pap. *(978-1-84905-807-0(5))* Kingsley, Jessica Ltd.

Martin, Rosemary. Top Tips for Asperger Students: How to Get the Most Out of University & College. 2010. (ENG., Illus.). 144p. pap. *(978-1-84905-140-8(2))* Kingsley, Jessica Ltd.

McCandless, Jaquelyn. Children with Starving Brains: A Medical Treatment Guide for Authism Spectrum Disorder. 4th ed. 2009. 407p. pap. 29.95 *(978-1-883647-17-9(7)*, Bramble Bks.) Bramble Co.

McCarthy, Jenny. Louder Than Words: A Mother's Journey in Healing Autism. l.t. ed. 2008. (Thorndike Nonfiction Ser.). (Illus.). 247p. 31.95 *(978-1-4104-0473-2(0))* Thorndike Pr.

—Mother Warriors: A Nation of Parents Healing Autism Against All Odds. l.t. ed. 2008. 509p. 31.95 *(978-1-4104-1003-0(X))* Thorndike Pr.

McCarthy, Jenny & Jerry, Kartzinel. Healing & Preventing Autism: A Complete Guide. 2009. (Playaway Adult Nonfiction Ser.). 59.99 *(978-1-4332-7096-3(X))* Findaway World, LLC.

McClannahan, Lynn E. & Krantz, Patricia J. Activity Schedules for Children with Autism: Teaching Independent Behavior. 2nd ed. 2010. (Illus.). 140p. pap. 19.95 *(978-1-60613-003-2(X))* Woodbine Hse.

McCoy, Kathleen M. Autism from the Teacher's Perspective: Strategies for Classroom Instruction. 2010. 464p. pap. 78.00 *(978-0-89108-348-1(0))* Love Publishing Co.

McNair, Frank. The Golden Rules for Managers: 119 Incredible Lessons for Leadership Success. 2009. (ENG.). 256p. 16.99 *(978-1-4022-1528-5(2))* Sourcebooks, Inc.

Miller, Arnold. The Miller Method: Developing the Capacities of Children on the Autism Spectrum. 2007. (ENG., Illus.). 32p. *(978-1-84310-722-4(8))* Kingsley, Jessica Ltd.

Miller, Eileen. The Girl Who Spoke with Pictures: Autism Through Art. 2008 (ENG., Illus.). 208p. *(978-1-84310-889-4(5))* Kingsley, Jessica Ltd.

Miller, Helen. The Educator's Guide to Teaching Students with Autism Spectrum Disorders. Ben-Arieh, Josefa & Miller, Helen J., eds. 2009. (Illus.). 176p. pap. 31.95 *(978-1-4129-5776-2(1)*, B57755P) Corwin Pr.

Miller, Kirsten. Children on the Bridge: A Story of Autism in South Africa. 2007. (ENG.). 240p. per. 21.00 *(978-1-77009-218-1(8))* Jacana Media ZAF. Dist: Independent Pubs. Group.

Miller, Suzy. Awesomism! A New Way to Understand the Diagnosis of Autism. 2008. 116p. pap. 15.95 *(978-1-4401-0285-1(6))* iUniverse, Inc.

Mills, Bruce & Cumberland, Debra, eds. Siblings & Autism: Stories Spanning Generations & Cultures. 2010. (ENG., Illus.). 240p. pap. *(978-1-84905-831-5(8))* Kingsley, Jessica Ltd.

Mirenda, Pat & Iacono, Teresa. Autism & Augmentative & Alternative Communication (AAC) 2008. (Illus.). 504p. 54.95 *(978-1-55766-953-7(8))* Brookes, Paul H. Publishing Co.

Moor, Julia & Moore, Julia. Playing, Laughing & Learning with Children on the Autism Spectrum 2008 A Practical Resource of Play Ideas for Parents & Carers. 2nd ed. 2008. (ENG., Illus.). 304p. (C). pap. *(978-1-84310-608-1(6))* Kingsley, Jessica Ltd.

Moore, Charlotte. George & Sam: Two Boys, One Family, & Autism. 2007. (ENG., Illus.). 320p. pap. 13.95 *(978-0-312-37424-2(0)*, St. Martin's Griffin) St. Martin's Pr.

Morgan, Hugh & Attfield, Elizabeth. Living with Autistic Spectrum Disorders: Guidance for Parents, Carers & Siblings. 2006. (Autistic Spectrum Disorder Support Kit Ser.). (Illus.). 96p. 58.00 *(978-1-4129-2328-6(X)*, B2328XC); per. 24.00 *(978-1-4129-2329-3(8)*, B2328XP) SAGE Pubns., Ltd. GBR. Dist: SAGE Pubns., Inc.

Moustafa. You Are Not Alone — A Message to Parents of Children with Autism. 2009. 238p. pap. 15.95 *(978-1-935118-71-8(4))* Bellissima Publishing, LLC.

Mukhopadhyay, Tito Rajarshi. The Gold of the Sunbeams: And Other Stories. 2011. (ENG.). 272p. pap. 14.95 *(978-1-61145-253-2(8)*, 611253, Arcade Publishing) Skyhorse Publishing Co., Inc.

—The Mind Tree: A Miraculous Child Breaks the Silence of Autism. 2011. (ENG.). 176p. pap. 14.95 *(978-1-61145-002-6(0)*, 611002, Arcade Publishing) Skyhorse Publishing Co., Inc.

Myers, Jennifer McIlwee. How to Teach Life Skills to Kids with Autism or Asperger's. 2010. (ENG.). 322p. pap. 19.95 *(978-1-935274-13-1(9))* Future Horizons, Inc.

Myles, Brenda Smith. The Comprehensive Autism Planning System [CAPS] for Individuals with Asperger Syndrome, Autism, & Related Disabilities: Integrating Best Practices Throughout the Student's Day. 2007. pap. 29.95 *(978-1-934575-03-1(8))* Autism Asperger Publishing Co.

Myles, Brenda Smith, et al. Autism Spectrum Disorders: A Handbook for Parents & Professionals, 2 vols. 2007. 544p. 200.00 *(978-0-313-33632-4(6)*, GR3632, Praeger Pubs.) Greenwood Publishing Group, Inc.

Nelson, Andrew. Foundation Role Plays for Autism: Role Plays for Working with Individuals with Autism Spectrum Disorders, Parents, Peers, Teachers, & Other Professionals. 2010. 160p. pap. 60.95 *(978-1-84905-063-0(5))* Kingsley, Jessica Ltd. GBR. Dist: Books International, Inc.

Nelson, Beth. Angels Unaware. 2011. 248p. 22.95 ***(978-1-4670-4016-7(9))***; pap. 12.95 ***(978-1-4670-4017-4(7))*** AuthorHouse.

Netty. Full Stop to the Rescue, a Big Red Border Book. 2010. 38p. pap. 11.00 *(978-1-60911-109-0(5)*, Strategic Bk. Publishing) AEG Literary Publishing Services, Inc.

Newell, Trauma Foundation. Alanis's Daily Routine. 2011. 28p. pap. 1.95 ***(978-1-935268-82-6(1))*** Halo Publishing International.

Nichols, Shana. Girls Growing up on the Autism Spectrum: What Parents & Professionals Should Know about the Pre-Teen & Teenage Years. 2008 (ENG., Illus.). 352p. pap. *(978-1-84310-855-9(0))* Kingsley, Jessica Ltd.

Nikopoulos, Christos & Keenan, Mickey. Video Modelling & Behaviour Analysis: A Guide for Teaching Social Skills to Children with Autism. 2006. (ENG., Illus.). 176p. per. *(978-1-84310-338-7(9))* Kingsley, Jessica Ltd.

Notbohm, Ellen. Ten Things Your Student with Autism Wishes You Knew. 2006. (ENG., Illus.). 117p. per. 14.95 *(978-1-932565-36-2(1))* Future Horizons, Inc.

Notbohm, Ellen & Zysk, Veronica. 1001 Great Ideas for Teaching & Raising Children with Autism Spectrum Disorders, 2nd Edition. 2nd rev. ed. 2010. (ENG.). 320p. pap. 24.95 *(978-1-935274-06-3(6))* Future Horizons, Inc.

O'Kelley, Sarah, et al. Diagnosis & Treatment of Children with Autism Spectrum Disorders. 2009. (ENG.). pap. 12.95 *(978-1-59363-372-1(6))* Prufrock Pr.

Page, Louise. An Autism Connection. 2008. 128p. pap. 24.49 *(978-1-4092-0564-7(9))* Lulu Enterprises Inc.

Palmer, Ann. A Friend's & Relative's Guide to Supporting the Family with Autism: How Can I Help? 2012. (ENG.). 224p. pap. ***(978-1-84905-877-3(6))*** Kingsley, Jessica Ltd.

Paradiz, Valerie. Elijah's Cup: A Family's Journey into the Community & Culture of High-Functioning Autism & Asperger's Syndrome. 2007. (ENG.). 256p. pap. 17.95 *(978-1-4165-6776-9(3)*, Free Pr.) Free Pr.

Parish, Robert, ed. Embracing Autism: Connecting & Communicating with Children in the Autism Spectrum. 2008. (ENG., Illus.). 208p. 24.95 *(978-0-7879-9586-7(X)*, Jossey-Bass) Wiley, John & Sons, Inc.

Park, Elizabeth. Montessori Pedagogy for a High-Functioning Autistic Child. 2008. 72p. pap. *(978-3-8364-8941-6(4))* VDM Verlag Dr. Mueller e.K.

Peete, Rodney & Morton, Danelle. Not My Boy! A Father, a Son, & One Family's Journey with Autism. 2010. (ENG.). 256p. 24.99 *(978-1-4013-2361-5(8))* Hyperion Pr.

Perry, Nancy. Adults on the Autism Spectrum Leave the Nest: Achieving Supported Independence. 2008. (ENG.). 288p. pap. *(978-1-84310-904-4(2))* Kingsley, Jessica Ltd.

Phillips, Nicky & Beavan, Liz. Teaching Play to Children with Autism: Practical Interventions Using Identiplay. 2007. (Lucky Duck Bks.). (Illus.). 80p. pap. 25.95 *(978-1-4129-2894-6(X)*, B2894XP) SAGE Pubns., Ltd. GBR. Dist: SAGE Pubns., Inc.

Phillips, Nicky & Beavan, Liz. Teaching Play to Children with Autism: Practical Interventions using Identiplay. 2nd ed. 2012. (Lucky Duck Bks.). 136p. pap. 50.00 ***(978-1-4462-0766-6(8)***, B07666P) SAGE Pubns., Ltd. GBR. Dist: SAGE Pubns., Inc.

Pierangelo, Roger & Giuliani, George. Teaching Students with Autism Spectrum Disorders: A Step-by-Step Guide for Educators. 2008. (Step-By-Step Guide for Educators Ser.). (Illus.). 224p. 82.95 *(978-1-4129-1707-0(7)*, B17077C) Corwin Pr.

Pierangelo, Roger & Giuliani, George A. Teaching Students with Autism Spectrum Disorders: A Step-by-Step Guide for Educators. 2008. (Step-By-Step Guide for Educators Ser.). (Illus.). 224p. pap. 36.95 *(978-1-4129-1708-7(5)*, B17077P) Corwin Pr.

Pittman, Mary. Helping Pupils with Autistic Spectrum Disorders to Learn. 2007. (Illus.). 144p. 65.00 *(978-1-4129-1965-4(7)*, B19654C); pap. 30.00 *(978-1-4129-1966-1(5)*, B19654P) SAGE Pubns., Ltd. GBR. Dist: SAGE Pubns., Inc.

Plimley, Lynn, et al. Autistic Spectrum Disorders in the Early Years. 2007. (Autistic Spectrum Disorder Support Kit Ser.). (Illus.). 112p. 94.00 *(978-1-4129-2314-9(X)*, B2314XC); per. 29.00 *(978-1-4129-2315-6(8)*, B2314XP) SAGE Pubns., Ltd. GBR. Dist: SAGE Pubns., Inc.

Powell, Craig M. & Monteggia, Lisa M. The Autisms: Molecules to Model Systems. 2012. (ENG.). 416p. 145.00 ***(978-0-19-974431-2(9))*** Oxford Univ. Pr., Inc.

Powell, Stuart & Jordan, Rita, eds. Autism & Learning. 2011. (ENG., Illus.). 168p. (C). pap. 40.95 *(978-0-415-68749-2(7))*; 155.00 *(978-0-415-68748-5(9))* Routledge.

Price, Marean J. Lord, Why Not Me? A Mother's Story of an Autistic Child. (Illus.). 104p. (Orig.). pap. 14.95 *(978-1-883372-00-2(3))* Rondelle Publishing Co.

Ravert, Melody & Ravert, Tim. Silent Angel: The Joys & Challenges in Raising an Autistic Child. 2006. 140p. per. 12.95 *(978-1-60002-224-1(3)*, 4109) Mountain Valley Publishing, LLC.

Rebeck, Theresa. Three Girls & Their Brother. 2008. (Playaway Adult Fiction Ser.). (ENG.). 64.99 *(978-1-60640-566-6(7))* Findaway World, LLC.

Rehfeldt, Ruth Anne & Barnes-Holmes, Yvonee. Derived Relational Responding Applications for Learners with Autism & Other Developmental Disabilities: A Progressive Guide to Change. 2009. (Professional Ser.). (ENG.). 400p. instr.'s gde. ed. 79.95 *(978-1-57224-536-5(0))* New Harbinger Pubns.

Reichow, Brian, et al, eds. Evidence-Based Practices & Treatments for Children with Autism. xviii, 408p. 2011. pap. 49.95 ***(978-1-4419-6974-3(8)***, 1441969748) 2010. 179.00 *(978-1-4419-6973-6(X)*, 144196973X) Springer.

Reynolds. Ab: A Brief Introduction to Teaching Children with Autism. 2011. 102p. pap. 12.95 ***(978-0-557-84591-0(2))*** Lulu Enterprises Inc.

Riegel, Courtney. Through a Mother's Eyes: A Spiral down the Autism Spectrum. 2006. 94p. per. 9.99 *(978-1-59886-590-5(0))* Tate Publishing & Enterprises, LLC.

Robertson, Randy. Finding Mary: One Family's Journey on the Road to Autism Recovery. 2010. 204p. pap. 17.95 *(978-1-4502-2302-7(8))* iUniverse, Inc.

Rogers, Sally J. & Dawson, Geraldine. Early Start Denver Model Curriculum Checklist for Young Children with Autism. 2009. (ENG.). 16p. pap. 50.00 *(978-1-60623-633-8(4))* Guilford Pubns., Inc.

—Early Start Denver Model for Young Children with Autism: Promoting Language, Learning, & Engagement. 2009. (ENG., Illus.). 297p. 75.00 *(978-1-60623-632-1(6))*; pap. 50.00 *(978-1-60623-631-4(8))* Guilford Pubns., Inc.

Romp, Julia. The Cat Who Came Back for Christmas: How a Cat Brought a Family the Gift of Love. 2012. (ENG.). 288p. (gr. 12). pap. 15.00 ***(978-0-452-29878-1(4)***, Plume) Penguin Group (USA) Inc.

Rosner, D. M. The China Doll. 2008. (ENG., Illus.). 28p. (J). 8.99 *(978-1-934340-98-1(7))* Jigsaw Pr.

Ross, Donna Satterlee & Jolly, Kelly Ann, eds. That's Life with Autism: Tales & Tips for Families with Autism. 2006. (ENG.). 28p. per. *(978-1-84310-829-0(1))* Kingsley, Jessica Ltd.

Rothenberg, Mira. The Children of Raquette Lake: One Summer That Helped Change the Course of Treatment for Autism. 2012. (ENG.). 256p. pap. 19.95 ***(978-1-58394-467-7(2))*** North Atlantic Bks.

Rudy, Lisa Jo. Get Out, Explore, & Have Fun! How Families of Children with Autism or Asperger Syndrome Can Get the Most Out of Community Activities. 2010. (ENG., Illus.). 256p. pap. 19.95 *(978-1-84905-809-4(1))* Kingsley, Jessica Ltd. GBR. Dist: Books International, Inc.

Sansosti, Frank J., et al. High-Functioning Autism - Asperger Syndrome in Schools: Assessment & Intervention. 2010. (Guilford Practical Intervention in Schools Ser.). (ENG., Illus.). 257p. (gr. k-12). pap. 40.00 *(978-1-60623-670-3(9))* Guilford Pubns., Inc.

Savarese, Ralph James. Reasonable People: A Memoir of Autism & Adoption: on the Meaning of Family & the Politics of Neurological Difference. annot. ed. 2007. (ENG.). 496p. 25.95 *(978-1-59051-129-9(8))* Other Pr., LLC.

Scanlan, Audrey & Snyder, Linda. Rhythms of Grace: Volume 1: A Worship & Faith-Formation Curriculum Resource for Children with Autism. 2010. 140p. pap. 30.00 *(978-1-60674-005-7(9))* Morehouse Education Resources.

Schetter, Patricia, et al. Homeschooling the Child with Autism: Answers to the Top Questions Parents & Professionals Ask. 2009. (ENG., Illus.). 288p. pap. 22.95 *(978-0-470-29256-3(3)*, Jossey-Bass) Wiley, John & Sons, Inc.

Schlieder, Mary, frwd. Friendly Facts: A Fun, Interactive Resource to Help Children Explore the Complexities of Friends & Friendship. 2010. (Illus.). 75p. (J). pap. 19.95 *(978-1-934575-61-1(5))* Autism Asperger Publishing Co.

Schneider, Cindy B. Acting Antics: A Theatrical Approach to Teaching Social Understanding to Kids & Teens with Asperger Syndrome. 2007. (ENG., Illus.). 224p. per. *(978-1-84310-845-0(3))* Kingsley, Jessica Ltd.

Schopler, Eric & Mesibov, Gary B., eds. Communication Problems in Autism. 2010. (Current Issues in Autism Ser.). 350p. pap. 109.00 *(978-1-4419-3203-7(8)*, 1441932038) Springer.

Schroeder, Ruth Knott. Coach Yourself Through the Autism Spectrum. 2009. (ENG., Illus.). 240p. pap. *(978-1-84905-801-8(6))* Kingsley, Jessica Ltd.

Scott, Elizabeth Burton. Raindrops on Roman: Overcoming Autism: A Message of Hope. Rakini, Kate, ed. 2009. 160p. pap. 14.95 *(978-1-934759-24-0(4))* Reed, Robert D. Pubs.

Scott, Robbyn Val. Scott Scott, 1 vol. 2010. 98p. pap. 16.95 *(978-1-61546-041-0(1))* PublishAmerica, Inc.

Seach, Diana. Interactive Play & Creative Activities for Children with Autism. 2015. (ENG.). 112p. pap. 35.95 *(978-0-415-48154-0(6))* Routledge.

Sell, Colleen, ed. A Cup of Comfort for Parents of Children with Autism: Stories of Hope & Everyday Success. 2007. (ENG., Illus.). 336p. per. 9.95 *(978-1-59337-683-3(9))* Adams Media Corp.

Senator, Susan. The Autism Mom's Survival Guide (For Dads, Too!) Creating a Balanced & Happy Life While Raising a Child with Autism. 2010. (ENG.). 208p. pap. 16.95 *(978-1-59030-753-3(4)*, Trumpeter) Shambhala Pubns., Inc.

—Making Peace with Autism: One Family's Story of Struggle, Discovery, & Unexpected Gifts. 2006. (ENG.). 272p. per. 14.00 *(978-1-59030-382-5(2)*, Trumpeter) Shambhala Pubns., Inc.

Sheahan, Bobbi & DeOrnellas, Kathy. What I Wish I'd Known about Raising a Child with Autism: A Mom & a Psychologist Offer Heartfelt Guidance for the First Five Years. 2011. (ENG.). 250p. pap. 14.95 *(978-1-935274-23-0(6))* Future Horizons, Inc.

Sheehan, Martin R., et al. Managing the Cycle of Meltdowns for Students with Autism Spectrum Disorder. 2012. 240p. pap. 27.16 ***(978-1-4129-9403-3(9)***, B94033P) Corwin Pr.

Sher, Barbara. Early Intervention Games: Fun, Joyful Ways to Develop Social & Motor Skills in Children with Autism Spectrum or Sensory Processing Disorders. 2009. (ENG., Illus.). 252p. pap. 16.95 *(978-0-470-39126-6(X)*, Jossey-Bass) Wiley, John & Sons, Inc.

Shumaker, Laura. A Regular Guy: Growing up with Autism. 2008. 225p. pap. 14.95 *(978-0-9801836-0-3(X))* Landscape Pr.

Sicile-Kira, Chantal. Autism Life Skills: From Communication & Safety to Self-Esteem & More- 10 Essential Abilities Every Child Needs & Deserves to Learn. 2008. (ENG.). 208p. (gr. 12-18). 14.95 *(978-0-399-53461-4(X)*, Perigee Trade) Penguin Group (USA) Inc.

Sicile-Kira, Chantal. What Is Autism? Understanding Life with Autism or Asperger's. rev. ed. 2012. (ENG.). 174p. pap. 14.95 ***(978-1-59652-842-0(7))*** Turner Publishing Co.

Siegel, Bryna. Helping Children with Autism Learn: Treatment Approaches for Parents & Professionals. 2007. (ENG.). 512p. per. 24.95 *(978-0-19-532506-5(0))* Oxford Univ. Pr., Inc.

Sigafoos, Jeff, et al. How to Use Video Modeling & Video Prompting. 2006. (PRO-ED Series on Autism Spectrum Disorders). 14.00 *(978-1-4164-0152-0(0))* PRO-ED, Inc.

Silberberg, Barrie. The Autism & ADHD Diet: A Step-by-Step Guide to Hope & Healing by Living Gluten Free & Casein Free (GFCF) & Other Interventions. 2009. (ENG.). 256p. pap. 14.99 *(978-1-4022-1845-3(1))* Sourcebooks, Inc.

Silva, Louisa/M. Helping Your Child with Autism: A Home Program from Chinese Medicine. 2010. (Illus.). 144p. pap. 25.00 *(978-0-9821280-0-8(2))* Qigong Sensory Training Institute.

Silverman, Chloe. Understanding Autism: Parents, Doctors, & the History of a Disorder. 2011. (ENG.). 360p. (C). 35.00 ***(978-0-691-15046-8(X))*** Princeton Univ. Pr.

Silverman, Stephan M. & Weinfeld, Rich. School Success for Children with Asperger's Syndrome. 2007. (ENG.). 229p. pap. 16.95 *(978-1-59363-215-1(0))* Prufrock Pr.

Simpson, Cynthia & Spencer, Vicky. Teaching Children with Autism: Strategies for Effective Inclusion & Instruction. 2009. (ENG.). 350p. pap. 39.95 *(978-1-59363-364-6(5))* Prufrock Pr.

Simpson, Richard L. & Myles, Brenda Smith. Educating Children & Youth with Autism: Strategies for Effective Practice. 2nd ed. 2007. 48.00 *(978-1-4164-0210-7(1))* PRO-ED, Inc.

Siri, Ken. 1,001 Tips for the Parents of Autistic Boys: Everything You Need to Know about Diagnosis, Doctors, Schools, Taxes, Vacations, Babysitters, Treatments, Food, & More. 2010. (ENG.). 480p. pap. 17.95 *(978-1-61608-105-8(8)*, 608105) Skyhorse Publishing Co., Inc.

Siri, Ken & Lyons, Tony. Cutting-Edge Therapies for Autism 2010-2011. 2010. (ENG.). 528p. pap. 17.95 *(978-1-61608-025-9(6)*, 608025) Skyhorse Publishing Co., Inc.

Slater, Amy E. & Norlin, John W. Autism Case Law: A Desktop Reference to Key Decisions. 2007. *(978-1-57834-094-1(2))* LRP Pubns.

Smith, Inga J. Gluten-Free Casein-Free Everyday: GFCF Recipes for Kids with Autism. 2008. 328p. per. 19.95 *(978-0-9727273-4-1(5))* Green Owl, Inc.

Smith, John, et al. Helping Children with Autism Spectrum Conditions through Everyday Transitions: Small Changes - Big Challenges. 2012. (ENG., Illus.). 192p. pap. ***(978-1-84905-275-7(1))*** Kingsley, Jessica Ltd.

Smith, Tristram. Making Inclusion Work for Students with Autism Spectrum Disorders: An Evidence-Based Guide. 2011. (ENG., Illus.). 380p. (gr. k-12). pap. 40.00 *(978-1-60623-932-2(5))* Guilford Pubns., Inc.

Smith, Veronica & Patterson, Stephanie Y. Getting into the Game: Sports Programs for Kids with Autism. 2012. (ENG.). 256p. pap. ***(978-1-84905-249-8(2))*** Kingsley, Jessica Ltd.

Solomon, Walter, et al. Autism & Understanding: The Waldon Approach to Child Development. 2012. 240p. 115.00 ***(978-1-4462-0923-3(7)***, B09233C); pap. 43.95 ***(978-1-4462-0924-0(5)***, B09233P) SAGE Pubns., Ltd. GBR. Dist: SAGE Pubns., Inc.

Stagliano, Kim. All I Can Handle - I'M No Mother Teresa: A Life Raising Three Daughters with Autism. 2011. (ENG., Illus.). 208p. pap. 14.95 *(978-1-61608-459-2(6)*, 608459) Skyhorse Publishing Co., Inc.

Stahmer, Aubyn C., et al. Classroom Pivotal Response Teaching for Children with Autism. 2011. (ENG., Illus.). 210p. (gr. -1-3). pap. 55.00 *(978-1-60918-241-0(3))* Guilford Pubns., Inc.

Stauth, Cameron & Bock, Kenneth. Healing the New Childhood Epidemics: Autism, ADHD, Asthma, & Allergies: The Groundbreaking Program for the 4-A Disorders. 2008. (ENG., Illus.). 480p. pap. 16.00 *(978-0-345-49451-1(2)*, Ballantine Bks.) Random House Publishing Group.

Stehli, Annabel. The Sound of a Miracle. 2010. 226p. pap. 14.95 *(978-0-8253-0533-7(0))* Beaufort Bks., Inc.

—The Sound of Falling Snow: Stories of Recovery from Autism & Related Conditions. 2010. 241p. pap. 14.95 *(978-0-8253-0532-0(2))* Beaufort Bks., Inc.

Stillman, William. The Autism Answer Book: More Than 300 of the Top Questions Parents Ask. 2007. (ENG.). 320p. per. 15.99 *(978-1-4022-0977-2(0))* Sourcebooks, Inc.

—Empowered Autism Parenting: Celebrating (And Defending) Your Child's Place in the World. 2009. (ENG.). 224p. pap. 16.95 *(978-0-470-47587-4(0)*, Jossey-Bass) Wiley, John & Sons, Inc.

Stillman William. The Everything Parent's Guide to Children with Asperger's Syndrome: The sound advice & reliable answers you need to help your child Succeed. 2nd ed. 2010. (ENG.). 320p. pap. 14.95 *(978-1-4405-0394-8(X))* Adams Media Corp.

Stillman, William. The Soul of Autism: Looking Beyond Labels to Unveil Spiritual Secrets of the Heart Savants. 2008. (ENG.). 1p. pap. 14.99 *(978-1-60163-005-6(0)*, New Page Bks.) Career Pr., Inc.

Strickland, Elizabeth. Eating for Autism: The 10-Step Nutrition Plan to Help Treat Your Child's Autism, Asperger's, or ADHD. 2009. (ENG.). 304p. pap. 17.95 *(978-0-7382-1243-2(1))* Da Capo Pr., Inc.

Stults, Kimberly J. Lessons from Lorena: Living with Autism. 2011. pap. 10.99 *(978-1-61739-079-1(8))* Tate Publishing & Enterprises, LLC.

Sturmey, Peter. How to Teach Verbal Behavior. 2008. (PRO-ED Series on Autism Spectrum Disorders). pap. 14.00 *(978-1-4164-0147-6(4))* PRO-ED, Inc.

Sullivan, Lori. Overcoming Autism: A Parent's Guide. 2009. 148p. 28.95 *(978-1-4490-2993-7(0))*; pap. 19.95 *(978-1-4490-2992-0(2))* AuthorHouse.

Sulzer-Azaroff, Beth. Applying Behavior Analysis Across the Autism Spectrum: A Field Guide for New Practitioners. 2nd ed. 2011. ***(978-1-59738-036-2(9))*** Sloan Publishing.

Sulzer-Azaroff, Beth. Applying Behavior Analysis Across the Autism Spectrum: A Guide for Practitioners. 2007. (C). pap. 30.00 net. *(978-1-59738-009-6(1))* Sloan Publishing.

Talmage, Karen Loden, text. Climbing Art Obstacles in Autism: Teaching Visual-Motor Skills through Visually Structured Art Activities. 2007. (Illus.). spiral bd. 39.95 *(978-1-934226-07-0(6))* Tasks Galore Publishing, Inc.

Taylor, Juliann & Taylor, Wes. Get the Skinny on Children with Autism. 2006. 100p. pap. 9.95 *(978-1-60037-039-7(X)*, 160037039X, Get The Skinny Books) Morgan James Publishing.

Telfer, J. Christopher's Story. 2007. 184p. per. *(978-1-84747-309-7(1))* Chipmunkapublishing.

—Christopher's Story Part Ii. 2008. 156p. pap. *(978-1-84747-378-3(4))* Chipmunkapublishing.

—Christphers Story. 2007. pap. *(978-1-84747-128-4(5))* Chipmunkapublishing.

The Health Experts of The Doctors' Prescription for Healthy Living, ed. New Hope for Autism. 2008. 96p. pap. 12.95 *(978-1-893910-53-9(9))* Freedom Pr., Inc., The.

Thompson, Charlotte & Tilton, Adelle Jameson. The Everything Parent's Guide to Children with Autism: Expert, reassuring advice to help your child at home, at school, & at Play. 2nd ed. 2010. (ENG.). 304p. pap. 14.95 *(978-1-4405-0392-4(3))* Adams Media Corp.

Thompson, Travis. Freedom from Meltdowns: Dr. Thompson's Solutions for Children with Autism. 2008. 304p. *(978-1-55766-986-5(4))* Brookes, Paul H. Publishing Co.

Tommey, Jonathan & Tommey, Polly. Autism: A Practical Guide to Improving Your Child's Quality of Life. 2012. (ENG.). 304p. pap. 19.95 ***(978-0-7499-4238-0(X))*** Piatkus Bks. GBR. Dist: Independent Pubs. Group.

Tucker, George. Teachers' Views on the Spiritual Development of Children with Autism. 2011. 112p. pap. ***(978-3-8443-1487-8(3))*** Lambert Academic Publishing.

UC Davis Mind Institute Staff. Educational Interventions for Students with Autism. Mundy, Peter & Mastergeorge, Ann, eds. 2012. (ENG.). 336p. pap. 30.00 ***(978-0-470-58486-6(6)***, Jossey-Bass) Wiley, John & Sons, Inc.

Van Der Post, Anna. Children & Teenagers with Aspergers. 2009. 356p. pap. *(978-1-84747-904-4(9))* Chipmunkapublishing.

Vandegrift, Berthajane. A Few Impertinent Questions: About Autism, Freudianism & Materialism. 2010. 200p. 24.99 *(978-1-4520-1646-7(1))*; pap. 14.49 *(978-1-4520-1645-0(3))* AuthorHouse.

Vicker, Beverly. Sharing Information about Your Child with Autism Spectrum Disorder: What Do Respite or Alternative Caregivers Need to Know? 2007. (Illus.). 228p. pap. 24.95 incl. cd-rom *(978-1-931282-40-6(4))* Autism Asperger Publishing Co.

Wagner, Sheila. Inclusive Programming for High School Students with Autism or Aspergers Syndrome: A Guide for Parents & Teachers. 2009. (ENG., Illus.). 392p. pap. 24.95 *(978-1-932565-57-7(4))* Future Horizons, Inc.

Wahlberg, Timothy. Finding the Gray: The Black & White World of Asperger's & Autism. 2010. pap. 19.95 *(978-0-615-35704-1(0))* Wahlberg & Assocs.

Wakefield, Andrew. Callous Disregard: Autism & Vaccines - The Truth Behind a Tragedy. 2010. pap. *(978-1-4507-1187-6(1))* Independent Pub.

—Callous Disregard: Autism & Vaccines - The Truth Behind a Tragedy. 2010. (ENG.). 288p. 26.95 *(978-1-61608-169-0(4)*, 608169) Skyhorse Publishing Co., Inc.

Wakefield, Andrew J. Callous Disregard: Austims & Vaccines - The Truth Behind a Tragedy. 2011. (ENG.). 288p. pap. 17.95 *(978-1-61608-323-6(9)*, 608323) Skyhorse Publishing Co., Inc.

Wakefield, Andrew J. Waging War on the Autistic Child: The Legacy of Baron von Munchausen. 2012. (ENG.). 272p. 26.95 ***(978-1-61608-614-5(9)***, 608614) Skyhorse Publishing Co., Inc.

Wall, Kate. Autism & Early Years Practice. 2nd ed. 2009. (Illus.). 176p. (C). 112.00 *(978-1-84787-507-5(6)*, B75075C); pap. 45.00 *(978-1-84787-508-2(4)*, B75075P) SAGE Pubns., Ltd. GBR. Dist: SAGE Pubns., Inc.

Walton, Susan. Discovering Family Fun with Autism. 2010. (ENG.). 224p. pap. 14.99 *(978-1-4022-4120-8(8))* Sourcebooks, Inc.

Way, Rhonda. Autism: Rebuilding with Builder Dan. 2008. (J). cd-rom 20.00 net. *(978-0-9740360-7-6(2))* Autism Research Institute.

Webber, Jo & Scheuermann, Brenda. Educating Students with Autism: A Quick Start Manual. 2008. 51.00 *(978-1-4164-0255-8(1))* PRO-ED, Inc.

Weiss, Mary Jane. Jumpstarting Communication Skills in Children with Autism: A Parents Guide to Applied Verbal Behavior. 2011. 200p. pap. ***(978-1-890627-70-6(4))*** Woodbine Hse.

Weiss, Mary Jane. Practical Solutions for Educating Young Children with High Functioning Autism & Asperger Syndrome. 2007. (Illus.). 242p. pap. 21.95 *(978-1-934575-14-7(3))* Autism Asperger Publishing Co.

Whalen, Christina. Real Life, Real Progress for Children with Autism Spectrum Disorders: Strategies for Successful Generalization in Natural Environments. 2009. (Illus.). 256p. pap. 29.95 *(978-1-55766-954-4(6))* Brookes, Paul H. Publishing Co.

Wheeler, Maria. Toilet Training for Individuals with Autism or Other Developmental Issues. 2nd ed. 2007. (ENG., Illus.). 133p. per. 19.95 *(978-1-932565-49-2(3))* Future Horizons, Inc.

Whiffen, Leeann. A Child's Journey Out of Autism: One Family's Story of Living in Hope & Finding a Cure. 2009. (ENG.). 336p. pap. 14.99 *(978-1-4022-1838-5(9))* Sourcebooks, Inc.

Whitman, Thomas L. & DeWitt, Nicole. Key Learning Skills for Children with Autism Spectrum Disorders: A Blueprint for Life. 2011. (ENG.). 304p. *(978-1-84905-864-3(4))* Kingsley, Jessica Ltd.

Widmer-Reyes, Debra. Treadmill for Students with Autism & Apraxia Protocol. 2009. pap. *(978-1-61584-444-9(9))* Independent Pub.

Williams, Keith E. & Foxx, Richard M. Eating Problems of Children with Autism Spectrum Disorders & Developmental Disabilities: Interventions for Professionals & Parents. 2008. xv, 204p. 55.00 *(978-1-4164-0248-0(9))* PRO-ED, Inc.

Willis, Clarissa. Teaching Young Children with Autism Spectrum Disorder. 2008. (ENG., Illus.). 224p. per. 24.95 *(978-0-87659-008-9(3))* Gryphon Hse., Inc.

Winner, Michelle Garcia. Thinking About You Thinking About Me. 2nd rev. ed. 2007. *(978-0-9701320-1-7(8)*, Social Cognitive Deficits) Think Social Publishing, Inc.

Wiseman, Nancy D. The First Year: Autism Spectrum Disorders - An Essential Guide for the Newly Diagnosed Child. 2009. (ENG.). 368p. pap. 16.95 *(978-1-60094-065-1(X))* Da Capo Pr., Inc.

Wolfberg, Pamela J. Peer Play & the Autism Spectrum: The Art of Guiding Children's Socialization & Imagination. (Illus.). v, 264p. 39.95 *(978-1-931282-17-8(X)*, 9921) Social Skills Solutions.

—Play & Imagination in Children with Autism. 2nd rev. ed. 2009. (ENG., Illus.). 216p. pap. 24.95 *(978-0-8077-4941-8(9))*; 56.00 *(978-0-8077-4942-5(7))* Teachers College Pr., Teachers College, Columbia Univ.

Woodcock, Linda & Page, Andrea. Managing Family Meltdown: The Low Arousal Approach & Autism. 2009. (ENG., Illus.). 208p. pap. *(978-1-84905-009-8(0))* Kingsley, Jessica Ltd.

Yoshida, Yuko. Raising Children with Asperger's Syndrome & High-Functioning Autism: Championing the Individual. Sanders, Esther & Hirano, Cathy, trs. from JPN. 2012. (ENG., Illus.). 256p. pap. ***(978-1-84905-317-4(0))*** Kingsley, Jessica Ltd.

Young, Ronnie. Asperger Syndrome Pocketbook. 2008. (Illus.). 128p. pap. *(978-1-903776-99-5(6)*, Teachers' Pocketbooks) Management Pocketbooks GBR. Dist: Ware-Pak, Inc.

Zager, Dianne, et al, eds. Educating Students with Autism. 2011. (ENG., Illus.). 352p. 150.00 *(978-0-415-87756-5(3))*; pap. 59.95 *(978-0-415-87757-2(1))* Routledge.

Ziegler, Martha Hanes. My Daughter, My Teacher: Mary Ann, Autistic in English & Spanish. 2010. 160p. pap. 14.95 *(978-1-4502-2916-6(6))* iUniverse, Inc.

AUTO COURTS

see Motels

AUTO MECHANICS

see Automobile Mechanics

AUTO THEFT

see Automobile Theft

AUTO WORKERS

see Automobile Industry Workers

AUTOBIOGRAPHICAL FICTION

Abad Faciolince, Héctor Joaquín & Abad Faciolince, Héctor. Traiciones de la Memoria. 2010. (SPA., Illus.). 265p. *(978-84-204-0574-2(4)*, Alfaguara) Santillana USA Publishing Co., Inc.

Blinko, Nick. The Primal Screamer. 2011. (ENG.). 144p. (Orig.). pap. 14.95 ***(978-1-60486-331-4(5))*** PM Pr.

Duras, Marguerite. Writing. Polizzotti, Mark, tr. from FRE. 2011. (ENG.). 128p. pap. 16.95 ***(978-0-8166-7753-5(0))*** Univ. of Minnesota Pr.

Jackson, Stewart. Writings of George Godwin: A Twentieth Century Romantic. 2011. 144p. pap. 14.90 *(978-1-4269-4990-6(1))* Trafford Publishing.

McClanahan, Ed. O the Clear Moment. 2009. (ENG.). 208p. pap. 14.95 *(978-1-58243-529-9(4)*, Counterpoint Pr.) Basic Bks. GBR. Dist: Perseus-PGW.

Roth, Henry & Davidson, Willing. An American Type. 2011. (ENG.). 273p. pap. 15.95 *(978-0-393-33992-5(0)*, 33992) Norton, W. W. & Co., Inc.

Whitinger, Raleigh, ed. Bekenntnisse Einer Giftmischerin, Von Ihr Selbst Geschrieben. 2009. (GER.). pap. 12.95 *(978-1-60329-064-7(8))* Modern Language Assn. of America.

AUTOBIOGRAPHICAL FICTION—HISTORY AND CRITICISM

Ballesteros, Isolina. Escritura Femenina y Discurso Autobiografico en la Nueva Novela Espanola. 2nd ed. (American University Studies: Vol. 207). (SPA.). 202p. 29.95 *(978-0-8204-6205-9(5))* Lang, Peter Publishing, Inc.

Boldrini, Lucia. Autobiographies of Others. 2012. (Routledge Studies in Twentieth-Century Literature Ser.). (ENG., Illus.). 244p. (C). 125.00 ***(978-0-415-50737-0(5))*** Routledge.

Bolln, Frauke, ed. Europaische Memoiren / Memoires Europeens: Festschrift f r Dolf Oehler. 2008. (GER.). 420p. (C). 77.00 *(978-3-89971-480-7(6))* Vandenhoeck & Ruprecht GmbH & Co. KG DEU. Dist: ISD.

Bronfen, Elisabeth. Dorothy Richardson's Art of Memory: Space, Identity, Text. 2011. (ENG.). 272p. pap. 30.00 *(978-0-7190-8326-6(5))* Manchester Univ. Pr. GBR. Dist: Macmillan.

Dufief-Sanchez, Véronique. Philosophie du roman personnel, de Chateaubriand a Fromentin 1802-1863. 2010. (HISTOIRE des IDeES et CRITIQUE LITTeRAIRE Ser.). (FRE.). 416p. (C). pap. 82.00 *(978-2-600-01326-0(1))* Droz, Librairie CHE. Dist: Brown, David Bk. Co., The.

Ferran, Ofelia. Working Through Memory: Writing & Remembrance in Contemporary Spanish Narrative. 2008. 370p. 75.00 *(978-0-8387-5658-4(1))* Bucknell Univ. Pr.

Gastanaga Ponce de Leon, Jose Luis. Caballero Noble Desbaratado: Autobiografia e Invencion en el Siglo XVI. 2011. (Purdue Studies in Romance Literatures Ser.). (SPA.). 198p. pap. 45.00 *(978-1-55753-602-0(3))* Purdue Univ. Pr.

Gibbs, Alan. Henry Roth's Semi-Autobiographical Tetralogy Mercy of a Rude Stream (1994-1998) The Second Career of an American Novelist. 2008. 276p. 109.95 *(978-0-7734-5101-8(3))* Mellen, Edwin Pr., The.

Hernández, Mark A. Figural Conquistadors: Rewriting the New World's Discovery & Conquest in Mexican & River Plate Novels of the 1980s & 1990s. 2006. (Bucknell Studies in Latin American Literature & Theory). (Illus.). 194p. 45.00 *(978-0-8387-5645-4(X))* Bucknell Univ. Pr.

Jackson, Anna. Diary Poetics: Form & Style in Writers' Diaries, 1915-1962. 2010. (Routledge Studies in Twentieth-Century Literature Ser.). (ENG.). 198p. (C). 125.00 *(978-0-415-99831-4(X))* Routledge.

Johansen, Jorgen & Sondergaard, Leif, eds. Fact, Fiction & Faction. 2010. 169p. pap. 32.25 *(978-87-7674-430-4(2))* Univ. Pr. of Southern Denmark DNK. Dist: International Specialized Bk. Services.

Larrier, Renee. Autofiction & Advocacy in the Francophone Caribbean. 2006. (ENG.). 200p. 59.95 *(978-0-8130-3005-0(6))* Univ. Pr. of Florida.

Lee, Ying S. Masculinity & the English Working Class: Studies in Victorian Autobiography & Fiction. 2007. (Literary Criticism & Cultural Theory Ser.). (ENG., Illus.). 284p. (C). 131.00 *(978-0-415-98146-0(8))* Routledge.

Leland, John. Why Kerouac Matters: The Lessons of on the Road (They're Not What You Think) 2008. (ENG.). 224p. (gr. 12-18). 15.00 *(978-0-14-311437-6(9)*, Penguin (Non-Classics)) Penguin Group (USA) Inc.

Maher, Paul, Jr. Jack Kerouac's American Journey: The Real-Life Odyssey of on the Road. 2007. (ENG.). 320p. per. 16.00 *(978-1-56025-991-6(4))* Da Capo Pr., Inc.

Martens, Lorna. The Diary Novel. 2009. (ENG., Illus.). 320p. (C). pap. 42.00 *(978-0-521-10825-6(X))* Cambridge Univ. Pr.

Mauldin, Joanne Marshall. Thomas Wolfe: When Do the Atrocities Begin? 2007. (Illus.). 352p. 38.00 *(978-1-57233-494-6(0))* Univ. of Tennessee Pr.

Miller, John E. Laura Ingalls Wilder & Rose Wilder Lane: Authorship, Place, Time, & Culture. 2008. (ENG., Illus.). 280p. (C). 39.95 *(978-0-8262-1823-0(7))* Univ. of Missouri Pr.

Mock, Roberta, ed. Walking, Writing & Performance: Autobiographical Texts by Deirdre Heddon, Carl Lavery & Phil Smith. 2009. (ENG., Illus.). 192p. pap. 35.00 *(978-1-84150-155-0(7))* Intellect, Ltd. GBR. Dist: Chicago Distribution Ctr.

Nicholas, Bims. Understanding Anthony Powell. 2011. (Understanding Contemporary British Literature Ser.). (ENG.). 408p. pap. 24.95 ***(978-1-61117-051-1(6))*** Univ. of South Carolina Pr.

Said, Edward W. & Said, Edward W. Joseph Conrad & the Fiction of Autobiography. 2008. (ENG.). 248p. (gr. 17). pap. 27.00 *(978-0-231-14005-8(3))*; (Illus.). 80.00 *(978-0-231-14004-1(5))* Columbia Univ. Pr.

Saunders, Max. Self Impression: Life-Writing, Autobiografiction, & the Forms of Modern Literature. 2010. (ENG., Illus.). 600p. 95.00 *(978-0-19-957976-1(8))* Oxford Univ. Pr., Inc.

Schmidt, Ulrich. Zwischen Aufbruch und Wende: Lebensgeschichten der sechziger und siebziger Jahre. (Studien und Texte zur Sozialgeschichte der Literatur Ser.). (GER.). VII, 307p. 210.00 ***(978-3-11-183898-4(6))*** De Gruyter, Walter Inc.

Steinig, Valeska. Abschied Von der DDR: Autobiografisches Schreiben Nach Dem Ende der Politischen Alternative. (GER.). 22p. pap. 46.95 *(978-3-631-56237-6(3))* Lang, Peter GmbH, Europaischer Verlag der Wissenschaften DEU. Dist: Lang, Peter Publishing, Inc.

Tarvas, Mari, ed. Tradition und Geschichte im literarischen und sprachwissenschaftlichen Kontext: Unter Mitwirkung von Sonja Pachali, Aigi Heero, Merle Jung, Heiju Ridali und Maris Saagpakk. 2008. 152p. pap. 49.95 *(978-3-631-57270-2(0))* Lang, Peter GmbH, Europaischer Verlag der Wissenschaften DEU. Dist: Lang, Peter.

Toro, Vera, et al. La Obsesión Del Yo: La Auto(R)ficción en la Literatura Española y Latinoamericana. 2010. (SPA.). 284p. pap. 36.00 *(978-84-8489-510-7(6))* Iberoamericana Vervuert Publishing Corp.

Walkowiak, Maciej. Ernst Von Salomons Autobiographische Romane Als Literarische Selbstgestaltungsstrategien Im Kontext der Historisch-Politischen Semantik. (GER.). 379p. pap. 68.95 *(978-3-631-56863-7(0))* Lang, Peter GmbH, Europaischer Verlag der Wissenschaften DEU. Dist: Lang, Peter Publishing, Inc.

AUTOBIOGRAPHICAL MEMORY

Here are entered works on memory of one's past experiences.

Assink, Marian & Schroots, Johannes J. F. The Dynamics of Autobiographical Memory Using the LIM/Lifeline Interview Method. 2010. (Illus.). 162p. pap. 69.00 *(978-0-88937-370-9(1))* Hogrefe Publishing.

Bauer, Patricia J. Remembering the Times of Our Lives: Memory in Infancy & Beyond. 2006. (Developing Mind Ser.). (ENG., Illus.). 448p. 110.00 *(978-0-8058-4040-7(0))*; per. 60.00 *(978-0-8058-5733-7(8))* Taylor & Francis Group GBR. (Psychology Press). Dist: Taylor & Francis Group.

Berntsen, Dorthe & Rubin, David C., eds. Understanding Autobiographical Memory: Theories & Approaches. 2012. (ENG., Illus.). 384p. pap. 38.99 ***(978-0-521-18933-0(0))*** Cambridge Univ. Pr.

Brown, Christopher A. After the Event. 2007. 188p. 30.99 *(978-1-4257-6534-7(3))*; per. 20.99 *(978-1-4257-6533-0(5))* Xlibris Corp.

Christensen, Madonna Dries. Toys Remembered: Men Recall Their Childhood Toys. 2011. 196p. pap. 18.95 *(978-1-4502-7543-9(5))* iUniverse, Inc.

Conway, M. A., et al, eds. Theoretical Perspectives on Autobiographical Memory. 2010. (NATO Science Series D: (closed) Ser.). 516p. pap. 439.00 *(978-90-481-4136-4(2)*, 9048141362) Springer.

Dalgleish. Autobiographical Memory & Emotional Disorder. Brewin, Chris, ed. 2008. (Special Issues of Memory Ser.). (ENG.). 136p. 54.50 *(978-1-84169-833-5(4)*, Psychology Press) Taylor & Francis Group GBR. Dist: Taylor & Francis Group.

Dawson, Graham. Making Peace with the Past? Memory, Trauma & the Irish Troubles. 2011. (ENG., Illus.). 416p. pap. 30.00 *(978-0-7190-5672-7(1))* Manchester Univ. Pr. GBR. Dist: Macmillan.

Della Sala, Sergio, ed. Forgetting. 2010. (Current Issues in Memory Ser.). (ENG., Illus.). 352p. 75.00 *(978-1-84872-012-1(2)*, Psychology Press) Taylor & Francis Group GBR. Dist: Taylor & Francis Group.

Dickson, Janet. Autobiographical Memory & Emotional Disorders. 2009. 192p. pap. *(978-3-639-12579-5(7))* VDM Verlag Dr. Mueller e.K.

DiGaetani, John Louis. Stages of Struggle: Modern Playwrights & Their Psychological Inspirations. 2008. (ENG., Illus.). 206p. per 35.00 *(978-0-7864-3157-1(1))* McFarland & Co., Inc. Pubs.

Douglas, Kate. Contesting Childhood: Autobiography, Trauma & Memory. 2010. (Rutgers Series in Childhood Studies). (ENG., Illus.). 208p. (C). pap. 23.95 *(978-0-8135-4664-3(8))* Rutgers Univ. Pr.

—Contesting Childhood: Autobiography, Trauma, & Memory. 2010. (Rutgers Series in Childhood Studies). (ENG., Illus.). 236p. (C). 72.00 *(978-0-8135-4663-6(X))* Rutgers Univ. Pr.

Estrade, Patrick. You Are What You Remember: A Pathbreaking Guide to Understanding & Interpreting Your Childhood Memories. 2008. (ENG.). 272p. pap. 16.95 *(978-0-60094-042-2(0)*, Da Capo Lifelong) Da Capo Pr., Inc.

Haight, Barbara & Haight, Barrett. The Handbook of Structured Life Review. 2007. 208p. per. *(978-1-932529-27-2(6))* Health Professions Pr.

Haustein, Katja. Regarding Lost Time: Photography, Identity & Affect in Proust, Benjamin, & Barthes. 2012. (Legenda Main Ser.). (ENG., Illus.). 206p. (C). 89.50 *(978-1-907747-91-5(5))* European Humanities Research Ctr. GBR. Dist: Brown, David Bk. Co., The.

Kenyon, Gary M., et al. Storying Later Life: Issues, Investigations, & Interventions in Narrative Gerontology. 2010. (ENG., Illus.). 424p. 49.95 *(978-0-19-539795-6(9))* Oxford Univ. Pr., Inc.

Lippincott, Sharon M. The Heart & Craft of Lifestory Writing: How to Transform Memories into Meaningful Stories. 2007. (Illus.). 275p. per. 16.95 *(978-0-9792998-0-3(2))* Lighthouse Point Pr.

Lynch, James A. A Boy Named Jim. 2011. 144p. pap. 11.95 ***(978-1-4582-0021-1(3)***, Abbott Pr.) Author Solutions, Inc.

Mace, John H., ed. The Act of Remembering: Toward an Understanding of How We Recall the Past. 2010. (New Perspectives in Cognitive Psychology Ser.: 2). (ENG., Illus.). 416p. 110.95 *(978-1-4051-8904-0(5))*; pap. 54.95 *(978-1-4051-8903-3(7))* Wiley, John & Sons, Inc. (Wiley-Blackwell).

Malo, Markus. Behauptete Subjektivität: Eine Skizze zur deutschsprachigen jüdischen Autobiographie im 20. Jahrhundert. 2009. (Conditio Judaica Ser.). (GER.). VI, 338p. pap. *(978-3-484-65174-6(1))* Verlag Max Niemeyer.

Markowitsch, Hans J. & Welzer, Harald. The Development of Autobiographical Memory. 2009. (ENG., Illus.). 288p. 75.00 *(978-1-84372-020-6(3)*, Psychology Press) Taylor & Francis Group GBR. Dist: Taylor & Francis Group.

Marsh, Jeffrey. Share Your Stories Father. 2011. 192p. pap. 14.99 *(978-1-59955-513-3(1))* Cedar Fort, Inc./CFI Distribution.

—Share Your Stories Grandfather. 2011. 192p. pap. 14.99 *(978-1-59955-514-0(X))* Cedar Fort, Inc./CFI Distribution.

—Share Your Stories Grandmother. 2011. 192p. pap. 14.99 *(978-1-59955-512-6(3))* Cedar Fort, Inc./CFI Distribution.

—Share Your Stories Mother. 2011. 192p. pap. 14.99 *(978-1-59955-511-9(5))* Cedar Fort, Inc./CFI Distribution.

McGaugh, James L. Memory & Emotion: The Making of Lasting Memories. 2006. (Maps of the Mind Ser.). (ENG., Illus.). 192p. (gr. 17). pap. 26.00 *(978-0-231-12023-4(0))* Columbia Univ. Pr.

Neisser, Ulric & Fivush, Robyn, eds. The Remembering Self: Construction & Accuracy in the Self-Narrative: Construction & Accuracy in the Self-Narrative. 2008. (Emory Symposia in Cognition Ser.). (ENG., Illus.). 316p. pap. 42.00 *(978-0-521-08791-9(0))* Cambridge Univ. Pr.

Paperno, Irina. Stories of the Soviet Experience: Memoirs, Diaries, Dreams. 2009. 256p. 57.95 *(978-0-8014-4839-3(5))*; pap. 22.95 *(978-0-8014-7590-0(2))* Cornell Univ. Pr.

Randall, William L. & McKim, Elizabeth. Reading Our Lives: The Poetics of Growing Old. 2008. (ENG.). 224p. 39.95 *(978-0-19-530687-3(2))* Oxford Univ. Pr., Inc.

Rutten, Owner/Designer Kristin. Scrapbooker's All-in-One Memory Logbook 2010. 2009. 392p. pap. 29.95 *(978-0-557-13228-7(2))* Lulu Enterprises Inc.

Sutton, John. Philosophy & Memory Traces: Descartes to Connectionism. 2007. (ENG.). 392p. pap. 79.00 *(978-0-521-03937-6(1))* Cambridge Univ. Pr.

Svaldi, Jennifer. The Impact of Mood & Self-Focus on Recall of Autobiographical Memories. 2008. 68p. pap. *(978-3-639-02004-5(9))* VDM Verlag Dr. Mueller e.K.

AUTOBIOGRAPHIES

Here are entered collections of autobiographies.

see also Diaries

also subdivision Biography under particular subjects and names of countries, cities, etc. e.g. Children—Biography, Scientists—Biography, United States—Biography; also names of persons for autobiographies of specific persons

Benedict, Elizabeth. Mentors, Muses & Monsters: 30 Writers on the People Who Changed Their Lives. 2009. (ENG., Illus.). 288p. 24.99 *(978-1-4391-0861-1(7)*, Free Pr.) Free Pr.

Christensen, Alicia, ed. American Lives: A Reader. 2010. (American Lives Ser.). (ENG.). 326p. pap. 16.95 *(978-0-8032-2805-4(8)*, Bison Bks.) Univ. of Nebraska Pr.

Christmas, Girard & Christmas, School Teacher (retired) Girard. Reports of My Death: Beyond-the-Grave Confessions of North American Writers. 2010. (ENG.). 688p. 50.02 *(978-0-557-26465-0(0))* Lulu Enterprises Inc.

Christmas, School Teacher (retired) Girard. Reports of My Death: Beyond-the-Grave Confessions of North American Writers. 2010. 688p. pap. 34.95 *(978-0-557-28457-3(0))* Lulu Enterprises Inc.

Dasberg, Lea. An Intimate History of Jewish Childhood in the Western World 1723-1953: According to Autobiographies. 2009. 448p. pap. 28.52 *(978-1-4269-1061-6(4))* Trafford Publishing.

Fellner, Steve. All Screwed Up. 2009. 181p. pap. 16.95 *(978-0-9815163-3-2(5))* Benu Pr.

Gale Cengage Publishing, creator. Something about the Author: Facts & Pictures about Authors & Illustrators of Books for Young People. 2008. (Something about the Author Ser.: Vol. 186). (ENG., Illus.). 240p. (J). 202.00 *(978-0-7876-9935-2(7))* Cengage Gale.

—Something about the Author: Facts & Pictures about Authors & Illustrators of Books of Young People. 2008. (Something about the Author Ser.). (ENG., Illus.). 384p. 202.00 *(978-0-7876-9934-5(9))* Cengage Gale.

—Something about the Author Volume 184: Facts & Pictures about Authors & Illustrators of Books for Young People. 2008. (Something about the Author Ser.: Vol. 184). (ENG., Illus.). 240p. 202.00 *(978-0-7876-9933-8(0))* Cengage Gale.

Gale Editors, ed. Something about the Author, Vol. 171. 2006. (Something about the Author Ser.). (ENG.). 352p. 202.00 *(978-0-7876-8795-3(2))* Cengage Gale.

Gray, John. John Gray Sears Journal. Date not set. 16.95 *(978-0-06-019408-6(1))* HarperCollins Pubs.

Kumar, Lisa. Something about the Author. 2008. (Something about the Author Ser.). (ENG.). 384p. 202.00 *(978-0-7876-9938-3(1))*; 368p. 202.00 *(978-0-7876-9936-9(5))*; 224p. 202.00 *(978-0-7876-9937-6(3))* Cengage Gale.

Kumar, Lisa, ed. Something about the Author. 2008. (Something about the Author Ser.). (ENG.). 368p. 202.00 *(978-0-7876-8807-3(X))* Cengage Gale.

lyrics, K. The Maturity of Changes. 2009. 73p. pap. 15.00 *(978-0-557-09659-6(6))* Lulu Enterprises Inc.

Macaulay, Zachary. Life & Letters of Zachary Macaulay. 2009. 438p. pap. *(978-0-217-50306-8(3))* Books LLC.

Pipkin, James W. Sporting Lives: Metaphor & Myth in American Sports Autobiographies. 2008. (Sports & American Culture Ser.). (ENG.). 176p. (C). 29.95 *(978-0-8262-1779-0(6))* Univ. of Missouri Pr.

Reid, Bill. Senior Citizens Writing II. 2009. 360p. pap. 30.00 *(978-1-60235-107-3(4))* Parlor Pr.

Rushton, Jack L. It's Good to Be Alive: Observations from a Wheelchair. 2010. 19.99 *(978-1-59955-408-2(9))* Cedar Fort, Inc./CFI Distribution.

Shaw, Margaret Dinzler. Memoirs in the Light of Day: An Essay Collection. 2008. vii, 210p. pap. *(978-0-9676130-5-5(1))* Lamberson Corona Pr.

Smith, Larry & Fershleiser, Rachel. I Can't Keep My Own Secrets: Six-Word Memoirs by Teens Famous & Obscure. 2009. (ENG., Illus.). 192p. (J). (gr. 8-18). pap. 8.99 *(978-0-06-172684-2(2)*, HarperTeen) HarperCollins Pubs.

—It All Changed in an Instant: More Six-Word Memoirs by Writers Famous & Obscure. 2010. (ENG.). 240p. pap. 12.00 *(978-0-06-171943-1(9)*, HarperPerennial) HarperCollins Pubs.

Smthng about Auth. 2008. (Something about the Author Ser.). (ENG.). 272p. 202.00 *(978-1-4144-2164-3(8))* Cengage Gale.

Something about the Author. (Something about the Author Ser.). (ENG.). 2008. 240p. 202.00 *(978-1-4144-2162-9(1))* 2008. 368p. 202.00 *(978-1-4144-2163-6(X))*196. 2009. 240p. 202.00 *(978-1-4144-2168-1(0))* Cengage Gale.

Taylor, Meadows. The Story of My Life. 2010. 504p. pap. 39.75 *(978-1-146-66548-3(2))*; 494p. pap. 38.75 *(978-1-146-76997-6(0))* BiblioBazaar.

—The Story of My Life. 2009. 294p. pap. *(978-1-150-17560-2(5))*; 306p. pap. *(978-0-217-37311-1(9))* Books LLC.

Taylor, Meadows & Bruce, Henry. The Story of My Life. 2010. 560p. pap. 42.75 *(978-1-146-98906-0(7))* BiblioBazaar.

Taylor, Meadows & Taylor, Alice M. The Story of My Life. 2010. 430p. pap. 35.75 *(978-1-178-34276-5(X))* BiblioBazaar.

Taylor, Meadows, et al. The Story of My Life. 2010. 558p. pap. 42.75 *(978-1-178-34688-6(9))* BiblioBazaar.

Thomson Gale, creator. Something about the Author: Facts & Pictures about Authors & Illustrators of Books for Young People, Vol. 170. 2006. (Something about the Author Ser.). (ENG., Illus.). 224p. 202.00 *(978-0-7876-8794-6(4))* Cengage Gale.

—Something about the Author: Volume 169, Vol. 169. 2006. (Something about the Author Ser.). (ENG., Illus.). 336p. 202.00 *(978-0-7876-8793-9(6))* Cengage Gale.

Wisdom Speaks. Whispers of Our Past. 2009. 178p. pap. 15.00 *(978-0-9792132-9-8(0))* Reflections Publishing, Inc.

Yost, Paula Stallings & McNees, Pat, eds. My Words Are Gonna Linger: The Art of Personal History. 2009. (Illus.). 320p. pap. 19.95 *(978-0-9820134-0-3(X))* Personal History Pr.

AUTOBIOGRAPHIES—BIBLIOGRAPHY

Ogunyemi, Christopher Babatunde. Male Autobiographical Narratives & Gender Imperatives in Nigeri. 2010. 104p. pap. *(978-3-639-25820-2(7))* VDM Verlag Dr. Mueller e.K.

AUTOBIOGRAPHY

Abercrombie, Barbara. Courage & Craft: Writing Your Life into Story. 2007. (ENG.). 160p. per. 16.95 *(978-1-57731-601-5(0))* New World Library.

—(WCS)Courage & Craft: Writing Your Life into Story. 2006. 162p. pap. 28.95 *(978-0-470-05424-6(7))* Wiley, John & Sons, Inc.

Adams, Timothy Dow. Telling Lies in Modern American Autobiography. 2011. (ENG.). 224p. pap. 40.00 *(978-0-8078-5995-7(8))* Univ. of North Carolina Pr.

Anderson, Dana. Identity's Strategy: Rhetorical Selves in Conversion. 2007. (Studies in Rhetoric/Communication Ser.). 209p. *(978-1-57003-706-1(X))* Univ. of South Carolina Pr.

Anderson, Linda. Autobiography. 2nd rev. ed. 2011. (New Critical Idiom Ser.). (ENG.). 176p. (C). 95.00 *(978-0-415-57213-2(4))*; pap. 22.95 *(978-0-415-57214-9(2))* Taylor & Francis Group GBR. (Routledge). Dist: Taylor & Francis Group.

Angier, Carole & Cline, Sally. Life Writing: Writing Biography, Autobiography & Memoir. 2010. (ENG.). 288p. pap. 24.95 *(978-1-4081-2418-5(1)*, Methuen Drama) A & C Black GBR. Dist: Macmillan.

Atkins, Kim & Mackenzie, Catriona, eds. Practical Identity & Narrative Agency. 2010. 312p. pap. 39.95 *(978-0-415-88391-7(1))* Routledge.

Atkinson, Kim, ed. Practical Identity & Narrative Agency. 2007. (Routledge Studies in Contemporary Philosophy Ser.). XI, 308p. 118.00 *(978-0-415-95847-9(4))* Routledge.

Ba U, U. My Burn: The Autobiography of A President. 2011. 220p. 44.95 ***(978-1-258-08700-5(6))*** Literary Licensing, LLC.

Baggerman, Arianne, et al. Controlling Time & Shaping Self: Developments in Autobiographical Writing since the Sixteenth Century. 2011. (Illus.). 532p. ***(978-90-04-19500-4(9))*** BRILL.

Baldwin, Christina. Storycatcher: Making Sense of Our Lives Through the Power & Practice of Story. 2007. (ENG.). 272p. per. 14.95 *(978-1-57731-603-9(7))* New World Library.

Balzer, Paula. Writing & Selling Your Memoir: How to Craft Your Life Story So That Somebody Else Will Actually Want to Read It. 2011. (ENG., Illus.). 240p. pap. 17.99 *(978-1-59963-135-6(0)*, Writer's Digest Bks.) F&W Media, Inc.

Bergstein, Frank D. Some Reminiscences of World War II. 2010. 100p. pap. 11.65 *(978-1-4269-3278-6(2))* Trafford Publishing.

Berman, Jeffrey. Companionship of Grief: Love & Loss in the Memoirs of C. S. Lewis, John Bayley, Donald Hall, & Calvin Trillin. 2010. 288p. pap. 26.95 *(978-1-55849-804-4(4))*; lib. bdg. 80.00 *(978-1-55849-803-7(6))* Univ. of Massachusetts Pr.

Bird, Carmel. Writing the Story of Your Life. 2007. 320p. *(978-0-7322-8456-5(2)*, Fourth Estate) HarperCollins Pubs. Australia.

Birkerts, Sven. Art of Time in Memoir: Then, Again. 2007. (Art Of... Ser.). (ENG.). 120p. pap. 12.00 *(978-1-55597-489-3(9))* Graywolf Pr.

Blasing, Mutlu Konuk. The Art of Life: Studies in American Autobiographical Literature. 2011. (ENG.). 222p. pap. 25.00 *(978-0-292-72932-2(4))* Univ. of Texas Pr.

Bolln, Frauke, ed. Europaische Memoiren / Memoires Europeens: Festschrift f r Dolf Oehler. 2008. (GER.). 420p. (C). 77.00 *(978-3-89971-480-7(6))* Vandenhoeck & Ruprecht GmbH & Co. KG DEU. Dist: ISD.

Boyle, Claire. Consuming Autobiographies: Reading & Writing the Self in Post-War France. 2007. (Legenda Main Ser.). 176p. 79.50 *(978-1-905981-10-6(4))* European Humanities Research Ctr. GBR. Dist: Brown, David Bk. Co., The.

Branch, Mabel Merriam. My Book: An Autobiography. 2011. 294p. 48.95 ***(978-1-258-08910-8(6))*** Literary Licensing, LLC.

Broadrick, Lawson. That's Just the Way It Was Back Then. 2009. 450p. pap. 19.95 *(978-1-4327-4385-7(6))* Outskirts Pr., Inc.

Broughton. Auto/Biography: Critical Concepts in LiteraryCultural Studi Vol1, 4 vols. 2006. *(978-0-415-34872-0(2))* Routledge.

—Auto/Biography: Critical Concepts in LiteraryCultural Studi Vol2, 4 vols. 2006. *(978-0-415-34873-7(0))* Routledge.

—Auto/Biography: Critical Concepts in LiteraryCultural Studi Vol3, 4 vols. 2006. *(978-0-415-34874-4(9))* Routledge.

—Auto/Biography: Critical Concepts in LiteraryCultural Studi Vol4, 4 vols. 2006. *(978-0-415-34875-1(7))* Routledge.

Broughton, Trev Lynn, ed. Autobiography, 4 vols. 2007. (Critical Concepts in Literary & Cultural Studies). 1600p. 1440.00 *(978-0-415-34871-3(4))* Routledge.

Brown, R. Alexander. Up from Harlem: A Pictorial Autobiography. 2009. 364p. pap. 22.49 *(978-1-4389-8128-4(7))* AuthorHouse.

Byrne, Robbie. Mulligan's Us: The Autobiography of Robbie Byrne. 2011. 324p. pap. 29.95 ***(978-1-4560-0557-3(X))*** PublishAmerica, Inc.

Cabral, Louise. Islands of Recall: Write Your Life Story. 2007. 168p. per. 15.95 *(978-0-595-43580-7(7))* iUniverse, Inc.

Cartwright, Peter & Strickland, William Peter. Autobiography of Peter Cartwright: The Backwoods Preacher. 2010. 540p. pap. 40.75 *(978-1-149-04839-9(5))*; pap. 40.75 *(978-1-145-60630-5(5))* BiblioBazaar.

Casemore, Brian. The Autobiographical Demand of Place: Curriculum Inquiry in the American South. 2007. (Complicated Conversation: A Book Ser. of Curriculum Studies). 160p. (C). pap. 25.95 *(978-0-8204-8805-9(4))* Lang, Peter Publishing, Inc.

Casey, Karen. My Story to Yours: A Guided Memoir for Writing Your Recovery Journey. 2011. E-Book ***(978-1-61649-163-5(9))***; (ENG.). 194p. pap. 14.95 ***(978-1-61649-094-2(2))*** Hazelden Publishing & Educational Services.

Chaney, Michael A. Graphic Subjects: Critical Essays on Autobiography & Graphic Novels. 2011. (Illus.). ix, 339p. E-Book *(978-0-299-25103-1(9))*; (ENG., 336p. pap. 26.95 *(978-0-299-25104-8(7))* Univ. of Wisconsin Pr.

Chang, Heewon. Autoethnography as Method. (Developing Qualitative Inquiry Ser.). (ENG., Illus.). 230p. (C). 2009. pap. 29.95 *(978-1-59874-123-0(3))* 2008. 94.00 *(978-1-59874-122-3(5))* Left Coast Pr., Inc.

Chisholm, Alison, et al. How to Write about Yourself. rev. ed. 2007. 208p. pap. 15.95 *(978-0-7490-0367-8(7))* Allison & Busby, Ltd. GBR. Dist: International Publishers Marketing.

Chudacoff, Sophie, et al. Stories from the Heart Vol. 3: More Enchanting Tales & Imagination Tools to Help You Write Better Memoirs. Hillebrandt, Ina S., ed. 2007. (Stories from the Heart Ser.: 3). (Illus.). 226p. per. 19.95 *(978-1-880882-12-2(4),* 978-1-880882-12-2) Pawpress.

Cohler, Bertram J. Writing Desire: Sixty Years of Gay Autobiography. 2007. (Wisconsin Studies in Autobiography Ser.). (ENG.). 272p. per. 24.95 *(978-0-299-22204-8(7))* Univ. of Wisconsin Pr.

Counihan, Beth. Mousepads & Memoirs. 2009. 124p. pap. *(978-3-639-14231-0(4))* VDM Verlag Dr. Mueller e.K.

Couser, G. Thomas. Memoir: An Introduction, 1 vol. 2011. (ENG.). 208p. 99.00 *(978-0-19-982690-2(0));* pap. 18.95 *(978-0-19-982692-6(7))* Oxford Univ. Pr., Inc.

—Signifying Bodies: Disability in Contemporary Life Writing. 2009. (Corporealities: Discourses of Disability Ser.). (ENG., Illus.). 216p. pap. 28.95 *(978-0-472-05069-7(9))* Univ. of Michigan Pr.

Crowley, Kimberly. My Mother, Her Self. 2010. 64p. pap. *(978-3-639-22906-6(1))* VDM Verlag Dr. Mueller e.K.

Cuffy, Beverly. The Mind of the Individual: My Autobiography. 2011. 152p. 24.95 ***(978-1-4620-6224-9(5));*** pap. 14.95 ***(978-1-4620-6222-5(9))*** iUniverse, Inc.

Dahlke, Birgit, et al, eds. German Life Writing in the Twentieth Century. 2010. (Studies in German Literature Linguistics & Culture Ser.: Volume 96). 222p. 75.00 *(978-1-57113-313-7(5))* Camden Hse.

D'Amore, Jonathan. American Authorship & Autobiographical Narrative: Mailer, Wideman, Eggers. 2012. (American Literature Readings in the Twenty-First Century Ser.). (ENG., Illus.). 224p. 80.00 ***(978-0-230-39067-6(6))*** Palgrave Macmillan.

Davis, Lloyd, et al, eds. Early Modern Autobiography: Theories, Genres, Practices. 2006. (ENG., Illus.). 320p. 85.00 *(978-0-472-09928-3(0))* Univ. of Michigan Pr.

—Early Modern Autobiography: Theories, Genres, Practices. 2006. (ENG., Illus.). 320p. per. 32.50 *(978-0-472-06928-6(4))* Univ. of Michigan Pr.

Davis, Lloyd, et al. Early Modern English Lives: Autobiography & Self-Representation 1500-1660. 2007. (Illus.). 250p. 114.95 *(978-0-7546-5295-3(5))* Ashgate Publishing Co.

DeMello, Margo, ed. Speaking for Animals: Animal Autobiographical Writing. 2012. (Routledge Advances in Sociology Ser.). (ENG., Illus.). 272p. (C). 125.00 ***(978-0-415-80899-6(5))*** Routledge.

Denbow, Carol. A Book Inside: How to Write, Publish, & Sell Your Story. 2008. 104p. pap. 18.95 *(978-0-615-19924-5(0))* Plain & Simple Bks.

Diamond, Suzanne. Compelling Confessions: The Politics of Personal Disclosure. 2010. 230p. (ENG.). 65.00 *(978-1-61147-042-0(0)); (978-0-8386-4265-8(9))* Fairleigh Dickinson Univ. Pr.

Diedrich, Lisa. Treatments: Language, Politics, & the Culture of Illness. 2007. 288p. 67.50 *(978-0-8166-4697-5(X));* per. 24.00 *(978-0-8166-4698-2(8))* Univ. of Minnesota Pr.

Douglass, Frederick. Narrative of the Life of Frederick Douglass: An American Slave & Incidents in the Life of a Slave Girl. 2007. pap. 6.99 *(978-1-59986-871-4(7))* Filiquarian Publishing, LLC.

Doyle, Paddy. Pure Grit. 2009. (Illus.). 200p. pap. 14.49 *(978-1-4389-9541-0(5))* AuthorHouse.

Eakin, Paul John. Living Autobiographically: How We Create Identity in Narrative. 2008. 208p. 60.95 *(978-0-8014-4724-2(0));* pap. 18.95 *(978-0-8014-7478-1(7))* Cornell Univ. Pr.

Edwards, Ali. Sharing Your Story: Recording Life's Details with Mini Books. 2008. (ENG.). 164p. pap. 19.99 *(978-1-933516-82-0(8),* Creating Keepsakes Magazine) Primedia Scrapbooking.

Edwards, Natalie. Shifting Subjects: Plural Subjectivity in Contemporary Francophone Women's Autobiography. 2011. (ENG.). 180p. 60.00 *(978-1-61149-030-5(8))* 2010. *(978-1-936249-02-2(2))* Univ. of Delaware Pr.

Edwards, Natalie, et al, eds. Textual & Visual Selves: Photography, Film, & Comic Art in French Autobiography. 2011. (ENG., Illus.). 288p. pap. 25.00 *(978-0-8032-3631-8(X))* Univ. of Nebraska Pr.

Egan, Susanna. Burdens of Proof: Faith, Doubt, & Identity in Autobiography. 2011. (Life Writing Ser.). 265p. (C). pap. 34.95 *(978-1-55458-333-1(0))* Wilfrid Laurier Univ. Pr. CAN. Dist: Univ. of Toronto Pr.

—Patterns of Experience in Autobiography. 2011. (ENG.). 240p. pap. 40.00 *(978-0-8078-6533-0(8))* Univ. of North Carolina Pr.

Ellis, Carolyn. Revision: Autoethnographic Reflections on Life & Work. 2008. (Writing Lives Ser.). (ENG.). 395p. 89.00 *(978-1-59874-039-4(3));* pap. 29.95 *(978-1-59874-040-0(7))* Left Coast Pr., Inc.

Equiano, Olaudah. The Life of Olaudah Equiano. 2008. 112p. per. *(978-956-291-606-6(5))* Editorial Benei Noaj.

Folger, Robert A. Writing as Poaching: Interpellation & Self-Fashioning in colonial relaciones de méritos y Servicios. 2011. (Medieval & Early Modern Iberian World Ser.). (Illus.). 208p. ***(978-90-04-21109-4(8))*** BRILL.

Ford, Henry. My Life & Work - Autobiography. 2007. (ENG.). 304p. per. 12.45 *(978-1-60424-146-4(2),* Book Jungle) Standard Pubns., Inc.

Foster, John. Essays in a Series of Letters. 2007. (ENG.). 336p. 45.95 *(978-0-548-06034-6(7))* Kessinger Publishing, LLC.

Franco, Carol & Lineback, Kent. The Legacy Guide: Capturing the Facts, Memories, & Meaning of Your Life. annot. ed. 2006. (ENG.). 400p. (gr. 12-18). 18.95 *(978-1-58542-516-7(8),* Tarcher) Penguin Group (USA) Inc.

Franklin, Cynthia G. Academic Lives: Memoir, Cultural Theory, & the University Today. 2009. (ENG.). 347p. pap. 24.95 *(978-0-8203-3343-4(3));* 368p. lib. bdg. 59.95 *(978-0-8203-3342-7(5))* Univ. of Georgia Pr.

Fuchs, Miriam & Howes, Craig, eds. Teaching Life Writing Texts. 2008. (ENG.). 400p. 40.00 *(978-0-87352-819-1(0))* Modern Language Assn. of America.

Gale, Maggie B., et al. Auto - Biography & Identity: Women, Theatre & Performance. Gale, Maggie B. & Gardner, Viv, eds. 2009. (Women, Theatre & Performance Ser.). (ENG., Illus.). 272p. pap. 24.95 *(978-0-7190-6333-6(7))* Manchester Univ. Pr. GBR. Dist: Macmillan.

Gallagher, Stephanie. True North: A Flickering soul in no man's land; Knut Utstein Kloster, father of the $20-billion-a-year modern cruise industry. 2009. 208p. 27.95 *(978-1-4401-7918-1(2));* pap. 17.95 *(978-1-4401-7917-4(4))* iUniverse, Inc.

Gastanaga Ponce de Leon, Jose Luis. Caballero Noble Desbaratado: Autobiografia e Invencion en el Siglo XVI. 2011. (Purdue Studies in Romance Literatures Ser.). (SPA.). 198p. pap. 45.00 *(978-1-55753-602-0(3))* Purdue Univ. Pr.

Gawthorpe, Ann. Teach Yourself How to Write Your Life Story. 2009. (Teach Yourself: Writing Ser.). (ENG.). 192p. pap. 14.95 *(978-0-07-162585-2(2),* 0071625852) McGraw-Hill Cos., The.

Gawthorpe, Anne. Write Your Life Story. 2011. (Teach Yourself Ser.). (ENG.). 192p. pap. 19.95 *(978-1-4441-0321-2(0),* Hodder & Stoughton) Hodder General Publishing Div. GBR. Dist: Independent Pubs. Group.

Gillies, Midge. Writing Lives: Literary Biography. 2009. (Cambridge Contexts in Literature Ser.). (ENG.). 128p. pap. 16.00 *(978-0-521-73231-4(X))* Cambridge Univ. Pr.

Goldberg, Natalie. Old Friend from Far Away: The Practice of Writing Memoir. 2009. (ENG., Illus.). 336p. pap. 15.00 *(978-1-4165-3503-4(9),* Free Pr.) Free Pr.

Granger, Benjamin. Legend in the Dreamer: My Life & Career Autobiography. 2011. 78p. pap. 19.95 ***(978-1-4626-1021-1(8))*** PublishAmerica, Inc.

Grantham, Unity. Beginning Early, Starting Late (an Autobiography) 2008. 204p. per. 20.95 *(978-1-84799-393-9(1))* Lulu Enterprises Inc.

Gray, Larry S. & Hart, Michael J. The Armageddon Project: Tales from the Kingdom Hall. 2009. 451p. pap. 18.95 *(978-1-4327-5014-5(3))* Outskirts Pr., Inc.

Grundner, Tom, frwd. Me Father Was the Keeper: John Smeaton & the Eddystone Light. 2008. 92p. per. 7.95 *(978-1-934757-28-4(4))* Fireship Pr.

Guerrero, Jane G. Casuratan Ti Biagco: Sinurat ni Don Sabas Gaerlan. 2009. 200p. pap. 14.49 *(978-1-4389-7920-5(7))* AuthorHouse.

Guerrero, Jane G., tr. Casuratan Ti Biagco: Sinurat ni Don Sabas Gaerlan. 2009. 200p. pap. 24.99 *(978-1-4389-7921-2(5))* AuthorHouse.

Hagberg, Garry L. Describing Ourselves: Wittgenstein & Autobiographical Consciousness. 2008. (ENG.). 240p. 74.00 *(978-0-19-923422-6(1))* Oxford Univ. Pr., Inc.

—Describing Ourselves: Wittgenstein & Autobiographical Consciousness. 2011. (ENG.). 284p. pap. 35.00 *(978-0-19-969842-4(2))* Oxford Univ. Pr., Inc.

Hainsworth, Peter & McLaughlin, Martin. Biographies & Autobiographies in Modern Italy: A Festschrift for John Woodhouse. 2006. (Legenda Main Ser.). (ENG., Illus.). 2p. (C). 74.00 *(978-1-905981-07-6(4))* European Humanities Research Ctr. GBR. Dist: Brown, David Bk. Co., The.

Halfin, Igal. Red Autobiographies: Initiating the Bolshevik Self. 2011. (ENG.). 224p. (C). pap. 30.00 *(978-0-295-99112-2(7))* Univ. of Washington Pr.

Hall, Calvin L. & Hall, Clavin L. African American Journalists: Autobiography as Memoir & Manifesto. 2009. (ENG.). 146p. pap. 40.00 *(978-0-8108-6930-1(6))* Scarecrow Pr., Inc.

Hamilton, Charles, Sr. From Darkness to Light. 2009. 377p. 24.95 *(978-1-4327-2112-1(7))* Outskirts Pr., Inc.

Hamilton, Nigel. How to Do Biography: A Primer. 2008. 400p. 22.95 *(978-0-674-02796-1(5))* Harvard Univ. Pr.

Hampl, Patricia & Tyler May, Elaine, eds. Tell Me True: Memoir, History, & Writing a Life. 2011. (ENG.). 240p. pap. 18.95 *(978-0-87351-815-4(2),* Borealis Bk.) Minnesota Historical Society Pr.

Harte, Liam, ed. Modern Irish Autobiography: Self, Nation & Society. 2007. (ENG.). 288p. 100.00 *(978-1-4039-1268-8(8))* Palgrave Macmillan.

Haustein, Katja. Regarding Lost Time: Photography, Identity & Affect in Proust, Benjamin, & Barthes. 2012. (Legenda Main Ser.). (ENG., Illus.). 206p. (C). 89.50 *(978-1-907747-91-5(5))* European Humanities Research Ctr. GBR. Dist: Brown, David Bk. Co., The.

Haynes, Rosetta R. Radical Spiritual Motherhood: Autobiography & Empowerment in Nineteenth-Century African American Women. 2011. 264p. 39.95 *(978-0-8071-3694-2(8))* Louisiana State Univ. Pr.

Helmuth, James L. Crossing the Bridge: From Mennonite Boy to Gay Man. 2009. 136p. pap. 13.95 *(978-1-4401-8846-6(7))* iUniverse, Inc.

Henfrey, Arthur. Botanical & Physiological Memoirs. 2009. 310p. pap. 27.64 *(978-1-150-65380-3(9))* General Bks. LLC.

Henfrey, Arthur, ed. Botanical & Physiological Memoirs. 2010. 610p. pap. 35.96 *(978-1-163-99250-0(X))* 2008. 608p. 59.95 *(978-0-548-99937-0(6))* 2007. (ENG.). 612p. per. 44.95 *(978-0-548-64714-1(3))* Kessinger Publishing, LLC.

Herrmann, Gina. Written in Red: The Communist Memoir in Spain. 2009. (Hispanisms Ser.). (ENG.). 272p. 45.00 *(978-0-252-03469-5(4))* Univ. of Illinois Pr.

Hindmarsh, D. Bruce. The Evangelical Conversion Narrative: Spiritual Autobiography in Early Modern England. 2008. (ENG.). 400p. per. 55.00 *(978-0-19-923671-8(2))* Oxford Univ. Pr., Inc.

Holden, Philip. Autobiography & Decolonization: Modernity, Masculinity, & the Nation-State. 2008. (Wisconsin Studies in Autobiography Ser.). 279p. 55.00 *(978-0-299-22610-7(7))* Univ. of Wisconsin Pr.

Holmgren, Beth, ed. The Russian Memoir: History & Literature. 2007. (Srlt Ser.). (ENG.). 264p. per. 27.95 *(978-0-8101-2428-8(9))* Northwestern Univ. Pr.

Hoomes, Eleanor W. Create-an-Autobiography No. 8: Writing from Experience. Date not set. (Illus.). tchr. ed. 9.95 *(978-1-56644-000-4(9),* 039-3AP) Educational Impressions.

Horsdal, Marianne. Telling Lives. 2011. (ENG.). 184p. (C). 150.00 *(978-0-415-68023-3(9));* pap. 39.95 *(978-0-415-68024-0(7))* Routledge.

Howes, Craig. Teaching Life Writing Texts. Fuchs, Miriam, ed. 2008. (ENG.). 400p. per. 25.00 *(978-0-87352-820-7(4))* Modern Language Assn. of America.

Huddart, David. Postcolonial Theory & Autobiography. 2007. (Routledge Research in Postcolonial Literatures Ser.). (ENG.). 208p. 120.00 *(978-0-415-35342-7(4))* Routledge.

Hunter, Allan G. Write Your Memoir: The Soul Work of Telling Your Story. 2010. (ENG.). 160p. pap. 14.95 *(978-1-84409-177-5(5))* Findhorn Pr. GBR. Dist: Independent Pubs. Group.

Iles, George. Little Masterpieces of Autobiography; Actors. 2010. (Illus.). 78p. pap. 20.00 *(978-1-153-73922-1(4))* General Bks. LLC.

Iles, George, ed. Little Masterpieces of Autobiography: Actors. 2007. 120p. per. *(978-1-4065-3407-8(2))* Dodo Pr.

Inscoe, John C. Writing the South through the Self: Explorations in Southern Autobiography. 2011. (ENG.). 268p. 59.95 *(978-0-8203-3767-8(6));* pap. 19.95 *(978-0-8203-3768-5(4))* Univ. of Georgia Pr.

James L. Helmuth. Crossing the Bridge: From Mennonite Boy to Gay Man. 2009. 136p. 23.95 *(978-1-4401-8848-0(3))* iUniverse, Inc.

Jeffrey, Julie Roy. Abolitionists Remember: Antislavery Autobiographies & the Unfinished Work of Emancipation. 2008. (ENG., Illus.). 352p. 66.50 *(978-0-8078-3208-0(1));* pap. 27.95 *(978-0-8078-5885-1(4))* Univ. of North Carolina Pr.

Jentsch, Mary Hunt. Trek: An American Woman, Two Small Children & Survival in World War II Germany. 2008. (ENG., Illus.). 250p. pap. 14.00 *(978-0-9755618-5-0(5))* McWitty Pr., Inc.

Jones, Elizabeth. Spaces of Belonging: Home, Culture & Identity in 20th-Century French Autobiography. 2007. 320p. per. 88.00 *(978-90-420-2283-6(3))* Rodopi.

Jurecic, Ann. Illness as Narrative. 2012. (Pitt Comp Literacy Culture Ser.). (ENG.). 224p. pap. 24.95 ***(978-0-8229-6190-1(3))*** Univ. of Pittsburgh Pr.

Kirby, Dawn Latta & Kirby, Dan. New Directions in Teaching Memoir: A Studio Workshop Approach. 2007. (Illus.). 208p. pap. 32.50 *(978-0-325-00668-0(7),* E00668) Heinemann.

Lara, Adair. Naked, Drunk, & Writing: Shed Your Inhibitions & Craft a Compelling Memoir or Personal Essay. 2010. (ENG., Illus.). 256p. pap. 14.99 *(978-1-58008-480-2(X))* Ten Speed Pr.

Larson, Thomas. The Memoir & the Memoirist: Reading & Writing Personal Narrative. 2007. 200p. 32.95 *(978-0-8040-1100-6(1));* per. 16.95 *(978-0-8040-1101-3(X))* Swallow Pr.

Lazar, David, ed. Truth in Nonfiction: Essays. 2008. (ENG., Illus.). 212p. pap. 19.95 *(978-1-58729-654-3(3))* Univ. of Iowa Pr.

Lebow, Alisa S. First Person Jewish. 2008. (Visible Evidence Ser.). (Illus.). 224p. pap. 22.50 *(978-0-8166-4355-4(5))* Univ. of Minnesota Pr.

—First Person Jewish. 2008. (Visible Evidence Ser.). (Illus.). 224p. 67.50 *(978-0-8166-4354-7(7))* Univ. of Minnesota Pr.

Ledoux, Denis. The Photo Scribe: A Writing Guide: How to Write the Stories Behind Your Photographs. 3rd ed. 2008. (Illus.). 127p. pap. 19.95 *(978-0-9742773-1-8(2))* Soleil Pr.

Lee, Ying. Masculinity & the English Working Class: Studies in Victorian Autobiography & Fiction. 2012. (Literary Criticism & Cultural Theory Ser.). (ENG.). 264p. (C). pap. 42.95 ***(978-0-415-54169-5(7))*** Routledge.

Lee, Ying S. Masculinity & the English Working Class: Studies in Victorian Autobiography & Fiction. 2007. (Literary Criticism & Cultural Theory Ser.). (ENG., Illus.). 264p. (C). 131.00 *(978-0-415-98146-0(8))* Routledge.

Lehmann, Jürgen. Bekennen - Erzählen - Berichten: Studien Zu Theorie und Geschichte der Autobiographie. (Studien zur deutschen Literatur Ser.). (GER., Illus.). VIII, 289p. 135.00 ***(978-3-11-183971-4(0))*** De Gruyter, Walter Inc.

Lippincott, Sharon M. The Heart & Craft of Lifestory Writing: How to Transform Memories into Meaningful Stories. 2007. (Illus.). 275p. per. 16.95 *(978-0-9792998-0-3(2))* Lighthouse Point Pr.

Lynch, Claire. Irish Autobiography: Stories of Self in the Narrative of a Nation. 2009. (Reimagining Ireland Ser.). (ENG.). 234p. pap. 49.95 *(978-3-03911-856-4(0))* Lang, Peter AG GBR. Dist: Lang, Peter.

Maan, Ajit. Internarrative Identity: Placing the Self. 2nd ed. 2009. (ENG.). 112p. pap. 20.99 *(978-0-7618-4967-4(X))* Univ. Pr. of America, Inc.

Maan, Ajit K. Internarrative Identity: Placing the Self. 2nd ed. 2010. xx, 90p. *(978-0-7618-4968-1(8))* Univ. Pr. of America, Inc.

Majeed, Javed. Autobiography, Travel & Postnational Identity: Gandhi, Nehru & Iqbal. 2007. (ENG.). 344p. 110.00 *(978-1-4039-8595-8(2))* Palgrave Macmillan.

Malo, Markus. Behauptete Subjektivität: Eine Skizze zur deutschsprachigen jüdischen Autobiographie im 20. Jahrhundert. 2009. (Conditio Judaica Ser.). (GER.). VI, 338p. pap. *(978-3-484-65174-6(1))* Verlag Max Niemeyer.

Marlow, L., ed. The Rhetoric of Biography: Narrating Lives in Persianate Societies. 2011. (Ilex Ser.). (ENG., Illus.). 184p. pap. 19.95 *(978-0-674-06066-1(0))* Harvard Univ., Ctr. for Hellenic Studies.

Maxwell, Roy & Vayne, Constance. From Poorhouse to Penthouse & Back. 2010. 517p. pap. 30.00 *(978-1-4452-9846-7(5))* Lulu Enterprises Inc.

Maynes, Mary Jo, et al. Telling Stories: The Use of Personal Narratives in the Social Sciences & History. 2008. 200p. 61.00 *(978-0-8014-4617-7(1));* pap. 19.95 *(978-0-8014-7392-0(6))* Cornell Univ. Pr.

McKenna, James. Last Exit from Bridgeton: An East End Childhood Remembered. 2nd enl. ed. 2006. (ENG.). 468p. per. *(978-1-84530-038-8(6))* Grimsay Pr.

McLeroy, Leigh. Treasured: Knowing God by the Things He Keeps. 2009. (ENG.). 224p. 14.99 *(978-1-4000-7481-5(9),* WaterBrook Pr.) Doubleday Religious Publishing Group, The.

Monteleone, Tom & Costello, Victoria. The Complete Idiot's Guide to Writing a Memoir. 2011. (Complete Idiot's Guide Ser.). (ENG.). 304p. (gr. 12). 15.95 *(978-1-61564-123-9(8),* Alpha Bks.) Penguin Group (USA) Inc.

Moore, Dinty W. Crafting the Personal Essay: A Guide for Writing & Publishing Creative Non-Fiction. 2010. (ENG., Illus.). 272p. pap. 17.99 *(978-1-58297-796-6(8),* Writer's Digest Bks.) F&W Media, Inc.

Moore-Gilbert, Bart, et al. Postcolonial Life-Writing: Culture, Politics, & Self-Representation. 2009. (Routledge Research in Postcolonial Literatures Ser.). (ENG.). 200p. 110.00 *(978-0-415-44299-2(0))* Routledge.

Morin, Cindy Lyn. My Sorry Life. 2011. 50p. pap. 16.95 ***(978-1-4626-0904-8(X))*** PublishAmerica, Inc.

Moscheles, Felix. Fragments of an Autobiography. 2009. 188p. pap. *(978-0-217-47935-6(9))* Books LLC.

—Fragments of an Autobiography. 2007. (ENG.). 372p. 48.95 *(978-0-548-15489-2(9));* pap. 33.95 *(978-1-4304-4919-5(5))* Kessinger Publishing, LLC.

Mullan, David George. Narratives of the Religious Self in Early-Modern Scotland. 2010. (St Andrews Studies in Reformation History Ser.). (Illus.). 464p. 134.95 *(978-0-7546-6832-9(0))* Ashgate Publishing Co.

Muncey, Tessa. Creating Autoethnographies. 2010. 168p. (C). 71.00 *(978-1-84787-472-6(X),* B74726C); pap. 26.00 *(978-1-84787-473-3(8),* B74726P) SAGE Pubns., Ltd. GBR. Dist: SAGE Pubns., Inc.

Myers, Linda. The Power of Memoir: How to Write Your Healing Story. 2010. (ENG., Illus.). 272p. pap. 16.95 *(978-0-470-50836-7(1),* Jossey-Bass) Wiley, John & Sons, Inc.

Nash, Geoffrey. The Anglo-Arab Encounter: Fiction & Autobiography by Arab Writers in English. 2007. 215p. pap. *(978-3-03911-026-1(8))* Lang, Peter AG.

Ni Riain, Noirin. Listen with the Ear of the Heart: An Autobiography. 2010. (ENG., Illus.). 202p. 28.95 *(978-1-84730-172-7(X))* Veritas Pubns. IRL. Dist: Dufour Editions, Inc.

Nickerson, Sarah. Don't Weep. 2009. 56p. pap. 12.99 *(978-1-4259-0008-3(9))* AuthorHouse.

Noonan, James, ed. Biography & Autobiography: Essays on Irish & Canadian History & Literature. (Illus.). 300p. pap. *(978-0-88629-209-6(3))* McGill-Queen's Univ. Pr.

Norton, Lisa D. & Norton, Lisa Dale. Shimmering Images: A Handy Little Guide to Writing Memoir. 2008. (ENG., Illus.). 144p. pap. 14.99 *(978-0-312-38292-6(8),* St. Martin's Griffin) St. Martin's Pr.

Novell, Pepa. La Memoria Sublevada: Autobiografía y Reivindicación Del Intelectual Ibérico Del Medio Siglo. 2009. (SPA.). 172p. pap. 24.80 *(978-84-8489-494-0(0))* Iberoamericana Vervuert Publishing Corp.

Nunan, Anna. Autobiographical Progression in the Writings of Christa Wolf: Nachdenken uber Christa T. (1968), Kindheitsmuster (1976), & ein Tag im Jahr (2003) 2011. 268p. 119.95 *(978-0-7734-1541-6(6))* Mellen, Edwin Pr., The.

Oberlander, Judy. 101 Ways (more or less) to Tell Your Life Story: The Unconventional Autobiography. 2008. (Illus.). 54p. spiral bd. *(978-0-9743770-1-8(5))* Bad Cat Pr.

Oke, Michael. Write Your Life Story: How to Organise & Record Your Memories for Family & Friends to Enjoy. 4th ed. 2010. (ENG.). 211p. pap. 26.00 *(978-1-84528-399-5(6))* How To Books GBR. Dist: Parkwest Pubns., Inc.

—Write Your Life Story 3e. 3rd ed. 2009. (Illus.). 336p. 26.00 *(978-1-84528-305-6(8))* How To Books GBR. Dist: Parkwest Pubns., Inc.

Oloimooja, Rev. Joseph. Angels Walk among Us: From Every Tribe, Kindred & Nation. 2011. 224p. pap. 19.00 ***(978-0-578-07850-2(3))*** Kindness Mission Inc.

Osborn, James M. The Beginnings of Autobiography in England: A Paper Delivered by James M. Osborn at the Fifth Clark Library Seminar, August 8 1959. 2011. 34p. 35.95 ***(978-1-258-09653-3(6))*** Literary Licensing, LLC.

Paperno, Irina. Stories of the Soviet Experience: Memoirs, Diaries, Dreams. 2009. 256p. 57.95 *(978-0-8014-4839-3(5));* pap. 22.95 *(978-0-8014-7590-0(2))* Cornell Univ. Pr.

Parker, F. Calvin. The Good Book Is Better Than It Used to Be: Eighty Years with the Bible. 2009. 198p. 26.95 *(978-1-4401-6010-3(4));* pap. 16.95 *(978-1-4401-6012-7(0))* iUniverse, Inc.

Pich, Edgard. Autobiographiques: Du Jugement. 2011. (FRE.). 244p. 119.95 *(978-0-7734-1467-9(3))* Mellen, Edwin Pr., The.

Poole, Fred. AUTHENTIC WRITING a memoir on creating Memoir. 2008. 204p. pap. 14.95 *(978-0-615-20492-5(9))* Tinker Street Pr.

Porter, Roger J. Bureau of Missing Persons: Writing the Secret Lives of Fathers. 2011. (Illus.). 224p. 35.00 *(978-0-8014-4987-1(1))* Cornell Univ. Pr.

Rasilla, Carmen Garcia de la. Salvador Dali's Literary Self-Portrait: Approaches to a Surrealist Autobiography. 2009. (Illus.). 196p. 48.50 *(978-0-8387-5723-9(5))* Bucknell Univ. Pr.

Rieder, Bernadette. Unter Beweis: Das Leben: Sechs Autobiographien Deutschsprachiger SchriftstellerInnen Aus Israel. 2008. (GER., Illus.). 395p. (C). 68.00 *(978-3-89971-460-9(1))* Vandenhoeck & Ruprecht GmbH & Co. KG DEU. Dist: ISD.

Roach Smith, Marion. The Memoir Project: A Thoroughly Non-Standardized Text for Writing & Life. 2011. (ENG.). 128p. pap., pap. 12.00 *(978-0-446-58484-5(3))* Grand Central Publishing.

Roorbach, Bill. Writing Life Stories: How to Make Memories into Memoirs, Ideas into Essays, & Life into Literature. 2nd ed. 2008. (ENG.). 304p. pap. 16.99 *(978-1-58297-527-6(2)*, Writer's Digest Bks.) F&W Media, Inc.

Root, Robert L., Jr., ed. & intro. Landscapes with Figures: The Nonfiction of Place. 2007. (ENG.). 294p. pap. 21.95 *(978-0-8032-5983-5(2)*, Bison Bks.) Univ. of Nebraska Pr.

Rosinsky, Natalie M. Write Your Own Autobiography. 2008. (Write Your Own Ser.). (ENG., Illus.). 64p. (gr. 6-7). lib. bdg. 33.99 *(978-0-7565-3525-4(5)*, Write Your Own) Compass Point Bks.

Sankara, Edgard. Postcolonial Francophone Autobiographies: From Africa to the Antilles. 2011. viii, 218p. E-Book **(978-0-8139-3176-0(2))**; (ENG.). 232p. (C). (gr. 13-17). pap. 24.50 **(978-0-8139-3172-2(X))**; (ENG., Illus.). 232p. (gr. 17). 55.00 **(978-0-8139-3171-5(1))** Univ. Pr. of Virginia.

Schneider, Myra & Killick, John. Writing Your Self: Transforming Personal Material. 2010. (ENG., Illus.). 270p. 24.95 *(978-1-84706-252-9(0))*; 90.00 *(978-1-84706-251-2(2))* Continuum International Publishing Group, Ltd. GBR. Dist: National Bk. Network.

Sellers, Stephanie A. Native American Autobiography Redefined: A Handbook. 2007. 144p. (C). pap. 29.95 *(978-0-8204-7944-6(6))* Lang, Peter Publishing, Inc.

Shamsai-Nejad, Vafa. Autobiography thru Blogs of Experience, Inspiration & Advice, 1 vol. 2010. 98p. pap. 16.95 *(978-1-4489-8504-3(8))* PublishAmerica, Inc.

Shumaker, Wayne. English Autobiography: Its Emergence, Materials, & Form. 2011. 276p. 47.95 **(978-1-258-07226-1(2))** Literary Licensing, LLC.

Silverman, Sue William. Fearless Confessions: A Writer's Guide to Memoir. 2009. (ENG.). 256p. pap. 19.95 *(978-0-8203-3166-9(X))* Univ. of Georgia Pr.

Skura, Meredith Anne. Tudor Autobiography: Listening for Inwardness. 2008. (ENG., Illus.). 272p. 45.00 *(978-0-226-76187-9(8))* Univ. of Chicago Pr.

Smith, Harold Ivan. Borrowed Narratives: Using Biographical & Historical Grief Narratives with the Bereaving. 2012. (ENG., Illus.). 299p. 39.95 *(978-0-415-89394-7(1))* Routledge.

Smith, Sidonie & Watson, Julia. Reading Autobiography: Interpreting Life Narratives. 2nd ed. 2010. 392p. pap., instr.'s gde. ed 19.50 *(978-0-8166-6986-8(4))*; instr.'s gde. ed. 58.50 *(978-0-8166-6985-1(6))* Univ. of Minnesota Pr.

Smith, Thomas R., ed. Lifewriting Annual: Biographical & Autobiographical Studies, Vol. 2. 2008. 316p. 115.00 *(978-0-404-63422-3(2))* AMS Pr., Inc.

Smyth, Adam. Autobiography in Early Modern England. 2010. (ENG., Illus.). 232p. 89.00 *(978-0-521-76172-7(7))* Cambridge Univ. Pr.

Spencer, Lauren. A Step-by-Step Guide to Personal Writing. 2009. (Library of Writing Skills Ser.). 48p. (gr. 5-8). 53.00 *(978-1-60853-987-1(3)*, Rosen Central) Rosen Publishing Group, Inc., The.

Spry, Tami. Body, Paper, Stage: Writing & Performing Autoethnography. 2011. (Qualitative Inquiry & Social Justice Ser.). (ENG.). 232p. 89.00 *(978-1-59874-486-6(0))*; pap. 34.95 *(978-1-59874-487-3(9))* Left Coast Pr., Inc.

Stauffer, Donald A. English Biography Before 1700. 2011. 410p. 54.95 **(978-1-258-07316-9(1))** Literary Licensing, LLC.

Stein, Daniel. Music Is My Life: Louis Armstrong, Autobiography, & American Jazz. 2012. (Jazz Perspectives Ser.). (ENG.). 360p. (C). 80.00 **(978-0-472-07180-7(7))**; (Illus.). pap. 45.00 **(978-0-472-05180-9(6))** Univ. of Michigan Pr.

Steinig, Valeska. Abschied Von der DDR: Autobiografisches Schreiben Nach Dem Ende der Politischen Alternative. (GER.). 22p. pap. 46.95 *(978-3-631-56237-6(3))* Lang, Peter GmbH, Europaischer Verlag der Wissenschaften DEU. Dist: Lang, Peter Publishing, Inc.

Stelzig, Eugene L. Romantic Autobiography in England. 2009. (Nineteenth Century Ser.). (Illus.). 232p. 99.95 *(978-0-7546-6366-9(3))* Ashgate Publishing Co.

Stelzig, Eugene L. Henry Crabb Robinson in Germany: A Study in Nineteenth-Century Life Writing. 2010. 137p. 36.00 *(978-0-8387-5763-5(4))*; (ENG.). 36.00 *(978-1-61148-350-5(6))* Bucknell Univ. Pr.

The Story System: The Guide to the Methodical Memoir. 2007. 77p. ring bd. 119.95 *(978-0-9764729-8-8(8))* Legacy Road Communications.

Straight, Nathan. Autobiography, Ecology, & the Well-Placed Self: The Growth of Natural Biography in Contemporary American Life Writing. 2011. 157p. (C). 70.95 **(978-1-4331-1225-6(6))** Lang, Peter Publishing, Inc.

Sturrock, John. The Language of Autobiography: Studies in the First Person Singular. 2010. (ENG.). 308p. (C). pap. 33.99 *(978-0-521-13163-6(4))* Cambridge Univ. Pr.

Suhrud, Tridip. An Autobiography or the Story of My Experiments with Truth: A Table of Concordance. 2010. (ENG., Illus.). 220p. (C). pap. 23.95 *(978-0-415-57142-5(1)*, Routledge India) Taylor & Francis Group GBR. Dist: Taylor & Francis Group.

Szabados, Bela. Ludwig Wittgenstein on Race, Gender, & Cultural Identity: Philosophy As a Personal Endeavour. 2010. 286p. 109.95 *(978-0-7734-3817-0(3))* Mellen, Edwin Pr., The.

Tarvas, Mari, ed. Tradition und Geschichte im literarischen und sprachwissenschaftlichen Kontext: Unter Mitwirkung von Sonja Pachall, Algi Heero, Merle Jung, Helju Ridali und Maris Saagpakk. 2008. 152p. pap. 49.95 *(978-3-631-57270-2(0))* Lang, Peter GmbH, Europaischer Verlag der Wissenschaften DEU. Dist: Lang, Peter.

Taylor, Max T. Many Lives, One Lifespan: An Autobiography. 2011. 354p. 29.99 **(978-1-4628-8798-9(8))**; pap. 19.99 **(978-1-4628-8797-2(X))** Xlibris Corp.

Thurston, Dawn & Thurston, Morris. Breathe Life into Your Life Story: How to Write a Story People Will Want to Read. 2007. (Illus.). 227p. pap. 22.95 *(978-1-56085-094-6(9))* Signature Bks., LLC.

Tomaselli, Keyan G. Writing in the San/D: Autoethnography among Indigenous Southern Africans. 2007. (Crossroads in Qualitative Inquiry Ser.: Vol. 7). (AFR & ENG., Illus.). 190p. 80.00 *(978-0-7591-0950-6(8))* AltaMira Pr.

—Writing in the San/d: Autoethnography among Indigenous Southern Africans. 2007. (Crossroads in Qualitative Inquiry Ser.: Vol. 7). (AFR & ENG., Illus.). 190p. per. 32.95 *(978-0-7591-0951-3(6))* AltaMira Pr.

Tomonari, Noboru. Constructing Subjectivities: Autobiographies in Modern Japan. 2008. (ENG.). 294p. 78.99 *(978-0-7391-1716-3(5))* Lexington Bks.

Traig, Jennifer. The Autobiographer's Handbook: The 826 National Guide to Writing Your Memoir. 2008. 256p. 15.00 *(978-1-4299-3092-5(6))*; (ENG.). pap. 15.00 *(978-0-8050-8713-0(3))* Holt, Henry & Co. (Holt Paperback).

Trotsky, Leon. My Life: An Attempt at an Autobiography. 2007. (Dover Value Editions Ser.). (ENG., Illus.). 624p. per. 18.95 *(978-0-486-45609-6(9))* Dover Pubns., Inc.

van Oort, J. & Wyrwa, D., eds. Autobiographie und Hagiographie in der christlichen Antike. 2009. (Patristic Studies). (GER.). 129p. (C). pap. 53.00 *(978-90-429-2212-9(5))* Peeters Pubs. & Booksellers BEL. Dist: Brown, David Bk. Co., The.

Voigt, Lisa. Writing Captivity in the Early Modern Atlantic: Circulations of Knowledge & Authority in the Iberian & English Imperial Worlds. 2009. (Published for the Omohundro Institute of Early American History & Culture, Williamsburg, VA Ser.). (ENG., Illus.). 352p. pap. 26.95 *(978-0-8078-5944-5(3))* Univ. of North Carolina Pr.

Walker, Madeline Ruth. The Trouble with Sauling Around: Conversion in Ethnic American Autobiography, 1965-2002. 2011. (ENG.). 240p. pap. 35.00 **(978-1-60938-063-2(0))** Univ. of Iowa Pr.

Warner, Chantelle. The Literary Pragmatics of Autobiography: Authenticity in Contemporary German Testimony. 2012. (Routledge Studies in Rhetoric & Stylistics Ser.). (ENG.). 208p. (C). 125.00 **(978-0-415-50130-9(X))** Routledge.

Warner, Elisha. A Country Printer: An Informal Autobiography of Elisha Warner. 2011. 192p. 42.95 **(978-1-258-06105-0(8))** Literary Licensing, LLC.

Wells, Matthew V. To Die & Not Decay: Autobiography & the Pursuit of Immortality in Early China. 2009. *(978-0-924304-58-3(8))* Assn. for Asian Studies, Inc.

Wells, Thomas. Behind the Curtains. 2008. 224p. pap. 26.50 *(978-1-84799-664-0(7))* Lulu Enterprises Inc.

Whitlock, Gillian. Soft Weapons: Autobiography in Transit. 2006. (Illus.). 216p. per. 22.50 *(978-0-226-89526-0(2))* Univ. of Chicago Pr.

Wiebe, Katie Funk. How to Write Your Personal or Family History: If You Don't Do It, Who Will?, 1 vol. 2009. (ENG.). 165p. pap. 11.95 *(978-1-56148-665-6(5))* Good Bks.

Wiltala, Geri Colozzi. Heather's Return. 2011. 216p. pap. 24.95 **(978-1-4489-7944-3(7))** PublishAmerica, Inc.

Williams, Andrew. The Toxic Morsel: T.E. Lawrence & the Mint. 2008. 185p. pap. 61.95 *(978-3-03911-010-0(1))* Lang, Peter AG GBR. Dist: Lang, Peter.

Williams, Harris. Bion's Dream: A Reading of the Autobiographies. 2010. 116p. pap. 21.95 *(978-1-85575-890-2(3))* Karnac Bks. GBR. Dist: Stylus Publishing, LLC.

Williams, Jim. A Message to the Children. 2007. 204p. per. *(978-0-7552-1065-7(4))* Authors OnLine, Ltd.

Winterowd, W. Ross. Senior Citizens Writing: A Workshop & Anthology, with an Introduction & Guide for Workshop Leaders. 2006. (ENG.). 288p. per. *(978-1-60235-000-7(0))* Parlor Pr.

Wright, J. Lenore. The Philosopher's I: Autobiography & the Search for the Self. 2006. 217p. 74.50 *(978-0-7914-6913-2(1))*; per. 29.95 *(978-0-7914-6914-9(X))* State Univ. of New York Pr.

Xu, Dejin. Race & Form: Towards a Contextualized Narratology of African American Autobiography. 226p. pap. 47.95 *(978-3-03911-003-2(9))* Lang, Peter Publishing, Inc.

Yagoda, Ben. Memoir: A History. 2010. (ENG.). 304p. (gr. 12). 16.00 *(978-1-59448-482-7(1)*, Riverhead Trade (Paperbacks)) Penguin Group (USA) Inc.

Zweig, Stefan, intro. Casanova, Stendhal, Tolstoy: Adepts in Self-Portraiture, 3. 2012. (ENG.). 410p. pap. 34.95 **(978-1-4128-4595-3(5))** Transaction Pubs.

AUTOBIOGRAPHY—BIBLIOGRAPHY

Long, Jeffrey E. Remembered Childhoods: A Guide to Autobiography & Memoirs of Childhood & Youth, 1 vol. 2007. (Illus.). 524p. 75.00 *(978-1-59158-174-1(5)*, LU1745) Libraries Unlimited, Inc.

O'Connor, Maureen. Life Stories: A Guide to Reading Interests in Memoirs, Autobiographies, & Diaries, 1 vol. 2011. (Real Stories Ser.). 723p. 60.00 **(978-1-59158-527-5(9)**, LU8527) Libraries Unlimited, Inc.

Reisner, Rosalind & Trott, Barry. Read on... Life Stories: Reading Lists for Every Taste, 1 vol. 2009. (Read on Ser.). 175p. pap. 30.00 *(978-1-59158-766-8(2)*, LU8766) Libraries Unlimited, Inc.

Roche, Rick. Read On — Biography: Reading Lists for Every Taste. 2012. E-Book **(978-1-61069-179-6(2))** Libraries Unlimited, Inc.

—Read On... Biography: Reading Lists for Every Taste, 1 vol. 2012. (Read on Ser.). 163p. pap. 30.00 **(978-1-59884-701-7(5)**, A3275P) Pearson Education GBR. Dist: ABC-CLIO, LLC.

AUTOBIOGRAPHY—HISTORY AND CRITICISM

see Autobiography

AUTOBIOGRAPHY—TECHNIQUE

see Autobiography

AUTOBIOGRAPHY—WOMEN AUTHORS

Adams, Katherine. Owning Up: Privacy, Property, & Belonging in U. S. Women's Life Writing, 1840-1890. 2009. (ENG., Illus.). 304p. 65.00 *(978-0-19-533680-1(1))* Oxford Univ. Pr., Inc.

Andersen, Corinne. Representing the Subject. 2008. 168p. pap. *(978-3-639-08168-8(4))* VDM Verlag Dr. Mueller e.K.

Autumn, Christine. All That I Am. 2006. 31.49 *(978-1-4259-6683-6(7))*; pap. 22.49 *(978-1-4259-6682-9(9))* AuthorHouse.

Beard, Laura J. Acts of Narrative Resistance: Women's Autobiographical Writings in the Americas. 2009. (New World Studies). (ENG., Illus.). 216p. (C). (gr. 13-17). pap. 21.50 *(978-0-8139-2863-0(X))*; (gr. 17). 55.00 *(978-0-8139-2862-3(1))* Univ. Pr. of Virginia.

Beyer, Susan Meredith. Above Reality: Where Miracles Happen & Healing Begins. 2007. 230p. pap. 14.95 *(978-0-9764822-8-4(2))* Beyer Printing, Inc.

Burns, Lasonia. Forbidden Fruit. 2010. 152p. pap. 11.99 *(978-1-4490-9787-5(1))* AuthorHouse.

Byron, Kristine A. Women, Revolution, & Autobiographical Writing in the Twentieth Century: Writing History, Writing the Self. 2007. 316p. *(978-0-7734-5367-8(9))* Mellen, Edwin Pr., The.

Cooke, Miriam, frwd. Arab Women's Lives Retold: Exploring Identity Through Writing. 2007. (Gender, Culture, & Politics in the Middle East Ser.). (Illus.). 271p. 45.00 *(978-0-8156-3122-4(7))* Syracuse Univ. Pr.

Downs, Molly. Letters to Siena. 2009. 83p. pap. 16.99 *(978-0-557-09655-8(3))* Lulu Enterprises Inc.

Dreher, Kwakiutl L. Dancing on the White Page: Black Women Entertainers Writing Autobiography. 2008. 225p. per. 29.95 *(978-0-7914-7284-2(1))* State Univ. of New York Pr.

—Dancing on the White Page: Black Women Entertainers Writing Autobiography, 1950-1990. 2008. 74.50 *(978-0-7914-7283-5(3))* State Univ. of New York Pr.

Eckhart, Cynthia. I'll Be There... A Story of Family, Friends, & Faith. 2010. 156p. 24.99 *(978-1-4520-7656-0(1))*; pap. 12.95 *(978-1-4520-7655-3(3))* AuthorHouse.

Edwards, Natalie. Shifting Subjects: Plural Subjectivity in Contemporary Francophone Women's Autobiography. 2011. (ENG.). 180p. 60.00 *(978-1-61149-030-5(8))* Univ. of Delaware Pr.

Etherington-Wright, Christine & Etherington-wright, Chris. Gender, Professions & Discourse: Early Twentieth-Century Women's Autobiography. 2008. (ENG., Illus.). 248p. 89.00 *(978-0-230-21992-2(6))* Palgrave Macmillan.

Finnegan, Jordana. Narrating the American West: New Forms of Historical Memory. 2008. 224p. 99.95 *(978-1-60497-519-2(9))* Cambria Pr.

Gandy-Wilson, Bren. Women Are Spiritual Bridges: One woman's incredible autobiographical journey out of darkness & into His marvelous Light. 2009. 528p. 33.99 *(978-1-4389-0981-3(0))*; pap. 23.49 *(978-1-4389-0980-6(2))* AuthorHouse.

Golley, Nawar Al-Hassan, frwd. Arab Women's Lives Retold: Exploring Identity Through Writing. 2007. (Gender, Culture, & Politics in the Middle East Ser.). (Illus.). 256p. pap. 22.95 *(978-0-8156-3147-7(2))* Syracuse Univ. Pr.

Havlicek, Brenda. It Started at the Church: Trapped in Love & Trouble. 2011. 140p. pap. 16.99 **(978-1-4634-2631-6(3))** AuthorHouse.

Hess, Louise A. Apple Blossom Time: An Autobiography in Prose & Poetry. 2011. 280p. 29.95 **(978-1-4575-0160-9(0))**; pap. 14.95 **(978-1-60844-421-2(X))** Dog Ear Publishing, LLC.

Hughes, Barbara. Between Literature & History: The Diaries & Memoires of Mary Leadbeater & Dorothea Herbert. 2010. (Reimagining Ireland Ser.). 255p. pap. 53.95 *(978-3-03911-889-2(7))* Lang, Peter AG GBR. Dist: Lang, Peter.

Larrisey, Gina. From Care to Somewhere. 2010. 296p. pap. 15.49 *(978-1-4520-9011-5(4))* AuthorHouse.

Marching, Soe Tjen. The Discrepancy Between the Public & the Private Selves of Indonesian Women: A Comparison of Published & Unpublished Autobiographies & Diaries. 2007. 268p. *(978-0-7734-5435-4(7))* Mellen, Edwin Pr., The.

Marshall, Brenda DeVore & Mayhead, Molly A. Telling Political Lives: The Rhetorical Autobiographies of Women Leaders in the United States. 2008. (Lexington Studies in Political Communication). (ENG.). 220p. 73.50 *(978-0-7391-1947-1(8))*; pap. 30.50 *(978-0-7391-1948-8(6))* Lexington Bks.

Martin, Lena C. Desperate for Love: Overcoming with Prayer. 2007. 436p. per. 18.95 *(978-1-4327-0209-0(2))* Outskirts Pr., Inc.

Mintz, Susannah B. Unruly Bodies: Life Writing by Women with Disabilities. 2007. (ENG.). 264p. per. 23.95 *(978-0-8078-5830-1(7))* Univ. of North Carolina Pr.

Montecino, Gina. My Search for Peace of Mind: A Compelling Autobiography. 2009. 368p. pap. 17.99 *(978-1-4343-2391-0(9))* AuthorHouse.

Muchiri, Jennifer. Women's Autobiography. 2010. 180p. pap. *(978-3-639-24302-4(1))* VDM Verlag Dr. Mueller e.K.

Murray, Lorraine. Confessions of an Ex-Feminist. 2008. 144p. per. 12.95 *(978-1-58617-225-1(5))* Ignatius Pr.

Peattie, Elia W. Painted Windows. 2008. 52p. pap. *(978-1-4099-1420-4(8))* Dodo Pr.

—Painted Windows. 2010. 48p. pap. *(978-1-4076-1893-7(8))* HardPr.

Peattie, Elia Wilkinson. Painted Windows. 2010. 132p. pap. 20.75 *(978-1-175-73004-6(1))* 2009. 122p. 21.99 *(978-1-110-00427-0(3))* 2009. 122p. pap. 15.99 *(978-1-110-00425-6(7))* BiblioBazaar.

—Painted Windows. 2010. (Illus.). 32p. pap. 14.14 *(978-1-153-73935-1(6))* General Bks. LLC.

Prenshaw, Peggy Whitman. Composing Selves: Southern Women & Autobiography. 2011. (Southern Literary Studies). 368p. 45.00 *(978-0-8071-3791-8(X))* Louisiana State Univ. Pr.

Rappe, Lillian Moira. Illegitimates I Have Slaved For. 2010. 216p. pap. 15.99 *(978-1-4520-9059-7(9))* AuthorHouse.

Robinson, Joyce A. I was a waif & child Servant... No Regrets. 2008. 492p. 30.99 *(978-1-4343-4730-5(3))* AuthorHouse.

Robinson, Kathy. My Many Faces. Date not set. per. 16.00 *(978-0-9673326-0-4(5))* Robinson, Kathy L.

Schell, Tina. Living in A Flip Flop World. 2010. 156p. pap. 38.99 *(978-1-4520-8393-3(2))* AuthorHouse.

Schwalen, Anja. Identity, Gender, & Memory in Ethnic Autobiography. 2010. 76p. pap. *(978-3-8383-7431-4(2))* Lambert Academic Publishing.

Scott, Adleyn. Goodbye, Mary Janes: Places in My Life & the Shoes That Took Me There. 2010. 112p. pap. 47.99 *(978-1-4520-6745-2(7))* AuthorHouse.

Sharpe, Elizabeth. Flame of God. 2007. 128p. 35.95 *(978-0-548-00188-2(X))* Kessinger Publishing, LLC.

Shockley, Megan Taylor. The Captain's Widow of Sandwich: Self-Invention & the Life of Hannah Rebecca Burgess, 1834-1917. 2010. (ENG., Illus.). 272p. 45.00 *(978-0-8147-8319-1(8))* New York Univ. Pr.

Sloboda, Noel. The Making of Americans in Paris: The Autobiographies of Edith Wharton & Gertrude Stein. 2008. (American University Studies XXIV: American Literature Ser.: Vol. 77). 206p. (C). 67.95 *(978-1-4331-0104-5(1))* Lang, Peter Publishing, Inc.

Spence, Catherine Helen. An Autobiography. l.t. ed. 2007. (ENG.). 174p. pap. 21.99 *(978-1-4264-1536-4(2))* BiblioBazaar.

Taber, Gladys. Another Path. 18.95 *(978-0-8488-0723-8(5))* Amereon LTD.

Virgo, L. Patricia. Island Girl. 2nd rev. ed. 2011. 220p. pap. 14.99 **(978-1-4634-1886-1(8))** AuthorHouse.

Wang, Jing M. When I Was Born: Women's Autobiography in Modern China. 2008. (Wisconsin Studies in Autobiography Ser.). (ENG.). 276p. 65.00 *(978-0-299-22510-0(0))* Univ. of Wisconsin Pr.

Wench, Gail & Bartell, Eugenia. Fourteen Doors & a Mattress. 2010. 148p. pap. 15.00 *(978-1-4490-8686-2(1))* AuthorHouse.

Wharton, Edith. A Backward Glance. 2007. (ENG.). 424p. per. *(978-1-4067-5364-6(5))* Read Bks.

Wilson, Susannah. Voices from the Asylum: Four French Women Writers, 1850-1920. 2010. (Oxford Modern Languages & Literature Monographs). (ENG.). 264p. 110.00 *(978-0-19-957935-8(0))* Oxford Univ. Pr., Inc.

Wright, Susan Briggs. Coping with Transition: Men, Motherhood, Money, & Magic - Memoirs from the Lives of Professional Women. 2011. 192p. pap. 24.95 **(978-1-933896-78-6(7))** Texas Review Pr.

AUTOBIOGRAPHY OF WOMEN

see Autobiography—Women Authors

AUTOCAD (COMPUTER PROGRAM)

Abbott, Dan. AutoCAD: Secrets Every User Should Know. 2007. (ENG., Illus.). 446p. per. 39.99 *(978-0-470-10993-5(9)*, Sybex) Wiley, John & Sons, Inc.

Ambrosius, Lee. AutoCAD 2008 3D Modeling Workbook for Dummies. 2007. (ENG., Illus.). 366p. pap. 29.99 *(978-0-470-09763-2(9)*, For Dummies) Wiley, John & Sons, Inc.

—AutoCAD 2009 & AutoCAD LT 2009 All-in-One Desk Reference for Dummies. 2nd ed. 2008. (ENG., Illus.). 792p. pap. 39.99 *(978-0-470-24378-7(3)*, For Dummies) Wiley, John & Sons, Inc.

Architectural Desktop 2007 Tutorial Series. 2007. 299.00 incl. cd-rom *(978-1-932931-31-0(7))* 4D Design Solutions, LLC.

Ashton, Tia, et al. AutoCAD Release 14. Moloney, Laurie, ed. (Version 1.0 Ser.). (FRE., Illus.). pap., tchr. ed. 25.00 *(979-1-890484-50-7(4)*, KnowledgeWorks) HTR, Inc.

—AutoCAD Release 14, Level II. McGowan, Mark, ed. Adreamine, Ltd. Staff, tr. Date not set. (FRE., Illus.). pap., stu. ed. 100.00 *(978-1-890484-40-8(7)*, KnowledgeWorks) HTR, Inc.

Aubin, Paul F. Autocad Architecture 2011. 2010. (ENG., Illus.). 984p. pap. 106.95 *(978-1-111-13795-3(1)*, AutoDesk Pr.) Delmar Cengage Learning.

—AutoCAD Architecture 2011. 2010. (ENG.). 8p. pap. 5.95 *(978-1-111-31059-2(9)*, AutoDesk Pr.) Delmar Cengage Learning.

—Mastering AutoCAD Architecture 2008. 6th rev. ed. 2007. (ENG., Illus.). 1164p. pap. 108.95 *(978-1-4283-1162-6(9)*, AutoDesk Pr.) Delmar Cengage Learning.

—Mastering AutoCAD Architecture 2010. 7th ed. 2009. (ENG., Illus.). 976p. pap. 108.95 *(978-1-4390-5729-2(X)*, AutoDesk Pr.) Delmar Cengage Learning.

Aubin, Paul F., et al. AutoCAD MEP 2010. 2009. (ENG., Illus.). 720p. pap. 93.95 *(978-1-4390-5766-7(4)*, AutoDesk Pr.) Delmar Cengage Learning.

—AutoCAD MEP 2011. 2010. (ENG., Illus.). 744p. pap. 90.95 *(978-1-111-13792-2(7)*, AutoDesk Pr.) Delmar Cengage Learning.

—CourseNotes for Aubin/McClelland/Schmid/Stanley's the Aubin Academy Master Series: AutoCAD MEP 2011. 2010. (ENG.). 8p. pap. 5.95 *(978-1-111-31053-0(X)*, AutoDesk Pr.) Delmar Cengage Learning.

Aubin, Paul F. (Paul F. Aubin). Revit Architecture 2012. 2011. (CAD New Releases Ser.). (ENG., Illus.). 752p. pap. 93.95 *(978-1-111-64848-0(4)*, AutoDesk Pr.) Delmar Cengage Learning.

AutoCAD 2006 with 2007 Updates Tutorial Series. 2007. 249.00 incl. cd-rom *(978-1-932931-30-3(9))* 4D Design Solutions, LLC.

AutoCAD 2007 Tutorial Series. 2007. 119.00 incl. cd-rom *(978-1-932931-29-7(5))* 4D Design Solutions, LLC.

AutoCAD LT 2007 Tutorial Series. 2007. 99.00 incl. cd-rom *(978-1-932931-32-7(5))* 4D Design Solutions, LLC.

A

AutoCAD Mechanical 2007 Tutorial Series. 2007. 89.00 incl. cd-rom (978-1-932931-28-0(7)) 4D Design Solutions, LLC.

Autodesk Inc Staff. AutoCAD LT 2009 Perpetural. 2008. (ENG.). (C). 663.65 (978-1-4354-6442-1(7), AutoDesk Pr.) Delmar Cengage Learning.

Autodesk Official Training Guide Staff. Learning AutoCAD 2010 & AutoCAD LT 2010. 2009. (ENG., Illus.). 928p. pap. 69.99 (978-1-897177-79-2(8), Sybex) Wiley, John & Sons, Inc.

—Learning AutoCAD Civil 3D 2010. 2009. (ENG., Illus.). 720p. pap. 79.99 (978-1-897177-77-8(1), Sybex) Wiley, John & Sons, Inc.

Banach, Daniel T., et al. Autodesk Inventor 2010 Essentials Plus. 2009. (ENG.). 768p. pap. 134.95 (978-1-4390-5572-4(6), AutoDesk Pr.) Delmar Cengage Learning.

Bethune, James D. Engineering Graphics with AutoCAD 2009. 2008. (ENG., Illus.). 752p. (C). 135.80 (978-0-13-500089-2(0), Prentice Hall) Prentice Hall PTR.

—Engineering Graphics with Autocad 2011. 2010. (ENG., Illus.). 744p. (C). 121.40 (978-0-13-801591-6(0), Prentice Hall) Prentice Hall PTR.

Bride, Mac. Teach Yourself Auto CAD 2007. 2nd ed. 2007. (Teach Yourself Ser.). (ENG., Illus.). 224p. per. 12.95 (978-0-07-149085-6(X), 007149085X) McGraw-Hill Cos., The.

Byrnes, David. AutoCAD 2008 for Dummies. 2007. (ENG., Illus.). 432p. per. 24.99 (978-0-470-11650-0(1), For Dummies) Wiley, John & Sons, Inc.

—AutoCAD 2009 for Dummies. 2008. (ENG., Illus.). 420p. pap. 24.99 (978-0-470-22977-4(2), For Dummies) Wiley, John & Sons, Inc.

—AutoCAD 2011 for Dummies. 2010. (ENG., Illus.). 532p. pap. 29.99 (978-0-470-59539-8(6), For Dummies) Wiley, John & Sons, Inc.

—AutoCAD 2012 for Dummies. 2011. (ENG., Illus.). 560p. pap. 29.99 (978-1-118-02440-9(0), For Dummies) Wiley, John & Sons, Inc.

Byrnes, David & Ambrosius, Lee. AutoCAD & AutoCAD LT All-in-One Desk Reference for Dummies. 2006. (ENG., Illus.). 786p. pap. 39.99 (978-0-471-75260-8(6), For Dummies) Wiley, John & Sons, Inc.

Byrnes, David & Byrnes. AutoCAD 2010 for Dummies. 2009. (ENG., Illus.). 456p. pap. 29.99 (978-0-470-43345-4(0), For Dummies) Wiley, John & Sons, Inc.

Chappell, Eric. AutoCAD Civil 3D 2012 Essentials. 2011. (ENG., Illus.). 384p. pap. 49.99 (978-1-118-01678-7(5), Sybex) Wiley, John & Sons, Inc.

Curry, Zane. AutoCAD 2009 for Interior Design: A 3D Modelling Approach. 2008. (ENG., Illus.). 448p. (C). pap. 112.60 (978-0-13-234276-6(6), Prentice Hall) Prentice Hall PTR.

Ding, Suining. Modeling & Visualization with AutoCAD. 2008. (Illus.). 400p. pap. 97.50 (978-1-56367-501-0(3)) Fairchild Bks.

Divino, Mj. The 18 Commandments: The Version-Independent Way to Creatively Design, Draw, & Draft with Autocad. rev. ed. 2008. (ENG.). 240p. spiral bd. 85.48 (978-0-7575-5156-7(4)) Kendall Hunt Publishing Co.

Dix, Mark & Riley, Paul. Discovering AutoCAD 2012. rev. ed. 2011. (ENG., Illus.). 696p. (C). pap. 100.20 (978-0-13-265824-9(0), Prentice Hall) Prentice Hall PTR.

Dix, Mark, et al. Discovering AutoCAD 2009. 2008. (ENG., Illus.). 624p. (C). pap. 104.27 (978-0-13-235875-0(1), Prentice Hall) Prentice Hall PTR.

—Discovering AutoCAD 2010. 2009. (ENG., Illus.). 600p. (C). pap. 112.60 (978-0-13-506998-1(X), Prentice Hall) Prentice Hall PTR.

—Discovering AutoCAD 2011. 2010. (ENG., Illus.). 624p. (C). pap. 98.60 (978-0-13-512204-4(X), Prentice Hall) Prentice Hall PTR.

Feng, Jin & Lu, Jiang. Basic CAD for Interior Designers: AutoCAD, Architectural Desktop, & Viz Render 2007. 2007. (ENG., Illus.). 368p. per. 112.60 (978-0-13-225183-9(3), Prentice Hall) Prentice Hall PTR.

Finkelstein, Ellen. AutoCAD 2007 & AutoCAD LT 2007 Bible. 2006. (Bible Ser.: 333). (ENG., Illus.). 1296p. pap. 49.99 (978-0-471-78886-7(4), Wiley) Wiley, John & Sons, Inc.

—AutoCAD 2008 & AutoCAD LT 2008 Bible. 2007. (Bible Ser.: 415). (ENG., Illus.). 1296p. pap. 49.99 (978-0-470-12049-1(5), Wiley) Wiley, John & Sons, Inc.

—AutoCAD 2009 & AutoCAD LT 2009. 2008. (ENG., Illus.). 1272p. pap. 49.99 (978-0-470-26017-3(3), Wiley) Wiley, John & Sons, Inc.

—AutoCAD 2010 & AutoCAD LT 2010. 2009. (Bible Ser.: 572). (ENG., Illus.). 1296p. pap. 49.99 (978-0-470-43640-0(9), Wiley) Wiley, John & Sons, Inc.

—AutoCAD 2012 & AutoCAD LT 2012: The Book You Need to Succeed! 2011. (Bible Ser.: 759). (ENG., Illus.). 1296p. pap. 49.99 (978-1-118-02221-4(1), Wiley) Wiley, John & Sons, Inc.

—AutoCAD & AutoCAD LT. 2010. (Bible Ser.: 667). (ENG., Illus.). 1296p. pap. 49.99 (978-0-470-60823-4(4), Wiley) Wiley, John & Sons, Inc.

Fiorello, Joseph A. CAD for Interiors: Beyond the Basics. 2010. (ENG., Illus.). 192p. pap. 55.00 (978-0-470-43885-5(1), Wiley) Wiley, John & Sons, Inc.

Gibbs, Carolyn. The Design Studio: Developing Technical & Creative Skills Using AutoCAD & ADT. 2008. (Illus.). 608p. pap. 90.00 (978-1-56367-442-6(4)) Fairchild Bks.

Gindis, Elliot. Up & Running with AutoCAD 2010. 2009. (ENG., Illus.). 520p. pap. 51.95 (978-0-12-375719-7(3), Academic Pr.) Elsevier Science & Technology Bks.

—Up & Running with AutoCAD 2011: 2D Drawing & Modeling. 2010. (ENG., Illus.). 510p. pap. 59.95 (978-0-12-375715-9(0), Academic Pr.) Elsevier Science & Technology Bks.

—Up & Running with AutoCAD 2012. 2011. (ENG.). 550p. pap. 59.95 (978-0-12-387683-6(4), Academic Pr.) Elsevier Science & Technology Bks.

—Up & Running with AutoCAD 2012: 2D & 3D Drawing & Modeling. (ENG., Illus.). 2010. 708p. pap. 79.95 (978-0-12-375717-3(7)) 2nd ed. 2011. 754p. pap. 79.95 (978-0-12-387029-2(1)) Elsevier Science & Technology Bks. (Academic Pr.).

Gladfelter, Donnie. AutoCAD 2011 & AutoCAD LT 2011: No Experience Required. 2010. (ENG., Illus.). 1008p. pap. 34.99 (978-0-470-60216-4(3), Sybex) Wiley, John & Sons, Inc.

—AutoCAD 2012 & AutoCAD LT 2012: No Experience Required. 2011. (ENG., Illus.). 1080p. pap. 39.99 (978-1-118-01677-0(7), Sybex) Wiley, John & Sons, Inc.

Goldberg, H. Frank. Revit Architecture 2011: A Comprehensive Guide. 2010. (ENG., Illus.). 648p. (C). pap. 106.20 (978-0-13-813483-9(9), Prentice Hall) Prentice Hall PTR.

Grabowski, Ralph. AutoCAD 2010: What's Inside? rev. ed. 2009. (ENG.). 128p. pap. 35.95 (978-1-4354-9302-5(8), AutoDesk Pr.) Delmar Cengage Learning.

—The Illustrated AutoCAD 2009. 2008. (ENG., Illus.). 1008p. pap. 66.95 (978-1-4354-0253-9(7), AutoDesk Pr.) Delmar Cengage Learning.

—The Illustrated AutoCAD 2010 Quick Reference. 2009. (ENG., Illus.). 1008p. pap. 66.95 (978-1-4390-5627-1(7), AutoDesk Pr.) Delmar Cengage Learning.

—Illustrated AutoCAD 2011 Quick Reference. 2010. (ENG.). 1104p. pap. 66.95 (978-1-111-12516-5(3), AutoDesk Pr.) Delmar Cengage Learning.

—Using AutoCAD 2008 Basics. 2007. (ENG., Illus.). 1224p. pap. 112.95 (978-1-4283-1159-6(9), AutoDesk Pr.) Delmar Cengage Learning.

—Using AutoCAD 2010. 2009. (ENG.). 1176p. pap. 135.95 (978-1-4390-5625-7(0), AutoDesk Pr.) Delmar Cengage Learning.

—Using AutoCAD 2011. 2010. (ENG., Illus.). 1168p. pap. 111.95 (978-1-111-12514-1(7), AutoDesk Pr.) Delmar Cengage Learning.

Grabowski, Ralph (Ralph Grabowski). The Illustrated AutoCAD 2012 Quick Reference Guide. 2011. (CAD New Releases Ser.). (ENG., Illus.). 1102p. pap. 66.95 (978-1-111-64849-7(2), AutoDesk Pr.) Delmar Cengage Learning.

Graham, Richard (Rick) & Holland, Louisa. Mastering AutoCAD Civil 3D 2012. 2011. (ENG., Illus.). 936p. pap. 79.99 (978-1-118-01681-7(5), Sybex) Wiley, John & Sons, Inc.

Hamad, Munir. AutoCAD 2009 Essentials. 2009. 323p. pap. 55.95 (978-0-7637-7377-9(8)) Jones & Bartlett Learning, LLC.

—AutoCAD 2010. 2010th ed. 2009. (ENG., Illus.). 702p. pap. 62.95 (978-0-7637-8004-3(9)) Jones & Bartlett Learning, LLC.

—AutoCAD 2010 3D Modeling Essentials. 2010. 254p. pap. 49.95 (978-0-7637-9794-2(4)) Jones & Bartlett Learning, LLC.

—AutoCAD 2010 Essentials. 2009. (ENG., Illus.). 370p. pap. 55.95 (978-0-7637-7629-9(7)) Jones & Bartlett Learning, LLC.

—Autocad 2011. 2010. 394p. pap. 51.95 (978-0-7637-9798-0(7)) Jones & Bartlett Learning, LLC.

—Autocad 2011 3D Modeling Essentials. 2010. 332p. pap. 51.95 (978-0-7637-9796-6(0)) Jones & Bartlett Learning, LLC.

—Autocad 2011 Essentials Comprehensive Edition. 2010. 734p. pap. 59.95 (978-0-7637-9800-0(2)) Jones & Bartlett Learning, LLC.

—AutoCAD(r) 2012 3D Modeling. 2011. (Illus.). 400p. pap. 41.95 (978-1-936420-21-6(X)) Mercury Learning & Information.

—AutoCAD(r) 2012 Beginning & Intermediate. 2011. (Illus.). 400p. pap. 39.95 (978-1-936420-20-9(1)) Mercury Learning & Information.

Hamad, Munir M. AutoCAD 2008 Essentials. 2007. (ENG., Illus.). 400p. pap. 55.95 (978-1-934015-06-3(7)) Jones & Bartlett Learning, LLC.

Jefferis, Alan, et al. AutoCAD 2008 for Architecture. 2007. (ENG., Illus.). 992p. per. 149.95 (978-1-4283-1161-9(0), AutoDesk Pr.) Delmar Cengage Learning.

Kalameja, Alan. Autocad 2009 Tutor for Engineering Graphics. 2008. (ENG.). 1248p. pap. 150.95 (978-1-4354-0256-0(1), AutoDesk Pr.) Delmar Cengage Learning.

Kalameja, Alan & Lang, Kevin. AutoCAD 2011 Tutor for Engineering Graphics. 2010. (ENG., Illus.). 1072p. pap. 128.95 (978-1-111-13589-8(4), AutoDesk Pr.) Delmar Cengage Learning.

—AutoCAD Tutor for Engineering Graphics 2012. 2011. (CAD New Releases Ser.). (ENG., Illus.). 1056p. pap. 121.95 (978-1-111-64852-7(2), AutoDesk Pr.) Delmar Cengage Learning.

Kalameja, Alan J. The AutoCAD 2008 Tutor for Engineering Graphics. 2007. (ENG., Illus.). 1312p. pap. 143.95 (978-1-4283-1155-8(6), AutoDesk Pr.) Delmar Cengage Learning.

—AutoCAD 2010 Tutor for Engineering Graphics. 2009. (ENG.). 1056p. pap. 140.95 (978-1-4354-8617-1(X), AutoDesk Pr.) Delmar Cengage Learning.

Kirkpatrick, Beverly L. & Kirkpatrick, James M. AutoCAD for Interior Design & Space Planning 2009. 2008. (ENG., Illus.). 640p. (C). pap. 112.60 (978-0-13-500099-1(8), Prentice Hall) Prentice Hall PTR.

—Design & Space Planning 2011. 2010. (ENG., Illus.). 672p. (C). pap. 106.20 (978-0-13-512464-2(6), Prentice Hall) Prentice Hall PTR.

Kirkpatrick, James M. & Kirkpatrick, Beverly L. AutoCAD 2010 for Interior Design & Space Planning. 2009. (ENG.). 696p. (C). pap. 96.80 (978-0-13-506992-9(0), Prentice Hall) Prentice Hall PTR.

Kogent, Inc. AutoCAD 2010 in Practice. 2009. 450p. pap. 52.95 (978-1-934015-39-1(3)) Jones & Bartlett Learning, LLC.

Koser, Gary, et al. Workplace Skills for Success with AutoCAD 2010: Advanced. 2009. (ENG.). 456p. (C). pap. 97.00 (978-0-13-700941-1(0), Prentice Hall) Prentice Hall PTR.

—Workplace Skills for Success with AutoCAD 2010: Basics. 2009. (ENG., Illus.). 408p. (C). pap. 97.00 (978-0-13-507156-4(9), Prentice Hall) Prentice Hall PTR.

—Workplace Skills for Success with AutoCAD 2010: Basics Through Advanced. 2009. (ENG., Illus.). 792p. (C). pap. 112.60 (978-0-13-507929-4(2), Prentice Hall) Prentice Hall PTR.

—Workplace Skills for Success with AutoCAD 2011: Basics. 2010. (ENG., Illus.). 432p. (C). pap. 91.00 (978-0-13-215080-4(8), Prentice Hall) Prentice Hall PTR.

Krishnan, G. V. AutoCad 2010. 2009. (ENG.). 6p. (C). 6.95 (978-1-4354-9894-5(1)) Delmar Cengage Learning.

Krishnan, G. V. & Stellman, Thomas A. AutoCAD 2011 Course Notes for for Krishnan/Stellman's Harnessing AutoCAD 2011. 2010. (ENG.). 8p. pap. 5.95 (978-1-111-13790-8(0), AutoDesk Pr.) Delmar Cengage Learning.

—Harnessing AutoCAD 2010. 2009. (ENG., Illus.). 1200p. pap. 140.95 (978-1-4390-5564-9(5), AutoDesk Pr.) Delmar Cengage Learning.

—Harnessing AutoCAD 2011. 2010. (ENG.). 1232p. pap. 136.95 (978-1-111-13788-5(9), AutoDesk Pr.) Delmar Cengage Learning.

Krishnan, G. V. (G. V. Krishnan) & Stellman, Thomas A. AutoCAD 2012. 2011. (ENG.). 8p. pap. 4.95 (978-1-133-01447-8(X), AutoDesk Pr.) Delmar Cengage Learning.

—Harnessing AutoCAD 2012. 2011. (CAD New Releases Ser.). (ENG.). 1200p. pap. 129.95 (978-1-111-64851-0(4), AutoDesk Pr.) Delmar Cengage Learning.

Kyles, Shannon R. AutoCAD Workbook for Architects & Engineers. 2008. (ENG., Illus.). 296p. pap. 52.95 (978-1-4051-8096-2(X), Wiley-Blackwell) Wiley, John & Sons, Inc.

Leach, James & Bledsaw, Thomas. AutoCAD 2012 Instructor. 7th ed. 2011. (ENG., Illus.). 1360p. (C). pap. 173.33 (978-0-07-337546-5(2), 0073375462, McGraw-Hill Science, Engineering & Mathematics) McGraw-Hill Higher Education.

Leach, James & Leach, James A. AutoCAD 2010 Instructor. 6th ed. 2009. (ENG., Illus.). 1344p. (C). pap. 173.33 (978-0-07-337541-0(1), 0073375411, McGraw-Hill Science, Engineering & Mathematics) McGraw-Hill Higher Education.

Leach, James A. AutoCad 2007 Instructor. 3rd ed. 2006. 1472p. (C). pap. 96.56 (978-0-07-352262-3(7), 9780073522623, McGraw-Hill Science, Engineering & Mathematics) McGraw-Hill Higher Education.

—AutoCad 2007 Instructor with Autodesk Inventor Software 06-07. 3rd rev. ed. 2006. (C). pap. 110.63 incl. cd-rom (978-0-07-331274-3(6), 9780073312743, McGraw-Hill Science, Engineering & Mathematics) McGraw-Hill Higher Education.

—AutoCAD 2008 Instructor. 4th rev. ed. 2007. 1472p. pap. 77.25 (978-0-07-352265-4(1)) McGraw-Hill Professional Publishing.

—AutoCAD 2008 Instructor: A Student Guide to Complete Coverage of AutoCAD's Commands & Features. 4th ed. 2007. pap. 150.00 (978-0-07-721608-5(3), 9780077216085, McGraw-Hill Science, Engineering & Mathematics) McGraw-Hill Higher Education.

—AutoCAD 2009 Instructor: A Student Guide to Complete Coverage of AutoCAD's Commands & Features. 5th ed. 2008. (Illus.). 1440p. (C). pap. 150.00 (978-0-07-337534-2(9), 9780073375342, McGraw-Hill Science, Engineering & Mathematics) McGraw-Hill Higher Education.

Leach, James A. & Dyer, James. AutoCAD 2008 Companion. 3rd ed. 2007. (McGraw-Hill Graphics Ser.). 702p. (C). pap. 70.63 (978-0-07-340246-8(X), 9780073402468, McGraw-Hill Science, Engineering & Mathematics) McGraw-Hill Higher Education.

Lombard, Matt. SolidWorks 2007 Bible. 2007. (Bible Ser.: 382). (ENG., Illus.). 1104p. pap. 49.99 (978-0-470-08013-9(2), Wiley) Wiley, John & Sons, Inc.

Madsen, David A. & Palma, Ron M. Architectural Desktop & It's Applications 2007. 2007. 70.00 (978-1-59070-796-8(6)) Goodheart-Willcox Pub.

—Architectural Drafting Using AutoCad 2010. 6th ed. 2009. (ENG.). 860p. 82.64 (978-1-60525-187-5(9)) Goodheart-Willcox Pub.

McFarland, Jon. AutoCAD 2009 & AutoCAD LT 2009: No Experience Required. 2nd ed. 2008. (ENG., Illus.). 840p. pap. 34.99 (978-0-470-26058-6(0), Sybex) Wiley, John & Sons, Inc.

McFarland, Jon & Mcfarland. AutoCAD 2010 & AutoCAD LT 2010: No Experience Required. 2009. (ENG., Illus.). 888p. pap. 34.99 (978-0-470-43868-8(1), Sybex) Wiley, John & Sons, Inc.

McFarlane, Bob. Beginning AutoCAD 2007. 2006. (ENG., Illus.). 392p. (C). per. 38.95 (978-0-7506-8323-4(6)) Routledge.

—Starting with AutoCAD LT. (Illus.). 200p. pap. (978-0-340-62543-9(0), Hodder Arnold) Hodder Education.

Moss, Elise. AutoCAD 2008 Fundamentals. 2007. (Illus.). 551p. per. 59.95 (978-1-58503-344-7(8), SDC Pubns.) Schroff Development Corp.

—Autodesk AutoCAD Architecture 2008 Fundamentals. 2007. 289p. per. 59.95 (978-1-58503-358-4(8), SDC Pubns.) Schroff Development Corp.

—Autodesk AutoCAD Architecture 2009: Fundamentals. 2008. (Illus.). pap. 59.95 (978-1-58503-449-9(5), SDC Pubns.) Schroff Development Corp.

Omura, George. Introducing AutoCAD 2008. 2007. (ENG., Illus.). 400p. per. 29.99 (978-0-470-12150-4(5), Sybex) Wiley, John & Sons, Inc.

—Introducing AutoCAD 2009 & AutoCAD LT 2009. 2008. (ENG., Illus.). 413p. pap. 34.99 (978-0-470-26060-9(2), Sybex) Wiley, John & Sons, Inc.

—Introducing AutoCAD 2010 & AutoCAD LT 2010. 2009. (ENG., Illus.). 400p. pap. 34.99 (978-0-470-43867-1(3), Sybex) Wiley, John & Sons, Inc.

—Mastering AutoCAD 2010 & AutoCAD LT 2010. 2009. (ENG., Illus.). 1224p. pap. 49.99 (978-0-470-46603-2(0), Sybex) Wiley, John & Sons, Inc.

—Mastering AutoCAD 2011 & AutoCAD LT 2011. 2010. (ENG., Illus.). 1248p. pap. 49.99 (978-0-470-62197-4(4), Sybex) Wiley, John & Sons, Inc.

—Mastering AutoCAD 2012 & AutoCAD LT 2012. 2011. (ENG., Illus.). 1152p. pap. 49.99 (978-0-470-95288-7(1), Sybex) Wiley, John & Sons, Inc.

Omura, George & Graham, Richard (Rick). Mastering AutoCAD for Mac. 2010. (ENG., Illus.). 768p. pap. 49.99 (978-0-470-93234-6(1), Sybex) Wiley, John & Sons, Inc.

Onstott, Scott. AutoCAD 2012 & AutoCAD LT 2012. 2011. (ENG., Illus.). 400p. pap. 49.99 (978-1-118-01679-4(3), Sybex) Wiley, John & Sons, Inc.

Onstott, Scott & Allen, Lynn. AutoCAD: Professional Tips & Techniques. 2006. (ENG., Illus.). 316p. per. 39.99 (978-0-470-08454-0(5), Sybex) Wiley, John & Sons, Inc.

Plantenberg, Kirstie. Engineering Graphics Essentials with AutoCAD 2008. 2007. 800p. per. 59.95 (978-1-58503-385-0(5), SDC Pubns.) Schroff Development Corp.

Puerta, Frank & Autodesk Inc Staff. AutoCAD 2010 In 3D: A Modern Approach. 2009. (ENG.). 672p. (C). pap. 112.60 (978-0-13-507160-1(7), Prentice Hall) Prentice Hall PTR.

Puerta, Frank & Autodesk Staff. AutoCAD 2011 In 3D: A Modern Perspective. 2010. (ENG.). 696p. (C). pap. 113.60 (978-0-13-512230-3(9), Prentice Hall) Prentice Hall PTR.

Richard, Paul & Fitzgerald, Jim. Introduction to AutoCAD 2012: A Modern Perspective. rev. ed. 2011. (ENG., Illus.). 960p. (C). pap. 100.20 (978-0-13-272517-0(7), Prentice Hall) Prentice Hall PTR.

Richard, Paul, et al. AutoCAD 2008. 2007. (ENG., Illus.). 1408p. (C). pap. 144.20 (978-0-13-514373-5(X), Prentice Hall) Prentice Hall PTR.

—Introduction to AutoCAD 2011: A Modern Perspective. 2010. (ENG.). 816p. (C). pap. 106.13 (978-0-13-801636-4(4), Prentice Hall) Prentice Hall PTR.

Richard, Paul F., et al. AutoCAD 2010 in 2D And 3D: A Modern Perspective. 2009. (ENG., Illus.). 1416p. (C). pap. 129.00 (978-0-13-507931-7(4), Prentice Hall) Prentice Hall PTR.

—Introduction to AutoCAD 2010: A Modern Perspective. 2009. (ENG., Illus.). 928p. (C). pap. 112.60 (978-0-13-507159-5(3), Prentice Hall) Prentice Hall PTR.

Saufley, Ted. AutoCAD LT 2000-2000i: Fundamentals & Applications: Solutions Manual. pap., tchr. ed. 16.00 (978-1-56637-747-8(1)) Goodheart-Willcox Pub.

Saufley, Ted & Schreiner, Paul B. AutoCAD LT Fundamentals: Drafting & Design Applications. 7th ed. 2007. (Illus.). 540p. (gr. 9-12). 46.50 (978-1-59070-777-7(X)) Goodheart-Willcox Pub.

—Autocad LT Fundamentals: Drafting & Design Applications. 8th ed. 2007. 66.64 (978-1-59070-871-2(7)) Goodheart-Willcox Pub.

Schrock, Cheryl. Advanced AutoCAD 2010 Exercise Workbook. 2009. 400p. (C). pap. 39.95 (978-0-8311-3400-6(3)) Industrial Pr., Inc.

—Advanced Autocad 2011 Exercise Workbook. 2010. 450p. (C). pap. 39.95 (978-0-8311-3417-4(8)) Industrial Pr., Inc.

—AutoCAD Pocket Reference. 2009. 300p. (C). pap. 21.95 (978-0-8311-3384-9(8)) Industrial Pr., Inc.

—Beginning Autocad 2011 Exercise Workbook. 2010. 550p. (C). pap. 39.95 (978-0-8311-3416-7(X)) Industrial Pr., Inc.

Schrock, Cheryl R. Advanced AutoCAD 2012 Exercise Workbook. 2011. 464p. (C). pap. 39.95 **(978-0-8311-3431-0(3))** Industrial Pr., Inc.

—AutoCAD Pocket Reference. 5th ed. 2011. 300p. (C). pap. 22.95 **(978-0-8311-3428-0(3))** Industrial Pr., Inc.

—Beginning AutoCAD 2012 Exercise Workbook. 2011. 560p. (C). pap. 39.95 **(978-0-8311-3430-3(5))** Industrial Pr., Inc.

Seidler, Douglas. Digital Drawing for Designers: A Visual Guide to AutoCAD. 2007. (Illus.). 223p. pap. 89.50 (978-1-56367-512-6(9)) Fairchild Bks.

Shih, Randy. AutoCAD 2008 Tutorial - Second Level: 3D Modeling. 2007. per. 59.95 (978-1-58503-363-8(4), SDC Pubns.) Schroff Development Corp.

—AutoCAD LT 2007 Tutorial. 2006. 309p. per. 59.95 (978-1-58503-294-5(8), SDC Pubns.) Schroff Development Corp.

—AutoCAD LT 2008 Tutorial. 2007. per. 59.95 (978-1-58503-369-0(3), SDC Pubns.) Schroff Development Corp.

—Tools for Design with FisherTechnik: AutoCAD 2011 & Autodesk Inventor 2011. 2010. 638p. pap. 59.95 (978-1-58503-615-8(3), SDC Pubns.) Schroff Development Corp.

Shih, Randy & Zecher, Jack. AutoCAD 2008 Tutorial - First Level: 2D Fundamentals. 2007. 297p. per. 59.95 (978-1-58503-361-4(8), SDC Pubns.) Schroff Development Corp.

Shrock, Cheryl. Exercise Workbook for Advanced AutoCAD 2007. 2006. 440p. (C). pap., wbk. ed. 39.95 (978-0-8311-3303-0(1)) Industrial Pr., Inc.

—Exercise Workbook for Advanced Autocad 2009. 2008. 448p. (C). pap. 36.95 (978-0-8311-3360-3(0)) Industrial Pr., Inc.

—Exercise Workbook for Beginning AutoCAD. 2007. (2008 Ser.). (Illus.). 400p. pap. 39.95 incl. cd-rom (978-0-8311-3341-2(4)) Industrial Pr., Inc.

Shrock, Cheryl & Shrock, Cheryl R. Beginning AutoCAD 2009 Exercise Workbook. 2008. (Illus.). 550p. (C). pap. 36.95 (978-0-8311-3359-7(7)) Industrial Pr., Inc.

Shrock, Cheryl R. Exercise Workbook For Advanced AutoCAD 2005, Learning Bundle Edition. cd-rom 34.95 (978-0-8311-3293-4(0)) Industrial Pr., Inc.

—Exercise Workbook for Advanced AutoCAD 2008. 2007. (AutoCAD Exercise Workbooks Ser.). (Illus.). 400p. pap. 39.95 (978-0-8311-3342-9(2)) Industrial Pr., Inc.

—Exercise Workbook for Advanced AutoCAD2005. 400p. pap. 29.95 (978-0-8311-3199-9(3)) Industrial Pr., Inc.

—Exercise Workbook for Beginning AutoCAD 2007. 2006. (AutoCAD Exercise Workbooks Ser.). 440p. (C). pap., wbk. ed. 39.95 (978-0-8311-3302-3(3)) Industrial Pr., Inc.

Shumaker, Terence & Madsen, David. AutoCAD & its Applications 2011 Instructor's Resource CD. 2010. cd-rom 90.00 (978-1-60525-331-2(6)) Goodheart-Willcox Pub.

—AutoCAD & its Applications 2011Companion Web Site on CD Site License. 2010. cd-rom 200.00 *(978-1-60525-347-3(2))* Goodheart-Willcox Pub.
—AutoCAD & its Applications 2011ExamView Assessment Suite. 2010. cd-rom 240.00 *(978-1-60525-332-9(4))* Goodheart-Willcox Pub.
Shumaker, Terence M. Autocad & Its Applications: Advanced Autocad 2008. 2007. 52.00 *(978-1-59070-832-3(6))* Goodheart-Willcox Pub.
Shumaker, Terence M. & Madsen, David A. AutoCAD & Its Applications: Basics 2007. 14th ed. 2007. (Illus.). 944p. (gr. 9-12). 45.00 *(978-1-59070-752-4(4))* Goodheart-Willcox Pub.
—AutoCad & Its Applications 2009. 17th ed. 2009. (ENG., Illus.). 1600p. 94.60 *(978-1-60525-163-9(1))* Goodheart-Willcox Pub.
Shumaker, Terence M., et al. Autocad & Its Applications: Comprehensive 2012. 19th ed. 2011. (ENG.). 1760p. (gr. 9-14). 102.64 *(978-1-60525-565-1(3))* Goodheart-Willcox Pub.
—AutoCad & Its Applications 2009. 16th ed. 2008. 82.00 *(978-1-59070-994-8(2))* 17th ed. 2009. (ENG.). 944p. 69.00 *(978-1-60525-161-5(5))* Goodheart-Willcox Pub.
—Autocad & Its Applications 2011. 18th ed. 2010. (ENG.). 1600p. pap. 99.00 *(978-1-60525-330-5(8))* Goodheart-Willcox Pub.
—AutoCad & Its Applications Advanced 2010. 17th ed. 2009. (ENG.). 656p. 57.00 *(978-1-60525-162-2(3))* Goodheart-Willcox Pub.
—Autocad & Its Applications Advanced 2011. 18th ed. 2010. (ENG.). 672p. 60.00 *(978-1-60525-329-9(4))* Goodheart-Willcox Pub.
—Autocad & Its Applications Advanced 2012. 19th ed. 2011. (ENG., Illus.). 704p. (gr. 9-14). 62.00 ***(978-1-60525-563-7(7))*** Goodheart-Willcox Pub.
—AutoCAD & Its Applications BASICS 2008. 15th ed. 2007. 62.64 *(978-1-59070-830-9(X))* Goodheart-Willcox Pub.
—AutoCAD & Its Applications Basics 2011. 18th ed. 2010. (ENG.). 944p. pap. 72.00 *(978-1-60525-328-2(6))* Goodheart-Willcox Pub.
—AutoCAD & Its Applications Basics 2012. 19th ed. 2011. (ENG.). 1056p. (gr. 9-14). 74.64 *(978-1-60525-561-3(0))* Goodheart-Willcox Pub.
—AutoCAD & Its Applications: Comprehensive. 14th ed. 2006. (Illus.). 88.00 incl. cd-rom *(978-1-59070-760-9(5))* Goodheart-Willcox Pub.
—Autocad & Its Applications Comprehensive 2008. 15th ed. 2007. 88.00 *(978-1-59070-834-7(2))* Goodheart-Willcox Pub.
Sinclair, James A. AutoCAD Fundamentals for Engineers & Architects: A Multimedia Step-by-Step Tutorial by the CD-Professor. 2nd ed. 2007. (ENG., Illus.). 100p. cd-rom 39.95 *(978-0-9753521-0-6(5))* ITTC Pubns.
Stellman, Thomas A. & Krishnan, G. V. Harnessing AutoCAD 2007. 2006. (ENG., Illus.). 1216p. (Orig.). 127.95 *(978-1-4180-4906-5(9))*, AutoDesk Pr.) Delmar Cengage Learning.
—Harnessing Autocad 2007. 2006. (ENG.). 416p. pap. 59.95 *(978-1-4180-4907-2(7))*, AutoDesk Pr.) Delmar Cengage Learning.
—Harnessing AutoCAD 2008 Exercise Manual. 2007. (Illus.). per. *(978-1-4283-1157-2(2))* Delmar Cengage Learning.
Stine, Daniel. Interior Design Using AutoCAD 2008. 2007. per. 59.95 *(978-1-58503-365-2(0))*, SDC Pubns.) Schroff Development Corp.
Stine, Daniel John. Interior Design using AutoCAD 2007. 2006. (Illus.). 300p. per. 59.95 *(978-1-58503-290-7(5))*, SDC Pubns.) Schroff Development Corp.
Sykes, Timothy Sean. AutoCAD 2008: One Step at a Time. 5th ed. 2007. (Illus.). 700p. per. 59.95 *(978-0-9778938-6-7(3))* Forager Pubns.
—AutoCAD 2009: One Step at a Time. 2008. (Illus.). 700p. pap. 64.22 *(978-0-9794155-2-4(7))* Forager Pubns.
—AutoCAD 2010: One Step at a Time. 2009. (Illus.). 704p. pap. 64.22 *(978-0-9794155-6-2(X))* Forager Pubns.
—AutoCAD 2011: One Step at a Time. 2010. (Illus.). 700p. pap. 64.22 *(978-0-9819867-2-2(2))* Forager Pubns.
—3D AutoCAD 2008: One Step at a Time. 5th ed. 2007. (Illus.). 328p. per. 49.95 *(978-0-9778938-8-1(X))* Forager Pubns.
—3D AutoCAD 2009: One Step at a Time. 2008. (Illus.). 336p. pap. 49.95 *(978-0-9794155-3-1(5))* Forager Pubns.
—3D AutoCAD 2011: One Step at a Time. 2010. (Illus.). 360p. pap. 49.95 *(978-0-9819867-3-9(0))*; (ENG., vii, 351p. pap. 19.95 *(978-0-9819867-5-3(7))* Forager Pubns.
Tickoo, Sham. AutoCAD 2009: A Problem-Solving Approach. 2008. (ENG., Illus.). 656p. pap. 140.95 *(978-1-4354-0258-4(8))*, AutoDesk Pr.) Delmar Cengage Learning.
—AutoCAD 2010: A Problem-Solving Approach. 2009. (ENG., Illus.). 1408p. pap. 139.95 *(978-1-4390-5567-0(X))*, AutoDesk Pr.) Delmar Cengage Learning.
—AutoCAD 2011: A Problem-Solving Approach. 2010. (ENG., Illus.). 1392p. pap. 114.95 *(978-1-111-12772-5(7))*, AutoDesk Pr.) Delmar Cengage Learning.
—Customizing AutoCAD 2011. 2010. (ENG.). 560p. pap. 107.95 *(978-1-111-12777-0(8))*, AutoDesk Pr.) Delmar Cengage Learning.
Ward, Harry O. & Autodesk Inc Staff. AutoCAD Civil 3D 2008: Procedures & Applications. 2007. (ENG., Illus.). 432p. pap. 104.00 *(978-0-13-159231-5(9))*, Prentice Hall) Prentice Hall PTR.
Ward, Harry O., et al. AutoCAD Civil 3D 2010: Procedures & Applictions. 2009. (ENG., Illus.). 432p. (C). pap. 112.60 *(978-0-13-507166-3(6))*, Prentice Hall) Prentice Hall PTR.
Wedding, James & Graham, Rick. Introducing AutoCAD Civil 3D 2010. 2009. (ENG., Illus.). 336p. pap. 49.99 *(978-0-470-48152-3(8))*, Sybex) Wiley, John & Sons, Inc.
Wedding, James & McEachron, Scott. Mastering AutoCAD Civil 3D 2010. 2009. (ENG., Illus.). 912p. pap. 69.99 *(978-0-470-47353-5(3))*, Sybex) Wiley, John & Sons, Inc.
—Mastering AutoCAD Civil 3D 2011. 2010. (ENG., Illus.). 936p. pap. 69.99 *(978-0-470-88418-8(5))*, Sybex) Wiley, John & Sons, Inc.
Wedding, James & Probert, Dana. Introducing AutoCAD Civil 3D 2009. 2008. (ENG., Illus.). 320p. pap. 39.99 *(978-0-470-37316-3(4))*, Sybex) Wiley, John & Sons, Inc.
Wedding, James, et al. Mastering AutoCAD Civil 3D 2008. 2007. (ENG., Illus.). 840p. pap. 69.99 *(978-0-470-16740-3(8))*, Sybex) Wiley, John & Sons, Inc.
—Mastering AutoCAD Civil 3D 2009. 2008. (ENG., Illus.). 864p. pap. 69.99 *(978-0-470-37315-6(6))*, Sybex) Wiley, John & Sons, Inc.
Whiteacre, Matthew. The Essentials of Autocad. 3rd rev. ed. 2009. (ENG.). 132p. pap. 61.60 *(978-0-7575-5337-0(0))* Kendall Hunt Publishing Co.
Winters, Jerry. VB. NET Programming for AutoCAD Customization: VB. NET Training for AutoCAD 2007 & AutoCAD 2008. 2007. spiral bd. *(978-1-892131-10-2(2))* VB CAD, Inc.
Wohlers, Terry. Applying AutoCAD(r) 2007. 14th ed. 2006. (ENG.). (C). pap., stu. ed. 71.04 *(978-0-07-877163-7(3))*, 0078771633) McGraw-Hill Higher Education.
—Applying AutoCAD 2011. 2nd ed. 2010. (ENG., Illus.). 800p. (C). pap. 95.67 *(978-0-07-337548-9(9))*, 0073375489, McGraw-Hill Science, Engineering & Mathematics) McGraw-Hill Higher Education.
—Applying AutoCAD 2012. 3rd ed. 2011. (ENG., Illus.). 800p. (C). pap. 95.67 *(978-0-07-337550-2(0))*, 0073375500, McGraw-Hill Science, Engineering & Mathematics) McGraw-Hill Higher Education.
Wohlers, Terry. Applying AutoCAD® 2013. 4th ed. 2012. (ENG., Illus.). 832p. (C). pap. 95.67 ***(978-0-07-337551-9(9))***, 0073375519, McGraw-Hill Science, Engineering & Mathematics) McGraw-Hill Higher Education.
Wohlers, Terry T. Applying AutoCAD. 2007. (ENG., Illus.). 812p. (C). per. 71.04 *(978-0-07-880153-2(2))*, 0078801532) McGraw-Hill Higher Education.
Wyatt, Sr.), William G(William GWyatt, Sr.). AutoCAD Architecture 2012 Course Notes for Wyatt's Accessing AUTOCAD Architecture 2012. 2011. (ENG.). 8p. 4.95 *(978-1-111-64833-6(6))*, AutoDesk Pr.) Delmar Cengage Learning.
Wyatt, William G. Accessing AutoCAD Architecture 2009. 2008. (ENG.). 1032p. pap. 140.95 *(978-1-4354-0262-1(6))*, AutoDesk Pr.) Delmar Cengage Learning.
—Accessing AutoCAD Architecture 2011. 2010. (ENG., Illus.). 928p. pap. 113.95 *(978-1-111-12685-8(2))*, AutoDesk Pr.) Delmar Cengage Learning.
—Accessing Autocad Architecture 2012. 2011. (CAD New Releases Ser.). (ENG., Illus.). 800p. pap. 113.95 *(978-1-111-64831-2(X))*, AutoDesk Pr.) Delmar Cengage Learning.
Yarwood, Alf. Introduction to AutoCAD 2008: 2D & 3D Design. 2007. (ENG., Illus.). 370p. pap. 41.95 *(978-0-7506-8512-2(3))*, Newnes) Elsevier Science & Technology Bks.
—Introduction to AutoCAD 2009: 2D & 3D Design. 2008. (ENG., Illus.). 428p. pap. 38.95 *(978-0-7506-8983-0(8))* Routledge.
—Introduction to AutoCAD 2010. 2009. (ENG., Illus.). 456p. (C). pap. 39.95 *(978-1-85617-868-6(4))* Routledge.
—Introduction to AutoCAD 2011. 2010. (ENG., Illus.). 416p. (C). pap. 41.95 *(978-0-08-096575-8(X))* Routledge.
—Introduction to AutoCAD 2012. 2011. (ENG., Illus.). 456p. (C). pap. 42.95 ***(978-0-08-096947-3(X))*** Routledge.
—Introduction to AutoCAD 2013. 2012. (ENG., Illus.). 448p. pap. 49.95 ***(978-0-415-53762-9(2))*** Routledge.
Zimmerman, Phillip J. Harnessing AutoCAD Civil 3D 2011. 2010. (ENG., Illus.). 432p. pap. 110.95 *(978-1-111-13791-5(9))*, AutoDesk Pr.) Delmar Cengage Learning.
Zirwas, Dean & Koser, Gary. Workplace Skills for Success Autocad 2008 Basics: A Layered Learning Approach. 2007. (ENG., Illus.). 360p. pap. 97.00 *(978-0-13-612701-7(0))*, Prentice Hall) Prentice Hall PTR.

AUTOCLAVES

see also Pressure Vessels

Goodwin, Harold. Laboratory Autoclaves, High Pressure & Hydrogenation Apparatus - Design & Construction. 2006. 164p. 59.95 *(978-1-4276-1406-3(7))* Wexford College Pr.

AUTOCODES

see Programming Languages (Electronic Computers)

AUTODESK ANIMATOR (COMPUTER PROGRAM)

Autodesk, Inc. Staff. Autodesk 3ds Max 2010: Foundation for Games. 2009. (ENG., Illus.). 345p. pap. 50.95 *(978-0-240-81194-9(1))*, Focal Pr.) Elsevier Science & Technology Bks.
Autodesk Maya Press Staff. Learning Autodesk Maya 2008: Foundation. 2007. (ENG., Illus.). 640p. pap. 69.99 *(978-1-897177-42-6(9))*, Sybex) Wiley, John & Sons, Inc.
Demchak, Greg, et al. Revit' Architecture 2010. 2009. (ENG., Illus.). 816p. pap. 59.99 *(978-0-470-45649-1(3))*, Sybex) Wiley, John & Sons, Inc.
Kermanikian, Ara. Introducing Mudbox. 2010. (ENG., Illus.). 416p. pap. 49.99 *(978-0-470-53725-1(6))*, Sybex) Wiley, John & Sons, Inc.
McFarland, Jon. Mastering AutoDesk VIZ 2008. 2007. (ENG., Illus.). 1008p. per. 69.99 *(978-0-470-14482-4(3))*, Sybex) Wiley, John & Sons, Inc.
Onstott, Scott. 3ds Max & VIZ for Architects (DVD-ROM) 2007. 463p. cd-rom *(978-0-9719583-9-5(4))* Onstott, Scott.
Virtual Training Company, prod. Autodesk Combustion 4. 2006. cd-rom 99.95 *(978-1-933736-55-6(0))* VTC, Inc.

AUTODESK INVENTOR (ELECTRONIC RESOURCE)

Autodesk Inventor 2008 Tutorial Series. 2007. 259.00 incl. cd-rom *(978-1-932931-38-9(4))* 4D Design Solutions, LLC.
Autodesk Official Training Guide Staff & Zimmerman, Jan. Learning Autodesk Inventor 2010. 2009. (ENG., Illus.). 1008p. pap. 79.99 *(978-1-897177-55-5(8))*, Sybex) Wiley, John & Sons, Inc.
Banach, Daniel T., et al. Autodesk Inventor 2011 Essentials Plus. 2010. (ENG., Illus.). 800p. pap. 122.95 *(978-1-111-13527-0(4))*, AutoDesk Pr.) Delmar Cengage Learning.
—Autodesk Inventor 2012 Essentials Plus. 2011. (CAD New Releases Ser.). (ENG., Illus.). 784p. pap. 123.95 *(978-1-111-64665-3(1))*, AutoDesk Pr.) Delmar Cengage Learning.
—Inventor Course Notes X 2012. 2011. (ENG.). 6p. 5.95 *(978-1-111-64666-0(X))*, AutoDesk Pr.) Delmar Cengage Learning.
—Inventor Coursenotes 2011. 2010. (ENG.). 6p. 5.95 *(978-1-111-13528-7(2))*, AutoDesk Pr.) Delmar Cengage Learning.
Bertoline, Gary R. Introduction to Graphics Communications for Engineers. 3rd ed. 2007. (Basic Engineering Series & Tools Ser.). pap. 71.56 *(978-0-07-722867-5(7))*, 9780077228675, McGraw-Hill Science, Engineering & Mathematics) McGraw-Hill Higher Education.
Bertoline, Gary Robert & Wiebe, Eric N. Fundamentals of Graphics Communication. 5th ed. 2007. (ENG.). 832p. (C). pap. 141.88 incl. cd-rom *(978-0-07-722868-2(5))*, 0077228685, McGraw-Hill Science, Engineering & Mathematics) McGraw-Hill Higher Education.
Bethune, James D. Engineering Design Graphics Inventor 2011. rev. ed. 2011. (ENG.). 792p. (C). pap. 111.00 *(978-0-13-273594-0(6))*, Prentice Hall) Prentice Hall PTR.
Bethune, James D. & AutoDesk Press Staff. Engineering Design & Graphics with Autodesk Inventor 2009. 2008. (Autodesk Design Institute Press Ser.). (Illus.). 704p. pap. *(978-0-13-615762-6(5))* Pearson Education Canada.
Ethier, Stephen J., et al. Instant Design: Fundamentals of Autodesk Inventor 2010. 2009. (ENG., Illus.). 224p. (C). pap. 97.00 *(978-0-13-506801-4(0))*, Prentice Hall) Prentice Hall PTR.
Grabowski, Ralph. Learning Autodesk Inventor 2008: The 2D to 3D Transition Handbook. 2007. (ENG., Illus.). 304p. (C). per. 76.95 *(978-1-4354-1329-0(6))* Delmar Cengage Learning.
Hansen, L. S. Learning & Applying Autodesk Inventor 2009. 2008. 450p. (C). pap. 42.95 *(978-0-8311-3365-8(1))* Industrial Pr., Inc.
Hansen, L. Scott. Applied Inventor 2007-2008. 2007. 500p. 42.95 *(978-0-8311-3340-5(6))* Industrial Pr., Inc.
Hansen, L. Scott. Autodesk Inventor. 2012. (ENG., Illus.). 500p. (C). pap. 88.00 ***(978-0-07-352270-8(8))***, 0073522708, McGraw-Hill Science, Engineering & Mathematics) McGraw-Hill Higher Education.
Leach, James A. AutoCAD 2008 Instructor: A Student Guide to Complete Coverage of AutoCAD's Commands & Features. 4th ed. 2007. pap. 150.00 *(978-0-07-721608-5(3))*, 9780077216085, McGraw-Hill Science, Engineering & Mathematics) McGraw-Hill Higher Education.
LoFaso, James P. Inventor for Parametric Modeling: Autodesk Inventor 2009. 3rd ed. 2008. 60.00 *(978-1-60525-000-7(7))* Goodheart-Willcox Pub.
Madsen, David P. Inventor & Its Applications. 2nd ed. 2009. 66.64 *(978-1-60525-002-1(3))* Goodheart-Willcox Pub.
Moss, Elise. The Power of Design; an Introduction to Autodesk Inventor 2008. 2007. 310p. per. 59.95 *(978-1-58503-372-0(3))*, SDC Pubns.) Schroff Development Corp.
Shih, Randy. Parametric Modeling with Autodesk Inventor 2008. 2007. 381p. per. 59.95 *(978-1-58503-371-3(5))*, SDC Pubns.) Schroff Development Corp.
—Tools for Design with FisherTechnik: AutoCAD 2011 & Autodesk Inventor 2011. 2010. 638p. pap. 59.95 *(978-1-58503-615-8(3))*, SDC Pubns.) Schroff Development Corp.
Short, Thomas & Dudek, Anthony. Learning Autodesk Inventor: A Process-Based Approach. 4th ed. 2007. 60.00 *(978-1-59070-864-4(4))* Goodheart-Willcox Pub.
—Learning Autodesk Inventor 2010. 6th ed. 2009. (ENG.). 476p. pap. 66.64 *(978-1-60525-267-4(0))* Goodheart-Willcox Pub.
Smith, Kevin D. & Tremblay, Thom. Autodesk Inventor 2010: No Experience Required. 2009. (ENG., Illus.). 528p. pap. 39.99 *(978-0-470-48169-1(2))* Sybex) Wiley, John & Sons, Inc.
Tremblay, Thom. Autodesk Inventor 2012 & Inventor LT 2012 Essentials. 2011. (ENG., Illus.). 400p. pap. 49.99 *(978-1-118-01680-0(7))*, Sybex) Wiley, John & Sons, Inc.
Waguespack, Curtis. Mastering Autodesk Inventor 2010. 2009. (ENG., Illus.). 816p. pap. 69.99 *(978-0-470-47830-1(6))*, Sybex) Wiley, John & Sons, Inc.
—Mastering Autodesk Inventor 2012 & Autodesk Inventor LT 2012. 2011. (ENG., Illus.). 1032p. pap. 79.99 *(978-1-118-01682-4(3))*, Sybex) Wiley, John & Sons, Inc.
Waguespack, Curtis. Mastering Autodesk Inventor & Inventor LT. 2012. (ENG.). 1008p. pap. 79.99 ***(978-1-118-27430-9(X))***, Sybex) Wiley, John & Sons, Inc.
Waguespack, Curtis & Tremblay, Thom. Mastering Autodesk Inventor & Autodesk Inventor LT 2011. 2010. (ENG., Illus.). 936p. pap. 69.99 *(978-0-470-88287-0(5))*, Sybex) Wiley, John & Sons, Inc.
Younis, Wasim. Up & Running with Autodesk Inventor Simulation 2010: A Step-by-Step Guide to Engineering Design Solutions. 2009. (ENG., Illus.). 384p. pap. 103.00 *(978-1-85617-694-1(0))*, Butterworth-Heinemann) Elsevier Science & Technology Bks.
—Up & Running with Autodesk Inventor Simulation 2011: A Step-by-Step Guide to Engineering Design Solutions. 2nd ed. 2010. (ENG., Illus.). 464p. pap. 92.95 *(978-0-12-382102-7(9))*, Butterworth-Heinemann) Elsevier Science & Technology Bks.

AUTOGENIC TRAINING

Antony, Martin M. & Rowa, Karen A. Overcoming Fear of Heights: How to Conquer Acrophobia & Live a Life Without Limits. 2007. (Pocket Phobia Ser.). (ENG.). 160p. per. 14.95 *(978-1-57224-456-6(9))* New Harbinger Pubns.
Bastaracherican, Rene A. Self-Hypnosis: Learn to Use Your Mental Power to Take Control of Your Life. 2009. (ENG.). 256p. pap. 9.95 *(978-1-59869-835-0(4))* Adams Media Corp.
Blair, Forbes Robbins. Self-Hypnosis Revolution: The Amazingly Simple Way to Use Self-Hypnosis to Change Your Life. 2007. (ENG.). 304p. per. 19.99 *(978-1-4022-0670-2(4))* Sourcebooks, Inc.
Copelan, Rachel. How to Hypnotize Yourself & Others. 2nd rev. ed. 2007. 240p. pap. *(978-0-8119-0758-3(9))* Lifetime Bks.
Coue, Emile. Self Mastery. 2007. (ENG.). 60p. per. 5.99 *(978-0-9794154-9-4(7))* Arc Manor.
—Some Notes on the Journey to Paris in October 1919. 2006. pap. 9.95 *(978-1-4286-8075-3(6))* Kessinger Publishing, LLC.
Elmer, Bruce N. Hypnotize Yourself Out of Pain Now! A Powerful, User-friendly Program for Anyone Searching for Immediate Pain Relief. 2nd rev. ed. 2008. 256p. pap. incl. audio compact disk *(978-1-84590-087-8(1))* Crown House Publishing, Whaley Bridge.
Goldberg, Bruce. Increase Athletic Performance. 2007. (ENG.). 13.00 incl. audio *(978-1-885577-63-4(X))* Goldberg, Bruce Inc.
Gurgevich, Steven. Hypnosis House Call A Complete Course in Mind-Body Healing. 2011. (ENG.). 208p. 17.95 *(978-1-4027-7747-9(7))* Sterling Publishing Co., Inc.
Gurgevich, Steven & Gurgevich, Joy. The Self-Hypnosis Diet: Use Your Subconscious Mind to Reach Your Perfect Weight. 2009. 232p. pap. 15.95 *(978-1-59179-672-5(5))* Sounds True, Inc.
Harris, Michael. 10 Minute Mental Vacation. 2007. (Sleepnosis Ser.). 253p. pap. 29.95 incl. audio compact disk *(978-1-887895-71-2(X))* Nazca Plains Corp., The.
Harrold, Glenn. Look Young Live Longer: The 7-Step Programme That Will Slow the Ageing Process & Improve the Quality of Your Life. 2010. (ENG.). 208p. pap. 14.95 *(978-0-7528-8610-7(X))* Orion Bks. Ltd. GBR. Dist: Sterling Publishing Co., Inc.
Havens, Ronald A. Self Hypnosis for Cosmic Consciousness: Achieving Altered States, Mystical Experiences, & Spiritual Enlightenment. 2007. 267p. pap. *(978-1-904424-54-3(6))* Crown House Publishing, Whaley Bridge.
Haymes, Gary. Go Beyond Stress: Twelve Self-Hypnotic Stress-Buster Sessions. 2007. 261p. pap. 27.95 *(978-1-4241-9528-2(4))* PublishAmerica, Inc.
Hepburn, Susan. Hypnodiet: Lose Weight, Feel Fabulous - The Stress-Free Way. 2010. (ENG., Illus.). 160p. pap. *(978-0-7499-5235-8(0))* Piatkus Bks. GBR. Dist: Hachette Bk. Group.
Hubert, Jean Pierre. La Sophrologie Analytique: La Sophranalyse. 2010. (FRE.). 341p. *(978-2-296-12960-3(9))* Harmattan Pr.
Jackson, Lisa. Adore Yourself Slim. 2011. (ENG., Illus.). 176p. 24.95 *(978-0-85720-162-1(X))* Simon & Schuster, Ltd. GBR. Dist: Independent Pubs. Group.
James, Ursula. You Can Think Yourself Thin: Transform Your Shape with Hypnosis. 2009. (ENG.). 208p. (gr. 12-18). 15.95 *(978-1-58542-727-7(6))*, Tarcher) Penguin Group (USA) Inc.
Johnson, Jim. Success Through Self-Hypnosis. 2008. 152p. pap. 12.95 *(978-1-59858-562-9(2))* Dog Ear Publishing, LLC.
LaBay, Mary Lee & Hogan, Kevin. Through the Open Door: Secrets of Self-Hypnosis, 1 vol. 2012. (ENG.). 272p. pap. 23.00 *(978-1-58980-891-1(6))* Pelican Publishing Co., Inc.
Lecron, Leslie M. Self-Hypnotism: The Technique & Its Use in Daily Living. pap. 4.95 *(978-0-13-803486-3(9))*, Reward Bks.) Prentice Hall PTR.
Mannarino M.A., Donald J. Mind over Platter: The Nationally Popular Self-Hypnotic Weight Loss Program-Think & Lose. 2009. 92p. pap. 11.95 *(978-1-4401-3843-0(5))* iUniverse, Inc.
McGill, Ormond. Hypnotism & Meditation. Mulder, Marleen, ed. 2008. mass mkt. *(978-1-933332-40-6(9))* Hypnotherapy Training Institute.
McKenna, Paul. I Can Make You Confident The Power to Go for Anything You Want! 2010. (ENG., Illus.). 224p. 22.95 *(978-1-4027-6922-1(9))* Sterling Publishing Co., Inc.
O'Briain, Cathal. Powerful Mind Through Self-hypnosis. 2010. (ENG.). 308p. pap. 24.95 *(978-1-84694-298-3(5))* Hunt, John Publishing Ltd. GBR. Dist: National Bk. Network.
Pearson, Judith E. Why Do I Keep Doing This!!? End Bad Habits, Negativity & Stress with Self-Hypnosis & NLP. 2012. (ENG.). 300p. pap. incl. audio compact disk ***(978-1-84590-732-7(9))*** Crown Hse. Publishing.
Simpkins, C. Alexander & Simpkins, Annellen M. Neuro-Hypnosis: Using Self-Hypnosis to Activate the Brain for Change. 2010. (ENG., Illus.). 288p. pap. 24.95 *(978-0-393-70625-3(7))*, 70625) Norton, W. W. & Co., Inc.
Slate, Joe H. & Weschcke, Carl Llewellyn. Doors to Past Lives & Future Lives: Practical Applications of Self-Hypnosis. 2011. (ENG.). 240p. pap. 15.95 *(978-0-7387-2797-4(0))* Llewellyn Pubns.
Sourcebooks, Inc. & Walden, Kelly Sullivan. Zone Golf. 2010. (ENG.). 272p. 18.99 *(978-1-4022-3964-9(5))* Sourcebooks, Inc.
Weschcke, Carl Llewellyn & Slate, Joe H. Self-Empowerment Through Self-Hypnosis: Harnessing the Enormous Potential of the Mind. 2010. (ENG.). 264p. pap. 15.95 *(978-0-7387-1928-3(5))* Llewellyn Pubns.

AUTOGENOUS WELDING

see Welding

AUTOGIROS

Federal Aviation Administration. Sport Pilot Practical Test Standards for Airplane, Weight-Shift Control, Powered Parachute, & Flight Instructor: FAA-S-8081-29 And 31. 2008. (Practical Test Standards Ser.). (ENG.). 196p. pap. 9.95 *(978-1-56027-725-5(4))* Aviation Supplies & Academics, Inc.

Federal Aviation Administration Staff & U.S. Department of Transportation, eds. Rotorcraft Flying Handbook. 2007. (Illus.). 208p. pap. 14.95 *(978-1-60239-060-7(6))* Skyhorse Publishing Co., Inc.

Gibbings, David. Fairey Rotodyne. 2009. (ENG., Illus.). 160p. pap. 32.95 *(978-0-7524-4916-6(8))* History Pr. Ltd.,The GBR. Dist: Independent Pubs. Group.

AUTOGRAPH LETTERS

see Autographs

AUTOGRAPHIC PROCESSES

see Copying Processes

AUTOGRAPHS

see also Books—Owners' Marks; Manuscripts

Cohen, Dan. Play Ball, Mr. President: A Century of Baseballs Signed by U. S. Presidents. 2008. (ENG.). 48p. pap. 19.99 *(978-1-60194-020-9(3),* Elevate) Advantage Media Group.

Draper, Lyman C. An Essay on the Autographic Collections of the Signers of the Declaration of Independence & the Constitution. 2007. (ENG.). 120p. 34.95 *(978-0-548-04234-2(9))* Kessinger Publishing, LLC.

Huth, Henry. The Huth Library. 2009. 168p. pap. *(978-0-217-08775-9(2))* Books LLC.

—The Huth Library a Catalogue of the Printed Books, Manuscripts , Autograph Letters, & Engravings. 2010. 312p. pap. *(978-1-152-96588-1(3));* 288p. pap. *(978-1-152-96584-3(0));* 332p. pap. *(978-1-152-96582-9(4))* Books LLC.

AUTOGRAPHS—COLLECTORS AND COLLECTING

Brewer, Susan. Collecting Autographs. 2011. (Illus.). 272p. pap. 29.95 ***(978-1-84468-070-2(3))*** Pen & Sword Bks. Ltd. GBR. Dist: Casemate Pubs. & Bk. Distributors, LLC.

Ellis, Bill. The Signs Are Good. 2011. 182p. pap. ***(978-1-908147-69-1(5))*** YouWriteOn.

Ellis, Lee, ed. The Celebrity Address Directory & Autograph Collector's Guide. 3rd ed. 2007. per. 39.95 *(978-0-9759569-2-2(2))* Americana Group Publishing.

Gilman, Caroline Howard. The Poetry of Travelling in the United States by Caroline Gilman with Additional Sketches, by a Few Friends; & a Week among Autographs, by Rev S. 2006. 444p. per. 26.99 *(978-1-4255-4826-1(1))* MPublishing.

Johnson, Brian. Rockers & Rollers: A Full-Throttle Memoir. 2011. (ENG.). 256p. 24.99 *(978-0-06-199063-0(3))* HarperCollins Pubs.

Liddell, Larry. Sign, Please! 2011. 122p. pap. 19.95 ***(978-1-4560-3126-8(0))*** PublishAmerica, Inc.

Raynor, Robert, compiled by. Raynors' Compendium of Autographs & Biographies of the High Command of the Confederate States of America. 2007. (Illus.). 262p. 69.95 *(978-0-9799447-0-3(8))* Raynors' Inventory Management Systems.

Saffro, Richard. The Sanders Autograph Price Guide, 7th Edition. 7th ed. 2009. (ENG.). 560p. pap. 24.95 *(978-0-615-26462-2(X))* Odyssey Pubns., Inc.

Wakeman, Stephen & Wakeman, Alice L. James. The Stephen H Wakeman Collection of Books of Nineteenth Century American Writers. 2011. 260p. 47.95 ***(978-1-258-04996-6(1))*** Literary Licensing, LLC.

AUTOGRAPHS—FACSIMILES

Baile De Laperriere, Charles & Murray, Lynda, eds. Who's Who in Art: Biographies of Leading Men & Women in the World of Art in Britain Today: Artists, Sculptors, Designers, Architects, Critics, Writers, Lecturers, Curators & Photographers. 33rd rev. ed. 2008. (Who's Who in Art Ser.). (Illus.). 1128p. *(978-0-904722-42-0(2))* Hilmarton Manor Pr.

Munn, Lewis C. The American Orator. 2007. (ENG.). 450p. 52.95 *(978-0-548-18094-5(6));* pap. 37.95 *(978-1-4304-8196-6(X))* Kessinger Publishing, LLC.

—The American Orator with an Appendix Containing the Declaration of Independence, with the Fac-Similes of the Autographs of the Signers; the Constitut. 2006. 452p. per. 26.99 *(978-1-4255-4965-7(9))* MPublishing.

AUTOHARP

Beatles, The. The Beatles for Autoharp. 2011. (ENG.). 64p. pap. 14.99 ***(978-1-4584-0762-7(4),*** 1458407624) Leonard, Hal Corp.

AUTOIMMUNE DISEASES

see also Chronic Active Hepatitis; Graves' Disease; Systemic Lupus Erythematosus

Abramovitz, Melissa, ed. Autoimmune Disorders. 2011. (Diseases & Disorders Ser.). (Illus.). 128p. (YA). (gr. 9-12). lib. bdg. 33.45 *(978-1-4205-0657-0(9))* Cengage Gale.

Altmann, A. & Theofilopoulos, Argyrios N., eds. Signal Transduction Pathways in Autoimmunity, Vol. 5. (Current Directions in Autoimmunity Ser.: Vol. 5). (Illus.). *(978-3-8055-7308-5(1))* Karger, S. AG.

Amor, Sandra & Huizinga, Ruth. Autoimmunity to Neuronal Proteins in Neurological Disorders. 2011. (Series: Neurology - Laboratory & Clinical Research Developments Ser.). 147p. pap. 47.00 *(978-1-61324-397-8(9))* Nova Science Pubs., Inc.

Asherson, Ronald, contrib. by. Endocrine Manifestations of Systemic Autoimmune Diseases. 2008. (Handbook of Systemic Autoimmune Diseases Ser.: 9). (ENG., Illus.). 340p. 195.00 *(978-0-444-53172-8(6),* Elsevier Science) Elsevier Science & Technology Bks.

Ballestar, Esteban, ed. Epigenetic Contributions in Autoimmune Disease. 2011. (Advances in Experimental Medicine & Biology Ser.). (ENG., Illus.). xvi, 178p. 189.00 *(978-1-4419-8215-5(9),* 1441982159) Springer.

Bradley, Mary Boyle. Up the Creek with a Paddle: Beat MS & All Autoimmune Disorders with Low Dose Naltrexone (LDN) 2009. 248p. pap. 16.95 *(978-1-4327-1150-4(4))* Outskirts Pr., Inc.

Brenner, Kyle J., ed. Autoimmune Diseases: Symptoms, Diagnosis & Treatment. 2010. (Immunology & Immune System Disorders Ser.). (Illus.). xiii, 465p. 195.00 *(978-1-61668-007-7(5))* Nova Science Pubs., Inc.

Brill, Alida & Lockshin, Michael D. Dancing at the River's Edge: A Patient & Her Doctor Negotiate Life with Chronic Illness. 3rd ed. (ENG.). 2010. 264p. pap. 16.95 *(978-0-9824332-7-0(1))* 2009. 224p. 23.95 *(978-0-9801394-0-2(6))* Schaffner Pr., Inc.

Brown, Ellen & Konopelski, Karen. Supercharge Your Immune System: 100 Ways to Help Your Body Fight Illness - One Glass at a Time. 2008. (ENG., Illus.). 208p. 14.95 *(978-1-59233-328-8(1),* 1592333281) Quayside.

Brown, Terwana J. Healed by Faith. 2010. 116p. pap. 15.00 *(978-0-557-28573-0(9))* Lulu Enterprises Inc.

Cassell, Dana K. & Rose, Noel. The Encyclopedia of Autoimmune Diseases. 2nd rev. ed. 2011. (Library of Health & Living Ser.). 75.00 *(978-0-8160-7722-9(3))* Facts On File, Inc.

Cervera, Ricard. Diagnostic Criteria in Autoimmune Diseases. 2008. (Illus.). 872p. 239.00 *(978-1-60327-427-2(8))* Humana Pr.

Chernajovsky, Yuti & Robbins, Paul D. Gene Therapy for Autoimmune & Inflammatory Diseases. 2010. (Milestones in Drug Therapy Ser.). (ENG., Illus.). 250p. 179.00 *(978-3-0346-0164-1(6),* 3034601646) Birkhauser Verlag AG CHE. Dist: Springer.

Cimaz, Rolando & Lehman, Thomas J. A., eds. Pediatrics in Systemic Autoimmune Diseases. 2007. (Handbook of Systemic Autoimmune Diseases Ser.: 6). (ENG., Illus.). 300p. 190.00 *(978-0-444-52971-8(3),* Elsevier Science) Elsevier Science & Technology Bks.

Costados. A Doença de Pessoa. 2010. (POR.). 38p. pap. 13.50 *(978-1-4452-9247-2(5))* Lulu Enterprises Inc.

Deister, Kelli. Shaky Ground: Living with Cogan's Syndrome, 1 vol. 2010. 84p. pap. 19.95 *(978-1-4489-3395-2(1))* PublishAmerica, Inc.

Delgado Gaitan, Concha. Prickly Cactus: Finding Sacred Meaning in Chronic Illness. 2009. pap. 14.95 *(978-1-879384-76-7(0))* Cypress Hse.

Dembowski, Sheila S. Leaning into the Light. 2011. 112p. pap. 12.95 *(978-1-4502-9733-2(1))* iUniverse, Inc.

Demoss, Whisper. My Book of Shadows. 2010. 249p. pap. 19.99 *(978-1-4500-9611-9(5))* Xlibris Corp.

Dickinson, Douglas. New Targets & Approaches to Autoimmune-Induced Salivary Hypofunction. 2011. (Immunology & Immune System Disorders Ser.). 49p. pap. 43.00 *(978-1-61122-307-1(5))* Nova Science Pubs., Inc.

Dubois, Quentin P. Autoantibodies Research Progress. 2008. (C). 185.00 *(978-1-60456-108-1(4))* Nova Science Pubs., Inc.

Elkon, Keith B. Apoptosis & Its Relevance to Autoimmunity, Vol. 9. (Current Directions in Autoimmunity Ser.: Vol. 9). (Illus.). 210p. *(978-3-8055-8036-6(3))* Karger, S. AG.

Gershwin, M. Eric & Shoenfeld, Yehuda, eds. Autoimmunity Pt. A: Basic Principles & New Diagnostic Tools. 2007. (Annals of the New York Academy of Sciences Ser.: 2). (ENG.). 400p. pap. 159.95 *(978-1-57331-663-7(6),* Wiley-Blackwell) Wiley, John & Sons, Inc.

—Autoimmunity, Part B: Novel Applications of Basic Research. 2007. (Annals of the New York Academy of Sciences Ser.: Vols. 1105-1108). (ENG., Illus.). 752p. per. 159.95 *(978-1-57331-709-2(8),* Wiley-Blackwell) Wiley, John & Sons, Inc.

Gilbere, Gloria. I Was Poisoned by My Body — I Have a Gut Feeling You Could Be, Too! The Odyssey of a Doctor Who Reversed Fibromyalgia, Leaky Gut Syndrome, Multiple Allergic Responses, Naturally & Her Life 10 Years after Recovery. 2nd ed. 2007. (Illus.). 303p. pap. *(978-0-9776300-6-6(4))* Lucky Pr., LLC.

Grewal, Iqbal S. Therapeutic Targets of the TNF Superfamily. 2008. (Advances in Experimental Medicine & Biology Ser.: Vol. 647). (Illus.). 252p. 159.00 *(978-0-387-89519-2(1))* Springer.

Grewal, Iqbal S., ed. Therapeutic Targets of the TNF Superfamily. 2010. (Advances in Experimental Medicine & Biology Ser.). (ENG., Illus.). xvii, 220p. pap. 159.00 *(978-1-4419-2799-6(9),* 1441927999) Springer.

Harrison, W. B. & Dijkmans, B. A. C., eds. Combination Treatment in Autoimmune Diseases. 2010. (ENG., Illus.). vi, 213p. pap. 137.00 *(978-3-642-07704-3(8),* 3642077048) Springer.

Hertl, Michael, ed. Autoimmune Diseases of the Skin: Pathogenesis, Diagnosis, Management. 3rd ed. 2010. (ENG., Illus.). xxii, 594p. 179.00 *(978-3-211-99224-1(3),* 3211992243) Springer.

Horwitz, Randy & Muller, Daniel. Integrative Rheumatology. 2010. (Weil Integrative Medicine Library). (ENG., Illus.). 350p. 39.95 *(978-0-19-531121-1(3))* Oxford Univ. Pr., Inc.

Hou, Wanzhu, ed. Treating Autoimmune Disease with Chinese Medicine. 2010. (ENG., Illus.). 320p. 73.95 *(978-0-443-06974-1(3),* Churchill Livingstone) Elsevier - Health Sciences Div.

Hughes, Graham & Sangle, Shirish. Hughes Syndrome: the Antiphospholipid Syndrome: A Guide for Students. 2011. (ENG., Illus.). xvii, 102p. pap. 29.95 *(978-0-85729-738-9(4),* 0857297384) Springer.

Hughes, Graham R. V. Understanding Hughes Syndrome: Case Studies for Patients. 2008. (Illus.). 88p. pap. 19.95 *(978-1-84800-375-0(7),* 1848003757) Springer.

Joffe, Rosalind & Friedlander, Joan. Women, Work, & Autoimmune Disease: Keep Working, Girlfriend! Mansfield, L. G., ed. 2008. (ENG.). 216p. pap. 18.95 *(978-1-932603-68-2(9))* Demos Medical Publishing, LLC.

Kalman, Bernadette & Brannagan, Thomas H., III, eds. Neuroimmunology in Clinical Practice. 2007. (ENG., Illus.). 280p. 199.95 *(978-1-4051-5840-4(9),* Wiley-Blackwell) Wiley, John & Sons, Inc.

Khamashta, M. A., ed. Hughes Syndrome: Antiphospholipid Syndrome. 2nd ed. 2010. (ENG., Illus.). xxii, 602p. pap. 169.00 *(978-1-84996-940-6(X),* 184996940X) Springer.

Khamashta, M. A. & Bertolaccini, Maria L. Antiphospholipid Syndrome Handbook. 2010. (Illus.). 128p. pap. 59.95 *(978-1-84628-522-6(4))* Springer.

Khamashta, Munther A. & Ramos-Casals, Manuel, eds. Autoimmune Diseases: Acute & Complex Situations. 2011. (ENG., Illus.). xii, 416p. 219.00 *(978-0-85729-357-2(5),* 0857293575) Springer.

Khamashta, Munther A., et al. Antiphospholipid Syndrome in Systemic Autoimmune Diseases. Cervera, R., ed. 2009. (Handbook of Systemic Autoimmune Diseases Ser.: 10). (ENG., Illus.). 266p. 205.00 *(978-0-444-53169-8(6),* Elsevier Science) Elsevier Science & Technology Bks.

Kuan, Anita. Antibody-Mediated Myocarditis. 2010. 112p. pap. *(978-3-8383-6604-3(2))* Lambert Academic Publishing.

Kuchroo, Vijay K., et al, eds. Cytokines & Autoimmune Diseases. 2010. (Illus.). 436p. pap. 150.00 *(978-1-61737-225-4(0),* 1617372250) Humana Pr.

Kyewski, B. & Suri-Payer, Elisabeth, eds. CD4+CD25+ Regulatory T Cells: Origin, Function & Therapeutic Potential: Origin, Function & Therapeutic Potential. 2010. (Current Topics in Microbiology & Immunology Ser.). (Illus.). xi, 330p. pap. 169.00 *(978-3-642-06376-3(4),* 3642063764) Springer.

Land, Lina. The Gift of Remission: A Journey into Multiple Sclerosis & Back Again Prevent, Stop & Recover from Autoimmune Disease. 2009. 128p. pap. 14.95 *(978-1-4327-4216-4(7))* Outskirts Pr., Inc.

Langwith, Jacqueline. Autoimmune Diseases. 2011. (Perspectives on Diseases & Disorders Ser.). 144p. lib. bdg. 37.10 *(978-0-7377-5251-9(3),* Greenhaven Pr., Inc.) Cengage Gale.

Levy, Michael J. & Chari, Suresh T., eds. Autoimmune (IgG4-Associated) Pancreatitis & Cholangitis. 2010. (ENG., Illus.). 270p. 139.00 *(978-1-4419-6429-8(0),* 1441964290) Springer.

Marie, Celia. Life in the Cave: Overcoming Grave's Disease. 2009. pap. 8.99 *(978-1-60799-984-3(6))* Tate Publishing & Enterprises, LLC.

Mason, Justin C. & Pusey, Charles D., eds. The Kidney in Systemic Autoimmune Diseases. 2007. (Handbook of Systemic Autoimmune Diseases Ser.: 7). (ENG., Illus.). 432p. 190.00 *(978-0-444-52972-5(1),* Elsevier Science) Elsevier Science & Technology Bks.

Miller, Aaron E. & DeAngelis, Tracy M. Neuroimmunology. 2012. (What Do I Do Now Ser.). (ENG., Illus.). 192p. pap. 34.99 ***(978-0-19-973292-0(2))*** Oxford Univ. Pr., Inc.

Miller, Msw. Julie's Story, My Life with Lupus. 2008. 104p. pap. 10.99 *(978-1-4389-2276-8(0))* AuthorHouse.

Molnár, Ildikó, ed. Nervous, Immune, Endocrine Regulatory Systems & Diseases Associated with Nerve Growth Factor Co-Secretion. 2010. (Endocrinology Research & Clinical Developments Ser.). 69.00 *(978-1-60876-780-9(9),* Nova Biomedical Bks.) Nova Science Pubs., Inc.

Murrell, Dédée F. Autoimmune Blistering Disease Part I, an Issue of Dermatologic Clinics. 2011. (Clinics: Dermatology Ser.: 29-3). (ENG., Illus.). 192p. 110.00 *(978-1-4557-1033-1(4),* Saunders) Elsevier - Health Sciences Div.

Murrell, Dédée F. Dermatologic Clinics Pt. 2: Autoimmune Blistering Diseases - Diagnosis & Management. 2011. (Clinics: Dermatology Ser.: 29-4). (ENG.). 110.00 ***(978-1-4557-1034-8(2),*** Saunders) Elsevier - Health Sciences Div.

Nakazawa, Donna Jackson. The Autoimmune Epidemic. 2009. (ENG.). 352p. pap. 15.99 *(978-0-7432-7776-1(7),* Touchstone) Touchstone.

—The Autoimmune Epidemic: Bodies Gone Haywire in a World Out of Balance — and the Cutting-Edge Science that Promises Hope. 2008. (ENG.). 352p. 25.00 *(978-0-7432-7775-4(9),* Touchstone) Touchstone.

Nickoloff, Brian J. & Nestle, F. O. Dermatologic Immunity. 2008. (Current Directions in Autoimmunity Ser.). (Illus.). 366p. (C). *(978-3-8055-8391-6(5))* Karger, S. AG.

Oksenberg, Jorge R. & Brassat, David, eds. Immunogenetics of Autoimmune Disease. 2006. (Medical Intelligence Unit Ser.). (Illus.). xiii, 158p. 189.00 *(978-0-387-36004-1(2),* 0387360042) Springer.

Organ, Steve, ed. Lupus: Complete Handbook. 2011. 132p. pap. 14.95 ***(978-1-937354-09-1(1))*** Rapid Publishing LLC.

Pearce, Simon & Pearce, Simon H. S. Autoimmune Endocrine Disorders, an Issue of Endocrinology Clinics. 2009. (Clinics: Internal Medicine Ser.: 38-2). (ENG., Illus.). 240p. 99.00 *(978-1-4377-0471-6(9),* Saunders) Elsevier - Health Sciences Div.

Pearson, Audrey. My Four-Year Pmr & Prednisone Challenge: How Amrit Yoga Helped Me Overcome PMR (Polymyalgia Rheumatica) & Helped Me Deal with the Side Effects & W. 2009. 308p. 31.95 *(978-1-4401-2312-2(8));* pap. 21.95 *(978-1-4401-2310-8(1))* iUniverse, Inc.

Petrelli, Claude T., ed. New Research on Autoantibodies. 2008. (Illus.). xi, 213p. 129.00 *(978-1-60456-055-8(X),* Nova Biomedical Bks.) Nova Science Pubs., Inc.

Petrov, Maria E. Autoimmune Disorders: Symptoms, Diagnosis & Treatment. 2011. (Immunology & Immune System Disorders Ser.). 129.00 *(978-1-61761-552-8(8),* Nova Biomedical Bks.) Nova Science Pubs., Inc.

Pollard, Kenneth Michael, ed. Autoantibodies & Autoimmunity: Molecular Mechanisms in Health & Disease. 2006. 633p. 230.00 *(978-3-527-60785-3(4),* Wiley-American Ceramic Society) Wiley, John & Sons, Inc.

Pourmand, R. R., ed. Immune-Mediated Neuromuscular Diseases. 2009. (Frontiers of Neurology & Neuroscience Ser.). (Illus.). 170p. *(978-3-8055-9141-6(1))* Karger, S. AG.

Prud'homme, Gerald J. Gene Therapy of Autoimmune Disease. 2010. (Medical Intelligence Unit Ser.). (Illus.). 149p. pap. 149.00 *(978-1-4419-3427-7(8),* 1441934278) Springer.

Radbruch, Andreas & Lipsky, Peter E. Current Concepts in Autoimmunity & Chronic Inflammation. 2010. (Current Topics in Microbiology & Immunology Ser.). (Illus.). x, 282p. pap. 169.00 *(978-3-642-06745-7(X),* 364206745X) Springer.

Ramos-Casals, Manuel, ed. Digestive Involvement in Systemic Autoimmune Diseases. 2008. (Handbook of Systemic Autoimmune Diseases Ser.: 8). (ENG., Illus.). 350p. 195.00 *(978-0-444-53168-1(8),* Elsevier Science) Elsevier Science & Technology Bks.

Reed, Kathy. Multiple Sclerosis: The Many Faces of the Disease. 2009. (Illus.). 64p. pap. 19.95 *(978-1-4327-3549-4(7))* Outskirts Pr., Inc.

Renz, Harald, ed. Autoimmune Diagnostics. 2012. (ENG.). 260p. 168.00 ***(978-3-11-175038-5(8))*** De Gruyter, Walter Inc.

—Autoimmune Diagnostics. 2012. (ENG., Illus.). 260p. 112.00 ***(978-3-11-022864-9(5))*** De Gruyter, Walter Inc.

Ryffel, Bernhard & Di Padova, Franco. Th17 Cells: Role in Inflammation & Autoimmune Disease. 2008. (Progress in Inflammation Research Ser.). (Illus.). 300p. 189.00 *(978-3-7643-8680-1(0))* Birkhauser Boston.

Schett, Georg. Infection & Rheumatic Diseases. 2009. 200p. 159.00 *(978-3-211-79281-0(3))* Springer.

Shoenfeld, Yehuda, et al, eds. Autoantibodies. 2nd ed. 2006. (ENG., Illus.). 872p. 195.00 *(978-0-444-52763-9(X),* Elsevier Science) Elsevier Science & Technology Bks.

Shoenfeld, Yehuda & Gershwin, M. Eric, eds. Autoimmunity Pt. C: The Mosaic of Autoimmunity. 2007. (Annals of the New York Academy of Sciences Ser.: Vols. 1105-1108). (ENG.). 400p. pap. 159.95 *(978-1-57331-662-0(8),* Wiley-Blackwell) Wiley, John & Sons, Inc.

—Autoimmunity Pt. D: Autoimmune Disease, Annus Mirabilis. 2007. (Annals of the New York Academy of Sciences Ser.: Vols. 1105-1108). (ENG.). 628p. pap. 159.95 *(978-1-57331-708-5(X),* Wiley-Blackwell) Wiley, John & Sons, Inc.

—Contemporary Challenges in Autoimmunity. 2009. (Annals of the New York Academy of Sciences Ser.). (ENG., Illus.). 400p. pap. 159.95 *(978-1-57331-762-7(4),* Wiley-Blackwell) Wiley, John & Sons, Inc.

Shoenfeld, Yehuda, et al. Diagnostic Criteria in Autoimmune Diseases. 2008. (Illus.). xviii, 593p. pap. *(978-1-60327-284-1(4))* Humana Pr.

Shurin, Michael R. & Smolkin, Yuri S., eds. Immune Mediated Diseases: From Theory to Therapy. 2007. (Advances in Experimental Medicine & Biology Ser.). (ENG., Illus.). xxii, 458p. 189.00 *(978-0-387-72004-3(9),* 0387720049) Springer.

Stohl, William. B Cell Trophic Factors & B Cell Antagonism in Autoimmune Disease, Vol. 8. (Current Directions in Autoimmunity Ser.: Vol. 8). (Illus.). *(978-3-8055-7851-6(2))* Karger, S. AG.

Udall, Kate Gilbert. Flaxseed & Flaxseed Oil. 3rd ed. 2011. (Woodland Health Ser.). 32p. pap. 4.95 ***(978-1-58054-203-6(4))*** Woodland Publishing, Inc.

Vogel, Fynn L. & Zimmermann, Lucas F. Autoimmunity: Role, Regulation, & Disorders. 2008. (Illus.). xiii, 309p. 129.00 *(978-1-60456-833-2(X))* Nova Science Pubs., Inc.

Wallace, Daniel J., ed. The Sjogren's Book, 1 vol. 4th ed. 2011. (ENG., Illus.). 448p. 35.00 *(978-0-19-973722-2(3))* Oxford Univ. Pr., Inc.

Weetman, Anthony P. Autoimmune Diseases in Endocrinology. 2007. (Contemporary Endocrinology (Humana Press) Ser.). (Illus.). 434p. 189.00 *(978-1-58829-733-4(0))* Humana Pr.

Weetman, Anthony P., ed. Autoimmune Diseases in Endocrinology. 2010. (Contemporary Endocrinology Ser.). (Illus.). xii, 434p. pap. 189.00 *(978-1-61737-747-1(3),* 1617377473) Humana Pr.

Wiersinga, Wilmar M., ed. The Thyroid & Autoimmunity: Proceedings Merck European Thyroid Symposium, June 2006. 2007. (ENG., Illus.). 208p. pap. 14.95 *(978-1-58890-606-9(X))* Thieme Medical Pubs., Inc.

Wilson, Brucene. Understanding Autoimmune Disease & Stress-Related Illness. 2009. 176p. pap. 14.95 *(978-0-557-11026-1(2))* Lulu Enterprises Inc.

Zhang, Jingwu, ed. Immune Regulation & Immunotherapy in Autoimmune Disease. (ENG., Illus.). xvi, 570p. 2010. pap. 139.00 *(978-1-4419-4209-8(2),* 1441942092) 2007. 139.00 *(978-0-387-36002-7(6),* 0387360026) Springer.

Zhang, Jingwu & Cohen, Irun R. T-Cell Vaccination. Zhang, Jingwu & Cohen, Irun R., eds. 2008. (Illus.). x, 171p. 79.00 *(978-1-60456-178-4(5),* Nova Biomedical Bks.) Nova Science Pubs., Inc.

Zouali, Moncef, ed. The Epigenetics of Autoimmune Diseases. 2009. (ENG., Illus.). 472p. 199.95 *(978-0-470-75861-8(9),* Wiley) Wiley, John & Sons, Inc.

AUTOIMMUNE HEPATITIS

see Chronic Active Hepatitis

AUTO-IONIZATION

see Auger Effect

AUTOLISP (COMPUTER PROGRAM LANGUAGE)
Krawczyk, Robert J. The Codewriting: Creating Computational Architecture in AutoLISP. 2008. (ENG., Illus.). 272p. pap., wbk. ed. 50.00 (978-1-56898-792-7(7)) Princeton Architectural Pr.

AUTOMATA
see Machine Theory

AUTOMATED ACCOUNTING SYSTEMS
see Accounting—Data Processing

AUTOMATED BATTLEFIELD
see Electronics in Military Engineering

AUTOMATED GUIDED VEHICLE SYSTEM
Rashidi, Hassan & Edward, Professor. Vehicle Scheduling in Port Automation. 2010. 212p. pap. (978-3-639-22992-9(4)) VDM Verlag Dr. Mueller e.K.
Verma, Shobhit. Precision Positioning of Automatically Guided Vehicles. 2010. 96p. pap. (978-3-639-25357-3(4)) VDM Verlag Dr. Mueller e.K.
Williams, Stefan B. Efficient Solutions to Autonomous Mapping & Navigation Problems. 2009. 192p. pap. (978-3-639-19947-5(2)), VDM Verlag Dr. Mueller e.K.

AUTOMATED INFORMATION NETWORKS
see Information Networks

AUTOMATED MAINTENANCE
see Automatic Checkout Equipment

AUTOMATED TELLERS
Kasera, Sumit. ATM Networks. 2006. (ENG., Illus.). 466p. 79.95 (978-0-07-147732-1(2), 0071477322) McGraw-Hill Professional Publishing.
Kausar, Khawaja. Customer Satisfaction Towards Technology: A Study on Atms. 2011. 68p. pap. **(978-3-639-33427-2(2))** VDM Verlag Dr. Mueller e.K.

AUTOMATED THEOREM PROVING
see Automatic Theorem Proving

AUTOMATED TYPESETTING
see Computerized Typesetting

AUTOMATIC BREAD MACHINES
Crocker, Betty. Best Bread Machine. Tlusty, Lois L., ed. 2009. (ENG.). 240p. pap. 17.95 (978-0-470-48007-6(6), Betty Crocker) Wiley, John & Sons, Inc.
Fertig, Judith. The Artisan Bread Machine: 250 Recipes for Breads, Rolls, Flatbreads & Pizzas. 2011. (ENG., Illus.). 320p. pap. 24.95 (978-0-7788-0264-8(7)) Rose, Robert Inc. CAN. Dist: Firefly Bks., Ltd.
Hawkins, Kathryn. Bread! Simple & Satisfying Recipes for Your Bread Machine, 1 vol. 2006. (ENG., Illus.). 176p. pap. 15.95 (978-1-56148-540-6(3)); spiral bd. 19.95 (978-1-56148-541-3(1)) Good Bks.
Humphries, Carolyn. Gluten-Free Bread & Cakes from Your Breadmaker from Your Breadmaker: With Full Details for Dairy or Lactose Intolerance. 2010. (ENG., Illus.). 160p. pap. 16.95 (978-0-572-03569-3(1)) Foulsham, W. Co., Ltd. GBR. Dist: APG Sales & Distribution Services.
Lewis, Sara. The Bread Book: The Definitive Guide to Making Bread by Hand or Machine. 2006. (ENG., Illus.). 200p. pap. 14.95 (978-0-600-61473-9(5), Hamlyn) Octopus Publishing Group GBR. Dist: Hachette Bk. Group.
—Bread Machine Easy: 70 Delicious Recipes that Make the Most of Your Machine. 2008. 144p. 17.95 (978-0-600-61837-9(4), Hamlyn) Octopus Publishing Group GBR. Dist: Jaguar Bk. Group.
—Bread Machine Easy: 70 Delicious Recipes That Make the Most of Your Machine. 2010. (ENG., Illus.). 144p. pap. 14.99 (978-0-600-62182-9(0), Hamlyn) Octopus Publishing Group GBR. Dist: Hachette Bk. Group.
Peoples, Jerome T. Lee's Bread Machines: The Father of Automated Bread Making. 2011. 67p. pap. 14.95 (978-1-4327-6337-4(7)) Outskirts Pr., Inc.
Roberts, Annalise G. Gluten-Free Baking Classics for the Bread Machine. 2009. (ENG., Illus.). 72p. pap. 14.95 (978-1-57284-104-8(4)) Surrey Bks.
Saunders, Karen. Tips for Your Breadmaker: Tips & Advice Every Breadmaker Owner Needs to Know. 2006. (ENG., Illus.). 144p. per. 9.95 (978-0-09-190912-3(0)) Random Hse. GBR. Dist: Independent Pubs. Group.
Shapter, Jennie. Getting the Best from your Bread Machine. 2012. (ENG., Illus.). 128p. pap. 16.99 **(978-1-78019-133-1(2))** Anness Publishing GBR. Dist: National Bk. Network.
—The Ultimate Bread Machine Cookbook. 2011. (ENG., Illus.). 256p. 35.00 (978-0-7548-2102-1(1)) Anness Publishing GBR. Dist: National Bk. Network.
Shapter, Jennie. 80 Bread Machine Best-Ever Recipes: Discover the potential of your bread machine with step-by-step recipes from around the world, illustrated in 300 Photographs. 2012. (ENG., Illus.). 128p. pap. 17.99 **(978-1-84476-870-7(8))** Anness Publishing GBR. Dist: National Bk. Network.
Sheasby, Anne. The Bread Machine Bible: More Than 100 Recipes for Delicious Home Baking with Your Bread Machine. 2009. (ENG., Illus.). 176p. 19.95 (978-1-84483-795-3(5)) Duncan Baird Pubs. GBR. Dist: Sterling Publishing Co., Inc.
Washburn, Donna & Butt, Heather. 300 Best Bread Machine Recipes. 2010. (ENG., Illus.). 448p. pap. 24.95 (978-0-7788-0244-0(2)) Rose, Robert Inc. CAN. Dist: Firefly Bks., Ltd.

AUTOMATIC CHECKOUT EQUIPMENT
see also Error-Correcting Codes (Information Theory)
Ahlstrand, Alan & Rendina, Ralph. General Motors Trailblazer 2002-2009. 2010. (ENG., Illus.). 384p. pap. 29.95 (978-1-56392-803-1(5)) Haynes,Chilton.
Wiseman Murray Staff. Reliability-Centered Knowledge Making Use of the Cmms Database. 2010. (Illus.). 129.95 (978-0-8493-9146-0(6)) CRC Pr. LLC.

AUTOMATIC COMPUTERS
see Computers

AUTOMATIC CONTROL
see also Automatic Pilot (Airplanes); Automatic Timers; Automation; Cybernetics; Delay Lines; Digital Control Systems; Electric Controllers; Error-Correcting Codes (Information Theory); Feedback Control Systems; Guidance Systems (Flight); Hydraulic Control; Intelligent Control Systems; Machine-Tools—Numerical Control; Pneumatic Control; Process Control; Real-Time Control; Servomechanisms; Switching Theory
Abu-Khalaf, Murad, et al. Nonlinear H2/H-Infinity Constrained Feedback Control: A Practical Design Approach Using Neural Networks. 2010. (Advances in Industrial Control Ser.). (Illus.). xx, 203p. pap. 159.00 (978-1-84996-584-2(6), 1849965846) Springer.
Acary, Vincent & Brogliato, Bernard. Numerical Methods for Nonsmooth Dynamical Systems: Applications in Mechanics & Electronics. 2010. (Lecture Notes in Applied & Computational Mechanics Ser.). (Illus.). xxii, 526p. pap. 269.00 (978-3-642-09464-4(3), 3642094643) Springer.
Ahmadian, Mehdi & Ghasemi Nejhad, M. N. Active & Passive Smart Structures & Integrated Systems 2009: 9-12 March 2009, San Diego, California, United States. 2009. (Proceedings of SPIE Ser.). (Illus.). 860p. pap. 160.00 (978-0-8194-7548-0(3)) SPIE.
Alamir, Mazen. Stabilization of Nonlinear Systems Using Receding-horizon Control Schemes: A Parametrized Approach for Fast Systems. 2006. (Lecture Notes in Control & Information Sciences Ser.: Vol. 339). (Illus.). xvii, 308p. pap. 159.00 (978-1-84628-470-0(8), 1846284708) Springer.
Albertos, Pedro & Mareels, Iven. Feedback & Control for Everyone. 2010. (ENG., Illus.). xviii, 350p. pap. 29.95 (978-3-642-03445-9(4), 3642034454) Springer.
Ali, Ahmad. Controller Design Methods for Linear Systems. 2010. 148p. pap. (978-3-639-09193-9(0)) VDM Verlag Dr. Mueller e.K.
Aly El-Naggar, Ayman & Atallah Salem, Farhan. Fundamentals of Automation & Industrial Control Systems Using Plc. 2011. 212p. pap. **(978-3-8443-9984-4(4))** Lambert Academic Publishing.
American Society of Mechanical Engineers Staff, et al. Mechatronics: The Integration of Engineering Design. (Illus.). 190p. 170.00 (978-0-85298-840-4(0)) Professional Engineering Publishing GBR. Dist: SAE Intl.
Andrade Cetto, Juan, et al, eds. Informatics in Control Automation & Robotics: Revised & Selected Papers from the International Conference on Informatics in Control Automation & Robotics 2009. 2011. (Lecture Notes in Electrical Engineering Ser.). (Illus.). xiv, 354p. 179.00 (978-3-642-19729-1(9), 3642197299) Springer.
Angelescu, Dan E. Highly Integrated Microfluidics Design. 2011. (Illus.). 268p. 119.00 (978-1-59693-979-0(6)) Artech Hse., Inc.
Astolfi, Alessandro & Marconi, Lorenzo, eds. Analysis & Design of Nonlinear Control Systems: In Honor of Alberto Isidori. (ENG., Illus.). xxviii, 483p. 2010. pap. 209.00 (978-3-642-09378-4(7), 3642093787) 2007. 209.00 (978-3-540-74357-6(X), 354074357X) Springer.
Aström, Karl J., et al. Computer-Controlled Systems: Theory & Design, Third Edition. 3rd ed. 2011. (Dover Books on Electrical Engineering Ser.). (ENG.). 576p. (C). pap. 29.95 **(978-0-486-48613-0(3))** Dover Pubns., Inc.
Athans, Michael & Falb, Peter L. Optimal Control: An Introduction to the Theory & Its Applications. 2006. (Dover Books on Engineering Ser.). (ENG., Illus.). 896p. per. 44.95 (978-0-486-45328-6(6)) Dover Pubns., Inc.
Avgoustinov, Nikolay. Modelling in Mechanical Engineering & Mechatronics: Towards Autonomous Intelligent Software Models. (ENG., Illus.). xxiv, 226p. 2010. pap. 169.00 (978-1-84996-673-3(7), 1849966737) 2007. 169.00 (978-1-84628-908-8(4), 1846289084) Springer.
Awrejcewicz, Jan. Modeling, Simulation & Control of Nonlinear Engineering Dynamical Systems: State-of-the-Art, Perspectives & Applications. 2008. (ENG., Illus.). xxiv, 336p. 179.00 (978-1-4020-8777-6(2), 1402087772) Springer London, Ltd. GBR. Dist: Springer.
Bagchi, Wriddhi. Design of Pid Controller Using Plc. 2011. 72p. pap. **(978-3-8443-2508-9(5))** Lambert Academic Publishing.
Bai, Ying, et al, eds. Advanced Fuzzy Logic Technologies in Industrial Applications. (Advances in Industrial Control Ser.). (Illus.). xxvi, 334p. 2010. pap. 189.00 (978-1-84996-606-1(0), 1849966060) 2006. 189.00 (978-1-84628-468-7(6), 1846284686) Springer.
Balasubramaniam, P., ed. Control, Computation & Information Systems: First International Conference on Logic, Information, Control & Computation, ICLICC 2011, Gandhigram, India, February 25-27, 2011, Proceedings. 2011. (Communications in Computer & Information Science Ser.). xiv, 328p. pap. 95.00 (978-3-642-19262-3(9), 3642192629) Springer.
Ballas, Rüdiger G. Piezoelectric Multilayer Beam Bending Actuators: Static & Dynamic Behavior & Aspects of Sensor Integration. 2010. (Microtechnology & MEMS Ser.). (Illus.). xxiv, 358p. pap. 249.00 (978-3-642-06910-9(X), 364206910X) Springer.
Ballhausen, Wolfram. Technikphilosophische Aspekte der Automatisierungstechnik. 2010. 138p. 43.95 (978-3-631-59667-8(7)) Lang, Peter GmbH, Europäischer Verlag der Wissenschaften DEU. Dist: Lang, Peter.
Bao, Jie & Lee, Peter L. Process Control: The Passive Systems Approach. 2010. (Advances in Industrial Control Ser.). (Illus.). xx, 253p. pap. 199.00 (978-1-84996-669-6(9), 1849966699) Springer.
Baocang, Ding, ed. Modern Predictive Control. 2009. (ENG., Illus.). 286p. 144.95 (978-1-4200-8530-3(1), CRC Press) Taylor & Francis Group GBR. Dist: Taylor & Francis Group.
Bar-Cohen, Yoseph. Electroactive Polymer Actuators & Devices (EAPAD) 2007: 19-22 March 2007, San Diego, California, USA. 2007. (Proceedings of SPIE Ser.). (Illus.). 644p. pap. 130.00 (978-0-8194-6645-7(X)) SPIE.
Bar-Cohen, Yoseph & Carpi, Federico. Electroactive Polymer Actuators & Devices (EAPAD) 2011. 2011. (Proceedings of SPIE Ser.). 912p. pap. 170.00 **(978-0-8194-8538-0(1))** SPIE.
Baranyi, Peter, et al. Tensor Product Model Transformation in Polytopic Model-Based Control. 2012. (Automation & Control Engineering Ser.). (ENG., Illus.). 250p. 129.95 (978-1-4398-1816-9(9), CRC Press) Taylor & Francis Group GBR. Dist: Taylor & Francis Group.
Barkalov, Alexander & Titarenko, Larysa. Logic Synthesis for Compositional Microprogram Control Units. 2010. (Lecture Notes in Electrical Engineering Ser.). (Illus.). xvi, 272p. pap. 139.00 (978-3-642-08879-7(1), 3642088791) Springer.
—Logic Synthesis for FSM-Based Control Units. 2009. (Lecture Notes in Electrical Engineering Ser.). (Illus.). xx, 236p. 159.00 (978-3-642-04308-6(9), 3642043089) Springer.
Bartelt, Terry L. M. Instrumentation & Process Control. 2006. (ENG.). 160p. (C). pap., lab manual ed. 83.95 (978-1-4180-6339-9(8)) Delmar Cengage Learning.
Bartolini, Giorgio. Modern Sliding Mode Control Theory. 2008. (Lecture Notes in Control & Information Sciences Ser.). spiral bd. 219.00 (978-3-540-79015-0(2)) Springer.
Bartoszewicz, Andrzej & Nowacka-Leverton, Aleksandra. Time-Varying Sliding Modes for Second & Third Order Systems. 2009. (Lecture Notes in Control & Information Sciences Ser.). (Illus.). x, 192p. pap. 139.00 (978-3-540-92216-2(4)) Springer.
Behera, Laxmidhar & Kar, Indrani. Intelligent Systems & Control Principles & Applications. 2010. (ENG., Illus.). 496p. 35.00 (978-0-19-806315-5(6)) Oxford Univ. Pr., Inc.
Belmiloudi, Aziz. Stabilization, Optimal & Robust Control: Theory & Applications in Biological & Physical Sciences. (Communications & Control Engineering Ser.). (Illus.). 2010. xxii, 502p. pap. 229.00 (978-1-84996-790-7(3), 1849967903) 2008. 526p. 229.00 (978-1-84800-343-9(9)) Springer.
Bemporad, Alberto, et al. Networked Control Systems. 2010. (Lecture Notes in Control & Information Sciences Ser.). (Illus.). xiv, 371p. pap. 159.00 (978-0-85729-032-8(0), 0857290320) Springer.
Ben-Asher, Joseph Z. Optimal Control Theory with Aerospace Applications. 2010. 89.95 (978-1-60086-732-3(4)) American Institute of Aeronautics & Astronautics.
Bevly, David M. & Cobb, Stewart. GNSS for Vehicle Control. 2010. 247p. 129.00 (978-1-59693-301-9(1)) Artech Hse., Inc.
Bevrani, Hassan. Robust Power System Frequency Control. (Power Electronics & Power Systems Ser.). (ENG., Illus.). xiv, 226p. 2010. pap. 129.00 (978-1-4419-4661-4(6), 1441946616) 2009. 129.00 (978-0-387-84877-8(0)) Springer.
Bhuyan, Manabendra. Intelligent Instrumentation. 2010. (ENG., Illus.). 547p. (C). 104.95 (978-1-4200-8953-0(6), CRC Press) Taylor & Francis Group GBR. Dist: Taylor & Francis Group.
Bicchi, Antonio, et al, eds. Control Problems in Robotics. 2010. (Springer Tracts in Advanced Robotics Ser.). xiv, 280p. pap. 159.00 (978-3-642-05535-5(4), 3642055354) Springer.
Billingsley, John. Essentials of Control Techniques & Theory. 2009. (ENG., Illus.). 339p. (C). 96.95 (978-1-4200-9123-6(9), CRC Press) Taylor & Francis Group GBR. Dist: Taylor & Francis Group.
Bittanti, Sergio & Colaneri, Patrizio. Periodic Systems: Filtering & Control. 2008. (Communications & Control Engineering Ser.). (ENG., Illus.). xix, 424p. 159.00 (978-1-84800-910-3(0), 1848009100) Springer.
Blanke, Mogens, et al. Diagnosis & Fault-Tolerant Control. 2nd ed. (ENG., Illus.). xix, 672p. 2010. pap. 159.00 (978-3-642-07136-2(8), 3642071368) 2006. 159.00 (978-3-540-35652-3(5), 3540356525) Springer.
Blondel, Vincent D., et al, eds. Recent Advances in Learning & Control. 2008. (Lecture Notes in Control & Information Sciences Ser.). (Illus.). 277p. pap. 159.00 (978-1-84800-154-1(1)) Springer.
Boukas, El-Kébir. Control of Singular Systems with Random Abrupt Changes. 2010. (Communications & Control Engineering Ser.). (Illus.). xiv, 267p. pap. 139.00 (978-3-642-09375-3(2), 3642093752) Springer.
Boukas, El-Kebir. Control of Singular Systems with Random Abrupt Changes. 2008. (Communications & Control Engineering Ser.). (Illus.). 267p. 139.00 (978-3-540-74344-6(8)) Springer.
Bozzano, Marco & Villafiorita, Adolfo. Design & Safety Assessment of Critical Systems. 2010. (ENG., Illus.). 297p. 89.95 (978-1-4398-0331-8(5)) Auerbach Pubs., Inc.
Brogliato, Bernard, et al. Dissipative Systems Analysis & Control: Theory & Applications. 2nd ed. (Communications & Control Engineering Ser.). (Illus.). 2010. xiv, 576p. pap. 199.00 (978-1-84996-618-4(4), 1849966184) 2006. 576p. 199.00 (978-1-84628-516-5(X), 184628516X) Springer.
Bullo, Francesco & Lewis, Andrew D. Geometric Control of Mechanical Systems: Modeling, Analysis, & Design for Simple Mechanical Control Systems. 2010. (Texts in Applied Mathematics Ser.). (Illus.). xviii, 726p. pap. 84.95 (978-1-4419-1968-7(6), 1441919686) Springer.
Buskey, Gregg. Helicopter Automation: Learning from Human Demonstration. 2011. 256p. pap. **(978-3-8443-2665-9(0))** Lambert Academic Publishing.
Cagnol, John & Zolesio, Jean-Paul, eds. System Modeling & Optimization: Proceedings of the 21st IFIP TC7 Conference held in July 21st - 25th, 2003, Sophia Antipolis, France. 2010. (IFIP Advances in Information & Communication Technology Ser.). (Illus.). xvi, 306p. pap. 175.00 (978-1-4419-5433-6(3), 1441954333) Springer.
Capehart, Barney L., et al, eds. Web Based Enterprise Energy & Building Automation Systems. 2007. (ENG., Illus.). 423p. 194.95 (978-0-8493-8235-2(1)) Fairmont Pr., Inc.
Castillo, Oscar, et al, eds. Soft Computing for Intelligent Control & Mobile Robotics. 2010. (Studies in Computational Intelligence Ser.). 499p. 179.00 (978-3-642-15533-8(2), 3642155332) Springer.
Chakraborty, Suman. Microfluidics & Microfabrication. 2010. (Illus.). xvi, 357p. **(978-1-4419-1543-6(5))** Springer.
Chen, Ben M. Robust & H-Infinity Control. 2010. (Communications & Control Engineering Ser.). (Illus.). xii, 452p. pap. 169.00 (978-1-84996-858-4(6), 1849968586) Springer.
Chen, Ran, ed. 2011 International Conference in Electrics, Communication & Automatic Control Proceedings, 2 vols. 2012. (Lecture Notes in Electrical Engineering Ser.). (ENG., Illus.). cxl, 1746p. 469.00 (978-1-4419-8848-5(3), 1441988483) Springer.
Cheng, Daizhan, et al. Analysis & Control of Boolean Networks: A Semi-tensor Product Approach. 2010. (Communications & Control Engineering Ser.). (Illus.). xvi, 470p. 159.00 (978-0-85729-096-0(7), 0857290967) Springer.
Choudhury, Ali Ahammad Shoukat, et al. Diagnosis of Process Nonlinearities & Valve Stiction: Data Driven Approaches. (Advances in Industrial Control Ser.). (Illus.). 2010. xx, 286p. pap. 149.00 (978-3-642-09810-9(X), 364209810X) 2008. 316p. 149.00 (978-3-540-79223-9(6), 3540792236) Springer.
Christofides, Panagiotis D., et al. Networked & Distributed Predictive Control: Methods & Applications to Nonlinear Process Networks. 2011. (Advances in Industrial Control Ser.). (Illus.). xxvii, 230p. 129.00 (978-0-85729-581-1(0) 0857295810) Springer.
Christophersen, Frank J. Optimal Control of Constrained Piecewise Affine Systems. 2007. (Lecture Notes in Control & Information Sciences Ser.). (Illus.). 189p. pap. 159.00 (978-3-540-72700-2(0)) Springer.
Clévy, Cédric, et al, eds. Signal Measurement & Estimation Techniques for Micro & Nanotechnology. 2011. (ENG., Illus.). x, 242p. 129.00 (978-1-4419-9945-0(0), 1441999450) Springer.
Coello, Carlos A. Coello, et al, eds. New Trends in Electrical Engineering, Automatic Control, Computing & Communication Sciences. 2010. 516p. pap. (978-3-8325-2429-6(0)) Logos Verlag Berlin.
Colnaric, M., et al. Distributed Embedded Control Systems: Improving Dependability with Coherent Design. 2007. (Advances in Industrial Control Ser.). (Illus.). 272p. 189.00 (978-1-84800-051-3(0), 1848000510) Springer.
Colnaric, MatjaA3/4 & Verber, Domen. Distributed Embedded Control Systems: Improving Dependability with Coherent Design. 2010. (Advances in Industrial Control Ser.). (Illus.). xviii, 250p. pap. 189.00 (978-1-84996-715-0(6), 1849967156) Springer.
Cox, S., ed. Precision Livestock Farming '07. 2007. (Illus.). 312p. 102.00 (978-90-8686-023-4(0)) Wageningen Academic Publishers NLD. Dist: Enfield Publishing & Distribution Co., Inc.
Coy, Andre. Like Humans Do: A Scene Analysis Approach to Improving Robustness in Automatic Speech Recognition. 2011. (Computer Science, Technology & Applications Ser.). (Illus.). viii, 195p. 129.00 (978-1-61209-228-7(4)) Nova Science Pubs., Inc.
Cram101 Textbook Reviews. Outlines & Highlights for Automatic Control Systems by Kuo & Golnaraghi, Isbn: 0471134767. 2011. 114p. pap. 28.95 **(978-1-61812-718-1(7))** Cram101 Inc.
Cram101 Textbook Reviews. Outlines & Highlights for Control Systems Engineering by Nise, Isbn: 9780471794752. 2010. 62p. pap. 27.95 (978-1-61654-342-6(6)) Cram101 Inc.
Cram101 Textbook Reviews & Cram101 Textbook Reviews. Outlines & Highlights for Modern Control Engineering by Katsuhiko Ogat. 2011. 76p. pap. 27.95 **(978-1-61830-816-0(5))** Cram101 Inc.
—Outlines & Highlights for System Dynamics by William Palm III, Isbn: 9780073529271 0073529273. 2011. 226p. pap. 30.95 **(978-1-61490-591-2(6))** Cram101 Inc.
Cychowski, Marcin. Robust Model Predictive Control. 2009. 148p. pap. (978-3-639-01086-2(8)) VDM Verlag Dr. Mueller e.K.
Dale, Chris & Anderson, Tom, eds. Making Systems Safer: Proceedings of the Eighteenth Safety-Critical Systems Symposium, Bristol, UK, 9-11th February 2010. 2009. (ENG., Illus.). x, 273p. pap. 149.00 (978-1-84996-085-4(2), 1849960852) Springer.
Das, Abhijit & Mukhopadhyay, Siddhartha. Nonlinear Autopilot Design for Aerospace Vehicles. 2010. 228p. pap. (978-3-639-24120-4(7)) VDM Verlag Dr. Mueller e.K.
Das, Vinu V., et al, eds. Power Electronics & Instrumentation Engineering: International Conference, PEIE 2010,Kochi, Kerala, India, September 7-9, 2010, Proceedings. 2010. (Communications in Computer & Information Science Ser.). x, 114p. pap. 84.00 (978-3-642-15738-7(6), 3642157386) Springer.
Datta, Aniruddha, et al. Structure & Synthesis of PID Controllers. 2010. (Advances in Industrial Control Ser.). (Illus.). xviii, 236p. pap. 129.00 (978-1-84996-889-8(6), 1849968896) Springer.
de Brito Alves, Rita Maria, et al, eds. 10th International Symposium on Process Systems Engineering - PSE2009, 2 vols., Pt. A. 2009. (Computer Aided Chemical Engineering Ser.). (Illus.). 1224p. 0.02 (978-0-444-53435-4(0), Elsevier Science) Elsevier Science & Technology Bks.
De Silva, Clarence W. Sensors & Actuators: Control System Instrumentation. 2007. (ENG., Illus.). 696p. (C). 115.95 (978-1-4200-4483-6(4), CRC Press) Taylor & Francis Group GBR. Dist: Taylor & Francis Group.

A

Denis, B., ed. Control Technology in Elementary Education. 2007. (NATO asi Series / Computer & Systems Sciences Ser.). (Illus.). 328p. 129.00 *(978-3-540-56710-3(0))* Springer.

Desosa, Jesus. Control Systems: Analysis & Realization. 2010. 192p. pap. 23.95 *(978-1-4502-1607-4(2))* iUniverse, Inc.

Ding, Steven X. Model-Based Fault Diagnosis Techniques: Design Schemes, Algorithms, & Tools. 2008. (Illus.). 473p. pap. 109.00 *(978-3-540-76303-1(1)*, 3540763031) Springer.

Dochain, Denis. Automatic Control of Bioprocesses. 2007. 256p. 150.00 *(978-1-905209-36-1(3))* ISTE/Hermes Science Publishing GBR. Dist: Independent Pubs. Group.

Doebelin, Ernest. Instrumentation Design Studies. 2010. (ENG., Illus.). 725p. 119.95 *(978-1-4398-1948-7(3)*, CRC Press) Taylor & Francis Group GBR. Dist: Taylor & Francis Group.

Dolgui, Alexandre, et al, eds. Information Control Problems in Manufacturing 2006: A Proceedings Volume from the 12th IFAC International Symposium, St Etienne, France, 17-19 May 2006, 3 vols. 2007. (IFAC Proceedings Volumes Ser.). (ENG., Illus.). 2480p. pap. 265.00 *(978-0-08-044654-7(X)*, Elsevier Science) Elsevier Science & Technology Bks.

Dragan, Vasile, et al. Mathematical Methods in Robust Control of Discrete-Time Linear Stochastic Systems. (Illus.). 2010. x, 346p. *(978-1-4419-0630-4(4))* 2009. (ENG., x, 348p. 119.00 *(978-1-4419-0629-8(0)*, 1441906290) Springer.

—Mathematical Methods in Robust Control of Linear Stochastic Systems. 2010. (Mathematical Concepts & Methods in Science & Engineering Ser.). (Illus.). xii, 312p. pap. 97.00 *(978-1-4419-2143-7(5)*, 1441921435) Springer.

Driankov, D., et al, eds. Fuzzy Logic & Fuzzy Control: IJCAI '91 Workshops on Fuzzy Logic & Fuzzy Control, Sydney, Australia, August 24, 1991. Proceedings. 2007. (Lecture Notes in Computer Science Ser.). 180p. per. 49.95 *(978-3-540-58279-3(7))* Springer.

Dua, Vivek, et al, eds. Multi-Parametric Model-Based Control: Theory & Applications. 2007. (Process Systems Engineering Ser.). (ENG., Illus.). 275p. 235.00 *(978-3-527-31692-2(2)*, Wiley-VCH) Wiley, John & Sons, Inc.

Duan, Guang-Ren. Analysis & Design of Descriptor Linear Systems. 2010. (Advances in Mechanics & Mathematics Ser.). (Illus.). xix, 494p. 84.95 *(978-1-4419-6396-3(0)*, 1441963960) Springer.

Ducard, Guillaume. Fault-tolerant Flight Control & Guidance Systems: Practical Methods for Small Unmanned Aerial Vehicles. 2009. (Advances in Industrial Control Ser.). (ENG., Illus.). xxii, 266p. 149.00 *(978-1-84882-560-4(9))* Springer.

Dukkipati, Rao V. Analysis & Design of Control Systems Using MATLAB. 2nd ed. 2009. (Illus.). xi, 449p. *(978-1-906574-19-2(7))* New Age Science, Ltd.

Eidson, John C. Measurement, Control, & Communication Using IEEE 1588. 2010. (Advances in Industrial Control Ser.). (Illus.). xviii, 283p. pap. 149.00 *(978-1-84996-565-1(X)*, 184996565X) Springer.

Espinosa Oviedo, Jairo Jose, et al. Fuzzy Logic, Identification & Predictive Control. 2010. (Advances in Industrial Control Ser.). (Illus.). xix, 263p. pap. 179.00 *(978-1-84996-931-4(0)*, 1849969310) Springer.

Famouri, Parviz, et al. Reduced Order Systems. 2006. (Lecture Notes in Control & Information Sciences Ser.). (Illus.). xiii, 202p. 159.00 *(978-3-540-34358-5(X)*, 354034358X) Springer.

Fang, Jiancheng & Wang, Zhongyu. Seventh International Symposium on Instrumentation & Control Technology: Optoelectronic Technology & Instruments, Control Theory & Automation, & Space Exploration: 10-13 October 2008, Beijing, China. 2008. (Proceedings of SPIE Ser.). (Illus.). 660p. pap. 130.00 *(978-0-8194-7363-9(4))* SPIE.

—Seventh International Symposium on Instrumentation & Control Technology: Sensors & Instruments, Computer Simulation, & Artificial Intelligence: 10-13 October, 2008, Beijing, China. 2008. (Proceedings of SPIE Ser.). (Illus.). 642p. pap. 130.00 *(978-0-8194-7361-5(8))* SPIE.

—Sixth International Symposium on Instrumentation & Control Technology: Sensors, Automatic Measurement, & Computer Simulation: 13-15 October, 2006, Beijing, China, 2 vols. 2006. (Proceedings of SPIE Ser.). (Illus.). 1266p. pap. 200.00 *(978-0-8194-6453-8(8))* SPIE.

Fehse, Wigbert. Automated Rendezvous & Docking of Spacecraft. 2008. (Cambridge Aerospace Ser.). (ENG.). 516p. pap. 105.00 *(978-0-521-08986-9(7))* Cambridge Univ. Pr.

Feng, Gang. Analysis & Synthesis of Fuzzy Control Systems: A Model Based Approach. 2010. (Automation & Control Engineering Ser.). (ENG., Illus.). 299p. 129.95 *(978-1-4200-9264-6(2)*, CRC Press) Taylor & Francis Group GBR. Dist: Taylor & Francis Group.

Fernandez de Canete, Javier, et al. System Engineering & Automation: An Interactive Educational Approach. 2011. (Illus.). xii, 256p. 129.00 *(978-3-642-20229-2(2)*, 3642202292) Springer.

Findeisen, Rolf, et al, eds. Assessment & Future Directions of Nonlinear Model Predictive Control. 2007. (Lecture Notes in Control & Information Sciences Ser.). xii, 642p. 239.00 *(978-3-540-72698-2(5))* Springer.

Flammini, Francesco, ed. Dependability Assurance of Real-Time Embedded Control Systems. 2009. (Applied Statistical Science Ser.). pap. 43.00 *(978-1-61728-502-8(1)*, Nova Novinka) Nova Science Pubs., Inc.

Fortuna, Luigi & Frasca, Mattia, eds. Optimal & Robust Control: Advanced Topics with Matlab(r). 2012. (ENG., Illus.). 251p. 99.95 ***(978-1-4665-0191-1(X)***, CRC Press) Taylor & Francis Group GBR. Dist: Taylor & Francis Group.

Fridman, Leonid, et al, eds. Sliding Modes after the first Decade of the 21st Century: State of the Art. 2011. (Lecture Notes in Control & Information Sciences Ser.). (ENG., Illus.). xxii, 598p. pap. 199.00 ***(978-3-642-22163-7(7)***, 3642221637) Springer.

Gabrys, Bogdan, et al. Knowledge-Based Intelligent Information & Engineering Systems: 10th International Conference, KES 2006, Bournemouth, UK, October 9-11 2006, Proceedings, Part I, 3 vols. 2007. (Lecture Notes in Computer Science Ser.). (Illus.). 1297p. pap. 149.00 *(978-3-540-46535-5(9)*, 3540465359) Springer.

—Knowledge-Based Intelligent Information & Engineering Systems: 10th International Conference, KES 2006, Bournemouth, UK, October 9-11 2006, Proceedings, Part II, 3 vols. 2006. (Lecture Notes in Computer Science Ser.). (Illus.). 1335p. pap. 159.00 *(978-3-540-46537-9(5)*, 3540465375) Springer.

—Knowledge-Based Intelligent Information & Engineering Systems: 10th International Conference, KES 2006, Bournemouth, UK, October 9-11, 2006 Proceedings, Part III, 3 vols. 2007. (Lecture Notes in Computer Science Ser.). (Illus.). 1301p. pap. 179.00 *(978-3-540-46542-3(1)*, 3540465421) Springer.

Gajic, Zoran & Lelic, M. Modern Control Systems Engineering. 2012. (Dover Books on Electrical Engineering Ser.). (ENG.). 448p. pap. 19.95 *(978-0-486-47455-7(0))* Dover Pubns., Inc.

Gajic, Zoran, et al. Optimal Control: Weakly Coupled Systems & Applications. 2008. (Automation & Control Engineering Ser.). (ENG., Illus.). 320p. (C). 145.95 *(978-0-8493-7429-6(4)*, CRC Press) Taylor & Francis Group GBR. Dist: Taylor & Francis Group.

Gao, Wei & Dian, Songyi. Precision Control of Planar Motion Stages. 2010. 160p. pap. *(978-3-639-22037-7(4))* VDM Verlag Dr. Mueller e.K.

Garnier, Hugues & Wang, Liuping, eds. Identification of Continuous-Time Models from Sampled Data. 2008. (Advances in Industrial Control Ser.). (ENG., Illus.). xxvi, 413p. 219.00 *(978-1-84800-160-2(6)*, 1848001606) Springer.

—Identification of Continuous-time Models from Sampled Data. 2010. (Advances in Industrial Control Ser.). (Illus.). xxvi, 413p. pap. 219.00 *(978-1-84996-740-2(7)*, 1849967407) Springer.

Gegov, Alexander. Distributed Fuzzy Control of Multivariable Systems. 2010. (International Series in Intelligent Technologies Ser.). 204p. pap. 219.00 *(978-90-481-4652-9(6)*, 9048146526) Springer.

Ghasemi-Nejhad, Mehrdad. Active & Passive Smart Structures & Integrated Systems 2010. 2010. (Proceedings of SPIE Ser.). 958p. pap. 180.00 ***(978-0-8194-8058-3(4))*** SPIE.

—Active & Passive Smart Structures & Integrated Systems 2011. 2011. (Proceedings of SPIE Ser.). 914p. pap. 160.00 ***(978-0-8194-8539-7(X))*** SPIE.

Giri, Fouad & Bai, Er-Wei, eds. Block-oriented Nonlinear System Identification. 2010. (Lecture Notes in Control & Information Sciences Ser.). (Illus.). xix, 431p. pap. 159.00 *(978-1-84996-512-5(9)*, 1849965129) Springer.

Giua, Alessandro, et al, eds. Analysis & Design of Hybrid Systems 2006: A Proceedings Volume from the 2nd Ifac Conference, Alghero, Italy, 7-9 June 2006. 2007. (IPV - IFAC Proceedings Volume Ser.). (ENG., Illus.). 448p. pap. 230.00 *(978-0-08-044613-4(2)*, Elsevier Science) Elsevier Science & Technology Bks.

Goble, William M. Control Systems Safety Evaluation & Reliability. 3rd rev. ed. 2010. (ENG.). 458p. pap. 109.00 *(978-1-934394-80-9(7))* ISA.

Golnaraghi, Farid & Kuo, Benjamin C. Automatic Control Systems. 9th ed. 2009. (ENG., Illus.). 800p. (C). 197.95 *(978-0-470-04896-2(4)*, Wiley) Wiley, John & Sons, Inc.

Gomis i Bellmunt, Oriol & Campanile, Flavio. Design Rules for Actuators in Active Mechanical Systems. 2010. (ENG., Illus.). xxiv, 205p. 129.00 *(978-1-84882-613-7(3)*, 1848826133) Springer.

Goodwin, Graham, et al. Constrained Control & Estimation: An Optimisation Approach. 2010. (Communications & Control Engineering Ser.). (Illus.). xviii, 411p. pap. 159.00 *(978-1-84996-883-6(7)*, 1849968837) Springer.

Graune, Uwe, et al. Logo! Practical Training. 2nd ed. 2009. (ENG., Illus.). 112p. pap. 22.50 *(978-3-89578-338-8(2)*, Wiley-VCH) Wiley, John & Sons, Inc.

Green, Michael, et al. Linear Robust Control. 2012. (Dover Books on Electrical Engineering Ser.). (ENG.). 560p. pap. 29.95 ***(978-0-486-48836-3(5))*** Dover Pubns., Inc.

Grüne, Lars & Pannek, Jargen. Nonlinear Model Predictive Control: Theory & Algorithms. 2011. (Communications & Control Engineering Ser.). (Illus.). xii, 370p. 159.00 *(978-0-85729-500-2(4)*, 0857295004) Springer.

Gulder, Jürgen, et al. Sliding Mode Control in Electro-Mechanical Systems. 2nd rev. ed. 2009. (Automation & Control Engineering Ser.). (ENG., Illus.). 503p. 154.95 *(978-1-4200-6560-2(2)*, CRC Press) Taylor & Francis Group GBR. Dist: Taylor & Francis Group.

Guo, Lei & Wang, Hong. Stochastic Distribution Control System Design: A Convex Optimization Approach. 2010. (Advances in Industrial Control Ser.). (ENG., Illus.). xvi, 182p. 149.00 *(978-1-84996-029-8(1)*, 1849960291) Springer.

Ha, Kwangtae. A Combined Piezoelectric & Composite Actuator. 2009. 124p. pap. *(978-3-639-15523-5(8))* VDM Verlag Dr. Mueller e.K.

Haber, Robert, et al. Predictive Control in Process Engineering: From the Basics to the Applications. 2011. (ENG., Illus.). 629p. 190.00 *(978-3-527-31492-8(X)*, Wiley-VCH) Wiley, John & Sons, Inc.

Haddad, Wassim M. Nonlinear Dynamical Systems & Control: A Lyapunov-Based Approach. 2008. (ENG., Illus.). 976p. (C). 115.00 *(978-0-691-13329-4(8))* Princeton Univ. Pr.

Halvarsson, Bjorn. Interaction Analysis in Multivariable Control Systems: Applications to Bioreactors for Nitrogen Removal. 2010. (Uppsala Dissertations from the Faculty of Science & Technology Ser.). (Illus.). 162p. pap. 52.50 *(978-91-554-7781-3(X))* Uppsala Universitet/Acta Universitatis Uppsaliensis SWE. Dist: Coronet Bks.

Hendricks, Elbert, et al. Linear Systems Control: Deterministic & Stochastic Methods. (ENG., Illus.). xx, 556p. 2010. pap. 129.00 *(978-3-642-09721-8(9)*, 3642097219) 2008. 129.00 *(978-3-540-78485-2(3)*, 3540784853) Springer.

Higuchi, Toshiro, et al, eds. Next-Generation Actuators Leading Breakthroughs. 2009. (ENG., Illus.). xxii, 438p. 169.00 *(978-1-84882-990-9(6)*, 1848829906) Springer.

Hippe, Peter. Windup in Control: Its Effects & Their Prevention. 2010. (Advances in Industrial Control Ser.). (Illus.). xviii, 314p. pap. 199.00 *(978-1-84996-579-8(X)*, 184996579X) Springer.

Hollender, Martin. Collaborative Process Automation Systems. 2009. (ENG.). 375p. pap. 99.00 *(978-1-936007-10-3(X))* ISA.

Hruz, B. & Zhou, M C. Modeling & Control of Discrete-Event Dynamic Systems: With Petri Nets & Other Tools. 2007. (Advanced Textbooks in Control & Signal Processing Ser.). (Illus.). 341p. per. 79.95 *(978-1-84628-872-2(X))* Springer.

Huang, Biao & Kadali, Ramesh. Dynamic Modeling, Predictive Control & Performance Monitoring: A Data-Driven Subspace Approach. 2008. (Lecture Notes in Control & Information Sciences Ser.). (Illus.). 272p. (C). 159.00 *(978-1-84800-232-6(7))* Springer.

Huang, Dan & Nguang, Sing Kiong. Robust Control for Uncertain Networked Control Systems with Random Delays. 2009. (Lecture Notes in Control & Information Sciences Ser.). (Illus.). xii, 162p. pap. 149.00 *(978-1-84882-677-9(X)*, 184882677X) Springer.

Huang, Sunan & Lee, Tong Heng. Applied Predictive Control. 2010. (Advances in Industrial Control Ser.). (Illus.). xvii, 264p. pap. 149.00 *(978-1-84996-864-5(0)*, 1849968640) Springer.

Hughes, John M. Real World Instrumentation with Python: Automated Data Acquisition & Control Systems. 2010. (ENG., Illus.). 624p. pap. 54.99 *(978-0-596-80956-0(5))* O'Reilly Media, Inc.

IEEE Staff. 2007 5th Student Conference on Research & Development. 2007. pap. 224.00 *(978-1-4244-1469-7(5))* IEEE.

—2007 International Conference on Control, Automation & Systems. 2007. pap. 1052.00 *(978-1-4244-1465-9(2))* IEEE.

—2008 IEEE International Conference on Automation Science & Engineering. 2008. pap. 354.00 *(978-1-4244-2022-3(9))* IEEE.

—2008 IEEE International Symposium on Computer-Aided Control System Design. 2008. pap. 206.00 *(978-1-4244-2221-0(3))* IEEE.

IEEE Staff, ed. 2007 IEEE Conference on Control Applications. 2007. pap. 412.00 *(978-1-4244-0442-1(8)*, 07CH37809) IEEE.

Institute of Electrical and Electronics Engineers Staff, contrib. by. 2007 International Symposium on Computational Intelligence in Robotics & Automation. 2007. pap. 296.00 *(978-1-4244-0789-7(3)*, 07EX1610) IEEE.

Intelligent Information Technology Application Research Association Staff & IEEE Computer Society Staff, contrib. by. CASE 2009: 2009 IITA International Conference on Control, Automation & Systems Engineering: Proceedings, 11-12 July 2009, Zhangjiajie, China. 2009. (Illus.). xix, 680p. pap. ***(978-0-7695-3728-3(6))*** IEEE Computer Society Pr.

ISA - Instrumentation Systems and Automation Society Staff, compiled by. Isa Expo 2006. 2007. 192p. pap. 186.00 *(978-1-60423-721-4(X))* Curran Assocs., Inc.

Jahanmir, Said. Proceedings of the ASME Dynamic Systems & Control Division: Presented at [the] 2006 ASME International Mechanical Engineering Congress & Exposition: November 5-10, 2006, Chicago, Illinois, 2 vols. 2007. (Illus.). pap. *(978-0-7918-4768-8(3))* American Society of Mechanical Engineers, The.

Jain, Lakhmi, ed. Knowledge-Based Intelligent Information & Engineering Systems: KES 2007 - WIRN 2007 Part I: 11th International Conference, KES 2007 XVII Italian Workshop on Neural Networks Vietri sul Mare, Italy, September 12-14, 2007 Proceedings, 3 vols. 2007. (Lecture Notes in Computer Science Ser.). (Illus.). 882p. pap. 149.00 *(978-3-540-74817-5(2))* Springer.

—Knowledge-Based Intelligent Information & Engineering Systems: KES 2007 - WIRN 2007 Part III: 11th International Conference, KES 2007 XVII Italian Workshop on Neural Networks Vietri sul Mare, Italy, September 12-14, 2007 Proceedings, 3 vols. 2007. (Lecture Notes in Computer Science Ser.). (Illus.). 1126p. pap. 169.00 *(978-3-540-74828-1(8))* Springer.

—Knowledge-Based Intelligent Information & Engineering Systems: KES 2007-WIRN 2007: 11th International Conference, KES 2007 XVII Italian Workshop on Neural Networks Vietri sul Mare, Italy, September 12-14, 2007 Proceedings, Part II, 3 vols. 2007. (Lecture Notes in Computer Science Ser.). (Illus.). 1380p. pap. 189.00 *(978-3-540-74826-7(1))* Springer.

Jairath, Anoop. Control Systems a State Variable Approach. 2008. (ENG.). 364p. 109.95 *(978-1-4200-7757-5(0)*, CRC Press) Taylor & Francis Group GBR. Dist: Taylor & Francis Group.

Janocha, Hartmut, ed. Actuators: Basics & Applications. 2010. (ENG., Illus.). xiv, 343p. pap. 209.00 *(978-3-642-08266-5(1)*, 3642082661) Springer.

—Adaptronics & Smart Structures: Basics, Materials, Design, & Applications. 2nd ed. 2010. (ENG., Illus.). xviii, 544p. pap. 239.00 *(978-3-642-09110-0(5)*, 3642091105) Springer.

Jantzen, Jan. Foundations of Fuzzy Control. 2007. (ENG., Illus.). 230p. 110.00 *(978-0-470-02963-3(3)*, Wiley) Wiley, John & Sons, Inc.

Jatuphol, Chawapatnakul. Redesign of Control Center for Supporting Operators' Efficiency: Discussion on Control Centers for Future Concept Improvement. 2011. 84p. pap. ***(978-3-639-33450-0(7))*** VDM Verlag Dr. Mueller e.K.

Johnson, Michael A. & Moradi, Mohammad H., eds. PID Control: New Identification & Design Methods. 2010. (Illus.). xxviii, 560p. pap. 149.00 *(978-1-84996-897-3(7)*, 1849968977) Springer.

Jung, Sooyong. The Gradient Based Nonlinear Model Predictive Control System. 2009. 136p. pap. *(978-3-639-21241-9(X))* VDM Verlag Dr. Mueller e.K.

Kaczorek, Tadeusz. Polynomial & Rational Matrices: Applications in Dynamical Systems Theory. 2006. (Communications & Control Engineering Ser.). (Illus.). 503p. 199.00 *(978-1-84628-604-9(2)*, 1846286042) Springer.

Karvinen, Kimmo & Karvinen, Tero. Make - Arduino Bots & Gadgets: Six Embedded Projects with Open Source Hardware & Software - Build Robots & Other Electronic Devices. 2011. (ENG., Illus.). 296p. pap. 34.99 *(978-1-4493-8971-0(6))* O'Reilly Media, Inc.

Khan, M. Saleem & Aslam, M. Applications of Fuzzy Logic Time Control in Industrial Automation: A Simplified Design Approach. 2011. 116p. pap. ***(978-3-639-34207-9(0))*** VDM Verlag Dr. Mueller e.K.

Koenig, David M. Practical Control Engineering: Guide for Engineers, Managers, & Practitioners. 2009. (ENG., Illus.). 508p. (C). 99.95 *(978-0-07-160613-4(0)*, 0071606130) McGraw-Hill Professional Publishing.

Kopacek, Peter, ed. Improving Stability in Developing Nations Through Automation 2006. 2007. (IPV - IFAC Proceedings Volume Ser.). (ENG., Illus.). 128p. pap. 96.95 *(978-0-08-045406-1(2)*, Elsevier Science) Elsevier Science & Technology Bks.

Krassi, Boris. Dynamic Virtual Prototyping for Control Engineering: Concepts, Methods, Applications. 2008. 196p. pap. *(978-3-639-08926-4(X))* VDM Verlag Dr. Mueller e.K.

Langner, Ralph. Robust Control System Networks: How to Achieve Reliable Control after Stuxnet. 2011. 206p. 79.95 ***(978-1-60650-300-3(6))*** Momentum Pr.

Laudon, Matthew & Romanowicz, Bart, eds. NSTI Nanotech: Technical Proceedings: Volume 1. 2007. (Illus.). 850p. per. 119.95 *(978-0-9767985-6-9(5))* Taylor & Francis Group.

—NSTI Nanotech: Technical Proceedings: Volume 2. 2007. (Illus.). 872p. per. 119.95 *(978-0-9767985-7-6(3))* Taylor & Francis Group.

Lee, Gary, ed. Advances in Automation & Robotics, Vol. 1: Selected papers from the 2011 International Conference on Automation & Robotics (ICAR 2011), Dubai, December 1-2 2011, 2 vols. 2011. (Lecture Notes in Electrical Engineering Ser.). (ENG., Illus.). xvi, 668p. 229.00 ***(978-3-642-25552-6(3)***, 3642255523) Springer.

—Advances in Automation & Robotics, Vol. 2: Selected papers from the 2011 International Conference on Automation & Robotics (ICAR 2011), Dubai, December 1-2 2011. 2011. (Lecture Notes in Electrical Engineering Ser.). (ENG., Illus.). xvi, 656p. 229.00 ***(978-3-642-25645-5(7)***, 3642256457) Springer.

Levine, William S. The Control Handbook: Control System Applications, 3 vols. 2nd rev. ed. 2010. (Electrical Engineering Handbook Ser.). (ENG., Illus.). 942p. 89.95 *(978-1-4200-7360-7(5)*, CRC Press) Taylor & Francis Group GBR. Dist: Taylor & Francis Group.

—The Control Handbook: Control System Fundamentals, 3 vols. 2nd rev. ed. 2010. (Electrical Engineering Handbook Ser.). (ENG., Illus.). 786p. 89.95 *(978-1-4200-7362-1(1)*, CRC Press) Taylor & Francis Group GBR. Dist: Taylor & Francis Group.

—The Control Systems Handbook: Control System Advanced Methods, 3 vols. 2nd rev. ed. 2010. (Electrical Engineering Handbook Ser.). (ENG., Illus.). 1798p. 149.95 *(978-1-4200-7364-5(8)*, CRC Press) Taylor & Francis Group GBR. Dist: Taylor & Francis Group.

Levine, William S., ed. The Control Handbook, 3 vols., Set. 2nd rev. ed. 2010. (Electrical Engineering Handbook Ser.). (ENG., Illus.). 3526p. 319.95 *(978-1-4200-7366-9(4)*, CRC Press) Taylor & Francis Group GBR. Dist: Taylor & Francis Group.

Lilly, John H. Fuzzy Control & Identification. 2010. (ENG., Illus.). 231p. 105.00 *(978-0-470-54277-4(2))*; 99.95 *(978-0-470-87424-0(4))* Wiley, John & Sons, Inc. (Wiley).

Lin, Feng. Robust Control Design: An Optimal Control Approach. 2007. (Rsp Ser.). (ENG., Illus.). 378p. 140.00 *(978-0-470-03191-9(3)*, Wiley-Interscience) Wiley, John & Sons, Inc.

Liu, Jinkun & Wang, Xinhua. Advanced Sliding Mode Control for Mechanical Systems: Design, Analysis & MATLAB Simulation. 2012. (ENG., Illus.). 360p. 169.00 *(978-3-642-20906-2(8)*, 3642209068) Springer.

Lokhorst, C. & Groot Koerkamp, P. W. G., eds. Precision livestock Farming '09. 2009. (Illus.). 368p. 108.00 *(978-90-8686-112-5(1))* Wageningen Academic Publishers NLD. Dist: Enfield Publishing & Distribution Co., Inc.

Louis, Jean-Paul. Control of Synchronous Actuators. 2011. (ENG., Illus.). 432p. 195.00 *(978-1-84821-273-2(9)*, Wiley-ISTE) Wiley, John & Sons, Inc.

Lunze, Jan & Lamnabhi-Lagarrigue, Françoise, eds. Handbook of Hybrid Systems Control: Theory, Tools, Applications. 2009. (ENG., Illus.). 582p. 99.00 *(978-0-521-76505-3(6))* Cambridge Univ. Pr.

Mackenroth, Uwe. Robust Control Systems: Theory & Case Studies. 2010. (ENG., Illus.). xvi, 519p. pap. 149.00 *(978-3-642-05891-2(4)*, 3642058914) Springer.

Magni, Lalo, et al, eds. Nonlinear Model Predictive Control: Towards New Challenging Applications. 2009. (Lecture Notes in Control & Information Sciences Ser.). (ENG., Illus.). xii, 572p. pap. 139.00 *(978-3-642-01093-4(8))* Springer.

Mahnke, Wolfgang, et al. OPC Unified Architecture. 2009. (ENG., Illus.). xxiii, 339p. 69.95 *(978-3-540-68898-3(6)*, 3540688986) Springer.

Manoonpong, Poramate. Neural Preprocessing & Control of Reactive Walking Machines: Towards Versatile Artificial Perception-Action Systems. (Cognitive Technologies Ser.). (Illus.). 2010. xvi, 188p. pap. 99.00 *(978-3-642-08835-3(X)*, 364208835X) 2007. 185p. 99.00 *(978-3-540-68802-0(1))* Springer.

McMillan, Gregory K. Essentials of Modern Measurements & Final Elements in the Process Industry. 2010. (ENG., Illus.). 571p. pap. 119.00 *(978-1-936007-23-3(1))* ISA.

Mellodge, Patricia. Model Abstraction in Dynamical Systems: Application to Mobile Robot Control. 2008. (Lecture Notes in Control & Information Sciences Ser.). (ENG., Illus.). xiv, 118p. pap. 129.00 *(978-3-540-70792-9(1)*, 3540707921) Springer.

Michel, Robert. Flexray Applications in Control Loops Focussing on Steer-by-Wire Models. 2008. 108p. pap. *(978-3-639-02985-7(2))* VDM Verlag Dr. Mueller e.K.

Michels, Kai, et al. Fuzzy Control: Fundamentals, Stability & Design of Fuzzy Controllers. 2010. (Studies in Fuzziness & Soft Computing Ser.). (Illus.). x, 411p. pap. 189.00 *(978-3-642-06863-8(4)*, 3642068634) Springer.

Michiels, Wim, et al. Stability & Stabilization of Time-Delay Systems: An Eigenvalue-Based Approach. 2007. (Advances in Design & Control Ser.). (ENG., Illus.). 400p. (C). pap. 99.00 *(978-0-89871-632-0(2))* Society for Industrial and Applied Mathematics.

Mignani. Sensors & Microsystems (10th Italian) 2008. 200.00 *(978-981-283-352-5(8))* World Scientific Publishing Co., Inc.

Mohammadpour, Javad & Scherer, Carsten W., eds. Control of Linear Parameter Varying Systems with Applications. 2012. (ENG., Illus.). xviii, 547p. 179.00 ***(978-1-4614-1832-0(1)***, 1461418321) Springer.

Monje, Concepción A., et al. Fractional-order Systems & Controls: Fundamentals & Applications. 2010. (Advances in Industrial Control Ser.). (Illus.). xxvi, 415p. 209.00 *(978-1-84996-334-3(7)*, 1849963347) Springer.

Morris, Alan S. & Langari, Reza. Measurement & Instrumentation: Theory & Application. 2011. (ENG., Illus.). 640p. (C). pap. 99.95 *(978-0-12-381960-4(1)*, Butterworth-Heinemann) Elsevier Science & Technology Bks.

Muhammad, Abubakr. Graphs, Simplicial Complexes, & Beyond. 2008. 192p. pap. *(978-3-8364-9186-0(9))* VDM Verlag Dr. Mueller e.K.

Murphy, Sean A., ed. Glow Discharges & Tokamaks. 2010. (Physics Research & Technology Ser.). (Illus.). xii, 434p. 145.00 *(978-1-61668-352-8(X))* Nova Science Pubs., Inc.

Nagrath, I. J. & Gopal, M. Control Systems Engineering. 5th ed. 2008. (ENG., Illus.). 900p. 95.00 *(978-1-84829-003-7(9))* Anshan GBR. Dist: Publishers Storage & Shipping.

Nano Science &, Tech Inst., ed. Technical Proceedings of the 2004 NSTI Nanotechnology Conference & Trade Show, Volume 3. 2007. 79.95 *(978-0-9728422-9-7(2))* Taylor & Francis Group.

—Technical Proceedings of the 2005 NSTI Nanotechnology Conference & Trade Show, Volume 1. 2007. 109.95 *(978-0-9767985-0-7(6))* Taylor & Francis Group.

—Technical Proceedings of the 2006, 2005, & 2004 Nanotechnology Conferences & Trade Shows. 2007. 950.00 *(978-1-4200-6369-1(3))* Taylor & Francis Group.

—Technical Proceedings of the 2006, 2005, & 2004 Nanotechnology Conferences & Trade Shows CD-ROMs. 2007. 750.00 *(978-1-4200-6370-7(7))* Taylor & Francis Group.

—Technical Proceedings of the 2006 NSTI Nanotechnology Conference & Trade Show on CD-ROM. 2007. ring bd. 299.95 *(978-0-9767985-9-0(X))* Taylor & Francis Group.

—Technical Proceedings of the 2006 NSTI Nanotechnology Conference & Trade Show, Volume 3. 2007. 119.95 *(978-0-9767985-8-3(1))* Taylor & Francis Group.

—Technical Proceedings of the 2007 Nanotechnology Conference & Trade Show, Nanotech 2007, Volume 4. 2007. 199.95 *(978-1-4200-6457-5(6))* Taylor & Francis Group.

Nano Science and Technology Institute, creator. NSTI Nanotech: Technical Proceedings: Volume 2. 2007. (Illus.). 788p. per. 109.95 *(978-0-9767985-1-4(4))* Taylor & Francis Group.

—NSTI Nanotech: Technical Proceedings: Volume 3. 2007. (Illus.). 766p. per. 109.95 *(978-0-9767985-2-1(2))* Taylor & Francis Group.

—NSTI Nanotech: Technical Proceedings, Volume 1: The Nanotechnology Conference & Trade Show: Boston, March 7-11 2004. 2007. (Illus.). 501p. per. 79.95 *(978-0-9728422-7-3(6))* Taylor & Francis Group.

—Nsti Nanotech: Technical Proceedings, Volume 2. 2007. (Illus.). 501p. per. 79.95 *(978-0-9728422-8-0(4))* Taylor & Francis Group.

Natale, Ciro. Interaction Control of Robot Manipulators: Six-degrees-of-freedom Tasks. 2010. (Springer Tracts in Advanced Robotics Ser.). (Illus.). xiv, 108p. pap. 99.00 *(978-3-642-05519-5(2)*, 3642055192) Springer.

Nath, Nitendra. Nonlinear Control Techniques for Robot Manipulators - Nonlinear Control of Mechatronic Systems with Applications in Robotics. 2008. 136p. pap. *(978-3-8364-8976-8(7))* VDM Verlag Dr. Mueller e.K.

Nersesov, Sergey G. & Haddad, Wassim M. Impulsive & Hybrid Dynamical Systems: Stability, Dissipativity, & Control. 2006. (Princeton Series in Applied Mathematics). (ENG., Illus.). 520p. (C). 87.50 *(978-0-691-12715-6(8))* Princeton Univ. Pr.

Nise, Norman S. Control Systems Engineering. 6th ed. 2010. (ENG.). 926p. (C). 196.95 *(978-0-470-54756-4(1)*, Wiley) Wiley, John & Sons, Inc.

—Control Systems Engineering, Sixth Edition Binder Ready Version. 2010. (ENG.). 944p. (C). ring bd. 123.95 *(978-0-470-91769-5(5)*, Wiley) Wiley, John & Sons, Inc.

Normey-Rico, Julio E. & Camacho, Eduardo F. Control of Dead-Time Processes. 2007. (Advanced Textbooks in Control & Signal Processing Ser.). (Illus.). 462p. per. 139.00 *(978-1-84628-828-9(2))* Springer.

Noura, Hassan, et al. Fault-tolerant Control Systems: Design & Practical Applications. 2009. (Advances in Industrial Control Ser.). (ENG., Illus.). xxi, 233p. 189.00 *(978-1-84882-652-6(4)*, 1848826524) Springer.

O'Brien, Wayne. Breakdowns in Controls in Automated Systems. 2008. 392p. pap. *(978-3-639-08727-7(5))* VDM Verlag Dr. Mueller e.K.

Ocampo-Martinez, Carlos. Model Predictive Control of Wastewater System. 2010. (Advances in Industrial Control Ser.). (Illus.). xxx, 217p. 149.00 *(978-1-84996-352-7(5)*, 1849963525) Springer.

O'Dwyer, Aidan. Pi & Pid Controller Tuning Rules. 3rd ed. 2009. (Illus.). 624p. instr.'s hndbk. ed. 201.00 *(978-1-84816-242-6(1))* Imperial College Pr. GBR. Dist: World Scientific Publishing Co., Inc.

Ogata, Katsuhiko. Control Engineers. 2007. (ENG.). 448p. (C). pap. 88.00 *(978-0-13-615077-0(2)*, Prentice Hall) Prentice Hall PTR.

—Modern Control Engineering. 5th ed. 2009. (ENG.). 912p. (C). 183.00 *(978-0-13-615673-4(8)*, Prentice Hall) Prentice Hall PTR.

Olalla, Carlos, et al. Robust Linear Control of Dc-Dc Converters. 2010. 224p. pap. *(978-3-639-24070-2(7))* VDM Verlag Dr. Mueller e.K.

Orlov, Yury V. & Orlov, IU V. Discontinuous Systems: Lyapunov Analysis & Robust Synthesis under Uncertainty Conditions. 2008. (Communications & Control Engineering Ser.). (ENG., Illus.). xx, 320p. 159.00 *(978-1-84800-983-7(6)*, 1848009836) Springer.

Ortega, Romeo, et al. Passivity-based Control of Euler-Lagrange Systems: Mechanical, Electrical & Electromechanical Applications. 2010. (Communications & Control Engineering Ser.). (Illus.). xxxiv, 543p. pap. 199.00 *(978-1-84996-852-2(7)*, 1849968527) Springer.

Ouyang, Hua. Networked Predictive Control Systems. 2010. 164p. pap. *(978-3-8383-5839-0(2))* Lambert Academic Publishing.

Page, Tom & Thorsteinsson, Gisli. Product Design Considerations for Automated Manufacturing. 2010. 60p. pap. *(978-3-8383-7713-1(3))* Lambert Academic Publishing.

Palm, Rainer, et al. Model Based Fuzzy Control: Fuzzy Gain Schedulers & Sliding Mode Fuzzy Controllers. 2010. (Illus.). xiii, 184p. pap. 74.95 *(978-3-642-08262-7(9)*, 3642082629) Springer.

Palm, William J., III. System Dynamics. 2nd ed. 2009. (ENG., Illus.). 848p. (C). 220.00 *(978-0-07-352927-1(3)*, 0073529273, McGraw-Hill Science, Engineering & Mathematics) McGraw-Hill Higher Education.

Pathak, Yashwant Vishnupant. Handbook of Nutraceuticals Vol. II: Scale-Up, Processing & Automation. 2011. (ENG., Illus.). 593p. 169.95 *(978-1-4398-2368-2(5)*, CRC Press) Taylor & Francis Group GBR. Dist: Taylor & Francis Group.

Patino Guevara, Diego Alejandro. Control of Limit Cycles in Hybrid Dynamical Systems. 2010. 172p. pap. *(978-3-8383-0252-2(4))* Lambert Academic Publishing.

Perdikaris, G. Computer Controlled Systems: Theory & Applications. 2010. (Intelligent Systems, Control & Automation: Science & Engineering Ser.). (Illus.). 492p. pap. 319.00 *(978-90-481-4100-5(1)*, 9048141001) Springer.

Pham, D. T. Innovative Production Machines & Systems: Fourth I*PROMS Virtual International Conference, 1-14 July 2008. Pham, D. T. et al, eds. 2009. (ENG., Illus.). 650p. 289.95 *(978-1-4398-0117-8(7))* Whittles Publishing GBR. Dist: Taylor & Francis Group.

Pham, D. T., et al, eds. Innovative Production Machines & Systems: Third I*PROMS Virtual International Conference, 2-13 July 2007. 2008. (Illus.). xxiii, 647p. 94.95 *(978-1-4200-7347-8(8))* Whittles Publishing GBR. Dist: Taylor & Francis Group.

Pipeleers, Goele, et al. Optimal Linear Controller Design for Periodic Inputs. 2009. (Lecture Notes in Control & Information Sciences Ser.). (Illus.). xvi, 164p. pap. 129.00 *(978-1-84882-974-9(4)*, 1848829744) Springer.

Piztek, Pavel, ed. Proceedings of the 16th IFAC World Congress. 2006. (ENG.). cd-rom 445.00 *(978-0-08-045108-4(X)*, Elsevier Science) Elsevier Science & Technology Bks.

Poznyak, Alex. Advanced Mathematical Tools for Automatic Control Engineers Vol. 2: Stochastic Systems. 2009. (ENG., Illus.). 500p. 205.00 *(978-0-08-044673-8(6)*, Elsevier Science) Elsevier Science & Technology Bks.

Poznyak, Alexander S. Advanced Mathematical Tools for Control Engineers: Volume 1: Deterministic Systems. 2008. (ENG., Illus.). 808p. 225.00 *(978-0-08-044674-5(4)*, Elsevier Science) Elsevier Science & Technology Bks.

Qiang Lu, et al. Nonlinear Control Systems & Power System Dynamics. 2010. (International Series on Asian Studies in Computer & Information Science Ser.). 400p. pap. 249.00 *(978-1-4419-4885-4(6)*, 1441948856) Springer.

Ramesh, S. & Sampath, P., eds. Next Generation Design & Verification Methodologies for Distributed Embedded Control Systems: Proceedings of the GM R&D Workshop, Bangalore, India, January 2007. (ENG.). xxii, 300p. 2010. pap. 175.00 *(978-90-481-7583-3(6)*, 9048175836) 2007. (Illus.). 175.00 *(978-1-4020-6253-7(2)*, 1402062532) Springer.

Rawlings, James Blake & Mayne, David Q. Model Predictive Control: Theory & Design. 2009. (Illus.). xli, 533p. ***(978-0-9759377-0-9(7))*** Nob Hill Publishing.

Re, Luigi del, ed. Automotive Model Predictive Control: Models, Methods & Applications. 2010. (Lecture Notes in Control & Information Sciences Ser.). (ENG., Illus.). viii, 312p. pap. 189.00 *(978-1-84996-070-0(4)*, 1849960704) Springer.

Redmill, Felix & Anderson, Tom, eds. Improvements in System Safety: Proceedings of the Sixteenth Safety-Critical Systems Symposium, Bristol, UK, 5-7 February 2008. 2008. (ENG., Illus.). x, 266p. per. 149.00 *(978-1-84800-099-5(5)*, 1848000995) Springer.

—The Safety of Systems: Proceedings of the Fifteenth Safety-Critical Systems Symposium, Bristol, UK, 13-15 February 2007. 2007. (ENG., Illus.). x, 262p. pap. 129.00 *(978-1-84628-805-0(3)*, 1846288053) Springer.

Ren, Wei & Beard, Randal. Distributed Consensus in Multi-vehicle Cooperative Control: Theory & Applications. 2010. (Communications & Control Engineering Ser.). (Illus.). xvi, 319p. pap. 159.00 *(978-1-84996-701-3(6)*, 1849967016) Springer.

—Distributed Consensus in Multi-Vehicle Cooperative Control: Theory & Applications. 2007. (Communications & Control Engineering Ser.). (Illus.). 320p. 159.00 *(978-1-84800-014-8(6)*, 1848000146) Springer.

Richalet, Jacques & O'Donovan, Donal. Predictive Functional Control: Principles & Industrial Applications. 2012. (Advances in Industrial Control Ser.). (ENG., Illus.). xxii, 222p. pap. 179.00 ***(978-1-84996-845-4(4)***, 1849968454) Springer.

Robyns, Benoît, et al. Vector Control of Induction Machines: Desensitisation & Optimisation Through Fuzzy Logic. 2012. (Power Systems Ser.). (ENG., Illus.). xxvi, 222p. 179.00 ***(978-0-85729-900-0(X)***, 085729900X) Springer.

Rosenwasser, Efim N. & Lampe, Bernhard P. Multivariable Computer-controlled Systems: A Transfer Function Approach. (Communications & Control Engineering Ser.). (Illus.). 2010. xviii, 478p. pap. 199.00 *(978-1-84996-600-9(1)*, 1849966001) 2006. XVIII, 478p. 199.00 *(978-1-84628-431-1(7)*, 1846284317) Springer.

Rouff, Christopher & Hinchey, Mike, eds. Experience from the DARPA Urban Challenge. 2011. (ENG., Illus.). xv, 320p. 179.00 *(978-0-85729-771-6(6)*, 0857297716) Springer.

Sánchez-Peña, Ricardo S., et al, eds. Identification & Control: The Gap Between Theory & Practice. 2007. (ENG., Illus.). xvi, 330p. 139.00 *(978-1-84628-898-2(3)*, 1846288983) Springer.

—Identification & Control: The Gap between Theory & Practice. 2010. (ENG., Illus.). xvi, 330p. pap. 139.00 *(978-1-84996-670-2(2)*, 1849966702) Springer.

Schmid, Ulrich, et al. Smart Sensors, Actuators, & MEMS V. 2011. (Proceedings of SPIE Ser.). 790p. pap. 160.00 ***(978-0-8194-8655-4(8))*** SPIE.

Schröder, Dierk, ed. Intelligent Observer & Control Design for Nonlinear Systems. 2010. (ENG., Illus.). xiii, 339p. pap. 159.00 *(978-3-642-08346-4(3)*, 3642083463) Springer.

Schuldt, Arne. Multiagent Coordination Enabling Autonomous Logistics. 2011. (ENG., Illus.). xvi, 272p. 129.00 *(978-3-642-20091-5(5)*, 3642200915) Springer.

Schuster, Alfons, ed. Robust Intelligent Systems. 2010. (ENG., Illus.). xii, 299p. pap. 139.00 *(978-1-84996-765-5(2)*, 1849967652) Springer.

Secchi, Cristian, et al. Control of Interactive Robotic Interfaces: A Port-Hamiltonian Approach. 2010. (Springer Tracts in Advanced Robotics Ser.). (Illus.). xxii, 233p. pap. 159.00 *(978-3-642-08061-6(8)*, 3642080618) Springer.

Segel, Joshua E. Piezoelectric Actuators. 2011. (Electrical Engineering Developments Ser.). (Illus.). 154p. 95.00 ***(978-1-61324-131-3(X))*** Nova Science Pubs., Inc.

Shestak, Vladimir. Robust Resource Allocation for Parallel Distributed Computing Systems. 2010. 156p. pap. *(978-3-8383-6672-2(7))* Lambert Academic Publishing.

Siciliano, Bruno & Dario, Paolo, eds. Experimental Robotics VIII: Proceedings of the 8th International Symposium ISER02. 2010. (Springer Tracts in Advanced Robotics Ser.). xvi, 669p. pap. 349.00 *(978-3-642-05559-1(1)*, 3642055591) Springer.

Simani, Silvio, et al. Model-based Fault Diagnosis in Dynamic Systems Using Identification Techniques. 2010. (Advances in Industrial Control Ser.). (Illus.). xiv, 282p. pap. 179.00 *(978-1-84996-895-9(0)*, 1849968950) Springer.

Sinha, Alok. Linear Systems: Optimal & Robust Control. 2007. (ENG., Illus.). 488p. (C). 115.95 *(978-0-8493-9217-7(9)*, 9217, CRC Press) Taylor & Francis Group GBR. Dist: Taylor & Francis Group.

Siouris, George M. Missile Guidance & Control Systems. 2010. (ENG., Illus.). xiv, 666p. pap. 419.00 *(978-1-4419-1835-2(3)*, 1441918353) Springer.

Siqueira, Adriano A. G., et al. Robust Control of Robots: Fault Tolerant Approaches. 2011. (ENG., Illus.). xvi, 228p. 129.00 ***(978-0-85729-897-3(6)***, 0857298976) Springer.

Slezak, Dominik, et al. Control & Automation: International Conference, CA 2009, Held as Part of the Future Generation Information Technology Conference, CA 2009, Jeju Island, Korea, December 10-12, 2009. Proceedings. 2009. (Communications in Computer & Information Science Ser.). xi, 87p. pap 89.95 *(978-3-642-10742-9(7)*, 3642107427) Springer.

Sousa, Leonel, et al, eds. Embedded Systems for Portable & Mobile Video Platforms. 2007. 80p. per. 14.00 *(978-977-5945-85-3(2))* Hindawi Publishing Corp.

Stoustrup, Jakob & Zhou, Kemin, eds. Robustness Issues in Fault Diagnosis & Fault Tolerant Control. 2007. 168p. pap. 26.00 *(978-977-454-025-7(5))* Hindawi Publishing Corp.

Sundararajan, N., et al. Fully Tuned Radial Basis Function Neural Networks for Flight Control. 2010. (International Series on Asian Studies in Computer & Information Science Ser.). 176p. pap. 279.00 *(978-1-4419-4915-8(1)*, 1441949151) Springer.

Sung, Su Whan, et al. Process Identification & PID Control. 2009. (ENG., Illus.). 352p. 152.00 *(978-0-470-82410-8(7)*, Wiley-IEEE Pr.) Wiley, John & Sons, Inc.

Szymkat, Maciej, ed. System Modeling & Optimization: 23rd IFIP TC 7 Conference, Cracow, Poland, July 23-27, 2007, Revised Selected Papers. 2009. (IFIP Advances in Information & Communication Technology Ser.). ix, 507p. 219.00 *(978-3-642-04801-2(3)*, 3642048013) Springer.

Söderholm, Mattias. Use of Barkhausen Noise for Grinding Quality Control. 2009. 68p. pap. *(978-3-639-14718-6(9))* VDM Verlag Dr. Mueller e.K.

Tan, Kok Kiong & Putra, Andi Sudjana. Drives & Control for Industrial Automation. 2010. (Advances in Industrial Control Ser.). (ENG., Illus.). xiv, 204p. 149.00 *(978-1-84882-424-9(6)*, 1848824246) Springer.

Tan, Kok Kiong, et al. Precision Motion Control: Design & Implementation. 2nd ed. 2007. (Advances in Industrial Control Ser.). (Illus.). 288p. 189.00 *(978-1-84800-020-9(0))* Springer.

Tan, Siew-Chong, et al. Sliding Mode Control of Switching Power Converters. 2011. (ENG., Illus.). 301p. 139.95 *(978-1-4398-3025-3(8)*, CRC Press) Taylor & Francis Group GBR. Dist: Taylor & Francis Group.

Tao, Gang, et al. Adaptive Control of Systems with Actuator Failures. 2010. (ENG., Illus.). xvi, 299p. pap. 159.00 *(978-1-84996-917-8(5)*, 1849969175) Springer.

Tarbouriech, Sophie, et al, eds. Advanced Strategies in Control Systems with Input & Output Constraints. 2006. (Lecture Notes in Control & Information Sciences Ser.). (Illus.). xvii, 462p. 289.00 *(978-3-540-37009-3(9)*, 3540370099) Springer.

Tarbouriech, Sophie, et al. Stability & Stabilization of Linear Systems with Saturating Actuators. 2011. (ENG., Illus.). xxi, 430p. 179.00 ***(978-0-85729-940-6(9)***, 0857299409) Springer.

Tatjewski, Piotr. Advanced Control of Industrial Processes: Structures & Algorithms. 2010. (Advances in Industrial Control Ser.). (Illus.). xx, 332p. pap. 199.00 *(978-1-84996-632-0(X)*, 184996632X) Springer.

Terrell, William J. Stability & Stabilization. 2009. (ENG., Illus.). 474p. (C). 78.50 *(978-0-691-13444-4(8))* Princeton Univ. Pr.

Tewari, Ashish. Automatic Control of Atmospheric & Space Flight Vehicles: Design & Analysis with Matlab & Simulink. 2011. (Control Engineering Ser.). (ENG., Illus.). xiv, 374p. 74.95 ***(978-0-8176-4863-3(1)***, 0817648631) Birkhauser Verlag AG CHE. Dist: Springer.

Tripathi, S. M. Modern Control Systems: An Introduction. 2008. (Illus.). 350p. pap. 88.95 *(978-1-934015-21-6(0))* Jones & Bartlett Learning, LLC.

Turner, Matthew C. & Bates, Declan G., eds. Mathematical Methods for Robust & Nonlinear Control: EPSRC Summer School. 2007. (Lecture Notes in Control & Information Sciences Ser.). (Illus.). XVI, 444p. pap. 189.00 *(978-1-84800-024-7(3)*, 1848000243) Springer.

Tzafestas, Spyros G. Human & Nature Minding Automation: An Overview of Concepts, Methods, Tools & Applications. 2009. (Intelligent Systems, Control & Automation: Science & Engineering Ser.). (Illus.). xx, 346p. 169.00 *(978-90-481-3561-5(3)*, 9048135613) Springer.

Varga, Andreas, et al, eds. Optimization Based Clearance of Flight Control Laws: A Civil Aircraft Application. 2011. (Lecture Notes in Control & Information Sciences Ser.). (ENG., Illus.). xxiv, 452p. pap. 159.00 ***(978-3-642-22626-7(4)***, 3642226264) Springer.

Vasseur, Jean-Philippe & Dunkels, Adam. Interconnecting Smart Objects with IP: The Next Internet. 2010. (ENG., Illus.). 432p. pap. 72.95 *(978-0-12-375165-2(9)*, Morgan Kaufmann) Elsevier Science & Technology Bks.

Velásquez, Juan D., et al. Knowledge-Based Intelligent Information & Engineering Systems: 13th International Conference, KES 2009, Santiago, Chile, September 28-30, 2009, Proceedings Part I, 2 vols. 2009. (Lecture Notes in Computer Science / Lecture Notes in Artificial Intelligence Ser.). (Illus.). xxx, 381p. pap. 95.00 *(978-3-642-04594-3(4)*, 3642045944) Springer.

—Knowledge-Based Intelligent Information & Engineering Systems: 13th International Conference, KES 2009, Santiago, Chile, September 28-30, 2009, Proceedings, Part II, 2 vols. 2009. (Lecture Notes in Computer Science / Lecture Notes in Artificial Intelligence Ser.). (Illus.). xxix, 873p. pap. 159.00 *(978-3-642-04591-2(X)*, 364204591X) Springer.

Veloni, Anastasia & Palamides, Alexandros. Control System Problems: Formulas, Matlab, & Solutions. 2011. (ENG., Illus.). 532p. 99.95 *(978-1-4398-6850-8(6)*, CRC Press) Taylor & Francis Group GBR. Dist: Taylor & Francis Group.

Vijver, G., ed. New Perspectives on Cybernetics: Self-Organization, Autonomy & Connectionism. 2010. (Synthese Library). 272p. pap. 229.00 *(978-90-481-4107-4(9)*, 9048141079) Springer.

Vilanova, Ramon & Visioli, Antonio, eds. PID Control in the Third Millennium: Lessons Learned & New Approaches. 2012. (Advances in Industrial Control Ser.). (ENG., Illus.). xiv, 599p. 229.00 ***(978-1-4471-2424-5(3)***, 1447124243) Springer.

Villani, Emilia, et al. Modelling & Analysis of Hybrid Supervisory Systems: A Petri Net Approach. (Advances in Industrial Control Ser.). (Illus.). xxii, 224p. 2010. pap. 179.00 *(978-1-84996-637-5(0)*, 1849966370) 2006. (ENG., 179.00 *(978-1-84628-650-6(6)*, 1846286506) Springer.

Vinter, R. B. Optimal Control. 2010. (Illus.). xvii, 507p. E-Book ***(978-0-8176-8086-2(1))*** Springer.

Vinter, Richard. Optimal Control. 2010. (Modern Birkhauser Classics Ser.). Orig. Title: Optimal Control. (Illus.). xx, 500p. pap. 69.95 *(978-0-8176-4990-6(5)*, 0817649905) Birkhauser Verlag AG CHE. Dist: Springer.

Virk, Shafqat Mumtaz, et al. Fault Prediction Analysis. 2010. 56p. pap. *(978-3-639-24862-3(7))* VDM Verlag Dr. Mueller e.K.

Visioli, Antonio. Practical PID Control. 2010. (Advances in Industrial Control Ser.). (Illus.). xviii, 310p. pap. 199.00 *(978-1-84996-622-1(2)*, 1849966222) Springer.

Visioli, Antonio & Zhong, Qing-Chang. Control of Integral Processes with Dead Time. 2010. (Advances in Industrial Control Ser.). (ENG., Illus.). xxvi, 268p. 129.00 *(978-0-85729-069-4(X)*, 085729069X) Springer.

Vukosavic, Slobodan N. Digital Control of Electrical Drives. 2007. (Power Electronics & Power Systems Ser.). (ENG., Illus.). xii, 352p. 139.00 *(978-0-387-25985-7(6)*, 0387259856) Springer.

Vyatkin, Valeriy. IEC 61499 Function Blocks for Embedded & Distributed Control Systems Design. 2007. (ENG.). 279p. pap. 89.00 *(978-0-9792343-0-9(1))* ISA.

Wang, Fei-Yue & Liu, Derong. Networked Control Systems: Theory & Applications. 2008. (ENG., Illus.). xviii, 344p. 139.00 *(978-1-84800-214-2(9)*, 1848002149) Springer.

Wang, Fei-Yue & Liu, Derong, eds. Networked Control Systems: Theory & Applications. 2010. (ENG., Illus.). xviii, 344p. pap. 139.00 *(978-1-84996-756-3(3)*, 1849967563) Springer.

Wang, Liuping. Model Predictive Control System Design & Implementation Using MATLAB(r). 2009. (Advances in Industrial Control Ser.). (ENG., Illus.). xxx, 376p. 209.00 *(978-1-84882-330-3(4))* Springer.

Wang, Zhengming, et al. Measurement Data Modeling & Parameter Estimation. 2011. (Systems Evaluation, Prediction, & Decision-Making Ser.). (ENG., Illus.). 553p. 119.95 *(978-1-4398-5378-8(9)*, CRC Press) Taylor & Francis Group GBR. Dist: Taylor & Francis Group.

Westervelt, Eric R., et al. Feedback Control of Dynamic Bipedal Robot Locomotion. 2007. (Control & Automation Ser.). (ENG., Illus.). 528p. 189.95 *(978-1-4200-5372-2(8)*, CRC Press) Taylor & Francis Group GBR. Dist: Taylor & Francis Group.

Wu, Min, et al. Stability Analysis & Robust Control of Time-Delay Systems. 2010. (ENG., Illus.). 335p. 129.00 *(978-3-642-03036-9(X)*, 364203036X) Springer.

Wu, Yanwen, ed. Advances in Computer, Communication, Control & Automation. 2011. (Lecture Notes in Electrical Engineering Ser.). (ENG., Illus.). xvi, 804p. 279.00 ***(978-3-642-25540-3(X)***, 364225540X) Springer.

Xia, Yuanqing, et al. Analysis & Synthesis of Networked Control Systems. 2011. (Lecture Notes in Control & Information Sciences Ser.). (Illus.). xvi, 200p. pap. 109.00 *(978-3-642-17924-2(X)*, 364217924X) Springer.

Xue, Dingyu, et al. Linear Feedback Control: Analysis & Design with MATLAB. 2007. (Advances in Design & Control Ser.). (ENG., Illus.). 370p. (C). pap. 99.00 *(978-0-89871-638-2(1))* Society for Industrial and Applied Mathematics.

Yan, Liang, et al. Design, Modeling & Experiments of 3-DOF Electromagnetic Spherical Actuators. 2011. (Mechanisms & Machine Science Ser.). (ENG., Illus.). xxii, 166p. 129.00 *(978-94-007-1645-2(1)*, 9400716451) Springer.

Yang, Guang-Hong & Ye, Dan. Reliable Control & Filtering of Linear Systems with Adaptive Mechanisms. 2010. (Automation & Control Engineering Ser.). (ENG., Illus.). 264p. 119.95 *(978-1-4398-3522-7(5)*, CRC Press) Taylor & Francis Group GBR. Dist: Taylor & Francis Group.

Yang, Woosung, et al. Biologically Inspired Robotic Systems Control. 2010. 164p. pap. *(978-3-639-23071-0(X))* VDM Verlag Dr. Mueller e.K.

Yang, Xianyong. Re Gong Guo Cheng Zi Dong Kong Zhi. 2nd ed. 2008. (CHI., Illus.). xi, 419p. *(978-7-302-16597-2(1))* Tsinghua Univ. Pr.

Yarin, L. P., et al. Fluid Flow, Heat Transfer & Boiling in Micro-Channels. 2010. (Heat & Mass Transfer Ser.). (Illus.). xiv, 481p. pap. 219.00 *(978-3-642-09754-6(5)*, 3642097545) Springer.

Youssef, Ahmed A. & Haslett, Jim. Nanometer CMOS RFICs for Mobile TV Applications. 2010. (Analog Circuits & Signal Processing Ser.). (ENG., Illus.). xv, 200p. 159.00 *(978-90-481-8603-7(X)*, 904818603X) Springer.

Yousuf, Muhammad Salman. Nonlinear Predictive Control Using Particle Swarm Optimization. 2010. 144p. pap. *(978-3-639-24966-8(6))* VDM Verlag Dr. Mueller e.K.

Yu, Cheng-Ching. Autotuning of PID Controllers: A Relay Feedback Approach. 2nd ed. 2012. (ENG., Illus.). xiv, 261p. pap. 149.00 *(978-1-84996-546-0(3)*, 1849965463) Springer.

—Autotuning of PID Controllers: Relay Feedback Approach. 2nd rev. ed. 2007. (Illus.). xiv, 261p. 149.00 *(978-1-84628-036-8(2)*, 1846280362) Springer.

Yu, Fei, et al. Proceedings, ISECS International Colloquium on Computing, Communication, Control, & Management: CCCM 2008, 4-5 August 2008, Guangzhou, China, 3 vols. 2008. (Illus.). *(978-0-7695-3290-5(X))* IEEE Computer Society Pr.

Zaccarian, L. Modern Anti-Windup Synthesis. 2011. (Princeton Series in Applied Mathematics Ser.). (ENG., Illus.). 304p. (C). 69.50 *(978-0-691-14732-1(9))* Princeton Univ. Pr.

Zhang, Chunlei & Ordóñez, Raúl. Extremum-Seeking Control & Applications: A Numerical Optimization-Based Approach. 2011. (Advances in Industrial Control Ser.). (ENG., Illus.). xviii, 203p. 129.00 ***(978-1-4471-2223-4(2)***, 1447122232) Springer.

Zhang, Hong-Yue, ed. Fault Detection Supervision & Safety of Technical Processes 2006: A Proceedings Volume from the 6th IFAC Symposium on Fault Detection, Supervision & Safety of Technical Processes, 2 vols. 2007. (IPV - IFAC Proceedings Volume Ser.). (ENG., Illus.). 1576p. pap. 290.00 *(978-0-08-044485-7(7)*, Elsevier Science) Elsevier Science & Technology Bks.

Zhang, Huanshui & Xie, Lihua. Control & Estimation of Systems with Input/Output Delays. 2007. (Lecture Notes in Control & Information Sciences Ser.). (Illus.). 213p. pap. 159.00 *(978-3-540-71118-6(X))* Springer.

Zhang, Peng. Industrial Control Technology: A Handbook for Engineers & Researchers. 2008. (ENG., Illus.). 900p. 310.00 *(978-0-8155-1571-5(5))* William Andrew, Inc.

Zhang, Runtong, et al. Fuzzy Control of Queuing Systems. 2010. (ENG., Illus.). x, 175p. pap. 159.00 *(978-1-84996-930-7(2)*, 1849969302) Springer.

Zhang, Tianbiao, ed. Future Computer, Communication, Control & Automation. 2011. (Advances in Intelligent & Soft Computing Ser.). (ENG., Illus.). xvi, 748p. pap. 399.00 ***(978-3-642-25537-3(X)***, 364225537X) Springer.

Zhong, Qing-Chang. Robust Control of Time-delay Systems. 2010. (ENG., Illus.). xxii, 231p. pap. 169.00 *(978-1-84996-566-8(8)*, 1849965668) Springer.

Zoitl, Alois. Real-Time Execution for IEC 61499. 2008. (ENG.). 276p. pap. 89.00 *(978-1-934394-27-4(0))* ISA.

2007 American Control Conference. 2007. pap. 1052.00 *(978-1-4244-0988-4(8)*, 07CH37877) IEEE.

2007 IEEE International Conference on Computational Intelligence for Measurement Systems & Applications. 2007. pap. 206.00 *(978-1-4244-0823-8(7)*, 07EX1621) IEEE.

2007 IEEE International Conference on Control & Automation. 2007. pap. 606.00 *(978-1-4244-0817-7(2)*, 07EX1625) IEEE.

2007 Mediterranean Conference on Control & Automation. 2007. pap. 412.00 *(978-1-4244-1281-5(1)*, 07EX1809) IEEE.

2008 IEEE Conference on Automation Science & Engineering: Arlington, Va, 23-26 August 2008, 2 vols. 2008. (Illus.). lxvi, 1030p. *(978-1-4244-2023-0(7))* IEEE Computer Society Pr.

AUTOMATIC CONTROL—BIBLIOGRAPHY

2005 InspecSearch Aid. (Inspec Database Ser.). cd-rom 195.00 *(978-0-86341-471-8(0)*, IP032) Institution of Engineering & Technology GBR. Dist: Books International, Inc.

2005 InspecSearch Aids. (Inspec Database Ser.). cd-rom 395.00 *(978-0-86341-472-5(9)*, IP033) Institution of Engineering & Technology GBR. Dist: Books International, Inc.

AUTOMATIC CONTROL—DICTIONARIES

Siemens A and D Translation Services Staff, ed. Wörterbuch Industrielle Elektrotechnik, Energie- und Automatisierungstechnik / Dictionary of Electrical Engineering, Power Engineering & Automation: CD-ROM Deutsch-Englisch / English-German. CD-ROM - Edition 2011, Pt. 1. 2011. (ENG.). 1042p. 115.00 *(978-3-89578-313-5(7)*, Wiley-VCH) Wiley, John & Sons, Inc.

AUTOMATIC COUNTING DEVICES

see Digital Counters

AUTOMATIC DATA COLLECTION SYSTEMS

Ansari, Farhad, ed. Sensing Issues in Civil Structural Health Monitoring. 2010. (ENG.). xx, 528p. pap. 259.00 *(978-90-481-6921-4(6)*, 9048169216) Springer.

Boginski, Vladimir L., et al, eds. Sensors: Theory, Algorithms, & Applications: Theory, Algorithms, & Applications. 2011. (Springer Optimization & Its Applications Ser.). (ENG., Illus.). x, 242p. 124.00 ***(978-0-387-88618-3(4)***, 0387886184) Springer.

Boller, Christian, et al, eds. Encyclopedia of Structural Health Monitoring, 5 vols. 2009. (ENG., Illus.). 2960p. 1695.00 *(978-0-470-05822-0(6)*, Wiley) Wiley, John & Sons, Inc.

Giurgiutiu, Victor. Structural Health Monitoring: With Piezoelectric Wafer Active Sensors. 2007. (ENG., Illus.). 760p. 143.00 *(978-0-12-088760-6(6)*, Academic Pr.) Elsevier Science & Technology Bks.

Institute of Electrical and Electronics Engineers Staff, contrib. by. 2007 International Conference on Information Acquisition. 2007. pap. 340.00 *(978-1-4244-1219-8(6)*, 07TH8959) IEEE.

Karbhari, V. M. Structural Health Monitoring of Civil Infrastructure Systems. 2009. (ENG., Illus.). 552p. 244.95 *(978-1-4398-0131-4(2)*, CRC Press) Taylor & Francis Group GBR. Dist: Taylor & Francis Group.

Karbhari, V. M. & Ansari, F., eds. Structural Health Monitoring of Civil Infrastructure Systems. 2009. (Illus.). 552p. *(978-1-84569-392-3(2))* Woodhead Publishing Ltd.

Kortuem, Gerd. Smart Sensing & Context. 2007. (Lecture Notes in Computer Science / Computer Communication Networks & Telecommunications Ser.). spiral bd. 79.95 *(978-3-540-75695-8(7))* Springer.

McBeath, Simon. Competition Car Data Logging: A Practical Handbook. 2nd ed. 2009. (ENG., Illus.). 176p. 49.95 *(978-1-84425-565-8(4)*, 1844255654) Haynes Publishing PLC GBR. Dist: MBI Distribution Services/Quayside Distribution.

Michael, Katina & Michael, M. G. Innovative Automatic Identification & Location-Based Services: From Bar Codes to Chip Implants. 2009. (Premier Reference Source Ser.). (Illus.). 544p. 165.00 *(978-1-59904-795-9(0)*, Information Science Publishing) IGI Global.

Neo, Wei Ren. Development of Data Acquisition System of Ntu Venture II. 2010. 88p. pap. *(978-3-8383-8514-3(4))* Lambert Academic Publishing.

Nsang, Augustine. Novel Approaches to Dimensionality Reduction & Applications. 2011. 204p. pap. ***(978-3-8454-0050-1(1))*** Lambert Academic Publishing.

Ogle, Jennifer Harper. Technologies for Improving Safety Data. 2007. (Illus.). 98p. 45.00 *(978-0-309-09785-7(1))* Transportation Research Board.

Ordys, Andrzej, et al, eds. Process Control Performance Assessment: From Theory to Implementation. 2010. (Advances in Industrial Control Ser.). (Illus.). xxii, 325p. pap. 199.00 *(978-1-84996-630-6(3)*, 1849966303) Springer.

Pazienza, Maria Teresa & Stellato, Armando. Semi-Automatic Ontology Development: Processes & Resources. 2012. ***(978-1-4666-0188-8(4))***; ***(978-1-4666-0190-1(6))*** IGI Global.

Ponzetto, S. P., ed. Knowledge Acquisition from a Collaboratively Generated Encyclopedia - Volume 327 Dissertations in Artificial Intelligence. 2010. 236p. pap. 73.00 *(978-1-60750-097-1(3))* IOS Pr., Inc.

Shaw, William T. Cybersecurity for Scada Systems. 2006. (Illus.). 562p. 89.00 *(978-1-59370-068-3(7))* PennWell Corp.

Spencer, Charles D. Digital Design for Computer Data Acquisition. 2009. (ENG., Illus.). 372p. pap. 63.00 *(978-0-521-10255-1(3))* Cambridge Univ. Pr.

Taylor, H. R. Data Acquisition for Sensor Systems. 2010. (ENG.). 344p. pap. 149.00 *(978-1-4419-4729-1(9)*, 1441947299) Springer.

AUTOMATIC DATA PROCESSING

see Electronic Data Processing

AUTOMATIC DATA PROCESSORS

see Computers

AUTOMATIC DATA STORAGE

see Information Storage and Retrieval Systems

AUTOMATIC DIGITAL COMPUTERS

see Electronic Digital Computers

AUTOMATIC DRAFTING

see Computer Graphics

AUTOMATIC FACTORIES

see Automation

AUTOMATIC INDEXING

Gaussier, E. Textual Information Access: Statistical Models. 2012. (Iste Ser.: 588). (ENG.). 175.00 ***(978-1-84821-322-7(0)***, Wiley-ISTE) Wiley, John & Sons, Inc.

Lairson, Michael D. Oracle CRM on Demand Embedded Analytics. 2011. (Oracle Press Ser.). (ENG., Illus.). 192p. pap. 30.00 *(978-0-07-174536-9(X)*, 007174536X) McGraw-Hill Osborne.

AUTOMATIC LANGUAGE PROCESSING

see Computational Linguistics

AUTOMATIC MACHINE-TOOLS

see Machine-Tools

AUTOMATIC MACHINERY

see also Automation; Coin-Operated Machines; Robots, Industrial

Harris, J. Fuzzy Logic Applications in Engineering Science. 2nd ed. 2010. (Intelligent Systems, Control & Automation: Science & Engineering Ser.). xviii, 221p. pap. 159.00 *(978-90-481-7034-0(6)*, 9048170346) Springer.

Melchiorri, Claudio & Biagiotti, Luigi. Trajectory Planning for Automatic Machines & Robots. 2008. (ENG., Illus.). xiv, 514p. 159.00 *(978-3-540-85628-3(5)*, 3540856285) Springer.

AUTOMATIC MUSICAL INSTRUMENTS

see Mechanical Musical Instruments

AUTOMATIC PILOT (AIRPLANES)

Ben-Asher, Joseph Z. Optimal Control Theory with Aerospace Applications. 2010. 89.95 *(978-1-60086-732-3(4))* American Institute of Aeronautics & Astronautics.

Casner, Stephen M. Cockpit Automation: For General Aviators & Future Airline Pilots. 2007. (ENG., Illus.). 188p. pap. 29.95 *(978-1-56027-636-4(3))* Aviation Supplies & Academics, Inc.

Zafar, Zain, et al. Autopilot System for an Unmanned Aerial Vehicle. 2011. 208p. pap. ***(978-3-8443-1560-8(8))*** Lambert Academic Publishing.

AUTOMATIC PILOT (SHIPS)

Fossen, Thor I. Handbook of Marine Craft Hydrodynamics & Motion Control. 2011. (ENG., Illus.). 596p. 200.00 *(978-1-119-99149-6(8)*, Wiley) Wiley, John & Sons, Inc.

Perez, Tristan. Ship Motion Control: Course Keeping & Roll Stabilisation Using Rudder & Fins. 2010. (Advances in Industrial Control Ser.). (Illus.). xxii, 300p. pap. 199.00 *(978-1-84996-978-9(7)*, 1849969787) Springer.

Schlaefer, Alexander & Blaurock, Ole, eds. Robotic Sailing: Proceedings of the 4th International Robotic Sailing Conference. 2011. (ENG., Illus.). x, 206p. 189.00 ***(978-3-642-22835-3(6)***, 3642228356) Springer.

Xiao, Chengmo & Nguang, Sing Kiong. Yacht Modelling & Adaptive Control. 2009. (Transportation Issues, Policies & R&D Ser.). (Illus.). xiii, 151p. 69.00 *(978-1-60741-430-8(9))* Nova Science Pubs., Inc.

AUTOMATIC PRODUCTION

see Automation

AUTOMATIC PROGRAMMING LANGUAGES

see Programming Languages (Electronic Computers)

AUTOMATIC SPEECH RECOGNITION

AbuZeina, Dia & Elshafei, Moustafa. Cross-Word Modeling for Arabic Speech Recognition. 2011. (SpringerBriefs in Electrical & Computer Engineering / SpringerBriefs in Speech Technology Ser.). (ENG & ARA., Illus.). x, 74p. 49.95 ***(978-1-4614-1212-0(9)***, 1461412129) Springer.

Akyol, Aydin. Increasing Robustness of Spoken Dialogue Systems. 2009. 104p. pap. *(978-3-8364-7678-2(9))* VDM Verlag Dr. Mueller e.K.

Asliyan, Rifat. Turkish Speech Recognition. 2010. 188p. pap. *(978-3-8383-5186-5(X))* Lambert Academic Publishing.

Beigi, Homayoon. Fundamentals of Speaker Recognition. 2011. (ENG., Illus.). lx, 942p. 119.00 *(978-0-387-77591-3(9)*, 0387775919) Springer.

Bendewald. Proving It. 159.60 *(978-0-9668434-2-2(8))* CompuTALK.

Cannistra, Robert M. CCNA Voice Portable Command Guide. rev. ed. 2012. (Portable Command Guide Ser.). (ENG.). 300p. pap. 34.99 ***(978-1-58720-442-5(8))*** Cisco Pr.

Carson-Berndsen, J. Time Map Phonology: Finite State Models & Event Logics in Speech Recognition. 2010. (Text, Speech & Language Technology Ser.). 264p. pap. 159.00 *(978-90-481-4969-8(X)*, 904814969X) Springer.

Chen, Fang. Designing Human Interface in Speech Technology. 2010. (ENG.). xxiii, 382p. pap. 99.00 *(978-1-4419-3697-4(1)*, 1441936971) Springer.

Coy, Andre. Emulating Human Speech Recognition: A Scene Analysis Approach to Improving Robustness in Automatic Speech Recognition. 2012. pap. ***(978-1-61942-914-7(4))*** Nova Science Pubs., Inc.

Coy, Andre. Like Humans Do: A Scene Analysis Approach to Improving Robustness in Automatic Speech Recognition. 2011. (Computer Science, Technology & Applications Ser.). (Illus.). viii, 195p. 129.00 *(978-1-61209-228-7(4))* Nova Science Pubs., Inc.

Cram101 Textbook Reviews & Cram101 Textbook Reviews. Outlines & Highlights for Speech & Language Processing: An Introduction to Natural Language Processing, Computational Linguistics, & Speech Recog. 2011. 504p. pap. 37.95 ***(978-1-61461-638-2(8))*** Cram101 Inc.

Dadvar, Maral. Who Spoke When? 2011. 68p. pap. ***(978-3-8443-8628-8(9))*** Lambert Academic Publishing.

Deng, Li & He, Xiaodong. Discriminative Learning for Speech Pr. 2008. (Synthesis Lectures on Speech & Audio Processing Ser.). 100p. pap. 40.00 *(978-1-59829-308-1(7))* Morgan & Claypool Pubs.

Deshpande, Mangesh & Holambe, Raghunath. Speaker Identification: New Spectral Feature Extraction Techniques. 2011. 152p. pap. ***(978-3-8454-0463-9(9))*** Lambert Academic Publishing.

Divenyi, Pierre, ed. Speech Separation by Humans & Machines. 2010. (ENG., Illus.). xxiv, 319p. pap. 119.00 *(978-1-4419-5460-2(0)*, 1441954600) Springer.

Dunn, Michael D. Pro Microsoft Speech Server 2007: Developing Speech Enabled Applications with . NET. 2007. (Expert's Voice In . Net Ser.). (ENG., Illus.). 275p. 59.99 *(978-1-59059-902-0(0))* Apress L. P.

Dybkjær, Laila, ed. Recent Trends in Discourse & Dialogue. 2010. (Text, Speech & Language Technology Ser.). xxxii, 312p. pap. 249.00 *(978-90-481-7734-9(0)*, 9048177340) Springer.

El-Samie, Fathi E. Abd. Information Security for Automatic Speaker Identification. 2011. (SpringerBriefs in Speech Technology Ser.). (ENG., Illus.). xiii, 122p. pap. 49.95 *(978-1-4419-9697-8(4)*, 1441996974) Springer.

Farrús, Mireia. Prosody in Automatic Speaker Recognition. 2010. 216p. pap. *(978-3-639-08991-2(X))* VDM Verlag Dr. Mueller e.K.

Fulop, Sean A. Speech Spectrum Analysis. 2011. (Signals & Communication Technology Ser.). (Illus.). xiii, 206p. 129.00 *(978-3-642-17477-3(9)*, 3642174779) Springer.

Gales, Mark & Young, Steve. The Application of Hidden Markov Models in Speech Recognition. 2008. (ENG.). 112p. pap. 80.00 net. *(978-1-60198-120-2(1))* Now Pubs.

Gardner-Bonneau, Daryle & Blanchard, Harry E., eds. Human Factors & Voice Interactive Systems. 2nd ed. (Signals & Communication Technology Ser.). (Illus.). 2010. xxvi, 469p. pap. 99.00 *(978-1-4419-3798-8(6)*, 1441937986) 2007. 468p. 99.00 *(978-0-387-25482-1(X)*, 038725482X) Springer.

Gibbon, Dafydd, ed. Natural Language Processing & Speech Technology: Results of the 3rd KONVENS Conference, Bielefeld, October 1996. (ENG.). X, 403p. 195.00 ***(978-3-11-187043-4(X))*** De Gruyter, Mouton DEU. Dist: de Gruyter, Walter GmbH & Co. KG.

Habernal, Ivan & Matousek, Vaclav, eds. Text, Speech & Dialogue: 14th International Conference, TSD 2011, Pilsen, Czech Republic, September 1-5, 2011, Proceedings. 2011. (Lecture Notes in Computer Science / Lecture Notes in Artificial Intelligence Ser.). (ENG., Illus.). xi, 444p. pap. 95.00 ***(978-3-642-23537-5(9)***, 3642235379) Springer.

Haque, Serajul. Auditory Features for Speech Recognition & Enhancement. 2009. 208p. pap. *(978-3-639-18396-2(7))* VDM Verlag Dr. Mueller e.K.

Hassanat, Ahmad. Automatic Lip-Reading System. 2011. 188p. pap. ***(978-3-8443-1079-5(7))*** Lambert Academic Publishing.

Herbig, Tobias, et al. Self-Learning Speaker Identification: A System for Enhanced Speech Recognition. 2011. (Signals & Communication Technology Ser.). (Illus.). xii, 172p. 129.00 *(978-3-642-19898-4(8)*, 3642198988) Springer.

International Speech Communication Association (ISCA) Staff, compiled by. INTERSPEECH 2006 & 9th International Conference on Spoken Language Processing. 2008. 2633p. pap. 295.00 *(978-1-60423-449-7(0))* Curran Assocs., Inc.

Jokinen, Kristina & McTear, Michael. Spoken Dialogue Systems. 2009. (Synthesis Lectures on Human Language Technologies Ser.). (Illus.). 151p. pap. 40.00 *(978-1-59829-599-3(3))* Morgan & Claypool Pubs.

Kafidi, Petrus. Touchtone & Speech Interfacing to a System, Which One to Choose. 2009. 108p. pap. *(978-3-639-10912-2(0))* VDM Verlag Dr. Mueller e.K.

Karat, John & Karat, Clare-Marie. Designing & Evaluating Usable Technology in Industrial Research. 2010. (Synthesis Lectures on Human-Centered Informatics Ser.). 118p. pap. 35.00 *(978-1-60845-053-4(8))* Morgan & Claypool Pubs.

Keshet, Joseph & Bengio, Samy, eds. Automatic Speech & Speaker Recognition: Large Margin & Kernel Methods. 2009. (ENG., Illus.). 268p. 140.00 *(978-0-470-69683-5(4)*, Wiley) Wiley, John & Sons, Inc.

Khan, Muhammad Afaq. Building Service-Aware Networks: The Next-Generation WAN/MAN. 2009. (Networking Technology Ser.). (Illus.). 336p. 60.00 *(978-1-58705-788-5(3))* Cisco Pr.

Kitapci, Kivanc. Effects of Speech Intelligibility on Computer-Based Task Performance. 2010. 100p. pap. *(978-3-8383-5163-6(0))* Lambert Academic Publishing.

Kolossa, Dorothea & Häb-Umbach, Reinhold, eds. Robust Speech Recognition of Uncertain or Missing Data: Theory & Applications. 2011. (ENG., Illus.). xiv, 380p. 129.00 *(978-3-642-21316-8(2)*, 3642213162) Springer.

Kraal, Ben. Considering Use & Design of Speech Recognition Systems. 2008. 220p. pap. *(978-3-639-06758-3(4))* VDM Verlag Dr. Mueller e.K.

Lee, Gary Geunbae, et al, eds. Spoken Dialogue Systems for Ambient Environments: Seond International Workshop, IWSDS 2010, Gotemba, Shizuoka, Japan, October 1-2, 2010. Proceedings. 2010. (Lecture Notes in

Computer Science / Lecture Notes in Artificial Intelligence Ser.). xi, 199p. pap. 72.00 *(978-3-642-16201-5(0)*, 3642162010) Springer.

Lewis, James R. Practical Speech User Interface Design. 2010. (Human Factors & Ergonomics Ser.). (ENG., Illus.). 344p. 89.95 *(978-1-4398-1584-7(4)*, CRC Press) Taylor & Francis Group GBR. Dist: Taylor & Francis Group.

Li, Junfeng. Noise Reduction Based on Microphone Array & Post-Filtering. 2009. 156p. pap. *(978-3-639-20483-4(2))* VDM Verlag Dr. Mueller e.K.

Li, Qi (Peter). Speaker Authentication. 2011. (Signals & Communication Technology Ser.). (ENG., Illus.). xxv, 237p. 129.00 ***(978-3-642-23730-0(4)***, 3642237304) Springer.

Liew, Alan Wee-Chung & Wang, Shilin. Visual Speech Recognition: Lip Segmentation & Mapping. 2009. (Illus.). 572p. 225.00 *(978-1-60566-186-5(4))* IGI Global.

Lindberg, Borge. Automatic Speech Recognition on Mobile Devices & over Communication Networks. Tan, Zheng-Hua, ed. 2008. (Advances in Pattern Recognition Ser.). (Illus.). XX, 404p. 109.00 *(978-1-84800-142-8(8)*, 1848001428) Springer.

Liu, Yaohe & Song, Tingxin. Yu Yin Shi Bie Yu Kong Zhi Ying Yong Ji Shu. 2008. (CHI., Illus.). vi, 201p. *(978-7-03-020982-5(6))* Science Pr.

Loehr, Andreas. Conversation-and-Control. 2007. 244p. per. *(978-3-8364-5719-4(9))* VDM Verlag Dr. Mueller e.K.

Luig, Johannes. Speech Features for Stress Recognition. 2010. 108p. pap. *(978-3-639-07779-7(2))* VDM Verlag Dr. Mueller e.K.

Maier, Andreas. Parallel Robust Speech Recognition. 2008. 92p. pap. *(978-3-8364-7706-2(8))* VDM Verlag Dr. Mueller e.K.

Makino, Shoji, et al, eds. Blind Speech Separation. (Signals & Communication Technology Ser.). 2010. xv, 432p. pap. 189.00 *(978-90-481-7651-9(4)*, 9048176514) 2007. (Illus.). 432p. 189.00 *(978-1-4020-6478-4(0)*, 1402064780) Springer.

Mary, Leena. Extraction & Representation of Prosody for Speaker, Speech & Language Recognition. 2011. (SpringerBriefs in Electrical & Computer Engineering / SpringerBriefs in Speech Technology Ser.). (ENG., Illus.). x, 61p. pap. 49.95 ***(978-1-4614-1158-1(0)***, 1461411580) Springer.

Misra, Hemant. Noise Robust Automatic Speech Recognition. 2009. 172p. pap. *(978-3-639-14960-9(2))* VDM Verlag Dr. Mueller e.K.

Möller, Sebastian Heinrich. Quality of Telephone-Based Spoken Dialogue Systems. 2010. (ENG., Illus.). xix, 469p. pap. 149.00 *(978-1-4419-3584-7(3)*, 1441935843) Springer.

Muller, Christian, ed. Speaker Classification I: Fundamentals, Features, & Methods. 2007. (Lecture Notes in Computer Science Ser.). (Illus.). 353p. per. 79.95 *(978-3-540-74186-2(0))* Springer.

—Speaker Classification II: Selected Projects. 2007. (Lecture Notes in Artificial Intelligence Ser.). (Illus.). 307p. pap. 79.95 *(978-3-540-74121-3(6))* Springer.

Nass, Clifford & Brave, Scott. Wired for Speech: How Voice Activates & Advances the Human-Computer Relationship. annot. ed. 2007. (ENG., Illus.). 319p. (gr. 17). per. 18.95 *(978-0-262-64065-7(1))* MIT Pr.

Neugebauer, Moritz. Constraint-Based Acoustic Modelling. 2007. (Computer Studies in Language & Speech Ser.). (Illus.). 215p. pap. *(978-3-631-56076-1(1))* Lang, Peter GmbH, Europaischer Verlag der Wissenschaften.

—Constraint-Based Acoustic Modelling. 2007. (Illus.). 215p. pap. 62.95 *(978-0-8204-8779-6(3))* Lang, Peter Publishing, Inc.

Neustein, Amy, ed. Advances in Speech Recognition: Mobile Environments, Call Centers & Clinics. 2010. (ENG., Illus.). xxvi, 370p. 179.00 *(978-1-4419-5950-8(5)*, 1441959505) Springer.

Neustein, Amy & Patil, Hemant A., eds. Forensic Speaker Recognition: Law Enforcement & Counter-Terrorism. 2011. (ENG., Illus.). xxi, 540p. 229.00 *(978-1-4614-0262-6(X)*, 146140262X) Springer.

Örücü, Feristah & DALKILIÇ, GÖKHAN. Characteristics of Contemporary Printed Turkish. 2010. 80p. pap. *(978-3-8383-8507-5(1))* Lambert Academic Publishing.

Peinado, Antonio & Segura, Jose. Speech Recognition over Digital Channels: Robustness & Standards. 2006. (ENG., Illus.). 274p. 140.00 *(978-0-470-02400-3(3))*, Wiley) Wiley, John & Sons, Inc.

Penn, Gerald & Zhu, Xiaodan. Speech Summarization. 2012. (Synthesis Lectures on Human Language Technologies Ser.). 100p. pap. 40.00 *(978-1-60845-056-5(2))* Morgan & Claypool Pubs.

Porzel, Robert. Contextual Computing: Models & Applications. 2010. (Cognitive Technologies Ser.). (Illus.). xii, 178p. 99.00 *(978-3-642-17395-0(0)*, 3642173950) Springer.

Purdy, Trevor. Automated Speech Recognition. 2008. 96p. pap. *(978-3-639-00667-4(4))* VDM Verlag Dr. Mueller e.K.

Raab, Martin. Language Modeling for Machine Translation. 2007. 104p. per. *(978-3-8364-5066-9(6))* VDM Verlag Dr. Mueller e.K.

Rayner, Manny, et al. Putting Linguistics into Speech Recognition: The Regulus Grammar Compiler. 2006. (Illus.). 305p. 65.00 *(978-1-57586-525-6(4))*; per. 25.00 *(978-1-57586-526-3(2))* CSLI Pubns.

Razak, Aishah Abdul. Voice Driven Emotion Reconstruction: for Virtual Reality Telecommunication. 2008. 104p. pap. *(978-3-639-09845-7(5))* VDM Verlag Dr. Mueller e.K.

Riedhammer, Korbinian. An Automatic Intelligibility Test. 2008. 92p. pap. *(978-3-639-01177-7(5))* VDM Verlag Dr. Mueller e.K.

Sadun, Erica & Sande, Steve. Talking to Siri: Learning the Language of Apple's Intelligent Assistant. 2012. (ENG.). 168p. pap. 14.99 ***(978-0-7897-4973-4(4))*** Que.

Sainath, Tara. Speech Recognition Using Broad Classes. 2010. 172p. pap. *(978-3-639-27976-4(X))* VDM Verlag Dr. Mueller e.K.

Sakti, Sakriani, et al. Incorporating Knowledge Sources into Statistical Speech Recognition. 2009. (Lecture Notes in Electrical Engineering Ser.). (ENG., Illus.). xxiv, 196p. 139.00 *(978-0-387-85829-6(6))* Springer.

Schroeder, Manfred R. Computer Speech: Recognition, Compression, Synthesis. 2nd ed. 2010. (Springer Series in Information Sciences Ser.). (Illus.). xxxiv, 375p. pap. 169.00 *(978-3-642-05956-8(2)*, 3642059562) Springer.

Stiefelhagen, Rainer & Garofolo, John, eds. Multimodal Technologies for Perception of Humans: First International Evaluation Workshop on Classification of Events, Activities & Relationships, CLEAR 2006, Southampton, UK, April 6-7, 2006, Revised Selected Papers. 2007. (Lecture Notes in Computer Science / Image Processing, Computer Vision, Pattern Recognition, & Graphics Ser.). (Illus.). xii, 360p. pap. 99.00 *(978-3-540-69567-7(2)*, 3540695672) Springer.

Stork, David G. & Hennecke, Marcus E., eds. Speechreading by Humans & Machines: Models, Systems, & Applications. 2010. (NATO asi Series / Computer & Systems Sciences Ser.). xv, 686p. pap. 359.00 *(978-3-642-08252-8(1)*, 3642082521) Springer.

Strauß, Petra-Maria & Minker, Wolfgang. Proactive Spoken Dialogue Interaction in Multi-Party Environments. 2010. (ENG., Illus.). xx, 180p. 129.00 *(978-1-4419-5991-1(2)*, 1441959912) Springer.

Tan, Tian Swee, et al. Malay Text to Speech Synthesis System: Malay Speech Synthesis System Design & Verification. 2011. 132p. pap. ***(978-3-639-34005-1(1))*** VDM Verlag Dr. Mueller e.K.

Tan, Zheng-Hua & Lindberg, Boerge, eds. Automatic Speech Recognition on Mobile Devices & over Communication Networks. 2010. (Advances in Computer Vision & Pattern Recognition Ser.). (Illus.). xx, 404p. pap. 109.00 *(978-1-84996-736-5(9)*, 1849967369) Springer.

Travieso-González, Carlos M. & Alonso-Hernández, Jesús, eds. Advances in Nonlinear Speech Processing: 5th International Conference on Nonlinear Speech Processing, NoLISP 2011, Las Palmas de Gran Canaria, Spain, November 7-9, 2011, Proceedings. 2011. (Lecture Notes in Computer Science / Lecture Notes in Artificial Intelligence Ser.). (ENG., Illus.). xiv, 280p. pap. 72.00 ***(978-3-642-25019-4(X)***, 364225019X) Springer.

Vogt, Thurid. Real-Time Automatic Emotion Recognition from Speech. 2011. 220p. pap. ***(978-3-8381-2545-9(2))*** Südwestdeutscher Verlag für Hochschulschriften AG & Co. KG.

Wahlster, Wolfgang, ed. SmartKom: Foundations of Multimodal Dialogue Systems: Foundations of Multimodal Dialogue Systems. 2010. (Cognitive Technologies Ser.). (Illus.). xviii, 644p. pap. 139.00 *(978-3-642-06266-7(0)*, 3642062660) Springer.

Wang, DeLiang & Brown, Guy J. Computational Auditory Scene Analysis: Principles, Algorithms & Applications. 2006. 533p. 89.95 *(978-0-470-04338-7(5)*, Wiley-IEEE Pr.) Wiley, John & Sons, Inc.

Will, Thomas. Creating a Dynamic Speech Dialogue - How to Implement Dialogue Initiatives & Question Selection Strategies with Voicexml Agents. 2007. 84p. per. *(978-3-8364-4990-8(0))* VDM Verlag Dr. Mueller e.K.

William Meisel. Speech in the User Interface: Lessons from Experience. 2010. 268p. pap. 10.00 *(978-1-4269-2622-8(7))* Trafford Publishing.

Woelfel, Matthias & McDonough, John. Distant Speech Recognition. 2009. (ENG., Illus.). 594p. 140.00 *(978-0-470-51704-8(2)*, Wiley) Wiley, John & Sons, Inc.

Zia-ul-Haque, Qazi & Zia-Ul-Haque, Qazi. Research Towards Socially Interactive Robots: Robots & Human. 2010. 144p. pap. *(978-3-639-28463-8(1))* VDM Verlag Dr. Mueller e.K.

AUTOMATIC TELLER MACHINES

see Automated Tellers

AUTOMATIC THEOREM PROVING

AI. Symbolic Computation & Education. 2007. 124.00 *(978-981-277-599-3(4))* World Scientific Publishing Co., Inc.

Altenkirch, Thosten, ed. Types for Proofs & Programs: International Workshop, Types 2006 Nottingham, UK, April 18-21, 2006 Revised Selected Papers. 2007. (Lecture Notes in Computer Science Ser.). (Illus.). 268p. pap. 69.95 *(978-3-540-74463-4(0))* Springer.

Automated Technology for Verification & Analysis. 2008. (Lecture Notes in Computer Science / Programming & Software Engineering Ser.). spiral bd. 89.95 *(978-3-540-88386-9(X)*, 354088386X) Springer.

Bü, et al. Application of the Automata Theory to Economic Systems. 2010. 168p. pap. *(978-3-8383-5054-7(5))* Lambert Academic Publishing.

Berardi, Stefano, et al. Types for Proofs & Programs: International Conference, TYPES 2008 Torino, Italy, March 26-29, 2008 Revised Selected Papers. 2009. (Lecture Notes in Computer Science / Theoretical Computer Science & General Issues Ser.). viii, 323p. pap. 79.95 *(978-3-642-02443-6(2)*, 3642024432) Springer.

Berghofer, Stefan, et al. Theorem Proving in Higher Order Logics: 22nd International Conference, TPHOLs 2009, Munich, Germany, August 17-20, 2009, Proceedings. 2009. (Lecture Notes in Computer Science / Theoretical Computer Science & General Issues Ser.). (ENG.). xi, 517p. pap. 109.00 *(978-3-642-03358-2(X)*, 364203358X) Springer.

Bertot, Yves & Castéran, Pierre. Interactive Theorem Proving & Program Development: Coq'Art: the Calculus of Inductive Constructions. 2010. (Texts in Theoretical Computer Science. an EATCS Ser.). xxv, 469p. pap. 109.00 *(978-3-642-05880-6(9)*, 3642058809) Springer.

Bibel, W. & Schmitt, P. H., eds. Automated Deduction - A Basis for Applications Volume I Foundations - Calculi & Methods Volume II Systems & Implementation Techniques Volume III Applications, 3 vols. 2010. (Applied Logic Ser.). 500p. pap. 389.00 *(978-90-481-5050-2(7)*, 9048150507); (ENG.). 346p. pap. 279.00 *(978-90-481-5052-6(3)*, 9048150523); (ENG.). 448p. pap. 349.00 *(978-90-481-5051-9(5)*, 9048150515) Springer.

Bjørner, Nikolaj & Sofronie-Stokkermans, Viorica, eds. Automated Deduction — CADE-23: 23rd International Conference on Automated Deduction, WrocÅ¿aw, Poland, July 31 — August 5, 2011, Proceedings. 2011. (Lecture Notes in Computer Science / Lecture Notes in Artificial Intelligence Ser.). (Illus.). xiii, 508p. pap. 107.00 ***(978-3-642-22437-9(7)***, 3642224377) Springer.

Bjorner, Nikolaj & Voronkov, Andrei, eds. Logic for Programming, Artificial Intelligence, & Reasoning: 18th International Conference, LPAR-18, Merida, Venezuela, March 11-15, 2012, Proceedings. 2012. (Lecture Notes in Computer Science / Theoretical Computer Science & General Issues Ser.: 7180). (ENG., Illus.). xi, 446p. pap. 95.00 ***(978-3-642-28716-9(6)***, 3642287166) Springer.

Bortin, Maksym. An Approach to the Extension of a Theorem Prover by Advanced Structuring Mechanisms. 2010. 235p. pap. *(978-3-8325-2502-6(5))* Logos Verlag Berlin.

Bouajjani, Ahmed & Chin, Wei-Ngan, eds. Automated Technology for Verification & Analysis: 8th International Symposium, ATVA 2010, Singapore, September 21-24, 2010, Proceedings. 2010. (Lecture Notes in Computer Science / Programming & Software Engineering Ser.). viii, 404p. pap. 95.00 *(978-3-642-15642-7(8)*, 3642156428) Springer.

Brannler, Kai & Metcalfe, George, eds. Automated Reasoning with Analytic Tableaux & Related Methods: 20th International Conference, TABLEAUX 2011, Bern, Switzerland, July 4-8, 2011, Proceedings. 2011. (Lecture Notes in Computer Science / Lecture Notes in Artificial Intelligence Ser.). (ENG., Illus.). viii, 279p. pap. 72.00 ***(978-3-642-22118-7(1)***, 3642221181) Springer.

Bultan, Tevfik & Hsiung, Pao-Ann, eds. Automated Technology for Verification & Analysis: 9th International Symposium, ATVA 2011, Taipei, Taiwan, October 11-14, 2011, Proceedings. 2011. (Lecture Notes in Computer Science / Programming & Software Engineering Ser.). (ENG., Illus.). xiv, 532p. pap. 107.00 ***(978-3-642-24371-4(1)***, 3642243711) Springer.

Caferra, Ricardo, et al. Automated Model Building. 2010. (Applied Logic Ser.). xi, 344p. pap. 219.00 *(978-90-481-6696-1(9)*, 9048166969) Springer.

Clarke, Edmund M. & Voronkov, Andrei, eds. Logic for Programming, Artificial Intelligence, & Reasoning: 16th International Conference, LPAR-16, Dakar, Senegal, April 25 — May 1, 2010, Revised Selected Papers. 2011. (Lecture Notes in Computer Science / Lecture Notes in Artificial Intelligence Ser.). (ENG.). x, 517p. pap. 107.00 *(978-3-642-17510-7(4)*, 3642175104) Springer.

D'Agostino, M., et al, eds. Handbook of Tableau Methods. 2010. (Illus.). 680p. pap. 439.00 *(978-90-481-5184-4(8)*, 9048151848) Springer.

Degano, Pierpaolo & ViganÃ², Luca. Foundations & Applications of Security Analysis: Joint Workshop on Automated Reasoning for Security Protocol Analysis & Issues in the Theory of Security, ARSPA-WITS 2009, York, UK, March 28-29, 2009, Revised Selected Papers. 2009. (Lecture Notes in Computer Science / Security & Cryptology Ser.). (ENG., Illus.). x, 223p. pap. 69.95 *(978-3-642-03458-9(6)*, 3642034586) Springer.

Dershowitz, Nachum & Voronkov, A. Logic for Programming, Artificial Intelligence, & Reasoning: 14th International Conference, LPAR 2007, Yerevan, Armenia, October 15-19, 2007: Proceedings. 2007. (Lecture Notes in Computer Science / Lecture Notes in Artificial Intelligence Ser.). (Illus.). xiii, 562p. 109.00 *(978-3-540-75558-6(6))* Springer.

Fermüller, Christian G. & Voronkov, Andrei, eds. Logic for Programming, Artificial Intelligence, & Reasoning: 17th International Conference, LPAR-17, Yogyakarta, Indonesia, October 10-15, 2010, Proceedings. 2010. (Lecture Notes in Computer Science / Theoretical Computer Science & General Issues Ser.). xii, 656p. pap. 119.00 *(978-3-642-16241-1(X)*, 364216241X) Springer.

Furbach, Ulrich & Shankar, Natarajan. Automated Reasoning: Third International Joint Conference, IJCAR 2006, Seattle, WA, USA, August 17-20, 2006: Proceedings. 2007. (Lecture Notes in Computer Science Ser.). (Illus.). XV, 680p. pap. 119.00 *(978-3-540-37187-8(7)*, 3540371877) Springer.

Giese, Martin & Waaler, Arild. Automated Reasoning with Analytic Tableaux & Related Methods: 18th International Conference, TABLEAUX 2009, Oslo, Norway, July 6-10, 2009, Proceedings. 2009. (Lecture Notes in Computer Science / Lecture Notes in Artificial Intelligence Ser.). xii, 341p. pap. 79.95 *(978-3-642-02715-4(6)*, 3642027156) Springer.

Giesl, Jürgen & Hähnle, Reiner, eds. Automated Reasoning: 5th International Joint Conference, IJCAR 2010, Edinburgh, UK, July 16-19, 2010, Proceedings. 2010. (Lecture Notes in Computer Science / Lecture Notes in Artificial Intelligence Ser.). xii, 534p. pap. 107.00 *(978-3-642-14202-4(8)*, 3642142028) Springer.

Goldreich, Oded. Probabilistic Proof Systems: A Primer. 2008. (ENG.). 104p. pap. 75.00 net. *(978-1-60198-152-3(X))* Now Pubs.

Gottlob, G., et al, eds. Computational Logic & Proof Theory: Third Kurt Gödel Colloquium, KGC'93, Brno, Czech Republic, August 24-27, 1993. Proceedings. 2007. (Lecture Notes in Computer Science Ser.). 376p. per. 59.95 *(978-3-540-57184-1(1))* Springer.

Graf, Susanne & Zhang, Wenhui. Automated Technology for Verification & Analysis: 4th International Symposium, ATVA 2006, Beijing, China, October 23-26, 2006, Proceedings. 2006. (Lecture Notes in Computer Science Ser.: Vol. 4218). (Illus.). 540p. pap. 109.00 *(978-3-540-47237-7(1)*, 3540472371) Springer.

Harrison, John. Handbook of Practical Logic & Automated Reasoning. 2009. (ENG., Illus.). 702p. 165.00 *(978-0-521-89957-4(5))* Cambridge Univ. Pr.

Hasan, Osman & Tahar, SofiFne. Probabilistic Analysis using Theorem Proving: A Higher-order Logic Based Approach. 2008. 164p. pap. *(978-3-639-09472-5(7))* VDM Verlag Dr. Mueller e.K.

Kamareddine, F. D., ed. Thirty Five Years of Automating Mathematics. 2010. (Applied Logic Ser.). 328p. pap. 199.00 *(978-90-481-6440-0(0)*, 9048164400) Springer.

Kammnller, Florian. Interactive Theorem Proving in Software Engineering. 2008. 120p. pap. *(978-3-8364-5769-9(5))* VDM Verlag Dr. Mueller e.K.

Kaufmann, Matt & Paulson, Lawrence C., eds. Interactive Theorem Proving: First International Conference, ITP 2010 Edinburgh, UK, July 11-14, 2010, Proceedings. 2010. (Lecture Notes in Computer Science / Theoretical Computer Science & General Issues Ser.). (Illus.). xi, 495p. pap. 109.00 *(978-3-642-14051-8(3)*, 3642140513) Springer.

Kohlenbach, Ulrich. Applied Proof Theory. 2008. (Springer Monographs in Mathematics Ser.). (C). 99.00 *(978-3-540-77532-4(3))* Springer.

—Applied Proof Theory: Proof Interpretations & their Use in Mathematics: Proof Interpretations & their Use in Mathematics. 2010. (Springer Monographs in Mathematics Ser.). xx, 536p. pap. 99.00 *(978-3-642-09627-3(1)*, 3642096271) Springer.

Laudet, M., et al, eds. Symposium on Automatic Demonstration. 2008. (Lecture Notes in Mathematics Ser.). 320p. pap. 59.95 *(978-3-540-04914-2(2)*, 3540049142) Springer.

Leitsch, Alexander & Baaz, Matthias. Methods of Cut-Elimination. 2011. (Trends in Logic Ser.). (ENG., Illus.). vi, 287p. 139.00 *(978-94-007-0319-3(8)*, 9400703198) Springer.

Liu, Zhiming & Ravn, Anders P. Automated Technology for Verification & Analysis: 7th International Symposium, ATVA 2009, Macao, China, October 14-16, 2009, Proceedings. 2009. (Lecture Notes in Computer Science / Programming & Software Engineering Ser.). xi, 414p. pap. 99.00 *(978-3-642-04760-2(2)*, 3642047602) Springer.

Miculan, Marino. Types for Proofs & Programs: International Conference, TYPES 2007, Cividale Del Friuli, Italy, May 2-5, 2007. 2008. (Lecture Notes in Computer Science / Theoretical Computer Science & General Issues Ser.). (Illus.). spiral bd. 69.95 *(978-3-540-68084-0(5)*, 3540680845) Springer.

Nakatsu, Robbie T. Diagrammatic Reasoning in AI. 2009. (ENG., Illus.). 330p. 122.00 *(978-0-470-33187-3(9)*, Wiley) Wiley, John & Sons, Inc.

Namjoshi, Kedar S. (Bell Laboratories). Automated Technology for Verification & Analysis. 2007. (Lecture Notes in Computer Science / Programming & Software Engineering Ser.). spiral bd. 109.00 *(978-3-540-75595-1(0)*, 3540755950) Springer.

Olivetti, Nicola. Automated Reasoning with Analytic Tableaux & Related Methods: 16th International Conference, Tableaux 2007, AIX en Provence, France, July 3-6, 2007, Proceedings. 2007. (Lecture Notes in Artificial Intelligence Ser.). (Illus.). 244p. per. 64.95 *(978-3-540-73098-9(2))* Springer.

Pfenning, Frank. Automated Deduction - CADE-21: 21st International Conference on Automated Deduction Bremen, Germany, July 17-20, 2007 Proceedings. 2007. (Lecture Notes in Computer Science Ser.). (Illus.). 522p. per. 99.00 *(978-3-540-73594-6(1))* Springer.

Recio, Tomas, ed. Automated Deduction in Geometry. 2008. (Lecture Notes in Computer Science Ser.). (Illus.). 211p. pap. 59.95 *(978-3-540-77355-9(X))* Springer.

Rossi, Francesca & Tsoukis, Alexis. Algorithmic Decision Theory: First International Conference, ADT 2009, Venice, Italy, October 2009, Proceedings. 2009. (Lecture Notes in Computer Science / Lecture Notes in Artificial Intelligence Ser.). xii, 460p. pap. 99.00 *(978-3-642-04427-4(1)*, 3642044271) Springer.

Schmidt, Renate A. Automated Deduction - CADE-22: 22nd International Conference on Automated Deduction, Montreal, Canada, August 2-7, 2009. Proceedings. 2009. (Lecture Notes in Computer Science / Lecture Notes in Artificial Intelligence Ser.). xiv, 504p. pap. 109.00 *(978-3-642-02958-5(2)*, 3642029582) Springer.

Schneider, Klaus & Brandt, Jens. Theorem Proving in Higher Order Logics: 20th International Conference, TPHOLs 2007 Kaiserslautern, Germany, September 10-13, 2007 Proceedings. 2007. (Lecture Notes in Computer Science Ser.). (Illus.). 399p. pap. 89.95 *(978-3-540-74590-7(4))* Springer.

Schreck, Pascal, et al, eds. Automated Deduction in Geometry: 8th International Workshop, ADG 2010, Munich, Germany, July 22-24, 2010, Revised Papers. 2011. (Lecture Notes in Computer Science / Lecture Notes in Artificial Intelligence Ser.). (Illus.). x, 259p. pap. 72.00 ***(978-3-642-25069-9(6)***, 3642250696) Springer.

Schumann, Johann M. Automated Theorem Proving in Software Engineering. 2010. (ENG., Illus.). xiv, 228p. pap. 109.00 *(978-3-642-08759-2(0)*, 3642087590) Springer.

Schwartz, Jacob T., et al. Computational Logic & Set Theory: Applying Formalized Logic to Analysis. 2011. (ENG., Illus.). xvii, 416p. 89.95 ***(978-0-85729-807-2(0)***, 0857298070) Springer.

Siekmann, Jörg H., ed. 8th International Conference on Automated Deduction. 2007. (Lecture Notes in Computer Science Ser.). 724p. per. 79.95 *(978-3-540-16780-8(3))* Springer.

Sturm, Thomas & Zengler, Christoph, eds. Automated Deduction in Geometry: 7th International Workshop, ADG 2008, Shanghai, China, September 22-24, 2008, Revised Papers. 2011. (Lecture Notes in Computer Science / Lecture Notes in Artificial Intelligence Ser.). (Illus.). ix, 225p. pap. 72.00 *(978-3-642-21045-7(7)*, 3642210457) Springer.

Suchanek, Fabian. Automated Reasoning & Common Sense. 2008. 72p. pap. *(978-3-639-00393-2(4))* VDM Verlag Dr. Mueller e.K.

A

Theorem Proving in Higher Order Logics. 2008. (Lecture Notes in Computer Science / Theoretical Computer Science & General Issues Ser.). spiral bd. 79.95 *(978-3-540-71065-3(5)*, 3540710655) Springer.

Van Eekelen, Marko, et al, eds. Interactive Theorem Proving: Second International Conference, ITP 2011, Berg en Dal, the Netherlands, August 22-25, 2011, Proceedings. 2011. (Lecture Notes in Computer Science / Theoretical Computer Science & General Issues Ser.). (ENG., Illus.). xi, 383p. pap. 83.00 ***(978-3-642-22862-9(3)***, 3642228623) Springer.

Voronkov, Andrei, ed. Logic for Programming, Artificial Intelligence, & Reasoning: 13th International Conference, Lpar 2006, Phnom Penh, Cambodia, November 13-17, 2006, Proceedings. 2007. (Lecture Notes in Computer Science Ser.). (Illus.). 588p. pap. 119.00 *(978-3-540-48281-9(4)*, 3540482814) Springer.

AUTOMATIC TIMERS

see also Delay Lines

Jay, Jen Chie. Time Synchronization Application in Wireless Sensor Network. 2008. 92p. pap. *(978-3-639-00957-6(6))* VDM Verlag Dr. Mueller e.K.

Monteiro, José & van Leuken, Rene. Integrated Circuit & System Design: Power & Timing Modeling, Optimization & Simulation: 19th International Workshop, PATMOS 2009, Delft, the Netherlands, September 9-11, 2009, Revised Selected Papers. 2010. (Lecture Notes in Computer Science / Theoretical Computer Science & General Issues Ser.). (Illus.). 370p. pap. 83.00 *(978-3-642-11801-2(1)*, 3642118011) Springer.

Shmaliy, Yuriy. GPS-based Optimal FIR Filtering of Clock Models. 2009. (Electrical Engineering Developments Ser.). 89.00 *(978-1-60741-835-1(5))* Nova Science Pubs., Inc.

Timing Issues . . . 1997: ACM International Workshop on Timing Issues in the Specification & Synthesis of Digital Systems Held December 4-5, 1997. Date not set. *(978-0-89791-967-8(X)*, 481971) Assn. for Computing Machinery.

AUTOMATIC TRANSLATING

see Machine Translating

AUTOMATIC TRANSMISSIONS, AUTOMOBILE

see Automobiles—Transmission Devices

AUTOMATION

see also Assembly-Line Methods; Automatic Checkout Equipment; Automatic Control; Automatic Machinery; Electronic Control; Feedback Control Systems; Robotics; Servomechanisms; Systems Engineering

Al. Information Computing & Automation, 3 vols. 2008. (Illus.). xxviii, 1554p. pap. 378.00 *(978-981-279-948-7(6))* World Scientific Publishing Co., Inc.

Alterovitz, Gil, et al. Automation in Proteomics & Genomics: An Engineering Case-Based Approach. 2009. (ENG., Illus.). 340p. 155.00 *(978-0-470-72723-2(3)*, Wiley) Wiley, John & Sons, Inc.

American Society of Mechanical Engineers Staff, ed. Getting Robots & Automation Systems to Work. (Illus.). 43p. *(978-0-85298-507-6(X))* Professional Engineering Publishing.

—Proceedings of DETC99, 25th Design Automation Conference. 1552p. 125.00 *(978-0-7918-1971-5(X))* ASME Pr.

Andrade-Cetto, Juan. Informatics in Control, Automation & Robotics: Selected Papers from the International Conference on Informatics in Control, Automation & Robotics. 2008. (Lecture Notes in Electrical Engineering Ser.). (ENG., Illus.). xxii, 374p. 139.00 *(978-3-540-79141-6(8)*, 3540791418) Springer.

Andrade Cetto, Juan, et al, eds. Informatics in Control Automation & Robotics: Revised & Selected Papers from the International Conference on Informatics in Control Automation & Robotics 2009. 2011. (Lecture Notes in Electrical Engineering Ser.). (Illus.). xiv, 354p. 179.00 *(978-3-642-19729-1(9)*, 3642197299) Springer.

—Informatics in Control Automation & Robotics: Revised & Selected Papers from the International Conference on Informatics in Control Automation & Robotics 2010. 2011. (Lecture Notes in Electrical Engineering Ser.). (Illus.). xiv, 366p. 129.00 *(978-3-642-19538-9(5)*, 3642195385) Springer.

—Informatics in Control, Automation & Robotics: Selcted Papers from the International Conference on Informatics in Control, Automation & Robotics 2008. 2009. (Lecture Notes in Electrical Engineering Ser.). (Illus.). xvi, 284p. 129.00 *(978-3-642-00270-0(6))* Springer.

—Informatics in Control Automation & Robotics: Selected Papers from the International Conference on Informatics in Control Automation & Robotics 2006. 2010. (Lecture Notes in Electrical Engineering Ser.). (Illus.). xxii, 374p. pap. 129.00 *(978-3-642-09803-1(7)*, 3642098037) Springer.

Ao, Sio-long, et al, eds. Intelligent Automation & Systems Engineering. 2011. (Lecture Notes in Electrical Engineering Ser.). (ENG., Illus.). x, 430p. 179.00 ***(978-1-4614-0372-2(3)***, 1461403723) Springer.

Badel, Stéphane & Leblebici, Yusuf. Design Automation for Differential MOS Current-Mode Logic Circuits. 2010. (ENG.). 200p. 139.00 *(978-90-481-3611-7(3)*, 9048136113) Springer.

Bartelt, Terry. Industrial Automated Systems: Instrumentation & Motion Control. 2010. (ENG.). 744p. (C). 151.95 *(978-1-4354-8888-5(1))* Delmar Cengage Learning.

Berger, Hans. Automating with SIMATIC: Controllers, Software, Programming, Data Communication Operator Control & Process Monitoring. 2nd ed. 2012. (ENG.). 300p. 60.00 ***(978-3-89578-387-6(0)***, Wiley-VCH) Wiley, John & Sons, Inc.

Braz, José, et al, eds. Informatics in Control, Automation & Robotics I. 2010. (ENG.). xiii, 290p. pap. 175.00 *(978-90-481-7055-5(9)*, 9048170559) Springer.

Bunch, Cody. Automating VSphere: With VMware vCenter Orchestrator. 2012. (VMware Press Ser.). (ENG.). 312p. pap. 39.99 ***(978-0-321-79991-3(7)***, Prentice Hall) Prentice Hall PTR.

Chase, Greg, et al. Applying Real-World BPM in an SAP Environment. 2010. (Illus.). 600p. 69.95 *(978-1-59229-343-8(3)*, SAP PR.) Galileo Pr., Inc.

Chen, Deji, et al. WirelessHART: Real-Time Mesh Network for Industrial Automation. 2010. (ENG., Illus.). xxii, 276p. 99.00 *(978-1-4419-6046-7(5)*, 1441960465) Springer.

Das, Vinu V., et al, eds. Power Electronics & Instrumentation Engineering: International Conference, PEIE 2010,Kochi, Kerala, India, September 7-9, 2010, Proceedings. 2010. (Communications in Computer & Information Science Ser.). x, 114p. pap. 84.00 *(978-3-642-15738-7(6)*, 3642157386) Springer.

Filipe, Joaquim. Informatics in Control, Automation & Robotics. 2008. (Lecture Notes in Electrical Engineering Ser.). (Illus.). 300p. spiral bd. 129.00 *(978-3-540-85639-9(0)*, 3540856390) Springer.

Filipe, Joaquim, et al, eds. Informatics in Control, Automation & Robotics II. (ENG.). xv, 243p. 2010. pap. 175.00 *(978-90-481-7412-6(0)*, 9048174120) 2007. (Illus.). 175.00 *(978-1-4020-5625-3(7)*, 1402056257) Springer.

Frohwerk, Arthur, et al. Best Practices in Planning Automation Restructuring. Date not set. pap. *(978-1-892942-01-2(1))* Clinical Laboratory Management Assn.

Gajbhiye, Dinil, et al. Low Cost Automation & Effective Material Handling Systems. 2011. 88p. pap. ***(978-3-8454-0825-5(1))*** Lambert Academic Publishing.

Gieras, Jacek F., et al. Linear Synchronous Motors. 2nd rev. ed. 2011. (Electric Power Engineering Ser.). (ENG., Illus.). 520p. 139.95 *(978-1-4398-4221-8(3)*, CRC Press) Taylor & Francis Group GBR. Dist: Taylor & Francis Group.

Guenthner, Wolfgang. Enhancing Cognitive Assistance Systems with Inertial Measurement Units. 2010. (Studies in Computational Intelligence Ser.). (Illus.). x, 144p. pap. 159.00 *(978-3-642-09572-6(0)*, 3642095720) Springer.

Gunn, John. Technique for Automation of Instantaneous Performance Optimization. 2009. 76p. pap. *(978-3-639-21758-2(6))* VDM Verlag Dr. Mueller e.K.

Gupta, Narayan, et al. Online Engineering. 2009. 79.00 *(978-1-60741-166-6(0))* Nova Science Pubs., Inc.

Haas, Christian. Optimierung der Koordinationsinstrumente internationaler Unternehmen: Konzeptionelle Gestaltung und praktische Umsetzung am Beispiel der ATS Automation Tooling Systems Munich GmbH. 2009. 62p. pap. *(978-3-639-18465-5(3))* VDM Verlag Dr. Mueller e.K.

Halder, Bibhrajit. Robust Nonlinear Fault Detection & Isolation of Robotic System. 2009. 140p. pap. *(978-3-639-12839-0(7))* VDM Verlag Dr. Mueller e.K.

Heckman, Davin. A Small World: Smart Houses & the Dream of the Perfect Day. 2008. (ENG., Illus.). 224p. (C). 79.95 *(978-0-8223-4134-5(4))*; per. 22.95 *(978-0-8223-4158-1(1))* Duke Univ. Pr.

Helland, Therese. Software Process Support: A Service-Oriented Approach. 2008. 224p. pap. *(978-3-639-09616-3(9))* VDM Verlag Dr. Mueller e.K.

Hester, Matthew & Dutkiewicz, Sarah. Automating Microsoft Windows Server 2008 R2 with Windows PowerShell 2. 0. 2011. (ENG., Illus.). 432p. pap. 49.99 *(978-1-118-01386-1(7)*, Sybex) Wiley, John & Sons, Inc.

Huang, De-Shuang, et al, eds. Intelligent Control & Automation: Emerging Intelligent Computing Technology & Applications. 2006. (Lecture Notes in Control & Information Sciences Ser.: Vol. 344). (Illus.). xxv, 1121p. 319.00 *(978-3-540-37255-4(5)*, 3540372555) Springer.

IEEE Computer Society Press Staff, ed. Computer & Automation Engineering, Proceedings. 2009. 369p. 222.00 *(978-0-7695-3569-2(0))* IEEE Computer Society Pr.

IEEE Staff. 2007 IEEE International Conference on Automation & Logistics. 2007. pap. 430.00 *(978-1-4244-1530-4(6))* IEEE.

—2007 International Conference on Control, Automation & Systems. 2007. pap. 1052.00 *(978-1-4244-1465-9(2))* IEEE.

—2007 International Conference on Intelligent Sensors, Sensor Networks & Information Processing. 2007. pap. 296.00 *(978-1-4244-1501-4(2))* IEEE.

—2008 7th World Congress on Intelligent Control & Automation. 2008. pap. 2016.00 *(978-1-4244-2113-8(6))* IEEE.

Ihrig, Colin J. & Jones, Alex K. Le Improving Performance & Reducing Power with Hardware Acceleration - Static Timing Analysis Based Transformations of Combinational Logic in a High. 2008. 96p. pap. *(978-3-639-10690-9(3))* VDM Verlag Dr. Mueller e.K.

Intelligent Information Technology Application Research Association Staff & IEEE Computer Society Staff, contrib. by. CASE 2009: 2009 IITA International Conference on Control, Automation & Systems Engineering: Proceedings, 11-12 July 2009, Zhangjiajie, China. 2009. (Illus.). xix, 680p. pap. ***(978-0-7695-3728-3(6))*** IEEE Computer Society Pr.

ISA, creator. ISA Directory of Automation: Products & Services. 2008. (ISA Directory of Automation Ser.). (Illus.). 287p. pap. 163.25 *(978-1-934394-71-7(8))* ISA.

Ito, Takayuki, et al, eds. Advances in Agent-Based Complex Automated Negotiations. 2009. (Studies in Computational Intelligence Ser.). (ENG., Illus.). viii, 216p. 179.00 *(978-3-642-03189-2(7)*, 3642031897) Springer.

John, Karl-Heinz & Tiegelkamp, Michael. IEC 61131-3: Programming Industrial Automation Systems: Concepts & Programming Languages, Requirements for Programming Systems, Decision-Making Aids. 2nd ed. 2010. (Illus.). vi, 376p. 179.00 *(978-3-642-12014-5(8)*, 3642120148) Springer.

Kim, Kwang J. & Tadokoro, Satoshi, eds. Electroactive Polymers for Robotic Applications: Artificial Muscles & Sensors. 2010. (ENG., Illus.). x, 281p. pap. 169.00 *(978-1-84996-590-3(0)*, 1849965900) Springer.

Kim, Tai-hoon, et al, eds. Control & Automation, & Energy System Engineering: International Conferences, CA & CES3 2011, Held as Part of the Future Generation Information Technology Conference, FGIT 2011, in Conjunction with GDC 2011, Jeju Island, Korea, December 8-10, 2011. Proceedings. 2011. (Communications in Computer & Information Science Ser.). (Illus.). xv, 392p. pap. 107.00 ***(978-3-642-26009-4(8)***, 3642260098) Springer.

Lee, Gary, ed. Advances in Automation & Robotics, Vol. 1: Selected papers from the 2011 International Conference on Automation & Robotics (ICAR 2011), Dubai, December 1-2 2011, 2 vols. 2011. (Lecture Notes in Electrical Engineering Ser.). (ENG., Illus.). xvi, 668p. 229.00 ***(978-3-642-25552-6(3)***, 3642255523) Springer.

—Advances in Automation & Robotics, Vol. 2: Selected papers from the 2011 International Conference on Automation & Robotics (ICAR 2011), Dubai, December 1-2 2011. 2011. (Lecture Notes in Electrical Engineering Ser.). (ENG., Illus.). xvi, 656p. 229.00 ***(978-3-642-25645-5(7)***, 3642256457) Springer.

Liu, Yang. Towards E-Automation. 2010. 92p. pap. *(978-3-8383-9791-7(6))* Lambert Academic Publishing.

Love, Jonathan. Process Automation Handbook: A Guide to Theory & Practice. 2007. (Illus.). 1093p. 399.00 *(978-1-84628-281-2(0)*, 1846282810) Springer.

Luo, Qi, ed. Recent Trends in Materials & Mechanical Engineering Materials, Mechatronics & Automation (Applied Mechanics & Materials) 2011. 2265p. pap. ***(978-3-03785-099-2(X))*** Trans Tech Pubns., Ltd.

Mahr, Bernd & Sheng, Huanye, eds. Autonomous Systems - Self-Organization, Management, & Control: Proceedings of the 8th International Workshop Held at Shanghai Jiao Tong University, Shanghai, China, October 6-7 2008. 2010. x, 186p. pap. 159.00 *(978-90-481-8017-2(1)*, 9048180171) Springer.

Markon, Sandor A., et al. Control of Traffic Systems in Buildings. 2010. (Advances in Industrial Control Ser.). (Illus.). xxii, 279p. pap. 179.00 *(978-1-84996-604-7(4)*, 1849966044) Springer.

—Control of Traffic Systems in Buildings: Applications of Modern Supervisory & Optimal Control. 2006. (Advances in Industrial Control Ser.). (Illus.). XXII, 279p. 179.00 *(978-1-84628-448-9(1)*, 1846284481) Springer.

Martin, H. Lee. Techonomics, Vol. 2. 2006. (Industrial Innovation Ser.). (ENG., Illus.). 256p. 102.95 *(978-0-8493-7067-0(1)*, 7067, CRC Press) Taylor & Francis Group GBR. Dist: Taylor & Francis Group.

Martin, Peter & Hale, Gregory. Automation Made Easy: Everything You Wanted to Know about Automation & Need to Ask. 2009. (ENG.). 218p. pap. 79.00 *(978-1-936007-06-6(1))* ISA.

Mathia, Karl. Robotics for Electronics Manufacturing: Principles & Applications in Cleanroom Automation. 2010. (ENG., Illus.). 250p. 130.00 *(978-0-521-87652-0(4))* Cambridge Univ. Pr.

Nof, Shimon Y., ed. Springer Handbook of Automation. 2009. (ENG., Illus.). lxxvi, 1812p. 199.00 *(978-3-540-78830-0(1)*, 3540788301) Springer.

Pang, Justin Chee Khiang, et al. Intelligent Diagnosis & Prognosis of Industrial Networked Systems. 2011. (Automation & Control Engineering Ser.). (ENG., Illus.). 332p. 139.95 *(978-1-4398-3933-1(6)*, CRC Press) Taylor & Francis Group GBR. Dist: Taylor & Francis Group.

Parker, Lynne E., et al, eds. Multi-Robot Systems. from Swarms to Intelligent Automata, Volume III: Proceedings from the 2005 International Workshop on Multi-Robot Systems. 2010. (ENG.). x, 302p. pap. 209.00 *(978-90-481-6849-1(X)*, 904816849X) Springer.

Pigan, Raimond & Metter, Mark. Automating with PROFINET: Industrial Communication Based on Industrial Ethernet. 2nd ed. 2008. (ENG., Illus.). 462p. 80.00 *(978-3-89578-294-7(7)*, Wiley-VCH) Wiley, John & Sons, Inc.

Qi, Luo, ed. Information & Automation: International Symposium, ISIA 2010, Guangzhou, China, November 10-11, 2010. Revised Selected Papers. 2011. (Communications in Computer & Information Science Ser.). (Illus.). xix, 758p. pap. 143.00 *(978-3-642-19852-6(X)*, 364219852X) Springer.

Rao, Ananth. HP QuickTest Professional WorkShop Series: Level 1: HP Quicktest. 2011. 254p. pap. 39.95 ***(978-1-4327-5340-5(1))*** Outskirts Pr., Inc.

Ratchev, Svetan, ed. Micro-Assembly Technologies & Applications: IFIP TC5 WG5. 5 Fourth International Precision Assembly Seminar (IPAS'2008) Chamonix, France, February 10-13 2008. 2010. (IFIP Advances in Information & Communication Technology Ser.). viii, 416p. pap. 149.00 *(978-1-4419-4591-4(1)*, 1441945911) Springer.

—Precision Assembly Technologies for Mini & Micro Products: Proceedings of the IFIP TC5 WG5. 5 Third International Precision Assembly Seminar (IPAS'2006), 19-21 February 2006, Bad Hofgastein, Austria. 2010. (IFIP Advances in Information & Communication Technology Ser.). xii, 336p. pap. 155.00 *(978-1-4419-4063-6(4)*, 1441940634) Springer.

Russ, Gerhard. Situation-Dependent Behavior in Building Automation. 2008. 192p. pap. *(978-3-639-07444-0(0))* VDM Verlag Dr. Mueller e.K.

Sasaki, Minoru. ICMIT 2007: Mechatronics, MEMS, & Smart Materials: 5-6 December 2007, Gifu, Japan, 2 vols. 2007. (Proceedings of SPIE Ser.). (Illus.). 1240p. pap. 190.00 *(978-0-8194-6959-5(9))* SPIE.

Shirase, Keiichi & Aoyagi, Seiji, eds. Service Robotics & Mechatronics: Selected papers of the International Conference on Machine Automation ICMA2008. 2009. (ENG., Illus.). x, 394p. 249.00 *(978-1-84882-693-9(1)*, 1848826931) Springer.

Siemens A and D Translation Services Staff. Dictionary of Electrical Engineering, Power Engineering & Automation / Wörterbuch Elektrotechnik, Energie- und Automatisierungstechnik: Part 2: English-German / Teil 2: Englisch-Deutsch, 2 vols., Pt. 2. 6th ed. 2009. (ENG & GER.). 994p. 145.00 *(978-3-89578-314-2(5)*, Wiley-VCH) Wiley, John & Sons, Inc.

Smit Sibinga, C. Th., et al, eds. Automation in Blood Transfusion. 2010. (Developments in Hematology & Immunology Ser.). 252p. pap. 329.00 *(978-1-4419-4744-4(2)*, 1441947442) Springer.

Sobh, Tarek, et al, eds. Innovative Algorithms & Techniques in Automation, Industrial Electronics & Telecommunications. (ENG.). xvi, 552p. 2010. pap. 139.00 *(978-90-481-7589-5(5)*, 9048175895) 2007. (Illus.). 139.00 *(978-1-4020-6265-0(6)*, 1402062656) Springer.

Sobh, Tarek & Elleithy, Khaled, eds. Novel Algorithms & Techniques in Telecommunications, Automation & Industrial Electronics. 2008. (ENG., Illus.). xvi, 585p. 179.00 *(978-1-4020-8736-3(5)*, 1402087365) Springer.

Tan, Honghua, ed. Informatics in Control, Automation & Robotics: Volume 1, 2 vols. 2011. (Lecture Notes in Electrical Engineering Ser.). (ENG., Illus.). xviii, 818p. 279.00 ***(978-3-642-25898-5(0)***, 3642258980) Springer.

Tan, Kok Kiong & Putra, Andi Sudjana. Drives & Control for Industrial Automation. 2010. (Advances in Industrial Control Ser.). (ENG., Illus.). xiv, 204p. 149.00 *(978-1-84882-424-9(6)*, 1848824246) Springer.

Tanik, Urcun. Architecting Automated Design Systems. 2008. 408p. pap. *(978-3-639-00255-3(5))* VDM Verlag Dr. Mueller e.K.

Tarn, Tzyh-Jong, et al, eds. Robotic Welding, Intelligence & Automation: Rwia - 2010. 2011. (Lecture Notes in Electrical Engineering Ser.). (Illus.). xii, 508p. 229.00 *(978-3-642-19958-5(5)*, 3642199585) Springer.

Technology Research Editors, ed. Welding & Automation, 2007 Ed. 2007. pap. 128.50 *(978-1-60030-622-8(5)*, Search-In-Print) CSA Journal Division.

ter Hofstede, Arthur H. M., et al, eds. Modern Business Process Automation: YAWL & its Support Environment. 2009. (ENG., Illus.). xviii, 676p. 99.00 *(978-3-642-03120-5(X)*, 364203120X) Springer.

Vyatkin, Valeriy, et al, eds. Embedded System Design in Intelligent Industrial Automation. 2008. 104p. pap. 17.00 *(978-977-454-029-5(8))* Hindawi Publishing Corp.

Wu, Yanwen, ed. Advances in Computer, Communication, Control & Automation. 2011. (Lecture Notes in Electrical Engineering Ser.). (ENG., Illus.). xvi, 804p. 279.00 ***(978-3-642-25540-3(X)***, 364225540X) Springer.

Xu, Lai. Monitoring Multi-Party Contracts for E-Business. 2008. 168p. pap. *(978-3-639-11484-3(1))* VDM Verlag Dr. Mueller e.K.

Yang, Dehuai, ed. Informatics in Control, Automation & Robotics: Volume 2, 2 vols. 2011. (Lecture Notes in Electrical Engineering Ser.). (ENG., Illus.). xviii, 838p. 279.00 ***(978-3-642-25991-3(X)***, 364225991X) Springer.

Zeng, Dehuai, ed. Advances in Information Technology & Industry Applications. 2012. (Lecture Notes in Electrical Engineering Ser.). (ENG., Illus.). xvi, 752p. 279.00 ***(978-3-642-26000-1(4)***, 3642260004) Springer.

Zhang, Helen, et al, eds. Advanced Research on Automation, Communication, Architectonics & Materials: Selected, Peer Reviewed Papers from the 2011 International Conference on ... June 18-19 (Advanced Materials Research) 2011. 1382p. pap. ***(978-3-03785-103-6(1))*** Trans Tech Pubns., Ltd.

Ziagos, Sotirius. Analysis of Signalling Effects. 2008. 104p. pap. *(978-3-639-03046-4(X))* VDM Verlag Dr. Mueller e.K.

Zuo, Dunwen, et al, eds. Functional Manufacturing Technologies & Ceesuro I. 2010. (Key Engineering Materials Ser.: Vols. 426-427). (Illus.). 720p. pap. 345.00 *(978-0-87849-300-5(X))* Translatons for Technology.

2007 IEEE International Conference on Automation Science & Engineering. 2007. pap. 340.00 *(978-1-4244-1153-5(X)*, 07EX1754) IEEE.

2007 Second IEEE Conference on Industrial Electronics & Applications. 2007. pap. 430.00 *(978-1-4244-0736-1(2)*, 07EX1593) IEEE.

AUTOMATION—BIBLIOGRAPHY

Devries, Kelly. Medieval Military Technology. 2nd ed. 2011. pap. *(978-1-55111-714-0(2))* Univ. of Toronto Pr.

AUTOMATION—DATA PROCESSING

Bissett, Brian. Automated Data Analysis Using Excel. 2007. (ENG., Illus.). 480p. pap. 67.95 *(978-1-58488-885-7(7)*, Chapman & Hall/CRC) CRC Pr. LLC.

Chen, Wai-Kai. Computer Aided Design & Design Automation. 3rd ed. 2009. (Circuits & Filters Handbook, 3rd Edition Ser.). (ENG., Illus.). 435p. 102.95 *(978-1-4200-5918-2(1)*, CRC Press) Taylor & Francis Group GBR. Dist: Taylor & Francis Group.

AUTOMATION—DICTIONARIES

Antoni, Thomas. Dictionary of Drives & Mechatronics / Wörterbuch Antriebstechnik und Mechatronik: Deutsch-Englisch / Englisch-Deutsch. 3rd ed. 2007. (GER & ENG.). 998p. 130.00 *(978-3-89578-282-4(3)*, Wiley-VCH) Wiley, John & Sons, Inc.

AUTOMATION—ECONOMIC ASPECTS

MacMillan, R. H. Automation, Friend or Foe? 2011. (ENG.). 118p. pap. 39.99 ***(978-1-107-65166-1(2))*** Cambridge Univ. Pr.

AUTOMATION—SOCIAL ASPECTS

Granter, Edward. Critical Social Theory & the End of Work. 2009. (Rethinking Classical Sociology Ser.). 212p. 99.95 *(978-0-7546-7697-3(8))* Ashgate Publishing Co.

MacMillan, R. H. Automation, Friend or Foe? 2011. (ENG.). 118p. pap. 39.99 ***(978-1-107-65166-1(2))*** Cambridge Univ. Pr.

Noble, David F. Forces of Production: A Social History of Industrial Automation. 2011. (ENG., Illus.). 427p. pap. 49.95 *(978-1-4128-1828-5(1))* Transaction Pubs.

AUTOMATISM

Adler, Jan Rosamomd & Oberon, Ron J. Many Planes Above: A Connection to the Universe & Universal Knowledge Book II, 2 vols., Vol. 2. 2007. (Illus.). 386p. pap. 22.95 *(978-0-615-14580-8(9))* Oberon, Ron & Assocs., LLC.

Adler, Jan Rosamond & Oberon, Ron J. Our Earth & Beyond: A Message from the Universe to 21st Century Earth Book I, 2 vols. 2007. (Illus.). 386p. pap. 22.95 *(978-0-615-13526-7(9))* Oberon, Ron & Assocs., LLC.

Bond, Frederick Blig. Hill of Vision A Forecast of the Great W. 2006. pap. 21.95 *(978-1-4286-5083-1(0))* Kessinger Publishing, LLC.

Bourduas, Paul-Emile, et al. Total Refusal - Refus Globa : The Complete 1948 Manifesto of the Montreal Automatists. 2010. (Exile Classics Ser.). (ENG., Illus.). 140p. pap. 18.95 *(978-1-55096-107-2(1))* Exile Editions, Ltd. CAN. Dist: Independent Pubs. Group.

Brandon, Wilfred. Incarnation: A Plea from the Masters. Ellis, Edith, tr. 2007. (ENG.). 200p. 39.95 *(978-0-548-08085-6(2))* Kessinger Publishing, LLC.

Burton, Eva. A Natural Bridge to Cross. 2007. (ENG.). 292p. 43.95 *(978-0-548-10839-0(0))* Kessinger Publishing, LLC.

—Your Unseen Forces. 2007. (ENG.). 300p. 43.95 *(978-0-548-12578-6(3))* 2006. pap. 28.95 *(978-1-4286-3555-5(6))* Kessinger Publishing, LLC.

Nasgaard, Roald & Ellenwood, Ray. The Automatiste Revolution: Montreal, 1941-1960. 2009. (ENG., Illus.). 160p. 50.00 *(978-1-55365-356-1(4))* D&M Pubs. Inc. CAN. Dist: Perseus-PGW.

Schopp, Robert F. Automatism, Insanity, & the Psychology of Criminal Responsibility: A Philosophical Inquiry. 2008. (Cambridge Studies in Philosophy & Law Ser.). (ENG.). 292p. (C). pap. 34.99 *(978-0-521-06133-9(4))* Cambridge Univ. Pr.

AUTOMATONS
see Robots

AUTOMOBILE ACCESSORIES
see Automobiles—Equipment and Supplies

AUTOMOBILE ACCIDENTS
see Traffic Accidents

AUTOMOBILE BATTERIES
see Automobiles—Batteries

AUTOMOBILE BRAKES
see Automobiles—Brakes

AUTOMOBILE BODIES
see Automobiles—Bodies

AUTOMOBILE BUYING
see Automobiles—Purchasing

AUTOMOBILE CLUB OF SOUTHERN CALIFORNIA

Hayes, Bill & Quattlebaum, Jim. The Original Wild Ones: Tales of the Boozefighters Motorcycle Club. 2009. (ENG., Illus.). 288p. pap. 17.99 *(978-0-7603-3537-6(0),* 0760335370, Motorbooks) MBI Publishing Co. LLC.

AUTOMOBILE COLLISION INSURANCE
see Automobile Insurance

AUTOMOBILE CONSTRUCTION WORKERS
see Automobile Industry Workers

AUTOMOBILE DRIVER EDUCATION
see also Traffic Safety—Study and Teaching

Azarela, Linda Ann. Learn How to Drive & Survive. 2010. 120p. 22.95 *(978-1-4502-3247-0(7));* (ENG.). pap. 12.95 *(978-1-4502-3246-3(9))* iUniverse, Inc.

Bartkowiak, Judy. So You Have Passed Your Driving Test - What Now? Advanced Driving Skills for Young Drivers. 2011. 86p. pap. ***(978-1-908218-37-7(1))*** MX Publishing, Ltd.

Berardelli, Phil. Safe Young Drivers: A Guide for Parents & Teens. 2008. (ENG., Illus.). spiral bd. 15.00 *(978-0-9814773-1-2(3))* Mountain Lake Pr.

—Safe Young Drivers: A Guide for Parents & Teens. 3rd rev. ed. 2006. (ENG.). spiral bd. 18.00 *(978-0-9675191-6-6(0))* Nautilus Communications, Inc.

Brock, John F., et al. Effectiveness of Commercial Motor Vehicle Driver Training Curricula & Delivery Methods. 2007. (Illus.). 34p. 34.00 *(978-0-309-09883-0(1))* Transportation Research Board.

Collins, Amy Fine. The God of Driving: How I Overcame Fear & Put Myself in the Driver's. 2011. (ENG.). 352p. pap. 21.99 *(978-1-4516-3169-2(3))* Simon & Schuster.

Crane, Colin. Become an Approved Driving Instuctor. 2009. 260p. pap. 30.00 *(978-1-84528-348-3(1),* How To Books GBR. Dist: Parkwest Pubns., Inc.

Damerst Publishing LLC Staff. Teen Driving Guides: Parent Guide & Teen Guide, vols. 2, vol. 2. Damerst, Douglas, ed. 2011. (ENG., Illus.). 108p. spiral bd. 29.95 ***(978-0-615-54526-4(2))*** Damerst Publishing LLC.

Dorn, Lisa, ed. Driver Behaviour & Training, Vol. 2. 2008. (Human Factors in Road & Rail Transport Ser.). (Illus.). 476p. 124.95 *(978-0-7546-7203-6(4))* Ashgate Publishing Co.

Goodwin, Arthur. Guidance for Implementation of the AASHTO Strategic Highway Safety Plan. 2007. (Illus.). pap. *(978-0-309-09908-0(0))* Transportation Research Board.

Hayes, Anne Marie. 3 Keys to Keeping Your Teen Alive: Lessons for Surviving the First Year of Driving. 2011. (ENG.). 290p. pap. 24.95 *(978-1-60037-884-3(6))* Morgan James Publishing.

Miller, Frank. Driverthink. 2009. 184p. pap. 14.95 *(978-1-59858-984-9(9))* Dog Ear Publishing, LLC.

Praxis II Exam Secrets Test Prep Staff, ed. Praxis II Safety/Driver Education (0860) Exam Secrets Study Guide: Praxis II Test Review for the Praxis II Subject Assessments. 2011. (C). 62.99 *(978-1-61403-706-4(X))* Mometrix Media LLC.

Rudman, Jack. Safety/Driver Education. (National Teacher Examination Ser.: NT-59). pap. 29.95 *(978-0-8373-8479-5(6),* Passbooks) National Learning Corp.

Scotti, Anthony. Professional Driving Techniques: The Essential Guide to Operating a Motor Vehicle with Confidence & Skill, 1. 4th rev. ed. 2007. Orig. Title: Driving Techniques. (Illus.). 310p. pap. 22.95 *(978-0-9793813-1-7(2),* sku PDT4) PhotoGraphics Publishing.

AUTOMOBILE DRIVERS
see also Automobile Drivers' Licenses; Automobile Driving; Drinking and Traffic Accidents; Police Pursuit Driving; Taxicab Drivers

Alexander, Jesse. Inside the Archives. 2010. (Illus.). 96p. 75.00 *(978-1-935007-10-4(6))* Bull, David Publishing, Inc.

Amundrud, Robert A. Explanations, Excuses, & Exhortations: Several Trucks, One Driver, & a Multitude of Experiences. 2010. 160p. pap. 19.95 *(978-1-4269-2304-3(X))* Trafford Publishing.

Argetsinger, Michael. Mark Donohue: His Life in Photographs. 2010. (Illus.). 244p. 39.95 *(978-1-935007-09-8(2))* Bull, David Publishing, Inc.

Armentrout, David & Armentrout, Patricia. Jimmie Johnson. 2006. (In the Fast Lane Ser.). (Illus.). 24p. (J). (gr. -1-3). lib. bdg. *(978-1-60044-217-9(X))* Rourke Publishing, LLC.

Arneson, Erik. John Force: The Straight Story of Drag Racing's 300-mph Superstar. 2009. (ENG., Illus.). 176p. pap. 19.99 *(978-0-7603-3566-6(4),* 0760335664, Motorbooks) MBI Publishing Co. LLC.

Arron, Simon & Hughes, Mark. The Complete Book of Formula One. 2008. (Complete Book Ser.). (ENG., Illus.). 492p. 60.00 *(978-0-7603-3456-0(0),* 0760334560, Motorbooks) MBI Publishing Co. LLC.

Barnard, Yvonne, et al, eds. The Safety of Intelligent Driver Support Systems: Design Evaluation & Social Perspectives. 2011. (Human Factors in Road & Rail Transport Ser.). (Illus.). 210p. 124.95 *(978-0-7546-7776-5(1))* Ashgate Publishing Co.

Bechtel, Mark. He Crashed Me So I Crashed Him Back: The True Story of the Year the King, Jaws, Earnhardt, & the Rest of NASCAR's Feudin', Fightin' Good Ol' Boys Put Stock Car Racing on the Map. 2011. (ENG., Illus.). 320p. pap. 14.99 *(978-0-316-03403-6(7),* Back Bay Bks.) Little Brown & Co.

Bergoffen, Gene, et al. Older Commercial Drivers, Do They Pose a Safety Risk? 2010. (Illus.). 28p. ***(978-0-309-14314-1(4))*** Transportation Research Board.

Bh. Secrets Exposed: Discrimination still exist in the nscs.inThe good ole boy racing seriesThe proof & the truth shall set you Free! 2009. 48p. pap. 9.95 *(978-1-4401-5296-2(9))* iUniverse, Inc.

Blount, Terry. The Blount Report: NASCAR's Most Overrated & Underrated Drivers, Cars, Teams, & Tracks. 2009. (ENG.). 240p. 24.95 *(978-1-60078-089-9(X))* Triumph Bks.

Bob, McClurg. Yenko: The Man, the Machines, the Legend. 2010. 192p. 39.95 *(978-1-932494-85-3(5))* CarTech, Inc.

Boehme, Michael L., ed. Roads & Drivers. 2010. (Transportation Infrastructure - Roads, Highways, Bridges, Airports & Mass Transit Ser.). 235.00 *(978-1-60741-999-0(8))* Nova Science Pubs., Inc.

Bouzanquet, Jean Francois. Fast Ladies: Female Racing Drivers 1888 To 1970. 2009. (ENG., Illus.). 176p. pap. 59.95 *(978-1-84584-225-3(1),* 1845842251) Veloce Publishing Ltd. GBR. Dist: MBI Distribution Services/Quayside Distribution.

Boyce, Doug. Grumpy's Toys: The Authorized History of Grumpy Jenkins' Cars. 2011. (Illus.). pap. 34.95 *(978-1-934709-27-6(1))* CarTech, Inc.

Broughton, Paul & Walker, Linda. Motorcycling & Leisure: Understanding the Recreational PTW Rider. 2009. (Human Factors in Road & Rail Transport Ser.). (Illus.). 216p. 124.95 *(978-0-7546-7501-3(7))* Ashgate Publishing Co.

Burgt, Andrew. Lewis Hamilton World Champion 2nd. 2nd ed. 2008. (Illus.). 236p. *(978-1-84425-699-0(5))* Haynes Publishing PLC.

Burn, Liz. Drag Racing: Through the eyes of a Woman. 2010. (Illus.). 120p. pap. 33.49 *(978-1-4490-3900-4(6))* AuthorHouse.

Bye, Chris. Crash Test. 2007. pap. *(978-0-9784402-6-8(9))* BPS Bks.

Cannell, Michael. The Limit: Life & Death on the 1961 Grand Prix Circuit. 1. ed. 2012. (ENG.). 415p. 31.99 ***(978-1-4104-4624-4(7))*** Thorndike Pr.

Castro, Candida & Hartley, Laurence R. Human Factors of Visual & Cognitive Performance in Driving. 2008. (ENG., Illus.). 296p. 97.95 *(978-1-4200-5530-6(5),* CRC Press) Taylor & Francis Group GBR. Dist: Taylor & Francis Group.

Castroneves, Helio. Victory Road: The Ride of My Life. 2010. (ENG.). 304p. (gr. 12). 24.95 *(978-0-451-22737-9(9))* Penguin Group (USA) Inc.

Clarke, Deborah. Driving Women: Fiction & Automobile Culture in Twentieth-Century America. 2007. (ENG., Illus.). 226p. (gr. 17). 49.00 *(978-0-8018-8550-1(7));* per. 27.00 *(978-0-8018-8617-1(1))* Johns Hopkins Univ. Pr.

Clarkson, Jeremy. Motorworld. 2006. (ENG., Illus.). 208p. (gr. 12-18). 16.00 *(978-0-14-101787-7(2),* Penguin Global) Penguin Group (USA) Inc.

Clarsen, Georgine. Eat My Dust: Early Women Motorists. 2008. (Johns Hopkins University Studies in Historical & Political Science Ser.: 126). (ENG., Illus.). 216p. (gr. 17). 52.00 *(978-0-8018-8465-8(9))* Johns Hopkins Univ. Pr.

Codling, Stuart. Real Racers: Formula 1 in the 1950s & 1960s: A Driver's Perspective. Rare & Classic Images from the Klemantaski Collection. 2011. (ENG., Illus.). 208p. 40.00 *(978-0-7603-3891-9(4),* 0760338914, Motorbooks) MBI Publishing Co. LLC.

Collings, Timothy & Edworthy, Sarah. The Formula One Years. 2009. (ENG., Illus.). 336p. 39.95 *(978-1-84732-166-4(6))* Carlton Bks., Ltd. GBR. Dist: Sterling Publishing Co., Inc.

Collins, Ben. The Man in the White Suit: The Stig, le Mans, the Fast Lane & Me. 2012. (ENG., Illus.). 352p. 12.95 ***(978-0-00-733169-7(X))*** HarperCollins Pubs. Ltd. GBR. Dist: Independent Pubs. Group.

Collins, Peter. British Touring Car Racing: The Crowd's Favourite - Late 1960s to 1990. 2009. (Those Were the Days Ser.). (ENG., Illus.). 96p. pap. 29.95 *(978-1-84584-247-5(2),* 1845842472) Veloce Publishing Ltd. GBR. Dist: MBI Distribution Services/Quayside Distribution.

Combating Distracted Driving: Managing Behavioral & Technological Risks: Hearing Before the Committee on Commerce, Science, & Transportation, United States Senate, One Hundred Eleventh Congress, First Session, October 28, 2009. 2010. iii, 41p. *(978-0-16-086161-1(6),* 552-070-41261-1) United States Government Printing Office.

Comfort, Ray. 101 Annoying Things about Other Drivers. 2007. (Illus.). 139p. per. *(978-0-89221-668-0(9))* New Leaf Pr., Inc.

Comte, Michel. Michael by Michel, 1 vol. ltd. ed. 2008. (ENG., Illus.). 120p. (gr. 13-18). 100.00 *(978-3-88243-898-7(3))* Steidl, Gerhard Druckerei und Verlag DEU. Dist: Innovative Logistics.

Cotter, Tom. TV Tommy Ivo: Drag Racing's Master Showman. 2011. (ENG., Illus.). 240p. 28.00 *(978-0-7603-3892-6(2),* 0760338922, Motorbooks) MBI Publishing Co. LLC.

Coulthard, David. It Is What It Is. 2008. (ENG., Illus.). 392p. pap. 18.95 *(978-0-7528-9334-1(3),* Orion Publishing Group, Ltd. GBR. Dist: Independent Pubs. Group.

Daly, Derek. Race to Win: How to Become a Complete Champion Driver. 2008. (ENG., Illus.). 256p. 25.95 *(978-0-7603-3185-9(5),* 0760331855, Motorbooks) MBI Publishing Co. LLC.

Davis, Gerry Hempel. Romancing the Roads: A Driving Diva's Firsthand Guide, Volume II West of the Mississippi. 2011. ***(978-1-58979-640-9(3))*** Taylor Trade Publishing.

—Romancing the Roads Vol. 2: A Driving Diva's Firsthand Guide, West of the Mississippi, Volume 2. 2012. (ENG.). 344p. pap. 18.95 ***(978-1-58979-639-3(X))*** Taylor Trade Publishing.

Davis, S. C. H. Sammy. My Life in Motorsport: His Final Autobiography. 2008. (ENG., Illus.). 192p. 44.95 *(978-1-906133-02-3(6),* 1906133026) Herridge & Sons Ltd.

De Lap, Adam John. Home James: Confessions from a Limousine Chauffer. 2011. 114p. pap. 19.95 ***(978-1-4560-9668-7(0))*** PublishAmerica, Inc.

Dieckman, Diane. Twentieth Century Drifter: The Life of Marty Robbins. 2012. (Music in American Life Ser.). (ENG., Illus.). 304p. 29.95 ***(978-0-252-03632-3(8)),*** Univ. of Illinois Pr.

Donovan, Brian. Hard Driving: The Wendell Scott Story. 2009. (ENG.). 328p. 16.99 *(978-1-58642-163-1(3))* Steerforth Pr.

Douglas, Richard. A Trucker's Diary. 2011. 144p. pap. 24.95 ***(978-1-4626-1188-1(5))*** PublishAmerica, Inc.

Duma, Tuncay. Madd, Drunk Driving Laws, & Deterrence. 2009. 124p. pap. *(978-3-639-13221-2(1))* VDM Verlag Dr. Mueller e.K.

Ecclestone, Bernie, frwd. The Official Formula 1 Season Review 2011. 2012. (ENG., Illus.). 272p. 49.95 ***(978-0-85733-108-3(6),*** 0857331086) Haynes Publishing PLC GBR. Dist: MBI Distribution Services/Quayside Distribution.

Ecclestone, Bernie, frwd. Official Formula1 Season Review 2010. 2011. (ENG., Illus.). 272p. 44.95 *(978-0-85733-001-7(2),* 0857330012) Haynes Publishing PLC GBR. Dist: MBI Distribution Services/Quayside Distribution.

Edelstein, Robert. Nascar Legends: Memorable Men, Moments, & Machines in Racing History. 2011. (ENG.). 320p. (gr. 12). 25.95 *(978-1-59020-184-8(1))* Overlook Pr., The.

Ellwanger, Steven J. Young Driver Accidentsand Delinquency: Modeling & General Theories of Crime. 2006. (Criminal Justice). (Illus.). 264p. lib. bdg. 70.00 *(978-1-59332-194-9(5))* LFB Scholarly Publishing LLC.

Evans, David, ed. Rallycourse 2007-2008: The World's Leading Rally Annual. 2008. (Rallycourse: the World's Leading Rally Annual Ser.). (ENG., Illus.). 192p. 49.95 *(978-1-905334-23-0(0),* 1905334230) Crash Media Grp. Ltd. GBR. Dist: MBI Distribution Services/Quayside Distribution.

—Rallycourse, 2008-2009. 2009. (ENG., Illus.). 192p. 49.95 *(978-1-905334-33-9(8),* 1905334338) Crash Media Grp. Ltd. GBR. Dist: MBI Distribution Services/Quayside Distribution.

Fielden, Greg & Auto Editors of Consumer Guide Staff. NASCAR Chronicle. 2008. (NASCAR Library Collection). (Illus.). 532p. 12.98 *(978-1-4127-7513-7(2))* Publications International, Ltd.

Finn, Joel E. American Road Racing: 1948-1950. 2007. (Illus.). 452p. 150.00 *(978-0-9647769-3-7(6))* Garnet Hill Publishing Co., Inc.

Ford, Ruth E. Your Driving Eye. 2011. 106p. 39.95 ***(978-1-258-08576-6(3))*** Literary Licensing, LLC.

Formula One Journalists Editors, ed. The Official Formula 1 Season Review 2007. 2008. (Official Formula One Season Review Ser.). (ENG., Illus.). 248p. 34.95 *(978-1-84425-453-8(4),* 1844254534) Haynes Publishing PLC GBR. Dist: MBI Distribution Services/Quayside Distribution.

Frilling, Christoph. Elly Beinhorn und Bernd Rosemeyer - Kleiner Grenzverkehr zwischen Resistenz und Kumpanei im Nationalsozialismus: Studien zu Habitus und Sprache prominenter Mitläufer. 2009. (GER.). 478p. pap. 107.95 *(978-3-631-58836-9(4))* Lang, Peter GmbH, Europaischer Verlag der Wissenschaften DEU. Dist: Lang, Peter.

Ganchy, Sally. Great Moments in NASCAR Racing. (Highlights of NASCAR Racing Ser.). 48p. (gr. 5-5). 2009. 53.00 *(978-1-61513-299-7(6),* Rosen Central) 2008. (Illus.). (YA). lib. bdg. 26.50 *(978-1-4042-1397-5(X))* Rosen Publishing Group, Inc., The.

Gillispie, Tom. Angel in Black: Remembering of Dale Earnhardt Sr. 2008. (ENG., Illus.). 304p. per. 19.99 *(978-1-58182-638-8(9),* Cumberland Hse.) Sourcebooks, Inc.

Goodwin, Carl. They Started in MGs: Profiles of Sports Car Racers of the 1950s. 2011. (ENG., Illus.). 291p. pap. 35.00 *(978-0-7864-6052-6(0))* McFarland & Co., Inc. Pubs.

Gurwell, Matt. Beyond Driving with Dignity: The Workbook for the Families of Older Drivers. 2010. 130p. pap. 27.99 *(978-0-615-38896-0(5))* Keeping us Safe, LLC.

Hamilton, Maurice. Chequered Conflict: The Inside Story on Two Explosive F1 World Championships. 2008. (ENG., Illus.). 320p. 34.95 *(978-1-84737-268-0(6))* Simon & Schuster, Ltd. GBR. Dist: Independent Pubs. Group.

Hansen, Arlen J. Gentleman Volunteers: The Story of the American Ambulance Drivers in the First World War. 2011. (ENG., Illus.). 256p. pap. 16.95 *(978-1-61145-099-6(3),* 611099, Arcade Publishing) Skyhorse Publishing Co., Inc.

Hartenbaum, Natalie P. The DOT Medical Examination: A Guide to Commercial Drivers' Medical Certification. 5th ed. 2010. *(978-1-883595-53-1(3),* OEM Pr.) OEM Health Information, Inc.

Hawley, Samuel. Speed Duel: The Inside Story of the Land Speed Record in the Sixties. 2010. (ENG., Illus.). 360p. pap. 24.95 *(978-1-55407-633-8(1))* Firefly Bks., Ltd.

Hayes, Anne Marie. 3 Keys to Keeping Your Teen Alive: Lessons for Surviving the First Year of Driving. 2011. (ENG.). 290p. pap. 24.95 *(978-1-60037-884-3(6))* Morgan James Publishing.

Hennessy, Dwight, ed. Traffic Psychology: An International Perspective. 2010. (Psychology Research Progress Ser.). (Illus.). xv, 352p. 195.00 *(978-1-61668-846-2(7))* Nova Science Pubs., Inc.

Henny, Phil Louis, as told by. Remembering Carroll Shelby. 2010. per. 59.00 *(978-0-9765247-2-4(4))* Editions Cotty.

Henry, Alan. Jenson Button: A World Champion's Story. 2009. (Illus.). 176p. *(978-1-84425-936-6(6))* Haynes Publishing PLC.

Hilbert, Richard C. Distracted Driving: Research & Prevention Efforts. 2011. (Transportation Infrastructure - Roads, Highways, Bridges, Airports & Mass Transit Ser.). 115.00 *(978-1-61209-278-2(0))* Nova Science Pubs., Inc.

Hilton, Christopher. Grand Prix Showdown! The Full Drama of Every Championship-Deciding Grand Prix since 1950. 2nd ed. 2010. (ENG., Illus.). 464p. 34.95 *(978-1-84425-709-6(6),* 1844257096) Haynes Publishing PLC GBR. Dist: MBI Distribution Services/Quayside Distribution.

—Memories of Clay Regazzoni. 2009. (ENG., Illus.). 192p. 59.95 *(978-1-84425-479-8(8),* 1844254798) Haynes Publishing PLC GBR. Dist: MBI Distribution Services/Quayside Distribution.

—Memories of Senna: Anecdotes & Insights from Those Who Knew Him. 2011. (ENG., Illus.). 256p. 24.95 ***(978-0-85733-229-5(5),*** 0857332295) Haynes Publishing PLC GBR. Dist: MBI Distribution Services/Quayside Distribution.

Hilton, Christopher. Michael Schumacher: The Whole Story. 2008. (ENG., Illus.). 472p. per. 16.95 *(978-1-84425-448-4(8),* 1844254488) Haynes Publishing PLC GBR. Dist: MBI Distribution Services/Quayside Distribution.

Hines, Martin. Every Split Second Counts: My Life with Fast Karts, Fast Women & F1 Superstars. 2008. (ENG., Illus.). 320p. 34.95 *(978-1-84454-658-9(6))* Blake, John Publishing, Ltd. GBR. Dist: Independent Pubs. Group.

Hole, Graham. The Psychology of Driving. 2006. (ENG., Illus.). 248p. per. 34.95 *(978-0-8058-5978-2(0),* Psychology Press) Taylor & Francis Group GBR. Dist: Taylor & Francis Group.

Hole, Graham J. The Psychology of Driving. 2006. (ENG., Illus.). 248p. 73.95 *(978-0-8058-4425-2(2),* Psychology Press) Taylor & Francis Group GBR. Dist: Taylor & Francis Group.

Hughes, Mark. The Unofficial Complete Encyclopedia of Formula One: An Illustrated Guide to the World's Fastest Sport. 2009. (ENG., Illus.). 256p. 29.99 *(978-0-7548-1959-2(0))* Anness Publishing GBR. Dist: National Bk. Network.

Ingram, Jonathan. Nascar in Photographs. 2007. (Illus.). 192p. *(978-1-84732-022-3(8))* Carlton Bks., Ltd.

Jalife, Carlos. Brothers Rodriguez. 2009. (Illus.). 592p. *(978-1-893618-89-3(7))* Bull, David Publishing, Inc.

Jennings, Charles. Burning Rubber: The Extraordinary Story of Formula One. 2011. (ENG., Illus.). 336p. 13.95 *(978-0-85738-125-5(3));* 256p. 27.95 *(978-1-84916-092-6(9))* Quercus GBR. Dist: Independent Pubs. Group.

Jones, Bruce. The Complete Encyclopedia of Formula One. 2010. (ENG., Illus.). 288p. pap. 29.95 *(978-1-84732-655-3(2))* Carlton Bks., Ltd. GBR. Dist: Sterling Publishing Co., Inc.

Kennedy, Pat. How Much Do You Really Know about the Indianapolis 500? 500+ Multiple-Choice Questions to Educate & Test Your Knowledge of the Hundred-Year History. 2011. 232p. pap. 16.95 *(978-1-4490-8894-1(5))* AuthorHouse.

Kiesbye, Stefan, ed. Distracted Driving. 2012. (At Issue Ser.). (ENG.). 128p. (gr. 10-12). pap. 33.70 ***(978-0-7377-5567-1(9),*** Greenhaven Pr., Inc.); (YA). (gr. 9-12). lib. bdg. 23.85 ***(978-0-7377-5566-4(0))*** Cengage Gale.

La Bella, Laura. Carl Edwards. 2009. (Behind the Wheel Ser.). (YA). (gr. 5-9). lib. bdg. 26.50 *(978-1-4042-1898-7(X))* Rosen Publishing Group, Inc., The.

—Carl Edwards: NASCAR Driver. 2009. (Behind the Wheel Ser.). 48p. (gr. 5-5). 53.00 *(978-1-61511-537-2(4),* Rosen Central) Rosen Publishing Group, Inc., The.

Larson, Jayne A. Driving the Saudis: Seven Weeks Behind the Wheel with Some of the World's Richest Princesses, Their Nannies, Servants, & One Royal Hairdresser. 2012. (ENG.). 224p. 23.00 ***(978-1-4516-4001-4(3),*** Free Pr.) Free Pr.

Law, Alexander & Winlaw, Susan. Car Advice for Women (and Smart Men) Reduce the Risk, Cost & Grief of Auto Ownership & Buying a New Car. 2008 312p. pap. *(978-0-9781931-0-2(5))* Consumer Automotive Media Services (CAMS).

Lee, Keith. Drag Bike Racing in Britain: From the Mid 60s to the Mid 80s. 2010. (Those were the Days... Ser.). (ENG., Illus.). 96p. pap. 25.95 *(978-1-84584-314-4(2)*, 1845843142) Veloce Publishing Ltd. GBR. Dist: MBI Distribution Services/Quayside Distribution.

Loughran, David S. & Seabury, Seth A. Estimating the Accident Risk of Older Drivers. 2007. 66p. pap. 23.00 *(978-0-8330-4139-5(8)*, tr-450) RAND Corp., The.

Ludvigsen, Karl. German Racing Silver: Drivers, Cars & Triumphs of German Motor Racing. 2009. (Racing Colours Ser.). (ENG., Illus.). 176p. 39.95 *(978-0-7110-3368-9(4))* Allan, Ian Publishing GBR. Dist: BookMasters Distribution Services (BDS).

Ludwig, Gary. Tommy Hinnershitz, the Life & Times of an Auto-Racing Legend. 2009. (Illus.). 252p. 29.95 *(978-0-9815099-4-5(0))* Basket Road Pr., Inc.

Madigan, Tom. Snake vs. Mongoose: How a Rivalry Changed Drag Racing Forever. 2009. (ENG., Illus.). 160p. 35.00 *(978-0-7603-3486-7(2)*, 0760334862, Motorbooks) MBI Publishing Co. LLC.

Madsen, William E. Crash Risks & Safety Issues among Older Drivers. 2011. (Aging Issues, Health & Financial Alternatives Ser.). 89.00 *(978-1-61209-348-2(5))* Nova Science Pubs., Inc.

McBeath, Simon. Official Formula 1 Season Review 2008. Formula Journalists Staff, ed. 2009. (ENG., Illus.). 272p. 49.95 *(978-1-84425-566-5(2)*, 1844255662) Haynes Publishing PLC GBR. Dist: MBI Distribution Services/Quayside Distribution.

McGinniss, Joe. They Call Him Cale: The Life & Career of NASCAR Legend Cale Yarborough. 2008. (ENG.). 256p. 24.95 *(978-1-60078-051-6(2))* Triumph Bks.

Miller, Leonard T. Racing While Black: How an African-American Stock Car Team Made Its Mark on NASCAR. 2010. (ENG.). 336p. 24.95 *(978-1-58322-896-8(9))* Seven Stories Pr.

Miller, Timothy & Milton, Steve. Nascar Now! 3rd ed. 2008. (ENG., Illus.). 176p. pap. 24.95 *(978-1-55407-340-5(5))* Firefly Bks., Ltd.

Molinaro, Martin. Hey, I'm Marty. I Drive the Bus! Book Ii: If You Have Ever Driven A Bus or Have Been A Passenger on A Bus; You Must Read This Book! 2010. 152p. 22.49 *(978-1-4520-6369-0(9))*; pap. 11.99 *(978-1-4520-6368-3(0))* AuthorHouse.

Montgomery, B. Broken White Line. 2007. 188p. per. 24.95 *(978-1-4241-8584-9(X))* PublishAmerica, Inc.

Needell, Tiff. Tiff Gear: The Autobiography of Tiff Needell. (ENG., Illus.). 2012. 384p. pap. 15.95 ***(978-0-85733-140-3(X)***, 085733140X) 2011. 320p. 29.95 *(978-0-85733-089-5(6)*, 0857330896) Haynes Publishing PLC GBR. Dist: MBI Distribution Services/Quayside Distribution.

Nevison, Tim. The Drivers: A Celebration of New Zealand Motor Sports' Greatest. 2007. (Illus.). 224p. *(978-1-86950-693-3(6))* HarperCollins Pubs. Australia.

Nowak, Patrick J. Forty Cars That Owned Me. 2007. 331p. pap. 19.95 *(978-0-7414-3736-5(8))* Infinity Publishing.

O' Leary, Mike. Mario Andretti: The Complete Record. 2007. (Illus.). 155p. reprint ed. pap. 17.00 *(978-1-4223-6640-0(5))* DIANE Publishing Co.

Odell, Morris. Older Road Users, Myths & Realities: A Guide for Medical & Legal Professionals. 2009. (Illus.). xvi, 302p. *(978-1-933264-70-7(5))* Lawyers & Judges Publishing Co., Inc.

Oxley, Mat. Valentino Rossi: Portrait of a Speed God. 3rd ed. 2010. (ENG., Illus.). 200p. 34.95 *(978-1-84425-833-8(5)*, 1844258335) Haynes Publishing PLC GBR. Dist: MBI Distribution Services/Quayside Distribution.

Parker, Chas. Brands Hatch: The Definitive History of Britain's Best-Loved Motor Racing Circuit. 2007. (ENG., Illus.). 240p. 54.95 *(978-1-84425-334-0(1)*, 1844253341) Haynes Publishing PLC GBR. Dist: MBI Distribution Services/Quayside Distribution.

—Motor Racing at Brands Hatch in the Eighties. 2009. (ENG., Illus.). 96p. pap. 15.95 *(978-1-84584-214-7(6)*, 1845842146) Veloce Publishing Ltd. GBR. Dist: MBI Distribution Services/Quayside Distribution.

Perkins, Lisa M. & White, Danielle J. Older Drivers Impaired by Multiple Medications. 2011. (Aging Issues, Health & Financial Alternatives Ser.). 195.00 *(978-1-61209-374-1(4))* Nova Science Pubs., Inc.

Porsche A.G Staff, contrib. by. Porsche Ladies. 2011. (ENG & GER., Illus.). 200p. 22.95 *(978-3-8321-9323-2(5))* DuMont DEU. Dist: D.A.P./Distributed Art Pubs.

Raby, Philip. Grand Prix: Driver by Driver. 2007. (ENG., Illus.). 240p. 27.99 *(978-1-905828-17-3(9)*, 1905828179) G2 Entertainment Ltd. GBR. Dist: MBI Distribution Services/Quayside Distribution.

Redshaw, Sarah. In the Company of Cars: Driving As a Social & Cultural Practice. 2008. (Human Factors in Road & Rail Transport Ser.). (Illus.). 208p. 124.95 *(978-0-7546-7198-5(4))* Ashgate Publishing Co.

Reyes, Steve. Fuel Altereds Forever. 2008. 192p. pap. 24.95 *(978-1-932494-75-4(8))* CarTech, Inc.

Rogers, Gareth. Lewis Hamilton the Story So Far. 2008. (ENG., Illus.). 200p. pap. 19.95 *(978-0-7524-4480-2(8))* History Pr. Ltd.,The GBR. Dist: Independent Pubs. Group.

Roper, Wendy Ward. Track Talk. 2010. (ENG., Illus.). 160p. per. 20.00 *(978-0-88962-863-2(7))* Mosaic Pr.

Roy, Alexander. The Driver: My Dangerous Pursuit of Speed & Truth in the Outlaw Racing World. 2008. (ENG.). 336p. pap. 14.95 *(978-0-06-137499-9(7))* HarperCollins Pubs.

Seymour, Miranda. The Bugatti Queen. Date not set. *(978-0-8050-7415-4(5)*, Holt, Henry & Co.) Holt, Henry & Co.

Shinar, David. Traffic Safety & Human Behavior. 2007. (Illus.). 813p. 111.95 *(978-0-08-045029-2(6))* Emerald Group Publishing Ltd. GBR. Dist: Turpin Distribution Services Ltd.

Soard, Todd, et al. Fleet Driver Safety. 2008. (ENG.). 71p. pap. 11.25 *(978-0-7637-5840-0(X))* Jones & Bartlett Learning, LLC.

Souter, Gerry. The Earnhardts: A Biography, 1 vol. 2009. (Greenwood Biographies Ser.). (Illus.). 138p. 35.00 *(978-0-313-35840-1(0)*, GR5840) Greenwood Publishing Group, Inc.

Spaulding, Jeffrey. Matt Kenseth: NASCAR Driver. 2009. (Behind the Wheel Ser.). (ENG., Illus.). 48p. (YA). (gr. 5-8). pap. 11.75 *(978-1-4358-5404-8(7))* Rosen Publishing Group, Inc., The.

Stewart, Jackie. Winning Is Not Enough: The Autobiography (US Edition) 2008. (ENG.). 495p. 27.95 *(978-0-7553-1829-2(3))* Headline Bk. Publishing GBR. Dist: Independent Pubs. Group.

Stone, Matt & Lerner, Preston. Winning: The Racing Life of Paul Newman. 2009. (ENG., Illus.). 176p. 30.00 *(978-0-7603-3706-6(3)*, 0760337063, Motorbooks) MBI Publishing Co. LLC.

Theeuwes, Jan, et al. Designing Safe Road Systems: A Human Factors Perspective. 2012. (Human Factors in Road & Rail Transport Ser.). (Illus.). 180p. 99.95 ***(978-1-4094-4388-9(4))*** Ashgate Publishing Co.

Thompson, Tamara. Senior Citizens & Driving. 2008. (At Issue Ser.). (ENG.). 80-128p. (gr. 10-12). 22.50 *(978-0-7377-4055-4(8)*, Greenhaven Pr., Inc.) Cengage Gale.

Thompson, Tamara, ed. Senior Citizens & Driving. 2008. (At Issue Ser.). (ENG., Illus.). 101p. (YA). (gr. 9-12). pap. 31.80 *(978-0-7377-4054-7(X))* Cengage Gale.

Timken, David S. & Milkman, Harvey B. Driving with Care — Education & Treatment of the Underage Impaired Driving Offender: An Adjunct Provider's Guide to Driving with Care - Education & Treatment of the Impaired Driving Offender — Strategies for Responsible Living & Change. Wanberg, Kenneth W., ed. 2010. (Illus.). 312p. pap. 56.00 *(978-1-4129-8782-0(2)*, B87820P) SAGE Pubns., Inc.

Toledo, Tomer. Integrated Model of Driving Behavior. 2008. 200p. per. *(978-3-8364-3556-7(X))* VDM Verlag Dr. Mueller e.K.

Tremayne, David. Jochen Rindt: Champion Lost. 2011. (ENG., Illus.). 256p. 69.95 *(978-1-84425-472-9(0)*, 1844254720) Haynes Publishing PLC GBR. Dist: MBI Distribution Services/Quayside Distribution.

—Lost Generation: The Brilliant but Tragic Lives of Rising British F1 Stars Roger Williamson, Tony Brise & Tom Pryce. 2010. (ENG., Illus.). 368p. pap. 17.95 *(978-1-84425-839-0(4)*, 1844258394) Haynes Publishing PLC GBR. Dist: MBI Distribution Services/Quayside Distribution.

Turbane, Ronnie Gale. A. R. T. -Accident Ready Trainer. 2007. (Illus.). 38p. spiral bd. 29.95 *(978-0-9797149-1-7(5))* Turbane, Ronnie Gale.

Turner, Stuart. Harnessing Horsepower: The Pat Moss Carlsson Story. 2011. (ENG., Illus.). 160p. 49.95 *(978-1-84584-306-9(1)*, 1845843061) Veloce Publishing Ltd. GBR. Dist: MBI Distribution Services/Quayside Distribution.

Vanderbilt, Tom. Traffic: Why We Drive the Way We Do (And What It Says about Us) (Vintage Ser.). (ENG.). 416p. 2009. pap. 16.00 *(978-0-307-27719-0(4)*, Vintage) 2008. 24.95 *(978-0-307-26478-7(5)*, Knopf) Knopf Doubleday Publishing Group.

Venables, David. British Racing Green: Drivers, Cars & Triumphs of British Motor Racing. 2009. (ENG., Illus.). 176p. 46.95 *(978-0-7110-3332-0(3))* Allan, Ian Publishing GBR. Dist: BookMasters Distribution Services (BDS).

Voie, Ellen & Layover. A Workbook for Professional Drivers & Teir Families. 2009. pap. 15.00 *(978-1-61623-474-4(1))* Independent Pub.

Wagstaff, Ian. The British at Indianapolis. 2010. (ENG., Illus.). 256p. 99.95 *(978-1-84584-246-8(4)*, 1845842464) Veloce Publishing Ltd. GBR. Dist: MBI Distribution Services/Quayside Distribution.

Walton, Jeremy. Gerry Marshall: His Authorised Biography. 2010. (ENG., Illus.). 256p. 59.95 *(978-1-84425-648-8(0)*, 1844256480) Haynes Publishing PLC GBR. Dist: MBI Distribution Services/Quayside Distribution.

Wanders, Ted. The Law & the Truck Driver. 2010. 800p. pap. 36.49 *(978-1-4520-5767-5(2))* AuthorHouse.

Wördenweber, Burkhard, et al. Automotive Lighting & Human Vision. 2010. (ENG & ABK., Illus.). xviii, 410p. pap. 139.00 *(978-3-642-07177-5(5)*, 3642071775) Springer.

Welch, Ian & Morgan, Charlie. The A-Z of Grand Prix: A Grand Prix A to Z. 2009. (Little Book Ser.). (ENG., Illus.). 128p. 9.99 *(978-1-906635-26-8(9)*, 1906635269) G2 Entertainment Ltd. GBR. Dist: MBI Distribution Services/Quayside Distribution.

Wells, Helen. The Fast & the Furious: Drivers Speed Cameras & Control in a Risk Society. 2011. (Human Factors in Road & Rail Transport Ser.). 244p. 99.95 ***(978-1-4094-3089-6(8))*** Ashgate Publishing Co.

West, David. Race Car Drivers. 2008. (Graphic Careers Ser.). (ENG., Illus.). 48p. (gr. 5-8). per. 14.05 *(978-1-4042-1453-8(4))*; (YA). lib. bdg. 29.25 *(978-1-4042-1452-1(6))* Rosen Publishing Group, Inc., The.

Wilson, Alan. Driven by Desire: The Desire Wilson Story. 2011. (ENG., Illus.). 160p. 49.95 *(978-1-84584-389-2(4)*, 1845843894) Veloce Publishing Ltd. GBR. Dist: MBI Distribution Services/Quayside Distribution.

Wood, Perry Allen. Declarations of Stock Car Independents: Interviews with Twelve Racers of the 1950s Through 1970s. 2010. (ENG., Illus.). 264p. pap. 35.00 *(978-0-7864-4764-0(8))* McFarland & Co., Inc. Pubs.

Worral, Frank & Worrall, Frank. Lewis Hamilton: The Biography. 2007. (ENG., Illus.). 306p. 29.95 *(978-1-84454-543-8(1))* Blake, John Publishing, Ltd. GBR. Dist: Independent Pubs. Group.

Worrall, Frank. Lewis Hamilton: Champion of the World - The Biography. 2009. (ENG., Illus.). 338p. pap. 14.95 *(978-1-84454-581-0(4))* Blake, John Publishing, Ltd. GBR. Dist: Independent Pubs. Group.

Wurld, C. C. What about Us? Tales from an Angry Mass Transit Bus Operator. 2011. 152p. pap. 16.00 ***(978-1-4634-1516-7(8))*** AuthorHouse.

ZIROGIANNIS, Attorney at Law Marc. The New York State Taxicab Driver's Companion. 2010. 73p. pap. 12.49 *(978-0-557-49730-0(2))* Lulu Enterprises Inc.

Zmud, Johanna & Arce, Carlos. Compilation of Public Opinion Data on Tolls & Road Pricing. 2008. 57p. 42.00 *(978-0-309-09800-7(9))* Transportation Research Board.

AUTOMOBILE DRIVERS' LICENSES

see also Automobile Drivers' Tests

Beckham, Diane. Transportation Code Crimes & License Suspensions. 2007. 170p. pap. 27.00 *(978-0-9796993-5-1(5))* Texas District & County Attorneys Assn.

Céré, Jean-Paul. Le Permis à Points. 4th ed. 2010. (FRE.). 117p. *(978-2-296-12289-5(2))* Editions L'Harmattan.

Hinchcliff, Reece. Research Use in Novice Driver Licensing Policy. 2011. 280p. pap. ***(978-3-8454-0130-0(3))*** Lambert Academic Publishing.

Identification Security: Reevaluating the REAL ID ACT: Hearing Before the Committee on Homeland Security & Governmental Affairs, United States Senate, of the One Hundred Eleventh Congress, First Session, July 15, 2009. 2011. (Illus.). iv, 170p. ***(978-0-16-088994-3(4)***, 552-070-43026-1) United States Government Printing Office.

LearningExpress Editors. Commercial Truck Drivers License Test Prep. 2008. (Complete Preparation Guides). (ENG.). 240p. pap. 26.95 *(978-1-57685-659-8(3))* LearningExpress, LLC.

Loughran, David S., et al. Regulating Older Drivers: Are New Policies Needed? 2007. (Illus.). 38p. per. 20.00 *(978-0-8330-4194-4(0)*, op-189) RAND Corp., The.

Meurer, Todd E. Traffic Law & Practice in Wisconsin. 4th ed. 2010. *(978-1-57862-281-8(6))* State Bar of Wisconsin.

Mike Byrnes and Associates. Barron's CDL Truck Driver's Test. 3rd rev. ed. 2010. (ENG.). 448p. pap. 18.99 *(978-0-7641-4382-3(4))* Barron's Educational Series, Inc.

Mosher, Matt & Research and Education Association Staff. CDL - Commerical Driver's License Exam. 5th ed. 2011. (CDL Test Preparation Ser.). (ENG.). 336p. pap. 18.95 *(978-0-7386-0907-2(2))* Research & Education Assn.

MVR 1995 Decoder Handbook. 290 ED#: 5p. pap. *(978-0-7605-1854-0(8))* Rector Pr., Ltd.

MVR 1995 Handbook. 275 ED#: 6p. pap. *(978-0-7605-1853-3(X))* Rector Pr., Ltd.

National Safety Compliance Services Staff. The Ctts Cdl Study Manual (English Version) 3rd rev. ed. 2009. (ENG.). 400p. pap. 36.00 *(978-0-7872-8175-5(1))* Kendall Hunt Publishing Co.

Phan, Allyson C. Teen Driver Safety & Graduated Driver Licenses. 2011. (Children's Issues, Laws & Programs Ser.). 195.00 *(978-1-61209-375-8(2))* Nova Science Pubs., Inc.

Sankey, Michael L., ed. The MVR Access & Decoder Digest: The Complete National Reference of Motor Vehicle Records Access, Content, & Conviction Code Tables. 2010. (MVR Access & Decoder Digest Ser.). 622p. pap. 31.95 *(978-1-879792-96-8(6))* BRB Pubns., Inc.

—The U. S. Motor Vehicle Reference Book. 2010. (U. S. Motor Vehicle Reference Book Ser.). (Illus.). 270p. pap. 14.95 *(978-1-879792-95-1(8))* BRB Pubns., Inc.

Sankey, Michael L., ed. The U. S. Motor Vehicle Reference Book 2011. 2011. (Illus.). 272p. pap. 14.95 ***(978-1-879792-97-5(4))*** BRB Pubns., Inc.

Social Security Disability Fraud: Case Studies in Federal Employees & Commercial Driver's Licenses: Hearing Before the Permanent Subcommittee on Investigations of the Committee on Homeland Security & Governmental Affairs, United States Senate, One Hundred Eleventh Congress, Second Session, August 4, 2010. 2011. (Illus.). iii, 181p. ***(978-0-16-088325-5(3)***, 552-070-42630-2) United States Government Printing Office.

Will Real ID Actually Make Us Safer? An Examination of Privacy & Civil Liberties Concerns: Hearing Before the Committee on the Judiciary, United States Senate, One Hundred Tenth Congress, First Session, May 8, 2007. 2007. (Illus.). iv, 247p. *(978-0-16-079239-7(8)*, 552-070-35346-7) United States Government Printing Office.

Wright, Yvonne. Secrets the Trucking Companies Don't Want You to Know! 2009. (ENG.). 60p. pap. 10.99 *(978-0-557-04375-0(1))* Lulu Enterprises Inc.

AUTOMOBILE DRIVERS' TESTS

AA Publishing. Theory Test: The Official Questions & Answers for Car Drivers & Motorcyclists, 2 vols. 12th ed. 2010. (AA Driving Test Ser.). (ENG., Illus.). 224p. pap. 12.95 *(978-0-7495-6716-3(3))* Automobile Assn. GBR. Dist: Independent Pubs. Group.

Bryans, Bill. Part 3 the Essential Knowledge Second Edition. 2010. 440p. pap. 52.50 *(978-1-4452-2259-2(0))* Lulu Enterprises Inc.

Hall, Diane. L of a Way 2 Pass. 2008. 240p. pap. 15.99 *(978-1-4389-0958-5(6))* AuthorHouse.

Hartenbaum, Natalie P. The DOT Medical Examination: A Guide to Commercial Drivers' Medical Certification. 4th ed. 2007. *(978-1-883595-48-7(7)*, OEM Pr.) OEM Health Information, Inc.

Montgomery, Donna & Adelson-Goldstein, Jayme. Driving in the City. Oxford Staff, ed. 2nd ed. 2008. (Oxford Picture Dictionary 2E Ser.). (ENG., Illus.). 32p. pap. 8.69 *(978-0-19-474031-9(5))* Oxford Univ. Pr., Inc.

AUTOMOBILE DRIVING

see also Automobile Driver Education

Adler, Dennis. 50 Cars to Drive. 2008. (ENG., Illus.). 256p. 45.00 *(978-1-59921-230-2(7)*, Lyons Pr.) Globe Pequot Pr., The.

Adler, Steffen. Analysing Long-Term Seating Comfort - the Relation Between Long-Term Seating Comfort & Driver Movement. 2008. 156p. pap. *(978-3-639-02054-0(5))* VDM Verlag Dr. Mueller e.K.

Allen, Jim. Four-Wheeler's Bible. 2nd ed. 2009. (Motorbooks Workshop Ser.). (ENG., Illus.). 256p. pap. 29.99 *(978-0-7603-3530-7(3)*, 0760335303, Motorbooks) MBI Publishing Co. LLC.

Atwell, Denise. To the Driving Test & Beyond- 2006. (Illus.). 128p. per. 17.37 *(978-1-4120-8423-9(7))* Trafford Publishing.

Bédard, Henri & Delashmit, Geraud, eds. Accidents: Causes, Analysis & Prevention. 2009. (Safety & Risk in Society Ser.). 129.00 *(978-1-60741-712-5(X))* Nova Science Pubs., Inc.

Bedsworth, Louise, et al. Driving Change: Reducing Vehicle Miles Traveled in California. 2011. *(978-1-58213-143-6(0))* Public Policy Institute of California.

Beretta, Joseph. Automotive Electricity: Electric Drive. 2010. (Iste Ser.: 375). (ENG., Illus.). 304p. 127.00 *(978-1-84821-095-0(7)*, Wiley-ISTE) Wiley, John & Sons, Inc.

Bevly, David M. & Cobb, Stewart. GNSS for Vehicle Control. 2010. 247p. 129.00 *(978-1-59693-301-9(1))* Artech Hse., Inc.

Boyle, Linda N. & Brown, Timothy, eds. Driving Simulation Conference - North America 2007. 2007. (Illus.). cd-rom 20.00 *(978-0-87414-160-3(5))* Univ. of Iowa, Pubns. Dept.

Brennan, Virginia. Gasoline Gypsies: David & Virginia's Life on the Road. 2009. 132p. pap. 14.95 *(978-1-4327-0391-2(9))* Outskirts Pr., Inc.

British Broadcasting Corporation Staff & Top Gear Staff. The Big Book of Top Gear 2010. 2010. (ENG., Illus.). 128p. 24.95 *(978-1-84607-824-8(5))* BBC Worldwide GBR. Dist: Independent Pubs. Group.

Buehler, Martin, et al, eds. The DARPA Urban Challenge: Autonomous Vehicles in City Traffic. 2009. (Springer Tracts in Advanced Robotics Ser.). (Illus.). xxxvi, 626p. 239.00 *(978-3-642-03990-4(1)*, 3642039901) Springer.

Castro, Candida & Hartley, Laurence R. Human Factors of Visual & Cognitive Performance in Driving. 2008. (ENG., Illus.). 296p. 97.95 *(978-1-4200-5530-6(5)*, CRC Press) Taylor & Francis Group GBR. Dist: Taylor & Francis Group.

Chramosta, Vladimir. Driving Is Fun or Is It? 2006. 80p. pap. 16.95 *(978-1-4137-6686-8(2))* PublishAmerica, Inc.

Christensen, Kathie. A Wise Dad's (And Mom'S) Cool Tips for the Road (And Some Cool Tips for the 'Road of Life' Too)... 2011. 48p. pap. 17.95 *(978-1-4497-0438-4(7)*, WestBow Pr.) Author Solutions, Inc.

Clarkson, Jeremy. Clarkson on Cars. 2006. (ENG., Illus.). 368p. (gr. 12-18). 16.00 *(978-0-14-101788-4(0)*, Penguin Global) Penguin Group (USA) Inc.

Comfort, Ray. 101 Annoying Things about Other Drivers. 2007. (Illus.). 139p. per. *(978-0-89221-668-0(9))* New Leaf Pr., Inc.

Croft, William. Old Trails & Frontiers: Driving the American Southwest. 2012. (Illus.). 207p. 33.95 ***(978-1-84624-655-5(5))*** Book Guild, Ltd. GBR. Dist: Trans-Atlantic Pubns., Inc.

Darden, Joe. The Book on Safe Driving. 2008. 103p. pap. 18.95 *(978-0-615-24737-3(7))* Darden, Joe Group, LLC.

Davidson, Jim. 75 Ways to Save Gas: Clean, Green Tips to Cut Costs at the Pump. 2011. (ENG.). 144p. (gr. 12). 8.99 ***(978-0-14-318605-2(1)***, Penguin (Non-Classics)) Penguin Group (USA) Inc.

Delmar Learning Staff. Trucking Tractor: Trailer Driver Computer Based Training 2010. (Automotive Multimedia Solutions Ser.). (ENG.). (C). 114.95 *(978-1-4354-5406-4(5))* Delmar Cengage Learning.

Dernaus, A. B. When the Aa Man Saluted. 2008. (ENG., Illus.). 160p. pap. 29.95 *(978-0-7509-4857-9(4))* History Pr. Ltd.,The GBR. Dist: Independent Pubs. Group.

Dewar, Robert E. & Olson, Paul L. Human Factors in Traffic Safety. 2007. *(978-1-933264-24-0(1))* Lawyers & Judges Publishing Co., Inc.

Doy, Penelope. Conducir Comodo y Seguro (Drive Comfortable & Safe) (SPA.). 200p. *(978-84-305-8744-5(6))* Susaeta Ediciones, S.A.

Dziadik, Steve. How's My Driving? Why Every Other Driver Doesn't Seem to Have a Clue! 2009. (Illus.). 210p. pap. 16.95 *(978-1-4327-4383-3(X))* Outskirts Pr., Inc.

Elford, Vic. Porsche High-Performance Driving Handbook. 2nd rev. ed. 2008. (ENG., Illus.). 176p. pap. 29.95 *(978-0-7603-2754-8(8)*, 0760327548, Motorbooks) MBI Publishing Co. LLC.

European Commission Staff, contrib. by. Analysis & Development of New Insight into Substitution of Short Car Trips by Cycling & Walking: Adonis. (Illus.). vi, 132p. *(978-92-828-4396-3(3))* European Commission BEL. Dist: Balogh International, Inc.

Fisher, Donald L. Handbook of Driving Simulation for Engineering, Medicine, & Psychology. Rizzo, Matthew et al, eds. 2011. (ENG., Illus.). 751p. 129.95 *(978-1-4200-6100-0(3)*, CRC Press) Taylor & Francis Group GBR. Dist: Taylor & Francis Group.

Garriott, James C. & Aguayo, Erik H. Garriott's Medicolegal Aspects of Alcohol. 5th ed. 2008. 536p. 139.00 *(978-1-933264-58-5(6))* Lawyers & Judges Publishing Co., Inc.

Gentile, Judith. Behind the Wheel. 2009. 260p. pap. 14.49 *(978-1-4389-3547-8(1))* AuthorHouse.

Green, Marc. Forensic Aspects of Vision & Highway Safety. 3rd ed. 2008. *(978-1-933264-54-7(3))* Lawyers & Judges Publishing Co., Inc.

Guadalupe River Valley Travel Guide: Driving Trip in the Texas Hill Country by way of Rte. 27 & Center Point River Road. 2nd enl. exp. ed. 2007. (Illus.). 27p. pap. 20.00 incl. audio compact disk *(978-0-9676931-5-6(2))* Skyline Ranch Pr.

Gustavsson, Filip N., ed. New Transportation Research Progress. 2008. (C). 185.00 (978-1-60456-032-9(0)) Nova Science Pubs., Inc.

Hammond, Richard & Wilman, Andy. Car Confidential: The Odd, the Mad, the Bad & the Curious. 2007. (ENG., Illus.). 144p. 19.95 (978-0-297-84445-7(8)) Orion Publishing Group, Ltd. GBR. Dist: Independent Pubs. Group.

Hartenbaum, Natalie P. The DOT Medical Examination: A Guide to Commercial Drivers' Medical Certification. 5th ed. 2010. (978-1-883595-53-1(3), OEM Pr.) OEM Health Information, Inc.

Harwood, Douglas W., et al. Passing Sight Distance Criteria. 2008. (Illus.). 93p. pap. 43.00 (978-0-309-09927-1(7)) Transportation Research Board.

Hennessy, Dwight, ed. Traffic Psychology: An International Perspective. 2010. (Psychology Research Progress Ser.). (Illus.). xv, 352p. 195.00 (978-1-61668-846-2(7)) Nova Science Pubs., Inc.

Henny, Phil Louis. Nenn mich einfach Carroll. 2009.Tr. of Nenn mich einfach Carroll. (GER., Illus.). 146p. (978-0-9765247-4-8(0)) Editions Cotty.

Hill, Phil. Phil Hill: A Driving Life. 2010. (Illus.). 192p. 75.00 (978-1-935007-07-4(6)) Bull, David Publishing, Inc.

Hole, Graham J. The Psychology of Driving. 2006. (ENG., Illus.). 248p. 73.95 (978-0-8058-4425-2(2), Psychology Press) Taylor & Francis Group GBR. Dist: Taylor & Francis Group.

Howard, Hal. Truckin' with Bubba ... & I Ain't Bubba. 2011. 152p. 24.95 (978-1-4502-7385-5(8)); pap. 14.95 (978-1-4502-7383-1(1)) iUniverse, Inc.

Hutchinson, Emily. Car & Driver. 2011. (21st Century Lifeskills Ser.). (ENG.). 48p. (gr. 9-12). pap., stu. ed. 14.95 (978-1-61651-115-9(X)) Saddleback Educational Publishing.

Jakle, John A. & Sculle, Keith A. Motoring: The Highway Experience in America. 2009. (ENG., Illus.). 288p. pap. 24.95 (978-0-8203-3415-8(4)) Univ. of Georgia Pr.

Käppler, Wolf Dieter. Smart Driver Training Simulation: Save Money. Prevent. (ENG., Illus.). x, 142p. 2010. pap. 99.00 (978-3-642-09579-5(8), 3642095798) 2008. 99.00 (978-3-540-77069-5(0), 3540770690) Springer.

Kauppi, Anu Irene & González, Narciso. The Psychophysiological Prediction of Driving Quality under Fatigue. 2008. 76p. pap. (978-3-639-07335-5(5)) VDM Verlag Dr. Mueller e.K.

Keller, J. J. Keller's Tractor-Trailer Driver Training Manual. 2nd ed. 2008. (Illus.). xiv, 586p. (978-1-60287-276-9(7)) Keller, J.J. & Assocs., Inc.

Lindsey, Jeffery & Patrick, Richard. Emergency Vehicle Operations. 2006. (ENG., Illus.). 304p. (C). per. 52.00 (978-0-13-118155-7(6), Prentice Hall) Prentice Hall PTR.

Lucas, Karen, et al. Auto Motives: Understanding Car Use Behaviours. Lucas, Karen et al, eds. 2011. (Illus.). 312p. 49.95 (978-0-85724-233-4(4)) Emerald Group Publishing Ltd. GBR. Dist: Turpin Distribution Services Ltd.

Martin, James. Driven: Cooking in the Fast Lane - My Story. 2009. (ENG., Illus.). 320p. 13.95 (978-0-00-729468-8(9)) HarperCollins Pubs. Ltd. GBR. Dist: Independent Pubs. Group.

Merriman, Peter. Driving Spaces. 2007. (RGS-IBG Book Ser.: 17). (ENG., Illus.). 320p. pap. 42.95 (978-1-4051-3072-1(5)); 92.95 (978-1-4051-3073-8(3)) Wiley, John & Sons, Inc. (Wiley-Blackwell).

Miller, Frank. Driverthink. 2009. 184p. pap. 14.95 (978-1-59858-984-9(9)) Dog Ear Publishing, LLC.

Miller, John & Stacey, Margaret. The Driving Instructor's Handbook. 14th ed. 2006. (Illus.). 400p. pap. (978-0-7494-4746-5(X)) Kogan Page, Ltd.

Mobil Travel Guide. Luxury Drives. 2008. (ENG.). 192p. pap. 17.95 (978-1-936010-14-1(3)) Five Star Travel Corp., The.

Morton, Paul. How to Drift: The Art of Oversteer. 2006. (S-A Design Ser.). (ENG., Illus.). 128p. pap. 24.95 (978-1-932494-23-5(5), S-A Design) CarTech, Inc.

Murray, Scott. Trucker's Tales. 2007. 99p. per. 9.99 (978-1-59886-900-2(0)) Tate Publishing & Enterprises, LLC.

Newlon, Michael. U S Route 395: Travel the Three Flags Highway in a Classic Sports Car. 2009. 81p. pap. 24.95 (978-1-4327-1705-6(7)) Outskirts Pr., Inc.

Newlon, Michael R. U. S. Route 95: Travel America's Desolation Highway in A Classic Sports Car. 2009. 88p. pap. 24.95 (978-1-4327-2472-6(X)) Outskirts Pr., Inc.

Noakes, Andrew P. 101 Ways to Beat the Gas Pump. 2007. 152p. per. 13.95 (978-0-595-44379-6(6)) iUniverse, Inc.

Olson, Paul L., et al. Forensic Aspects of Driver Perception & Response. 3rd ed. 2010. (978-1-933264-78-3(0)) Lawyers & Judges Publishing Co., Inc.

O'Rourke, P. J. Driving Like Crazy: Thirty Years of Vehicular Hell-Bending, Celebrating America the Way It's Supposed to Be - With an Oil Well in Every Backyard, a Cadillac Escalade in Every Carport, & the Chairman of the Federal Reserve Mowing Our Lawn. 2010. (ENG.). 288p. pap. 14.00 (978-0-8021-4479-9(9), Grove Pr.) Grove/Atlantic, Inc.

O'Toole, Randal. Gridlock: Why We're Stuck in Traffic & What to Do about It. 2010. (ENG.). 232p. 24.95 (978-1-935308-23-2(8)) Cato Institute.

Owen Valley High Project Ignition, compiled by. Shifting Gears: Alert today, alive Tomorrow. 2007. 96p. per. 15.95 (978-0-9800429-1-7(7)) Pen & Publish Inc.

Prion Books UK. For the World's Best Driver: A Glovebox Full of Fun for the Expert Behind the Wheel. 2010. (ENG., Illus.). 192p. 18.95 (978-1-85375-765-5(9)) Prion GBR. Dist: Independent Pubs. Group.

Puyal, Robert. Behind the Wheel: The Great Automobile Aficionados. 2010. (ENG., Illus.). 240p. 49.95 (978-2-08-030154-3(3)) Flammarion et Cie FRA. Dist: Random Hse., Inc.

Redshaw, Sarah. In the Company of Cars: Driving As a Social & Cultural Practice. 2008. (Human Factors in Road & Rail Transport Ser.). (Illus.). 208p. 124.95 (978-0-7546-7198-5(4)) Ashgate Publishing Co.

Robbins, David. Driving South. 250p. 19.95 (978-1-86812-467-1(3)) Southern Bk. Pubs. ZAF. Dist: Continental Enterprises Group, Inc. (CEG).

Schultheis, Maria T., et al. Handbook for the Assessment of Driving Capacity. Schultheis, Maria T. et al, eds. 2008. (ENG., Illus.). 256p. 80.95 (978-0-12-631255-3(9), Academic Pr.) Elsevier Science & Technology Bks.

Scotti, Anthony. Professional Driving Techniques: The Essential Guide to Operating a Motor Vehicle with Confidence & Skill. 1. 4th rev. ed. 2007. Orig. Title: Driving Techniques. (Illus.). 310p. pap. 22.95 (978-0-9793813-1-7(2), sku PDT4) PhotoGraphics Publishing.

Scotti, Anthony J. Driver's Education Teacher's Guide: For use with Professional Driving Techniques 4th Ed. 2008. 106p. pap. 35.00 (978-0-9793813-2-4(0)) PhotoGraphics Publishing.

Stewart, Gerry. Driving Tips from Grampa: Prevent Tomorrow's Accidents Today by Reading. 2007. 120p. per. 10.99 (978-1-60247-255-2(5)) Tate Publishing & Enterprises, LLC.

Stuart, Ronald J. A Parent's Worst Nightmare: Rites of Passage - A Teacher¿s Manual for Parents on Teaching Their Children to Drive. 2008. 52p. pap. 16.95 (978-1-60672-231-2(X)) PublishAmerica, Inc.

Takeda, Kazuya, et al, eds. In-Vehicle Corpus & Signal Processing for Driver Behavior. 2010. (ENG., Illus.). xiv, 286p. pap. 129.00 (978-1-4419-4640-9(3), 1441946403) Springer.

Takeda, Kazuya (University of Nagoya & Takeda, Kazuya. In-Vehicle Corpus & Signal Processing for Driver Behavior. Takeda, Kazuya et al, eds. 2008. (Illus.). xiv, 286p. 129.00 (978-0-387-79581-2(2)) Springer.

Taylor, Charles. Help! My Teenager Wants to Drive. stu. ed. (978-1-56857-004-4(X)) Noble Publishing Assocs.

Toledo, Tomer. Integrated Model of Driving Behavior. 2008. 200p. per. (978-3-8364-3556-7(X)) VDM Verlag Dr. Mueller e.K.

Top Gear Staff & British Broadcasting Corporation Staff. The Big Book of Top Gear 2011. 2010. (ENG., Illus.). 128p. 24.95 (978-1-84990-061-4(2)) BBC Worldwide GBR. Dist: Independent Pubs. Group.

Vanderbilt, Tom. Traffic: Why We Drive the Way We Do (And What It Says about Us) (Vintage Ser.). (ENG.). 416p. 2009. pap. 16.00 (978-0-307-27719-0(4), Vintage) 2008. 24.95 (978-0-307-26478-7(5), Knopf) Knopf Doubleday Publishing Group.

Walsh, Lorrin. Drive Your Motorhome Like a Pro. 2006. (ENG., Illus.). 64p. per. 12.95 (978-0-9785788-0-0(5)) Drive Smart.

Weiers, Ronald. Gas Smarts: Hundreds of Small Ways to Save Big Time at the Pump. 2011. (ENG.). 256p. pap. 11.95 (978-1-4405-0049-7(5)) Adams Media Corp.

Weiers, Ronald M. Ga$ Smart$ 2011. E-Book (978-1-4405-1081-6(4)) Adams Media Corp.

Wells, Charles A. ATV Trails Guide: Colorado Central Mountains. 2007. (Illus.). 168p. pap. 19.95 (978-0-9664976-9-4(4)) FunTreks Guidebooks.

Wright, Yvonne. Secrets the Trucking Companies Don't Want You to Know! 2009. (ENG.). 60p. pap. 10.99 (978-0-557-04375-0(1)) Lulu Enterprises Inc.

Zad, Morad A. The Untold Rules of Driving. 2010. 100p. pap. 14.95 (978-1-60844-609-4(3)) Dog Ear Publishing, LLC.

AUTOMOBILE DRIVING—SAFETY MEASURES

see Traffic Safety

AUTOMOBILE ENGINEERING

Ahmadian, M., ed. Advanced Automotive Technologies 1993. 419p. pap. 75.00 (978-0-7918-1046-2(1)) American Society of Mechanical Engineers, The.

American Society of Mechanical Engineers Staff, ed. Computers in Engine Technology. (Illus.). 288p. 178.00 (978-0-85298-765-0(X)); 332p. 76.00 (978-0-85298-625-7(4)) Professional Engineering Publishing GBR. Dist: SAE Intl.

—Diesel Fuel Injection Systems. 156p. 84.00 (978-0-85298-708-7(0)); (Illus.). 181p. 128.00 (978-0-85298-980-7(6)); (Illus.). 160p. 130.00 (978-0-85298-814-5(1)) Professional Engineering Publishing GBR. Dist: SAE Intl.

—Disc Brakes for Commercial Vehicles. 158p. 76.00 (978-0-85298-662-2(9)) Professional Engineering Publishing GBR. Dist: SAE Intl.

—Electronic Braking Systems. (Illus.). 234p. 63.00 (978-1-86058-036-9(X)) Professional Engineering Publishing GBR. Dist: SAE Intl.

—Engine Transient Performance. (Illus.). 74p. 78.00 (978-0-85298-753-7(6)) Professional Engineering Publishing GBR. Dist: SAE Intl.

—Managing the Vehicle on the Road. 192p. 126.00 (978-0-85298-690-5(4)) Professional Engineering Publishing GBR. Dist: SAE Intl.

—New Developments in Power Train & Chassis Engineering. 618p. 242.00 (978-0-85298-689-9(0)) Professional Engineering Publishing GBR. Dist: SAE Intl.

—Quiet Revolutions: Powertrain & Vehicle Noise Refinement. 208p. 110.00 (978-0-85298-724-7(2)) Professional Engineering Publishing GBR. Dist: SAE Intl.

Arafat, Rahman. A Text Book of Automobile Engineering: A Text Book for B. Sc Engineering Degree, Diploma in Mechanical Engineering & Diploma in Automobile Engineering. 2011. 220p. pap. **(978-3-639-33562-0(7))** VDM Verlag Dr. Mueller e.K.

Bishop, Michael. They Found Our Engineer: The Story of Arthur Goddard, the Land Rover's first Engineer. 2011. 152p. pap. 22.02 **(978-1-4567-7758-6(0))** AuthorHouse.

Bonnick, Allan. Automotive Science & Mathematics. 2008. (ENG., Illus.). 264p. (C). pap. 33.95 (978-0-7506-8522-1(0)) Routledge.

Cantor, Brian, et al, eds. Automotive Engineering: Lightweight, Functional, & Novel Materials. 2008. (Series in Material Science & Engineering Ser.). (ENG., Illus.). 296p. 162.95 (978-0-7503-1001-7(4), IP155, Taylor & Francis) Taylor & Francis Group GBR. Dist: Taylor & Francis Group.

Christian, Paar. Energy Management in Hybrid Electric Vehicles Using Co-Simulation: Using Co-Simulation for the Development of Energy Management Algorithms in Hybrid Electric Vehicles. 2011. 88p. pap. **(978-3-639-33112-7(5))** VDM Verlag Dr. Mueller e.K.

Dacey, Karen H. The Stanleys of Newton: Yankee Tinkerers in the Gilded Age. 2009. (978-1-886727-16-8(3)); pap. (978-1-886727-15-1(5)) Stanley Museum, Inc.

Delmar Learning Staff. Auxiliary Power Systems Installation & Repair Test E3. 2012. (ENG.). 164p. pap. 23.95 (978-1-4354-3937-5(6)) Delmar Cengage Learning.

Duffy, James E. Modern Automotive Technology. 7th ed. 2008. (ENG., Illus.). 1613p. (gr. 9-14). 96.64 (978-1-59070-956-6(X)) Goodheart-Willcox Pub.

Hamilton, Maurice. Williams: The Legendary Story of Frank Williams & His F1 Team in Their Own Words. 2010. (ENG., Illus.). 384p. 39.95 (978-0-09-193267-1(X)) Ebury Publishing GBR. Dist: Independent Pubs. Group.

Jurgen, Ronald K. Automotive Microcontrollers. 2008. (Illus.). vi, 443p. 79.99 (978-0-7680-2067-0(0)) SAE Intl.

Kaya, Serhat. Advanced Processes for Formability Improvement of Lightweight Sheet. 2010. 156p. pap. (978-3-639-23249-3(6)) VDM Verlag Dr. Mueller e.K.

Manish, Choudhary. Evaluation & Modification of Static Head Restraint Testing Machine: And Creating a Conceptual Design for Making It Fmvss 202A Enabled. 2011. 100p. pap. **(978-3-639-32347-4(5))** VDM Verlag Dr. Mueller e.K.

Mansor, Muhammad Na,fal & Intan Suraya Murat, Bibi. Vehicle Monitoring Using Vibration Characteristic. 2011. 80p. pap. **(978-3-8443-2781-6(9))** Lambert Academic Publishing.

Muthuraman, S. Reduced Knocking in Petrol Engines: Octane Enhancing Petrol Additives in Proper Development of Power with Less Knocking. 2011. 252p. pap. **(978-3-639-33864-5(2))** VDM Verlag Dr. Mueller e.K.

Ozguner, Umit, et al. Autonomous Ground Vehicles. 2011. (Illus.). 212p. 109.00 (978-1-60807-192-0(8)) Artech Hse., Inc.

Pavkovic, Danijel & Deur, Joško. Modeling & Control of Electronic Throttle Drive. 2011. 188p. pap. **(978-3-8443-1628-5(0))** Lambert Academic Publishing.

Perry, David, photos by. Hot Rod Kings: Top Traditional Rod & Custom Builders. 2007. (ENG., Illus.). 160p. 34.95 (978-0-7603-2738-8(6), 0760327386, Motorbooks) MBI Publishing Co. LLC.

Reddy, B. Hemanjaneya. Interfacial Fracture Response of Rubber Composites. 2010. 160p. pap. (978-3-639-24834-0(1)) VDM Verlag Dr. Mueller e.K.

Reimpell, Jornsen. The Automotive Chassis: Engineering Principles. (Illus.). 368p. (978-0-340-61443-3(9), Hodder Arnold) Hodder Education.

Sensors & Actuators. 2007. (C). 109.95 **(978-1-4200-4484-3(2)**, CRC Press) Taylor & Francis Group GBR. Dist: Taylor & Francis Group.

Smith, Paul D. Merchants of Speed: The Men Who Built America's Performance Industry. 2009. (ENG., Illus.). 240p. 40.00 (978-0-7603-3567-3(2), 0760335672, Motorbooks) MBI Publishing Co. LLC.

Stauber, R. & Vollrath, L. Plastics in Automotive Engineering: Exterior Applications. 2007. (978-1-56990-406-0(5)) Hanser Pubns.

Subramonian, P. Eng. Tire Inflation Technology Existing & an Evolution to Be. 2010. 68p. pap. (978-3-8383-8502-0(0)) Lambert Academic Publishing.

Trapp, Martin & Chen, Feng. Automotive Buzz, Squeak & Rattle: Mechanisms, Analysis, Evaluation & Prevention. Chen, Frank, ed. 2011. (ENG., Illus.). 296p. 99.95 (978-0-7506-8496-5(8), Butterworth-Heinemann) Elsevier Science & Technology Bks.

Wellnitz, Joerg, et al. Sustainable Automotive Technologies 2010: Proceedings of the 2nd International Conference. 2009. 301p. 189.00 (978-3-642-10796-2(6), 3642107966) Springer.

Xie. Intelligent Vehicle: Perception, Decision & Action. 2011. 88.00 (978-981-4271-63-9(2)) World Scientific Publishing Co., Inc.

AUTOMOBILE EXHAUST GAS

see Automobiles—Motors—Exhaust Gas

AUTOMOBILE FILLING STATIONS

see Service Stations

AUTOMOBILE FUEL SYSTEMS

see Automobiles—Fuel Systems

AUTOMOBILE GUIDES

see Automobile Travel—Guidebooks

AUTOMOBILE INDUSTRY AND TRADE

see also Automobiles—Prices; Service Stations; Used Car Trade

Amoo, Edwina. Information Technology in the Automobile Industry. 2011. 72p. pap. **(978-3-8433-9084-2(3))** Lambert Academic Publishing.

Anand, Joseph Sahaya. Intermetallic Nickel Aluminides for Automotive Body Applications. 2011. 100p. pap. **(978-3-8443-9835-9(X))** Lambert Academic Publishing.

Andrews, Brad. How to Land a Top-Paying Retail Sales & Automobile Dealer Services Job: Your Complete Guide to Opportunities, Resumes & Cover Letters, Interviews, Salaries, Promotions, What to Expect from Recruiters & More! 2010. (ADY.). 156p. pap. (978-1-74244-613-4(2)) Emereo Pty Ltd.

Atkinson, Kevin. The Singer Story: Cars, Commercial Vehicles, Bicycles, Motorcycles. 2008. (ENG., Illus.). 256p. 120.00 (978-1-874105-52-7(9), 1874105529) Veloce Publishing Ltd. GBR. Dist: MBI Distribution Services/Quayside Distribution.

Becker, Helmut. High Noon in the Automotive Industry. 2010. (ENG., Illus.). xii, 261p. pap. 99.00 (978-3-642-06523-1(6), 3642065236) Springer.

Berres, Sr. No Thanks, I'm Just Looking! Reflections of a Car Salesman. 2009. 108p. 21.49 (978-1-4490-4314-8(3)) AuthorHouse.

Bhatia, Sanket. Competence-Based Decision Support for the Offshoring of Automotive Product Development Processes to Indi. 2011. 174p. pap. **(978-3-640-90928-5(3))** Hammer, Patrick, Tanja Hammer, Matthias Knoop, Julius Mittenzwei, Georg Steinbach u. Michael Teltscher. GRIN Verlag GbR.

BIA. Key Automobile Dealers & Service Companies of Russia. 6th rev. ed. 2006. 398p. (J). pap. 249.00 (978-1-4187-4516-5(2)) Business Information Agency.

—Key Russian Manufacturers & Suppliers of Automobile & Accessories. 6th rev. ed. 2006. 376p. (J). pap. 249.00 (978-1-4187-4500-4(6)) Business Information Agency.

—Major Automobile Dealers of the World. 6th rev. ed. 2006. 400p. (J). pap. 249.00 (978-1-4187-4313-0(5)) Business Information Agency.

—Major Transportation Equipment Manufacturers of the World. 6th rev. ed. 2006. 400p. (J). pap. 249.00 (978-1-4187-4278-2(3)) Business Information Agency.

Binder, Mario & Clegg, Ben, eds. Sustainable Supplier Management in the Automotive Industry: Leading the 3rd Revolution through Collaboration. 2010. (Transportation Issues, Policies & R&D Ser.). 158p. pap. 38.70 (978-1-61668-675-8(8)) Nova Science Pubs., Inc.

Blum, Andreas. Co-Opetition in the Automotive Industry. 2009. (Illus.). 88p. pap. (978-3-639-17079-5(2)) VDM Verlag Dr. Mueller e.K.

Blum, Petra, et al. Motoring the Future: VW & Toyota Vying for Pole Position. 2011. (ENG., Illus.). 288p. 40.00 (978-0-230-29955-9(5)) Palgrave Macmillan.

Brinkley, Douglas. Wheels for the World: Henry Ford, His Company, & a Century of Progress, 1903-2003. 858p. 2009. (ENG.). pap. 18.00 (978-1-4379-6550-6(4)) 2006. (Illus.). reprint ed. 35.00 (978-1-4223-5456-8(3)) DIANE Publishing Co.

Calabrese, Giuseppe, ed. The Greening of the Automotive Industry. 2012. (ENG., Illus.). 336p. 105.00 **(978-0-230-36909-2(X))** Palgrave Macmillan.

Callahan, John. Empowering Consumers with How Totorials. 2007. pap. 39.95 (978-1-59800-971-2(0)) Outskirts Pr., Inc.

Camandrett, Sebas. Gilera Motorcycles in Argentina. 2010. 101p. pap. 40.00 (978-0-557-45182-1(5)) Lulu Enterprises Inc.

Ciravegna, Luciano, ed. Sustaining Industrial Competitiveness after the Crisis: Lessons from the Automotive Industry. 2012. (ENG., Illus.). 288p. 95.00 **(978-0-230-34816-5(5))** Palgrave Macmillan.

Dzholev, Boris. Mini-A Rebirth of an Iconic Brand. 2011. 68p. pap. **(978-3-8443-3058-8(5))** Lambert Academic Publishing.

Fijalkowski, B. T. Automotive Mechatronics: Operational & Practical Issues: Volume I, 2 vols. 2010. (Intelligent Systems, Control & Automation: Science & Engineering Ser.). (Illus.). xvii, 593p. 229.00 (978-94-007-0408-4(9), 9400704089) Springer.

—Automotive Mechatronics: Operational & Practical Issues: Volume II, 2 vols. 2011. (Intelligent Systems, Control & Automation: Science & Engineering Ser.). (Illus.). xiii, 523p. 229.00 (978-94-007-1182-2(4), 9400711824) Springer.

GM & Chrysler Dealership Closures: Protecting Dealers & Consumers: Hearing Before the Committee on Commerce, Science, & Transportation, United States Senate, One Hundred Eleventh Congress, First Session, June 3, 2009. 2010. (Illus.). iv, 130p. **(978-0-16-087147-4(6)**, 552-070-41990-0) United States Government Printing Office.

Golinska, Paulina, ed. Environmental Issues in Automotive Industry. 2012. (EcoProduction. Environmental Issues in Logistics & Manufacturing Ser.). (ENG.). 400p. 179.00 **(978-3-642-23836-9(X)**, 364223836X) Springer.

Golrang, Mehdi & RAHMANDOUST, Mohsen. Recycling Capabilities by Rapid Manufacturing. 2011. 88p. pap. **(978-3-8443-9605-8(5))** Lambert Academic Publishing.

Gomes, Emanuel, et al. Mergers & Acquisitions as Strategic Methods of Business Development in the Global Automobile Industry: An Analysis of Five Cases. 2010. (Illus.). ix, 222p. (978-0-7734-3740-1(1)) Mellen, Edwin Pr., The.

Gondal, Farrukh. Wireless Sensor Network for Automobile Tire Health Monitoring. 2009. 128p. pap. (978-3-639-16367-4(2)) VDM Verlag Dr. Mueller e.K.

Grismer, Phillip. Apples, Oranges & Lemons: Surviving the Automobile Business. 2007. 548p. 43.95 (978-0-595-69066-4(1)); per. 33.95 (978-0-595-43604-0(8)) iUniverse, Inc.

Guo, Huaqun, ed. Automotive Informatics & Communicative Systems: Principles in Vehicular Networks & Data Exchange. 2009. 364p. 195.00 (978-1-60566-338-8(7)) IGI Global.

Hall, William & Lee, Moses. Chrysler: From Bankruptcy to Rebirth. 2010. (C). pap. 20.00 (978-1-61674-422-9(7)) Davidson, William Institute At The Univ. of Michigan, The.

Hirtzman, Philippe, ed. The Private Car of the Future: Technological & Corporate Strategies. 2011. 190p. pap. 33.00 (978-2-7472-1647-0(0)) Eska, Editions FRA. Dist: International Publishers Marketing.

Hordeski, Michael F. Alternative Fuels: The Future of Hydrogen. 2nd ed. 2008. x, 286p. (978-0-88173-595-6(7)) Fairmont Pr., Inc.

Hordeski, Michael Frank. Alternative Fuels: The Future of Hydrogen. 2nd rev. ed. 2008. (ENG.). x, 286p. 125.95 (978-1-4200-8016-2(4), CRC Press) Taylor & Francis Group GBR. Dist: Taylor & Francis Group.

James, Wanda. Driving from Japan: Japanese Cars in America. alt. ed. 2007. (ENG., Illus.). 320p. per. 39.95 (978-0-7864-3116-8(4)) McFarland & Co., Inc. Pubs.

Johnson, H. Thomas. Profit Beyond Measure. 2008. (ENG.). 280p. pap. 18.95 (978-1-4391-2462-8(0), Free Pr.) Free Pr.

Jost, Andreas. Modellgestütztes Management von Prozessinnovationen: Ein methodisches Konzept zur Unterstützung von Prozessinnovationen in der automobilen Produktentstehung auf Basis systemdynamischer Modellierung und Simulation. 2008. (Schriften zur Unternehmensplanung Ser.). 370p. pap. 81.95 *(978-3-631-58513-9(6))* Lang, Peter GmbH, Europäischer Verlag der Wissenschaften DEU. Dist: Lang, Peter.

Kö, et al. What Determines the Number of Cars? 2010. 48p. pap. *(978-3-8383-5765-2(5))* Lambert Academic Publishing.

Kaplan, Len. Automotive Industry. 2009. (ENG.). 136p. pap. 18.44 *(978-0-557-06473-1(2))* Lulu Enterprises Inc.

Kaseke, Nyasha. Hyperinflation- Reasons for Staying in an Organisation. 2011. 68p. pap. ***(978-3-8433-8891-7(1))*** Lambert Academic Publishing.

Kemp, William H. The Zero-Carbon Car: Building the Car the Auto Industry Can't Get Right. 2007. (ENG., Illus.). 500p. per. 24.95 *(978-0-9733233-4-4(5))* Aztext Pr. CAN. Dist: Consortium Bk. Sales & Distribution.

Kucuk Yilmaz, Ayse & Yilmaz, Mehmet. Auto Wars. 2008. 168p. pap. *(978-3-8364-9261-4(X))* VDM Verlag Dr. Mueller e.K.

Kymal, Chad. Conducting Effective Process-Based Audits: A Handbook for ISO/TS 16949. 2007. *(978-1-932828-13-9(3))* Paton Professional.

Lahnalampi, Nita. Red One Plus Ltd: For the satisfaction of customers & Nature. 2010. 92p. pap. *(978-3-8383-6785-9(5))* Lambert Academic Publishing.

Lancaster, Phil A. Merchandising New & Used Cars. 15.95 *(978-0-87359-030-3(9),* AM 202) Northwood Univ. Pr.

Lansbury. Globalization Employment Relations in the Auto Assembly Industry. 2008. pap. 139.00 *(978-90-411-2698-6(8))* Wolters Kluwer Law & Business.

Lansbury, Russell D., et al. The Global Korean Motor Industry. 2007. (Routledge Advances in Korean Studies). (ENG., Illus.). 144p. (C). 158.00 *(978-0-415-41366-4(4))* Routledge.

Latin American Business: Equity Distortion in Regional Resource Allocation in Brazil. 2007. (ENG., Illus.). 242p. 135.00 *(978-0-7890-3535-6(9));* per. 87.95 *(978-0-7890-3536-3(7))* Routledge.

Lee, Dong Wook. An Innovative Inflatable Morphing Vehicle Structure: Concept & Analytical Design Model for Crashworthiness. 2008. 192p. pap. *(978-3-639-10223-9(1))* VDM Verlag Dr. Mueller e.K.

Lepetun, Jan. Flowing with the Current. 2011. 52p. pap. ***(978-3-8433-9264-8(1))*** Lambert Academic Publishing.

Lewin, Tony. The A-Z of 21st-Century Cars. 2011. (ENG., Illus.). 540p. pap. 39.95 *(978-1-85894-525-5(9))* Merrell Pubs. Ltd. GBR. Dist: Perseus Distribution.

LexisNexis Staff, compiled by. Mealey's Executive Summary: Personal Injury & Liability in the Auto Industry Update. 2007. pap. 295.00 *(978-1-59579-428-4(X))* LexisNexis Mealey's.

Lightweight Materials in Transportation. 2007. per. 4250.00 *(978-1-59623-289-1(7))* BCC Research.

Liker, Jeffrey & Ogden, Timothy N. Toyota Under Fire: Lessons for Turning Crisis into Opportunity. 2011. (ENG., Illus.). 208p. 20.00 *(978-0-07-176299-1(X),* 007176299X) McGraw-Hill Cos., The.

Lipowsky, Hansjörg & Arpaci, Emin. Copper in the Automotive Industry. 2007. (ENG.). 191p. 95.00 *(978-3-527-31769-1(4),* Wiley-VCH) Wiley, John & Sons, Inc.

Lopez, Ray. Inside the Minds of Car Dealers: How to Buy Your Next Car Without Fear. 2009. *(978-1-58985-156-6(0))* Five Star Pubns., Inc.

Maxwell, Gordan A. & Drummond, Stuart K., eds. Automotive Industry: Technical Challenges, Design Issues & Global Economic Crisis. 2010. (American Political, Economic, & Security Issues Ser.). 258p. 145.00 *(978-1-60876-143-2(6))* Nova Science Pubs., Inc.

Mikler, John. Greening the Car Industry: Varieties of Capitalism & Climate Change. 2009. (Illus.). 296p. 145.00 *(978-1-84720-652-7(2))* Elgar, Edward Publishing, Inc.

Mongkhonvanit, Jomphong. Regional Development in Knowledge Economy. 2009. 240p. pap. *(978-3-639-13678-4(0))* VDM Verlag Dr. Mueller e.K.

Morgan, Peter. Porsche Boxster & Cayman All Models 1996 to 2007. 3rd ed. 2007. (ENG., Illus.). 104p. pap. 14.95 *(978-0-9549990-6-3(1),* 0954999061, PMM Bks.) Morgan, Peter Media Ltd. GBR. Dist: MBI Distribution Services/Quayside Distribution.

Motavalli, Jim. High Voltage: The Fast Track to Plug in the Auto Industry. 2011. (ENG.). 272p. 24.99 *(978-1-60529-263-2(X))* Rodale Pr., Inc.

Mueller, Markus, et al. Automotive SPICE in Practice: Surviving Interpretation & Assessment. 2008. (Rockynook Computing Ser.). (ENG., Illus.). 304p. pap. 54.95 *(978-1-933952-29-1(6))* Rocky Nook.

Ncube, Mfowabo. Impact of Tpm on Manufacturing Performance. 2009. 104p. pap. *(978-3-639-19606-1(6))* VDM Verlag Dr. Mueller e.K.

Niall, Todd. Bambina: The Fiat 500 in New Zealand = Quando la Nuova Zelanda Fabbricava Fiat 500. 2007. (ITA & ENG., Illus.). 126p. pap. *(978-0-473-11885-3(8))* Iconic Publishing.

Niechwiadowicz, John. An Industry in Crisis: A Comparative Analysis of Collision Repair Labor Rates. 2009. (Illus.). 25p. ring bd. *(978-0-9793772-6-6(9))* Mechling Bookbindery.

Niederstadt, Joseph. Standardized Work for Noncyclical Processes. 2010. (ENG., Illus.). 120p. pap. 39.95 *(978-1-4398-2550-1(5))* Productivity Pr.

Parment, Anders. Automobile Marketing: Distribution Strategies for Competitiveness. 2009. 408p. pap. *(978-3-639-20249-6(X))* VDM Verlag Dr. Mueller e.K.

Parry, Glenn & Graves, Andrew. Build to Order: The Road to the 5-Day Car. 2008. (ENG., Illus.). xx, 438p. 69.95 *(978-1-84800-224-1(6),* 1848002246) Springer.

Pavlinek, Petr. A Successful Transformation? Restructuring of the Czech Automobile Industry. 2010. (Contributions to Economics Ser.). (ENG., Illus.). xiv, 296p. pap. 139.00 *(978-3-7908-2553-4(0),* 3790825530) Physica-Verlag DEU. Dist: Springer.

Pavlinek, Petr. A Successful Transformation? 2008. (Contributions to Economics Ser.). 139.00 *(978-3-7908-2039-3(3))* Physica-Verlag DEU. Dist: Springer.

Plunkett, Jack W. Plunkett's Automobile Industry Almanac 2007 (E-Book) Automobile, Truck & Specialty Vehicle Industry Market Research, Statistics, Trends & Leading Companies. Plunkett, Jack W., ed. 2006. 574p. E-Book 499.99 incl. cd-rom *(978-1-59392-401-0(1))* Plunkett Research, Ltd.

Plunkett's Automobile Industry Almanac: The Only Comprehensive Guide to Automotive Companies & Trends. annuals 2006. (Plunkett's Automobile Industry Almanac Ser.). (Illus.). 557p. pap. 299.99 incl. cd-rom *(978-1-59392-059-3(8))* Plunkett Research, Ltd.

Poth, Ulrich. Automotive Coatings Formulations. 2008. (ENG.). 237p. 205.00 *(978-0-8155-1565-4(0))* Vincentz, Curt R. DEU. Dist: Elsevier Science & Technology Bks.

Price, Barrie. Lea-Francis Story. (Illus.). 160p. lthr. *(978-1-901295-23-8(0))* Veloce Publishing Ltd. GBR. Dist: MBI Distribution Services/Quayside Distribution.

Price, Jerry. Let's Go for A Ride. 2007. per. 15.00 *(978-0-9768477-3-1(6))* Windjammer Adventure Publishing.

Pulignano, Valeria. Flexibility at Work: Critical Developments in the International Automobile Industry. Pulignano, Valeria et al, eds. 2008. (ENG., Illus.). 224p. 95.00 *(978-1-4039-0041-8(8))* Palgrave Macmillan.

Raimey, Michael D. Car Selling 101: The Basics. Raimey, Ro'Derick R., ed. Date not set. (Illus.). 229p. (Orig.). pap. 17.75 *(978-0-9657902-0-8(7))* Me-Me Bks.

Rasiah, Rajah, et al, eds. Multinationals Technology & Localization in Automotive Firms in Asia. 2009. 176p. pap. 39.95 *(978-0-415-57464-8(1))* Routledge.

Rezin, Andrew. Automotive Service Management. 2nd rev. ed. 2012. (ENG.). 336p. (C). 106.67 ***(978-0-13-272540-8(1),*** Prentice Hall) Prentice Hall PTR.

Rona, J. Michael. Leading the Health Care Revolution Using the Toyota Production Systems: Lessons from the Frontline. 2009. (Illus.). 225p. pap. 49.95 *(978-1-4200-9967-6(1))* Productivity Pr.

Rotermann, Stefan. Ekanban & Barcode Implementation in an Automotive Supplier Plant. 2009. 132p. pap. *(978-3-639-14258-7(6))* VDM Verlag Dr. Mueller e.K.

Rother, Sven. Prozesscontrolling im Autohaus: Am Beispiel des Geschäftsprozesses 'Service' 2010. 140p. pap. *(978-3-639-22343-9(8))* VDM Verlag Dr. Mueller e.K.

Roxborough, Ian. Unions & Politics in Mexico: The Case of the Automobile Industry. 2009. (Cambridge Latin American Studies). (ENG., Illus.). 224p. pap. 31.99 *(978-0-521-10268-1(5))* Cambridge Univ. Pr.

Russmann, Roland. Collaborative Engineering in Partnernetzwerken der Automobilindustrie: Die Schwierigkeit, verschiedene PDM/CAD-Systeme unterschiedlicher Partner zu verwalten und zu synchronisieren. 2009. 148p. pap. *(978-3-639-21511-3(7))* VDM Verlag Dr. Mueller e.K.

Saint Martin C Staff. Transforming Health Care: Virginia Mason Medical Center's Pursuit of the Perfect Patient Experience. 2010. (ENG., Illus.). 248p. 41.95 *(978-1-56327-375-9(6))* Productivity Pr.

Sammer, Gerald. Succesful Automotive Testing. 2008. 224p. pap. *(978-3-639-07079-8(8))* VDM Verlag Dr. Mueller e.K.

Schratz, Wilhelm. Theory & Practice of Knowledge Management. 2008. 144p. pap. *(978-3-639-03659-6(X))* VDM Verlag Dr. Mueller e.K.

Seitz. Supply Chain Performance, Collaboration, & Stability Measurement: Development of a Model for the Automotive Industry. 2007. 100p. per. *(978-3-8364-0242-2(4))* VDM Verlag Dr. Mueller e.K.

Shaharudin, Mohd Rizaimy, et al. Purchase Intention of Motorcycle/Scooter in Malaysi. 2011. 100p. pap. ***(978-3-8443-9023-0(5))*** Lambert Academic Publishing.

Shishoo, Roshan. Textile Advances in the Automotive Industry. Shishoo, Roshan, ed. 2008. (ENG., Illus.). 320p. 249.95 *(978-1-4200-9000-0(3),* CRC Press) Taylor & Francis Group GBR. Dist: Taylor & Francis Group.

Siegelbaum, Lewis H. Cars for Comrades: The Life of the Soviet Automobile. (Illus.). 2011. 328p. pap. 24.95 *(978-0-8014-7721-8(2))* 2008. 309p. 39.95 *(978-0-8014-4638-2(4))* Cornell Univ. Pr.

Siggerud, Katherine. Passenger Vehicle Fuel Economy: Preliminary Observations on Corporate Average Fuel Economy Standards. 2007. (Illus.). 17p. (C). pap. 15.00 *(978-1-4223-1584-2(3))* DIANE Publishing Co.

Slutsky, Adam. Nothing Runs: Misadventures in the Classic, Collectable & Exotic Car Biz. 2012. (ENG., Illus.). 144p. pap. 14.95 *(978-1-84584-344-1(4),* 1845843444) Veloce Publishing Ltd. GBR. Dist: MBI Distribution Services/Quayside Distribution.

Sly, David. Transport Effort. 2008. 116p. pap. *(978-3-639-07526-7(9))* VDM Verlag Dr. Mueller e.K.

SPANOTES Mathematics - Bilingual CD: A bilingual study aid for secondary school Mathematics. 2009. (SPA & ENG., Illus.). 146p. cd-rom 24.95 *(978-1-884730-02-3(7))* InterLingua.com, Inc.

Spatz, Julius & Nunnenkamp, Peter. Globalisierung der Automobilindustrie: Wettbewerbsdruck, Arbeitsmarkteffekte und Anpassungsreaktionen. (Kieler Studien - Kiel Studies). (GER., Illus.). 136p. 52.66 *(978-3-540-43535-8(2),* 3540435352) Springer.

Stern, Philip Van Doren. Tin Lizzie: The Story of the Fabulous Model T Ford. 2011. 180p. 42.95 ***(978-1-258-05841-8(3))*** Literary Licensing, LLC.

Streather, Adrian. Monsieur Bernar Nahum: A Pioneer of Turkey's Automotive Industry. 2011. (ENG., Illus.). 392p. pap. 22.95 ***(978-9944-424-85-1(4))*** Citlembik/Nettleberry Pubns. TUR. Dist: National Bk. Network.

Subic, Aleksandar, et al, eds. Sustainable Automotive Technologies 2012: Proceedings of the 4th International Conference. 2012. (ENG., Illus.). xii, 404p. 199.00 ***(978-3-642-24144-4(1),*** 3642241441) Springer.

Suryanarayana, Gargeshwari. Aerodynamic Drag Reduction of Bluff Bodies. 2010. 180p. pap. *(978-3-8383-1103-6(5))* Lambert Academic Publishing.

Taneja, Nawal K. Looking Beyond the Runway: Airlines Innovating with Best Practices While Facing Realities. 2010. (Illus.). 354p. 64.95 *(978-1-4094-0099-8(9))* Ashgate Publishing Co.

Technology Research Editors, ed. NDT/NDE in the Automotive Industry, 2007 Ed. 2007. pap. 128.50 *(978-1-60030-253-4(X),* Search-In-Print) CSA Journal Division.

—Weight Reduction in the Automotive Industry, 2007 Ed. 2007. pap. 128.50 *(978-1-60030-202-2(5),* Search-In-Print) CSA Journal Division.

Tuncay Çelikel, Asli. Research & Development Collaborations: Turkish Automotive Industry. 2010. 184p. pap. *(978-3-639-23096-3(5))* VDM Verlag Dr. Mueller e.K.

Utterback. Foundational Thinking about Innovation. 2011. 300p. 93.00 *(978-981-279-051-4(9))* World Scientific Publishing Co., Inc.

Van Boxtel, Ed. A Practical Systematic ASpproach to Selling Automotive Vehicles. 2007. *(978-0-9772315-2-2(6))* Minuteman Pr. of Green Bay.

Wells, P. E. The Automotive Industry in a ERA of Eco-Austerity: Creating an Industry As If the Planet Mattered. 224p. 2012. pap. 39.95 ***(978-1-84980-623-7(3))*** 2010. (Illus.). 112.00 *(978-1-84844-967-1(4))* Elgar, Edward Publishing, Inc.

Wolfe, Joel. Autos & Progress: The Brazilian Search for Modernity, 1 vol. 2010. (ENG., Illus.). 288p. 99.00 *(978-0-19-517457-1(7))* Oxford Univ. Pr., Inc.

Wolfe, Joel, contrib. by. Autos & Progress: The Brazilian Search for Modernity, 1 vol. 2010. (ENG., Illus.). 288p. pap. 21.95 *(978-0-19-517456-4(9))* Oxford Univ. Pr., Inc.

Wynn-Williams, Michael S. & Wynn-Williams, Michael. Surfing the Global Tide: Automotive Giants & How to Survive Them. 2009. (ENG., Illus.). 270p. 59.00 *(978-0-230-57924-8(8))* Palgrave Macmillan.

Ziegler, Oliver. Global Compact Membership & the Automobile Industry - a U S - German Comparison. 2008. 104p. per. *(978-3-8364-6813-8(1))* VDM Verlag Dr. Mueller e.K.

AUTOMOBILE INDUSTRY AND TRADE—USED CARS

see Used Car Trade

AUTOMOBILE INDUSTRY AND TRADE—AUSTRALIA

Beer, Andrew. The Impacts of Automotive Plant Closure. Beer, Andrew & Thomas, Holli, eds. 2009. (Regions & Cities Ser.). (ENG.). 132p. 125.00 *(978-0-415-54334-7(7))* Routledge.

Kitainge, Kisilu Mashtakh. Balancing the Forces for Training Programs & Work Alignment: A Study of Automotive Retail, Service & Repair Industries in Kenya & Australia. 2011. 312p. pap. ***(978-3-639-32971-1(6))*** VDM Verlag Dr. Mueller e.K.

AUTOMOBILE INDUSTRY AND TRADE—CANADA

Anastakis, Dimitry. Car Nation: An Illustrated History of Canada's Transformation Behind the Wheel. 2008. (ENG., Illus.). 96p. pap. 24.95 *(978-1-55277-005-4(2))* Lorimer, James & Co., Ltd., Pubs. CAN. Dist: Casemate Pubs. & Bk. Distributors, LLC.

Arculus, Paul. Durant's Right-Hand Man. 2011. 368p. ***(978-1-77067-782-1(8));*** pap. ***(978-1-77067-783-8(6))*** FriesenPress.

Digest of Motor Laws 2007 Edition. 2007. pap. *(978-1-59508-206-0(9))* AAA.

Edmonston, Louis-Philippe. Lemon-Aid New Cars & Trucks 2012. 2011. (ENG., Illus.). 526p. pap. 29.99 *(978-1-4597-0046-8(5))* Dundurn CAN. Dist: Ingram Pub. Services.

Edmonston, Phil. Lemon-Aid New Cars & Trucks 2011. 2010. (ENG., Illus.). 536p. pap. 28.99 *(978-1-55488-790-3(9))* Dundurn CAN. Dist: Ingram Pub. Services.

Edmonston, Phil. Lemon-Aid Used Cars & Trucks 2012-2013. 2012. (ENG., Illus.). 624p. pap. 29.99 ***(978-1-4597-0234-9(4))*** Dundurn CAN. Dist: Ingram Pub. Services.

Fuss, Melvyn A. & Waverman, Leonard. Costs & Productivity in Automobile Production: The Challenge of Japanese Efficiency. 2006. (ENG., Illus.). 256p. pap. 53.00 *(978-0-521-03175-2(3))* Cambridge Univ. Pr.

McCredie, Andrew & Reisner, Paula. Intermeccanica: The Story of the Prancing Bull. 2010. (ENG., Illus.). 192p. 79.95 *(978-1-84584-249-9(9),* 1845842499) Veloce Publishing Ltd. GBR. Dist: MBI Distribution Services/Quayside Distribution.

Russell, Jason. Our Union: UAW/ CAW Local 27 from 1950 To 1990. 2012. (ENG., Illus.). 300p. pap. 32.95 *(978-1-926836-43-0(X))* UBC Pr. CAN. Dist: Univ. of Washington Pr.

Spencer, Zack. Motormouth: The Complete Canadian Car-Buying Guide 2010 Edition. 2009. (ENG.). 320p. pap. 23.95 ***(978-0-470-16026-8(8),*** Wiley) Wiley, John & Sons, Inc.

Spencer, Zack. Motormouth: The Complete Canadian Car Guide. 2011th ed. 2011. (ENG., Illus.). 352p. pap. 24.95 *(978-0-470-96404-0(9),* Wiley) Wiley, John & Sons, Inc.

AUTOMOBILE INDUSTRY AND TRADE—CHINA

Baker, Kevin. Economic Tsunami: China's Car Industry Will Sweep Away Western Car Makers. 2007. (Illus.). 360p. (C). pap. 29.95 *(978-1-877058-56-1(4))* Rosenberg Publishing Pty, Ltd. AUS. Dist: International Specialized Bk. Services.

Calkins, Martin. King Car & the Ethics of Automobile Proponents' Strategies in China & India. 2011. (Transportation Issues, Policies & R&D Ser.). 180p. 69.00 *(978-1-61761-271-8(5))* Nova Science Pubs., Inc.

Chin, Gregory T. China's Automotive Modernization: The Party-State & Multinational Corporations. 2010. (International Political Economy Ser.). (ENG., Illus.). 304p. 100.00 *(978-0-230-22060-7(6))* Palgrave Macmillan.

Dassi, Alberto. The Chinese Automotive Industry. 2011. 112p. pap. ***(978-3-8454-1554-3(1))*** Lambert Academic Publishing.

Dunne, Robert R. & Dunne, Michael. American Wheels, Chinese Roads: The Story of General Motors in China. 2011. (ENG.). 227p. 29.95 *(978-0-470-82861-8(7),* Wiley) Wiley, John & Sons, Inc.

Garibaldo, Francesco, et al, eds. Is China a Risk or an Opportunity for Europe? An Assessment of the Automobile, Steel & Shipbuilding Sectors. 2007. (Illus.). 125p. pap. 32.95 *(978-3-631-57474-4(6))* Lang, Peter Publishing, Inc.

Matousek, David. Marketing of a Foreign Automotive Brand: The Case of Skoda in Taiwan. 2009. 76p. pap. *(978-3-639-16234-9(X))* VDM Verlag Dr. Mueller e.K.

McGunagle, Doreen. The Chinese Auto Industry. 2007. 116p. per. *(978-3-8364-1632-0(8))* VDM Verlag Dr. Mueller e.K.

Meier, Nicola. China - the New Developmental State? An Empirical Analysis of the Automotive Industry. 2009. (Hohenheimer volkswirtschaftliche Schriften Ser.). 362p. pap. 81.95 *(978-3-631-58284-8(6))* Lang, Peter GmbH, Europäischer Verlag der Wissenschaften DEU. Dist: Lang, Peter.

Posth, Martin. 1,000 Days in Shanghai: The Volkswagen Story - The First Chinese-German Car Factory. Travis, Ian, tr. from GER. 2008. (ENG., Illus.). 250p. pap. 24.95 *(978-0-470-82388-0(7),* Wiley) Wiley, John & Sons, Inc.

Thun, Eric. Changing Lanes in China: Foreign Direct Investment, Local Governments, & Auto Sector Development. 2008. (ENG., Illus.). 346p. pap. 30.99 *(978-0-521-72409-8(0))* Cambridge Univ. Pr.

Wu, Facheng. Qi Che Jiang Guo Zhi Meng. 2009. (Illus.). *(978-7-5011-8739-3(8))* Xinhua Publishing Hse.

Zhao, Chao. Aging in China & Its Impact on Vehicle Design. 2009. 272p. pap. *(978-3-639-13287-8(4))* VDM Verlag Dr. Mueller e.K.

AUTOMOBILE INDUSTRY AND TRADE—DEVELOPING COUNTRIES

Lansbury, Russell D., et al. The Global Korean Motor Industry: The Hyundai Motor Company's Global Strategy. 2012. (Routledge Advances in Korean Studies). (ENG., Illus.). 144p. (C). pap. 42.95 ***(978-0-415-54279-1(0))*** Routledge.

AUTOMOBILE INDUSTRY AND TRADE—EUROPE

BIA. Essential Transportation Equipment Manufacturers of Western Europe. 6th rev. ed. 2006. 400p. (J). pap. 249.00 *(978-1-4187-4385-2(3))* Business Information Agency.

Calabrese, Giuseppe. La Filiera Dello Stile e le Politiche Industriali per L'automotive in Piemonte e in Europa. 2010. (ITA.). 218p. *(978-88-568-2275-5(X))* Angeli.

Chapman, Giles. The Ford Transit Story. 2011. (Story Ser.). (ENG., Illus.). 128p. 16.95 ***(978-0-7524-6283-7(0))*** History Pr. Ltd.,The GBR. Dist: Independent Pubs. Group.

Chilton Automotive Editorial Staff. European Mechanical Service Manual 2006. 2006. (Chilton Mechanical Manuals Ser.). (ENG., Illus.). 1152p. 89.95 *(978-1-4180-0604-4(1))* Delmar Cengage Learning.

Dolski, Joerg. Standardisierung im Internationalen Marketing: Entwicklung eines Analyseschemas. 2010. (Europäische Hochschulschriften. Reihe 5: Volks- und Betriebswirtschaft Ser.). (GER.). 224p. pap. 66.95 *(978-3-631-58990-8(5))* Lang, Peter GmbH, Europäischer Verlag der Wissenschaften DEU. Dist: Lang, Peter.

European Commission Staff, contrib. by. Examination of Current & Future Excess Capacity in the European Automobile Industry. (Illus.). 41p. *(978-92-828-0612-8(X))* European Commission BEL. Dist: Balogh International, Inc.

Kelly, Maurice A. Russian Motor Vehicles: Soviet Limousines 1930-2003. 2011. (ENG., Illus.). 128p. 49.95 *(978-1-84584-300-7(2),* 1845843002) Veloce Publishing Ltd. GBR. Dist: MBI Distribution Services/Quayside Distribution.

—Russian Motor Vehicles: The Czarist Period 1784 to 1917. 2009. (ENG., Illus.). 112p. 24.95 *(978-1-84584-213-0(8),* 1845842138) Veloce Publishing Ltd. GBR. Dist: MBI Distribution Services/Quayside Distribution.

Ludvigsen, Karl, intro. Ford's Feisty Capri: European Sporting Coupes 1969-1987. 2009. (Ludvigsen Library Ser.). (ENG., Illus.). 128p. pap. 29.95 *(978-1-58388-251-1(0),* 1583882510) Iconografix, Inc.

Siegelbaum, Lewis H., ed. The Socialist Car: Automobility in the Eastern Bloc. 2011. (Illus.). 248p. 65.00 ***(978-0-8014-4991-8(X));*** pap. 24.95 ***(978-0-8014-7738-6(7))*** Cornell Univ. Pr.

Thomas, Hugh & Thomas, H. Eduardo Barreiros & the Recovery of Spain. 2009. (ENG., Illus.). 448p. 45.00 *(978-0-300-12109-4(1))* Yale Univ. Pr.

Welfens, Paul J. J., ed. Clusters in Automotive & Information & Communication Technology: Innovation, Multinationalization & Networking Dynamics. 2012. (ENG., Illus.). xix, 289p. 139.00 ***(978-3-642-25815-2(8),*** 3642258158) Springer.

AUTOMOBILE INDUSTRY AND TRADE—FRANCE

Bellu, Serge. Louis Vuitton: The Art of the Automobile. 2008. (ENG., Illus.). 256p. 75.00 *(978-0-8109-9551-2(4))* Abrams.

Berk, Gijsbert-Paul. Andre Lefebre: And the Cars He Created at Voisin & Citroen. 2009. (ENG., Illus.). 144p. 39.95 *(978-1-84584-244-4(8),* 1845842448) Veloce Publishing Ltd. GBR. Dist: MBI Distribution Services/Quayside Distribution.

Boddy, William 'Bill'. Montlhery: The Story of the Paris Autodrome. 2007. (Classic Reprint Ser.). (ENG., Illus.). 232p. 35.95 *(978-1-84584-052-5(6),*

1845840526) Veloce Publishing Ltd. GBR. Dist: MBI Distribution Services/Quayside Distribution.

Clarke, R. M., contrib. by. Hispano Suiza - Road Test Portfolio. 2011. (Illus.). 182p. pap. 39.95 (978-1-58850-160-8(4)) Veloce Enterprises, Inc.

Kewley, Stuart. Toyota's French Connection: Trends in Franco-Japanese Automotive Relations. 60p. pap. 14.95 (978-1-86203-121-0(5)) Chatham Hse. GBR. Dist: Brookings Institution Pr.

AUTOMOBILE INDUSTRY AND TRADE—GERMANY

Fuss, Melvyn A. & Waverman, Leonard. Costs & Productivity in Automobile Production: The Challenge of Japanese Efficiency. 2006. (ENG., Illus.). 256p. pap. 53.00 (978-0-521-03175-2(3)) Cambridge Univ. Pr.

Gantriis, Peter. The Art of BMW: 85 Years of Motorcycling Excellence. 2008. (Illus.). 192p. 40.00 (978-0-7603-3315-0(7), 0760333157, Motorbooks) MBI Publishing Co. LLC.

Jürgens, Ulrich, et al. Breaking from Taylorism: Changing Forms of Work in the Automobile Industry. 2009. (ENG., Illus.). 464p. pap. 58.00 (978-0-521-10253-7(7)) Cambridge Univ. Pr.

Meredith, Laurence. Ferdinand Porsche & the Legacy of Genius. 2010. 268p. (978-1-904408-67-3(2)) Bank House Bks.

Muth, Hendrik. Mehrmarkenhandel in der Automobilbranche: Eine Betrachtung aus Kundensicht. 2008. (Marktorientierte Unternehmensführung Ser.). 362p. pap. 81.95 (978-3-631-57640-3(4)) Lang, Peter GmbH, Europaischer Verlag der Wissenschaften DEU. Dist: Lang, Peter.

Richartz, Jörg. Anreizsysteme zur Steuerung der Hersteller-Händler-Beziehung in der Automobilindustrie. 2009. (Strategisches Marketingmanagement Ser.). (GER.). 338p. pap. 86.95 (978-3-631-59194-9(2)) Lang, Peter GmbH, Europaischer Verlag der Wissenschaften DEU. Dist: Lang, Peter.

Robson, Graham. Inside the BMW Factories: Building the Ultimate Driving Machine. 2008. (ENG., Illus.). 192p. 40.00 (978-0-7603-3463-8(3), 0760334633, Motorbooks) MBI Publishing Co. LLC.

Schlegelmilch, Rainer W. Mercedes. 2008. (Transportation Ser.). (Illus.). 599p. per. 24.95 (978-0-8416-0283-0(2)) American Map Corp.

Trajanov, Romy. The Impact of Cultural Differences on Cross-Border Merger Processes - the Example of Daimlerchrysler. 2007. 144p. per. (978-3-8364-2810-1(5)) VDM Verlag Dr. Mueller e.K.

Walker, Mick. Nsu: The Complete Story, 1 vol. 2010. (ENG., Illus.). 240p. 44.95 (978-1-84797-148-7(2), 1847971482) Crowood Pr., Ltd. GBR. Dist: MBI Distribution Services/Quayside Distribution.

Welzel, Mirko. Kooperation und vertikale Wettbewerbsbeschränkungen in selektiven Vertriebssystemen: Das Beispiel des europäischen Automobilvertriebs. 2008. (Europäische Hochschulschriften. Reihe 5: Volks- und Betriebswirtschaft Ser.). 266p. pap. 65.95 (978-3-631-57972-5(1)) Lang, Peter GmbH, Europaischer Verlag der Wissenschaften DEU. Dist: Lang, Peter.

AUTOMOBILE INDUSTRY AND TRADE—GREAT BRITAIN

Aamidor, Abe. Shooting Star: The Rise & Fall of the British Motorcycle Industry. 2009. (ENG., Illus.). 176p. 29.95 (978-1-55022-900-4(1)) ECW Pr. CAN. Dist: Independent Pubs. Group.

Abbiss, Reg. Rolls-Royce from the Inside: The Humour, the Myths, the Truths. 2007. (ENG.). 240p. pap. 37.95 (978-0-7524-4324-9(0)) History Pr. Ltd., The GBR. Dist: Independent Pubs. Group.

Astley, Rick. Classic British Car Electrical Systems: Your guide to understanding, repairing & improving the electrical components & systems that were typical of British cars from 1950 To 1980. 2009. (Essential Ser.). (ENG., Illus.). 176p. pap. 49.95 (978-1-84584-215-4(4), 1845842154) Veloce Publishing Ltd. GBR. Dist: MBI Distribution Services/Quayside Distribution.

Beer, Andrew. The Impacts of Automotive Plant Closure. Beer, Andrew & Thomas, Holli, eds. 2009. (Regions & Cities Ser.). (ENG.). 132p. 125.00 (978-0-415-54334-7(7)) Routledge.

Bez, Ulrich. Mr. Aston Martin. 2012. (ENG & GER., Illus.). 408p. 110.00 **(978-3-8327-9542-9(1))** teNeues Publishing Co.

Bickerstaff, J. P. Original Vincent Motorcycle: The Restorer's Guide to postwar singles & Twins. 2009. (Original Ser.). (ENG., Illus.). 128p. 49.95 (978-1-906133-14-6(X), 190613314X) Herridge & Sons, Ltd. GBR. Dist: MBI Distribution Services/Quayside Distribution.

Chapman, Giles. 100 Cars Britain Can Be Proud Of. 2010. (ENG., Illus.). 192p. pap. 18.95 (978-0-7524-5686-7(5)) History Pr. Ltd., The GBR. Dist: Independent Pubs. Group.

Clarke, R., compiled by. TVR Limited Edition Ultra: 1959-1985. 2009. (Limited Edition Ultra Ser.). (ENG., Illus.). 208p. pap. 37.95 (978-1-85520-853-7(9), 1855208539) Brooklands Bks. GBR. Dist: MBI Distribution Services/Quayside Distribution.

Crane, Colin. Become an Approved Driving Instuctor. 2009. 260p. pap. 30.00 (978-1-84528-348-3(1)) How To Books GBR. Dist: Parkwest Pubns., Inc.

Day, Kenneth. Alvis: Story of the Red Triangle. 4th ed. 2009. (ENG., Illus.). 448p. 90.00 (978-1-84425-524-5(7), 1844255247) Haynes Publishing PLC GBR. Dist: MBI Distribution Services/Quayside Distribution.

Dunnett, Peter. The Decline of the British Motor Industry (Routledge Revivals) 2011. (Routledge Revivals Ser.). (ENG.). 208p. 110.00 (978-0-415-67938-1(9)) Routledge.

Dymock, Eric. Ford in Britain: Centenary File. 2011. 304p. 69.50 (978-0-9554909-3-4(6)) Dove Publishing GBR. Dist: Trans-Atlantic Pubns., Inc.

Gauäÿ, Philipp. The Electric Car & Britain. 2011. 32p. pap. **(978-3-640-70595-5(5))** Hammer, Patrick, Tanja Hammer, Matthias Knoop, Julius Mittenzwei, Georg Steinbach u. Michael Teltscher. GRIN Verlag GbR.

Gomes, Emanuel. Acquisitions in the Uk Car Industry. 2009. (Illus.). 208p. pap. (978-3-639-15442-9(6)) VDM Verlag Dr. Mueller e.K.

Hadland, Tony. Raleigh: Ups & Downs of the Iconic Bicycle Brand. 2011. (Cycling Resources Ser.). (Illus.). 360p. 49.95 (978-1-892495-68-6(6)) Cycle Publishing/Van Der Plas Pubns.

Hayter, Teresa & Harvey, David. The Factory & the City. (Illus.). xii, 308p. pap. (978-0-7201-2215-2(5), Burns & Oates) Continuum International Publishing Group, Ltd.

Jürgens, Ulrich, et al. Breaking from Taylorism: Changing Forms of Work in the Automobile Industry. 2009. (ENG., Illus.). 464p. pap. 58.00 (978-0-521-10253-7(7)) Cambridge Univ. Pr.

Killip, Chris, photos by. Chris Killip: Pirelli Work, 1 vol. 2006. (ENG., Illus.). 128p. 50.00 (978-3-86521-317-4(0)) Steidl, Gerhard Druckerei und Verlag DEU. Dist: Innovative Logistics.

Liversidge, T. J. Excelsior the lost Pioneer: The story of Excelsior motor Cycles. 2010. (Illus.). 72p. pap. 10.49 (978-1-4490-7678-8(5)) AuthorHouse.

Mynard, Dennis C. Salmons & Sons: The Tickford Coachbuilders. 2007. (ENG.). 192p. 49.95 (978-1-86077-422-5(9)) History Pr. Ltd., The GBR. Dist: Independent Pubs. Group.

Newell, Ray. The Morris Minor. 2009. (Shire Library). (ENG., Illus.). 48p. pap. 12.95 (978-0-7478-0762-9(0)) Shire Pubns., Ltd. GBR. Dist: Random Hse., Inc.

Peck, Colin. British Woodies: From the 1920's to the 1950's. 2008. (Those Were the Days Ser.). (ENG., Illus.). 96p. pap. 25.95 (978-1-84584-169-0(7), 1845841697) Veloce Publishing Ltd. GBR. Dist: MBI Distribution Services/Quayside Distribution.

Poynting, Roy. The Sammy Miller Museum Collection: Road Machines. 2010. (Illus.). 228p. pap. (978-0-9555278-3-8(X)) Redline Bks.

Pritchard, Anthony. British Family Cars of the 1950s And 60s. 2009. (Shire Library). (ENG., Illus.). 64p. pap. 12.95 (978-0-7478-0712-4(4)) Shire Pubns., Ltd. GBR. Dist: Random Hse., Inc.

Robson, Graham. The Book of the Standard Motor Company. 2011. (ENG., Illus.). 208p. 69.95 (978-1-84584-343-4(6), 1845843436) Veloce Publishing Ltd. GBR. Dist: MBI Distribution Services/Quayside Distribution.

Schlegelmilch, Rainer W. & Lehbrink, Hartmut. British Sports Cars. 2008. (Transportation Ser.). (Illus.). 439p. pap. 24.95 (978-0-8416-0276-2(X)) American Map Corp.

Skilleter, Paul & Porter, Philip. Sir William Lyons: The Official Biography. 2011. (ENG., Illus.). 384p. pap. 17.95 (978-0-85733-106-9(X), 085733106X) Haynes Publishing PLC GBR. Dist: MBI Distribution Services/Quayside Distribution.

Stewart, Paul, et al. We Sell Our Time No More: Workers' Struggles Against Lean Production in the British Car Industry. 2009. (ENG., Illus.). 272p. 95.00 (978-0-7453-2868-3(7)); pap. 35.00 (978-0-7453-2867-6(9)) Pluto Pr. GBR. Dist: Macmillan.

Stokoe, Noel. Jowett - A Century of Memories. 2010. (ENG., Illus.). 176p. pap. 24.95 (978-1-4456-0087-1(0)) Amberley Publishing GBR. Dist: Casemate Pubs. & Bk. Distributors, LLC.

Taylor, James. Family Cars of the 1970s And 80s. 2012. (Shire Library). (ENG., Illus.). 64p. pap. 12.95 **(978-0-7478-1149-7(0))** Shire Pubns., Ltd. GBR. Dist: Random Hse., Inc.

Taylor, S. AC Heritage. Date not set. (Illus.). 128p. pap. 18.95 (978-1-85532-549-4(7)) Osprey Publishing, Ltd. GBR. Dist: Stackpole Bks.

Vessey, Alan. By Precision into Power: A Bicentennial Record of D. Napier & Son. 2006. (ENG., Illus.). 288p. pap. 39.95 (978-0-7524-3888-7(3)) History Pr. Ltd., The GBR. Dist: Independent Pubs. Group.

Walker, Mick. British Motorcycles of the 1940s And 50s. 2010. (Shire Library). (ENG., Illus.). 64p. pap. 12.95 (978-0-7478-0805-3(8)) Shire Pubns., Ltd. GBR. Dist: Random Hse., Inc.

Walker, Nick. A-Z British Coachbuilders, 1919-1960: And the Development of Styles & Techniques. 2nd rev. enl. ed. 2007. (ENG., Illus.). 224p. 59.95 (978-0-9549981-6-5(2), 0954998162) Herridge & Sons, Ltd. GBR. Dist: MBI Distribution Services/Quayside Distribution.

Watts, Martin. Classic Dormobile Camper Vans: A Guide to the Camper Vans of Martin Walter & Dormobile. 2009. (ENG., Illus.). 128p. 39.95 (978-1-84797-083-1(4), 1847970834) Crowood Pr., Ltd. GBR. Dist: MBI Distribution Services/Quayside Distribution.

Webb, Martyn. Morgan, Malvern & Motoring. 2008. (ENG., Illus.). 288p. 49.95 (978-1-84797-039-8(7), 1847970397) Crowood Pr., Ltd. GBR. Dist: MBI Distribution Services/Quayside Distribution.

Wood, Jonathan. The British Motor Industry. 2010. (Shire Library). (ENG., Illus.). 64p. pap. 12.95 (978-0-7478-0768-1(X)) Shire Pubns., Ltd. GBR. Dist: Random Hse., Inc.

AUTOMOBILE INDUSTRY AND TRADE—INDIA

Aziz Rizvi, Syed Nasir & Mukherji, Debroto. Study of Global Competitiveness of Indian & Chinese. 2011. 252p. pap. **(978-3-8433-9062-0(2))** Lambert Academic Publishing.

Becker-Ritterspach, Florian & Becker-Ritterspac, Florian. Hybridization of MNE Subsidiaries: The Automotive Sector in India. 2009. (ENG.). 256p. (C). 100.00 (978-0-230-20669-4(7)) Palgrave Macmillan.

Calkins, Martin. King Car & the Ethics of Automobile Proponents' Strategies in China & India. 2011. (Transportation Issues, Policies & R&D Ser.). 180p. 69.00 (978-1-61761-271-8(5)) Nova Science Pubs., Inc.

Gupta, Ashu, et al. Simulation Software. 2011. 292p. pap. **(978-3-8454-0295-6(4))** Lambert Academic Publishing.

Lansbury, Russell D., et al. The Global Korean Motor Industry: The Hyundai Motor Company's Global Strategy. 2012. (Routledge Advances in Korean Studies). (ENG., Illus.). 144p. (C). pap. 42.95 **(978-0-415-54279-1(0))** Routledge.

Spaliviero, Giovanni. The Joint Venture Between Fiat & Tata Motors. 2011. 84p. pap. **(978-3-8443-9443-6(5))** Lambert Academic Publishing.

AUTOMOBILE INDUSTRY AND TRADE—INDIANA

Aamidor, Abe & Evanoff, Ted. At the Crossroads: Middle America & the Battle to Save the Car Industry. 2010. (ENG., Illus.). 404p. 24.95 (978-1-55022-904-2(4)) ECW Pr. CAN. Dist: Independent Pubs. Group.

AUTOMOBILE INDUSTRY AND TRADE—IRELAND

Nyhan, Miriam A. Are You Still Below? A History of the Ford Marina Plant, Cork, 1917-84. 2008. (ENG., Illus.). 158p. 44.95 (978-1-905172-49-8(4)) Collins Pr., The IRL. Dist: Dufour Editions, Inc.

AUTOMOBILE INDUSTRY AND TRADE—ITALY

Carugati, Decio G. & Carugati, D. G. R. Pininfarina. 2010. (ENG., Illus.). 240p. 150.00 (978-88-370-7360-2(7), Mondadori Electa (Acc)) Antique Collectors' Club GBR. Dist: National Bk. Network.

Clark, Jennifer. Mondo Agnelli: Fiat, Chrysler, & the Power of a Dynasty. 2011. (ENG., Illus.). 368p. 29.95 **(978-1-118-01852-1(4)**, Wiley) Wiley, John & Sons, Inc.

Cloesen, Ulrich (Uli) Peter. Italian Custom Motorcycles: The Italian Chop - Choppers, Cruisers, Bobbers, Trikes & Quads. 2012. (ENG., Illus.). 128p. 39.95 **(978-1-84584-394-6(0)**, 1845843940) Veloce Publishing Ltd. GBR. Dist: MBI Distribution Services/Quayside Distribution.

Curami, Andrea. Alfa Romeo & Mille Miglia. 2010. (ENG.). 160p. 44.95 (978-88-7911-496-7(4)); (Illus.). 44.95 (978-88-7911-504-9(9), 8879115049) Giorgio Nada Editore ITA. Dist: MBI Distribution Services/Quayside Distribution.

D'Alessio, Paolo & Boni, Valerio. Ducati: The Two-Wheels Red. 2011. 192p. 12.95 (978-90-79761-87-6(7)) Tectum B.V.B.A. BEL. Dist: Innovative Logistics.

Davies, Peter. The Lambretta Scooter Bible: Covers All Lambretta Models Built in Italy Between 1947 & 1971. 2008. (Bible Ser.). (ENG., Illus.). 160p. reprint ed. 59.95 (978-1-84584-086-0(0), 1845840860) Veloce Publishing Ltd. GBR. Dist: MBI Distribution Services/Quayside Distribution.

Falloon, Ian. The Laverda: Twins & Triples Bible: 650 & 750cc Twins: 1000 & 1200cc Triples. 2007. (Bible Ser.). (ENG., Illus.). 160p. 59.95 (978-1-84584-058-7(5), 1845840585) Veloce Publishing Ltd. GBR. Dist: MBI Distribution Services/Quayside Distribution.

Museum Staff, ed. The Museo Nazionale Dell' Automobile in Turin. 2012. (ENG., Illus.). 164p. 42.00 **(978-88-422-1993-4(2))** Allemandi, Umberto & Co. GBR. Dist: Antique Collectors' Club.

Nada, Giorgio Editor, ed. Zagato Milano 1919-2009: The Official Book. 2010. (ENG., Illus.). 160p. 64.95 (978-88-7911-487-5(5), 8879114875) Giorgio Nada Editore ITA. Dist: MBI Distribution Services/Quayside Distribution.

Rizzo, Enzo, text. Legendary Italian Cars. 2010. (ENG., Illus.). 304p. 39.95 (978-88-544-0492-2(6)) White Star ITA. Dist: Random Hse., Inc.

Zumbrunn & Heseltine, Richard. Italian Auto Legends: Classics of Style & Design. 2008. (Illus.). 296p. pap. 22.95 (978-1-85894-431-9(7)) Merrell Pubs. Ltd. GBR. Dist: Perseus Distribution.

AUTOMOBILE INDUSTRY AND TRADE—JAPAN

Alexander, Jeffrey W. Japan's Motorcycle Wars: B an Industry History. 2008. pap. 30.00 (978-0-8248-3328-2(7)) Univ. of Hawaii Pr.

Chambers, K. Dennis. Toyota. 2008. (Corporations That Changed the World Ser.). (Illus.). 180p. 45.00 (978-0-313-35032-0(9), GR5032, Greenwood Pr.) Greenwood Publishing Group, Inc.

Clarke, R. M., compiled by. Audi TT Performance Portfolio 1998-2006. 2007. (Performance Portfolio Ser.). (ENG., Illus.). 120p. pap. 24.95 (978-1-85520-732-5(X), 185520732X) Brooklands Bks. GBR. Dist: MBI Distribution Services/Quayside Distribution.

Cleary, Peter. Run, Run as Fast As you Can. 2009. 312p. pap. 23.50 (978-1-4269-0959-7(4)) Trafford Publishing.

Coffey. The Myth of Japanese Efficiency: The World Car Industry in a Globalizing Age. 2007. (Illus.). 208p. (C). 119.00 (978-1-84542-041-3(1)) Elgar, Edward Publishing, Inc.

Danko, James. Import-Export Business Secrets of the Japanese Used Car Export Market. 2009. 271p. pap. 24.99 (978-0-557-07041-1(4)) Lulu Enterprises Inc.

DeLorenzo, Peter. The United States of Toyota: How Detroit Squandered its Legacy & Enabled Toyota to Become America's Car Company. 2007. (ENG.). 308p. 37.95 (978-1-59299-302-4(8)) Inkwater Pr.

Fujimoto, Takahiro & Miller, Brian. Competing to Be Really, Really Good: The Behind-The-Scenes Drama of Capability-Building Competition in the Autopobile Industry. 2007. (Illus.). xi, 156p. (978-4-924971-21-9(9)) International House of Japan, Incorporated, The.

Fuss, Melvyn A. & Waverman, Leonard. Costs & Productivity in Automobile Production: The Challenge of Japanese Efficiency. 2006. (ENG., Illus.). 256p. pap. 53.00 (978-0-521-03175-2(3)) Cambridge Univ. Pr.

Hemsworth, Gregory B., ed. Automobile Trade with South Korea & Japan. 2011. (Trade Issues, Policies & Laws Transportation Issues, Policies & R&D Ser.). 93p. pap. 43.00 (978-1-61209-820-3(7)) Nova Science Pubs., Inc.

Hoeft, Steven E. Stories from My Sensei: Two Decades of Lessons Learned Implementing Toyota-Style Systems. 2009. (ENG., Illus.). 180p. 32.95 (978-1-4398-1654-7(9)) Productivity Pr.

Irawati, Dessy. Knowledge Transfer in the Automobile Industry: Global-Local Production Networks. 2011. (Routledge Studies in the Modern World Economy Ser.). (ENG., Illus.). 232p. (C). 152.00 (978-0-415-68060-8(3)) Routledge.

Kewley, Stuart. Toyota's French Connection: Trends in Franco-Japanese Automotive Relations. 60p. pap. 14.95 (978-1-86203-121-0(5)) Chatham Hse. GBR. Dist: Brookings Institution Pr.

Kriska, Laura. The Accidental Office Lady: An American Woman in Corporate Japan. 2011. (ENG.). 256p. pap. 15.95 (978-4-8053-1156-1(8)) Tuttle Publishing.

May, Matthew E. The Elegant Solution: Toyota's Formula for Mastering Innovation. 2011. (ENG.). 256p. pap. 16.99 **(978-0-7432-9019-7(4)**, Free Pr.) Free Pr.

Miyoshi, Hiroaki & Kii, Masanobu, eds. Technological Innovation & Public Policy: The Automotive Industry. 2011. (Palgrave Macmillan Asian Business Ser.). (ENG., Illus.). 208p. 95.00 (978-0-230-23076-7(8)) Palgrave Macmillan.

Monden, Yasuhiro. Toyota Production System: An Integrated Approach to Just-in-Time. 4th rev. ed. 2011.Tr. of Shin Toyota Shisutemu. (ENG., Illus.). 566p. 69.95 (978-1-4398-2097-1(X)) Productivity Pr.

Osono, Emi, et al. Extreme Toyota: Radical Contradictions That Drive Success at the World's Best Manufacturer. Bigelow, Susan J., ed. 2008. (ENG., Illus.). 320p. 27.95 (978-0-470-26762-2(3), Wiley) Wiley, John & Sons, Inc.

Planning, Alpha, ed. New Exhibition Design: Tokyo Motor Show CEATEC Japan. 2008. (ENG., Illus.). 256p. 65.00 (978-4-568-50343-2(4)) Azur Corp. JPN. Dist: Antique Collectors' Club.

Sato, Masaaki. The Honda Myth: The Genius & His Wake. 2006. (ENG.). 480p. 24.95 (978-1-932234-26-8(8)) Rizzoli International Pubns., Inc.

Shimokawa, Koichi. Japan & the Global Automotive Industry. 2010. (ENG., Illus.). 352p. 95.00 (978-0-521-86687-3(1)) Cambridge Univ. Pr.

Staples, Andrew. Responses to Regionalism in East Asia: Japanese Production Networks in the Automotive Sector. Hasegawa, Harukiyo, ed. 2008. (ENG., Illus.). 240p. 95.00 (978-0-230-51625-0(4)) Palgrave Macmillan.

Womack, James P., et al. The Machine That Changed the World: The Story of Lean Production — Toyota's Secret Weapon in the Global Car Wars That Is Now Revolutionizing World Industry. 2007. (ENG., Illus.). 352p. pap. 15.95 (978-0-7432-9979-4(5), Free Pr.) Free Pr.

AUTOMOBILE INDUSTRY AND TRADE—KENTUCKY

Ambrose, William. The Lexington Motor Car: Bred in Old Kentucky. 2007. (Illus.). 96p. 30.00 (978-0-9799158-0-2(5)) Ambrose, William.

AUTOMOBILE INDUSTRY AND TRADE—MEXICO

Gachú, et al. The Impact of NAFTA on the Automotive Industry in Mexico: An Analysis in Political Economy. 2008. 304p. pap. (978-3-639-09150-2(7)) VDM Verlag Dr. Mueller e.K.

AUTOMOBILE INDUSTRY AND TRADE—MICHIGAN

Dewar, Robert J. A Savage Factory: An Eyewitness Account of the Auto Industry's Self-Destruction. 2009. 240p. pap. 18.49 (978-1-4389-5293-2(7)) AuthorHouse.

Ganem, Jennifer Czerwick. Dearborn Inn. 2011. (Images of America Ser.). (ENG., Illus.). 128p. pap. 21.99 **(978-0-7385-8270-2(0))** Arcadia Publishing.

Taylor, Alex, III. Sixty to Zero: An Inside Look at the Collapse of General Motors — and the Detroit Auto Industry. 2011. (ENG.). 272p. pap. 17.00 (978-0-300-17151-8(X)) Yale Univ. Pr.

AUTOMOBILE INDUSTRY AND TRADE—MINNESOTA

Schwab, Randall. Wind Spirit. 2009. 80p. pap. 15.50 (978-1-60844-171-6(7)) Dog Ear Publishing, LLC.

AUTOMOBILE INDUSTRY AND TRADE—TENNESSEE

McCall, Walter. Weller Brothers of Memphis. 2010. (American Coachbuilders Ser.). (ENG., Illus.). 128p. pap. 19.95 (978-1-58388-257-3(X), 158388257X) Iconografix, Inc.

AUTOMOBILE INDUSTRY AND TRADE—TEXAS

Hemphill, Hugh. San Antonio on Wheels: The Alamo City Learns to Drive. 2009. (Illus.). 88p. pap. 18.95 (978-1-893271-49-4(8)) Maverick Publishing Co.

AUTOMOBILE INDUSTRY AND TRADE—UNITED STATES

Aamidor, Abe & Evanoff, Ted. At the Crossroads: Middle America & the Battle to Save the Car Industry. 2010. (ENG., Illus.). 404p. 24.95 (978-1-55022-904-2(4)) ECW Pr. CAN. Dist: Independent Pubs. Group.

After the Financial Crisis: Ongoing Challenges Facing Delphi Retirees: Field Hearing Before the Subcommittee on Oversight & Investigations of the Committee on Financial Services, U.S. House of Representatives, One Hundred Eleventh Congress, Second Session, July 13, 2010. 2010. (Illus.). vi, 161p. **(978-0-16-087424-6(6)**, 552-070-42117-3) United States Government Printing Office.

Alexander, Jack. The caterpillar's Roots. 2010. 442p. pap. 36.10 (978-0-557-30521-6(7)) Lulu Enterprises Inc.

Arute, Jack. Tales from the Indianapolis 500: A Collection of the Greatest Indy 500 Stories Ever Told. 2012. (Tales from the Team Ser.). (ENG., Illus.). 208p. 19.95 **(978-1-61321-044-4(2)**, 613044) Skyhorse Publishing Co., Inc.

Auto Editors of Consumer Guide Staff. American Cars of The 1950's. 2007. (Illus.). 320p. 12.98 (978-1-4127-1997-1(6)) Publications International, Ltd.

Automobile Arbitration Fairness ACT of 2008: Hearing Before the Subcommittee on Commercial & Administrative Law of the Committee on the Judiciary, House of Representatives, One Hundred Tenth Congress, Second Session, on H.R. 5312, March 6, 2008. 2009. iv, 109p. (978-0-16-082583-5(0), 552-070-38604-1) United States Government Printing Office.

Bartlett, Tom. Motor Wheels & Flyers. 2010. 81p. pap. 11.50 (978-0-557-61669-5(7)) Lulu Enterprises Inc.

Basch, Harry & Slater, Shirley. RV Vacations. 5th ed. 2010. (Dummies Travel Ser.: 140). (ENG., Illus.). 456p. pap. 19.99 (978-0-470-64378-5(1), For Dummies) Wiley, John & Sons, Inc.

Battery & EV Industry Review 2005. 2006. per. 1950.00 (978-1-59623-207-5(2)) BCC Research.

Beamish, Anne. Learning from Work: Designing Organizations for Learning & Communication. 2007. (ENG., Illus.). 176p. 55.00 (978-0-8047-5715-7(1)); per. 21.95 (978-0-8047-5716-4(X)) Stanford Univ. Pr. (Stanford Business Bks.).

Beecroft, David. History of the American Automobile Industry. 2009. 97p. pap. 19.95 (978-0-557-05575-3(X)) Lulu Enterprises Inc.

Bergman, Garry D., ed. Cash for Clunkers & the Auto Industry: Background, Lessons & Results. 2010. (Business Issues, Competition & Entrepreneurship Ser.). 89.00 (978-1-61728-918-7(3)) Nova Science Pubs., Inc.

Bertram, Barry. White Trucks of The 1950s. 2009. (At Work Ser.). (ENG., Illus.). 128p. pap. 19.95 (978-1-58388-230-6(8), 1583882308) Iconografix, Inc.

Borg, Kevin L. Auto Mechanics: Technology & Expertise in Twentieth-Century America. (Studies in Industry & Society Ser.). (ENG., Illus.). 280p. (gr. 17). 2010. pap. 32.00 (978-0-8018-9485-5(9)) 2007. 50.00 (978-0-8018-8606-5(6)) Johns Hopkins Univ. Pr.

Bowling, Brad. Ford Mustang. 2010. (First Gear Ser.). (ENG., Illus.). 240p. pap. 19.99 (978-0-7603-3808-7(6), 0760338086, Motorbooks) MBI Publishing Co. LLC.

Bromley, Michael L. William Howard Taft & the First Motoring Presidency, 1909-1913. alt. ed. 2007. (ENG., Illus.). 447p. per. 45.00 (978-0-7864-2952-3(6)) McFarland & Co., Inc. Pubs.

Calabro, Marian. The Pep Boys Company History Book. 2006. (978-1-57990-636-8(2)) Lark Bks.

Cathcart, Alan. American Dream Bikes. 2010. (ENG.). 240p. 40.00 (978-1-935350-01-9(3), Parker Hse. Publishing Inc.,Csi) Continental Sales, Inc.

Clark, Jennifer. Mondo Agnelli: Fiat, Chrysler, & the Power of a Dynasty. 2011. (ENG., Illus.). 368p. 29.95 **(978-1-118-01852-1(4)**, Wiley) Wiley, John & Sons, Inc.

Clarke, Sally. Trust & Power: Consumers, the Modern Corporation, & the Making of the United States Automobile Market. 2007. (ENG., Illus.). 314p. 60.00 (978-0-521-86878-5(5)) Cambridge Univ. Pr.

Clarke, Sally H. Trust & Power: Consumers, the Modern Corporation, & the Making of the United States Automobile Market. 2009. (ENG.). 316p. pap. 42.00 (978-0-521-12038-8(1)) Cambridge Univ. Pr.

Collier, Peter & Horowitz, David. Los Ford. (SPA.). 464p. (978-84-7223-175-7(5), 6020) Tusquets Editores.

Corner, Colin. The Complete Book of Shelby Automobiles: Cobras, Mustangs, & Super Snakes. 2009. (Complete Book Ser.). (ENG., Illus.). 256p. 45.00 (978-0-7603-3578-9(8), 0760335788, Motorbooks) MBI Publishing Co. LLC.

Congressional Oversight Panel September Oversight Report: The Use of TARP Funds in the Support & Reorganization of the Domestic Automotive Industry. 2009. iii, 176p. (978-0-16-084400-3(2), 552-070-39942-9) United States Government Printing Office.

Cook, Marc. Ducati 1098/1198: The Superbike Redefined. 2010. (Illus.). 176p. 39.95 (978-1-935007-06-7(8)) Bull, David Publishing, Inc.

Crumm, Thomas A. What Is Good for General Motors? Solving America's Industrial Conundrum. 2010. 288p. pap. 33.95 (978-0-87586-778-6(2)) 2009. pap. 23.95 (978-0-87586-777-9(4)) Algora Publishing.

Dalton, Curt, et al. Miami Valley's Marvelous Motor Cars. 2007. (Illus.). 96p. per. 19.95 (978-0-9715702-9-0(9)) Dalton, Curt.

De Lorenzo, Peter M. Witch Hunt: Essays on the U.S. Auto Industry & the Blithering Idiots Who Almost Killed It. Putman, Janice J., ed. 2011. 384p. 37.95 (978-0-9821733-7-4(7)) Octane Pr.

DeLorenzo, Peter. The United States of Toyota: How Detroit Squandered its Legacy & Enabled Toyota to Become America's Car Company. 2007. (ENG.). 308p. 37.95 (978-1-59299-302-4(8)) Inkwater Pr.

Dewhurst. Harley-Davidson 100 Years of the American Motorcycle -Crestline. 192p. 24.98 (978-0-7603-1759-4(3)) MBI Publishing Co. LLC.

Digest of Motor Laws 2007 Edition. 2007. pap. (978-1-59508-206-0(9)) AAA.

Eisinger, Douglas S. Smog Check: Science, Federalism, & the Politics of Clean Air. 2010. (ENG., Illus.). 252p. 99.95 (978-1-933115-71-9(8), RFF Pr.) Earthscan LLC.

Elliot, James R. The U. S. Auto Industry & the Role of Federal Assistance. 2010. (Business Issues, Competition & Entrepreneurship Ser.). (Illus.). 197p. 130.00 (978-1-60741-322-6(1)) Nova Science Pubs., Inc.

Endelman, Judith E., ed. The Model T Reconsidered: Proceedings of the World of the Model T Conference. 2008. (Illus.). 132p. pap. 39.95 (978-0-933728-07-3(7)) Ford, Henry The.

Erskine, Albert Russel. History of the Studebaker Corporation. 2009. 98p. pap. 19.95 (978-0-557-05279-0(3)) Lulu Enterprises Inc.

Examining the Delphi Bankruptcy's Impact on Workers & Retirees: Hearing Before the Subcommittee on Health, Employment, Labor, & Pensions, Committee on Education & Labor, U.S. House of Representatives, One Hundred Eleventh Congress, First Session, Hearing Held in Washington, DC, December 2, 2009. 2010. (Illus.). iii, 54p. (978-0-16-085950-2(6), 552-070-41141-1) United States Government Printing Office.

Flory, J. "Kelly", Jr. American Cars, 1946-1959: Every Model, Year by Year. 2008. (ENG., Illus.). 1047p. 75.00 (978-0-7864-3229-5(2)) McFarland & Co., Inc. Pubs.

—American Cars, 1973-1980: Every Model, Year by Year. 2012. (ENG., Illus.). 75.00 (978-0-7864-4352-9(9)) McFarland & Co., Inc. Pubs.

Ford, Henry. My Life & Work. 2008. 268p. 28.99 (978-0-554-22394-0(5)); 25.99 (978-0-554-31697-0(8)) BiblioBazaar.

—My Life & Work. 2009. 200p. pap. (978-0-217-25960-6(X)) Books LLC.

—My Life & Work. 2007. 296p. 21.50 (978-1-60206-935-0(2)) Cosimo, Inc.

—My Life & Work. 2010. 302p. pap. 11.50 (978-1-57898-916-4(7)) Martino Publishing.

Ford, Henry & Crowther, Samuel. My Life & Work. 2007. (ENG.). 312p. 22.99 (978-1-59986-693-2(5)) Filiquarian Publishing, LLC.

Foster, Patrick. Studebaker: The Complete History. 2008. (ENG., Illus.). 192p. 40.00 (978-0-7603-3287-0(8), 0760332878, Motorbooks) MBI Publishing Co. LLC.

Foster, Patrick R. Kaiser-Frazer 1947-1955 Photo Archive. 2009. (Photo Archive Ser.). (ENG., Illus.). 128p. pap. 32.95 (978-1-58388-239-9(1), 1583882391) Iconografix, Inc.

Franz, Kathleen. Tinkering: Consumers Reinvent the Early Automobile. 2011. (Illus.). 232p. (C). pap. 24.95 (978-0-8122-2158-9(3)) Univ. of Pennsylvania Pr.

Full Committee Hearing on the Role of Small Business Suppliers & Manufacturers in the Domestic Auto Industry: Hearing Before the Committee on Small Business, United States House of Representatives, One Hundred Eleventh Congress, First Session, Hearing Held May 13, 2009. 2009. v, 96p. (978-0-16-084162-0(3), 552-070-39763-9) United States Government Printing Office.

Fuss, Melvyn A. & Waverman, Leonard. Costs & Productivity in Automobile Production: The Challenge of Japanese Efficiency. 2006. (ENG., Illus.). 256p. pap. 53.00 (978-0-521-03175-2(3)) Cambridge Univ. Pr.

Gabrick, Robert. Federal Trucks Photo Archive. 2008. (Photo Archive Ser.). (ENG., Illus.). 128p. pap. 19.95 (978-1-58388-223-8(5), 1583882235) Iconografix, Inc.

—Go the Greyhound Way: The Romance of the Road. 2009. (ENG., Illus.). 160p. pap. 34.95 (978-1-58388-246-7(4), 1583882464) Iconografix, Inc.

Geithner, Timothy F. Treasury Secretary Timothy F. Geithner: Hearing Before the Congressional Oversight Panel, One Hundred Eleventh Congress, First Session, September 10, 2009. 2009. iii, 85p. (978-0-16-084662-5(5), 552-070-40155-5) United States Government Printing Office.

Glasscock, Carl Burgess. The Gasoline Age: The Story of the Men Who Made It. 2011. 382p. 53.95 **(978-1-258-08313-7(2))** Literary Licensing, LLC.

Goddard, Stephen B. Colonel Albert Pope & His American Dream Machines: The Life & Times of a Bicycle Tycoon Turned Automotive Pioneer. alt. ed. 2008. (ENG.). 263p. pap. 39.95 (978-0-7864-4089-4(9)) McFarland & Co., Inc. Pubs.

Gordon, Whitby. Earning the American Dream. 2009. (Illus.). 347p. pap. 39.95 (978-1-4276-4036-9(X)) Aardvark Global Publishing.

Gregg, John T. & Mears, Patrick E. Auto Supplier Insolvencies & Bankruptcies: Issues for Suppliers & Customers of Financially Troubled Auto Suppliers. 2006. 270p. per. 25.00 (978-0-9785292-4-6(3)) American Bankruptcy Institute.

Hadsall, Guy & Foster, Patrick R. Mister Javelin: Guy Hadsall Jr. at American Motors. 2007. (Illus.). vi, 95p. pap. (978-0-9662019-2-5(2)) Olde Milford Pr., The.

Harbour, James E. & Higgins, James V. Factory Man: How Jim Harbour Discovered Toyota's Quality & Productivity Methods & Helped the U.S. Auto Industry Get Competitive. 2009. (Illus.). xvi, 170p. (978-0-87263-860-0(X)) Society of Manufacturing Engineers.

Headrick Jr, Robert J. Cadillac: The Tailfin Years. 2008. (ENG., Illus.). 128p. pap. 34.95 (978-1-58388-212-2(X), 158388212X) Iconografix, Inc.

Heitmann, John Alfred. The Automobile & American Life. 2009. (ENG., Illus.). 260p. pap. 39.95 (978-0-7864-4013-9(9)) McFarland & Co., Inc. Pubs.

Hemsworth, Gregory B., ed. Automobile Trade with South Korea & Japan. 2011. (Trade Issues, Policies & Laws Transportation Issues, Policies & R&D Ser.). 93p. pap. 43.00 (978-1-61209-820-3(7)) Nova Science Pubs., Inc.

Hesselbart, Al. The Dumb Things Sold Just Like That: A History of the Recreational Vehicle Industry in America. 2007. per. 19.95 (978-0-9796976-0-9(3)) Legacy Ink Publishing.

Hoffman, Bryce G. American Icon: Alan Mulally & the Fight to Save Ford Motor Company. 2012. (ENG., Illus.). 432p. 26.00 **(978-0-307-88605-7(0)**, Crown Business) Crown Publishing Group.

Holmstrom, Darwin & Newhardt, David. Gto: Pontiac's Great One. rev. ed. 2011. (ENG., Illus.). 336p. pap. 29.99 (978-0-7603-3985-5(6), 0760339856, Motorbooks) MBI Publishing Co. LLC.

Holstein, William. Why GM Matters: Inside the Race to Transform an American Icon. 2009. (ENG., Illus.). 288p. 26.00 (978-0-8027-1718-4(7)) Walker & Co.

Horton, David Earl. I Was a Teenage Car Columnist: A Boomer's Scrapbook of mid-60's Cars & Stories. Edwards, Agnes, ed. 2008. (Illus.). 120p. per. 19.95 (978-0-9800990-4-1(8)) Thunderboomer Media LLC.

Hybrid Cars: Increasing Fuel Efficiency & Reducing Oil Dependence: Hearing Before the Subcommittee on Energy & Resources of the Committee on Government Reform, House of Representatives, One Hundred Ninth Congress, Second Session, July 20, 2006. 2007. (Illus.). iii, 89p. (978-0-16-079131-4(6), 552-070-36226-6) United States Government Printing Office.

Ingrassia, Paul. Crash Course: The American Automobile Industry's Road from Glory to Disaster. 2011. (Illus.). 336p. pap. 17.00 (978-0-8129-8075-2(1), Random Hse. Trade Paperbacks) Random House Publishing Group.

Innovation, Jobs, & Energy Independence: Reinvigorating the Domestic Auto Industry: Hearing Before the Select Committee on Energy Independence & Global Warming, House of Representatives, One Hundred Tenth Congress, Second Session, December 9, 2008. 2010. iii, 105p. (978-0-16-087177-1(8), 552-070-42019-3) United States Government Printing Office.

Jürgens, Ulrich, et al. Breaking from Taylorism: Changing Forms of Work in the Automobile Industry. 2009. (ENG., Illus.). 464p. pap. 58.00 (978-0-521-10253-7(7)) Cambridge Univ. Pr.

Kimes, Beverly Rae & Cox, James H. Walter L. Marr: Buick's Amazing Engineer. 2007. (Illus.). 214p. (978-0-9766683-4-3(3)) Racemaker Pr.

Klier, Thomas H. & Rubenstein, James M. Who Really Made Your Car? Restructuring & Geographic Change in the Auto Industry. 2008. 419p. 40.00 (978-0-88099-334-0(0)); pap. 20.00 (978-0-88099-333-3(2)) Upjohn, W.E. Institute for Employment Research.

Knecht, Paul. Tears on Henry Ford's Face. 2007. 175p. per. 12.99 (978-1-59886-656-8(7)) Tate Publishing & Enterprises, LLC.

Kousakis, James S. & Leonard, John Peter. General Motors & Chrysler: Assistance & Exit from the Troubled Asset Relief Program. 2012. **(978-1-61942-072-4(4))** Nova Science Pubs., Inc.

Krevsky, Margery. Sirens of Chrome: The Enduring Allure of Auto Show Models. 2008. (Illus.). 24.95 (978-1-879094-84-0(3)) Momentum Bks., LLC.

Laurel, William C. U. S. & Asian Motor Vehicle Industry in the Global Economy. 2011. (Business Issues, Competition & Entrepreneurship Ser.). 195.00 (978-1-61728-828-9(4)) Nova Science Pubs., Inc.

Lee, J. Edward. John Gary Anderson & His Maverick Motor Company: The Rise & Fall of Henry Ford's Rock Hill Rival. 2007. (Illus.). 126p. pap., per. 19.99 (978-1-59629-229-1(6)) History Pr., The.

Lunn, Roy. The World Crisis It All Started With 9/11. 2009. 212p. pap. 12.95 (978-1-936051-66-3(4)) Peppertree Pr., The.

Lutz, Bob. Car Guys vs. Bean Counters: The Battle for the Soul of American Business. 2011. (ENG., Illus.). 256p. (gr. 12). 26.95 (978-1-59184-400-6(2), Portfolio (Hardcover)) Penguin Group (USA) Inc.

Lyons, Dan. Muscle Car the Art of Power. 2008. (ENG., Illus.). 192p. 27.99 (978-0-89689-617-8(X)) Krause Pubns.

Magee, David. Crash: Why the Big Three Failed & the Future of America's Automotive Industry. 2009. (ENG.). 256p. pap. 16.95 (978-0-9800164-5-1(2)) Jefferson Pr.

—Turnaround. Date not set. 256p. pap. 14.99 (978-0-06-051486-0(8)) HarperCollins Pubs.

Marquis, Samuel S. Henry Ford: An Interpretation. 2011. 220p. 44.95 **(978-1-258-02577-9(9))** Literary Licensing, LLC.

—Henry Ford: An Interpretation. 2007. (Great Lakes Bks.). 24.95 (978-0-8143-3367-9(2)) Wayne State Univ. Pr.

Martin, Terry. Packard: The Warren Years. 2009. (Illus.). 182p. pap. (978-1-893619-61-6(3)) Historical Publishing Network.

McCarthy, Tom. Auto Mania: Cars, Consumers, & the Environment. 2009. (ENG., Illus.). 368p. pap. 20.00 (978-0-300-15848-9(3)) Yale Univ. Pr.

McPherson, Thomas A. The Henney Motor Company: The Complete History. 2009. (ENG., Illus.). 288p. 79.95 (978-1-58388-233-7(2), 1583882332) Iconografix, Inc.

—Miller-Meteor: The Complete Illustrated History. 2010. (ENG., Illus.). 320p. 79.95 (978-1-58388-258-0(8), 1583882588) Iconografix, Inc.

McPherson, Thomas A. & McCall, Walter. Cadillac Fleetwood Seventy-Five Series Limousines 1937-1987 Photo Archive. 2009. (Photo Archive Ser.). (ENG., Illus.). 128p. pap. 32.95 (978-1-58388-248-1(0), 1583882480) Iconografix, Inc.

Miller, Jeanine Head. A History of the Henry Ford: Telling America's Story. 2009. (Illus.). 216p. (978-1-57864-577-0(8)) Donning Co. Pubs.

Miller, Larry H. & Robinson, Doug. Driven: An Autobiography. 2012. pap. 18.99 **(978-1-60908-916-0(2))** 2010. (978-1-60641-656-3(1)) Deseret Bk. Co.

Miller, Steve. The Turnaround Kid: What I Learned Rescuing America's Most Troubled Companies. 2008. (ENG., Illus.). 272p. 25.95 (978-0-06-125127-6(5), Collins) HarperCollins Pubs.

Morey, Bruce. Automotive 2030, North America. 2011. **(978-0-7680-5727-0(2))** SAE Intl.

Moriarty, Frank. Top Speed: Dodge & Plymouth Stock Car Racing. 2007. 188p. per. 16.95 (978-0-595-45617-8(0)) iUniverse, Inc.

Morris, Charles. Factory Lightweights: Detroit's Drag Racing Specials of The '60s. 2007. (ENG., Illus.). 160p. pap. 24.95 (978-1-932494-44-0(8)) CarTech, Inc.

Mort, Norm. American 'Independent' Automakers: AMC to Willys 1945 to 1960. 2010. (Those Were the Days Ser.). (ENG., Illus.). 96p. pap. 29.95 (978-1-84584-239-0(1), 1845842391) Veloce Publishing Ltd. GBR. Dist: MBI Distribution Services/Quayside Distribution.

—American Trucks of The 1960s. 2010. (Those Were the Days Ser.). (ENG., Illus.). 96p. pap. 29.95 (978-1-84584-228-4(6), 1845842286) Veloce Publishing Ltd. GBR. Dist: MBI Distribution Services/Quayside Distribution.

Mroz, Albert. American Cars, Trucks & Motorcycles of World War I: Illustrated Histories of 225 Manufacturers. 2010. (ENG., Illus.). 428p. pap. 45.00 (978-0-7864-3967-6(X)) McFarland & Co., Inc. Pubs.

Munroe, Brian. Car Buying Revealed: How to Buy a Car & Not Get Taken for a Ride. 2008. (ENG., Illus.). 213p. pap. 19.95 (978-1-60037-400-5(X)) Morgan James Publishing.

Musselman, M. M. Get a Horse! the Story of the Automobile in Americ. 2011. 336p. 50.95 **(978-1-258-06413-6(8))** Literary Licensing, LLC.

Nada Official Used Car Guide Co, creator. NADA Official Used Car Guide: Passenger Cars, Light-Duty Trucks. 2009. (NADA Official Used Car Guide: Consumer Edition Ser.). 284p. pap. 9.95 (978-1-881406-67-9(9)) N.A.D.A. Official Used Car Guide Co.

Nelson, R. Dave, et al. Powered by Hond: Developing Excellence in the Global Enterprise. 2007. 288p. per. 21.95 (978-0-595-47262-8(1), Backinprint.com) iUniverse, Inc.

Newhardt, David. Art of the Muscle Car. 2009. (ENG., Illus.). 240p. 40.00 (978-0-7603-3591-8(5), 0760335915, Motorbooks) MBI Publishing Co. LLC.

O'Callaghan, Timothy J. Ford in the Service of America: Mass Production for the Military During the World Wars. 2009. (ENG., Illus.). 206p. pap. 35.00 (978-0-7864-4485-4(1)) McFarland & Co., Inc. Pubs.

Oversight of TARP Assistance to the Automobile Industry: Field Hearing Before the Congressional Oversight Panel, One Hundred Eleventh Congress, First Session, Hearing Held in Detroit, Michigan, July 27, 2009. 2009. (Illus.). iii, 150p. (978-0-16-084597-0(1), 552-070-40103-2) United States Government Printing Office.

Parkhurst, Scott. V-8 Horsepower Performance Handbook. 2009. (Motorbooks Workshop Ser.). (ENG., Illus.). 160p. pap. 24.99 (978-0-7603-3552-9(4), 0760335524, Motorbooks) MBI Publishing Co. LLC.

Paulose, John & Kihara, Zhou. Recalls of Automobiles & Medical Devices: Federal Oversight. 2011. **(978-1-62100-122-5(9))** Nova Science Pubs., Inc.

Pound, Arthur & Babcock, James M. The Automobile & an American City. 2011. 34p. 35.95 **(978-1-258-04381-0(5))** Literary Licensing, LLC.

Publications International Staff, creator. Cars of The 1960s. 2007. (Illus.). 192p. 24.95 (978-1-4127-1554-6(7)) Publications International, Ltd.

Quattlebaum, Julian K. The Great Savannah Races. 2011. (ENG., Illus.). 152p. pap. 24.95 **(978-0-8203-3813-2(3))** Univ. of Georgia Pr.

Ragsdale, Mark P. Car Wreck. 2010. 256p. pap. 15.95 (978-1-934938-65-2(3), Langdon Street Pr.) Hillcrest Publishing Group, Inc.

Ramifications of Auto Industry Bankruptcies: Hearing Before the Committee on the Judiciary, House of Representatives, One Hundred Eleventh Congress, First Session, May 21, 2009. 2009. iv, 178p. (978-0-16-084379-2(0), 552-070-39922-4) United States Government Printing Office.

Ramifications of Auto Industry Bankruptcies: Hearing Before the Subcommittee on Commercial & Administrative Law of the Committee on the Judiciary, House of Representatives, One Hundred Eleventh Congress, First Session, July 21, 2009. 2010. iv, 71p. (978-0-16-085264-0(1), 552-070-40605-1) United States Government Printing Office.

Ramifications of Auto Industry Bankruptcies: Hearing Before the Subcommittee on Commercial & Administrative Law of the Committee on the Judiciary, House of Representatives, One Hundred Eleventh Congress, First Session, July 22, 2009. 2010. (Illus.). iv, 282p. (978-0-16-085324-1(9), 552-070-40654-9) United States Government Printing Office.

Rattner, Steven. Overhaul: An Insider's Account of the Obama Administration's Emergency Rescue of the Auto Industry. (ENG., Illus.). 2011. 384p. pap. 15.95 (978-0-547-57742-5(7), Mariner Bks.) 2010. 352p. 27.00 (978-0-547-44321-8(8)) Houghton Mifflin Harcourt Trade & Reference Pubs.

Reforming Corporate Average Fuel Economy (CAFE) Standards: Hearing Before the Subcommittee on Surface Transportation & Merchant Marine of the Committee on Commerce, Science, & Transportation, United States Senate, One Hundred Ninth Congress, Second Session, May 9, 2006. 2011. (Illus.). iii, 85p. **(978-0-16-088301-9(6)**, 552-070-42606-0) United States Government Printing Office.

Review of Industry Plans to Stabilize the Financial Condition of the American Automobile Industry: Hearing Before the Committee on Financial Services, U.S. House of Representatives, One Hundred Tenth Congress, Second Session, December 5, 2008. 2009. (Illus.). iv, 296p. (978-0-16-082968-0(2), 552-070-38879-6) United States Government Printing Office.

Robert J. Dewar Staff. A Savage Factory. 2009. 240p. 25.99 (978-1-4389-5294-9(5)) AuthorHouse.

Robson, Graham. Inside the BMW Factories: Building the Ultimate Driving Machine. 2008. (ENG., Illus.). 192p. 40.00 (978-0-7603-3463-8(3), 0760334633, Motorbooks) MBI Publishing Co. LLC.

Rodengen, Jeffrey L. The Legend of General Parts: Proudly Serving a World in Motion. Lewin, Heather & Murphy, Mickey, eds. 2007. (Illus.). 328p. 39.95 (978-0-945903-79-6(0)) Write Stuff Enterprises, Inc.

Rubenstein, James M. Making & Selling Cars: Innovation & Change in the U. S. Automotive Industry. 2008. (ENG., Illus.). 416p. (gr. 17). pap. 38.00 (978-0-8018-8853-3(0)) Johns Hopkins Univ. Pr.

Russ, Jonathan S. Global Motivations: Honda Toyota. 2008. (ENG.). 170p. pap. 32.99 (978-0-7618-3931-6(3)) Univ. Pr. of America, Inc.

—Global Motivations: Honda, Toyota, & the Drive Toward American Manufacturing. 2008. (ENG.). 170p. 63.99 (978-0-7618-3930-9(5)) Univ. Pr. of America, Inc.

Russell, Jason. Our Union: UAW/ CAW Local 27 from 1950 To 1990. 2012. (ENG., Illus.). 300p. pap. 32.95 (978-1-926836-43-0(X)) UBC Pr. CAN. Dist: Univ. of Washington Pr.

Schreiber, Hermann, ed. Gasoline Prices & their Effects on Behavior. 2010. (America in the 21st Century: Political & Economic Issues Ser.). pap. 43.00 (978-1-60741-351-6(5)) Nova Science Pubs., Inc.

Segal, Howard P. Recasting the Machine Age: Henry Ford's Village Industries. 2008. (ENG., Illus.). 244p. pap. 26.95 (978-1-55849-642-2(4)) Univ. of Massachusetts Pr.

Shiers, Will. Roadside Relics: America's Abandoned Automobiles. 2010. (ENG., Illus.). 208p. pap. 21.99 (978-0-7603-3984-8(8), 0760339848, Motorbooks) MBI Publishing Co. LLC.

Shotwel, Gregg. Live Bait & Ammo: Autoworkers under the Gun. 2012. (ENG., Illus.). 246p. pap. 17.00 ***(978-1-60846-142-4(4))*** Haymarket Bks.
Smith, Kim. Auto Dealerships. 2009. v, 228p. pap. *(978-0-87218-833-4(7))* National Underwriter Co.
Smith, Paul D. Merchants of Speed: The Men Who Built America's Performance Industry. 2009. (ENG., Illus.). 240p. 40.00 *(978-0-7603-3567-3(2),* 0760335672, Motorbooks) MBI Publishing Co. LLC.
Spitzer, Alan & Spitzer, Alison. Grand Theft Auto. 2011. (ENG.). 244p. 21.95 *(978-1-935547-31-0(3))*; 280p. 28.95 *(978-1-935547-27-3(5))* New Year Publishing.
Stanley, Richard A. Custom Built by Mcfarlan: A History of the Carriage & Automobile Manufacturer, 1856-1928. 2011. (ENG., Illus.). 277p. 55.00 *(978-0-7864-4457-1(6))* McFarland & Co., Inc. Pubs.
The State of the Domestic Automobile Industry: Impact of Federal Assistance: Hearing Before the Committee on Banking, Housing, & Urban Affairs, United States Senate, One Hundred Eleventh Congress, First Session, on Examining the Role of the Federal Government's Auto Task Force in the Restructuring of America's Automobile Industry, June 10, 2009. 2010. iii, 60p. *(978-0-16-085132-2(7),* 552-070-40486-4) United States Government Printing Office.
Stevenson, Heon. American Automobile Advertising, 1930-1980: An Illustrated History. 2008. (ENG., Illus.). 294p. 75.00 *(978-0-7864-3685-9(9))* McFarland & Co., Inc. Pubs.
Street, Brian Jeffrey. Half a Step Ahead: Learning My Way Around a Motor Scooter. 2009. 128p. pap. 11.00 *(978-0-557-04713-0(7))* Lulu Enterprises Inc.
Teutul, Paul. The Ride of a Lifetime: Doing Business the Orange County Choppers Way. 2010. (ENG.). 208p. pap. 16.95 *(978-0-470-56342-7(7),* Wiley) Wiley, John & Sons, Inc.
Turner, Tim. One Team on All Levels: Stories from Toyota Team Members. 2nd rev. ed. 2011. (ENG., Illus.). 322p. pap. 29.95 *(978-1-4398-6067-0(X))* Productivity Pr.
Vlasic, Bill. Once upon a Car: The Fall & Resurrection of America's Big Three Auto Makers — GM, Ford, & Chrysler. 2012. (ENG.). 400p. pap. 15.99 ***(978-0-06-184563-5(9),*** William Morrow Paperbacks) 2011. 394p. E-Book 21.99 ***(978-0-06-204222-4(X),*** Morrow, William & Co.) 2011. (ENG.). 400p. 26.99 *(978-0-06-184562-8(0),* Morrow, William & Co.) 2011. (ENG.). 624p. pap. 26.99 *(978-0-06-208860-4(2),* HarperLuxe) HarperCollins Pubs.
Vuic, Jason. The Yugo: The Rise & Fall of the Worst Car in History, 1 vol. 2011. (ENG., Illus.). 272p. pap. 14.00 *(978-0-8090-9895-8(4),* Hill & Wang) Farrar, Straus & Giroux.
Walcott, Samantha E. & Capaldi, Jason A. TARP on the U. S. Automotive Industry: Impact & Implications. 2011. (Series: Economic Issues, Problems & Perspectives Ser.). 257p. 215.00 *(978-1-61324-363-3(4))* Nova Science Pubs., Inc.
Watts, Steven. The People's Tycoon: Henry Ford & the American Century. 2006. (Vintage Ser.). (ENG., Illus.). 656p. pap. 18.00 *(978-0-375-70725-4(5),* Vintage) Knopf Doubleday Publishing Group.
Wentland, Kenneth. Ford Flexes Back. 2008. 164p. 25.95 *(978-1-60693-222-3(5),* Strategic Bk. Publishing) AEG Literary Publishing Services, Inc.
Who's Buying Transportation. 2007. 133p. pap. 59.95 *(978-1-933588-63-6(2))* New Strategist Pubns., Inc.
Wilkins, Mira & Hill, Frank Ernest. American Business Abroad: Ford on Six Continents. 2011. (ENG., Illus.). 572p. 99.00 ***(978-1-107-00797-0(6))***; 574p. pap. 36.99 ***(978-1-107-40023-8(6))*** Cambridge Univ. Pr.
Wyatt, Dan H. Signs of a Wreck. 2009. pap. 49.97 *(978-1-61584-064-9(8))* Independent Pub.
Yanik, Anthony J. Maxwell Motor & the Making of Chrysler Corporation. 2009. (Illus.). 189p. 34.95 *(978-0-8143-3423-2(7))* Wayne State Univ. Pr.
Young, Jan. Studebaker & the Railroads - Volume 1. 2009. 263p. pap. 29.95 *(978-0-557-09291-8(4))* Lulu Enterprises Inc.
—Studebaker & the Railroads - Volume 2. 2009. 201p. pap. 27.95 *(978-0-557-09383-0(X))* Lulu Enterprises Inc.
$4 Gasoline & Fuel Economy: Auto Industry at a Crossroads: Hearing Before the Select Committee on Energy Independence & Global Warming, House of Representatives, One Hundred Tenth Congress, Second Session, June 26, 2008. 2010. (Illus.). iii, 515p. ***(978-0-16-087784-1(9),*** 552-070-42295-1) United States Government Printing Office.

AUTOMOBILE INDUSTRY AND TRADE—UNITED STATES—DIRECTORIES

McCall, Walter. The Illustrated Encyclopedia of American Fire Engine Manufacturers. 2009. (ENG., Illus.). 304p. pap. 19.95 *(978-1-58388-252-8(9),* 1583882529) Iconografix, Inc.
Plunkett, Jack W. Plunkett's Automobile Industry Almanac 2008: Automobile, Truck & Specialty Vehicle Industry Market Research, Statistics, Trends & Leading Companies. annuals Plunkett, Jack W., ed. 2007. 575p. pap. 299.99 incl. cd-rom *(978-1-59392-094-4(6))*; 586p. E-Book 299.99 incl. cd-rom *(978-1-59392-437-9(2))* Plunkett Research, Ltd.

AUTOMOBILE INDUSTRY AND TRADE—WISCONSIN

Oosterwal, Dantar P. The Lean Machine: How Harley-Davidson Drove Top-Line Growth & Profitability with Revolutionary Lean Product Development, 1 vol. 2010. (ENG., Illus.). 272p. 27.95 *(978-0-8144-1378-4(1))* Amacom.

AUTOMOBILE INDUSTRY WORKERS

see also Automobile Mechanics

Anner, Mark S. Solidarity Transformed: Labor Responses to Globalization & Crisis in Latin America. 2011. (Illus.). 240p. 59.95 *(978-0-8014-4959-8(6))*; pap. 21.95 *(978-0-8014-7673-0(9))* Cornell Univ. Pr. (ILR Pr.).
Examining the Delphi Bankruptcy's Impact on Workers & Retirees: Hearing Before the Subcommittee on Health, Employment, Labor, & Pensions, Committee on Education & Labor, U.S. House of Representatives, One Hundred Eleventh Congress, First Session, Hearing Held in Washington, DC, December 2, 2009. 2010. (Illus.). iii, 54p. *(978-0-16-085950-2(6),* 552-070-41141-1) United States Government Printing Office.
Ferrante, Marco. Marchionne: L'uomo Che Comprò la Chrysler. 2009. (ITA.). 123p. *(978-88-04-58145-1(X))* Mondadori.
Glucksmann, Miriam. Women on the Line. 2009. (ENG., Illus.). 232p. (C). pap. 35.95 *(978-0-415-47642-3(9))* Routledge.
Glucksmann, Miriam & Glucksmann Aka Ruth Ca, Miriam. Women on the Line. 2009. (ENG., Illus.). 232p. (C). 140.00 *(978-0-415-47641-6(0))* Routledge.
Hayter, Teresa & Harvey, David. The Factory & the City. (Illus.). xii, 308p. pap. *(978-0-7201-2215-2(5),* Burns & Oates) Continuum International Publishing Group, Ltd.
Holmstrom, Darwin & Keefe, Melinda, eds. Life Is a Highway: A Century of Great Automotive Writing. 2010. (ENG., Illus.). 288p. 25.00 *(978-0-7603-3858-2(2),* 0760338582, Motorbooks) MBI Publishing Co. LLC.
Jackson, Carlton. Child of the Sit-Downs: The Revolutionary Life of Genora Dollinger. 2008. (Illus.). 39.00 *(978-0-87338-944-0(1))* Kent State Univ. Pr.
Pulignano, Valeria. Flexibility at Work: Critical Developments in the International Automobile Industry. Pulignano, Valeria et al, eds. 2008. (ENG., Illus.). 224p. 95.00 *(978-1-4039-0041-8(8))* Palgrave Macmillan.
Roxborough, Ian. Unions & Politics in Mexico: The Case of the Automobile Industry. 2009. (Cambridge Latin American Studies). (ENG., Illus.). 224p. pap. 31.99 *(978-0-521-10268-1(5))* Cambridge Univ. Pr.

Russell, Jason. Our Union: UAW/ CAW Local 27 from 1950 To 1990. 2012. (ENG., Illus.). 300p. pap. 32.95 *(978-1-926836-43-0(X))* UBC Pr. CAN. Dist: Univ. of Washington Pr.
Shotwel, Gregg. Live Bait & Ammo: Autoworkers under the Gun. 2012. (ENG., Illus.). 246p. pap. 17.00 ***(978-1-60846-142-4(4))*** Haymarket Bks.
Walker, Charles Rumford & Guest, Robert H. The Man on the Assembly Line. 2011. 202p. 44.95 ***(978-1-258-08641-1(7))*** Literary Licensing, LLC.

AUTOMOBILE INSURANCE

see also No-Fault Automobile Insurance

Auto Injury Insurance Claims: Countrywide Patterns in Treatment, Cost, & Compensation - 2008 Edition. 2008. 93p. pap. 250.00 *(978-1-56594-049-9(0))* Insurance Research Council.
Berk, Jon & Jainchill, Michael C. 2007 Supplement, Connecticut Law of Uninsured & Underinsured Motorist Coverage. 2007. 156p. pap. 74.00 *(978-1-878698-98-8(2))* Atlantic Law Bk. Co.
Bunnell, Randall. Utah Auto Law: Utah Law of Motor Vehicle Insurance & Accident Liability. 2009. *(978-1-4224-7087-9(3))* LexisNexis Matthew Bender.
Continuing Education of the Bar. California Uninsured Motorist Practice: August 2007 Update. 2nd ed. 2007. 252p. ring bd. 88.00 *(978-0-7626-1282-6(7))* Continuing Education of the Bar-California.
Denuit, Michel, et al. Actuarial Modelling of Claim Counts: Risk Classification, Credibility & Bonus-Malus Systems. 2007. (ENG.). 384p. 130.00 *(978-0-470-02677-9(4),* Wiley-Interscience) Wiley, John & Sons, Inc.
Florida Bar, Continuing Legal Education Staff, contrib. by. Florida Automobile Insurance Law. 7th ed. 2010. (Illus.). *(978-1-4224-4116-9(4))* Florida Bar Continuing Legal Education Pubns., The.
French, Patterson H. Automobile Compensation Plan. (Columbia University, Studies in the Social Sciences: No. 393). reprint ed. 32.50 *(978-0-404-51393-1(X))* AMS Pr., Inc.
Heaton, Paul. Auto Insurance Reform in Michigan: What Can the Data Tell Us? 2010. 8p. pap. 15.00 *(978-0-8330-4955-1(0),* op-293) RAND Corp., The.
Holloway, M L. Everything You Need to Know after Being in an Auto Accident: How to Represent Yourself after Being in an Auto Accident. 2007. 80p. per. 10.95 *(978-1-4327-1435-2(X))* Outskirts Pr., Inc.
Ibn Saeed, Bashiru Imoro. Regression Model for Motor Insurance Claims. 2011. 120p. pap. ***(978-3-8443-1607-0(8))*** Lambert Academic Publishing.
Insurance Research Council Staff, contrib. by. Florida Auto Injury Insurance Claim Environment, 2007 Final Report. 2007. (Illus.). 71p. pap. 100.00 *(978-1-56594-044-4(X),* IRC169) Insurance Research Council.
Lemaire, Jean. Automobile Insurance: Actuarial Models. 2010. (Huebner International Series on Risk, Insurance & Economic Security Ser.). (ENG.). 272p. pap. 249.00 *(978-90-481-5814-0(1),* 9048158141) Springer.
Lynch, Arthur. New York No-Fault Threshold, Vol. 1. 2007. *(978-1-58012-123-1(3))* James Publishing.
Noctor, Cathleen & Lyons, Richard. The MIBI Agreements & the Law: A Guide to Irish Law. 2nd ed. 2012. 400p. 195.00 ***(978-1-84766-992-6(1),*** Bloomsbury Professional) Bloomsbury Publishing Plc GBR. Dist: International Specialized Bk. Services.
Public Attitude Monitor 2006, Issue 2: Influence of Coastal Proximity on Natural Disaster Preparedness & Planning. 2006. 32p. pap. 50.00 *(978-1-56594-043-7(1),* IRC168) Insurance Research Council.
Rodengen, Jeffrey L. Amica: A Century of Service 1907-2007. Fernandez, Elizabeth & Gambill, Jill, eds. 2007. (Illus.). 144p. 39.95 *(978-1-932022-14-8(7),* Write Stuff) Write Stuff Enterprises, Inc.
Smith, Kim. Auto Dealerships. 2009. v, 228p. pap. *(978-0-87218-833-4(7))* National Underwriter Co.
Staten, Frederick & Lee, Aleta. Maximum Recovery - Insurance Claims Demystified: A 40 year veteran of the industry clarifies the Process. 2010. 156p. pap. 14.95 *(978-1-4502-3638-6(3))* iUniverse, Inc.
Tarlington, Martin H. Credit-Based Insurance Scores: Impacts on Consumers of Automobile Insurance. 2009. 79.00 *(978-1-60692-914-8(3))* Nova Science Pubs., Inc.
TheStreet. com Ratings Consumer Guide to Automobile Insurance. 2007. pap. 49.00 *(978-1-58773-375-8(7))*; pap. 49.00 *(978-1-58773-374-1(9))* TheStreet.com Ratings, Inc.
Walker, Corey J. L. How to Buy Car Insurance to Protect Your Family: 5 Insurance Company Secrets Revealed. 2007. per. 14.95 *(978-1-59872-759-3(1))* Instant Pub.
Weiss Ratings' Consumer Guide to Automobile Insurance. 2006. pap. 49.00 *(978-1-58773-305-5(6))*; pap. 49.00 *(978-1-58773-304-8(8))* TheStreet.com Ratings, Inc.

AUTOMOBILE INSURANCE, NO-FAULT

see No-Fault Automobile Insurance

AUTOMOBILE LAW

see Automobiles—Law and Legislation

AUTOMOBILE LICENSE PLATES

Mazzulo, Michelle. Vanity Plate Puzzles: A Puzzle Book Where You Solve the Vanity Plates. 2008. (ENG.). 96p. pap. 8.95 *(978-1-59580-038-1(7))* Santa Monica Pr.
Moss, Dave. Number Plates: A History of Vehicle Registration in Britain. 2008. (Shire Library). (ENG., Illus.). 32p. pap. 11.95 *(978-0-7478-0566-3(0))* Shire Pubns., Ltd. GBR. Dist: Random Hse., Inc.
Northup, John. License Plates of America: The official guide to the license plates of the United States, Canada & Mexico. 2008. (Illus.). 144p. pap. 16.95 *(978-0-9758805-8-6(6))* River Pointe Pubns.
2007 License Plate Guide: Current Standard Passenger Vehicle License Plates for the United States & Canada. 2007. (J). 14.95 *(978-0-9766236-2-5(5))* KGS America LLC.

AUTOMOBILE MAINTENANCE

see Automobiles—Maintenance and Repair

AUTOMOBILE MECHANICS

Borg, Kevin L. Auto Mechanics: Technology & Expertise in Twentieth-Century America. (Studies in Industry & Society Ser.). (ENG., Illus.). 280p. (gr. 17). 2010. pap. 32.00 *(978-0-8018-9485-5(9))* 2007. 50.00 *(978-0-8018-8606-5(6))* Johns Hopkins Univ. Pr.
Bryant, Peter. Can-Am Challenger: The Cockney F1 Mechanic Who Designed & Built America's Best Can-Am Cars. 2007. (Illus.). 400p. 49.95 *(978-1-893618-86-2(2))* Bull, David Publishing, Inc.
Cdx Global Staff. Natef Automotive Task Sheets. rev. ed. 2010. 74p. pap. 26.95 *(978-0-7637-8512-3(1))* Jones & Bartlett Learning, LLC.
—Natef Automotive Task Sheets: Auto Transmission. rev. ed. 2010. 76p. pap. 26.95 *(978-0-7637-8499-7(0))* Jones & Bartlett Learning, LLC.
Chek-Chart Staff. Auto Mechanics Refresher Course. (C). stu. ed. 42.00 *(978-0-88098-078-4(8),* Gousha, H. M. Maps & Atlases) Prentice Hall Bks.
Delmar. Professional Truck Technician Training Series: Medium/Heavy Duty Truck Electricity & Electronics CBT - Bilingual. 2010. (ENG.). 114.95 *(978-1-4390-6027-8(4))* Delmar Cengage Learning.
Delmar, Cengage Learning. ASE Test Prep- T8 Preventive Maintenance. 5th ed. 2012. (ENG.). 256p. pap. 23.95 *(978-1-111-12904-0(5))* Delmar Cengage Learning.
Delmar Learning. ASE Test Preparation - P2 Parts Specialist. 5th ed. 2012. (ENG.). 224p. pap. 23.95 *(978-1-111-12714-5(X))* Delmar Cengage Learning.

—Test H1: Compressed Natural Gas Engines. 2010. (ENG.). 240p. pap. 23.95 *(978-1-4354-3939-9(2))* Delmar Cengage Learning.
Delmar Learning Staff. ASE Test Preparation: Transit Bus H5, Suspension & Steering. 2009. (ENG.). 128p. pap. 23.95 *(978-1-4283-4011-4(4))* Delmar Cengage Learning.
—ASE Test Preparation - T1 Gasoline Engines. 5th ed. 2011. (ENG.). 192p. pap. 23.95 *(978-1-111-12897-5(9))* Delmar Cengage Learning.
—ASE Test Preparation - T4 Brakes. 5th ed. 2012. (ENG.). 192p. pap. 23.95 *(978-1-111-12900-2(2))* Delmar Cengage Learning.
—ASE Test Preparation - T6 Electrical & Electronic System. 5th ed. 2011. (ENG.). 224p. pap. 23.95 *(978-1-111-12902-6(9))* Delmar Cengage Learning.
—ASE Test Preparation - T7 Heating, Ventilation, & Air Condition. 5th ed. 2011. (ENG.). 196p. pap. 23.95 *(978-1-111-12903-3(7))* Delmar Cengage Learning.
—ASE Test Preparation - Truck Equipment Series: Electrical/Electronic Systems Installation & Repair, E2. 2009. (ENG.). 112p. pap. 23.95 *(978-1-4354-3936-8(8))* Delmar Cengage Learning.
—Diesel Engines. 2010. (ENG.). 114.95 *(978-1-4354-4141-5(9))* Delmar Cengage Learning.
—Preventive Maintenance Computer Based Training (CBT) 2009. (ENG.). 114.95 *(978-1-4390-6025-4(8))* Delmar Cengage Learning.
—Preventive Maintenance Test H8. 2010. (ENG.). 160p. pap. 23.95 *(978-1-4354-3938-2(4))* Delmar Cengage Learning.
Gordon, Michael. P2 Automobile Parts Specialist: Motor Age Training Self-Study Guide for ASE Certification. 2007. spiral bd. 24.95 *(978-1-933180-79-3(X))* Advanstar Communications, Inc.
Grady, Michael. A1 Automotive Engine Repair: Motor Age Training Self-Study Guide for ASE Certification. 2006. spiral bd. 22.95 *(978-1-933180-71-7(4))* Advanstar Communications, Inc.
—A7 Heating & Air Conditioning: Motor Age Self-Study Guide for ASE Certification. 2007. spiral bd. 22.95 *(978-1-933180-82-3(X))* Advanstar Communications, Inc.
Hinzmann, Randy. Best of Mechanics Corner. 2011. 164p. pap. 19.99 ***(978-1-4568-8595-3(2))*** Xlibris Corp.
Janisin, Matthew. Snap - On Diagnostic. 2012. (ENG.). 528p. (C). pap. 67.00 *(978-1-4354-8379-8(0))* Delmar Cengage Learning.
Johanson, Chris. Auto Brakes: A5 Shop Manual. abr. ed. 2007. (Illus.). 192p. (gr. 9-12). per. 18.00 *(978-1-59070-724-1(9))* Goodheart-Willcox Pub.
Jones and Bartlett Publishers Staff & Cdx Global Staff. Brakes Tasksheet Manual for NATEF Proficiency. rev. ed. 2009. 82p. pap. 26.95 *(978-0-7637-8507-9(5))* Jones & Bartlett Learning, LLC.
Kellogg, Randall. The Complete Guide Towards Starting Your Own Paintless Dent Removal Business. 2010. 92p. pap. 34.99 *(978-1-4520-0032-9(8))* AuthorHouse.
Knowles, Don. Medium/Heavy Duty Truck Technician Certification Test Preparation Manual. 2nd rev. ed. 2007. (ENG., Illus.). 736p. per. 67.95 *(978-1-4180-6600-0(1))* Delmar Cengage Learning.
Martin, Isaac. Ford Windsor Small-Block Performance. 2010. (ENG.). 192p. (gr. 12). 21.95 *(978-1-55788-558-6(3),* HP Trade) Penguin Group (USA) Inc.
Nash, Federick. Fundamentos de Mecanica Automotriz.Tr. of Fundamentals of Auto Mechanics. (SPA.). 17.98 *(978-968-13-0865-0(4))* Editorial Diana, S.A. MEX. Dist: Continental Bk. Co., Inc.
Norville, Norman. S3 Drive Train: Motor Age Self-Study Guide for ASE Certification. 2007. spiral bd. 22.95 *(978-1-933180-83-0(8))* Advanstar Communications, Inc.
—S4 School Bus Brakes: Motor Age Self-Study Guide for ASE Certification. 2006. spiral bd. 22.95 *(978-1-933180-70-0(6))* Advanstar Communications, Inc.
—T4 Med/Hvy Truck Brakes. 2007. spiral bd. 22.95 *(978-1-933180-81-6(1))* Advanstar Communications, Inc.
—T5 Med/Hvy Truck Steering & Suspension. 2006. spiral bd. 22.95 *(978-1-933180-72-4(2))* Advanstar Communications, Inc.
—T8 Med/Hvy Truck Preventive Maintenance & Inspection (PMI) 2006. spiral bd. 22.95 *(978-1-933180-78-6(1))* Advanstar Communications, Inc.
Oliver, Michael. Tales from the Toolbox: A Collection of Behind-the-Scenes Tales from Grand Prix Mechanics. 2010. (ENG., Illus.). 176p. pap. 24.95 *(978-1-84584-199-7(9),* 1845841999) Veloce Publishing Ltd. GBR. Dist: MBI Distribution Services/Quayside Distribution.
Parks, Lew Jeff Carla & Parks, Chad. Win from the Back: Memoirs of A Racecar Mechanic. 2011. 540p. pap. 29.99 ***(978-1-4634-5248-3(9))*** AuthorHouse.
Prague, Nick. L1 Automotive Advanced Engine Performance Specialist: Motor Age Training Self-Study Guide for ASE Certification. 2006. spiral bd. 25.95 *(978-1-933180-77-9(3))* Advanstar Communications, Inc.
Prentice-Hall, Inc Staff, creator. Interior & Rear Section Damage Analysis Program 4. 2007. (Illus.). 41p. pap. *(978-0-13-243121-7(1),* Prentice Hall) Pearson Education Canada.
Seyfer, Donny. C1 Automobile Service Consultant: Motor Age Training Self-Study Guide for ASE Certification. 2007. spiral bd. 22.95 *(978-1-933180-85-4(4))* Advanstar Communications, Inc.

AUTOMOBILE OPERATION

see Automobile Driving

AUTOMOBILE OWNERSHIP

see also Automobiles—Purchasing

Balish, Chris. How to Live Well Without Owning a Car: Save Money, Breathe Easier, & Get More Mileage Out of Life. 2006. (ENG., Illus.). 224p. pap. 12.95 *(978-1-58008-757-5(4))* Ten Speed Pr.
Calkins, Martin. King Car & the Ethics of Automobile Proponents' Strategies in China & India. 2011. (Transportation Issues, Policies & R&D Ser.). 160p. 69.00 *(978-1-61761-271-8(5))* Nova Science Pubs., Inc.
Clarsen, Georgine. Eat My Dust: Early Women Motorists. 2008. (Johns Hopkins University Studies in Historical & Political Science Ser.: 126). (ENG., Illus.). 216p. (gr. 17). 52.00 *(978-0-8018-8465-8(9))* Johns Hopkins Univ. Pr.
Ferrari Life Staff, compiled by. Ferrari Life Buyers Portfolio. 2007. (Buyer's Portfolio Ser.). (ENG., Illus.). 136p. 29.95 *(978-1-85520-747-9(8),* 1855207478) Brooklands Bks. GBR. Dist: MBI Distribution Services/Quayside Distribution.
Ladd, Brian. Autophobia: Love & Hate in the Automotive Age. (Illus.). 2011. (ENG.). 240p. pap. 15.00 *(978-0-226-46729-0(5))* 2008. 236p. 22.50 *(978-0-226-46741-2(4))* Univ. of Chicago Pr.

AUTOMOBILE OWNERSHIP—PSYCHOLOGICAL ASPECTS

Lamm, Jay. You Are What You Drive: What Your Car Says about You. 2008. (ENG., Illus.). 144p. pap. 19.99 *(978-0-7603-3263-4(0),* 0760332630, Motorbooks) MBI Publishing Co. LLC.
Overstake, T. J. For Love of the Car: Memories of a True Car Guy. 2009. 159p. pap. 11.95 *(978-1-4327-3594-4(2))* Outskirts Pr., Inc.

AUTOMOBILE PARKING

Arrington, G. B. & Cervero, Robert. Effects of TOD on Housing, Parking, & Travel. 2008. (Illus.). 66p. pap. 42.00 *(978-0-309-11748-7(8))* Transportation Research Board.
Ben-Joseph, Eran. Rethinking a Lot: The Design & Culture of Parking. 2012. (ENG., Illus.). 184p. (gr. 17). 24.95 ***(978-0-262-01733-6(4))*** MIT Pr.
Camporeale, Louis. The New York City Motorists' Parking Survival Guide: How to Avoid & Deal with Parking Tickets Effectively. 2nd exp. ed. 2008. (New York City Parking Survival Guide: How to Avoid & Deal With Ser.). (ENG., Illus.). 168p. pap. 14.95 *(978-0-9664678-2-6(5))* Parking Pal Co., Inc.
Colozzi, Jacqueline, ed. Lots NYC: The Definitive Guide to Parking Lots & Garages. 2007. (Illus.). 392p. 9.95 *(978-0-9758849-0-4(5))* Lots Pubns., LLC.

Institute of Transportation Engineers Staff, contrib. by. Parking Generation: An Informational Report of the Institute of Transportation Engineers. 4th ed. 2010. *(978-1-933452-55-5(2))* Institute of Transportation Engineers.
Keil, Uta, et al. Parking Structures, 1 vol. 2012. (ENG., Illus.). 240p. 99.95 *(978-3-938666-95-1(1))* DOM Pubs. DEU. Dist: Innovative Logistics.
Lots Publications, creator. Lots: Guide to Parking Lots & Garages in New York City. 2008. (Lots NYC: the Definitive Guide to Parking Lots & Garages Ser.). (Illus.). 400p. 9.95 *(978-0-8416-0301-1(4))* American Map Corp.
Marusek, Sarah. Politics of Parking: Rights Identity & Property. 2012. (Illus.). 180p. 104.95 ***(978-0-7546-7971-4(3))*** Ashgate Publishing Co.
Ricondo & Associates Staff, et al, contrib. by. Handbook to Assess the Impacts of Constrained Parking at Airports. 2010. (Illus.). 101p. pap. ***(978-0-309-15496-3(0))*** Transportation Research Board.
Shimmin, Rogan. Street Parking for Cars. 2009. 80p. pap. *(978-3-639-17607-0(3))* VDM Verlag Dr. Mueller e.K.
Shoup, Donald. The High Cost of Free Parking. 2011. (ENG.). 776p. pap. 34.95 *(978-1-932364-96-5(X))* American Planning Assn.
Tohn, Margot. Park It! NYC: Complete Guide to Parking Garages. 2007. (Park It NYC: Complete Guide to Parking Garages Ser.). (Illus.). 355p. per. 13.95 *(978-0-9790281-0-6(8))*; 2nd ed. (ENG., 360p. per. 13.95 *(978-0-9790281-1-3(6))* Park It! Guides.
Urban Land Institute & National Parking Association. The Dimensions of Parking. 5th ed. 2009. (ENG., Illus.). 170p. 89.95 *(978-0-87420-120-8(9))* Urban Land Institute.
Zeiger, Sheldon. Stick It to Your Ticket: The Unofficial Guide to Beating Your Parking Ticket in Chicago. 2009. 79p. pap. 12.95 *(978-0-9822346-0-0(0))* Zeiger.

AUTOMOBILE-PARKING METERS
see Parking Meters

AUTOMOBILE PRICES
see Automobiles—Prices

AUTOMOBILE PURCHASING
see Automobiles—Purchasing

AUTOMOBILE RACING
see also Automobiles, Racing; Drag Racing; Indianapolis Speedway Race; Karting; Le Mans Endurance Race; Model Car Racing; Sports Car Events; Stock Car Racing; Watkins Glen Grand Prix Race

Alexander, Jesse. Inside the Archives. 2010. (Illus.). 96p. 75.00 *(978-1-935007-10-4(6))* Bull, David Publishing, Inc.
—Portraits. 2008. (Illus.). 96p. 75.00 *(978-1-893618-98-5(6))* Bull, David Publishing, Inc.
Allison, Mike & Browning, Peter. The Works MGs: Their Story in Pre-War & Post-War Races, Rallies, Trials & Record-Breaking. 2nd ed. 2011. (ENG., Illus.). 296p. 49.95 *(978-0-85733-014-7(4)*, 0857330144) Haynes Publishing PLC GBR. Dist: MBI Distribution Services/Quayside Distribution.
Arute, Jack. Tales from the Indianapolis 500: A Collection of the Greatest Indy 500 Stories Ever Told. 2012. (Tales from the Team Ser.). (ENG., Illus.). 208p. 19.95 ***(978-1-61321-044-4(2)***, 613044) Skyhorse Publishing Co., Inc.
Autocar Staff, compiled by. Subaru Impreza Turbo. 2008. (Autocar Collection). (ENG., Illus.). 160p. 39.95 *(978-1-84425-497-2(6)*, 1844254976) Haynes Publishing PLC GBR. Dist: MBI Distribution Services/Quayside Distribution.
Baggott, John. Big Healeys in Competition: Austin-Healy 100, 3000 & Jensen Healey in Race & Rally. 2006. (Crowood Autoclassics Ser.). (ENG., Illus.). 200p. 34.95 *(978-1-86126-828-0(9)*, 1861268289) Crowood Pr., Ltd. GBR. Dist: MBI Distribution Services/Quayside Distribution.
Bamford, Robert & Jarvis, John. Homes of British Speedway. 2nd ed. 2006. (ENG., Illus.). 288p. pap. 39.95 *(978-0-7524-4004-0(7))* History Pr. Ltd.,The GBR. Dist: Independent Pubs. Group.
Bamsey, Ian. Sauber-Mercedes C9: The Return of the Silver Arrows. 2007. (ENG., Illus.). 200p. 34.95 *(978-1-86126-836-5(X)*, 186126836X) Crowood Pr., Ltd. GBR. Dist: MBI Distribution Services/Quayside Distribution.
Beaver, Dale. Before the Thunder Rolls: Devotions for NASCAR Fans. 2007. 109p. per. 5.00 *(978-0-8170-1521-3(3))* Judson Pr.
Ben-Ari, Dani & Frissell, Susan. Girls Go Racing: Driving to Esteems. 2009. 120p. pap. 12.49 *(978-1-4490-0738-6(4))* AuthorHouse.
Bentley, Ross. Ultimate Speed Secrets: The Complete Guide to High-Performance & Race Driving. 2011. (Speed Secrets Ser.). (ENG., Illus.). 336p. pap. 25.99 *(978-0-7603-4050-9(1)*, 0760340501, Motorbooks) MBI Publishing Co. LLC.
Bentley, Ross & Schroeder, Per. Winning Autocross Techniques. rev. ed. 2009. (Speed Secrets Ser.). (ENG., Illus.). 160p. pap. 19.99 *(978-0-7603-3156-9(1)*, 0760331561, Motorbooks) MBI Publishing Co. LLC.
Blount, Terry. The Blount Report: NASCAR's Most Overrated & Underrated Drivers, Cars, Teams, & Tracks. 2009. (ENG.). 240p. 24.95 *(978-1-60078-089-9(X))* Triumph Bks.
Bouzanquet, Jean Francois. Fast Ladies: Female Racing Drivers 1888 To 1970. 2009. (ENG., Illus.). 176p. pap. 59.95 *(978-1-84584-225-3(1)*, 1845842251) Veloce Publishing Ltd. GBR. Dist: MBI Distribution Services/Quayside Distribution.
Boyer, Arlynda Lee. Buddha on the Backstretch: The Spiritual Wisdom of Driving 200 MPH. 2009. 160p. 27.00 *(978-0-88146-174-9(1))* Mercer Univ. Pr.
Breslin, Mike. The Track Day Manual. 2008. (ENG., Illus.). 176p. 36.95 *(978-1-84425-482-8(8)*, 1844254828) Haynes Publishing PLC GBR. Dist: MBI Distribution Services/Quayside Distribution.
Burgess-Wise, David & Venables, David. French Racing Blue: Drivers, Cars & Triumphs of French Motor Racing. 2009. (Racing Colours Ser.). (ENG., Illus.). 176p. 39.95 *(978-0-7110-3369-6(2))* Allan, Ian Publishing GBR. Dist: BookMasters Distribution Services (BDS).
Carter, Anthony. Motor Racing: The Pursuit of Victory 1930-1962. 2011. (ENG., Illus.). 176p. 59.95 *(978-1-84584-279-6(0)*, 1845842790) Veloce Publishing Ltd. GBR. Dist: MBI Distribution Services/Quayside Distribution.
Castle, Paul. Psychology of Motorsport Success: How to improve your performance with mental skills Training. 2008. (ENG., Illus.). 232p. 39.95 *(978-1-84425-495-8(X)*, 184425495X) Haynes Publishing PLC GBR. Dist: MBI Distribution Services/Quayside Distribution.
Charters, David A. The Chequered Past: Sports Car Racing & Rallying in Canada, 1951-1991. 2007. (ENG., Illus.). 382p. *(978-0-8020-9093-5(1))*; pap. *(978-0-8020-9394-3(9))* Univ. of Toronto Pr.
Clemens, Kevin. A Lap of the Globe: Behind the Wheel of a Vintage Mercedes in the World's Longest Auto Race. 2006. (ENG., Illus.). 231p. per. 25.00 *(978-0-7864-2561-7(X))* McFarland & Co., Inc. Pubs.
Collings, Timothy & Edworthy, Sarah. The Formula One Years. 2009. (ENG., Illus.). 336p. 39.95 *(978-1-84732-166-4(6))* Carlton Bks., Ltd. GBR. Dist: Sterling Publishing Co., Inc.
Collins, Ben. The Man in the White Suit: The Stig, le Mans, the Fast Lane & Me. 2012. (ENG., Illus.). 352p. 12.95 ***(978-0-00-733169-7(X))*** HarperCollins Pubs. Ltd. GBR. Dist: Independent Pubs. Group.
Collins, Peter. British Touring Car Racing: The Crowd's Favourite - Late 1960s to 1990. 2009. (Those Were the Days Ser.). (ENG., Illus.). 96p. pap. 29.95 *(978-1-84584-247-5(2)*, 1845842472) Veloce Publishing Ltd. GBR. Dist: MBI Distribution Services/Quayside Distribution.
Collins, S S & Ireland, Gavin D. Speedway: Auto Racing's Ghost Tracks. 2010. (ENG., Illus.). 176p. 34.95 *(978-1-84584-241-3(3)*, 1845842413) Veloce Publishing Ltd. GBR. Dist: MBI Distribution Services/Quayside Distribution.
Collins, Sam S. & Page, David. Superprix: The Story of Birmingham's Motor Race. 2010. (Those Were the Days Ser.). (ENG., Illus.). 96p. pap. 29.95 *(978-1-84584-242-0(1)*, 184584242I) Veloce Publishing Ltd. GBR. Dist: MBI Distribution Services/Quayside Distribution.
Colombo, Ercole & Allievi, Pino. I Love Ferrari. 2010. (ITA & ENG., Illus.). 120p. 120.00 *(978-88-7200-289-6(3))* Vianello Libri ITA. Dist: Antique Collectors' Club.
Culver, Chad & Culver, Wayne. Delaware Auto Racing. 2012. (Images of Sports Ser.). (ENG., Illus.). 128p. pap. 21.99 ***(978-0-7385-9207-7(2))*** Arcadia Publishing.
Curami, Andrea. Alfa Romeo & Mille Miglia. 2010. (ENG.). 160p. 44.95 *(978-88-7911-496-7(4))*; (Illus.). 44.95 *(978-88-7911-504-9(9)*, 8879115049) Giorgio Nada Editore ITA. Dist: MBI Distribution Services/Quayside Distribution.
—Mercedes-Benz & Mille Miglia. 2008. (ITA & ENG., Illus.). 160p. 39.95 *(978-88-7911-359-5(3)*, 8879113593) Giorgio Nada Editore ITA. Dist: MBI Distribution Services/Quayside Distribution.
Daly, Derek. Race to Win: How to Become a Complete Champion Driver. 2008. (ENG., Illus.). 256p. 25.95 *(978-0-7603-3185-9(5)*, 0760331855, Motorbooks) MBI Publishing Co. LLC.
Davey, Arnold. Lagonda 2, 3 & 3 1/2 Litre: Including 16/80, 1925-1935. 2008. (In Detail Ser.). (ENG., Illus.). 176p. 59.95 *(978-0-9549981-8-9(9)*, 0954998189) Herridge & Sons Ltd.
Davis, Larry. Super Stock: Drag Racing the Family Sedan. 2010. (ENG., Illus.). 210p. pap. 29.95 *(978-1-934709-48-1(4))* CarTech, Inc.
Despain, Dave. Wind Tunnel: Talking Racing with Dave Despain. 2010. (ENG., Illus.). 256p. 26.00 *(978-0-7603-3013-5(1)*, Motorbooks) MBI Publishing Co. LLC.
Diniz Sanches, Joao. Driving Games Manual: The Ultimate Guide to All Car-Based Computer & Video Games. 2009. (ENG., Illus.). 224p. 39.95 *(978-1-84425-526-9(3)*, 1844255263) Haynes Publishing PLC GBR. Dist: MBI Distribution Services/Quayside Distribution.
Domenjoz, Luc. The Formula One Yearbook 2008 - 2009. 2009. (ENG., Illus.). 224p. 19.95 *(978-2-84707-154-2(7)*, 2847071547) Chronosports, editeur CHE. Dist: MBI Distribution Services/Quayside Distribution.
Domenjoz, Luc, ed. Formula 1 Yearbook. 2008. (Formula One Yearbook Ser.). (ENG., Illus.). 224p. 19.95 *(978-2-84707-139-9(3)*, 2847071393) Chronosports, editeur CHE. Dist: MBI Distribution Services/Quayside Distribution.
Edmondson, Pete, compiled by. Guide to Alabama & Georgia ATV & Dirt Bike Trails. 2nd ed. 2007. (Illus.). 78p. 14.95 *(978-0-9796304-0-8(1))* Atvtrails.org.
Elford, Vic. Vic Elford: Reflections on a Golden Era in Motorsports. 2006. (Illus.). 288p. 39.95 *(978-1-893618-52-7(8))* Bull, David Publishing, Inc.
Evans, David. Autocourse 2008-2009. Henry, Alan, ed. 2009. (ENG., Illus.). 336p. 59.95 *(978-1-905334-31-5(1)*, 1905334311) Crash Media Grp. Ltd. GBR. Dist: MBI Distribution Services/Quayside Distribution.
Evans, David, ed. Rallycourse 2006-2007: The World's Leading Rally Annual. 2007. (Rallycourse: the World's Leading Rally Annual Ser.). (ENG., Illus.). 248p. 44.95 *(978-1-905334-18-6(4)*, 1905334184) Crash Media Grp. Ltd. GBR. Dist: MBI Distribution Services/Quayside Distribution.
—Rallycourse 2007-2008: The World's Leading Rally Annual. 2008. (Rallycourse: the World's Leading Rally Annual Ser.). (ENG., Illus.). 192p. 49.95 *(978-1-905334-23-0(0)*, 1905334230) Crash Media Grp. Ltd. GBR. Dist: MBI Distribution Services/Quayside Distribution.
Eyston, George & Lyndon, Barre. Motor Racing & Record Breaking. 2007. 224p. per. *(978-1-905217-89-2(7))* Mills, Jeremy Publishing.
Fielden, Greg. Forty Years of Stock Car Racing, 5 vols. Incl. Beginning, 1949-1958. 336p. 1987. 24.95 *(978-0-9621580-2-5(X))*; Big Bucks & Boycotts, 1965-1971. 368p. 1989. 24.95 *(978-0-9621580-3-2(8))*; Forty Plus Four, 1990-1993. 336p. 1994. suppl. ed. 34.95 *(978-1-885016-01-0(8))*; Modern Era, 1972-1989. 688p. 1990. 39.95 *(978-0-9621580-4-9(6))*; Superspeedway Boom, 1959-1964. 320p. 1988. 24.95 *(978-0-9621580-1-8(1))*; (Illus.). 149.75 *(978-1-885016-02-7(6))* Galfield Pr., The.
Finn, Joel E. American Road Racing: 1948-1950. 2007. (Illus.). 452p. 150.00 *(978-0-9647769-3-7(6))* Garnet Hill Publishing Co., Inc.
Fleishman, Bill & Pearce, Al. The Unauthorized Nascar Fan Guide: 2004. rev. ed. (Illus.). 576p. pap. *(978-0-681-27587-4(1))* Visible Ink Pr.
Frazetta, Frank. Frazetta johnny comet Deluxe, 1 vol. 2011. (ENG.). 264p. 69.95 ***(978-1-934331-48-4(1))*** Vanguard Productions.
Frey, J. Louis. Armchair Racers Guide to Greatness. 2007. 101p. pap. 10.95 *(978-0-7414-3852-2(6))* Infinity Publishing.
Fuller, Michael J. & Martin, J. A. Inside IMSA's Legendary GTP Race Cars: The Prototype Experience. rev. ed. 2008. (ENG., Illus.). 256p. 50.00 *(978-0-7603-3069-2(7)*, 0760330697, Motorbooks) MBI Publishing Co. LLC.
Garnier, Peter. The Art of Gordon Crosby. 2009. (ENG., Illus.). 96p. 59.95 *(978-1-906133-09-2(3)*, 1906133093) Herridge & Sons Ltd.
Goodwin, Colin. The Racing Driver's Pocket Book: The British Double-Twelve Hour Race. 2011. (ENG., Illus.). 160p. 12.95 *(978-1-84486-134-7(1)*, Conway Maritime Pr.) Anova Bks. GBR. Dist: Sterling Publishing Co., Inc.
Gran, Dave. Go Ahead Take the Wheel: Road Racing on Your Budget. 2008. (Illus.). 188p. per. 16.95 *(978-0-9777860-0-8(5))* Dragon Publishing.
Grant-Braham, Bruce. Motor Racing at Thruxton in The 1970s. 2012. (Those Were the Days Ser.). (ENG., Illus.). 96p. pap. 29.95 ***(978-1-84584-370-0(3)***, 1845843703) Veloce Publishing Ltd. GBR. Dist: MBI Distribution Services/Quayside Distribution.
Gregoire, Francoise-Michel. Who Works in Formula One 2006. 2006. (Illus.). 515p. 99.50 *(978-1-901711-42-4(0))* Who Works Publications, Ltd. GBR. Dist: Trans-Atlantic Pubns., Inc.
Gross, Bonnie S. All about Car Racing. 2011. 110p. pap. 19.99 ***(978-1-4568-3949-9(7))*** Xlibris Corp.
Hamilton, Maurice. Chequered Conflict: The Inside Story on Two Explosive F1 World Championships. 2008. (ENG., Illus.). 320p. 34.95 *(978-1-84737-268-0(6))* Simon & Schuster, Ltd. GBR. Dist: Independent Pubs. Group.
Hamilton, Maurice. McLaren the Art of Racing. 2012. (Illus.). 304p. 160.00 ***(978-3-7913-5195-7(8))*** Prestel Publishing.
Hart, Lou. Drag Racing Funny Cars: Factory Flyers to Flip-top Fuelers. 2008. (Photo Gallery Ser.). (ENG., Illus.). 160p. pap. 19.95 *(978-1-58388-220-7(0)*, 1583882200) Iconografix, Inc.
Heinfeld, Robert. Daredevils on Dirt: Early Years at the New Bremen Speedway. 2007. (Illus.). 61p. *(978-1-933197-35-7(8))* Orange Frazer Pr.
Hembree, Mike M. Racing with Giants: How God Can Steer You to the Winner's Circle, 0 vols. 2009. 160p. 15.99 *(978-1-4041-8701-6(4))* Nelson, Thomas Inc.
Herbst, Keith S. Daredevils of the Frontier. 2006. (Illus.). 192p. 39.95 *(978-0-9709854-0-8(1))* Coastal 181.
Hilton, Christopher. Grand Prix Battlegrounds: A Comprehensive Guide to All Formula 1 Circuits Since 1950. 2010. (ENG., Illus.). 288p. 69.95 *(978-1-84425-694-5(4)*, 1844256944) Haynes Publishing PLC GBR. Dist: MBI Distribution Services/Quayside Distribution.
—Memories of Senna: Anecdotes & Insights from Those Who Knew Him. 2011. (ENG., Illus.). 256p. 24.95 ***(978-0-85733-229-5(5)***, 0857332295) Haynes Publishing PLC GBR. Dist: MBI Distribution Services/Quayside Distribution.
Hilton, Christopher. Michael Schumacher: The Whole Story. 2008. (ENG., Illus.). 472p. per. 16.95 *(978-1-84425-448-4(8)*, 1844254488) Haynes Publishing PLC GBR. Dist: MBI Distribution Services/Quayside Distribution.
Holtzclaw, Kenneth M. & Del Mar Thoroughbred Club. Del Mar Racetrack. 2006. (Images of Sports Ser.). (ENG., Illus.). 128p. per. 21.99 *(978-0-7385-3146-5(4))* Arcadia Publishing.
Hornsey, David. Race & Track Day Driving Techniques. 2011. (SpeedPro Ser.). (ENG., Illus.). 128p. pap. 29.95 *(978-1-84584-355-7(X)*, 184584355X) Veloce Publishing Ltd. GBR. Dist: MBI Distribution Services/Quayside Distribution.
Horsman, John. Racing in the Rain: My Years with Brilliant Drivers, Legendary Sports Cars, & a Dedicated Team. 2006. (Illus.). 250p. 49.95 *(978-1-893618-71-8(4))* Bull, David Publishing, Inc.
House, Kirk W. & Mitchell, Charles R. Watkins Glen Racing. 2008. 128p. pap. 19.99 *(978-0-7385-5666-6(1))* Arcadia Publishing.
Hunt, Rod, illus. Top Gear - Where's Stig: The World Tour. 2011. (ENG.). 40p. 16.95 *(978-1-84990-052-2(3))* BBC Worldwide GBR. Dist: Independent Pubs. Group.
Hylton, Pete. Ghost Tracks: A Historic Look at America's Lost Road Racing Tracks. 2007. 128p. per. 34.95 *(978-0-9796976-1-6(1))* Legacy Ink Publishing.
Ireland, Gavin. Le Mans Panoramic. 2012. (ENG., Illus.). 224p. 69.95 *(978-1-84584-243-7(X)*, 184584243X) Veloce Publishing Ltd. GBR. Dist: MBI Distribution Services/Quayside Distribution.
Jacobs, Norman. Out of the Frying Pan: The Story of New Cross Speedway. 2008. (ENG.). 160p. pap. 30.95 *(978-0-7524-4476-5(X))* History Pr. Ltd.,The GBR. Dist: Independent Pubs. Group.
Jaliffe, Carlos. Brothers Rodriguez. 2009. (Illus.). 592p. *(978-1-893618-89-3(7))* Bull, David Publishing, Inc.
Jones, Bruce. Grand Prix 2011: The World's Best-Selling Formula One Guide. 2011. (ENG., Illus.). 112p. pap. 17.95 *(978-1-84732-728-4(1))* Carlton Bks., Ltd. GBR. Dist: Sterling Publishing Co., Inc.
Jones, Bruce. World Motor Sports Facts & Records. 2011. (ENG., Illus.). 320p. pap. 12.95 ***(978-1-84732-774-1(5))*** Carlton Bks., Ltd. GBR. Dist: Independent Pubs. Group.
Jones, Bruce, ed. The Official Formula 1 Season Review. 2007. (ENG., Illus.). 256p. 34.95 *(978-1-84425-345-6(7)*, 1844253457) Haynes Publishing PLC GBR. Dist: MBI Distribution Services/Quayside Distribution.
Joubin, Philippe. Rally Yearbook 2006: World Rally Championship. Waldron, David, tr. 2007. (Rally Yearbook: World Rally Championship Ser.). (ENG., Illus.). 176p. 19.95 *(978-2-84707-114-6(8)*, 2847071148) Chronosports, editeur CHE. Dist: MBI Distribution Services/Quayside Distribution.
Kalwasinski, Stan & Beck, Samuel. Blue Island's Raceway Park. 2010. (Images of America Ser.). (ENG., Illus.). 128p. pap. 21.99 *(978-0-7385-7743-2(X))* Arcadia Publishing.
Kerr, Phil. To Finish First: My Years Inside Formula One, Can-Am & Indy 500. 2008. (ENG., Illus.). 384p. 59.50 *(978-1-899870-81-3(4)*, 1899870814) Motor Racing Pubns., Ltd. GBR. Dist: MBI Distribution Services/Quayside Distribution.
Keyser, Michael. A French Kiss with Death: Steve Mcqueen & the Making of le Mans. 2008. (Illus.). 464p. pap. 39.95 *(978-0-8376-1552-3(6))* Bentley Pubs.
Kroplick, Howard. Vanderbilt Cup Races of Long Island. 2008. (Images of Sports Ser.). (Illus.). 127p. per. 21.99 *(978-0-7385-5751-9(X))* Arcadia Publishing.
Lancaster, Nicholas. Brooklands: Cradle of British Motor Racing & Aviation. 2009. (Shire Library). (ENG., Illus.). 56p. pap. 12.95 *(978-0-7478-0707-0(8))* Shire Pubns., Ltd. GBR. Dist: Random Hse., Inc.
Langenscheidt Publishers Staff, contrib. by. Motor Racing: The Early Years/Die Anfange des Motorsports/les Debuts de la Course Automobile. 2008. (Transportation: the Early Years Ser.). (Illus.). 351p. 49.95 *(978-0-8416-0281-6(6))* American Map Corp.
Lawrence, M. Brabham Ralt Honda the Ron Tauranac Story. 2011. (Illus.). 290p. pap. 29.95 ***(978-1-58850-159-2(0))*** Veloce Enterprises, Inc.
Lee, Brian R. For the Love of Cars: The Growth of the Old Car Hobby. 2008. 104p. pap. 28.99 *(978-1-4389-0459-7(2))* AuthorHouse.
Lee, Cory. Drag Racing Collectibles. 2011. (ENG., Illus.). 128p. pap. 29.95 *(978-1-58388-279-5(0)*, 1583882790) Iconografix, Inc.
Leerhsen, Charles. Blood & Smoke: A True Tale of Mystery, Mayhem & the Birth of the Indy 500. 2012. (ENG., Illus.). 288p. pap. 15.00 ***(978-1-4391-4905-8(4))*** Simon & Schuster.
Leslie-Pelecky, Diandra. The Physics of NASCAR: How to Make Steel + Gas + Rubber = Speed. 2008. (ENG., Illus.). 304p. (gr. 12-18). 25.95 *(978-0-525-95053-0(2)*, Dutton Adult) Penguin Group (USA) Inc.
Lier, Alexandra. Speedseekers. 2008. 274p. *(978-1-58423-315-2(X))*; (Illus.). *(978-1-58423-314-5(1))* Gingko Pr., Inc.
Lier, Alexandra, et al. Speedseekers. 2008. (Illus.). 273p. *(978-1-58423-326-8(5))* Gingko Pr., Inc.
Linn, Stephen. The Ultimate Tailgater's Racing Guide, 0 vols. 2007. (Illus.). 224p. per. 14.99 *(978-1-4016-0334-2(3))* Nelson, Thomas Inc.
—The Ultimate Tailgater's Travel Guide: More Than 20 Great Road Trips, 0 vols. 2006. (Illus.). 224p. per. 14.99 *(978-1-4016-0258-1(4))* Nelson, Thomas Inc.
Long, Brian. Porsche Racing Cars1976 to 2005. 2008. (ENG., Illus.). 272p. 89.95 *(978-1-904788-45-4(9)*, 1904788459) Veloce Publishing Ltd. GBR. Dist: MBI Distribution Services/Quayside Distribution.
Ludvigsen, Karl. German Racing Silver: Drivers, Cars & Triumphs of German Motor Racing. 2009. (Racing Colours Ser.). (ENG., Illus.). 176p. 39.95 *(978-0-7110-3368-9(4))* Allan, Ian Publishing GBR. Dist: BookMasters Distribution Services (BDS).
—Porsche 956 And 962: Immortal Endurance Racers 1982-1994. 2010. (ENG., Illus.). 128p. pap. 32.95 *(978-1-58388-269-6(3)*, 1583882693) Iconografix, Inc.
—Porsche Spyders, 1956-1964: Type 550A, RSK & 718. 2007. (Ludvigsen Library Ser.). (ENG., Illus.). 128p. pap. 29.95 *(978-1-58388-200-9(6)*, 1583882006) Iconografix, Inc.
Ludvigsen, Karl E. Porsche: Excellence Was Expected: The Comprehensive History of the Company, Its Cars & Its Racing Heritage, 3 vols. 2nd ed. 2008. (Illus.). 1688p. 299.95 *(978-0-8376-0235-6(1))* Bentley Pubs.
McBeath, Simon. Competition Car Data Logging: A Practical Handbook. 2nd ed. 2009. (ENG., Illus.). 176p. 49.95 *(978-1-84425-565-8(4)*, 1844255654) Haynes Publishing PLC GBR. Dist: MBI Distribution Services/Quayside Distribution.
McCarter, Mark. The Racetracks Book: A Journey Around the Tracks Where Stock Cars Roar. 2007. (Illus.). 229p. pap. 20.00 *(978-1-4223-6636-3(7))* DIANE Publishing Co.
McClurg, Bob. Fire, Nitro, Rubber, & Smoke: Bob Mcclurg's Drag Racing Memories. 2007. (ENG., Illus.). 160p. pap. 29.95 *(978-1-932494-37-2(5))* CarTech, Inc.
McFadyen, Peter. Motor Racing at Oulton Park in The 1960s. 2007. (Those were the Days... Ser.). (ENG., Illus.). 96p. pap. 24.95 *(978-1-84584-038-9(0)*, 1845840380) Veloce Publishing Ltd. GBR. Dist: MBI Distribution Services/Quayside Distribution.
—Motor Racing at Oulton Park in The 1970s. 2008. (Those were the Days... Ser.). (ENG., Illus.). 96p. pap. 25.95 *(978-1-84584-164-5(6)*, 1845841646) Veloce Publishing Ltd. GBR. Dist: MBI Distribution Services/Quayside Distribution.
McGee, David M. Tales of Bristol Motor Speedway. 2011. (Illus.). 130p. pap. 19.99 ***(978-1-60949-145-1(9))*** History Pr., The.

McKenna, Kevin. How to Drag Race. 2008. 144p. pap. 24.95 *(978-1-932494-47-1(2))* CarTech, Inc.

Meredith, Laurence. Porsche: the Rally Story. 2008. (ENG., Illus.). 256p. 89.95 *(978-1-84584-109-6(3)*, 1845841093) Veloce Publishing Ltd. GBR. Dist: MBI Distribution Services/Quayside Distribution.

Miller, Timothy & Milton, Steve. Nascar Now! 3rd ed. 2008. (ENG., Illus.). 176p. pap. 24.95 *(978-1-55407-340-5(5))* Firefly Bks., Ltd.

Montagna, Paolo. Monza: A Glorious History. 2008. (ENG., Illus.). 176p. 44.95 *(978-88-7911-356-8(5)*, 8879113585) Giorgio Nada Editore ITA. Dist: MBI Distribution Services/Quayside Distribution.

Morgan, David. Seven Fifty Motor Club: The Birthplace of Modern British Motorsport. 2010. (ENG., Illus.). 224p. 52.95 *(978-1-84425-716-4(9)*, 1844257169) Haynes Publishing PLC GBR. Dist: MBI Distribution Services/Quayside Distribution.

Moses, Sam. Fast Guys, Rich Guys, & Idiots: A Racing Odyssey on the Border of Obsession. 2007. (ENG., Illus.). 348p. pap. 21.95 *(978-0-8032-1096-7(5)*, Bison Bks.) Univ. of Nebraska Pr.

Nye, Doug. The Goodwood Revival: The First Ten Years. 2008. (Illus.). 288p. 70.00 *(978-1-85894-449-4(X))* Merrell Pubs. Ltd. GBR. Dist: Perseus Distribution.

Olvey, Stephen. Rapid Response: My Inside Story as a Motor Racing Life-Saver. 2010. (ENG., Illus.). 288p. pap. 15.95 *(978-1-84425-982-3(X)*, 184425982X) Haynes Publishing PLC GBR. Dist: MBI Distribution Services/Quayside Distribution.

O'Malley, J. Daytona 24 Hours. 2009. *(978-1-935007-00-5(9))* Bull, David Publishing, Inc.

O'Neil, Terry. Motor Racing at Nassau in the 1950s And 1960s. 2008. (Those were the Days... Ser.). (ENG., Illus.). 96p. pap. 25.95 *(978-1-84584-198-0(0)*, 1845841980) Veloce Publishing Ltd. GBR. Dist: MBI Distribution Services/Quayside Distribution.

—Northeast American Sports Car Races 1950-1959. 2010. (ENG., Illus.). 432p. 200.00 *(978-1-84584-254-3(5)*, 1845842545) Veloce Publishing Ltd. GBR. Dist: MBI Distribution Services/Quayside Distribution.

—Runways & Racers: Sports Car Races Held on Military Airfields in America, 1952-1954. 2011. (ENG., Illus.). 208p. 69.95 *(978-1-84584-255-0(3)*, 1845842553) Veloce Publishing Ltd. GBR. Dist: MBI Distribution Services/Quayside Distribution.

Parker, Chas. Brands Hatch: The Definitive History of Britain's Best-Loved Motor Racing Circuit. 2007. (ENG., Illus.). 240p. 54.95 *(978-1-84425-334-0(1)*, 1844253341) Haynes Publishing PLC GBR. Dist: MBI Distribution Services/Quayside Distribution.

—Endurance Racing at Silverstone in the 1970s & 1980s. 2010. (Those Were the Days Ser.). (ENG., Illus.). 96p. pap. 29.95 *(978-1-84584-277-2(4)*, 1845842774) Veloce Publishing Ltd. GBR. Dist: MBI Distribution Services/Quayside Distribution.

—Motor Racing at Brands Hatch in the Eighties. 2009. (ENG., Illus.). 96p. pap. 15.95 *(978-1-84584-214-7(6)*, 1845842146) Veloce Publishing Ltd. GBR. Dist: MBI Distribution Services/Quayside Distribution.

Parker, Paul. Sports Car Racing in Camera 1950-1959. 2011. (ENG., Illus.). 240p. 59.95 *(978-1-84425-552-8(2)*, 1844255522) Haynes Publishing PLC GBR. Dist: MBI Distribution Services/Quayside Distribution.

—Sports Car Racing in Camera 1960-69. 2007. (ENG., Illus.). 240p. 59.95 *(978-1-84425-400-2(3)*, 1844254003) Haynes Publishing PLC GBR. Dist: MBI Distribution Services/Quayside Distribution.

—Sports Car Racing in Camera, 1970-79. 2008. (ENG., Illus.). 240p. 59.95 *(978-1-84425-471-2(2)*, 1844254712) Haynes Publishing PLC GBR. Dist: MBI Distribution Services/Quayside Distribution.

Parks, Peggy J. Street Racing. 2007. (Ripped from the Headlines Ser.). (YA). (gr. 7-12). 23.95 *(978-1-60217-019-3(3))* Erickson Pr.

Piola, Giorgio. Formula 1 2010/2011 Technical Analysis. 2011. (ENG., Illus.). 120p. pap. 44.95 *(978-88-7911-526-1(X)*, 887911526X) Giorgio Nada Editore ITA. Dist: MBI Distribution Services/Quayside Distribution.

Prima Games Staff & Mazurek, Jim. Forza Motorsport 3: Prima Official Game Guide. 2009. (ENG.). 256p. pap. 19.99 *(978-0-7615-6338-9(5)*, Prima Games) Random Hse. Information Group.

Pritchard, Anthony. Mille Miglia: The World's Greatest Road Race. 2007. (ENG., Illus.). 256p. 64.95 *(978-1-84425-139-1(X)*, 184425139X) Haynes Publishing PLC GBR. Dist: MBI Distribution Services/Quayside Distribution.

—Silver Arrows in Camera, 1934-39: A Photographic History of the Mercedes-Benz & Auto Union. 2008. (ENG., Illus.). 480p. 150.00 *(978-1-84425-467-5(4)*, 1844254674) Haynes Publishing PLC GBR. Dist: MBI Distribution Services/Quayside Distribution.

Punnett, Dick. Beach Racers: Daytona Before NASCAR. 2008. (ENG., Illus.). 168p. per. 25.00 *(978-0-8130-3260-3(1))* Univ. Pr. of Florida.

Purves, Bryan & Brenchley, Tim. The Last Works Minis: The End of a Legend. 2007. (ENG., Illus.). 192p. 59.95 *(978-1-84584-087-7(9)*, 1845840879) Veloce Publishing Ltd. GBR. Dist: MBI Distribution Services/Quayside Distribution.

Pyle, Michael. Side by Side: Life According to Racing. 2008. 60p. pap. 9.95 *(978-0-7414-4634-3(0))* Infinity Publishing.

Quattlebaum, Julian K. The Great Savannah Races. 2011. (ENG., Illus.). 152p. pap. 24.95 ***(978-0-8203-3813-2(3))*** Univ. of Georgia Pr.

Rand McNally, creator. The Ultimate NASCAR Road Trip Guide: The Road Tripper's Guide to All 31 NASCAR-Sanctioned Tracks. 2007. (Ultimate NASCAR Road Trip Guide Ser.). (Illus.). 384p. per. 14.95 *(978-0-528-93830-6(4))* Rand McNally.

Ravaioli, Fabio. Touring Car World 2006. 12th ed. 2006. (ENG., Illus.). 272p. pap. *(978-88-7911-394-6(1)*, 8879113941) Giorgio Nada Editore ITA. Dist: MBI Distribution Services/Quayside Distribution.

Rawlinson, Colin C. The 500cc Racing Car. 2008. (Shire Library). (ENG., Illus.). 32p. pap. 11.95 *(978-0-7478-0555-7(5))* Shire Pubns., Ltd. GBR. Dist: Random Hse., Inc.

Reinke, Phillip C. Pinewood Winning by the Rules. 2010. 64p. pap. 9.99 *(978-1-60911-153-3(2)*, Eloquent Bks.) AEG Literary Publishing Services, Inc.

Reuss, Eberhard. Hitler's Motor Racing Battles: The Silver Arrows under the Swastika. 2008. (ENG., Illus.). 368p. 49.95 *(978-1-84425-476-7(3)*, 1844254763) Haynes Publishing PLC GBR. Dist: MBI Distribution Services/Quayside Distribution.

Robson, Graham. British Touring Car Racing in Camera: A photographic celebration of 50 Years. 2008. (ENG., Illus.). 240p. 59.95 *(978-1-84425-469-9(0)*, 1844254690) Haynes Publishing PLC GBR. Dist: MBI Distribution Services/Quayside Distribution.

—Cosworth & Ford: The Road Cars. 2006. (Crowood Autoclassics Ser.). (ENG., Illus.). 200p. 34.95 *(978-1-86126-838-9(6)*, 1861268386) Crowood Pr., Ltd. GBR. Dist: MBI Distribution Services/Quayside Distribution.

—Monte Carlo Rally: The Golden Age, 1911-1980. 2007. (ENG., Illus.). 240p. 59.95 *(978-1-906133-00-9(X)*, 190613300X) Herridge & Sons, Ltd. GBR. Dist: MBI Distribution Services/Quayside Distribution.

Rogers, Gareth. Lewis Hamilton the Story So Far. 2008. (ENG., Illus.). 200p. pap. 19.95 *(978-0-7524-4480-2(8))* History Pr. Ltd.,The GBR. Dist: Independent Pubs. Group.

Rogers, Gareth. 100 Years of the British Automobile Racing Club. 2012. (ENG., Illus.). 168p. 45.00 ***(978-0-7524-6180-9(X))*** History Pr. Ltd.,The GBR. Dist: Independent Pubs. Group.

Roy, Alexander. The Driver: My Dangerous Pursuit of Speed & Truth in the Outlaw Racing World. (ENG.). 336p. 2008. pap. 14.95 *(978-0-06-137499-9(7))* 2007. (Illus.). 25.95 *(978-0-06-122793-6(5))* HarperCollins Pubs.

Royal, William N. & Royal, Ted. Checkered Flag: Favorite Auto-Racing Stories of Great Drivers & Owners. Date not set. (Illus.). 240p. (Orig.). pap. 24.95 *(978-1-57488-146-2(9))* Potomac Bks., Inc.

Salmon, Dick. Brm: A Mechanic's Tale. 2007. (ENG., Illus.). 224p. 74.95 *(978-1-84584-082-2(8)*, 1845840828) Veloce Publishing Ltd. GBR. Dist: MBI Distribution Services/Quayside Distribution.

Schild, Jim & Schild, James J. Proving Ground: A History of Dodge, Chrysler, & Plymouth Racing. 2009. (ENG., Illus.). 192p. 40.00 *(978-0-7603-3458-4(7)*, 0760334587, Motorbooks) MBI Publishing Co. LLC.

Schlegelmilch, Rainer, photos by. Formula 1: World Champions. 2012. (GER & ENG., Illus.). 256p. 95.00 ***(978-3-8327-9612-9(6))*** teNeues Publishing Co.

Seneca, Michael J. The Fairmount Park Motor Races, 1908-1911. alt. ed. 2010. (ENG., Illus.). 238p. pap. 39.95 *(978-0-7864-4592-9(0))* McFarland & Co., Inc. Pubs.

Shakespeare, Paul. Building a Dune Buggy: The Essential Manual. 2006. (Essential Manual Ser.). (ENG., Illus.). 144p. pap. 49.95 *(978-1-904788-73-7(4)*, 1904788734) Veloce Publishing Ltd. GBR. Dist: MBI Distribution Services/Quayside Distribution.

Smart, Hamish. Track Days: A Glovebox Guide. 2009. (ENG., Illus.). 128p. pap. 19.95 *(978-1-84797-111-1(3)*, 1847971113) Crowood Pr., Ltd. GBR. Dist: MBI Distribution Services/Quayside Distribution.

Smith, Roger. Analysing Formula 1: Innovative Insights into Winners & Winning in Grand Prix Racing since 1950. 2008. (ENG., Illus.). 304p. *(978-1-84425-447-7(X)*, 184425447X) Haynes Publishing PLC GBR. Dist: MBI Distribution Services/Quayside Distribution.

Smith, Roy. Alpine & Renault: The Sports Prototypes 1973 to 1978. 2010. (ENG., Illus.). 224p. 69.95 *(978-1-84584-226-0(X)*, 184584226X) Veloce Publishing Ltd. GBR. Dist: MBI Distribution Services/Quayside Distribution.

—Amedee Gordini: A True Racing Legend. 2012. (ENG., Illus.). 288p. 89.95 *(978-1-84584-317-5(7)*, 1845843177) Veloce Publishing Ltd. GBR. Dist: MBI Distribution Services/Quayside Distribution.

Smith, Roy P. Alpine & Renault: The Sports Prototypes 1963 To 1969. 2010. (ENG., Illus.). 208p. 69.95 *(978-1-84584-191-1(3)*, 1845841913) Veloce Publishing Ltd. GBR. Dist: MBI Distribution Services/Quayside Distribution.

South Boston Speedway: The FIRST 50 Years. 2007. (ENG., Illus.). 160p. per. 19.95 *(978-0-9789261-3-7(7))* Coastal 181.

Spurring, Quentin. Jim Clark: A photographic Portrait. 2008. (ENG., Illus.). 256p. 59.95 *(978-1-84425-501-6(8)*, 1844255018) Haynes Publishing PLC GBR. Dist: MBI Distribution Services/Quayside Distribution.

—Le Mans, 1960-69: The Official History of the World's Greatest Motor Race. 2010. (ENG., Illus.). 352p. 70.00 *(978-1-84425-584-9(0)*, 1844255840) Haynes Publishing PLC GBR. Dist: MBI Distribution Services/Quayside Distribution.

—Le Mans 24 Hours: the Official History 1970-79. 2011. (ENG., Illus.). 352p. 70.00 *(978-1-84425-539-9(5)*, 1844255395) Haynes Publishing PLC GBR. Dist: MBI Distribution Services/Quayside Distribution.

Starkey, John. Porsche 911r, Rs & Rsr. 4th ed. (Illus.). 272p. lthr. *(978-1-901295-89-4(3))* Veloce Publishing Ltd. GBR. Dist: MBI Distribution Services/Quayside Distribution.

Stewart, Mark & Kennedy, Mike. NASCAR Safety on the Track. 2008. (Science of NASCAR Ser.). (Illus.). 48p. (YA). (gr. 4-7). lib. bdg. 27.93 *(978-0-8225-8742-2(4))* Lerner Publishing Group.

—Nascar Safety on the Track. 2009. pap. 52.95 *(978-0-8225-9339-3(4))* Lerner Publishing Group.

Stokoe, Noel. Sporting Jowetts. 2009. (ENG., Illus.). 256p. pap. 34.95 *(978-0-7524-4775-9(0))* History Pr. Ltd.,The GBR. Dist: Independent Pubs. Group.

Teaters, Matthew. Formula One Famous Failures. 2009. 96p. pap. 13.99 *(978-1-4251-8528-2(2))* Trafford Publishing.

Thompson, Neal. Driving with the Devil: Southern Moonshine, Detroit Wheels, & the Birth of NASCAR. 2007. (ENG.). 432p. pap. 14.95 *(978-1-4000-8226-1(9)*, Three Rivers Pr.) Crown Publishing Group.

Tibballs, Geoff. Motor Racing's Strangest Races: Extraordinary but True Stories from over a Century of Motor Racing. 2012. (ENG., Illus.). 168p. 15.95 ***(978-1-907554-65-0(3))*** Anova Bks. GBR. Dist: Independent Pubs. Group.

Tipler, Johnny & Ramirez, Jo. La Carrera Panamericana: The World's Greatest Road Race! 2008. (ENG., Illus.). 272p. 89.95 *(978-1-84584-170-6(0)*, 1845841700) Veloce Publishing Ltd. GBR. Dist: MBI Distribution Services/Quayside Distribution.

Tremayne, David, ed. Formula One: 50 Golden Years. (Illus.). 116p. *(978-0-9531900-2-7(1))* Apex Marketing, Ltd. GBR. Dist: Vine Hse. Distribution.

Upton, Larry, et al. The Historic Manzanita Speedway in Phoenix. 2012. (Images of America Ser.). (ENG., Illus.). 128p. pap. 21.99 ***(978-0-7385-8517-8(3))*** Arcadia Publishing.

Ursic, Billy. Supercross Unleashed: The Joy of SX. 2007. (ENG., Illus.). 160p. pap. 24.95 *(978-0-7603-2995-5(8)*, 0760329958, Motorbooks) MBI Publishing Co. LLC.

Venables, David. British Racing Green: Drivers, Cars & Triumphs of British Motor Racing. 2009. (ENG., Illus.). 176p. 46.95 *(978-0-7110-3332-0(3))* Allan, Ian Publishing GBR. Dist: BookMasters Distribution Services (BDS).

—Brooklands: The Official Centenary History. 2007. (ENG., Illus.). 256p. 54.95 *(978-1-84425-329-6(5)*, 1844253295) Haynes Publishing PLC GBR. Dist: MBI Distribution Services/Quayside Distribution.

—The Classic Motor Racing Circuits of Europe. 2010. (ENG., Illus.). 176p. 39.95 *(978-0-7110-3481-5(8))* Allan, Ian Publishing GBR. Dist: BookMasters Distribution Services (BDS).

Wagstaff, Ian. The British at Indianapolis. 2010. (ENG., Illus.). 256p. 99.95 *(978-1-84584-246-8(4)*, 1845842464) Veloce Publishing Ltd. GBR. Dist: MBI Distribution Services/Quayside Distribution.

—The British at le Mans: 85 Years of Endeavour. 2006. (ENG., Illus.). 280p. 79.95 *(978-1-899870-80-6(6)*, 1899870806) Motor Racing Pubns., Ltd. GBR. Dist: MBI Distribution Services/Quayside Distribution.

Walton, Jeremy. Audi Quattro: A Celebration of the World's First Turbocharged 4x4 Coupe. 2007. (Haynes Great Cars Ser.). (ENG., Illus.). 160p. 32.95 *(978-1-84425-330-2(9)*, 1844253309) Haynes Publishing PLC GBR. Dist: MBI Distribution Services/Quayside Distribution.

Ward, David. The Smart One: Winning the Cannonball Run. 2010. (Illus.). 134p. 32.95 *(978-1-84624-404-9(8))* Book Guild, Ltd. GBR. Dist: Trans-Atlantic Pubns., Inc.

Welch, Ian & Morgan, Charlie. The A-Z of Grand Prix: A Grand Prix A to Z. 2009. (Little Book Ser.). (ENG., Illus.). 128p. 9.99 *(978-1-906635-26-8(9)*, 1906635269) G2 Entertainment Ltd. GBR. Dist: MBI Distribution Services/Quayside Distribution.

West, David. Race Car Drivers. 2008. (Graphic Careers Ser.). (ENG., Illus.). 48p. (gr. 5-8). per. 14.05 *(978-1-4042-1453-8(4))*; (YA). lib. bdg. 29.25 *(978-1-4042-1452-1(6))* Rosen Publishing Group, Inc., The.

White, Ben. NASCAR Racers. 2009. (First Gear Ser.). (ENG., Illus.). 256p. pap. 19.99 *(978-0-7603-3577-2(X)*, 076033577X, Motorbooks) MBI Publishing Co. LLC.

Wiley, Lana. 360 Degrees of Tailgaiting. 2007. 232p. spiral bd. *(978-0-9800495-0-3(4))* Checkered Flag Productions Inc.

Willerth, Jeffrey. Racing School Directory. 6th rev. ed. lib. bdg. 11.95 *(978-0-9644044-1-0(9))* Erthbound Entertainment.

Williams, David D. Turbine Racing in Seattle. 2007. (Images of Sports Ser.). (Illus.). 127p. per. 19.99 *(978-0-7385-4891-3(X))* Arcadia Publishing.

Wimpffen, Janos. Spyders & Silhouettes: The World Manufacturers & Sports Car Championships in Photographs, 1972-1981. 2007. (Illus.). 400p. 149.95 *(978-1-893618-83-1(8))* Bull, David Publishing, Inc.

Woods, Dave & Rose, Geoff. Bristol Bulldogs. (ENG., Illus.). 128p. pap. 22.99 *(978-0-7524-2231-2(6))* History Pr. Ltd.,The GBR. Dist: Trafalgar Square Publishing.

Wyatt, Steve & Carter, Anthony. Motor Racing: The Pursuit of Victory, 1963-1972. 2012. (ENG., Illus.). 272p. 89.95 *(978-1-84584-285-7(5)*, 1845842855) Veloce Publishing Ltd. GBR. Dist: MBI Distribution Services/Quayside Distribution.

Zwart, Jeffrey. Three Points of Contact. 2008. (Illus.). 156p. *(978-1-893618-99-2(4))* Bull, David Publishing, Inc.

AUTOMOBILE RACING—BIOGRAPHY

Ackroyd, John. Jet Blast & the Hand of Fate: Adventures with Land Speed Cars & Record Balloons. 2007. (ENG., Illus.). 288p. 66.95 *(978-0-9544357-8-3(8))* Redline Bks. GBR. Dist: MBI Distribution Services/Quayside Distribution.

Allen, James. Michael Schumacher: The Edge of Greatness. 2009. (ENG., Illus.). 416p. pap. 14.95 *(978-0-7553-1650-2(9))* Headline Bk. Publishing GBR. Dist: Independent Pubs. Group.

Argabright, Dave. Lone Wolf: One of Auto Racing's most compelling characters tells his Story. 2007. (Illus.). 352p. 32.50 *(978-0-9719639-4-8(0))* American Scene Pr., LLC.

Argetsinger, Michael. Mark Donohue. 2009. 320p. 39.95 *(978-1-935007-02-9(5))* Bull, David Publishing, Inc.

—Mark Donohue: His Life in Photographs. 2010. (Illus.). 244p. 39.95 *(978-1-935007-09-8(2))* Bull, David Publishing, Inc.

Belcher Foundation (Belcher, Ky.) Staff, contrib. by. Fastest of the First: A Complete History of the Inaugural 1911 Indianapolis 500, Including the Driving of the Fastest Laps by Fred W. Belcher. 2008. (Illus.). 263p. *(978-0-9816476-1-6(8))* Belcher Foundation, Inc.

Bell, Derek & Henry, Alan. Derek Bell: My Racing Life. 2011. (ENG., Illus.). 288p. 54.95 *(978-0-85733-088-8(8)*, 0857330888) Haynes Publishing PLC GBR. Dist: MBI Distribution Services/Quayside Distribution.

Bh. Secrets Exposed: Discrimination still exist in the nscs,inThe good ole boy racing seriesThe proof & the truth shall set you Free! 2009. 48p. pap. 9.95 *(978-1-4401-5296-2(9))* iUniverse, Inc.

Bob, McClurg. Yenko: The Man, the Machines, the Legend. 2010. 192p. 39.95 *(978-1-932494-85-3(5))* CarTech, Inc.

Bourcier, Bones, ed. Steady Eddie: Memories of Ed Flemke, Modified Racing's Fastest Professor. 2007. (Illus.). 256p. per. 23.95 *(978-0-9789261-1-3(0))* Coastal 181.

Brooks, Tony. Tony Brooks - Poetry in Motion: Autobiography of a Supreme Grand Prix Driver. 2012. (ENG., Illus.). 276p. 89.50 ***(978-1-899870-83-7(0)***, 1899870830) Motor Racing Pubns., Ltd. GBR. Dist: MBI Distribution Services/Quayside Distribution.

Burford, Brian. Moran Brothers. (ENG., Illus.). 224p. pap. 35.00 *(978-0-7524-2424-8(6))* History Pr. Ltd.,The GBR. Dist: Trafalgar Square Publishing.

Burgt, Andrew. Lewis Hamilton World Champion 2nd. 2nd ed. 2008. (Illus.). 236p. *(978-1-84425-699-0(5))* Haynes Publishing PLC.

Button, Jenson. My Championship Year. 2010. (ENG.). 224p. pap. 24.99 *(978-0-297-86012-9(7))*; (Illus.). 37.99 *(978-0-297-86011-2(9))* Orion Publishing Group, Ltd. GBR. (Weidenfeld & Nicolson). Dist: Hachette Bk. Group.

Bye, Chris. Crash Test. 2007. pap. *(978-0-9784402-6-8(9))* BPS Bks.

Cameron, James. Independent Pasts: Three brothers, forty years a healing motorcycle Journey. 2009. (ENG.). 512p. pap. 20.49 *(978-1-4490-3516-7(7))* AuthorHouse.

Chimits, Xavier. Grand Prix Racers: Portraits of Speed. 2008. (ENG., Illus.). 224p. 40.00 *(978-0-7603-3430-0(7)*, 0760334307, Motorbooks) MBI Publishing Co. LLC.

Comte, Michel. Michael by Michel, 1 vol. ltd. ed. 2008. (ENG., Illus.). 120p. (gr. 13-18). 100.00 *(978-3-88243-898-7(3))* Steidl, Gerhard Druckerei und Verlag DEU. Dist: Innovative Logistics.

Cooper, Adam. Piers Courage: Last of the Gentlemen Racers. 2nd ed. 2010. (ENG., Illus.). 384p. pap. 17.95 *(978-1-84425-863-5(7)*, 1844258637) Haynes Publishing PLC GBR. Dist: MBI Distribution Services/Quayside Distribution.

Coulthard, David. It Is What It Is. 2008. (ENG., Illus.). 392p. pap. 18.95 *(978-0-7528-9334-1(3))* Orion Publishing Group, Ltd. GBR. Dist: Independent Pubs. Group.

Cremonesi, Andrea & Degl'Innocenti, Marco. Meet Sebastian Vettel: The Story of Formula One's Youngest Champion. 2012. (ENG., Illus.). 160p. pap. 21.95 ***(978-0-285-64085-6(2))*** Souvenir Pr. Ltd. GBR. Dist: Independent Pubs. Group.

Davis, S. C. H. Sammy. My Life in Motorsport: His Final Autobiography. 2008. (ENG., Illus.). 192p. 44.95 *(978-1-906133-02-3(6)*, 1906133026) Herridge & Sons Ltd.

Deloriea, Wayne. Coach Without a Whistle. 2009. 132p. pap. 14.99 *(978-1-60791-202-6(3))* Xulon Pr., Inc.

DeLoriea, Wayne. Coach Without A Whistle. 2009. *(978-1-60791-301-6(1))* Xulon Pr., Inc.

Diekman, Diane. Twentieth Century Drifter: The Life of Marty Robbins. 2012. (Music in American Life Ser.). (ENG., Illus.). 304p. 29.95 ***(978-0-252-03632-3(8))*** Univ. of Illinois Pr.

Donovan, Brian. Hard Driving: The Wendell Scott Story. 2009. (ENG.). 328p. 16.99 *(978-1-58642-160-1(3))* Steerforth Pr.

Doodson, Mike. Nigel Mansell: A Photographic Portrait. 2008. (ENG., Illus.). 256p. 54.95 *(978-1-84425-631-0(6)*, 1844256316) Haynes Publishing PLC GBR. Dist: MBI Distribution Services/Quayside Distribution.

Elliott, Bill & Millard, Chris. Awesome Bill from Dawsonville: My Life in NASCAR. 2007. (ENG., Illus.). 336p. per. 13.95 *(978-0-06-112574-4(1))* HarperCollins Pubs.

Finke, Don & Finke, Nikki. Imagine That: Over 45 Years of Auto Racing Experiences. 2010. 432p. 33.95 *(978-1-4490-8750-0(7))*; pap. 24.95 *(978-1-4490-8752-4(3))* AuthorHouse.

Gale Editor, ed. Jeff Gordon. 2011. (People in the News Ser.). (Illus.). 128p. lib. bdg. 33.45 *(978-1-4205-0606-8(4)*, Lucent Bks.) Cengage Gale.

Ganchy, Sally. Great Moments in NASCAR Racing. 2009. (Highlights of NASCAR Racing Ser.). 48p. (gr. 5-5). 53.00 *(978-1-61513-299-7(6)*, Rosen Central) Rosen Publishing Group, Inc., The.

Gauld, Graham. From the Fells to Ferrari: The Official Biography of Cliff Allison. 2008. (ENG., Illus.). 144p. 22.95 *(978-1-84584-150-8(6)*, 1845841506) Veloce Publishing Ltd. GBR. Dist: MBI Distribution Services/Quayside Distribution.

—Gentleman Jack: The Official Biography of Jack Sears. 2008. (ENG., Illus.). 160p. 49.95 *(978-1-84584-151-5(4)*, 1845841514) Veloce Publishing Ltd. GBR. Dist: MBI Distribution Services/Quayside Distribution.

Goodwin, Tony. Doctor on the Grid. 2012. (ENG., Illus.). 184p. 64.95 ***(978-1-899870-84-4(9)***, 1899870849) Motor Racing Pubns., Ltd. GBR. Dist: MBI Distribution Services/Quayside Distribution.

Gould, Todd. For Gold & Glory: Charlie Wiggins & the African-American Racing Car Circuit. 2007. (ENG., Illus.). 240p. pap. 14.95 (978-0-253-21962-6(0), 0253219620) Indiana Univ. Pr.

Gregoire, Francois-Michel. Who Works in Motorsports 2006: A Complete Guide to Motor Sports Worldwide. 2006. (Illus.). 600p. 99.50 (978-1-901711-43-1(9)) Who Works Publications, Ltd. GBR. Dist: Trans-Atlantic Pubns., Inc.

Henny, Phil Louis. Bob Bondurant: Des Cobra a la Formule 1... . la meme Passion! ltd. ed. 2007. Orig. Title: Bob Bondurant America's uncrowned world driving Champion. (FRE., Illus.). 192p. per. 45.00 (978-0-9765247-3-1(2)) Editions Cotty.

—Nenn mich einfach Carroll. 2009.Tr. of Nenn mich einfach Carroll. (GER., Illus.). 146p. (978-0-9765247-4-8(0)) Editions Cotty.

Henny, Phil Louis, as told by. Remembering Carroll Shelby. 2010. per. 59.00 (978-0-9765247-2-4(4)) Editions Cotty.

Henry, Alan & Moss, Stirling. Stirling Moss: All My Races. 2010. (ENG., Illus.). 352p. 52.95 (978-1-84425-700-3(2), 1844257002) Haynes Publishing PLC GBR. Dist: MBI Distribution Services/Quayside Distribution.

Henry, Alan & Spurring, Quentin. Ronnie Peterson: A Photographic Portrait. 2009. (ENG., Illus.). 240p. 54.95 (978-1-84425-548-1(4), 1844255484) Haynes Publishing PLC GBR. Dist: MBI Distribution Services/Quayside Distribution.

Hilton, Christopher. The Brawn Story: The Man & the Team That Turned Formula 1 Upside-Down. 2009. (Illus.). 256p. (978-1-84425-937-3(4)) Haynes Publishing PLC.

—The Brawn Story: The Man & the Team That Turned Formula 1 Upside-Down. 2nd ed. 2010. (ENG., Illus.). 336p. pap. 15.95 (978-1-84425-999-1(4), 1844259994) Haynes Publishing PLC GBR. Dist: MBI Distribution Services/Quayside Distribution.

—Memories of Clay Regazzoni. 2009. (ENG., Illus.). 192p. 59.95 (978-1-84425-479-8(8), 1844254798) Haynes Publishing PLC GBR. Dist: MBI Distribution Services/Quayside Distribution.

—The Toleman Story: Last Romantics in Formula 1. 2010. (ENG., Illus.). 208p. 69.95 (978-1-84584-217-8(0), 1845842170) Veloce Publishing Ltd. GBR. Dist: MBI Distribution Services/Quayside Distribution.

Hines, Martin. Every Split Second Counts: My Life with Fast Karts, Fast Women & F1 Superstars. 2008. (ENG., Illus.). 320p. 34.95 (978-1-84454-658-9(6)) Blake, John Publishing, Ltd. GBR. Dist: Independent Pubs. Group.

Hughes, Jonathan. Motorsports America, the Men & Machines of American Motorsports 2007-2008. 2008. (Illus.). 100p. 29.00 (978-0-929323-29-9(7)) Autosport International, Inc.

Hughes, Mark. The Unofficial Complete Encyclopedia of Formula One: An Illustrated Guide to the World's Fastest Sport. 2009. (ENG., Illus.). 256p. 29.99 (978-0-7548-1959-2(0)) Anness Publishing GBR. Dist: National Bk. Network.

Hummel, Alan. Penske Racing Team: 40 Years of Excellence. 2007. (ENG., Illus.). 272p. 19.95 (978-1-58388-195-8(6), 1583881956) Iconografix, Inc.

Kennedy, Pat. How Much Do You Really Know about the Indianapolis 500? 500+ Multiple-Choice Questions to Educate & Test Your Knowledge of the Hundred-Year History. 2011. 232p. pap. 16.95 (978-1-4490-8894-1(5)) AuthorHouse.

Kenny, John. The Dirty Dozen: Ireland's Motor-sport Legends. 2007. (ENG., Illus.). 272p. pap. 15.95 **(978-1-84717-050-7(1))** O'Brien Pr., Ltd., The IRL. Dist: Dufour Editions, Inc.

Kirby, Gordon. Rick Mears * Thanks: The Story of Rick Mears & the Mears Gang. 2008. (ENG., Illus.). 264p. pap. 39.95 (978-1-905334-30-8(3), 1905334303) Icon Pubng. Ltd. GBR. Dist: MBI Distribution Services/Quayside Distribution.

La Bella, Laura. Carl Edwards. 2009. (Behind the Wheel Ser.). (YA). (gr. 5-9). lib. bdg. 26.50 (978-1-4042-1898-7(X)) Rosen Publishing Group, Inc., The.

Leuthauser, Karl & Leuthauser, Kyle. The Driving Force: Living Life & Full Speed. 2009. (Illus.). 80p. pap. 9.99 (978-0-7644-3749-6(6)) Group Publishing, Inc.

Lovell, Terry. Bernie Ecclestone: King of Sport. (ENG., Illus.). 2010. 420p. pap. 13.95 (978-1-84454-826-2(0)) 2008. 288p. 34.95 (978-1-84454-623-7(3)) Blake, John Publishing, Ltd. GBR. Dist: Independent Pubs. Group.

Ludvigsen, Karl. Colin Chapman: Inside the Innovator. 2010. (ENG., Illus.). 208p. 59.95 (978-1-84425-413-2(5), 1844254135) Haynes Publishing PLC GBR. Dist: MBI Distribution Services/Quayside Distribution.

Ludwig, Gary. Tommy Hinnershitz, the Life & Times of an Auto-Racing Legend. 2009. (Illus.). 252p. 29.95 (978-0-9815099-4-5(0)) Basket Road Pr., Inc.

Madigan, Tom. Hurricane! The Bob Hannah Story. 2008. (ENG., Illus.). 176p. 35.00 (978-0-7603-3300-6(9), 0760333009, Motorbooks) MBI Publishing Co. LLC.

Manson, David. Freddie Dixon. 2009. (ENG., Illus.). 184p. 49.95 (978-1-84425-540-5(9), 1844255409) Haynes Publishing PLC GBR. Dist: MBI Distribution Services/Quayside Distribution.

McBride, Simon. Kris Meeke: Intercontinental Rally Challenge Champion. 2010. (ENG., Illus.). 160p. 39.95 (978-1-84584-071-6(2), 1845840712) Veloce Publishing Ltd. GBR. Dist: MBI Distribution Services/Quayside Distribution.

Miller, Leonard T. Racing While Black: How an African-American Stock Car Team Made Its Mark on NASCAR. 2010. (ENG.). 336p. 24.95 (978-1-58322-896-8(9)) Seven Stories Pr.

Miller, Timothy. Drag Racing: The World's Fastest Sport. 2009. (ENG., Illus.). 208p. 34.95 (978-1-55407-446-4(0)) Firefly Bks., Ltd.

Nevison, Tim. The Drivers: A Celebration of New Zealand Motor Sports' Greatest. 2007. (Illus.). 224p. (978-1-86950-693-3(6)) HarperCollins Pubs. Australia.

Norwood, John, text. Motorsports America, the Men & Machines of American Motorports 2006-2007. 2007. (Illus.). 200p. 29.00 (978-0-929323-28-2(9)) Autosport International, Inc.

O' Leary, Mike. Mario Andretti: The Complete Record. 2007. (Illus.). 155p. reprint ed. pap. 17.00 (978-1-4223-6640-0(5)) DIANE Publishing Co.

Osborne, Mark. Rebel Speedway. 2007. pap. 16.00 (978-0-8059-8954-0(4)) Dorrance Publishing Co., Inc.

Otto, Edgar & Biondi, Joann. Ed Otto: NASCAR's Silent Partner. 2008. (Illus.). 208p. 29.95 (978-0-9789261-4-4(5)) Coastal 181.

Parker, Paul. Races, Faces, Places: The motor racing photography of Michael Cooper. 2009. (ENG., Illus.). 352p. 79.95 (978-1-84425-508-5(5), 1844255085) Haynes Publishing PLC GBR. Dist: MBI Distribution Services/Quayside Distribution.

Patrick, Danica. Danica: Crossing the Line. 2007. (ENG., Illus.). 240p. pap. 17.95 (978-0-7432-9830-8(6), Touchstone) Touchstone.

Priaulx, Andy. Andy Priaulx: The Autobiography of the Three-time World Touring Car Champion. 2008. (ENG., Illus.). 288p. 36.95 (978-0-00-728117-6(X)) HarperCollins Pubs. Ltd. GBR. Dist: Independent Pubs. Group.

Pritchard, Anthony. Ferrari: Men from Maranello: The biographical A-Z of all significant Ferrari racing People. 2009. (ENG., Illus.). 384p. 70.00 (978-1-84425-414-9(3), 1844254143) Haynes Publishing PLC GBR. Dist: MBI Distribution Services/Quayside Distribution.

Pulford, John & Winn, Allan. 100 Years of Brooklands: The Birthplace of British Motorsport & Aviation. Temple, Julian, ed. 2007. (ENG., Illus.). 192p. 45.00 (978-0-9551020-6-6(5)) Touchstone Bks. Ltd. GBR. Dist: Independent Pubs. Group.

Roy, Alexander. The Driver: My Dangerous Pursuit of Speed & Truth in the Outlaw Racing World. 2007. (ENG., Illus.). 336p. 25.95 (978-0-06-122793-6(5)) HarperCollins Pubs.

Scott, Michael. Motorcycle Workd Champions: The Inside Story of History's Heroes. 2008. (ENG., Illus.). 224p. 44.95 (978-1-84425-454-5(2), 1844254542) Haynes Publishing PLC GBR. Dist: MBI Distribution Services/Quayside Distribution.

Shirley, Phil. The Last British Hero: The Mysterious Death of Grand Prix Legend Richard Seaman. Date not set. (ENG., Illus.). 288p. 35.00 (978-1-84018-584-3(8)) Mainstream Publishing Co., Ltd. GBR. Dist: Independent Pubs. Group.

Southgate, Tony. Tony Southgate from Drawing Board to Chequered Flag: The Autobiography of One of Motorsport's Most Prolific & Versatile Racing Car Designers. 2010. (ENG., Illus.). 256p. 79.95 (978-1-899870-82-0(2), 1899870822) Motor Racing Pubns., Ltd. GBR. Dist: MBI Distribution Services/Quayside Distribution.

Spaulding, Jeffrey. Matt Kenseth: NASCAR Driver. 2009. (Behind the Wheel Ser.). (ENG., Illus.). 48p. (YA). (gr. 5-8). pap. 11.75 (978-1-4358-5404-8(7)) Rosen Publishing Group, Inc., The.

Stafford, Ian. Lewis Hamilton: New Kid on the Grid. 2007. (ENG., Illus.). 224p. 32.95 (978-1-84596-338-5(5)) Mainstream Publishing Co., Ltd. GBR. Dist: Independent Pubs. Group.

Stewart, Jackie. Winning Is Not Enough: The Autobiography. 2010. (ENG., Illus.). 576p. pap. 13.95 (978-0-7553-1539-0(1)) Headline Bk. Publishing GBR. Dist: Independent Pubs. Group.

—Winning Is Not Enough: The Autobiography (US Edition) 2008. (ENG.). 495p. 27.95 (978-0-7553-1829-2(3)) Headline Bk. Publishing GBR. Dist: Independent Pubs. Group.

Stone, Matt & Lerner, Preston. Winning: The Racing Life of Paul Newman. 2009. (ENG., Illus.). 176p. 30.00 (978-0-7603-3706-6(3), 0760337063, Motorbooks) MBI Publishing Co. LLC.

Sullivan, Patrick. Brick by Brick: The Story of Auto Racing Pioneer Joie Ray. 2008. (Illus.). 208p. pap. 22.50 (978-0-9719639-5-5(9)) American Scene Pr., LLC.

Take It to the Limit: The Dave Mungenast Way. 2006. 206p. 24.95 (978-0-9788817-0-2(2)) Motohistory.

Tremayne, David. Jochen Rindt: Champion Lost. 2011. (ENG., Illus.). 256p. 69.95 (978-1-84425-472-9(0), 1844254720) Haynes Publishing PLC GBR. Dist: MBI Distribution Services/Quayside Distribution.

—The Lost Generation: The Brilliant but Tragic Lives of Rising British F1 Stars Roger Williamson, Tony Brise & Tom Pryce. 2007. (ENG., Illus.). 240p. 54.95 (978-1-84425-205-3(1), 1844252051) Haynes Publishing PLC GBR. Dist: MBI Distribution Services/Quayside Distribution.

Tulloch, Andrew. Jim Clark: Grand Prix Legend. 2009. (ENG., Illus.). 240p. (978-0-297-85440-1(2), Weidenfeld & Nicolson) Orion Publishing Group, Ltd. GBR. Dist: Sterling Publishing Co., Inc.

Turner, Stuart. Harnessing Horsepower: The Pat Moss Carlsson Story. 2011. (ENG., Illus.). 160p. 49.95 (978-1-84584-306-9(1), 1845843061) Veloce Publishing Ltd. GBR. Dist: MBI Distribution Services/Quayside Distribution.

Van de Burgt, Andrew. Lewis Hamilton: A Portrait of Britain's New F1 Star. 2008. (ENG., Illus.). 160p. 27.95 (978-1-84425-480-4(1)) Haynes Publishing PLC GBR. Dist: MBI Distribution Services/Quayside Distribution.

Walker, Mick. Derek Minter: King of Brands. 2008. (ENG., Illus.). 240p. (978-1-85983-601-9(1), 1859836011) DB Publishing.

Walton, Jeremy. Gerry Marshall: His Authorised Biography. 2010. (ENG., Illus.). 256p. 59.95 (978-1-84425-648-8(0), 1844256480) Haynes Publishing PLC GBR. Dist: MBI Distribution Services/Quayside Distribution.

—Life of Spice: The Autobiography of Gordon Spice. 2009. (ENG., Illus.). 256p. 49.95 (978-1-84425-568-9(9), 1844255689) Haynes Publishing PLC GBR. Dist: MBI Distribution Services/Quayside Distribution.

Waltrip, Darrell. Sundays Will Never Be the Same: Racing, Tragedy, & Redemption — My Life in America's Fastest Sport. 2012. (ENG., Illus.). 256p. 24.99 **(978-1-4516-4489-0(2)**, Free Pr.) Free Pr.

Waltrip, Michael & Henican, Ellis. In the Blink of an Eye: Dale, Daytona, & the Day that Changed Everything. 2011. (ENG.). 420p. pap. 14.99 **(978-0-7868-9139-9(4))** Hyperion Pr.

Waltrip, Michael & Henican, Ellis. In the Blink of an Eye: Dale, Daytona, & the Day That Changed Everything. 2011. (ENG.). 240p. 24.99 (978-1-4013-2431-5(2)) Hyperion Pr.

Wheeler, Humpy & Golenbock, Peter. Growing up NASCAR: Racing's Most Outrageous Promoter Tells All. 2010. (ENG., Illus.). 304p. 25.00 (978-0-7603-3775-2(6), 0760337756, Motorbooks) MBI Publishing Co. LLC.

White, Gordon Eliot. AB & Marvin Jenkins: The Studebaker Connection & the Mormon Meteors. 2006. (ENG., Illus.). 160p. pap. 32.95 (978-1-58388-173-6(5), 1583881735) Iconografix, Inc.

Wilson, Alan. Driven by Desire: The Desire Wilson Story. 2011. (ENG., Illus.). 160p. 49.95 (978-1-84584-389-2(4), 1845843894) Veloce Publishing Ltd. GBR. Dist: MBI Distribution Services/Quayside Distribution.

Worral, Frank & Worrall, Frank. Lewis Hamilton: The Biography. 2007. (ENG., Illus.). 306p. 29.95 (978-1-84454-543-8(1)) Blake, John Publishing, Ltd. GBR. Dist: Independent Pubs. Group.

Worrall, Frank. Lewis Hamilton: Champion of the World - The Biography. 2009. (ENG., Illus.). 338p. pap. 14.95 (978-1-84454-581-0(4)) Blake, John Publishing, Ltd. GBR. Dist: Independent Pubs. Group.

Yates, Brock. Umbrella Mike: The True Story of the Chicago Gangster Behind the Indy 500. 2007. (ENG., Illus.). 224p. per. 14.95 (978-1-56025-966-4(3)) Da Capo Pr., Inc.

Young, Eoin. Memories of the Bear: A Biography of Denny Hulme. 2008. (ENG., Illus.). 416p. 34.95 (978-1-84425-208-4(6), 1844252086) Haynes Publishing PLC GBR. Dist: MBI Distribution Services/Quayside Distribution.

AUTOMOBILE RACING—JUVENILE LITERATURE

Georgiou, Tyrone. Indy Cars. 2011. (Fast Lane: Open-Wheel Racing Ser.). (Illus.). 24p. (J). (gr. 2-5). pap. 8.15 (978-1-4339-5756-7(6), Stevens, Gareth Learning Library) Stevens, Gareth Publishing LLLP.

—Pro Stock Motorcycle Dragsters. 2011. (Fast Lane: Drag Racing Ser.). (Illus.). 24p. (J). (gr. 2-5). pap. 8.15 (978-1-4339-4704-9(8), Stevens, Gareth Learning Library) Stevens, Gareth Publishing LLLP.

AUTOMOBILE RADIOS

see Automobiles—Radio Equipment

AUTOMOBILE RALLIES

Arnold, Ronnie. American Rally Action 2. 2007. (Illus.). 159p. (978-0-9778320-1-9(5)) Speed-Pics Publishing.

Autocar Staff, compiled by. Subaru Impreza Turbo. 2008. (Autocar Collection). (ENG., Illus.). 160p. 39.95 (978-1-84425-497-2(6), 1844254976) Haynes Publishing PLC GBR. Dist: MBI Distribution Services/Quayside Distribution.

Baggott, John. Big Healeys in Competition: Austin-Healy 100, 3000 & Jensen Healey in Race & Rally. 2006. (Crowood Autoclassics Ser.). (ENG., Illus.). 200p. 34.95 (978-1-86126-828-0(9), 1861268289) Crowood Pr., Ltd. GBR. Dist: MBI Distribution Services/Quayside Distribution.

Charters, David A. The Chequered Past: Sports Car Racing & Rallying in Canada, 1951-1991. 2007. (ENG., Illus.). 382p. (978-0-8020-9093-5(1)); pap. (978-0-8020-9394-3(9)) Univ. of Toronto Pr.

Collins, Peter. Lancia 037: The Development & Rally History of a World Champion. 2008. (ENG., Illus.). 192p. 79.95 (978-1-84584-076-1(3), 1845840763) Veloce Publishing Ltd. GBR. Dist: MBI Distribution Services/Quayside Distribution.

Evans, David, ed. Rallycourse 2006-2007: The World's Leading Rally Annual. 2007. (Rallycourse: the World's Leading Rally Annual Ser.). (ENG., Illus.). 248p. 44.95 (978-1-905334-18-6(4), 1905334184) Crash Media Grp. Ltd. GBR. Dist: MBI Distribution Services/Quayside Distribution.

—Rallycourse, 2008-2009. 2009. (ENG., Illus.). 192p. 49.95 (978-1-905334-33-9(8), 1905334338) Crash Media Grp. Ltd. GBR. Dist: MBI Distribution Services/Quayside Distribution.

Holmes, Martin. Pirelli World Rallying 30. 2007. (Illus.). 208p. 67.50 (978-0-9545433-4-1(3)) Holmes, Martin Rallying GBR. Dist: Trans-Atlantic Pubns., Inc.

Joubin, Philippe & Bourret, Jerome. Rally Yearbook 2007-2008: World Rally Championship. 2008. (Rally Yearbook: World Rally Championship Ser.). (ENG., Illus.). 176p. 19.95 (978-2-84707-140-5(7), 2847071407) Chronosports, editeur CHE. Dist: MBI Distribution Services/Quayside Distribution.

Joubin, Philippe & Vennin, Jean-Philippe. Rally Yearbook 2001-2002. rev. ed. (Illus.). 164p. (978-2-940125-84-5(8)) Chronosports, editeur CHE. Dist: Vine Hse. Distribution.

Konemann Staff. Safari Rally. Date not set. (Illus.). 260p. 29.95 (978-3-8290-5027-2(5), 810206) Konemann.

McBride, Simon. Kris Meeke: Intercontinental Rally Challenge Champion. 2010. (ENG., Illus.). 160p. 39.95 (978-1-84584-071-6(2), 1845840712) Veloce Publishing Ltd. GBR. Dist: MBI Distribution Services/Quayside Distribution.

Moreton, Mike. Rallye Sport Fords: The Inside Story. 2007. (ENG., Illus.). 160p. 49.95 (978-1-84584-115-7(8), 1845841158) Veloce Publishing Ltd. GBR. Dist: MBI Distribution Services/Quayside Distribution.

Robson, Graham. Austin Healey 100-6 & 3000. 2007. (Rally Giants Ser.). (ENG., Illus.). 128p. pap. 29.95 (978-1-84584-128-7(X), 184584128X) Veloce Publishing Ltd. GBR. Dist: MBI Distribution Services/Quayside Distribution.

—The Daily Mirror World Cup Rally 40: The World's Toughest Rally in Retrospect. 2010. (ENG., Illus.). 208p. 69.95 (978-1-84584-271-0(5), 1845842715) Veloce Publishing Ltd. GBR. Dist: MBI Distribution Services/Quayside Distribution.

—Peugeot 205 T16. 2007. (Rally Giants Ser.). (ENG., Illus.). 128p. pap. 29.95 (978-1-84584-129-4(8), 1845841298) Veloce Publishing Ltd. GBR. Dist: MBI Distribution Services/Quayside Distribution.

—Toyota Celicia GT-Four. 2009. (Rally Giants Ser.). (ENG., Illus.). 128p. pap. 29.95 (978-1-84584-184-3(0), 1845841840) Veloce Publishing Ltd. GBR. Dist: MBI Distribution Services/Quayside Distribution.

Young, Philip. How to Build a Successful Low-Cost Rally Car. 2009. (SpeedPro Ser.). (ENG., Illus.). 96p. pap. 33.95 (978-1-84584-208-6(1), 1845842081) Veloce Publishing Ltd. GBR. Dist: MBI Distribution Services/Quayside Distribution.

AUTOMOBILE REPAIR

see Automobiles—Maintenance and Repair

AUTOMOBILE SERVICE STATIONS

see Service Stations

AUTOMOBILE SPEED RECORDS

see Automobiles, Racing—Speed Records

AUTOMOBILE STEALING

see Automobile Theft

AUTOMOBILE THEFT

Bender, Michael. The Fast, the Fraudulent & the Fatal: The Dangerous & Dark side of Illegal Street Racing, Drifting & Modified Cars. 2009. 204p. pap. 24.99 (978-1-4343-0146-8(X)) AuthorHouse.

Levy, Marissa Potchak. Opportunity, Environmental Characteristics, & Crime: An Analysis of Auto Theft Patterns. 2008. (Criminal Justice). (Illus.). 230p. 65.00 (978-1-59332-327-1(1)) LFB Scholarly Publishing LLC.

AUTOMOBILE TIRES

see Automobiles—Tires

AUTOMOBILE TOURING

see Automobile Travel

AUTOMOBILE TRAILERS

see Automobiles—Trailers

AUTOMOBILE TRANSMISSION

see Automobiles—Transmission Devices

AUTOMOBILE TRAVEL

see also Games for Travelers

Algeo, Matthew. Harry Truman's Excellent Adventure: The True Story of a Great American Road Trip. (ENG.). 2011. 288p. pap. 16.95 (978-1-56976-707-8(6)) 2009. (Illus.). 272p. 24.95 (978-1-55652-777-7(2)) Chicago Review Pr., Inc.

Asensio, Miguel & Asensio, Valerie. Ride Texas: Motorcycling Ride Guide for the Roads of Texas, 2 vols., vol. 1. 3rd rev. ed. 2007. spiral bd. 20.99 (978-0-9772242-0-3(1)) Motoventure, Inc.

Barzini, Luigi. Peking to Paris. 2007. (Illus.). 416p. per. 24.95 (978-0-9789563-1-8(1)) Demontreville Pr., Inc.

Blackman, Jeffrey E. Out of Gas: Pumps & Pickups from the Golden Age of Gas. 2009. (ENG., Illus.). 96p. 19.95 (978-0-88150-853-6(5), 150853) Countryman Pr.

Bold, Brian. Road Works Drives of A Lifetime. 2007. (Illus.). 242p. pap. 18.08 (978-1-84753-033-2(8)) Lulu Enterprises Inc.

Boye, Alan. Nebraska. 2nd ed. 2007. (ENG., Illus.). 496p. (Orig.). pap. 24.95 (978-0-8032-5968-3(9), Bison Bks.) Univ. of Nebraska Pr.

Brennan, Virginia. Gasoline Gypsies: David & Virginia's Life on the Road. 2009. 132p. pap. 14.95 (978-1-4327-0391-2(9)) Outskirts Pr., Inc.

Browne, Byron. Driving Southwest Texas: On the Road in Big Bend Country. 2010. (978-1-60949-072-0(X)) History Pr., The.

Butko, Brian. Lincoln Highway Companion: A Guide to Americas First Coast-to-Coast Road. 2008. (ENG., Illus.). 192p. pap. 26.95 (978-0-8117-3547-6(8)) Stackpole Bks.

Byron, M. Christine & Wilson, Thomas R. Vintage Views along the West Michigan Pike: From Sand Trails to US-31. 2011. 35.00 (978-1-933926-30-8(9)) Arbutus Pr.

Byron, Robert. Europe in the Looking Glass. 2012. (ENG.). 200p. pap. 16.95 **(978-1-84391-357-3(7))** Hesperus Pr. GBR. Dist: Independent Pubs. Group.

Cable, Ted T. & Cadden, LuAnn M. Driving Across Missouri: A Guide to I-70. 2010. 15.95 (978-0-7006-1697-8(7)) Univ. Pr. of Kansas.

Carson, Dean, et al. Drive Tourism: Trends & Emerging Markets. 2010. (Advances in Tourism Ser.). (ENG., Illus.). 400p. (C). 168.00 (978-0-415-49149-5(5)) Routledge.

Chase, Harold B. Auto-Biography: Recollections of A Pioneer Motorist, 1896-1911. 2011. 186p. 42.95 **(978-1-258-06774-8(9))** Literary Licensing, LLC.

Clarkson, Jeremy. Motorworld. 2006. (ENG., Illus.). 208p. (gr. 12-18). 16.00 (978-0-14-101787-7(2), Penguin Global) Penguin Group (USA) Inc.

Corfield, David. Roads with a View: Scotland's Greatest Views & How to Find Them by Road. 2012. (ENG., Illus.). 144p. 45.00 (978-1-84584-367-0(3), 1845843673) Veloce Publishing Ltd. GBR. Dist: MBI Distribution Services/Quayside Distribution.

Croyle, Wanda F. My First Limo. 2009. 28p. pap. 15.99 (978-1-4415-3466-8(0)) Xlibris Corp.

Davis, Gerry Hempel. Romancing the Roads: A Driving Diva's Firsthand Guide, Volume II West of the Mississippi. 2011. **(978-1-58979-640-9(3))** Taylor Trade Publishing.

—Romancing the Roads Vol. 2: A Driving Diva's Firsthand Guide, West of the Mississippi, Volume 2. 2012. (ENG.). 344p. pap. 18.95 **(978-1-58979-639-3(X))** Taylor Trade Publishing.

Davis, Walt & Davis, Isabel. Exploring the Edges of Texas. 2010. (ENG., Illus.). 304p. 24.95 (978-1-60344-153-7(0)) Texas A&M Univ. Pr.

Dickinson, Janet & Lumsdon, Les. Slow Travel & Tourism. 2010. (Tourism Environment & Development Ser.). (ENG., Illus.). 240p. 130.00 (978-1-84971-112-8(7)) Routledge.

Dobson, Patrick. Seldom Seen: A Journey into the Great Plains. 2009. (ENG.). 296p. 29.95 (978-0-8032-1616-7(5)) Univ. of Nebraska Pr.

Domm, Robert W. Lake Michigan Backroads: Your Guide to Wild & Scenic Adventures in Michigan, Wisconsin, Illinois, & Indiana. 2008. (ENG., Illus.). 160p. pap. 21.99 (978-0-7603-2980-1(X), 076032980X, Voyageur Pr) MBI Publishing Co. LLC.

Douglass, Frazier. Lightweight Camping for Motorcycle Travel: Revised Edition. 2009. 348p. 33.95 (978-1-4401-7647-0(7)); pap. 23.95 (978-1-4401-7645-6(0)) iUniverse, Inc.

Dubreil, Adriane. Crossing the Sands. 2007. (Illus.). 193p. 65.00 (978-1-85443-222-3(2)) Dalton Watson Fine Bks.

Dunmire, William W. New Mexico's Living Landscapes. 2012. (ENG., Illus.). 136p. pap. 29.95 (978-0-89013-543-3(6)) Museum of New Mexico Pr.

Eddy, Arthur Jerome. Two Thousand Miles on an Automobile. (Travel in America Ser.). (ENG.). 336p. 2007. 49.95 (978-1-4290-0536-4(X)) 2007. per. 24.95 (978-1-4290-0537-1(8)) 2006. per. 19.95 (978-1-55709-924-2(3)) Applewood Bks.

—Two Thousand Miles on an Automobile. 2008. 244p. 24.99 (978-0-554-39737-5(4)); 27.99 (978-0-554-30434-2(1)) BiblioBazaar.

—Two Thousand Miles on an Automobile. 2007. 216p. per. (978-1-4065-1630-2(9)) Dodo Pr.

—Two Thousand Miles on an Automobile. 2007. (ENG.). 164p. per. (978-1-4068-5002-4(0)) Echo Library.

Forster, Matt. Michigan: Drives, Day Trips & Weekend Excursions. 2009. (Backroads & Byways Ser.). (ENG., Illus.). 256p. pap. 18.95 (978-0-88150-831-4(4), 150831) Countryman Pr.

Franklin, Paul M. & Mikula, Nancy Joyce. Backroads of Florida: Your Guide to Great Day Trips & Weekend Getaways. 2009. (ENG., Illus.). 160p. pap. 21.99 (978-0-7603-3226-9(6), 0760332266, Voyageur Pr) MBI Publishing Co. LLC.

Ginnodo, Bill & Ginnodo, Celia. Seven Perfect Days in Arizona: A Guided Driving Tour. 2009. (978-0-9656587-4-4(0)) Pride Publications, Inc.

Godfrey, Jonnie & Karslake, Elizabeth. Eastern Crete. 4th ed. (Illus.). 136p. pap. 14.95 (978-1-85691-197-9(7)) Hunter Publishing, Inc.

Gough, Laurie. Kiss the Sunset Pig: An American Road Trip with Exotic Detours. 2008. (ENG.). 344p. (gr. 12-18). 20.00 (978-0-14-305615-7(8), Penguin Global) Penguin Group (USA) Inc.

Green, Stewart M. Scenic Driving Arizona. 3rd ed. 2009. (Scenic Driving Ser.). (ENG., Illus.). 224p. pap. 15.95 (978-0-7627-5054-2(5), Falcon Guides) Globe Pequot Pr., The.

—Scenic Driving New England. 2nd ed. 2006. (Scenic Driving Ser.). (ENG., Illus.). 328p. per. 16.95 (978-0-7627-4060-4(4), Falcon Guides) Globe Pequot Pr., The.

Hale, Louis C. We Discover the Old Dominion. (Illus.). 374p. reprint ed. lib. bdg. 98.00 (978-0-7222-4667-2(6)) Library Reprints, Inc.

Hawk, Diane. Touring the Old Redwood Highway - Del Norte County. 2006. (Illus.). 150p. per. 20.95 (978-0-9672162-5-6(7)) Hawk Mountaintop Publishing.

Helm, Michael, compiled by. Exploring Colorado Highways: Trip Trivia. 2007. pap. 19.95 (978-0-9777301-0-0(7)) Travel Organization Network Exchange.

—Exploring Illinois Highways: Trip Trivia. 2007. pap. 19.95 (978-0-9744358-4-8(8)) Travel Organization Network Exchange.

—Exploring Indiana Highways: Trip Trivia. 2007. pap. 19.95 (978-0-9744358-3-1(X)) Travel Organization Network Exchange.

—Exploring Iowa Highways: Trip Trivia. 2007. pap. 19.95 (978-0-9744358-5-5(6)) Travel Organization Network Exchange.

—Exploring Kansas Highways: Trip Trivia. 2007. pap. 19.95 (978-0-9744358-6-6(0)) Travel Organization Network Exchange.

—Exploring Missouri Highways: Trip Trivia. 2007. pap. 19.95 (978-0-9744358-6-2(4)) Travel Organization Network Exchange.

—Exploring Nebraska Highways: Trip Trivia. 2007. pap. 19.95 (978-0-9744358-7-9(2)) Travel Organization Network Exchange.

—Exploring Oklahoma Highways: Trip Trivia. 2007. pap. 19.95 (978-0-9777301-2-4(3)) Travel Organization Network Exchange.

Hilton, Kathryn M. The Happy Traveler: Cross Country Trips. 2007. 152p. per. 20.99 (978-1-4257-6188-2(7)) Xlibris Corp.

Howard, Lynna. Backcountry Roads — Idaho. 2008. (ENG., Illus.). 240p. pap. 27.95 (978-0-87004-459-5(1)) Caxton Pr.

Hvattum, Mari, et al. Routes Roads & Landscapes. 2011. (Illus.). 266p. 124.95 (978-1-4094-0820-8(5)) Ashgate Publishing Co.

Ihlenfeld, Dave. Dog Days: A Year in the Oscar Mayer Weinermobile. 2011. (ENG., Illus.). 232p. pap. 14.95 (978-1-4027-7610-6(1)) Union Square Pr.

Ihlenfeld, Dave. Dog Days: A Year in the Oscar Mayer Wienermobile. 2011. (ENG., Illus.). 232p. pap. 14.95 (978-1-4027-9803-0(2)) Sterling Publishing Co., Inc.

Jackson, Gram & Reader's Digest Editors. The Most Scenic Drives in America: 120 Spectacular Road Trips. rev. ed. 2012. (ENG.). 400p. (gr. 12). 35.00 (978-1-60652-359-2(9)) Reader's Digest Assn., Inc., The.

Jakle, John A. & Sculle, Keith A. Motoring: The Highway Experience in America. 2009. (ENG., Illus.). 288p. pap. 24.95 (978-0-8203-3415-8(4)) Univ. of Georgia Pr.

Jenner, Paul & Smith, Christine. Landscapes of the Pyrenees. 3rd ed. (Illus.). 136p. 14.95 (978-1-85691-211-2(6)) Sunflower Bks. (UK) GBR. Dist: Hunter Publishing, Inc.

Knowles, Drew. Route 66 Quick Reference Encyclopedia. 2008. (ENG., Illus.). 224p. pap. 12.95 (978-1-59580-034-3(4), 1282840) Santa Monica Pr.

Krug, Larry. The 1924 Coolidge-Dawes Lincoln Tour. 2007. (Illus.). 160p. pap. 29.95 (978-0-7643-2763-6(1)) Schiffer Publishing, Ltd.

Lindahl, Larry, photos by. Arizona Kicks on Route 66. 2012. pap. (978-1-933855-76-9(2), Rio Nuevo Pubs.) Rio Nuevo Pubs.

Llewellin, Phil. The Road to Muckle Flugga: Great Drives in Five Continents. 2011. (ENG., Illus.). 384p. pap. 15.95 (978-0-85733-003-1(9), 0857330039) Haynes Publishing PLC GBR. Dist: MBI Distribution Services/Quayside Distribution.

Lockhart, Douglas. Malta, Gozo & Comino: Car Tours & Walks. 4th ed. (Illus.). 136p. pap. 14.99 (978-1-85691-246-4(9)) Sunflower Bks. (UK) GBR. Dist: Hunter Publishing, Inc.

Lowry, Amy Gillis & Tucker Parks, Abbie. North Georgia's Dixie Highway. 2007. (Images of America Ser.). (ENG., Illus.). 128p. per. 21.99 (978-0-7385-4431-1(0)) Arcadia Publishing.

Lumsdon, Les & Dickinson, Janet. Slow Travel & Tourism. 2010. (Tourism Environment & Development Ser.). (ENG., Illus.). 240p. pap. 39.95 (978-1-84971-113-5(5)) Routledge.

Marks, Christine. Interstate 75 & the 401: A Traveler's Guide Between Toronto & Miami. 4th ed. 2009. (ENG., Illus.). 240p. spiral bd. 24.95 (978-1-55046-526-6(0)) Boston Mills Pr. CAN. Dist: Firefly Bks., Ltd.

Martin, Paul. Travels with Bertha: Two Years Travelling Around Australia in a 1978 Ford Falcon. 2012. (ENG.). 256p. pap. 29.95 (978-1-907593-42-0(X)) Liberties Pr. IRL. Dist: Dufour Editions, Inc.

Massing, Conni L. Roadtripping: On the Move with the Buffalo Gals, 1 vol. 2010. (ENG., Illus.). 264p. pap. (978-1-897142-47-9(1)) Brindle & Glass Publishing.

McBrien, Judith P. Pocket Guide to Los Angeles Architecture. 2009. (Pocket Guides). (ENG., Illus.). 143p. pap. 24.95 (978-0-393-73190-3(1), 73190) Norton, W. W. & Co., Inc.

McCarthy, Kevin M. Caloosahatchee River Guidebook. 2012. (ENG.). 256p. pap. 14.95 (978-1-56164-507-7(9)) Pineapple Pr., Inc.

Melville, Greg. Greasy Rider: Two Dudes, One Fry-Oil-Powered Car, & a Cross-Country Search for a Greener Future. 2008. (ENG.). 257p. pap. 15.95 (978-1-56512-595-7(9), 1565125959) Algonquin Bks. of Chapel Hill.

Milepost Editors. The Milepost: Legendary Alaska Trip Planner & Alaska Travel Guide to the Highways, Roads, Ferries, Lodgings, Recreation, Sightseeing Attractions & Services along the Alaska Highway to & Within Alaska, Including Alberta, British Columbia, Northwest Territories & the Yukon. 63rd ed. 2011. 784p. pap. 29.95 (978-1-892154-28-6(5)) Milepost, The.

Misuraca, Karen. Backroads of the California Coast: Your Guide to Scenic Getaways & Adventures. 2009. (ENG., Illus.). 256p. pap. 21.99 (978-0-7603-3343-3(2), 0760333432, Voyageur Pr) MBI Publishing Co. LLC.

MONACO BOOKS, compiled by. Discover France, 1 vol. 2011. (ENG., Illus.). 464p. pap. 29.95 (978-3-89944-635-7(6), Monaco Bks.) Verlag Wolfgang Kunth GmbH & Co. KG DEU. Dist: Innovative Logistics.

Mueller, Michael. Mustang: An American Classic. 2009. (ENG., Illus.). 288p. 50.00 (978-0-7893-1885-5(7)) Universe Publishing.

Parent, Laurence. Scenic Driving North Carolina. 2nd ed. 2006. (Scenic Driving Ser.). (ENG., Illus.). 240p. per. 15.95 (978-0-7627-4061-1(2), Falcon Guides) Globe Pequot Pr., The.

Petrov, Evgeny, et al. Ilf & Petrov's American Road Trip: The 1935 Travelogue of Two Soviet Writers. Wolf, Erika, ed. Fisher, Anne O., tr. from RUS. 2006. (ENG., Illus.). 176p. 24.95 (978-1-56898-600-5(9)) Princeton Architectural Pr.

Pierce, Wendi & Steed, Rick. Historic Day Trips from Dallas/Fort Worth. 2010. (ENG., Illus.). 176p. pap. 19.99 (978-1-59629-081-5(1)) History Pr., The.

Post, Emily. By Motor to the Golden Gate. 2009. 392p. 33.99 (978-1-116-67457-6(2)); 38.99 (978-1-116-67456-9(4)); pap. 33.75 (978-1-116-67458-3(0)) BiblioBazaar.

—By Motor to the Golden Gate. 2008. 390p. 48.95 (978-0-548-99154-1(5)) 2007. (ENG.). 392p. per. 33.95 (978-0-548-65543-6(X)) Kessinger Publishing, LLC.

—By Motor to the Golden Gate. 2007. (ENG.). 388p. per. (978-1-4067-7982-0(2)) Read Bks.

Progress, Michael Davis & Stephen Moore. 2006. per. 24.95 (978-0-9771696-2-7(6)) Grand Central Pr.

Rea, Amy C. Backroads & Byways of Minnesota: Drives, Day Trips & Weekend Excursions. 2011. (Backroads & Byways Ser.). (ENG.). 256p. pap. 18.95 (978-0-88150-932-8(9), 150932) Countryman Pr.

Reader's Digest Association Staff, contrib. by. The Most Scenic Drives in America: 120 Spectacular Road Trips. 2012. (978-1-60652-389-6(9)); (978-1-60652-390-2(2)) Reader's Digest Assn., Inc., The.

Revolinski, Kevin. Backroads & Byways of Wisconsin: Drives, Day Trips & Weekend Excursions. 2009. (Backroads & Byways Ser.). (ENG., Illus.). 256p. pap. 18.95 (978-0-88150-816-1(0), 150816) Countryman Pr.

Richards, Steve. Driving a Big Truck, the Adventure Continues from a Different Perspective. 2008. 243p. pap. 14.95 (978-1-4327-3844-0(5)) Outskirts Pr., Inc.

Rodriquez, JoAnn. Legallay Driving the 50 States of the USA — CA: All the information you need to make your California car trip safe & hassle Free! 2007. 2p. (YA). pap. 9.95 (978-0-9800246-0-9(9)) Lucre Publishing.

Roth, Anna. West Coast Road Eats: The Best Road Food from San Diego to the Canadian Border. 2011. (ENG., Illus.). 368p. pap. 22.95 (978-1-57061-690-7(6)) Sasquatch Bks.

Schuffert, Robert. Scenic Tennessee: A Travel Guide to Tennessee's Hidden Natural Treasures. 2008. (ENG., Illus.). 216p. spiral bd. 34.99 (978-0-9744781-2-8(1)) Schuffert, Robert Studios.

Scott, Chris. Overlanders' Handbook: Worldwide Route & Planning Guide - Car, 4wd, Van, Truck. 2011. (ENG., Illus.). 672p. 39.95 (978-1-905864-07-2(8)) Trailblazer Pubns. GBR. Dist: Globe Pequot Pr., The.

Scotto, Emilio. The Longest Ride: My Ten-Year 500,000 Mile Motorcycle Journey. rev. ed. 2007. (ENG., Illus.). 224p. 34.95 (978-0-7603-2632-9(0), 0760326320, Motorbooks) MBI Publishing Co. LLC.

Sloman, Lynn. Car Sick: Solutions for Our Car-Addicted Culture. 2006. (ENG., Illus.). 192p. per. 20.00 (978-1-903998-76-2(X)) Green Bks. GBR. Dist: Chelsea Green Publishing.

Smith, Laura Massino. Tour of Frank Gehry & Other L. A. Architecture. 2007. (Illus.). 112p. pap. 14.95 (978-0-7643-2715-5(1)) Schiffer Publishing, Ltd.

Sonderman, Joe. Route 66 in Arizona. 2010. (Images of America Ser.). (ENG., Illus.). 128p. pap. 21.99 (978-0-7385-7942-9(4)) Arcadia Publishing.

Strand, Ginger Gail. Killer on the Road: Violence & the American Interstate. 2012. (ENG., Illus.). 222p. 25.00 (978-0-292-72637-6(6)) Univ. of Texas Pr.

Sutcliffe, Andrea. Touring the Shenandoah Valley Backroads. 2nd ed. 2010. (Illus.). xii, 286p. (978-0-89587-393-4(1)) Blair, John F. Pub.

The Clark Group & Back Home In Kentucky, compiled by. Kentucky One Tank Trips V2 (Hazard Cover) 2007. 107p. pap. 9.95 (978-1-883589-83-7(5)) Clark Publishing, Inc.

Time Out Guides Staff. Time Out Flight Free Europe: Great Breaks by Rail, Road & Sea. 2008. (Time Out Guides). (ENG., Illus.). 336p. pap. 22.95 (978-1-84670-087-3(6)) Time Out Guides Ltd. GBR. Dist: Perseus-PGW.

Travel, Michelin. Quebec. 7th rev. ed. 2009. (Green Guide Ser.). (ENG., Illus.). 448p. pap. 21.99 (978-1-906261-44-3(X)) Michelin Travel & Lifestyle.

Wallis, Michael. Lincoln Highway. 2007. 39.95 (978-0-7930-5938-6(0)) Norton, W. W. & Co., Inc.

—The Lincoln Highway: Coast to Coast from Times Square to the Golden Gate. 2011. (ENG., Illus.). 304p. pap. 19.95 (978-0-393-34130-0(5), 34130) Norton, W. W. & Co., Inc.

Walsh, Dan. Endless Horizon: A Very Messy Motorcycle Journey Around the World. 2009. (ENG., Illus.). 384p. 28.00 (978-0-7603-3604-5(0), 0760336040, Motorbooks) MBI Publishing Co. LLC.

Weaver, Alistair. A Drive on the Wild Side. 2007. (ENG., Illus.). 176p. 59.95 (978-1-84584-100-3(X), 184584100X) Veloce Publishing Ltd. GBR. Dist: MBI Distribution Services/Quayside Distribution.

Weeks, Michael. The Complete Civil War Road Trip Guide: More than 400 Civil War Sites, from Antietam to Zagonyi's Charge. 2009. (ENG., Illus.). 504p. pap. 19.95 (978-0-88150-860-4(8), 150860) Countryman Pr.

Williamson, Michael S., photos by. The Lincoln Highway: Coast to Coast from Times Square to the Golden Gate. 2007. (ENG., Illus.). 304p. 39.95 (978-0-393-05938-0(3), 5938) Norton, W. W. & Co., Inc.

Woolley, Ivan M. Off to Mt Hood: An Autobiography of the Old Road. 2011. 110p. 39.95 (978-1-258-10080-3(0)) Literary Licensing, LLC.

Youngblood, Wayne. The Open Road. 2008. (Way We Were Ser.). 160p. (978-0-7858-2443-5(X), Chartwell) Book Sales, Inc.

Zimmerman, Karla & Zimmerman. Chicago: Day Trips, Weekend Getaways, Easy Planning, Quick Access, Best Places to Visit. 2009. (Great Escapes Ser.). (ENG., Illus.). 172p. pap. 16.95 (978-0-88150-844-4(6), 150844) Countryman Pr.

AUTOMOBILE TRAVEL—GUIDEBOOKS

Adams, Kevin. Backroads of North Carolina: Your Guide to Great Day Trips & Weekend Getaways. 2009. (ENG., Illus.). 160p. pap. 21.99 (978-0-7603-2592-6(8), 0760325928, Voyageur Pr) MBI Publishing Co. LLC.

American Automobile Association Staff. Northeastern Tour Book. (Illus.). 656p. reprint ed. lib. bdg. 128.00 (978-0-7222-0564-8(3)) Library Reprints, Inc.

—Southeastern Tour Book. (Illus.). 408p. reprint ed. lib. bdg. 98.00 (978-0-7222-0565-5(1)) Library Reprints, Inc.

Annino, Jan Godown. Scenic Driving Florida: Your Indispensable Highway Companion. 3rd ed. 2010. (Scenic Driving Ser.). (ENG., Illus.). 240p. pap. 16.95 (978-0-7627-5055-9(3)) Globe Pequot Pr., The.

Arrow Maps, creator. New England Road Atlas: Connecticut, Massachusetts, Rhode Island, Maine, New Hampshire, Vermont. 2007. (American Map Ser.). 80p. 10.95 (978-1-55751-321-2(X)) Arrow Map, Inc.

Atkins, Leslie. Backroads & Byways of Maryland: Drives, Day Trips & Weekend Excursions. 2011. (Backroads & Byways Ser.). (ENG.). 224p. pap. 18.95 (978-0-88150-926-7(4), 150926) Countryman Pr.

Axline, Jon & Bradshaw, Glenda Clay. Montana's Historical Highway Markers, 4th. 2008. (ENG., Illus.). 224p. pap. 13.95 (978-0-9759196-4-4(4)) Montana Historical Society Pr.

Baird, David. Back Roads of Southern Spain: 25 Great Car Trips Around Andalusia. 2006. (SPA., Illus.). 287p. pap. 28.95 (978-84-89954-23-6(2)) Academy Chicago Pubs., Ltd.

Balaz, Christine & Balaz, Karen. Backroads & Byways of Utah: Drives, Day Trips & Weekend Excursions. 2011. (Backroads & Byways Ser.). (ENG., Illus.). 232p. pap. 18.95 (978-0-88150-906-9(X), 150906) Countryman Pr.

Beckius, Kim Knox. Backroads of New England: Your Guide to Scenic Getaways & Adventures. 2nd ed. 2012. (ENG., Illus.). 256p. pap. 22.99 (978-0-7603-4239-8(3), 0760342393, Voyageur Pr) MBI Publishing Co. LLC.

Beckius, Kim Knox. Backroads of New York: Your Guide to New York's Most Scenic Backroad Adventures. 2007. (Backroads Of ... Ser.). (ENG., Illus.). 160p. pap. 21.95 (978-0-7603-2955-9(9), 0760329559, Voyageur Pr) MBI Publishing Co. LLC.

Blond, Becca, et al. Arizona, New Mexico & the Grand Canyon Trips. 2009. (Regional Guide Ser.). (ENG., Illus.). 352p. pap. 19.99 (978-1-74179-729-9(2)) Lonely Planet Pubns.

Bonney, Lorraine G. The Big Thicket Guidebook: Exploring the Backroads & History of Southeast Texas. Gunter, Pete A. Y. & Johnston, Maxine, eds. 2011. (Temple Big Thicket Ser.). (Illus.). 848p. 29.95 (978-1-57441-318-2(X)) Univ. of North Texas Pr.

Bostwick, Mark. The Four-Wheeler's Companion: The Off-Road Guide to Southwestern BC. 3rd rev. ed. (ENG., Illus.). 206p. pap. 24.95 (978-1-55017-118-1(6)) Harbour Publishing Co., Ltd. CAN. Dist: Ingram Pub. Services.

British Auto Association. Frommer's 25 Great Drives in France. 9th ed. 2011. (Best Loved Driving Tours Ser.). (ENG.). 208p. pap. 19.99 (978-0-470-90448-0(8), Frommers) Wiley, John & Sons, Inc.

British Auto Association & Duncan, Paul. Frommer's 25 Great Drives in Italy. 10th ed. 2011. (Best Loved Driving Tours Ser.). (ENG.). 208p. pap. 19.99 (978-0-470-90447-3(X), Frommers) Wiley, John & Sons, Inc.

British Auto Association & Williams, David. Frommer's 25 Great Drives in Scotland. 2nd ed. 2011. (Best Loved Driving Tours Ser.). (ENG.). 208p. pap. 19.99 (978-0-470-90449-7(6), Frommers) Wiley, John & Sons, Inc.

British Auto Association, et al. Frommer's 23 Great Drives in New England. 8th ed. 2011. (Best Loved Driving Tours Ser.). (ENG.). 208p. pap. 19.99 (978-0-470-90450-3(X), Frommers) Wiley, John & Sons, Inc.

Brown, Amy K. Backroads & Byways of Texas: Drives, Day Trips & Weekend Excursions. 2008. (Backroads & Byways Ser.). (ENG., Illus.). 256p. pap. 16.95 (978-0-88150-786-7(5), 150786) Countryman Pr.

Brown, Tricia. The World-Famous Alaska Highway: A Guide to the Alcan & Other Wilderness Roads of the North. 4th ed. 2011. (ENG.). 288p. pap. 22.95 (978-1-55591-749-4(6)) Fulcrum Publishing.

Browning, Peter. Exploring the Back Roads: 28 Day Trips in the Greater Bay Area. 2006. (Illus.). 125p. per. 12.95 (978-0-944220-21-4(5)) Great West Bks.

Bryan, Liz. Country Roads of Alberta: Exploring the Routes Less Travelled, 1 vol. 2007. (ENG., Illus.). 160p. pap. (978-1-894974-29-5(8)) Heritage Hse.

—Country Roads of British Columbia: Exploring the Interior, 1 vol. rev. ed. 2008. (ENG., Illus.). 192p. pap. (978-1-894974-43-1(3)) Heritage Hse.

Campanile, Robert. Mohawk Trail. 2007. (Postcard History Ser.). (ENG., Illus.). 128p. per. 19.99 (978-0-7385-5007-7(8)) Arcadia Publishing.

Church, Mike & Church, Terri. Camping Mexico's Baja: Explore Baja & Puerto Peñasco with Your RV or Tent. 4th ed. 2008. (Traveler's Guide Ser.). (ENG., Illus.). 256p. pap. 16.95 (978-0-9749471-8-1(0)) Rolling Homes Pr.

Clark, Gary. Enjoying Big Bend National Park: A Friendly Guide to Adventures for Everyone. 2009. (W.L. Moody, Jr., Natural History Ser.: No. 41). (ENG., Illus.). 128p. pap. 17.95 (978-1-60344-101-8(8)) Texas A&M Univ. Pr.

Clark, Gregor, et al. New England Trips. 2009. (Regional Guide Ser.). (ENG., Illus.). 360p. pap. 19.99 (978-1-74179-728-2(4)) Lonely Planet Pubns.

Corfield, David. Roads with a View: England's Greatest Views & How to Find Them by Road. 2010. (ENG., Illus.). 144p. 45.00 (978-1-84584-350-2(9), 1845843509) Veloce Publishing Ltd. GBR. Dist: MBI Distribution Services/Quayside Distribution.

Couper, Jim. The Long & Winding Road: Discovering the Pleasures & Treasures of Highway 97, 1 vol. 2010. (ENG., Illus.). 208p. per. (978-1-894974-12-7(3)) Heritage Hse.

Cullen, Michael. Southern Peloponnese. 2nd ed. (Illus.). 136p. pap. 15.99 (978-1-85691-310-2(4)) Hunter Publishing, Inc.

Dahlgren, Dorothy & Kincaid, Simone. Roads Less Traveled Through the Coeur D'Alenes: Historical Driving Tours of Benewah, Kootenai & Shoshone Counties. 2007. (Illus.). 280p. per. 12.95 (978-0-9723356-7-6(6)) Museum of North Idaho.

Dalby, Ron. Guide to the Alaska Highway. 2nd ed. 2011. (ENG., Illus.). 288p. pap. 19.95 (978-0-89732-926-2(0)) Menasha Ridge Pr., Inc.

D'Arcy, David. Civil War Tours of the Low Country: Beaufort, Hilton Head, & Bluffton, South Carolina. 2008. (Illus.). 144p. pap. 16.95 (978-0-7643-2790-2(9)) Schiffer Publishing, Ltd.

Davis, Gerry. Romancing the Roads: A Driving Diva's Firsthand Guide, Volume I: East of the Mississippi. 2011. (978-1-58979-620-1(9)) Taylor Trade Publishing.

Davis, Gerry Hempel. Romancing the Roads Vol. 1: Driving Diva's Firsthand Guide - East of the Mississippi. 2011. (ENG.). 416p. pap. 18.95 (978-1-58979-619-5(5)) Taylor Trade Publishing.

Dishner, Jackie, et al. Arizona: Drives, Day Trips & Weekend Excursions. 2009. (Backroads & Byways Ser.). (ENG., Illus.). 216p. pap. 17.95 (978-0-88150-815-4(2), 150815) Countryman Pr.

Eaton, Diane & Eaton, Allison. Exploring the BC Coast by Car. 2nd unabr. rev. ed. 2008. (ENG., Illus.). 400p. pap. 24.95 (978-1-55017-415-1(0)) Harbour Publishing Co., Ltd. CAN. Dist: Ingram Pub. Services.

Ernst, Chloe. Scenic Driving Atlantic Canada: Nova Scotia, New Brunswick, Prince Edward Island, Newfoundland, & Labrador. 2011. (Scenic Driving Ser.). (ENG., Illus.). 264p. pap. 15.95 (978-0-7627-6481-5(3)) Globe Pequot Pr., The.

Federal Writers' Project of the Works Progress Administration for the State of New Jersey Staff, contrib. by. New Jersey, a Guide to Its Present & Past. 2007. (978-1-60354-029-2(6)) U. S. History Publishers.

Freeman, Rich & Freeman, Sue. Take Your Bike: Family Rides in New York's Finger Lakes Region. 2nd rev. ed. 2006. (Illus.). 224p. per. 19.95 (978-1-930480-22-3(9)) Footprint Pr., Inc.

A

Fugate, Francis L. & Fugate, Roberta B. Roadside History of Oklahoma. (Roadside History Ser.). (Illus.). 472p. pap. 20.00 *(978-0-87842-272-2(2),* 259) Mountain Pr. Publishing Co., Inc.

Fuller, Steven & Schmidt, Jeremy. National Geographic Yellowstone & Grand Teton National Parks Road Guide: The Essential Guide for Motorists. 2nd rev. ed. 2010. (ENG., Illus.). 96p. pap. 9.95 *(978-1-4262-0597-2(X),* National Geographic) National Geographic Society.

Gibbons, Bob & Pritchard-Jones, Siân. Africa Overland, 5th: 4x4, Motorbike, Bicycle, Truck. 5th rev. ed. 2009. (ENG., Illus.). 320p. pap. 25.99 *(978-1-84162-283-5(4))* Bradt Travel Guides GBR. Dist: Globe Pequot Pr., The.

Gibson, John. Maine's Most Scenic Roads, 2nd Edition: 25 Routes off the Beaten Path. 2nd ed. 2011. (ENG.). 192p. pap. 14.95 *(978-0-89272-942-5(2))* Down East Bks.

Ginnodo, Bill & Ginnodo, Celia. Seven Perfect Days in Colorado: A Guided Driving Tour. 2nd ed. 2007. *(978-0-9656587-3-7(2))* Pride Publications, Inc.

—Seven Perfect Days in Northern California: A Guided Driving Tour. 2007. (Illus.). 158p. *(978-0-9656587-2-0(4))* Pride Publications, Inc.

Green, Stewart M. Scenic Driving Colorado. 3rd ed. 2008. (Scenic Driving Ser.). (ENG., Illus.). 320p. pap. 15.95 *(978-0-7627-4791-7(9),* Falcon Guides) Globe Pequot Pr., The.

Greene, Donald. Americas Overland - the Driving Handbook. 2008. 368p. pap. 29.95 *(978-0-557-00712-7(7))* Lulu Enterprises Inc.

Gregston, Brent. Bavaria & the Austrian Tyrol. 3rd ed. 2009. (Drive Around - Thomas Cook Ser.). (ENG., Illus.). 288p. pap. 26.95 *(978-1-84157-999-3(8))* Cook, Thomas Publishing GBR. Dist: Globe Pequot Pr., The.

Hammond, Karen T. Backroads & Byways of New England: Drives, Day Trips & Weekend Excursions. 2011. (Backroads & Byways Ser.). (ENG.). 240p. pap. 18.95 *(978-0-88150-901-4(9),* 150901) Countryman Pr.

Harvard Student Agencies, Inc. Let's Go Roadtripping USA: The Student Travel Guide. 2010. (Let's Go Ser.). (ENG., Illus.). 1024p. pap. 24.95 *(978-1-59880-321-1(2),* Let's Go) Avalon Travel Publishing.

Harvey, Michael. TopGear Top Drives: Road Trips of a Lifetime in the World's Most Dramatic Locations. 2009. (ENG., Illus.). 224p. pap. 24.95 *(978-1-84607-464-6(9))* BBC Worldwide GBR. Dist: Independent Pubs. Group.

Hasenwinkel Road Travel Guide: Drive the Texas Hill Country by way of Hasenwinkel Road. 2nd enl. exp. ed. 2007. (Illus.). 24p. pap. 20.00 incl. audio compact disk *(978-0-9676931-7-0(9))* Skyline Ranch Pr.

Hawk, Diane. Touring the Old Redwood Highway: Humboldt County: 2ed Printing Revised. 2007. (Illus.). 199p. per. 23.95 *(978-0-9672162-8-7(1))* Hawk Mountaintop Publishing.

Hermann Sons Road Travel Guide: Driving Trip in the Texas Hill Country y way of Hermann Sons Road. 2007. (Illus.). 28p. pap. 20.00 incl. audio compact disk *(978-0-9676931-6-3(0))* Skyline Ranch Pr.

Hinckley, Jim. Route 66 Backroads: Your Guide to Scenic Side Trips & Adventures from the Mother Road. 2008. (ENG., Illus.). 208p. pap. 24.99 *(978-0-7603-2817-0(X),* 076032817X, Voyageur Pr) MBI Publishing Co. LLC.

Hoffman, James L. Day Trips from Raleigh-Durham: Getaway Ideas for the Local Traveler. 4th ed. 2011. (Day Trips Ser.). (ENG., Illus.). 256p. pap. 14.95 *(978-0-7627-6007-7(9))* Globe Pequot Pr., The.

Hoobler, James A. A Guide to Historic Nashville, Tennessee. 2008. (Illus.). 168p. pap. 19.99 *(978-1-59629-404-2(3))* History Pr., The.

Huegel, Tony. California Desert Byways: 68 of California's Best Backcountry Drives. 3rd rev. ed. 2006. (ENG.). 200p. pap. 18.95 *(978-0-89997-413-2(9))* Wilderness Pr.

—Sierra Nevada Byways: 51 of the Sierra Nevada's Best Backcountry Drives. 3rd ed. 2008. (ENG., Illus.). 184p. pap. 18.95 *(978-0-89997-473-6(2))* Wilderness Pr.

—Utah Byways: 65 of Utah's Best Backcountry Drives. 3rd rev. ed. 2006. (ENG.). 224p. pap. 18.95 *(978-0-89997-424-8(4))* Wilderness Pr.

Hunt, Lindsay & Thomas Cook Publishing Staff. England & Wales: Your Guide to Great Drives. Top 25 Tours. 3rd ed. 2009. (Drive Around - Thomas Cook Ser.). (ENG., Illus.). 288p. pap. 26.95 *(978-1-84848-065-0(2))* Cook, Thomas Publishing GBR. Dist: Globe Pequot Pr., The.

Janssen, Peter. Touring the Natural Wonders of New Zealand: Over 45 Spectacular Routes. 2009. (Illus.). 176p. *(978-1-86966-234-9(2))* New Holland Pubs. (NZ) Ltd.

Jenks, Jim. A Guide to Historic Bozeman. 4th ed. 2007. (Montana Mainstreets Ser.). (ENG., Illus.). 176p. per. 12.95 *(978-0-9721522-3-5(7))* Montana Historical Society Pr.

Jensen, Jamie. Road Trip USA: Cross-Country Adventures on America's Two-Lane Highways. 5th ed. 2009. (Road Trip USA Ser.). (ENG.). 928p. pap. 29.95 *(978-1-59880-101-9(5))* Westview Pr.

—Road Trip USA Appalachian Trail. 2010. (Road Trip USA Ser.). (ENG.). 128p. pap. 9.95 *(978-1-59880-579-6(7))* Avalon Travel Publishing.

—Road Trip USA Great River Road. 2010. (Road Trip USA Ser.). (ENG.). 128p. pap. 9.95 *(978-1-59880-581-9(9))* Avalon Travel Publishing.

—Road Trip USA Route 66. 2009. (Road Trip USA Ser.). (ENG.). 128p. pap. 9.95 *(978-1-59880-205-4(4))* Avalon Travel Publishing.

Johnson, Paul Eric. Backroads of New Jersey: Your Guide to New Jersey's Most Scenic Backroad Adventures. rev. ed. 2007. (Backroads Of ... Ser.). (ENG., Illus.). 160p. pap. 21.95 *(978-0-7603-2954-2(0),* 0760329540, Voyageur Pr) MBI Publishing Co. LLC.

Karras, Christy. Scenic Driving Utah, 3rd. 2011. (Scenic Driving Ser.). (ENG., Illus.). 288p. pap. 15.95 *(978-0-7627-6482-2(1))* Globe Pequot Pr., The.

Karras, Christy & Zusy, Stephen. Motorcycle Touring in the Pacific Northwest: The Region's Best Rides. 2010. (Motorcycle Touring Ser.). (ENG., Illus.). 400p. pap. 18.95 *(978-0-7627-5727-5(2))* Globe Pequot Pr., The.

Keats, Robert. The Border Guide: A Guide to Living, Working, & Investing in the United States. 10th ed. 2009. (ENG.). 368p. pap. 23.95 *(978-1-55180-855-0(2))* Self-Counsel Pr., Inc. CAN. Dist: National Bk. Network.

Kentucky One Tank Trips V2. 2007. 112p. pap. 9.95 *(978-1-883589-82-0(7))* Clark Publishing, Inc.

King, Mona. Frommer's 25 Great Drives in Spain. 9th ed. 2010. (Best Loved Driving Tours Ser.). (ENG., Illus.). pap. 19.99 *(978-0-470-56041-9(X),* Frommers) Wiley, John & Sons, Inc.

Knowles, Drew. Route 66 Adventure Handbook: Turbocharged Fourth Edition. 4th ed. 2011. (ENG., Illus.). 432p. pap. 19.95 *(978-1-59580-059-6(X))* Santa Monica Pr.

Knox Beckius, Kim. The New England Coast: The Most Spectacular Sights & Destinations. 2008. (ENG., Illus.). 160p. 30.00 *(978-0-7603-3064-7(6),* 0760330646, Voyageur Pr) MBI Publishing Co. LLC.

Lambert, Anthony. Switzerland Without a Car. 4th ed. 2009. (ENG., Illus.). 432p. pap. 22.99 *(978-1-84162-281-1(8))* Bradt Travel Guides GBR. Dist: Globe Pequot Pr., The.

Lang, Sandy, et al. Scenic Driving South Carolina. 2nd ed. 2011. (Scenic Driving Ser.). (ENG., Illus.). 360p. pap. 14.95 *(978-0-7627-4792-4(7))* Globe Pequot Pr., The.

Langlieb, David. Backroads & Byways of Pennsylvania: Drives, Day Trips & Weekend Excursions. 2011. (Backroads & Byways Ser.). (ENG.). 240p. pap. 18.95 *(978-0-88150-903-8(5),* 150903) Countryman Pr.

Lee, John, et al. Pacific Northwest Trips. 2009. (Regional Guide Ser.). (ENG., Illus.). 352p. pap. 19.99 *(978-1-74179-732-9(2))* Lonely Planet Pubns.

Leon, Harmon & National Lampoon Editors. National Lampoon Road Trip USA. 2007. (ENG., Illus.). 320p. per. *(978-0-9788323-0-8(2))* National Lampoon.

Let's Go, Inc. Staff. Roadtripping USA: The Complete Coast-to-Coast Guide to America. 3rd ed. 2009. (ENG.). 1024p. pap. 27.99 *(978-0-312-38583-5(8),* Let's Go Pubns.) St. Martin's Pr.

Linn, Stephen. The Ultimate Tailgater's Travel Guide: More Than 20 Great Road Trips, 0 vols. 2006. (Illus.). 224p. per. 14.99 *(978-1-4016-0258-1(4))* Nelson, Thomas Inc.

Livingston, Jill. That Ribbon of Highway II: Highway 99 from Sacramento to the Mexican Border. 2nd ed. 2009. *(978-0-9768321-2-6(7))* Living Gold Pr.

Lonely Planet Staff, et al. USA's Best Trips. 2010. (Regional Guide Ser.). (ENG., Illus.). 708p. pap. 24.99 *(978-1-74179-735-0(7))* Lonely Planet Pubns.

Massey, Peter. Backcountry Adventures Southern California. 2008. 44.95 *(978-1-930193-33-8(5))* Adler Publishing Co.

Massey, Peter & Wilson, Jeanne. California Trails Northern Sierra Region. 2006. (Illus.). 359p. per. 19.95 *(978-1-930193-23-9(8))* Adler Publishing Co.

—Utah Trails Central Region. 2007. (Illus.). 199p. per. 16.95 *(978-1-930193-31-4(9))* Adler Publishing Co.

—Utah Trails Moab Region. 2006. (Illus.). 209p. per. 19.95 *(978-1-930193-09-3(2))* Adler Publishing Co.

—Utah Trails Northern Region. 2007. (Illus.). 228p. per. 16.95 *(978-1-930193-30-7(0))* Adler Publishing Co.

—Utah Trails Southwest Region. 2006. (Illus.). 211p. per. 19.95 *(978-1-930193-10-9(6))* Adler Publishing Co.

Massey, Peter, et al. Arizona Trails Northeast Region. 2007. (Illus.). 255p. per. 19.95 *(978-1-930193-02-4(5))* Adler Publishing Co.

—Arizona Trails South Region. 2007. (Trails Ser.). (Illus.). 225p. per. 24.95 *(978-1-930193-03-1(3))* Adler Publishing Co.

—Arizona Trails West Region. 2006. (Illus.). 201p. per. 19.95 *(978-1-930193-00-0(9))* Adler Publishing Co.

—California Trails Central Mountains Region. 2006. (Illus.). 305p. per. 19.95 *(978-1-930193-19-2(X))* Adler Publishing Co.

—California Trails Desert Region. 2006. (Illus.). 337p. per. 19.95 *(978-1-930193-20-8(3))* Adler Publishing Co.

—California Trails High Sierra Region. 2006. (Illus.). 249p. per. 19.95 *(978-1-930193-21-5(1))* Adler Publishing Co.

—California Trails North Coast Region. 2006. (Illus.). 247p. per. 19.95 *(978-1-930193-22-2(X))* Adler Publishing Co.

—California Trails South Coast Region. 2006. (Illus.). 254p. per. 19.95 *(978-1-930193-24-6(6))* Adler Publishing Co.

—Colorado Trails Southwest Region. 2007. (Trails Ser.). (Illus.). 336p. per. 24.95 *(978-1-930193-07-9(6))* Adler Publishing Co.

—Nevada Trails Southern Region: Backroads & 4-Wheel Drive Trails. 2011. (ENG.). 320p. per. 24.95 *(978-1-930193-14-7(9))* Adler Publishing Co.

—Nevada Trails Western Region. 2008. (ENG., Illus.). 272p. per. 24.95 *(978-1-930193-15-4(7))* Adler Publishing Co.

Maynard, Charles W. Blue Ridge Parkway: An Extraordinary Journey along the World's Oldest Mountains. 2012. (ENG., Illus.). 120p. 24.95 *(978-0-9844218-0-0(7))* Mountain Trail Pr. LLC.

Meredith, Richard. Driven Together: Historic First Crossing of Asia's New Highway to the West. 2008. (Illus.). 224p. *(978-0-9541432-4-4(8))* Mercury Bks.

Mitchell, Roger & Mitchell, Loris. Southern CA SUV Trails, Vol. 2. 2007. 360p. pap. 21.95 *(978-0-9789978-0-9(8))* Track & Trail Pubns.

Mobil Travel Guide. Luxury Drives. 2008. (ENG.). 192p. pap. 17.95 *(978-1-936010-14-1(3))* Five Star Travel Corp., The.

Monaco Books, ed. Dream Routes of Europe, 1 vol. 2010. (ENG., Illus.). 336p. 29.95 *(978-3-89944-575-6(9),* Monaco Bks.) Verlag Wolfgang Kunth GmbH & Co. KG DEU. Dist: Innovative Logistics.

—Dream Routes of USA & Canada, 1 vol. 2010. (ENG., Illus.). 256p. 29.95 *(978-3-89944-576-3(7),* Monaco Bks.) Verlag Wolfgang Kunth GmbH & Co. KG DEU. Dist: Innovative Logistics.

National Geographic Society (U.S.), Book Division Staff, contrib. by. Drives of a Lifetime: 500 of the World's Most Spectacular Trips. 2010. (Illus.). 319p. *(978-1-4262-0773-0(5))* National Geographic Society.

National Geographic Society Staff. Scenic Highways & Byways: The 275 Best Drives in the U. S. 3rd ed. 2007. (National Geographic Traveler Ser.). (ENG., Illus.). 464p. pap. 26.00 *(978-1-4262-0056-4(0),* National Geographic) National Geographic Society.

NC Department of Cultural Resources & NC Cooperative Extension. Homegrown Handmade: Art Roads & Farm Trails. 2008. (Illus.). 387p. pap. 19.95 *(978-0-89587-355-2(9))* Blair, John F. Pub.

Negri, Sam. Arizona Highways: the Back Roads. 5th ed. 2007. (Arizona Highways: Travel Arizona Collection). (Illus.). 248p. pap. 19.95 *(978-1-932082-77-7(8))* Arizona Highways.

Neider, Susan M. Golden Country: Touring Scenic California. 2007. (ENG., Illus.). 128p. pap. 19.95 *(978-0-7627-4303-2(4),* Falcon Guides) Globe Pequot Pr., The.

The Old No. 9 Travel Guide: Driving Trip in the Texas Hill Country by way of the Old No. 9 Highway. 2007. (Illus.). 32p. pap. 20.00 incl. audio compact disk *(978-0-9676931-3-2(6))* Skyline Ranch Pr.

Olson Steve & Bobbi. Marking Time. 2007. 144p. 29.95 *(978-0-9789364-2-6(6))* Nebraska Life Publishing, Inc.

Parent, Laurence. Scenic Driving New Mexico. 3rd ed. 2011. (Scenic Driving Ser.). (ENG., Illus.). 224p. pap. 14.95 *(978-0-7627-6044-2(3))* Globe Pequot Pr., The.

—Scenic Driving Texas, 3rd. 2011. (Scenic Driving Ser.). (ENG., Illus.). 256p. pap. 15.95 *(978-0-7627-4889-1(3))* Globe Pequot Pr., The.

Paxton, Mark. Ford Capri: All Models (Except RS), 1969 to 1987. 2009. (Essential Buyer's Guide Ser.). (ENG., Illus.). 64p. pap. 19.95 *(978-1-84584-205-5(7),* 1845842057) Veloce Publishing Ltd. GBR. Dist: MBI Distribution Services/Quayside Distribution.

Perich, Shawn. Backroads of Minnesota: Your Guide to Scenic Getaways & Adventures. 2011. (ENG., Illus.). 256p. pap. 21.99 *(978-0-7603-4066-0(8),* 0760340668, Voyageur Pr) MBI Publishing Co. LLC.

Phenix, Penny. Frommer's 25 Great Drives in Ireland. 8th ed. 2010. (Best Loved Driving Tours Ser.). (ENG., Illus.). pap. 19.99 *(978-0-470-56024-2(X),* Frommers) Wiley, John & Sons, Inc.

Posner, Stan & Phillips-Posner, Sandra. Drive I-95: Exit by Exit Info, Maps, History, & Trivia. 4th ed. 2007. (Illus.). 208p. pap. 23.95 *(978-1-894979-88-7(5))* Travelsmart Publishing CAN. Dist: Partners Bk. Distributing, Inc.

Rand McNally, creator. The Ultimate NASCAR Road Trip Guide. 2007. (Ultimate NASCAR Road Trip Guide Ser.). (Illus.). 384p. per. 14.95 *(978-0-528-94172-6(0))* Rand McNally.

Rand McNally Staff. Road Atlas. 2010. 13.95 *(978-0-528-35528-8(7))* Rand McNally.

Rau, Fred. Motorcycle Touring Bible. 2011. (ENG., Illus.). 224p. pap. 29.99 *(978-0-7603-3741-7(1),* 0760337411, Motorbooks) MBI Publishing Co. LLC.

Rice, Melanie & Rice, Christopher. Brittany & Normandy. 3rd ed. 2009. (Drive Around - Thomas Cook Ser.). (ENG., Illus.). 288p. pap. 26.95 *(978-1-84848-012-4(1))* Cook, Thomas Publishing GBR. Dist: Globe Pequot Pr., The.

Robinson, Charles M., III. Roadside History of Louisiana. 2007. (Roadside History Ser.). (Illus.). 351p. per. 20.00 *(978-0-87842-531-0(4))* Mountain Pr. Publishing Co., Inc.

Roy, Sally. Frommer's 25 Great Drives in Northern Italy. 5th ed. 2010. (Best Loved Driving Tours Ser.). (ENG., Illus.). pap. 19.99 *(978-0-470-56025-9(8),* Frommers) Wiley, John & Sons, Inc.

Sakowski, Carolyn. Touring the Western North Carolina Backroads. 3rd ed. 2011. (Illus.). xviii, 316p. E-Book ***(978-0-89587-560-0(8))***; (ENG.). 320p. pap. 19.95 *(978-0-89587-559-4(4))* Blair, John F. Pub.

Sanger, Andrew. Burgundy & the Rhone Valley. 3rd ed. 2009. (Drive Around - Thomas Cook Ser.). (ENG., Illus.). 288p. pap. 26.95 *(978-1-84848-013-1(X))* Cook, Thomas Publishing GBR. Dist: Globe Pequot Pr., The.

Satterfield, Archie. Backroads & Byways of Missouri: Drives, Day Trips & Weekend Excursions. 2008. (Backroads & Byways Ser.). (ENG., Illus.). 256p. pap. 16.95 *(978-0-88150-775-1(X),* 150775) Countryman Pr.

Spinzia, Raymond E., et al. Long Island: A Guide to New York's Suffolk & Nassau Counties. 3rd ed. 2008. (ENG., Illus.). 496p. pap. *(978-0-7818-1213-9(5))* Hippocrene Bks., Inc.

Spitzer, Rick. Colorado Mountain Passes: Photos & History from the High Points on Colorado Roadways. 2008. 265p. pap. 23.95 *(978-1-56579-598-3(9))* Westcliffe Pubs.

St. John, Alan D. Oregon's Dry Side: Exploring East of the Cascade Crest. 2007. (ENG., Illus.). 324p. pap. 29.95 *(978-0-88192-829-7(1),* 0881928291) Timber Pr., Inc.

Stern, Jane & Stern, Michael. Roadfood: The Coast-to-Coast Guide to 800 of the Best Barbecue Joints, Lobster Shacks, Ice Cream Parlors, Highway Diners, & Much, Much More. 2011. 592p. pap. 21.99 *(978-0-307-59124-1(7),* Clarkson Potter) Crown Publishing Group.

Strandoo, Orv. The Essential Driving Guide for England, Scotland & Ireland. 2007. (Illus.). 112p. per. 14.95 *(978-1-887542-59-3(0))* Book Pubs. Network.

—The Essential Driving Guide for Italy: A No-Nonsense Guide to the Ins & Outs of Driving in Italy & Sicily. 2007. (Essential Guide to Driving in Europe Ser.). (Illus.). 66p. per. 12.95 *(978-1-887542-47-0(7))* Book Pubs. Network.

—The Essential Guide for Driving in France: A No-Nonsense Guide to the Ins & Outs of Driving in France. 2007. (Essential Driving Guides in Europe Ser.). (Illus.). 104p. per. 14.95 *(978-1-887542-53-1(1))* Book Pubs. Network.

Stroeve, Wilbert & Akerman, James R., photos by. Chicago to Lake Geneva, Then & Now: Retracing the Route of H. Sargent Michaels' 1905 Photographic Guide for Motorists. 2008. (Illus.). 160p. pap. 17.95 *(978-0-911028-82-9(X))* Newberry Library.

Sullivan, Richard. Driving & Discovering Hawaii, Maui, & Molokai. 2007. 164p. pap. 19.95 *(978-0-9636828-0-2(6))* Montgomery Ewing Pubs.

Sullivan, Richard, photos by. Driving & Discovering Hawaii: Oahu, Honolulu, & Waikiki. rev. ed. 2010. (ENG., Illus.). 144p. pap. *(978-1-59700-813-6(3))* Island Heritage Publishing.

Tennis, Joe. Beach to Bluegrass: Places to Brake on Virginia's Longest Road. 2007. (ENG., Illus.). 200p. per. 17.95 *(978-1-57072-323-0(0))* Overmountain Pr.

Thomas Cook Publishing. Drive Around Canadian Rockies, 3rd: Your guide to great drives. Top 25 Tours. 2009. (Drive Around - Thomas Cook Ser.). (ENG., Illus.). 288p. pap. 26.95 *(978-1-84848-202-9(7))* Cook, Thomas Publishing GBR. Dist: Globe Pequot Pr., The.

—Drive Around New England, 3rd: Your guide to great drives. Top 25 Tours. 2009. (Drive Around - Thomas Cook Ser.). (ENG., Illus.). 288p. pap. 26.95 *(978-1-84848-203-6(5))* Cook, Thomas Publishing GBR. Dist: Globe Pequot Pr., The.

—Driving Guides Northern Italy, 4th. 4th ed. 2011. (Drive Around - Thomas Cook Ser.). (ENG., Illus.). 288p. pap. 26.95 *(978-1-84848-379-8(1))* Cook, Thomas Publishing GBR. Dist: Globe Pequot Pr., The.

—New Zealand: Your Guide to Great Drives. Top 15 Tours. 3rd ed. 2009. (Drive Around - Thomas Cook Ser.). (ENG., Illus.). 288p. pap. 26.95 *(978-1-84848-204-3(3))* Cook, Thomas Publishing GBR. Dist: Globe Pequot Pr., The.

—Washington DC: Your Guide to Great Drives. Top 25 Tours. 3rd ed. 2009. (Drive Around - Thomas Cook Ser.). (ENG., Illus.). 288p. pap. 26.95 *(978-1-84848-205-0(1))* Cook, Thomas Publishing GBR. Dist: Globe Pequot Pr., The.

Thomas Cook Publishing Staff. Driving Guides Catalonia & the Spanish Pyrenees. 4th ed. 2011. (Drive Around - Thomas Cook Ser.). (ENG., Illus.). 288p. pap. 26.95 *(978-1-84848-377-4(5))* Cook, Thomas Publishing GBR. Dist: Globe Pequot Pr., The.

—Driving Guides Dordogne. 4th ed. 2011. (Drive Around - Thomas Cook Ser.). (ENG., Illus.). 288p. pap. 26.95 *(978-1-84848-357-6(0))* Cook, Thomas Publishing GBR. Dist: Globe Pequot Pr., The.

—Driving Guides Ireland. 4th ed. 2011. (Drive Around - Thomas Cook Ser.). (ENG., Illus.). 288p. pap. 26.95 *(978-1-84848-378-1(3))* Cook, Thomas Publishing GBR. Dist: Globe Pequot Pr., The.

—Driving Guides Languedoc. 4th ed. 2011. (Drive Around - Thomas Cook Ser.). (ENG., Illus.). 288p. pap. 26.95 *(978-1-84848-358-3(9))* Cook, Thomas Publishing GBR. Dist: Globe Pequot Pr., The.

—Driving Guides Portugal. 4th ed. 2011. (Drive Around - Thomas Cook Ser.). (ENG., Illus.). 288p. pap. 26.95 *(978-1-84848-380-4(5))* Cook, Thomas Publishing GBR. Dist: Globe Pequot Pr., The.

—Driving Guides Scotland. 4th ed. 2011. (Drive Around - Thomas Cook Ser.). (ENG., Illus.). 288p. pap. 26.95 *(978-1-84848-381-1(3))* Cook, Thomas Publishing GBR. Dist: Globe Pequot Pr., The.

—Driving Guides Tuscany & Umbria. 4th ed. 2011. (Drive Around - Thomas Cook Ser.). (ENG., Illus.). 288p. pap. 26.95 *(978-1-84848-382-8(1))* Cook, Thomas Publishing GBR. Dist: Globe Pequot Pr., The.

—Loire Valley Driving Guide. 4th ed. 2011. (Drive Around - Thomas Cook Ser.). (ENG., Illus.). 288p. pap. 26.95 *(978-1-84848-359-0(7))* Cook, Thomas Publishing GBR. Dist: Globe Pequot Pr., The.

—Provence & the Cote D'Azur Driving Guide. 4th ed. 2011. (Drive Around - Thomas Cook Ser.). (ENG., Illus.). 288p. pap. 26.95 *(978-1-84848-360-6(0))* Cook, Thomas Publishing GBR. Dist: Globe Pequot Pr., The.

TL Enterprises Staff & Trailer Life Books Publishibg Staff. 2011 Exit Now: Interstate Exit Directory. 2011. (ENG., Illus.). 600p. pap. 24.95 *(978-0-9824894-4-4(7),* Trailer Life Bks.) TL Enterprises, Inc.

Ver Berkmoes, Ryan, et al. Lonely Planet California Trips. 2009. (Regional Guide Ser.). (ENG., Illus.). 416p. pap. 19.99 *(978-1-74179-727-5(6))* Lonely Planet Pubns.

Ware, Jane, ed. Particular Places: A Traveler's Guide to Ohio's Best Road Trips. 2008. (Orange Frazer Roadbook Ser.). (Illus.). 223p. pap. 16.95 *(978-1-933197-44-9(7))* Orange Frazer Pr.

Watson, Mark. The Next Exit: USA Interstate Highway Exit Directory. 2007. (Next Exit: the Most Complete Interstate Highway Guide Ever Printed Ser.). (Illus.). 542p. per. 14.95 *(978-0-9714073-6-7(3))* Next Exit, Inc.

Welsch, Jeff & Moore, Sherry L. Backroads & Byways of Montana: Drives, Day Trips & Weekend Excursions. 2011. (Backroads & Byways Ser.). (ENG.). 224p. pap. 18.95 *(978-0-88150-899-4(3),* 150899) Countryman Pr.

Whitehorne, Stephen. Sunflower Guide Landscapes of the Scottish Highlands & the Isle of Skye: A Countryside Guide. 2nd ed. 2007. (Sunflower Guides Scottish Highlands & the Isle of Skye Ser.). (Illus.). 136p. pap. 17.99 *(978-1-85691-287-7(6))* Hunter Publishing, Inc.

Wilson, Jeanne, et al. Arizona Trails Central Region. 2006. (Illus.). 251p. per. 19.95 *(978-1-930193-01-7(7))* Adler Publishing Co.

Wood, Crystal. Backroads & Byways of Oregon: Drives, Day Trips & Weekend Excursions. 2010. (Backroads & Byways Ser.). (ENG., Illus.). 208p. pap. 18.95 *(978-0-88150-835-2(7),* 150835) Countryman Pr.
Wurzer, Cathy. The WPA Guide to the Minnesota Arrowhead Country: The Federal Writers' Project Guide to 1930s Minnesota. 2008. (ENG.). 272p. pap. 16.95 *(978-0-87351-634-1(6))* Minnesota Historical Society Pr.
Zelade, Richard. Lone Star Guide to Central Texas. 2011. (ENG., Illus.). 424p. pap. 18.95 *(978-1-58979-604-1(7))* Taylor Trade Publishing.
—Lone Star Guide to the Texas Hill Country. 6th ed. 2011. (ENG., Illus.). 392p. pap. 18.95 *(978-1-58979-609-6(8))* Taylor Trade Publishing.

AUTOMOBILE TRAVELING
see Automobile Travel

AUTOMOBILE TRUCKS
see Trucks

AUTOMOBILE WORKERS
see Automobile Mechanics

AUTOMOBILES
see also Alfa Romeo Automobile; American Motors Automobiles; Antique and Classic Cars; Aston Martin Automobile; Audi Automobile; BLMC Automobiles; BMW Automobiles; Bugatti Automobile; Chrysler Automobile; Citroen Automobile; Cord Automobile; Ferrari Automobile; Fiat Automobiles; Ford Automobile; Honda Automobile; Hydrogen Cars; Hyundai Automobile; Isuzu Automobile; Jaguar Automobile; Lamborghini Automobile; Lancia Automobile; Lotus Automobiles; Maserati Automobile; Mazda Automobiles; Mercedes Automobile; Mitsubishi Automobile; Morgan Automobiles; Muscle Cars; Nissan Automobile; Packard Automobile; Peugeot Automobile; Porsche Automobiles; Renault Automobile; Rolls-Royce Automobile; Rover Automobile; Saab Automobile; Sports Cars; Studebaker Automobile; Subaru Automobile; Suzuki Automobile; Toyota Automobiles; Triumph Automobile; Used Cars; Volkswagen Automobiles; Volvo Automobile
also headings beginning with the word Automobile

Alberer, Daniel, et al, eds. Identification for Automotive Systems. 2011. (Lecture Notes in Control & Information Sciences Ser.). (ENG., Illus.). xvi, 356p. pap. 179.00 ***(978-1-4471-2220-3(8),*** 1447122208) Springer.
American Society of Mechanical Engineers Staff, ed. Automobile Emissions & Combustion. (IMechE Seminar Publication Ser.: Vol. 1). (Illus.). 200p. 172.00 *(978-0-85298-892-3(3))* Professional Engineering Publishing GBR. Dist: SAE Intl.
Anastakis, Dimitry. Car Nation: An Illustrated History of Canada's Transformation Behind the Wheel. 2008. (ENG., Illus.). 96p. pap. 24.95 *(978-1-55277-005-4(2))* Lorimer, James & Co., Ltd., Pubs. CAN. Dist: Casemate Pubs. & Bk. Distributors, LLC.
Auto Mechanics. cd-rom 910.95 *(978-1-56191-793-8(1));* cd-rom 910.95 *(978-1-56191-794-5(X))* Films Media Group.
Automobile Quarterly 46-4, volume 46 issue 4. 2007. lib. bdg. 24.95 *(978-1-59613-052-4(0))* Automobile Heritage Publishing & Communications, LLC.
Automobile Quarterly 47-1, volume 47 issue 1. 2007. lib. bdg. 24.95 *(978-1-59613-053-1(9))* Automobile Heritage Publishing & Communications, LLC.
AWS D8. 1M-2007, Specification for Automotive Weld Quality — Resistance Spot Welding of Steel. 2007. *(978-0-87171-065-9(X))* American Welding Society.
AWS D8. 8M-2007, Specification for Automotive Weld Quality — Arc Welding of Steel. 2007. *(978-0-87171-019-2(6))* American Welding Society.
Baldwin, Nick. Proprietary Engines for Vehicles. 2006. (Shire Albums Ser.). (ENG., Illus.). 40p. pap. 11.95 *(978-0-7478-0496-3(6))* Shire Pubns., Ltd. GBR. Dist: Random Hse., Inc.
Balish, Chris. How to Live Well Without Owning a Car: Save Money, Breathe Easier, & Get More Mileage Out of Life. 2006. (ENG., Illus.). 224p. pap. 12.95 *(978-1-58008-757-5(4))* Ten Speed Pr.
Bell, A. Graham. Four-Stroke Performance Tuning: A Practical Guide. 3rd ed. 2006. (ENG., Illus.). 376p. 34.95 *(978-1-84425-314-2(7),* 1844253147) Haynes Publishing PLC GBR. Dist: MBI Distribution Services/Quayside Distribution.
Bouaziz, Samir, et al, eds. Embedded Systems for Intelligent Vehicles. 2007. 108p. per. 17.00 *(978-977-5945-98-3(4))* Hindawi Publishing Corp.
Brimax Publishing, creator. My Little Book of Cars. 2008. (Illus.). 24p. (gr. -1-1). bds. *(978-1-905279-33-3(7))* Brimax Books Ltd.
Bryant, Jefferson. How to Build a Killer Street Mach ne. 2010. (Motorbooks Workshop Ser.). (ENG., Illus.). 192p. pap. 29.99 *(978-0-7603-3549-9(4),* 0760335494, Motorbooks) MBI Publishing Co. LLC.
Cacciabue, Pietro C. Modelling Driver Behaviour in Automotive Environments: Critical Issues in Driver Interactions with Intelligent Transport Systems. 2007. (ENG., Illus.). xiv, 428p. 149.00 *(978-1-84628-617-9(4),* 1846286174) Springer.
Card, Peter W. Motor Car Mascots & Badges. 2nd ed. 2008. (Shire Library). (ENG., Illus.). 56p. pap. 12.95 *(978-0-7478-0629-5(2))* Shire Pubns., Ltd. GBR. Dist: Random Hse., Inc.
Cars: Mit coolen Stickern aus Cars, die zeigen, wie schnell du wächst. (Disney Storybooks Bilingual Ser.). 48p. *(978-1-4054-8495-4(0));* 64p. pap. *(978-1-4075-0913-6(6));* 24p. pap. *(978-1-4054-9724-4(6))* Parragon, Inc.
Cars: Mit coolen Stickern aus Cars, die zeigen, wie schnell du wächst. 2007. (Illus.). 10p. (J). (ENG.). 29.99 *(978-1-934514-59-6(1));* (ENG., 39.99 *(978-1-934514-78-8(0));* 14.99 *(978-1-934514-13-9(6))* Senario LLC.
Chapman, Giles. TV Cars: Star Cars from the World of Television. 2011. (ENG., Illus.). 128p. pap. 12.95 *(978-0-85733-087-1(X),* 085733087X) Haynes Publishing PLC GBR. Dist: MBI Distribution Services/Quayside Distribution.
Chapman, Giles & Porter, Richard. My Dad Had One of Those. 2008. (ENG., Illus.). 160p. 19.95 *(978-0-563-53919-3(4))* BBC Worldwide GBR. Dist: Independent Pubs. Group.
Cherrett, Angela. Alfa Romeo Modello 8c 2300. ltd ed. (Illus.). 192p. lthr. *(978-1-874105-02-2(2))* Veloce Publishing Ltd. GBR. Dist: MBI Distribution Services/Quayside Distribution.
Chiras, Dan. Green Transportation Basics. 2010. (Green Energy Guide Ser.). (ENG., Illus.). 192p. pap. 12.95 ***(978-0-86571-619-3(6),*** 9780865716193) New Society Pubs., Ltd. CAN. Dist: Consortium Bk. Sales & Distribution.
Chiu, Imes. The Evolution from Horse to Automobile: A Comparative International Study. 2008. 328p. 109.95 *(978-1-60497-546-8(6))* Cambria Pr.
Christensen, Lisa. About Cars: An Easy Guide to Car Maintenance & Repair. rev. ed. 2007. (Clueless Ser.). (ENG., Illus.). 176p. per. 16.95 *(978-1-55407-333-7(2))* Firefly Bks., Ltd.
Clarke, R. M. Checker Automobiles. 2010. (Road Test Portfolio Ser.). (ENG., Illus.). 140p. pap. 36.95 *(978-1-85520-898-8(9),* 1855208989) Brooklands Bks. GBR. Dist: MBI Distribution Services/Quayside Distribution.
Clarkson, Jeremy. Clarkson on Cars. 2006. (ENG., Illus.). 368p. (gr. 12-18). 16.00 *(978-0-14-101788-4(0),* Penguin Global) Penguin Group (USA) Inc.
—Motorworld. 2006. (ENG., Illus.). 208p. (gr. 12-18). 16.00 *(978-0-14-101787-7(2),* Penguin Global) Penguin Group (USA) Inc.
Clarkson, Wensley. Car Trouble: A Childhood on Four Wheels. 2011. (ENG., Illus.). 224p. pap. 16.95 *(978-1-84596-612-6(3))* Mainstream Publishing Co. Ltd. GBR. Dist: Independent Pubs. Group.
Classic Cars From Around The World. Date not set. (Illus.). 96p. 6.98 *(978-0-7525-9636-5(5))* Parragon, Inc.
Committee on Review of the FreedomCAR and Fuel Research Program, Phase 3 & National Research Council. Review of the Research Program of the FreedomCAR & Fuel Partnership: Third Report. 2010. (ENG.). 228p. pap. 49.75 *(978-0-309-15683-7(1))* National Academies Pr.
Cox, Roy L. Engineered Tribological Composites: The Art of Friction Material Development. 2011. ***(978-0-7680-3485-1(X))*** SAE Intl.
Davis, Patrick. Selling Cars: The Handbook of the Professional. Clifton, Larry, ed. 84p. pap. 10.95 *(978-1-885640-66-6(8))* Insight Publishing.
De Fabianis, Valeria Manferto, ed. Cars. Ponting, Sarah, tr. 2010. (MiniCube Ser.). (ENG., Illus.). 768p. 6.95 *(978-88-544-0315-4(6))* White Star ITA. Dist: Sterling Publishing Co., Inc.
De Lorenzo, Matt. Automobiles: Elegance on Wheels. 2008. (ENG., Illus.). 208p. 35.00 *(978-88-544-0424-3(1))* White Star ITA. Dist: Random Hse., Inc.
Desapriya, Ediriweera. Head Restraints & Whiplash: The Past, Present & Future. 2010. (Transportation Issues, Policies & R&D Ser.). 110p. pap. 43.00 *(978-1-61668-150-0(0))* Nova Science Pubs., Inc.
Design Law: Are Special Provisions Needed to Protect Unique Industries?: Hearing Before the Subcommittee on Courts, the Internet, & Intellectual Property of the Committee on the Judiciary, House of Representatives, One Hundred Tenth Congress, Second Session, February 14, 2008. 2008. (Illus.). iii, 96p. *(978-0-16-081773-1(0),* 552-070-37981-9) United States Government Printing Office.
Doherty, Richard. Humber Light Reconnaissance Car 1941-45. 2011. (New Vanguard Ser.). (ENG., Illus.). 48p. pap. 17.95 *(978-1-84908-310-2(X))* Osprey Publishing, Ltd. GBR. Dist: Random Hse., Inc.
Dolski, Joerg. Standardisierung im Internationalen Marketing: Entwicklung eines Analyseschemas. 2010. (Europäische Hochschulschriften Reihe 5: Volks- und Betriebswirtschaft Ser.). (GER.). 224p. pap. 66.95 *(978-3-631-58990-8(5))* Lang, Peter GmbH, Europaischer Verlag der Wissenschaften DEU. Dist: Lang, Peter.
Dregni, Eric & Godollei, Ruthann. Road Show: Art Cars & the Museum of the Streets. 2009. (ENG., Illus.). 160p. 22.95 *(978-1-933108-17-9(7),* Speck Pr.) Fulcrum Publishing.
Dunne, Bradley L. Corporate Average Fuel Economy (CAFE) Standards & the Environmental Impact. 2011. (Energy Policies, Politics & Prices Ser.). 295.00 *(978-1-61122-767-3(4))* Nova Science Pubs., Inc.
Dwivedi, Sharada. Automobiles of the Maharajas. 2010. (Illus.). 324p. 50.00 *(978-88-544-0421-2(7))* White Star ITA. Dist: Random Hse., Inc.
Egan, Peter. Peter Egan on the Road: Americas Favorite Automotive Writer Says off the Interstate. 2008. (ENG.). 356p. 26.95 *(978-0-9817270-0-4(X),* Parker Hse. Publishing Inc.,Csi) Continental Sales, Inc.
Eskandarian, Azim, ed. Handbook of Intelligent Vehicles, 2 vols. 2012. (ENG., Illus.). 1675p. 949.00 *(978-0-85729-084-7(3),* 0857290843) Springer.
Freyssenet, Michel. The Second Automobile Revolution: Trajectories of the World Carmakers in the 21st Century. Freyssenet, Michel, ed. 2009. (ENG., Illus.). 450p. 137.00 *(978-0-230-21971-7(3))* Palgrave Macmillan.
Gandari, Jonathan. The Sinking Hummer. 2011. 80p. pap. ***(978-3-8443-8095-8(7))*** Lambert Academic Publishing.
George Teke, Forbid. Sustainable Management of Automobile Waste. 2010. 148p. pap. *(978-3-639-25496-9(1))* VDM Verlag Dr. Mueller e.K.
Gordon, Robert. Intelligent Freeway Transportation Systems: Functional Design. 2009. (ENG., Illus.). xii, 218p. 129.00 *(978-1-4419-0732-5(7),* 1441907327) Springer.
Gosson, Scotty. America's Coolest Station Wagons. 2011. *(978-1-934709-45-0(X))* CarTech, Inc.
Hendry, Maurice D. & GodShall, Jeffrey I. Cadillac vols. 1 & 2: Legacy of Leadership. 7th rev. ed. 2009. (ENG., Illus.). 555p. *(978-1-59613-016-6(4),* 1596130164) Automobile Heritage Publishing & Communications, LLC.
Hill, Phil. Phil Hill: A Driving Life. 2010. (Illus.). 192p. 75.00 *(978-1-935007-07-4(6))* Bull, David Publishing, Inc.
Hobbs, George & Elliot, Ben. The Gasoline Automobile. 2011. (Illus.). 276p. pap. 19.95 ***(978-1-935700-53-1(7))*** Periscope Film, LLC.
Hollander Interchange Manual: Body Parts I. 72nd ed. 2006. (Illus.). 1536p. pap. 50.00 *(978-1-58132-121-0(X))* Hollander.
Hollander Interchange Manual: Body Parts II. 72nd ed. 2006. (Illus.). 1296p. pap. 75.00 *(978-1-58132-122-7(8))* Hollander.
Hollander Interchange Manual: Body Parts III. 72nd ed. 2006. (Illus.). 1552p. pap. 75.00 *(978-1-58132-123-4(6))* Hollander.
Hollander Interchange Manual: Body Parts Set. 72nd ed. 2006. (Illus.). 4384p. pap. 235.00 *(978-1-58132-132-6(5))* Hollander.
Hollander Interchange Manual: Complete Set. 72nd ed. 2006. (Illus.). 12216p. pap. 449.00 *(978-1-58132-136-4(8))* Hollander.
Hollander Interchange Manual: Identification Set. 72nd ed. 2006. (Illus.). 1320p. pap. 200.00 *(978-1-58132-135-7(X))* Hollander.
Institute of Electrical and Electronics Engineers Staff, contrib. by. 2007 IEEE Intelligent Transportation Systems Conference. 2007. pap. 376.00 *(978-1-4244-1395-9(8),* 07TH8964) IEEE.
Jensen, Todd A. Automotive Websites. 2nd rev. ed. 2006. (ENG., Illus.). 219p. per. 35.00 *(978-0-7864-2802-1(3))* McFarland & Co., Inc. Pubs.
Jodidio, Philip. Architecture & Automobiles. 2011. (ENG., Illus.). 228p. 60.00 *(978-1-86470-330-6(X))* Images Publishing Group AUS. Dist: National Bk. Network.
Johnson, Alan. How to Pinstripe. rev. ed. 2007. (Motorbooks Workshop Ser.). (ENG., Illus.). 160p. pap. 25.95 *(978-0-7603-2749-4(1),* 0760327491, Motorbooks) MBI Publishing Co. LLC.
Jones, Ernest B. Basic Car Care & Emergency Preparedness. 2010. 76p. pap. 12.99 *(978-1-4520-7707-9(X))* AuthorHouse.
Kemp, Roger L., ed. Cities & Cars: A Handbook of Best Practices. 2007. (ENG., Illus.). 278p. per. 39.95 *(978-0-7864-2919-6(4))* McFarland & Co., Inc. Pubs.
Key, Jimmy. What's Ya Name? 2006. pap. 9.00 *(978-0-8059-6556-8(4))* Dorrance Publishing Co., Inc.
Kidston, Simon & Sonnery, Marc. Miura 360°: The World's First Supercar. 2012. (ENG.). 208p. 180.00 *(978-0-9817270-3-5(4),* Parker Hse. Publishing Inc.,Csi) Continental Sales, Inc.
Kimble, David & Endres, Christopher P. Cutaway: The Automotive Art of David Kimble. 2011. ***(978-1-934709-84-9(0))*** CarTech, Inc.
Knight, David. Tron: Evolution - Prima Essential Guide: Prima Official Game Guide. 2010. (ENG.). 192p. pap. 14.99 *(978-0-307-47083-6(0),* Prima Games) Random Hse. Information Group.
Lanham, Stephen. Little Book of Car Mascots. 2011. (Little Book Of Ser.). (ENG.). 128p. 11.99 *(978-1-907803-44-0(0))* G2 Entertainment Ltd. GBR. Dist: BookMasters Distribution Services (BDS).
Lawlor, John & Hancock, William. Auto Math Handbook HP1554: Easy Calculations for Engine Builders, Auto Engineers, Racers, Students, & Performance Enthusiasts. 2011. (ENG., Illus.). 128p. (gr. 12). 23.95 *(978-1-55788-554-8(0),* HP Trade) Penguin Group (USA) Inc.
Linde, Arvid. How Your Car Works: Your Guide to the Components & Systems of Modern Cars, Including Hybrid & Electric Vehicles. 2011. (ENG., Illus.). 128p. pap. 24.95 *(978-1-84584-390-8(8),* 1845843908) Veloce Publishing Ltd. GBR. Dist: MBI Distribution Services/Quayside Distribution.
Louter, David. Windshield Wilderness: Cars, Roads, & Nature in Washington's National Parks. 2010. (Weyerhaeuser Environmental Bks.). (ENG.). 288p. pap. 24.95 *(978-0-295-99021-7(X))* Univ. of Washington Pr.
Lumley. The Potential for Cost & Weight Reduction in Transport Applications through the use of Heat Treated Aluminum High Pressure Diecastings. 2011. (Materials Science & Technologies Ser.). 53p. pap. 43.00 *(978-1-61761-798-0(9),* Nova Novinka) Nova Science Pubs., Inc.
Maat, K., ed. Built Environment & Car Travel: Analyses of Interdependencies. 2009. 184p. pap. 65.00 *(978-1-60750-064-3(7))* IOS Pr., Inc.
Master, Matt. Daft Cars. 2009. (ENG., Illus.). 128p. 17.95 *(978-1-84607-807-1(5))* BBC Worldwide GBR. Dist: Independent Pubs. Group.
Mega Machines. 256p. *(978-1-4054-8655-2(4))* Parragon, Inc.
Mikler, John. Greening the Car Industry: Varieties of Capitalism & Climate Change. 2009. (Illus.). 296p. 145.00 *(978-1-84720-652-7(2))* Elgar, Edward Publishing, Inc.
Morey, Bruce. Automotive 2030, North America. 2011. ***(978-0-7680-5727-0(2))*** SAE Intl.
Nye, Doug. British Cars of the Sixties. 2008. (ENG.). 240p. 40.00 *(978-0-9796891-6-1(3),* Parker Hse. Publishing Inc.,Csi) Continental Sales, Inc.
Okada, Akira. Innovative Materials for Automotive Industry. 2010. (Materials Science & Technologies Ser.). pap. 43.00 *(978-1-61668-237-8(X))* Nova Science Pubs., Inc.
O'Rourke, P. J. Driving Like Crazy: Thirty Years of Vehicular Hell-Bending, Celebrating America the Way It's Supposed to Be - With an Oil Well in Every Backyard, a Cadillac Escalade in Every Carport, & the Chairman of the Federal Reserve Mowing Our Lawn. 2010. (ENG.). 288p. pap. 14.00 *(978-0-8021-4479-9(9),* Grove Pr.) Grove/Atlantic, Inc.
Pellow, Harry C. The Maestro Chronicles. 1984p. per. 19.50 *(978-0-941210-08-9(1))* HCP Research.
Pemberton, Max. Ward's 1994 Worldwide Vehicle Parc. (Illus.). (Orig.). (C). pap. 950.00 *(978-0-910589-50-5(X))* Ward's Communications, Inc.
Portman, Michael. Torinos. 2011. (Wild Wheels Ser.). (Illus.). 32p. (gr. 3-6). pap. 10.50 *(978-1-4339-4756-8(0),* Stevens, Gareth Learning Library) Stevens, Gareth Publishing LLLP.
Prokhorov, Danil. Computational Intelligence in Automotive Applications. 2009. (Studies in Computational Intelligence Ser.). 199.00 *(978-3-540-79256-7(2))* Springer.
Rashidi, Waleed & Yoe, Craig. NASCAR Learn to Draw Race Cars: Discover All You Need to Know to Begin Drawing Your Favorite NASCAR Race Cars. 2011. (Learn to Draw Favorite Characters Ser.). (Illus.). 32p. (J). (gr. k-3). 28.50 *(978-1-936309-33-7(5))* Foster, Walter Publishing, Inc.
Reddie, John. Cars I Loved & Lost. 2011. 128p. pap. 13.95 ***(978-1-4620-4517-4(0))*** iUniverse, Inc.
Reed, T., et al. Gengas: The Swedish Classic on Wood Fueled Vehicles. 340p. pap. 30.00 *(978-1-890607-01-2(0))* Biomass Energy Foundation.
Rive Box, Rob de la. Classic Cars. (Complete Encyclopedia Ser.). (Illus.). 320p. *(978-90-366-1597-6(6))* Rebo International B.V.
Ross, Daniel Alexander, et al, eds. Cars Now!, Vol. 1. 2011. (ENG, FRE & GER., Illus.). 448p. pap. 39.99 *(978-3-8365-1984-7(4))* TASCHEN DEU. Dist: Ingram Pub. Services.
Sheng, Gang. Vehicle Noise, Vibration, & Sound Quality. 2012. ***(978-0-7680-3484-4(1))*** SAE Intl.
Siegelbaum, Lewis H. Cars for Comrades: The Life of the Soviet Automobile. 2011. (Illus.). 328p. pap. 24.95 *(978-0-8014-7721-8(2))* Cornell Univ. Pr.
Sobey, Ed. A Field Guide to Automotive Technology. 2009. (ENG., Illus.). 208p. pap. 14.95 *(978-1-55652-812-5(4))* Chicago Review Pr., Inc.
Society of Plastics Engineers (SPE) Staff, compiled by. SPE Automotive TPO Global Conference 2006. 2007. 290p. pap. 187.00 *(978-1-60423-699-6(X))* Curran Assocs., Inc.
Sousa, Leonel, et al, eds. Embedded Systems for Portable & Mobile Video Platforms. 2007. 80p. per. 14.00 *(978-977-5945-85-3(2))* Hindawi Publishing Corp.
Sparrow, David & Sparrow, Andrea. Bubblecars & Microcars - The Colour Family Album. (Illus.). 96p. *(978-1-874105-29-9(4))* Veloce Publishing Ltd. GBR. Dist: MBI Distribution Services/Quayside Distribution.
Stone, Matt. My First Car: Recollections of First Cars from Jay Leno, Tony Stewart, Carroll Shelby, Dan Ackroyd, Tom Wolfe & Many More! 2011. (ENG., Illus.). 224p. 25.00 *(978-0-7603-3534-5(6),* 0760335346, Motorbooks) MBI Publishing Co. LLC.
Der Taschen Brockhaus Band 1: Autos. (GER., Illus.). *(978-3-7653-1771-2(3))* Brockhaus, F. A., GmbH DEU. Dist: International Bk. Import Service, Inc.
Tipler, Johnny. Lotus Elise, 1995-2007. 2011. (Ultimate Owner's Guide Ser.). (ENG., Illus.). 80p. pap. 19.95 *(978-1-906712-09-9(3),* 1906712093, PMM Bks.) Morgan, Peter Media Ltd. GBR. Dist: MBI Distribution Services/Quayside Distribution.
Travers, Jim. Extreme Cars. 2007. (Extreme Wonders Ser.). (ENG., Illus.). 224p. pap. 15.95 *(978-0-06-089144-2(0),* HarperPerennial) HarperCollins Pubs.
Trout, Tim, ed. Beckett Racing Coll Price Gd-#19. 2011. 432p. pap. 24.95 *(978-1-930692-97-8(8))* Beckett Media LLP.
Ulrich, Finger. 2007 7th International Conference on ITS Telecommunications. 2007. pap. 340.00 *(978-1-4244-1177-1(7),* 07EX1765) IEEE.
United States, Congress Senate Committee on Energy and Natural Resources Staff, contrib. by. Transportation Sector Fuel Efficiency: Hearing Before the Committee on Energy & Natural Resources, United States Senate, One Hundred Tenth Congress, First Session, on Transportation Sector Fuel Efficiency, Including Challenges to & Incentives for Increased Oil Savings Through Technological Innovation Including Plug-In Hybrids, January 30, 2007. 2007. iii, 72p. *(978-0-16-078490-3(5),* 552-070-35771-8) United States Government Printing Office.
Urban Land Institute & National Parking Association. The Dimensions of Parking. 5th ed. 2009. (ENG., Illus.). 170p. 89.95 *(978-0-87420-120-8(9))* Urban Land Institute.
Varat, Michael S. Crash Reconstruction Research: 20 Years of Progress, 1988-2007. 2008. (Illus.). iv, 756p. 119.95 *(978-0-7680-2052-6(2))* SAE Intl.
VDI Wissensforum Staff, contrib. by. Plastics in Automotive Engineering. 2009. (Illus.). 427p. pap. *(978-3-18-234304-2(1))* VDI-Verlag GmbH.
Wang, Xu, ed. Vehicle noise & Vibration Refinement. 2010. (Illus.). 452p. 255.00 *(978-1-84569-497-5(X))* Woodhead Publishing Ltd. GBR. Dist: Taylor & Francis Group.
Wood, Paul K. C. Strain Rate Testing of Metallic Materials & their Modeling for use in CAE based Automotive Crash Simulation Tools. 2009. (Handbook Ser.). (Illus.). vii, 93p. *(978-1-84735-374-0(6))* Smithers Rapra Publishing.
Yaknin, Judy. Driving It Home: 100 years of car Advertising. 2008. (Popular Culture Ser.). 132p. pap. 23.00 *(978-1-904750-35-2(4))* Libri Publishing Ltd GBR. Dist: Independent Pubs. Group.
$4 Gasoline & Fuel Economy: Auto Industry at a Crossroads: Hearing Before the Select Committee on Energy Independence & Global Warming, House of Representatives, One Hundred Tenth Congress, Second Session, June 26, 2008. 2010. (Illus.). iii, 515p. ***(978-0-16-087784-1(9),*** 552-070-42295-1) United States Government Printing Office.

AUTOMOBILES—ACCESSORIES
see Automobiles—Equipment and Supplies

AUTOMOBILES—ACCIDENTS
see Traffic Accidents

AUTOMOBILES—AERODYNAMICS
The Best of Automotive CFD - Proceedings of the 3rd EACC 2007. 2007. 0.00 net. *(978-0-9719532-1-5(X))* Fluent, Inc.

Stein, Jonathan A., ed. Curves of Steel: Streamlined Automobile Design. 2nd rev. ed. 2009. (ENG., Illus.). 192p. 75.00 (978-0-9779809-6-3(0)) Coachbuilt Pr.

Technology Research Editors, ed. Automotive Aerodynamics, 2007 Ed. 2007. pap. 128.50 (978-1-60030-236-7(X), Search-In-Print) CSA Journal Division.

AUTOMOBILES—AIR CONDITIONING

Birch, Tom. Automotive Heating & Air Conditioning. 5th ed. 2009. (ENG & SPA., Illus.). 528p. (C). pap. 122.80 (978-0-13-505136-8(3), Prentice Hall) Prentice Hall PTR.

Birch, Tom & Duvic, Marten. NATEF Correlated Task Sheets for Automotive Heating & Air Conditioning. 6th ed. 2011. (ENG.). 168p. (C). pap. 27.80 **(978-0-13-254047-6(9)**, Prentice Hall) Prentice Hall PTR.

Birch, Tom & Duvic, Martin. Automotive Heating & Air Conditioning. 6th rev. ed. 2011. (ENG & SPA., Illus.). 480p. (C). pap. 118.00 (978-0-13-255153-3(5), Prentice Hall) Prentice Hall PTR.

Chisenhall, Jack L. & Davis, Norman. How to Air Condition. 2010. (Hot Rod Basics Ser.). (ENG., Illus.). 144p. pap. 27.95 (978-1-929133-44-4(8), 1929133448) Wolfgang Pubns., Inc.

Daly, Steven. Automotive Air Conditioning & Climate Control Systems. 2006. (ENG., Illus.). 432p. (C). per. 57.95 (978-0-7506-6955-9(1), Butterworth-Heinemann) Elsevier Science & Technology Bks.

Delmar Learning Staff. Heating, Ventilation, Air-Conditioning & Refrigeration: Computer Based Training. 2009. (ENG.). 114.95 (978-1-4283-2144-1(6)) Delmar Cengage Learning.

Delmar Learning, Thomson. ASE Test Preparation - A7 Heating & Air Conditioning. 5th ed. 2011. (ENG., Illus.). 176p. pap. 23.95 (978-1-111-12709-1(3)) Delmar Cengage Learning.

Erjavec, Jack. Brakes: Natef Standards Job Sheets. 3rd ed. 2009. (ENG.). 208p. (C). pap. 40.95 (978-1-4354-8320-0(0)) Delmar Cengage Learning.

—NATEF Standards Job Sheets Area A7. 3rd ed. 2009. (ENG.). 176p. (C). pap. 40.95 (978-1-4354-8322-4(7)) Delmar Cengage Learning.

Grady, Michael. A7 Heating & Air Conditioning: Motor Age Self-Study Guide for ASE Certification. 2007. spiral bd. 22.95 (978-1-933180-82-3(X)) Advanstar Communications, Inc.

Haynes Manuals Editors. Automotive Heating & Air Conditioning. 2011. (Haynes Techbook Ser.). (ENG., Illus.). 254p. pap. 24.95 (978-1-56392-913-7(9), 1563929139) Haynes Manuals, Inc.

Institution of Mechanical Engineers Staff, contrib. by. Proceedings of the IMechE's VTMS8 - Vehicle Thermal: Management Systems Conference. 2007. (ENG., Illus.). 756p. per. (978-1-84334-348-6(7), Chandos Publishing) Woodhead Publishing Ltd.

Rehkopf, Jeffrey. Automotive Heating & Air Conditioning. 2008. (978-0-13-158308-5(5)) Pearson Bks.

Schnubel, Mark. Today's Technician: Automotive Heating & Air Conditioning, 2 vols. 4th ed. 2008. (ENG., Illus.). 976p. (C). pap. 161.95 (978-1-4283-8324-1(7)) Delmar Cengage Learning.

Schnubel, Mark. Today's Technician: Automotive Heating & Air Conditioning Classroom Manual & Shop Manual, 2 vols. 5th ed. 2012. (Today's Technician Ser.). (ENG.). 250p. (C). pap. 147.95 **(978-1-133-01745-5(2))** Delmar Cengage Learning.

AUTOMOBILES—BATTERIES

Stienecker, Adam. Hybrid Energy Storage Systems. 2009. 68p. pap. (978-3-639-13994-5(1)) VDM Verlag Dr. Mueller e.K.

AUTOMOBILES—BIBLIOGRAPHY

Young, Jan. Studebaker Bibliography. 2009. 103p. pap. 19.95 (978-0-557-05750-4(7)) Lulu Enterprises Inc.

AUTOMOBILES—BODIES

American Society of Mechanical Engineers Staff, ed. Chassis Frames: Passenger Car & Light Truck. 20p. 32.00 (978-0-7918-2292-0(3)) ASME Pr.

Calabrese, Giuseppe. La Filiera Dello Stile e le Politiche Industriali per L'automotive in Piemonte e in Europa. 2010. (ITA.). 218p. (978-88-568-2275-5(X)) Angeli.

Clymer, Floyd. How to Build a Fiberglass Car. 2010. 90p. pap. 24.95 (978-1-58850-098-4(5)) Veloce Enterprises, Inc.

Cram101 Textbook Reviews. Outlines & Highlights for Collision Repair Fundamentals by James E Duffy. 2011. 234p. pap. 31.95 **(978-1-61905-974-0(6))** Cram101 Inc.

Davies, Geoffrey. Materials for Automobile Bodies. 2nd ed. 2012. (ENG.). 110.00 (978-0-08-096979-4(8), Butterworth-Heinemann) Elsevier Science & Technology Bks.

Duffy, James E. Collision Repair Fundamentals. 2007. (ENG., Illus.). 576p. (C). 101.95 (978-1-4180-1336-3(6)) Delmar Cengage Learning.

Gross, Ken. The Allure of the Automobile: Driving in Style, 1930-1965. 2010. 40.00 (978-1-932543-34-6(1)) High Museum of Art.

Haajanen, Lennart W. Illustrated Dictionary of Automobile Body Styles. alt. ed. 2007. (ENG., Illus.). 175p. per. 39.95 (978-0-7864-3737-5(5)) McFarland & Co., Inc. Pubs.

Joseph, Matt. Automotive Bodywork & Rust Repair. 2009. 144p. pap. 24.95 (978-1-932494-97-6(9), S-A Design) CarTech, Inc.

—Automotive Sheet Metal Forming & Fabrication. 2011. (Illus.). 144p. pap. 24.95 (978-1-934709-36-8(0), S-A Design) CarTech, Inc.

Labaco, Ronald T. & Gross, Ken. Allure of the Automobile: Driving in Style, 1930-1965. 2010. (ENG., Illus.). 144p. 40.00 (978-0-8478-3495-2(6), Skira) Rizzoli International Pubns., Inc.

Lammon, Kurt. How to Repair Plastic Bodywork: Practical, Money-Saving Techniques for Cars, Motorcycles, Trucks, ATVs, & Snowmobiles. 2009. (ENG., Illus.). 144p. pap. 20.00 (978-1-884313-80-6(9), 1884313809) Whitehorse Pr.

Malen, Donald E. Fundamentals of Automobile Body Structure Design. 2011. (Illus.). 450p. (978-0-7680-2169-1(3)) SAE Intl.

Morello, L., et al. The Automotive Body: Volume I: Components Design, 2 vols. 2010. (Mechanical Engineering Ser.). Orig. Title: La Carrozzeria. (ENG., Illus.). xxii, 670p. 119.00 (978-94-007-0512-8(3), 9400705123) Springer.

—The Automotive Body: Volume II: System Design. 2010. (Mechanical Engineering Ser.). (ENG., Illus.). x, 570p. 119.00 (978-94-007-0515-9(8), 9400705158) Springer.

Nada, Giorgio Editor, ed. Zagato Milano 1919-2009: The Official Book. 2010. (ENG., Illus.). 160p. 64.95 (978-88-7911-487-5(5), 8879114875) Giorgio Nada Editore ITA. Dist: MBI Distribution Services/Quayside Distribution.

Omar, Mohammed A. The Automotive Body Manufacturing Systems & Processes. 2011. (ENG., Illus.). 392p. 120.00 (978-0-470-97633-3(0), Wiley) Wiley, John & Sons, Inc.

Palmer, Kris. Fix It! How to Repair Automotive Dents, Scratches, Tears & Stains. 2011. (Motorbooks Workshop Ser.). (ENG., Illus.). 144p. pap. 24.99 (978-0-7603-3989-3(9), 0760339899, Motorbooks) MBI Publishing Co. LLC.

Parks, Dennis W. The Complete Guide to Auto Body Repair. 2008. (Motorbooks Workshop Ser.). (ENG., Illus.). 192p. pap. 29.95 (978-0-7603-3278-8(9), 0760332789, Motorbooks) MBI Publishing Co. LLC.

Porter, Lindsay. Classic Car Bodywork Restoration Manual (4th Edition) The Complete Illustrated Step-by-Step Guide. 4th ed. 2010. (ENG., Illus.). 288p. 39.95 (978-1-84425-829-1(7), 1844258297) Haynes Publishing PLC GBR. Dist: MBI Distribution Services/Quayside Distribution.

Prentice-Hall, Inc Staff, creator. Interior & Rear Section Damage Analysis Program 4. 2007. (Illus.). 41p. pap. (978-0-13-243121-7(1), Prentice Hall) Pearson Education Canada.

Remus, Timothy. How to Chop Tops. 2008. (Old Skool Skills Ser.). (ENG., Illus.). 144p. pap. 24.95 (978-1-929133-49-9(9), 1929133499) Wolfgang Pubns., Inc.

Richardson, Jim & Horvath, Tom. Pro Paint & Body. 2011. (ENG.). 160p. (gr. 12). 21.95 (978-1-55788-563-0(X), HP Trade) Penguin Group (USA) Inc.

Uttrachi, Gerald. Advanced Automotive Welding. 2012. (ENG., Illus.). 160p. pap. 29.95 **(978-1-934709-96-2(4))** CarTech, Inc.

Zurschmeide, Jeffery. Automotive Welding: A Practical Guide. 2009. (Illus.). 144p. pap. 24.95 (978-1-932494-86-0(3)) CarTech, Inc.

AUTOMOBILES—BRAKES

American Society of Mechanical Engineers Staff, ed. Automotive Braking: Recent Developments & Future Trends. (Illus.). 304p. 186.00 (978-1-86058-131-1(5)) Professional Engineering Publishing GBR. Dist: SAE Intl.

Breuer, Bert & Bill, Karlheinz H. Brake Technology Handbook. 2008. 119.95 (978-0-7680-1787-8(4)) SAE Intl.

Delmar. ASE Test Preparation - A5 Brakes. 5th ed. 2011. (ENG., Illus.). 240p. pap. 23.95 (978-1-111-12707-7(7)) Delmar Cengage Learning.

Delmar Cengage Learning Staff. DATO: Diagnostic Scenarios for Brake Systems. 2011. (Automotive Multimedia Solutions Ser.). (ENG.). (C). 41.95 (978-1-111-03480-1(X)) Delmar Cengage Learning.

Delmar Learning. Brakes: Computer Based Training. 2007. (ENG.). 114.95 (978-1-4283-2110-6(1)) Delmar Cengage Learning.

Delmar Learning Staff. Suspension & Steering. 2008. (ENG.). 114.95 (978-1-4283-2093-2(8)) Delmar Cengage Learning.

Gkikas, Nikolaos. Ergonomics of Intelligent Vehicle Braking Systems. 2011. (Illus.). 256p. pap. **(978-3-8443-9392-7(7))** Lambert Academic Publishing.

Halderman, James D. Automotive Brake Systems. 5th ed. 2009. (ENG., Illus.). 488p. (C). pap. 118.00 (978-0-13-507934-8(9), Prentice Hall) Prentice Hall PTR.

Halderman, James D. & Mitchell, Chase. Automotive Brake Systems. 4th ed. 2007. (ENG.). 504p. (C). pap. 122.80 (978-0-13-174803-3(3), Prentice Hall) Prentice Hall PTR.

Hammill, Des. How to Build & Modify Sportscar & Kitcar Suspension & Brakes: For Road & Track - Revised & Updated 2nd Edition. 3rd ed. 2008. (SpeedPro Ser.). (ENG., Illus.). 128p. pap. 39.95 (978-1-84584-207-9(3), 1845842073) Veloce Publishing Ltd. GBR. Dist: MBI Distribution Services/Quayside Distribution.

Hollander Interchange Manual: Chassis I. 72nd ed. 2006. (Illus.). 864p. pap. 75.00 (978-1-58132-124-1(4)) Hollander.

Hollander Interchange Manual: Chassis II. 72nd ed. 2006. (Illus.). 1288p. pap. 75.00 (978-1-58132-125-8(2)) Hollander.

Hollander Interchange Manual: Chassis III. 72nd ed. 2006. (Illus.). 728p. pap. 75.00 (978-1-58132-126-5(0)) Hollander.

Hollander Interchange Manual: Chassis Set. 72nd ed. 2006. (Illus.). 2880p. pap. 235.00 (978-1-58132-133-3(3)) Hollander.

Hollander Interchange Manual: Identification I. 72nd ed. 2006. (Illus.). 472p. pap. 100.00 (978-1-58132-130-2(9)) Hollander.

Hollander Interchange Manual: Identification II. 72nd ed. 2006. (Illus.). 848p. pap. 100.00 (978-1-58132-131-9(7)) Hollander.

Johanson, Chris. Auto Brakes: A5 Shop Manual. abr. ed. 2007. (Illus.). 192p. (gr. 9-12). per. 18.00 (978-1-59070-724-1(9)) Goodheart-Willcox Pub.

Johanson, Chris & Stockel, Martin T. Auto Brakes. 2007. (Illus.). 512p. 66.64 (978-1-59070-838-5(5)) Goodheart-Willcox Pub.

Johnson, Ann. Hitting the Brakes: Engineering Design & the Production of Knowledge. 2009. (ENG., Illus.). 232p. 79.95 (978-0-8223-4526-8(9)); pap. 22.95 (978-0-8223-4541-1(2)) Duke Univ. Pr.

Limpert, Rudolf. Brake Design & Safety. 3rd ed. 2011. **(978-0-7680-3438-7(8))** SAE Intl.

Norville, Norman. T4 Med/Hvy Truck Brakes. 2007. spiral bd. 22.95 (978-1-933180-81-6(1)) Advanstar Communications, Inc.

Owen, Cliff & Varis, Lee. Automotive Brake Systems: Classroom Manual. 5th ed. 2010. (ENG.). 832p. (C). pap. 147.95 (978-1-4354-8655-3(2)) Delmar Cengage Learning.

Owen, Clifton E. Classroom Manual for Automotive Brake Systems. 5th ed. 2010. (ENG., Illus.). xvi, 285p. (C). pap. 110.95 **(978-1-4354-8657-7(9))** Delmar Cengage Learning.

Owen, Clifton E. & Eichhorn, Lane. Shop Manual for Automotive Brake Systems. 5th ed. 2010. (ENG., Illus.). xx, 498p. (C). pap. 110.95 (978-1-4354-8656-0(0)) Delmar Cengage Learning.

Rahim Abu Bakar, Abd. Disk Brake Squeal. 2008. 196p. per. (978-3-8364-3591-8(8)) VDM Verlag Dr. Mueller e.K.

Rehkopf, Jeffrey J. & Mitchell, Chase D. Automotive Brake Systems. 2007. (General Motors Fundamental Curriculum Ser.). 432p. (C). pap. 73.33 (978-0-13-158246-0(1), Prentice Hall) Prentice Hall PTR.

Robert Bosch GmbH Staff. Bosch Technical Instruction: Symbols for Compressed-Air Brake Systems. (Illus.). pap. 14.95 (978-0-8376-0597-5(0)) Bentley Pubs.

Savaresi, Sergio M. & Tanelli, Mara. Active Braking Control Systems Design for Vehicles. 2010. (Advances in Industrial Control Ser.). (Illus.). xxii, 255p. 149.00 (978-1-84996-349-7(5), 1849963495) Springer.

Technology Research Editors, ed. Motor Vehicle Brake Systems, 200 Ed. 2007. pap. 128.50 (978-1-60030-251-0(3), Search-In-Print) CSA Journal Division.

Thompson, James K. Brake NVH: Testing & Measurements. 2011. (Illus.). 156p. (978-0-7680-3480-6(9)) SAE Intl.

Walker, James, Jr. High-Performance Brake Systems: Design, Selection, & Installation. 2007. (S-A Design Ser.). (ENG., Illus.). 144p. pap. 24.95 (978-1-932494-32-7(4), S-A Design) CarTech, Inc.

Zausner, Robert. Bad Brake: Ford Trucks, Deadly When Parked. 2011. **(978-1-933822-39-6(2))** Camino Bks., Inc.

AUTOMOBILES—COLLECTORS AND COLLECTING

see also Antique and Classic Cars; Automobiles—History

Berg, Phil. Ultimate Garages II. 2007. (Illus.). 191p. 34.95 (978-1-893618-74-9(9)) Bull, David Publishing, Inc.

Berg, Phil. Ultimate Garages III. 2011. 191p. 39.95 **(978-0-9845891-0-4(4))** Mallard Service Inc.

Bertilsson, Bo. Hot Rods & Custom Cars. Date not set. (Illus.). 176p. 24.95 (978-0-7603-1585-9(X)) MBI Publishing Co. LLC.

Brooks, Jackson. Cars I Could've, Should've, Kept: Memoir of a Life Restoring Classic Sports Cars. 2007. (ENG., Illus.). 263p. per. 25.00 (978-0-7864-2810-6(4)) McFarland & Co., Inc. Pubs.

Budano, Rob & Kerr, Richard. Tomy AF-X. Kevin, Timothy, ed. (Collector's Quick Reference Ser.: Vol. 4). 100p. (Orig.). pap. 14.95 (978-0-88379-608-5(2)) What It Is! Publishing.

Cotter, Tom. The Corvette in the Barn: More Great Stories of Automotive Archaeology. 2010. (ENG., Illus.). 256p. 26.00 (978-0-7603-3797-4(7), 0760337977, Motorbooks) MBI Publishing Co. LLC.

Cummings, Christopher W. The Cadillac That Followed Me Home: Memoir of a V-16 Dream Realized. 2006. (ENG., Illus.). 243p. per. 25.00 (978-0-7864-2808-3(2)) McFarland & Co., Inc. Pubs.

Garvey, Scott. The Tractor in the Haystack: Great Stories of Tractor Archaeology. 2008. (ENG., Illus.). 256p. 22.00 (978-0-7603-3295-5(9), 0760332959, Voyageur Pr) MBI Publishing Co. LLC.

Gillham, Roger. Scalextric: Ultimate Guide. 7th ed. 2009. (ENG., Illus.). 400p. 69.95 (978-1-84425-536-8(0), 1844255360) Haynes Publishing PLC GBR. Dist: MBI Distribution Services/Quayside Distribution.

Guzzardi, Giuseppe & Rizzo, Enzo. Convertibles. 2007. (978-1-57215-483-4(7), JG Pr.) World Pubns. Group, Inc.

Horton, David Earl. I Was a Teenage Car Columnist: A Boomer's Scrapbook of mid-60's Cars & Stories. Edwards, Agnes, ed. 2008. (Illus.). 120p. per. 19.95 (978-0-9800990-4-1(8)) Thunderboomer Media LLC.

Johnson, Brian. Rockers & Rollers: A Full-Throttle Memoir. 2012. (ENG.). 256p. pap. 14.99 **(978-0-06-199084-7(1))** HarperCollins Pubs.

Keister, Douglas, photos by. Teardrops & Tiny Trailers, 1 vol. 2008. (ENG., Illus.). 160p. 19.99 (978-1-4236-0274-3(9)) Gibbs Smith, Publisher.

Kowalke, Ron. 2011 Collector Car Price Guide. 5th ed. 2010. (ENG., Illus.). 760p. pap. 19.99 (978-1-4402-1285-7(6)) Krause Pubns.

—2012 Collector Car Price Guide. 6th ed. 2011. (ENG.). 760p. pap. 21.99 (978-1-4402-2377-8(7)) Krause Pubns.

Laumann, Lloyd L., ed. A Collector's Guide to Classic Mighty Tonkas. 2006. (Illus.). 160p. spiral bd. 39.95 (978-0-9787888-0-3(X)) M & MV Bks.

Lee, Brian R. For the Love of Cars: The Growth of the Old Car Hobby. 2008. 104p. pap. 28.99 (978-1-4389-0459-7(2)) AuthorHouse.

Linden, Steve. Car Collecting: Everything You Need to Know. 2008. (Everything You Need to Know Ser.). (ENG., Illus.). 160p. per. 24.95 (978-0-7603-2809-5(9), 0760328099, Motorbooks) MBI Publishing Co. LLC.

Mack, Charlie. Lesney's Matchbox(r) Toys: The Superfast Years, 1969-1982. 3rd rev. ed. 2009. (Illus.). 128p. pap. 19.99 (978-0-7643-3321-7(6)) Schiffer Publishing, Ltd.

Macmillan, Don. The Bigger Book of John Deere Tractors: The Complete Model-by-Model Encyclopedia ... Plus Classic Toys, Brochures, & Collectibles, 2nd Edition. 2nd rev. ed. 2010. (Big Book Ser.). (ENG., Illus.). 288p. 40.00 (978-0-7603-3653-3(9), 0760336539, Voyageur Pr) MBI Publishing Co. LLC.

Martin, Keith & Sports Car Market Magazine Editors. Keith Martin's Guide to Car Collecting. 2009. (Illus.). 304p. pap. 21.99 (978-0-7603-3749-3(7), 0760337497, Motorbooks) MBI Publishing Co. LLC.

Morgan, Peter. Collector's Originality Guide Porsche 911. rev. ed. 2010. (Collector's Originality Guide Ser.). (ENG., Illus.). 200p. 40.00 (978-0-7603-3575-8(3), 0760335753, Motorbooks) MBI Publishing Co. LLC.

Nourmand, Tony. Stars & Cars. 2009. (ENG., Illus.). 192p. 52.50 (978-0-7522-2645-3(2), Boxtree) Pan Macmillan GBR. Dist: Trans-Atlantic Pubns., Inc.

Nowak, Patrick J. Forty Cars That Owned Me. 2007. 331p. pap. 19.95 (978-0-7414-3736-5(8)) Infinity Publishing.

Overstake, T. J. For Love of the Car: Memories of a True Car Guy. 2009. 159p. pap. 11.95 (978-1-4327-3594-4(2)) Outskirts Pr., Inc.

Palmer, Kris. Survivor: The Unrestored Collector Car. 2008. (ENG.). 216p. 30.00 (978-0-9817270-1-1(8), Parker Hse. Publishing Inc.,Csi) Continental Sales, Inc.

Passmore, Michael. The AA: History, Badges & Memorabilia. 2008. (Shire Library). (ENG., Illus.). 40p. pap. 11.95 (978-0-7478-0552-6(0)) Shire Pubns., Ltd. GBR. Dist: Random Hse., Inc.

Publications International Staff. Chevy Classics. 2008. 128p. 10.98 (978-1-4127-1524-9(5)) Publications International, Ltd.

Ralston, Andrew. Diecast Toy Cars of the 1950s & 1960s. collector's ed. 2009. (ENG., Illus.). 128p. pap. 19.95 (978-1-84584-180-5(8), 1845841808) Veloce Publishing Ltd. GBR. Dist: MBI Distribution Services/Quayside Distribution.

Ralston, Andrew & Ralston, Andrew G. Plastic Toy Cars of the 1950s & 1960s: The Collector's Guide. 2008. (ENG., Illus.). 128p. pap. 39.95 (978-1-84584-125-6(5), 1845841255) Veloce Publishing Ltd. GBR. Dist: MBI Distribution Services/Quayside Distribution.

Robinson, Jon G. Standard Catalog of 1950s Chrysler. 2006. (ENG., Illus.). 224p. per. 24.99 (978-0-89689-249-1(2), Antique Trader) Krause Pubns.

Roy, Rex. Motor City Dream Garages: Amazing Collections from Americas Greatest Car City. rev. ed. 2007. (ENG., Illus.). 192p. 34.95 (978-0-7603-2989-4(3), 0760329893, Motorbooks) MBI Publishing Co. LLC.

Schild, Jim. Challenger & Barracuda, 1970-74. 2010. (Collector's Originality Guide Ser.). (ENG., Illus.). 128p. pap. 24.99 (978-0-7603-3788-2(8), 0760337888, Motorbooks) MBI Publishing Co. LLC.

Tucker, Malcolm. Rust in Peace: Photographs from the Mike Worthington-Williams Archives. 2008. (ENG., Illus.). 256p. 49.00 (978-1-85443-225-4(7), 1854432257) Dalton Watson Fine Bks.

Wood, Jonathan. Coachbuilding: The Hand-Crafted Car Body. 2009. (Shire Library). (ENG., Illus.). 48p. pap. 12.95 (978-0-7478-0688-2(8)) Shire Pubns., Ltd. GBR. Dist: Random Hse., Inc.

—MG. 2008. (Shire Library). (ENG., Illus.). 56p. pap. 12.95 (978-0-7478-0674-5(8)) Shire Pubns., Ltd. GBR. Dist: Random Hse., Inc.

AUTOMOBILES—CONSERVATION AND RESTORATION

Adams, Bruce, ed. Mercedes-Benz 190SL 1955-1963 Restoration & Ownership - Volume 2, 2. 2007. 75.00 (978-0-9729420-1-0(7)) International 190SL Group.

Brownell, Tom & Scott, Jason. How to Restore Your Collector Car. 2nd rev. ed. 2009. (Motorbooks Workshop Ser.). (ENG., Illus.). 272p. pap. 29.99 (978-0-7603-3541-3(9), 0760335419, Motorbooks) MBI Publishing Co. LLC.

Cummings, Christopher W. The Cadillac That Followed Me Home: Memoir of a V-16 Dream Realized. 2006. (ENG., Illus.). 243p. per. 25.00 (978-0-7864-2808-3(2)) McFarland & Co., Inc. Pubs.

Date, Colin. Collector's Originality Guide Mustang 1964-1-2-1966. 2009. (Collector's Originality Guide Ser.). (ENG., Illus.). 128p. pap. 24.99 (978-0-7603-3745-5(4), 0760337454, Motorbooks) MBI Publishing Co. LLC.

Falconer, Tom. Collector's Originality Guide Corvette 1968-1982. 2010. (Collector's Originality Guide Ser.). (ENG., Illus.). 144p. pap. 24.99 (978-0-7603-3747-9(0), 0760337470, Motorbooks) MBI Publishing Co. LLC.

Frohwerk, Arthur, et al. Best Practices in Planning Automation Restructuring. Date not set. pap. (978-1-892942-01-2(1)) Clinical Laboratory Management Assn.

Gunnell, John. How to Restore Automotive Trim & Hardware. 2009. (Motorbooks Workshop Ser.). (ENG., Illus.). 160p. pap. 24.99 (978-0-7603-3531-4(1), 0760335311, Motorbooks) MBI Publishing Co. LLC.

Hardier, Ghislain. La Jeep Dans Tous Ses Etats. 2008. 176p. 44.95 (978-2-84048-236-9(3)) Editions Heimdal FRA. Dist: Casemate Pubs. & Bk. Distributors, LLC.

Joseph, Matt. Automotive Bodywork & Rust Repair. 2009. 144p. pap. 24.95 (978-1-932494-97-6(9), S-A Design) CarTech, Inc.

Lyles, Larry. Project Mustang: The Step-by-Step Restoration of a Popular Vintage Car. 2007. (ENG., Illus.). 192p. per. 24.95 (978-1-933958-03-3(0)) BowTie Pr.

Mustang Monthly Editors and Publishers Staff. Classic Mustang: Restoration, Repair & Upgrades. 2011. (ENG.). 224p. (gr. 12). 21.95 (978-1-55788-556-2(7), HP Trade) Penguin Group (USA) Inc.

National Association of Road Transport Museums Staff. Buses Restored 2008. 2008. (Illus.). 128p. 26.95 (978-0-7110-3319-1(6)) Allan, Ian Publishing GBR. Dist: Casemate Pubs. & Bk. Distributors, LLC.

Petris, Chris. How to Restore Your Corvette: 1963-1967. 2012. (ENG., Illus.). 192p. pap. 29.95 **(978-1-934709-76-4(X))** CarTech, Inc.

Porter, Lindsay. Classic Car Bodywork Restoration Manual (4th Edition) The Complete Illustrated Step-by-Step Guide. 4th ed. 2010. (ENG., Illus.). 288p. 39.95 (978-1-84425-829-1(7), 1844258297) Haynes Publishing PLC GBR. Dist: MBI Distribution Services/Quayside Distribution.

Prince, Richard. Corvette 1968-1982 Restoration Guide. 2nd ed. 2011. (Motorbooks Workshop Ser.). (ENG., Illus.). 224p. pap. 29.99 *(978-0-7603-4057-8(9)*, 0760340579, Motorbooks) MBI Publishing Co. LLC.

The Rebuilder's Data Book for Popular British Cars: Professional Edition, 1945-1986 Models. *(978-1-890700-34-8(7))* Imported Car, The.

The Rebuilder's Data Book for Popular European Cars: Professional Edition, 1945-1986 Models. *(978-1-890700-35-5(5))* Imported Car, The.

The Rebuilder's Data Book for Popular Import Cars: 1945-1986 Models. lib. bdg. *(978-1-890700-33-1(9))* Imported Car, The.

The Rebuilder's Data Book for Popular Japanese Cars: Professional Edition, 1945-1986 Models. *(978-1-890700-36-2(3))* Imported Car, The.

Sessions, Ron. Classic Camaro HP1564: Repair, Restoration & Upgrades. 2011. 176p. 21.95 *(978-1-55788-564-7(8)*, HP Trade) Penguin Group (USA) Inc.

Thorley, Nigel. Original Jaguar Mk I/Mk II Vol. 8: The Restorer's Guide to Mk1, Mk11, 240/340 & Daimler. 2008. (Original Ser.). (ENG., Illus.). 96p. 44.95 *(978-1-906133-04-7(2)*, 1906133042) Herridge & Sons Ltd.

Williams, Roger. How to Restore Triumph TR2, 3, 3A, 4 & 4A: Body, Trim & Mechanical Restoration. 2009. (Enthusiast's Restoration Manuals Ser.). (ENG., Illus.). 192p. pap. 69.95 *(978-1-84584-263-5(4)*, 1845842634) Veloce Publishing Ltd. GBR. Dist: MBI Distribution Services/Quayside Distribution.

—How to Restore Triumph TR5/250 & TR6. 2010. (Enthusiast's Restoration Manuals Ser.). (ENG., Illus.). 192p. pap. 59.95 *(978-1-903706-46-6(7)*, 1903706467) Veloce Publishing Ltd. GBR. Dist: MBI Distribution Services/Quayside Distribution.

Yost, Spencer. How to Keep Your Classic Tractor Alive. 2009. (ENG., Illus.). 240p. pap. 23.99 *(978-0-7603-2951-1(6)*, 0760329516, Voyageur Pr) MBI Publishing Co. LLC.

Zimmerman, Mark. How to Restore Your Motorcycle: Second Edition. 2nd ed. 2010. (Motorbooks Workshop Ser.). (ENG., Illus.). 192p. pap. 29.99 *(978-0-7603-3772-1(1)*, 0760337721, Motorbooks) MBI Publishing Co. LLC.

AUTOMOBILES—CONSTRUCTION

see Automobiles—Design and Construction

AUTOMOBILES—CUSTOMIZING

Alig, Joseph & Kilmer, Stephan. East vs. West: Rods, Customs & Rails: Rods, Customs & Rails. 2012. (Illus.). 160p. pap. 29.95 ***(978-1-934709-75-7(1))*** CarTech, Inc.

Allen, Jim. Jeep 4x4 Performance Handbook. 2nd rev. ed. 2007. (Motorbooks Workshop Ser.). (ENG., Illus.). 224p. pap. 29.95 *(978-0-7603-2687-9(8)*, 0760326878, Motorbooks) MBI Publishing Co. LLC.

Bonk, Aaron. High-Performance Sport Compact Heads & Cams. 2007. (ENG., Illus.). 128p. pap. 24.95 *(978-1-932494-35-8(9)*, S-A Design) CarTech, Inc.

Borties, JoAnn. The Custom Painting Idea Book: Cars, Motorcycles, Trucks. 2008. (Motorbooks Workshop Ser.). (ENG., Illus.). 160p. pap. 25.95 *(978-0-7603-3169-9(3)*, 0760331693, Motorbooks) MBI Publishing Co. LLC.

Caldwell, Bruce. How to Paint Flames. 2nd ed. 2011. (Motorbooks Workshop Ser.). (ENG., Illus.). 160p. pap. 24.99 *(978-0-7603-4136-0(2)*, 0760341362, Motorbooks) MBI Publishing Co. LLC.

Eccles, David. VW Camper Inspirational Interiors: Bespoke & Custom Interior Designs. 2009. (ENG., Illus.). 224p. 44.95 *(978-1-84797-070-1(2)*, 1847970702) Crowood Pr., Ltd. GBR. Dist: MBI Distribution Services/Quayside Distribution.

Fotojoost, et al, photos by. Top Tuning. 2007. (ENG., Illus.). 252p. *(978-90-76886-35-0(0))* Tectum B.V.B.A.

Ganahl, Pat. Custom Painting. 2008. (Performance How-to Ser.). (Illus.). 144p. pap. 24.95 *(978-1-932494-58-7(8))* CarTech, Inc.

Garber, Bette S. Ultra-Custom Semi Trucks. 2008. (Gallery Ser.). (ENG., Illus.). 192p. pap. 17.95 *(978-0-7603-3292-4(4)*, 0760332924, Motorbooks) MBI Publishing Co. LLC.

Hale, James. How to Modify Volkswagen Bus Suspension, Brakes & Chassis for High Performance. enl. ed. 2011. (ENG., Illus.). 144p. pap. 49.95 *(978-1-84584-262-8(6)*, 1845842626) Veloce Publishing Ltd. GBR. Dist: MBI Distribution Services/Quayside Distribution.

Hartman, Jeff. Supercharging Performance Handbook. 2011. (Motorbooks Workshop Ser.). (ENG., Illus.). 224p. pap. 29.99 *(978-0-7603-3938-1(4)*, 0760339384, Motorbooks) MBI Publishing Co. LLC.

Henderson, Shawn. Chevy LS Engine Conversion Handbook. 2011. (ENG.). 192p. 23.95 *(978-1-55788-566-1(4)*, HP Trade) Penguin Group (USA) Inc.

Holder, Bill & Kunz, Phil. Resto-Mod Muscle Cars: A Showcase of the World's Best Builds, Plus Ideas for Designing Your Own. 2008. (ENG., Illus.). 176p. pap. 24.99 *(978-0-89689-616-1(1))* Krause Pubns.

Kluczyk, Barry. High-Performance New Hemi Builder's Guide: 2003-Present. 2007. (S-A Design Ser.). (ENG., Illus.). 144p. pap. 24.95 *(978-1-932494-39-6(1)*, S-A Design) CarTech, Inc.

Leffingwell, Randy. Shelby Mustang: Racer for the Street. 2011. (ENG., Illus.). 192p. pap. 24.99 *(978-0-7603-3945-9(7)*, 0760339457, Motorbooks) MBI Publishing Co. LLC.

Lier, Alexandra. Speedseekers. 2008. 274p. *(978-1-58423-315-2(X))*; (Illus.). *(978-1-58423-314-5(1))* Gingko Pr., Inc.

Mangus, Ron & Smith, Gary D. Chevy Tri-Five Custom Interiors: 1955, 1956 1957. 2008. (Ron Mangus' Custom Hot Rod Interiors Ser.). (ENG., Illus.). 160p. pap. 27.95 *(978-1-931128-25-4(1)*, 1931128251) California Bill's Automotive Handbooks.

Martinez, Herb, ed. Pinstripe Planet II: More Fine Lines from the World's Best. 2010. (ENG.). 192p. 37.95 *(978-0-9558336-2-5(0))* Korero Books LLP GBR. Dist: Independent Pubs. Group.

Mayes, Alan. Custom Cars: Coupes, Sedans, Pickups. 2010. (Idea Book Ser.). (ENG., Illus.). 160p. pap. 24.99 *(978-0-7603-3760-8(8)*, 0760337608, Motorbooks) MBI Publishing Co. LLC.

Miller, Dick. How to Hook & Launch: Traction Mods for Street & Strip. 2012. (ENG., Illus.). 128p. pap. 24.95 ***(978-1-934709-35-1(2))*** CarTech, Inc.

Nason, Douglas, et al. King of the Kustomizers: The Art of George Barris. 2012. (ENG., Illus.). 200p. 39.95 *(978-0-86719-740-2(4))* Last Gasp of San Francisco.

Newton, Richard. Autocross Performance Handbook. rev. ed. 2007. (Motorbooks Workshop Ser.). (ENG., Illus.). 160p. pap. 25.95 *(978-0-7603-2788-3(2)*, 0760327882, Motorbooks) MBI Publishing Co. LLC.

Noakes, Andrew. The Ford Cosworth DFV: The Inside Story of F1's Greatest Engine. 2007. (ENG., Illus.). 192p. 44.95 *(978-1-84425-337-1(6)*, 1844253376) Haynes Publishing PLC GBR. Dist: MBI Distribution Services/Quayside Distribution.

Pettitt, Joe & Banks, Gale. High-Performance Diesel Builder's Guide. 2007. (S-A Design Ser.). (ENG., Illus.). 128p. pap. 24.95 *(978-1-932494-34-1(0)*, S-A Design) CarTech, Inc.

Pinstripers, Collection of 25. Pinstriping Masters II: More Techniques, Tricks, & Special F/X for Laying down the Line. 2008. (ENG., Illus.). 168p. pap. 29.95 *(978-0-9637336-4-1(8)*, 0963733648) Airbrush Action, Inc.

Remus, Timothy. How to Chop Tops. 2008. (Old Skool Skills Ser.). (ENG., Illus.). 144p. pap. 24.95 *(978-1-929133-49-9(9)*, 1929133499) Wolfgang Pubns., Inc.

Seume, Keith. The Story of the California Look VW. 2009. (ENG., Illus.). 144p. pap. 29.95 *(978-1-906133-08-5(5)*, 1906133085) Herridge & Sons, Ltd. GBR. Dist: MBI Distribution Services/Quayside Distribution.

Taylor, Thom. Kustomland: The Custom Car Photography of James Potter, 1955-1959. 2008. (ENG., Illus.). 128p. 24.95 *(978-0-7603-2259-8(7)*, 0760322597, Motorbooks) MBI Publishing Co. LLC.

Thurn, Walt. High-Performance C5 Corvette Builder's Guide. 2007. (S-A Design Ser.). (ENG., Illus.). 144p. pap. 24.95 *(978-1-932494-33-4(2)*, S-A Design) CarTech, Inc.

Warner, Mark. The Electric Vehicle Conversion Handbook HP1568. 2011. (ENG.). 192p. (gr. 12). 21.95 *(978-1-55788-568-5(0)*, HP Trade) Penguin Group (USA) Inc.

Zurschmeide, Jeffrey. High-Performance Subaru Builder's Guide: Includes the Impreza, Legacy, Forester, Outback, WRX & STI. 2007. (S-A Design Ser.). (ENG., Illus.). 144p. pap. 24.95 *(978-1-932494-51-8(0)*, S-A Design) CarTech, Inc.

AUTOMOBILES—DESIGN AND CONSTRUCTION

see also Automobiles—Bodies

Ahmed, Ammar. Vehicle Architecture. 2010. 123p. pap. 45.00 *(978-0-557-41437-6(7))* Lulu Enterprises Inc.

Aird, Forbes. Fiberglass & Other Composite MaterialsHP1498: A Guide to High Performance Non-Metallic Materials for AutomotiveRacing & Marine Use. Includes Fiberglass, Kevlar, Carbon Fiber,Molds, Structures An. rev. ed. 2006. (ENG., Illus.). 160p. (gr. 12-18). 21.95 *(978-1-55788-498-5(6)*, HP Trade) Penguin Group (USA) Inc.

American Society of Mechanical Engineers Staff, ed. Automotive Manufacturing (Autotech '97) (Illus.). 68p. 59.00 *(978-1-86058-023-9(8))* Professional Engineering Publishing GBR. Dist: SAE Intl.

—Engineering for the Customer (Fisita Proceedings), 5 vols. (Illus.). 179p. 90.00 *(978-0-85298-836-7(2))* Professional Engineering Publishing GBR. Dist: SAE Intl.

—Integration of Design & Manufacture (Fisita Proceedings), 5 vols. (Illus.). 300p. 120.00 *(978-0-85298-835-0(4))* Professional Engineering Publishing GBR. Dist: SAE Intl.

Atkins, Richard D. An Introduction to Engine Testing & Development. 2009. 79.95 *(978-0-7680-2099-1(9))* SAE Intl.

Austin, Jorg & Walter, Sigmund. Porsche 911 Source Book: The Full Specification History, 1963 To 2010. 2011. (ENG., Illus.). 384p. 44.95 *(978-1-84425-969-4(2)*, 1844259692) Haynes Publishing PLC GBR. Dist: MBI Distribution Services/Quayside Distribution.

Balfour, Christopher. Bristol Cars: A Very British Story. 2010. (ENG., Illus.). 320p. 62.95 *(978-1-84425-407-1(0)*, 1844254070) Haynes Publishing PLC GBR. Dist: MBI Distribution Services/Quayside Distribution.

Bayley, Stephen. Cars: Freiheit - Stil - Sex - Power - Bewegung - Farbe. 2009. (ENG., Illus.). 384p. 65.00 *(978-1-84091-504-4(8)*, Conran Octopus) Octopus Publishing Group GBR. Dist: Hachette Bk. Group.

Benfield, Matt. Radio Control Car Manual: The Complete Guide to Buying, Building & Maintaining. 2008. (ENG., Illus.). 176p. 36.95 *(978-1-84425-470-5(4)*, 1844254704) Haynes Publishing PLC GBR. Dist: MBI Distribution Services/Quayside Distribution.

Berk, Gijsbert-Paul. Andre Lefebre: And the Cars He Created at Voisin & Citroen. 2009. (ENG., Illus.). 144p. 39.95 *(978-1-84584-244-4(8)*, 1845842448) Veloce Publishing Ltd. GBR. Dist: MBI Distribution Services/Quayside Distribution.

Bertilsson, Bo. Roy Brizio Street Rods: Modern Hot Rods Defined. 2009. (ENG., Illus.). 160p. 35.00 *(978-0-7603-3544-4(3)*, 0760335443, Motorbooks) MBI Publishing Co. LLC.

Bertsche, Bernd. Reliability in Automotive & Mechanical Engineering. 2008. (VDI-Buch Ser.). (Illus.). 506p. 139.00 *(978-3-540-33969-4(8)*, 3540339698) Springer.

—Reliability in Automotive & Mechanical Engineering: Determination of Component & System Reliability. 2011. (VDI-Buch Ser.). (ENG., Illus.). xi, 500p. pap. 139.00 *(978-3-642-07049-5(3)*, 3642070493) Springer.

Bhise, Vivek D. Ergonomics in the Automotive Design Process. 2011. (ENG., Illus.). 329p. 89.95 *(978-1-4398-4210-2(8)*, CRC Press) Taylor & Francis Group GBR. Dist: Taylor & Francis Group.

Blank, Harrod. Art Cars: The cars, the artists, the obsession, the Craft. 2nd exp. ed. 2007. (Illus.). 160p. (YA). pap. 19.95 *(978-0-933621-92-3(2))* Blank Bks.

Bolofo, Koto. Vroom! Vroom! 2010. (ENG., Illus.). 96p. 75.00 *(978-3-86521-961-9(6))* Steidl, Gerhard Druckerei und Verlag DEU. Dist: D.A.P./Distributed Art Pubs.

Bongers, Marc. Porsche Data Book: The Definitive Reference to Specifications & Statistics. 2006. (ENG., Illus.). 400p. 49.95 *(978-1-84425-316-6(3)*, 1844253163) Haynes Publishing PLC GBR. Dist: MBI Distribution Services/Quayside Distribution.

Bonnick, Allan. Automotive Science & Mathematics. 2008. (ENG., Illus.). 264p. (C). pap. 33.95 *(978-0-7506-8522-1(0))* Routledge.

—A Practical Approach to Motor Vehicle Engineering & Maintenance. 3rd rev. ed. 2011. (ENG., Illus.). 504p. pap. 41.95 *(978-0-08-096998-5(4))* Routledge.

Booth, Gavin. Buses by Design. 2008. (ENG., Illus.). 160p. 46.95 *(978-0-7110-3326-9(9))* Allan, Ian Publishing GBR. Dist: BookMasters Distribution Services (BDS).

Boyle, Linda N., et al, compiled by. Proceedings of the 4th International Driving Symposium on Human Factors in Driver Assessment, Training, & Vehicle Design. 2007. (Illus.). 598p. (C). per. 75.00 *(978-0-87414-158-0(3))* Univ of Iowa, Pubns. Dept.

Bridgewater, Julian, et al. The Soapbox Bible: How to Build Your Own Soapbox, Buggy, or Go-Cart. 2010. (ENG., Illus.). 160p. 16.95 *(978-1-4027-6682-4(3))* Sterling Publishing Co., Inc.

Brown, Stewart J. Volvo Ailsa. 2011. (ENG., Illus.). 96p. 32.95 *(978-0-7110-3514-0(8))* Allan, Ian Publishing GBR. Dist: BookMasters Distribution Services (BDS).

Browning, Jaclyn E. & McMann, Alexander K. Computational Engineering: Design, Development & Applications. 2011. (Engineering Tools, Techniques & Tables Ser.). 89.00 *(978-1-61122-806-9(9))* Nova Science Pubs., Inc.

Broy, Manfred. Model-Driven Development of Reliable Automotive Services: Second Automotive Software Workshop, ASWSD 2006, San Diego, CA, USA, March 15-17, 2006, Revised Selected Papers. 2008. (Lecture Notes in Computer Science / Programming & Software Engineering Ser.). xvii, 183p. pap. 69.95 *(978-3-540-70929-9(0))* Springer.

Bryant, Jefferson. How to Design & Install in Car Entertainment Systems. 2009. (Illus.). 144p. pap. 24.95 *(978-1-932494-94-5(4)*, S-A Design) CarTech, Inc.

Carroll, John & Stuart, Garry. The Ultimate Guide to Choppers. 2007. (Illus.). 447p. pap. 12.99 *(978-0-7858-2249-3(6)*, Chartwell) Book Sales, Inc.

Cathcart, Alan. American Dream Bikes. 2010. (ENG.). 240p. 40.00 *(978-1-935350-01-9(3)*, Parker Hse. Publishing Inc.,Csi) Continental Sales, Inc.

Cdx Global Staff & Jones and Bartlett Publishers Staff. Suspension & Steering Tasksheet Manual for Natef Proficiency. rev. ed. 2010. 98p. pap. 26.95 *(978-0-7637-8467-6(2))* Jones & Bartlett Learning, LLC.

Chase, Brian. Still Unsafe at Any Speed. 2009. pap. 29.99 *(978-1-61584-575-0(5))* Independent Pub.

Cheetham, Craig. World's Worst Cars. (World's Worst: from Innovation to Disaster Ser.). 80p. 2009. (gr. 8-8). 61.20 *(978-1-60854-858-3(9))* 2008. (Illus.). 30.60 *(978-1-4042-1844-4(0))* Rosen Publishing Group, Inc., The.

Chu, Hsiao-Yun & Jenkins, David, eds. Buckminster Fuller: Dymaxion Car. 2011. (SPA & ENG., Illus.). 224p. 75.00 *(978-0-9564339-3-0(5))* Ivory Pr. ESP. Dist: D.A.P./Distributed Art Pubs.

Circle Track Magazine Editors, ed. Dirt Track Chassis & Suspension: Advanced Setup & Design Technology for Dirt Track Racing. 2007. (ENG., Illus.). 128p. (gr. 12-18). 19.95 *(978-1-55788-511-1(7)*, HP Trade) Penguin Group (USA) Inc.

Clymer, Floyd. How to Build a Racing Car. 2010. 86p. pap. 24.95 *(978-1-58850-150-9(7))* Veloce Enterprises, Inc.

Copping, Richard. VW Camper & Microbus. 2009. (Shire Library). (ENG., Illus.). 64p. pap. 12.95 *(978-0-7478-0709-4(4))* Shire Pubns., Ltd. GBR. Dist: Random Hse., Inc.

Cotter, Tom. Dean Jeffries: 50 Fabulous Years in Hot Rods, Racing & Film. 2009. (ENG., Illus.). 192p. 40.00 *(978-0-7603-3346-4(7)*, 0760333467, Motorbooks) MBI Publishing Co. LLC.

Crolla, David, ed. Automotive Engineering: Powertrain, Chassis System & Vehicle Body. 2009. (ENG., Illus.). 850p. 155.00 *(978-1-85617-577-7(4)*, Butterworth-Heinemann) Elsevier Science & Technology Bks.

Curami, Andrea. Alfa Romeo & Mille Miglia. 2010. (ENG.). 160p. 44.95 *(978-88-7911-496-7(4))*; (Illus.). 44.95 *(978-88-7911-504-9(9)*, 8879115049) Giorgio Nada Editore ITA. Dist: MBI Distribution Services/Quayside Distribution.

Cusumano, Michael A. & Kentaro, Nobeoka. Thinking Beyond Lean: How Multi Project Management Is Transforming Produ. 2008. (ENG., Illus.). 272p. pap. 18.95 *(978-1-4391-0177-3(9)*, Free Pr.) Free Pr.

Design Museum Staff. Fifty Cars That Changed the World. 2010. (ENG., Illus.). 110p. 20.00 *(978-1-84091-536-5(6)*, Conran Octopus) Octopus Publishing Group GBR. Dist: Hachette Bk. Group.

Dewey, Adrian. How to Illustrate & Design Concept Cars. 2009. (ENG., Illus.). 128p. reprint ed. pap. 35.95 *(978-1-84584-220-8(0)*, 1845842200) Veloce Publishing Ltd. GBR. Dist: MBI Distribution Services/Quayside Distribution.

Dickinson, Gene D. GDT Speedster from Dream to Reality. 2008. 179p. pap. 82.70 *(978-0-615-16515-8(X))* GDT Speedster, LLC.

Dixon, John. Modern Diesel Technology: Heating, Ventilation, Air Conditioning & Refrigeration. 2006. (ENG., Illus.). 304p. (C). per. 123.95 *(978-1-4018-7849-8(0))* Delmar Cengage Learning.

Dodds, Alastair. Making Cars. Date not set. (Scotland's Past in Action Ser.). (Illus.). 88p. pap. 4.95 *(978-0-948636-81-3(5)*, 6815) NMS Enterprises Ltd. - Publishing GBR. Dist: Weatherhill, Inc.

Dolcini, Pietro J., et al. Dry Clutch Control for Automated Manual Transmission Vehicles. 2010. (Advances in Industrial Control Ser.). (ENG., Illus.). 144p. 149.00 *(978-1-84996-067-0(4)*, 1849960674) Springer.

Donaldson, Bruce K. Analysis of Aircraft Structures. 2nd rev. ed. 2008. (Cambridge Aerospace Ser.). (ENG., Illus.). 974p. (C). 155.00 *(978-0-521-86583-8(2))* Cambridge Univ. Pr.

Down, Barrie. Art Deco & British Car Design: The Airline Cars of the 1930s. 2010. (ENG., Illus.). 144p. reprint ed. 44.95 *(978-1-84584-252-9(9)*, 1845842529) Veloce Publishing Ltd. GBR. Dist: MBI Distribution Services/Quayside Distribution.

Dron, Tony & de Burton, Simon. The Bentley Brooklands. 2010. (ENG., Illus.). 208p. pap. 195.00 *(978-1-85894-549-1(6))* Merrell Pubs. Ltd. GBR. Dist: Perseus Distribution.

Duncan, John. Any Colour - So Long As It's Black: Designing the Model T Ford, 1906-1908. 2010. (ENG., Illus.). 128p. 21.00 *(978-1-877437-15-1(8))* Exisle Publishing Ltd. NZL. Dist: BookMasters Distribution Services (BDS).

Edmondson, Chuck. Fast Car Physics. 2011. (ENG., Illus.). 248p. (gr. 17). 75.00 *(978-0-8018-9822-8(6))*; pap. 29.95 *(978-0-8018-9823-5(4))* Johns Hopkins Univ. Pr.

Edsall, Larry. Chevrolet Volt: Charging into the Future. 2010. (ENG., Illus.). 144p. 30.00 *(978-0-7603-3893-3(0)*, 0760338930, Motorbooks) MBI Publishing Co. LLC.

Electromecanica Automotriz. 2006th ed. 2006. (SPA.). training bk. ed. 150.00 *(978-0-9759696-2-5(5))* Vargas, Eduardo.

Elford, Vic. Porsche High-Performance Driving Handbook. 2nd rev. ed. 2006. (ENG., Illus.). 176p. pap. 29.95 *(978-0-7603-2754-8(8)*, 0760327548, Motorbooks) MBI Publishing Co. LLC.

Eliasson, Olafur. The Climate Car: Your mobile expectations: BMW H2R Project. 2008. (Illus.). 320p. 44.95 *(978-3-03778-117-3(3)*, 3037781173) Springer.

Elliott, Sue. Automotive Custom Interiors. 2009. (Idea Book Ser.). (ENG., Illus.). 160p. pap. 24.99 *(978-0-7603-3288-7(6)*, 0760332886, Motorbooks) MBI Publishing Co. LLC.

Emerson, Seth & Fisher, Bill. Performance Corvairs: How to Hotrod the Corvair Engine & Chassis. 2012. (ENG., Illus.). 176p. pap. 27.95 *(978-1-931128-22-3(7)*, 1931128227) California Bill's Automotive Handbooks.

European Automobile Engineers Cooperation (EAEC) Staff, compiled by. 10th EAEC European Automotive Congress (EAEC 2005) 2007. 1512p. pap. 306.00 *(978-1-60423-604-0(3))* Curran Assocs., Inc.

Evenden, Helen. Moving Foward: New Directions in Transport Design. 2007. (ENG., Illus.). 128p. pap. 35.00 *(978-1-85177-491-3(2))* V & A Pubns. GBR. Dist: Hachette Bk. Group.

Farameh, Patrice & Simonian, John. Timepiece Machines, 1 vol. 2010. (FRE, DUT & ENG., Illus.). 304p. 49.95 *(978-90-79761-45-6(1))* Tectum B.V.B.A. BEL. Dist: Innovative Logistics.

Finkbeiner, Andy. How to Build Max-Performance Mopar Big Blocks. 2009. 144p. pap. 24.95 *(978-1-934709-03-0(4)*, S-A Design) CarTech, Inc.

Gahan, Andrew. 3D Automotive Modeling: An Insider's Guide to 3D Car Modeling & Design for Games & Film. 2010. (ENG., Illus.). 472p. pap. 49.95 *(978-0-240-81428-5(2)*, Focal Pr.) Elsevier Science & Technology Bks.

Genta, G. & Morello, L. The Automotive Chassis, 2 vols. 2008. (Mechanical Engineering Ser.). (ENG., Illus.). xxiv, 628p. 99.00 *(978-1-4020-8674-8(1))* Springer.

Genta, Giancarlo. The Automotive Chassis, 2 vols. 2008. (Mechanical Engineering Ser.). (Illus.). 99.00 *(978-1-4020-8673-1(3))* Springer.

Gerst, Matthias. Harley-Davidson: All the Motorcycles, 1903-1983. 2010. (ENG., Illus.). 404p. 42.95 *(978-1-84425-676-1(6)*, 1844256766) Haynes Publishing PLC GBR. Dist: MBI Distribution Services/Quayside Distribution.

Gibbs, Chris. Build Your Own Single-Seater: On a Budget. 2013. (ENG., Illus.). 176p. pap. 29.95 *(978-1-84425-639-6(1)*, 1844256391) Haynes Publishing PLC GBR. Dist: MBI Distribution Services/Quayside Distribution.

—Build Your Own Sports Car: On a Budget. 2007. (ENG., Illus.). 208p. 32.95 *(978-1-84425-391-3(0)*, 1844253910) Haynes Publishing PLC GBR. Dist: MBI Distribution Services/Quayside Distribution.

Gingerelli, Dain. Hot Rods: Roadsters, Coupes, Customs. 2009. (Idea Book Ser.). (ENG., Illus.). 160p. pap. 24.99 *(978-0-7603-3516-1(8)*, 0760335168, Motorbooks) MBI Publishing Co. LLC.

Grist, Peter. Virgil Exner, Visioneer: The Official Biography of Virgil M. Exner, Designer Extraordinaire. 2007. (ENG., Illus.). 160p. 49.95 *(978-1-84584-118-8(2)*, 1845841182) Veloce Publishing Ltd. GBR. Dist: MBI Distribution Services/Quayside Distribution.

Gross, Ken. Art of the Hot Rod. 2008. (ENG., Illus.). 240p. 40.00 *(978-0-7603-2282-6(1)*, 0760322821, Motorbooks) MBI Publishing Co. LLC.

Halderman, James D. Automotive Technology. 4th ed. 2011. (ENG.). (C). 94.40 ***(978-0-13-276966-2(2))***; (Illus.). 1664p. 124.80 ***(978-0-13-254261-6(7))*** Prentice Hall PTR. (Prentice Hall).

Hamon, Abdollahifakhr & Ceyhun, Sengul. Automatic Design of Wiring Pattern for Car Seat Heaters: Design Automation. 2011. 88p. pap. ***(978-3-639-33687-0(9))*** VDM Verlag Dr. Mueller e.K.

Handzel, Will. How to Build High-Performance Chevy LS1/LS6 V-8s: Modifying & Tuning Gen3 Engines for GM Cars & Pickups. 2008. 160p. pap. 24.95 *(978-1-932494-88-4(X))* CarTech, Inc.

Hiller, M. & Schramm, D. Dynamics of Road Vehicles. 2008. 400p. pap. 109.00 *(978-3-540-36044-5(1))* Springer.

Hirz, Mario & Dietrich, Wilhelm. 3D-CAD Design Methods in Vehicle & Engine Development Processes. 2011. (VDI-Buch Ser.). (ENG., Illus.). 300p. 159.95 *(978-3-642-11939-2(5)*, 3642119395) Springer.

Hoag, Kevin L. Vehicular Engine Design. 2006. (Fahrzeugantrieb/Powertrain Ser.). (Illus.). x, 223p. 139.00 *(978-3-211-21130-4(6)*, 3211211306) Springer.

Holmstrom, Darwin & Newhardt, David. Gto: Pontiac's Great One. 2009. (ENG., Illus.). 336p. 50.00 *(978-0-7603-3515-4(X)*, 076033515X, Motorbooks) MBI Publishing Co. LLC.

Hu, Shilian. Surface Finish Analysis of Composite Automotive Panels. 2008. 164p. pap. *(978-3-639-03702-9(2))* VDM Verlag Dr. Mueller e.K.

Humphrey, Kristin L., ed. Demolition Derby. rev. ed. (Illus.). 150p. pap. 9.95 *(978-0-9718708-1-9(0))* Humphrey, Mark.

Hung, Steve, et al, eds. Sustainable Automotive Technologies 2011: Proceedings of the 3rd International Conference. 2011. (ENG., Illus.). ix, 150p. 199.00 *(978-3-642-19052-0(9)*, 3642190529) Springer.

Hylton, Stuart. The Horseless Carriage: The Birth of the Motor Age. 2009. (ENG., Illus.). 192p. pap. 27.95 *(978-0-7524-5078-0(6))* History Pr. Ltd.,The GBR. Dist: Independent Pubs. Group.

Inam Ahmed, Muhammad. Design & Performance Optimization of a Car Radiator. 2010. 112p. pap. *(978-3-8383-4360-0(3))* Lambert Academic Publishing.

Institution of Mechanical Engineers (Great Britain), Automobile Division Staff, contrib. by. IPDS 2006: Integrated Powertrain & Driveline Systems 2006: 14-15 June 2006, Ford Motor Company, Dunton, Essex, Institution of Mechanical Engineers Automobile Division. (Illus.). 208p. pap. *(978-1-84569-197-4(0))* Woodhead Publishing Ltd.

Jacobus, John L., ed. Inside the Fisher Body Craftsman's Guild: Contestants Recall the Great General Motors Talent Search. 2011. (ENG.). 336p. pap. 35.00 ***(978-0-7864-4861-6(X))*** McFarland & Co., Inc. Pubs.

Johnson, Ann. Hitting the Brakes: Engineering Design & the Production of Knowledge. 2009. (ENG., Illus.). 232p. 79.95 *(978-0-8223-4526-8(9))*; pap. 22.95 *(978-0-8223-4541-1(2))* Duke Univ. Pr.

Jurgen, Ronald K. Object Detection, Collision Warning & Avoidance Systems, Vol. 2. 2007. 419p. 89.95 *(978-0-7680-1810-3(2))* SAE Intl.

Kaul, Sudhir. Modeling Techniques for Vibration Isolation in Motorcycles. 2011. 232p. pap. ***(978-3-8443-0127-4(5))*** Lambert Academic Publishing.

Kieser, Ulrich, et al. Future Cars: Bio Fuel, Hybrid, Electric, Hydrogen, Fuel Economy in All Shapes & Sizes/ Bio-Treibstoff, Hybrid, Elektro, Wasserstoff, Sparsame Autos in Allen Klassen und Formen. 2008. (GER & ENG., Illus.). 168p. 44.00 *(978-3-89986-098-6(5)*, Avedition Gmbh,Csi) Continental Sales, Inc.

Kluczyk, Barry. How to Rebuild Any Automotive Engine Videobook. 2009. 144p. pap. 39.95 *(978-1-934709-11-5(5)*, S-A Design) CarTech, Inc.

Kupnik, Mario. Ultrasonic Transit-Time Gas Flowmeter for Automotive Applications - a Monitoring Tool for Exhaust Emission Control. 2008. 220p. pap. *(978-3-639-00789-3(1))* VDM Verlag Dr. Mueller e.K.

Kymal, Chad. Conducting Effective Process-Based Audits: A Handbook for ISO/TS 16949. 2007. *(978-1-932828-13-9(3))* Paton Professional.

Kymmell, Willem. Building Information Modeling: Planning & Managing Construction Projects. 2008. (Construction Ser.). (ENG., Illus.). 270p. 79.95 *(978-0-07-149453-3(7)*, 0071494537) McGraw-Hill Professional Publishing.

Laban, Brian. The Mini: Celebrating 50 Years of a Modern Motoring Icon. 2009. (ENG., Illus.). 208p. 34.95 *(978-1-84732-373-6(1))* Carlton Bks., Ltd. GBR. Dist: Sterling Publishing Co., Inc.

Lamm, John. Exotic Cars. 2008. (Gallery Ser.). (ENG., Illus.). 256p. pap. 19.99 *(978-0-7603-3261-0(4)*, 0760332614, Motorbooks) MBI Publishing Co. LLC.

Lee, Dong Wook. An Innovative Inflatable Morphing Vehicle Structure: Concept & Analytical Design Model for Crashworthiness. 2008. 192p. pap. *(978-3-639-10223-9(1))* VDM Verlag Dr. Mueller e.K.

Lehbrink, Hartmut. Bmw-Rev. 2010. 384p. pap. 29.99 *(978-0-8416-7163-8(X))* Langenscheidt Publishing Group.

Leitman, Seth. Build Your Own Plug-in Hybrid Electric Vehicle. 2009. (ENG., Illus.). 320p. pap. 24.95 *(978-0-07-161473-3(7)*, 0071614737, TAB/Electronics) McGraw-Hill Professional Publishing.

Leitman, Seth & Brant, Bob. Build Your Own Electric Vehicle. 2nd ed. 2008. (ENG., Illus.). 327p. pap. 29.95 *(978-0-07-154373-6(2)*, 0071543732, TAB/Electronics) McGraw-Hill Professional Publishing.

Leonardi, Paul M. Car Crashes Without Cars: Simulation Technology & Organizational Change in Automotive Engineering. 2012. ***(978-0-262-01784-8(9))*** MIT Pr.

Lewin, Tony. The A-Z of 21st-Century Cars. 2011. (ENG., Illus.). 540p. pap. 39.95 *(978-1-85894-525-5(9))* Merrell Pubs. Ltd. GBR. Dist: Perseus Distribution.

—How to Design Cars Like a Pro. (Illus.). 128p. 34.95 *(978-0-7603-1704-4(6)*, Motorbooks) MBI Publishing Co. LLC.

Lewin, Tony & Borroff, Ryan. How to Design Cars Like a Pro. 2010. (Illus.). 208p. pap. 29.99 *(978-0-7603-3695-3(4)*, 0760336954, Motorbooks) MBI Publishing Co. LLC.

Lightweight Materials in Transportation. 2007. per. 4250.00 *(978-1-59623-289-1(7))* BCC Research.

Limpert, Rudolf. Brake Design & Safety. 3rd ed. 2011. ***(978-0-7680-3438-7(8))*** SAE Intl.

Linde, Arvid. Preston Tucker & Others: Tales of Brilliant Automotive Innovations. 2011. (ENG., Illus.). 160p. pap. 39.95 *(978-1-84584-017-4(8)*, 1845840178) Veloce Publishing Ltd. GBR. Dist: MBI Distribution Services/Quayside Distribution.

Liu, Yucheng. Simplified Modeling for Crashworthiness Analysis. 2008. 164p. pap. *(978-3-639-00671-1(2))* VDM Verlag Dr. Mueller e.K.

Lyons, Dan. Muscle Car the Art of Power. 2008. (ENG., Illus.). 192p. 27.99 *(978-0-89689-617-8(X))* Krause Pubns.

Malen, Donald E. Fundamentals of Automobile Body Structure Design. 2011. (Illus.). 450p. *(978-0-7680-2169-1(3))* SAE Intl.

Mallick, P. K., ed. Materials, Design & Manufacturing for Lightweight Vehicles. 2010. (Illus.). 384p. 230.00 *(978-1-84569-463-0(5))* Woodhead Publishing Ltd. GBR. Dist: Taylor & Francis Group.

—Materials Design & Manufacturing for Lightweight Vehicles. 2010. (Illus.). xii, 369p. 209.95 *(978-1-4398-2972-1(1))* CRC Pr. LLC.

Mat Saman, Muhamad Zameri. Design for End of Life Value. 2009. 304p. pap. *(978-3-639-14770-4(7))* VDM Verlag Dr. Mueller e.K.

Maxwell, Gordan A. & Drummond, Stuart K., eds. Automotive Industry: Technical Challenges, Design Issues & Global Economic Crisis. 2010. (American Political, Economic, & Security Issues Ser.). 258p. 145.00 *(978-1-60876-143-2(6))* Nova Science Pubs., Inc.

Mayes, Alan. Custom Cars: Coupes, Sedans, Pickups. 2010. (Idea Book Ser.). (ENG., Illus.). 160p. pap. 24.99 *(978-0-7603-3760-8(8)*, 0760337608, Motorbooks) MBI Publishing Co. LLC.

—Old School Customs: Top Traditional Custom Car Builders. 2009. (ENG., Illus.). 160p. 35.00 *(978-0-7603-3457-7(9)*, 0760334579, Motorbooks) MBI Publishing Co. LLC.

McCall, Walter. Weller Brothers of Memphis. 2010. (American Coachbuilders Ser.). (ENG., Illus.). 128p. pap. 19.95 *(978-1-58388-257-3(X)*, 158388257X) Iconografix, Inc.

McMahon, David. Quantum Field Theory: A Self-Teaching Guide. 2008. (Demystified Ser.). (ENG., Illus.). 299p. per. 24.95 *(978-0-07-154382-8(1)*, 0071543821) McGraw-Hill Professional Publishing.

McPherson, Dale. Modern Diesel Technology: Electrical/Electronic Systems & Heating, Ventilation, Air Conditioning Systems Job Sheets. 2006. (ENG.). 144p. (C). pap. 34.95 *(978-1-4180-6338-2(X))* Delmar Cengage Learning.

Mead, Syd, frwd. Cosmic Motors: Spaceships, Cars & Pilots of Another Galaxy. 2007. (ENG., Illus.). 171p. 46.95 *(978-1-933492-28-5(7))* Design Studio Pr.

Meade, David. Winning the Pinewood Derby: Ultimate Speed Secrets for Building the Fastest Car. 2006. (ENG., Illus.). 106p. pap. 12.95 *(978-1-56523-291-4(7))* Fox Chapel Publishing Co., Inc.

Miller, Jay K. Turbo: Real World High-Performance Turbocharger Systems. 2008. 144p. pap. 24.95 *(978-1-932494-29-7(4))* CarTech, Inc.

Morello, L., et al. The Automotive Body: Volume I: Components Design, 2 vols. 2010. (Mechanical Engineering Ser.). Orig. Title: La Carrozzeria. (ENG., Illus.). xxii, 670p. 119.00 *(978-94-007-0512-8(3)*, 9400705123) Springer.

—The Automotive Body: Volume II: System Design. 2010. (Mechanical Engineering Ser.). (ENG., Illus.). x, 570p. 119.00 *(978-94-007-0515-9(8)*, 9400705158) Springer.

Morey, Bruce. Automotive 2030, North America. 2011. ***(978-0-7680-5727-0(2))*** SAE Intl.

Mueller, Markus, et al. Automotive SPICE in Practice: Surviving Interpretation & Assessment. 2008. (Rockynook Computing Ser.). (ENG., Illus.). 304p. pap. 54.95 *(978-1-933952-29-1(6))* Rocky Nook.

Nada, Giorgio Editor, ed. Zagato Milano 1919-2009: The Official Book. 2010. (ENG., Illus.). 160p. 64.95 *(978-88-7911-487-5(5)*, 8879114875) Giorgio Nada Editore ITA. Dist: MBI Distribution Services/Quayside Distribution.

Nappo, Donato & Vairelli, Stefania. 2cv, 1 vol. 2010. (ITA, ENG & FRE., Illus.). 186p. 12.95 *(978-90-79761-60-9(5))* Tectum B.V.B.A. BEL. Dist: Innovative Logistics.

Nedbal, Richard. How to Build Max-Performance Hemi Engines. 2009. (Illus.). 144p. pap. 24.95 *(978-1-932494-95-2(2)*, S-A Design) CarTech, Inc.

Negrone, Jos Bendinelli. 500 Love: The Fiat 500 Story. 2008. (ITA, GER & ENG., Illus.). 120p. 59.95 incl. lp *(978-3-940004-42-0(1))* Edel Classica Gmbh.

Newbury. The Car Design Yearbook 5: The Definitive Annual Guide to All New Concept & Production Cars Worldwide the Definitive Annual Guide to All New Concept & Production Cars. (Illus.). 288p. *(978-1-85894-338-1(8))* Merrell Pubs. Ltd.

Newbury, Stephen. The Car Design Yearbook 3 Vol. 3: The Definitive Annual Guide to All New Concept & Production Cars Worldwide. rev. ed. (Illus.). 304p. *(978-1-85894-241-4(1))* Merrell Pubs. Ltd.

—The Car Design Yearbook 4: The Definitive Annual Guide to All New Concept & Production Cars Worldwide. (Illus.). 288p. *(978-1-85894-285-8(3))* Merrell Pubs. Ltd.

—The Car Design Yearbook 5: The Definitive Annual Guide to All New Concept & Production Cars Worldwide. (Illus.). 288p. *(978-1-85894-318-3(3))* Merrell Pubs. Ltd.

Newbury, Stephen & Lewin, Tony. All New Concept & Production Cards Worldwide. annuals 2009. (Car Design Yearbook Ser.). (ENG.). 304p. 44.95 *(978-1-85894-477-7(5))* Merrell Pubs. Ltd. GBR. Dist: Perseus Distribution.

—The Car Design Yearbook 7. 2008. 320p. 44.95 *(978-1-85894-419-7(8))* Merrell Pubs. Ltd. GBR. Dist: Perseus Distribution.

Newell, Ray. Morris Minor: 60 Years on the Road. 2008. (ENG., Illus.). 160p. pap. 49.95 *(978-1-84584-157-7(3)*, 1845841573) Veloce Publishing Ltd. GBR. Dist: MBI Distribution Services/Quayside Distribution.

—Original Morris Minor: The Restorer's Guide to All Saloon, Tourer, Convertible, Traveller & Light Commercial Models. 2008. (Original Ser.). (ENG., Illus.). 128p. 49.95 *(978-1-906133-03-0(4)*, 1906133034) Herridge & Sons Ltd.

Noakes, Keith. Successful Composite Techniques: A Practical Introduction to the Use of Modern Composite Materials. 4th ed. 2008. (ENG., Illus.). 176p. pap. 29.95 *(978-1-84797-054-1(0)*, 1847970540) Crowood Pr., Ltd. GBR. Dist: MBI Distribution Services/Quayside Distribution.

Nunney, M. J. Light & Heavy Vehicle Technology. 4th rev. ed. 2006. (ENG., Illus.). 688p. per. 48.95 *(978-0-7506-8037-0(7))* Routledge.

Omar, Mohammed A. The Automotive Body Manufacturing Systems & Processes. 2011. (ENG., Illus.). 392p. 120.00 *(978-0-470-97633-3(0)*, Wiley) Wiley, John & Sons, Inc.

Orel, Frank & Brummer, Elmar, eds. Porsche Icons Collector's Edition. 2010. 160p. 2200.00 *(978-3-8327-9392-0(5))* teNeues Publishing Co.

Parkin, David. Talk to Me. 2008. pap. 10.00 *(978-0-8059-7922-0(0))* Dorrance Publishing Co., Inc.

Parks, Dennis W. Hot Rod Body & Chassis Builder's Guide. 2009. (Motorbooks Workshop Ser.). (ENG., Illus.). 176p. pap. 25.99 *(978-0-7603-3532-1(X)*, 076033532X, Motorbooks) MBI Publishing Co. LLC.

Petroleum Equipment Institute, compiled by. Recommended Practices for Installation of Underground Liquid Storage Systems: Rp100: Rp100. 2000th ed. 2011. pap. 95.00 *(978-0-9642638-5-7(8))* Petroleum Equipment Institute.

—Recommended Practices for the Inspection & Maintenance of UST Systems: Rp900: Rp900. 2008. (ENG., Illus.). 52p. pap. 90.00 *(978-0-9642638-8-8(2))* Petroleum Equipment Institute.

Planning, Alpha, ed. New Exhibition Design: Tokyo Motor Show CEATEC Japan. 2008. (ENG., Illus.). 256p. 65.00 *(978-4-568-50343-2(4))* Azur Corp. JPN. Dist: Antique Collectors' Club.

Plugging into Energy Independence with 150 MPG Vehicles: Hearing Before the Select Committee on Energy Independence & Global Warming, House of Representatives, One Hundred Tenth Congress, First Session, July 12, 2007. 2010. iii, 61p. *(978-0-16-086627-2(8)*, 552-070-41605-6) United States Government Printing Office.

Potak, Joseph. How to Build & Modify GM LS-Series Engines. 2009. (Motorbooks Workshop Ser.). (ENG., Illus.). 176p. pap. 27.99 *(978-0-7603-3543-7(5)*, 0760335435, Motorbooks) MBI Publishing Co. LLC.

Powell, Tracy. American Auto Legends: Classics of Style & Design. 2010. (Auto Legends Ser.). (ENG., Illus.). 288p. 49.95 *(978-1-85894-516-3(X))* Merrell Pubs. Ltd. GBR. Dist: Perseus Distribution.

—General Motors Styling 1927-1958: Genesis of the World's Largest Design Studios. 2007. lib. bdg. 29.95 *(978-0-9709195-1-9(4))* Powell House Publishing.

Price, Barrie & Arbey, Jean-Louis. Bugatti: The 8-Cylinder Touring Cars 1920-1934 - Types 28, 30, 38, 38a, 44 & 49. 2007. (ENG., Illus.). 144p. 59.95 *(978-1-901295-95-5(8)*, 1901295958) Veloce Publishing Ltd. GBR. Dist: MBI Distribution Services/Quayside Distribution.

Reed, Matthew P. & Klinich, Kathleen D. Child Anthropometry for Improved Vehicle Occupant Safety. 2010. (Illus.). vii, 416p. pap. *(978-0-7680-2172-1(3))* SAE Intl.

Reid, George. Ford Engine Parts Interchange. 2010. (Illus.). 160p. pap. 24.95 *(978-1-934709-19-1(0)*, S-A Design) CarTech, Inc.

—How to Rebuild the Small-Block Ford. 2008. 144p. pap. 24.95 *(978-1-932494-89-1(8))* CarTech, Inc.

Reinke, Phillip C. Pinewood Winning by the Rules. 2010. 84p. pap. 9.99 *(978-1-60911-153-3(2)*, Eloquent Bks.) AEG Literary Publishing Services, Inc.

Remus, Timothy. How to Chop Tops. 2008. (Old Skool Skills Ser.). (ENG., Illus.). 144p. pap. 24.95 *(978-1-929133-49-9(9)*, 1929133499) Wolfgang Pubns., Inc.

Robert Bosch Gmbh. Bosch Automotive Handbook. 7th ed. 2007. (Illus.). 1192p. vinyl bd. 49.95 *(978-0-8376-1540-0(2))* Bentley Pubs.

Robert Bosch GmbH Staff. Automotive Handbook. 8th ed. 2011. (ENG., Illus.). 1266p. 65.00 ***(978-1-119-97556-4(5)***, Wiley) Wiley, John & Sons, Inc.

SAE Transmission/Axle/Driveline Forum Committee Staff, contrib. by. Design Practices — Passenger Car Automatic Transmissions. 4th ed. 2012. ***(978-0-7680-1125-8(6))*** SAE Intl.

Sannia, Alessandro. Alfa Romeo, 1 vol. 2010. (ENG & FRE., Illus.). 192p. 12.95 *(978-90-79761-50-0(8))* Tectum B.V.B.A. BEL. Dist: Innovative Logistics.

—Fiat 500, 1 vol. 2010. (ITA, ENG & FRE., Illus.). 192p. 12.95 *(978-90-79761-61-6(3))* Tectum B.V.B.A. BEL. Dist: Innovative Logistics.

—Mercedes-Benz, 1 vol. 2011. (ITA, ENG & FRE., Illus.). 192p. 12.95 *(978-90-79761-51-7(6))* Tectum B.V.B.A. BEL. Dist: Innovative Logistics.

—Mini, 1 vol. 2008. (ENG & FRE., Illus.). 192p. 12.95 *(978-90-79761-55-5(9))* Tectum B.V.B.A. BEL. Dist: Innovative Logistics.

Sannia, Alessandro. Porsche. 2010. (ITA, ENG & FRE., Illus.). 192p. 12.95 ***(978-90-79761-52-4(4))*** Tectum B.V.B.A. BEL. Dist: Innovative Logistics.

Sannia, Alessandro & Boni, Valerio. Vespa, 1 vol. 2007. (ITA, ENG & FRE., Illus.). 192p. 12.95 *(978-90-79761-56-2(7))* Tectum B.V.B.A. BEL. Dist: Innovative Logistics.

Sannia, Alessandro & D'Alessio, Paolo. Ferrari, 1 vol. 2011. (ENG & FRE., Illus.). 192p. 12.95 *(978-90-79761-53-1(2))* Tectum B.V.B.A. BEL. Dist: Innovative Logistics.

Schorr, Martyn L. Motion Performance: Tales of a Muscle Car Builder. 2009. (ENG., Illus.). 176p. 35.00 *(978-0-7603-3538-3(9)*, 0760335389, Motorbooks) MBI Publishing Co. LLC.

Schunk, Rick. Harley-Davidson Panhead Restoration. 2009. (ENG., Illus.). 144p. pap. 34.95 *(978-1-929133-81-9(2)*, 1929133812) Wolfgang Pubns., Inc.

Scraba, Wayne. Practical Fabrication & Assembly Techniques: Automotive, Motorcycle, Racing. 2010. (Motorbooks Workshop Ser.). (ENG., Illus.). 144p. pap. 24.99 *(978-0-7603-3800-1(0)*, 0760338000, Motorbooks) MBI Publishing Co. LLC.

Sehanobish, Kalyan. Engineering Plastics & Plastic Composites in Automotive Applications. 2009. 199.00 *(978-0-7680-1933-9(8))* SAE Intl.

Sehgal, Shankar, et al. Active Device Development for Automobiles. 2011. 100p. pap. ***(978-3-8454-2478-1(8))*** Lambert Academic Publishing.

Sensors & Actuators. 2007. (C). 109.95 ***(978-1-4200-4484-3(2)***, CRC Press) Taylor & Francis Group GBR. Dist: Taylor & Francis Group.

Somers, Dan. Birth of a New Machine: Building a Cobra Replica. 2008. (Illus.). 82p. spiral bd. 19.95 *(978-0-615-19604-6(7))* Somehow Publishing.

Stein, Jonathan A., ed. Curves of Steel: Streamlined Automobile Design. 2nd rev. ed. 2009. (ENG., Illus.). 192p. 75.00 *(978-0-9779809-6-3(0))* Coachbuilt Pr.

Stroud, John. Concept Cars. 2010. (ENG., Illus.). 304p. 14.95 *(978-88-544-0461-8(6))* White Star ITA. Dist: Random Hse., Inc.

Sven, Voelker. Go Faster: The Graphic Design of Racing Cars. 2010. 144p. 40.00 *(978-3-89955-279-9(2))* Die Gestalten Verlag DEU. Dist: Prestel Publishing.

Tanner, Keith. How to Build a High-Performance Mazda Miata MX-5. 2010. (Motorbooks Workshop Ser.). (ENG., Illus.). 192p. pap. 29.99 *(978-0-7603-3705-9(5)*, 0760337055, Motorbooks) MBI Publishing Co. LLC.

Technology Research Editors, ed. Adhesives & Adhesive Bonding for Automotive Applications, 2007 Ed. 2007. pap. 128.50 *(978-1-60030-159-9(2)*, Search-In-Print) CSA Journal Division.

—Advanced Materials for Automotive Components: World Business Brief, 2007 Ed. 2007. pap. 68.50 *(978-1-60030-235-0(1)*, Search-In-Print) CSA Journal Division.

—Automotive Applications of Spot Welding, 2007 Ed. 2007. pap. 128.50 *(978-1-60030-238-1(6)*, Search-In-Print) CSA Journal Division.

—Coating of Automobile & Automotive Components, 2007 Ed. 2007. pap. 128.50 *(978-1-60030-241-1(6)*, Search-In-Print) CSA Journal Division.

—Corrosion of Automobiles & Their Components, 2007 Ed. 2007. pap. 128.50 *(978-1-60030-242-8(4)*, Search-In-Print) CSA Journal Division.

—Cost Issues in Automobile & Automotive Component Manufacturing, 2007 Ed. 2007. pap. 128.50 *(978-1-60030-212-1(2)*, Search-In-Print) CSA Journal Division.

—Failure of Automotive Components, 2007 Ed. 2007. pap. 128.50 *(978-1-60030-245-9(9)*, Search-In-Print) CSA Journal Division.

—Magnesium & Magnesium Base Alloys in Automotive Applications, 2007 Ed. 2007. pap. 128.50 *(978-1-60030-218-3(1)*, Search-In-Print) CSA Journal Division.

—Market Developments: Magnesium in Automotive Applications, 2007 Ed. 2007. pap. 68.50 *(978-1-60030-220-6(3)*, Search-In-Print) CSA Journal Division.

—Welding of Aluminum Automotive Components, 2007 Ed. 2007. pap. 128.50 *(978-1-60030-204-6(1)*, Search-In-Print) CSA Journal Division.

Thompson, Andy. Cars of Eastern Europe: The Definitive History. 2011. (ENG., Illus.). 400p. 57.95 *(978-1-84425-991-5(9)*, 1844259919) Haynes Publishing PLC GBR. Dist: MBI Distribution Services/Quayside Distribution.

Thompson, Brian. How to Build Your Own Supercar. 2008. (Essential Manual Ser.). (ENG., Illus.). 112p. pap. 19.95 *(978-1-84584-166-9(2)*, 1845841662) Veloce Publishing Ltd. GBR. Dist: MBI Distribution Services/Quayside Distribution.

Thorley, Nigel. Jaguar XK: A celebration of Jaguar's 1950s Classic. 2008. (Haynes Great Cars Ser.). (ENG., Illus.). 160p. 39.95 *(978-1-84425-332-6(5)*, 1844253325) Haynes Publishing PLC GBR. Dist: MBI Distribution Services/Quayside Distribution.

Ulsoy, A. Galip, et al. Automotive Control Systems. 2012. (ENG., Illus.). 384p. (C). 125.00 ***(978-1-107-01011-6(X))*** Cambridge Univ. Pr.

Vale, Matthew. Triumph Twenty-One to Daytona: The C Class 350cc & 500cc Twins. 2008. (ENG., Illus.). 192p. 34.95 *(978-1-86126-997-3(8)*, 1861269978) Crowood Pr., Ltd. GBR. Dist: MBI Distribution Services/Quayside Distribution.

Vizard, David. How to Build Max-Performance Chevy Big-Blocks on a Budget. 2011. (Illus.). 144p. *(978-1-934709-38-2(7))* CarTech, Inc.

Vogel, Carl. Build Your Own Electric Motorcycle. 2009. (ENG., Illus.). 384p. pap. 24.95 *(978-0-07-162293-6(4)*, 0071622934, TAB/Electronics) McGraw-Hill Professional Publishing.

Walker, Mick. Aermacchi: Harley-Davidson Motorcycles. 2006. (Enthusiasts Ser.). (ENG., Illus.). 216p. pap. 46.95 *(978-0-9544357-6-9(1))* Redline Bks. GBR. Dist: MBI Distribution Services/Quayside Distribution.

Walker, Nick. A-Z British Coachbuilders, 1919-1960: And the Development of Styles & Techniques. 2nd rev. enl. ed. 2007. (ENG., Illus.). 224p. 59.95 *(978-0-9549981-6-5(2)*, 0954998162) Herridge & Sons, Ltd. GBR. Dist: MBI Distribution Services/Quayside Distribution.

Warner, Mark. The Electric Vehicle Conversion Handbook HP1568. 2011. (ENG.). 192p. (gr. 12). 21.95 *(978-1-55788-568-5(0)*, HP Trade) Penguin Group (USA) Inc.

White, Jason. Old School Viscom: 20 Renderings in 20 Steps, 2010. (ENG., Illus.). 258p. (C). pap. 44.95 *(978-0-9846220-0-9(4))* White, Jason.

Williamson, Dan. Factory-Original Sporting Mk2 Escorts: The Originality Guide to the Sporting Variants of the Ford Escort Mk2. 2012. (Factory Original Ser.). (ENG., Illus.). 128p. 59.95 *(978-1-906133-29-0(8)*, 1906133298) Herridge & Sons, Ltd. GBR. Dist: MBI Distribution Services/Quayside Distribution.

Winkowski, Frederic & Sullivan, Frank D. Carchitecture: Frames, Fenders, & Fins. 2008. (ENG., Illus.). 352p. 25.00 *(978-0-9793384-8-9(4))* Glitterati, Inc.

Wong, J. Y. Terramechanics & Off-Road Vehicle Engineering: Terrain Behaviour, Off-Road Vehicle Performance & Design. 2nd ed. 2009. (ENG., Illus.). 488p. 145.00 *(978-0-7506-8561-0(1)*, Butterworth-Heinemann) Elsevier Science & Technology Bks.

Wurth, Peter, ed. Mini: the Book. 2007. (Illus.). 191p. 42.00 *(978-3-89955-180-8(X))* Die Gestalten Verlag DEU. Dist: Prestel Publishing.

Zazarine, Paul. The Collector's Guide to GTO 1964-1974. 2007. (ENG., Illus.). 128p. pap. 19.95 *(978-1-58388-196-5(4)*, 1583881964) Iconografix, Inc.

Zhao, Chao. Aging in China & Its Impact on Vehicle Design. 2009. 272p. pap. *(978-3-639-13287-8(4))* VDM Verlag Dr. Mueller e.K.

Zumbrunn & Heseltine, Richard. Italian Auto Legends: Classics of Style & Design. 2008. (Illus.). 296p. pap. 22.95 *(978-1-85894-431-9(7))* Merrell Pubs. Ltd. GBR. Dist: Perseus Distribution.

Zurschmeide, Jeffrey. High-Performance Subaru Builder's Guide: Includes the Impreza, Legacy, Forester, Outback, WRX & STI. 2007. (S-A Design Ser.). (ENG., Illus.). 144p. pap. 24.95 *(978-1-932494-51-8(0)*, S-A Design) CarTech, Inc.

AUTOMOBILES—*DICTIONARIES*

Clough, Albert L. A Dictionary of Automobile *Terms*. 2009. 360p. pap. 30.45 *(978-1-4446-1722-1(2))* Research Pr.

Haajanen, Lennart W. Illustrated Dictionary of Automobile Body Styles. alt. ed. 2007. (ENG., Illus.). 175p. per. 39.95 *(978-0-7864-3737-5(5))* McFarland & Co., Inc. Pubs.

Lewin, Tony. The A-Z of 21st-Century Cars. 2011. (ENG., Illus.). 540p. pap. 39.95 *(978-1-85894-525-5(9))* Merrell Pubs. Ltd. GBR. Dist: Perseus Distribution.

Publications International Staff. Ency of Amer Cars. 2006. (Illus.). 848p. 34.98 (978-1-4127-1354-2(4), 1261319, PIL Kids) Publications International, Ltd.

AUTOMOBILES—DIESEL MOTORS

see Automobiles—Motors

AUTOMOBILES—DRIVE TRAINS

see Automobiles—Power Trains

AUTOMOBILES—DRIVERS' LICENSES

see Automobile Drivers' Licenses

AUTOMOBILES—DRIVING

see Automobile Driving

AUTOMOBILES—DYNAMICS

Abe, Masato. Vehicle Handling Dynamics: Theory & Application. 2009. (ENG., Illus.). 296p. 104.00 (978-1-85617-749-8(1), Butterworth-Heinemann) Elsevier Science & Technology Bks.

Azad, et al. Articulated Steer Vehicles: Dynamics & Control - Fundamentals in Modeling, Stability Analysis & Controller Development. 2010. 204p. pap. (978-3-8364-5665-4(6)) VDM Verlag Dr. Mueller e.K.

Crolla, David & Mashadi, Behrooz. Vehicle Powertrain Systems: Integration & Optimization. 2012. (ENG., Illus.). 560p. 105.00 (978-... 652p. 99.95 Wiley) Wiley, John & Sons, Inc.

Dukkipati, Rao V. Road Vehicle Dynamics, 2 vols. 2009. (Illus.). viii, 542p. (978-0-7680-1643-7(6)) SAE Intl.

—Road Vehicle Dynamics: Problems & Solutions. (Illus.). 248p. (gr. 17). 69.95 (978-0-7680-2051-9(4)) SAE Intl.

Edmondson, Chuck. Fast Car Physics. 2011. ... (978-0-8018-9823-5(4)) Johns Hopkins Univ. Pr. (978-0-8018-9822-8(6)); pap. 29.95 ...

Ellis, J. R. Vehicle Handling Dynamics. ... 208p. ... Staff, ed. (Illus.) ... Engineering ... Gras.). xi, 270p. 189.00 ...

Genta, Giampiero & Morello, Lorenzo. ... Non-Smooth Problems in Vehicle Systems Dynamics: Proceedings of the Euromech Colloquium. 2009. (ENG., Illus.). 1300p. ... 642-01355-3(4), 3642013553 ... 3322-4(9), CRC Press) Taylor & Francis Group.

Mastinu, Giampiero & Ploechl, Manfred, eds. Road & Off-Road Vehicle System Dynamics Handbook. 2nd ed. 189.95 ... Taylor & Francis Group GBR. Dist: Taylor & Francis Group, LLC.

Newton, Richard. Autocross Performance Handbook. 2007. (Motorbooks Workshop Ser.). (ENG., Illus.). ... (978-0-7603-2788-3(2), 0760327882, MBI ...

Rajamani, Rajesh. Vehicle Dynamics & Control. 2nd ed. ... xxv, 47... 129.00 (978-1-4419-3889-3(3), 139.00 **(978-1-4614-1432-2(6)**, Springer) Springer.

... Road Vehicle Dynamics. 2011. (ENG., Illus.). 361p. 99.95 (978-1-4398-3898-... CRC Press) Taylor & Francis Group GBR. Dist: Taylor & Francis Group.

Rosenbluth, William. ... Application & Interpretation of Black Box Data & Crash Dynamics. 20... (978-0-8031-7003-2(3)) American Society for Testing & Materials.

Schiehlen, W. Dynamical Analysis of Vehicle Systems. 2008. (CISM International Centre for Mechanical Sciences Ser.). 169.00 (978-3-211-76... Springer.

Schiehlen, W., ed. Dynamical Analysis of Vehicle Systems: Theoretical Foundations & Advanced Applications. 2010. (CISM International Centre for Mechanical Sciences Ser.). (Illus.). vii, 304p. pap. 169... (978-3-211-99919-6(1), 3211999191) Springer.

Wong, J. Y. Terramechanics & Off-Road Vehicle Engineering: Terrain Behaviour, Off-Road Vehicle Performance & Design. 2nd ed. 2009. (ENG., Illus.). 488p. 145.00 (978-0-7506-8561-0(1), Butterworth-Heinemann) Elsevier Science & Technology Bks.

AUTOMOBILES—ELECTRIC EQUIPMENT

Autodata. 2007 Key Programming & Service Indicators (Coverage 96-07) 2006. pap. 83.95 (978-1-893026-37-...)) Delmar Cengage Learning.

Candela, Tony. Automotive Electrical Performance Projects. 2011. (Illus.). 192p. pap. 29.95 (978-1-934709-55-9(7)) CarTech, Inc.

—Automotive Wiring & Electrical Systems. 2009. 144p. pap. 24.95 (978-1-932494-87-7(1)) CarTech, Inc.

Chapman, Norm. Principles of Electricity & Electronics for the Automotive Technician. 2nd ed. 2008. (ENG.). 608p. (C). pap. 156.95 (978-1-4283-6121-8(9)) Delmar Cengage Learning.

Day, John. Automotive E/E Reliability: Strategies for Keeping Pace in a Feature-Rich World. 2011. **(978-0-7680-3499-8(X))** SAE Intl.

Delmar Learning Staff. ASE Test Preparation - A6 Electricity & Electronics. 2011. (ENG., Illus.). 256p. pap. 23.95 (978-1-111-12708-4(5)) Delmar Cengage Learning.

—Electricity & Electronics: Computer Based Training. 2007. (ENG.). 114.95 (978-1-4283-2095-6(4)) Delmar Cengage Learning.

—Truck Equipment Installation & Repair, Test E1. 2012. (ENG.). 164p. pap. 23.95 (978-1-4354-3935-1(X)) Delmar Cengage Learning.

Denton, Tom. Automobile Electrical & Electronic Systems: Automotive Technology - Vehicle Maintenance & Repair. 4th rev. ed. 2012. (ENG., Illus.). 744p. (C). pap. 47.95 (978-0-08-096942-8(9)) Routledge.

—Automobile Electrical & Electronic Systems: Automotive Technology: Vehicle Maintenance & Repair. 4th ed. 2012. (Illus.). xxxv, 703p. E-Book **(978-0-08-096943-5(7))** Routledge.

Denton, Tom. Automobile Electrical & Electronic Systems: Automotive Technology: Vehicle Maintenance & Repair. 2011. (... pap. 36.95 (978-0-08-096945-9(3)) Routledge.

Duffy, James E. Auto Electricity & Electronics Instructor's Guide. 2009. pap. 90.00 *(978-1-59070-913-9(6))* Goodheart-Willcox Pub.

Erjavec, Jack. Elecrical & Elecronic Systems: NATEF Standards Job Sheets. 3rd ed. 2009. (ENG.). 240p. (C). pap. 40.95 *(978-1-4354-8321-7(9))* Delmar Cengage Learning.

Fornel, Bernard de & Louis, Jean-Paul. Electrical Actuators: Applications & Performance. 2010. (Iste Ser.: 376). (ENG., Illus.). 528p. 184.00 *(978-1-84821-096-7(5)*, Wiley-ISTE) Wiley, John & Sons, Inc.

Halderman, James D. Advanced Automotive Electricity & Electronics. rev. ed. 2012. (ENG.). 480p. (C). pap. 110.93 ***(978-0-13-254262-3(5)**, Prentice Hall)* Prentice Hall PTR.

—Automotive Electricity & Electronics. 3rd ed. 2010. (ENG., Illus.). 544p. (C). pap. 118.00 *(978-0-13-512406-2(9))* Pearson Education Canada CAN. Dist: Pearson Education.

—Diagnosis & Troubleshooting of Automotive Electrical, Electronic, & Computer Systems. 5th rev. ed. 2010. (ENG., Illus.). 528p. (C). pap. 118.00 *(978-0-13-255155-7(1)*, Prentice Hall) Prentice Hall PTR.

—NATEF Correlated Task Sheets for Diagnosis & Troubleshooting of Automotive Electrical, Electronic, & Computer Systems. (ENG.). (C). 5th ed. 2009. 624p. pap. 36.20 *(978-0-13-506899-1(1))* 6th rev. ed. 2011. 264p. pap. 29.00 *(978-0-13-255220-2(5))* Prentice Hall PTR. (Prentice Hall).

Hatch, Steve V. Computerized Engine Controls. 9th ed. 2011. (New Automotive & Truck Technology Titles! Ser.). (ENG.). 688p. (C). pap. 149.95 *(978-1-111-13490-7(1))* Delmar Cengage Learning.

Hollembeak, Barry. Today's Technician: Automotive Electricity & Electronics Classroom & Shop Manual Pack. 5th ed. 2010. (ENG.). 1296p. (C). pap. 147.95 *(978-1-4354-7010-1(9))* Delmar Cengage Learning.

Hu, Jia-Sheng & Tsa, Mi-Ching. Control & Fault Diagnosis of an Auto-balancingTwo-wheeled Cart: Remote pilot & sensor/actuator fault diagnosis for coaxial two-wheeled electric vehicle. 2008. 144p. pap. *(978-3-639-10631-2(8))* VDM Verlag Dr. Mueller e.K.

IEEE Staff. 2009 IEEE Workshop on Computational Intelligence in Vehicles & Vehicular Systems. 2009. pap. 196.00 *(978-1-4244-2770-3(3))* IEEE.

Jones and Bartlett Publishers Staff & Cdx Global Staff. Electrical & Electronic Systems Tasksheet Manual for NATEF Proficiency. rev. ed. 2010. 75p. pap. 26.95 *(978-0-7637-8508-6(3))* Jones & Bartlett Learning, LLC.

Kershaw, John F. & Halderman, James D. Automotive Electrical & Electronic Systems. 5th ed. 2007. (ENG., Illus.). (C). 416p. pap. 62.40 *(978-0-13-238884-9(7))*; 384p. per. 80.60 (978-0-13-238883-2(9)) Prentice Hall PTR. (Prentice Hall).

McPherson, Dale. Modern Diesel Technology: Electrical/Electronic Systems & Heating, Ventilation, Air Conditioning Systems Job Sheets. 2006. (ENG.). 144p. (C). pap. 34.95 *(978-1-4180-6338-2(X))* Delmar Cengage Learning.

Meyer, Gereon & Valldorf, Jürgen, eds. Advanced Microsystems for Automotive Applications 2011: Smart Systems for Electric, Safe & Networked Mobility. 2011. (VDI-Buch Ser.). (Illus.). x, 344p. 259.00 *(978-3-642-21380-9(4)*, 3642213804) Springer.

Munday, Frank. Custom Auto Electrickery: How to Work with & Understand Auto *Electrical* Systems. 2006. (Hot Rod Handbooks Ser.). (ENG., Illus.). 256p. per. 29.95 *(978-0-949398-35-2(7)*, 0949398357) Graffiti Pubns. AUS. *Dist:* MBI Distribution Services/Quayside Distribution.

Prague, Nick. Automotive Electrical Systems. 2007. 84p. per. 10.95 *(978-0-595-46747-1(4))* iUniverse, Inc.

Ribbens, William. Understanding Automotive Electronics. 7th ed. 2012. (ENG.). 520p. 99.95 *(978-0-08-097097-4(4)*, Butterworth-Heinemann) Elsevier Science & Technology Bks.

Robert Bosch GmbH. Automotive Electrics: Systems & Components: Networking, Hybrid Drive. 5th ed. 2007. (Automotive Electronics Ser.). (Illus.). 530p. 59.95 (978-0-8376-1541-7(0)) Bentley Pubs.

—Bosch Automotive Networking: Expert Know-How on Automotive Technology. 2007. (Illus.). 119p. per. 24.95 *(978-0-8376-1547-9(X)) Bentley Pubs.*

—Bosch Technical Instruction: Alternators. (Illus.). *pap. 14.95 (978-0-8376-0479-4(6)) Bentley Pubs.*

—Bosch Technical Instruction: Graphical Symbols & Circuit Diagrams for Automotive Electrics. (Illus.). pap. 14.95 *(978-0-8376-0493-0(1))* Bentley Pubs.

—Bosch Technical Instruction: Symbols for Compressed-Air Brake Systems. (Illus.). pap. 14.95 *(978-0-8376-0597-5(0))* Bentley Pubs.

Rudman, Jack. Automotive Electrical - Electronics. (Dantes *Subject* Standardized Tests Ser.: Vol. 39). 49.95 *(978-0-8373-6539-8(2))* National Learning Corp.

Stienecker, Adam. Hybrid Energy Storage Systems. 2009. 68p. pap. *(978-3-639-13994-5(1))* VDM Verlag Dr. Mueller e.K.

Strong, Matt. Custom Auto Wiring & Electrical: Oem Electrical Systems, Premade & Custom Wiring Kits, & Car Audio Installations for Street Rods, *Muscle Cars*, Race Cars, Trucks & Restorations. 2009. (ENG.). *192p.* (gr. 12-18). pap. 21.95 *(978-1-55788-545-6(1)*, HP Trade) Penguin Group (USA) Inc.

AUTOMOBILES—ELECTRIC WIRING

Beretta, Joseph. Automotive Electricity: Electric Drive. 2010. (Iste Ser.: 375). (ENG., Illus.). 304p. 127.00 *(978-1-84821-095-0(7)*, Wiley-ISTE) Wiley, John & Sons, Inc.

Candela, Tony. Automotive Electrical Performance Projects. 2011. (Illus.). *192p.* pap. 29.95 *(978-1-934709-55-9(7))* CarTech, Inc.

—Automotive Wiring & Electrical Systems. *2009.* 144p. pap. 24.95 *(978-1-932494-87-7(1))* CarTech, Inc.

Parrholser, Dennis. Wiring: A Detailed How-to Guide. 2011. (Hot Rod Basics Ser.). (ENG., Illus.). 144p. pap. 27.95 *(978-1-929133-98-7(7)*, 1929133987, ArtKulture) *Wolfgang* Pubns., Inc.

Parks, *Dennis* W. Automotive Wiring: A Practical Guide to Wiring Your Hot Rod or Custom Car. 2011. *(Motorbooks Workshop Ser.).* (ENG., Illus.). *144p. pap.* 24.99 *(978-0-7603-3992-3(9), 0760339929, Motorbooks) MBI* Publishing Co. LLC.

Strong, Matt. Custom Auto Wiring & Electrical: Oem Electrical Systems, Premade & Custom Wiring Kits, & Car Audio Installations for Street Rods, Muscle Cars, Race Cars, Trucks & Restorations. 2009. (ENG.). 192p. (gr. 12-18). pap. 21.95 *(978-1-55788-545-6(1)*, HP Trade) Penguin Group (USA) Inc.

AUTOMOBILES—ELECTRONIC EQUIPMENT

see also *Automobiles—Radio Equipment*

Abut, Huseyin, et al, eds. Advances for in-Vehicle & *Mobile* Systems: Challenges for International Standards. 2010. (Illus.). xvi, 284p. pap. 139.00 (978-1-4419-4131-2(2), 1441941312) Springer.

—Digital Signal Processing for in-Vehicle & *Mobile* Systems II. 2007. (Illus.). XVI, 334p. 39.00 *(978-0-387-33503-2(X)*, 038733503X) Springer.

Autodata. 2007 Domestic Diagnostic Trouble Code Manual (1994-2007) 3rd ed. 2006. pap. 83.95 *(978-1-893026-35-3(3))* Delmar Cengage Learning.

—2007 Import Diagnostic Trouble Code Manual (1994-2007) 3rd ed. 2006. *pap.* 83.95 *(978-1-893026-36-0(1))* Delmar Cengage Learning.

Bringing Theory into Practice: Fundamentals of Power Semiconductors for Automotive Applications. 2006. 59.95 (978-0-9789866-0-5(1)) Infineon Technologies AG.

Broy, Manfred. Model-Driven Development of Reliable Automotive Services: Second Automotive Software Workshop, ASWSD 2006, San Diego, CA, USA, March 15-17, 2006, Revised Selected Papers. 2008. (Lecture Notes in Computer Science / Programming & Software Engineering Ser.). xviii, 183p. pap. 64.95 *(978-3-540-70929-9(0))* Springer.

Casier, Herman. Analog Circuit Design: Sensors, Actuators & Power Drivers - Integrated Power Amplifiers from Wireline to RF - Very High Frequency Front Ends. 2008. (ENG.). x, 362p. 189.00 *(978-1-4020-8262-7(2)*, 1402082622) Springer.

Casier, Herman, et al, eds. Analog Circuit Design: Sensors, Actuators & Power Drivers; Integrated Power Amplifiers from Wireline to RF; Very High Frequency Front Ends. 2010. (ENG.). x, 362p. pap. 189.00 *(978-90-481-7824-7(X)*, 904817824X) Springer.

Chapman, Norm. Principles of Electricity & Electronics for the Automotive Technician. 2nd ed. 2008. (ENG.). 608p. (C). pap. 156.95 *(978-1-4283-6121-8(9))* Delmar Cengage Learning.

Chen, Jiann-Liang & Chang, Yao-Chung. Telematics Communication Technologies & Vehicular Networks: Wireless Architectures & Applications. Huang, Chung-Ming & Chen, Yuh-Shyan, eds. 2009. 414p. 180.00 *(978-1-60566-840-6(0))* IGI Global.

Chilton Automotive Editorial Staff. Asian Diagnostic Service Manual 2006, Vol. 3. 2006. (Chilton Diagnostic Manuals Ser.). (ENG., Illus.). 1032p. 79.95 *(978-1-4180-2915-9(7))* Delmar Cengage Learning.

—European Diagnostic Service 2006. 2006. (Chilton Diagnostic Manuals Ser.). (ENG., Illus.). 888p. 79.95 *(978-1-4180-2924-1(6))* Delmar Cengage Learning.

Chilton Editors. Chilton 2006 Asian Diagnostic Service Vol. 1, Vol. 1. 2006. (Chilton Diagnostic Manuals Ser.). (ENG., Illus.). 768p. 79.95 *(978-1-4180-2913-5(0))* Delmar Cengage Learning.

—Chilton Asian Diagnostic Service Manual 2006, Vol. 2. 2006. (Chilton Diagnostic Manuals Ser.). (ENG., Illus.). 984p. 79.95 *(978-1-4180-2914-2(9))* Delmar Cengage Learning.

Cram101 Textbook Reviews *Staff.* Outlines & Highlights for Computerized Engine Controls Be by Steve V Hatch, Isbn: 9781428399969. 2009. 148p. pap. 29.95 *(978-1-4288-7502-9(6))* Cram101 Inc.

Delmar Learning Staff. ASE Test Preparation - A6 Electricity & Electronics. 5th ed. 2011. (ENG., Illus.). 256p. pap. 23.95 (978-1-111-12708-4(5)) Delmar Cengage Learning.

—Electricity & Electronics: Computer Based Training. 2007. (ENG.). 114.95 *(978-1-4283-2095-6(4))* Delmar Cengage Learning.

—Truck Equipment Installation & Repair, Test E1. 2012. (ENG.). 164p. pap. 23.95 *(978-1-4354-3935-1(X))* Delmar Cengage Learning.

Denton, Tom. Automobile Electrical & Electronic Systems: Automotive Technology - Vehicle Maintenance & Repair. 4th rev. ed. 2012. (ENG., Illus.). 744p. (C). pap. 47.95 (978-0-08-096942-8(9)) Routledge.

Denton, Tom. Automobile Electrical & Electronic Systems: *Automotive* Technology: Vehicle Maintenance & Repair. *4th ed. 2012. (Illus.).* xxxv, 703p. E-Book **(978-0-08-096943-5(7))** Routledge.

Dorries, Elisabeth H. Today's Technician: *Advanced Automotive* Electronic. 2010. (ENG.). (C). *pap. 110.95 (978-1-4180-6080-0(1))* Delmar Cengage Learning.

Fuentes, *Andy. Automotive Electronics: Components* & Test Equipment - *U.S. Markets, Technologies & Opportunities*; 1994 to 2000 Analysis. *Archdeacon, Tim, ed.* 200p. 1900.00 (978-1-883742-10-2(2)) Allied *Business* Intelligence, Inc.

Gabler, Hampton Clay, et al. Event Data Recorders: *A Decade of Innovation.* 2008. (Illus.). ix, 477p. *89.99 (978-0-7680-2066-3(2))* SAE Intl.

Goel, Asvin. *Fleet Telematics: Real-Time Management & Planning of Commercial Vehicle Operations.* 2007. (Operations Research Computer Science Interfaces Ser.). (Illus.). xiv, 184p. 149.00 (978-0-387-75104-7(1), 0387751041) Springer.

Halderman, James D. Advanced Automotive *Electricity & Electronics.* rev. ed. 2012. (ENG.). 480p. (C). pap. *110.93 **(978-0-13-254262-3(5)**,* Prentice Hall) Prentice Hall PTR.

—*Automotive Electricity & Electronics.* 3rd ed. 2010. (ENG., Illus.). 544p. (C). pap. *118.00* (978-0-13-512406-2(9)) Pearson Education Canada CAN. Dist: Pearson Education.

—Automotive Electricity & Electronics. 2008. *(978-0-13-613743-6(1))*; 2nd ed. (ENG., Illus.). 528p. (C). pap. 113.33 *(978-0-13-502950-3(3)*, Prentice Hall) Prentice Hall PTR.

—Diagnosis & *Troubleshooting* of Automotive Electrical, Electronic, & Computer *Systems. 5th ed.* 2008. (ENG., Illus.). 832p. (C). pap. 122.80 *(978-0-13-506696-6(4)*, Prentice Hall) Prentice Hall PTR.

—NATEF Correlated Task Sheets for Diagnosis & Troubleshooting of Automotive Electrical, Electronic, & Computer Systems. (ENG.). (C). *5th ed. 2009. 624p.* pap. 36.20 (978-0-13-506899-1(1)) *6th rev. ed. 2011. 264p. pap. 29.00 (978-0-13-255220-2(5)) Prentice Hall PTR. (Prentice Hall).*

Hollembeak, Barry. *Advanced Automotive Electronic Systems: Classroom Manual. 2010.* (Today's Technician Ser.). (ENG.). 912p. (C). pap. 147.95 *(978-1-111-03814-4(7))* Delmar Cengage Learning.

—Today's Technician: Automotive Electricity & Electronics Classroom & Shop Manual Pack. 5th ed. 2010. (ENG.). 1296p. (C). pap. 147.95 *(978-1-4354-7010-1(9))* Delmar Cengage *Learning.*

IEEE Staff. 2008 Fifth Annual *Conference on Wireless on demand Network* Systems & *Services. 2008. pap. 188.00 (978-1-4244-1958-6(1))* IEEE.

Institute *of Electrical and* Electronics Engineers, Inc. Staff, et al, contrib. by. 2007 *Fourth* Annual Conference on Wireless on Demand Network Systems & Services. 2007. (Illus.). vii, 171p. pap. 180.00 (978-1-4244-0860-3(1), 07EX1629) IEEE.

Jurgen, Ronald K. Automotive Electronics Reliability. 2nd ed. 2010. (Illus.). iv, 369p. **(978-0-7680-3492-9(2))** SAE Intl.

—Infotainment Systems on *Fast Forward. 2007. (Illus.). vi, 726p. 69.99 (978-0-7680-1943-8(5)) SAE Intl.*

—X-By *Wire Automotive* Systems. 2009. (Illus.). vi, 427p. *(978-0-7680-2100-4(6)) SAE Intl.*

Kershaw, John F. & Halderman, James D. Automotive Electrical & Electronic Systems. 5th ed. 2007. (ENG., Illus.). (C). 416p. pap. 62.40 *(978-0-13-238884-9(7))*; 384p. per. 80.60 (978-0-13-238883-2(9)) Prentice Hall PTR. (Prentice Hall).

Larses, Ola. *Architecting & Modeling Automotive Embedded Systems: Technology, Methods & Management. 2008. 316p. pap. (978-3-639-09870-9(6))* VDM Verlag *Dr. Mueller e.K.*

Lemke, Kerstin, et al, eds. Embedded Security in Cars: Securing Current & Future Automotive IT Applications. 2010. (ENG., Illus.). x, 273p. *pap. 89.95 (978-3-642-06659-7(3)*, 3642066593) Springer.

McPherson, Dale. Modern Diesel Technology: Electrical/Electronic Systems & Heating, Ventilation, Air Conditioning Systems Job Sheets. 2006. (ENG.). 144p. (C). pap. 34.95 *(978-1-4180-6338-2(X))* Delmar Cengage Learning.

Navet, Nicolas & Simonot-Lion, Francoise. Automotive Embedded Systems Handbook. Navet, Nicolas & Simonot-Lion, Francoise, eds. 2008. (Industrial Information Technology Ser.). (ENG., Illus.). 488p. 162.95 *(978-0-8493-8026-6(X)*, CRC Press) Taylor & Francis Group GBR. Dist: Taylor & Francis Group.

Olatunde, Adebukola O. A Tensioner for the Belt-Driven Integrated Starter-Generator. 2009. 196p. pap. *(978-3-639-16216-5(1))* VDM Verlag Dr. Mueller e.K.

Parise, George, et al. The Haynes Computer Codes & Electronic Engine Management Systems Manual. (Illus.). *(978-1-56392-274-3(5))* Haynes Manuals, Inc.

Pavkovic, Danijel & Deur, Joako. Modeling & Control of Electronic Throttle Drive. 2011. 188p. pap. ***(978-3-8443-1628-5(0))*** Lambert Academic Publishing.

Prague, Nick. L2 Med/Hvy Vehicle Electronic Diesel Engine Diagnostic Specialist: Motor Age Self-Study Guide for ASE Certification. 2006. spiral bd. 28.95 (978-1-933180-58-8(7)) Advanstar Communications, Inc.

Rabinovich, Victor, et al. Automotive Antenna Design & Applications. 2010. (ENG., Illus.). 330p. 129.95 (978-1-4398-0407-0(9), CRC Press) Taylor & Francis Group GBR. Dist: Taylor & Francis Group.

Rettberg, Achim, et al, eds. From Specification to Embedded Systems Application. 2010. (IFIP Advances in Information & Communication Technology Ser.). (Illus.). xii, 320p. pap. 149.00 (978-1-4419-3899-2(0), 1441938990) Springer.

Robert Bosch GmbH Staff. Automotive Electrics: Systems & Components: Networking, Hybrid Drive. 5th ed. 2007. (Automotive Electronics Ser.). (Illus.). 530p. 59.95 (978-0-8376-1541-7(0)) Bentley Pubs.

—Bosch Automotive Networking: Expert Know-How on Automotive Technology. 2007. (Illus.). 119p. per. 24.95 (978-0-8376-1547-9(X)) Bentley Pubs.

—Bosch Technical Instruction: Engine Electronics. (Illus.). pap. 14.95 (978-0-8376-0475-6(3)) Bentley Pubs.

—Bosch Technical Instruction: Interference Suppression. (Illus.). pap. 14.95 (978-0-8376-0476-3(1)) Bentley Pubs.

Rosenbluth, William. Application & Interpretation of Black Box Data & Crash Dynamics. 2009. (978-0-8031-7003-2(3)) American Society for Testing & Materials.

Rudman, Jack. Automotive Electrical - Electronics. (Dantes Subject Standardized Tests Ser.: Vol. 39). 49.95 (978-0-8373-6539-8(2)) National Learning Corp.

Steyaert, Michiel, et al, eds. Analog Circuit Design: High-speed Clock & Data Recovery, High-performance Amplifiers, Power Management. 2010. (ENG.). xii, 360p. pap. 209.00 (978-90-481-8032-5(5), 9048180325) Springer.

Syner, Jason. How to Install Automotive Mobile Electronic Systems. 2010. (Motorbooks Workshop Ser.). (ENG., Illus.). 192p. pap. 29.99 (978-0-7603-3177-4(4), 0760331774, Motorbooks) MBI Publishing Co. LLC.

Takeda, Kazuya, et al, eds. In-Vehicle Corpus & Signal Processing for Driver Behavior. 2010. (ENG., Illus.). xiv, 286p. pap. 129.00 (978-1-4419-4640-9(3), 1441946403) Springer.

Takeda, Kazuya (University of Nagoya & Takeda, Kazuya. In-Vehicle Corpus & Signal Processing for Driver Behavior. Takeda, Kazuya et al, eds. 2008. (Illus.). xiv, 286p. 129.00 (978-0-387-79581-2(2)) Springer.

Valldorf, Jargen & Gessner, Wolfgang, eds. Advanced Microsystems for Automotive Applications 2005. 2010. (VDI-Buch Ser.). (Illus.). xviii, 554p. pap. 179.00 (978-3-642-06371-8(3), 3642063713) Springer.

—Advanced Microsystems for Automotive Applications 2006. 2010. (VDI-Buch Ser.). (Illus.). xviii, 516p. pap. 219.00 (978-3-642-07004-4(3), 3642070043) Springer.

—Advanced Microsystems for Automotive Applications 2008. 2010. (VDI-Buch Ser.). (Illus.). xvi, 308p. pap. 189.00 (978-3-642-09683-9(2), 3642096832) Springer.

2007 IEEE International Conference on Vehicular Electronics & Safety. 2007. pap. 234.00 (978-1-4244-1265-5(X), 07EX1802) IEEE.

AUTOMOBILES—EMISSION CONTROL DEVICES

see Automobiles—Pollution Control Devices

AUTOMOBILES—ENGINES

see Automobiles—Motors

AUTOMOBILES—EQUIPMENT AND SUPPLIES

BIA. Key Russian Manufacturers & Suppliers of Automobile & Accessories. 6th rev. ed. 2006. 376p. (J). pap. 249.00 (978-1-4187-4500-4(6)) Business Information Agency.

Calabro, Marian. The Pep Boys Company History Book. 2006. (978-1-57990-636-8(2)) Lark Bks.

Cheong, Woo-Jae. Development of a Protective Coating on the Magnesium Az91d Alloy. 2009. 312p. pap. (978-3-639-16166-3(1)) VDM Verlag Dr. Mueller e.K.

Chilton Automotive Editorial Staff. Chilton Asian Mechanical Service: Subaru-Toyota. 2006. (Chilton Mechanical Manuals Ser.). (ENG., Illus.). 1944p. 79.95 (978-1-4180-0949-6(0)) Delmar Cengage Learning.

—Chilton Asian Mechanical Service Vol. II: Kia-Nissan. 2006. (Chilton Mechanical Manuals Ser.). (ENG., Illus.). 1872p. 79.95 (978-1-4180-0948-9(2)) Delmar Cengage Learning.

Edmondson, Chuck. Fast Car Physics. 2011. (ENG., Illus.). 248p. (gr. 17). 75.00 (978-0-8018-9822-8(6)); pap. 29.95 (978-0-8018-9823-5(4)) Johns Hopkins Univ. Pr.

Gordon, Michael. P2 Automobile Parts Specialist: Motor Age Training Self-Study Guide for ASE Certification. 2007. spiral bd. 24.95 (978-1-933180-79-3(X)) Advanstar Communications, Inc.

Henderson, Bob & Haynes, John H. OBD-II & Sistemas de Control Electrónico del Motor. 2006. (Haynes Repair Manuals Ser.). (ENG., Illus.). 272p. per. 26.95 (978-1-56392-612-9(1), 1563926121) Haynes Manuals, Inc.

Jain, Vipul & Heydari, Payam, eds. Automotive Radar Sensors in Silicon Technologies: Circuits & Systems. 2012. (ENG.). x, 240p. 129.00 (978-1-4419-6774-9(5), 1441967745) Springer.

Klier, Thomas H. & Rubenstein, James M. Who Really Made Your Car? Restructuring & Geographic Change in the Auto Industry. 2008. 419p. 40.00 (978-0-88099-334-0(0)); pap. 20.00 (978-0-88099-333-3(2)) Upjohn, W.E. Institute for Employment Research.

Larses, Ola. Architecting & Modeling Automotive Embedded Systems: Technology, Methods & Management. 2008. 316p. pap. (978-3-639-09870-9(6)) VDM Verlag Dr. Mueller e.K.

Mavrigian, Mike. High Performance Fasteners & Plumbing: A Guide to Nuts, Bolts, Fuel, Brake, Oil & Coolant Lines, Hoses, Clamps, Racinghardware & Plumbing Techniques. 2008. (ENG., Illus.). 176p. (gr. 12-18). 19.95 (978-1-55788-523-4(0), HP Trade) Penguin Group (USA) Inc.

Morgan, Sally. Old Cars. 2007. (Dealing with Waste/Watts Ser.). (Illus.). 30p. (J). (gr. 4-7). lib. bdg. (978-1-59920-010-1(4), Harwood Academic Pubs.) Black Rabbit Bks.

Newcomb, Doug. Car Audio for Dummies. 2008. (ENG., Illus.). 310p. pap. 24.99 (978-0-470-15158-7(7), For Dummies) Wiley, John & Sons, Inc.

Petroleum Equipment Institute, compiled by. Recommended Practices for Installation of Underground Liquid Storage Systems: Rp100: Rp100. 2000th ed. 2011. pap. 95.00 (978-0-9642638-5-7(8)) Petroleum Equipment Institute.

—Recommended Practices for the Inspection & Maintenance of UST Systems: Rp900: Rp900. 2008. (ENG., Illus.). 52p. pap. 90.00 (978-0-9642638-8-8(2)) Petroleum Equipment Institute.

Rasiah, Rajah. Multinationals, Technology & Localization in Automotive Firms in Asia. 2008. pap. 40.00 (978-0-415-49558-5(X)) Routledge.

Robert Bosch GmbH Staff. Bosch Technical Instruction: Starting Systems. (Illus.). pap. 14.95 (978-0-8376-0480-0(X)) Bentley Pubs.

Robert Bosch GmbH Staff, creator. Safety, Comfort & Convenience Systems: Function, Regulation & Components. 2006. (Illus.). 399p. 59.95 (978-0-8376-1391-8(4), H013) Bentley Pubs.

Sly, David. Transport Effort. 2008. 116p. pap. (978-3-639-07526-7(9)) VDM Verlag Dr. Mueller e.K.

Smith, Paul D. Merchants of Speed: The Men Who Built America's Performance Industry. 2009. (ENG., Illus.). 240p. 40.00 (978-0-7603-3567-3(2), 0760335672, Motorbooks) MBI Publishing Co. LLC.

Timothy, Kevin. The Pocket Parts Pal: The Complete Guide to Ho Scale Car Parts. Collison, Joanne, ed. 3rd ed. (Illus.). 72p. (Orig.). pap. 4.95 (978-88-379-6059-9(X)) What It Is! Publishing.

Vokins, Stephen. Nodding Dogs & Vinyl Roofs: The Weird World of Quirky Car Accessories. (ENG., Illus.). 2010. 120p. pap. 9.95 (978-1-84425-712-6(6), 1844257126) 2008. 128p. 14.95 (978-1-84425-422-4(4), 1844254224) Haynes Publishing PLC GBR. Dist: MBI Distribution Services/Quayside Distribution.

White, Harvey. How to Keep Your Muscle Car Alive. 2009. (Motorbooks Workshop Ser.). (ENG., Illus.). 224p. pap. 29.99 (978-0-7603-3546-8(X), 076033546X, Motorbooks) MBI Publishing Co. LLC.

AUTOMOBILES—EXHAUST CONTROL DEVICES

see Automobiles—Pollution Control Devices

AUTOMOBILES—[illegible]

see also Carburetors

American Society of Mechanical Engineers Staff, ed. Automotive Power Systems: Environment & Conservation. 228p. 130.00 (978-0-85298-721-[illegible]) Professional Engineering Publishing GBR. Dist: SAE Intl.

Bennett, Sean. Medium/Heavy Duty Truck Engines, Fuel & Computerized Management Systems. 3rd ed. 2008. (ENG.). 960p. (C). 201.95 (978-1-4283-6666-4(0)) Delmar Cengage Learning.

—Medium/Heavy Duty Truck Engines, Fuel, Computer Management. 3rd ed. 2008. (ENG.). 272p. (C). pap., wbk. ed. 54.95 (978-1-4283-6661-9(X)) Delmar Cengage Learning.

Bovair, Jennifer L. & Arent, Douglas Jay. Alternative Transportation Fuels & Vehicle Technologies: Challenges & Opportunities: A Report of the CSIS Energy & National Security Program, CSIS Global Strategy Institute, & National Renewable Energy Laboratory. 2008. pap. (978-0-8920-[illegible]-542-4(7)) Ctr. for Strategic & International Studies.

Committee on Review of the FreedomCAR and Fuel Research Program, Phase 2 & National Research Council. Review of the Research Program of the FreedomCAR & Fuel Partnership: Second Report. 2008. (ENG.). 166p. pap. 38.75 (978-0-309-11634-3(1)) National Academies Pr.

Davidson, Jim. 75 Ways to Save Gas: Clean, Green Tips to Cut Costs at the Pump. 2011. (ENG.). 144p. (gr. 12). 8.99 (978-0-14-318605-2(1), Penguin (Non-Classics)) Penguin Group (USA) Inc.

Fortune, Luke. UFO How-to Vol VII - Esoteric Power Systems. 2009. 615p. pap. 49.95 (978-0-557-06796-1(0)) Lulu Enterprises Inc.

Genat, Robert. Fuelies: Fuel Injected Corvettes 1957-1965. 2008. (Cartech Ser.). (Illus.). 192p. pap. 29.95 (978-1-932494-52-5(9)) CarTech, Inc.

Halderman, James D. Automotive Fuel & Emissions Systems, Automotive Fuel & Emissions Control Systems: NATEF Correlated Task Sheets. 2nd ed. 2008. (ENG.). 390p. (C). pap. 36.20 (978-0-13-506011-7(7), Prentice Hall) Prentice Hall PTR.

Halderman, James D. & Linder, James. Automotive Fuel & Emissions Control Systems. (ENG.). (C). 2nd ed. 2008. 576p. pap. 122.80 (978-0-13-505481-9(8)) 3rd ed. 2011. (Illus.). 480p. pap. 118.00 (978-0-13-254292-0(7)) Prentice Hall PTR. (Prentice Hall).

—NATEF Correlated Task Sheets for Automotive Fuel & Emissions Control Systems. 3rd rev. ed. 2011. (ENG.). 336p. (C). pap. 21.80 (978-0-13-254510-5(1), Prentice Hall) Prentice Hall PTR.

Halderman, James D. & Martin, Tony. NATEF Correlated Job Sheets for Hybrid & Alternative Fuel Vehicles. 3rd ed. 2012. (ENG.). 96p. (C). pap. 26.67 (978-0-13-278538-9(2), Prentice Hall) Prentice Hall PTR.

Hartman, Jeff. Nitrous Oxide Performance Handbook. 2009. (Motorbooks Workshop Ser.). (ENG., Illus.). 224p. pap. 29.99 (978-0-7603-2624-4(X), 076032624X, Motorbooks) MBI Publishing Co. LLC.

IEEE Staff, ed. 2007 IEEE Vehicle Power & Propulsion Conference. 2007. pap. 412.00 (978-0-7803-9760-6(6), 07EX1461) IEEE.

Institution of Mechanical Engineers. Innovations in Fuel Economy & Sustainable Road Transport. 2012. (ENG., Illus.). 240p. pap. 330.00 (978-0-85709-213-7(8)) Woodhead Publishing Ltd. GBR. Dist: Ingram Pub. Services.

Institution of Mechanical Engineers (IMechE). Injection Systems for IC Engine Conference: Institution of Mechanical Engineers (IMechE) conference May 2009. 2009. (Illus.). 300p. (978-1-84334-561-9(7), Chandos Publishing) Woodhead Publishing Ltd.

McClurg, Bob. How to Install & Tune Nitrous Oxide Systems. 2012. (Illus.). 144p. pap. 24.95 (978-1-934709-34-4(4)) CarTech, Inc.

McMann, Denise M., ed. Unintended or Sudden Acceleration in Automobiles. 2010. (Transportation Issues, Policies & R&D Ser.). pap. 43.00 (978-1-61728-983-5(3), Nova Novinka) Nova Science Pubs., Inc.

Michael, Stephen A. Poor Man Hydrogen Generator on Demand: SMCS HHO Stephens Multi Cell Systems Hydrogen Generator on Demand. 2011. 68p. pap. 29.99 (978-1-4567-1992-0(0)) AuthorHouse.

Moss, Dave. The Efficient Driver's Handbook: Your Guide to Fuel Efficient Driving Techniques & Car Choice. 2010. (ENG., Illus.). 96p. pap. 19.95 (978-1-84584-351-9(7), 1845843517) Veloce Publishing Ltd. GBR. Dist: MBI Distribution Services/Quayside Distribution.

Orrigo, Craig A., ed. Toyota Automobiles & Unintended Acceleration. 2011. (Series: Transportation Issues, Policies & R&D Ser.). 207p. 185.00 (978-1-61324-275-9(1)) Nova Science Pubs., Inc.

Papasavva, Stella, et al, eds. Life-Cycle Analysis Tools for "Green" Materials & Process Selection: Proceedings: Symposium on Life-Cycle Analysis Tools for "Green" Materials & Process Selection (2005: Boston, MA) 2009. (Symposium Proceedings Ser.: Vol. 895). (Illus.). 189p. 90.00 (978-1-55899-850-6(0)) Materials Research Society.

Porche, Isaac R., III & Bernstein, Mark A. An Approach to Assessing the Technical Feasibility & Market Potential of a New Automotive Device. 2007. 76p. pap. 23.00 (978-0-8330-4162-3(2), tr313) RAND Corp., The.

Reforming Corporate Average Fuel Economy (CAFE) Standards: Hearing Before the Subcommittee on Surface Transportation & Merchant Marine of the Committee on Commerce, Science, & Transportation, United States Senate, One Hundred Ninth Congress, Second Session, May 9, 2006. 2011. (Illus.). iii, 85p. (978-0-16-088301-9(6), 552-070-42606-0) United States Government Printing Office.

Robert Bosch Gmbh. Bosch Diesel Fuel-Injection Systems Unit Injector System & Unit Pump System: Technical Instruction Booklet. 2007. (Illus.). 78p per. 24.95 (978-0-8376-1550-9(X)) Bentley Pubs.

Robert Bosch GmbH Staff. Bosch Technical Instruction: Diesel Fuel-Injection — An Overview. (Illus.). pap. 14.95 (978-0-8376-0494-7(X)) Bentley Pubs.

—Bosch Technical Instruction: Diesel Fuel-Injection Pumps Types PE-P. (Illus.). pap. 14.95 (978-0-8376-0496-1(6)) Bentley Pubs.

—Bosch Technical Instruction: Distributor Fuel-Injection Pump Type VE. Illus.). pap. 14.95 (978-0-8376-0495-4(8)) Bentley Pubs.

Teene, Eero. Modeling of a Liquid Phase Lpg Fuel Injection System Development Modeling, & Experimentation. 2008. 152p. pap. (978-3-639-09612-(6)) VDM Verlag Dr. Mueller e.K.

The Hightower Report, prod. Commodity Trading Guide 2008. 2007. 56. 20.00 (978-0-9789285-1-3(2)) Hightower Report, The.

Vehicle Fuel Economy. 2008. 70p. (C). pap. 39.00 (978-1-60692-057-2(X)) Nova Science Pubs., Inc.

Weiers, Ronald. Gas Smarts: Hundreds of Small Ways to Save Big Tim at the Pump. 2011. (ENG.). 256p. pap. 11.95 (978-1-4405-0049-7(5)) Adams Media Corp.

Weiers, Ronald M. Ga$ Smart$ 2011. E-Book (978-1-4405-1081-6(4)) Adams Media Corp.

Zhao, H., ed. Advanced Direct Injection Combustion Engine Technologies & Development: Diesel Engines, 2 vols., 2. 2009. (Illus.). 756p. 290.00 (978-1-84569-744-0(8)) Woodhead Publishing Ltd. GBR. Dist: Taylor & Francis Group.

—Advanced Direct Injection Combustion Engine Technologies & Development: Science & Technology, 2 vols. 2009. (Illus.). 840p. (978-1-84569-389-3(2))

Zhao Hua Staff. Homogeneous Charge Compression [illegible] (Hcci) [illegible] Aut. 2007. (ENG.). 524p. 289.95 (978-1-4200-4459-1(1), CRC Press) Taylor & Francis Group GBR. Dist: Taylor & Francis Group.

AUTOMOBILES—GEARING

see Automobiles—Transmission Devices

AUTOMOBILES—GUIDEBOOKS

see Automobile Travel—Guidebooks

AUTOMOBILES—HANDBOOKS, MANUALS, ETC.

Ahlstrand, [illegible] Benz C-Class: 2001 Thru 2007. 2010. [illegible] 1985-2007 [illegible] 45.45 (978-1-56392-667-9(3), [illegible]737-9(3)) Haynes,Chilton.

Ahlstrand, Alan, et al. Honda XR50R, XR70R, XR80R, XR100R, CRF50F, CRF70F, CRF80F, CRF100F, 1985 Thru 2007 [illegible] 450, 500 Twins & Ninja 250, Manual Ser.). (ENG., Illus.). 160p. per. 33.95 [illegible] (ENG., Illus.). 240p. pap. 1563926571) Haynes Manuals, Inc. [illegible] Manuals, Inc.

—Yamaha YFS200 Blaster ATV 1988 Thru 2006, 200cc. 2008. (Owners Workshop Manual Ser.). (ENG., Illus.). 128p. per. 36.45 (978-1-56392-688-4(1), 1563926881) Haynes Manuals, Inc.

Anderson, Bruce. Porsche 911 Performance Handbook, 1963-1998. 3rd ed. 2009. (Motorbooks Workshop Ser.). (ENG., Illus.). 304p. pap. 34.99 (978-0-7603-3180-4(4), 0760331804, Motorbooks) MBI Publishing Co. LLC.

Antonellis, Michael. The Car Owner's Manual You REALLY Need. 2009. 96p. pap. 14.99 (978-0-557-08839-3(9)) Lulu Enterprises Inc.

[illegible]ooks, creator. Mercedes-Benz 220b 1959-1965 Owners Workshop Manual. [illegible] 192p. pap. 34.95 (978-1-58850-093-9(4)) Veloce Enterprises, Inc.

[illegible]ishers. Audi TT Service Manual: 1. 8L turbo, 3. 2L; including roadster [illegible]

—BMW [illegible]000-2006. 2006. (Illus.). 978p. pap. 99.95 (978-0-8376-1500-4(3), Servic[illegible] Pubs.

[illegible] 2008 [illegible] Service Manual (E90, E91, E92, E93) 2006, 2007, 2008, 2009 [illegible] Pubs.

—Mercedes-Benz [illegible] 325xi, 328i, 328xi, 330i, 330xi, 335i, 335xi: 2006, 2007, Kompressor, C2[illegible]). 1256p. pap. 129.95 (978-0-8376-1608-7(5)) Bentley Bentley Pubs.

—MINI Cooper - Diagnosis [illegible] 2) Service Manual: C220, C230, C230 [illegible]6p. pap. 59.95 (978-0[illegible]). 1216p. pap. 129.95 (978-0-8376-1572-1(0))

—Mi[illegible] Cooper (R55, R56, R57) [illegible]sswork: Cooper, Cooper S. 2009. (Illus.). [illegible] JSW), including Clubm[illegible](2)) Bentley Pubs.

—Volkswa[illegible] 11. (Illus.). 1058p. 139.9[illegible] [illegible]ual: Cooper, Cooper S, John Cooper [illegible]soline Jetta (A5) S[illegible]ice Manual[illegible]tible: 2007, 2008, 2009, 2010 [illegible] 2 [illegible] including TDI, g[illegible] 12200[illegible] 2006, 2007, 20[illegible] [illegible]1671-1(9)) Bentley Pubs.

—Volksw[illegible] (978-0-8376-1616-2(6)) [illegible]09 2010. 2[illegible] diesel, 2. 0L & 2. 5L Includ[illegible] Jetta (A5) Service Manual[illegible] Pubs. (978-0-[illegible]

—Volkswagen [illegible] Sportwagen 2008. (ENG[illegible] 5 - 2008: [illegible] 2007, 2008, 2009 1640p. pap. [illegible]-5(5)) Bentley Pubs. [illegible] 952p. lib. bdg.

British Leyland Motor[illegible] [illegible]le Service Manual: Including Convertible. 20[illegible]. (Illus.). (Illus.). 50p. (Orig.). [illegible]8376-15[illegible](3)) Bentley Pubs. [illegible]). 1016p. pap. [illegible] 2. 5L,

—MGB Tuning Handbook [illegible] Tourer & G[illegible] (978-0-8376-0506-7(7)) Bentley [illegible]8376-0504-[illegible] Handbook, 1975-1980.

[illegible]GC Driver's Handbook: 1967-1[illegible]-1974. (Illus.) [illegible] (978-0-8376-0503-6(2)) Bentley Pubs.

[illegible] Triumph Spitfire MK III Driver's Handbook [illegible] 64p. 16.00 [illegible] 16.00

—Tri[illegible] (978-0-8376-0527-2(X)) Bentley Pubs.

[illegible] Stag Workshop Manual: 1971-1973. (Illus.) [illegible] 80p. (Orig.). 16.00

—Trium[illegible] (978-0-8376-0508-1(3)) Bentley Pubs.

[illegible] Driver's Handbook (U. S. Spec), 1975. [illegible] 40p. 70.00 (978-0-8376-0550-0(4)) Bentley Pubs. [illegible] 16.00

Chilton. Chilton Asian Service Manual Vol. 3: Infiniti, Nissan, 5 vols. 2011. (ENG., Illus.). 1[illegible]

—Chilton Euro[illegible] Service Manual 2010: Audi, BMW, Mercedes-Benz, Mini, Saab, Volks[illegible] Volvo. 2011. (ENG., Illus.). 2304p. 99.95 [illegible] 95 (978-1-111-03766-6(3)) Delmar Cengage Learning. (978-1-111-0[illegible]

Chilton, (Chilton). C[illegible]) Delmar Cengage Learning. (ENG., Illus.). 15[illegible] Asian Service Manual, 2010, 5 vols., Vol. 1. 2011. Learning. [illegible] 95 (978-1-111-03764-2(7)) Delmar Cengage

—Chilton Asian Service Manual 2010: Hyundai, Kia, Lexus, Vol. 2. 2011. (ENG., Illus.). 2424p. 79.95 (978-1-111-03765-9(5)) Delmar Cengage Learning.

—Chilton Asian Service Manual 2010 Vol. 4: Mazda, Mitsubishi, Subaru, Suzuki, 5 vols. 2011. (ENG., Illus.). 244[illegible] 79.95 (978-1-111-03767-3(1)) Delmar Cengage Learning.

—Chilton Asian Service Manual 2010 Vol. 5: Scion, Toyota. 2011. (ENG.). 2040p. [illegible].95 (978-1-111-03768-0(X)) Delmar Cengage Learning.

[illegible] Automotive Editorial Staff. Chilton Labor Guide 2010. 2009. (ENG.). [illegible]8p. 219.95 (978-1-111-03608-9(X)) Delmar Cengage Learning.

[illegible]bility Manual Asian, 1992-94, European. 2304p. 112.00 [illegible]-0-8019-8553-9(6)) Nichols Publishing Co.

[illegible]an Mechanical Service Manual 2006. 2006. (Chilton Mechanical [illegible]als Ser.). (ENG., Illus.). 1152p. 89.95 (978-1-4180-0604-4(1)) Delmar [illegible]age Learning.

[illegible]tors. Chilton 2006 Asian Diagnostic Service Vol. 1, Vol. 1. 2006. [illegible]n Diagnostic Manuals Ser.). (ENG., Illus.). 768p. 79.95 [illegible]4180-291[illegible](0)) Delmar Cengage Learning.

[illegible]vin. VW GTI, Golf, & Jetta, Mk III & IV: Find It. Fix It. Trick It. rev. ed. [illegible]otorbooks Workshop Ser.). (ENG., Illus.). 160p. per. 24.95 [illegible]03-2595-7(2), 0760325952, Motorbooks) MBI Publishing Co. LLC.

[illegible]ew & Mather, Phil. Suzuki: SV650 & SV650S '99 to '08. Haynes, [illegible] ed. 2009. (Haynes Service & Repair Manual Ser.). (ENG., Illus.). (978-1-84425-767-6(3), 1844257673) Haynes Manuals, Inc.

[illegible]ishi Magna/Dimante 1991 To 2005: Automobile Repair Manual. [illegible]lus.). 521p. pap. 34.95 (978-1-876720-09-4(3), 1876720093) [illegible] AUS. Dist: MBI Distribution Services/Quayside Distribution.

[illegible]ven, Greg. Water-Cooled VW Performance Handbook: 3rd [illegible]011. (Motorbooks Workshop Ser.). (ENG., Illus.). 208p. pap. [illegible]-3766-0(7), 0760337667, Motorbooks) MBI Publishing Co.

[illegible]tef Standards Job Sheets. 3rd ed. 2009. (ENG.). 208p. [illegible]6-4354-8320-0(0)) Delmar Cengage Learning.

The check digit for ISBN-10 appears in parentheses after the full ISN-13

Wong, J. Y. Terramechanics & Off-Road Vehicle Engineering: Terrain Behaviour, Off-Road Vehicle Performance & Design. 2nd ed. 2009. (ENG., Illus.). 488p. 145.00 *(978-0-7506-8561-0(1)*, Butterworth-Heinemann) Elsevier Science & Technology Bks.

Wurth, Peter, ed. Mini: the Book. 2007. (Illus.). 191p. 42.00 *(978-3-89955-180-8(X))* Die Gestalten Verlag DEU. Dist: Prestel Publishing.

Zazarine, Paul. The Collector's Guide to GTO 1964-1974. 2007. (ENG., Illus.). 128p. pap. 19.95 *(978-1-58388-196-5(4)*, 1583881964) Iconografix, Inc.

Zhao, Chao. Aging in China & Its Impact on Vehicle Design. 2009. 272p. pap. *(978-3-639-13287-8(4))* VDM Verlag Dr. Mueller e.K.

Zumbrunn & Heseltine, Richard. Italian Auto Legends: Classics of Style & Design. 2008. (Illus.). 296p. pap. 22.95 *(978-1-85894-431-9(7))* Merrell Pubs. Ltd. GBR. Dist: Perseus Distribution.

Zurschmeide, Jeffrey. High-Performance Subaru Builder's Guide: Includes the Impreza, Legacy, Forester, Outback, WRX & STI. 2007. (S-A Design Ser.). (ENG., Illus.). 144p. pap. 24.95 *(978-1-932494-51-8(0)*, S-A Design) CarTech, Inc.

AUTOMOBILES—DICTIONARIES

Clough, Albert L. A Dictionary of Automobile Terms. 2009. 360p. pap. 30.45 *(978-1-4446-1722-1(2))* Research Pr.

Haajanen, Lennart W. Illustrated Dictionary of Automobile Body Styles. alt. ed. 2007. (ENG., Illus.). 175p. per. 39.95 *(978-0-7864-3737-5(5))* McFarland & Co., Inc. Pubs.

Lewin, Tony. The A-Z of 21st-Century Cars. 2011. (ENG., Illus.). 540p. pap. 39.95 *(978-1-85894-525-5(9))* Merrell Pubs. Ltd. GBR. Dist: Perseus Distribution.

Publications International Staff. Ency of Amer Cars. 2006. (Illus.). 848p. 34.98 *(978-1-4127-1354-2(4)*, 1261319, PIL Kids) Publications International, Ltd.

AUTOMOBILES—DIESEL MOTORS

see Automobiles—Motors

AUTOMOBILES—DRIVE TRAINS

see Automobiles—Power Trains

AUTOMOBILES—DRIVERS' LICENSES

see Automobile Drivers' Licenses

AUTOMOBILES—DRIVING

see Automobile Driving

AUTOMOBILES—DYNAMICS

Abe, Masato. Vehicle Handling Dynamics: Theory & Application. 2009. (ENG., Illus.). 296p. 104.00 *(978-1-85617-749-8(1)*, Butterworth-Heinemann) Elsevier Science & Technology Bks.

Azad, et al. Articulated Steer Vehicles: Dynamics & Control - Fundamental Issues in Modeling, Stability Analysis & Controller Development. 2008. (Illus.). 204p. pap. *(978-3-8364-6665-4(6))* VDM Verlag Dr. Mueller e.K.

Crolla, David & Mashadi, Behrooz. Vehicle Powertrain Systems: Integration & Optimization. 2012. (ENG., Illus.). 560p. 105.00 ***(978-0-470-66602-9(1)***, Wiley) Wiley, John & Sons, Inc.

Dukkipati, Rao V. Road Vehicle Dynamics, 2 vols. 2008. (Illus.). xxii, 852p. 99.95 *(978-0-7680-1643-7(6))* SAE Intl.

—Road Vehicle Dynamics: Problems & Solutions, 2 vols. 2009. (Illus.). viii, 542p. 69.95 *(978-0-7680-2051-9(4))* SAE Intl.

Edmondson, Chuck. Fast Car Physics. 2011. (ENG., Illus.). 248p. (gr. 17). 75.00 *(978-0-8018-9822-8(6))*; pap. 29.95 *(978-0-8018-9823-5(4))* Johns Hopkins Univ. Pr.

Ellis, J. R. Vehicle Handling Dynamics. American Society of Mechanical Engineers Staff, ed. (Illus.). 208p. 46.00 *(978-0-85298-885-5(0))* Professional Engineering Publishing GBR. Dist: SAE Intl.

Grove Thomsen, Per & True, Hans, eds. Non-Smooth Problems in Vehicle Systems Dynamics: Proceedings of the Euromech Colloquium. 2009. (ENG., Illus.). xi, 270p. 189.00 *(978-3-642-01355-3(4)*, 3642013554) Springer.

Mastinu, Giampiero & Ploechl, Manfred, eds. Road Vehicle Dynamics. 2013. (ENG., Illus.). 1300p. instr.'s hndbk. ed. 189.95 *(978-0-8493-3322-4(9)*, CRC Press) Taylor & Francis Group GBR. Dist: Taylor & Francis Group.

Newton, Richard. Autocross Performance Handbook. rev. ed. 2007. (Motorbooks Workshop Ser.). (ENG., Illus.). 160p. pap. 25.95 *(978-0-7603-2788-3(2)*, 0760327882, Motorbooks) MBI Publishing Co. LLC.

Rajamani, Rajesh. Vehicle Dynamics & Control. 2011. (Mechanical Engineering Ser.). (ENG., Illus.). xxv, 471p. pap. 129.00 *(978-1-4419-3889-3(3)*, 1441938893); 2nd ed. xxv, 496p. 139.00 ***(978-1-4614-1432-2(6)***, 1461414326) Springer.

Rill, Georg. Road Vehicle Dynamics. 2011. (ENG., Illus.). 361p. 99.95 ***(978-1-4398-3898-3(4)***, CRC Press) Taylor & Francis Group GBR. Dist: Taylor & Francis Group.

Rosenbluth, William. Application & Interpretation of Black Box Data & Crash Dynamics. 2009. *(978-0-8031-7003-2(3))* American Society for Testing & Materials.

Schiehlen, W. Dynamical Analysis of Vehicle Systems. 2008. (CISM International Centre for Mechanical Sciences Ser.). 169.00 *(978-3-211-76665-1(0))* Springer.

Schiehlen, W., ed. Dynamical Analysis of Vehicle Systems: Theoretical Foundations & Advanced Applications. 2010. (CISM International Centre for Mechanical Sciences Ser.). (Illus.). vii, 304p. pap. 169.00 *(978-3-211-99919-6(1)*, 3211999191) Springer.

Wong, J. Y. Terramechanics & Off-Road Vehicle Engineering: Terrain Behaviour, Off-Road Vehicle Performance & Design. 2nd ed. 2009. (ENG., Illus.). 488p. 145.00 *(978-0-7506-8561-0(1)*, Butterworth-Heinemann) Elsevier Science & Technology Bks.

AUTOMOBILES—ELECTRIC EQUIPMENT

Autodata. 2007 Key Programming & Service Indicators (Coverage 96-07) 2006. pap. 83.95 *(978-1-893026-37-7(X))* Delmar Cengage Learning.

Candela, Tony. Automotive Electrical Performance Projects. 2011. (Illus.). 192p. pap. 29.95 *(978-1-934709-55-9(7))* CarTech, Inc.

—Automotive Wiring & Electrical Systems. 2009. 144p. pap. 24.95 *(978-1-932494-87-7(1))* CarTech, Inc.

Chapman, Norm. Principles of Electricity & Electronics for the Automotive Technician. 2nd ed. 2008. (ENG.). 608p. (C). pap. 156.95 *(978-1-4283-6121-8(9))* Delmar Cengage Learning.

Day, John. Automotive E/E Reliability: Strategies for Keeping Pace in a Feature-Rich World. 2011. ***(978-0-7680-3499-8(X))*** SAE Intl.

Delmar Learning Staff. ASE Test Preparation - A6 Electricity & Electronics. 5th ed. 2011. (ENG., Illus.). 256p. pap. 23.95 *(978-1-111-12708-4(5))* Delmar Cengage Learning.

—Electricity & Electronics: Computer Based Training. 2007. (ENG.). 114.95 *(978-1-4283-2095-6(4))* Delmar Cengage Learning.

—Truck Equipment Installation & Repair, Test E1. 2012. (ENG.). 164p. pap. 23.95 *(978-1-4354-3935-1(X))* Delmar Cengage Learning.

Denton, Tom. Automobile Electrical & Electronic Systems: Automotive Technology - Vehicle Maintenance & Repair. 4th rev. ed. 2012. (ENG., Illus.). 744p. (C). pap. 47.95 *(978-0-08-096942-8(9))* Routledge.

—Automobile Electrical & Electronic Systems: Automotive Technology: Vehicle Maintenance & Repair. 4th ed. 2012. (Illus.). xxxv, 703p. E-Book ***(978-0-08-096943-5(7))*** Routledge.

Denton, Tom. Automobile Mechanical & Electrical Systems: Automotive Technology: Vehicle Maintenance & Repair. 2011. (ENG.). 528p. (C). pap. 36.95 *(978-0-08-096945-9(3))* Routledge.

Duffy, James E. Auto Electricity & Electronics Instructor's Guide. 2009. pap. 90.00 *(978-1-59070-913-9(6))* Goodheart-Willcox Pub.

Erjavec, Jack. Electrical & Electronic Systems: NATEF Standards Job Sheets. 3rd ed. 2009. (ENG.). 240p. (C). pap. 40.95 *(978-1-4354-8321-7(9))* Delmar Cengage Learning.

Fornel, Bernard de & Louis, Jean-Paul. Electrical Actuators: Applications & Performance. 2010. (Iste Ser.: 376). (ENG., Illus.). 528p. 184.00 *(978-1-84821-096-7(5)*, Wiley-ISTE) Wiley, John & Sons, Inc.

Halderman, James D. Advanced Automotive Electricity & Electronics. rev. ed. 2012. (ENG.). 480p. (C). pap. 110.93 ***(978-0-13-254262-3(5)***, Prentice Hall) Prentice Hall PTR.

—Automotive Electricity & Electronics. 3rd ed. 2010. (ENG., Illus.). 544p. (C). pap. 118.00 *(978-0-13-512406-2(9))* Pearson Education Canada CAN. Dist: Pearson Education.

—Diagnosis & Troubleshooting of Automotive Electrical, Electronic, & Computer Systems. 6th rev. ed. 2010. (ENG., Illus.). 528p. (C). pap. 118.00 *(978-0-13-255155-7(1)*, Prentice Hall) Prentice Hall PTR.

—NATEF Correlated Task Sheets for Diagnosis & Troubleshooting of Automotive Electrical, Electronic, & Computer Systems. (ENG.). (C). 5th ed. 2009. 624p. pap. 36.20 *(978-0-13-506899-1(1))* 6th rev. ed. 2011. 264p. pap. 29.00 *(978-0-13-255220-2(5))* Prentice Hall PTR. (Prentice Hall).

Hatch, Steve V. Computerized Engine Controls. 9th ed. 2011. (New Automotive & Truck Technology Titles! Ser.). (ENG.). 688p. (C). pap. 149.95 *(978-1-111-13490-7(1))* Delmar Cengage Learning.

Hollembeak, Barry. Today's Technician: Automotive Electricity & Electronics Classroom & Shop Manual Pack. 5th ed. 2010. (ENG.). 1296p. (C). pap. 147.95 *(978-1-4354-7010-1(9))* Delmar Cengage Learning.

Hu, Jia-Sheng & Tsai, Mi-Ching. Control & Fault Diagnosis of an Auto-balancingTwo-wheeled Cart: Remote pilot & sensor/actuator fault diagnosis for coaxial two-wheeled electric vehicle. 2008. 144p. pap. *(978-3-639-10631-2(8))* VDM Verlag Dr. Mueller e.K.

IEEE Staff. 2009 IEEE Workshop on Computational Intelligence in Vehicles & Vehicular Systems. 2009. pap. 196.00 *(978-1-4244-2770-3(3))* IEEE.

Jones and Bartlett Publishers Staff & Cdx Global Staff. Electrical & Electronic Systems Tasksheet Manual for NATEF Proficiency. rev. ed. 2010. 75p. pap. 26.95 *(978-0-7637-8508-6(3))* Jones & Bartlett Learning, LLC.

Kershaw, John F. & Halderman, James D. Automotive Electrical & Electronic Systems. 5th ed. 2007. (ENG., Illus.). (C). 416p. pap. 62.40 *(978-0-13-238884-9(7))*; 384p. per. 80.60 *(978-0-13-238883-2(9))* Prentice Hall PTR. (Prentice Hall).

McPherson, Dale. Modern Diesel Technology: Electrical/Electronic Systems & Heating, Ventilation, Air Conditioning Systems Job Sheets. 2006. (ENG.). 144p. (C). pap. 34.95 *(978-1-4180-6338-2(X))* Delmar Cengage Learning.

Meyer, Gereon & Valldorf, Jürgen, eds. Advanced Microsystems for Automotive Applications 2011: Smart Systems for Electric, Safe & Networked Mobility. 2011. (VDI-Buch Ser.). (Illus.). x, 344p. 259.00 *(978-3-642-21380-9(4)*, 3642213804) Springer.

Munday, Frank. Custom Auto Electrickery: How to Wire & Understand Auto Electrical Systems. 2006. (Hot Rod Handbooks Ser.). (ENG., Illus.). 256p. per. 29.95 *(978-0-949398-35-2(7)*, 0949398357) Graffiti Pubns. AUS. Dist: MBI Distribution Services/Quayside Distribution.

Prague, Nick. Automotive Electrical Systems. 2007. 84p. per. 10.95 *(978-0-595-46747-1(4))* iUniverse, Inc.

Ribbens, William. Understanding Automotive Electronics. 7th ed. 2012. (ENG.). 520p. 99.95 *(978-0-08-097097-4(4)*, Butterworth-Heinemann) Elsevier Science & Technology Bks.

Robert Bosch GmbH Staff. Automotive Electrics: Systems & Components: Networking, Hybrid Drive. 5th ed. 2007. (Automotive Electronics Ser.). (Illus.). 530p. 59.95 *(978-0-8376-1541-7(0))* Bentley Pubs.

—Bosch Automotive Networking: Expert Know-How on Automotive Technology. 2007. (Illus.). 119p. per. 24.95 *(978-0-8376-1547-9(X))* Bentley Pubs.

—Bosch Technical Instruction: Alternators. (Illus.). pap. 14.95 *(978-0-8376-0479-4(6))* Bentley Pubs.

—Bosch Technical Instruction: Graphical Symbols & Circuit Diagrams for Automotive Electrics. (Illus.). pap. 14.95 *(978-0-8376-0493-0(1))* Bentley Pubs.

—Bosch Technical Instruction: Symbols for Compressed-Air Brake Systems. (Illus.). pap. 14.95 *(978-0-8376-0597-5(0))* Bentley Pubs.

Rudman, Jack. Automotive Electrical - Electronics. (Dantes Subject Standardized Tests Ser.: Vol. 39). 49.95 *(978-0-8373-6539-8(2))* National Learning Corp.

Stienecker, Adam. Hybrid Energy Storage Systems. 2009. 68p. pap. *(978-3-639-13994-5(1))* VDM Verlag Dr. Mueller e.K.

Strong, Matt. Custom Auto Wiring & Electrical: Oem Electrical Systems, Premade & Custom Wiring Kits, & Car Audio Installations for Street Rods, Muscle Cars, Race Cars, Trucks & Restorations. 2009. (ENG.). 192p. (gr. 12-18). pap. 21.95 *(978-1-55788-545-6(1)*, HP Trade) Penguin Group (USA) Inc.

AUTOMOBILES—ELECTRIC WIRING

Beretta, Joseph. Automotive Electricity: Electric Drive. 2010. (Iste Ser.: 375). (ENG., Illus.). 304p. 127.00 *(978-1-84821-095-0(7)*, Wiley-ISTE) Wiley, John & Sons, Inc.

Candela, Tony. Automotive Electrical Performance Projects. 2011. (Illus.). 192p. pap. 29.95 *(978-1-934709-55-9(7))* CarTech, Inc.

—Automotive Wiring & Electrical Systems. 2009. 144p. pap. 24.95 *(978-1-932494-87-7(1))* CarTech, Inc.

Overholser, Dennis. Wiring: A Detailed How-to Guide. 2011. (Hot Rod Basics Ser.). (ENG., Illus.). 144p. pap. 27.95 *(978-1-929133-98-7(7)*, 1929133987, ArtKulture) Wolfgang Pubns., Inc.

Parks, Dennis W. Automotive Wiring: A Practical Guide to Wiring Your Hot Rod or Custom Car. 2011. (Motorbooks Workshop Ser.). (ENG., Illus.). 144p. pap. 24.99 *(978-0-7603-3992-3(9)*, 0760339929, Motorbooks) MBI Publishing Co. LLC.

Strong, Matt. Custom Auto Wiring & Electrical: Oem Electrical Systems, Premade & Custom Wiring Kits, & Car Audio Installations for Street Rods, Muscle Cars, Race Cars, Trucks & Restorations. 2009. (ENG.). 192p. (gr. 12-18). pap. 21.95 *(978-1-55788-545-6(1)*, HP Trade) Penguin Group (USA) Inc.

AUTOMOBILES—ELECTRONIC EQUIPMENT

see also Automobiles—Radio Equipment

Abut, Huseyin, et al, eds. Advances for In-Vehicle & Mobile Systems: Challenges for International Standards. 2010. (Illus.). xv, 284p. pap. 139.00 *(978-1-4419-4131-2(2)*, 1441941312) Springer.

—Digital Signal Processing for In-Vehicle & Mobile Systems II. 2007. (Illus.). XVI, 284p. 139.00 *(978-0-387-33503-2(X)*, 038733503X) Springer.

Autodata. 2007 Domestic Diagnostic Trouble Code Manual (1994-2007) 3rd ed. 2006. pap. 83.95 *(978-1-893026-35-3(3))* Delmar Cengage Learning.

—2007 Import Diagnostic Trouble Code Manual (1994-2007) 3rd ed. 2006. pap. 83.95 *(978-1-893026-36-0(1))* Delmar Cengage Learning.

Bridging Theory into Practice: Fundamentals of Power Semiconductors for Automotive Applications. 2006. 59.95 *(978-0-9789866-0-5(1))* Infineon Technologies AG.

Broy, Manfred. Model-Driven Development of Reliable Automotive Services: Second Automotive Software Workshop, ASWSD 2006, San Diego, CA USA, March 15-17, 2006, Revised Selected Papers. 2008. (Lecture Notes in Computer Science / Programming & Software Engineering Ser.). xvii, 183p. pap. 69.95 *(978-3-540-70929-9(0))* Springer.

Casier, Herman. Analog Circuit Design: Sensors, Actuators & Power Drivers - Integrated Power Amplifiers from Wireline to RF - Very High Frequency Front Ends. 2008. (ENG.). x, 362p. 189.00 *(978-1-4020-8262-7(2)*, 1402082622) Springer.

Casier, Herman, et al, eds. Analog Circuit Design: Sensors, Actuators & Power Drivers; Integrated Power Amplifiers from Wireline to RF; Very High Frequency Front Ends. 2010. (ENG.). x, 362p. pap. 189.00 *(978-90-481-7824-7(X)*, 904817824X) Springer.

Chapman, Norm. Principles of Electricity & Electronics for the Automotive Technician. 2nd ed. 2008. (ENG.). 608p. (C). pap. 156.95 *(978-1-4283-6121-8(9))* Delmar Cengage Learning.

Chen, Jiann-Liang & Chang, Yao-Chung. Telematics Communication Technologies & Vehicular Networks: Wireless Architectures & Applications. Huang, Chung-Ming & Chen, Yuh-Shyan, eds. 2009. 414p. 180.00 *(978-1-60566-840-5(0))* IGI Global.

Chilton Automotive Editorial Staff. Asian Diagnostic Service Manual 2006, Vol. 3. 2006. (Chilton Diagnostic Manuals Ser.). (ENG., Illus.). 1032p. 79.95 *(978-1-4180-2915-9(7))* Delmar Cengage Learning.

—European Diagnostic Service 2006. 2006. (Chilton Diagnostic Manuals Ser.). (ENG., Illus.). 888p. 79.95 *(978-1-4180-2924-1(6))* Delmar Cengage Learning.

Chilton Editors. Chilton 2006 Asian Diagnostic Service Vol. 1, Vol. 1. 2006. (Chilton Diagnostic Manuals Ser.). (ENG., Illus.). 768p. 79.95 *(978-1-4180-2913-5(0))* Delmar Cengage Learning.

—Chilton Asian Diagnostic Service Manual 2006, Vol. 2. 2006. (Chilton Diagnostic Manuals Ser.). (ENG., Illus.). 984p. 79.95 *(978-1-4180-2914-2(9))* Delmar Cengage Learning.

Cram101 Textbook Reviews Staff. Outlines & Highlights for Computerized Engine Controls 8e by Steve V Hatch, Isbn: 9781428399969. 2009. 148p. pap. 29.95 *(978-1-4288-7502-9(6))* Cram101 Inc.

Delmar Learning Staff. ASE Test Preparation - A6 Electricity & Electronics. 5th ed. 2011. (ENG., Illus.). 256p. pap. 23.95 *(978-1-111-12708-4(5))* Delmar Cengage Learning.

—Electricity & Electronics: Computer Based Training. 2007. (ENG.). 114.95 *(978-1-4283-2095-6(4))* Delmar Cengage Learning.

—Truck Equipment Installation & Repair, Test E1. 2012. (ENG.). 164p. pap. 23.95 *(978-1-4354-3935-1(X))* Delmar Cengage Learning.

Denton, Tom. Automobile Electrical & Electronic Systems: Automotive Technology - Vehicle Maintenance & Repair. 4th rev. ed. 2012. (ENG., Illus.). 744p. (C). pap. 47.95 *(978-0-08-096942-8(9))* Routledge.

Denton, Tom. Automobile Electrical & Electronic Systems: Automotive Technology: Vehicle Maintenance & Repair. 4th ed. 2012. (Illus.). xxxv, 703p. E-Book ***(978-0-08-096943-5(7))*** Routledge.

Dorries, Elisabeth H. Today's Technician: Advanced Automotive Electronic. 2010. (ENG.). (C). pap. 110.95 *(978-1-4180-6080-0(1))* Delmar Cengage Learning.

Fuertes, Andy. Automotive Electronics: Components & Test Equipment - U. S. Markets, Technologies & Opportunities: 1994 to 2000 Analysis. Archdeacon, Tim, ed. 200p. 1900.00 *(978-1-883742-10-2(2))* Allied Business Intelligence, Inc.

Gabler, Hampton Clay, et al. Event Data Recorders: A Decade of Innovation. 2008. (Illus.). ix, 477p. 89.99 *(978-0-7680-2066-3(2))* SAE Intl.

Goel, Asvin. Fleet Telematics: Real-Time Management & Planning of Commercial Vehicle Operations. 2007. (Operations Research Computer Science Interfaces Ser.). (Illus.). xiv, 184p. 149.00 *(978-0-387-75104-7(1)*, 0387751041) Springer.

Halderman, James D. Advanced Automotive Electricity & Electronics. rev. ed. 2012. (ENG.). 480p. (C). pap. 110.93 ***(978-0-13-254262-3(5)***, Prentice Hall) Prentice Hall PTR.

—Automotive Electricity & Electronics. 3rd ed. 2010. (ENG., Illus.). 544p. (C). pap. 118.00 *(978-0-13-512406-2(9))* Pearson Education Canada CAN. Dist: Pearson Education.

—Automotive Electricity & Electronics. 2008. *(978-0-13-613743-6(1))*; 2nd ed. (ENG., Illus.). 528p. (C). pap. 113.33 *(978-0-13-502950-3(3)*, Prentice Hall) Prentice Hall PTR.

—Diagnosis & Troubleshooting of Automotive Electrical, Electronic, & Computer Systems. 5th ed. 2008. (ENG., Illus.). 832p. (C). pap. 122.80 *(978-0-13-506696-6(4)*, Prentice Hall) Prentice Hall PTR.

—NATEF Correlated Task Sheets for Diagnosis & Troubleshooting of Automotive Electrical, Electronic, & Computer Systems. (ENG.). (C). 5th ed. 2009. 624p. pap. 36.20 *(978-0-13-506899-1(1))* 6th rev. ed. 2011. 264p. pap. 29.00 *(978-0-13-255220-2(5))* Prentice Hall PTR. (Prentice Hall).

Hollembeak, Barry. Advanced Automotive Electronic Systems: Classroom Manual. 2010. (Today's Technician Ser.). (ENG.). 912p. (C). pap. 147.95 *(978-1-111-03814-4(7))* Delmar Cengage Learning.

—Today's Technician: Automotive Electricity & Electronics Classroom & Shop Manual Pack. 5th ed. 2010. (ENG.). 1296p. (C). pap. 147.95 *(978-1-4354-7010-1(9))* Delmar Cengage Learning.

IEEE Staff. 2008 Fifth Annual Conference on Wireless on demand Network Systems & Services. 2008. pap. 188.00 *(978-1-4244-1958-6(1))* IEEE.

Institute of Electrical and Electronics Engineers, Inc. Staff, et al, contrib. by. 2007 Fourth Annual Conference on Wireless on Demand Nework Systems & Services. 2007. (Illus.). vii, 171p. pap. 180.00 *(978-1-4244-0860-3(1)*, 07EX1629) IEEE.

Jurgen, Ronald K. Automotive Electronics Reliability. 2nd ed. 2010. (Illus.). iv, 369p. ***(978-0-7680-3492-9(2))*** SAE Intl.

—Infotainment Systems on Fast Forward. 2007. (Illus.). vi, 726p. 69.99 *(978-0-7680-1943-8(5))* SAE Intl.

—X-By Wire Automotive Systems. 2009. (Illus.). vi, 427p. *(978-0-7680-2100-4(6))* SAE Intl.

Kershaw, John F. & Halderman, James D. Automotive Electrical & Electronic Systems. 5th ed. 2007. (ENG., Illus.). (C). 416p. pap. 62.40 *(978-0-13-238884-9(7))*; 384p. per. 80.60 *(978-0-13-238883-2(9))* Prentice Hall PTR. (Prentice Hall).

Larses, Ola. Architecting & Modeling Automotive Embedded Systems: Technology, Methods & Management. 2008. 316p. pap. *(978-3-639-09870-9(6))* VDM Verlag Dr. Mueller e.K.

Lemke, Kerstin, et al, eds. Embedded Security in Cars: Securing Current & Future Automotive IT Applications. 2010. (ENG., Illus.). x, 273p. pap. 89.95 *(978-3-642-06659-7(3)*, 3642066593) Springer.

McPherson, Dale. Modern Diesel Technology: Electrical/Electronic Systems & Heating, Ventilation, Air Conditioning Systems Job Sheets. 2006. (ENG.). 144p. (C). pap. 34.95 *(978-1-4180-6338-2(X))* Delmar Cengage Learning.

Navet, Nicolas & Simonot-Lion, Francoise. Automotive Embedded Systems Handbook. Navet, Nicolas & Simonot-Lion, Francoise, eds. 2008. (Industrial Information Technology Ser.). (ENG., Illus.). 488p. 162.95 *(978-0-8493-8026-6(X)*, CRC Press) Taylor & Francis Group GBR. Dist: Taylor & Francis Group.

Olatunde, Adebukola O. A Tensioner for the Belt-Driven Integrated Starter-Generator. 2009. 196p. pap. *(978-3-639-16216-5(1))* VDM Verlag Dr. Mueller e.K.

Parise, George, et al. The Haynes Computer Codes & Electronic Engine Management Systems Manual. (Illus.). *(978-1-56392-274-9(6))* Haynes Manuals, Inc.

Pavkovic, Danijel & Deur, Josko. Modeling & Control of Electronic Throttle Drive. 2011. 188p. pap. ***(978-3-8443-1628-5(0))*** Lambert Academic Publishing.

Prague, Nick. L2 Med/Hvy Vehicle Electronic Diesel Engine Diagnostic Specialist: Motor Age Self-Study Guide for ASE Certification. 2006. spiral bd. 28.95 *(978-1-933180-58-8(7))* Advanstar Communications, Inc.

Rabinovich, Victor, et al. Automotive Antenna Design & Applications. 2010. (ENG., Illus.). 330p. 129.95 *(978-1-4398-0407-0(9)*, CRC Press) Taylor & Francis Group GBR. Dist: Taylor & Francis Group.

Rettberg, Achim, et al, eds. From Specification to Embedded Systems Application. 2010. (IFIP Advances in Information & Communication Technology Ser.). (Illus.). xii, 320p. pap. 149.00 *(978-1-4419-3899-2(0)*, 1441938990) Springer.

Robert Bosch GmbH Staff. Automotive Electrics: Systems & Components: Networking, Hybrid Drive. 5th ed. 2007. (Automotive Electronics Ser.). (Illus.). 530p. 59.95 *(978-0-8376-1541-7(0))* Bentley Pubs.

—Bosch Automotive Networking: Expert Know-How on Automotive Technology. 2007. (Illus.). 119p. per. 24.95 *(978-0-8376-1547-9(X))* Bentley Pubs.

—Bosch Technical Instruction: Engine Electronics. (Illus.). pap. 14.95 *(978-0-8376-0475-6(3))* Bentley Pubs.

—Bosch Technical Instruction: Interference Suppression. (Illus.). pap. 14.95 *(978-0-8376-0476-3(1))* Bentley Pubs.

Rosenbluth, William. Application & Interpretation of Black Box Data & Crash Dynamics. 2009. *(978-0-8031-7003-2(3))* American Society for Testing & Materials.

Rudman, Jack. Automotive Electrical - Electronics. (Dantes Subject Standardized Tests Ser.: Vol. 39). 49.95 *(978-0-8373-6539-8(2))* National Learning Corp.

Steyaert, Michiel, et al, eds. Analog Circuit Design: High-speed Clock & Data Recovery, High-performance Amplifiers, Power Management. 2010. (ENG.). xii, 360p. pap. 209.00 *(978-90-481-8032-5(5)*, 9048180325) Springer.

Syner, Jason. How to Install Automotive Mobile Electronic Systems. 2010. (Motorbooks Workshop Ser.). (ENG., Illus.). 192p. pap. 29.99 *(978-0-7603-3177-4(4)*, 0760331774, Motorbooks) MBI Publishing Co. LLC.

Takeda, Kazuya, et al, eds. In-Vehicle Corpus & Signal Processing for Driver Behavior. 2010. (ENG., Illus.). xiv, 286p. pap. 129.00 *(978-1-4419-4640-9(3)*, 1441946403) Springer.

Takeda, Kazuya (University of Nagoya & Takeda, Kazuya. In-Vehicle Corpus & Signal Processing for Driver Behavior. Takeda, Kazuya et al, eds. 2008. (Illus.). xiv, 286p. 129.00 *(978-0-387-79581-2(2))* Springer.

Valldorf, Jargen & Gessner, Wolfgang, eds. Advanced Microsystems for Automotive Applications 2005. 2010. (VDI-Buch Ser.). (Illus.). xviii, 554p. pap. 179.00 *(978-3-642-06371-8(3)*, 3642063713) Springer.

—Advanced Microsystems for Automotive Applications 2006. 2010. (VDI-Buch Ser.). (Illus.). xviii, 516p. pap. 219.00 *(978-3-642-07004-4(3)*, 3642070043) Springer.

—Advanced Microsystems for Automotive Applications 2008. 2010. (VDI-Buch Ser.). (Illus.). xvi, 308p. pap. 189.00 *(978-3-642-09683-9(2)*, 3642096832) Springer.

2007 IEEE International Conference on Vehicular Electronics & Safety. 2007. pap. 234.00 *(978-1-4244-1265-5(X)*, 07EX1802) IEEE.

AUTOMOBILES—EMISSION CONTROL DEVICES

see Automobiles—Pollution Control Devices

AUTOMOBILES—ENGINES

see Automobiles—Motors

AUTOMOBILES—EQUIPMENT AND SUPPLIES

BIA. Key Russian Manufacturers & Suppliers of Automobile & Accessories. 6th rev. ed. 2006. 376p. (J). pap. 249.00 *(978-1-4187-4500-4(6))* Business Information Agency.

Calabro, Marian. The Pep Boys Company History Book. 2006. *(978-1-57990-636-8(2))* Lark Bks.

Cheong, Woo-Jae. Development of a Protective Coating on the Magnesium Az91d Alloy. 2009. 312p. pap. *(978-3-639-16166-3(1))* VDM Verlag Dr. Mueller e.K.

Chilton Automotive Editorial Staff. Chilton Asian Mechanical Service: Subaru-Toyota. 2006. (Chilton Mechanical Manuals Ser.). (ENG., Illus.). 1944p. 79.95 *(978-1-4180-0949-6(0))* Delmar Cengage Learning.

—Chilton Asian Mechanical Service Vol. II: Kia-Nissan. 2006. (Chilton Mechanical Manuals Ser.). (ENG., Illus.). 1872p. 79.95 *(978-1-4180-0948-9(2))* Delmar Cengage Learning.

Edmondson, Chuck. Fast Car Physics. 2011. (ENG., Illus.). 248p. (gr. 17). 75.00 *(978-0-8018-9822-8(6))*; pap. 29.95 *(978-0-8018-9823-5(4))* Johns Hopkins Univ. Pr.

Gordon, Michael. P2 Automobile Parts Specialist: Motor Age Training Self-Study Guide for ASE Certification. 2007. spiral bd. 24.95 *(978-1-933180-79-3(X))* Advanstar Communications, Inc.

Henderson, Bob & Haynes, John H. OBD-II & Sistemas de Control Electrónico del Motor. 2006. (Haynes Repair Manuals Ser.). (ENG., Illus.). 272p. per. 26.95 *(978-1-56392-612-9(1)*, 1563926121) Haynes Manuals, Inc.

Jain, Vipul & Heydari, Payam, eds. Automotive Radar Sensors in Silicon Technologies: Circuits & Systems. 2012. (ENG.). x, 240p. 129.00 *(978-1-4419-6774-9(5)*, 1441967745) Springer.

Klier, Thomas H. & Rubenstein, James M. Who Really Made Your Car? Restructuring & Geographic Change in the Auto Industry. 2008. 419p. 40.00 *(978-0-88099-334-0(0))*; pap. 20.00 *(978-0-88099-333-3(2))* Upjohn, W.E. Institute for Employment Research.

Larses, Ola. Architecting & Modeling Automotive Embedded Systems: Technology, Methods & Management. 2008. 316p. pap. *(978-3-639-09870-9(6))* VDM Verlag Dr. Mueller e.K.

Mavrigian, Mike. High Performance Fasteners & Plumbing: A Guide to Nuts, Bolts, Fuel, Brake, Oil & Coolant Lines, Hoses, Clamps, Racinghardware & Plumbing Techniques. 2008. (ENG., Illus.). 176p. (gr. 12-18). 19.95 *(978-1-55788-523-4(0)*, HP Trade) Penguin Group (USA) Inc.

Morgan, Sally. Old Cars. 2007. (Dealing with Waste/Watts Ser.). (Illus.). 30p. (J). (gr. 4-7). lib. bdg. *(978-1-59920-010-1(4)*, Harwood Academic Pubs.) Black Rabbit Bks.

Newcomb, Doug. Car Audio for Dummies. 2008. (ENG., Illus.). 310p. pap. 24.99 *(978-0-470-15158-7(7)*, For Dummies) Wiley, John & Sons, Inc.

Petroleum Equipment Institute, compiled by. Recommended Practices for Installation of Underground Liquid Storage Systems: Rp100: Rp100. 2000th ed. 2011. pap. 95.00 *(978-0-9642638-5-7(8))* Petroleum Equipment Institute.

—Recommended Practices for the Inspection & Maintenance of UST Systems: Rp900: Rp900. 2008. (ENG., Illus.). 52p. pap. 90.00 *(978-0-9642638-8-8(2))* Petroleum Equipment Institute.

Rasiah, Rajah. Multinationals, Technology & Localization in Automotive Firms in Asia. 2008. pap. 40.00 *(978-0-415-49558-5(X))* Routledge.

Robert Bosch GmbH Staff. Bosch Technical Instruction: Starting Systems. (Illus.). pap. 14.95 *(978-0-8376-0480-0(X))* Bentley Pubs.

Robert Bosch GmbH Staff, creator. Safety, Comfort & Convenience Systems: Function, Regulation & Components. 2006. (Illus.). 399p. 59.95 *(978-0-8376-1391-8(4)*, H013) Bentley Pubs.

Sly, David. Transport Effort. 2008. 116p. pap. *(978-3-639-07526-7(9))* VDM Verlag Dr. Mueller e.K.

Smith, Paul D. Merchants of Speed: The Men Who Built America's Performance Industry. 2009. (ENG., Illus.). 240p. 40.00 *(978-0-7603-3567-3(2)*, 0760335672, Motorbooks) MBI Publishing Co. LLC.

Timothy, Kevin. The Pocket Parts Pal: The Complete Guide to Ho Scale Car Parts. Collison, Joanne, ed. 2010. (Illus.). 72p. (Orig.). pap. 4.95 *(978-88-379-6059-9(X))* What It Is! Publishing.

Vokins, Stephen. Nodding Dogs & Vinyl Roofs: The Weird World of Quirky Car Accessories. (ENG., Illus.). 2010. 120p. pap. 9.95 *(978-1-84425-712-6(6)*, 1844257126) 2008. 128p. 14.95 *(978-1-84425-422-4(4)*, 1844254224) Haynes Publishing PLC GBR. Dist: MBI Distribution Services/Quayside Distribution.

White, Harvey. How to Keep Your Muscle Car Alive. 2009. (Motorbooks Workshop Ser.). (ENG., Illus.). 224p. pap. 29.99 *(978-0-7603-3546-8(X)*, 076033546X, Motorbooks) MBI Publishing Co. LLC.

AUTOMOBILES—EXHAUST CONTROL DEVICES

see Automobiles—Pollution Control Devices

AUTOMOBILES—EXHAUST GAS

see Automobiles—Motors—Exhaust Gas

AUTOMOBILES—FUEL SYSTEMS

see also Carburetors

American Society of Mechanical Engineers Staff, ed. Automotive Power Systems: Environment & Conservation. 228p. 130.00 *(978-0-85298-721-6(8))* Professional Engineering Publishing GBR. Dist: SAE Intl.

Bennett, Sean. Medium/Heavy Duty Truck Engines, Fuel & Computerized Management Systems. 3rd ed. 2008. (ENG.). 960p. (C). 201.95 *(978-1-4283-6666-4(0))* Delmar Cengage Learning.

—Medium/Heavy Duty Truck Engines, Fuel, Computer Management. 3rd ed. 2008. (ENG.). 272p. (C). pap., wbk. ed. 54.95 *(978-1-4283-6661-9(X))* Delmar Cengage Learning.

Bovair, Jennifer L. & Arent, Douglas Jay. Alternative Transportation Fuels & Vehicle Technologies: Challenges & Opportunities: A Report of the CSIS Energy & National Security Program, CSIS Global Strategy Institute, & National Renewable Energy Laboratory. 2008. pap. *(978-0-89206-542-4(7))* Ctr. for Strategic & International Studies.

Committee on Review of the FreedomCAR and Fuel Research Program, Phase 2 & National Research Council. Review of the Research Program of the FreedomCAR & Fuel Partnership: Second Report. 2008. (ENG.). 166p. pap. 38.75 *(978-0-309-11634-3(1))* National Academies Pr.

Davidson, Jim. 75 Ways to Save Gas: Clean, Green Tips to Cut Costs at the Pump. 2011. (ENG.). 144p. (gr. 12). 8.99 ***(978-0-14-318605-2(1)***, Penguin (Non-Classics)) Penguin Group (USA) Inc.

Fortune, Luke. UFO How-to Vol VII - Esoteric Power Systems. 2009. 615p. pap. 49.95 *(978-0-557-06796-1(0))* Lulu Enterprises Inc.

Genat, Robert. Fuelies: Fuel Injected Corvettes 1957-1965. 2008. (Cartech Ser.). (Illus.). 192p. pap. 29.95 *(978-1-932494-52-5(9))* CarTech, Inc.

Halderman, James D. Automotive Fuel & Emissions Systems, Automotive Fuel & Emissions Control Systems: NATEF Correlated Task Sheets. 2nd ed. 2008. (ENG.). 390p. (C). pap. 36.20 *(978-0-13-506011-7(7)*, Prentice Hall) Prentice Hall PTR.

Halderman, James D. & Linder, James. Automotive Fuel & Emissions Control Systems. (ENG.). (C). 2nd ed. 2008. 576p. pap. 122.80 *(978-0-13-505481-9(8))* 3rd ed. 2011. (Illus.). 480p. pap. 118.00 *(978-0-13-254292-0(7))* Prentice Hall PTR. (Prentice Hall).

—NATEF Correlated Task Sheets for Automotive Fuel & Emissions Control Systems. 3rd rev. ed. 2011. (ENG.). 336p. (C). pap. 21.80 *(978-0-13-254510-5(1)*, Prentice Hall) Prentice Hall PTR.

Halderman, James D. & Martin, Tony. NATEF Correlated Job Sheets for Hybrid & Alternative Fuel Vehicles. 3rd ed. 2012. (ENG.). 96p. (C). pap. 26.67 ***(978-0-13-278538-9(2)***, Prentice Hall) Prentice Hall PTR.

Hartman, Jeff. Nitrous Oxide Performance Handbook. 2009. (Motorbooks Workshop Ser.). (ENG., Illus.). 224p. pap. 29.99 *(978-0-7603-2624-4(X)*, 076032624X, Motorbooks) MBI Publishing Co. LLC.

IEEE Staff, ed. 2007 IEEE Vehicle Power & Propulsion Conference. 2007. pap. 412.00 *(978-0-7803-9760-6(6)*, 07EX1461) IEEE.

Institution of Mechanical Engineers. Innovations in Fuel Economy & Sustainable Road Transport. 2012. (ENG., Illus.). 240p. pap. 330.00 ***(978-0-85709-213-7(8))*** Woodhead Publishing Ltd. GBR. Dist: Ingram Pub. Services.

Institution of Mechanical Engineers (IMechE). Injection Systems for IC Engines Conference: Institution of Mechanical Engineers (IMechE) conference May 2009. 2009. (Illus.). 300p. *(978-1-84334-561-9(7)*, Chandos Publishing) Woodhead Publishing Ltd.

McClurg, Bob. How to Install & Tune Nitrous Oxide Systems. 2012. (Illus.). 144p. pap. 24.95 ***(978-1-934709-34-4(4))*** CarTech, Inc.

McMann, Denise M., ed. Unintended or Sudden Acceleration in Automobiles. 2010. (Transportation Issues, Policies & R&D Ser.). pap. 43.00 *(978-1-61728-983-5(3)*, Nova Novinka) Nova Science Pubs., Inc.

Michael, Stephen A. Poor Man Hydrogen Generator on Demand: SMCS HHO Stephens Multi Cell Systems Hydrogen Generator on Demand. 2011. 68p. pap. 29.99 *(978-1-4567-1992-0(0))* AuthorHouse.

Moss, Dave. The Efficient Driver's Handbook: Your Guide to Fuel Efficient Driving Techniques & Car Choice. 2010. (ENG., Illus.). 96p. pap. 19.95 *(978-1-84584-351-9(7)*, 1845843517) Veloce Publishing Ltd. GBR. Dist: MBI Distribution Services/Quayside Distribution.

Orrigo, Craig A., ed. Toyota Automobiles & Unintended Acceleration. 2011. (Series: Transportation Issues, Policies & R&D Ser.). 207p. 185.00 *(978-1-61324-275-9(1))* Nova Science Pubs., Inc.

Papasavva, Stella, et al, eds. Life-Cycle Analysis Tools for "Green" Materials & Process Selection: Proceedings: Symposium on Life-Cycle Analysis Tools for "Green" Materials & Process Selection (2005: Boston, MA) 2009. (Symposium Proceedings Ser.: Vol. 895). (Illus.). 189p. 90.00 *(978-1-55899-850-6(0))* Materials Research Society.

Porche, Isaac R., III & Bernstein, Mark A. An Approach to Assessing the Technical Feasibility & Market Potential of a New Automotive Device. 2007. 76p. pap. 23.00 *(978-0-8330-4162-3(2)*, tr313) RAND Corp., The.

Reforming Corporate Average Fuel Economy (CAFE) Standards: Hearing Before the Subcommittee on Surface Transportation & Merchant Marine of the Committee on Commerce, Science, & Transportation, United States Senate, One Hundred Ninth Congress, Second Session, May 9, 2006. 2011. (Illus.). iii, 85p. ***(978-0-16-088301-9(6)***, 552-070-42606-0) United States Government Printing Office.

Robert Bosch Gmbh. Bosch Diesel Fuel-Injection Systems Unit Injector System & Unit Pump System: Technical Instruction Booklet. 2007. (Illus.). 78p. per. 24.95 *(978-0-8376-1550-9(X))* Bentley Pubs.

Robert Bosch GmbH Staff. Bosch Technical Instruction: Diesel Fuel-Injection — An Overview. (Illus.). pap. 14.95 *(978-0-8376-0494-7(X))* Bentley Pubs.

—Bosch Technical Instruction: Diesel Fuel-Injection Pumps Types PE-PF. (Illus.). pap. 14.95 *(978-0-8376-0496-1(6))* Bentley Pubs.

—Bosch Technical Instruction: Distributor Fuel-Injection Pump Type VE. (Illus.). pap. 14.95 *(978-0-8376-0495-4(8))* Bentley Pubs.

Teene, Eero. Modeling of a Liquid Phase Lpg Fuel Injection System Development, Modeling, & Experimentation. 2008. 152p. pap. *(978-3-639-09612-5(6))* VDM Verlag Dr. Mueller e.K.

The Hightower Report, prod. Commodity Trading Guide 2008. 2007. 56p. 20.00 *(978-0-9789285-1-3(2))* Hightower Report, The.

Vehicle Fuel Economy. 2008. 70p. (C). pap. 39.00 *(978-1-60692-057-2(X))* Nova Science Pubs., Inc.

Weiers, Ronald. Gas Smarts: Hundreds of Small Ways to Save Big Time at the Pump. 2011. (ENG.). 256p. pap. 11.95 *(978-1-4405-0049-7(5))* Adams Media Corp.

Weiers, Ronald M. Ga$ Smart$ 2011. E-Book *(978-1-4405-1081-6(4))* Adams Media Corp.

Zhao, H., ed. Advanced Direct Injection Combustion Engine Technologies & Development: Diesel Engines, 2 vols., 2. 2009. (Illus.). 756p. 290.00 *(978-1-84569-744-0(8))* Woodhead Publishing Ltd. GBR. Dist: Taylor & Francis Group.

—Advanced Direct Injection Combustion Engine Technologies & Development: Science & Technology, 2 vols. 2009. (Illus.). 840p. *(978-1-84569-389-3(2))* Woodhead Publishing Ltd.

Zhao Hua Staff. Homogeneous Charge Compression Ignition (Hcci) & Controlled Aut. 2007. (ENG.). 524p. 289.95 *(978-1-4200-4459-1(1)*, CRC Press) Taylor & Francis Group GBR. Dist: Taylor & Francis Group.

AUTOMOBILES—GEARING

see Automobiles—Steering-Gear; Automobiles—Transmission Devices

AUTOMOBILES—GUIDES

see Automobile Travel—Guidebooks

AUTOMOBILES—HANDBOOKS, MANUALS, ETC.

Ahlstrand, Alan. Mercedes-Benz C-Class: 2001 Thru 2007. 2010. (ENG., Illus.). 432p. pap. 29.95 *(978-1-56392-737-9(3))* Haynes,Chilton.

Ahlstrand, Alan & Freund, Ken. Kawasaki EN450, 500 Twins & Ninja 250, 1985-2007. 2007. (Automotive Repair Manual Ser.). (ENG., Illus.). 240p. pap. 45.45 *(978-1-56392-667-9(9)*, 1563926679) Haynes Manuals, Inc.

Ahlstrand, Alan, et al. Honda XR50R, XR70R, XR80R, XR100R & CRF50F, CRF70F, CRF80F, CRF100F, 1985 Thru 2007. 2007. (Motorcycle Repair Manual Ser.). (ENG., Illus.). 160p. per. 33.95 *(978-1-56392-657-0(1)*, 1563926571) Haynes Manuals, Inc.

—Yamaha YFS200 Blaster ATV: 1988 Thru 2006, 200cc. 2008. (Owners Workshop Manual Ser.). (ENG., Illus.). 128p. per. 36.45 *(978-1-56392-688-4(1)*, 1563926881) Haynes Manuals, Inc.

Anderson, Bruce. Porsche 911 Performance Handbook, 1963-1998. 3rd ed. 2009. (Motorbooks Workshop Ser.). (ENG., Illus.). 304p. pap. 34.99 *(978-0-7603-3180-4(4)*, 0760331804, Motorbooks) MBI Publishing Co. LLC.

Antonellis, Michael. The Car Owner's Manual You REALLY Need. 2009. 96p. pap. 14.99 *(978-0-557-08839-3(9))* Lulu Enterprises Inc.

Autobooks, creator. Mercedes-Benz 220b 1959-1965 Owners Workshop Manual. 2010. 192p. pap. 34.95 *(978-1-58850-093-9(4))* Veloce Enterprises, Inc.

Bentley Publishers. Audi TT Service Manual: 1. 8L turbo, 3. 2L; including roadster & Quattro: 2000-2006. 2006. (Illus.). 978p. pap. 99.95 *(978-0-8376-1500-4(3)*, AT06) Bentley Pubs.

—BMW 3 Series Service Manual (E90, E91, E92, E93) 2006, 2007, 2008, 2009 Service Manual: 325i, 325xi, 328i, 328xi, 330i, 330xi, 335i, 335xi: 2006, 2007, 2008 2009. 2009. (Illus.). 1256p. pap. 129.95 *(978-0-8376-1608-7(5))* Bentley Pubs.

—Mercedes-Benz C-Class (W202) Service Manual: C220, C230, C230 Kompressor, C280. 2009. (Illus.). 1216p. pap. 129.95 *(978-0-8376-1572-1(0))* Bentley Pubs.

—MINI Cooper - Diagnosis Without Guesswork: Cooper, Cooper S. 2009. (Illus.). 336p. pap. 59.95 *(978-0-8376-1571-4(2))* Bentley Pubs.

—MINI Cooper (R55, R56, R57) Service Manual: Cooper, Cooper S, John Cooper Works (JSW), including Clubman & Convertible: 2007, 2008, 2009, 2010 2011. 2011. (Illus.). 1058p. 139.95 ***(978-0-8376-1671-1(9))*** Bentley Pubs.

—Volkswagen Jetta (A5) Service Manual: 1. 9L & 2. 0L diesel, 2. 0L & 2. 5L gasoline; including TDI, gli & SportWagen: 2005, 2006, 2007, 2008, 2009 2010: 2005, 2006, 2007, 2008, 2009 2010. 2009. (Illus.). 1352p. lib. bdg. 129.95 *(978-0-8376-1616-2(6))* Bentley Pubs.

—Volkswagen Jetta (A5) Service Manual 2005 - 2008: 1. 9L TDI, 2. 0L FSI, 2. 5L, Including gli & Sportwagen. 2008. (ENG., Illus.). 1016p. pap. 99.95 *(978-0-8376-1558-5(5))* Bentley Pubs.

—Volkswagen New Beetle Service Manual: Including Convertible. 2008. (Illus.). 1640p. pap. 109.95 *(978-0-8376-1559-2(3))* Bentley Pubs.

British Leyland Motors Staff. MGB Tourer & GT Tuning Handbook, 1975-1980. (Illus.). 50p. (Orig.). 16.00 *(978-0-8376-0504-3(0))* Bentley Pubs.

—MGB Tuning Handbook (1800cc), 1962-1974. (Illus.). 50p. (Orig.). 16.00 *(978-0-8376-0506-7(7))* Bentley Pubs.

—MGC Driver's Handbook: 1967-1969. (Illus.). 64p. 16.00 *(978-0-8376-0503-6(2))* Bentley Pubs.

—Triumph Spitfire MK III Driver's Handbook (1964) 80p. (Orig.). 16.00 *(978-0-8376-0527-2(X))* Bentley Pubs.

—Triumph Stag Workshop Manual: 1971-1973. (Illus.). 640p. 70.00 *(978-0-8376-0508-1(3))* Bentley Pubs.

—Triumph TR6 Driver's Handbook (U. S. Spec), 1975. 72p. 16.00 *(978-0-8376-0550-0(4))* Bentley Pubs.

Chilton. Chilton Asian Service Manual Vol. 3: Infiniti, Nissan, 5 vols. 2011. (ENG., Illus.). 1680p. 79.95 *(978-1-111-03766-6(3))* Delmar Cengage Learning.

—Chilton European Service Manual 2010: Audi, BMW, Mercedes-Benz, Mini, Saab, Volkswagen, Volvo. 2011. (ENG., Illus.). 2304p. 99.95 *(978-1-111-03769-7(8))* Delmar Cengage Learning.

Chilton, (Chilton). Chilton Asian Service Manual, 2010, 5 vols., Vol. 1. 2011. (ENG., Illus.). 1536p. 79.95 *(978-1-111-03764-2(7))* Delmar Cengage Learning.

—Chilton Asian Service Manual 2010: Hyundai, Kia, Lexus, Vol. 2. 2011. (ENG., Illus.). 2424p. 79.95 *(978-1-111-03765-9(5))* Delmar Cengage Learning.

—Chilton Asian Service Manual 2010 Vol. 4: Mazda, Mitsubishi, Subaru, Suzuki, 5 vols. 2011. (ENG., Illus.). 2448p. 79.95 *(978-1-111-03767-3(1))* Delmar Cengage Learning.

—Chilton Asian Service Manual 2010 Vol. 5: Scion, Toyota. 2011. (ENG.). 2040p. 79.95 *(978-1-111-03768-0(X))* Delmar Cengage Learning.

Chilton Automotive Editorial Staff. Chilton Labor Guide 2010. 2009. (ENG.). 2688p. 219.95 *(978-1-111-03608-9(X))* Delmar Cengage Learning.

—Driveability Manual Asian, 1992-94, European. 2304p. 112.00 *(978-0-8019-8553-9(6))* Nichols Publishing Co.

—European Mechanical Service Manual 2006. 2006. (Chilton Mechanical Manuals Ser.). (ENG., Illus.). 1152p. 89.95 *(978-1-4180-0604-4(1))* Delmar Cengage Learning.

Chilton Editors. Chilton 2006 Asian Diagnostic Service Vol. 1, Vol. 1. 2006. (Chilton Diagnostic Manuals Ser.). (ENG., Illus.). 768p. 79.95 *(978-1-4180-2913-5(0))* Delmar Cengage Learning.

Clemens, Kevin. VW GTI, Golf, & Jetta, Mk III & IV: Find It. Fix It. Trick It. rev. ed. 2006. (Motorbooks Workshop Ser.). (ENG., Illus.). 160p. per. 24.95 *(978-0-7603-2595-7(2)*, 0760325952, Motorbooks) MBI Publishing Co. LLC.

Coombs, Matthew & Mather, Phil. Suzuki: SV650 & SV650S '99 to '08. Haynes, Max, ed. 3rd ed. 2009. (Haynes Service & Repair Manual Ser.). (ENG., Illus.). 336p. 45.45 *(978-1-84425-767-6(3)*, 1844257673) Haynes Manuals, Inc.

Ellery, Max. Mitsubishi Magna/Dimante 1991 To 2005: Automobile Repair Manual. 2008. (ENG., Illus.). 521p. pap. 34.95 *(978-1-876720-09-4(3)*, 1876720093) Renniks Pubns. AUS. Dist: MBI Distribution Services/Quayside Distribution.

Erickson, Chad & Raven, Greg. Water-Cooled VW Performance Handbook: 3rd Edition. 3rd ed. 2011. (Motorbooks Workshop Ser.). (ENG., Illus.). 208p. pap. 29.99 *(978-0-7603-3766-0(7)*, 0760337667, Motorbooks) MBI Publishing Co. LLC.

Erjavec, Jack. Brakes: Natef Standards Job Sheets. 3rd ed. 2009. (ENG.). 208p. (C). pap. 40.95 *(978-1-4354-8320-0(0))* Delmar Cengage Learning.

—Elecrical & Elecronic Systems: NATEF Standards Job Sheets. 3rd ed. 2009. (ENG.). 240p. (C). pap. 40.95 *(978-1-4354-8321-7(9))* Delmar Cengage Learning.

—NATEF Standards Job Sheets Area A2. 3rd ed. 2009. (ENG.). 192p. (C). pap. 40.95 *(978-1-4354-8317-0(0))* Delmar Cengage Learning.

—NATEF Standards Job Sheets Area A3. 3rd ed. 2009. (ENG.). 208p. (C). pap. 40.95 *(978-1-4354-8318-7(9))* Delmar Cengage Learning.

—NATEF Standards Job Sheets Area A7. 3rd ed. 2009. (ENG.). 176p. (C). pap. 40.95 *(978-1-4354-8322-4(7))* Delmar Cengage Learning.

—NATEF Standards Job Sheets Area A8. 3rd ed. 2009. (ENG.). 256p. (C). pap. 40.95 *(978-1-4354-8323-1(5))* Delmar Cengage Learning.

—Suspension & Steering: Natef Standards Job Sheets. 3rd ed. 2009. (ENG.). 240p. (C). pap. 40.95 *(978-1-4354-8319-4(7))* Delmar Cengage Learning.

Godfrey, Eric. Chrysler LH-Series: 1998 Thru 2004. 2010. (ENG.). 400p. pap. 29.95 *(978-1-56392-733-1(0))* Haynes,Chilton.

—VW Passat & Audi A4: VW Passat, 1998 thru 2005 & Audi A4, 1996 Thru 2001. 2009. (ENG.). 480p. pap. 29.95 *(978-1-56392-748-5(9))* Haynes,Chilton.

Hadfield, Chris. Automotive Service Job Sheets for NATEF Task Mastery. 2nd ed. 2011. (New Automotive & Truck Technology Titles! Ser.). (ENG., Illus.). 816p. (C). pap. 89.95 *(978-1-111-13798-4(6))* Delmar Cengage Learning.

Hadfield, Christopher & Dorries, Elisabeth H. Shop Manual for Automotive Engine Repair & Rebuilding. 4th ed. 2010. (Illus.). xix, 650p. pap. *(978-1-4354-2827-0(7))* Delmar Cengage Learning.

Hamilton, Joe L. Chilton's Chrysler 300/Charger/Magnum: 2005-07 Repair Manual. 2008. (ENG., Illus.). 384p. pap. 29.95 *(978-1-56392-685-3(7))* Haynes,Chilton.

—General Motors Cobalt/G5: 2005 Through 2007. 2008. (ENG., Illus.). 320p. pap. 29.95 *(978-1-56392-687-7(3))* Haynes,Chilton.

—Toyota/Lexus: Highlander 2001-06 RX 300/330 1999-06 Repair Manual. 2007. (Chilton's Total Car Care Repair Manuals Ser.). (ENG., Illus.). 368p. per. 29.95 *(978-1-56392-624-2(5))* Haynes,Chilton.

Hansen, Graham. How to Build Big-Inch Chevy Small Blocks. 2011. pap. 24.95 *(978-1-934709-66-5(2)*, S-A Design) CarTech, Inc.

Haynes Editors & Freund, Ken. Honda Foreman & Rubicon ATVs, 1995 Thru 2007. 2007. (Motorcycle Repair Manual Ser.). (ENG., Illus.). 208p. pap. 36.45 *(978-1-56392-656-3(3)*, 1563926563) Haynes Manuals, Inc.

Haynes Manuals Editors. Mazda Mazda3 2004 Thru 2011. 2011. (Haynes Repair Manual Ser.). (ENG., Illus.). 272p. pap. 26.95 ***(978-1-56392-915-1(5)***, 1563929155) Haynes Manuals, Inc.

—Toyota RAV4 1996 Thru 2010. 2011. (Haynes Repair Manual Ser.). (ENG., Illus.). 336p. pap. 26.95 ***(978-1-56392-937-3(6)***, 1563929376) Haynes Manuals, Inc.

Haynes, Max. Dodge Pick-ups: 2002 Thru 2008. 2009. (Haynes Repair Manual Ser.). (ENG., Illus.). 288p. pap. 26.95 *(978-1-56392-742-3(X)*, 156392742X) Haynes Manuals, Inc.

—Ford Focus 2000 Thru 2007. 2009. (Haynes Repair Manual Ser.). (ENG., Illus.). 336p. 26.95 *(978-1-56392-754-6(3)*, 1563927543) Haynes Manuals, Inc.

—Toyota Camry 2002-2006 Repair Manual. 2009. (Haynes Repair Manual Ser.). (ENG., Illus.). 288p. pap. 26.95 *(978-1-56392-762-1(4)*, 1563927624) Haynes Manuals, Inc.

Henderson, Bob. Chilton's General Motors Deville/Seville: 1999-05 Repair Manual. 2007. (Chilton's Total Car Care Repair Manuals Ser.). (ENG., Illus.). 432p. per. 29.95 *(978-1-56392-659-4(8))* Haynes,Chilton.

Henderson, Bob & Haynes, J. H. Toyota Hi-Lux & 4 Runner Automotive Repair Manual. 2nd ed. (Illus.). 272p. *(978-1-56392-256-5(3))* Haynes Manuals, Inc.

Heritage Information Systems. Illustrated Powerstroke Diagnostics: 2006-07 6. 0L E250-450 & F250-550. 2008. (Illus.). 544p. per. 89.95 *(978-0-9725784-1-7(2))* Heritage Technical LLC.

Holder, Bill & Kunz, Phil. Resto-Mod Muscle Cars: A Showcase of the World's Best Builds, Plus Ideas for Designing Your Own. 2008. (ENG., Illus.). 176p. pap. 24.99 *(978-0-89689-616-1(1))* Krause Pubns.

Hyland, Sean. How to Build Max-Performance 4. 6-Liter Ford Engines. 2007. (Cartech Ser.). (ENG., Illus.). 144p. pap. 24.95 *(978-1-932494-68-6(5)*, S-A Design) CarTech, Inc

Imhoff, Tim. Chilton's Toyota Prius 2001-08 Repair Manual. 2009. (ENG., Illus.). 304p. pap. 29.95 *(978-1-56392-691-4(1))* Haynes,Chilton.

—Nissan Altima: 2007-2010. 2011. (ENG.). 352p. pap. 29.95 *(978-1-56392-907-6(4))* Haynes,Chilton.

Imhoff, Tim & Haynes, J. H. Holden Commodore Automotive Repair Manual. (Illus.). 208p. *(978-1-56392-258-9(4))* Haynes Manuals, Inc.

Jaguar Cars Staff. The Jaguar E-Type 4.2 Series 2 Driver's Handbook (1969-1971) (Illus.). 80p. (Orig.). 30.00 *(978-0-8376-0534-0(2))* Bentley Pubs.

—The Jaguar MK 2 Models, 3.8 Litre Driver's Handbook (1960-1966) (Illus.). 84p. 30.00 *(978-0-8376-0502-9(4))* Bentley Pubs.

Jeffrey, Zurschmeide. The New Mini Performance Handbook. 2010. (ENG., Illus.). 144p. pap. 24.95 *(978-1-934709-14-6(X)*, S-A Design) CarTech, Inc.

Jorgensen, Eric & Ahlstrand, Alan. Ford Ranger Pick-Ups: 2000-05 Repair Manual. 2007. (Chilton's Total Car Care Repair Manuals Ser.). (ENG., Illus.). 384p. per. 29.95 *(978-1-56392-641-9(5))* Haynes,Chilton.

Killingsworth, Jeff & Haynes, J. H. Toyota Corolla & Holden Nova Automotive Repair Manual. (Illus.). 288p. *(978-1-56392-254-1(1))* Haynes Manuals, Inc.

Lake, Charles S. The Motor Cyclist's Handbook the Classic 1911 Guide to the Construction & Management of Motorcycles. 2007. 342p. pap. 29.95 *(978-1-4303-1131-7(2))* Lulu Enterprises Inc.

LeDoux, L. Alan & Haynes, J. H. Ford Laser & Mazda 323 Automotive Repair Manual. (Illus.). 304p. *(978-1-56392-264-0(9))* Haynes Manuals, Inc.

Legg, A. K. & Drayton, Spencer. Nissan Pulsar Automotive Repair Manual. (Illus.). 240p. *(978-1-56392-272-5(X))* Haynes Manuals, Inc.

Maddox, Robert. General Motors Malibu, 2004-07. 2010. (ENG., Illus.). 336p. pap. 29.95 *(978-1-56392-678-5(4))* Haynes,Chilton.

Maddox, Robert & Haynes, John H. Ford Mustang: 1994 Thru 2004. Freund, Ken, ed. 2008. (Haynes Automotive Repair Manual Ser.). (ENG., Illus.). 288p. per. 26.95 *(978-1-56392-676-1(8)*, 1563926768) Haynes Manuals, Inc.

Maddox, Robert & Heinrich, George B., III. Ford Mustang 1994-04 Repair Manual: Covers U. S. & Canadian Models of Ford Mustang. 2007. (Chilton's Total Car Care Ser.). (ENG., Illus.). 432p. per. 29.95 *(978-1-56392-649-5(0))* Haynes,Chilton.

Mihalyi, Eric Michael & Ryan, Mark. Ford Crown Victoria/Grand Marquis: 1989 Through 2010. 2011. (ENG.). 400p. pap. 29.95 ***(978-1-56392-904-5(X))*** Haynes,Chilton.

Mihalyi, Eric Michael & Storer, Jay. Ford Pick-Ups/Expedition/Navigator: 1997-30 Repair Manual. 2007. (ENG., Illus.). 432p. per. 29.95 *(978-1-56392-655-6(5))* Haynes,Chilton.

Motor Interior Panel Removal Guide: Includes Door Panels, Door Handles, Door Latches, Exterior Rearview Mirrors, Floor Consoles & Instrument Panels. 4th ed. 2007. (Illus.). *(978-1-58251-264-8(7))* Motor Information Systems.

Newton, Richard. Autocross Performance Handbook. rev. ed. 2007. (Motorbooks Workshop Ser.). (ENG., Illus.). 160p. pap. 25.95 *(978-0-7603-2788-3(2)*, 0760327882, Motorbooks) MBI Publishing Co. LLC.

Overholser, Dennis. Wiring: A Detailed How-to Guide. 2011. (Hot Rod Basics Ser.). (ENG., Illus.). 144p. pap. 27.95 *(978-1-929133-98-7(7)*, 1929133987, ArtKulture) Wolfgang Pubns., Inc.

Popular Science Monthly. Auto Kinks: Handy Manual of Short Cuts & Ingenious Ways of Keeping A Motor Car in Condition & Doing Emergency Repair Jobs. 2011. 192p. 42.95 ***(978-1-258-06659-8(9))*** Literary Licensing, LLC.

Reid, George. Ford Engine Parts Interchange. 2010. (Illus.). 160p. pap. 24.95 *(978-1-934709-19-1(0)*, S-A Design) CarTech, Inc.

Robert Bentley, contrib. by. Audi A6 Service Manual: 1998, 1999, 2000, 2001, 2002, 2003, 2004 Including S6, Allroad Quattro, RS6. 2006. (Illus.). 946p. per. 99.95 *(978-0-8376-1499-1(6)*, A604) Bentley Pubs.

Robert Bentley, inc Staff, contrib. by. Volkswagen Passat Service Manual: 1998, 1999, 2000, 2001, 2002, 2003, 2004, 2005 1. 8L Turbo, 2. 8L V6, 4. 0L W8 Including Wagon And 4Motion. 2007. (Illus.). 1872p. per. 129.95 *(978-0-8376-1483-0(X)*, VP05) Bentley Pubs.

Robert Bosch Gmbh. Bosch Automotive Handbook. 7th ed. 2007. (Illus.). 1192p. vinyl bd. 49.95 *(978-0-8376-1540-0(2),* Bentley Pubs.

Robert Bosch GmbH Staff. Automotive Handbook. Bauer, Horst, ed. 5th ed. 962p. *(978-0-7680-0669-8(4))* Bow Historical Bks.

Robert Bosch GmbH Staff. Automotive Handbook. 8th ed. 2011. (ENG., Illus.). 1266p. 65.00 ***(978-1-119-97556-4(5)***, Wiley) Wiley, John & Sons, Inc.

Robert Bosch GmbH Staff, creator. Safety, Comfort & Convenience Systems: Function, Regulation & Components. 2006. (Illus.). 399p. 59.95 *(978-0-8376-1391-8(4)*, H013) Bentley Pubs.

Santini, Al. OBD-II: Functions, Monitors & Diagnostic Techniques. 2010. (ENG.). 176p. (C). pap. 69.95 *(978-1-4283-9000-3(6))* Delmar Cengage Learning.

Santucci, Leo. Chevrolet Inline Six-Cylinder Power Manual 2nd Edition. 2011. (ENG., Illus.). 224p. pap. 29.95 *(978-1-931128-27-8(8)*, 1931128278) California Bill's Automotive Handbooks.

Sheeky, Christine L. & Stubblefield, Mike. General Motors: Buick/Oldsmobile/Pontiac Fwd 1985-05 Repair Manual. 2007. (Chilton's Total Car Care Repair Manuals Ser.). (ENG., Illus.). 352p. per. 29.95 *(978-1-56392-627-3(X))* Haynes,Chilton.

Staffel, Ed. Chevrolet Small Block Parts Interchange Manual. 2010. (Illus.). 144p. pap. 24.95 *(978-1-934709-23-8(9)*, S-A Design) CarTech, Inc.

Stolwijk, Henri. Haynes Car Guide: The Facts, The Figures, The Knowledge. 2008. (Haynes Car Guide Ser.). (ENG., Illus.). 400p. pap. 19.95 *(978-1-84425-455-2(0)*, 1844254550) Haynes Publishing PLC GBR. Dist: MBI Distribution Services/Quayside Distribution.

—Haynes Car Guide 2007: The Facts, the Figures, the Knowledge. 2007. (Haynes Car Guide Ser.). (ENG., Illus.). 400p. pap. 17.95 *(978-1-84425-399-9(6)*, 1844253996) Haynes Publishing PLC GBR. Dist: MBI Distribution Services/Quayside Distribution.

Storer, Jay. Nissan 350Z & Infiniti G35: 2003 Thru 2008. 2010. (ENG., Illus.). 416p. pap. 29.95 *(978-1-56392-731-7(4))* Haynes,Chilton.

Storer, Jay, et al. Saturn Ion 2003 Thru 2007. 2007. (Automotive Repair Manual Ser.). (ENG., Illus.). 320p. pap. 24.95 *(978-1-56392-664-8(4)*, 1563926644) Haynes Manuals, Inc.

The Chilton Editors. Toyota Sienna 1998-2009. 2011. (ENG.). 320p. pap. 29.95 ***(978-1-56392-905-2(8))*** Haynes,Chilton.

Ward, Charlotte, et al. Auto Suggestions: Heal Your Carma, Fix Your Car. 2007. pap. 14.95 *(978-0-9646842-2-5(5))* Purposeful Pr.

Wegmann, John A. Chilton's Honda Pilot/Acura MDX 2001-07 Repair Manual: Covers All U.S. & Canadian Models of Honda Pilot (2003 Through 2007) & Acura MDX (2001 Through 2007) 2009. (ENG., Illus.). 432p. pap. 29.95 *(978-1-56392-692-1(X))* Haynes,Chilton.

Woods Dual Power: Manual on Woods Automobile. (Illus.). 24p. reprint ed. pap. 10.00 *(978-0-8466-6019-4(9)*, U19) Shorey's Bookstore.

AUTOMOBILES—HEATING AND VENTILATION

see also Automobiles—Air Conditioning

Birch, Tom. Automotive Heating & Air Conditioning. 5th ed. 2009. (ENG & SPA., Illus.). 528p. (C). pap. 122.80 *(978-0-13-505136-8(3)*, Prentice Hall) Prentice Hall PTR.

Birch, Tom & Duvic, Marten. NATEF Correlated Task Sheets for Automotive Heating & Air Conditioning. 6th ed. 2011. (ENG.). 168p. (C). pap. 27.80 ***(978-0-13-254047-6(9)***, Prentice Hall) Prentice Hall PTR.

Birch, Tom & Duvic, Martin. Automotive Heating & Air Conditioning. 6th rev. ed. 2011. (ENG & SPA., Illus.). 480p. (C). pap. 118.00 *(978-0-13-255153-3(5)*, Prentice Hall) Prentice Hall PTR.

Daly, Steven. Automotive Air Conditioning & Climate Control Systems. 2006. (ENG., Illus.). 432p. (C). per. 57.95 *(978-0-7506-6955-9(1)*, Butterworth-Heinemann) Elsevier Science & Technology Bks.

Delmar Cengage Learning Staff. Dato: Diagnostic Scenarios for Heating. 2011. (Automotive Multimedia Solutions Ser.). (ENG.). (C). 33.95 *(978-1-111-03489-4(3))* Delmar Cengage Learning.

Delmar Learning, Thomson. ASE Test Preparation - A7 Heating & Air Conditioning. 5th ed. 2011. (ENG., Illus.). 176p. pap. 23.95 *(978-1-111-12709-1(3))* Delmar Cengage Learning.

Erjavec, Jack. Brakes: Natef Standards Job Sheets. 3rd ed. 2009. (ENG.). 208p. (C). pap. 40.95 *(978-1-4354-8320-0(0))* Delmar Cengage Learning.

—NATEF Standards Job Sheets Area A7. 3rd ed. 2009. (ENG.). 176p. (C). pap. 40.95 *(978-1-4354-8322-4(7))* Delmar Cengage Learning.

Grady, Michael. A7 Heating & Air Conditioning: Motor Age Self-Study Guide for ASE Certification. 2007. spiral bd. 22.95 *(978-1-933180-82-3(X))* Advanstar Communications, Inc.

Haynes Manuals Editors. Automotive Heating & Air Conditioning. 2011. (Haynes Techbook Ser.). (ENG., Illus.). 254p. pap. 24.95 *(978-1-56392-913-7(9)*, 1563929139) Haynes Manuals, Inc.

Rehkopf, Jeffrey. Automotive Heating & Air Conditioning. 2008. *(978-0-13-158308-5(5))* Pearson Bks.

Salah, Mohammad. Nonlinear Control for Advanced Vehicle Thermal Management Systems. 2010. 124p. pap. *(978-3-639-23904-1(0))* VDM Verlag Dr. Mueller e.K.

Schnubel, Mark. Today's Technician: Automotive Heating & Air Conditioning, 2 vols. 4th ed. 2008. (ENG., Illus.). 976p. (C). pap. 161.95 *(978-1-4283-8324-1(7))* Delmar Cengage Learning.

Schnubel, Mark. Today's Technician: Automotive Heating & Air Conditioning Classroom Manual & Shop Manual, 2 vols. 5th ed. 2012. (Today's Technician Ser.). (ENG.). 250p. (C). pap. 147.95 ***(978-1-133-01745-5(2))*** Delmar Cengage Learning.

AUTOMOBILES—HISTORY

see also Automobiles—Collectors and Collecting

Adler, Dennis. Convertibles. 2011. (First Gear Ser.). (ENG., Illus.). 240p. pap. 19.99 *(978-0-7603-4020-2(X)*, 076034020X, Motorbooks) MBI Publishing Co. LLC.

—Mercedes-Benz. 2008. (Gallery Ser.). (ENG., Illus.). 256p. pap. 19.99 *(978-0-7603-3372-3(6)*, 0760333726, Motorbooks) MBI Publishing Co. LLC.

Auto Editors of Consumer Guide, ed. American Cars of The 1950s. 2010. 320p. 12.98 *(978-1-4508-0642-8(2))* Publications International, Ltd.

—American Cars of The 1960s. 2010. 320p. 12.98 *(978-1-4508-0641-1(4))* Publications International, Ltd.

Auto Editors of Consumer Guide Staff. American Cars of The 1950's. 2007. (Illus.). 320p. 12.98 *(978-1-4127-1997-1(6))* Publications International, Ltd.

—Corvette Sports Car Superstar. 2007. (Illus.). 447p. 24.98 *(978-1-4127-1993-3(3))* Publications International, Ltd.

Automobile Year No. 38: 1990-1991. 280p. 39.95 *(978-2-88324-012-4(4)*, 3-AQ-0078) Automobile Quarterly, Inc.

Banks, Michael. Crosley: A Fine Car. 2012. (ENG., Illus.). 128p. pap. 37.95 *(978-1-58388-293-1(6)*, 1583882936) Iconografix, Inc.

Bayley, Stephen. Cars: Freiheit - Stil - Sex - Power - Bewegung - Farbe. 2011. (ENG., Illus.). 384p. 19.99 *(978-1-84091-535-8(8)*, Conran Octopus) Octopus Publishing Group GBR. Dist: Hachette Bk. Group.

Beckman, Andrew. The Studebaker National Museum... over a Century on Wheels. 2008. (Illus.). 160p. lib. bdg. 42.50 *(978-1-934729-02-1(7))* M.T. Publishing Co., Inc.

Bishop, Michael. They Found Our Engineer: The Story of Arthur Goddard. the Land Rover's first Engineer. 2011. 152p. pap. 22.02 ***(978-1-4567-7758-6(0))*** AuthorHouse.

Black, Edwin. Internal Combustion: How Corporations & Governments Addicted the World to Oil & Derailed the Alternatives. 2008. (ENG.). 432p. 10.00 *(978-0-914153-11-5(0))* Dialog Pr.

Booij, Jeroen. Maximum Mini: The Definitive Book of Cars Based on the Original Mini. 2009. (ENG., Illus.). 128p. pap. 49.95 *(978-1-84584-154-6(9)*, 1845841549) Veloce Publishing Ltd. GBR. Dist: MBI Distribution Services/Quayside Distribution.

Brown, Stewart J. Volvo Ailsa. 2011. (ENG., Illus.). 96p. 32.95 *(978-0-7110-3514-0(8))* Allan, Ian Publishing GBR. Dist: BookMasters Distribution Services (BDS).

Buckley, David Joss. Ultimate Autos of the Fifties. 2008. (Ultimate Autos of The... Ser.). (Illus.). 160p. 12.99 *(978-0-7858-2368-1(9)*, Chartwell) Book Sales, Inc.

Car and Driver Editorial Staff. Car & Driver Porsche: Iconic Cars. 2011. (ENG.). 128p. 24.99 *(978-1-936297-50-4(7))* Filipacchi Publishingsan.

—Iconic Cars. 2011. (ENG.). 128p. 24.99 *(978-1-936297-49-8(3))* Filipacchi Publishingsan.

Carugati, Decio G. & Carugati, D. G. R. Pininfarina. 2010. (ENG., Illus.). 240p. 150.00 *(978-88-370-7360-2(7)*, Mondadori Electa (Acc)) Antique Collectors' Club GBR. Dist: National Bk. Network.

Casey, Robert H. The Model T: A Centennial History. 2008. (ENG., Illus.). 168p. 26.95 *(978-0-8018-8850-2(6))* Johns Hopkins Univ. Pr.

Chapman, Giles. The Ford Transit Story. 2011. (Story Ser.). (ENG., Illus.). 128p. 16.95 ***(978-0-7524-6283-7(0))*** History Pr. Ltd.,The GBR. Dist: Independent Pubs. Group.

Chapman, Giles. The Worst Cars Ever Sold. 2007. (ENG., Illus.). 160p. per. 18.95 *(978-0-7509-4714-5(4))* Sutton Publishing.

Cheetham, Craig. World's Worst Cars. 2009. (World's Worst: from Innovation to Disaster Ser.). 80p. (gr. 8-8). 61.20 *(978-1-60854-858-3(9))* Rosen Publishing Group, Inc., The.

Clarke, R. M. Mercury Comet & Cyclone Limited Edition Extra 1960-1975. 2006. (Limited Edition Extra Ser.). (ENG., Illus.). 128p. pap. 24.95 *(978-1-85520-713-4(3)*, 1855207133) Brooklands Bks. GBR. Dist: MBI Distribution Services/Quayside Distribution.

—Mercury Gold Portfolio 1947-1966. 2006. (Gold Portfolio Ser.). (ENG., Illus.). 176p. pap. 32.95 *(978-1-85520-714-1(1)*, 1855207141) Brooklands Bks. GBR. Dist: MBI Distribution Services/Quayside Distribution.

—TVR Performance Portfolio 2000-2005. 2006. (Performance Portfolio Ser.). (ENG., Illus.). 128p. pap. 24.95 *(978-1-85520-717-2(6)*, 1855207176) Brooklands Bks. GBR. Dist: MBI Distribution Services/Quayside Distribution.

Clarke, R. M., compiled by. Allard Limited Edition Ultra. 2009. (Limited Edition Ultra Ser.). (ENG., Illus.). 212p. pap. 37.95 *(978-1-85520-832-2(6)*, 1855208326) Brooklands Bks. GBR. Dist: MBI Distribution Services/Quayside Distribution.

—VW Corrado Limited Edition Premier. 2008. (Limited Edition Premier Ser.). (ENG., Illus.). 160p. pap. 32.95 *(978-1-85520-829-2(6)*, 1855208296) Brooklands Bks. GBR. Dist: MBI Distribution Services/Quayside Distribution.

Copping, Richard. Volkswagen Beetle: A Celebration of the World's Most Popular Car. 2011. (Haynes Great Cars Ser.). (ENG., Illus.). 160p. 39.95 *(978-1-84425-966-3(8)*, 1844259668) Haynes Publishing PLC GBR. Dist: MBI Distribution Services/Quayside Distribution.

Copping, Richard & Screaton, Brian. Volkswagen Transporter: The First 60 Years. 2009. (ENG., Illus.). 400p. 62.95 *(978-1-84425-579-5(4)*, 1844255794) Haynes Publishing PLC GBR. Dist: MBI Distribution Services/Quayside Distribution.

Cotter, Tom. The Corvette in the Barn: More Great Stories of Automotive Archaeology. 2010. (ENG., Illus.). 256p. 26.00 *(978-0-7603-3797-4(7)*, 0760337977, Motorbooks) MBI Publishing Co. LLC.

Cutting, Robert. King of Wheels. 2007. (Timeline Ser.). (Illus.). 48p. pap. 8.99 *(978-1-4190-4396-3(X))* Houghton Mifflin Harcourt Supplemental Pubs.

Dalton, Curt, et al. Miami Valley's Marvelous Motor Cars. 2007. (Illus.). 96p. per. 19.95 *(978-0-9715702-9-0(9))* Dalton, Curt.

Davey, Arnold. Lagonda, 1899-1999. (Images of Transportation Ser.). (Illus.). 128p. 22.00 *(978-0-7524-1713-4(4))* History Pr. Ltd.,The GBR. Dist: Trafalgar Square Publishing.

DeLorenzo, Peter. The United States of Toyota: How Detroit Squandered its Legacy & Enabled Toyota to Become America's Car Company. 2007. (ENG.). 308p. 37.95 *(978-1-59299-302-4(8))* Inkwater Pr.

Dickirson, Gene D. GDT Speedster from Dream to Reality. 2008. 179p. pap. 82.70 *(978-0-615-16515-8(X))* GDT Speedster, LLC.

Dorling Kindersley Publishing Staff. Car: A Definitive Visual History of the Automobile. 2011. (ENG.). 360p. 40.00 *(978-0-7566-7167-9(1))* Dorling Kindersley Publishing, Inc.

Edsall, Larry. Miata 20 Years. 2008. (ENG., Illus.). 176p. 25.00 *(978-0-7603-3386-0(6)*, 0760333866, Motorbooks) MBI Publishing Co. LLC.

Fiat (Firm) Staff. Fiat 500: The Autobiography. 2012. (ENG., Illus.). 144p. 45.00 *(978-0-8478-3720-5(3))* Rizzoli International Pubns., Inc.

Flory, J. "Kelly", Jr. American Cars, 1946-1959: Every Model, Year by Year. 2008. (ENG., Illus.). 1047p. 75.00 *(978-0-7864-3229-5(2))* McFarland & Co., Inc. Pubs.

Foster, Patrick R. Hudson Automobiles. 2010. (Illustrated History Ser.). (ENG., Illus.). 128p. pap. 34.95 *(978-1-58388-266-5(9)*, 1583882669) Iconografix, Inc.

—Kaiser-Frazer 1947-1955 Photo Archive. 2009. (Photo Archive Ser.). (ENG., Illus.). 128p. pap. 32.95 *(978-1-58388-239-9(1)*, 1583882391) Iconografix, Inc.

Franz, Kathleen. Tinkering: Consumers Reinvent the Early Automobile. 2011. (Illus.). 232p. (C). pap. 24.95 *(978-0-8122-2158-9(3))* Univ. of Pennsylvania Pr.

Fria, Robert A. Mustang Genesis: The Creation of the Pony Car. 2010. (ENG., Illus.). 208p. 45.00 *(978-0-7864-5840-0(2))* McFarland & Co., Inc. Pubs.

Genat, Robert & Newhardt, David. American Cars of The 1950s. rev. ed. 2007. (Gallery Ser.). (ENG., Illus.). 192p. pap. 14.95 *(978-0-7603-3230-6(4)*, 0760332304, Motorbooks) MBI Publishing Co. LLC.

Gingerelli, Dain. Harley-Davidson Museum Masterpieces. 2010. (First Gear Ser.). (ENG., Illus.). 240p. pap. 19.99 *(978-0-7603-3894-0(9)*, 0760338949, Motorbooks) MBI Publishing Co. LLC.

Giucci, Guillermo. The Cultural Life of the Automobile: Roads to Modernity. Mayagoitia, Anne & Nagao, Debra, trs. from POR. 2012. (ENG & SPA., Illus.). 260p. 55.00 ***(978-0-292-72872-1(7))*** Univ. of Texas Pr.

Goetz, Robert. Holt Cat, 1933-2008: Seventy-Five Years of Making the Earth Move. 2008. *(978-1-893271-47-0(1))* Maverick Publishing Co.

Grafton, Carol Belanger, ed. Vintage Automobile Ads & Posters. 2010. (Dover Electronic Clip Art Ser.). (ENG., Illus.). 48p. pap. 19.95 *(978-0-486-99099-6(0))* Dover Pubns., Inc.

Hadland, Tony. Raleigh: Ups & Downs of the Iconic Bicycle Brand. 2011. (Cycling Resources Ser.). (Illus.). 360p. 49.95 *(978-1-892495-68-6(6))* Cycle Publishing/Van Der Plas Pubns.

Hart, Lou. Kings of the Quarter-Mile: Rail-Jobs, Slingshots & Mid-Engine Dragsters. 2009. (Photo Gallery Ser.). (ENG., Illus.). 160p. pap. 19.95 *(978-1-58388-234-4(0)*, 1583882340) Iconografix, Inc.
Harvey, Jonathan. VW Beetle. 2009. (Haynes Enthusiast Guide Ser.). (ENG., Illus.). 160p. 39.95 *(978-1-84425-434-7(8)*, 1844254348) Haynes Publishing PLC GBR. Dist: MBI Distribution Services/Quayside Distribution.
Hayes, Russell. Tvr: Ever the Extrovert. 2009. (Haynes Classic Makes Ser.). (ENG., Illus.). 160p. 34.95 *(978-1-84425-507-8(7)*, 1844255077) Haynes Publishing PLC GBR. Dist: MBI Distribution Services/Quayside Distribution.
Holloway, Hilton & Buckley, Martin. The A-Z of Cars: The Century's Classic Automobiles. 2009. (ENG., Illus.). 400p. 39.95 *(978-1-84732-150-3(X))* Carlton Bks., Ltd. GBR. Dist: Sterling Publishing Co., Inc.
Holmes, Mark. Ultimate Classic Cars: The World's Greatest Automobiles. 2007. (Illus.). 160p. 12.99 *(978-0-7858-2302-5(6)*, Chartwell) Book Sales, Inc.
—Ultimate Convertibles: Roofless Beauty. 2007. (Illus.). 160p. 12.99 *(978-0-7858-2286-8(0)*, Chartwell) Book Sales, Inc.
Hylton, Pete. Ghost Tracks: A Historic Look at America's Lost Road Racing Tracks. 2007. 128p. per. 34.95 *(978-0-9796976-1-6(1))* Legacy Ink Publishing.
Hylton, Stuart. The Horseless Carriage: The Birth of the Motor Age. 2009. (ENG., Illus.). 192p. pap. 27.95 *(978-0-7524-5078-0(6))* History Pr. Ltd.,The GBR. Dist: Independent Pubs. Group.
Kelly, Maurice A. Russian Motor Vehicles: The Czarist Period 1784 to 1917. 2009. (ENG., Illus.). 112p. 24.95 *(978-1-84584-213-0(8)*, 1845842138) Veloce Publishing Ltd. GBR. Dist: MBI Distribution Services/Quayside Distribution.
Knowles, David. Triumph TR7: The Untold Story. 2008. (ENG., Illus.). 256p. 44.95 *(978-1-86126-891-4(2)*, 1861268912) Crowood Pr., Ltd. GBR. Dist: MBI Distribution Services/Quayside Distribution.
Laban, Brian. Cars: Die Anfänge des Automobils, 1 vol. 2011. (GER, FRE & ENG.). 352p. 19.99 ***(978-3-8331-6184-1(1))*** h.f.ullmann DEU. Dist: Innovative Logistics.
—Cars: The Early Years/Die Anfange des Automobils/les Premieres Annees de L'Automobile. 2008. (Transportation: the Early Years Ser.). (Illus.). 349p. 49.95 *(978-0-8416-0279-3(4))* American Map Corp.
—The Mini: Celebrating 50 Years of a Modern Motoring Icon. 2009. (ENG., Illus.). 208p. 34.95 *(978-1-84732-373-6(1))* Carlton Bks., Ltd. GBR. Dist: Sterling Publishing Co., Inc.
Leffingwell, Randy. Porsche: A History of Excellence. 2011. (ENG., Illus.). 348p. pap. 30.00 *(978-0-7603-4016-5(1)*, 0760340161, Motorbooks) MBI Publishing Co. LLC.
Lintelmann, Reinhard. 1000 Automoviles: Historia, Clasicos, Detalles. 2007. (Illus.). 359p. *(978-3-625-00035-8(0))* Negev Importing Co., Ltd.
Locke, William S. Elcar & Pratt Automobiles: The Complete History. alt. ed. 2007. (ENG., Illus.). 346p. per. 45.00 *(978-0-7864-3254-7(3))* McFarland & Co., Inc. Pubs.
Ludvigsen, Karl, intro. Ford's Feisty Capri: European Sporting Coupes 1969-1987. 2009. (Ludvigsen Library Ser.). (ENG., Illus.). 128p. pap. 29.95 *(978-1-58388-251-1(0)*, 1583882510) Iconografix, Inc.
Magazine, Car. Best of Car: The '70s & '80s. Oliver, Ben, ed. 2008. (ENG.). 160p. 19.95 *(978-1-906032-49-4(1))* Anova Bks. GBR. Dist: Independent Pubs. Group.
McCall, Walter & McPherson, Thomas A. Carved-Panel Hearses: An Illustrated History, 1933-1948. 2011. (ENG., Illus.). 128p. pap. 39.95 *(978-1-58388-281-8(2)*, 1583882812) Iconografix, Inc.
McCarthy, Tom. Auto Mania: Cars, Consumers, & the Environment. 2009. (ENG., Illus.). 368p. pap. 20.00 *(978-0-300-15848-9(3))* Yale Univ. Pr.
Mccausey, Gregory. Chrysler Front Wheel Drive Performance: 1983-1992. 2009. pap. 19.00 *(978-1-61584-912-3(2))* Independent Pub.
McPherson, Thomas A. The Henney Motor Company: The Complete History. 2009. (ENG., Illus.). 288p. 79.95 *(978-1-58388-233-7(2)*, 1583882332) Iconografix, Inc.
—Miller-Meteor: The Complete Illustrated History. 2010. (ENG., Illus.). 320p. 79.95 *(978-1-58388-258-0(8)*, 1583882588) Iconografix, Inc.
Morgan, Charlie & Fowler, Stan. Little Book of Land Rover. 2008. (Little Book Ser.). (ENG., Illus.). 128p. 9.99 *(978-1-906229-10-8(4)*, 1906229104) G2 Entertainment Ltd. GBR. Dist: MBI Distribution Services/Quayside Distribution.
Mort, Norm. American 'Independent' Automakers: AMC to Willys 1945 to 1960. 2010. (Those Were the Days Ser.). (ENG., Illus.). 96p. pap. 29.95 *(978-1-84584-239-0(1)*, 1845842391) Veloce Publishing Ltd. GBR. Dist: MBI Distribution Services/Quayside Distribution.
—American Station Wagons: The Golden Era, 1950-1975. 2010. (Those Were the Days Ser.). (ENG., Illus.). 96p. pap. 29.95 *(978-1-84584-268-0(5)*, 1845842685) Veloce Publishing Ltd. GBR. Dist: MBI Distribution Services/Quayside Distribution.
—American Woodies 1928-1953. 2011. (Those Were the Days Ser.). (ENG., Illus.). 96p. pap. 29.95 *(978-1-84584-269-7(3)*, 1845842693) Veloce Publishing Ltd. GBR. Dist: MBI Distribution Services/Quayside Distribution.
Mort, Norman. American Trucks of The 1950s. 2010. (Those Were the Days Ser.). (ENG., Illus.). 96p. pap. 29.95 *(978-1-84584-227-7(8)*, 1845842278) Veloce Publishing Ltd. GBR. Dist: MBI Distribution Services/Quayside Distribution.
Mort, Norman & Mort, Norm. Anglo-American Cars: From the 1930s to The 1970s. 2010. (Those were the Days... Ser.). (ENG., Illus.). 96p. pap. 29.95 *(978-1-84584-233-8(2)*, 1845842332) Veloce Publishing Ltd. GBR. Dist: MBI Distribution Services/Quayside Distribution.
Mroz, Albert. American Cars, Trucks & Motorcycles of World War I: Illustrated Histories of 225 Manufacturers. 2010. (ENG., Illus.). 428p. pap. 45.00 *(978-0-7864-3967-6(X))* McFarland & Co., Inc. Pubs.
Mueller, Mike. The Complete Book of Mustang: Every Model Since 1964-1/2. 2010. (Complete Book Ser.). (ENG., Illus.). 360p. pap. 29.99 *(978-0-7603-3830-8(2)*, 0760338302, Motorbooks) MBI Publishing Co. LLC.
—Ford Pickup Trucks. 2008. (Gallery Ser.). (ENG., Illus.). 192p. pap. 17.95 *(978-0-7603-3262-7(2)*, 0760332622, Motorbooks) MBI Publishing Co. LLC.
—Mustang 1964 1/2-1973. 2008. (Motorbooks Classic Ser.). (ENG., Illus.). 168p. pap. 24.95 *(978-0-7603-3452-2(8)*, 0760334528, Motorbooks) MBI Publishing Co. LLC.
Musselman, M. M. Get a Horse! the Story of the Automobile in Americ. 2011. 336p. 50.95 ***(978-1-258-06413-6(8))*** Literary Licensing, LLC.
Narus, Don. Chrysler- the Golden Age 1940-1949. 2009. 130p. pap. 22.95 *(978-0-578-01121-9(2))* New Albany Bks.
—Chrysler's Land Yacht-Twon & Country Convertibles 1942-1986. 2009. pap. 22.95 *(978-1-61623-211-5(0))* Independent Pub.
Nelson, Kevin. Wheels of Change from Zero to 600 M.P.H: The Amazing Story of California & the Automobile. 2009. pap. 24.95 *(978-1-59714-113-0(5))* Heyday.
Orel, Frank & Brummer, Elmar, eds. Generation Porsche. 2009. 400p. pap. 45.00 *(978-3-8327-9031-8(4))* teNeues Publishing Co.
Parker, Paul. Sports Car Racing in Camera 1960-69. 2007. (ENG., Illus.). 240p. 59.95 *(978-1-84425-400-2(3)*, 1844254003) Haynes Publishing PLC GBR. Dist: MBI Distribution Services/Quayside Distribution.
Parrish, Kent. Ford Fire Trucks. 2010. (ENG., Illus.). 144p. pap. 34.95 *(978-1-58388-254-2(5)*, 1583882545) Iconografix, Inc.
Patton, Phil. Cars of the 20th Century: 100 Years of Automotive Ads, 1900-1999. Heimann, Jim, ed. 2009. (FRE, GER & ENG., Illus.). 400p. 39.99 *(978-3-8365-1463-7(X))* TASCHEN DEU. Dist: Ingram Pub. Services.
Peck, Colin. The Last Real Austins: 1946 To 1959. 2009. (Those Were the Days Ser.). (ENG., Illus.). 96p. pap. 29.95 *(978-1-84584-193-5(X)*, 184584193X) Veloce Publishing Ltd. GBR. Dist: MBI Distribution Services/Quayside Distribution.
Peters, Eric. Road Hogs: Detroit's Big, Beautiful Luxury Performance Cars of the 1960s & 1970s. 2011. (ENG., Illus.). 160p. 35.00 *(978-0-7603-3764-6(0)*, 0760337640, Motorbooks); *(978-0-7603-3388-4(2))* MBI Publishing Co. LLC.
Phillips, Lou. Cars: 1895-1965. 2011. 696p. 34.99 *(978-1-4568-9293-7(2))*; pap. 23.99 ***(978-1-4568-9292-0(4))*** Xlibris Corp.
Porter, Richard & Chapman, Giles. My Dad Wished He Had One of Those. 2008. (ENG., Illus.). 192p. 19.95 *(978-0-340-96324-1(7)*, Hodder & Stoughton) Hodder General Publishing Div. GBR. Dist: Independent Pubs. Group.
Posth, Martin. 1,000 Days in Shanghai: The Volkswagen Story - The First Chinese-German Car Factory. Travis, Ian, tr. from GER. 2008. (ENG., Illus.). 250p. pap. 24.95 *(978-0-470-82388-0(7)*, Wiley) Wiley, John & Sons, Inc.
Powley, Adam. My Dad's Motors. 2011. (ENG., Illus.). 144p. 12.95 *(978-0-85733-042-0(X)*, 085733042X) Haynes Publishing PLC GBR. Dist: MBI Distribution Services/Quayside Distribution.
Pressnell, Jon. Mini: The Definitive History. 2009. (ENG., Illus.). 272p. 54.95 *(978-1-84425-475-0(5)*, 1844254755) Haynes Publishing PLC GBR. Dist: MBI Distribution Services/Quayside Distribution.
Publications International Staff. Ency of Amer Cars. 2006. (Illus.). 848p. 34.98 *(978-1-4127-1354-2(4)*, 1261319, PIL Kids) Publications International, Ltd.
Publications International Staff, creator. Cars of The 1960s. 2007. (Illus.). 192p. 24.95 *(978-1-4127-1554-6(7))* Publications International, Ltd.
Publishers of Old Cars Weekly. 50s Flashback: Fabulous Cars We'll Never Forget. 2010. 144p. pap. 12.99 *(978-1-4402-1412-7(3))* Krause Pubns.
Puyal, Robert. Behind the Wheel: The Great Automobile Aficionados. 2010. (ENG., Illus.). 240p. 49.95 *(978-2-08-030154-3(3))* Flammarion et Cie FRA. Dist: Random Hse., Inc.
Queener, Charles W. The Alphabet & the Automobile. 2006. (Illus.). 48p. 17.95 *(978-1-893618-77-0(3))* Bull, David Publishing, Inc.
Quellin, Adam. The Little Book of Microcars. 2010. (ENG., Illus.). 96p. pap. 9.95 *(978-1-84584-278-9(2)*, 1845842782) Veloce Publishing Ltd. GBR. Dist: MBI Distribution Services/Quayside Distribution.
—Microcars at Large! 2007. (ENG., Illus.). 112p. pap. 29.95 *(978-1-84584-092-1(5)*, 1845840925) Veloce Publishing Ltd. GBR. Dist: MBI Distribution Services/Quayside Distribution.
Rawlinson, Colin C. The 500cc Racing Car. 2008. (Shire Library). (ENG., Illus.). 32p. pap. 11.95 *(978-0-7478-0555-7(5))* Shire Pubns., Ltd. GBR. Dist: Random Hse., Inc.
Rees, Chris. The Magnificent 7: The Enthusiasts' Guide to All Models of Lotus & Caterham Seven. 2nd ed. 2007. (ENG., Illus.). 184p. 36.95 *(978-1-84425-410-1(0)*, 1844254100) Haynes Publishing PLC GBR. Dist: MBI Distribution Services/Quayside Distribution.
Richardson, James. Volkswagen Golf GTI. 2009. (ENG., Illus.). 192p. 34.95 *(978-1-84797-048-0(6)*, 1847970486) Crowood Pr., Ltd. GBR. Dist: MBI Distribution Services/Quayside Distribution.
Robson, Graham. The Ford Cortina. 2008. (Shire Library). (ENG., Illus.). 32p. pap. 11.95 *(978-0-7478-0519-9(9))* Shire Pubns., Ltd. GBR. Dist: Random Hse., Inc.
Ruch, Peter. Legendary German Cars. 2010. (ENG., Illus.). 304p. 39.95 *(978-88-544-0447-2(0))* White Star ITA. Dist: Random Hse., Inc.
Scheller, Bill & Scheller, William. Porsche: The Fine Art of the Sports Car. 2008. (ENG., Illus.). 384p. 24.95 *(978-0-7893-9978-6(4))* Universe Publishing.
Schild, Jim. Chevrolet Camaro: 1970-1981. 2008. (Collector's Originality Guide Ser.). (ENG., Illus.). 144p. 37.95 *(978-0-7603-3134-7(0)*, 0760331340, Motorbooks) MBI Publishing Co. LLC.
Schlegelmilch, Rainer W. & Lehbrink, Hartmut. Porsche. 2008. (Transportation Ser.). (Illus.). 399p. 49.95 *(978-0-8416-0300-4(6))* American Map Corp.
Siegelbaum, Lewis H. Cars for Comrades: The Life of the Soviet Automobile. 2008. (Illus.). 309p. 39.95 *(978-0-8014-4638-2(4))* Cornell Univ. Pr.
Sneed, Geoffrey. Carburettors to Catseyes: A Brief History of Motoring Inventions. 2011. (Illus.). 115p. 33.95 ***(978-1-84624-660-9(1))*** Book Guild, Ltd. GBR. Dist: Trans-Atlantic Pubns., Inc.
Stanley, Richard A. The Lexington Automobile: A Complete History. alt. ed. 2012. (ENG., Illus.). 263p. pap. 35.00 ***(978-0-7864-6934-5(X))*** McFarland & Co., Inc. Pubs.
Starkey, John. Lola - The Illustrated History 1957-1977. (Illus.). 192p. lthr. *(978-1-901295-21-4(4))* Veloce Publishing Ltd. GBR. Dist: MBI Distribution Services/Quayside Distribution.
—Lola - The Illustrated History from 1978. (Illus.). 176p. lthr. *(978-1-901295-17-7(6))* Veloce Publishing Ltd. GBR. Dist: MBI Distribution Services/Quayside Distribution.
Stein, Jonathan A. The Performing Art of the American Automobile: The Hendricks Collection on Exhibit at the Gateway Colorado Auto Museum. 2011. (ENG., Illus.). 272p. 60.00 *(978-0-9779809-0-1(1)*, 977980) Coachbuilt Pr.
Stein, Jonathan A., ed. Curves of Steel: Streamlined Automobile Design. 2nd rev. ed. 2009. (ENG., Illus.). 192p. 75.00 *(978-0-9779809-6-3(0))* Coachbuilt Pr.
Stokoe, Noel. Sporting Jowetts. 2009. (ENG., Illus.). 256p. pap. 34.95 *(978-0-7524-4775-9(0))* History Pr. Ltd.,The GBR. Dist: Independent Pubs. Group.
Stokoe, Noel, ed. My Car Was a Jowett. (Illus.). 160p. 27.50 *(978-0-7524-2796-6(2))* History Pr. Ltd.,The GBR. Dist: Trafalgar Square Publishing.
Stroud, John. Concept Cars. 2010. (ENG., Illus.). 304p. 14.95 *(978-88-544-0461-8(6))* White Star ITA. Dist: Random Hse., Inc.
Sucher, Harry V. The Iron Redskin: The History of the Indian Motorcycle. 2010. (ENG., Illus.). 304p. 52.95 *(978-1-84425-500-9(X)*, 184425500X) Haynes Publishing PLC GBR. Dist: MBI Distribution Services/Quayside Distribution.
Tabucchi, Maurizio. Alfa Romeo: 100 Years. 2010. (ENG., Illus.). 144p. 79.95 *(978-88-7911-495-0(6))* Giorgio Nada Editore ITA. Dist: MBI Distribution Services/Quayside Distribution.
—Alfa Romeo, from 1910 to 2010. 2010. (ENG., Illus.). 144p. 79.95 *(978-88-7911-503-2(0)*, 8879115030) Giorgio Nada Editore ITA. Dist: MBI Distribution Services/Quayside Distribution.
Tres, Miquel. Harley Davidson. (SPA., Illus.). 210p. *(978-84-96137-23-3(6))* A. Asppan, S.L. Distribuidora Internacional de Libros y Revistas.
Tumminelli, Paolo, creator. Car Design America: Myths, Brands, People. 2012. (ENG, GER & SPA., Illus.). 392p. 65.00 ***(978-3-8327-9596-2(0))*** teNeues Publishing Co.
Tumminello, Paolo, photos by. Car Design Europe. 2011. (ENG, GER & FRE., Illus.). 392p. 65.00 *(978-3-8327-9459-0(X))* teNeues Publishing Co.
Turner, Paul. Automobile Memories: 44 Vehicles in 50 Years. Date not set. 142p. pap. 12.00 *(978-1-57636-054-5(7))* SunRise Publishing.
Vagg, Jon. Ultimate Autos of the Sixties. 2008. (Ultimate Autos of The... Ser.). (Illus.). 160p. 12.99 *(978-0-7858-2369-8(7)*, Chartwell) Book Sales, Inc.
Van Boggart, Angelo. Just 30s. 2011. (ENG.). 144p. pap. 12.99 *(978-1-4402-1428-8(X))* Krause Pubns.
Vokins, Stephen. Weird Cars: A Century of the World's Strangest Cars. 2nd ed. 2012. (ENG., Illus.). 288p. pap. 20.95 ***(978-0-85733-237-0(6)***, 0857332376) Haynes Publishing PLC GBR. Dist: MBI Distribution Services/Quayside Distribution.
Walker, Nick. A-Z British Coachbuilders, 1919-1960: And the Development of Styles & Techniques. 2nd rev. enl. ed. 2007. (ENG., Illus.). 224p. 59.95 *(978-0-9549981-6-5(2)*, 0954998162) Herridge & Sons, Ltd. GBR. Dist: MBI Distribution Services/Quayside Distribution.
Walton, Jeremy. Audi Quattro: A Celebration of the World's First Turbocharged 4x4 Coupé. 2007. (Haynes Great Cars Ser.). (ENG., Illus.). 160p. 32.95 *(978-1-84425-330-2(9)*, 1844253309) Haynes Publishing PLC GBR. Dist: MBI Distribution Services/Quayside Distribution.
White, Ben. NASCAR Then & Now. 2010. (ENG., Illus.). 144p. 25.00 *(978-0-7603-3814-8(0)*, 0760338140, Motorbooks) MBI Publishing Co. LLC.
Wilson, Steve. Triumph Bonneville - T120/T140. 2nd ed. 2009. (Haynes Great Bikes Ser.). (ENG., Illus.). 176p. 39.95 *(978-1-84425-549-8(2)*, 1844255492) Haynes Publishing PLC GBR. Dist: MBI Distribution Services/Quayside Distribution.
Witzel, Michael Karl & Steil, Tim. Americana: Roadside Memories. (Illus.). 285p. pap. *(978-0-681-62683-6(6)*, Lowe & B. Hould Pubs.) Borders Pr.
Wood, Jonathan. The Austin Seven. 2008. (Album Ser.: Vol. 343). (ENG., Illus.). 32p. pap. 11.95 *(978-0-7478-0416-1(8))* Shire Pubns., Ltd. GBR. Dist: Random Hse., Inc.
Young, Anthony. Camaro. (Illus.). 156p. pap. *(978-0-681-20005-0(7)*, Lowe & B. Hould Pubs.) Borders Pr.
Zumbrunn, Michel. British Auto Legends: Classics of Style & Design. 2009. (Illus.). 288p. pap. *(978-1-85894-494-4(5))* Merrell Pubs. Ltd.
—British Auto Legends: Classics of Style & Design. 2007. (Auto Legends Ser.). (ENG., Illus.). 288p. 49.95 *(978-1-85894-412-8(0))* Merrell Pubs. Ltd. GBR. Dist: Perseus Distribution.
Zumbrunn, Michel & Heseltine, Richard. Ferrari Legends: Classics of Style & Design. 2008. (Illus.). 288p. 49.95 *(978-1-85894-432-6(5))* Merrell Pubs. Ltd. GBR. Dist: Perseus Distribution.

AUTOMOBILES—IGNITION

see also Spark Plugs

Hammill, Des. How to Build & Power Tune Distributor-Type Ignition Systems: New 3rd Edition! 3rd ed. 2009. (Speedpro Ser.). (ENG., Illus.). 64p. pap. 33.95 *(978-1-84584-186-7(7)*, 1845841867) Veloce Publishing Ltd. GBR. Dist: MBI Distribution Services/Quayside Distribution.
Lake, Charles S. The Motorcyclist's Handbook. 2011. 344p. pap. 29.95 ***(978-1-935700-55-5(3))*** Periscope Film, LLC.
Mcintyre, Dustin. Laser Spark Plug Development & Engine Testing - Design of a Diode Side Pumped Solid State Passively Q-Switched Laser for Use As an Ignition Source F. 2008. 224p. pap. *(978-3-639-11362-4(4))* VDM Verlag Dr. Mueller e.K.
Robert Bosch GmbH Staff. Bosch Technical Instruction: Battery Ignition. (Illus.). pap. 14.95 *(978-0-8376-0477-0(X))* Bentley Pubs.
—Bosch Technical Instruction: Motronic Combined Ignition & Fuel-Injection System. (Illus.). pap. 14.95 *(978-0-8376-0471-8(0))* Bentley Pubs.
Ryden, Todd. How to Build High-Performance Ignition Systems. 2008. (Sa Design Ser.). (Illus.). 144p. pap. 24.95 *(978-1-932494-71-6(5))* CarTech, Inc.
Zhao Hua Staff. Homogeneous Charge Compression Ignition (Hcci) & Controlled Aut. 2007. (ENG.). 524p. 289.95 *(978-1-4200-4459-1(1)*, CRC Press) Taylor & Francis Group GBR. Dist: Taylor & Francis Group.

AUTOMOBILES—JUVENILE LITERATURE

Dorling Kindersley Publishing Staff. Driven Mad. 2012. (ENG.). 96p. (J). (gr. 2-7). 16.99 ***(978-0-7566-9013-7(7))*** Dorling Kindersley Publishing, Inc.
Peppas, Lynn. Tractors at Work. 2010. (Vehicles on the Move Ser.). (ENG.). 32p. (J). (gr. k-3). lib. bdg. *(978-0-7787-3050-7(6))* Crabtree Publishing Co.
Portman, Michael. Chargers. 2011. (Wild Wheels Ser.). (Illus.). 32p. (J). (gr. 3-6). pap. 10.50 *(978-1-4339-4740-7(4)*, Stevens, Gareth Learning Library) Stevens, Gareth Publishing LLLP.

AUTOMOBILES—LAW AND LEGISLATION

Automobile Arbitration Fairness ACT of 2008: Hearing Before the Subcommittee on Commercial & Administrative Law of the Committee on the Judiciary, House of Representatives, One Hundred Tenth Congress, Second Session, on H.R. 5312, March 6, 2008. 2009. iv, 109p. *(978-0-16-082583-5(0)*, 552-070-38604-1) United States Government Printing Office.
Brownell, Tom & Scott, Jason. How to Restore Your Collector Car. 2nd rev. ed. 2009. (Motorbooks Workshop Ser.). (ENG., Illus.). 272p. pap. 29.99 *(978-0-7603-3541-3(9)*, 0760335419, Motorbooks) MBI Publishing Co. LLC.
Butterworth Staff, compiled by. Butterworths Legislation Service: Motor Vehicle Accidents Act 84 of 1986. Date not set. *(978-0-409-01433-4(8)*, MICHIE) LEXIS Publishing.
—Butterworths Legislation Service: Multilateral Motor Vehicle Accidents Fund Act 93 of 1989. Date not set. *(978-0-409-01434-1(6)*, MICHIE) LEXIS Publishing.
Button, James & Button, James T. H. Button on Taxis: Licensig Law & Practice. 3rd ed. 2009. 1120p. pap. 165.00 *(978-1-84766-055-8(X)*, Bloomsbury Professional) Bloomsbury Publishing Plc GBR. Dist: International Specialized Bk. Services.
Coorpender, Bruce, ed. Pocket Guide to Georgia Traffic Laws. 2011. (ENG.). 166p. per. 8.99 *(978-1-884493-70-6(X))* Pocket Pr., Inc.
Design Patents & Auto Replacement Parts: Hearing Before the Committee on the Judiciary, House of Representatives, One Hundred Eleventh Congress, Second Session, March 22, 2010. 2010. (Illus.). iii, 139p. *(978-0-16-087075-0(5)*, 552-070-41932-2) United States Government Printing Office.
Digest of Motor Laws 2007 Edition. 2007. pap. *(978-1-59508-206-0(9))* AAA.
Examining S. 3302, the Motor Vehicle Safety ACT of 2010: Hearing Before the Committee on Commerce, Science, & Transportation, United States Senate, One Hundred Eleventh Congress, Second Session, May 19, 2010. 2011. (Illus.). iii, 98p. ***(978-0-16-089042-0(X)***, 552-070-43074-1) United States Government Printing Office.
Gould Publications Staff. California Vehicle Code. annuals. stu. ed. 6.00 *(978-0-87526-292-5(9))* Gould Pubns., Inc.
Grange, Janet L., et al, eds. Car, Travel & Entertainment & Home Office Deductions CPE Course. 2006th rev. ed. 2006. (Illus.). 301p. per. 47.50 *(978-0-8080-1485-0(4)*, 0-5996-400) Toolkit Media Group.
Huse, Harry C. Motor Vehicle Laws of the State of Washington. 109p. reprint ed. lib. bdg. 88.00 *(978-0-7222-0589-1(9))* Library Reprints, Inc.
Identification Security: Reevaluating the REAL ID ACT: Hearing Before the Committee on Homeland Security & Governmental Affairs, United States Senate, of the One Hundred Eleventh Congress, First Session, July 15, 2009. 2011. (Illus.). iv, 170p. ***(978-0-16-088994-3(4)***, 552-070-43026-1) United States Government Printing Office.
Kenney, Raymond J. & Farris, Teresa J. Motor Vehicle Law & Practice: And Related Topics with Forms, 2 vols. 4th ed. 2008. (Massachusetts Practice Ser.: Vols. 11-12). (Illus.). *(978-0-314-99907-8(8))*; *(978-0-314-99908-5(6))* West Publishing Co., College & Schl. Div.
Looseleaf Law Publications, creator. Vehicle & Traffic Laws, NYS Paperback. 2010. 674p. pap. 19.95 *(978-1-932777-59-8(8)*, LLP) Looseleaf Law Pubns., Inc.
Looseleaf Law Publications, suppl. CT Motor Vehicles Law Condensed Guide. 2011. (ENG.). 10.95 *(978-0-930137-68-7(X)*, LLP) Looseleaf Law Pubns., Inc.
—Vehicle & Traffic Law Condensed Guide. 2009. (New York State Ser.). ring bd. 9.95 *(978-0-930137-17-5(5))* Looseleaf Law Pubns., Inc.
—Vehicle & Traffic Law/ NYC Traffic Rules. 2010. ring bd. 36.95 *(978-0-930137-77-9(9)*, LLP) Looseleaf Law Pubns., Inc.

New Jersey Motor Vehicles - Condensed Guide. 2009. ring bd. 9.95 *(978-0-930137-93-9(0))* Looseleaf Law Pubns., Inc.

Nichols, James L. & Ledingham, Katherine A. The Impact of Legislation, Enforcement, & Sanctions on Safety Belt Use. 2008. (Illus.). 68p. pap. 41.00 *(978-0-309-09912-7(9))* Transportation Research Board.

Noshita, Fumio. Shitsumu Shiryo Doro Kotsuho Kaisetsu. 15th ed. 2010. (JPN., Illus.). 10p. *(978-4-8090-1237-2(9))* Tokyo Horei Shuppan.

OECD Staff, ed. Moving Freight with Better Trucks. 2011. (Illus.). 356p. pap. ***(978-92-821-0293-0(9))*** Organization for Economic Cooperation & Development.

Pierse, Robert. Road Traffic Law: The 1961-2011 Road Traffic Acts - Annotated Legislation. 3rd ed. 2011. 688p. pap. 235.00 ***(978-1-84766-734-2(1)***, Bloomsbury Professional) Bloomsbury Publishing Plc GBR. Dist: International Specialized Bk. Services.

Pocket Press. Pocket Guide to Kentucky Traffic Laws. 2011. (ENG.). 120p. per. 8.99 net. *(978-1-884493-94-2(7))* Pocket Pr., Inc.

Pocket Press, ed. Pocket Guide to Alabama Traffic Laws. 2004th ed. 2011. (ENG.). 144p. pap. 8.99 *(978-1-884493-52-2(1))* Pocket Pr., Inc.

—Pocket Guide to Arizona Traffic Laws. 2011. (ENG.). 132p. per. 8.99 *(978-1-884493-95-9(5))* Pocket Pr., Inc.

—Pocket Guide to Louisiana Traffic Laws. 2011. (ENG.). 164p. per. 8.99 net. *(978-1-884493-97-3(1))* Pocket Pr., Inc.

—Pocket Guide to Michigan Traffic Laws. 2012. (ENG.). 148p. per. 8.99 net. *(978-1-884493-93-5(9))* Pocket Pr., Inc.

—Pocket Guide to New Jersey Traffic Laws. 2004th ed. 2012. (ENG.). 194p. pap. 8.99 *(978-1-884493-55-3(6))* Pocket Pr., Inc.

—Pocket Guide to New York Traffic Laws. 2012. (ENG.). 164p. pap. 8.99 *(978-1-884493-98-0(X))* Pocket Pr., Inc.

—Pocket Guide to Oregon Traffic Laws. 2004th ed. 2012. (ENG.). 224p. per. 8.99 *(978-1-884493-29-4(7))* Pocket Pr., Inc.

—Pocket Guide to Tennessee Traffic Laws. 2004th ed. 2011. (ENG.). 176p. pap. 8.99 *(978-1-884493-51-5(3))* Pocket Pr., Inc.

—Pocket Guide to Virginia Traffic Laws. 2011. (ENG.). 160p. per. 8.99 net. *(978-1-884493-85-0(8))* Pocket Pr., Inc.

—Pocket Guide to Washington Traffic Laws. 2004th ed. 2011. (ENG.). 208p. pap. 8.99 *(978-1-884493-43-0(2))* Pocket Pr., Inc.

Sandalow, David B., ed. Plug-in Electric Vehicles: What Role for Washington? 2009. (ENG., Illus.). 260p. 29.95 *(978-0-8157-0305-1(8))* Brookings Institution Pr.

Sullivan, Ronald T. CT Motor Vehicle Field Manual: Blue Book. 2011. 166p. ring bd. 10.95 *(978-0-930137-74-8(4)*, LLP) Looseleaf Law Pubns., Inc.

Utah Criminal. Motor Vehicles & Related Statutes. annuals rev. ed. 630p. (C). pap. 24.95 *(978-0-87526-558-2(8))* Gould Pubns., Inc.

Welzel, Mirko. Kooperation und vertikale Wettbewerbsbeschränkungen in selektiven Vertriebssystemen: Das Beispiel des europäischen Automobilvertriebs. 2008. (Europäische Hochschulschriften. Reihe 5: Volks- und Betriebswirtschaft Ser.). 266p. pap. 65.95 *(978-3-631-57972-5(1))* Lang, Peter GmbH, Europäischer Verlag der Wissenschaften DEU. Dist: Lang, Peter.

2010 Vehicle Code Abridge CA- 2010. 368p. pap. 19.99 *(978-1-56325-155-9(8))* Lawtech Publishing Co., Ltd.

2010 Vehicle Code Unabridged CA- 2010. 672p. pap. 23.99 *(978-1-56325-158-0(2))* Lawtech Publishing Co., Ltd.

2010 Vehicle Qwik-Code CA- 2010. 96p. pap. 15.99 *(978-1-56325-151-1(5))* Lawtech Publishing Co., Ltd.

AUTOMOBILES—LEASING

see Automobiles, Rental

AUTOMOBILES—LICENSES

see also Automobile Drivers' Licenses; Automobile License Plates

2007 License Plate Guide: Current Standard Passenger Vehicle License Plates for the United States & Canada. 2007. (J). 14.95 *(978-0-9766236-2-5(5))* KGS America LLC.

AUTOMOBILES—LIGHTING

Berghmans, Francis. Optical Sensors 2008: 7-10 April 2008, Strasbourg, France. 2008. (Proceedings of SPIE Ser.). (Illus.). 746p. pap. 165.00 *(978-0-8194-7201-4(8))* SPIE.

Card, Peter W. Early Vehicle Lighting. 2nd ed. 2008. (Shire Library). (ENG., Illus.). 56p. pap. 12.95 *(978-0-7478-0585-4(7))* Shire Pubns., Ltd. GBR. Dist: Random Hse., Inc.

Wördenweber, Burkhard, et al. Automotive Lighting & Human Vision. 2010. (ENG & ABK., Illus.). xviii, 410p. pap. 139.00 *(978-3-642-07177-5(5)*, 3642071775) Springer.

Wördenweber, Burkard, et al. Automotive Lighting & Human Vision. 2007. (ENG., Illus.). xviii, 410p. 139.00 *(978-3-540-36696-6(2)*, 3540366962) Springer.

AUTOMOBILES—LUBRICATION

American Society of Mechanical Engineers Staff, ed. Gearbox Noise & Vibration. 200p. 104.00 *(978-0-85298-718-6(8))* Professional Engineering Publishing GBR. Dist: SAE Intl.

Chek-Chart Staff. Master Lubrication Handbook, 1985. (Illus.). 1000p. stu. ed. 90.00 *(978-0-88098-059-3(1))*; suppl. ed. 85.45 *(978-0-88098-075-3(3))* Prentice Hall Bks. (Gousha, H. M. Maps & Atlases).

Lube Recommendations & Capacities Booklet, 1986. 48p. stu. ed. 5.55 *(978-0-88098-084-5(2)*, Gousha, H. M. Maps & Atlases) Prentice Hall Bks.

Master Lubrication Handbook. rev. ed. (Illus.). 900p. stu. ed. 90.00 *(978-0-88098-079-1(6)*, Gousha, H. M. Maps & Atlases) Prentice Hall Bks.

Master Lubrication Handbook, 1987. rev. ed. stu. ed. 96.80 *(978-0-88098-095-1(8)*, Gousha, H. M. Maps & Atlases) Prentice Hall Bks.

Master Lubrication Handbook Supplement. rev. ed. stu. ed. 74.25 *(978-0-88098-080-7(X)*, Gousha, H. M. Maps & Atlases) Prentice Hall Bks.

Master Lubrication Handbook Supplement, 1987. rev. ed. stu. ed. 76.50 *(978-0-88098-094-4(X)*, Gousha, H. M. Maps & Atlases) Prentice Hall Bks.

Tractor & Farm Implement & Lubrication Guide, 1986. (Illus.). 192p. stu. ed. 39.40 *(978-0-88098-082-1(6)*, Gousha, H. M. Maps & Atlases) Prentice Hall Bks.

Truck Lubrication Guide, 1986. (Illus.). 96p. stu. ed. 34.75 *(978-0-88098-083-8(4)*, Gousha, H. M. Maps & Atlases) Prentice Hall Bks.

AUTOMOBILES—MAINTENANCE AND REPAIR

Ahlstrand, Alan. Ford Escort & Tracer: 1991 Thru 2000. 2009. (ENG.). 384p. pap. 29.95 *(978-1-56392-783-6(7))* Haynes,Chilton.

—Mazda MX-5 Miata: 1990 Thru 2009. 2010. (ENG.). 400p. pap. 29.95 *(978-1-56392-886-4(8))* Haynes,Chilton.

—Mitsubishi Eclipse: 1999 Thru 2005. 2009. (ENG.). 512p. pap. 29.95 *(978-1-56392-738-6(1))* Haynes,Chilton.

Ahlstrand, Alan & Freund, Ken. Kawasaki EN450, 500 Twins & Ninja 250, 1985-2007. 2007. (Automotive Repair Manual Ser.). (ENG., Illus.). 240p. pap. 45.45 *(978-1-56392-667-9(9)*, 1563926679) Haynes Manuals, Inc.

Ahlstrand, Alan, et al. Honda XR50R, XR70R, XR80R, XR100R & CRF50F, CRF70F, CRF80F, CRF100F, 1985 Thru 2007. 2007. (Motorcycle Repair Manual Ser.). (ENG., Illus.). 160p. per. 33.95 *(978-1-56392-657-0(1)*, 1563926571) Haynes Manuals, Inc.

—Toyota Corolla & Holden Nova Automotive Repair Manual. (Illus.). 288p. *(978-1-56392-260-2(6))* Haynes Manuals, Inc.

Allwood, Mel & Hopkins, Jenn. Maintaining Mountain Bikes: The Do-It-Yourself Guide. 2nd ed. 2010. (ENG., Illus.). 256p. pap. 29.95 *(978-1-55407-604-8(8))* Firefly Bks., Ltd.

Astley, Rick. Classic British Car Electrical Systems: Your guide to understanding, repairing & improving the electrical components & systems that were typical of British cars from 1950 To 1980. 2009. (Essential Ser.). (ENG., Illus.). 176p. pap. 49.95 *(978-1-84584-215-4(4)*, 1845842154) Veloce Publishing Ltd. GBR. Dist: MBI Distribution Services/Quayside Distribution.

—MGB Electricals Systems. 2009. (Essential Manual Ser.). (ENG., Illus.). 192p. pap. 54.95 *(978-1-84584-229-1(4)*, 1845842294) Veloce Publishing Ltd. GBR. Dist: MBI Distribution Services/Quayside Distribution.

Atherton, Larry & Schreib, Larry. How to Rebuild the Small Block Chevrolet. 2nd rev. ed. 2009. 160p. pap. 24.95 *(978-1-934709-00-9(X)*, S-A Design) CarTech, Inc.

Augenstein, David M. The Shop Environmental Awareness Training Guide for Mechanics & Technicians: A Self-Study Guide of Environmental Rules & Practices for Vehicle/Equipment Maintenance & Refueling Operations. Date not set. 45p. (C). pap. 17.80 *(978-0-9644663-3-3(3))* Environmental Development Corp.

Augenstein, David M. & Swartz, George, eds. Shop Safety/OSHA Compliance Guide for Managers of Motor Vehicle/Equipment Maintenance & Refueling Operations: A Standard Industry Reference on OSHA Compliance & Recommended Safety Practices. Date not set. (Illus.). 358p. (C). pap. 239.00 *(978-0-9644663-4-0(1))* Environmental Development Corp.

Auto Mechanics. cd-rom 910.95 *(978-1-56191-793-8(1))*; cd-rom 910.95 *(978-1-56191-794-5(X))* Films Media Group.

Autobooks, creator. Fiat 128 1969-1982 Owners Workshop Manual. 2008. 144p. pap. 34.95 *(978-1-58850-008-3(X))* Veloce Enterprises, Inc.

—Fiat 1300, 1500 1961-1967 Owners Workshop Manual. 2008. (Illus.). 156p. pap. 34.95 *(978-1-58850-010-6(1))* Veloce Enterprises, Inc.

—Mercedes-Benz 280 1968-1972 Owners Workshop Manual. 2010. (Illus.). 198p. pap. 34.95 *(978-1-58850-096-0(9))* Veloce Enterprises, Inc.

Autodata. 2007 Domestic Diagnostic Trouble Code Manual (1994-2007) 3rd ed. 2006. pap. 83.95 *(978-1-893026-35-3(3))* Delmar Cengage Learning.

—2007 Import Diagnostic Trouble Code Manual (1994-2007) 3rd ed. 2006. pap. 83.95 *(978-1-893026-36-0(1))* Delmar Cengage Learning.

—2007 Key Programming & Service Indicators (Coverage 96-07) 2006. pap. 83.95 *(978-1-893026-37-7(X))* Delmar Cengage Learning.

Banish, Greg. Engine Management: Advanced Tuning. 2007. (S-A Design Ser.). (ENG., Illus.). 128p. pap. 24.95 *(978-1-932494-42-6(1)*, S-A Design) CarTech, Inc.

Ben-Ari, Dani. Car Ownership for Women. 2010. 88p. pap. 10.49 *(978-1-4520-1527-9(9))* AuthorHouse.

Benfield, Matt. Radio Control Car Manual: The Complete Guide to Buying, Building & Maintaining. 2008. (ENG., Illus.). 176p. 36.95 *(978-1-84425-470-5(4)*, 1844254704) Haynes Publishing PLC GBR. Dist: MBI Distribution Services/Quayside Distribution.

Benford, Tom. Weekend Projects for Your Classic Corvette 1953-1982. 2010. (Motorbooks Workshop Ser.). (ENG., Illus.). 224p. pap. 29.99 *(978-0-7603-3758-5(6)*, 0760337586, Motorbooks) MBI Publishing Co. LLC.

—Weekend Projects for Your Modern Corvette: C4, C5, & C6. 2009. (Motorbooks Workshop Ser.). (ENG., Illus.). 224p. pap. 29.99 *(978-0-7603-3540-6(0)*, 0760335400, Motorbooks) MBI Publishing Co. LLC.

Bennett, Mark. Porsche Boxster & Cayman: Everything You Need to Know about Your Boxster or Cayman. 2010. (Ultimate Buyers' Guide Ser.). (ENG., Illus.). 104p. pap. 35.95 *(978-1-906712-01-3(8)*, 1906712018, PMM Bks.) Morgan, Peter Media Ltd. GBR. Dist: MBI Distribution Services/Quayside Distribution.

Bentley Publishers. Audi A4 (B6, B7) Service Manual: 1. 8L turbo, 2. 0L turbo, 3. 0L, 3. 2L, including Avant & Cabriolet: 2002, 2003, 2004, 2005, 2006, 2007 2008. 2010. (Illus.). 1430p. 149.95 *(978-0-8376-1574-5(7))* Bentley Pubs.

—Audi TT Service Manual: 1. 8L turbo, 3. 2L; including roadster & Quattro: 2000-2006. 2006. (Illus.). 978p. pap. 99.95 *(978-0-8376-1500-4(3)*, AT06) Bentley Pubs.

—BMW 3 Series Service Manual (E90, E91, E92, E93) 2006, 2007, 2008, 2009 Service Manual: 325i, 325xi, 328i, 328xi, 330i, 330xi, 335i, 335xi: 2006 2007, 2008 2009. 2009. (Illus.). 1256p. pap. 129.95 *(978-0-8376-1608-7(5))* Bentley Pubs.

—BMW 5 Series Service Manual: 525i, 528i, 530i, 535i, 545i, 550i: 2004, 2005, 2006, 2007, 2008, 2009 2010: 2004, 2005, 2006, 2007, 2008, 2009 2010. 2010. (Illus.). 1734p. 149.95 *(978-0-8376-1621-6(2))* Bentley Pubs.

—Mercedes-Benz C-Class (W202) Service Manual: C220, C230, C230 Kompressor, C280. 2009. (Illus.). 1216p. pap. 129.95 *(978-0-8376-1572-1(0))* Bentley Pubs.

—MINI Cooper - Diagnosis Without Guesswork: Cooper, Cooper S. 2009. (Illus.). 336p. pap. 59.95 *(978-0-8376-1571-4(2))* Bentley Pubs.

—MINI Cooper (R55, R56, R57) Service Manual: Cooper, Cooper S, John Cooper Works (JSW), including Clubman & Convertible: 2007, 2008, 2009, 2010 2011. 2011. (Illus.). 1058p. 139.95 ***(978-0-8376-1671-1(9))*** Bentley Pubs.

—Volkswagen Jetta (A5) Service Manual: 1. 9L & 2. 0L diesel, 2. 0L & 2. 5L gasoline; including TDI, gli & SportWagen: 2005, 2006, 2007, 2008, 2009 2010: 2005, 2006, 2007, 2008, 2009 2010. 2009. (Illus.). 1352p. lib. bdg. 129.95 *(978-0-8376-1616-2(6))* Bentley Pubs.

—Volkswagen Jetta (A5) Service Manual 2005 - 2008: 1. 9L TDI, 2. 0L FSI, 2. 5L, Including gli & Sportwagen. 2008. (ENG., Illus.). 1016p. pap. 99.95 *(978-0-8376-1558-5(5))* Bentley Pubs.

—Volkswagen New Beetle Service Manual: Including Convertible. 2008. (Illus.). 1640p. pap. 109.95 *(978-0-8376-1559-2(3))* Bentley Pubs.

—Volkswagen Rabbit, GTI (A5) Service Manual: 2. 0l Fsi, 2. 5l: 2006-2009. 2008. (Illus.). pap. 109.95 *(978-0-8376-1560-8(7))* Bentley Pubs.

Bentley Publishers, creator. BMW X5 Service Manual: 3. 0i, 4. 4i, 4. 6is, 4. 8is. 2008. (Illus.). 1240p. per. 129.95 *(978-0-8376-1534-9(8))* Bentley Pubs.

—Mini Cooper Service Manual 2002-2006: Cooper, Cooper S, Including Convertible. 2007. (Illus.). 1084p. per. 119.95 *(978-0-8376-1511-0(9)*, MC06) Bentley Pubs.

—Toyota Prius Repair & Maintenance Manual. 2008. (Illus.). 600p. 69.95 *(978-0-8376-1553-0(4))* Bentley Pubs.

Bill, Trovato. How to Build Max Performance Oldsmobile V-8s. 2010. 128p. pap. 24.95 *(978-1-934709-04-7(2)*, S-A Design) CarTech, Inc.

Birch, Thomas W. Automatic Transmissions & Transaxles. 5th rev. ed. 2011. (ENG., Illus.). 576p. (C). pap. 118.00 ***(978-0-13-262227-1(0)***, Prentice Hall) Prentice Hall PTR.

BMW. Bmw Motorcycles Factory Workshop Manual R26 R27. 2007. 164p. per. 29.95 *(978-1-58850-068-7(3))* Veloce Enterprises, Inc.

Bonnick, Allan. A Practical Approach to Motor Vehicle Engineering & Maintenance. 3rd rev. ed. 2011. (ENG., Illus.). 504p. pap. 41.95 *(978-0-08-096998-5(4))* Routledge.

Borg, Kevin L. Auto Mechanics: Technology & Expertise in Twentieth-Century America. (Studies in Industry & Society Ser.). (ENG., Illus.). 280p. (gr. 17). 2010. pap. 32.00 *(978-0-8018-9485-5(9))* 2007. 50.00 *(978-0-8018-8606-5(6))* Johns Hopkins Univ. Pr.

Bracken, Bob. Hot Rods, Pink-Bellies & Hank Ballard. 2008. 139p. pap. 24.95 *(978-1-60563-600-9(2))* PublishAmerica, Inc.

Brand, Paul. How to Repair Your Car. rev. ed. 2006. (Motorbooks Workshop Ser.). (ENG., Illus.). 224p. pap. 21.99 *(978-0-7603-2273-4(2)*, 0760322732, Motorbooks) MBI Publishing Co. LLC.

—How to Repair Your Pickup or SUV. 2008. (Motorbooks Workshop Ser.). (ENG., Illus.). 224p. pap. 19.99 *(978-0-7603-3320-4(3)*, 0760333203, Motorbooks) MBI Publishing Co. LLC.

Breslin, Mike. The Track Day Manual. 2008. (ENG., Illus.). 176p. 36.95 *(978-1-84425-482-8(8)*, 1844254828) Haynes Publishing PLC GBR. Dist: MBI Distribution Services/Quayside Distribution.

Brewer, Wesley C. & Brewer, Annie M. The Glove Box Auto Reviver. (Illus.). 350p. (Orig.). spiral bd. 24.95 *(978-0-938641-01-8(8))* Chaparral Productions.

Brice, Alwyn. Something for the Weekend? 2010. 154p. 29.99 *(978-1-4535-1457-3(0))*; pap. 19.99 *(978-1-4535-1456-6(2))* Xlibris Corp.

British Leyland Motors Staff. MGB Tourer, GT & V8 Parts Catalogue 1962-1976. (Illus.). 440p. (Orig.). 60.00 *(978-0-8376-0505-0(9))* Bentley Pubs.

—Range Rover Workshop Manual, 1986-1989. (Illus.). pap. 90.00 *(978-0-8376-0606-4(3)*, YVW3) Bentley Pubs.

—Range Rover Workshop Manual, 1990-1994. (Illus.). pap. 90.00 *(978-0-8376-0607-1(1)*, YVW4) Bentley Pubs.

—Triumph GT6 Mk III Parts Catalogue: 1971-1973. 140p. 40.00 *(978-0-8376-0523-4(7))* Bentley Pubs.

—The Triumph TR2 & TR3 Spare Parts Catalogue, 1953-1963. 374p. 55.00 *(978-0-8376-0533-3(4))* Bentley Pubs.

—Triumph TR250 Spare Parts Catalogue, 1968. 259p. 55.00 *(978-0-8376-0507-4(5))* Bentley Pubs.

—Triumph TR4 Spare Parts Catalogue, 1961-1964. 319p. 55.00 *(978-0-8376-0546-3(6))* Bentley Pubs.

—Triumph TR4A Spare Parts Catalogue, 1965-1967. 336p. (Orig.). 55.00 *(978-0-8376-0556-2(3))* Bentley Pubs.

—Triumph TR6 Driver's Handbook (U. S. Spec), 1970. 16.00 *(978-0-8376-0562-3(8))* Bentley Pubs.

—Triumph TR6 Spare Parts Catalogue, 1974-1976. 280p. 55.00 *(978-0-8376-0553-1(9))* Bentley Pubs.

—Triumph TR7 Spare Parts Catalogue, 1979-1981. (Illus.). 420p. 60.00 *(978-0-8376-0567-8(9))* Bentley Pubs.

Brooklands Books & VelocePress, prods. Bugatti - Road Test Portfolio. 2010. 482p. pap. 89.95 *(978-1-58850-099-1(3))* Veloce Enterprises, Inc.

Bunzer, Gary. RV Owner's Handbook. 4th ed. 2009. (ENG.). 338p. pap. 24.95 *(978-0-7627-5141-9(X))* Globe Pequot Pr., The.

Burt, William. How to Rebuild the Small-Block Mopar. 2008. (Sa Design Ser.). (Illus.). 144p. pap. 24.95 *(978-1-932494-54-9(5))* CarTech, Inc.

Car Care Guide, 1986. rev. ed. (Illus.). 424p. stu. ed. 39.95 *(978-0-88098-081-4(8)*, Gousha, H. M. Maps & Atlases) Prentice Hall Bks.

Carter, Carolyn L., et al. Automobile Fraud: Odometer Tampering, Lemon Laundering, & Concealment of Salvage or Other Adverse History. 3rd ed. 2007. (Illus.). xxxv, 636p. pap. *(978-1-60248-011-7(7))* National Consumer Law Ctr., The.

Cdx Global Staff. Natef Automotive Task Sheets. rev. ed. 2010. 74p. pap. 26.95 *(978-0-7637-8512-3(1))* Jones & Bartlett Learning, LLC.

—Natef Automotive Task Sheets: Auto Transmission. rev. ed. 2010. 76p. pap. 26.95 *(978-0-7637-8499-7(0))* Jones & Bartlett Learning, LLC.

—Natef Automotive Task Sheets: Manual Drive Train. rev. ed. 2010. 114p. pap. 26.95 *(978-0-7637-8511-6(3))* Jones & Bartlett Learning, LLC.

Cerich, Jose, et al. Jeep Cherokee, Wagoneer & Comanche 1984 Al 2000. 2007. (Manual de Reparacion Ser.). (SPA & ENG., Illus.). 368p. per. 24.95 *(978-1-56392-492-7(7)*, 1563924927) Haynes Manuals, Inc.

Chilton. Chilton 2012 Labor Guide: Domestic & Imported Vehicles - CD-ROM. 2011. (ENG.). 234.95 ***(978-1-4354-6154-3(1))*** Delmar Cengage Learning.

—Chilton Asian Service Manual Vol. 3: Infiniti, Nissan, 5 vols. 2011. (ENG., Illus.). 1680p. 79.95 *(978-1-111-03766-6(3))* Delmar Cengage Learning.

—Chilton Asian Service Manuals. 2008. 5731p. 299.95 *(978-1-4283-2214-1(0))*; 2064p. 99.95 *(978-1-4283-2220-2(5))* Delmar Cengage Learning.

—Chilton European Service Manual 2010: Audi, BMW, Mercedes-Benz, Mini, Saab, Volkswagen, Volvo. 2011. (ENG., Illus.). 2304p. 99.95 *(978-1-111-03769-7(8))* Delmar Cengage Learning.

—Chilton Total Car Care Domestic Vehicles. 2006. (Chilton Total Car Care Series CDs Ser.). (ENG.). 19.95 *(978-1-4180-3202-9(6))* Delmar Cengage Learning.

—Chilton 2006 Asian Diagnostic Service Manual Series. 2006. (Chilton Diagnostic Manuals Ser.). 239.85 *(978-1-4180-2986-9(6))* Delmar Cengage Learning.

—General Motors Astro/Safari 1985-2005 Repair Manual. 2009. (ENG.). 432p. pap. 29.95 *(978-1-56392-697-6(0))* Haynes,Chilton.

Chilton, (Chilton). Chilton Asian Service Manual 2008. 2008. (ENG.). Vol. 1. 1728p. 79.95 *(978-1-4283-2215-8(9))* Vol. 4. 1968p. 79.95 *(978-1-4283-2218-9(3))* Delmar Cengage Learning.

—Chilton Asian Service Manual, 2010, 5 vols., Vol. 1. 2011. (ENG., Illus.). 1536p. 79.95 *(978-1-111-03764-2(7))* Delmar Cengage Learning.

—Chilton Asian Service Manual 2010: Hyundai, Kia, Lexus, Vol. 2. 2011. (ENG., Illus.). 2424p. 79.95 *(978-1-111-03765-9(5))* Delmar Cengage Learning.

—Chilton Asian Service Manual 2010 Vol. 4: Mazda, Mitsubishi, Subaru, Suzuki, 5 vols. 2011. (ENG., Illus.). 2448p. 79.95 *(978-1-111-03767-3(1))* Delmar Cengage Learning.

—Chilton Asian Service Manual 2010 Vol. 5: Scion, Toyota. 2011. (ENG.). 2040p. 79.95 *(978-1-111-03768-0(X))* Delmar Cengage Learning.

—Chilton Chrysler Service Manual, 2010 Edition (2 Volume Set) 2010. (ENG.). 2016p. 149.95 *(978-1-111-03654-6(3))* Delmar Cengage Learning.

—Chilton General Motors Service Manual 2008, Vol. 1 & 2. 2007. (ENG.). 2264p. 169.95 *(978-1-4283-2211-0(6))* Delmar Cengage Learning.

—Chilton Labor Guide 2008: Domestic & Import Set. 2007. (ENG.). 2536p. 199.95 *(978-1-4283-2035-2(0))* Delmar Cengage Learning.

—Chilton Labor Guide 2009 Set: Domestic & Imported Vehicles. 2008. (ENG.). 209.95 *(978-1-4354-6965-5(8))* Delmar Cengage Learning.

Chilton Automotive Editorial Staff. Asian Diagnostic Service Manual 2006, Vol. 3. 2006. (Chilton Diagnostic Manuals Ser.). (ENG., Illus.). 1032p. 79.95 *(978-1-4180-2915-9(7))* Delmar Cengage Learning.

—Chilton Asian Mechanical Service: Subaru-Toyota. 2006. (Chilton Mechanical Manuals Ser.). (ENG., Illus.). 1944p. 79.95 *(978-1-4180-0949-6(0))* Delmar Cengage Learning.

—Chilton Asian Mechanical Service Vol. II: Kia-Nissan. 2006. (Chilton Mechanical Manuals Ser.). (ENG., Illus.). 1872p. 79.95 *(978-1-4180-0948-9(2))* Delmar Cengage Learning.

—Chilton Asian Service Manual 2008. 2008. (ENG.). Vol. 2. 1920p. 79.95 *(978-1-4283-2216-5(7))* Vol. 3. 2256p. 79.95 *(978-1-4283-2217-2(5))* Delmar Cengage Learning.

—Chilton Daimler Chrysler Service Manual 2008, Vol. 1 & 2, Set. 2007. (ENG.). 2400p. 149.95 *(978-1-4283-2204-2(3))* Delmar Cengage Learning.

—Chilton Ford Service Manual 2008, 2 vols., Vols. 1 & 2. 2008th ed. 2007. (ENG.). 250p. 159.95 *(978-1-4283-2208-0(6))* Delmar Cengage Learning.

—Chilton Ford Service Manual, 2010 Edition (2 Volume Set) 2010. (ENG.). 2672p. 159.95 *(978-1-111-03657-7(8))* Delmar Cengage Learning.

—Chilton General Motors Service Manual, 2010 Edition (3 Volume Set) 2010. (ENG.). 3576p. 189.95 *(978-1-111-03661-4(6))* Delmar Cengage Learning.

—Chilton Labor Guide. 2010. (ENG.). 229.95 *(978-1-111-03611-9(X))* Delmar Cengage Learning.

—Chilton Labor Guide 2008. 2007. (ENG.). 199.95 *(978-1-4283-2041-3(5))* Delmar Cengage Learning.

—Domestic & Import Labor Guide, 1982-96. 1800p. 147.00 *(978-0-8019-8724-3(5))* Nichols Publishing Co.

—Domestic Auto Service Manual, 1992-96. 2504p. 100.00 *(978-0-8019-8726-7(1))* Nichols Publishing Co.
—Domestic Labor Guide & Parts Manual, 1992-96. 1632p. 97.00 *(978-0-8019-8727-4(X))* Nichols Publishing Co.
—European Diagnostic Service 2006. 2006. (Chilton Diagnostic Manuals Ser.). (ENG., Illus.). 888p. 79.95 *(978-1-4180-2924-1(6))* Delmar Cengage Learning.
—European Mechanical Service Manual 2006. 2006. (Chilton Mechanical Manuals Ser.). (ENG., Illus.). 1152p. 89.95 *(978-1-4180-0604-4(1))* Delmar Cengage Learning.
—Import Service Manual, 1991-95. 2304p. 100.00 *(978-0-8019-8696-3(6))* Nichols Publishing Co.
Chilton Editors. Chilton 2006 Asian Diagnostic Service Vol. 1, Vol. 1. 2006. (Chilton Diagnostic Manuals Ser.). (ENG., Illus.). 768p. 79.95 *(978-1-4180-2913-5(0))* Delmar Cengage Learning.
—Chilton Asian Diagnostic Service Manual 2006, Vol. 2. 2006. (Chilton Diagnostic Manuals Ser.). (ENG., Illus.). 984p. 79.95 *(978-1-4180-2914-2(9))* Delmar Cengage Learning.
Chittenden, Gordon. Performance Tuning the Sunbeam Tiger. 2006. (Illus.). 140p. per. 39.95 *(978-1-58850-062-5(4))* Veloce Enterprises, Inc.
Clarke & Beadle, R. M. & T., creator. Delahaye - Road Test Portfolio. 2010. 142p. pap. 29.95 *(978-1-58850-095-3(0))* Veloce Enterprises, Inc.
Clarke, R. M., compiled by. Jaguar XK8 & XKR Performance Portfolio 1996-2005. 2008. (Performance Portfolio Ser.). (ENG., Illus.). 128p. pap. 24.95 *(978-1-85520-757-8(5)*, 1855207575) Brooklands Bks. GBR. Dist: MBI Distribution Services/Quayside Distribution.
—VW Corrado Limited Edition Premier. 2008. (Limited Edition Premier Ser.). (ENG., Illus.). 160p. pap. 32.95 *(978-1-85520-829-2(6)*, 1855208296) Brooklands Bks. GBR. Dist: MBI Distribution Services/Quayside Distribution.
Clemens, Kevin. VW GTI, Golf, & Jetta, Mk III & IV: Find It. Fix It. Trick It. rev. ed. 2006. (Motorbooks Workshop Ser.). (ENG., Illus.). 160p. per. 24.95 *(978-0-7603-2595-7(2)*, 0760325952, Motorbooks) MBI Publishing Co. LLC.
Clymer, F. Austin-Healey Owner's Handbook for the Maintenance & Repair of the 6-Cylinder Models 1956-1968. 2007. 264p. per. 39.95 *(978-1-58850-074-8(8))* Veloce Enterprises, Inc.
—Volkswagen Transporter 1950 - 1979 1200cc - 1600cc Workshop Manual. 2010. 410p. pap. 24.95 *(978-1-58850-152-3(3))* Veloce Enterprises, Inc.
Clymer, Floyd. Bmw Motorcycles Workshop Manual R50 R50s R60 R69s. 2007. (MUL.). 180p. per. 34.95 *(978-1-58850-067-0(5))* Veloce Enterprises, Inc.
—Porsche 356 Owners Workshop Manual 1948-1965. 2008. 216p. pap. 34.95 *(978-1-58850-100-4(0))* Veloce Enterprises, Inc.
—Porsche 912 Workshop Manual 1965-1968. 2008. 308p. pap. 29.95 *(978-1-58850-101-1(9))* Veloce Enterprises, Inc.
—Volvo 1944-1968 Workshop Manual Pv444, Pv544 , P1800, Pv445, P122 , P210, P130, P220, 144, 142 And 145. 2008. (Illus.). 464p. pap. 34.95 *(978-1-58850-067-6(1))* Veloce Enterprises, Inc.
Clymer Publications Staff. BMW K1200RS, LT & LT 1998-2010. 2011. pap. 51.95 ***(978-1-59969-412-2(3))*** Clymer Publishing.
—Honda TRX250 Recon & Recon ES, 1997-2007. 2008. pap. 34.95 *(978-1-59969-176-3(0))* Clymer Publishing.
—Honda Trx250 Recon & Recon Es 1997-2011. 2011. pap. 34.95 ***(978-1-59969-388-0(7))*** Clymer Publishing.
—Honda TRX400EX Fourtrax & Sportrax 1999-2007. 2008. pap. 34.95 *(978-1-59969-251-7(1))* Clymer Publishing.
—Honda TRX450R & TRX450ER 2004-2009. 2011. pap. 34.95 ***(978-1-59969-411-5(5))*** Clymer Publishing.
—Kawasaki Bayou KLF220 & KLF250 1988-2010. 2011. pap. 34.95 *(978-1-59969-376-7(3))* Clymer Publishing.
—Polaris 400, 450 & 500 Sportsman 1996-2008. 2008. pap. 45.95 *(978-1-59969-242-5(2))* Clymer Publishing.
—Polaris Magnum & Big Boss ATVs, 1996-1999. 2008. pap. 34.95 *(978-1-59969-224-1(4))* Clymer Publishing.
—Polaris Predator 2003-2007. 2008. pap. 34.95 *(978-1-59969-261-6(9))* Clymer Publishing.
—Suzuki GSX-R1000, 2005-2006. Grooms, James & Arens, Rick, eds. 2008. (Clymer Color Wiring Diagrams Ser.). (Illus.). 403p. per. 35.95 *(978-1-59969-195-4(7))* Clymer Publishing.
—Yamaha V-Star 1300 2007-2010. 2011. pap. 36.95 *(978-1-59969-379-8(8))* Clymer Publishing.
—Yamaha YFM80 Moto-4, Badger & Raptor 2001-2008. 2008. pap. 34.95 *(978-1-59969-236-4(8))* Clymer Publishing.
Clymer Staff. Clymer Yamaha V-Star 1100 1999-2007. 2007. (Clymer Color Wiring Diagrams Ser.). (Illus.). 403p. per. 34.95 *(978-1-59969-156-5(6))* Clymer Publishing.
Coombs, Matthew & Freund, Ken. Aprilia RSV 1000 Mille (inc. RSV-R) '98 To '03. 2007. (Haynes Service & Repair Manual Ser.). (ENG., Illus.). 256p. 45.45 *(978-1-84425-255-8(8)*, 1844252558) Haynes Manuals, Inc.
Coombs, Matthew & Mather, Phil. Suzuki: SV650 & SV650S '99 to '08. Haynes, Max, ed. 3rd ed. 2009. (Haynes Service & Repair Manual Ser.). (ENG., Illus.). 336p. 45.45 *(978-1-84425-767-6(3)*, 1844257673) Haynes Manuals, Inc.
Cooper, Towanda D. 99 Things Women Wish They Knew Before... Servicing Their Car: A Woman's Guide to Avoinding CostlyMaintenence Fees. 2010. (ENG.). 200p. pap. 12.95 *(978-1-60037-711-2(4))* Morgan James Publishing.
Cram101 Textbook Reviews. Outlines & Highlights for Collision Repair & Refinishing: A Foundation Course for Technicians by Alfred Thomas, ISBN. 2010. 320p. pap. 33.95 *(978-1-61654-565-9(8))* Cram101 Inc.
Cram101 Textbook Reviews. Outlines & Highlights for Collision Repair Fundamentals by James E Duffy. 2011. 234p. pap. 31.95 ***(978-1-61905-974-0(6))*** Cram101 Inc.
Cram101 Textbook Reviews & Cram101 Textbook Reviews. Outlines & Highlights for Modern Diesel Technology: Diesel Engines by Sean Bennett. 2011. 158p. pap. 29.95 ***(978-1-61830-941-9(2))*** Cram101 Inc.
Criswell, Jack. Porsche 911 (993) Carrera, Turbo & RS. 2010. (Ultimate Buyers' Guide Ser.). (ENG., Illus.). 160p. pap. 35.95 *(978-1-906712-06-8(9)*, 1906712069, PMM Bks.) Morgan, Peter Media Ltd. GBR. Dist: MBI Distribution Services/Quayside Distribution.
Delmar. ASE Test Preparation - A5 Brakes. 5th ed. 2011. (ENG., Illus.). 240p. pap. 23.95 *(978-1-111-12707-7(7))* Delmar Cengage Learning.
Delmar, (Delmar). ASE Test Preparation - A9 Light Vehicle Diesel Engines. 2011. (ENG., Illus.). 224p. pap. 23.95 *(978-1-111-12711-4(5))* Delmar Cengage Learning.
—ASE Test Preparation - C1 Service Consultant. 5th ed. 2011. (ENG.). 176p. pap. 23.95 *(978-1-111-12712-1(3))* Delmar Cengage Learning.
Delmar Cengage Learning. DATO: Diagnostic Scenarios for Electricity - Electronics. 2011. (Automotive Multimedia Solutions Ser.). (ENG.). (C). 49.95 *(978-1-111-03474-0(5))* Delmar Cengage Learning.
Delmar Cengage Learning Staff. DATO: Diagnostic Scenarios for Engine Performance. 2010. (Automotive Multimedia Solutions Ser.). (ENG.). (C). 49.95 *(978-1-111-03477-1(X))* Delmar Cengage Learning.
—DATO: Diagnostic Scenarios for Engine Repair. 2011. (Automotive Multimedia Solutions Ser.). (ENG.). (C). 41.95 *(978-1-111-03486-3(9))* Delmar Cengage Learning.
Delmar Learning Staff. Advanced Engine Performance Computer Based Training (CBT) 2008. (ENG.). 114.95 *(978-1-4283-2097-0(0))* Delmar Cengage Learning.
—ASE Test Preparation - A1 Engine Repair. 5th ed. 2011. (ENG.). 256p. pap. 23.95 *(978-1-111-12703-9(4))* Delmar Cengage Learning.
—ASE Test Preparation - A2 Automatic Transmissions & Transaxles. 5th ed. 2011. (ENG.). 176p. pap. 23.95 *(978-1-111-12704-6(2))* Delmar Cengage Learning.
—ASE Test Preparation - A3 Manual Drive Trains & Axles. 5th ed. 2011. (ENG., Illus.). 208p. pap. 23.95 *(978-1-111-12705-3(0))* Delmar Cengage Learning.
—ASE Test Preparation - A4 Suspension & Steering. 5th ed. 2011. (ENG., Illus.). 176p. pap. 23.95 *(978-1-111-12706-0(9))* Delmar Cengage Learning.
—ASE Test Preparation - A6 Electricity & Electronics. 5th ed. 2011. (ENG., Illus.). 256p. pap. 23.95 *(978-1-111-12708-4(5))* Delmar Cengage Learning.
—ASE Test Preparation - A8 Engine Performance. 5th ed. 2011. (ENG.). 192p. pap. 23.95 *(978-1-111-12710-7(7))* Delmar Cengage Learning.
—ASE Test Preparation - T2 Diesel Engines. 5th ed. 2011. (ENG.). 256p. pap. 23.95 *(978-1-111-12898-2(7))* Delmar Cengage Learning.
—ASE Test Preparation - T3 Drive Train. 5th ed. 2012. (ENG.). 176p. pap. 23.95 *(978-1-111-12899-9(5))* Delmar Cengage Learning.
—ASE Test Preparation - Transit Bus H2, Diesel Engines. 2007. (ENG., Illus.). 224p. per. 23.95 *(978-1-4180-6570-6(6))* Delmar Cengage Learning.
—ASE Test Preparation - Transit Bus H7, Heating, Ventilation, & Air Conditioning. 2007. (ENG.). 112p. pap. 23.95 *(978-1-4180-6571-3(4))* Delmar Cengage Learning.
—ASE Test Preparation - X1 Exhaust Systems. 5th ed. 2011. (ENG.). 176p. pap. 23.95 *(978-1-111-12715-2(8))* Delmar Cengage Learning.
—ASE Test Preparation Collision Repair & Refinish- Test B4: Structural Analysis & Damage Repair. 3rd rev. ed. 2006. (ENG., Illus.). 112p. per. 23.95 *(978-1-4018-3666-5(6))* Delmar Cengage Learning.
—Damage Analysis & Estimating Test B6. 3rd rev. ed. 2007. (ASE Test Prep for Collision Ser.). (ENG., Illus.). 144p. per. 23.95 *(978-1-4018-3668-9(2))* Delmar Cengage Learning.
—Engine Performance Classroom Manual, Vol 1 & Shop Manual, Vol. 2. 2007. (ENG.). 114.95 *(978-1-4180-4239-4(0))* Delmar Cengage Learning.
—Mechanical & Electrical Components Test B5. 3rd rev. ed. 2007. (ASE Test Prep for Collision Ser.). (ENG., Illus.). 176p. per. 23.95 *(978-1-4018-3667-2(4))* Delmar Cengage Learning.
—Preventive Maintenance Test H8. 2010. (ENG.). 160p. pap. 23.95 *(978-1-4354-3938-2(4))* Delmar Cengage Learning.
—Test B2 - Painting & Refinishing. 3rd rev. ed. 2006. (ASE Test Prep for Collision Ser.). (ENG., Illus.). 112p. per. 23.95 *(978-1-4018-3664-1(X))* Delmar Cengage Learning.
Delmar Learning Staff & Cengage Delmar Learning. Service Consultant. 2008. (ENG.). 114.95 *(978-1-4180-4247-9(1))* Delmar Cengage Learning.
Delmar Learning, Thomson. ASE Test Preparation - A7 Heating & Air Conditioning. 5th ed. 2011. (ENG., Illus.). 176p. pap. 23.95 *(978-1-111-12709-1(3))* Delmar Cengage Learning.
—ASE Test Preparation - L1 Advanced Engine Performance. 5th ed. 2011. (ENG.). 224p. pap. 23.95 *(978-1-111-12713-8(1))* Delmar Cengage Learning.
Dempsey, Wayne R. 101 Performance Projects for Your BMW 3 Series 1982-2000. rev. ed. 2006. (Motorbooks Workshop Ser.). (ENG., Illus.). 272p. pap. 34.95 *(978-0-7603-2695-4(9)*, 0760326959, Motorbooks) MBI Publishing Co. LLC.
—101 Projects for Your Porsche Boxster. 2011. (Motorbooks Workshop Ser.). (ENG., Illus.). 312p. pap. 34.99 *(978-0-7603-3554-3(0)*, 0760335540, Motorbooks) MBI Publishing Co. LLC.
Denton, Tom. Advanced Automotive Fault Diagnosis: Automotive Technology - Vehicle Maintenance & Repair. 3rd rev. ed. 2011. (ENG., Illus.). 456p. (C). pap. 41.95 *(978-0-08-096955-8(0))* Routledge.
—Automobile Mechanical & Electrical Systems: Automotive Technology: Vehicle Maintenance & Repair. 2011. (ENG.). 528p. (C). pap. 36.95 *(978-0-08-096945-9(3))* Routledge.
Derrick, Martin. Atlas of Automobiles. (Illus.). 240p. pap. *(978-81-84406-028-3(4))* Taj Bks., Ltd.
Dixon, John. Modern Diesel Technology: Preventive Maintenance & Inspection. 2008. (ENG.). 408p. (C). pap. 116.95 *(978-1-4180-5391-8(0))* Delmar Cengage Learning.
Donny Petersen. Donny's Unauthorized Technical Guide to Harley-Davidson, 1936 to Present: Volume III. 2010. 740p. 49.95 *(978-1-4502-0820-8(7))*; pap. 39.95 *(978-1-4502-0818-5(5))* iUniverse, Inc.
Dorries, Elisabeth H. Today's Technician: Advanced Automotive Electronic. 2010. (ENG.). (C). pap. 110.95 *(978-1-4180-6080-0(1))* Delmar Cengage Learning.
Duffy, James E. Auto Body Repair Technology. 5th ed. 2008. (ENG.). (C). 480p. pap. 68.95 *(978-1-4180-7354-1(7))*; (Illus.). 1056p. 194.95 *(978-1-4180-7353-4(9))* Delmar Cengage Learning.
—Auto Engine Repair. 5th ed. 2009. (ENG.). 592p. 96.00 *(978-1-60525-193-6(3))* Goodheart-Willcox Pub.
—Collision Repair Fundamentals. 2007. (ENG., Illus.). 576p. (C). 101.95 *(978-1-4180-1336-3(6))* Delmar Cengage Learning.
Dummies Press Staff, et al. Bike Repair & Maintenance for Dummies. 2009. (ENG., Illus.). 360p. pap. 19.99 *(978-0-470-41580-1(0)*, For Dummies) Wiley, John & Sons, Inc.
Eichelberger, John & Haefner, Ronald G. Automotive Technology: For General Service Technicians. 2007. (ENG.). 128p. (C). pap. 34.95 *(978-1-4180-1342-4(0))* Delmar Cengage Learning.
Ellery, Max. Mitsubishi Magna/Dimante 1991 To 2005: Automobile Repair Manual. 2008. (ENG., Illus.). 521p. pap. 34.95 *(978-1-876720-09-4(3)*, 1876720093) Renniks Pubns. AUS. Dist: MBI Distribution Services/Quayside Distribution.
Ellery Publications Editors, ed. Mitsubishi Pajero 2000 To 2010. 2009. (ENG., Illus.). 528p. pap. 34.95 *(978-1-876720-21-6(2)*, 1876720212) Renniks Pubns. AUS. Dist: MBI Distribution Services/Quayside Distribution.
Emanuel, Dave. How to Rebuild & Modify Carter/Edelbrock Carburetors: Performance, Street, & off-Road Applications. 2007. (ENG., Illus.). 136p. pap. 24.95 *(978-1-932494-36-5(7)*, S-A Design) CarTech, Inc.
Erickson, Chad & Raven, Greg. Water-Cooled VW Performance Handbook: 3rd Edition. 3rd ed. 2011. (Motorbooks Workshop Ser.). (ENG., Illus.). 208p. pap. 29.99 *(978-0-7603-3766-0(7)*, 0760337667, Motorbooks) MBI Publishing Co. LLC.
Erjavec & Erjavec, Jack. Manual Transmissions & Transaxles: Manual Transmissions/Transaxles Classrm Mnl 5e, 2 vols. 5th ed. 2010. (ENG., Illus.). (C). pap. 110.95 *(978-1-4354-2685-6(1))* CENGAGE Learning.
Erjavec, Jack. Automotive Technology: A Systems Approach. 5th ed. 2009. (ENG.). 1664p. (C). 149.95 *(978-1-4283-1149-7(1))* Delmar Cengage Learning.
—Brakes: Natef Standards Job Sheets. 3rd ed. 2009. (ENG.). 208p. (C). pap. 40.95 *(978-1-4354-8320-0(0))* Delmar Cengage Learning.
—Elecrical & Elecronic Systems: NATEF Standards Job Sheets. 3rd ed. 2009. (ENG.). 240p. (C). pap. 40.95 *(978-1-4354-8321-7(9))* Delmar Cengage Learning.
—Manual Transmissions & Transaxles, 2 vols. 5th ed. 2011. (Illus.). ***(978-1-4354-2835-5(8))*** Delmar Cengage Learning.
—NATEF Standards Job Sheets Area A1. 3rd ed. 2009. (ENG.). 240p. (C). pap. 40.95 *(978-1-4354-8316-3(2))* Delmar Cengage Learning.
—NATEF Standards Job Sheets Area A2. 3rd ed. 2009. (ENG.). 192p. (C). pap. 40.95 *(978-1-4354-8317-0(0))* Delmar Cengage Learning.
—NATEF Standards Job Sheets Area A3. 3rd ed. 2009. (ENG.). 208p. (C). pap. 40.95 *(978-1-4354-8318-7(9))* Delmar Cengage Learning.
—NATEF Standards Job Sheets Area A7. 3rd ed. 2009. (ENG.). 176p. (C). pap. 40.95 *(978-1-4354-8322-4(7))* Delmar Cengage Learning.
—NATEF Standards Job Sheets Area A8. 3rd ed. 2009. (ENG.). 256p. (C). pap. 40.95 *(978-1-4354-8323-1(5))* Delmar Cengage Learning.
—Suspension & Steering: Natef Standards Job Sheets. 3rd ed. 2009. (ENG.). 240p. (C). pap. 40.95 *(978-1-4354-8319-4(7))* Delmar Cengage Learning.
Esterline, Stephanie. This Girls First Car: Teenage Girls Guide to Safe Car Care & Easy Maintenance Tips. 2006. (Illus.). 100p. (YA). per. 14.95 net. *(978-0-9787690-3-1(1))* GI Engineering Co., LLC.
Falconer, Tom. Corvette Sting Ray, 1963-1967. Hughes, Mark, ed. collector's ed. 2008. (Original Ser.). (ENG., Illus.). 112p. pap. 24.95 *(978-0-7603-3304-4(1)*, 0760333041, Motorbooks) MBI Publishing Co. LLC.
Fix, Lauren. Lauren Fix's Guide to Loving Your Car: Everything You Need to Know to Take Charge of Your Car & Get on with Your Life. 2008. (ENG., Illus.). 224p. pap. 18.99 *(978-0-312-37079-4(2)*, St. Martin's Griffin) St. Martin's Pr.
Freund, Ken. Honda Pilot Acura MDX: Honda Pilot - 2003 thru 2007 - Acura MDX - 2001 Thru 2007. 2008. (Haynes Repair Manual Ser.). (ENG., Illus.). 352p. pap. 26.95 *(978-1-56392-690-7(3)*, 1563926903) Haynes Manuals, Inc.
—VW New Beetle 1998 Thru 2005. 2008. (Haynes Repair Manual Ser.). (ENG., Illus.). 352p. pap. 26.95 *(978-1-56392-683-9(0)*, 1563926830) Haynes Manuals, Inc.
Freund, Ken, et al. Chevrolet Astro & GMC Safari 1985 Thru 2005. 2007. (Haynes Repair Manual Ser.). (ENG., Illus.). per. 26.95 *(978-1-56392-696-9(2)*, 1563926962) Haynes Manuals, Inc.
Fry, Trevor. Caring for Your Car: How to Maintain & Service Your Car. 2011. (ENG., Illus.). 120p. pap. 19.95 *(978-1-84584-396-0(7)*, 1845843967) Veloce Publishing Ltd. GBR. Dist: MBI Distribution Services/Quayside Distribution.
Gaines, Tharran E. How to Restore Ford Tractors: The Ultimate Guide to Rebuilding & Restoring N-Series & Later Tractors 1939-1962. 2008. (ENG., Illus.). 224p. pap. 29.99 *(978-0-7603-2620-6(7)*, 0760326207, Voyageur Pr) MBI Publishing Co. LLC.
Gales, W. M. Taking Care of Your Car. 2007. 10.00 *(978-0-8059-8337-1(6))* Dorrance Publishing Co., Inc.
Gilles, Tim. Automotive Service: Inspection, Maintenance, Repair. (ENG.). (C). 3rd ed. 2007. 672p. pap. 65.95 *(978-1-4180-3759-8(1))* 3rd rev. ed. 2007. (Illus.). 1488p. 130.95 *(978-1-4180-3758-1(3))* 4th ed. 2011. 672p. pap. 65.95 *(978-1-111-12862-3(6))* 4th ed. 2011. 1568p. 130.95 *(978-1-111-12861-6(8))* Delmar Cengage Learning.
Godfrey, Eric. Chrysler LH-Series: 1998 Thru 2004. 2010. (ENG.). 400p. pap. 29.95 *(978-1-56392-733-1(0))* Haynes,Chilton.
Godfrey, Eric, et al. VW Passat & Audi A4: Passat (1998 Thru 2005) & Audi A4 (1996 Thru 2001) 1. 8l 4-Cylinder Turbo & 2. 8l V6 Engines. 2008. (Haynes Manuals Ser.). (ENG., Illus.). 334p. per. 26.95 *(978-1-56392-703-4(9)*, 1563927039) Haynes Manuals, Inc.
Gordon, Michael. P2 Automobile Parts Specialist: Motor Age Training Self-Study Guide for ASE Certification. 2007. spiral bd. 24.95 *(978-1-933180-79-3(X))* Advanstar Communications, Inc.
Grady, Michael. A1 Automotive Engine Repair: Motor Age Training Self-Study Guide for ASE Certification. 2006. spiral bd. 22.95 *(978-1-933180-71-7(4))* Advanstar Communications, Inc.
—A7 Heating & Air Conditioning: Motor Age Self-Study Guide for ASE Certification. 2007. spiral bd. 22.95 *(978-1-933180-82-3(X))* Advanstar Communications, Inc.
Grainger, Rod & Shoemark, Pete. Mazda Miata MX-5 Eunos Roadster 1. 6: Enthusiast's Workshop Manual. 2006. (ENG., Illus.). 368p. reprint ed. pap. 49.95 *(978-1-84584-083-9(6)*, 1845840836) Veloce Publishing Ltd. GBR. Dist: MBI Distribution Services/Quayside Distribution.
—Mazda Miata MX-5 Eunos Roadster 1. 8: Enthuasiast's Shop Manual. 2006. (ENG., Illus.). 300p. reprint ed. pap. 49.95 *(978-1-84584-090-7(9)*, 1845840909) Veloce Publishing Ltd. GBR. Dist: MBI Distribution Services/Quayside Distribution.
—Mazda Mx-5 1.6 Litre Enthusiast's Workshop Manual. (Illus.). 368p. pap. *(978-1-901295-25-2(7))* Veloce Publishing Ltd. GBR. Dist: MBI Distribution Services/Quayside Distribution.
Graves, Dan. Smart Car ForTwo Maintenance & Service Manual on CD: Smart Car ForTwo Manual. 2007.Tr. of Smart Car ForTwo Manual. (Illus.). cd-rom 89.00 *(978-0-9798214-0-0(1))* Graves, Dan.
Gray, Michael E. & Gray, Linda E. Auto Upkeep: Basic Car Care, Maintenance, & Repair. 2nd rev. exp. ed. 2007. (ENG., Illus.). 192p. (YA). 69.95 *(978-0-9740792-6-4(X))*; pap. 34.95 *(978-0-9740792-1-9(9)*, 9780974079219) Rolling Hills Publishing.
—Auto Upkeep (Homeschool Paperback Text Curriculum Kit) Basic Car Care, Maintenance, & Repair, 2 bks. 2nd ed. 2007. (ENG., Illus.). 336p. (YA). 75.95 *(978-0-9740792-5-7(1))* Rolling Hills Publishing.
—Auto Upkeep (Instructor CD) Basic Car Care, Maintenance, & Repair. 2nd ed. 2007. (ENG.). (YA). cd-rom 99.95 *(978-0-9740792-3-3(5))* Rolling Hills Publishing.
—Auto Upkeep (Textbook Paperback/Workbook Set) Basic Car Care, Maintenance, & Repair, 2 bks. 2nd ed. 2007. (ENG., Illus.). 336p. (YA). 60.90 *(978-0-9740792-4-0(3))* Rolling Hills Publishing.
—Auto Upkeep (Workbook) Basic Car Care, Maintenance, & Repair. 2nd ed. 2007. (ENG., Illus.). 144p. (YA). pap. 25.95 *(978-0-9740792-2-6(7))* Rolling Hills Publishing.
Hadfield, Chris. Automotive Service Job Sheets for NATEF Task Mastery. 2nd ed. 2011. (New Automotive & Truck Technology Titles! Ser.). (ENG., Illus.). 816p. (C). pap. 89.95 *(978-1-111-13798-4(6))* Delmar Cengage Learning.
—Today's Technician: Automotive Engine Repair & Rebuilding. 4th ed. 2009. (ENG.). 1008p. (C). pap. 147.95 *(978-1-4354-2824-9(2))* Delmar Cengage Learning.
Hadfield, Christopher & Dorries, Elisabeth H. Classroom Manual for Automotive Engine Repair & Rebuilding. 4th ed. 2010. (Illus.). xiv, 316p. pap. *(978-1-4354-2606-1(1))* Delmar Cengage Learning.
—Shop Manual for Automotive Engine Repair & Rebuilding. 4th ed. 2010. (Illus.). xix, 650p. pap. *(978-1-4354-2827-0(7))* Delmar Cengage Learning.
Haefner, Ron & Leathers, Paul. Automotive Technology: For General Service Technicians. 2007. (ENG., Illus.). 976p. (C). 116.95 *(978-1-4180-1340-0(4))* Delmar Cengage Learning.
Haefner, Ronald G. Automotive Technology: For General Service Technicians. 2007. (ENG.). 608p. (C). pap., wbk. ed. 34.95 *(978-1-4180-1341-7(2))* Delmar Cengage Learning.
—The Car Care Book. 4th ed. 2008. (ENG.). 464p. (C). 152.95 *(978-1-4283-4293-4(1))*; pap. 129.95 *(978-1-4283-4295-8(8))* Delmar Cengage Learning.
Halderman, James. Automotive Engines: Theory & Servicing. 7th rev. ed. 2010. (ENG., Illus.). 608p. (C). pap. 118.00 *(978-0-13-510383-8(5)*, Prentice Hall) Prentice Hall PTR.
Halderman, James D. Advanced Automotive Electricity & Electronics. rev. ed. 2012. (ENG.). 480p. (C). pap. 110.93 ***(978-0-13-254262-3(5)***, Prentice Hall) Prentice Hall PTR.
—Advanced Engine Performance Diagnosis. 5th ed. 2011. (ENG., Illus.). 432p. (C). pap. 118.00 *(978-0-13-254009-4(6)*, Prentice Hall) Prentice Hall PTR.
—Automotive Electricity & Electronics. 3rd ed. 2010. (ENG., Illus.). 544p. (C). pap. 118.00 *(978-0-13-512406-2(9))* Pearson Education Canada CAN. Dist: Pearson Education.

—Automotive Engine Performance. 2008. *(978-0-13-158358-0(1))* 2nd ed. 2006. (ENG., Illus.). 560p. (C). pap. 122.80 *(978-0-13-198935-1(9)*, Prentice Hall) 3rd ed. 2009. (ENG., Illus.). 540p. (C). pap. 118.00 *(978-0-13-508504-2(7)*, Prentice Hall) Prentice Hall PTR.

—Automotive Engine Performance Worktext. 2nd ed. 2006. (ENG., Illus.). 448p. (C). pap. 36.20 *(978-0-13-199129-3(9)*, Prentice Hall) Prentice Hall PTR.

—Automotive Technology. 4th ed. 2011. (ENG.). (C). 94.40 ***(978-0-13-276966-2(2))***; (Illus.). 1664p. 124.80 ***(978-0-13-254261-6(7))*** Prentice Hall PTR. (Prentice Hall).

—Diagnosis & Troubleshooting of Automotive Electrical, Electronic, & Computer Systems. 6th rev. ed. 2010. (ENG., Illus.). 528p. (C). pap. 118.00 *(978-0-13-255155-7(1)*, Prentice Hall) Prentice Hall PTR.

—NATEF Correlated Job Sheets for Automotive Chassis Systems. 5th ed. 2009. (ENG.). 240p. (C). pap. 36.20 *(978-0-13-509377-1(5)*, Prentice Hall) Prentice Hall PTR.

—NATEF Correlated Job Sheets for Automotive Chassis Systems: Principles, Diagnosis, & Service. (ENG.). (C). 3rd ed. 2008. 400p. pap. 41.60 *(978-0-13-237944-1(9))* 4th ed. 2007. 348p. pap. 34.40 *(978-0-13-238488-9(4))* Prentice Hall PTR. (Prentice Hall).

—NATEF Correlated Task Sheets for Advanced Engine Performance Diagnosis. 5th ed. 2011. (ENG.). (C). pap. 29.00 *(978-0-13-254516-7(0)*, Prentice Hall) Prentice Hall PTR.

—NATEF Correlated Task Sheets for Automotive Brake Systems. 5th ed. 2009. (ENG.). 400p. (C). pap. 36.20 *(978-0-13-507935-5(7)*, Prentice Hall) Prentice Hall PTR.

—NATEF Correlated Task Sheets for Automotive Electricity & Electronics. 3rd ed. 2010. (ENG.). 256p. (C). pap. 27.20 *(978-0-13-705263-9(4)*, Prentice Hall) Prentice Hall PTR.

—NATEF Correlated Task Sheets for Automotive Engine Performance. 3rd ed. 2009. (ENG.). 448p. (C). pap. 36.20 *(978-0-13-509350-4(3)*, Prentice Hall) Prentice Hall PTR.

—Natef Correlated Task Sheets for Automotive Engines: Theory & Servicing. 7th ed. 2010. (ENG.). 75p. (C). pap. 36.20 *(978-0-13-512392-8(5)*, Prentice Hall) Prentice Hall PTR.

—NATEF Correlated Task Sheets for Diagnosis & Troubleshooting of Automotive Electrical, Electronic, & Computer Systems. (ENG.). (C). 5th ed. 2009. 624p. pap. 36.20 *(978-0-13-506899-1(1))* 6th rev. ed. 2011. 264p. pap. 29.00 *(978-0-13-255220-2(5))* Prentice Hall PTR. (Prentice Hall).

—NATEF Task Sheets for Automotive Steering, Suspension & Alignment. 5th ed. 2009. (ENG.). 75p. (C). pap. 36.20 *(978-0-13-508500-4(4)*, Prentice Hall) Prentice Hall PTR.

—Worktext for Advanced Engine Performance Diagnosis. 4th ed. 2008. (ENG.). 400p. (C). pap. 36.20 *(978-0-13-506039-1(7)*, Prentice Hall) Prentice Hall PTR.

Halderman, James D. & Deeter, Darrell D. Study Guide for Introduction to Automotive Service. rev. ed. 2012. (ENG.). 576p. (C). pap. 33.33 ***(978-0-13-298827-8(5)***, Prentice Hall) Prentice Hall PTR.

Halderman, James D. & Mitchell, Chase. Advanced Engine Performance Diagnosis. 4th ed. 2008. (ENG.). 528p. (C). pap. 122.80 *(978-0-13-503688-4(7)*, Prentice Hall) Prentice Hall PTR.

Halderman, James D. & Trinidad, Omar D. NATEF Correlated Task Sheets for Introduction to Automotive Service. 2012. (ENG.). 264p. (C). pap. 33.33 ***(978-0-13-254991-2(3)***, Prentice Hall) Prentice Hall PTR.

Halderman, James D., et al. Introduction to Automotive Service. rev. ed. 2012. (ENG.). 432p. (C). pap. 100.00 ***(978-0-13-254008-7(8)***, Prentice Hall) Prentice Hall PTR.

Hall, Lynne L. Geek's Guide to Auto Maintenance: Don't Be a Dummy. Get Twice as Smart for Half the Price. 2007. (Geek's Guides Ser.). (ENG.). 192p. pap. *(978-1-57587-277-3(3))* Crane Hill Pubs.

Hamilton, Joe L. Chilton's Chrysler 300/Charger/Magnum: 2005-07 Repair Manual. 2008. (ENG., Illus.). 384p. pap. 29.95 *(978-1-56392-685-3(7))* Haynes,Chilton.

—Chrysler 300 & Dodge Charger & Magnum: 2005 - 2009. 2011. (ENG., Illus.). 384p. pap. 29.95 *(978-1-56392-911-3(2))* Haynes,Chilton.

—General Motors Cobalt/G5: 2005 Through 2007. 2008. (ENG., Illus.). 320p. pap. 29.95 *(978-1-56392-687-7(3))* Haynes,Chilton.

—Kia Sephia & Spectra. 2010. (ENG.). 384p. pap. 29.95 *(978-1-56392-839-0(6))* Haynes,Chilton.

—Toyota Tacoma: 2005 Thru 2009. 2010. (ENG.). 416p. pap. 29.95 *(978-1-56392-780-5(2))* Haynes,Chilton.

—Toyota/Lexus: Highlander 2001-06 RX 300/330 1999-06 Repair Manual. 2007. (Chilton's Total Car Care Repair Manuals Ser.). (ENG., Illus.). 368p. per. 29.95 *(978-1-56392-624-2(5))* Haynes,Chilton.

Hamilton, Patrick, et al. Light Vehicle Maintenance & Repair Level 2. 2nd ed. 2011. (ENG.). 352p. (C). pap. 37.99 *(978-1-4080-1162-1(X))* Cengage Learning GBR. Dist: CENGAGE Learning.

Hammill, Des. How to Build & Modify Sportscar & Kitcar Suspension & Brakes: For Road & Track - Revised & Updated 2nd Edition. 3rd ed. 2008. (SpeedPro Ser.). (ENG., Illus.). 128p. pap. 39.95 *(978-1-84584-207-9(3)*, 1845842073) Veloce Publishing Ltd. GBR. Dist: MBI Distribution Services/Quayside Distribution.

—SU Carburettor High-Performance Manual. 2007. (SpeedPro Ser.). (ENG., Illus.). 96p. reprint ed. per. 29.95 *(978-1-84584-073-0(9)*, 1845840739) Veloce Publishing Ltd. GBR. Dist: MBI Distribution Services/Quayside Distribution.

—The 4-Cylinder Engine Short Block High-Performance Manual: Updated & Revised New Colour Edition. 2012. (ENG., Illus.). 112p. pap. 32.95 *(978-1-84584-414-1(9)*, 1845844149) Veloce Publishing Ltd. GBR. Dist: MBI Distribution Services/Quayside Distribution.

Hansen, Courtney. The Garage Girl's Guide to Everything You Need to Know about Your Car. 2007. (ENG., Illus.). 284p. per. 18.95 *(978-1-58182-519-0(6))* Turner Publishing Co.

Hansen, Graham. How to Build Big-Inch Chevy Small Blocks. 2011. pap. 24.95 *(978-1-934709-66-5(2)*, S-A Design) CarTech, Inc.

Hardiman, Paul. Mazda MX-5 Renovation Manual: 1989-2005 Includes Miata & Eunos. 2011. (ENG., Illus.). 192p. 32.95 *(978-0-85733-006-2(3)*, 0857330063) Haynes Publishing PLC GBR. Dist: MBI Distribution Services/Quayside Distribution.

—Mini (1989-2000) A practical guide to renovation on a Budget. 2008. (Do It Up! Ser.). (ENG., Illus.). 192p. 39.95 *(978-1-84425-424-8(0)*, 1844254240) Haynes Publishing PLC GBR. Dist: MBI Distribution Services/Quayside Distribution.

Hartman, Jeff. Supercharging Performance Handbook. 2011. (Motorbooks Workshop Ser.). (ENG., Illus.). 224p. pap. 29.99 *(978-0-7603-3938-1(4)*, 0760339384, Motorbooks) MBI Publishing Co. LLC.

Haynes Editors. BMW 3-Series,1999 Thru 2005. 2012. (Haynes Repair Manual Ser.). (ENG., Illus.). 336p. pap. 26.95 ***(978-1-56392-966-3(X)***, 156392966X) Haynes Manuals, Inc.

—Ford Fusion & Mercury Milan, 2006 Thru 2010. 2012. (Haynes Repair Manual Ser.). (ENG., Illus.). 320p. pap. 26.95 ***(978-1-56392-890-1(6)***, 1563928906) Haynes Manuals, Inc.

—Mazda Mazda6, 2003 Thru 2011. 2012. (Haynes Repair Manual Ser.). (ENG., Illus.). 320p. pap. 26.95 ***(978-1-56392-916-8(3)***, 1563929163) Haynes Manuals, Inc.

—Nissan: Titan 2004 Thru 2009, Armada 2005 Thru 2010. 2012. (Haynes Repair Manual Ser.). (ENG., Illus.). 272p. pap. 26.95 ***(978-1-56392-816-1(7)***, 1563928167) Haynes Manuals, Inc.

Haynes Editors, ed. General Motors Buick Regal, Chevrolet Lumina,Olds Cutlass Supreme,Pontiac Grand Prix, 1988-2007. 2009. (ENG., Illus.). 416p. pap. 26.95 *(978-1-56392-726-3(8)*, 1563927268) Haynes Manuals, Inc.

—Mazda MPV 1989-1998. 2008. (Haynes Service & Repair Manual Ser.). (ENG., Illus.). 320p. pap. 26.95 *(978-1-56392-727-0(6)*, 1563927276) Haynes Manuals, Inc.

—Nissan 350Z & Infiniti G35, 2003-2008. 2008. (Haynes Repair Manual Ser.). (ENG., Illus.). 336p. pap. 26.95 *(978-1-56392-723-2(3)*, 1563927233) Haynes Manuals, Inc.

Haynes Editors & Freund, Ken. Honda Foreman & Rubicon ATVs, 1995 Thru 2007. 2007. (Motorcycle Repair Manual Ser.). (ENG., Illus.). 208p. pap. 36.45 *(978-1-56392-656-3(3)*, 1563926563) Haynes Manuals, Inc.

—Yamaha Kodiak & Grizzlys ATVS: 2-wheel drive & 4-wheel drive 1993 To 2005. 2007. (Owners Workshop Manual Ser.). (ENG., Illus.). 240p. pap. 36.45 *(978-1-56392-567-2(2)*, 1563925672) Haynes Manuals, Inc.

Haynes, J. H. & Warren, Larry. Haynes Ford Aerostar Mini-Vans Owners Workshop Manual, No. 1476: 1986-1990. (Haynes Automotive Repair Manual Ser.). (Illus.). 300p. pap. 16.95 *(978-1-56392-032-5(8))* Haynes Manuals, Inc.

Haynes, J. J. GM Cobalt/G5 Automotive Repair Manual. 2012. (ENG., Illus.). 256p. pap. 26.95 ***(978-1-56392-974-8(0)***, 1563929740) Haynes Manuals, Inc.

—Hyundai Elantra: 1996 Thru 2010. 2011. (Haynes Repair Manual Ser.). (ENG., Illus.). 282p. pap. 26.95 ***(978-1-56392-927-4(9)***, 1563929279) Haynes Manuals, Inc.

—Kia Spectra/Sephia/Sportage 1994 Thru 2010. 2011. (Haynes Repair Manual Ser.). (ENG., Illus.). 288p. pap. 26.95 *(978-1-56392-908-3(2)*, 1563929082) Haynes Manuals, Inc.

—Toyota Sienna 1998 Thru 2009: All Models. 2010. (ENG., Illus.). 320p. pap. 26.95 *(978-1-56392-808-6(6)*, 1563928086) Haynes Manuals, Inc.

Haynes, J. J., ed. Saturn Vue, '02-'07. 2009. (Haynes Repair Manual Ser.). (ENG., Illus.). 352p. pap. 26.95 *(978-1-56392-764-5(0)*, 1563927640) Haynes Manuals, Inc.

Haynes, John. Chevrolet & GMC Full-Size Vans: 1996 Thru 2010. 2011. (Haynes Repair Manual Ser.). (ENG., Illus.). 288p. pap. 24.95 ***(978-1-56392-887-1(6)***, 1563928876) Haynes Manuals, Inc.

—Chevrolet Impala & Monte Carlo: 2006 Thru 2010. 2011. (Haynes Repair Manual Ser.). (ENG., Illus.). 288p. pap. 24.95 *(978-1-56392-894-9(9)*, 1563928949) Haynes Manuals, Inc.

—Mitsubishi Galant 1994 Thru 2010. 2011. (Haynes Repair Manual Ser.). (ENG., Illus.). 320p. pap. 24.95 *(978-1-56392-853-6(1)*, 1563928531) Haynes Manuals, Inc.

—Nissan Altima, 2007 Thru 2010. 2011. (Haynes Repair Manual Ser.). (ENG., Illus.). 307p. pap. 26.95 *(978-1-56392-896-3(5)*, 1563928965) Haynes Manuals, Inc.

—Nissan Sentra And 200SX: 1995 Thru 2006. 2010. (Haynes Repair Manual Ser.). (ENG., Illus.). 288p. pap. 26.95 *(978-1-56392-802-4(7)*, 1563928027) Haynes Manuals, Inc.

—Toyota Corolla 2003 Thru 2008. 2010. (Haynes Repair Manual Ser.). (ENG., Illus.). 320p. pap. 26.95 *(978-1-56392-807-9(8)*, 1563928078) Haynes Manuals, Inc.

—Toyota Corolla Automotive Repair Manual. 2012. (ENG.). 256p. pap. 26.95 ***(978-1-56392-978-6(3)***, 1563929783) Haynes Manuals, Inc.

—Toyota Highlander Lexus RX 300/330 1999 Thru 2007. 2010. (Haynes Repair Manual Ser.). (ENG., Illus.). 304p. pap. 26.95 *(978-1-56392-860-4(4)*, 1563928604) Haynes Manuals, Inc.

—Toyota Tundra (2000 thru 2006) & Sequoia (2000-2007) All 2WD & 4WD Models. 2010. (Haynes Repair Manual Ser.). (ENG., Illus.). 288p. pap. 26.95 *(978-1-56392-848-2(5)*, 1563928485) Haynes Manuals, Inc.

—Yamaha ATVs Timberwolf, Bruin, Bear Tracker, 350ER & Big Bear: 1987 To 2009. 2010. (Haynes Service & Repair Manual Ser.). (ENG., Illus.). 208p. pap. 45.45 *(978-1-56392-842-0(6)*, 1563928426) Haynes Manuals, Inc.

Haynes, John, ed. Toyota 4Runner, '03-'09. 2009. (Haynes Repair Manual Ser.). (ENG., Illus.). 320p. pap. 24.95 *(978-1-56392-758-4(6)*, 1563927585) Haynes Manuals, Inc.

—Toyota Matrix & Pontiac Vibe, '03-'08. 2009. (Haynes Repair Manual Ser.) (ENG., Illus.). 272p. pap. 26.95 *(978-1-56392-766-9(7)*, 1563927667) Haynes Manuals, Inc.

Haynes, John H. Ford Escape/Mazda Tribute Automotive Repair Manual. 2012. (ENG.). 320p. pap. 26.95 ***(978-1-56392-954-0(6)***, 1563929546) Haynes Manuals, Inc.

—Mitsubishi Eclipse & Eagle Talon 1995 Thru 2005. 2008. (Haynes Repair Manual Ser.). (ENG., Illus.). 282p. pap. 26.95 *(978-1-56392-707-2(1)*, 1563927071) Haynes Manuals, Inc.

—Nissan Altima 1993 Thru 2006. 2008. (Haynes Repair Manual Ser.). (ENG., Illus.). 282p. pap. 26.95 *(978-1-56392-722-5(5)*, 1563927225) Haynes Manuals, Inc.

—Nissan Frontier & Xterra, '05-'08. 2008. (Automotive Repair Manual Ser.). (ENG., Illus.). 304p. pap. 26.95 *(978-1-56392-702-7(0)*, 1563927020) Haynes Manuals, Inc.

—VW Golf & Jetta 1993 Thru 1998. 2008. (Haynes Repair Manual Ser.). (ENG., Illus.). 282p. pap. 26.95 *(978-1-56392-712-6(8)*, 1563927128) Haynes Manuals, Inc.

—VW Golf, GTI, & Jetta, '99-'05. 2008. (Automotive Repair Manual Ser.) (ENG., Illus.). 336p. pap. 26.95 *(978-1-56392-708-9(X)*, 156392708X) Haynes Manuals, Inc.

Haynes Manuals Editors. BMW 3-Series 2006 Thru 2010: 325i, 325xi, 330i, 330xi (2006), 328i, 328xi (2007 Thru 2010) 2011. (Haynes Repair Manual Ser.). (ENG., Illus.). 304p. pap. 26.95 ***(978-1-56392-914-4(7)***, 1563929147) Haynes Manuals, Inc.

—Chrysler PT Cruiser, 2001 Thru 2010 All Model. 2011. (Haynes Repair Manual Ser.). (ENG., Illus.). 320p. pap. 26.95 ***(978-1-56392-963-2(5)***, 1563929635) Haynes Manuals, Inc.

—Ford Pick-ups: 2004 Thru 2010. 2011. (Haynes Repair Manual Ser.). (ENG., Illus.). 304p. pap. 26.95 ***(978-1-56392-951-9(1)***, 1563929511) Haynes Manuals, Inc.

—Mazda Mazda3 2004 Thru 2011. 2011. (Haynes Repair Manual Ser.). (ENG., Illus.). 272p. pap. 26.95 ***(978-1-56392-915-1(5)***, 1563929155) Haynes Manuals, Inc.

—Nissan Murano 2003 Thru 2010: All Models. 2011. (Haynes Repair Manual Ser.). (ENG., Illus.). 288p. pap. 26.95 ***(978-1-56392-921-2(X)***, 156392921X) Haynes Manuals, Inc.

—Toyota RAV4 1996 Thru 2010. 2011. (Haynes Repair Manual Ser.). (ENG., Illus.). 336p. pap. 26.95 ***(978-1-56392-937-3(6)***, 1563929376) Haynes Manuals, Inc.

Haynes Manuals Editors, compiled by. Ford Pick-ups 1997 thru 2003 Expedition 1997 Thru 2009. 2007. (Haynes Repair Manual Ser.). (ENG., Illus.). 318p. pap. 26.95 *(978-1-56392-781-2(0)*, 1563927810) Haynes Manuals, Inc.

—Pontiac G6 2005 Thru 2009. 2009. (Haynes Repair Manual Ser.). (ENG., Illus.). 304p. pap. 26.95 *(978-1-56392-782-9(9)*, 1563927829) Haynes Manuals Inc.

Haynes Manuals Editors, ed. Acura TL 1999 Thru 2008. 2009. (Automotive Repair Manual Ser.). (ENG., Illus.). 336p. pap. 26.95 *(978-1-56392-744-7(6)*, 1563927446) Haynes Manuals, Inc.

—Chrysler LHS,Concorde,300M,Dodge Intrepid, 1998-2004. 2009. (Haynes Repair Manual Ser.). (ENG., Illus.). 320p. pap. 26.95 *(978-1-56392-732-4(2)*, 1563927322) Haynes Manuals, Inc.

—Honda Rancher, Recon & TRX250EX ATV's. 2010. (Owners Workshop Manual Ser.). (ENG., Illus.). 208p. pap. 33.95 *(978-1-56392-778-2(0)*, 1563927780) Haynes Manuals, Inc.

—Hyundai Sonata 1999 Thru 2008. 2009. (Automotive Repair Manual Ser.). (ENG., Illus.). 288p. pap. 26.95 *(978-1-56392-736-2(5)*, 1563927365) Haynes Manuals, Inc.

—Mercedes-Benz C-Class 2001 Thru 2007. 2009. (Automotive Repair Manual Ser.). (ENG., Illus.). 352p. pap. 26.95 *(978-1-56392-735-5(7)*, 1563927357) Haynes Manuals, Inc.

—Toyota Tacoma 2005-2009. 2009. (Haynes Repair Manual Ser.). (ENG., Illus.). 352p. pap. 26.95 *(978-1-56392-770-6(5)*, 1563927705) Haynes Manuals, Inc.

Haynes Manuals, Editors of. Chevrolet Silverado & GMC Sierra, 2007 Thru 2012. 2012. (Haynes Repair Manual Ser.). (ENG., Illus.). 384p. pap. 26.95 ***(978-1-56392-972-4(4)***, 1563929724) Haynes Manuals, Inc.

—Mazda Protege Automotive Repair Manual. 2012. (Haynes Repair Manual Ser.). (ENG., Illus.). 320p. pap. 26.95 ***(978-1-56392-968-7(6)***, 1563929686) Haynes Manuals, Inc.

Haynes, Max. Audi A4: 2002 Thru 2008. 2011. (Haynes Repair Manual Ser.). (ENG., Illus.). 352p. pap. 26.95 *(978-1-56392-837-6(X)*, 156392837X) Haynes Manuals, Inc.

—Chevrolet Colorado GMC Canyon 2004 Thru 2010. 2011. (ENG., Illus.). 300p. pap. 24.95 *(978-1-56392-898-7(1)*, 1563928981) Haynes Manuals, Inc.

—Dodge Pick-ups: 2002 Thru 2008. 2009. (Haynes Repair Manual Ser.). (ENG., Illus.). 288p. pap. 26.95 *(978-1-56392-742-3(X)*, 156392742X) Haynes Manuals, Inc.

—Ford Explorer 2002 Thru 2010: Includes Mercury Mountineer. 2010. (Haynes Repair Manual Ser.). (ENG., Illus.). 282p. pap. 26.95 *(978-1-56392-811-6(6)*, 1563928116) Haynes Manuals, Inc.

—Ford Focus 2000 Thru 2007. 2009. (Haynes Repair Manual Ser.). (ENG., Illus.). 336p. 26.95 *(978-1-56392-754-6(3)*, 1563927543) Haynes Manuals, Inc.

—Ford Full-Size Vans 1992 Thru 2010. 2011. (Haynes Repair Manual Ser.). (ENG., Illus.). 336p. pap. 24.95 *(978-1-56392-922-9(8)*, 1563929228) Haynes Manuals, Inc.

—Ford Windstar & Freestar 1995 Thru 2007. 2010. (Haynes Repair Manual Ser.). (ENG., Illus.). 286p. pap. 26.95 *(978-1-56392-765-2(9)*, 1563927659) Haynes Manuals, Inc.

—General Motors Chevrolet Malibu 2004 Thru 2010. 2011. (ENG., Illus.). 272p. pap. 26.95 *(978-1-56392-895-6(7)*, 1563928957) Haynes Manuals, Inc.

—Hundai Excel & Accent 1986 Thru 2009: All Models. 2010. (Haynes Repair Manual Ser.). (ENG., Illus.). 308p. pap. 26.95 *(978-1-56392-804-8(3)*, 1563928043) Haynes Manuals, Inc.

—Jeep Wrangler 1987 Thru 2008. 2009. (Haynes Repair Manual Ser.). (ENG., Illus.). 180p. pap. 26.95 *(978-1-56392-796-6(9)*, 1563927959) Haynes Manuals, Inc.

—Lincoln Rear-Wheel Drive Models, 1970 Thru 2005. 2010. (Haynes Repair Manual Ser.). (ENG., Illus.). 399p. pap. 24.95 *(978-1-56392-812-3(4)*, 1563928124) Haynes Manuals, Inc.

—Suzuki Intruder, Marauder, Volusia & Boulevard '85 To '09. 2010. (ENG., Illus.). 248p. 45.45 *(978-1-56392-779-9(9)*, 1563927799) Haynes Manuals, Inc.

—Toyota Camry 2002-2006 Repair Manual. 2009. (Haynes Repair Manual Ser.). (ENG., Illus.). 288p. pap. 26.95 *(978-1-56392-762-1(4)*, 1563927624) Haynes Manuals, Inc.

Haynes, Max, ed. Honda Accord 2003-2007. 2009. (Haynes Repair Manual Ser.). (ENG., Illus.). 288p. pap. 26.95 *(978-1-56392-740-9(3)*, 1563927403) Haynes Manuals, Inc.

Haynes Publishing, compiled by. The Classic Cutaways. 2009. (ENG., Illus.). 208p. 49.95 *(978-1-84425-570-2(0)*, 1844255700) Haynes Publishing PLC GBR. Dist: MBI Distribution Services/Quayside Distribution.

Heick, Terry. Toyota MR2 Performance: A Practical Owner's Guide for Everyday Maintenance, Upgrades & Performance Modifications. Covers 1985-2005, All Makes & Models. 2009. (ENG.). 208p. (gr. 12-18). 21.95 *(978-1-55788-553-1(2)*, HP Trade) Penguin Group (USA) Inc.

Henderson, Bob. Chilton's General Motors Deville/Seville: 1999-05 Repair Manual. 2007. (Chilton's Total Car Care Repair Manuals Ser.). (ENG., Illus.). 432p. per. 29.95 *(978-1-56392-659-4(8))* Haynes,Chilton.

—Chilton's Toyota Rav4, 1996-05 Repair Manual: Covers U.S. & Canadian Models of Toyota Rav4 Models. 2009. (ENG., Illus.). 400p. pap. 29.95 *(978-1-56392-759-1(4))* Haynes,Chilton.

—Chilton's Volkswagen New Beetle 1998-05 Repair Manual: Covers U.S. & Canadian Models of Volkswagen New Beetle Gasoline & 1.9L ECOdiesel Engines. 2008. (ENG., Illus.). 432p. pap. 29.95 *(978-1-56392-711-9(X))* Haynes,Chilton.

—Nissan Maxima Repair Manual. 2006. (Chilton's Total Car Care Ser.). (ENG., Illus.). 464p. per. 29.95 *(978-1-56392-604-4(0))* Haynes,Chilton.

Henderson, Bob & Haynes, J. H. Toyota Hi-Lux & 4 Runner Automotive Repair Manual. 2nd ed. (Illus.). 272p. *(978-1-56392-256-5(8))* Haynes Manuals, Inc.

Henderson, Bob & Haynes, John H. OBD-II & Sistemas de Control Electrónico del Motor. 2006. (Haynes Repair Manuals Ser.). (ENG., Illus.). 272p. per. 26.95 *(978-1-56392-612-9(1)*, 1563926121) Haynes Manuals, Inc.

Henderson, Bob, et al. General Motors Chevrolet Venture, Oldsmobile Silhouette, Pontiac Trans Sport & Montana 1997 Thru 2005. 2007. (Haynes Repair Manuals Ser.). (ENG., Illus.). 256p. per. 26.95 *(978-1-56392-636-5(9)*, 1563926369) Haynes Manuals, Inc.

Henderson, John. Car Buying & Ownership 2010. 2010. (Teach Yourself Ser.). (ENG., Illus.). 192p. pap. 19.95 *(978-1-4441-0752-4(6)*, Hodder & Stoughton) Hodder General Publishing Div. GBR. Dist: Independent Pubs. Group.

Heritage Information Systems. Illustrated Powerstroke Diagnostics: 2006-07 6. 0L E250-450 & F250-550. 2008. (Illus.). 544p. per. 89.95 *(978-0-9725784-1-7(2))* Heritage Technical LLC.

Holdener, Richard. Building Honda K-Series Engine Performance. 2007. (Cartech Ser.). (ENG., Illus.). 160p. pap. 24.95 *(978-1-932494-41-9(3)*, S-A Design) CarTech, Inc.

Hole, Steve. A to Z of Kit Cars. 2012. (ENG., Illus.). 176p. 49.95 *(978-1-84425-677-8(4)*, 1844256774) Haynes Publishing PLC GBR. Dist: MBI Distribution Services/Quayside Distribution.

Hollaway, M L. Everything You Need to Know after Being in an Auto Accident How to Represent Yourself after Being in an Auto Accident. 2007. 80p. per. 10.95 *(978-1-4327-1435-2(X))* Outskirts Pr., Inc.

Holembeak, Barry. Advanced Automotive Electronic Systems: Classroom Manual. 2010. (Today's Technician Ser.). (ENG.). 912p. (C). pap. 147.95 *(978-1-111-03814-4(7))* Delmar Cengage Learning.

—Today's Technician: Automotive Electricity & Electronics Classroom & Shop Manual Pack. 5th ed. 2010. (ENG.). 1296p. (C). pap. 147.95 *(978-1-4354-7010-1(9))* Delmar Cengage Learning.

Horler, Terry. MG/A-H Midget/Sprite: Your Expert Guide to Common Problems & How to Fix Them. 2012. (ENG., Illus.). 128p. pap. 24.95 ***(978-1-84584-402-8(5)***, 1845844025) Veloce Publishing Ltd. GBR. Dist: MBI Distribution Services/Quayside Distribution.

Imhoff, Tim. Chilton's Toyota Prius 2001-08 Repair Manual. 2009. (ENG., Illus.). 304p. pap. 29.95 *(978-1-56392-691-4(1))* Haynes,Chilton.

—General Motors Equinox & Torrent: 2005 Thru 2009. 2010. (ENG.). 352p. pap. 29.95 *(978-1-56392-810-9(8))* Haynes,Chilton.

—Hyundai Sonata: 1999 Thru 2008. 2010. (ENG., Illus.). 368p. pap. 29.95 *(978-1-56392-739-3(X))* Haynes,Chilton.

—Nissan Altima: 2007-2010. 2011. (ENG.). 352p. pap. 29.95 *(978-1-56392-907-6(4))* Haynes,Chilton.

—Nissan Murano: 2003 Thru 2010. 2011. (Illus.). 352p. pap. 29.95 ***(978-1-56392-935-9(X))*** Haynes,Chilton.

Imhoff, Tim. Saturn Vue. 2010. (ENG.). 432p. pap. 29.95 *(978-1-56392-772-0(1))* Haynes,Chilton.

Imhoff, Tim & Haynes, J. H. Holden Commodore Automotive Repair Manual. (Illus.). 208p. *(978-1-56392-258-9(4))* Haynes Manuals, Inc.

Imhoff, Tim & Haynes, John H. Toyota Prius, 2001-2008. Freund, Ken, ed. 2008. (Haynes Repair Manuals Ser.). (ENG., Illus.). 320p. per. 26.95 *(978-1-56392-680-8(6)*, 1563926806) Haynes Manuals, Inc.

Jaguar Cars Staff. Jaguar 420 Spare Parts Catalogue, 1967-1968. (Illus.). 340p. (Orig.). ring bd. 70.00 *(978-0-8376-0551-7(2))* Bentley Pubs.

—The Jaguar E-Type 4.2 Series 1 Spare Parts Catalogue (1965-1968) (Illus.). 295p. (Orig.). ring bd. 60.00 *(978-0-8376-0548-7(2))* Bentley Pubs.

Janus. Caring for Your Car. 64p. pap. 8.95 *(978-0-8224-5053-5(4))* Globe Fearon Educational Publishing.

Jeffrey, Zurschmeide. The New Mini Performance Handbook. 2010. (ENG., Illus.). 144p. pap. 24.95 *(978-1-934709-14-6(X)*, S-A Design) CarTech, Inc.

Johanson & Johanson, Chris. Auto Engine Performance & Drivability. 3rd ed. 2009. (ENG.). 218p. pap., wbk. ed. 24.00 *(978-1-60525-053-3(8))* Goodheart-Willcox Pub.

Johanson, Chris. Auto Brakes: A5 Shop Manual. abr. ed. 2007. (Illus.). 192p. (gr. 9-12). per. 18.00 *(978-1-59070-724-1(9))* Goodheart-Willcox Pub.

Johanson, Chris & Duffy, James E. Automatic Transmissions & Transaxles. 3rd ed. 2009. (ENG.). 495p. 96.00 *(978-1-60525-203-2(4))* Goodheart-Willcox Pub.

Jones and Bartlett Publishers Staff & Cdx Global Staff. Brakes Tasksheet Manual for NATEF Proficiency. rev. ed. 2009. 82p. pap. 26.95 *(978-0-7637-8507-9(5))* Jones & Bartlett Learning, LLC.

—Electrical & Electronic Systems Tasksheet Manual for NATEF Proficiency. rev. ed. 2010. 75p. pap. 26.95 *(978-0-7637-8508-6(3))* Jones & Bartlett Learning, LLC.

Jorgensen, Eric & Ahlstrand, Alan. Ford Ranger Pick-Ups: 2000-05 Repair Manual. 2007. (Chilton's Total Car Care Repair Manuals Ser.). (ENG., Illus.). 384p. per. 29.95 *(978-1-56392-641-9(5))* Haynes,Chilton.

—Ford Ranger Pick-ups: 2000-2008. 2009. (ENG.). 384p. pap. 29.95 *(978-1-56392-752-2(7))* Haynes,Chilton.

Joseph, Matt. Automotive Bodywork & Rust Repair. 2009. 144p. pap. 24.95 *(978-1-932494-97-6(9)*, S-A Design) CarTech, Inc.

—Automotive Sheet Metal Forming & Fabrication. 2011. (Illus.). 144p. pap. 24.95 *(978-1-934709-36-8(0)*, S-A Design) CarTech, Inc.

Kartalamakis, Jim. The Alfa Romeo V6 Engine High-Performance Manual. 2011. (SpeedPro Ser.). (ENG., Illus.). 156p. pap. 59.95 *(978-1-84584-021-1(6)*, 1845840216) Veloce Publishing Ltd. GBR. Dist: MBI Distribution Services/Quayside Distribution.

Kershaw, John F. & Halderman, James D. Automotive Electrical & Electronic Systems. 5th ed. 2007. (ENG., Illus.). (C). 416p. pap. 62.40 *(978-0-13-238884-9(7))*; 384p. per. 80.60 *(978-0-13-238883-2(9))* Prentice Hall PTR. (Prentice Hall).

Kibler, Jeff, et al. Chevrolet Lumina, Monte Carlo & Impala (FWD) 1995 Thru 2005. 2007. (Haynes Repair Manuals Ser.). (ENG., Illus.). 288p. per. 26.95 *(978-1-56392-632-7(6)*, 1563926326) Haynes Manuals, Inc.

—Toyota Land Cruiser Automotive Repair Manual. (Illus.). 352p. *(978-1-56392-259-6(2))* Haynes Manuals, Inc.

Killingsworth, Jeff & Haynes, J. H. Ford Falcon & Fairlane Automotive Repair Manual. (Illus.). 224p. *(978-1-56392-263-3(0))*; 224p. *(978-1-56392-262-6(2))*; 240p. *(978-1-56392-261-9(4))* Haynes Manuals, Inc.

—Toyota Corolla & Holden Nova Automotive Repair Manual. (Illus.). 288p. *(978-1-56392-254-1(1))* Haynes Manuals, Inc.

—Toyota Corolla RWD Automotive Repair Manual. (Illus.). 240p. *(978-1-56392-273-2(8))* Haynes Manuals, Inc.

Kitainge, Kisilu Mashtakh. Balancing the Forces for Training Programs & Work Alignment: A Study of Automotive Retail, Service & Repair Industries in Kenya & Australia. 2011. 312p. pap. ***(978-3-639-32971-1(6))*** VDM Verlag Dr. Mueller e.K.

Knight, Nigel. Selling Your Car: How to Make Your Car Look Great & Advice on the Best Selling Methods. 2012. (RAC Handbook Ser.). (ENG., Illus.). 96p. pap. 19.95 ***(978-1-84584-450-9(5)***, 1845844505) Veloce Publishing Ltd. GBR. Dist: MBI Distribution Services/Quayside Distribution.

Knowles, Don. Automotive Suspension & Steering Systems, 2 vols. 4th rev. ed. 2006. (ENG., Illus.). 432p. (C). pap. 153.95 *(978-1-4018-9682-9(0))* Delmar Cengage Learning.

—Automotive Technician Certification: Test Preparation Manual. 3rd rev. ed. 2006. (ENG., Illus.). 704p. per. 81.95 *(978-1-4180-4926-3(3))* Delmar Cengage Learning.

—Automotive Technician Certification Test Preparation Manual. 4th ed. 2009. (ENG.). 704p. pap. 75.95 *(978-1-4283-2101-4(2))* Delmar Cengage Learning.

—Medium/Heavy Duty Truck Technician Certification Test Preparation Manual. 2nd rev. ed. 2007. (ENG., Illus.). 736p. per. 67.95 *(978-1-4180-6600-0(1))* Delmar Cengage Learning.

—Today's Technician: Automotive Suspension & Steering Systems. 5th ed. 2010. (ENG.). 1040p. (C). pap. 147.95 *(978-1-4354-8118-3(6))* Delmar Cengage Learning.

Lamm, John. Velocity: Supercar Revolution. rev. ed. 2006. (ENG., Illus.). 352p. 50.00 *(978-0-7603-2596-4(0)*, 0760325960, Motorbooks) MBI Publishing Co. LLC.

Lammon, Kurt. How to Repair Plastic Bodywork: Practical, Money-Saving Techniques for Cars, Motorcycles, Trucks, ATVs, & Snowmobiles. 2009. (ENG., Illus.). 144p. pap. 20.00 *(978-1-884313-80-6(9)*, 1884313809) Whitehorse Pr.

Law, Alexander & Winlaw, Susan. Car Advice for Women (and Smart Men) Reduce the Risk, Cost & Grief of Auto Ownership & Buying a New Car. 2008. 312p. pap. *(978-0-9781931-0-2(5))* Consumer Automotive Media Services (CAMS).

Lee, Christian. High-Performance Jeep Wrangler TJ Builder's Guide, 1997-2006. 2007. (S-A Design Ser.: Vol. 120). (ENG., Illus.). 144p. pap. 24.95 *(978-1-932494-26-6(X)*, S-A Design) CarTech, Inc.

Line, Mommies. CAR OWNERSHIP for Mommies. 2008. 96p. pap. 12.95 *(978-0-557-01323-4(2))* Lulu Enterprises Inc.

Livesey, Andrew. Advanced Motorsport Engineering. 2012. (Illus.). xiv, 220p. ***(978-0-08-094333-6(0))*** Routledge.

Long, Brian. Celica & Supra: The Book of Toyota's Sports Coupés. 2007. (ENG., Illus.). 208p. pap. 39.95 *(978-1-904788-13-3(0)*, 1904788130) Veloce Publishing Ltd. GBR. Dist: MBI Distribution Services/Quayside Distribution.

Lynn, Vyvyan & Molla, Tony. The Complete Idiot's Guide to Auto Repair. 2007. (Complete Idiot's Guide Ser.). (ENG., Illus.). 368p. (gr. 12-18). 19.95 *(978-1-59257-495-7(5)*, Alpha Bks.) Penguin Group (USA) Inc.

Maddox, Rob. Acura TL: 1999 Thru 2008. 2009. (ENG.). 400p. pap. 29.95 *(978-1-56392-757-7(8))* Haynes,Chilton.

Maddox, Robert. Ford Explorer & Mercury Mountaineer, 2002-06: Covers U. S. & Canadian Models of Ford Explorer & Mercury Mountaineer - Does Not Include Information on Sport Trac Models. 2008. (ENG., Illus.). 416p. pap. 29.95 *(978-1-56392-684-6(9))* Haynes,Chilton.

—General Motors Malibu, 2004-07. 2010. (ENG., Illus.). 336p. pap. 29.95 *(978-1-56392-678-5(4))* Haynes,Chilton.

—Honda Civic & CR-V, 2001-2006. 2009. (Chilton's Total Car Care Repair Manuals Ser.). (ENG., Illus.). 320p. pap. 24.95 *(978-1-56392-750-8(0))* Haynes,Chilton.

—Subaru Legacy & Forester: 2000-2006 Repair Manual. 2007. (Haynes Repair Manuals Ser.). (ENG., Illus.). 480p. per. 29.95 *(978-1-56392-623-5(7))* Haynes,Chilton.

Maddox, Robert & Haynes, John. Toyota Previa, 1991 Thru 1995. 2nd ed. 2006. (Haynes Repair Manuals Ser.). (ENG., Illus.). 328p. pap. 26.95 *(978-1-56392-211-4(8)*, 1563922118) Haynes Manuals, Inc.

Maddox, Robert & Haynes, John H. Ford Mustang: 1994 Thru 2004. Freund, Ken, ed. 2008. (Haynes Automotive Repair Manual Ser.). (ENG., Illus.). 288p. per. 26.95 *(978-1-56392-676-1(8)*, 1563926768) Haynes Manuals, Inc.

Maddox, Robert & Heinrich, George B., III. Ford Mustang 1994-04 Repair Manual: Covers U. S. & Canadian Models of Ford Mustang. 2007. (Chilton's Total Car Care Ser.). (ENG., Illus.). 432p. per. 29.95 *(978-1-56392-649-5(0))* Haynes,Chilton.

Maddox, Robert, et al. Subaru Legacy & Forester 2000 Thru 2006. 2007. (Haynes Repair Manuals Ser.). (ENG., Illus.). 400p. per. 26.95 *(978-1-56392-619-8(9)*, 1563926199) Haynes Manuals, Inc.

Magliozzi, Tom. Ask Click & Clack: Answers from Car Talk. 2008. (ENG.). 208p. pap. 16.95 *(978-0-8118-6477-0(4))* Chronicle Bks. LLC.

Manley, Pat. The Diesel Companion. 2006. (ENG., Illus.). 24p. pap. 14.95 *(978-1-898660-91-0(3)*, 135235AE, Wiley) Wiley, John & Sons, Inc.

Marion, Doug. Chevy II Nova: Production Details, History & Performance for Every Model. 2008. (ENG., Illus.). 224p. pap. 24.99 *(978-0-89689-658-1(7))* Krause Pubns.

Martin, Tracy. How to Use Automotive Diagnostic Scanners. rev. ed. 2008. (Motorbooks Workshop Ser.). (ENG., Illus.). 192p. per. 29.95 *(978-0-7603-2800-2(5)*, 0760328005, Motorbooks) MBI Publishing Co. LLC.

Mavrigian, Mike. Building the Chevy LS Engine: Rebuilding & Performance Modifications for Chevy Ls Engines, Featuring a Buildup of an Ls2. Includes Added Information on Ls3, Ls7, & Ls9. 2010. (ENG.). 208p. (gr. 12). 21.95 *(978-1-55788-559-3(1)*, HP Trade) Penguin Group (USA) Inc.

—High Performance Fasteners & Plumbing: A Guide to Nuts, Bolts, Fuel, Brake, Oil & Coolant Lines, Hoses, Clamps, Racinghardware & Plumbing Techniques. 2008. (ENG., Illus.). 176p. (gr. 12-18). 19.95 *(978-1-55788-523-4(0)*, HP Trade) Penguin Group (USA) Inc.

—How to Rebuild Big-Block Chevy Engines, 1991-2000 Gen V & Gen VI: Step-by-Step Disassembly, Reconditioning & Final Assembly. 2009. (ENG.). 208p. (gr. 12-18). 21.95 *(978-1-55788-550-0(8)*, HP Trade) Penguin Group (USA) Inc.

McCord, Keith. Automotive Diagnostic Systems: Understanding OBD I & OBD II. 2011. (Illus.). 144p. pap. *(978-1-934709-06-1(9))* CarTech, Inc.

McKinney, Mac. What Every Automobile Owner Should Know: The Little Book That Can Save You Big Money. 2010. pap. 7.99 *(978-1-61739-045-6(3))* Tate Publishing & Enterprises, LLC.

McNicholl, George. How to Rebuild Corvette Rolling Chassis 1963-1982. rev. ed. 2007. (Motorbooks Workshop Ser.). (ENG., Illus.). 224p. pap. 34.95 *(978-0-7603-3014-2(X)*, 076033014X, Motorbooks) MBI Publishing Co. LLC.

Meredith, Laurence. Original VW Bus: The Restorer's Guide to All Bus, Panel Van & Pick-Up Models, 1950-1979. 2011. (Original Ser.). (ENG., Illus.). 128p. 49.95 ***(978-1-906133-35-1(2)***, 1906133352) Herridge & Sons, Ltd. GBR. Dist: MBI Distribution Services/Quayside Distribution.

Meyer, William C. The Complete Guide to Rv Electrical, Computer, Solar & Communications Systems Working & Living Independently on the Road. 2009. 228p. pap. 24.95 *(978-1-60844-040-5(0))* Dog Ear Publishing, LLC.

Mihalyi, Eric Michael & Ryan, Mark. Chilton's Ford Crown Victoria 1989-06 Repair Manual. 2007. (Chilton's Total Car Care Repair Manuals Ser.). (ENG., Illus.). 400p. pap. 29.95 *(978-1-56392-671-6(7))* Haynes,Chilton.

Mihalyi, Eric Michael & Ryan, Mark. Ford Crown Victoria/Grand Marquis: 1989 Through 2010. 2011. (ENG.). 400p. pap. 29.95 ***(978-1-56392-904-5(X))*** Haynes,Chilton.

Mihalyi, Eric Michael & Storer, Jay. Ford Pick-ups, Expedition & Navigator: 1997 Thru 2009. 2009. (ENG.). 448p. pap. 29.95 *(978-1-56392-792-8(6))* Haynes,Chilton.

—Ford Pick-Ups/Expedition/Navigator: 1997-30 Repair Manual. 2007. (ENG., Illus.). 432p. per. 29.95 *(978-1-56392-655-6(5))* Haynes,Chilton.

Mills, Rinsey. Ac Sports Cars in Detail: Six-Cylinder Models 1933-1963. 2009. (In Detail Ser.). (ENG., Illus.). 192p. 79.95 *(978-0-9549981-7-2(0)*, 0954998170) Herridge & Sons Ltd.

Morgan, Andrew. Routemaster Bus: 1954 Onwards (All Marks) 2011. (Owners Workshop Manual Ser.). (ENG., Illus.). 160p. 29.95 *(978-1-84425-938-0(2)*, 1844259382) Haynes Publishing PLC GBR. Dist: MBI Distribution Services/Quayside Distribution.

Morgan, Dave. Door Slammers: The Chassis Book. (Illus.). 188p. (Orig.). reprint ed. pap. 30.00 *(978-0-9631217-0-7(7))* Lamplighter Productions.

Morris, Charles. How to Rebuild Big-Block Ford Engines. 2009. 144p. pap. 24.95 *(978-1-932494-92-1(8)*, S-A Design) CarTech, Inc.

Motor Interior Panel Removal Guide: Includes Door Panels, Door Handles, Door Latches, Exterior Rearview Mirrors, Floor Consoles & Instrument Panels. 4th ed. 2007. (Illus.). *(978-1-58251-264-8(7))* Motor Information Systems.

Muscle Mustangs and Fast Fords Magazine Staff & Smith, Evan J. Ford Engine Buildups. 2008. (ENG., Illus.). 160p. (gr. 12-18). 19.95 *(978-1-55788-531-9(1)*, HP Trade) Penguin Group (USA) Inc.

Mustang Monthly Editors and Publishers Staff. Classic Mustang: Restoration, Repair & Upgrades. 2011. (ENG.). 224p. (gr. 12). 21.95 *(978-1-55788-556-2(7)*, HP Trade) Penguin Group (USA) Inc.

Neal, Grant. Porsche 911(996) All Models Including Turbo & GT 1997 to 2005. 2009. (Ultimate Buyers' Guide Ser.). (ENG., Illus.). 160p. pap. 35.95 *(978-1-906712-10-5(7)*, 1906712107, PMM Bks.) Morgan, Peter Media Ltd. GBR. Dist: MBI Distribution Services/Quayside Distribution.

Newton, Richard. Wheel & Tire Performance Handbook. rev. ed. 2007. (Motorbooks Workshop Ser.). (ENG., Illus.). 160p. pap. 25.95 *(978-0-7603-3144-6(8)*, 0760331448, Motorbooks) MBI Publishing Co. LLC.

Niechwiadowicz, John. An Industry in Crisis: A Comparative Analysis of Collision Repair Labor Rates. 2009. (Illus.). 25p. ring bd. *(978-0-9793772-6-6(9))* Mechling Bookbindery.

Owen, Cliff & Varis, Lee. Automotive Brake Systems: Classroom Manual. 5th ed. 2010. (ENG.). 832p. (C). pap. 147.95 *(978-1-4354-8655-3(2))* Delmar Cengage Learning.

Owen, Clifton E. Classroom Manual for Automotive Brake Systems. 5th ed. 2010. (ENG., Illus.). xvi, 285p. (C). pap. 110.95 ***(978-1-4354-8657-7(9))*** Delmar Cengage Learning.

Owen, Clifton E. Today's Technician: Basic Automotive Service & Systems. 4th ed. 2010. (ENG.). (C). pap. 147.95 *(978-1-4354-5384-5(0))* Delmar Cengage Learning.

Owen, Clifton E. & Eichhorn, Lane. Shop Manual for Automotive Brake Systems. 5th ed. 2010. (ENG., Illus.). xx, 498p. (C). pap. 110.95 *(978-1-4354-8656-0(0))* Delmar Cengage Learning.

Palmer, Kris. Fix It! How to Repair Automotive Dents, Scratches, Tears & Stains. 2011. (Motorbooks Workshop Ser.). (ENG., Illus.). 144p. pap. 24.99 *(978-0-7603-3989-3(9)*, 0760339899, Motorbooks) MBI Publishing Co. LLC.

Parise, George, et al. The Haynes Computer Codes & Electronic Engine Management Systems Manual. (Illus.). *(978-1-56392-274-9(6))* Haynes Manuals, Inc.

Parkhurst, Scott. V-8 Horsepower Performance Handbook. 2009. (Motorbooks Workshop Ser.). (ENG., Illus.). 160p. pap. 24.99 *(978-0-7603-3552-9(4)*, 0760335524, Motorbooks) MBI Publishing Co. LLC.

Parks, Dennis W. The Complete Guide to Auto Body Repair. 2008. (Motorbooks Workshop Ser.). (ENG., Illus.). 192p. pap. 29.95 *(978-0-7603-3278-8(9)*, 0760332789, Motorbooks) MBI Publishing Co. LLC.

Paul, Cangailosi. How to Rebuild & Modify High-Performance Manual Transmissions. 2010. 144p. pap. 24.95 *(978-1-934709-29-0(8)*, S-A Design) CarTech, Inc.

Paul, Eddie. Eddie Paul's Paint & Bodywork Handbook: Secrets from a Master Customizer. 2007. (ENG., Illus.). 176p. per. 24.99 *(978-0-89689-233-0(6))* Krause Pubns.

—Sheet Metal Fabrication: Techniques & Tips for Beginners & Pros. rev. ed. 2008. (Motorbooks Workshop Ser.). (ENG., Illus.). 160p. pap. 25.95 *(978-0-7603-2794-4(7)*, 0760327947, Motorbooks) MBI Publishing Co. LLC.

Paxton, Mark. How to Restore Volkswagen Bus. 2008. (Enthusiast's Restoration Manuals Ser.). (ENG., Illus.). 272p. pap. 74.95 *(978-1-84584-093-8(3)*, 1845840933) Veloce Publishing Ltd. GBR. Dist: MBI Distribution Services/Quayside Distribution.

Pearson, creator. Drive Lines, U-Joints & Axle Shafts. 2007. (Illus.). 31p. pap. *(978-0-536-10873-9(0))* Pearson Education Canada.

Pearson Education Staff & Pearson, Nina. Automotive Steering Suspension Alignment, Kit. 2009. (ENG.). (C). 34.80 *(978-0-13-510695-2(8)*, Prentice Hall) Prentice Hall PTR.

Petersen, Donny. Donny's Unauthorized Technical Guide to Harley Davidson 1936-2008 Vol. 1: The Twin Cam. 2007. 456p. 37.95 *(978-0-595-89601-1(4))*; Vol. 1. per. 27.95 *(978-0-595-43902-7(0))* iUniverse, Inc.

Peterson, David. Modifying Your Mitsubishi Powered DSM & EVO's 4G63. 2006. 100p. per. 19.95 *(978-0-9771482-7-1(0)*, Ithaca Pr.) Authors & Artists Publishers of New York, Inc.

Peterson, John C. & deKryger, William. Math for the Automotive Trade. 5th ed. 2011. (New Automotive & Truck Technology Titles! Ser.). (ENG., Illus.). 368p. (C). pap. 121.95 *(978-1-111-31823-9(9))* Delmar Cengage Learning.

Pollard, Dave. A Practical Guide to Renovation On a Budget. 2006. (Revive Your Ser.). (ENG.). 192p. 34.95 *(978-1-84425-244-2(2))* Haynes Publishing PLC GBR. Dist: MBI Distribution Services/Quayside Distribution.

Popular Mechanics Press Editors. Popular Mechanics Complete Car Care Manual. 2008. (ENG., Illus.). 352p. per. 19.95 *(978-1-58816-723-1(2))* Hearst Communications, Inc.

Popular Science Monthly. Auto Kinks: Handy Manual of Short Cuts & Ingenious Ways of Keeping A Motor Car in Condition & Doing Emergency Repair Jobs. 2011. 192p. 42.95 ***(978-1-258-06659-8(9))*** Literary Licensing, LLC.

Porter, Lindsay. Classic Car Bodywork Restoration Manual (4th Edition) The Complete Illustrated Step-by-Step Guide. 4th ed. 2010. (ENG., Illus.). 288p. 39.95 *(978-1-84425-829-1(7)*, 1844258297) Haynes Publishing PLC GBR. Dist: MBI Distribution Services/Quayside Distribution.

Potak, Joseph. GM LS-Series Engines: The Complete Swap Manual. 2011. (Motorbooks Workshop Ser.). (ENG., Illus.). 192p. pap. 27.99 *(978-0-7603-3609-0(1)*, 0760336091, Motorbooks) MBI Publishing Co. LLC.

Prague, Nick. L1 Automotive Advanced Engine Performance Specialist: Motor Age Training Self-Study Guide for ASE Certification. 2006. spiral bd. 25.95 *(978-1-933180-77-9(3))* Advanstar Communications, Inc.

Prentice-Hall, Inc Staff, creator. Interior & Rear Section Damage Analysis Program 4. 2007. (Illus.). 41p. pap. *(978-0-13-243121-7(1)*, Prentice Hall) Pearson Education Canada.

Price Digest Staff. Official Tractor Blue Book 2008. 2007. pap. *(978-1-59969-161-9(2))* Penton Media, Inc.

Price Digests. Clymer Powersport Vehicle Blue Book Spring/Summer 2007. 2007. pap. *(978-1-59969-114-5(0))* Penton Media, Inc.

Primedia Business Magazines and Media Staff. Oliver I & T Timeless Collection Edition - Series 2050 2150. (Illus.). reprint ed. pap. 34.95 *(978-0-87288-150-1(4)*, O22) Penton Media, Inc.

Protecting the Consumer from Flooded & Salvage Vehicle Fraud: Hearing Before the Subcommittee on Consumer Affairs, Product Safety, & Insurance of the Committee on Commerce, Science, & Transportation, United States Senate, One Hundred Ninth Congress, First Session, November 16, 2005. 2011. iii, 66p. ***(978-0-16-088452-8(7)***, 552-070-42664-7) United States Government Printing Office.

Pugliese, Michael A. The Ultimate 7.62 X 39 mm SKS-AK-47-MAX 90 Muffler Pipe Silencer Plans. Pugliese, Michael A., ed. (Illus.). 28p. (Orig.). pap. *(978-1-886774-00-1(5))* M & M Engineering.

—The Ultimate SKS Full Auto Plans. Pugliese, Michael A., ed. (Illus.). 28p. (Orig.). pap. *(978-1-886774-01-8(3))* M & M Engineering.

Ramsey, Dan, et al. Car Care & Maintenance. 2009. (Teach Yourself VISUALLY Consumer Ser.). (ENG., Illus.). 224p. pap. 21.99 *(978-0-470-37727-7(5)*, Visual) Wiley, John & Sons, Inc.

Rehkopf, Jeffrey. Automotive Engine Repair & Rebuilding. 4th ed. 2006. (ENG., Illus.). 384p. (C). pap. 89.40 *(978-0-13-048236-5(6))*; spiral bd. 69.40 *(978-0-13-048206-8(4))* Prentice Hall PTR. (Prentice Hall).

Reid, George. How to Rebuild & Modify Ford C4 & C6 Automatic Transmissions. 2012. (Illus.). 160p. pap. 24.95 ***(978-1-934709-82-5(4))*** CarTech, Inc.

Rendle, Steve. The Car Book: Everything You Need to Know about Owning, Enjoying, & Maintaining Your Car. 2010. (ENG., Illus.). 176p. pap. 17.95 *(978-1-84425-841-3(6)*, 1844258416) Haynes Publishing PLC GBR. Dist: MBI Distribution Services/Quayside Distribution.

—The Car Book: The Essential Guide to Buying, Owning, Enjoying & Maintaining a Car. 2006. (ENG., Illus.). 176p. pap. 29.95 *(978-1-84425-311-1(2)*, 1844253112) Haynes Publishing PLC GBR. Dist: MBI Distribution Services/Quayside Distribution.

—Nissan Pulsar & Holden Astra Automotive Repair Manual. (Illus.). 224p. *(978-1-56392-271-8(1))* Haynes Manuals, Inc.

Rezin, Andrew A. Automotive Service Management: Principles into Practice. 2008. (ENG., Illus.). 400p. (C). 106.67 *(978-0-13-199863-6(3)*, Prentice Hall) Prentice Hall PTR.

Richardson, Jim & Horvath, Tom. Pro Paint & Body. 2011. (ENG.). 160p. (gr. 12). 21.95 *(978-1-55788-563-0(X)*, HP Trade) Penguin Group (USA) Inc.

Robert Bentley, contrib. by. Audi A6 Service Manual: 1998, 1999, 2000, 2001, 2002, 2003, 2004 Including S6, Allroad Quattro, RS6. 2006. (Illus.). 946p. per. 99.95 *(978-0-8376-1499-1(6)*, A604) Bentley Pubs.

Robert Bentley, inc Staff, contrib. by. Volkswagen Passat Service Manual: 1998, 1999, 2000, 2001, 2002, 2003, 2004, 2005 1. 8L Turbo, 2. 8L V6, 4. 0L W8 Including Wagon And 4Motion. 2007. (Illus.). 1872p. per. 129.95 *(978-0-8376-1483-0(X)*, VP05) Bentley Pubs.

Robert Bosch GmbH Staff. Automotive Handbook. Bauer, Horst, ed. 5th ed. 962p. *(978-0-7680-0669-8(4))* Bow Historical Bks.

—Bosch Automotive Networking: Expert Know-How on Automotive Technology. 2007. (Illus.). 119p. per. 24.95 *(978-0-8376-1547-9(X))* Bentley Pubs.

Robert Bosch GmbH Staff, creator. Safety, Comfort & Convenience Systems: Function, Regulation & Components. 2006. (Illus.). 399p. 59.95 *(978-0-8376-1391-8(4),* H013) Bentley Pubs.

Robson, Graham. Mini Cooper. 2009. (Rally Giants Ser.). (ENG., Illus.). 128p. pap. 29.95 *(978-1-84584-183-6(2),* 1845841832) Veloce Publishing Ltd. GBR. Dist: MBI Distribution Services/Quayside Distribution.

Rockwood, Chuck & Birch, Tom. Automatic Transmissions & Transaxles. 4th ed. 2009. (ENG., Illus.). 600p. (C). pap. 122.80 *(978-0-13-505135-1(5),* Prentice Hall) Prentice Hall PTR.

Ron Roland, Roland & Ron Roland. Restored by Hand: The Nuts & Bolts of Porsche 356 Restoration. 2010. 276p. pap. 29.95 *(978-1-4269-0718-0(4))* Trafford Publishing.

Rotella, Rocky. How to Rebuild Pontiac V-8s. 2011. (ENG., Illus.). 144p. *(978-1-934709-41-2(7))* CarTech, Inc.

Rudman, Jack. Auto Body Repair. (Occupational Competency Examination Ser.: Vol. 5). (Orig.). 49.95 *(978-0-8373-5755-3(1),* Passbooks) National Learning Corp.

—Auto Mechanics. (Occupational Competency Examination Ser.: Vol. 7). 49.95 *(978-0-8373-5757-7(8),* Passbooks) National Learning Corp.

—Automotive Workbook. (Workbook Ser.: Vol. 2820). 49.95 *(978-0-8373-7926-5(1),* Passbooks) National Learning Corp.

Ruggles, Cliff. GM Automatic Overdrive Transmission Builder's & Swapper's Guide. 2008. (S-A Design Ser.). 128p. pap. 24.95 *(978-1-932494-50-1(2))* CarTech, Inc.

—How to Rebuild & Modify GM Turbo Hydra-Matic 400 Transmissions. 2011. (Illus.). 144p. pap. 24.95 *(978-1-934709-20-7(4),* S-A Design) CarTech, Inc.

—How to Rebuild & Modify Rochester Quadrajet Carburetors. 2006. (ENG., Illus.). 128p. pap. 24.95 *(978-1-932494-18-1(9),* S-A Design) CarTech, Inc.

Sahota, Gurcharn. Caring for Your Car's Bodywork & Interior. 2012. (ENG., Illus.). 80p. pap. 19.95 *(978-1-84584-388-5(6),* 1845843886) Veloce Publishing Ltd. GBR. Dist: MBI Distribution Services/Quayside Distribution.

Sandlin, Eileen Figure. How to Open & Operate a Financially Successful Car Detailing Business: With Companion CD-ROM. 2010. (ENG.). 288p. pap. 39.95 *(978-1-60138-279-5(0))* Atlantic Publishing Co.

Santini, Al. OBD-II: Functions, Monitors & Diagnostic Techniques. 2010. (ENG.). 176p. (C). pap. 69.95 *(978-1-4283-9000-3(6))* Delmar Cengage Learning.

Santucci, Leo. Chevrolet Inline Six-Cylinder Power Manual 2nd Edition. 2011. (ENG., Illus.). 224p. pap. 29.95 *(978-1-931128-27-8(8),* 1931128278) California Bill's Automotive Handbooks.

Schnubel, Mark. Today's Technician: Automotive Heating & Air Conditioning, 2 vols. 4th ed. 2008. (ENG., Illus.). 976p. (C). pap. 161.95 *(978-1-4283-8324-1(7))* Delmar Cengage Learning.

Schnubel, Mark. Today's Technician: Automotive Heating & Air Conditioning Classroom Manual & Shop Manual, 2 vols. 5th ed. 2012. (Today's Technician Ser.). (ENG.). 250p. (C). pap. 147.95 ***(978-1-133-01745-5(2))*** Delmar Cengage Learning.

Sclar, Deanna. Auto Repair for Dummies. 2nd ed. 2008. (ENG., Illus.). 552p. pap. 21.99 *(978-0-7645-9902-6(X),* For Dummies) Wiley, John & Sons, Inc.

Scott, Ed & Clymer Publications Staff. Clymer Harley-Davidson VRSC Series 2002-2007. 2007. (Clymer Color Wiring Diagrams Ser.). (Illus.). 659p. per. 47.95 *(978-1-59969-189-3(2))* Clymer Publishing.

Scott, Jason. How to Rebuild & Modify Your Muscle Car. rev. ed. 2006. (Motorbooks Workshop Ser.). (ENG., Illus.). 176p. per. 24.95 *(978-0-7603-2775-3(0),* 0760327750, Motorbooks) MBI Publishing Co. LLC.

Scraba, Wayne. How to Build a Winning Drag Race Chassis & Suspension. 2007. (ENG., Illus.). 192p. (gr. 12-18). 23.95 *(978-1-55788-462-6(5),* HP Trade) Penguin Group (USA) Inc.

Seloc. Suzuki Outboards 1996-2007 All 4 Stroke Models. 2008. (ENG.). 1p. pap. 38.95 *(978-0-89330-073-9(X))* Delmar Cengage Learning.

Seloc, (Seloc). Volvo Penta Stern Drives, 2003-2007. 2008. (ENG.). 1p. pap. 38.95 *(978-0-89330-074-6(8))* Delmar Cengage Learning.

Sessions, Ron. Classic Camaro HP1564: Repair, Restoration & Upgrades. 2011. 176p. 21.95 *(978-1-55788-564-7(8),* HP Trade) Penguin Group (USA) Inc.

Seyfer, Donny. C1 Automobile Service Consultant: Motor Age Training Self-Study Guide for ASE Certification. 2007. spiral bd. 22.95 *(978-1-933180-85-4(4))* Advanstar Communications, Inc.

Sformo, Larry & Sformo, Todd. Practical Problems in Mathematics for Automotive Technicians. 7th ed. 2008. (Applied Mathematics Ser.). (ENG.). 256p. pap. 65.95 *(978-1-4283-3524-0(2))* Delmar Cengage Learning.

Shaw, Steven E. Cheating the Dealer: Classified: Author Reveals the Top Secrets to Saving Thousands on Your Car Repair. 2011. (ENG.). 136p. pap. 14.00 *(978-1-60037-844-7(7))* Morgan James Publishing.

Sheeky, Christine L. & Stubblefield, Mike. General Motors: Buick/Oldsmobile/Pontiac Fwd 1985-05 Repair Manual. 2007. (Chilton's Total Car Care Repair Manuals Ser.). (ENG., Illus.). 352p. per. 29.95 *(978-1-56392-627-3(X))* Haynes,Chilton.

Shepard, Larry. How to Rebuild & Modify Chrysler 426 Hemi Engines: New Technology for 1964 to 1971 Classic Hemis & Today's Modern Crate Engines. 2007. (ENG., Illus.). 240p. (gr. 12-18). 19.95 *(978-1-55788-525-8(7),* HP Trade) Penguin Group (USA) Inc.

Starbuck, Jon & Harper, Gavin D. J. Run Your Diesel Vehicle on Biofuels: A Do-It-Yourself Manual. 2008. (ENG., Illus.). 248p. pap. 24.95 *(978-0-07-160043-9(4),* 0071600434, TAB/Electronics) McGraw-Hill Professional Publishing.

Storer, Jay. BMW 3-series: 2006 Thru 2010. 2011. (Illus.). 363p. pap. 29.95 ***(978-1-56392-930-4(9))*** Haynes,Chilton.

—Chilton's Saturn Ion 2003-07 Repair Manual. 2008. (ENG., Illus.). 304p. pap. 29.95 *(978-1-56392-675-4(X))* Haynes,Chilton.

—Mustang, 1964 1/2 Thru 1970. 2011. (ENG., Illus.). 320p. pap. 26.95 ***(978-1-56392-957-1(0),*** 1563929570) Haynes Manuals, Inc.

—Nissan 350Z & Infiniti G35: 2003 Thru 2008. 2010. (ENG., Illus.). 416p. pap. 29.95 *(978-1-56392-731-7(4))* Haynes,Chilton.

—Nissan Titan & Armada 2004 Thru 2010. 2011. (ENG.). 336p. pap. 29.95 *(978-1-56392-841-3(8))* Haynes,Chilton.

—Toyota Camry: 2002-2006. 2009. (ENG.). 368p. pap. 29.95 *(978-1-56392-797-3(7))* Haynes,Chilton.

—Toyota Matrix & Pontiac Vibe: 2003 Thru 2008. 2010. (ENG.). 320p. pap. 29.95 *(978-1-56392-773-7(X))* Haynes,Chilton.

—Toyota Sienna. 2010. (ENG.). 268p. pap. 29.95 *(978-1-56392-777-5(2))* Haynes,Chilton.

—Volkswagen Golf/Jetta/GTI: 1999 Through 2005. 2010. (ENG., Illus.). 416p. pap. 29.95 *(978-1-56392-718-8(7))* Haynes,Chilton.

Storer, Jay & Haynes, John H. Pontiac G6 — 2005 Thru 2009. 2010. (ENG.). 240p. pap. 29.95 *(978-1-56392-805-5(1))* Haynes,Chilton.

Storer, Jay & Kibler, Jeff. Ford Windstar & Freestar: 1995 Thru 2007. 2010. (ENG.). 400p. pap. 29.95 *(978-1-56392-809-3(4))* Haynes,Chilton.

Storer, Jay & Stubblefield, Mike. Ford Fusion & Mercury Milan: 2006 Thru 2010. 2011. (ENG., Illus.). 384p. pap. 29.95 *(978-1-56392-902-1(3))* Haynes,Chilton.

Storer, Jay, et al. Buick Century, 1997 Thru 2005: All Models. 2007. (Haynes Repair Manuals Ser.). (ENG., Illus.). 256p. per. 26.95 *(978-1-56392-628-0(8),* 1563926288) Haynes Manuals, Inc.

—Saturn Ion 2003 Thru 2007. 2007. (Automotive Repair Manual Ser.). (ENG., Illus.). 320p. pap. 24.95 *(978-1-56392-664-8(4),* 1563926644) Haynes Manuals, Inc.

Stubblefield, Mike. Chilton Ford Mustang: 2005-07 Repair Manual. 2007. (Chilton's Total Car Care Repair Manuals Ser.). (ENG., Illus.). 352p. pap. 29.95 *(978-1-56392-674-7(1))* Haynes,Chilton.

—Ford Escape, Mazda Tribute & Mercury Mariner: 2001 Thru 2007. 2009. (ENG.). 320p. pap. 29.95 *(978-1-56392-700-3(4))* Haynes,Chilton.

—General Motors Impala & Monte Carlo. 2009. (ENG., Illus.). 352p. pap. 29.95 *(978-1-56392-709-6(8))* Haynes,Chilton.

—GM Full-Size Van: 1998 Thru 2007. 2010. (ENG.). 384p. pap. 29.95 *(978-1-56392-725-6(X))* Haynes,Chilton.

—Jeep Wrangler: 1987 Thru 2008. 2010. (ENG., Illus.). 496p. pap. 29.95 *(978-1-56392-843-7(4))* Haynes,Chilton.

—Toyota Tundra/Sequoia, 2000-2006. 2009. (ENG.). 448p. pap. 29.95 *(978-1-56392-761-4(6))* Haynes,Chilton.

Stubblefield, Mike, et al. Buick, Oldsmobile & Pontiac Full-Size Models 1985 Thru 2005: Front-Wheel Drive. rev. ed. 2007. (Haynes Repair Manuals Ser.). (ENG., Illus.). 256p. per. 26.95 *(978-1-56392-625-9(3),* 1563926253) Haynes Manuals, Inc.

—Honda TRX300EX & TRX400EX & TRX450R/ER ATVs: 1993 Thru 2006 282cc, 397cc, 449cc. 2007. (Haynes Repair Manuals Ser.). (ENG., Illus.). 272p. per. 36.45 *(978-1-56392-611-2(3),* 1563926113) Haynes Manuals, Inc.

—Subaru Legacy 1990 Thru 1999: Includes Legacy Outback & Legacy Brighton. 2007. (Haynes Repair Manual Ser.). (ENG., Illus.). 320p. per. 26.95 *(978-1-56392-646-4(6),* 1563926466) Haynes Manuals, Inc.

Swike, Tim. Beginner intermediate & advanced hot rod techniques for guitar a fender stratocaster wiring Guide. 2008. 243p. pap. 19.95 *(978-0-615-21813-7(X))* Swike, Tim.

Taylor, Bruce. Alfa Romeo Montreal: The Dream Car That Came True. 2009 (ENG., Illus.). 208p. 79.95 *(978-1-84584-218-5(9),* 1845842189) Veloce Publishing Ltd. GBR. Dist: MBI Distribution Services/Quayside Distribution.

The Chilton Editors. Toyota Sienna 1998-2009. 2011. (ENG.). 320p. pap. 29.95 ***(978-1-56392-905-2(8))*** Haynes,Chilton.

Thomas, Kenneth W. & Thomas, Alfred. Collision Repair & Refinishing: A Foundation Course for Technicians. 2009. (ENG.). 496p. (C). pap. 33.95 *(978-1-4180-0102-5(3))* Delmar Cengage Learning.

Thomas, Kenneth W., et al. Collision Repair & Refinishing: A Foundation Course for Technicians. 2009. (ENG.). 920p. (C). 146.95 *(978-1-4018-8994-4(8),* Delmar Cengage Learning.

Thomson Delmar Learning Staff. Painting & Refinishing Test B2. 3rd ed. 2007. (ASE Test Prep for Collision Ser.). (ENG., Illus.). pap. 98.95 *(978-1-4018-5120-0(7),* Delmar Learning) Delmar Cengage Learning.

Thomson Delmar Learning Staff, creator. Chilton Asian Diagnostics, 2006 Edition, 3 vols., Set. 2006. 1176p. 239.85 *(978-1-4180-3212-8(3))* Delmar Cengage Learning.

—Non-Structural Analysis & Damage Repair Test B3. 3rd rev. ed. 2006. (ENG., Illus.). 120p. pap. 23.95 *(978-1-4018-3665-8(8))* Delmar Cengage Learning.

Tirovic, Marko. Vehicle Performance: The Fundamentals of Predicting & Optimising the Performance of Road, off-Road & Race Vehicles. 2009. (ENG., Illus.). 384p. pap. 79.95 *(978-0-7506-8116-2(0),* Butterworth-Heinemann) Elsevier Science & Technology Bks.

Torbjornsen, Thomas. How to Make Your Car Last Forever: Avoid Expensive Repairs, Improve Fuel Economy, Understand Your Warranty, Save Money. 2010. (Motorbooks Workshop Ser.). (ENG., Illus.). 176p. pap. 24.99 *(978-0-7603-3796-7(9),* 0760337969, Motorbooks) MBI Publishing Co. LLC.

Transactions. 2010. (ENG.). 312p. pap. 29.75 *(978-1-172-19218-2(9));* 327p. pap. 31.75 *(978-1-172-19228-1(6));* 355p. pap. 32.75 *(978-1-172-19207-6(3))* BiblioBazaar.

Transactions. 2009. 284p. pap. *(978-0-217-40758-8(7));* 184p. pap. *(978-0-217-40740-3(4));* 140p. pap. *(978-0-217-40737-3(4));* 196p. pap. *(978-0-217-96810-2(4));* 404p. pap. *(978-0-217-96880-5(5));* 412p. pap. *(978-1-4589-4601-0(0));* 312p. pap. *(978-1-4589-4607-2(X));* 252p. pap. *(978-1-4589-4610-2(X))* Books LLC.

The Triumph GT6 & Vitesse 2 Litre Workshop Manual, 1967-1973: 1967-1973. 45.00 *(978-0-8376-0571-5(7))* Bentley Pubs.

Uttrachi, Gerald. Advanced Automotive Welding. 2012. (ENG., Illus.). 160p. pap. 29.95 ***(978-1-934709-96-2(4))*** CarTech, Inc.

Van Bogart, Angelo. Automobile Digest. 2010. (ENG.). 352p. pap. 24.99 *(978-1-4402-1665-7(7))* Krause Pubns.

Van Boggart, Angelo. Just Packards. 2010. (ENG.). 144p. pap. 12.99 *(978-1-4402-1427-1(1))* Krause Pubns.

Vincent, Peter, photos by. Hot Rod Garages. 2009. (ENG., Illus.). 224p. 40.00 *(978-0-7603-2696-1(7),* 0760326967, Motorbooks) MBI Publishing Co. LLC.

Vitale, Mike. Complete Guide to Repairing & Restoring Aurora Slot Cars. Lane, Mike, ed. (Illus.). 72p. (Orig.). pap. 9.95 *(978-88-379-6067-4(0))* What It Is! Publishing.

Vizard, David. How to Port & Flow Test Cylinder Heads. 2012. (ENG., Illus.). 144p. pap. 24.95 *(978-1-934709-64-1(6))* CarTech, Inc.

Ward, Charlotte, et al. Auto Suggestions: Heal Your Carma, Fix Your Car. 2007. pap. 14.95 *(978-0-9646842-2-5(5))* Purposeful Pr.

Ware, Pat. Ferguson Tractor Manual: An Insight into Owning, Restoring & Using the World's Most Well-Known Tractor. 2011. (Owners Workshop Manual Ser.). (ENG., Illus.). 160p. 32.95 *(978-0-85733-010-9(1),* 0857330101) Haynes Publishing PLC GBR. Dist: MBI Distribution Services/Quayside Distribution.

—Military Jeep: 1940 Onwards (Ford, Willys & Hotchkiss) 2011. (Owners Workshop Manual Ser.). (ENG., Illus.). 160p. 34.95 *(978-1-84425-933-5(1),* 1844259331) Haynes Publishing PLC GBR. Dist: MBI Distribution Services/Quayside Distribution.

Warner, Mark. Street Rotary: How to Build Maximum Horsepower & Reliability into Mazda's 12a, 13b & Renesis Engines. 2009. (ENG.). 176p. (gr. 12-18). pap. 23.95 *(978-1-55788-549-4(4),* HP Trade) Penguin Group (USA) Inc.

Warren, Larry. Chilton's Dodge Neon 2000-05 Repair Manual. 2007. (Chilton's Total Car Care Repair Manuals Ser.). (ENG., Illus.). 320p. pap. 29.95 *(978-1-56392-670-9(9))* Haynes,Chilton.

Warren, Larry, et al. Dodge & Plymouth Neon 2000 Thru 2005. 2007. (Haynes Repair Manuals Ser.). (ENG., Illus.). 256p. per. 24.95 *(978-1-56392-596-2(6),* 1563925966) Haynes Manuals, Inc.

Weber, James J. 101 Jeep Performance Projects. 2009. (Motorbooks Workshop Ser.). (ENG., Illus.). 256p. pap. 34.99 *(978-0-7603-3164-4(2),* 0760331642, Motorbooks) MBI Publishing Co. LLC.

Wegmann, John A. Chilton's Dodge Pick-Ups 2002-08 Repair Manual: Covers U. S. & Canadian Models of Dodge Full-size Pick-ups. 2009. (Chilton Automotive Books). (ENG.). 432p. pap. 29.95 *(978-1-56392-763-8(2))* Haynes,Chilton.

—Chilton's Honda Pilot/Acura MDX 2001-07 Repair Manual: Covers All U.S. & Canadian Models of Honda Pilot (2003 Through 2007) & Acura MDX (2001 Through 2007) 2009. (ENG., Illus.). 432p. pap. 29.95 *(978-1-56392-692-1(X))* Haynes,Chilton.

—Chrysler Caravan/Voyager/Town & Country 2003-06 Repair Manual: Covers U. S. & Canadian Models of Dodge Caravan, Chrysler Voyager & Town & Country. 2007. (Haynes Repair Manuals Ser.). (ENG., Illus.). 384p. per. 29.95 *(978-1-56392-621-1(0))* Haynes,Chilton.

Wegmann, John A., et al. Chrysler Sebring, Dodge Stratus & Avenger 1995 Thru 2005. rev. ed. 2007. (Automotive Repair Manual Ser.). (ENG., Illus.). pap. 26.95 *(978-1-56392-654-9(7),* 1563926547) Haynes Manuals, Inc.

White, Harvey. How to Keep Your Muscle Car Alive. 2009. (Motorbooks Workshop Ser.). (ENG., Illus.). 224p. pap. 29.99 *(978-0-7603-3546-8(X),* 076033546X, Motorbooks) MBI Publishing Co. LLC.

Williams, Roger. How to Restore Triumph TR2, 3, 3A, 4 & 4A: Body, Trim & Mechanical Restoration. 2009. (Enthusiast's Restoration Manuals Ser.). (ENG., Illus.). 192p. pap. 69.95 *(978-1-84584-263-5(4),* 1845842634) Veloce Publishing Ltd. GBR. Dist: MBI Distribution Services/Quayside Distribution.

—How to Restore Triumph TR5/250 & TR6. 2010. (Enthusiast's Restoration Manuals Ser.). (ENG., Illus.). 192p. pap. 59.95 *(978-1-903706-46-6(7),* 1903706467) Veloce Publishing Ltd. GBR. Dist: MBI Distribution Services/Quayside Distribution.

Wingrove, Gordon. Porsche 911 Carrera 3.2: Every Thing You Need to Know about Your 1983 to 1989 Porsche 911. 2009. (Ultimate Buyers' Guide Ser.). (ENG., Illus.). 160p. pap. 35.95 *(978-1-906712-02-0(6),* 1906712026, FMM Bks.) Morgan, Peter Media Ltd. GBR. Dist: MBI Distribution Services/Quayside Distribution.

Zurschmeide, Jeffery. Automotive Welding: A Practical Guide. 2009. (Illus.). 144p. pap. 24.95 *(978-1-932494-86-0(3))* CarTech, Inc.

AUTOMOBILES—MISCELLANEA

Bellu, Serge. Louis Vuitton: The Art of the Automobile. 2008. (ENG., Illus.). 256p. 75.00 *(978-0-8109-9551-2(4))* Abrams.

British Broadcasting Corporation Staff & Top Gear Staff. The Big Book of Top Gear 2010. 2010. (ENG., Illus.). 128p. 24.95 *(978-1-84607-824-6(5))* BBC Worldwide GBR. Dist: Independent Pubs. Group.

Chapman, Giles. Chapman's Car Compendium: The Essential Book of Car Facts & Trivia. 2007. (ENG., Illus.). 187p. 16.95 *(978-1-85894-414-2(7))* Merrell Pubs. Ltd. GBR. Dist: Perseus Distribution.

Dorling Kindersley Publishing Staff. Illustrated Encyclopedia of Extraordinary Automobiles. 2012. (ENG.). 360p. 15.95 ***(978-0-7566-9576-7(7))*** Dorling Kindersley Publishing, Inc.

Magliozzi, Tom. Ask Click & Clack: Answers from Car Talk. 2008. (ENG.). 208p. pap. 16.95 *(978-0-8118-6477-0(4))* Chronicle Bks. LLC.

Miller, Stephan A. The World's Most Complete Guide to Saving Gas (and Money) 2008. 100p. pap. 23.95 *(978-1-4357-0972-0(1))* Lulu Enterprises Inc.

Puyal, Robert. Behind the Wheel: The Great Automobile Aficionados. 2010. (ENG., Illus.). 240p. 49.95 *(978-2-08-030154-3(3))* Flammarion et Cie FRA. Dist: Random Hse., Inc.

Raby, Philip. The Little Book of Aston Martin. 2007. (Little Book Ser.). (ENG., Illus.). 128p. 11.99 *(978-1-905828-87-6(X),* 190582887X) G2 Entertainment Ltd. GBR. Dist: BookMasters Distribution Services (BDS).

Stone, Matt. McQueen's Machines: The Cars & Bikes of a Hollywood Icon. 2010. (ENG., Illus.). 184p. pap. 19.99 *(978-0-7603-3895-7(7),* 0760338957, Motorbooks) MBI Publishing Co. LLC.

Tagliaferri, Mariarosaria. Cars & Stars: 50 Years of Dreams, 1 vol. 2009. (ENG., DUT & FRE., Illus.). 208p. pap. 55.00 *(978-90-76886-00-8(6),)* Tectum B.V.B.A. BEL. Dist: Innovative Logistics.

Top Gear Staff & British Broadcasting Corporation Staff. The Big Book of Top Gear 2011. 2010. (ENG., Illus.). 128p. 24.95 *(978-1-84990-061-4(2))* BBC Worldwide GBR. Dist: Independent Pubs. Group.

AUTOMOBILES—MODELS

see also Model Car Racing

Clark, Jack & Wicker, Robert. Hot Wheels the Ultimate Redline Guide Companion, 1968-1977. rev. ed. 2007. (Hot Wheels the Ultimate Redline Guide Ser.). (ENG., Illus.). 272p. 29.95 *(978-1-57432-539-3(6),* 1574325396) Collector Bks.

David, Dennis. It's Delightful! It's Delovely! It's... Desoto Automobiles. 2006. (ENG., Illus.). 128p. pap. 39.95 *(978-1-58388-172-9(7),* 1583881727) Iconografix Inc.

Fold-n-Roll GS Guide. 2007. spiral bd. 24.95 *(978-1-58651-933-9(6))* Pitsco/Pitsco LEGO Dacta.

Gillham, Roger. Scalextric: A Race Through Time. 50th ed. 2007. (ENG., Illus.). 144p. *(978-1-84425-415-6(1),* 1844254151) Haynes Publishing PLC GBR. Dist: MBI Distribution Services/Quayside Distribution.

Irvine, Mat. Scale Car Modelling. 2011. (ENG., Illus.). 160p. pap. 29.95 ***(978-1-84797-291-0(8),*** 1847972918) Crowood Pr., Ltd. GBR. Dist: MBI Distribution Services/Quayside Distribution.

Laumann, Lloyd L., ed. A Collector's Guide to Classic Mighty Tonkas. 2006. (Illus.). 160p. spiral bd. 39.95 *(978-0-9787898-0-3(X))* M & MV Bks.

Liu, Yucheng. Simplified Modeling for Crashworthiness Analysis. 2008. 164p. pap. *(978-3-639-00671-1(2))* VDM Verlag Dr. Mueller e.K.

Mack, Charlie. Lesney's Matchbox(r) Toys: The Superfast Years, 1969-1982. 3rd rev. ed. 2009. (Illus.). 128p. pap. 19.99 *(978-0-7643-3321-7(6))* Schiffer Publishing, Ltd.

Macmillan, Don. The Bigger Book of John Deere Tractors: The Complete Model-by-Model Encyclopedia ... Plus Classic Toys, Brochures, & Collectibles, 2nd Edition. 2nd rev. ed. 2010. (Big Book Ser.). (ENG., Illus.). 288p. 40.00 *(978-0-7603-3653-3(9),* 0760336539, Voyageur Pr) MBI Publishing Co. LLC.

Maplegate Media Editorial Staff, ed. Radio Control Tips & Tricks: Essentials for the Track, Bench & Beyond. 2008. (Illus.). 82p. pap. 17.95 *(978-0-9817995-0-6(7))* Maplegate Media Group, Inc.

Morgan, Peter. Porsche Boxster & Cayman All Models 1996 to 2007. 3rd ed. 2007. (ENG., Illus.). 104p. pap. 14.95 *(978-0-9549990-6-3(1),* 0954999061 PMM Bks.) Morgan, Peter Media Ltd. GBR. Dist: MBI Distribution Services/Quayside Distribution.

Publications International Staff. Classic Cars Pontiac. 2010. 128p. 11.98 *(978-1-60553-376-6(9))* Publications International, Ltd.

Ralston, Andrew. Diecast Toy Cars of the 1950s & 1960s. collector's ed. 2009. (ENG., Illus.). 128p. pap. 19.95 *(978-1-84584-180-5(8),* 1845841808) Veloce Publishing Ltd. GBR. Dist: MBI Distribution Services/Quayside Distribution.

—Tinplate Toy Cars of the 1950s & 1960s from Japan. 2008. (ENG., Illus.). 160p. *(978-1-84584-126-3(3),* 1845841263) Veloce Publishing Ltd. GBR. Dist: MBI Distribution Services/Quayside Distribution.

Ralston, Andrew & Ralston, Andrew G. Plastic Toy Cars of the 1950s & 1960s: The Collector's Guide. 2008. (ENG., Illus.). 128p. pap. 39.95 *(978-1-84584-125-6(5),* 1845841255) Veloce Publishing Ltd. GBR. Dist: MBI Distribution Services/Quayside Distribution.

Sahakangas, Kimmo, et al. Encyclopedia of Small-Scale Diecast Motor Vehicle Manufacturers. 2006. (ENG., Illus.). 144p. pap. 19.95 *(978-1-58388-174-3(3),* 1583881743) Iconografix, Inc.

Schleicher, Robert S. Slot Car Racing in the Digital Age. 2008. (ENG., Illus.). 240p. pap. 31.99 *(978-0-7603-3235-1(5),* 0760332355, Voyageur Pr) MBI Publishing Co. LLC.

Starkey, John. Lola T70. 3rd ed. (Illus.). 160p. lthr. *(978-1-903706-52-7(1))* Veloce Publishing Ltd. GBR. Dist: MBI Distribution Services/Quayside Distribution.

Thorne, Troy. Pinewood Derby Designs & Patterns: The Ultimate Guide to Creating the Coolest Car. 2010. (ENG.). 118p. pap. 12.95 *(978-1-56523-341-6(7))* Fox Chapel Publishing Co., Inc.

Ultimate RC Projects. 2007. (Illus.). 144p. *(978-0-911295-73-3(9))* Air Age, Inc.

Walker, Nick. A-Z British Sports & Thoroughbred Motor Cars: 1919-1939. 2007. (ENG., Illus.). 304p. 59.95 *(978-1-906133-01-6(8),* 1906133018) Herridge & Sons, Ltd. GBR. Dist: MBI Distribution Services/Quayside Distribution.

Wigman, Nick J., et al. The Car Modeller's Handbook. 2007. (ENG., Illus.). 160p. per. 29.95 *(978-1-86126-893-8(9)*, 1861268939) Crowood Pr., Ltd. GBR. Dist: MBI Distribution Services/Quayside Distribution.
Windrow, Richard. Displaying your Model. 2009. (Osprey Modelling Ser.). (ENG., Illus.). 80p. pap. 19.95 *(978-1-84603-416-9(7))* Osprey Publishing, Ltd. GBR. Dist: Random Hse., Inc.
Zarnock, Michael & Van Bogart, Angelo. Hot Wheels, Warman's Companion. 2nd ed. 2009. (ENG., Illus.). 288p. pap. 18.99 *(978-0-89689-843-1(1))* Krause Pubns.

AUTOMOBILES—MOTORS

see also Automobiles, Racing—Motors; Automotive Gas Turbines

American Society of Mechanical Engineers Staff, ed. Engine Transient Performance. (Illus.). 74p. 78.00 *(978-0-85298-753-7(6))* Professional Engineering Publishing GBR. Dist: SAE Intl.
—Experimental Methods in Engine Research & Development. (Illus.). 168p. 60.00 *(978-0-85298-674-5(2))*; 180p. 150.00 *(978-0-85298-792-6(7))* Professional Engineering Publishing GBR. Dist: SAE Intl.
—Lean Burn Combustion Engines. (Illus.). 250p. 155.00 *(978-1-86058-037-6(8))* Professional Engineering Publishing GBR. Dist: SAE Intl.
Arcoumanis, C. & Kamimoto, Take, eds. Flow & Combustion in Reciprocating Engines. 2010. (Experimental Fluid Mechanics Ser.). (Illus.). ix, 420p. pap. 129.00 *(978-3-642-08385-3(4)*, 3642083854) Springer.
Arcoumanis, Constantine, ed. Flow & Combustion in Automotive Engines. 2006. (Experimental Fluid Mechanics Ser.). 350p. (C). 129.00 *(978-3-540-64142-1(4)*, 3540641424) Springer.
Atherton, Larry & Schreib, Larry. How to Rebuild the Small Block Chevrolet. 2nd rev. ed. 2009. 160p. pap. 24.95 *(978-1-934709-00-9(X)*, S-A Design) CarTech, Inc.
Atkins, Richard D. An Introduction to Engine Testing & Development. 2009. 79.95 *(978-0-7680-2099-1(9))* SAE Intl.
Autodata. 2007 Domestic Diagnostic Trouble Code Manual (1994-2007) 3rd ed. 2006. pap. 83.95 *(978-1-893026-35-3(3))* Delmar Cengage Learning.
—2007 Import Diagnostic Trouble Code Manual (1994-2007) 3rd ed. 2006. pap. 83.95 *(978-1-893026-36-0(1))* Delmar Cengage Learning.
Baechtel, John. Performance Automotive Engine Math. 2011. (Illus.). 160p. *(978-1-934709-47-4(6))* CarTech, Inc.
—Small-Block Chevy Performance 1955-1996. 2006. (ENG., Illus.). 144p. pap. 19.95 *(978-1-932494-15-0(4)*, S-A Design) CarTech, Inc.
Banish, Greg. Designing & Tuning High-Performance Fuel Injection Systems. 2009. 128p. pap. 24.95 *(978-1-932494-90-7(1)*, S-A Design) CarTech, Inc.
—Engine Management: Advanced Tuning. 2007. (S-A Design Ser.). (ENG., Illus.). 128p. pap. 24.95 *(978-1-932494-42-6(1)*, S-A Design) CarTech, Inc.
Barry, Robotnik. How to Build Max-Performance Ford FE Engines. 2010. 144p. pap. 24.95 *(978-1-934709-15-3(8)*, S-A Design) CarTech, Inc.
Bell, A. Graham. Four-Stroke Performance Tuning. 4th ed. 2012. (ENG., Illus.). 512p. 40.00 ***(978-0-85733-125-0(6)***, 0857331256) Haynes Publishing PLC GBR. Dist: MBI Distribution Services/Quayside Distribution.
Bennett, Sean. Medium/Heavy Duty Truck Engines, Fuel & Computerized Management Systems. 3rd ed. 2008. (ENG.). 960p. (C). 201.95 *(978-1-4283-6666-4(0))* Delmar Cengage Learning.
Benty, Cam & Super Chevy Magazine Editors. Chevy LS Engine Buildups HP1567. 2011. (ENG.). 224p. (gr. 12). 21.95 *(978-1-55788-567-8(2)*, HP Trade) Penguin Group (USA) Inc.
Bettes, Harold & Hancock, Bill. Dyno Testing & Tuning. 2008. (Performance How-to Ser.). (Illus.). 144p. pap. 24.95 *(978-1-932494-49-5(9))* CarTech, Inc.
Bill, Trovato. How to Build Max Performance Oldsmobile V-8s. 2010. 128p. pap. 24.95 *(978-1-934709-04-7(2)*, S-A Design) CarTech, Inc.
Bonk, Aaron. Honda Engine Swaps. 2007. (S-A Design Ser.). (ENG., Illus.). 128p. pap. 24.95 *(978-1-932494-56-3(1)*, S-A Design) CarTech, Inc.
Borah, Debajit. Ecologically Important Microbes in Automobile Engines. 2011. 76p. pap. ***(978-3-8443-0091-8(0))*** Lambert Academic Publishing.
Bryant, Jefferson. How to Swap GM LS-Series Engines into Almost Anything. 2009. (ENG., Illus.). 144p. pap. 24.95 *(978-1-932494-81-5(2))* CarTech, Inc.
Burt, William. How to Rebuild the Small-Block Mopar. 2008. (Sa Design Ser.). (Illus.). 144p. pap. 24.95 *(978-1-932494-54-9(5))* CarTech, Inc.
Cdx Global Staff. Natef Automotive Task Sheets. rev. ed. 2010. 74p. pap. 26.95 *(978-0-7637-8512-3(1))* Jones & Bartlett Learning, LLC.
—Natef Automotive Task Sheets: Auto Transmission. rev. ed. 2010. 76p. pap. 26.95 *(978-0-7637-8499-7(0))* Jones & Bartlett Learning, LLC.
Clark, Nigel N., et al. Assessment of Hybrid-Electric Transit Bus Technology. 2009. (Illus.). 77p. *(978-0-309-11803-3(4))* Transportation Research Board.
Clarke, R. M., compiled by. Ford Small Block. 2008. (ENG., Illus.). 108p. pap. 19.95 *(978-1-85520-773-8(7)*, 1855207737) Brooklands Bks. GBR. Dist: MBI Distribution Services/Quayside Distribution.
Colesworthy, Robert L. Reher-Morrison Championship Engine Assembly. 2007. (Illus.). 400p. per. *(978-0-9723432-8-2(8))* IQ Learning Systems, Inc.
Cramer, Matt & Hoffmann, Jerry. Performance Fuel Injection Systems HP1557: How to Design, Build, Modify, & Tune EFI & ECU Systems. Covers Components, Sensors, Fuel & Ignition Requirements, Standalone Units, Drag Strip A. 2010. (ENG.). 160p. (gr. 12). 23.95 *(978-1-55788-557-9(5)*, HP Trade) Penguin Group (USA) Inc.
Cram101 Textbook Reviews & Cram101 Textbook Reviews. Outlines & Highlights for Medium / Heavy Duty Truck Engines, Fuel, Computerized Management Systems by Sean Bennett. 2011. 82p. pap. 27.95 ***(978-1-61830-946-4(3))*** Cram101 Inc.
—Outlines & Highlights for Modern Diesel Technology: Diesel Engines by Sean Bennett. 2011. 158p. pap. 29.95 ***(978-1-61830-941-9(2))*** Cram101 Inc.
Delmar, (Delmar). ASE Test Preparation - A9 Light Vehicle Diesel Engines. 2011. (ENG., Illus.). 224p. pap. 23.95 *(978-1-111-12711-4(5))* Delmar Cengage Learning.
Delmar Learning Staff. ASE Test Preparation - A1 Engine Repair. 5th ed. 2011. (ENG.). 256p. pap. 23.95 *(978-1-111-12703-9(4))* Delmar Cengage Learning.
—ASE Test Preparation - A8 Engine Performance. 5th ed. 2011. (ENG.). 192p. pap. 23.95 *(978-1-111-12710-7(7))* Delmar Cengage Learning.
—ASE Test Preparation - T2 Diesel Engines. 5th ed. 2011. (ENG.). 256p. pap. 23.95 *(978-1-111-12898-2(7))* Delmar Cengage Learning.
—Engine Performance Classroom Manual, Vol. 1 & Shop Manual, Vol. 2. 2007. (ENG.). 114.95 *(978-1-4180-4239-4(0))* Delmar Cengage Learning.
Delmar Learning, Thomson. ASE Test Preparation - L1 Advanced Engine Performance. 5th ed. 2011. (ENG.). 224p. pap. 23.95 *(978-1-111-12713-8(1))* Delmar Cengage Learning.
Denton, Tom. Automobile Mechanical & Electrical Systems: Automotive Technology: Vehicle Maintenance & Repair. 2011. (ENG.). 528p. (C). pap. 36.95 *(978-0-08-096945-9(3))* Routledge.
Duffy, James E. Auto Engine Repair. 5th ed. 2009. (ENG.). 592p. 96.00 *(978-1-60525-193-6(3))* Goodheart-Willcox Pub.
Dunn-Rankin, Derek, ed. Lean Combustion: Technology & Control. 2007. (ENG., Illus.). 280p. 90.95 *(978-0-12-370619-5(X)*, Academic Pr.) Elsevier Science & Technology Bks.
Emanuel, Dave. How to Rebuild & Modify Carter/Edelbrock Carburetors: Performance, Street, & off-Road Applications. 2007. (ENG., Illus.). 136p. pap. 24.95 *(978-1-932494-36-5(7)*, S-A Design) CarTech, Inc.
Emerson, Seth & Fisher, Bill. Performance Corvairs: How to Hotrod the Corvair Engine & Chassis. 2012. (ENG., Illus.). 176p. pap. 27.95 *(978-1-931128-22-3(7)*, 1931128227) California Bill's Automotive Handbooks.
Finkbeiner, Andy. How to Build Max-Performance Mopar Big Blocks. 2009. 144p. pap. 24.95 *(978-1-934709-03-0(4)*, S-A Design) CarTech, Inc.
Fortune, Luke. UFO How-to Vol VII - Esoteric Power Systems. 2009. 615p. pap. 49.95 *(978-0-557-06796-1(0))* Lulu Enterprises Inc.
Genat, Robert. Hemi: The Ultimate American V-8. (ENG.). 168p. 2009. 14.99 *(978-0-7858-2584-5(3)*, 0785825843, Crestline) 2007. (Illus.). pap. 24.95 *(978-0-7603-2747-0(5)*, 0760327475, Motorbooks) MBI Publishing Co. LLC.
Gilles, Tim. Automotive Engines: Diagnosis, Repair, Rebuilding. 6th ed. 2010. (ENG.). 752p. (C). pap. 155.95 *(978-1-4354-8641-6(2))* Delmar Cengage Learning.
Grady, Michael. A1 Automotive Engine Repair: Motor Age Training Self-Study Guide for ASE Certification. 2006. spiral bd. 22.95 *(978-1-933180-71-7(4))* Advanstar Communications, Inc.
Guzzella, Lino & Sciarretta, Antonio. Vehicle Propulsion Systems: Introduction to Modeling & Optimization. 2nd ed. 2010. (ENG., Illus.). xii, 338p. pap. 109.00 *(978-3-642-09415-6(5)*, 3642094155) Springer.
Hadfield, Chris. Today's Technician: Automotive Engine Repair & Rebuilding. 4th ed. 2009. (ENG.). 1008p. (C). pap. 147.95 *(978-1-4354-2824-9(2))* Delmar Cengage Learning.
Hadfield, Christopher & Dorries, Elisabeth H. Classroom Manual for Automotive Engine Repair & Rebuilding. 4th ed. 2010. (Illus.). xiv, 316p. pap. *(978-1-4354-2606-1(1))* Delmar Cengage Learning.
—Shop Manual for Automotive Engine Repair & Rebuilding. 4th ed. 2010. (Illus.). xix, 650p. pap. *(978-1-4354-2827-0(7))* Delmar Cengage Learning.
Halderman, James. Automotive Engines: Theory & Servicing. 7th rev. ed. 2010. (ENG., Illus.). 608p. (C). pap. 118.00 *(978-0-13-510383-8(5)*, Prentice Hall) Prentice Hall PTR.
Halderman, James D. Automotive Engine Performance. 2008. *(978-0-13-158358-0(1))* 2nd ed. 2006. (ENG., Illus.). 560p. (C). pap. 122.80 *(978-0-13-198935-1(9)*, Prentice Hall) 3rd ed. 2009. (ENG., Illus.). 540p. (C). pap. 118.00 *(978-0-13-508504-2(7)*, Prentice Hall) Prentice Hall PTR.
—Automotive Engine Performance Worktext. 2nd ed. 2006. (ENG., Illus.). 448p. (C). pap. 36.20 *(978-0-13-199129-3(9)*, Prentice Hall) Prentice Hall PTR.
—Automotive Engines: Theory & Servicing. 6th ed. 2008. (ENG.). 440p. (C). spiral bd. 36.20 *(978-0-13-505494-9(X)*, Prentice Hall) Prentice Hall PTR.
—NATEF Correlated Task Sheets for Advanced Engine Performance Diagnosis. 5th ed. 2011. (ENG.). (C). pap. 29.00 *(978-0-13-254516-7(0)*, Prentice Hall) Prentice Hall PTR.
—Worktext for Advanced Engine Performance Diagnosis. 4th ed. 2008. (ENG.). 400p. (C). pap. 36.20 *(978-0-13-506039-1(7)*, Prentice Hall) Prentice Hall PTR.
Halderman, James D. & Mitchell, Chase. Advanced Engine Performance Diagnosis. 4th ed. 2008. (ENG.). 528p. (C). pap. 122.80 *(978-0-13-503688-4(7)*, Prentice Hall) Prentice Hall PTR.
—Automotive Engines: Theory & Servicing. 6th ed. 2008. (ENG., Illus.). 696p. (C). pap. 122.80 *(978-0-13-503689-1(5)*, Prentice Hall) Prentice Hall PTR.
Hammill, Des. Ford Cleveland 335-Series V8 Engine 1970 To 1982. 2011. (Essential Source Book Ser.). (ENG., Illus.). 80p. pap. 29.95 *(978-1-84584-349-6(5)*, 1845843495) Veloce Publishing Ltd. GBR. Dist: MBI Distribution Services/Quayside Distribution.
—SU Carburettor High-Performance Manual. 2007. (SpeedPro Ser.). (ENG., Illus.). 96p. reprint ed. per. 29.95 *(978-1-84584-073-0(9)*, 1845840739) Veloce Publishing Ltd. GBR. Dist: MBI Distribution Services/Quayside Distribution.
Handzel, Will. How to Build High-Performance Chevy LS1/LS6 V-8s: Modifying & Tuning Gen3 Engines for GM Cars & Pickups. 2008. 160p. pap. 24.95 *(978-1-932494-88-4(X))* CarTech, Inc.
Hansen, Graham. High-Performance Chevy Small-Block Cylinder Heads. 2007. (Cartech Ser.). (ENG., Illus.). 144p. pap. 24.95 *(978-1-932494-31-0(6)*, S-A Design) CarTech, Inc.
Hartman, Jeff. Turbocharging Performance Handbook. rev. ed. 2007. (Motorbooks Workshop Ser.). (ENG., Illus.). 272p. pap. 29.95 *(978-0-7603-2805-7(6)*, 0760328056, Motorbooks) MBI Publishing Co. LLC.
Haynes, Max & Freund, Ken. Engine Performance: GM, Ford, Chrysler More Muscle under Your Hood! 2008. (Haynes Techbook Ser.). (ENG., Illus.). 238p. pap. 26.95 *(978-1-56392-693-8(8)*, 1563926938) Haynes Manuals, Inc.
Hege, John B. The Wankel Rotary Engine: A History. alt. ed. 2006. (ENG., Illus.). 182p. per. 35.00 *(978-0-7864-2905-9(4))* McFarland & Co., Inc. Pubs.
Henderson, Shawn. Chevy LS Engine Conversion Handbook. 2011. (ENG.). 192p. 23.95 *(978-1-55788-566-1(4)*, HP Trade) Penguin Group (USA) Inc.
Hillion, Mathieu. Transient Combustion Control of Internal Combustion Engines. 2010. 164p. pap. *(978-3-8383-8214-2(5))* Lambert Academic Publishing.
Hirz, Mario & Dietrich, Wilhelm. 3D-CAD Design Methods in Vehicle & Engine Development Processes. 2011. (VDI-Buch Ser.). (ENG., Illus.). 300p. 159.95 *(978-3-642-11939-2(5)*, 3642119395) Springer.
Holdener, Richard. Building Honda K-Series Engine Performance. 2007. (Cartech Ser.). (ENG., Illus.). 160p. pap. 24.95 *(978-1-932494-41-9(3)*, S-A Design) CarTech, Inc.
—Dyno-Proven GM LS1 Thru LS7 Performance Parts. 2007. (S-A Design Ser.). (ENG., Illus.). 160p. pap. 24.95 *(978-1-932494-40-2(5)*, S-A Design) CarTech, Inc.
—Xtreme Honda B-Series Engines HP1552: Dyno-Tested Performance Parts Combos, Supercharging, Turbocharging & Nitrousoxide — Includes B16A1/2/3 (Civic, Del Sol), B17A (GSR), B18C (GSR), B18C. 2009. (ENG.). 160p. (gr. 12-18). 21.95 *(978-1-55788-552-4(4)*, HP Trade) Penguin Group (USA) Inc.
Hollander Interchange Manual: Engine I. 72nd ed. 2006. (Illus.). 760p. pap. 75.00 *(978-1-58132-127-2(9))* Hollander.
Hollander Interchange Manual: Engine II. 72nd ed. pap. 75.00 *(978-1-58132-128-9(7))* Hollander.
Hollander Interchange Manual: Engine III. 72nd ed. 2006. (Illus.). 1160p. pap. 75.00 *(978-1-58132-129-6(5))* Hollander.
Hollander Interchange Manual: Engine Set, 3 vols. 72nd ed. 2006. 2528p. pap. 235.00 *(978-1-58132-134-0(1))* Hollander.
Huntimer, Tony. How to Rebuild the Big-Block Chevrolet. 2009. 144p. pap. 24.95 *(978-1-932494-53-2(7))* CarTech, Inc.
Hyland, Sean. How to Build Max-Performance 4. 6-Liter Ford Engines. 2007. (Cartech Ser.). (ENG., Illus.). 144p. pap. 24.95 *(978-1-932494-68-6(5)*, S-A Design) CarTech, Inc.
Institution of Mechanical Engineers (IMechE). Injection Systems for IC Engines Conference: Institution of Mechanical Engineers (IMechE) conference May 2009. 2009. (Illus.). 300p. *(978-1-84334-561-9(7)*, Chandos Publishing) Woodhead Publishing Ltd.
Institution of Mechanical Engineers Staff, contrib. by. Proceedings of the IMechE's VTMS8 - Vehicle Thermal: Management Systems Conference. 2007. (ENG., Illus.). 756p. per. *(978-1-84334-348-6(7)*, Chandos Publishing) Woodhead Publishing Ltd.
Johanson & Johanson, Chris. Auto Engine Performance & Drivability. 3rd ed. 2009. (ENG.). 218p. pap., wbk. ed. 24.00 *(978-1-60525-053-3(8))* Goodheart-Willcox Pub.
Kartalamakis, Jim. The Alfa Romeo V6 Engine High-Performance Manual. 2011. (SpeedPro Ser.). (ENG., Illus.). 156p. pap. 59.95 *(978-1-84584-021-1(6)*, 1845840216) Veloce Publishing Ltd. GBR. Dist: MBI Distribution Services/Quayside Distribution.
Kim, Stephan & Kim, Stephen. How to Build Big-Inch GM LS-Series Engines. 2011. (Illus.). 144p. pap. *(978-1-934709-44-3(1))* CarTech, Inc.
Kluczyk, Barry. How to Rebuild Any Automotive Engine Videobook. 2009. 144p. pap. 39.95 *(978-1-934709-11-5(5)*, S-A Design) CarTech, Inc.
—How to Supercharge & Turbocharge GM LS-Series Engines. 2010. (Illus.). 144p. pap. 24.95 *(978-1-934709-12-2(3)*, S-A Design) CarTech, Inc.
Lab-Volt Ltd. Staff. AC/DC Motors & Generators. Date not set. *(978-2-89289-403-5(4))* Lab-Volt Systems, Inc.
Lafontaine, Pierre & Lewis, David. Chevy Small-Block V-8 Interchange Manual. 2nd ed. 2009. (Motorbooks Workshop Ser.). (ENG., Illus.). 176p. pap. 24.99 *(978-0-7603-3166-8(9)*, 0760331669, Motorbooks) MBI Publishing Co. LLC.
Lee, Christian. High-Performance Jeep Wrangler TJ Builder's Guide, 1997-2006. 2007. (S-A Design Ser.: Vol. 120). (ENG., Illus.). 144p. pap. 24.95 *(978-1-932494-26-6(X)*, S-A Design) CarTech, Inc.
Martin, Isaac. Ford Windsor Small-Block Performance. 2010. (ENG.). 192p. (gr. 12). 21.95 *(978-1-55788-558-6(3)*, HP Trade) Penguin Group (USA) Inc.
Mavrigian, Mike. Building the Chevy LS Engine: Rebuilding & Performance Modifications for Chevy Ls Engines, Featuring a Buildup of an Ls2. Includes Added Information on Ls3, Ls7, & Ls9. 2010. (ENG.). 208p. (gr. 12). 21.95 *(978-1-55788-559-3(1)*, HP Trade) Penguin Group (USA) Inc.
Maynard, Chris & Scheller, Bill. Manifold Destiny: The One! the Only! Guide to Cooking on Your Car Engine! 2008. (ENG., Illus.). 160p. pap. 14.00 *(978-1-4165-9623-3(2))* Simon & Schuster.
McClurg, Bob. How to Install & Tune Nitrous Oxide Systems. 2012. (Illus.). 144p. pap. 24.95 ***(978-1-934709-34-4(4))*** CarTech, Inc.
McCord, Keith. Automotive Diagnostic Systems: Understanding OBD I & OBD II. 2011. (Illus.). 144p. pap. *(978-1-934709-06-1(9))* CarTech, Inc.
Miller, Jay K. Turbo: Real World High-Performance Turbocharger Systems. 2008. 144p. pap. 24.95 *(978-1-932494-29-7(4))* CarTech, Inc.
Morris, Charles. How to Rebuild Big-Block Ford Engines. 2009. 144p. pap. 24.95 *(978-1-932494-92-1(8)*, S-A Design) CarTech, Inc.
Muscle Mustangs and Fast Fords Magazine Staff & Smith, Evan J. Ford Engine Buildups. 2008. (ENG., Illus.). 160p. (gr. 12-18). 19.95 *(978-1-55788-531-9(1)*, HP Trade) Penguin Group (USA) Inc.
Na. How to Rebuild the Big-Block Mopar. 2012. (ENG., Illus.). 144p. pap. 24.95 ***(978-1-934709-37-5(9))*** CarTech, Inc.
Nedbal, Richard. How to Build Max-Performance Hemi Engines. 2009. (Illus.). 144p. pap. 24.95 *(978-1-932494-95-2(2)*, S-A Design) CarTech, Inc.
Palazollo, Joe. High-Performance Differentials, Axels, & Drivelines. 2009. (Illus.). 144p. pap. 24.95 *(978-1-934709-02-3(6)*, S-A Design) CarTech, Inc.
Parkhurst, Scott. V-8 Horsepower Performance Handbook. 2009. (Motorbooks Workshop Ser.). (ENG., Illus.). 160p. pap. 24.99 *(978-0-7603-3552-9(4)*, 0760335524, Motorbooks) MBI Publishing Co. LLC.
Pashley, Tony. How to Build Motorcycle-engined Racing Cars. 2008. (SpeedPro Ser.). (ENG., Illus.). 144p. pap. 49.95 *(978-1-84584-123-2(9)*, 1845841239) Veloce Publishing Ltd. GBR. Dist: MBI Distribution Services/Quayside Distribution.
Passini, John. Weber Carburettors Tuning Tips & Techniques. 2008. (ENG., Illus.). 128p. pap. 19.95 *(978-1-85520-759-2(1)*, 1855207591) Brooklands Bks. GBR. Dist: MBI Distribution Services/Quayside Distribution.
Petralia, Mike. Small-Block Chevy Bolt-on Horsepower. 2006. (ENG.). 144p. pap. 24.95 *(978-1-932494-17-4(0)*, S-A Design) CarTech, Inc.
Pickerill, Ken. Today's Technician: Automotive Engine Performance. 5th ed. 2009. (ENG.). 1208p. (C). pap. 147.95 *(978-1-4354-2823-2(4))* Delmar Cengage Learning.
Potak, Joseph. GM LS-Series Engines: The Complete Swap Manual. 2011. (Motorbooks Workshop Ser.). (ENG., Illus.). 192p. pap. 27.99 *(978-0-7603-3609-0(1)*, 0760336091, Motorbooks) MBI Publishing Co. LLC.
—How to Build & Modify GM LS-Series Engines. 2009. (Motorbooks Workshop Ser.). (ENG., Illus.). 176p. pap. 27.99 *(978-0-7603-3543-7(5)*, 0760335435, Motorbooks) MBI Publishing Co. LLC.
Prague, Nick. L1 Automotive Advanced Engine Performance Specialist: Motor Age Training Self-Study Guide for ASE Certification. 2006. spiral bd. 25.95 *(978-1-933180-77-9(3))* Advanstar Communications, Inc.
Rakopoulos, Constantine D. & Giakoumis, Evangelos G. Diesel Engine Transient Operation: Principles of Operation & Simulation Analysis. 2009. (ENG., Illus.). xx, 390p. 169.00 *(978-1-84882-374-7(6)*, 1848823746) Springer.
Rehkopf, Jeffrey. Automotive Engine Repair & Rebuilding. 4th ed. 2006. (ENG., Illus.). 384p. (C). pap. 89.40 *(978-0-13-048236-5(6))*; spiral bd. 69.40 *(978-0-13-048206-8(4))* Prentice Hall PTR. (Prentice Hall).
Rehkopf, Jeffrey J. & Mitchell, Chase D. Automotive Engines. 2007. (General Motors Fundamental Curriculum Ser.). (Illus.). 432p. (C). pap. 73.33 *(978-0-13-241143-1(1)*, Prentice Hall) Prentice Hall PTR.
Reid, George. Ford Engine Parts Interchange. 2010. (Illus.). 160p. pap. 24.95 *(978-1-934709-19-1(0)*, S-A Design) CarTech, Inc.
—How to Rebuild the 4. 6-/5. 4-liter Ford Engines. 2009. (Illus.). 144p. pap. 24.95 *(978-1-932494-80-8(4))* CarTech, Inc.
Reyes, Steve. Slingshot Spectacular: The Front-Engine Dragster Era. 2007. (ENG., Illus.). 192p. pap. 24.95 *(978-1-932494-64-8(2))* CarTech, Inc.
Rogers, David. Engine Combustion: Pressure Measurement & Analysis. 2010. (Illus.). 270p. 79.95 *(978-0-7680-1963-6(X))* SAE Intl.
Ruggles, Cliff. How to Rebuild & Modify Rochester Quadrajet Carburetors. 2006. (ENG., Illus.). 128p. pap. 24.95 *(978-1-932494-18-1(9)*, S-A Design) CarTech, Inc.
Santucci, Leo. Chevrolet Inline Six-Cylinder Power Manual 2nd Edition. 2011. (ENG., Illus.). 224p. pap. 29.95 *(978-1-931128-27-8(8)*, 1931128278) California Bill's Automotive Handbooks.
Sciarretta, Antonio & Guzzella, Lino. Vehicle Propulsion Systems: Introduction to Modeling & Optimization. 2nd ed. 2007. (ENG., Illus.). xii, 338p. 109.00 *(978-3-540-74691-1(9)*, 3540746919) Springer.
Sessler, Peter C. Ultimate American V-8 Engine. 2nd ed. 2010. (Motorbooks Workshop Ser.). (ENG., Illus.). 240p. pap. 29.99 *(978-0-7603-3681-6(4)*, 0760336814, Motorbooks) MBI Publishing Co. LLC.
Shepard, Larry. How to Rebuild & Powertune Carter - Edelbrock Carburetors: Covers AFB, AVS & TQ Models for Street, Performance & Racing. 2010. (ENG.). 176p. (gr. 12-18). 21.95 *(978-1-55788-555-5(9)*, HP Trade) Penguin Group (USA) Inc.
—The Mopar Six-Pack Engine Handbook: How to Rebuild & Modify the 440 6-Barrel & 340 6-Barrel or Convert Your la Small-Block (318-360 C. I.), Mopar Big Block (383-440 C. I.) or Magnum (5. 2L-5. 9L) to 6-Barrel Induction. 2008. (ENG., Illus.). 256p. (gr. 12-18). 19.95 *(978-1-55788-528-9(1)*, HP Trade) Penguin Group (USA) Inc.
Siu, Jason. How to Rebuild Honda B-Series Engines. 2008. (Illus.). 144p. pap. 24.95 *(978-1-932494-78-5(2))* CarTech, Inc.
Stapleton, Daniel. The MG Midget & Austin Healey Sprite High Performance Manual. 3rd ed. 2008. (SpeedPro Ser.). (ENG., Illus.). 176p. pap. 49.95 *(978-1-84584-142-3(5)*, 1845841425) Veloce Publishing Ltd. GBR. Dist: MBI Distribution Services/Quayside Distribution.
Stotsky, Alexander A. Automotive Engines: Control, Estimation, Statistical Detection. 2009. (ENG., Illus.). xii, 215p. 159.00 *(978-3-642-00163-5(7)*, 3642001637) Springer.
Szilagyi, Jim. How to Build Big-Inch Mopar Small Blocks. 2007. (ENG., Illus.). 144p. pap. 24.95 *(978-1-932494-57-0(X)*, S-A Design) CarTech, Inc.

Taeschner, Mark R. 289 Hipo Engine Build-up 40 Years Later. 2011. 60p. pap. 24.95 *(978-1-4567-2163-3(1))* AuthorHouse.

Technology Research Editors, ed. Materials Selection for Automotive Engines, 2007 Ed. 2007. pap. 128.50 *(978-1-60030-185-8(1),* Search-In-Print) CSA Journal Division.

Vizard, David. David Vizard's How to Build Horsepower. 2010. *(978-1-934709-17-7(4))* CarTech, Inc.

—How to Build Max-Performance Chevy Small Blocks on a Budjet! 2009. 160p. pap. 24.95 *(978-1-932494-84-6(7))* CarTech, Inc.

—How to Port & Flow Test Cylinder Heads. 2012. (ENG., Illus.). 144p. pap. 24.95 *(978-1-934709-64-1(6))* CarTech, Inc.

Wang, Yushu. Introduction to Engine Valvetrains: Yushu Wang. 2006. (Illus.). xiv, 586p. 89.95 *(978-0-7680-1079-4(9))* SAE Intl.

Weertman, Willem L. Chrysler Engines 1922-1998. 2007. 69.95 *(978-0-7680-1642-0(8))* SAE Intl.

Werner, Chris. HT Rebuild GM LS Series Engine. 2008. 144p. pap. 24.95 *(978-1-932494-60-0(X))* CarTech, Inc.

Zazarine, Paul. The Collector's Guide to GTO 1964-1974. 2007. (ENG., Illus.). 128p. pap. 19.95 *(978-1-58388-196-5(4),* 1583881964) Iconografix, Inc.

Zhang, Xi & Mi, Chris. Vehicle Power Management: Modeling, Control & Optimization. 2011. (Power Systems Ser.). (ENG., Illus.). xiv, 346p. 179.00 *(978-0-85729-735-8(X),* 085729735X) Springer.

Zhao, Fuquan. Technologies for Near-Zero-Emission Gasoline-Power Vehicles. 2006. (Illus.). xvi, 464p. 119.95 *(978-0-7680-1461-7(1))* SAE Intl.

Zhao, H., ed. Advanced Direct Injection Combustion Engine Technologies & Development: Diesel Engines, 2 vols., 2. 2009. (Illus.). 756p. 290.00 *(978-1-84569-744-0(8))* Woodhead Publishing Ltd. GBR. Dist: Taylor & Francis Group.

—Advanced Direct Injection Combustion Engine Technologies & Development: Science & Technology, 2 vols. 2009. (Illus.). 840p. *(978-1-84569-389-3(2))* Woodhead Publishing Ltd.

—Advanced Direct Injection Combustion Engine Technologies & Development Vol. 2: Diesel Engines, 2 vols. 2010. (ENG., Illus.). 560p. 269.95 *(978-1-4398-2475-7(4),* CRC Press) Taylor & Francis Group GBR. Dist: Taylor & Francis Group.

AUTOMOBILES—MOTORS—CONTROL SYSTEMS

Azad, et al. Articulated Steer Vehicles: Dynamics & Control - Fundamental Issues in Modeling, Stability Analysis & Controller Development. 2008. (Illus.). 204p. pap. *(978-3-8364-5665-4(6))* VDM Verlag Dr. Mueller e.K.

Beretta, Joseph. Automotive Electricity: Electric Drive. 2010. (Iste Ser.: 375). (ENG., Illus.). 304p. 127.00 *(978-1-84821-095-0(7),* Wiley-ISTE) Wiley, John & Sons, Inc.

Bishop, Richard. Safety Impacts of Speed Limiter Device Installations on Commercial Trucks & Buses: A Synthesis of Safety Practice. 2008. (Illus.). 43p. *(978-0-309-09827-4(0))* Transportation Research Board.

Cram101 Textbook Reviews Staff. Outlines & Highlights for Computerized Engine Controls 8e by Steve V Hatch, Isbn: 9781428399969. 2009. 148p. pap. 29.95 *(978-1-4288-7502-9(6))* Cram101 Inc.

Hatch, Steve V. Computerized Engine Controls. 9th ed. 2011. (New Automotive & Truck Technology Titles! Ser.). (ENG.). 688p. (C). pap. 149.95 *(978-1-111-13490-7(1))* Delmar Cengage Learning.

Holzmann, Édéric. Adaptive Cooperation between Driver & Assistant System: Improving Road Safety. 2010. (ENG., Illus.). xiv, 226p. pap. 159.00 *(978-3-642-09388-3(4),* 3642093884) Springer.

Holzmann, Frederic. Adaptive Cooperation Between Driver & Assistant System: Improving Road Safety. 2007. (ENG., Illus.). xiv, 226p. 159.00 *(978-3-540-74473-3(8),* 3540744738) Springer.

Ihsan, Sany. Semiactive Control Policies. 2011. 140p. pap. ***(978-3-8443-8417-8(0))*** Lambert Academic Publishing.

Kiencke, Uwe & Nielsen, Lars. Automotive Control Systems: For Engine, Driveline, & Vehicle. 2nd ed. 2010. (ENG., Illus.). xviii, 512p. pap. 89.95 *(978-3-642-06211-7(3),* 3642062113) Springer.

Li, Li & Wang, Fei-Yue. Advanced Motion Control & Sensing for Intelligent Vehicles. 2007. (Illus.). 448p. 179.00 *(978-0-387-44407-9(6))* Springer.

Linton, Charlie. Fast Track Driving: A Private Tutor's Guide. 2010. (ENG., Illus.). 164p. pap. 40.49 *(978-1-4490-6980-3(0))* AuthorHouse.

Parise, George, et al. The Haynes Computer Codes & Electronic Engine Management Systems Manual. (Illus.). *(978-1-56392-274-9(6))* Haynes Manuals, Inc.

Robert Bosch GmbH Staff. Gasoline-Engine Management. 3rd ed. 2006. (Illus.). 358p. 59.95 *(978-0-8376-1390-1(6),* H012) Bentley Pubs.

—Gasoline-Engine Management: Systems & Components - New - Biofuel-Motronic. 3rd rev. ed. 2006. (ENG., Illus.). 364p. 65.00 *(978-0-470-05757-5(2),* Wiley) Wiley, John & Sons, Inc.

Salah, Mohammad. Nonlinear Control for Advanced Vehicle Thermal Management Systems. 2010. 124p. pap. *(978-3-639-23904-1(0))* VDM Verlag Dr. Mueller e.K.

Santini, Al. OBD-II: Functions, Monitors & Diagnostic Techniques. 2010. (ENG.). 176p. (C). pap. 69.95 *(978-1-4283-9000-3(6))* Delmar Cengage Learning.

Ulsoy, A. Galip, et al. Automotive Control Systems. 2012. (ENG., Illus.). 384p. (C). 125.00 ***(978-1-107-01011-6(X))*** Cambridge Univ. Pr.

AUTOMOBILES—MOTORS—EXHAUST GAS

see also Automobiles—Pollution Control Devices

Birgersson, Henrik. Regeneration Methods for Commercial Automotive Three-Way Catalysts: Development & Assessment of Regeneration Methods for Commercial Automotive Three-Way Catalysts. 2008. 76p. pap. *(978-3-639-10510-0(9))* VDM Verlag Dr. Mueller e.K.

Burgdoerfer, Carolynne D., ed. Cars, Climate & the EPA: Issues in Regulating Greenhouse Gas Emissions. 2010. (Environmental Science, Engineering & Technology Ser.). 89.00 *(978-1-61728-963-7(9))* Nova Science Pubs., Inc.

Delmar Learning Staff. ASE Test Preparation - X1 Exhaust Systems. 5th ed. 2011. (ENG.). 176p. pap. 23.95 *(978-1-111-12715-2(8))* Delmar Cengage Learning.

—Fuels, Emissions & Exhaust. 2010. (ENG.). 114.95 *(978-1-4354-4148-4(6))* Delmar Cengage Learning.

Eastwood, Peter. Particulate Emissions from Vehicles. 2008. 493p. 169.95 *(978-0-7680-2060-1(3))* IEEE Computer Society Pr.

—Particulate Emissions from Vehicles. 2008. (Rsp Ser.). (ENG., Illus.). 512p. pap. 145.00 *(978-0-470-72455-2(2),* Wiley) Wiley, John & Sons, Inc.

Eisinger, Douglas S. Smog Check: Science, Federalism, & the Politics of Clean Air. 2010. (ENG., Illus.). 252p. 99.95 *(978-1-933115-71-9(8))*; pap. 34.95 *(978-1-933115-72-6(6))* Earthscan LLC. (RFF Pr.).

Gruden, Dusan. Traffic & Environment. 2010. (Handbook of Environmental Chemistry / Anthropogenic Compounds Ser.). (Illus.). xiv, 294p. pap. 279.00 *(978-3-642-05506-5(0),* 3642055060) Springer.

Hughes, Peter. Personal Transport & the Greenhouse Effect. 2009. (Energy & Infrastructure Set Ser.). (ENG., Illus.). 190p. 110.00 *(978-1-84407-981-0(3))* Routledge.

Khare, Mukesh & Nagendra, S. M. Shiva. Artificial Neural Networks in Vehicular Pollution Modelling. 2010. (Studies in Computational Intelligence Ser.). (Illus.). xvi, 242p. pap. 149.00 *(978-3-642-07222-2(4),* 3642072224) Springer.

Knafl, Alexander. Advanced Diesel Combustion & Aftertreatment. 2008. 164p. pap. *(978-3-8364-6575-5(2))* VDM Verlag Dr. Mueller e.K.

Koirala, Rishi Raj. Assessment of Policy Measures in Controlling the Vehicular Pollution. 2011. 120p. pap. ***(978-3-8443-2737-3(1))*** Lambert Academic Publishing.

Kupnik, Mario. Ultrasonic Transit-Time Gas Flowmeter for Automotive Applications - a Monitoring Tool for Exhaust Emission Control. 2008. 220p. pap. *(978-3-639-00789-3(1))* VDM Verlag Dr. Mueller e.K.

McConnell, Virginia & Harrington, Winston, eds. Controlling Automobile Air Pollution. 2007. (International Library of Environmental Economics & Policy Ser.). (Illus.). 580p. 325.00 *(978-0-7546-2658-9(X))* Ashgate Publishing Co.

Organisation for Economic Co-operation and Development Staff. Itf Round Tables No. 142: The Cost & Effectiveness of Policies to Reduce Vehicle Emissions. 2009. 184p. pap. 92.00 *(978-92-821-0212-1(2))* Organization for Economic Cooperation & Development.

—Transports et éMissions de CO2: Quels Progrès ? 2007. pap. *(978-92-821-2379-9(0))* European Conference of Ministers of Transportation.

Pacific Institute, et al. Paying with Our Health: The Real Cost of Freight Transport in California. Hart, Ian, ed. 2006. (Illus.). 40p. pap. *(978-1-893790-14-8(2))* Pacific Institute for Studies in Development, Environment & Security.

Rakopoulos, Constantine D. & Giakoumis, Evangelos G. Diesel Engine Transient Operation: Principles of Operation & Simulation Analysis. 2009. (ENG., Illus.). xx, 390p. 169.00 *(978-1-84882-374-7(6),* 1848823746) Springer.

Sigel, Gabrielle. Emerging Issues in Environmental Law & Climate Change. 2008. pap. *(978-1-4224-2622-7(X))* LexisNexis Matthew Bender.

Towards Ecological Taxation: The Efficacy of Emissions- Related Motor Taxation Regimes. 2011. (Corporate Social Responsibility Ser.). (Illus.). 256p. 124.95 *(978-0-566-08979-4(3),* Gower Publishing Co., Ltd.) Ashgate Publishing, Ltd. GBR. Dist: Ashgate Publishing Co.

AUTOMOBILES—OWNERSHIP

see Automobile Ownership

AUTOMOBILES—PAINTING

Bortles, JoAnn. The Custom Painting Idea Book: Cars, Motorcycles, Trucks. 2008. (Motorbooks Workshop Ser.). (ENG., Illus.). 160p. pap. 25.95 *(978-0-7603-3169-9(3),* 0760331693, Motorbooks) MBI Publishing Co. LLC.

—How to Master Airbrush Painting Techniques. rev. ed. 2007. (Motorbooks Workshop Ser.). (ENG., Illus.). 192p. pap. 24.95 *(978-0-7603-2399-1(2),* 0760323992, Motorbooks) MBI Publishing Co. LLC.

Fraser, Craig. Automotive Cheap Tricks & Special F/X II: Learn How to Paint Cars, Trucks, Motorcycles, Musical Instruments, Surfboards, & R. C. Cars. 2010. (ENG., Illus.). 216p. pap. 34.95 *(978-0-9637336-7-2(2),* 0963733672) Airbrush Action, Inc.

Ganahl, Pat. Custom Painting. 2008. (Performance How-to Ser.). (Illus.). 144p. pap. 24.95 *(978-1-932494-58-7(8))* CarTech, Inc.

Gardiner, Tony. How to Draw & Paint Cars. 2008. (ENG., Illus.). 128p. pap. 35.95 *(978-1-84584-124-9(7),* 1845841247) Veloce Publishing Ltd. GBR. Dist: MBI Distribution Services/Quayside Distribution.

Gesterkamp, Stefan R. How to Paint Your Show Car. 2008. (Motorbooks Workshop Ser.). (ENG., Illus.). 192p. pap. 29.99 *(978-0-7603-3275-7(4),* 0760332754, Motorbooks) MBI Publishing Co. LLC.

Kosmoski, Jon. Kosmoski's New Kustom Painting Secrets. 2012. (Paint Expert Ser.). (ENG., Illus.). 144p. pap. 27.95 *(978-1-929133-83-3(9),* 1929133839) Wolfgang Pubns., Inc.

Layos, Juan & de Dios Catena, Juan. F. A. Q. Frequently Asked Questions about Techniques Used for Painting Cars & Motorcycles. 2008. (Modelling Manuals Ser.). (Illus.). 159p. pap. 49.95 *(978-84-96658-08-0(2))* Andrea Pr. ESP. Dist: Casemate Pubs. & Bk. Distributors, LLC.

Makhlouf, Abdel Salam Hamdy, ed. High Performance Coatings for Automotive & Aerospace Industries. 2010. (Materials Science & Technologies Ser.). (Illus.). vi, 413p. 145.00 *(978-1-60876-579-9(2))* Nova Science Pubs., Inc.

Martinez, Herb. Herb Martinez's Guide to Pinstriping. 2007. (ENG., Illus.). 176p. per. 24.99 *(978-0-89689-244-6(1))* Krause Pubns.

Mehran, Mark Whitney. Basic Hot Rod Pinstriping Techniques with Hot Rod Surf. 2006. (Illus.). 26p. per. 16.95 *(978-0-9786756-1-5(4))* HOT ROD SURF Publishing.

—Hot Rod Surf 100 % Genuine Book. collector's ed. 2006. (Illus.). 152p. per. 24.95 *(978-0-9786756-0-8(6))* HOT ROD SURF Publishing.

Paul, Eddie. Eddie Paul's Paint & Bodywork Handbook: Secrets from a Master Customizer. 2007. (ENG., Illus.). 176p. per. 24.99 *(978-0-89689-233-0(6))* Krause Pubns.

Perewitz, Dave & Remus, Timothy. Advanced Custom Motorcycle Painting. 2008. (Paint Expert Ser.). (ENG., Illus.). 144p. pap. 27.95 *(978-1-929133-53-6(7),* 1929133537) Wolfgang Pubns., Inc.

Pinstripers, Collection of 25. Pinstriping Masters II: More Techniques, Tricks, & Special F/X for Laying down the Line. 2008. (ENG., Illus.). 168p. pap. 29.95 *(978-0-9637336-4-1(8),* 0963733648) Airbrush Action, Inc.

Remus, Timothy. How to Paint Tractors & Trucks. 2008. (Home Shop Ser.). (ENG., Illus.). 144p. pap. *(978-1-929133-47-5(2),* 1929133472) Wolfgang Pubns., Inc.

Richardson, Jim & Horvath, Tom. Pro Paint & Body. 2011. (ENG.). 160p. (gr. 12). 21.95 *(978-1-55788-563-0(X),* HP Trade) Penguin Group (USA) Inc.

Shanteau, Pamela & Shanteau, Donn. Custom Automotive & Motorcycle Airbrushing 101. 2007. per. 34.95 *(978-0-9671643-1-1(1))* Iwata Medea, Inc.

Streitberger, Hans-Joachim & Dossel, Karl-Friedrich, eds. Automotive Paints & Coatings. 2nd ed. 2008. (ENG.). 517p. 249.00 *(978-3-527-30971-9(3),* Wiley-VCH) Wiley, John & Sons, Inc.

AUTOMOBILES—PARKING

see Automobile Parking

AUTOMOBILES—PICTORIAL WORKS

Acerbi, Leonardo. Ferrari All the Cars: A Complete Guide. 2012. (ENG., Illus.). 436p. pap. 26.95 *(978-88-7911-523-0(5),* 8879115235) Giorgio Nada Editore ITA. Dist: MBI Distribution Services/Quayside Distribution.

Adams, Ron. The Long Haul: American Trucking Companies. 2008. (ENG., Illus.). 208p. pap. 34.95 *(978-1-58388-211-5(1),* 1583882111) Iconografix, Inc.

—Semi-Trucks of the 1950s. 2008. (Photo Gallery Ser.). (ENG., Illus.). 160p. pap. 29.95 *(978-1-58388-187-3(5),* 1583881875) Iconografix, Inc.

Adler, Dennis. Convertibles. 2011. (First Gear Ser.). (ENG., Illus.). 240p. pap. 19.99 *(978-0-7603-4020-2(X),* 076034020X, Motorbooks) MBI Publishing Co. LLC.

—50 Cars to Drive. 2008. (ENG., Illus.). 256p. 45.00 *(978-1-59921-230-2(7),* Lyons Pr.) Globe Pequot Pr., The.

Alexander, Jesse. Ferrari Grand Prix Moments: Formula One Photographs, 1954-1966. 2007. (Illus.). 96p. 75.00 *(978-1-893618-84-8(6))* Bull, David Publishing, Inc.

Auto Editors of Consumer Guide Staff. American Cars of The 1950's. 2007. (Illus.). 320p. 12.98 *(978-1-4127-1997-1(6))* Publications International, Ltd.

—Corvette Sports Car Superstar. 2007. (Illus.). 447p. 24.98 *(978-1-4127-1993-3(3))* Publications International, Ltd.

Autocar Staff, contrib. by. Aston Martin since 1994. 2008. (Autocar Collection). (ENG., Illus.). 176p. 39.95 *(978-1-84425-445-3(3),* 1844254453) Haynes Publishing PLC GBR. Dist: MBI Distribution Services/Quayside Distribution.

—New Mini. 2008. (ENG., Illus.). 176p. 39.95 *(978-1-84425-444-6(5),* 1844254445) Haynes Publishing PLC GBR. Dist: MBI Distribution Services/Quayside Distribution.

Barany, Les, ed. Carnivora. 2008. 176p. pap. 29.95 *(978-0-9795132-1-3(9))* Scapegoat Publishing.

Bayley, Stephen. Cars: Freiheit - Stil - Sex - Power - Bewegung - Farbe. (ENG., Illus.). 384p. 2011. 19.99 *(978-1-84091-535-8(8))* 2009. 65.00 *(978-1-84091-504-4(8))* Octopus Publishing Group GBR. (Conran Octopus). Dist: Hachette Bk. Group.

Benford, Tom. Weekend Projects for Your Modern Corvette: C4, C5, & C6. 2009. (Motorbooks Workshop Ser.). (ENG., Illus.). 224p. pap. 29.99 *(978-0-7603-3540-6(0),* 0760335400, Motorbooks) MBI Publishing Co. LLC.

Bertolino, Jon. Vintage Snowmobiles: The Golden Years 1968-1982. 2007. (Photo Gallery Ser.). (ENG., Illus.). 128p. pap. 37.95 *(978-1-58388-193-4(X),* 158388193X) Iconografix, Inc.

Bill, Jon. Auburn Cord Duesenberg Racers & Record-Setters Photo Archive. 2010. (Photo Archive Ser.). (ENG., Illus.). 128p. pap. 32.95 *(978-1-58388-247-4(2),* 1583882472) Iconografix, Inc.

Blaettel, Werner. Lancia Delta HF Integrale: The Story of a Champion. Albrecht, Peter L., tr. 2007. (ENG., Illus.). 208p. 79.95 *(978-1-84584-132-4(8),* 1845841328) Veloce Publishing Ltd. GBR. Dist: MBI Distribution Services/Quayside Distribution.

Bobbitt, Malcolm. British Lorries of The 1950s. 2009. (Those Were the Days Ser.). (ENG., Illus.). 96p. pap. 29.95 *(978-1-84584-209-3(X),* 184584209X) Veloce Publishing Ltd. GBR. Dist: MBI Distribution Services/Quayside Distribution.

Bolofo, Koto. Vroom! Vroom! 2010. (ENG., Illus.). 96p. 75.00 *(978-3-86521-961-9(6))* Steidl, Gerhard Druckerei und Verlag DEU. Dist: D.A.P./Distributed Art Pubs.

Boni, Valerio. Vespa. 2007. (ENG., Illus.). 185p. 16.95 *(978-0-8478-2936-1(7))* Rizzoli International Pubns., Inc.

Booij, Jeroen. Maximum Mini: The Definitive Book of Cars Based on the Original Mini. 2009. (ENG., Illus.). 128p. pap. 49.95 *(978-1-84584-154-6(9),* 1845841549) Veloce Publishing Ltd. GBR. Dist: MBI Distribution Services/Quayside Distribution.

Booth, Gavin. Buses by Design. 2008. (ENG., Illus.). 160p. 46.95 *(978-0-7110-3326-9(9))* Allan, Ian Publishing GBR. Dist: BookMasters Distribution Services (BDS).

Bouzanquet, Jean Francois. Fast Ladies: Female Racing Drivers 1888 To 1970. 2009. (ENG., Illus.). 176p. pap. 59.95 *(978-1-84584-225-3(1),* 1845842251) Veloce Publishing Ltd. GBR. Dist: MBI Distribution Services/Quayside Distribution.

Bowling, Brad. Ford Mustang. 2010. (First Gear Ser.). (ENG., Illus.). 240p. pap. 19.99 *(978-0-7603-3808-7(6),* 0760338086, Motorbooks) MBI Publishing Co. LLC.

Breslin, Mike. The Track Day Manual. 2008. (ENG., Illus.). 176p. 36.95 *(978-1-84425-482-8(8),* 1844254828) Haynes Publishing PLC GBR. Dist: MBI Distribution Services/Quayside Distribution.

Burgt, Andrew. Lewis Hamilton World Champion 2nd. 2nd ed. 2008. (Illus.). 236p. *(978-1-84425-699-0(5))* Haynes Publishing PLC.

Bush, Andrew. Drive. 2008. (ENG., Illus.). 146p. 65.00 *(978-0-300-13648-7(X))* Yale Univ. Pr.

Car and Driver Editorial Staff, ed. American Road Warriors: Classic Muscle Cars. 2008. (ENG., Illus.). 128p. 24.99 *(978-1-933231-37-2(8))* Filipacchi Publishingsan.

Car Magazine Staff & Anova Books Staff. Best of Car Magazine: The '60s & '70s. 2007. (ENG., Illus.). 160p. 19.95 *(978-1-906032-20-3(3))* Anova Bks. GBR. Dist: Independent Pubs. Group.

Chambers, Jerry. Cruisin' down Your Streets. 2008. 112p. pap. 31.99 *(978-1-4389-3199-9(9))* AuthorHouse.

Chapman, Giles. My Dad's Cortina. 2009. (ENG., Illus.). 120p. pap. 16.95 *(978-1-84425-696-9(0),* 1844256960) Haynes Publishing PLC GBR. Dist: MBI Distribution Services/Quayside Distribution.

—The Worst Cars Ever Sold. 2007. (ENG., Illus.). 160p. per. 18.95 *(978-0-7509-4714-5(4))* Sutton Publishing.

Chauveau, C. L' Aube du Tracteur en France. 2008. (Petite Encyclopedie Agricole Ser.). (Illus.). 248p. 44.95 *(978-2-35250-060-5(5))* Histoire et Collections FRA. Dist: Casemate Pubs. & Bk. Distributors, LLC.

Clarke, R. M., ed. Brooklands Jensen Cars: Jensen-Healey 1972-76. (Illus.). 100p. pap. 16.95 *(978-1-870642-67-5(8))* MBI Publishing Co. LLC.

Clausager, Anders Ditlev. Factory Original Jaguar E-Type: The Originality Guide to the Jaguar E-Type Mk2. 2012. (Factory Original Ser.). (ENG., Illus.). 160p. 49.95 *(978-1-906133-36-8(0),* 1906133360) Herridge & Sons, Ltd. GBR. Dist: MBI Distribution Services/Quayside Distribution.

—Jaguar XK140/150 in Detail. 2008. (In Detail Ser.). (ENG., Illus.). 192p. 59.95 *(978-1-906133-07-8(7),* 1906133077) Herridge & Sons Ltd.

Codling, Stuart. Art of the Formula 1 Race Car. 2010. (ENG., Illus.). 208p. 45.00 *(978-0-7603-3731-8(4),* 0760337314, Motorbooks) MBI Publishing Co. LLC.

—Form Follows Function: The Art of the Supercar. 2011. (ENG., Illus.). 224p. 40.00 *(978-0-7603-4116-2(8),* 0760341168, Motorbooks) MBI Publishing Co. LLC.

—Real Racers: Formula 1 in the 1950s & 1960s: A Driver's Perspective. Rare & Classic Images from the Klemantaski Collection. 2011. (ENG., Illus.). 208p. 40.00 *(978-0-7603-3891-9(4),* 0760338914, Motorbooks) MBI Publishing Co. LLC.

Collins, Peter. British Touring Car Racing: The Crowd's Favourite - Late 1960s to 1990. 2009. (Those Were the Days Ser.). (ENG., Illus.). 96p. pap. 29.95 *(978-1-84584-247-5(2),* 1845842472) Veloce Publishing Ltd. GBR. Dist: MBI Distribution Services/Quayside Distribution.

Colombo, Ercole & Allievi, Pino. I Love Ferrari. 2010. (ITA & ENG., Illus.). 120p. 120.00 *(978-88-7200-289-6(3))* Vianello Libri ITA. Dist: Antique Collectors' Club.

Corner, Colin. The Complete Book of Shelby Automobiles: Cobras, Mustangs, & Super Snakes. 2009. (Complete Book Ser.). (ENG., Illus.). 256p. 45.00 *(978-0-7603-3578-9(8),* 0760335788, Motorbooks) MBI Publishing Co. LLC.

Consumer Guide Editors, ed. Mustang an American Classic. 2007. (Illus.). 320p. 12.98 *(978-1-4127-1998-8(4))* Publications International, Ltd.

Corbetta, Luigi. Legendary Motorcycles. 2011. (ENG., Illus.). 304p. 39.95 *(978-88-544-0393-2(8))* White Star ITA. Dist: Random Hse., Inc.

Cotter, Tom. Dean Jeffries: 50 Fabulous Years in Hot Rods, Racing & Film. 2009. (ENG., Illus.). 192p. 40.00 *(978-0-7603-3346-4(7),* 0760333467, Motorbooks) MBI Publishing Co. LLC.

Culver, Bruce. Schutzenpanzer. 2008. (ENG., Illus.). 229p. 69.95 *(978-1-930571-29-7(1))* Ryton Pubns.

Davey, Arnold. Lagonda, 1899-1999. (Images of Transportation Ser.). (Illus.). 128p. 22.00 *(978-0-7524-1713-4(4))* History Pr. Ltd., The GBR. Dist: Trafalgar Square Publishing.

David Fetherston Publishing. Show Car Dreams: Sixty Years of Indoor Car Show Art & Color. 1500th ed. 2010. (Illus.). 250.00 *(978-0-615-38734-5(9))* GP/Publishing.

Davison, Stephen. Between the Hedges: A Celebration of 40 Years of Road Racing. 2011. (ENG., Illus.). 146p. 38.95 *(978-0-85640-856-4(5))* Blackstaff Pr., Ltd. GBR. Dist: Dufour Editions, Inc.

De Baeck, Philippe. Mini Car Bible, 1 vol. 2009. (ENG., Illus.). 384p. 24.95 *(978-90-79761-24-1(9))* Tectum B.V.B.A. BEL. Dist: Innovative Logistics.

Deganello, Elvio & Rizzoli, Arturo. Abarth: All the Cars. 2009. (ENG., Illus.). 192p. pap. 49.95 *(978-88-7911-464-6(6),* 8879114646) Giorgio Nada Editore ITA. Dist: MBI Distribution Services/Quayside Distribution.

DeMauro, Thomas, photos by. Collector's Originality Guide Pontiac GTO 1964-1974. 2008. (Collector's Originality Guide Ser.). (ENG., Illus.). 128p.

pap. 24.99 *(978-0-7603-3558-1(3)*, 0760335583, Motorbooks) MBI Publishing Co. LLC.

Dorling Kindersley Publishing Staff. Car: A Definitive Visual History of the Automobile. 2011. (ENG.). 360p. 40.00 *(978-0-7566-7167-9(1))* Dorling Kindersley Publishing, Inc.

Doyle, David. WWII Jeep. 2009. (Illus.). 48p. pap. ***(978-0-89747-585-3(2))*** Squadron Signal Pubns.

Dron, Tony & de Burton, Simon. The Bentley Brooklands. 2010. (ENG., Illus.). 208p. pap. 195.00 *(978-1-85894-549-1(6))* Merrell Pubs. Ltd. GBR. Dist: Perseus Distribution.

Edsall, Larry. Chevrolet Volt: Charging into the Future. 2010. (ENG., Illus.). 144p. 30.00 *(978-0-7603-3893-3(0)*, 0760338930, Motorbooks) MBI Publishing Co. LLC.

—Ferrari. 2011. (First Gear Ser.). (ENG., Illus.). 240p. pap. 19.99 *(978-0-7603-4058-5(7)*, 0760340587, Motorbooks) MBI Publishing Co. LLC.

—Legendary Cars: Cars That Made History from the Early Days to the 21st Century. 2010. (Genius Ser.). (ENG., Illus.). 288p. 39.95 *(978-88-544-0081-8(5))* White Star ITA. Dist: Sterling Publishing Co., Inc.

Elias, Jamal J. On Wings of Diesel: Trucks, Identity & Culture in Pakistan. 2011. (ENG., Illus.). 320p. 90.00 *(978-1-85168-749-7(1))* Oneworld Pubns. GBR. Dist: National Bk. Network.

Ellis, Chris. 101 Brockbank Cartoons. 2009. (ENG., Illus.). 112p. pap. 12.95 *(978-1-84425-647-1(2)*, 1844256472) Haynes Publishing PLC GBR. Dist: MBI Distribution Services/Quayside Distribution.

Falloon, Ian. Moto Guzzi Story: Racing & production models from 1921 to the Present. 2nd ed. 2008. (ENG., Illus.). 224p. 49.95 *(978-1-84425-505-4(0)*, 1844255050) Haynes Publishing PLC GBR. Dist: MBI Distribution Services/Quayside Distribution.

Farameh, Patrice, photos by. Luxury Toys: Top of the World. 2011. 220p. pap. 19.95 *(978-3-8327-9407-1(7))* teNeues Publishing Co.

Feist, Uwe. Panzerspahwagen. 2008. (ENG., Illus.). 150p. 49.95 *(978-1-930571-30-3(5))* Ryton Pubns.

Foster, Patrick R. Kaiser-Frazer 1947-1955 Photo Archive. 2009. (Photo Archive Ser.). (ENG., Illus.). 128p. pap. 32.95 *(978-1-58388-239-9(1)*, 1583882391) Iconografix, Inc.

Friedlander, Lee, photos by. America by Car. 2010. (ENG.). 200p. 395.00 *(978-1-935202-08-0(1))* D.A.P./Distributed Art Pubs.

—Lee Friedlander: America by Car. 2010. (ENG., Illus.). 200p. 49.95 *(978-1-935202-07-3(3))* D.A.P./Distributed Art Pubs.

Friedlander, Lee, photos by. Lee Friedlander: The New Cars 1964, 1 vol. 2011. (ENG.). 85p. 49.95 ***(978-1-881337-31-7(6))*** Fraenkel Gallery.

Gabrick, Robert. Federal Trucks Photo Archive. 2008. (Photo Archive Ser.). (ENG., Illus.). 128p. pap. 19.95 *(978-1-58388-223-8(5)*, 1583882235) Iconografix, Inc.

—Reo Trucks, 1910-1966. 2006. (Photo Archive Ser.). (ENG., Illus.). 128p. pap. 19.95 *(978-1-58388-181-1(6)*, 1583881816) Iconografix, Inc.

Gingerelli, Dain. Hot Rods: Roadsters, Coupes, Customs. 2009. (Idea Book Ser.). (ENG., Illus.). 160p. pap. 24.99 *(978-0-7603-3516-1(8)*, 0760335168, Motorbooks) MBI Publishing Co. LLC.

Gorodji, Dennis. Nissan GT-R Supercar: Born to Race. 2010. (ENG., Illus.). 226p. 39.95 *(978-1-84584-221-5(9)*, 1845842219) Veloce Publishing Ltd. GBR. Dist: MBI Distribution Services/Quayside Distribution.

Grafton, Carol Belanger, ed. Vintage Automobile Ads & Posters. 2010. (Dover Electronic Clip Art Ser.). (ENG., Illus.). 48p. pap. 19.95 *(978-0-486-99099-6(0))* Dover Pubns., Inc.

Green, Simon. Garage Life: # 1 The Offbeat Import Car Shop. 2010. (Life in the Garage Ser.). (ENG.). 240p. 36.00 *(978-1-935350-03-3(X)*, Parker Hse. Publishing Inc.,Csi) Continental Sales, Inc.

Grist, Peter. Dodge Challenger Plymouth Barracuda: Chrysler's Potent Pony Cars. 2009. (ENG., Illus.). 196p. 59.95 *(978-1-84584-105-8(0)*, 1845841050) Veloce Publishing Ltd. GBR. Dist: MBI Distribution Services/Quayside Distribution.

Grubb, Scooter. Sturgis 70th Anniversary. 2011. (ENG., Illus.). 144p. pap. 27.95 *(978-1-929133-96-3(0)*, 1929133960) Wolfgang Pubns., Inc.

Gunnell, John. How to Restore Automotive Trim & Hardware. 2009. (Motorbooks Workshop Ser.). (ENG., Illus.). 160p. pap. 24.99 *(978-0-7603-3531-4(1)*, 0760335311, Motorbooks) MBI Publishing Co. LLC.

Hardin, Drew. Hot Rod Magazine All the Covers. Hot Rod Magazine Staff, ed. 2010. (ENG., Illus.). 256p. 35.00 *(978-0-7603-3817-9(5)*, 0760338175, Motorbooks) MBI Publishing Co. LLC.

Hart, Lou. Drag Racing Funny Cars: Factory Flyers to Flip-top Fuelers. 2008. (Photo Gallery Ser.). (ENG., Illus.). 160p. pap. 19.95 *(978-1-58388-220-7(0)*, 1583882200) Iconografix, Inc.

—Kings of the Quarter-Mile: Rail-Jobs, Slingshots & Mid-Engine Dragsters. 2009. (Photo Gallery Ser.). (ENG., Illus.). 160p. pap. 19.95 *(978-1-58388-234-4(0)*, 1583882340) Iconografix, Inc.

—Volkswagen Drag Racing. 2012. (Photo Archive Ser.). (ENG., Illus.). 128p. pap. 29.95 *(978-1-58388-294-8(4)*, 1583882944) Iconografix, Inc.

Hart, Lou & Lee, Cory. Drag Racing's Exhibition Attractions: From Rockets to Ramp-Jumps. 2008. (ENG., Illus.). 96p. pap. 12.95 *(978-1-58388-208-5(1)*, 1583882081) Iconografix, Inc.

Hart, Roger. Postcards from Detroit: Remembering Formula 1 in the Motor City. 2006. (Illus.). 96p. 24.95 *(978-1-893618-72-5(2))* Bull, David Publishing, Inc.

Haskew, Michael E. Tanks Inside Out. 2010. (ENG., Illus.). 320p. 34.95 *(978-1-60710-110-9(6)*, Thunder Bay Pr.) Advantage Pubs. Group.

Hayes, Russell. Ford Cortina: The Complete History. 2012. (ENG., Illus.). 288p. 56.95 ***(978-1-84425-988-5(9)***, 1844259889) Haynes Publishing PLC GBR. Dist: MBI Distribution Services/Quayside Distribution.

Hayes, Russell. Tvr: Ever the Extrovert. 2009. (Haynes Classic Makes Ser.). (ENG., Illus.). 160p. 34.95 *(978-1-84425-507-8(7)*, 1844255077) Haynes Publishing PLC GBR. Dist: MBI Distribution Services/Quayside Distribution.

Haynes Publishing, compiled by. The Classic Cutaways. 2009. (ENG., Illus.). 208p. 49.95 *(978-1-84425-570-2(0)*, 1844255700) Haynes Publishing PLC GBR. Dist: MBI Distribution Services/Quayside Distribution.

Headrick Jr, Robert J. Cadillac: The Tailfin Years. 2008. (ENG., Illus.). 128p. pap. 34.95 *(978-1-58388-212-2(X)*, 158388212X) Iconografix, Inc.

Heasley, Jerry. Corvette Masterpieces: Dream Cars You'd Love to Own. 2007. (ENG.). 352p. 40.00 *(978-0-89689-554-6(8))* Krause Pubns.

Heimann, Jim, ed. Cars of the 50s. 25th ed. 2009. (ENG., Illus.). 192p. 7.99 *(978-3-8365-1427-9(3))* TASCHEN DEU. Dist: Ingram Pub. Services.

Herlocher, Rusty & Gunnell, John. The Best of Auto Wreck Photos - Vintage Car Wrecks 1950-1979 & CRASH. 2009. (ENG.). cd-rom 19.99 *(978-1-4402-0826-3(3))* Krause Pubns.

Ireland, Gavin. Le Mans Panoramic. 2012. (ENG., Illus.). 224p. 69.95 *(978-1-84584-243-7(X)*, 184584243X) Veloce Publishing Ltd. GBR. Dist: MBI Distribution Services/Quayside Distribution.

Iverson, Richard J. A Pictorial View from the Bear Shops at Indianapolis. 2006. lib. bdg. 20.00 *(978-0-9742668-2-4(5))* Pitstop Bks.

Jones, Brian & Jones, Sierra. The Car Show Book. 2011. 378p. pap. 24.99 ***(978-0-557-71107-9(X))*** Lulu Enterprises Inc.

Keister, Douglas, photos by. Teardrops & Tiny Trailers, 1 vol. 2008. (ENG., Illus.). 160p. 19.99 *(978-1-4236-0274-3(9))* Gibbs Smith, Publisher.

Kelly, Maurice A. Russian Motor Vehicles: Soviet Limousines 1930-2003. 2011. (ENG., Illus.). 128p. 49.95 *(978-1-84584-300-7(2)*, 1845843002) Veloce Publishing Ltd. GBR. Dist: MBI Distribution Services/Quayside Distribution.

Kennedy, Steve. Northeastern Modified Stock Car Racing. 2012. (Photo Gallery Ser.). (ENG., Illus.). 160p. pap. 39.95 *(978-1-58388-284-9(7)*, 1583882847) Iconografix, Inc.

Killen, William D. Firefighting with Henry's Model T. 2008. (Illus.). 135p. *(978-0-615-22303-2(6))* Killen, William D.

Knowles, David. Triumph TR7: The Untold Story. 2008. (ENG., Illus.). 256p. 44.95 *(978-1-86126-891-4(2)*, 1861268912) Crowood Pr., Ltd. GBR. Dist: MBI Distribution Services/Quayside Distribution.

Kreipke, Robert. The Model T: A Pictorial Chronology of the Most Famous Car in the World. 2008. (Illus.). 156p. lib. bdg. 37.50 *(978-1-932439-93-9(5))* M.T. Publishing Co., Inc.

Krevsky, Margery. Sirens of Chrome: The Enduring Allure of Auto Show Models. 2008. (Illus.). 24.95 *(978-1-879094-84-0(3))* Momentum Bks., LLC.

Laban, Brian. The Mini: Celebrating 50 Years of a Modern Motoring Icon. 2009. (ENG., Illus.). 208p. 34.95 *(978-1-84732-373-6(1))* Carlton Bks., Ltd. GBR. Dist: Sterling Publishing Co., Inc.

Lamm, John. Exotic Cars. 2008. (Gallery Ser.). (ENG., Illus.). 256p. pap. 19.99 *(978-0-7603-3261-0(4)*, 0760332614, Motorbooks) MBI Publishing Co. LLC.

—Velocity: Supercar Revolution. rev. ed. 2006. (ENG., Illus.). 352p. 50.00 *(978-0-7603-2596-4(0)*, 0760325960, Motorbooks) MBI Publishing Co. LLC.

Laughing Elephant Publishing Staff, compiled by. Cars from the 50s Postcard Book. 2010. (ENG., Illus.). 30p. pap. 9.95 *(978-1-59583-390-7(0)*, Darling & Co.) Laughing Elephant.

Layos, Juan & de Dios Catena, Juan. F. A. Q. Frequently Asked Questions about Techniques Used for Painting Cars & Motorcycles. 2008. (Modelling Manuals Ser.). (Illus.). 159p. pap. 49.95 *(978-84-96658-08-0(2))* Andrea Pr. ESP. Dist: Casemate Pubs. & Bk. Distributors, LLC.

Lehbrink, Hartmut. Bmw-Rev. 2010. 384p. pap. 29.99 *(978-0-8416-7163-8(X))* Langenscheidt Publishing Group.

—Ferrari (Lct) 2010. 4p. pap. 29.99 *(978-0-8416-7155-3(9))* Langenscheidt Publishing Group.

Lehbrink, Hartmut & Schlegelmilch, Rainer W. British Sports Cars. 2008. (ENG., Illus.). 440p. 24.95 *(978-3-8331-1154-9(2))* h.f.ullmann DEU. Dist: Innovative Logistics.

Lehbrink, Hartmut & Von Osterroth, Jochen. Bmw. Schlegelmilch, Rainer W., ed. rev. ed. 2010. (ENG., Illus.). 480p. 49.95 ***(978-3-8331-1059-7(7))*** h.f.ullmann DEU. Dist: Innovative Logistics.

Lehbrink, Hartmut, et al. BMW, 1 vol. 2010. (ENG., Illus.). 384p. spiral bd. 19.99 *(978-3-8331-5291-7(5))* h.f.ullmann DEU. Dist: Innovative Logistics.

Lewin, Tony. The A-Z of 21st-Century Cars. 2011. (ENG., Illus.). 540p. pap. 39.95 *(978-1-85894-525-5(9))* Merrell Pubs. Ltd. GBR. Dist: Perseus Distribution.

Lintelmann, Reinhard. 1000 Automoviles: Historia, Clasicos, Detalles. 2007. (Illus.). 359p. *(978-3-625-00035-8(0))* Negev Importing Co., Ltd.

Long, Brian. The Book of the Jaguar XJ-S. 2012. (ENG., Illus.). 160p. 69.95 *(978-1-84584-401-1(7)*, 1845844017) Veloce Publishing Ltd. GBR. Dist: MBI Distribution Services/Quayside Distribution.

Ludvigsen, Karl. Porsche Spyders, 1956-1964: Type 550A, RSK & 718. 2007. (Ludvigsen Library Ser.). (ENG., Illus.). 128p. pap. 29.95 *(978-1-58388-200-9(6)*, 1583882006) Iconografix, Inc.

—White Racers from Zuffenhausen: Porsche 904, 906, 907, 908, 909, 910. 2008. (Ludvigsen Library Ser.). (ENG., Illus.). 128p. pap. 29.95 *(978-1-58388-218-4(9)*, 1583882189) Iconografix, Inc.

Macmillan, Don, ed. The John Deere Tractor Legacy: The Complete Illustrated History from Tractors & Machinery to Deere's Role in Farm Life, 1837 to Today. 2012. (ENG., Illus.). 256p. pap. 24.99 *(978-0-7603-4014-1(5)*, 0760340145, Voyageur Pr) MBI Publishing Co. LLC.

Manferto de Fabianus, Valeria & Rizzo, Enzo. Cube Book: Motocicletas. 2008. (Illus.). 736p. 19.95 *(978-970-718-673-6(9)*, Numen) Advanced Marketing, S. de R. L. de C. V. MEX. Dist: Perseus-PGW.

Marek, Bjoern. Sleeping Beauties USA: Abandoned Classic Cars & Trucks. 2011. (ENG., Illus.). 96p. 24.95 *(978-1-84584-346-5(0)*, 1845843460) Veloce Publishing Ltd. GBR. Dist: MBI Distribution Services/Quayside Distribution.

Marie. Amer Car Ad Coll. *(978-4-7663-3190-5(7))* Green Arrow Publishing.

Markham, Louk. Crown Coach Corporation: School Buses, Fire Trucks & Custom Coaches. 2011. (ENG., Illus.). 128p. pap. 34.95 *(978-1-58388-275-7(8)*, 1583882758) Iconografix, Inc.

Martinez, Diosdado. Havana City Classic Cars. 2009. 220p. pap. *(978-1-926609-00-3(X))* Bermuda Library.

Mayes, Alan. Hot Rods. 2010. (First Gear Ser.). (ENG., Illus.). 240p. pap. 19.99 *(978-0-7603-3861-2(2)*, 0760338612, Motorbooks) MBI Publishing Co. LLC.

—Old School Customs: Top Traditional Custom Car Builders. 2009. (ENG., Illus.). 160p. 35.00 *(978-0-7603-3457-7(9)*, 0760334579, Motorbooks) MBI Publishing Co. LLC.

McCall, Walt & McPherson, Tom. Classic American Ambulances & Funeral Vehicles: 1900-1980 Photo Archives. 2007. (Photo Archive Ser.). (ENG., Illus.). 256p. pap. 19.95 *(978-1-58388-206-1(5)*, 1583882065) Iconografix, Inc.

McCall, Walter. Funeral Service & Flower Cars Photo Archive. 2008. (Photo Archive Ser.). (ENG., Illus.). 128p. pap. 29.95 *(978-1-58388-227-6(8)*, 1583882278) Iconografix, Inc.

Mccausey, Gregory. Chrysler Front Wheel Drive Performance: 1983-1992. 2009. pap. 19.00 *(978-1-61584-912-3(2))* Independent Pub.

McCausland, Evan T. Rapid Transit Series Buses: General Motors & Beyond. 2008. (Enthusiast's Reference Ser.). (ENG., Illus.). 160p. pap. 32.95 *(978-1-58388-209-2(X)*, 158388209X) Iconografix, Inc.

McFadyen, Peter. Motor Racing at Oulton Park in The 1970s. 2008. (Those were the Days... Ser.). (ENG., Illus.). 96p. pap. 25.95 *(978-1-84584-164-5(6)*, 1845841646) Veloce Publishing Ltd. GBR. Dist: MBI Distribution Services/Quayside Distribution.

Moloney, James H. Mercury Automobiles, 1939-1959. 2007. (Photo Archive Ser.). (ENG., Illus.). 128p. pap. 29.95 *(978-1-58388-205-4(7)*, 1583882057) Iconografix, Inc.

Moore, Moe. Guzzi Girls. 2007. (Illus.). 159p. 29.95 *(978-3-936709-30-8(0))* Goliath DEU. Dist: SCB Distributors.

Moylan, Brian. MG's Abingdon Factory. 2007. (Those Were the Days Ser.). (ENG., Illus.). 96p. reprint ed. pap. 24.95 *(978-1-84584-114-0(X)*, 184584114X) Veloce Publishing Ltd. GBR. Dist: MBI Distribution Services/Quayside Distribution.

Mueller, Mike. El Camino by Chevrolet. 2008. (ENG., Illus.). 112p. pap. 24.95 *(978-1-58388-215-3(4)*, 1583882154) Iconografix, Inc.

—The Corvette Factories: Building America's Sports Car. 2009. (ENG., Illus.). 192p. 40.00 *(978-0-7603-3551-2(6)*, 0760335516, Motorbooks) MBI Publishing Co. LLC.

—Muscle Cars. 2010. (First Gear Ser.). (ENG., Illus.). 240p. pap. 19.99 *(978-0-7603-3837-7(X)*, 076033837X, Motorbooks) MBI Publishing Co. LLC.

Narus, Don. Chrysler's Land Yacht-Twon & Country Convertibles 1942-1986. 2009. pap. 22.95 *(978-1-61623-211-5(0))* Independent Pub.

Negrone, Jos Bendinelli. VW Bus: Road to Freedom. 2009. (ENG., Illus.). 120p. 49.95 incl. lp *(978-3-940004-55-0(3))* Edel Classica Gmbh.

Newhardt, David. Art of the Muscle Car. 2009. (ENG., Illus.). 240p. 40.00 *(978-0-7603-3591-8(5)*, 0760335915, Motorbooks) MBI Publishing Co. LLC.

Nishio, Tetsuya & Kopec, Rick. World Registry of Cobras. 4th ed. 2009. (ENG.). 1618p. 225.00 *(978-1-935350-07-1(2)*, Parker Hse. Publishing Inc.,Csi) Continental Sales, Inc.

Nourmand, Tony. Stars & Cars. 2009. (ENG., Illus.). 192p. 52.50 *(978-0-7522-2645-3(2)*, Boxtree) Pan Macmillan GBR. Dist: Trans-Atlantic Pubns., Inc.

Olson, Randall. GM in Miniature. 2008. (ENG., Illus.). 128p. pap. *(978-1-84584-156-0(5)*, 1845841565) Veloce Publishing Ltd. GBR. Dist: MBI Distribution Services/Quayside Distribution.

Orel, Frank, ed. The Porsche Book. 2010. (GER, CHI, RUS & FRE., Illus.). 296p. 125.00 *(978-3-8327-9377-7(1))* teNeues Publishing Co.

O'Toole, Larry. Classic Hot Rod Style: Traditional Hot Rods with New Millennium Make-Over. 2008. (ENG., Illus.). 140p. pap. 24.95 *(978-0-949398-59-8(4)*, 0949398594) Graffiti Pubns. AUS. Dist: MBI Distribution Services/Quayside Distribution.

Palmer, Michael. Morgan 4/4: The First 75 Years. 2011. (ENG., Illus.). 192p. 39.95 ***(978-1-84797-288-0(8)***, 1847972888) Crowood Pr., Ltd. GBR. Dist: MBI Distribution Services/Quayside Distribution.

Parker, Paul. Formula 1 in Camera 1950-59. 2011. (ENG., Illus.). 240p. 49.95 *(978-1-84425-553-5(0)*, 1844255530) Haynes Publishing PLC GBR. Dist: MBI Distribution Services/Quayside Distribution.

—Races, Faces, Places: The motor racing photography of Michael Cooper. 2009. (ENG., Illus.). 352p. 79.95 *(978-1-84425-508-5(5)*, 1844255085) Haynes Publishing PLC GBR. Dist: MBI Distribution Services/Quayside Distribution.

—Sports Car Racing in Camera 1950-1959. 2011. (ENG., Illus.). 240p. 59.95 *(978-1-84425-552-8(2)*, 1844255522) Haynes Publishing PLC GBR. Dist: MBI Distribution Services/Quayside Distribution.

—Sports Car Racing in Camera 1960-69. 2007. (ENG., Illus.). 240p. 59.95 *(978-1-84425-400-2(3)*, 1844254003) Haynes Publishing PLC GBR. Dist: MBI Distribution Services/Quayside Distribution.

—Sports Car Racing in Camera, 1970-79. 2008. (ENG., Illus.). 240p. 59.95 *(978-1-84425-471-2(2)*, 1844254712) Haynes Publishing PLC GBR. Dist: MBI Distribution Services/Quayside Distribution.

Peck, Colin. The Last Real Austins: 1946 To 1959. 2009. (Those Were the Days Ser.). (ENG., Illus.). 96p. pap. 29.95 *(978-1-84584-193-5(X)*, 184584193X) Veloce Publishing Ltd. GBR. Dist: MBI Distribution Services/Quayside Distribution.

Petit, Jacques. Cars on Vinyl: 500 Superb Record Covers Dedicated to the Automobile. 2010. (ENG., Illus.). 160p. pap. 27.95 *(978-1-84425-726-3(6)*, 1844257266) Haynes Publishing PLC GBR. Dist: MBI Distribution Services/Quayside Distribution.

Polidori, Robert. Heroes of the Revolution: American Cars & Cuban Beats. 2006. (ENG.). 14.95 incl. lp *(978-3-937406-53-4(0))* Edel Classica Gmbh.

Porsche AG, Ing. h. c. F., ed. Porsche Museum: Die Autos / The Cars. 2010. (ENG., Illus.). 256p. 22.95 *(978-3-8321-9297-6(2))* DuMont DEU. Dist: D.A.P./Distributed Art Pubs.

Porter, Philip. Collector's Originality Guide Jaguar E-Type. 2008. (Collector's Originality Guide Ser.). (ENG., Illus.). 96p. pap. 24.99 *(978-0-7603-3560-4(5)*, 0760335605, Motorbooks) MBI Publishing Co. LLC.

Porter, Richard & Chapman, Giles. My Dad Wished He Had One of Those. 2008. (ENG., Illus.). 192p. 19.95 *(978-0-340-96324-1(7)*, Hodder & Stoughton) Hodder General Publishing Div. GBR. Dist: Independent Pubs. Group.

Powell, Tracy. American Auto Legends: Classics of Style & Design. 2010. (Auto Legends Ser.). (ENG., Illus.). 288p. 49.95 *(978-1-85894-516-3(X))* Merrell Pubs. Ltd. GBR. Dist: Perseus Distribution.

Powley, Adam. My Dad's Motors. 2011. (ENG., Illus.). 144p. 12.95 *(978-0-85733-042-0(X)*, 085733042X) Haynes Publishing PLC GBR. Dist: MBI Distribution Services/Quayside Distribution.

Presland, Willi & Presland, William A. Aston Martin V8. 2009. (ENG., Illus.). 208p. 44.95 *(978-1-84797-066-4(4)*, 1847970664) Crowood Pr., Ltd. GBR. Dist: MBI Distribution Services/Quayside Distribution.

Press, Ammonite, ed. 100 Years of Motorcycles. 2010. (ENG.). 300p. pap. 19.95 *(978-1-906672-53-9(9)*, Ammonite Pr.) AE Pubns. GBR. Dist: BookMasters Distribution Services (BDS).

Pressnell, Jon. Mini: The Definitive History. 2009. (ENG., Illus.). 272p. 54.95 *(978-1-84425-475-0(5)*, 1844254755) Haynes Publishing PLC GBR. Dist: MBI Distribution Services/Quayside Distribution.

—Morris Minor: the Official Photo Album. 2008. (ENG., Illus.). 160p. 39.95 *(978-1-84425-518-4(2)*, 1844255182) Haynes Publishing PLC GBR. Dist: MBI Distribution Services/Quayside Distribution.

Price, Barrie & Arbey, Jean-Louis. Bugatti: The 8-Cylinder Touring Cars 1920-1934 - Types 28, 30, 38, 38a, 44 & 49. 2007. (ENG., Illus.). 144p. 59.95 *(978-1-901295-95-5(8)*, 1901295958) Veloce Publishing Ltd. GBR. Dist: MBI Distribution Services/Quayside Distribution.

Pripps, Robert N. & Brock, Harold L. The Big Book of Ford Tractors. 2nd ed. 2008. (ENG., Illus.). 192p. pap. 25.99 *(978-0-7603-3490-4(0)*, 0760334900, Voyageur Pr) MBI Publishing Co. LLC.

Pritchard, Anthony. British Family Cars of the 1950s And 60s. 2009. (Shire Library). (ENG., Illus.). 64p. pap. 12.95 *(978-0-7478-0712-4(4))* Shire Pubns., Ltd. GBR. Dist: Random Hse., Inc.

—Silver Arrows in Camera, 1934-39: A Photographic History of the Mercedes-Benz & Auto Union. 2008. (ENG., Illus.). 480p. 150.00 *(978-1-84425-467-5(4)*, 1844254674) Haynes Publishing PLC GBR. Dist: MBI Distribution Services/Quayside Distribution.

Publications International Staff. Ency of Amer Cars. 2006. (Illus.). 848p. 34.98 *(978-1-4127-1354-2(4)*, 1261319, PIL Kids) Publications International, Ltd.

Publications International Staff, creator. Cars of The 1960s. 2007. (Illus.). 192p. 24.95 *(978-1-4127-1554-6(7))* Publications International, Ltd.

Purves, Bryan & Brenchley, Tim. The Last Works Minis: The End of a Legend. 2007. (ENG., Illus.). 192p. 59.95 *(978-1-84584-087-7(9)*, 1845840879) Veloce Publishing Ltd. GBR. Dist: MBI Distribution Services/Quayside Distribution.

Quinn, Edward, photos by. Stars & Cars of The '50s. 2011. 256p. pap. 39.95 *(978-3-8327-9450-7(6))* teNeues Publishing Co.

Ratcliffe, David. International Train-Ferry Wagons in Colour for the Modeller & Historian. 2009. (ENG., Illus.). 96p. pap. 27.95 *(978-0-7110-3404-4(4))* Allan, Ian Publishing GBR. Dist: BookMasters Distribution Services (BDS).

Ratti, Diego. Bugatti Type 32 Tank. 2008. 102p. 126.50 *(978-1-4092-2487-7(2))* Lulu Enterprises Inc.

Reyes, Steve. Slingshot Spectacular: The Front-Engine Dragster Era. 2007. (ENG., Illus.). 192p. pap. 24.95 *(978-1-932494-64-8(2))* CarTech, Inc.

Rizzo, Enzo. Automoviles. 2007. (Cube Bks.). (Illus.). 735p. 19.95 *(978-970-718-440-4(X)*, Numen) Advanced Marketing, S. de R. L. de C. V. MEX. Dist: Perseus-PGW.

—Cars. 2010. (Cube Bks.). (ENG., Illus.). 736p. 14.95 *(978-88-544-0172-3(2))* White Star ITA. Dist: Sterling Publishing Co., Inc.

Robertson, Scott, ed. Start Your Engines: Surface Vehicle Sketches & Renderings from the Drawthrough Collection. 2006. (ENG., Illus.). 139p. pap. 29.95 *(978-1-933492-13-1(9))* Design Studio Pr.

Robson, Graham. British Touring Car Racing in Camera: A photographic celebration of 50 Years. 2008. (ENG., Illus.). 240p. 59.95 *(978-1-84425-469-9(0)*, 1844254690) Haynes Publishing PLC GBR. Dist: MBI Distribution Services/Quayside Distribution.

—Ford Capri. 2008. (Crowood Autoclassics Ser.). (ENG., Illus.). 192p. 34.95 *(978-1-86126-978-2(1)*, 1861269781) Crowood Pr., Ltd. GBR. Dist: MBI Distribution Services/Quayside Distribution.

—Jaguar XK8: The Complete Story. 2009. (ENG., Illus.). 192p. 39.95 *(978-1-84797-074-9(5)*, 1847970745) Crowood Pr., Ltd. GBR. Dist: MBI Distribution Services/Quayside Distribution.

Ruch, Peter. Legendary German Cars. 2010. (ENG., Illus.). 304p. 39.95 *(978-88-544-0447-2(0))* White Star ITA. Dist: Random Hse., Inc.

Sanders, Ralph W. The Farm Tractor: 100 Years of North American Tractors. rev. ed. 2007. (ENG., Illus.). 384p. 40.00 *(978-0-7603-3074-6(3)*, 0760330743, Voyageur Pr) MBI Publishing Co. LLC.

Sannia, Alessandro. Bmw, 1 vol. 2011. (ENG & FRE., Illus.). 192p. 12.95 *(978-90-79761-90-6(7))* Tectum B.V.B.A. BEL. Dist: Innovative Logistics.

Schlegelmilch, Rainer W., et al. Bmw. 2008. (Transportation Ser.). (Illus.). 479p. 49.95 *(978-0-8416-0274-8(3))* American Map Corp.

Schlegelmilch, Rainer W. & Lehbrink, Hartmut. Porsche. 2008. (Transportation Ser.). (Illus.). 399p. 49.95 *(978-0-8416-0300-4(6))* American Map Corp.

Scrogham, Cole. Porsche 911 Engine Assembly Guide. 2010. 45p. pap. 29.95 *(978-0-557-20389-5(9))* Lulu Enterprises Inc.

Shiers, Will. Roadside Relics: America's Abandoned Automobiles. 2010. (ENG., Illus.). 208p. pap. 21.99 *(978-0-7603-3984-8(8)*, 0760339848, Motorbooks) MBI Publishing Co. LLC.

Siu, Jason. How to Digitally Photograph Cars. 2009. 144p. pap. 24.95 *(978-1-932494-99-0(5))* CarTech, Inc.

Smale, Glen. Ferrari Design: The Definitive Study. 2010. (ENG., Illus.). 272p. 69.95 *(978-1-84425-487-3(9)*, 1844254879) Haynes Publishing PLC GBR. Dist: MBI Distribution Services/Quayside Distribution.

—Porsche 917: The Complete Photographic History. 2009. (ENG., Illus.). 480p. 150.00 *(978-1-84425-426-2(7)*, 1844254267) Haynes Publishing PLC GBR. Dist: MBI Distribution Services/Quayside Distribution.

—Porsche at le Mans: Sixty Years of Porsche Participation in the World's Greatest Motor Race. 2011. (ENG., Illus.). 352p. 72.95 *(978-1-84425-995-3(1)*, 1844259951) Haynes Publishing PLC GBR. Dist: MBI Distribution Services/Quayside Distribution.

Smith, Greg, illus. Extreme Trucks. 2009. (ENG.). 96p. pap. 9.99 *(978-0-7603-3393-6(9)*, 0760333939, Motorbooks) MBI Publishing Co. LLC.

Smith, Michael Paul, photos by. Elgin Park: An Ideal American Town. 2011. (Illus.). 144p. 35.00 *(978-3-7913-4548-2(6))* Prestel Publishing.

Smith, Roy P. Alpine & Renault: The Sports Prototypes 1963 To 1969. 2010. (ENG., Illus.). 208p. 69.95 *(978-1-84584-191-1(3)*, 1845841913) Veloce Publishing Ltd. GBR. Dist: MBI Distribution Services/Quayside Distribution.

Speed Kings. 2007. (Illus.). 128p. 48.00 *(978-3-89955-197-6(4))* Die Gestalten Verlag DEU. Dist: Prestel Publishing.

Spurring, Quentin. Jim Clark: A photographic Portrait. 2008. (ENG., Illus.). 256p. 59.95 *(978-1-84425-501-6(8)*, 1844255018) Haynes Publishing PLC GBR. Dist: MBI Distribution Services/Quayside Distribution.

—Le Mans, 1960-69: The Official History of the World's Greatest Motor Race. 2010. (ENG., Illus.). 352p. 70.00 *(978-1-84425-584-9(0)*, 1844255840) Haynes Publishing PLC GBR. Dist: MBI Distribution Services/Quayside Distribution.

Stein, Jonathan A., ed. Curves of Steel: Streamlined Automobile Design. 2nd rev. ed. 2009. (ENG., Illus.). 192p. 75.00 *(978-0-9779809-6-3(0))* Coachbuilt Pr.

Stokoe, Noel, ed. My Car Was a Jowett. (Illus.). 160p. 27.50 *(978-0-7524-2796-6(2))* History Pr. Ltd.,The GBR. Dist: Trafalgar Square Publishing.

Stone, Matt & Matras, John L. 365 Cars You Must Drive. rev. ed. 2006. (ENG., Illus.). 320p. pap. 19.95 *(978-0-7603-2414-1(X)*, 076032414X, Motorbooks) MBI Publishing Co. LLC.

Swager, Nick. Secrets of Speed: Today's Techniques for 4-Stroke Engine Blueprinting & Tuning. 2010. (SpeedPro Ser.). (ENG., Illus.). 128p. pap. 39.95 *(978-1-84584-297-0(9)*, 1845842979) Veloce Publishing Ltd. GBR. Dist: MBI Distribution Services/Quayside Distribution.

Tagliaferri, Mariarosaria. Cars & Stars: 50 Years of Dreams, 1 vol. 2009. (ENG, DUT & FRE., Illus.). 208p. pap. 55.00 *(978-90-76886-00-8(8))* Tectum B.V.B.A. BEL. Dist: Innovative Logistics.

—Motorcycles & Stars, 1 vol. 2010. (FRE, DUT & ENG., Illus.). 208p. 49.95 *(978-90-79761-44-9(3))* Tectum B.V.B.A. BEL. Dist: Innovative Logistics.

Taylor, Blaine. Hitler's Chariots Vol. 1: Mercedes-Benz G-4 Cross-Country Touring Car. 2009. (Illus.). 160p. bds. 49.99 *(978-0-7643-3236-4(8))* Schiffer Publishing, Ltd.

Taylor, James. Land Rover: 60 Years of the 4x4 Workhorse. 2008. (ENG., Illus.). 270p. 49.95 *(978-1-86126-965-2(X)*, 186126965X) Crowood Pr., Ltd. GBR. Dist: MBI Distribution Services/Quayside Distribution.

—Range Rover: 40 Years of the 4x4 Icon, 1 vol. 2010. (ENG., Illus.). 192p. 44.95 *(978-1-84797-184-5(9)*, 1847971849) Crowood Pr., Ltd. GBR. Dist: MBI Distribution Services/Quayside Distribution.

Taylor, Thom. Kustomland: The Custom Car Photography of James Potter, 1955-1959. 2008. (ENG., Illus.). 128p. 24.95 *(978-0-7603-2259-8(7)*, 0760322597, Motorbooks) MBI Publishing Co. LLC.

Temple, David W. Full-Size Fords: 1955-1970. 2010. 144p. pap. 29.95 *(978-1-934709-08-5(5))* CarTech, Inc.

teNeues. 125 Years of Automobiles: Illustrated Chronicle of Daimler AG. 2010. (Illus.). 304p. 59.95 *(978-3-8327-9442-2(5))* teNeues Publishing Co.

Teters, K. Scott. Illustrated Corvette Series. 2010. *(978-1-934709-46-7(8))* CarTech, Inc.

Thompson, Mark. Motocross & Off-Road Motorcycle: Setup Guide. 2010. (Motorbooks Workshop Ser.). (ENG., Illus.). 144p. pap. 24.99 *(978-0-7603-3596-3(6)*, 0760335966, Motorbooks) MBI Publishing Co. LLC.

Tucker, Malcolm. Rust in Peace: Photographs from the Mike Worthington-Williams Archives. 2008. (ENG., Illus.). 256p. 49.00 *(978-1-85443-225-4(7)*, 1854432257) Dalton Watson Fine Bks.

Van Boggart, Angelo. Just 30s. 2011. (ENG.). 144p. pap. 12.99 *(978-1-4402-1428-8(X))* Krause Pubns.

Venables, David. The Classic Motor Racing Circuits of Europe. 2010. (ENG., Illus.). 176p. 39.95 *(978-0-7110-3481-5(8))* Allan, Ian Publishing GBR. Dist: BookMasters Distribution Services (BDS).

Wagstaff, Ian. The British at Indianapolis. 2010. (ENG., Illus.). 256p. 99.95 *(978-1-84584-246-8(4)*, 1845842464) Veloce Publishing Ltd. GBR. Dist: MBI Distribution Services/Quayside Distribution.

Waldner, Raffael. Car Crash Studies, 2001-2010. 2010. (ENG & GER., Illus.). 96p. 35.00 *(978-3-03764-114-9(2))* JRP Ringier Kunstverlag AG CHE. Dist: D.A.P./Distributed Art Pubs.

Wharmby, Matthew. The London Titan. 2008. (ENG., Illus.). 176p. 36.95 *(978-0-7110-3299-6(8))* Allan, Ian Publishing GBR. Dist: BookMasters Distribution Services (BDS).

Wharmby, Matthew & Rixon, Geoff. Routemaster Omnibus. 2007. (ENG., Illus.). 288p. 37.95 *(978-0-7110-3314-6(5))* Allan, Ian Publishing GBR. Dist: BookMasters Distribution Services (BDS).

Williams, Jan & Raupp, Guenther. Ferrari: 25 Years of Calendar Images. 2008. 95.00 *(978-3-8327-9283-1(X))* teNeues Publishing Co.

Wimpffen, Janos. Spyders & Silhouettes: The World Manufacturers & Sports Car Championships in Photographs, 1972-1981. 2007. (Illus.). 400p. 149.95 *(978-1-893618-83-1(8))* Bull, David Publishing, Inc.

Wingrove, Gordon. Porsche 917: The Undercover Story. 2006. (ENG., Illus.). 208p. 74.95 *(978-0-9549990-2-5(9)*, 0954999029, PMM Bks.) Morgan, Peter Media Ltd. GBR. Dist: MBI Distribution Services/Quayside Distribution.

Wyatt, Steve & Carter, Anthony. Motor Racing: The Pursuit of Victory, 1963-1972. 2012. (ENG., Illus.). 272p. 89.95 *(978-1-84584-285-7(5)*, 1845842855) Veloce Publishing Ltd. GBR. Dist: MBI Distribution Services/Quayside Distribution.

Wyss, Wallace A. Cobra & Shelby Mustang 1962-2007 Photo Archive: Including Prototypes & Clones. 2007. (Photo Archive Ser.). (ENG., Illus.). 128p. pap. 34.95 *(978-1-58388-198-9(0)*, 1583881980) Iconografix, Inc.

Zumbrunn. Italian Auto Legends: Classics of Style & Design. 2006. (Auto Legends Ser.). (ENG., Illus.). 288p. 49.95 *(978-1-85894-336-7(1))* Merrell Pubs. Ltd. GBR. Dist: Perseus Distribution.

Zumbrunn & Heseltine, Richard. Italian Auto Legends: Classics of Style & Design. 2008. (Illus.). 296p. pap. 22.95 *(978-1-85894-431-9(7))* Merrell Pubs. Ltd. GBR. Dist: Perseus Distribution.

Zumbrunn, Michel, photos by. Auto Legends: Classics of Style & Design. 2006. (Auto Legends Ser.). (ENG., Illus.). 296p. pap. 22.95 *(978-1-85894-348-0(5))* Merrell Pubs. Ltd. GBR. Dist: Perseus Distribution.

—Ferrari Legends: Classics of Style & Design. 2010. (Auto Legends Ser.). (ENG., Illus.). 288p. pap. 24.95 *(978-1-85894-533-0(X))* Merrell Pubs. Ltd. GBR. Dist: Perseus Distribution.

AUTOMOBILES—POLLUTION CONTROL DEVICES

see also Automobiles—Motors—Exhaust Gas

Birgersson, Henrik. Regeneration Methods for Commercial Automotive Three-Way Catalysts: Development & Assessment of Regeneration Methods for Commercial Automotive Three-Way Catalysts. 2008. 76p. pap. *(978-3-639-10510-0(9))* VDM Verlag Dr. Mueller e.K.

Busawon, Roshan. The Software Model Calmob6- Transportation Emission & Fuel Consumption Inventories. 2007. 304p. per. *(978-3-8364-2637-4(4))* VDM Verlag Dr. Mueller e.K.

Halderman, James D. Automotive Fuel & Emissions Systems, Automotive Fuel & Emissions Control Systems: NATEF Correlated Task Sheets. 2nd ed. 2008. (ENG.). 390p. (C). pap. 36.20 *(978-0-13-506011-7(7)*, Prentice Hall) Prentice Hall PTR.

Halderman, James D. & Linder, James. Automotive Fuel & Emissions Control Systems. (ENG.). (C). 2nd ed. 2008. 576p. pap. 122.80 *(978-0-13-505481-9(8))* 3rd ed. 2011. (Illus.). 480p. pap. 118.00 *(978-0-13-254292-0(7))* Prentice Hall PTR. (Prentice Hall).

—NATEF Correlated Task Sheets for Automotive Fuel & Emissions Control Systems. 3rd rev. ed. 2011. (ENG.). 336p. (C). pap. 21.80 *(978-0-13-254510-5(1)*, Prentice Hall) Prentice Hall PTR.

Khare, Mukesh & Nagendra, Shiva. Artificial Neural Networks in Vehicular Pollution Modelling. 2007. (Studies in Computational Intelligence Ser.). (Illus.). xvi, 242p. 149.00 *(978-3-540-37417-6(5)*, 3540374175) Springer.

Lahnalampi, Nita. Red One Plus Ltd: For the satisfaction of customers & Nature. 2010. 92p. pap. *(978-3-8383-6785-9(5))* Lambert Academic Publishing.

Organisation for Economic Co-operation and Development Staff. Tables Rondes Fit No. 142: Le Coût et l'Efficacité des Mesures Visant à réDuire les éMissions de VéHicules. 2009. 200p. pap. 92.00 *(978-92-821-0214-5(5))* Organization for Economic Cooperation & Development.

Palocz-Andresen, Michael. Decreasing of Fuel Consumption & Emissions: Sensing, Control & Reduction of Emissions. 2012. (Green Energy & Technology Ser.). (ENG., Illus.). 300p. 189.00 *(978-3-642-11975-0(1)*, 3642119751) Springer.

Ponce, Micaela Inés. Reducing Greenhouse Gas Emissions Via Telecommuting. 2010. 152p. pap. *(978-3-639-23465-7(0))* VDM Verlag Dr. Mueller e.K.

Porche, Isaac R., III & Bernstein, Mark A. An Approach to Assessing the Technical Feasibility & Market Potential of a New Automotive Device. 2007. 76p. pap. 23.00 *(978-0-8330-4162-3(2)*, tr313) RAND Corp., The.

Uzkan, Teoman, ed. Recent Developments on Engine Emissions: Proceedings of the Spring Technical Conference of the ASME Internal Combustion Engine Division 1996, Youngstown, OH, Set. Date not set. 269p. pap. 204.00 *(978-0-7918-1766-7(0)*, TJ1075) American Society of Mechanical Engineers, The.

Yantovsky, Evgeny & Gorski, J. Zero Emissions Power Cycles. 2009. (ENG., Illus.). 282p. 154.95 *(978-1-4200-8791-8(6)*, CRC Press) Taylor & Francis Group GBR. Dist: Taylor & Francis Group.

AUTOMOBILES—POWER TRAINS

see also Automobiles—Motors; Automobiles—Transmission Devices; Automobiles—Wheels

Birch, Tom & Rockwood, Chuck. Manual Drivetrains & Axles: NATEF Correlated Task Sheets. 5th ed. 2007. (ENG., Illus.). 160p. (C) spiral bd. 34.80 *(978-0-13-199406-5(9))* Pearson Education Canada CAN. Dist: Pearson Education.

Cdx Global Staff. Natef Automotive Task Sheets: Manual Drive Train. rev. ed. 2010. 114p. pap. 26.95 *(978-0-7637-8511-6(3))* Jones & Bartlett Learning, LLC.

Crolla, David & Mashadi, Behrooz. Vehicle Powertrain Systems: Integration & Optimization. 2012. (ENG., Illus.). 560p. 105.00 ***(978-0-470-66602-9(1)***, Wiley) Wiley, John & Sons, Inc.

Delmar Learning Staff. ASE Test Preparation - A3 Manual Drive Trains & Axles. 5th ed. 2011. (ENG., Illus.). 208p. pap. 23.95 *(978-1-111-12705-3(0))* Delmar Cengage Learning.

—ASE Test Preparation - T3 Drive Train. 5th ed. 2012. (ENG.). 176p. pap. 23.95 *(978-1-111-12896-9(5))* Delmar Cengage Learning.

Guzzomi, Andrew Louis. Torsional Vibration of Powertrains. 2009. 152p. pap. *(978-3-639-16133-5(5))* VDM Verlag Dr. Mueller e.K.

Hellgren, Jonas. Cost Effective Design of Hybrid Powertrains. 2010. 112p. pap. *(978-3-8383-2141-7(3))* Lambert Academic Publishing.

Heritage Information Systems. Illustrated Powerstroke Diagnostics: 2006-07 6. 0L E250-450 & F250-550. 2008. (Illus.). 544p. per. 89.95 *(978-0-9725784-1-7(2))* Heritage Technical LLC.

Rehkopf, Jeffrey. Manual Drivetrains & Axles. 2009. 432p. pap. *(978-0-13-158307-8(7))* Pearson Bks.

Rockwood, Chuck & Birch, Thomas S. Natef Correlated Task Sheets for Manual Drivetrain & Axles. 6th ed. 2011. (ENG.). 168p. (C). pap. 29.00 ***(978-0-13-512415-1(6)***, Prentice Hall) Prentice Hall PTR.

Rockwood, Chuck & Birch, Tom. Manual Drivetrains & Axles. 5th ed. 2007. (ENG., Illus.). 552p. (C). pap. 122.80 *(978-0-13-199405-8(0)*, Prentice Hall) Prentice Hall PTR.

—Manual Drivetrains & Axles. 6th rev. ed. 2011. (ENG., Illus.). 552p. (C). pap. 118.00 *(978-0-13-512362-1(3)*, Prentice Hall) Prentice Hall PTR.

Seherr-Thoss, Hans-Christoph, et al. Universal Joints & Driveshafts: Analysis, Design, Applications. Tipper, J. A. & Hill, S. J., trs. 2nd ed. 2010. (ENG., Illus.). xxii, 351p. pap. 139.00 *(978-3-642-06766-2(2)*, 3642067662) Springer.

AUTOMOBILES—PRICES

Apen, John, ed. The Gold Book: Older Vehicles 1945-1980: April-May-June 1997, Vol. 18, No. 2. Date not set. 195p. ring bd. 20.00 *(978-1-57033-033-9(6))* Gold Bk., The.

Crespin, Peter. Jaguar XJ-S: All 6 & 12 Cylinder Models 1975 to 1996. 2008. (Essential Buyer's Guide Ser.). (ENG., Illus.). 64p. pap. 19.95 *(978-1-84584-161-4(1)*, 1845841611) Veloce Publishing Ltd. GBR. Dist: MBI Distribution Services/Quayside Distribution.

Grasso, Sandy. Watch Those Car Guys: Eve Used an Apple... These Guys Used Steel. 2010. 536p. 33.99 *(978-1-4520-3085-2(5))*; pap. 23.49 *(978-1-4520-3086-9(3))* AuthorHouse.

Gunnell, John. Standard Catalog of Chevy, 1912-2001: 90 Years of History, Photos, Technical Data & Pricing. 2011. (ENG.). 448p. pap. 24.99 ***(978-1-4402-3051-6(X))*** Krause Pubns.

—Standard Catalog of Ford, 1903-2002: 100 Years of History, Photos, Technical Data & Pricing. 2011. (ENG.). 384p. pap. 24.99 ***(978-1-4402-3036-3(6))*** Krause Pubns.

Heilig, Rudy A. Citroen DS & ID: All Models 1966 to 1975. 2008. (Essential Buyer's Guide Ser.). (ENG., Illus.). 64p. pap. 19.95 *(978-1-84584-138-6(7)*, 1845841387) Veloce Publishing Ltd. GBR. Dist: MBI Distribution Services/Quayside Distribution.

Hobbs, David. Subaru Impreza: All Turbo Models 1992 to 2007. 2008. (Essential Buyer's Guide Ser.). (ENG., Illus.). 64p. pap. 19.95 *(978-1-84584-163-8(8)*, 1845841638) Veloce Publishing Ltd. GBR. Dist: MBI Distribution Services/Quayside Distribution.

Kowalke, Ron. 2011 Collector Car Price Guide. 5th ed. 2010. (ENG., Illus.). 760p. pap. 19.99 *(978-1-4402-1285-7(6))* Krause Pubns.

—2012 Collector Car Price Guide. 6th ed. 2011. (ENG.). 760p. pap. 21.99 *(978-1-4402-2377-8(7))* Krause Pubns.

Luikens, Jim & Hedberg, Mary. Standard Catalog of Mercedes-Benz. 2009. (ENG., Illus.). 224p. pap. 24.99 *(978-0-89689-703-8(6))* Krause Pubns.

Zarnock, Michael & Van Bogart, Angelo. Hot Wheels, Warman's Companion. 2nd ed. 2009. (ENG., Illus.). 288p. pap. 18.99 *(978-0-89689-843-1(1))* Krause Pubns.

AUTOMOBILES—PURCHASING

see also Automobile Ownership

Atmajian. Buying a Car for Your Teenager. 2008. 73p. pap. 16.95 *(978-1-4241-1660-7(0))* PublishAmerica, Inc.

Baden, D. A. How to Buy a New Car Like You Practically Stole It! 2008. 57p. pap. 20.00 *(978-0-615-21738-3(9))* Integrity Arts, LLC.

Barker, John & Horler, Terry. MG Midget & Austin Healey Sprite: All Models. 2011. (Essential Buyer's Guide Ser.). (ENG., Illus.). 64p. pap. 19.95 *(978-1-84584-354-0(1)*, 1845843541) Veloce Publishing Ltd. GBR. Dist: MBI Distribution Services/Quayside Distribution.

Bass, Chris. Mercedes Benz Pagoda' 230, 250 And 280SL: The Essential Buyer's Guide. 2007. (Essential Buyer's Guide Ser.). (ENG., Illus.). 64p. pap. 19.95 *(978-1-84584-113-3(1)*, 1845841131) Veloce Publishing Ltd. GBR. Dist: MBI Distribution Services/Quayside Distribution.

Batchelor, Dean & Leffingwell, Randy. Porsche. 5th ed. 2010. (ENG., Illus.). 240p. pap. 24.99 *(978-0-7603-3606-9(7)*, 0760336067, Motorbooks) MBI Publishing Co. LLC.

Ben-Ari, Dani. Car Ownership for Women. 2010. 88p. pap. 10.49 *(978-1-4520-1527-9(9))* AuthorHouse.

Benjamins, Rene. The World of Car Sales: What Everyone Buying a Car Should Know. 2008. 68p. pap. 12.95 *(978-1-4327-2554-9(8))* Outskirts Pr., Inc.

Bild Buch Staff. Ratgeber Auto: Mit diesen Tipps fahren Sie Gut. (GER.). 230p. pap. *(978-3-548-42034-9(6))* Ullstein-Taschenbuch-Verlag DEU. Dist: International Bk. Import Service, Inc.

Blackburn, Jon. Peugeot 205 GTI. 2011. (Essential Buyer's Guide Ser.). (ENG., Illus.). 64p. pap. 19.95 *(978-1-84584-283-3(9)*, 1845842839) Veloce Publishing Ltd. GBR. Dist: MBI Distribution Services/Quayside Distribution.

Bobbitt, Malcolm. Rolls-Royce Silver Shadow Bentley T-Series: Including Corniche, Camargue, Silver Shadow II & Bentley T2 - 1965 to 1995. 2008. (Essential Buyer's Guide Ser.). (ENG., Illus.). 64p. pap. 19.95 *(978-1-84584-146-1(8)*, 1845841468) Veloce Publishing Ltd. GBR. Dist: MBI Distribution Services/Quayside Distribution.

Car Buying Secrets Exposed. 2007. per. *(978-1-59916-164-8(8))* Printing Systems.

Case, Ron. Trade Secrets Revealed: Automobiles. 2007. 60p. per. 8.95 *(978-1-4327-0499-5(0))* Outskirts Pr., Inc.

Chek Chart Manual Transmission (Shop) & Transaxles. (Illus.). 240p. pap. *(978-1-57932-001-0(5))* Prentice Hall PTR.

Consumer Reports Editors. New Car Buying Guide 2008. 2008. (Consumer Reports New Car Buying Guide Ser.). (ENG.). 264p. pap. 9.99 *(978-1-933524-18-4(9))* Consumer Reports Bks.

Consumer Reports Staff, creator. New Car Buying Guide. 2007. (Consumer Reports New Car Buying Guide Ser.). (ENG., Illus.). 264p. pap. 9.99 *(978-1-933524-09-2(X))* Consumer Reports Bks.

—Used Car Buying Guide 2007. 2008. (Consumer Reports Used Car Buying Guide Ser.). (ENG., Illus.). 240p. pap. 9.99 *(978-1-933524-16-0(2))* Consumer Reports Bks.

Cool Solutions First-Time Used Car Byers. 2006. 75.00 net. *(978-1-932795-02-8(2))* Filene Research Institute, Inc.

Copping, Richard & Cservenka, Kenneth. Volkswagen Golf GTI. 2009. (Essential Buyer's Guide Ser.). (ENG., Illus.). 64p. pap. 19.95 *(978-1-84584-188-1(3)*, 1845841883) Veloce Publishing Ltd. GBR. Dist: MBI Distribution Services/Quayside Distribution.

Crespin, Peter. Jaguar E-Type V12 5.3 Litre. 2007. (Essential Buyer's Guide Ser.). (ENG., Illus.). 64p. pap. 19.95 *(978-1-84584-077-8(1)*, 1845840771) Veloce Publishing Ltd. GBR. Dist: MBI Distribution Services/Quayside Distribution.

—Jaguar/Daimler XJ: All Models (Inc. Vcp) 1994 to 2003. 2009. (Essential Buyer's Guide Ser.). (ENG., Illus.). 64p. pap. 19.95 *(978-1-84584-200-0(6)*, 1845842006) Veloce Publishing Ltd. GBR. Dist: MBI Distribution Services/Quayside Distribution.

—Jaguar/Daimler XJ40: The Essential Buyer's Guide. 2009. (Essential Buyer's Guide Ser.). (ENG., Illus.). 64p. pap. 19.95 *(978-1-84584-192-8(1)*, 1845841921) Veloce Publishing Ltd. GBR. Dist: MBI Distribution Services/Quayside Distribution.

Crook, Carla. Mazda MX-5 Miata: Mk1 1989-97 & Mk2, 1998-2001. 2011. (Essential Buyer's Guide Ser.). (ENG., Illus.). 64p. pap. 19.95 *(978-1-84584-231-4(6)*, 1845842316) Veloce Publishing Ltd. GBR. Dist: MBI Distribution Services/Quayside Distribution.

Davis, G. L. A Salesman's Secrets: The Inside Scoop-Things You Need to Know Before Purchasing Your Next Car. 2008. 88p. pap. 16.95 *(978-1-60672-489-7(4))* PublishAmerica, Inc.

Day, S. E. How to Legally Steal Your Next Vehicle & Save $1000s: A Consumer Informational Guide to Effective Automobile Negotiations. 2010. 66p. pap. 14.99 *(978-1-60911-985-0(1)*, Eloquent Bks.) AEG Literary Publishing Services, Inc.

Edmonston, Louis-Philippe. Lemon-Aid New Cars & Trucks 2012. 2011. (ENG., Illus.). 526p. pap. 29.99 *(978-1-4597-0046-8(5))* Dundurn CAN. Dist: Ingram Pub. Services.

Edmonston, Phil. Lemon-Aid New Cars & Trucks 2010. 2009. (ENG., Illus.). 466p. pap. 28.99 *(978-1-55488-442-1(X)*, Dundurn Pr.) Dundurn CAN. Dist: Ingram Pub. Services.

—Lemon-Aid New Cars & Trucks 2011. 2010. (ENG., Illus.). 536p. pap. 28.99 *(978-1-55488-790-3(9))* Dundurn CAN. Dist: Ingram Pub. Services.

—Lemon-Aid Used Cars & Trucks 2010-2011. 2010. (ENG., Illus.). 576p. pap. 28.99 *(978-1-55488-721-7(6))* Dundurn CAN. Dist: Ingram Pub. Services.

—Lemon-Aid Used Cars & Trucks 2011-2012. 2011. (ENG., Illus.). 624p. pap. 29.99 *(978-1-55488-951-8(0)*, Dundurn Pr.) Dundurn CAN. Dist: Ingram Pub. Services.

Edwards, Stephen. Questions When Buying a Car. 2006. (50 Plus One Ser.). (ENG.). 213p. pap. *(978-1-933766-05-8(0))* Encouragement Pr., 2nd Edition, LLC.

Elwins, Dannie. Car Buying Tips That Will Streamline the Car Buying Process. 2009. 44p. pap. 16.99 (978-0-557-15562-0(2)) Lulu Enterprises Inc.

—How to Buy A Car & Get A Great Deal on It. 2009. 40p. pap. 16.99 (978-0-557-15547-7(9)) Lulu Enterprises Inc.

—How to Purchase or Buy A Car with Bad or No Credit. 2009. 40p. pap. 16.99 (978-0-557-15549-1(5)) Lulu Enterprises Inc.

Falconer, Tom. Corvette C2 Sting Ray: 1963-1967. 2011. (Essential Buyer's Guide Ser.). (ENG., Illus.). 64p. pap. 19.95 (978-1-84584-329-8(0), 1845843290) Veloce Publishing Ltd. GBR. Dist: MBI Distribution Services/Quayside Distribution.

Field, Christopher. Tax Saving Tactics for Motorists: A Guide for Company Owners, Sole Traders & Landlords. 2011. 236p. pap. **(978-1-907302-49-7(2))** Taxcafe UK Ltd.

Gelber, Steven M. Horse Trading in the Age of Cars: Men in the Marketplace. 2008. (Gender Relations in the American Experience Ser.). (ENG., Illus.). 248p. (gr. 17). 51.00 (978-0-8018-8997-4(9)) Johns Hopkins Univ. Pr.

Green, Simon. Garage Life: # 1 The Offbeat Import Car Shop. 2010. (Life in the Garage Ser.). (ENG.). 240p. 36.00 (978-1-935350-03-3(X), Parker Hse. Publishing Inc.,Csi) Continental Sales, Inc.

Haefner, Ronald G. The Car Care Book. 4th ed. 2008. (ENG.). 464p. (C). 152.95 (978-1-4283-4293-4(1)) Delmar Cengage Learning.

Harmon, Daniel E. First Car Smarts. 2009. 77.70 (978-1-4358-5545-8(0)); pap. 12.95 (978-1-4358-5544-1(2)); (Illus.). 64p. (J). (gr. 7-12). lib. bdg. 29.25 (978-1-4358-5269-3(9)) Rosen Publishing Group, Inc., The.

Heathouse, Harry William. How to Buy a Car: Save Thousands on Your Next Car. 2007. 60p. per. 16.95 (978-1-4241-8112-4(7)) PublishAmerica, Inc.

Henderson, John. Car Buying & Ownership 2010. 2010. (Teach Yourself Ser.). (ENG., Illus.). 192p. pap. 19.95 (978-1-4441-0752-4(6), Hodder & Stoughton) Hodder General Publishing Div. GBR. Dist: Independent Pubs. Group.

Henshaw, Peter. Hinckley Triumph Triples & Fours 750, 900. 2010. (Essential Buyer's Guide Ser.). (ENG., Illus.). 64p. pap. 19.95 (978-1-84584-287-1(1), 1845842871) Veloce Publishing Ltd. GBR. Dist: MBI Distribution Services/Quayside Distribution.

Herfel, George E. Wheel'in & Deal'in: Make BIG PROFITS buying & selling Classic Cars & MORE. 2009. 56p. pap. 11.95 (978-1-4327-3663-7(9)) Outskirts Pr., Inc.

Kelley Blue Book, creator. Kelley Blue Book Used Car Guide: 1992-2006 Used Car & Truck. 2006. (Kelley Blue Book Used Car Guide Ser.). 383p. per. (978-1-883392-63-5(2)) Kelley Blue Bk.

—Kelley Blue Book Used Car Guide: Consumer Edition: 1992-2006 Models. 2007. (Kelley Blue Book Used Car Guide Ser.). 384p. per. 9.95 (978-1-883392-66-6(7)) Kelley Blue Bk.

Ker, Rod. Classic Japanese Motorcycle Guide. 2007. (ENG., Illus.). 240p. pap. 29.95 (978-1-84425-335-7(X), 184425335X) Haynes Publishing PLC GBR. Dist: MBI Distribution Services/Quayside Distribution.

Kramon, James M. Como Comprar un Automovil. 2006. (Guias Practicas Ser.). (ESP & ENG.). 128p. per. 8.95 (978-1-57248-546-4(9), Sphinx Publishing) Sourcebooks, Inc.

Law, Alexander & Winlaw, Susan. Car Advice for Women (and Smart Men) Reduce the Risk, Cost & Grief of Auto Ownership & Buying a New Car. 2008. 312p. pap. (978-0-9781931-0-2(5)) Consumer Automotive Media Services (CAMS).

Line, Mommies. CAR OWNERSHIP for Mommies. 2008. 96p. pap. 12.95 (978-0-557-01323-4(2)) Lulu Enterprises Inc.

Long, David. Classic Cars: How Choose Your Dream Car. 2009. 176p. 39.99 (978-1-84468-052-8(5)) Pen & Sword Bks. Ltd. GBR. Dist: Casemate Pubs. & Bk. Distributors, LLC.

Moran, Pat & Hartmann, Steve. The Smarter Deal. 2009. 93p. pap. 16.72 (978-0-557-18580-1(7)) Lulu Enterprises Inc.

Moser, Curtis C. How to Save Thousands When You Buy a Mobile Home. rev. ed. 96p. pap. 14.95 (978-0-9628152-0-1(9)) CCM Advertising.

Munroe, Brian. Car Buying Revealed: How to Buy a Car & Not Get Taken for a Ride. 2008. (ENG., Illus.). 213p. pap. 19.95 (978-1-60037-400-5(X)) Morgan James Publishing.

Muth, Hendrik. Mehrmarkenhandel in der Automobilbranche: Eine Betrachtung aus Kundensicht. 2008. (Marktorientierte Unternehmensführung Ser.). 362p. pap. 81.95 (978-3-631-57640-3(4)) Lang, Peter GmbH, Europaischer Verlag der Wissenschaften DEU. Dist: Lang, Peter.

Nichol, Pres. Scott J. Who's Negotiating Your Next Vehicle Purchase/Lease. 2008. 128p. pap. 12.97 (978-0-615-18247-6(X)) Nichol, Scott J.

Paxton, Mark. Citroen 2CV. 2007. (Essential Buyer's Guide Ser.). (ENG., Illus.). 64p. 19.95 (978-1-84584-099-0(2), 1845840992) Veloce Publishing Ltd. GBR. Dist: MBI Distribution Services/Quayside Distribution.

—Mini: The Essential Buyer's Guide. 2009. (Essential Buyer's Guide Ser.). (ENG., Illus.). 64p. pap. 19.95 (978-1-84584-204-8(9), 1845842049) Veloce Publishing Ltd. GBR. Dist: MBI Distribution Services/Quayside Distribution.

—Vespa Scooters - Classic 2-Stroke Models, 1960-2008. 2010. (Essential Buyer's Guide Ser.). (ENG., Illus.). 64p. pap. 19.95 (978-1-84584-334-2(7), 1845843347) Veloce Publishing Ltd. GBR. Dist: MBI Distribution Services/Quayside Distribution.

Robinson, Bill. The Insider's Guide to Buying a Car. (Illus.). 156p. pap. 19.99 (978-0-7090-6393-3(8)) Hale, Robert Ltd. GBR. Dist: Trafalgar Square Publishing.

Sass, Robert. Ran When Parked: Insider's Secrets of Buying, Selling & Enjoying Classic Cars on a Budget. 2010. (ENG.). 160p. pap. 30.00 (978-0-9817270-4-2(2), Parker Hse. Publishing Inc.,Csi) Continental Sales, Inc.

Sheakley, Art "Moe". Do Car Salesmen Go to Heaven? The Truth, the Whole Truth, & Nothing but the Truth about the Automobile Business. 2006. 204p. pap. 17.99 (978-1-4141-0791-2(9)) Pleasant Word.

Sommer, Garland F. Buying Used Vehicles. 2007. 72p. per. 10.50 (978-1-59858-505-6(3)) Dog Ear Publishing, LLC.

Spencer, Zack. Motormouth: The Complete Canadian Car-Buying Guide 2010 Edition. 2009. (ENG.). 320p. pap. 23.95 **(978-0-470-16026-8(8)**, Wiley) Wiley, John & Sons, Inc.

Spencer, Zack. Motormouth: The Complete Canadian Car Guide. 2011th ed. 2011. (ENG., Illus.). 352p. pap. 24.95 (978-0-470-96404-0(9), Wiley) Wiley, John & Sons, Inc.

Sutton, Remar. Don't Get Taken Every Time: The Ultimate Guide to Buying or Leasing a Car, in the Showroom or on the Internet. 6th rev. ed. 2007. (ENG.). 496p. (gr. 12-18). 15.00 (978-0-14-303888-7(5), Penguin (Non-Classics)) Penguin Group (USA) Inc.

Terrell, J. The New Car Games: Trips, Tricks, Traps. 2007. 56p. per. 16.95 (978-1-4241-8542-9(4)) PublishAmerica, Inc.

Thompson, Travis. High-Performance Ford Mustang Buyer's Guide 1979-Present. 2006. (ENG., Illus.). 128p. pap. 24.95 (978-1-932494-16-7(2), S-A Design) CarTech, Inc.

Thurman, Maurice. Land Rover Series I, II & IIA. 2011. (Essential Buyer's Guide Ser.). (ENG., Illus.). 64p. pap. 19.95 (978-1-84584-348-9(7), 1845843487) Veloce Publishing Ltd. GBR. Dist: MBI Distribution Services/Quayside Distribution.

Thurman, Maurice & Jones, Barrie. MG TD, TF & TF1500, 1949-1955. 2011. (Essential Buyer's Guide Ser.). (ENG., Illus.). 64p. pap. 19.95 (978-1-84584-352-6(5), 1845843525) Veloce Publishing Ltd. GBR. Dist: MBI Distribution Services/Quayside Distribution.

Williams, L. D. The Car Buyer: An Insiders Guide to Buying A Vehicle. 2009. 108p. pap. 15.95 (978-1-4327-4447-2(X)) Outskirts Pr., Inc.

Williams, Roger. Triumph TR7 & TR8. 2010. (Essential Buyer's Guide Ser.). (ENG., Illus.). 64p. pap. 19.95 (978-1-84584-316-8(9), 1845843169) Veloce Publishing Ltd. GBR. Dist: MBI Distribution Services/Quayside Distribution.

Yost, Spencer. How to Keep Your Classic Tractor Alive. 2009. (ENG., Illus.). 240p. pap. 29.99 (978-0-7603-2951-1(6), 0760329516, Voyageur Pr) MBI Publishing Co. LLC.

Zazarine, Paul. The Collector's Guide to GTO 1964-1974. 2007. (ENG., Illus.). 128p. pap. 19.95 (978-1-58388-196-5(4), 1583881964) Iconografix, Inc.

AUTOMOBILES—RADIO EQUIPMENT

Rabinovich, Victor, et al. Automotive Antenna Design & Applications. 2010. (ENG., Illus.). 330p. 129.95 (978-1-4398-0407-0(9), CRC Press) Taylor & Francis Group GBR. Dist: Taylor & Francis Group.

Silva, Paulo & Huijsing, Johan H. High-Resolution IF-to-Baseband SigmaDelta ADC for Car Radios. 2010. (Analog Circuits & Signal Processing Ser.). xii, 220p. pap. 159.00 (978-90-481-7788-2(X), 904817788X) Springer.

Silva, Paulo G. R. & Huijsing, Johan H. High-Resolution If-to-Baseband Sigmadelta Adc for Car Radios. 2008. (Analog Circuits & Signal Processing Ser.). XII, 220p. 159.00 (978-1-4020-8163-7(4), 1402081634) Springer.

Yoder, Andrew. Auto Audio. 3rd rev. ed. 2008. (Illus.). 384p. pap. 32.95 (978-0-07-147753-6(5), 9780071477536, TAB/Electronics) McGraw-Hill Professional Publishing.

AUTOMOBILES—RENTING

see Automobiles, Rental

AUTOMOBILES—REPAIRING

see Automobiles—Maintenance and Repair

AUTOMOBILES—RESTORATION

see Automobiles—Conservation and Restoration

AUTOMOBILES—ROAD GUIDES

see Automobile Travel—Guidebooks

AUTOMOBILES—SAFETY MEASURES

American Society of Mechanical Engineers Staff, ed. Engineering for the Customer (Fisita Proceedings), 5 vols. (Illus.). 179p. 90.00 (978-0-85298-836-7(2)) Professional Engineering Publishing GBR. Dist: SAE Intl.

—Safety & the Automobile. (IMechE Seminar Publication Ser.: Vol. 3). (Illus.). 298p. 92.00 (978-0-85298-894-7(X)) Professional Engineering Publishing GBR. Dist: SAE Intl.

—Safety, the Vehicle & the Road (Fisita Proceedings), 5 vols. (Illus.). 648p. 92.00 (978-0-85298-837-4(0)) Professional Engineering Publishing GBR. Dist: SAE Intl.

Bernard, Chris. Moon Spotlight Maine Biking. 2010. (Moon Spotlight Ser.). (ENG.). 90p. pap. 8.95 (978-1-59880-566-6(5)) Avalon Travel Publishing.

Bose, Dipan. Pre-Crash Occupant Characterization. 2010. 200p. pap. (978-3-639-26181-3(X)) VDM Verlag Dr. Mueller e.K.

Brezger, Friedrich. Segmentierung: von unbewegten Objekten aus monoskopischen Farbbildsequenzen. 2009. 126p. pap. (978-3-639-18473-0(4)) VDM Verlag Dr. Mueller e.K.

Chase, Brian. Still Unsafe at Any Speed. 2009. pap. 29.99 (978-1-61584-575-0(5)) Independent Pub.

Corte, Joseph Da, ed. Motorcycle Safety & Crashes. 2010. (Transportation Issues, Policies & R&D Ser.). (Illus.). xi, 175p. 115.00 (978-1-60741-884-9(3)) Nova Science Pubs., Inc.

Egan, Peter. Side Glances 4: The Best from America's Most Popular Automotive Writer. 2006. (ENG., Illus.). 304p. 24.95 (978-1-85520-728-8(1), 1855207281) Brooklands Bks. GBR. Dist: MBI Distribution Services/Quayside Distribution.

Eisinger, Douglas S. Smog Check: Science, Federalism, & the Politics of Clean Air. 2010. (ENG., Illus.). 252p. 99.95 (978-1-933115-71-9(8), RFF Pr.) Earthscan LLC.

Ferraro, Christina N., ed. Traffic Safety. 2010. (Transportation Issues, Policies & R&D Ser.). (Illus.). xii, 318p. 129.00 (978-1-61761-120-9(4)) Nova Science Pubs., Inc.

Hoffmann Ed.D P.E., Arthur W. Don't Be a Dummy: Primer on Automotive Safety by an Engineering Expert Witness. 2009. 104p. pap. 11.95 (978-1-4401-3556-9(8)) iUniverse, Inc.

Johnson, Otis E. The Big Trucks & Safety: A View from the Cab. 2009. 130p. pap. 17.95 (978-1-4489-9327-7(X)) PublishAmerica, Inc.

Kapoor, Tanya. Child Occupant Protection in Vehicles. 2009. 364p. pap. (978-3-639-14776-6(6)) VDM Verlag Dr. Mueller e.K.

Kissinger, Dietmar. Millimeter-Wave Receiver Concepts for 77 GHz Automotive Radar in Silicon-Germanium Technology. 2012. (SpringerBriefs in Electrical & Computer Engineering Ser.). (ENG., Illus.). xiv, 111p. pap. 49.95 **(978-1-4614-2289-1(2)**, 1461422892) Springer.

Kody, Matin F. Automobiles: Performance, Safety Assessment, & Energy Consumption. 2010. (Transportation Issues, Policies & R&D Ser.). 233p. 89.00 (978-1-61668-218-7(3)) Nova Science Pubs., Inc.

Kowalick, Thomas M. Black Box: Event Data Recorder Rulemaking & Analysis. 2007. (Illus.). 473p. per. 40.00 (978-0-9787171-2-4(0)) MICAH.

Line, Mommies. CAR OWNERSHIP for Mommies. 2008. 96p. pap. 12.95 (978-0-557-01323-4(2)) Lulu Enterprises Inc.

Mahmood, Hikmat F., et al, eds. Crashworthiness & Occupant Protection in Transportation Systems: ASME International Mechanical Engineering Congress & Exposition (1996: Atlanta, Georgia) (AMD Ser.: Vol. 218). 200p. pap. 30.00 (978-0-7918-1554-0(4)) ASME Pr.

Manish, Choudhary. Evaluation & Modification of Static Head Restraint Testing Machine: And Creating a Conceptual Design for Making It Fmvss 202A Enabled. 2011. 100p. pap. **(978-3-639-32347-4(5))** VDM Verlag Dr. Mueller e.K.

Manual de la Tecnica del Automovil. 3rd ed. (SPA., Illus.). 893p. 44.95 (978-0-8376-0612-5(8), H301) Bentley Pubs.

Paulose, John & Kihara, Zhou. Recalls of Automobiles & Medical Devices: Federal Oversight. 2011. **(978-1-62100-122-5(9))** Nova Science Pubs., Inc.

Pecheux, Kelley Klaver. Guidebook for Mitigating Fixed-Route Bus-And-Pedestrian Collisions. 2008. (Illus.). 65p. 38.00 (978-0-309-09915-8(3)) Transportation Research Board.

Rising Highway Fatalities:: Hearing Before a Subcommittee of the Committee on Appropriations, United States Senate, One Hundred Tenth Congress, First Session, Special Hearing, April 19, 2007, Washington, DC. 2007. (Illus.). iii, 43p. (978-0-16-079834-4(5), 552-070-36728-4) United States Government Printing Office.

Robert Bosch GmbH Staff, creator. Safety, Comfort & Convenience Systems: Function, Regulation & Components. 2006. (Illus.). 399p. 59.95 (978-0-8376-1391-8(4), H013) Bentley Pubs.

Seiffert, Ulrich & Wech, Lothar. Automotive Safety Handbook. 2nd ed. 2007. 99.95 (978-0-7680-1798-4(X)) SAE Intl.

Technology Research Editors, ed. Protection of Automotive Components, 2007 Ed. 2007. pap. 128.50 (978-1-60030-194-0(0), Search-In-Print) CSA Journal Division.

Wheel Safety Activity Book. 26.50 (978-1-56230-897-1(1)) Syndistar, Inc.

2007 IEEE International Conference on Vehicular Electronics & Safety. 2007. pap. 234.00 (978-1-4244-1265-5(X), 07EX1802) IEEE.

AUTOMOBILES—SEAT BELTS

Nichols, James L. & Ledingham, Katherine A. The Impact of Legislation, Enforcement, & Sanctions on Safety Belt Use. 2008. (Illus.). 68p. pap. 41.00 (978-0-309-09912-7(9)) Transportation Research Board.

AUTOMOBILES—SERVICE STATIONS

see Service Stations

AUTOMOBILES—SERVICING

see Automobiles—Maintenance and Repair

AUTOMOBILES—SMOG CONTROL DEVICES

see Automobiles—Pollution Control Devices

AUTOMOBILES—SOCIAL ASPECTS

see also Automobile Industry and Trade; Transportation, Automotive

Blanke, David. Hell on Wheels: The Promise & Peril of America's Car Culture, 1900-1940. 2007. (Culture America Ser.). (Illus.). 266p. 34.95 (978-0-7006-1515-5(6)) Univ. Pr. of Kansas.

Böhm, Steffen, et al, eds. Against Automobility. 2006. (Sociological Review Monographs). (ENG., Illus.). 268p. per. 39.95 (978-1-4051-5270-9(2), Wiley-Blackwell) Wiley, John & Sons, Inc.

Borg, Kevin L. Auto Mechanics: Technology & Expertise in Twentieth-Century America. (Studies in Industry & Society Ser.). (ENG., Illus.). 280p. (gr. 17). 2010. pap. 32.00 (978-0-8018-9485-5(9)) 2007. 50.00 (978-0-8018-8606-5(6)) Johns Hopkins Univ. Pr.

Bromley, Michael L. William Howard Taft & the First Motoring Presidency, 1909-1913. alt. ed. 2007. (ENG., Illus.). 447p. per. 45.00 (978-0-7864-2952-3(6)) McFarland & Co., Inc. Pubs.

Chappell, Ben. Lowrider Space: Aesthetics & Politics of Mexican American Custom Cars. 2012. (ENG., Illus.). 272p. 55.00 **(978-0-292-73786-0(6))** Univ. of Texas Pr.

Clarke, Deborah. Driving Women: Fiction & Automobile Culture in Twentieth-Century America. 2007. (ENG., Illus.). 226p. (gr. 17). 49.00 (978-0-8018-8550-1(7)); per. 27.00 (978-0-8018-8617-1(1)) Johns Hopkins Univ. Pr.

Copping, Richard. VW Camper & Microbus. 2009. (Shire Library). (ENG., Illus.). 64p. pap. 12.95 (978-0-7478-0709-4(4)) Shire Pubns., Ltd. GBR. Dist: Random Hse., Inc.

Drake, Albert. The Age of Hot Rods: Essays on Rods, Custom Cars & Their Drivers from the 1950s to Today. 2008. (ENG., Illus.). 207p. pap. 39.95 (978-0-7864-3404-6(X)) McFarland & Co., Inc. Pubs.

Engler, Yves & Mugyenyi, Bianca. Stop Signs: Cars & Capitalism on the Road to Economic, Social & Ecological Decay. 2011. (ENG.). 252p. pap. 19.95 (978-1-55266-384-4(1)) Fernwood Publishing Co., Ltd. CAN. Dist: Independent Pubs. Group.

Falconer, Tim. Drive: A Road Trip Through Our Complicated Affair with the Automobile. 2009. (ENG.). 288p. (gr. 12-18). 35.00 (978-0-670-06569-1(2), Penguin Global) Penguin Group (USA) Inc.

Fleming, Dan & Sturm, Damion. Media, Masculinities & the Machine: F1, Transformers & Fantasizing Technology at Its Limits. 2011. (ENG., Illus.). 248p. 120.00 (978-1-4411-1554-6(4)) Continuum International Publishing Group, Ltd. GBR. Dist: National Bk. Network.

Flonneau, Mathieu. Automobile, les Cartes du Désamour: Généalogies de L'anti-Automobilisme. 2009. (FRE & ENG., Illus.). 220p. (978-2-84446-155-1(7)) Descartes et Cie.

Geels, Frank, et al, eds. Automobility in Transition? A Socio-Technical Analysis of Sustainable Transport. 2011. (Routledge Studies in Sustainability Transitions Ser.). (ENG., Illus.). 410p. (C). 50.00 (978-0-415-88505-8(1)) Routledge.

Genat, Robert. Woodward Avenue: Cruising the Legendary Strip. 2010. (Illus.). 160p. 34.95 (978-1-932494-91-4(X)) CarTech, Inc.

Giucci, Guillermo. The Cultural Life of the Automobile: Roads to Modernity. Mayagoitia, Anne & Nagao, Debra, trs. from POR. 2012. (ENG & SPA., Illus.). 260p. 55.00 **(978-0-292-72872-1(7))** Univ. of Texas Pr.

Hylton, Stuart. The Horseless Carriage: The Birth of the Motor Age. 2009. (ENG., Illus.). 192p. pap. 27.95 (978-0-7524-5078-0(6)) History Pr. Ltd., The GBR. Dist: Independent Pubs. Group.

Krevsky, Margery. Sirens of Chrome: The Enduring Allure of Auto Show Models. 2008. (Illus.). 24.95 (978-1-879094-84-0(3)) Momentum Bks., LLC.

Ladd, Brian. Autophobia: Love & Hate in the Automotive Age. (Illus.). 2011. (ENG.). 240p. pap. 15.00 (978-0-226-46729-0(5)) 2008. 236p. 22.50 (978-0-226-46741-2(4)) Univ. of Chicago Pr.

Lutz, Catherine & Lutz Fernandez, Anne. Carjacked: The Culture of the Automobile & Its Effect on Our Lives. 2010. (ENG., Illus.). 272p. 28.00 (978-0-230-61813-8(8)) Palgrave Macmillan.

Mclaren, Arlene Tigar & Conley, Jim. Car Troubles: Critical Studies of Auto-Mobility. 2009. (Transport & Society Ser.). (Illus.). 272p. 124.95 (978-0-7546-7772-7(9)) Ashgate Publishing Co.

Museum Tinguely (Basel, Switzerland) Staff, ed. Car Fetish: I Drive Therefore I Am. 2011. (ENG., Illus.). 300p. pap. 65.00 **(978-3-86828-228-3(9))** Kehrer Verlag Heidelberg, Klaus Kehrer DEU. Dist: Consortium Bk. Sales & Distribution.

Nelson, Kevin. Wheels of Change from Zero to 600 M.P.H: The Amazing Story of California & the Automobile. 2009. pap. 24.95 (978-1-59714-113-0(5)) Heyday.

Packer, Jeremy. Mobility Without Mayhem: Safety, Cars, & Citizenship. 2008. (ENG., Illus.). 360p. 94.95 (978-0-8223-3952-6(8)); per. 25.95 (978-0-8223-3963-2(3)) Duke Univ. Pr.

Paterson, Matthew. Automobile Politics: Ecology & Cultural Political Economy. 2007. (ENG., Illus.). 284p. per. 35.99 (978-0-521-69130-7(3)); 107.00 (978-0-521-87080-1(1)) Cambridge Univ. Pr.

Seiler, Cotten. Republic of Drivers: A Cultural History of Automobility in America. 2008. (Illus.). 240p. 52.00 (978-0-226-74563-3(5)); pap. 19.00 (978-0-226-74564-0(3)) Univ. of Chicago Pr.

Sheppard, Steve & Seinfeld, Jerry. Car-O-Scope. 2007. 207p. pap. 10.95 (978-0-9777196-0-0(X)) Cohort Pr.

Siegelbaum, Lewis H., ed. The Socialist Car: Automobility in the Eastern Bloc. 2011. (Illus.). 248p. 65.00 (978-0-8014-4991-8(X)); pap. 24.95 **(978-0-8014-7738-6(7))** Cornell Univ. Pr.

Stavitsky, Gail & Warhol, Andy. Warhol & Cars: American Icons. 2011. (978-0-615-41922-0(4)) Montclair Art Museum.

Tatum, Charles M. Lowriders in Chicano Culture: From Low to Slow to Show, 1 vol. 2011. (Illus.). 223p. 55.00 (978-0-313-38149-2(6), A2584C) Greenwood Publishing Group, Inc.

Uffelen, Van Chris. Automobile Architecture. 2011. (Architecture in Focus Ser.). (ENG., Illus.). 424p. 99.95 (978-3-03768-073-5(3), Braun Publish,Csi) Continental Sales, Inc.

Wolfe, Joel. Autos & Progress: The Brazilian Search for Modernity, 1 vol. 2010. (ENG., Illus.). 288p. 99.00 (978-0-19-517457-1(7)) Oxford Univ. Pr., Inc.

Wolfe, Joel, contrib. by. Autos & Progress: The Brazilian Search for Modernity, 1 vol. 2010. (ENG., Illus.). 288p. pap. 21.95 (978-0-19-517456-4(9)) Oxford Univ. Pr., Inc.

AUTOMOBILES—SPEED

see also Automobiles, Racing—Speed Records

Fijol, Robert. Factors Involved in Commercial Vehicle Fatalities Related to Speed. 2008. 76p. pap. (978-3-8364-8884-6(1)) VDM Verlag Dr. Mueller e.K.

Fisher, Bill. Ford Speed Manual. 2007. (ENG., Illus.). 128p. per. 19.95 *(978-1-931128-06-3(5)*, 1931128065) California Bill's Automotive Handbooks.

Mason, Nick & Hales, Mark. Passion for Speed: Twenty-Four Classic Cars that Shaped a Century of Motor Sport. 2010. (ENG., Illus.). 208p. 39.95 *(978-1-84732-639-3(0))* Carlton Bks., Ltd. GBR. Dist: Sterling Publishing Co., Inc.

Morrison, Kevin M. The Complete Book on Speed Enforcement: A Practical Guide to Understanding Speed Enforcement Concepts & Devices. 2012. (Illus.). 182p. pap. 29.95 ***(978-0-398-08733-3(4))*** Thomas, Charles C. Pub., Ltd.

Scott, Michael & Maddox, with David. Speeding in Residential Areas, 2nd Edition. 2010. 60p. pap. *(978-1-935676-02-7(4))* U.S. Dept. of Justice-COPS.

AUTOMOBILES—SPRINGS AND SUSPENSION

Delmar Learning Staff. Suspension & Steering. 2007. (ENG.). 114.95 *(978-1-4180-4237-0(4))* Delmar Cengage Learning.

Dixon, John. Suspension Geometry & Computation. 2009. (ENG., Illus.). 434p. 135.00 *(978-0-470-51021-6(8)*, Wiley) Wiley, John & Sons, Inc.

Ebrahimi, Babak. Electromagnetic Dampers in Vehicle Suspension Systems. 2009. 196p. pap. *(978-3-639-21394-2(7))* VDM Verlag Dr. Mueller e.K.

Erjavec, Jack. Suspension & Steering: Natef Standards Job Sheets. 3rd ed. 2009. (ENG.). 240p. (C). pap. 40.95 *(978-1-4354-8319-4(7))* Delmar Cengage Learning.

Guglielmino, Emanuele, et al. Semi-Active Suspension Control: Improved Vehicle Ride & Road Friendliness. 2008. (ENG., Illus.). xvi, 294p. 139.00 *(978-1-84800-230-2(0)*, 1848002300) Springer.

Halderman, James D. Automotive Steering, Suspension, & Alignment. 4th ed. 2007. (ENG.). 504p. (C). pap. 122.80 *(978-0-13-222905-0(6)*, Prentice Hall) Prentice Hall PTR.

—Automotive Steering, Suspension & Alignment. 5th ed. 2009. (ENG., Illus.). 492p. (C). pap. 118.00 *(978-0-13-610001-0(5)*, Prentice Hall) Prentice Hall PTR.

—Steering, Suspension, & Alignment. 2007. (General Motors Fundamental Curriculum Ser.). (Illus.). 457p. per. 73.33 *(978-0-13-241131-8(8))* Pearson Education.

Hammill, Des. How to Build & Modify Sportscar & Kitcar Suspension & Brakes: For Road & Track - Revised & Updated 2nd Edition. 3rd ed. 2008. (SpeedPro Ser.). (ENG., Illus.). 128p. pap. 39.95 *(978-1-84584-207-9(3)*, 1845842073) Veloce Publishing Ltd. GBR. Dist: MBI Distribution Services/Quayside Distribution.

Hollander Interchange Manual: Chassis I. 72nd ed. 2006. (Illus.). 864p. pap. 75.00 *(978-1-58132-124-1(4))* Hollander.

Hollander Interchange Manual: Chassis II. 72nd ed. 2006. (Illus.). 1288p. pap. 75.00 *(978-1-58132-125-8(2))* Hollander.

Hollander Interchange Manual: Chassis III. 72nd ed. 2006. (Illus.). 728p. pap. 75.00 *(978-1-58132-126-5(0))* Hollander.

Hollander Interchange Manual: Chassis Set. 72nd ed. 2006. (Illus.). 2880p. pap. 235.00 *(978-1-58132-133-3(3))* Hollander.

Hollander Interchange Manual: Identification I. 72nd ed. 2006. (Illus.). 472p. pap. 100.00 *(978-1-58132-130-2(9))* Hollander.

Hollander Interchange Manual: Identification II. 72nd ed. 2006. (Illus.). 848p. pap. 100.00 *(978-1-58132-131-9(7))* Hollander.

Ihsan, Sany. Semiactive Control Policies. 2011. 140p. pap. ***(978-3-8443-8417-8(0))*** Lambert Academic Publishing.

Johanson, Chris & Stockel, Martin T. Auto Suspension & Steering Technology. 136p. tchr. ed. 28.00 *(978-1-56637-700-3(5))*; 2nd ed. 186p. pap., wbk. ed. 14.00 *(978-1-56637-699-0(8))* Goodheart-Willcox Pub.

Knowles, Don. Automotive Suspension & Steering Systems, 2 vols. (ENG., Illus.). (C). 4th rev. ed. 2006. 432p. pap. 153.95 *(978-1-4018-9682-9(0))* 5th ed. 2010. pap. 110.95 ***(978-1-4354-8115-2(1))*** 5th ed. 2010. spiral bd. 110.95 ***(978-1-4354-8114-5(3))*** Delmar Cengage Learning.

—Automotive Suspension & Steering Systems Classroom Manual. 5th ed. 2011. (ENG.). pap., pap. 295.95 ***(978-1-111-65568-6(5))*** Delmar Cengage Learning.

Knowles, Don. Today's Technician: Automotive Suspension & Steering Systems. 5th ed. 2010. (ENG.). 1040p. (C). pap. 147.95 *(978-1-4354-8118-3(6))* Delmar Cengage Learning.

McGee, Trenton. 4x4 Suspension Handbook. 2008. (Sa Design Ser.). (Illus.). 144p. pap. 24.95 *(978-1-932494-48-8(0))* CarTech, Inc.

Miller, Dick. How to Hook & Launch: Traction Mods for Street & Strip. 2012. (ENG., Illus.). 128p. pap. 24.95 ***(978-1-934709-35-1(2))*** CarTech, Inc.

Noakes, Keith. Motorcycle Road & Racing Chassis: A Modern Review of the Best Independents. 2007. (ENG., Illus.). 176p. pap. 39.95 *(978-1-84584-130-0(1)*, 1845841301) Veloce Publishing Ltd. GBR. Dist: MBI Distribution Services/Quayside Distribution.

Norville, Norman. T5 Med/Hvy Truck Steering & Suspension. 2006. spiral bd. 22.95 *(978-1-933180-72-4(2))* Advanstar Communications, Inc.

Pearson Education Staff & Pearson, Nina. Automotive Steering Suspension Alignment, Kit. 2009. (ENG.). (C). 34.80 *(978-0-13-510695-2(8)*, Prentice Hall) Prentice Hall PTR.

Tann, Jeff. The Complete Builder's Guide to Hot Rod Chassis & Suspensions. 2010. (Illus.). 144p. pap. 24.95 *(978-1-934709-18-4(2)*, S-A Design) CarTech, Inc.

Technology Research Editors, ed. Motor Vehicle Suspension Systems: Vibrational Effects & Stability, 2007 Ed. 2007. pap. 128.50 *(978-1-60030-252-7(1)*, Search-In-Print) CSA Journal Division.

AUTOMOBILES—STEERING-GEAR

Delmar Cengage Learning Staff. Dato: Diagnostic Scenarios for Suspension/Steering. 2011. (Automotive Multimedia Solutions Ser.). (ENG.). (C). 33.95 *(978-1-111-03483-2(4))* Delmar Cengage Learning.

Delmar Learning Staff. Suspension & Steering. (ENG.). 2008. 114.95 *(978-1-4283-2093-2(8))* 2007. 114.95 *(978-1-4180-4237-0(4))* Delmar Cengage Learning.

Erjavec, Jack. Suspension & Steering: Natef Standards Job Sheets. 3rd ed. 2009. (ENG.). 240p. (C). pap. 40.95 *(978-1-4354-8319-4(7))* Delmar Cengage Learning.

Halderman, James D. Automotive Steering, Suspension, & Alignment. 4th ed. 2007. (ENG.). 504p. (C). pap. 122.80 *(978-0-13-222905-0(6)*, Prentice Hall) Prentice Hall PTR.

—Automotive Steering, Suspension & Alignment. 5th ed. 2009. (ENG., Illus.). 492p. (C). pap. 118.00 *(978-0-13-610001-0(5)*, Prentice Hall) Prentice Hall PTR.

—Steering, Suspension, & Alignment. 2007. (General Motors Fundamental Curriculum Ser.). (Illus.). 457p. per. 73.33 *(978-0-13-241131-8(8))* Pearson Education.

Hollander Interchange Manual: Chassis I. 72nd ed. 2006. (Illus.). 864p. pap. 75.00 *(978-1-58132-124-1(4))* Hollander.

Hollander Interchange Manual: Chassis II. 72nd ed. 2006. (Illus.). 1288p. pap. 75.00 *(978-1-58132-125-8(2))* Hollander.

Hollander Interchange Manual: Chassis III. 72nd ed. 2006. (Illus.). 728p. pap. 75.00 *(978-1-58132-126-5(0))* Hollander.

Hollander Interchange Manual: Chassis Set. 72nd ed. 2006. (Illus.). 2880p. pap. 235.00 *(978-1-58132-133-3(3))* Hollander.

Hollander Interchange Manual: Identification I. 72nd ed. 2006. (Illus.). 472p. pap. 100.00 *(978-1-58132-130-2(9))* Hollander.

Hollander Interchange Manual: Identification II. 72nd ed. 2006. (Illus.). 848p. pap. 100.00 *(978-1-58132-131-9(7))* Hollander.

Johanson, Chris & Stockel, Martin T. Auto Suspension & Steering Technology. 136p. tchr. ed. 28.00 *(978-1-56637-700-3(5))*; 2nd ed. 186p. pap., wbk. ed. 14.00 *(978-1-56637-699-0(8))* Goodheart-Willcox Pub.

Knowles, Don. Automotive Suspension & Steering Systems, 2 vols. 5th ed. 2010. (ENG., Illus.). (C). pap. 110.95 ***(978-1-4354-8115-2(1))***; spiral bd. 110.95 ***(978-1-4354-8114-5(3))*** Delmar Cengage Learning.

—Automotive Suspension & Steering Systems Classroom Manual. 5th ed. 2011. (ENG.). pap., pap. 295.95 ***(978-1-111-65568-6(5))*** Delmar Cengage Learning.

Knowles, Don. Today's Technician: Automotive Suspension & Steering Systems. 5th ed. 2010. (ENG.). 1040p. (C). pap. 147.95 *(978-1-4354-8118-3(6))* Delmar Cengage Learning.

Norville, Norman. T5 Med/Hvy Truck Steering & Suspension. 2006. spiral bd. 22.95 *(978-1-933180-72-4(2))* Advanstar Communications, Inc.

Pearson Education Staff & Pearson, Nina. Automotive Steering Suspension Alignment, Kit. 2009. (ENG.). (C). 34.80 *(978-0-13-510695-2(8)*, Prentice Hall) Prentice Hall PTR.

AUTOMOBILES—TESTING

American Society of Mechanical Engineers Staff, ed. Automotive Diagnostics. 142p. 104.00 *(978-0-85298-728-5(5))*; 640p. 174.00 *(978-0-85298-697-4(1))* Professional Engineering Publishing GBR. Dist: SAE Intl.

Atkins, Richard D. An Introduction to Engine Testing & Development. 2009. 79.95 *(978-0-7680-2099-1(9))* SAE Intl.

Bettes, Harold & Hancock, Bill. Dyno Testing & Tuning. 2008. (Performance How-to Ser.). (Illus.). 144p. pap. 24.95 *(978-1-932494-49-5(9))* CarTech, Inc.

Chilton Automotive Editorial Staff. Asian Diagnostic Service Manual 2006, Vol. 3. 2006. (Chilton Diagnostic Manuals Ser.). (ENG., Illus.). 1032p. 79.95 *(978-1-4180-2915-9(7))* Delmar Cengage Learning.

—European Diagnostic Service 2006. 2006. (Chilton Diagnostic Manuals Ser.). (ENG., Illus.). 888p. 79.95 *(978-1-4180-2924-1(6))* Delmar Cengage Learning.

Chilton Editors. Chilton 2006 Asian Diagnostic Service Vol. 1, Vol. 1. 2006. (Chilton Diagnostic Manuals Ser.). (ENG., Illus.). 768p. 79.95 *(978-1-4180-2913-5(0))* Delmar Cengage Learning.

—Chilton Asian Diagnostic Service Manual 2006, Vol. 2. 2006. (Chilton Diagnostic Manuals Ser.). (ENG., Illus.). 984p. 79.95 *(978-1-4180-2914-2(9))* Delmar Cengage Learning.

Denton, Tom. Advanced Automotive Fault Diagnosis: Automotive Technology - Vehicle Maintenance & Repair. 3rd rev. ed. 2011. (ENG., Illus.). 456p. (C). pap. 41.95 *(978-0-08-096955-8(0))* Routledge.

Nordhoff, Lawrence S., ed. Human Subject Crash Testing: Innovations & Advances. 2007. 929p. pap. 119.95 *(978-0-7680-1931-5(1))* SAE Intl.

Oldham, Joe. Muscle Car Confidential: Confessions of a Muscle Car Test Driver. rev. ed. 2007. (ENG., Illus.). 176p. 34.95 *(978-0-7603-2831-6(5)*, 0760328315, Motorbooks) MBI Publishing Co. LLC.

Plint, Michael James & Martyr, Tony. Engine Testing: Theory & Practice. 2007. 468p. pap. 99.95 *(978-0-7680-1850-9(1))* SAE Intl.

Sammer, Gerald. Succesful Automotive Testing. 2008. 224p. pap. *(978-3-639-07079-8(8))* VDM Verlag Dr. Mueller e.K.

Seiffert, Ulrich & Wech, Lothar. Automotive Safety Handbook. 2nd ed. 2007. 99.95 *(978-0-7680-1798-4(X))* SAE Intl.

Technology Research Editors, ed. Failure of Automotive Components, 2007 Ed. 2007. pap. 128.50 *(978-1-60030-245-9(9)*, Search-In-Print) CSA Journal Division.

Thompson, James K. Brake NVH: Testing & Measurements. 2011. (Illus.). 156p. *(978-0-7680-3480-6(9))* SAE Intl.

AUTOMOBILES—THEFT

see Automobile Theft

AUTOMOBILES—TIRES

Giapponi, Thomas R. Tire Forensic Investigation: Analyzing Tire Failure. 2008. 79.95 *(978-0-7680-1955-1(9))* SAE Intl.

Heuston, C. Randall. Bandag Revolutions: Bandag's 50 Years of Innovation in the Tire Industry. 2007. *(978-0-9793779-2-1(7))* WDG Publishing.

Siggerud, Katherine A. Underinflated Tires in the U. S. 2007. (Illus.). 17p. (C). pap. 15.00 *(978-1-4223-1519-4(3))* DIANE Publishing Co.

AUTOMOBILES—TOURING

see Automobile Travel

AUTOMOBILES—TRAILERS

see also Mobile Homes; Trailer Camps

Littlefield, Bruce & Brown, Simon. Airstream Living. 2007. (ENG., Illus.). 160p. pap. 19.95 *(978-0-06-115164-4(5)*, Collins Design) HarperCollins Pubs.

Newton, Richard. The Complete Trailer Handbook. 2008. (Motorbooks Workshop Ser.). (ENG., Illus.). 160p. pap. 19.99 *(978-0-7603-3371-6(8)*, 0760333718, Motorbooks) MBI Publishing Co. LLC.

AUTOMOBILES—TRANSMISSION DEVICES

American Society of Mechanical Engineers Staff, ed. Automobile Transmissions. (IMechE Seminar Publication Ser.: Vol. 2). (Illus.). 138p. 126.00 *(978-0-85298-893-0(1))* Professional Engineering Publishing GBR. Dist: SAE Intl.

—Gearbox Noise & Vibration. 200p. 104.00 *(978-0-85298-718-6(8))* Professional Engineering Publishing GBR. Dist: SAE Intl.

Birch, Thomas W. Automatic Transmissions & Tranaxles. 5th rev. ed. 2011. (ENG., Illus.). 576p. (C). pap. 118.00 ***(978-0-13-262227-1(0)***, Prentice Hall) Prentice Hall PTR.

Birch, Thomas W. & Rockwood, Chuck. NATEF Correlated Task Sheets for Automatic Transmissions & Tranaxles. 5th rev. ed. 2011. (ENG.). 144p. (C). pap. 36.20 ***(978-0-13-260608-0(9)***, Prentice Hall) Prentice Hall PTR.

Birch, Tom D., et al. NATEF Correlated Task Sheets for Automatic Transmissions & Tranaxles. 4th ed. 2009. (ENG.). 60p. (C). pap. 36.20 *(978-0-13-506953-0(X)*, Prentice Hall) Prentice Hall PTR.

Delmar Cengage Learning. DATO: Diagnostic Scenarios for Automatic Transmissions. 2011. (Automotive Multimedia Solutions Ser.). (ENG.). (C). 41.95 *(978-1-111-03492-4(3))* Delmar Cengage Learning.

Delmar Cengage Learning, (Delmar Cengage Learning). DATO: Diagnostic Scenarios for Manual Transmissions. 2011. (Automotive Multimedia Solutions Ser.). (ENG.). (C). 33.95 *(978-1-111-03495-5(8))* Delmar Cengage Learning.

Delmar Learning Staff. ASE Test Preparation - A2 Automatic Transmissions & Transaxles. 5th ed. 2011. (ENG.). 176p. pap. 23.95 *(978-1-111-12704-6(2))* Delmar Cengage Learning.

—Automatic Transmissions. 2007. (ENG.). 114.95 *(978-1-4180-4243-1(9))* Delmar Cengage Learning.

Dolcini, Pietro J., et al. Dry Clutch Control for Automated Manual Transmission Vehicles. 2010. (Advances in Industrial Control Ser.). (ENG., Illus.). 144p. 149.00 *(978-1-84996-067-0(4)*, 1849960674) Springer.

Erjavec & Erjavec, Jack. Manual Transmissions & Transaxles: Manual Transmissions/Transaxles Classrm Mnl 5e, 2 vols. 5th ed. 2010. (ENG., Illus.). (C). pap. 110.95 *(978-1-4354-2685-6(1))* CENGAGE Learning.

Erjavec, Jack. Manual Transmissions & Transaxles, 2 vols. 5th ed. 2011. (Illus.). ***(978-1-4354-2835-5(8))*** Delmar Cengage Learning.

—NATEF Standards Job Sheets Area A2. 3rd ed. 2009. (ENG.). 192p. (C). pap. 40.95 *(978-1-4354-8317-0(0))* Delmar Cengage Learning.

—NATEF Standards Job Sheets Area A3. 3rd ed. 2009. (ENG.). 208p. (C). pap. 40.95 *(978-1-4354-8318-7(9))* Delmar Cengage Learning.

—NATEF Standards Job Sheets Area A8. 3rd ed. 2009. (ENG.). 256p. (C). pap. 40.95 *(978-1-4354-8323-1(5))* Delmar Cengage Learning.

—Shop Manual for Automatic Transmissions & Transaxles. 5th ed. 2010. (ENG., Illus.). xx, 583p. (C). pap. 110.95 *(978-1-4354-8104-6(6))* Delmar Cengage Learning.

—Today's Technician: Manual Transmissions & Transaxles. 5th ed. 2010. (ENG.). 928p. (C). pap. 147.95 *(978-1-4354-3933-7(3))* Delmar Cengage Learning.

—Today's Technician: Automatic Transmissions & Transaxles. 5th ed. 2010. (ENG.). 1040p. (C). pap. 147.95 *(978-1-4354-8105-3(4))* Delmar Cengage Learning.

Halderman, James D. Automatic Transmissions & Transaxles. 2007. (General Motors Fundamental Curriculum Ser.). 432p. (C). pap. 73.33 *(978-0-13-158232-3(1)*, Prentice Hall) Prentice Hall PTR.

—Automotive Chassis Systems. 5th ed. 2009. (ENG., Illus.). 784p. (C). pap. 118.00 *(978-0-13-508503-5(9)*, Prentice Hall) Prentice Hall PTR.

Halderman, James D. NATEF Correlated Task Sheets for Automotive Technology. 4th ed. 2011. (ENG.). 700p. (C). pap. 26.00 ***(978-0-13-254010-0(X)***, Prentice Hall) Prentice Hall PTR.

Institution of Mechanical Engineers (Great Britain), Automobile Division Staff, contrib. by. IPDS 2006: Integrated Powertrain & Driveline Systems 2006: 14-15 June 2006, Ford Motor Company, Dunton, Essex, Institution of Mechanical Engineers Automobile Division. (Illus.). 208p. pap. *(978-1-84569-197-4(0))* Woodhead Publishing Ltd.

Johanson, Chris & Duffy, James E. Automatic Transmissions & Transaxles. 3rd ed. 2009. (ENG.). 495p. 96.00 *(978-1-60525-203-2(4))* Goodheart-Willcox Pub.

Naunheimer, Harald, et al. Automotive Transmissions: Fundamentals, Selection, Design & Application. Kuchle, Aaron, tr. from GER. 2nd ed. 2010. (ENG., Illus.). xxiv, 718p. 229.00 *(978-3-642-16213-8(4)*, 3642162134) Springer.

Noakes, Keith. Motorcycle Road & Racing Chassis: A Modern Review of the Best Independents. 2007. (ENG., Illus.). 176p. pap. 39.95 *(978-1-84584-130-0(1)*, 1845841301) Veloce Publishing Ltd. GBR. Dist: MBI Distribution Services/Quayside Distribution.

Padgett, Marty. Bobcat: Fifty Years of Opportunity 1958-2008. 2007. *(978-0-7603-3212-2(6))* MBI Publishing Co. LLC.

Paul, Cangialosi. How to Rebuild & Modify High-Performance Manual Transmissions. 2010. 144p. pap. 24.95 *(978-1-934709-29-0(8)*, S-A Design) CarTech, Inc.

Reid, George. How to Rebuild & Modify Ford C4 & C6 Automatic Transmissions. 2012. (Illus.). 160p. pap. 24.95 ***(978-1-934709-82-5(4))*** CarTech, Inc.

Rockwood, Chuck & Birch, Tom. Automatic Transmissions & Transaxles. 4th ed. 2009. (ENG., Illus.). 600p. (C). pap. 122.80 *(978-0-13-505135-1(5)*, Prentice Hall) Prentice Hall PTR.

Ruggles, Cliff. How to Rebuild & Modify GM Turbo Hydra-Matic 400 Transmissions. 2011. (Illus.). 144p. pap. 24.95 *(978-1-934709-20-7(4)*, S-A Design) CarTech, Inc.

SAE Transmission/Axle/Driveline Forum Committee Staff, contrib. by. Design Practices — Passenger Car Automatic Transmissions. 4th ed. 2012. ***(978-0-7680-1125-8(0))*** SAE Intl.

Viroj Wiwanitkit. Traffic & Industrial Environmental Problem: New Concern for Developing Countries. 2009. 42.00 *(978-1-60692-473-0(7))* Nova Science Pubs., Inc.

Voith Power Transmission: 100 Years of the Fottinger Principle. 2007. (Illus.). 320p. 89.95 *(978-3-540-68784-9(X))* Springer.

AUTOMOBILES—TRAVELING

see Automobile Travel

AUTOMOBILES—VENTILATION

see Automobiles—Heating and Ventilation

AUTOMOBILES—WHEELS

Halderman, James D. Automotive Steering, Suspension, & Alignment. 4th ed. 2007. (ENG.). 504p. (C). pap. 122.80 *(978-0-13-222905-0(6)*, Prentice Hall) Prentice Hall PTR.

—Automotive Steering, Suspension & Alignment. 5th ed. 2009. (ENG., Illus.). 492p. (C). pap. 118.00 *(978-0-13-610001-0(5)*, Prentice Hall) Prentice Hall PTR.

—Steering, Suspension, & Alignment. 2007. (General Motors Fundamental Curriculum Ser.). (Illus.). 457p. per. 73.33 *(978-0-13-241131-8(8))* Pearson Education.

Pearson Education Staff & Pearson, Nina. Automotive Steering Suspension Alignment, Kit. 2009. (ENG.). (C). 34.80 *(978-0-13-510695-2(8)*, Prentice Hall) Prentice Hall PTR.

Steve, Magnante. How to Build Altered Wheelbase Cars. 2010. 144p. pap. 29.95 *(978-1-934709-26-9(3)*, S-A Design) CarTech, Inc.

Technology Research Editors, ed. Automotive Wheels, 2007 Ed. 2007. pap. 128.50 *(978-1-60030-239-8(4)*, Search-In-Print) CSA Journal Division.

Wheels. (Early Intervention Levels Ser.). 23.10 *(978-0-7362-0032-5(0))*; Vol. 4. 3.85 *(978-1-56334-980-5(9))* Hampton-Brown Bks.

AUTOMOBILES—YEARBOOKS

Newbury, Stephen & Lewin, Tony. All New Concept & Production Cars Worldwide. annuals 2009. (Car Design Yearbook Ser.). (ENG.). 304p. 44.95 *(978-1-85894-477-7(5))* Merrell Pubs. Ltd. GBR. Dist: Perseus Distribution.

—The Car Design Yearbook 7. 2008. 320p. 44.95 *(978-1-85894-419-7(8))* Merrell Pubs. Ltd. GBR. Dist: Perseus Distribution.

AUTOMOBILES, ANTIQUE

see Antique and Classic Cars

AUTOMOBILES, CLASSIC

see Antique and Classic Cars

AUTOMOBILES, COMPANY

Bradford, Francis H. & Dias, Ric A. Hall-Scott: The Untold Story of a Great American Engine-Maker. 2007. 49.95 *(978-0-7680-1660-4(6))* SAE Intl.

Does de Willebois, Emile van der. The Misuse of Corporate Vehicles: How the Corrupt Use Legal Structures to Hide Their Wealth & What to Do about It. 2011. ***(978-0-8213-8896-9(7))*** World Bank Pubns.

Towards Ecological Taxation: The Efficacy of Emissions- Related Motor Taxation Regimes. 2011. (Corporate Social Responsibility Ser.). (Illus.). 256p. 124.95 *(978-0-566-08979-4(3)*, Gower Publishing Co., Ltd.) Ashgate Publishing, Ltd. GBR. Dist: Ashgate Publishing Co.

van der Does de Willebois, Emile, et al. The Misuse of Corporate Vehicles: How the Corrupt Use Legal Structures to Hide Their Wealth & What to Do about It. 2011. (StAR Initiative Ser.). (ENG.). 240p. pap. 25.00 ***(978-0-8213-8894-5(0)***, 9780821388945) World Bank Pubns.

AUTOMOBILES, DIESEL

see Automobiles—Motors

AUTOMOBILES, ELECTRIC

Anderson, Curtis D. & Anderson, Judy. Electric & Hybrid Cars: A History. 2nd rev. ed. 2010. (ENG., Illus.). 267p. pap. 45.00 *(978-0-7864-3301-8(9))* McFarland & Co., Inc. Pubs.

Astley, Rick. Classic British Car Electrical Systems: Your guide to understanding, repairing & improving the electrical components & systems that were typical of British cars from 1950 To 1980. 2009. (Essential Ser.). (ENG., Illus.). 176p.

pap. 49.95 *(978-1-84584-215-4(4)*, 1845842154) Veloce Publishing Ltd. GBR. Dist: MBI Distribution Services/Quayside Distribution.

Awedikian, Roy. Quality of the Design of Test Cases for Automotive Software. 2011. 316p. pap. ***(978-3-8443-2990-2(0))*** Lambert Academic Publishing.

Battery & EV Industry Review 2005. 2006. per. 1950.00 *(978-1-59623-207-5(2))* BCC Research.

Billmaier, James. Jolt! The Impending Dominance of the Electric Car & Why America Must Take Charge. 2010. (ENG.). 236p. 22.99 *(978-1-59932-220-9(X))* Advantage Media Group.

Boschert, Sherry. Plug-in Hybrids: The Cars That Will Recharge America. 2006. (ENG., Illus.). 231p. per. 16.95 *(978-0-86571-571-4(8)*, 0865715718) New Society Pubs., Ltd. CAN. Dist: Consortium Bk. Sales & Distribution.

Ehsani/Gao/Emad. Modern Electric, Hybrid Electrc, & Fuel Cell Vehicles. 2nd rev. ed. 2009. (Power Electronics & Applications Ser.). (ENG., Illus.). 557p. 139.95 *(978-1-4200-5398-2(1)*, CRC Press) Taylor & Francis Group GBR. Dist: Taylor & Francis Group.

Gauäy, Philipp. The Electric Car & Britain. 2011. 32p. pap. ***(978-3-640-70595-5(5))*** Hammer, Patrick, Tanja Hammer, Matthias Knoop, Julius Mittenzwei, Georg Steinbach u. Michael Teltscher. GRIN Verlag GbR.

Halderman, James D. & Martin, Tony. NATEF Correlated Job Sheets for Hybrid & Alternative Fuel Vehicles. 3rd ed. 2012. (ENG.). 96p. (C). pap. 26.67 ***(978-0-13-278538-9(2)***, Prentice Hall) Prentice Hall PTR.

Hummel, Christopher B. Plug-in Hybrid Electric Vehicles & Energy Use. 2011. (Energy Science, Engineering & Technology Ser.). 185.00 ***(978-1-61470-633-5(6))*** Nova Science Pubs., Inc.

Hybrid Cars: Increasing Fuel Efficiency & Reducing Oil Dependence: Hearing Before the Subcommittee on Energy & Resources of the Committee on Government Reform, House of Representatives, One Hundred Ninth Congress, Second Session, July 20, 2006. 2007. (Illus.). iii, 89p. *(978-0-16-079131-4(6)*, 552-070-36226-6) United States Government Printing Office.

Institution of Mechanical Engineers. Innovations in Fuel Economy & Sustainable Road Transport. 2012. (ENG., Illus.). 240p. pap. 330.00 ***(978-0-85709-213-7(8))*** Woodhead Publishing Ltd. GBR. Dist: Ingram Pub. Services.

Isaacs, David & Linde, Arvid. Electric Cars the Future Is Now! Your Guide to the Cars You Can Buy Now & What the Future Holds. 2010. (ENG., Illus.). 128p. pap. 24.95 *(978-1-84584-310-6(X)*, 184584310X) Veloce Publishing Ltd. GBR. Dist: MBI Distribution Services/Quayside Distribution.

Kadirov, Djavlonbek. Sustainable Marketing Systems. 2010. 212p. pap. *(978-3-639-23710-8(2))* VDM Verlag Dr. Mueller e.K.

Liu, Guangfu & Hu, Dongxue. Lü Se Ji Shu Yu Jian Li Lun Yu Fang Fa: Yi Xin Neng Yuan Qi Che Wei Dui Xiang. 2009. (CHI., Illus.). 204p. *(978-7-122-05869-0(7))* Chemical Industry Pr.

Mitchell, William J., et al. Reinventing the Automobile: Personal Urban Mobility for the 21st Century. 2010. (ENG., Illus.). 240p. (gr. 17). 21.95 *(978-0-262-01382-6(7))* MIT Pr.

Motavalli, Jim. High Voltage: The Fast Track to Plug in the Auto Industry. 2011. (ENG.). 272p. 24.99 *(978-1-60529-263-2(X))* Rodale Pr., Inc.

Mountfort, Jon. Scalextric. 2009. (Shire Library). (ENG., Illus.). 56p. pap. 12.95 *(978-0-7478-0747-6(7))* Shire Pubns., Ltd. GBR. Dist: Random Hse., Inc.

Opportunities & Challenges Presented in Increasing the Number of Electric Vehicles in the Light Duty Automotive Sector: Hearing Before a Subcommittee of the Committee on Appropriations, United States Senate, One Hundred Eleventh Congress, Second Session, Special Hearing, February 23, 2010, Washington, DC. 2011. (Illus.). iv, 87p. ***(978-0-16-087823-7(3)***, 552-070-42327-3) United States Government Printing Office.

Terpstra, Philip. 1995 Worldwide Electric Vehicle Directory. 7th ed. (Illus.). 79p. pap. 20.00 *(978-1-883063-05-4(1))* Spirit Pubns.

Thacher, Eric F. A Solar Car Primer. 2011. (Energy Science, Engineering & Technology Ser.). 387p. pap. 39.00 *(978-1-60876-161-6(4))* Nova Science Pubs., Inc.

Virk, Shafqat Mumtaz, et al. Fault Prediction Analysis. 2010. 56p. pap. *(978-3-639-24862-3(7))* VDM Verlag Dr. Mueller e.K.

AUTOMOBILES, FOREIGN

Chilton. Chilton Asian Service Manuals. 2008. 5731p. 299.95 *(978-1-4283-2214-1(0))*; 2064p. 99.95 *(978-1-4283-2220-2(5))* Delmar Cengage Learning.

—Chiton 2006 Asian Diagnostic Service Manual Series. 2006. (Chilton Diagnostic Manuals Ser.). 239.85 *(978-1-4180-2986-9(6))* Delmar Cengage Learning.

Chilton, (Chilton). Chilton Asian Service Manual 2008. 2008. (ENG.). Vol. 1. 1128p. 79.95 *(978-1-4283-2215-8(9))* Vol. 4. 1968p. 79.95 *(978-1-4283-2218-9(3))* Delmar Cengage Learning.

Chilton Automotive Editorial Staff. Asian Diagnostic Service Manual 2006, Vol. 3. 2006. (Chilton Diagnostic Manuals Ser.). (ENG., Illus.). 1032p. 79.95 *(978-1-4180-2915-9(7))* Delmar Cengage Learning.

—Chilton Asian Service Manual 2008. 2008. (ENG.). Vol. 2. 1920p. 79.95 *(978-1-4283-2216-5(7))* Vol. 3. 2256p. 79.95 *(978-1-4283-2217-2(5))* Delmar Cengage Learning.

—European Diagnostic Service 2006. 2006. (Chilton Diagnostic Manuals Ser.). (ENG., Illus.). 888p. 79.95 *(978-1-4180-2924-1(6))* Delmar Cengage Learning.

Chilton Editors. Chilton 2006 Asian Diagnostic Service Vol. 1, Vol. 1. 2006. (Chilton Diagnostic Manuals Ser.). (ENG., Illus.). 768p. 79.95 *(978-1-4180-2913-5(0))* Delmar Cengage Learning.

—Chilton Asian Diagnostic Service Manual 2006, Vol. 2. 2006. (Chilton Diagnostic Manuals Ser.). (ENG., Illus.). 984p. 79.95 *(978-1-4180-2914-2(9))* Delmar Cengage Learning.

Clarke, R. M., compiled by. Mini Performance Portfolio 2001-2006. 2007. (Performance Portfolio Ser.). (ENG., Illus.). 120p. pap. 24.95 *(978-1-85520-734-9(6)*, 1855207346) Brooklands Bks. GBR. Dist: MBI Distribution Services/Quayside Distribution.

European Commission Staff, contrib. by. Examination of Current & Future Excess Capacity in the European Automobile Industry. (Illus.). 41p. *(978-92-828-0612-8(X))* European Commission BEL. Dist: Balogh International, Inc.

Long, Brian. Daimler SP250. 2nd ed. 2008. (Classic Reprint Ser.). (ENG., Illus.). 208p. 34.95 *(978-1-904788-77-5(7)*, 1904788777) Veloce Publishing Ltd. GBR. Dist: MBI Distribution Services/Quayside Distribution.

The Rebuilder's Data Book for Popular British Cars: Professional Edition, 1945-1986 Models. *(978-1-890700-34-8(7))* Imported Car, The.

The Rebuilder's Data Book for Popular European Cars: Professional Edition, 1945-1986 Models. *(978-1-890700-35-5(5))* Imported Car, The.

The Rebuilder's Data Book for Popular Import Cars: 1945-1986 Models. lib. bdg. *(978-1-890700-33-1(9))* Imported Car, The.

The Rebuilder's Data Book for Popular Japanese Cars: Professional Edition, 1945-1986 Models. *(978-1-890700-36-2(3))* Imported Car, The.

Taylor, S. AC Heritage. Date not set. (Illus.). 128p. pap. 18.95 *(978-1-85532-549-4(7))* Osprey Publishing, Ltd. GBR. Dist: Stackpole Bks.

Vuic, Jason. The Yugo: The Rise & Fall of the Worst Car in History, 1 vol. 2011. (ENG., Illus.). 272p. pap. 14.00 *(978-0-8090-9895-8(4)*, Hill & Wang) Farrar, Straus & Giroux.

AUTOMOBILES, FOREIGN—MAINTENANCE AND REPAIR

see Automobiles—Maintenance and Repair

AUTOMOBILES, GAS-TURBINE

Lehto, Steve. Chrysler's Turbine Car: The Rise & Fall of Detroit's Coolest Creation. (ENG.). 2012. 240p. pap. 16.95 ***(978-1-61374-345-4(9))*** 2010. (Illus.). 224p. 24.95 *(978-1-56976-549-4(9))* Chicago Review Pr., Inc.

Masters, Timothy & Lehto, Steve. Drawn to Injustice: The Wrongful Conviction of Timothy Masters. 2012. (ENG.). 448p. (gr. 12). pap. 9.99 ***(978-0-425-24792-1(9)***, Berkley) Penguin Group (USA) Inc.

AUTOMOBILES, GAS-TURBINE—MOTORS

see Automotive Gas Turbines

AUTOMOBILES, RACING

see also Hot Rods; Sports Cars

also names of specific racing automobiles, e.g. Austin-Healey Automobile

Arneson, Erik. Mickey Thompson: The Fast Life & Tragic Death of a Racing Legend. 2011. (ENG., Illus.). 304p. pap. 17.99 *(978-0-7603-4015-8(3)*, 0760340153, Motorbooks) MBI Publishing Co. LLC.

Arron, Simon & Hughes, Mark. The Complete Book of Formula One. 2008. (Complete Book Ser.). (ENG., Illus.). 492p. 60.00 *(978-0-7603-3456-0(0)*, 0760334560, Motorbooks) MBI Publishing Co. LLC.

Barrett, Frank & Jaynes, Boyd. Shelby Cars in Detail. 2008. (Illus.). 272p. *(978-1-893618-94-7(3))* Bull, David Publishing, Inc.

Blount, Terry. The Blount Report: NASCAR's Most Overrated & Underrated Drivers, Cars, Teams, & Tracks. 2009. (ENG.). 240p. 24.95 *(978-1-60078-089-9(X))* Triumph Bks.

Boddy, William 'Bill'. Montlhery: The Story of the Paris Autodrome. 2007. (Classic Reprint Ser.). (ENG., Illus.). 232p. 35.95 *(978-1-84584-052-5(6)*, 1845840526) Veloce Publishing Ltd. GBR. Dist: MBI Distribution Services/Quayside Distribution.

Boyce, Doug. Grumpy's Toys: The Authorized History of Grumpy Jenkins' Cars. 2011. (Illus.). pap. 34.95 *(978-1-934709-27-6(1))* CarTech, Inc.

Boyd, Lew. Paved Track Dirt Track: Racing at Old Bridge Stadium & Nazareth Raceway. 2006. (Illus.). 232p. per. 23.95 *(978-0-9709854-9-1(5))* Coastal 181.

Breslin, Mike. The Track Day Manual. 2008. (ENG., Illus.). 176p. 36.95 *(978-1-84425-482-8(8)*, 1844254828) Haynes Publishing PLC GBR. Dist: MBI Distribution Services/Quayside Distribution.

Brown, Christopher. Making Sense of Squiggly Lines: The Basic Analysis of Race Car Data Acquisition. 2011. (ENG., Illus.). 144p. pap. 44.95 *(978-0-9832593-1-2(3))* CB-Racing.

Bryant, Peter. Can-Am Challenger: The Cockney F1 Mechanic Who Designed & Built America's Best Can-Am Cars. 2007. (Illus.). 400p. 49.95 *(978-1-893618-86-2(2))* Bull, David Publishing, Inc.

Byrd, Tommy Lee. Street Sleepers: The Art of the Deceptively Fast Car. 2011. (Illus.). 144p. pap. 24.95 *(978-1-934709-58-0(1))* CarTech, Inc.

Codling, Stuart. Art of the Formula 1 Race Car. 2010. (ENG., Illus.). 208p. 45.00 *(978-0-7603-3731-8(4)*, 0760337314, Motorbooks) MBI Publishing Co. LLC.

Colesworthy, Robert L. Reher-Morrison Championship Engine Assembly. 2007. (Illus.). 400p. per. *(978-0-9723432-8-2(8))* IQ Learning Systems, Inc.

Collins, Peter. Lancia 037: The Development & Rally History of a World Champion. 2008. (ENG., Illus.). 192p. 79.95 *(978-1-84584-076-1(3)*, 1845840763) Veloce Publishing Ltd. GBR. Dist: MBI Distribution Services/Quayside Distribution.

Colombo, Ercole & Allievi, Pino. I Love Ferrari. 2010. (ITA & ENG., Illus.). 120p. 120.00 *(978-88-7200-289-6(3))* Vianello Libri ITA. Dist: Antique Collectors' Club.

Dawson, Sam. GT: The World's Best GT Cars 1953-1973. 2007. (ENG., Illus.). 144p. 49.95 *(978-1-84584-060-0(7)*, 1845840607) Veloce Publishing Ltd. GBR. Dist: MBI Distribution Services/Quayside Distribution.

Domenjoz, Luc. The Formula One Yearbook 2008 - 2009. 2009. (ENG., Illus.). 224p. 19.95 *(978-2-84707-154-2(7)*, 2847071547) Chronosports, editeur CHE. Dist: MBI Distribution Services/Quayside Distribution.

Dorling Kindersley Publishing Staff & Chapman, Niles. Illustrated Encyclopedia of Extraordinary Automobiles. 2009. (ENG.). 360p. (gr. 12). 23.00 *(978-0-7566-4980-7(3))* Dorling Kindersley Publishing, Inc.

Fodisch, Jorg Thomas, et al. Porsche 908: The Long Distance Runner. 2009. (ENG., Illus.). 240p. 89.95 *(978-1-84584-201-7(4)*, 1845842014) Veloce Publishing Ltd. GBR. Dist: MBI Distribution Services/Quayside Distribution.

Formula One Journalists Editors, ed. The Official Formula 1 Season Review 2007. 2008. (Official Formula One Season Review Ser.). (ENG., Illus.). 248p. 34.95 *(978-1-84425-453-8(4)*, 1844254534) Haynes Publishing PLC GBR. Dist: MBI Distribution Services/Quayside Distribution.

Fuller, Michael J. & Martin, J. A. Inside IMSA's Legendary GTP Race Cars: The Prototype Experience. rev. ed. 2008. (ENG., Illus.). 256p. 50.00 *(978-0-7603-3069-2(7)*, 0760330697, Motorbooks) MBI Publishing Co. LLC.

Georgiou, Tyrone. Sprint Cars. 2011. (Fast Lane: Open-Wheel Racing Ser.). 24p. (gr. 2-5). pap. 8.15 *(978-1-4339-5768-0(X))*; (Illus.). lib. bdg. 22.60 *(978-1-4339-5766-6(3))* Stevens, Gareth Publishing LLLP. (Stevens, Gareth Learning Library).

Gibson, John. Extreme Action Sports-Crestline. 176p. pap. 15.98 *(978-0-7603-1728-0(3))* MBI Publishing Co. LLC.

Gillham, Roger. Scalextric: Ultimate Guide. 7th ed. 2009. (ENG., Illus.). 400p. 69.95 *(978-1-84425-536-8(0)*, 1844255360) Haynes Publishing PLC GBR. Dist: MBI Distribution Services/Quayside Distribution.

—Scalextric: A Race Through Time. 50th ed. 2007. (ENG., Illus.). 144p. *(978-1-84425-415-6(1)*, 1844254151) Haynes Publishing PLC GBR. Dist: MBI Distribution Services/Quayside Distribution.

Goodwin, Carl. They Started in MGs: Profiles of Sports Car Racers of the 1950s. 2011. (ENG., Illus.). 291p. pap. 35.00 *(978-0-7864-6052-6(0))* McFarland & Co., Inc. Pubs.

Hart, Lou & Lee, Cory. Drag Racing's Exhibition Attractions: From Rockets to Ramp-Jumps. 2008. (ENG., Illus.). 96p. pap. 12.95 *(978-1-58388-208-5(1)*, 1583882081) Iconografix, Inc.

John-Neil, Richard. Backtrack: The Golden Years of Oval Racing. 2006. (ENG.). 96p. pap. 29.95 *(978-0-7524-4080-4(2))* History Pr. Ltd.,The GBR. Dist: Independent Pubs. Group.

Kennedy, Steve. Northeastern Modified Stock Car Racing. 2012. (Photo Gallery Ser.). (ENG., Illus.). 160p. pap. 39.95 *(978-1-58388-284-9(7)*, 1583882847) Iconografix, Inc.

Krumm, Michael. Driving on the Edge: The Art & Science of Race Driving. 2011. (ENG., Illus.). 192p. 39.95 ***(978-1-905334-63-6(X)***, 190533463X) Icon Pubng. Ltd. GBR. Dist: MBI Distribution Services/Quayside Distribution.

Langenscheidt Publishers Staff, contrib. by. Motor Racing: The Early Years/Die Anfange des Motorsports/les Debuts de la Course Automobile. 2008. (Transportation: the Early Years Ser.). (Illus.). 351p. 49.95 *(978-0-8416-0281-6(6))* American Map Corp.

Lawes, Jon. Competition Car Electrics. 2006. (ENG., Illus.). 192p. 44.95 *(978-1-84425-302-9(3)*, 1844253023) Haynes Publishing PLC GBR. Dist: MBI Distribution Services/Quayside Distribution.

Lehbrink, Hartmut. Mercedes Sport. 2008. (Transportation Ser.). (Illus.). 399p. 49.95 *(978-0-8416-0284-7(0))* American Map Corp.

Lier, Alexandra. Speedseekers. 2008. 274p. *(978-1-58423-315-2(X))*; (Illus.). *(978-1-58423-314-5(1))* Gingko Pr., Inc.

Livesey, Andrew. Advanced Motorsport Engineering. 2012. (Illus.). xiv, 220p. ***(978-0-08-094333-6(0))*** Routledge.

Long, Brian. Porsche Racing Cars: 1953 To 1975. 2008. (ENG., Illus.). 208p. 89.95 *(978-1-904788-44-7(0)*, 1904788440) Veloce Publishing Ltd. GBR. Dist: MBI Distribution Services/Quayside Distribution.

Lorenzo, Jorge & Roberts, Matt. Jorge Lorenzo: The New King of MotoGP. 2011. (ENG., Illus.). 240p. 39.95 *(978-0-85733-095-6(0)*, 0857330950) Haynes Publishing PLC GBR. Dist: MBI Distribution Services/Quayside Distribution.

Ludvigsen, Karl. BMW Racing Cars: 328 to Racing V12. 2007. (Ludvigsen Library Ser.). (ENG., Illus.). 128p. pap. 29.95 *(978-1-58388-201-6(4)*, 1583882014) Iconografix, Inc.

—Brm V16: How Britain's Auto Makers Built a Grand Prix Car to Beat the World. 2007. (ENG., Illus.). 96p. *(978-1-84584-037-2(2)*, 1845840372) Veloce Publishing Ltd. GBR. Dist: MBI Distribution Services/Quayside Distribution.

—German Racing Silver: Drivers, Cars & Triumphs of German Motor Racing. 2009. (Racing Colours Ser.). (ENG., Illus.). 176p. 39.95 *(978-0-7110-3368-9(4))* Allan, Ian Publishing GBR. Dist: BookMasters Distribution Services (BDS).

—The Incredible Blitzen Benz. 2006. (Illus.). 170p. 69.00 *(978-1-85443-223-0(0))* Dalton Watson Fine Bks.

—White Racers from Zuffenhausen: Porsche 904, 906, 907, 908, 909, 910. 2008. (Ludvigsen Library Ser.). (ENG., Illus.). 128p. pap. 29.95 *(978-1-58388-218-4(9)*, 1583882189) Iconografix, Inc.

Mangus, Ron & Smith, Gary D. Ford Roadsters Custom Interiors. 2008. (Ron Mangus' Custom Hot Rod Interiors Ser.). (ENG., Illus.). 160p. pap. 27.95 *(978-1-931128-26-1(X)*, 193112826X) California Bill's Automotive Handbooks.

McBeath, Simon. Competition Car Aerodynamics: A Practical Handbook. 2nd ed. 2011. (ENG., Illus.). 296p. 39.95 *(978-0-85733-007-9(1)*, 0857330071) Haynes Publishing PLC GBR. Dist: MBI Distribution Services/Quayside Distribution.

—Competition Car Composites: A Practical Handbook. 2nd ed. 2010. (ENG., Illus.). 208p. 44.95 *(978-1-84425-701-0(0)*, 1844257010) Haynes Publishing PLC GBR. Dist: MBI Distribution Services/Quayside Distribution.

—Competition Car Data Logging: A Practical Handbook. 2nd ed. 2009. (ENG., Illus.). 176p. 49.95 *(978-1-84425-565-8(4)*, 1844255654) Haynes Publishing PLC GBR. Dist: MBI Distribution Services/Quayside Distribution.

—Official Formula 1 Season Review 2008. Formula Journalists Staff, ed. 2009. (ENG., Illus.). 272p. 49.95 *(978-1-84425-566-5(2)*, 1844255662) Haynes Publishing PLC GBR. Dist: MBI Distribution Services/Quayside Distribution.

—The Official Formula 1 Season Review 2009. 2010. (ENG., Illus.). 256p. pap. 44.95 *(978-1-84425-721-8(5)*, 1844257215) Haynes Publishing PLC GBR. Dist: MBI Distribution Services/Quayside Distribution.

McCarthy, Todd. Fast Women: The Legendary Ladies of Racing. 2007. (Illus.). 320p. 23.95 *(978-1-4013-5202-8(2))* Miramax Bks.

McFadyen, Peter. Motor Racing at Oulton Park in The 1970s. 2008. (Those were the Days... Ser.). (ENG., Illus.). 96p. pap. 25.95 *(978-1-84584-164-5(6)*, 1845841646) Veloce Publishing Ltd. GBR. Dist: MBI Distribution Services/Quayside Distribution.

Miller, Timothy. Drag Racing: The World's Fastest Sport. 2009. (ENG., Illus.). 208p. 34.95 *(978-1-55407-446-4(0))* Firefly Bks., Ltd.

Moreton, Mike. Rallye Sport Fords: The Inside Story. 2007. (ENG., Illus.). 160p. 49.95 *(978-1-84584-115-7(8)*, 1845841158) Veloce Publishing Ltd. GBR. Dist: MBI Distribution Services/Quayside Distribution.

Moretti, Valerio. Nuvolari - When Nuvolari Raced... lthr. *(978-1-874105-38-1(3))* Veloce Publishing Ltd. GBR. Dist: MBI Distribution Services/Quayside Distribution.

Newton, Richard. Autocross Performance Handbook. rev. ed. 2007. (Motorbooks Workshop Ser.). (ENG., Illus.). 160p. pap. 25.95 *(978-0-7603-2788-3(2)*, 0760327882, Motorbooks) MBI Publishing Co. LLC.

Noble, Butch & Sports Car Racing Association of the Monterey Peninsula. Mazda Raceway Laguna Seca. 2009. (Images of Sports Ser.). (ENG., Illus.). 128p. pap. 21.99 *(978-0-7385-6925-3(9))* Arcadia Publishing.

Olvey, Stephen. Rapid Response: My Inside Story as a Motor Racing Life-Saver. rev. ed. 2011. (ENG., Illus.). 320p. pap. 15.95 *(978-0-85733-112-0(4)*, 0857331124) Haynes Publishing PLC GBR. Dist: MBI Distribution Services/Quayside Distribution.

Parker, Paul. Sports Car Racing in Camera, 1970-79. 2008. (ENG., Illus.). 240p. 59.95 *(978-1-84425-471-2(2)*, 1844254712) Haynes Publishing PLC GBR. Dist: MBI Distribution Services/Quayside Distribution.

Pritchard, Anthony. Porsche: The Sports Racing Cars 1953-72. 2008. (ENG., Illus.). 272p. 64.95 *(978-1-84425-333-3(3)*, 1844253333) Haynes Publishing PLC GBR. Dist: MBI Distribution Services/Quayside Distribution.

—Silver Arrows in Camera, 1934-39: A Photographic History of the Mercedes-Benz & Auto Union. 2008. (ENG., Illus.). 480p. 150.00 *(978-1-84425-467-5(4)*, 1844254674) Haynes Publishing PLC GBR. Dist: MBI Distribution Services/Quayside Distribution.

Purves, Bryan & Brenchley, Tim. The Last Works Minis: The End of a Legend. 2007. (ENG., Illus.). 192p. 59.95 *(978-1-84584-087-7(9)*, 1845840879) Veloce Publishing Ltd. GBR. Dist: MBI Distribution Services/Quayside Distribution.

Rashidi, Waleed & Yoe, Craig. NASCAR Learn to Draw Race Cars: Discover All You Need to Know to Begin Drawing Your Favorite NASCAR Race Cars. 2011. (Learn to Draw Favorite Characters Ser.). (Illus.). 32p. (J). (gr. k-3). 28.50 *(978-1-936309-33-7(5))* Foster, Walter Publishing, Inc.

Rawlinson, Colin C. The 500cc Racing Car. 2008. (Shire Library). (ENG., Illus.). 32p. pap. 11.95 *(978-0-7478-0555-7(5))* Shire Pubns., Ltd. GBR. Dist: Random Hse., Inc.

Reyes, Steve. Funny Car Fever: The Birth of Drag Racing's Wildest Class. 2007. (ENG., Illus.). 192p. pap. 24.95 *(978-1-932494-43-3(X))* CarTech, Inc.

Reynolds, Harry C. Formula III Racing in North America. 2010. (ENG., Illus.). 272p. pap. 19.95 *(978-1-58388-242-9(1)*, 1583882421) Iconografix, Inc.

Robson, Graham. Peugeot 205 T16. 2007. (Rally Giants Ser.). (ENG., Illus.). 128p. pap. 29.95 *(978-1-84584-129-4(8)*, 1845841298) Veloce Publishing Ltd. GBR. Dist: MBI Distribution Services/Quayside Distribution.

—Toyota Celicia GT-Four. 2009. (Rally Giants Ser.). (ENG., Illus.). 128p. pap. 29.95 *(978-1-84584-184-3(0)*, 1845841840) Veloce Publishing Ltd. GBR. Dist: MBI Distribution Services/Quayside Distribution.

Schlegelmilch, Rainer W., photos by. Formula 1: The Roaring '70s. 2011. (ENG, GER, FRE, SPA & ITA., Illus.). 216p. 85.00 ***(978-3-8327-9537-5(5))*** teNeues Publishing Co.

Segers, Jorge. Analysis Techniques for Racecar Data Acquisition. 2008. 79.95 *(978-0-7680-1655-0(X))* SAE Intl.

Smart, Hamish. Track Days: A Glovebox Guide. 2009. (ENG., Illus.). 128p. pap. 19.95 *(978-1-84797-111-1(3)*, 1847971113) Crowood Pr., Ltd. GBR. Dist: MBI Distribution Services/Quayside Distribution.

Smith, Roger. Analysing Formula 1: Innovative Insights into Winners & Winning in Grand Prix Racing since 1950. 2010. (ENG., Illus.). 232p. pap. 27.95 *(978-1-84425-840-6(8)*, 1844258408) Haynes Publishing PLC GBR. Dist: MBI Distribution Services/Quayside Distribution.

—The Book of Formula 1 Top Tens. (ENG., Illus.). 2010. 200p. pap. 12.95 *(978-1-84425-847-5(5)*, 1844258475) 2009. 208p. 19.95 *(978-1-84425-571-9(9)*, 1844255719) Haynes Publishing PLC GBR. Dist: MBI Distribution Services/Quayside Distribution.

Smith, Roy P. Alpine & Renault: The Development of the Revolutionary Turbo F1 Car 1968-1979. 2008. (ENG., Illus.). 224p. 44.95 *(978-1-84584-177-5(8)*,

1845841778) Veloce Publishing Ltd. GBR. Dist: MBI Distribution Services/Quayside Distribution.

Stewart, Mark & Kennedy, Mike. NASCAR Safety on the Track. 2008. (Science of NASCAR Ser.). (Illus.). 48p. (YA). (gr. 4-7). lib. bdg. 27.93 *(978-0-8225-8742-2(4))* Lerner Publishing Group.

Templeman, Graham. The Competition Car Data Logging Manual. 2008. (SpeedPro Ser.). (ENG., Illus.). 128p. pap. 39.95 *(978-1-84584-162-1(X),* 184584162X) Veloce Publishing Ltd. GBR. Dist: MBI Distribution Services/Quayside Distribution.

Tipler, John. Lotus 78 & 79: The Ground-Effect Cars. 2009. (ENG., Illus.). 216p. 29.95 *(978-1-84797-143-2(1),* 1847971431) Crowood Pr., Ltd. GBR. Dist: MBI Distribution Services/Quayside Distribution.

Tipler, Johnny & Ramirez, Jo. La Carrera Panamericana: The World's Greatest Road Race! 2008. (ENG., Illus.). 272p. 89.95 *(978-1-84584-170-6(0),* 1845841700) Veloce Publishing Ltd. GBR. Dist: MBI Distribution Services/Quayside Distribution.

Tobia, Ernest Riveras. Jorge Lorenzo: My Story So Far. Roberts, Matt, tr. from SPA. 3rd ed. 2011. (ENG., Illus.). 448p. pap. 14.95 *(978-0-85733-100-7(0),* 0857331000) Haynes Publishing PLC GBR. Dist: MBI Distribution Services/Quayside Distribution.

Venables, David. Bentley: A Racing History. 2011. (ENG., Illus.). 304p. 59.95 *(978-0-85733-021-5(7),* 0857330217) Haynes Publishing PLC GBR. Dist: MBI Distribution Services/Quayside Distribution.

—British Racing Green: Drivers, Cars & Triumphs of British Motor Racing. 2009. (ENG., Illus.). 176p. 46.95 *(978-0-7110-3332-0(3))* Allan, Ian Publishing GBR. Dist: BookMasters Distribution Services (BDS).

Williams, Roger. MG MGB & MGB GT. 2006. (Essential Buyer's Guide Ser.). (ENG., Illus.). 64p. reprint ed. pap. 19.95 *(978-1-84584-029-7(1),* 1845840291) Veloce Publishing Ltd. GBR. Dist: MBI Distribution Services/Quayside Distribution.

Zimmerman, John. Dan Gurneys Eagle Racing Cars: The Technical History of the Machines Designed & Built by All American Racers. 2007. (Illus.). 208p. 75.00 *(978-1-893618-82-4(X))* Bull, David Publishing, Inc.

40 Years of Champions: The drivers who have helped make Michigan International Speedway Great. 2008. (Illus.). 136p. 24.95 *(978-0-9815030-0-4(4))* Jackson Citizen Patriot.

AUTOMOBILES, RACING—DESIGN AND CONSTRUCTION

Bolles, Bob. Advanced Race Car Chassis Technology: Winning Chassis Design & Setup for Circle Track & Road Race Cars. 2010. (ENG.). 192p. (gr. 12). 21.95 *(978-1-55788-562-3(1),* HP Trade) Penguin Group (USA) Inc.

Clarke, R. M., compiled by. Porsche Sports Racers Ultimate Portfolio, 1952-1968. 2007. (Ultimate Portfolio Ser.). (ENG., Illus.). 208p. per. 37.95 *(978-1-85520-730-1(3),* 1855207303) Brooklands Bks. GBR. Dist: MBI Distribution Services/Quayside Distribution.

Horsman, John. Racing in the Rain: My Years with Brilliant Drivers, Legendary Sports Cars, & a Dedicated Team. 2006. (Illus.). 250p. 49.95 *(978-1-893618-71-8(4))* Bull, David Publishing, Inc.

Huneycutt, Jeff. How to Build Chevy Small-Block Circle-Track Racing Engines. 2007. (Performance How-to Ser.). (ENG., Illus.). 128p. per. 24.95 *(978-1-932494-27-3(8),* S-A Design) CarTech, Inc.

Livesey, Andrew. Advanced Motorsport Engineering: Units for Study at Level 3. 2012. (ENG., Illus.). 240p. pap. 44.95 *(978-0-7506-8908-3(0))* Routledge.

—Basic Motorsport Engineering: Units for Study at Level 2. 2011. (ENG., Illus.). 288p. pap. 36.95 *(978-0-7506-8909-0(9))* Routledge.

Ludvigsen, Karl & Ludvigsen, Karl E. Red-Hot Rivals: Ferrari vs Maserati - Epic Clashes for Supremacy. 2008. (ENG., Illus.). 240p. 54.95 *(978-1-84425-412-5(7),* 1844254127) Haynes Publishing PLC GBR. Dist: MBI Distribution Services/Quayside Distribution.

Monroe, Tom. The Racing Engine Builder's Handbook: How to Build Winning Drag, Circle Track, Marine & Road Racing Engines. 2006. (ENG., Illus.). 208p. (gr. 12-18). 23.95 *(978-1-55788-492-3(7),* HP Trade) Penguin Group (USA) Inc.

Noakes, Keith. Motorcycle Road & Racing Chassis: A Modern Review of the Best Independents. 2007. (ENG., Illus.). 176p. pap. 39.95 *(978-1-84584-130-0(1),* 1845841301) Veloce Publishing Ltd. GBR. Dist: MBI Distribution Services/Quayside Distribution.

Pashley, Tony. How to Build Motorcycle-engined Racing Cars. 2008. (SpeedPro Ser.). (ENG., Illus.). 144p. pap. 49.95 *(978-1-84584-123-2(9),* 1845841239) Veloce Publishing Ltd. GBR. Dist: MBI Distribution Services/Quayside Distribution.

Piola, Giorgio. Formula 1 Technical Analysis 2008-2009. 2010. (ENG., Illus.). 120p. pap. 39.95 *(978-88-7911-466-0(2),* 8879114662) Giorgio Nada Editore ITA. Dist: MBI Distribution Services/Quayside Distribution.

Purves, Bryan & Brenchley, Tim. The Last Works Minis: The End of a Legend. 2007. (ENG., Illus.). 192p. 59.95 *(978-1-84584-087-7(9),* 1845840879) Veloce Publishing Ltd. GBR. Dist: MBI Distribution Services/Quayside Distribution.

Rendle, Steve. Red Bull Racing F 1 Car: An Insight into the Technology, Engineering, Maintenance & Operation of Red Bull Racing RB6. 2011. (Owners Workshop Manual Ser.). (ENG., Illus.). 160p. 29.95 *(978-0-85733-099-4(3),* 0857330993) Haynes Publishing PLC GBR. Dist: MBI Distribution Services/Quayside Distribution.

Smith, Carroll. Carroll Smith's Engineer to Win. 280p. pap. 24.95 *(978-0-7603-1624-5(4))* MBI Publishing Co. LLC.

Southgate, Tony. Tony Southgate from Drawing Board to Chequered Flag: The Autobiography of One of Motorsport's Most Prolific & Versatile Racing Car Designers. 2010. (ENG., Illus.). 256p. 79.95 *(978-1-899870-82-0(2),* 1899870822) Motor Racing Pubns., Ltd. GBR. Dist: MBI Distribution Services/Quayside Distribution.

Spalding, Neil. MotoGP Technology. 2nd ed. 2010. (ENG., Illus.). 272p. 39.95 *(978-1-84425-834-5(3),* 1844258343) Haynes Publishing PLC GBR. Dist: MBI Distribution Services/Quayside Distribution.

Staniforth, Allan. Competition Car Suspension: A Practical Handbook. 4th ed. 2006. (ENG., Illus.). 240p. 44.95 *(978-1-84425-328-9(7),* 1844253287) Haynes Publishing PLC GBR. Dist: MBI Distribution Services/Quayside Distribution.

Thorne, Troy. Pinewood Derby Designs & Patterns: The Ultimate Guide to Creating the Coolest Car. 2010. (ENG.). 118p. pap. 12.95 *(978-1-56523-341-6(7))* Fox Chapel Publishing Co., Inc.

Tremayne, David. The Science of Formula 1 Design. 3rd ed. 2010. (ENG., Illus.). 192p. 34.95 *(978-1-84425-718-8(5),* 1844257185) Haynes Publishing PLC GBR. Dist: MBI Distribution Services/Quayside Distribution.

Young, Philip. How to Build a Successful Low-Cost Rally Car. 2009. (SpeedPro Ser.). (ENG., Illus.). 96p. pap. 33.95 *(978-1-84584-208-6(1),* 1845842081) Veloce Publishing Ltd. GBR. Dist: MBI Distribution Services/Quayside Distribution.

AUTOMOBILES, RACING—JUVENILE LITERATURE

Gifford, C. Racing Cars. (Big MacHines Ser.). 32p. (J). 14.99 *(978-1-58086-834-1(7))* EDC Publishing.

AUTOMOBILES, RACING—MOTORS

Bowen, Robert. How to Build Max-Performance Mitsubishi 4G63t Engines. 2009. 144p. pap. 24.95 *(978-1-932494-62-4(6))* CarTech, Inc.

Elliott, Sue. Street Machines: Classics, Muscle Cars, Modern. 2010. (Idea Book Ser.). (ENG., Illus.). 160p. pap. 24.99 *(978-0-7603-3907-7(4),* 0760339074, Motorbooks) MBI Publishing Co. LLC.

Huneycutt, Jeff. How to Build Chevy Small-Block Circle-Track Racing Engines. 2007. (Performance How-to Ser.). (ENG., Illus.). 128p. per. 24.95 *(978-1-932494-27-3(8),* S-A Design) CarTech, Inc.

McClurg, Bob. How to Install & Tune Nitrous Oxide Systems. 2012. (Illus.). 144p. pap. 24.95 ***(978-1-934709-34-4(4))*** CarTech, Inc.

Monroe, Tom. How to Build Small-Block Ford Racing Engines HP1536: Parts, Blueprinting, Modifications, & Dyno Testing for Drag, Circle Track,Road, Off-Road, & Boat Racing. 2010. (ENG.). 192p. (gr. 12). 21.95 *(978-1-55788-536-4(2),* HP Trade) Penguin Group (USA) Inc.

Nye, Doug & Rudd, Tony. B. R. M. - The Saga of British Racing Motors Vol. 3: Monocoque V8 Cars, 1963-1969. 2008. (ENG., Illus.). 368p. 160.00 *(978-1-899870-64-6(4),* 1899870644) Motor Racing Pubns., Ltd. GBR. Dist: MBI Distribution Services/Quayside Distribution.

Parker, Paul. Races, Faces, Places: The motor racing photography of Michael Cooper. 2009. (ENG., Illus.). 352p. 79.95 *(978-1-84425-508-5(5),* 1844255085) Haynes Publishing PLC GBR. Dist: MBI Distribution Services/Quayside Distribution.

Vokins, Stephen. Extreme Cars: The Fastest, Wildest, Craziest, Oddest Cars Ever. 2010. (ENG., Illus.). 144p. pap. 17.95 *(978-1-84425-846-8(7),* 1844258467) Haynes Publishing PLC GBR. Dist: MBI Distribution Services/Quayside Distribution.

Williams, Roger. How to Improve MGB, MGC & MGB, Vol. 8. 2nd ed. 2009. (SpeedPro Ser.). (ENG., Illus.). 224p. pap. 34.95 *(978-1-84584-187-4(5),* 1845841875) Veloce Publishing Ltd. GBR. Dist: MBI Distribution Services/Quayside Distribution.

AUTOMOBILES, RACING—SPEED RECORDS

Ackroyd, John. Jet Blast & the Hand of Fate: Adventures with Land Speed Cars & Record Balloons. 2007. (ENG., Illus.). 288p. 66.95 *(978-0-9544357-8-3(8))* Redline Bks. GBR. Dist: MBI Distribution Services/Quayside Distribution.

Hawley, Samuel. Speed Duel: The Inside Story of the Land Speed Record in the Sixties. 2010. (ENG., Illus.). 360p. pap. 24.95 *(978-1-55407-633-8(1))* Firefly Bks., Ltd.

AUTOMOBILES, RENTAL

End Discriminatory State Taxes for Automobile Renters ACT of 2009: Hearing Before the Subcommittee on Commercial & Administrative Law of the Committee on the Judiciary, House of Representatives, One Hundred Eleventh Congress, Second Session, on H.R. 4175, June 15, 2010. 2010. iv, 124p. ***(978-0-16-087132-0(8),*** 552-070-41977-2) United States Government Printing Office.

International Wealth Success, compiled by. Auto & Truck Leasing Kit. 2007. ring bd. 100.00 *(978-1-56150-815-0(2))* International Wealth Success, Inc.

AUTOMOBILES, RENTAL—GREAT BRITAIN

Georgano, G. N. & Munro, Bill. The London Taxi. 2009. (Shire Library). (ENG., Illus.). 64p. pap. 12.95 *(978-0-7478-0692-9(6))* Shire Pubns., Ltd. GBR. Dist: Random Hse., Inc.

AUTOMOBILES, STEAM

see also Stanley Steamer Automobile

Norris, William. Modern Steam Road Wagons. 2007. 188p. per. 27.45 *(978-1-4086-0917-0(7))* Audubon Pr. & Christian Bk. Service.

—Modern Steam Road Wagons. 2008. 190p. 37.95 *(978-1-4366-2954-6(3));* 192p. pap. 22.95 *(978-0-548-90375-9(1))* Kessinger Publishing, LLC.

AUTOMOBILES, TURBINE POWERED

see Automobiles, Gas-Turbine

AUTOMOBILES, USED

see Used Cars

AUTOMOBILES, VINTAGE

see Antique and Classic Cars

AUTOMOBILES IN ART

Barany, Les, ed. Carnivora. 2008. 176p. pap. 29.95 *(978-0-9795132-1-3(9))* Scapegoat Publishing.

Bretzel, Giacomo. Grand Prix. 2009. (ENG.). 64p. 45.00 *(978-2-7572-0209-8(X),* Art Stock Bks. Ltd/Csi) Continental Sales, Inc.

Dejanoff, Plamen, photos by. Dejanoff. 2008. (ENG., Illus.). 160p. pap. 49.00 *(978-3-905701-58-6(8))* JRP Ringier Kunstverlag AG CHE. Dist: D.A.P./Distributed Art Pubs.

Dixon, David. Watts My Line? The Life & Work of Editorial Artist, Lawrie Watts. 2007. (ENG., Illus.). 216p. pap. 46.95 *(978-0-9544357-7-6(X))* Redline Bks. GBR. Dist: MBI Distribution Services/Quayside Distribution.

Earle, Joe. Buriki: Japanese Tin Toys from the Golden Age of the American Automobile. 2009. (ENG., Illus.). 96p. pap. 19.95 *(978-0-300-15157-2(8))* Japan Society Gallery.

Gardiner, Tony. How to Draw & Paint Cars. 2008. (ENG., Illus.). 128p. pap. 35.95 *(978-1-84584-124-9(7),* 1845841247) Veloce Publishing Ltd. GBR. Dist: MBI Distribution Services/Quayside Distribution.

Garnier, Peter. The Art of Gordon Crosby. 2009. (ENG., Illus.). 96p. 59.95 *(978-1-906133-09-2(3),* 1906133093) Herridge & Sons Ltd.

Kimble, David & Endres, Christopher P. Cutaway: The Automotive Art of David Kimble. 2011. ***(978-1-934709-84-9(0))*** CarTech, Inc.

KIT Publishers. Betsabee Romero: Cars & Traces. 2010. 160p. pap. 30.00 *(978-94-6022-123-1(6))* Royal Tropical Institute Pr. (KIT (Koninklijk Instituut voor de Tropen) NLD. Dist: Stylus Publishing, LLC.

Museum Tinguely (Basel, Switzerland) Staff, ed. Car Fetish: I Drive Therefore I Am. 2011. (ENG., Illus.). 300p. pap. 65.00 ***(978-3-86828-228-3(9))*** Kehrer Verlag Heidelberg, Klaus Kehrer DEU. Dist: Consortium Bk. Sales & Distribution.

op de Weegh, Ard & Hottendorff, Kay. The Fate of the Sleeping Beauties. 2010. (ENG., Illus.). 160p. 59.95 *(978-1-84584-070-9(4),* 1845840704) Veloce Publishing Ltd. GBR. Dist: MBI Distribution Services/Quayside Distribution.

Petit, Jacques. Cars on Vinyl: 500 Superb Record Covers Dedicated to the Automobile. 2010. (ENG., Illus.). 160p. pap. 27.95 *(978-1-84425-726-3(6),* 1844257266) Haynes Publishing PLC GBR. Dist: MBI Distribution Services/Quayside Distribution.

Stavitsky, Gail & Warhol, Andy. Warhol & Cars: American Icons. 2011. *(978-0-615-41922-0(4))* Montclair Art Museum.

Taylor, Thom & Newton, Ed. How to Draw Crazy Cars & Mad Monsters Like a Pro. rev. ed. 2007. (Motorbooks Studio Ser.). (ENG., Illus.). 144p. pap. 19.95 *(978-0-7603-2471-4(9),* 0760324719, Motorbooks) MBI Publishing Co. LLC.

Thompson, Keith. 50 Fantasy Vehicles to Draw & Paint: Create Awe-Inspiring Crafts for Comics, Computer Games, & Graphic Novels. 2007. (ENG., Illus.). 128p. pap. 21.99 *(978-0-7641-3522-4(8))* Barron's Educational Series, Inc.

Torres, Jickie. Harley-Davidson Motorcycles: A Step-by-Step Guide to Drawing the Steel, Rubber, Leather, & Chrome of America's Hottest Motorcycle. 2010. (Licensed How to Draw Ser.). (ENG., Illus.). 48p. pap. 8.95 *(978-1-60058-177-9(3),* 1600581773) Foster, Walter Publishing, Inc.

Veysey, Paul. Motor Movies - the Posters: "Art & the Automobile Combined in over 240 Fabulously Evocative Poster Images" 2007. (ENG., Illus.). 224p. 29.95 *(978-1-84584-127-0(1),* 1845841271) Veloce Publishing Ltd. GBR. Dist: MBI Distribution Services/Quayside Distribution.

Warhol, Andy. Cars: Andy Warhol, Sylvie Fleury, Robert Longo, Vincent Szarek. 2010. (ENG & GER., Illus.). 248p. 60.00 *(978-3-7757-2582-8(2))* Hatje Cantz Verlag GmbH & Co KG DEU. Dist: D.A.P./Distributed Art Pubs.

AUTOMOBILES IN MOTION PICTURES

Brun, Frédéric. Steve Mcqueen: A Passion for Speed. 2011. (ENG., Illus.). 192p. 40.00 *(978-0-7603-4248-0(2),* 0760342482, Motorbooks) MBI Publishing Co. LLC.

Veysey, Paul. Motor Movies - the Posters: "Art & the Automobile Combined in over 240 Fabulously Evocative Poster Images" 2007. (ENG., Illus.). 224p. 29.95 *(978-1-84584-127-0(1),* 1845841271) Veloce Publishing Ltd. GBR. Dist: MBI Distribution Services/Quayside Distribution.

AUTOMORPHIC FORMS

Behrens, Mark & Lawson, Tyler. Topological Automorphic Forms. 2010. (Memoirs of the American Mathematical Society Ser.). (Illus.). 136p. pap. 74.00 *(978-0-8218-4539-4(X))* American Mathematical Society.

Borel, Armand. Automorphic Forms on SL2 (R) 2008. (Cambridge Tracts in Mathematics Ser.). (ENG.). 208p. pap. 48.00 *(978-0-521-07212-0(3))* Cambridge Univ. Pr.

Bruggeman, R. W. Fourier Coefficients of Automorphic Forms. 2008. (Lecture Notes in Mathematics Ser.). 212p. pap. 59.95 *(978-3-540-10839-9(4))* Springer.

Bruggeman, Roelof W. Families of Automorphic Forms. 2009. (Modern Birkhäuser Classics Ser.). Orig. Title: 978-3-7643-5046-8 (mma). (ENG.). 328p. pap. 59.95 *(978-3-0346-0335-5(5),* 3034603355) Birkhauser Verlag AG CHE. Dist: Springer.

Bump, D. Automorphic Forms on GL (3,TR) 2008. (Lecture Notes in Mathematics Ser.). pap. 39.95 *(978-3-540-13864-8(1))* Springer.

Bump, Daniel, et al, eds. Multiple Dirichlet Series, L-functions & Automorphic Forms. 2012. (Progress in Mathematics Ser.). (ENG., Illus.). viii, 388p. 129.00 ***(978-0-8176-8333-7(X),*** 081768333X) Birkhauser Verlag AG CHE. Dist: Springer.

Elstrodt, Juergen, et al. Groups Acting on Hyperbolic Space: Harmonic Analysis & Number Theory. 2010. (Springer Monographs in Mathematics Ser.). (ENG.). xv, 524p. pap. 139.00 *(978-3-642-08302-0(1),* 3642083021) Springer.

Explicit Constructions of Automorphic L-Functions. 2008. (Lecture Notes in Mathematics Ser.). pap. 39.95 *(978-3-540-17848-4(1))* Springer.

Flicker, Y. Z. The Trace Formula & Base Change for GL (3) 2008. (Lecture Notes in Mathematics Ser.). pap. 46.00 *(978-3-540-11500-7(5))* Springer.

Gelbart, Stephen S. Automorphic Forms & L-Functions I. Global Aspects. Ginzburg, David et al, eds. 2009. (Contemporary Mathematics Ser.). (Illus.). 285p. pap. 89.00 *(978-0-8218-4706-0(6))* American Mathematical Society.

—Automorphic Forms & L-Functions II: Local Aspects. Ginzburg, David et al, eds. 2009. (Contemporary Mathematics Ser.). (Illus.). 313p. pap. 99.00 *(978-0-8218-4708-4(2))* American Mathematical Society.

Gerritzen, L. & Put, M. van der. Schottky Groups & Mumford Curves. 2008. (Lecture Notes in Mathematics Ser.). 332p. pap. 59.95 *(978-3-540-10229-8(9))* Springer.

Getz, Jayce & Goresky, Mark. Hilbert Modular Forms with Coefficients in Intersection Homology & Quadratic Base Change. 2012. (Progress in Mathematics Ser.: 298). (ENG., Illus.). xiii, 256p. 109.00 ***(978-3-0348-0350-2(8),*** 3034803508) Birkhauser Verlag AG CHE. Dist: Springer.

Goldfeld, Dorian & Hundley, Joseph. Automorphic Representations & L-Functions for the General Linear Group, 2 vols., Vol. 1. 2011. (Cambridge Studies in Advanced Mathematics Ser.). (ENG., Illus.). 570p. 105.00 *(978-0-521-47423-8(X))* Cambridge Univ. Pr.

—Automorphic Representations & L-Functions for the General Linear Group, 2 vols., Vol. 2. 2011. (Cambridge Studies in Advanced Mathematics Ser.). (ENG., Illus.). 208p. 82.00 *(978-1-107-00799-4(2))* Cambridge Univ. Pr.

Hamahata, Yoshinori. Geometry & Analysis of Automorphic Forms of Several Variables - Proceedings of the International Symposium in Honor of Takayuki Oda on the Occasion of His 60th Birthday. Hamahata, Yoshinori et al, eds. 2011. 388p. 128.00 ***(978-981-4355-59-9(3))*** World Scientific Publishing Co., Inc.

Hejhal, Dennis A. The Selberg Trace Formula for Psl. 2008. (Lecture Notes in Mathematics Ser.). 524p. pap. 39.95 *(978-3-540-07988-0(2))* Springer.

Jacquet, H. Automorphic Forms on GL (2) Part 2. 2008. (Lecture Notes in Mathematics Ser.). 164p. pap. 39.95 *(978-3-540-05931-8(8),* 3540059318) Springer.

Jacquet, H. & Langlands, R. P. Automorphic Forms on GL (2) Part 2. 2008. (Lecture Notes in Mathematics Ser.). 560p. pap. 69.95 *(978-3-540-04903-6(7))* Springer.

Ji, Lizhen, et al, eds. Lie Groups & Automorphic Forms. 2006. (AMS/IP Studies in Advanced Mathematics: Vol. 37). (Illus.). 239p. pap. 61.00 *(978-0-8218-4198-3(X))* American Mathematical Society.

Jian-Shu Li, et al, eds. Harmonic Analysis, Group Representations, Automorphic Forms, & Invariant Theory: In Honor of Roger E. Howe. 2008. (Lecture Notes Series, Institute for Mathematical Sciences Ser.). 429p. 124.00 *(978-981-277-078-3(X))* World Scientific Publishing Co., Inc.

Klevång, Oscar. Automorphic Forms. 2011. 132p. pap. ***(978-3-8443-1690-2(6))*** Lambert Academic Publishing.

Kobayashi, Toshiyuki, et al, eds. Representation Theory & Automorphic Forms. 2007. (Progress in Mathematics Ser.). (Illus.). 210p. 99.00 *(978-0-8176-4505-2(5),* 0817645055) Springer.

Labesse, J. P. Cohomology of Arithmetic Groups & Automorphic Forms: Proceedings of a Conference held in Luminy/Marseille, France, May 22-27, 1989. 2008. (Lecture Notes in Mathematics Ser.). pap. 59.95 *(978-3-540-53422-8(9))* Springer.

Langlands, Robert P. On the Functional Equations Satisfied by Eisenstein Series. 2008. (Lecture Notes in Mathematics Ser.). 344p. pap. 46.00 *(978-3-540-07872-2(X))* Springer.

Moeglin, C. & Waldspurger, J. L. Spectral Decomposition & Eisenstein Series: A Paraphrase of the Scriptures. Schneps, Leila, tr. from FRE. 2008. (Cambridge Tracts in Mathematics Ser.). (ENG., Illus.). 368p. pap. 69.00 *(978-0-521-07035-5(X))* Cambridge Univ. Pr.

Ray, Urmie. Automorphic Forms & Lie Superalgebras. 2007. (Algebra & Applications Ser.). (Illus.). x, 290p. (C). 129.00 *(978-1-4020-5009-1(7),* 1402050097) Springer.

Roberts, Brooks & Schmidt, Ralf. Local Newforms for GSp(4) 2007. (Lecture Notes in Mathematics Ser.). (Illus.). 307p. per. 79.95 *(978-3-540-73323-2(X))* Springer.

Sarnak, Peter & Shahidi, Freydoon, eds. Automorphic Forms & Applications. 2007. (IAS/Park City Mathematics Ser.: Vol. 12). (Illus.). 427p. (C). 79.00 *(978-0-8218-2873-1(8))* American Mathematical Society.

Shimura, Goro. Arithmeticity in the Theory of Automorphic Forms. 2010. (Mathematical Surveys & Monographs). 302p. pap. 80.00 *(978-0-8218-4961-3(1))* American Mathematical Society.

Unterberger, André. Quantization & Arithmetic. 2008. (Pseudo-Differential Operators Ser.). (Illus.). 160p. spiral bd. 59.95 *(978-3-7643-8790-7(4))* Birkhauser Boston.

AUTOMORPHIC FUNCTIONS

see also Automorphic Forms

Accola, R. D. M. Riemann Surfaces, Theta Functions, & Abelian Automorphisms Groups. 2008. (Lecture Notes in Mathematics Ser.). 116p. pap. 39.95 *(978-3-540-07398-7(1))* Springer.

Christian, U. Selberg's Zeta, L, & Eisensteinseries. 2008. (Lecture Notes in Mathematics Ser.). pap. 26.00 *(978-3-540-12701-7(1))* Springer.

Cogdell, James W., et al. Lectures on Automorphic L-Functions. 2009. (Fields Institute Monographs Ser.). 283p. pap. 87.00 *(978-0-8218-4800-5(3))* American Mathematical Society.

Gan, Wee Teck, et al, eds. Eisenstein Series & Applications. 2008. (Progress in Mathematics Ser.). (Illus.). 314p. 89.95 *(978-0-8176-4496-3(2)*, 0817644962) Springer.

Gelbart, Stephen S. Automorphic Forms & L-Functions I. Global Aspects. Ginzburg, David et al, eds. 2009. (Contemporary Mathematics Ser.). (Illus.). 285p. pap. 89.00 *(978-0-8218-4706-0(6))* American Mathematical Society.

—Automorphic Forms & L-Functions II: Local Aspects. Ginzburg, David et al, eds. 2009. (Contemporary Mathematics Ser.). (Illus.). 313p. pap. 99.00 *(978-0-8218-4708-4(2))* American Mathematical Society.

Jorgenson, Jay & Lang, Serge. Heat Eisenstein Series on SLn (C) 2009. (Memoirs of the American Mathematical Society Ser.). 127p. pap. 67.00 *(978-0-8218-4044-3(4))* American Mathematical Society.

N'Guérékata, Gaston M. Almost Automorphic & Almost Periodic Functions in Abstract Spaces. 2010. 148p. pap. 139.00 *(978-1-4419-3373-7(5)*, 1441933735) Springer.

—Topics in Almost Automorphy. 2010. xii, 168p. pap. 99.00 *(978-1-4419-3561-8(4)*, 1441935614) Springer.

Sarnak, Peter & Shahidi, Freydoon, eds. Automorphic Forms & Applications. 2007. (IAS/Park City Mathematics Ser.: Vol. 12). (Illus.). 427p. (C). 79.00 *(978-0-8218-2873-1(8))* American Mathematical Society.

Shahidi, Freydoon. Eisenstein Series & Automorphic L-Functions. 2010. (Colloquium Publications). (Illus.). 210p. 55.00 *(978-0-8218-4989-7(1))* American Mathematical Society.

Shi, J. The Kazhdan-Lusztig Cells in Certain Affine Weyl Groups. 2008. (Lecture Notes in Mathematics Ser.). pap. 59.95 *(978-3-540-16439-5(1))* Springer.

Shimura, Goro. Automorphic Functions & Number Theory. 2007. (Lecture Notes in Mathematics Ser.). 76p. per. 39.95 *(978-3-540-04224-2(5))* Springer.

—Collected Papers: Volume IV: 1989-2001. 2010. (ENG.). xiv, 754p. pap. 169.00 *(978-1-4419-2991-4(6)*, 1441929916) Springer.

Shimura, Goro. Modular Forms: Basics & Beyond: Basics & Beyond. 2011. (Springer Monographs in Mathematics Ser.). (ENG.). x, 175p. 99.00 ***(978-1-4614-2124-5(1)**, 1461421241)* Springer.

Steuding, Jörn. Value Distributions of L-Functions. 2007. (Lecture Notes in Mathematics Ser.). (Illus.). XIV, 322p. pap. 79.95 *(978-3-540-26526-9(0)*, 3540265260) Springer.

AUTOMOTIVE FLEETS

see Motor Vehicle Fleets

AUTOMOTIVE FUEL SYSTEMS

see Automobiles—Fuel Systems

AUTOMOTIVE FUELS

see Motor Fuels

AUTOMOTIVE GAS-TURBINE ENGINES

see Automotive Gas Turbines

AUTOMOTIVE GAS TURBINES

McIntyre, Dustin. Laser Spark Plug Development & Engine Testing - Design of a Diode Side Pumped Solid State Passively Q-Switched Laser for Use As an Ignition Source F. 2008. 224p. pap. *(978-3-639-11362-4(4))* VDM Verlag Dr. Mueller e.K.

AUTOMOTIVE MEDICINE

see also Automobiles—Safety Measures; Crash Injuries; Traffic Accidents

Babizhayev, Mark A. Tragic Accident with Princess Diana: The Effects of Glare & Visual Disability on Driving. 2010. (Transportation Issues, Policies & R&D Ser.). pap. 47.00 *(978-1-61728-270-6(7)*, Nova Novinka) Nova Science Pubs., Inc.

Green, Marc. Forensic Aspects of Vision & Highway Safety. 3rd ed. 2008. *(978-1-933264-54-7(3))* Lawyers & Judges Publishing Co., Inc.

Verster, Joris C. Drugs, Driving, & Traffic Safety. 2009. (Illus.). xx, 559p. E-Book *(978-3-7643-9923-8(6))* Birkhauser Verlag AG.

AUTOMOTIVE TRANSPORT WORKERS

see Highway Transport Workers

AUTOMOTIVE TRANSPORTATION

see Transportation, Automotive

AUTOMOTIVE VEHICLES

see Motor Vehicles

AUTOMUTILATION

see Self-Mutilation

AUTONOMIC DRUGS

see also Sympathomimetic Agents

Cruickshank, John Malcolm. The Modern Role of Beta-Blockers in Cardiovascular Medicine. 2010. (Illus.). 271p. pap. *(978-1-60795-108-7(8))* PMPH-USA, Ltd.

AUTONOMIC NERVOUS SYSTEM

see Nervous System, Autonomic

AUTONOMY

see also Home Rule; Self-Determination, National

Adams, Harry. Justice for Children: Autonomy Development & the State. 2009. 264p. pap. 29.95 *(978-0-7914-7332-0(5))* 2008. 254p. 70.00 *(978-0-7914-7331-3(7))* State Univ. of New York Pr.

Arellano-Gault, David. Community-Based Organizations in Mexico. 2010. 312p. pap. *(978-3-639-27784-5(8))* VDM Verlag Dr. Mueller e.K.

Backhaus, Jürgen G., ed. Two Centuries of Local Autonomy. 2011. (European Heritage in Economics & the Social Sciences Ser.). (ENG., Illus.). x, 114p. 119.00 *(978-1-4614-0292-3(1)*, 1461402921) Springer.

Barad Singiri, Meenakshi. Promoting Learner Autonomy in Writing. 2010. 112p. pap. *(978-3-8383-7971-5(3))* Lambert Academic Publishing.

Bates, Merrelyn. Preparing Professionals for Autonomy. 2008. 344p. per. *(978-3-8364-3605-2(1))* VDM Verlag Dr. Mueller e.K.

Ben-Ishai, Elizabeth. Fostering Autonomy: A Theory of Citizenship, the State, & Social Service Delivery. 2012. (ENG.). 208p. ***(978-0-271-05217-5(1))*** Pennsylvania State Univ. Pr.

Bernstein, Steven & Coleman, William D., eds. Unsettled Legitimacy: Political Community, Power, & Authority in a Global Era. 2010. (ENG.). 408p. (C). pap. 35.95 *(978-0-7748-1718-9(6))* UBC Pr. CAN. Dist: Univ. of Washington Pr.

Bono, James, et al, eds. A Time for the Humanities: Futurity & the Limits of Autonomy. 2008. (ENG., Illus.). 250p. 65.00 *(978-0-8232-2919-2(X))* Fordham Univ. Pr.

Bono, James J. A Time for the Humanities: Futurity & the Limits of Autonomy. Dean, Tim & Ziarek, Ewa Plonowska, eds. 4th ed. 2008. (ENG.). 250p. pap. 26.00 *(978-0-8232-2920-8(3))* Fordham Univ. Pr.

Boudreau, George. Independence: A Guide to Revolutionary Philadelphia. 2011. (ENG., Illus.). 416p. 24.95 *(978-1-59416-143-8(7))* Westholme Publishing.

Casalta Nabais, José. Estudos Sobre Autonomias Territoriais, Institucionais e Cívicas. 2010. 222p. *(978-972-40-4224-4(3))* Almedina, Livraria.

Cepaluni, Gabriel & Vigevani, Tullo. Brazilian Foreign Policy in Changing Times: The Quest for Autonomy from Sarney to Lula. Moura, Leandro, tr. 2012. (ENG.). 190p. (gr. 17). pap. 29.99 ***(978-0-7391-2882-4(5))*** Lexington Bks.

Chen, Yu-Wen. Transnational Cooperation of Ethnopolitical Mobilization: A Survey Analysis of European Ethnopolitical Groups. 2009. (Europäische Hochschulschriften. Reihe 31: Politikwissenschaft Ser.). 242p. pap. 57.95 *(978-3-631-58948-9(4))* Lang, Peter GmbH, Europaischer Verlag der Wissenschaften DEU. Dist: Lang, Peter.

Chiang, Mark. The Cultural Capital of Asian American Studies: Autonomy & Representation in the University. 2009. (ENG.). 272p. 78.00 *(978-0-8147-1700-4(4))*; pap. 23.00 *(978-0-8147-1701-1(2))* New York Univ. Pr.

Church, Jeffrey. Infinite Autonomy: The Divided Individual in the Political Thought of G. W. F. Hegel & Friedrich Nietzsche. 2011. 288p. 64.95 ***(978-0-271-05075-1(6))*** Pennsylvania State Univ. Pr.

Clarke, Simon R. Foundations of Freedom: Welfare-Based Arguments against Paternalism. 2012. (Routledge Studies in Contemporary Philosophy Ser.). (ENG., Illus.). 152p. (C). 125.00 ***(978-0-415-62237-0(9))*** Routledge.

Colomer. Great Empires, Small Nations. 2007. (Illus.). 128p. 170.00 *(978-0-415-43774-5(1))*; pap. 39.95 *(978-0-415-43775-2(X))* Routledge.

Cossa, José Augusto. Power, Politics, & Higher Education in Southern Africa: International Regimes, Local Governments, & Educational Autonomy. 2008. (Illus.). 252p. (C). 104.95 *(978-1-60497-515-4(6))* Cambria Pr.

D. White, Nigel & Collins, Richard, eds. International Organisations & the Idea of Autonomy. 2011. (Routledge Research in International Law Ser.). 464p. 125.00 *(978-0-415-55088-8(2))* Routledge.

Davis, Marvin. Independence vs Submission vs You: In an Anxious Heaven & a Patient Hell. 2009. 132p. pap. 14.95 *(978-1-4327-3523-4(3))* Outskirts Pr., Inc.

Gagnon, Alain-G & Keating, Michael, eds. Political Autonomy & Divided Societies: Imagining Democratic Alternatives in Complex Settings. 2012. (Comparative Territorial Politics Ser.). (ENG., Illus.). 288p. 95.00 ***(978-0-230-36425-7(X))*** Palgrave Macmillan.

Galetta, Diana-Urania. Procedural Autonomy of Eu Member States - Paradise Lost? A Study on the Functionalized Procedural Competence of Eu Member States. 2010. (ENG.). xvi, 200p. 119.00 *(978-3-642-12546-1(8)*, 3642125468) Springer.

Ganguly, Rajat. Autonomy & Ethnic Conflict in South & South-East Asia. 2012. (Asian Security Studies). (ENG.). 176p. (C). 135.00 *(978-0-415-57016-9(6))* Routledge.

Gardner, Anne-Marie. Democratic Governance & Non-State Actors. 2011. (ENG., Illus.). 206p. 89.00 *(978-0-230-10874-5(1))* Palgrave Macmillan.

Gribenas, Rick, ed. Participatory Autonomy. 2008. (ENG.). 114p. pap. 14.95 *(978-1-57027-190-8(9))* Autonomedia.

Hlongwane, Siphiwe. From State to 'Independent' Regulation in South Afric. 2010. 148p. pap. *(978-3-639-19007-6(6))* VDM Verlag Dr. Mueller e.K.

Jelinek, Robert, ed. OFFSHORE CENSUS: The Citizens of the State of Sabotage. 2011. (GER., Illus.). 410p. 59.95 *(978-3-7091-0533-7(1)*, 3709105331) Springer Wien AUT. Dist: Springer.

Jennings, Ivor. The Approach to Self-Government. 2011. (ENG.). 214p. pap. 22.99 ***(978-0-521-24191-5(X))*** Cambridge Univ. Pr.

Kangas, Lari. Namibian Democracy Consolidated? 2008. 168p. pap. *(978-3-8364-7958-5(3))* VDM Verlag Dr. Mueller e.K.

Lamb, Terry & Reinders, Hayo. Learner & Teacher Autonomy: Concepts, Realities, & Responses. 2008. (Illus.). (C). *(978-90-272-0517-9(5))* Benjamins, John Publishing Co.

Leipoldt, Erik. Euthanasia And Disability Perspective: An Investigation In The Netherlands And Australia. 2010. 292p. pap. *(978-3-639-24715-2(9))* VDM Verlag Dr. Mueller e.K.

Maclean, Alasdair. Autonomy, Informed Consent & Medical Law: A Relational Challenge. 2009. (Cambridge Law, Medicine & Ethics Ser.). (ENG., Illus.). 316p. 114.00 *(978-0-521-89693-1(2))* Cambridge Univ. Pr.

Marshall, Jill. Personal Freedom Through Human Rights Law: Autonomy, Identity, & Integrity under the European Convention on Human Rights. 2008. (International Studies in Human Rights Ser.). 240p. (C). *(978-90-04-17059-9(6))* BRILL.

Mayr, Ernst. What Makes Biology Unique? Considerations on the Autonomy of a Scientific Discipline. 2007. (ENG.). 246p. per. 19.99 *(978-0-521-70034-4(5))* Cambridge Univ. Pr.

Mtsweni, Sipho. Salutogenic Functioning Amongst University Administrative Staff. 2010. 140p. pap. *(978-3-8383-7891-6(1))* Lambert Academic Publishing.

Ong, Aihwa. Neoliberalism as Exception: Mutations in Citizenship & Sovereignty. 2006. (ENG., Illus.). 304p. (C). 89.95 *(978-0-8223-3736-2(3))*; per. 24.95 *(978-0-8223-3748-5(7))* Duke Univ. Pr.

Othman, Awras. Learner Autonomy. 2011. 280p. pap. ***(978-3-8443-2473-0(9))*** Lambert Academic Publishing.

Pradhan, D. S. Third World Attitudes Toward International Law. 2010. 275p. 59.50 *(978-81-7533-311-6(1))* M. D. Pubns. Pvt, Ltd. IND. Dist: Coronet Bks.

Rasmussen, Claire Elaine. The Autonomous Animal: Self-Governance & the Modern Subject. 2011. (ENG., Illus.). 248p. 75.00 *(978-0-8166-6956-1(2))*; pap. 25.00 *(978-0-8166-6957-8(0))* Univ. of Minnesota Pr.

Sellers, Mortimer, ed. Autonomy in the Law. (Ius Gentium: Comparative Perspectives on Law & Justice Ser.). 2008. XII, 180p. 109.00 *(978-1-4020-8284-9(3)*, 1402082843) 2007. 179p. per. 79.95 *(978-1-4020-6489-0(6))* Springer.

Streeter, Stephen, et al, eds. Empires & Autonomy: Moments in the History of Globalization. 2010. (ENG.). 394p. pap. 32.95 *(978-0-7748-1600-7(7))* Univ. of Washington Pr.

Suksi, Markku. Sub-State Governance Through Territorial Autonomy: A Comparative Study in Constitutional Law of Powers, Procedures & Institutions. 2011. (ENG., Illus.). xxxiii, 685p. 239.00 *(978-3-642-20047-2(8)*, 3642200478) Springer.

United States, Congress House Committee on Foreign Affairs Staff, contrib. by. Tibet: Status of the Sino-Tibetan Dialogue: Hearing Before the Committee on Foreign Affairs, House of Representatives, One Hundred Tenth Congress, First Session, March 13, 2007. 2007. iii, 59p. *(978-0-16-078745-4(9)*, 552-070-35954-1) United States Government Printing Office.

Vigevani, Tullo & Cepaluni, Gabriel. Brazilian Foreign Policy in Changing Times: The Quest for Autonomy from Sarney to Lula. 2009. (ENG., Illus.). 182p. 68.50 *(978-0-7391-2881-7(7))* Lexington Bks.

Weller, Marc & Nobbs, Katherine, eds. Asymmetric Autonomy & the Settlement of Ethnic Conflicts. 2010. (National & Ethnic Conflict in the 21st Century Ser.). 360p. (C). 59.95 *(978-0-8122-4230-0(0))* Univ. of Pennsylvania Pr.

Weller, Marc & Wolff, Stefan, eds. Autonomy, Self Governance & Conflict Resolution: Innovative approaches to Institutional Design in Divided Societies. 2008. 272p. 41.95 *(978-0-415-47959-2(2))* Routledge.

AUTONOMY (PHILOSOPHY)

Aboulafia, Mitchell. Transcendence: On Self-Determination & Cosmopolitanism. 2010. (ENG.). 216p. 55.00 *(978-0-8047-7019-4(0))*; pap. 21.95 *(978-0-8047-7020-0(4))* Stanford Univ. Pr.

Banerjee, Paula & Das, Samir Kumar, eds. Autonomy: Beyond Kant & Hermeneutics. 2008. (Anthem Press India Ser.). (ENG.). 296p. 80.00 *(978-1-84331-743-2(5))* Anthem Pr. GBR. Dist: Books International, Inc.

Benson, Philip. Teaching & Researching: Autonomy in Language Learning. 2nd ed. 2011. (Applied Linguistics in Action Ser.). (ENG., Illus.). 296p. (C). pap. 42.07 *(978-1-4082-0501-3(7))* Prentice Hall, ESL Dept.

Böhm, Steffen, et al, eds. Against Automobility. 2006. (Sociological Review Monographs). (ENG., Illus.). 268p. per. 39.95 *(978-1-4051-5270-9(2)*, Wiley-Blackwell) Wiley, John & Sons, Inc.

Bojanowski, Jochen. Kants Theorie der Freiheit: Rekonstruktion und Rehabilitierung. (Kantstudien-Ergänzungshefte Ser.).Tr. of Kant's Theory of Freedom. (GER.). XIII, 314p. 225.00 ***(978-3-11-181310-3(X))*** De Gruyter, Walter Inc.

Bratman, Michael. Structures of Agency: Essays. 2007. (ENG.). 336p. per. 30.00 *(978-0-19-518771-7(7))* Oxford Univ. Pr., Inc.

Brett, Stephen F. The Law of Love: From Autonomy to Communion. 2010. (ENG.). 195p. pap. 18.00 *(978-1-58966-207-0(5))* Univ. of Scranton Pr.

Christman, John. The Politics of Persons: Individual Autonomy & Socio-historical Selves. (ENG.). 2011. 286p. pap. 55.00 ***(978-1-107-40229-4(8))*** 2009. 284p. 93.00 *(978-0-521-76056-0(9))* Cambridge Univ. Pr.

Christman, John & Anderson, Joel, eds. Autonomy & the Challenges to Liberalism: New Essays. 2009. (ENG.). 400p. pap. 53.00 *(978-0-521-12031-9(4))* Cambridge Univ. Pr.

Colburn, Ben. Autonomy & Liberalism. 2010. (Routledge Studies in Contemporary Philosophy Ser.). (ENG.). 176p. (C). 125.00 *(978-0-415-87596-7(X))* Routledge.

Corrigan, Oonagh. The Limits of Consent: A Socio-Ethical Approach to Human Subject Research in Medicine. Corrigan, Oonagh et al, eds. 2009. (ENG., Illus.). 256p. 98.50 *(978-0-19-923146-1(X))* Oxford Univ. Pr., Inc.

Davenport, John J. Narrative Identity & Autonomy: A Kierkegaardian Defense. 2012. (Routledge Studies in Contemporary Philosophy Ser.). (ENG.). 256p. (C). 125.00 *(978-0-415-89413-5(1))* Routledge.

Day-Sclater, Shelley, et al, eds. Regulating Autonomy: Sex, Reproduction & Family. 2009. (ENG.). 267p. pap. 72.00 *(978-1-84113-946-3(7))* Hart Publishing Ltd. GBR. Dist: International Specialized Bk. Services.

Deligiorgi, Katerina. The Scope of Autonomy: Kant & the Morality of Freedom. 2012. (ENG.). 256p. 75.00 ***(978-0-19-964615-9(5))*** Oxford Univ. Pr., Inc.

Gardner, Susan T. Thinking Your Way to Freedom: A Guide to Owning Your Own Practical Reasoning. 2009. (ENG., Illus.). 296p. pap. 46.95 *(978-1-59213-867-8(5))* Temple Univ. Pr.

Gemes, Ken & May, Simon. Nietzsche on Freedom & Autonomy. 2011. (ENG.). 294p. pap. 35.00 *(978-0-19-969468-6(0))* Oxford Univ. Pr., Inc.

Gemes, Ken & May, Simon, eds. Nietzsche on Freedom & Autonomy. 2009. (ENG.). 296p. 85.00 *(978-0-19-923156-0(7))* Oxford Univ. Pr., Inc.

Grant, Colin B. Post-Transcendental Communication: Contexts of Human Autonomy. 2008. 186p. pap. 54.95 *(978-3-03911-032-2(2))* Lang, Peter AG GBR. Dist: Lang, Peter.

Höffe, Otfried. Can Virtue Make Us Happy? The Art of Living & Morality. McGaughey, Douglas R., tr. from GER. 2010. (ENG.). 384p. 39.95 *(978-0-8101-2545-2(5))* Northwestern Univ. Pr.

Kekes, John. The Enlargement of Life: Moral Imagination at Work. 2010. 256p. pap. 24.95 *(978-0-8014-7627-3(5))* 2006. 236p. 52.50 *(978-0-8014-4511-8(6)*, Comstock Publishing Assocs.) Cornell Univ. Pr.

Klooger, J. B. & Klooger, Jeff. Castoriadis: Psyche, Society, Autonomy. 2009. (Social & Critical Theory Ser.). 368p. *(978-90-04-17529-7(6))* BRILL.

Lumer, Christoph & Nannini, Sandro, eds. Intentionality Deliberation & Autonomy: The Action- Theoretic Basis of Practical Philosophy. 2007. 326p. 134.95 *(978-0-7546-6058-3(3))* Ashgate Publishing Co.

Marshall, J. D. Michel Foucault: Personal Autonomy & Education: Personal Autonomy & Education. 2010. (Philosophy & Education Ser.). 254p. pap. 239.00 *(978-90-481-4697-0(6)*, 9048146976) Springer.

May, T. Autonomy, Authority & Moral Responsibility. 2010. (Law & Philosophy Library). 204p. pap. 219.00 *(978-90-481-4949-0(5)*, 9048149495) Springer.

Oshana, Marina. Personal Autonomy in Society. 2006. 204p. 99.95 *(978-0-7546-5670-8(5))* Ashgate Publishing Co.

Rabbani, Martha Jalali. The Development & Antidevelopment Debate: Critical Reflections on the Philosophical Foundations. 2011. 196p. 99.95 *(978-1-4094-0997-7(X))* Ashgate Publishing Co.

Seeskin, Kenneth. Autonomy in Jewish Philosophy. 2009. (ENG.). 268p. pap. 38.99 *(978-0-521-11462-2(4))* Cambridge Univ. Pr.

Shell, Susan Meld. Kant & the Limits of Autonomy. 2009. 444p. 58.00 *(978-0-674-03333-7(7))* Harvard Univ. Pr.

Taylor, James St & Taylor, James Stacey. Practical Autonomy & Bioethics. 2009. (Routledge Annals of Bioethics Ser.). (ENG.). XVI, 212p. 126.00 *(978-0-415-99740-9(2))* Routledge.

Yoran, Hanan. Between Utopia & Dystopia: Erasmus, Thomas More, & the Humanist Republic of Letters. 2010. (ENG.). 264p. 68.50 *(978-0-7391-3647-8(X))* Lexington Bks.

AUTONOMY (PSYCHOLOGY)

see also Free Will and Determinism

Arneil, Barbara, et al, eds. Sexual Justice/Cultural Justice: Critical Perspectives in Political Theory & Practice. annot. ed. 2007. (Routledge Innovations in Political Theory Ser.: Vol. 23). 238p. 150.00 *(978-0-415-77092-7(0))* Routledge.

Bavetta, Sebastiano & Navarra, Pietro. The Economics of Freedom: Theory, Measurement, & Policy Implications. 2012. (ENG., Illus.). 224p. 99.00 ***(978-1-107-01784-9(X))*** Cambridge Univ. Pr.

Benbenishty, Julie. Autonomy End of Life Decisions Experiencing Life Threatening Event. 2010. 72p. pap. *(978-3-8383-5646-4(2))* Lambert Academic Publishing.

Bergsma, J. & Thomasma, David C. Autonomy & Clinical Medicine: Renewing the Health Professional Relation with the Patient. 2010. (International Library of Ethics, Law, & the New Medicine Ser.). 224p. pap. 169.00 *(978-90-481-5413-5(8)*, 9048154138) Springer.

Biegler, Paul. The Ethical Treatment of Depression: Autonomy Through Psychotherapy. 2011. (Philosophical Psychopathology Ser.). (ENG., Illus.). 232p. (gr. 17). 35.00 *(978-0-262-01549-3(8))* MIT Pr.

Brunn, Frank Martin. Selbstbestimmung in der Perspektive theologischer Ethik; [Self-determination from the Perspective of Theological Ethics]. Alexander Dietz & Frank Martin Brunn, eds. 2011. (Marburger Theologische Studien Ser.). (GER.). 168p. (C). pap. 39.00 ***(978-3-374-02888-7(8))*** Evangelische Verlagsanstalt GmbH DEU. Dist: Brown, David Bk. Co., The.

Chandler, Steve & Black, Duane. The Hands-off Manager: How to Mentor People & Allow Them to Be Successful. (ENG.). 2012. 224p. pap. 14.99 ***(978-1-60163-223-4(1))*** 2007. 1p. 19.99 *(978-1-56414-950-3(1))* Career Pr., Inc.

—The Hands-Off Manager: How to Mentor People & Allow Them to Be Successful. 2012. E-Book ***(978-1-60163-592-1(3))*** Career Pr., Inc.

Chirkov, Valery, et al, eds. Human Autonomy in Cross-Cultural Context: Perspectives on the Psychology of Agency, Freedom, & Well-Being. 2010. (Cross-Cultural Advancements in Positive Psychology Ser.). (Illus.). xiv, 283p. 139.00 *(978-90-481-9666-1(3)*, 9048196663) Springer.

Clarke, Desmond M. Church & State: Essays in Political Philosophy. 275p. *(978-0-902561-29-8(4))*; pap. *(978-0-902561-30-4(8))* Cork Univ. Pr.

Cleveland, Jeri. Empowered: An Activity Based Self-Determination Curriculum for Students with Visual Impairments. 2007. *(978-1-880366-39-4(8))* Texas Schl. for the Blind & Visually Impaired.

Durbin, Sam. You're Not the Boss of Me: Stories of Self-Determination. 2007. 60p. per. 15.00 *(978-1-929830-18-3(1))* Innovations Pr.
Erhard-Weiss, Dana. Mothers' & Fathers' Judgments about Young Children's Autonomy. 2008. 92p. pap. *(978-3-8364-3858-2(5))* VDM Verlag Dr. Mueller e.K.
Finley, Guy. The Courage to Be Free: Discover Your Original Fearless Self. 2010. (ENG.). 1p. 16.95 *(978-1-57863-475-0(X))* Red Wheel/Weiser.
Fondren, Gloria. Adolescents' Perceptions about Ways They Develop Autonomy. 2010. 184p. pap. *(978-3-8383-5252-7(1))* Lambert Academic Publishing.
Gruen, Arno. The Insanity of Normality: Toward Understanding Human Destructiveness. Hannum, Hildegarde & Hannum, Hunter, trs. 2007. 244p. per. 24.00 *(978-0-9669908-4-3(6))* Human Development Bks.
Hague, Ros. Autonomy, Identity & Feminism: The Politics of Who We Are. 2011. (Routledge Innovations in Political Theory Ser.). (ENG.). 200p. (C). 138.00 *(978-0-415-58468-5(X))* Routledge.
Hinton, James. Nine Wartime Lives: Mass Observation & the Making of the Modern Self. (ENG., Illus.). 272p. 2011. pap. 29.95 *(978-0-19-960515-6(7))* 2010. 45.00 *(978-0-19-957466-7(9))* Oxford Univ. Pr., Inc.
Homrich, Barbara J. Autonomy Disturbance As a Psychological Characteristic in Anorexi. 2008. 164p. pap. *(978-3-639-02739-6(6))* VDM Verlag Dr. Mueller e.K.
Jinsei, Juna. 100 Worlds to the Inner Cosmos: Gain Power, Control, & Freedom. 2009. 264p. pap. 13.95 *(978-1-4327-4491-5(7))* Outskirts Pr., Inc.
Knox, Jean. Self-Agency in Psychotherapy: Attachment, Autonomy, & Intimacy. 2010. (Norton Series on Interpersonal Neurobiology Ser.). (ENG., Illus.). 256p. 35.00 *(978-0-393-70559-1(5)*, 70559) Norton, W. W. & Co., Inc.
Landgraf, Edgar. Improvisation as Art: Conceptual Challenges, Historical Perspectives. 2011. (ENG.). 176p. 110.00 *(978-1-4411-4694-6(6))* Continuum International Publishing Group, Ltd. GBR. Dist: National Bk. Network.
Macken, John. The Autonomy Theme in the Church Dogmatics: Karl Barth & his Critics. 2008. (ENG.). 244p. (C). pap. 34.99 *(978-0-521-07237-3(9))* Cambridge Univ. Pr.
Magolda, Marcia B. Baxter. Authoring Your Life: Developing an Internal Voice to Navigate Life's Challenges. 2009. 400p. 29.95 *(978-1-57922-271-0(4))* Stylus Publishing, LLC.
Mithaug, Dennis E. Self-instruction Pedagogy: How to Teach Self-Determined Learning. 2007. 242p. (YA). *(978-0-398-07722-8(3))*; pap. *(978-0-398-07723-5(1))* Thomas, Charles C. Pub., Ltd.
Nedelsky, Jennifer. Law's Relations: A Relational Theory of Self, Autonomy, & Law, 1 vol. 2011. (ENG.). 560p. 65.00 *(978-0-19-514796-4(0))* Oxford Univ. Pr., Inc.
Nys, Thomas, et al. Autonomy & Paternalism: Reflections on the Theory & Practice of Health Care. Denier, Y. et al, eds. 2007. (Ethical Perspectives Ser.). (ENG.). 184p. (C). pap. 66.00 *(978-90-429-1880-1(2))* Peeters Pubs. & Booksellers BEL. Dist: Brown, David Bk. Co., The.
Radoilska, Lubomira, ed. Autonomy & Mental Disorder. 2012. (ENG.). 328p. pap. 75.00 ***(978-0-19-959542-6(9))*** Oxford Univ. Pr., Inc.
Reiff, Henry B. Self-Advocacy Skills for Students with Learning Disabilities: Making It Happen in College & Beyond: A Resource for Students, Parents, & Guidance Counselors. 2007. pap. 19.95 *(978-1-934032-06-0(9)*, Dude Publishing) National Professional Resources, Inc.
Richardson, Janice. Freedom Autonomy & Privacy. 2013. (ENG.). 208p. 120.00 *(978-0-415-57243-9(6))* Routledge.
Russell, Cathriona. Autonomy & Food Biotechnology in Theological Ethics. 2009. 290p. pap. 54.95 *(978-3-03911-838-0(2))* Lang, Peter AG GBR. Dist: Lang, Peter.
Sampson, Edward. Celebrating the Other: A Dialogic Account of Human Nature. 2008. (ENG.). x, 207p. pap. 28.00 *(978-0-9819076-0-4(1))* Taos Institute Pubns.
Santoro, Emilio. Autonomy, Freedom & Rights: A Critique of Liberal Subjectivity. 2010. (Law & Philosophy Library). 304p. pap. 219.00 *(978-90-481-6330-4(7)*, 9048163307) Springer.
Schermer, M. The Different Faces of Autonomy: Patient Autonomy in Ethical Theory & Hospital Practice. 2010. (Library of Ethics & Applied Philosophy Ser.). 232p. pap. 159.00 *(978-90-481-6161-4(4)*, 9048161614) Springer.
Seeskin, Kenneth. Autonomy in Jewish Philosophy. 2009. (ENG.). 268p. pap. 38.99 *(978-0-521-11462-2(4))* Cambridge Univ. Pr.
Showden, Carisa Renae. Choices Women Make: Agency in Domestic Violence, Assisted Reproduction, & Sex Work. 2011. 304p. 75.00 *(978-0-8166-5595-3(2))*; pap. 25.00 *(978-0-8166-5596-0(0))* Univ. of Minnesota Pr.
Shulman, Helene & Watkins, Mary. Towards Psychologies of Liberation. 2010. (Critical Theory & Practice in Psychology & the Human Sciences Ser.). (ENG.). 352p. pap. 31.00 *(978-0-230-53769-9(3))* Palgrave Macmillan.
Strawson, Galen. Freedom & Belief. rev. ed. 2010. (ENG., Illus.). 320p. 99.00 *(978-0-19-924749-3(8))* Oxford Univ. Pr., Inc.
Taylor, James Stacey, ed. Personal Autonomy: New Essays on Personal Autonomy & its Role in Contemporary Moral Philosophy. 2008. (ENG.). 360p. (C). pap. 24.99 *(978-0-521-73234-5(4))* Cambridge Univ. Pr.
Topivala, Candrakanta. Maro Atamarama: Angata Lekhanono Sañcaya. 2009. 200p. *(978-93-80294-02-5(6)*, Library of Congress — New Delhi Overseas Office) Parshva Pubn.
Watkins, Mary & Shulman, Helene. Toward Psychologies of Liberation. 2008. (ENG.). 408p. 110.00 *(978-0-230-53768-2(5))* Palgrave Macmillan.

AUTOPILOT

see Automatic Pilot (Airplanes)

AUTOPOIESIS

Here are entered works on spontaneously generated phenomena in physical, biological, and social sciences.

Clarke, Bruce & Hansen, Mark B. N., eds. Emergence & Embodiment: New Essays on Second-Order Systems Theory. 2009. (Science & Cultural Theory Ser.). (ENG., Illus.). 296p. 84.95 *(978-0-8223-4581-7(1))*; pap. 23.95 *(978-0-8223-4600-5(1))* Duke Univ. Pr.
Hayim, Gila J. Instability, Complexity, & Cultural Change: An Autopoiesis Approach. 2006. 220p. *(978-0-7734-5745-4(3))* Mellen, Edwin Pr., The.
Hidalgo-Capitá, et al. Self-Regulation of the World Economic System. 2011. 72p. pap. ***(978-3-8454-1664-9(5))*** Lambert Academic Publishing.
Klinger, Chris. Bootstrapping Reality from the Limitations of Logic. 2010. 348p. pap. *(978-3-639-25009-1(5))* VDM Verlag Dr. Mueller e.K.
Philippopoulos-Mihalopoulos, An. Absent Environments: Theorising Environmental Law & the City. 2009. 260p. pap. 39.95 *(978-0-415-57443-3(9)*, Routledge Cavendish) Taylor & Francis Group GBR. Dist: Taylor & Francis Group.
Philippopoulos-Mihalopoulos, Andreas, ed. Law & Ecology. 2011. (Law, Justice & Ecology Ser.). (ENG., Illus.). 256p. 125.00 *(978-0-415-58713-6(1))* Routledge.
Schumacher, Patrik S. The Autopoiesis of Architecture: A New Framework for Architecture. 2011. (ENG., Illus.). 478p. pap. 50.00 *(978-0-470-77298-0(0)*, Wiley) Wiley, John & Sons, Inc.
—The Autopoiesis of Architecture: A New Framework for Architecture. 2011. (ENG., Illus.). 478p. 130.00 *(978-0-470-77299-7(9)*, Wiley) Wiley, John & Sons, Inc.
—The Autopoiesis of Architecture Vol. 2: A New Agenda for Architecture. 2012. (ENG., Illus.). 784p. pap. 50.00 ***(978-0-470-66616-6(1)***, Wiley) Wiley, John & Sons, Inc.
—The Autopoiesis of Architecture Vol. II: A New Agenda for Architecture. 2012. (ENG., Illus.). 784p. 145.00 ***(978-0-470-66615-9(3)***, Wiley) Wiley, John & Sons, Inc.

AUTOPSY

see also Death—Causes; Medical Examiners (Law)

Adams, J. Hume & Murray, Margaret F. Atlas of Post-Mortem Techniques in Neuropathology. 2009. (ENG., Illus.). 156p. pap. 38.99 *(978-0-521-10568-2(4))* Cambridge Univ. Pr.
Adams, Vernard Irvine. Guidelines for Reports by Autopsy Pathologists. (ENG., Illus.). xvi, 128p. 2010. pap. 54.95 *(978-1-61737-900-0(X)*, 161737900X) 2008. 54.95 *(978-1-60327-472-2(3)*, 1603274723) Humana Pr.
Burke, Michael P. Forensic Pathology: Postmortem CT Scanning, Fractures, & Mechanism of Injury. 2011. (ENG., Illus.). 273p. 189.95 ***(978-1-4398-8148-4(0)***, CRC Press) Taylor & Francis Group GBR. Dist: Taylor & Francis Group.
Burton, Julian L. & Rutty, Guy. The Hospital Autopsy: A Manual of Fundamental Autopsy Practice. 3rd ed. 2010. (ENG., Illus.). 336p. 149.50 *(978-0-340-96514-6(2))* Hodder Arnold Pubs.
Cox, Margaret, et al, eds. Scientific Investigation of Mass Graves: Towards Protocols & Standard Operating Procedures. 2007. (ENG., Illus.). 592p. 203.00 *(978-0-521-86587-6(5))* Cambridge Univ. Pr.
Finkbeiner, Walter E., et al. Autopsy Pathology: A Manual & Atlas. 2nd ed. 2009. (ENG., Illus.). 441p. 199.00 *(978-1-4160-5453-5(7)*, Saunders) Elsevier - Health Sciences Div.
Gilbert-Barness, Enid & Debich-Spicer, Diane E. Handbook of Pediatric Autopsy Pathology. 2010. (Illus.). 544p. pap. 259.00 *(978-1-61737-433-3(4)*, 1617374334) Humana Pr.
Goodson, Jr. Autopsy, Anatomy of Survival: The Autobiography of Thomas (Tommy) Hugh Goodson, Jr. 2009. 460p. pap. 39.95 *(978-1-4401-1198-3(7))* iUniverse, Inc.
Houser, Stuart Lair. The Operated Heart at Autopsy. 2009. (ENG., Illus.). x, 238p. 189.00 *(978-1-60327-807-2(9)*, 1603278079) Humana Pr.
Kammen, Michael G. Digging up the Dead: A History of Notable American Reburials. 2010. (Illus.). 272p. 25.00 *(978-0-226-42329-6(8))* Univ. of Chicago Pr.
Karch, Steven B., ed. Postmortem Toxicology of Abused Drugs. 2007. (ENG., Illus.). 216p. 89.95 *(978-1-4200-5451-4(1)*, CRC Press) Taylor & Francis Group GBR. Dist: Taylor & Francis Group.
Koehler, Steven A. Postmortem: Establishing the Cause of Death. 2006. (ENG., Illus.). 176p. pap. 24.95 *(978-1-55407-220-0(4))* Firefly Bks., Ltd.
Lecomte, Dominique. La Maison du Mort. 2010. (FRE.). 202p. *(978-2-213-60932-4(2))* Fayard, Artheme, Librairie.
McCracken-Flesher, Caroline. The Doctor Dissected: A Cultural Autopsy of the Burke & Hare Murders, 1 vol. 2012. (ENG., Illus.). 304p. 65.00 ***(978-0-19-976682-6(7))*** Oxford Univ. Pr., Inc.
McNamee, Lakshini. Learning from Autopsies. 2011. 88p. pap. ***(978-3-8454-0708-1(5))*** Lambert Academic Publishing.
Mitchell, Piers. Anatomical Dissection in Enlightenment Britain & Beyond: Autopsy, Pathology & Display. 2012. (History of Medicine in Context Ser.). (Illus.). 175p. 114.95 ***(978-1-4094-1886-3(3))*** Ashgate Publishing Co.
National Center for Health Statistics (U.S.) Staff, contrib. by. Autopsy Patterns in 2003. 2007. (DHHS Publication Ser.: Nos. 2005-1851). (Illus.). iv, 19p. *(978-0-8406-0613-6(3)*, Centers for Disease Control & Prevention) United States Government Printing Office.
Pomara, Cristoforo. Forensic Autopsy. Fineschi, Vittorio & Karch, Steven B., eds. 2010. (ENG., Illus.). 161p. instr.'s hndbk. ed. 189.95 *(978-1-4398-0064-5(2)*, CRC Press) Taylor & Francis Group GBR. Dist: Taylor & Francis Group.
Prayson, Richard A. Autopsy: Learning from the Dead. 2007. (Cleveland Clinic Guides). (ENG., Illus.) 150p. per. 14.95 *(978-1-59624-045-2(8))* Cleveland Clinic Pr.
Roach, Mary. Stiff: The Curious Lives of Human Cadavers. 2009. 13.46 *(978-0-7848-3006-2(1)*, Everbind) Marco Bk. Co.
Rutty, Guy N., ed. Essentials of Autopsy Practice: Current Methods & Modern Trends. 2011. (ENG., Illus.). x, 246p. pap. 179.00 *(978-1-84996-979-6(5)*, 1849969795) Springer.
—Essentials of Autopsy Practice: New Advances, Trends & Developments. 2010. (Illus.). x, 190p. pap. 219.00 *(978-1-84996-657-3(5)*, 1849966575) Springer.
—Essentials of Autopsy Practice: Tropical Developments, Trends & Advances. 2007. (Illus.). 187p. 219.00 *(978-1-84628-834-0(7))* Springer.
Sheaff, Michael T. & Hopster, Deborah J. Post Mortem Technique Handbook. 2nd ed. 2011. (ENG., Illus.) xiv, 452p. pap. 179.00 *(978-1-84996-927-7(2)*, 1849969272) Springer.
Shkrum, Michael J. & Ramsay, David A. Forensic Pathology of Trauma: Common Problems for the Pathologist. 2007. (Forensic Science & Medicine Ser.). (Illus.). 648p. 299.00 incl. cd-rom *(978-1-58829-458-6(7)*, 1588294587) Humana Pr.
Sperling, Daniel. Posthumous Interests: Legal & Ethical Perspectives. 2011. (Cambridge Law, Medicine & Ethics Ser.). (ENG.). 304p. pap. 60.00 *(978-0-521-18766-4(4))* Cambridge Univ. Pr.
Thomas, A. R. A Practical Guide for Making Post-Mortem Examinations, & for the Study of Morbid Anatomy, with Directions for Embalming the Dead, & for the Preser. 2006. (Illus.). 336p. per. 23.99 *(978-1-4255-3455-4(4))* MPublishing.
Timmermans, Stefan. Postmortem: How Medical Examiners Explain Suspicious Deaths. annot. ed. 2007. (Fieldwork Encounters & Discoveries Ser.). 384p. per. 18.00 *(978-0-226-80399-9(6))* Univ. of Chicago Pr.
Vuitaggione, Julie M. & Forester, Kyle N. Pathology: New Research. 2012. pap. ***(978-1-62100-698-5(0))*** Nova Science Pubs., Inc.
Waters, Brenda L. Handbook of Autopsy Practice. 4th ed. 2009. (Illus.). 608p. 179.00 *(978-1-58829-841-6(8))* Humana Pr.
World Health Organization. Normes d'autopsie Verbale: Etablissement et attribution de la cause de Décès. 2010. 131p. pap. 24.00 *(978-92-4-254721-4(2))* World Health Organization.
—Verbal Autopsy Standards: Ascertaining & Attributing Cause of Death. 2007. (Nonserial Publication). (ENG.). 117p. pap. 24.00 *(978-92-4-154721-5(9))* World Health Organization.
Zugibe, Frederick & Carroll, David L. Dissecting Death: Secrets of a Medical Examiner. 2006. (Illus.). 256p. pap. 14.00 *(978-0-7679-1880-0(0)*, Broadway) Broadway Bks.

AUTOSUGGESTION

see Hypnotism; Mental Suggestion

AUTRY, GENE, 1907-1998

Bond, Johnny. Thirty Years on the Road with Gene Autry: Recollections. 2007. (Illus.). 288p. 29.95 *(978-1-880756-18-8(8))* Riverwood Pr.
George-Warren, Holly. Public Cowboy No. 1: The Life & Times of Gene Autry. 2009. (ENG., Illus.). 480p. pap. 17.95 *(978-0-19-537267-0(0))* Oxford Univ. Pr., Inc.

AUTUMN

Blacklock, Judith. Judith Blacklocks flower recipes for Autumn. 2008. (ENG.). 112p. 29.95 *(978-0-9552391-4-4(1)*, Falcon Guides) Globe Pequot Pr., The.
Bowles, E. A. My Garden in Autumn & Winter. 2008. (ENG.). 352p. pap. 24.95 *(978-1-60469-043-9(7)*, 1604690437) Timber Pr., Inc.
Clarke, Ethne. Autumn Gardens. (Illus.). 168p. *(978-0-7153-0701-4(0))* David & Charles Pubs. GBR. Dist: David & Charles Pubs.
Dunne, Pete. Arctic Autumn: A Journey to Season's Edge. 2011. (ENG., Illus.). 272p. 24.00 *(978-0-618-82221-8(6))* Houghton Mifflin Harcourt Trade & Reference Pubs.
Ernst, Tim. Arkansas Autumn: Spectacular Fall Photos of the Natural State. 2010. (Illus.). 144p. 34.95 *(978-1-882906-70-3(5))* Cloudland.net Publishing.
Finch. Autumn Trees. Date not set. (Illus.). 80p. pap. 129.15 *(978-0-582-18162-5(3))* Addison-Wesley Longman, Ltd. GBR. Dist: Trans-Atlantic Pubns., Inc.
Gooseberry Patch. Classics Collection Fall Favorites with Sunmaid: Scrumptious Recipes to Share with Family & Friends. 2007. (ENG., Illus.). 32p. 4.95 *(978-1-933494-42-5(5))* Gooseberry Patch.
Hanna, Rod, photos by. Colorado's Seasons of Gold. 2010. (Illus.). 220p. 48.00 *(978-0-615-32464-7(9))* Hanna Enterprises.
Ideals Thanksgiving 2008. 2008. (ENG.). 64p. pap. 6.99 *(978-0-8249-1319-9(1))* Ideals Pubns.
Máté, Ferenc. A New England Autumn: A Sentimental Journey. 2008. (ENG., Illus.). 160p. 25.00 *(978-0-920256-55-8(4)*, 25655) Albatross Publishing CAN. Dist: Norton, W. W. & Co., Inc.
Pickering, Samuel F. Autumn Spring. 2007. (ENG.). 152p. per. 19.95 *(978-1-57233-596-7(3))* Univ. of Tennessee Pr.
Ritt, Thomas Francis. A D, V2, No 3, Autumn 1951. Ritt, Thomas Francis et al, eds. 2011. 134p. 40.95 ***(978-1-258-02268-6(0))*** Literary Licensing, LLC.
Thoreau, Henry David. Autumn. 2009. 242p. pap. *(978-0-217-44255-8(2))* Books LLC.
Thoreau, Henry David. October, or Autumnal Tints. 2012. (ENG., Illus.). 128p. 17.95 ***(978-0-393-08188-6(5)***, 8188) Norton, W. W. & Co., Inc.

AUTUMN—JUVENILE LITERATURE

Enslow, Brian. Fall Colors. 2011. (All About Colors of the Seasons Ser.). (Illus.). 24p. (J). (gr. k-3). lib. bdg. 21.26 *(978-0-7660-3909-4(9))* Enslow Pubs., Inc.

AUVERGNE (FRANCE)

Michelin, creator. Auvergne Rhône Valley. 4th rev. ed. 2007. (Michelin Green Guide Auvergne & the Rhone Valley Ser.). (Illus.). 678p. 21.95 *(978-2-06-712336-6(X))* Michelin.

AUXIN

Estelle, Mark, et al, eds. Auxin Signaling. 2010. (Illus.). 253p. 135.00 *(978-0-87969-898-0(5))* Cold Spring Harbor Laboratory Pr.
Keller, Andrew H. & Fallon, Michelle D., eds. Auxins: Structure, Biosynthesis & Functions. 2012. ***(978-1-62100-504-9(6))*** Nova Science Pubs., Inc.

AVA (PLANT)

see Kava Plant

AVALANCHES

see also Landslides

Bolognesi, Robert. Avalanche! Understand & Reduce the Risks from Avalanches. 2007. (Illus.). 112p. pap. 12.95 *(978-1-85284-473-8(6))* Cicerone Pr. GBR. Dist: Midpoint Trade Bks., Inc.
Brooks-Range Mountaineering. Avalanche Information Card: US & International contact information for up-to-date mountaineering Info. 2007. (Illus.). 1p. 4.95 *(978-0-9798276-2-4(0))* Brooks-Range Mountaineering Equipment Co.
—Ski Guide Cards Set. 2011. (ENG., Illus.). 36p. 24.95 *(978-0-9798276-0-0(4))* Brooks-Range Mountaineering Equipment Co.
Daffern, Tony. Backcountry Avalanche Safety: Skiers, Climbers, Boarders & Snowshoers, 1 vol. 3rd rev. ed. 2009. (ENG., Illus.). 208p. pap. *(978-1-897522-54-7(1))* Rocky Mountain Bks.
De Wrachien, D., et al, eds. Monitoring, Simulation, Prevention & Remediation of Dense & Debris Flows II. 2008. (WIT Transactions on Engineering Sciences Ser.: 60). (Illus.). 240p. 158.00 *(978-1-84564-118-4(3))* WIT Pr GBR. Dist: WIT Pr.
Djuidje Kenmoe, Germaine. Frictional Stick-Slip Phenomen. 2011. 104p. pap. ***(978-3-8443-0973-7(X))*** Lambert Academic Publishing.
Feist, Holger & Kurzeder, Tobias. PowderGuide. 160p. pap. 18.95 *(978-0-9717748-7-2(0)*, 958) Mountain Pr. Publishing Co., Inc.
Fredston, Jill. Snowstruck: In the Grip of Avalanches. 2007. (ENG., Illus.). 352p. pap. 14.00 *(978-0-15-603254-4(6)*, Mariner Bks.) Houghton Mifflin Harcourt Trade & Reference Pubs.
—Untitled Avalanche Book. Date not set. *(978-0-86547-663-9(2)*, North Point Pr.) Farrar, Straus & Giroux.
Howley, Emma. Snow Avalanche Prediction in Grasdalen, Norway: Application of Statistical Methods. 2008. 128p. pap. *(978-3-639-07135-1(2))* VDM Verlag Dr. Mueller e.K.
Hutter, Kolumban & Pudasaini, Shiva P. Avalanche Dynamics: Dynamics of Rapid Flows of Dense Granular Avalanches. 2006. (ENG., Illus.). xxiv, 602p. 209.00 *(978-3-540-32686-1(3)*, 3540326863) Springer.
Krist, Gary. The White Cascade: The Great Northern Railway Disaster & America's Deadliest Avalanche. 2008. (ENG., Illus.). 352p. pap. 17.00 *(978-0-8050-8329-3(4)*, Holt Paperback) Holt, Henry & Co.
McClung, David & Schaerer, Peter. The Avalanche Handbook. 3rd rev. ed. 2006. (ENG., Illus.). 342p. per. 21.95 *(978-0-89886-809-8(2))* Mountaineers Bks., The.
Moynier, John. Avalanche Aware: The Essential Guide to Avalanche Safety. 2nd ed. 2006. (Falcon Guide Ser.). (ENG., Illus.). 104p. pap. 7.95 *(978-0-7627-3803-8(0)*, Falcon Guides) Globe Pequot Pr., The.
Pudasaini, S. P. & Hutter, Kolumban. Avalanche Dynamics: Dynamics of Rapid Flows of Dense Granular Avalanches. 2010. (ENG., Illus.). xxiv, 602p. pap. 209.00 *(978-3-642-06919-2(3)*, 3642069193) Springer.
Schaefer, Marius. Shear Evolution in Small Scale Avalanches. 2011. 96p. pap. ***(978-3-8381-2738-5(2))*** Südwestdeutscher Verlag für Hochschulschriften AG & Co. KG.
Spilsbury, Louise & Spilsbury, Richard. Landslides & Avalanches in Action. 2009. (Natural Disasters in Action Ser.). (ENG., Illus.). 48p. (gr. 5-8). pap. 11.75 *(978-1-4358-5138-2(2)*, Rosen Central) Rosen Publishing Group, Inc., The.
Spilsbury, Richard & Spilsbury, Louise. Landslides & Avalanches in Action. 2008. (Illus.). 48p. lib. bdg. 26.50 *(978-1-4042-1868-0(8))* Rosen Publishing Group, Inc., The.
Takahashi, Tamotsu, ed. Debris Flow: Mechanics, Prediction & Countermeasures. 2007. (ENG., Illus.). 448p. (C). 129.95 *(978-0-415-43552-9(8)*, Taylor & Francis) Taylor & Francis Group GBR. Dist: Taylor & Francis Group.
Tremper, Bruce. Staying Alive in Avalanche Terrain. 2nd ed. 2008. (ENG.). 304p. pap. 18.95 *(978-1-59485-084-4(4))* Mountaineers Bks., The.
Waitt, Richard B. & Beget, James E. Volcanic Processes & Geology of Augustine Volcano, Alaska. 2009. (Illus.). vii, 78p. *(978-1-4113-2411-4(0))* United States Geological Survey.
Woodlief, Jennifer. A Wall of White: The True Story of Heroism & Survival in the Face of a Deadly Avalanche. 2010. (ENG., Illus.). 256p. pap. 16.99 *(978-1-4165-4694-8(4)*, Beyond Words/Atria Bks.) Atria Bks.
World Book, Inc Staff, contrib. by. Landslides, Mudslides & Avalanches. 2007. *(978-0-7166-9810-4(2))* World Bk., Inc.
—Landslides, Mudslides, & Avalanches. 2nd ed. 2009. (Illus.). 47p. *(978-0-7166-9826-5(9))* World Bk., Inc.

AVANKI (ASIAN PEOPLE)

see Evenki (Asian People)

AVANT-GARDE (AESTHETICS)

see also Avant-Garde (Music); Literature, Experimental; Postmodernism

Acquaviva, Frederic. Gil J. Wolman. I am immortal & Alive. 2010. 184p. pap. 39.95 *(978-84-92505-40-1(0))* Museu d'Art Contemporani de Barcelona ESP. Dist: Actar Birkhauser Distribution.

Adamson, Walter. Embattled Avant-Gardes: Modernism's Resistance to Commodity Culture in Europe. 2007. 448p. 60.00 *(978-0-520-25270-7(5))* Univ. of California Pr.

Adamson, Walter L. Embattled Avant-Gardes: Modernism's Resistance to Commodity Culture in Europe. 2009. (ENG.). 448p. pap. 31.95 *(978-0-520-26153-2(4))* Univ. of California Pr.

Ades, Dawn & Baker, Simon. Undercover Surrealism: Georges Bataille & Documents. 2006. (Illus.). 271p. pap. *(978-0-262-51197-1(5))*; (ENG., 272p. (gr. 17). pap. 40.00 *(978-0-262-01230-0(8))* MIT Pr.

Albiñana, Salvador. Mexico Illustrated 1920-1950. 2011. (SPA & ENG., Illus.). 288p. 65.00 *(978-84-92480-87-6(4))* RM Verlag, S.L. ESP. Dist: D.A.P./Distributed Art Pubs.

Albiñana, Salvador, ed. México Ilustrado: Libros, Revistas y Carteles, 1920-1950. 2010. (SPA., Illus.). 376p. *(978-607-7515-56-2(6))* R.M. Editorial, S.A. de C.V.

Andrews, Colman. Ferran: The Inside Story of el Bulli & the Man Who Reinvented Food. 2011. (ENG.). 336p. (gr. 12). 16.00 *(978-1-59240-668-5(8)*, Gotham) Penguin Group (USA) Inc.

Antliff, Allan. Anarchist Modernism: Art, Politics, & the First American Avant-Garde. 2007. (Illus.). 314p. per. 45.00 *(978-0-226-02104-1(1))* Univ. of Chicago Pr.

Antliff, Mark. Avant-Garde Fascism: The Mobilization of Myth, Art, & Culture in France, 1909-1939. 2007. (ENG., Illus.). 376p. 94.95 *(978-0-8223-4015-7(1))*; pap. 25.95 *(978-0-8223-4034-8(8))* Duke Univ. Pr.

Ascunce, Aranzazu. Barcelona & Madrid: Social Networks of the Avant-Garde. 2012. (ENG.). 254p. (gr. 17). 75.00 ***(978-1-61148-424-3(3))*** Bucknell Univ. Pr.

Baker, George. The Artwork Caught by the Tail: Francis Picabia & Dada in Paris. (October Bks.). (ENG., Illus.). 496p. (gr. 17). 2010. pap. 24.95 *(978-0-262-51486-6(9))* 2007. 41.95 *(978-0-262-02618-5(X))* MIT Pr.

Barbaro, Luca M. & Pola, Francesca, eds. A Roma, la Nostra Era Avanguardia. 2010. (ENG & ITA.). 192p. pap. 62.50 *(978-88-370-7488-3(3))* Electa ITA. Dist: Trans-Atlantic Pubns., Inc.

Barbero, Luca Massimo & Widenheim, Cecilia. Milan-Turin 1958-1968 No. 2. 2008. (ENG., Illus.). 112p. pap. 50.00 *(978-3-86521-639-7(0))* Steidl, Gerhard Druckerei und Verlag DEU. Dist: D.A.P./Distributed Art Pubs.

Bataille, Georges. The Absence of Myth: Writings on Surrealism. Richardson, Michael, ed. & tr. by. from FRE. 2006. (ENG.). 224p. per. 19.95 *(978-1-84467-560-9(2)*, 844560) Verso Bks. GBR. Dist: Norton, W. W. & Co., Inc.

Beekman, Klaus & Vries, Jan De, eds. Avant-Garde & Criticism. 2007. (Avant Garde Critical Studies: 21). (ENG., Illus.). 368p. 95.00 *(978-90-420-2152-5(7))* Rodopi.

Bennett, Robert. Deconstructing Post-Wwii New York City. 2011. 142p. pap. 39.95 ***(978-0-415-80689-3(5))*** Routledge.

Berghaus, Ginter & Berghaus, Günter. Theatre, Performance, & the Historical Avant-garde. 2009. (Palgrave Studies in Theatre & Performance History Ser.). (ENG., Illus.). 400p. pap. 35.00 *(978-0-230-61752-0(2))* Palgrave Macmillan.

Berghaus, Gunter, ed. Futurism & the Technological Imagination. 2009. (Illus.). 402p. 120.00 *(978-90-420-2747-3(9))* Rodopi.

Berghuis, Thomas J. Writing on the Wall: Chinese New Realism & Avant-Garde in the Eighties & Nineties. 2008. (ENG., Illus.). 152p. pap. 40.00 *(978-90-5662-542-9(X))* NAi Uitgevers / Publishers Stichting NLD. Dist: D.A.P./Distributed Art Pubs.

Best, Susan. Visualizing Feeling: Affect & the Feminine Avant-garde. 2011. (ENG., Illus.). 224p. 90.00 *(978-1-84885-851-0(5))* I. B. Tauris & Co., Ltd. GBR. Dist: Macmillan.

Bing, Xu. Xu Bing, 1 vol. 2012. (ENG., Illus.). 280p. 85.00 ***(978-0-9568670-0-1(6))*** Albion Editions GBR. Dist: D.A.P./Distributed Art Pubs.

Bohn, Willard. Apollinaire on the Edge: Modern Art, Popular Culture, & the Avant-Garde. 2010. (Illus.). 143p. pap. 38.00 *(978-90-420-3108-1(5))* Rodopi.

Bray, Joe, et al, eds. Routledge Companion to Experimental Literature. 2012. (Routledge Companions Ser.). (ENG., Illus.). 560p. 175.00 *(978-0-415-57000-8(X))* Routledge.

Breitwieser, Sabine & Switek, Gabriela, eds. Avant-Garde in the Bloc. 2010. (POL & ENG., Illus.). 528p. pap. 35.00 *(978-3-03764-094-4(4))* JRP Ringier Kunstverlag AG CHE. Dist: D.A.P./Distributed Art Pubs.

Brenner, Anita. Avant-Garde Art & Artists in Mexico: Anita Brenner's Journals of the Roaring Twenties. Glusker, Susannah Joel, ed. 2010. (ENG., Illus.). 901p. 125.00 *(978-0-292-72184-5(6))* Univ. of Texas Pr.

Bru, Sascha, et al, eds. Europa! Europa? The Avant-Garde, Modernism & the Fate of the Continent. 2009. (European Avant-Garde & Modernism Studies). (ENG, GER & FRE., Illus.). XII, 534p. 140.00 *(978-3-11-021771-1(6))* De Gruyter, Walter Inc.

Buhr, Elke. Begegnung Bauhaus: Kurt Schmidt und Künstler der Avantgarde Von Kandinsky Bis Vasarely: Kunstsammlung Gera, 25. März Bis 28. Juni 2009. 2009. (Illus.). 159p. pap. *(978-3-910051-52-2(9))* Glaux Verlag Christine Jager KG.

Burgess, Gelett. Le Petit Journal des Refusées. 2009. *(978-0-89263-013-4(2))*; *(978-0-89263-012-7(4))*; *(978-0-89263-014-1(0))* Rice Univ. Pr.

Bury, Stephen. Breaking the Rules: The Printed Face of the European Avant Garde 1900-1937. 2008. (ENG., Illus.). 176p. 60.00 *(978-0-7123-0975-2(6))* British Library, The GBR. Dist: Chicago Distribution Ctr.

—Breaking the Rules: The Printed Face of the European Avant Garde 1900-1937. 2008. (ENG., Illus.). 128p. pap. 30.00 *(978-0-7123-0980-6(2))* British Library, The GBR. Dist: Chicago Distribution Ctr.

Carrick, Jill. Nouveau Réalisme, 1960s France, & the Neo-Avant-Garde: Topographies of Chance & Return. 2010. (Illus.). 184p. 104.95 *(978-0-7546-6141-2(5))* Ashgate Publishing Co.

Carson, Juli, ed. & text. Exile of the Imaginary: Politics Aesthetics Love, 1 vol. 2007. (ENG., Illus.). 184p. pap. 29.00 *(978-3-86560-211-4(8))* Verlag der Buchhandlung Walther Konig DEU. Dist: D.A.P./Distributed Art Pubs.

Chicuri, Abelardo Mena, et al. Cuba Avant-Garde: Contemporary Cuban Art from the Farber Collection / Arte Contemporaneo Cubano de la Coleccion Farber. Delson, Susan, ed. Lizarraga, Felix, tr. 2007. (SPA & ENG., Illus.). 188p. pap. 29.95 *(978-0-9762552-5-3(1))* Univ. Pr. of Florida.

—Cuba Avant-Garde: Contemporary Cuban Art from the Farber Collection /Arte Contemporaneo Cubano de la Coleccion Farber. Delson, Susan, ed. Lizarraga, Felix, tr. 2007. (SPA & ENG., Illus.). 188p. 59.95 *(978-0-9762552-4-6(3))* Univ. Pr. of Florida.

Coen, Ester, ed. Futurismo 100: Illuminazioni. 2009. (ITA., Illus.). 450p. 142.50 *(978-88-370-6777-9(1))* Electa ITA. Dist: Trans-Atlantic Pubns., Inc.

Cooper, John Xiros. Modernism & the Culture of Market Society. 2009. (ENG.). 300p. pap. 44.00 *(978-0-521-12011-1(X))* Cambridge Univ. Pr.

Dantini, Michele. Modern & Contemporary Art. 2008. (ENG., Illus.). 192p. pap. 14.95 *(978-1-4027-5921-5(5))* Sterling Publishing Co., Inc.

de Canales, Francisco Gonzalez. Experiments with Life Itself. 2012. (ENG., Illus.). 152p. pap. *(978-84-92861-65-1(7))* Actar Birkhauser Distribution.

Doherty, Claire, ed. Situation. 2009. (Documents of Contemporary Art Ser.). (ENG.). 238p. (gr. 17). pap. 24.95 *(978-0-262-51305-0(6))* MIT Pr.

Duchting, Hajo. The Blaue Reiter. Wolf, Norbert, ed. 2009. (ENG., Illus.). 96p. pap. 9.99 *(978-3-8228-5580-5(4))* TASCHEN DEU. Dist: Ingram Pub. Services.

Eckmann, Sabine, et al. Reality Bites: Making Avant-garde Art in Post-Wall Germany. 2007.Tr. of Reality Bites: Kunst nach dem Mauerfall. (GER.). per. 55.00 *(978-0-936316-21-5(7))* Washington Univ., Mildred Lane Kemper Art Museum.

Fargo, Matthew, tr. from JPN. Hyperart: Thomasson. 2010. (ENG., Illus.). 352p. pap. 17.95 *(978-1-885030-46-7(0))* Muae Publishing, Inc.

Ferrari, Rossella. Pop Goes the Avant-Garde: Experimental Theater in Contemporary China. 2012. (Seagull Books - Enactments Ser.). (ENG., Illus.). 344p. pap. 25.00 ***(978-0-85742-045-9(3))*** Seagull Bks. GBR. Dist: Chicago Distribution Ctr.

Firmin, Sandra. Artpark: 1974-1984. 2011. *(978-0-9842518-1-0(2))* Princeton Architectural Pr.

FitzGerald, Michael. Picasso & American Art. 2006. (ENG., Illus.). 400p. 65.00 *(978-0-300-11452-2(4))* Yale Univ. Pr.

FitzGerald, Michael C. & Boddewyn, Julia May. Picasso & American Art. 2006. (Illus.). 400p. pap. *(978-0-87427-154-6(1))* Whitney Museum of American Art.

Fleckner, Uwe. The Invention of the 20th Century: Carl Einstein & the Avant-Gardes. 2009. 324p. pap. 65.00 *(978-84-8026-386-3(5))* Museo Nacional Centro de Arte Reina Sofia ESP. Dist: Actar Birkhauser Distribution.

Froula, Christine. Virginia Woolf & the Bloomsbury Avant-Garde: War, Civilization, Modernity. 2007. (Gender & Culture Ser.). (ENG.). 432p. (gr. 17). pap. 26.50 *(978-0-231-13445-3(2))* Columbia Univ. Pr.

Furlani, Andre. Guy Davenport: Postmodern & After. 2007. (Avant-Garde & Modernism Studies Ser.). (ENG.). 296p. 59.95 *(978-0-8101-2385-4(1))* Northwestern Univ. Pr.

—Guy Davenport: Postmodernism & After. 2007. (Avant-Garde & Modernism Studies). (ENG.). 296p. per. 27.95 *(978-0-8101-2389-2(4))* Northwestern Univ. Pr.

Gallo, Rubén. Mexican Modernity: The Avant-Garde & the Technological Revolution. 2010. (ENG., Illus.). 280p. (gr. 17). pap. 17.95 *(978-0-262-51496-5(6))* MIT Pr.

Giunta, Andrea. Avant-Garde, Internationalism, & Politics: Argentine Art in the Sixties. Kahn, Peter, tr. from SPA. 2007. (Latin America Otherwise Ser.). (ENG., Illus.). 432p. per. 27.95 *(978-0-8223-3893-2(9))*; 99.95 *(978-0-8223-3877-2(7))* Duke Univ. Pr.

Graf, Alexander & Scheunemann, Dietrich, eds. Avant-Garde Film. 2007. (Illus.). 405p. 11700.00 *(978-90-420-2305-5(8))* Rodopi.

Gurianova, Nina. The Aesthetics of Anarchy: Art & Ideology in the Early Russian Avant-Garde. 2012. (ENG., Illus.). 343p. 49.95 ***(978-0-520-26876-0(8))*** Univ. of California Pr.

Harte, Timothy. Fast Forward: The Aesthetics & Ideology of Speed in Russian Avant-Garde Culture, 1910-1930. 2009. (ENG., Illus.). 328p. pap. 29.95 *(978-0-299-23324-2(3))* Univ. of Wisconsin Pr.

Hopkins, David, ed. Neo-avant-garde. 2006. (Avant Garde Critical Studies: 20). (Illus.). 464p. *(978-90-420-2125-9(X))* Rodopi.

Hung, Wu, text. Making History: Wu Hung on Contemporary Art. 2009. (ENG., Illus.). 278p. 50.00 *(978-988-99617-0-1(9))* Timezone 8 Ltd. HKG. Dist: D.A.P./Distributed Art Pubs.

Jennison, Ruth. The Zukofsky Era: Modernity, Margins, & the Avant-Garde. 2012. (Hopkins Studies in Modernism Ser.). (ENG., Illus.). 248p. (gr. 17). 60.00 ***(978-1-4214-0529-2(6))*** Johns Hopkins Univ. Pr.

Jeon, Joseph Jonghyun. Racial Things, Racial Forms: Objecthood in Avant-Garde Asian American Poetry. 2012. (Contemporary North American Poetry Ser.). (ENG., Illus.). 240p. pap. 39.95 ***(978-1-60938-086-1(X))*** Univ. of Iowa Pr.

Johnson, Dominic. Glorious Catastrophe: Jack Smith, Performance & Visual Culture. 2012. (ENG., Illus.). 272p. 95.00 ***(978-0-7190-8299-3(4))*** Manchester Univ. Pr. GBR. Dist: Macmillan.

Johnson, Jeffrey. Haiku Poetics in Twentieth Century Avant-Garde Poetry. 2011. (Illus.). viii, 248p. ***(978-0-7391-7104-2(6))***; (ENG., 262p. 70.00 ***(978-0-7391-4876-1(1))*** Lexington Bks.

Jolas, Eugene. Eugene Jolas: Critical Writings, 1924-1951. 2009. 300p. *(978-0-8101-1771-6(1))* Northwestern Univ. Pr.

Joseph, Branden W. Beyond the Dream Syndicate - Tony Conrad & the Arts after Cage. 2011. (ENG., Illus.). 480p. (gr. 17). pap. 22.95 ***(978-1-890951-87-0(0))*** Zone Bks.

Joseph, Branden W. Random Order: Robert Rauschenberg & the Neo-Avant-Garde. 2007. (October Bks.). (ENG., Illus.). 432p. (gr. 17). pap. 20.95 *(978-0-262-60071-2(4))* MIT Pr.

Joseph, Branden Wayne. Beyond the Dream Syndicate: Tony Conrad & the Arts after Cage. 2008. (ENG., Illus.). 480p. (gr. 17). 34.95 *(978-1-890951-86-3(2))* Zone Bks.

Kabakov, Ilya & Kabakov, Emilia, illus. Under the Snow/Unter Dem Schnee. 2008. (ENG.). 100p. 42.00 *(978-3-86560-348-7(3))* Verlag der Buchhandlung Walther Konig DEU. Dist: D.A.P./Distributed Art Pubs.

Knabb, Ken, ed. Situationist International Anthology. enl. ed. 2007. 532p. per. 20.00 *(978-0-939682-04-1(4))* Bureau of Public Secrets.

Kostelanetz, Richard. More Complete Audio Writing (Nineteen Eighty-Seven) Kostelanetz, Richard, ed. 424p. 500.00 incl. audio *(978-0-932360-84-7(X))* Archae Editions.

Kotynek, Roy & Cohassey, John. American Cultural Rebels: Avant-Garde & Bohemian Artists, Writers & Musicians from the 1850s Through the 1960s. 2008. (ENG.). 262p. per. 39.95 *(978-0-7864-3709-2(X))* McFarland & Co., Inc. Pubs.

Kovtun, Evgueny. Russian Avant-Garde. 2007. (Art of Century Ser.). (ENG., Illus.). 199p. pap. 19.95 *(978-1-85995-678-6(5))* Parkstone International GBR. Dist: Ingram Pub. Services.

Le Coultre, Martijn F. & Purvis, Alston W. Jan Tschichold: Plakate der Avantgarde. 2007. (Illus.). 239p. pap. 48.48 *(978-3-7643-7603-1(1)*, 3764376031) Birkhauser Boston.

Leger, Marc James. Brave New Avant Garde: Essays on Contemporary Art & Politics. 2012. (ENG., Illus.). 208p. pap. 22.95 ***(978-1-78099-050-7(2))*** Hunt, John Publishing Ltd. GBR. Dist: National Bk. Network.

Levine, Caroline. Provoking Democracy: Why We Need the Arts. 2007. (Blackwell Manifestos Ser.: 12). (ENG., Illus.). 256p. pap. 39.95 *(978-1-4051-5927-2(8))*; 104.95 *(978-1-4051-5926-5(X))* Wiley, John & Sons, Inc. (Wiley-Blackwell).

Madson, Jerry. Bog Walk Pitcher Plants Meet Implicate Polysynthesis. 2007. 100p. pap. 44.50 *(978-1-4303-2883-4(5))* Lulu Enterprises Inc.

Maffei, Giorgio & Picciau, Maura, eds. The Book As A Work of Art, 1 vol. 2007. (ENG., Illus.). 160p. pap. 55.00 *(978-88-7570-037-9(0))* Corraini ITA. Dist: D.A.P./Distributed Art Pubs.

Mangini, Shirley. Maruja Mallo & the Spanish Avant-Garde. 2010. (Ashgate Studies in Surrealism Ser.). (Illus.). 272p. 119.95 *(978-0-7546-6932-6(7))* Ashgate Publishing Co.

Marcus, Greil. Lipstick Traces: A Secret History of the Twentieth Century. 20th annot. ed. 2009. (Illus.). 496p. pap. 26.50 *(978-0-674-03480-8(5)*, Belknap Pr.) Harvard Univ. Pr.

Meffre, Liliane & Salazar-Ferrer, Olivier, eds. Carl Einstein et Benjamin Fondane: Avant-gardes et émigration dans le Paris des Années 1920-1930. 2008. (Comparatisme et Société / Comparatism & Society Ser.). (FRE & GER., Illus.). 224p. pap. 52.95 *(978-90-5201-445-6(0))* PIE - Peter Lang BEL. Dist: Lang, Peter.

Merewether, Charles & Hiro, Rika Iezumi, eds. Art, Anti-Art, Non-Art: Experimentations in the Public Sphere in Postwar Japan, 1950-1970. 2007. (ENG., Illus.). 158p. 45.00 *(978-0-89236-866-2(7))* Oxford Univ. Pr., Inc.

Mertins, Detlef & Jennings, Michael William. G: An Avant-Garde Journal of Art, Architecture, Design, & Film, 1923-1926. 2010. (ENG.). 280p. 40.00 *(978-1-60606-039-1(2))* Getty Pubns.

Miller, Tyrus. Singular Examples: Artistic Politics & the Neo-Avant-Garde. 2009. (Avant-Garde & Modernism Studies). (ENG.). 270p. pap. 34.95 *(978-0-8101-2512-4(9))*; (Illus.). 69.95 *(978-0-8101-2511-7(0))* Northwestern Univ. Pr.

Mitter, Partha. The Triumph of Modernism: India's Artists & the Avant-Garde, 1922-1947. 2007. (ENG., Illus.). 256p. pap. 45.00 *(978-1-86189-318-5(3))* Reaktion Bks., Ltd. GBR. Dist: Chicago Distribution Ctr.

Montilla, Patricia M. Parody, the Avant-Garde, & the Poetics of Subversion in Oliverio Girondo. 2007. (Latin America: Interdisciplinary Studies). (Illus.). 168p. (C). 61.95 *(978-0-8204-7897-5(0))* Lang, Peter Publishing, Inc.

Morris, Catherine, ed. 9 Evenings Reconsidered: Art, Theatre, & Engineering 1966, 1 vol. 2006. (ENG., Illus.). 88p. per. 25.00 *(978-0-938437-69-7(0))* Massachusetts Institute of Technology, List Visual Arts Ctr.

Nel, Philip. The Avant-Garde & American Postmodernity: Small Incisive Shocks. 2009. (ENG.). 265p. pap. 25.00 *(978-1-60473-252-8(0))* Univ. Pr. of Mississippi.

Novero, Cecilia. Antidiets of the Avant-Garde: From Futurist Cooking to Eat Art. 2010. (ENG., Illus.). 368p. 82.50 *(978-0-8166-4600-5(7))*; pap. 27.50 *(978-0-8166-4601-2(5))* Univ. of Minnesota Pr.

Parcerisas, Pila, ed. Viennese Actionism. 2008. 440p. pap. *(978-84-96954-44-1(7))* Actar Birkhauser Distribution.

Pare, Richard. The Lost Vanguard: Russian Modernist Architecture, 1922-1932. 2007. (ENG., Illus.). 348p. 85.00 *(978-1-58093-185-4(5))* Monacelli Pr., Inc.

Parton, Anthony. Goncharova: The Art & Design of Natalia Goncharova. 2010. (ENG., Illus.). 520p. *(978-1-85149-605-1(X)*, Antique Collectors Club Dist) Antique Collectors' Club.

Pearlman, Ellen. Nothing & Everything: The Influence of Buddhism on the American Avant-Garde, 1942 - 1962. 2012. (ENG., Illus.). 264p. pap. 21.95 ***(978-1-58394-363-2(3))*** North Atlantic Bks.

Perchuk, Andrew & Singh, Rani, eds. Harry Smith: The Avant-Garde in the American Vernacular. 2010. (Issues & Debates Ser.). (ENG., Illus.). 296p. pap. 35.00 *(978-0-89236-735-1(0))* Oxford Univ. Pr., Inc.

Petersen, Stephen. Space-Age Aesthetics: Lucio Fontana, Yves Klein, & the Postwar European Avant-Garde. 2009. (Refiguring Modernism Ser.). (ENG.). 320p. pap. 75.00 *(978-0-271-03342-6(8))* Pennsylvania State Univ. Pr.

Petrova, E. A. & Petrova, Yevgenia, eds. Abstraction in Russia, 2 vols. 2006. (ENG., Illus.). pap. 160.00 *(978-3-935298-50-6(1)*, Palace Editions) Mandala Publishing.

Piotrowski, Piotr. In the Shadow of Yalta: Art & the Avant-garde in Eastern Europe, 1945-1989. 2011. (Illus.). 488p. pap. 30.00 *(978-1-86189-863-0(0))* Reaktion Bks., Ltd. GBR. Dist: Chicago Distribution Ctr.

—In the Shadow of Yalta: Art & the Avant-Garde in Eastern Europe, 1945-1989. Piotrowski, Piotr, tr. from POL. 2009. (ENG., Illus.). 498p. 55.00 *(978-1-86189-438-0(4))* Reaktion Bks., Ltd. GBR. Dist: Chicago Distribution Ctr.

Platzer, Monika. Wiener Kinetismus: eine bewegte ModerneViennese Kineticism: Modernism in Motion: Eine Bewegte Moderne Viennese Kineticism: Modernism in Motion. Bast, Gerald, ed. 2011. (ENG.). 256p. 69.95 *(978-3-211-99143-5(3))* Springer Wien AUT. Dist: Actar Birkhauser Distribution.

Poggi, Christine. Inventing Futurism: The Art & Politics of Artificial Optimism. 2008. (ENG., Illus.). 392p. (C). 46.95 *(978-0-691-13370-6(0))* Princeton Univ. Pr.

Rabaté, Jean-Michel. Given: 1' Art 2' Crime: Modernity, Murder & Mass Culture. 2007. (ENG.). 228p. 67.50 *(978-1-84519-111-5(0))* Sussex Academic Pr. GBR. Dist: International Specialized Bk. Services.

—Given 1-Degree Art 2-Degrees Crime: Modernity, Murder & Mass Culture. 2007. (ENG.). 228p. pap. 29.95 *(978-1-84519-112-2(9))* Sussex Academic Pr. GBR. Dist: International Specialized Bk. Services.

Rabinow, Rebecca A., et al, eds. Cezanne to Picasso: Ambroise Vollard, Patron of the Avant-Garde. 2006. (Metropolitan Museum of Art Publications). (ENG., Illus.). 464p. 65.00 *(978-0-300-11779-0(5))* Yale Univ. Pr.

Rashkin, Elissa. Stridentist Movement in Mexico: The Avant-Garde & Cultural Change in the 1920s. 2011. (ENG.). 288p. pap. 32.95 *(978-0-7391-3157-2(5))* Lexington Bks.

Rashkin, Elissa J. Stridentist Movement in Mexico: The Avant-Garde & Cultural Change in the 1920s. 2009. (ENG., Illus.). 278p. 78.99 *(978-0-7391-3156-5(7))* Lexington Bks.

Reviakin, Sergei. The Russian Experiment Continues. 2010. 88p. pap. *(978-3-8383-7925-8(X))* Lambert Academic Publishing.

Ronduda, Lukasz & Zeyfang, Florian, eds. 1,2,3... Avant-Gardes: Film/Art between Experiment & Archive. 2007. (ENG & GER., Illus.). 224p. pap. 29.95 *(978-1-933128-24-5(0))* Sternberg Pr.

Saletnik, Jeffrey & Schuldenfrei, Robin, eds. Bauhaus Construct: Fashioning Identity, Discourse & Modernism. 2009. (ENG., Illus.). 288p. (C). 165.00 *(978-0-415-77835-0(2))*; pap. 49.95 *(978-0-415-77836-7(0))* Routledge.

Sandler, Irving. From Avant-Garde to Pluralism: An on-the-Spot History. 2008. 292p. 30.00 *(978-1-889097-68-8(3))* Hard Pr. Editions.

—A Sweeper-Up after Artists: A Memoir. 2009. (ENG.). 382p. pap. 18.95 *(978-0-500-28767-5(8))* Thames & Hudson.

Sanouillet, Michel & Sanouillet, M. Dada in Paris. Ganguly, Sharmila, tr. from FRE. rev. ed. 2009. (ENG.). 720p. (gr. 17). 39.95 *(978-0-262-01303-1(7))* MIT Pr.

Sant, Toni. Franklin Furnace & the Spirit of the Avant-Garde: A History of the Future. 2011. (ENG., Illus.). 184p. pap. 25.00 *(978-1-84150-371-4(1))* Intellect, Ltd. GBR. Dist: Chicago Distribution Ctr.

Schammah Gesser, Silvina. Madrid's Forgotten Avante-Garde: Between Essentialism & Modernity. 2012. (ENG.). 240p. 74.95 *(978-1-84519-384-3(9))* Sussex Academic Pr. GBR. Dist: International Specialized Bk. Services.

Scholz, Dieter. Pinsel & Dolch: Anarchistische Ideen in Kunst & Kunsttheorie 1840-1920. (GER., Illus.). 477p. *(978-3-496-01199-6(8))* Reimer, Dietrich.

Schramm, Helmar, et al. Spuren der Avantgarde: Theatrum Anatomicum: Frühe Neuzeit und Moderne Im Kulturvergleich. 2011. (GER., Illus.). 591p. 168.00 ***(978-3-11-024578-3(7))*** De Gruyter, Walter Inc.

Schwartz, Jorge. Las Vanguardias Latinoamericanas: Textos Programáticos y Críticos. 2006. (Tierra Firme Ser.). (SPA., Illus.). 748p. pap. 39.99 *(978-968-16-5621-8(0))* Fondo de Cultura Economica USA.

Selby. Art & Text. Monem, Nadine, ed. 2009. (ENG., Illus.). 288p. 45.00 *(978-1-906155-65-0(8))* Black Dog Publishing Ltd. GBR. Dist: Perseus Distribution.

Sell, Mike. Avant-Garde Performance & the Limits of Criticism: Approaching the Living Theatre, Happenings/Fluxus, & the Black Arts Movement. 2008. (Theater: Theory/Text/Performance Ser.). (ENG., Illus.). 336p. pap. 29.95 *(978-0-472-03307-2(7))* Univ. of Michigan Pr.

Silverman, Renée M., ed. The Popular Avant-Garde. 2010. (Illus.). 324p. 88.00 *(978-90-420-3160-9(3))* Rodopi.

Sonn, Richard David. Sex, Violence, & the Avant-Garde: Anarchism in Interwar France. 2010. 232p. 65.00 *(978-0-271-03663-2(X))* Pennsylvania State Univ. Pr.

Soto, Michael. The Modernist Nation: Generation, Renaissance, & Twentieth-Century American Literature. 2007. (ENG.). 256p. per. 24.95 *(978-0-8173-5467-1(0))* Univ. of Alabama Pr.

Specht, Benjamin. Physik als Kunst: Die Poetisierung der Elektrizität Um 1800. 2010. (Studien zur deutschen Literatur Ser.).Tr. of Physics as Art. the Poeticisation of Electricity Around 1800. (GER., Illus.). X, 448p. ***(978-3-484-18193-9(1))*** Verlag Max Niemeyer.

Spira, Andrew. The Avant-Garde Icon: Russian Avant-Garde Art & the Icon Painting Tradition. 2008. (Illus.). 224p. 100.00 *(978-0-85331-975-7(8),* Lund Humphries Pubs.) Ashgate Publishing, Ltd. GBR. Dist: Ashgate Publishing Co.

Sternstein, Malynne M. The Will to Chance: Necessity & Arbitrariness in the Czech Avant-Garde from Poetism to Surrealism. 2007. (ENG.). 226p. pap. *(978-0-89357-323-2(X))* Slavica Pubs.

Tang, Xiaobing. Origins of the Chinese Avant-Garde: The Modern Woodcut Movement. 2007. (Illus.). 300p. 65.00 *(978-0-520-24909-7(7))* Univ. of California Pr.

Terraroli, Valerio, ed. The Avant-Garde Movements 1900-1919, 5 vols. 2006. (Art of the Twentieth Century Ser.). (ENG., Illus.). 456p. 60.00 *(978-88-7624-504-3(5))* Skira Editore ITA. Dist: Random Hse., Inc.

Tiampo, Ming. Gutai: Decentering Modernism. 2011. (ENG., Illus.). 264p. 99.00 *(978-0-226-80165-0(9));* pap. 39.00 *(978-0-226-80166-7(7))* Univ. of Chicago Pr.

Touchon, Cecil. Natural Born Fluxus - Childhood Event Scores by Fluxus Artists. 2009. 279p. pap. 24.51 *(978-0-578-00333-7(3))* Ontological Museum Pubns.

Tupitsyn, Margarita, ed. Rodchenko & Popova: Defining Constructivism. 2009. (ENG., Illus.). 192p. pap. 39.95 *(978-1-85437-796-8(5))* Tate Publishing, Ltd. GBR. Dist: Hachette Bk. Group.

Tupitsyn, Victor. The Museological Unconscious. 2009. (ENG., Illus.). 352p. (gr. 17). 34.95 *(978-0-262-20173-5(9))* MIT Pr.

Tupitsyn, Victor. The Museological Unconscious: Communal (Post)Modernism in Russia. 2012. (ENG., Illus.). 352p. (gr. 17). pap. 17.95 *(978-0-262-51751-5(5))* MIT Pr.

van Crevel, Maghiel. Chinese Poetry in Times of Mind, Mayhem & Money. 2011. 518p. pap. *(978-90-04-20563-5(2))* BRILL.

Van Lieshout, Atelier, illus. Atelier Van Lieshout, 1 vol. 2007. (ENG.). 272p. pap. 55.00 *(978-90-5662-482-8(2))* NAi Uitgevers / Publishers Stichting NLD. Dist: D.A.P./Distributed Art Pubs.

Weber, Nicholas Fox. The Bauhaus Group: Six Masters of Modernism. 2009. (ENG., Illus.). 544p. 40.00 *(978-0-307-26836-5(5),* Knopf) Knopf Doubleday Publishing Group.

Weissweiler, Lilli. Futuristen Auf Europa-Tournee: Zur Vorgeschichte, Konzeption und Rezeption der Ausstellungen Futuristischer Malerei (1911-1913) 2009. (Illus.). 287p. pap. *(978-3-8376-1205-9(8))* Transcript Verlag.

Williams, Raymond. Politics of Modernism: Against the New Conformists. 2007. (Radical Thinkers Ser.: Vol. 23). (ENG.). 208p. per. 12.95 *(978-1-84467-580-7(7),* 844580) Verso Bks. GBR. Dist: Norton, W. W. & Co., Inc.

Witkovsky, Matthew. Avant-Garde Art in Everyday Life: Early Twentieth-Century European Modernism. 2011. (ENG., Illus.). 160p. 50.00 *(978-0-300-16609-5(5))* Art Institute of Chicago.

Zanetta, Maria Alejandra. La Otra Cara de la Vanguardia: Estudio Comparativo de la Obra Artistica de Maruja Mallo, Angeles Santos y Remedios Varo. 2006. (ENG & SPA., Illus.). 280p. 109.95 *(978-0-7734-5721-8(6))* Mellen, Edwin Pr., The.

Zeller, Christoph. A'sthetik des Authentischen: Literatur und Kunst Um 1970. 2010. (Spectrum Literaturwissenschaft / spectrum Literature Ser.).Tr. of Aesthetics of the Authentic. (GER., Illus.). IX, 333p. 140.00 *(978-3-11-022720-8(7))* De Gruyter, Walter Inc.

AVANT-GARDE (MUSIC)

Adlington, Robert. Sound Commitments: Avant-Garde Music & the Sixties. 2009. (ENG., Illus.). 336p. 99.00 *(978-0-19-533664-1(X))* Oxford Univ. Pr., Inc.

—Sound Commitments: Avant-Garde Music & the Sixties. Adlington, Robert, ed. 2009. (ENG., Illus.). 336p. pap. 29.95 *(978-0-19-533665-8(8))* Oxford Univ. Pr., Inc.

Austin, Larry, et al, eds. Source: Music of the Avant-Garde, 1966-1973. 2011. (ENG., Illus.). 440p. pap. 34.95 *(978-0-520-26745-9(1));* 400p. 70.00 *(978-0-520-25748-1(0))* Univ. of California Pr.

Bernstein, David W., ed. The San Francisco Tape Music Center: 1960s Counterculture & the Avant-Garde. 2008. (Illus.). 286p. 70.00 *(978-0-520-24892-2(9));* pap. 31.95 *(978-0-520-25617-0(4))* Univ. of California Pr.

Byrne, David, et al, texts. New York Noise: Art & Music from the New York Underground 1978-88, 1 vol. 2007. (ENG., Illus.). 203p. pap., pap. 39.95 *(978-0-9554817-0-3(8))* Soul Jazz Records GBR. Dist: D.A.P./Distributed Art Pubs.

Cohen, Brigid. Stefan Wolpe & the Avant-Garde Diaspora. 2012. (New Perspectives in Music History & Criticism Ser.). (ENG., Illus.). 376p. 99.00 *(978-1-107-00300-2(8))* Cambridge Univ. Pr.

Demers, Joanna Teresa. Listening Through the Noise: The Aesthetics of Experimental Electronic Music. 2010. (ENG.). 248p. pap. 24.95 *(978-0-19-538766-7(X))* Oxford Univ. Pr., Inc.

Haskins, Rob. Anarchic Societies of Sounds. 2009. 280p. pap. *(978-3-639-13209-0(2))* VDM Verlag Dr. Mueller e.K.

Hicks, Michael & Asplund, Christian. Christian Wolff. 2012. (American Composers Ser.). (ENG.). 144p. 80.00 *(978-0-252-03706-1(5))* Univ. of Illinois Pr.

Huckvale, David. Hammer Film Scores & the Musical Avant-Garde. 2008. (ENG., Illus.). 235p. pap. 39.95 *(978-0-7864-3456-5(2))* McFarland & Co., Inc. Pubs.

Joseph, Branden W. Beyond the Dream Syndicate - Tony Conrad & the Arts after Cage. 2011. (ENG., Illus.). 480p. (gr. 17). pap. 22.95 *(978-1-890951-87-0(0))* Zone Bks.

Joseph, Branden Wayne. Beyond the Dream Syndicate: Tony Conrad & the Arts after Cage. 2008. (ENG., Illus.). 480p. (gr. 17). 34.95 *(978-1-890951-86-3(2))* Zone Bks.

Jurging, Stefan. Die Tradition des Traditionsbruches: John Cages Amerikanische Asthetik. (Beitrage Aus Anglistik und Amerikanistik Ser.: Vol. 11). (GER.). 201 S.p. 30.95 *(978-3-631-39446-5(2))* Lang, Peter Publishing, Inc.

Kelly, Caleb & Kelly, C. Cracked Media: The Sound of Malfunction. 2009. (ENG., Illus.). 400p. (gr. 17). 26.95 *(978-0-262-01314-7(2))* MIT Pr.

Kutschke, Beate. Musikkulturen in der Revolte: Studien zu Rock, Avantgarde und Klassik im Umfeld von 1968. 2008. (ENG & GER., Illus.). 249p. (C). pap. 74.00 *(978-3-515-09085-8(1))* Steiner, Franz Verlag Wiesbaden GmbH DEU. Dist: Brown, David Bk. Co., The.

Lawrence, Tim. Hold on to Your Dreams: Arthur Russell & the Downtown Music Scene, 1973-1992. 2009. (ENG., Illus.). 448p. 94.95 *(978-0-8223-4466-7(1));* pap. 25.95 *(978-0-8223-4485-8(8))* Duke Univ. Pr.

Maconie, Robin. Avant Garde: An American Odyssey from Gertrude Stein to Pierre Boulez. 2012. (ENG.). 340p. (gr. 17). 75.00 *(978-0-8108-8312-3(0))* Scarecrow Pr., Inc.

Moore, Thurston & Coley, Byron. No Wave: Post-Punk - Underground - New York, 1976-1980. 2008. (ENG., Illus.). 144p. 27.50 *(978-0-8109-9543-7(3),* Abrams Image) Abrams.

Piekut, Benjamin. Experimentalism Otherwise: The New York Avant-Garde & Its Limits. 2011. (California Studies in 20th-Century Music Ser.). (ENG., Illus.). 296p. 65.00 *(978-0-520-26850-0(4));* pap. 24.95 *(978-0-520-26851-7(2))* Univ. of California Pr.

Rogers, Holly. Visualising Music. 2010. 248p. pap. *(978-3-8383-5056-1(1))* Lambert Academic Publishing.

Saunders, James. The Ashgate Research Companion to Experimental Music. 2009. (Illus.). 412p. 149.95 *(978-0-7546-6282-2(9))* Ashgate Publishing Co.

Schechner, Richard. Decline & Fall of the Avant Garde. 2008. 120.00 *(978-0-415-34367-1(4))* Routledge.

AVANT-GARDE FICTION

see Experimental Fiction

AVANT-GARDE FILMS

see Experimental Films

AVANT-GARDE LITERATURE

see Literature, Experimental

AVANTI AUTOMOBILE

Hull, John. Avanti: Studebaker & Beyond. 2011. (ENG., Illus.). 96p. pap. 29.95 *(978-1-58388-273-3(1),* 1583882731) Iconografix, Inc.

AVARICE

Buchanan, Patrick J. Day of Reckoning: How Hubris, Ideology, & Greed are Tearing America Apart. 2009. (ENG.). 304p. pap. 14.95 *(978-0-312-53938-2(X),* St. Martin's Griffin) St. Martin's Pr.

Folbre, Nancy. Greed Lust & Gender: A History of Economic Ideas. 2010. (ENG.). 272p. 34.95 *(978-0-19-923842-2(1))* Oxford Univ. Pr., Inc.

Gasparino, Charles. The Sellout: How Three Decades of Wall Street Greed & Government Mismanagement Destroyed the Global Financial System. 2010. (ENG.). 576p. pap. 16.99 *(978-0-06-169717-3(6),* Harper Paperbacks) HarperCollins Pubs.

Girling, Richard. Greed. 2009. (ENG.). 368p. pap. 24.95 *(978-0-385-61328-6(8))* Transworld Publishers Ltd. GBR. Dist: Independent Pubs. Group.

jestrow, robert. The avaricious Personality. 2008. 172p. pap. 17.50 *(978-1-4357-1430-4(X))* Lulu Enterprises Inc.

Keener, John Christian. Post-Oak Circuit by a Member of the Red River Conference Ed by Thos O Summers, D D. 2006. 288p. per. 23.99 *(978-1-4255-2580-4(6))* MPublishing.

Levi, Steven C. The Clara Nevada: Gold, Greed, Murder & Alaska's Inside Passage. 2011. (Illus.). 128p. pap. 19.99 *(978-1-60949-288-5(9))* History Pr., The.

Nowak, Mark. Shut Up, Shut Down. 2008. (ENG., Illus.). 161p. pap. 16.00 *(978-1-56689-163-9(9))* Coffee Hse. Pr.

Quinn, Kay. How Much Does God Co$T? 2009. 120p. 21.49 *(978-1-4490-3998-1(7));* pap. 14.95 *(978-1-4490-3997-4(9))* AuthorHouse.

Robinson, Matthew, et al. Greed Is Good: Maximization & Elite Deviance in America. 2008. (ENG.). 150p. 75.00 *(978-0-7425-6070-3(8));* pap. 26.95 *(978-0-7425-6071-0(6))* Rowman & Littlefield Publishers, Inc.

Rosner, Brian S. Greed as Idolatry: The Origin & Meaning of a Pauline Metaphor. 2007. 214p. per. 22.00 *(978-0-8028-3374-7(8))* Eerdmans, William B. Publishing Co.

Sarna, David E. Y. History of Greed: Financial Fraud from Tulip Mania to Bernie Madoff. 2010. (ENG.). 398p. 29.95 *(978-0-470-60180-8(9),* Wiley) Wiley, John & Sons, Inc.

Slover, Ron. The Buffet Syndrome: A Wakeup Call for America! 2007. (Illus.). 136p. per. 13.99 *(978-1-891774-00-3(X))* Path Publishing, Inc.

Toynbee, Polly & Walker, David. Unjust Rewards: Ending the Greed that Is Bankrupting Britain. 2008. (ENG.). 256p. pap. 15.95 *(978-1-84708-096-7(0))* Granta Bks. GBR. Dist: Independent Pubs. Group.

AVATARS (COMPUTER GRAPHICS)

Adrian, Angela. Law & Order in Virtual Worlds: Exploring Avatars, Their Ownership & Rights. 2010. 356p. 180.00 *(978-1-61520-795-4(3))* IGI Global.

Albion, Acedia. Avatar Fashion Volume VII. 2009. 48p. pap. 21.50 *(978-0-615-15343-8(7))* Studio SFO.

Ar-Raqib, Akil & Roche, Edward M. Virtual Worlds Real Terrorism. 2010. 355p. 73.95 *(978-0-578-03222-1(8))* Barraclough Ltd.

Cardy, Andrew. Me, My Virtual-Self & I. 2009. 56p. pap. *(978-3-639-17363-5(5))* VDM Verlag Dr. Mueller e.K.

Heaton, Jeff. Introduction to Textures, Animation Audio & Sculpting in Second Life. 2007. (Illus.). 108p. per. 19.99 *(978-1-60439-002-5(6))* Heaton Research, Inc.

Ludlow, Peter & Wallace, Mark. The Second Life Herald: The Virtual Tabloid That Witnessed the Dawn of the Metaverse. 2007. (ENG., Illus.). 312p. (gr. 17). 29.95 *(978-0-262-12294-8(4))* MIT Pr.

Ludlow, Peter, et al. The Second Life Herald: The Virtual Tabloid that Witnessed the Dawn of the Metaverse. 2009. (ENG., Illus.). 312p. (gr. 17). pap. 15.95 *(978-0-262-51322-7(6))* MIT Pr.

Meadows, Mark Stephen. I, Avatar: The Culture & Consequences of Having a Second Life. 2007. (ENG., Illus.). 144p. per. 34.99 *(978-0-321-53339-5(9))* New Riders Publishing.

Morrison, Connie. Who Do They Think They Are? Teenage Girls & Their Avatars in Spaces of Social Online Communication. 2009. (New Literacies & Digital Epistemologies Ser.). (Illus.). 246p. pap. 32.95 *(978-1-4331-0552-4(7))* Lang, Peter Publishing, Inc.

Morrison, Rodger. Archetypal Symbols, Avatars, & Trust. 2009. 176p. pap. *(978-3-639-19300-8(8))* VDM Verlag Dr. Mueller e.K.

Online Virtual Worlds: Applications & Avatars in a User-Generated Medium: Hearing Before the Subcommittee on Telecommunications & the Internet of the Committee on Energy & Commerce, House of Representatives, One Hundred Tenth Congress, Second Session, April 1, 2008. 2008. (Illus.). v, 82p. *(978-0-16-084502-4(5),* 552-070-40025-7) United States Government Printing Office.

Percival, Sean. Second Life In-World Travel Guide. 2007. (ENG., Illus.). 216p. per. 26.99 *(978-0-7897-3730-4(2))* Que.

Schroeder, Ralph & Axelsson, Ann-Sofie, eds. Avatars at Work & Play: Collaboration & Interaction in Shared Virtual Environments. 2010. (Computer Supported Cooperative Work Ser.). xv, 277p. pap. 149.00 *(978-90-481-6989-4(5),* 9048169895) Springer.

Waggoner, Zach. My Avatar, My Self: Identity in Video Role-Playing Games. 2009. (ENG., Illus.). 207p. pap. 35.00 *(978-0-7864-4109-9(7))* McFarland & Co., Inc. Pubs.

AVATARS (RELIGION)

see also Incarnation

Armstrong, Jeffrey. Spiritual Teachings of the Avatar: Ancient Wisdom for a New World. 2010. (ENG., Illus.). 240p. 22.00 *(978-1-58270-281-0(0),* Beyond Words/Atria Bks.) Atria Bks.

—Spiritual Teachings of the Avatar: Ancient Wisdom for a New World. 2010. pap. *(978-1-58270-282-7(9))* Beyond Words Publishing, Inc.

AVE MARIA (MUSIC)

Murray, Paul. The Hail Mary: On the Threshold of Grace. 2010. 78p. *(978-0-7648-1962-9(3))* Liguori Pubns.

AVEBURY (ENGLAND)

Gillings, Mark, et al. Landscape of the Megaliths: Excavation & Fieldwork on the Avebury Monuments 1997-2003. 2010. (ENG., Illus.). 416p. (C). pap. 70.00 *(978-1-84217-971-0(3))* Oxbow Bks., Ltd. GBR. Dist: Brown, David Bk. Co., The.

Mann, Nicholas. Avebury & the Cosmos of our Ancestors. 2011. (ENG., Illus.). 369p. pap. 24.95 *(978-1-84694-680-6(8))* Hunt, John Publishing Ltd. GBR. Dist: National Bk. Network.

AVEDON, RICHARD, 1923-2004

Avedon, Richard. Avedons Kennedys. 40.00 *(978-1-59258-031-6(9))* Hylas Publishing.

Avedon, Richard, photos by. Avedon Fashion 1944-2000. 2009. (ENG., Illus.). 372p. 100.00 *(978-0-8109-8389-2(3))* Abrams.

—Richard Avedon: Photographs 1946-2004, 1 vol. 2007. (ENG., Illus.). 192p. 70.00 *(978-87-91607-49-3(3))* Louisana DNK. Dist: D.A.P./Distributed Art Pubs.

Stevens, Norma, et al. Performance. 2008. (ENG., Illus.). 304p. 100.00 *(978-0-8109-7268-9(3))* Abrams.

AVERAGE

American Society of Civil Engineers Staff, contrib. by. Standard Guideline for the Geostatistical Estimation & Block-Averaging of Homogeneous & Isotropic Saturated Hydraulic Conductivity: Asce/ewri 54-10. 2010. (ENG.). 30p. pap. 59.00 *(978-0-7844-1092-9(5))* American Society of Civil Engineers.

Hudson, N. Geoffrey & Harvey, Michael. The York-Antwerp Rules: The Principles & Practice of General Average Adjustment. 3rd rev. ed. 2010. (Illus.). 459p. 486.00 *(978-1-84311-886-2(6))* Informa Professional GBR. Dist: International Specialized Bk. Services.

Kagan, R. L. Averaging of Meteorological Fields. Gandin, Lev S. & Smith, Thomas M., eds. 2010. (Atmospheric & Oceanographic Sciences Library). 296p. pap. 189.00 *(978-90-481-4936-0(3),* 9048149363) Springer.

MacCullough, Deborah. A Study of Experts Understanding of Arithmetic Mean. 2008. 216p. pap. *(978-3-639-09710-8(6))* VDM Verlag Dr. Mueller e.K.

Thorndike, Edward Lee. An Introduction to the Theory of Mental & Social Measurements. 2009. 296p. 24.99 *(978-1-103-85458-5(5));* pap. 18.99 *(978-1-103-85453-0(4))* BiblioBazaar.

—An Introduction to the Theory of Mental & Social Measurements. Wozniak, Robert H., ed. (Classics in Psychology Ser.). (Illus.). 228p. *(978-1-85506-689-2(0),* Burns & Oates) Continuum International Publishing Group, Ltd.

AVERROES, 1126-1198

Belo, Catarina. Chance & Determinism in Avicenna & Averroes. 2007. 252p. *(978-90-04-15587-9(2))* BRILL.

Bonmariage, C., et al, eds. Lulle et la Condamnation De 1277: La Declaration de Raymond ecrite sous forme de Dialogue. 2006. (Philosophes Medievaux Ser.). (ENG.). 196p. (C). pap. 109.00 *(978-90-429-1592-3(7))* Peeters Pubs. & Booksellers BEL. Dist: Brown, David Bk. Co., The.

Fakhry, Majid. Islamic Occasionalism: And Its Critique by Averroes & Aquinas. 2007. 224p. 165.00 *(978-0-415-44873-4(5))* Routledge.

Nielsen, Lauge O., et al. Thomas Wylton: On the Intellectual Soul. 2011. (ENG & LAT.). 240p. 75.00 *(978-0-19-726461-4(1))* Oxford Univ. Pr., Inc.

Sonnebom, Liz. Averroes (Ibn Rushd) Muslim Scholar, Philosopher, & Physician of the Twelfth Century. 2009. (Great Muslim Philosophers & Scientists of the Middle Ages Ser.). 112p. (gr. 6-6). 66.50 *(978-1-61513-179-2(5),* Rosen Central) Rosen Publishing Group, Inc., The.

Wohlman, Avital. Al-Ghazali, Averroes & the Interpretation of the Qur'an: Common Sense & Philosophy in Islam. 2009. (Culture & Civilization in the Middle East Ser.). (ENG.). 130p. 110.00 *(978-0-415-55720-7(8))* Routledge.

Zanner, Markus. Konstruktionsmerkmale der Averroes-Rezeption: Ein Religionswissenschaftlicher Beitrag zur Rezeptionsgeschichte des islamischen Philosophen Ibn Ruschd. (Regensburger Studien zur Theologie Ser.: Vol. 61). (GER., Illus.). 181p. 28.95 *(978-3-631-36629-5(9))* Lang, Peter Publishing, Inc.

AVERY, MILTON, 1885-1965

Hobbs, Robert & Hobbs, Robert. Milton Avery. 2007. (ENG., Illus.). 264p. 85.00 *(978-0-933920-95-8(4))* Hudson Hills Pr. LLC.

Willers, Karl. Milton Avery & the End of Modernism. 2011. 80p. pap. 20.00 *(978-0-615-40181-2(3),* Suny Pr.) State Univ. of New York Pr.

AVESTA

Darmesteter, James. The Zend-Avesta. 2010. 392p. pap. 33.75 *(978-1-142-77712-9(8))* BiblioBazaar.

—The Zend-Avesta. 2009. 236p. pap. 31.82 *(978-1-150-17879-5(5))* General Bks. LLC.

Forrest, Satnam Mendoza. Witches, Whores, & Sorcerers: The Concept of Evil in Early Iran. 2011. (ENG.). 245p. 55.00 *(978-0-292-72687-1(2))* Univ. of Texas Pr.

Pirart, Eric & Tremblay, Xavier, eds. Zarathustra entre l'Inde et L'Iran: Etudes indo-iraniennes et indo-europeennes offertes a Jean Kellens a loccasion de son 65e Anniversaire. 2009. (Beitrage zur Iranistik Ser.). (ENG, FRE & GER., Illus.). 390p. (C). 187.00 *(978-3-89500-651-7(3))* Reichert, Ludwig Dr. DEU. Dist: Brown, David Bk. Co., The.

Remmer, Ulla. Frauennamen Im Rigveda und Im Avesta: Studien Zur Onomastik des ältesten Indischen und Iranischen. 2006. (Iranische Onomastik Ser.). (GER.). 288p. (C). pap. 89.00 *(978-3-7001-3737-5(0))* Austrian Academy of Sciences Press AUT. Dist: Brown, David Bk. Co., The.

Schuyler, Montgomery. Index Verborum of the Fragments of the "Avesta" (Columbia University, Indo-Iranian Ser.: No. 4). reprint ed. 31.50 *(978-0-404-50474-8(4))* AMS Pr., Inc.

AVESTAN LANGUAGE

Panaino, Antonio & Sadovski, Velizar. Disputationes Iranologicae Vindobonenses. 2007. (Veroffentlichungen zur Iranistik Ser.). (ITA & GER.). 108p. (C). pap. 41.00 *(978-3-7001-3963-8(2))* Austrian Academy of Sciences Press AUT. Dist: Brown, David Bk. Co., The.

Remmer, Ulla. Frauennamen Im Rigveda und Im Avesta: Studien Zur Onomastik des ältesten Indischen und Iranischen. 2006. (Iranische Onomastik Ser.). (GER.). 288p. (C). pap. 89.00 *(978-3-7001-3737-5(0))* Austrian Academy of Sciences Press AUT. Dist: Brown, David Bk. Co., The.

Sims-Williams, Nicholas. Bactrian Documents, Part II. 2007. (Studies in the Khalili Collections). 328p. (C). *(978-1-874780-90-8(0),* Khalili Collections) I. B. Tauris & Co., Ltd.

Sims-Williams, Nicholas & Sims-williams, Nicholas. Bactarian Documents 1. 2007. (Studies in the Khalili Collection). (ENG.). 256p. 65.00 *(978-1-874780-73-1(0),* Khalili Collections) I. B. Tauris & Co., Ltd. GBR. Dist: Macmillan.

West, Martin L. Old Avestan Syntax & Stylistics: With an edition of the Texts. 2011. (Abhandlungen der Akademie der Wissenschaften zu Göttingen. Neue Folge Ser.). XII, 184p. (ENG., Illus.). 210.00 *(978-3-11-218937-5(X));* (AVE & ENG.). 140.00 *(978-3-11-025308-5(9))* De Gruyter, Walter Inc.

AVIAN PESTS

see Bird Pests

AVIATION

see Aeronautics

AVIATION ACCIDENTS

see Aircraft Accidents

AVIATION ELECTRONICS

see Avionics

AVIATION FUELS

see Airplanes—Fuel

AVIATION GASOLINE

see Airplanes—Fuel

AVIATION INDUSTRY

see Aircraft Industry; Airlines

AVIATION INSURANCE

Fobe. Aviation Products & Insurance in the EU Legal Aspects Ins 2e Rev. 2010. 152.00 (978-90-411-2803-4(4)) Wolters Kluwer Law & Business.

Gowdy, Rex. Crashing Las Vegas: Memoirs of an Aircraft Crash Investigator in the Heyday of Las Vegas. 2007. 76p. per. 16.95 (978-1-4241-9541-1(1)) PublishAmerica, Inc.

Wells, Alexander T. & Chadbourne, Bruce D. Introduction to Aviation Insurance & Risk Management. 3rd ed. 2007. (Illus.). xi, 548p. (978-1-57524-274-3(5)) Krieger Publishing Co.

AVIATION LAW

see Aeronautics—Law and Legislation

AVIATION MECHANICS (PERSONS)

Crane, Dale. Aviation Maintenance Technician: Airframe: Volume 2: Systems. 3rd ed. 2007. (Aviation Maintenance Technician Ser.). (ENG., Illus.). 492p. pap. 49.95 (978-1-56027-549-7(9)) Aviation Supplies & Academics, Inc.

—Aviation Mechanic Handbook. 5th ed. 2006. (ENG., Illus.). 376p. spiral bd. 16.95 (978-1-56027-591-6(X)) Aviation Supplies & Academics, Inc.

Federal Aviation Administration. Far/amt 2012: Federal Aviation Regulations for Aviation Maintenance Technicians. 2011. (FAR/AIM Ser.). (ENG.). 925p. pap. 24.95 (978-1-56027-860-3(9)) Aviation Supplies & Academics, Inc.

Loschiavo, Vincent, compiled by. Avionics Technician General Radiotelephone Operators License & Radar Endorsement Study Guide. 2006. ring bd. (978-0-9791441-0-3(8)) Loschiavo, Vincent.

Rudman, Jack. Airframe & Powerplant Mechanics. (Occupational Competency Examination Ser.). 49.95 (978-0-8373-5752-2(7), OLE-2, Passbooks) National Learning Corp.

Tomter Pedersen, Peter. Make it Safe! 2008. 322p. pap. 57.50 (978-1-84799-454-7(7)) Lulu Enterprises Inc.

AVIATION MEDICINE

see also Anoxemia; Decompression Sickness; Flight—Physiological Aspects; Space Medicine

ASTNA. ASTNA Patient Transport: Principles & Practice. Holleran, Renee S., ed. 4th ed. 2009. (ENG., Illus.). 848p. 99.95 (978-0-323-05749-3(7), Mosby) Elsevier - Health Sciences Div.

Blazevic, Ivana. Effect of Homoeopathic Complex on Leg Oedema During Long Air Flights. 2010. 120p. pap. (978-3-8383-5806-2(6)) Lambert Academic Publishing.

Campbell, Patricia M. Manual of In-Flight Medical Care. 2nd ed. 2008. (Illus.). vii, 208p. 24.49 (978-0-7575-4978-6(0)); (978-0-7575-5376-9(1)) Kendall Hunt Publishing Co.

Civil Aviation Medical Institute Staff. Pilot Medical Handbook: Human Factors for Successful Flying. 2009. (ENG., Illus.). 100p. pap. 16.95 (978-1-56027-717-0(3)) Aviation Supplies & Academics, Inc.

Culkin, Jennifer. A Final Arc of Sky: A Memoir of Critical Care. (ENG.). 248p. 2010. pap. 16.00 (978-0-8070-7329-2(6)) 2009. 24.95 (978-0-8070-7285-1(0)) Beacon Pr.

Davis, Jeffrey R. Fundamentals of Aerospace Medicine. Davis, Jeffrey R. et al, eds. 4th rev. ed. 2008. (ENG., Illus.). 754p. 238.99 (978-0-7817-7466-6(7)) Lippincott Williams & Wilkins.

Hudson, Janice. Trauma Junkie: Memoirs of an Emergency Flight Nurse. 2nd enl. ed. 2010. (ENG., Illus.). 272p. pap. 19.95 (978-1-55407-614-7(5)) Firefly Bks., Ltd.

Martin, Terence & Glanfield, Mike. Aeromedical Transportation: A Clinical Guide. 2nd rev. ed. 2006. (Illus.). 312p. pap. 60.00 (978-0-7546-4148-3(1)) Ashgate Publishing Co.

Nicholson, Anthony. The Neurosciences & the Practice of Aviation Medicine. 2011. (Illus.). 524p. 170.00 **(978-0-7546-7292-0(1))** Ashgate Publishing Co.

Reinhart, Richard O. Basic Flight Physiology. 3rd rev. ed. 2007. (ENG., Illus.). 311p. (C). pap. 59.95 (978-0-07-149488-5(X), 007149488X) McGraw-Hill Professional Publishing.

World Health Organization. A Guide to Hygiene & Sanitation in Aviation. 3rd rev. ed. 2010. (Nonserial Publication Ser.). 71p. pap. 24.00 (978-92-4-154777-2(4)) World Health Organization.

AVIATION PSYCHOLOGY

see also Fear of Flying

Bor, Robert & Hubbard, Todd. Handbook of Aviation Mental Health: Psychological Implications for Air Transportation. 2006. (Illus.). 376p. 130.00 (978-0-7546-4371-5(9)) Ashgate Publishing Co.

Campbell, Patricia M. Manual of In-Flight Medical Care. 2nd ed. 2008. (Illus.). vii, 208p. (978-0-7575-5376-9(1)); 24.49 (978-0-7575-4978-6(0)) Kendall Hunt Publishing Co.

Harris, Don. Human Performance on the Flight Deck. 2011. (Illus.). 384p. 144.95 **(978-1-4094-2339-3(5))**; pap. 69.95 **(978-1-4094-2338-6(7))** Ashgate Publishing Co.

Langewiesche, William. Aloft. 2010. (Vintage Departures Ser.). (ENG.). 272p. pap. 15.00 (978-0-307-74148-6(6), Vintage) Knopf Doubleday Publishing Group.

Leonhardt, Jorg & Vogt, Joachim, eds. Critical Incident Stress Management in Aviation. 2006. (Illus.). 194p. 120.00 (978-0-7546-4738-6(2)) Ashgate Publishing Co.

MARTINUSSEN, Monica. Aviation Psychology & Human Factors. 2009. (ENG., Illus.). 240p. 92.95 (978-1-4398-0843-6(0), CRC Press) Taylor & Francis Group GBR. Dist: Taylor & Francis Group.

Olsen, W. Scott. Never Land: Adventures, Wonder, & One World Record in a Very Small Plane. 2010. (ENG., Illus.). 202p. 24.95 (978-0-8032-1750-8(1)) Univ. of Nebraska Pr.

Voogt, Alex De & D'Oliveira, Teresa C. Mechanisms in the Chain of Safety: Research & Operational Experiences in Aviation Psychology. 2012. (Illus.). 150p. 99.95 **(978-1-4094-1254-0(7))** Ashgate Publishing Co.

Wright State University Conferences and Events Staff, compiled by. International Symposium on Aviation Psychology 2007. 2007. 784p. pap. 118.00 (978-1-60423-304-9(4)) Curran Assocs., Inc.

AVIATION REGULATIONS

see Aeronautics—Law and Legislation

AVIATORS

see Air Pilots

AVICENNA, 980-1037

Avicenna. The Physics of the Healing: A Parallel English-Arabic, 2 vols. Davis, Morgan, ed. McGinnis, Jon, tr. from ARA. 2010. (Brigham Young University - Islamic Translation Ser.). (Illus.). 1168p. 49.95 (978-0-8425-2747-7(8), Maxwell, Neal A. Institute for Religious Scholarship) Brigham Young Univ.

Belo, Catarina. Chance & Determinism in Avicenna & Averroes. 2007. 252p. (978-90-04-15587-9(2)) BRILL.

Elkaisy-Friemuth, Maha. God & Humans in Islamic Thought: Abd Al-Jabbar, Ibn Sina & Al-Ghazali. (ENG.). 2011. 224p. pap. 39.95 **(978-0-415-66388-5(1))** 2006. 240p. 160.00 (978-0-415-40028-2(7)) Routledge.

Hasse, Dag Nikolaus & Bertolacci, Amos, eds. The Arabic, Hebrew & Latin Reception of Avicenna's Metaphysics. 2012. (Scientia Graeco-Arabica Ser.). (ENG., Illus.). VIII, 398p. (gr. 17). E-Book 210.00 **(978-3-11-173654-9(7))** De Gruyter, Walter Inc.

Khan, Aisha. Avicenna (Ibn Sina) Muslim Physician & Philosopher of the Eleventh Century. 2009. (Great Muslim Philosophers & Scientists of the Middle Ages Ser.). 112p. (gr. 6-6). 66.50 (978-1-61513-180-8(9), Rosen Central) Rosen Publishing Group, Inc., The.

Koutzarova, Tiana. Das Transzendentale Bei Ibn Sina: Zur Metaphysik Als Wissenschaft Erster Begriffs- und Urteilsprinzipien. 2009. (GER.). (978-90-04-17123-7(1)) BRILL.

McGinnis, Jon. Avicenna, 1 vol. 2010. (Mediev Thinkers Ser.). (Illus.). 320p. pap. 29.95 (978-0-19-533148-6(6)) Oxford Univ. Pr., Inc.

Paavilainen, Helena M. Medieval Pharmacotherapy — Continuity & Change: Case Studies from Ibn Sina & Some of His Late Medieval Commentators. 2009. xix, 795p. (978-90-04-17119-0(3)) BRILL.

Treiger, Alexander. Inspired Knowledge in Islamic Thought. 2011. (Culture & Civilization in the Middle East Ser.). (ENG., Illus.). 200p. (C). 125.00 (978-0-415-78307-1(0)) Routledge.

AVICULTURE

see also Birds—Breeding; Game Bird Culture; Ornamental Birds; Poultry

Butler, Arthur G. Foreign Finches in Captivity. 2010. 282p. pap. 49.95 (978-1-61646-011-2(3)) Coachwhip Pubns.

Duncan, Ian J. H. & Hawkins, Penny, eds. The Welfare of Domestic Fowl & Other Captive Birds. 2010. (Animal Welfare Ser.). (ENG., Illus.). xi, 298p. 199.00 (978-90-481-3649-0(0), 9048136490) Springer.

Glatz, Phil, et al, eds. The Welfare of Farmed Ratites. 2011. (Animal Welfare Ser.). (Illus.). xvii, 263p. 189.00 (978-3-642-19296-8(3), 3642192963) Springer.

Holland, Glenn S. Encyclopedia of Aviculture, Vol. 1. 2007. (Illus.). 832p. 100.00 (978-0-88839-460-6(8)) Hancock Hse. Pubs.

AVID MCXPRESS (COMPUTER PROGRAM)

see Avid Xpress (Computer Program)

AVID XPRESS (COMPUTER PROGRAM)

Kauffmann, Sam. Avid Editing: A Guide for Beginning & Intermediate Users. 4th ed. 2009. (ENG., Illus.). 408p. pap. 49.95 (978-0-240-81080-5(5), Focal Pr.) Elsevier Science & Technology Bks.

Kauffmann, Sam & Kennedy, Ashley. Avid Editing: A Guide for Beginning & Intermediate Users. 5th ed. 2012. (ENG.). 448p. (C). pap. 49.95 **(978-0-240-81856-6(3)**, Focal Pr.) Elsevier Science & Technology Bks.

Staten, Greg & Bayes, Steve. The Avid Handbook: Advanced Techniques, Strategies, & Survival Information for Avid Editing Systems. 5th ed. 2008. (ENG., Illus.). 368p. pap. 49.95 (978-0-240-81081-2(3), Focal Pr.) Elsevier Science & Technology Bks.

AVIGATION

see Navigation (Aeronautics)

AVIGNON (FRANCE)

Bonechi, Casa. Avignon: English Edition. 64p. pap. (978-88-7009-107-6(4)) Casa Editrice Bonechi.

Locken, E. Travel Journal Avignon. 2010. 192p. pap. 19.99 (978-0-557-34216-7(3)) Lulu Enterprises Inc.

Rollo-Koster, Joelle. The People of Curialavignon: A Critical Edition of the Liber Divisionis & the Matriculae of Notre Dame la Majonr. 2009. (Illus.). 468p. 129.95 (978-0-7734-4680-9(X)) Mellen, Edwin Pr., The.

AVILA (SPAIN)

Arsuaga, Ana Echevarria. City of the Three Mosques: Avila & Its Muslims in the Middle Ages. 2011. (ENG.). 168p. (C). 132.00 **(978-3-89500-829-0(X))** Reichert, Ludwig Dr. DEU. Dist: Brown, David Bk. Co., The.

Rees, Margaret A. The Spiritual Diaries of Doña María Vela Y Cueto Volume One: Libro de las Mercedes, 2 vols. 2007. (SPA., Illus.). 160p. (C). 109.95 (978-0-7734-5517-7(5)) Mellen, Edwin Pr., The.

AVIONICS

see also Airplanes—Electronic Equipment; Astrionics

American Society of Mechanical Engineers Staff, ed. Avionic Systems Design & Software. (Illus.). 106p. 83.00 (978-1-86058-045-1(9)) Professional Engineering Publishing GBR. Dist: SAE Intl.

Boulanger, Jean-Louis. Security of Computer Architectures. 2010. (Iste Ser.: 477). (ENG., Illus.). 512p. 95.00 (978-1-84821-197-1(X), Wiley-ISTE) Wiley, John & Sons, Inc.

Casos, David G. Unmanned Aircraft Systems: Strengths & Weaknesses. 2009. (Defense, Security & Strategies Ser.). 69.00 (978-1-60741-114-7(8)) Nova Science Pubs., Inc.

Collinson, R. P. G. Introduction to Avionics Systems. (Illus.). 2nd rev. ed. 2006. 504p. 169.00 (978-1-4020-7278-9(3), 1402072783) 3rd ed. 2011. (ENG., xvi, 525p. 89.95 (978-94-007-0707-8(X), 940070707X) Springer.

Cossement, Mark. Development of a Simulator for the Testing of Avionics Displays. 2009. 128p. pap. (978-3-639-20477-3(8)) VDM Verlag Dr. Mueller e.K.

Eismin, Thomas K. Aircraft: Electricity & Electronics. 5th ed. 2007. (ENG.). (C). pap., pap., pap. 133.33 (978-0-07-723152-1(X), 007723152X) McGraw-Hill Higher Education.

Federal Aviation Administration. Advanced Avionics Handbook: Faa-h-8083-6. 2009. (FAA Handbooks Ser.). (ENG.). 114p. pap. 19.95 (978-1-56027-758-3(0)) Aviation Supplies & Academics, Inc.

Federal Aviation Administration (U.S.), ed. Advanced Avionics Handbook. 2009. (ENG.). 100p. pap. 42.00 (978-0-16-083123-2(7), Federal Aviation Administration) United States Government Printing Office.

Federal Aviation Administration Staff. Advanced Avionics Handbook: Faa-h-8083-6. 2012. (ENG., Illus.). 128p. pap. 16.95 **(978-1-61608-533-9(9)**, 608533) Skyhorse Publishing Co., Inc.

Feher, Lambert E. Energy Efficient Microwave Systems: Materials Processing Technologies for Avionic, Mobility & Environmental Applications. 2009. (ENG., Illus.). xvi, 114p. 159.00 (978-3-540-92121-9(4)) Springer.

Ginger, Helen. Tech Careers: Avionics. 2009. (Tech Careers Ser.). 111p. pap. 14.95 (978-1-934302-47-7(3)) Texas State Technical College Publishing.

Helfrick, Albert D. Principles of Avionics - 4th Edition. 4th exp. ed. 2007. per. 89.00 (978-1-885544-26-1(X)) Avionics Communications, Inc.

Hilderman, Vance & Baghi, Tony. Avionics Certification: A complete Guide to DO-178 (Software), DO-254 (Hardware) 2007. (ENG., Illus.). 244p. per. 95.00 (978-1-885544-25-4(1)) Avionics Communications, Inc.

Institute of Electrical and Electronics Engineers Staff, contrib. by. 2007 IEEE Avionics, Fiber-Optics & Photonics Technology Conference. 2007. pap. 198.00 (978-1-4244-0936-5(5), 07EX1663) IEEE.

Jane's Avionics: In-Depth Assessment of Airborne Electronic Equipment. 510.00 (978-0-7106-2311-9(9)) Jane's Information Group, Inc.

Janzen, Ryan E. Winged Messengers. 2008. 56p. pap. (978-3-639-04406-5(1)) VDM Verlag Dr. Mueller e.K.

McShea, Robert. Test & Evaluation of Aircraft Avionics & Weapons Systems. 2010. (ENG., Illus.). 700p. 149.00 (978-1-891121-90-6(1)) SciTech Publishing, Inc.

McShea, Robert E. Test & Evaluation of Aircraft Avionics & Weapon Systems. 2010. 124.95 (978-1-60086-760-6(X)) SciTech Publishing, Inc.

Nagabhushana, S. & Sudha, L. K. Aircraft Instrumentation & Systems. 2010. (Illus.). 410p. (C). (978-93-80578-35-4(0)) I.K. International Publishing House Pvt. Ltd.

R, Spitzer Cary. Digital Avionics Handbook, 2 vols. 2nd rev. ed. 2006. (ENG., Illus.). 680p. 179.95 (978-0-8493-5008-5(5), CRC Press) Taylor & Francis Group GBR. Dist: Taylor & Francis Group.

Reeves-Hardcastle. Avionics for Aerospace Engineers. Date not set. 320p. pap. 56.95 (978-0-7506-5152-3(0), Butterworth-Heinemann) Elsevier Science & Technology Bks.

Spitzer, Cary R., ed. Digital Avionics Handbook: Development & Implementation, 2 vols. 2nd ed. 2006. (Electrical Engineering Handbook Ser.). (ENG., Illus.). 232p. 124.95 (978-0-8493-8441-7(9), CRC Press) Taylor & Francis Group GBR. Dist: Taylor & Francis Group.

—Digital Avionics Handbook: Elements, Software & Functions, 2 vols. 2nd ed. 2006. (Avionics Handbook, Second Edition Ser.). (ENG., Illus.). 448p. 124.95 (978-0-8493-8438-7(9), CRC Press) Taylor & Francis Group GBR. Dist: Taylor & Francis Group.

2007 IEEE Autotestcon. 2007. pap. 274.00 (978-1-4244-1238-9(2), 07CH37906) IEEE.

AVITAMINOSIS

see also Rickets; Vitamin B1 Deficiency

Allison-Francis, Emily. Correcting the Vitamin D Deficiency Dilemma: Strategies to Fight Diseases & Prolong Life for Black People. 2011. **(978-0-912444-49-9(5))** Dare Bks.

Carlson, Laurie Winn. The Sunlight Solution: What More Sun Exposure & Vitamin D Are Essential to Your Health. 2009. (ENG.). 248p. pap. 19.98 (978-1-59102-701-0(2)) Prometheus Bks., Pubs.

Eleftheriadis, Theodoros & Liakopoulos, Vassilios. Vitamin D Receptor Agonists & Kidney Diseases. 2010. (Nephrology Research & Clinical Developments Ser.). pap. 47.00 (978-1-61668-860-8(2), Nova Biomedical Bks.) Nova Science Pubs., Inc.

Foo, Leng Huat. Vitamin D Status in Adolescent Girls. 2011. 80p. pap. **(978-3-8433-6997-8(6))** Lambert Academic Publishing.

Frankenburg, Frances R. Vitamin Discoveries & Disasters: History, Science, & Controversies, 1 vol. 2009. (Praeger Series on Contemporary Health & Living Ser.). (Illus.). 143p. 34.95 (978-0-313-35475-5(8), C35475, Praeger Pubs.) Greenwood Publishing Group, Inc.

Lerner, Vladimir & Miodownik, Chanoch. Vitamin D Deficiency. 2011. (Nutrition & Diet Research Progress Ser.). 95.00 **(978-1-61470-964-0(5)**, Nova Biomedical Bks.) Nova Science Pubs., Inc.

Malone, Stephanie R., ed. Vitamin D: Nutrition, Side Effects & Supplements. 2009. (Nutrition & Diet Research Progress Ser.). (Illus.). xii, 234p. 129.00 (978-1-61728-601-8(X)) Nova Science Pubs., Inc.

Miranda, Andrés. Vitamin C: Nutritional Role, Supplementation in Pathophysiological States & Side Effects. Rodrigo, Ramon, ed. 2010. (Nutrition & Diet Research Progress Ser.). (Illus.). 103p. pap. 43.00 (978-1-61728-950-7(7), Nova Biomedical Bks.) Nova Science Pubs., Inc.

Pacholok, Sally M. & Stuart, Jeffrey J. Could It Be B12? An Epidemic of Misdiagnoses. 2nd ed. 2011. (ENG.). 324p. pap. 14.95 (978-1-884995-69-9(1)) Linden Publishing Co., Inc.

Stafford, Diane & Dowd, James. The Vitamin D Cure. 2009. (ENG., Illus.). 272p. pap. 14.95 (978-0-470-45575-3(6), Wiley) Wiley, John & Sons, Inc.

AVOCADO

El Aguacate.Tr. of Avocado. (SPA.). 11.95 (978-968-29-4481-9(3)) Direccion General de Publicaciones del Consejo Nacional para la Cultura y las Artes MEX. Dist: AIMS International Bks., Inc.

AVOCATIONS

see Hobbies

AVOT

see Mishnah—Avot

AVRO (AIRPLANE)

Darling, Kev. Avro Vulcan Part1. 2007. 132p. pap. 39.95 (978-1-84799-237-6(4)) Lulu Enterprises Inc.

Fildes, David W. Avro Vulcan: Design & Development. 2011. (Illus.). 328p. 60.00 **(978-1-84884-284-7(8))** Pen & Sword Bks. Ltd. GBR. Dist: Casemate Pubs. & Bk. Distributors, LLC.

Gainor, Chris. Who Killed the Avro Arrow? 2007. (ENG., Illus.). 256p. pap. (978-1-894864-68-8(9)) Folklore Publishing CAN. Dist: Lone Pine Publishing.

AWA

see Kava Plant

AWAKENING (BUDDHISM)

see Enlightenment (Buddhism)

AWAKENING, GREAT

see Great Awakening

AWARDS

see Arbitration and Award; Rewards (Prizes, etc.)

AWARENESS

see also Race Awareness

Albers, Susan. Eat, Drink, & Be Mindful: How to End Your Struggle with Mindless Eating & Start Savoring Food with Intention & Joy. 2009. (Workbook Ser.). (ENG.). 208p. pap. 19.95 (978-1-57224-615-7(4)) New Harbinger Pubns.

Albers, Susan. Eating Mindfully, Second Edition: How to End Mindless Eating & Enjoy a Balanced Relationship with Food. 2nd ed. 2012. (ENG.). 312p. pap. 16.95 **(978-1-60882-330-7(X))** New Harbinger Pubns.

Allen, Jon G., et al. Mentalizing in Clinical Practice. 2008. (Illus.). 403p. 67.00 (978-1-58562-306-8(7)) American Psychiatric Publishing, Inc.

Anders, Christina Ada. Perceptual Dialectology: Neue Wege der Dialektologie. Anders, Christina Ada et al, eds. 2010. (Linguistik - Impulse & Tendenzen Ser.).Tr. of Perceptual Dialectology. (GER., Illus.). XXI, 449p. 140.00 **(978-3-11-022751-2(7))** De Gruyter, Walter Inc.

Anders, Christina Ada. Wahrnehmungsdialektologie: Das Obersächsische im Alltagsverständnis von Laien. 2010. (Linguistik - Impulse & Tendenzen Ser.).Tr. of Perceptual Dialectology. (GER., Illus.). X, 466p. 168.00 (978-3-11-022133-6(0)) De Gruyter, Walter Inc.

Andersson, Kjell. Transparency & Accountability in Science & Politics: The Awareness Principle. 2008. (ENG., Illus.). 272p. 95.00 (978-0-230-54217-4(4)) Palgrave Macmillan.

Arthur, J. d. Salvia Divinorum: Doorway to Thought-Free Awareness. 2010. (ENG.). 1p. pap. 14.95 (978-1-59477-347-1(5), Park Street Pr.) Inner Traditions International, Ltd.

Asante, Molefi Kete. Maulana Karenga: An Intellectual Portrait. 2009. (ENG.). 224p. pap. 19.95 (978-0-7456-4828-6(2)) Polity Pr. GBR. Dist: Wiley, John & Sons, Inc.

Bar, Moshe, ed. Predictions in the Brain: Using Our Past to Generate a Future, 1 vol. 2011. (ENG., Illus.). 400p. 99.95 (978-0-19-539551-8(4)) Oxford Univ. Pr., Inc.

Barkhuysen, Iris. Diamond Light Awareness. 2010. 270p. pap. 23.95 (978-0-557-27109-2(6)) Lulu Enterprises Inc.

Bateman, Anthony W. & Fonagy, Peter, eds. Handbook of Mentalizing in Mental Health Practice. 2011. (ENG., Illus.). 617p. pap. 69.00 (978-1-58562-372-3(5)) American Psychiatric Publishing, Inc.

Bays, Jan Chozen. How to Train a Wild Elephant: And Other Adventures in Mindfulness. 2011. (ENG.). 224p. pap. 14.00 (978-1-59030-817-2(4)) Shambhala Pubns., Inc.

Boyce, Barry, ed. The Mindfulness Revolution: Leading Psychologists, Scientists, Artists, & Meditation Teachers on the Power of Mindfulness in Daily Life. 2011. (Shambhala Sun Book Ser.). (ENG.). 288p. pap. 16.95 (978-1-59030-889-9(1)) Shambhala Pubns., Inc.

Briant, Ed. Be Still & Know Thyself: A Guide To Becoming Aware. 2007. 48p. pap. 15.00 (978-1-4303-2609-0(3)) Lulu Enterprises Inc.

Brooks, Charles V. W. & Selver, Charlotte. Reclaiming Vitality & Presence: Sensory Awareness as a Practice for Life. Laeng-Gilliatt, Stefan & Lowe, Richard, eds. 2nd rev. ed. 2007. (ENG., Illus.). 288p. pap. 19.95 *(978-1-55643-641-3(6))* North Atlantic Bks.

Brown, Michael. The Presence Process: A Journey into Present Moment Awareness. 2010. (ENG.). 325p. pap. 19.95 *(978-1-897238-46-2(0))* Namaste Publishing, Inc. CAN. Dist: Perseus-PGW.

Bruce, Peter J. Understanding Decision-Making Processes in Airline Operations Control. 2011. (Illus.). 206p. 99.95 ***(978-1-4094-1148-2(6))*** Ashgate Publishing Co.

Butkovic, Hrvoje. Living Deliberately. 2010. *(978-1-58982-771-4(6))* American Bk. Publishing Group.

Carter, Carol & Kravits, Sarah. Cultural Awareness & Global Citizenship. rev. ed. 2011. (ENG.). 32p. (C). pap. 13.33 ***(978-0-13-285023-0(0)***, Prentice Hall) Prentice Hall PTR.

Chapman, Susan Gillis. The Five Keys to Mindful Communication: Using Deep Listening & Mindful Speech to Strengthen Relationships, Heal Conflicts, & Accomplish Your Goals. 2012. (ENG.). 224p. pap. 15.95 ***(978-1-59030-941-4(3))*** Shambhala Pubns., Inc.

Clare, Linda & Halligan, Peter W., eds. Pathologies of Awareness: Bridging the Gap Between Theory & Practice. 2007. (Special Issues of Neuropsychological Rehabilitation Ser.). (ENG., Illus.). 156p. 79.95 *(978-1-84169-810-6(5)*, Psychology Press) Taylor & Francis Group GBR. Dist: Taylor & Francis Group.

Clay, James. Just One Thing. 2011. 152p. pap. 14.95 ***(978-1-257-06089-4(9))*** Lulu Enterprises Inc.

Cochran, Margaret. What Are You Afraid Of? 2010. 113p. pap. 11.00 *(978-0-557-59765-9(X))* Lulu Enterprises Inc.

Conner, Janet. My Soul Pages: A Companion to Writing down Your Soul. 2011. 192p. 17.95 *(978-1-57324-496-1(1)*, Conari Pr.) Red Wheel/Weiser.

Crenshaw, Neil. You Can Develop Pure Awareness: Incorporate Principles of Science, Spirituality, Psychology & Eastern Philosophy to Open Your Life into Cosmic Cons. 2009. (Illus.). 132p. pap. 15.95 *(978-1-4327-3202-8(1))* Outskirts Pr., Inc.

Cuhulain, Kerr & Douglas, Janet. The Safe Approach: Controlling Risk for Workers in the Helping Professions. 2007. *(978-1-930461-03-1(8))* Idyll Arbor, Inc.

Dalrymple, Alfred John. I. 2007. 50p. pap. 6.00 *(978-0-9673338-5-4(7))* Dalrymple Bks.

D'Arcy, Paula. Waking up to This Day: Seeing the Beauty Right Before Us. 2009. 144p. pap. 17.00 *(978-1-57075-849-2(2))* Orbis Bks.

Dash, P. African Caribbean Pupils in Art Education. 2010. 242p. *(978-94-6091-049-4(1))*; (Illus.). pap. *(978-94-6091-048-7(3))* Sense Pubs.

de Anca, Celia. Beyond Tribalism: Managing Identities in a Diverse World. 2012. (IE Business Publishing Ser.). (ENG., Illus.). 320p. 40.00 ***(978-0-230-27694-9(6))*** Palgrave Macmillan.

Department of Defense's Work with States, Universities, & Students to Transform the Nation's Foreign Language Capacity: Hearing Before the Oversight & Investigations Subcommittee of the Committee on Armed Services, House of Representatives, One Hundred Tenth Congress, Second Session, Hearing Held September 23, 2008. 2009. (Illus.). iv, 128p. *(978-0-16-085140-7(8)*, 552-070-40494-5) United States Government Printing Office.

Diamond, Elizabeth. 7 Mindsets to Master Self-Awareness. 2010. 188p. (ENG.). 24.99 *(978-1-4520-4624-2(7))*; pap. 14.99 *(978-1-4520-4623-5(9))* AuthorHouse.

Dimaggio, Giancarlo & Lysaker, Paul, eds. Metacognition & Severe Adult Mental Disorders: From Research to Treatment. 2010. (ENG., Illus.). 344p. (C). 49.95 *(978-0-415-48423-7(5))* Routledge.

Donskis, Leonidas. Troubled Identity & the Modern World. 2009. (ENG.). 240p. 89.00 *(978-0-230-60770-5(5))* Palgrave Macmillan.

The Electric Empire: Electricity & Polarity As Related to Our Awareness. Date not set. pap. *(978-0-9658557-2-3(4))* Loizos, Tom.

Elpel, Thomas J. Roadmap to Reality: Consciousness, Worldviews, & the Blossoming of the Human Spirit. 2010. (ENG., Illus.). 272p. pap. 30.00 *(978-1-892784-29-2(7))* HOPS Pr., LLC.

Epstein, Mark. Going on Being: Life at the Crossroads of Buddhism & Psychotherapy. 2009. (ENG.). 225p. pap. 16.95 *(978-0-86171-569-5(1))* Wisdom Pubns.

Eschholz, Paul, et al. Language Awareness: Readings for College Writers. 10th ed. 2009. (ENG.). 736p. (C). pap. 62.95 *(978-0-312-46316-8(2))*; (Illus.). xxii, 650p. 60.95 *(978-0-312-46341-0(3))* Bedford/Saint Martin's.

Estep, M. A Theory of Immediate Awareness: Self-Organization & Adaptation in Natural Intelligence. 2010. 310p. pap. 129.00 *(978-90-481-6251-2(3)*, 9048162513) Springer.

Fenner, Peter. Radiant Mind: Awakening Unconditioned Awareness. 2007. 291p. 22.95 *(978-1-59179-577-3(X)*, BK01133) Sounds True, Inc.

—Radiant Mind: Teachings & Practices to Awaken Unconditioned Awareness. 2007. (Illus.). 7p. audio compact disk 69.95 *(978-1-59179-607-7(5)*, AF01132D) Sounds True, Inc.

Ferguson, Gaylon. Natural Wakefulness: Discovering the Wisdom We Were Born With. 2010. (ENG.). 224p. pap. 15.95 *(978-1-59030-769-4(0))* Shambhala Pubns., Inc.

Ferguson, Gaylon & Ferguson, Gaylon Jules. Natural Wakefulness: Discovering the Wisdom We Were Born With. 2009. (ENG.). 224p. 21.95 *(978-1-59030-657-4(0))* Shambhala Pubns., Inc.

Fernandez, Jaime. Overcoming the Enemy Within: A Journey to Enlightenment. 2011. 95p. pap. 14.95 ***(978-1-4327-7770-8(X))*** Outskirts Pr., Inc.

Frankel, Tamar. The Ponzi Scheme Puzzle: How Victims Get Caught in the Net & How Self Awareness Can Help Protect Them. 2012. (ENG.). 224p. 35.00 ***(978-0-19-992661-9(1))*** Oxford Univ. Pr., Inc.

Fresh, Cecelia. The Creative Footprint. 2010. 60p. pap. *(978-3-8383-4119-4(8))* Lambert Academic Publishing.

Görnitz, Thomas & Görnitz, Brigitte. Die Evolution des Geistigen: Quantenphysik - Bewusstsein - Religion. 2010. (GER., Illus.). 372p. (C). 68.00 *(978-3-525-56717-3(0))* Vandenhoeck & Ruprecht GmbH & Co. KG DEU. Dist: ISD.

Greer, John. Seeing, Knowing, Being: A Guide to Sacred Awakenings. 2012. (ENG.). 256p. pap. 14.95 ***(978-0-615-52183-1(5))*** True Compass Pr.

Grudin, Robert. American Vulgar: The Politics of Manipulation Versus the Culture of Awareness. 2006. (ENG.). 240p. per. 15.00 *(978-1-59376-102-8(3))* Counterpoint LLC.

Hanh, Thich Nhat. You Are Here: Discovering the Magic of the Present Moment. McLeod, Melvin, ed. Kohn, Sherab Chodzin, tr. from FRE. 2010. (ENG.). 160p. pap. 14.00 *(978-1-59030-838-7(7))* Shambhala Pubns., Inc.

Harp, David. Mindfulness to Go: How to Meditate While You're on the Move. 2011. (ENG.). 224p. pap. 16.95 *(978-1-57224-989-9(7))* New Harbinger Pubns.

Harris, Gabrielle. Touching Animal Souls - Developing Awareness Through the Animal World. 2011. 274p. pap. ***(978-0-9869858-3-6(X))*** Kima Global Pubs.

Haven, Girard. Notes from a Conscious Teaching. Date not set. 164p. 10.00 *(978-0-9645782-1-0(2))* Ulysses Bks.

Hawn, Goldie. 10 Mindful Minutes: Giving Our Children — And Ourselves — The Social & Emotional Skills to Reduce Stress & Anxiety for Healthier, Happy Lives. 2011. (ENG.). 256p. (gr. 12). 24.00 *(978-0-399-53606-9(X)*, Perigee Trade) Penguin Group (USA) Inc.

Hawn, Goldie & Holden, Wendy. 10 Mindful Minutes: Giving Our Children — and Ourselves — the Social & Emotional Skills to Reduce Stress & Anxiety for Healthier, Happy Lives. 2012. (ENG.). 256p. (gr. 12). pap. 14.00 ***(978-0-399-53772-1(4)***, Perigee Trade) Penguin Group (USA) Inc.

Heer, Dr Dain & Heer, Dain. Being You, Changing the World. 2011. 316p. pap. 24.95 ***(978-0-9845088-1-5(3))*** Big Country Publishing, LLC.

Henning, Tim. Person sein und Geschichten Erzählen: Eine Studie aber personale Autonomie und narrative Grande. 2009. (Quellen und Studien zur Philosophie Ser.).Tr. of Being a Person & Telling a Story: Personal Autonomy, Biographical Knowledge & Narrative Reasons. (GER.). VIII, 289p. 210.00 ***(978-3-11-173713-3(6))*** De Gruyter, Walter Inc.

Henning, Tim. Person sein und Geschichten erzählen: Eine Studie über personale Autonomie und narrative Gründe. 2009. (Quellen und Studien zur Philosophie Ser.).Tr. of Being a Person & Telling a Story: Personal Autonomy, Biographical Knowledge & Narrative Reasons. (GER.). VIII, 289p. 137.00 *(978-3-11-020569-5(6))* De Gruyter, Walter Inc.

Hick, Steven F. & Bien, Thomas, eds. Mindfulness & the Therapeutic Relationship. (ENG.). 240p. 2010. pap. 25.00 *(978-1-60918-019-5(4))* 2008. 50.00 *(978-1-59385-820-9(5))* Guilford Pubns., Inc.

Hill, Anthony Wakefield. The Knowledge of Everything: According to the Voice of Silence. 2010. 520p. *(978-1-84748-447-5(6))* Athena Pr.

Holmes-Eber, Paula, et al. Applications in Operational Culture: Perspectives from the Field: Perspectives from the Field. Marine Corps University Press (U.S.), ed. 2012. (ENG., Illus.). 197p. pap. 20.00 ***(978-0-16-090106-5(5)***, Marine Corps) United States Government Printing Office.

Hutslar, Julie. The Mask, the Mirror, & the Illusion: Awakening to the Knowledge of Who You Truly Are. 2008. 252p. pap. 15.00 *(978-0-9753000-0-8(8))* Luminous Epinoia Pr.

Indermaur, Scott. Revealed: Personal Visions of Transformation & Discovery. 2011. pap. ***(978-1-935656-10-4(4))*** Little Red Tree Publishing LLC.

Joshi, Vasant. If It Could Happen to Buddha, Why Not You: Understanding the Ancient Secrets of Self Awareness. 2010. (ENG.). 152p. pap. 9.95 *(978-81-8328-156-0(7))* Wisdom Tree IND. Dist: SCB Distributors.

Kabat-Zinn, Jon. Mindfulness for Beginners: Reclaiming the Present Moment — and Your Life. 2011. 120p. 21.95 incl. audio compact disk ***(978-1-60407-653-5(5))*** Sounds True, Inc.

Kaparo, Risa. Awakening Somatic Intelligence: The Art & Practice of Embodied Mindfulness. 2012. (ENG., Illus.). 352p. pap. 21.95 ***(978-1-58394-417-2(6))*** North Atlantic Bks.

Kardaras, Nicholas. How Plato & Pythagoras Can Save Your Life: The Ancient Greek Prescription for Health & Happiness. 2011. 256p. 21.95 *(978-1-57324-475-6(9)*, Conari Pr.) Red Wheel/Weiser.

King, Bill. 7 Days to Inner Peace: The Building Blocks of Awareness. 2008. (Illus.). 163p. per. 19.95 *(978-0-9801206-0-8(8))* posiTRACT Solutions, LLC.

Kinslow, Frank J. Eufeeling! The Art of Creating Inner Peace & Outer Prosperity. 2012. (ENG.). pap. 14.95 ***(978-1-4019-3399-9(8))*** Hay Hse., Inc.

—The Secret of Instant Healing. 2011. (ENG.). pap. 14.95 *(978-1-4019-3194-0(4))* Hay Hse., Inc.

Kinslow, Frank J. The Secret of Quantum Living. 2012. (Illus.). xii, 280p. ***(978-1-4019-3197-1(9))***; (ENG.). 312p. pap. 16.95 ***(978-1-4019-3196-4(0))*** Hay Hse., Inc.

Kott, Alexander. Battle of Cognition: The Future Information-Rich Warfare & the Mind of the Commander, 1 vol. 2007. (Praeger Security International Ser.). (Illus.). 272p. 59.95 *(978-0-313-34995-9(9)*, C34995, Praeger Security International) Greenwood Publishing Group, Inc.

Kravets, Jewgeni. Coordination Aware Service Monitoring. 2008. 132p. pap. *(978-3-639-00116-7(8))* VDM Verlag Dr. Mueller e.K.

Kundtz, David. Awakened Mind: One-Minute Wake up Calls to a Bold & Mindful Life. 2009. (ENG.). 320p. pap. 14.95 *(978-1-57324-360-5(4)*, Conari Pr.) Red Wheel/Weiser.

Lai, Simon C. H. Book of Spells. 2010. 116p. pap. 16.00 *(978-1-60976-197-4(9)*, Eloquent Bks.) AEG Literary Publishing Services, Inc.

—Book of Spells II. 2010. 92p. pap. 15.50 *(978-1-60976-489-0(7)*, Eloquent Bks.) AEG Literary Publishing Services, Inc.

Lana Tracy Lewis. Living Life Consciously. 2009. 396p. pap. 19.97 *(978-1-4343-4137-2(2))* AuthorHouse.

Lang, Stefan. Spontaneität des Selbst. 2010. (Neue Studien zur Philosophie Ser.). (GER.). 144p. (C). 48.00 *(978-3-89971-774-7(0))* Vandenhoeck & Ruprecht GmbH & Co. KG DEU. Dist: ISD.

Lawrence, Richard. Unlock Your Psychic Powers. 2008. (ENG., Illus.). 208p. pap. 19.95 *(978-1-84694-088-0(5))* Hunt, John Publishing Ltd. GBR. Dist: National Bk. Network.

Leff, David K. Deep Travel: In Thoreau's Wake on the Concord & Merrimack. 2009. (American Land & Life Ser.). (ENG., Illus.). 230p. 32.00 *(978-1-58729-739-2(2))* Univ. of Iowa Pr.

Leicester, Mal. Special Stories for Disability Awareness: Stories & Activities for Teachers, Parents & Professionals. 2006. (ENG., Illus.). 128p. per. *(978-1-84310-390-5(7))* Kingsley, Jessica Ltd.

Liu, JeeLoo & Perry, John, eds. Consciousness & the Self: New Essays. 2011. (ENG., Illus.). 270p. 90.00 ***(978-1-107-00075-9(0))*** Cambridge Univ. Pr.

Locke, Simeon. Consciousness, Self-Consciousness, & the Science of Being Human, 1 vol. 2007. 172p. 34.95 *(978-0-313-35006-1(X)*, C35006, Praeger Pubs.) Greenwood Publishing Group, Inc.

Loizos, Tom. Metaphysically Yours: A Scrutiny of the "Core Concepts" Housed in Our Awareness. Date not set. pap. *(978-0-9658557-1-6(6))* Loizos, Tom.

Malkani, Vikas. The Little Manual of Enlightenment: 7 Valuable Tips for Those in Search of Awareness. 2009. (ENG.). 144p. pap. 14.95 *(978-1-84694-163-4(6))* Hunt, John Publishing Ltd. GBR. Dist: National Bk. Network.

Margulis, Lynn, et al, eds. Chimeras & Consciousness: Evolution of the Sensory Self. 2011. (ENG., Illus.). 344p. (gr. 17). 58.00 *(978-0-262-01539-4(0))*; pap. 29.00 *(978-0-262-51583-2(0))* MIT Pr.

Markopoulos, Panos, et al, eds. Awareness Systems: Advances in Theory, Methodology & Design. 2009. (Human-Computer Interaction Ser.). (ENG., Illus.). xvi, 470p. 149.00 *(978-1-84882-476-8(9)*, 1848824769) Springer.

Mashour, George, ed. Consciousness, Awareness, & Anesthesia. 2010. (ENG., Illus.). 272p. 89.00 *(978-0-521-51822-2(9))* Cambridge Univ. Pr.

McCracken, Lance M. Mindfulness & Acceptance in Behavioral Medicine: Current Theory & Practice. 2011. (Context Press Mindfulness & Acceptance Practica Ser.). (ENG., Illus.). 400p. pap. 49.95 *(978-1-57224-731-4(2))* New Harbinger Pubns.

McQuarrie, Lynn. Phonology & Deaf Readers: New Insights On An Old Debate. 2008. 120p. pap. *(978-3-639-07966-1(3))* VDM Verlag Dr. Mueller e.K.

Millward, Scott. Understanding the Shared Situation Awareness Process. 2008. 120p. pap. *(978-3-639-04804-9(0))* VDM Verlag Dr. Mueller e.K.

Molesko, Norman. RETIRING & SENIOR LIVING... Experiencing the Second Half of Life. 2010. 202p. pap. 19.98 *(978-0-557-41811-4(9))* Lulu Enterprises Inc.

Molinary, Rosie. Beautiful You: A Daily Guide to Radical Self-Acceptance. 2010. (ENG.). 440p. pap. 16.95 *(978-1-58005-331-0(9))* Seal Pr.

Mordasini, Don. Princes & Ogres: Integration of Psyche & Soul. 2012. (Illus.). 244p. ***(978-1-58982-825-4(9)***, Millennial Mind Publishing) American Bk. Publishing Group.

Morrison, Gerald. Spiritual Journey. 2008. 96p. pap. 10.95 *(978-1-4327-2079-7(1))* Outskirts Pr., Inc.

Moss, Richard. Inside-Out Healing: Transforming Your Life Through the Power of Presence. 2011. (ENG.). 256p. 15.95 *(978-1-4019-2758-5(0))* Hay Hse., Inc.

O'Brien, Lucy. Self-Knowing Agents. 2007. (ENG.). 256p. 85.00 *(978-0-19-926148-2(2))* Oxford Univ. Pr., Inc.

Onwubiko, Cyril & Owens, Thomas. Situational Awareness in Computer Network Defense: Principles, Methods & Applications. 2012. ***(978-1-4666-0106-2(X))***; E-Book ***(978-1-4666-0105-5(1))*** IGI Global.

Pappas, Nicholas J. On Awareness: A Collection of Philosophical Dialogues. 2011. 202p. pap. 19.95 ***(978-0-87586-840-0(1))***; pap. 29.95 ***(978-0-87586-841-7(X))***; pap. 19.35 ***(978-0-87586-842-4(8))*** Algora Publishing.

Perkams, Matthias. Selbstbewusstsein in der Spatantike: Die Neuplatonischen Kommentare Zu Aristoteles' de Anima. 2008. (Quellen und Studien Zur Philosophie Ser.). (GER.). XIV, 468p. 147.00 *(978-3-11-020492-6(4))* De Gruyter, Walter Inc.

Pippin, Robert. Hegel on Self Consciousness - Desire & Death in the Phenomenology of Spirit. 2010. (Princeton Monographs in Philosophy Ser.). (ENG.). 120p. (C). 29.95 *(978-0-691-14851-9(1))* Princeton Univ. Pr.

Prigatano, George P., ed. The Study of Anosognosia. 2010. (ENG., Illus.). 560p. 89.95 *(978-0-19-537909-9(8))* Oxford Univ. Pr. GBR. Dist: Rittenhouse Bk. Distributors.

Ralston, Peter. The Book of Not Knowing: Exploring the True Nature of Self, Mind, & Consciousness. 2010. (ENG.). 600p. pap. 24.95 *(978-1-55643-857-8(5))* North Atlantic Bks.

Reagan, Leslie J. Dangerous Pregnancies: Mothers, Disabilities, & Abortion in Modern America. 2010. (ENG., Illus.). 396p. 29.95 *(978-0-520-25903-4(3))* Univ. of California Pr.

Rödl, Sebastian. Self-Consciousness. 2007. 222p. 46.00 *(978-0-674-02494-6(X))* Harvard Univ. Pr.

Sabzevary, Amir. Choiceless Awareness. 2010. 132p. pap. *(978-3-8383-0385-7(7))* Lambert Academic Publishing.

Salas, Eduardo & Dietz, Aaron S., eds. Situational Awareness. 2011. (Critical Essays on Human Factors in Aviation Ser.). 544p. 260.00 ***(978-0-7546-2973-3(2))*** Ashgate Publishing Co.

Sears, Richard W., et al. Mindfulness in Clinical Practice. 2011. *(978-1-56887-126-4(0))*; (Illus.). xxi, 183p. ***(978-1-56887-136-3(8))*** Professional Resource Exchange, Inc. (Professional Resource Pr.).

Selby, John. Executive Genius. 2008. (ENG.). 1p. 21.99 *(978-1-56414-986-2(2))* Career Pr., Inc.

Shannon, Christopher C., et al. Finding the Shape of Space. 2011. ***(978-1-58566-208-1(9))*** Air University Pr.

Sher, George. Who Knew?: Responsibility Without Awareness. 2009. (ENG.). 168p. 99.00 *(978-0-19-538919-7(0))*; pap. 24.95 *(978-0-19-538920-3(4))* Oxford Univ. Pr., Inc.

Siegel, Daniel J. The Mindful Brain. 2007. 26.95 *(978-0-7937-0470-5(7))* Norton, W. W. & Co., Inc.

—The Mindful Therapist: A Clinician's Guide to Mindsight & Neural Integration. 2010. (ENG., Illus.). 320p. 27.95 *(978-0-393-70645-1(1)*, 70645) Norton, W. W. & Co., Inc.

Simone, Lalania. Urban Soul Warrior: Self Mastery in the Midst of the Metropolis. 2008. (ENG.). 256p. pap. 15.95 *(978-1-59376-212-4(7)*, Soft Skull Pr.) Counterpoint LLC.

Smith, Kenneth. Shamanism for the Age of Science. 2011. (ENG.). 1p. pap. 18.00 *(978-1-59143-119-0(0))* Bear & Co.

Smith, Kenneth. Shamanism for the Age of Science: Awakening the Energy Body. 2011. E-Book ***(978-1-59143-977-6(9))*** Bear & Co.

Stevens, John O. Awareness: Exploring, exprimenting, Experiencing. 2007. pap. 33.00 *(978-0-939266-44-9(X))* Gestalt Journal Pr.

Taplin, Barry. Mind Your Head UK Awareness Stress & Confidence. 2008. 90p. pap. 19.95 *(978-0-9556935-0-2(0))* Mind Your Head UK GBR. Dist: Lulu Enterprises Inc.

Tisdale, Stacey & Kennedy, Paula Boyer. The True Cost of Happiness: The Real Story Behind Managing Your Money. (ENG., Illus.). 288p. 2009. pap. 16.95 *(978-0-470-49657-2(6))* 2007. 24.95 *(978-0-470-13906-6(4))* Wiley, John & Sons, Inc. (Wiley).

Tougas, Cecile. The Phenomena of Awareness. 2012. (ENG., Illus.). 152p. (C). 105.00 ***(978-0-415-68590-0(7))***; pap. 36.95 ***(978-0-415-68591-7(5))*** Routledge.

Tracol, Henri. The Real Question Remains: Gurdjieff - A Living Call. 2009. (ENG.). 236p. pap. 16.95 *(978-1-59675-032-6(4))* Morning Light Pr.

Van Rossum, Melissa. All You've Ever Known: The Way in to Your Authentic Self Lies in Your Own Two Hands. 2007. 256p. per. 28.95 *(978-0-9792265-0-2(3))* MetaPublishing.

Ward, Caroline T. The Four Faces of Woman: Restoring Your Authentic Power, Recovering Your Eternal Beauty. 2008. (ENG., Illus.). 256p. pap. 19.95 *(978-1-84694-086-6(9))* Hunt, John Publishing Ltd. GBR. Dist: National Bk. Network.

Wilson, Marie-Claire. Seasonal Awareness & Wellbeing: Looking & Feeling Better the Easy Way. 2011. (ENG.). 211p. pap. 22.95 ***(978-1-84694-469-7(4))*** Hunt, John Publishing Ltd. GBR. Dist: National Bk. Network.

Xu, Changmo. Han Yu Yu Yan Jie Gou Yi Zheng: Li Lun Yu Jiao Xue Ying Yong. 2010. (CHI., Illus.). viii, 291p. *(978-986-6923-96-8(7))* Le Jin Bks., Ltd.

AWNINGS

Cryder, Jo. 1000 Shutters & Awnings. 2007. (Illus.). 160p. pap. 29.95 *(978-0-7643-2711-7(9))* Schiffer Publishing, Ltd.

AWOLOWO, OBAFEMI, 1909-1987

Nolte, Insa. Obafemi Awolowo & the Making of Remo: The Local Politics of a Nigerian Nationalist. 2010. *(978-1-59221-755-7(9))*; pap. *(978-1-59221-756-4(7))* Africa World Pr.

—Obafemi Awolowo & the Making of Remo: The Local Politics of a Nigerian Nationalist. 2009. (International African Library). (ENG., Illus.). 296p. (gr. 17). 75.00 *(978-0-7486-3895-6(4))* Edinburgh Univ. Pr. GBR. Dist: Columbia Univ. Pr.

AXES

Davis, Vin & Edmonds, Mark, eds. Stone Axe Studies III. 2011. (ENG., Illus.). 448p. (C). 96.00 *(978-1-84217-421-0(5))* Oxbow Bks., Ltd. GBR. Dist: Brown, David Bk. Co., The.

Goren-Inbar, N. & Sharon, Gonen. Axe Age: Acheulian Toolmaking - from Quarry to Discard. 2006. (Approaches to Anthropological Archaeology Ser.). (ENG., Illus.). 608p. (C). 95.00 *(978-1-84553-138-6(8))* Equinox Publishing Ltd. GBR. Dist: ISD.

Leakey, M. D. Olduvai Gorge. 2009. (ENG.). 376p. pap. 51.00 *(978-0-521-10518-7(8))* Cambridge Univ. Pr.

AXIAL FLOW COMPRESSORS

see Compressors

AXIOLOGY

see Values

AXIOMATIC SET THEORY

Bell, John L. The Axiom of Choice. 2009. (Illus.). 264p. pap. *(978-1-904987-54-3(0))* College Pubns.

Berto, Francesco, et al. The Mathematics of the Models of Reference. 2010. 186p. pap. *(978-1-84890-011-0(2))* College Pubns.

Felgner, U. Models of Zf-Set Theory. 2008. (Lecture Notes in Mathematics Ser.). 188p. pap. 39.95 *(978-3-540-05591-4(6)*, 3540055916) Springer.

Fremlin, D. H. Consequences of Martin's Axiom. 2008. (Cambridge Tracts in Mathematics Ser.). (ENG.). 340p. pap. 61.00 *(978-0-521-08954-8(9))* Cambridge Univ. Pr.

Jech, Thomas J. The Axiom of Choice. 2008. (Dover Books on Mathematics Ser.). (ENG.). 224p. pap. 14.95 *(978-0-486-46624-8(8))* Dover Pubns., Inc.

Liu, Xiaodong & Pedrycz, Witold. Axiomatic Fuzzy Set Theory & Its Applications. 2009. (Studies in Fuzziness & Soft Computing Ser.). (Illus.). xviii, 514p. 199.00 *(978-3-642-00401-8(6))* Springer.

Lubansky, Raymond. Axiomatic Spectral Theory in Banach Algebras. 2010. 140p. pap. *(978-3-8383-5097-4(9))* Lambert Academic Publishing.

Maddy, Penelope. Defending the Axioms: On the Philosophical Foundations of Set Theory. 2011. (ENG.). 144p. 45.00 *(978-0-19-959618-8(2))* Oxford Univ. Pr., Inc.

McGrane, Joshua. Unfolding Ambivalence. 2010. 228p. pap. *(978-3-8383-4786-8(2))* Lambert Academic Publishing.

Peters, H. J. Axiomatic Bargaining Game Theory. 2010. (Theory & Decision Library C Ser.). (ENG.). 256p. pap. 239.00 *(978-90-481-4178-4(8),* 9048141788) Springer.

AXIOMS

Bryant, James W. Proverbial Wisdom: (Daily Reader) 2011. 158p. pap. 24.95 ***(978-1-4626-2626-7(2))*** PublishAmerica, Inc.

Carson, Emily & Huber, Renate, eds. Intuition & the Axiomatic Method. 2010. (Western Ontario Series in Philosophy of Science Ser.). xiii, 324p. pap. 199.00 *(978-90-481-7019-7(2),* 9048170192) Springer.

Fetisov, A. I. & Dubnov, Ya. S. Proof in Geometry: With Mistakes in Geometric Proofs. 2006. (Dover Books on Mathematics Ser.). (ENG., Illus.). 128p. per. 9.95 *(978-0-486-45354-5(5))* Dover Pubns., Inc.

Fishburn, Peter C., et al. The Mathematics of Preference, Choice & Order: Essays in Honor of Peter C. Fishburn. 2008. (Studies in Choice & Welfare Ser.). (Illus.). 430p. 179.00 *(978-3-540-79127-0(2))* Springer.

Fremlin, D. H. Consequences of Martin's Axiom. 2008. (Cambridge Tracts in Mathematics Ser.). (ENG.). 340p. pap. 61.00 *(978-0-521-08954-8(9))* Cambridge Univ. Pr.

Herrlich, Horst. Axiom of Choice. 2006. (Lecture Notes in Mathematics Ser.). (Illus.). XIV, 194p. pap. 69.95 *(978-3-540-30989-5(6),* 3540309896) Springer.

Kanovei, Vladimir & Reeken, Michael. Nonstandard Analysis, Axiomatically. 2010. (Springer Monographs in Mathematics Ser.). xvi, 408p. pap. 135.00 *(978-3-642-06077-9(3),* 3642060773) Springer.

Laurenzana, Federico. Anvía. 2009. (SPA.). 200p. pap. 16.70 *(978-0-557-03879-4(0))* Lulu Enterprises Inc.

Moore, Gregory H. & Mathematics. Zermelo's Axiom of Choice: Its Origins, Development, & Influence. 2012. (Dover Books on Mathematics Ser.). (ENG.). 432p. pap. 24.95 ***(978-0-486-48841-7(1))*** Dover Pubns., Inc.

Rudeanu. Axioms for Lattices & Boolean Algebras. 2008. 77.00 *(978-981-283-454-6(0))* World Scientific Publishing Co., Inc.

AXLES

see also Bearings (Machinery)

Birch, Tom & Rockwood, Chuck. Manual Drivetrains & Axles: NATEF Correlated Task Sheets. 5th ed. 2007. (ENG., Illus.). 160p. (C). spiral bd. 34.80 *(978-0-13-199406-5(9))* Pearson Education Canada CAN. Dist: Pearson Education.

Pearson, creator. Drive Lines, U-Joints & Axle Shafts. 2007. (Illus.). 31p. pap. *(978-0-536-10873-9(0))* Pearson Education Canada.

AYASOFYA MUSEZI

Stuhlman, Byron. The Initiatory Process in the Byzantine Tradition. 2009. 95.00 *(978-1-60724-430-1(6))* Gorgias Pr., LLC.

AYCKBOURN, ALAN, 1939-

Mandala, Susan. Twentieth-Century Drama Dialogue As Ordinary Talk: Speaking Between the Lines. 2007. 152p. 99.95 *(978-0-7546-5105-5(3))* Ashgate Publishing Co.

AYCOCK, CHARLES BRANTLEY, 1859-1912

Connor, R. D. W. & Poe, Clarence. The Life & Speeches of Charles Brantley Aycock. (ENG.). 408p. 2007. 49.95 *(978-0-548-12555-7(4))* 2006. per. 34.95 *(978-1-4286-3530-2(0))* Kessinger Publishing, LLC.

AYDELOTTE, FRANK, 1880-1956

Hesperides. An Adventure in Education - Swarthmore College under Frank Aydelotte. 2007. 252p. per. *(978-1-4067-5043-0(3),* Hesperides Pr.) Read Bks.

Wood, Ruth Shoemaker. Transforming Campus Culture: Frank Aydelotte's Honors Experiment at Swarthmore College. 2011. (ENG.). 148p. 65.00 ***(978-1-61149-371-9(4))*** Univ. of Delaware Pr.

AYRSHIRE (SCOTLAND)

Carroll, David. Burns Country. 2009. (ENG., Illus.). 128p. pap. 24.95 *(978-0-7524-4956-2(7))* History Pr. Ltd., The GBR. Dist: Independent Pubs. Group.

Dobson, David. Scotland During the Plantation of Ulster: The People of Ayrshire, 1600-1699. 2008. (Illus.). 138p. pap. 21.50 *(978-0-8063-5391-3(0))* Clearfield Co.

Paterson, James. History of the Counties of Ayr & Wigton. 2009. (Illus.). 318p. pap. 25.79 *(978-1-150-22198-9(4))* General Bks. LLC.

Shelley, Henry C. The Ayrshire Homes & Haunts of Burns. 2010. 172p. 30.99 *(978-1-140-52948-4(X))*; pap. 21.75 *(978-1-140-52949-1(8))* BiblioBazaar.

AYURVEDIC MEDICINE

see Medicine, Ayurvedic

AZANDE (AFRICAN PEOPLE)

see Zande (African People)

AZALEAS

Halliday, Robert. Practical Azalea Culture. 2008. (Gardening in America Ser.). (ENG.). 120p. pap. 10.95 *(978-1-4290-1282-9(X))* Applewood Bks.

AZANA, MANUEL, 1880-1940

Villar, Arturo del. Manuel Azaña y Valladolid. 2010. (SPA.). 63p. *(978-84-613-9471-5(2),* LearnVerbs.com) Tsunami Systems S. L.

AZEOTROPES

Luyben, William L. & Chien, I-Lung. Design & Control of Distillation Systems for Separating Azeotropes. 2010. (ENG., Illus.). 472p. 132.00 *(978-0-470-44862-5(8))* American Institute of Chemical Engineers.

AZERBAIJAN—BIOGRAPHY

Oldfield, Anna C. Azerbaijani Women Poet-Minstrels: Women "Ashiqs" from the Eighteenth Century to the Present. 2008. (Illus.). 242p. 129.95 *(978-0-7734-4990-9(6))* Mellen, Edwin Pr., The.

AZERBAIJAN—DESCRIPTION AND TRAVEL

Elliott, Mark. Azerbaijan: With Excursions to Georgia. 4th rev. ed. 2010. (ENG., Illus.). 368p. pap. 24.95 *(978-1-905864-23-2(X))* Trailblazer Pubns. GBR. Dist: Globe Pequot Pr., The.

Holding, Nicholas. Armenia. 3rd ed. 2011. (Bradt Travel Guide Ser.). (ENG., Illus.). 256p. pap. 25.99 *(978-1-84162-345-0(8))* Bradt Travel Guides GBR. Dist: Globe Pequot Pr., The.

Illis, Ben. A Hedonist's Guide to Baku. 2010. (ENG., Illus.). 176p. im. lthr. 18.00 *(978-1-905428-46-5(4),* HG2) Filmer Ltd. GBR. Dist: Perseus-PGW.

Karanian, Matthew & Kurkjian, Robert. Armenia & Karabagh: The Stone Garden Guide. 2nd ed. 2006. per. 24.95 *(978-0-9672120-9-8(X))* Stone Garden Productions.

Locken, E. Travel Journal Azerbaijan. 2010. 192p. pap. 19.99 *(978-0-557-43261-5(8))* Lulu Enterprises Inc.

Noble, John. Georgia, Armenia & Azerbaijan. 4th rev. ed. 2012. (Multi Country Guide Ser.). (ENG., Illus.). 328p. pap. 25.99 ***(978-1-74179-403-8(X))*** Lonely Planet Pubns.

Noble, John, et al. Georgia, Armenia & Azerbaijan. 3rd rev. ed. 2008. (Lonely Planet Georgia, Armenia & Azerbaijan Ser.). (ENG., Illus.). 364p. pap. 24.99 *(978-1-74104-477-5(4))* Lonely Planet Pubns.

Time Out Guides Staff, ed. Baku: And the Best of Azerbaijan. 2012. (Time Out Guides). (ENG., Illus.). 256p. pap. 19.95 ***(978-1-84670-246-4(1))*** Time Out Guides Ltd. GBR. Dist: Perseus-PGW.

AZERBAIJAN—ECONOMIC CONDITIONS

Ahadov, Isa. The Negative Impacts of the State Capture & Business Capture. 2010. 72p. pap. *(978-3-8383-4570-3(3))* Lambert Academic Publishing.

Cornell, Svante E. Azerbaijan since Independence. 2010. (Studies of Central Asia & the Caucasus Ser.). (ENG., Illus.). 512p. 99.95 *(978-0-7656-3002-5(8))*; pap. 39.95 *(978-0-7656-3003-2(6))* Sharpe, M.E. Inc.

Icon Group International, Inc. Staff, compiled by. The 2006 Economic & Product Market Databook for Baku, Azerbaijan. 2006. 618p. ring bd. 95.00 *(978-0-497-80124-3(8))* Icon Group International, Inc.

—The 2006 Economic & Product Market Databook for Gyandzha, Azerbaijan. 2006. 618p. ring bd. 95.00 *(978-0-497-80632-3(0))* Icon Group International, Inc.

—The 2006 Economic & Product Market Databook for Lenkoran, Azerbaijan. 2006. 618p. ring bd. 95.00 *(978-0-497-80840-2(4))* Icon Group International, Inc.

—The 2006 Economic & Product Market Databook for Mingechaur, Azerbaijan. 2006. 618p. ring bd. 95.00 *(978-0-497-81025-2(5))* Icon Group International, Inc.

—The 2006 Economic & Product Market Databook for Nakhichevan, Azerbaijan. 2006. 618p. ring bd. 95.00 *(978-0-497-81086-3(7))* Icon Group International, Inc.

—The 2006 Economic & Product Market Databook for Sheki, Azerbaijan. 2006. 618p. ring bd. 95.00 *(978-0-497-81519-6(2))* Icon Group International, Inc.

—The 2006 Economic & Product Market Databook for Shemakha, Azerbaijan. 2006. 618p. ring bd. 95.00 *(978-0-497-81520-2(6))* Icon Group International, Inc.

—The 2006 Economic & Product Market Databook for Stepanakert, Azerbaijan. 2006. 618p. ring bd. 95.00 *(978-0-497-81567-7(2))* Icon Group International, Inc.

—The 2006 Economic & Product Market Databook for Sumgait, Azerbaijan. 2006. 618p. ring bd. 95.00 *(978-0-497-81588-2(5))* Icon Group International, Inc.

Lerman, Zvi. Rural Transition in Azerbaijan. 2010. (Rural Economies in Transition Ser.). (ENG., Illus.). 187p. 68.50 *(978-0-7391-4316-2(6))* Lexington Bks.

Mogilevskii, P. I. & Ermolov, P. N. The 1823 Russian Survey of the Karabagh Province: A Primary Source on the Demography & Economy of Karabagh in the Early 19th Century. 2011. (Illus.). ***(978-1-56859-173-5(X))*** Mazda Pubs., Inc.

Wakeman-Linn, John, ed. Managing Oil Wealth: The Case of Azerbaijan. (RUS.). pap. 20.00 *(978-1-58906-357-0(0),* ISIRA0022004) International Monetary Fund.

AZERBAIJAN—FOREIGN RELATIONS

Cornell, Svante E. Azerbaijan since Independence. 2010. (Studies of Central Asia & the Caucasus Ser.). (ENG., Illus.). 512p. 99.95 *(978-0-7656-3002-5(8))*; pap. 39.95 *(978-0-7656-3003-2(6))* Sharpe, M.E. Inc.

Cox, Caroline, et al. Heroes & Zeros: Bible Discovery for Families. 2010. (Illus.). 48p. (J). pap. *(978-1-873166-79-6(6))* Good Bk. Co.

Huseynov, Tabib. Resolving Ethno-Territorial Conflicts. 2008. 56p. pap. *(978-3-639-01827-1(3))* VDM Verlag Dr. Mueller e.K.

Ideals vs. Reality in Human Rights & U.S. Foreign Policy: The Cases of Azerbaijan, Cuba, & Egypt: Hearing Before the Subcommittee on International Organizations, Human Rights, & Oversight of the Committee on Foreign Affairs, House of Representatives, One Hundred Tenth Congress, First Session, July 12, 2007. 2007. (Illus.). iii, 72p. *(978-0-16-079302-8(5),* 552-070-36381-5) United States Government Printing Office.

Mahmudov, Yagub. Azerbaijan & Europe: Medieval Diplomatic Relations. 2010. 408p. pap. 23.99 *(978-1-4535-5575-0(7))* Xlibris Corp.

Murinson, Alexander. Turkey's Entente with Israel & Azerbaijan: State Identity & Security in the Middle East & Causcasus. 2010. (Routledge Studies in Middle Eastern Politics Ser.). (ENG., Illus.). 226p. 130.00 *(978-0-415-77892-3(1))* Routledge.

Overland, Indra, et al, eds. Caspian Energy Politics. 2011. (ENG., Illus.). 208p. pap. 42.95 ***(978-0-415-69320-2(9))*** Routledge.

Overland, Indra, et al, eds. Petroleum Politics of the Caspian. 2010. (Central Asian Studies). (ENG., Illus.). 208p. 130.00 *(978-0-415-54916-5(7))* Routledge.

Pashaev, Kh M. Racing up Hill: Selected Papers of Azerbaijan's First Ambassador to the United States of America. 2006. (Illus.). xviii, 339p. pap. *(978-1-59267-065-9(2))* Global Scholarly Pubns.

AZERBAIJAN—HISTORY

Aliyev, Sarkhan. Three Colors of Azerbaijani Identity. 2008. 76p. pap. *(978-3-639-06142-0(X))* VDM Verlag Dr. Mueller e.K.

Bolukbasi, Suha. Azerbaijan: A Political History. 2011. (International Library of Caucasus Ser.). (ENG., Illus.). 304p. 90.00 *(978-1-84885-620-2(2))* I. B. Tauris & Co., Ltd. GBR. Dist: Macmillan.

Cox, Caroline, et al. Heroes & Zeros: Bible Discovery for Families. 2010. (Illus.). 48p. (J). pap. *(978-1-873166-79-6(6))* Good Bk. Co.

Esayi Hasan Jalaleants & Bournoutian, George A. A Brief History of the Aghuank Region: Patmutiwn Hamarot Aghuanits Erkri: A History of Karabagh & Ganje from 1702-1723. 2009. (ARM & ENG., Illus.). xi, 124p. *(978-1-56859-171-1(3))* Mazda Pubs., Inc.

Fawcett, Louise L. Estrange. Iran & the Cold War: The Azerbaijan Crisis Of 1946. 2009. (Cambridge Middle East Library). (ENG.). 240p. pap. 34.99 *(978-0-521-10473-9(4))* Cambridge Univ. Pr.

Haroyan, Lusine. Nagorno Karabagh Conflict. 2009. 64p. pap. *(978-3-639-08615-7(5))* VDM Verlag Dr. Mueller e.K.

Isgenderli, Anar. Realities of Azerbaijan 1917-1920. 2011. 238p. 29.99 ***(978-1-4568-7954-9(5))***; pap. 19.99 ***(978-1-4568-7953-2(7))*** Xlibris Corp.

Kazimova, Nikki. Azerbaijan - Culture Smart! The Essential Guide to Customs & Culture. 2011. (Culture Smart! Ser.). (ENG., Illus.). 168p. pap. 9.95 *(978-1-85733-544-6(9))* Kuperard Pubs. GBR. Dist: Random Hse., Inc.

Taylor, Paul Michael. Past & Future Heritage in the Pipelines Corridor: Azerbaijan, Georgia, Turkey. 2011. (AZE & ENG., Illus.). 239p. ***(978-0-9724557-6-3(0))***; pap. ***(978-0-9724557-4-9(4))*** Smithsonian Institution, Asian Cultural History Program.

AZERBAIJAN—POLITICS AND GOVERNMENT

Bolukbasi, Suha. Azerbaijan: A Political History. 2011. (International Library of Caucasus Ser.). (ENG., Illus.). 304p. 90.00 *(978-1-84885-620-2(2))* I. B. Tauris & Co., Ltd. GBR. Dist: Macmillan.

Cornell, Svante E. Azerbaijan since Independence. 2010. (Studies of Central Asia & the Caucasus Ser.). (ENG., Illus.). 512p. 99.95 *(978-0-7656-3002-5(8))*; pap. 39.95 *(978-0-7656-3003-2(6))* Sharpe, M.E. Inc.

Mehdiyeva, Nazrin. Power Games in the Caucasus: Azerbaijan's Foreign & Energy Policy Towards the West, Russia & the Middle East. 2011. (Library of International Relations Ser.). (ENG., Illus.). 288p. 92.50 *(978-1-84885-426-0(9),* Tauris Academic Studies) I. B. Tauris & Co., Ltd. GBR. Dist: Macmillan.

Sattarov, Rufat. Islam, State, & Society in Independent Azerbaijan: Between Historical Legacy & Post-Soviet Reality (with special reference to Baku & its Environs) 2009. (Kaukasienstudien Ser.). (Illus.). 394p. (C). 105.00 *(978-3-89500-692-0(0))* Reichert, Ludwig Dr. DEU. Dist: Brown, David Bk. Co., The.

Swietochowski, Tadeusz. Azerbaijan: Legacies of the Past & the Trials of Independence. 2009. (Postcommunist States & Nations Ser.). (ENG.). 192p. 130.00 *(978-0-415-27411-1(7))* Routledge.

Torjesen, Stina & Øverland, Indra. International Election Observers in Post-Soviet Azerbaijan: Geopolitical Pawns or Agents of Change? 2007. (ENG.). 232p. per. *(978-3-89821-743-9(4))* ibidem-Verlag.

Willerton, John P. Patronage & Politics in the USSR. 2009. (Cambridge Russian, Soviet & Post-Soviet Studies). 324p. pap. 42.00 *(978-0-521-12133-0(7))* Cambridge Univ. Pr.

AZERBAIJAN—SOCIAL CONDITIONS

Aliyev, Sarkhan. Three Colors of Azerbaijani Identity. 2008. 76p. pap. *(978-3-639-06142-0(X))* VDM Verlag Dr. Mueller e.K.

Cornell, Svante E. Azerbaijan since Independence. 2010. (Studies of Central Asia & the Caucasus Ser.). (ENG., Illus.). 512p. 99.95 *(978-0-7656-3002-5(8))*; pap. 39.95 *(978-0-7656-3003-2(6))* Sharpe, M.E. Inc.

Cox, Caroline, et al. Heroes & Zeros: Bible Discovery for Families. 2010. (Illus.). 48p. (J). pap. *(978-1-873166-79-6(6))* Good Bk. Co.

Kazimova, Nikki. Azerbaijan - Culture Smart! The Essential Guide to Customs & Culture. 2011. (Culture Smart! Ser.). (ENG., Illus.). 168p. pap. 9.95 *(978-1-85733-544-6(9))* Kuperard Pubs. GBR. Dist: Random Hse., Inc.

Lerman, Zvi. Rural Transition in Azerbaijan. 2010. (Rural Economies in Transition Ser.). (ENG., Illus.). 187p. 68.50 *(978-0-7391-4316-2(6))* Lexington Bks.

AZERBAIJANI LANGUAGE

Euro Talk. Talk Now! Azeri. 2008. 29.99 *(978-1-84352-424-3(4))* TOPICS Entertainment.

Householder, Fred W. & Lotfi, Mansour. Basic course in Azerbaijani. (Uralic & Altaic Ser.). (ENG.). XIII, 275p. 210.00 ***(978-3-11-207672-9(9))***; 135.00 ***(978-3-11-102434-9(2))*** De Gruyter, Mouton DEU. Dist: de Gruyter, Walter GmbH & Co. KG.

Icon Group International, Inc. Staff, compiled by. Webster's Azerbaijani - English Thesaurus Dictionary. 2008. 75p. ring bd. 28.95 incl. audio compact disk *(978-0-497-83432-6(4))* Icon Group International, Inc.

AZERI LANGUAGE

see Azerbaijani Language

AZIDES

Al-Ghamdi, Khalid. Structural Stability & Vibrational Spectra of Some Organoazides. 2010. 184p. pap. *(978-3-8383-3951-1(7))* Lambert Academic Publishing.

Bräse, Stefan & Banert, Klaus, eds. Organic Azides: Syntheses & Applications. 2010. (ENG., Illus.). 536p. 200.00 *(978-0-470-51998-1(3),* Wiley) Wiley, John & Sons, Inc.

AZO COMPOUNDS

see also Azo Dyes

Ikeda, Tomiki. Smart Light-Responsive Materials: Azobenzene-Containing Polymers & Liquid Crystals. Zhao, Yue & Ikeda, Tomiki, eds. 2009. (ENG., Illus.). 522p. 166.00 *(978-0-470-17578-1(8),* Wiley-Interscience) Wiley, John & Sons, Inc.

AZO DYES

Atacag Erkurt, Hatice, ed. Biodegradation of Azo Dyes. 2010. (Handbook of Environmental Chemistry Ser.). (ENG., Illus.). xiv, 214p. 259.00 *(978-3-642-11846-3(1),* 3642118461) Springer.

Erler Kubilay, Yesim. Dye Treatment with Fungi. 2009. 184p. pap. *(978-3-639-03372-4(8))* VDM Verlag Dr. Mueller e.K.

AZOLE

see Pyrrol

AZOREANS

Bolton, Mary H. Dream Garden: An Immigrant's Story. 2007. (Illus.). vii, 125p. *(978-0-9763106-5-5(1))* Abecedarian Bks.

Leal, João. Azorean Identity in Brazil & the United States: Arguments about History, Culture, & Transnational Connections. Graca, Wendy, tr. from POR. 2011. (Portuguese in the Americas Ser.). 192p. pap. 24.95 *(978-1-933227-31-3(1))* Tagus Pr.

Williams, Jerry R. In Pursuit of Their Dreams: A History of Azorean Immigration to the United States. 2nd ed. 2007. (Portuguese in the Americas Ser.). (Illus.). 216p. pap. 22.95 *(978-1-933227-19-1(2))* Tagus Pr.

AZORES

Costa, Susana Goulart & Adão, Deolinda Maria. Azores: Nine Islands, One History = Açores: Nove Ilhas, Uma Historia. 2008. (POR & ENG.). *(978-0-9819336-0-3(2))* Univ. of California, Institute of Governmental Studies.

AZORES—DESCRIPTION AND TRAVEL

Murray, Charles Augustus. Murray's Travels in North America: During the Years 1834, 1835 & 1836, Including a Summer Residence with the Pawnee Tribe of Indians in the Remote Prairies of ... & the Azore Islands. 2007. (Travel in America Ser.). (ENG.). 496p. 49.95 *(978-1-4290-0210-3(7))* Applewood Bks.

—Murray's Travels in North America 1839: During the Years 1834, 1835 & 1836, Including a Summer Residence with the Pawnee Tribe of Indians in the Remote Prairies of the Missouri & a Visit to Cuba & the Azore Islands. 2007. (Travel in America Ser.). (ENG.). 496p. per. 24.95 *(978-1-4290-0211-0(5))* Applewood Bks.

Sayers, David. Azores. 4th rev. ed. 2010. (Bradt Travel Guide Ser.). (ENG., Illus.). 272p. pap. 23.99 *(978-1-84162-328-3(8))* Bradt Travel Guides GBR. Dist: Globe Pequot Pr., The.

Stieglitz, Andreas. The Azores. 2nd ed. (Illus.). 136p. pap. 14.95 *(978-1-85691-170-2(5))* Sunflower Bks. (UK) GBR. Dist: Hunter Publishing, Inc.

—Landscapes of the Azores: A Countryside Guide. 4th ed. 2006. (Illus.). 136p. pap. 15.99 *(978-1-85691-308-9(2))* Hunter Publishing, Inc.

AZTEC ART

Diel, Lori Boornazian. The Tira de Tepechpan: Negotiating Place under Aztec & Spanish Rule. 2008. (ENG., Illus.). 208p. (C). 65.00 *(978-0-292-71831-9(4))* Univ. of Texas Pr.

Douglas, Eduardo de J. In the Palace of Nezahualcoyotl: Painting Manuscripts, Writing the Pre-Hispanic Past in Early Colonial Period Tetzcoco, Mexico. 2010. (ENG., Illus.). 288p. 60.00 *(978-0-292-72168-5(4))* Univ. of Texas Pr.

Henderson, Lucia. Producer of the Living, Eater of the Dead: Revealing Tlaltecuhtli, the Two-Faced Aztec Earth. 2007. (Bar S Ser.). (Illus.). iv, 71p. (C). pap. 62.50 *(978-1-4073-0083-2(0))* British Archaeological Reports Ltd. GBR. Dist: Brown, David Bk. Co., The.

Marsden, Allish. Frisbee. 2010. 177p. pap. 16.00 *(978-1-4461-3381-1(8))* Lulu Enterprises Inc.

Peperstraete, Sylvie, ed. Image & Ritual in the Aztec World. 2009. (Bar S Ser.). (SPA & ENG., Illus.). 134p. (C). 75.00 *(978-1-4073-0378-9(3))* British Archaeological Reports Ltd. GBR. Dist: Brown, David Bk. Co., The.

Rabasa, José. Tell Me the Story of How I Conquered You: Elsewheres & Ethnosuicide in the Colonial Mesoamerican World. 2011. (ENG., Illus.). 280p. 55.00 *(978-0-292-72875-2(1))* Univ. of Texas Pr.

Villela, Khristaan D. & Miller, Mary, eds. The Aztec Calendar Stone. 2010. (ENG., Illus.). 344p. 49.00 *(978-1-60606-004-9(X)*, Getty Research Institute) Getty Pubns.

AZTEC CALENDAR

Bowditch, Charles P. Mexican & Central American Antiquities, Calendar Systems, & History. 682p. reprint ed. 128.00 *(978-0-7222-9682-0(7))* Library Reprints, Inc.

Nuttall, Zelia. Fundamental Principles of Old & New World Civilization. (HU PMP Ser.: Vol. 2). 65.00 *(978-0-527-01190-1(8))* Periodicals Service Co.

Villela, Khristaan D. & Miller, Mary, eds. The Aztec Calendar Stone. 2010. (ENG., Illus.). 344p. 49.00 *(978-1-60606-004-9(X)*, Getty Research Institute) Getty Pubns.

AZTEC GODS

see also Quetzalcoatl (Aztec Deity)

Henderson, Lucia. Producer of the Living, Eater of the Dead: Revealing Tlaltecuhtli, the Two-Faced Aztec Earth. 2007. (Bar S Ser.). (Illus.). iv, 71p. (C). pap. 62.50 *(978-1-4073-0083-2(0))* British Archaeological Reports Ltd. GBR. Dist: Brown, David Bk. Co., The.

Olivier, Guilhem. Mockeries & Metamorphoses of an Aztec God: Tezcatlipoca, Lord of the Smoking Mirror. Besson, Michel, tr. 2008. (Mesoamerican Worlds Ser.). Orig. Title: Moqueries et Metamorphoses d'un Dieu Azteque. (ENG., Illus.). 403p. pap. 45.00 *(978-0-87081-907-0(0))* Univ. Pr. of Colorado.

AZTEC LANGUAGE

see Nahuatl Language

AZTEC LITERATURE

see Nahuatl Literature

AZTECS

Asselbergs, Florine G. L. Conquered Conquistadors: The Lienzo de Quauhquechollan: A Nahua Vision of the Conquest of Guatemala. 2008. (Mesoamerican Worlds Ser.). (ENG., Illus.). 400p. pap. 45.00 *(978-0-87081-899-8(6))* Univ. Pr. of Colorado.

Ballou, Maturin Murray. Aztec Land. 2010. 376p. pap. 33.75 *(978-1-177-67354-9(1))*; 372p. pap. 32.75 *(978-1-143-52607-7(4))*; 376p. pap. 33.75 *(978-1-141-97008-7(2))* BiblioBazaar.

—Aztec Land. 2009. 188p. pap. *(978-0-217-18061-0(2))*; pap. *(978-1-4590-9460-4(3))* Books LLC.

—Aztec Land. 2009. 258p. pap. *(978-1-4099-8699-7(3))* Dodo Pr.

—Aztec Land. 2010. (Illus.). 156p. pap. 24.39 *(978-1-153-82145-2(1))* General Bks. LLC.

Balutet, Nicolas. Homosexualité et Imaginaire Sexuel Chez les Aztèques. 2008. (Bar S Ser.). (FRE., Illus.). 193p. (C). pap. 87.50 *(978-1-4073-0309-3(0))* British Archaeological Reports Ltd. GBR. Dist: Brown, David Bk. Co., The.

Bandelier, Adolph F. A. On the Social Organization & Mode of Government of the Ancient Mexicans. 699p. reprint ed. 128.00 *(978-0-7222-9695-0(9))* Library Reprints, Inc.

Bateman, Dewayne. Aztec Indians. 2010. 48p. pap. 15.99 *(978-1-4500-6484-2(1))* Xlibris Corp.

Berger, Uta. Die Anatomie der Azteken: Bernardino de Sahagúns anatomischer Bericht aus dem Codex Florentinus, Buch 10, Kapitel 27. 2010. (Marburger Schriften zur Medizingeschichte Ser.). (GER.). 268p. 67.95 *(978-3-631-61266-8(4))* Lang, Peter GmbH, Europaischer Verlag der Wissenschaften DEU. Dist: Lang, Peter.

Biart, Lucien. The Aztecs: Their History, Manners, & Customs. 2010. 354p. pap. 32.75 *(978-1-149-16413-6(1))* 2008. 352p. 28.99 *(978-0-554-42107-0(0))* 2008. 352p. pap. 31.75 *(978-0-554-42105-6(4))* 2008. 352p. 29.99 *(978-0-554-42097-4(X))* 2008. 352p. pap. 32.75 *(978-0-554-42099-8(6))* BiblioBazaar.

Bierhorst, John. Codex Chimalpopoca: The Text in Nahuatl with a Glossary & Grammatical Notes. 2011. (ENG.). 210p. pap. 29.95 *(978-0-8165-0245-5(5))* Univ. of Arizona Pr.

Billingslea, Wesley. The Aztecs. 2007. (Lost Cultures Ser.). (Illus.). 108p. per. 14.95 *(978-0-9791644-0-8(0))* Teotl Publishing, Inc.

Brumfiel, Elizabeth M. & Feinman, Gary M. The Aztec World. Brumfiel, Elizabeth M. & Feinman, Gary M., eds. 2008. (ENG., Illus.). 272p. 55.00 *(978-0-8109-7278-0(6))* Abrams.

—The Aztec World. 2008. (Illus.). xix, 252p. pap. 26.95 *(978-0-8109-8309-0(5))* Abrams.

Brundage, Burr Cartwright. A Rain of Darts. 2012. (ENG.). 372p. pap. 30.00 ***(978-0-292-73993-2(1))*** Univ. of Texas Pr.

Carrasco, David. The Aztecs. 2011. (Very Short Introductions Ser.). (ENG., Illus.). 160p. pap. 11.95 ***(978-0-19-537938-9(1))*** Oxford Univ. Pr., Inc.

Carrasco, David & Sessions, Scott. Daily Life of the Aztecs, 1 vol. 2nd rev. ed. (Greenwood Press Daily Life Through History Ser.). (Illus.). 288p. 49.95 *(978-0-313-37744-0(8)*, GR7744) Greenwood Publishing Group, Inc.

Carrasco, David & Sessions, Scott. Daily Life of the Aztecs: People of the Sun & Earth. 2008. 304p. (C). reprint ed. pap. 14.95 *(978-0-87220-933-6(4))* Hackett Publishing Co., Inc.

Carrasco, David, et al. Breaking Through Mexico's Past: Digging the Aztecs with Eduardo Matos Moctezuma. 2007. (ENG., Illus.). 195p. 34.95 *(978-0-8263-3831-0(3))* Univ. of New Mexico Pr.

Chipman, Donald E. Moctezuma's Children: Aztec Royalty under Spanish Rule, 1520-1700. 2010. (ENG., Illus.). 224p. pap. 25.00 *(978-0-292-72597-3(3))* Univ. of Texas Pr.

Clendinnen, Inga. The Cost of Courage in Aztec Society: Essays on Mesoamerican Society & Culture. 2010. (ENG., Illus.). 224p. (C). 85.00 *(978-0-521-51811-6(3))*; pap. 24.99 *(978-0-521-73207-9(7))* Cambridge Univ. Pr.

Cline, Sarah L. Colonial Culhuacan, 1580-1600: A Social History of an Aztec Town. 280p. 2009. 56.00 *(978-1-59740-346-7(6))* 2008. pap. 28.00 *(978-1-59740-664-2(3))* ACLS Humanities E-Book.

Connell, William F. After Moctezuma: Indigenous Politics & Self-Government in Mexico City, 1524-1730. 2011. (ENG., Illus.). 352p. (C). 45.00 *(978-0-8061-4175-6(1))* Univ. of Oklahoma Pr.

Cruz Garcia, Alvaro. Los Aztecas. 2008. (Vida y costumbres en la Antiguedad Ser.). (ENG.). 192p. 9.95 *(978-84-9764-836-3(6))* Edimat Libros, S. A. ESP. Dist: Independent Pubs. Group.

Deane, Zain. Mexico's Aztec & Maya Empires - An Explorer's Guide. 2011. (Explorer's Complete Ser.). (ENG., Illus.). 400p. pap. 21.95 *(978-1-58157-107-3(0)*, 157107) Countryman Pr.

Domenici, Davide. The Aztecs: History & Treasures of an Ancient Civilization. (ENG., Illus.). 208p. 2009. 19.98 *(978-88-544-0459-5(4)*, White Star Promotional) 2007. 35.00 *(978-88-544-0239-3(7)*, White Star) Rizzoli International Pubns., Inc.

Dossick, Philip. Aztecs: Epoch of Social Revolution. 2011. 212p. 27.95 *(978-1-4502-9719-6(6))*; pap. 17.95 *(978-1-4502-9718-9(8))* iUniverse, Inc.

Douglas, Eduardo de J. In the Palace of Nezahualcoyotl: Painting Manuscripts, Writing the Pre-Hispanic Past in Early Colonial Period Tetzcoco, Mexico. 2010. (ENG., Illus.). 288p. 60.00 *(978-0-292-72168-5(4))* Univ. of Texas Pr.

Elliott, J. H., intro. William H. Prescott's History of the Conquest of Mexico. 2009. (Continuums Histories Ser.). (ENG.). 160p. pap. 16.95 *(978-1-4411-4699-1(7))* Continuum International Publishing Group, Ltd. GBR. Dist: National Bk. Network.

Endredy, James. The Flying Witches of Veracruz: A Shaman's True Story of Indigenous Witchcraft, Devil's Weed, & Trance Healing in Aztec Brujeria. 2011. (ENG.). 240p. pap. 14.95 *(978-0-7387-2756-1(3))* Llewellyn Pubns.

Hagen, Victor W. Von. The Ancient Sun Kingdoms of the Americas: Aztec, Maya, Inca. 2011. 650p. 63.95 ***(978-1-258-04155-7(3))*** Literary Licensing, LLC.

Headrick, Annabeth. The Teotihuacan Trinity: The Sociopolitical Structure of an Ancient Mesoamerican City. 2010. (ENG., Illus.). 230p. pap. 30.00 *(978-0-292-72309-2(1))* Univ. of Texas Pr.

Izeki, Mutsumi, ed. Conceptualization of 'Xihuitl' History, Environment & Cultural Dynamics in Postclassic Mexica Cognition. 2008. (Bar S Ser.). (Illus.). 191p. (C). 87.50 *(978-1-4073-0346-8(5))* British Archaeological Reports Ltd. GBR. Dist: Brown, David Bk. Co., The.

Knab, Timothy J. The Dialogue of Earth & Sky: Dreams, Souls, Curing, & the Modern Aztec Underworld. 2009. (ENG.). 179p. pap. 21.95 *(978-0-8165-2880-6(2))* Univ. of Arizona Pr.

Lara, Jaime. Christian Texts for Aztecs: Art & Liturgy in Colonial Mexico. 2008. (ENG., Illus.). 336p. 75.00 *(978-0-268-03379-8(X))* Univ. of Notre Dame Pr.

Lee, Jongsoo. The Allure of Nezahualcoyotl: Pre-Hispanic History, Religion, & Nahua Poetics. 2008. (ENG., Illus.). 294p. 45.00 *(978-0-8263-4337-6(6))* Univ. of New Mexico Pr.

Leon-Portillo, Miguel. The Broken Spears 2007: The Aztec Account of the Conquest of Mexico. 2nd rev. ed. 2006. (ENG., Illus.). 264p. per. 19.00 *(978-0-8070-5500-7(X))* Beacon Pr.

Madsen, William. Christo-Paganism: A Study of Mexican Religious Syncretism. 2011. 76p. 37.95 ***(978-1-258-02011-8(4))*** Literary Licensing, LLC.

—The Virgin's Children: Life in an Aztec Village Today. 2011. 266p. 47.95 ***(978-1-258-08563-6(1))*** Literary Licensing, LLC.

Medin, Tzvi. Mito y Pragmatismo e Imperialismo: La Conciencia Social en la Conquista Del Imperio Azteca. 2009. (SPA.). 298p. pap. 24.80 *(978-84-8489-416-2(9))* Iberoamericana Vervuert Publishing Corp.

Mould, Paul, ed. Sayola: The Conquest of the Aztecs. 2008. 291p. pap. 24.00 *(978-1-58690-081-6(1))* Mould, Paul Publishing GBR. Dist: Gazelle Bk.Services Ltd.

Olivier, Guilhem. Mockeries & Metamorphoses of an Aztec God: Tezcatlipoca, Lord of the Smoking Mirror. Besson, Michel, tr. 2008. (Mesoamerican Worlds Ser.). Orig. Title: Moqueries et Metamorphoses d'un Dieu Azteque. (ENG., Illus.). 403p. pap. 45.00 *(978-0-87081-907-0(0))* Univ. Pr. of Colorado.

Pennock, Caroline Dodds. Bonds of Blood: Gender, Lifecycle, & Sacrifice in Aztec Culture. 2008. (Early Modern History: Society & Culture Ser.). (ENG., Illus.). 256p. 85.00 *(978-0-230-00330-9(3))* Palgrave Macmillan.

Peperstraete, Sylvie, et al. La "Chronique X" Reconstitution et Analyse D'une Source Perdue Fondamentale Sur la Civilisation Aztèque, D'après L'Historia de Las Indias de Nueva España de D. Durán (1581) et la Crónica Mexicana de F.A. Tezozomoc (Ca. 1598) 2007. (Bar S Ser.). (FRE & SPA., Illus.). 602p. (C). 132.50 *(978-1-4073-0044-3(X))* British Archaeological Reports Ltd. GBR. Dist: Brown, David Bk. Co., The.

Pohl, John & Lyons, Claire. The Aztec Pantheon & the Art of Empire. 2010. (Illus.). 104p. 25.00 *(978-1-60606-007-0(4))* Getty Pubns.

Prescott, William Hickling. History of the Conquest of Mexico. 2009. 456p. pap. *(978-0-217-25446-5(2))*; 372p. pap. *(978-0-217-49516-5(8))*; 288p. pap. *(978-0-217-49519-6(2))*; 312p. pap. *(978-0-217-93504-3(4))*; 420p. pap. *(978-0-217-93074-1(3))*; 332p. pap. *(978-0-217-22571-7(3))*; 420p. pap. *(978-0-217-22573-1(X))*; 396p. pap. *(978-0-217-25876-0(X))* Books LLC.

—History of the Conquest of Mexico. 2008. (ENG.). 532p. per. *(978-1-4086-4399-0(5))* Read Bks.

Prescott, William Hickling & Kirk, John Foster. HISTORY OF THE CONQUEST OF MEXICO. 2008. xxviii, 1010p. pap. ***(978-1-4351-1346-6(2))*** Barnes & Noble, Inc.

Saville, Marshall H. Narrative of Some Things of New Spain & of the Great City of Temestitan Mexico. 2009. 98p. pap. 18.75 *(978-1-115-94012-2(0))*; pap. 18.75 *(978-1-115-94011-5(2))* BiblioBazaar.

Sider, Sandra. Handbook to Life in Renaissance Europe. 2007. (ENG., Illus.). 410p. per. 25.00 *(978-0-19-533084-7(6))* Oxford Univ. Pr., Inc.

Smith, Michael E. Aztec City-State Capitals. 2008. (Ancient Cities of the New World Ser.). (ENG., Illus.). 256p. pap. 27.95 *(978-0-8130-3245-0(8))* Univ. Pr. of Florida.

Smith, Michael E. The Aztecs. 3rd ed. 2012. (Peoples of America Ser.). (ENG., Illus.). 416p. pap. 36.95 ***(978-1-4051-9497-6(9)***, Wiley-Blackwell) Wiley, John & Sons, Inc.

Thomson, Hugh. Tequila Oil: Getting Lost in Mexico. 2010. (ENG., Illus.). 240p. 16.95 *(978-0-7538-2694-2(1)*, Phoenix) Orion Publishing Group, Ltd. GBR. Dist: Independent Pubs. Group.

Tinker, Clif. The Aztec Theater: San Antonio's Grand Illusion. 2011. (ENG.). 224p. pap. 17.95 *(978-0-916727-48-2(3))* Wings Pr.

Tomlinson, Gary. The Singing of the New World: Indigenous Voice in the Era of European Contact. 2009. (New Perspectives in Music History & Criticism Ser.). (ENG., Illus.). 232p. pap. 34.99 *(978-0-521-11017-4(3))* Cambridge Univ. Pr.

Tomo, Grandes de, ed. Los Grandes - Cuauhtemoc. 2007. 128p. pap. 5.95 *(978-970-666-950-6(7))* Grupo Editorial Tomo, S.A. de C.V. MEX. Dist: Giron Bks.

Townsend, Richard. The Aztecs. 3rd rev. ed. 2009. (Ancient Peoples & Places Ser.). (ENG., Illus.). 256p. pap. 24.95 *(978-0-500-28791-0(0)*, 528791) Thames & Hudson.

Wertheimer, Eric. Imagined Empires: Incas, Aztecs, & the New World of American Literature, 1771-1876. 2009. (Cambridge Studies in American Literature & Culture Ser.). (ENG.). 256p. (C). pap. 38.00 *(978-0-521-11007-5(6))* Cambridge Univ. Pr.

Wolf, Gerhard & Connors, Joseph, eds. Colors Between Two Worlds: The Florentine Codex of Bernardino de Sahagún. 2012. (Villa I Tatti Ser.: 28). (ENG., Illus.). 506p. 70.00 ***(978-0-674-06462-1(3))*** Villa I Tatti.

AZTECS—ART

see Aztec Art

AZTECS—CALENDAR

see Aztec Calendar

AZTECS—FOLKLORE

Meza, Otilia. Leyendas Mexicas y Mayas.Tr. of Mexican/Mayan Legends. (SPA., Illus.). 163p. 12.98 *(978-968-38-0241-5(9))* Panorama Editorial MEX. Dist: Continental Bk. Co., Inc.

AZTECS—LEGENDS

see Aztecs—Folklore

AZUELA, MARIANO, 1873-1952

Azuela, Arturo. Prisma de Mariano Azuela. 2009. (SPA., Illus.). 346p. 27.00 *(978-970-722-013-3(9))* Plaza y Valdes, S.A. de C.V. MEX. Dist: Sony Electronics.

Azuela, Mariano. Los de Abajo.Tr. of Underdogs. (SPA.). 7.50 *(978-956-13-0579-3(8))* Bello, Andres CHL. Dist: AIMS International Bks., Inc.

B

B CELLS

see also Burkitt's Lymphoma

Basu, Subhendu. Somatic Hypermutation in Peyers Patch Germinal Centers & the Gut Environment. 2008. 180p. pap. *(978-3-639-05917-5(4))* VDM Verlag Dr. Mueller e.K.

Bronner, Felix, et al, eds. Bone Resorption. 2010. (Topics in Bone Biology Ser.). (Illus.). xiv, 189p. pap. 329.00 *(978-1-84996-926-0(4)*, 1849969264) Springer.

Cancro, Michael P., ed. BLyS Ligands & Receptors. 2009. (Contemporary Immunology Ser.). (ENG., Illus.). 300p. 189.00 *(978-1-60327-012-0(4))* Humana Pr.

Cherry, Daniel A. & Jelic, Tomislav M. Bone Marrow: A Practical Manual. 2011. (ENG., Illus.). 210p. pap. 45.00 *(978-1-57059-708-4(1))* Landes Bioscience.

De Ceuninck, édéric, et al, eds. Cartilage & Osteoarthritis. 2010. (Methods in Molecular Medicine Ser.). (Illus.). 360p. pap. 159.00 *(978-1-61737-606-1(X)*, 161737606X) Humana Pr.

Gibbins, Jonathan M. & Mahaut-Smith, Martyn P., eds. Platelets & Megakaryocytes: Volume 1: Functional Assays. 2010. (Methods in Molecular Biology Ser.). (Illus.). 408p. pap. 179.00 *(978-1-61737-356-5(7)*, 1617373567) Humana Pr.

—Platelets & Megakaryocytes: Volume 2: Perspectives & Techniques. 2010. (Methods in Molecular Biology Ser.). (Illus.). 500p. pap. 199.00 *(978-1-61737-305-3(2)*, 1617373052) Humana Pr.

Gu, Hua & Rajewsky, Klaus, eds. B Cell Protocols. 2010. (Methods in Molecular Biology Ser.). (Illus.). 304p. pap. 149.00 *(978-1-61737-510-1(1)*, 1617375101) Humana Pr.

Hauge, Helena. Gene Expression Analysis in Diffuse Large B-Cell Lymphom. 2011. 72p. pap. ***(978-3-8433-7476-7(7))*** Lambert Academic Publishing.

Hauser, Jannek. Regulation of B Cell Development by Antigen Receptors. 2011. 64p. pap. ***(978-3-8443-2501-0(8))*** Lambert Academic Publishing.

Helfrich, Miep H. & Ralston, Stuart H., eds. Bone Research Protocols. 2010. (Methods in Molecular Medicine Ser.). (Illus.). 468p. pap. 159.00 *(978-1-61737-321-3(4)*, 1617373214) Humana Pr.

Hu, Jiancheng. Regulation of B Cell Migration & Antigen Receptor Signaling by Lsc. 2010. 136p. pap. *(978-3-639-27472-1(5))* VDM Verlag Dr. Mueller e.K.

Klandt, Sigrun. An Immunotoxin for the Depletion of Autoreactive B Cells in Ms. 2010. 80p. pap. *(978-3-639-28253-5(1))* VDM Verlag Dr. Mueller e.K.

Lonial, Sagar. Myeloma Therapy: Pursuing the Plasma Cell. 2008. (Contemporary Hematology Ser.). (Illus.). 550p. 159.00 *(978-1-934115-82-4(7))* Humana Pr.

Manser, Tim. Specialization & Complementation of Humoral Immune Responses to Infection. 2007. (Current Topics in Microbiology & Immunology Ser.). (Illus.). 159p. 139.00 *(978-3-540-73899-2(1))* Springer.

Moehler, Thomas & Goldschmidt, Hartmut. Multiple Myeloma. 2010. (Recent Results in Cancer Research Ser.). (Illus.). 200p. 219.00 *(978-3-540-85771-6(0)*, 3540857710) Springer.

Monroe, John G. & Rothenberg, Ellen, eds. The Molecular Biology of B-Cell & T-Cell Development. 2010. (Contemporary Immunology Ser.). 608p. pap. 239.00 *(978-1-61737-065-6(7)*, 1617370657) Humana Pr.

Nemazee, David Ahmad, ed. B Cell Biology in Autoimmunity, Vol. 6. (Current Directions in Autoimmunity Ser.: Vol. 6). (Illus.). *(978-3-8055-7454-9(1))* Karger, S. AG.

Pulendran, Bali & Ahmed, Rafi. From Innate Immunity to Immunological Memory. 2006. (Current Topics in Microbiology & Immunology Ser.). (Illus.). x, 184p. 199.00 *(978-3-540-32635-9(9)*, 3540326359) Springer.

Sabatini, Massimo, et al, eds. Cartilage & Osteoarthritis. 2010. (Methods in Molecular Medicine Ser.). (Illus.). 376p. pap. 154.00 *(978-1-61737-450-0(4)*, 1617374504) Humana Pr.

Salem, Dalia. Detection of Minimal Residual Disease in Precursor B-Cell Neoplasms. 2011. 108p. pap. ***(978-3-8443-2014-5(8))*** Lambert Academic Publishing.

Stoltz, J. F., ed. Mechanobiology: Cartilage & Chondrocyte - Volume 5 - Volume 73 Biomedical & Health Research - Book Edition of Biorheology. 2008. (Illus.). 104p. 240.00 *(978-1-58603-927-1(X))* IOS Pr., Inc.

Tariman, Joseph D. Multiple Myeloma: A Textbook for Nurses. 2010. (Illus.). 285p. *(978-1-890504-93-9(9))* Oncology Nursing Society.

Toeh, Gerrard K. H. Towards Individualized Therapy for Multiple Myeloma: A Guide for Choosing Treatment That Best Fits Patients. 2009. 200p. pap. 58.00 *(978-981-283-579-6(2))* World Scientific Publishing Co., Inc.

B-FIFTY-TWO BOMBER

Holmes, Charles/W & Holmes, Merelyn. Big BUF: Tales the B52 Bomber & the Sac Pilots Who Flew them in the Era of the Vietnam War. 2011. (Illus.). 280p. pap. 18.95 ***(978-1-59630-073-6(6)***, BeachHouse Bks.) Science & Humanities Pr.

B-SEVENTEEN BOMBER

Ayers, Travis L. The Bomber Boys: Heroes Who Flew the B17s in World War II. l.t. ed. 2010. (ENG.). 418p. 31.50 *(978-1-4104-2569-0(X))* Thorndike Pr.

Best, Gary A. Belle of the Brawl: Letters Home from a B-17 Bombardier. 2010. (ENG.). 422p. pap. 24.95 *(978-1-59299-489-2(X))* Inkwater Pr.

Douglas, Graeme. Boeing B-17 Flying Fortress Manual: 1935 Onwards. 2011. (ENG., Illus.). 160p. 28.00 *(978-0-7603-4077-6(3)*, 0760340773, Zenith Pr.) MBI Publishing Co. LLC.

Foxx, Sly & Poling, Sylvester. No Names Please. 2010. 272p. pap. 17.48 *(978-1-4269-0754-8(0))* Trafford Publishing.

Frater, Stephen. Hell above Earth: The Incredible True Story of an American WWII Bomber Commander & the Copilot Ordered to Kill Him. 2012. (ENG., Illus.). 320p. 25.99 ***(978-0-312-61792-9(5))*** St. Martin's Pr.

Listemann, Phil H. Boeing Fortress Mk.I. 2009. (Illus.). 40p. pap. 20.95 *(978-2-9532544-2-6(0))* Listemann, Philippe FRA. Dist: Casemate Pubs. & Bk. Distributors, LLC.

Pitts, Jesse Richard. Return to Base: Memoirs of a B-17 Co-Pilot Kimbolton: England, 1943-1944. 2006. (ENG., Illus.). 288p. pap. 24.95 *(978-0-7524-4025-5(X))* History Pr. Ltd.,The GBR. Dist: Independent Pubs. Group.

Simons, Graham S. & Friedman, Harry. B-17 - the Fifteen Ton Flying Fortress. 2011. (Illus.). 256p. 39.95 ***(978-1-84884-538-1(3))*** Pen & Sword Bks. Ltd. GBR. Dist: Casemate Pubs. & Bk. Distributors, LLC.

Sly Foxx, Foxx & Poling, Sylvester. No Names Please. 2010. 272p. 27.48 *(978-1-4269-0755-5(9))* Trafford Publishing.

Webster, George. The Savage Sky. 2007. (Stackpole Military History Ser.). (ENG., Illus.). 256p. pap. 16.95 *(978-0-8117-3388-5(2))* Stackpole Bks.

B-TWENTY-FOUR BOMBER

Armstrong, Robert H. & Newby, Leroy W. Angel on Our Wing. (Illus.). 360p. 24.95 *(978-0-9632257-0-2(7))* Armstrong, Robert H.

Auton, Jim. RAF Liberator over the Eastern Front: A Bomb Aimer's Second World War & Cold War Story. 2008. (Illus.). 224p. 39.95 *(978-1-84415-729-7(6))* Pen & Sword Bks. Ltd. GBR. Dist: Casemate Pubs. & Bk. Distributors, LLC.

Bodie, Peter. Liberators in England in World War II: Rare Photographs from Wartime Archives. 2009. (Illus.). 144p. pap. 25.99 *(978-1-84415-821-8(7))* Pen & Sword Bks. Ltd. GBR. Dist: Casemate Pubs. & Bk. Distributors, LLC.

Craig, Bruce Galvin. Survival: Self & Country, WWII: Combat Adventures of a B24 Navigator. 2011. 272p. 28.99 ***(978-1-4670-3521-7(1))***; pap. 19.95 ***(978-1-4670-3519-4(X))*** AuthorHouse.

Davis, James M. In Hostile Skies: An Americn B-24 Pilot in World War II. Snead, David L., ed. 2007. (North Texas Military Biography & Memoir Ser.). (ENG., Illus.). 256p. per. 14.95 *(978-1-57441-239-0(6))* Univ. of North Texas Pr.

Freeland, Kent. A Street Called Darwin. 2008. 164p. pap. 15.95 *(978-0-595-53112-7(1))* iUniverse, Inc.

Griffith, Alan. Consolidated Mess: The Illustrated Guide to Nose-Turreted B-24 Production Variants in USAAF Combat Service. 2010. (Illus.). 156p. pap. 59.00 *(978-83-61421-16-0(5))* Stratus, Wydawnictwo, Juszczak, Artur POL. Dist: Casemate Pubs. & Bk. Distributors, LLC.

Scearce, Phil. Finish Forty & Home: The Untold World War II Story of B-24s in the Pacific. 2011. (Mayborn Literary Nonfiction Ser.). (Illus.). 352p. 29.95 ***(978-1-57441-316-8(3))*** Univ. of North Texas Pr.

B-TWENTY-NINE BOMBER

Abernathy, Jack N. We Called Ourselves Sailgers. 2010. 60p. pap. 10.49 *(978-1-4490-7158-5(9))* AuthorHouse.

Campbell, Richard H. The Silverplate Bombers: A History & Registry of the Enola Gay & Other B-29s Configured to Carry Atomic Bombs. alt. ed. 2012. (ENG., Illus.). 245p. pap. 25.00 ***(978-0-7864-6907-9(2))*** McFarland & Co., Inc. Pubs.

Harris, Samuel R. B-29s over Japan 1944-1945: A Group Commander's Diary. Mann, Robert A., ed. 2011. (ENG., Illus.). 267p. pap. 35.00 *(978-0-7864-6297-1(3))* McFarland & Co., Inc. Pubs.

Mann, Robert A. The B-29 Superfortress Chronology, 1934-1960. 2009. (ENG.). 319p. pap. 49.95 *(978-0-7864-4274-4(3))* McFarland & Co., Inc. Pubs.

Wolk, Herman S. Cataclysm: General Hap Arnold & the Defeat of Japan. 2010. (ENG., Illus.). 344p. 24.95 *(978-1-57441-281-9(7))* Univ. of North Texas Pr.

BAAL (DEITY)

B. O'Brien Books Staff. The First Church of Baal at Ferguson, MO. 400p. pap. 12.00 *(978-0-9703598-0-3(2))* O'Brien, Bill.

Harfouche, Christian. Battles of the Elohim: They walked as Men. 2010. (ENG.). 280p. *(978-1-888966-14-5(9))* M.E.D.I.A. Group.

Harfouche, Christian & Harfouche, Robin. Battles of the Elohim: They Walked As Men. 2011. (ENG.). 240p. 24.99 *(978-0-7684-3783-6(0))* Destiny Image Pubs.

Ortlund, Eric. Theophany & Chaoskampf: The Interpretation of Theophanic Imagery in the Baal Epic, Isaiah, & the Twelve. 2010. 104.00 *(978-1-61719-160-2(4))* Gorgias Pr., LLC.

Smith, Mark S. T. & Pitard, Wayne, eds. The Ugaritic Baal Cycle: Volume II. Introduction with Text, Translation & Commentary of KTU/CAT 1. 3-1. 4. 2008. (Vetus Testamentum Supplements Ser.). 840p. *(978-90-04-15348-6(9))* BRILL.

BAAL SHEM TOV, CA. 1700-1760

Buxbaum, Yitzhak & Buxbaum. Light & Fire of the Baal Shem Tov. 2006. (ENG.). 448p. pap. 24.95 *(978-0-8264-1888-3(0))* Continuum International Publishing Group, Ltd. GBR. Dist: National Bk. Network.

Cohn, Tzvi Meir. Baal Shem Tov Numbers: Mystical Stories of the Legendary Kaballah Master, Vol. 4. 2012. Orig. Title: Faith Love Joy. (ENG.). pap. 14.95 *(978-0-9792865-5-1(7))* BST Publishing.

Cohn, Tzvi Meir, adapted by. Baal Shem Tov Leviticus: Mystical Stories on the Weekly Torah Portion. 2012. Orig. Title: Faith Love Joy. (ENG.). pap. 14.95 *(978-0-9792865-4-4(9))* BST Publishing.

Etkes, Immanuel. The Besht: Magician, Mystic, & Leader. 2012. (Tauber Institute Series for the Study of European Jewry Ser.). (ENG.). 350p. pap. 40.00 ***(978-1-61168-308-0(4)***, Brandeis University Press) Univ. Pr. of New England.

Feinstein, Michoel, ed. Baal Shem Tov Heart of Prayer: Rabbi Yisrael Ben Eliezer, vols. 3, no. 3. Shore, Eliezer, tr. 2010. (ENG.). 239p. pap. 14.95 *(978-0-9792865-6-8(5))* BST Publishing.

Glazer, Aubrey L., ed. Pillar of Prayer: Guidance in Contemplative Prayer, Sacred Study, & the Spiritual Life, from the Baal Shem Tov & His Circle. Kallus, Menachem, tr. 2011. (Fons Vitae Spiritual Affinities Ser.). (ENG.). 372p. pap. 24.95 ***(978-1-891785-79-5(6))*** Fons Vitae of Kentucky, Inc.

Kornblau, Yitcho. A Never Ending Tale: Illustrated Parables of the Ba'al Shem Tov & His Disciples. 2009. 57p. 21.99 *(978-1-59826-318-3(8))* Feldheim Pubs.

BAALSRUD, JAN, 1917-1988

Howarth, David. We Die Alone: A WWII Epic of Escape & Endurance. 2007. (ENG., Illus.). 232p. pap. 16.95 *(978-1-59921-063-6(0)*; Lyons Pr.) Globe Pequot Pr., The.

Scott, Astrid Karlsen & Haug, Tore. Defiant Courage: A WWII Epic of Escape & Endurance. 2010. (ENG., Illus.). 368p. pap. 16.95 *(978-1-61608-160-7(0)*, 608160) Skyhorse Publishing Co., Inc.

BAB, 1819-1850

see Bab, Ali Muhammad Shirazi, 1819-1850

BAB, ALI MUHAMMAD SHIRAZI, 1819-1850

Kerr, Gordon. Tarikh IJadid or New History of Mirza Al. 2006. 344p. per. *(978-1-4067-0118-0(1)*, Hesperides Pr.) Read Bks.

Lawson, Todd. Babism & the Qur'an: The Literary Beginnings of the Babi Movement. 2012. (Iranian Studies). (ENG., Illus.). 240p. (C). 135.00 *(978-0-415-49539-4(3))* Routledge.

Saiedi, Nader. Gate of the Heart: Understanding the Writings of the Bfb. 2010. (Bahf#237; Studies). (Illus.). 432p. pap. 42.95 *(978-1-55458-056-9(0))* Wilfrid Laurier Univ. Pr. CAN. Dist: Univ. of Toronto Pr.

BABAR, EMPEROR OF HINDUSTAN, 1483-1530

Grenard, Fernand. Baber First of the Moguls. 2007. (ENG.). 286p. 43.95 *(978-0-548-01502-5(3))* Kessinger Publishing, LLC.

Lane-Poole, Stanley. Babar. 2007. (ENG.). 208p. 39.95 *(978-0-548-05039-2(2))* Kessinger Publishing, LLC.

BABAR (FICTITIOUS CHARACTER)

Nelson, Christine. Drawing Babar: Early Drafts & Watercolors. 2008. (Illus.). xi, 150p. *(978-0-87598-151-2(8))*; pap. *(978-0-87598-152-9(6))* Pierpont Morgan Library.

BABBAGE, CHARLES, 1792-1871

Babbage, Charles. Babbage's Calculating Engines: Being a Collection of Papers Relating to them; their History & Construction. Babbage, Henry P., ed. 2010. (Cambridge Library Collection - Mathematics Ser.). (ENG.). 388p. pap. 31.99 *(978-1-108-00096-3(7))* Cambridge Univ. Pr.

—Decline of Science in England. 2007. 108p. per. *(978-1-4068-1228-2(5))* Echo Library.

—Science & Reform: Selected Works of Charles Babbage. Hyman, Anthony, ed. 2007. (ENG.). 368p. pap. 74.00 *(978-0-521-03676-4(3))* Cambridge Univ. Pr.

BABBITT, IRVING, 1865-1933

Babbitt, Irving. Spanish Character & Other Essays: With a Bibliography of His Publications & an Index to His Collected Works. Manchester, Frederick et al, eds. reprint ed. 34.50 *(978-0-404-20013-8(3))* AMS Pr., Inc.

Levin, Harry. Irving Babbitt & the Teaching of Literature. 2011. 30p. 35.95 ***(978-1-258-02374-4(1))*** Literary Licensing, LLC.

McKean, Keith F. The Moral Measure of Literature. 2011. 136p. 40.95 ***(978-1-258-07346-6(3))*** Literary Licensing, LLC.

BABEL, I. (ISAAK), 1894-1941

Babel, Isaac. Isaac Babel's Selected Writings. Freidin, Gregory, ed. Constantine, Peterr, tr. from RUS. 2009. (Norton Critical Edition Ser.). (ENG., Illus.). 520p. (C). pap. 16.00 net. *(978-0-393-92703-0(2)*, 92703) Norton, W. W. & Co., Inc.

Balke, Florian. Europäische Oper und russische Moderne: Musiktheatralisches in den Texten Innokentij Annenskijs, Michail Kuzmins und Isaak Babels. 2009. (Slavische Literaturen. Texte und Abhandlungen Ser.). (GER.). 652p. pap. 141.95 *(978-3-631-58383-8(4))* Lang, Peter GmbH, Europaischer Verlag der Wissenschaften DEU. Dist: Lang, Peter.

Blake, Patricia. The Unfinished Life & Work of Isaac Babel. 2007. *(978-0-374-28151-9(3))* Farrar, Straus & Giroux.

Freidin, Gregory, ed. The Enigma of Isaac Babel: Biography, History, Context. 2009. (ENG., Illus.). 288p. 60.00 *(978-0-8047-5903-8(0))* Stanford Univ. Pr.

Stanton, Rebecca Jane. Isaac Babel & the Self-Invention of Odessan Modernism. 2012. (Srit Ser.). (ENG., Illus.). 186p. 45.00 ***(978-0-8101-2832-3(2))*** Northwestern Univ. Pr.

Vinokur, Val. The Trace of Judaism: Dostoevsky, Babel, Mandelstam, Levinas. 2009. (Srit Ser.). (ENG.). 216p. pap. 24.95 *(978-0-8101-2585-8(4))*; (Illus.). 69.95 *(978-0-8101-5208-3(8))* Northwestern Univ. Pr.

Zholkovskii, A. K. & IAmpolskii, M. B. Babel. (RUS.). 441p. *(978-5-900504-08-7(5))* Fraza.

BABEL, TOWER OF

Bentolila, Alain. Parle à Ceux Que Tu N'aimes Pas: Le Défi de Babel. 2010. (FRE.). 233p. pap. *(978-2-7381-2544-6(1))* Jacob, Odile.

De Lafayette, Maximillien. Baalbeck: The Anunnaki's City & Afrit Undergound. 2010. 80p. pap. 16.49 *(978-0-557-62407-2(X))* Lulu Enterprises Inc.

LaCocque, Andre. The Captivity of Innocence: Babel & the Yahwist. 2010. 206p. pap. 23.00 *(978-1-60899-353-6(1))* Wipf & Stock Pubs.

McConkie, Clay & McConkie, John, illus. A Man Named Peleg: An Exploration into the Days of Peleg. 2007. 139p. per. 13.99 *(978-1-59955-024-4(5))* Cedar Fort, Inc./CFI Distribution.

Rebuilding the Tower of Babel: The Dark side of Rick Warren's Purpose Driven Church. 2007. pap. *(978-0-9768167-1-3(7))* Cutting Edge Ministries.

BABIES

see Infants

BABIES, TEST TUBE

see Fertilization in Vitro, Human

BABISM

see also Bahai Faith

Kerr, Gordon. Tarikh IJadid or New History of Mirza Al. 2006. 344p. per. *(978-1-4067-0118-0(1)*, Hesperides Pr.) Read Bks.

Ketab Corp. Panj Maghale: Gooshehayee az tarikhe ayeene babi va Bahaie. 2007.Tr. of Five Articles. (PER.). 86p. pap. *(978-1-59584-116-2(4))* Ketab Corp.

MacEoin, Denis. The Messiah of Shiraz: Studies in Early & Middle Babism. 2008. (Iran Studies). (Illus.). 528p. *(978-90-04-17035-3(9))* BRILL.

Nabil, Azam. Dawn-Breakers. 2007. pap. 25.00 *(978-0-9762780-4-7(9))* Best Publishing.

Towfigh, Stephan Anis, et al. Ain-I Bahai: Nigarishi Kutah Bih Tarikh Va Taalim. 2010. (PER., Illus.). 169p. ***(978-3-942426-00-8(5))*** Ketab Corp.

BABOONS

Cheney, Dorothy L. & Seyfarth, Robert M. Baboon Metaphysics: The Evolution of a Social Mind. (Illus.). 358p. 2008. pap. 18.00 *(978-0-226-10244-3(0))* 2007. 27.50 *(978-0-226-10243-6(2))* Univ. of Chicago Pr.

D'Hooghe, T. M., et al, eds. The Baboon As a Nonhuman Primate Model for the Study of Human Reproduction: Serono Symposia International Conference, Nairobi, January 2004, Vol. 57. (Illus.). 56p. *(978-3-8055-7588-1(2))* Karger, S. AG.

Smuts, Barbara B. & Smuts, Barbara. Sex & Friendship in Baboons. 2007. (ENG., Illus.). 319p. pap. 29.95 *(978-0-202-30973-6(8))* Aldine Transaction.

Swedell, Larissa & Leigh, Steven R., eds. Reproduction & Fitness in Baboons: Behavioral, Ecological, & Life History Perspectives. 2006. (Developments in Primatology: Progress & Prospects Ser.). (Illus.). 322p. 179.00 *(978-0-387-30688-9(9*, 0387306889) Springer.

—Reproduction & Fitness in Baboons: Behavioral, Ecological, & Life History Perspectives: Behavioral, Ecological, & Life History Perspectives. 2010. (Developments in Primatology: Progress & Prospects Ser.). (Illus.). viii, 322p. pap. 179.00 *(978-1-4419-4036-0(7)*, 1441940367) Springer.

BABUR, EMPEROR OF HINDUSTAN, 1483-1530

Anooshahr, Ali. The Ghazi Sultans & the Frontiers of Islam: A Comparative Study of the Late Medieval & Early Modern Periods. 2008. (Routledge Studies in Middle Eastern History Ser.). (ENG.). 208p. (C). 140.00 *(978-0-415-46360-7(2))* Routledge.

Gupta, Aditya. Babur & Humayun: Modern Learning Organisation. 2008. 94p. pap. 15.95 *(978-0-557-00896-4(4))* Lulu Enterprises Inc.

BABY ANIMALS

see Animals—Infancy

BABY BOOKS

Here are entered journals or scrapbooks specifically designed to record the progress of children from birth through roughly two years of age.

Better Homes and Gardens Books Staff. Scrapbooking for Baby. 2010. (Better Homes & Gardens Crafts Ser.: 11). (ENG., Illus.). 192p. pap. 14.99 *(978-0-470-54802-8(9)*, Wiley) Wiley, John & Sons, Inc.

Bild Buch Staff. Unser Baby: Der Ratgeber fuer die ersten 12 Monate. (GER.). 128p. pap. *(978-3-548-42024-0(9))* Ullstein-Taschenbuch-Verlag DEU. Dist: International Bk. Import Service, Inc.

Blue Baby Record Book. Date not set. (Baby Record Bks.). 56p. 7.98 *(978-0-7525-7644-2(5))* Parragon, Inc.

Bosh, Amber. Baby's Journal. 2010. (YA). pap. 13.98 *(978-1-61704-001-6(0))* River Styx Publishing Co.

Chang, Tessa. 1st Timers: My Book of Firsts. 2010. 44p. pap. 21.99 *(978-1-4535-1364-4(7))* Xlibris Corp.

Deseret Book, ed. Baby Keepsake Album Blue: From Birth to Baptism. 2007. 48p. 19.95 *(978-1-59038-774-0(0))* Deseret Bk. Co.

—Baby Keepsake Album Pink: From Birth to Baptism. 2007. 48p. 19.95 *(978-1-59038-773-3(2))* Deseret Bk. Co.

Good Books Staff. Baby's Days: A Record Book of Baby's First Year, 1 vol. 2008. (ENG., Illus.). 40p. 15.95 *(978-1-56148-606-9(X))* Good Bks.

Greenaway, Kate, illus. Kate Greenaway Baby Book: A Record of the First Five Years. 3rd rev. ed. 2011. (ENG.). 60p. 15.00 *(978-1-873329-42-9(3))* Sheldrake Pr. GBR. Dist: Interlink Publishing Group, Inc.

Harper, Lisa. Welcome Home Little Baby. 2008. (ENG.). 16p. 8.99 *(978-1-4389-1310-0(9))* AuthorHouse.

Holmes, Tot. Baby Blue Book, 1998. Date not set. pap. 6.00 *(978-0-943716-29-9(2))* Holmes Publishing.

Kinne, Laura. Baby steps - Preemie Milestones - Blue. 2009. 32p. pap. 9.28 *(978-0-557-06634-6(4))* Lulu Enterprises Inc.

—Baby steps - Preemie Milestones - Pink. 2009. 32p. pap. 9.28 *(978-0-557-06734-3(0))* Lulu Enterprises Inc.

—Baby steps - Preemie Milestones - Purple. 2009. 32p. pap. 9.28 *(978-0-557-06562-2(3))* Lulu Enterprises Inc.

Koh, Me Ra. Your Baby in Pictures: The New Parents' Guide to Photographing Your Baby's First Year. 2011. (ENG., Illus.). 144p. pap. 19.99 *(978-0-8174-0003-3(6)*, Amphoto Bks.) Watson-Guptill Pubns., Inc.

Lluch, Elizabeth & Lluch, Alex. Keepsake of Love Baby Journal: Preserving Memories from the Happiest Days of Your Life! 2007. (ENG., Illus.). 98p. 19.95 *(978-1-887169-76-9(8))* WS Publishing.

—Snuggle Bears Baby Journal Organizer & Keepsake. 2007. (ENG., Illus.). 100p. 24.95 *(978-1-887169-82-0(2))* WS Publishing.

McClure, Nikki. The First 1000 Days: A Baby Journal. 2006. (ENG., Illus.). 128p. pap. 12.95 *(978-1-57061-508-5(X))* Sasquatch Bks.

Morgenthal, Deborah & Lark Books Staff. For My Daughter: Special Memories of Our Life Together. 2010. (AARP Ser.). (ENG., Illus.). 112p. 12.95 *(978-1-60059-504-2(9))* Lark Bks.

—For My Son: Special Memories of Our Life Together. 2010. (AARP Ser.). (ENG., Illus.). 112p. 12.95 *(978-1-60059-503-5(0))* Lark Bks.

My Baby Book. Date not set. 14.95 *(978-0-88271-557-5(7)*, 10344); 1410p. 14.95 *(978-0-88271-135-5(0)*, 1415) Regina Pr., Malhame & Co.

Peterson, Pamela. Baby's First Year: Magical Moments & Milestones. 2007. 40p. 30.00 *(978-0-9749198-0-5(2))* Melody Pr.

Pink Baby Record Book. Date not set. (Baby Record Bks.). 56p. 7.98 *(978-0-7525-7645-9(3))* Parragon, Inc.

Precious Moments Baby Record Book: Catholic Ed. Date not set. 17.95 *(978-0-88271-289-5(6)*, 1940) Regina Pr., Malhame & Co.

Rasmussen, Dani & Perez, Antoinette. Essential Baby Organizer: Birth to One YEar. 2008. 162p. pap. 19.95 *(978-0-9766479-5-9(8))* Mango Media, Inc.

Rastall, Natalie. Simply A Boy. 2007. 24.99 net. *(978-1-60402-336-7(8))* Independent Pub.

Taylor, Erin E. Preemie Book of Memories. 2007. spiral bd. 19.99 *(978-0-9792977-0-0(2))* Kenzie's Hat.

BABY BOOM GENERATION

Here are entered works on members of the generation born following World War II, especially between 1947 and 1961, who came of age and joined the work force in the 1970's.

see also Church Work with the Baby Boom Generation

Abele, Joyce L. Sixties Kid. 2008. 139p. pap. 24.95 *(978-1-60610-775-1(5))* PublishAmerica, Inc.

Altilia, Tony. I Wish Someone Had Told Me That: Ten Kernals of Experience for Those Starting Their Careers from Those Ending Theirs. 2008. *(978-0-9809231-7-9(4))* BPS Bks.

Amacher, Ryan C. A Baby Boomer's Guide to Their Second Sixties. 2012. pap. ***(978-0-86534-855-4(3))*** Sunstone Pr.

Anderson, Christopher. What Happened to the Love Generation? How the Boomers Blew It. 2011. 204p. pap. 14.95 ***(978-1-4327-7420-2(4))*** Outskirts Pr., Inc.

Anneli, Ulla & Alsop, C. Scott. A Boomer's Health Guide: It's Now or Never! 2007. 176p. pap. 19.95 *(978-1-4251-1712-2(0))* Trafford Publishing.

Arquilla, John. Troubled Quest for Military T. 2009. (ENG.). 208p. 24.95 *(978-1-56663-724-4(4))* Dee, Ivan R. Pub.

Azzarelli, Jim. One Way Out: The Story of a Baby Boomer Chasing His American Dream. 2009. 200p. pap. 17.95 *(978-1-4401-2786-1(7))* iUniverse, Inc.

Berit, Kari. The Unexpected Caregiver: How Boomers Can Keep Mom & Dad Active, Safe & Independent. 2007. 192p. pap. 19.00 *(978-1-57861-606-0(9))* Attainment Co., Inc.

Bibby, Reginald W. The Boomer Factor: What Canada's Most Famous Generation Is Leaving Behind. 2006. (ENG.). 192p. pap. *(978-0-9780554-4-8(6))* ECW Pr. CAN. Dist: Independent Pubs. Group.

Blair, Seabury, Jr. The Creaky Knees Guide Washington: The 100 Best Easy Hikes in the State. 2009. (ENG., Illus.). 320p. pap. 16.95 *(978-1-57061-582-5(9))* Sasquatch Bks.

Bober, Melody. Generations — Baby Boomers (1964 — 1974) 25 Songs That Defined the Times. 2011. (Generations Ser.). (ENG.). 104p. pap. 14.99 *(978-0-7390-6551-8(3))* Alfred Publishing Co., Inc.

Boomers & the Budget: What Does It Mean for America's Seniors?: Hearing Before the Special Committee on Aging, United States Senate, One Hundred Tenth Congress, First Session, Washington, DC, February 15, 2007. 2007. (Illus.). iii, 65p. *(978-0-16-079400-1(5)*, 552-070-36412-9) United States Government Printing Office.

Brockman, Chris. Growing up in Boom Times. 2011. 164p. 22.95 ***(978-1-4567-6829-4(8))***; pap. 13.95 ***(978-1-4567-6830-0(1))*** AuthorHouse.

Brown, Mary & Orsborn, Carol. Boom: Marketing to the Ultimate Power Consumer — The Baby-Boomer Woman. 2006. (ENG., Illus.). 256p. 24.00 *(978-0-8144-7390-0(3))* Amacom.

Burke, Arlene. Nothin Like I Thought: A Baby-Boomer's Look in the Rear View Mirror. 2007. 272p. per. 15.95 *(978-0-9794844-3-8(X))* Emersonstreet Bks.

Bush, Lawrence. Waiting for God: The Spiritual Explorations of a Reluctant Atheist. 2008. 194p. per. 16.95 *(978-0-9789980-5-9(7))* Yehuda, Ben Pr.

Byham, William C. 70: The New 50: Retirement Management: Retaining the Energy & Expertise of Experienced Employees. 2007. 30.00 *(978-0-9761514-3-2(X))* Development Dimensions International, Inc.

—70 the New 50: Retirement Management Retaining the Energy & Expertise of Experienced Employees. 2006. pap. 30.00 *(978-0-9761514-2-5(1))* Development Dimensions International, Inc.

Chaston, Ian. Boomer Marketing: Selling to a Recession Resistant Market. 2009. (ENG., Illus.). 268p. 47.95 *(978-0-415-48963-6(6))*; 153.00 *(978-0-415-48962-1(8))* Routledge.

Checchi, Mary Jane. The 50+ Dog Owner: Complete Dog Parenting for Baby Boomers & Beyond, 1 vol. 2010. (ENG.). 272p. 24.95 *(978-0-7938-0643-0(7))* TFH Pubns., Inc.

Chiocchi, Roger. Baby Boomer Bust? How the Generation of Promise Became the Generation of Panic. 2010. (ENG.). 212p. pap. 17.95 *(978-1-60037-751-8(3))* Morgan James Publishing.

Cochran, Lynda J., et al. Leisure Programming for Baby Boomers. 2009. (ENG., Illus.). 224p. (C). (gr. 13-16). pap. 32.00 *(978-0-7360-7363-9(9))* Human Kinetics Pubs.

Coker, Don. Fins, Friends & Fireflies: A Nostalgic Journey Back to Adolescent Life in North Central Texas in The 1950s. 2011. 154p. pap. 14.95 ***(978-1-61434-231-1(8))*** Booklocker.com, Inc.

Cook, Jere & Cook, Patricia A. Fitness for Boomers: Strength - Flexibility - Endurance - Balance. 2011. 128p. pap. 14.95 *(978-1-4120-5380-8(3))* Trafford Publishing.

Cooper, Sherry. The New Retirement: How It Will Change Our Future. 2008. (ENG.). 256p. (gr. 12-18). 23.50 *(978-0-670-06688-9(5)*, Penguin Global) Penguin Group (USA) Inc.

Corbridge, Carol. The Boomer's Guide to Lightweight Backpacking: New Gear for Old People, 1 vol. 2008. (ENG., Illus.). 102p. pap. 18.95 *(978-1-57188-442-8(4))* Amato, Frank Pubns., Inc.

Coulmas, Florian & Conrad, Harald, eds. The Demographic Challenge: A Handbook about Japan. 2008. (Illus.). 1242p. *(978-90-04-15477-3(9))* BRILL.

Cravit, David. The New Old: How the Boomers Are Changing Everything... Again. 2008. (ENG., Illus.). 300p. pap. 19.95 *(978-1-55022-843-4(9))* ECW Pr. CAN. Dist: Independent Pubs. Group.

Custer, Chuck. I Did My Damnedest. 2007. 384p. pap. 18.36 *(978-0-615-16011-5(5))* Neymeyer, Colleen.

Damen, Margaret May & McCuistion, Niki Nicastro. Women, Wealth & Giving: The Virtuous Legacy of the Boom Generation. 2009. (ENG., Illus.). 256p. 49.95 *(978-0-470-23064-0(9)*, Wiley) Wiley, John & Sons, Inc.

Dana, Gordon J. Road to Retirement for Baby Boomers. 2011. 168p. 29.99 ***(978-1-4568-8236-5(8))***; pap. 19.99 ***(978-1-4568-8235-8(X))*** Xlibris Corp.

Davidson, Sara. Leap! What Will We Do with the Rest of Our Lives? l.t. ed. 2007. (Readers Circle Ser.). 431p. 31.95 *(978-1-60285-044-6(5))* Ctr. Point Large Print.

—Leap! What Will We Do with the Rest of Our Lives? 2008. (ENG.). 336p. pap. 15.00 *(978-0-345-47809-2(6)*, Ballantine Bks.) Random House Publishing Group.

Dean, Malcolm & Cann, Paul, eds. Unequal Ageing: The untold story of exclusion in old Age. 2009. (Illus.). 192p. 80.00 *(978-1-84742-412-9(0))*; pap. 29.95 *(978-1-84742-411-2(2))* Policy Pr. GBR. Dist: Chicago Distribution Ctr.

Elwins, Dannie. Health & Wealth Tips for Baby Boomers. 2009. 32p. pap. 16.99 *(978-0-557-15430-2(8))* Lulu Enterprises Inc.

Farmer Sr., Karl V. I Know Life's Not Supposed to Be Fair. 2011. 68p. pap. 15.99 ***(978-1-4568-7162-8(5))*** Xlibris Corp.

Farrell, Kathy. Until I Get It Right. 2007. per. 19.95 *(978-0-9795125-0-6(6))* Kettle Cove Pubns., Inc.

Fixler, Jill Friedman & Steinhorn, Beth. Boomer Volunteer Engagement: Facilitator's Tool Kit. 2010. 216p. pap. 24.95 *(978-1-4520-1537-8(6))* AuthorHouse.

Folkerth, Michael. The Biggest Lie Ever Believed. 2007. pap. 13.95 *(978-0-9779965-3-7(0))* Lifetime Chronicle Pr.

Fraser, Roy. Jill's Date. 2008. 198p. pap. 24.95 *(978-1-60474-677-8(7))* PublishAmerica, Inc.

Fraunfelder, Frederick T. & Gilbaugh, James H., Jr. Retire Right: 8 Scientifically Proven Traits You Need for a Happy, Fulfilling Retirement. 2009. (ENG.). 208p. (gr. 8-18). 15.00 *(978-1-58333-346-4(0)*, Avery) Penguin Group (USA) Inc.

Freedman, Marc. Encore: Finding Work that Matters in the Second Half of Life. 2008. (ENG., Illus.). 272p. pap. 14.95 *(978-1-58648-634-1(9))* Perseus Bks. Group.

Furlong, Mary. Turning Silver into Gold: How to Profit in the New Boomer Marketplace. 2007. (ENG.). 304p. pap. 34.99 *(978-0-13-231199-1(2))* FT Press.

Gates, Donna & Schrecengost, Lyndi. The Baby Boomer Diet: Body Ecology's Guide to Growing Younger: Anti-Aging Wisdom for Every Generation. 2011. (ENG.). 27.95 *(978-1-4019-3545-0(1))* Hay Hse., Inc.

Gerou, Tom. Generations — Baby Boomers (1964 — 1974) Bk. 2: 25 Songs That Defined the Times. 2011. (Generations Ser.). (ENG.). 92p. pap. 14.99 *(978-0-7390-6557-0(2))* Alfred Publishing Co., Inc.

Geyman, John. The Cancer Generation: Baby Boomers Facing a Perfect Storm. 2009. (ENG.). 375p. pap. 18.95 *(978-1-56751-398-1(0))* Common Courage Pr.

Gitlin, Martin. The Baby Boomer Encyclopedia, 1 vol. 2011. (Illus.). 231p. 55.00 *(978-0-313-38218-5(2)*, A2646C) Greenwood Publishing Group, Inc.

Gitlin, Marty. The Baby Boomer Encyclopedia. 2011. (Illus.). xxiv, 231p. E-Book ***(978-0-313-38219-2(0)***, Greenwood Pr.) Greenwood Publishing Group, Inc.

Goldsmith, Jeff Charles. The Long Baby Boom: An Optimistic Vision for a Graying Generation. 2008. (ENG., Illus.). 232p. 25.95 *(978-0-8018-8851-9(4))* Johns Hopkins Univ. Pr.

Grupe, Robert Charles. Building Sand Castles: A Baby Boomer's Journey Through Addictions. 2007. (Illus.). 148p. per. 12.95 *(978-0-9662278-5-7(9))* Grupe, Robert C. & Assocs.

Haas, Donald Ray. How to Plan for Baby Boomers. 2nd ed. 2007. 262p. per. 34.95 *(978-0-87218-923-2(6))* National Underwriter Co.

Haberland, Kathleen Mulhall. Lost in the Crowd: Memoir of the First Baby Boomer. 2010. 180p. 24.99 *(978-1-4520-7387-3(2))*; pap. 14.49 *(978-1-4520-7386-6(4))* AuthorHouse.

Hall, Julie. The Boomer Burden: Dealing with Your Parents' Lifetime Accumulation of Stuff, 0 vols. 2008. 256p. pap. 14.99 *(978-0-7852-2825-7(X))* Nelson, Thomas Inc.

Hargrave, Terry. Boomers on the Edge: Three Realities That Will Change Your Life Forever, 1 vol. 2008. (ENG.). 272p. pap. 14.99 *(978-0-310-27659-3(4))* Zondervan.

Harper, Christopher. Flyover Country: Baby Boomers & Their Stories. 2010. (ENG.). 150p. pap. 25.00 *(978-0-7618-5332-9(4))* Hamilton Bks.

Harris, Leslie M. & Edelman, Michelle, eds. After Sixty: Marketing to Baby Boomers Reaching Their Big Transition Years. 2006. (Illus.). 190p. kivar 39.95 *(978-0-9786602-0-8(X))* Paramount Market Publishing, Inc.

Haymon, Sandra W. Baby Boomers: Sandwiched Between Retirement & Caregiving. 2009. pap. 29.99 *(978-1-60696-861-1(0))* Tate Publishing & Enterprises, LLC.

Hodge, Gerald. The Geography of Aging: Preparing Communities for the Surge in Seniors. 2008. (ENG., Illus.). 336p. (C). *(978-0-7735-3429-2(6))*; pap. *(978-0-7735-3430-8(X))* McGill-Queen's Univ. Pr.

Hood, Jacky. Happy about Working to Stay Young: Expanded Careers for Boomers & Seniors. 2007. (Happy About... Ser.). 103p. per. 16.95 *(978-1-60005-035-0(2))* Happy About.

Hovanec, Margret & Shilton, Elizabeth. Redefining Retirement: New Realities for Boomer Women, 1 vol. 2007. (ENG., Illus.). 288p. pap. 24.95 *(978-1-897187-21-0(1))* Second Story Pr. CAN. Dist: Univ. of Toronto Pr.

Howard, Steve. Boomer Selling: Helping the Wealthiest Generation in History Own Your Premium Products & Services. 2009. 208p. pap. 15.95 *(978-0-9821911-0-1(3))* ACT Group, Inc., The.

Hudson, Robert B. & Hudson, Robert B. Boomer Bust? Economic & Political Issues of the Graying Society, 2 vols. 2008. (Illus.). 576p. 200.00 *(978-0-275-99549-2(6)*, C9549, Praeger Pubs.) Greenwood Publishing Group, Inc.

Ingram, Jerry G. Baby Boomers & Retirement Planning- a Multifactor Approach. 2007. 192p. per. *(978-3-8364-2137-9(2))* VDM Verlag Dr. Mueller e.K.

Isay, Jane. Walking on Eggshells: Navigating the Delicate Relationship Between Adult Children & Parents. 2008. (ENG.). 256p. pap. 15.00 *(978-0-7679-2085-8(6))* Broadway Bks.

—Walking on Eggshells: Navigating the Delicate Relationship Between Adult Children & Their Parents. l.t. ed. 2007. (Thorndike Health, Home & Learning Ser.). 315p. 29.95 *(978-0-7862-9663-7(1))* Thorndike Pr.

Izard, Mary Beth. BoomerPreneurs: How Baby Boomers Can Start Their Own Business, Make Money & Enjoy Life. 2010. 286p. pap. 25.95 *(978-0-9728748-3-0(6))* Acheve Consulting, Inc.

Johnson, Jeff & Forman, Paula. Hourglass Solution. 2013. (ENG.). 240p. pap. 16.00 *(978-0-7382-1384-2(5))* Da Capo Pr., Inc.

—The Hourglass Solution: A Boomer's Guide to the Rest of Your Life. 2009. (ENG.). 240p. 25.00 *(978-0-7382-1246-3(6))* Perseus Bks. Group.

Johnson, Valinda. In My Father's House Again. 2011. 168p. pap. 13.96 ***(978-1-4269-7506-6(6))*** Trafford Publishing.

Joyann. Ink Splatters. 2011. 108p. 23.99 ***(978-1-4670-3922-2(5))***; pap. 14.95 ***(978-1-4670-3923-9(3))*** AuthorHouse.

Judd, Naomi. Naomi's Guide to Aging Gratefully: Facts, Myths, & Good News for Boomers. 2008. (ENG.). 272p. pap. 17.99 *(978-0-7432-7516-3(0))* Simon & Schuster.

JWT Mature Market Group & C&R Research, compiled by. The Boomer Heartbeat: Capturing the Heartbeat of Baby Boomers Now & in the Future. 2006. 71p. pap. 75.00 *(978-0-9766973-9-8(4)*, 1035) Paramount Market Publishing, Inc.

Keliher, Evan. Boomers! (A Survival Guide for the Future) 2007. 224p. pap. 12.95 *(978-0-9648859-7-4(2))* Pedagogue Pr.

Keller, Jon. The Bluest State: How Democrats Created the Massachusetts Blueprint for American Political Disaster. 2008. (ENG.). 272p. pap. 16.99 *(978-0-312-38490-6(4)*, St. Martin's Griffin) St. Martin's Pr.

Kennedy, Kay. Looking Back: Boomers Remember History from the 40's to the Present. 2007. 216p. pap. 17.95 *(978-1-60145-286-3(1))* Booklocker.com, Inc.

Kitcho, Catherine. Happy about Being a Baby Boomer: Facing Our Newfound Longevity. 2007. 116p. per. *(978-1-60005-063-3(8))* Happy About.

Labenske, Victor. Generations — Baby Boomers (1964 — 1974) 25 Songs That Defined the Times. 2011. (Generations Ser.). (ENG.). 112p. pap. 14.99 *(978-0-7390-6553-2(X))* Alfred Publishing Co., Inc.

Leber, David. The Future for Baby Boomers (As I See It) 2006. 71p. per. 10.00 *(978-1-59824-324-6(1))* E-BookTime LLC.

Letendre, Denis. The Power of Freedom. 2011. 112p. 22.95 *(978-1-4502-7660-3(1))*; pap. 12.95 *(978-1-4502-7658-0(X))* iUniverse, Inc.

Lindsay, Jeanne Warren. Four Little Lindsays & How They Grew 1957-1959. 2010. (ENG.). 176p. pap. 14.95 *(978-1-932538-99-1(2))* Morning Glory Pr., Inc.

Lloyd Billingsley. Our Time after a While: Reflections of a Borderline Baby Boomer. 2010. 148p. pap. 14.95 *(978-1-4502-0464-4(3))* iUniverse, Inc.

Long, Mike & Clyde, John. Lawyers at Midlife: A Retirement Planner for Boomer Attorneys. 2007. pap. *(978-0-940675-59-9(5))* LawyerAvenue Pr.

Losey, Bill. Retire in a Weekend! The Baby Boomer's Guide to Making Work Optional. 2008. (Illus.). 170p. pap. 29.95 incl. cd-rom *(978-0-9798554-1-2(1))* Love Your Life.

Loyd, Gerald G. The God of the Baby Boomers. 2009. 212p. pap. 15.99 *(978-1-60791-914-8(1))* Xulon Pr., Inc.

Lunchbucket, Joe. The Joe Lunchbucket Chronicles: Tales & Travels of an Aging Boomer. 2010. 115p. pap. 12.95 *(978-1-4327-5744-1(X))* Outskirts Pr., Inc.

Lynch, Frederick R. One Nation under AARP: The Fight over Medicare, Social Security, & America's Future. 2011. (ENG., Illus.). 288p. 60.00 *(978-0-520-25653-8(0))*; pap. 25.95 *(978-0-520-26828-9(8))* Univ. of California Pr.

MacKay, Carleen, et al. Return of the Boomers: Crossing the Bridge to the Future with the Help of the Mature Workforce. 2008. 185p. pap. 19.95 *(978-0-9773408-2-8(1))* Cambridge Media, LLC.

Malikow, Max. It's Not Too Late! Making the Most of the Rest of Your Life. 2007. (ENG.). 96p. per. 24.50 *(978-0-7618-3774-9(4))* Univ. Pr. of America, Inc.

Marano, Anthony F. My Play Ground-the Bronx: My Memoirs. 2008. 332p. 32.95 *(978-0-595-51775-6(7))*; pap. 22.95 *(978-0-595-52955-1(0))* iUniverse, Inc.

Mathews, Albert J. Wake up Americ: It's Not Illegal to Think. 2008. 300p. pap. 22.99 *(978-1-4389-2995-8(1))* AuthorHouse.

Matz, Carol. Generations — Baby Boomers (1964 — 1974) Bk. 2: 25 Songs That Defined the Times. 2011. (Generations Ser.). (ENG.). 88p. pap. 14.99 *(978-0-7390-6555-6(6))* Alfred Publishing Co., Inc.

Mauterstock, Robert B. Can We Talk? a Financial Guide for Baby Boomers Assisting Their Elderly Parents. 2008. (ENG.). 144p. pap. 20.00 *(978-0-9771403-9-8(3))* Soar With Eagles.

May, Elaine Tyler. Homeward Bound: American Families in the Cold War Era. 20th ed. 2008. (ENG.). 320p. pap. 19.95 *(978-0-465-01020-2(2))* Perseus Bks. Group.

Mazer, Gwen. Wise Talk, Wild Women. 2007. (ENG., Illus.). 144p. 24.95 *(978-1-885171-87-0(0)*, Wildcat Canyon) Council Oak Bks.

McAllister, Michelle D. Baby Boomers & Beyond: The Who, What, When, & Where Guide to Health & Spirituality. 2010. 84p. pap. 10.95 *(978-0-595-52479-2(6))* iUniverse, Inc.

McFarland, Barbara & Watson-Rouslin, Virginia. My Mother Was Right: How Today's Women Reconcile with Their Mothers. 2nd ed. 2009. (ENG.). 278p. pap. 18.95 *(978-0-470-62335-0(7)*, Jossey-Bass) Wiley, John & Sons, Inc.

Miller, Ron. Kateri Lodge: The Years We Lived. 2011. pap. 22.99 *(978-1-61777-021-0(3))* Tate Publishing & Enterprises, LLC.

Mills, Mark & Mills, Nancy Fernandez. Boomers! Funding Your Future in an Age of Uncertainty. l.t. ed. 2008. (Thorndike Health, Home & Learning Ser.). (Illus.). 483p. 30.95 *(978-1-4104-0397-1(1))* Thorndike Pr.

Monhollon, Rusty, ed. Baby Boom: People & Perspectives, 1 vol. 2010. (Perspectives in American Social History Ser.). 246p. 85.00 *(978-1-59884-105-3(X)*, BABBOO1C) ABC-CLIO, LLC.

Moore, Frank. Dismantling the Myths: The Connection Between Faith & Morality. 2008. (ENG., Illus.). 224p. pap. 16.99 *(978-0-8341-2376-2(2)*, 9780834123762) Beacon Hill Pr. of Kansas City.

Moschis, George & Mathur, Anil. Baby Boomers & Their Parents: Surprising Findings about Their Lifestyles, Mindsets, & Well-Being. 2007. 231p. 47.50 *(978-0-9786602-4-6(2))* Paramount Market Publishing, Inc.

Moseley, Arthur M., Jr. Baby Boomer Memories: The First Fifty Years. 2009. 289p. pap. 19.95 *(978-1-4327-4603-2(0))* Outskirts Pr., Inc.

Moss, Ron. New Town Boy. 2010. 184p. pap. 17.50 *(978-1-4461-3868-7(2))* Lulu Enterprises Inc.

Nathanson, Bradley. American Departures: The Curious Plight of a Uniquely Privileged, Quietly Desperate Baby Boomer. 2007. 310p. pap. 17.95 *(978-0-9794031-7-0(0))* Airtime Entertainment Corp.

Novelli, Bill & Workman, Boe. Fifty Plus: Give Meaning & Purpose to the Best Time of Your Life. 2007. (ENG.). 256p. pap. 16.99 *(978-0-312-35478-7(9)*, St. Martin's Griffin) St. Martin's Pr.

Nyren, Chuck. Advertising to Baby Boomers. 2007. 182p. per. 24.95 *(978-0-9786602-3-9(4)*, 1025) Paramount Market Publishing, Inc.

O'CONNOR, Kaori. Lycra: How a Fiber Shaped America. 2011. (Routledge Series for Creative Teaching & Learning in Anthropology Ser.). (ENG., Illus.). 192p. pap. 19.95 *(978-0-415-80437-0(X))* Routledge.

O'Leary, Marilyn & Gaffney, Sylvia. Keep Choosing, Keep Living: Three Cousins Invite You to a Conversation about Coming of Older Age. 2009. 100p. pap. 13.95 *(978-1-4327-1694-3(8))* Outskirts Pr., Inc.

Osborne, Jack. Makers of Mischief: A Boomer's Adventures in Childhood. 2007. 384p. 26.95 *(978-0-9798798-0-7(9))* DreamAway Bks. Inc.

Osenton, Tom. Boomer Destiny: Leading the U. S. through the Worst Crisis since the Great Depression, 1 vol. 2009. (Illus.). 210p. 39.95 *(978-0-313-35604-9(1)*, C35604, Praeger Pubs.) Greenwood Publishing Group, Inc.

Pagano, Lou. A Baby Boomer's Journey: From Mommy's Care to Medicare. 2011. 56p. pap. 16.95 ***(978-1-4560-4981-2(X))*** PublishAmerica, Inc.

Pang, Ha-Nam. Han'guk Peibibum Sedae Ui Kullo Saengae (Work Life) Yon'gu. 2010. (KOR., Illus.). iv, 179p. *(978-89-7356-810-9(8))* Korea Labor Institute.

Pargman, David. Boomercise: Exercising as You Age. 2011. (ENG., Illus.). 229p. pap. 16.95 *(978-1-935412-32-8(9))* Fitness Information Technology, Inc.

Pearce. Growing up Boomer & Beyond. 2009. 144p. pap. 11.95 *(978-1-59330-617-5(2))* Aventine Pr.

Perreault, Inge. For Women Only the 50 Plus Roller Coaster. 2007. 168p. per. 15.95 *(978-0-595-46387-9(8))* iUniverse, Inc.

Piergeorge, MS, RD, RD, Susan M., Susan M. Boomer Be Well! Rebel Against Aging Through Food, Nutrition & Lifestyle. 2011. (ENG.). 301p. pap. 25.00 ***(978-0-9846006-0-1(4))*** Asante Pubns., LLC.

Potter, Beverly A. Youth Extension A to Z. 2010. (ENG., Illus.). 192p. pap. 14.95 *(978-1-57951-090-9(6))* Ronin Publishing.

Raleigh, Donald J. Soviet Baby Boomers: An Oral History of Russia's Cold War Generation, 1 vol. 2011. (Oxford Oral History Ser.). (ENG., Illus.). 432p. 34.95 *(978-0-19-974434-3(3))* Oxford Univ. Pr., Inc.

Reauthorizing the Older Americans ACT: Encouraging Healthy Living As Baby Boomers Age: Field Hearing Before the Special Committee on Aging, United States Senate, One Hundred Eleventh Congress, Second Session, Pueblo, CO, August 27, 2010. 2011. iii, 55p. ***(978-0-16-088013-1(0)***, 552-070-42437-7) United States Government Printing Office.

Retirement Decisions. 2008. 87p. 39.00 *(978-1-60456-812-7(7))* Nova Science Pubs., Inc.

Rightmyer, Marty. Close the Door We Live in a Barn. 2009. 248p. pap. 15.95 *(978-1-4389-4922-2(7))* AuthorHouse.

Roos, Stephen. A Boomer's Guide to the 12 Steps. 2009. (ENG.). 128p. pap. 13.95 *(978-1-59285-696-1(9))* Hazelden Publishing & Educational Services.

Roszak, Theodore. The Making of an Elder Culture: Reflections on the Future of America's Most Audacious Generation. 2009. (ENG.). 320p. pap. 18.95 *(978-0-86571-661-2(7)*, 9780865716612) New Society Pubs., Ltd. CAN. Dist: Consortium Bk. Sales & Distribution.

Rowe, Heidemarie. Boomers & Beyond, Prescription for the Golden Years. 2007. 204p. per. 16.95 *(978-1-934246-82-5(4))* Peppertree Pr., The.

Salsbury, Gregory. Retirementology: Rethinking the American Dream in a New Economy. 2010. (ENG., Illus.). 240p. pap. 19.99 *(978-0-13-705653-8(2))* FT Press.

Scarpa, Carmine J. Save Me a Seat by the Drummer. 2008. 90p. pap. 11.95 *(978-1-4303-2826-1(6))* Lulu Enterprises Inc.

Schriener, Judy & Kephart, Mike. Building for Boomers: Guide Design & Construction. 2010. (ENG., Illus.). 304p. instr.'s gde. ed. 59.95 *(978-0-07-159981-8(9)*, 0071599819) McGraw-Hill Professional Publishing.

Schulz, James H. & Binstock, Robert H. Aging Nation: The Economics & Politics of Growing Older in America, 1 vol. 2006. (Illus.). 296p. 49.95 *(978-0-275-98415-1(X)*, C8415, Praeger Pubs.) Greenwood Publishing Group, Inc.

—Aging Nation: The Economics & Politics of Growing Older in America. 2008. (ENG., Illus.). 304p. (C). (gr. 13-17). pap. 28.00 *(978-0-8018-8864-9(6))* Johns Hopkins Univ. Pr.

Schwalbe, Robert. Sixty, Sexy, & Successful: A Guide for Aging Male Baby Boomers, 1 vol. 2008. (Sex, Love, & Psychology Ser.). (Illus.). 320p. 49.95 *(978-0-275-99928-5(9)*, C9928, Praeger Pubs.) Greenwood Publishing Group, Inc.

Scott, Joan Fitting. Skinning the Cat: A Baby Boomer's Guide to the New Retiree Lifestyles. 2006. (ENG.). 96p. per. 9.95 *(978-0-7414-3358-9(3))* Infinity Publishing.

Semones, JoAnn. Eye Remember. 2008. 92p. pap. 14.95 *(978-1-59393-250-3(2))* BearManor Media.

Shah, Vijay. Nivruttini Pravrutti: Fun life of Retirement. 2010. 184p. pap. 50.00 *(978-1-4490-4649-1(5))* AuthorHouse.

Sills, Judith. Getting Naked Again: Dating, Romance, Sex, & Love When You've Been Divorced, Widowed, Dumped, or Distracted. 2010. (ENG.). 288p. pap. 14.99 *(978-0-446-55180-9(5)*, Springboard Pr.) Grand Central Publishing.

Smith, J. Walker & Clurman, Ann. Generation Ageless: How Baby Boomers Are Changing the Way We Live Today & They're Just Getting Started. 2007. (ENG., Illus.). 272p. 24.95 *(978-0-06-112898-1(8)*, Collins) HarperCollins Pubs.

Social Structures: Demographic Changes & the Well-Being of Older Persons. 2007. (Societal Impact on Aging Ser.). (Illus.). 314p. 90.00 *(978-0-8261-2407-4(0))* Springer Publishing Co., Inc.

Spector, Stan. Baby Boomers' Official Guide to Retirement Income. 2007. 128p. per. 16.95 *(978-1-59858-342-7(5))* Dog Ear Publishing, LLC.

Speir, Cynthia A. & Speir, James A. Baby Boomers Express: From Long Hair to Silver Hair. 2008. 194p. 29.95 *(978-1-59930-103-7(2))* LifeSuccess Publishing.

St. Louis Post-Dispatch. St. Louis Baby Boomers. 2008. 34.95 *(978-0-9796054-4-4(X))* St. Louis Post-Dispatch.

Stallworth, Catherine R. Power & Grace: Healing with Yoga for Boomers & Beyond. 2009. 131p. pap. 21.95 *(978-1-4327-4131-0(4))* Outskirts Pr., Inc.

Steinhorn, Leonard. Greater Generation: In Defense of the Baby Boom Legacy. Date not set. mass mkt. *(978-0-312-99597-3(0)*, St. Martin's Paperbacks) St. Martin's Pr.

Stella, Vince. Interview with a Boomer. 2011. 200p. pap. 24.95 ***(978-1-59095-766-0(0))*** TotalRecall Pubns., Inc.

Stoner, Gregg. The Yellow Footprints to Hell & Back: The starting point for every Marine. 2008. 180p. 26.95 *(978-0-595-50120-5(6))*; 184p. pap. 16.95 *(978-0-595-48422-5(0))* iUniverse, Inc.

Sturniolo, Joseph S. & Christopherson, Daniel. The Caterpillar That Roared: Awakening the Lion Within. 2008. (ENG., Illus.). 146p. pap. 11.95 *(978-1-60037-343-5(7))* Morgan James Publishing.

—The Caterpillar That Roared: Awakening the Lion Within - A Parable about the Journey Toward a More Meaningful Life. 2008. (ENG., Illus.). 146p. 21.95 *(978-1-60037-342-8(9))* Morgan James Publishing.

Sumner, Brian R. The Lucky Generation: The Life, Loves & Times of a (Slightly Mad) Baby Boomer. 2011. 188p. pap. 17.09 ***(978-1-4567-7921-4(4))*** AuthorHouse.

Tagliaferre, Lewis. Baby Boomer Lamentations: Metaphysical Essays to Die For. 2011. 404p. 35.95 ***(978-1-4620-1035-6(0))***; pap. 25.95 ***(978-1-4620-1034-9(2))*** iUniverse, Inc.

Tanner, Ken. The Boomers' Career Survival Guide: Achieving Success & Contentment from Middle Age through Retirement, 1 vol. 2009. (Illus.). 165p. 29.95 *(978-0-313-36521-8(0)*, C36521, Praeger Pubs.) Greenwood Publishing Group, Inc.

Textor-Black, Sharon. Elsa's Own Blue Zone: America's Centenarian Sweetheart's Insights for Positive Aging & Living. 2009. (ENG., Illus.). 162p. pap. 14.95 *(978-1-60037-579-8(0))* Morgan James Publishing.

The I AM Foundation & Viglione, Steve. The Bridge: A Seven Stage Map to Redefine Your Life & Purpose. 2008. pap. 16.95 *(978-0-9645224-5-9(4))* I AM Foundation, The.

The Rev. Cynthia Vold Forde Staff. The Spirit in the South. 2009. 388p. pap. 50.00 *(978-1-4343-5554-3(X))* AuthorHouse.

Thornhill, Matt & Martin, John. Boomer Consumer: Ten New Rules for Marketing to America's Largest, Wealthiest & Most Influential Group. 2007. (Illus.). 218p. 24.95 *(978-0-9842386-7-1(5))* LINX Corp.

Valentin, Ric. Baby Boomer's Facts & Trivia. 2006. (ENG.). 164p. per. 11.95 *(978-1-59800-731-2(9))* Outskirts Pr., Inc.

Venneberg, Donald L. & Eversole, Barbara Weiss. The Boomer Retirement Time Bomb: How Companies Can Avoid the Fallout from the Coming Skills Shortage, 1 vol. 2010. 147p. 34.95 *(978-0-313-37538-5(0)*, C37538, Praeger Pubs.) Greenwood Publishing Group, Inc.

B

Walsh, Gregory & Lavery, Michael. Whole Brain Power: the Fountain of Youth for the Mind & Body. 2008. 308p. pap. 19.95 *(978-0-557-00514-7(0))* Lulu Enterprises Inc.

Watts, Bruce. Memories from a Baby Boomer: The Early Years. 2007. 48p. per. 16.95 *(978-1-4241-8025-7(2))* PublishAmerica, Inc.

Welch, Anne Stuart. What Can I Say? I'm A Product of The 60's. 2011. 160p. 22.23 ***(978-1-4567-6721-1(6))*** AuthorHouse.

—What Can I Say? I'm A Product of The 60's. 2011. 160p. pap. 12.50 ***(978-1-4567-6723-5(2))*** AuthorHouse.

West, Hal. The Pickled Priest & the Perishing Parish: Boomer Pastors Bouncing Back. 2011. 140p. 28.95 ***(978-1-61507-928-5(9))***; pap. 11.95 ***(978-1-61507-915-5(7))*** Cross Bks. Publishing.

Wintroub, Barbara. Fighting Gravity: A Guide to Extending the Warranty on Your Body. 2011. 132p. pap. 16.95 ***(978-1-4525-3652-1(X))*** Get Published.

Wissman, Jennifer. Training Methods for Older Adults. 2009. 64p. pap. *(978-3-639-17774-9(6))* VDM Verlag Dr. Mueller e.K.

Woodman, Becky. Love, Peace, & Flower Power: Memoirs of a Baby Boomer. 2011. 166p. pap. 24.95 ***(978-1-4626-1041-9(2))*** PublishAmerica, Inc.

Zelinsky, Edward A. The Origins of the Ownership Society: How the Defined Contribution Paradigm Changed America, 1 vol. 2012. (ENG.). 192p. pap. 29.95 ***(978-0-19-991408-1(7))*** Oxford Univ. Pr., Inc.

BABY BOOMERS

see Baby Boom Generation

BABY BUST GENERATION

see Generation X

BABY FOODS

Adamkin, David H. Nutritional Strategies for the Very Low Birthweight Infant. 2009. (ENG., Illus.). 208p. pap. 44.99 *(978-0-521-73246-8(8))* Cambridge Univ. Pr.

Agostoni, Carlo & Brunser, Oscar. Issues in Complementary Feeding. 2007. (Nestlé Nutrition Workshop Series: Pediatric Program Ser.). (Illus.). 264p. *(978-3-8055-8283-4(8))* Karger, S. AG.

Ansel, Karen & Ferreira, Charity. The Baby & Toddler Cookbook: Fresh, Homemade Foods for a Healthy Start. 2011. (ENG.). 176p. lib. bdg. 24.95 *(978-1-74089-980-2(6))* Weldon Owen, Inc.

Australian Women's Weekly Staff. Baby Food. (Australian Women's Weekly Parenting Guides). (Illus.). 64p. pap. 5.95 *(978-1-86396-224-7(7))* ACP Publishing Pty, Ltd. AUS. Dist: Graphic Arts Ctr. Publishing Co.

Baby Food Market: Companies-Products-Services. 175p. (Orig.). pap. *(978-0-7605-2221-9(9))* Rector Pr., Ltd.

Baby Foods International Market: Companies-Products-Services. 250p. (Orig.). pap. *(978-0-7605-2223-3(5))* Rector Pr., Ltd.

Bailey, Christine. The Top 100 Baby Foods: Easy Purees & First Foods for 6-12 Months. 2011. (Top 100 Recipes Ser.). (ENG., Illus.). 144p. pap. 9.95 *(978-1-84483-930-8(3))* Duncan Baird Pubs. GBR. Dist: Sterling Publishing Co., Inc.

Barnes, Lisa. Cooking for Baby: Wholesome, Homemade, Delicious Foods for 6 to 18 Months. 2009. (ENG., Illus.). 128p. 19.99 *(978-1-4165-9918-0(5)*, Touchstone) Touchstone.

Bessinger, Jeannette L. & Yabon-Brenner, Tracee. Best Food for Your Baby & Toddler: From First Foods to Meals Your Child Will Love. 2010. (Great Expectations Ser.). (ENG., Illus.). 384p. pap. 14.95 *(978-1-4027-3618-6(5))* Sterling Publishing Co., Inc.

Binet, M. & Jadfard, R. Comidas Sanas y Nutritivas para el Bebe. (SPA.). 224p. *(978-84-95456-01-4(X)*, 87114) Ediciones Oniro S.A.

Boyd, Lara. First Foods Fast: How to Prepare Delicious Simple Meals for Your Baby, from First Tastes to One Year. 2nd ed. 2006. (ENG., Illus.). 80p. pap. 9.95 *(978-1-905222-46-9(7))* Luath Pr. Ltd. GBR. Dist: Ingram Pub. Services.

Bramley, Lauren & Bradshaw, Brenda. The Baby's Table: Revised & Updated. 2010. (ENG., Illus.). 240p. pap. 19.50 *(978-0-307-35883-7(6)*, Random Hse CAN) Random Hse. of Canada, Ltd. CAN. Dist: Random Hse., Inc.

Buck, Angela. Organic Cooking for Baby & Toddler: 300 Naturally Delicious Recipes to Get Your Child off to a Healthy Start. 2008. (ENG.). 288p. pap. 15.95 *(978-1-59869-926-5(1))* Adams Media Corp.

Carden, Jennifer. Toddler Café: Fast, Recipes, & Fun Ways to Feed Even the Pickiest Eater. 2008. (ENG., Illus.). 132p. per. 14.95 *(978-0-8118-5927-1(4))* Chronicle Bks. LLC.

Carenco, Jenny. Les Petits Plats Francais: Baby Gourmet. 2012. (Petits Plats Francais Ser.). (ENG., Illus.). 72p. 12.95 ***(978-0-85720-593-3(5))*** Simon & Schuster, Ltd. GBR. Dist: Independent Pubs. Group.

Cigale, Jennifer. Newborn Necessities: Book 2. 2011. pap. 8.99 *(978-1-61739-652-6(4))* Tate Publishing & Enterprises, LLC.

Daulter, Anni & Lanay, Shanté. Organically Raised: Conscious Cooking for Babies & Toddlers. 2010. (ENG., Illus.). 224p. pap. 21.99 *(978-1-60529-643-2(0))* Rodale Pr., Inc.

Dixon, Keith. Cooking for Gracie: The Making of a Parent from Scratch. 2012. (ENG.). 224p. pap. 14.00 ***(978-0-307-59188-3(3))*** Broadway Bks.

—Cooking for Gracie: The Making of a Parent from Scratch. 2011. 224p. 22.00 *(978-0-307-59187-6(5)*, Crown) Crown Publishing Group.

Duffy, Nikki. River Cottage Baby & Toddler Cookbook. 2012. (ENG., Illus.). 256p. 34.00 ***(978-1-4088-0756-9(4))*** Bloomsbury Publishing.

Food and Agriculture Organization of the United Nations Staff, contrib. by. Enterobacter Sakazakii & Salmonella in Powdered Infant Formula: Meeting Report. 2006. (Nonserial Publication). (ENG.). 115p. pap. 34.80 *(978-92-4-156331-4(1))* World Health Organization.

Gardner, Tamika L. 201 Organic Baby Purees: The Freshest, Most Wholesome Food Your Baby Can Eat! 2012. (ENG.). 240p. pap. 16.95 ***(978-1-4405-2899-6(3))*** Adams Media Corp.

Glock, Beverly. 500 Baby & Toddler Dishes: Nutritious Make-Ahead Meals for Baby's First Foods & Beyond. 2011. (Illus.). 288p. 16.95 *(978-1-4162-0635-4(3))* Sellers Publishing, Inc.

Graimes, Nicola. Weaning & First Foods. 2011. (ENG., Illus.). 144p. pap. 18.95 *(978-1-904760-75-7(9))* Carroll & Brown Pubs., Ltd. GBR. Dist: Independent Pubs. Group.

Grant, Amanda. Baby & Toddler Healthy Eating Planner: The New Way to Feed Your Child a Balanced Diet Every Day, Featuring over 350 Recipes, Meal Planners, Charts & Nutrition Guides. 2006. (ENG., Illus.). 216p. pap. 19.95 *(978-1-84533-449-9(3)*, Mitchell Beazley) Octopus Publishing Group GBR. Dist: Hachette Bk. Group.

Healthy Meals for Babies & Toddlers. 2008. 96p. *(978-1-4075-3926-3(4))* Parragon, Inc.

Hill, Rachael Anne. Baby & Toddler Cookbook. 2008. (ENG., Illus.). 144p. *(978-1-84597-588-3(X))* CICO Bks.

Ibclc, Rachael Austin Rm C&Fhn. Feeding Baby: A Definitive Guide to the Science & Wisdom of Infant Feeding Choices. 2011. 102p. pap. 15.99 ***(978-1-4568-8315-7(1))*** Xlibris Corp.

Kalnins, Daina & Saab, Joanne. Better Baby Food: Your Essential Guide to Nutrition, Feeding & Cooking for All Babies & Toddlers. 2nd ed. 2008. (ENG., Illus.). 304p. pap. 24.95 *(978-0-7788-0195-5(0))* Rose, Robert Inc. CAN. Dist: Firefly Bks., Ltd.

Karmel, Annabel. The Healthy Baby Meal Planner: Mom-Tested, Child-Approved Recipes for Your Baby & Toddler. 2009. (ENG., Illus.). 208p. (Orig.). pap. 17.00 *(978-1-4391-0278-7(3)*, Beyond Words/Atria Bks.) Atria Bks.

—Starting Solids: Everyday Help for Introducing Your Baby's First Foods, with More Than 50 All-New Recipes. 2010. (ENG.). 128p. 16.00 *(978-0-7566-6214-1(1))* Dorling Kindersley Publishing, Inc.

—SuperFoods: For Babies & Children. 2011. (ENG., Illus.). 192p. pap. 17.99 *(978-0-7432-7524-8(1)*, Beyond Words/Atria Bks.) Atria Bks.

—Top 100 Finger Foods: 100 Recipes for a Healthy, Happy Child. 2010. (ENG., Illus.). 160p. 18.00 *(978-0-7434-9371-0(0)*, Beyond Words/Atria Bks.) Atria Bks.

Karmel, Annabel & Sullivan, Karen. First Meals & More: Your Questions Answered. 2009. (ENG., Illus.). 224p. (gr. 12-18). 22.00 *(978-0-7566-4284-6(1))* Dorling Kindersley Publishing, Inc.

Knight, Karin & Ruggiero, Tina. The Best Homemade Baby Food on the Planet: Know What Goes into Every Bite with More Than 200 of the Most Deliciously Nutritious Homemade Baby Food Recipes - Includes More Than 60 Purees Your Baby Will Love. 2010. (ENG., Illus.). 240p. pap. 19.99 *(978-1-59233-423-0(7)*, 1592334237) Quayside.

Koss, Ron & Koss, Arnie. The Earth's Best Story: A Bittersweet Tale of Twin Brothers Who Sparked an Organic Revolution. 2010. (ENG.). 384p. pap. 19.95 *(978-1-60358-239-1(8))* Chelsea Green Publishing.

Lewis, Sara. Healthy Home-Made Food for Babies & Toddlers. 2009. (ENG., Illus.). 264p. pap. 20.99 *(978-1-84476-874-5(0))* Anness Publishing GBR. Dist: National Bk. Network.

Lidman, Leonida. Controlling Fluctuations of Diabetes Blood Glucose, Healing & Preventing Nerve Damage with Baby's Milk. 2nd ed. 2009. 112p. pap. *(978-1-926585-63-5(1)*, CCB Publishing) CCB Publishing.

Linardakis, Constantina. The Baby Gourmet Cookbook. Linardakis, Nikos M., ed. Date not set. (Illus.). pap. 14.95 *(978-1-884084-16-4(8))* Michaelis Medical Publishing Corp.

Meade, Maggie. The Wholesome Baby Food Guide: Over 150 Easy, Delicious, & Healthy Recipes from Purees to Solids. 2012. (ENG.). 336p. pap. 15.99 *(978-0-446-58410-4(X))* Grand Central Publishing.

More, Judy. Happy Toddler Mealtimes. 2011. (Teach Yourself Ser.). (ENG., Illus.). 192p. pap. 15.95 ***(978-1-4441-0747-0(X)***, Hodder & Stoughton) Hodder General Publishing Div. GBR. Dist: Independent Pubs. Group.

O'Donnell, Norah & Tracy, Geoff. Baby Love: Healthy, Easy, Delicious Meals for Your Baby & Toddler. 2010. (ENG., Illus.). 160p. 19.99 *(978-0-312-62192-6(2)*, St. Martin's Griffin) St. Martin's Pr.

Parenting Magazine Staff & Chronicle Books Staff. Love in Spoonfuls. 2010. (ENG.). 160p. pap. 19.95 *(978-0-8118-7131-0(2))* Chronicle Bks. LLC.

Phillipson-Webb, Lianne. Sprout Right: Nutrition from Tummy to Toddler. 2010. (ENG., Illus.). 292p. pap. 20.00 *(978-0-14-317350-2(2)*, Penguin Global) Penguin Group (USA) Inc.

Preston, Penny. Toddler Menus: A Mix-and-Match Guide to Healthy Eating. 2007. (ENG.). 128p. pap. 16.95 *(978-1-59869-563-2(0))* Adams Media Corp.

Priwer, Shana & Phillips, Cynthia. The Everything Cooking for Baby & Toddler Book: 300 Delicious, Easy Recipes to Get Your Child off to a Healthy Start. 2nd ed. 2006. (ENG., Illus.). 304p. per. 15.95 *(978-1-59337-691-8(X))* Adams Media Corp.

Rapley, Gill & Murkett, Tracey. Baby-Led Weaning: The Essential Guide to Introducing Solid Foods - And Helping Your Baby to Grow up a Happy & Confident Eater. 2010. (ENG.). 264p. pap. 14.95 *(978-1-61519-021-8(X)*, 161519021X) Experiment LLC, The.

Rubin, Jacqueline. Naturally Healthy First Foods for Baby: The Best Nutrition for the First Year & Beyond. 2008. (ENG.). 288p. pap. 12.95 *(978-1-4022-1124-9(4))* Sourcebooks, Inc.

Schmidt, Christina. The Baby Bistro: Child-Approved Recipes & Expert Nutrition Advice for the First Year. 2009. (ENG.). 144p. pap. 16.95 *(978-1-933503-18-9(1))* Bull Publishing Co.

Splichal, Joachim & Splichal, Christine. Feeding Baby: Everyday Recipes for Healthy Infants & Toddlers. 2nd rev. ed. 2008. (ENG., Illus.). 144p. pap. 14.95 *(978-1-58761-317-3(4)*, Celestial Arts) Ten Speed Pr.

Super Baby Food: Your Complete Guide to What, When & How to Feed Your Baby & Toddler. 3rd ed. 2011. 608p. 19.95 *(978-0-9652603-2-9(1))* Roberts, F.J. Publishing.

Tolstoshev, Nirelle. Healthy Baby Food. 2010. (ENG., Illus.). 160p. pap. 16.95 *(978-1-74257-033-4(X))* New Holland Pubs. Pty, Ltd. AUS. Dist: Tuttle Publishing.

Wagman, Jordan & Hillhouse, Jill. Easy Gourmet Baby Food: 150 Recipes for Homemade Goodness. 2008. (ENG., Illus.). 272p. pap. 21.95 *(978-0-7788-0182-5(9))* Rose, Robert Inc. CAN. Dist: Firefly Bks., Ltd.

Young, Nicole & Day, Nadine. Blender Baby Food: Over 175 Recipes for Healthy Homemade Meals. 2nd ed. 2011. (ENG., Illus.). 216p. pap. 19.95 *(978-0-7788-0262-4(0))* Rose, Robert Inc. CAN. Dist: Firefly Bks., Ltd.

BABY NAMES

see Names, Personal

BABY SITTERS

see Babysitters

BABY SITTING

see Babysitting

BABYLON (EXTINCT CITY)

Cancik-Kirschbaum, Eva, et al, eds. Babylon: Wissenskultur in Orient und Okzident / Science Culture Between Orient & Occident. 2011. (Topoi Ser.). (GER & ENG., Illus.). XXII, 379p. 112.00 *(978-3-11-022211-1(6))* De Gruyter, Walter Inc.

Dougherty, Raymond Philip. Nabonidus & Belshazzar: A Study of the Closing Events of the Neo-Babylonian Empire. 2008. (Ancient near East: Ser.). 230p. pap. 20.00 *(978-1-55635-956-9(X)*, Wipf and Stock) Wipf & Stock Pubs.

Gallagher, Steve. Intoxicated with Babylon: The Seduction of God's People in the Last Days. annot. ed. 2007. (ENG.). 240p. per. 13.99 *(978-0-9758832-4-2(0))* Pure Life Ministries.

Hirmer Verlag, ed. Babylon: Mythos und Wahrheit. Bd. 1: Wahrheit, Bd. 2: Mythos, 2 vols. 2008. (GER., Illus.). 900p. (C). 88.00 *(978-3-7774-5005-6(7))* Hirmer Verlag GmbH DEU. Dist: Brown, David Bk. Co., The.

Kriwaczek, Paul. Babylon: Mesopotamia & the Birth of Civilization. 2012. (ENG., Illus.). 320p. 27.99 ***(978-1-250-00007-1(6)***, Dunne, Thomas Bks.) St. Martin's Pr.

Layard, Austen Henry. Discoveries in the Ruins of Nineveh & Babylon: With Travels in Armenia, Kurdistan & the Desert: Being the Result of a Second Expedition Undertaken for the Trustees of the British Museum. 2010. (Cambridge Library Collection - Archaeology Ser.). (Illus.). 392p. (ENG.). pap. 31.99 *(978-1-108-01678-0(2))*; pap. 31.99 *(978-1-108-01677-3(4))* Cambridge Univ. Pr.

—Discoveries in the Ruins of Nineveh & Babylon; with Travels in Armenia, Kurdistan, & the Desert. 2007. (Gorgias Classic Archaeological Reprints Ser.: 3). 68.00 *(978-1-59333-636-3(5))* Gorgias Pr., LLC.

Leick, Gwendolyn. The Babylonian World. 2009. (Routledge Worlds Ser.). (ENG., Illus.). 616p. pap. 49.95 *(978-0-415-49783-1(3))* Routledge.

McKinney, Edward. From Nebuchadnezzar to Gorbachev, the Story of Babylon, Book 1 Of 3. 2010. 268p. pap. 29.95 *(978-0-557-26850-4(8))* Lulu Enterprises Inc.

Mystical Babylon. 31p. (Orig.). pap. 0.95 *(978-0-937408-21-6(2))* GMI Pubns.

Oviesa, Prince. Prayer: The Timeless Relevance. 2010. pap. 9.99 *(978-1-61566-312-5(6))* Tate Publishing & Enterprises, LLC.

Scaife, Gladys. Babylon the Great Rise & Fall: No Subtitle. 2008. 136p. pap. 13.99 *(978-1-60647-387-0(5))* Xulon Pr., Inc.

Seymour, Michael. Babylon: The History of a Legend & its Afterlives. 2012. (ENG., Illus.). 352p. 96.00 ***(978-1-84885-701-8(2))*** I. B. Tauris & Co., Ltd. GBR. Dist: Macmillan.

Slotsky, Alice Louise & Wallenfels, Ronald. Tallies & Trends: The Late Babylonian Commodity Price Lists. 2009. *(978-1-934309-23-0(0)*, CDL Pr.) Univ. Pr. of Maryland.

Wartke, Ralf-B. Auf dem Weg nach Babylon: Robert Koldewey - Ein Archäologenleben. Wartke, Ralf-B., ed. 2008. (Illus.). 192p. (C). 38.00 *(978-3-8053-3918-6(6))* Zabern, Philipp von Verlag, GmbH DEU. Dist: Brown, David Bk. Co., The.

BABYLONIA

see also Sumer

Budge, E. A. Wallis. Babylonian Life & History. 2010. 196p. pap. 23.75 *(978-1-148-65158-3(6))*; 172p. pap. 21.75 *(978-1-141-40704-0(3))* BiblioBazaar.

—Babylonian Life & History. 2010. 82p. pap. 20.00 *(978-1-153-35712-8(7))* 2009. 106p. pap. 14.14 *(978-1-150-64938-7(0))* General Bks. LLC.

—Babylonian Life & History. 2007. (ENG.). 164p. per. *(978-1-4067-5356-1(4))* Read Bks.

De Lafayette, Maximillien. Description & Explanation of Anunnaki, Babylonian, Sumerian, Akkadian, Assyrian, Phoenician Slabs, Seals, Inscriptions, Statues, Tablets & Secret Symbols. 4th Edition. 2010. 400p. pap. 29.50 *(978-0-557-45240-8(6))* Lulu Enterprises Inc.

Holtz, Shalom. Neo-Babylonian Decision Records & Related Documents: Typological, Procedural, & Comparative Aspects. 2009. *(978-90-04-17496-2(6))* BRILL.

Leick. The Babylonian World. 2007. *(978-0-415-43625-0(7))*; (Illus.). MXXXVIIIp. *(978-0-415-43626-7(5))* Taylor & Francis Group. (Routledge).

Maximillien de Lafayette, Germain Lumiere/. Description & Explanation of Anunnaki, Babylonian, Sumerian, Akkadian, Assyrian, Phoenician Slabs, Seals, Inscriptions, Statues, Tablets & Secret Symbols. 2010. 400p. pap. 29.50 *(978-0-557-44178-5(1))* Lulu Enterprises Inc.

Shoesmith, Bernard. The Fall of Babylon. 2010. 152p. pap. 14.00 *(978-1-59755-239-4(9)*, Advantage Inspirational) Advantage Bks.

BABYLONIA—ANTIQUITIES

Baikie, James. The Life of the Ancient East: Being Some Chapters of the Romance of Modern Excavation 1923. 2007. 540p. 57.95 *(978-0-548-05401-7(0))* Kessinger Publishing, LLC.

British Museum, Department of Egyptian and Assyrian Art Staff. Babylonian Boundary-Stones & Memorial Tablets in the British Museum, 2 vols., Set. King, Leonard W., ed. (Ancient Mesopotamian Texts & Studies). reprint ed. 85.00 *(978-0-404-18166-6(X))* AMS Pr., Inc.

Foster, Benjamin & Foster, Karen Polinger. Civilizations of Ancient Iraq. 2011. (ENG., Illus.). 312p. (C). pap. 16.95 *(978-0-691-14997-4(6))* Princeton Univ. Pr.

Foster, Benjamin R. & Foster, Karen Polinger. Civilizations of Ancient Iraq. 2009. (ENG., Illus.). 312p. (C). 26.95 *(978-0-691-13722-3(6))* Princeton Univ. Pr.

Frahm, Eckart & Jursa, Michael. Neo-Babylonian Letters & Contracts from the Eanna Archive. 2011. (Yale Oriental Series, Babylonian Texts). (ENG., Illus.). 226p. 125.00 *(978-0-300-16959-1(0))* Yale Univ. Pr.

Hilprecht, H. V. Drought, Famine, Plague & Pestilence. 2009. 294p. pap. *(978-1-4590-7310-4(X))* Books LLC.

—Drought, Famine, Plague & Pestilence. 2007. (Gorgias Classic Archaeological Reprints Ser.: 9). 88.00 *(978-1-59333-640-0(3))*;2 of 2. 44.00 *(978-1-59333-650-9(0))* Gorgias Pr., LLC.

Hilprecht, H. V. & Robertson, Warren. Drought, Famine, Plague & Pestilence, 1 of 2. 2010. (Gorgias Classic Archaeological Reprints Ser.: 9). pap. 130.00 *(978-1-59333-649-3(7))* Gorgias Pr., LLC.

Hilprecht, Hermann Vollrat, ed. The Excavations in Assyria & Babylonia. 2011. (Cambridge Library Collection - Archaeology Ser.). (Illus.). 688p. pap. 48.00 *(978-1-108-02564-5(1))* Cambridge Univ. Pr.

King, L. W. Legends of Babylon & Egypt in Relation to Hebrew Tradition. 2007. 172p. per. *(978-1-4065-1948-8(0))* Dodo Pr.

Maiocchi, Massimo. Classical Sargonic Tablets Chiefly from Adab in the Cornell University Collections. 2009. *(978-1-934309-12-4(5)*, CDL Pr.) Univ. Pr. of Maryland.

Maiocchi, Massimo & Visicato, Giuseppe. Classical Sargonic Tablets Chiefly from Adab in the Cornell University Collections. 2012. ***(978-1-934309-40-7(0)***, CDL Pr.) Univ. Pr. of Maryland.

McEwan, G. J. The Late Babylonian Tablets in the Royal Ontario Museum, Vol. 2. (Illus.). 312p. pap. *(978-0-88854-282-3(8))* BRILL.

Richardson, Seth Francis Corning. Texts from the Late Old Babylonian Period. 2010. (Journal of Cuneiform Studies Supplement Ser.). (ENG.). 232p. (C). 75.00 *(978-0-89757-084-8(7))* American Schls. of Oriental Research.

Rizza, Alfredo. Assyrians & Babylonians: History & Treasures of an Ancient Civilization. 2010. (ENG.). 19.98 *(978-88-544-0457-1(8))* White Star ITA. Dist: Random Hse., Inc.

University of Pennsylvania, Babylonian Expedition Staff, Babylonian Expedition. The Babylonian Expedition of the University of Pennsylvani. 2009. 112p. 39.95 *(978-1-4181-7571-9(4))* MPublishing.

Visicato, Giuseppe & Westenholz, Aage. Early Dynastic & Early Sargonic Tablets from Adab in the Cornell University Collections. 2010. *(978-1-934309-10-0(9)*, CDL Pr.) Univ. Pr. of Maryland.

BABYLONIA—COMMERCE

Jones, Tom B. Sumerian Economic Texts from the Third Ur Dynasty. 2009. (ENG.). 441p. pap. 60.00 *(978-0-8166-6040-7(9))* Univ. of Minnesota Pr.

Lau, Robert J. Old Babylonian Temple Records. (Columbia University, Oriental Studies: No. 3). reprint ed. 39.50 *(978-0-404-50493-9(0))* AMS Pr., Inc.

Lau, Robert Julius. Old Babylonian Temple Records. 2007. 69.00 *(978-1-59333-632-5(2))* Gorgias Pr., LLC.

Nesbit, William M. Sumerian Records from Drehem. (Columbia University, Oriental Studies: No. 8). (Illus.). reprint ed. 32.50 *(978-0-404-50498-4(1))* AMS Pr., Inc.

Slotsky, Alice Louise & Wallenfels, Ronald. Tallies & Trends: The Late Babylonian Commodity Price Lists. 2009. *(978-1-934309-23-0(0)*, CDL Pr.) Univ. Pr. of Maryland.

Ungnad, Arthur. Selected Business Documents of the Neo-Babylonian Period. 2008. 85p. pap. 7.00 *(978-1-60608-352-9(X)*, Wipf and Stock) Wipf & Stock Pubs.

BABYLONIA—HISTORY

Blakeslee, Michael. The Exile. 2009. 444p. pap. 22.99 *(978-1-61579-380-8(1))* Xulon Pr., Inc.

Charpin, Dominique. Hammurabi of Babylon. 2012. (ENG., Illus.). 312p. 82.50 ***(978-1-84885-752-0(7))*** I. B. Tauris & Co., Ltd. GBR. Dist: Macmillan.

Dalley, Stephanie. Mari & Karana, Two Old Babylonian Cities: With a New Introduction by the Author. 2007. (Gorgias Classic Archaeological Reprints Ser.: 10). 74.00 *(978-1-59333-634-9(9))* Gorgias Pr., LLC.

Dougherty, Raymond Philip. Nabonidus & Belshazzar: A Study of the Closing Events of the Neo-Babylonian Empire. 2008. (Ancient near East: Ser.). 230p. pap. 20.00 *(978-1-55635-956-9(X)*, Wipf and Stock) Wipf & Stock Pubs.

Fisher, Clarence. The Mycenaean Palace at Nippur. 2009. pap. 20.44 *(978-1-60724-506-3(X))* Gorgias Pr., LLC.

Frame, Grant & van Zoest, C. H. Babylonia 689-627 B.C. A Political History. 2007. 358p. pap. 65.00 *(978-90-6258-069-9(6))* Netherlands Institute for the Near East NLD. Dist: Eisenbrauns, Inc.

Goodspeed, George Stephen. A History of the Babylonians & Assyrians. 2009. 572p. pap. *(978-0-217-42615-2(8))* Books LLC.

Grice, Ettalene Mears. Chronology of the Larsa Dynasty. 2009. 48p. pap. 16.75 *(978-1-116-89652-7(4))* BiblioBazaar.

Hirmer Verlag, ed. Babylon: Mythos und Wahrheit. Bd. 1: Wahrheit, Bd. 2: Mythos, 2 vols. 2008. (GER., Illus.). 900p. (C). 88.00 *(978-3-7774-5005-6(7))* Hirmer Verlag GmbH DEU. Dist: Brown, David Bk. Co., The.

Jones, C. H. W. Ancient Babylonia. 2012. (ENG.). 178p. pap. 19.99 ***(978-1-107-60572-5(5))*** Cambridge Univ. Pr.

King, Leonard W. History of Babylon from the Foundations of the Monarchy to the Persian Conquest. reprint ed. 49.50 *(978-0-404-03694-2(5))* AMS Pr., Inc.

Leick, Gwendolyn, ed. The Babylonian World. 2007. (Routledge Worlds Ser.). (Illus.). 590p. 250.00 *(978-0-415-35346-5(7))* Routledge.

Ragozin, Zénaïde Alexeïevna. Chaldea from the Earliest Times to the Rise of Assyria. 2008. (Illus.). 204p. pap. *(978-1-84830-940-1(6))*, Wildhern Pr.) Echo Library.

—Media Babylon & Persia. 2006. 476p. per. *(978-1-4067-2215-4(4))*, Hesperides Pr.) Read Bks.

Rawlinson, George. The Chronicle of Michael the Great in French Translation. 2008. 304p. 28.99 *(978-0-554-34833-9(0))*; 196p. 22.99 *(978-0-554-34829-2(2))*; 200p. 22.99 *(978-0-554-34831-5(4))*; 196p. 25.99 *(978-0-554-25526-2(X))*; 200p. 25.99 *(978-0-554-25528-6(6))*; 304p. 29.99 *(978-0-554-25530-9(8))*; (Illus.). 460p. 31.99 *(978-0-554-34834-6(9))*; (Illus.). 368p. 29.99 *(978-0-554-34832-2(2))*; (Illus.). 368p. 31.99 *(978-0-554-25529-3(4))*; (Illus.). 460p. 33.99 *(978-0-554-25531-6(6))* BiblioBazaar.

—The Chronicle of Michael the Great in French Translation. Chabot, Jean-Baptiste, tr. 2011. (Gorgias Classic Archaeological Reprints Ser.: 4). (FRE.). 350.00 *(978-1-59333-637-0(3))* Gorgias Pr., LLC.

—The Chronicle of Michael the Great in French Translation. 2007. (Gorgias Classic Archaeological Reprints Ser.: 4). 1 of 3. 51.33 *(978-1-59333-646-2(2))*2 of 3. 51.33 *(978-1-59333-647-9(0))*3 of 3. 51.33 *(978-1-59333-648-6(9))* Gorgias Pr., LLC.

—Five Great Monarchies of the Ancient Eas. 2006. pap. 43.95 *(978-1-4286-4769-5(4))* Kessinger Publishing, LLC

—Seven Great Monarchies of the Ancient Ea. 2006. pap. 54.95 *(978-1-4286-4794-7(5))*; pap. 54.95 *(978-1-4286-4792-3(9))* Kessinger Publishing, LLC.

—The Seven Great Monarchies of the Ancient Eastern World: Babylon, Vol. 4. I.t. ed. 2007. (ENG.). 196p. pap. 21.99 *(978-1-4264-9273-0(1))* BiblioBazaar.

—The Seven Great Monarchies of the Ancient Eastern World: Media: Media. 2007. (ENG.). 142p. pap. 18.99 *(978-1-4346-0109-4(9))*; 154p. pap. 21.99 *(978-1-4346-0118-6(8))* BiblioBazaar.

—The Seven Great Monarchies of the Ancient Eastern World, Part I. 2007. (Illus.). 180p. per. *(978-1-4065-4248-6(2))* Dodo Pr.

—The Seven Great Monarchies of the Ancient Eastern World Volume 1: Chaldaea. 2007. (ENG.). 178p. pap. 19.99 *(978-1-4264-9214-3(6))* BiblioBazaar.

—The Seven Great Monarchies of the Ancient Eastern World Volume 4 Babylon. 2007. (ENG.). 176p. pap. 19.99 *(978-1-4264-9216-7(2))* BiblioBazaar.

—The Seven Great Monarchies of the Ancient Eastern World Volume 7: The Sassanian or New Persian Empire. 2007. 414p. pap. 16.99 *(978-1-4264-9219-8(7))* BiblioBazaar.

Rizza, Alfredo. Assyrians & Babylonians: History & Treasures of an Ancient Civilization. 2010. (ENG.). 19.98 *(978-88-544-0457-1(8))* White Star ITA. Dist: Random Hse., Inc.

—The Assyrians & the Babylonians: History & Treasures of an Ancient Civilization. 2007. (ENG., Illus.). 208p. 35.00 *(978-88-544-0268-3(0))*, White Star) Rizzoli International Pubns., Inc.

Sigrist, Marcel. On the Third Dynasty of Ur: Studies in Honor of Marcel Sigrist. Michalowski, Piotr, ed. & tr. by. 2008. (Journal of Cuneiform Studies Supplement Ser.). (ENG., Illus.). 313p. (C). 75.00 *(978-0-89757-080-0(4))* American Schls. of Oriental Research.

BABYLONIA—HISTORY—SOURCES

Baker, Heather D., et al, eds. Your Praise Is Sweet: A Memorial Volume for Jeremy Black from Students, Colleagues & Friends. 2010. (ENG.). 472p. (C). 70.00 *(978-0-903472-28-9(7))* British Schl. of Archaeology in Iraq GBR. Dist: Brown, David Bk. Co., The.

Dalley, Stephanie. Babylonian Tablets from the First Sealand Dynasty in the Schoyen Collection. 2009. *(978-1-934309-08-7(7))*, CDL Pr.) Univ. Pr. of Maryland.

Grayson, A. Kirk. Assyrian & Babylonian Chronicles. 2008. (Texts from Cuneiform Sources Ser.: Vol. 5). 300p. 79.50 *(978-1-57506-049-1(3))* Eisenbrauns, Inc.

Hilprecht, H. V. The Earliest Version of the Babylonian Deluge Story & the Temple Library of Nippur. 2009. 84p. pap. 17.95 *(978-1-120-75734-0(7))* Kessinger Publishing, LLC.

King, L. W., ed. The Letters & Inscriptions of Hammurabi, King of Babylon About. 2006. (ENG.). 444p. per. 36.95 *(978-1-4286-3423-7(1))* Kessinger Publishing, LLC.

Richardson, Seth Francis Corning. Texts from the Late Old Babylonian Period. 2010. (Journal of Cuneiform Studies Supplement Ser.). (ENG.). 232p. (C). 75.00 *(978-0-89757-084-8(7))* American Schls. of Oriental Research.

Ungnad, Arthur. Alt Babylonische Briefe aus dem Museum zu Philadelphia. (Ancient Mesopotamian Texts & Studies). reprint ed. 34.50 *(978-0-404-18226-7(7))* AMS Pr., Inc.

Visicato, Giuseppe & Westenholz, Aage. Early Dynastic & Early Sargonic Tablets from Adab in the Cornell University Collections. 2010. *(978-1-934309-10-0(9))*, CDL Pr.) Univ. Pr. of Maryland.

Westenholz, Joan & Westenholz, Aage. Cuneiform Inscriptions in the Collection of the Bible Lands Museum Jerusalem: The Old Babylonian Inscriptions. 2006. (Illus.). *(978-90-04-14710-2(1))* BRILL.

BABYLONIAN CIVILIZATION

see Civilization, Assyro-Babylonian

BABYLONIAN INSCRIPTIONS

see Cuneiform Inscriptions

BABYLONIAN LANGUAGE

see Akkadian Language

BABYLONIAN LETTERS

see Assyro-Babylonian Letters

BABYLONIAN LITERATURE

see Assyro-Babylonian Literature

BABYLONIAN MATHEMATICS

see Mathematics, Babylonian

BABYLONIAN MYTHOLOGY

see Mythology, Assyro-Babylonian

BABYSITTERS

Forman-Brunell, Miriam. Babysitter: An American History. 2009. (ENG., Illus.). 326p. 65.00 *(978-0-8147-2759-1(X))* New York Univ. Pr.

Nolte, Lysne. Big Sister Babysitter: I'm going to be a WHAT?! 2011. 90p. pap. 8.95 ***(978-1-257-76114-2(5))*** Lulu Enterprises Inc.

BABYSITTING

Boucher, Michelle. Bon Voyage: Leaving the Kids Home, the Complete Guide to Overnight Childcare. Date not set. (Illus.). 110p. (Orig.). pap. 10.00 *(978-0-9658110-1-9(8))* Hands of the Sun Publishing.

Forman-Brunell, Miriam. Babysitter: An American History. 2011. (ENG., Illus.). 326p. pap. 25.00 ***(978-0-8147-2895-6(2))*** New York Univ. Pr.

BACA, ELFEGO, 1864-1945

Crichton, Kyle. Law & Order, Ltd: The Rousing Life of Elfego Baca of New Mexico: Facsimile of 1928 Edition with a New Foreword by Stan Sager. 2008. 284p. pap. 26.95 *(978-0-86534-668-0(2))* Sunstone Pr.

Sager, Stan. ¡Viva Elfego! The Case for Elfego Baca, Hispanic Hero. 2008. 280p. pap. 24.95 *(978-0-86534-608-6(9))* Sunstone Pr.

BACA FAMILY

La Farge, Oliver. Behind the Mountains. 2009. 228p. pap. 24.95 *(978-0-86534-676-5(3))* Sunstone Pr.

Lucero, Donald L. The Adobe Kingdom: New Mexico, 1598-1958, As Experienced by the Families Lucero de Godoy y Baca. 2nd ed. 2009. 384p. pap. 26.95 *(978-0-86534-669-7(0))* Sunstone Pr.

BACALL, LAUREN, 1924-

Bacall, Lauren & Bacall, Lauren. By Myself & Then Some. 2006. (ENG.). 512p. pap. 15.99 *(978-0-06-112791-5(4))* HarperCollins Pubs.

BACCALAUREATE ADDRESSES

Campbell, James V. Law & Lawyers in Society an Address Delivered Before the Graduating Class of the Law Department of the University of Michigan, March 28, 1866 by J. 2011. 22p. pap. 11.99 ***(978-1-4181-9129-0(9))*** MPublishing.

Chimsky-Lustig, Mark, ed. Creating a Life You'll Love: Notable Achievers Offer Their Secrets for Happiness. 2009. 248p. pap. 15.95 *(978-1-4162-0536-4(5))* Sellers Publishing, Inc.

Committee for Improved Measurement of High School Dropout and Completion Rates: Expert Guidance on Next Steps for Research and Policy Workshop, et al. High School Dropout, Graduation, & Completion Rates: Better Data, Better Measures, Better Decisions. Koenig, Judith Anderson & Hauser, Robert M., eds. 2011. (ENG.). 154p. pap. 36.75 *(978-0-309-16307-1(2))* National Academies Pr.

Duffield, D. Bethune. The Lawyer's Oath an Address Delivered Before the Class of 1867, of the Law Department, University of Michigan, March 27th, 1867, by D Bethune Duffi. 2011. 26p. pap. 11.99 ***(978-1-4181-9238-9(4))*** MPublishing.

Hopkins, Mark. Baccalaureate Sermons, & Occasional Discourses, by Mark Hopkins. 2006. 400p. per. 26.99 *(978-1-4255-4290-0(5))* MPublishing.

Llamas, Edmundo. Tareas para el Examen de Admisión. 2011. 200p. pap. 23.95 ***(978-1-257-17350-1(2))*** Lulu Enterprises Inc.

Miscamble, Wilson D., ed. Go Forth & Do Good: Memorable Notre Dame Commencement Addresses. 2012. (ENG.). 312p. pap. 25.00 ***(978-0-268-03525-9(3))*** Univ. of Notre Dame Pr.

Shapiro, Neil, illus. Wisdom & Wack for the Graduate. 2007. (ENG.). 72p. 14.95 *(978-1-933176-15-4(6))* Red Rock Pr., Inc.

BACCHUS (GREEK DEITY)

see Dionysus (Greek Deity)

BACH, CARL PHILIPP EMANUEL, 1714-1788

Cornelison, Paul E., et al. Er Ist der Vater, Wir Sind Die Bub'n: Essays in Honor of Christoph Wolff. 2010. *(978-0-9819850-1-5(7))* Steglein Publishing, Inc.

Lee, Sun Young. Studien Zur Kirchenmusik Von Carl Philipp Emanuel Bach (1714-1788) 2011. (Europäische Hochschulschriften. Reihe 36: Musikwissenschaft Ser.). (GER.). 244p. pap. 67.95 *(978-3-631-61148-7(X))* Lang, Peter GmbH, Europaischer Verlag der Wissenschaften DEU. Dist: Lang, Peter.

Richards, Annette, ed. C. P. E. Bach Studies. (Cambridge Composer Studies). (ENG., Illus.). 2009. 284p. pap. 42.00 *(978-0-521-12043-2(8))* 2006. 280p. 106.99 *(978-0-521-83629-6(8))* Cambridge Univ. Pr.

BACH, EDWARD, 1886-1936

Fabrocini, Vicenzo. Flores de Bach (The Bach Flowers) (SPA.). 96p. *(978-84-315-1713-7(1))* De Vecchi, Editorial, S.A.

Guastela, Evelina. El Gran Libro de las Flores de Bach.Tr. of Book of Bach Flowers. (SPA.). pap. *(978-84-315-1826-4(X))* De Vecchi, Editorial, S.A.

McCabe, Vinton. The Healing Bouquet: Exploring Bach Flower Remedies, 1 vol. 2008. (ENG., Illus.). 240p. pap. *(978-1-59120-072-7(5))* Basic Health Pubns., Inc.

PallasDowney, Rhonda. Flower Essences: Discover the Healing Powers of Flowers. 2010. 36p. pap. 4.95 *(978-1-58054-129-9(1))* Woodland Publishing, Inc.

Salmon, Philip. Dr Bachs Flower Remedies & the Chakras. 3rd ed. 2006. pap. *(978-1-905367-04-7(X))* North Atlantic Bks.

Salmon, Philip & Jeoffroy, Anna. Dr. Bach's Flower Remedies: Tapping into the Positive Emotional Qualities of the Chakras. 3rd ed. 2007. (ENG., Illus.). 128p. pap. 22.95 *(978-1-55643-640-6(8))* North Atlantic Bks.

Webb-De Sisto, Marion. Turning to Nature: The Healing Flower Remedies Created by Dr. Edward Bach. 2009. 116p. pap. 13.95 *(978-1-60145-873-5(8))* Booklocker.com, Inc.

BACH, JOHANN CHRISTIAN, 1735-1782

Böß, Reinhard. Die ungleich schwebende originalstimmung von johann sebastian bach das wohl tem perirte Clavier. 2009. (GER.). 220p. pap. 60.95 *(978-3-631-58441-5(5))* Lang, Peter GmbH, Europaischer Verlag der Wissenschaften DEU. Dist: Lang, Peter.

Siblin, Eric. The Cello Suites: J. S. Bach, Pablo Casals, & the Search for a Baroque Masterpiece. 2011. (ENG.). 336p. pap. 15.95 *(978-0-8021-4524-6(8))*, Grove Pr.) Grove/Atlantic, Inc.

Terry, Charles Sanford. John Christian Bach. 2009. (Illus.). 436p. pap. *(978-1-906857-32-5(6))* Travis & Emery Music Bookshop.

BACH, JOHANN SEBASTIAN, 1685-1750

Alexander, Peter Lawrence. Street Smart Guide to the Bach Chorales. 2009. 296p. pap. 29.95 *(978-0-939067-92-3(7))* Alexander Publishing.

Alfred Publishing Staff. Shredding Bach: Book & CD. 2010. (National Guitar Workshop Ser.). (ENG.). 64p. pap. 16.99 *(978-0-7390-6951-6(9))* Alfred Publishing Co., Inc.

Bach - Brandenburg Concertos 1-3. 2008. (ENG.). 124p. pap. 16.99 incl. audio compact disk *(978-3-7957-6502-6(1))*, 3795765021) Schott Musik International GmbH & Co. KG DEU. Dist: Leonard, Hal Corp.

Bach - Brandenburg Concertos 4-6. 2008. (ENG.). 164p. pap. 17.99 incl. audio compact disk *(978-3-7957-6503-3(X))*, 379576503X) Schott Musik International GmbH & Co. KG DEU. Dist: Leonard, Hal Corp.

Bach - Overtures Nos. 1-2. 2008. (ENG.). 58p. pap. 12.99 incl. audio compact disk *(978-3-7957-6513-2(7))*, 3795765137) Schott Musik International GmbH & Co. KG DEU. Dist: Leonard, Hal Corp.

Bach - Overtures Nos. 3-4. 2008. (ENG.). 116p. pap. 14.99 incl. audio compact disk *(978-3-7957-6514-9(5))*, 3795765145) Schott Musik International GmbH & Co. KG DEU. Dist: Leonard, Hal Corp.

Bach, Carl Philipp Emanuel & Agricola, Johann Friedrich. Nekrolog or Obituary Notice of Johann Sebastian Bach. Emery, Walter, tr. from GER. 2009. 268p. *(978-1-906857-79-0(2))* Travis & Emery Music Bookshop.

Bach, Carl Philipp Emanuel, et al. Nekrolog, or, Obituary Notice of Johann Sebastian Bach. 2010. xx, 231p. pap. *(978-1-906857-80-6(6))* Travis & Emery Music Bookshop.

Bach, Johann Sebastian. Triple Concerto BMV 1044 for Flute, Violin & Harpsichord in Full Score. 2007. (Dover Orchestral Scores Ser.). (ENG., Illus.). 64p. pap. 9.95 *(978-0-486-45728-4(1))* Dover Pubns., Inc.

Berger, Karol. Bach's Cycle, Mozart's Arrow: An Essay on the Origins of Musical Modernity. (Illus.). 2008. 432p. pap. 25.95 *(978-0-520-25797-9(9))* 2007. 420p. 39.95 *(978-0-520-25091-8(5))* Univ. of California Pr.

Biographiq. Johann Sebastian Bach - German Composer & Organist. 2008. 72p. pap. 9.99 *(978-1-59986-374-0(X))*, Biographiq) Filiquarian Publishing, LLC.

Blumenberg, Hans. Matthduspassion. *(978-0-8047-4067-8(4))*; pap. *(978-0-8047-4068-5(2))* Stanford Univ. Pr.

Butler, Gregory ed. Bach Perspectives, Volume 6: J. S. Bach's Concerted Ensemble Music, the Ouverture. 2007. (Bach Perspectives (BP) Ser.). (Illus.). 176p. 52.00 *(978-0-252-03042-0(7))* Univ. of Illinois Pr.

Butler, Gregory G. J. S. Bach's Concerted Ensemble Music Vol. 7: The Concerto. Butler, Gregory, ed. 2007. (Bach Perspectives Ser.: Vol. 7). (Illus.). 136p. 62.00 *(978-0-252-03165-6(2))* Univ. of Illinois Pr.

Butt, John. Bach's Dialogue with Modernity: Perspectives on the Passions. 2010. (ENG., Illus.). 330p. 104.00 *(978-0-521-88356-6(3))* Cambridge Univ. Pr.

Cantoni, Angelo. La Reference a Bach dans les Oeuvres Neo-Classiques de Stravinsky, Vol. 8. Date not set. (GER & FRE., Illus.). iv, 358p. *(978-3-487-10598-7(5))* Olms, Georg Verlag AG.

Carrell, Norman. Bach's Brandenburg Concerts. reprint ed. lib. bdg. 59.00 *(978-0-403-08968-0(9))* Scholarly Pr., Inc.

Carrington, Jerome. Trills in the Bach Cello Suites: A Handbook for Performers. 2009. (ENG.). 216p. (C). 40.00 *(978-0-8061-4001-8(1))* Univ. of Oklahoma Pr.

Castle, Joseph. Best of Bach for Classic Guitar, 1 vol. 2008. (ENG.). 20p. pap. 4.95 *(978-1-56222-134-8(5)*, 93453) Mel Bay Pubns., Inc.

Cervino, Alessandro & Laws, Catherine. The Practice of Practising. 2012. (ENG., Illus.). 92p. pap. 34.00 ***(978-90-5867-848-5(2))*** Leuven Univ. Pr. BEL. Dist: Cornell Univ. Pr.

Chafe, Eric Thomas. J. S. Bach's Johannine Theology: The St. John Passion & the Cantatas for Spring 1725. 2011. *(978-0-19-977334-3(3))* Oxford Univ. Pr., Inc.

Connor, John Bosco. Gregorian Chant & Medieval Hymn Tunes in the Works of J S Bach. 2011. 198p. 44.95 ***(978-1-258-02741-4(0))*** Literary Licensing, LLC.

Dürr, Alfred. The Cantatas of J. S. Bach: With Their Librettos in German-English Parallel Text. Jones, Richard D. P., tr. from GER. 2006. (ENG., Illus.). 984p. per. 99.00 *(978-0-19-929776-4(2))* Oxford Univ. Pr., Inc.

Dutkanicz, David, ed. My First Book of Bach: Favorite Pieces in Easy Piano Arrangements. 2007. (Dover Music for Piano Ser.). (ENG.). 48p. pap. 4.95 *(978-0-486-45737-6(0))* Dover Pubns., Inc.

Dykstra, Elaine S. Deducing the Original Sounds of Bach's Organ Works: An Historical Account of the Musical Capabilities of the Organs That Bach Knew. 2007. 188p. 99.95 *(978-0-7734-5254-1(0))* Mellen, Edwin Pr., The.

Elie, Paul. Soundabout: Reinventing Bach, 1 vol. 2012. (ENG., Illus.). 496p. 30.00 ***(978-0-374-28107-6(6))*** Farrar, Straus & Giroux.

Erickson, Raymond & Hal Leonard Corporation Staff. The Worlds of Johann Sebastian Bach, 1 vol. 2009. (ENG., Illus.). 348p. 34.99 *(978-1-57467-166-7(9))*, 1574671669, Amadeus Press) Leonard, Hal Corp.

Franklin, Don O. Bach Studies. 2008. (ENG., Illus.). 380p. pap. 53.00 *(978-0-521-08832-9(1))* Cambridge Univ. Pr.

Geck, Martin. Johann Sebastian Bach: Life & Work. Hargraves, John, tr. from GER. 2006. (ENG., Illus.). 752p. 40.00 *(978-0-15-100648-9(2))* Houghton Mifflin Harcourt Trade & Reference Pubs.

Hal Leonard Corporation Staff. Unlocking the Masters Set: Bach's Keyboard Music, Beethoven's Symphonies, & Brahms - A Listener's Guide. deluxe ed. 2010. (ENG.). 500p. pap. 55.00 incl. audio compact disk *(978-1-57467-192-6(8))*, 1574671928, Amadeus Press) Leonard, Hal Corp.

Harper, Paula, contrib. by. Elena Presser: Works on the Music of Johann Sebastian Bach. 16p. (Orig.). (C). *(978-0-9630869-2-1(8))* Univ. of Wyoming Art Museum.

Hecksher, Martin A., frwd. The Universal Bach: Lectures Celebrating the Tercentenary of Bach's Birthday. 2006. (Illus.). 94p. reprint ed. 25.00 *(978-1-4223-8006-2(8))* DIANE Publishing Co.

Hofstadter, Douglas R. Godel, Escher, Bach: Un Eterno y Gracil Bucle. 2007. (Fabula (Tusquets Editores) Ser.) (Illus.). 882p. pap. *(978-84-8383-024-6(8))* Tusquets Editores.

Jones, Gordon. Bach's Choral Music. 2009. (Unlocking the Masters Ser.: No. 20). (ENG.). 224p. pap. 22.99 incl. audio compact disk *(978-1-57467-180-3(4))*, 1574671804, Amadeus Press) Leonard, Hal Corp.

Jones, Richard. The Creative Development of Johann Sebastian Bach: Music to Delight the Spirit Volume 1: 1695-1717, 2 vols. 2007. (ENG., Illus.). 352p. 199.00 *(978-0-19-816440-1(8))* Oxford Univ. Pr., Inc.

Kelly, Thomas Forrest & Gallagher, Sean, eds. The Century of Bach & Mozart: Perspectives on Historiography, Composition, Theory & Performance. 2009. (Isham Library Papers: 7). (Illus.). 427p. pap. 39.95 *(978-0-9640317-5-3(2))* Harvard Univ., Dept. of Music.

Kempen, Suzanne van. Bach - musikpädagogisch Betrachtet. 2009. (Beiträge zur europäischen Musikgeschichte Ser.). (GER.). 340p. 79.95 *(978-3-631-59325-7(2))* Lang, Peter GmbH, Europaischer Verlag der Wissenschaften DEU. Dist: Lang, Peter.

Leahy, Anne. J. S. Bach's Leipzig Chorale Preludes: Music, Text, Theology. 2011. (Contextual Bach Studies). (ENG., Illus.). 326p. (gr. 17). 80.00 *(978-0-8108-8181-5(0))* Scarecrow Pr., Inc.

Leahy, Anne & Leaver, Robin A. J. S. Bach's "Leipzig" Chorale Preludes: Music, Text, Theology. 2011. (Illus.). xxviii, 295p. E-Book *(978-0-8108-8182-2(9))* Scarecrow Pr., Inc.

Ledbetter, David. The Baroque Composers, 5 vols., Set. 2011. (Baroque Composers Ser.). 2948p. 1250.00 *(978-0-7546-2903-0(1))* Ashgate Publishing Co.

Lederer, Victor. Bach's Keyboard Music. 2010. (ZUN & ENG.). 200p. pap. 22.99 incl. audio compact disk *(978-1-57467-182-7(0))*, 1574671820, Amadeus Press) Leonard, Hal Corp.

—Bach's St. Matthew Passion: A Closer Look. 2008. (Magnum Opus Ser.). (ENG.). 144p. pap. 19.95 *(978-0-8264-2940-7(8))* Continuum International Publishing Group, Ltd. GBR. Dist: National Bk. Network.

Leiter, E. J. The Performance of Bach's Keyboard Works on the Piano. 2010. (Illus.). 187p. 70.00 *(978-0-615-35109-4(3))* Edition Caos.

Melamed, Daniel R., ed. Bach Perspectives, Volume 8: J. S. Bach & the Oratorio Tradition. 2011. (Bach Perspectives Ser.). (ENG., Illus.). 168p. 60.00 *(978-0-252-03584-5(4))* Univ. of Illinois Pr.

—Bach Studies 2. 2006. (ENG., Illus.). 256p. pap. 53.00 *(978-0-521-02891-2(4))* Cambridge Univ. Pr.

Mellers, Wilfrid. Bach & the Dance of God. 336p. 2009. *(978-1-904331-87-2(4))* 2007. (ENG.). per. *(978-1-904331-21-6(1))* Travis & Emery Music Bookshop.

Mooney, Sharon F. & Stapert, Calvin R. J. S. Bach. 2010. (History Makers Ser.). (ENG., Illus.). 192p. pap. 16.95 *(978-0-7459-5286-4(0))* Lion Hudson PLC GBR. Dist: Independent Pubs. Group.

Phillips, Mark, contrib. by. 50 Solos for Classical Guitar. 2006. (ENG.). 88p. pap. 16.95 incl. audio compact disk *(978-1-57560-885-3(5))*, 1575608855) Cherry Lane Music Co.

Shuckburgh, Julian. Harmony & Discord: The Real Life of Johann Sebastian Bach. 2010. (ENG., Illus.). 320p. (gr. 8). 35.00 *(978-1-905847-85-3(8))* Old Street Publishing GBR. Dist: Consortium Bk. Sales & Distribution.

Siblin, Eric. The Cello Suites: J. S. Bach, Pablo Casals, & the Search for a Baroque Masterpiece. 2009. (ENG.). 336p. 24.00 *(978-0-8021-1929-2(8)*, Atlantic Monthly Pr.) Grove/Atlantic, Inc.

Stauffer, George, et al, eds. About Bach. 2008. (ENG., Illus.). 232p. 38.00 *(978-0-252-03344-5(2))* Univ. of Illinois Pr.

Stinson, Russell. The Reception of Bach's Organ Works from Mendelssohn to Brahms, 1 vol. 2010. (ENG., Illus.). 240p. pap. 35.00 *(978-0-19-974703-0(2))* Oxford Univ. Pr., Inc.

Tomita, Yo, ed. Bach. 2011. (Baroque Composers Ser.). (GER & ENG., Illus.). 612p. 250.00 *(978-0-7546-2891-0(4))* Ashgate Publishing Co.

Travis &. Emery, &. Emery & Terry, Charles Sanford. Bach's Chorals Part 1 - the Hymns & Hymn Melodies of the Passions & Oratorios [Facsimile of 1915 Edition]. 2010. 102p. pap. *(978-1-906857-26-4(1))* Travis & Emery Music Bookshop.

—Bach's Chorals Part 2 - the Hymns & Hymn Melodies of the Cantatas & Motetts [Facsimile of 1917 Edition, Part II]. 2010. 638p. pap. *(978-1-906857-28-8(8))* Travis & Emery Music Bookshop.

—Bach's Chorals Part 3 - the Hymns & Hymn Melodies of the Organ Works [Facsimile of 1921 Edition, Part III]. 2010. 388p. pap. *(978-1-906857-30-1(X))* Travis & Emery Music Bookshop.

Van Geem, Jack. Percussion Master Class on Works by Schwantner, Schuller & Bach. Cirone, Anthony J., ed. 2011. (ENG.). 62p. pap. 24.95 *(978-1-57463-119-7(5)*, 1574631195) Meredith Music Pubns.

White, Andrew. Good Invention Repaid with Interest. 2010. 392p. pap. *(978-3-8383-1749-6(1))* Lambert Academic Publishing.

Williams, Peter. J. S. Bach: A Life in Music. (ENG., Illus.). 2011. 417p. pap. 24.99 *(978-0-521-30683-6(3))* 2007. 418p. 38.00 *(978-0-521-87074-0(7))* Cambridge Univ. Pr.

Williams, Peter, ed. Bach, Handel, Scarlatti, 1685-1985. 2008. (ENG., Illus.). 384p. pap. 48.00 *(978-0-521-08213-6(7))* Cambridge Univ. Pr.

Winold, Allen. Bach's Cello Suites: Analyses & Explorations, 2 vols. 2007. (Illus.). pap. *(978-0-253-21885-8(3))* Indiana Univ. Pr.

Wolff, Christoph & Zepf, Markus. The Organs of J. S. Bach: A Handbook. 2012. (ENG., Illus.). 240p. pap. 30.00 ***(978-0-252-07845-3(4))*** Univ. of Illinois Pr.

Wolff, Christoph, et al. The Organs of J. S. Bach: A Handbook. 2012. (ENG., Illus.). 240p. 85.00 ***(978-0-252-03684-2(0))*** Univ. of Illinois Pr.

Yearsley, David. Bach & the Meanings of Counterpoint. 2008. (New Perspectives in Music History & Criticism Ser.). (ENG., Illus.). 276p. pap. 37.99 *(978-0-521-09099-5(7))* Cambridge Univ. Pr.

Yearsley, David. Bach's Feet: The Organ Pedals in European Culture. 2012. (Musical Performance & Reception Ser.). (ENG., Illus.). 312p. 99.00 ***(978-0-521-19901-8(8))*** Cambridge Univ. Pr.

Zager, Daniel, ed. Music & Theology: Essays in Honor of Robin A. Leaver. 2006. (ENG., Illus.). 296p. 116.00 *(978-0-8108-5414-7(7))* Scarecrow Pr., Inc.

BACH FAMILY

Terry, Charles Sanford. The Origin of the Family of Bach Musicians Ursprung der Musicalisch-Bachischen Familie. 2009. 76p. pap. *(978-1-906857-22-6(9))* Travis & Emery Music Bookshop.

BACHE, A. D. (ALEXANDER DALLAS), 1806-1867

Jansen, Axel. Alexander Dallas Bache: Building the American Nation Through Science & Education in the 19th Century. 2011. (Illus.). 340p. pap. 49.00 *(978-3-593-39355-1(7))* Campus Verlag GmbH DEU. Dist: Chicago Distribution Ctr.

BACHE, BENJAMIN FRANKLIN, 1769-1798

Fay, Bernard. Two Franklins. reprint ed. 31.50 *(978-0-404-02372-0(X))* AMS Pr., Inc.

BACHELARD, GASTON, 1884-1962

Bulcão, Marly. Promenade Brésilienne Dans la Poétique de Gaston Bachelard. 2010. (FRE.). 111p. *(978-2-296-12686-2(3))* Editions L'Harmattan.

Crocenzi, Gina. Literature & the Science of the Unknowable. 2010. 212p. pap. *(978-3-8383-0757-2(7))* Lambert Academic Publishing.

Jäger, Klaus. Die Phänomenologie der poetischen Imagination bei Gaston Bachelard. 2009. (Miroir et Image. Philosophische Abhandlungen Ser.). (GER.). 184p. 57.95 *(978-3-631-59158-1(6))* Lang, Peter GmbH, Europaischer Verlag der Wissenschaften DEU. Dist: Lang, Peter.

Kennedy, Miles. A Bachelardian Concrete Metaphysics. 2011. (ENG.). 186p. pap. 55.95 *(978-3-03911-990-5(7))* Lang, Peter GmbH, Europaischer Verlag der Wissenschaften DEU. Dist: Lang, Peter.

BACHELORS

see also Unmarried Fathers

Boyer, David. Bachelor Party Confidential: A Real-Life Peek Behind the Closed-Door Tradition. 2007. (ENG., Illus.). 240p. pap. 16.95 *(978-1-4169-2808-9(1))* Gallery Pr., The IRL. Dist: Simon & Schuster, Inc.

Carns, Chad. The Gourmet Bachelor: Global Flavor, Local Ingredients. 2010. (Illus.). 193p. 34.50 *(978-0-615-22980-5(8))* Carns Concepts.

Johnson, R. M. Why Men Fear Marriage: The Surprising Truth Behind Why So Many Men Can't Commit. 2011. (ENG.). 256p. pap. 15.00 *(978-1-4391-0150-6(7)*, Gallery Books/Karen Hunter Publishing) Gallery Books/Karen Hunter Publishing.

McCurdy, John Gilbert. Citizen Bachelors: Manhood & the Creation of the United States. 2009. (Illus.). 320p. 35.00 *(978-0-8014-4788-4(7))* Cornell Univ. Pr.

Miller, Terry L. Cooking Bachelor Style: Life Beyond the Freezer Section. 2010. pap. 15.99 *(978-1-61566-628-7(1))* Tate Publishing & Enterprises, LLC.

Naylor, Sharon. The Smart Guide to Bachelorette Parties. 2011. (Smart Guides). (ENG.). 272p. pap. 18.95 ***(978-0-9785341-0-3(7))*** Smart Guide Pubns., Inc.

Parada Nuñez, Raquel. A grammar Guide for the 2nd level of ESO Students. 2009. (SPA.). 37p. pap. 16.95 *(978-1-4092-6541-2(2))* Lulu Enterprises Inc.

Womanizer: Thee Uncomfortable Truth about Men & Marriage. 2008. 76p. pap. 10.99 *(978-0-9703881-4-8(4))* Manage Me Productions, LLC.

BACILLARIOPHYTA

see Diatoms

BACILLUS

see Bacillus (Bacteria)

BACILLUS (BACTERIA)

see also Bacillus Subtilis

Bergman, Nicholas H., ed. Bacillus Anthracis & Anthrax. 2010. (ENG., Illus.). 337p. 129.95 *(978-0-470-41011-0(6)*, Wiley-Blackwell) Wiley, John & Sons, Inc.

Charles, J. F., et al, eds. Entomopathogenic Bacteria: from Laboratory to Field Application: From Laboratory to Field Application. 2010. 548p. pap. 379.00 *(978-90-481-5542-2(8)*, 9048155428) Springer.

François-Xavier, Etoa. Heat-Induced Resistance in Bacillus Spores. 2011. 168p. pap. ***(978-3-8433-9259-4(5))*** Lambert Academic Publishing.

Graumann, Peter, ed. Bacillus: Cellular & Molecular Biology. 2007. (Illus.). 454p. (C). 319.00 *(978-1-904455-12-7(3))* 2nd ed. 2012. 412p. 360.00 ***(978-1-904455-97-4(2))*** Caister Academic Pr. GBR. Dist: International Specialized Bk. Services.

Horikoshi, Koki. Alkaliphiles: Genetic Properties & Applications of Enzymes. 2006. (ENG., Illus.). 270p. 199.00 *(978-3-540-33372-2(X)*, 354033372X) Springer.

Kausar, Malik. Genetic Improvement of a Local Isolate of Bacillus Thuringiensis. 2011. 124p. pap. ***(978-3-639-34447-9(2))*** VDM Verlag Dr. Mueller e.K.

Kaushal, Rajeev & S.S. Kanwar. In Vitro Studies of a New Lipase of Bacillus. 2011. 220p. pap. ***(978-3-8443-1726-8(0))*** Lambert Academic Publishing.

King, Leslie. A Clinical Laboratories Response to a Terrorist Assault with Anthrax. 2009. 172p. pap. *(978-3-639-19724-2(0))* VDM Verlag Dr. Mueller e.K.

Sansinenea, Estibaliz, ed. Bacillus thuringiensis Biotechnology. 2012. (ENG., Illus.). xvi, 392p. 209.00 ***(978-94-007-3020-5(9)***, 9400730209) Springer.

Takami, Hideto. Genomic Diversity of Bacillus-Related Species. 2008. (Illus.). 99p. pap. 39.00 *(978-1-60456-396-2(6)*, Nova Biomedical Bks.) Nova Science Pubs., Inc.

Vuppu, Dr. Suneetha & Vuppu, Suneetha. Screening of Keratinolytic Bacteria from Poultry Waste. 2011. 108p. pap. ***(978-3-8443-2787-8(8))*** Lambert Academic Publishing.

BACILLUS SUBTILIS

Kaushish Lily, Dr. Madhuri, et al. Benzo-A-Pyrene Degradation by Bacillus Subtilis Bmt4i. 2011. 160p. pap. ***(978-3-8443-2455-6(0))*** Lambert Academic Publishing.

Pan, Zhiwei. Metabolic Engineering of Bacillus. 2009. 144p. pap. *(978-3-639-17234-8(5))* VDM Verlag Dr. Mueller e.K.

BACK PACKING

see Backpacking

BACK PAIN

see Backache

BACKACHE

Abdul Aziz, Faieza. Using Semi Immersive Virtual Environments to Reduce Lower Back Pain. 2010. 172p. pap. *(978-3-639-27248-2(X))* VDM Verlag Dr. Mueller e.K.

Adams, Michael A. The Biomechanics of Back Pain. 3rd ed. 2012. (ENG., Illus.). 336p. 79.95 ***(978-0-7020-4313-0(3)***, Churchill Livingstone) Elsevier - Health Sciences Div.

Adams, Michael A., et al. The Biomechanics of Back Pain. 2nd rev. ed. 2006. (ENG., Illus.). 336p. 77.95 *(978-0-443-10068-0(3)*, Churchill Livingstone) Elsevier - Health Sciences Div.

American College of Physicians (ACP). Low Back Pain GUIDELINES Pocketcard 2011. 2011. 10p. pap. 9.95 ***(978-0-9846423-0-4(7))*** International Guidelines Ctr., Inc.

Ayanniyi, Olusola. Effects of the Mckenzie Protocol on Back Pain in Pregnant Subjects. 2011. 164p. pap. ***(978-3-639-32289-7(4))*** VDM Verlag Dr. Mueller e.K.

Brown, Mark D. Conquer Back & Neck Pain: Walk It Off! A Spine Doctor's Proven Solutions for Finding Relief Without Pills or Surgery. 2008. (Illus.). 164p. pap. 11.95 *(978-1-934716-01-4(4))* Sunrise River Pr.

Chapman, Jens R., et al. Spine Outcomes Measures & Instruments. 2007. (ENG., Illus.). 300p. 179.99 *(978-1-60406-000-3(X))* Thieme Medical Pubs., Inc.

Chevan. Management of Low Back Pain. rev. ed. 2011. (Illus.). 348p. pap. 59.95 *(978-0-7637-7945-0(8))* Jones & Bartlett Learning, LLC.

Clarke, Andrew, et al, eds. ABC of Spinal Disorders. 2010. (ABC Ser.: 141). (ENG., Illus.). 72p. pap. 39.95 *(978-1-4051-7069-7(7))* Wiley, John & Sons, Inc.

Condron, Declan. Back Strengthening for Health & Fitness. 2008. *(978-1-4027-5974-1(6)*, Sterling Innovation) Sterling Publishing Co., Inc.

Corenman, Donald Steven. Everything You Wanted to Know about the Back: A Consumers Guide to the Diagnosis & Treatment of Lower Back Pain. 2011. 170p. 29.99 ***(978-1-4363-3746-5(1))*** Xlibris Corp.

Cox, James M. Low Back Pain: Mechanism, Diagnosis & Treatment. 7th rev. ed. 2011. (ENG.). 736p. 139.00 ***(978-1-60831-002-9(7))*** Lippincott Williams & Wilkins.

Depalma, Michael & DePalma, Michael J. ISpine: Evidence-Based Interventional Spine Care. 2011. 544p. 135.00 *(978-1-933864-71-6(0))* Demos Medical Publishing, LLC.

Dickson, Robert A. & Butt, W. Paul. The Medico-Legal Back: an Illustrated Guide. 2011. (ENG., Illus.). 226p. pap. 45.00 *(978-0-521-28320-5(5))* Cambridge Univ. Pr.

DiNubile, Nicholas A. & Scali, Bruce. Framework for the Lower Back: A 6-Step Plan for a Healthy Lower Back. 2nd rev. ed. 2010. (ENG., Illus.). 192p. pap. 18.99 *(978-1-60529-197-0(8))* Rodale Pr., Inc.

Dorling Kindersley Publishing Staff. Essential Back Care. 2011. (ENG.). 224p. pap. 17.95 *(978-0-7566-8264-4(9))* Dorling Kindersley Publishing, Inc.

Fishman, Loren & Ardman, Carol. Yoga for Back Pain. 2012. (ENG.). 208p. pap. 19.95 ***(978-0-393-34312-0(X)***, 34312) Norton, W. W. & Co., Inc.

Girasole, Gerard & Hartman, Cara. The 7-Minute Back Pain Solution: 7 Simple Exercises to Heal Your Back Without Drugs or Surgery in Just Minutes a Day. 2012. (ENG.). 272p. pap. ***(978-0-373-89258-7(6))*** Harlequin Enterprises, Ltd.

Goodman, Eric & Park, Peter. Foundation: Redefine Your Core, Conquer Back Pain, & Move with Confidence. 2011. (ENG., Illus.). 288p. pap. 22.99 *(978-1-60961-100-2(4))* Rodale Pr., Inc.

Greenhalgh, Sue & Selfe, James. Red Flag II: A Guide to Solving Serious Pathology of the Spine. 2009. (Physiotherapy Pocketbooks Ser.). (ENG., Illus.). 256p. (C). pap. 41.95 *(978-0-443-06914-7(X)*, Churchill Livingstone) Elsevier - Health Sciences Div.

Guarino, Anthony H. Get Your Lower Back Pain under Control - And Get on with Life. 2010. (ENG., Illus.). 200p. pap. 18.95 *(978-0-8018-9731-3(9))*; (gr. 17). 45.00 *(978-0-8018-9730-6(0))* Johns Hopkins Univ. Pr.

Gutknecht, David R. Low Back Pain FAQs. 2007. (FAQs (Frequently Asked Questions) Ser.). (Illus.). 58p. per. *(978-1-55009-319-3(3))* Decker Publishing.

Hansen, Mark Victor, et al. Back Pain. 2006. (Chicken Soup for the Soul Ser.). (ENG.). 144p. mass mkt. 4.99 *(978-0-7573-0522-1(9))* Health Communications, Inc.

Hasenbring, Monika I., et al, eds. From Acute to Chronic Back Pain: Risk Factors, Mechanisms, & Clinical Implications. 2012. (ENG., Illus.). 624p. 165.00 ***(978-0-19-955890-2(6))*** Oxford Univ. Pr., Inc.

Hiatt-Coblentz, Ruth & Stanton, Andra Fischgrund. Pilates for Fragile Backs: Recovering Strength & Flexibility after Surgery, Injury, or Other Back Problems. 2006. (ENG., Illus.). 176p. pap. 18.95 *(978-1-57224-466-5(6))* New Harbinger Pubns.

Hong, Youlian, ed. Load Carriage in School Children: Epidemiology & Exercise Science. 2010. (Children's Issues, Laws & Programs Ser.). 160.00 *(978-1-61668-622-2(7))* Nova Science Pubs., Inc.

Ingham, Penny. The Well Tuned Body. 2007. (ENG., Illus.). 1111p. pap. 10.95 ***(978-1-84024-578-3(6))*** Summerdale Pubs. GBR. Dist: Independent Pubs. Group.

Jansson, Maja C. & Lindberg, William J. Low Back Pain: New Research. 2008. (Illus.). xii, 182p. (C). 185.00 *(978-1-60456-532-4(2))* Nova Science Pubs., Inc.

Key, Josephine. Back Pain - A Movement Problem: A Clinical Approach Incorporating Relevant Research & Practice. 2010. (ENG., Illus.). 400p. 67.95 *(978-0-7020-3079-6(1)*, Churchill Livingstone) Elsevier - Health Sciences Div.

Kraus, Hans. Backache, Stress, & Tension: Understanding Why You Have Back Pain & Simple Exercises to Prevent & Treat It. 2012. (ENG., Illus.). 244p. pap. 14.95 ***(978-1-61608-341-0(7)***, 608341) Skyhorse Publishing Co., Inc.

Lee, John, et al. Back Pain. 2009. (Facts Ser.). (ENG., Illus.). 176p. pap. 19.95 *(978-0-19-956107-0(9))* Oxford Univ. Pr., Inc.

Maigne, Jean-Ives & Maigne, Jean-Yves. El Dolor de Espalda (Back Pain) (SPA.). 152p. *(978-84-8019-194-4(5))* Paidotribo, Editorial S.L.

Malanga, Gerard A. Low Back Pain, an Issue of Occupational & Environmental Clinics. 2006. (Clinics: Internal Medicine Ser.). 240p. 54.00 *(978-1-4160-3932-7(5)*, Elsevier Espana) Elsevier - Health Sciences Div.

Mannion, Jamie. Functional Characteristics of the Hamstring Muscles in Low Back Pain. 2010. 96p. pap. *(978-3-8383-3935-1(5))* Lambert Academic Publishing.

Marras, William S. The Working Back: A Systems View. 2008. (ENG., Illus.). 309p. 111.00 *(978-0-470-13405-4(4)*, Wiley-Interscience) Wiley, John & Sons, Inc.

McAvoy Aquatic & Sports Therapy. Aqua-gym. 2007. (Illus.). 66p. spiral bd. *(978-0-9712257-2-5(9))* McAvoy, Rick.

McCarthy, Christopher. Combined Movement Theory: Rational Mobilization & Manipulation of the Vertebral Column. 2010. (ENG., Illus.). 226p. pap. 85.95 *(978-0-443-06857-7(7)*, Churchill Livingstone) Elsevier - Health Sciences Div.

McGill, Stuart M. Low Back Disorders: Evidenced Based Prevention & Rehabilitation. 2nd rev. ed. 2007. (ENG., Illus.). 328p. 67.00 *(978-0-7360-6692-1(6))* Human Kinetics Pubs.

Morrone, Lisa. Overcoming Back & Neck Pain: A Proven Program for Recovery & Prevention. 2008. 250p. pap. 12.99 *(978-0-7369-2168-8(0))* Harvest Hse. Pubs.

Nelson, Jason M. Miserable Joy: Chronic Pain in the Christian Life. 2007. per. *(978-0-8100-1749-8(0))* Northwestern Publishing Hse.

Pereira da Silva, Jose Antonio & Woolf, Anthony D. Rheumatology of the Lower Limbs in Clinical Practice. 2011. (ENG., Illus.). viii, 179p. pap. 59.95 ***(978-1-4471-2252-4(6)***, 1447122526) Springer.

Petrone, Elaine. Miracle Ball Method for Pregnancy: Relieve Back Pain & Labor Pain, Regain a Flat Belly, & More. 2011. (ENG., Illus.). 288p. pap. 19.95 *(978-0-7611-6097-7(3)*, 0761160973) Workman Publishing Co., Inc.

—The Portable Miracle Ball Method: Relieve Your Pain, Reduce Your Stress. 2006. (ENG., Illus.). 296p. pap. 14.95 *(978-0-7611-4382-6(3)*, 0761143823) Workman Publishing Co., Inc.

Resnick, Daniel K., et al. Surgical Management of Low Back Pain: A Co-Publication of Thieme & the American Association of Neurological Surgeons. 2nd ed. 2008. (ENG., Illus.). 232p. 149.99 *(978-1-60406-035-5(2))* Thieme Medical Pubs., Inc.

Rosenblatt, Marc. Low Back Pain: What You Need to Know. 2008. 156p. pap. 19.95 *(978-1-933889-03-0(9))* Ctr. Path Publishing.

Sahrmann, Shirley. Movement System Impairment Syndromes of the Extremities, Cervical & Thoracic Spines. 2010. (ENG., Illus.). 568p. (C). 74.95 *(978-0-323-05342-6(4)*, Mosby) Elsevier - Health Sciences Div.

Sarno, John E. Healing Back Pain: The Mind-Body Connection. 2010. (ENG.). 240p. pap. 6.99 *(978-0-446-55768-9(4)*, Wellness Central) Grand Central Publishing.

Sauer, Sharon & Biancalana, Mary. Trigger Point Therapy for Low Back Pain. 2010. (Workbook Ser.). (ENG., Illus.). 280p. pap., wbk. ed. 24.95 *(978-1-57224-563-1(8))* New Harbinger Pubns.

Silverman, Gerald M. Your Miraculous Back: A Step-by-Step Guide to Relieving Neck & Back Pain. 2006. (New Harbinger Self-Help Workbook Ser.). (ENG., Illus.). 184p. per. 18.95 *(978-1-57224-452-8(6))* New Harbinger Pubns.

Sinett, Sheldon, DC & Sinett, Todd, DC. The Truth about Back Pain: A Revolutionary, Individualized Approach to Diagnosing & Healing Back Pain. 2009. (ENG.). 224p. (gr. 12-18). 15.00 *(978-0-399-53485-0(7)*, Perigee Trade) Penguin Group (USA) Inc.

Smith, Roxanne M. Struck down but Not Destroyed: Finding Hope in the Maze of Suffering. 2008. 16.95 *(978-1-934363-17-1(0))* Zoe Life Publishing.

Smith, William. Back Pain: The Complete Reference Guide to Caring for Your Back Through Fitness. 2009. (Exercises For Ser.). (ENG., Illus.). 160p. pap. 15.00 *(978-1-57826-304-2(2))* Hatherleigh Co., Ltd., The.

Stretch away low back pain, second Edition. 2006. cd-rom 17.95 *(978-0-9789455-0-3(6))* Stretch Away Pain, LLC.

Szpalski, Marek, et al, eds. Surgery for Low Back Pain. 2010. (ENG., Illus.). xiv, 285p. 139.00 *(978-3-642-04546-2(4)*, 3642045464) Springer.

Taber, Douglas J., DC & Van Vorst, Douglas, DC. Spinal Stabilization: A Functional Rehab Program. 2010. 56p. pap. 15.49 *(978-0-557-15847-8(8))* Lulu Enterprises Inc.

Taber, Douglas. The Spinal Answer Exercise Protocol. 2010. 32p. pap. 23.95 *(978-0-557-27871-8(6))* Lulu Enterprises Inc.

—Spinal Decompression Stabilization Protocol. 2009. 32p. pap. 48.60 *(978-0-557-05050-5(2))* Lulu Enterprises Inc.

Taylor, Martin T. My Neck Hurts! Nonsurgical Treatments for Neck & Upper Back Pain. 2010. (Johns Hopkins Press Health Book Ser.). (ENG., Illus.). 192p. pap. 19.95 *(978-0-8018-9666-8(5))*; (gr. 17). 40.00 *(978-0-8018-9665-1(7))* Johns Hopkins Univ. Pr.

Theodoridis, Theodoros & Krämer, Jürgen. Spinal Injection Techniques. 2009. (ENG., Illus.). 253p. 199.99 *(978-3-13-145071-5(1))* Thieme Medical Pubs., Inc.

Vleeming, Andry, et al. Movement, Stability & Lumbopelvic Pain: Integration of Research & Therapy. 2nd rev. ed. 2007. (ENG., Illus.). 672p. pap. 134.00 *(978-0-443-10178-6(7)*, Churchill Livingstone) Elsevier - Health Sciences Div.

White, Augustus A. Your Aching Back: A Doctor's Guide to Relief. 2010. (ENG., Illus.). 368p. pap. 22.99 *(978-1-4165-9301-0(2))* Simon & Schuster.

Winsor, Jodie. Gentle Yoga for Back Pain: A Safe & Easy Approach to Better Health & Well-Being through Yoga. Krusinski, Anna, ed. 2012. (ENG.). 112p. pap. 12.50 *(978-1-57826-390-5(5))* Hatherleigh Co., Ltd., The.

Wong, David A. & Transfeldt, Ensor. Macnab's Backache. 4th rev. ed. 2006. (Illus.). 304p. 158.99 *(978-0-7817-6085-0(2))* Lippincott Williams & Wilkins.

50 Ways to Ease Back Pain. 9.98 *(978-0-7853-0679-5(X))* Publications International, Ltd.

BACKACHE—PREVENTION

Adedoyin, Rufus Adesoji. Reference Values for Isometric Lumber: Extensors' Endurance & Spinal Extension Flexibility in Apparently Healthy Adults. 2011. 96p. pap. ***(978-3-639-33353-4(5))*** VDM Verlag Dr. Mueller e.K.

Borenstein, David G. Heal Your Back: Your Complete Prescription for Preventing, Treating, & Eliminating Back Pain. 2011. *(978-1-59077-186-0(9))* Evans, M. & Co., Inc.

Borentstein, David. Heal Your Back: Your Complete Prescription for Preventing, Treating, & Eliminating Back Pain. 2011. (ENG.). 296p. pap. 15.95 *(978-1-59077-185-3(0))* Evans, M. & Co., Inc.

Jaffe, Michael. Play Golf Forever: Treating Low Back Pain & Improving Your Golf Swing Through Fitness. 2010. 208p. pap. 14.99 *(978-1-4389-8831-3(1))* AuthorHouse.

King, Janie. Back Labor No More: What Every Woman Should Know Before Labor. 2nd ed. 2008. (Illus.). 134p. pap. *(978-0-926218-07-9(7))* Plenary Systems, Inc.

Murinson, Beth. Take Back Your Back: Everything You Need to Know to Effectively Reverse & Manage Back Pain. 2011. (ENG., Illus.). 272p. pap. 21.99 *(978-1-59233-406-3(7)*, 1592334067) Quayside.

Norris, Christopher M. Back Stability: Integrating Science & Therapy. 2nd ed. 2008. (ENG., Illus.). 360p. 54.00 *(978-0-7360-7017-1(6))* Human Kinetics Pubs.

Rippel, Stefan. Healing Your Spine: Learn to Live Without Back Pain. 2008. (ENG.). 320p. pap. 24.95 *(978-1-84694-137-5(7))* Hunt, John Publishing Ltd. GBR. Dist: National Bk. Network.

The check digit for ISBN-10 appears in parentheses after the full ISBN-13

Time-Life Books Staff, contrib. by. Fit Back: Pain Relief & Prevention. (Illus.). 144p. 20.00 *(978-1-84447-162-1(4))* Time Life Value GBR. Dist: Mercury Bks. Ltd.

Warson, James & Hendrickson, Ami. The Rider's Pain-Free Back: Overcome Chronic Soreness, Injury, & Aging, & Stay in the Saddle for Years to Come. 2007. (ENG., Illus.). 184p. pap. 29.95 *(978-1-57076-371-7(2))* Trafalgar Square Bks.

—The Rider's Pain-Free Back Book: Overcoming & Preventing Back Pain to Get You Back in the Saddle. 2007. *(978-1-57076-367-0(4))* Trafalgar Square Publishing.

50 Things You Can Do to Save Your Back. Date not set. (Illus.). 6p. *(978-0-945100-74-4(4))* Parlay International.

BACKACHE—TREATMENT

Amziev, Alexis. El Dolonde Espalda. (SPA.). 412p. *(978-84-7927-331-6(3))* Robinbk., Ediciones S.L. ESP. Dist: Lectorum Pubns., Inc.

Auday F.A.C.S. Jose H. When to Bypass Back Surgery. 2009. 100p. pap. 15.99 *(978-1-4363-8387-2(0))* Xlibris Corp.

Borenstein, David G. Heal Your Back: Your Complete Prescription for Preventing, Treating, & Eliminating Back Pain. 2011. *(978-1-59077-186-0(9))* Evans, M. & Co., Inc.

Borentstein, David. Heal Your Back: Your Complete Prescription for Preventing, Treating, & Eliminating Back Pain. 2011. (ENG.). 296p. pap. 15.95 *(978-1-59077-185-3(0))* Evans, M. & Co., Inc.

Brenholz, Avi. A Patient's Guide to Backache Relief Acupressure & Medication. Date not set. (Illus.). 50p. pap. 2.48 *(978-1-889958-03-3(4))* Ben Aur, Avraham Inc.

Busch, Richard E., III. Surgery Not Included: Freedom from Chronic Neck & Back Pain. 2009. 200p. pap. 29.95 *(978-0-9819398-4-1(8))* Ultimate Publishing Hse., The.

Chong, Sam, et al, eds. Back Pain. 2012. (ENG.). 160p. pap. 24.99 ***(978-0-19-950977-2(2))*** Oxford Univ. Pr., Inc.

Craig, Gary & Tanney. EFT for Back Pain. 2009. pap. 14.95 *(978-1-60415-032-2(7))* Energy Psychology Pr.

Cram101 Textbook Reviews & Cram101 Textbook Reviews. Outlines & Highlights for Conservative Management of Low Back Syndromes by Craig E Morris, Isbn: 9780071374729. 2011. 682p. pap. 41.95 ***(978-1-61461-412-8(1))*** Cram101 Inc.

Craze, Richard. Beat Back Pain with Alexander Technique. 2011. (Teach Yourself Ser.). (ENG., Illus.). 156p. pap. 15.95 *(978-1-4441-0102-7(1))*, Hodder & Stoughton) Hodder General Publishing Div. GBR. Dist: Independent Pubs. Group.

Dagenais, Simon & Haldeman, Scott. Evidenced-Based Management of Low Back Pain. 2011. (ENG., Illus.). 496p. 115.00 *(978-0-323-07293-9(3)*, Mosby) Elsevier - Health Sciences Div.

Ekman, Per. Fusion for Chronic Low-Back Pain. 2010. 72p. pap. *(978-3-639-22081-0(1))* VDM Verlag Dr. Mueller e.K.

Ferguson, Fraser. A Pocketbook of Managing Lower Back Pain. 2009. (Physiotherapy Pocketbooks Ser.). (ENG., Illus.). 288p. (C). pap. 49.95 *(978-0-443-06846-1(7))*, Churchill Livingstone) Elsevier - Health Sciences Div.

Fortanasce, Vincent, et al. End Back & Neck Pain. 2011. (ENG., Illus.). 224p. pap. 19.95 *(978-0-7360-9528-0(4))* Human Kinetics Pubs.

Gillanders, Ann. Reflexology for Back Pain: Healing Your Back in a Safe & Successful Way. 2009. (ENG.). 128p. pap. 15.00 *(978-1-4379-6564-3(4))* DIANE Publishing Co.

Gokaslan, Ziya L. & Riley, Lee Hunter. The Back Book. 2008. (Johns Hopkins Press Health Book Ser.). (ENG., Illus.). 168p. 45.00 *(978-0-8018-9042-0(X))*; pap. 16.95 *(978-0-8018-9043-7(8))* Johns Hopkins Univ. Pr.

Gokhale, Esther & Adams, Susan. 8 Steps to a Pain-Free Back: Natural Posture Solutions for Pain in the Back, Neck, Shoulder, Hip, Knee, & Foot. Adams, Susan, ed. 2008. (ENG., Illus.). 244p. pap. 24.95 *(978-0-9793036-0-9(5))* Pendo Pr.

Gonzalez, Carlos M. Hanging Out for the Health of It: One Minute a Day to a Healthier, Happier, & Longer Life. 2008. (ENG.). 232p. pap. 14.99 *(978-1-59932-058-8(4))* Advantage Media Group.

Gray, Scot. Good Back, Bad Back: The 10 Things Women Must Know to Eliminate Back Pain & Look & Feel Younger. 2011. (ENG.). 100p. pap. 11.99 *(978-1-59932-202-5(1))* Advantage Media Group.

Gupta, Subodh. Simplified Yoga for Backache. 2008. 68p. pap. *(978-0-9556882-4-9(8))* Gupta, Subodh.

Hadler, Nortin M. Stabbed in the Back: Confronting Back Pain in an Overtreated Society. 2009. (ENG., Illus.). 224p. 27.00 *(978-0-8078-3348-3(7))* Univ. of North Carolina Pr.

Hainline, Brian. Back Pain Understood: A Cutting-Edge Approach to Healing Your Back. 2007. (Illus.). 230p. per. 14.95 *(978-0-9787727-0-3(9))* Medicus Pr., Inc.

Haronian, Edwin. Back Surgery: Is It Right for You? 2007. (ENG.). 192p. pap. 17.95 *(978-0-7570-0275-2(5))* Square One Pubs.

Henson, Frances, ed. Equine Back Pathology: Diagnosis & Treatment. 2009. (ENG., Illus.). 280p. 162.99 *(978-1-4051-5492-5(6)*, Wiley-Blackwell) Wiley, John & Sons, Inc.

Highsmith, Jason & Milvojevic, Jovanka JoAnn. The Complete Idiot's Guide to Back Pain. 2011. (Complete Idiot's Guide Ser.). (ENG.). 304p. (gr. 12). 16.95 *(978-1-61564-068-3(1)*, Alpha Bks.) Penguin Group (USA) Inc.

Jaffe, Michael, et al. Play Golf Forever: Treating Low Back Pain & Improving Your Golf Swing Through Fitness. 2008. (Illus.). 220p. pap. 17.95 *(978-1-933669-14-4(4))* Literary Architects, LLC.

Jesse, Cannone. The 7-Day Back Pain Cure: How Thousands of People Got Relief Without Doctors, Drugs, or Surgery. 2009. 212p. pap. 14.95 *(978-0-9764624-8-4(6))* Innovation Pr.

Karl, Gary A. Dynamics of Back Pain: Helpful Hints to Becoming Pain-Free. 2008. 96p. pap. 14.99 *(978-1-4389-1838-9(0))* AuthorHouse.

Katz, Jeffrey N. & Parkinson, Gloria. Heal Your Aching Back: What a Harvard Doctor Wants You to Know about Finding Relief & Keeping Your Back Strong. 2007. (Harvard Medical School Guides). (ENG., Illus.). 272p. per. 14.95 *(978-0-07-146755-0(3)*, 0071467653) McGraw-Hill Cos., The.

Low-Back Pain: Healing Your Aching Back. 2008. 26.00 *(978-1-933812-48-9(6))* Harvard Medical Schl., Harvard Health Pubns.

Mathis, John & Golovac, Stanley, eds. Image-Guided Spine Interventions. 2nd ed. 2011. (Illus.). xii, 403p. pap. 99.00 ***(978-1-4614-0525-2(4)***, 1461405254) Springer.

Mathis, John M. & Golovac, Stanley. Image-Guided Spine Interventions. 2nd ed. 2010. (Illus.). 415p. 199.00 *(978-1-4419-0351-8(8)*, 1441903518) Springer.

McCarberg, Bill, et al. Back & Neck Pain. 2012. (ENG.). 144p. pap. 34.99 *(978-0-19-539457-3(7))* Oxford Univ. Pr., Inc.

Meeks, Sara. Walk Tall! An Exercise Program for the Prevention & Treatment of Back Pain, Osteoporosis & the Postural Changes of Aging. 2010. (ENG., Illus.). 160p. spiral bd. 24.95 *(978-0-937404-71-3(3))* Triad Publishing Co.

Murinson, Beth. Take Back Your Back: Everything You Need to Know to Effectively Reverse & Manage Back Pain. 2011. (ENG., Illus.). 272p. pap. 21.99 *(978-1-59233-406-3(7)*, 1592334067) Quayside.

Norris, Christopher M. Back Stability: Integrating Science & Therapy. 2nd ed. 2008. (ENG., Illus.). 360p. 54.00 *(978-0-7360-7017-1(6))* Human Kinetics Pubs.

Pujari, Astrid & Alton, Nancy Schatz. The Healthy Back Book: A Guide to Whole Healing for Outdoor Enthusiasts & Other Active People. 2010. (ENG.). 192p. pap. 14.95 *(978-1-59485-012-7(7)*, Skipstone) Mountaineers Bks., The.

Ramos Vieira, Edgar. Low Back Disorders in Heavy Jobs & Their Control. 2008. 252p. pap. *(978-3-639-06136-9(5))* VDM Verlag Dr. Mueller e.K.

Resnick, Daniel K., et al. Surgical Management of Low Back Pain: A Co-Publication of Thieme & the American Association of Neurological Surgeons. 2nd ed. 2008. (ENG., Illus.). 232p. 149.99 *(978-1-60406-035-5(2))* Thieme Medical Pubs., Inc.

Rona, Donna C. Acute Care - Homeopathy for Back Injuries. 2009. 119p. pap. 12.95 *(978-0-557-10563-2(3))* Lulu Enterprises Inc.

—Acute Care - Homeopathy for Knee Injuries & Pain. 2009. 112p. pap. 12.95 *(978-0-557-10558-8(7))* Lulu Enterprises Inc.

Sacchi, Franca. Vencer el Dolor de Espalda (Conquer Your Backache) (SPA.). 128p. *(978-84-315-1088-6(9))* De Vecchi, Editorial, S.A.

Santaguida, Pasqualina & Gross, Anita. Complementary & Alternative Medicine in Back Pain Utilization Report. 2009. (Illus.). ix, 149p. *(978-1-58763-372-0(8))* Agency for Healthcare Research & Quality.

Smith, Tom. Living with Back Pain. 112p. *(978-0-85969-883-2(1)*, Sheldon Press) SPCK Publishing.

Souter, Keith. 50 Things You Can Do Today to Manage Back Pain. 2011. (Personal Health Guides). (ENG., Illus.). 128p. pap. 10.95 ***(978-1-84953-120-7(X))*** Summersdale Pubs. GBR. Dist: Independent Pubs. Group.

Stout, Alison. Low Back Pain, an Issue of Physical Medicine & Rehabilitation Clinics. 2010. (Clinics: Orthopedics Ser.: 21-4). (ENG., Illus.). xii, 660p. 105.00 *(978-1-4377-2484-4(1)*, Saunders) Elsevier - Health Sciences Div.

Sullivan, Karen. Collins Gem 5-Minute Back Relief: Beat Backache Instantly. 2008. (Collins Gem Ser.). (ENG., Illus.). 192p. pap. 6.95 *(978-0-00-725159-9(9))* HarperCollins Pubs. Ltd. GBR. Dist: Independent Pubs. Group.

Thakur, Bharat. Yoga for Backache Relief. 2007. (Illus.). 99p. pap. 7.95 *(978-81-8328-006-8(4))* Wisdom Tree IND. Dist: SCB Distributors.

Time-Life Books Staff, contrib. by. Fit Back: Pain Relief & Prevention. (Illus.). 144p. 20.00 *(978-1-84447-162-1(4))* Time Life Value GBR. Dist: Mercury Bks. Ltd.

Wang, Dongchun. Interstate Variations in Medical Practice Patterns for Low Back Conditions. 2008. *(978-1-934224-91-5(X))* Workers Compensation Research Institute.

Weiner, Debra K. & Mitchell, Deborah. What Your Doctor May Not Tell You about Back Pain: The 6-Step Program for Lasting Relief. Breuer, Paula, ed. 2007. (ENG., Illus.). 320p. per. 18.99 *(978-0-446-69495-7(9))* Grand Central Publishing.

Wexler, Barbara. Natural Guide to Back Pain. 2007. (Woodland Health Ser.). (Illus.). 36p. pap. 4.95 *(978-1-58054-457-3(6))* Woodland Publishing, Inc.

Winter, Robert B. & Bach, Marilyn L. Living Well with Back Pain: What Your Doctor Doesn't Tell You... That You Need to Know. 2006. (Living Well (Collins) Ser.). (Illus.). 368p. pap. 14.95 *(978-0-06-079227-5(2)*, William Morrow Paperbacks) HarperCollins Pubs.

BACKBONE

see Spine

BACKGAMMON

Ballard, Nack & Weaver, Paul. Backgammon Openings, Book A. 2007. 39.00 net. *(978-0-9797053-0-4(4))* Backgammon Pr., The.

Beadles, Patti & Crane, Michael. 52 Great Backgammon Tips: At Home, Tournament & Online. 2007. (ENG., Illus.). 144p. pap. 12.95 *(978-0-7134-9064-0(0)*, Batsford, B. T. Ltd.) Anova Bks. GBR. Dist: Sterling Publishing Co., Inc.

Bray, Chris. Backgammon for Blood: A Guide for Those Who Like to Play but Love to Win. 2nd ed. 2011. (ENG., Illus.). 176p. pap. 12.95 *(978-1-61608-126-3(0)*, 608126) Skyhorse Publishing Co., Inc.

—Backgammon for Dummies. 2008. (ENG., Illus.). 280p. pap. 14.99 *(978-0-470-77085-6(6)*, For Dummies) Wiley, John & Sons, Inc.

Crane, Michael. Teach Yourself Backgammon. 2007. (Teach Yourself Ser.). (ENG., Illus.). 176p. per. 10.95 *(978-0-07-148260-8(1)*, 0071482601) McGraw-Hill Cos., The.

Gannon, Joe. The Backgammon Book: All You Need to Know to Play the World's Oldest Board Game. 2010. (Illus.). 47p. ***(978-1-60311-242-0(1))*** Mud Puddle, Inc.

Gibson, Walter Brown. Fell's Guide to Winning Backgammon. 2008. (Illus.). 166p. pap. *(978-0-8119-0235-9(8))* Lifetime Bks.

Jones, Chris. The Little Book of Backgammon Tips. 2008. (Little Book Ser.). (ENG.). 112p. pap. 4.95 *(978-1-904573-93-7(2))* Absolute Pr. GBR. Dist: Independent Pubs. Group.

Nevaer, Louis E. V. Backgammon: A Cultural History of the World's Favorite Game. 2011. *(978-0-8118-6537-1(1))* Chronicle Bks. LLC.

BACKOFFICE (COMPUTER PROGRAM)

see Microsoft BackOffice (Computer Program)

BACKPACKING

Absolon, Molly. Backpacker magazine's Hiking & Backpacking with Kids: Proven Strategies for Fun Family Adventures. 2012. (Backpacker Magazine Ser.). (ENG., Illus.). 112p. pap. 12.95 *(978-0-7627-7295-7(6)*, Falcon Guides) Globe Pequot Pr., The.

—Backpacker magazine's Trailside Recipes: Simple & Tasty Backcountry Fare. 2012. (Backpacker Magazine Ser.). (ENG., Illus.). 128p. pap. 12.95 *(978-0-7627-7297-1(2)*, Falcon Guides) Globe Pequot Pr., The.

Anderson, Dave. Backpacker magazine's Outdoor Hazards: Avoiding Trouble in the Backcountry. 2012. (Backpacker Magazine Ser.). (ENG., Illus.). 128p. pap. 12.95 *(978-0-7627-7296-4(4)*, Falcon Guides) Globe Pequot Pr., The.

Baggett, Jennifer, et al. The Lost Girls: Three Friends. Four Continents. One Unconventional Detour Around the World. (ENG.). 304p. 2011. pap. 15.99 *(978-0-06-168907-9(6)*, HarperPerennial) 2010. 24.99 *(978-0-06-168906-2(8))* HarperCollins Pubs.

Beffort, Brian. Joy of Backpacking: Your Complete Guide to Attaining Pure Happiness in the Outdoors. 2007. (ENG., Illus.). 336p. per. 19.95 *(978-0-89997-405-7(8))* Wilderness Pr.

Berry, Thomas. The Dream of the Earth. 2nd ed. 2006. (ENG.). 264p. pap. 14.95 *(978-1-57805-135-9(5))* Sierra Club Bks.

Black, Teresa "Dicentra". One Pan Wonders ~ Backcountry Cooking at its Finest. 2008. 95p. pap. 13.95 *(978-0-615-24676-5(1))* Black Mountain Pubns.

Bubenik, Jenifer. Thoughts from the Chicken Bus. 2009. 220p. pap. 15.00 *(978-1-60844-052-8(4))* Dog Ear Publishing, LLC.

Carter, David E., et al. The Big Book of Packaging. 2011. (ENG., Illus.). 384p. 49.99 *(978-0-06-200989-0(3)*, Collins Design) HarperCollins Pubs.

Clelland, Mike. Ultralight Backpackin' Tips: 153 Amazing & Inexpensive Tips for Extremely Lightweight Camping. 2011. (ENG., Illus.). 144p. pap. 14.95 *(978-0-7627-6384-9(1)*, Falcon Guides) Globe Pequot Pr., The.

Conners, Tim & Conners, Christine. The Scout's Backpacking Cookbook. 2012. (ENG., Illus.). 192p. pap. 16.95 ***(978-0-7627-7910-9(1)***, Falcon Guides) Globe Pequot Pr., The.

Corbridge, Carol. The Boomer's Guide to Lightweight Backpacking: New Gear for Old People, 1 vol. 2008. (ENG., Illus.). 102p. pap. 18.95 *(978-1-57188-442-8(4))* Amato, Frank Pubns., Inc.

Daney, Dave. Packing with Burros. 2010. *(978-0-87961-280-1(0))*; (Illus.). xii, 142p. pap. *(978-978-087-961-7(7))* Naturegraph Pubs., Inc.

Davis, Brew. 46 Days: Keeping up with Jennifer Pharr Davis on the Appalachian Trail. 2011. 208p. pap. 12.95 ***(978-0-8253-0678-5(7))*** Beaufort Bks., Inc.

Densmore, Lisa. Predicting Weather: Forecasting, Planning, & Preparing. 2010. (Backpacker Magazine Ser.). (ENG., Illus.). 96p. pap. 12.95 *(978-0-7627-5656-8(X)*, Falcon Guides) Globe Pequot Pr., The.

Dodge, Kathleen. John Muir Trail. 2007. (Day & Section Hikes Ser.). (ENG., Illus.). 160p. per. 13.95 *(978-0-89732-963-7(5))* Menasha Ridge Pr., Inc.

DuFresne, Jim. Isle Royale National Park. 4th ed. 2011. pap. 16.95 *(978-0-9830150-0-0(7))* MichiganTrailMaps.com.

Eberhart, M. J. Ten Million Steps: Nimblewill Nomad's Epic 10-Month Trek from the Florida Keys to Quebec. 2007. (ENG., Illus.). 544p. pap. 16.95 *(978-0-89732-979-8(1))* Menasha Ridge Pr., Inc.

Friend, Sandra. Explorer's Guide 50 Hikes in Central Florida. 2nd ed. 2011. (50 Hikes Ser.). (ENG.). 272p. pap. 19.95 *(978-0-88150-902-1(7)*, 150902) Countryman Pr.

Gadd, Ben. The Canadian Hiker's & Backpacker's Handbook: Your How-To Guide for Hitting the Trails, Coast to Coast to Coast. 2008. (ENG., Illus.). 369p. pap. 29.95 *(978-1-55285-917-9(7))* Whitecap Bks., Ltd. CAN. Dist: Midpoint Trade Bks., Inc.

Gilford, Judith. The Packing Book: Secrets of the Carry-on Traveler. 4th rev. ed. 2006. (Packing Book: Secrets of the Carry-on Traveler Ser.). (ENG., Illus.). 288p. pap. 14.99 *(978-1-58008-783-4(3))* Ten Speed Pr.

Gilman, Susan Jane. Undress Me in the Temple of Heaven. 2010. (ENG.). 320p. pap. 13.99 *(978-0-446-69693-7(5))* Grand Central Publishing.

Goldenberg, Marni & Martin, Bruce. Hiking & Backpacking. 2007. (ENG., Illus.). 272p. per. 20.95 *(978-0-7360-6801-7(5))* Human Kinetics Pubs.

Hannam, Kevin & Ateljevic, Irena. Backpacker Tourism: Concepts & Profiles. Hannam, Kevin & Ateljevic, Irena, eds. 2007. (Tourism & Cultural Change Ser.). (ENG., Illus.). 280p. 159.95 *(978-1-84541-078-0(5))* Channel View Pubns., Ltd. GBR. Dist: Univ. of Toronto Pr.

Hannam, Kevin & Ateljevic, Irena, eds. Backpacker Tourism: Concepts & Profiles. 2007. (Tourism & Cultural Change Ser.). (ENG.). 280p. 59.95 *(978-1-84541-077-3(7))* Channel View Pubns., Ltd. GBR. Dist: Univ. of Toronto Pr.

Hannam, Kevin & Diekmann, Anya, eds. Beyond Backpacker Tourism: Mobilities & Experiences. 2010. (Illus.). 248p. E-Book *(978-1-84541-132-9(3))* Channel View Pubns., Ltd.

—Beyond Backpacker Tourism: Mobilities & Experiences. 2010. (Tourism & Cultural Change Ser.). (ENG., Illus.). 248p. 109.95 *(978-1-84541-131-2(5))*; pap. 54.95 *(978-1-84541-130-5(7))* Channel View Pubns., Ltd. GBR. Dist: Univ. of Toronto Pr.

Hauserman, Tim. Monsters in the Woods: Backpacking with Children. 2007. (ENG., Illus.). 152p. per. 15.95 *(978-0-87417-711-4(1))* Univ. of Nevada Pr.

Heid, Matt. AMC's Best Backpacking in New England. 2008. (ENG., Illus.). 320p. per. 18.95 *(978-1-929173-74-7(1))* Appalachian Mountain Club Bks.

Jahangir, Tahir. A Travel Companion to the Northern Areas of Pakistan. 2nd ed. 2012. (ENG., Illus.). 226p. pap. 29.95 ***(978-0-19-547778-8(2))*** Oxford Univ. Pr., Inc.

Jardine, Ray. Trail Life: Ray Jardine's Lightweight Backpacking. 2009. (Illus.). 400p. pap. 24.95 *(978-0-9632359-7-8(4))* AdventureLore Pr.

Johnson-Eluwole, Mindi S. Travel: the Well-Known Secret: Travel Stories & Life Lessons. 2011. 244p. 24.95 ***(978-1-4567-4520-2(4))***; pap. 16.95 ***(978-1-4567-4521-9(2))*** AuthorHouse.

Kemsley, William & Kemsley, William, Jr. Backpacker & Hiker's Handbook. 2008. (ENG., Illus.). 304p. per. 24.95 *(978-0-8117-3462-2(5))* Stackpole Bks.

King, Suzanne & Robertson, Elaine. The Backpacker's Bible: Your Essential Guide to Round the World Travel. (ENG.). 336p. 2012. pap. 15.95 ***(978-1-907554-21-6(1))*** 2008. pap. 17.95 *(978-1-906032-27-2(0))* Anova Bks. GBR. Dist: Independent Pubs. Group.

Klein, Karin. Orange County. 2010. (50 Hikes Ser.). (ENG.). 256p. pap. 18.95 *(978-0-88150-872-7(1)*, 150872) Countryman Pr.

Lipker, Kim. Smart & Savvy Hiking: What Every Woman Needs to Know on the Trail. 2008. (ENG., Illus.). 224p. pap. 15.95 *(978-0-89732-671-1(7))* Menasha Ridge Pr., Inc.

Lorain, Douglas. Backpacking Oregon: From Rugged Coastline to Mountain Meadow. 2nd ed. 2007. (Backpacking Ser.). (ENG., Illus.). 276p. pap. 18.95 *(978-0-89997-441-5(4))* Wilderness Pr.

—Backpacking Washington: From Volcanic Peaks to Rainforest Valleys. 2nd rev. ed. 2007. (Backpacking Ser.). (ENG., Illus.). 288p. per. 17.95 *(978-0-89997-423-1(6))* Wilderness Pr.

—100 Classic Hikes in Oregon: Oregon Coast, Columbia Gorge, Cascades, Eastern Oregon, Wallowas. 2nd ed. 2011. (ENG.). 256p. pap. 21.95 *(978-1-59485-492-7(0))* Mountaineers Bks., The.

Lorain, Douglas, photos by. Backpacking Wyoming: From Towering Granite Peaks to Steaming Geyser Basins. 2010. (ENG., Illus.). 288p. pap. 18.95 *(978-0-89997-505-4(4))* Wilderness Pr.

Maloney, Lisa. 50 Hikes Around Anchorage. 2010. (50 Hikes Ser.). (ENG., Illus.). 232p. pap. 18.95 *(978-0-88150-905-2(1)*, 150905) Countryman Pr.

March, Laurie Ann. Another Fork in the Trail: Vegetarian & Vegan Recipes for the Backcountry. 2011. (ENG.). 224p. pap. 17.95 *(978-0-89997-506-1(2))* Wilderness Pr.

Mayberger, James. A Summer Odyssey: Forging America's Great Western Trail. 2nd ed. 2009. (Illus.). ix, 246p. *(978-1-60702-327-2(X))* Independent Pub.

McIntosh, Fiona. Slack Packing: A Guide to South Africa's Top Leisure Trails. 2007. (Illus.). 160p. pap. 71.00 *(978-1-919938-72-1(9))* Sunbird Publishing ZAF. Dist: International Publishers Marketing.

Miller, Joe. Backpacking North Carolina: The Definitive Guide to 43 Can't-Miss Trips from Mountains to Sea. 2011. (Southern Gateways Guides). (ENG., Illus.). 256p. pap. 20.00 *(978-0-8078-7183-6(4))*; 45.00 *(978-0-8078-3455-8(6))* Univ. of North Carolina Pr.

Molloy, Johnny. Day & Overnight Hikes: Shenandoah National Park. 3rd ed. 2007. (Day & Overnight Hikes Ser.). (ENG., Illus.). 200p. per. 15.95 *(978-0-89732-634-6(2))* Menasha Ridge Pr., Inc.

—50 Hikes in Alabama. 2010. (50 Hikes Ser.). (ENG.). 240p. pap. 18.95 *(978-0-88150-878-9(0)*, 150878) Countryman Pr.

Noy, Chaim. A Narrative Community: Voices of Israeli Backpackers. 2006. (Raphael Patai Series in Jewish Folklore & Anthropology). (Illus.). 238p. per. 29.95 *(978-0-8143-3176-7(9))* Wayne State Univ. Pr.

Paris, Cody. The Backpacker Market. 2008. 84p. pap. *(978-3-639-07468-0(8))* VDM Verlag Dr. Mueller e.K.

Paterson, Penny & Paterson, Caroline. The Backpacker's Kitchen. 2010. (ENG., Illus.). 152p. spiral bd. 15.95 *(978-0-7090-8952-0(X))* Hale, Robert Ltd. GBR. Dist: Independent Pubs. Group.

Pegram, Tim. The Blue Ridge Parkway by Foot: A Park Ranger's Memoir. 2007. (Contributions to Southern Appalachian Studies). (ENG., Illus.). 324p. per. 29.95 *(978-0-7864-3140-3(7))* McFarland & Co., Inc. Pubs.

Roach, Gerry. Colorado's Fourteeners: From Hikes to Climbs. 3rd ed. 2011. (ENG.). 336p. pap. 22.95 *(978-1-55591-746-3(1))* Fulcrum Publishing.

Roberts, Harry & Schneider, Russ. Basic Illustrated Backpacking. 2008. (Basic Essentials Ser.). (ENG., Illus.). 64p. pap. 9.95 *(978-0-7627-4757-3(9)*, Falcon Guides) Globe Pequot Pr., The.

Rogers, Jim. Masters on the Trail ~ a Backpack Primer for Folks over Fifty. 2010. 156p. pap. 14.49 *(978-1-935125-76-1(1))* Robertson Publishing.

Romano, Craig. Backpacking Washington: Overnight & Multi-Day Routes. 2011. (ENG.). 288p. pap. 18.95 *(978-1-59485-110-0(7))* Mountaineers Bks., The.

—Backpacking Washington: Overnight & Multiday Routes. 2011. E-Book *(978-1-59485-413-2(0))* Mountaineers Bks., The.

Romano, Jeff. New England. 2009. (ENG.). 256p. pap. 21.95 (978-1-59485-100-1(X)) Mountaineers Bks., The.

Schneider, Bill. Bear Country Behavior: Essential Skills & Safety Tips for Hikers. 2012. (Backpacker Magazine Ser.). (ENG., Illus.). 104p. pap. 12.95 (978-0-7627-7294-0(8), Falcon Guides) Globe Pequot Pr., The.

Sherman, Steve & Older, Julia. Appalachian Odyssey: Walking the Trail from Georgia to Maine. 2009. 268p. pap. 19.95 (978-1-4401-1530-1(3)) iUniverse, Inc.

Shillington, Ben & Sandiford, Rebecca. Winter Backpacking: Your Guide to Safe & Warm Winter Camping & Day Trips. 2011. (ENG., Illus.). 160p. pap. 19.95 (978-1-56523-636-3(X)) Fox Chapel Publishing Co., Inc.

Soares, John R. & Soares, Mark. 100 Classic Hikes in Northern California. 3rd ed. 2007. (ENG.). 240p. pap. (978-1-59485-062-2(3)) Mountaineers Bks., The.

Soles, Clyde. Backpacker magazine's Backpacking Basics: Planning, Preparing, & Packing. 2011. (Backpacker Magazine Ser.). (ENG., Illus.). 96p. pap. 12.95 (978-0-7627-5549-3(0), Falcon Guides) Globe Pequot Pr., The.

Stevenson, Jason. The Complete Idiot's Guide to Backpacking & Hiking. 2010. (Complete Idiot's Guide Ser.). (ENG.). 368p. (gr. 12-18). 16.95 (978-1-59257-960-0(4), Alpha Bks.) Penguin Group (USA) Inc.

Tilton, Buck. Backcountry First Aid & Extended Care. 5th ed. 2007. (Falcon Guide Ser.). (ENG., Illus.). 128p. (Orig.). per. 5.95 (978-0-7627-4357-5(3), Falcon Guides) Globe Pequot Pr., The.

—Hiking & Backpacking. 2009. (Knack: Make It Easy Ser.). (ENG., Illus.). 256p. pap., instr.'s gde. ed. 19.95 (978-1-59921-400-9(8), Knack) Globe Pequot Pr., The.

Townsend, Chris. The Backpacker's Handbook. 4th ed. 2011. (ENG., Illus.). 480p. pap. 21.00 (978-0-07-175489-7(X), 007175489X, International Marine/Ragged Mountain Pr.) McGraw-Hill Professional Publishing.

Uney, Graham. Backpacker's Britain: Northern Scotland. 2009. (Illus.). 288p. pap. 19.95 (978-1-85284-458-5(2)) Cicerone Pr. GBR. Dist: Midpoint Trade Bks., Inc.

—Backpacker's Britain - Central & Southern Scottish Highlands, Vol. 4. 2009. (Backpacker's Britain Ser.). (Illus.). 240p. pap. 19.95 (978-1-85284-527-8(9)) Cicerone Pr. GBR. Dist: Midpoint Trade Bks., Inc.

Warren, Scott S. & Gascoyne, John. Colorado: Great Plains/Front Range/Rocky Mountains/Colorado Plateau. 3rd rev. ed. 2008. (100 Classic Hikes Ser.). (ENG., Illus.). 96p. pap. 21.95 (978-1-59485-024-0(0)) Mountaineers Bks., The.

Wilderness Press. Backpacking California: Mountain, Foothill, Coastal & Desert Adventures in the Golden State. 2nd ed. 2008. (Backpacking Ser.). (ENG., Illus.). 490p. pap. 24.95 (978-0-89997-446-0(5)) Wilderness Pr.

BACKUS, ISAAC, 1724-1806

Hovey, Alvah. A Memoir of the Life & Times of the Rev Isaac Backus, a M. 2009. 274p. pap. (978-0-217-15993-7(1)) Books LLC.

—A Memoir of the Life & Times of the Rev Isaac Backus, a M. 2006. 384p. per. 26.99 (978-1-4255-4132-3(1)) MPublishing.

BACKWARD CHILDREN

see Slow Learning Children

BACON, FRANCIS, 1561-1626

Abbott, Edwin A. Bacon & Essex: A Sketch of Bacon's Earlier Life. 2007. (ENG.). 332p. 45.95 (978-0-548-12271-6(7)) Kessinger Publishing, LLC.

—Bacon's Essays, Vol. 1. 2006. pap. 28.95 (978-1-4286-4258-4(7)) Kessinger Publishing, LLC.

—Francis Bacon: An Account of His Life & Works. 2007. (ENG.). 552p. 57.95 (978-0-548-10021-9(7)) Kessinger Publishing, LLC.

Allen, Charles. Notes on the Bacon-Shakespeare Question. 2009. 324p. 36.99 (978-1-117-48771-7(7)); (ENG.). 323p. pap. 29.75 (978-1-117-48772-4(5)); 324p. 25.99 (978-1-103-01724-9(1)); 324p. pap. 19.99 (978-1-103-01720-1(9)) BiblioBazaar.

—Notes on the Bacon-Shakespeare Question. 2009. 184p. pap. 19.99 (978-1-150-46631-1(6)) General Bks. LLC.

—Notes on the Bacon-Shakespeare Question. 2009. 324p. 45.95 (978-1-104-16503-1(1)); pap. 30.95 (978-1-104-14805-8(6)) Kessinger Publishing, LLC.

Arya, Rina. Francis Bacon: Critical & Theoretical Perspectives. 2012. (Illus.). 224p. pap. 49.50 (978-1-84519-383-6(0)) Sussex Academic Pr. GBR. Dist: International Specialized Bk. Services.

Bacon, Francis. Certain Miscellanious Works of the Right Honorable Francis Lo. Verulam, Viscount S. Alban. reprint ed. lib. bdg. 98.00 (978-0-7426-2024-7(7)) Classic Bks.

—The Confession of Faith. reprint ed. lib. bdg. 98.00 (978-0-7426-2019-3(0)) Classic Bks.

—The Essays of Sir Francis Bacon. 2009. 204p. pap. 17.95 (978-1-58509-332-8(7)) Book Tree, The.

—The Letters & the Life of Francis Bacon Including All His Occasional Works, Namely Letters, Speeches, Tracts, State Papers, Memorials, Devices & All Authentic Writing Not Already Printed among His Philosophical, Literary, or Professional Works, 7 Vols. reprint ed. lib. bdg. 686.00 (978-0-7426-2032-2(8)) Classic Bks.

—The Philosophical Works of Francis Bacon, Baron of Verulam, Viscount St. Albans, & Lord High Chancellor of England; Methodized, & Made English, from the Orginals, with Occasional Notes, to Explain What is Obscure, 3 Vols. reprint ed. lib. bdg. 294.00 (978-0-7426-2029-2(8)) Classic Bks.

—Sir Francis Bacon, His Apology, in Certain Imputations Concerning the Late Earl of Essex: Written to the Right Honorable, His Very Good Lord, the Earl of Devonshire, Lord Lieutenant of Ireland. reprint ed. lib. bdg. 98.00 (978-0-7426-2004-9(2)) Classic Bks.

—Summi Angliae Cancellarii Instauration Magna. reprint ed. lib. bdg. 98.00 (978-0-7426-2010-0(7)) Classic Bks.

—Thoughts on the Nature of Things. 2006. pap. 12.95 (978-1-4286-6959-8(0)) Kessinger Publishing, LLC.

—Topics of the Inquiry Concerning Light & the Matter of Light. 2006. pap. 9.95 (978-1-4286-6927-7(2)) Kessinger Publishing, LLC.

Bacon, Francis. The Works of Francis Bacon, Volume 4. Spedding, James et al, eds. 2011. (Cambridge Library Collection - Philosophy Ser.). (ENG.). 520p. pap. 37.99 **(978-1-108-04076-1(4))**; 670p. pap. 45.00 **(978-1-108-04077-8(2))**; 414p. pap. 31.99 **(978-1-108-04072-3(1))**; 844p. pap. 53.00 **(978-1-108-04070-9(5))**; 682p. pap. 48.00 **(978-1-108-04068-6(3))**; 438p. pap. 32.99 **(978-1-108-04073-0(X))**; 450p. pap. 32.99 **(978-1-108-04075-4(6))**; 512p. pap. 37.99 **(978-1-108-04067-9(5))**; 784p. pap. 50.00 **(978-1-108-04069-3(1))**; 438p. pap. 32.99 **(978-1-108-04071-6(3))**; 456p. pap. 34.99 **(978-1-108-04074-7(8))**; 850p. pap. 53.00 **(978-1-108-04066-2(7))**; 706p. pap. 48.00 **(978-1-108-04065-5(9))**; (Illus.). 876p. pap. 53.00 **(978-1-108-04064-8(0))** Cambridge Univ. Pr.

Begley, W. Is It Shakespeare? the Great Question of Elizabethan Literature Answered. 2007. (ENG.). 404p. 49.95 (978-0-548-03922-9(4)) Kessinger Publishing, LLC.

Biographiq. Sir Francis Bacon - English Philosopher & Statesman. 2008. 56p. pap. 9.99 (978-1-59986-100-5(3), Biographiq) Filiquarian Publishing, LLC.

Bompas, George C. The Problem of the Shakespeare Plays. 2009. 96p. pap. 14.14 (978-1-4589-3377-5(6)) General Bks. LLC.

Bozeman, Theodore Dwight. Protestants in an Age of Science: The Baconian Ideal & Antebellum American Religious Thought. 2011. (ENG.). 254p. pap. 40.00 **(978-0-8078-9626-6(8))** Univ. of North Carolina Pr.

Church, R. W. Bacon: English Men of Letters. Morley, John, ed. 2007. (ENG.). 168p. per. (978-1-4065-1372-1(5)) Dodo Pr.

Church, Richard. Bacon. 2007. (ENG.). 234p. 41.95 (978-0-548-04958-7(0)) Kessinger Publishing, LLC.

Church, Richard W. Bacon. Morley, John, ed. reprint ed. 41.50 (978-0-404-51704-5(8)) AMS Pr., Inc.

Church, Richard William. Bacon. 2011. (Cambridge Library Collection - English Men of Letters Ser.). (ENG.). 240p. pap. 22.99 **(978-1-108-03443-2(8))** Cambridge Univ. Pr.

Church, Richard William. Bacon: English Men of Letters. 2007. (ENG.). 182p. pap. 19.99 (978-1-4346-2406-2(4)); 204p. pap. 22.99 (978-1-4346-2452-9(8)) BiblioBazaar.

Corneanu, Sorana. Regimens of the Mind: Boyle, Locke, & the Early Modern Cultura Animi Tradition. 2012. (ENG.). 320p. 50.00 (978-0-226-11639-6(5)) Univ. of Chicago Pr.

Dawkins, Peter. Bacon's Shakespeare: Facts Pointing to Francis Bacon as Author of the Shakespeare Poems & Plays. 2007. (Illus.). 56p. pap. (978-0-86293-012-7(X)) Bacon, Francis Research Trust.

Desroches, Dennis. Francis Bacon & the Limits of Scientific Knowledge. 2006. (Continuum Studies in British Philosophy). (ENG.). 208p. 155.00 (978-0-8264-8681-3(9)) Continuum International Publishing Group, Ltd. GBR. Dist: National Bk. Network.

Donnelly, Ignatius. The Cipher in the Plays & on the Tombstone. 2010. 400p. pap. 33.75 (978-1-141-94065-3(5)) BiblioBazaar.

—The Cipher in the Plays & on the Tombstone. 2008. 384p. 48.95 (978-1-4365-6587-5(1)) 2007. (ENG.). 388p. per. 33.95 (978-0-548-75176-3(5)) Kessinger Publishing, LLC.

Du Maurier, Daphne. Golden Lads: A Study of Anthony Bacon, Francis & Their Friends. 22.95 (978-0-88411-544-1(5)) Amereon LTD.

—Golden Lads: A Study of Anthony Bacon, Francis & Their Friends. 2008. (ENG.). 352p. pap. 15.95 (978-1-84408-073-1(0), Virago Press) Little, Brown Bk. Group Ltd. GBR. Dist: Independent Pubs. Group.

Eiseley, Loren Corey. Francis Bacon & the Modern Dilemm. 2011. 106p. 39.95 **(978-1-258-10306-4(0))** Literary Licensing, LLC.

Fowler, Thomas. Bacon. 2009. 156p. pap. (978-0-217-33752-6(X)); 124p. pap. (978-1-4590-9491-8(3)) Books LLC.

Funari, Anthony J. Francis Bacon & the Seventeenth-Century Intellectual Discourse. 2011. (ENG., Illus.). 192p. 80.00 (978-0-230-11684-9(1)) Palgrave Macmillan.

Hall, Manly Palmer. Francis Bacon the Concealed Poet. 2006. pap. 16.95 (978-1-4286-3605-7(6)) Kessinger Publishing, LLC.

Harrison, Martin & Daniels, Rebecca. Francis Bacon: Incunabula. 2009. (ENG., Illus.). 256p. 75.00 (978-0-500-09344-3(X), 509344) Thames & Hudson.

Jardine, Lisa. Francis Bacon: Discovery & the Art of Discourse. 2009. (ENG.). 276p. pap. 38.00 (978-0-521-10908-6(6)) Cambridge Univ. Pr.

Kiernan, Michael. The Oxford Francis Bacon VIII: The Historie of the raigne of King Henry the seventh & other works of The 1620s. 2012. (Oxford Francis Bacon Ser.). (ENG., Illus.). 832p. 160.00 (978-0-19-925666-2(7)) Oxford Univ. Pr., Inc.

Kim, Shi-Hyong. Bacon und Kant: Ein Erkenntnistheoretischer Vergleich Zwischen Dem Novum Organum und der Kritik der Reinen Vernunft. 2008. (Kantstudien-Ergänzungshefte Ser.). (GER.). XII, 372p. 119.00 (978-3-11-020212-0(3)) De Gruyter, Walter Inc.

Laing, Francis Henry. Lord Bacon's Philosophy Examined: to Which Is Added, the Mental. 2007. (ENG.). 188p. per. 22.95 (978-1-4304-4657-6(9)) Kessinger Publishing, LLC.

Lang, Andrew. Shakespeare, Bacon & the Great Unknown. reprint ed. 40.00 (978-0-404-03871-7(9)) AMS Pr., Inc.

—Shakespeare, Bacon & the Great Unknown. 2008. 184p. 22.99 (978-0-554-31221-7(2)) 2008. 184p. 25.99 (978-0-554-21918-9(2)) 2006. 186p. pap. 19.99 (978-1-4264-1221-9(5)) 2006. (ENG.). 180p. pap. 21.99 (978-1-4264-1264-6(9)) BiblioBazaar.

—Shakespeare, Bacon & the Great Unknown. 2009. 146p. pap. (978-1-150-28735-0(7)) Books LLC.

—Shakespeare, Bacon & the Great Unknown. 2007. (ENG.). 184p. per. (978-1-4065-2645-5(2)) Dodo Pr.

—Shakespeare, Bacon & the Great Unknown. 2007. (ENG.). 360p. 46.95 (978-0-548-00501-9(X)) Kessinger Publishing, LLC.

Lerner, Ralph. Playing the Fool: Subversive Laughter in Troubled Times. 2009. (ENG.). 144p. 32.50 (978-0-226-47315-4(5)) Univ. of Chicago Pr.

Lochithea. Baconian Reference Book: Commentarius Solutus. 2009. 828p. pap. 58.95 (978-1-4401-3844-7(3)) iUniverse, Inc.

Martin, Julian. Francis Bacon, the State & the Reform of Natural Philosophy. 2007. (ENG.). 252p. pap. 51.00 (978-0-521-03566-8(X)) Cambridge Univ. Pr.

Matthews, Steven. Theology & Science in the Thought of Francis Bacon. 2008. 164p. 114.95 (978-0-7546-6252-5(7)) Ashgate Publishing Co.

Minkov, Svetozar. Francis Bacon's "Inquiry Touching Human Nature" Virtue, Philosophy, & the Relief of Man's Estate. 2010. ix, 151p. (978-0-7391-4483-1(9)) Lexington Bks.

—Francis Bacon's Inquiry Touching Human Virtue: Virtue, Philosophy, & the Relief of Man's Estate. 2010. (ENG.). 158p. 62.99 (978-0-7391-4481-7(2)) Lexington Bks.

Nichol, John. Francis Bacon: His Life & Philosophy. 2009. 224p. 28.99 (978-1-113-10818-0(5)); pap. 24.75 (978-1-113-10816-6(9)) BiblioBazaar.

Owen, Orville W. Sir Francis Bacon's Cipher Story. 2009. 204p. 39.95 (978-1-120-79547-2(8)); pap. 24.95 (978-1-120-70794-9(3)) Kessinger Publishing, LLC.

Patrick, Dave & Dawkins, Peter. The View Beyond: Sir Francis Bacon: Alchemy, Science, Mystery. 2011. (View Ser.). (ENG., Illus.). 288p. pap. 19.95 (978-1-905398-22-5(0)) Polair Publishing GBR. Dist: SCB Distributors.

Pott, Constance M. Francis Bacon & His Secret Society. 2008. (ENG.). pap. 31.95 (978-1-934935-18-7(2), Cornerstone Bk. Publishers) Poll, Michael Publishing.

Pott, Henry. Francis Bacon & His Secret Society. 2009. 420p. 30.99 (978-1-113-72746-6(2)) BiblioBazaar.

—Francis Bacon & His Secret Society. 2007. (ENG.). 424p. 49.95 (978-0-548-28051-5(7)) Kessinger Publishing, LLC.

Rees, Graham & Fattori, Marta, eds. The Reception of Francis Bacon in Europe. 2007. (Reception of Writers in Europe Ser.). (ENG.). 400p. 250.00 (978-0-8264-7037-9(8)) Continuum International Publishing Group, Ltd. GBR. Dist: National Bk. Network.

Robertson, John M., ed. The Philiosophical Works of Frances Bacon (Routledge Revivals) 2011. (Routledge Revivals Ser.). (ENG.). 942p. 250.00 (978-0-415-67955-8(9)) Routledge.

Sacks, David, ed. Selected Works of Sir Francis Bacon. 2006. (ENG.). 416p. 40.00 (978-0-300-11238-2(6)) Yale Univ. Pr.

Smedley, William. The Mystery of Francis Bacon. 2007. 148p. per. 14.99 (978-1-59547-765-1(9)) NuVision Pubns., LLC.

Smedley, William T. How Francis Bacon Marked Books with the Publication of Which He. 2006. pap. 12.95 (978-1-4304-2452-9(4)) Kessinger Publishing, LLC.

—The Mystery of Francis Bacon. 2009. 204p. 23.99 (978-1-103-44692-6(4)); pap. 17.99 (978-1-103-44690-2(8)) BiblioBazaar.

Steeves, George Walter. Francis Bacon: A Sketch of His Life, Works & Literary Friends, Chiefly from A Bibliographical Point of View. 2008. 292p. per. 28.95 (978-1-4086-6521-3(2)) Audubon Pr. & Christian Bk. Service.

Stewart, Alan, ed. The Oxford Francis Bacon I: Early Writings 1584-1586. 2012. (Oxford Francis Bacon Ser.). (ENG., Illus.). 1152p. 299.00 **(978-0-19-818313-6(5))** Oxford Univ. Pr., Inc.

Stopes, Charlotte Carmichael. The Bacon-Shakspere Question Answered. 2010. (Cambridge Library Collection - Women's Writing Ser.). 294p. pap. 23.99 (978-1-108-02190-6(5)) Cambridge Univ. Pr.

Strinati, Claudio Massimo, et al. Caravaggio Bacon. 2010. (ITA & ENG., Illus.). 224p. 60.00 (978-88-7179-623-9(3), Ore Cultura Srl (Acc)) Antique Collectors' Club GBR. Dist: National Bk. Network.

Tudhope, George V. Francis Bacon & the Masonic Term: the Symbol G & Geometry - 2006. pap. 9.95 (978-1-4304-3019-3(2)) Kessinger Publishing, LLC.

Udny, E. Francis. Francis Rakoczi II of Transylvania & the Count St Germain - 2006. pap. 9.95 (978-1-4304-3045-2(1)) Kessinger Publishing, LLC.

Vickers, Brian. Francis Bacon & Renaissance Prose. Vickers, Brian, ed. 2009. (ENG.). 332p. pap. 36.99 (978-0-521-11496-7(9)) Cambridge Univ. Pr.

Waters, Robert. William Shakespeare Portrayed by Himself: A Revelation of the Poet in the Career & Character of One of His Own Dramatic Heroes. 2007. (ENG.). 354p. 46.95 (978-0-548-01879-8(0)) Kessinger Publishing, LLC.

Wormald, Brian Harvey Goodwin. Francis Bacon: History, Politics & Science, 1561-1626. 2006. (ENG.). 424p. pap. 56.00 (978-0-521-03145-5(1)) Cambridge Univ. Pr.

Zittel, Claus & Nanni, Romano, eds. Philosophies of Technology: Francis Bacon & his Contemporaries, 2 vols. 2008. (Intersections Ser.). (C). (978-90-04-17050-6(2)) BRILL.

BACON, FRANCIS, 1909-1992

Arya, Rina. Francis Bacon: Painting in a Godless World. 2012. (Illus.). 176p. 80.00 **(978-1-84822-044-7(8)**, Lund Humphries Pubs.) Ashgate Publishing, Ltd. GBR. Dist: Ashgate Publishing Co.

Bacon, Francis. Francis Bacon - A Terrible Beauty, 1 vol. 2009. (ENG., Illus.). 208p. pap. 34.95 (978-3-86930-027-6(2)) Steidl, Gerhard Druckerei und Verlag DEU. Dist: Innovative Logistics.

Brighton, Andrew. Francis Bacon. 2010. (ENG., Illus.). 80p. pap. 16.50 (978-1-85437-307-6(2)) Tate Publishing, Ltd. GBR. Dist: Hachette Bk. Group.

Brunet, Lynn. A Course of Severe & Arduous Trials: Bacon, Beckett & Spurious Freemasonry in Early Twentieth-Century Ireland. 2009. (Reimagining Ireland Ser.). (ENG.). 210p. pap. 46.95 (978-3-03911-854-0(4)) Lang, Peter AG GBR. Dist: Lang, Peter.

Chare, Nicholas. After Frances Bacon: Synaesthesia & Sex in Paint. 2012. (Illus.). 192p. 114.95 **(978-1-4094-1170-3(2))** Ashgate Publishing Co.

Chiappini, Rudy, ed. Bacon. 2008. (ENG., Illus.). 176p. 90.00 (978-88-6130-293-8(9)) Skira Editore ITA. Dist: Random Hse., Inc.

Deleuze, Gilles & Deleuze. Francis Bacon: The Logic of Sensation. (Illus.). 228p. 90.00 (978-0-8264-6647-1(8)) Continuum International Publishing Group, Ltd. GBR. Dist: National Bk. Network.

Ficacci, Luigi. Bacon. 25th ed. 2010. (25 Ser.). (ENG., Illus.). 96p. 14.99 (978-3-8365-2544-2(5)) TASCHEN DEU. Dist: Ingram Pub. Services.

Gale, Matthew & Stephens, Chris, eds. Francis Bacon. 2009. (ENG., Illus.). 288p. 30.00 (978-0-8478-3275-0(9)) Rizzoli International Pubns., Inc.

Harrison, Martin. In Camera - Francis Bacon: Photography, Film & the Practice of Painting. 2006. (ENG., Illus.). 256p. pap. 39.95 (978-0-500-28624-1(8)) Thames & Hudson.

Harrison, Martin, ed. New Studies: Centenary Essays, 1 vol. 2010. (ENG., Illus.). 272p. 58.00 (978-3-86521-946-6(2)) Steidl, Gerhard Druckerei und Verlag DEU. Dist: Innovative Logistics.

Hunter, Sam. Francis Bacon. 2009. (ENG., Illus.). 96p. 25.00 (978-84-343-1202-9(6)) Polígrafa, Ediciones, S. A. ESP. Dist: D.A.P./Distributed Art Pubs.

Leiris, Michel. Francis Bacon. 2008. (ENG., Illus.). 256p. 55.00 (978-84-343-1190-9(9)) Polígrafa, Ediciones, S. A. ESP. Dist: D.A.P./Distributed Art Pubs.

Marini, Francesca. Francis Bacon. 2009. (Skira MINI Artbooks Ser.). (ENG., Illus.). 96p. pap. 8.99 (978-88-6130-709-4(4)) Skira Editore ITA. Dist: Random Hse., Inc.

Miles, P. T. Francis Bacon: Painter of the Invisible. 2011. 104p. pap. 16.77 (978-1-4520-9723-7(2)) AuthorHouse.

Peppiatt, Michael. Francis Bacon: Anatomy of an Enigma. 2009. (ENG., Illus.). 464p. pap. 16.95 (978-1-60239-762-0(7), 239762) Skyhorse Publishing Co., Inc.

—Francis Bacon: Studies for a Portrait. 2008. (ENG., Illus.). 272p. 35.00 (978-0-300-14255-6(2)) Yale Univ. Pr.

—Francis Bacon in the 1950s. 2009. (ENG., Illus.). 224p. pap. 33.00 (978-0-300-15121-3(7)) Yale Univ. Pr.

Riley, Andrew. Let us Face the Future: British Art 1945-1968. 2011. (ENG & SPA.). 283p. 54.95 (978-84-937610-8-0(7)) Fundacio Joan Miro ESP. Dist: Actar Birkhauser Distribution.

Schmied. Francis Bacon: Commitment & Conflict. (Illus.). 192p. 19.95 (978-3-7913-3472-1(7)) Prestel Publishing.

Steffen, Barbara & Bryson, Norman, eds. Francis Bacon und die Bildtradition: Katalog zur Ausstellung in der Fondation Beyeler, 8.2.-20.6.2004. (Illus.). 272p. 60.00 (978-88-8491-881-9(2)) Skira Editore ITA. Dist: Rizzoli International Pubns., Inc.

Weiland, Anna Maria. Francis Bacon: Living Art. 2009. (Illus.). 128p. pap. 14.95 (978-3-7913-4202-3(9)) Prestel Publishing.

BACON, ROGER, 1214-1294

Bacon, Roger. The Opus Majus of Roger Bacon. Bridges, John Henry, ed. 2010. (Cambridge Library Collection - Physical Sciences Ser.). (LAT.). 784p. pap. 50.00 (978-1-108-01443-4(7)); (Illus.). 608p. pap. 43.00 (978-1-108-01442-7(9)) Cambridge Univ. Pr.

Bridges, John H. The Life & Work of Roger Bacon. Jones, H. Gordon, ed. reprint ed. 27.50 (978-0-404-18450-6(2)) AMS Pr., Inc.

Charpentier, Jarl. William of Rubruck & Roger Bacon. 2010. (LAT.). 81.80 (978-1-61143-120-9(4)) Gorgias Pr., LLC.

Hirsch, S. A. A Book of Essays. 2007. (ENG.). 368p. 48.95 (978-0-548-05314-0(6)) Kessinger Publishing, LLC.

Westacott. Roger Bacon. (978-0-8022-1853-7(9)) Philosophical Library, Inc.

BACON-SHAKESPEARE CONTROVERSY

see Shakespeare, William, 1564-1616—Authorship

BACON'S REBELLION, 1676

Andrews, Charles M., ed. Narratives of the Insurrections 1675 To 1690. 2007. 432p. 51.95 (978-0-548-03501-6(6)) Kessinger Publishing, LLC.

Andrews, Charles McLean. Narratives of the Insurrections, 1675-1690. 2009. 300p. pap. (978-1-151-12254-4(8)); 368p. pap. (978-0-217-51640-2(8)) Books LLC.

—Narratives of the Insurrections, 1675-1690. (Original Narratives of Early American History Ser.). 414p. reprint ed. 98.00 (978-0-7222-6521-5(2)) Library Reprints, Inc.

Bayne, Howard R. A Rebellion in the Colony of Virginia. (Illus.). 16p. reprint ed. lib. bdg. 88.00 (978-0-7222-4605-4(6)) Library Reprints, Inc.

Stanard, Mary. Story of Bacon's Rebellion. reprint ed. 150.00 (978-0-7222-6638-0(3)) Library Reprints, Inc.

Wiseman, Samuel. Samuel Wiseman's Bk of Recor. Oberg, Michael, ed. 2009. (ENG.). 304p. pap. 34.99 (978-0-7391-3530-3(9)) Lexington Bks.

BACTERIA

Here are entered works on bacteria. Works on the science of studying bacteria are entered under the heading Bacteriology.

see also Actinomycetales; Anaerobic Bacteria; Bacteria, Nitrifying; Bacterial Cell Walls; Gram-Negative Bacteria; Gram-Positive Bacteria; L-Form Bacteria; Pathogenic Bacteria

Afroz, Amber. Protein Profiling & Genetic Improvement of Tomato. 2010. 280p. pap. (978-3-8383-9396-4(1)) Lambert Academic Publishing.

Ahmed, Iftikhar & FUJIWARA, Toru. Boron-Tolerance in Bacteri. 2010. 84p. pap. (978-3-639-25890-5(8)) VDM Verlag Dr. Mueller e.K.

Al-Qadiri, Hamzah. Fourier Transform Infrared Spectroscopy. 2011. 204p. pap. **(978-3-8383-6060-7(5))** Lambert Academic Publishing.

Alvarez, Héctor M., ed. Biology of Rhodococcus. 2010. (Microbiology Monographs). (Illus.). xi, 300p. 239.00 (978-3-642-12936-0(6), 3642129366) Springer.

An, Yuehuei H. & Friedman, Richard J. eds. Handbook of Bacterial Adhesion: Principles, Methods, & Applications. 2010. (ENG.). 672p. pap. 199.00 (978-1-61737-192-9(0), 1617371920) Humana Pr.

Barredo, José-Luis, ed. Microbial Carotenoids from Bacteria & Microalgae: Methods & Protocols. 2012. (Methods in Molecular Biology Ser.: 892). (ENG., Illus.). x, 352p. 139.00 **(978-1-61779-878-8(9)**, 1617798789) Humana Pr.

Barton, Larry L. & Hamilton, W. Allan, eds. Sulphate-Reducing Bacteria: Environmental & Engineered Systems. (ENG., Illus.). 2009. 552p. pap. 67.00 (978-0-521-12399-0(2)) 2007. 562p. 208.00 (978-0-521-85485-6(7)) Cambridge Univ. Pr.

Blum, Paul, ed. Archaea: New Models for Prokaryotic Biology. 2008. (Illus.). 255p. (C). 319.00 (978-1-904455-27-1(1)) Caister Academic Pr. GBR. Dist: International Specialized Bk. Services.

Boone, David R. & Castenholz, Richard W., eds. Bergey's Manual of Systematic Bacteriology: Volume One: the Archaea & the Deeply Branching & Phototrophic Bacteria. 2nd ed. 2012. (ENG., Illus.). xxi, 721p. pap. 159.00 (978-1-4419-3159-7(7), 1441931597) Springer.

Brahma, Nitosh Kumar. Bacterial Adherence. 2011. (Immunology & Immune System Disorders Ser.). 145.00 (978-1-61209-225-6(X)) Nova Science Pubs., Inc.

Cohen, G. N. Microbial Biochemistry. 2010. (Illus.). xv, 333p. pap. 239.00 (978-90-481-6390-8(0), 9048163900) Springer.

Collin, M. & Schuch, R., eds. Bacterial Sensing & Signaling. 2009. (Contributions to Microbiology Ser.). (ENG., Illus.). 230p. (978-3-8055-9132-4(2)) Karger, S. AG.

Cram101 Textbook Reviews. Outlines & Highlights for Emerging Cancer Therapy: Microbial Approaches & Biotechnological Tools by A. Fialho. 2011. 116p. pap. 28.95 **(978-1-61905-346-5(2))** Cram101 Inc.

Cullimore, D. Roy. Practical Atlas for Bacterial Identification. 2nd rev. ed. 2010. (ENG., Illus.). 327p. 139.95 (978-1-4200-8797-0(5), CRC Press) Taylor & Francis Group GBR. Dist: Taylor & Francis Group.

Dahl, Christiane & Friedrich, Cornelius G., eds. Microbial Sulfur Metabolism. 2007. (ENG., Illus.). xxii, 308p. 189.00 (978-3-540-72679-1(9), 3540726799) Springer.

Dhewa, Tejpal. Lactic Acid Bacteria As Probiotics: Applications & Safety Issues. 2011. 108p. pap. **(978-3-8433-9199-3(8))** Lambert Academic Publishing.

Ditty, Jayna L., et al, eds. Bacterial Circadian Programs. 2009. (ENG., Illus.). xi, 333p. 229.00 (978-3-540-88430-9(0), 3540884300) Springer.

Dundon, William. Malicious Microbes. 2007. 152p. per. (978-0-7552-1052-7(2)) Authors OnLine, Ltd.

Dworkin, Martin. The Prokaryotes: A Handbook on the Biology of Bacteria: Vol. 3: Archaea & Bacteria: Firmicutes, Actinomycetes, 7 vols. 3rd ed. 2006. (Illus.). LIV, 1146p. 875.00 (978-0-387-33489-9(C), 0387334890) Springer.

Edwards, Clive, ed. Environmental Monitoring of Bacteria. 2010. (Methods in Biotechnology Ser.). 344p. pap. 149.00 (978-1-61737-077-9(0), 1617370770) Humana Pr.

El-Sharoud, Walid, ed. Bacterial Physiology: A Molecular Approach. 2007. (Illus.). 371p. 359.00 (978-3-540-74920-2(9)) Springer.

Ellis, David. Iron Bacteria - Organisms & Their Identification - Illustrated. 2006. (Illus.). 216p. 34.95 (978-1-933998-40-4(7), Merchant Bks.) Rough Draft Printing.

Feurer, Carole. Development of a Genomic Approach for the Study of Coryneform Bacteri. 2009. 120p. pap. (978-3-639-19673-3(2)) VDM Verlag Dr. Mueller e.K.

Filloux, Alain A.M., ed. Bacterial Regulatory Networks. 2012. 400p. 360.00 **(978-1-908230-03-4(7))** Caister Academic Pr. GBR. Dist: International Specialized Bk. Services.

Franklin, Trevor J. & Snow, George Alan. Biochemistry & Molecular Biology of Antimicrobial Drug Action. 6th ed. 2010. (ENG., Illus.). x, 182p. pap. 134.00 (978-1-4419-3549-6(5), 1441935495) Springer.

Fuller, R. & Perdigón, G., eds. Probiotics 3: Immunomodulation by the Gut Microflora & Probiotics. 2010. 280p. pap. 151.00 (978-90-481-5429-6(4), 9048154294) Springer.

Ganguli, B. N. & Deshmukh, S. K., eds. Fungi: Multifaceted Microbes. 2006. (ENG., Illus.). 321p. 167.95 (978-1-4200-4328-0(5), CRC Press) Taylor & Francis Group GBR. Dist: Taylor & Francis Group.

Garrity, George. Bergey's Manual(r) of Systematic Bacteriology: The Proteobacteria, Part A Introductory Essays, Vol. 2. 2nd ed. 2010. Orig. Title: Bergey's Manual Trust. (Illus.). xxvi, 304p. pap. 74.95 (978-1-4419-3695-0(5), 1441936955) Springer.

Garrity, George M. Bergey's Manual of Systematic Bacteriology/George M. Garrity, Editor-In-Chief. 2nd ed. (Illus.). 2010. (ENG.). 974p. 219.00 (978-0-387-95042-6(7), 0387950427) 2009. 349.00 (978-0-387-95043-3(5)) Springer.

Gottschalk, Gerhard. Discover the World of Microbes: Bacteria, Archaea, & Viruses. 2012. (ENG., Illus.). 400p. pap. 79.95 **(978-3-527-32845-1(9)**, Wiley-VCH) Wiley, John & Sons, Inc.

Greenwood, David. Medical Microbiology: A Guide to Microbial Infections: Pathogenesis, Immunity, Laboratory Diagnosis, & Control. 17th ed. 2007. (978-0-443-10210-3(4), Churchill Livingstone) Elsevier Health Sciences.

Greenwood, David, et al. Medical Microbiology: A Guide to Microbial Infections - Pathogenesis, Immunity, Laboratory Diagnosis & Control. 17th rev. ed. 2007. (ENG., Illus.). 752p. pap. 94.95 (978-0-443-10209-7(0), Churchill Livingstone) Elsevier - Health Sciences Div.

Grimm, Bernhard, et al, eds. Chlorophylls & Bacteriochlorophylls: Biochemistry, Biophysics, Functions & Applications. 2010. (Advances in Photosynthesis & Respiration Ser.). (Illus.). xxix, 603p. pap. 449.00 (978-90-481-7140-8(7), 9048171407) Springer.

Gunde-Cimerman, Nina, et al, eds. Adaptation to Life at High Salt Concentrations in Archaea, Bacteria, & Eukarya. 2010. (Cellular Origin, Life in Extreme Habitats & Astrobiology Ser.). xii, 577p. pap. 319.00 (978-90-481-6914-6(3), 9048169143) Springer.

Gupta, Vijai Kumar & Ayyachamy, Manimaran. Biotechnology of Microbial Enzymes. 2011. **(978-1-62100-131-7(8)**, Nova Science Pubs., Inc.

Hackstein, Johannes H. P. (Endo)symbiotic Methanogenic Archaea. Hackstein, Johannes H. P., ed. 2010. (Microbiology Monographs). (Illus.). xiv, 240p. 219.00 (978-3-642-13614-6(1), 3642136141) Springer.

Hallenbeck, Patrick C. Recent Advances in Phototrophic Prokaryotes. 2010. (Illus.). xv, 359p. E-Book (978-1-4419-1528-3(1)) Springer.

Hallenbeck, Patrick C., ed. Recent Advances in Phototrophic Prokaryotes. 2010. (Advances in Experimental Medicine & Biology Ser.). (ENG., Illus.). xv, 359p. 209.00 (978-1-4419-1527-6(3), 1441915273) Springer.

Herwald, Heiko & Russell, Wayne. Concepts in Bacterial Virulence, Vol. 12. (Contributions to Microbiology Ser.: Vol. 12). (Illus.). (978-3-8055-7786-1(9)) Karger, S. AG.

Hunter, C. Neil. The Purple Phototrophic Bacteria. 2008. (Advances in Photosynthesis & Respiration Ser.). (Illus.). 1000p. 629.00 (978-1-4020-8814-8(0)) Springer.

Kato, Sakura Y. Archaea: Structure, Habitats & Ecological Significance. 2011. (Microbiology Research Advances Ser.). 98.00 (978-1-61761-932-8(9), Nova Biomedical Bks.) Nova Science Pubs., Inc.

Keshk, Sherif. Scope on Bacterial Cellulose Production. 2011. 72p. pap. **(978-3-8443-0211-0(5))** Lambert Academic Publishing.

Khan, Abdul Arif, ed. Bacteria & Cancer. 2012. (ENG., Illus.). vi, 278p. 189.00 **(978-94-007-2584-3(1)**, 9400725841) Springer.

Kim, Byung Hong & Gadd, Geoffrey Michael. Bacterial Physiology & Metabolism. 2008. (ENG., Illus.). 552p. (C). per. 83.00 (978-0-521-71230-9(0)) Cambridge Univ. Pr.

Kim, Minjun. Bacterial Microfluidics. 2008. 116p. per. (978-3-8364-3592-5(6)) VDM Verlag Dr. Mueller e.K.

Koch, A. L. Bacterial Growth & Form. 2nd ed. 2011. (ENG., Illus.). 480p. pap. 309.00 (978-90-481-5844-7(3), 9048158443) Springer.

Koch, Arthur L. The Bacteria: Their Origin, Structure, Function & Antibiosis. 2007. (Illus.). 224p. pap. 69.95 (978-1-4020-6625-2(2)) Springer.

Kotb, Essam. Toxigenic Bacterial Proteases & Their Inhibitors. 2011. 176p. pap. **(978-3-8433-9176-4(9))** Lambert Academic Publishing.

Krämer, Reinhard & Jung, Kirsten, eds. Bacterial Signaling. 2010. (ENG., Illus.). 513p. 169.95 (978-3-527-32365-4(1), Wiley-VCH) Wiley, John & Sons, Inc.

Linke, Dirk & Goldman, Adrian, eds. Bacterial Adhesion: Chemistry, Biology & Physics. 2011. (Advances in Experimental Medicine & Biology Ser.). (Illus.). xiv, 374p. 189.00 (978-94-007-0939-3(0), 9400709390) Springer.

Lyte, Mark & Freestone, Primrose P. E., eds. Microbial Endocrinology: Interkingdom Signaling in Infectious Disease & Health. 2010. (ENG., Illus.). xvi, 316p. 209.00 (978-1-4419-5575-3(5), 1441955755) Springer.

Maczulak, Anne. Allies & Enemies: How the World Depends on Bacteria. 2010. (FT Press Science Ser.). (ENG., Illus.). 224p. 24.99 (978-0-13-701546-7(1)) FT Press.

Mahrous, Hoda, et al. Functionalities of Lactic Acid Bacteri. 2010. 192p. pap. (978-3-639-23871-6(0)) VDM Verlag Dr. Mueller e.K.

Materials Research Society ( ) Staff, compiled by. Biofilm-Material Interactions: New Tools, Technologies, & Opportunities. 2007. (Materials Research Society Symposium Proceedings Ser.). 31p. pap. 40.00 (978-1-60423-410-7(5)) Curran Assocs., Inc.

Mendez-Vilas, A., ed. Science & Technology Against Microbial Pathogens: Research, Development & Evaluation: Proceedings of the International Conference on Antimicrobial Research (ICAR2010), Valladolid, Spain, 3-5 November 2010. 2011. (ENG., Illus.). 432p. 130.00 **(978-981-4354-85-1(6))** World Scientific Publishing Co., Inc.

Monif, Gilles R. A Physician's Guide for the Collection of Bacteriological & Viral Specimens. 55p. 7.95 (978-1-880906-73-6(2)) IDI Publishing.

Mukhopadhyay, Mahuya & K.Paul, Amal. Potentials of Purple Non Sulfur Phototrophic Bacteri. 2011. 148p. pap. **(978-3-8443-1242-3(0))** Lambert Academic Publishing.

Musat, Niculina. Symbioses Between Worms & Bacteria in Shallow Marine Sediments. 2008. 140p. pap. (978-3-639-03400-4(7)) VDM Verlag Dr. Mueller e.K.

Nickerson, Cheryl A. & Schurr, Michael, eds. Molecular Paradigms of Infectious Disease: A Bacterial Perspective. 2010. (Emerging Infectious Diseases of the 21st Century Ser.). (Illus.). xii, 645p. pap. 279.00 (978-1-4419-4042-1(1), 1441940421) Springer.

Nies, Dietrich H. & Silver, S. Molecular Microbiology of Heavy Metals. 2007. (Microbiology Monographs). (Illus.). viii, 460p. 259.00 (978-3-540-69770-1(5), 3540697705) Springer.

Nies, Dietrich H. & Silver, Simon. Molecular Microbiology of Heavy Metals. 2010. (Microbiology Monographs). (Illus.). viii, 460p. pap. 259.00 (978-3-642-08916-9(X), 364208916X) Springer.

Pescatore, Fred & Gazella, Karolyn A. Boost Your Health with Bacteria. 2009. 250p. pap. 15.95 (978-1-935297-21-5(X)) Better Nutrition Magazine.

Pinero, Daniel. De las Bacterias al Hombre: La Evolucion. (Ciencia para Todos Ser.). (SPA.). pap. 6.99 (978-968-16-2540-5(4)) Fondo de Cultura Economica USA.

Radolf, Justin & Samuels, D. Scott, eds. Borrelia: Molecular Biology, Host Interaction & Pathogenesis. 2010. (Illus.). 574p. 319.00 (978-1-904455-58-5(1)) Caister Academic Pr. GBR. Dist: International Specialized Bk. Services.

Reid, Christopher W., et al, eds. Bacterial Glycomics: Current Research, Technology & Applications. 2012. (Illus.). 280p. 319.00 **(978-1-904455-95-0(6))** Caister Academic Pr. GBR. Dist: International Specialized Bk. Services.

Rescigno, Maria, ed. Dendritic Cell Interactions with Bacteria. 2007. (Advances in Molecular & Cellular Microbiology Ser.: Vol. 14). (ENG., Illus.). 266p. 162.99 (978-0-521-85586-0(1)) Cambridge Univ. Pr.

Robinson, Mark W. & Dalton, John P., eds. Cysteine Proteases of Pathogenic Organisms. 2011. (Advances in Experimental Medicine & Biology Ser.). (ENG., Illus.). xx, 222p. 189.00 (978-1-4419-8413-5(5), 1441984135) Springer.

Rogers, Kara. Bacteria & Viruses. 2011. (Biochemistry, Cells, & Life Ser.). (ENG.). 240p. (YA). lib. bdg. 40.00 (978-1-61530-306-9(5)) Rosen Publishing Group, Inc., The.

Rogers, Kara, ed. Bacteria & Viruses. 2011. (Biochemistry, Cells, & Life Ser.). (Illus.). 240p. (YA). 80.00 (978-1-61530-420-2(7)) Rosen Publishing Group, Inc., The.

Romeo, Tony. Bacterial Biofilms. (Current Topics in Microbiology & Immunology Ser.). (Illus.). xii, 296p. 2010. pap. 219.00 (978-3-642-09469-9(4), 3642094694) 2008. (ENG., 219.00 (978-3-540-75417-6(2), 3540754172) Springer.

Rosenzweig, Amy & Ragsdale, Stephen W., eds. Methods in Methane Metabolism Pt. A: Methanogenesis, 2 vols. 2011. (ENG., Illus.). 424p. 187.00 (978-0-12-385112-3(2), Academic Pr.) Elsevier Science & Technology Bks.

Rumbaugh, Kendra P., ed. Quorum Sensing: Methods & Protocols. 2010. (Methods in Molecular Biology Ser.). (Illus.). xvi, 310p. 139.00 (978-1-60761-970-3(9), 1607619709) Humana Pr.

Rushford, Jaime Salas & Benno DVM, Yoshimi. Morinaga BB536: Japan's Leading Clinically Proven Probiotic. 2011. (Woodland Health Ser.). 52p. pap. 4.95 **(978-1-58054-206-7(9))** Woodland Publishing, Inc.

Sachs, Jessica Snyder. Good Germs, Bad Germs: Health & Survival in a Bacterial World. 2008. (ENG., Illus.). 304p. pap. 15.00 (978-0-8090-1642-6(7), Hill & Wang) Farrar, Straus & Giroux.

Saier, M. H., ed. The P-Type ATPase Superfamily. 2010. (Illus.). 104p. pap. (978-3-8055-9597-1(2)) Karger, S. AG.

Saldmann, Frédérick. Wash Your Hands! The Dirty Truth about Germs, Viruses & Epidemics... And the Simple Ways to Protect Yourself in a Dangerous World. 2008. (ENG.). 208p. pap. 12.95 (978-1-60286-049-0(1)) Perseus Bks. Group.

Salminen, Seppo, et al, eds. Lactic Acid Bacteria. 4th rev. ed. 2011. (ENG., Illus.). 798p. 189.95 **(978-1-4398-3577-4(9)**, CRC Press) Taylor & Francis Group GBR. Dist: Taylor & Francis Group.

Scarpignato, C. & Lanas, A. Bacterial Flora in Digestive Disease: Focus on Rifaximin, Vol. 73. (Illus.). 156p. (978-3-8055-8083-0(5)) Karger, S. AG.

Scarpignato, Carmelo & Lanas, Angel, eds. Bacterial Flora in Digestive Disease: Focus on Rifaximin, Vol. 73. (Digestion Ser.). (Illus.). 152p. pap. (978-3-8055-8078-6(9)) Karger, S. AG.

Schüler, Dirk. Magnetoreception & Magnetosomes in Bacteria. 2010. (Microbiology Monographs). (Illus.). viii, 319p. pap. 239.00 (978-3-642-07224-6(0), 3642072240) Springer.

Schüler, Dirk, ed. Magnetoreception & Magnetosomes in Bacteria. 2007. (Microbiology Monographs). (Illus.). 319p. 239.00 (978-3-540-37467-1(1)) Springer.

Shapiro, Lucy & Losick, Richard M., eds. Cell Biology of Bacteria. 2010. (Illus.). 285p. 135.00 (978-0-87969-907-9(8)) Cold Spring Harbor Laboratory Pr.

Sleator, Roy & Hill, Colin. Patho-Biotechnology. Sleator, Roy & Hill, Colin, eds. 2008. (978-1-58706-304-6(2)) Landes Bioscience.

Spencer, John F. T. & Alicia L. Ragout de Spencer, eds. Environmental Microbiology: Methods & Protocols. 2010. (Methods in Biotechnology Ser.). (Illus.). 448p. pap. 199.00 (978-1-61737-370-1(2), 1617373702) Humana Pr.

Spicer, W. John. Clinical Microbiology & Infectious Diseases: An Illustrated Colour Text. 2nd rev. ed. 2007. (Illustrated Colour Text Ser.). (ENG., Illus.). 264p. (C). pap. 64.95 (978-0-443-10303-2(8), Churchill Livingstone) Elsevier - Health Sciences Div.

Spiro, Stephen & Dixon, Ray, eds. Sensory Mechanisms in Bacteria: Molecular Aspects of Signal Recognition. 2010. (Illus.). 287p. 319.00 (978-1-904455-69-1(7)) Caister Academic Pr. GBR. Dist: International Specialized Bk. Services.

Srivastava, S. Understanding Bacteria. 2010. 492p. pap. 389.00 (978-90-481-6429-5(X), 904816429X) Springer.

Steinka, Izabela. Lactic Acid Cheese Safety. 2008. (Illus.). vi, 114p. pap. 39.00 (978-1-60456-244-6(7)) Nova Science Pubs., Inc.

Taylor, Frank S. Conquest of a Bacteria. (978-0-8022-1697-7(8)) Philosophical Library, Inc.

Tenney, Deanne. Tea Tree Oil. 2nd ed. 2011. (Woodland Health Ser.). 32p. pap. 4.95 **(978-1-58054-208-1(5))** Woodland Publishing, Inc.

Topley, W. W. C. Microbiology & Microbial Infections, 8 vols., Set. 10th ed. 2006. (ENG.). 3500p. 2600.00 (978-0-470-68638-6(3), Wiley) Wiley, John & Sons, Inc.

Vladimirov, Nikita, et al. Multiscale Modeling of Bacterial Chemotaxis. 2010. 132p. pap. (978-3-8383-4246-7(1)) Lambert Academic Publishing.

Volova, Tatiana G. Hydrogen-Based Biosynthesis. 2009. 145.00 (978-1-60876-053-4(7)) Nova Science Pubs., Inc.

Wassenaar, Trudy M. Bacteria: The Benign, the Bad, & the Beautiful. 2011. (ENG., Illus.). 232p. pap. 39.95 **(978-1-118-10766-9(7)**, Wiley-Blackwell) Wiley, John & Sons, Inc.

Wen, Yu-Mei. Recent Works on Microbes & Infections in China: Selected from the Journal of Microbes & Infections (China) 2009. 336p. 144.00 (978-981-283-566-6(0)) World Scientific Publishing Co., Inc.

Wilson, Michael. Bacteriology of Humans: An Ecological Perspective. 2008. (ENG., Illus.). 360p. 119.95 (978-1-4051-6165-7(5), Wiley-Blackwell) Wiley, John & Sons, Inc.

Wilson, Samual J. Microbes & Health. 2009. 240p. pap. 25.75 (978-1-110-51264-5(3)) BiblioBazaar.

Winans, Stephen C. & Bassler, Bonnie L., eds. Chemical Communication among Bacteria. 2008. (Illus.). 483p. 170.00 (978-1-55581-404-5(2)) ASM Pr.

Yamanaka, Tateo. Chemolithoautotrophic Bacteria: Biochemistry & Environmental Biology. 2010. (ENG., Illus.). xiv, 157p. pap. 189.00 (978-4-431-99850-1(0), 4431998500) Springer.

Yokota, Akira, et al. Alicyclobacillus: Thermophilic Acidophilic Bacilli. 2007. (Illus.). 180p. 189.00 (978-4-431-69849-4(3), 4431698493) Springer.

Zourob, Mohammed, et al. Principles of Bacterial Detection: Biosensors, Recognition Receptors & Microsystems. 2008. (ENG., Illus.). xxxii, 970p. 137.00 (978-0-387-75112-2(2), 0387751122) Springer.

BACTERIA—CULTURES AND CULTURE MEDIA

see Microbiology—Cultures and Culture Media

BACTERIA—GENETICS

see Bacterial Genetics

BACTERIA, AEROBIC

Hardarson, Gudni G. & Broughton, William J., eds. Molecular Microbial Ecology of the Soil: Results from an FAO/IAEA Co-ordinated Research Programme, 1992-1996. 2010. (Developments in Plant & Soil Sciences Ser.). (Illus.). 184p. pap. 179.00 (978-90-481-5099-1(X), 904815099X) Springer.

Ibrahim, Ahmed. Salicylic Acid Biosynthetic Genes Expressed in Rhizobium. 2010. 164p. pap. (978-3-639-26969-7(1)) VDM Verlag Dr. Mueller e.K.

Jones, Huw D. & Shewry, P. R. Transgenic Wheat, Barley & Oats: Production & Characterization Protocols. 2008. (Methods in Molecular Biology Ser.). (Illus.). x, 349p. 129.00 (978-1-58829-961-1(9)) Humana Pr.

Tzfira, Tzvi & Citovsky, Vitaly, eds. Agrobacterium: From Biology to Biotechnology. 2008. (ENG., Illus.). xxxiv, 750p. 169.00 (978-0-387-72289-4(0), 0387722890) Springer.

—Agrobacterium: from Biology to Biotechnology: From Biology to Biotechnology. 2010. (ENG., Illus.). xxxiv, 750p. pap. 169.00 (978-1-4419-2473-5(6), 1441924736) Springer.

Wang, Kan, ed. Agrobacterium Protocols: Volume I. 2nd ed. 2010. (Methods in Molecular Biology Ser.). (Illus.). 512p. pap. 209.00 (978-1-61737-628-3(0), 1617376280) Humana Pr.

—Agrobacterium Protocols: Volume II. 2nd ed. 2010. (Methods in Molecular Biology Ser.). (Illus.). 512p. pap. 209.00 (978-1-61737-803-4(8), 1617378038) Humana Pr.

BACTERIA, ANAEROBIC

see Anaerobic Bacteria

BACTERIA, BLUE-GREEN

see Cyanobacteria

BACTERIA, NITRIFYING

Wong, Tommy S. W. Overland Flow & Surface Runoff. 2011. (Hydrological Science & Engineering Ser.). 358p. 129.00 (978-1-61122-868-7(9)) Nova Science Pubs., Inc.

BACTERIA, PATHOGENIC

see Pathogenic Bacteria

BACTERIA, PHYTOPATHOGENIC

see Phytopathogenic Bacteria

BACTERIA, SPOREFORMING

see also Spores (Bacteria)

Logan, Niall A. & Vos, Paul De, eds. Endospore-forming Soil Bacteria. 2011. (Soil Biology Ser.). (ENG., Illus.). xv, 347p. 209.00 (978-3-642-19576-1(8), 3642195768) Springer.

B

BACTERIAL CELL WALLS

Camesano, Terri A. & Mello, Charlene M. Microbial Surfaces: Structure, Interactions, & Reactivity. 2008. (ACS Symposium Ser.). (ENG., Illus.). 130.00 *(978-0-8412-7430-3(4))* American Chemical Society.

Daffé, Mamadou & Reyrat, Jean-Marc. The Mycobacterial Cell Envelope. 2008. (Illus.). 400p. (C). 200.00 *(978-1-55581-468-7(9))* ASM Pr.

Ivanova, Elena P. Surface Structure & Properties of Microbial Cells on a Nanometer Scale. 2006. (Illus.). 267p. 129.00 *(978-1-60021-242-0(5))* Nova Science Pubs., Inc.

Koch, Arthur L. The Bacteria: Their Origin, Structure, Function & Antibiosis. 2007. (Illus.). 224p. pap. 69.95 *(978-1-4020-6625-2(2))* Springer.

König, Helmut, et al. Prokaryotic Cell Wall Compounds: Structure & Biochemistry. 2010. (ENG., Illus.). xvii, 517p. 209.00 *(978-3-642-05061-9(1)*, 3642050611) Springer.

Mattman Lida H Staff. Cell Wall Deficient Forms Stealth Pathogens Fourth Edition. 2009. 149.95 *(978-0-8493-3578-5(7))* CRC Pr. LLC.

Seltmann, Guntram & Holst, Otto. The Bacterial Cell Wall. 2010. (ENG., Illus.). ix, 280p. pap. 209.00 *(978-3-642-07648-0(3)*, 3642076483) Springer.

BACTERIAL CULTURES

see Microbiology—Cultures and Culture Media

BACTERIAL DISEASES

see also Anthrax; Gram-Negative Bacterial Infections; Listeriosis; Necrotizing Fasciitis; Pathogenic Bacteria; Rickettsial Diseases

Abedon, Stephen T. Bacteriophages & Biofilms: Ecology, Phage Therapy, Plaques. 2011. (Bacteriology Research Developments Ser.). (Illus.). ii, 138p. pap. 69.00 *(978-1-61761-588-7(9)*, Nova Biomedical Bks.) Nova Science Pubs., Inc.

Ahmad, Iqbal & Aqil, Farrukh, eds. New Strategies Combating Bacterial Infection. 2008. (ENG., Illus.). 322p. 209.95 *(978-3-527-32206-0(X)*, Wiley-VCH) Wiley, John & Sons, Inc.

Austin, B. & Austin, D. A. Bacterial Fish Pathogens: Disease of Farmed & Wild Fish. 4th ed. (Springer Praxis Books / Environmental Sciences Ser.). xxviii, 552p. 2010. pap. 309.00 *(978-90-481-7526-0(7)*, 9048175267) 2007. (Illus.). 309.00 *(978-1-4020-6068-7(8))* Springer.

Balaban, Naomi, ed. Control of Biofilm Infections by Signal Manipulation. (Springer Series on Biofilms Ser.). (Illus.). 2010. xvi, 175p. pap. 159.00 *(978-3-642-09309-8(4)*, 3642093094) 2008. 175p. 159.00 *(978-3-540-73852-7(5))* Springer.

Bauman & Bauman, Robert W. Microbiology with Diseases by Body System with MasteringMicrobiology#8482; with Current Issues in Microbiology Vols 1 And 2. 3rd ed. 2011. (ENG.). (C). pap., pap. 192.47 ***(978-0-321-77839-0(1))*** Benjamin-Cummings Publishing Co.

Bauman, Robert W. Diseases by Body System. 3rd ed. 2011. (ENG.). (C). 57.20 *(978-0-321-71637-8(X))* Benjamin-Cummings Publishing Co.

—Microbiology: With Diseases by Body System. 3rd rev. ed. 2011. (ENG.). 928p. (C). 192.47 *(978-0-321-71271-4(4))* Benjamin-Cummings Publishing Co.

—Microbiology with Diseases by Body System. 3rd ed. 2011. (MasteringMicrobiology Ser.). (ENG.). 928p. (C). 192.47 *(978-0-321-69429-4(5))*; ring bd. 125.53 *(978-0-321-72236-2(1))* Benjamin-Cummings Publishing Co.

—Microbiology with Diseases by Body System, Books a la Carte Edition. 3rd ed. 2011. (ENG.). 928p. (C). ring bd. 115.53 *(978-0-321-71005-5(3))* Benjamin-Cummings Publishing Co.

—Microbiology with Diseases by Taxonomy. 3rd ed. 2010. (ENG.). 896p. (C). ring bd. 113.73 *(978-0-321-67740-2(4))* Benjamin-Cummings Publishing Co.

Bauman, Robert W., et al. Study Guide for Microbiology with Diseases by Body System. 3rd ed. 2011. (ENG.). 312p. (C). pap. 59.33 *(978-0-321-71629-3(9))* Benjamin-Cummings Publishing Co.

Bjarnsholt, Thomas, ed. Biofilm Infections. 2010. (ENG., Illus.). 350p. 209.00 *(978-1-4419-6083-2(X)*, 144196083X) Springer.

Brook, Itzhak. Anaerobic Infections: Diagnosis & Management. 2007. (Infectious Disease & Therapy Ser.: Vol. 46). (ENG., Illus.). 440p. 150.00 *(978-0-8493-8257-4(2)*, Informa Healthcare) Taylor & Francis Group GBR. Dist: Taylor & Francis Group.

Chanishvili, Nina. A Literature Review of the Practical Application of Bacteriophage Research. 2012. (Bacteriology Research Developments Virology Research Progress Ser.). 312p. 165.00 ***(978-1-62100-851-4(7))*** Nova Science Pubs., Inc.

Ciancio, A. & Mukerji, K. G. Integrated Management of Diseases Caused by Fungi, Phytoplasma & Bacteria. Mukerji, K. G. & Ciancio, Aurelio, eds. 2008. (Integrated Management of Plant Pests & Diseases Ser.). (ENG., Illus.). xxvi, 422p. 229.00 *(978-1-4020-8570-3(2)*, 1402085702) Springer.

Ck, Venil. Antimicrobial Properties of Acorus Calamus. 2011. 60p. pap. ***(978-3-8443-8063-7(9))*** Lambert Academic Publishing.

Cram101 Textbook Reviews. Outlines & Highlights for Alcamos Fundamentals of Microbiology: Body Systems by Jeffrey, C. Pommerville, ISBN. 2010. 282p. pap. 32.95 *(978-1-61698-636-0(0))* Cram101 Inc.

Cram101 Textbook Reviews. Outlines & Highlights for Antibacterial Therapy & Newer Agents, an Issue of Infectious Disease Clinics by Keith S Kaye, Isbn: 9781437712322. 2011. 174p. pap. 29.95 ***(978-1-61461-911-6(5))*** Cram101 Inc.

Cram101 Textbook Reviews Staff. Outlines & Highlights for Microbiology with Diseases by Body System by Robert W Bauman, Isbn: 9780321513410. 2009. 190p. pap. 30.95 *(978-1-4288-8226-3(X))* Cram101 Inc.

Crawford, Dorothy H. Deadly Companions: How Microbes Shaped Our History. 2009. (ENG., Illus.). 272p. pap. 19.95 *(978-0-19-956144-5(3))* Oxford Univ. Pr., Inc.

Cunha, Burke A. Antibiotic Essentials. 10th ed. 2011. 778p. pap. 24.95 *(978-1-4496-2431-6(6))* Jones & Bartlett Learning, LLC.

—Antibiotic Essentials 2009. 7th rev. ed. 2008. pap. 21.95 *(978-0-7637-6118-9(4))* 8th ed. 2009. 368p. pap. 28.95 *(978-0-7637-7219-2(4))* Jones & Bartlett Learning, LLC.

—Antibiotics Essentials 2010. 9th rev. ed. 2010. 732p. pap. 28.95 *(978-0-7637-9214-5(4))* Jones & Bartlett Learning, LLC.

Dawson, Paul, et al. Bacterial Transfer During Eating. 2010. 64p. pap. *(978-3-639-21838-1(8))* VDM Verlag Dr. Mueller e.K.

DeLeo, Frank & Otto, Michael, eds. Bacterial Pathogenesis: Methods & Protocols. 2010. (Methods in Molecular Biology Ser.). (Illus.). xvi, 320p. pap. 129.00 *(978-1-61737-751-8(1)*, 1617377511) Humana Pr.

DeLeo, Frank R. & Otto, Michael, eds. Bacterial Pathogenesis: Methods & Protocols. 2008. (Methods in Molecular Biology Ser.). (Illus.). 311p. 129.00 *(978-1-58829-740-2(3))* Humana Pr.

Emergence of the Superbug: Antimicrobial Resistance in the United States: Hearing of the Committee on Health, Education, Labor, & Pensions, United States Senate, One Hundred Tenth Congress, Second Session, on Examining the Public Health Impacts of Antimicrobial Resistant Bacterial Infections in the United States, Focusing on Current Antimicrobials & Continued Development of New Solutions for the Future Protection Agains. 2010. iv, 113p. *(978-0-16-085123-0(8)*, 552-070-40479-1) United States Government Printing Office.

Fatmi, M'Barek. Pseudomonas Syringae Pathovars & Related Pathogens: Identification, Epidemiology & Genomics. Collmer, Alan et al, eds. 2008. (ENG., Illus.). xi, 433p. 369.00 *(978-1-4020-6900-0(6)*, 1402069006) Springer.

Fazio, Joseph. Aberrant Cell Biology in Cystic Fibrosis Cells. 2009. 132p. pap. *(978-3-639-16646-0(9))* VDM Verlag Dr. Mueller e.K.

File, Thomas & Stevens, Dennis L. Contemporary Diagnosis & Management of Skin & Soft-Tissue Infections. 3rd ed. 2009. (Illus.). 176p. *(978-1-935103-11-0(3))* Assocs. in Medical Marketing Co., Inc.

Finn, Adam & Pollard, Andrew J., eds. Hot Topics in Infection & Immunity in Children IV. 2007. (Advances in Experimental Medicine & Biology Ser.). (Illus.). 238p. 159.00 *(978-0-387-73959-5(9))* Springer.

Forum on Microbial Threats & Institute of Medicine. Antibiotic Resistance: Implications for Global Health & Novel Intervention Strategies: Workshop Summary. 2010. (ENG.). 496p. pap. 95.00 *(978-0-309-15611-0(4))* National Academies Pr.

Gillespie, Stephen H., ed. Management of Multiple Drug-Resistant Infections. 2010. (Infectious Disease Ser.). (Illus.). 428p. pap. 149.00 *(978-1-61737-438-8(5)*, 1617374385) Humana Pr.

Giordano, Lorenzo S. & Moretti, Marco A. Salmonella Infections: New Research. 2008. (Illus.). x, 160p. 98.00 *(978-1-60456-735-9(X))* Nova Science Pubs., Inc.

Griffiths, Jeffrey, et al, eds. Public Health & Infectious Diseases. 2010. (ENG.). 512p. 103.00 *(978-0-12-381506-4(1))* Elsevier Science & Technology Bks.

Hager, Thomas. The Demon under the Microscope: From Battlefield Hospitals to Nazi Labs, One Doctor's Heroic Search for the World's First Miracle Drug. 2007. (ENG.). 352p. pap. 15.00 *(978-1-4000-8214-8(5)*, Three Rivers Pr.) Crown Publishing Group.

Hauser, Alan R. Antibiotic Basics for Clinicians: Choosing the Right Antibacterial Agent. 2nd rev. ed. 2012. 336p. pap. 47.95 ***(978-1-4511-1221-4(1))*** Lippincott Williams & Wilkins.

Hensel, Michael & Schmidt, Herbert, eds. Horizontal Gene Transfer in the Evolution of Pathogenesis. 2008. (Advances in Molecular & Cellular Microbiology Ser.). (ENG., Illus.). 342p. 140.00 *(978-0-521-86297-4(3))* Cambridge Univ. Pr.

Huttunen, Reetta. Factors Associated with Susceptibility to & Outcome of Bacteraemia with Reference to Staphylococcus aureus, Streptococcus pneumoniae, B- haemolytic streptococcus & Escherichia coli Bacteraemias. 2010. (Acta Universitatis Tamperensis Ser.). 139p. pap. 79.50 *(978-951-44-8032-4(5))* Tampere Univ. Pr. FIN. Dist: Coronet Bks.

Jones Chris Staff. Carbohydrate Vaccines Against Bacterial Diseases. 2008. 1050p. 169.95 *(978-1-57444-452-0(2))* CRC Pr. LLC.

Joseph, Warren S. Handbook of Lower Extremity Infections. 3rd ed. 2009. *(978-1-57400-131-0(0))* Data Trace Publishing, Co.

Kaye, Donald & Kaye, Keith S. Antibacterial Therapy & Newer Agents, an Issue of Infectious Disease Clinics. 2009. (Clinics: Internal Medicine Ser.: 23-4). (ENG., Illus.). xiv, 758p. 99.00 *(978-1-4377-1232-2(0)*, Saunders) Elsevier - Health Sciences Div.

Knoll, Torsten. MRSA Killer Bacteria from the Operating Room. 2008. 52p. pap. 11.50 *(978-1-4092-2246-0(2))* Lulu Enterprises Inc.

Kumar, Anand. Optimizing Antimicrobial Therapy of Life-threatening Infection, Sepsis & Septic Shock, an Issue of Critical Care Clinics. 2010. (Clinics: Internal Medicine Ser.: 27-1). (ENG., Illus.). 232p. 110.00 *(978-1-4557-0431-6(8)*, Saunders) Elsevier - Health Sciences Div.

Lesch, John E., ed. The First Miracle Drugs: How the Sulfa Drugs Transformed Medicine. 2006. (ENG., Illus.). 376p. 29.95 *(978-0-19-518775-5(X))* Oxford Univ. Pr., Inc.

Liu, Dongyou, ed. Molecular Detection of Human Bacterial Pathogens. 2011. (ENG., Illus.). 1278p. 199.95 *(978-1-4398-1238-9(1)*, CRC Press) Taylor & Francis Group GBR. Dist: Taylor & Francis Group.

Lutsenko, Andriy & Palahniuk, Vasyl, eds. Water Microbiology: Types, Analyses & Disease-causing Microorganisms. 2009. (Microbiology Research Advances Ser.). (Illus.). xiii, 364p. 145.00 *(978-1-60741-273-1(X))* Nova Science Pubs., Inc.

Lydyard. Case Studies in Infectious Diseases. 2009. (Illus.). 350p. pap. 59.00 *(978-0-8153-4142-0(3)*, Garland Science) Taylor & Francis Group.

Lyte, Mark & Freestone, Primrose P. E., eds. Microbial Endocrinology: Interkingdom Signaling in Infectios Disease & Health. 2010. (ENG., Illus.). xvi, 316p. 209.00 *(978-1-4419-5575-3(5)*, 1441955755) Springer.

Magdalenic, Vjera. Chlamydia Pneumoniae Immunology. 2009. 224p. pap. *(978-3-639-14327-0(2))* VDM Verlag Dr. Mueller e.K.

McKenzie, Hamish, et al. Infectious Disease: Clinical Cases Uncovered. 2009. (Clinical Cases Ser.: 32). (ENG., Illus.). 168p. pap. 41.95 *(978-1-4051-6891-5(9)*, Wiley-Blackwell) Wiley, John & Sons, Inc.

Moriarty, T. Fintan, et al, eds. Biomaterials Associated Infection: Immunological Aspects & Antimicrobial Strategies. 2012. (ENG., Illus.). 320p. 159.00 ***(978-1-4614-1030-0(4)***, 1461410304) Springer.

Mrsa: Strategies to Turn the Tide in Hospitals & the Community. 2007. per. *(978-1-933040-75-2(0))* AHC Media, LLC.

Oelschlaeger, Tobias A. & Hacker, Jörg H., eds. Bacterial Invasion into Eukaryotic Cells. 2010. (Subcellular Biochemistry Ser.). 682p. pap. 359.00 *(978-1-4419-3330-0(1)*, 1441933301) Springer.

Ouaissi, Ali, ed. Immunology & Molecular Biology of Protozoan Infections. 2007. 76p. per. 13.00 *(978-977-454-011-0(5))* Hindawi Publishing Corp.

Philpott, Dana & Ebel, Frank, eds. E. Coli: Shiga Toxin Methods & Protocols. 2010. (Methods in Molecular Medicine Ser.). (Illus.). 368p. pap. 149.00 *(978-1-61737-264-3(1)*, 1617372641) Humana Pr.

Pokharel, Swechha. Biological Hazards Associated with Street Foods of Nepal. 2011. 116p. pap. ***(978-3-8443-0969-0(1))*** Lambert Academic Publishing.

Pollard, Andrew J. & Finn, Adam, eds. Hot Topics in Infection & Immunity in Children II. 2010. (Advances in Experimental Medicine & Biology Ser.). (Illus.). xxx, 234p. pap. 179.00 *(978-1-4419-3786-5(2)*, 1441937862) Springer.

Pommerville, Jeffrey. Alcamo's Fundamentals of Microbiology: Body Systems. 2009. 1032p. 188.95 *(978-0-7637-6259-9(8))* Jones & Bartlett Learning, LLC.

Pommerville, Jeffrey C. & Alcamo, I. Edward. Alcamo's Fundamentals of Microbiology. 2nd ed. 2012. ***(978-1-4496-0594-0(X))*** Jones & Bartlett Publishers.

Randbone, Jonathan M., ed. Encyclopedia of Infection Research, 3 vols. 2012. (Series: Bacteriology Research Developments Ser.). 1131p. 395.00 *(978-1-61324-311-4(1))* Nova Science Pubs., Inc.

Rescigno, Maria, ed. Dendritic Cell Interactions with Bacteria. 2007. (Advances in Molecular & Cellular Microbiology Ser.: Vol. 14). (ENG., Illus.). 266p. 162.99 *(978-0-521-85586-0(1))* Cambridge Univ. Pr.

Reynolds, L. A. Superbugs & Superdrugs. 2008. (Illus.). 172p. pap. *(978-0-85484-114-1(8))* Wellcome Institute for the History of Medicine.

Robinson, D. Ashley, et al, eds. Bacterial Population Genetics in Infectious Disease. 2010. (ENG., Illus.). 428p. 145.95 *(978-0-470-42474-2(5)*, Wiley-Blackwell) Wiley, John & Sons, Inc.

Ronco, C., et al, eds. Endotoxemia & Endotoxin Shock: Disease, Diagnosis & Therapy. 2010. (Contributions to Nephrology Ser.). (SPA & ENG., Illus.). 130p. *(978-3-8055-9484-4(4))* Karger, S. AG.

Rotbart, Harley A. Germ Proof Your Kids: The Complete Guide to Protecting (Without Overprotecting) Your Family from Infections. 2008. (Illus.). 380p. per. 37.50 *(978-1-55581-427-4(1))* ASM Pr.

Salyers, Abigail A., et al. Bacterial Pathogenesis: A Molecular Approach. 3rd ed. 2011. (ENG., Illus.). 540p. pap. ***(978-1-55581-418-2(2))*** ASM Pr.

Schlossberg, David & Samuel, Rafik. Antibiotics Manual. 2011. 500p. pap. *(978-1-60795-084-4(7))* PMPH-USA. Ltd.

Scientific American Editors. Infectious Disease. 2008. (Scientific American Readers Ser.). (ENG., Illus.). 368p. 65.00 *(978-0-226-74263-2(6))* Univ. of Chicago Pr.

Scientific American Staff. Infectious Disease. 2008. (Scientific American Readers Ser.). (ENG., Illus.). 368p. pap. 22.50 *(978-0-226-74264-9(4))* Univ. of Chicago Pr.

Sheen, Barbara. MRSA. 2009. (Diseases & Disorders Ser.). (Illus.). 128p. (YA). (gr. 7-12). 32.45 *(978-1-4205-0144-5(5))* Cengage Gale.

Shirtliff, Mark & Leid, Jeff. The Role of Biofilms in Device-Related Infections. 2009. (Springer Series on Biofilms Ser.). (ENG., Illus.). xii, 272p. 189.00 *(978-3-540-68113-7(2))* Springer.

Slonczewski, Joan L. & Foster, John W. Microbiology: An Evolving Science. 2nd ed. 2010. (ENG., Illus.). 1097p. (C). 142.00 net. *(978-0-393-93447-2(0)*, 93447) Norton, W. W. & Co., Inc.

Southwick, Frederick S. Infectious Diseases: A Clinical Short Course. 2nd ed. 2007. (LANGE Clinical Medicine Ser.). (ENG., Illus.). 464p. (C). per. 62.00 *(978-0-07-147722-2(5)*, 0071477225) McGraw-Hill Professional Publishing.

Spicer, W. John. Clinical Microbiology & Infectious Diseases: An Illustrated Colour Text. 2nd rev. ed. 2007. (Illustrated Colour Text Ser.). (ENG., Illus.). 264p. (C). pap. 64.95 *(978-0-443-10303-2(8)*, Churchill Livingstone) Elsevier - Health Sciences Div.

Weigelt, John A., ed. MRSA, Second Edition. 2nd ed. 2009. (Illus.). 250p. 150.00 *(978-1-4398-1879-4(7)*, Informa Healthcare) Taylor & Francis Group.

Wilson, Samual J. Microbes & Health. 2009. 240p. pap. 25.75 *(978-1-110-51264-5(3))* BiblioBazaar.

Woodford, Neil & Johnson, Alan, eds. Molecular Bacteriology: Protocols & Clinical Applications. 2010. (Methods in Molecular Medicine Ser.). 692p. pap. 179.00 *(978-1-61737-053-3(3)*, 1617370533) Humana Pr.

BACTERIAL DISEASES IN ANIMALS

see Veterinary Bacteriology

BACTERIAL GENETICS

Abdelhaleem, Mohamed M., ed. Helicases: Methods & Protocols. 2009. (Methods in Molecular Biology Ser.). (ENG., Illus.). xii, 404p. 129.00 *(978-1-60327-354-1(9)*, 1603273549) Humana Pr.

Adams, Horace T. Contemporary Trends in Bacteriophage Research. 2009. (Illus.). 447p. 129.00 *(978-1-60692-181-4(9))* Nova Science Pubs., Inc.

Bhunia, Arun. Foodborne Microbial Pathogens: Mechanisms & Pathogenesis. 2010. (Food Science Text Ser.). (Illus.). xviii, 276p. pap. 79.95 *(978-1-4419-2562-6(7)*, 1441925627) Springer.

Bhunia, Arun K. Foodborne Microbial Pathogens: Mechanisms & Pathogenesis. 2008. (Food Science Texts Ser.). (ENG., Illus.). xviii, 276p. 79.95 *(978-0-387-74536-7(X)*, 038774536X) Springer.

Birge, Edward A. Bacterial & Bacteriophage Genetics. 5th ed. 2010. (ENG., Illus.). xx, 580p. pap. 115.00 *(978-1-4419-2019-5(6)*, 1441920196) Springer.

Chan, V. L. Ricky, et al. Bacterial Genomes & Infectious Diseases. 2006. (Illus.). 288p. 159.00 *(978-1-58829-496-8(X)*, 158829496X) Humana Pr.

Cox III, Robert Sidney & Cox Iii, Robert Sidney. Combinatorial Genetic Logic. 2010. 220p. pap. *(978-3-8383-0053-5(X))* Lambert Academic Publishing.

Cram101 Textbook Reviews Staff. Outlines & Highlights for Molecular Genetics of Bacteria by Larry Snyder, Isbn: 9781555813994. 2009. 68p. pap. 27.95 *(978-1-4288-9704-5(6))* Cram101 Inc.

de Reuse, H. & Bereswill, S., eds. Microbial Pathogenomics. 2009. (Genome Dynamics Ser.). (Illus.). 214p. *(978-3-8055-9192-8(6))* Karger, S. AG.

DeLeo, Frank & Otto, Michael, eds. Bacterial Pathogenesis: Methods & Protocols. 2010. (Methods in Molecular Biology Ser.). (Illus.). xvi, 320p. pap. 129.00 *(978-1-61737-751-8(1)*, 1617377511) Humana Pr.

DeLeo, Frank R. & Otto, Michael, eds. Bacterial Pathogenesis: Methods & Protocols. 2008. (Methods in Molecular Biology Ser.). (Illus.). 311p. 129.00 *(978-1-58829-740-2(3))* Humana Pr.

El-Sharoud, Walid, ed. Bacterial Physiology: A Molecular Approach. 2007. (Illus.). 371p. 359.00 *(978-3-540-74920-2(9))* Springer.

Fuxelius, Hans-Henrik. Methods & Applications in Comparative Bacterial Genomics - Studying Microevolution in Action. 2008. 72p. pap. *(978-3-8364-7580-8(4))* VDM Verlag Dr. Mueller e.K.

Hackworth, Cheryl. Understanding Mechanisms of Agrobacterium Tumefaciens Transformation. 2009. 152p. pap. *(978-3-639-13745-3(0))* VDM Verlag Dr. Mueller e.K.

Hecker, Michael & Jungblut, Peter R., eds. Proteomics of Microbial Pathogens. 2007. (ENG., Illus.). 343p. 245.00 *(978-3-527-31759-2(7)*, Wiley-VCH) Wiley, John & Sons, Inc.

Klipp, Werner, et al, eds. Genetics & Regulation of Nitrogen Fixation in Free-Living Bacteria. 2010. (Nitrogen Fixation: Origins, Applications, & Research Progress Ser.). xix, 300p. pap. 289.00 *(978-90-481-6607-7(1)*, 9048166071) Springer.

Knudsen, Walter D. & Bruns, Sam S. Bacterial DNA, DNA Polymerase & DNA Helicases. 2009. (Genetics - Research & Issues Ser.). 129.00 *(978-1-60741-094-2(X)*, Nova Biomedical Bks.) Nova Science Pubs., Inc.

Konings, W. N., et al, eds. Lactic Acid Bacteria: Genetics, Metabolism & Applications: Genetics, Metabolism & Applications. 2010. 420p. pap. 263.00 *(978-90-481-5312-1(3)*, 9048153123) Springer.

Maloy, Stanley R., ed. Advanced Bacterial Genetics: Use of Transposons & Phage for Genomic Engineering. 2007. (Methods in Enzymology Ser.). (ENG., Illus.). 320p. 187.00 *(978-0-12-373749-6(4)*, Academic Pr.) Elsevier Science & Technology Bks.

Mullany, Peter, ed. The Dynamic Bacterial Genome. 2010. (Advances in Molecular & Cellular Microbiology Ser.). (ENG.). 444p. pap. 83.00 *(978-0-521-12961-9(3))* Cambridge Univ. Pr.

Palacios, Rafael & Newton, William E., eds. Genomes & Genomics of Nitrogen-fixing Organisms. 2010. (Nitrogen Fixation: Origins, Applications, & Research Progress Ser.). xvii, 246p. pap. 309.00 *(978-90-481-6778-4(7)*, 9048167787) Springer.

Pallen, Mark J., et al, eds. Bacterial Pathogenomics. 2007. (Illus.). 453p. 190.00 *(978-1-55581-451-9(4))* ASM Pr.

Parish, Tanya & Stoker, Neil G., eds. Mycobacterium Tuberculosis Protocols. 2010. (Methods in Molecular Medicine Ser.). (Illus.). 424p. pap. 209.00 *(978-1-61737-184-4(X)*, 161737184X) Humana Pr.

Perry, Robert Donald & Fetherson, Jacqueline D. The Genus Yersinia: From Genomics to Function. 2007. (Advances in Experimental Medicine & Biology Ser.: Vol. 603). (Illus.). xxiv, 432p. 159.00 *(978-0-387-72123-1(1))* Springer.

Robinson, D. Ashley, et al, eds. Bacterial Population Genetics in Infectious Disease. 2010. (ENG., Illus.). 428p. 145.95 *(978-0-470-42474-2(5)*, Wiley-Blackwell) Wiley, John & Sons, Inc.

Schumann, Wolfgang. Dynamics of the Bacterial Chromosome: Structure & Function. 2006. (ENG., Illus.). 448p. 239.95 *(978-3-527-30496-7(7)*, Wiley-VCH) Wiley, John & Sons, Inc.

Siezen, Roland J., et al, eds. Lactic Acid Bacteria: Genetics, Metabolism & Applications: Genetics, Metabolism & Applications. 2010. 450p. pap. 149.00 *(978-90-481-6141-6(X)*, 904816141X) Springer.

Storz, G. Bacterial Stress Responses. 2nd ed. 2011. (ENG., Illus.). 580p. ***(978-1-55581-621-6(5))*** ASM Pr.

Tsakalidou, Effie & Papadimitriou, Konstantinos, eds. Stress Response in Lactic Acid Bacteria. 2011. (Food Microbiology & Food Safety Ser.). (ENG., Illus.). 300p. 239.00 *(978-0-387-92770-1(0)*, 0387927700) Springer.

Tscherwizek, Sandra. 16S Ribosomal RNA Gene Sequencing: Establishment of a Method for the Identification of Microorganisms in Biopharmaceutical Production Areas. 2008. 80p. pap. *(978-3-639-10903-0(1))* VDM Verlag Dr. Mueller e.K.

Ullrich, Matthias S., ed. Bacterial Polysaccharides: Current Innovations & Future Trends. 2009. (Illus.). 358p. 319.00 *(978-1-904455-45-5(X))* Caister Academic Pr. GBR. Dist: International Specialized Bk. Services.

Walk, S. Population Genetics of Bacteria - A Tribute to Thomas S. Whittam. 2011. (ENG., Illus.). 320p. ***(978-1-55581-535-6(9))*** ASM Pr.

Wilson, Van, ed. SUMO Regulation of Cellular Processes. 2009. (ENG., Illus.). x, 338p. 199.00 *(978-90-481-2648-4(7),* 9048126487) Springer.

Woodford, Neil & Johnson, Alan P., eds. Genomics, Proteomics, & Clinical Bacteriology: Methods & Reviews. 2010. (Methods in Molecular Biology Ser.). (Illus.). 408p. pap. 119.00 *(978-1-61737-428-9(8),* 1617374288) Humana Pr.

BACTERIAL INFECTIONS
see Bacterial Diseases

BACTERIAL LEACHING

Donati, Edgardo R., et al, eds. Biohydrometallurgy 2009: A Meeting Point Between Microbial Ecology, Metal Recovery Processes & Environmental Remediation. 2009. (Advanced Materials Research Ser.: Vol. 71-73). (Illus.). 782p. *(978-0-87849-322-7(0))* Trans Tech Pubns., Ltd.

Gaylarde, Christine C. & Videla, Hector A., eds. Bioextraction & Biodeterioration of Metals. 2009. (Biology of World Resources Ser.). (ENG., Illus.). 392p. pap. 52.00 *(978-0-521-12235-1(X))* Cambridge Univ. Pr.

Rawlings, Douglas E. & Johnson, D. Barrie, eds. Biomining. 2006. (ENG., Illus.). xx, 314p. 219.00 *(978-3-540-34909-9(X),* 354034909X) Springer.

Tyagi, R. D. & Blais, J. F. Bacterial Leaching of Metals from Sewage Sludge. Date not set. 139.00 *(978-0-8493-4888-4(9))* CRC Pr. LLC.

BACTERIAL MEMBRANES
see Bacterial Cell Walls

BACTERIAL METABOLISM
see Microbial Metabolism

BACTERIAL RESISTANCE TO ANTIBIOTICS
see Drug Resistance in Microorganisms

BACTERIAL SPORES
see Spores (Bacteria)

BACTERIAL WARFARE
see Biological Warfare

BACTERIOCIDAL AGENTS
see Anti-Infective Agents

BACTERIOLOGICAL WARFARE
see Biological Warfare

BACTERIOLOGISTS

Caruana, Gastone. Fragments of a Life. 2008. (Illus.). 304p. per. *(978-1-84748-212-9(0))* Athena Pr.

Freney, Jean, et al. The Pioneers of Bacteriology: The Great Scientists of the Infinitesimal. 2012. 230p. pap. 24.95 *(978-2-7472-1546-6(6))* Eska, Editions FRA. Dist: International Publishers Marketing.

BACTERIOLOGY

Here are entered works on the science of studying bacteria. Works on bacteria are entered under Bacteria.

see also Bacterial Genetics; Biological Products; Disinfection and Disinfectants; Fermentation; Germ Theory of Disease; Immunity; Medicine, Preventive; Sanitary Microbiology; Veterinary Bacteriology

also subdivision Microbiology under particular subjects, e.g. Milk—Microbiology

ABBE Research Division Staff. Drinking Water Bacteriology & Microbiology Are Hazards in Any Nation on Planet Earth with Index & Medical Analysis of New Research Information. 2007. (Illus.). 160p. 69.95 *(978-0-7883-4504-3(4),* 0-7883-4504-4) ABBE Pubs. Assn. of Washington, D.C.

Beach, Bennett S. Histology, Pathology, & Bacteriology: A Manual for Students & Practitioners. 2009. 164p. pap. 16.99 *(978-1-103-87958-8(8))* BiblioBazaar.

Coenye, Tom & Vandamme, Peter, eds. Burkholderia: Molecular Microbiology & Genomics. 2007. (ENG., Illus.). 350p. (C). 272.00 *(978-1-904933-28-1(9),* Taylor & Francis) Taylor & Francis Group GBR. Dist: Taylor & Francis Group.

Collier, Leslie H. Topley & Wilson's Principles of Bacteriology, Virology & Immunity, 5 vols. 8th ed. (Illus.). 736p. *(978-0-7131-4592-2(7),* Hodder Arnold) Hodder Education.

Conn, H. W. The Story of Germ Life. 2009. 204p. 28.99 *(978-1-110-60944-4(2));* pap. 23.75 *(978-1-110-60942-0(6))* BiblioBazaar.

—The Story of Germ Life. 2007. 124p. per. *(978-1-4065-1480-3(2))* Dodo Pr.

Diagnostic Bacteriology. instr.'s gde. ed. *(978-0-8036-0536-7(6))* Davis, F. A. Co.

Ernst, Joel & Stendahl, Olle, eds. Phagocytosis of Bacteria & Bacterial Pathogenicity. 2006. (Advances in Molecular & Cellular Microbiology Ser.: Vol. 12). (ENG., Illus.). 296p. 165.99 *(978-0-521-84569-4(6))* Cambridge Univ. Pr.

Herbert William Conn. The Story of Germ Life. 2007. (ENG.). 138p. pap. 18.99 *(978-1-4346-3912-7(6));* 150p. pap. 19.99 *(978-1-4346-3913-4(4))* BiblioBazaar.

Krasner, Robert. 20th Century Microbe Hunters. 2007. 199p. (C). pap. 57.95 *(978-0-7637-4201-0(5))* Jones & Bartlett Learning, LLC.

Linton, Alan H. Topley & Wilson's Principles of Bacteriology, Virology & Immunity, 5 vols. 8th ed. (Illus.). 484p. *(978-0-7131-4589-2(7),* Hodder Arnold) Hodder Education.

Mcisaac, Isabel. Bacteriology for Nurses. 2008. (Illus.). 191p. 22.99 *(978-0-554-72485-0(5))* BiblioBazaar.

Parker, M. T. Topley & Wilson's Principles of Bacteriology, Virology & Immunity, 5 vols., Set. 8th ed. (Illus.). 2742p. *(978-0-7131-4594-6(3),* Hodder Arnold) Hodder Education.

Parker, Tom. Topley & Wilson's Principles of Bacteriology, Virology & Immunity, 5 vols. 8th ed. (Illus.). 724p. *(978-0-7131-4590-8(0),* Hodder Arnold) Hodder Education.

Sachs, Jessica Snyder. Good Germs, Bad Germs: Health & Survival in a Bacterial World. 2008. (ENG., Illus.). 304p. pap. 15.00 *(978-0-8090-1642-6(7),* Hill & Wang) Farrar, Straus & Giroux.

Sansonetti, Philippe, ed. Bacterial Virulence: Basic Principles, Models & Global Approaches. 2010. (Infection Biology (VCH) Ser.). (ENG., Illus.). 340p. 209.95 *(978-3-527-32326-5(0),* Wiley-VCH) Wiley, John & Sons, Inc.

Smith, Geoffrey R. Topley & Wilson's Principles of Bacteriology, Virology & Immunity, 5 vols. 8th ed. (Illus.). 746p. *(978-0-7131-4591-5(9),* Hodder Arnold) Hodder Education.

Srivastava, S. Understanding Bacteria. 2010. 492p. pap. 389.00 *(978-90-481-6429-5(X),* 904816429X) Springer.

Toman, Rudolf, et al, eds. Coxiella burnetii: Recent Advances & New Perspectives in Research of the Q Fever Bacterium: Recent Advances & New Perspectives in Research of the Q Fever Bacterium. 2012. (Advances in Experimental Medicine & Biology Ser.). (ENG., Illus.). x, 430p. 209.00 ***(978-94-007-4314-4(9),*** 9400743149) Springer.

Topley, W. W. C. & Wilson, Graham S. Topley & Wilson's Principles of Bacteriology, Virology & Immunity, 5 vols. 8th ed. 124p. *(978-0-7131-4593-9(5),* Hodder Arnold) Hodder Education.

Woodford, Neil & Johnson, Alan, eds. Molecular Bacteriology: Protocols & Clinical Applications. 2010. (Methods in Molecular Medicine Ser.). 692p. pap. 179.00 *(978-1-61737-053-3(3),* 1617370533) Humana Pr.

Zourob, Mohammed, et al. Principles of Bacterial Detection: Biosensors, Recognition Receptors & Microsystems. 2008. (ENG., Illus.). xxxii, 970p. 137.00 *(978-0-387-75112-2(2),* 0387751122) Springer.

BACTERIOLOGY—HISTORY

Berger, Silvia. Bakterien in Krieg und Frieden: Eine Geschichte der medizinischen Bakteriologie in Deutschland, 1890-1933. 2009. (GER., Illus.). 476p. pap. *(978-3-8353-0556-4(5))* Wallstein-Verlag GmbH Verlag und Werbung.

Gradmann, Christoph. Laboratory Disease: Robert Koch's Medical Bacteriology. Forster, Elborg, tr. from GER. 2009. (ENG., Illus.). 328p. (gr. 17). 37.00 *(978-0-8018-9313-1(5))* Johns Hopkins Univ. Pr.

BACTERIOLOGY—LABORATORY MANUALS

Oâ€(tm)Connor, Louise, ed. Diagnostic Bacteriology Protocols. 2nd ed. 2010. (Methods in Molecular Biology Ser.). (Illus.). 236p. pap. 149.00 *(978-1-61737-666-5(3),* 1617376663) Humana Pr.

Shodja, Mary Michelle. Bacteriology for CLS & MLT. 2010. 104p. pap. 38.12 *(978-1-4269-4052-1(1))* Trafford Publishing.

BACTERIOLOGY—TECHNIQUE
see also Sterilization

Oâ€(tm)Connor, Louise, ed. Diagnostic Bacteriology Protocols. 2nd ed. 2010. (Methods in Molecular Biology Ser.). (Illus.). 236p. pap. 149.00 *(978-1-61737-666-5(3),* 1617376663) Humana Pr.

Woodford, Neil & Johnson, Alan P., eds. Genomics, Proteomics, & Clinical Bacteriology: Methods & Reviews. 2010. (Methods in Molecular Biology Ser.). (Illus.). 408p. pap. 119.00 *(978-1-61737-428-9(8),* 1617374288) Humana Pr.

BACTERIOLOGY, VETERINARY
see Veterinary Bacteriology

BACTERIOPHAGES

Abedon, Stephen T. Bacteriophages & Biofilms: Ecology, Phage Therapy, Plaques. 2011. (Bacteriology Research Developments Ser.). (Illus.). ii, 138p. pap. 69.00 *(978-1-61761-588-7(9),* Nova Biomedical Bks.) Nova Science Pubs., Inc.

Abedon, Stephen T., ed. Bacteriophage Ecology: Population Growth, Evolution, & Impact of Bacterial Viruses. 2008. (Advances in Molecular & Cellular Microbiology Ser.). (ENG., Illus.). 526p. 147.00 *(978-0-521-85845-8(3))* Cambridge Univ. Pr.

Adams, Horace T. Contemporary Trends in Bacteriophage Research. 2009. (Illus.). 447p. 129.00 *(978-1-60692-181-4(9))* Nova Science Pubs., Inc.

Aitken, Robert, ed. Antibody Phage Display: Methods & Protocols. 2nd ed. 2009. (Methods in Molecular Biology Ser.). (ENG., Illus.). x, 242p. 149.00 *(978-1-60327-301-5(8),* 1603273018) Humana Pr.

Birge, Edward A. Bacterial & Bacteriophage Genetics. 5th ed. 2010. (ENG., Illus.). xx, 580p. pap. 115.00 *(978-1-4419-2019-5(6),* 1441920196) Springer.

Camazza, Santina. Phage Display as a Tool for Synthetic Biology. Guglielminc, Salvatore, ed. 2010. (Nanotechnology Science & Technology Ser.). 93p. pap. 43.00 *(978-1-60876-987-2(9))* Nova Science Pubs., Inc.

Catalano, Carlos E., ed. Viral Genome Packaging: Genetics, Structure, & Mechanism: Genetics, Structure, & Mechanism. 2010. (Molecular Biology Intelligence Unit Ser.). (Illus.). x, 153p. pap. 159.00 *(978-1-4419-3432-1(4),* 1441934324) Springer.

Clokie, Martha, ed. Bacteriophages: Methods & Protocols, 2 vols. 2009. (Methods in Molecular Biology Ser.). (Illus.). 350p. 139.00 *(978-1-58829-682-5(2))* Humana Pr.

Clokie, Martha R. J. & Kropinski, Andrew M. Bacteriophages, 2 vols. 2009. (Methods in Molecular Biology Ser.). (Illus.). 320p. 119.00 *(978-1-60327-564-4(9))* Humana Pr.

Comeau, Andrt M. The Ecology of Vibriophages. 2008. 136p. pap. *(978-3-639-04151-4(8))* VDM Verlag Dr. Mueller e.K.

Elshayeb, Ayman. In Vitro Tests for Bacteriophages Against Sudanese Bacteria Species. 2010. 120p. pap. *(978-3-8383-8603-4(5))* Lambert Academic Publishing.

Häusler, Thomas. Viruses vs. Superbugs: A Solution to the Antibiotics Crisis? 2nd rev. ed. 2007. (ENG., Illus.). 256p. pap. 14.95 *(978-0-230-55193-0(9))* Palgrave Macmillan.

Kuchment, Anna. The Forgotten Cure: The Past & Future of Phage Therapies. 2011. (ENG., Illus.). xvi, 131p. 19.95 *(978-1-4614-0250-3(6),* 146140250€) Springer.

Lobocka, Malgorzata & Syzbalski, Waclaw T. Bacteriophages, Part A. 2012. (ENG.). 416p. 161.00 ***(978-0-12-394621-8(2),*** Academic Pr.) Elsevier Science & Technology Bks.

McGrath, Stephen & Van Sinderen, Douwe, eds. Bacteriophage: Genetics & Molecular Biology. 2007. (Illus.). 344p. 319.00 *(978-1-904455-14-1(X))* Caister Academic Pr. GBR. Dist: International Specialized Bk. Services.

Pasharawipas, Tirasak. Bacteriophage. 2011. 92p. pap. ***(978-3-8443-9739-0(6))*** Lambert Academic Publishing.

Petrenko, Valery & Smith, George P., eds. Phage Bionanotechnology. 2011. (RSC Nanoscience & Nanotechnology Ser.). (ENG., Illus.). 288p. 195.00 ***(978-0-85404-184-8(2))*** Royal Society of Chemistry, The GBR. Dist: Ingram Pub. Services.

Reinheimer, Jorge Alberto. Bacteriophages in Dairy Processing. del Luján Quiberoni, Andrea, ed. 2012. (Advances in Food Safety & Food Microbiology (Series Editors: Dr. Anderson de Souza Sant'Ana & Dr. Bernadette D. G. M. Franco) Biotechnology in Agriculture, Industry & Medicine Ser.). 321p. 165.00 ***(978-1-61324-517-0(3))*** Nova Science Pubs., Inc.

Sabour Rouhaghdam, Alireza. Bacteriophages in the Detection & Control of Foodborne Pathogens. 2010. (Illus.). 400p. ***(978-1-55581-502-8(2))*** ASM Pr.

Sankaran, Neeraja. Frank Macfarlane Burnet & the Nature of theBacteriophage, 1924-1937. 2008. 296p. pap. *(978-3-639-07520-5(X))* VDM Verlag Dr. Mueller e.K.

Sillankorva, Sanna, et al. Use of Bacteriophages to Control Biofilms. 2011. 192p. pap. ***(978-3-8454-0611-4(9))*** Lambert Academic Publishing.

Slavcev, Ph. D. MBA Roderick & Slavcev. Tackling a Legendary Scientific Mystery. 2010. 264p. pap. *(978-3-8383-1963-6(X))* Lambert Academic Publishing.

Villa, Tomas G. & Crespo, Patricia Veiga, eds. Enzybiotics: Antibiotic Enzymes as Drugs & Therapeutics. 2010. (ENG., Illus.). 284p. 111.00 *(978-0-470-37655-3(4),* Wiley) Wiley, John & Sons, Inc.

BACTERIOSTATIC AGENTS
see Anti-Infective Agents

BACTRIA

Benjamin, C. The Yuezhi: Origin, Migration & the Conquest of Northern Bactria. 2007. (Silk Road Studies). (ENG.). 245p. (C). pap. 73.00 *(978-2-503-52429-0(X))* Brepols Pubs. BEL. Dist: ISD.

Naveh, Joseph. Ancient Aramaic Documents from Bactria: 4th Century B. C. E. Naveh, Joseph & Shaked, Shaul, eds. 2008. (Studies in the Khalili Collection). (ENG.). 224p. 81.00 *(978-1-874780-74-8(9),* Khalili Collections) I. B. Tauris & Co., Ltd. GBR. Dist: Macmillan.

Rawlinson, Hugh G. Bactria: The History of a Forgotten Empire. reprint ed. 32.50 *(978-0-404-05227-0(4))* AMS Pr., Inc.

BACTRIAN LANGUAGE (OLD BACTRIAN)
see Avestan Language

BACULOVIRUSES

Kawaoka, Yoshihiro. Biology of Negative Strand RNA Viruses: the Power of Reverse Genetics: The Power of Reverse Genetics. 2010. (Current Topics in Microbiology & Immunology Ser.). (Illus.). ix, 347p. pap. 219.00 *(978-3-642-07375-5(1),* 3642073751) Springer.

Murhammer, David W. Baculovirus & Insect Cell Expression Protocols. 2nd ed. 2007. (Methods in Molecular Biology Ser.). (Illus.). 470p. 209.00 *(978-1-58829-537-8(0),* 1588295370) Humana Pr.

Murhammer, David W., ed. Baculovirus & Insect Cell Expression Protocols. 2nd ed. 2010. (Methods in Molecular Biology Ser.). (Illus.). xiv, 470p. pap. 209.00 *(978-1-61737-629-0(9),* 1617376299) Humana Pr.

BAD BREATH

Sterer, Nir & Rosenberg, Mel. Breath Odors: Origin, Diagnosis, & Management. 2011. (Illus.). ix, 116p. 139.00 *(978-3-642-19311-8(0),* 3642193110) Springer.

BAD DREAMS
see Nightmares

BAD FAITH (LAW)

Barker, William T. & Appleman, John Alan. New Appleman Insurance Bad Faith Litigation. 2nd ed. 2009. *(978-1-4224-7514-0(X))* LexisNexis Matthew Bender.

Friedman, Rick & Malone, Patrick. Rules of the Road: A Plaintiff Lawyer's Guide to Proving Liability. 2nd ed. 2010. 320p. 95.00 *(978-1-934833-17-9(7))* 2007. (ENG.). 316p. 95.00 *(978-0-9743248-6-9(8))* Trial Guides LLC.

McGonigle, Richard L., Jr. Insurance Bad Faith in Pennsylvania. Shotsberger, Amanda, ed. 2008. (Guide Books Ser.). (ENG.). 1042p. pap. 81.00 *(978-1-57786-224-6(4))* Incisive Media.

McMonigle, Richard L., Jr. Insurance Bad Faith in Pennsylvania. 2011. (ENG.). 1042p. pap. 85.00 *(978-1-57786-129-4(9))* Incisive Media.

McMonigle, Richard L., Jr., et al. Insurance Bad Faith in Pennsylvania. 2010. (ENG.). 1200p. pap. 89.95 *(978-1-57786-365-6(8))* Incisive Media.

BADEN (GERMANY)—HISTORY

Maciejewski, Jürgen. Amtsmannvertreibungen in Baden im März und April 1848: Bürokratiekritik, bürokratiekritischer Protest und Revolution Von 1848/49. 2010. (Europäische Hochschulschriften. Reihe 3: Geschichte und ihre Hilfswissenschaften Ser.). (GER., Illus.). 510p. pap. 115.95 *(978-3-631-57768-4(0))* Lang, Peter GmbH, Europäischer Verlag der Wissenschaften DEU. Dist: Lang, Peter.

BADEN-POWELL OF GILWELL, ROBERT STEPHENSON SMYTH BADEN-POWELL, BARON, 1857-1941

Baden-Powell, Heather. Baden-Powell: A Family Album. 2008. (ENG., Illus.). 224p. pap. 34.95 *(978-0-7509-4441-0(2))* History Pr. Ltd.,The GBR. Dist: Independent Pubs. Group.

Baden-Powell, Robert. Playing the Game: A Baden-Powell Compendium. Sica, Mario, ed. (ENG., Illus.). 2008. 448p. pap. 17.95 *(978-0-330-44235-0(X))* 2007. 368p. 29.95 *(978-1-4050-8827-5(3))* Macmillan Pubs., Ltd. GBR. Dist: Independent Pubs. Group.

Begbie, Harold. The Story of Baden-Powell: 'The Wolf that never Sleeps' 2007. (Illus.). 120p. per. *(978-1-4065-3743-7(8))* Dodo Pr.

—Story of BadenPowell. 2006. 25.95 *(978-1-4218-2962-3(2));* (ENG.). pap. 10.95 *(978-1-4218-3062-9(0))* 1st World Publishing, Inc.

Jeal, Tim. Baden-Powell: Founder of the Boy Scouts. 2007. (ENG., Illus.). 720p. pap. 19.00 *(978-0-300-12513-9(5))* Yale Univ. Pr.

Scott, David C. & Murphy, Brendan. The Scouting Party: Pioneering & Preservation, Progressivism & Preparedness in the Making of the Boy Scouts of America. 2010. (Illus.). 285p. *(978-0-9789836-3-5(7),* Red Honor Pr.) PenlandScott Pubs.

BADER, DOUGLAS, 1910-1982

Frayn-Turner, John. The Bader Wing. 2007. (Illus.). 153p. 39.95 *(978-1-84415-544-6(7))* Pen & Sword Bks. Ltd. GBR. Dist: Casemate Pubs. & Bk. Distributors, LLC.

Mackenzie, S. P. Bader's War: 'Have a Go at Everything' 2008. (ENG., Illus.). 192p. 42.95 *(978-1-86227-467-9(3))* History Pr. Ltd.,The GBR. Dist: Independent Pubs. Group.

Saunders, Andy. Bader's Last Fight: An In-Depth Investigation of a Great WWII Mystery. 2007. (Illus.). 160p. 39.95 *(978-1-904943-96-9(9))* Grub Street GBR. Dist: Casemate Pubs. & Bk. Distributors, LLC.

Turner, John Frayn. Douglas Bader: The Biography. 2009. (Illus.). 256p. 39.99 *(978-1-84415-909-3(4))* Pen & Sword Bks. Ltd. GBR. Dist: Casemate Pubs. & Bk. Distributors, LLC.

BADGER DOGS, GERMAN
see Dachshunds

BADGERS

Clark, Michael. Badgers. rev. ed. (Illus.). 128p. 19.95 *(978-0-905483-65-8(0))* Whittet Bks., Ltd. GBR. Dist: Diamond Farm Bk. Pubs.

Pearce, George/ E. Badger Behaviour, Conservation & Rehabilitation: 70 Years of Getting to Know Badgers. 2011. (Illus.). 175p. *(978-1-907807-03-9(9))* Pelagic Publishing Ltd.

Roper, Tim. Badger. 2010. (Collins New Naturalist Ser.). (ENG., Illus.). 400p. 75.00 *(978-0-00-732041-7(8))* HarperCollins Pubs. Ltd. GBR. Dist: Independent Pubs. Group.

BADGES OF HONOR
see Decorations of Honor; Medals

BADMINTON (GAME)

Brahms, Bernd-Vol. Badminton Handbook. 2010. (Illus.). 160p. pap. 18.95 *(978-1-84126-298-7(6))* Meyer & Meyer Sport, Ltd. GBR. Dist: Cardinal Pubs. Group.

Chen, Gong & Chen, Carol. Coaching Badminton 101. 2009. (Illus.). 170p. pap. 19.95 *(978-1-60679-038-0(2))* Coaches Choice.

Davidson, Kenneth. How to Improve Your Badminton. 2011. 70p. pap. 26.45 ***(978-1-4474-2673-8(3))*** Barclay Pr., Inc.

Grice, Tony. Badminton. 6th ed. 2009. (ENG., Illus.). 165p. (Orig.). pap. 14.95 *(978-0-89641-472-3(3))* American Pr.

—Badminton. 2nd rev. ed. 2007. (ENG., Illus.). 200p. (Orig.). per. 19.95 *(978-0-7360-7229-8(2))* Human Kinetics Pubs.

Thomas, George. The Art of Badminton. 2008. (Illus.). 200p. *(978-1-4437-3781-4(X),* Home Farm Bks.) Read Bks.

Thomas, George. Badminton. 2011. 58p. pap. 26.45 ***(978-1-4474-2669-1(X))*** Audubon Pr. & Christian Bk. Service.

BAEZ, JOAN, 1941-

Baez, Joan. And a Voice to Sing With: A Memoir. 2009. (ENG., Illus.). 400p. pap. 24.99 *(978-1-4391-6964-3(0))* Simon & Schuster.

Hajdu, David. Positively 4th Street: The Lives & Times of Joan Baez, Bob Dylan, Mimi Baez Fariña & Richard Fariña. 2011. (ENG., Illus.). 352p. pap. 18.00 *(978-0-312-68069-5(4))* Picador.

BAGANDA (AFRICAN PEOPLE)
see Ganda (African People)

BAGASSE

Amin Salehi, Farnaz. Bagasse As a Fuel for Combined Heat & Power. 2011. 132p. pap. ***(978-3-8454-1483-6(9))*** Lambert Academic Publishing.

BAGBY, GEORGE WILLIAM, 1828-1883

King, Joseph L. Doctor George William Bagby. reprint ed. 20.00 *(978-0-404-03693-5(7))* AMS Pr., Inc.

BAGDAD
see Baghdad (Iraq)

B

BAGEHOT, WALTER, 1826-1877

Bagehot, Walter. Literary Studies (Miscellaneous Essays) Hutton, Richard H., ed. (Works of Walter Bagehot, 1826-1877). 357p. reprint ed. lib. bdg. 49.00 *(978-0-7812-0893-2(9))* Reprint Services Co.

Irvine, William. Walter Bagehot. 2006. (ENG.). 316p. per. *(978-1-4067-0946-9(8),* Hesperides Pr.) Read Bks.

Prochaska, Frank. Eminent Victorians on American Democracy: The View from Albion. 2012. (ENG.). 184p. 45.00 ***(978-0-19-964061-4(0))*** Oxford Univ. Pr., Inc.

BAGELS

Balinska, Maria. The Bagel: The Surprising History of a Modest Brand. 2008. (ENG., Illus.). 240p. 24.00 *(978-0-300-11229-0(7))* Yale Univ. Pr.

—The Bagel: The Surprising History of a Modest Bread. 2009. (ENG., Illus.). 240p. pap. 16.00 *(978-0-300-15820-5(3))* Yale Univ. Pr.

BAGHDAD (IRAQ)

Ciezadlo, Annia. Day of Honey: A Memoir of Food, Love, & War. 2011. (ENG.). 400p. 26.00 *(978-1-4165-8393-6(9),* Free Pr.) Free Pr.

Gilman, Arthur. The Saracens, from the Earliest Times to the Fall of Bagdad. 2009. (Illus.). 316p. pap. *(978-1-150-73255-3(5))* Books LLC.

Hassanein, Ahmed Taher, et al. Baghdad Arts Deco: Architectural Brickwork, 19201950. 2011. (ENG.). 608p. 39.95 *(978-977-416-356-2(7))* American Univ. in Cairo Pr. EGY. Dist: Oxford Univ. Pr., Inc.

Kirtikar, Margo. Once upon a Time in Baghdad. 2011. 308p. pap. 19.99 ***(978-1-4568-5375-4(9))*** Xlibris Corp.

Levy, Reuben. A Baghdad Chronicle. 2011. (ENG.). 298p. pap. 23.99 *(978-1-107-60054-6(5))* Cambridge Univ. Pr.

Mahir, Zaid. The Way to Baghdad: Day 18 of the War. 2011. 196p. 24.95 ***(978-1-4269-6460-2(9))***; pap. 14.95 ***(978-1-4269-6461-9(7))*** Trafford Publishing.

Osborn, Robert Durie. Islam under the Khalifs of Baghdad. 2009. 426p. 30.99 *(978-1-116-56789-2(X))*; pap. 34.75 *(978-1-116-56791-5(1))*; pap. 35.75 *(978-1-116-56790-8(3))* BiblioBazaar.

—Islam under the Khalifs of Baghdad. 2009. 200p. pap. *(978-0-217-49435-9(8))* Books LLC.

—Islam under the Khalifs of Baghdad. 2007. (ENG.). 424p. 51.95 *(978-0-548-13575-4(4))* 2006. pap. 36.95 *(978-1-4286-4703-9(1))* Kessinger Publishing, LLC.

Poole, Oliver. Red Zone: Five Bloody Years in Baghdad. 2009. (ENG.). 336p. pap. *(978-0-9558302-5-9(7))* Reportage Pr.

Sassoon, David. History of the Jews in Baghdad. 2nd ed. 2006. (Illus.). per. *(978-1-84356-002-9(X))* Wallenberg, Simon Pr.

Stark, Freya. Baghdad Sketches: Journeys Through Iraq. 2011. (Freya Stark Collection). (ENG., Illus.). 184p. 16.00 *(978-1-84885-655-4(5),* Tauris Parke Paperbacks) I. B. Tauris & Co., Ltd. GBR. Dist: Macmillan.

Sypeck, Jeff. Becoming Charlemagne: Europe, Baghdad, & the Empires of A. D. 800. 2006. (ENG., Illus.). 256p. 25.95 *(978-0-06-079706-5(1),* Ecco) HarperCollins Pubs.

Tholib, Udjang. The Reign of the 'Abbasid Caliph Al-Qadir Billah. 2009. 340p. pap. *(978-3-639-21748-3(9))* VDM Verlag Dr. Mueller e.K.

Zigan, Mike. Ignition. 2007. 344p. (ENG.). 27.99 *(978-1-60266-886-7(8))*; per. 17.99 *(978-1-60266-885-0(X))* Xulon Pr., Inc.

BAGPIPE

Cannon, Roderick D. The Highland Bagpipe & Its Music. 2008. (ENG., Illus.). 205p. pap. 19.95 *(978-1-84158-666-3(8))* Birlinn, Ltd. GBR. Dist: Interlink Publishing Group, Inc.

Cheape, Hugh. Bagpipes: A National Collection of a National Instrument. 2nd ed. 2011. (Illus.). 160p. pap. 19.95 *(978-1-905267-55-2(X))* NMS Enterprises Ltd. - Publishing GBR. Dist: National Bk. Network.

Dickson, Joshua. The Highland Bagpipe: Music, History, Tradition. 2009. (Ashgate Popular & Folk Music Ser.). (Illus.). 408p. 79.95 *(978-0-7546-6669-1(7))* Ashgate Publishing Co.

Gibson, John G. Old & New World Highland Bagpiping. 2011. (McGill-Queen's Studies in Ethnic History Ser.). (ENG., Illus.). 448p. (C). pap. ***(978-0-7735-3923-5(9))*** McGill-Queen's Univ. Pr.

MacPherson, Hugh D. A Piper's American Odyssey, Book 1: Contemporary Compositions for the Bagpipe. 2008. (Illus.). 69p. pap. incl. audio compact disk *(978-1-894131-95-7(9))* Penumbra Pr.

Millington, Iain, compiled by. Sullivan Ross Collection of Pipe Music. 2007. (Illus.). 148p. pap. 20.00 *(978-0-9796600-0-9(9))* Ross, David.

BAHA ALLAH, 1817-1892

Momen, Moojan. Baha'u'llah: A Short Biography. 2007. (ENG., Illus.). 192p. pap. 16.95 *(978-1-85168-469-4(7))* Oneworld Pubns. GBR. Dist: National Bk. Network.

Safai, Maryam. Tului Digar. 2nd ed. 2008. (PER., Illus.). 130p. *(978-1-59584-196-4(2))* Ketab Corp.

Sears, William. The Prisoner & the Kings: How One Man Changed the Course of History. 2nd ed. 2007. 259p. per. *(978-1-931847-41-4(X),* Gaia Books) Baha'i Publishing.

Terry, Peter. Baha'u'llah in His Own Words. 2009. 274p. pap. 19.95 *(978-0-557-05821-1(X))* Lulu Enterprises Inc.

BAHA ULLAH, 1817-1892

see Baha Allah, 1817-1892

BAHAI FAITH

see also Babism

Abdu'l-Baha. First Prayers: For Tender Plants: Prayers. 2011. ***(978-0-87743-715-4(7))*** Baha'i Publishing Trust, U.S.

Abdul-Baha. Paris Talks: Addresses Given by Abdul-Baha In 1911. 2006. 249p. per. 12.00 *(978-1-931847-32-2(0))* Baha'i Publishing.

Abdu'l-Baha. Paris Talks: Addresses Given by Abdul-Bahá in 1911. 2011. ***(978-1-931847-90-2(8))*** Baha'i Publishing Trust, U.S.

—The Promulgation of Universal Peace: Talks Delivered by Abdul-Bahá During His Visit to the United States & Canada in 1912. 2007. xxvi, 707p. *(978-0-87743-335-4(6))* Baha'i Publishing Trust, U.S.

—Selections from the Writings of Abdul-Bahá. 2010. ix, 483p. *(978-1-931847-74-2(6))* Baha'i Publishing Trust, U.S.

—Talks by Abdul-Bahá: The Eternal Covenant. 2011. *(978-1-931847-82-7(7))* Baha'i Publishing Trust, U.S.

Abdu'l-Baha. Talks by Abdul-Bahá: Universal Education. 2011. 178p. ***(978-1-931847-87-2(8))*** Baha'i Publishing.

Adamson, Hugh C. The A to Z of the Bahai Faith. 2009. (A to Z Guide Ser.: No. 70). (ENG.). 528p. pap. 34.45 *(978-0-8108-6853-3(9))* Scarecrow Pr., Inc.

—Historical Dictionary of the Baha'i Faith. 2nd ed. 2006. (Historical Dictionaries of Religions, Philosophies, & Move Ser.). (ENG., Illus.). 720p. 145.00 *(978-0-8108-5096-5(6))* Scarecrow Pr., Inc.

Afnan, Mirza Habibu'llah, ed. The Genesis of Babi-Baha'i Faiths in Shiraz & Fars. Rabbani, Ahang, tr. from PER. 2008. 430p. *(978-90-04-17054-4(5))* BRILL.

Agis, Derya. Training of the Bahá'í Child Educators. 2011. 84p. pap. ***(978-3-8443-1882-1(8))*** Lambert Academic Publishing.

Avnery, Uri. 1948: A Soldier's Tale: The Bloody Road to Jerusalem. Costello, Christopher, tr. from HEB. 2008. (ENG., Illus.). 400p. pap. 19.95 *(978-1-85168-629-2(0))* Oneworld Pubns. GBR. Dist: National Bk. Network.

Ayyam-i Ha & the Fast: A Compilation. Date not set. 14.95 *(978-0-933770-89-8(8))* Kalimat Pr.

Baha, Abdu'L. The Secret of Divine Civilization. Gail, Marzieh, tr. 2011. 130p. 40.95 ***(978-1-258-05543-1(0))*** Literary Licensing, LLC.

Bahá'í National Center Staff, contrib. by. Messages of Hope & Assurance. 2008. *(978-1-931847-37-7(1))* Baha'i Publishing Trust, U.S.

Baha'i Publishing, compiled by. Illumine My Family: Bahai Prayers & Meditations from the Bahai Faith. 2009. 241p. pap. 12.00 *(978-1-931847-62-9(2))* Baha'i Publishing Trust, U.S.

Baha'i Publishing, creator. Meditations: Selections from Baha'i Scripture. 2008. 163p. pap. 19.00 *(978-1-931847-56-8(8))* Baha'i Publishing.

Bahai Publishing, et al. Spirit of Faith: The Oneness of Humanity. 2011. 137p. ***(978-1-931847-86-5(X))*** Baha'i Publishing Trust, U.S.

Bahá'í Publishing Trust Staff, contrib. by. Illumine My Being: Bahá'í Prayers & Meditations for Health. 2010. *(978-1-931847-69-8(X))* Baha'i Publishing.

Baháulláh. Fountain of Wisdom: A Collection of Writings from Baháulláh. 2010. *(978-1-931847-80-3(0))* Baha'i Publishing.

—Las Palabras Ocultas. 2008. (SPA.). *(978-0-87743-339-2(9))* Baha'i Publishing Trust, U.S.

—Pasajes de Los Escritos de Baháullah. 2008. (SPA.). *(978-0-87743-340-8(2))* Baha'i Publishing Trust, U.S.

—The Pen of Glory: Selected Works of Baháullah. 2008. *(978-1-931847-55-1(X))* Baha'i Publishing.

Baha'u'llah. The Summons of the Lord of Hosts: Tablets of Baha'u'llah. 2006. 409p. per. 14.00 *(978-1-931847-33-9(9))* Baha'i Publishing.

Baha'u'llah & Abdu'l-Baha. Illumine My Heart: Baha'i Prayers for Every Occasion. 2008. 193p. pap. 12.00 *(978-1-931847-53-7(3))* Baha'i Publishing Trust, U.S.

—The Universal Principles of the Reform Bahai Faith. Glaysher, Frederick, ed. 2008. 148p. (ENG.). 19.99 *(978-0-9670421-3-8(5))*; pap. 11.99 *(978-0-9670421-0-7(0))* Earthrise Pr. (Reform Bahai Pr.).

Baháulláh, et al. Baháí Prayers: A Selection of Prayers. 2009. 344p. ***(978-0-87743-345-3(3))***; ***(978-0-87743-346-0(1))***; pap. ***(978-0-87743-344-6(5))*** Baha'i Publishing Trust, U.S.

—Illumine My World: Bahá'í Prayers & Meditations for Peace. 2009. *(978-1-931847-65-0(7))* Baha'i Publishing.

—The Oneness of God. 2010. 157p. *(978-1-931847-76-6(2))* Baha'i Publishing Trust, U.S.

—Oraciones Baháís: Selección de Oraciones. 2008. (SPA.). pap. *(978-0-87743-341-5(0))* Baha'i Publishing Trust, U.S.

—Spirit of Faith: The Oneness of Religion. 2011. *(978-1-931847-81-0(9))* Baha'i Publishing Trust, U.S.

Baha'u'llah & the New Era: An Introduction to the Baha'i Faith. 2006. 333p. per. 14.00 *(978-1-931847-27-8(4))* Baha'i Publishing.

Blecker, Lisa. Blessed Is the Spot: A Prayer, 1 vol., 1 DVD. 2007. (Illus.). bds. 14.95 incl. DVD *(978-1-931492-08-9(5))* Discover Writing Pr.

Brookshaw, Dominic Parviz & Fazel, Seena B., eds. The Baha'Is of Iran. 2010. 240p. pap. 39.95 *(978-0-415-58322-0(5))* Routledge.

Browne, Edward G., ed. A Traveller's Narrative Written to Illustrate the Episode of the Báb: Volume 1, Persian Text: Edited in the Original Persian, & Translated into English, with an Introduction & Explanatory Notes. 2012. (ENG.). 214p. pap. 34.99 ***(978-1-107-68562-8(1))*** Cambridge Univ. Pr.

—A Traveller's Narrative Written to Illustrate the Episode of the Báb: Volume 2, English Translation & Notes: Edited in the Original Persian, & Translated into English, with an Introduction & Explanatory Notes, 2 vols. 2012. (ENG.). 504p. pap. 39.99 ***(978-1-107-63304-9(4))*** Cambridge Univ. Pr.

Caldwell, Jenabe E. Follow the Instructions. 2008. 176p. pap. 15.00 *(978-0-9762780-6-1(5))* Best Publishing.

Cheyne, Thomas Kelly. The Reconciliation of Races & Religion. l.t. ed. 2007. (ENG.). 162p. pap. 21.99 *(978-1-4346-0536-8(1))* BiblioBazaar.

—The Reconciliation of Races & Religions. 2008. 164p. 25.99 *(978-0-554-26136-2(7))*; 22.99 *(978-0-554-35439-2(X))* BiblioBazaar.

—The Reconciliation of Races & Religions. 2007. (ENG.). 104p. per. *(978-1-4068-4546-4(9))* Echo Library.

—The Reconciliation of Races & Religions: The Reconciliation of Races & Religions. 2007. (ENG.). 146p. pap. 18.99 *(978-1-4346-0532-0(9))* BiblioBazaar.

—Reconciliation of Races & Religions Do. 2007. pap. *(978-1-4065-1445-2(4))* Dodo Pr.

Chubinah, Bahram. Duktur Muhammad Musaddiq Va Bahayiyan. 2009. 74p. *(978-1-59584-234-3(9))*; *(978-1-59584-235-0(7))* Ketab Corp.

Danesh, John. Baha'i Faith in Words & Images. 2015. (ENG., Illus.). 160p. 30.00 *(978-1-85168-216-4(3))*; pap. 19.95 *(978-1-85168-219-5(8))* Oneworld Pubns. GBR. Dist: National Bk. Network.

Day of the Covenant: A Compilation. Date not set. 14.95 *(978-0-933770-88-1(X))* Kalimat Pr.

Douglas, Kim. High Desert: A Journey of Survival & Hope. 2009. vii, 270p. *(978-1-931847-59-9(2))* Baha'i Publishing Trust, U.S.

Echevarria, Lynn. Life Histories of Bahá'í Women in Canada: Constructing Religious Identity in the Twentieth Century. 2011. ix, 229p. (C). 78.95 ***(978-1-4331-1457-1(7))*** Lang, Peter Publishing, Inc.

Eschraghi, Armin, et al. Baha'u'llah, Brief an den Sohn des Wolfes: Lauh-i Ibn-i Dhi'b. 2010. (GER.). 679p. *(978-3-458-70029-6(3))* Insel Verlag Anton Kippenberg.

Esslemont, J. E. Baha Uliahand the New Era. 2006. 316p. per. *(978-1-4067-2235-2(9),* Hesperides Pr.) Read Bks.

Fazel, Seena. Baha Is of Iran. Brookshaw, Dominic Parviz, ed. 2007. (Routledge Advances in Middle East & Islamic Studies). (ENG., Illus.). 304p. 160.00 *(978-0-415-35673-2(3))* Routledge.

Ford, Mary Hanford. Oriental Rose or the Teachings of Abdul. 2006. pap. 24.95 *(978-1-4286-4893-7(3))* Kessinger Publishing, LLC.

Garlington, William. The Baha'i Faith in America, 1 vol. 248p. pap. 27.95 *(978-0-275-98991-0(7),* B8991) Greenwood Publishing Group, Inc.

—The Baha'i Faith in America. 2008. (ENG., Illus.). 248p. per. 27.95 *(978-0-7425-6234-9(4))* Rowman & Littlefield Publishers, Inc.

Glaysher, Frederick. Letters from the American Desert: Signposts of a Journey, A Vision. 2008. 172p. 19.99 *(978-0-9670421-1-4(9))* Earthrise Pr.

Hanna, Nabil I. Promises Fulfilled: Christianity, Islam, & the Baha'i Faith. 2010. *(978-1-931847-77-3(0))* Baha'i Publishing Trust, U.S.

Harper, Jane E. The Universe Within Us: A Guide to the Purpose of Life. 2009. *(978-1-931847-58-2(4))* Baha'i Publishing Trust, U.S.

Hatcher, J., compiled by. The Meaning of Suffering & the Mystery of Sacrifice. 2007. 48p. per. *(978-988-97451-6-5(X))* Juxta Publishing Ltd.

Hatcher, John. The Face of God among Us: How the Creator Educates Humanity. 2010. (Illus.). xv, 333p. *(978-1-931847-70-4(3))* Baha'i Publishing Trust, U.S.

Holley, Horace. Bahai: The Spirit of the Age. 2007. (ENG.). 228p. 41.95 *(978-0-548-10822-2(6))* Kessinger Publishing, LLC.

Illumine My Spirit: Bahá'í Prayers & Meditations for Women. 2008. (Illus.). vi, 234p. pap. *(978-1-931847-57-5(6))* Baha'i Publishing.

Ives, Howard Colby. Portals to Freedom. 2012. ***(978-1-931847-99-5(1))*** Baha'i Publishing.

Ketab Corp. Panj Maghale: Gooshehayee az tarikhe ayeene babi va Bahaie. 2007.Tr. of Five Articles. (PER.). 86p. pap. *(978-1-59584-116-2(4))* Ketab Corp.

Khan, Janet A. Heritage of Light: The Spiritual Destiny of America. 2009. 235p. 17.00 *(978-1-931847-73-5(8))* Baha'i Publishing Trust, U.S.

Kurzius, Brian. Hidden Gifts: Finding Blessings in the Struggles of Life. 2007. 139p. pap. *(978-1-931847-48-3(7))* Baha'i Publishing.

Lample, Paul. Revelation & Social Reality: Learning to Translate What Is Written into Reality. 2009. vii, 293p. ***(978-1-890101-70-1(2))*** Palabra Pubns.

Lawson, Todd. Babism & the Qur'an: The Literary Beginnings of the Babi Movement. 2012. (Iranian Studies). (ENG., Illus.). 240p. (C). 135.00 *(978-0-415-49539-4(3))* Routledge.

Lee, Anthony A. The Baha'i Faith in Africa: Establishing a New Religious Movement, 1952-1962. 2011. (Illus.). xii, 279p. ***(978-90-04-20684-7(1))*** BRILL.

Lepard, Brian D. In the Glory of the Father: The Baha'i Faith & Christianity. 2008. x, 246p. *(978-1-931847-34-6(7))* Baha'i Publishing Trust, U.S.

Markaz-i Asnad-i Huquq-i Bashar-I Iran. Diyanati Mamnu: Azar Va Taqib-I Bahayiyan Dar Iran: Va Jamiahi Dar Tangna: Sharh-I Mashaqqat-I Bahayiyan-I Shiraz. 2009. (Illus.). 297p. *(978-1-59584-193-3(8))* Ketab Corp.

Medina, John Fitzgerald. America's Sacred Calling: Building a New Spiritual Reality. 2010. *(978-1-931847-79-7(7))* Baha'i Publishing Trust, U.S.

—Faith, Physics, & Psychology: Rethinking Society & the Human Spirit. 2006. 537p. per. 17.00 *(978-1-931847-30-8(4))* Baha'i Publishing.

Miller, Daun E. Children of the Kingdom: A Baha'i Approach to Spiritual Parenting. 2010. xi, 249p. pap. *(978-1-931847-75-9(4))* Baha'i Publishing Trust, U.S.

Momen, Moojan. The Baha'i Faith: A Beginner's Guide. 2007. (Beginner's Guides (Oneworld) Ser.). (ENG.). 160p. per. 14.95 *(978-1-85168-563-9(4))* Oneworld Pubns. GBR. Dist: National Bk. Network.

—Baha'u'llah: A Short Biography. 2007. (ENG., Illus.). 192p. pap. 16.95 *(978-1-85168-469-4(7))* Oneworld Pubns. GBR. Dist: National Bk. Network.

Muhammad Hasan Khan, et al. Bahaiyan-I Nur-I Mazandaran: Bar Asas-I Sih Nuskhah-I Khatti. 2007. (PER., Illus.). 214p. *(978-1-59584-136-0(9))* Ketab Corp.

Nabil, Azam. Dawn-Breakers. 2007. pap. 25.00 *(978-0-9762780-4-7(9))* Best Publishing.

Pryse, James. The Apocalypse Unsealed. 2007. 236p. per. 13.95 *(978-1-60206-247-4(1))* Cosimo, Inc.

Quds Jurabchi, Ala al-Din. Baha Allah: Bunyanguzar-I Ain-I Bahai. 2nd ed. 2010. (PER.). 208p. ***(978-1-59584-243-5(8))*** Ketab Corp.

Renshaw, Amy. Voyage of Love. 2010. pap. *(978-0-87743-714-7(9))* Baha'i Publishing Trust, U.S.

Ring, Phyllis Edgerly. Life at First Sight: Finding the Divine in the Details. 2009. x, 240p. pap. 15.00 *(978-1-931847-67-4(3))* Baha'i Publishing Trust, U.S.

Rohani, Parviz & Ehsan, Shahin. The Qur'an & the Eternal Covenant of God. 2011. 274p. 22.95 ***(978-1-936401-70-3(3))*** Two Harbors Pr., Inc.

Ruhe-Schoen, Janet. Rejoice in My Gladness: The Life of Táhirih. 2011. xiii, 383p. *(978-1-931847-84-1(3))* Baha'i Publishing Trust, U.S.

Rutstein, Carol, ed. From a Gnat to an Eagle: The Story of Nathan Rutstein. 2008. 234p. pap. 18.00 *(978-1-931847-46-9(0))* Baha'i Publishing.

Rutstein, Nathan. A Way Out of the Trap: A Ten-Step Program for Spiritual Growth. 2007. vii, 238p. pap. *(978-1-931847-40-7(1))* Baha'i Publishing.

Safai, Maryam. Tului Digar. 2nd ed. 2008. (PER., Illus.). 130p. *(978-1-59584-196-4(2))* Ketab Corp.

Saiedi, Nader. Gate of the Heart: Understanding the Writings of the Bfb. 2010. (Bahf#237; Studies). (Illus.). 432p. pap. 42.95 *(978-1-55458-056-9(0))* Wilfrid Laurier Univ. Pr. CAN. Dist: Univ. of Toronto Pr.

Scharbrodt, Oliver. Islam & the Baha'i Faith: A Comparative Study of Muhammad 'Abduh & 'Abdul-Baha 'Abbas. 2011. (ENG., Illus.). 256p. pap. 39.95 ***(978-0-415-66403-5(9))*** Routledge.

Scharbrodt, Oliver. Islam & the Baha'i Faith: A Comparative Study of Muhammad Abduh & Abdul-Baha Abbas. 2008. (Culture & Civilization in the Middle East Ser.). (ENG., Illus.). 256p. (C). 150.00 *(978-0-415-77441-3(1))* Routledge.

Shahvar, Soli. The Forgotten Schools: The Baha'Is & Modern Education in Iran, 1899-1934. 2009. (ENG., Illus.). 288p. 92.50 *(978-1-84511-683-5(6),* Tauris Academic Studies) I. B. Tauris & Co., Ltd. GBR. Dist: Macmillan.

Shoghi. Family Life: A Compilation of Extracts from the Bahá'í Writings & from Letters Written by & on Behalf of Shoghi Effendi & the Universal House of Justice. 2008. 92p. pap. *(978-0-87743-354-5(2))* Baha'i Publishing.

Smith, Peter. An Introduction to the Baha'i Faith. 2008. (Introduction to Religion Ser.). (ENG., Illus.). 256p. (C). 81.00 *(978-0-521-86251-6(5))*; pap. 30.99 *(978-0-521-68107-0(3))* Cambridge Univ. Pr.

Terry, Peter. Proofs of the Prophets. 2008. 224p. pap. 19.95 *(978-1-4357-1346-8(X))* Lulu Enterprises Inc.

Universal House of Justice Staff, contrib. by. Messages from the Universal House of Justice, 1986-2001. 2010. *(978-0-87743-356-9(9))* Baha'i Publishing.

Warburg, Margit. Citizens of the World: A History & Sociology of the Bahais in a Globalisation Perspective. 2006. (Illus.). 550p. *(978-90-04-14373-9(4))* BRILL.

Wilson, Samuel G. Bahaism & Its Claims. reprint ed. 39.50 *(978-0-404-06995-7(9))* AMS Pr., Inc.

BAHAISM

see Bahai Faith

BAHAMAS

Johnson, Whittington B. Post-Emancipation Race Relations in the Bahamas. 2006. (ENG., Illus.). 192p. 59.95 *(978-0-8130-2994-8(5))* Univ. Pr. of Florida.

2007 Bahamas Handbook. 2007. 39.95 *(978-0-914755-83-8(8))* Routledge.

BAHAMAS—BIOGRAPHY

Carlisle, Sandee. Forgetting the Hurt, Remember the Hope: A Memoir of Endurance. 2008. 308p. pap. 13.95 *(978-1-59800-376-5(3))* Outskirts Pr., Inc.

Charles, Apostle Wislet. Hell Is Real. 2011. 56p. pap. 15.00 ***(978-1-4634-0263-1(5))*** AuthorHouse.

Cooper, Havard S. My Story ... His Glory: The Life & Experience of a Bahamian Son: Havard S. Cooper Sr. 2010. 200p. 26.95 *(978-1-4502-5679-7(1))*; pap. 16.95 *(978-1-4502-5678-0(3))* iUniverse, Inc.

Dreishpoon, Georgene S. Pursuit of Paradise: Memoir of a Bahama Mama. 2010. 220p. 26.95 *(978-1-4502-4760-3(1))*; pap. 16.95 *(978-1-4502-4758-0(X))* iUniverse, Inc.

Pflueger, Charles. Island Fever: Life Adventures in Search of Island Paradise. 2011. 408p. 35.95 *(978-1-4502-8794-4(8))*; pap. 25.95 *(978-1-4502-8792-0(1))* iUniverse, Inc.

Roberts, J. Rodney. An Apostolic Father. 2009. 96p. pap. 10.99 *(978-1-60791-528-7(6))* Xulon Pr., Inc.

Sears-Muschett, Regina. Held Hostage in the Bahamas: Rediscovering Home. 2007. 240p. per. 14.50 *(978-1-4259-9179-1(3))* AuthorHouse.

Sylvester, Geraldine. The Reluctant Innkeeper. 2008. 320p. pap. 16.95 *(978-1-934937-14-3(2))* Mill City Pr., Inc.

Wohlfelder, Peter. My Missionary Adventure: A True Story. 2009. 100p. pap. 14.00 *(978-1-4490-3646-1(5))* AuthorHouse.

Woodard, Colin. The Republic of Pirates: Being the True & Surprising Story of the Caribbean Pirates & the Man Who Brought Them Down. 2008. (ENG., Illus.). 400p. pap. 15.00 *(978-0-15-603462-3(X),* Mariner Bks.) Houghton Mifflin Harcourt Trade & Reference Pubs.

BAHAMAS—DESCRIPTION AND TRAVEL

Aubertin, J. A Fight with Distances: The States, the Hawaiian Islands, Canada, British Columbia, Cuba, the Bahamas. 2007. (Travel in America Ser.). (ENG.). 436p. 49.95 *(978-1-4290-0484-8(3))*; per. 24.95 *(978-1-4290-0485-5(1))* Applewood Bks.

Bonechi, Casa. Bahamas. (Illus.). 64p. *(978-88-7009-213-4(5))* Casa Editrice Bonechi.

Brownlee, John. Bahamas Boating & Fishing Guide. 2007. (Illus.). 224p. pap. 19.95 *(978-1-60239-068-3(1))* Skyhorse Publishing Co., Inc.

Charles, Ron. Open Road's Best of the Bahamas: Your Passport to the Perfect Trip! & Includes One-Day, Weekend One-Week & Two-Week Trips. 2008. (ENG., Illus.). 224p. pap. 14.95 *(978-1-59360-100-3(X))* Open Road Publishing.

Cleare, Angela B. History of Tourism in the Bahamas. 2007. 636p. 38.99 *(978-1-4257-3670-5(X))* Xlibris Corp.

—History of Tourism in the Bahamas: A Global Perspective. 2007. 636p. per. 28.99 *(978-1-4257-3669-9(6))* Xlibris Corp.

Dold, Gaylord, et al. Bahamas. 2nd ed. 2007. (Rough Guide Travel Guides Ser.). (ENG., Illus.). 408p. pap. 20.99 *(978-1-84353-776-2(1))* Rough Guides, Ltd. GBR. Dist: Dorling Kindersley Publishing, Inc.

Fodor's Travel Publications, Inc. Staff. Fodor's Bahamas: Plus Turks & Caicos. 28th ed. 2011. (Full-Color Gold Guides). (ENG.). 416p. pap. 19.99 *(978-0-679-00937-5(X),* Fodor's) Fodor's Travel Pubns.

Gale, Dave. Below Another Sky: A Bahama Memoir. 2011. ***(978-0-9661448-6-4(4))*** Caribe Communications.

Henderson, James. Caribbean & the Bahamas. 6th ed. (Country & Regional Guides). (ENG., Illus.). 340p. per. 22.95 *(978-1-86011-212-6(9))* Cadogan Guides GBR. Dist: Globe Pequot Pr., The.

Howard, Blair. Adventure Guide to the Islands of the Bahamas & Turks & Caicos. 4th ed. 2007. (Adventure Guide to the Bahamas, Turks & Caicos Ser.). (Illus.). 576p. pap. 9.99 *(978-1-58843-589-7(X))* Hunter Publishing, Inc.

Jung, C. G., et al. Frommer's Portable Bahamas. 8th ed. 2011. (Frommer's Portable Ser.: 273). (ENG.). 192p. pap. 12.99 *(978-1-118-02883-4(X),* Frommers) Wiley, John & Sons, Inc.

Klingel, Gilbert. Inagua. 2010. pap. 19.95 *(978-0-7414-5851-3(9))* Infinity Publishing.

Locken, E. Travel Journal Bahamas. 2010. 192p. pap. 19.99 *(978-0-557-43262-2(6))* Lulu Enterprises Inc.

McCulloch, Janelle. Dream Hotels: Architectural Hideaways. 2011. (ENG.). 248p. 60.00 ***(978-1-86470-367-2(9))*** Images Publishing Group AUS. Dist: National Bk. Network.

Pavlidis, Stephen J. The Exuma Guide: A Cruising Guide to the Exuma Cays. 3rd ed. 2009. pap. *(978-1-892399-31-1(8))* Seaworthy Pubns., Inc.

Philpott, Don. Bahamas. (Illus.). 96p. pap. 12.95 *(978-1-901522-00-6(8))* Hunter Publishing, Inc.

Porter, Darwin & Prince, Danforth. Frommer's Bahamas 2012. 7th ed. 2011. (Frommer's Complete Guides). (ENG., Illus.). 320p. pap. 18.99 *(978-1-118-00425-8(6),* Frommers) Wiley, John & Sons, Inc.

Robertson, Jessica, et al. Must Sees the Bahamas Michelin. 2009. (Must Sees Ser.). (ENG., Illus.). 192p. pap. 11.99 *(978-1-906261-62-7(8))* Michelin Travel & Lifestyle.

Sweeting, Lawrence. A Better Bahamas Begins with You. Date not set. (Illus.). 80p. (Orig.). pap. 10.00 *(978-0-9643786-8-1(X))* Media Publishing.

Sylvester, Geraldine. The Reluctant Innkeeper. 2008. 320p. pap. 16.95 *(978-1-934937-14-3(2))* Mill City Pr., Inc.

Walton, Chelle Koster. The Bahamas. 2010. (Great Destinations Ser.). (ENG., Illus.). 264p. pap. 19.95 *(978-1-58157-125-7(9),* 157125) Countryman Pr.

Wood, Lawson. Dive the Bahamas: Complete Guide to Diving & Snorkelling. 2007. (Dive Ser.). (ENG., Illus.). 176p. pap. 20.00 *(978-1-56656-705-3(X))* Interlink Publishing Group, Inc.

BAHAMAS—ECONOMIC CONDITIONS

Icon Group International, Inc. Staff, compiled by. The 2006 Economic & Product Market Databook for Freeport, Bahamas. 2006. 618p. ring bd. 95.00 *(978-0-497-80556-2(1))* Icon Group International, Inc.

—The 2006 Economic & Product Market Databook for Nassau, Bahamas. 2006. 618p. ring bd. 95.00 *(978-0-497-81105-1(7))* Icon Group International, Inc.

Johnson, Dexter, Sr. Crisis in Paradise the Bahamas at the Start of the Post-Tourism Era. 2009. (ENG.). 234p. pap. 25.00 *(978-0-9822338-6-3(8))* Terenshad Publishing Co.

Strachan, Cheryl C. Flying the Pride. 2010. 74p. pap. 33.99 *(978-1-60957-223-5(8))* Xulon Pr., Inc.

Wilchcombe, Monique. Countdown: A Handbook for Senior High School Students - Bahamas. 2009. 185p. pap. 26.41 *(978-1-4357-0912-6(8))* Lulu Enterprises Inc.

BAHAMAS—HISTORY

Baker, Harrison Scott. American Prisoners of War Held at Barbados, New Providence, & Newfoundland During the War of 1812. 2007. iii, 199p. pap. *(978-0-7884-4498-2(0))* Heritage Bks.

Bethell, A. Talbot. The Early Settlers of the Bahamas & Colonists of North America. 2007. 238p. reprint ed. pap. 23.00 *(978-0-7884-1249-3(3),* B173) Heritage Bks.

Cash & Maples. Making of the Bahamas. Date not set. (Illus.). 64p. pap. 59.75 *(978-0-582-02805-0(1))* Addison-Wesley Longman, Ltd. GBR. Dist: Trans-Atlantic Pubns., Inc.

Cleare, Angela B. History of Tourism in the Bahamas. 2007. 636p. 38.99 *(978-1-4257-3670-5(X))* Xlibris Corp.

—History of Tourism in the Bahamas: A Global Perspective. 2007. 636p. per. 28.99 *(978-1-4257-3669-9(6))* Xlibris Corp.

Craton, Michael. A-Z of Bahamas Heritage. 2007. (MacMillan Caribbean Ser.). (ENG., Illus.). 424p. pap. 24.95 *(978-1-4050-0242-4(5))* Macmillan Caribbean GBR. Dist: Interlink Publishing Group, Inc.

Johnson, Dexter/ Reno. An Introduction to Critical Problems in Bahamian Constitutional Law. 2008. (ENG.). 147p. pap. 15.00 *(978-0-9822338-4-9(1))* Terenshad Publishing Co.

—An Introduction to the Law & Legal System of the Commonwealth of the Bahamas. 2008. (ENG.). 145p. pap. 15.00 *(978-0-9822338-3-2(3))* Terenshad Publishing Co.

Neely, Wayne. The Great Bahamas Hurricane Of 1866: The Story of One of the Greatest & Deadliest Hurricanes to Ever Impact the Bahamas. 2011. 260p. 29.95 ***(978-1-4620-1103-2(9))***; pap. 19.95 ***(978-1-4620-1102-5(0))*** iUniverse, Inc.

Rommen, Timothy. Funky Nassau: Roots, Routes, & Representation in Bahamian Popular Music. 2011. (Music of the African Diaspora Ser.). (ENG., Illus.). 304p. 60.00 *(978-0-520-26568-4(6))*; pap. 26.95 *(978-0-520-26569-1(6))* Univ. of California Pr.

BAHAMAS—SOCIAL LIFE AND CUSTOMS

Herzing, Denise & Herzing, Denise L. Dolphin Diaries: My 25 Years with Spotted Dolphins in the Bahamas. 2011. (ENG., Illus.). 336p. 26.99 *(978-0-312-60896-5(9))* St. Martin's Pr.

Herzing, Denise L. Dolphin Diaries: My 25 Years with Spotted Dolphins in the Bahamas. 2012. (ENG.). 336p. pap. 16.99 ***(978-1-250-00691-2(0),*** St. Martin's Griffin) St. Martin's Pr.

Ingraham, Clarice P. Maternal Morbidity & Mortality in the Bahamas. 2011. 108p. pap. 39.28 *(978-1-4269-5183-1(3))* Trafford Publishing.

Jenkins, Olga Culmer. Bahamian Memories: Island Voices of the Twentieth Century. 2008. (ENG., Illus.). 320p. pap. 29.95 *(978-0-8130-3272-6(5))* Univ. Pr. of Florida.

Tinker, Keith L. The Migration of Peoples from the Caribbean to the Bahamas. 2011. (ENG., Illus.). 168p. 69.95 *(978-0-8130-3531-4(7))* Univ. Pr. of Florida.

BAHAMIAN COOKING

see Cooking, Bahamian

BAHASA INDONESIA

see Indonesian Language

BAHAULLAH, 1817-1892

see Baha Allah, 1817-1892

BAHAWALPUR (PAKISTAN)

Dar, Shujaat Zamir. Sights in the Sands of Cholistan: Bahawalpur's History & Architecture. Dar, Shujaat Zamir, ed. 2007. (ENG., Illus.). 250p. 85.00 *(978-0-19-547353-7(1))* Oxford Univ. Pr., Inc.

BAHIA (BRAZIL: STATE)

Despland, Michel. Bastide on Religion: The Invention of Candomblé. 2008. (Key Thinkers in the Study of Religion Ser.). (ENG.). 224p. (C). 95.00 *(978-1-84553-365-6(8))*; pap. 29.95 *(978-1-84553-366-3(6))* Equinox Publishing Ltd. GBR. Dist: ISD.

Harris, Richard. Hidden Puerto Vallarta: Including the Bahia de Banderas & Sierra Madre Mountains. 2009. (Hidden Travel Ser.). (ENG., Illus.). 232p. pap. 16.95 *(978-1-56975-571-6(X))* Ulysses Pr.

Pinho, Patricia de Santana. Mama Africa: Reinventing Blackness in Bahia. Langdon, Elena, tr. from POR. 2010. (ENG., Illus.). 280p. 84.95 *(978-0-8223-4654-8(0))*; pap. 23.95 *(978-0-8223-4646-3(X))* Duke Univ. Pr.

Robinson, Alex. Bahia: The Heart of Brazil's Northeast. 2011. (Bradt Travel Guide Ser.). (ENG., Illus.). 192p. pap. 25.99 *(978-1-84162-329-0(6))* Bradt Travel Guides GBR. Dist: Globe Pequot Pr., The.

—Bahia & Salvador Footprint Focus. 2011. (Footprint Focus Ser.). (ENG., Illus.). 112p. pap. 11.95 *(978-1-908206-12-1(8))* Footprint Handbooks GBR. Dist: Globe Pequot Pr., The.

Romo, Anadelia A. Brazil's Living Museum: Race, Reform, & Tradition in Bahia. 2010. (ENG., Illus.). 272p. 59.95 *(978-0-8078-3382-7(7))*; 240p. pap. 24.95 *(978-0-8078-7115-7(X))* Univ. of North Carolina Pr.

Selka, Stephen. Religion & the Politics of Ethnic Identity in Bahia, Brazil. 2009. (New World Diasporas Ser.). (ENG., Illus.). 192p. pap. 29.95 *(978-0-8130-3387-7(X))* Univ. Pr. of Florida.

Sommers, Michael. Salvador & Bahia. 2009. (Moon Spotlight Ser.). (ENG.). 85p. pap. 7.95 *(978-1-59880-538-3(X))* Avalon Travel Publishing.

BAHRAIN—DESCRIPTION AND TRAVEL

Explorer, Explorer. Bahrain Mini Explorer. 2008. (ENG.). 200p. pap. 11.95 *(978-9948-03-319-6(1))* Explorer Publishing UAE. Dist: Globe Pequot Pr., The.

Explorer Publishing (UAE) Staff. Bahrain Explorer. 2005th ed. 2007. (Explorer - Residents' Guides). (ENG., Illus.). 430p. pap. 24.95 *(978-976-8182-52-4(0))* Explorer Publishing UAE. Dist: Globe Pequot Pr., The.

Locken, E. Travel Journal Bahrain. 2010. 192p. pap. 19.99 *(978-0-557-43266-0(9))* Lulu Enterprises Inc.

Tripp, Harvey. CultureShock! Bahrain. 2007. (Illus.). 200p. pap. 15.95 *(978-981-232-893-9(9))* Marshall Cavendish International (Asia) Private Ltd. SGP. Dist: Marshall Cavendish Corp.

Tripp, Harvey, et al. Bahrain, 1 vol. 2008. (CultureShock! Ser.). (ENG., Illus.). 200p. pap. 15.95 *(978-0-7614-5473-1(X))* Marshall Cavendish Corp.

BAHRAIN—ECONOMIC CONDITIONS

Dew, Philip. Bahrain's Business Environment. 2008. (ENG.). pap. 75.00 *(978-1-84673-086-3(4),* GMB Publishing Ltd.) Blue Ibex Ltd. GBR. Dist: Ingram Pub. Services.

Icon Group International, Inc. Staff, compiled by. The 2006 Economic & Product Market Databook for Al Hidd, Bahrain. 2006. 618p. ring bd. 95.00 *(978-0-497-80014-7(4))* Icon Group International, Inc.

—The 2006 Economic & Product Market Databook for Isa Town, Bahrain. 2006. 618p. ring bd. 95.00 *(978-0-497-81931-6(7))* Icon Group International, Inc.

—The 2006 Economic & Product Market Databook for Jidd Hafs, Bahrain. 2006. 618p. ring bd. 95.00 *(978-0-497-81946-0(5))* Icon Group International, Inc.

—The 2006 Economic & Product Market Databook for Manama, Bahrain. 2006. 618p. ring bd. 95.00 *(978-0-497-80936-2(2))* Icon Group International, Inc.

—The 2006 Economic & Product Market Databook for Muharraq, Bahrain. 2006. 618p. ring bd. 95.00 *(978-0-497-81069-6(7))* Icon Group International, Inc.

Kadhem, S. Mohamed. Developing Motivational & Coaching Skills in Telecom Companies. 2010. 100p. pap. *(978-3-8383-7015-6(5))* Lambert Academic Publishing.

BAHRAIN—HISTORY

Etheredge, Laura S., ed. Persian Gulf States: Kuwait, Qatar, Bahrain, Oman, & the United Arab Emirates. 2011. (Middle East: Region in Transition Ser.). (Illus.). 184p. (YA). 80.00 *(978-1-61530-454-7(1))* Rosen Publishing Group, Inc., The.

Gunning, Jeroen, et al. The Handbook of Bahrain. 2008. 50.00 *(978-0-7103-1388-1(8))* Kegan Paul International, Ltd. GBR. Dist: Columbia Univ. Pr.

BAHRAIN—POLITICS AND GOVERNMENT

Bashmi, Ibrahim. Mashru Al-Bahrayn Al-Islahi: Ishkaliyat Ghiyab Thaqafat Al-Dimuqratiyah: Ruyah Naqdiyah Lil-Tahawwulat Al-Siyasiyah. (ARA.). 140p. *(978-99901-02-52-9(X))* Markaz al-Bahrayn lil-Dirasat wa-al-Buhuth.

Kadhem, S. Mohamed. The Conceptual Metaphors of Gulf War II in Bahraini Journalism. 2010. 96p. pap. *(978-3-8383-7290-7(5))* Lambert Academic Publishing.

Nakhleh, Emile A. Bahrain: Political Development in a Modernizing Society. 2011. (ENG.). 212p. pap. 27.95 *(978-0-7391-6858-5(4))* Lexington Bks.

Niethammer, Katja. Political Reform in Bahrain: Institutional Transformation, Identity Conflict & Democracy. 2013. (History & Society in the Islamic World Ser.). (ENG.). 224p. (C). 130.00 *(978-0-415-55914-0(6))* Routledge.

BAHRAIN—SOCIAL CONDITIONS

Gardner, Andrew. City of Strangers: Gulf Migration & the Indian Community in Bahrain. 2010. (Illus.). 216p. 59.95 *(978-0-8014-4882-9(4))*; pap. 19.95 *(978-0-8014-7602-0(X))* Cornell Univ. Pr. (ILR Pr.).

BAHUTU

see Hutu (African People)

BAIL

see also Bail Bondsmen

Bail Bond Fairness ACT of 2007: Hearing Before the Subcommittee on Crime, Terrorism, & Homeland Security of the Committee on the Judiciary, House of Representatives, One Hundred Tenth Congress, First Session, on H.R. 2286, June 7, 2007. 2008. iii, 61p. *(978-0-16-081750-2(1),* 552-070-37958-4) United States Government Printing Office.

De Haas, Elsa. Antiquities of Bail: Origin & Historical Development in Criminal Cases to the Year 1275. reprint ed. 20.00 *(978-0-404-02067-5(4))* AMS Pr., Inc.

Verrochi, Richard. How to Start a Bail Bond Business & Become a Bail Bondsman, 1. 2006. 153p. 29.95 *(978-0-9789569-0-5(7),* 1) Verrochi, Richard.

BAIL—GREAT BRITAIN

Hucklesby, Anthea. Bail. 2013. (ENG.). 320p. 150.00 *(978-0-415-48911-9(3))* Routledge.

—Bail Support Schemes for Adults. 2011. (Illus.). 120p. pap. 28.95 *(978-1-84742-954-4(8))* Policy Pr. GBR. Dist: Chicago Distribution Ctr.

BAIL BONDSMEN

Verrochi, Richard. How to Start A Bail Bond Business & Become A Bail Bondsman. 2006. 152p. per. 29.95 *(978-0-9789569-1-2(5))* Verrochi, Richard.

BAIL JUMPING

see Bail

BAILEY, ALICE, 1880-1949

Bailey, Alice A. Unfinished Autobiography. 2009. (ENG., Illus.). 304p. pap. 20.00 *(978-0-85330-124-0(7))* Lucis Publishing Co.

BAILIE, JOSEPH, 1860-1935

Garner, Michael. Romanticism & the Gothic: Genre, Reception, & Canon Formation. 2006. (Cambridge Studies in Romanticism Ser.). (ENG.). 276p. pap. 45.00 *(978-0-521-02693-2(8))* Cambridge Univ. Pr.

BAILIFFS

Rudman, Jack. Bailiff. (Career Examination Ser.: C-3693). pap. 23.95 *(978-0-8373-3693-0(7))* National Learning Corp.

Schneider, Zoë A. The King's Bench: Bailiwick Magistrates & Local Governance in Normandy, 1670-1740. 2008. (Changing Perspectives on Early Modern Europe Ser.: Volume 11). (Illus.). 340p. 75.00 *(978-1-58046-292-1(8))* Univ. of Rochester Pr.

BAILLIE, GRIZEL (HUME), LADY, 1665-1746

Tytler, Sarah. The Songstresses of Scotland. 2009. 136p. pap. *(978-1-151-12828-7(7))* Books LLC.

—The Songstresses of Scotland, 2 Vols. reprint ed. 125.00 *(978-0-7222-1497-8(9))* Library Reprints, Inc.

Tytler, Sarah & Watson, Jean L. The Songstresses of Scotland. 2009. 680p. 39.99 *(978-1-115-87964-4(2))*; 46.99 *(978-1-115-87963-7(4))*; pap. 47.75 *(978-1-115-87965-1(0))*; pap. 46.75 *(978-1-115-87966-8(9))* BiblioBazaar.

BAILLIE, JOANNA, 1762-1851

Mclean, Thomas, ed. Further Letters of Joanna Baillie. 2010. 296p. *(978-0-8386-4149-1(0))* Fairleigh Dickinson Univ. Pr.

Tytler, Sarah. The Songstresses of Scotland. 2009. 136p. pap. *(978-1-151-12828-7(7))* Books LLC.

Tytler, Sarah & Watson, Jean L. The Songstresses of Scotland. 2009. 680p. 46.99 *(978-1-115-87963-7(4))*; 39.99 *(978-1-115-87964-4(2))*; pap. 47.75 *(978-1-115-87965-1(0))*; pap. 46.75 *(978-1-115-87966-8(9))* BiblioBazaar.

BAILLY, JEAN SYLVAIN, 1736-1793

Kelly, George Armstrong. Victims, Authority, & Terror: The Parallel Deaths of D'Orleans, Custine, Bailly, & Malesherbes. 2011. (ENG.). 404p. pap. 50.00 *(978-0-8078-9698-3(5))* Univ. of North Carolina Pr.

BAILMENTS

see also Auctions; Carriers; Freight Forwarders; Hotels—Law and Legislation; Liens; Pawnbroking; Pledges (Law); Possession (Law)

Jones, William. An Essay on the Law of Bailments. 2009. 166p. pap. 19.99 *(978-1-150-20470-8(2))* General Bks. LLC.

Jones, William & Balmanno, John. An Essay on the Law of Bailments. 2009. (ENG.). 311p. pap. 28.75 *(978-1-117-59095-0(X))* BiblioBazaar.

Story, Joseph. Commentaries on the Law of Bailments: With Illustrations from the Civil & Foreign Law. 2007. 95.00 *(978-1-58477-778-6(8))* Lawbook Exchange, Ltd., The.

BAINBRIDGE, BERYL, 1933-2010

Grubisic, Brett Josef. Understanding Beryl Bainbridge. 2008. 208p. 39.95 *(978-1-57003-756-6(6))* Univ. of South Carolina Pr.

BAIT

see also Fishing Lures

Blaha, Francisco. Development of a Bait for the Longlining Fishery of Snapper. 2010. 68p. pap. *(978-3-8383-6081-2(8))* Lambert Academic Publishing

BAJA CALIFORNIA (MEXICO: PENINSULA)

Diez, Carlos. Bien Salud: A Guide to Baja's Medical Services. Warren, Sam ed. Date not set. (Illus.). 200p. (Orig.). pap. 16.95 *(978-0-945949-08-4(1))* Warren Communications.

Hill, Herman. Baja's Hidden Gold: Treasure along the Mission Trail. 2008. 188p. pap. 16.95 *(978-1-934248-72-0(X))* Mill City Pr., Inc.

Koch, Rod. When the Green Flag Drops. 2011. 498p. 34.99 ***(978-1-4568-5863-6(7))***; pap. 23.99 ***(978-1-4568-5862-9(9))*** Xlibris Corp.

Minch, John, et al. Roadside Geology & Biology of Baja California. Date not set. (Illus.). 194p. 19.95 *(978-0-9631090-1-9(4))* Minch, John & Assocs., Inc.

Reyes, Bárbara O. Private Women, Public Lives: Gender & the Missions of the Californias. 2010. (ENG., Illus.). 245p. pap. 25.00 *(978-0-292-72347-4(4))* Univ. of Texas Pr.

BAJA CALIFORNIA (MEXICO: PENINSULA)—DESCRIPTION AND TRAVEL

Axelrod, Alan, et al. Best Guide: Loreto: Baja California Sur, Mexico. 2007. (Illus.). 200p. per. 23.95 *(978-0-9700455-8-4(1))* Benevon Pubns.

Bancroft, Hubert Howe. California Pastoral. 2007. (ENG.). 816p. per. 55.95 *(978-0-548-50158-0(0))* Kessinger Publishing, LLC.

Church, Mike & Church, Terri. Camping Mexico's Baja: Explore Baja & Puerto Peñasco with Your RV or Tent. 4th ed. 2008. (Traveler's Guide Ser.). (ENG., Illus.). 256p. pap. 16.95 *(978-0-9749471-8-1(0))* Rolling Homes Pr.

Delgado, Kevin. Los Cabos & Baja California Sur. 2nd ed. 2011. (Great Destinations Ser.). (ENG., Illus.). 224p. pap. 19.95 *(978-1-58157-121-9(6),* 157121) Countryman Pr.

Ensenada, Baja Mexico: You Decide Travel Gd. 2006. 124p. pap. 15.95 *(978-0-9708898-9-8(5))* Sunbelt Pubns., Inc.

Fodor's Travel Publications, Inc. Staff. Los Cabos & the Baja Peninsula. 2nd ed. 2010. (Full-Color Gold Guides). (ENG., Illus.). 308p. pap. 19.99 *(978-1-4000-0438-6(1),* Fodor's) Fodor's Travel Pubns.

Fowler, Peter. Good Info for Gringos Living in Baja. 2007. 106p. pap. 9.95 *(978-0-9791017-1-7(9))* Fowler, Peter.

Gatch, Tom. Hooked on Baja: Where & How to Fish Mexico's Legendary Waters. 2007. (ENG., Illus.). 224p. per. 21.95 *(978-0-88150-726-3(1))* Countryman Pr.

Healey, Elizabeth L. Baja, Mexico/Baja California y Baja California Sur: Through the Eyes of an Honest Lens/Por Los Ojos de un Lente Honesto. 2006. (Illus.). 156p. 39.95 *(978-1-4276-0945-8(4))* Aardvark Global Publishing.

Hepp, Joy & Hamilton, Valerie. Frommer's Los Cabos & Baja. 4th ed. 2011. (Frommer's Complete Guides). (ENG., Illus.). 224p. pap. 17.99 ***(978-1-118-08604-9(X),*** Frommers) Wiley, John & Sons, Inc.

Itoi, Nikki Goth. Moon Baja: Including Cabo San Lucas. 2011. (Moon Handbooks Ser.). (ENG., Illus.). 492p. pap. 19.99 *(978-1-59880-889-6(3))* Avalon Travel Publishing.

—Moon Cabo: Including la Paz & Todos Santos. 2011. (Moon Handbooks Ser.). (ENG., Illus.). 304p. pap. 16.99 *(978-1-59880-890-2(7))* Avalon Travel Publishing.

Martone, Laura. Baja RV Camping. 2008. (Moon Outdoors Ser.). (ENG.). 300p. pap. 17.95 *(978-1-59880-148-4(1))* Avalon Travel Publishing.

Mayo, C. M. Miraculous Air: Journey of a Thousand Miles Through Baja California, the Other Mexico. 2007. (ENG., Illus.). 390p. per. 15.00 *(978-1-57131-304-1(4))* Milkweed Editions.

National Geo Maps Staff. Map North Baja Ca. 2009. 11.95 *(978-1-56695-243-9(3))* National Geographic Maps.

—Map South Baja Ca. 2009. 11.95 *(978-1-56695-244-6(1))* National Geographic Maps.

La Paz, Baja Mexico: You Decide Travel Gd. 2006. 114p. pap. 15.95 *(978-0-9708898-8-1(7))* Sunbelt Pubns., Inc.

Puckett, George E. Baja Diaries - Chronicles of a Paradise Lost. 2008. 180p. pap. 14.95 *(978-1-4343-4601-8(3))* AuthorHouse.

B

Salvadori, Clement. Motorcycle Journeys Through California & Baja. 2nd ed. 2007. (Motorcycle Journeys Ser.). (ENG., Illus.). 352p. per. 29.95 *(978-1-884313-60-8(4)*, 1884313604) Whitehorse Pr.
Swaim, Bernie. Think You Know Baja. 2006. pap. 16.95 *(978-0-9721863-2-2(8))* Sunbelt Pubns., Inc.
Ventura, Jesse. Don't Start the Revolution Without Me! 2009. (ENG., Illus.). 320p. pap. 14.95 *(978-1-60239-716-3(3)*, 239716) Skyhorse Publishing Co., Inc.
Vernon, Edward W. A Maritime History of Baja California. 2010. (ENG., Illus.). 307p. 49.95 *(978-0-578-03668-7(1))* Univ. of New Mexico Pr.

BAKED PRODUCTS
see also Biscuits; Bread; Cake; Muffins; Pastry
Anastacio, Aileen. Home Café: 100 Recipes for Irresistible Coffees & Delectable Desserts, 1 vol. 2010. (ENG., Illus.). 224p. pap. 26.00 *(978-981-4276-09-2(X))* Marshall Cavendish International (Asia) Private Ltd. SGP. Dist: Marshall Cavendish Corp.
Atkinson, Catherine. 500 Cookies, Biscuits & Bakes: An Irresistible Collection of Cookies, Scones, Bars, Brownies, Slices, Muffins, Cup Cakes, Flapjacks, Shortbread, Savoury Crackers & More, Shown in 500 Fabulous Photographs. 2008. (ENG., Illus.). 256p. 29.99 *(978-0-7548-1837-3(3))* Anness Publishing GBR. Dist: National Bk. Network.
—500 Cookies, Biscuits & Bakes: An irresistible collection of cookies, scones, bars, brownies, slices, muffins, shortbread, cup cakes, flapjacks, savory crackers & more, shown in 500 fabulous Photographs. 2011. (ENG., Illus.). 264p. pap. 18.99 *(978-1-78019-001-3(8))* Anness Publishing GBR. Dist: National Bk. Network.
Baked Goods Market: Companies-Products-Services. 173p. (Orig.). pap. *(978-0-7605-2205-9(7))* Rector Pr., Ltd.
Bakery Products Market: Companies-Products-Services. 60p. (Orig.). pap. *(978-0-7605-2203-5(0))* Rector Pr., Ltd.
Bakery Snacks Market: Companies-Products-Services. 200p. (Orig.). pap. *(978-0-7605-2204-2(9))* Rector Pr., Ltd.
Bent, A. J., et al. Technology of Cakemaking. 6th ed. 2010. (ENG., Illus.). 421p. pap. 249.00 *(978-1-4419-4742-0(6)*, 1441947426) Springer.
Berry, Mary. Mary Berry's Baking Bible: Over 250 Classic Recipes. 2010. (ENG., Illus.). 400p. 44.95 *(978-1-84607-785-2(0))* BBC Worldwide GBR. Dist: Independent Pubs. Group.
Blake, Susannah, ed. Perfect Pancakes & Crepes: More Than 20 Delicious Recipes, from Pancakes, Wraps & Fruit-Filled Crepes to Latkes & Scones, Shown Step by Step in over 125 Photographs. 2012. (ENG., Illus.). 64p. 9.99 ***(978-0-7548-2481-7(0))*** Anness Publishing GBR. Dist: National Bk. Network.
Bread Market: Companies-Products-Services. 200p. (Orig.). pap. *(978-0-7605-2207-3(3))* Rector Pr., Ltd.
Brown, Warren. CakeLove in the Morning: Recipes for Muffins, Scones, Pancakes, Waffles, Biscuits, Frittatas, & Other Breakfast Treats. 2012. (ENG., Illus.). 208p. 24.95 ***(978-1-58479-894-1(7))*** Stewart, Tabori & Chang.
Cauvain, S.P. & Young, L. S. More Baking Problems Solved. 2009. (Illus.). 252p. *(978-1-84569-382-4(5))* Woodhead Publishing Ltd.
Cauvain, Stanley. More Baking Problems Solved. 2009. 256p. 209.95 *(978-1-4398-0108-6(8))* CRC Pr. LLC.
Cauvain, Stanley P. & Young, Linda S. Bakery Food Manufacture & Quality: Water Control & Effects. 2nd ed. 2008. (ENG., Illus.). 304p. 219.95 *(978-1-4051-7613-2(X)*, Wiley-Blackwell) Wiley, John & Sons, Inc.
Clements, Carole. Best-Ever Home Baking: A wonderful collection of irresistible home bakes & cakes, with 70 classic recipes shown in 300 step-by-step Photographs. 2011. (ENG., Illus.). 96p. pap. 16.99 *(978-1-84476-976-6(3))* Anness Publishing GBR. Dist: National Bk. Network.
—Easy Home Baking: 70 Fabulous Cakes, Cookies, Breads, Pies & Muffins SHown Step by Step in Over 300 Photographs. 2008. (ENG., Illus.). 96p. pap. 9.99 *(978-1-84476-584-3(9))* Anness Publishing GBR. Dist: National Bk. Network.
CQ Products. Class Treats, Bake Sales & Birthday Parties. 2010. (ENG.). 128p. spiral bd. 10.00 *(978-1-56383-138-6(4))* G & R Publishing.
Culinary Institute of America Staff. Baking & Pastry: Mastering the Art & Craft. 2nd ed. 2009. (ENG., Illus.). 108p. pap., pupil's gde. ed. 35.00 *(978-0-470-25868-2(3)*, Wiley) Wiley, John & Sons, Inc.
Cuthbert, Pippa, et al. The Big Book of Sweet Treats. 2012. (ENG., Illus.). 304p. 14.95 *(978-1-84773-550-8(9))* New Holland Pubs., Ltd. GBR. Dist: Sterling Publishing Co., Inc.
Eckberg, John. Have a Crumby: A Collection of Wit & Whimsy from Cincinnati's Favorite Bakery. 2007. (ENG., Illus.). 160p. pap. 17.95 *(978-1-57860-306-0(4))* Clerisy Pr.
Edwards, W. P. The Science of Bakery Products. 2007. (ENG., Illus.). 274p. 40.00 *(978-0-85404-486-3(8))* Royal Society of Chemistry, The GBR. Dist: Ingram Pub. Services.
Ferguson, Valerie. Sweet Delights: A Superb Box Collection of Delectable Recipes in 10 Irresistible Cookbooks, 10 vols. 2010. (Illus.). 640p. 30.00 *(978-0-7548-2019-2(X))* Anness Publishing GBR. Dist: National Bk. Network.
—The Teatime Cookbook: 150 Homemade Cakes, Bakes & Party Treats. 2010. (ENG., Illus.). 320p. 16.99 *(978-0-7548-2163-2(3))* Anness Publishing GBR. Dist: National Bk. Network.
Fortnum, et al. Tea at Fortnum & Mason. 2012. (ENG., Illus.). 128p. 17.95 ***(978-0-09-193768-3(X))*** Ebury Publishing GBR. Dist: Independent Pubs. Group.
Fraser, Linda. 60 Easy Low Fat Baking Recipes: Healthy & Delicious Low-Fat, Low Cholesterol Cookies, Scones, Cakes & Bakes, Shown Step-by-Step in 300 Beautiful Photographs. 2011. (ENG., Illus.). 96p. pap. 16.99 *(978-1-84476-801-1(5))* Anness Publishing GBR. Dist: National Bk. Network.
Good Food Magazine Staff. Good Food: 201 Perfect Cakes & Bakes. 2011. (ENG., Illus.). 192p. pap. 23.95 ***(978-1-84990-143-7(0))*** BBC Worldwide GBR. Dist: Independent Pubs. Group.
Helou, Anissa. Savory Baking from the Mediterranean: Focaccias, Flatbreads, Rusks, Tarts, & Other Breads. 2007. (ENG., Illus.). 304p. 29.95 *(978-0-06-054219-1(5)*, Morrow, William Cookbooks) HarperCollins Pubs.
Hornby, Jane, et al. Good Food 101: Cupcakes & Small Bakes - Triple-Tested Recipes. 2010. (ENG., Illus.). 216p. pap. 9.95 *(978-1-84607-915-3(2))* BBC Worldwide GBR. Dist: Independent Pubs. Group.
Hui, Y. H., et al, eds. Bakery Products: Science & Technology. 2006. (ENG., Illus.). 586p. 249.95 *(978-0-8138-0187-2(7)*, Wiley-Blackwell) Wiley, John & Sons, Inc.
Leisure Arts. Celebrating Quick Breads & Pastries. 2011. (Celebrating Cookbooks Ser.). (ENG., Illus.). 144p. pap. 14.95 *(978-1-60900-116-2(8))* Leisure Arts, Inc.
Lerouet, Michael. Laduree: The Savory Recipes. 2011. (ENG.). 392p. *(978-2-8123-0458-3(8))* Hachette Livre UK.
Lewis, Fay. From My Oven: A Step-by-Step Guide to Successful Baking. 2008. (Illus.). 224p. 28.00 *(978-1-77007-564-1(X))* Struik Pubs. ZAF. Dist: International Publishers Marketing.
Lewis, Matt & Poliafito, Renato. Baked: New Frontiers in Baking. 2008. (ENG., Illus.). 208p. 29.95 *(978-1-58479-721-0(5))* Stewart, Tabori & Chang.
Magee, David. MoonPie: Biography of an Out-Of-This-World Snack. 2007. (ENG., Illus.). 192p. per. 14.95 *(978-0-8130-3157-6(5))* Univ. Pr. of Florida.
Mq Publications. Homemade Baking. 2006. 19.95 *(978-1-84601-143-6(4))* M Q Pubns. GBR. Dist: Ingram Pub. Services.
New Holland Australia, creator. Baking. 2007. (Illus.). 222p. per. 19.95 *(978-1-74110-547-6(1))* New Holland Pubs. Pty, Ltd. AUS. Dist: National Bk. Network.
Novak Bull, Lorena. The Everything Vegan Baking Cookbook: 300 Recipes for Any Occasion! 2012. (ENG.). 304p. pap. 16.95 ***(978-1-4405-2997-9(3))*** Adams Media Corp.
Osborne, Catherine, ed. Just Liked My Mother Used to Bake. 2008. (ENG., Illus.). 64p. *(978-1-84597-600-2(2))* CICO Bks.
Pellegrini, Matteo. The Art of Baking Bread: What You Really Need to Know to Make Great Bread. 2012. (ENG., Illus.). 192p. 24.95 ***(978-1-61608-537-7(1)***, 608537) Skyhorse Publishing Co., Inc.
Peterson, James. Baking: 300 Recipes, 2,000 Photographs, 1 Baking Education. 2009. (ENG., Illus.). 400p. 40.00 *(978-1-58008-991-3(7))* Ten Speed Pr.
Pettigrew, Jane. Good Old-Fashioned Teatime Treats. 2010. (ENG., Illus.). 112p. 12.95 *(978-1-905400-90-4(X))* National Trust, Aylesbury GBR. Dist: Independent Pubs. Group.
Quinn, Janie. Essential Eating Sprouted Baking: With Whole Grain Flours That Digest as Vegetables. 2008. (ENG.). 192p. 27.95 *(978-0-9679843-3-9(5))* Azure Moon Publishing.
Ratcliffe, Janine. 101 Brilliant Baking Ideas. 2010. (Olive Magazine Ser.). (ENG., Illus.). 216p. pap. 9.95 *(978-1-84607-812-5(1))* BBC Worldwide GBR. Dist: Independent Pubs. Group.
Robbins, Jill. Allergen Free Baking: Baked Treats for All Occasions. 2007. (ENG., Illus.). 150p. pap. 18.95 *(978-0-9776836-1-1(3))* Book Publishing Co.
Romy Lewis & Victoria Jos. Making Cupcakes with Lola. 2011. (ENG., Illus.). 144p. *(978-1-84975-186-5(2))* Ryland Peters & Small.
Scurfield, George & Scurfield, Cecilia. Home Baked: A little book of bread, cake & biscuit Recipes. 2009. (Illus.). 144p. 24.95 *(978-1-906502-37-9(4))* Grub Street GBR. Dist: Casemate Pubs. & Bk. Distributors, LLC.
Simmons, Jessica, ed. Women's Institute: Vintage Teatime. 2012. (ENG., Illus.). 112p. pap. 18.95 ***(978-0-85720-859-0(4))*** Simon & Schuster, Ltd. GBR. Dist: Independent Pubs. Group.
Strauss, Elisa & Matheson, Christie. Confetti Cakes for Kids: Delightful Cookies, Cakes, & Cupcakes from New York City's Famed Bakery. 2nd ed. 2008. (ENG., Illus.). 224p. 29.99 *(978-0-316-11829-3(X))* Little Brown & Co.
Talbot, G. Technology of Coated & Filled Chocolate, Confectionery, Bakery Products & Ice Cream. Talbot, G., ed. 2009. (Illus.). 384p. 239.95 *(978-1-4398-0136-9(3))* CRC Pr. LLC.
Talbot, G., ed. Science & Technology of Enrobed & Filled Chocolate, Confectionery & Bakery Products. 2009. (Illus.). 468p. *(978-1-84569-390-9(6))* Woodhead Publishing Ltd.
Trivuncic, Sarah. Bake Me I'm Yours... Sweet Bitesize Bakes: 25 Miniature Baking & Cake Decorating Projects. 2012. (ENG., Illus.). 128p. 14.99 ***(978-1-4463-0183-8(4))*** David & Charles Pubs. GBR. Dist: F&W Media, Inc.
Young, Linda S. & Cauvain, Stanley P. Baked Products: Science, Technology & Practice. 2006. (ENG., Illus.). 240p. 230.00 *(978-1-4051-2702-8(3)*, Wiley-Blackwell) Wiley, John & Sons, Inc.

BAKER, BOBBY, 1950-
Baker, Bobby. Diary Drawings. 2010. (ENG., Illus.). 224p. pap. 22.95 ***(978-1-84668-374-9(2))*** Profile Bks. Ltd. GBR. Dist: Consortium Bk. Sales & Distribution.
Baker, Bobby, ed. Bobby Baker. 2007. (Illus.). 288p. 140.00 *(978-0-415-44410-1(1))* Routledge.
Barrett, Michaéle. Bobby Baker: Redeeming Features of Daily Life. 2007. (Illus.). 288p. 46.95 *(978-0-415-44411-8(X))* Routledge.

BAKER, EDWARD DICKINSON, 1811-1861
Kennedy, Elijah Robinson. The Contest for California in 1861: How Colonel E.d. Baker Saved the Pacific States in the Union. 361p. reprint ed. 98.00 *(978-0-7222-8044-7(0))* Library Reprints, Inc.

BAKER, GEORGE, CA. 1875-1965
see Father Divine

BAKER, JOSEPHINE, 1906-1975
Cheng, Anne Anlin & Baker, Josephine. Second Skin: Josephine Baker & the Modern Surface, 1 vol. 2011. (ENG., Illus.). 224p. 24.95 *(978-0-19-538705-6(8))* Oxford Univ. Pr., Inc.
Jules-Rosette, Bennetta. Josephine Baker in Art & Life: The Icon & the Image. 2007. (Illus.). 392p. pap. 26.00 *(978-0-252-07412-7(2))*; 368p. 60.00 *(978-0-252-03157-1(1))* Univ. of Illinois Pr.

BAKER, NEWTON DIEHL, 1871-1937
Cramer, C. H. & Baker, Newton D. Newton D Baker: A Biography. 2011. 322p. 50.95 ***(978-1-258-08767-8(7))*** Literary Licensing, LLC.

BAKER, RAY STANNARD, 1870-1946
Peterson, Merrill D. The President & His Biographer: Woodrow Wilson & Ray Stannard Baker. 2007. (ENG.). 248p. 29.95 *(978-0-8139-2654-4(8))* Univ. Pr. of Virginia.

BAKER, RUSSELL, 1925-
Bidinger, Elizabeth. The Ethics of Working Class Autobiography: Representation of Family by Four American Authors. 2006. (ENG.). 212p. per. 45.00 *(978-0-7864-2576-1(8))* McFarland & Co., Inc. Pubs.

BAKER, MOUNT
Hodge, Paul William. The Mt. Baker Book. 2006. (Illus.). 154p. per. 14.95 *(978-0-9753496-6-3(X))* Sound & Mountains Publishing.
McQuaide, Mike. Insiders' Guide to Bellingham & Mount Baker. 2006. (Insiders' Guide Ser.). (ENG., Illus.). 224p. per. 17.95 *(978-0-7627-3845-8(6))* Globe Pequot Pr., The.

BAKERS AND BAKERIES
see also Baked Products
Baked Goods Market: Companies-Products-Services. 173p. (Orig.). pap. *(978-0-7605-2205-9(7))* Rector Pr., Ltd.
Bakery Products Market: Companies-Products-Services. 60p. (Orig.). pap. *(978-0-7605-2203-5(0))* Rector Pr., Ltd.
Bakery Snacks Market: Companies-Products-Services. 200p. (Orig.). pap. *(978-0-7605-2204-2(9))* Rector Pr., Ltd.
Baking Market: Companies-Products-Services. 150p. (Orig.). pap. *(978-0-7605-2206-6(5))* Rector Pr., Ltd.
Beischel, Cynthia Kuhn & Thie, Tom. Virginia Bakery Remembered. 2010. 240p. pap. 24.99 *(978-1-60949-114-7(9))* History Pr., The.
BIA. Major Bakery, Candy & Chocolate Manufacturers of the World. 6th rev. ed. 2006. 400p. (J). pap. 249.00 *(978-1-4187-4238-6(4))* Business Information Agency.
—Major Candy & Chocolate Wholesalers of the World. 6th rev. ed. 2006. 400p. (J). pap. 249.00 *(978-1-4187-4322-2(4))* Business Information Agency.
Bread Market: Companies-Products-Services. 200p. (Orig.). pap. *(978-0-7605-2207-3(3))* Rector Pr., Ltd.
Crump, A. K. & TasteTV, eds. The Chocolate Guide: To Local Chocolatiers, Chocolate Makers, Boutiques, Patisseries, Cafes & Shops. 2008. (ENG., Illus.). 192p. pap., instr.'s gde. ed. 15.95 *(978-0-9767682-9-6(1))* TCB-Cafe Publishing.
Davis, Detra Denay. How to Start a Home-Based Bakery Business. 2011. (Home-Based Business Ser.). 192p. pap. 18.95 *(978-0-7627-6082-4(6))* Globe Pequot Pr., The.
Etcell, Pamela May. Our Daily Bread - the Field Bakery & the Anzac Legend. 2008. 308p. pap. *(978-3-639-01982-7(2))* VDM Verlag Dr. Mueller e.K.
Howard, Beth M. Making Piece: A Memoir of Love, Loss & Pie. 2012. (ENG.). 320p. ***(978-0-373-89257-0(8))*** Harlequin Enterprises, Ltd.
Laskin, Avner. Celebrating Cobblers & Pies. 2010. (ENG.). 144p. pap. 14.95 *(978-1-60900-009-7(9))* Leisure Arts, Inc.
Malgieri, Nick. Bake! Essential Techniques for Perfect Baking. 2010. (ENG.). 224p. 29.95 *(978-1-906868-23-9(9))* Cathie, Kyle Ltd. GBR. Dist: National Bk. Network.
Malouf, Tarek. The Hummingbird Bakery Cookbook. 2009. (ENG., Illus.). 144p. *(978-1-84597-831-0(5))* Ryland Peters & Small.
Scheele, Charel. Old World Breads & the History of A Flemish Baker. 2011. 104p. pap. 11.95 ***(978-1-4620-5471-8(4))*** iUniverse, Inc.
Swift, Martha & Thomas, Lisa. Cupcakes from the Primrose Bakery. 2010. (ENG.). 144p. pap. 18.95 *(978-1-906868-08-6(5))* Cathie, Kyle Ltd. GBR. Dist: National Bk. Network.
TasteTV & Crump, A. K. The Chocolate Guide: To Local Chocolatiers, Chocolate Makers, Boutiques, Patisseries & Shops. 2008. (ENG., Illus.). 192p. pap. 15.95 *(978-0-9798640-0-1(3))* TCB-Cafe Publishing.
Valastro, Buddy. Cake Boss: Stories & Recipes from Mia Famiglia. (ENG.). 272p. 2012. pap. 16.99 *(978-1-4516-1034-5(3))* 2010. (Illus.). 25.99 *(978-1-4391-8351-9(1))* Free Pr. (Free Pr.).
Wells, Robert. The Modern Practical Bread Baker. 2008. (Cooking in America Ser.). (ENG.). 152p. pap. 11.95 *(978-1-4290-1253-9(6))* Applewood Bks.
Whitley, Andrew. Bread Matters: The State of Modern Bread & a Definitive Guide to Baking Your Own. 2009. (ENG.). 416p. 34.99 *(978-0-7407-7373-0(9))* Andrews McMeel Publishing.

BAKERS AND BAKERIES—VOCATIONAL GUIDANCE
see Baking—Vocational Guidance

BAKERY PRODUCTS
see Baked Products

BAKHTIN, M. M. (MIKHAIL MIKHAILOVICH), 1895-1975
Ambrosia-Conn, Kristina. Reading Bakhtin in the Novels of Robert Mclam Wilson. 2010. 68p. pap. *(978-3-8383-4562-8(2))* Lambert Academic Publishing.
Baxter, Leslie A. Voicing Relationships: A Dialogic Perspective. 2010. 224p. (C). pap. 41.00 *(978-1-4129-2785-7(4)*, B27846P) SAGE Pubns., Inc.
Baxter, Leslie A., ed. Voicing Relationships: A Dialogic Perspective. 2010. 224p. (C). 79.00 *(978-1-4129-2784-0(6)*, B27846C) SAGE Pubns., Inc.
Beasley-Murray, Tim & Beasley-murray, Tim. Mikhail Bakhtin & Walter Benjamin: Experience & Form. 2008. (ENG.). 256p. 100.00 *(978-0-230-53535-0(6))* Palgrave Macmillan.
Blevins, Jacob. Dialogism & Lyric Self-Fashioning: Bakhtin & the Voices of a Genre. 2008. (ENG., Illus.). 265p. 60.00 *(978-1-57591-120-5(5))* Susquehanna Univ. Pr.
Boer, Roland. Bakhtin & Genre Theory in Biblical Studies. 2007. (SBL - Semeia Studies). *(978-90-04-15737-8(9))* BRILL.
Boer, Roland, ed. Bakhtin & Genre Theory in Biblical Studies. 2007. 248p. per. 25.95 *(978-1-58983-276-3(0))* Society of Biblical Literature.
Chappell, Brian. The Ultimate Threshold Dialogue. 2010. 76p. pap. *(978-3-8383-8039-1(8))* Lambert Academic Publishing.
Darwesh, Rachel Pollard. Dialogued Desire. 2008. (United Kingdom Council for Psychotherapy Ser.). 256p. pap. 38.95 *(978-1-85575-449-2(5))* Karnac Bks. GBR. Dist: Stylus Publishing, LLC.
Easley, Keith. Dickens & Bakhtin: Authoring & Dialogism in Dickens's Novels, 1849-1861. 2012. ***(978-0-404-64478-9(3))*** AMS Pr., Inc.
Graham, Pechey. Mikhail Bakhtin: The Word in the World. 2007. (Critics of the Twentieth Century Ser.). 238p. 110.00 *(978-0-415-42420-2(8))* Routledge.
—Mikhail Bakhtin: The Word in the World. 2007. (Critics of the Twentieth Century Ser.). 238p. per. 35.95 *(978-0-415-42419-6(4))* Taylor & Francis Group.
Haynes, Deborah J. Bakhtin & the Visual Arts. 2008. (Cambridge Studies in New Art History & Criticism Ser.). (ENG., Illus.). 240p. pap. 36.99 *(978-0-521-06604-4(2))* Cambridge Univ. Pr.
Herrick, Tim. The Philosophical Affiliations of Mikhail Bakhtin & Jacques Derrid. 2010. 288p. pap. *(978-3-639-24600-1(4))* VDM Verlag Dr. Mueller e.K.
Manderson, Desmond. Kangaroo Courts & the Rule of Law - the Legacy of Modernism. 2012. (ENG.). 248p. pap. 42.95 ***(978-0-415-52951-8(4))*** Routledge.
Nikiforov, Vladimir. The Collapse of Philosophy & its Rebirth: An Intellectual History with Special Attention to Husserl, Richert, & Bakhtin. 2006. 456p. 129.95 *(978-0-7734-5594-8(9))* Mellen, Edwin Pr., The.
Peeren, Esther. Intersubjectivities & Popular Culture: Bakhtin & Beyond. 2007. (Cultural Memory in the Present Ser.). (ENG.). 304p. 60.00 *(978-0-8047-5669-3(4))* Stanford Univ. Pr.
Platter, Charles. Aristophanes & the Carnival of Genres. 2006. (Arethusa Bks.). (ENG.). 272p. (gr. 17). 59.00 *(978-0-8018-8527-3(2))* Johns Hopkins Univ. Pr.
RENFREW. Mikhail Bakhtan. 2008. 95.00 *(978-0-415-31968-3(4))* Routledge.
Renfrew. Mikhail Bakhtan. 2008. (Routledge Critical Thinkers Ser.). pap. 22.95 *(978-0-415-31969-0(2))* Routledge.
Sackville-West, Vita. Twelve Days in Persia: Across the Mountains with the Bakhtiari Tribe. 2009. (ENG., Illus.). 144p. pap. 17.00 *(978-1-84511-933-1(9)*, Tauris Parke Paperbacks) I. B. Tauris & Co., Ltd. GBR. Dist: Macmillan.
San Juan, E., Jr. Critique & Social Transformation: Lessons from Antonio Gramsci, Mikhail Bakhtin, & Raymond Williams. 2009. 304p. 119.95 *(978-0-7734-4778-3(4))* Mellen, Edwin Pr., The.
Sharland, Suzanne. Horace in Dialogue: Bakhtinian Readings in the Satires. 2009. 359p. pap. 70.95 *(978-3-03911-946-2(X))* Lang, Peter AG GBR. Dist: Lang, Peter.
Shields, Carolyn M. Bakhtin Primer. 2007. (Peter Lang Primer Ser.). 189p. pap. 18.95 *(978-0-8204-8188-3(2))* Lang, Peter Publishing, Inc.
Traficante, Antonio. D.H. Lawrence's Italian Travel Literature & Translations of Giovanni Verga: A Bakhtinian Reading. 2007. (Illus.). 216p. (C). 68.95 *(978-0-8204-8817-2(8))* Lang, Peter Publishing, Inc.
Visquerra Tischler, Serbio. Tiempo Y Emancipación. Mijaíl Bajtín Y Walter Benjamin En La Selva Lacandona., Vol. 3. 2008. (SPA.). 80p. pap. *(978-99922-61-73-6(0))* F & G Editores.
Webb, Geoff R. Mark at the Threshold: Applying Bakhtinian Categories to Markan Characterisation. 2008. 276p. *(978-90-04-16774-2(9))* BRILL.
White, E. Jayne & Peters, Michael A. Bakhtinian Pedagogy: Opportunities & Challenges for Research, Policy & Practice in Education Across the Globe. 2011. E-Book ***(978-1-4539-0144-1(2))*** Lang, Peter GmbH, Europaischer Verlag der Wissenschaften.
White, Jayne. Bakhtinian Pedagogy: Opportunities & Challenges for Research, Policy & Practice in Education Across the Globe. 2011. xii, 272p. (C). 149.95 ***(978-1-4331-1354-3(6))***; pap. 35.95 ***(978-1-4331-1353-6(8))*** Lang, Peter Publishing, Inc.
Zbinden, Karine. Bakhtin between East & West: Cross-Cultural Transmission. 2006. (Legenda Main Ser.). (ENG.). 197p. (C). 69.00 *(978-1-904350-54-5(2))* European Humanities Research Ctr. GBR. Dist: Brown, David Bk. Co., The.

BAKING
see also Baked Products; Dutch Oven Cooking; Pizza; Souffles
Aiken, Tammy. Tammy's Kitchen Recipes: Simple & Easy Recipes to Compliment Any Season. 2011. (Illus.). 168p. pap. 49.95 ***(978-1-4327-7144-7(2))*** Outskirts Pr., Inc.

Alexander, William. 52 Loaves. 2011. (ENG.). 352p. pap. 15.95 (978-1-61620-050-3(2), 1616200502) Algonquin Bks. of Chapel Hill.
Anderson, Jean. The Big Book of Southern Baking. 2012. (ENG., Illus.). 272p. 32.50 (978-1-118-06775-8(4), Wiley) Wiley, John & Sons, Inc.
Appel, Jennifer. Buttercup Bakes at Home: More Than 75 New Recipes from Manhattan's Premier Bake Shop for Tempting Homemade Sweets. 2006. (ENG., Illus.). 144p. 26.00 (978-0-7432-7122-6(X)) Simon & Schuster.
Appel, Jennifer & Torey, Allysa. The Complete Magnolia Bakery Cookbook: Recipes from the World-Famous Bakery & Allysa Torey's Home Kitchen. 2009. (ENG., Illus.). 240p. pap. 19.99 (978-1-4391-7564-4(0)) Simon & Schuster.
Arrick, David, et al. The Butch Bakery Cookbook. 2011. (ENG., Illus.). 192p. 19.99 (978-0-470-93088-5(8), Wiley) Wiley, John & Sons, Inc.
Ashcraft, Stephanie. Cake Mix Cooking for Kids, 1 vol. 2011. (ENG., Illus.). 80p. 14.99 (978-1-4236-1917-8(X)) Gibbs Smith, Publisher.
—200 Cake Mix Creations, 1 vol. 2010. (ENG.). 208p. 12.99 (978-1-4236-1705-1(3)) Gibbs Smith, Publisher.
Atkinson, Catherine, et al. 300 Chocolate & Coffee Recipes: Delicious, easy-to-make recipes for total indulgence, from bakes to desserts, shown step by step in more than 1300 glorious Photographs. 2012. (ENG., Illus.). 512p. pap. 18.99 (978-1-78019-075-4(1)) Anness Publishing GBR. Dist: National Bk. Network.
Australian Women's Weekly Staff. Café Cakes & Puddings. Coleman, Mary, ed. (Illus.). 64p. pap. 5.95 (978-1-86396-230-8(1)) ACP Publishing Pty, Ltd. AUS. Dist: Graphic Arts Ctr. Publishing Co.
—Muffins, Scones & Breads, Vol. 2. Blacker, Maryanne, ed. 2nd ed. (ENG., Illus.). 120p. pap. 12.95 (978-1-86396-161-5(5)) ACP Publishing Pty, Ltd. AUS. Dist: Graphic Arts Ctr. Publishing Co.
Australian Women's Weekly Staff, contrib. by. Children's Birthday Cakes: Step-by-Step to the Perfect Birthday Cake. (Illus.). 120p. pap. 12.95 (978-1-86396-281-0(6)) ACP Publishing Pty, Ltd. AUS. Dist: Graphic Arts Ctr. Publishing Co.
Baking. Date not set. 256p. 7.98 (978-0-7525-9946-5(1)); 48p. pap. 4.98 (978-1-4054-0839-4(1)); 240p. (978-1-4075-2621-8(9)); 48p. pap. (978-1-4075-1094-1(0)) Parragon, Inc.
Baking with Brother Boniface. 10.00 (978-0-941711-49-4(8), Wyrick) Gibbs Smith, Publisher.
Baking with the Motivator: Making Money Using Wal-Mart Product. 2006. (978-0-9790979-0-4(8)) Rodgers, Milo T.
Barbone, Elizabeth. Easy Gluten-Free Baking. 2006. per. 24.94 (978-0-9786672-0-7(4)) Gluten-Free Baking & More.
Bardi, Carla, et al. The Golden Book of Baking: Over 300 Great Recipes. 2009. (ENG.). 704p. 29.99 (978-0-7641-6272-5(1)) Barron's Educational Series, Inc.
Barricelli, John. The Seasonal Baker: Easy Recipes from My Home Kitchen to Make Year-Round. 2012. (ENG., Illus.). 288p. 35.00 (978-0-307-95187-8(1), Clarkson Potter) Crown Publishing Group.
Barricelli, John. The Sono Baking Company Cookbook: The Best Sweet & Savory Recipes for Every Occasion. 2010. (ENG., Illus.). 288p. 35.00 (978-0-307-44945-0(9), Clarkson Potter) Crown Publishing Group.
Barton, Miriam. The Pioneer Cookbook: Recipes for Today's Kitchen. 2011. (ENG., Illus.) 184p. pap. 17.95 (978-1-59992-142-6(1)) Leatherwood Pr.
Beeton, Isabella. Mrs Beeton's Cakes & Baking. 2006. (ENG., Illus.). 256p. 11.95 (978-0-304-36829-7(6)) Cassell P L C GBR. Dist: Independent Pubs. Group.
Beischel, Cynthia Kuhn & Thie, Tom. Virginia Bakery Remembered. 2010. 240p. pap. 24.99 (978-1-60949-114-7(9)) History Pr., The.
Berry, Mary. 100 Sweet Treats & Puds. 2011. (My Kitchen Table Ser.). (ENG., Illus.). 208p. pap. 13.95 (978-1-84990-336-3(0)) BBC Worldwide GBR. Dist: Independent Pubs. Group.
Bester, Tina. Bake. 2012. (ENG., Illus.). 152p. 19.95 (978-1-86205-898-9(9)) Chrysalis Children's Bks. GBR. Dist: Independent Pubs. Group.
Better Homes and Gardens Books Staff. Anyone Can Bake. 2009. (ENG., Illus.). 352p. 24.95 (978-0-470-50059-0(X), Wiley) Wiley, John & Sons, Inc.
The Big Book of Baking. 2008. 320p. (978-1-4075-3967-6(1)) Parragon, Inc.
Birthday Cakes. 96p. (978-1-4054-9579-0(0)) Parragon, Inc.
Blair, Louise. Great Gluten-Free Baking: Over 80 Delicious Cakes & Bakes. (ENG., Illus.). 144p. 2010. pap. 14.99 (978-0-600-62183-6(9)) 2007. 24.95 (978-0-600-61633-7(9)) Octopus Publishing Group GBR. (Hamlyn). Dist: Hachette Bk. Group.
Blakeslee, Robert. Your Time to Bake: A Novice's Guide to Baking Cakes, Cookies, Pies, & More. 2011. (ENG.). 416p. 29.95 (978-0-7570-0355-4(9)) Square One Pubs.
Bloom, Carole. The Essential Baker: The Comprehensive Guide to Baking with Chocolate, Fruit, Nuts, Spices, & Other Ingredients. 2007. (ENG., Illus.). 672p. 40.00 (978-0-7645-7645-4(3), Wiley) Wiley, John & Sons, Inc.
Bolger, Erin. The Happy Baker: A Girl's Guide to Emotional Baking. 2010. 160p. pap. (978-0-373-89241-9(1)) Harlequin Enterprises, Ltd.
Boston Common Press Staff. The America's Test Kitchen Family Baking Book. 2008. (ENG.). 552p. pap. 34.95 (978-1-933615-22-6(2)) America's Test Kitchen.
—The Best Cover & Bake Recipes. 2008. (Best Recipe Ser.). (ENG., Illus.). 338p. pap. 19.95 (978-1-933615-31-8(1)) America's Test Kitchen.
Boyce, Kimberly. Good to the Grain: Baking with Whole-Grain Flours. 2010. (ENG., Illus.). 208p. 29.95 (978-1-58479-830-9(0)) Stewart, Tabori & Chang.
Braker, Flo. Baking for All Occasions. 2008. (ENG., Illus.). 320p. 35.00 (978-0-8118-4547-2(8)) Chronicle Bks. LLC.
Brass, Marilynn & Brass, Sheila. Heirloom Baking with the Brass Sisters: More Than 100 Years of Recipes Discovered & Collected by the Queens of Comfort Food" 2011. (ENG., Illus.). 312p. pap. 19.95 (978-1-57912-881-4(5), 1579128815) Black Dog & Leventhal Pubs., Inc.
Briggs, Janet. Baking Classics. 2008. (Illus.). 416p. (978-0-89821-612-7(5)) Reiman Pubns., L.P.
Brody, Esther. 1500 Best Bars, Cookies, Muffins, Cakes, & More. 2008. (ENG., Illus.). 624p. pap. 27.95 (978-0-7788-0194-8(2)) Rose, Robert Inc. CAN. Dist: Firefly Bks., Ltd.
Bullock-Prado, Gesine. Confections of a Closet Master Baker: A Sweet Journey of Starting over, One Cake at a Time. 2009. (ENG., Illus.). 240p. 24.00 (978-0-7679-3268-4(4)) Broadway Bks.
—My Life from Scratch: A Sweet Journey of Starting over, One Cake at a Time. 2010. (ENG.). 240p. pap. 14.00 (978-0-7679-3273-8(0)) Broadway Bks.
Byrn, Anne. The Cake Mix Doctor Bakes Gluten-Free. 2010. (ENG., Illus.). 352p. 26.95 (978-0-7611-6107-3(4), 0761161074); pap. 14.95 (978-0-7611-6098-4(1), 0761160981) Workman Publishing Co., Inc.
Cakes & Bakes. 96p. (978-1-4054-7231-9(6)) Parragon, Inc.
Campbell, Georgina. The Best of Irish Breads & Baking: Traditional, Contemporary & Festive. 2007. (ENG., Illus.). 166p. pap. 16.95 (978-1-903164-25-9(7)) Georgina Campbell's Guides Ltd. IRL. Dist: Interlink Publishing Group, Inc.
Canadian Living & Baird, Elizabeth. The Complete Canadian Living Baking Book: The Essentials of Home Baking. 2008. (ENG., Illus.). 352p. 34.95 (978-0-9809924-2-7(7)) Transcontinental Bks. CAN. Dist: Random Hse., Inc.
Castella, Krystina. Crazy about Cupcakes. 2006. (Crazy About Ser.). (ENG., Illus.). 256p. pap. 17.95 (978-1-4027-1994-3(9)) Sterling Publishing Co., Inc.
—A World of Cake: 150 Recipes for Sweet Traditions from Cultures near & Far - Honey Cakes to Flat Cakes, Fritters to Chiffons, Meringues to Mooncakes, Tartes to Tortes, Fruit Cakes to Spice Cakes. 2010. (ENG., Illus.). 352p. pap. 24.95 (978-1-60342-576-6(4), 1603425764) Storey Publishing, LLC.
Catalano, Ania. Baking with Agave Nectar: Over 100 Recipes Using Nature's Ultimate Sweetener. 2008. (ENG., Illus.). 144p. pap. 15.99 (978-1-58761-321-0(2), Celestial Arts) Ten Speed Pr.
Cauvain, S.P. & Young, L. S. More Baking Problems Solved. 2009. (Illus.). 252p. (978-1-84569-382-4(5)) Woodhead Publishing Ltd.
Cauvain, Stanley. More Baking Problems Solved. 2009. 256p. 209.95 (978-1-4398-0108-6(8)) CRC Pr. LLC.
Cech, Mary. The Art of Savory Baking: 75 Recipes for Breads, Biscuits, Pastries, Popovers, Tarts, Turnovers, & More. 2010. (978-1-4521-0023-4(3)) Chronicle Bks. LLC.
Chang, Joanne & Matheson, Christie. Flour: Spectacular Recipes from Boston's Flour Bakery + Cafe. 2010. (ENG., Illus.). 320p. 35.00 (978-0-8118-6944-7(X)) Chronicle Bks. LLC.
Charlotte Peyk. Scandinavian Baking Without Eggs. 2011. 144p. pap. 39.50 (978-87-7114-608-0(3)) Bks. on Demand.
Chattman, Lauren. The Baking Answer Book. 2009. (ENG., Illus.). 378p. pap. 14.95 (978-1-60342-439-4(3), 1603424393) Workman Publishing Co., Inc.
—Mom's Big Book of Baking: 200 Simple, Foolproof Family Favorites for Birthday Parties, Bake Sales, & More. 2008. (ENG.). 288p. reprint ed. 21.95 (978-1-55832-395-7(3)) Harvard Common Pr.
Chocolate Chip Cookies. (Little Book Practice Reader). (978-0-8136-5381-5(9)) Modern Curriculum Pr.
Cholagh, Samira Yako. A Baking Journey: From Samira's Kitchen to Yours. 2011. pap. 37.99 (978-1-61739-558-1(7)) Tate Publishing & Enterprises, LLC.
Clark, Lindy. Lindy's Gluten-Free Goodies & More! 2009. (Illus.). 118p. pap. (978-0-9842181-4-1(9), Orbit Books) DLC Media.
Clements, Carole. Baking: Over 200 Irresistible Home-Made Cakes, Pies, Muffins, Tarts, Buns, Bread & Cookies. 2011. (ENG., Illus.). 264p. pap. 18.99 (978-1-78019-005-1(0)) Anness Publishing GBR. Dist: National Bk. Network.
—Best-Ever Home Baking: A wonderful collection of irresistible home bakes & cakes, with 70 classic recipes shown in 300 step-by-step Photographs. 2011. (ENG., Illus.). 96p. pap. 16.99 (978-1-84476-976-6(3)) Anness Publishing GBR. Dist: National Bk. Network.
—Easy Home Baking: 70 Fabulous Cakes, Cookies, Breads, Pies & Muffins SHown Step by Step in Over 300 Photographs. 2008. (ENG., Illus.). 96p. pap. 9.99 (978-1-84476-584-3(9)) Anness Publishing GBR. Dist: National Bk. Network.
Collister, Linda. Easy Baking. 2008. (ENG., Illus.). 240p. pap. (978-1-84597-745-0(9)) Ryland Peters & Small.
—Great British Bake Off Bk. 2: How to Bake - The Perfect Victoria Sponge & Other Baking Secrets. 2011. (ENG., Illus.). 320p. 36.95 (978-1-84990-268-7(2)) BBC Worldwide GBR. Dist: Independent Pubs. Group.
Collister, Linda. Sweet Treats from My Mother's Kitchen. 2010. (ENG., Illus.). 176p. (978-1-84597-950-8(8)) Ryland Peters & Small.
Cookbook Resources, contrib. by. Simple Old-Fashioned Baking: The Best Recipes from Grandma's Kitchen. 2008. 288p. (978-1-59769-032-4(5)) Cookbook Resources, LLC.
Cookbook Resources, ed. Quick & Easy Family Baking: Cakes, Cookies Pies & Breads Anyone Can Bake! 2011. (ENG.). 384p. pap. (978-1-59769-109-3(7)) Cookbook Resources, LLC.
Cookies. Date not set. (Essentials Collection Cooking). 96p. 5.98 (978-1-4054-2021-1(9)) Parragon, Inc.
Cookies. 2008. (ENG., Illus.). 32p. (978-1-84510-281-4(9)) Top That! Publishing PLC.
Cooking Light Magazine Staff. Cooking Light Way to Bake: The Complete Visual Guide to Light Baking. 2011. (ENG., Illus.). 424p. 29.95 (978-0-8487-3475-6(0)) Oxmoor Hse., Inc.
Cook's Illustrated Magazine Editors. Baking Illustrated: The Ultimate Kitchen Companion for the Home Baker with 375 Foolproof Recipes. (ENG., Illus.). 528p. 35.00 (978-0-936184-75-3(2)) America's Test Kitchen.
Coppedge, Richard J., Jr. & Chookazian, George. Gluten-Free Baking with the Culinary Institute of America: 150 Flavorful Recipes from the World's Premier Culinary College. 2008. (ENG., Illus.). 288p. pap. 18.95 (978-1-59869-613-4(0)) Adams Media Corp.
Corriher, Shirley O. BakeWise: The Hows & Whys of Successful Baking with over 200 Magnificent Recipes. (978-0-688-16742-4(X)) Hearst Bks.
—BakeWise: The Hows & Whys of Successful Baking with over 200 Magnificent Recipes. 2008. (ENG., Illus.). 544p. 40.00 (978-1-4165-6078-4(5), Scribner) Scribner.
Cotman. Bake the Scottish Way. rev. ed. (Scottish Cooking Ser.). (Illus.). 32p. pap. 3.95 (978-0-7117-0228-8(4)) Jarrold Publishing GBR. Dist: 7 Hills Bk. Distributors.
Country Living Editors. Country Living Little Book of Pies & Tarts: 50 Easy Homemade Favorites to Bake & Share. 2011. (ENG., Illus.). 144p. spiral bd. 12.95 (978-1-58816-856-6(5)) Hearst Communications, Inc.
Crocker, Betty. Betty Crocker Baking Basics: Recipes & Tips to Bake with Confidence. 2nd ed. 2009. (ENG., Illus.). 272p. 25.95 (978-0-470-28661-6(X), Betty Crocker) Wiley, John & Sons, Inc.
Culinary Institute of America Staff. Baking & Pastry: Mastering the Art & Craft. 2nd ed. 2009. (ENG., Illus.). 944p. 70.00 (978-0-470-05591-5(X), Wiley) Wiley, John & Sons, Inc.
Cupcakes, Muffins & Baked Goods. 2008. 240p. (978-1-4075-3960-7(4)) Parragon, Inc.
Czech This Out. Czech This Out Vol. 2: Authentic Czech Cookies & more, Czech strudel, fruit dumplings, things for kids to make, eat, do, Parenting styles, tips/insights for parenting, Czech proverbs & inspirational insights. 2007. 163p. spiral bd. 12.95 (978-0-9789012-2-6(3)) Niemann, Carol.
Daley, Regan. In the Sweet Kitchen. 2010. (ENG., Illus.). 704p. pap. 24.95 (978-1-57965-427-6(4), 1579654274) Artisan.
Davis, Piper & Jackson, Ellen. The Grand Central Baking Book: Breakfast Pastries, Cookies, Pies, & Satisfying Savories from the Pacific Northwest's Celebrated Bakery. 2009. (ENG., Illus.). 208p. 30.00 (978-1-58008-953-1(4)) Ten Speed Pr.
Day, Martha. Traditional Afternoon Tea. 2012. (ENG., Illus.). 64p. 9.99 (978-0-7548-2170-0(6)) Anness Publishing GBR. Dist: National Bk. Network.
Day, Martha. 101 Best-Ever Cakes: A Card Deck of Delicious Step-by-Step Recipes. 2012. (ENG.). 52p. pap. 14.99 (978-0-7548-1847-2(0)) Anness Publishing GBR. Dist: National Bk. Network.
Day, Martin. Baking: Breads Muffins Cakes Pies Tarts Cookies & Bars over 400 Step-by-Step Recipes with over 1500 Photographs. 2012. (ENG.). 512p. 29.99 (978-0-7548-2249-3(4)) Anness Publishing GBR. Dist: National Bk. Network.
Denzer, Kiko. Build Your Own Earth Oven: A Low-Cost, Wood-Fired Mud Oven, Simple Sourdough Bread, Perfect Loaves. 3rd rev. ed. 2007. (ENG., Illus.). 132p. per. 17.95 (978-0-9679846-7-4(X)) Hand Print Pr.
Diegel, Donna. The Complete Idiot's Guide to Vegan Baking. 2011. (Complete Idiot's Guide Ser.). (ENG.). 336p. (gr. 12). 16.95 (978-1-61564-057-7(6), Alpha Bks.) Penguin Group (USA) Inc.
DiResta, David, et al. The Toaster Oven Cookbook. rev. ed. 2006. (Nitty Gritty Cookbooks Ser.). (ENG., Illus.). 176p. pap. 8.95 (978-1-55867-326-7(1)) Bristol Publishing Enterprises.
Dodge, Abigail Johnson. The Weekend Baker: Irresistible Recipes, Simple Techniques, & Stress-Free Strategies for Busy People. 2008. (ENG.). 384p. pap. 24.95 (978-0-393-33139-4(3), 33139) Norton, W. W. & Co., Inc.
Dorling Kindersley Publishing Staff. Cakes & Cupcakes. 2010. (ENG.). 224p. 20.00 (978-0-7566-6731-3(3)) Dorling Kindersley Publishing, Inc.
—Step-by-Step Baking. 2011. (ENG., Illus.). 544p. 35.00 (978-0-7566-8679-6(2)) Dorling Kindersley Publishing, Inc.
Douglas, Tom. The Dahlia Bakery Cookbook: Sweetness in Seattle. 2012. (ENG.). 288p. 35.00 (978-0-06-218374-3(5), Morrow, William Cookbooks) HarperCollins Pubs.
Easy to Bake, Easy to Make. (978-1-930560-95-6(8)) International Masters Pubs., Inc.
Eicher, Lovina & Williams, Kevin. The Amish Cook's Baking Book. 2009. (ENG.). 224p. 29.99 (978-0-7407-8547-4(8)) Andrews McMeel Publishing.
Eppenbach, Sarah. Baked Alaska. 2011. (ENG.). 96p. pap. 14.95 (978-0-88240-835-4(6), Alaska Northwest Bks.) Graphic Arts Ctr. Publishing Co.
Ettinger, John. Bob's Red Mill Baking Book: More Than 400 Recipes Featuring Whole & Healthy Grains. 2006. (ENG., Illus.). 496p. 29.95 (978-0-7624-2744-4(2)) Running Pr. Bk. Pubs.
Farris, Emily. Casserole Crazy: Hot Stuff for Your Oven! 2008. (ENG.). 208p. (gr. 12-18). 15.95 (978-1-55788-535-7(4), HP Trade) Penguin Group (USA) Inc.
Farrow, Joanna. Dress Your Gingerbread: Bake Them! Dress Them! Eat Them! 2010. (ENG., Illus.). 128p. pap. 14.99 (978-1-84601-369-0(0), Spruce) Octopus Publishing Group GBR. Dist: Hachette Bk. Group.
—Kinky Cupcakes. 2010. (ENG., Illus.). 96p. 12.99 (978-1-84601-364-5(X), Spruce) Octopus Publishing Group GBR. Dist: Hachette Bk. Group.
Field, Carol. The Italian Baker, Revised: The Classic Tastes of the Italian Countryside — Its Breads, Pizza, Focaccia, Cakes, Pastries, & Cookies. 2011. (ENG., Illus.). 432p. 35.00 (978-1-60774-106-0(7)) Ten Speed Pr.
Figoni, Paula I. How Baking Works: Exploring the Fundamentals of Baking Science. 3rd ed. 2010. (ENG., Illus.). 528p. pap. 45.00 (978-0-470-39267-6(3), Wiley) Wiley, John & Sons, Inc.
Figoni, Paula I. How Baking Works: Exploring the Fundamentals of Baking Science, Third Edition Set. 3rd ed. 2011. pap. 110.00 (978-1-118-13234-0(3), Wiley) Wiley, John & Sons, Inc.
Flodin, Lisa & Perez, Camilla. Baking with Kids: Inspiring a Love of Cooking with Recipes for Bread, Cupcakes, Cheesecake, & More! 2012. (ENG., Illus.). 72p. 16.95 (978-1-61608-684-8(X), 608684) Skyhorse Publishing Co., Inc.
Fox, Mindy & DeMasco, Karen. The Craft of Baking: Cakes, Cookies, & Other Sweets with Ideas for Inventing Your Own. 2009. (ENG., Illus.). 256p. 35.00 (978-0-307-40810-5(8), Clarkson Potter) Crown Publishing Group.
Fraser, Linda. Low-Fat Baking for Every Day. 2012. (ENG., Illus.). 160p. pap. 17.99 (978-1-84476-968-1(2)) Anness Publishing GBR. Dist: National Bk. Network.
Fulton, Margaret. Margaret Fulton Baking: The Ultimate Sweet & Savoury Baking Collection. 2012. (ENG., Illus.). 480p. 49.95 (978-1-74270-028-1(4)) Rizzoli International Pubns., Inc.
Geary, George. The Complete Baking Cookbook: 350 Recipes from Cookies & Cakes to Muffins & Pies. 2007. (ENG., Illus.). 448p. 34.95 (978-0-7788-0176-4(4)); pap. 24.95 (978-0-7788-0165-8(9)) Rose, Robert Inc. CAN. Dist: Firefly Bks., Ltd.
Ginsberg, Stanley & Berg, Norman. Inside the Jewish Bakery: Recipes & Memories from the Golden Age of Jewish Baking. 2011. (978-1-933822-23-5(6)) Camino Bks., Inc.
Gisslen, Wayne. Professional Baking. (ENG.). 5th ed. 2008. 188.95 (978-0-470-48637-5(6)) 5th ed. 2008. (Illus.). 800p. (C). 119.95 (978-0-471-78348-0(X), Wiley) 5th ed. 2008. 145.95 (978-0-470-31652-8(7), Wiley) 5th ed. 2008. (Illus.). 704p. 65.00 (978-0-471-78349-7(8), Wiley) 6th ed. 2012. (Illus.). 800p. (C). 102.95 (978-1-118-08374-1(1), Wiley) 6th ed. 2012. (Illus.). 192p. (C). pap., pupil's gde. ed. 38.95 (978-1-118-15833-3(4), Wiley) Wiley, John & Sons, Inc.
—Professional Baking 5th Edition College Version w/CD-ROM Student Study Guide Prof Baking Method Cards Pkg & How Baking Works 3rd Edition Set. 2011. (C). 223.90 (978-1-118-08329-1(6)) Wiley, John & Sons, Inc.
Gisslen, Wayne. Professional Baking 5th Edition College Version w/CD-ROM with How Baking Works 3rd Edition & Prof Baking Methods Cards Set. 5th ed. 2011. (C). 181.95 (978-1-118-13191-6(6)) Wiley, John & Sons, Inc.
Gisslen, Wayne & Griffin, Mary Ellen. Study Guide to Accompany Professional Baking. 5th ed. 2008. (ENG., Illus.). 220p. pap. 43.95 (978-0-471-78350-3(1), Wiley) Wiley, John & Sons, Inc.
Glander, Amy. Taste of Home Cupcakes! Muffins & More: 130 Scrumptious Delights. 2008. (Illus.). 112p. (978-0-89821-624-0(9)) Reiman Pubns., L.P.
Goldman, Duff & Goldman, Willie. The Ace of Cakes: Inside the World of Charm City Cakes. 2009. (ENG.). 256p. 35.00 (978-0-06-170301-0(X), Morrow, William Cookbooks) HarperCollins Pubs.
Goldman, Marcy. The New Best of Betterbaking. Com: 200 Classic Recipes from the Beloved Baker's Website. 2009. (Illus.). 456p. pap. 26.95 (978-1-77050-002-0(2)) Whitecap Bks., Ltd. CAN. Dist: Midpoint Trade Bks., Inc.
—A Treasury of Jewish Holiday Baking. 10th anniv. ed. 2009. 400p. pap. 23.95 (978-1-77050-003-7(0)) Whitecap Bks., Ltd. CAN. Dist: Midpoint Trade Bks., Inc.
Goldman, Marcy & Cooking Light Magazine Staff. A Passion for Baking: Bake to Celebrate, Bake to Nourish, Bake for Fun. rev. ed. 2007. (ENG., Illus.). 320p. 29.95 (978-0-8487-3179-3(4)) Oxmoor Hse., Inc.
Goldstein, Darra. Baking Boot Camp: Five Days of Basic Training at the Culinary Institute of America. 2007. (ENG., Illus.). 288p. 29.95 (978-0-7645-7279-1(2), Wiley) Wiley, John & Sons, Inc.
Good Housekeeping Editors, ed. Good Housekeeping the Great Bake Sale Cookbook: 75 Sure-Fire Fund-Raising Favorites. 2009. (ENG., Illus.). 192p. spiral bd. 12.95 (978-1-58816-787-3(9)) Hearst Communications, Inc.
Gordon, Kathryn & McBride, Anne E. Les Petits Macarons: Colorful French Confections to Make at Home. 2011. (ENG., Illus.). 270p. 18.00 (978-0-7624-4258-4(1)) Running Pr. Bk. Pubs.
Gordon, Teresa. Daily Harvest Bakery & Deli Cookbook, 1 vol. 2008. (ENG., Illus.). 176p. 19.95 (978-1-58980-606-1(9)) Pelican Publishing Co., Inc.
Gorton, L. A. Baking Science & Technology Volume II: Formulation & Production. 2010. (Illus.). 782p. pap. (978-0-9820239-1-4(X)) Sosland Publishing Co.
Gottlieb, Michael. Gottlieb's Bakery: Savannah's Sweetest Tradition. 2011. 132p. pap. 16.99 (978-1-60949-416-2(4)) History Pr., The.
Green, Aliza. Starting with Ingredients: Baking - Quintessential Recipes for the Way We Really Bake. 2008. (ENG., Illus.). 800p. 39.95 (978-0-7624-3158-8(X)) Perseus Bks. Group.
Greenspan, Dorie. Baking: From My Home to Yours. 2006. (ENG., Illus.). 528p. 40.00 (978-0-618-44336-9(3)) Houghton Mifflin Harcourt Publishing Co.
Greve, Della. Itty Bitty Baking. 2010. 32p. mass mkt. 9.99 (978-1-60380-070-9(0)) becker&mayer! books.
Harris, Inge & Harris, Gillian. A Celebration of Gluten Free Baking. 2009. 136p. pap. 15.90 (978-0-557-21667-3(2)) Lulu Enterprises Inc.
Haugen, Tiffany. The Power of Flour: Cooking with Non-traditional Flours. 2009. (Illus.). 134p. spiral bd. 19.95 (978-1-57188-445-9(9)) Amato, Frank Pubns., Inc.

B

Haynes, Linda. More from Ace Bakery: Recipes for & with Bread. 2010. (Ace Bakery Ser.). (ENG., Illus.). 192p. pap. 24.95 (978-1-55285-808-0(1)) Whitecap Bks., Ltd. CAN. Dist: Midpoint Trade Bks., Inc.
Heatter, Maida. Maida Heatter's Cakes. 2011. (ENG.). 368p. pap. 19.99 (978-1-4494-0114-6(7)) Andrews McMeel Publishing.
—Maida Heatter's Cookies. 2011. (ENG.). 336p. pap. 19.99 (978-1-4494-0115-3(5)) Andrews McMeel Publishing.
Hedh, Jan. Artisan Breads: Practical Recipes & Detailed Instructions for Baking the World's Finest Loaves. 2011. (ENG., Illus.). 240p. 24.95 (978-1-61608-487-5(1), 608487) Skyhorse Publishing Co., Inc.
Hertzberg, Jeff & François, Zoë. Artisan Bread in Five Minutes a Day: The Discovery That Revolutionizes Home Baking. 2007. (ENG., Illus.). 256p. 27.99 (978-0-312-36291-1(9), Dunne, Thomas Bks.) St. Martin's Pr.
Hitz, Ciril. Baking Artisan Pastries & Breads: Sweet & Savory Baking for Breakfast, Brunch, & Beyond. 2009. (ENG., Illus.). 176p. pap. 24.99 (978-1-59253-564-4(X), 159253564X) Quayside.
Holechek, Kris. The 100 Best Vegan Baking Recipes: Amazing Cookies, Cakes, Muffins, Pies, Brownies & Breads. 2009. (ENG., Illus.). 144p. pap. 14.95 (978-1-56975-714-7(3)) Ulysses Pr.
Holt, Geraldene. Geraldene Holt's Cakes. 2011. (ENG., Illus.). 304p. (C). pap. 36.00 (978-1-903018-75-0(7)) Prospect Bks. GBR. Dist: Brown, David Bk. Co., The.
How to Bake Bread: Five Families of Bread. 2011. (Illus.). 525p. pap. 23.95 (978-0-615-23129-7(2)) Red Seal Bks.
Hui, Y. H., et al, eds. Bakery Products: Science & Technology. 2006. (ENG., Illus.). 586p. 249.95 (978-0-8138-0187-2(7), Wiley-Blackwell) Wiley, John & Sons, Inc.
Jacob, Cheryl. Anyone Can Cook & Bake the Easy Way: 50 Easy, Step-by-Step Recipes That Taste the Best & Will Impress Your Guests: Most Recipes Contain Only 4 & 5 Ingredients. 2011. (ENG.). 92p. pap. 18.95 (978-1-4662-2513-8(0)) CreateSpace.
Jensen, Kir. Sugar Cube: 50 Deliciously Twisted Treats from the Sweetest Little Food Cart on the Planet. 2012. (ENG., Illus.). 144p. 24.95 (978-1-4521-0126-2(4)) Chronicle Bks. LLC.
Jerome, Helen. Concerning Cake Making. 2008. 268p. (978-1-4437-3287-1(7)) 2007. 264p. per. (978-1-4067-8935-5(6)) Read Bks. (Vintage Cookery Bks.).
Johnson & Wales University, College of Culinary Arts Educational Task Force Staff, contrib. by. Baking & Pastry Formulas. 3rd ed. 2008. (978-0-13-236484-3(0)) Prentice Hall PTR.
Johnson & Wales University, College of Culinary Arts Educational Task Force Staff & Johnson & Wales University, International Baking and Pastry Institute Staff, contrib. by. Baking & Pastry, 2 vols. 3rd ed. 2009. (Illus.). (978-0-13-513358-3(0)) Prentice Hall PTR.
Johnson, Marjorie. The Road to Blue Ribbon Baking with Marjorie. 2007. 256p. 29.95 (978-1-59298-195-3(X)) Beaver's Pond Pr., Inc.
Jones, Holly & David. Wood-Fired Oven Cookbook: '70 recipes for incredible stone-baked pizzas & breads, roasts, cakes & desserts, all specially devised for the outdoor oven & illustrated in over 400 Photographs. 2012. (ENG., Illus.). 128p. 17.99 (978-1-903141-94-6(X)) Anness Publishing GBR. Dist: National Bk. Network.
Katzinger, Jennifer. Flying Apron's Gluten-Free & Vegan Baking Book. 2009. (ENG., Illus.). 192p. pap. 23.95 (978-1-57061-629-7(9)) Sasquatch Bks.
Kayser, Eric & Yosefi, Yair. New French Recipes. 2009. (ENG., Illus.). 160p. 34.95 (978-2-08-030095-9(4)) Flammarion et Cie FRA. Dist: Random Hse., Inc.
Kelly, Carla. Quick & Easy Vegan Bake Sale: More Than 150 Delicious Sweet & Savory Vegan Treats Perfect for Sharing. 2011. (ENG., Illus.). 296p. pap. 17.95 (978-1-61519-026-3(0), 1615190260) Experiment LLC, The.
Kerr, Gordon & Winston, Robert P. Baking Bible. 2008. (ENG., Illus.). 704p. (gr. 12-18). 40.00 (978-0-14-300825-5(0), Penguin Global) Penguin Group (USA) Inc.
King Arthur Flour Staff. King Arthur Flour Whole Grain Baking: Delicious Recipes Using Nutritious Whole Grains. 2006. (King Arthur Flour Cookbooks Ser.). (ENG., Illus.). 544p. 35.00 (978-0-88150-719-5(9), 150719) Countryman Pr.
Labensky, Sarah R. Study Guide for on Baking: A Textbook of Baking & Pastry Fundamentals. 2nd ed. 2008. (ENG.). 240p. (C). pap. 29.00 (978-0-13-235775-3(5), Prentice Hall) Prentice Hall PTR.
Labensky, Sarah R., et al. On Baking. 3rd rev. ed. 2012. (ENG.). 864p. (C). 121.00 (978-0-13-237456-9(0), Prentice Hall) Prentice Hall PTR.
Labensky, Sarah R., et al. On Baking: A Textbook of Baking & Pastry Fundamentals. 2nd ed. 2008. (ENG., Illus.). 848p. (C). 125.87 (978-0-13-157923-1(1), Prentice Hall) Prentice Hall PTR.
Laris, David & Brettschneider, Dean. The Menu: An Inspiring Collection of 15 Five-Course Menus for Any Occasion, 1 vol. 2009. (ENG.). 216p. 37.50 (978-981-261-623-4(3)) Marshall Cavendish International (Asia) Private Ltd. SGP. Dist: Marshall Cavendish Corp.
Laskin, Avner. Celebrating Cobblers & Pies. 2010. (ENG.). 144p. pap. 14.95 (978-1-60900-009-7(9)) Leisure Arts, Inc.
Lawrence, Sue. Sue Lawrence's Book of Baking: More Than 120 Glorious Breads, Biscuits, Cakes & Tarts. 2008. (ENG., Illus.). 192p. pap. 24.95 (978-0-7553-1212-2(0)) Headline Bk. Publishing GBR. Dist: Independent Pubs. Group.
Leader, Daniel. Local Breads. 2007. 35.00 (978-0-7930-5055-0(3)) Norton, W. W. & Co., Inc.
Lee, Sandra. Bake Sale Cookbook. 2011. (ENG., Illus.). 240p. pap. 19.95 (978-0-470-64559-8(8), Wiley) Wiley, John & Sons, Inc.
Lepard, Dan & Whittington, Richard. Baking with Passion: Exceptional Recipes for Real Breads, Cakes & Pastries. (ENG., Illus.). 1p. pap. 19.95 (978-1-84400-034-0(6)) Quadrille Publishing, Ltd. GBR. Dist: Graphic Arts Ctr. Publishing Co.
Levy, Sarah. Sweetness: Delicious Baked Treats for Every Occasion. 2009. (ENG., Illus.). 144p. 20.00 (978-1-57284-093-5(5)) Surrey Bks.
Lewis, Fay. From My Oven: A Step-by-Step Guide to Successful Baking. 2008. (Illus.). 224p. 28.00 (978-1-77007-564-1(X)) Struik Pubs. ZAF. Dist: International Publishers Marketing.
Lewis, Jenny. Midwest Sweet Baking History: Delectable Classics Around Lake Michigan. 2011. 160p. pap. 19.99 (978-1-60949-344-8(3)) History Pr., The.
Lewis, Matt & Poliafito, Renato. Baked: New Frontiers in Baking. 2008. (ENG., Illus.). 208p. 29.95 (978-1-58479-721-0(5)) Stewart, Tabori & Chang.
—Baked Explorations: Classic American Desserts Reinvented. 2010. (ENG., Illus.). 208p. 29.95 (978-1-58479-850-7(5)) Stewart, Tabori & Chang.
Lewis, Sara. 200 Cakes & Bakes: Hamlyn All Color. 2009. (ENG.). 240p. pap. 7.99 (978-0-600-61871-3(4), Hamlyn) Octopus Publishing Group GBR. Dist: Hachette Bk. Group.
Lindholm, Leila. Sweet & Savory Swedish Baking. 2009. (ENG., Illus.). 224p. 29.95 (978-1-60239-798-9(8), 239798) Skyhorse Publishing Co., Inc.
Lion House Staff. Lion House Bakery. 2009. (Illus.). 128p. 25.95 (978-1-60641-137-7(3)) Deseret Bk. Co.
Luchetti, Emily & Weiss, Lisa. The Fearless Baker: Scrumptious Cakes, Pies, Cobblers, Cookies, & Quick Breads That You Can Make to Impress Your Friends & Yourself. 2011. (ENG., Illus.). 288p. 29.99 (978-0-316-07428-5(4)) Little Brown & Co.
Magnier Moreno, Marianne. Cooking from above - Baking. 2009. (ENG., Illus.). 224p. pap. 24.99 (978-0-600-61998-7(2), Hamlyn) Octopus Publishing Group GBR. Dist: Hachette Bk. Group.
Malgieri, Nick. Bake! Essential Techniques for Perfect Baking. 2010. (ENG.). 224p. 29.95 (978-1-906868-23-9(9)) Cathie, Kyle Ltd. GBR. Dist: National Bk. Network.
—The Modern Baker: Time-Saving Techniques for Breads, Tarts, Pies, Cakes & Cookies. 2nd ed. 2011. (ENG., Illus.). 320p. 22.95 (978-0-7566-8914-8(7)) Dorling Kindersley Publishing, Inc.
Malouf, Tarek. The Hummingbird Bakery Cookbook. 2009. (ENG., Illus.). 144p. (978-1-84597-831-0(5)) Ryland Peters & Small.
Marcotte, Michele. Handbook of Baking Science & Engineering. 2008. 720p. 199.95 (978-0-8493-1504-6(2), 1504) Taylor & Francis Group.
Mari-Louis Guy, Callie Maritz and. Cakebread, Pudding & Pie. 2011. (Illus.). 192p. 27.00 (978-1-77007-852-9(5)) Random Hse. Struik (Pty.), Ltd. ZAF. Dist: International Publishers Marketing.
Marianne & Jean-Michel. The Vegan Boulangerie: The best of traditional French baking... egg & Dairy-free. 2010. 144p. pap. (978-1-4269-2659-4(6)) Trafford Publishing (UK) Ltd.
Martin, Laura C. Green Market Baking Book: 100 Delicious Recipes for Naturally Sweet & Savory Treats. 2011. (ENG., Illus.). 224p. 17.95 (978-1-4027-5997-0(5)) Sterling Publishing Co., Inc.
Masi, Noble, et al. Baking Fundamentals. 2006. (ENG., Illus.). 624p. (C). 125.87 (978-0-13-118351-3(6), Prentice Hall) Prentice Hall PTR.
Maugans, Debby. Small-Batch Baking for Chocolate Lovers. 2011. (ENG., Illus.). 352p. pap. 21.99 (978-0-312-61224-5(9), St. Martin's Griffin) St. Martin's Pr.
McAuley, Jo. Brownies, Bars & Goodies Galore. 2010. (ENG., Illus.). 192p. pap. 16.95 (978-1-84601-373-7(9), Spruce) Octopus Publishing Group GBR. Dist: Hachette Bk. Group.
McCrea, Billie & Carlyle-Gauthier, Rachel. Gluten Free Mama's Best Baking Recipes. 2007. 152p. per. 15.99 (978-1-60266-409-8(9)) Xulon Pr., Inc.
MCP Staff & Australian Women's Weekly Staff. Muffins. (ENG., Illus.). 80p. pap. 5.95 (978-1-86396-249-0(2)) ACP Publishing Pty, Ltd. AUS. Dist: Graphic Arts Ctr. Publishing Co.
McQuillan, Susan & Sesame Workshop Staff. B Is for Baking: 50 Yummy Dishes to Make Together. 2011. (ENG., Illus.). 128p. 16.99 (978-0-470-63886-6(9), Wiley) Wiley, John & Sons, Inc.
Meyer, Arthur L. Danish Cooking & Baking Traditions. 2011. (ENG., Illus.). 256p. 32.00 (978-0-7818-1262-7(3)) Hippocrene Bks., Inc.
Mezo, Frances Elizabeth. A Bake-A-Holic's 40 Favorite Recipes. 2010. 83p. pap. 19.95 (978-0-557-41494-9(6)) Lulu Enterprises Inc.
Mill, Hodgson. Hodgson Mill Whole Grain Baking: 400 Healthy & Delicious Recipes for Muffins, Breads, Cookies, & More. 2007. (ENG., Illus.). 480p. per. 19.95 (978-1-59233-261-8(7), 1592332617, Fair Winds Press) Quayside.
Mink, Miisa & Wahlsten, Marianna. Nordic Bakery Cookbook. 2011. (ENG., Illus.). 144p. (978-1-84975-096-7(3)) Ryland Peters & Small.
Miura, Muriel. Cookies from Hawaii's Kitchen. 2006. 14.95 (978-1-56647-815-1(4)) Mutual Publishing LLC.
Moon, Jan & Southern Living Magazine Editors. Southern Living Big Book of Cupcakes: 150 Brilliantly Delicious Dreamcakes. 2011. (ENG., Illus.). 256p. pap. 19.95 (978-0-8487-3437-4(8)) Oxmoor Hse., Inc.
Murphy, Melissa. The Sweet Melissa Baking Book: Recipes from the Beloved Bakery for Everyone's Favorite Treats. 2008. (ENG., Illus.). 256p. (gr. 12-18). 27.00 (978-0-670-01874-1(0), Studio) Penguin Group (USA) Inc.
Mushet, Cindy & Sur La Table Staff. The Art & Soul of Baking. 2008. (ENG., Illus.). 464p. 40.00 (978-0-7407-7334-1(8)) Andrews McMeel Publishing.
Nguyen, Andrea. Asian Dumplings: Mastering Gyoza, Spring Rolls, Samosas, & More. 2009. (ENG., Illus.). 240p. 30.00 (978-1-58008-975-3(5)) Ten Speed Pr.
Niall, Mani. Sweet! From Agave to Turbinado, Home Baking with Every Kind of Natural Sugar & Sweetener. 2008. (ENG., Illus.). 288p. pap. 18.95 (978-1-60094-004-0(8)) Perseus Bks. Group.
Nilsen, Angela, et al. Cakes & Cake Decorating: Two Perfect Books for Bakers: over 600 Recipes for Fabulous Decorated Cakes, with Step-by-Step Techniques & More Than 1250 Photographs, 2 vols. 2012. (ENG., Illus.). 264p. 25.00 (978-0-7548-2375-9(X)) Anness Publishing GBR. Dist: National Bk. Network.
Novak Bull, Lorena. The Everything Vegan Baking Cookbook: 300 Recipes for Any Occasion! 2012. (ENG.). 304p. pap. 16.95 (978-1-4405-2997-9(3)) Adams Media Corp.
Old Farmer's Almanac Staff. The Old Farmer's Almanac Everyday Cookbook. 2008. (ENG., Illus.). 336p. 19.95 (978-1-57198-463-0(1)) Yankee Publishing, Inc.
Old Farmer's Almanac Staff, creator. The Old Farmer's Almanac Best Home Baking: Irresistible Recipes from America's Blue Ribbon Bakers. 2nd rev. ed. 2006. (ENG., Illus.). 192p. 14.95 (978-1-57198-385-5(6)) Yankee Publishing, Inc.
Olson, Anna. Back to Baking: 200 Timeless Recipes to Bake, Share, & Enjoy. 2011. 356p. 40.00 (978-1-77050-063-1(4)) Whitecap Bks., Ltd. CAN. Dist: Midpoint Trade Bks., Inc.
Orton, Mildred Ellen. Cooking with Wholegrains: The Basic Wholegrain Cookbook. 2010. (ENG., Illus.). 80p. pap. 12.00 (978-0-374-53261-1(3)) Farrar, Straus & Giroux.
Owens, Robert & Owens, Donna. Grandpa & grandma's sweet treat Book. 2008. 39p. pap. 14.96 (978-1-4357-4482-0(9)) Lulu Enterprises Inc.
Pappas, Lou Seibert & Williams-Sonoma. Baking. Williams, Chuck, ed. rev. ed. 2006. (Food Made Fast Ser.). (ENG., Illus.). 112p. 17.95 (978-0-8487-3138-0(7)) Oxmoor Hse., Inc.
Pascal, Cybele. The Allergen-Free Baker's Handbook: How to Bake Without Gluten, Wheat, Dairy, Eggs, Soy, Peanuts, Tree Nuts, & Sesame. 2009. (ENG., Illus.). 200p. pap. 25.00 (978-1-58761-348-7(4), Celestial Arts) Ten Speed Pr.
The Passionate Baker. 2006. per. 24.00 (978-0-9791625-0-3(5)) Homeniuk, Paul.
Patent, Greg. A Baker's Odyssey: Celebrating Time-Honored Recipes from America's Rich Immigrant Heritage. 2007. (ENG., Illus.). 416p. 34.95 (978-0-7645-7281-4(4), Wiley) Wiley, John & Sons, Inc.
Patric. Cook Your Way to a Happy Ending: An Accumulation of Recipes off the Beaten Path. 2009. 196p. pap. 46.49 (978-1-4389-1788-7(0)) AuthorHouse.
Patten, Marguerite. Baking Handbook: All You Need to Know to Bake Successful Cakes, Biscuits, Breads & Pastries. 2008. (BASIC BASICS Ser.). 192p. pap. (978-1-904010-11-1(3)) Grub Street.
Petersan, Doron. Sticky Fingers' Sweets: 100 Super-Secret Vegan Recipes. 2012. (ENG., Illus.). 304p. (gr. 12). 27.50 (978-1-58333-463-8(7), Avery) Penguin Group (USA) Inc.
Peterson, James. Baking: 300 Recipes, 2,000 Photographs, 1 Baking Education. 2009. (ENG., Illus.). 400p. 40.00 (978-1-58008-991-3(7)) Ten Speed Pr.
Peyton, Oliver & Byrne. British Baking. 2012. (ENG., Illus.). 288p. 35.00 (978-0-224-08661-5(8)) Random Hse. GBR. Dist: Independent Pubs. Group.
Pillsbury Company Staff, contrib. by. Best of the Bake-Off Cookbook: Recipes from America's Favorite Cooking Contest. 2nd ed. 2008. (ENG., Illus.). 368p. 29.95 (978-0-470-19442-3(1), Wiley) Wiley, John & Sons, Inc.
Pillsbury Editors. Holiday Baking: Treats Filled with Cheer for a Magical Time of Year. 2007. (ENG., Illus.). 223p. 19.95 (978-0-470-08062-7(0), Wiley) Wiley, John & Sons, Inc.
—Pillsbury Bake-off Winners: 100 Top Recipes from the 42nd Pillsbury Bake-off Contest. 2007. (ENG., Illus.). 224p. pr. 18.95 (978-0-470-08061-0(2), Wiley) Wiley, John & Sons, Inc.
—Pillsbury Baking. 2006. (ENG., Illus.). 272p. 24.95 (978-0-471-78088-5(X), Wiley) Wiley, John & Sons, Inc.
—Pillsbury Best of the Bake-Off Desserts. 2007. (ENG., Illus.). 160p. pap. 17.95 (978-0-471-78720-4(5), Wiley) Wiley, John & Sons, Inc.
Popovic, Isidora. Popina Book of Baking. 2010. (Illus.). 144p. (978-1-84597-965-2(6)) Ryland Peters & Small.
Publications International Staff. Concealed Spiral Splenda. 2008. 128p. 10.98 (978-1-4127-2959-8(9)) Publications International, Ltd.
—3 in 1 Jello, Bakers, Philadelphia. 2008. 288p. spiral bd. 14.98 (978-1-4127-9580-7(X)) Publications International, Ltd.
—3 in 1 Weeknight Meals, Pot Luck, Bake Sale. 2008. 288p. spiral bd. 14.98 (978-1-4127-2911-6(4)) Publications International, Ltd.
Publications International Staff, contrib. by. Favorite Brand Name Baking. 2007. (Illus.). 383p. 16.98 (978-1-4127-2602-3(6)) Publications International, Ltd.
Publications International Staff, creator. America's Favorites Bake Sale. 2007. (America's Favorites Ser.). (Illus.). 160p. 10.98 (978-1-4127-2983-3(1)) Publications International, Ltd.
Publications International Staff, ed. Kitchen-Aid. 2008. ring bd. 12.98 (978-1-4127-2917-8(3)) Publications International, Ltd.
—100 Best Bake Sale. 2007. spiral bd. 12.98 (978-1-4127-2545-3(3)) Publications International, Ltd.
Pyler, E. J. & Gorton, L. A. Baking Science & Technology. 4th ed. 2008. (Illus.). (978-0-9820239-0-7(1)) Sosland Publishing Co.
Randell, Sarah. Weekend Baking. 2010. (ENG., Illus.). 144p. (978-1-84975-033-2(5)) Ryland Peters & Small.
Ray, Meg & Miette Cakes Staff. Miette: Recipes from San Francisco's Most Charming Pastry Shop. 2011. (ENG., Illus.). 224p. 27.50 (978-0-8118-7504-2(0)) Chronicle Bks. LLC.
Read-Baldry, Hannah & Leech, Christine. Everything Alice: The Wonderland Book of Makes & Bakes. 2011. (ENG.). 144p. pap. 24.99 (978-1-4403-1440-7(3), North Light Bks.) F&W Media, Inc.
Rees, Nicole. Baking Unplugged. 2009. (ENG.). 272p. 29.95 (978-0-470-14911-9(6), Wiley) Wiley, John & Sons, Inc.
Reilly, Rebecca. Gluten-Free Baking: More Than 125 Recipes for Delectable Sweet & Savory Baked Goods, Including Cakes, Pies, Quick Breads, Muffins, Cookies, & Other Delights. 2007. (ENG., Illus.). 240p. pap. 18.99 (978-1-4165-3599-7(3)) Simon & Schuster.
Ridenour, Lisa. A Cookie in Each Hand: Decadent, Easy-to-Make Recipes for the Home Cook. 2007. 132p. per. 13.95 (978-0-595-45527-0(1)) iUniverse, Inc.
Rinsky, Glenn & Rinsky, Laura Halpin. The Pastry Chef's Companion: A Comprehensive Resource Guide for the Baking & Pastry Professional. 2008. (ENG., Illus.). 384p. per. 19.95 (978-0-470-00955-0(1), Wiley) Wiley, John & Sons, Inc.
Roberts, Annalise G. Gluten-Free Baking Classics. 2nd ed. 2008. (ENG.). 250p. pap. 17.95 (978-1-57284-099-7(4)) Surrey Bks.
—Gluten-Free Baking Classics for the Bread Machine. 2009. (ENG., Illus.). 72p. pap. 14.95 (978-1-57284-104-8(4)) Surrey Bks.
Rosen, Zilly. Zombie Cupcakes: From the Grave to the Table with 16 Cupcake Corpses. 2011. (ENG.). 80p. pap. 14.99 (978-1-4494-0112-2(0)) Andrews McMeel Publishing.
RPS Staff. Cinnamon, Spice & Warm Apple Pie. 2006. 144p. (978-1-84975-054-7(8)) Ryland Peters & Small.
Rps Stationery. The Hummingbird Bakery Baking Organizer. 2010. (ENG.). 128p. (978-1-84975-118-6(8)) Ryland Peters & Small.
Rudnicki, Kelly. The Food Allergy Mama's Baking Book: Great Dairy-, Egg-, & Nut-Free Treats for the Whole Family. 2009. (ENG., Illus.). 176p. pap. 19.95 (978-1-57284-102-4(8)) Surrey Bks.
—Vegan Baking Classics: Delicious, Easy-to-Make Traditional Favorites. 2010. (ENG., Illus.). 144p. pap. 17.95 (978-1-57284-112-3(5)) Surrey Bks.
Ryland Peters & Small and CICO Books, creator. Easy Cakes & Bakes: Cupcakes, brownies, muffins, loaves & More. 2012. (ENG., Illus.). 240p. (978-1-84975-212-1(5)) Ryland Peters & Small.
Sahin, Serpil & Sumnu, Servet Gulum, eds. Food Engineering Aspects of Baking Sweet Goods. 2008. (Contemporary Food Engineering Ser.). (ENG., Illus.). 304p. 185.95 (978-1-4200-5274-9(8), CRC Press) Taylor & Francis Group GBR. Dist: Taylor & Francis Group.
Sandler, Lori. The Divvies Bakery Cookbook: No Nuts. No Eggs. No Dairy. Just Delicious! 2010. (ENG., Illus.). 176p. 25.99 (978-0-312-60528-5(5)) St. Martin's Pr.
Sands, Brinna & King Arthur Flour Staff. The Original King Arthur Flour Cookbook. 2010. (King Arthur Flour Cookbooks Ser.). (ENG., Illus.). 624p. ring bd. 35.00 (978-0-88150-940-3(X), 150940) Countryman Pr.
Sannar, Micki. Olive Oil Desserts: Delicious & Healthy Heart Smart Baking. Martin, Megan, ed. 2009. (ENG., Illus.). 152p. 24.95 (978-0-9801349-0-2(0)) Mikko International.
Scherber, Amy & Dupree, Toy Kim. The Sweeter Side of Amy's Bread: Cakes, Cookies, Bars, Pastries & More from New York City's Favorite Bakery. 2008. (ENG., Illus.). 272p. 34.95 (978-0-470-17074-8(3), Wiley) Wiley, John & Sons, Inc.
Scurfield, George & Scurfield, Cecilia. Home Baked: A little book of bread, cake & biscuit Recipes. 2009. (Illus.). 144p. 24.95 (978-1-906502-37-9(4)) Grub Street GBR. Dist: Casemate Pubs. & Bk. Distributors, LLC.
Sember, Brette. The Muffin Tin Cookbook: 200 Fast, Delicious Mini-Pies, Pasta Cups, Gourmet Pockets, Veggie Cakes, & More! 2012. (ENG.). 224p. pap. 17.95 (978-1-4405-3216-0(8)) Adams Media Corp.
Shirazi, Kate & Blake, Susannah. Baking Magic. 2010. (ENG., Illus.). 288p. 22.95 (978-1-86205-889-7(X)) Chrysalis Children's Bks. GBR. Dist: Independent Pubs. Group.
Shoyer, Paula. The Kosher Baker: Over 160 Dairy-Free Recipes from Traditional to Trendy. 2010. (HBI Series on Jewish Women Ser.). (Illus.). 348p. 35.00 (978-1-58465-835-1(5), Brandeis University Press) Univ. Pr. of New England.
Shu-ling, Chou. Cake Recipes. (Illus.). 120p. (978-957-629-204-0(2)) Hilit Publishing Co., Ltd.
Simmons, Jessica, ed. Women's Institute: Vintage Teatime. 2012. (ENG., Illus.). 112p. pap. 18.95 (978-0-85720-859-0(4)) Simon & Schuster, Ltd. GBR. Dist: Independent Pubs. Group.
Sinclair, Pat. Baking Basics & Beyond: Learn These Simple Techniques & Bake Like a Pro. 2011. (ENG., Illus.). 320p. pap. 19.95 (978-1-57284-126-0(5)) Surrey Bks.
Smith, Beth. Double Baked. 2011. 56p. pap. 16.95 (978-1-4626-4372-1(8)) PublishAmerica, Inc.
Smith, Laura L., et al. Gluten-Free Baking for Dummies. 2011. (ENG.). 392p. pap. 19.99 (978-1-118-07773-3(3), For Dummies) Wiley, John & Sons, Inc.
Smith, Lindy. Bake Me I'm Yours... Cookie. 2008. (ENG., Illus.). 128p. pap. 14.99 (978-0-7153-2926-9(X)) David & Charles Pubs. GBR. Dist: F&W Media, Inc.
—Bake Me I'm Yours... Cupcake Love. 2010. (ENG., Illus.). 128p. 14.99 (978-0-7153-3781-3(5)) David & Charles Pubs. GBR. Dist: F&W Media, Inc.
Staib, Walter. City Tavern: Recipes from the Birthplace of American Cuisine. 2009. (ENG.). 392p. 35.00 (978-0-7624-3417-6(1)) Perseus Bks. Group.
Sunset Books Staff, et al. Baking: Recipes & Techniques for Successful Home Baking. rev. ed. 2008. (ENG., Illus.). 320p. 34.95 (978-0-8487-3258-5(8)) Oxmoor Hse., Inc.
Taste of Home Staff. Taste of Home Baking: From the World's Number One Food & & Entertaining Magazine. 2011. (ENG.). 510p. (gr. 12). 29.95 (978-0-89821-846-6(2)) Reader's Digest Assn., Inc., The.

Taylor, Anna. Alexia Renée's - Bake Fresh- Muffins, Breads, Biscuits Etc... 2008. 100p. pap. 19.95 *(978-1-4357-0734-4(6))* Lulu Enterprises Inc.
Tee, Susanna. Whoopies! Fabulous Seasonal Mix-and-Match Recipes for Whoopie Pies. 2011. (ENG., Illus.). 96p. pap. 12.95 *(978-1-4027-8647-1(6))* Sterling Publishing Co., Inc.
The Culinary Institute of America. Baking & Pastry: Mastering the Art & Craft with Art of the Chocolatier Pastry Chef's Companion & Tasting Success Set. 2nd ed. 2011. 194.90 ***(978-1-118-12749-0(8)**, Wiley)* Wiley, John & Sons, Inc.
The Culinary Institute of America (CIA). Baking & Pastry: Mastering the Art & Craft 2nd Edition with Art of the Chocolatier & Pastry Chef's Companion Set. 2nd ed. 2011. 154.95 ***(978-1-118-13201-2(7)**, Wiley)* Wiley, John & Sons, Inc.
Thebault, Rachel. Sweet Chic: Stylish Treats to Dress Up for Any Occasion. 2010. (ENG., Illus.). 208p. 28.00 *(978-0-345-51655-8(9)*, Ballantine Bks.) Random House Publishing Group.
Tillie, Karlene. The Impatient Baker: Simple, Streamlined & Speedy Recipes for Classic American Style Cookies, Cakes, Brownies, Breakfast & Fruit Desserts. 2007. 204p. per. 17.95 *(978-0-595-45187-5(X))* iUniverse, Inc.
Trivuncic, Sarah. Bake Me I'm Yours... Sweet Bitesize Bakes: 25 Miniature Baking & Cake Decorating Projects. 2012. (ENG., Illus.). 128p. 14.99 ***(978-1-4463-0183-8(4))*** David & Charles Pubs. GBR. Dist: F&W Media, Inc.
Turnbull, Wendy. Gems of Gluten-Free Baking: Breads & Irresistible Treats Everyone Can Enjoy. 2nd ed. 2010. (ENG., Illus.). 198p. pap. 29.95 *(978-1-77050-016-1(9))* Whitecap Bks., Ltd. CAN. Dist: Midpoint Trade Bks., Inc.
Tye, Diane. Baking as Biography: A Life Story in Recipes. 2010. 288p. (ENG.). (C). *(978-0-7735-3724-8(4))*; pap. *(978-0-7735-3725-5(2))* McGill-Queen's Univ. Pr.
Valastro, Buddy. Cake Boss: Stories & Recipes from Mia Famiglia. (ENG.). 272p. 2012. pap. 16.99 *(978-1-4516-1034-5(3))* 2010. (Illus.). 25.99 *(978-1-4391-8351-9(1))* Free Pr. (Free Pr.).
Vickery, Phil. Gluten-Free Baking. 2011. (ENG., Illus.). 173p. pap. 24.95 *(978-1-55407-811-0(3))* Firefly Bks., Ltd.
Walden, Hilaire & Clements, Carole. The Cookies & Baking Bookbox, 2 vols. 2012. (ENG., Illus.). 528p. 25.00 *(978-0-7548-2013-0(0))* Anness Publishing GBR. Dist: National Bk. Network.
Walter, Carole. Great Cakes, Pies, Cookies, Muffins & More: Secrets for Sensational Sweets & Fabulous Favorite Recipes. 2009. (Illus.). iii, 396p. *(978-1-60529-781-1(X))* Rodale Pr., Inc.
—Great Coffee Cakes, Sticky Buns, Muffins & More: 200 Anytime Treats & Special Sweets for Morning to Midnight. 2007. (ENG., Illus.). 416p. 35.00 *(978-0-307-23755-2(9)*, Clarkson Potter) Crown Publishing Group.
Washburn, Donna & Butt, Heather. The Gluten-Free Baking Book: 250 Small-Batch Recipes for Everything from Brownies to Cheesecake. 2011. (ENG., Illus.). 320p. pap. 24.95 *(978-0-7788-0274-7(4))* Rose, Robert Inc. CAN. Dist: Firefly Bks., Ltd.
Whitley, Andrew. Bread Matters: The State of Modern Bread & a Definitive Guide to Baking Your Own. 2009. (ENG.). 416p. 34.99 *(978-0-7407-7373-0(9))* Andrews McMeel Publishing.
Williams-Sonoma. The Williams-Sonoma Baking Book: Essential Recipes for Today's Home Baker. 2010. (ENG., Illus.). 416p. 34.95 *(978-1-60320-107-0(6))* Oxmoor Hse., Inc.
Wilson, Dede. The Birthday Cake Book: 75 Recipes for Candle-Worthy Creations. 2008. (ENG.) 176p. 27.95 *(978-1-55832-381-0(3))*; (Illus.). pap. 14.95 *(978-1-55832-382-7(1))* Harvard Common Pr.
Wilson, Joy. Joy the Baker Cookbook: 100 Simple & Comforting Recipes. 2012. (ENG., Illus.). 208p. pap. 19.99 ***(978-1-4013-1060-8(5))*** Hyperion Pr.
Wolf, Bonny. Talking with My Mouth Full: Crab Cakes, Bundt Cakes, & Other Kitchen Stories. 2007. (ENG.). 272p. pap. 15.99 *(978-0-312-37385-6(6)*, St. Martin's Griffin) St. Martin's Pr.
Wolf, Laurie Goldrich, et al. The Only Bake Sale Cookbook You'll Ever Need: 201 Mouthwatering, Kid-Pleasing Treats. 2008. (ENG.). 272p. pap. 14.95 *(978-0-06-123383-8(8)*, Morrow, William Cookbooks) HarperCollins Pubs.
Yockelson, Lisa. Baking by Flavor. 2011. (ENG.). 592p. pap. 24.99 ***(978-1-118-16967-4(0)**, Wiley)* Wiley, John & Sons, Inc.
Yockelson, Lisa. Baking Style: Art, Craft, Recipes. 2011. (ENG., Illus.). 528p. 45.00 *(978-0-470-43702-5(2)*, Wiley) Wiley, John & Sons, Inc.

BAKING—VOCATIONAL GUIDANCE

Favorite Brand Name Recipes Editors. Kitchen Aid Baking Basics: Techniques for Perfect Baking. 2010. 192p. spiral bd. 12.98 *(978-1-4508-0049-5(1))* Publications International, Ltd.
Felder, Amy. Savory Sweets: From Ingredients to Plated Desserts. 2007. (Wiley Desktop Editions Ser.). (ENG., Illus.). 272p. pap. 35.00 *(978-0-471-74058-2(6)*, Wiley) Wiley, John & Sons, Inc.
Pascal, Cybele. The Allergen-Free Baker's Handbook: How to Bake Without Gluten, Wheat, Dairy, Eggs, Soy, Peanuts, Tree Nuts, & Sesame. 2009. (ENG., Illus.). 200p. pap. 25.00 *(978-1-58761-348-7(4)*, Celestial Arts) Ten Speed Pr.

BAKONGO (AFRICAN PEOPLE)

see Kongo (African People)

BAKUBA (AFRICAN PEOPLE)

see Kuba (African People)

BAKUNIN, MIKHAIL ALEKSANDROVITCH, 1814-1876

Goodwin, James. Confronting Dostoevsky's Demons: Anarchism & the Specter of Bakunin in Twentieth-Century Russia. 2010. (Middlebury Studies in Russian Language & Literature Ser.). 262p. (C). 77.95 *(978-1-4331-0883-9(6))* Lang, Peter Publishing, Inc.
Leier, Mark. Bakunin: A Biography. Date not set. pap. *(978-0-312-30539-0(7))*; mass mkt. *(978-0-312-98512-7(6)*, St. Martin's Paperbacks) St. Martin's Pr.
—Bakunin: The Creative Passion-A Biography. 2009. (ENG.). 384p. pap. 17.95 *(978-1-58322-894-4(2))* Seven Stories Pr.
Randolph, John. The House in the Garden: The Bakunin Family & the Romance of Russian Idealism. 2007. (Illus.). 287p. 46.00 *(978-0-8014-4542-2(6))* Cornell Univ. Pr.

BALAAM (BIBLICAL FIGURE)

Gadol, Kohen Ben. Last Sounding of Shofar. 2010. pap. 24.95 *(978-0-7414-6126-1(9))* Infinity Publishing.
Kooten, Geurt Hendrik van & Ruiten, J. Van. The Prestige of the Pagan Prophet Balaam in Judaism, Early Christianity & Islam. Kooten, George H. van & Ruiten, Jacques van, eds. 2008. (Themes in Biblical Narrative Ser.). 344p. *(978-90-04-16564-9(9))* BRILL.
Levine, Baruch A. & Gross, Andrew. In Pursuit of Meaning: Collected Studies of Baruch A. Levine. 2011. 109.50 *(978-1-57506-206-3(2))*; *(978-1-57506-207-5(0))*; *(978-1-57506-208-2(9))* Eisenbrauns, Inc.

BALAENOPTERA

see Whales

BALAKLAVA, BATTLE OF, BALAKLAVA, UKRAINE, 1854

Bancroft, James W. Echelon: The Light Brigade Action at Balaclava - A New Perspective. 2011. (ENG., Illus.). 192p. 29.95 ***(978-0-7524-6207-3(5))*** History Pr. Ltd., The GBR. Dist: Independent Pubs. Group.
Buttery, David. Messenger of Death: Captain Nolan & the Charge of the Light Brigade. 2008. (Illus.). 256p. 39.95 *(978-1-84415-756-3(3))* Pen & Sword Bks. Ltd. GBR. Dist: Casemate Pubs. & Bk. Distributors, LLC.
Trow, M. J. The Pocket Hercules: Captain Morris & the Charge of the Light Brigade. 2006. (Illus.). 170p. 39.95 *(978-1-84415-378-7(9))* Pen & Sword Bks. Ltd. GBR. Dist: Casemate Pubs. & Bk. Distributors, LLC.

BALANCE

see Balances (Weighing Instruments); Equilibrium

BALANCE (ART)

see Proportion (Art)

BALANCE (PHYSICS)

see Equilibrium

BALANCE (PHYSIOLOGY)

see Equilibrium (Physiology)

BALANCE OF NATURE

see Ecology

BALANCE OF PAYMENTS

see also Balance of Trade; Capital Movements; International Liquidity

Becker, Torbjörn. Country Insurance: The Role of Domestic Policies. 2007. (Illus.). v, 36p. *(978-1-58906-607-6(3))* International Monetary Fund.
Brakman, Steven & Marrewijk, Charles van. The Economics of International Transfers. 2009. (ENG., Illus.). 232p. pap. 36.99 *(978-0-521-11872-9(7))* Cambridge Univ. Pr.
Brender, Anton & Pisani, Florence. Global Imbalances & the Collapse of Globalised Finance. 2010. (ENG., Illus.). 150p. pap. 16.00 *(978-92-9079-943-6(9))* Ctr. for European Policy Studies BEL. Dist: Brookings Institution Pr.
Caves, Richard E., et al. World Trade & Payments: An Introduction. 10th rev. ed. 2006. (ENG., Illus.). 712p. (C). pap. 93.33 *(978-0-321-22660-0(7))* Addison Wesley.
Chang, Tse Chun. Cyclical Movements in the Balance of Payments. 2011. (ENG., Illus.). 252p. pap. 23.99 *(978-1-107-61522-9(4))* Cambridge Univ. Pr.
Clarida, Richard H., ed. G7 Current Account Imbalances: Sustainability & Adjustment. 2007. (National Bureau of Economic Research Conference Report). (Illus.). 448p. 107.50 *(978-0-226-10726-4(4))* Univ. of Chicago Pr.
Cram101 Textbook Reviews. Outlines & Highlights for International Economics by Robert C Feenstr. 2011. 414p. pap. 35.95 ***(978-1-4672-6672-7(8))*** Cram101 Inc.
Cram101 Textbook Reviews & Cram101 Textbook Reviews. Outlines & Highlights for Essentials of International Economics by Robert C Feenstr. 2011. 414p. pap. 35.95 ***(978-1-61830-159-8(4))*** Cram101 Inc.
Dunaway, Steven. Global Imbalances & the Financial Crisis: Council Special Report No. 44, March 2009. 2009. (ENG., Illus.). 56p. pap. 10.00 *(978-0-87609-428-0(0))* Council on Foreign Relations.
Dyker, David A. Yugoslavia: Socialism, Development & Debt. 2011. (Routledge Revivals Ser.). (ENG.). 216p. 115.00 *(978-0-415-61568-6(2))* Routledge.
Elitok, Secil Pacaci. Growth & Balance of Payments Constraint: The Case of Turkey. 2008. 120p. pap. *(978-3-639-05432-3(6))* VDM Verlag Dr. Mueller e.K.
Feenstra, Robert C. & Taylor, Alan M. International Economics. 2009. (ENG.). 900p. (C). 118.95 *(978-1-4292-3957-8(3))* Worth Pubs., Inc.
International Monetary Fund. Balance of payments & international investment position Manual. 2009. (Illus.). 369p. pap. ***(978-1-58906-812-4(2))*** International Monetary Fund.
Kester, Anne Y. International Reserves & Foreign Currency Liquidity: Guidelines for a Data Template. (ARA.). pap. 23.00 *(978-1-58906-102-6(0)*, IRFCAA0012001); (CHI.). pap. 23.00 *(978-1-58906-195-8(0)*, IRFCCA0012001) International Monetary Fund.
McGuire, Shayne. Buy Gold Now: How a Real Estate Bust, Our Bulging National Debt, & the Languishing Dollar Will Push Gold to Record Highs. 2008. (ENG., Illus.). 240p. 34.95 *(978-0-470-18588-9(0)*, Wiley) Wiley, John & Sons, Inc.
Peláez, Carlos M. & Peláez, Carlos A. The Global Recession Risk: Dollar Devaluation & the World Economy. 2007. (ENG., Illus.). 276p. 116.00 *(978-0-230-52150-6(9))* Palgrave Macmillan.
Prati, Alessandro. External Performance in Low-Income Countries. 2011. 64p. pap. ***(978-1-61635-053-6(9))*** International Monetary Fund.
Scatigna, Louis. Financial Physician. 2009. (ENG.). 1p. pap. 14.99 *(978-1-60163-098-8(0))* Career Pr., Inc.
Siddaiah, Thummuluri. International Financial Management. 2009. pap. *(978-81-317-1720-2(8))* Pearson Bks.
Statistics Department Staff. Balance of Payments Textbook. (ARA.). 150p. pap. 25.00 *(978-1-58906-292-4(2)*, BPTAA) International Monetary Fund.
Stern, Robert M. Balance of Payments: Theory & Economic Policy. 2007. (ENG., Illus.). 451p. (gr. 11). pap. 34.95 *(978-0-202-30893-7(6))* Aldine Transaction.
United Nations. Trade & Development Report 2008: (Russian Language) 2009. (RUS.). 280p. pap. 55.00 *(978-92-1-411033-0(6))* United Nations Pubns.
United Nations Staff. Trade & Development Report 2008: (Chinese Language) 2009. (CHI.). 192p. pap. 55.00 *(978-92-1-730155-1(8))* United Nations Pubns.

BALANCE OF PAYMENTS—EUROPE

Funke, Katja. Balance of Payments Issues in Central & Eastern European Countries' Run-Up to Euro Area Accession. 2007. (Studien zu Internationalen Wirschaftsbeziehungen Ser.: Vol. 9). 241p. pap. 51.95 *(978-0-8204-8723-6(6))* Lang, Peter Publishing, Inc.
—Balance of Payments Issues in Central & Eastern European Countrie's Run-up to Euro Area Accession. (Illus.). 241p. pap. 51.95 *(978-3-631-55694-8(2))* Lang, Peter GmbH, Europaischer Verlag der Wissenschaften DEU. Dist: Lang, Peter Publishing, Inc.
Wandhöfer, Ruth. EU Payments Integration: The Tale of SEPA, PSD & Other Milestones along the Road. 2010. (Palgrave Macmillan Studies in Banking & Financial Institutions Ser.). (ENG., Illus.). 320p. 110.00 *(978-0-230-24347-7(9))* Palgrave Macmillan.

BALANCE OF PAYMENTS—GREAT BRITAIN

Office for Humanities Communication Staff, et al. United Kingdom Balance of Payments 2006. Bundey, John, ed. 2006. (ENG., Illus.). 208p. pap. 85.00 *(978-1-4039-9387-8(4))* Palgrave Macmillan.
Office for National Statistics Staff. United Kingdom Balance of Payments 2010: The Pink Book. 2010. (ENG.). 224p. pap. 85.00 *(978-0-230-24377-4(0))* Palgrave Macmillan.
Price, Deborah & Office for National Statistics Staff. United Kingdom Balance of Payments 2009. 2010. (ENG.). 170p. pap. 85.00 *(978-0-230-57610-0(9))* Palgrave Macmillan.
The Office for National Statistics. United Kingdom Balance of Payments 2008: The Pink Book. 2009. (ENG.). 170p. pap. 85.00 *(978-0-230-54565-6(3))* Palgrave Macmillan.

BALANCE OF POWER

Ahrari, Ehsan M. The Great Powers Versus the Hegemon. 2011. (ENG., Illus.). 256p. 85.00 *(978-0-230-27891-2(4))* Palgrave Macmillan.
Bacevich, Andrew J. The Limits of Power: The End of American Exceptionalism. 2009. (American Empire Project Ser.). (ENG.). 224p. pap. 14.00 *(978-0-8050-9016-1(9)*, Holt Paperback) Holt, Henry & Co.
Berenskoetter. Power in World Politics. 2008. (ENG., Illus.). 328p. (C). 160.00 *(978-0-415-42113-3(6))* Routledge.
Berenskoetter, Felix. Power in World Politics. Williams, M. J., ed. 2007. (ENG., Illus.). 328p. (C). 44.95 *(978-0-415-42114-0(4))* Routledge.
Bo, Zhiyue. China's Elite Politics: Governance & Democratization. 2009. (Illus.). 350p. 111.00 *(978-981-283-672-4(1))* World Scientific Publishing Co., Inc.
Bozo, Frederic. Visions of the End of the Cold War. 2012. E-Book ***(978-0-85745-370-9(X))*** Berghahn Bks., Inc.
Brawley, Mark R. Political Economy & Grand Strategy: A Neoclassical Realist View. 2009. (Routledge Global Security Studies). (ENG., Illus.). 176p. (C). 130.00 *(978-0-415-49367-3(6))* Routledge.
Bromley, Simon. American Power & the Prospects for International Order. 2008. (ENG.). 288p. 74.95 *(978-0-7456-4238-3(1))*; pap. 29.95 *(978-0-7456-4239-0(X))* Polity Pr. GBR. Dist: Wiley, John & Sons, Inc.
Brooks, Stephen G. & Wohlforth, William Curti. World Out of Balance: International Relations & the Challenge of American Primacy. 2008. (ENG., Illus.). 225p. (C). pap. 24.95 *(978-0-691-13784-1(6))* Princeton Univ. Pr.
Brzezinski, Zbigniew. Strategic Vision: America & the Crisis of Global Power. 2012. (ENG., Illus.). 224p. (gr. 13). 26.00 ***(978-0-465-02954-9(X))*** Basic Bks.
Bukovansky, Mlada, et al. Special Responsibilities: Global Problems & American Power. 2012. (ENG.). 312p. 85.00 ***(978-1-107-02135-8(9))***; pap. 29.99 ***(978-1-107-69169-8(9))*** Cambridge Univ. Pr.
Byers, Michael & Nolte, Georg, eds. United States Hegemony & the Foundations of International Law. 2008. (ENG.). 552p. (C). pap. 69.00 *(978-0-521-05086-9(3))* Cambridge Univ. Pr.
Chaimowicz, Thomas. Antiquity as the Source of Modernity: Freedom & Balance in the Thought of Montesquieu & Burke. 2008. (ENG.). 151p. 49.95 *(978-1-4128-0771-5(9))* Transaction Pubs.
Chan, Steve. Looking for Balance: China, the United States, & Power Balancing in East Asia. 2012. (Studies in Asian Security Ser.). (ENG.). 304p. 50.00 *(978-0-8047-7820-6(5))* Stanford Univ. Pr.
Chan. War, Peace & Hegemony in a Globalized World: The Changing Balance of Power in the Twenty-first Century. 2007. (Routledge Advances in International Relations & Global Politics Ser.). (Illus.). 256p. 160.00 *(978-0-415-43577-2(3))* Routledge.
Cordesman, Anthony H. & Gagel, Andrew. The Korean Military Balance: Comparative Korean Forces & the Forces of Key Neighboring States: Main Report. 2011. pap. ***(978-0-89206-632-2(6))*** Ctr. for Strategic & International Studies.
Craig, Gordon A. Tact & Intelligence: Essays on Diplomatic History & International Relations. Thompson, Bruce, ed. 2008. (ENG., Illus.). 330p. per. *(978-0-930664-26-8(4))* Society for the Promotion of Science & Scholarship, Inc.
Cui, Shunji. Sino-Japanese Relations & a 'security Regime' in East Asi. 2010. 276p. pap. *(978-3-8383-9178-6(0))* Lambert Academic Publishing.
David, Charles-Philippe & Grondin, David. Hegemony or Empire? The Redefinition of US Power under George W. Bush. 2006. (Illus.). 256p. 120.00 *(978-0-7546-4774-4(9))* Ashgate Publishing Co.
Emmott, Bill. Rivals: How the Power Struggle Between China, India & Japan Will Shape Our Next Decade. 2008. (ENG., Illus.). 352p. 26.00 *(978-0-15-101503-0(1))* Houghton Mifflin Harcourt Trade & Reference Pubs.
—Rivals: How the Power Struggle Between China, India, & Japan Will Shape Our Next Decade. 2009. (ENG.). 352p. pap. 15.95 *(978-0-15-603362-6(3)*, Mariner Bks.) Houghton Mifflin Harcourt Trade & Reference Pubs.
Felix, David. America Rising: Power & Political Economy in the First Nation. 2008. (ENG., Illus.). 265p. 39.95 *(978-1-4128-0811-8(1))* Transaction Pubs.
Fels, Enrico, et al, eds. Power in the 21st Century: International Security & International Political Economy in a Changing World. 2012. (Global Power Shift Ser.). (ENG., Illus.). xviii, 319p. 139.00 ***(978-3-642-25081-1(5)**, 3642250815)* Springer.
Gill, Stephen. Power & Resistance in the New World Order. 2nd rev. ed. 2008. (ENG.). 304p. 152.00 *(978-0-230-20369-3(8))*; pap. 40.00 *(978-0-230-20370-9(1))* Palgrave Macmillan.
Holslag, Jonathan. Trapped Giant. 2011. (Adelphi Ser.). (ENG., Illus.). 160p. (C). pap. 19.95 *(978-0-415-66989-4(8))* Routledge.
Hook, Steven W. US Foreign Policy: the Paradox of World Power, 00 vols. 2nd rev. ed. 2010. (Illus.). 564p. pap. 88.00 *(978-1-60426-609-2(0))* CQ Pr.
Horowitz, Michael C. The Diffusion of Military Power: Causes & Consequences for International Politics. 2010. (ENG., Illus.). 286p. (C). 75.00 *(978-0-691-14395-8(1))*; pap. 26.95 *(978-0-691-14396-5(X))* Princeton Univ. Pr.
Ikenberry, G. John, et al, eds. International Relations Theory & the Consequences of Unipolarity. 2011. (ENG., Illus.). 392p. 95.00 *(978-1-107-01170-0(1))* Cambridge Univ. Pr.
Kalyvas, Andreas. Democracy & the Politics of the Extraordinary: Max Weber, Carl Schmitt, & Hannah Arendt. 2008. (ENG.). 336p. 85.00 *(978-0-521-87768-8(7))* Cambridge Univ. Pr.
Kanishka Jayasuriya, 30 Sutcliffe St. Reconstituting the Global Liberal Order: Legitimacy, Regulation & Security. 2009. 170p. pap. 37.50 *(978-0-415-45977-4(1))* Routledge.
Kapur, S. Paul. Dangerous Deterrent: Nuclear Weapons Proliferation & Conflict in South Asia. 2007. (Studies in Asian Security Ser.). (ENG.). 280p. 65.00 *(978-0-8047-5549-8(3))*; per. 24.95 *(978-0-8047-5550-4(7))* Stanford Univ. Pr.
Kaufman, Stuart. The Balance of Power in World History. Kaufman, Stuart et al, eds. 2007. (ENG., Illus.). 288p. pap. 41.00 *(978-0-230-50711-1(5))* Palgrave Macmillan.
Kaufman, Stuart J. & Kaufman, Stuart. The Balance of Power in World History. Little, Richard & Wohlforth, William C., eds. 2007. (ENG., Illus.). 374p. 137.00 *(978-0-230-50710-4(7))* Palgrave Macmillan.
Khanna, Parag. The Second World: Empires & Influence in the New Global Order. 2009. (ENG., Illus.). 496p. 16.00 *(978-0-8129-7984-8(2)*, Random Hse. Trade Paperbacks) Random House Publishing Group.
Kissane Dylan & Kissane, Dylan. Tracking Power & Predicting Conflict: Reformulating Power Cycle Theory for the 21st Century. 2008. 116p. pap. *(978-3-639-09704-7(1))* VDM Verlag Dr. Mueller e.K.
Kowner, Rotem, ed. The Impact of the Russo-Japanese War. annot. ed. 2006. (Routledge Studies in the Modern History of Aisa Ser.). (Illus.). 348p. 170.00 *(978-0-415-36824-7(3))* Routledge.
Kupchan, Charles. How Enemies Become Friends: The Sources of Stable Peace. 2010. (Princeton Studies in International History & Politics Ser.). (ENG., Illus.). 448p. 29.95 *(978-0-691-14265-4(3))* Princeton Univ. Pr.
Kupchan, Charles. How Enemies Become Friends - the Sources of Stable Peace. 2012. (Princeton Studies in International History & Politics Ser.). (ENG., Illus.). 448p. (C). pap. 24.95 ***(978-0-691-15438-1(4))*** Princeton Univ. Pr.
Lee, Dong Sun. Power Shifts, Strategy & War: Declining States & International Conflict. 2007. (Routledge Global Security Studies). (ENG., Illus.). 224p. (C). 150.00 *(978-0-415-77338-6(5))* Routledge.
Lennon, Alexander T. J. & Kozlowski, Amanda, eds. Global Powers in the 21st Century: Strategies & Relations. 2008. (Washington Quarterly Readers Ser.). (ENG., Illus.). 456p. (gr. 17). pap. 30.00 *(978-0-262-62218-9(1))* MIT Pr.
Leonard, Mark. Why Europe Will Run the 21st Century. annot. ed. 2006. (ENG.). 192p. per. 11.95 *(978-1-58648-424-8(9))* PublicAffairs.
Levin, Michael L. The Next Great Clash: China & Russia vs. the United States, 1 vol. 2007. (Praeger Security International Ser.). (Illus.). 216p. 44.95 *(978-0-313-34592-0(9)*, C34592, Praeger Security International) Greenwood Publishing Group, Inc.
Lieber, Robert J. The American Era: Power & Strategy for the 21st Century. annot. ed. 2007. (ENG.). 306p. per. 22.99 *(978-0-521-69738-5(7))* Cambridge Univ. Pr.

B

Little, Richard. The Balance of Power in International Relations. 2007. (ENG., Illus.). 328p. (C). 94.99 *(978-0-521-87488-5(2))* Cambridge Univ. Pr.

—The Balance of Power in International Relations: Metaphors, Myths & Models. 2007. (ENG., Illus.). 328p. (C). per. 35.99 *(978-0-521-69760-6(3))* Cambridge Univ. Pr.

Mearsheimer & Cram101 Textbook Reviews Staff. The Tragedy of Great Power Politics. 2007. 128p. per. 11.95 *(978-1-4288-2364-8(6))* Cram101 Inc.

Niederberger, Andreas. Demokratie unter Bedingungen der Weltgesellschaft? Normative Grundlagen legitimer Herrschaft in einer globalen politischen Ordnung. 2009. (Ideen & Argumente Ser.).Tr. of Democracy under the conditions of a world Society? (GER.). X, 523p. 84.00 *(978-3-11-021410-9(5))*; 126.00 ***(978-3-11-173310-4(6))*** De Gruyter, Walter Inc.

Odgaard, Liselotte. The Balance of Power in Asia-Pacific Security. 2009. 278p. pap. 39.95 *(978-0-415-54702-4(4))* Routledge.

—The Balance of Power in Asia-Pacific Security: Us-China Policies on Regional Order. 2007. (Politics in Asia Ser.). (Illus.). 272p. 170.00 *(978-0-415-41591-0(8))* Routledge.

Okoth, Simon. A 'seat at the Table' 2010. 240p. pap. *(978-3-8383-5115-5(0))* Lambert Academic Publishing.

Ordeshook, Peter, et al. Balance of Power. 2007. (ENG.). 368p. pap. 74.00 *(978-0-521-37615-0(7))* Cambridge Univ. Pr.

Panzner, Michael J., et al. When Giants Fall: An Economic Roadmap for the End of the American Era. 2009. (ENG.). 288p. 27.95 *(978-0-470-31043-4(X)*, Wiley) Wiley, John & Sons, Inc.

Pelopidas, Benoit, et al. When Empire Meets Nationalism: Power Politics in the US & Russia. 2009. 226p. 114.95 *(978-0-7546-7805-2(9))* Ashgate Publishing Co.

Pineo, Ronn F. Ecuador & the United States: Useful Strangers. 2007. (United States & the Americas Ser.). (ENG., Illus.). 276p. 59.95 *(978-0-8203-2970-3(3))*; per. 24.95 *(978-0-8203-2971-0(1))* Univ. of Georgia Pr.

Porter, Gareth. Perils of Dominance: Imbalance of Power & the Road to War in Vietnam. 2006. 403p. per. 24.95 *(978-0-520-25004-8(4))* Univ. of California Pr.

Power & International Relations. *(978-0-394-44776-6(X))* Knopf, Alfred A. Inc.

Rees, John. Timelines. 2012. (ENG., Illus.). 222p. 125.00 ***(978-0-415-69102-4(8))***; pap. 31.95 ***(978-0-415-69103-1(6))*** Routledge.

Renard, Thomas & Biscop, Sven. The European Union & Emerging Powers in the 21st Century: How Europe Can Shape a New Global Order. 2012. 203p. 99.95 ***(978-1-4094-1956-3(8))*** Ashgate Publishing Co.

Rogerson, Barnaby. The Last Crusaders: The Hundred-Year Battle for the Center of the World. (ENG.). 512p. (gr. 12). 2011. 19.95 *(978-1-59020-440-5(9))* 2010. 35.00 *(978-1-59020-286-9(4))* Overlook Pr., The.

Rosato, Sebastian. Europe United: Power Politics & the Making of the European Community. 2011. (Cornell Studies in Security Affairs Ser.). (Illus.). 280p. 35.00 *(978-0-8014-4935-2(9))* Cornell Univ. Pr.

Roth, Ariel Ilan. Leadership in International Relations: The Balance of Power & the Origins of World War II. 2010. (ENG.). 214p. 89.00 *(978-0-230-10690-1(0))* Palgrave Macmillan.

Rother, Bernd. Visions of the End of the Cold War in Europe, 1945-1990. Bozo, Frederic et al, eds. 2012. (ENG.). 352p. 95.00 ***(978-0-85745-288-7(6))*** Berghahn Bks., Inc.

Saltzman, Ilai Z. Securitizing Balance of Power Theory: A Polymorphic Reconceptualization. 2011. (ENG., Illus.). 328p. (gr. 17). 85.00 ***(978-0-7391-7071-7(6))*** Lexington Bks.

—Securitizing Balance of Power Theory: A Polymorphic Reconceptualization. 2011. ***(978-0-7391-7072-4(4))*** Lexington Bks.

Schweller, Randall L. Unanswered Threats: Political Constraints on the Balance of Power. 2008. (Princeton Studies in International History & Politics). (ENG.). 200p. (C). pap. 27.95 *(978-0-691-13646-2(7))* Princeton Univ. Pr.

Singh, Daljit. By Design or Accident: Reflections on Asian Security. 2010. 176p. ***(978-981-4279-71-0(4))*** Institute of Southeast Asian Studies.

Skaff, Jonathan Karam. Sui-Tang China & Its Turko-Mongol Neighbors: Culture, Power, & Connections, 580-800, 1 vol. 2012. (Oxford Studies in Early Empires Ser.). (ENG., Illus.). 416p. 85.00 ***(978-0-19-973413-9(5))*** Oxford Univ. Pr., Inc.

Stuart, P. D. Codeword Barbelon - Danger in the Vatican: The Sons of Loyola & Their Plans for World Domination, 2 vols. 2007. (Illus.). 550p. pap. *(978-0-9543596-6-9(6))* Lux-Verbi Bks.

Thompson, William R., ed. Systemic Transitions: Past, Present, & Future. 2008. (Evolutionary Processes in World Politics Ser.). (ENG., Illus.). 304p. 105.00 *(978-0-230-60846-7(9))* Palgrave Macmillan.

Van Wyk, Barry. The Balance of Power & the Transition to Democracy in South Afric. 2009. 208p. pap. *(978-3-639-17939-2(0))* VDM Verlag Dr. Mueller e.K.

Vanevera & Cram101 Textbook Reviews Staff. Causes of War: Power & the Roots of Conflict. 2007. 124p. per. 28.95 *(978-1-4288-2486-7(3))* Cram101 Inc.

Vedrine, Hubert. History Strikes Back: How States, Nations, & Conflicts Are Shaping the 21st Century. Gordon, Philip H., tr. from FRE. 2008. (ENG.). 143p. 22.95 *(978-0-8157-8984-0(X))* Brookings Institution Pr.

Vinci, Anthony. Armed Groups & the Balance of Power: The International Relations of Terrorists, Warlords & Insurgents. 2010. (ENG.). 178p. pap. 39.95 *(978-0-415-59067-9(1))* 2008. 192p. 140.00 *(978-0-415-46622-6(9))* Routledge.

Walker, William. Weapons of Mass Destruction & Global Order. 2011. (Routledge Global Security Studies). (ENG., Illus.). 256p. (C). 145.00 *(978-0-415-42105-8(5))*; pap. 39.95 *(978-0-415-42106-5(3))* Routledge.

Walsh, David M. The Military Balance in the Cold War: US Perceptions & Policy, 1976-85. 2007. (Cold War History (Routledge) Ser.). (ENG.). 304p. (C). 170.00 *(978-0-415-42619-0(7))* Routledge.

Walt, Stephen M. Taming American Power: The Global Response to U. S. Primacy. 2006. (ENG.). 320p. per. 16.95 *(978-0-393-32919-3(4)*, 32919) Norton, W. W. & Co., Inc.

Walton, C. Dale. Geopolitics & the Great Powers in the 21st Century: Multipolarity & the Revolution in Strategic Perspective. 2007. (Geopolitical Theory Ser.). (Illus.). 141p. 160.00 *(978-0-415-35853-8(1))* Routledge.

Yoshihara, Susan & Sylva, Douglas A., eds. Population Decline & the Remaking of Great Power Politics. 2011. 304p. 35.00 ***(978-1-59797-550-6(8))*** Potomac Bks., Inc.

Zhiyue, Bo. China's Elite Politics: Political Transition & Power Balancing. 2007. (Series on Contemporary China Ser.). (Illus.). 449p. 113.00 *(978-981-270-041-4(2))* World Scientific Publishing Co., Inc.

BALANCE OF TRADE

see also Balance of Payments; Mercantile System

Assessing China's Behavior & Its Impact on U.S. Interests: Briefing Before the Committee on Foreign Affairs, House of Representatives, One Hundred Twelfth Congress, First Session, January 19, 2011. 2011. (Illus.). iii, 66p. ***(978-0-16-088142-8(0)***, 552-070-42559-4) United States Government Printing Office.

Caldwell, Andrew J. U. S. Trade, Protectionism & the Global Economic Downturn. 2010. (Global Economic Studies). 144p. 69.00 *(978-1-60876-966-7(6))* Nova Science Pubs., Inc.

Chandler, Marc. Making Sense of the Dollar: Exposing Dangerous Myths about Trade & Foreign Exchange. 2009. (Bloomberg Ser.: 18). (ENG., Illus.). 240p. 27.95 *(978-1-57660-321-5(0)*, Bloomberg Pr.) Wiley, John & Sons, Inc.

Chung, Chul. Han'guk Ui Kyoyok Kujo Wa Kyongsang Suji Pyondong Yoin Punsok. 2008. (KOR., Illus.). 229p. *(978-89-322-1285-2(6))* Korea Institute for International Economic Policy.

Dunaway, Steven. Global Imbalances & the Financial Crisis: Council Special Report No. 44, March 2009. 2009. (ENG., Illus.). 56p. pap. 10.00 *(978-0-87609-428-0(0))* Council on Foreign Relations.

Haddad, Mona & Shepherd, Ben. Managing Openness: Trade & Outward-Oriented Growth after the Crisis. 2011. *(978-0-8213-8632-3(8))* World Bank Pubns.

Haddad, Mona & Shepherd, Ben, eds. Managing Openness: Trade & Outward-Oriented Growth after the Crisis. 2011. (Trade & Development Ser.). (ENG., Illus.). 348p. pap. 49.95 *(978-0-8213-8631-6(X)*, 9780821386316) World Bank Pubns.

Hoeffner, George D. Relationship Between the Dollar, Price of Oil & the U. S. Trade Deficit. 2010. 98.00 *(978-1-61728-686-5(9))* Nova Science Pubs., Inc.

Loton, Tony. Financial Trading Patterns. 2007. (Illus.). 128p. per. 15.50 *(978-0-9556764-2-0(8))* Lulu Enterprises Inc.

Massari, Marilyn G. & Lutz, Karl J. Globalization: Trade Agreements, Global Health & United Nations Involvement. 2011. (Global Economic Studies). 140.00 ***(978-1-61470-327-3(2))*** Nova Science Pubs., Inc.

Meade, James E. A Geometry of International Trade (Routledge Revivals) 2012. (Routledge Revivals Ser.). (ENG.). 116p. 80.00 ***(978-0-415-52630-2(2))*** Routledge.

Mun, Thomas. England's Treasure by Forraign Trade. 2008. 140p. 21.99 *(978-0-559-19458-0(7))*; pap. 19.75 *(978-0-559-19456-6(0))* BiblioBazaar.

—England's Treasure by Forraign Trade. 2009. 72p. pap. 20.00 *(978-1-151-52944-2(3))* General Bks. LLC.

Ozga, S. A. The Rate of Exchange & the Terms of Trade. 2007. (ENG.). 116p. (gr. 11). pap. 18.95 *(978-0-202-36154-3(3))* Aldine Transaction.

Prati, Alessandro. External Performance in Low-Income Countries. 2011. 64p. pap. ***(978-1-61635-053-6(9))*** International Monetary Fund.

Richman, Raymond L. & Richman, Howard B. Trading Away Our Future: How to Fix Our Government-Driven Trade Defecits & Faulty Tax System Before It's Too Late. 2008. (Illus.). 230p. pap. 12.95 *(978-0-929446-05-9(4))* Pennsylvania Homeschoolers.

Sato, Ryuzo & Rizzo, John A., eds. Unkept Promises, Unclear Consequences: US Economic Policy & the Japanese Response. 2006. (ENG.). 212p. pap. 48.00 *(978-0-521-02766-3(7))* Cambridge Univ. Pr.

The Office for National Statistics. United Kingdom Balance of Payments 2008: The Pink Book. 2009. (ENG.). 170p. pap. 85.00 *(978-0-230-54565-6(3))* Palgrave Macmillan.

Wondimu, Lulit Assefa. Trade Balance & Exchange Rate: Ethiopian Case: The Impact of Exchange Rates on the Trade Balance - the Case of Ethiopia 1992 - 2007. 2011. 84p. pap. ***(978-3-639-33071-7(4))*** VDM Verlag Dr. Mueller e.K.

Yankovich, Carl T., ed. U. S. Trade Deficit Issues. 2010. 79.00 *(978-1-60692-090-9(1))* Nova Science Pubs., Inc.

BALANCE SHEETS

see Financial Statements

BALANCES (WEIGHING INSTRUMENTS)

Krayer, Peter Joseph. The Use & Care of a Balance. 2009. 48p. pap. 16.75 *(978-1-113-36022-9(4))* BiblioBazaar.

BALANCHINE, GEORGE, 1904-1983

Charles, Joseph & Joseph, Charles M. Stravinsky & Balanchine: A Journey of Invention. 2011. (ENG., Illus.). 464p. pap. 45.00 ***(978-0-300-17697-1(X))*** Yale Univ. Pr.

Costas, ed. & photos by. Balanchine: Celebrating a Life in Dance. 2009. (Illus.). 256p. pap. 29.95 *(978-1-55949-847-0(1))* Tide-Mark Pr., Ltd.

Fisher, Barbara Milberg & Fisher, Barbara. In Balanchine's Company: A Dancer's Memoir. 2006. (ENG., Illus.). 236p. 25.95 *(978-0-8195-6807-6(4))* Wesleyan Univ. Pr.

Goldner, Nancy. Balanchine Variations. 2008. (ENG., Illus.). 160p. pap. 24.95 *(978-0-8130-3226-9(1))* Univ. Pr. of Florida.

Gottlieb, Robert. George Balanchine: The Ballet Maker. 2010. (Eminent Lives Ser.). (ENG., Illus.). 224p. pap. 13.99 *(978-0-06-075071-8(5)*, HarperPerennial) HarperCollins Pubs.

Teachout, Terry. All in the Dances: A Brief Life of George Balanchine. 2007. (Illus.). 185p. *(978-1-4223-6715-5(0))* DIANE Publishing Co.

BALANCING (GYMNASTICS)

see Acrobats and Acrobatism

BALANCING (PHYSICS)

see Equilibrium

BALBOA, VASCO NUNEZ DE, 1475-1519

Mitchinson, Martin. The Darien Gap: Travels in the Rainforest of Panama. unabr. ed. 2008. (ENG., Illus.). 284p. pap. 26.95 *(978-1-55017-421-2(5))* Harbour Publishing Co., Ltd. CAN. Dist: Ingram Pub. Services.

BALCH, EMILY GREENE, 1867-1961

Gwinn, Kristen E. Emily Greene Balch: The Long Road to Internationalism. 2010. (ENG., Illus.). 232p. 45.00 *(978-0-252-03578-4(X))* Univ. of Illinois Pr.

BALCHEN, BERNT, 1899-1973

Knight, Clayton & Durham, Robert C. Hitch Your Wagon: The Story of Bernt Balchen. 2011. 362p. 51.95 ***(978-1-258-07828-7(7))*** Literary Licensing, LLC.

BALD EAGLE

Carrick, Doug. The Eagles of Hornby Island: My Tree-Top Neighbours. 2007. (Illus.). 112p. pap. 14.95 ***(978-0-88839-649-5(X))*** Hancock Hse. Pubs.

Guidry, Jeff. An Eagle Named Freedom: My True Story of a Remarkable Friendship. 2011. (ENG.). 224p. pap. 14.99 *(978-0-06-201550-1(8)*, Harper Paperbacks) 2010. 224p. 21.99 *(978-0-06-182674-0(X)*, Morrow, William & Co.) 2010. (ENG.). 240p. pap. 21.99 *(978-0-06-194572-4(2)*, HarperLuxe) HarperCollins Pubs.

Schempf, Philip F. & Wright, Bruce A. Bald Eagles in Alaska. 2010. 438p. pap. 29.95 ***(978-0-88839-695-2(3))*** Hancock Hse. Pubs.

Tekiela, Stan. Majestic Eagles: Compelling Facts & Images of the Bald Eagle. 2007. (Illus.). 144p. pap. 14.95 *(978-1-59193-200-0(9))* Adventure Pubns., Inc.

BALDNESS

Atul, Tripathi, et al. Dermo-Follicular Proliferation: A Scientific Study. 2011. 160p. pap. ***(978-3-639-32400-6(5))*** VDM Verlag Dr. Mueller e.K.

Avram, Marc R. & Rogers, Nicole E. Hair Transplantation. 2009. (ENG., Illus.). 128p. 175.00 *(978-0-521-87967-5(1))* Cambridge Univ. Pr.

Culvert, L. Lee. Women & Alopecia: Managing Unexplained Hair Loss. 2009. 188p. pap. 29.95 *(978-1-4269-0014-3(7))* Trafford Publishing.

Hoffmann, Candace. Breaking the Silence on Women's Hair Loss. 2007. 176p. per. 16.95 *(978-1-58054-469-6(X))* Woodland Publishing, Inc.

Hurwitz, Sam. Hair Loss: The Best Thing That Ever Happened to Me. 2007. 120p. pap. 9.99 *(978-0-9711902-9-0(1))* S H P Publishing.

Kingsley, David H. The Hair-Loss Cure: A Self-Help Guide. 2009. 144p. pap. 14.95 *(978-1-935278-04-7(5)*, iUniverse Star) iUniverse, Inc.

Martin, David Lozell. Soluciones Naturales a la Calvicie. (SPA.). 228p. *(978-84-7927-339-2(9))* Robinbk., Ediciones S.L. ESP. Dist: Lectorum Pubns., Inc.

Panagotacos, Peter J. The Complete Book of Hair Loss Answers: Your Comprehensive Guide to the Latest & Best Techniques. 2nd ed. 2010. (Illus.). 320p. per. 15.00 *(978-0-9720028-7-5(1)*, Elite Bks.) Author's Publishing Cooperative.

Peters, Ken & Waddell, Nick. Healthy Body: Healthy Hair: A Natural Guide to Healthy Hair & Hair Loss Prevention. 2007. (Illus.). 89p. per. 8.95 *(978-1-896817-30-9(0))* Apple Publishing Co., Ltd.

Price, Vera & Mirmirani, Paradi, eds. Cicatricial Alopecia: An Approach to Diagnosis & Management. 2011. (ENG., Illus.). 104p. 139.00 *(978-1-4419-8398-5(8)*, 1441983988) Springer.

Rathi, Vaishali & Rathi, Jagdish. Plants for Hair Growth Promotion. 2010. 68p. pap. *(978-3-8383-3793-7(X))* Lambert Academic Publishing.

Segrave, Kerry. Baldness: A Social History. alt. ed. 2008. (ENG.). 222p. pap. 35.00 *(978-0-7864-4079-5(1))* McFarland & Co., Inc. Pubs.

Willemsen, Ria & Vanderlinden, Johan. Alopecia Areat: Stress & Hypnosis. 2010. 156p. pap. *(978-3-8383-5463-7(X))* Lambert Academic Publishing.

Women's Hair Loss: An Expert Physician's Strategic Guide for Women Who Suffer from (or Live in Fear of) Losing Their Hair: the Hidden Epidemic. 2009. (Illus.). 49.99 *(978-0-615-30969-9(0))* Lock & Mane.

BALDRIDGE NATIONAL QUALITY AWARD

see Malcolm Baldridge National Quality Award

BALDRIGE, LETITIA

King, Joseph, ed. Strategic Leadership: Leading Change in a New Age. 2011. 60p. 29.95 ***(978-1-4269-7535-6(X))***; pap. 19.95 ***(978-1-4269-7534-9(1))*** Trafford Publishing.

BALDWIN, JAMES, 1924-1987

Baldwin, James. The Cross of Redemption: Uncollected Writings. Kenan, Randall, ed. 2011. (Vintage International Original Ser.). (ENG.). 400p. pap. 16.00 *(978-0-307-27596-7(5)*, Vintage) Knopf Doubleday Publishing Group.

—The Devil Finds Work. 2011. (Vintage International Ser.). (ENG.). 144p. pap. 14.00 *(978-0-307-27595-0(7)*, Vintage) Knopf Doubleday Publishing Group.

—No Name in the Street. 2007. (Vintage International Ser.). (ENG.). 208p. pap. 14.00 *(978-0-307-27592-9(2)*, Vintage) Knopf Doubleday Publishing Group.

—Notes of a Native Son. 2012. (ENG.). 192p. pap. 15.00 *(978-0-8070-0623-8(8))* Beacon Pr.

Blight, David W. American Oracle: The Civil War in the Civil Rights Era. 2011. (ENG., Illus.). 328p. 27.95 *(978-0-674-04855-3(5)*, Belknap Pr.) Harvard Univ. Pr.

Bloom, Harold, ed. James Baldwin. 2nd rev. ed. 2007. (Modern Critical Views Ser.). 240p. (C). (gr. 9-12). 45.00 *(978-0-7910-9365-8(4)*, Chelsea Hse.) Facts On File, Inc.

Boyd, Herb. Baldwin's Harlem: A Biography of James Baldwin. 2008. (ENG.). 272p. pap. 17.99 *(978-0-7432-9308-2(8)*, Beyond Words/Atria Bks.) Atria Bks.

Clegg, Joshua W. The Observation of Human Systems: Lessons from the History of Anti-Reductionistic Empirical Psychology. Clegg, Joshua, ed. 2008. (ENG.). 312p. 59.95 *(978-1-4128-0838-5(3))* Transaction Pubs.

Dickstein, Morris. James Baldwin. 2010. (Critical Insights Ser.). 455p. (C). 85.00 *(978-1-58765-701-6(5))* Salem Pr., Inc.

Field, Douglas. A Historical Guide to James Baldwin. 2009. (History Gds American Ser.). (ENG., Illus.). 304p. pap. 27.95 *(978-0-19-536654-9(9))* Oxford Univ. Pr., Inc.

—James Baldwin. 2012. (Writers & Their Work Ser.). (ENG.). 128p. (C). 80.00 *(978-0-7463-1202-5(4))*; pap. 26.00 *(978-0-7463-1207-0(5))* Northcote Hse. Publishers, Ltd. GBR. Dist: Brown, David Bk. Co., The.

Garcia, Jay. Psychology Comes to Harlem: Rethinking the Race Question in Twentieth-Century America. 2012. (New Studies in American Intellectual & Cultural History Ser.). (ENG.). 232p. (gr. 17). 50.00 ***(978-1-4214-0519-3(9))*** Johns Hopkins Univ. Pr.

Gerstner, David A. Queer Pollen: White Seduction, Black Male Homosexuality, & the Cinematic. 2011. (New Black Studies Ser.). (ENG., Illus.). 216p. 80.00 *(978-0-252-03590-6(9))*; pap. 25.00 *(978-0-252-07787-6(3))* Univ. of Illinois Pr.

Hardy, Clarence. James Balwins God. 2009. (ENG.). 168p. pap. 19.95 *(978-1-57233-692-6(7))* Univ. of Tennessee Pr.

Henderson, Carol E. James Baldwin's Go Tell It on the Mountain: Historical & Critical Essays. 2006. 180p. (C). 63.95 *(978-0-8204-8158-6(0))* Lang, Peter Publishing, Inc.

Kaplan, Cora & Schwarz, Bill. James Baldwin: America & Beyond. 2011. (Illus.). 288p. E-Book ***(978-0-472-02761-3(1))*** Univ. of Michigan Pr.

King, Lovalerie. James Baldwin & Toni Morrison: Comparative Critical & Theoretical Essays. King, Lovalerie & Scott, Lynn Orilla, eds. 2009. (ENG.). 352p. pap. 29.00 *(978-0-230-61972-2(X))* Palgrave Macmillan.

King, Lovalerie & Scott, Lynn Orilla, eds. James Baldwin & Toni Morrison: Comparative Critical & Theoretical Essays. 2006. (ENG.). 312p. 89.00 *(978-1-4039-7073-2(4))* Palgrave Macmillan.

Miller, D. Quentin. A Criminal Power: James Baldwin & the Law. 2012. 224p. 45.95 ***(978-0-8142-1175-5(5))***; (ENG.). cd-rom 14.95 ***(978-0-8142-9276-1(3))*** Ohio State Univ. Pr.

Muyumba, Walton M. The Shadow & the Act: Black Intellectual Practice, Jazz Improvisation, & Philosophical Pragmatism. 2009. (ENG.). 232p. 48.00 *(978-0-226-55423-5(6))*; pap. 18.00 *(978-0-226-55424-2(4))* Univ. of Chicago Pr.

Odhiambo, George. Faces of Christianity. 2011. 152p. pap. ***(978-3-8443-1652-0(3))*** Lambert Academic Publishing.

O'Hara, Daniel T. Visions of Global America & the Future of Critical Reading. 2009. (ENG.). 192p. 54.95 *(978-0-8142-1104-5(6))*; cd-rom 14.95 *(978-0-8142-9202-0(X))* Ohio State Univ. Pr.

Reddinger, Amy. Domestic Inversions, Domestic Interventions. 2008. 176p. pap. *(978-3-8364-7369-9(0))* VDM Verlag Dr. Mueller e.K.

Röckl, Barbara. Through A Glass Darkly: The Mirror Metaphor in Texts by Richard Wright, James Baldwin, & Ralph Ellison. 2009. (Europäische Hochschulschriften. Reihe 14: Angelsächsische Sprache und Literatur Ser.). 290p. pap. 72.95 *(978-3-631-59214-4(0))* Lang, Peter GmbH, Europaischer Verlag der Wissenschaften DEU. Dist: Lang, Peter.

Schwarz, Bill & Kaplan, Cora. James Baldwin: America & Beyond. 2011. (ENG., Illus.). 268p. (C). 80.00 *(978-0-472-07152-4(1))*; pap. 29.95 *(978-0-472-05152-6(0))* Univ. of Michigan Pr.

Zaborowska, Magdalena J. James Baldwin's Turkish Decade: Erotics of Exile. 2009. (ENG., Illus.). 416p. 94.95 *(978-0-8223-4144-4(1))* Duke Univ. Pr.

Zaborowska, Magdalena J. & Zaborowska, Magdalena. James Baldwin's Turkish Decade: Erotics of Exile. 2009. (ENG., Illus.). 416p. pap. 26.95 *(978-0-8223-4167-3(0))* Duke Univ. Pr.

BALDWIN, JAMES MARK, 1861-1934

Baldwin, James M. Between Two Wars, Eighteen Sixty-One to Nineteen Twenty-One: Being Memories, Opinion & Letters Received by James Mark Baldwin, 2 vols., Set. reprint ed. 115.00 *(978-0-404-59013-0(6))* AMS Pr., Inc.

Weber, Bruce H. & DePew, David J., eds. Evolution & Learning: The Baldwin Effect Reconsidered. 2007. (Life & Mind: Philosophical Issues in Biology & Psychology Ser.). (ENG., Illus.). 352p. (gr. 17). per. 26.00 *(978-0-262-73181-2(9))* MIT Pr.

BALDWIN, STANLEY BALDWIN, EARL, 1867-1947

Jenkins, Roy. Baldwin. 2012. (Illus.). 220p. pap. *(978-1-4482-0068-9(7)*, 142602, Bloomsbury Reader) Bloomsbury Publishing Plc.

Perkins, Anne. Baldwin. 2006. (British Prime Ministers of the 20th Century Ser.). (ENG., Illus.). 170p. pap. 16.95 *(978-1-904950-60-8(4))* Haus Publishing GBR. Dist: Consortium Bk. Sales & Distribution.

Williamson, Philip. Stanley Baldwin: Conservative Leadership & National Values. 2007. (ENG., Illus.). 408p. pap. 62.00 *(978-0-521-43812-4(8))* Cambridge Univ. Pr.

Williamson, Philip & Baldwin, Edward, eds. Baldwin Papers: A Conservative Statesman, 1908-1947. 2009. (ENG.). 560p. pap. 53.00 *(978-0-521-11847-7(6))* Cambridge Univ. Pr.

BALDWIN LOCOMOTIVE WORKS

Solomon, Brian. Baldwin Locomotives. 2010. (ENG., Illus.). 160p. 40.00 *(978-0-7603-3589-5(3)*, 0760335893, Voyageur Pr) MBI Publishing Co. LLC.

BALDWIN LOCOMOTIVES

Baldwin Locomotives. 2009. (Illus.). 328p. bds. 39.99 *(978-0-7643-3376-7(3))* Schiffer Publishing, Ltd.

Solomon, Brian. Baldwin Locomotives. 2010. (ENG., Illus.). 160p. 40.00 *(978-0-7603-3589-5(3)*, 0760335893, Voyageur Pr) MBI Publishing Co. LLC.

BALEARIC ISLANDS (SPAIN)—DESCRIPTION AND TRAVEL

Davis, Elena. Witches, Oranges & Slingers: Half a Century on Mallorca. 2007. 196p. per. 16.43 *(978-1-4251-0725-3(7))* Trafford Publishing.

Hutt, Graham & RCC Pilotage Foundation. Islas Baleares: Ibiza, Formentera, Mallorca, Cabrera & Menorca. 9th rev. ed. 2011. (ENG., Illus.). 264p. ***(978-1-84623-283-1(X))*** Imray, Laurie, Norie & Wilson, Ltd.

Jens, Detlef. Balearics: Cruising Companion. 2009. 256p. 49.95 *(978-0-470-75430-6(3)*, Wiley) Wiley, John & Sons, Inc.

BALFOUR, ARTHUR JAMES BALFOUR, EARL OF, 1848-1930

Green, E. H. H. Balfour. 2006. (British Prime Ministers of the 20th Century Ser.). (ENG., Illus.). 170p. pap. 16.95 *(978-1-904950-55-4(8))* Haus Publishing GBR. Dist: Consortium Bk. Sales & Distribution.

Lewis, Geoffrey. Balfour & Weizmann: The Zionist, the Zealot & the Emergence of Israel. 2009. (ENG., Illus.). 224p. 32.95 *(978-1-84725-040-7(8))* Continuum International Publishing Group, Ltd GBR. Dist: National Bk. Network.

O'Callaghan, Margaret. British High Politics. (Illus.). 256p. pap. *(978-1-85918-002-0(7))* Cork Univ. Pr.

—British High Politics & a Nationalist Ireland: Criminality & the Law under Forster & Balfour. (Illus.). 256p. *(978-1-85918-001-3(9))* Cork Univ. Pr.

Raleigh, Lord. Lord Balfour & his Relation to Science. 2012. (ENG.). 56p. pap. 35.99 ***(978-1-107-61644-8(1))*** Cambridge Univ. Pr.

Zebel, Sydney H. Balfour: A Political Biography. 2008. (Conference on British Studies Biographica Ser.). (ENG.). 324p. pap. 42.00 *(978-0-521-08881-7(X))* Cambridge Univ. Pr.

BALFOUR DECLARATION

Renton, James. The Zionist Masquerade: The Birth of the Anglo-Zionist Alliance, 1914-18. 2007. (ENG., Illus.). 256p. 95.00 *(978-0-230-54718-6(4))* Palgrave Macmillan.

Stein, Leonard. The Balfour Declaration. 2008. 704p. pap. 70.00 *(978-1-59740-475-4(6))* ACLS Humanities E-Book.

BALI ISLAND (INDONESIA)

Covarrubias, Miguel. Island of Bali. 2006. (ENG.). 528p. per. *(978-1-4067-0174-6(2)*, Hesperides Pr.) Read Bks.

Lansing, J. Stephen. Priests & Programmers: Technologies of Power in the Engineered Landscape of Bali. 2007. (ENG., Illus.). 216p. (C). per. 23.95 *(978-0-691-13066-8(3))* Princeton Univ. Pr.

Lewis, Jeff & Lewis, Belinda. Bali's Silent Crisis: Desire, Tragedy, & Transition. 2009. (ENG., Illus.). 252p. 68.50 *(978-0-7391-2820-6(5))* Lexington Bks.

Vickers, Adrian. Journeys of Desire: A Study of the Balinese Text Malat. 2010. (Verhandelingen Van Het Koninklijk Instituut Voor Taal-, Land Ser.). (ENG., Illus.). 396p. per. 44.00 *(978-90-6718-137-2(4))* KITLV Pr. NLD. Dist: Univ. of Hawaii Pr.

BALI ISLAND (INDONESIA)—DESCRIPTION AND TRAVEL

Berger, Asa. Bali Tourism. 2012. (ENG., Illus.). 164p. 95.00 *(978-0-7890-3519-6(7))*; pap. 39.95 *(978-0-7890-3520-2(0))* Routledge.

Berkmoes, Ryan Ver. Bali. 2nd rev. ed. 2010. (Encounter Ser.). (ENG., Illus.). 160p. pap. 12.99 *(978-1-74179-717-6(9))* Lonely Planet Pubns.

Berkmoes, Ryan Ver & Carroll, Marian. Bali & Lombok. 13th rev. ed. 2011. (Regional Guide Ser.). (ENG., Illus.). 404p. pap. 23.99 *(978-1-74179-704-6(7))* Lonely Planet Pubns.

Copeland, Jonathan & Wayan Murni, Ni. Secrets of Bali: Fresh Light on the Morning of the World. 2010. (ENG., Illus.). 407p. pap. 30.00 *(978-974-524-118-3(0))* Orchid Pr. THA. Dist: National Bk. Network.

Covarrubias, Miguel. Island of Bali. 2008. 532p. *(978-1-4437-2082-3(8)*, Hesperides Pr.) Read Bks.

Covarrubias, Miguel & Vickers, Adrian. Island of Bali. 2008. (Periplus Classics Ser.). (ENG.). 480p. pap. 24.95 *(978-0-7946-0562-9(1)*, PeriplusEdition) Tuttle Publishing.

Dixon, Paul. Bali & Lombok Footprint Focus. 2012. (Footprint Focus Ser.). (ENG., Illus.). 128p. pap. 12.95 *(978-1-903206-45-9(4))* Footprint Handbooks GBR. Dist: Globe Pequot Pr., The.

Fodor's Travel Publications, Inc. Staff. Bali. 2009. (In Focus Ser.). 192p. pap. 10.95 *(978-1-4000-0884-1(0)*, Fodor's) Fodor's Travel Pubns.

Gruschwitz, Bernd F. Bali Lombok: An Up-to-Date Travel Guide with 147 Color Photos & 17 Maps. 2nd ed. (Nelles Guides). (Illus.). 256p. pap. 14.95 *(978-3-88618-114-8(6))* Nelles Verlag DEU. Dist: 7 Hills Bk. Distributors.

Gstaltmayr, Heiner. Bali Baedeker Guide. 2012. (Baedeker Guides Ser.). (ENG., Illus.). 258p. pap. 20.00 ***(978-3-8297-6552-7(5))*** Marco Polo Travel Publishing GBR. Dist: Innovative Logistics.

Inglis, Kim. Bali Home: Inspirational Design Ideas. 2010. (ENG., Illus.). 144p. 24.95 *(978-0-8048-3982-2(4))* Tuttle Publishing.

Insight Guides. INS Step by Step Bali. 2011. (Step by Step Ser.). (ENG., Illus.). 112p. pap. 16.99 *(978-981-282-245-1(3))* APA Publications Services SGP. Dist: Ingram Pub. Services.

Periplus Editions. Bali Street Atlas Third Edition. 3rd ed. 2011. (ENG.). 144p. pap. 19.95 *(978-0-7946-0703-6(9))* Tuttle Publishing.

Periplus Editors, ed. Bali: The Ultimate Guide to the World's Most Famous Tropical Island. 2012. (Periplus Adventure Guides) (ENG., Illus.). 352p. pap. 24.95 ***(978-0-8048-4206-8(X))*** Tuttle Publishing.

Pickell, David & Siagian, Wally. Diving Bali: The Underwater Jewel of Southeast Asia. 2nd ed. 2010. (ENG., Illus.). 240p. pap. 24.95 *(978-0-7946-0600-8(8))* Tuttle Publishing.

Pratiwi, Wiwik. Tourism in Traditional Bali Settlement. 2009. 420p. pap. *(978-3-639-12966-3(0))* VDM Verlag Dr. Mueller e.K.

Rata, Ida Bagus. Bali. Fabbri, Patrizia & Giorgi, Simonetta, eds. Melville, Diane, tr. from ITA. (Illus.). 128p. *(978-88-8029-580-8(2))* Casa Editrice Bonechi.

Reichle, Natasha. Bali: Art Ritual Performance. 2011. (ENG., Illus.). 376p. 49.50 *(978-0-939117-55-0(X))* Asian Art Museum of San Francisco.

Reynolds, Betty. An Artist's Journey to Bali: The Island of Art, Magic & Mystery. 2010. (ENG., Illus.). 48p. 16.95 *(978-0-8048-4043-9(1))* Tuttle Publishing.

Shepherd, Robert J. Partners in Paradise: Tourism Practices, Heritage Policies, & Anthropological Sites. 2012. 141p. E-Book ***(978-1-4539-0193-9(0))*** Lang, Peter GmbH, Europaischer Verlag der Wissenschaften.

Smart Guide Bali. 2009. (SMART GUIDE Ser.). 12.95 *(978-981-282-120-1(1))* Insight Guides.

Smith, Lynne Maree. Bali. 3rd ed. (Illus.). 224p. pap. 14.95 *(978-1-86315-108-5(7))* Little Hills Pr. AUS. Dist: CPG Publishing, Inc.

Thomas Cook Publishing Staff & Lerner, Alison. Bali & Lombok. 2nd ed. 2009. (Travellers - Thomas Cook Ser.). (ENG., Illus.). 176p. pap. 16.95 *(978-1-84848-164-0(0))* Cook, Thomas Publishing GBR. Dist: Globe Pequot Pr., The.

Thomasson-Croll, Mary Justice. Frommer's Bali & Lombok. 2010. (Frommer's Portable Ser.). (ENG., Illus.). 384p. pap. 19.99 *(978-0-470-49776-0(9)*, Frommers) Wiley, John & Sons, Inc.

Thomasson-Croll, Mary Justice, et al. Frommer's Bali & Lombok. 2nd ed. 2012. (Frommer's Complete Guides). (ENG.). 384p. pap. 21.99 ***(978-1-118-09600-0(2)***, Frommers) Wiley, John & Sons, Inc.

BALI ISLAND (INDONESIA)—RELIGION

Fox, Richard. Critical Reflections on Religion & Media in Contemporary Bali. 2010. (Illus.). 340p. *(978-90-04-17649-2(7))* BRILL.

Howe, Leo. The Changing World of Bali. 2009. 164p. pap. 39.95 *(978-0-415-54674-4(5))* Routledge.

Reuter, Thomas. Global Trends in Religion & the Reaffirmation of Hindu Identity in Bali. 2008. 24p. pap. 9.95 *(978-1-876924-63-8(2)*, Monash Univ. Pr.) Monash Univ. Publishing AUS. Dist: International Specialized Bk. Services.

BALI ISLAND (INDONESIA)—SOCIAL LIFE AND CUSTOMS

Amin, Helle & Meikle, David. Reunited in the Desert. 2008. (ENG., Illus.). 272p. pap. 16.95 *(978-1-84454-606-0(3))* Blake, John Publishing, Ltd. GBR. Dist: Independent Pubs. Group.

Copeland, Jonathan & Wayan Murni, Ni. Secrets of Bali: Fresh Light on the Morning of the World. 2010. (ENG., Illus.). 407p. pap. 30.00 *(978-974-524-118-3(0))* Orchid Pr. THA. Dist: National Bk. Network.

de Neefe, Janet. Fragrant Rice: My Continuing Love Affair with Bali. 2006. (ENG., Illus.). 336p. per. 19.95 *(978-0-7946-5028-5(7)*, PeriplusEdition) Tuttle Publishing.

Eiseman, Fred B., Jr., et al. Bali: Sekala & Niskala. 2009. (ENG.). 392p. pap. 24.95 *(978-0-8048-4098-9(9))* Tuttle Publishing.

Eldridge, Paul. Sex, Drugs & Techno. 2011. 214p. pap. 22.95 ***(978-1-84694-511-3(9))*** O Bks., John Hunt.

Francione, Gianni, et al. Bali Living: Innovative Tropical Design. 2008. (ENG., Illus.). 224p. 44.95 *(978-0-7946-0567-4(2)*, PeriplusEdition) Tuttle Publishing.

Lewis, Jeff & Lewis, Belinda. Bali's Silent Crisis: Desire, Tragedy, & Transition. 2009. (ENG., Illus.). 252p. 68.50 *(978-0-7391-2820-6(5))* Lexington Bks.

Lindsey, Timothy. The Romance of K'Tut Tantri & Indonesia. 2010. 406p. pap. 29.95 *(978-979-3780-63-4(0))* Equinox Publishing IDN. Dist: Univ. of Hawaii Pr.

Reynolds, Betty. An Artist's Journey to Bali: The Island of Art, Magic & Mystery. 2010. (ENG., Illus.). 48p. 16.95 *(978-0-8048-4043-9(1))* Tuttle Publishing.

Shepherd, Robert. Partners in Paradise: Tourism Practices, Heritage Policies, & Anthropological Sites. 2011. (Asian Thought & Culture Ser.). 152p. (C). pap. 68.95 ***(978-1-4331-1609-4(X))*** Lang, Peter Publishing, Inc.

Slattum, Judy. Balinese Masks: Spirits of an Ancient Drama. 2011. (ENG., Illus.). 128p. pap. 18.95 *(978-0-8048-4184-9(5))* Tuttle Publishing.

Vickers, Ph.D., Adrian. Bali: A Paradise Created. 2nd ed. 2012. (ENG., Illus.). 1p. pap. 16.95 ***(978-0-8048-4260-0(4))*** Tuttle Publishing.

BALINESE ART

see Art, Balinese

BALINESE MUSIC

see Music, Balinese

BALKAN PENINSULA

Alexandrov, Vesselin, ed. Global Environmental Change - Challenges to Science & Society in Southeastern Europe. 2010. (ENG.). xxi, 350p. 129.00 *(978-90-481-8694-5(3)*, 9048186943) Springer.

Radovich, Eugene. Land of Destiny. A Tale of the Balkans. 2011. 122p. 39.95 ***(978-1-258-07574-3(1))*** Literary Licensing, LLC.

Stoianovich, Traian. Between East & West: The Balkan & Mediterranean Worlds, 4 vols., Set. 350.00 *(978-0-89241-525-0(8))* Caratzas, Aristide D. Pub.

BALKAN PENINSULA—ANTIQUITIES

Chapman, John, et al. Parts & Wholes: Fragmentation in Prehistoric Context. 2006. (ENG., Illus.). 264p. (C). pap. 60.00 *(978-1-84217-222-3(0))* Oxbow Bks., Ltd. GBR. Dist: Brown, David Bk. Co., The.

Darlas, Andreas & Mihailovic, Dusan. The Palaeolithic of the Balkans. 2008. (Bar S Ser.). (ENG., Illus.). 116p. (C). pap. 72.50 *(978-1-4073-0305-5(8))* British Archaeological Reports Ltd. GBR. Dist: Brown, David Bk. Co., The.

Forenbaher, Staso. A Connecting Sea: Maritime Interaction in Adriatic Prehistory. 2009. (Bar S Ser.). (ENG., Illus.). 155p. (C). pap. 87.50 *(978-1-4073-0614-8(6))* British Archaeological Reports Ltd. GBR. Dist: Brown, David Bk. Co., The.

Hofsten, Helène Whittaker von. The Aegean Bronze Age in Relation to the Wider European Context: Papers from a Session at the Eleventh Annual Meeting of the European Association of Archaeologists, Cork, 5-11 September 2005. 2008. (Bar S Ser.). (ENG., Illus.). 170p. (C). pap. 60.00 *(978-1-4073-0187-7(X))* British Archaeological Reports Ltd. GBR. Dist: Brown, David Bk. Co., The.

Kozowski, Janusz Krzysztof & Nowak, Marek. Mesolithic/Neolithic Interactions in the Balkans & in the Middle Danube Basin. 2008. (Bar S Ser.). (Illus.). vi, 115p. (C). pap. 65.00 *(978-1-4073-0168-6(3))* British Archaeological Reports Ltd. GBR. Dist: Brown, David Bk. Co., The.

Manassero, Niccolò. Rhyta e Corni Potori Dall'Età Del Ferro All'epoca Sasanide: Libagioni Pure e Misticismo Tra la Grecia e il Mondo Iranico. 2008. (Bar S Ser.). (ITA., Illus.). 279p. (C). pap. 125.00 ***(978-1-4073-0210-2(8))*** British Archaeological Reports Ltd. GBR. Dist: Brown, David Bk. Co., The.

BALKAN PENINSULA—DESCRIPTION AND TRAVEL

Booth, Felicity & Roshi, Elenita. Gjirokastra: The Essential Guide. 2010. (ENG., Illus.). 95p. (C). pap. 15.95 *(978-99956-747-0-0(X))* Butrint Foundation GBR. Dist: Brown, David Bk. Co., The.

Cartwright, Garth. Princes Amongst Men: Journeys with Gypsy Musicians. 2011. (ENG., Illus.). 320p. pap. 15.95 ***(978-1-85242-483-1(4))*** Serpent's Tail Ltd. GBR. Dist: Consortium Bk. Sales & Distribution.

Durham, Edith M. Twenty Years of Balkan Tangle. 2007. 244p. (ENG.). 43.99 *(978-1-4280-7545-0(3))*; per. 36.99 *(978-1-4280-7544-3(5))* IndyPublish.com.

Durham, Mary Edith. Twenty Years of Balkan Tangle. 2008. 304p. 25.99 *(978-0-554-36837-5(4))* 2008. 304p. 28.99 *(978-0-554-27534-5(1))* 2007. (ENG.). 268p. pap. 21.99 *(978-1-4346-3426-9(4))* 2007. (ENG.). 300p. pap. 23.99 *(978-1-4346-3427-6(2))* BiblioBazaar.

Gordon, Lynn. Two Vagabonds in the Balkans. 2007. 190.00 *(978-0-7103-1124-5(9))* Taylor & Francis Group.

Hammond, Andrew. The Debated Lands: British & American Representations of the Balkans. 2007. 238p. 85.00 *(978-0-7083-1965-9(3))* Univ. of Wales Pr. GBR. Dist: Chicago Distribution Ctr.

Isenberg, Robert. The Archipelago: A Balkan Passage. 2011. 208p. pap. 19.95 *(978-1-932870-44-2(X))* Autumn Hse. Pr.

Lear, Edward, et al. Edward Lear in Albania: Journals of a Landscape Painter in the Balkans. 2008. (ENG., Illus.). 256p. 41.00 *(978-1-84511-602-6(X))* I. B. Tauris & Co., Ltd. GBR. Dist: Macmillan.

Lonely Planet Staff & McAdam, Marika. Western Balkans. 2nd rev. ed. 2009. (Multi Country Guide Ser.). (ENG., Illus.). 452p. pap. 24.99 *(978-1-74104-729-5(3))* Lonely Planet Pubns.

Meckfessel, Shon. Suffled How It Gush: A North American Anarchist in the Balkans. 2009. (ENG., Illus.). 260p. pap. 16.95 *(978-1-904859-85-7(2))* AK Pr. GBR. Dist: Consortium Bk. Sales & Distribution.

Montini, Massimiliano, ed. Developing CDM Projects in the Western Balkans: Legal & Technical Issues Compared. 2009. (ENG.). xxiv, 202p. 129.00 *(978-90-481-3391-8(2)*, 9048133912) Springer.

Powell, E. Alexander. The New Frontiers of Freedom from the Alps to The Ægean. 2007. (ENG.). 154p. pap. 19.99 *(978-1-4346-0821-5(2))*; 170p. pap. 21.99 *(978-1-4346-0895-6(6))* BiblioBazaar.

Sobolev, Andrei N. Malyi Dialektologicheskii Atlas Balkanskikh Iazykov. 2009. (RUS., Illus.). *(978-5-02-025277-6(8))* NBD - Biblion B.V.

Sobolev, Andrei N. & Domosiletskaia, M. V. Malyi Dialektologicheskii Atlas Balkanskikh Iazykov. 2009. (RUS., Illus.). *(978-5-02-025278-3(6))*; *(978-3-86688-040-5(5))* NBD - Biblion B.V.

BALKAN PENINSULA—ECONOMIC CONDITIONS

Bartlett, William. Europe's Troubled Region: Economic Development, Institutional Reform & Social Welfare in the Western Balkans. 2008. (Routledge Studies in Development Economics Ser.). (Illus.). 288p. 160.00 *(978-0-415-19350-4(8))* Routledge.

Bateman, Milford, ed. Confronting Microfinance: Undermining Sustainable Development. 2011. (Illus.). 274p. 75.00 *(978-1-56549-342-1(7))* Stylus Publishing, LLC.

Bitzenis, Aristidis. The Balkans: FDI & EU Accession. 2009. (Transition & Development Ser.). (Illus.). 424p. 144.95 *(978-0-7546-4566-5(5))* Ashgate Publishing Co.

Central & South Eastern Europe 2009. 9th rev. ed. 2008. (ENG., Illus.). 852p. 700.00 *(978-1-85743-466-8(8))* Routledge.

Central & South Eastern Europe 2010. 10th rev. ed. 2009. (ENG.). 860p. 750.00 *(978-1-85743-524-5(9))* Routledge.

Circa. A Political & Economic Dictionary of Central & South-Eastern Europe. 2008. 320p. 260.00 *(978-1-85743-359-3(9))* Routledge.

Cviic, Christopher, ed. In Search of the Balkan Recovery: The Political & Economic Reemergence of South Eastern Europe. 2010. (Columbia/Hurst Ser.). (ENG.). 244p. (gr. 17). 45.00 *(978-0-231-70170-9(5))* Columbia Univ. Pr.

Dallago, Bruno, ed. Transformation & European Integration: The Local Dimension. 2006. (Studies in Economic Transition). (ENG., Illus.). 336p. 137.00 *(978-1-4039-4781-9(3))* Palgrave Macmillan.

Europa Central & South-Eastern Europe. 7th rev. ed. 2006. (ENG., Illus.). 828p. 575.00 *(978-1-85743-372-2(6))* Routledge.

Europa Publications, ed. Central & South-Eastern Europe 2012. 12th rev. ed. 2011. (ENG.). 900p. 815.00 *(978-1-85743-617-4(2))* Routledge.

Europa Publications, ed. Central & South-Eastern Europe 2013. 13th rev. ed. 2012. (ENG.) 900p. 815.00 ***(978-1-85743-650-1(4))*** Routledge.

Europa Publications Staff. Central & South-Eastern Europe 2008. 8th rev. ed. 2007. 819p. 640.00 *(978-1-85743-422-4(6))* Routledge.

Friedman, Morris G., ed. Economics & Politics of the Balkans Region. 2008. (Illus.). (C). 69.00 *(978-1-60456-043-5(6))* Nova Science Pubs., Inc.

Handjiski, Borko, et al. Enhancing Regional Trade Integration in Southeast Europe. 2010. (World Bank Working Papers: 185). (ENG., Illus.). 96p. pap. 25.00 *(978-0-8213-8259-2(4)*, 9780821382592) World Bank Pubns.

Inotai, András. The European Union & Southeastern Europe: Troubled Waters Ahead? 2007. (Illus.). 447p. pap. 80.95 *(978-90-5201-071-7(4))* Lang, Peter Publishing, Inc.

International Energy Agency Staff. Energy in the Western Balkans: The Path to Reform & Reconstruction. 2008. (Illus.). 412p. pap. 63.00 *(978-92-64-04218-6(0))* Organization for Economic Cooperation & Development.

Kusic, Sinisa & Grupe, Claudia, eds. The Western Balkans on Their Way to the EU? 2007. 156p. (C). pap. 35.95 *(978-3-631-55896-6(1))* Lang, Peter Publishing, Inc.

McGowan, Bruce. Economic Life in Ottoman Europe: Taxation, Trade & the Struggle for Land, 1600-1800. 2010. (Studies in Modern Capitalism Ser.). (ENG.). 240p. pap. 27.99 *(978-0-521-13536-8(2))* Cambridge Univ. Pr.

McTernan, Benedict, ed. Political Risk Yearbook - 2007 Vol. 7: East Europe. 2007. per. *(978-1-933539-35-5(6))* PRS Group Inc., The.

Mitrovic, Ljubisa R. Tranzicija U Periferni Kapitalizam: Ogledi Iz Sociologije Globalnih I Regionalnih Promena = Transition to Peripheral Capitalism: Essays on the Sociology of Global & Regional Change. 2009. (Illus.). 263p. *(978-86-7419-199-6(1))* Institut za politicke studije.

O'brennan. The Eu & the Western Balkans. 2008. (Europe & the Nation State Ser.). (ENG.) 224p. (C). 130.00 *(978-0-415-42608-4(1))* Routledge.

Organisation for Economic Co-operation and Development. Investment Reform Index 2010: Monitoring Policies & Institutions for Direct Investment in South East Europe. 2010. (Illus.). 319p. pap. 37.00 *(978-92-64-07957-1(2))* Organization for Economic Cooperation & Development.

Organisation for Economic Co-operation and Development Staff. Progress in Policy Reforms to Improve the Investment Climate in South East Europe: Investment Reform Index 2006. 2008. pap. 63.00 *(978-92-64-03723-6(3))* Organization for Economic Cooperation & Development.

Pallai, Katalin. Who Decides? Development, Planning, Services, & Vulnerable Groups. 2009. pap. 32.95 *(978-963-9719-14-9(5))* Institute for Local Government & Public Service, Open Soc. Institute HUN. Dist: Books International, Inc.

Parveva, Stefka. Village, Town & People in the Ottoman Balkans, 16th-mid-19th Century. 2010. 108.44 *(978-1-61719-098-8(5))* Gorgias Pr., LLC.

Sanjay, Kathuria & Kathuria, Sanjay. Western Balkan Integration & the EU: An Agenda for Trade & Growth. 2008. (Directions in Development Ser.). (ENG., Illus.). 184p. pap. 30.00 *(978-0-8213-7472-6(9)*, 9780821374726) World Bank Pubns.

Sergi, Bruno S., et al. The Political Economy of Southeast Europe from 1990 to the Present: Challenges & Opportunities. 2008. (ENG., Illus.). 208p. 110.00 *(978-0-8264-2867-7(3))* Continuum International Publishing Group, Ltd. GBR. Dist: National Bk. Network.

Shaqiri, Albinot. The Economic Well-Being of Albanians: Trust & Social Capital - How do Cultural Values & the Levels of Trust Affect Social Capital & the Robustne. 2008. 92p. pap. *(978-3-639-11536-9(8))* VDM Verlag Dr. Mueller e.K.

Sjöberg, Örjan & Wyzan, Michael L. Economic Change in the Balkan States. (Illus.). x, 173p. *(978-0-86187-055-4(7)*, Burns & Oates) Continuum International Publishing Group, Ltd.

Sternad, Dietmar & Döring, Thomas, eds. Handbook of Doing Business in South East Europe. 2011. (ENG., Illus.). 560p. 185.00 *(978-0-230-27865-3(5))* Palgrave Macmillan.

Tiltman, H. Hessell. Peasant Europe. 2006. (Illus.). 338p. 250.00 *(978-0-7103-1155-9(9))* Taylor & Francis Group.

BALKAN PENINSULA—ETHNIC RELATIONS

Colovic, Ivan. The Balkans: the Terror of Culture: Essays in Political Anthropology. 2011. 196p. pap. 43.00 *(978-3-8329-6303-3(0))* Nomos Verlagsgesellschaft DEU. Dist: International Specialized Bk. Services.

Koktsidis, Ioannis. Strategic Rebellion: Ethnic Conflict in FYR Macedonia & the Balkans. 2012. (Nationalisms across the Globe Ser.). (ENG.). 261p. pap. 54.95 **(978-3-0343-0148-0(0))** Lang, Peter AG GBR. Dist: Lang, Peter.

Madgearu, Alexandru. The Wars of the Balkan Peninsula: Their Medieval Origins. Gordon, Martin, ed. 2007. (ENG., Illus.). 244p. per. 64.00 (978-0-8108-5846-6(0)) Scarecrow Pr., Inc.

Mulaj, Klejda. Politics of Ethnic Cleansing: Nation-State Building & Provision of in/Security in Twentieth-Century Balkans. 2008. (ENG.). 216p. 73.50 (978-0-7391-1782-8(3)) Lexington Bks.

Parveva, Stefka. Village, Town & People in the Ottoman Balkans, 16th-mid-19th Century. 2010. 108.44 (978-1-61719-098-8(5)) Gorgias Pr., LLC.

Roth, Klaus & Brunnbauer, Ulf, eds. Region, Regional Identity & Regionalism in Southeastern Europe, Pt. 1. 2011. (ENG.). 304p. pap. 44.95 (978-3-8258-1387-1(8)) Lit Verlag DEU. Dist: Transaction Pubs.

Shay, Shaul. Islamic Terror & the Balkans. (ENG.). 231p. 2008. pap. 24.95 (978-1-4128-0868-2(5)) 2006. (Illus.). (gr. 11). 39.95 (978-0-7658-0347-4(X)) Transaction Pubs.

BALKAN PENINSULA—FOREIGN RELATIONS

Bechev, Dimitar. Constructing South East Europe: The Politics of the Balkan Regional Cooperation. 2011. (St. Antony's Ser.). (ENG., Illus.). 224p. 85.00 (978-0-230-23972-2(2)) Palgrave Macmillan.

Braniff, Maire. Integrating the Balkans: Conflict Resolution & the Impact of EU Expansion. 2011. (Library of European Studies). (ENG.). 256p. 92.00 (978-1-84885-669-1(5), Tauris Academic Studies) I. B. Tauris & Co., Ltd. GBR. Dist: Macmillan.

Bugajski, Janusz. Are Europe & NATO Still Widening? Western Balkan Policy Review: A Report of the CSIS Lavrentis Lavrentiadis Chair in Southeast European Studies. 2010. pap. (978-0-89206-602-5(4)) Ctr. for Strategic & International Studies.

Deacon, Bob. International Actors & Social Policy in South East Europe. Stubbs, Paul, ed. 2007. 272p. (C). 127.00 (978-1-84720-096-9(6)) Elgar, Edward Publishing, Inc.

Debardeleben, Joan. The Boundaries of EU Enlargement: Finding a Place for Neighbours. DeBardeleben, Joan, ed. 2008. (Studies in Central & Eastern Europe Ser.). (ENG., Illus.). 300p. 95.00 (978-0-230-52124-7(X)) Palgrave Macmillan.

Deliso, Christopher. The Coming Balkan Caliphate: The Threat of Radical Islam to Europe & the West, 1 vol. 2007. (Praeger Security International Ser.). 240p. 39.95 (978-0-275-99525-6(9), C9525, Praeger Security International) Greenwood Publishing Group, Inc.

Despot, Andrea. Amerikas Weg auf den Balkan: Zur Genese der Beziehungen zwischen den USA und Südosteuropa 1820-1920. 2010. (Balkanologische Veroffentlichungen des Osteuropa-Instituts an der Freien Universitat Berlin Ser.). (GER.). 346p. (C). pap. 102.00 (978-3-447-06188-9(X)) Harrassowitz, Otto Verlag DEU. Dist: ISD.

Dodds, Brandon. Victory Dance. 2008. 97p. pap. 16.95 (978-0-578-00047-3(4)) Southern Cross Publishing.

Elbasani, Arolda, ed. Europeanization Integration & the Western Balkans Balkans. 2012. (Routledge/UACES Contemporary European Studies). (ENG.). 256p. (C). 130.00 (978-0-415-59452-3(9)) Routledge.

Hatzopoulos, Pavlos. The Balkans Beyond Nationalism & Identity: International Relations & Ideology. 2008. (ENG.). 288p. 89.00 (978-1-84511-503-6(1)) I. B. Tauris & Co., Ltd. GBR. Dist: Macmillan.

Human Rights, Democracy, & Integration in South-Central Europe: Hearing Before the Commission on Security & Cooperation in Europe, One Hundred Ninth Congress, Second Session, June 15, 2006. 2007. iv, 96p. (978-0-16-079775-0(6), 552-070-36690-3) United States Government Printing Office.

Kissoudi, Penelope. The Balkan Games & Balkan Politics in the Interwar Years 1929-1939: Politicians in Pursuit of Peace. 2009. (Sport in the Global Society Ser.). (ENG., Illus.). 224p. (C). 150.00 (978-0-415-48645-3(9)) Routledge.

Kovic, Milos. Disraeli & the Eastern Question. 2010. (ENG., Illus.). 368p. 115.00 (978-0-19-957460-5(X)) Oxford Univ. Pr., Inc.

Kusic, Sinisa & Grupe, Claudia, eds. The Western Balkans on Their Way to the EU? 2007. 156p. (C). pap. 35.95 (978-3-631-55896-6(1)) Lang, Peter Publishing, Inc.

Livanios, Dimitris. The Macedonian Question: Britain & the Southern Balkans 1939-1949. 2008. (Oxford Historical Monographs). (ENG., Illus.). 280p. 125.00 (978-0-19-923768-5(9)) Oxford Univ. Pr., Inc.

MacShane, MP, Dennis. Why Kosovo Matters. 2012. (ENG., Illus.). 120p. 14.95 **(978-1-907822-39-1(9))** Haus Publishing GBR. Dist: Consortium Bk. Sales & Distribution.

Marko, Joseph & Petrusic, Antonija. European Integration & Its Effects on Minority Protection in the Western Balkan Countries. Lantschner, Emma, ed. 2008. 382p. (C). pap. 86.00 (978-3-8329-3080-6(9)) Nomos Verlagsgesellschaft DEU. Dist: International Specialized Bk. Services.

O'brennan. The Eu & the Western Balkans. 2008. (Europe & the Nation State Ser.). (ENG.). 224p. (C). 130.00 (978-0-415-42608-4(1)) Routledge.

Pettifer, James & Vickers, Miranda. The Albanian Question: Reshaping the Balkans. 2009. (ENG., Illus.). 288p. pap. 26.95 (978-1-84885-095-8(6)) I. B. Tauris & Co., Ltd. GBR. Dist: Macmillan.

Trauner, Florian. The Europeanisation of the Western Balkans: EU Justice & Home Affairs in Croatia & Macedonia. 2011. (Europe in Change Ser.). (ENG., Illus.). 224p. 90.00 (978-0-7190-8345-7(1)) Manchester Univ. Pr. GBR. Dist: Macmillan.

BALKAN PENINSULA—HISTORY

Akgün, Seçil. 27 Mays: Bir Ihtilal, Bir Devrim, Bir Anayasa. 2009. (TUR., Illus.). viii, 291p. (978-9944-344-77-7(X)) Odtu Gelistirme Vakfi Yayincilik ve Iletisim AS.

Bideleux, Robert & Jeffries, Ian. Balkans Contemporary History. 2006. (Illus.). 640p. (C). (ENG.). 44.95 (978-0-415-22963-0(4)); 145.00 (978-0-415-22962-3(6)) Routledge.

Biondich, Mark. The Balkans: Revolution, War, & Political Violence Since 1878. 2011. (ENG., Illus.). 352p. 99.00 (978-0-19-929905-8(6)) Oxford Univ. Pr., Inc.

Bjelic, Dusan I. Normalizing the Balkans: Geopolitics of Psychoanalysis & Psychiatry. 2011. (Illus.). 200p. 99.95 **(978-1-4094-3315-6(3))** Ashgate Publishing Co.

Chitan, Simona. 30 de Interviuri Eveniment. 2008. (RUM.). 174p. (978-973-733-299-8(7)) Tritonic.

Colovic, Ivan. The Balkans: the Terror of Culture: Essays in Political Anthropology. 2011. 196p. pap. 43.00 (978-3-8329-6303-3(0)) Nomos Verlagsgesellschaft DEU. Dist: International Specialized Bk. Services.

Demirci, Sevtap. British Public Opinion Towards the Ottoman Empire During the Two Crises. 2010. 87.68 (978-1-61719-136-7(1)) Gorgias Pr., LLC.

Destani, Bejtullah & Elsie, Robert, eds. The Balkan Wars: British Consular Reports from Macedonia in the Final Years of the Ottoman Empire. 2013. (ENG., Illus.). 288p. 96.00 **(978-1-78076-076-6(0))** I. B. Tauris & Co., Ltd. GBR. Dist: Macmillan.

Dimou, Augusta. 'Transition' & the Politics of History Education in Southeastern Europe. Dimou, Augusta, ed. 2009. (Eckert. Die Schriftenreihe Ser.). (ENG., Illus.). 402p. (C). pap. 63.00 (978-3-89971-531-6(4)) Vandenhoeck & Ruprecht GmbH & Co. KG DEU. Dist: ISD.

Durham, Edith M. Twenty Years of Balkan Tangle. 2007. 244p. (ENG.). 43.99 (978-1-4280-7545-0(3)); per. 36.99 (978-1-4280-7544-3(5)) IndyPublish.com.

Durham, M. Edith. The Blaze in the Balkans: Selected Writings 1903-1941. Elsie, Robert & Destani, Bejtullah, eds. 2012. (ENG.). 224p. 40.00 (978-1-84885-710-0(1)) I. B. Tauris & Co., Ltd. GBR. Dist: Macmillan.

Durham, Mary Edith. Twenty Years of Balkan Tangle. 2008. 304p. 28.99 (978-0-554-27534-5(1)) 2008. 304p. 25.99 (978-0-554-36837-5(4)) 2007. (ENG.). 268p. pap. 21.99 (978-1-4346-3426-9(4)) 2007. (ENG.). 300p. pap. 23.99 (978-1-4346-3427-6(2)) BiblioBazaar.

Elgood, Robert. The Arms of Greece: And Her Balkan Neighbours in the Ottoman Period. 2009. (ENG., Illus.). 336p. 60.00 (978-0-500-25157-7(6), 525157) Thames & Hudson.

Emmert, Thomas & Ingrao, Charles W., eds. Conflict in South-Eastern Europe at the End of the Twentieth Century: A Scholars' Initiative Assesses Some of the Controversies. 2006. (Nations & Nationalism of Eastern Europe & the Former USSR Ser.). (ENG., Illus.). 232p. 150.00 (978-0-415-39925-8(4)) Routledge.

Forbes, Nevill & Toynbee, Arnold J. The Balkans. 2008. 332p. 28.99 (978-0-554-33326-7(0)); 29.99 (978-0-554-24023-7(8)) BiblioBazaar.

Goltz, Thomas. The Chalk Circle: The Other Balkan Wars. Date not set. (978-0-312-27796-3(2)) St. Martin's Pr.

Gordon, Jan. A Balkan Freebooter: Being the True Exploits of the Serbian Outlaw & Comitaj Petko Moritch. 2007. (ENG.). 336p. 45.95 (978-0-548-14522-7(9)) Kessinger Publishing, LLC.

Grandits, Hannes, et al, eds. Conflicting Loyalties in the Balkans: The Great Powers, the Ottoman Empire & Nation-Building. 2011. (Library of Ottoman Studies). (ENG., Illus.). 320p. 99.00 (978-1-84885-477-2(3), Tauris Academic Studies) I. B. Tauris & Co., Ltd. GBR. Dist: Macmillan.

Grubacic, Andrej. Don't Mourn, Balkanize! Essays after Yugoslavia. 2010. (ENG.). 272p. pap. 20.00 (978-1-60486-302-4(1)) PM Pr.

Grumeza, Ion. Roots of Balkanization: Eastern Europe C. E. 500-1500. 2010. (ENG.). 260p. pap. 35.00 (978-0-7618-5134-9(8)) Univ. Pr. of America, Inc.

Hall, Richard C. The Modern Balkans: A History. 2011. (ENG., Illus.). 208p. 40.00 (978-1-86189-810-4(X)) Reaktion Bks., Ltd. GBR. Dist: Chicago Distribution Ctr.

Heppner, Harald & Barbarics-Hermanik, Zsuzsa, eds. Türkenangst und Festungsbau: Wirklichkeit und Mythos. 2009. (Neue Forschungen zur ostmittel- und südosteuropäischen Geschichte. New Researches on East Central & South East European History. Recherches nouvelles sur l'histoire de l'Europe centrale et orientale Ser.). (GRE.). 254p. 64.95 (978-3-631-59303-5(1)) Lang, Peter GmbH, Europaischer Verlag der Wissenschaften DEU. Dist: Lang, Peter.

Hutchinson, T. S. An American Soldier under the Greek Flag at Bezanie. 2007. (ENG.). 312p. 45.95 (978-0-548-03835-2(X)) Kessinger Publishing, LLC.

Ingrao, Charles, et al, eds. Peace of Passarowitz 1718. 2011. (Central European Studies). (Illus.). 310p. pap. 39.95 (978-1-55753-594-8(9)) Purdue Univ. Pr.

Janzekovic, John. The Use of Force in Humanitarian Intervention: Morality & Practicalities. 2006. (Illus.). 238p. 120.00 (978-0-7546-4850-5(8)) Ashgate Publishing Co.

Jordan, David Starr. War's Aftermath: A Preliminary Study of the Eugenics of War As Illustrated by the Civil War of the United States And the Late Wars in the Balkans. 103p. reprint ed. 88.00 (978-0-7222-8000-3(9)) Library Reprints, Inc.

Jowett, Philip. Armies of the Balkan Wars 1912-13: The Priming Charge for the Great War. 2011. (Men-at-Arms Ser.). (ENG., Illus.). 48p. pap. 17.95 (978-1-84908-418-5(1)) Osprey Publishing, Ltd. GBR. Dist: Random Hse., Inc.

Kolovous, Elias, et al, eds. The Ottoman Empire, the Balkans, the Greek Lands. 2010. 123.32 (978-1-61719-099-5(3)) Gorgias Pr., LLC.

Krott, Rob. Save the Last Bullet for Yourself: A Soldier of Fortune in the Balkans & Somalia. 2008. (Illus.). 256p. 32.95 (978-1-932033-95-3(5)) Casemate Pubs. & Bk. Distributors, LLC.

Kuftinec, Sonja Arsham. Theatre, Facilitation, & Nation Formation in the Balkans & Middle East. 2009. (Studies in International Performance Ser.). (ENG., Illus.). 224p. 89.00 (978-0-230-00539-6(X)) Palgrave Macmillan.

Lauer, Reinhard, ed. Erinnerungskultur in Südosteuropa. 2011. (Abhandlungen der Akademie der Wissenschaften zu Göttingen. Neue Folge Ser.). (GER.). XVIII, 438p. 168.00 **(978-3-11-025304-7(6))** De Gruyter, Walter Inc.

Lóczy, Dénes, et al, eds. Recent Landform Evolution: The Carpatho-Balkan-Dinaric Region. 2012. (Springer Geography Ser.). (ENG., Illus.). xxi, 460p. 179.00 **(978-94-007-2447-1(0)**, 9400724470) Springer.

Madgearu, Alexandru. The Wars of the Balkan Peninsula: Their Medieval Origins. Gordon, Martin, ed. 2007. (ENG., Illus.). 244p. per. 64.00 (978-0-8108-5846-6(0)) Scarecrow Pr., Inc.

Malian, Stan (Stojan). History & Religion of Macedoni: Gateway to Europe. 2009. 200p. 24.99 (978-1-4389-7764-5(6)); pap. 14.69 (978-1-4389-7763-8(8)) AuthorHouse.

Michail, Eugene. British & the Balkans: Forming Images of Foreign Lands, 1900-1945. 2011. (ENG.). 224p. 120.00 (978-0-8264-2268-2(3)) Continuum International Publishing Group, Ltd. GBR. Dist: National Bk. Network.

Milojkovic-Djuric, Jelena, ed. Balkan Cultural Legacies: Historical, Literary, & Fine Arts Perceptions. 2011. (ENG., Illus.). 250p. (gr. 17). 50.00 (978-0-88033-674-1(9)) Eastern European Monographs.

Mojzes, Paul. Balkan Genocides: Holocaust & Ethnic Cleansing in the 20th Century. 2011. (Studies in Genocide: Religion, History, & Human Rights Ser.). (ENG.). 316p. 42.95 **(978-1-4422-0663-2(2))** Rowman & Littlefield Publishers, Inc.

—Balkan Genocides: Holocaust & Ethnic Cleansing in the Twentieth Century. 2011. **(978-1-4422-0665-6(9))** Rowman & Littlefield Publishers, Inc.

Murray, William S. Making of the Balkan States. (Columbia University, Studies in the Social Sciences: No. 102). reprint ed. 24.50 (978-0-404-51102-9(3)) AMS Pr., Inc.

Murvar, Vatro. The Vlachs of the Balkans: A Submerged Nation Existing Throughout the Millennia. 155p. 30.00 (978-0-931635-02-1(0)); pap. 16.00 (978-0-931635-03-8(9)) Foundation for the Sociological Study of the Stateless Submerged Nations.

Nevill Forbes. The Balkans: A History of Bulgaria — Serbia — Greece — Rumania — Tu. l.t. ed. 2007. 636p. pap. 24.99 (978-1-4264-5637-4(9)) BiblioBazaar.

Parveva, Stefka. Village, Town & People in the Ottoman Balkans, 16th-mid-19th Century. 2010. 108.44 (978-1-61719-098-8(5)) Gorgias Pr., LLC.

Pavlowitch, Steven. Hitler's New Disorder: The Second World War in Yugoslavia. 2008. (Columbia/Hurst Ser.). (ENG., Illus.). 256p. (gr. 17). 37.50 (978-0-231-70050-4(4)) Columbia Univ. Pr.

Petersen, Roger Dale. Western Intervention in the Balkans: The Strategic Use of Emotion in Conflict. 2011. (Cambridge Studies in Comparative Politics Ser.). (ENG., Illus.). 352p. pap. 32.99 **(978-0-521-28126-3(1))**; 99.00 **(978-1-107-01066-6(7))** Cambridge Univ. Pr.

Roth, Brunnbauer. Urban Life & Culture in Southeastern Europe: Anthropological & Historical Perspectives. Roth, Klaus & Brunnbauer, Ulf, eds. 2008. (Ethnologia Balkanica Ser.). (ENG., Illus.). 368p. pap. 49.95 (978-3-8258-9903-5(9)) Lit Verlag DEU. Dist: Transaction Pubs.

Roth, Klaus & Lauth Bacas, Jutta. Migration In, From, & to Southeastern Europe: Ways & Strategies of Migrating. 2011. 312p. pap. 49.95 **(978-3-643-10896-8(6))** Lit Verlag DEU. Dist: Transaction Pubs.

Shepard, Jonathan. Emergent Elites & Byzantium in the Balkans & East-Central Europe. 2011. (Variorum Collected Studies). (Illus.). 434p. 190.00 (978-1-4094-0364-7(5)) Ashgate Publishing Co.

Sonnichsen, Albert. Confessions of a Macedonian Bandit: A Californian in the Balkan Wars. 2007. (ENG.). 224p. per. 12.15 (978-1-60206-153-8(X)) Cosimo, Inc.

Stephenson, Paul. Byzantium's Balkan Frontier: A Political Study of the Northern Balkans, 900-1204. 2006. (ENG.). 368p. pap. 74.00 (978-0-521-02756-4(X)) Cambridge Univ. Pr.

Stojanovic, Mihailo D. The Great Powers & the Balkans 1875-1878. 2008. (ENG.). 312p. pap. 42.00 (978-0-521-08934-0(4)) Cambridge Univ. Pr.

Todorova, Maria. Imagining the Balkans. rev. ed. 2009. (ENG.). 304p. pap. 24.95 (978-0-19-538786-5(4)) Oxford Univ. Pr., Inc.

Vàsàry, István. Cumans & Tatars: Oriental Military in the Pre-Ottoman Balkans, 1185-1365. 2009. (ENG., Illus.). 248p. pap. 38.00 (978-0-521-12028-9(4)) Cambridge Univ. Pr.

Wachtel, Andrew. The Balkans in World History. 2008. (New Oxford World History Ser.). (ENG., Illus.). 176p. pap. 19.95 (978-0-19-533801-0(4)); (YA). 60.00 (978-0-19-515849-6(0)) Oxford Univ. Pr., Inc.

Wakefield, Alan & Moody, Simon. Under the Devil's Eye. 2011. (Illus.). 272p. 50.00 **(978-1-84884-461-2(1))** Pen & Sword Bks. Ltd. GBR. Dist: Casemate Pubs. & Bk. Distributors, LLC.

Wirthwein, Walter G. Britain & the Balkan Crisis Eighteen Seventy-Five to Eighteen Seventy-Eight. (Columbia University, Studies in the Social Sciences: No. 407). reprint ed. 36.50 (978-0-404-51407-5(3)) AMS Pr., Inc.

Yavuz, M. Hakan, ed. War & Diplomacy: The Russo-Turkish War of 1877-1878 & the Treaty of Berlin. 2011. (ENG., Illus.). 616p. (gr. 12). 40.00 **(978-1-60781-150-3(2))** Univ. of Utah Pr.

BALKAN PENINSULA—LANGUAGES

Joseph, Brian D. The Synchrony & Diachrony of the Balkan Infinitive: A Study in Areal, General & Historical Linguistics. 2009. (Cambridge Studies in Linguistics Ser.). (ENG.). 356p. pap. 48.00 (978-0-521-10533-0(1)) Cambridge Univ. Pr.

Kallulli, Dalina & Tasmowski, Liliane, eds. Clitic Doubling in Balkan Languages. 2008. (Linguistik Aktuell/Linguistics Today Ser.: Vol. 130). (Illus.). 341p. 173.00 (978-90-272-5513-6(X)) Benjamins, John Publishing Co.

Kononen, Mija & Nuorluoto, Juhani, eds. Europe — Evropa: Cross-Cultural Dialogues Between the West, Russia, & Southeastern Europe. 2010. (Studia Multiethnica Upsaliensia Ser.). (Illus.). 324p. pap. 82.50 (978-91-554-7697-7(X)) Uppsala Universitet/Acta Universitatis Upsaliensis SWE. Dist: Coronet Bks.

Tomic, Olga M. Balkan Sprachbund Morpho-Syntactic Features. 2010. (Studies in Natural Language & Linguistic Theory Ser.). xxi, 749p. pap. 439.00 (978-90-481-7135-4(0), 9048171350) Springer.

Tomic, Olga Miseska. Balkan Sprachbund Morpho-Syntactic Features. 2006. (Studies in Natural Language & Linguistic Theory Ser.). (Illus.). xxi, 749p. 439.00 (978-1-4020-4487-8(9), 1402044879) Springer.

BALKAN PENINSULA—POLITICS AND GOVERNMENT

Bache, Ian & Andreou, George, eds. Cohesion Policy & Multi-Level Governance in South East Europe. 2010. (ENG.). 136p. (C). 125.00 (978-0-415-59419-6(7)) Routledge.

Baer, Josette. From Post-Communism Toward the Third Millennium: Aspects of Political & Economic Development in Eastern & South-Eastern Europe from 2000-2005. 2011. (Interdisciplinary Studies on Central & Eastern Europe Ser.). (ENG.). 270p. pap. **(978-3-03911-773-4(4))** Lang, Peter.

Biondich, Mark. The Balkans: Revolution, War, & Political Violence Since 1878. 2011. (ENG., Illus.). 352p. 99.00 (978-0-19-929905-8(6)) Oxford Univ. Pr., Inc.

Braniff, Maire. Integrating the Balkans: Conflict Resolution & the Impact of EU Expansion. 2011. (Library of European Studies). (ENG.). 256p. 92.00 (978-1-84885-669-1(5), Tauris Academic Studies) I. B. Tauris & Co., Ltd. GBR. Dist: Macmillan.

Bugajski, Janusz. Are Europe & NATO Still Widening? Western Balkan Policy Review: A Report of the CSIS Lavrentis Lavrentiadis Chair in Southeast European Studies. 2010. pap. (978-0-89206-602-5(4)) Ctr. for Strategic & International Studies.

Bunjevac, Nina & jukic Pranjic, Irena. Balkan Comics: Women on the Fringe. 2012. (ENG., Illus.). 240p. 50.00 **(978-1-935613-50-3(2))** Batty, Mark Pub., LLC.

Circa. A Political & Economic Dictionary of Central & South-Eastern Europe. 2008. 320p. 260.00 (978-1-85743-359-3(9)) Routledge.

Cohen, Lenard J. & Lampe, John R. Embracing Democracy in the Western Balkans: From Post-Conflict Struggles Toward European Integration. 2011. (ENG., Illus.). 560p. (gr. 17). 70.00 **(978-1-4214-0382-3(X))**; pap. 29.95 **(978-1-4214-0433-2(8))** Johns Hopkins Univ. Pr.

Cviic, Christopher, ed. In Search of the Balkan Recovery: The Political & Economic Reemergence of South Eastern Europe. 2010. (Columbia/Hurst Ser.). (ENG.). 244p. (gr. 17). 45.00 (978-0-231-70170-9(5)) Columbia Univ. Pr.

Deacon, Bob. International Actors & Social Policy in South East Europe. Stubbs, Paul, ed. 2007. 272p. (C). 127.00 (978-1-84720-096-9(6)) Elgar, Edward Publishing, Inc.

Duvold, Kjetil. Making Sense of Baltic Democracy. 2010. 292p. pap. (978-3-8383-2017-5(4)) Lambert Academic Publishing.

Emerson, Peter. Party Politics in the Western Balkans. Emerson, Peter & Stojarová, Vera, eds. 2009. (Routledge Research in Comparative Politics Ser.). (ENG., Illus.). 256p. 128.00 (978-0-415-55099-4(8)) Routledge.

Europa Central & South-Eastern Europe. 7th rev. ed. 2006. (ENG., Illus.). 828p. 575.00 (978-1-85743-372-2(6)) Routledge.

Europa Publications, ed. Central & South-Eastern Europe 2012. 12th rev. ed. 2011. (ENG.). 900p. 815.00 (978-1-85743-617-4(2)) Routledge.

Europa Publications Staff. Central & South-Eastern Europe 2008. 8th rev. ed. 2007. 819p. 640.00 (978-1-85743-422-4(6)) Routledge.

Farkas, Richard P. Democratization in the Balkans: Prescription for a Badly Scarred Body Politic. 2008. (Northeastern Series on Democratization & Political Development Ser.). (ENG., Illus.). 150p. pap. 29.95 (978-1-55553-691-6(3), Northeastern University Pr.) Univ. Pr. of New England.

Fischer, Bernd J., ed. Balkan Strongmen: Dictators & Authoritarian Rulers of Southeast Europe. 2007. (Central European Studies). (ENG., Illus.). 494p. 39.95 (978-1-55753-455-2(1)) Purdue Univ. Pr.

Fluri, Philipp H., et al, eds. The Evolution of Civil-Military Relations in South East Europe: Continuing Democratic Reform & Adapting to the Needs of Fighting Terrorism. 2010. (ENG.). xii, 276p. pap. 89.95 (978-3-7908-2524-4(7), 3790825247) Physica-Verlag DEU. Dist: Springer.

Friedman, Morris G., ed. Economics & Politics of the Balkans Region. 2008. (Illus.). (C). 69.00 (978-1-60456-043-5(6)) Nova Science Pubs., Inc.

Gallagher. The Balkans in the New Millennium. 2007. pap. 41.95 (978-0-415-46001-9(8)) Routledge.

Glenny, Misha. The Balkans: Nationalism, War, & the Great Powers, 1804-2011. 2012. (ENG.). 752p. (gr. 12). pap. 25.00 **(978-0-14-242256-4(8)**, Penguin (Non-Classics)) Penguin Group (USA) Inc.

Goltz, Thomas. The Chalk Circle: The Other Balkan Wars. Date not set. (978-0-312-27796-3(2)) St. Martin's Pr.

Grandits, Hannes, et al, eds. Conflicting Loyalties in the Balkans: The Great Powers, the Ottoman Empire & Nation-Building. 2011. (Library of Ottoman Studies). (ENG., Illus.). 320p. 99.00 (978-1-84885-477-2(3), Tauris Academic Studies) I. B. Tauris & Co., Ltd. GBR. Dist: Macmillan.

Hatzopoulos, Pavlos. The Balkans Beyond Nationalism & Identity: International Relations & Ideology. 2008. (ENG.). 288p. 89.00 *(978-1-84511-503-6(1))* I. B. Tauris & Co., Ltd. GBR. Dist: Macmillan.

Human Rights, Democracy, & Integration in South-Central Europe: Hearing Before the Commission on Security & Cooperation in Europe, One Hundred Ninth Congress, Second Session, June 15, 2006. 2007. iv, 96p. *(978-0-16-079775-0(6)*, 552-070-36390-3) United States Government Printing Office.

Inotai, András. The European Union & Southeastern Europe: Troubled Waters Ahead? 2007. (Illus.). 447p. pap. 80.95 *(978-90-5201-071-7(4))* Lang, Peter Publishing, Inc.

Izvorski, Ivalo V. & Kahkonen, Satu, eds. Public Expenditure Policies in Southeast Europe. 2008. (World Bank Working Papers: 134). (ENG., Illus.). 120p. per. 20.00 *(978-0-8213-7450-4(8)*, 9780821374504) World Bank Pubns.

Kavalski, Emilian. Extending the European Security Community: Constructing Peace in the Balkans. 2008. (ENG., Illus.). 272p. 89.00 *(978-1-84511-497-8(3)*, Tauris Academic Studies) I. B. Tauris & Co., Ltd. GBR. Dist: Macmillan.

Kissoudi, Penelope. The Balkan Games & Balkan Politics in the Interwar Years 1929-1939: Politicians in Pursuit of Peace. 2009. (Sport in the Global Society Ser.). (ENG., Illus.). 224p. (C). 150.00 *(978-0-415-48545-3(9))* Routledge.

Koktsidis, Ioannis. Strategic Rebellion: Ethnic Conflict in FYR Macedonia & the Balkans. 2012. (Nationalisms across the Globe Ser.). (ENG.). 261p. pap. 54.95 ***(978-3-0343-0148-0(0))*** Lang, Peter AG GBR. Dist: Lang, Peter.

Kostovicova, Denisa. Transnationalism in the Balkans. Bojicic-Dzelilovic, Vesna, ed. 2008. (Association for the Study of Nationalities Ser.). VI, 122p. 140.00 *(978-0-415-46446-8(3))* Routledge.

MacKellar, Landis & Repansek, Jana. Pension Reform in Southeastern Europe: Linking to Labor & Financial Market Reforms. Holzmann, Robert, ed. 2008. (Directions in Development Ser.). (ENG., Illus.). 480p. pap. 45.00 *(978-0-8213-7558-7(X)*, 9780821375587) World Bank Pubns.

Mäder, Ueli & Simko, Dusan. Stabilization & Progress in the Western Balkans: Proceedings of the Symposium 2010, Basel, Switzerland, September 17-19. 2011. 198p. pap. ***(978-3-0343-0640-9(7))*** Lang, Peter Publishing, Inc.

Madgearu, Alexandru. The Wars of the Balkan Peninsula: Their Medieval Origins. Gordon, Martin, ed. 2007. (ENG., Illus.). 244p. per. 64.00 *(978-0-8108-5846-6(0))* Scarecrow Pr., Inc.

Marko, Joseph & Petrusic, Antonija. European Integration & Its Effects on Minority Protection in the Western Balkan Countries. Lantschner, Emma, ed. 2008. 382p. (C). pap. 86.00 *(978-3-8329-3080-6(9))* Nomos Verlagsgesellschaft DEU. Dist: International Specialized Bk. Services.

McTernan, Benedict, ed. Political Risk Yearbook - 2007 Vol. 7: East Europe. 2007. per. *(978-1-933539-35-5(6))* PRS Group Inc., The.

Meckfessel, Shon. Suffled How It Gush: A North American Anarchist in the Balkans. 2009. (ENG., Illus.). 260p. pap. 16.95 *(978-1-904859-85-7(2))* AK Pr. GBR. Dist: Consortium Bk. Sales & Distribution.

Mulaj, Klejda. Politics of Ethnic Cleansing: Nation-State Building & Provision of in/Security in Twentieth-Century Balkans. 2008. (ENG.). 216p. 73.50 *(978-0-7391-1782-8(3))* Lexington Bks.

Noutcheva, Gergana. European Foreign Policy & the Challenges of Balkan Accession. 2012. (Routledge/UACES Contemporary European Studies). (ENG., Illus.). 256p. (C). 130.00 *(978-0-415-59684-8(X))* Routledge.

O'brennan. The Eu & the Western Balkans. 2008. (Europe & the Nation State Ser.). (ENG.). 224p. (C). 130.00 *(978-0-415-42608-4(1))* Routledge.

Petersen, Roger Dale. Western Intervention in the Balkans: The Strategic Use of Emotion in Conflict. 2011. (Cambridge Studies in Comparative Politics Ser.). (ENG., Illus.). 352p. pap. 32.99 ***(978-0-521-28126-3(1))***; 99.00 ***(978-1-107-01066-6(7))*** Cambridge Univ. Pr.

Pond, Elizabeth. Endgame in the Balkans: Regime Change, European Style. 2006. (ENG., Illus.). 412p. 29.95 *(978-0-8157-7160-9(6))* Brookings Institution Pr.

Ramet, Sabrina P., ed. Central & Southeast European Politics Since 1989. 2010. (ENG., Illus.). 600p. (C). 100.00 *(978-0-521-88810-3(7))*; pap. 36.99 *(978-0-521-71616-1(0))* Cambridge Univ. Pr.

Sanjay, Kathuria & Kathuria, Sanjay. Western Balkan Integration & the EU: An Agenda for Trade & Growth. 2008. (Directions in Development Ser.). (ENG., Illus.). 184p. pap. 30.00 *(978-0-8213-7472-6(9)*, 9780821374726) World Bank Pubns.

Saric, Ljiljana, et al, eds. Contesting Europe's Eastern Rim: Cultural Identities in Public Discourse. 2010. (Multilingual Matters Ser.). (Illus.). 264p. 129.95 *(978-1-84769-324-2(5))* Multilingual Matters GBR. Dist: Univ. of Toronto Pr.

Sergi, Bruno S., et al. The Political Economy of Southeast Europe from 1990 to the Present: Challenges & Opportunities. 2008. (ENG., Illus.). 208p. 110.00 *(978-0-8264-2867-7(3))* Continuum International Publishing Group, Ltd. GBR. Dist: National Bk. Network.

Simic, Olivera, et al, eds. Peace Psychology in the Balkans: Mapping the Pathways to Peace. 2011. (Peace Psychology Book Ser.). (ENG.). 450p. 129.00 ***(978-1-4614-1947-1(6)***, 1461419476) Springer.

Trauner, Florian. The Europeanisation of the Western Balkans: EU Justice & Home Affairs in Croatia & Macedonia. 2011. (Europe in Change Ser.). (ENG., Illus.). 224p. 90.00 *(978-0-7190-8345-7(1))* Manchester Univ. Pr. GBR. Dist: Macmillan.

van Meurs, Wim & Mungiu-Pippidi, Alina, eds. Ottomans into Europeans: State & Institution-Building in South Eastern Europe. 2010. (Columbia/Hurst Ser.). (ENG.). 320p. (gr. 17). 50.00 *(978-0-231-70168-6(3))* Columbia Univ. Pr.

WHO Regional Office for Europe. Health & Economic Development in South-eastern Europe. 2006. (Euro Nonserial Publication). (ENG.). 138p. pap. 30.00 *(978-92-890-2295-8(7))* World Health Organization.

BALKAN PENINSULA—RELIGION

Gerov, Georgi. Christian Art Icons from Melnik & the Melnik Region, Bulgaria. 2007. (Series Christian Art Ser.). 180p. 110.00 *(978-954-642-285-9(1))* Pensoft Pubs. BGR. Dist: Coronet Bks.

Kitromilides, Paschalis M. An Orthodox Commonwealth: Symbolic Legacies & Culture Encounters in Southeastern Europe. 2007. (Variorum Collected Studies). (Illus.). 276p. 144.95 *(978-0-7546-5963-1(1))* Ashgate Publishing Co.

Malian, Stan (Stojan). History & Religion of Macedoni: Gateway to Europe. 2009. 200p. 24.99 *(978-1-4389-7764-5(6))*; pap. 14.69 *(978-1-4389-7763-8(8))* AuthorHouse.

Merdjanova, Ina & Brodeur, Patrice. Religion as a Conversation Starter: Interreligious Dialogue for Peacebuilding in the Balkans. 2011. (Continuum Advances in Religious Studies). (ENG.). 194p. (gr. 17). pap. 44.95 ***(978-1-4411-9438-1(X))*** Continuum International Publishing Group, Ltd. GBR. Dist: National Bk. Network.

Merdjanova, Ina & Brodeur, Patrice. Religion as a Conversation Starter: Interreligious Dialogue for Peacekeeping in the Balkans. 2010. (Continuum Advances in Religious Studies). (ENG., Illus.). 208p. 120.00 *(978-0-8264-3902-4(0))* Continuum International Publishing Group, Ltd. GBR. Dist: National Bk. Network.

Veronis, Luke A. Go Forth: Stories of Missions & Resurrection in Albania. 2010. 232p. pap. 18.95 *(978-0-9822770-6-5(7))* Conciliar Pr.

Voss, Christian & Telbizova-Sack, Jordanka. Islam und Muslime in (Südost)Europa Im Kontext Von Transformation und EU-Erweiterung. 2010. (GER & ENG., Illus.). 222p. *(978-3-86688-104-4(5))* Sagner, Otto.

BALKAN PENINSULA—SOCIAL CONDITIONS

Arachchige Don, Neville & Mitovic, Ljubisa. The balkans in Transitions. 2007. 23.50 *(978-0-9792762-0-0(9))* International Research Foundation for Development.

Friman, H. Richard & Reich, Simon. Human Trafficking, Human Security, & the Balkans. Friman, H. Richard & Reich, Simon, eds. 2007. (Pitt Security Continuum Ser.). (ENG.). 208p. (C). per. 19.95 *(978-0-8229-5974-8(7))* Univ. of Pittsburgh Pr.

Goltz, Thomas. The Chalk Circle: The Other Balkan Wars. Date not set. *(978-0-312-27796-3(2))* St. Martin's Pr.

Gordon, Jan. Balkan Freebooter Being the True Exploit. 2006. pap. 30.95 *(978-1-4286-5826-4(2))* Kessinger Publishing, LLC.

Gordon, Lynn. Two Vagabonds in the Balkans. 2007. 190.00 *(978-0-7103-1124-5(9))* Taylor & Francis Group.

Grandits, Hannes, et al, eds. Conflicting Loyalties in the Balkans: The Great Powers, the Ottoman Empire & Nation-Building. 2011. (Library of Ottoman Studies). (ENG., Illus.). 320p. 99.00 *(978-1-84885-477-2(3)*, Tauris Academic Studies) I. B. Tauris & Co., Ltd. GBR. Dist: Macmillan.

Izvorski, Ivalo V. & Kahkonen, Satu, eds. Public Expenditure Policies in Southeast Europe. 2008. (World Bank Working Papers: 134). (ENG., Illus.). 120p. per. 20.00 *(978-0-8213-7450-4(8)*, 9780821374504) World Bank Pubns.

Kafkalas, Grigoris. Overcoming Fragmentation in Southeast Europe: Spatial Development Trends & Integration Potential. Getimis, Panayiotis, ed. 2007. (Urban & Regional Planning & Development Ser.). (Illus.). 354p. 134.95 *(978-0-7546-4796-6(X))* Ashgate Publishing Co.

Mazaj, Meta. Once upon a Time There Was a Country - National & Cynicism in the Post-1990s Balkan Cinem. 2008. 176p. pap. *(978-3-8364-2880-4(6))* VDM Verlag Dr. Mueller e.K.

Meckfessel, Shon. Suffled How It Gush: A North American Anarchist in the Balkans. 2009. (ENG., Illus.). 260p. pap. 16.95 *(978-1-904859-85-7(2))* AK Pr. GBR. Dist: Consortium Bk. Sales & Distribution.

Milojkovic-Djuric, Jelena, ed. Balkan Cultural Legacies: Historical, Literary, & Fine Arts Perceptions. 2011. (ENG., Illus.). 250p. (gr. 17). 50.00 *(978-0-88033-674-1(9))* Eastern European Monographs.

Mitrovic, Ljubisa R. Tranzicija U Periferni Kapitalizam: Ogledi Iz Sociologije Globalnih I Regionalnih Promena = Transition to Peripheral Capitalism: Essays on the Sociology of Global & Regional Change. 2009. (Illus.). 263p. *(978-86-7419-199-6(1))* Institut za politicke studije.

Pallai, Katalin. Who Decides? Development, Planning, Services, & Vulnerable Groups. 2009. pap. 32.95 *(978-963-9719-14-9(5))* Institute for Local Government & Public Service, Open Soc. Institute HUN. Dist: Books International, Inc.

Parveva, Stefka. Village, Town & People in the Ottoman Balkans, 16th-mid-19th Century. 2010. 108.44 *(978-1-61719-098-8(5))* Gorgias Pr., LLC.

Prezelj, Iztok. The Fight Against Terrorism & Crisis Management in the Western Balkans. 2008. xii, 223p. 161.00 *(978-1-58603-823-6(0))* IOS Pr., Inc.

Roth, Klaus & Hayden, Robert. Migration In, From, & to Southeastern Europe: Ways & Strategies of Migrating. 2011. 304p. pap. 49.95 ***(978-3-643-10895-1(8))*** Lit Verlag DEU. Dist: Transaction Pubs.

Roth, Klaus & Lauth Bacas, Jutta. Migration In, From, & to Southeastern Europe: Ways & Strategies of Migrating. 2011. 312p. pap. 49.95 ***(978-3-643-10896-8(6))*** Lit Verlag DEU. Dist: Transaction Pubs.

Shaqiri, Albinot. The Economic Well-Being of Albanians: Trust & Social Capital - How do Cultural Values & the Levels of Trust Affect Social Capital & the Robustne. 2008. 92p. pap. *(978-3-639-11536-9(8))* VDM Verlag Dr. Mueller e.K.

van Weenen, John. Task Force Albania. (Illus.). 280p. *(978-0-9517660-8-8(2))*; 292p. pap. *(978-0-9517660-7-1(4))* Van Weenen, John GBR. Dist: Vine Hse. Distribution.

Vitale, Ksenija, ed. Environmental & Food Safety & Security for South-East Europe & Ukraine. 2012. (NATO Science for Peace & Security Series C: Environmental Security Ser.). (ENG., Illus.). xvi, 272p. 189.00 ***(978-94-007-2952-0(9)***, 9400729529) Springer.

BALKAN QUESTION

see Eastern Question (Balkan)

BALKAN STATES

see Balkan Peninsula

BALL, LUCILLE, 1911-1989

Edwards, Elisabeth. I Love Lucy: A Celebration of All Things Lucy - Inside the World of Television's First Great Sitcom. 2011. (ENG., Illus.). 256p. 30.00 *(978-0-7624-3976-8(9))* Running Pr. Bk. Pubs.

Monush, Barry & Sheridan, James. Lucille Ball FAQ: Everything Left to Know about America's Favorite Redhead. 2011. (ENG., Illus.). 500p. pap. 19.99 *(978-1-61774-082-4(9)*, 1617740829, Applause Theatre & Cinema) Leonard, Hal Corp.

Running Press, ed. I Love Lucy: Lucy & Ricky. 2011. (ENG.). 32p. pap. 8.95 *(978-0-7624-4025-2(2))* Running Pr. Bk. Pubs.

Sanders, Coyne S. & Gilbert, Tom. Desilu: The Story of Lucille Ball & Desi Arnaz. 2011. (ENG.). 400p. pap. 16.99 *(978-0-06-202001-7(3))* HarperCollins Pubs.

BALL-BEARINGS

see also Roller Bearings

Harris, Tedric A. & Kotzalas, Michael N. Essential Concepts of Bearing Technology, 2 vols., Vol. 1. 5th rev. ed. 2006. (Rolling Bearing Analysis, Fifth Edition Ser.). (ENG., Illus.). 392p. 149.95 *(978-0-8493-7183-7(X)*, CRC Press) Taylor & Francis Group GBR. Dist: Taylor & Francis Group.

Harris Tedric a Staff. Rolling Bearing Analysis Fifth Edition - Two Volume Set, 2 vols., Vol. 2. 5th rev. ed. 2006. (Rolling Bearing Analysis, Fifth Edition Ser.). (ENG., Illus.). 760p. 229.95 *(978-0-8493-8167-6(3)*, CRC Press) Taylor & Francis Group GBR. Dist: Taylor & Francis Group.

BALL GAMES

see also Baseball; Basketball; Billiards; Bowling; Bowls (Game); Cricket; Croquet; Field Hockey; Football; Golf; Handball; Lacrosse; Polo; Racquetball; Table Tennis; Tennis; Volleyball; Water Polo

Alderson, Alf. A Load of Old Balls: Round Things to Hit, Kick, Throw, Pot, Pass, Smash & Catch. 2011. (ENG., Illus.). 160p. 14.95 ***(978-1-84818-404-6(2))*** Pitch Publishing (Brighton) Ltd. GBR. Dist: Independent Pubs. Group.

Braun, Jerry, et al. The Complete Guide to Paintball. 4th rev. ed. 2007. (Complete Guide to Paintball Ser.). (ENG., Illus.). 432p. per. 22.95 *(978-1-57826-254-0(2)*, Hatherleigh Pr.) Hatherleigh Co., Ltd., The.

Chetwynd, Josh. The Secret History of Balls: The Stories Behind the Things We Love to Catch, Whack, Throw, Kick, Bounce & Bat. 2011. (ENG., Illus.). 240p. (gr. 12). 13.95 *(978-0-399-53674-8(4)*, Perigee Trade) Penguin Group (USA) Inc.

D'Angelo, Chris. If you got the Guts, we got the Balls: A book about Dodgeball. 2008. 52p. pap. 24.95 *(978-0-615-24370-2(3))* Dangerous Chris Print.

DiSorbo, Dan & Applebaum, Ben. The Book of Beer Pong: The Official Guide to the Sport of Champions. 2009. (ENG.). 160p. 15.95 *(978-0-8118-6632-3(7))* Chronicle Bks. LLC.

Elwell, Kathy. Your Quick Reference Guide into the World of Sports. 2007. 86p. (YA). spiral bd. 18.95 *(978-0-9792279-1-2(7)*, QRG912) Elite Comfort, Inc.

Fox, John. The Ball: Discovering the Object of the Game. 2012. (P. S. Ser.). (ENG.). 400p. pap. 14.99 ***(978-0-06-188179-4(1)***, HarperPerennial) HarperCollins Pubs.

Heidi Linden, Das Ballspiel in Kult und Mythologie der Meso-Amerikanischen Völker, Band 1. (Supplement-Reihe/Supplement-Ser.). (GER.). vi, 138p. 58.00 *(978-3-615-00076-4(5))* Weidmann DEU. Dist: Lubrecht & Cramer, Ltd.

Hermann, Michael. Wiffle Ball: The Ultimate Guide. 2010. (ENG.). 160p. pap. 12.95 *(978-1-60078-361-6(9))* Triumph Bks.

Horgan, Tim. Christy Ring: Hurling's Greatest. 2008. (ENG., Illus.). 374p. 49.95 *(978-1-905172-44-3(3))* Collins Pr., The IRL. Dist: Dufour Editions, Inc.

—Christy Ring: Hurlings Greatest. 2008. (ENG., Illus.). 382p. pap. 33.95 *(978-1-905172-74-0(5))* Collins Pr., The IRL. Dist: Dufour Editions, Inc.

Martin, Henry. Unlimited Heartbreak: The Inside Story of Limerick Hurling. 2010. (ENG., Illus.). 408p. pap. 36.95 *(978-1-84889-014-5(1))* Collins Pr., The IRL. Dist: Dufour Editions, Inc.

Riegel, Ralph. Three Kings: Cork, Kilkenny, Tipperary: The Battle for Hurling Supremacy. 2008. (ENG., Illus.). 256p. 19.95 ***(978-1-84717-102-3(8))*** O'Brien Pr., Ltd., The IRL. Dist: Dufour Editions, Inc.

Strong, Todd & DeKoven, Bernie. Great Games for Big Activity Balls. 2009. (ENG., Illus.). 240p. (gr. k-6). pap. 20.00 *(978-0-7360-7481-0(3))* Human Kinetics Pubs.

BALL ROOM DANCING

see Ballroom Dancing

BALLADS

see also Folk Songs; Political Ballads and Songs

Agee, Roy. Play Ballads with a Band: Music Minus One Trombone. 2009. (ENG.). 24p. pap. 19.98 incl. audio compact disk *(978-1-59615-798-9(4)*, 1596157984) Music Minus One.

Arnold, Jeff. Jazz Ballads: Jazz Guitar Chord Melody Solos. 2006. (ENG., Illus.). 48p. pap. 14.99 *(978-1-4234-0587-0(0)*, 1423405870) Leonard, Hal Corp.

Ballades. pap. 8.00 *(978-0-7935-5974-9(X))* Leonard, Hal Corp.

Ballads from Manuscripts, Vol. 1, Pts. 1-2. (Ballad Society Ser.: Nos. 1, 2, 3 & 10). reprint ed. 57.50 *(978-0-404-50821-0(9))* AMS Pr., Inc.

Ballads from Manuscripts: A Poor Man's Pittance; Ballads Relating Chiefly to the Reign of Queen Elizabeth, Vol. 2, Parts 1-2. (Ballad Society Ser.: Nos. 1, 2, 3 & 10). reprint ed. *(978-0-404-50822-7(7))* AMS Pr., Inc.

Chart Toppers - Ballads. 18.95 *(978-1-85909-613-0(1)*, Warner Bros. Pubns.) Alfred Publishing Co., Inc.

Chen, I-Chen. Narrative in the Ballades of Fryderyk Chopin. 2009. 160p. pap. *(978-3-639-16759-7(7))* VDM Verlag Dr. Mueller e.K.

Coates, Dan. Top 50 Ballads: Easy Piano. 2011. (Top 50 Ser.). (ENG.). 196p. pap. 19.99 ***(978-0-7390-7788-7(0))*** Alfred Publishing Co., Inc.

Coates, Dan, contrib. by. The World's Most Beautiful Music. 2010. (ENG.). 148p. pap. 19.99 *(978-0-7390-6834-2(2))* Alfred Publishing Co., Inc.

Coxe, Arthur Cleveland. Christian Ballads by the Reverend Arthur Cleveland Coxe. 2007. (ENG.). 268p. 42.95 *(978-0-548-03787-4(6))* Kessinger Publishing, LLC.

Gary Moore Ballads & Blues. 21.95 *(978-1-85909-234-7(9))* Warner Chappell Music Ltd. GBR. Dist: Warner Bros. Pubns.

Gilbert, William S. More Bab Ballads. 2006. (ENG.). 144p. pap. 18.99 *(978-1-4264-0691-1(6))*; 150p. pap. 19.99 *(978-1-4264-0672-0(X))* BiblioBazaar.

Graham, Charles A. Boomer Ballads of the High North. 2011. 112p. 39.95 ***(978-1-258-07048-9(0))*** Literary Licensing, LLC.

Gummere, Francis B. The Popular Ballad. 2009. 378p. 29.99 *(978-1-113-87114-5(8))*; pap. 26.99 *(978-1-113-87112-1(1))* BiblioBazaar.

—The Popular Ballad. 2008. 374p. 48.95 *(978-1-4365-6539-4(1))* 2007. (ENG.). 376p. per. 33.95 *(978-0-548-76250-9(3))* Kessinger Publishing, LLC.

Haag, John L., proc. The Ballad Songs: Awesome Top Ten Soft Rock Including Ten #1 Songs! 2008. (Critics Choice Ser.). 128p. pap. 21.95 *(978-1-933657-51-6(0))* Professional Music Institute.

Hal Leonard Corp., creator. Contemporary Piano Repertoire - Level 4: Rock, Swing, Blues, Ballads, & More! 2010. (ENG.). 64p. pap. 9.99 *(978-1-4234-9818-6(6)*, 1423498186) Leonard, Hal Corp.

—Contemporary Piano Repertoire - Level 5: Rock, Swing, Blues, Ballads, & More! 2010. (ENG.). 80p. pap. 10.99 *(978-1-4234-9819-3(4)*, 1423498194) Leonard, Hal Corp.

—Cool Love Songs: Love Ballads from the Heart. 2010. (ENG.). 80p. pap. 12.99 *(978-1-4234-9741-7(4)*, 1423497414) Leonard, Hal Corp.

Hal Leonard Corp., creator. Disney's Fairy Tale Weddings. 2011. (ENG.). 66p. pap. 14.99 ***(978-1-4584-1327-7(6)***, 1458413276) Leonard, Hal Corp.

Hal Leonard Corporation Staff, creator. Beautiful Ballads. 2010. (E-Z Play Today Ser.: Vol. 302). (ENG.). 240p. pap. 16.99 *(978-1-4234-8653-4(6)*, 1423486536) Leonard, Hal Corp.

—Contemporary Wedding Ballads. 2010. (ENG.). 64p. pap. 16.99 incl. audio compact disk *(978-1-4234-8862-0(8)*, 1423488628) Leonard, Hal Corp.

—Inspirational Ballads: 20 Songs of Faith, Hope & Love. 2008. (ENG.). 120p. pap. 12.95 *(978-1-4234-3831-1(0)*, 1423438310) Leonard, Hal Corp.

—Inspirational Ballads: 26 Songs of Faith, Hope & Love. 2008. (ENG.). 162p. pap. 14.95 *(978-1-4234-3830-4(2)*, 1423438302) Leonard, Hal Corp.

—Inspirational Ballads: E-Z Play Today #34. 2008. (ENG.). 88p. pap. 10.95 *(978-1-4234-3832-8(9)*, 1423438329) Leonard, Hal Corp.

—Jazz Ballads. 2009. (Jazz Piano Solos Ser.: Vol. 10). (ENG.). 96p. pap. 15.99 *(978-1-4234-5915-6(6)*, 1423459156) Leonard, Hal Corp.

—Play Ballads with a Band: Music Minus One Alto Sax. 2009. (ENG.). 24p. pap. 19.98 incl. audio compact disk *(978-1-59615-797-2(6)*, 1596157976) Music Minus One.

—Play Ballads with a Band: Music Minus One Bb Trumpet. 2009. (ENG.). 24p. pap. 19.98 incl. audio compact disk *(978-1-59615-794-1(1)*, 1596157941) Music Minus One.

—Play Ballads with a Band: Music Minus One Tenor Sax. 2009. (ENG.). 24p. pap. 19.98 incl. audio compact disk *(978-1-59615-623-4(6)*, 1596156236) Music Minus One.

—Rock Ballads. 2007. (Keyboard Play-along Ser.: Vol. 6). (ENG.). 48p. pap. 14.95 incl. audio compact disk *(978-1-4234-1796-5(8)*, 1423417968) Leonard, Hal Corp.

Jewett, Sophie. Folk Ballads of Southern Europe. 2007. (ENG.). 312p. 45.95 *(978-0-548-04477-3(5))* Kessinger Publishing, LLC.

Kernis, Aaron Jay. Ballad: For Cello & Piano. 2006. pap. 12.95 *(978-1-4234-1822-1(0)*, 1423418220) Leonard, Hal Corp.

Lang, Andrew. A Collection of Ballads. 2007. 266p. pap. 21.99 *(978-1-4346-1430-8(1))*; (ENG.). 310p. pap. 24.99 *(978-1-4346-1524-4(3))* BiblioBazaar.

Maidment, James, ed. A New Book of Old Ballads. 2009. 68p. pap. 16.95 *(978-1-104-59806-8(X))* Kessinger Publishing, LLC.

Morley, Henry. A Bundle of Ballads. 2010. (Illus.). 142p. pap. 23.00 *(978-1-153-58140-0(X))* General Bks. LLC.

—A Bundle of Ballads. 2010. 268p. 34.36 *(978-1-169-30717-9(5))*; pap. 22.36 *(978-1-162-64773-9(6))*; 42.95 *(978-1-161-41638-1(2))* Kessinger Publishing, LLC.

Ogilvie, Brian. Play Ballads with a Band: For B-flat Clarinet. 2009. (ENG.). 24p. pap. 19.98 incl. audio compact disk *(978-1-59615-795-8(X)*, 159615795X) Music Minus One.

Pound, Louise. Poetic Origins & the Ballad. 2009. 260p. pap. 26.75 *(978-1-116-42017-3(1))*; pap. 27.75 *(978-1-116-42016-6(3))*; 30.99 *(978-1-116-42015-9(5))*; 34.99 *(978-1-116-42014-2(7))*; 24.99

B

(978-1-103-31401-0(7)); pap. 18.99 (978-1-103-31400-3(9)); 24.99 (978-1-103-10619-6(8)); pap. 18.99 (978-1-103-10616-5(3)) BiblioBazaar.

—Poetic Origins & the Ballad. 2009. 196p. pap. 19.99 (978-0-217-78558-7(1)) General Bks. LLC.

—Poetic Origins & the Ballad. 2007. (ENG.). 256p. 42.95 (978-0-548-15891-3(6)); per. 27.95 (978-1-4304-5413-7(X)) Kessinger Publishing, LLC.

Sanborn, Jan. Wedding Performer — Ballads for Wedding Receptions: 9 Romantic Selections for Piano Solo. 2009. (Wedding Performer Ser.). (ENG.). 40p. pap. 12.95 (978-0-7390-5187-0(3)) Alfred Publishing Co., Inc.

Taylor, Mark & Roberts, Jim, contrib. by. Classic Jazz Ballads: 10 Favorite Tunes. 2007. (Jazz Play-along Ser.). (ENG., Illus.). 48p. pap. 15.99 incl. audio compact disk (978-1-4234-2615-8(0), 1423426150) Leonard, Hal Corp.

BALLADS—BIBLIOGRAPHY

Child, Francis James. English & Scottish Ballads. 2009. 336p. 25.99 (978-1-103-85863-7(7)) 2009. 336p. pap. 19.99 (978-1-103-85855-2(6)) 2009. 484p. 28.99 (978-1-103-22010-6(1)) 2009. 484p. pap. 22.99 (978-1-103-22007-6(1)) 2009. 356p. 26.99 (978-1-103-18437-8(7)) 2009. 340p. 25.99 (978-1-103-11927-1(3)) 2009. 368p. 26.99 (978-0-559-91091-3(6)) 2009. 304p. 25.99 (978-1-103-11175-6(2)) 2009. 368p. pap. 20.99 (978-0-559-91090-6(8)) 2009. 304p. pap. 19.99 (978-1-103-11173-2(6)) 2009. 356p. pap. 20.99 (978-1-103-18435-4(0)) 2009. 340p. pap. 19.99 (978-1-103-11925-7(7)) 2008. 412p. 30.99 (978-0-559-78224-4(1)) 2008. 412p. pap. 33.75 (978-0-559-78221-3(7)) 2008. 340p. 28.99 (978-0-559-43550-8(9)) 2008. 340p. pap. 30.75 (978-0-559-43548-5(7)) 2008. 404p. 30.99 (978-0-554-51869-5(4)) 2008. 404p. 32.99 (978-0-554-51857-2(0)) 2008. 404p. pap. 33.75 (978-0-554-51867-1(8)) 2008. 404p. pap. 34.75 (978-0-554-51861-9(9)) BiblioBazaar.

—English & Scottish Ballads. 2009. 246p. pap. (978-0-217-71631-4(8)); 298p. pap. (978-0-217-71628-4(8)) Books LLC.

—English & Scottish Ballads Ed by Francis James Child. 2006. (ENG.). 356p. per. 26.99 (978-1-4255-3629-9(8)); (ENG.). 336p. per. 23.99 (978-1-4255-3396-0(5)); 488p. per. 29.99 (978-1-4255-5440-8(7)); (ENG.). 420p. per. 26.99 (978-1-4255-4599-4(8)); (ENG.). 364p. per. 26.99 (978-1-4255-3767-8(7)); (ENG.). 364p. per. 26.99 (978-1-4255-3817-0(7)); (ENG.). 332p. per. 23.99 (978-1-4255-3315-1(9)); (ENG.). 304p. per. 23.99 (978-1-4255-2892-8(9)); (ENG.). 364p. per. 26.99 (978-1-4255-3847-7(9)) MPublishing.

BALLADS—HISTORY AND CRITICISM

Gilbert, Suzanne. Ballad. 2008. 200p. 95.00 (978-0-415-22225-9(7)); pap. 21.95 (978-0-415-22226-6(5)) Routledge.

Henderson, T. F. The Ballad in Literature. 2012. (ENG.). 140p. pap. 19.99 **(978-1-107-60577-0(6))** Cambridge Univ. Pr.

McNair, Alexander J., ed. Romancero Viejo. 2006. (European Masterpieces Ser.: Vol. 23). (SPA.). 244p. (C). per. 16.95 (978-1-58977-034-8(X), ROMANCERO, European Masterpieces) LinguaText, Ltd.

Middlebrook, Leah. Imperial Lyric: New Poetry & New Subjects in Early Modern Spain. 2009. (Penn State Romance Studies). (ENG.). 176p. 60.00 (978-0-271-03517-8(X)); pap. 35.00 (978-0-271-03518-5(8)) Pennsylvania State Univ. Pr.

Vega, Gabriel Laso de la. Critical Editions of Spanish Artistic Ballads (Romanceros Artisticos) Primera Parte del Romancero y Tragedias (1587) de Gabriel Laso de la Vega. Mortenson, Barbara, ed. 2006. (SPA.). 508p. 139.95 (978-0-7734-5781-2(X)) Mellen, Edwin Pr., The.

BALLADS, AMERICAN

see also Folk Songs, American

Boersma, Susan Bentall & Martin, Joseph M. Give Me a Grateful Heart: SATB or Two-Part Mixed. 2011. 12p. pap. 1.95 **(978-1-4291-2539-0(X))** Lorenz Corp., The.

Brewster, Paul G. Ballads & Songs of Indiana. 376p. reprint ed. lib. bdg. 98.00 (978-0-7222-0377-4(2)) Library Reprints, Inc.

—Ballads & Songs of Indiana. 2007. (ENG.). 376p. per. (978-1-4067-5376-9(9)) Read Bks.

Dobie, J. Frank, ed. Follow de Drinkin' Gou'd. 2007. 204p. per. 24.95 (978-1-4325-7459-8(0)) Kessinger Publishing, LLC.

The Forget Me Not Songster. 2009. 164p. pap. (978-1-150-78600-6(0)) Books LLC.

Gaultier, Bon. The Book of Ballads. 2007. (ENG.). 336p. 45.95 (978-0-548-04336-3(1)) Kessinger Publishing, LLC.

Gaultier, Bon, ed. The Book of Ballads. 2008. 216p. 27.99 (978-0-554-56184-4(0)); 24.99 (978-0-554-56188-2(3)); pap. 24.75 (978-0-554-56185-1(9)); pap. 23.75 (978-0-554-56187-5(5)) BiblioBazaar.

Gilbert, W. S. Bab Ballads & Savoy Songs. 2007. (Illus.). 164p. per. (978-1-4065-2845-9(5)) Dodo Pr.

Jackson, George P., ed. Spiritual Folk Songs of Early America. 2008. 26.75 (978-0-8446-2297-2(4)) Smith, Peter Pub., Inc.

Lucas, Harry A. Ballads of Arizona & the Old West. 2011. 144p. 40.95 **(978-1-258-02088-0(2))** Literary Licensing, LLC.

Pound, Louise. American Ballads & Songs. 2010. (ENG.). 316p. pap. 30.75 (978-1-171-76814-2(1)) 2010. (ENG.). 316p. pap. 30.75 (978-1-176-17664-5(1)) 2009. 296p. 24.99 (978-1-103-95676-0(0)) 2009. 296p. pap. 18.99 (978-1-103-95670-8(1)) BiblioBazaar.

—American Ballads & Songs. 2009. 352p. pap. (978-1-4590-2617-9(9)) Books LLC.

—American Ballads & Songs. Pound, Louise, ed. 2010. 302p. pap. 23.16 (978-1-163-78203-3(3)) Kessinger Publishing, LLC.

Pound, Louise, ed. American Ballads & Songs. 2007. 304p. 43.95 (978-0-548-54107-4(8)); (ENG.). per. 28.95 (978-0-548-49914-6(4)) Kessinger Publishing, LLC.

Scollard, Clinton. Ballads of American Bravery. 2010. (ENG.). 246p. pap. 26.75 (978-1-176-21156-8(0)); 244p. pap. 26.75 (978-1-147-68372-1(7)); 246p. pap. 26.75 (978-1-145-53383-7(3)) BiblioBazaar.

—Ballads of American Bravery. 2009. 242p. pap. (978-0-217-17912-6(6)) Books LLC.

Scollard, Clinton, ed. Ballads of American Bravery. 2010. 244p. pap. 21.56 (978-1-163-94146-1(8)) 2008. 242p. 41.95 (978-0-548-95459-1(3)) 2007. 244p. per. 26.95 (978-0-548-62968-0(4)) Kessinger Publishing, LLC.

Thompson, Harold W., ed. A Pioneer Songster: Texts from the Stevens-Douglass Manuscript of Western New York, 1841-1856. 2011. 224p. 44.95 **(978-1-258-09910-7(1))** Literary Licensing, LLC.

Woodworth, Samuel. Melodies, Duets, Trios, Songs, & Ballads, Pastoral, Amatory, Sentimental, Patriotic, Religious, & Miscellaneous Together with Metrical Epistles. 2006. 300p. per. 23.99 (978-1-4255-2761-7(2)) MPublishing.

BALLADS, AMERICAN—HISTORY AND CRITICISM

Nelson, Scott Reynolds. Steel Drivin' Man -John Henry- The Untold Story of an American Legend. 2008. (ENG., Illus.). 224p. pap. 14.95 (978-0-19-534119-5(8)) Oxford Univ. Pr., Inc.

BALLADS, DANISH

Olrik, Axel. The Heroic Legends of Denmark. 2009. 332p. pap. (978-0-217-11769-2(4)) Books LLC.

—The Heroic Legends of Denmark. Hollander, Lee M., tr. 2007. 546p. 57.95 (978-0-548-16247-7(6)); 548p. per. 42.95 (978-1-4304-5845-6(3)) Kessinger Publishing, LLC.

BALLADS, ENGLISH

see also Folk Songs, English

Allingham, William. The Ballad Book: A Selection of the Choicest British Ballads. 2010. 408p. pap. 34.75 (978-1-148-48581-2(3)) 2010. 452p. pap. 36.75 (978-1-147-00157-0(X)) 2010. 408p. pap. 34.75 (978-1-142-69081-6(4)) 2009. 448p. 27.99 (978-0-559-92412-5(7)) 2009. 432p. 27.99 (978-0-559-92910-6(2)) 2009. 448p. pap. 21.99 (978-0-559-92409-5(7)) 2009. 432p. pap. 21.99 (978-0-559-92907-6(2)) BiblioBazaar.

—The Ballad Book: A Selection of the Choicest British Ballads. 2010. 442p. 41.56 (978-1-163-22543-1(6)); pap. 29.56 (978-1-162-79070-1(9)) Kessinger Publishing, LLC.

—The Ballad Book: A selection of the choicest British Ballads. 2010. 456p. pap. 36.75 (978-1-177-77876-3(9)) BiblioBazaar.

—The Ballad Book: A Selection of the Choicest Old Ballads. 2010. 450p. pap. 36.75 (978-1-146-12767-7(7)) BiblioBazaar.

—The Ballad Book; a Selection of the Choicest British Ballads. 2010. 450p. pap. 36.75 **(978-1-177-74387-7(6))** BiblioBazaar.

—The Ballad Book; a Selection of the Choicest British Ballads. 2010. 184p. pap. 18.01 (978-1-151-90926-8(2)) General Bks. LLC.

—The Ballad Book; a Selection of the Choicest Old Ballads. 2010. 452p. pap. 36.75 (978-1-177-93229-5(6)) BiblioBazaar.

Ashton, John. Modern Street Ballads. 2008. 424p. 30.99 (978-0-559-47861-1(5)); pap. 34.75 (978-0-559-47860-4(7)) BiblioBazaar.

—Modern Street Ballads. 2009. 276p. pap. (978-0-217-31788-7(X)) Books LLC.

—Modern Street Ballads. 456p. 2008. 52.95 (978-1-4365-9482-0(0)) 2007. per. 37.95 (978-0-548-79615-3(7)) Kessinger Publishing, LLC.

Bagford, Ballads. Bagford Ballads, 2 vols. Ebsworth, J. W., ed. (Ballad Society, London Publications: Nos. 14-17 & 20). (Illus.). reprint ed. 187.50 (978-0-404-50830-2(8)) AMS Pr., Inc.

Ballad Society. Publications of the Ballad Society, 14 vols., Set, Nos. 1-38. (Ballad Society Ser.: Nos. 1-38). reprint ed. 1315.00 (978-0-404-50820-3(0)) AMS Pr., Inc.

Belden, Henry H., ed. Ballads & Songs. 530p. reprint ed. lib. bdg. 98.00 (978-0-7222-0369-9(1)) Library Reprints, Inc.

Bell, Robert. Ancient Poems, Ballads, & Songs of the Peasantry of England. l.t. ed. 2006. (ENG.). 378p. pap. 26.99 (978-1-4264-0725-3(4)) BiblioBazaar.

Bell, Robert, ed. Ancient Poems, Ballads, & Songs of the Peasantry of England. 2007. (ENG.). 300p. per. (978-1-4065-4994-2(0)) Dodo Pr.

Buchan, David & Moreira, James, eds. The Glenbuchat Ballads. annot. ed. 2007. (ENG.). 274p. 60.00 (978-1-57806-972-9(6)) Univ. Pr. of Mississippi.

Campbell, O. D. & Sharp, C. J. English Folk Songs from the Southern Appalachians. 341p. reprint ed. lib. bdg. 98.00 (978-0-7222-4950-5(0)) Library Reprints, Inc.

Chappell, W. & Ebsworth, J. W., eds. The RoxBurghe Ballads, 8 vols., Set. reprint ed. 935.00 (978-0-404-50840-1(5)) AMS Pr., Inc.

Chappell, William. Old English Popular Music. 2009. 360p. 26.99 (978-1-103-30239-0(6)); pap. 20.99 (978-1-103-30236-9(1)) BiblioBazaar.

Child, Francis James. English & Scottish Ballads. 2009. 336p. 25.99 (978-1-103-85863-7(7)) 2009. 336p. pap. 19.99 (978-1-103-85855-2(6)) 2009. 484p. 28.99 (978-1-103-22010-6(1)) 2009. 484p. pap. 22.99 (978-1-103-22007-6(1)) 2009. 356p. 26.99 (978-1-103-18437-8(7)) 2009. 340p. 25.99 (978-1-103-11927-1(3)) 2009. 304p. 25.99 (978-1-103-11175-6(2)) 2009. 368p. 26.99 (978-0-559-91091-3(6)) 2009. 340p. pap. 19.99 (978-1-103-11925-7(7)) 2009. 356p. pap. 20.99 (978-1-103-18435-4(0)) 2009. 304p. pap. 19.99 (978-1-103-11173-2(6)) 2009. 368p. pap. 20.99 (978-0-559-91090-6(8)) 2008. 412p. 30.99 (978-0-559-78224-4(1)) 2008. 412p. pap. 33.75 (978-0-559-78221-3(7)) 2008. 340p. 28.99 (978-0-559-43550-8(9)) 2008. 340p. pap. 30.75 (978-0-559-43548-5(7)) 2008. 404p. 30.99 (978-0-554-51869-5(4)) 2008. 404p. 32.99 (978-0-554-51857-2(0)) 2008. 404p. pap. 34.75 (978-0-554-51861-9(9)) 2008. 404p. pap. 33.75 (978-0-554-51867-1(8)) BiblioBazaar.

—English & Scottish Ballads. 2009. 246p. pap. (978-0-217-71631-4(8)); 298p. pap. (978-0-217-71628-4(8)) Books LLC.

—English & Scottish Ballads Ed by Francis James Child. 2006. (ENG.). 364p. per. 26.99 (978-1-4255-3847-7(9)); (ENG.). 420p. per. 26.99 (978-1-4255-4599-4(8)); 488p. per. 29.99 (978-1-4255-5440-8(7)); (ENG.). 364p. per. 26.99 (978-1-4255-3817-0(7)); (ENG.). 336p. per. 23.99 (978-1-4255-3396-0(5)); (ENG.). 304p. per. 23.99 (978-1-4255-2892-8(9)); (ENG.). 364p. per. 26.99 (978-1-4255-3767-8(7)); (ENG.). 356p. per. 26.99 (978-1-4255-3629-9(8)); (ENG.). 332p. per. 23.99 (978-1-4255-3315-1(9)) MPublishing.

—The English & Scottish Popular Ballads. 2009. 262p. 34.99 (978-1-117-27879-7(4)); pap. 26.75 (978-1-117-27880-3(8)) BiblioBazaar.

—The English & Scottish Popular Ballads. 2009. 332p. pap. (978-1-151-47001-0(5)); 514p. pap. (978-1-151-47004-1(X)); 294p. pap. (978-1-151-47007-2(4)); 306p. pap. (978-1-151-47010-2(4)) Books LLC.

—The English & Scottish Popular Ballads, 5 vols., Vol. 4. Heiman, Mark F. & Heiman, Laura Saxton, eds. 2nd rev. ed. 2008. (ENG.). 531p. pap. 24.95 (978-0-9707020-8-1(6)) Loomis Hse. Pr.

—The English & Scottish Popular Ballads, 5 vols., Vol.5. 2nd ed. 2011. 572p. 34.95 **(978-1-935243-16-8(0))**; pap. 24.95 **(978-1-935243-15-1(2))** Loomis Hse. Pr.

Crosland, T. W. H., compiled by. English Songs & Ballads. 2007. (ENG.). 430p. pap. 26.99 (978-1-4346-5699-5(3)) BiblioBazaar.

Edwards, George Wharton. The Book of Old English Ballads. 2009. 148p. 24.99 (978-0-559-07360-1(7)); 21.99 (978-0-559-07370-0(4)); pap. 20.75 (978-0-559-07368-7(2)); pap. 21.75 (978-0-559-07363-2(1)) BiblioBazaar.

Garrett, Edmund H. Victorian Songs: Lyrics of the Affections & Nature. 2007. (ENG.). 308p. 43.95 (978-0-548-04330-1(2)) Kessinger Publishing, LLC.

Garrett, Edmund H., ed. & illus. Victorian Songs: Lyrics of the Affections & Nature. 2008. 208p. pap. (978-1-4099-4601-4(0)) Dodo Pr.

Gilbert, W. S. The Bab Ballads. 2008. 156p. 25.99 (978-0-554-21681-2(7)); 22.99 (978-0-554-30984-2(X)) BiblioBazaar.

—The Bab Ballads. 2007. 124p. per. (978-1-4065-2844-2(7)) Dodo Pr.

Greenway, John. American Folk Songs of Protest. 2011. 358p. 51.95 **(978-1-258-06822-6(2))** Literary Licensing, LLC.

Gregory, Isabella Augusta. The Kiltartan History Book. 2007. (ENG.). 76p. per. 16.95 (978-0-548-71488-1(6)) Kessinger Publishing, LLC.

Gummere, Francis Barton. Old English Ballads. 2009. 376p. pap. (978-1-4588-3560-4(X)) Books LLC.

Hale, Edward E. New England History in Ballads. 182p. reprint ed. 88.00 (978-0-7222-6405-8(4)) Library Reprints, Inc.

Hindley, Charles. The Life & Times of James Catnach, (Late of Seven Dials), Ballad Monger. 2011. (Cambridge Library Collection - Literary Studies). (ENG., Illus.). 456p. pap. 34.99 **(978-1-108-03942-0(1))** Cambridge Univ. Pr.

Huntington, Gale, ed. Sam Henry's Songs of the People. 2010. (ENG.). 672p. pap. 34.95 (978-0-8203-3625-1(4)) Univ. of Georgia Pr.

Laneham, Robert. Captain Cox, His Ballads & Books, or Robert Laneham's Letter. Furnivall, Frederick J., ed. (Ballad Society, London Publications: No. 7). reprint ed. 30.00 (978-0-404-50823-4(5)) AMS Pr., Inc.

Mackay, Charles, ed. The Cavalier Songs & Ballads of England from 1642 To 1684. 2007. 288p. per. (978-1-4065-4558-6(9)) Dodo Pr.

Mariah Carey - the Ballads. 2009. (ENG.). 106p. pap. 16.99 (978-1-4234-7451-7(1), 1423474511) Leonard, Hal Corp.

McPartland, Joe. The Ulster Reciter: Ballads, Poems & Recitations for Every Occation. 2nd rev. ed. 2008. (ENG., Illus.). 96p. pap. 12.95 (978-0-85640-829-8(8)) Blackstaff Pr., Ltd. GBR. Dist: Dufour Editions, Inc.

Paterson, Andrew Barton 'Banjo'. The Old Bush Songs. 2007. 128p. per. (978-1-4068-2319-6(8)) Echo Library.

Paterson, Andrew Barton 'Banjo', ed. The Old Bush Songs. 2007. (ENG.). 128p. per. (978-1-4065-4124-3(9)) Dodo Pr.

Percy, Thomas. Reliques of Ancient English Poetry. 2010. 426p. pap. 35.75 (978-1-144-37772-2(2)) 2008. 440p. 30.99 (978-0-559-72170-0(6)) 2008. 436p. 30.99 (978-0-559-87544-1(4)) 2008. 440p. pap. 34.75 (978-0-559-72167-0(6)) 2008. 436p. pap. 34.75 (978-0-559-87542-7(8)) 2008. 432p. 30.99 (978-0-559-52911-5(2)) 2008. 432p. pap. 34.75 (978-0-559-52910-8(4)) 2008. 492p. 31.99 (978-0-559-20462-3(0)) 2008. 492p. 31.99 (978-0-559-35401-4(0)) 2008. 492p. pap. 37.75 (978-0-559-20459-3(0)) 2008. 492p. pap. 37.75 (978-0-559-35400-7(2)) BiblioBazaar.

—Reliques of Ancient English Poetry. 2009. 394p. pap. (978-0-217-98340-2(5)); 154p. pap. (978-0-217-98343-3(X)); 322p. pap. (978-0-217-98336-5(7)); 362p. pap. (978-0-217-74959-6(3)); 326p. pap. (978-0-217-27442-5(0)); 362p. pap. (978-0-217-27447-0(1)) Books LLC.

—Reliques of Ancient English Poetry. 2009. 288p. pap. 19.99 (978-1-150-08811-7(7)); 394p. pap. 20.86 (978-0-217-98330-3(8)); 322p. pap. 19.99 (978-0-217-98334-1(0)) General Bks. LLC.

—Reliques of Ancient English Poetry V1: Consisting of Old Heroic Ballads, Songs & Other Pieces of Our Earlier Poets. Prichard, J. V., ed. 2007. 516p. 55.95 (978-0-548-18209-3(4)) Kessinger Publishing, LLC.

Percy, Thomas & Prichard, J. V. Reliques of Ancient English Poetry: Consisting of Old Heroic Ballads, Songs, & Other Pieces of Our Earlier Poets, Together with Some Few of Later Date. Prichard, J. V., ed. 2007. 520p. per. 40.95 (978-1-4304-8359-5(8)) Kessinger Publishing, LLC.

Poetry, English. Reliques of Ancient English Poetry. 2009. 388p. pap. 20.68 (978-0-217-27444-9(7)) General Bks. LLC.

Quiller-Couch, Arthur Thomas, ed. The Oxford Book of Ballads, 2 vols in 1. 800p. reprint ed. 55.00 (978-0-403-08625-2(6)) Somerset Pubs., Inc.

Robinson, Clement. A Handful of Pleasant Delights. 2009. 96p. pap. 18.95 (978-1-120-11871-4(9)) Kessinger Publishing, LLC.

Rollins, Hyder E., ed. A Pepysian Garland: Black-Letter Broadside Ballads of the Years 1595-1639 Chiefly from the Collection of Samuel Pepys. 2012. (ENG.). 526p. pap. 39.99 **(978-1-107-60775-0(2))** Cambridge Univ. Pr.

Scollard, Clinton. Ballads of Valor & Victory Being Stori. 2006. pap. 20.95 (978-1-4286-5453-2(4)) Kessinger Publishing, LLC.

Shoemaker, Henry W. North Pennsylvania Minstrelsy: As Sung in the Backwood Settlements, Hunting Cabins & Lumber Camps in Northern Pennsylvania, 1840-1910. 2011. (ENG., Illus.). 168p. pap. 22.95 (978-0-271-04881-9(6), Metalmark) Pennsylvania State Univ. Pr.

Tinsley, Jim Bob. He Was Singin' This Song: A Collection of Forty-Eight Traditional Songs of the American Cowboy, with Words, Music, Pictures, & Stories. 2nd ed. 2007. (ENG., Illus.). 244p. 50.00 incl. audio compact disk (978-1-57424-222-5(9), 1574242229); 242p. pap. 35.00 incl. audio compact disk (978-1-57424-220-1(2), 1574242202) Centerstream Publishing.

Walters, Richard, ed. Folksongs in Recital - 14 Concert Arrangements: High Voice. 2007. (ENG.). 88p. pap. 19.95 incl. audio compact disk (978-1-4234-2134-4(5), 1423421345) Leonard, Hal Corp.

—Folksongs in Recital - 14 Concert Arrangements: Low Voice. 2007. (ENG.). 88p. pap. 19.95 incl. audio compact disk (978-1-4234-2135-1(3), 1423421353) Leonard, Hal Corp.

BALLADS, ENGLISH—BIBLIOGRAPHY

Hindley, Charles. History of the Catnach Press: At Berwick-upon-Tweed, Alnwick & Newcastle-upon-Tyne, in Northumberland, & Seven Dials, London. 2010. (Cambridge Library Collection - Printing & Publishing History Ser.). (Illus.). 360p. pap. 29.99 (978-1-108-00909-6(3)) Cambridge Univ. Pr.

BALLADS, ENGLISH—HISTORY AND CRITICISM

Brown, Mary Ellen. Child's Unfinished Masterpiece: The English & Scottish Popular Ballads. 2011. (ENG., Illus.). 296p. 45.00 (978-0-252-03594-4(1)) Univ. of Illinois Pr.

Davis, John Paul, ed. Robin Hood: The Last Templar? 2009. (ENG.). 256p. pap. 23.95 (978-0-7206-1339-1(6)) Owen, Peter Ltd. GBR. Dist: Independent Pubs. Group.

de Vos, Gail. Stories from Songs: Ballads as Literary Fictions for Young Adults, 1 vol. 2008. (Illus.). 500p. pap. 45.00 (978-1-59158-424-7(8), LU4248) Libraries Unlimited, Inc.

Gregory, E. David. The Late Victorian Folksong Revival: The Persistence of English Melody, 1878-1903. 2010. (ENG., Illus.). 600p. (gr. 17). 84.00 (978-0-8108-6988-2(8)) Scarecrow Pr., Inc.

Gummere, Francis Barton. The Popular Ballad. 2009. 376p. 26.99 (978-1-103-72668-4(4)); 376p. pap. 20.99 (978-1-103-72667-7(6)); 380p. 26.99 (978-0-559-90451-6(7)); 380p. pap. 20.99 (978-0-559-90449-3(5)) BiblioBazaar.

—The Popular Ballad. 2009. 216p. pap. (978-1-4589-3180-1(3)) Books LLC.

Hodgart, M. J. C. Ballads. 2006. 208p. per. (978-1-4067-2465-3(3), Hesperides Pr.) Read Bks.

McLane, Maureen N. Balladeering, Minstrelsy, & the Making of British Romantic Poetry. 2008. (Cambridge Studies in Romanticism Ser.). (ENG., Illus.). 314p. 109.00 (978-0-521-89576-7(6)) Cambridge Univ. Pr.

Newman, Steve. Ballad Collection, Lyric, & the Canon: The Call of the Popular from the Restoration to the New Criticism. annot. ed. 2007. (Illus.). 304p. (C). 65.00 (978-0-8122-4009-2(X)) Univ. of Pennsylvania Pr.

Odell, George Clinton Densmore. Simile & Metaphor in the English & Scottish Ballads. 2008. 108p. 34.95 (978-0-548-90912-6(1)) 2007. (ENG.). 112p. per. 19.95 (978-0-548-60000-9(7)) Kessinger Publishing, LLC.

Pollard, A. J. Imagining Robin Hood: The Late-Medieval Stories in Historical Context. 2007. (ENG., Illus.). 288p. per. 27.95 (978-0-415-40493-8(2)) Routledge.

Spencer, Scott B. The Ballad Collectors of North America: How Gathering Folksongs Transformed Academic Thought & American Identity. 2012. E-Book **(978-0-8108-8156-3(X))** 2011. (ENG.). 246p. (gr. 17). 65.00 **(978-0-8108-8155-6(1))** Scarecrow Pr., Inc.

Walsh, John Evangelist. The Night Casey Was Born: The True Story Behind the Great American Ballad Casey at the Bat. 2007. (ENG., Illus.). 256p. (gr. 12). 25.00 (978-1-58567-893-8(7)) Overlook Pr., The.

Würzbach, Natascha. The Rise of the English Street Ballad, 1550-1650. Walls, Gayna, tr. from GER. 2011. (European Studies in English Literature Ser.). (ENG., Illus.). 372p. pap. 39.99 (978-0-521-17744-3(8)) Cambridge Univ. Pr.

BALLADS, FRENCH

Wilkins, Nigel, ed. One Hundred Ballades, Rondeaux & Virelais from the Late Middle Ages. 2009. (ENG.). 224p. pap. 33.99 (978-0-521-11032-7(7)) Cambridge Univ. Pr.

BALLADS, HUNGARIAN

see also Folk Songs, Hungarian

Leader, Ninon A. M. Hungarian Classical Ballads: And Their Folklore. 2010. (ENG.). 380p. pap. 36.99 (978-0-521-15786-5(2)) Cambridge Univ. Pr.

BALLADS, IRISH

see also Folk Songs, Irish

Ellis, Hercules. Romances & Ballads of Ireland. 2010. 472p. pap. 37.75 *(978-1-144-52084-5(3))* BiblioBazaar.

Gregory, Lady I. A. Kiltartan History Book. l.t. ed. 2006. pap. *(978-1-4068-3268-6(5))* Echo Library.

Hal Leonard Corporation Staff, creator. Irish Ballads. 2006. (ENG., Illus.). 144p. per. 14.95 *(978-1-4234-1137-6(4)*, 1423411374) Leonard, Hal Corp.

Mel Bay Publications Inc, creator. Great Irish Songs & Ballads, Volume 1: Piano, Vocal & Guitar Chords. 2007. (Illus.). 48p. pap. 9.95 *(978-0-7866-1596-4(6))* Mel Bay Pubns., Inc.

BALLADS, JAPANESE

see also Folk Songs, Japanese

Tamaki, Masami. Ryukyu Kayoron. 2010. (JPN.). 548p. *(978-4-7904-1206-9(7))* Sunagoya Shobo.

BALLADS, SCOTTISH

see also Folk Songs, Scots

Barnard, Anne L. Auld Robin Gray. Scott, Walter, Sr., ed. (Bannatyne Club, Edinburgh Publications: No. 9). reprint ed. 28.00 *(978-0-404-52709-9(4))* AMS Pr., Inc.

Buchan, David & Moreira, James, eds. The Glenbuchat Ballads. annot. ed. 2007. (ENG.). 274p. 60.00 *(978-1-57806-972-9(6))* Univ. Pr. of Mississippi.

Buchan, Peter. Ancient Ballads & Songs of the North of Scotland. 2009. 48p. pap. *(978-0-217-77735-3(X))* Books LLC.

—The High-Kilted Muse: Peter Buchan & His Secret Songs of Silence. Shoolbraid, Murray, ed. 2010. (ENG.). 336p. 55.00 *(978-1-60473-417-1(5))* Univ. Pr. of Mississippi.

Chambers, Robert. The Scottish Ballads. 2010. 422p. pap. 34.75 *(978-1-146-49492-2(0))*; 420p. pap. 34.75 *(978-1-145-44223-8(4))* BiblioBazaar.

Chambers, Robert, ed. The Scottish Ballads. 2007. 412p. 49.95 *(978-0-548-33074-1(0))*; per. 34.95 *(978-0-548-32420-2(4))* Kessinger Publishing, LLC.

—The Songs of Scotland Prior to Burns. reprint ed. 57.50 *(978-0-404-08627-5(6))* AMS Pr., Inc.

Child, Francis James. English & Scottish Ballads. 2009. 336p. 25.99 *(978-1-103-85863-7(7))* 2009. 336p. pap. 19.99 *(978-1-103-85855-2(6))* 2009. 484p. 28.99 *(978-1-103-22010-6(1))* 2009. 484p. pap. 22.99 *(978-1-103-22007-6(1))* 2009. 356p. 26.99 *(978-1-103-18437-8(7))* 2009. 340p. 25.99 *(978-1-103-11927-1(3))* 2009. 368p. 26.99 *(978-0-559-91091-3(6))* 2009. 304p. 25.99 *(978-1-103-11175-6(2))* 2009. 368p. pap. 20.99 *(978-0-559-91090-6(8))* 2009. 340p. pap. 19.99 *(978-1-103-11925-7(7))* 2009. 356p. pap. 20.99 *(978-1-103-18435-4(0))* 2009. 304p. pap. 19.99 *(978-1-103-11173-2(6))* 2008. 412p. 30.99 *(978-0-559-78224-4(1))* 2008. 412p. pap. 33.75 *(978-0-559-78221-3(7))* 2008. 340p. 28.99 *(978-0-559-43550-8(9))* 2008. 340p. pap. 30.75 *(978-0-559-43548-5(7))* 2008. 404p. 32.99 *(978-0-554-51857-2(0))* 2008. 404p. 30.99 *(978-0-554-51869-5(4))* 2008. 404p. pap. 34.75 *(978-0-554-51861-9(9))* 2008. 404p. pap. 33.75 *(978-0-554-51867-1(8))* BiblioBazaar.

—English & Scottish Ballads. 2009. 246p. pap. *(978-0-217-71631-4(8))*; 298p. pap. *(978-0-217-71628-4(8))* Books LLC.

—English & Scottish Ballads Ed by Francis James Child. 2006. (ENG.). 304p. per. 23.99 *(978-1-4255-2892-8(9))*; (ENG.). 332p. per. 23.99 *(978-1-4255-3315-1(9))*; (ENG.). 336p. per. 23.99 *(978-1-4255-3396-0(5))*; (ENG.). 356p. per. 26.99 *(978-1-4255-3629-9(8))*; (ENG.). 364p. per. 26.99 *(978-1-4255-3767-8(7))*; (ENG.). 364p. per. 26.99 *(978-1-4255-3817-0(7))*; (ENG.). 364p. per. 26.99 *(978-1-4255-3847-7(9))*; (ENG.). 420p. per. 26.99 *(978-1-4255-4599-4(8))*; 488p. per. 29.99 *(978-1-4255-5440-8(7))* MPublishing.

—The English & Scottish Popular Ballads. 2009. 262p. 34.99 *(978-1-117-27879-7(4))*; pap. 26.75 *(978-1-117-27880-3(8))* BiblioBazaar.

—The English & Scottish Popular Ballads. 2009. 514p. pap. *(978-1-151-47004-1(X))*; 306p. pap. *(978-1-151-47010-2(4))*; 294p. pap. *(978-1-151-47007-2(4))*; 332p. pap. *(978-1-151-47001-0(5))* Books LLC.

—The English & Scottish Popular Ballads, 5 vols., Vol. 4. Helman, Mark F. & Helman, Laura Saxton, eds. 2nd rev. ed. 2008. (ENG.). 531p. pap. 24.95 *(978-0-9707020-8-1(6))* Loomis Hse. Pr.

—The English & Scottish Popular Ballads, 5 vols., Vol.5. 2nd ed. 2011. 572p. 34.95 ***(978-1-935243-16-8(0))***; pap. 24.95 ***(978-1-935243-15-1(2))*** Loomis Hse. Pr.

Cunningham, Allan. The Songs of Scotland, Ancient & Modern. 2009. 362p. 33.99 *(978-1-116-16891-4(X))* 2009. 362p. 38.99 *(978-1-116-16890-7(1))* 2009. 362p. pap. 31.75 *(978-1-116-16893-8(6))* 2008. 380p. 29.99 *(978-0-559-73642-1(8))* 2008. 380p. pap. 32.75 *(978-0-559-73639-1(8))* BiblioBazaar.

—The Songs of Scotland, Ancient & Modern. 2009. 372p. pap. *(978-0-217-13259-6(6))*; 474p. pap. *(978-0-217-13256-5(1))*; 326p. pap. *(978-0-217-61369-9(1))*; 700p. pap. *(978-0-217-89606-1(5))*; 322p. pap. *(978-0-217-39766-7(2))* Books LLC.

—The Songs of Scotland, Ancient & Modern. 2009. 318p. pap. 19.99 *(978-1-4589-8354-1(4))* General Bks. LLC.

Hogg, James & Hogg, James. The Forest Minstrel. Garside, Peter et al, eds. 2006. (Collected Works of James Hogg Ser.). (ENG., Illus.). 420p. (gr. 17). 98.00 *(978-0-7486-2288-7(8))* Edinburgh Univ. Pr. GBR. Dist: Columbia Univ. Pr.

Maidment, James. Scottish Ballads & Songs, Historical & Traditionary. 2010. 384p. pap. 33.75 *(978-1-147-25235-4(1))*; pap. 33.75 *(978-1-142-75084-8(1))* BiblioBazaar.

—Scottish Ballads & Songs, Historical & Traditionary. 2010. (Illus.). 190p. pap. 19.99 *(978-1-154-05929-8(4))* 2009. 202p. pap. 28.66 *(978-1-151-21893-3(6))* General Bks. LLC.

Pinkerton, John. Select Scottish Ballads. 2010. 478p. pap. 37.75 *(978-1-145-27574-4(5))* BiblioBazaar.

Pinkerton, John, ed. Select Scottish Ballads, 2 vols. 2nd enl. ed. reprint ed. 20.00 *(978-0-404-08674-9(8))* AMS Pr., Inc.

Rieuwerts, Sigrid, ed. The Ballad Repertoire of Anna Gordon, Mrs Brown of Falkland. 2011. (Scottish Text Society Fifth Ser.: Volume 8). (Illus.). 354p. 60.00 *(978-1-897976-32-6(1))* Scottish Text Society GBR. Dist: Boydell & Brewer, Inc.

Scott, Walter, Sr. Minstrelsy of the Scottish Border. 2008. 344p. 29.99 *(978-0-554-24375-7(X))* 2008. 344p. 28.99 *(978-0-554-33678-7(2))*1. 2006. (ENG.). 296p. pap. 21.99 *(978-1-4264-6392-1(8))*1. 2006. (ENG.). 342p. pap. 24.99 *(978-1-4264-6466-9(5))* BiblioBazaar.

—Minstrelsy of the Scottish Border. 2008. Vol. 1. 272p. pap. *(978-1-4065-7469-2(4))* Vol. 2. 348p. pap. *(978-1-4065-7470-8(8))* Dodo Pr.

Scottish Songs, Ballads, & Popular Rhymes (ES 4-vol. Set) 2011. 1025.00 *(978-4-902454-65-9(3))* Synapse, Edition JPN. Dist: Taylor & Francis Group.

Sinclair, Charles. Scotland's Bloody Ballads. 2011. (ENG., Illus.). 96p. pap. 7.95 ***(978-1-899874-54-5(2))*** Goblinshead GBR. Dist: Dufour Editions, Inc.

BALLADS, SCOTTISH—HISTORY AND CRITICISM

Ainslie, Hew. Scottish Songs, Ballads, & Poems. 2010. (ENG.). 224p. pap. 25.75 *(978-1-177-55001-7(6))*; 212p. pap. 24.75 *(978-1-146-63967-5(8))* BiblioBazaar.

—Scottish Songs, Ballads, & Poems. 2010. (Illus.). 114p. pap. 20.49 *(978-1-150-83687-9(3))*; 72p. pap. 20.00 *(978-1-154-84166-4(9))* General Bks. LLC.

—Scottish Songs, Ballads, & Poems. 2006. 220p. per. 20.99 *(978-1-4255-1814-1(1))* MPublishing.

Brown, Mary Ellen. Child's Unfinished Masterpiece: The English & Scottish Popular Ballads. 2011. (ENG., Illus.). 296p. 45.00 *(978-0-252-03594-4(1))* Univ. of Illinois Pr.

Clyne, Norval. The Romantic Scottish Ballads & the Lady Wardlaw Heresy. 2009. 52p. pap. 16.75 *(978-1-116-88880-5(7))*; pap. 15.75 *(978-1-116-88881-2(5))* BiblioBazaar.

—The Romantic Scottish Ballads & the Lady Wardlaw Heresy. 2009. 54p. pap. 9.19 *(978-0-217-72789-1(1))* General Bks. LLC.

—The Romantic Scottish Ballads & the Lady Wardlaw Heresy. 2009. 48p. pap. 15.95 *(978-1-104-32691-3(4))* Kessinger Publishing, LLC.

Cunningham, Allan. The Songs of Scotland, Ancient & Modern. 2009. 362p. 33.99 *(978-1-116-16891-4(X))* 2009. 362p. 38.99 *(978-1-116-16890-7(1))* 2009. 362p. pap. 31.75 *(978-1-116-16893-8(6))* 2008. 380p. 29.99 *(978-0-559-73642-1(8))* 2008. 380p. pap. 32.75 *(978-0-559-73639-1(8))* BiblioBazaar.

—The Songs of Scotland, Ancient & Modern. 2009. 322p. pap. *(978-0-217-39766-7(2))*; 372p. pap. *(978-0-217-13259-6(6))*; 474p. pap. *(978-0-217-13256-5(1))*; 326p. pap. *(978-0-217-61369-9(1))*; 700p. pap. *(978-0-217-89606-1(5))* Books LLC.

—The Songs of Scotland, Ancient & Modern. 2009. 318p. pap. 19.99 *(978-1-4589-8354-1(4))* General Bks. LLC.

Gummere, Francis Barton. The Popular Ballad. 2009. 376p. 26.99 *(978-1-103-72668-4(4))*; 376p. pap. 20.99 *(978-1-103-72667-7(6))*; 380p. 26.99 *(978-0-559-90451-6(7))*; 380p. pap. 20.99 *(978-0-559-90449-3(5))* BiblioBazaar.

—The Popular Ballad. 2009. 216p. pap. *(978-1-4589-3180-1(3))* Books LLC.

Hodgart, M. J. C. Ballads. 2006. 208p. per. *(978-1-4067-2465-3(3)*, Hesperides Pr.) Read Bks.

Lang, Andrew. Sir Walter Scott & the Border Minstrelsy. 2009. 172p. 26.99 *(978-1-110-53353-4(5))*; pap. 20.75 *(978-1-110-53352-7(7))* BiblioBazaar.

—Sir Walter Scott & the Border Minstrelsy. 2009. 90p. pap. *(978-1-151-68488-2(0))* Books LLC.

—Sir Walter Scott & the Border Minstrelsy. 2007. (ENG.). 120p. per. *(978-1-4065-2647-9(9))* Dodo Pr.

—Sir Walter Scott & the Border Minstrelsy. 2008. 170p. 37.95 *(978-1-4371-9466-1(4))*; pap. 22.95 *(978-1-4370-6420-9(5))* Kessinger Publishing, LLC.

Newman, Steve. Ballad Collection, Lyric, & the Canon: The Call of the Popular from the Restoration to the New Criticism. annot. ed. 2007. (Illus.). 304p. (C). 65.00 *(978-0-8122-4009-2(X))* Univ. of Pennsylvania Pr.

Odell, George Clinton Densmore. Simile & Metaphor in the English & Scottish Ballads. 2008. 108p. 34.95 *(978-0-548-90912-6(1))* 2007. (ENG.). 112p. per. 19.95 *(978-0-548-60000-9(7))* Kessinger Publishing, LLC.

Stewart, Elizabeth. Up Yon Wide & Lonely Glen: Travellers' Songs, Stories & Tunes of the Fetterangus Stewarts. 2012. (ENG.). 305p. 70.00 ***(978-1-61703-314-8(6))***; pap. 35.00 ***(978-1-61703-308-7(1))*** Univ. Pr. of Mississippi.

BALLADS, SERBIAN

Low, David Halyburton. The Ballads of Marko Kraljevic. 2009. 158p. pap. *(978-1-151-91013-4(9))* Books LLC.

BALLADS, SPANISH

see also Folk Songs, Spanish

Díaz Roig, Mercedes. Del Romancero Hispánico. 2008. (Estudios Lingüísticos y Literarios Ser.). (SPA.). 146p. pap. 21.99 *(978-968-12-1363-3(7))* El Colegio de México, A.C., Biblioteca Miguel Cosio Villegas MEX. Dist: Fondo de Cultura Economica USA.

Garvin, Mario. Scripta Manent: Hacia una Edicion Critica Del Romancero Impreso (Siglo XVI) 2007. (SPA.). 327p. pap. 75.00 *(978-84-8489-307-3(3))* Iberoamericana Vervuert Publishing Corp.

Gaultier, Bon. The Book of Ballads. 2007. (ENG.). 336p. 45.95 *(978-0-548-04336-3(1))* Kessinger Publishing, LLC.

Gaultier, Bon, ed. The Book of Ballads. 2008. 216p. 27.99 *(978-0-554-56184-4(0))*; 24.99 *(978-0-554-56188-2(3))*; pap. 23.75 *(978-0-554-56187-5(5))*; pap. 24.75 *(978-0-554-56185-1(9))* BiblioBazaar.

Griffin, Nigel, et al, eds. The Spanish Ballad in the Golden Age. 2008. (Monografías A Ser.: Volume 264). (Illus.). 284p. 90.00 *(978-1-85566-172-1(1)*, Tamesis Bks.) Boydell & Brewer, Ltd. GBR. Dist: Boydell & Brewer, Inc.

Lockhart, J. G. Ancient Spanish Ballads; Historical & Romantic Tr by J G Lockhart, Esq. 2006. 160p. per. 18.99 *(978-1-4255-1233-0(X))* MPublishing.

McNair, Alexander J., ed. Romancero Viejo. 2006. (European Masterpieces Ser.: Vol. 23). (SPA.). 244p. (C). per. 16.95 *(978-1-58977-034-8(X)*, ROMANCERO, European Masterpieces) LinguaText, Ltd.

Middlebrook, Leah. Imperial Lyric: New Poetry & New Subjects in Early Modern Spain. 2009. (Penn State Romance Studies). (ENG.). 176p. 60.00 *(978-0-271-03517-8(X))*; pap. 35.00 *(978-0-271-03518-5(8))* Pennsylvania State Univ. Pr.

Rennert, Hugo Albert. The Spanish Pastoral Romances. 2009. 210p. 32.99 *(978-1-116-85728-3(6))*; 28.99 *(978-1-116-85729-0(4))*; pap. 23.75 *(978-1-116-85731-3(6))*; pap. 24.75 *(978-1-116-85730-6(8))* BiblioBazaar.

—The Spanish Pastoral Romances. 2009. 158p. pap. 19.99 *(978-1-151-14446-1(0))* General Bks. LLC.

Smith, C. Spanish Ballads. 2nd ed. 2008. (Spanish Texts Ser.). (SPA & ENG., Illus.). 224p. pap. 19.95 *(978-1-85399-445-6(6))* Bristol Classical Pr. GBR. Dist: International Publishers Marketing.

Vega, Gabriel Laso de la. Critical Editions of Spanish Artistic Ballads (Romanceros Artisticos) Primera Parte del Romancero y Tragedias (1587) de Gabriel Laso de la Vega. Mortenson, Barbara, ed. 2006. (SPA.). 508p. 139.95 *(978-0-7734-5781-2(X))* Mellen, Edwin Pr., The.

BALLADS, WELSH

see also Folk Songs, Welsh

Borrow, George Henry. Welsh Poems & Ballads. (Celtic Language & Literature Ser.: Goidelic & Brythonic). reprint ed. 37.50 *(978-0-404-17537-5(6))* AMS Pr., Inc.

Jones, Ffion Mair. Welsh Ballads of the French Revolution. 2012. (University of Wales Press - Wales & the French Revolution Ser.). (ENG & WEL., Illus.). 490p. pap. 40.00 ***(978-0-7083-2461-5(4))*** Univ. of Wales Pr. GBR. Dist: Chicago Distribution Ctr.

BALLANTYNE, R. M. (ROBERT MICHAEL), 1825-1894

Ballantyne, R. M. Personal Reminiscences in Book Making. 2007. (ENG.). 140p. per. *(978-1-4065-5844-9(3))* Dodo Pr.

BALLAST (SHIPS)

see also Ships—Cargo

Alexander, Jeff. Pandora's Locks: The Opening of the Great Lakes-St. Lawrence Seaway. 2009. (ENG., Illus.). 431p. 29.95 *(978-0-87013-857-7(X))* Michigan State Univ. Pr.

Committee on Assessing Numeric Limits for Living Organisms in Ballast Water & National Research Council. Assessing the Relationship Between Propagule Pressure & Invasion Risk in Ballast Water. 2011. (ENG.). 156p. pap. 37.25 ***(978-0-309-21562-6(5))*** National Academies Pr.

Discharges Incidental to the Normal Operation of a Commercial Vessel: Hearing Before the Subcommittee on Water Resources & Environment of the Committee on Transportation & Infrastructure, House of Representatives, One Hundred Tenth Congress, Second Session, June 12, 2008. 2008. xiii, 201p. *(978-0-16-083802-6(9)*, 552-070-39504-1) United States Government Printing Office

Lighthouse Press, prod. Ballast Water (90 Days) 2007. pap. 9.00 *(978-1-57785-641-2(4)*, Lighthouse Pr.) ProStar Pubns., Inc.

Wouters, Clara E., ed. Protecting the Great Lakes from Invasive & Nonindigenous Species. 2010. (Environmental Science, Engineering & Technology Ser.). 130.00 *(978-1-61728-103-7(4))* Nova Science Pubs., Inc.

BALLET

Here are entered works on the ballet. Ballet scores are entered under the heading Ballets.

see also Choreography; Pantomime

Aukhanov, Bulat. Aukhanov: Dance, Folklore & the Ballet in Kazakhstan. 2008. (Illus.). 200p. 127.50 *(978-0-7103-1384-3(5))* Kegan Paul International, Ltd. GBR. Dist: Columbia Univ. Pr.

Barth, Kathrin & Romer, Sigrid. Learning Ballet. 2007. (Learning ... Training ... Ser.). (Illus.). 152p. pap. 14.95 *(978-1-84126-224-6(2))* Meyer & Meyer Sport, Ltd. GBR. Dist: Cardinal Pubs. Group.

Bingham, Jane. Ballet. 2008. (Dance Ser.). (ENG., Illus.). 48p. (gr. 1-11). 32.00 *(978-1-4329-1374-8(3)*, NA-h) Heinemann-Raintree.

Bocharinkova, Y., et al. The Bolshoi Ballet Story. 2011. 144p. 40.95 ***(978-1-258-04915-7(5))*** Literary Licensing, LLC.

Brodovitch, Alexey, photos by. Alexey Brodovitch: Ballet. 2011. (ENG., Illus.). 142p. 39.95 *(978-1-935004-22-6(0))* Errata Editions.

Charles, Joseph & Joseph, Charles M. Stravinsky & Balanchine: A Journey of Invention. 2011. (ENG., Illus.). 464p. pap. 45.00 ***(978-0-300-17697-1(X))*** Yale Univ. Pr.

De Warren, Robert. Destiny's Waltz, in Step with Giants. 2009. 412p. 36.50 *(978-1-60860-457-9(8)*, Eloquent Bks.) AEG Literary Publishing Services, Inc.

Dixon, Melanye Young. Marion D. Cuyjet & Her Judimar School of Dance: Training Ballerinas in Black Philadelphia 1948-1971. 2011. (Illus.) 232p. 119.95 ***(978-0-7734-1592-8(0))*** Mellen, Edwin Pr., The.

Ebers, John. Seven Years of the King's Theatre. 2009. 148p. pap. *(978-1-150-28713-8(6))* Books LLC.

—Seven Years of the King's Theatre. 2010. (Illus.). 128p. pap. 21.79 *(978-1-154-84564-8(8))* General Bks. LLC.

—Seven Years of the King's Theatre. 436p. 2010. 41.56 *(978-1-163-41465-1(4))* 2010. pap. 29.56 *(978-1-162-95528-5(7))* 2007. (ENG.). 51.95 *(978-0-548-10704-1(1))* Kessinger Publishing, LLC.

Ellison, Nancy. In Classic Style: The Splendor of American Ballet Theatre. 2008. (ENG., Illus.). 240p. 50.00 *(978-0-8478-3041-1(1))* Rizzoli International Pubns., Inc.

Foster, Rory. Ballet Pedagogy: The Art of Teaching. 2010. (ENG., Illus.). 176p. pap. 26.95 *(978-0-8130-3459-1(0))* Univ. Pr. of Florida.

Hurok, S. Leningrad Kirov Ballet. 2011. 62p. 36.95 ***(978-1-258-02668-4(6))*** Literary Licensing, LLC.

Leick, Laura, IV. The World Made Flesh: The World of Literary Ballet. 2006. 256p. 30.00 *(978-0-300-11099-9(5))* Yale Univ. Pr.

Levy, Morris S. & Ward, John Milton. The King's Theatre Collection: Ballet & Italian Opera in London, 1706-1883. 2nd rev. ed. 2006. (John Milton & Ruth Neils Ward Collection, Harvard Theatre Collection). (Illus.). 553p. per. 75.00 *(978-0-9765472-2-8(8))* Harvard Univ. Pr.

Ludden, Ken. Mfab Catalog 2011-2012. 2011. 260p. pap. 24.95 ***(978-1-257-05377-3(9))*** Lulu Enterprises Inc.

Mara, Thalia. Do's & Don'ts of Ballet Center Practice. 2011. 48p. pap. 35.95 ***(978-1-258-02115-3(3))*** Literary Licensing, LLC.

McLean, Adrienne L. Dying Swans & Madmen: Ballet, the Body, & Narrative Cinema. 2008. (Na Ser.). (ENG., Illus.). 320p. per. 26.95 *(978-0-8135-4280-5(4))* Rutgers Univ. Pr.

Messerer, Asaf & Briansky, Oleg. Classes in Classical Ballet. 2007. (ENG.). 400p. pap. 20.00 *(978-0-87910-344-6(2)*, 0879103442, Limelight Editions) Leonard, Hal Corp.

Midgelow, Vida L. Reworking the Ballet: Counter Narratives & Alternative Bodies. 2007. (ENG., Illus.). 240p. (C). 33.95 *(978-0-415-97603-9(0))* Routledge.

—Reworking the Ballet: Counter-Narratives & Alternative Bodies. 2007. (Illus.). 240p. 125.00 *(978-0-415-97602-2(2))* Routledge.

Norton, Leslie & Franklin, Frederic. Frederic Franklin: A Biography of the Ballet Star. 2007. (ENG., Illus.). 235p. per. 45.00 *(978-0-7864-3051-2(6))* McFarland & Co., Inc. Pubs.

Nunn, Michael & Trevitt, Billy. Ballet Boyz. 2011. (ENG., Illus.). 96p. pap. 40.95 ***(978-1-84943-050-0(0))*** Oberon Bks., Ltd. GBR. Dist: Consortium Bk. Sales & Distribution.

Robert, Grace. The Borzoi Book of Ballets. 2007. (ENG.). 438p. 51.95 *(978-0-548-06807-6(0))* Kessinger Publishing, LLC.

Ryman, Rhonda. Foundations of Classical Ballet Technique. (Illus.). 120p. *(978-0-9524648-2-0(X))* Royal Academy of Dancing GBR. Dist: Vine Hse. Distribution.

Tchaikovsky, Peter Illich. Tchaikovsky's the Nutcracker: F Horn. 2007. (ENG.). 16p. pap. 10.95 incl. audio compact disk *(978-1-57560-966-9(5)*, 1575609665) Cherry Lane Music Co.

Turnage, Melissa. A Morning Cup of Ballet. 2009. 80p. 12.95 *(978-1-57587-299-5(4))* Crane Hill Pubs.

Uferas, Gerard. In the Company of Stars: The Paris Opera Ballet. 2007. (Illus.). 160p. 50.00 *(978-2-08-030000-3(8))* Flammarion et Cie FRA. Dist: Random Hse., Inc.

White, John, Jr. Advanced Principles in Teaching Classical Ballet. 2009. (ENG.). 200p. pap. 29.95 *(978-0-8130-3297-9(0))* Univ. Pr. of Florida.

BALLET—COSTUME

Purvis, Alston, et al, eds. The Ballets Russes & the Art of Design. 2009. (ENG., Illus.). 208p. 50.00 *(978-1-58093-254-7(1))* Monacelli Pr., Inc.

BALLET—DICTIONARIES

Grant, Gail. Technical Manual & Dictionary of Classical Ballet. 2008. 156p. pap. *(978-1-60796-031-7(1))* Editorial Benei Noaj.

BALLET—HISTORY

Birmingham Royal Ballet Staff, contrib. by. Birmingham Royal Ballet: A Cinderella Story. 2011. (ENG., Illus.). 150p. 50.00 ***(978-1-84943-097-5(7))*** Oberon Bks., Ltd. GBR. Dist: Consortium Bk. Sales & Distribution.

Burden, Michael & Thorp, Jennifer, eds. The Ballet de la Nuit: Rothschild B1/16/6. 2009. (ENG., Illus.). 360p. 86.00 *(978-1-57647-143-2(8))* Pendragon Pr.

Caddy, Davinia. The Ballets Russes & Beyond: Music & Dance in Belle-époque Paris. 2012. (New Perspectives in Music History & Criticism Ser.: 22). (ENG., Illus.). 254p. 99.00 ***(978-1-107-01440-4(9))*** Cambridge Univ. Pr.

Cowart, Georgia J. & Cowart, Georgia. The Triumph of Pleasure: Louis XIV & the Politics of Spectacle. 2008. (Illus.). 336p. 55.00 *(978-0-226-11638-9(7))* Univ. of Chicago Pr.

Dorris, George E., ed. The Royal Swedish Ballet. (Illus.). 160p. pap. 21.95 *(978-1-85273-069-7(2))* Dance Bks., Ltd. GBR. Dist: Princeton Bk. Co. Pubs.

Eliot, Karen. Dancing Lives: Five Female Dancers from the Ballet d'Action to Merce Cunningham. 2010. (ENG., Illus.). 216p. pap. 22.00 *(978-0-252-07779-1(2))* Univ. of Illinois Pr.

Fleming-Markarian, Margaret. Symbolism in Nineteenth-Century Ballet: Giselle, Coppélia, the Sleeping Beauty & Swan Lake. 2012. (ENG.). 272p. pap. 72.95 ***(978-3-0343-0267-8(3))*** Lang, Peter AG GBR. Dist: Lang, Peter.

Goldner, Nancy. Balanchine Variations. 2008. (ENG., Illus.). 160p. pap. 24.95 *(978-0-8130-3226-9(1))* Univ. Pr. of Florida.

—More Balanchine Variations. 2011. (ENG., Illus.). 160p. pap. 24.95 *(978-0-8130-3753-0(0))* Univ. Pr. of Florida.

Grammeniati, Barbara. Seventeenth-Century Ballet a Multi-Art Spectacle. 2011. 132p. 29.99 ***(978-1-4568-8198-6(1))***; pap. 19.99 ***(978-1-4568-8197-9(3))*** Xlibris Corp.

Guest, Ivor F. Adventures of a Ballet Historian. 2011. (Illus.). 132p. ***(978-0-903102-69-8(2))*** Dance Bks., Ltd.

Günsür Yüceil, Zeynep. Modernization Through Dancing Bodies in Turkey. 2010. 360p. pap. *(978-3-8383-4931-2(8))* Lambert Academic Publishing.

Homans, Jennifer. Apollo's Angels: A History of Ballet. (ENG., Illus.). 672p. 2011. pap. 20.00 *(978-0-8129-6874-3(3)*, Random Hse. Trade Paperbacks) 2010. 40.00 *(978-1-4000-6060-3(5)*, Random House) Random House Publishing Group.

Hurok, Sol. S Hurok Presents: A Memoir of the Dance World. 2011. 368p. 53.95 ***(978-1-258-02292-1(3))*** Literary Licensing, LLC.

Jones, E. Michael. Ballet Parking: Performing the Nutcracker as Counter-Revolutionary Act. 2009. (ENG.). 29.00 *(978-0-929891-08-8(2))* Fidelity Pr.

Kant, Marion, ed. The Cambridge Companion to Ballet. 2007. (Cambridge Companions to Music Ser.). (ENG., Illus.). 394p. 101.00 *(978-0-521-83221-2(7))*; pap. 29.99 *(978-0-521-53986-9(2))* Cambridge Univ. Pr.

Lieven, Peter. The Birth of Ballets-Russes. 2010. (Illus.). 377p. pap. ***(978-1-906830-23-6(1))*** Noverre Pr., The.

Martens, Frederick H. The Book of the Opera & the Ballet & the History of the Opera. reprint ed. 37.50 *(978-0-404-18857-3(5))* AMS Pr., Inc.

Nye, Edward. Mime, Music & Drama on the Eighteenth-Century Stage: The Ballet D'action. 2011. (ENG., Illus.). 344p. 99.00 *(978-1-107-00549-5(3))* Cambridge Univ. Pr.

O'Brien, Victoria. A History of Irish Ballet, 1927-1963. 2011. (Reimagining Ireland Ser.). (ENG.). 208p. pap. 55.95 *(978-3-03911-873-1(0))* Lang, Peter GmbH, Europaischer Verlag der Wissenschaften DEU. Dist: Lang, Peter.

Pawlick, Catherine E. Vaganova Today: The Preservation of Pedagogical Tradition. 2011. (ENG., Illus.). 208p. 29.95 *(978-0-8130-3697-7(6))* Univ. Pr. of Florida.

Poll, Heinz. A Time to Dance: The Life of Heinz Poll. Poll, Heinz & Schubert, Barbara, eds. 2008. (Ohio History & Culture Ser.). (ENG., Illus.). 212p. pap. 19.95 *(978-1-931968-52-2(7))* Univ. of Akron Pr., The.

Poll, Heinz & Schubert, Barbara, eds. A Time to Dance: The Life of Heinz Poll. 2008. (Ohio History & Culture Ser.). (Illus.). 212p. 29.95 *(978-1-931968-51-5(9))* Univ. of Akron Pr., The.

Roca, Octavio. Cuban Ballet, 1 vol. 2010. (ENG., Illus.). 240p. 40.00 *(978-1-4236-0758-8(9))* Gibbs Smith, Publisher.

Scheijen, Sjeng. Diaghilev: A Life, 1 vol. 2010. (ENG., Illus.). 560p. 39.95 *(978-0-19-975149-5(8))* Oxford Univ. Pr., Inc.

Siegel, Marcia B. Mirrors & Scrims: The Life & Afterlife of Ballet. 2010. (ENG., Illus.). 416p. (C). lib. bdg. 85.00 *(978-0-8195-6875-5(9))*; pap. 27.95 *(978-0-8195-6926-4(7))* Wesleyan Univ. Pr.

Sistenich, Frank & Theobald, Christine. Malakhov's Sleeping Beauty. 2007. (ENG.). 160p. 50.00 *(978-3-7957-0557-2(6)*, 3795705576) Schott Music Corp.

Slonimsky, Juri. The Soviet Ballet. *(978-0-8022-1587-1(4))* Philosophical Library, Inc.

Smith, Marian. Ballet & Opera in the Age of Giselle. 2010. (Princeton Studies in Opera Ser.). (ENG., Illus.). 288p. (C). pap. 27.95 *(978-0-691-14649-2(7))* Princeton Univ. Pr.

Stoneley, Peter. A Queer History of the Ballet. 2006. (Illus.). 206p. per. 35.95 *(978-0-415-97280-2(9))*; 120.00 *(978-0-415-97279-6(5))* Routledge.

Vaughan, David. Frederick Ashton & His Ballets. 2nd ed. (Illus.). 570p. 59.95 *(978-1-85273-062-8(5))* Princeton Bk. Co. Pubs.

Volynsky, Akim. Ballet's Magic Kingdom: Selected Writings on Dance in Russia, 1911-1925. Rabinowitz, Stanley J., ed. (ENG., Illus.). 352p. 2010. pap. 23.00 *(978-0-300-16449-7(1))* 2008. 35.00 *(978-0-300-12462-0(7))* Yale Univ. Pr.

BALLET—JUVENILE LITERATURE

Cady, Jennifer. Jose Limon. 2006. (High-Interest Ser.). (ENG.). 48p. (gr. 5-8). pap. 11.75 *(978-1-4042-0643-4(4)*, Rosen Classroom Bks. & Materials) Rosen Publishing Group, Inc., The.

BALLET—STAGE-SETTING AND SCENERY

Purvis, Alston, et al, eds. The Ballets Russes & the Art of Design. 2009. (ENG., Illus.). 208p. 50.00 *(978-1-58093-254-7(1))* Monacelli Pr., Inc.

BALLET DANCERS

see Dancers

BALLET DANCING

Franchi, Cristina, ed. Kenneth MacMillan at the Royal Opera House. 2006. (Illus.). 136p. pap. 40.00 *(978-1-84002-623-8(5))* Oberon Bks., Ltd. GBR. Dist: Consortium Bk. Sales & Distribution.

Hammond, Sandra Noll. Ballet: Beyond the Basics. 2011. (Illus.). 154p. (C). pap. 24.95 *(978-1-57766-718-6(2))* Waveland Pr., Inc.

Hecht, Thom. Emotionally Intelligent Ballet Training- Facilitating Emotional Intelligence in Vocational Dance Training. 2007. 224p. per. *(978-3-8364-4495-8(X))* VDM Verlag Dr. Mueller e.K.

Laws, Kenneth. Physics & the Art of Dance: Understanding Movement. 2nd ed. 2008. (ENG., Illus.). 288p. pap. 39.95 *(978-0-19-534101-0(5))* Oxford Univ. Pr., Inc.

Lille, Dawn. Equipoise: The Life & Work of Alfredo Corvino. 2009. 24.95 *(978-1-4358-9124-1(4))* Rosen Publishing Group, Inc., The.

Mara, Thalia. So You Want to Be a Ballet Dancer. 2011. 178p. 42.95 ***(978-1-258-04193-9(6))*** Literary Licensing, LLC.

Neufeld, James. Passion to Dance: The National Ballet of Canada. 2011. (ENG., Illus.). 480p. 50.00 *(978-1-4597-0121-2(6))* Dundurn CAN. Dist: Ingram Pub. Services.

O'Connor, Eileen. Flexing for Ballet. 2011. 54p. 36.95 ***(978-1-258-02130-6(7))*** Literary Licensing, LLC.

Papa, Lisa. Boutique Tutu Instructions. 2007. 40p. per. 21.99 *(978-1-4257-9599-3(4))* Xlibris Corp.

Reece, Kim Taylor. Eternal Dance. 2006. 204p. 55.00 *(978-1-59779-028-4(1))* Reece, Kim Taylor Prodns. LLC.

Sanchez, Ricardo B. Bullfight: The Pas de Seux. 2012. (ENG.). 176p. 60.00 ***(978-0-9832702-1-8(X))*** Glitterati, Inc.

Savino, Jo. Jo Savino a Dream, Love & Dedication: Dancing on Four Continents. 2011. 168p. pap. 46.49 *(978-1-4567-3296-7(X))* AuthorHouse.

Serrebrenikov, Nicolai & Lawson, Joan. Art of Pas de Deux. 2011. (Illus.). 84p. pap. ***(978-0-903102-84-1(6))*** Dance Bks., Ltd.

Sistenich, Frank & Theobald, Christine. Malakhov's Sleeping Beauty. 2007. (ENG.). 160p. 50.00 *(978-3-7957-0557-2(6)*, 3795705576) Schott Music Corp.

Speer, Dean. On Technique. 2010. (ENG., Illus.). 288p. 29.95 *(978-0-8130-3438-6(8))* Univ. Pr. of Florida.

Stanwood, Tamara. Classical Ballet: Combinations for Ten Complete Advanced Classes. 2009. 92p. pap. 20.00 *(978-0-557-09319-9(8))* Lulu Enterprises Inc.

Storelli, Patricia. The Magic Pointe Shoes. 2011. 372p. pap. 25.95 ***(978-1-60594-691-7(5)***, Llumina Pr.) Aeon Publishing Inc.

White, John, Jr. Advanced Principles in Teaching Classical Ballet. 2009. (ENG.). 200p. pap. 29.95 *(978-0-8130-3297-9(0))* Univ. Pr. of Florida.

BALLET DANCING—WOUNDS AND INJURIES

see Dancing Injuries

BALLETS

Betly: Opera Comica in One Act. 2011. (Critical Edition of the Operas of Gaetano Donizetti: Operas Ser.). (Illus.). 650p. 400.00 *(978-88-7592-888-9(6))* Casa Ricordi ITA. Dist: Chicago Distribution Ctr.

Copland, Aaron. Aaron Copeland: Suite from the Appalachian Spring in Six Movements: For Violin & Piano. 2007. 34p. per. 16.95 *(978-1-4234-2984-5(2)*, 1423429842) Leonard, Hal Corp.

—Appalachian Spring Suite. 2007. (ENG.). 28p. pap. 14.95 *(978-1-4234-5476-2(6)*, 1423454766) Boosey & Hawkes, Inc.

—Appalachian Spring Suite: For Violin & Piano. 2007. (ENG.). 36p. pap. 16.95 *(978-1-4234-5184-6(8)*, 1423451848) Boosey & Hawkes, Inc.

—Ballet Music for Piano. 2011. (ENG.). 144p. pap. 19.99 *(978-1-61780-548-6(3)*, 1617805483) Boosey & Hawkes, Inc.

Fox, Daniel, ed. Worlds Greatest Orchestra Opera Ballet. 2006. (World's Greatest Ser.). (ENG.). 128p. pap. 16.95 *(978-0-7390-4379-0(X))* Alfred Publishing Co., Inc.

Grammeniati, Barbara. Filippo d'Agliè's Ballets (1604-1667) 2011. 188p. pap. 34.30 *(978-1-4567-7317-5(8))* AuthorHouse.

Joseph, Charles M. Stravinsky's Ballets. (Yale Music Masterworks Ser.). 2012. (Illus.). 320p. 40.00 *(978-0-300-11872-8(4))* 2011. *(978-83-00-11872-4(1))* Yale Univ. Pr.

Legris, Manuel. Romeo & Juliet - Paris Opera & Ballet - Blu-ray. 2010. 39.99 *(978-0-7697-8952-1(8)*, Kultur) Kultur International Films.

Pritchard, Jane & Marsh, Geoffrey, eds. Diaghilev & the Golden Age of the Ballet Russes 1909-1929. 2010. (ENG., Illus.). 240p. 55.00 *(978-1-85177-613-9(3))* V & A Pubns. GBR. Dist: Hachette Bk. Group.

Scheijen, Sjeng. Diaghilev: A Life, 1 vol. 2012. (ENG., Illus.). 560p. pap. 27.95 ***(978-0-19-989178-8(8))*** Oxford Univ. Pr., Inc.

Tchaikovsky, Peter Illich. Tchaikovsky's the Nutcracker: Alto Sax. 2007. (Play along (Cherry Lane Music) Ser.). (ENG.). 16p. pap. 10.95 incl. audio compact disk *(978-1-57560-968-3(1)*, 1575609681) Cherry Lane Music Co.

—Tchaikovsky's the Nutcracker: Clarinet. 2007. (ENG.). 16p. pap. 10.95 incl. audio compact disk *(978-1-57560-960-7(6)*, 1575609606) Cherry Lane Music Co.

—Tchaikovsky's the Nutcracker: Flute. 2007. (ENG.). 16p. per. 10.95 *(978-1-57560-953-9(3)*, 1575609533) Cherry Lane Music Co.

—Tchaikovsky's the Nutcracker: Tenor Sax. 2007. (ENG.). 16p. pap. 10.95 incl. audio compact disk *(978-1-57560-961-4(4)*, 1575609614) Cherry Lane Music Co.

—Tchaikovsky's the Nutcracker: Trombone. 2007. (ENG.). 16p. pap. 10.95 incl. audio compact disk *(978-1-57560-967-6(3)*, 1575609673) Cherry Lane Music Co.

—Tchaikovsky's the Nutcracker: Trumpet. 2007. (ENG.). 16p. pap. 10.95 incl. audio compact disk *(978-1-57560-965-2(7)*, 1575609657) Cherry Lane Music Co.

—Tchaikovsky's the Nutcracker: Viola. 2007. (ENG.). 16p. pap. 10.95 incl. audio compact disk *(978-1-57560-963-8(0)*, 1575609630) Cherry Lane Music Co.

Tchaikovsky, Peter Ilyich. The Nutcracker Suite Teacher's Handbook: A Mini-Musical Based on Tchaikovsky's Famous Ballet for Unison & 2-Part Voices. 2007. (ENG., Illus.). 52p. pap. 34.99 *(978-0-7390-4541-1(5))* Alfred Publishing Co., Inc.

—Tchaikovsky's the Nutcracker: Cello. 2007. (Play along (Cherry Lane Music) Ser.). (ENG.). 16p. pap. 10.95 incl. audio compact disk *(978-1-57560-964-5(9)*, 1575609649) Cherry Lane Music Co.

—Tchaikovsky's the Nutcracker: Violin. 2007. (ENG.). 16p. pap. 10.95 incl. audio compact disk *(978-1-57560-962-1(2)*, 1575609622) Cherry Lane Music Co.

Temin, Christine. Behind the Scenes at Boston Ballet. 2009. (ENG., Illus.). 240p. 34.00 *(978-0-8130-3353-2(5))* Univ. Pr. of Florida.

Townley, Wyatt. Kansas City Ballet. 2007. pap. 29.95 *(978-1-933466-43-9(X))* Kansas City Star Bks.

Tregulova, Zelfira & Bowlt, John E., eds. A Festival of Wonders: Serghei Diaghilev & the Ballets Russes. 2009. (ENG., Illus.). 320p. 60.00 *(978-88-572-0090-3(6))* Skira Editore ITA. Dist: Random Hse., Inc.

BALLETS—SCORES

Edwards, Matthew, ed. The Nutcracker Suite, Op. 71a. 2009. (ENG.). 48p. pap. 12.99 incl. audio compact disk *(978-1-4234-5800-5(1)*, 1423458001, G Schirmer, Inc.) Leonard, Hal Corp.

Khachaturian, Aram. Adagio from Spartacus. 2009. (ENG.). 12p. pap. 4.99 *(978-1-4234-6276-7(9)*, 1423462769, G Schirmer, Inc.) Leonard, Hal Corp.

—Selected Piano Works Vol. 2085. 2010. (ENG.). 64p. pap. 12.99 *(978-1-4234-9020-3(7)*, 1423490207, G Schirmer, Inc.) Leonard, Hal Corp.

Leonard, Hal. Suite from the Ballet - Homage to the Queen Op. 42a 1953: Study Score. 2010. (ENG.). 112p. pap. 63.00 *(978-1-84938-400-1(2)*, 1849384002) Novello & Co.

Schmidt, Johann Christoph. Johann Christoph Schmidt: Chaconne from les quatre Saisons. Goebel, Reinhard, ed. 2011. pap. 15.00 net. *(978-0-89579-697-4(X))* A-R Editions, Inc.

Tchaikovsky, Peter Illich. Tchaikovsky's the Nutcracker Suite: Stylish Arrangements from the Holiday Classic. 2007. (ENG.). 40p. pap. 9.95 *(978-1-4234-3167-1(7)*, 1423431677) Leonard, Hal Corp.

BALLETS—STORIES, PLOTS, ETC.

Angus, David. Ballet Stories: Swan Lake, Coppelia, Sleeping Beauty, Nutcracker, Giselle. 2007. (Junior Classics (Playaway) Ser.). (J). 34.99 *(978-1-59895-983-3(2))* Findaway World, LLC.

Krokover, Rosalyn. The New Borzoi Book of Ballets. 2011. 384p. 53.95 ***(978-1-258-08609-1(3))*** Literary Licensing, LLC.

Maynard, Olga. The Ballet Companion. 2011. 176p. 42.95 ***(978-1-258-04352-0(1))*** Literary Licensing, LLC.

Thibodeaux, Kathy. A Christmas Dream. 2007. (Illus.). 68p. (J). 25.00 *(978-0-9799864-0-6(0))* Magnificat! Publishing Co.

BALLIN, ALBERT, 1857-1918

Huldermann, Bernhard. Albert Ballin (German Edition) 2009. (ENG.). 336p. 36.99 *(978-1-117-56420-3(7))*; pap. 30.75 *(978-1-117-56421-0(5))* BiblioBazaar.

—Albert Ballin (German Edition) 2008. 420p. 49.95 *(978-1-4369-9689-1(9))*; pap. 34.95 *(978-1-4367-6325-7(8))* Kessinger Publishing, LLC.

BALLISTIC MISSILES

see also Fleet Ballistic Missile Weapons Systems; Intercontinental Ballistic Missiles

also names of specific missiles

American Foreign Policy Council, creator. Missile Defenses & American Security 2004: The International Dimension. 2008. (ENG.). 60p. pap. 20.99 *(978-0-7618-3988-0(7))* Univ. Pr. of America, Inc.

Azure, Kevin C., ed. Sea-Based Ballistic Missile Defense: Background & Issues. 2010. (Defense, Security & Strategy Ser.). ix, 102p. pap. 43.00 *(978-1-60741-982-2(3))* Nova Science Pubs., Inc.

Blank, Stephen J. Russia & Arms Control: Are There Opportunities for the Obama Administration? 2009. pap. *(978-1-58487-381-5(7))* Strategic Studies Institute, U.S. Army War College Commandant (AWCC-DSI/Pubns.).

Boord, Warren & Hoffman, John B. Air & Missile Defense Systems Engineering. 2012. (ENG., Illus.). 240p. 129.95 *(978-1-4398-0670-8(5)*, CRC Press) Taylor & Francis Group GBR. Dist: Taylor & Francis Group.

Bormann, Natalie. National Missile Defence & the Politics of US Identity: A Poststructural Critique. 2008. (ENG.). 192p. 89.00 *(978-0-7190-7470-7(3))* Manchester Univ. Pr. GBR. Dist: Macmillan.

Boyes, John. Project Emily: Thor IRBM & the RAF. 2008. (ENG., Illus.). 192p. pap. 42.95 *(978-0-7524-4611-0(8))* History Pr. Ltd., The GBR. Dist: Independent Pubs. Group.

Breaking the Cycle of North Korean Provocations: Hearing Before the Committee on Foreign Relations, United States Senate, One Hundred Twelfth Congress, First Session, March 1, 2011. 2011. iii, 80p. ***(978-0-16-089623-1(1)***, 552-070-43512-3) United States Government Printing Office.

Burns, Richard Dean. The Missile Defense Systems of George W. Bush: A Critical Assessment, 1 vol. 2010. (Praeger Security International Ser.). (Illus.). 198p. 44.95 *(978-0-313-38466-0(5)*, A2925C, Praeger Pubs.) Greenwood Publishing Group, Inc.

Buteux, Paul. The Politics of Nuclear Consultation in NATO, 1965-1980. 2011. (LSE Monographs in International Studies). (ENG.). 308p. pap. 24.99 *(978-0-521-15482-6(0))* Cambridge Univ. Pr.

Butler, Jeffrey T. The Influence of Politics, Technology, & Asia on the Future of US Missile Defense. 2007. (Illus.). xiv, 81p. pap. *(978-1-58566-167-1(8))* Air University Pr.

Carpenter, Lee. Memoirs of a Cold Warrior: The Struggle for Nuclear Parity. 2009. 33.95 *(978-0-87586-703-8(0))*; pap. 23.95 *(978-0-87586-702-1(2))* Algora Publishing.

Cimbala, Stephen & Cimbala, Stephen J. Shield of Dreams: Missile Defense & U.S.-Russian Nuclear Strategy. 2008. (Illus.). 256p. 48.00 *(978-1-59114-116-7(8))* Naval Institute Pr.

—Shield of Dreams: Missile Defense in US & Russian Nuclear Strategy. 2008. 256p. pap. 24.00 *(978-1-59114-117-4(6))* Naval Institute Pr.

Congressional Budget Office (U.S.), compiled by. Options for Deploying Missile Defenses in Europe. 2009. (ENG., Illus.). 82p. pap. 15.00 *(978-0-16-082738-9(8)*, Congressional Budget Office) United States Government Printing Office.

Do the United States & Europe Need a Missile Defense System? Joint Hearing Before the Subcommittee on Europe & the Subcommittee on Terrorism, Nonproliferation, & Trade of the Committee on Foreign Affairs, House of Representatives, One Hundred Tenth Congress, First Session, May 3, 2007. 2007. v, 30p. *(978-0-16-079046-1(8)*, 552-070-36152-9) United States Government Printing Office.

Dominguez, Jayden A. & Moreno, Benjamin T. U. S. Prompt Global Strike Mission Options. 2011. (Defense, Security & Strategies Ser.). 95.00 ***(978-1-62100-047-1(8))*** Nova Science Pubs., Inc.

Fergusson, James G. Canada & Ballistic Missile Defence, 1954-2009: Déjà Vu All over Again. 2010. (ENG., Illus.). 352p. (C). pap. 37.95 *(978-0-7748-1751-6(8))* Univ. of British Columbia Pr. CAN. Dist: Univ. of Washington Pr.

Francis, Paul. Defense Acquisitions: Missile Defense Agency Fields Initial Capability but Falls Short of Original Goals. 2006. (Illus.). 84p. (C). pap. 25.00 *(978-1-4223-0710-6(7))* DIANE Publishing Co.

—Defense Acquisitions: Missile Defense Needs a Better Balance between Flexibility & Accountability: Congressional Testimony. 2007. 14p. (C). pap. 15.00 *(978-1-4223-1548-4(7))* DIANE Publishing Co.

The Future of Missile Defense Testing: Hearing Before the Strategic Forces Subcommittee of the Committee on Armed Services, House of Representatives, One Hundred Eleventh Congress, First Session, Hearing Held, February 25, 2009. 2010. (Illus.). iv, 164p. *(978-0-16-086279-3(5)*, 552-070-41370-7) United States Government Printing Office.

Future Roles & Missions of the Missile Defense Agency: Hearing Before the Strategic Forces Subcommittee of the Committee on Armed Services, House of Representatives, One Hundred Eleventh Congress, First Session, Hearing Held, March 26, 2009. 2010. iii, 81p. *(978-0-16-085913-7(1)*, 552-070-41109-7) United States Government Printing Office.

Gallais, Patrick. Atmospheric Re-Entry Vehicle Mechanics. (ENG., Illus.). xxii, 354p. 2010. pap. 109.00 *(978-3-642-09281-7(0)*, 3642092810) 2007. 109.00 *(978-3-540-73646-2(8)*, 3540736468) Springer.

Gormley, Dennis. Missile Contagion. 2010. 0288p. pap. 21.95 *(978-1-59114-332-1(2))* Naval Institute Pr.

Gormley, Dennis M. Missile Contagion: Cruise Missile Proliferation & the Threat to International Security, 1 vol. 2008. (Praeger Security International Ser.). (Illus.). 272p. 54.95 *(978-0-275-99836-3(3)*, C9836, Praeger Security International) Greenwood Publishing Group, Inc.

Han, Zipeng. Dan Jian Wai Dan Dao Xue. 2008. (CHI., Illus.). *(978-7-5640-1618-0(3))* Beijing Institute of Technology Pr.

Hearing on National Defense Authorization ACT for Fiscal Year 2008 & Oversight of Previously Authorized Programs Before the Committee on Armed Services, House of Representatives, One Hundred Tenth Congress, First Session: Strategic Forces Subcommittee Hearing on Budget Request for Missile Defense Programs, Hearing Held, March 27, 2007. 2008. iii, 122p. *(978-0-16-082020-5(0)*, 552-070-38181-3) United States Government Printing Office.

Hearing on National Defense Authorization ACT for Fiscal Year 2009 & Oversight of Previously Authorized Programs Before the Committee on Armed Services, House of Representatives, One Hundred Tenth Congress, Second Session: Strategic Forces Subcommittee Hearing on Budget Request for Missile Defense Programs, Hearing Held, April 17, 2008. 2009. (Illus.). iii, 130p. *(978-0-16-083867-5(3)*, 552-070-39562-8) United States Government Printing Office.

Hey, Nigel. The Star Wars Enigma: Behind the Scenes of the Cold War Race for Missile Defense. 2006. (Illus.). 288p. 27.95 *(978-1-57488-981-9(8))* Potomac Bks., Inc.

Holden, Simon R. North Korea's Nuclear & Ballistic Weapons. 2010. (Weapons of Mass Destruction Ser.). 117p. pap. 43.00 *(978-1-60876-844-8(9))* Nova Science Pubs., Inc.

Hughes, Christopher W. Japan's Security Policy & Ballistic Missile Defence. 2006. (Sheffield Centre for Japanese Studies/Routledge Ser.). 216p. 150.00 *(978-0-415-29888-9(1)*, RU25483) Taylor & Francis Group.

Issues Affecting Naval Force Structure: Hearing Before the Seapower & Expeditionary Forces Subcommittee of the Committee on Armed Services, House of Representatives, One Hundred Eleventh Congress, Second Session, Hearing Held January 20, 2010. 2010. (Illus.). iii, 98p. ***(978-0-16-086884-9(X)***, 552-070-41794-0) United States Government Printing Office.

Kaufmann, J. E. Fortress America: The Forts That Defended America, 1600 to the Present. 2007. (ENG., Illus.). 416p. per. 22.95 *(978-0-306-81550-8(8))* Da Capo Pr., Inc.

Miller, Debra A. Nuclear Armament. 2011. ***(978-0-7377-6113-9(X))***; pap. ***(978-0-7377-6114-6(8))*** Cengage Gale. (Greenhaven Pr., Inc.).

Owenstein, Joshua A., ed. Iran: Social, Economic & Political Developments. 2010. (Politics & Economics of the Middle East Ser.). 115.00 *(978-1-60741-552-7(6))* Nova Science Pubs., Inc.

Peoples, Columba. Justifying Ballistic Missile Defence: Technology, Security & Culture. 2009. (Cambridge Studies in International Relations Ser.). (ENG.). 318p. 85.00 *(978-0-521-11329-8(6))*; pap. 33.00 *(978-0-521-13041-7(7))* Cambridge Univ. Pr.

Pinkston, Daniel A. The North Korean Ballistic Missile Program. 2008. (Demystifying North Korea Ser.). lib. bdg. *(978-1-58487-342-6(6))* Strategic Studies Institute, U.S. Army War College Commandant (AWCC-DSI/Pubns.).

Polmar, Norman & Norris, Robert S. The U. S. Nuclear Arsenal: A History of Weapons & Delivery Systems since 1945. 2009. (Illus.). 240p. 49.95 *(978-1-55750-681-8(7))* Naval Institute Pr.

The President's Decision on Missile Defense in Europe: Hearing Before the Committee on Armed Services, United States Senate, One Hundred Eleventh Congress, First Session, September 24, 2009. 2010. iii, 94p. *(978-0-16-085291-6(9)*, 552-070-40630-1) United States Government Printing Office.

Report on the Ballistic Missile Defense Review & the Fiscal Year 2011 National Defense Authorization Budget Request for Missile Defense Programs: Hearing Before the Subcommittee on Strategic Forces of the Committee on Armed Services, House of Representatives, One Hundred Eleventh Congress, Second Session, Hearing Held April 15, 2010. 2010. iii, 111p. ***(978-0-16-087226-6(X)***, 552-070-42064-9) United States Government Printing Office.

Sauer, Tom. Eliminating Nuclear Weapons: The Role of Missile Defence. 2011. (Columbia/Hurst Ser.). (ENG.). 224p. (gr. 17). 30.00 *(978-0-231-70266-9(3))* Columbia Univ. Pr.

Scobell, Andrew & Sanford, John M. North Korea's Military Threat: Pyongyang's Conventional Forces, Weapons of Mass Destruction, & Ballistic Missiles. 2007. (Demystifying North Korea Ser.). pap. *(978-1-58487-286-3(1))* Strategic Studies Institute, U.S. Army War College Commandant (AWCC-DSI/Pubns.).

Simons, Jason D. Nuclear Weapons Policy. 2011. (Series: Weapons of Mass Destruction Ser.). pap. 43.00 *(978-1-61122-007-0(6))*, Nova Science Pubs., Inc.

Staples, Steven. Missile Defence: Round One. 2006. (ENG., Illus.). 248p. pap. *(978-1-55028-929-9(2))* Lorimer, James & Co., Ltd., Pubs. CAN. Dist: Casemate Pubs. & Bk. Distributors, LLC.

United States, Congress House Committee on Armed Services Strategic Forces Subcommittee Staff, contrib. by. Hearings on National Defense Authorization ACT for Fiscal Year 2006 & Oversight of Previously Authorized Programs Before the Committee on Armed Services, House of Representatives, One Hundred Ninth Congress, First Session: Strategic Forces Subcommittee Hearing on Budget Request for Missile Defense Programs, Hearing Held March 15, 2005. 2007. iii, 144p. *(978-0-16-077933-6(2)*, 552-070-35368-2) United States Government Printing Office.

Van Riper, A. Bowdoin. Rockets & Missiles: The Life Story of a Technology. 2007. (ENG., Illus.). 192p. (C). (gr. 13-17). per. 21.95 *(978-0-8018-8792-5(5))* Johns Hopkins Univ. Pr.

What Are the Prospects? What Are the Costs? Oversight of Ballistic Missile Defense (Part 2): Hearing Before the Subcommittee on National Security & Foreign Affairs of the Committee on Oversight & Government Reform, House of Representatives, One Hundred Tenth Congress, Second Session, April 16, 2008. 2009. (Illus.). iii, 130p. *(978-0-16-083393-9(0)*, 552-070-39206-8) United States Government Printing Office.

Wilson, Jim. Launch Pad Uk. 2009. (Illus.). 208p. 39.99 *(978-1-84415-799-0(7))* Pen & Sword Bks. Ltd. GBR. Dist: Casemate Pubs. & Bk. Distributors, LLC.

Zarchan, Paul. Tactical & Strategic Missile Guidance. 5th ed. 2007. (Progress in Astronautics & Aeronautics Ser.). (Illus.). 888p. *(978-1-56347-874-1(9))* American Institute of Aeronautics & Astronautics.

BALLISTICS

see also Gunnery

Baker, Ernest & Templeton, Douglas, eds. Ballistics 2011: 26th International Symposium on Ballistics. 2011. (Illus.). 2226p. 319.50 ***(978-1-60595-052-5(1))*** DEStech Pubns., Inc.

Ballistic Resistance of Body Armor. 2009. 78p. pap. 49.00 *(978-1-60692-295-8(5))* Nova Science Pubs., Inc.

Ballistics '95: 15th International Symposium on Ballistics, 3 vols., Set. Incl. Vol. 1. pap. *(978-0-9618156-0-8(4))*; Vol. 2. pap. *(978-0-9618156-1-5(2))*; Vol. 3. pap. *(978-0-9618156-2-2(0))*; (Illus.). 1995. 300.00 *(978-0-9618156-4-6(7))* American Defense Preparedness Assn.

Brebbia, Carlos A. & Motta, A. A., eds. Computational Ballistics III. 2007. (WIT Transactions on Modelling & Simulation Ser.: 45). (Illus.). 256p. 165.00 *(978-1-84564-077-4(2))* WIT Pr GBR. Dist: WIT Pr.

Bredsten, George B. Handgun Bullet Stopping Power: Beyond the Hyperbole of Cartridge Advocacy. 2008. (Illus.). 212p. pap. *(978-1-926585-03-1(8)*, CCB Publishing) CCB Publishing.

Broyles, Janell. Careers in Ballistics Investigation. 2008. (Careers in Forensics Ser.). (Illus.). 64p. lib. bdg. 29.25 *(978-1-4042-1345-6(7))* Rosen Publishing Group, Inc., The.

Burstein, Joseph. Precise Numerical Analysis for Nonlinear Dynamics: Basic Problem of Exterior Ballistics & Primary Problem of Celestial Mechanics. 2007. (Illus.). v, 94p. *(978-0-9765949-4-9(3))* Metrics Pr.

Carlucci, Donald E. & Jacobson, Sidney S. Ballistics: Theory & Design of Guns & Ammunition. 2007. (ENG., Illus.). 512p. 149.95 *(978-1-4200-6618-0(8)*, CRC Press) Taylor & Francis Group GBR. Dist: Taylor & Francis Group.

Chambers, G. Paul. Head Shot. 2012. (ENG., Illus.). 260p. pap. 18.00 ***(978-1-61614-561-3(7))*** Prometheus Bks., Pubs.

Chambers, G. Paul. Head Shot: The Science Behind the JFK Assassination. 2010. (ENG., Illus.). 240p. 25.00 ***(978-1-61614-209-4(X))*** Prometheus Bks., Pubs.

Denny, Mark. Their Arrows Will Darken the Sun: The Evolution & Science of Ballistics. 2011. (ENG., Illus.). 248p. (gr. 17). 65.00 *(978-0-8018-9856-3(0))*; pap. 30.00 *(978-0-8018-9857-0(9))* Johns Hopkins Univ. Pr.

Forker, Bob. Ammo & Ballistics 4 — For Hunters, Shooters, & Collectors: Ballistic Data Out to 1,000 Yards for over 169 Calibers & over 2,400 Different Loads — Includes Data on Centerfire & Rimfire Cartridges for All Handguns & Rifles. 4th ed. 2009. (ENG.). 440p. pap. 26.95 *(978-1-57157-345-2(3))* Safari Pr., Inc.

Gurstelle, William. Backyard Ballistics: Build Potato Cannons, Paper Match Rockets, Cincinnati Fire Kites, Tennis Ball Mortars, & More Dynamite Devices. 2nd ed. 2012. (ENG.). 240p. pap. 16.95 ***(978-1-61374-064-4(6))*** Chicago Review Pr., Inc.

Haag, Michael G. & Haag, Lucien C. Shooting Incident Reconstruction. 2nd ed. 2011. (ENG.). 440p. 99.95 *(978-0-12-382241-3(6)*, Academic Pr.) Elsevier Science & Technology Bks.

Hall, A. R. Ballistics in the Seventeenth Century: A Study in the Relations of Science & War with Reference Principally to England. 2009. (ENG.). 204p. pap. 29.99 *(978-0-521-11650-3(3))* Cambridge Univ. Pr.

Halstead, Tom. Reduced Load Ballistics Research Manual. 2011. pap. 12.95 ***(978-0-7414-6516-0(7))*** Infinity Publishing.

Klimi, Gjergj. Exterior Ballistics of Small Arms. 2009. 280p. 29.99 *(978-1-4415-0602-3(0))*; pap. 19.99 *(978-1-4415-0601-6(2))* Xlibris Corp.

Kneubuehl, Beat P., ed. Wound Ballistics: Basics & Applications. 2011. (ENG., Illus.). 500p. 229.00 *(978-3-642-20355-8(8)*, 3642203558) Springer.

Meloan, Clifton E., et al. Lab Manual for Criminalistics: An Introduction to Forensic Science. 10th ed. 2010. (ENG.). 352p. (C). pap. 83.60 *(978-0-13-509944-5(7)*, Prentice Hall) Prentice Hall PTR.

Meyers, Charles. Silent Evidence. 2007. per. 19.95 *(978-1-59712-099-9(5))* Catawba Publishing Co.

Pejsa, Arthur J. New Exact Small Arms Ballistics: The Source Book for Riflemen. 2008. (Illus.). 220p. 24.95 *(978-0-9749902-6-2(4))* Kenwood Publishing.

Rosenberg, Zvi & Dekel, Erez. Terminal Ballistics. 2012. (ENG., Illus.). xiii, 323p. 129.00 ***(978-3-642-25304-1(0)***, 3642253040) Springer.

Technology Research Editors, ed. Advanced Materials for Ballistic Protection, 2007 Ed. 2007. pap. 128.50 *(978-1-60030-205-3(X)*, Search-In-Print) CSA Journal Division.

van Zwoll, Wayne. The Shooter's Bible Guide to Rifle Ballistics. 103rd ed. 2011. (ENG., Illus.). 224p. pap. 19.95 *(978-1-61608-224-6(0)*, 608224) Skyhorse Publishing Co., Inc.

West, David. Detective Work with Ballistics. (Graphic Forensic Science Ser.). 48p. (gr. 5-5). 2009. (ENG.). (YA). 58.50 *(978-1-61512-950-8(2)*, Rosen Central) 2008. (Illus.). per. 14.05 *(978-1-4042-1435-4(6))* 2008. (ENG., Illus.). (YA). lib. bdg. 29.25 *(978-1-4042-1434-7(8))* Rosen Publishing Group, Inc., The.

BALLOON ANGIOPLASTY

see Transluminal Angioplasty

BALLOON ASCENSIONS

Marion, Fulgence. Wonderful Balloon Ascents. 2009. 158p. pap. *(978-1-4589-5237-0(1))* Books LLC.

McConnell, Thomas S. Balloon Safety Seminars. 2009. pap. 20.00 *(978-1-890689-45-2(9)*, Rio Grande Bks.) LPD Pr.

Wilkinson, Alec. The Ice Balloon: S. A. Andrée & the Heroic Age of Arctic Exploration. 2012. (ENG., Illus.). 256p. 25.95 ***(978-0-307-59480-8(7)***, Knopf) Knopf Doubleday Publishing Group.

Yeatman, John. Daffodil & Golden Eagle. (Illus.). 165p. reprint ed. 19.95 *(978-0-89388-110-8(4))* Okpaku Communications Corp.

BALLOONING

Balloon Flying Handbook. 2007. (Illus.). 128p. per. 12.95 *(978-1-60239-069-0(X))* Skyhorse Publishing Co., Inc.

Crouch, Tom D. Lighter Than Air: An Illustrated History of Balloons & Airships. 2009. (ENG., Illus.). 192p. 37.00 *(978-0-8018-9127-4(2))* Johns Hopkins Univ. Pr.

Dutcher, Russell K. Union Army Balloon Corps: Operations During the War of the Rebellion, 1861-1863. 2009. (Illus.). xx, 186p. *(978-0-7884-8062-1(6))*; 206p. pap. 22.00 *(978-0-7884-4785-3(8))* Heritage Bks.

Kotar, S. I. & Gessler, J. E. Ballooning: A History, 1782-1900. 2010. (ENG., Illus.). 303p. pap. 45.00 *(978-0-7864-4941-5(1))* McFarland & Co., Inc. Pubs.

Lynn, Michael R. The Sublime Invention: Ballooning in Europe, 1783-1820, 1 vol. 2010. (Enlightenment World Ser.). (ENG., Illus.). 256p. 99.00 *(978-1-84893-016-2(X))* Pickering & Chatto Pubs., Ltd. GBR. Dist: Ashgate Publishing Co.

Magni, Roberto & Comi, Daniela, photos by. Hot Air Balloons: History, Evolution & Great Adventures. 2011. (ENG., Illus.). 304p. 39.95 *(978-88-544-0489-2(6))* White Star ITA. Dist: Sterling Publishing Co., Inc.

McConnell, Thomas S. Balloon Safety Seminars. 2009. pap. 20.00 *(978-1-890689-45-2(9)*, Rio Grande Bks.) LPD Pr.

National Monuments Record (England) Staff, contrib. by. Mata Hari's Glass Eye & Other Stories: Pioneers of Aerial Photography. 2007. (Illus.). 20p. 50.00 *(978-1-905624-01-0(8))* English Heritage GBR. Dist: Brown, David Bk. Co., The.

Rolt, L. T. C. The Balloonists: The History of the First Aeronauts. 2006. (ENG., Illus.). 272p. per. 19.95 *(978-0-7509-4202-7(9))* Sutton Publishing.

Vesely, Kim, et al. The World Comes to Albuquerque: The Dream Takes Flight Celebrating 40 Years of the Albuquerque International Balloon Fiesta. 2011. *(978-1-890689-76-6(9))*; pap. *(978-1-890689-97-1(1))* LPD Pr. (Rio Grande Bks.).

BALLOONS

see also Aeronautics; Airships; Balloon Ascensions; Hot Air Balloons

Balloons. Date not set. 64p. 5.98 *(978-1-4054-0320-7(9))* Parragon, Inc.

Müller, Ingo & Strehlow, Peter. Rubber & Rubber Balloons: Paradigms of Thermodynamics. 2010. (Lecture Notes in Physics Ser.). (ENG., Illus.). viii, 123p. pap. 89.95 *(978-3-642-05782-3(9)*, 3642057829) Springer.

BALLOONS—HISTORY

Bacon, J. M. The Dominion of the Air. 2007. 176p. per. *(978-1-4068-2382-0(1))* Echo Library.

Crouch, Tom D. Lighter Than Air: An Illustrated History of Balloons & Airships. 2009. (ENG., Illus.). 192p. 37.00 *(978-0-8018-9127-4(2))* Johns Hopkins Univ. Pr.

Rev. J. M. Bacon. The Dominion of the Air: The Story of Aerial Navigation. 2006. (ENG.). 252p. pap. 21.99 *(978-1-4264-0067-4(5))* BiblioBazaar.

BALLOONS, DIRIGIBLE

see Airships

BALLOU, ADIN, 1803-1890

Ballou, Adin. Autobiography of Adin Ballou, 1803-1890. 2009. 418p. pap. *(978-0-217-44223-7(4))* Books LLC.

—Autobiography of Adin Ballou 1803-1890: Containing an Elaborate. Heywood, William Sweetzer, ed. 2007. pap. 44.95 *(978-1-4304-4930-0(6))* Kessinger Publishing, LLC.

BALLOU, HOSEA, 1771-1852

Ballou, Maturin Murray. Biography of Rev Hosea Ballou. 2007. (ENG.). 406p. 49.95 *(978-0-548-14938-6(0))*; 408p. per. 34.95 *(978-1-4304-4247-9(6))* Kessinger Publishing, LLC.

—Biography of Rev Hosea Ballou by His Youngest Son, Maturin M Ballou. 2006. 412p. per. 26.99 *(978-1-4255-4479-9(7))* MPublishing.

BALLROOM DANCING

see also names of individual dances, e.g. Tango (Dance); Waltz

Allen, Jeffrey. Ballroom Dancing - The Complete Idiot's Guide. 2nd ed. 2006. (Complete Idiot's Guide Ser.). (ENG., Illus.). 304p. (gr. 12-18). 24.95 *(978-1-59257-577-0(3)*, Alpha Bks.) Penguin Group (USA) Inc.

Baker, Kele & Schiller, Ralf. Strictly Come Dancing: Dance Yourself Fit with the Beginner's Guide to All the Dances from the Show. 2009. (ENG., Illus.). 112p. pap. 18.95 *(978-1-84607-765-4(6))* BBC Worldwide GBR. Dist: Independent Pubs. Group.

Balbuena Gutiérrez, Bárbara. El Casino y la Salsa en Cuba. 2008. (Illus.). 139p. *(978-959-10-0997-5(6))* Books on Demand GmbH.

Bottomer, Paul. Ballroom Dancing. 2012. (ENG., Illus.). 264p. pap. 17.99 ***(978-1-78019-130-0(8))*** Anness Publishing GBR. Dist: National Bk. Network.

Bottomer, Paul. Ballroom Dancing Step-by-Step: Learn to Waltz, Quickstep, Foxtrot, Tango & Jive in over 400 Easy-to-Follow Colour Photographs & Diagrams. 2006. (ENG., Illus.). 96p. pap. 8.99 *(978-1-84476-276-7(9))* Anness Publishing GBR. Dist: National Bk. Network.

C/o Ssp, Shane. Easy & Elementary Ballroom Dancing: Where Boys Become Gentlemen & Girls Become Ladies. 2007. (Illus.). 130p. (J). spiral bd. 19.99 *(978-0-9764570-3-9(2))* Skull Stone Publishing.

Causey, Gregory. Dancing with Natasha. 2007. pap. 16.00 *(978-1-934446-00-3(9))* Romance Divine LLC.

Classen, Bonnie. Willowbrook Ballroom. 2011. (Images of America Ser.). (ENG., Illus.). 128p. pap. 21.99 ***(978-0-7385-8399-0(5))*** Arcadia Publishing.

Durang, Charles. Fashionable Dancers Casket or the BallRo. 2006. (Illus.). 192p. per. *(978-1-4067-9535-6(6)*, Pomona Pr.) Read Bks.

Ericksen, Julia. Dance with Me: Ballroom Dancing & the Promise of Instant Intimacy. 2011. (ENG., Illus.). 294p. 27.95 ***(978-0-8147-2266-4(0))*** New York Univ. Pr.

Ericksen, Julia A. Dance with Me: Ballroom Dancing & the Promise of Instant Intimacy. 2011. E-Book ***(978-0-8147-2285-5(7))***; E-Book ***(978-0-8147-2298-5(9))*** New York Univ. Pr.

Eyer, Richard C. Marriage Is Like Dancing. 2007. (Illus.). 175p. pap. 15.49 *(978-0-7586-1302-8(4))* Concordia Publishing Hse.

Giordano, Ralph G. Satan in the Dance Hall: Rev. John Roach Straton, Social Dancing, & Morality in 1920s New York City. 2008. (ENG.). 304p. pap. 60.00 *(978-0-8108-6146-6(1))* Scarecrow Pr., Inc.

—Social Dancing in America: A History & Reference, 2 vols. 2006. (Illus.). 808p. 149.95 *(978-0-313-33756-7(X)*, GR3756, Greenwood Pr.) Greenwood Publishing Group, Inc.

—Social Dancing in America Volume One Fair Terpsichore to the Ghost Dance, 1607-1900: A History & Reference, 2 vols. 2006. (Illus.). 358p. 85.00 *(978-0-313-33403-0(X)*, GR3403, Greenwood Pr.) Greenwood Publishing Group, Inc.

—Social Dancing in America Volume Two Lindy Hop to Hip Hop, 1901-2000: A History & Reference, 2 vols. 2006. (Illus.). 403p. 85.00 *(978-0-313-33352-1(1)*, GR3352, Greenwood Pr.) Greenwood Publishing Group, Inc.

Golden, Eve. Vernon & Irene Castle's Ragtime Revolution. 2007. (ENG., Illus.). 360p. 40.00 *(978-0-8131-2459-9(X))* Univ. Pr. of Kentucky.

Hansmann, Arthur J. Ballroom & Latin Dancing for Today: A Dissertation & Instruction in Choreography & Technique. 2007. (Illus.). vi, 220p. *(978-1-60461-139-7(1))* Culter, Robert Bks.

Hodge, Susie. Latin & Ballroom. 2008. (Dance Ser.). (ENG., Illus.). 48p. (gr. 1-11). 32.00 *(978-1-4329-1377-9(8)*, NA-h) Heinemann-Raintree.

Horwood, Craig Revel. Ballroom Dancing. 2011. (Teach Yourself Ser.). (ENG., Illus.). 302p. pap. 19.95 *(978-1-4441-0273-4(7)*, Hodder & Stoughton) Hodder General Publishing Div. GBR. Dist: Independent Pubs. Group.

Hughes, Maureen. The Pocket Guide to Ballroom Dancing. 2010. (Illus.). 192p. pap. 19.95 *(978-1-84468-082-5(7))* Pen & Sword Bks. Ltd. GBR. Dist: Casemate Pubs. & Bk. Distributors, LLC.

Katalin, Lányi. Same-Sex Ballroom Dance - a Challenge to Patriarchal Gender Order. 2008. 56p. pap. *(978-3-639-01298-9(4))* VDM Verlag Dr. Mueller e.K.

Kerr, Gordon. Old Time & Sequence Dances - Descriptions Standardised by the Official Board of Ballroom Dancing. 2007. 76p. per. *(978-1-4067-8862-4(7)*, Pomona Pr.) Read Bks.

Knowles, Mark. The Wicked Waltz & Other Scandalous Dances: Outrage at Couple Dancing in the 19th & Early 20th Centuries. 2009. (ENG., Illus.). 272p. pap. 39.95 *(978-0-7864-3708-5(1))* McFarland & Co., Inc. Pubs.

Maloney, Alison, ed. Strictly Come Dancing 2009. annuals 2008. (ENG., Illus.). 128p. 24.95 *(978-1-84607-611-4(0))* BBC Worldwide GBR. Dist: Independent Pubs. Group.

Marion, Jonathan S. Ballroom: Culture & Costume in Competitive Dance. 2008. (Dress, Body, Culture Ser.). (ENG., Illus.). 224p. 109.95 *(978-1-84520-799-1(8))*; pap. 39.95 *(978-1-84520-800-4(5))* Berg Pubs. GBR. Dist: Macmillan.

McMains, Juliet E. Glamour Addiction: Inside the American Ballroom Dance Industry. 2006. (Illus.). xvii, 245p. *(978-0-8195-6775-8(2))* Wesleyan Univ. Pr.

McMains, Juliet E. & McMains, Juliet. Glamour Addiction: Inside the American Ballroom Dance Industry. 2006. (ENG., Illus.). 268p. 29.95 *(978-0-8195-6774-1(4))* Wesleyan Univ. Pr.

Moore, Alex. Ballroom Dancing. 2008. 324p. *(978-1-4437-3443-1(8)*, Pomona Pr.) Read Bks.

Mouvet, Maurice. Maurice's Art of Dancing. 2009. 56p. pap. *(978-0-217-23342-2(2))* Books LLC.

Munday, John S. Beauty in Partnership. 2011. 180p. pap. 14.95 *(978-0-615-46112-0(3))* MAW Pr.

Murray, Arthur. Arthur Murray's Let's Dance. 2011. 82p. 37.95 ***(978-1-258-01368-4(1))*** Literary Licensing, LLC.

—Ballroom Dancing. 2011. 80p. 37.95 ***(978-1-258-01327-1(4))*** Literary Licensing, LLC.

—The Modern Dances: Advanced Course, Parts 2-3. 2011. 64p. 36.95 ***(978-1-258-05404-5(3))*** Literary Licensing, LLC.

Murray, Johann P. C. Dancing Like a Star: 32 Ballroom Dance Lessons. rev. ed. 2010. (ENG.). 350p. pap. 79.00 *(978-0-7575-8596-8(5))* Kendall Hunt Publishing Co.

Raurell, Lydia. The Year of Dancing Dangerously: One Woman's Journey from Beginner to Winner. 2008. (ENG.). 160p. (gr. 12). 24.95 *(978-1-59020-127-5(2))* Overlook Pr., The.

Rosanova, Angela M. Ballroom Dancing Made Easy: Dance Your Way to Better Health & Social Recognition. 2011. 138p. 40.95 ***(978-1-258-06828-8(1))*** Literary Licensing, LLC.

Rose, Jamie. Shut up & Dance! The Joy of Letting Go of the Lead on the Dance Floor & Off. 2011. (ENG.). 240p. (gr. 12). 16.95 *(978-1-58542-889-2(2)*, Tarcher) Penguin Group (USA) Inc.

Silvester, Victor. Modern Ballroom Dancing. 2008. 172p. pap. *(978-1-4097-2656-2(8))* Read Bks.

—Theory & Technique of Ballroom Dancing. 2008. 192p. *(978-1-4437-3645-9(7)*, Hesperides Pr.) Read Bks.

Simon, Jaimee. Learn & Master Ballroom Dancing. 2010. (ENG.). 75p. pap. 149.00 incl. audio compact disk *(978-0-9774004-3-0(3)*, 0977400433) Legacy Learning Systems, Inc.

Tanaka, Patrice. Becoming Ginger Rogers: How Ballroom Dancing Made Me a Happier Woman, Better Partner, & Smarter CEO. 2011. (ENG., Illus.). 288p. pap. 14.95 *(978-1-936661-03-9(9))* BenBella Bks.

Tourville, Tom & Peters, Rebecca. Remembering Okoboji: The Rock & Roll Years. 2010. (Illus.). 90p. 14.99 *(978-0-578-05560-2(0))* Midwest Pubns.

White, Geogina. Light Fantastic: Dance Floor Courtship in New Zealand. 2007. (Illus.). 207p. pap. *(978-1-86950-619-3(7))* HarperCollins Pubs. Australia.

Williams, Jeffrey C. Home of Happy Dancers: A Pictorial Scrapbook History of Bridgeport, Connecticut's Ritz Ballroom. 2011. ***(978-1-57864-722-4(3))*** Donning Co. Pubs.

Zona, Christine & George, Chris. Gotta Ballroom. 2008. (ENG., Illus.). 224p. 27.95 *(978-0-7360-5907-7(5))* Human Kinetics Pubs.

BALLROOM DANCING—GREAT BRITAIN

Goodman, Len. Better Late Than Never: From Barrow Boy to Ballroom. 2009. (ENG., Illus.). 336p. pap. 15.95 *(978-0-09-192803-2(6))* Ebury Publishing GBR. Dist: Independent Pubs. Group.

—Better Late Than Never: My Story. 2008. (ENG., Illus.). 320p. 29.95 *(978-0-09-192802-5(8))* Ebury Publishing GBR. Dist: Independent Pubs. Group.

BALLS (SPORTING GOODS)

see also Golf Balls

Berke, Kai-Lee, et al. The Creative Curriculum for Preschool Teaching Guide Featuring the Balls Study. 2010. *(978-1-60617-383-1(9))* Teaching Strategies, Inc.

—El Currículo Creativo para Educación Preescolar Guía de Enseñanza Estudio de Las Pelotas, Bolas y Balones. 2012. (SPA & ENG.). *(978-1-60617-410-4(X))* Teaching Strategies, Inc.

Chetwynd, Josh. The Secret History of Balls: The Stories Behind the Things We Love to Catch, Whack, Throw, Kick, Bounce & Bat. 2011. (ENG., Illus.). 240p. (gr. 12). 13.95 *(978-0-399-53674-8(4)*, Perigee Trade) Penguin Group (USA) Inc.

FunSway. BALL,CUP & ME. 2008. 194p. pap. 39.95 *(978-0-557-03789-6(1))* Lulu Enterprises Inc.

Knight, Lucy. Exercise Ball for Weight Loss. 2011. (ENG., Illus.). 144p. (gr. k-2). pap. 19.95 ***(978-0-85783-011-1(2))*** Kyle Bks. GBR. Dist: National Bk. Network.

Strong, Todd & DeKoven, Bernie. Great Games for Big Activity Balls. 2009. (ENG., Illus.). 240p. (gr. k-6). pap. 20.00 *(978-0-7360-7481-0(3))* Human Kinetics Pubs.

BALOCH

see Baluchi (Southwest Asian People)

BALOCHI LANGUAGE

see Baluchi Language

BALSAM FIR

Bakuzis, E. V. & Hansen, H. L. Balsam Fir: A Monographic Review. 2009. (ENG.). 468p. pap. 60.00 *(978-0-8166-5701-8(7))* Univ. of Minnesota Pr.

BALTHUS, 1908-2001

Blocklehurst, John, et al. Balthus: Works, Interviews. 2008. (ENG., Illus.). 160p. 45.00 *(978-84-343-1165-7(8))* Poligrafa, Ediciones, S. A. ESP. Dist: D.A.P./Distributed Art Pubs.

Rewald, Sabine, ed. Balthus: Time Suspended: Paintings & Drawings 1932-1960. 2007. (Illus.). 163p. 79.95 *(978-3-8296-0321-8(5))* Schirmer/Mosel Verlag GmbH DEU. Dist: Prestel Publishing.

Shinoyama, Kishin. Balthus - Das Haus des Malers. The Painter's House: Baltus im Grand Chalet. Baltus at the Grand Chalet. 2007. 104p. pap. 19.95 *(978-3-8296-0320-1(7))* Schirmer/Mosel Verlag GmbH DEU. Dist: Prestel Publishing.

BALTIC LANGUAGES

see also Latvian Language; Lithuanian Language

Ewels, Andrea-Eva. Areallinguistik und Sprachtypologie im Ostseeraum: Die phonologisch relevante Vokal- und Konsonantenquantität. 2009. (Studien in nordeuropäischer und baltischer Linguistik. Studies in North European & Baltic Linguistics Ser.). (GER.). 266p. 67.95 *(978-3-631-57786-8(9))* Lang, Peter GmbH, Europäischer Verlag der Wissenschaften DEU. Dist: Lang, Peter.

Icon Group International, Inc. Staff, compiled by. The 2009-2014 World Outlook for Parts & Attachments for Small Household Electric Appliances. 2008. 544p. ring bd. 28.95 incl. audio compact disk *(978-0-497-83573-6(8))* Icon Group International, Inc.

Kortlandt, Frederik. Baltica & Balto-Slavica. 2009. (Illus.). 456p. 126.00 *(978-90-420-2652-0(9))* Rodopi.

Kortlandt, Frederik. Selected Writings on Slavic & General Linguistics. 2011. (ENG., Illus.). 484p. 144.00 ***(978-90-420-3363-4(0))*** Rodopi.

Olander, Thomas. Balto-Slavic Accentual Mobility. 2009. (Trends in Linguistics. Studies & Monographs [TiLSM] Ser.). (ENG.). XI, 274p. 123.00 *(978-3-11-020397-4(9))*; 196.00 ***(978-3-11-173247-3(9))*** De Gruyter, Mouton DEU. Dist: de Gruyter, Walter GmbH & Co. KG.

Petit. Untersuchungen zu den baltischen Sprachen. 2010. (Brill's Studies in Indo-European Languages & Linguistics Ser.). (GER.). 340p. *(978-90-04-17836-6(8))* BRILL.

Pronk, Tijmen & Derksen, Rick, eds. Accent Matters: Papers on Balto-Slavic Accentology. 2011. (Illus.). 373p. 104.00 *(978-90-420-3332-0(0))* Rodopi.

BALTIC MYTHOLOGY

see Mythology, Baltic

BALTIC PEOPLES

see Balts (Indo-European People)

BALTIC QUESTION

see Baltic States

BALTIC REPUBLICS

see Baltic States

BALTIC SEA

BACC Author Team. Assessment of Climate Change for the Baltic Sea Basin. 2010. (Regional Climate Studies). (Illus.). xxii, 474p. pap. 309.00 *(978-3-642-09189-6(X)*, 364209189X) Springer.

BACC Author Team, creator. Assessment of Climate Change for the Baltic Sea Basin. 2008. (Regional Climate Studies). (Illus.). 473p. 309.00 *(978-3-540-72785-9(X))* Springer.

Bes, Lennart & Frankot, Edda, eds. Baltic Connections: Archival Guide to the Maritime Relations of the Countries around the Baltic Sea (including the Netherlands) 1450-1800, 3 vols., Set. 2007. (Northern World Ser.). 2415p. *(978-90-04-16429-1(4))* BRILL.

Blomqvist, E. M., et al, eds. Biological, Physical & Geochemical Features of Enclosed & Semi-enclosed Marine Systems. 2011. (Developments in Hydrobiology Ser.). (ENG., Illus.). 296p. pap. 189.00 *(978-90-481-5250-6(X)*, 904815250X) Springer.

Dablin, Guy-Paul. Escapades Maritimes en Scandinavie - les Secrets de la Mer Baltique. 2010. 66p. pap. *(978-1-899820-95-5(7))* Paragon Publishing, Rothersthorpe.

Engberg, Nils. Archaeology of Medieval Towns in the Baltic & North Sea Area. 2009. (Illus.). 218p. 42.00 *(978-87-7602-131-3(9))* Univ. Pr. of Southern Denmark DNK. Dist: International Specialized Bk. Services.

Feistel, Rainer, et al. State & Evolution of the Baltic Sea, 1952-2005: A Detailed 50-Year Survey of Meteorology & Climate, Physics, Chemistry, Biology, & Marine Environment. 2008. (ENG., Illus.). 712p. 247.00 *(978-0-471-97968-5(6)*, Wiley-Interscience) Wiley, John & Sons, Inc.

Fuhrer, Armin. Die Todesfahrt der 'Gustloff' Porträts von Überlebenden der größten Schiffskatastrophe aller Zeiten. 2007. (GER., Illus.). 288p. pap. *(978-3-7892-8235-5(9))* Olzog Verlag GmbH.

Håkanson, Lars & Bryhn, Andreas C. Eutrophication in the Baltic Sea: Present Situation, Nutrient Transport Processes, Remedial Strategies. 2010. (Environmental Science & Engineering Ser.). (Illus.). viii, 264p. pap. 159.00 *(978-3-642-08990-9(9)*, 3642089909) Springer.

—Tools & Criteria for Sustainable Coastal Ecosystem Management: Examples from the Baltic Sea & Other Aquatic Systems. 2010. (Environmental Science & Engineering / Environmental Science Ser.). (Illus.). viii, 292p. pap. 179.00 *(978-3-642-09707-2(3)*, 3642097073) Springer.

Håkanson, Lars, et al. The Fish Production Potential of the Baltic Sea: A New General Approach for Optimizing Fish Quota Including a Holistic Management Plan Based on Ecosystem Modelling. 2010. (Environmental Science & Engineering / Environmental Science Ser.). (ENG., Illus.). x, 340p. 199.00 *(978-3-642-11561-5(6)*, 3642115616) Springer.

Harff, Jan, et al, eds. The Baltic Sea Basin. 2011. (Central & Eastern European Development Studies (CEEDES) Ser.). (ENG., Illus.). xiii, 449p. 179.00 *(978-3-642-17219-9(9)*, 3642172199) Springer.

Kautsky, Hans & Snoeijs, Pauli, eds. Biology of the Baltic Sea. 2011. (Developments in Hydrobiology Ser.). (ENG.). 284p. pap. 189.00 *(978-90-481-6550-6(4)*, 9048165504) Springer.

Leppäranta, Matti & Myrberg, Kai. Physical Oceanography of the Baltic Sea. 2009. (Springer Praxis Books / Geophysical Sciences Ser.). (Illus.). 300p. 269.00 *(978-3-540-79702-9(5))* Springer.

MacGregor, John. The Rob Roy on the Baltic: A Canoe Cruise. 2009. (Illus.). 236p. pap. 14.99 *(978-1-929516-20-9(7))* Dixon-Price Publishing.

Madsen, Kristine S. Recent & Future Climatic Changes of the North Sea & the Baltic Se. 2011. 160p. pap. ***(978-3-8443-1270-6(6))*** Lambert Academic Publishing.

Nelson, Jack A. Flashes in the Night: The Sinking of the Estonia. 2010. *(978-1-934074-21-3(7))* Apprentice Hse.

Pempkowiak, Janusz & Kulinski, Karol. Carbon Cycling in the Baltic Sea. 2012. (Geoplanet: Earth & Planetary Sciences Ser.). (ENG., Illus.). xiv, 129p. 129.00 *(978-3-642-19387-3(0)*, 3642193870) Springer.

Ransome, Arthur. Racundra's First Cruise. Hammett, Brian, ed. 2006. (ENG., Illus.). 256p. 32.95 *(978-1-898660-96-5(4)*, Wiley) Wiley, John & Sons, Inc.

Rathkolb, Oliver & Sooman, Imbi, eds. Geschichtspolitik im erweiterten Ostseeraum und ihre aktuellen Symptome / Historical Memory Culture in the Enlarged Baltic Sea Region & its Symptoms Today. 2011. (Zeitgeschichte im Kontext Ser.). (GER & ENG.). 214p. (C). 51.00 ***(978-3-89971-803-4(8))*** Vandenhoeck & Ruprecht GmbH & Co. KG DEU. Dist: ISD.

Reckermann, Marcus. Climate Impacts on the Baltic Sea: from Science to Policy: School of Environmental Research - Organized by the Helmholtz-Zentrum Geesthacht. Brander, Keith et al, eds. 2012. (Springer Earth System Sciences Ser.). (ENG., Illus.). xiv, 216p. 139.00 ***(978-3-642-25727-8(5)***, 3642257275) Springer.

Scheibner, J. Baltic Sea. 2010. (ENG.). 160p. 34.95 *(978-3-8003-1678-6(1)*, Art Stock Bks. Ltd/Csi) Continental Sales, Inc.

Schernewski, Gerald & Schiewer, Ulrich, eds. Baltic Coastal Ecosystems: Structure, Function & Coastal Zone Management. 2012. (Central & Eastern European Development Studies (CEEDES) Ser.). (ENG., Illus.). ix, 397p. pap. 189.00 *(978-3-642-07690-9(4)*, 3642076904) Springer.

Thomas Cook Publishing Staff. Traveller Guides Baltic Cruising. 2nd ed. 2011. (Travellers - Thomas Cook Ser.). (ENG., Illus.). 176p. pap. 16.95 *(978-1-84848-388-0(0))* Cook, Thomas Publishing GBR. Dist: Globe Pequot Pr., The.

Tuvikene, Rando. Seaweed Polysaccharides. 2010. 152p. pap. *(978-3-8383-5462-0(1))* Lambert Academic Publishing.

Wulff, F. V., et al, eds. A Systems Analysis of the Baltic Sea. 2010. (Ecological Studies). (Illus.). xx, 460p. pap. 259.00 *(978-3-642-08727-1(2)*, 3642087272) Springer.

BALTIC STATES

Pick, Frederick W. The Baltic Nations: Estonia, Latvia, & Lithuania. reprint ed. 32.50 *(978-0-404-20202-6(0))* AMS Pr., Inc.

BALTIC STATES—COMMERCE

BIA. Essential Baltic Manufacturers: Food, Textile, Clothing, & Chemical Companies. 6th rev. ed. 2006. 300p. (J). pap. 249.00 *(978-1-4187-4203-4(1))* Business Information Agency.

Browne, William Hand. George Calvert & Cecilius Calvert, Barons Baltimore of Baltimore. (Makers of America Ser.). 181p. reprint ed. 88.00 *(978-0-7222-9027-9(6))* Library Reprints, Inc.

Fedorowicz, J. K. England's Baltic Trade in the Early Seventeenth Century: A Study in Anglo-Polish Commercial Diplomacy. 2008. (Cambridge Studies in Economic History Ser.). (ENG.). 352p. pap. 46.00 *(978-0-521-07388-2(X))* Cambridge Univ. Pr.

BALTIC STATES—DESCRIPTION AND TRAVEL

Bousfield, Jonathan & Rough Guides Staff. The Rough Guide to Estonia, Latvia & Lithuania. 3rd ed. 2011. (ENG., Illus.). 392p. 24.99 *(978-1-84836-888-0(7))* Rough Guides, Ltd. GBR. Dist: Dorling Kindersley Publishing, Inc.

Hutton, Marcelline. Falling in Love with the Baltics: A Travel Memoir. 2009. 96p. pap. 35.99 *(978-1-4343-7031-0(3))* AuthorHouse.

Imray, Laurie & Wilson, Ltd., creator. The Baltic Sea: Germany, Denmark, Sweden, Finland, Russia, Poland, Kaliningrad, Lithuania, Latvia, Estonia. 3rd rev. ed. 2010. (Illus.). 376p. *(978-1-84623-187-2(6))* Imray, Laurie, Norie & Wilson, Ltd.

Lonely Planet Staff & Bain, Carolyn. Estonia, Latvia & Lithuania. 5th rev. ed. 2009. (Multi Country Guide Ser.). (ENG., Illus.). 456p. pap. 25.99 *(978-1-74104-770-7(6))* Lonely Planet Pubns.

Mckelvie, Robin & McKelvie, Jenny. Baltic States. 2008. (Globetrotter Travel Packs Ser.). (ENG., Illus.). 128p. 14.95 *(978-1-84773-201-9(1)*, Globetrotter) New Holland Pubs., Ltd. GBR. Dist: Globe Pequot Pr., The.

Taylor, Neil. Baltic Cities. 2008. (Bradt Travel Guide Ser.). (ENG., Illus.). 320p. pap. 25.99 *(978-1-84162-247-7(8))* Bradt Travel Guides GBR. Dist: Globe Pequot Pr., The.

BALTIC STATES—ECONOMIC CONDITIONS

Donskis, Leonidas. A Litmus Test Case of Modernity: Examining Modern Sensibilities & the Public Domain in the Baltic States at the Turn of the Century. 2009. (Interdisciplinary Studies on Central & Eastern Europe Ser.). 312p. pap. *(978-3-0343-0335-4(1))* Lang, Peter.

Elletson, Harold. Baltic Independence & Russian Foreign Energy Policy. 2006. (Russian Foreign Energy Policy Ser.). (ENG.). 40p. pap. 180.00 *(978-1-905050-36-9(4)*, GMB Publishing Ltd.) Blue Ibex Ltd. GBR. Dist: Ingram Pub. Services.

Fedotov, Alexander. From Union to Union. 2011. 272p. pap. ***(978-3-8443-8918-0(0))*** Lambert Academic Publishing.

Holt-Jensen, Arild & Pollock, Eric, eds. Urban Sustainability & Governance: New Challengers in Nordic-Baltic Housing Policies. 2008. 89.00 *(978-1-60456-886-8(0))* Nova Science Pubs., Inc.

Madumarov, Eldar. External Factors of Economic Growth. 2008. 260p. pap. *(978-3-639-07643-1(5))* VDM Verlag Dr. Mueller e.K.

Mandre, Mihkel. Payout Concept for Pension Systems in Baltic Countries. 2010. 92p. pap. *(978-3-8383-6428-5(7))* Lambert Academic Publishing.

Mikeladze, Davit. Russian-Speaking Population in the Baltic States. 2010. 68p. pap. *(978-3-8383-7188-7(7))* Lambert Academic Publishing.

Paas, T. & Eamets, Raul. Labor Market Flexibility, Flexicurity & Employment: Lessons of the Baltic States. 2006. (Illus.). (C). 169.00 *(978-1-60021-416-5(9))* Nova Science Pubs., Inc.

Paci, Pierella, et al. Internal Labor Mobility in Central Europe & the Baltic Region. 2007. (World Bank Working Papers: 105). (ENG.). 100p. pap. 15.00 *(978-0-8213-7090-2(1)*, 9780821370902) World Bank Pubns.

Rieter, Heinz & Zweynert, Joachim, eds. Economic Styles in the Process of EU Eastern Enlargement. 2009. 345p. pap. 93.00 *(978-3-8329-4684-5(5))* Nomos Verlagsgesellschaft DEU. Dist: International Specialized Bk. Services.

BALTIC STATES—FOREIGN RELATIONS

Archer, Clive B. New Security Issues in Northern Europe. 2007. (Routledge/UACES Contemporary European Studies). (ENG., Illus.). 256p. (C). 150.00 *(978-0-415-39340-9(X))* Routledge.

Dahl, Ann-Sofie. Us Policy in the Nordic-Baltic Region: During the Cold War & After. 2008. 116p. per. *(978-91-7335-009-9(5))* Santerus Forlag.

Elletson, Harold. Baltic Independence & Russian Foreign Energy Policy. 2006. (Russian Foreign Energy Policy Ser.). (ENG.). 40p. pap. 180.00 *(978-1-905050-36-9(4)*, GMB Publishing Ltd.) Blue Ibex Ltd. GBR. Dist: Ingram Pub. Services.

Fonnesberg-Schmidt, Iben. The Popes & the Baltic Crusades 1147-1254. 2006. (Northern World Ser.: Vol. 26). (Illus.). 287p. *(978-90-04-15502-2(3))* BRILL.

Hedegaard, Lars & Lindström, Bjarne, eds. The NEBI YEARBOOK 2001/2002: North European & Baltic Sea Integration. 2010. xiii, 486p. pap. 114.00 *(978-3-642-07700-5(5)*, 3642077005) Springer.

Hiden, John, et al, eds. The Baltic Question During the Cold War. 2009. 210p. pap. 39.95 *(978-0-415-56934-7(6))* Routledge.

Hiden, John & Housden, Martyn. Neighbours or Enemies? Germans, the Baltic & Beyond. 2008. 164p. per. *(978-90-420-2349-9(X))* Rodopi B.V. Editions.

Jacobsson, Bengt. The European Union & the Baltic States: Changing forms of Governance. 2009. (Europe & the Nation State Ser.). (ENG.). 208p. 140.00 *(978-0-415-48276-9(3))* Routledge.

Leivyte, Janina. Russia's European Agenda & the Baltic States. 2010. (Routledge Contemporary Russia & Eastern Europe Ser.). (ENG., Illus.). 228p. 145.00 *(978-0-415-55400-8(4))* Routledge.

Mälksoo, Maria. The Politics of Becoming European: A Study of Polish & Baltic Post-Cold War Security Imaginaries. 2009. (New International Relations Ser.). (ENG.). 224p. (C). 128.00 *(978-0-415-49997-2(6))* Routledge.

Mole. The Baltic States. 2012. (BASEES/Routledge Series on Russian & East European Studies). (ENG., Illus.). 216p. (C). 150.00 *(978-0-415-39497-0(X))* Routledge.

Mole, Richard C. M. The Baltic States from the Soviet Union to the European Union: Identity, Discourse & Power in the Post-Communist Transition of Estonia, Latvia & Lithuania. 2012. E-Book ***(978-0-203-12149-8(X))*** Earthscan.

Ponomarjovs, Dmitrijs. The Eu-Russia Relationship Dynamics. 2009. 60p. pap. *(978-3-639-20536-7(7))* VDM Verlag Dr. Mueller e.K.

Rislakki, Jukka. The Case for Latvia. Disinformation Campaigns Against a Small Nation: Fourteen Hard Questions & Straight Answers about a Baltic Country. 2008. 296p. 90.00 *(978-90-420-2423-6(2))* Rodopi.

—The Case for Latvia Disinformation Campaigns Against a Small Nation: Fourteen Hard Questions & Straight Answers about a Baltic Country. 2008. 296p. pap. *(978-90-420-2424-3(0))* Rodopi B.V. Editions.

Statiev, Alexander. The Soviet Counterinsurgency in the Western Borderlands. 2010. (ENG., Illus.). 384p. 90.00 *(978-0-521-76833-7(0))* Cambridge Univ. Pr.

Van Elsuwege, P. From Soviet Republics to EU Member States. A Legal & Political Assessment of the Baltic States' Accession to the EU, 2 vols. 2008. (Studies in EU External Relations Ser.). 519p. *(978-90-04-16945-6(8))* BRILL.

BALTIC STATES—HISTORY

Barrett, Michael B. Operation Albion: The German Conquest of the Baltic Islands. 2008. (Twentieth-Century Battles Ser/ Ser). (ENG., Illus.). 312p. 29.95 *(978-0-253-34969-9(9)*, 0253349699) Indiana Univ. Pr.

Baxter, Ian. Battle in the Baltics 1944-45: The Fighting for Latvia, Lithuania & Estonia, a Photographic History. 2009. (Illus.). 112p. 59.95 *(978-1-906033-33-0(1))* Helion & Co., Ltd. GBR. Dist: Casemate Pubs. & Bk. Distributors, LLC.

Bennich-Björkman, Li & Aarelaid-Tart, Aili, eds. Baltic Biographies at Historical Crossroads. 2011. (Routledge/ESA Studies in European Societies Ser.). (ENG., Illus.). 240p. (C). 130.00 *(978-0-415-68110-0(3))* Routledge.

Darieva, Tsypylma & Kaschuba, Wolfgang. Representations on the Margins of Europe: Politics & Identities in the Baltic & South Caucasian States. Darieva, Tsypylma & Kaschuba, Wolfgang, eds. 2008. (Illus.). 350p. pap. 50.00 *(978-3-593-38241-8(5))* Campus Verlag GmbH DEU. Dist: Chicago Distribution Ctr.

Donnert, Erich. Agrarfrage und Aufklärung in Lettland und Estland: Livland, Estland und Kurland im 18. und beginnenden 19. Jahrhundert. 2008. 238p. pap. 55.95 *(978-3-631-57021-0(X))* Lang, Peter GmbH, Europäischer Verlag der Wissenschaften DEU. Dist: Lang, Peter.

Fonnesberg-Schmidt, Iben. The Popes & the Baltic Crusades 1147-1254. 2006. (Northern World Ser.: Vol. 26). (Illus.). 287p. *(978-90-04-15502-2(3))* BRILL.

Frey, Axel, compiled by. Baltischer Biographischer Index. 2nd ed. 2008. (GER.). LXXXVIII, 2135p. *(978-3-598-35346-8(4))* Saur, K. G. Verlag GmbH & Co.

Hiden, John, et al, eds. The Baltic Question During the Cold War. 2009. 210p. pap. 39.95 *(978-0-415-56934-7(6))* Routledge.

Housden, Martyn & Smith, David J., eds. Forgotten Pages in Baltic History: Diversity & Inclusion. 2011. (ENG., Illus.). 340p. pap. 95.00 *(978-90-420-3315-3(0))* Rodopi.

Jensen, Carsten Selch, et al. Crusading & Chronicle Writing in the Medieval Baltic Frontier: A Companion to the Chronicle of Henry of Livonia. 2011. (Illus.). 522p. 134.95 ***(978-0-7546-6627-1(1))*** Ashgate Publishing Co.

Kasekamp, Andres. A History of the Baltic States. 2010. (Palgrave Essential Histories Ser.). (ENG., Illus.). 296p. 85.00 *(978-0-230-01940-9(4))*; pap. 28.00 *(978-0-230-01941-6(2))* Palgrave Macmillan.

Kotljarchuk, Andrej. Making the Baltic Union - the 1655 Federation of Kedainiai Between Sweden & the Grand Duchy of Lithuani. 2008. 348p. pap. *(978-3-639-04331-0(6))* VDM Verlag Dr. Mueller e.K.

Murray, Alan V., ed. The Clash of Cultures on the Medieval Baltic Frontier. 2009. (Illus.). 394p. 134.95 *(978-0-7546-6483-3(X))* Ashgate Publishing Co.

Palmer, Alan. The Baltic: A New History of the Region & Its People. 2007. (ENG., Illus.). 464p. (gr. 12). per. 19.95 *(978-1-58567-863-1(5))* Overlook Pr., The.

Plakans, Andrejs. A Concise History of the Baltic States. 2011. (Cambridge Concise Histories Ser.). (ENG., Illus.). 490p. 75.00 *(978-0-521-83372-1(8))*; pap. 27.99 *(978-0-521-54155-8(7))* Cambridge Univ. Pr.

Rathkolb, Oliver & Sooman, Imbi, eds. Geschichtspolitik im erweiterten Ostseeraum und ihre aktuellen Symptome / Historical Memory Culture in the Enlarged Baltic Sea Region & its Symptoms Today. 2011. (Zeitgeschichte im Kontext Ser.). (GER & ENG.). 214p. (C). 51.00 ***(978-3-89971-803-4(8))*** Vandenhoeck & Ruprecht GmbH & Co. KG DEU. Dist: ISD.

Seydel, Renate. Hiddensee. Ein Lesebuch. (GER.). pap. *(978-3-548-24963-6(9))* Ullstein-Taschenbuch-Verlag DEU. Dist: International Bk. Import Service, Inc.

Wheaton, Paul M., ed. Labor Market in the Baltic Region. 2012. (European Political, Economic, & Security Issues Ser.). 235p. 89.00 *(978-1-61209-952-1(1))* Nova Science Pubs., Inc.

BALTIC STATES—POLITICS AND GOVERNMENT

Agarin, Timofey. A cat¿s Lick: Democratisation & minority communities in the post-Soviet Baltic. 2010. (Illus.). 391p. 112.00 *(978-90-420-2989-7(7))* Rodopi.

Donskis, Leonidas. A Litmus Test Case of Modernity: Examining Modern Sensibilities & the Public Domain in the Baltic States at the Turn of the Century. 2009. (Interdisciplinary Studies on Central & Eastern Europe Ser.). 312p. pap. *(978-3-0343-0335-4(1))* Lang, Peter.

Gebhard, Carmen. Unravelling the Baltic Sea Conundrum: Regionalism & European Integration Revisited. 2009. 279p. pap. 55.00 *(978-3-8329-4084-3(7))* Nomos Verlagsgesellschaft DEU. Dist: International Specialized Bk. Services.

Jacobsson, Bengt. The European Union & the Baltic States: Changing forms of Governance. 2009. (Europe & the Nation State Ser.). (ENG.). 208p. 140.00 *(978-0-415-48276-9(3))* Routledge.

Joas, Marko, et al, eds. Governing a Common Sea: Environmental Policies in the Baltic Sea Region. 2008. (ENG., Illus.). 256p. (C). 117.00 *(978-1-84407-537-9(0))* Routledge.

Kirchner, Walther. The Rise of the Baltic Question: University of Delaware Monograph Series No. 3. 2011. 294p. 48.95 ***(978-1-258-05541-7(4))*** Literary Licensing, LLC.

Meleshevich, Andrey A. Party Systems in Post-Soviet Countries: A Comparative Study of Political Institutionalization in the Baltic States, Russia, & Ukraine. 2007. (ENG.) 280p. 89.00 *(978-1-4039-7449-5(7))* Palgrave Macmillan.

Mole. The Baltic States. 2012. (BASEES/Routledge Series on Russian & East European Studies). (ENG., Illus.). 216p. (C). 150.00 *(978-0-415-39497-0(X))* Routledge.

Mole, Richard C. M. The Baltic States from the Soviet Union to the European Union: Identity, Discourse & Power in the Post-Communist Transition of Estonia, Latvia & Lithuania. 2012. E-Book ***(978-0-203-12149-8(X))*** Earthscan.

Organisation for Economic Co-operation and Development Staff. Local Economic & Employment Development Baltic Partnerships: Integration, Growth & Local Governance in the Baltic Sea Region. 2007. pap. 54.00 *(978-92-64-02928-6(1))* Organization for Economic Cooperation & Development.

Pettai, Eva-Clarita, ed. Memory & Pluralism in the Baltic States. 2011. (ENG.). 160p. (C). 125.00 *(978-0-415-66841-5(7))* Routledge.

Pssbo, Heiko. Great Power's Dependency Policies in a Geostrategic Subregion. 2009. 124p. pap. *(978-3-639-16331-5(1))* VDM Verlag Dr. Mueller e.K.

BALTICS (STATES)

see Baltic States

BALTIMORE (MD.)

ADC, the Map People Staff, creator. Baltimore City & County, Maryland. 28th ed. 2006. (Street Map Bks.). (Illus.). 84p. 12.95 *(978-0-87530-800-5(7))* ADC The Map People.

Bagnoli, Martina & Gerry, Kathryn B. The Medieval World: The Walters Art Museum. 2011. (ENG., Illus.). 208p. 45.00 *(978-1-904832-96-6(2))* Giles, D. Ltd. GBR. Dist: Antique Collectors' Club.

Friedrichs, Jargen & Goodman, Allen C. The Changing Downtown: A Comparative Study of Baltimore & Hamburg. (ENG.). X, 254p. 210.00 ***(978-3-11-177816-7(9))*** De Gruyter, Walter Inc.

Grivno, Max. Gleanings of Freedom: Free & Slave Labor along the Mason-Dixon Line, 1790-1860. 2011. (Working Class in American History Ser.). (ENG., Illus.). 296p. 50.00 ***(978-0-252-03652-1(2))*** Univ. of Illinois Pr.

Howard, George W. The Monumental City V2: Its Past History & Present Resources. 2007. (ENG.). 452p. per. 37.95 *(978-1-4304-4241-7(7))* Kessinger Publishing, LLC.

Mencken, H. L. Happy Days: Mencken's Autobiography, 1880-1892, Volume 1. 2006. (ENG.). 336p. pap. 27.00 *(978-0-8018-8531-0(0))* Johns Hopkins Univ. Pr.

Moskos, Peter. Cop in the Hood: My Year Policing Baltimore's Eastern District. 2009. (ENG., Illus.). 280p. (C). pap. 16.95 *(978-0-691-14386-6(2))* Princeton Univ. Pr.

Richardson, Odel, Jr. The Long Way "Home" The Spirit... the Life... the Purpose... 2009. 656p. 36.49 *(978-1-4490-0413-2(X))* AuthorHouse.

—The Long Way "Home" The Spirit... the Life... the Purpose... 2009. 656p. pap. 27.99 *(978-1-4490-0412-5(1))* AuthorHouse.

Thomas, Thaddeus P. The City Government of Baltimore. 2009. (ENG.). 52p. pap. 16.99 *(978-1-117-29715-6(2)*, BiblioLife); pap. 16.75 *(978-1-117-29714-9(4))* BiblioBazaar.

BALTIMORE (MD.)—DESCRIPTION AND TRAVEL

ADC, the Map People Staff. Atlas Baltimore City County MD. 2008. 120p. 14.95 *(978-0-87530-608-7(X))* ADC The Map People.

ADC, the Map People Staff, creator. Baltimore, Maryland City & County Street Atlas. 2007. (Illus.). 64p. 12.95 *(978-0-87530-899-9(6))* ADC The Map People.

—Baltimore, Maryland Pocket Atlas. 2007. 128p. 9.95 *(978-0-87530-891-3(0))* ADC The Map People.

Balkan, Evan L. & Balkan, Evan. 60 Hikes Within 60 Miles: Baltimore: Including Anne Arundel, Carroll, Harford, & Howard Counties. 2nd ed. 2009. (60 Hikes within 60 Miles Ser.). (ENG., Illus.). 336p. pap. 17.95 *(978-0-89732-692-6(X))* Menasha Ridge Pr., Inc.

Blake, Allison. Baltimore, Annapolis & the Chesapeake Bay. 2010. (Great Destinations Ser.). (ENG., Illus.). 320p. pap. 19.95 *(978-1-58157-112-7(7)*, 157112) Countryman Pr.

Brown, Geoff. Baltimore. 2009. (Moon Handbooks Ser.). (ENG.). 250p. pap. 17.95 *(978-1-56691-984-5(3))* Westview Pr.

Colbert, Judy. Baltimore. 6th ed. 2010. (Insiders' Guide Ser.). (ENG., Illus.). 208p. pap. 18.95 *(978-0-7627-5670-4(5)*, Insiders' Guide) Globe Pequot Pr., The.

Dickon, Chris. Chesapeake Bay Steamers. 2006. (Images of America Ser.). (ENG., Illus.). 128p. per. 21.99 *(978-0-7385-4373-4(X))* Arcadia Publishing.

Entertainment Publications, Inc. Staff, compiled by. Baltimore 2009 Entertainment Book. 2008. pap. 30.00 *(978-1-59878-617-0(2))* Entertainment Pubns., Inc.

Hayward, Mary Ellen. Baltimore's Alley Houses: Homes for Working People since the 1780s. 2008. (Creating the North American Landscape Ser.). (ENG., Illus.). 328p. (gr. 17). 47.00 *(978-0-8018-8834-2(4))* Johns Hopkins Univ. Pr.

Kelly, Cindy. Outdoor Sculpture in Baltimore: A Historical Guide to Public Art in the Monumental City. 2011. (ENG., Illus.). 416p. (gr. 17). 44.95 *(978-0-8018-9722-1(X))* Johns Hopkins Univ. Pr.

Lanman, Barry A. Baltimore County: Celebrating A Legacy 1659-2009. 2009. *(978-1-60743-522-8(5))* Independent Pub.

—Baltimore County: Celebrating a Legacy 1659-2009. 2009. pap. *(978-1-60743-523-5(3))* Independent Pub.

MacKay, Bryan. Baltimore Trails: A Guide for Hikers & Mountain Bikers. 2nd ed. 2008. (ENG., Illus.). 288p. pap. 19.95 *(978-0-8018-9070-3(5))* Johns Hopkins Univ. Pr.

Miller, Roger & Pilling, Ron. Baltimore Portrait. 4th ed. 2006. 168p. 39.95 *(978-0-911897-50-0(X))* Image Publishing, Ltd.

Mitchell, Alexander D., IV. Baltimore Then & Now (Compact) 2009. (Then & Now Thunder Bay Ser.). (ENG.). 144p. pap. 12.95 *(978-1-59223-964-1(1)*, Thunder Bay Pr.) Advantage Pubs. Group.

Okonowicz, Ed. Baltimore Ghosts: History, Mystery, Legends & Love. 2nd ed. 2007. 144p. pap. 11.95 *(978-1-890690-18-2(X))* Myst & Lace Pubs., Inc.

O'Prey, Maureen. Brewing in Baltimore. 2011. (Images of America Ser.). (ENG., Illus.). 128p. pap. 21.99 ***(978-0-7385-8813-1(X))*** Arcadia Publishing.

Roseberry, D. P. Spooky Creepy Baltimore County. 2009. (Illus.). 160p. pap. 14.99 *(978-0-7643-3254-8(6))* Schiffer Publishing, Ltd.

Schehlein, Melissa. Towson. 2011. (Then & Now Ser.). (Illus.). 96p. pap. 21.99 *(978-0-7385-8734-9(6))* Arcadia Publishing.

Walston, Mark. Historic Photos of Baltimore. 2008. (Historic Photos Ser.). (ENG.). 206p. 39.95 *(978-1-59652-316-6(6))* Turner Publishing Co.

—Remembering Baltimore. 2010. (Remembering Ser.). (ENG.). 134p. pap. 16.95 *(978-1-59652-699-0(8))* Turner Publishing Co.

Zagat Survey Staff. Washington, DC - Baltimore Restaurants 2010. 2009. (ENG.). 288p. pap. 14.95 *(978-1-60478-164-9(5))* Zagat Survey.

Zagat Survey Staff, creator. Zagat Survey Washington, DC/Baltimore Restaurants. 2006. (Zagat Survey: Washington, D. C. /Baltimore Restaurants Ser.). (ENG.). 256p. per. 13.95 *(978-1-57006-803-4(8))* Zagat Survey.

Zagat Survey Staff, ed. 2009 Washington DC/Baltimore Book Pack. 2008. (ENG.). 29.95 *(978-1-60478-025-3(8))* Zagat Survey.

BALTIMORE (MD.)—HISTORY

see also Baltimore, Battle of, Baltimore, Md., 1814

Alexander, Gregory J. & Williams, Paul Kelsey. A Brief History of Charles Village. 2008. (Brief Histories Ser.). 21.99 *(978-1-59629-618-3(6))* History Pr., The.

Augsburger, Leonard. Treasure in the Cellar: A Tale of Gold in Depression-Era Baltimore. 2008. (ENG., Illus.). 208p. (gr. 17). pap. 26.00 *(978-0-938420-97-2(6))* Maryland Historical Society.

Barnes, Robert W. Biographical Data from Baltimore Newspapers, 1817-1819. 2011. 202p. pap. 24.00 ***(978-0-8063-5525-2(5))*** Clearfield Co.

Baum, Howell S. Brown in Baltimore: School Desegregation & the Limits of Liberalism. 2010. (Illus.). 272p. pap. 24.95 *(978-0-8014-7652-5(6))* Cornell Univ. Pr.

Bell, Madison Smartt. Charm City: A Walk Through Baltimore. 2007. (Crown Journeys Ser.). (ENG., Illus.). 240p. 16.95 *(978-0-307-34206-5(9)*, Crown) Crown Publishing Group.

Bowditch, Eden Unger & Draddy, Anne. Druid Hill Park: The Heart of Historic Baltimore. 2008. (Illus.). 160p. pap. 19.99 *(978-1-59629-209-3(1))* History Pr., The.

Brown, George William. The Origin & Growth of Civil Liberty in Maryland a Discourse Delivered by Geo Wn Brown, Before the Maryland Historical Society, Baltimore, April. 2006. 364p. per. 26.99 *(978-1-4255-3783-8(9))* MPublishing.

Brown, George Williams. Baltimore & the Nineteenth of April 1861. (Johns Hopkins University Studies in Historical & Political Science). 176p. reprint ed. 88.00 *(978-0-7222-8320-2(2))* Library Reprints, Inc.

Brown, Robert P. & Olson, Steven P. Some Gave All: A History of Baltimore Police Officers Killed in the Line of Duty, 1808-2007. 2007. (Illus.). 232p. 25.00 *(978-0-9635159-5-7(0))* Chesapeake Bk. Co.

Clark, William & Sosa, Maria. Federal Hill. 2012. (Images of America Ser.). (ENG., Illus.). 128p. pap. 21.99 ***(978-0-7385-9206-0(4))*** Arcadia Publishing.

Duff, Charles & Clark, Tracey. Baltimore Architecture. 2006. (Then & Now Ser.). (ENG., Illus.). 96p. per. 21.99 *(978-0-7385-4281-2(4))* Arcadia Publishing.

Elfenbein, Jessica, et al. Baltimore '68: Riots & Rebirth in an American City. 2011. (ENG., Illus.). 294p. pap. 29.95 *(978-1-4399-0662-0(9))* Temple Univ. Pr.

Ezratty, Harry A. Baltimore in the Civil War: The Pratt Street Riot & a City Occupied. 2010. (ENG., Illus.). 128p. pap. 19.99 *(978-1-60949-003-4(7))* History Pr., The.

Flynn, Tom. Baseball in Baltimore. 2008. (Images of Baseball Ser.). (ENG., Illus.). 128p. per. 21.99 *(978-0-7385-5325-2(5))* Arcadia Publishing.

Helton, Gary. Baltimore's Streetcars & Buses. 2008. (Images of America Ser.). (ENG., Illus.). 128p. pap. 21.99 *(978-0-7385-5369-6(7))* Arcadia Publishing.

—Highlandtown. 2006. (Images of America Ser.). (ENG., Illus.). 128p. per. 21.99 *(978-0-7385-4338-3(1))* Arcadia Publishing.

Holcomb, Eric. The City as Suburb. 2007. 288p. pap. 24.50 *(978-1-930066-59-5(7))* Univ. Pr. of Virginia.

Holcomb, Eric L. The City as Suburb: A History of Northeast Baltimore Since 1660. 2nd rev. ed. 2008. (Center Bks.). (ENG., Illus.). 273p. (C). (gr. 13-17). pap. 24.50 *(978-1-930066-73-1(2))* Univ. Pr. of Virginia.

—The City As Suburb: A History of Northeast Baltimore since 1660. 2nd rev. ed. 2008. (Center Bks.). (ENG., Illus.). 294p. (gr. 17). 49.50 *(978-1-930066-72-4(4))* Univ. Pr. of Virginia.

Martin, Mary L. & Wolfgang-Price, Nathaniel. Baltimore: A History in Postcards. 2006. (Illus.). 128p. pap. 24.95 *(978-0-7643-2489-5(6))* Schiffer Publishing, Ltd.

Mitchell, Alexander D., IV. Baltimore Then & Now (Compact) 2009. (Then & Now Thunder Bay Ser.). (ENG.). 144p. pap. 12.95 *(978-1-59223-964-1(1)*, Thunder Bay Pr.) Advantage Pubs. Group.

Nix, Elizabeth. Baltimore '68: Riots & Rebirth in an American City. Elfenbein, Jessica & Hollowak, Thomas, eds. 2011. (ENG., Illus.). 294p. 74.50 *(978-1-4399-0661-3(0))* Temple Univ. Pr.

O'Prey, Maureen. Brewing in Baltimore. 2011. (Images of America Ser.). (ENG., Illus.). 128p. pap. 21.99 ***(978-0-7385-8813-1(X))*** Arcadia Publishing.

Orser, W. Ed. Gwynns Falls. 2008. 160p. pap. 19.99 *(978-1-59629-476-9(0))* History Pr., The.

Ross, Joseph. Arundel Burning: The Maryland Oyster Roast Fire Of 1956. 2008. (Illus.). 208p. pap. 18.00 *(978-0-9635159-7-1(7))* Chesapeake Bk. Co.

Ruppert, Gary B. Obstetrical Casebooks of Dr. Ferdinand E. Chatard: An Alternative Genealogical Resource for Baltimore City [Maryland], 1829-1883. 2007. pap. 25.50 *(978-0-7884-4331-2(3))* Heritage Bks.

Sandler, Gilbert. Home Front Baltimore: An Album of Stories from World War II. 2011. (ENG., Illus.). 176p. (gr. 17). 29.95 *(978-0-8018-9983-6(4))* Johns Hopkins Univ. Pr.

Schehlein, Melissa. Towson. 2011. (Then & Now Ser.). (Illus.). 96p. pap. 21.99 *(978-0-7385-8734-9(6))* Arcadia Publishing.

Schultheis, Patricia. Baltimore's Lexington Market. 2007. (Images of America Ser.). (ENG., Illus.). 128p. per. 21.99 *(978-0-7385-4361-1(6))* Arcadia Publishing.

Shalhope, Robert E. The Baltimore Bank Riot: Political Upheaval in Antebellum Maryland. 2009. (ENG.). 208p. 50.00 *(978-0-252-03480-0(5))* Univ. of Illinois Pr.

Shivers, Frank R., Jr. Bolton Hill: Classic Baltimore Neighborhood. 2010. (ENG., Illus.). 228p. (gr. 17). 35.00 *(978-0-938420-95-8(X))* Maryland Historical Society.

Silberman, Lauren R. The Jewish Community of Baltimore. 2008. (Images of America Ser.). (ENG., Illus.). 128p. pap. 19.99 *(978-0-7385-5397-9(2))* Arcadia Publishing.

Silberman, Lauren R. Wicked Baltimore: Charm City Sin & Scandal. 2011. 160p. pap. 19.99 ***(978-1-60949-108-6(4))*** History Pr., The.

The Fabulous Dell Brothers. I've Seen Things Go This Bad for Six Months in A Row: (Then Turn Right Around & Get Worse) 2011. 224p. pap. 15.95 ***(978-1-4634-1992-9(9))*** AuthorHouse.

Walston, Mark. Remembering Baltimore. 2010. (Remembering Ser.). (ENG.). 134p. pap. 16.95 *(978-1-59652-699-0(8))* Turner Publishing Co.

Weiner, Deborah R., et al. Voices of Lombard Street: A Century of Change in East Baltimore. 2007. (Illus.). 170p. pap. *(978-1-883312-08-4(6))* Jewish Museum of Maryland.

Wight Wise, Marsha. Baltimore Neighborhoods. 2009. (Postcard History Ser.). (ENG., Illus.). 128p. pap. 21.99 *(978-0-7385-5290-3(9))* Arcadia Publishing.

Zanow, Lois & Johnston, Sally. Monuments to Heaven: Baltimore's Historic Houses of Worship. 2010. 128p. pap. 38.49 *(978-1-4520-8537-1(4))* AuthorHouse.

BALTIMORE (MD.)—POLITICS AND GOVERNMENT

Argersinger, Jo Ann E. Toward a New Deal in Baltimore: People & Government in the Great Depression. 2011. (ENG.). 304p. pap. 40.00 *(978-0-8078-5724-3(6))* Univ. of North Carolina Pr.

BALTIMORE, BATTLE OF, BALTIMORE, MD., 1814

Brodie, Jeffrey, et al. The Star-Spangled Banner: The Making of an American Icon. 2008. 192p. 29.95 *(978-0-06-088562-5(9))* Smithsonian Institution Pr.

Davis, Paris M. The Four Principal Battles of the Late War: A Full Detailed Account of the Battle of Chippeway, Fall & Destruction of the City of Washington, Battles of Baltimore & New Orleans. (Magazine of History with Notes & Queries Ser.). 54p. reprint ed. 88.00 *(978-0-7222-7832-1(2))* Library Reprints, Inc.

Wilhelm, Lewis Webb. Sir George Calvert, Baron of Baltimore: A Paper Read Before the Maryland Historical Society, April 14th, 1884. (Maryland Historical Society Fund Ser.). 172p. reprint ed. 88.00 *(978-0-7222-3029-3(2))* Library Reprints, Inc.

BALTIMORE AND OHIO RAILROAD COMPANY

Collins, Darrell L. The Jones-Imboden Raid: A Confederate Attempt to Destroy the Baltimore & Ohio Railroad & Retake West Virginia. 2007. (ENG., Illus.). 220p. pap. 39.95 *(978-0-7864-3070-3(2))* McFarland & Co., Inc. Pubs.

Dixon Jr, Thomas W. Baltimore & Ohio's Cincinnatian. 2008. (ENG., Illus.). 80p. pap. 20.95 *(978-0-939487-85-1(3)*, 0939487853) TLC Publishing, Inc.

Expositor. The Western Maryland Railroad & His Honor the Mayor of Baltimore, Versus the Balt & Ohio Railroad. 2011. 18p. pap. 11.99 ***(978-1-4181-9027-9(6))*** MPublishing.

Greco, Thomas J. & Spence, Karl D. Dining on the B & O: Recipes & Sidelights from a Bygone Age. 2009. (ENG., Illus.). 208p. 34.95 *(978-0-8018-9323-0(2))* Johns Hopkins Univ. Pr.

Mellander, Deane. B & O Thunder in the Alleghenies. (Hobby Book Ser.: No. C 97). 84p. 13.95 *(978-0-911868-97-5(6))* Carstens Pubns., Inc.

Reizenstein, Milton. The Economic History of the Baltimore & Ohio Railroad. 1827-1853. (Johns Hopkins University. Studies in the Social Sciences. Thirtieth Ser.: 7-8). reprint ed. 32.50 *(978-0-404-61114-9(1))* AMS Pr., Inc.

Reynolds, Kirk & Oroszi, Dave. Baltimore & Ohio Railroad. 2008. (MBI Railroad Color History Ser.). (ENG., Illus.). 160p. 37.00 *(978-0-7603-2929-0(X)*, 076032929X, Voyageur Pr) MBI Publishing Co. LLC.

Smith, William, abr. The Book of the Great Railway Celebrations of 1857. 2009. (Transportation Ser.). (ENG.). 552p. pap. 32.95 *(978-1-4290-2004-6(0))* Applewood Bks.

Welsh, Joe. Baltimore & Ohio's Capitol Limited & National Limited. rev. ed. 2007. (Great Passenger Trains Ser.). (ENG., Illus.). 160p. 36.95 *(978-0-7603-2533-9(2)*, 0760325332, Voyageur Pr) MBI Publishing Co. LLC.

Withers, Bob. Baltimore & Ohio Facilities in Color. 2008. (Illus.). *(978-1-58248-273-6(X))*; *(978-1-58248-243-9(8))*; ***(978-1-58248-297-2(7))*** Morning Sun Bks., Inc.

—The Baltimore & Ohio Railroad in West Virginia. 2007. (Images of Rail Ser.). (ENG., Illus.). 128p. per. 21.99 *(978-0-7385-5283-5(6))* Arcadia Publishing.

BALTIMORE CATECHISM

Carter, Karen. Creating Catholics: Catechism & Primary Education in Early Modern France. 2011. (ENG., Illus.). 328p. pap. 40.00 *(978-0-268-02304-1(2))* Univ. of Notre Dame Pr.

Drinkwater, F. Catechism Stories. 2007. 512p. per. 27.95 *(978-0-9782985-3-1(5))* Catholic Authors Pr.

Kelly, William Roswell, et al. Living in God's Grace: Living My Religion Series, Book 3. 2011. 364p. 51.95 ***(978-1-258-09316-7(2))*** Literary Licensing, LLC.

—Living in God's Holiness: Living My Religion Series, Book 8. 2011. 368p. 53.95 ***(978-1-258-09317-4(0))*** Literary Licensing, LLC.

—Living in God's Love: Living My Religion Series, Book 1. 2011. 162p. 41.95 ***(978-1-258-09150-7(X))*** Literary Licensing, LLC.

Kinkead, Thomas L. An Explanation of the Baltimore Catechism of Christian Doctrine. 2009. 404p. 32.99 *(978-1-115-70674-2(8))*; pap. 27.99 *(978-1-115-70676-6(4))*; pap. 21.99 *(978-1-115-70677-3(2))* BiblioBazaar.

—An Explanation of the Baltimore Catechism of Christian Doctrine. 2007. 340p. per. *(978-1-4065-2893-0(5))* Dodo Pr.

Lovasik, Lawrence G. Catechism in Stories. 2011. 314p. 50.95 ***(978-1-258-07533-0(4))*** Literary Licensing, LLC.

MacKendrick, Karmen. Fragmentation & Memory: Meditations on Christian Doctrine. 2008. (ENG.). 192p. 75.00 *(978-0-8232-2949-9(1))*; 3rd ed. pap. 28.00 *(978-0-8232-2950-5(5))* Fordham Univ. Pr.

McNeill, Leon A. & Aaron, Madeleine. The Words of Truth. 2011. 222p. 44.95 ***(978-1-258-05219-5(9))*** Literary Licensing, LLC.

BALTIMORE COLTS (FOOTBALL TEAM)

Bowden, Mark. The Best Game Ever: Giants vs. Colts, 1958, & the Birth of the Modern NFL. 2008. 64.99 *(978-1-60514-554-9(8))* Findaway World, LLC.

—The Best Game Ever: Giants vs. Colts, 1958, & the Birth of the Modern NFL. 2009. (ENG.). 340p. pap. 14.00 *(978-0-8021-4412-6(8)*, Grove Pr.) Grove/Atlantic, Inc.

Gifford, Frank & Richmond, Peter. The Glory Game: How the 1958 NFL Championship Changed Football Forever. 2009. (ENG.) 320p. pap. 14.99 *(978-0-06-154257-2(1)*, Harper Paperbacks) 2008. 304p. 25.95 *(978-0-06-154255-8(5))* HarperCollins Pubs.

Klein, Dave. The Game of Their Lives: The 1958 NFL Championship. 50th anniv. ed. 2008. (ENG.). 288p. pap. 16.95 *(978-1-58979-384-2(6))* Taylor Trade Publishing.

Krauss, Barry & Moore, Joe M. Ain't Nothin' but a Winner: Bear Bryant, the Goal Line Stand, & a Chance of a Lifetime. 2nd ed. 2006. (ENG., Illus.). 152p. 26.95 *(978-0-8173-1541-2(1))* Univ. of Alabama Pr.

Olesker, Michael. The Colts' Baltimore: A City & Its Love Affair in The 1950s. 2008. (ENG., Illus.). 240p. 25.95 *(978-0-8018-9062-8(4))* Johns Hopkins Univ. Pr.

Sahadi, Lou. One Sunday in December: The 1958 NFL Championship Game & How It Changed Professional Football. 2008. (ENG., Illus.). 224p. pap. 14.95 *(978-1-59921-320-0(6)*, Lyons Pr.) Globe Pequot Pr., The.

BALTIMORE COUNTY (MD.)

Helton, Gary. Sparrows Point. 2007. (Images of America Ser.). (Illus.). 127p. per. 19.99 *(978-0-7385-4429-8(9))* Arcadia Publishing.

Orser, W. Ed. Gwynns Falls. 2008. 160p. pap. 19.99 *(978-1-59629-476-9(0))* History Pr., The.

BALTIMORE ORIOLES (BASEBALL TEAM)

Berney, Louis. Game of My Life: Baltimore Orioles: Memorable Stories of Orioles Baseball. 2006. (Game of My Life Ser.). (Illus.). 256p. 24.95 *(978-1-59670-272-1(9))* Sports Publishing, LLC.

—Tales from the Orioles Dugout. 2007. (Illus.). 202p. per. 15.95 *(978-1-59670-223-3(0))* Sports Publishing, LLC.

Epstein, Brad M. Baltimore Orioles 101: My First Team-Board-Book. Lt. ed. 2007. (101 — My First Text-Board Books). (Illus.). 22p. (J). pap. *(978-1-932530-87-2(8)*, 101 Bk.) Michaelson Entertainment.

Felber, Bill. A Game of Brawl: The Orioles, the Beaneaters, & the Battle for the 1897 Pennant. 2007. (ENG., Illus.). 320p. 24.95 *(978-0-8032-1135-0(8))* Univ. of Nebraska Pr.

Fox, Bucky. The Orioles Fan's Little Book of Wisdom. 2008. (ENG.). 112p. pap. 7.95 *(978-1-58979-346-0(3))* Taylor Trade Publishing.

Gesker, Mike, et al. The Orioles Encyclopedia: A Half Century of History & Highlights. 2009. (ENG., Illus.). 896p. 56.00 *(978-0-8018-9114-4(0))* Johns Hopkins Univ. Pr.

Loverro, Thom. Orioles Essential: Everything You Need to Know to Be a Real Fan! 2007. (Essential (Triumph) Ser.). (ENG., Illus.). 208p. 19.95 *(978-1-57243-832-3(0))* Triumph Bks.

Lynch, Frank. Orioles Rise from the Ashes: Baltimore's Journey to the Majors. 2006. (ENG.). 88p. per. 16.95 *(978-1-4241-6034-1(0))* PublishAmerica, Inc.

Millikin, Mark R. The Glory of the 1966 Orioles & Baltimore. 2006. pap. 24.95 *(978-1-878282-46-0(8))* St. Johann Pr.

Ripken, Cal, Jr. & Phillips, Donald T. Get in the Game: 8 Elements of Perseverance That Make the Difference. 2008. (ENG.). 272p. (gr. 12-18). 15.00 (978-1-59240-280-9(1), Gotham) Penguin Group (USA) Inc.

Society for American Baseball Research (SABR). Pitching, Defense, & Three-Run Homers: The 1970 Baltimore Orioles. Armour, Mark & Allen, Malcolm, eds. 2012. (Memorable Teams in Baseball History Ser.). (ENG., Illus.). 288p. pap. 24.95 **(978-0-8032-3993-7(9))** Univ. of Nebraska Pr.

BALTIMORE RAVENS (FOOTBALL TEAM)

Feinstein, John. Next Man Up: A Year Behind the Lines in Today's NFL. 2006. (ENG., Illus.). 544p. pap. 16.99 (978-0-316-01328-4(5), Back Bay Bks.) Little Brown & Co.

Oher, Michael. I Beat the Odds: From Homelessness, to the Blind Side, & Beyond. 2012. (ENG.). 288p. (gr. 12). 16.00 **(978-1-59240-638-8(6)**, Gotham) Penguin Group (USA) Inc.

Oher, Michael & Yaeger, Don. I Beat the Odds: From Homelessness, to the Blind Side & Beyond. 2011. (ENG.). 272p. (gr. 12). 26.00 (978-1-59240-612-8(2), Gotham) Penguin Group (USA) Inc.

BALTIMORE SUN

see Sun (Baltimore, Md.: 1837)

BALTO-SLAVIC LANGUAGES

see Baltic Languages; Slavic Languages

BALTO-SLAVIC PHILOLOGY

see Slavic Philology

BALTS (INDO-EUROPEAN PEOPLE)

see also Lithuanians

Mole, Richard C. M. The Baltic States from the Soviet Union to the European Union: Identity, Discourse & Power in the Post-Communist Transition of Estonia, Latvia & Lithuania. 2012. E-Book **(978-0-203-12149-8(X))** Earthscan.

BALUCHI (SOUTHWEST ASIAN PEOPLE)

Akbar, Malik Siraj. The Redefined Dimensions of Baloch Nationalist Movement. 2011. 346p. 29.99 **(978-1-4568-9532-7(X))**; pap. 19.99 **(978-1-4568-9531-0(1))** Xlibris Corp.

Axenov, Serge. Balochi Language of Turkmenistan: A Corpus-Based Grammatical Description. 2006. (Studia Iranica Upsaliensia Ser.: 10). 335p. (Orig.). pap. 77.50 (978-91-554-6766-1(0)) Uppsala Universitet/Acta Universitatis Uppsaliensis SWE. Dist: Coronet Bks.

Axmann, Martin. Back to the Future: The Khanate of Kalat & the Genesis of Baluch Nationalism 1915-1955. 2008. (ENG.). 360p. 21.95 (978-0-19-547645-3(X)) Oxford Univ. Pr., Inc.

BALUCHI LANGUAGE

Axenov, Serge. Balochi Language of Turkmenistan: A Corpus-Based Grammatical Description. 2006. (Studia Iranica Upsaliensia Ser.: 10). 335p. (Orig.). pap. 77.50 (978-91-554-6766-1(0)) Uppsala Universitet/Acta Universitatis Uppsaliensis SWE. Dist: Coronet Bks.

Sabir, Abdurrazzaq. Balochi Reader. 2010. (BAL & ENG.). xv, 296p. (978-1-931546-79-9(7)) Dunwoody Pr.

BALUYIA (AFRICAN PEOPLE)

see Luyia (African People)

BALZAC, HONORE DE, 1799-1850

Baker, Geoffrey. Realism's Empire: Empiricism & Enchantment in the Nineteenth-Century Novel. 2009. (ENG.). 288p. 61.95 (978-0-8142-1098-7(8)); cd-rom 14.95 (978-0-8142-9196-2(1)) Ohio State Univ. Pr.

Balzac, Honoré de. Journey from Paris to Java. 2010. (ENG.). 68p. pap. 14.95 (978-981-4260-14-5(2), Didier Millet,Csi) Continental Sales, Inc.

Bourgeois, Louise, et al. Moi, Eugénie Grandet. 2010. (FRE., Illus.). 135p. (978-2-07-013101-3(7)) Gallimard, Editions.

Brunetiere, Ferdinand. Honore de Balzac. 2007. 320p. 32.95 (978-1-4344-8399-7(1)); per. 19.95 (978-1-4344-8398-0(3)) Wildside Pr., LLC.

Carter, David. Honore de Balzac. 2008. (Brief Lives Ser.). (ENG.). 96p. pap. 13.95 (978-1-84391-908-7(7)) Hesperus Pr. GBR. Dist: Independent Pubs. Group.

Cerfberr, Anatole & Christophe, Jules François. Repertory of the Comedie Humaine A - Z. 2007. 504p. pap. 30.99 (978-1-4346-1185-7(X)); (ENG.). 554p. pap. 32.99 (978-1-4346-1256-4(2)) BiblioBazaar.

Cerfberr, Anatole & Frantois, Jules. Repertory of the Comedie Humaine, Complete, A — Z. 2007. 368p. per. (978-1-4068-4452-8(7)) Echo Library.

Faguet, Emile. Balzac. 2008. 272p. 42.95 (978-1-4366-3985-9(9)); pap. 27.95 (978-0-548-85487-7(4)) Kessinger Publishing, LLC.

—Balzac. 2008. 272p. pap. (978-1-4097-8556-9(4)); pap. (978-1-4097-8555-2(6)) Read Bks.

Fargeau. Balzac et la Recherche de l'Absolu. 32.95 (978-0-7859-0616-2(9), F56660) French & European Pubns., Inc.

Floyd, Juanita H. Women in the Life of Balzac. 2010. 194p. pap. 18.36 (978-1-162-71768-5(8)); 30.36 **(978-1-169-28286-5(5))**; 37.95 (978-1-161-48632-2(1)) Kessinger Publishing, LLC.

Floyd, Juanita Helm. Women in the Life of Balzac. 2010. (ENG.). 380p. pap. 33.75 (978-1-171-68673-6(0)) 2010. 366p. pap. 32.75 **(978-1-178-29228-2(2))** 2010. 388p. pap. 33.75 (978-1-177-87419-9(9)) 2010. (ENG.). 384p. pap. 33.75 (978-1-177-28045-7(0)) 2010. 380p. pap. 33.75 (978-1-149-10750-8(2)) 2009. 376p. 38.99 (978-1-117-09622-3(X)) 2009. (ENG.). 375p. pap. 32.75 (978-1-117-09623-0(8)) 2009. 380p. 26.99 (978-1-103-80078-0(7)) 2009. 380p. pap. 20.99 (978-1-103-80070-4(1)) BiblioBazaar.

—Women in the Life of Balzac. 2008. 212p. pap. (978-1-4099-4672-4(X)) Dodo Pr.

—Women in the Life of Balzac. 2010. (Illus.). 144p. pap. 23.19 (978-1-153-73406-6(0)) 2009. 174p. pap. 23.19 (978-1-151-26284-4(6)) General Bks. LLC.

—Women in the life of Balzac. 2009. (ENG.). 375p. pap. 25.99 (978-1-117-09624-7(6), BiblioLife) BiblioBazaar.

Giraud, Raymond. The Unheroic Hero in the Novels of Stendhal, Balzac, & Flaubert. 2011. 248p. 46.95 **(978-1-258-05855-5(3))** Literary Licensing, LLC.

Gribble, Francis. Balzac: The Man & the Lover. 292p. 2008. 43.95 (978-1-4366-8569-6(9)) 2007. (ENG.). per. 28.95 (978-1-4325-8283-8(6)) Kessinger Publishing, LLC.

Heathcote, Owen. Balzac & Violence: Representing History, Space, Sexuality & Death in la Comédie Humaine. 2009. (French Studies of the Eighteenth & Nineteenth Centuries Ser.). (Illus.). 293p. pap. 54.95 (978-3-03910-551-9(5)) Lang, Peter AG GBR. Dist: Lang, Peter.

Horton, Merrill. Hunting the Sun: Faulkner's Borrowings from Balzac's the Human Comedy & Droll Stories. 2010. (Modern American Literature: New Approaches Ser.). 290p. (C). 80.95 (978-1-4331-1003-0(2)) Lang, Peter Publishing, Inc.

James, Henry. The Question of Our Speech: The Lesson of Balzac, Two Lectures. reprint ed. pap. 75.00 (978-1-4047-3464-7(3)) Classic Textbooks.

Keim, Albert. Honore de Balzac. 2007. (Illus.). 140p. per. (978-1-4065-1868-9(9)) Dodo Pr.

—Honore de Balzac. 2010. (Illus.). 80p. pap. 20.00 (978-1-153-62917-1(8)) General Bks. LLC.

—Honort de Balzac. 2007. 88p. per. (978-1-4068-2500-8(X)) Echo Library.

Keim, Albert & Lumet, Louis. Honoré de Balzac. 2010. 284p. pap. 28.75 (978-1-147-55341-3(6)) BiblioBazaar.

—Honoré de Balzac. 2010. 104p. pap. 15.96 (978-1-162-66663-1(3)); 34.95 (978-1-161-43528-3(X)) Kessinger Publishing, LLC.

Keim, Albert, et al. Honoré de Balzac. 2010. 284p. (ENG.). pap. 28.75 (978-1-171-63911-4(2)); pap. 28.75 (978-1-176-71091-7(5)) BiblioBazaar.

Lawton, Frederick. Balzac. 2007. (ENG.). 260p. per. (978-1-4065-3620-1(2)) Dodo Pr.

—Balzac. 2007. (ENG.). 200p. per. (978-1-4068-1812-3(7)) Echo Library.

Mazaheri, John H. Essais Sur la Religiosite N'Honore De Balzac. 2008. (FRE.). 168p. 99.95 (978-0-7734-4968-8(X)) Mellen, Edwin Pr., The.

Mortimer, Armine Kotin. For Love or for Money: Balzac's Rhetorical Realism. 2011. (Illus.). 346p. 52.95 **(978-0-8142-1169-4(0))**; 368p. cd-rom 14.95 **(978-0-8142-9268-6(2))** Ohio State Univ. Pr.

Muhlstein, Anka. Balzac's Omelette: A Delicious Tour of French Food & Culture with Honore'de Balzac. 2011. (ENG., Illus.). 256p. 19.95 (978-1-59051-473-3(4)) Other Pr., LLC.

Saltus, Edgar E. Balzac. reprint ed. 34.50 (978-0-404-01959-4(5)) AMS Pr., Inc.

Sanders, Mary F. Honore de Balzac His Life & Writings. 2008. 284p. 25.99 (978-0-554-36167-3(1)) 2008. 284p. 28.99 (978-0-554-26864-4(7)) 2007. 254p. pap. 21.99 (978-1-4346-2030-9(1)) 2007. (ENG.). 282p. pap. 23.99 (978-1-4346-2059-0(X)) BiblioBazaar.

Vachon, Stephane. Balzac: Une Poetique du Roman. (FRE., Illus.). 460p. (978-2-89261-170-0(9)) Bow Historical Bks.

Wedmore, Frederick. Life of Honore de Balzac. 2007. (ENG.). 160p. 36.95 (978-0-548-15089-4(3)); per. 21.95 (978-1-4304-4433-6(9)) Kessinger Publishing, LLC.

Yousif, Keri. Balzac Grandville & the Rise of Book Illustration. 2012. (Illus.). 200p. 99.95 **(978-1-4094-1808-5(1))** Ashgate Publishing Co.

Zweig, Stefan. Balzac, Dickens, Dostoevsky: Master Builders of the Spirit. 2009. (ENG.). 291p. pap. 34.95 (978-1-4128-1047-0(7)) Transaction Pubs.

BAMANA (AFRICAN PEOPLE)

see Bambara (African People)

BAMBARA (AFRICAN PEOPLE)

Colleyn, Jean-Paul. Bamana. 2008. (ENG., Illus.). 144p. pap. 34.95 (978-88-7439-348-0(2)) 5 Continents ITA. Dist: Hachette Bk. Group.

—The Horses of Satire: The Kcrdugaw of Mali. 2011. 160p. 40.00 (978-2-35340-093-5(0)) Gourcuff Gradenigo FRA. Dist: National Bk. Network.

Colleyn, Jean-Paul, et al. Boli. 2010. (FRE & ENG., Illus.). 176p. 50.00 (978-2-35340-075-1(2)) Gourcuff Gradenigo FRA. Dist: National Bk. Network.

Rovine, Victoria L. Bogolan: Shaping Culture through Cloth in Contemporary Mali. 2nd ed. 2008. (African Expressive Cultures Ser.). (ENG., Illus.). 200p. pap. 24.95 (978-0-253-22029-5(7), 0253220297) Indiana Univ. Pr.

Wooten, Stephen R. The Art of Livelihood: Creating Expressive Agri-Culture in Rural Mali. 2009. 206p. pap. 30.00 (978-1-59460-731-8(1)) Carolina Academic Pr.

BAMBARA LANGUAGE

Icon Group International, Inc. Staff, compiled by. Webster's Bamanankan - English Thesaurus Dictionary. 2008. 57p. ring bd. 28.95 incl. audio compact disk (978-0-497-83433-3(2)) Icon Group International, Inc.

BAMBARA TRIBE

see Bambara (African People)

BAMBATHA REBELLION, 1906

see Zulu Rebellion, 1906

BAMBOO

Arber, Agnes. The Gramineae: A Study of Cereal, Bamboo & Grass. 2010. (Cambridge Library Collection - Life Sciences Ser.). (Illus.). 506p. pap. 37.99 (978-1-108-01731-2(2)) Cambridge Univ. Pr.

Awadh, Asma. Bamboo Micro-Enterprises in Nairobi City, Keny. 2011. 116p. pap. **(978-3-8443-2179-1(9))** Lambert Academic Publishing.

Bell, Michael. The Gardener's Guide to Growing Temperate Bamboos. (Gardener's Guides). (Illus.). 160p. (978-0-7153-0859-2(9)) David & Charles Pubs. GBR. Dist: David & Charles Pubs.

Bhattacharya, Samik. Tropical Bamboo: Molecular Profiling & Genetic Diversity Study. 2010. 220p. pap. (978-3-8383-7422-2(3)) Lambert Academic Publishing.

Crompton, David. Ornamental Bamboos. 2006. (ENG., Illus.). 306p. 39.95 (978-0-88192-790-0(2), 0881927902) Timber Pr., Inc.

Earle, Joe. New Bamboo: Contemporary Japanese Masters. 2008. (Illus.). 128p. 25.00 (978-0-300-14141-2(6)) Japan Society Gallery.

Gierach, John. Fishing Bamboo: An Angler's Passion for the Traditional Fly Rod. 2007. (ENG., Illus.). 128p. per. 14.95 (978-1-59921-217-3(X), Lyons Pr.) Globe Pequot Pr., The.

Min, Shen. Bamboo in China: Arts, Crafts & a Cultural History. Lee, Yawtsong, tr. 2011. (ENG., Illus.). 128p. 16.95 (978-1-60220-132-3(3)) BetterLink Pr., Inc.

Minke, Gernot. Building with Bamboo: Design & Technology of a Sustainable Architecture. 2012. (ENG.). 160p. pap. 69.95 (978-3-0346-0748-3(2)) Birkhauser Verlag AG CHE. Dist: Actar Birkhauser Distribution.

Okada, Koichiro, et al. Masters of Bamboo: Artistic Lineages in the Lloyd Cotsen Japanese Basket Collection. 2008. (ENG., Illus.). 144p. pap. 25.00 (978-0-939117-40-6(1)) Asian Art Museum of San Francisco.

Squire, David. The Bamboo, Grass & Palm Specialist: The Essential Guide to Selecting, Growing & Propagating Bamboos, Grasses & Palms. Bridgewater, Alan & Bridgewater, Gill, eds. 2007. (Specialist Ser.). (ENG., Illus.). 80p. pap. 9.95 (978-1-84537-483-9(5)) New Holland Pubs., Ltd. GBR. Dist: Sterling Publishing Co., Inc.

Stangler, Carol. The Craft & Art of Bamboo, Revised & Updated: 30 Eco-Friendly Projects to Make for Home & Garden. 2009. (ENG., Illus.). 160p. pap. 17.95 (978-1-60059-339-0(9)) Lark Bks.

Stanley, Lawrence. The Friendly Bamboo Revolution: Landscaping with Bamboo - A Practical Guide. 2008. (Illus.). 188p. pap. 39.95 (978-0-9801697-0-6(4)) Bamboo4Sale.com.

Whittaker, Paul. Practical Bamboos: The 50 Best Plants for Screens, Containers & More. 2010. (ENG., Illus.). 176p. pap. 19.95 (978-1-60469-056-9(9), 1604690569) Timber Pr., Inc.

Xiao, Yan, et al. Modern Bamboo Structures: Proceedings of First International Conference on Modern Bamboo Structures (ICBS-2007), Changsha, China, 28-30 October 2007. Xiao, Yan et al, eds. 2008. (ENG., Illus.). 312p. 157.95 (978-0-415-47597-6(X), Taylor & Francis) Taylor & Francis Group GBR. Dist: Taylor & Francis Group.

Yoshikawa, Isao & Suzuki, Osamu. Bamboo Fences. 2009. (ENG., Illus.). 160p. 40.00 (978-1-56898-834-4(6)) Princeton Architectural Pr.

Yu, Xiaobing. Bamboo. 2008. 196p. pap. (978-3-8364-8365-0(3)) VDM Verlag Dr. Mueller e.K.

BANACH ALGEBRAS

see also C Algebras; Function Algebras; Harmonic Analysis; Von Neumann Algebras

Aiena, Pietro. Fredholm & Local Spectral Theory, with Applications to Multipliers. 2010. xiv, 444p. pap. 149.00 (978-90-481-6522-3(9), 9048165229) Springer.

Allan, Graham & Dales, H. Garth. Introduction to Banach Spaces & Algebras. 2010. (Oxford Graduate Texts in Mathematics Ser.). (ENG.). 384p. pap. 62.50 (978-0-19-920654-4(6)); (Illus.). 125.95 (978-0-19-920653-7(8)) Oxford Univ. Pr., Inc.

Aupetit, B. Proprietes Spectrales des Algebres de Banach. 2008. (Lecture Notes in Mathematics Ser.). (FRE.). 208p. pap. 26.00 (978-3-540-09531-6(4)) Springer.

Bachar, J. M., ed. Radical Banach Algebras & Automatic Continuity: Proceedings of a Conference Held at California State University Long Beach, July 17-31, 1981. 2008. (Lecture Notes in Mathematics Ser.). pap. 59.00 (978-3-540-11985-2(X)) Springer.

Dales, H. G., et al. Banach Algebras on Semigroups & on Their Compactifications. 2010. (Memoirs of the American Mathematical Society Ser.). 165p. pap. 74.00 (978-0-8218-4775-6(9)) American Mathematical Society.

Derighetti, Antoine. Convolution Operators on Groups. 2011. (Lecture Notes of the Unione Matematica Italiana Ser.). (ENG.). xii, 171p. pap. 49.95 (978-3-642-20655-9(7), 3642206557) Springer.

Donner, K. Extension of Positive Operators & Korovkin Theorems. 2008. (Lecture Notes in Mathematics Ser.). pap. 26.00 (978-3-540-11183-2(2)) Springer.

Doran, R. S. Approximate Identities & Factorization in Banach Modules. 2008. (Lecture Notes in Mathematics Ser.). pap. 46.00 (978-3-540-09725-9(2)) Springer.

Eckmann, J. P. & Guenin, M. Methodes Algebriques en Mecanique Statistique. 2007. (Lecture Notes in Mathematics Ser.). (FRE.). 144p. per. 26.00 (978-3-540-04249-5(0)) Springer.

Fell, J. M. G. Induced Representations & Banach*-Algebraic Bundles. 2008. (Lecture Notes in Mathematics Ser.). pap. 46.00 (978-3-540-08147-0(X)) Springer.

Handelman, D. Positive Polynomials, Convex Integral Polytopes, & a Random Walk Problem. 2008. (Lecture Notes in Mathematics Ser.). pap. 39.95 (978-3-540-18400-3(7)) Springer.

Harpe, P. De La. Classical Banach-Lie Algebras & Banach-Lie Groups of Operators in Hilbert Space. 2008. (Lecture Notes in Mathematics Ser.). 172p. pap. 39.95 (978-3-540-05984-4(9)) Springer.

Huijsmans, C. B. & Luxemburg, Wilhelm A. J., eds. Positive Operators & Semigroups on Banach Lattices. 2010. 164p. pap. 179.00 (978-90-481-4205-7(9), 9048142059) Springer.

Jarosz, K. Perturbation of Banach Algebras. 2008. (Lecture Notes in Mathematics Ser.). pap. 39.95 (978-3-540-15218-7(0)) Springer.

Jorgensen, Palle E. T., et al. Representations, Wavelets & Frames: A Celebration of the Mathematical Work of Lawrence Baggett. 2008. (Applied & Numerical Harmonic Analysis Ser.). (Illus.). 350p. 89.95 (978-0-8176-4682-0(5)) Springer.

Kaniuth, Eberhard. A Course in Commutative Banach Algebras. 2007. (Graduate Texts in Mathematics Ser.). 368p. 69.95 (978-0-387-72475-1(3)) Springer.

Kone, Namadzavho Bernard. Functional Analysis: Quasinilpotent Equivalence in Banach Algebras. 2010. 60p. pap. (978-3-8383-5707-2(8)) Lambert Academic Publishing.

Larsen, R. The Multiplier Problem. 2008. (Lecture Notes in Mathematics Ser.). 296p. pap. 46.00 (978-3-540-04624-0(0), 3540046240) Springer.

Lubansky, Raymond. Axiomatic Spectral Theory in Banach Algebras. 2010. 140p. pap. (978-3-8383-5097-4(9)) Lambert Academic Publishing.

Muller, Vladimir. Spectral Theory of Linear Operators: And Spectral Systems in Banach Algebras. 2nd ed. 2007. (Operator Theory: Advances & Applications Ser.). 439p. 179.00 (978-3-7643-8264-3(3)) Springer.

Palmer, Theodore W. Banach Algebras & the General Theory of *-Algebras 2 Part Set: Volume 2, *-Algebras, 2 vols. 2009. (Encyclopedia of Mathematics & its Applications Ser.). (ENG.). 835p. pap. 140.00 (978-0-521-15261-7(5)) Cambridge Univ. Pr.

—Banach Algebras & the General Theory of *-Algebras: Volume 1, Algebras & Banach Algebras. 2009. (Encyclopedia of Mathematics & its Applications Ser.). (ENG.). 812p. pap. 140.00 (978-0-521-12410-2(7)) Cambridge Univ. Pr.

Roch, Steffen, et al. Non-Commutative Gelfand Theories: A Tool-kit for Operator Theorists & Numerical Analysts. 2010. (Universitext Ser.). (Illus.). xiv, 383p. pap. 74.95 (978-0-85729-182-0(3), 0857291823) Springer.

Silverman, Joseph H. Moduli Spaces & Arithmetic Dynamics. 2012. (CRM Monograph Ser.). (Illus.). 140p. 59.00 **(978-0-8218-7582-7(5))** American Mathematical Society.

Tian, Jianjun Paul. Evolution Algebras & Their Applications. 2007. (Lecture Notes in Mathematics Ser.). (Illus.). 125p. per. 69.95 (978-3-540-74283-8(2)) Springer.

Wapner, Leonard M. The Pea & the Sun: A Mathematical Paradox. 2007. (ENG., Illus.). 232p. pap. 24.95 (978-1-56881-327-1(9)) AK Peters, Ltd.

BANACH RINGS

see Banach Algebras

BANACH SPACES

see also Banach Algebras; Hilbert Space; Normed Linear Spaces

Akin, Ethan. The Metric Theory of Banach Manifolds. 2008. (Lecture Notes in Mathematics Ser.). 336p. pap. 46.00 (978-3-540-08915-5(2)) Springer.

Albiac, Fernando & Kalton, Nigel J. Topics in Banach Space Theory. 2010. (Graduate Texts in Mathematics Ser.). xii, 376p. pap. 84.95 (978-1-4419-2099-7(4), 1441920994) Springer.

Allan, Graham & Dales, H. Garth. Introduction to Banach Spaces & Algebras. 2010. (Oxford Graduate Texts in Mathematics Ser.). (ENG.). 384p. pap. 62.50 (978-0-19-920654-4(6)); (Illus.). 125.95 (978-0-19-920653-7(8)) Oxford Univ. Pr., Inc.

Baker, J., et al, eds. Banach Spaces of Analytic Functions. Proceedings of the Pelzczynski Conference Held at Kent State University, July 12-16, 1976. 2008. (Lecture Notes in Mathematics Ser.). 148p. pap. 26.00 (978-3-540-08356-6(1)) Springer.

Banach, Stefan. Theory of Linear Operations. Jellett, F., tr. from FRE. 2009. (Dover Books on Mathematics Ser.). (ENG.). 256p. pap. 14.95 (978-0-486-46983-6(2)) Dover Pubns., Inc.

Barbu, Viorel. Nonlinear Differential Equations of Monotone Types in Banach Spaces. 2010. x, 272p. **(978-1-4419-5542-5(9))** Springer.

Barbu, Viorel & Precupanu, Teodor. Convexity & Optimization in Banach Spaces. 4th ed. 2012. (Springer Monographs in Mathematics Ser.). (ENG.). xii, 368p. 124.00 **(978-94-007-2246-0(X)**, 940072246X) Springer.

Bastero, J. Probability & Banach Spaces: Proceedings of a Conference held in Zaragoza, June 17-21, 1985. 2008. (Lecture Notes in Mathematics Ser.). pap. 46.00 (978-3-540-17186-7(X)) Springer.

Beck, A., ed. Probability in Banach Spaces II: Proceedings of the Second International Conference on Probability in Banach Spaces, 18-24 June 1978, Oberwolfach, Germany. 2008. (Lecture Notes in Mathematics Ser.). 216p. pap. 46.00 (978-3-540-09242-1(0)) Springer.

—Probability in Banach Spaces III: Proceedings of the Third International Conference on Probability in Banach Spaces, Held at Tufts University, Medford, USA, August 4-16, 1980. 2008. (Lecture Notes in Mathematics Ser.). 340p. pap. 46.00 (978-3-540-10822-1(X)) Springer.

—Probability in Banach Spaces V: Proceedings of the International Conference held in Medford, USA, July 16-27, 1984. 2008. (Lecture Notes in Mathematics Ser.). pap. 59.00 (978-3-540-15704-5(2)) Springer.

Beck, A. & Jacobs, K., eds. Probability in Banach Spaces IV: Proceedings of the Seminar Held in Oberwolfach, FRG, July 1982. 2008. (Lecture Notes in Mathematics Ser.). pap. 46.00 (978-3-540-12295-1(8)) Springer.

Beck, Anatole, ed. Probability in Banach Spaces. 2008. (Lecture Notes in Mathematics Ser.). 304p. 46.00 (978-3-540-07793-0(6)) Springer.

Behrends, E. M-Structure & the Banach-Stone Theorem. 2008. (Lecture Notes in Mathematics Ser.). 228p. pap. 46.00 *(978-3-540-09533-0(0))* Springer.
Behrends, E., et al. _P-Structure in Real Banach Spaces. 2008. (Lecture Notes in Mathematics Ser.). 124p. pap. 26.00 *(978-3-540-08441-9(X))* Springer.
Blei, R. C., ed. Banach Spaces, Harmonic Analysis, & Probability Theory: Proceedings of the Special Year in Analysis, held at the University of Connecticut 1980-1981. 2008. (Lecture Notes in Mathematics Ser.). pap. 39.95 *(978-3-540-12314-9(8))* Springer.
Bourgin, R. D. Geometric Aspects of Convex Sets with the Radon - Nikodym Property. 2008. (Lecture Notes in Mathematics Ser.). 59.00 *(978-3-540-12296-8(6))* Springer.
Castillo, Jesus M. F. & Johnson, William B., eds. Methods in Banach Space Theory: Proceedings of the V Conference on Banach Spaces, Cáceres, Spain, 13-18 September, 2004. 2007. (London Mathematical Society Lecture Note Ser.: Vol. 337). (ENG., Illus.). 370p. per. 102.00 *(978-0-521-68568-9(0))* Cambridge Univ. Pr.
Chao, J. A. & Woyczynski, W. A., eds. Martingale Theory in Harmonic Analysis & Banach Spaces: Proceedings of the NSF-CBMS Conference Held at the Cleveland State University, Cleveland, Ohio, July 13-17, 1981. 2008. (Lecture Notes in Mathematics Ser.). pap. 46.00 *(978-3-540-11569-4(2))* Springer.
Chidume, Charles. Geometric Properties of Banach Spaces & Nonlinear Iterations. 2009. (Lecture Notes in Mathematics Ser.). xvii, 326p. pap. 89.95 *(978-1-84882-189-7(1))* Springer.
Cram101 Textbook Reviews. Outlines & Highlights for from Hahn-Banach to Monotonicity by Stephen Simons, Isbn: 9781402069185 1402069189. 2011. 60p. pap. 26.95 ***(978-1-61490-176-1(7))*** Cram101 Inc.
Diagana, Toka. Non-Archimedean Linear Operators & Applications. 2008. (Illus.). xiii, 92p. pap. 45.00 ***(978-1-60456-494-5(6))*** 2006. 92p. (C). 110.00 *(978-1-60021-405-9(3))* Nova Science Pubs., Inc.
Diagana, Toka. Pseudo Almost Periodic Functions in Banach Spaces. 2007. 125.00 *(978-1-50021-637-4(4))* Nova Science Pubs., Inc.
Diestel, J. Geometry of Banach Spaces - Selected Topics. 2008. (Lecture Notes in Mathematics Ser.). 304p. pap. 59.95 *(978-3-540-07402-1(3))* Springer.
Diestel, Joe, et al. The Metric Theory of Tensor Products: Grothendieck's Résumé Revisited. 2008. (Illus.). 278p. (C). 81.00 *(978-0-8218-4440-3(7))* American Mathematical Society.
Dodos, Pandelis. Banach Spaces & Descriptive Set Theory: Selected Topics: Selected Topics. 2010. (Lecture Notes in Mathematics Ser.). (ENG., Illus.). x, 160p. pap. 49.95 *(978-3-642-12152-4(7),* 3642121527) Springer.
Edmunds, David E., et al. Bounded & Compact Integral Operators. 2010. (Mathematics & Its Applications Ser.). 660p. pap. 319.00 *(978-90-481-6018-1(9),* 9048160189) Springer.
Engel, Klaus-Jochen & Nagel, Rainer. A Short Course on Operator Semigroups. 2010. (Universitext Ser.). (Illus.). xii, 247p. pap. 74.95 *(978-1-4419-2174-1(5),* 1441921745) Springer.
Erdelyi, I. & Lange, R. Spectral Decompositions on Banach Spaces. 2008. (Lecture Notes in Mathematics Ser.). 132p. pap. 26.00 *(978-3-540-08525-6(4))* Springer.
Fabian, Marián, et al. Banach Space Theory: The Basis for Linear & Nonlinear Analysis. 2010. (CMS Books in Mathematics Ser.). (Illus.). xiv, 822p. 129.00 *(978-1-4419-7514-0(4),* 1441975144) Springer.
Fabian, Marian, et al. Functional Analysis & Infinite-Dimensional Geometry. 2011. (CMS Books in Mathematics Ser.). (ENG.). ix, 451p. pap. 99.00 *(978-1-4419-2912-9(6),* 1441929126) Springer.
Favini, A. Differential Equations in Banach Spaces: Proceedings of a Conference held in Bologna, July 2-5, 1985. 2008. (Lecture Notes in Mathematics Ser.). pap. 46.00 *(978-3-540-17191-1(6))* Springer.
Geometric Aspects of Functional Analysis: Israel Seminar (GAFA) 1986-87. 2008. (Lecture Notes in Mathematics Ser.). pap. 46.00 *(978-3-540-19353-1(7))* Springer.
Geometrical & Statistical Aspects of Probability in Banach Spaces: Actes des Journees SMF de Calcul des Probabilites dans les Espaces de Banach, organisees a Strasbourg les 19 et 20 Juin 1985. 2008. (Lecture Notes in Mathematics Ser.). pap. 26.00 *(978-3-540-16487-6(1))* Springer.
Hajek, Petr, et al. Biorthogonal Systems in Banach Spaces. (CMS Books in Mathematics Ser.). 2010. xviii, 342p. pap. 89.95 *(978-1-4419-2395-0(0),* 1441923950) 2007. (Illus.). 339p. 89.95 *(978-0-387-68914-2(1))* Springer.
Harmand, P., et al. M-Ideals in Banach Spaces & Banach Algebras. 2008. (Lecture Notes in Mathematics Ser.). (Illus.). 395p. pap. 69.95 *(978-3-540-56814-8(X))* Springer.
Helemskii, A. Ya. Quantum Functional Analysis: Non-Coordinate Approach. 2010. (University Lecture Ser.). (Illus.). 241p. pap. 51.00 *(978-0-8218-5254-5(X))* American Mathematical Society.
Heyer, Herbert. Structural Aspects in the Theory of Probability, Vol. 8. 2nd ed. 2009. 424p. 111.00 *(978-981-4282-48-2(0))* World Scientific Publishing Co., Inc.
Hoffman, Kenneth. Banach Spaces of Analytic Functions. 2007. (Dover Books on Mathematics Ser.). (ENG.). 224p. per. 13.95 *(978-0-486-45874-8(1))* Dover Pubns., Inc.
Junge, Marius & Parcet, Javier. Mixed-Norm Inequalities & Operator Space Lp Embedding Theory. 2010. (Memoirs of the American Mathematical Society Ser.). 155p. pap. 74.00 *(978-0-8218-4655-1(8))* American Mathematical Society.
Kalton, N. & Saab, E, eds. Banach Spaces. 2008. (Lecture Notes in Mathematics Ser.). pap. 39.95 *(978-3-540-16051-9(5))* Springer.
Kantorovitz, S. Spectral Theory of Banach Space Operators: Ck-Classification, Abstract Volterra Operators, Similarity, Spectrality, Local Spectral Analysis. 2008. (Lecture Notes in Mathematics Ser.). pap. 26.00 *(978-3-540-12673-7(2))* Springer.
Ki Sik Ha. Nonlinear Functional Evolutions in Banach Spaces. 2010. 364p. pap. 152.00 *(978-90-481-6204-8(1),* 9048162041) Springer.
Kuo, H. H. Gaussian Measures in Banach Spaces. 2008. (Lecture Notes in Mathematics Ser.). 236p. pap. 59.95 *(978-3-540-07173-0(3))* Springer.
Lacey, H. Elton, ed. Notes in Banach Spaces. 2012. (ENG.). 448p. pap. 50.00 ***(978-0-292-74125-6(1))*** Univ. of Texas Pr.
Ledoux, Michel. Probability in Banach Spaces: Isoperimetry & Processes. 2010. (Ergebnisse der Mathematik und ihrer Grenzgebiete. 3. Folge A Series of Modern Surveys in Mathematics Ser.). (ENG., Illus.). xii, 480p. pap. 259.00 *(978-3-642-08087-6(1),* 3642080871) Springer.
Ledoux, Michel & Talagrand, Michel. Probability in Banach Spaces: Isoperimetry & Processes. 2011. (Classics in Mathematics Ser.). (ENG., Illus.). xii, 480p. pap. 74.95 *(978-3-642-20211-7(X),* 364220211X) Springer.
Lian, Zeng & Lu, Kening. Lyapunov Exponents & Invariant Manifolds for Random Dynamical Systems in a Banach Space. 2010. (Memoirs of the American Mathematical Society Ser.). 106p. pap. 68.00 *(978-0-8218-4656-8(6))* American Mathematical Society.
Light, W. & Cheney, E. Approximation Theory in Tensor Product Spaces. 2008. (Lecture Notes in Mathematics Ser.). pap. 39.95 *(978-3-540-16057-1(4))* Springer.
Lindenstrauss, J. & Tzafriri, L. Classical Banach Spaces. 2008. (Lecture Notes in Mathematics Ser.). 260p. pap. 46.00 *(978-3-540-06408-4(7),* 3540064087) Springer.
Lindenstrauss, Joram. Fréchet Differentiability of Lipschitz Functions & Porous Sets in Banach Spaces. 2012. (Annals of Mathematics Studies). (ENG.). 424p. (C). 165.00 ***(978-0-691-15355-1(8))*** Princeton Univ. Pr.
Lindenstrauss, Joram, et al. Fréchet Differentiability of Lipschitz Functions & Porous Sets in Banach Spaces. 2012. (Annals of Mathematics Studies). (ENG.). 424p. (C). pap. 75.00 ***(978-0-691-15356-8(6))*** Princeton Univ. Pr.
Ludkovsky, Sergey. Quasi-Invariant & Pseduo-Differentiable Measures in Banach Spaces. 2009. 198p. 145.00 *(978-1-60692-734-2(5))* Nova Science Pubs., Inc.
Lukes, Jaroslav, et al. Integral Representation Theory: Applications to Convexity, Banach Spaces & Potential Theory. 2010. (De Gruyter Studies in Mathematics Ser.). (ENG.). XVI, 715p. 129.95 *(978-3-11-020320-2(0))* De Gruyter, Walter Inc.
MacGregor, Thomas H. Banach Spaces of Analytic Functions. Hibschweiler, Rita A., ed. 2008. (Contemporary Mathematics Ser.). 147p. (C). pap. 61.00 *(978-0-8218-4268-3(4))* American Mathematical Society.
Michor, P. W. Functors & Categories of Banach Spaces. 2008. (Lecture Notes in Mathematics Ser.). 112p. pap. 39.95 *(978-3-540-08764-9(8))* Springer.
Milman, Vitali D. & Schechtman, Gideon, eds. Geometric Aspects of Functional Analysis: Israel Seminar 2004-2005. 2007. (Lecture Notes in Mathematics Ser.). 326p. per. 79.95 *(978-3-540-72052-2(9))* Springer.
Mujica, Jorge. Complex Analysis in Banach Spaces. 2010. (Dover Books on Mathematics Ser.). (ENG.). 464p. pap. 17.95 *(978-0-486-47466-3(6))* Dover Pubns., Inc.
Non-Spectral Asymptotic Analysis of One-Parameter Operator Semigroups. 2007. (Operator Theory: Advances & Applications Ser.). (Illus.). 174p. 109.00 *(978-3-7643-8095-3(0),* 3764380950) Birkhauser Verlag AG CHE. Dist: Springer.
Odell, E. W. Functional Analysis: Proceedings of the Seminar at the University of Texas at Austin, 1986-87. 2008. (Lecture Notes in Mathematics Ser.). pap. 46.00 *(978-3-540-50018-6(9))* Springer.
Odyniec, W. Minimal Projections in Banach Spaces: Problems of Existence & Uniqueness & their Application. 2008. (Lecture Notes in Mathematics Ser.). pap. 39.95 *(978-3-540-53197-5(1))* Springer.
Pietsch, A., ed. Banach Space Theory & its Applications: Proceedings of the First Romanian GDR Seminar Held at Bucharest, Romania, August 31 - September 6, 1981. 2008. (Lecture Notes in Mathematics Ser.). pap. 46.00 *(978-3-540-12298-2(2))* Springer.
Pietsch, Albrecht. History of Banach Spaces & Linear Operators. 2007. (ENG., Illus.). xxii, 855p. 160.00 *(978-0-8176-4367-6(2),* 0817643672) Birkhauser Boston.
Pietsch, Albrecht & Wenzel, Jörg. Orthonormal Systems & Banach Space Geometry. 2008. (Encyclopedia of Mathematics & its Applications Ser.). (ENG., Illus.). 564p. pap. 60.00 *(978-0-521-05431-7(1))* Cambridge Univ. Pr.
Pisier, Gilles. Complex Interpolation Between Hilbert, Banach & Operator Spaces. 2010. (Memoirs of the American Mathematical Society Ser.). 78p. pap. 64.00 *(978-0-8218-4842-5(9))* American Mathematical Society.
Pyatkov, Sergei G. Operator Theory. Nonclassical Problems. (Inverse & Ill-Posed Problems Ser.). (ENG.). XIV, 347p. 538.00 ***(978-3-11-182612-7(0))*** De Gruyter, Walter Inc.
Randrianantoanina, Beata & Randrianantoanina, Narcisse, eds. Banach Spaces & Their Applications in Analysis: In Honor of Nigel Kalton's 60th Birthday. 2007. (De Gruyter Proceedings in Mathematics Ser.). (ENG., Illus.). IX, 453p. 210.00 *(978-3-11-019449-4(X))* De Gruyter, Walter Inc.
Randrianantoanina, Beata & Randrianantoanina, Narcisse, eds. Banach Spaces & their Applications in Analysis: In Honor of Nigel Kalton's 60th Birthday. 2007. (De Gruyter Proceedings in Mathematics Ser.). (ENG.). IX, 453p. 321.00 ***(978-3-11-183395-8(X))*** De Gruyter, Walter Inc.
Ryan, Raymond A. Introduction to Tensor Products of Banach Spaces. 2010. (Springer Monographs in Mathematics Ser.). (Illus.). xiv, 225p. pap. 109.00 *(978-1-84996-872-0(1),* 1849968721) Springer.
Schwartz, L. Geometry & Probability in Banach Spaces. 2008. (Lecture Notes in Mathematics Ser.). pap. 39.95 *(978-3-540-10691-3(X))* Springer.
Simons, S. From Hahn-Banach to Monotonicity. 2nd ed. 2008. (Lecture Notes in Mathematics Ser.). (Illus.). xiv, 241p. (C). 69.95 *(978-1-4020-6918-5(9))* Springer.
Tolstonogov, Alexander. Differential Inclusions in a Banach Space. 2010. (Mathematics & Its Applications Ser.). 320p. pap. 179.00 *(978-90-481-5580-4(0),* 9048155800) Springer.
Trebels, W. Multipliers for -Bounded Fourier Expansions in Banach Spaces & Approximation Theory. 2008. (Lecture Notes in Mathematics Ser.). 116p. pap. 26.00 *(978-3-540-06357-5(9))* Springer.
Tsirelson's Space. 2008. (Lecture Notes in Mathematics Ser.). pap. 59.95 *(978-3-540-50678-2(0))* Springer.
Weron, A, ed. Probability Theory on Vector Spaces. 2008. (Lecture Notes in Mathematics Ser.). 288p. pap. 46.00 *(978-3-540-08846-2(6))* Springer.
—Probability Theory on Vector Spaces II: Proceedings, Blazejewko, Poland, September 17-23, 1979. 2008. (Lecture Notes in Mathematics Ser.). 340p. pap. 46.00 *(978-3-540-10253-3(1))* Springer.
Zaslavski, Alexander J. Optimization on Metric & Normed Spaces. 2010. (Springer Optimization & Its Applications Ser.). xiii, 434p. 149.00 *(978-0-387-88620-6(6),* 0387886206) Springer.

BANANA

Adams, Frederick Upham. Conquest of the Tropics: The Story of the Creative Enterprises Conducted by the United Fruit Company. 2009. 384p. 33.99 *(978-1-110-10824-4(9));* pap. 32.75 *(978-1-110-10822-0(2))* BiblioBazaar.
Chapman, Peter. Bananas: How the United Fruit Company Shaped the World. 2009. (ENG.). 240p. pap. 14.00 *(978-1-84767-194-3(2))* Canongate Bks. GBR. Dist: Perseus-PGW.
Cohen, Alisha E., ed. Bananas: Nutrition, Diseases & Trade Issues. 2010. (Food Science & Technology Ser.). 129.00 *(978-1-61761-124-7(7),* Nova Biomedical Bks.) Nova Science Pubs., Inc.
Davara, Paresh & C. Patel, N. Post Harvest Practices for Banana Followed in Gujarat. 2011. 124p. pap. ***(978-3-8443-0573-9(4))*** Lambert Academic Publishing.
Fm, Prof Dr Bilqees, et al. Nematodes Associated with Banana in Karachi, Sindh, Pakistan: Nematodes in Banana Root. 2011. 148p. pap. ***(978-3-639-32498-3(6))*** VDM Verlag Dr. Mueller e.K.
Frundt, Henry J. Fair Bananas! Farmers, Workers, & Consumers Strive to Change an Industry. 2009. (Illus.). 256p. (C). 65.00 *(978-0-8165-2720-5(2));* (ENG.), pap. 26.95 *(978-0-8165-2836-3(5))* Univ. of Arizona Pr.
Katungi, Enid. The Role of Social Capital in Technology Adoption by Small Farmers. 2011. 256p. pap. ***(978-3-8443-2415-0(1))*** Lambert Academic Publishing.
Koeppel, Dan. Banana: The Fate of the Fruit That Changed the World. (ENG., Illus.). (gr. 12-18). 2008. 304p. 16.00 *(978-0-452-29008-2(2),* Plume) 2007. 288p. 23.95 *(978-1-59463-038-5(0),* Hudson Street Pr.) Penguin Group (USA) Inc.
Moberg & Moberg, Mark. Slipping Away: Banana Politics & Fair Trade in the Eastern Caribbean. 2009. (Illus.). 272p. 90.00 *(978-1-84545-145-5(7))* Berghahn Bks., Inc.
Nithya Devi, Alagarsamy & Ponnuswamy, V. Screening of Banana Germplasm for Resistance & Tolerance to Nematode. 2011. 212p. pap. ***(978-3-8433-9492-5(X))*** Lambert Academic Publishing.
Pillay, Michael. Banana Breeding Progress & Challenges. 2011. (ENG., Illus.). 383p. 139.95 *(978-1-4398-0017-1(0),* CRC Press) Taylor & Francis Group GBR. Dist: Taylor & Francis Group.
Pillay, Michael, et al, eds. Genetics Genomics & Breeding of Bananas. 2012. (ENG., Illus.). 350p. 119.95 ***(978-1-57808-788-4(0))*** BIOS Scientific Publishers Ltd. GBR. Dist: Taylor & Francis Group.
Robinson, J. C. & Saúco, V. Galán. Bananas & Plantains. 2nd ed. 2010. (Crop Production Science in Horticulture Ser.). (Illus.). 320p. pap. 70.00 *(978-1-84593-658-7(2))* CABI GBR. Dist: Stylus Publishing, LLC.
Roche. The International Banana Trade. (Illus.). 192p. ***(978-1-85573-405-0(2))*** Woodhead Publishing Ltd.
Shafique, Umer & Anwar, Jamil. Bananas: A Concise Account. 2011. (Agriculture Issues & Policies Ser.). pap. 43.00 *(978-1-61761-745-4(8),* Nova Novinka) Nova Science Pubs., Inc.
Smale, Melinda & Tushemereirwe, W. An Economic Assessment of Banana Genetic Improvement & Innovation in the Lake Victoria Region of Uganda & Tanzania. 2007. *(978-0-89629-164-5(2))* International Food Policy Research Institute.
Tajudeen Adebayo, Adeniji. Nutrients in Musa & Manihot from II T. 2011. 144p. pap. ***(978-3-8433-8101-7(1))*** Lambert Academic Publishing.
Talwana, Herbert. Plant-Parasitic Nematodes & Banana Root Systems Interactions. 2010. 188p. pap. *(978-3-8383-7011-8(2))* Lambert Academic Publishing.
Wiley, James. The Banana: Empires, Trade Wars, & Globalization. 2010. (At Table Ser.). (ENG., Illus.). 316p. pap. 29.95 *(978-0-8032-3285-3(3))* Univ. of Nebraska Pr.
Wiley, James & Wiley, James R. Banana: Empires, Trade Wars, & Globalization. 2008. (At Table Ser.). (ENG., Illus.). 314p. 29.95 *(978-0-8032-1577-1(0))* Univ. of Nebraska Pr.

BANARAS (INDIA)
see Varanasi (India)

BANBURY (ENGLAND)

Yurdan, Marilyn. Banbury in Old Photographs. 2011. (Britain in Old Photographs Ser.). (ENG., Illus.). 128p. pap. 23.95 *(978-0-7524-5606-5(7))* History Pr. Ltd., The GBR. Dist: Independent Pubs. Group.

BANCROFT, GEORGE, 1800-1891

Greene, George Washington. The Life of Nathanael Greene: A Major-General in the Army of the Revolution. (Library of American Biographies). 403p. reprint ed. 98.00 *(978-0-7222-8550-3(7))* Library Reprints, Inc.

BANCROFT, HUBERT HOWE, 1832-1918

Bancroft, Hubert Howe. Works. 2009. 644p. pap. *(978-0-217-65784-6(2));* 560p. pap. *(978-0-217-65901-7(2));* 572p. pap. *(978-1-4589-5564-7(8))* Books LLC.
—Works. 2010. 440p. pap. 32.89 *(978-1-152-12823-1(X))* 2010. 470p. pap. 32.89 *(978-1-152-12820-0(5))* 2010. 438p. pap. 32.89 *(978-1-152-12817-0(5))* 2010. 484p. pap. 32.89 *(978-1-152-12811-8(6))* 2010. 456p. pap. 32.89 *(978-1-152-12814-9(0))* 2009. 630p. pap. 44.45 *(978-1-4589-5488-6(9))* General Bks. LLC.

BAND MUSIC
see also Military Music; Orchestral Music; Wind Ensembles

Alfred Publishing Staff. Record Deal in a Box — Album Edition: Boxed Set. 2011. (ENG.). pap. 49.99 ***(978-0-7390-8109-9(8))*** Alfred Publishing Co., Inc.
—Record Deal in a Box — Single Edition: Boxed Set. 2011. (ENG.). pap. 24.99 ***(978-0-7390-8110-5(1))*** Alfred Publishing Co., Inc.
—10 for 10 Sheet Music Big Band Classics: Piano Solos. 2012. (10 for 10 Sheet Music Ser.). (ENG.). 36p. pap. 10.00 ***(978-0-7390-7330-8(3))*** Alfred Publishing Co., Inc.
Amis, Kenneth. The Brass Player's Cookbook: Creative Recipes for a Successful Performance. 2006. (ENG.). 148p. pap. 24.95 *(978-1-57463-075-6(X),* 157463075X) Meredith Music Pubns.
Arnold, Malcolm. Flourish for Band: Score & Parts. 2010. (Faber Edition: Faber Wind Band Ser.). (ENG.). 187p. pap. 76.25 *(978-0-571-56513-9(1),* 0571565131) Faber & Faber, Ltd. GBR. Dist: Alfred Publishing Co., Inc.
—The Pre-Goodman Rag: Score & Parts. 2010. (Faber Edition: Faber Wind Band Ser.). (ENG.). pap. 60.25 *(978-0-571-56490-3(9))* Faber & Faber, Ltd. GBR. Dist: Alfred Publishing Co., Inc.
Bartok, Bela. Stravinsky, Bartok & More - Low Brass, Vol. 8. 2007. (Orchestra Musician's CD-ROM Library: Vol. 8). (ENG.). 8p. cd-rom 19.95 *(978-1-4234-3286-9(X),* 142343286X) Leonard, Hal Corp.
Battisti, Frank L. & Musgrave, Bruce. The Best We Can Be: A History of the Ithaca High School Band 1955-67. 2010. (ENG.). 208p. pap. 34.95 *(978-1-57463-159-3(4),* 1574631594) Meredith Music Pubns.
Boysen, Andrew, Jr., et al. Composers on Composing for Band, 3. Camphouse, Mark, ed. 2007. 328p. 29.95 *(978-1-57999-631-4(0),* 2007) G I A Pubns., Inc.
Brahms, Johannes. Johannes Brahms - Waltzes, Op. 39: Adapted for Brass Quintet by Chris Coletti & Brandon Ridenour Score & Parts. 2012. (ENG.). 40p. pap. 60.00 ***(978-1-4584-1857-9(X),*** 145841857X) Leonard, Hal Corp.
Bremel, Derek. Ides March: Score & Parts. 2010. (Faber Edition: Faber Wind Band Ser.). (ENG.). pap. 60.25 *(978-0-571-56488-0(7))* Faber & Faber, Ltd. GBR. Dist: Alfred Publishing Co., Inc.
Burch-Pesses, Michael. Canadian Band Music: A Qualitative Guide to Canadian Composers & Their Works for Band. 2008. (ENG.). 182p. pap. 24.95 *(978-1-57463-087-9(3),* 1574630873) Meredith Music Pubns.
Crider, Paula & Saunders, Jack. Essential Musicianship for Band - Masterwork Studies: Alto Clarinet. 2007. (ENG.). 80p. pap. 14.95 incl. audio compact disk *(978-0-634-08860-5(2),* 0634088602) Leonard, Hal Corp.
—Essential Musicianship for Band - Masterwork Studies: Bassoon. 2007. (ENG.). 80p. pap. 14.95 incl. audio compact disk *(978-0-634-08858-2(0),* 0634088580) Leonard, Hal Corp.
—Essential Musicianship for Band - Masterwork Studies: Clarinet. 2007. (ENG.). 88p. pap. 14.95 incl. audio compact disk *(978-0-634-08859-9(9),* 0634088599) Leonard, Hal Corp.
—Essential Musicianship for Band - Masterwork Studies: Conductor Score. 2007. (ENG.). 232p. spiral bd. 49.95 *(978-0-634-08855-1(6),* 0634088556) Leonard, Hal Corp.
—Essential Musicianship for Band - Masterwork Studies: Flute. 2007. (ENG.). 84p. pap. 14.95 incl. audio compact disk *(978-0-634-08856-8(4),* 0634088564) Leonard, Hal Corp.
—Essential Musicianship for Band - Masterwork Studies: Oboe. 2007. (ENG.). 80p. pap. 14.95 incl. audio compact disk *(978-0-634-08857-5(2),* 0634088572) Leonard, Hal Corp.
Curnow, James. The Beginning Band Collection: Full Score. 2007. (ENG.). 170p. spiral bd. 24.95 *(978-90-431-2627-4(6),* 9043126276) Leonard, Hal Corp.
Daugherty, Michael. Asclepius: Fanfare for Brass & Percussion Full Score. 2008. (ENG.). 40p. pap. 17.95 *(978-1-4234-6573-7(3),* 1423465733) Boosey & Hawkes, Inc.
—Raise the Roof: For Timpani & Symphonic Band. 2007. (ENG.). 90p. pap. 29.99 *(978-1-4234-5582-0(7),* 1423455827) Boosey & Hawkes, Inc.
Dobson, Simon. The Dreaded Groove & Hook: Score. 2010. (Faber Edition: Faber Brass Band Ser.). (ENG.). pap. 13.80 *(978-0-571-57001-0(1))* Faber & Faber, Ltd. GBR. Dist: Alfred Publishing Co., Inc.
Dobson, Simon, contrib. by. Clarion Alarum: Score & Parts. 2010. (Faber Edition: Faber Brass Band Ser.). (ENG.). pap. 30.25 *(978-0-571-57002-7(X))* Faber & Faber, Ltd. GBR. Dist: Alfred Publishing Co., Inc.
—The Dreaded Groove & Hook: Score & Parts. 2010. (Faber Edition: Faber Brass Band Ser.). (ENG.). pap. 60.25 *(978-0-571-57000-3(3))* Faber & Faber, Ltd. GBR. Dist: Alfred Publishing Co., Inc.

B

Erickson, Frank. Arranging for the Concert Band Workbook. 2009. 118p. pap. 24.95 *(978-0-910927-06-2(5))* Alfred Publishing Co., Inc.

Fidyk, Steve. Big Band Drumming at First Sight: Book & CD. 2011. (ENG.). 72p. pap. 19.99 ***(978-0-7390-7882-2(8))*** Alfred Publishing Co., Inc.

Frederickson, Matthew. Standards in the Studio. 2010. 256p. pap. *(978-3-8383-3440-0(X))* Lambert Academic Publishing.

Green, Eddie, et al. Ensemble Concepts for Band - Fundamental Level: Alto Clarinet. 2006. (ENG.). 19p. pap. 4.95 *(978-0-634-09452-1(1),* 0634094521) Leonard, Hal Corp.

—Ensemble Concepts for Band - Fundamental Level: Alto Saxophone. 2006. (ENG.). 16p. pap. 4.95 *(978-0-634-09454-5(8),* 0634094548) Leonard, Hal Corp.

—Ensemble Concepts for Band - Fundamental Level: Baritone Saxophone. 2006. (ENG.). 16p. pap. 4.95 *(978-0-634-09456-9(4),* 0634094564) Leonard, Hal Corp.

—Ensemble Concepts for Band - Fundamental Level: Baritone T. C. 2006. (ENG.). 16p. pap. 4.95 *(978-0-634-09461-3(0),* 0634094610) Leonard, Hal Corp.

—Ensemble Concepts for Band - Fundamental Level: Bass Clarinet. 2006. (ENG.). 16p. pap. 4.95 *(978-0-634-09453-8(X),* 063409453X) Leonard, Hal Corp.

—Ensemble Concepts for Band - Fundamental Level: F Horn. 2006. (ENG.). 16p. pap. 4.95 *(978-0-634-09458-3(0),* 0634094580) Leonard, Hal Corp.

—Ensemble Concepts for Band - Fundamental Level: Percussion. 2006. (ENG.). 36p. pap. 7.95 *(978-0-634-09464-4(5),* 0634094645) Leonard, Hal Corp.

—Ensemble Concepts for Band - Fundamental Level: Tenor Saxophone. 2006. (ENG.). 16p. pap. 4.95 *(978-0-634-09455-2(6),* 0634094556) Leonard, Hal Corp.

—Ensemble Concepts for Band - Fundamental Level: Trombone. 2006. (ENG.). 16p. pap. 4.95 *(978-0-634-09459-0(9),* 0634094599) Leonard, Hal Corp.

—Ensemble Concepts for Band - Fundamental Level: Trumpet. 2006. (ENG.). 16p. pap. 4.95 *(978-0-634-09457-6(2),* 0634094572) Leonard, Hal Corp.

—Ensemble Concepts for Band - Fundamental Level: Tuba. 2006. (ENG.). 16p. pap. 4.95 *(978-0-634-09462-0(9),* 0634094629) Leonard, Hal Corp.

Hal Leonard Corp., creator. The Piano Masters: Transcriptions of Songs by 80 Piano Artists from the Big Band Era. 2010. (ENG.). 110p. pap. 19.99 *(978-1-4234-9589-5(6),* 1423495896) Leonard, Hal Corp.

Hal Leonard Corporation Staff, creator. Best of Kenny Wayne Shepherd Band. 2006. (Guitar Recorded Versions Ser.). (ENG.). 136p. pap. 19.95 *(978-1-4234-0159-9(X),* 142340159X) Leonard, Hal Corp.

—Concert Pieces for Trumpet & Concert Band. 2006. (ENG.). 23p. pap. 19.98 incl. audio compact disk *(978-1-59615-102-4(1),* 1596151021) Music Minus One.

—Top of the Charts: Trombone. 2007. (ENG.). 16p. pap. 10.95 incl. audio compact disk *(978-1-57560-877-8(4),* 1575608774) Cherry Lane Music Co.

—Top of the Charts: Trumpet. 2007. (ENG.). 16p. pap. 10.95 incl. audio compact disk *(978-1-57560-870-9(7),* 1575608707) Cherry Lane Music Co.

—Torch Songs: Women's Edition. 2008. (Hal Leonard Pro Vocal Ser.). (ENG.). 40p. pap. 14.95 incl. audio compact disk *(978-1-4234-3192-3(8),* 1423431928) Leonard, Hal Corp.

—Torch Songs, Volume 29: Men's Edition. 2008. (Hal Leonard Pro Vocal Ser.: Vol. 29). (ENG.). 32p. pap. 14.95 incl. audio compact disk *(978-1-4234-3193-0(6),* 1423431936) Leonard, Hal Corp.

—The World's Most Famous Melodies: F Horn Play-along Book/CD Pack. 2007. (ENG.). 20p. pap. 10.95 incl. audio compact disk *(978-1-57560-904-1(5),* 1575609045) Cherry Lane Music Co.

—The World's Most Famous Melodies: Trumpet Play-along Book/CD Pack. 2007. (ENG.). 20p. pap. 10.95 incl. audio compact disk *(978-1-57560-903-4(7),* 1575609037) Cherry Lane Music Co.

Hesketh, Kenneth, contrib. by. Elegy: Score. 2010. (Faber Edition: Faber Brass Band Ser.). (ENG.). pap. 13.80 *(978-0-571-56989-2(7))* Faber & Faber, Ltd. GBR. Dist: Alfred Publishing Co., Inc.

—Elegy: Score & Parts. 2010. (Faber Edition: Faber Brass Band Ser.). (ENG.). pap. 35.25 *(978-0-571-56988-5(9))* Faber & Faber, Ltd. GBR. Dist: Alfred Publishing Co., Inc.

Hess, Nigel. Congestion Charge: Score & Parts, Score & Parts. 2010. (Faber Edition: Faber Wind Band Ser.). (ENG.). pap. 96.25 *(978-0-571-56773-7(8))* Faber & Faber, Ltd. GBR. Dist: Alfred Publishing Co., Inc.

—New London Pictures: Score & Parts, Score & Parts. 2010. (Faber Edition: Faber Wind Band Ser.). (ENG.). pap. 180.25 *(978-0-571-56767-6(3))* Faber & Faber, Ltd. GBR. Dist: Alfred Publishing Co., Inc.

—Thames Journey: Score. 2010. (Faber Edition: Faber Wind Band Ser.). (ENG.). pap. 15.25 *(978-0-571-55867-4(4))* Faber & Faber, Ltd. GBR. Dist: Alfred Publishing Co., Inc.

Hess, Nigel, contrib. by. London Eye: Score & Parts. 2010. (Faber Edition: Faber Brass Band Ser.). (ENG.). pap. 35.25 *(978-0-571-56789-8(4))* Faber & Faber, Ltd. GBR. Dist: Alfred Publishing Co., Inc.

Hinton, Eric L. The Art & Craft of Conducting: Realising Expressive Potential Through Physical Gestures in Selected Works for the Wind Orchestra. 2008. 99.95 *(978-1-60497-559-8(8))* Cambria Pr.

Hogan, Ed. Creative Carols for Brass Quartet, Volume 1: Traditional Carols with a Popular Twist. 2010. (ENG.). 36p. cd-rom 59.99 *(978-0-8341-7811-3(7),* 0834178117) Lillenas Publishing Co.

Igoe, Tommy. Groove Essentials: The Play-Along. 2008. (ENG.). 118p. pap. 39.95 incl. audio compact disk *(978-1-4234-6704-5(3),* 1423467043) Hudson Music, Ltd.

Kinder, Keith William. Prophetic Trumpets: Homage, Worship, & Celebration in the Wind Band Music of Franz Liszt & Richard Wagner. 2009. (ENG., Illus.). 265p. 54.00 *(978-1-57647-151-7(9))* Pendragon Pr.

Kitchener, Lord. Flag Woman: For a Minimum of Five Steel Drums, Drumset, & Optional Bass Guitar, Conductor Score & Parts. 2011. (Alfred's Steel Drum Ensemble Ser.). (ENG.). 20p. pap. 17.99 ***(978-0-7390-8106-8(3))*** Alfred Publishing Co., Inc.

Knight, John W. The Interpretive Wind Band Conductor. 2007. (Illus.). viii, 168p. *(978-1-57463-082-4(2),* Debolsillo) Meredith Music Pubns.

Neidig, Kenneth L., ed. Performance-Study Guides of Essential Works for Band. 2008. (ENG.). 80p. pap. 19.95 *(978-1-57463-107-4(1),* 1574631071) Meredith Music Pubns.

Nicholson, Chad. Great Music for Wind Band: A Guide to the Top 100 Works in Grades IV, V, VI, 1 vol. 2009. (ENG.). 196p. pap. 19.99 *(978-1-57463-092-3(X),* 157463092X) Meredith Music Pubns.

Pallhuber, Herman. Titan's Progress: Score. 2010. (Faber Edition: Faber Brass Band Ser.). (ENG.). pap. 16.25 *(978-0-571-56978-6(1))* Faber & Faber, Ltd. GBR. Dist: Alfred Publishing Co., Inc.

—Titan's Progress: Score & Parts. 2010. (Faber Edition: Faber Brass Band Ser.). (ENG.). pap. 125.80 *(978-0-571-56967-0(6))* Faber & Faber, Ltd. GBR. Dist: Alfred Publishing Co., Inc.

Paul, Timothy A. & Paul, Phyllis M. Winds & Hymns: Resource Guide to Hymns, Chorales & Spirituals in Selected Wind Literature. 2010. (ENG.). 224p. pap. 34.95 *(978-1-57463-116-6(0),* 1574631160) Meredith Music Pubns.

Ramsey, Gordon. Music, Emotion & Identity in Ulster Marching Bands: Flutes, Drums & Loyal Sons. 2011. 334p. pap. 73.95 ***(978-3-0343-0742-0(X))*** Lang, Peter AG GBR. Dist: Lang, Peter.

Salzman, Timothy, ed. A Composer's Insight - Volume 4: Thoughts, Analysis & Commentary on Contemporary Masterpieces for Wind Band. 2009. (ENG.). 276p. pap. 39.99 *(978-1-57463-154-8(3),* 1574631543) Meredith Music Pubns.

Schardein, James L. The Legendary Sousa Band: 40 Years from Plainfield to Atlantic City, 1892-1931. 2009. 259p. pap. 30.95 *(978-1-4327-4105-1(5))* Outskirts Pr., Inc.

Schwantner, Joseph. Recoil: For Wind Ensemble - Full Score. 2007. (ENG.). 66p. pap. 50.00 *(978-1-4234-5137-2(6),* 1423451376) European American Music Distributors Corp.

Smith, Robert W. At the Crossroads. 7.00 *(978-0-7692-8095-0(1),* Warner Bros. Pubns.) Alfred Publishing Co., Inc.

So, Mark. Bangs. 2009. 48p. pap. 8.00 *(978-0-557-06068-9(0))* Lulu Enterprises Inc.

Sosin, Donald, contrib. by. Trombone: the World's Most Famous Melodies. 2007. (Play along (Cherry Lane Music) Ser.). (ENG., Illus.). 20p. pap. 10.95 incl. audio compact disk *(978-1-57560-905-8(3),* 1575609053) Cherry Lane Music Co.

Stansell, Fritz. Blue Lake: The Early Years. 2007. (Illus.). 260p. 23.95 *(978-1-57143-161-5(6))* RDR Bks.

Stern, Mike. Mike Stern Live: The Paris Concert. 2008. (ENG.). 19.95 *(978-1-4234-3865-6(5),* 1423438655) Leonard, Hal Corp.

Stith, Gary. Score & Rehearsal Preparation: A Realistic Approach for Instrumental Conductors. 2011. (ENG.). 96p. pap. 19.95 *(978-1-57463-175-3(6),* 1574631756) Meredith Music Pubns.

Team Brass- Trumpet/Cmt B/Cd. 13.95 incl. audio compact disk *(978-1-85909-883-7(5),* Warner Bros. Pubns.) Alfred Publishing Co., Inc.

University of Pennsylvania Band Archives, The. The University of Pennsylvania Band. 2006. (Images of America Ser.). (Illus.). 128p. per. 19.99 *(978-0-7385-4557-8(0))* Arcadia Publishing.

Weiner, Howard T. Early Twentieth-Century Brass Idioms: Art, Jazz, & Other Popular Traditions - Proceedings of the International Conference Presented by the Institute of Jazz Studies of Rutgers University & the Historic Brass Society November 4-5, 2005. 2008. (Studies in Jazz Ser.). (ENG.). 186p. 58.00 *(978-0-8108-6245-6(X))* Scarecrow Pr., Inc.

Yeo, Young-Hwan. Interactive Motion for Brass Quintet & Tape. 2009. 96p. pap. *(978-3-639-15598-3(X))* VDM Verlag Dr. Mueller e.K.

BAND SAWS

American Society of Mechanical Engineers Staff, ed. Specifications for Band Saw Blades. 24p. 32.00 *(978-0-7918-2591-4(4))* ASME Pr.

Birkey, Steve. Making Puzzleboxes Using a Bandsaw. 2009. (Illus.). 95p. 61.99 *(978-1-4415-4267-0(1))* Xlibris Corp.

Duginske, Mark. The New Complete Guide to the Band Saw: Everything You Need to Know about the Most Important Saw in the Shop. 2007. (ENG., Illus.). 187p. pap. 19.95 *(978-1-56523-318-8(2))* Fox Chapel Publishing Co., Inc.

Graves, Eric. Success with Bandsaws. 2007. (Success with Woodworking Ser.). (ENG., Illus.). 176p. pap. 19.95 *(978-1-86108-473-6(0))* Guild of Master Craftsman Pubns., Ltd. GBR. Dist: Sterling Publishing Co., Inc.

Johnson, Roland. Taunton's Complete Illustrated Guide to Bandsaws. 2010. (Complete Illustrated Guides). (ENG., Illus.). 208p. pap. 24.95 *(978-1-60085-096-7(0))* Taunton Pr., Inc.

Kelsey, John, ed. Bandsaw: The Tool Information You Need at Your Fingertips. 2011. (Missing Shop Manual Ser.). (ENG., Illus.). 112p. pap. 12.95 *(978-1-56523-492-5(8))* Fox Chapel Publishing Co., Inc.

Ventura, Lois. Sculpted Band Saw Boxes: Design, Inspiration & Construction. 2008. (ENG., Illus.). 128p. pap. 24.99 *(978-1-55870-829-7(4),* Popular Woodworking Bks.) F&W Media, Inc.

BAND THEORY OF SOLIDS

see Energy-Band Theory of Solids

BANDAGES AND BANDAGING

see also Plaster Casts, Surgical; Splints (Surgery)

Abell, Brad & Abell, Brad A. Taping & Wrapping Made Simple, 3 vols. 2009. (ENG., Illus.). 192p. pap. 39.99 *(978-0-7817-6994-5(9))* Lippincott Williams & Wilkins.

Beam, Joel. Orthopedic Taping, Wrapping, Bracing, & Padding. 2nd rev. ed. 2011. (Illus.). 480p. pap. 84.95 ***(978-0-8036-2558-7(8))*** Davis, F. A. Co.

Castro, Marcelo, et al. Computational Hemodynamics of Cerebral Aneurysms: Assessing the Risk of Rupture from Hemodynamic Patterns. 2008. 184p. pap. *(978-3-639-09441-1(7))* VDM Verlag Dr. Mueller e.K.

Elsner, Peter, et al, eds. Textiles & the Skin, Vol. 31. (Current Problems in Dermatology Ser.: Vol. 31). (Illus.). *(978-3-8055-7438-9(X))* Karger, S. AG.

Gooch, Jan W. Biocompatible Polymeric Materials & Tourniquets for Wounds. 2010. (Topics in Applied Chemistry Ser.). (Illus.). xvi, 200p. 129.00 *(978-1-4419-5583-8(6),* 1441955836) Springer.

Hewetson, Tom, et al. An Illustrated Guide to Taping Techniques: Principles & Practice. 2nd ed. 2009. (ENG., Illus.). 240p. (C). pap. 74.95 *(978-0-7234-3482-5(4),* Mosby) Elsevier - Health Sciences Div.

Kennedy John F Staff. Medical Textiles 2007 Proceedings of the Fourth International con. 2008. 349.95 *(978-1-4200-4447-8(8))* CRC Pr. LLC.

Kumbrink, Birgit. K Taping: An Illustrated Guide. Basics, Techniques, Indications. 2011. Orig. Title: K-Taping. (ENG., Illus.). viii, 208p. pap. 69.95 *(978-3-642-12931-5(5),* 3642129315) Springer.

Macdonald, Rose, ed. Pocketbook of Taping Techniques. 2009. (Physiotherapy Pocketbooks Ser.). (ENG., Illus.). 318p. (C). pap. 49.95 *(978-0-7020-3027-7(9),* Churchill Livingstone) Elsevier - Health Sciences Div.

Macdonald, Sumaira & Stansby, Gerald. Practical Carotid Artery Stenting: I 2009. (ENG., Illus.). xiv, 208p. 119.00 *(978-1-84800-298-2(X),* 184800298X) Springer.

Marks, Susan. Stuck on You: The Indispensable History of Band-Aid Brand Bandages. 2007. *(978-1-933112-49-7(2))* Collectors Pr., Inc.

Palmer, Margaret D. Lessons on Massage. 2008. (Illus.). pap. *(978-1-84830-065-1(4),* Wildhern Pr.) Echo Library.

Perrin, David H. Athletic Taping & Bracing. 3rd ed. 2012. (Illus.). 152p. pap. 54.00 ***(978-1-4504-1352-7(8))*** Human Kinetics Pubs.

Prentice-Hall Staff. Consumer Reports Testing: Bandaids. 6.47 *(978-0-13-800475-0(7))* Prentice Hall (Schl. Div.).

Renberg, Walter C., et al. Small Animal Bandaging, Casting, & Splinting Techniques. 2011. (ENG., Illus.). 144p. pap. 52.99 *(978-0-8138-1962-4(8),* Wiley-Blackwell) Wiley, John & Sons, Inc.

BANDBOXES

Cholmeley-Jones, Edwina. Bandboxes: Tips, Tools, & Techniques for Learning the Craft. 2009. (Heritage Crafts Ser.). (ENG., Illus.). 132p. 24.95 *(978-0-8117-0503-5(X))* Stackpole Bks.

BANDELLO, MATTEO, 1480-1561

Bandello, Matteo. Certain Tragical Discourses of Bandello, 2 vols. Fenton, Geffraie, tr. (Tudor Translations, First Ser.: Nos. 19-20). reprint ed. 115.00 *(978-0-404-51900-1(8))* AMS Pr., Inc.

—Certain Tragical Discourses of Bandello. 2010. 342p. pap. 31.75 *(978-1-144-97737-3(1));* 332p. pap. 31.75 *(978-1-142-47085-2(7))* BiblioBazaar.

—Certain Tragical Discourses of Bandello. 2009. 236p. pap. *(978-0-217-69568-8(X));* 234p. pap. *(978-0-217-18893-7(1))* Books LLC.

—Certain Tragical Discourses of Bandello. 2010. (Illus.). 198p. pap. 20.59 *(978-1-154-07791-9(8))* 2010. 196p. pap. 20.59 *(978-1-152-63249-3(3))* 2010. 194p. pap. 20.59 *(978-1-152-63245-5(0))* 2010. 196p. pap. 20.59 *(978-1-152-63247-9(7))* 2009. 232p. pap. 20.40 *(978-0-217-96271-1(8))* General Bks. LLC.

Bandello, Matteo & Fenton, Geoffrey. Certain Tragical Discourses of Bandello. 2010. 330p. pap. 31.75 *(978-1-178-24012-2(6))* 2010. (ENG.). 342p. pap. 32.75 *(978-1-176-53769-9(5))* 2010. 334p. pap. 31.75 *(978-1-148-03171-2(5))* 2009. 336p. 29.99 *(978-1-115-24047-5(1))* 2009. 336p. 32.99 *(978-1-115-24045-1(5))* 2009. 336p. pap. 30.75 *(978-1-115-24041-3(2))* 2009. 336p. pap. 31.75 *(978-1-115-24043-7(9))* BiblioBazaar.

Bromilow, Pollie. Models of Women in Sixteenth-Century French Literature: Female Exemplarity in the Histoires Tragiques (1559) & the Heptaméron (1559) 2007. 224p. *(978-0-7734-5332-6(6))* Mellen, Edwin Pr., The.

BANDING OF BIRDS

see Bird Banding

BANDITS

see Brigands and Robbers

BANDMASTERS

see Conductors (Music)

BANDS (MUSIC)

see also Big Bands; Conducting; Dance Orchestras; Drum Majors; Instrumentation and Orchestration; Orchestra; Wind Instruments

Alfred Publishing Staff. Sound Innovations for Concert Band, Bk 2: A Revolutionary Method for Early-Intermediate Musicians (Conductor's Score), Score. 2011. (Sound Innovations Ser.). (ENG.). 400p. pap. 54.99 ***(978-0-7390-6743-7(5))*** Alfred Publishing Co., Inc.

—Sound Innovations for Concert Band, Bk 2: A Revolutionary Method for Early-Intermediate Musicians (Oboe), Book, CD & DVD. 2011. (Sound Innovations Ser.). (ENG.). 48p. pap. 8.99 ***(978-0-7390-6745-1(1))*** Alfred Publishing Co., Inc.

Atkins, Martin. Tour - Smart: And Break the Band. 2007. (ENG., Illus.). 592p. per. 29.95 *(978-0-9797313-0-3(5))* Soluble, LLC.

Barden & Barden, Wendy. Performance Assessment in Band. 2009. (Illus.). 48p. pap. ***(978-0-8497-2610-1(7),*** Wiley-Blackwell) Kjos, Neil A. Music Co.

Barylick, John. Killer Show: The Station Nightclub Fire, America's Deadliest Rock Concert. 2012. (ENG., Illus.). 320p. 27.95 ***(978-1-61168-265-6(7))*** Univ. Pr. of New England.

Brown 'Diamond Dean', Bryan D. How to Start a Band. 2008. 52p. pap. 16.95 *(978-1-60474-884-0(2))* PublishAmerica, Inc.

Brown, Maxine. Looking Back to See: A Country Music Memoir. 2010. pap. 19.95 *(978-1-55728-934-6(4))* Univ. of Arkansas Pr.

Burns, Mick. Keeping the Beat on the Street: The New Orleans Brass Band Renaissance. 2008. (Illus.). 197p. per. 17.95 *(978-0-8071-3333-0(7))* Louisiana State Univ. Pr.

Buyer, Paul. Marching Bands & Drumlines: Secrets of Success from the Best of the Best. 2009. (ENG.). 118p. pap. 19.95 *(978-1-57463-151-7(9),* 1574631519) Meredith Music Pubns.

Campo, David. Original Music for Wind Band in the Latter Half ofthe 1950s: A Historical Perspective. 2008. 180p. pap. *(978-3-639-06713-2(4))* VDM Verlag Dr. Mueller e.K.

Carter, Elliott. Call: Fanfare for Two Trumpets & Horn - Score & Parts. 2008. (ENG.). 8p. pap. 16.95 *(978-1-4234-6424-2(9),* 1423464249) Boosey & Hawkes, Inc.

—Mosaic: For Ensemble Full Score. 2010. (ENG.). 32p. pap. 19.99 *(978-1-61774-216-3(3),* 1617742163) Boosey & Hawkes, Inc.

Chlouber, Carla. The Oklahoma Cowboy Band. 2008. (Images of America Ser.). (Illus.). 128p. pap. 19.99 *(978-0-7385-5245-3(3))* Arcadia Publishing.

Coachman, Frank. Marching Band. (Team Spirit! Ser.). 2009. 64p. (gr. 6-6). 53.00 *(978-1-60853-271-1(2))* 2006. 68p. (gr. 8-12). pap. 26.50 *(978-1-4358-3768-3(1))* 2006. (Illus.). 64p. (YA). (gr. 8-12). lib. bdg. 26.50 *(978-1-4042-0730-1(9))* Rosen Publishing Group, Inc., The.

Colaneri, Christopher. Incorporating Total Percussion into the Middle School Band Program. 2009. 108p. pap. *(978-3-639-13642-5(X))* VDM Verlag Dr. Mueller e.K.

Corbisier, Isabelle. Music for Vagabonds - the Tuxedomoon Chronicles. 2008. 476p. per. *(978-1-906496-08-1(0))* Nute Publishing, Ltd.

Crider, Paula & Saunders, Jack. Essential Musicianship for Band - Masterwork Studies: Alto Saxophone. 2007. (ENG.). 84p. pap. 14.95 incl. audio compact disk *(978-0-634-08862-9(9),* 0634088629) Leonard, Hal Corp.

—Essential Musicianship for Band - Masterwork Studies: Baritone Saxophone. 2007. (ENG.). 80p. pap. 14.95 incl. audio compact disk *(978-0-634-08864-3(5),* 0634088645) Leonard, Hal Corp.

—Essential Musicianship for Band - Masterwork Studies: Tenor Saxophone. 2007. (ENG.). 80p. pap. 14.95 incl. audio compact disk *(978-0-634-08863-6(7),* 0634088637) Leonard, Hal Corp.

Daugherty, Michael. Asclepius: Fanfare for Brass & Percussion Score & Parts. 2008. (ENG.). 96p. pap. 50.00 *(978-1-4234-6634-5(9),* 1423466349) Boosey & Hawkes, Inc.

Dobson, Simon, contrib. by. Clarion Alarum: Score. 2010. (Faber Edition: Faber Brass Band Ser.). (ENG.). pap. 13.25 *(978-0-571-57003-4(8))* Faber & Faber, Ltd. GBR. Dist: Alfred Publishing Co., Inc.

Dust, Thomas J. & Dust, Laura Jane. Band AIDS: A Program Guide for the New Band Director. 2012. pap. ***(978-1-61233-073-0(8))*** Universal Pubs.

Fennell, Frederick. A Conductor's Interpretive Analysis of Masterworks for Band. 2008. (ENG.). 64p. pap. 19.95 *(978-1-57463-094-7(6),* 1574630946) Meredith Music Pubns.

Foutz, Colt. Building the Green Machine. 2008. 450p. 29.99 *(978-1-932714-39-5(1));* pap. 19.95 *(978-1-932714-59-3(6))* Savas Beatie.

Girls Aloud. Dreams That Glitter. 2008. (ENG., Illus.). 256p. 29.95 *(978-0-593-06122-0(5))* Transworld Publishers Ltd. GBR. Dist: Independent Pubs. Group.

Green, Eddie, et al. Ensemble Concepts for Band - Fundamental Level: Baritone B. C. 2006. (ENG.). 16p. pap. 4.95 *(978-0-634-09460-6(2),* 0634094602) Leonard, Hal Corp.

—Ensemble Concepts for Band - Fundamental Level: Bassoon. 2006. (ENG.). 16p. pap. 4.95 *(978-0-634-09450-7(5),* 0634094505) Leonard, Hal Corp.

—Ensemble Concepts for Band - Fundamental Level: Clarinet. 2006. (ENG.). 16p. pap. 4.95 *(978-0-634-09451-4(3),* 0634094513) Leonard, Hal Corp.

—Ensemble Concepts for Band - Fundamental Level: Conductor. 2006. (ENG.). 52p. pap. 12.95 *(978-0-634-09447-7(5),* 0634094475) Leonard, Hal Corp.

—Ensemble Concepts for Band - Fundamental Level: Electric Bass. 2006. (ENG.). 16p. pap. 4.95 *(978-0-634-09463-7(7),* 0634094637) Leonard, Hal Corp.

—Ensemble Concepts for Band - Fundamental Level: Flute. 2006. (ENG.). 16p. pap. 4.95 *(978-0-634-09448-4(3),* 0634094483) Leonard, Hal Corp.

—Ensemble Concepts for Band - Fundamental Level: Oboe. 2006. (ENG.). 16p. pap. 4.95 *(978-0-634-09449-1(1),* 0634094491) Leonard, Hal Corp.

—Ensemble Concepts for Band - Fundamental Level: Percussion. 2006. (ENG.). 36p. pap. 7.95 *(978-0-634-09464-4(5),* 0634094645) Leonard, Hal Corp.

Hal Leonard Corp., creator. Shenandoah: Brass Quintet with optional offstage Trumpets. 2010. (ENG.). 16p. pap. 30.00 *(978-1-4234-9836-0(4),* 1423498364) Leonard, Hal Corp.

Hatherley, Owen. Uncommon. 2011. (ENG., Illus.). 135p. pap. 19.95 *(978-1-84694-877-0(0))* Hunt, John Publishing Ltd. GBR. Dist: National Bk. Network.

The Heeey Baby Days of Beach Music: Stories & Remembrances of a Southern Music Genre. 2006. 59.95 *(978-0-9786047-0-7(9))* Haynes, Greg.

Hess, Nigel, contrib. by. Congestion Charge: Score & Parts. 2010. (Faber Edition: Faber Brass Band Ser.). (ENG.). pap. 60.25 *(978-0-571-56791-1(6))* Faber & Faber, Ltd. GBR. Dist: Alfred Publishing Co., Inc.

Homan, Shane. Access All Eras: Tribute Bands & Global Pop Culture. 2006. 272p. (C). 101.95 *(978-0-335-21691-8(9)*, 9780335216918, Open University Pr.) McGraw-Hill Education GBR. Dist: McGraw-Hill Cos., The.

—Access All Eras: Tribute Bands & Global Pop Culture. 2006. (Illus.). 272p. (C). pap. 61.00 *(978-0-335-21690-1(0)*, 0335216900, Open University Pr.) McGraw-Hill Education GBR. Dist: McGraw-Hill Cos., The.

Huston, Jenny. In Bloom: Irish Bands Now. 2010. (ENG., Illus.). 192p. pap. 36.95 *(978-1-85607-985-3(6))* Currach Pr. IRL. Dist: Dufour Editions, Inc.

Jones, Stephen E. Ritual & Music of North China: Shawm Bands in Shanxi. 2007. (SOAS Musicology Ser.). (Illus.). 148p. 59.95 *(978-0-7546-6163-4(6))* Ashgate Publishing Co.

—Ritual & Music of North China Vol. 2: Shaanbei. 2009. (SOAS Musicology Ser.). (Illus.). 272p. 79.95 *(978-0-7546-6590-8(9))* Ashgate Publishing Co.

Kearns, Ronald. Quick Reference for Band Directors. 2011. (ENG.). 266p. 75.00 ***(978-1-61048-345-2(6))***; pap. 36.95 ***(978-1-61048-346-9(4))*** Rowman & Littlefield Education.

Kearns, Ronald E. Quick Reference for Band Directors. 2011. ***(978-1-61048-347-6(2))*** Rowman & Littlefield Education.

Lane, Tom. The Worship Band Book: Training & Empowering Your Worship Band. 2012. (ENG., Illus.). 160p. spiral bd. 16.99 ***(978-1-4584-1817-3(0)***, 1458418170) Leonard, Hal Corp.

MacDonald, Darach. Blood & Thunder: Inside an Ulster Protestant Band. 2010. (ENG., Illus.). 352p. pap. 23.95 *(978-1-85635-672-5(8))* Mercier Pr., Ltd., The IRL. Dist: Dufour Editions, Inc.

Marcone, Stephen. Managing Your Band: Artist Management: the Ultimate Responsibility. 4th rev. ed. 2006. (ENG., Illus.). 272p. per. 29.95 *(978-0-9651250-4-8(1)*, 0965125041) HiMarks Publishing Co.

Markworth, Wayne. The Dynamic Marching Band. 2008. pap. 49.95 *(978-0-9787472-3-7(2))* Ajoyin Publishing, Inc.

Martin, Greg. Marching Fundamentals. 2007. (ENG.). 24.95 *(978-0-7390-4451-3(6))* Alfred Publishing Co., Inc.

Moonalice (Musical group) Staff, contrib. by. The Moonalice Legend: Posters & Words. 2008. (Illus.). *(978-0-9793314-6-5(3))* Rock Out Bks.

Navarre, Randy. Instrumental Music Teacher's Survival Kit: Ready-to-Use Guidelines, Lessons, & Exercises for Teaching Beginning Band Instruments. 2nd exp. ed. 2007. 344p. per. *(978-0-9765798-9-4(3))* Northeastern Music Pubns. Inc.

Norberg, John. Heartbeat of the University: 125 Years of Purdue Bands. 2011. (Founders Ser.). 190p. 49.95 *(978-1-55753-596-2(5))* Purdue Univ. Pr.

Oser, Bodhi. Band ID: The Ultimate Book of Band Logos. 2008. (ENG., Illus.). 420p. 40.00 *(978-0-8118-6049-9(3))* Chronicle Bks. LLC.

Owen, Randy & Rucker, Allen. Born Country: How Faith, Family, & Music Brought Me Home. 2009. (ENG.). 320p. pap. 15.99 *(978-0-06-167315-3(3)*, HarperOne) HarperCollins Pubs.

Owsinski, Bobby. How to Make Your Band Sound Great. 2009. (ENG., Illus.). 272p. pap. 29.99 *(978-1-4234-4190-8(7)*, 1423441907) Leonard, Hal Corp.

—The Musician's Ultimate Toolbox: How to Make Your Band Sound Great & the Studio Musician's Handbook, 2 vols. 2010. (ENG.). 552p. pap. 52.00 *(978-1-4234-9398-3(2)*, 1423493982) Leonard, Hal Corp.

Palm, Carl. Bright Lights Dark Shadows: The Real Story of ABBA. 2008. (ENG., Illus.). 568p. pap. 24.95 *(978-1-84772-419-9(1)*, OP52459) Omnibus Pr.

Pearson, Greg. Second Place Heroes. 2010. 220p. pap. 19.00 *(978-1-4461-5333-8(9))* Lulu Enterprises Inc.

Pool, Jeannie Gayle. Peggy Gilbert & Her All-Girl Band. 2008. (ENG., Illus.). 300p. per. 47.00 *(978-0-8108-6102-2(X))* Scarecrow Pr., Inc.

Porterfield, Jason. Band Front: Color Guards, Drum Majors, & Majorettes. 2009. (Team Spirit! Ser.). 64p. (gr. 6-6). 53.00 *(978-1-60853-266-7(6))* Rosen Publishing Group, Inc., The.

Raskin, Joyce. Aching to Be. 2007. 208p. pap. 13.95 *(978-0-615-17221-7(0))* Number One Fan Pr.

Taylor, Shawn & Taylor. People's Instinctive Travels & the Paths of Rhythm. 2007. (33 1/3 Ser.). (ENG.). 128p. pap. 14.95 *(978-0-8264-1923-1(2))* Continuum International Publishing Group, Ltd. GBR. Dist: National Bk. Network.

Thiam, Pascal. I Play in the School Band therefore, I am Smart: Effects of School Band Experience on the Motivation of High School Students. 2008. 140p. pap. *(978-3-639-09898-3(6))* VDM Verlag Dr. Mueller e.K.

Thomas, Dale A. A Band in Every School: Portraits of Historically Black School Bands in Florida. 2009. (Illus.). 168p. 30.00 *(978-0-9787299-0-5(0))* Harmonie Publishing, LLC.

Thompson, T. T. Tyler. Horns Up!! College Bands of the Arkansas Heartland. 2007. (Illus.). 383p. 30.00 *(978-0-9766007-2-9(1))* Phoenix International, Inc.

Walsh, Michael J. K. Runaway Dreams: The Story of Mama's Boys & Celtus. 2011. 282p. ***(978-1-84921-110-9(8))***; pap. ***(978-1-84921-096-6(9))*** Kennedy & Boyd.

Ware, David N. & Ware, David. Interviews with Sixteen Band Directors at Historically Black Colleges: Their Attitudes, Opinions, & Methods. 2008. 176p. 99.95 *(978-0-7734-5005-9(X))* Mellen, Edwin Pr., The.

Waring, Virginia. Fred Waring & the Pennsylvanians. 2007. (Music in American Life Ser.). (Illus.). 464p. pap. 30.95 *(978-0-252-07444-8(0))* Univ. of Illinois Pr.

Weaver, John Lawson, 3rd. The Lyncoya Rag - A Creek Indian March & Two Step (SHEET MUSIC) 2008. (Illus.). 6p. pap. 4.00 *(978-0-9771323-2-4(3))* Stargold Music Co.

Williamson, John E. Rehearsing the Band. Neidig, Kenneth L., ed. 2007. (ENG.). 104p. pap. 19.95 *(978-1-57463-093-0(8)*, 1574630938) Meredith Music Pubns.

Wooley Jr, Rex. So you want to be in a Band. 2010. 40p. pap. 10.00 *(978-0-557-60637-5(3))* Lulu Enterprises Inc.

BANDS, ROCK

see Rock Groups

BANG CHAN (THAILAND)

Goldsen, Rose K. & Ralis, Max. Factors Related to Acceptance of Innovations in Bang Chan, Thailand. 2011. 92p. 38.95 ***(978-1-258-10319-4(2))*** Literary Licensing, LLC.

BANGALA LANGUAGE

see Lingala Language

BANGKOK (THAILAND)

Bonechi, Casa. Golden Book of Bangkok. (Illus.). 96p. pap. *(978-88-7009-475-6(8))* Casa Editrice Bonechi.

Bush, Austin. Bangkok. 12 vols. 3rd rev. ed. 2011. (Encounter Ser.). (ENG., Illus.). 200p. pap. 12.99 *(978-1-74179-821-0(3))* Lonely Planet Pubns.

Cole, Jon. Bangkok Hard Time: The Surreal True Story of How a WesternTeenager Came of Age in 1960s Bangkok, Turned International Drug Smuggler & Walked the Prison Yards of Thailandrsquos Notorious Bangkok Hilton. 2012. (ENG., Illus.). 232p. pap. 16.95 ***(978-981-4358-32-3(0))*** Monsoon Bks. Pte. Ltd.

Cornwel-Smith, Philip. Very Bangkok: Neighbourhoods, Networks, Tribes. 2012. (ENG., Illus.). 336p. pap. 30.00 ***(978-974-9863-50-3(X))*** River Bks. THA. Dist: Antique Collectors' Club.

Cornwel-Smith, Philip & Time Out Guides Staff. Time Out Bangkok: And Beach Escapes. Cornwel-Smith, Philip, ed. 3rd ed. 2007. (Time Out Guides). (ENG., Illus.). 256p. per. 19.95 *(978-1-84670-021-7(3))* Time Out Guides Ltd. GBR. Dist: Perseus-PGW.

DK PUBLISHING. Top 10 Bangkok. 2012. (Eyewitness top 10 travel Guide Ser.). (ENG.). 128p. pap. 14.00 ***(978-0-7566-8545-4(1))*** Dorling Kindersley Publishing, Inc.

Dorling Kindersley Publishing Staff. Bangkok. 2010. (Eyewitness top 10 travel Guide Ser.). (ENG.). 128p. 14.00 *(978-0-7566-6186-1(2))* Dorling Kindersley Publishing, Inc.

Fodor's Travel Publications, Inc. Staff. Fodor's Bangkok's 25 Best, 5th Edition. 2009. (25 Best Ser.). (ENG.). 128p. pap. 11.99 *(978-1-4000-0376-1(8)*, Fodor's) Fodor's Travel Pubns.

Hopkins, Jerry. Bangkok Babylon: The Real-Life Exploits of Bangkok's Legendary Expatriates are Often Stranger Than Fiction. 2009. (ENG.). 224p. pap. 14.95 *(978-0-8048-4077-4(6))* Tuttle Publishing.

Insight Guides. Bangkok Insight City Guide. 5th ed. 2011. (City Guide Ser.). (ENG., Illus.). 256p. pap. 19.99 *(978-981-282-316-8(6))* APA Publications Services SGP. Dist: Ingram Pub. Services.

Insight Step by Step Bangkok. 2nd ed. 2012. (Step by Step Ser.). (Illus.). 128p. pap. 16.99 ***(978-1-78005-056-0(9))*** APA Publications Services SGP. Dist: Ingram Pub. Services.

Jackson, Peter A., ed. Queer Bangkok: 21st Century Markets, Media, & Rights. 2011. (Queer Asia Ser.). (ENG., Illus.). 320p. (gr. 17). 50.00 *(978-988-8083-04-6(X))*; pap. 25.00 *(978-988-8083-05-3(8))* Hong Kong Univ. Pr. HKG. Dist: Columbia Univ. Pr.

Johnson, Alan R. Leadership in A Slum: A Bangkok Case Study. 2010. (Regnum Studies in Mission Ser.). 258p. pap. 28.00 *(978-1-60899-407-6(4)*, Wipf and Stock) Wipf & Stock Pubs.

Kerr, Alex, et al. Bangkok Found: Reflections on the City. 2010. (ENG., Illus.). 316p. pap. *(978-974-9863-92-3(5)*, River Bks. Pr. Dist A C) Antique Collectors' Club.

Leroy, Joakim. Urban Bangkok: Contemporary Reflections. 2010. (ENG., Illus.). 210p. 40.00 *(978-974-524-126-5(1))* Orchid Pr. THA. Dist: National Bk. Network.

Locken, E. Travel Journal Bangkok. 2010. 192p. pap. 19.99 *(978-0-557-44415-1(2))* Lulu Enterprises Inc.

Lonely Planet Staff, et al. Bangkok. 9th ed. 2010. (City Guide Ser.). (ENG., Illus.). 296p. pap. 19.99 *(978-1-74179-587-5(7))* Lonely Planet Pubns.

McKelpin, Janet, ed. Lost & Found Bangkok. 2011. (Lost & Found Ser.). (ENG.). 240p. pap. 19.95 *(978-1-934159-21-7(2))* ThingsAsian Pr.

Ngcheong-Lum, Roseline. Bangkok. 1 vol. 2006. (Not Just A Good Food Guide Ser.). (ENG., Illus.). 200p. pap. 10.50 *(978-981-232-921-9(8))* Marshall Cavendish International (Asia) Private Ltd. SGP. Dist: Marshall Cavendish Corp.

O'Neil, Maryvelma. Bangkok: A Cultural History. 2008. (Cityscapes Ser.). (ENG., Illus.). 256p. pap. 16.95 *(978-0-19-534252-9(6))* Oxford Univ. Pr., Inc.

Osborne, Lawrence. Naked Tourist: In Search of Adventure & Beauty in the Age of the Airport Mall. 2007. (ENG.). 288p. pap. 20.00 *(978-0-86547-741-4(8)*, North Point Pr.) Farrar, Straus & Giroux.

Periplus Staff, ed. Bangkok Street Atlas. 2009. (ENG.). 336p. pap. 24.95 *(978-0-7946-0087-7(5)*, PeriplusEdition) Tuttle Publishing.

Rough Guides Staff, et al. Bangkok. 5th ed. 2010. (ENG., Illus.). 256p. 19.99 *(978-1-84836-261-1(7))* Rough Guides, Ltd. GBR. Dist: Dorling Kindersley Publishing, Inc.

Sheehan, Sean. Globetrotter the Best of Bangkok. 2007. (Globetrotter Best of Ser.). (ENG., Illus.). 96p. pap. 8.95 *(978-1-84537-446-4(0))* New Holland Pubs., Ltd. GBR. Dist: Globe Pequot Pr., The.

Suksri, Naengnoi & Piammattawat, Paisarn. Grand Palace & Rattanakosin Island. 2012. (ENG., Illus.). 230p. pap. 30.00 *(978-974-9863-41-1(0))* River Bks. THA. Dist: Antique Collectors' Club.

Time Out Guides Staff. Time Out Shortlist Bangkok. 2010. (Time Out Shortlist Ser.). (ENG., Illus.). 188p. pap. 12.95 *(978-1-84670-147-4(3))* Time Out Guides Ltd. GBR. Dist: Perseus-PGW.

Wallpaper Magazine Editors, ed. Wallpaper City Guide - Bangkok. 2011. (ENG.). 128p. pap. 9.95 ***(978-0-7148-6278-1(9))*** Phaidon Pr., Inc.

BANGLADESH—ANTIQUITIES

Salles, J. F. & Bovagne, M., eds. Pundranagara, cite antique du Bengale. Fouilles de Mahasthan: Rapport Preliminaire 1993-1999. 2007. (Indicopleustoi Ser.). (Illus.). 436p. (C). 136.00 *(978-2-503-99108-5(4))* Brepols Pubs. BEL. Dist: Brown, David Bk. Co., The.

Westland, J. A Report of the District of Jessore - Its Antiquities, Its History, & Its Commerce. 2009. 316p. pap. 29.95 *(978-1-4446-2420-5(2)*, Kent Pr.) Kent Communications, Ltd.

BANGLADESH—BIOGRAPHY

Dil, Anwar S. Bangladesh, an Intercultural Memoir. 2011. (Illus.). 342p. ***(978-984-20-0169-7(5))*** Intercultural Forum.

—Bangladesh, an Intercultural Panorama. 2011. (Illus.). 407p. ***(978-984-20-0167-3(9))*** Intercultural Forum.

Hoque, Azm Fazlul. My Life Through Six Continents. 2011. 474p. 34.99 ***(978-1-4568-8414-7(X))***; pap. 23.99 ***(978-1-4568-8413-0(1))*** Xlibris Corp.

Khan, Adil. The Destiny of a Child Is the Mystery of Creation. 2009. 160p. pap. 11.99 *(978-1-4389-8920-4(2))* AuthorHouse.

Khan, Misbahuddin. Atmasmrti. 2009. (BEN., Illus.). 384p. *(978-7-02-960003-9(7))* Bangladesh Charcha.

Nabi, Nuran. Bullets Of '71: A Freedom Fighter's Story. 2010. 496p. 40.00 *(978-1-4520-4377-7(9))*; pap. 30.00 *(978-1-4520-4378-4(7))* AuthorHouse.

BANGLADESH—COMMERCE

Selim, Shahpar. Ecological Modernisation & Environmental Compliance. 2011. (ENG.). (C). 130.00 *(978-0-415-59619-4(2)*, Routledge India) Taylor & Francis Group GBR. Dist: Taylor & Francis Group.

Westland, J. A Report of the District of Jessore - Its Antiquities, Its History, & Its Commerce. 2009. 316p. pap. 29.95 *(978-1-4446-2420-5(2)*, Kent Pr.) Kent Communications, Ltd.

BANGLADESH—DESCRIPTION AND TRAVEL

Glass, Jack. How Not to Travel India, Sri Lanka, Bangladesh & Nepal & Still Enjoy Yourself. 2008. (Illus.). 352p. pap. *(978-1-84549-309-7(5))* arima publishing.

Gudzowaty, Tomasz. Shipwreckers, 1 vol. 2012. (ENG., Illus.). 88p. pap. 65.00 *(978-3-86930-125-9(2))* Steidl, Gerhard Druckerei und Verlag DEU. Dist: Innovative Logistics.

Hollick, Julian Crandall. Ganga: A Journey down the Ganges River. 2007. (ENG., Illus.). 296p. 30.00 *(978-1-59726-385-3(9)*, Shearwater Bks.) Island Pr.

Leung, Mikey & Meggitt, Belinda. Bangladesh. 2009. (Bradt Travel Guide Ser.). (ENG., Illus.). 288p. pap. 25.99 *(978-1-84162-293-4(1))* Bradt Travel Guides GBR. Dist: Globe Pequot Pr., The.

Locken, E. Travel Journal Bangladesh. 2010. 192p. pap. 19.99 *(978-0-557-43267-7(7))* Lulu Enterprises Inc.

Lonely Planet Staff & Butler, Stuart. Bangladesh. 6th rev. ed. 2008. (Country Guide Ser.). (ENG., Illus.). 200p. pap. 26.99 *(978-1-74104-547-5(9))* Lonely Planet Pubns.

Pal, P. & Haque, E. Bengal: Sites & Sights. 2006. (Illus.). 152p. 66.00 *(978-81-85026-59-6(9))* Marg Pubns. IND. Dist: National Bk. Network.

Rahman, Saidur. Analysis of Travel Behavior in Dhaka City. 2011. 244p. pap. ***(978-3-8383-3933-7(9))*** Lambert Academic Publishing.

Siddique, Abu Bakar. Applications of Gis in Transit Network Development. 2010. 64p. pap. *(978-3-639-27563-5(2))* VDM Verlag Dr. Mueller e.K.

Trojanow, Ilija. Along the Ganges. 2011. (Armchair Traveller Ser.). (ENG.). 266p. 11.95 ***(978-1-906598-91-4(6))*** Haus Publishing GBR. Dist: Consortium Bk. Sales & Distribution.

BANGLADESH—ECONOMIC CONDITIONS

Ahmad, Abu Umar Faruq. Developments in Islamic Banking Practice: The Experience of Bangladesh. 2010. 228p. pap. 25.95 *(978-1-59942-828-4(8))* Universal Pubs.

Akhter, Nargis, et al. Workers' Participation in Management. 2011. 80p. pap. ***(978-3-8433-7241-1(1))*** Lambert Academic Publishing.

Ali Meerza, Syed Imran. Role of Rural-Urban Migration in Increasing Rural Child Labor. 2010. 64p. pap. *(978-3-639-25809-7(6))* VDM Verlag Dr. Mueller e.K.

Amin, Rabiul. Technology Transfer. 2009. 208p. pap. *(978-3-639-16447-3(4))* VDM Verlag Dr. Mueller e.K.

Ashraf, Mohammad. Demystifying Income/Nonparticipation in Mfis: Towards a Paradigm Shift. 2011. 168p. pap. ***(978-3-8454-1768-4(4))*** Lambert Academic Publishing.

—Microfinance or Debt Trap: Case for Yunus' Grameen Bank in Bangladesh. 2011. 80p. pap. ***(978-3-8443-1253-9(6))*** Lambert Academic Publishing.

Bertuzzo, Elisa T. Fragmented Dhaka: Analysing everyday life with Henri Lefebvres Theory of Production of Space. 2009. (Sozialgeographische Bibliothek Ser.). (ENG., Illus.). 246p. (C). pap. 89.00 *(978-3-515-09404-7(0))* Steiner, Franz Verlag Wiesbaden GmbH DEU. Dist: Brown, David Bk. Co., The.

Binta Samad, Rokshana. Improving Municipal Finance Through Revenue Generation of Dhaka City. 2010. 164p. pap. *(978-3-639-27693-0(0))* VDM Verlag Dr. Mueller e.K.

Chakraborty, Susmita & Rahman, Mostahidur. Water Pricing Stratagey. 2011. 120p. pap. ***(978-3-8433-7724-9(3))*** Lambert Academic Publishing.

Chopra, Kanchan, et al. Biodiversity Land Use Change & Human Well-Being: A Study of Aquaculture in the Indian Sunderbans. 2009. (ENG., Illus.). 360p. 49.95 *(978-0-19-806021-5(1))* Oxford Univ. Pr., Inc.

Chowdhury, Md. Ashraful & Chowdhury, Ashraful. Tourism Industry of Bangladesh. 2010. 284p. pap. *(978-3-8383-8344-6(3))* Lambert Academic Publishing.

Faruque, Cathleen Jo. The Invisible People: Poverty & Resiliency in the Dhaka Slums. 2008. 188p. pap. 24.95 *(978-1-60672-798-0(2))* PublishAmerica, Inc.

Fujita, Koichi. Re-Thinking Economic Development: The Green Revolution, Agrarian Structure & Transformation in Bangladesh. 2010. 316p. 89.95 *(978-1-920901-16-5(7)*, Trans Pacific Pr. AUS. Dist: International Specialized Bk. Services.

Gardner, Katy. The Gas Field: Discordant Developments & the Politics of Survival in Bangladesh, 1 vol. 2012. (Anthropology, Culture & Society Ser.). (ENG.). 280p. 32.00 ***(978-0-7453-3149-2(1))***; 216p. lib. bdg. 95.00 ***(978-0-7453-3150-8(5))*** Pluto Pr. GBR. Dist: Macmillan.

Huq, Muhammad Jahedul. Poverty, Livelihood & Environmental Performance: A Case of Bangladesh. 2011. 220p. pap. ***(978-3-639-31885-2(4))*** VDM Verlag Dr. Mueller e.K.

Husain, Mohammed Shahadat. Remittance & Socio-Economic Upliftment of Bangladesh. 2009. 68p. pap. *(978-3-639-21390-4(4))* VDM Verlag Dr. Mueller e.K.

Icon Group International, Inc. Staff, compiled by. The 2006 Economic & Product Market Databook for Barisal, Bangladesh. 2006. 618p. ring bd. 95.00 *(978-0-497-80145-8(0))* Icon Group International, Inc.

—The 2006 Economic & Product Market Databook for Chittagong, Bangladesh. 2006. 618p. ring bd. 95.00 *(978-0-497-80369-8(0))* Icon Group International, Inc.

—The 2006 Economic & Product Market Databook for Comilla, Bangladesh. 2006. 618p. ring bd. 95.00 *(978-0-497-80400-8(X))* Icon Group International, Inc.

—The 2006 Economic & Product Market Databook for Jessore, Bangladesh. 2006. 618p. ring bd. 95.00 *(978-0-497-81945-3(7))* Icon Group International, Inc.

—The 2006 Economic & Product Market Databook for Khulna, Bangladesh. 2006. 618p. ring bd. 95.00 *(978-0-497-81993-4(7))* Icon Group International, Inc.

—The 2006 Economic & Product Market Databook for Mymensingh, Bangladesh. 2006. 618p. ring bd. 95.00 *(978-0-497-81076-4(X))* Icon Group International, Inc.

—The 2006 Economic & Product Market Databook for Narayanganj, Bangladesh. 2006. 618p. ring bd. 95.00 *(978-0-497-81099-3(9))* Icon Group International, Inc.

—The 2006 Economic & Product Market Databook for Rajshahi, Bangladesh. 2006. 618p. ring bd. 95.00 *(978-0-497-81326-0(2))* Icon Group International, Inc.

—The 2006 Economic & Product Market Databook for Rangpur, Bangladesh. 2006. 618p. ring bd. 95.00 *(978-0-497-81332-1(7))* Icon Group International, Inc.

—The 2006 Economic & Product Market Databook for Saidpur, Bangladesh. 2006. 618p. ring bd. 95.00 *(978-0-497-81384-0(X))* Icon Group International, Inc.

—The 2006 Economic & Product Market Databook for Sylhet, Bangladesh. 2006. 618p. ring bd. 95.00 *(978-0-497-61596-7(6))* Icon Group International, Inc.

Islam, Kazi Saiful. Spatial Distribution of Urban Poverty: A Study of Khulna City, Bangladesh. 2011. 100p. pap. ***(978-3-639-32894-3(9))*** VDM Verlag Dr. Mueller e.K.

Jahan, Nusrat. Evaluation of Satisfaction of Employees with Performance Appraisal. 2010. 76p. pap. *(978-3-639-25796-0(0))* VDM Verlag Dr. Mueller e.K.

Kamruzzaman, Mohammad. Performance of Bangladesh Construction Industry in Economic Growth. 2011. 116p. pap. ***(978-3-8454-0812-5(X))*** Lambert Academic Publishing.

Karim, Iftekhar Ul. Effective Team Management of Gtz Bangladesh: Analyzing Team Effectiveness (TE) As a Part of Effective Team Management of Gtz Dhaka (Bangladesh) 2011. 72p. pap. ***(978-3-639-34278-9(X))*** VDM Verlag Dr. Mueller e.K.

Lewis, David. Bangladesh: Politics, Economy & Civil Society. 2011. (ENG., Illus.). 248p. (C). pap. 28.99 ***(978-0-521-71377-1(3))***; 95.00 ***(978-0-521-88612-3(0))*** Cambridge Univ. Pr.

Mahmud, Kazi Tanvir. Small Credit for Big Hope. 2011. 136p. pap. ***(978-3-8443-9525-9(3))*** Lambert Academic Publishing.

Mahmud, Mallik Sezan. Potential Economic Sector. 2011. 96p. pap. ***(978-3-8383-9585-2(9))*** Lambert Academic Publishing.

Mintoo, Abdul Awal. Bangladesh: Anatomy of Change. 2006. (Illus.). 496p. pap. *(978-1-84401-656-3(0))* Athena Pr.

Mollah, Sabur. Dividend Policy & Behavior in an Emerging Market. 2010. 308p. pap. *(978-3-8383-3731-9(X))* Lambert Academic Publishing.

Ms, Azizunnesa, et al. Sustainable Dairy Farming in Bangladesh: Economic Survey Model. 2011. 60p. pap. ***(978-3-639-32315-3(7))*** VDM Verlag Dr. Mueller e.K.

B

Naher, Ainoon. Gender, Religion & Development in Rural Bangladesh. 2008. 244p. pap. (978-3-8364-8312-4(2)) VDM Verlag Dr. Mueller e.K.
Rahman, Syed Ohidur. Investigation of Relationship Marketing Practice. 2010. 116p. pap. (978-3-639-23199-1(6)) VDM Verlag Dr. Mueller e.K.
Rana, Abdur Razzak. Alleviate Electricity Crisis in Bangladesh. 2010. 60p. pap. (978-3-8383-8311-8(7)) Lambert Academic Publishing.
Salequzzaman. Promote the Sustainability in Integrated Coastal Development. 2010. 368p. pap. (978-3-8383-2683-2(0)) Lambert Academic Publishing.
Selim, Reza, et al. A Study of Home Based Industry in Selected Slum Area: Dhaka, Bangladesh. 2011. 92p. pap. (978-3-639-28552-9(2)) VDM Verlag Dr. Mueller e.K.
Shafi Uddin, Mohammed. The Impact of Trade Liberalization on Economic Performance. 2011. 88p. pap. (978-3-8383-4672-4(6)) Lambert Academic Publishing.
Shakur, Parisa. Contra-Powerment? 2011. 68p. pap. (978-3-8443-8191-7(0)) Lambert Academic Publishing.
Shamsad, Sadah. Socio-Economic Dynamics of Microcredit Program in Informal Settlements. 2010. 156p. pap. (978-3-8383-2120-2(0)) Lambert Academic Publishing.
Ullah, Mamin. Corporate Governance Practices in Bangladesh. 2010. 80p. pap. (978-3-639-26963-5(2)) VDM Verlag Dr. Mueller e.K.
Ullah, Safi. Impact of Microfinance. 2010. 84p. pap. (978-3-639-27101-0(7)) VDM Verlag Dr. Mueller e.K.
United Nations. Assessment of Development Results: Bangladesh. 2012. (ENG.). pap. 18.00 (978-92-1-126296-4(8)) United Nations Pubns.
Wadud, Ikm Mokhtarul. Trade Arrangements, Productivity Growth & Firm Level Efficiency. 2010. 340p. pap. (978-3-639-25997-1(1)) VDM Verlag Dr. Mueller e.K.
Wakil, Md. Abdul, et al. Employment Status, Economic Structure & Quality of Life of Dhak. 2010. 184p. pap. (978-3-8383-8822-9(4)) Lambert Academic Publishing.

BANGLADESH—ECONOMIC POLICY

Ali, S. Mahmud. Understanding Bangladesh. 2010. (Columbia/Hurst Ser.). (ENG.). 288p. (gr. 17). 29.50 (978-0-231-70143-3(8)) Columbia Univ. Pr.
Hossain, Akhter. Fiscal Decentralization & Local Economic Development. 2010. 152p. pap. (978-3-8383-6636-4(0)) Lambert Academic Publishing.
Najneen, Farhana. Citizen Feedback & Satisfaction on the Services to Reduce Poverty. 2011. 72p. pap. (978-3-8454-1283-2(6)) Lambert Academic Publishing.
Nath, Tapan Kumar. Participatory Forest Management & Livelihoods of Ethnic People: Empirical Analysis from Bangladesh. 2009. (Illus.). x, 191p. 79.00 (978-1-60692-391-7(9)) Nova Science Pubs., Inc.
Shadat, Wasel Bin, et al. Trade Liberalisation, Manufacturing Growth, & Employment in Bangladesh. 2011. (Illus.). 220p. pap. 29.95 (978-81-7188-819-1(4)) Academic Foundation IND. Dist: Independent Pubs. Group.

BANGLADESH—FOREIGN RELATIONS

Gautam, P. K. Operation Bangladesh. 2007. (Illus.). 192p. (978-81-7049-273-3(4)) Manas Pubns.
Haider, Mohammed. Bangladesh Textile & Garment Industry. 2009. 168p. pap. (978-3-639-19230-8(3)) VDM Verlag Dr. Mueller e.K.
Karim, Iftekhar Ul. Effective Team Management of Gtz Bangladesh: Analyzing Team Effectiveness (TE) As a Part of Effective Team Management of Gtz Dhaka (Bangladesh) 2011. 72p. pap. (978-3-639-34278-9(X)) VDM Verlag Dr. Mueller e.K.
Milam, William B. Bangladesh & Pakistan: Flirting with Failure in South Asia. 2009. (Columbia/Hurst Ser.). (ENG.). 256p. (gr. 17). 35.00 (978-0-231-70066-5(0)) Columbia Univ. Pr.
Stromberg, Brandon E. Bangladesh & Burma: Background & Issues. 2011. (Asian Political, Economic & Security Issues Ser.). 158p. 89.00 (978-1-61761-219-0(7)) Nova Science Pubs., Inc.
Ullah, Ahsan & Panday, Pranab Kumar. Theorizing International Migration. 2008. 152p. pap. (978-3-639-04520-8(3)) VDM Verlag Dr. Mueller e.K.

BANGLADESH—HISTORY

see also India-Pakistan Conflict, 1971

Akash, Jahangir Alam. Pain. 2011. 478p. pap. 23.99 (978-1-4568-5802-5(5)) Xlibris Corp.
Ali, S. Mahmud. Understanding Bangladesh. 2010. (Columbia/Hurst Ser.). (ENG.). 288p. (gr. 17). 29.50 (978-0-231-70143-3(8)) Columbia Univ. Pr.
Arephina, E. Esa Ema Samachula. Bangladesh Documents, 1971, 4 vols. (978-7-03-660000-8(4)) Science Pr.
Bose, Sarmila. Dead Reckoning: Memories of the 1971 Bangladesh War. 2011. (Columbia/Hurst Ser.). (ENG.). 288p. (gr. 17). 37.50 (978-0-231-70164-8(0)) Columbia Univ. Pr.
Choudhury, Ziauddin M. Fight for Bangladesh. 2011. 78p. 24.99 (978-1-4568-4578-0(0)); pap. 15.99 (978-1-4568-4577-3(2)) Xlibris Corp.
Cochrane, Iain. The Causes of the Bangladesh War. 2009. 109p. pap. 20.95 (978-1-4452-4043-5(2)) Lulu Enterprises Inc.
Gautam, P. K. Operation Bangladesh. 2007. (Illus.). 192p. (978-81-7049-273-3(4)) Manas Pubns.
Goldrick, James, contrib. by. No Easy Answers: The Development of the Navies of India, Pakistan, Bangladesh, & Sri Lanka, 1945-1996. (Illus.). xiii, 225p. (978-1-897829-02-8(7)) Spantech & Lancer.
Husain, Syed Shahid. What was once East Pakistan. 2010. (ENG.). 350p. 29.95 (978-0-19-547715-3(4)) Oxford Univ. Pr., Inc.
Hussain, Mohammed D. It Was Glorious: Not A Cheap Shot. 2010. 284p. pap. 17.89 (978-1-4269-3693-7(1)) Trafford Publishing.
Hussain, Mohammed D. You May Get Sold but Don't Sell My Country. 2011. 216p. 29.99 (978-1-4628-8884-9(4)); 210p. pap. 19.99 (978-1-4628-8883-2(6)) Xlibris Corp.
Rahman, Syedur & Baxter, Craig. Historical Dictionary of Bangladesh, Vol. 75. 4th rev. ed. 2010. (Historical Dictionaries of Asia, Oceania, & the Middle East Ser.). (ENG.). 510p. 121.00 (978-0-8108-6766-6(4)) Scarecrow Pr., Inc.
Saikia, Yasmin. Women, War, & the Making of Bangladesh: Remembering 1971. 2011. (ENG., Illus.). 336p. 89.95 (978-0-8223-5021-7(1)); pap. 24.95 (978-0-8223-5038-5(6)) Duke Univ. Pr.
Stewart, Frank & Kumar, Sukrita Paul, eds. Crossing Over: Partition Literature from India, Pakistan, & Bangladesh. 2007. (Illus.). 219p. per. 16.00 (978-0-8248-3227-8(2)) Univ. of Hawaii Pr.
Tan & Kudaisya. Partition & Post-Colonial South Asia. 2007. Vol. 1. 496p. (978-0-415-35955-9(4)) Vol. 2. 400p. (978-0-415-35956-6(2)) Vol. 3. 326p. (978-0-415-35957-3(0)) Routledge.
van Schendel, Willem. A History of Bangladesh. 2009. (ENG., Illus.). (C). 376p. 80.00 (978-0-521-86174-8(8)); 374p. pap. 26.99 (978-0-521-67974-9(5)) Cambridge Univ. Pr.
Westland, J. A Report of the District of Jessore - Its Antiquities, Its History, & Its Commerce. 2009. 316p. pap. 29.95 (978-1-4446-2420-5(2), Kent Pr.) Kent Communications, Ltd.
Yunus, Mohammed. Bhutto & the Breakup of Pakistan. 2012. (ENG.). 148p. 20.00 (978-0-19-906379-6(6)) Oxford Univ. Pr., Inc.

BANGLADESH—POLITICS AND GOVERNMENT

Ahmed, Sabrina. Engaging Communities in City Planning. 2010. 68p. pap. (978-3-8383-7583-0(1)) Lambert Academic Publishing.
Akash, Jahangir Alam. Pain. 2011. 478p. pap. 23.99 (978-1-4568-5802-5(5)) Xlibris Corp.
Ali, S. Mahmud. Understanding Bangladesh. 2010. (Columbia/Hurst Ser.). (ENG.). 288p. (gr. 17). 29.50 (978-0-231-70143-3(8)) Columbia Univ. Pr.
Asian Indigenous & Tribal Peoples Network Staff, contrib. by. Sajek, Burnt to Ashes: Emblematic of Bangladesh's Policy Towards Indigenous Jumma Peoples. 2008. (Illus.). 31p. (978-81-902318-4-8(7)) Asian Indigenous & Tribal People Network.
Dil, Anwar S. & Dil, Afia. Bengali Language Movement & Creation of Bangladesh. 2011. (Illus.). 774p. (978-984-20-0170-3(9)) Intercultural Forum.
Fernando, Jude L. The Political Economy of NGOs: State Formation in Sri Lanka & Bangladesh, 1 vol. 2011. (ENG.). 352p. lib. bdg. 100.00 (978-0-7453-2172-1(0)); 30.00 (978-0-7453-2171-4(2)) Pluto Pr. GBR. Dist: Macmillan.
Hussain, Mohammed D. It Was Glorious: Not A Cheap Shot. 2010. 284p. pap. 17.89 (978-1-4269-3693-7(1)) Trafford Publishing.
Hussain, Mohammed D. You May Get Sold but Don't Sell My Country. 2011. 216p. 29.99 (978-1-4628-8884-9(4)); 210p. pap. 19.99 (978-1-4628-8883-2(6)) Xlibris Corp.
Islamist Militancy in Bangladesh. 2010. pap. 39.95 (978-0-415-57669-7(5)) Routledge.
Khan, Saleque. Performing the Nation: A Bangladesh Mise-en-scFnce. 2009. 164p. pap. (978-3-639-15880-9(6)) VDM Verlag Dr. Mueller e.K.
Lewis, David. Bangladesh: Politics, Economy & Civil Society. 2011. (ENG., Illus.). 248p. (C). pap. 28.99 (978-0-521-71377-1(3)); 95.00 (978-0-521-88612-3(0)) Cambridge Univ. Pr.
Mahiuddin, K. M. The Parliamentary Committee System in Bangladesh. 2009. 284p. pap. (978-3-639-19799-0(2)) VDM Verlag Dr. Mueller e.K.
Milam, William B. Bangladesh & Pakistan: Flirting with Failure in South Asia. 2011. (Columbia/Hurst Ser.). (ENG.). 256p. (gr. 17). pap. 26.50 (978-0-231-70067-2(9)) Columbia Univ. Pr.
Mintoo, Abdul Awal. Bangladesh: Anatomy of Change. 2006. (Illus.). 496p. pap. (978-1-84401-656-3(0)) Athena Pr.
Nath, Tapan Kumar. Participatory Forest Management & Livelihoods of Ethnic People: Empirical Analysis from Bangladesh. 2009. (Illus.). x, 191p. 79.00 (978-1-60692-391-7(9)) Nova Science Pubs., Inc.
Pamini, Syeda Naushin. Foreign Aid & Poverty Reduction in Bangladesh: The Problem of Good Governance. 2010. 109.95 (978-0-7734-3596-4(4)) Mellen, Edwin Pr., The.
—Public Sector Reform & Good Governance. 2010. 160p. pap. (978-3-639-24954-5(2)) VDM Verlag Dr. Mueller e.K.
Parua, Pranab Kumar. The Ganges: Analysis of the Farakka Barrage. 2009. (Water Science & Technology Library). (ENG.). xxviii, 391p. 199.00 (978-90-481-3102-0(2), 9048131022) Springer.
Quamruzzaman, Amm. The Militia Movement in Bangladesh. 2010. 224p. pap. (978-3-8383-7416-1(9)) Lambert Academic Publishing.
Rahman, Taiabur. Parliamentary Control & Government Accountability in South Asia: A Comparative Analysis of Bangladesh, India & Sri Lanka. (ENG., Illus.). 272p. 2012. pap. 42.95 (978-0-415-53318-8(X)) 2007. 160.00 (978-0-415-40498-3(3)) Routledge.
Riaz, Ali & Fair, Christine, eds. Political Islam & Governance in Bangladesh. 2010. (Routledge Contemporary South Asia Ser.). (ENG., Illus.). 200p. (C). 130.00 (978-0-415-57673-4(3), Routledge) Taylor & Francis Group GBR. Dist: Taylor & Francis Group.
Siraj, Sanjida. The Impact of European Aid on Poverty Alleviation & Governance. 2010. 268p. pap. (978-3-8383-2167-7(7)) Lambert Academic Publishing.
Stromberg, Brandon E. Bangladesh & Burma: Background & Issues. 2011. (Asian Political, Economic & Security Issues Ser.). 158p. 89.00 (978-1-61761-219-0(7)) Nova Science Pubs., Inc.
Ullah, Ahsan & Panday, Pranab Kumar. Theorizing International Migration. 2008. 152p. pap. (978-3-639-04520-8(3)) VDM Verlag Dr. Mueller e.K.

BANGLADESH—SOCIAL CONDITIONS

Adnan, Sarfaraz & Mostafizur Rahman. Spatial Structure of Dhaka City from Sustainability Perspective. 2010. 160p. pap. (978-3-8383-7184-9(4)) Lambert Academic Publishing.
Ahiduzzaman. Production & Use of Biomass Briquette Fuel in Bangladesh. 2011. 124p. pap. (978-3-8433-9159-7(9)) Lambert Academic Publishing.
Ahmed, Akhter U. Comparing Food & Cash Transfers to the Ultra-Poor in Bangladesh. 2009. (978-0-89629-173-7(1)) International Food Policy Research Institute.
Ahmed, Imtiaz. The Plight of the Stateless Rohingyas: Responses of the State, Society & the International Community. 2010. (Illus.). xvii, 220p. (978-984-506-015-8(3)) Univ. Pr. of America, Inc.
Akash, Jahangir Alam. Pain. 2011. 478p. pap. 23.99 (978-1-4568-5802-5(5)) Xlibris Corp.
Asian Indigenous & Tribal Peoples Network Staff, contrib. by. Sajek, Burnt to Ashes: Emblematic of Bangladesh's Policy Towards Indigenous Jumma Peoples. 2008. (Illus.). 31p. (978-81-902318-4-8(7)) Asian Indigenous & Tribal People Network.
Banik, Bijoy. Inclusion or Exclusion of the Urban Poor? 2010. 92p. pap. (978-3-8383-4260-3(7)) Lambert Academic Publishing.
Bertuzzo, Elisa T. Fragmented Dhaka: Analysing everyday life with Henri Lefebvres Theory of Production of Space. 2009. (Sozialgeographische Bibliothek Ser.). (ENG., Illus.). 246p. (C). pap. 89.00 (978-3-515-09404-7(0)) Steiner, Franz Verlag Wiesbaden GmbH DEU. Dist: Brown, David Bk. Co., The.
Billah, Masuma. Old Age Livelihood Planning of Sex Workers: Bangladesh Experience. 2011. 64p. pap. (978-3-8443-0235-6(2)) Lambert Academic Publishing.
Chowdhury, Ataharul Huq. Having a System Does Not Make a Home of It. 2010. 176p. pap. (978-3-639-27648-0(5)) VDM Verlag Dr. Mueller e.K.
Chowdhury, Newaz Ahmed. Rural Development Management by Village Based Co-Operative Society. 2010. 108p. pap. (978-3-8383-7473-4(8)) Lambert Academic Publishing.
Coupe, Stuart, et al. Voices from the Margins: Consensus Building & Planning with the Poor in Bangladesh. 2008. (ENG., Illus.). 100p. pap. 29.95 (978-1-85339-624-3(9)) Intermediate Technology Development Group of North America.
Daisy, Naznin Sultana & Rahman, Naima. Travel Pattern & Influential Factors of Mode Choice. 2011. 72p. pap. (978-3-8443-8708-7(0)) Lambert Academic Publishing.
Farid, Luthmela. Cross-Cultural Consumer Behaviour of Apparels. 2010. 84p. pap. (978-3-639-13762-0(0)) VDM Verlag Dr. Mueller e.K.
Faruque, Cathleen Jo. The Invisible People: Poverty & Resiliency in the Dhaka Slums. 2008. 188p. pap. 24.95 (978-1-60672-798-0(2)) PublishAmerica, Inc.
Fateha Sultana, Umme Busra. Gender, Sexualities & the Image Reflections. 2010. 108p. pap. (978-3-8383-5948-9(8)) Lambert Academic Publishing.
Ferdous, Tamanna. Malnutrition among Bangladeshi Elderly: Determinants & Consequences. 2010. 88p. pap. (978-3-8383-0478-6(0)) Lambert Academic Publishing.
Hakim, Sheikh Serajul. Of the Rough Waters & onto the City. 2010. 160p. pap. (978-3-8383-5710-2(8)) Lambert Academic Publishing.
Harder, Hans. Sufism & Saint Veneration in Contemporary Bangladesh. 2011. (Routledge Advances in South Asian Studies). (ENG., Illus.). 392p. (C). 148.00 (978-0-415-58170-7(2)) Routledge.
Hofer, Thomas & Messerli, Bruno. Floods in Bangladesh: History, Dynamics & Rethinking the Role of the Himalayas. 2006. (ENG., Illus.). 450p. pap. 45.00 (978-92-808-1121-6(5)) United Nations Pubns.
Hossain, Khandaker. Road Accident in Highways of Bangladesh: A Temporal Study. 2010. 80p. pap. (978-3-8383-8405-4(9)) Lambert Academic Publishing.
Hossain, Mallik Akram. Sanitation for the Urban Poor in Bangladesh Cities. 2010. 300p. pap. (978-3-8383-2042-7(5)) Lambert Academic Publishing.
Hossain, Shahadat. Urban Poverty in Bangladesh: Slum Communities, Migration & Social Integration. 2010. (Library of Development Studies). (ENG., Illus.). 288p. 96.00 (978-1-84885-470-3(6), Tauris Academic Studies) I. B. Tauris & Co., Ltd. GBR. Dist: Macmillan.
Hossain, Sheikh. A Gis Network Application on Public Water Supply System. 2010. 112p. pap. (978-3-639-25754-0(5)) VDM Verlag Dr. Mueller e.K.
Hossain, Zakir. Development of Some Demographic Models & Implementation in Bangladesh. 2010. 164p. pap. (978-3-8383-9328-5(7)) Lambert Academic Publishing.
Husain, Mohammed Shahadat. Remittance & Socio-Economic Upliftment of Bangladesh. 2009. 68p. pap. (978-3-639-21390-4(4)) VDM Verlag Dr. Mueller e.K.
Hussain, Mohammed D. You May Get Sold but Don't Sell My Country. 2011. 216p. 29.99 (978-1-4628-8884-9(4)); 210p. pap. 19.99 (978-1-4628-8883-2(6)) Xlibris Corp.
Hussain, Raja Rizwan & FERDOUS AHMED, Engr. Harvested Rainwater. 2010. 80p. pap. (978-3-639-16942-3(5)) VDM Verlag Dr. Mueller e.K.
Islam, Anwarul & Panda, K. C. It in Libraries. 2010. 256p. pap. (978-3-8383-1619-2(3)) Lambert Academic Publishing.
Islam, Mohammad Amirul. Male Involvement in Reproductive Health in Bangladesh: A Multilevel Analysis. 2008. 176p. pap. (978-3-639-10225-3(8)) VDM Verlag Dr. Mueller e.K.
Islam, Sabina. Some Demographic Models & Their Applications for Bangladesh. 2010. 148p. pap. (978-3-8383-8546-4(2)) Lambert Academic Publishing.
Islam, Shafirul. Disability & Poverty. 2009. 124p. pap. (978-3-639-16428-2(8)) VDM Verlag Dr. Mueller e.K.
Islam, Sharmin. Ideal Images of Womanhood & Adolescent Girls. 2010. 64p. pap. (978-3-8383-6815-3(0)) Lambert Academic Publishing.
Islam, Sirajul. Role of Microfinance Tools in Disaster Risk Reduction. 2010. 124p. pap. (978-3-8383-8367-5(2)) Lambert Academic Publishing.
Kabir, Kazi Shahdat. Civil Society in a Weak State. 2010. 212p. pap. (978-3-8383-5145-2(2)) Lambert Academic Publishing.
Kabir Shah & Kabir, Shah. THE IRAQ WAR IN BANGLADESHI NEWSPAPERS. 2008. 132p. pap. (978-3-639-08914-1(6)) VDM Verlag Dr. Mueller e.K.
Kamrujjaman & Tulshi Kumar Das, Professor. Survival Pattern of Flood Affected People. 2011. 96p. pap. (978-3-8443-0212-7(3)) Lambert Academic Publishing.
Khan, Saleque. Performing the Nation: A Bangladesh Mise-en-scFnce. 2009. 164p. pap. (978-3-639-15880-9(6)) VDM Verlag Dr. Mueller e.K.
Khanam, Rasheda. Child Labour & Schooling in Bangladesh. 2011. 204p. pap. (978-3-8443-1855-5(0)) Lambert Academic Publishing.
Lewis, David. Bangladesh: Politics, Economy & Civil Society. 2011. (ENG., Illus.). 248p. (C). pap. 28.99 (978-0-521-71377-1(3)); 95.00 (978-0-521-88612-3(0)) Cambridge Univ. Pr.
Liss, Carolin. Oceans of Crime: Maritime Piracy & Transnational Security in Southeast Asia & Bangladesh. 2010. (Illus.). xviii, 425p. pap. (978-981-4279-46-8(3)) Institute of Southeast Asian Studies.
Mahali, Shuvro Chandan & Monjurul Alam. Cyclone Resistant Village Development Plan for Coastal Region. 2011. 104p. pap. (978-3-639-33372-5(1)) VDM Verlag Dr. Mueller e.K.
Mahmud, Ilias. Health Seeking Behaviour of Disabled People in Bangladesh. 2011. 64p. pap. (978-3-8433-6229-0(7)) Lambert Academic Publishing.
Mamun, Sajed. Seismic Vulnerability Assessment in Chittagong City Corporation Are. 2010. 232p. pap. (978-3-8383-8993-6(X)) Lambert Academic Publishing.
Maroof, Abu & Jahan, Shamima. Problems & Prospects of 'Vabodaho' in Livelihood Crisis Management. 2010. 88p. pap. (978-3-639-28079-1(2)) VDM Verlag Dr. Mueller e.K.
Miller, Doug. Last Nightshift in Savar: The Story of the Spectrum Sweater Factory Collapse. 2012. (ENG., Illus.). 264p. pap. 28.95 (978-0-85716-039-3(7)) Northumbria University Press GBR. Dist: Independent Pubs. Group.
Morshed, Nahid. A Study on the Recycling of Inorganic Waste. 2011. 64p. pap. (978-3-8454-1106-4(6)) Lambert Academic Publishing.
Mursheda Farhana, Khandaker. Socio-Cultural Adjustment of Poor Migrants in Urban Bangladesh. 2011. 240p. pap. (978-3-8443-2311-5(2)) Lambert Academic Publishing.
Naher, Ainoon. Gender, Religion & Development in Rural Bangladesh. 2008. 244p. pap. (978-3-8364-8312-4(2)) VDM Verlag Dr. Mueller e.K.
Rahman, Mohammad Aminur. Disaster Risk Management in Dhaka City. 2011. 92p. pap. (978-3-8454-1834-6(6)) Lambert Academic Publishing.
Rahman, Pk. Motiur, et al. The Chronically Poor in Rural Bangladesh: Livelihood Constraints & Capabilities. (Routledge Studies in Development Economics Ser.). (Illus.). 208p. 2012. (ENG.). (C). pap. 42.95 (978-0-415-54315-6(0)) 2008. 160.00 (978-0-415-46468-0(4)) Routledge.
Rana, Abdur Razzak. Alleviate Electricity Crisis in Bangladesh. 2010. 60p. pap. (978-3-8383-8311-8(7)) Lambert Academic Publishing.
Randau, Karen, ed. Country Profile - Bangladesh: A Social Studies/Mission Unit. Date not set. (Teaching Your Child God's Love for the World - Uganda Ser.). 9.99 (978-0-939989-10-2(7)) Food for the Hungry, Inc.
Reza, Farhadur. Impact of Urbanization on Groundwater. 2011. 116p. pap. (978-3-8443-9526-6(1)) Lambert Academic Publishing.
Riaz, Ali. Islamist Militancy in Bangladesh: A Complex Web. 2007. (Routledge Contemporary South Asia Ser.). (Illus.). 192p. 160.00 (978-0-415-45172-7(8)) Routledge.
Rubayet Rahaman, Khan & Arifur Rahaman. An Assessment of Railways Level of Services. 2010. 72p. pap. (978-3-8383-4999-2(7)) Lambert Academic Publishing.
Selim, Reza, et al. A Study of Home Based Industry in Selected Slum Area: Dhaka, Bangladesh. 2011. 92p. pap. (978-3-639-28552-9(2)) VDM Verlag Dr. Mueller e.K.
Shabnam, Nourin, et al. Rural-Urban Disparity in Bangladesh. 2010. 196p. pap. (978-3-639-24028-3(6)) VDM Verlag Dr. Mueller e.K.
Shams, Shahriar. Arsenic Evaluation & Mitigation Using Gis & Expert System. 2011. 76p. pap. (978-3-8443-0636-1(6)) Lambert Academic Publishing.
Shamsad, Sadah. Socio-Economic Dynamics of Microcredit Program in Informal Settlements. 2010. 156p. pap. (978-3-8383-2120-2(0)) Lambert Academic Publishing.
Siddiqui, Kamal, et al. Social Formation in Dhaka, 1985-2005: A Longitudinal Study of Society in a Third World Megacity. 2010. (Illus.). 420p. 124.95 (978-1-4094-1103-1(6)) Ashgate Publishing Co.
Sifat, Sharmin. Child Mortality Risk Factors with Associated Socio-Economic Inequality: A Case Study of Bangladeshi Children. 2011. 72p. pap. (978-3-639-32449-5(8)) VDM Verlag Dr. Mueller e.K.

Togawa, Masahiko, et al, eds. Minorities & the State: Changing Social & Political Landscape of Bengal. 2011. (Illus.). 244p. (C). 43.00 ***(978-81-321-0589-3(3)***, B10589C) SAGE Pubns., Inc.
Touhid, Abul Baker. Physically Challenged People in Bangladesh. 2010. 148p. pap. *(978-3-639-27251-2(X))* VDM Verlag Dr. Mueller e.K.
Uddin, Jaber. Conflict Management for the Farakka Barrage. 2011. 64p. pap. ***(978-3-8443-0391-9(X)***, Lambert Academic Publishing.
—Hazardous Air Pollution: Contribution of Transport Sector in Dhaka City. 2011. 120p. pap. ***(978-3-8433-8765-1(6))*** Lambert Academic Publishing.
Uddin, Jalal. Arrack Drinking. 2011. 56p. pap. ***(978-3-8433-9291-4(9))*** Lambert Academic Publishing.
Uddin, M. S, et al. Land Reclamation & Township Development. 2011. 120p. pap. ***(978-3-8443-2610-9(3))*** Lambert Academic Publishing.
Wakil, Md. Abdul, et al. Employment Status, Economic Structure & Quality of Life of Dhak. 2010. 184p. pap. *(978-3-8383-5822-9(4))* Lambert Academic Publishing.

BANGLADESH—SOCIAL LIFE AND CUSTOMS

Callan, Alyson. Patients & Agents: Mental Illness, Modernity & Islam in Sylhet, Bangladesh. 2012. (ENG.). 252p. 85.00 ***(978-0-85745-488-1(9))*** Berghahn Bks., Inc.
Raju, Zakir Hossain. Bangladesh Cinema & National Identity: In Search of the Modern? 2012. (Routledge Contemporary South Asia Ser.). (ENG., Illus.). 240p. (C). 170.00 *(978-0-415-46544-1(3))* Routledge.
Shehabuddin, Elora. Reshaping the Holy: Democracy, Development, & Muslim Women in Bangladesh. 2008. (ENG., Illus.). 304p. (gr. 17). 85.00 *(978-0-231-14156-7(4))*; pap. 28.50 *(978-0-231-14157-4(2))* Columbia Univ. Pr.
Uddin, Emaj. Cross-Cultural Alcohol & Arrack Drinking. 2011. 148p. pap. ***(978-3-8443-0208-0(5))*** Lambert Academic Publishing.

BANGLADESHI COOKING

see Cooking, Bangladeshi

BANG'S DISEASE

see Brucellosis in Cattle

BANJO

Andrews, Lee (Drew). Children's Banjo Chord Book, 1 vol. 2008. (ENG.). 24p. pap. 5.95 *(978-0-7866-7617-0(5))* Mel Bay Pubns., Inc.
Bay, William. Banjo G Tuning Photo Chord Book, 1 vol. 2006. (ENG., Illus.). 52p. pap. 12.95 *(978-0-7866-7627-9(2)*, 20297dp) Mel Bay Pubns., Inc.
Carlin, Bob. The Birth of the Banjo: Joel Walker Sweeney & Early Minstrelsy. 2007. (ENG., Illus.). 203p. per. 35.00 *(978-0-7864-2874-8(0))* McFarland & Co., Inc. Pubs.
Carr, Joe. First Lessons Tenor Banjo, 1 vol. 2006. (Mel Bay's First Lessons Ser.). (ENG., Illus.). 32p. pap. 14.95 *(978-0-7866-7611-8(6)*, 21011set) Mel Bay Pubns., Inc.
—Mel Bay's First Lessons Tenor Banjo, 1 vol. 2006. (Mel Bay's First Lessons Ser.). (ENG., Illus.). 32p. pap. 7.95 *(978-0-7866-7520-3(9)*, 21011bcd) Mel Bay Pubns., Inc.
Collins, Eddie. Introduction to Bluegrass Banjo, 1 vol. 2007. (ENG., Illus.). 112p. spiral bd. 22.95 *(978-0-7866-7290-5(0))* Mel Bay Pubns., Inc.
Davis, Janet. Mel Bay's School of Banjo: Bluegrass Melodic Style. 2011. (ENG.). 94p. audio compact disk 19.99 ***(978-0-7866-8270-6(1))*** Mel Bay Pubns., Inc.
Evans, Bill. Banjo. 2006. (Absolute Beginners Ser.). (ENG., Illus.). 44p. pap. 12.99 incl. audio compact disk *(978-0-8256-3499-4(7)*, 0825634997) Music Sales Corp.
—Banjo for Dummies. 2007. (ENG., Illus.). 360p. pap. 24.99 *(978-0-470-12762-9(7)*, For Dummies) Wiley, John & Sons, Inc.
Garner, Steve. American Banjo: Three-Finger & Scruggs Style, 1 vol. 2007. (Smithsonian Folkways Ser.). (ENG.). 74p. spiral bd. 14.95 *(978-0-7866-5127-6(X))* Mel Bay Pubns., Inc.
Gelling, Peter. Banjo: For Beginners. 2006. (Progressive (Progressive) Ser.). (Illus.). 56p. pap. incl. audio compact disk *(978-1-86469-260-0(X)*, 256-656) Koala Music Publications.
—Banjo Chords: For Beginners. 2008. 96p. pap. incl. audio compact disk *(978-1-86469-379-9(7))* Koala Music Publications.
Godbey, Marty. Crowe on the Banjo: The Music Life of J. D. Crowe. 2011. (Music in American Life Ser.). (ENG., Illus.). 272p. pap. 19.95 *(978-0-252-07825-5(X))* Univ. of Illinois Pr.
Maclachlan, Iain. Celtic Tune Encyclopedia for 5-String Banjo, 1 vol. 2009. (ENG.). 96p. spiral bd. 17.95 *(978-0-7866-7694-1(9))* Mel Bay Pubns., Inc.
McGill, Terry. Alternate Tunings for Five-String Banjo Played Bluegrass Style, 1 vol. 2008. (ENG.). 72p. pap. 19.95 *(978-0-7866-7438-1(5))* Mel Bay Pubns., Inc.
Mills, Jim. Gibson Mastertone: Flathead 5-String Banjos of the 1930s And 1940s. 2009. (ENG.). 168p. pap. 45.00 *(978-1-57424-246-1(6)*, 1574242466) Centerstream Publishing.
Munde, Alan. Getting into Bluegrass Banjo, 1 vol. 2007. (Getting Into Ser.). (ENG., Illus.). 96p. pap. 17.95 *(978-0-7866-7557-9(8))* Mel Bay Pubns., Inc.
O'Brien, Colin. Play Banjo Today! Level One: A Complete Guide to the Basics. 2008. (ENG.). 48p. pap. 9.95 incl. audio compact disk *(978-1-4234-1993-8(6)*, 1423419936) Leonard, Hal Corp.
Pardee, Peter W., contrib. by. Banjo Picking: A Complete Method, 1 vol. 2006. (ENG.). 125p. spiral bd. 24.95 *(978-0-7866-7480-0(6)*, 20743bcd) Mel Bay Pubns., Inc.
Roller, Robin. Starting Bluegrass Banjo: The Definitive Step-by-Step Guide to Playing 5-String Banjo. 2007. (Illus.). 47p. pap. 14.95 incl. audio compact disk *(978-0-8256-0352-5(8)*, Oak Pubns.) Music Sales Corp.
Schmid, Will, et al. Hal Leonard Banjo Method - Book 2: For 5-String Banjo. 2nd rev. ed. 2011. (ENG.). 64p. pap. 16.99 incl. audio compact disk ***(978-1-4234-6318-4(8)***, 1423463188) Leonard, Hal Corp.
Senyak, Zhenya Gene. Banjo Camp! Learning, Picking & Jamming with Bluegrass & Old-Time Greats. 2008. (ENG., Illus.). 152p. 21.95 *(978-1-60059-282-9(1))* Lark Bks.
Shealy, Alexander. Picture Chords for 5-String Banjo. pap. 6.95 *(978-0-8256-5360-5(6))* Music Sales Corp.
Spottswood, Dick. Banjo on the Mountain: Wade Mainer's First Hundred Years. 2010. (American Made Music Ser.). (ENG., Illus.). 128p. 55.00 *(978-1-60473-577-2(5))*; pap. 30.00 *(978-1-60473-498-0(1))* Univ. Pr. of Mississippi.
Trischka, Tony. Tony Trischka - Banjo Bundle Pack: Tony Trischka Teaches 20 Easy Banjo Solos (Book/CD Pack) with Classic Bluegrass Banjo Solos (DVD) 2009. (ENG.). 29p. pap. 44.95 incl. audio compact disk *(978-1-4234-3668-3(7)*, 1423436687) Homespun Video.
Weissman, Dick. Banjo A to Z. 2008. (ENG.). 104p. pap. 19.95 *(978-0-7390-5260-0(8))* Alfred Publishing Co., Inc.

BANJO MUSIC

Here are entered composition not in a specific form or of a specific type for solo banjo, and collection of compositions in several forms or types for solo banjo.

Alfred Publishing Staff. Banjo: Piano/Vocal/Guitar, Sheet. 2012. (Original Sheet Music Edition Ser.). (ENG.). 8p. pap. 3.99 ***(978-0-7390-8930-9(7))*** Alfred Publishing Co., Inc.
—The Big Easy Banjo TAB Songbook: 62 Songs — Rock, Pop, Jazz, & Holiday Favorites! 2011. (Big Easy Songbook Ser.). 208p. pap. 24.99 *(978-0-7390-7696-5(5))* Alfred Publishing Co., Inc.
—Just for Fun: Classic Rock Banjo. 2010. (Just for Fun Ser.). (ENG.). 64p. pap. 14.99 *(978-0-7390-6459-7(2))* Alfred Publishing Co., Inc.
—Just for Fun: Easy Rock Banjo. 2010. (Just for Fun Ser.). (ENG.). 56p. pap. 14.99 *(978-0-7390-6463-4(0))* Alfred Publishing Co., Inc.
—Just for Fun: Rock & Pop Banjo. 2010. (Just for Fun Ser.). (ENG.). 64p. pap. 14.99 *(978-0-7390-6467-2(3))* Alfred Publishing Co., Inc.
—Just for Fun: Swingin' Jazz Banjo. 2010. (Just for Fun Ser.). (ENG.). 40p. pap. 14.99 *(978-0-7390-6471-9(1))* Alfred Publishing Co., Inc.
Alfred Publishing Staff. Just for Fun — Pop-Rock Banjo: 12 Great Recent Hits. 2011. (Just for Fun Ser.). (ENG.). 80p. pap. 14.99 ***(978-0-7390-8307-9(4))*** Alfred Publishing Co., Inc.
Beatles Staff & Sokolow, Fred. The Beatles for Banjo. 2009. (ENG.). 80p. pap. 14.99 *(978-1-4234-5653-7(X)*, 142345653X) Leonard, Hal Corp.
Bruce, Dix & Evans, Bill. Parking Lot Picker's Songbook: Banjo Edition, 1 vol. 2007. (ENG., Illus.). 304p. spiral bd. 29.95 *(978-0-7866-7491-6(1))* Mel Bay Pubns., Inc.
Carlin, Bob. Bob Carlin - Fiddle Tunes for Clawhammer Banjo. 2009. (ENG.). 60p. pap. 19.99 incl. audio compact disk *(978-1-57424-250-8(4)*, 1574242504) Centerstream Publishing.
Collins, Eddie. ASAP Fiddle Tunes Made Easy for Bluegrass Banjo: Learn How to Play the Bluegrass Way. 2010. (ENG.). 44p. pap. 19.99 incl. audio compact disk *(978-1-57424-260-7(1)*, 1574242601) Centerstream Publishing.
—Forty Gospel Greats for Banjo. 2010. (ENG.). 68p. pap. 19.99 incl. audio compact disk *(978-1-57424-263-8(6)*, 1574242636) Centerstream Publishing.
Costello, Patrick. The Outlaws & Scalawags Songbook. 2007. 54p. 24.95 *(978-0-9744190-3-9(6))* Pik-Ware Publishing.
Flesher, Bob. String Band Classics: Banjo, 1 vol. 2006. (ENG.). 48p. pap. 17.95 *(978-0-7866-4931-0(3)*, 96688bcd) Mel Bay Pubns., Inc.
Foster, Stephen. With My Banjo on My Knee: The Minstrel Songs of Stephen Foster. 2008. (ENG., Illus.). 64p. pap. 19.95 incl. audio compact disk *(978-1-57424-229-4(6)*, 1574242296) Centerstream Publishing.
Glaser, Matt & Hollender, Dave. Beyond Bluegrass Banjo: Etudes & Ideas for the Modern Banjo Player. 2011. (ENG.). 72p. pap. 19.99 incl. audio compact disk *(978-0-87639-118-1(8)*, 0876391188, Berklee Pr.) Leonard, Hal Corp.
Goggin, Jim. Sal Carson: The Life of a Big Band Leader. 2009. 340p. pap. 23.65 *(978-1-4269-1411-9(3))* Trafford Publishing.
Griner, Kelly. Irish Pub Songs for the 5-String Banjo Volume 1. 2010. 64p. pap. 19.95 *(978-0-578-05863-4(4))* Mondas Publishing.
Hal Leonard Corp., creator. Play Banjo Today! Level 2. 2011. (ENG.). 48p. pap. 9.99 incl. audio compact disk ***(978-1-4234-6642-0(X)***, 142346642X) Leonard, Hal Corp.
Kaufman, Steve. My First Banjo Picking Songs. 2011. (ENG.). 38p. audio compact disk 17.99 ***(978-0-7866-8350-5(3))*** Mel Bay Pubns., Inc.
Keefer, Jane. Old Time Stringband Workshop for Clawhammer Banjo: 40 Tunes Including Hoedowns, Jigs, Waltzes & More. Prohaska, Terry & Weissman, Dick, eds. 2011. (Illus.). 72p. pap. 19.99 ***(978-0-7866-8317-8(1)***, Bill's Music Shelf) Mel Bay Pubns., Inc.
Leftwich, Brad. Old-Time Fiddle: Round Peak Style: History, Tips, & Techniques. 2011. (Illus.). 128p. pap. 24.99 inc. audio compact disk ***(978-0-7866-8294-2(9))*** Mel Bay Pubns., Inc.
Levenson, Dan. Gospel Tunes for Clawhammer Banjo, 1 vol. 2008. (ENG.). 48p. pap. 17.95 *(978-0-7866-7576-0(4))* Mel Bay Pubns., Inc.
—Old Time Festival Tunes for Clawhammer Banjo, 1 vol. 2006. (ENG.). 248p. spiral bd. 29.95 *(978-0-7866-7519-7(5)*, 20313bcd) Mel Bay Pubns., Inc.
Maclachlan, Iain. Celtic Tune Encyclopedia for 5-String Banjo, 1 vol. 2009. (ENG.). 96p. spiral bd. 17.95 *(978-0-7866-7694-1(9))* Mel Bay Pubns., Inc.
Martin, Steve & Trischka, Tony. The Crow: New Songs for the Five-String Banjo. 2009. (ENG.). 42p. pap. 19.95 *(978-1-59773-277-2(X)*, 159773277X) Homespun Video.
McCabe, Larry. Easiest Banjo Tunes for Children, 1 vol. 2007. (Easiest Tunes for Children Ser.). (ENG., Illus.). 32p. pap. 14.95 *(978-0-7866-7575-3(6))* Mel Bay Pubns., Inc.
—101 Three-Chord Country & Bluegrass Songs: For Guitar, Banjo & Uke, 1 vol. 2008. (ENG.). 144p. pap. 14.95 *(978-0-7866-7708-5(2))* Mel Bay Pubns., Inc.
—101 Three-Chord Hymns & Gospel Songs: For Guitar, Banjo & Uke, 1 vol. 2008. (ENG.). 136p. pap. 14.95 *(978-0-7866-7654-5(X))* Mel Bay Pubns., Inc.
Nickerson, Ross, contrib. by. Christmas Music for Banjo Made Easy, 1 vol. 2007. (ENG., Illus.). 32p. pap. 14.95 *(978-0-7866-7702-3(3))* Mel Bay Pubns., Inc.
O'Brien, Colin. Play Banjo Today! Beginner's Pack: Level 1 Book/CD/DVD Pack. 2011. (ENG.). 48p. pap. 19.95 incl. audio compact disk *(978-1-61774-245-3(7)*, 1617742457) Leonard, Hal Corp.
Taylor, Todd. Pickin' over the Speed Limit: Presented by Todd Taylor, Guinness World Records' Fastest Banjo Player. 2011. (ENG.). 36p. pap. 19.99 incl. audio compact disk *(978-1-57424-262-1(8)*, 1574242628) Centerstream Publishing.
Triggs, Bill. Harry Reser: Tenor Banjo Legend: 26 Virtuoso Solos for Tenor Banjo, 1 vol. 2006. (ENG.). 136p. spiral bd. 24.95 *(978-0-7866-6050-6(3)*, 97057) Mel Bay Pubns., Inc.
Trischka, Tony. All-Star Bluegrass Jam-along: For Banjo. 2007. (ENG.). 43p. pap. 19.95 incl. audio compact disk *(978-1-59773-125-6(0)*, 1597731250) Homespun Video.
50 Solos for Irish Tenor Banjo. 2006. (Illus.). 48p. audio compact disk 23.95 *(978-1-85720-148-2(5)*, wm1371cd) Mel Bay Pubns., Inc.

BANK ACCEPTANCES

see Acceptances

BANK BILLS

see Bank Notes

BANK CLERKS

see Bank Employees

BANK CORRESPONDENCE

see Banks and Banking—Records and Correspondence

BANK CURRENCY

see Bank Notes

BANK DEPOSIT INSURANCE

see Deposit Insurance

BANK DEPOSITS

Dermine, Jean. Bank Valuation & Value-Based Management: Deposit & Loan Pricing, Performance Evaluation, & Risk Management. 2009. (ENG., Illus.). 432p. 95.00 *(978-0-07-162499-2(6)*, 0071624996) McGraw-Hill Cos., The.
Tyndale, Walter. Fundamentals of Offshore Banking: How to Open Accounts Almost Anywhere. 2009. 127p. pap. 19.95 *(978-0-557-06326-0(4))* Lulu Enterprises Inc.

BANK DIRECTORS

Bahin, Charlotte M. Bank Board Members Manual. 12th ed. 2007. pap. *(978-0-9785771-9-3(1))* America's Community Bankers.
Congressional Oversight Panel February Oversight Report: Executive Compensation Restrictions in the Troubled Asset Relief Program. 2011. (Illus.). iii, 105p. ***(978-0-16-088312-3(1)***, 552-070-42617-5) United States Government Printing Office.
Hamilton, James & Trautmann, Ted. Responsibilities of Corporate Officers & Directors under Federal Securities Law. rev. ed. 260p. (C). pap. 60.00 *(978-0-8080-0387-8(9))* Toolkit Media Group.
Hoover, Jewell & Ghiglieri, Catherine. The Ultimate Guide for Bank Directors. 2011. 96p. pap. 24.95 *(978-1-4520-8816-7(0))* AuthorHouse.
Milligan, Jack. The Guidebook to Effective Bank Board Committees. 2nd ed. 2006. 125.00 *(978-0-9785771-1-7(6))* America's Community Bankers.
Villa, John K. Bank Directors' Officers' & Lawyers' Civil Liabilities. 2nd ed. 2011. ***(978-1-4548-0108-5(5)***, Aspen Pubs.) Wolters Kluwer Law & Business.

BANK DISCOUNT

see Discount

BANK EMPLOYEES

Ali, Anees Janee & Nawari Hasan, Ali. Organizational Commitment among Bank Employees. 2010. 104p. pap. *(978-3-8383-9267-7(1))* Lambert Academic Publishing.
Amir Ishak, Noormala. Justice, Innovativeness & Organizational Citizenship Behavior. 2009. 172p. pap. *(978-3-639-21576-2(1))* VDM Verlag Dr. Mueller e.K.
Ashmole, Alan. Sand, Oil & Dollars: The adventures of an expatriate British Bank Manager in the Middle East in the 1950s, 1960s And 1970s. 2010. 152p. 25.49 *(978-1-4490-6449-5(3))*; pap. 13.49 *(978-1-4490-6448-8(5))* AuthorHouse.
Chavez, Joseph. Morality & Moral Reasoning in the Banking Industry. 2008. 108p. pap. *(978-3-639-08819-9(0))* VDM Verlag Dr. Mueller e.K.
Leeamornsiri, Joseph Nantawut. Hrd Competency Used During the Mergers. 2009. 228p. pap. *(978-3-639-20816-0(1))* VDM Verlag Dr. Mueller e.K.
Morris, Tim. Innovations in Banking, Volume 22. 2012. (ENG.). 152p. 100.00 ***(978-0-415-52667-8(1))*** Routledge.
Sampa, Saha, et al. Job Satisfaction of Bank Employees in Bangladesh: An Analysis of Satisfaction Factors. 2011. 160p. pap. ***(978-3-639-30241-7(9))*** VDM Verlag Dr. Mueller e.K.
Singh, Dr. Ripudaman, et al. Stress among Bank Employees. 2011. 72p. pap. ***(978-3-8454-1499-7(5))*** Lambert Academic Publishing.
Zafrul, Allam. Involvement & Burnout of Banking Professionals: Job Involvement & Job Burnout of Banking Professionals. 2011. 148p. pap. ***(978-3-639-33567-5(8))*** VDM Verlag Dr. Mueller e.K.

BANK EXAMINATION

Aicpa. AICPA Audit & Accounting Guide Depositories & Lending Institutions. 2007. pap. 86.25 *(978-0-87051-662-7(0))* American Institute of Certified Public Accountants.
—Audit Risk Alert Bank, Credit Union, & Other Depository & Lending Institution Industry Developments-2007. 2007. pap. 48.75 *(978-0-87051-696-2(5))* American Institute of Certified Public Accountants.
Donaldson, Deborah. Financial Institutions Internal Audit Desk Reference. 2nd ed. 2007. cd-rom 325.00 *(978-0-9799077-5-3(6))* Financial Managers Society, Inc.
DSST Exam Secrets Test Prep Staff, ed. DSST Money & Banking Exam Secrets Study Guide: DSST Test Review for the Dantes Subject Standardized Tests. 2011. 62.99 *(978-1-61403-529-9(6))* Mometrix Media LLC.
Shams, Heba & Butler, Mark. A Banker's Compliance Guide to Preventing Money Laundering & Terrorist Financing. 2011. *(978-0-8213-8571-5(2))* World Bank Pubns.
Steiner, Howard & Marini, Stephen. Independent Review for MSBs - the Complete BSA/AML Audit Workbook. 2009. 165p. pap. 119.95 *(978-0-615-23992-7(7))* ImpactAML-INX3 Financial Pr.

BANK FAILURES

Accountability for the Troubled Asset Relief Program: The Second Report of the Congressional Oversight Panel. 2009. iii, 61p. *(978-0-16-082692-4(6)*, 552-070-38709-9) United States Government Printing Office.
Ali, Tariq. A Banker for All Seasons: Bank of Crooks & Cheats Incorporated. 2007. (ENG., Illus.). 264p. 24.95 *(978-1-905422-65-4(2))* Seagull Bks. GBR. Dist: Chicago Distribution Ctr.
Aliber, Robert Z. & Zoega, Gylfi, eds. Preludes to the Icelandic Financial Crisis. 2011. (ENG., Illus.). 320p. 110.00 *(978-0-230-27692-5(X))* Palgrave Macmillan.
Allison, Herbert M. Hearing with Herbert M. Allison, Jr., Assistant Secretary of the Treasury for Financial Stability: Hearing Before the Congressional Oversight Panel, One Hundred Eleventh Congress, First Session, October 22, 2009. 2009. (Illus.). iii, 56p. *(978-0-16-085051-6(7)*, 552-070-40408-2) United States Government Printing Office.
—Herb Allison, Assistant Secretary of the Treasury for Financial Stability: Hearing Before the Congressional Oversight Panel, One Hundred Eleventh Congress, First Session, Hearing Held in Washington, D.C., June 24, 2009. 2009. iii, 49p. *(978-0-16-084493-5(2)*, 552-070-40016-8) United States Government Printing Office.
Bartiromo, Maria. The Weekend That Changed Wall Street: And How the Fallout Is Still Impacting Our World. 2011. (ENG.). 256p. (gr. 12). 15.00 *(978-1-59184-436-5(3)*, Portfolio Trade) Penguin Group (USA) Inc.
Brummer, Alex. The Crunch: How Greed & Incompetence Sparked the Credit Crisis. 2009. (ENG.). 286p. 14.95 ***(978-1-84794-009-4(9))*** Random Hse. GBR. Dist: Independent Pubs. Group.
Bryfonski, Dedria. The Banking Crisis. 2010. (Opposing Viewpoints Ser.). 240p. (J). pap. 26.75 *(978-0-7377-4855-0(9))*; (Illus.). 38.50 *(978-0-7377-4854-3(0))* Cengage Gale. (Greenhaven Pr., Inc.).
Carmassi, Jacopo, et al. Overcoming Too-Big-to-Fail: A Regulatory Framework to Limit Moral Hazard & Free Riding in the Financial Sector. 2010. (ENG.). 98p. pap. 30.00 *(978-92-9079-974-0(9))* Ctr. for European Policy Studies BEL. Dist: Brookings Institution Pr.
The Causes & Effects of the Lehman Brothers Bankruptcy: Hearing Before the Committee on Oversight & Government Reform, House of Representatives, One Hundred Tenth Congress, Second Session, October 6, 2008. 2010. (Illus.). iii, 251p. *(978-0-16-086105-5(5)*, 552-070-41215-8) United States Government Printing Office.
Ciro, Tony. The Global Financial Crisis: Triggers Responses & Aftermath. 2012. (Illus.). 266p. 124.95 ***(978-1-4094-1139-0(7))*** Ashgate Publishing Co.
Cohan, William D. House of Cards: A Tale of Hubris & Wretched Excess on Wall Street. (ENG.). 2010. 608p. pap. 16.95 *(978-0-7679-3089-5(4)*, Anchor) 2009. 480p. 27.95 *(978-0-385-52826-9(4)*, Doubleday) Knopf Doubleday Publishing Group.
—House of Cards: A Tale of Hubris & Wretched Excess on Wall Street. lt. ed. 2009. 819p. 32.95 *(978-1-4104-1835-7(9))* Thorndike Pr.
The Condition of Financial Institutions: Examining the Failure & Seizure of an American Bank: Hearing Before the Subcommittee on Financial Institutions & Consumer Credit of the Committee on Financial Services, U.S. House of Representatives, One Hundred Eleventh Congress, Second Session, January 21, 2010. 2010. v, 174p. *(978-0-16-086342-4(2)*, 552-070-41426-6) United States Government Printing Office.
Congressional Oversight Panel April Oversight Report: Assessing Treasury's Strategy: Six Months of TARP. 2009. (Illus.). iii, 134p. *(978-0-16-083194-3(9)*, 552-070-39030-8) United States Government Printing Office.
Congressional Oversight Panel July Oversight Report: TARP Repayments, Including the Repurchase of Stock Warrants. 2009. iii, 94p. *(978-0-16-083904-7(1)*, 552-070-39593-8) United States Government Printing Office.
Crowley, Robert W., ed. Unique Treatment of GMAC under TARP. 2010. (Financial Institutions & Services Ser.). (Illus.). ix, 176p. 115.00 *(978-1-61728-305-5(3))* Nova Science Pubs., Inc.

B

Davies, Howard. The Financial Crisis: Who Is to Blame? 2010. (ENG.). 240p. 69.95 *(978-0-7456-5163-7(1))*; pap. 19.95 *(978-0-7456-5164-4(X))* Polity Pr. GBR. Dist: Wiley, John & Sons, Inc.

Does the Dodd-Frank ACT End "Too Big to Fail?" Hearing Before the Subcommittee on Financial Institutions & Consumer Credit of the Committee on Financial Services, U.S. House of Representatives, One Hundred Twelfth Congress, First Session, June 14, 2011. 2011. v, 103p. ***(978-0-16-089633-0(9)***, 552-070-43522-1) United States Government Printing Office.

Duffie, Darrell. How Big Banks Fail, & What to Do about It. 2010. (ENG., Illus.). 112p. (C). 29.95 *(978-0-691-14885-4(6))* Princeton Univ. Pr.

Erdint, Didar. Bank Behavior & Crisis under MacRoeconomic Uncertainty. 2008. 304p. pap. *(978-3-639-01894-3(X))* VDM Verlag Dr. Mueller e.K.

Farrell, Greg. Crash of the Titans: Greed, Hubris, the Fall of Merrill Lynch, & the near-Collapse of Bank of America. 2011. (ENG.). 512p. pap. 17.00 *(978-0-307-71787-0(9)*, Crown Business) Crown Publishing Group.

FDIC Oversight: Examining & Evaluating the Role of the Regulator During the Financial Crisis & Today: Hearing Before the Subcommittee on Financial Institutions & Consumer Credit of the Committee on Financial Services, U.S. House of Representatives, One Hundred Twelfth Congress, First Session, May 26, 2011. 2011. v, 137p. ***(978-0-16-089516-6(2)***, 552-070-43475-5) United States Government Printing Office.

Felton, Andrew & Reinhart, Carmen M., eds. The First Global Financial Crisis of the 21st Century. 2009. (Illus.). 193p. pap. *(978-0-9557009-3-4(0))* Ctr. for Economic Policy Research.

Fuller, Robert Lynn. Phantom of Fear: The Banking Panic Of 1933. 2011. (ENG.). 287p. pap. 49.95 ***(978-0-7864-6510-1(7))*** McFarland & Co., Inc. Pubs.

Geithner, Timothy F. Treasury Secretary Timothy F. Geithner: Hearing Before the Congressional Oversight Panel, One Hundred Eleventh Congress, First Session, April 21, 2009. 2009. iii, 66p. *(978-0-16-084083-8(X)*, 552-070-39699-3) United States Government Printing Office.

Gray, Joanna & Akseli, Orkun. Financial Regulation in Crisis? The Role of Law & the Failure of Northern Rock. Gray, Joanna & Akseli, Orkun, eds. 2011. (Elgar Financial Law Ser.). 128p. 110.00 ***(978-1-84844-554-3(7))*** Elgar, Edward Publishing, Inc.

Green, Stephen. Good Value: Reflections on Money, Morality & an Uncertain World. (ENG.). 2011. 256p. pap. 14.95 *(978-0-8021-4525-3(6)*, Grove Pr.) 2010. 288p. 25.00 *(978-0-8021-1917-9(4)*, Atlantic Monthly Pr.) Grove/Atlantic, Inc.

Grind, Kirsten. The Lost Bank: The Story of Washington Mutual— The Biggest Bank Failure in American History. 2012. pap. ***(978-1-4516-1793-1(3))*** Simon & Schuster.

—The Lost Bank: The Story of Washington Mutual-The Biggest Bank Failure in American History. 2012. (ENG.). 400p. 27.00 ***(978-1-4516-1792-4(5))*** Simon & Schuster.

Grossman, Richard S. Unsettled Account: The Evolution of Banking in the Industrialized World since 1800. 2010. (Princeton Economic History of the Western World Ser.). (ENG., Illus.). 400p. (C). 39.50 *(978-0-691-13905-0(9))* Princeton Univ. Pr.

Hoelscher, David S. Bank Restructuring & Resolution. Hoelscher, David S., ed. 2006. (ENG., Illus.). 416p. 137.00 *(978-0-230-01900-3(5))* Palgrave Macmillan.

Hoelscher, David S. & Quintyn, Marc, contrib. by. Managing Systemic Banking Crises. (CHI.). *(978-7-5049-3541-0(7)*, S224CA) China Financial Publishing Hse.

Isaac, William M. Senseless Panic: How Washington Failed America. 2010. (ENG.). 190p. 24.95 *(978-0-470-64036-4(7)*, Wiley) Wiley, John & Sons, Inc.

Johnson, Simon & Kwak, James. 13 Bankers: The Wall Street Takeover & the Next Financial Meltdown. (Vintage Ser.). (ENG.). 2011. 336p. pap. 15.95 *(978-0-307-47660-9(X)*, Vintage) 2010. (Illus.). 320p. 26.95 *(978-0-307-37905-4(1)*, Pantheon) Knopf Doubleday Publishing Group.

Kelly, Kate. Street Fighters: The Last 72 Hours of Bear Sterns, the Toughest Firm on Wall Street. 2010. (ENG.). 256p. (gr. 12-18). 16.00 *(978-1-59184-318-4(9)*, Portfolio Trade) Penguin Group (USA) Inc.

LaBrosse, John, et al. Financial Crisis Management & Bank Resolution. 2009. 338p. 342.00 *(978-1-84311-838-1(6))* Informa Professional GBR. Dist: International Specialized Bk. Services.

Lastra, Rosa. Cross-Border Bank Insolvency. 2011. (ENG., Illus.). 592p. 250.00 *(978-0-19-957707-1(2))* Oxford Univ. Pr., Inc.

Mare, Davide Salvatore. MacRoeconomic Factors & Small Bank Failures. 2011. 76p. pap. ***(978-3-8443-8816-9(8))*** Lambert Academic Publishing.

McKinley, Vern. Financing Failure: A Century of Bailouts. 2012. (ENG.). 384p. 29.95 ***(978-1-59813-053-9(6))*** Independent Institute, The.

—Financing Failure: A History of Bailouts. 2012. (ENG.). 384p. pap. 19.95 ***(978-1-59813-049-2(8))*** Independent Institute, The.

Milne, Alistair. The Fall of the House of Credit: What Went Wrong in Banking & What can be Done to Repair the Damage? 2009. (ENG., Illus.). 380p. 30.00 *(978-0-521-76214-4(6))* Cambridge Univ. Pr.

Moosa, Imad A. The Myth of Too Big to Fail. 2010. (Palgrave Macmillan Studies in Banking & Financial Institutions Ser.). (ENG., Illus.). 256p. 105.00 *(978-0-230-27776-2(4))* Palgrave Macmillan.

Nadler, Marcus & Bogen, Jules. The Banking Crisis, Volume 24. 2012. (ENG.). 224p. 115.00 ***(978-0-415-52812-2(7))*** Routledge.

Park, Sangkyun. Contagion of Bank Failures (Rle Banking & Finance), Volume 26. 2012. (ENG.). 216p. 115.00 ***(978-0-415-52875-7(5))*** Routledge.

Parker, David C. & International Monetary Fund. Closing a Failed Bank: Resolution Practices & Procedures. 2011. (Illus.). 244p. pap. ***(978-1-61635-027-7(X))*** International Monetary Fund.

Quagliariello, Mario, ed. Stress-testing the Banking System: Methodologies & Applications. 2009. (ENG., Illus.). 354p. 139.00 *(978-0-521-76730-9(X))* Cambridge Univ. Pr.

Rochet, Jean-Charles. Why Are There So Many Banking Crises? The Politics & Policy of Bank Regulation. 2008. (ENG., Illus.). 336p. (C). 65.00 *(978-0-691-13146-7(5))* Princeton Univ. Pr.

Schubert, Aurel. The Credit-Anstalt Crisis Of 1931. 2006. (Studies in Macroeconomic History Ser.). (ENG., Illus.). 224p. pap. 48.00 *(978-0-521-03029-8(3))* Cambridge Univ. Pr.

Shalhope, Robert E. The Baltimore Bank Riot: Political Upheaval in Antebellum Maryland. 2009. (ENG.). 208p. 50.00 *(978-0-252-03480-0(5))* Univ. of Illinois Pr.

Smit, Jeroen. The Perfect Prey: The Fall of Abn Amro, or What Went Wrong in the Banking Industry. 2010. (ENG., Illus.). 480p. pap. 23.95 *(978-1-84916-268-5(9))* Quercus GBR. Dist: Independent Pubs. Group.

Stern, Gary H. & Feldman, Ron J. Too Big to Fail: The Hazards of Bank Bailouts. 2009. (ENG.). 230p. pap. 22.95 *(978-0-8157-0304-4(X))* Brookings Institution Pr.

Systemic Regulation, Prudential Matters, Resolution Authority, & Securitization: Hearing Before the Committee on Financial Services, U.S. House of Representatives, One Hundred Eleventh Congress, First Session, October 29, 2009. 2010. (Illus.). iv, 386p. ***(978-0-16-086125-3(X)***, 552-070-41231-0) United States Government Printing Office.

TARP Accountability & Oversight: Achieving Transparency: Hearing Before the Joint Economic Committee, Congress of the United States, One Hundred Eleventh Congress, First Session, March 11, 2009. 2009. iii, 76p. *(978-0-16-084354-9(5)*, 552-070-39897-0) United States Government Printing Office.

TARP Oversight: A 6-Month Update: Hearing Before the Committee on Finance, United States Senate, One Hundred Eleventh Congress, First Session, March 31, 2009. 2009. iii, 116p. ***(978-0-16-088303-3(2)***, 552-070-42608-6) United States Government Printing Office.

Taylor, John B. Ending Government Bailouts as We Know Them. Scott, Kenneth E. & Shultz, George P., eds. 2010. (Hoover inst press Publication). (ENG.). 338p. 19.95 *(978-0-8179-1124-9(3))* Hoover Institution Pr.

Toktas-Palut, Peral. Predicting Bank Failures. 2010. 252p. pap. *(978-3-8383-5292-3(0))* Lambert Academic Publishing.

Too Big to Fail? The Role of Antitrust Law in Government-Funded Consolidation in the Banking Industry: Hearing Before the Subcommittee on Courts & Competition Policy of the Committee on the Judiciary, House of Representatives, One Hundred Eleventh Congress, First Session, March 17, 2009. 2009. (Illus.). iii, 87p. *(978-0-16-084890-2(3)*, 552-070-40286-1) United States Government Printing Office.

Vickers, Raymond. Panic in the Loop: Chicago's Banking Crisis of 1932. 2011. (ENG.). 348p. 80.00 ***(978-0-7391-6640-6(9))*** Lexington Bks.

Vickers, Raymond B. Panic in Paradise: Florida's Banking Crash Of 1926. 2007. (Illus.). 336p. per. 36.00 *(978-0-8173-5414-5(X))* Univ. of Alabama Pr.

Vickers, Raymond B. Panic in the Loop: Chicago's Banking Crisis of 1932. 2011. ***(978-0-7391-6642-0(5))*** Lexington Bks.

Villa, John K. Bank Directors' Officers' & Lawyers' Civil Liabilities. 2nd ed. 2011. ***(978-1-4548-0108-5(5)***, Aspen Pubs.) Wolters Kluwer Law & Business.

Wall Street & the Financial Crisis: The Role of Bank Regulators: Hearing Before the Permanent Subcommittee on Investigations of the Committee on Homeland Security & Governmental Affairs, United States Senate, One Hundred Eleventh Congress, Second Session, April 16, 2010. 2010. (Illus.). xi, 685p. *(978-0-16-087094-1(1)*, 552-070-41950) United States Government Printing Office.

Ward, Vicky. The Devil's Casino: Friendship, Betrayal, & the High-Stakes Games Played Inside Lehman Brothers. 2011. (ENG., Illus.). 270p. pap. 16.95 *(978-1-118-01149-2(X)*, Wiley) Wiley, John & Sons, Inc.

Yavlinsky, Grigory. Realeconomik: The Hidden Cause of the Great Recession (and How to Avert the Next One) Bouis, Antonina W., tr. 2011. (ENG.). 192p. 26.00 *(978-0-300-15910-3(2))* Yale Univ. Pr.

BANK FEES

see Banks and Banking—Service Charges

BANK FRAUD

Barta, Dan, et al. Bank Fraud: Using Technology to Combat Losses. 2012. (Wiley & SAS Business Ser.: 25). (ENG.). 256p. 65.00 ***(978-0-470-49439-4(5)***, Wiley) Wiley, John & Sons, Inc.

Carey, Leon. Scammers among Us Beware: Scammers & Frauds. 2009. 60p. pap. 9.95 *(978-1-60693-983-3(1)*, Eloquent Bks.) AEG Literary Publishing Services, Inc.

Folami, Olakunle Michael. Crime in the Banking Sector & the Nation's Economy. 2011. 140p. pap. ***(978-3-8433-9320-1(6))*** Lambert Academic Publishing.

Geiger, Mark W. Financial Fraud & Guerrilla Violence in Missouri's Civil War, 1861-1865. 2010. (Yale Series in Economic & Financial History Ser.). (Illus.). 320p. 55.00 *(978-0-300-15151-0(9))* Yale Univ. Pr.

McDaniel, Herman. Bank Robbers Now Use Computers. 2007. 260p. per. 17.95 *(978-1-4327-0450-6(8))* Outskirts Pr., Inc.

Oversight of the SEC Inspector General's Report on the "Investigation of the SEC's Response to Concerns Regarding Robert Allen Stanford's Alleged Ponzi Scheme" & Improving SEC Performance: Hearing Before the Committee on Banking, Housing, & Urban Affairs, United States Senate, One Hundred Eleventh Congress, Second Session, on Examining the Oversight of the SEC Inspector General's Report on the "Investigation of the SEC's Response to Concerns Regarding Robert Allen Stanford's Alleged Ponzi Scheme" & Improving SEC Performance, September 22, 2010. 2011. iii, 72p. ***(978-0-16-088949-3(9)***, 552-070-42989-1) United States Government Printing Office.

Richard, Christine. Confidence Game: How a Hedge Fund Manager Called Wall Street's Bluff. 2010. (ENG., Illus.). 352p. *(978-1-57660-337-6(7)*, Bloomberg Pr.) Wiley, John & Sons, Inc.

The Role of Inspectors General: Minimizing & Mitigating Waste, Fraud, & Abuse: Hearing Before the Subcommittee on Oversight & Investigations of the Committee on Financial Services, U.S. House of Representatives, One Hundred Eleventh Congress, First Session, May 5, 2009. 2009. v, 62p. *(978-0-16-084131-6(3)*, 552-070-39738-8) United States Government Printing Office.

Shams, Heba & Butler, Mark. A Banker's Compliance Guide to Preventing Money Laundering & Terrorist Financing. 2011. *(978-0-8213-8571-5(2))* World Bank Pubns.

Stephenson, J. r. Broken Promises, Betrayals & Barefaced Lies. 2008. 144p. pap. *(978-0-9558557-0-2(5))* ShieldCrest.

Vander Weyer, Martin. Fortune's Spear: The Story of the Blue-Blooded Rogue Behind the Most Notorious City Scandal of the 1920s. 2012. (ENG.). 368p. 29.95 ***(978-1-907642-31-9(5))*** Elliott & Thompson, Ltd. GBR. Dist: Independent Pubs. Group.

BANK HOLDING COMPANIES

Chung, Eek-June. Risk & Bank Expansion into Nonbanking Businesses, Volume 4. 2012. (ENG.). 160p. 100.00 ***(978-0-415-52811-5(9))*** Routledge.

Congressional Oversight Panel July Oversight Report: TARP Repayments, Including the Repurchase of Stock Warrants. 2009. iii, 94p. *(978-0-16-083904-7(1)*, 552-070-39593-8) United States Government Printing Office.

Congressional Oversight Panel June Oversight Report: Stress Testing & Shoring up Bank Capital. 2009. (Illus.). iii, 142p. *(978-0-16-083525-4(9)*, 552-070-39248-3) United States Government Printing Office.

Crowley, Robert W., ed. Unique Treatment of GMAC under TARP. 2010. (Financial Institutions & Services Ser.). (Illus.). ix, 176p. 115.00 *(978-1-61728-305-5(3))* Nova Science Pubs., Inc.

Fein, Melanie L. & Heller, Pauline B. Federal Bank Holding Company Law. 3rd ed. 2011. ***(978-1-58852-177-4(X)***, Law Journal Pr.) Incisive Media.

Prohibiting Certain High-Risk Investment Activities by Banks & Bank Holding Companies: Hearing Before the Committee on Banking, Housing, & Urban Affairs, United States Senate, One Hundred Eleventh Congress, Second Session, on Examining Recent Restrictions Placed on Commercial Banks & Bank Holding Companies' High-Risk Investment Activities, February 2, 2010. 2010. iii, 71p. ***(978-0-16-087802-2(0)***, 552-070-42306-1) United States Government Printing Office.

BANK INSURANCE

Here are entered works on the insurance coverage of general banking activities. Works on the insurance business activities conducted by banks are entered under Banks and Banking—Insurance Business.

Augustinos, Theodore P. & Emmanuel, John N. Bank Insurance Sales Methods: Central Region. Smith, Carole, ed. 144p. pap. 389.00 *(978-0-8080-0397-7(6))* Toolkit Media Group.

—Bank Insurance Sales Methods: Northeast Region. Smith, Carole, ed. 152p. pap. 389.00 *(978-0-8080-0395-3(X))* Toolkit Media Group.

—Bank Insurance Sales Methods: Southern Region. Smith, Carole, ed. 176p. pap. 389.00 *(978-0-8080-0396-0(8))* Toolkit Media Group.

—Bank Insurance Sales Methods: Western Region. Smith, Carole, ed. 152p. pap. 389.00 *(978-0-8080-0398-4(4))* Toolkit Media Group.

Bakas, Adjiedj & Peverelli, Roger. The Future of Finance: Megatrends Beyond the Crisis. 2009. (Business & Finance Ser.). (Illus.). 320p. 25.00 *(978-1-906821-01-2(1))* Infinite Ideas GBR. Dist: Sony Electronics.

Bank Insurance Survey Report. Date not set. (Annual Ser.). (C). 140.00 *(978-0-89982-011-8(5))* American Bankers Assn.

Lin, Hong-Jen. It & Efficiency Analysis in Commercial Banks & Insurance Firms. 2009. 100p. pap. *(978-3-639-16144-1(0))* VDM Verlag Dr. Mueller e.K.

Schroeder, Gilbert J. & Tomaine, John J. Loan Loss Coverage under Financial Institution Bonds. 2007. xxv, 693p. *(978-1-59031-943-7(5))* American Bar Assn.

Simmonds, Scott. Simmonds on Bank Insurance. 2007. pap. *(978-0-9774015-2-9(9))* Insurance Consultants of Maine.

World Bank Staff, contrib. by. The World Bank Group Guarantee Instruments, 1990-2007. 2009. (Independent Evaluation Group Studies). (ENG., Illus.). 152p. pap. 30.00 *(978-0-8213-7679-9(9)*, 9780821376799) World Bank Pubns.

BANK INSURANCE ACTIVITIES

see Banks and Banking—Insurance Business

BANK INVESTMENTS

American Brokerage Consultants Staff. 1996 Survey Reports on Bank Retail Investment Services. Date not set. (1996 Bank Representative Compensation Survey Ser.: Vol. 2). *(978-0-89982-021-7(2))*; (1996 Banker's Report Card on Ihino-Party Marketing Companies Ser.: Vol. 3). *(978-0-89982-022-4(0))*; (1996 Bank Representative Compensaion Survey Ser.: Vol. 4). *(978-0-89982-023-1(9))* American Bankers Assn.

Andreassen, Ole. Getting Credit. 2008. 192p. pap. *(978-3-639-08775-8(5))* VDM Verlag Dr. Mueller e.K.

Baum, Daniel J. The Investment Function of Canadian Financial Institutions. 2007. (ENG.). 292p. per. 22.95 *(978-0-595-47425-7(X)*, Backinprint.com) iUniverse, Inc.

Duncan, Bradley S. & Brenshaw, Alicia M., eds. Proprietary Trading & Investment Restrictions under the Volcker Role. 2011. (Business Issues, Competition & Entrepreneurship Ser.). 112p. pap. 47.00 *(978-1-61324-066-3(X))* Nova Science Pubs., Inc.

Nicole A. Garcia. Banks, Securities & the Volcker Rule: Background & Issues. 2011. (Series: Financial Institutions & Services Ser.). 89.00 *(978-1-61761-988-5(4))* Nova Science Pubs., Inc.

Taranto Aldo & Taranto, Aldo. Modelling the Nature of Close-out Netting on Bank Portfolios: An Analysis of how Financial Institutions can Minimize their FX Exposures via Close-out Netting their Interbank Lending & Derivative Deals. 2008. 152p. pap. *(978-3-639-09571-5(5))* VDM Verlag Dr. Mueller e.K.

BANK LOANS

see Loans

BANK MANAGEMENT

Al Manaseer, Mousa. Bank Profitability. 2009. 260p. pap. *(978-3-639-17148-8(9))* VDM Verlag Dr. Mueller e.K.

American Bankers Association. Banking Today: Handbook. 2007. (Illus.). 134p. (C). pap. 79.00 *(978-0-89982-604-2(0))* American Bankers Assn.

—Banking Today: Leader's Guide. 2007. 108p. (C). pap. 55.00 *(978-0-89982-605-9(9))* American Bankers Assn.

America's Community Bankers Staff, contrib. by. America's Community Bankers: Celebrating 115 Years of Leadership Through the Decades. 2007. *(978-0-9791229-8-9(8))* America's Community Bankers.

Arora, Rashmi Umesh. Bank Credit & Development. 2009. 304p. pap. *(978-3-639-13948-8(8))* VDM Verlag Dr. Mueller e.K.

Bahin, Charlotte M. Bank Board Members Manual. 12th ed. 2007. pap. *(978-0-9785771-9-3(1))* America's Community Bankers.

Barth, James R., et al. Rethinking Bank Regulation: Till Angels Govern. 2007. (ENG., Illus.). 448p. (C). pap. 36.99 *(978-0-521-70930-9(X))* Cambridge Univ. Pr.

Berkelaar, Arjan Bastiaan, et al, eds. Interest Rate Models, Asset Allocation & Quantitative Techniques for Central Banks & Sovereign Wealth Funds. 2010. (ENG., Illus.). 432p. 116.00 *(978-0-230-24012-4(7))* Palgrave Macmillan.

Bexley, James B. Selling Financial Products. 2011. (ENG.). 192p. (C). pap. 77.33 ***(978-0-13-275213-8(1)***, Prentice Hall) Prentice Hall PTR.

—Selling Financial Products: A Practical Guide for Successful Bank Sales with Case Studies. 2012. (Illus.). xxi, 161p. ***(978-0-13-275218-3(2))*** Pearson Bks.

Bhati, Shyam. Role of Trust in Bank Lending. 2011. 308p. pap. ***(978-3-8443-2504-1(2))*** Lambert Academic Publishing.

Bhattacharya, Hrishikes. Banking Strategy, Credit Appraisal, & Lending Decisions: A Risk-Return Framework. 2nd ed. 2011. (ENG., Illus.). 632p. pap. 50.00 ***(978-0-19-807410-6(7))*** Oxford Univ. Pr., Inc.

Bikker, Jacob & Bos, J. W. B. Bank Performance. 2009. 154p. pap. 39.95 *(978-0-415-56961-3(3))* Routledge.

Blanpain. Globalization & Employment Relations in Retail Banking. 2007. pap. *(978-90-411-2620-7(1))* Kluwer Law International.

Cebotari, Igor. Banking Risk & Profitability in Republic of Moldov. 2010. 80p. pap. *(978-3-8383-7167-2(4))* Lambert Academic Publishing.

Chibaya Mbuya, John. Advanced Credit Risk Management in the Banking Industry. 2010. 300p. pap. *(978-3-8383-8674-4(4))* Lambert Academic Publishing.

—Bank Securities Management. 2010. 108p. pap. *(978-3-8383-8542-6(X))* Lambert Academic Publishing.

—The Bible of Banking: Volume 1. 2010. 664p. pap. *(978-3-8383-9485-5(2))* Lambert Academic Publishing.

—The Bible of Banking: Volume II. 2010. 636p. pap. *(978-3-8383-9645-3(6))* Lambert Academic Publishing.

—The Rise & Fall of South Africa's Fifth Largest Bank. 2010. 168p. pap. *(978-3-8383-7369-0(3))* Lambert Academic Publishing.

Chorafas, Dimitris N. Stress Testing for Risk Control under Basel II. 2006. (ENG., Illus.). 360p. 86.95 *(978-0-7506-8305-0(8)*, Butterworth-Heinemann) Elsevier Science & Technology Bks.

Claessens, Roger & Wiertz, Philippe. Bank Branch Management. 2006. *(978-2-87974-069-0(X))* Promoculture sarl.

Collardi, Boris F. J. World Class Private Banking: Building a Culture of Excellence. 2012. (Wiley Finance Ser.: 681). (ENG.). 256p. 120.00 *(978-0-470-82437-5(9)*, Wiley) Wiley, John & Sons, Inc.

Cram101 Textbook Reviews. Outlines & Highlights for Bank Management by Timothy W Koch, Isbn: 9780324655780. 2010. 344p. pap. 33.95 *(978-1-61698-028-3(1))* Cram101 Inc.

Cram101 Textbook Reviews & Cram101 Textbook Reviews. Outlines & Highlights for Global Bank Regulation: Principles & Policies by Heidi Mandanis Schooner. 2011. 350p. pap. 33.95 ***(978-1-61830-376-9(7))*** Cram101 Inc.

Cram101 Textbook Reviews Staff. Outlines & Highlights for Bank Management & Financial Services by Peter, Isbn: 007304623x. 2008. 192p. pap. 13.95 *(978-1-4288-5950-0(0))* Cram101 Inc.

Davis, Steven I. Banking in Turmoil: Strategies for Sustainable Growth. 2009. (ENG., Illus.). 256p. 110.00 *(978-0-230-23571-7(9))* Palgrave Macmillan.

Donatien, Hainaut. Asset Liability Management. Individual & institutional approaches. 2008. 220p. pap. *(978-3-8364-9178-5(8))* VDM Verlag Dr. Mueller e.K.

Duttweiler, Rudolf. Managing Liquidity in Banks: A Top down Approach. 2009. (ENG., Illus.). 304p. 75.00 *(978-0-470-74046-0(9)*, Wiley) Wiley, John & Sons, Inc.

Erdint, Didar. Bank Behavior & Crisis under MacRoeconomic Uncertainty. 2008. 304p. pap. *(978-3-639-01894-3(X))* VDM Verlag Dr. Mueller e.K.

GARP (Global Association of Risk Professionals), et al. Foundations of Banking Risk: An Overview of Banking, Banking Risks, & Risk-Based Banking Regulation. 2009. (Wiley Finance Ser.: 507). (ENG., Illus.). 264p. pap. 95.00 *(978-0-470-44219-7(0)*, Wiley) Wiley, John & Sons, Inc.

Glantz, Morton & Mun, Johnathan. Credit Engineering for Bankers: A Practical Guide for Bank Lending. 2nd ed. 2010. (ENG.). 556p. 89.95 *(978-0-12-378585-5(5)*, Academic Pr.) Elsevier Science & Technology Bks.

Goble, Jeff. More Yield, Less Risk - Better Sleep! A common sense guide to managing your bank's bond Portfolio. 2007. (Illus.). 122p. pap. 49.00 *(978-0-9799077-4-6(8))* Financial Managers Society, Inc.

Greenbaum, Stuart I. & Thakor, Anjan V. Contemporary Financial Intermediation. 2nd rev. ed. 2007. (Academic Press Advanced Finance Ser.). (ENG., Illus.). 672p. 103.00 *(978-0-12-299053-3(E)*, Academic Pr.) Elsevier Science & Technology Bks.

Greuning, Hennie van, et al. Analyzing Banking Risk: A Framework for Assessing Corporate Governance & Financial Risk. 3rd rev. ed. 2009. (World Bank Training Ser.). (ENG., Illus.). 440p. pap. 55.00 *(978-0-8213-7728-4(0)*, 9780821377284) World Bank Pubns.

Gup, B. E. & Gup, Benton E. Handbook for Directors of Financial Institutions. 2008. (Elgar Original Reference Ser.). (Illus.). 200p. (C). 173.00 *(978-1-84720-469-1(4))* Elgar, Edward Publishing, Inc.

Hens, Thorsten, et al. Behavioural Finance for Private Banking. 2009. (Wiley Finance Ser.). (ENG., Illus.). 270p. 80.00 *(978-0-470-77999-6(3)*, Wiley) Wiley, John & Sons, Inc.

Herrmann, Heinz. Designing Central Banks. Mayes, David & Wood, Geoffrey E., eds. 2009. (Routledge International Studies in Money & Banking Ser.). (ENG., Illus.). 272p. (C). 160.00 *(978-0-415-47616-4(X))* Routledge.

Hoelscher, David S. Bank Restructuring & Resolution. Hoelscher, David S., ed. 2006. (ENG., Illus.). 416p. 137.00 *(978-0-230-01900-3(5))* Palgrave Macmillan.

Hoflich, Peter. Banks at Risk: Global Best Practices in an Age of Turbulence. 2011. (ENG., Illus.). 256p. 65.00 *(978-0-470-82719-2(X)*, Wiley) Wiley, John & Sons, Inc.

Hong Kong Institute of Bankers Staff. Bank Asset & Liability Management. 2012. (ENG.). 256p. pap. 50.00 *(978-0-470-82753-6(X)*, Wiley) Wiley, John & Sons, Inc.

Iqbal, Zamir & Greuning, Hennie van. Risk Analysis for Islamic Banks. 2007. (Stand Alones Ser.). (ENG., Illus.). 328p. per. 50.00 *(978-0-8213-7141-1(X)*, 9780821371411) World Bank Pubns.

Janssen, Sven. British & German Banking Strategies. 2009. (Palgrave Macmillan Studies in Banking & Financial Institutions Ser.). (ENG., Illus.). 256p. (C). 116.00 *(978-0-230-22048-5(7))* Palgrave Macmillan.

Joshi, Vinay V. & Joshi, Vasant C. Managing Indian Banks: The Challenges Ahead. 3rd ed. 2009. (Response Bks.). (Illus.). 364p. (C). pap. 39.95 *(978-81-7829-852-8(X)*, B98528P) SAGE Pubns., Inc.

Kaleem, Ahmad. Monetary Stability under Dual Banking System. 2009. 202p. pap. *(978-3-639-18181-4(6))* VDM Verlag Dr. Mueller e.K.

Kaye, Jane & Stranger, Mark. Principles & Practice in Biobank Governance. 2009. (Illus.). 316p. 124.95 *(978-0-7546-7825-0(3))* Ashgate Publishing Co.

King, Brett. Bank 2. 0: How Customer Behaviour & Technology Will Change the Future of Financial Services, 1 vol. 2011. (ENG., Illus.). 360p. 39.99 *(978-981-4302-07-4(4))* Marshall Cavendish International (Asia) Private Ltd. SGP. Dist: Marshall Cavendish Corp.

Klaassen, Peter & Eeghen, Idzard van. Economic Capital: How It Works, & What Every Manager Needs to Know. 2009. (ENG., Illus.). 304p. (C). 82.95 *(978-0-12-374901-7(8)*, Elsevier Science) Elsevier Science & Technology Bks.

Koch and MacDonald. Bank Management. 2006. pap. 20.95 *(978-1-4288-0869-0(8))* Cram101 Inc.

Koch, Timothy W. & MacDonald, S. Scott. Bank Management. 7th ed. 2009. (ENG., Illus.). 888p. (C). 208.95 *(978-0-324-65578-0(9))* Cengage South-Western.

Kroner, Niels. A Blueprint for Better Banking: Svenska Handelsbanken & a proven model for more stable & profitable Banking. 2011. (ENG.). 218p. pap. 60.00 ***(978-0-85719-097-0(0))*** Harriman Hse. Publishing GBR. Dist: Ingram Pub. Services.

Leicht, Tanja. Change of Management - Management of Change - an Analysis of the Future Orientation of the Management of Cooperative Banks Consequences for the Hrm. 2008. 160p. pap. *(978-3-639-03124-9(5))* VDM Verlag Dr. Mueller e.K.

Lepinay, Vincent Antonin. Codes of Finance - Engineering Derivatives in a Global Bank. 2011. (ENG., Illus.). 304p. (C). 39.50 ***(978-0-691-15150-2(4))*** Princeton Univ. Pr.

Matz, Leonard, et al, eds. Liquidity Risk Measurement & Management: A Practitioner's Guide to Global Best Practices. 2006. (Wiley Finance Ser.). (ENG., Illus.). 350p. 160.00 *(978-0-470-82182-4(5)*, Wiley) Wiley, John & Sons, Inc.

Mazlad, Samar. Monetary Frameworks in Emerging Markets. 2010. 260p. pap. *(978-3-8383-4560-1(2))* Lambert Academic Publishing.

Michel, Alexandra & Wortham, Stanton. Bullish on Uncertainty: How Organizational Cultures Transform Participants. 2008. (ENG.). 278p. 78.99 *(978-0-521-86996-6(X))*; (Illus.). pap. 28.99 *(978-0-521-69019-5(6))* Cambridge Univ. Pr.

Milligan, Jack. The Guidebook to Effective Bank Board Committees. 2nd ed. 2006. 125.00 *(978-0-9785771-1-7(6))* America's Community Bankers.

Molyneux, Philip, ed. Bank Performance, Risk & Firm Financing. 2011. (Palgrave Macmillan Studies in Banking & Financial Institutions Ser.). (ENG., Illus.). 296p. 105.00 *(978-0-230-31335-4(3))* Palgrave Macmillan.

Musch. New basel capital Accord. 2008. (ENG.). 80p. pap. 19.95 *(978-92-9079-528-2(6))* Ctr. for European Policy Studies BEL. Dist: Brookings Institution Pr.

Nazvanov, Greg. Ontological Coaching for Bank Managers. 2010. 98p. pap. 17.44 *(978-1-4457-2213-9(5))* Lulu Enterprises Inc.

Nilsen, Henrik. Corporate Social Responsibility in Banking. 2011. 88p. pap. ***(978-3-8443-0227-1(1))*** Lambert Academic Publishing.

Organisation for Economic Co-operation and Development Staff. Bank Profitability: Financial Statements of Banks, 1996-2005. 2008. (Illus.). 596p. pap. 63.00 *(978-92-64-04154-7(0))* Organization for Economic Cooperation & Development.

Pond, Keith. Retail Banking. 3rd rev. ed. 2007. (Illus.). 184p. per. 29.95 *(978-0-85297-777-4(8))* Financial World Publishing GBR. Dist: Stylus Publishing, LLC.

Rose & Hudgins. Bank Management & Financial Services. 9th ed. 2012. (ENG., Illus.). 768p. (C). 215.33 ***(978-0-07-803467-1(1)***, 0078034671) McGraw-Hill Cos., The.

Rose, Peter S. & Hudgins, Sylvia Conway. Bank Management & Financial Services. 7th ed. 2006. (McGraw-Hill/Irwin Series in Finance, Insurance, & Real Estate). (Illus.). 752p. (C). 145.94 *(978-0-07-304623-5(X)*, 9780073046235) McGraw-Hill Cos., The.

—Bank Management & Financial Services. 8th ed. 2009. (ENG., Illus.). 768p. (C). 215.33 *(978-0-07-338243-2(4)*, 0073382434, McGraw-Hill/Irwin) McGraw-Hill Higher Education.

Saita, Francesco. Value at Risk & Bank Capital Management: Risk Adjusted Performances, Capital Management & Capital Allocation Decision Making. 2007. (Academic Press Advanced Finance Ser.). (ENG., Illus.). 280p. 90.95 *(978-0-12-369466-9(3)*, Academic Pr.) Elsevier Science & Technology Bks.

Satyanath, Shanker. Globalization, Politics, & Financial Turmoil: Asia's Banking Crisis. 2009. (Political Economy of Institutions & Decisions Ser.). (ENG., Illus.). 176p. pap. 26.99 *(978-0-521-10743-3(1))* Cambridge Univ. Pr.

Saunders, Anthony. Financial Institutions, in & Out of Crisis: Reflections by Anthony Saunders. 2011. 644p. 150.00 ***(978-981-4374-01-9(6))***; ***(978-981-4374-02-6(4))*** World Scientific Publishing Co., Inc.

Saunders, Anthony & Allen, Linda. Credit Risk Management in & Out of the Financial Crisis: New Approaches to Value at Risk & Other Paradigms. 3rd ed. 2010. (Wiley Finance Ser.: 528). (ENG., Illus.). 380p. 95.00 *(978-0-470-47834-9(9)*, Wiley) Wiley, John & Sons, Inc.

Scandizzo, Sergio. The Operational Risk Manager's Guide: Tools & Techniques of the Trade. 2007. (Illus.). 108p. pap. *(978-1-904339-75-5(1))* Risk Bks.

Shah, Mahmood & Clarke, Steve. E-Banking Management: Issues, Solutions, & Strategies. 2009. (Illus.). 310p. 165.00 *(978-1-60566-252-7(6))* IGI Global.

Shanmugam, B. Bank Management. 529p. *(978-0-471-33477-4(4))* Wiley, John & Sons, Inc.

Sironi, Andrea & Resti, Andrea. Risk Management & Shareholders' Value in Banking: From Risk Measurement Models to Capital Allocation Policies. 2007. (Wiley Finance Ser.: 421). (ENG., Illus.). 808p. 100.00 *(978-0-470-02978-7(1)*, Wiley) Wiley, John & Sons, Inc.

Smolo, Edib. Al-Bay' Bithaman Ajil, Musharakah Mutanaqisah & Ijarah Sukuk. 2010. 152p. pap. *(978-3-8383-5041-7(3))* Lambert Academic Publishing.

Somoza, Antonio. The Application of Insolvency Prediction Models to the Smes. 2009. 516p. pap. *(978-3-639-12209-1(7))* VDM Verlag Dr. Mueller e.K.

Spitzeck, Heiko, et al, eds. Banking with Integrity: The Winners of the Financial Crisis? 2012. (Humanism in Business Ser.). (ENG., Illus.). 232p. 90.00 ***(978-0-230-28995-6(9))*** Palgrave Macmillan.

Strang, David. Learning by Example: Imitation & Innovation at a Global Bank. 2010. (ENG., Illus.). 304p. (C). 35.00 *(978-0-691-14218-0(1))* Princeton Univ. Pr.

Terada-Hagiwara, Akiko & Pasadilla, Gloria. Experience of Asian Asset Management Companies: Do They Increase Moral Hazard? — Evidence from Thailand. 2007. (Illus.). 28p. (C). reprint ed. pap. 15.00 *(978-1-4223-1388-6(3))* DIANE Publishing Co.

Uppal, R., ed. Customer Relationship Management in Indian Banking Industry. 2008. 246p. (C). 36.50 *(978-81-7708-152-7(7))* New Century Publications IND. Dist: International Specialized Bk. Services.

Van Greuning, Hennie & Brajovic-Bratanovic, Sonja. Analyzing Banking Risk: A Framework for Assessing Corporate Governance & Risk Management. 3rd rev. ed. 2010. (ENG.). pap. 41.25 *(978-0-8213-8107-6(5))* World Bank Pubns.

Van Hoose, David. The Industrial Organization of Banking: Bank Behavior, Market Structure, & Regulation. 2010. (ENG., Illus.). viii, 257p. 139.00 *(978-3-642-02820-5(9)*, 3642028209) Springer.

BANK MARKETING

Borthayre, Blaire. Marketing Retail Financial Services to the Hispanic Community. 2008. (Marketing to the Hispanic Community Ser.). 208p. 39.95 incl. cd-rom *(978-0-470-15266-9(4)*, Wiley) Wiley, John & Sons, Inc.

Budd, Christopher Houghton. Finance at the Threshold: Rethinking the Real & Financial Economies. 2011. (Transformation & Innovation Ser.). (Illus.). 258p. 124.95 *(978-0-566-09211-4(5)*, Gower Publishing Co., Ltd.) Ashgate Publishing, Ltd. GBR. Dist: Ashgate Publishing Co.

Carner, William. Community Bank Marketing Manual. 1154p. ring bd. 355.00 *(978-1-55827-063-3(9)*, C34, Sheshunoff) Sheshunoff Information Services.

Levitt, Theodore. Marketing Myopia. 2008. (Harvard Business Review Classics Ser.). (ENG.). 90p. pap. 8.95 *(978-1-4221-2601-1(3))* Harvard Business Review Pr.

Long, Borareaksmey. Relationship Marketing in the Banking Industry. 2011. (Illus.). 80p. pap. ***(978-3-8433-8052-2(X))*** Lambert Academic Publishing.

Maxwell, Dennis D. The Great Eclipse: A Dream Design Bankrupted by Marketing & Mismanagement & Saved by a Sensible Business Strategy. 2011. 342p. pap. 24.95 ***(978-1-4575-0297-2(6))*** Dog Ear Publishing, LLC.

Stauber, Christina. Multi-Channel Banking - neue Wege zum Kunden: Ein Blick in die Vergangenheit und Zukunft innovativer Vertriebskanäle. 2010. 136p. pap. *(978-3-639-12321-0(2))* VDM Verlag Dr. Mueller e.K.

BANK MERGERS

Amihud, Yakov & Miller, Geoffrey, eds. Bank Mergers & Acquisitions. 2010. (New York University Salomon Center Series on Financial Markets & Institutions Ser.). (Illus.). 264p. pap. 209.00 *(978-1-4419-5187-8(3)*, 1441951873) Springer.

Andersen, Thomas. Bank Mergers & Acquisitions in Central Eastern Europe. 2011. 112p. pap. ***(978-3-8443-1148-8(3))*** Lambert Academic Publishing.

Ayadi, Rym. Assessing Performance Banking M & As E. 2007. (ENG., Illus.). 84p. pap. 30.00 *(978-92-9079-732-6(0))* Ctr. for European Policy Studies BEL. Dist: Brookings Institution Pr.

Bank of America & Merrill Lynch: How Did a Private Deal Turn into a Federal Bailout?: Joint Hearing Before the Committee on Oversight & Government Reform & the Subcommittee on Domestic Policy, House of Representatives, One Hundred Eleventh Congress, First Session. 2009. (Illus.). *(978-0-16-085853-6(4)*, 552-070-40789-8 (pt.1)); *(978-0-16-085526-9(8)*, 552-070-40789-8 (pt.1)); *(978-0-16-085857-4(7)*, 552-070-40789-8 (pt.1)); *(978-0-16-085921-2(2)*, 552-070-40789-8 (pt.1)) United States Government Printing Office.

Chung, Eek-June. Risk & Bank Expansion into Nonbanking Businesses, Volume 4. 2012. (ENG.). 160p. 100.00 ***(978-0-415-52811-5(9))*** Routledge.

Cornwall, Linda M., ed. New Developments in Banking & Finance. 2007. 129.00 *(978-1-60021-576-6(9))* Nova Science Pubs., Inc.

Fethi, Meryem Duygun. Financial Services: Efficiency & Risk Management. 2012. (Studies in Financial Optimization & Risk Management - Ser.). 252p. 140.00 ***(978-1-62100-560-5(7))*** Nova Science Pubs., Inc.

Keisers, Maximilian. Selected Essays on the Success of Mergers & Acquisitions: Evidence from the Banking & REIT Industries. 2009. (Europäische Hochschulschriften. Reihe 5: Volks- und Betriebswirtschaft Ser.). 150p. pap. 49.95 *(978-3-631-57320-4(0))* Lang, Peter GmbH, Europaischer Verlag der Wissenschaften DEU. Dist: Lang, Peter.

Leeamornsiri, Joseph Nantawut. Hrd Competency Used During the Mergers. 2009. 228p. pap. *(978-3-639-20816-0(1))* VDM Verlag Dr. Mueller e.K.

Leicht, Tanja. Change of Management - Management of Change - an Analysis of the Future Orientation of the Management of Cooperative Banks Consequences for the Hrm. 2008. 160p. pap. *(978-3-639-03124-9(5))* VDM Verlag Dr. Mueller e.K.

McGrath, Michael. The Banking M&A Integration Handbook. 2008. 72p. pap. 46.50 *(978-0-9559859-0-4(0))* Hibernia GBR. Dist: Lulu Enterprises Inc.

Rezaee, Zabihollah & Menon, Ram. Financial Services Firms: Governance, Regulations, Valuations, Mergers, & Acquisitions. 3rd ed. 2011. (Wiley Corporate F&a Ser.: 14). (ENG., Illus.). 582p. 125.00 *(978-0-470-60447-2(6)*, Wiley) Wiley, John & Sons, Inc.

Smit, Jeroen. The Perfect Prey: The Fall of Abn Amro, or What Went Wrong in the Banking Industry. 2010. (ENG., Illus.). 480p. pap. 23.95 *(978-1-84916-268-5(9))* Quercus GBR. Dist: Independent Pubs. Group.

The State of Community Banking: Opportunities & Challenges: Hearing Before the Subcommittee on Financial Institutions & Consumer Protection of the Committee on Banking, Housing, & Urban Affairs, United States Senate, One Hundred Twelfth Congress, First Session, on Examining the Current Economic & Regulatory Environment Facing Community Banks, April 6, 2011. 2011. (Illus.). iii, 101p. ***(978-0-16-089779-5(3)***, 552-070-43631-6) United States Government Printing Office.

BANK NOTES

see also Legal Tender; National Bank Notes

Acton, Johnny. Minted: The Story of the World's Money. Think Books Staff, ed. 2008. (ENG., Illus.). 156p. 17.95 *(978-1-84525-047-8(8))* Sterling Publishing Co., Inc.

Azpiazu. The Official Guidebook of Modern Federal Reserve Notes, Series 1963-2009. 2010. 448p. mass mkt. 49.95 *(978-0-7948-3237-7(7))* Whitman Publishing LLC.

Dauer, J. C., et al. Australian History 1901 - 2001 As Seen Through Banknotes. 2007. (Illus.). ***(978-0-9728466-1-5(1))*** Dauer, M.D., Edward A.

Hewitt, R. Shawn. A History & Catalog of Minnesota Obsolete Bank Notes & Scrip: A Comprehensive Guide to Minnesota Paper Money from the ERA of Minnesota Territory to the Great Depression. 2007. (Illus.). xx, 600p. *(978-0-9710821-4-4(6))* Spink USA, Inc.

MacKenzie, A. D. The Bank of England Note: A History of its Printing. 2011. (ENG.). 208p. pap. 22.99 *(978-0-521-17207-3(1))* Cambridge Univ. Pr.

Mihm, Stephen. A Nation of Counterfeiters: Capitalists, con Men, & the Making of the United States. (Illus.). 480p. 2009. pap. 21.00 *(978-0-674-03244-6(6))* 2007. 29.95 *(978-0-674-02657-5(8))* Harvard Univ. Pr.

National Research Council Staff, creator. A Path to the Next Generation of U. S. Banknotes: Keeping Them Real. 2007. (ENG., Illus.). 328p. per. 57.00 *(978-0-309-10578-1(1))* National Academies Pr.

Ricardo, David. Ricardos High Price of Bullion Including. 2006. pap. 14.95 *(978-1-59605-928-3(1)*, Cosimo Classics) Cosimo, Inc.

Sieber, Arlyn G. Warman's U. S. Coins & Currency Field Guide. 3rd ed. 2009. (ENG.). 512p. pap. 14.99 *(978-1-4402-0365-7(2))* Krause Pubns.

—Warman's U. S. Coins & Currency Field Guide: Values & Identification. 4th ed. 2011. (ENG., Illus.). 512p. pap. 14.99 *(978-1-4402-1698-5(3))* Krause Pubns.

Stahl, Alan M. Money on Paper: Bank Notes & Related Graphic Arts from the Collections of Vsevolod Onyshkevych & Princeton University. 2010. (ENG., Illus.). 81p. (C). pap. 29.95 *(978-0-87811-054-4(2))* Princeton Univ. Library.

Tomasko, Mark D. The Feel of Steel: The Art & History of Bank-Note Engraving in the United States. 2nd ed. 2012. ***(978-0-89722-321-8(7))*** American Numismatic Society.

BANK OF AMERICA

Bank of America & Merrill Lynch: How Did a Private Deal Turn into a Federal Bailout?: Joint Hearing Before the Committee on Oversight & Government Reform & the Subcommittee on Domestic Policy, House of Representatives, One Hundred Eleventh Congress, First Session. 2009. (Illus.). *(978-0-16-085853-6(4)*, 552-070-40789-8 (pt.1)); *(978-0-16-085526-9(8)*, 552-070-40789-8 (pt.1)); *(978-0-16-085921-2(2)*, 552-070-40789-8 (pt.1)); *(978-0-16-085857-4(7)*, 552-070-40789-8 (pt.1)) United States Government Printing Office.

Conrads, Margaret C., ed. Romancing the West: Alfred Jacob Miller in the Bank of America Collection. 2010. (ENG., Illus.). 136p. pap. 34.95 *(978-0-615-35171-1(9))* Nelson-Atkins Museum of Art, The.

Farrell, Greg. Crash of the Titans: Greed, Hubris, the Fall of Merrill Lynch, & the near-Collapse of Bank of America. (ENG.). 2011. 512p. pap. 17.00 *(978-0-307-71787-0(9))* 2010. 480p. 27.00 *(978-0-307-71786-3(0))* Crown Publishing Group. (Crown Business).

Rothacker, Rick. Banktown: The Rise & Struggles of Charlotte's Big Banks. 2010. (Illus.). 336p. 26.95 *(978-0-89587-381-1(8))* Blair, John F. Pub.

BANK OF CREDIT AND COMMERCE INTERNATIONAL

Ali, Tariq. A Banker for All Seasons: Bank of Crooks & Cheats Incorporated. 2007. (ENG., Illus.). 264p. 24.95 *(978-1-905422-65-4(2))* Seagull Bks. GBR. Dist: Chicago Distribution Ctr.

Block, A., ed. The Organized Criminal Activities of the Bank of Credit & Commerce International: Essays & Documentation: In memoriam David Whitby. 2010. 180p. pap. 113.00 *(978-90-481-5731-0(5)*, 9048157315) Springer.

BANK OF ENGLAND

Adams, Henry. Historical Essays. 2011. 422p. 90.00 ***(978-1-60449-120-3(5))*** Gaunt, Inc.

—Historical Essays. 422p. reprint ed. 98.00 *(978-0-7222-1941-6(5))* Library Reprints, Inc.

Antonella Anna, Porcelluzzi. Walter Bagehot & the Open Money Supply Approach to Monetary Theory. 2009. 268p. pap. *(978-3-639-02000-7(6))* VDM Verlag Dr. Mueller e.K.

Capie, Forrest. The Bank of England, from the 1950s to 1979. 2010. (Studies in Macroeconomic History Ser.). (ENG., Illus.). 920p. (C). 150.00 *(978-0-521-19282-8(X))* Cambridge Univ. Pr.

Chapman, Richard A. Decision Making: A Case Study of the Decision to Raise the Bank Rate in September 1957. 2011. (Routledge Revivals Ser.). (ENG.). 128p. 90.00 ***(978-0-415-50817-9(7))*** Routledge.

Clapham, John. Bank of England 2 Volume Set, 2 vols. 2008. (ENG., Illus.). 897p. pap. 116.00 *(978-0-521-73811-8(3))* Cambridge Univ. Pr.

Dunn, Chris. Good Trader Vi: Old Lady's Mean Machine 2007. 2007. 156p. per. 15.50 *(978-1-84426-428-5(9))* Upfront Publishing Ltd. GBR. Dist: Printondemand-worldwide.com.

Fforde, John. The Bank of England & Public Policy, 1941-1958. 2011. (ENG.). 883p. pap. 76.00 *(978-0-521-29452-2(5))* Cambridge Univ. Pr.

Hennessy, Elizabeth. A Domestic History of the Bank of England, 1930-1960. 2008. (ENG.). 472p. pap. 58.00 *(978-0-521-07358-5(6))* Cambridge Univ. Pr.

MacKenzie, A. D. The Bank of England Note: A History of its Printing. 2011. (ENG.). 208p. pap. 22.99 *(978-0-521-17207-3(1))* Cambridge Univ. Pr.

Murphy, Anne L. The Origins of English Financial Markets: Investment & Speculation before the South Sea Bubble. 2009. (Cambridge Studies in Economic History - Second Ser.). (ENG., Illus.). 298p. 107.00 *(978-0-521-51994-6(2))* Cambridge Univ. Pr.

Palk, Deirdre. Prisoners' Letters to the Bank of England, 1781-1827. 2007. (London Record Society Ser.: Volume 42). 332p. 34.95 *(978-0-900952-42-5(3))* London Record Society GBR. Dist: Boydell & Brewer, Inc.

Richards, Richard D. The Early History of Banking in England (Rle Banking & Finance), Volume 30. 2012. (ENG.). 344p. 130.00 ***(978-0-415-52878-8(X))*** Routledge.

Tempest, Paul. The Bank of England, 1694-2008: Adventures, Escapes & Memories, 3 vols. 2008. (ENG., Illus.). 241p. 25.00 *(978-1-905299-89-8(3)*, Stacey International) Stacey Publishing GBR. Dist: Midpoint Trade Bks., Inc.

Wood, John H. A History of Central Banking in Great Britain & the United States. 2008. (Studies in Macroeconomic History Ser.). (ENG., Illus.). 458p. pap. 36.99 *(978-0-521-74131-6(9))* Cambridge Univ. Pr.

B

BANK OF NORTH AMERICA

Moulton, R. K. The Constitutional Guide, Comprising the Constitution of the United States; with Notes & Commentaries from the Writings of Justice Story, Chancellor Kent, James Madison, & Other Distinguished American Citizens: [with] Legislative & Documentary History of the Banks of the United States from the Time of Establishing the Bank of North America, 1781, to October, 1834: With Notes & Comments. 2007. (978-1-58477-754-0(0)) Lawbook Exchange, Ltd., The.

—Legislative & Documentary History of the Banks of the United States from the Time of Establishing the Bank of North America, 1781, to October 1834: With Notes & Comments. 2007. 232p. 95.00 (978-1-58477-873-8(3)) Lawbook Exchange, Ltd., The.

BANK OF THE UNITED STATES, 1816-1836

Catterall, Ralph Charles Henry. The Second Bank of the United States. 2010. 360p. pap. (978-1-152-03926-1(1)) Books LLC.

Downing, J. Letters of J Downing Major Downingville. 2006. pap. 31.95 (978-1-4286-5642-0(1)) Kessinger Publishing, LLC.

Moulton, R. K. The Constitutional Guide, Comprising the Constitution of the United States; with Notes & Commentaries from the Writings of Justice Story, Chancellor Kent, James Madison, & Other Distinguished American Citizens: [with] Legislative & Documentary History of the Banks of the United States from the Time of Establishing the Bank of North America, 1781, to October, 1834: With Notes & Comments. 2007. (978-1-58477-754-0(0)) Lawbook Exchange, Ltd., The.

—Legislative & Documentary History of the Banks of the United States from the Time of Establishing the Bank of North America, 1781, to October 1834: With Notes & Comments. 2007. 232p. 95.00 (978-1-58477-873-8(3)) Lawbook Exchange, Ltd., The.

BANK RECORDS

see Banks and Banking—Records and Correspondence

BANK RESERVES

Bakker, Age F. P., et al. Central Bank Reserve Management: New Trends, from Liquidity to Return. 2007. (Illus.). 272p. (C). 127.00 (978-1-84542-957-7(5)) Elgar, Edward Publishing, Inc.

Stolz, Stéphanie. Bank Capital & Risk-Taking. 2007. (Kieler Studien - Kiel Studies). (Illus.). xiv, 150p. (C). 139.00 (978-3-540-48544-5(9), 3540485449) Springer.

BANK ROBBERIES

Biber, Katherine. Captive Images: Race, Crime, Photography. 2007. (ENG., Illus.). 160p. (C). per. 41.95 (978-0-415-42039-6(3), Routledge Cavendish) Taylor & Francis Group GBR. Dist: Taylor & Francis Group.

—Captive Images: Race, Crime, Photography. 2006. (Illus.). 137p. 150.00 (978-1-904385-72-1(9), Routledge) Taylor & Francis Group GBR. Dist: Taylor & Francis Group.

Clark, Jerry & Palattella, Ed. Pizza Bomber. 2012. (ENG., Illus.). 448p. (gr. 12). mass mkt. 9.99 **(978-0-425-25055-6(5)**, Berkley) Penguin Group (USA) Inc.

Conway, J. North. King of Heists: The Sensational Bank Robbery of 1878 That Shocked America. (ENG., Illus.). 240p. 2010. pap. 14.95 (978-1-59921-995-0(6)) 2009. 24.95 (978-1-59921-538-9(1)) Globe Pequot Pr., The. (Lyons Pr.).

Cooper, Ken. Held Hostage: A Serial Bank Robber's Road to Redemption. 2009. 320p. pap. 14.99 (978-0-8007-9456-9(7)) Chosen Bks.

De Santis, Richard. Field of Schemes, 1 vol. 2009. 52p. pap. 16.95 (978-1-60703-989-1(3)) PublishAmerica, Inc.

Ernst, Donna B. The Sundance Kid: The Life of Harry Alonzo Longabaugh. 2009. (ENG., Illus.). 264p. (C). 29.95 (978-0-8061-3982-1(X)) Univ. of Oklahoma Pr.

Escott, John. Dead Man's Money. 3rd ed. 2011. (ENG.). 48p. pap. 9.38 **(978-0-19-479365-0(6))** Oxford Univ. Pr., Inc.

Habarta, Ken. Bank Notes. 2009. 176p. pap. 16.99 (978-0-557-09592-6(1)) Lulu Enterprises Inc.

Macintyre, Ben. The Napoleon of Crime: The Life & Times of Adam Worth, Master Thief. 2011. 384p. pap. 15.00 (978-0-307-88646-0(8)) Broadway Bks.

McDaniel, Herman. Bank Robbers Now Use Computers. 2007. 260p. per. 17.95 (978-1-4327-0450-6(8)) Outskirts Pr., Inc.

Modern-Day Bank Robberies. 2007. per. 6.00 net. (978-0-9795921-1-9(9)) Postmodern Library.

Moore, Chris. Ripe for the Picking: The Inside Story of the Northern Bank Robbery. 2006. (Illus.). 224p. pap. 15.95 (978-0-7171-4001-5(6)) Gill & MacMillan, Ltd. IRL. Dist: Irish Bks. & Media, Inc.

Pedley, Derek. The Outlaw's Story. 2007. (ENG., Illus.). 328p. per. 19.95 (978-1-84454-418-9(4)) Blake, John Publishing, Ltd. GBR. Dist: Independent Pubs. Group.

Pound, Richard W. Unlucky to the End: The Story of Janise Marie Gamble. 2007. (ENG., Illus.). 272p. pap. (978-0-7735-3300-4(1)) McGill-Queen's Univ. Pr.

Rubinstein, Julian. Ballad of the Whiskey Robber: A True Story of Bank Heists, Ice Hockey, Transylvanian Pelt Smuggling, Moonlighting Detectives, & Broken Hearts. 2008. (ENG.). 319p. 24.00 (978-1-4379-6479-0(6)) DIANE Publishing Co.

Sperry, Paul. The Great American Bank Robbery: The Cost & Causes of the New Depression¿How Race-Based Lending & Other Multi-Cultural Schemes Make Us All Poorer, 0 vols. 2011. (Illus.). 320p. pap. 14.99 (978-1-59555-270-9(7)) Nelson, Thomas Inc.

Younger, Cole. The Story of Cole Younger. (Illus.). 123p. reprint ed. lib. bdg. 88.00 (978-0-7222-0724-6(7)) Library Reprints, Inc.

BANK STATEMENTS

see Banks and Banking—Accounting

BANKED BLOOD

see Blood Banks

BANKERS

see also Banks and Banking—Vocational Guidance; Women Bankers

Baer, Hans J. It's Not All about Money: Memoirs of a Private Banker. 2008. (Illus.). 528p. 29.95 (978-0-8253-0547-4(0)) Beaufort Bks., Inc.

Brummer, Alex. The Crunch: How Greed & Incompetence Sparked the Credit Crisis. 2009. (ENG.). 288p. 14.95 **(978-1-84794-009-4(9))** Random Hse. GBR. Dist: Independent Pubs. Group.

Bullard, Melissa Meriam. Filippo Strozzi & the Medici: Favor & Finance in Sixteenth-Century Florence & Rome. 2008. (Cambridge Studies in Early Modern History Ser.). (ENG., Illus.). 208p. pap. 32.99 (978-0-521-08816-9(X)) Cambridge Univ. Pr.

Campbell, Persia Crawford. Mary Williamson Harriman. 2011. 102p. 39.95 **(978-1-258-07689-4(6))** Literary Licensing, LLC.

Cannadine, David. Mellon: An American Life. 2008. (Vintage Ser.). (ENG., Illus.). 832p. pap. 23.00 (978-0-307-38679-3(1), Vintage) Knopf Doubleday Publishing Group.

Carter H. Golembe. But I Never Made a Loan: My Career in Banking - the Early Years. 2009. 164p. 25.95 (978-1-4401-7473-5(3)); pap. 15.95 (978-1-4401-7475-9(X)) iUniverse, Inc.

Cassis, Youssef. City Bankers, 1890-1914. Rocques, Margaret, tr. from FRE. 2009. (ENG., Illus.). 368p. pap. 38.99 (978-0-521-10521-7(8)) Cambridge Univ. Pr.

Chankowski, V., et al, eds. Pistoi dia ten technen. Bankers, Loans & Archives in the Ancient World: Studies in Honour of Raymond Bogaert. 2008. (Studia Hellenistica Ser.). (FRE.). 482p. (C). pap. 122.00 (978-90-429-1996-9(5)) Peeters Pubs. & Booksellers BEL. Dist: Brown, David Bk. Co., The.

Cohan, William D. The Last Tycoons: The Secret History of Lazard Frères & Co. 2007. (ENG.). 752p. 29.95 (978-0-385-51451-4(4), Doubleday) Doubleday Religious Publishing Group, The.

Coleman, Ewell R. A Life on the Black River in Arkansas: A Pioneering Banker's Memoir. 2008. 124p. pap. 16.95 (978-1-935106-06-7(6)) Butler Ctr. for Arkansas Studies.

Cooley, Richard & Boreson, Ann. Searching Through My Prayer List: A Memoir about Family, Career, & a Meaningful Retirement. 2010. (Illus.). 256p. 24.95 (978-1-933245-19-5(0)) Documentary Media LLC.

de Waal, Edmund. The Hare with Amber Eyes: A Hidden Inheritance. 2011. (ENG., Illus.). 368p. pap. 16.00 (978-0-312-56937-2(8)) Picador.

Dinkelspiel, Frances. Towers of Gold: How One Jewish Immigrant Named Isaias Hellman Created California. 2010. (ENG., Illus.). 400p. pap. 16.99 (978-0-312-35527-2(0), St. Martin's Griffin) St. Martin's Pr.

Driscoll Sr., Robert Edward. Diary of a Country Banker. 2011. 140p. 40.95 **(978-1-258-07298-8(X))** Literary Licensing, LLC.

Dufries, Courtney. Ten Lessons Bankers Never Learn: How Banks Operate & Why Bankers Screw Up. 2011. 440p. 38.95 **(978-1-4620-3325-6(3))**; pap. 28.95 **(978-1-4620-3324-9(5))** iUniverse, Inc.

Felton, Andrew & Reinhart, Carmen M., eds. The First Global Financial Crisis of the 21st Century. 2009. (Illus.). 193p. pap. (978-0-9557009-3-4(0)) Ctr. for Economic Policy Research.

Ferguson, Niall. High Financier: The Lives & Time of Siegmund Warburg. (ENG.). (gr. 12). 2011. 576p. 22.00 (978-0-14-311940-1(0), Penguin (Non-Classics)) 2010. (Illus.). 352p. 35.00 (978-1-59420-246-9(X), Penguin Pr. HC, The) Penguin Group (USA) Inc.

Fisher, June Breton. When Money Was in Fashion: Henry Goldman, Goldman Sachs, & the Founding of Wall Street. (ENG., Illus.). 288p. 2011. pap. 19.00 (978-0-230-11405-0(9)) 2010. 27.00 (978-0-230-61750-6(6)) Palgrave Macmillan.

Flint, Priscilla E. I Look Back & Wonder How I Got Over. 2010. 114p. pap. 11.99 (978-1-60957-897-8(X)) Xulon Pr., Inc.

Floor, Willem M. Guilds, Merchants & Ulama in Nineteenth-Century Iran. 2009. 280p. pap. (978-1-933823-31-7(3)) Mage Pubs., Inc.

Galuteria, Peter. Heart of a Hero: Charles Reed Bishop. 2009. (Illus.). xiv, 176p. (J). pap. (978-1-58178-094-9(X)) Bishop Museum Pr.

García Dimas, Alda & Turrent Díaz, Eduardo. Raúl Martínez Ostos: Leyes, Finanzas y Diplomacia para el Desarrollo, 1907-1993. 2008. (Vida y Pensamiento de México Ser.). (SPA., Illus.). 389p. (978-968-16-8580-5(6)); pap. (978-968-16-8581-2(4)) Fondo de Cultura Economica.

Hill, Vernon. Fans, Not Customers: How Commerce Bank Created a Super-Growth Business in a No-Growth Industry. 2007. 256p. (gr. 12). 24.95 (978-1-59184-173-9(9), Portfolio (Hardcover)) Penguin Group (USA) Inc.

Hunt, James L. Relationship Banker: Eugene W. Stetson, Wall Street, & American Business, 1916-1959. 2009. (Illus.). 400p. 35.00 (978-0-86554-915-9(X)) Mercer Univ. Pr.

Iskan, Dahlan. No Such Thing As Can't. 2011. 220p. pap. 17.95 **(978-1-4620-1923-6(4))** iUniverse, Inc.

—No Such Thing as Can't: One Man's Journey Across the Southern Seas, through Poverty & Ordeals, to become one of Indonesia's Most Prominent Bankers. 2011. 220p. 27.95 **(978-1-4620-1924-3(2))** iUniverse, Inc.

Kaplan, Herbert. Nathan Mayer Rothschild & the Creation of a Dynasty: The Critical Years 1806-1816. 2010. (ENG.). 224p. pap. 21.95 (978-0-8047-7361-4(0)) Stanford Univ. Pr.

Kimbrell, Jody D. Bankers: the Only Profession That Drove Jesus to Violence: A True Story of Lies, Deceit, & Deception. 2011. pap. 9.99 (978-1-61739-164-4(6)) Tate Publishing & Enterprises, LLC.

Kirkland, Kate Sayen. Captain James A. Baker of Houston, 1857-1941. 2012. **(978-1-60344-800-0(4))** Texas A&M Univ. Pr.

Kudkinski, Jim. The Tarnished Fed: Behind Closed Doors: Forty Years of Successes, Failures, Mystique, & Humor. 2010. 250p. pap. 16.95 (978-0-533-16318-2(8)) Vantage Pr., Inc.

Lindgren, Håkan. Jacob Wallenberg 1892-1980: Swedish Banker & International Negotiator. 2009. (Illus.). 556p. (978-91-7353-317-1(3)) Atlantis-Verlag AG.

Love, Ben F. Ben Love: My Life in Texas Commerce. 2008. (Kenneth E. Montague Series in Oil & Business History Ser.). (Illus.). 352p. pap. 23.95 (978-1-60344-049-3(6)) Texas A&M Univ. Pr.

Magomola, Gaby. Robben Island to Wall Street. 2009. 334p. pap. 33.00 (978-1-86888-570-1(4)) Unisa Press / Uitgewers GBR. Dist: International Specialized Bk. Services.

Marden, Orison Swett. A Darius Ogden Mills: a Self-Made Man Who Strives to Give Others. 2006. pap. 12.95 (978-1-4304-1070-6(1)) Kessinger Publishing, LLC.

McMaster, John Bach. Life & Times of Stephen Girard V1 Marl. 2006. pap. 38.95 (978-1-4286-3753-5(2)) Kessinger Publishing, LLC.

—Life & Times of Stephen Girard V2 Marl. 2006. pap. 38.95 (978-1-4286-3754-2(0)) Kessinger Publishing, LLC.

Milne, Alistair. The Fall of the House of Credit: What Went Wrong in Banking & What can be Done to Repair the Damage? 2009. (ENG., Illus.). 380p. 30.00 (978-0-521-76214-4(6)) Cambridge Univ. Pr.

O'Brien, D. P. & Creedy, John. Darwin's Clever Neighbour: George Warde Norman & His Circle. 2010. 512p. 165.00 (978-1-84844-557-4(1)) Elgar, Edward Publishing, Inc.

Pohl, Hans & Beckers, Thorsten. Deutsche Bankiers des 20. Jahrhunderts. 2008. (GER., Illus.). 488p. (C). 59.00 (978-3-515-08954-8(3)) Steiner, Franz Verlag Wiesbaden GmbH DEU. Dist: Brown, David Bk. Co., The.

Rhodes, William R. Banker to the World: Leadership Lessons from the Front Lines of Global Finance. 2011. xxxiii, 249p. E-Book **(978-0-07-170424-3(8))** McGraw-Hill Cos., The.

Rohatyn, Felix G. Dealings: A Political & Financial Life. 2010. (ENG., Illus.). 304p. 27.00 (978-1-4391-8196-6(9)) Simon & Schuster.

Rooyen, Pieter Van. Business Unusual. 2010. 490p. 34.99 (978-1-4500-5783-7(7)); pap. 23.99 (978-1-4500-5782-0(9)) Xlibris Corp.

Sanford, Helen Behr. Starboard at Midnight. 2011. (ENG., Illus.). 308p. 24.95 **(978-0-87850-200-4(9)**, Darwin Bks.) Darwin Pr., Inc., The.

Shaw, Peter. Hole. 2007. (Illus.). 272p. pap. (978-1-905170-72-2(6)) Accent Pr. Ltd.

Tait, Jeremy. The Obedient Banker: From Bombay to Beverly Hills (A revealing insight into the unusual life of a colonial Banker) 2011. (Illus.). 236p. pap. 28.06 (978-1-4567-7139-3(6)) AuthorHouse.

Tritton, Alan. Half-Closed Door. 2008. 572p. 39.95 (978-1-84624-271-7(1)) Book Guild, Ltd. GBR. Dist: Trans-Atlantic Pubns., Inc.

Trust, Graham. John Moss of Otterspool (1782-1858) Railway Pioneer Slave Owner Banker. 2010. (Illus.). 272p. pap. 15.49 (978-1-4520-0444-0(7)) AuthorHouse.

Tyler, Daniel. WD Farr: Cowboy in the Boardroom. 2011. (ENG., Illus.). 312p. 29.95 (978-0-8061-4193-0(X)) Univ. of Oklahoma Pr.

Valentine, Rebecca & Thompson, Travis. Beyond the Land of Gold: The Life & Times of Perry A. Burgess. 2010. (Illus.). 528p. (ENG.). 34.95 (978-0-9827089-1-0(2)); pap. 24.95 (978-0-9827089-0-3(4)) Thompson Media.

Weintraub, Stanley. Charlotte & Lionel: A Rothschild Love Story. 2007. (ENG.). 336p. pap. 22.95 (978-1-4165-7332-6(1), Free Pr.) Free Pr.

Wingate, J. Opportunity Is Everywhere: The Story of America's Supermarket Banker. 2007. 180p. 24.95 (978-0-9773365-2-4(2)) Interview You, LLC.

Wolfensohn, James D. A Global Life: My Journey among Rich & Poor, from Sydney to Wall Street to the World Bank. 2010. (ENG., Illus.). 480p. 29.95 (978-1-58648-255-8(6)) PublicAffairs.

BANKHEAD, TALLULAH, 1903-1968

Lobenthal, Joel. Tallulah! The Life & Times of a Leading Lady. 2008. (Illus.). 592p. pap. 17.95 (978-0-06-098906-4(8)) HarperCollins Pubs.

BANKING

see Banks and Banking

BANKING LAW

see also Discount; Negotiable Instruments

also topics in the field of banking, e.g. Trust Companies

Akhan, Jafor. Non-Banking Financial Companies (NBFCs) in India: Functioning & Reforms. 2010. 224p. 35.50 (978-81-7708-229-6(9)) New Century Publications IND. Dist: International Specialized Bk. Services.

Al-Roubaie, Amer & Alvi, Shafiq. Islamic Banking & Finance V1, 4 vols. 2010. (Illus.). 400p. (978-0-415-48874-7(5)) Routledge.

—Islamic Banking & Finance V2, 4 vols. 2010. (Illus.). 400p. (978-0-415-48873-0(7)) Routledge.

—Islamic Banking & Finance V3, 4 vols. 2010. (Illus.). 400p. (978-0-415-48872-3(9)) Routledge.

—Islamic Banking & Finance V4, 4 vols. 2010. (Illus.). 400p. (978-0-415-48871-6(0)) Routledge.

Al-roubaie, Amer & Alvi, Shafiq, eds. Islamic Banking & Finance, 4 vols. 2010. (Critical Concepts in Economics Ser.). (ENG., Illus.). 1672p. 1140.00 (978-0-415-48576-0(2)) Routledge.

Aldohni, Abdul Karim. The Legal & Regulatory Aspects of Islamic Banking: A Comparative Look at the United Kingdom & Malaysia. 2011. (Routledge Research in Finance & Banking Law Ser.). (ENG.). 264p. 135.00 (978-0-415-55515-9(9)) Routledge.

American Bankers Association. Banking Today: Handbook. 2007. (Illus.). 134p. (C). pap. 79.00 (978-0-89982-604-2(0)) American Bankers Assn.

—Banking Today: Leader's Guide. 2007. 108p. (C). pap. 55.00 (978-0-89982-605-9(9)) American Bankers Assn.

—Law & Banking. 6th ed. 2008. (Illus.). 569p. (C). pap. 119.00 (978-0-89982-612-7(1)) American Bankers Assn.

Andreassen, Ole. Getting Credit. 2008. 192p. pap. (978-3-639-08775-8(5)) VDM Verlag Dr. Mueller e.K.

Aspatore Books Staff, compiled by. Banking & Finance Client Strategies in Asia, 2010 Ed: Leading Lawyers on Understanding the Impact of Global Banking Reform, Navigating Regional Banking Laws, & Meeting the Needs of Today's Clients (Inside the Minds) 2010. (Illus.). 316p. pap. 100.00 (978-0-314-26821-1(9)) Aspatore Bks.

Aspatore Books Staff, compiled by. Navigating Banking & Finance Law in the Asia-Pacific: Leading Lawyers on Responding to the Latest Laws, Trends, & Client Needs (Inside the Minds) 2011. (ENG.). 268p. pap. 90.00 **(978-0-314-27884-5(2))** Aspatore Bks.

Aspen/Cch. Banking Laws & Regulations Deskbook Starter Kit (3 Volumes) 2010. ring bd. (978-0-7355-9925-3(4), Aspen Pubs.) Wolters Kluwer Law & Business.

Augustinos, Theodore P. & Emmanuel, John N. Bank Insurance Sales Methods: Requirements, Restrictions & Guidelines - Southern States. 510p. pap. 389.00 (978-0-8080-0604-6(5)) Toolkit Media Group.

Avery, Martha, et al, eds. China's Emerging Financial Markets: Challenges & Global Impact. 2009. (Wiley Finance Ser.: 782). (ENG., Illus.). 400p. 170.00 (978-0-470-82249-4(X), Wiley) Wiley, John & Sons, Inc.

Ayadi, Rym, et al. Convergence of Banking Sector Regulations on International Norms in the Southern Mediterranean: Impact on Bank Performance & Growth. 2011. (ENG.). 160p. pap. 29.95 **(978-94-6138-086-9(0))** Ctr. for European Policy Studies BEL. Dist: Brookings Institution Pr.

Baamir, Abdulrahman Y. Shari'a Law in Commercial & Banking Arbitration: Law & Practice in Saudi Arabia. 2010. 230p. 114.95 (978-1-4094-0377-7(7)) Ashgate Publishing Co.

Balthazar, Laurent. From Basel 1 to Basel 3: The Integration of State-of-the-Art Risk Modeling in Banking Regulation. 2006. (Finance & Capital Markets Ser.). (ENG., Illus.). 256p. 268.00 (978-1-4039-4888-5(7)) Palgrave Macmillan.

Bancroft-Whitney Company Staff, contrib. by. Financial Code Annotated of the State of California: Adopted May 15, 1951, with Amendments Through Chapter 948 of the 2006 Session of the 2005-2006 Legislature, 3 vols. 2007. (978-1-4224-4549-5(6)) LEXIS Publishing.

Banking & Finance Client Strategies in Central & South America: Leading Lawyers on Interpreting International Banking Laws, Advising Clients on Entering Latin American Capital Markets, & Predicting Financial Market Development & Stability (Inside the Minds) 2009. 248p. pap. 110.00 (978-0-314-20830-9(5)) Aspatore Bks.

Banking & Finance Law Client Strategies: Leading Lawyers on Understanding the Client's Goals, Working with Regulators, & Developing a Transactional Strategy in a Changing Marketplace (Inside the Minds) 2009. (Inside the Minds Ser.). 184p. pap. 80.00 (978-0-314-90421-8(2)) Aspatore Bks.

Banking & Finance Litigation Strategies: Leading Lawyers on Working with Clients, Managing Documentation, & Negotiating Settlements (Inside the Minds) 2009. 120p. pap. 90.00 (978-0-314-20736-4(8)) Aspatore Bks.

Banking Industry Perspectives on the Obama Administration's Financial Regulatory Reform Proposals: Hearing Before the Committee on Financial Services, U.S. House of Representatives, One Hundred Eleventh Congress, First Session, July 15, 2009. 2010. (Illus.). iii, 247p. (978-0-16-085239-8(0), 552-070-40581-0) United States Government Printing Office.

Barth, James R., et al. Rethinking Bank Regulation: Till Angels Govern. 2007. (ENG., Illus.). 448p. (C). pap. 36.99 (978-0-521-70930-9(X)) Cambridge Univ. Pr.

Benjamin, Joanna. Financial Law. 2008. (ENG., Illus.). 700p. 493.75 (978-0-19-928293-7(5)) Oxford Univ. Pr., Inc.

Blair QC, William & Brent, Richard, eds. Banks & Financial Crime: The Law of Tainted Money. 2008. (ENG.). 450p. 357.50 (978-0-19-929172-4(1)) Oxford Univ. Pr., Inc.

Blasi, Ronald W. U. S. Master Bank Tax Guide. 2007. (U. S. Master Ser.). 936p. per. 239.00 (978-0-8080-1767-7(5)) Toolkit Media Group.

Blunden, Tony & Thirlwell, John. Mastering Operational Risk: A Practical Guide to Understanding Operational Risk & How to Manage It. 2010. (Financial Times Ser.). (ENG., Illus.). 344p. (C). pap. 79.99 (978-0-273-72732-3(X)) FT Press.

Broome, Lissa L. & Markham, Jerry W. Regulation of Bank Financial Service Activities: Cases & Materials. 3rd rev. ed. 2008. (American Casebook Ser.). 984p. 153.00 (978-0-314-18413-9(9), West Legalworks) West.

—Regulation of Bank Financial Service Activities: Cases & Materials. 4th ed. 2011. xxxvi, 1043p. **(978-0-314-26616-3(X))** West Publishing Co., College & Schl. Div.

—Regulation of Bank Financial Service Activities: Cases & Materials, 4th. 4th rev. ed. 2010. (American Casebook Ser.). 1083p. 175.00 (978-0-314-26608-8(9), West Legalworks) West.

—Regulation of Bank Financial Service Activities: Selected Statutes & Regulations. 2008. (American Casebook Ser.). 659p. 50.00 (978-0-314-18411-5(2), West Legalworks) West.

—Regulation of Bank Financial Service Activities: Selected Statutes & Regulations, 4th. 4th rev. ed. 2010. (American Casebook Ser.). 782p. 58.00 (978-0-314-26852-5(9), West Legalworks) West.

—Regulation of Bank Financial Services, Cases & Materials. 2nd rev. ed. 2006. 100p. pap. 17.00 *(978-0-314-17713-1(2)*, West Legalworks) West.

Bryfonski, Dedria. The Banking Crisis. 2010. (Opposing Viewpoints Ser.). 240p. (J). pap. 26.75 *(978-0-7377-4855-0(9))*; (Illus.). 38.50 *(978-0-7377-4854-3(0))* Cengage Gale. (Greenhaven Pr., Inc.).

Busch, Andreas. Banking Regulation & Globalization. (ENG.). 2012. 304p. pap. 45.00 ***(978-0-19-965557-1(X))*** 2009. (Illus.). 288p. 125.00 *(978-0-19-921881-3(1))* Oxford Univ. Pr., Inc.

Byrne, James E. The Official Commentary on the International Standby Practice. Barnes, James G., ed. Date not set. xx, 353p. 129.00 *(978-1-888870-17-6(6))* Institute of International Banking Law & Practice, Inc.

Cao, Jin. Banking Regulation & the Financial Crisis. 2012. (Routledge International Studies in Money & Banking Ser.). (ENG., Illus.). 240p. (C). 125.00 *(978-0-415-60780-3(9))* Routledge.

Caprio, Gerard, Jr., et al, eds. Cross-Border Banking: Regulatory Challenges. 2006. (World Scientific Studies in International Economics). (Illus.). 477p. 150.00 *(978-981-256-829-8(8))* World Scientific Publishing Co., Inc.

Carnell. The Law of Banking & Financial Institutions 2009 Statutory Supp. pap. 38.50 *(978-0-7355-8986-5(0))* Wolters Kluwer Law & Business.

Carnell, Richard Scott, et al. The Law of Banking & Financial Institutions. 4th ed. 2009. xxxii, 796p. *(978-0-7355-5286-9(X))* Kluwer Law International.

CCH Incorporated. Wall Street Reform & Consumer Protection Act Of 2010: Law, Explanation & Analysis. 2010. 1623p. pap. 129.00 *(978-0-8080-2164-3(8)*, CCH) Wolters Kluwer Tax & Accounting.

CFA Institute, compiled by. A Primer on Islamic Finance. 2009. pap. *(978-1-934667-24-8(2))* Research Foundation of CFA Institute.

Chankowski, V., et al, eds. Pistoi dia ten technen. Bankers, Loans & Archives in the Ancient World: Studies in Honour of Raymond Bogaert. 2008. (Studia Hellenistica Ser.). (FRE.). 482p. (C). pap. 122.00 *(978-90-429-1996-9(5))* Peeters Pubs. & Booksellers BEL. Dist: Brown, David Bk. Co., The.

Cheatham, Anne J. Guide to Check 21 Implementation & Operations. *(978-1-55827-950-6(4))* Alex eSolutions, Inc.

Community & Consumer Advocates' Perspectives on the Obama Administration's Financial Regulatory Reform Proposals: Hearing Before the Committee on Financial Services, U.S. House of Representatives, One Hundred Eleventh Congress, First Session, July 16, 2009. 2009. (Illus.). iii, 211p. *(978-0-16-084937-4(3)*, 552-070-40328-1) United States Government Printing Office.

The Consideration of Regulatory Relief Proposals: Hearing Before the Committee on Banking, Housing, & Urban Affairs, United States Senate, One Hundred Ninth Congress, First Session, on Proposals to Reduce Unnecessary Regulatory Burden on Depository Institutions Insured by the Federal Deposit Insurance Corporation, June 21, 2005. 2007. (Illus.). v, 226p. *(978-0-16-079109-3(X)*, 552-070-36206-1) United States Government Printing Office.

Cowell, Lawrence P. Modernizing Financial Regulation. 2010. (Financial Institutions & Services Ser.). 193p. 115.00 *(978-1-60741-442-1(2))* Nova Science Pubs., Inc.

Cranston, Ross. Principles of Banking Law. 3rd rev. ed. 2013. (ENG.). 520p. pap. 74.00 *(978-0-19-927608-0(0))* Oxford Univ. Pr., Inc.

Credit Card Fair Fee ACT of 2009: Hearing Before the Committee on the Judiciary, House of Representatives, One Hundred Eleventh Congress, Second Session, on H.R. 2695, April 28, 2010. 2010. (Illus.). iii, 157p. *(978-0-16-086743-9(6)*, 552-070-41365-0) United States Government Printing Office.

Cross, Richard F. & Gillette, Clayton P. Self-Paced Security & Fraud Training for Banks. *(978-1-55827-386-3(7))* Sheshunoff Information Services.

Dai, Jianzhong. Bank Restructuring & Economic Growth. 2011. 96p. pap. ***(978-3-8454-0905-4(3))*** Lambert Academic Publishing.

Dar, Humayon & Moghul, Umar, eds. Legal Shari'A Aspects of Islamic Finance. 2010. (ENG., Illus.). 372p. pap. 190.00 *(978-1-899217-09-0(6))* Harriman Hse. Publishing GBR. Dist: Ingram Pub. Services.

Davis, Brian. Basel I & Basel II. 2008. 244p. pap. *(978-3-639-09183-0(3))* VDM Verlag Dr. Mueller e.K.

de Restre, Lucía Montoya Cadavid. El Debate Sobre la Banca Central Independiente: El Caso Colombiano. 2007. (SPA.). 176p. pap. 17.00 *(978-958-710-261-1(4))* Universidad Externado de Colombia COL. Dist: Siglo del Hombre.

Debari, James. How to Make Money Providing Default Mortgage Field Services. 2011. (Illus.). 116p. pap. 14.99 ***(978-1-4269-6520-3(6))*** Trafford Publishing.

Dewatripont, Mathias & Tirole, Jean. The Prudential Regulation of Banks. 2009. (Walras-Pareto Lectures). (ENG.). 272p. (gr. 17). pap. 30.00 *(978-0-262-51386-9(2))* MIT Pr.

Duffie, Darrell. How Big Banks Fail, & What to Do about It. 2010. (ENG., Illus.). 112p. (C). 29.95 *(978-0-691-14885-4(6))* Princeton Univ. Pr.

Dunbar, Charles F., ed. Laws of the United States Relating to Currency, Finance & Banking from 1789 to 1891. 309p. reprint ed. lib. bdg. 22.50 *(978-0-8371-4585-3(6)*, DULU, Greenwood Pr.) Greenwood Publishing Group, Inc.

Duncan, Bradley S. & Brenshaw, Alicia M., eds. Proprietary Trading & Investment Restrictions under the Volcker Role. 2011. (Business Issues, Competition & Entrepreneurship Ser.). 112p. pap. 47.00 *(978-1-61324-066-3(X))* Nova Science Pubs., Inc.

Eijffinger, Sylvester C. W. & Masciandaro, Donato, eds. Handbook of Central Banking, Financial Regulation & Supervision: After the Financial Crisis. 2012. (Elgar Original Reference Ser.). (Illus.). 672p. 295.00 ***(978-1-84980-313-7(7))*** Elgar, Edward Publishing, Inc.

Ekstrom, Leif. The Bank Secrecy Act: Information Sharing & Security Efforts. 2010. (Banking & Banking Developments Ser.). 89.00 *(978-1-60741-983-9(1))* Nova Science Pubs., Inc.

El-Gamal, Mahmoud A. Islamic Finance: Law, Economics, & Practice. (ENG., Illus.). 240p. 2008. pap. 31.99 *(978-0-521-74126-2(2))* 2006. 74.00 *(978-0-521-86414-5(3))* Cambridge Univ. Pr.

Ellinger, Peter & Neo, Dora. The Law & Practice of Documentary Letters of Credit. 2010. (ENG.). 429p. 190.00 *(978-1-84113-673-8(5))* Hart Publishing Ltd. GBR. Dist: International Specialized Bk. Services.

et al., compiled by. Banking & Finance Client Strategies in Asia: Leading Lawyers on Educating Clients, Understanding Key Rules & Regulations, & Navigating Recent Cases & Developments, Inside the Minds. 2009. 696p. pap. 125.00 *(978-0-314-90824-7(2))* Aspatore Bks.

Gleeson, Simon. International Regulation of Banking: Basel II, Capital & Risk Requirements. 2010. (ENG., Illus.). 350p. 395.00 *(978-0-19-921534-8(0))* Oxford Univ. Pr., Inc.

Gliha, John. Winning the Collection Game: Mortgage Foreclosure Dismissed! 2011. 182p. 29.99 ***(978-1-4628-9108-5(X))***; pap. 19.99 ***(978-1-4628-9107-8(1))*** Xlibris Corp.

Goodhart, Charles A.E. The Regulatory Response to the Financial Crisis. 2009. (Illus.). 168p. 119.00 *(978-1-84844-451-5(6))* Elgar, Edward Publishing, Inc.

Great Dominion Publishing, Dominion Publ & Great Dominion Publishing. Pressing Questions: A Collection of Political, Economic & Legal Perspectives. 2010. 172p. pap. 13.49 *(978-1-4490-6073-2(0))* AuthorHouse.

Gruson, Michael & Reisner, Ralph. Regulation of Foreign Banks, Vol. 1. 4th rev. ed. 2007. 142.00 *(978-0-327-16435-7(2))* LexisNexis Matthew Bender.

—Regulation of Foreign Banks, & Affiliates in the United States. 5th ed. 2008. *(978-1-4224-2882-5(6))* LexisNexis Matthew Bender.

Gup, Benton E., ed. Corporate Governance in Banking: A Global Perspective. 2007. (Illus.). 320p. (C). 137.00 *(978-1-84542-940-9(0))* Elgar, Edward Publishing, Inc.

Hardy, Peter D. Criminal Tax, Money Laundering, & Bank Secrecy ACT Litigation. 2010. (Illus.). xl, 1671p. *(978-1-57018-856-5(4))* Bureau of National Affairs, Inc., (BNA), The.

Haynes, Andrew. The Law Relating to International Banking. 2010. (Illus.). 558p. pap. 170.00 *(978-1-84766-679-6(5)*, Bloomsbury Professional) Bloomsbury Publishing Plc GBR. Dist: International Specialized Bk. Services.

Heaton, W. H. Quick Index - Banking Regulations. 1000p. *(978-1-881057-15-4(1))* Heaton Pubns.

Hkib. Fundamentals of Accounting & Law in Banking. 2011. 256p. pap. 50.50 *(978-0-470-82659-1(2)*, Wiley) Wiley, John & Sons, Inc.

Hong Kong Institute of Bankers Staff. Banking Law & Practice. 2012. (ENG.). 256p. pap. 50.00 *(978-0-470-82751-1(0)*, Wiley) Wiley, John & Sons, Inc.

Hopt, Klaus J. & Grundmann, Stefan. Festschrift Für Klaus J. Hopt Zum 70. Geburtstag Am 24. August 2010: Unternehmen, Markt und Verantwortung, 2 vols. 2010. (GER., Illus.). xxix, 3447p. 839.00 ***(978-3-89949-628-4(0))***; E-Book 839.00 ***(978-3-89949-632-1(9))*** De Gruyter, Walter Inc.

House (U.S.), Office of the Law Revision Counsel Staff, compiled by. United States Code, 2006, V. 6, Title 11, Bankruptcy to Title 12, Banks & Banking, Sections 1-1750jj. 2008. (ENG.). 1000p. 100.00 *(978-0-16-080001-6(3)*, Office of the Law Revision Counsel) United States Government Printing Office.

H.R. 2382, the Credit Card Interchange Fees ACT of 2009; & H.R. 3639, the Expedited Card Reform for Consumers ACT of 2009: Hearing Before the Committee on Financial Services House of Representatives, One Hundred Eleventh Congress, First Session, October 8, 2009. 2010. (Illus.). iv, 282p. *(978-0-16-085864-2(X)*, 552-070-41076-7) United States Government Printing Office.

H.R. 627, the Credit Cardholders' Bill of Rights ACT of 2009; & H.R. 1456, the Consumer Overdraft Protection Fair Practices ACT of 2009: Hearing Before the Subcommittee on Financial Institutions & Consumer Credit of the Committee on Financial Services, U.S. House of Representatives, One Hundred Eleventh Congress, First Session, March 19, 2009. 2009. (Illus.). v, 229p. *(978-0-16-083948-1(3)*, 552-070-39637-3) United States Government Printing Office.

Huang, Yi. Yin Hang Jian Guan Fa Lü Yan Jiu: Legal Thoughts on Banking Regulation. 2009. (CHI., Illus.). 10p. *(978-7-5036-9700-5(8))* Law Publishing Hse., The.

INCORPORATED, CCH. Practical Guide to Bank Compliance. 2007. pap. *(978-0-8080-1738-7(1))* Wolters Kluwer Law & Business.

Jones, Yvonne D. Bank Secrecy Act: Opportunities Exist for Fincen & the Banking Regulators to Further Strengthen the Framework for Consistent BSA Oversight. 2006. (Illus.). 127p. (C). pap. 35.00 *(978-1-4223-0792-2(1))* DIANE Publishing Co.

Kaufman, George G., et al, eds. International Financial Instability: Global Banking & National Regulation. 2008. (World Scientific Studies in International Economics). (Illus.). 479p. 150.00 *(978-981-270-763-5(8))* World Scientific Publishing Co., Inc.

Kehl, James E. Code Section 199 Compliance & Planning Manual. 2008. 400p. pap. 249.00 *(978-0-8080-1876-6(0))* Toolkit Media Group.

Kettell. Introduction to Islamic Banking & Finance. 2010. (Illus.). 100p. pap. 45.00 *(978-0-9558351-0-0(0))* Harriman Hse. Publishing GBR. Dist: Ingram Pub. Services.

Kettell, Brian B. A Guide to Islamic Investing. 2013. (Wiley Finance Ser.). (ENG.). 256p. 45.00 *(978-0-470-97802-3(3)*, Wiley) Wiley, John & Sons, Inc.

Khandelwal, Sunil Kumar, et al. Financial Risk Management for Islamic Banking & Finance. 2008. (Finance & Capital Markets Ser.). (ENG., Illus.). 300p. 247.00 *(978-0-230-55381-1(8))* Palgrave Macmillan.

Killenbeck, Mark Robert. McCulloch V. Maryland: Securing a Nation. 2006. (Landmark Law Cases & American Society Ser.). 227p. 35.00 *(978-0-7006-1472-1(9))* Univ. Pr. of Kansas.

—M'Culloch V. Maryland: Securing a Nation. 2006. (Landmark Law Cases & American Society Ser.). 227p. per. 16.95 *(978-0-7006-1473-8(7))* Univ. Pr. of Kansas.

Klein, Lilian E. Bank Secrecy ACT: Background, Statute, & Interpretation. 2006. 161p. 69.00 *(978-1-60021-472-1(X))* Nova Science Pubs., Inc.

—Bank Secrecy Act/Anti-Money Laundering. 2008. vi, 118p. pap. 50.00 *(978-1-60456-624-6(8))* Nova Science Pubs., Inc.

LaBrosse, John, et al. Financial Crisis Management & Bank Resolution. 2009. 338p. 342.00 *(978-1-84311-838-1(6))* Informa Professional GBR. Dist: International Specialized Bk. Services.

Lastra. Central Banking & Banking Regulation. 2nd rev. ed. 2011. *(978-90-411-2480-7(2))* Kluwer Law International.

Lastra, Rosa. Cross-Border Bank Insolvency. 2011. (ENG., Illus.). 592p. 250.00 *(978-0-19-957707-1(2))* Oxford Univ. Pr., Inc.

Lastra, Rosa Maria. Legal Foundations of International Monetary Stability. 2006. (ENG.). 600p. 291.50 *(978-0-19-926934-1(3))* Oxford Univ. Pr., Inc.

Laws of Virginia Related to Financial Institutions, 1999 Supplement. 97p. *(978-0-327-09716-7(7)*, 3550312) LEXIS Publishing.

Lee, Dellas W. & Zinnecker, Timothy R. Payment Systems, Banking, & Documentary Transactions: Problems, Cases, Comments, Second Edition. 2nd ed. 2007. (Carolina Academic Press Law Casebook Ser.). 356p. 50.00 *(978-1-59460-429-4(0))* Carolina Academic Pr.

Lücke, Tobias. Bankaufsichtsrechtliche Anerkennung Interner Kreditportfoliomodelle. 2011. (Europäische Hochschulschriften. Reihe 5: Volks- und Betriebswirtschaft Ser.). (GER.). 317p. pap. 83.95 ***(978-3-631-61810-3(7))*** Lang, Peter GmbH, Europaischer Verlag der Wissenschaften DEU. Dist: Lang, Peter.

Macey & Carnell, Richard Scott. The Law of Banking & Financial Institutions. 4th rev. ed. 2008. xxxii, 796p. 152.00 *(978-0-7355-5285-2(1)*, Aspen Pubs.) Wolters Kluwer Law & Business.

MacNeil, Iain G. & O'Brien, Justin. The Future of Financial Regulation. Justin O'Brien, ed. 2010. (ENG., Illus.). 488p. pap. 100.00 *(978-1-84113-910-4(6))* Hart Publishing Ltd. GBR. Dist: International Specialized Bk. Services.

Mailänder, Peter O. Festschrift Für Karl Peter Mailänder Zum 70. Geburtstag Am 23. Oktober 2006. Geiss, Karlmann et al, eds. 2006. (GER., Illus.). XIV, 653p. 335.00 *(978-3-89949-316-0(8))* De Gruyter, Walter Inc.

Malloy. International Banking, Second Edition, 2007-2008 Supplement. 2007. 242p. per. 25.00 *(978-1-59460-466-9(5))* Carolina Academic Pr.

Malloy, Michael P. Anatomy Meltdown: Financial Biography Subprime Mortgage Meltdown. 2010. pap., stu. ed. 39.00 *(978-0-7355-9458-6(9)*, Aspen Pubs.) Wolters Kluwer Law & Business.

—Banking & Financial Services Law: Cases, Materials, & Problems. 3rd ed. 2011. (Illus.). 842p. 95.00 ***(978-1-61163-097-8(5))*** Carolina Academic Pr.

—Banking & Financial Services Law, Second Edition, Supplement: 2007-2008. 2007. 374p. per. 37.00 *(978-1-59460-471-3(1))* Carolina Academic Pr.

Malloy, Michael P. Banking Law & Regulation. 2nd ed. 2011. ***(978-0-7355-5275-3(4))***; ***(978-0-7355-5274-6(6))***; ***(978-0-7355-5276-0(2))*** Wolters Kluwer Law & Business. (Aspen Pubs.).

Mannino, Edward F. Lender Liability & Banking Litigation. rev. ed. 800p. *(978-1-58852-050-0(1)*, Law Journal Pr.) Incisive Media.

Marin, Matej & Vlahu, Razvan. The Economics of Bank Bankruptcy Law. 2011. (ENG., Illus.). xiii, 158p. 139.00 ***(978-3-642-21806-4(7)***, 3642218067) Springer.

McCleskey, Scott. When Free Markets Fail: Saving the Market When It Can't Save Itself. 2010. (ENG.). 198p. 39.95 *(978-0-470-60336-9(4)*, Wiley) Wiley, John & Sons, Inc.

Misawa. Current Business & Legal Issues in Japan's Banking & Finance Industry. 2006. (Illus.). xii, 451p. 82.00 *(978-981-256-859-5(X))* World Scientific Publishing Co., Inc.

Misawa, Mitsuru. Current Business & Legal Issues in Japan's Banking & Finance Industry. 2nd ed. 2010. 530p. 85.00 *(978-981-4291-01-9(3))* World Scientific Publishing Co., Inc.

Moosa, Imad A. & A., Imad. Quantification of Operational Risk under Basel II: The Good, Bad & Ugly. 2008. (ENG., Illus.). 240p. 247.00 *(978-0-230-22266-3(8))* Palgrave Macmillan.

Morriss, Andrew P. Offshore Financial Centers & Regulatory Competition. 2010. (ENG.). 200p. (C). (gr. 13-17). 49.95 *(978-0-8447-4324-0(0)*, AEI Pr.) American Enterprise Institute for Public Policy Research.

Moulton, R. K. Legislative & Documentary History of the Banks of the United States from the Time of Establishing the Bank of North America, 1781, to October 1834: With Notes & Comments. 2007. 232p. 95.00 *(978-1-58477-873-8(3))* Lawbook Exchange, Ltd., The.

Mueller, Sebastian. Hawala: An Informal Payment System & Its Use to Finance Terrorism. 2007. 84p. per. *(978-3-86550-656-6(9))* VDM Verlag Dr. Mueller e.K.

Neate, F. W. Neate & Godfrey: Bank Confidentiality. Griffiths, Gwendoline & Godfrey, Gwendoline, eds. 5th rev. ed. 2011. 1004p. 395.00 *(978-1-84766-694-9(9)*, Bloomsbury Professional) Bloomsbury Publishing Plc GBR. Dist: International Specialized Bk. Services.

Nicole A. Garcia. Banks, Securities & the Volcker Rule: Background & Issues. 2011. (Series: Financial Institutions & Services Ser.). 89.00 *(978-1-61761-988-5(4))* Nova Science Pubs., Inc.

Office of the Federal Register (U.S.), compiled by. Code of Federal Regulations, Title 12, Banks & Banking, Pt. 1-199, Revised as of January 1 2011. rev. ed. 2011. (ENG.). 542p. pap. 39.00 *(978-0-16-087549-6(8)*, Office of the Federal Register) United States Government Printing Office.

—Code of Federal Regulations, Title 12, Banks & Banking, Pt. 1-199, Revised as of January 1 2012. rev. ed. 2012. (ENG.). 542p. pap. 39.00 ***(978-0-16-090083-9(2)***, Office of the Federal Register) United States Government Printing Office.

—Code of Federal Regulations, Title 12, Banks & Banking, Pt. 200-219, Revised as of January 1 2011. rev. ed. 2011. (ENG.). 569p. pap. 42.00 *(978-0-16-087550-2(1)*, Office of the Federal Register) United States Government Printing Office.

—Code of Federal Regulations, Title 12, Banks & Banking, Pt. 200-219, Revised as of January 1 2012. rev. ed. 2012. (ENG.). 569p. pap. 42.00 ***(978-0-16-090084-6(0)***, Office of the Federal Register) United States Government Printing Office.

—Code of Federal Regulations, Title 12, Banks & Banking, Pt. 220-229, Revised as of January 1 2012. rev. ed. 2012. (ENG.). 1301p. pap. 67.00 ***(978-0-16-090085-3(9)***, Office of the Federal Register) United States Government Printing Office.

—Code of Federal Regulations, Title 12, Banks & Banking, Pt. 220-299, Revised as of January 1 2011. rev. ed. 2011. (ENG.). 1301p. pap. 67.00 *(978-0-16-087551-9(X)*, Office of the Federal Register) United States Government Printing Office.

—Code of Federal Regulations, Title 12, Banks & Banking, Pt. 300-499, Revised as of January 1 2011. rev. ed. 2011. (ENG.). 783p. pap. 53.00 *(978-0-16-087552-6(8)*, Office of the Federal Register) United States Government Printing Office.

—Code of Federal Regulations, Title 12, Banks & Banking, Pt. 300-499, Revised as of January 1 2012. rev. ed. 2012. (ENG.). 783p. pap. 53.00 ***(978-0-16-090087-7(5)***, Office of the Federal Register) United States Government Printing Office.

—Code of Federal Regulations, Title 12, Banks & Banking, Pt. 500-599, Revised as of January 1 2011. rev. ed. 2011. (ENG.). 620p. pap. 44.00 *(978-0-16-087553-3(6)*, Office of the Federal Register) United States Government Printing Office.

—Code of Federal Regulations, Title 12, Banks & Banking, Pt. 500-599, Revised as of January 1 2012. rev. ed. 2012. (ENG.). 614p. pap. 44.00 ***(978-0-16-090088-4(3)***, Office of the Federal Register) United States Government Printing Office.

—Code of Federal Regulations, Title 12, Banks & Banking, Pt. 600-899, Revised as of January 1 2011. rev. ed. 2011. (ENG.). 1087p. pap. 62.00 *(978-0-16-087554-0(4)*, Office of the Federal Register) United States Government Printing Office.

—Code of Federal Regulations, Title 12, Banks & Banking, Pt. 600-899, Revised as of January 1 2012. rev. ed. 2012. (ENG.). 1087p. pap. 62.00 ***(978-0-16-090089-1(1)***, Office of the Federal Register) United States Government Printing Office.

—Code of Federal Regulations, Title 12, Banks & Banking, Pt. 900-End, Revised as of January 1 2011. rev. ed. 2011. (ENG.). 721p. pap. 56.00 *(978-0-16-087555-7(2)*, Office of the Federal Register) United States Government Printing Office.

Office of the Federal Register (U.S.), compiled by. Code of Federal Regulations, Title 12, Banks & Banking, Pt. 900-End, Revised as of January 1 2012. rev. ed. 2012. (ENG.). 721p. pap. 56.00 ***(978-0-16-090090-7(5)***, Office of the Federal Register) United States Government Printing Office.

Office of the Federal Register (U.S.), ed. Code of Federal Regulations, Title 12, Banks & Banking, Pt. 230-299, Revised as of January 1 2012. 2012. (ENG.). 451p. pap. 67.00 ***(978-0-16-090086-0(7)***, Office of the Federal Register) United States Government Printing Office.

Ozdemir, Bogie & Miu, Peter. Basel II Implementation: A Guide to Developing & Validating a Compliant, Internal Risk Rating System. 2008. (ENG., Illus.). 480p. 125.00 *(978-0-07-159130-0(3)*, 0071591303) McGraw-Hill Cos., The.

Pattison, John. Regulatory Compliance & Behaviour in Global Markets. 2007. 150p. pap. *(978-1-894611-28-2(4))* G-7 Report, Inc., The.

Pearson, Gail. Financial Services Law & Compliance in Australia. 2009. (ENG.). 628p. pap. 108.00 *(978-0-521-61784-0(7))* Cambridge Univ. Pr.

Peláez, Carlos M. & Peláez, Carlos A. Financial Regulation after the Global Recession. 2009. (ENG., Illus.). 208p. 100.00 *(978-0-230-23902-9(1))* Palgrave Macmillan.

Pelato-Shinar, Ruth. Dine Bankaut: Hovat Ha-Emun Ha-Bankait. 2010. (HEB.). 756p. *(978-965-7322-17-8(0))* Israel BAR Publishing Hse., The.

Practising Law Institute Staff, contrib. by. Subprime Credit Crisis: Everything You Need to Know Now. 2008. (Illus.). 1278p. pap. *(978-1-4024-1047-5(6))* Practising Law Institute.

Quintyn, Marc & Taylor, Michael W. Should Financial Sector Regulators Be Independent? (CHI.). *(978-1-58906-313-6(9)*, EIICA032); (ARA.). *(978-1-58906-312-9(0)*, EIIAA032); (SPA.). *(978-1-58906-311-2(2)*, EIISA032); (RUS.). *(978-1-58906-314-3(7)*, EIIRA032); (FRE.). *(978-1-58906-310-5(4)*, EIIFA032) International Monetary Fund.

Redenbach, Sven. The German Banking Sector. 2008. 60p. per. *(978-3-8364-6377-5(6))* VDM Verlag Dr. Mueller e.K.

B

Reference Guide to Regulatory Compliance. (ENG., Illus.). 2009. 872p. ring bd. 359.00 *(978-0-89982-628-8(8))* 2009. 872p. cd-rom 269.00 *(978-0-89982-638-7(5))* 2008. 806p. spiral bd. 379.00 *(978-0-89982-609-7(1))* American Bankers Assn.

Richmond Law & Tax Ltd., ed. Banking Regulators. 2nd rev. ed. 2006. 500p. pap. *(978-1-904501-76-3(1))* Richmond Law & Tax Ltd.

—Financial Services Regulators in Offshore Financial Centres. 2nd rev. ed. 2006. 250p. pap. *(978-1-904501-75-6(3))* Richmond Law & Tax Ltd.

Rosenberg, Arnold S. Stored Value Cards & Other New Payment Devices. 2008. 24p. pap. *(978-1-4224-2881-8(8))* LexisNexis Matthew Bender.

Rouse, Nick. Bankers' Lending Techniques. 3rd rev. ed. 2010. 300p. pap. 35.00 *(978-1-906403-00-3(7))* Lessons Professional Publishing GBR. Dist: Stylus Publishing, LLC.

Russell, Ellen. New Deal Banking Reforms & Keynesian Welfare State Capitalism. 2012. (New Political Economy Ser.). (ENG.). 158p. pap. 42.95 ***(978-0-415-54181-7(6))*** Routledge.

Russell, Ellen D. New Deal Banking Reforms & Keynesian Welfare State Capitalism. 2007. (New Political Economy Ser.). (ENG.). 158p. 125.00 *(978-0-415-95661-1(7))* Routledge.

Satyanath, Shanker. Globalization, Politics, & Financial Turmoil: Asia's Banking Crisis. 2009. (Political Economy of Institutions & Decisions Ser.). (ENG., Illus.). 176p. pap. 26.99 *(978-0-521-10743-3(1))* Cambridge Univ. Pr.

Schroeder, Gilbert J. & Tomaine, John J. Loan Loss Coverage under Financial Institution Bonds. 2007. xxv, 693p. *(978-1-59031-943-7(5))* American Bar Assn.

Scott, Hal S. International Finance, Transactions, Policy, & Regulation, 16th Edition. 16th rev. ed. 2009. (University Casebook Ser.). 1186p. 149.00 *(978-1-59941-719-6(7)*, Foundation Pr.) West.

Sharman, J. C. The Money Laundry: Regulating Criminal Finance in the Global Economy. 2011. (Cornell Studies in Political Economy Ser.). (Illus.). 224p. 29.95 ***(978-0-8014-5018-1(7))*** Cornell Univ. Pr.

Sigmond, Karen B. Mexican Banking Laws. 2008. 192p. pap. *(978-3-639-08230-2(3))* VDM Verlag Dr. Mueller e.K.

Singer, David Andrew. Regulating Capital: Setting Standards for the International Financial System. (Cornell Studies in Money Ser.). (Illus.). 2010. 176p. pap. 21.00 *(978-0-8014-7671-6(2))* 2007. 163p. 52.50 *(978-0-8014-4525-5(6))* Cornell Univ. Pr.

Singh, Dr Jasvinder, et al. Hand Book on Dishonour of Cheque Part- 2011. 380p. pap. ***(978-3-8443-1838-8(0))*** Lambert Academic Publishing.

—Hand Book on Dishonour of Cheque Part-B,C. 2011. 628p. pap. ***(978-3-8443-2045-9(8))*** Lambert Academic Publishing.

Skeel, David. The New Financial Deal: Understanding the Dodd-Frank Act & Its (Unintended) Consequences. 2010. (ENG., Illus.). 220p. 34.95 *(978-0-470-94275-8(4)*, Wiley) Wiley, John & Sons, Inc.

Southworth, Shirley Donald. Branch Banking in the United States. 2007. pap. 28.95 *(978-1-4067-5584-8(2))* Southworth Pr.

Steiner, Howard & Marini, Stephen. Independent Review for MSBs - the Complete BSA/AML Audit Workbook. 2009. 165p. pap. 119.95 *(978-0-615-23992-7(7))* ImpactAML-INX3 Financial Pr.

Tarullo, Daniel & Tarullo, Daniel K. Banking on Basel: The Future of International Financial Regulation. 2008. (Illus.). 256p. (C). pap. 26.95 *(978-0-88132-423-5(X))* Peterson Institute for International Economics.

Taylor, John. Construction Construed & Constitutions Vindicated 1820. 2009. 348p. 32.95 *(978-1-886363-43-4(9))* Lawbook Exchange, Ltd., The.

Torp, Jeffrey. BSA/Anti-Money Laundering Question & Answer Book. 2007. *(978-1-55827-442-6(1))* Sheshunoff Information Services.

Torp, Jeffrey & Hyde, Lorraine. Identity Theft Prevention Program. 2007. (Illus.). *(978-1-55827-962-9(8))* Sheshunoff Information Services.

Treasury Dept. (U.S.), compiled by. The Department of the Treasury Blueprint for a Modernized Financial Regulatory Structure. 2008. (ENG.). 212p. pap. 24.00 *(978-0-16-080645-2(3)*, Treasury Dept.) United States Government Printing Office.

Trinh Quang, Anh. Banking Supervision Moves Ahead in the New Er. 2010. 164p. pap. *(978-3-8383-7445-1(2))* Lambert Academic Publishing.

United States, Congress House Committee on Financial Services Subcommittee on Financial Institutions and Consumer Credit Staff, contrib. by. ILC's — A Review of Charter, Ownership, & Supervision Issues: Hearing Before the Subcommittee on Financial Institutions & Consumer Credit of the Committee on Financial Services, U.S. House of Representatives, One Hundred Ninth Congress, Second Session, July 12, 2006. 2007. vi, 296p. *(978-0-16-078213-8(9)*, 552-070-35597-9) United States Government Printing Office.

—A Review of Regulatory Proposals on Basel Capital & Commercial Real Estate: Hearing Before the Subcommittee on Financial Institutions & Consumer Credit of the Committee on Financial Services, U.S. House of Representatives, One Hundred Ninth Congress, Second Session, September 14, 2006. 2007. (Illus.). vi, 464p. *(978-0-16-078575-7(8)*, 552-070-35839-1) United States Government Printing Office.

Various Authors. Islamic Finance: Instruments & Markets. 2011. (ENG., Illus.). 320p. 85.00 *(978-1-84930-017-9(8))* Bloomsbury Publishing.

Villa, John K. Bank Directors' Officers' & Lawyers' Civil Liabilities. 2nd ed. 2011. ***(978-1-4548-0108-5(5)****, Aspen Pubs.)* Wolters Kluwer Law & Business.

Walker, George. European Banking Law: Policy & Programme Construction (Sir Joseph Gold Memorial Series Volume Six) 2007. (International Financial Law Ser.: Vol. 6). 435p. (C). pap. 165.00 *(978-0-903067-78-2(1))* British Institute of International & Comparative Law GBR. Dist: International Specialized Bk. Services.

Wall Street to Main Street: Is the Credit Crisis over & What Can the Federal Government Do to Prevent Unnecessary Systemic Risk in the Future?: Hearing Before the Joint Economic Committee, Congress of the United States, One Hundred Tenth Congress, Second Session, May 14, 2008. 2009. iii, 68p. *(978-0-16-082730-3(2)*, 552-070-38740-4) United States Government Printing Office.

Warren, et al. Payments & Credits, 8th. 8th rev. ed. 2010. 471p. 174.00 *(978-1-59941-746-2(4)*, Foundation Pr.) West.

Whittaker, Andrew M., et al, eds. Financial Services: Law & Practice. (Illus.). ring bd. *(978-0-406-99866-8(3)*, FSLPASET, MICHIE) LEXIS Publishing.

Wymeersch, Eddy, ed. Further Perspectives in Financial Integration in Europe: Reports presented at the Brussels meeting of the International Faculty for Corporate Market Law & Securities Regulations 26 - 30 April 1993. (ENG.). XVI, 281p. 374.00 ***(978-3-11-177848-8(7))*** De Gruyter, Walter Inc.

Zhou. Banking Laws in China: Theory & Practice. 2007. *(978-90-411-2519-4(1))* Kluwer Law International.

The 15th Replenishment of the International Development Association (IDA) & the 11th Replenishment of the African Development Fund (AfDF) Hearing Before the Committee on Financial Services, U.S. House of Representatives, One Hundred Tenth Congress, Second Session, June 18, 2008. 2008. iii, 111p. *(978-0-16-081944-5(X)*, 552-070-38117-1) United States Government Printing Office.

BANKING LAW—AFRICA

Donzo, Fonsia M. Banking Supervision in Liberi: How Adequate & Effective? 2011. 124p. pap. ***(978-3-8443-0872-3(5))*** Lambert Academic Publishing.

Goldface-Irokalibe, I. Law of Banking Nigeria. 2007. 376p. pap. *(978-978-023-225-2(7))* Malthouse Press Ltd, Nigeria NGA. Dist: Michigan State Univ. Pr.

Murinde, Victor, ed. Bank Regulatory Reforms in Africa. 2012. (Palgrave Macmillan Studies in Banking & Financial Institutions Ser.). (ENG., Illus.). 216p. 90.00 ***(978-0-230-31333-0(7))*** Palgrave Macmillan.

BANKING LAW—EUROPE

Apathy, Peter, et al, eds. Österreichisches Bankvertragsrecht 1: Geschäftsbeziehung. 2nd ed. 2006. (Springers Handbücher der Rechtswissenschaft Ser.). XXIV, 391p. 99.95 *(978-3-211-36962-3(7)*, 3211369627) Springer.

—Österreichisches Bankvertragsrecht 6: Kapitalmarkt. 2nd ed. 2007. (Springers Handbücher der Rechtswissenschaft Ser.). XXIII, 419p. 89.00 *(978-3-211-37040-7(4)*, 3211370404) Springer.

Blömer, Ulrike. Grenzüberschreitende Sachverhalte im Bankenaufsichtsrecht. 2010. (Frankfurter wirtschaftsrechtliche Studien Ser.). (GER.). 276p. 79.95 *(978-3-631-60413-7(0))* Lang, Peter GmbH, Europaischer Verlag der Wissenschaften DEU. Dist: Lang, Peter.

Dixon, Robert. Banking in Europe (Rle Banking & Finance), Volume 10. 2012. (ENG.). 160p. 100.00 ***(978-0-415-53022-4(9))*** Routledge.

Dragomir, Larisa. European Prudential Banking Regulation & Supervision: The Legal Dimension. 2012. (ENG.). 422p. pap. 44.95 ***(978-0-415-63147-1(5))*** Routledge.

—European Prudential Banking Regulation & Supervision: The Legal Dimension. 2010. (Routledge Research in Finance & Banking Law Ser.). (ENG.). 448p. 125.00 *(978-0-415-49656-8(X)*, Routledge) Taylor & Francis Group GBR. Dist: Taylor & Francis Group.

García Alcubilla, Raquel & Ruiz del Pozo, Javier. Credit Rating Agencies on the Watch List: Analysis of European Regulation. 2012. (ENG., Illus.). 320p. 99.00 ***(978-0-19-960886-7(5))*** Oxford Univ. Pr., Inc.

Gkoutzinis, Apostolos Ath. Internet Banking & the Law in Europe: Regulation, Financial Integration & Electronic Commerce. 2010. (ENG.). 404p. pap. 39.99 *(978-0-521-15323-2(9))* Cambridge Univ. Pr.

Insam, A. Suspicion of Money Laundering: In the Crossfire of International Due Diligence Obligations. 2006. 374p. 54.50 *(978-90-5095-594-2(0))* Intersentia Uitgevers N.V. BEL. Dist: International Specialized Bk. Services.

Johnston. Arthur Cox Banking Law Handbook Irish. 2007. 1154p. 252.00 *(978-1-84592-047-0(3)*, Bloomsbury Professional) Bloomsbury Publishing Plc GBR. Dist: International Specialized Bk. Services.

Johnston, William. Banking & Security Law in Ireland. 2nd rev. ed. 2012. 800p. 220.00 ***(978-1-84766-668-0(X)****,* Bloomsbury Professional) Bloomsbury Publishing Plc GBR. Dist: International Specialized Bk. Services.

Massari, Philipp. Das Wettbewerbsrecht: Die Regulierung des Wettbewerbs der Banken Durch Kartellrecht, Bankaufsichtsrecht und Lauterkeitsrecht. 2006. (Schriften Zum Europäischen und Internationalen Privat-, Bank- und Wirtschaftsrecht Ser.). (GER.). XXIII, 215p. 105.00 *(978-3-89949-366-5(4))* De Gruyter, Walter Inc.

Nordestgaard, Malene. Crisis Communication at Kaupthing Bank. 2010. 68p. pap. *(978-3-639-24091-7(X))* VDM Verlag Dr. Mueller e.K.

Pérez-Bustamante, David. Depósitos Bancarios y Crisis Financieras. 2009. (SPA.). 341p. *(978-84-9849-453-2(2))* Dykinson, S.L.

Szép, Davide. Mifid: Markets in Financial Instruments Directives. 2011. 292p. pap. ***(978-3-8443-9289-0(0))*** Lambert Academic Publishing.

Van De Vijver Staff. Financial & Banking: Regulation in Netherlands. 2011. xvi, 194p. *(978-90-411-2863-8(8))* Wolters Kluwer Law & Business.

BANKING LAW—GREAT BRITAIN

Byrne, Hugh & McEntagart, Louis. The National Asset Management Agency Act 2009: Annotations & Commentary: A Guide to Irish Law. 2010. 546p. pap. 160.00 *(978-1-84766-504-1(7)*, Bloomsbury Professional) Bloomsbury Publishing Plc GBR. Dist: International Specialized Bk. Services.

Chambers, Clare. Financial Exclusion & Banking Regulation in the Uk. 2010. 352p. pap. *(978-3-8383-5071-4(5))* Lambert Academic Publishing.

Crerar. Banking Law in Scotland. 2nd ed. 2007. 754p. pap. 210.00 *(978-1-84592-151-4(8)*, Bloomsbury Professional) Bloomsbury Publishing Plc GBR. Dist: International Specialized Bk. Services.

Ellinger, E. P., et al. Ellinger's Modern Banking Law. 5th ed. 2009. (ENG.). 885p. (C). pap. 85.00 *(978-0-19-923209-3(1))* Oxford Univ. Pr., Inc.

Fullarton, John. On the Regulation of Currencies. 2009. 146p. pap. 19.99 *(978-1-150-58041-3(0))* General Bks. LLC.

—On the Regulation of Currencies. 2008. 234p. pap. 26.95 *(978-1-4370-8653-9(5))* Kessinger Publishing, LLC.

Gray, Joanna & Akseli, Orkun. Financial Regulation in Crisis? The Role of Law & the Failure of Northern Rock. Gray, Joanna & Akseli, Orkun, eds. 2011. (Elgar Financial Law Ser.). 128p. 110.00 ***(978-1-84844-554-3(7))*** Elgar, Edward Publishing, Inc.

Keay, Andrew & Walton, Peter. Insolvency Law: Corporate & Personal. 2nd rev. ed. 2008. (ENG.). 738p. pap. *(978-1-84661-119-3(9))* Jordan Publishing, Ltd.

Levaggi, Peter, et al. Property Insolvency. 2009. (ENG., Illus.). 402p. incl. cd-rom *(978-1-84661-151-3(2))* Jordan Publishing, Ltd.

McNab, Helen. Consumer Credit Risk Management. 2008. (Illus.). 394p. (C). pap. 49.95 *(978-1-906403-21-8(X))* Lessons Professional Publishing GBR. Dist: Stylus Publishing, LLC.

Melville, Alan. Taxation. 15th ed. 2009. (ENG.). 640p. pap. *(978-0-273-73015-6(0))* Financial Times Business Enterprises, Ltd.

—Taxation. 13th rev. ed. 2007. 656p. pap. 110.00 *(978-0-273-71232-9(2)*, Financial Times/Prentice Hall) Pearson Education, Ltd. GBR. Dist: Trans-Atlantic Pubns., Inc.

Montagu, Gerald & Paul, Colin. Banking & Capital Markets Companion. 5th rev. ed. 2011. (ENG., Illus.). 632p. pap. 95.00 *(978-1-84766-308-5(7)*, Bloomsbury Professional) Bloomsbury Publishing Plc GBR. Dist: International Specialized Bk. Services.

Mugasha, Agasha. The Law of Multi-Bank Financing: Syndicated Loans & the Secondary Loan Market. 2008. (ENG., Illus.). 650p. 434.50 *(978-0-19-928912-7(3))* Oxford Univ. Pr., Inc.

Russen, Jonathan. Financial Services: Authorisation, Supervision & Enforcement: A Litigator's Guide. 2006. (ENG.). 432p. 345.00 *(978-0-19-929665-1(0))* Oxford Univ. Pr., Inc.

Singh, Dalvinder. Banking Regulations of UK Financial Markets. 2007. 238p. 124.95 *(978-0-7546-3971-8(1))* Ashgate Publishing Co.

Story, Joseph & Thorndike, John Larkin. Commentaries on the Law of Promissory Notes, & Guaranties of Notes, & Checks on Banks & Bankers. 2010. (ENG.). 812p. pap. 55.75 *(978-1-171-79476-9(2))* BiblioBazaar.

Walker, George & Blair, Michael, eds. Financial Markets & Exchanges Law. 2007. (ENG.). 674p. 467.50 *(978-0-19-928580-8(2))* Oxford Univ. Pr., Inc.

Walker, George, et al. Financial Services Law. 2nd ed. 2009. (ENG.). 1050p. 531.25 *(978-0-19-956418-7(3))* Oxford Univ. Pr., Inc.

Watson-Gandy, Mark. Personal Insolvency Practice: Litigation, Procedure & Precedents. 2011. (ENG.). 400p. 143.00 ***(978-0-85490-082-4(9))*** Gaunt, Inc.

BANKING LAW—JAPAN

Kawahigashi, Kenji. Fando to Kinyu Shohin Torihikiho. 2010. (JPN., Illus.). xi, 377p. *(978-4-7857-1773-5(4))* Shojihomu Co Ltd.

Takahashi, Yasufumi & Kobayashi, Takaaki. Chikujo Kaisetsu Shikin Kessaiho. 2010. (JPN., Illus.). vii, 388p. *(978-4-322-11553-6(5))*; *(978-4-322-11711-0(2))* Kinzai.

Watanabe, Masayuki & Inoue, Shinichiro. QandA Shikin Kessaiho Kaisei Kappu Hanbaiho: Atarashii Kessai Sabisu ni Kansuru Hosei No Odanteki Kaisetsu. 2010. (JPN.). 11p. *(978-4-322-11701-1(5))* Kinzai.

BANKNOTES

see Bank Notes

BANKRUPTCY

see also Corporate Reorganizations; Liquidation

Adapting to Changes in Bankruptcy Law: Leading Lawyers on Understanding Recent Bankruptcy Trends, Analyzing Changing Laws, & Developing Client Strategies (Inside the Minds) 2009. 196p. pap. 90.00 *(978-0-314-21424-9(0))* Aspatore Bks.

Alderman, M. Chapter 11 Business Reorganizations: For Business Leaders, Accountants & Lawyers. 2006. 200p. pap. 39.95 *(978-1-59800-413-7(1))* Outskirts Pr., Inc.

Allen, Mitchell. A Survival Guide to Debt: How to Overcome Tough Times & Restore Your Financial Health. 2009. (Illus.). 224p. pap. 14.95 *(978-1-929774-70-8(2)*, Greenleaf Book Group Pr.) Greenleaf Book Group.

American College of Bankruptcy Staff, contrib. by. 2007 Circuit Review & Best Practices Reports. 2007. 225.00 *(978-1-4224-1918-2(5))* LexisNexis Matthew Bender.

American Workers in Crisis: Does the Chapter 11 Business Bankruptcy Law Treat Employees & Retirees Fairly?: Hearing Before the Subcommittee on Commercial & Administrative Law of the Committee on the Judiciary, House of Representatives, One Hundred Tenth Congress, First Session, September 6, 2007. 2008. iii, 62p. *(978-0-16-082282-7(3)*, 552-070-38346-8) United States Government Printing Office.

Amr, Ahmed. The Sheep & the Guardians: Diary of a SEC Sanctioned Swindle. 2009. 324p. pap. 23.99 *(978-1-4269-1031-9(2))* Trafford Publishing.

Anders, Brett. The Devil's Dictionary of Bankruptcy Terms for Commercial Lenders. 2007. (Illus.). v, 179p. *(978-0-9793690-0-1(2))* Peppercorn Pr.

Anderson, John. Spark Law Bankruptcy. 2008. per. 17.95 *(978-0-9801482-2-0(7))* Mclaren Legal Pubs. LLC.

Aspatore Books Staff, compiled by. Bankruptcy Law Client Strategies in Europe: Leading Lawyers on Analyzing the European Bankruptcy Process, Developing Creative Strategies for Clients, & Understanding the Latest Laws & Trends (Inside the Minds) 2010. (Illus.). 192p. pap. 100.00 *(978-0-314-26774-0(3))* Aspatore Bks.

—Bankruptcy Law Client Strategies in South America: Leading Lawyers on Navigating the South American Bankruptcy Process, Working with Local Governments, & Developing Successful Strategies (Inside the Minds) 2011. 328p. pap. 90.00 *(978-0-314-27484-7(7))* Aspatore Bks.

—Bankruptcy Law Client Strategies in the Middle East & Africa: Leading Lawyers on Examining Local Bankruptcy Systems, Analyzing Recent & Proposed Changes to Laws, & Preparing Successful Client Strategies (Inside the Minds) 2011. (Illus.). 248p. pap. 90.00 *(978-0-314-27412-0(X))* Aspatore Bks.

—Bankruptcy Litigation & Dispute Resolution: Leading Lawyers on Key Case Strategies, Risk Assessment, & Settlement Considerations (Inside the Minds) 2008. (Inside the Minds Ser.). 316p. pap. 150.00 *(978-0-314-98676-4(6))* Aspatore Bks.

—Bankruptcy Restructuring Strategies: Leading Lawyers on Evaluating Bankruptcy Alternatives, Protecting the Client, & Developing Negotiation Strategies (Inside the Minds) 2008. pap. *(978-0-314-19553-1(X))* Aspatore Bks.

—Best Practices for Bankruptcy Law in China: Leading Lawyers on Interpreting New Legislation, Representing Distressed Companies, & Communicating with Debtors & Creditors. 2008. 240p. 105.00 *(978-0-314-19461-9(4))* Aspatore Bks.

—Best Practices for Distressed Company Workouts: Leading Lawyers on Evaluating Alternatives, Assembling a Workout Team, & Forecasting Possible Outcomes (Inside the Minds) 2008. 148p. pap. 80.00 *(978-0-314-20287-1(0))* Aspatore Bks.

—Best Practices for Filing Chapter 13: Leading Lawyers on Counseling the Client, Interpreting New Legislation, & Communicating with Creditors. 2008. (Inside the Minds Ser.). 152p. 75.00 *(978-0-314-19460-2(6))* Aspatore Bks.

—Best Practices for Filing Chapter 13, 2011 Ed: Leading Lawyers on Analyzing Today's Chapter 13 Filings, Preparing Clients, & Implementing Effective Strategies (Inside the Minds) 2011. (Illus.). 144p. pap. 80.00 *(978-0-314-27411-3(1))* Aspatore Bks.

—Buying & Selling Distressed Businesses: Leading Lawyers on Evaluating Assets & Identifying Buyers, Negotiating Deals, & Advising Directors & Officers on Fiduciary Duties (Inside the Minds) 2009. 452p. pap. 90.00 *(978-0-314-20785-2(6))* Aspatore Bks.

—Buying & Selling Distressed Businesses, 2010 Ed: Leading Lawyers on Navigating Recent Distressed Business Transactions, Understanding the Sales Process, & Developing Deal Strategies (Inside the Minds) 2010. (Illus.). 352p. pap. 95.00 *(978-0-314-27092-4(2))* Aspatore Bks.

—Chapter 11 Bankruptcy & Restructuring Strategies: Leading Lawyers on Developing a Case Strategy, Working with Key Players, & Achieving a Client's Goals. 2008. 400p. pap. 150.00 *(978-0-314-98707-5(X))* Aspatore Bks.

—Chapter 11 Bankruptcy & Restructuring Strategies, 2010 Ed: Leading Lawyers on Navigating Recent Chapter 11 Cases & Understanding Current Challenges Facing Debtors & Creditors (Inside the Minds) 2010. (Illus.). 344p. pap. 100.00 *(978-0-314-26781-8(6))* Aspatore Bks.

—Chapter 7 Consumer Bankruptcy Strategies: Leading Lawyers on Communicating with Clients, Evaluating Alternatives, & Understanding the Current Consumer Bankruptcy Climate (Inside the Minds) 2009. (Inside the Minds Ser.). 188p. pap. 75.00 *(978-0-314-20528-5(4))* Aspatore Bks.

—Chapter 9 Bankruptcy Strategies: Leading Lawyers on Navigating the Chapter 9 Filing Process, Counseling Municipalities, & Analyzing Recent Trends & Cases (Inside the Minds) 2011. (ENG.). 340p. pap. 95.00 ***(978-0-314-27931-6(8))*** Aspatore Bks.

—Creditors' Rights in Chapter 11 Cases: Leading Lawyers on Navigating the Reorganization Process, Exercising Creditors' Rights, & Understanding the Impact of Current Developments (Inside the Minds) 2009. 384p. pap. 110.00 *(978-0-314-20529-2(2))* Aspatore Bks.

—The Industries Most at Risk in Bankruptcy: Legal & Financial Experts on What to Expect, Avoiding Financial Trouble, & Thoughts on the Future (Inside the Minds) 2008. 152p. pap. 110.00 *(978-0-314-19911-9(X))* Aspatore Bks.

—Managing Environmental Liabilities in Bankruptcy: Leading Lawyers on Identifying Environmental Risks, Implementing Emerging Risk Transfer Strategies, & Navigating Current Trends in U. S. Environmental Liability (Inside the Minds) 2010. (Illus.). 184p. pap. 90.00 *(978-0-314-26853-2(7))* Aspatore Bks.

—Navigating Recent Bankruptcy Law Trends: Leading Lawyers on Implementing Innovative Bankruptcy Practices, Advising Clients, & Evaluating the Latest Trends & Cases (Inside the Minds) 2010. 200p. pap. 90.00 *(978-0-314-27201-0(1))* Aspatore Bks.

—Recent Developments in Bankruptcy Law in China: Leading Lawyers on Navigating Current Trends, Advising Clients on Common Legal Issues, & Understanding the Political & Economic Environment in China (Inside the Minds) 2010. 164p. pap. 90.00 *(978-0-314-26854-9(5))* Aspatore Bks.

—The Role of Creditors' Committees in Chapter 11 Bankruptcies (Inside the Minds) 2008. 124p. pap. 110.00 *(978-0-314-19914-0(4))* Aspatore Bks.

—Trends in Commercial Bankruptcy Filings: Leading Lawyers on Preparing Clients to File, Navigating Recent Liquidations & Sales, & Revising Existing Bankruptcy Strategies (Inside the Minds) 2010. (Illus.). 132p. pap. 90.00 (978-0-314-26855-6(3)) Aspatore Bks.

—Trends in Consumer Bankruptcy Filings: Leading Lawyers on Understanding the Current Bankruptcy Landscape, Navigating the Filing Process, & Educating Clients (Inside the Minds) 2010. 188p. pap. 75.00 (978-0-314-27344-4(1)) Aspatore Bks.

—Winning Legal Strategies for Emerging from Bankruptcy: Leading Lawyers on Establishing Realistic Objectives, Working with Key Players, & Navigating Each Stage of the Process. 2008. 188p. pap. 125.00 (978-0-314-99179-9(4)) Aspatore Bks.

Atlantic Publishing Group. How to File for Your Own Personal Bankruptcy: Everything You Need to Know Explained Easily Without an Attorney (with Companion CD-ROM) 2012. (ENG.). 288p. pap. 29.95 (978-1-60138-618-2(4)) Atlantic Publishing Co.

Attinger, Barbara Jeanne. Der Mittelpunkt der hauptsächlichen Interessen nach der EuInsVo - erfolgreiches Konzept oder Quelle der Rechtsunsicherheit? Eine Auseinandersetzung mit dem Zuständigkeitskriterium der Europäischen Insolvenzverordnung unter Heranziehung der Erkenntnisse der ökonomischen Analyse des Rechts. 2008. (Saarbrücker Studien zum Privat- und Wirtschaftsrecht Ser.). 337p. pap. 81.95 (978-3-631-57911-4(X)) Lang, Peter GmbH, Europäischer Verlag der Wissenschaften DEU. Dist: Lang, Peter.

Ayer, Jack D. & Bernstein, Michael L. Bankruptcy in Practice, Fourth Edition. 4th rev. ed. 2007. 512p. per. 99.95 (978-0-9785292-6-0(X)) American Bankruptcy Institute.

Baird, Douglas G. & Eisenberg, Theodore. Commercial & Debtor-Creditor Law: Selected Statutes, 2008. 2008. (University Casebook Ser.). 2025p. pap. 43.00 (978-1-59941-526-0(7), Foundation Pr.) West.

—Commercial & Debtor-Creditor Law: Selected Statutes 2009 Edition. 2009th rev. ed. 2009. 2042p. pap. 45.00 (978-1-59941-682-3(4), Foundation Pr.) West.

Baird, Douglas G. & Eisenberg, Theodore. Commercial & Debtor-Creditor Law: Selected Statutes 2011. 2011. 2138p. pap. 49.00 **(978-1-59941-948-0(3)**, Foundation Pr.) West.

Baird, Douglas G. & Jackson, Thomas H., compiled by. Commercial & Debtor-Creditor Law: Selected Statutes. 2007th rev. ed. 2007. (Academic Statutes Ser.). 2047p. per. 42.00 (978-1-59941-266-5(7), Foundation Pr.) West.

Baker, Sandy Ann. The Complete Bankruptcy Guide for Consumers & Small Businesses: Everything You Need to Know Explained So You Can Understand It. 2011. (ENG.). 288p. pap. 24.95 (978-1-60138-310-5(X)) Atlantic Publishing Co.

Bankruptcy Code & Related Materials for Law Students. 2008. (Student Guides). (Illus.). 403p. per. 39.00 (978-0-314-19069-7(4), West Legalworks) West.

Bankruptcy Judgeship Needs: Hearing Before the Subcommittee on Commercial & Administrative Law of the Committee on the Judiciary, House of Representatives, One Hundred Eleventh Congress, First Session, June 16, 2009. 2010. (Illus.). iii, 151p. (978-0-16-085231-2(5), 552-070-40573-9) United States Government Printing Office.

Bankruptcy Law Isn't Just for Bankruptcy Lawyers, 1997. Date not set. 90p. pap. 15.00 (978-1-56986-038-0(6), BK4-97-90) Federal Bar Assn.

Bankruptcy Law Update. pap. (978-0-660-16766-4(2)) Canadian Government Publishing.

Bankruptcy Reform: Hearing Before the Committee on the Judiciary, United States Senate, One Hundred Ninth Congress, First Session, February 10, 2005. 2008. (Illus.). iv, 265p. (978-0-16-081310-8(7), 552-070-37699-2) United States Government Printing Office.

Bankruptcy Trustee Compensation: Hearing Before the Subcommittee on Commercial & Administrative Law of the Committee on the Judiciary, House of Representatives, One Hundred Tenth Congress, Second Session, September 16, 2008. 2009. iii, 42p. (978-0-16-083172-0(5), 552-070-39019-7) United States Government Printing Office.

Bartell, Laura B. Visualizing Bankruptcy. 2011. **(978-1-4224-8229-2(4))** LexisNexis Matthew Bender.

Beale, Simon Russe. Insolvency & Restructuring Manual. 2009. (ENG.). 266p. pap. 168.00 (978-1-84766-148-7(3), Bloomsbury Professional) Bloomsbury Publishing Plc GBR. Dist: International Specialized Bk. Services.

Becker, Eugene S., et al. Commercial Fraud Manual. Lebowitz, David P. & Harwood, Bruce A., eds. 2010. pap. 55.00 (978-0-9824026-4-1(3)) American Bankruptcy Institute.

Berman, Geoffrey L. General Assignments for the Benefit of Creditors: The ABCs of ABCs. 2nd rev. ed. 2006. 118p. per. 25.00 (978-0-9785292-7-7(8)) American Bankruptcy Institute.

Bernstein, Stanley B., et al. Business Bankruptcy Essentials. 12th ed. 2010. (ENG.). 256p. pap. 89.95 (978-1-59031-812-6(9)) American Bar Assn.

Besser, Andrew. Real Property Receivership. 2nd ed. 2011. 200p. pap. 110.00 (978-1-84766-343-6(5), Bloomsbury Professional) Bloomsbury Publishing Plc GBR. Dist: International Specialized Bk. Services.

Best Practices for Filing Chapter 13, 2010 Ed: Leading Lawyers on Navigating the Current Bankruptcy Environment, Communicating with Clients, & Anticipating Future Trends (Inside the Minds) 2009. 152p. pap. 75.00 (978-0-314-22872-7(1)) Aspatore Bks.

Beyer, William G., et al. ABI's Pension Manual: A Practical Guide to Pension Issues Arising in Business Bankruptcy Cases. 2007. 354p. per. 25.00 (978-0-9785292-8-4(6)) American Bankruptcy Institute.

Bierman, Masten. Guerilla GT Bankruptcy. Date not set. pap. (978-0-312-20411-2(6), St. Martin's Griffin) St. Martin's Pr.

Blum, Brian A. Bankruptcy & Debtor/Creditor. 5th ed. 2010. pap., stu. ed. 45.95 (978-0-7355-8851-6(1)) Wolters Kluwer Law & Business.

Bowen, Anne-Marie L. Bankruptcy... Because Life Happens: Conquering Debt after the Bankruptcy Law Changed. Schmadebeck, Ross E., ed. 2008. 108p. pap. 18.95 (978-0-9793732-0-6(4)) Afresh Publishing LLC.

Branch, Ben & Ray, Hugh. Bankruptcy Investing - How to Profit from Distressed Companies. 2007. 328p. per. 44.95 (978-1-58798-291-0(9)) Beard Bks., Inc.

Brodie, Sean & Stephens, Jack. Diary of a Bankruptcy Bailout: The Recovery Obama Didn't Give You. 2010. 123p. pap. 12.95 (978-1-4327-4640-7(5)) Outskirts Pr., Inc.

Brubaker, Ralph, et al, eds. A Debtor World: Interdisciplinary Perspectives on Debt. 2012. 320p. 85.00 **(978-0-19-987372-2(0))** Oxford Univ. Pr., Inc.

Buchbinder. Basic Bankruptcy Law for Paralegals (Abridged) 2e. 2nd ed. 2011. pap. (978-0-7355-9879-9(7), Aspen Pubs.) Wolters Kluwer Law & Business.

Buchbinder, David L. Basic Bankruptcy Law for Paralegals. 8th ed. 2011. (Illus.). xxv, 569p. **(978-0-7355-0786-9(4)); (978-0-7355-0787-6(2))** Kluwer Law International.

Buchbinder, David L. Pearson: Basic Bankruptcy Law for Paralegals 6e. 2007. (C). pap. (978-0-7355-6794-8(8), Aspen Pubs.) Wolters Kluwer Law & Business.

Buchbinder, David L. & Cooper, Robert J. Basic Bankruptcy Law for Paralegals. 2nd ed. 2011. (Illus.). xxii, 363p. pap. **(978-0-7355-9880-5(0))** Kluwer Law International.

—Basic Bankruptcy Law for Paralegals. 2009. (Illus.). xxi, 361p. pap. (978-0-7355-7240-9(2), Aspen Pubs.) Wolters Kluwer Law & Business.

Buchegger, Walter, ed. Osterreichisches Insolvenzrecht: Kommentar. Auf der Grundlage der 3. Auflage des von Robert Bartsch und Rudolf Pollak begrundeten Werks. Band IV: $$ 96 bis 139 KO. 4th ed. 2006. (GER.). LXV, 739p. 209.00 (978-3-211-83892-1(9), 3211838929) Springer.

—Osterreichisches Insolvenzrecht: Kommentar. Band II: A?A? 44 Bis 62 Konkursordnung. 4th ed. 2007. 149.00 (978-3-211-83893-8(7), 3211838937) Springer.

Buchegger, Walter & Hanisch, Peter, eds. Österreichisches Insolvenzrecht: Kommentar. Zusatzband 1. 2007. 169.00 (978-3-211-83617-0(9), 3211836179) Springer.

Bufford, Samuel L. United States International Insolvency Law 2008-2009. 2009. (ENG.). 400p. 275.00 (978-0-19-534078-5(7)) Oxford Univ. Pr., Inc.

Burke, James & Comyn, Amanda-Jayne. Personal Insolvency Law. 2012. 350p. pap. 225.00 (978-1-84766-486-0(5), Bloomsbury Professional) Bloomsbury Publishing Plc GBR. Dist: International Specialized Bk. Services.

Burkhard, Ralf. Der Einfluss der Schuldrechtsreform auf von § 103 InsO erfasste Kaufverträge. 2010. (Schriften zum Verfahrensrecht Ser.). (GER.). 256p. pap. 65.95 (978-3-631-56942-9(4)) Lang, Peter GmbH, Europäischer Verlag der Wissenschaften DEU. Dist: Lang, Peter.

Bussel, Daniel & Bussel, Daniel. Bankruptcy, 7th Edition, 2007 Supplement. 7th rev. ed. 2007. (University Casebook Ser.). 151p. pap. 19.00 (978-1-59941-407-2(4), Foundation Pr.) West.

Butterworth Staff, compiled by. Butterworths Legislation Service: Insolvency Act 24 of 1936. Date not set. (978-0-409-01417-4(6), MICHIE) LEXIS Publishing.

Butterworths Redaksie Staff. Butterworths Wetgewingsdiens: Insolvensiewet: 24 van 1936. Scott, G.H., ed. Date not set. (AFR.). (978-0-409-01512-6(1), MICHIE) LEXIS Publishing.

Calnan, Richard. Proprietary Rights & Insolvency. 2010. (ENG., Illus.). 500p. 354.75 (978-0-19-922858-4(2)) Oxford Univ. Pr., Inc.

Carlson, David Gray. Consumer Bankruptcy. 2011. 642p. 84.95 **(978-1-60042-147-1(4))** 2009. 570p. 79.95 (978-1-60042-094-8(X)) Vandeplas Publishing.

Carr, Tracy. How to Survive & Prosper after a Financial Misfortune: A Complete Guide to Your Legal Rights after Bankruptcy, Foreclosure, Repossession, & Eviction. 2011. (ENG.). 336p. pap. 24.95 (978-1-60138-298-6(7)) Atlantic Publishing Co.

Carroll, Stephen J. & Clancy, Noreen. The Bankruptcy Abuse Prevention & Consumer Protection Act Of 2005: Evaluation of the Effects of Using IRS Expense Standards to Calculate a Debtor's. 2007. 66p. pap. 23.00 (978-0-8330-4183-6(5), TR-483) RAND Corp., The.

—The Effects of the Changes in Chapter 7 Debtors' Lien-Avoidance Rights under the Bankruptcy Abuse Prevention & Consumer Protection Act Of 2005. 2007. 44p. pap. 20.00 (978-0-8330-4207-1(6), TR484) RAND Corp., The.

Casenotes Publishing Co., Inc. Staff. Bankruptcy: Warren & Bussel. 8th ed. 2010. pap., stu. ed. 36.95 (978-0-7355-8941-4(0)) Wolters Kluwer Law & Business.

Chapman, Peter. The Last of the Imperious Rich: Lehman Brothers, 1844-2008. 2010. (ENG.). 320p. (gr. 12). 27.95 (978-1-59184-309-2(X), Portfolio (Hardcover)) Penguin Group (USA) Inc.

Chapter 7 Commercial Bankruptcy Strategies: Leading Lawyers on Counseling Clients, Filing a Proof of Claim, & Understanding the Benefits & Challenges of Bankruptcy (Inside the Minds) 2009. (Inside the Minds Ser.). 168p. pap. (978-0-314-19945-4(4)) Aspatore Bks.

Chapter 7 Consumer Bankruptcy Strategies, 2010 Ed: Leading Lawyers on Preparing a Chapter 7 Filing, Establishing Effective Client Strategies, & Understanding Recent Trends (Inside the Minds) 2010. (ENG.). 256p. pap. 85.00 (978-0-314-26650-7(X)) Aspatore Bks.

Chomsky, Carol L. & Kunz, Christina L. Selected Commercial Statutes for Secured Transactions Courses 2011. 2011. 1344p. pap. 46.00 **(978-0-314-27507-3(X))** West Publishing Co., College & Schl. Div.

Chomsky, Carol L., et al. Selected Commercial Statutes for Secured Transactions Courses. 2007th rev. ed. 2007. (Academic Statutes Ser.). 1561p. per. 39.00 (978-0-314-18075-9(3)) West.

Circuit City Unplugged: Why Did Chapter 11 Fail to Save 34,000 Jobs?: Hearing Before the Subcommittee on Commercial & Administrative Law of the Committee on the Judiciary, House of Representatives, One Hundred Eleventh Congress, First Session, March 11 2009. 2009. iv, 187p. (978-0-16-083529-2(1), 552-070-39252-1) United States Government Printing Office.

Clancy, Noreen & Carroll, Stephen J. Identifying Fraud, Abuse, & Error in Personal Bankruptcy Filings. 2007. 67p. pap. 23.00 (978-0-8330-4170-6(3), mg586) RAND Corp., The.

—Prebankruptcy Credit Counseling. 2007. 36p. per. 20.00 (978-0-8330-4205-7(X), tr-509) RAND Corp., The.

Clark, Ken, CFP. Getting Out of Debt - The Complete Idiot's Guide. 2009. (Complete Idiot's Guide Ser.). (ENG.). 352p. (gr. 12-18). 16.95 (978-1-59257-847-4(0), Alpha Bks.) Penguin Group (USA) Inc.

Clark, Leif M. & Glosband, Daniel M. Ancillary & Other Cross-Border Insolvency Cases under Chapter 15 of the Bankruptcy Code. 2008. pap. (978-1-4224-2421-6(9)) LexisNexis Matthew Bender.

Collier Bankruptcy Case Update. 320.00 (978-0-8205-3500-5(1)) LexisNexis Matthew Bender.

Consumer Debt: Are Credit Cards Bankrupting Americans?: Hearing Before the Subcommittee on Commercial & Administrative Law of the Committee on the Judiciary, House of Representatives, One Hundred Eleventh Congress, First Session, April 2, 2009. 2009. (Illus.). iii, 91p. (978-0-16-083546-9(1), 552-070-39269-6) United States Government Printing Office.

Consumer Protection & the Credit Crisis: Hearing Before the Committee on Commerce, Science, & Transportation, United States Senate, One Hundred Eleventh Congress, First Session, February 26, 2009. 2009. (Illus.). iii, 84p. (978-0-16-083564-3(X), 552-070-39282-3) United States Government Printing Office.

Continuing Education of the Bar. Personal & Small Business Bankruptcy Practice in California: September 2007 Update. 2007. 1750p. ring bd. 154.00 (978-0-7626-1319-9(X)) Continuing Education of the Bar-California.

Cook. Bankruptcy Litigation Manual 2010-2011e. 2010. ring bd. (978-0-7355-9382-4(5), Aspen Pubs.) Wolters Kluwer Law & Business.

Cook, Michael L. Bankruptcy Litigation Manual 2009-2010. 2009. ring bd. 379.00 (978-0-7355-8242-2(4)) Wolters Kluwer Law & Business.

Cook, Michael L., ed. Bankruptcy Litigation Manual. annuals 1065p. ring bd. 165.00 (978-1-56706-733-0(6), 63350, Aspen Pubs.) Wolters Kluwer Law & Business.

Cooper, Philip. No Access to Justice. 2009. (ENG., Illus.). 80p. pap. 10.00 (978-1-4349-0325-9(7)) Dorrance Publishing Co., Inc.

Corbett QC, James & Prudhoe, Tim. Insolvency & the Law of Offshore Trusts. 2012. (ENG.). 280p. 270.00 (978-0-19-957627-2(0)) Oxford Univ. Pr., Inc.

Cornell, John R. Employee Benefits & Executive Compensation in Corporate Bankruptcy. 2nd ed. 2010. pap. (978-1-4224-8043-4(7)) LexisNexis Matthew Bender.

—Employee Benefits & Executive Compensation in Corporate Bankruptcy: A Collier Monograph. 2008. pap. (978-1-4224-2420-9(0)) LexisNexis Matthew Bender.

Could Bankruptcy Reform Help Preserve Small Business Jobs? Hearing Before the Subcommittee on Administrative Oversight & the Courts of the Committee on the Judiciary, United States Senate, One Hundred Eleventh Congress, Second Session, March 17, 2010. 2010. (Illus.). iii, 147p. **(978-0-16-087420-8(3)**, 552-070-42113-1) United States Government Printing Office.

Craig, Les. The Kingdom of Honey Hill Pond. 2011. 62p. pap. **(978-1-908447-52-4(4))** Grosvenor Hse. Publishing Ltd.

Cram101 Textbook Reviews. Outlines & Highlights for Business Valuation & Bankruptcy by Ian Ratner. 2011. 120p. pap. 28.95 **(978-1-61905-185-0(0))** Cram101 Inc.

Cram101 Textbook Reviews Staff. Outlines & Highlights for Secured Credit: A Systems Approach, Sixth Edition by Lynn M. Lopucki, Elizabeth Warren, ISBN. 2009. 56p. pap. 26.95 (978-1-4288-7903-4(X)) Cram101 Inc.

Czaja, Lothar. Umsetzung der Kooperationsvorgaben durch die Europäische Insolvenzverordnung im deutschen Insolvenzverfahren. 2009. (Schriften zum Verfahrensrecht Ser.). (GER.). 306p. 83.95 (978-3-631-59511-4(5)) Lang, Peter GmbH, Europäischer Verlag der Wissenschaften DEU. Dist: Lang, Peter.

Dahl, Michael, et al, eds. European Insolvency Law: A Commentary. 2012. 500p. 400.00 (978-1-84113-219-8(5)) Hart Publishing Ltd. GBR. Dist: International Specialized Bk. Services.

Daniels, Philippa, et al. Personal Insolvency: A User's Guide. 2012. (ENG.). 800p. pap. 200.00 incl. cd-rom (978-1-84661-135-3(0)) Jordan Publishing, Ltd. GBR. Dist: International Specialized Bk. Services.

Dasoff, Glenn D. & Felton, Jim. Bankruptcy Litigation Trends in California: Understanding Changes to Bankruptcy Filings & Cases in the Economic Downturn. 2010. 20p. pap. (978-0-314-26710-8(7)) Aspatore Bks.

Davis, Anthony. Taxation in Corporate Insolvency & Rescue. 6th rev. ed. 2009. (ENG.). 374p. pap. 290.00 (978-1-84592-193-4(3), Bloomsbury Professional) Bloomsbury Publishing Plc GBR. Dist: International Specialized Bk. Services.

Debtor-in-Possession & Exit Financing: Leading Lawyers on Securing Funding & Analyzing Recent Trends in Bankruptcy Financing (Inside the Minds) 2010. 252p. pap. 100.00 (978-0-314-26362-9(4)) Aspatore Bks.

DeGiacomo, Mark G. A Practical Guide to Consumer Bankruptcy. 2010. pap. 125.00 (978-1-57589-591-8(9)) 2007. pap. 125.00 (978-1-57589-471-3(8)) Massachusetts Continuing Legal Education, Inc.

Donoher, William J. Corporate Bankruptcy: Fundamental Principles & Processes. 2011. 125p. pap. 29.95 **(978-1-60649-143-0(1))** Business Expert Pr.

Doyle, Louis, et al. Insolvency Legislation: Annotations & Commentary 2009. 3rd rev. ed. 2009. (ENG.). 1862p. pap. (978-1-84661-156-8(3)) Jordan Publishing, Ltd.

DUKE, S. P., SRP. ALL about BANKRUPTCY & YOU. 2008. 126p. pap. 20.50 (978-1-4357-0778-8(8)) Lulu Enterprises Inc.

Duke, S. R., SRP & Gardner, Mayo. Bankruptcy Is the Answer. 2010. 128p. pap. 22.95 (978-0-557-53502-6(6)) Lulu Enterprises Inc.

Dunscomb, S. Whitney, Jr. Bankruptcy: A Study in Comparative Legislation. (Columbia University, Studies in the Social Sciences: No. 6). reprint ed. 29.50 (978-0-404-51006-0(X)) AMS Pr., Inc.

Ehricke, Ulrich. Insolvenzrecht. 2008. (Springer-Lehrbuch Ser.). 350p. pap. 21.92 (978-3-540-42502-1(0), 3540425020) Springer.

Eisenberg, Theodore. Bankruptcy & Debtor Creditor Law, Cases & Materials, 4th. 4th rev. ed. 2010. (University Casebook Ser.). 833p. 177.00 (978-1-59941-436-2(8), Foundation Pr.) West.

Elias, Stephen. The New Bankruptcy: Will It Work for You? 4th rev. ed. 2011. (ENG.). 416p. pap. 24.99 (978-1-4133-1391-8(4)) NOLO.

Elias, Stephen & Laurence, Bethany. Bankruptcy for Small Business Owners: How to File for Chapter 7. 2010. (ENG.). 593p. pap. 39.99 (978-1-4133-1080-1(X)) NOLO.

Elias, Stephen & Leonard, Robin. Chapter 13 Bankruptcy: Keep Your Property & Repay Debts over Time. 10th rev. ed. 2010. (ENG.). 486p. pap. 39.99 (978-1-4133-1069-6(9)) NOLO.

Elias, Stephen, et al. Chapter 13 Bankruptcy: Keep Your Property & Repay Debts over Time. 11th rev. ed. 2012. (ENG.). 486p. pap. 39.99 **(978-1-4133-1712-1(X))** NOLO.

Elias, Stephen, et al. How to File for Chapter 7 Bankruptcy. 17th rev. ed. 2011. (ENG.). 458p. pap. 39.99 (978-1-4133-1633-9(6)) NOLO.

Enyi, Enyi. Detecting, Predicting & Preventing Corporate Failure. 2010. 140p. pap. (978-3-8383-4863-6(X)) Lambert Academic Publishing.

Epstein, David G. Epstein's A Student's Guide to Article 9 of the Uniform Commercial Code. 2008. 493p. pap. 37.00 (978-0-314-15082-0(X), West Legalworks) West.

Epstein, David G. Students' Guide to Article 9 & Related Statutes. 3rd rev. ed. 2011. 608p. pap. 42.00 **(978-0-314-27670-4(X))** West Publishing Co., College & Schl. Div.

Epstein, David G. & Nickles, Steve H. Bankruptcy: Materials & Cases, 3d. 3rd rev. ed. 2010. (American Casebook Ser.). 513p. 163.00 (978-0-314-91155-1(3), West Legalworks) West.

—Bankruptcy Code & Related Source Materials, 2010-2011. 2010. 442p. 41.00 (978-0-314-26305-6(5), West Legalworks) West.

—Bankruptcy Code & Related Source Materials, 2011-2012. 2011. 450p. pap. 31.00 **(978-0-314-27511-0(8))** West.

Epstein, David G. & Nickles, Steve H. Bankruptcy Code & Related Source Materials for Law Students, 2007-2008 Edition. 2007. 398p. pap. 33.00 (978-0-314-18032-2(X)) West.

Epstein, Lita. Personal Bankruptcy - The Complete Idiot's Guide. 2010. (Complete Idiot's Guide Ser.). (ENG.). 320p. (gr. 12-18). 16.95 (978-1-59257-947-1(7), Alpha Bks.) Penguin Group (USA) Inc.

Executive Compensation in Chapter 11 Bankruptcy Cases: How Much Is Too Much?: Hearing Before the Subcommittee on Commercial & Administrative Law of the Committee on the Judiciary, House of Representatives, One Hundred Tenth Congress, First Session, April 17, 2007. 2007. iv, 49p. (978-0-16-078959-5(1), 552-070-36077-8) United States Government Printing Office.

Ezon. E-Z Rules for the Bankruptcy Code. 2009. (Illus.). xi, 383p. pap., stu. ed. 31.95 (978-0-7355-7197-6(X)) Wolters Kluwer Law & Business.

Faber, Dennis, et al. Commencement of Insolvency Proceedings. Richter, Tomás, ed. 2012. (ENG.). 856p. 350.00 **(978-0-19-964422-3(5))** Oxford Univ. Pr., Inc.

Federal Courts - U. S. Districts & Bankruptcy Handbook: Companies-Products-Services. 675p. (Orig.). pap. 145.00 (978-0-7605-1855-7(6)) Rector Pr., Ltd.

Feeney, J. N. The Road Out of Debt: Bankruptcy & Other Solutions to Your Financial Problems. 2010. (ENG., Illus.). 385p. 29.95 (978-0-470-49866-6(2), Wiley) Wiley, John & Sons, Inc.

Ferriell, Jeffrey Thomas & Janger, Edward J. Understanding Bankruptcy. 2nd ed. 2007. 37.00 (978-1-4224-1182-7(6)) LexisNexis Matthew Bender.

Finch, Vanessa. Corporate Insolvency Law: Perspectives & Principles. 2nd ed. 2009. (ENG.). 918p. 205.00 (978-0-521-87810-4(1)); pap. 84.00 (978-0-521-70182-2(1)) Cambridge Univ. Pr.

Finn, Paul. Insolvency in Business. (ENG., Illus.). 1p. (978-0-304-31797-4(7), Burns & Oates) Continuum International Publishing Group, Ltd.

Flaaten, Gerhard. Lehman Brothers. 2010. 96p. pap. (978-3-639-25065-7(6)) VDM Verlag Dr. Mueller e.K.

Fletcher, Ian F. Insolvency in Private International Law. 2nd ed. 2007. (Oxford Private International Law Ser.). (ENG., Illus.). 160p. pap., suppl. ed. 75.00 (978-0-19-928873-1(9)) Oxford Univ. Pr., Inc.

Florida Bar, Continuing Legal Education Staff, contrib. by. Chapter 7 Bankruptcy: Straight Liquidation for the Debtor. 6th ed. 2008. (Illus.). pap. (978-1-4224-5095-6(3)) Florida Bar Continuing Legal Education Pubns., The.

B

Fourier, Charles. The Hierarchies of Cuckoldry & Bankruptcy. Longnecker, Geoffrey, tr. 2011. (ENG., Illus.). 94p. pap. 12.95 ***(978-0-9841155-5-6(2))*** Wakefield Pr.

Frey, Martin A. & Swinson, Sidney K. Introduction to Bankruptcy Law. 6th ed. 2012. (ENG.). 672p. (C). pap. 187.95 ***(978-1-4354-4080-7(3))*** Delmar Cengage Learning.

Friedland, Jonathan P., et al. Chapter 11 - 101: The Nuts & Bolts of Chapter 11 Practice. 2007. cd-rom 18.00 *(978-0-9792742-2-0(2))* American Bankruptcy Institute.

Frost, Christopher W., et al. Corporate Governance in Insolvency & Bankruptcy: A Collier Monograph. 2011. pap. ***(978-1-4224-8922-2(1))*** LexisNexis Matthew Bender.

GARDNER, Mayo. A Personal Guide to: Chapter 7 or 13 BANKRUPTCY. 2010. 95p. pap. 16.95 *(978-0-557-52675-8(2))* Lulu Enterprises Inc.

Garrido, José María. Out-Of-Court Debt Restructuring. 2011. ***(978-0-8213-8956-0(4))*** World Bank Pubns.

Gensor, Joe. Chapter 11 Analysis & Financial Restructuring: the Case of Pierre Foods & Oaktree Capital. 2009. 296p. pap. 49.98 *(978-0-578-03613-7(4))* Gensor, Joe.

Getzler, Joshua & Payne, Jennifer, eds. Company Charges: Spectrum & Beyond. 2006. (ENG.). 336p. 280.50 *(978-0-19-929993-5(5))* Oxford Univ. Pr., Inc.

Ginsberg, Robert E. & Kelley, Susan V. Ginsberg & Martin on Bankruptcy, 3 vols. 5th ed. 2008. ring bd. 675.00 *(978-0-7355-7552-3(5))* Wolters Kluwer Law & Business.

Gmb Publishing, creator. Insolvency Law in South East Europe. 2008. (ENG.). 48p. pap. 180.00 *(978-1-84673-143-3(7)*, GMB Publishing Ltd.) Blue Ibex Ltd. GBR. Dist: Ingram Pub. Services.

Gold, Charles H. Hatching Ruin , or Mark Twain's Road to Bankruptcy. 2011. (MARK TWAIN & HIS CIRCLE Ser.). (ENG., Illus.). 184p. (C). (gr. 13). pap. 25.00 *(978-0-8262-1959-6(4))* Univ. of Missouri Pr.

Golio, D. J. Bankrupting Joe the Taxpayer: With No One to Bail Him Out. 2009. 200p. 26.95 *(978-1-4389-7855-0(3))*; pap. 19.85 *(978-1-4389-7854-3(5))* AuthorHouse.

Gregg, John T. & Mears, Patrick E. Auto Supplier Insolvencies & Bankruptcies: Issues for Suppliers & Customers of Financially Troubled Auto Suppliers. 2006. 270p. per. 25.00 *(978-0-9785292-4-6(3))* American Bankruptcy Institute.

Hall, William & Lee, Moses. Chrysler: From Bankruptcy to Rebirth. 2010. (C). pap. 20.00 *(978-1-61674-422-9(7))* Davidson, William Institute At The Univ. of Michigan, The.

Halliday, Terence, et al. Bankrupt: Global Lawmaking & Systemic Financial Crisis. 2009. (ENG., Illus.). 536p. 90.00 *(978-0-8047-6074-4(8))*; pap. 29.95 *(978-0-8047-6075-1(6))* Stanford Univ. Pr.

Haman, Edward A. The Complete Chapter 13 Personal Bankruptcy Guide. 2007. (ENG., Illus.). 272p. per. 18.95 *(978-1-57248-595-2(7)*, Sphinx Publishing) Sourcebooks, Inc.

—Complete Chapter 7 Personal Bankruptcy Guide. 2007. (ENG., Illus.). 272p. per. 18.95 *(978-1-57248-594-5(9)*, Sphinx Publishing) Sourcebooks, Inc.

Harrell, Alvin C. & Miller, Fred H. The ABCs of the UCC: Related Insolvency Law. 2nd ed. 2007. (ABCs of the Ucc Ser.). (ENG.). 209p. per. 39.95 *(978-1-59031-682-5(7))* American Bar Assn.

Harris, Peggy. Growing up in the Great Depression. 2010. 220p. pap. 19.99 *(978-0-557-49121-6(5))* Lulu Enterprises Inc.

Helping Families Save Their Homes in Bankruptcy ACT of 2009 & the Emergency Homeownership & Equity Protection ACT: Hearing Before the Committee on the Judiciary, House of Representatives, One Hundred Eleventh Congress, First Session, on H.R. 200 & H.R. 225, January 22, 2009. 2009. (Illus.). iv, 170p. *(978-0-16-083581-0(X)*, 552-070-39299-8) United States Government Printing Office.

Henderson, Gordon D. & Goldring, Stuart J. Tax Planning for Troubled Corporations (2012) 2011. 1090p. pap. 397.50 ***(978-0-8080-2787-4(5)***, CCH) Wolters Kluwer Tax & Accounting.

Henry, Sally M. The New Bankruptcy Code: Cases, Developments, & Practice Insights since BAPCPA. 2nd ed. 2007. (ENG., Illus.). 672p. per. 75.95 *(978-1-59031-870-6(6))* American Bar Assn.

Henry, Sally M. Ordin on Contesting Confirmation. 4th ed. 2011. ***(978-1-4548-0118-4(2)***, Aspen Pubs.) Wolters Kluwer Law & Business.

Hillman, William C. & Crouch, Margaret M. Bankruptcy Deskbook. 4th rev. ed. 2006. (ENG., Illus.). 1703p. ring bd. 325.00 *(978-1-4024-0772-7(6))* Practising Law Institute.

—Personal Bankruptcy Answer Book. 2010. (ENG.). 410p. pap. 145.00 *(978-1-4024-1393-3(9)*, 26277) Practising Law Institute.

Hinger, Cathérine. Die Bauunternehmerinsolvenz: Die Sicherungs- und Vertragslösungsrechte zum Schutz der Vermögensinteressen des privaten Auftraggebers im Kontext von § 103 InsO. 2010. (Studien zum deutschen und europäischen Gesellschafts- und Wirtschaftsrecht Ser.). (GER.). 278p. 79.95 *(978-3-631-59868-9(8))* Lang, Peter GmbH, Europaischer Verlag der Wissenschaften DEU. Dist: Lang, Peter.

Hoffman, Andrew, et al. Molten Metal Technology. 2010. (C). pap. 7.00 *(978-1-61674-517-2(7))*; pap. 20.00 *(978-1-61674-515-8(0))* Davidson, William Institute At The Univ. of Michigan, The.

House (U.S.), Committee on the Judiciary, ed. Federal Rules of Bankruptcy Procedure, December 1 2010. 2011. (ENG.). 127p. pap. 13.00 ***(978-0-16-088523-5(X)***, Committee on the Judiciary) United States Government Printing Office.

—Federal Rules of Bankruptcy Procedure, December 1 2011. 2012. (ENG.). 126p. pap. 14.00 ***(978-0-16-090050-1(6)***, Committee on the Judiciary) United States Government Printing Office.

House (U.S.), Committee on the Judiciary Staff, ed. Federal Rules of Bankruptcy Procedure (December 2009) 2010. (ENG.). 127p. pap. 13.00 *(978-0-16-086218-2(3)*, Committee on the Judiciary) United States Government Printing Office.

House (U.S.), Office of the Law Revision Counsel Staff, compiled by. United States Code, 2006, V. 6, Title 11, Bankruptcy to Title 12, Banks & Banking, Sections 1-1750jj. 2008. (ENG.). 1000p. 100.00 *(978-0-16-080001-6(3)*, Office of the Law Revision Counsel) United States Government Printing Office.

Hovatter, Debra Lee. Bankruptcy Fundamentals for the Financial Services Industry: A Handbook for Non-Lawyers. Cauthen, George B. et al, eds. 2007. 176p. per. 25.00 *(978-0-9792742-6-8(5))* American Bankruptcy Institute.

Howard, Margaret. Cases & Materials on Bankruptcy, 5th. 5th rev. ed. 2011. (American Casebook Ser.). 173.00 ***(978-0-314-27767-1(6)***, West Legalworks) West.

Hunter, Muir. Going Bust? How to Resist & Survive Bankruptcy & Winding Up. 2007. 223p. pap. *(978-1-85811-368-5(7))* EMIS Professional Publishing.

Hurd, Heidi M. & Brubaker, Ralph. Debts & the Demands of Conscience: The Virtue of Bankruptcy. 2012. (ENG.). 250p. 70.00 ***(978-0-19-964296-0(6))*** Oxford Univ. Pr., Inc.

The Impact of the Subprime Mortgage Crisis: Leading Lawyers on Understanding the Factors Responsible, Minimizing the Financial Impact for Clients, & Recognizing the Effects of the Recession on Bankruptcy Law (Inside the Minds) 2009. 116p. pap. 90.00 *(978-0-314-90645-8(2))* Aspatore Bks.

Jaecks, Jörg. Konzernverrechnungsklauseln und Verwandte Einseitige Verrechnungsbefugnisse Im Mehrpersonenverhältnis. 2011. (Veröffentlichungen des Instituts für deutsches und europäisches Wirtschafts-, Wettbewerbs- und Regulierungsrecht der Freien Universität Berlin Ser.). (GER.). 396p. 98.95 *(978-3-631-61093-0(9))* Lang, Peter GmbH, Europaischer Verlag der Wissenschaften DEU. Dist: Lang, Peter.

Jasper, Margaret C. Dealing with Debt. 2006. (Legal Almanac Ser.). (ENG., Illus.). 240p. 47.00 *(978-0-19-532363-4(7))* Oxford Univ. Pr., Inc.

—Individual Bankruptcy & Restructuring. 2nd ed. 2006. (Legal Almanac Ser.). (ENG., Illus.). 230p. 47.00 *(978-0-19-532156-2(1))* Oxford Univ. Pr., Inc.

Johnston, William & Werlen, Thomas. Set-off Law & Practice: An International Handbook. 2nd ed. 2010. (ENG.). 660p. 445.50 *(978-0-19-957971-6(7))* Oxford Univ. Pr., Inc.

Jones, Grant & Knight, Andrew. Asset-Based Lending & Insolvency. 2012. 420p. pap. 145.00 *(978-1-904905-62-2(5))* Spiramus Pr. GBR. Dist: International Specialized Bk. Services.

Jones, Stewart & Hensher, David A., eds. Advances in Credit Risk Modelling & Corporate Bankruptcy Prediction. (Quantitative Methods for Applied Economics & Business Research Ser.). (ENG., Illus.). 312p. 2008. 108.00 *(978-0-521-86928-7(5))* 2006. pap. 50.99 *(978-0-521-68954-0(6))* Cambridge Univ. Pr.

Keay, Andrew R. Avoidance Provisions in Insolvency Law. 390p. *(978-0-455-21499-3(9))* LBC Information Services.

Keen, Samantha, et al. Solvent Liquidations. 2013. (ENG.). 500p. pap. 190.00 *(978-1-84661-092-9(3))* Jordan Publishing, Ltd. GBR. Dist: International Specialized Bk. Services.

Keijser, Thomas Rudolf Maria Pius. Financial Collateral Arrangements. 2006. (Law of Business & Finance Set Ser.). (Illus.). 430p. *(978-90-411-2556-9(6))* Kluwer Law International.

Kenadjian, Patrick S., ed. Too Big To Fail - Brauchen wir ein Sonderinsolvenzrecht für Banken? 2011. (Institute for Law & Finance Ser.).Tr. of Too Big to Fail ndash; Do we need a Special Insolvency Law for Banks? (GER., Illus.). XIV, 236p. E-Book 154.00 ***(978-3-11-027252-9(0))*** De Gruyter, Walter Inc.

Kilborn, Jason. Comparative Consumer Bankruptcy. 2007. 128p. pap. 20.00 *(978-1-59460-147-7(X))* Carolina Academic Pr.

Kimberlin-Murphy, Barbara Gail. Secrets Revealed by a Medical Collector, the Patient's Guide to Avoiding Bankruptcy. 2008. 108p. 28.99 *(978-1-4389-2465-6(8))*; pap. 18.99 *(978-1-4389-2464-9(X))* AuthorHouse.

Klee, Kenneth N. Bankruptcy & the Supreme Court. 2009. *(978-1-4224-2751-4(X))* LexisNexis Matthew Bender.

Klinck, Fabian. Die Grundlagen der besonderen Insolvenzanfechtung: Gläubiger und Vertrauensschutz im Übergang vom Prioritäts- zum Gleichbehandlungsgrundsatz. 2010. (GER.). 544p. 168.00 *(978-3-89949-803-5(8))* De Gruyter Rechtswissenschaften Verlags GmbH DEU. Dist: de Gruyter, Walter GmbH & Co. KG.

Koehler, Christoph Thomas. Lastschriftverfahren in der Insolvenz des Schuldners: Im Lichte der neuen BGH-Rechtsprechung. 2010. (Saarbrücker Studien zum Privat- und Wirtschaftsrecht Ser.). (GER.). 266p. 75.95 *(978-3-631-60161-7(1))* Lang, Peter GmbH, Europaischer Verlag der Wissenschaften DEU. Dist: Lang, Peter.

Krumm, Marcel. Steuervollzug und formelle Insolvenz. 2009. (Bochumer Schriften zum Steuerrecht Ser.). (GER.). 288p. 79.95 *(978-3-631-59169-7(1))* Lang, Peter GmbH, Europaischer Verlag der Wissenschaften DEU. Dist: Lang, Peter.

Kuney, George. Mastering Bankruptcy. 2008. per. 26.00 *(978-1-59460-393-8(6))* Carolina Academic Pr.

Lawall, Francis J. Debt Adjustments for Municipalities under Chapter 9 of the Bankruptcy Code. 2012. pap. ***(978-0-7698-4842-6(7))*** LexisNexis Matthew Bender.

Legal Intelligencer Staff. Bankruptcy Court Rules. 2011. (Illus.). 400p. pap. 99.00 *(978-1-57786-376-2(3))* Incisive Media.

Lehman Brothers, Sharper Image, Bennigan's & Beyond: Is Chapter 11 Bankruptcy Working?: Hearing Before the Subcommittee on Commercial & Administrative Law of the Committee on the Judiciary, House of Representatives, One Hundred Tenth Congress, Second Session, September 26, 2008. 2009. (Illus.). iii, 74p. *(978-0-16-083314-4(0)*, 552-070-39139-8) United States Government Printing Office.

Leibowitz, David. Filing for Chapter 13 Bankruptcy: What You Need to Know (Quick Prep) 2010. 176p. pap. 30.00 *(978-0-314-27208-9(9))* Aspatore Bks.

Levaggi, Peter, et al. Property Insolvency. 2009. (ENG., Illus.). 402p. incl. cd-rom *(978-1-84661-151-3(2))* Jordan Publishing, Ltd.

Levin, Richard B. Fundamentals of Bankruptcy Law. 6th ed. 2006. 566p. *(978-0-8318-0869-3(1)*, BK46) American Law Institute.

—Fundamentals of Bankruptcy Law, Seventh Edition. 2010. 452p. pap. *(978-0-8318-9977-6(8))* American Law Institute.

Loefton, Erolye P., ed. Emerging Business Issues. 2008. (Illus.). 244p. (C). 98.00 *(978-1-60456-511-9(X))* Nova Science Pubs., Inc.

LoPucki, Lynn M. & Doherty, Joseph W. Professional Fees in Corporate Bankruptcies: Data, Analysis, & Evaluation, 1 vol. 2011. (ENG., Illus.). 342p. 85.00 *(978-0-19-533772-3(7))* Oxford Univ. Pr., Inc.

LoPucki, Lynn M. & Mirick, Christopher R. Strategies for Creditors in Bankruptcy Proceedings. 5th ed. 2006. 955p. 290.00 *(978-0-7355-6057-4(9)*, Aspen Pubs.) Wolters Kluwer Law & Business.

LoPucki, Lynn M. & Warren, Elizabeth. Secured Credit: A Systems Approach. 7th ed. 2012. xxxv, 719p. ***(978-1-4548-0401-7(7))*** 2011. ***(978-1-4548-0400-0(9))*** Kluwer Law International.

—Secured Credit: A Systems Approach. 6th ed. 2009. (Illus.). xxxv, 708p. pap. *(978-0-7355-7650-6(5)*, Aspen Pubs.) Wolters Kluwer Law & Business.

Loukeris, Nikos. Bankruptcy Prediction, Portfolio Selection & Artificial Intelligence. 2010. 100p. pap. *(978-3-8433-5403-5(0))* Lambert Academic Publishing.

Lubben, Stephen J. Measuring the Costs of Chapter 11 Cases: Professional Fees in American Corporate Bankruptcy Cases. 2010. 90p. pap. 71.00 *(978-90-8974-370-1(7))* Eleven International Publishing NLD. Dist: International Specialized Bk. Services.

Mack, Michael G. How to Instantly Elimate Credt Card Debt: Without Bankruptcy. 2006. 160p. pap. 24.95 *(978-0-9772909-0-1(5))* Microdebt.

Maeda, Martha. How to Legally Settle Your Personal Credit Card Debt for Pennies on the Dollar: Without Filing Bankruptcy. 2010. 288p. pap. 24.95 *(978-1-60138-328-0(2))* Atlantic Publishing Co.

Mandatory Mediation Programs: Can Bankruptcy Courts Help End the Foreclosure Crisis?: Hearing Before the Subcommittee on Administrative Oversight & the Courts of the Committee on the Judiciary, United States Senate, One Hundred Eleventh Congress, Second Session, October 28, 2010. 2011. (Illus.). iii, 120p. ***(978-0-16-088577-8(9)***, 552-070-42753-8) United States Government Printing Office.

Mann, Bruce H. Republic of Debtors: Bankruptcy in the Age of American Independence. 2009. (Illus.). 358p. pap. 20.00 *(978-0-674-03241-5(1))* Harvard Univ. Pr.

Margret, Julie E. Solvency in Financial Accounting. 2011. (Routledge Studies in Accounting Ser.). (ENG., Illus.). 278p. (C). 125.00 *(978-0-415-89582-8(0))* Routledge.

Marin, Matej & Vlahu, Razvan. The Economics of Bank Bankruptcy Law. 2011. (ENG., Illus.). xiii, 158p. 139.00 ***(978-3-642-21806-4(7)***, 3642218067) Springer.

Marry, Blegen. Financial Distress Costs & Bankruptcy. 2010. 140p. pap. *(978-3-8383-4012-8(4))* Lambert Academic Publishing.

Martin, Nathalie. The Glannon Guide to Bankruptcy: Learning Bankruptcy Through Multiple-Choice Questions & Analysis. 3rd ed. 2011. ***(978-0-7355-0728-9(7)***, Aspen Pubs.) Wolters Kluwer Law & Business.

Martin, Nathalie & Tama, Ocean. Inside Bankruptcy Law: What Matters & Why. 2nd ed. 2011. (Illus.). xxiii, 249p. *(978-0-7355-0753-1(8)*, Aspen Pubs.) Wolters Kluwer Law & Business.

Mason, Paul. Meltdown: The End of the Age of Greed. 2009. (ENG.). 198p. pap. 14.95 *(978-1-84467-396-4(0)*, 844396) Verso Bks. GBR. Dist: Norton, W. W. & Co., Inc.

Maxwell, Dennis D. The Great Eclipse: A Dream Design Bankrupted by Marketing & Mismanagement & Saved by a Sensible Business Strategy. 2011. 342p. pap. 24.95 ***(978-1-4575-0297-2(6))*** Dog Ear Publishing, LLC.

Mbanwie, Gilbert & EDMOND, Ngam. Explaining & Predicting Financial Distress Using Financial Ratios. 2011. 64p. pap. ***(978-3-8443-8385-0(9))*** Lambert Academic Publishing.

McCormack, Gerard. Corporate Rescue Law - an Anglo-American Perspective. 2008. (Corporations, Globalisation & the Law Ser.). 336p. 144.00 *(978-1-84720-274-1(8))* Elgar, Edward Publishing, Inc.

McLoughlin, Patrick. Commercial Leases & Insolvency. 4th rev. ed. 2008. 298p. pap. 148.00 *(978-1-84766-147-0(5)*, Bloomsbury Professional) Bloomsbury Publishing Plc GBR. Dist: International Specialized Bk. Services.

Medical Bankruptcy Fairness ACT: Hearing Before the Subcommittee on Commercial & Administrative Law of the Committee on the Judiciary, House of Representatives, One Hundred Eleventh Congress, Second Session, on H.R. 901, July 15, 2010. 2010. iv, 194p. ***(978-0-16-087426-0(2)***, 552-070-42119-0) United States Government Printing Office.

Medical Debt: Can Bankruptcy Reform Facilitate a Fresh Start?: Hearing Before the Subcommittee on Administrative Oversight & the Courts of the Committee on the Judiciary, United States Senate, One Hundred Eleventh Congress, First Session, October 20, 2009. 2010. (Illus.). iv, 468p. *(978-0-16-085966-3(2)*, 552-070-41157-1) United States Government Printing Office.

Medical Debt: Is Our Healthcare System Bankrupting Americans?: Hearing Before the Subcommittee on Commercial & Administrative Law of the Committee on the Judiciary, House of Representatives, One Hundred Eleventh Congress, First Session, July 28, 2009. 2010. (Illus.). iii, 102p. *(978-0-16-085270-1(6)*, 552-070-40611-5) United States Government Printing Office.

Mevorach, Irit. Insolvency Within Multinational Enterprise Groups. 2009. (ENG., Illus.). 300p. 165.00 *(978-0-19-954472-1(7))* Oxford Univ. Pr., Inc.

Meynell, Robin. Book of Bankruptcy: The simple guide to bankruptcy & other remedies to Debt. 2009. 132p. pap. 13.99 *(978-1-4389-4629-0(5))* AuthorHouse.

Minar, Jan. Effective Us-Czech Stock Portfolio Allocation. 2010. 108p. pap. *(978-3-8383-5768-3(X))* Lambert Academic Publishing.

Moore, Marc. Company Law Statutes 2011-2012. 3rd rev. ed. 2011. (Routledge Student Statutes Ser.). (ENG.). 592p. (C). pap. 37.95 ***(978-0-415-68745-4(4))*** Routledge.

Moss, Gabriel S., et al. The EC Regulation on Insolvency Proceedings: A Commentary & Annotated Guide. 2nd ed. 2009. (ENG.). 550p. 341.00 *(978-0-19-921508-9(1))* Oxford Univ. Pr., Inc.

National Guard & Reservists Debt Relief ACT of 2008: Hearing Before the Subcommittee on Commercial & Administrative Law of the Committee on the Judiciary, House of Representatives, One Hundred Tenth Congress, Second Session, on H.R. 4044, April 1, 2008. 2009. (Illus.). iv, 143p. *(978-0-16-083230-7(6)*, 552-070-39058-8) United States Government Printing Office.

Nclc, et al. Bankruptcy Basics: A Step-By-Step Guide for Pro Bono Attorneys, General Practitioners, & Legal Services Offices. 2007. (Illus.). xiii, 408p. pap. *(978-1-60248-009-4(5))* National Consumer Law Ctr., The.

Newton, Grant W. Bankruptcy & Insolvency Accounting, 2 vols., Vols. 1 & 2, Set. 7th ed. 2009. (ENG., Illus.). 2016p. 283.95 *(978-0-471-78763-1(9)*, Wiley) Wiley, John & Sons, Inc.

—Bankruptcy & Insolvency Accounting: Forms & Exhibits, 2 vols. 7th ed. 2009. (ENG., Illus.). 1128p. 157.95 *(978-0-471-78762-4(0)*, Wiley) Wiley, John & Sons, Inc.

—Bankruptcy & Insolvency Accounting Vol. 1: Practice & Procedure, 2 vols., Volume 1. 7th ed. 2009. (ENG., Illus.). 888p. 157.95 *(978-0-471-78761-7(2)*, Wiley) Wiley, John & Sons, Inc.

Newton, Grant W. & Liquerman, Robert. Bankruptcy & Insolvency Taxation. 4th ed. 2012. (Wiley Corporate F&a Ser.: 576). (ENG., Illus.). 740p. 225.00 ***(978-1-118-00077-9(3)***, Wiley) Wiley, John & Sons, Inc.

Nickles. Friedmans Bankruptcy. 2010. pap., stu. ed. *(978-0-7355-9853-9(3)*, Aspen Pubs.) Wolters Kluwer Law & Business.

Niemi, Johanna, et al, eds. Consumer Credit, Debt & Bankruptcy: Comparative & International Perspectives. 2009. (ENG., Illus.). 453p. 124.00 *(978-1-84113-258-7(6))* Hart Publishing Ltd. GBR. Dist: International Specialized Bk. Services.

Olivares-Caminal, Rodrigo. Expedited Debt Restructuring: An International Comparative Analysis. 2007. *(978-90-411-2485-2(3))* Kluwer Law International.

Olson, Jim. The Little Red Box of Management Tools: That Would Have Helped Us Avoid the Financial Crisis. 2010. pap. 11.99 *(978-1-61663-840-5(0))* Tate Publishing & Enterprises, LLC.

Omar, Paul J., ed. International Insolvency Law. 2008. (Markets & the Law Ser.). (Illus.). 452p. 134.95 *(978-0-7546-2427-1(7))* Ashgate Publishing Co.

Onaran, Yalman. Zombie Banks: How Broken Banks & Debtor Nations Are Crippling the Global Economy. 2011. (Bloomberg Ser.: 160). (ENG., Illus.). 184p. 34.95 ***(978-1-118-09452-5(2)***, Bloomberg Pr.) Wiley, John & Sons, Inc.

Organisation for Economic Co-operation and Development Staff. Legal & Institutional Reforms of Asian Insolvency Systems. 2007. pap. 78.00 *(978-92-64-03832-5(9))* Organization for Economic Cooperation & Development.

Ostrowick, John. Biting off More Than You Can Chew. 2008. 103p. pap. 16.95 *(978-1-4092-1385-7(4))* Lulu Enterprises Inc.

Parks, Linda, et al, eds. Kansas Bankruptcy Handbook. 3rd rev. ed. 2009. ring bd. 225.00 *(978-1-890452-21-6(1))* Kansas Bar Assn.

Parry, Rebecca. Corporate Rescue: An Overview of Recent Developments. 2nd ed. 2006. (Illus.). xvii, 406p. *(978-90-411-2414-2(4))* Kluwer Law International.

Parry, Rebecca, et al. Transaction Avoidance in Insolvencies. 2nd ed. 2011. (ENG.). 768p. 350.00 *(978-0-19-958379-9(X))* Oxford Univ. Pr., Inc.

Parsons. Abc Debt: Case Study Approach Debtor Creditor Relation 2e. 2010. pap. *(978-0-7355-9881-2(9)*, Aspen Pubs.) Wolters Kluwer Law & Business.

Parsons, Stephen P. The ABCs of Debt: A Case Study Approach to Debtor/Creditor Relations & Bankruptcy Law. (Illus.). 2009. xxv, 437p. *(978-0-7355-7138-9(4)*, Aspen Pubs.) 2008. xxv, 437p. pap. 83.95 *(978-0-7355-7137-2(6))* 2nd ed. 2011. xxviii, 513p. *(978-0-7355-9882-9(7)*, Aspen Pubs.) Wolters Kluwer Law & Business.

Paskay, Alexander L. Creditors' Rights. 4th rev. ed. 2006. 964p. 124.95 *(978-1-60042-007-8(9))* Vandeplas Publishing.

Pehn, Franz. Financial Distress & Bankruptcy. 2009. 76p. pap. *(978-3-639-12921-2(0))* VDM Verlag Dr. Mueller e.K.

Pelc, Matthew. When You Have to File for Bankruptcy: Step-by-Step Instructions to Take Control of Your Financial Future. 2008. (ENG.). 288p. per. 24.95 *(978-1-60138-209-2(X))* Atlantic Publishing Co.

Peretore, Frank & Peretore, Janis Migliorise. Workouts & Enforcement for the Secured Creditor & Equipment Lessor. 2008. (ENG.). 544p. 225.50 *(978-0-19-533647-4(X))* Oxford Univ. Pr., Inc.

Pernick, Norman L. Bankruptcy Deadline Checklist. 4th ed. 2011. (ENG.). pap. 99.95 incl. cd-rom *(978-1-60442-621-2(7))* American Bar Assn.

Phelps, Kathy Bazoian & Rhodes, Steven W. The Ponzi Book: A Legal Resource for Unraveling Ponzi Schemes. 2012. pap. ***(978-0-7698-4657-6(2))*** AK Pr.

Pirraglia, Bill. LifeTips 101 Bankruptcy Tips. 2007. 9.99 *(978-1-60275-009-8(2))* LifeTips.

Pollard, David. Corporate Insolvency: Employment & Pension Rights. 4th rev. ed. 2009. (ENG., Illus.). 715p. 278.00 *(978-1-84766-307-8(9),* Bloomsbury Professional) Bloomsbury Publishing Plc GBR. Dist: International Specialized Bk. Services.

Porter, Katherine, ed. Broke: How Debt Bankrupts the Middle Class. 2012. (Studies in Social Inequality Ser.). (ENG., Illus.). 320p. 80.00 ***(978-0-8047-7700-1(4))***; pap. 24.95 ***(978-0-8047-7701-8(2))*** Stanford Univ. Pr.

Press, Daniel M. & Weiss, Brett. Chapter 11 for Individual Debtors. 2012. ***(978-0-7698-4829-7(X))*** LexisNexis Matthew Bender.

Private Student Loan Bankruptcy Fairness ACT of 2010: Hearing Before the Subcommittee on Commercial & Administrative Law of the Committee on the Judiciary, House of Representatives, One Hundred Eleventh Congress, Second Session, on H.R.5043, April 22, 2010. 2010. iv, 72p. *(978-0-16-086202-1(7),* 552-070-41300-6) United States Government Printing Office.

Protecting Employees & Retirees in Business Bankruptcies ACT of 2010: Hearing Before the Subcommittee on Commercial & Administrative Law of the Committee on the Judiciary, House of Representatives, One Hundred Eleventh Congress, Second Session, on H.R.4677, May 25, 2010. 2010. (Illus.). iv, 368p. ***(978-0-16-087139-9(5),*** 552-070-41984-5) United States Government Printing Office.

Protecting Employees in Airline Bankruptcies: Hearing Before the Subcommittee on Commercial & Administrative Law of the Committee on the Judiciary, House of Representatives, One Hundred Eleventh Congress, First Session, December 16, 2009. 2010. iv, 155p. *(978-0-16-085489-7(X),* 552-070-40740-5) United States Government Printing Office.

Ramifications of Auto Industry Bankruptcies: Hearing Before the Committee on the Judiciary, House of Representatives, One Hundred Eleventh Congress, First Session, May 21, 2009. 2009. iv, 178p. *(978-0-16-084379-2(0),* 552-070-39922-4) United States Government Printing Office.

Ramifications of Auto Industry Bankruptcies: Hearing Before the Subcommittee on Commercial & Administrative Law of the Committee on the Judiciary, House of Representatives, One Hundred Eleventh Congress, First Session, July 21, 2009. 2010. iv, 71p. *(978-0-16-085264-0(1),* 552-070-40605-1) United States Government Printing Office.

Ramifications of Auto Industry Bankruptcies: Hearing Before the Subcommittee on Commercial & Administrative Law of the Committee on the Judiciary, House of Representatives, One Hundred Eleventh Congress, First Session, July 22, 2009. 2010. (Illus.). iv, 282p. *(978-0-16-085324-1(9),* 552-070-40654-9) United States Government Printing Office.

Rasmussen, Scott. The People's Money: How Voters Will Balance the Budget & Eliminate the Federal Debt. 2012. (ENG., Illus.). 288p. 26.00 ***(978-1-4516-6610-6(1),*** Threshold Editions) Threshold Editions.

Rasmussen, Scott W. The People's Money: How Voters Would Balance the Budget & Eliminate the Federal Debt. 2013. (ENG.). 288p. pap. 16.00 ***(978-1-4516-6611-3(X),*** Threshold Editions) Threshold Editions.

Ratner, Ian, et al. Business Valuation & Bankruptcy. 2009. (Wiley Finance Ser.: 521). (ENG., Illus.). 262p. 95.00 *(978-0-470-46238-6(8),* Wiley) Wiley, John & Sons, Inc.

Rattner, Steven. Overhaul: An Insider's Account of the Obama Administration's Emergency Rescue of the Auto Industry. 2011. (ENG., Illus.). 384p. pap. 15.95 *(978-0-547-57742-5(7),* Mariner Bks.) Houghton Mifflin Harcourt Trade & Reference Pubs.

Reed, Meryl L., et al. Guide to Troubled Businesses & Bankruptcies, 2 vols. 3rd ed. Incl. Vol. 2. ring bd. *(978-1-56433-819-8(3))*; Vol. 1. ring bd. *(978-1-56433-820-4(7))*; 1995. 140.00 *(978-1-56433-818-1(5))* Practitioners Publishing Co.

Reichelt, Silvia. Untreue und Bankrott: Zum Problem Einer Strafrechtlichen Doppelhaftung des GeschäFtsfüHrers der Gmbh in der Insolvenz. 2011. (GER.). 216p. 69.95 ***(978-3-631-61773-1(9))*** Lang, Peter GmbH, Europaischer Verlag der Wissenschaften DEU. Dist: Lang, Peter.

Rhodes, Robbin & Lambert, Pete J., eds. Bankruptcy Exemptions: Homestead & Firearm Laws. 2012. 230p. pap. ***(978-1-61942-381-7(2))*** Nova Science Pubs., Inc.

Richard, Christine. Confidence Game: How a Hedge Fund Manager Called Wall Street's Bluff. 2010. (ENG., Illus.). 352p. *(978-1-57660-337-6(7),* Bloomberg Pr.) Wiley, John & Sons, Inc.

Ringe, Wolf-Georg, et al, eds. Current Issues in European Financial & Insolvency Law: Perspectives from France & the UK. 2009. (ENG.). 244p. 94.00 *(978-1-84113-935-7(1))* Hart Publishing Ltd. GBR. Dist: International Specialized Bk. Services.

Robinson, Jerry. Bankruptcy of Our Nation: 12 Key Strategies for Protecting Your Finances in These Uncertain Times. 2009. (Illus.). 272p. pap. 13.99 *(978-0-89221-693-2(X))* New Leaf Pr., Inc.

Roe, Mark J. Bankruptcy & Corporate Reorganization: Legal & Financial Materials. 2nd rev. ed. 2007. (University Casebook Ser.). (Illus.). 707p. 145.00 *(978-1-58778-775-1(X),* Foundation Pr.) West.

Roe, Mark J. Roe's Bankruptcy & Corporate Reorganization, Legal & Financial Materials, 3d. 3rd rev. ed. 2011. 720p. 167.00 ***(978-1-59941-774-5(X),*** Foundation Pr.) West.

Rosenberg, Robert J., et al. A Lender's Participation in a Chapter 11 Case. 2009. vii, 124p. *(978-1-4224-7343-6(0))* LexisNexis Matthew Bender.

Rothammer, Thomas. Die Insolvenzrechtliche Restschuldbefreiung - Probleme und Lösungen. 2008. (Schriften zum Verfahrensrecht Ser.). 170p. pap. 56.95 *(978-3-631-58087-5(8))* Lang, Peter GmbH, Europaischer Verlag der Wissenschaften DEU. Dist: Lang, Peter.

Roßkopf, Stefan. Die Aufrechnung im deutschen und englischen Insolvenzrecht: Eine rechtsvergleichende Untersuchung. 2008. (Schriften zum Verfahrensrecht Ser.). 220p. pap. 56.95 *(978-3-631-57572-7(6))* Lang, Peter GmbH, Europaischer Verlag der Wissenschaften DEU. Dist: Lang, Peter.

Salerno, Thomas J. Bankruptcy Litigation & Practice: Prac Gde 4e (2 Vol) W/Cd. 2007. ring bd. 450.00 *(978-0-7355-6193-9(1),* Aspen Pubs.) Wolters Kluwer Law & Business.

Salerno, Thomas J. & Kroop, Jordan A. Bankruptcy Litigation & Practice: A Practitioner's Guide. 4th ed. 2007. (Illus.). *(978-0-7355-7100-6(7))*; *(978-0-7355-7101-3(5))* Wolters Kluwer Law & Business. (Aspen Pubs.).

Samet, Joseph. Recent Developments in Distressed Debt, Restructurings & Workouts: Fallout from the Credit Crunch 2008. 2008. (Illus.). 674p. pap. *(978-1-4024-1188-5(X))* Practising Law Institute.

Scarberry, Mark S. & Klee, Kenneth N. Business Reorganization in Bankruptcy. 4th rev. ed. 2011. (American Casebook Ser.). 1250p. 173.00 ***(978-0-314-27130-3(9),*** West Legalworks) West.

Schaefer, Anna-Maja. Das autonome internationale Insolvenzrecht Spaniens im Vergleich zum deutschen Recht. 2008. (Schriften der Deutsch-Spanischen Juristenvereinigung Ser.). 276p. pap. 74.95 *(978-3-631-58024-0(X))* Lang, Peter GmbH, Europaischer Verlag der Wissenschaften DEU. Dist: Lang, Peter.

Schmüser, Gunnar Lennart. Das Zusammenspiel zwischen Haupt- und Sekundärinsolvenzverfahren nach der EuInsVO. 2009. (Internationalrechtliche Studien. Beiträge zum Internationalen Privatrecht, zum Einheitsrecht und zur Rechtsvergleichung Ser.). (GER.). 184p. 60.95 *(978-3-631-58677-8(9))* Lang, Peter GmbH, Europaischer Verlag der Wissenschaften DEU. Dist: Lang, Peter.

Schnyder, A. European Banking & Insurance Law. 2009. 500p. 224.00 *(978-90-5095-708-3(0))* Intersentia Uitgevers N.V. BEL. Dist: International Specialized Bk. Services.

Schofield, Gareth, et al. Bankruptcy & Divorce: A Practical Guide for the Family Lawyer. 3rd rev. ed. 2010. (ENG.). 320p. pap. *(978-1-84661-206-0(3))* Jordan Publishing, Ltd.

Schollander, Wendell & Schollander, Wes. Bankruptcy for Small Business, 2E: Know Your Legal Rights & Recover from Mistakes & Start over Successfully. 2nd ed. 2008. (ENG.). 272p. pap. 22.95 *(978-1-57248-665-2(1),* Sphinx Publishing) Sourcebooks, Inc.

—Personal Bankruptcy: Practical Answers to More Than 150 Questions on Bankruptcy. 2009. (ENG.). 288p. pap. 16.99 *(978-1-57248-746-8(1),* Sphinx Publishing) Sourcebooks, Inc.

Second Anniversary of the Enactment of the Bankruptcy Abuse Prevention & Consumer Protection ACT of 2005: Are Consumers Really Being Protected ?: Hearing Before the Subcommittee on Commercial & Administrative Law of the Committee on the Judiciary, House of Representatives, One Hundred Tenth Congress, First Session, May 1, 2007. 2007. (Illus.). iv, 265p. *(978-0-16-078992-2(3),* 552-070-36107-3) United States Government Printing Office.

Selected Statutes Vol. 1: Statue of Frauds Uniform Laws National Bankruptcy Act & Others. 2007. 357p. 80.00 *(978-1-56169-926-1(8))* Gaunt, Inc.

Sepinuck, Stephen L. & Rusch, Linda J. Problems & Materials on Bankruptcy Law & Practice. 2007. (American Casebook Ser.). (Illus.). lxviii, 578p. *(978-0-314-17173-3(8))* West Publishing Co., College & Schl. Div.

Serra Coelho, Luís M. The Aftermath of Chapter 11 Bankruptcy. 2011. 212p. pap. ***(978-3-8443-2265-1(5))*** Lambert Academic Publishing.

Shen, Hengliang. Das Absonderungsrecht in der Insolvenz: Erfahrungen aus Deutschland und die Praxis in China. 2009. (Schriften zum Verfahrensrecht Ser.). (GER.). 126p. 40.95 *(978-3-631-59280-9(9))* Lang, Peter GmbH, Europaischer Verlag der Wissenschaften DEU. Dist: Lang, Peter.

Shepard's Bankruptcy Citations. spiral bd. 2598.00 *(978-0-7698-3885-4(5))* Shepard's.

Siemonsen, Johanna. Die deutschen Ausführungsvorschriften zur Europäischen Insolvenzverordnung: Art. 102 EGInsO. 2009. (Internationalrechtliche Studien. Beiträge zum Internationalen Privatrecht, zum Einheitsrecht und zur Rechtsvergleichung Ser.). (GER.). 204p. 64.95 *(978-3-631-59480-3(1))* Lang, Peter GmbH, Europaischer Verlag der Wissenschaften DEU. Dist: Lang, Peter.

Singleton, Susan. Retention of Title. 2010. (Thorogood Reports). 100p. pap. 240.00 *(978-1-85418-703-1(1))* Thorogood GBR. Dist: Stylus Publishing, LLC.

Smart, Philip & 3-4 South Square Staff. Cross Border Insolvency. Sheldon, Richard, ed. 3rd rev. ed. 2011. (ENG.). 710p. *(978-1-84592-104-0(6),* Bloomsbury Professional) Bloomsbury Publishing Plc.

Somoza, Antonio. The Application of Insolveny Prediction Models to the Smes. 2009. 516p. pap. *(978-3-639-12209-1(7))* VDM Verlag Dr. Mueller e.K.

Soral, Bartu. Banking Crises & Bankruptcy for Profit in Turkey. 2008. 96p. pap. *(978-3-639-06085-0(7))* VDM Verlag Dr. Mueller e.K.

Stark, Robert J., et al. Contested Valuation in Corporate Bankruptcy. 2011. pap. ***(978-1-4224-9383-0(0))*** LexisNexis Matthew Bender.

Steinfeld, Shayna M. & Steinfeld, Bruce R. Family Lawyer's Guide to Bankruptcy. 2nd ed. 2009. (ENG.). pap. 129.95 incl. lp *(978-1-59031-962-8(1))* American Bar Assn.

Stieber, Christoph. Der gesicherte Geld- und Warenkredit in der Insolvenz: Das Insolvenzverwalterwahlrecht nach § 103 InsO und dessen Wirkungen auf die Sicherungsübereignung und den Eigentumsvorbehalt. 2009. (Schriften zum Verfahrensrecht Ser.). (GER.). 220p. 69.95 *(978-3-631-58767-6(8))* Lang, Peter GmbH, Europaischer Verlag der Wissenschaften DEU. Dist: Lang, Peter.

Straightening Out the Mortgage Mess: How Can We Protect Home Ownership & Provide Relief to Consumers in Financial Distress? 2009. iv, 166p. *(978-0-16-083327-4(2),* 552-070-39151-7) United States Government Printing Office.

Strochak, Adam P., et al. Environmental Issues in Bankruptcy Cases. 2009. pap. *(978-1-4224-7340-5(6))* LexisNexis Matthew Bender.

Stuerz, Waldemar. Banking System Risk in the United States of America & Europe. 2011. 96p. pap. ***(978-3-8443-0839-6(3))*** Lambert Academic Publishing.

Symes, Christopher F. Statutory Priorities in Corporate Insolvency Law: An Analysis of Preferred Creditor Status. 2008. (Markets & the Law Ser.). 314p. 134.95 *(978-0-7546-7519-8(X))* Ashgate Publishing Co.

Tabb, Charles Jordan & Brubaker, Ralph. Bankruptcy Law: Principles, Policies, & Practice. 3rd ed. 2010. *(978-1-4224-7898-1(X))* LexisNexis Matthew Bender.

The World Bank. Out-of-Court Debt Restructuring. 2012. (World Bank Studies). (ENG.). 72p. pap. 22.00 ***(978-0-8213-8983-6(1),*** 9780821389836) World Bank Pubns.

Thomson West, creator. Bankruptcy Code, Rules & Official Forms. 2007th rev. ed. 2007. 967p. per. 38.00 *(978-0-314-17207-5(6))* West.

Tomasic, Roman, ed. Insolvency Law in East Asia. 2006. (Illus.). 574p. 190.00 *(978-0-7546-2125-6(1))* Ashgate Publishing Co.

Too Big to Fail: The Inside Story of How Wall Street & Washington Fought to Save the Financial System - & Themselves. 2010. (Illus.). iv, 334p. *(978-0-16-085355-5(9),* 552-070-40681-6) United States Government Printing Office.

Too Big to Fail: The Role for Bankruptcy & Antitrust Law in Financial Regulation Reform. 2010. iii, 139p. *(978-0-16-086867-2(X),* 552-070-41779-6) United States Government Printing Office.

Too Big to Fail? The Role of Antitrust Law in Government-Funded Consolidation in the Banking Industry: Hearing Before the Subcommittee on Courts & Competition Policy of the Committee on the Judiciary, House of Representatives, One Hundred Eleventh Congress, First Session, March 17, 2009. 2009. (Illus.). iii, 87p. *(978-0-16-084890-2(3),* 552-070-40286-1) United States Government Printing Office.

Toube, Felicity, ed. International Asset Tracing in Insolvency. 2010. (ENG.). 462p. 437.50 *(978-0-19-957623-4(8))* Oxford Univ. Pr., Inc.

Trejos, Nancy. Hot (Broke) Messes: How to Have Your Latte & Drink It Too. 2010. (ENG.). 320p. pap. 13.99 *(978-0-446-55542-5(8),* Business Plus) Grand Central Publishing.

Tufts, Bill & Fairbanks, Lee. Pension Ponzi: How Public Sector Unions Are Bankrupting Canada's Health Care, Education & Your Retirement. 2011. (ENG.). 256p. pap. 26.95 ***(978-1-118-09873-8(0),*** Wiley) Wiley, John & Sons, Inc.

Turnwald, Gene F. Consumer Bankruptcy Protection in Michigan. 2010. 172p. pap. 14.50 *(978-1-60860-394-7(6),* Eloquent Bks.) AEG Literary Publishing Services, Inc.

U. S. Bankruptcy Code & Rules Booklet: January 2007 Black Line Edition. 2007. 400p. (C). per. 20.00 *(978-0-9773729-7-3(9))* LegalPub.com, Inc.

Understanding the Effects of BAPCPA: Leading Lawyers on Examining BAPCPA Changes, Adopting New Filing Strategies, & Analyzing Consumer Bankruptcy Trends (Inside the Minds) 2010. 176p. pap. 85.00 *(978-0-314-26651-4(8))* Aspatore Bks.

United States, Congress Senate Committee on the Judiciary Subcommittee on Administrative Oversight and the Courts Staff, contrib. by. Oversight of the Implementation of the Bankruptcy Abuse Prevention & Consumer Protection ACT: Hearing Before the Subcommittee on Administrative Oversight & the Courts of the Committee on the Judiciary, United States Senate, One Hundred Ninth Congress, Second Session, December 6, 2006. 2007. (Illus.). iv, 234p. *(978-0-16-078655-6(X),* 552-070-335897-8) United States Government Printing Office.

United States, Government Accountability Office Staff, contrib. by. Bankruptcy Implementation of Reform Act's Debt Reaffirmation Agreement Provisions. 2008. (Illus.). 90p. pap. 50.00 *(978-1-60456-656-7(6))* Nova Science Pubs., Inc.

United States Trustee Program: Watchdog or Attack Dog?: Hearing Before the Subcommittee on Commercial & Administrative Law of the Committee on the Judiciary, House of Representatives, One Hundred Tenth Congress, First Session, October 2, 2007. 2009. iii, 270p. *(978-0-16-083017-4(6),* 552-070-38915-6) United States Government Printing Office.

U.S. Bankruptcy Court & U.S. Securities and Exchange Commission. Bankruptcy Basics: What Happens When Public Companies Go Bankrupt - What Every Investor Should Know... 2008. 84p. pap. *(978-1-60796-011-0(1))* Editorial Benei Noaj.

Uzanas, Raymond A. True Grits: Tough Times, Tough People. 2011. 204p. pap. 14.95 ***(978-1-4670-3903-1(9))*** AuthorHouse.

Vaughan, Vikkie. Bankruptcy: File with God Not with Man. 2007. (Illus.). 150p. pap. 17.95 *(978-0-9774419-2-1(X))* New Writers' Ink.

Wakem, Mitchell. How to Get Credit after Filing Bankruptcy: The Complete Guide to Getting & Keeping Your Credit under Control. 2007. (ENG.). 288p. per. 24.95 *(978-1-60138-137-8(9))* Atlantic Publishing Co.

Warren, Elizabeth. Reorganizing American Business. 2008. xiv, 212p. pap. 19.50 *(978-0-7355-7654-4(8))* Wolters Kluwer Law & Business.

Warren, William D. & Bussel, Daniel J. Bankruptcy. 8th ed. 2009. (Illus.). xliii, 928p. *(978-1-59941-659-5(X))* West.

—Bankruptcy, 2008. 7th rev. ed. 2008. (University Casebook Ser.). 190p. pap. 21.00 *(978-1-59941-516-1(X),* Foundation Pr.) West.

—Bankruptcy, 2011 Supplement. 8th rev. ed. 2011. 208p. pap. 26.00 ***(978-1-60930-086-9(6),*** Foundation Pr.) West.

Warren, William D. & Bussel, Daniel J. Bankruptcy, 8th, 2010 Supplement. 8th rev. ed. 2010. (University Casebook Ser.). 120p. 26.00 *(978-1-59941-906-0(9),* Foundation Pr.) West.

Watson-Gandy, Mark. Corporate Insolvency Practice: Litigation, Procedure & Precedents. 2010. (Illus.). 389p. 134.50 *(978-0-85490-046-6(2))* Gaunt, Inc.

Watson-Gandy, Mark. Personal Insolvency Practice: Litigation Procedure & Precedents. 2011. (ENG.). 400p. 143.00 ***(978-0-85490-082-4(9))*** Gaunt, Inc.

Webster and Boy, Lauren. Practical Bankruptcy Law for Paralegals. 2006. pap. 11.95 *(978-1-4288-1012-9(9))* Cram101 Inc.

Weil, Gotshal & Manges Staff & American Bar Association, Section of Business Law Staff, contrib. by. Reorganizing Failing Businesses: A Comprehensive Review & Analysis of Financial Restructuring & Business Reorganization. rev. ed. 2007. (ENG.). 1200p. spiral bd. 290.95 *(978-1-59031-714-3(9))* American Bar Assn.

Weiland, Stefan. Par condicio Creditorum: Der insolvenzrechtliche Gleichbehandlungsgrundsatz und seine Durchbrechungen zugunsten öffentlich-rechtlicher Gläubiger. 2010. (Saarbrücker Studien zum Privat- und Wirtschaftsrecht Ser.). (GER.). 434p. 108.95 *(978-3-631-60303-1(7))* Lang, Peter GmbH, Europaischer Verlag der Wissenschaften DEU. Dist: Lang, Peter.

Wessels & Wessels, B. Cross-Border Insolvency Law: International Instruments & Commentary. 2007. *(978-90-411-2526-2(4))* Kluwer Law International.

Wessels, Bob. International Insolvency Law. 2007. xxxii, 670p. *(978-90-411-2502-3(3))* Kluwer Law International.

West. Bankruptcy Code, Rules & Official Forms, June 2008. 2008. 1151p. pap. 39.00 *(978-0-314-18036-0(2),* West Legalworks) West.

—Bankruptcy Code Rules & Official Forms, June 2009 Law School Edition. 2009. 1188p. pap. 42.00 *(978-0-314-19145-8(3),* West Legalworks) West.

West & West Law School. Bankruptcy Code, Rules & Official Forms, 2010 Law School Edition. 2010th rev. ed. 2010. 1158p. pap. *(978-0-314-91158-2(8),* West Legalworks) West.

West Law School. Bankruptcy Code, Rules & Official Forms, June 2011 Law School Edition. 2011. 1222p. pap. 47.00 ***(978-0-314-92324-0(1))*** West.

Westbrook, Jay Lawrence. A Global View of Business Insolvency Systems. 2010. xvi, 300p. *(978-90-04-18025-3(7))* 2009. pap. *(978-0-8213-8103-8(2))* BRILL.

Whaley, Douglas J. Problems & Materials on Debtor & Creditor Law. 4th rev. ed. 2009. 145.00 *(978-0-7355-7778-7(1))* Wolters Kluwer Law & Business.

Wickouski, Stephanie. Bankruptcy Crimes. 2007. 436p. 79.95 *(978-1-58798-272-9(2))* Beard Bks., Inc.

Wijkman, Anders & Rockstrom, Johan. Bankrupting Nature: Denying Our Planetary Boundaries. 2012. (ENG., Illus.). 256p. 44.95 ***(978-0-415-53969-2(2))*** Routledge.

Wilcox, J. Blake. The Surety & Bankruptcy. 2011. (ENG.). 320p. pap. 120.95 *(978-1-60442-943-5(7))* American Bar Assn.

Williamson, Deborah D., et al. Bankruptcy Litigation Manual: What Civil Litigators Need to Know. 2007. 100p. per. 25.00 *(978-0-9792742-4-4(9))* American Bankruptcy Institute.

Williamson, John Harvey. The Bankruptcy Issues Handbook. 4th ed. 2007. ix, 340p. pap. ***(978-1-880730-39-3(1))*** Argyle Publishing Co.

Winston. Complete Guide to Credit & Collection Law 2009-2010. 2009. pap. 170.00 *(978-0-7355-8079-4(0))* Wolters Kluwer Law & Business.

—Credit & Collection Law 2010-2011. 2010. pap. *(978-0-7355-9284-1(5),* Aspen Pubs.) Wolters Kluwer Law & Business.

Witt, Fred T., Jr., et al. Collier on Bankruptcy Taxation. 3rd rev. ed. 2007. ring bd., ring bd. 329.00 *(978-0-8205-2149-7(3))* LexisNexis Matthew Bender.

Wood, Joanne. Bankrupt 130 Of 2006. 2009. 220p. pap. 14.49 *(978-1-4389-3362-7(2))* AuthorHouse.

Working Families in Financial Crisis: Medical Debt & Bankruptcy: Hearing Before the Subcommittee on Commercial & Administrative Law of the Committee on the Judiciary, House of Representatives, One Hundred Tenth Congress, First Session, July 17, 2007. 2008. (Illus.). iv, 277p. *(978-0-16-081376-4(X),* 552-070-37754-9) United States Government Printing Office.

World Bank. A Global View of Business Insolvency Systems. 2010. (Law, Justice, & Development Ser.). (ENG.). 318p. pap. 35.00 *(978-0-8213-8261-5(6),* 9780821382615) World Bank Pubns.

The Worsening Foreclosure Crisis: Is It Time to Reconsider Bankruptcy Reform?: Hearing Before the Subcommittee on Administrative Oversight & the Courts of the Committee on the Judiciary, United States Senate, One Hundred Eleventh Congress, First Session, July 23, 2009. 2010. (Illus.). iii, 148p. *(978-0-16-085603-7(5),* 552-070-40845-2) United States Government Printing Office.

B

Wright, Joanne, ed. Insolvency Law. 2009. (Illus.). 182p. pap. 130.00 *(978-1-84766-104-3(1),* Bloomsbury Professional) Bloomsbury Publishing Plc GBR. Dist: International Specialized Bk. Services.

Yi, Sun-Dong. Ch'aekwonja Ch'wisokwon. 2010. 540p. *(978-89-7214-177-8(1))* Yug-Beobsa.

BANKS, JOSEPH, 1743-1820

Banks, Joseph. Endeavour Journal of Sir Joseph Banks. 2006. pap. *(978-1-4068-0051-7(1))* Echo Library.

—Journal of the Right Hon. Sir Joseph Banks Bart. , K. B. , P. R. S. During Captain Cook's First Voyage in H. M. S. Endeavour in 1768-71 to Terra del Fuego, Otahite, New Zealand, Australia, the Dutch East Indies, Etc. Hooker, Joseph Dalton, ed. 2011. (Cambridge Library Collection - Travel & Exploration Ser.). (ENG., Illus.). 532p. pap. 39.99 *(978-1-108-02916-2(7))* Cambridge Univ. Pr.

Chambers, Neil. Joseph Banks & the British Museum: The World of Collecting, 1770-1830, 1 vol. 2007. (ENG., Illus.). 210p. 99.00 *(978-1-85196-858-9(X))* Pickering & Chatto Pubs., Ltd. GBR. Dist: Ashgate Publishing Co.

Chambers, Neil, ed. The Indian & Pacific Correspondence of Sir Joseph Banks, 1 vol., Vol. 1. 2008. (Pickering Masters Ser.). (ENG.). 464p. 180.00 *(978-1-85196-835-0(0))* Pickering & Chatto Pubs., Ltd. GBR. Dist: Ashgate Publishing Co.

—The Indian & Pacific Correspondence of Sir Joseph Banks, 1768-1820, 1 vol. (Pickering Masters Ser.). (ENG.). Vol. 2. 2009. 480p. 180.00 *(978-1-85196-836-7(9))* Vol. 3. 2010. 528p. 180.00 *(978-1-85196-837-4(7))* Vol. 4. 2011. 672p. 180.00 *(978-1-85196-838-1(5))* Vol. 5. 2012. 400p. 180.00 *(978-1-85196-839-8(3))* Vol. 6. 2013. 400p. 180.00 *(978-1-85196-840-4(7))* Pickering & Chatto Pubs., Ltd. GBR. Dist: Ashgate Publishing Co.

—The Scientific Letters of Sir Joseph Banks, 1743-1820, 6 vols. 2007. (Pickering Masters Ser.). (ENG., Illus.). 3088p. 1050.00 *(978-1-85196-766-7(4))* Pickering & Chatto Pubs., Ltd. GBR. Dist: Ashgate Publishing Co.

Gascoigne, John. Science in the Service of Empire: Joseph Banks, the British State & the Uses of Science in the Age of Revolution. 2011. (ENG.). 255p. pap. 35.99 *(978-0-521-18136-5(4))* Cambridge Univ. Pr.

Holmes, Richard. The Age of Wonder: How the Romantic Generation Discovered the Beauty & Terror of Science. 2009. (Illus.). 576p. 40.00 *(978-0-375-42222-5(6),* Pantheon) Knopf Doubleday Publishing Group.

—The Age of Wonder: The Romantic Generation & the Discovery of the Beauty & Terror of Science. 2010. (Vintage Ser.). (ENG., Illus.). 576p. pap. 17.95 *(978-1-4000-3187-0(7),* Vintage) Knopf Doubleday Publishing Group.

Paris, John Ayrton. The Life of Sir Humphry Davy. 2011. (Cambridge Library Collection - Life Sciences Ser.). (ENG.). 474p. pap. 34.99 *(978-1-108-07319-6(0));* (Illus.). 446p. pap. 32.99 *(978-1-108-07318-9(2))* Cambridge Univ. Pr.

Smith, Edward. The Life of Sir Joseph Banks. 2009. 264p. pap. *(978-0-217-55841-9(0));* 286p. pap. *(978-0-217-12908-4(0))* Books LLC.

—The Life of Sir Joseph Banks: President of the Royal Society, with Some Notices of his Friends & Contemporaries. 2011. (Cambridge Library Collection - Life Sciences Ser.). (ENG., Illus.). 402p. pap. 31.99 *(978-1-108-03112-7(9))* Cambridge Univ. Pr.

BANKS, NATHANIEL PRENTICE, 1816-1894

Dupree, Stephen A. Planting the Union Flag in Texas: The Campaigns of Major General Nathaniel P. Banks in the West. 2008. (Red River Valley Bks.). (ENG., Illus.). 314p. 40.00 *(978-1-58544-641-4(6))* Texas A&M Univ. Pr.

Smith, Ned. The 22nd Maine Volunteer Infantry in the Civil War: A History & Roster. 2010. (ENG., Illus.). 260p. pap. 35.00 *(978-0-7864-4893-7(8))* McFarland & Co., Inc. Pubs.

BANKS, CENTRAL

see Banks and Banking, Central

BANKS, COIN

see Coin Banks

BANKS AND BANKING

see also Acceptances; Bank Deposits; Bank Employees; Bank Examination; Bank Failures; Bank Holding Companies; Bank Reserves; Bankers; Banks and Banking, Central; Banks and Banking, Cooperative; Bills of Exchange; Checks; Clearinghouses; Consumer Credit; Correspondent Banks; Development Banks; Discount; Foreign Exchange; Interest; Internet Banking; Investment Banking; Liquidity (Economics); Money; Negotiable Instruments; Savings Banks; Syndicates (Finance); Trust Companies; Usury

Abdelaziz, Gamal Sayed. Service Quality Dimensions. 2010. 436p. pap. *(978-3-8383-7284-6(0))* Lambert Academic Publishing.

Ahmed, Zafar. Balanced Scorecard & Its Application in Banking Sector of Pakistan. 2010. 180p. pap. *(978-3-639-23831-0(1))* VDM Verlag Dr. Mueller e.K.

Aichhorn, Ulrike, ed. Geld- und Kreditwesen im Spiegel der Wissenschaft. (GER., Illus.). XXI, 471p. pap. 129.00 *(978-3-211-23875-2(1),* 3211238751) Springer.

Al-Muharrami, Saeed. Arab Banking. 2010. 144p. pap. *(978-3-639-24692-6(6))* VDM Verlag Dr. Mueller e.K.

—Arab Gcc Banking. 2010. 120p. pap. *(978-3-639-13331-8(5))* VDM Verlag Dr. Mueller e.K.

Aldohni, Abdul Karim. The Legal & Regulatory Aspects of Islamic Banking: A Comparative Look at the United Kingdom & Malaysia. 2011. (Routledge Research in Finance & Banking Law Ser.). (ENG.). 264p. 135.00 *(978-0-415-55515-9(9))* Routledge.

Alessandrini, Pietro, et al, eds. The Changing Geography of Banking & Finance. (ENG., Illus.). xii, 300p. 2010. pap. 139.00 ***(978-1-4419-4720-8(5),*** 1441947205) 2009. 139.00 *(978-0-387-98077-5(6),* 0387980776) Springer.

Alinvi, Fatima. Customers' Expectations of Banks Becoming Cashless. 2010. 104p. pap. *(978-3-639-27571-7(X))* VDM Verlag Dr. Mueller e.K.

Ameresekere, Nihal Sri. Derivatives/Hedging Deals: By Citibank U. S. A Standard Charter Bank U. K Deutsche Bank Germany. 2011. (Illus.). 536p. pap. 101.88 ***(978-1-4567-7204-8(X))*** AuthorHouse.

American Bankers Association. Money & Banking. 6th ed. 2008. (Illus.). 349p. (C). pap. 129.00 *(978-0-89982-610-3(5))* American Bankers Assn.

—Principles of Banking: 9th Edition, 1. 9th ed. 2007. (ENG., Illus.). 366p. (C). pap. 99.00 *(978-0-89982-602-8(4))* American Bankers Assn.

—Principles of Banking Instructor's Manual: 9th Edition. 9th ed. 2007. (ENG., Illus.). (C). cd-rom 65.00 *(978-0-89982-603-5(2))* American Bankers Assn.

Anderloni, Luisa, et al, eds. New Frontiers in Banking Services: Emerging Needs & Tailored Products for Untapped Markets. (ENG., Illus.). xii, 377p. 2010. pap. 135.00 *(978-3-642-07984-9(9),* 3642079849) 2006. 135.00 *(978-3-540-46497-6(2),* 3540464972) Springer.

Ariff, Mohamed & Iqbal, Munawar. The Foundations of Islamic Banking: Theory, Practice & Education. Ariff, Mohamed & Iqbal, Munawar, eds. 2011. (Illus.). 296p. 125.00 *(978-1-84980-792-0(2))* Elgar, Edward Publishing, Inc.

Atack, Jeremy & Neal, Larry. The Origin & Development of Financial Markets & Institutions: From the Seventeenth Century to the Present. Atack, Jeremy & Neal, Larry, eds. 2009. (ENG., Illus.). 496p. 108.00 *(978-0-521-89517-0(0))* Cambridge Univ. Pr.

Atack, Jeremy & Neal, Larry, eds. The Origins & Development of Financial Markets & Institutions: From the Seventeenth Century to the Present. 2010. (ENG.). 496p. pap. 45.00 *(978-0-521-15476-5(6))* Cambridge Univ. Pr.

Baker, William. Endless Money: The Moral Hazards of Socialism. 2009. (ENG., Illus.). 417p. 29.95 *(978-0-470-47615-4(X),* Wiley) Wiley, John & Sons, Inc.

Ball, Laurence. Money, Banking, & Financial Markets. (ENG.). (C). 2009. 256p. pap., stu. ed. 42.95 *(978-1-4292-0600-6(4))* 2008. 608p. 105.95 *(978-1-4292-5709-1(1))* 2008. 608p. 174.95 *(978-0-7167-5934-8(9))* Worth Pubs., Inc.

—Money, Banking & Financial Markets. 2nd ed. 2011. (ENG., Illus.). 608p. (C). 174.95 *(978-1-4292-4409-1(7))* Worth Pubs., Inc.

Bank & Finance Handbook: Moody's. 500p. (Orig.). pap. 1795.00 *(978-0-7605-1804-5(1))* Rector Pr., Ltd.

Banking Technology Competition Handbook: Companies-Products-Services. 125p. (Orig.). pap. 695.00 *(978-0-7605-1868-7(8))* Rector Pr., Ltd.

Barth, James R., et al. Global Banking Regulation & Supervision: What are the Issues & What Are the Practices? 2009. pap. 37.00 *(978-1-60741-315-8(9))* Nova Science Pubs., Inc.

Barth, James R., et al. Guardians of Finance: Making Regulators Work for Us. 2012. (ENG., Illus.). 256p. (gr. 17). 27.95 ***(978-0-262-01739-8(3))*** MIT Pr.

Baum, Daniel J. The Banks of Canada in the Commonwealth Caribbean: Economic Nationalism & Multinational Enterprises of a Medium Power. 2007. 176p. per. 16.95 *(978-0-595-47603-9(1),* Backinprint.com) iUniverse, Inc.

Bauwens, Luc, et al. Handbook of Volatility Models & Their Applications. 2012. (Wiley Handbooks in Financial Engineering & Econometrics Ser.: 3). (ENG., Illus.). 568p. 149.95 ***(978-0-470-87251-2(9),*** Wiley) Wiley, John & Sons, Inc.

Benedikter, Roland. Social Banking & Social Finance: Answers to the Economic Crisis. 2011. (SpringerBriefs in Business Ser.). (ENG., Illus.). xiii, 133p. pap. 49.95 *(978-1-4419-7773-1(2),* 1441977732) Springer.

Benston, George J. & Rosenfeld, James. The Selected Works of George J. Benston: Banking & Financial Services, 1 vol. 2010. (ENG., Illus.). 376p. 99.00 *(978-0-19-538901-2(8))* Oxford Univ. Pr., Inc.

Berger, Allen N., et al, eds. The Oxford Handbook of Banking. (Oxford Handbooks Ser.). (ENG., Illus.). 2012. 1040p. 49.95 ***(978-0-19-964093-5(9))*** 2010. 976p. 150.00 *(978-0-19-923661-9(5))* Oxford Univ. Pr., Inc.

Bergström, Maria, et al, eds. Securitization, Accountability & Risk Management: Transforming the Public Security Domain. 2012. (PRIO New Security Studies). (ENG., Illus.). 192p. (C). 130.00 *(978-0-415-68014-1(X))* Routledge.

Bessis, Joël. Risk Management in Banking. 3rd ed. 2010. (ENG.). 840p. 135.00 *(978-0-470-01912-2(3),* Wiley) Wiley, John & Sons, Inc.

—Risk Management in Banking. 3rd ed. 2010. (ENG., Illus.). 840p. pap. 60.00 *(978-0-470-01913-9(1),* Wiley) Wiley, John & Sons, Inc.

Bikker, Jacob & Bos, J. W. B. Bank Performance. 2009. 154p. pap. 39.95 *(978-0-415-56961-3(3))* Routledge.

Bikker, Jacob A. & Bos, J. W. B. Bank Performance: A Theoretical & Empirical Framework for the Analysis of Profitability, Competition & Efficiency. 2007. (Routledge International Studies in Money & Banking Ser.). (Illus.). 256p. 140.00 *(978-0-415-39766-7(9))* Routledge.

Blenman, Lloyd P. Banking & Capital Markets: New International Perspectives. 2010. 400p. 130.00 *(978-981-4273-60-2(0))* World Scientific Publishing Co., Inc.

Bliss, R., et al. Banking Resolution & Crisis Management. 2009. 315.00 *(978-1-84311-825-1(4))* Informa Professional GBR. Dist: International Specialized Bk. Services.

Bluemke, Andreas. How to Invest in Structured Products: A Guide for Investors & Asset Managers. 2009. (Wiley Finance Ser.: 459). (ENG., Illus.). 384p. 85.00 *(978-0-470-74679-0(3),* Wiley) Wiley, John & Sons, Inc.

Boberski, Vincent. Community Banking Strategies: Steady Growth, Safe Portfolio Management, & Lasting Client Relationships. 2010. (Bloomberg Financial Ser.: 97). (ENG., Illus.). 178p. 60.00 *(978-1-57660-369-7(5),* Bloomberg Pr.) Wiley, John & Sons, Inc.

Bol, G., et al. Risk Assessment: Decisions in Banking & Finance. 2008. (Contributions to Economics Ser.). 270p. 139.00 *(978-3-7908-2049-2(0))* Physica-Verlag DEU. Dist: Springer.

Boleat, Mark J. Mortgage Market (RLE Banking & Finance) Theory & Practice of Housing Finance, Volume 2. 2012. (ENG.). 192p. 100.00 ***(978-0-415-53787-2(8))*** Routledge.

Burton, Maureen. Cram101 Textbook Outlines to Accompany the Financial System & the Economy, Burton & Lombra, 3rd Edition. 2006. (ENG.). 487p. pap. 19.95 *(978-1-4288-0744-0(6))* Cram101 Inc.

Burton, Maureen & Brown, Bruce. The Financial System & the Economy: Principles of Money & Banking. 5th rev. ed. 2009. (ENG., Illus.). 720p. (C). pap. 129.95 *(978-0-7656-2246-4(7))* Sharpe, M.E. Inc.

—The Financial System of the Economy: Principles of Money & Banking. 5th ed. 2009. pap. *(978-0-7656-2247-1(5))* Sharpe, M.E. Inc.

Capie, Forrest & Webber, Alan. Finance, Money & Banking, Set J. 2006. (Illus.). xii, 366p. 2575.00 *(978-0-415-37850-5(8))* Routledge.

Carter H. Golembe. But I Never Made a Loan: My Career in Banking - the Early Years. 2009. 164p. 25.95 *(978-1-4401-7473-5(3));* pap. 15.95 *(978-1-4401-7475-9(X))* iUniverse, Inc.

Case, Phil. Environmental Risk Management & Corporate Lending: A Global Perspective. (Illus.). xiv, 274p. *(978-1-85573-436-4(2))* Woodhead Publishing Ltd.

Cassidy, John. How Markets Fail: The Logic of Economic Calamities. 2009. (ENG., Illus.). 400p. 28.00 *(978-0-374-17320-3(6))* Farrar, Straus & Giroux.

—How Markets Fail: The Logic of Economic Calamities. 2010. (ENG.). 416p. pap. 16.00 *(978-0-312-43004-7(3))* Picador.

Castillo, Jerilyn J. & McAniff, Peter J. The Practitioner's Guide to Investment Banking, Mergers & Acquisitions, Corporate Finance. 2007. (ScoopBooks). 740p. 95.00 *(978-0-9761548-0-8(3),* ScoopBooks) Circinus Business Pr.

Casu, Barbara, et al. Introduction to Banking. 2006. (ENG., Illus.). 560p. (C). per. 100.00 *(978-0-273-69302-4(6),* Prentice Hall) Prentice Hall PTR.

Cecchetti, Stephen G. Money, Banking, & Financial Markets. 2nd ed. 2007. (ENG., Illus.). 672p. (C). 192.67 *(978-0-07-352309-5(7),* 0073523097, McGraw-Hill/Irwin) McGraw-Hill Higher Education.

Cecchetti, Stephen G. & Schoenholtz, Kermit L. Money, Banking & Financial Markets. 3rd ed. 2010. (ENG., Illus.). 704p. (C). 192.67 *(978-0-07-337590-8(X),* 007337590X, McGraw-Hill/Irwin) McGraw-Hill Higher Education.

Center for Financial Training. Banking Systems. 2nd ed. 2009. (Finance Ser.). (ENG.). 448p. (C). pap. 67.95 *(978-0-538-44928-1(4))* Cengage South-Western.

CFA Institute, compiled by. A Primer on Islamic Finance. 2009. pap. *(978-1-934667-24-8(2))* Research Foundation of CFA Institute.

Chambers, Don. Money Basics for Young Adults: High School Edition. 2006. (ENG.). (YA). 16.99 *(978-0-9722071-4-0(7))* Healthy Wealth.

Chaudri, Amer. Diatribe: A scathing journey into the heart of the Financial & Banking corporate culture (and related Digressions) 2010. 268p. pap. 16.95 *(978-1-60844-474-8(0))* Dog Ear Publishing, LLC.

Chibaya Mbuya, John. The Bible of Banking: Volume 1. 2010. 664p. pap. *(978-3-8383-9485-5(2))* Lambert Academic Publishing.

—The Bible of Banking: Volume II. 2010. 636p. pap. *(978-3-8383-9645-3(6))* Lambert Academic Publishing.

Choudhry, Moorad. Bank Asset & Liability Management: Strategy, Trading, Analysis. 2007. (ENG., Illus.). 1440p. 115.00 *(978-0-470-82135-0(3),* Wiley) Wiley, John & Sons, Inc.

—An Introduction to Banking: Liquidity Risk & Asset-Liability Management. 2011. (Securities Institute Ser.: 20). (ENG., Illus.). 384p. pap. 60.00 *(978-0-470-68725-3(8),* Wiley) Wiley, John & Sons, Inc.

Choudhry, Moorad & Landuyt, Gino. The Future of Finance: A New Model for Banking & Investment. 2010. (Wiley Finance Ser.: 576). (ENG., Illus.). 198p. 80.00 *(978-0-470-57229-0(9),* Wiley) Wiley, John & Sons, Inc.

Clavero Rasero, Beatriz. Credit Rating. 2008. 140p. pap. *(978-3-639-06160-4(8))* VDM Verlag Dr. Mueller e.K.

Clowers, A. Nicole & McCool, Thomas J. Bank Regulation: Modified Prompt Corrective Action Framework Would Improve Effectiveness. 2011. 92p. (C). pap. 25.00 ***(978-1-4379-8816-1(4))*** DIANE Publishing Co.

Colwell, Stephen. The Ways & Means of Payment; a Full Analysis of the Credit System, with Its Various Modes of Adjustment. 2006. 664p. per. 36.99 *(978-1-4255-6764-4(9))* MPublishing.

Congdon, Tim. Money in a Free Society: Keynes, Friedman, & the New Crisis in Capitalism. 2011. (ENG., Illus.). 486p. 29.95 *(978-1-59403-524-1(5))* Encounter Bks.

Conti, Vittorio & Hamaui, Rony, eds. Financial Markets Liberalisation & the Role of Banks. 2009. (ENG., Illus.). 400p. pap. 42.00 *(978-0-521-11190-4(0))* Cambridge Univ. Pr.

Cornwall, Linda M., ed. New Developments in Banking & Finance. 2007. 129.00 *(978-1-60021-576-6(9))* Nova Science Pubs., Inc.

Corrigan, James P., ed. International Perspectives on Financial Market Supervision. 2010. (Economic Issues, Problems & Perspectives Ser.). pap. 80.10 *(978-1-61728-006-1(2))* Nova Science Pubs., Inc.

Cram101 Textbook Reviews. Outlines & Highlights for Banking Systems by Center for Financial Training, Isbn: 9780538449281. 2010. 188p. pap. 30.95 *(978-1-61698-051-1(6))* Cram101 Inc.

—Outlines & Highlights for Money & Banking: An International Text by Robert Eyler. 2011. 172p. pap. 29.95 ***(978-1-4672-6606-2(X))*** Cram101 Inc.

—Outlines & Highlights for Money Bank & Fin Mrkts 2e by Laurence Ball. 2011. 334p. pap. 33.95 ***(978-1-4672-6600-0(0))*** Cram101 Inc.

—Outlines & Highlights for Money, Banking, & Financial Markets by Stephen Cecchetti. 2011. 272p. pap. 32.95 ***(978-1-4672-6627-7(2))*** Cram101 Inc.

—Outlines & Highlights for Money, Banking, & the Financial System by R Glenn Hubbard. 2011. 420p. pap. 35.95 ***(978-1-4672-6601-7(9))*** Cram101 Inc.

Cram101 Textbook Reviews & Cram101 Textbook Reviews. Outlines & Highlights for Economics of Banking by John Thompson. 2011. 566p. pap. 39.95 ***(978-1-61830-138-3(1))*** Cram101 Inc.

Cram101 Textbook Reviews Staff. Outlines & Highlights for Economics of Money, Banking & Financial Markets, Alternate Edition by Frederic S Mishkin, Isbn: 9780321427809. 2009. 386p. pap. 34.95 *(978-1-4288-3381-4(1))* Cram101 Inc.

—Outlines & Highlights for Economics of Money, Banking & Financial Markets by Frederic S Mishkin, Isbn: 9780321415059. 2009. 216p. pap. 30.95 *(978-1-4288-2773-8(0));* 156p. pap. 29.95 *(978-1-4288-9032-9(7))* Cram101 Inc.

—Outlines & Highlights for Money, Banking, & Financial Markets by Roger Leroy Miller, David D VanHoose, Isbn: 9780324320039. 2009. 310p. pap. 32.95 *(978-1-4288-3297-8(1))* Cram101 Inc.

—Outlines & Highlights for Money, Banking & Financial Markets by Stephen G Cecchetti, Isbn: 9780073523095. 2009. 238p. pap. 31.95 *(978-1-4288-2511-6(8));* 178p. pap. 29.95 *(978-1-4288-8947-7(7))* Cram101 Inc.

Dar, Humayon & Moghul, Umar, eds. Legal Shari'A Aspects of Islamic Finance. 2010. (ENG., Illus.). 372p. pap. 190.00 *(978-1-899217-09-0(6))* Harriman Hse. Publishing GBR. Dist: Ingram Pub. Services.

Darko-Amankrah, Christopher. Investors Perception of Financial Statements & Performance. 2011. 80p. pap. ***(978-3-8443-9060-5(X))*** Lambert Academic Publishing.

Davies, Virginia. Banking for Growth. 2008. 412p. pap. *(978-3-639-02667-2(5))* VDM Verlag Dr. Mueller e.K.

Davis, J. Maximum Yield: Opimizing Customer Value in Retail Banking. 2007. 208p. 29.95 *(978-0-470-07385-8(3),* Wiley) Wiley, John & Sons, Inc.

Davis, Steven I. Banking in Turmoil: Strategies for Sustainable Growth. 2009. (ENG., Illus.). 256p. 110.00 *(978-0-230-23571-7(9))* Palgrave Macmillan.

Dawes, Charles G. The Banking System of the United States & Its Relation to the Money & Business of the Country. 2010. 86p. pap. 18.75 *(978-1-140-18144-6(0))* BiblioBazaar.

Degryse, Hans, et al. Microeconometrics of Banking: Methods, Applications, & Results. 2009. (ENG., Illus.). 240p. 59.95 *(978-0-19-534047-1(7))* Oxford Univ. Pr., Inc.

Diamond, Douglas W. Banks & Liquidity Creation: A Simple Exposition of the Diamond-Dybvig Model: A Reprint from the Federal Reserve Bank of Richmond Economic Quarterly. 2007. (Illus.). 12p. (C). pap. 15.00 *(978-1-4223-1734-1(X))* DIANE Publishing Co.

Dilley, Deborah K. Essentials of Banking. 2008. (ENG., Illus.). 274p. pap. 47.50 *(978-0-470-17088-5(3),* Wiley) Wiley, John & Sons, Inc.

Dixon, Simon. Student to Ceo. 2011. 160p. pap. ***(978-1-907722-18-9(1))*** Ecademy Pr. Ltd.

Dobos, Ned, et al, eds. Global Financial Crisis: the Ethical Issues. 2011. (ENG., Illus.). 240p. 90.00 *(978-0-230-27663-5(6))* Palgrave Macmillan.

Drotskie, Adri. Customer Experience As a Strategic Differentiator. 2011. 340p. pap. ***(978-3-8443-9656-0(X))*** Lambert Academic Publishing.

Dufries, Courtney. Ten Lessons Bankers Never Learn: How Banks Operate & Why Bankers Screw Up. 2011. 440p. 38.95 ***(978-1-4620-3325-6(3));*** pap. 28.95 ***(978-1-4620-3324-9(5))*** iUniverse, Inc.

Dunkman, William E. Qualitative Credit Control. (Columbia University, Studies in the Social Sciences: No. 395). reprint ed. 32.50 *(978-0-404-51395-5(6))* AMS Pr., Inc.

Ehrlich, Sean D. Access Points: An Institutional Theory of Policy Bias & Policy Complexity, 1 vol. 2011. (ENG., Illus.). 208p. 99.00 ***(978-0-19-973753-6(3));*** pap. 27.95 ***(978-0-19-973754-3(1))*** Oxford Univ. Pr., Inc.

Einzig, Paul. Montagu Norman (RLE Banking & Finance) A Study in Financial Statemanship, Volume 11. 2012. (ENG.). 272p. 115.00 ***(978-0-415-53944-9(7))*** Routledge.

El-Hawary, Dahlia. Access to Finance, Banking Market Power & Institutional Development. 2011. 156p. pap. ***(978-3-8433-5641-1(6))*** Lambert Academic Publishing.

Essvale Corporation Limited Staff. Business Knowledge for IT in Retail Banking: A complete handbook for IT Professionals. 2007. pap. 98.02 *(978-0-9554124-2-4(0))* Essvale Corp. GBR. Dist: Silvermine International Bks., LLC.

Eyler & Eyler, Robert. Money & Banking: An International Text. 2009. (ENG., Illus.). 256p. 190.00 *(978-0-415-77546-5(9))* Routledge.

Eyler, Robert. Money & Banking. 2009. (ENG., Illus.). 256p. 59.95 *(978-0-415-77547-2(7))* Routledge.

Farrall, Cate & Lindsley, Marianne. Marketing. 2008. (ENG., Illus.). 144p. pap. 25.00 *(978-0-521-70269-0(0))* Cambridge Univ. Pr.

Farrell, Kathlyn. Reference Guide to Regulatory Compliance. 16th ed. 2006. 680p. 350.00 *(978-0-89982-586-1(9))* American Bankers Assn.

Fiordelisi, Franco. Merger & Aquisition in European Banking. Molyneux, Philip, ed. 2009. (Palgrave Macmillan Studies in Banking & Financial Institutions Ser.). (ENG., Illus.). 240p. (C). 100.00 *(978-0-230-53719-4(7))* Palgrave Macmillan.

First National Bank Vita Craft Now, contrib. by. First National Bank Vita Craft Now: 1997. (Illus.). *(978-0-620-21105-5(9))* Internet Clinic CC.

Floquet, Keegan. Capital Structure & Risk Dynamics among Banks. 2011. 280p. pap. ***(978-3-8443-1205-8(6))*** Lambert Academic Publishing.

Freixas, Xavier & Rochet, Jean-Charles. Microeconomics of Banking. 2nd ed. 2008. (ENG., Illus.). 392p. 65.00 *(978-0-262-06270-1(4))* MIT Pr.
Friedman, Jeffrey & Kraus, Wladimir. Engineering the Financial Crisis: Systemic Risk & the Failure of Regulation. 2011. (Illus.). 224p. (C). 45.00 ***(978-0-8122-4357-4(9))*** Univ. of Pennsylvania Pr.
Fuchs, Emma J. & Braun, Finn, eds. Emerging Topics in Banking & Finance. 2008. (Illus.). xi, 223p. 185.00 *(978-1-60456-550-8(0))*, Nova Science Pubs., Inc.
Gardner, James A. Innovation & the Future Proof Bank: A Practical Guide to Doing Different Business-as-Usual. 2009. (ENG., Illus.). 334p. 75.00 *(978-0-470-71419-5(0)*, Wiley) Wiley, John & Sons, Inc.
Ghosh, Amalendu. Managing Risks in Commercial & Retail Banking. 2012. (ENG.). 480p. 90.00 ***(978-1-118-10353-1(X)***, Wiley) Wiley, John & Sons, Inc.
Gilliland, Debbie & Maguire, Alison. Managing Corporate & Business Relationships: Bank / Customer Relationships. 2008. 250p. pap. 49.95 *(978-1-906403-26-3(0))* Global Professional Publishing GBR. Dist: Stylus Publishing, LLC.
Glantz, Morton & Mun, Johnathan. The Banker's Handbook on Credit Risk: Implementing Basel II. 2008. (ENG., Illus.). 432p. 86.95 *(978-0-12-373666-6(8)*, Academic Pr.) Elsevier Science & Technology Bks.
Gottschalk, Ricardo, ed. The Basel Capital Accords in Developing Countries: Challenges for Development Finance. 2010. (ENG., Illus.). 256p. 105.00 *(978-0-230-22224-3(2))* Palgrave Macmillan.
Green, Stephen. Good Value: Reflections on Money, Morality & an Uncertain World. (ENG.). 2011. 256p. pap. 14.95 *(978-0-8021-4525-3(6)*, Grove Pr.) 2010. 288p. 25.00 *(978-0-8021-1917-9(4)*, Atlantic Monthly Pr.) Grove/Atlantic, Inc.
Greenberg, Theodore S., et al. Politically Exposed Persons: A Guide on Preventive Measures for the Banking Sector. 2010. (ENG., Illus.). 124p. pap. 29.95 *(978-0-8213-8249-3(7)*, 9780821382493) World Bank Pubns.
Greene, William B. Mutual Banking. 2009. 68p. pap. 16.75 *(978-1-110-91390-9(7))* BiblioBazaar.
Gregoriou, Greg N., ed. The Banking Crisis Handbook. 2009. (ENG., Illus.). 628p. 92.95 *(978-1-4398-1853-4(3)*, CRC Press) Taylor & Francis Group GBR. Dist: Taylor & Francis Group.
Gumbo, Victor. The Libor Market Model & Its Application in the Safex-Jibar Market. 2011. 100p. pap. ***(978-3-8383-5372-2(2))*** Lambert Academic Publishing.
Gup, Benton E., ed. Corporate Governance in Banking: A Global Perspective. 2007. (Illus.). 320p. (C). 137.00 *(978-1-84542-940-9(0))* Elgar, Edward Publishing, Inc.
Gup, Benton E., et al. Commercial Banking: The Management of Risk. 2007. ix, 583p. pap. *(978-0-470-81072-9(6))* Wiley, John & Sons, Inc.
Hakes, Davide & Gamber, Edward. The Economics of Money, Banking & Financial Markets. 9th ed. 2009. (ENG.). 468p. (C). pap., pupil's gde. ed. 46.67 *(978-0-321-60001-1(0)*, Prentice Hall) Prentice Hall PTR.
Hakes, Davide S., et al. Study Guide for the Economics of Money, Banking, & Financial Markets & the Economics of Money, Banking, & Financial Markets Business School Edition. 10th rev. ed. 2012. (ENG.). 554p. (C). pap. 46.67 ***(978-0-13-276942-6(5)***, Prentice Hall) Prentice Hall PTR.
Handa, Jagdish. Monetary Economics. 2nd ed. 2008. (Illus.). (ENG.). 872p. 240.00 *(978-0-415-77209-9(5))*; XXVIII, 844p. pap. 95.00 *(978-0-415-77210-5(9))* Routledge.
Heges, Joseph E. Commercial Banking & the Stock Market Before 1863. (Johns Hopkins University. Studies in the Social Sciences, Thirtieth Ser.: 1). reprint ed. 37.50 *(978-0-404-61279-5(2))* AMS Pr., Inc.
Hellmuth, James G. & Sylla, Richard, eds. Banker's Diary & Guide: 1998 Edition. Date not set. 40.95 *(978-1-57987-014-0(7))* Faulkner & Gray, Inc.
Hoelscher, David S. & Quintyn, Marc, contrib. by. Managing Systemic Banking Crises. (CHI.). *(978-7-5049-3541-0(7)*, S224CA) China Financial Publishing Hse.
Hool, George. Banking Models: International Disclosure & Stock Returns. 2008. 64p. pap. *(978-3-8364-9946-0(0))* VDM Verlag Dr. Mueller e.K.
Hubbard, R. Glenn. Money: The Financial System & the Economy. 5th ed. 2006. pap. 19.95 *(978-1-4288-1113-3(3))* Cram101 Inc.
—Money, the Financial System, & the Economy. 6th ed. 2007. (ENG., Illus.). 768p. (C). pap. 206.67 *(978-0-321-42670-3(3))* Addison Wesley.
Hubbard, R. Glenn & O'Brien, Anthony Patrick. Money, Banking, & the Financial System. 2010. (ENG.). 640p. (C). 206.67 *(978-0-13-255345-2(7)*, Prentice Hall) Prentice Hall PTR.
Hunter, Todd Stephen. Sales Tips You Can Bank On. 2008. 64p. pap. 10.49 *(978-1-4389-1770-2(8))* AuthorHouse.
Jickling, Mark, et al. Government-Sponsored Organizations: Regulation. 2008. 73p. (C). 50.00 *(978-1-60456-524-9(1))* Nova Science Pubs., Inc.
Jones, Grant & Knight, Andrew. Asset-Based Lending & Insolvency. 2012. 420p. pap. 145.00 *(978-1-904905-62-2(5))* Spiramus Pr. GBR. Dist: International Specialized Bk. Services.
Jones, Thatcher C. Clearings & Collections: Foreign & Domestic. (Columbia University, Studies in the Social Sciences: No. 347). reprint ed. 29.50 *(978-0-404-51347-4(6))* AMS Pr., Inc.
Karasik, Paul. 22 Keys to Sales Success: How to Make it Big in Financial Services. 2009. pap. 30.00 *(978-1-61623-055-5(X))* Independent Pub.
Karim, Shafiel A. The Islamic Moral Economy: A Study of Islamic Money & Financial Instruments. 2010. 160p. pap. 25.95 *(978-1-59942-539-9(4)*, Brown Walker Pr.) Universal Pubs.
Karsone, Charles V., ed. Finance & Banking Developments. 2010. (Banking & Banking Developments Ser.). 354p. 129.00 *(978-1-60876-329-0(3))* Nova Science Pubs., Inc.
Keith Dickinson, Keith Checkley &. So you want to borrow Money? 2010. 110p. pap. 16.95 *(978-1-4461-6168-5(4))* Lulu Enterprises Inc.
Kemp, Malcolm. Market Consistency: Model Calibration in Imperfect Markets. 2009. (Wiley Finance Ser.). (ENG., Illus.). 376p. 80.00 *(978-0-470-77088-7(0)*, Wiley) Wiley, John & Sons, Inc.
Kettell, Brian B. Islamic Banking & Finance Set: Introduction to Islamic Banking & Finance, 2 vols. 2011. (Wiley Finance Ser.). (ENG.). 344p. pap., wbk. ed. 90.00 *(978-1-119-98995-0(7)*, Wiley) Wiley, John & Sons, Inc.
—Islamic Finance, 3 vols, Set. 2011. (ENG.). 536p. pap. 150.00 *(978-1-119-98996-7(5)*, Wiley) Wiley, John & Sons, Inc.
Keynes, John Maynard. A Treatise on Money: The Pure Theory of Money & the Applied Theory of Money. Complete Set. 2011. 816p. pap. 24.50 ***(978-1-61427-042-3(2))*** Martino Publishing.
—A Treatise on Money: Two Volumes Complete in One. 2011. 816p. pap. 35.00 ***(978-1-61427-011-9(2))*** Martino Publishing.
Khanna, Ayesha. Straight Through Processing for Financial Services: The Complete Guide. 2007. (Complete Technology Guides for Financial Services Ser.). (ENG., Illus.). 264p. per. 79.95 *(978-0-12-466470-8(9)*, Academic Pr.) Elsevier Science & Technology Bks.
Kim, Pyong-Yon & Lim, C.H. Financial Sector Reform in Transition Economies: Implications for North Korea. 2009. (Illus.). xxv, 320p. *(978-89-521-1064-0(1)*, Seoul National Univ.) Graduate Schl. of International & Studies.
Kinley, David. The Use of Credit Instruments in Payments in the United States. 2008. 236p. 24.99 *(978-0-559-52998-6(8))*; pap. 25.75 *(978-0-559-52995-5(3))* BiblioBazaar.
Koch, Elmar B. Challenges at the Bank for International Settlements: An Economist's (Re)View. (ENG., Illus.). xiv, 357p. 2010. pap. 129.00 *(978-3-642-09190-2(3)*, 3642091903) 2007. 129.00 *(978-3-540-72789-7(2)*, 3540727892) Springer.
Konzelmann, Suzanne J. & Fovargue-Davies, Marc, eds. Banking Systems in the Crisis. 2012. (Routledge Critical Studies in Finance & Stability Ser.). (ENG., Illus.). 304p. (C). 130.00 ***(978-0-415-51789-8(3))*** Routledge.
Koslowski, Peter. The Ethics of Banking: Conclusions from the Financial Crisis. 2011. (Issues in Business Ethics Ser.). (ENG.). xv, 214p. 139.00 *(978-94-007-0655-2(3)*, 9400706553) Springer.
Kovzanadze, Irakli. Systemic & Borderline Banking Crises: Lessons Learned for Future Prevention. 2010. 220p. 29.95 *(978-1-4502-3062-9(8))*; pap. 19.95 *(978-1-4502-3060-5(1))* iUniverse, Inc.
Kroner, Niels. A Blueprint for Better Banking: Svenska Handelsbanken & a Proven Model for Post-Crash Banking. 2009. (ENG.). 196p. 75.00 *(978-1-905659-31-8(1))* Harriman Hse. Publishing GBR. Dist: Ingram Pub. Services.
Kuhlmann, Arkadi & Philp, Bruce. The Orange Code: How ING Direct Succeeded by Being a Rebel with a Cause. 2008. (ENG., Illus.). 272p. 27.95 *(978-0-470-28723-1(3)*, Wiley) Wiley, John & Sons, Inc.
Kühn, Jochen. Optimal Risk-Return Trade-Offs of Commercial Banks: And the Suitability of Profitability Measures. 2006. (Lecture Notes in Economics & Mathematical Systems Ser.). (Illus.). x, 152p. (C). pap. 109.00 *(978-3-540-34819-1(0)*, 3540348190) Springer.
Laurentis, Giacomo De, ed. Strategy & Organization of Corporate Banking. 2010. (ENG., Illus.). ix, 191p. pap. 109.00 *(978-3-642-06158-5(3)*, 3642061583) Springer.
Lépineux, François & De Bettignies, Henri-Claude, eds. Finance for a Better World: The Shift Toward Sustainability. 2009. (ENG., Illus.). 288p. 105.00 *(978-0-230-55130-5(0))* Palgrave Macmillan.
Lipovyanov, Petar. Rules vs. Discretion in Setting Bond Underwriting Fees. 2011. 60p. pap. ***(978-3-8454-1510-9(X))*** Lambert Academic Publishing.
Lobb, Nancy. Steps to Independent Living: How to Use Money Wisely. 3rd rev. ed. 2008. (YA). pap. 14.99 *(978-0-8251-6493-4(1))* Walch Education.
Macesich, George. Issues in Money & Banking. 2006. pap. 9.95 *(978-1-4288-1056-3(0))* Cram101 Inc.
MacNeil, Iain G. & O'Brien, Justin. The Future of Financial Regulation. Justin O'Brien, ed. 2010. (ENG., Illus.). 488p. pap. 100.00 *(978-1-84113-910-4(6))* Hart Publishing Ltd. GBR. Dist: International Specialized Bk. Services.
Mars-Proietti, Laura, ed. TheStreet.com Ratings' Guide to Banks & Thrifts: Winter 2007/08. 2007. pap. 249.00 *(978-1-59237-246-1(5))* Grey Hse. Publishing.
Mason, Paul. Meltdown: The End of the Age of Greed. 2009. (ENG.). 198p. pap. 14.95 *(978-1-84467-396-4(0)*, 844396) Verso Bks. GBR. Dist: Norton, W. W. & Co., Inc.
Matthäus-Maier, Ingrid & Pischke, J. D. von, eds. EU Accession - Financial Sector Opportunities & Challenges for Southeast Europe. 2010. (ENG., Illus.). xx, 367p. pap. 69.95 *(978-3-642-06245-2(8)*, 3642062458) Springer.
Matthews, Kent & Thompson, John. The Economics of Banking. 2nd ed. 2008. (ENG., Illus.). 306p. pap. 74.95 *(978-0-470-51964-6(9)*, Wiley) Wiley, John & Sons, Inc.
Mayo, Herbert B. Basic Finance: An Introduction to Financial Institutions, Investments & Management. 10th ed. 2011. (ENG.). 720p. (C). pap. 209.95 *(978-1-111-82063-3(5))* Cengage South-Western.
McKernan, Signe-Mary & Sherraden, Michael. Asset Building & Low-Income Families. 2008. 300p. pap. 29.50 *(978-0-87766-754-4(3))* Urban Institute Pr.
Mekonnen Awoke, Habtamu. The Quality of Service Delivery & Customer Satisfaction. 2010. 88p. pap. *(978-3-639-28080-7(6))* VDM Verlag Dr. Mueller e.K.
Mellor, Mary. The Future of Money: From Financial Crisis to Public Resource, 1 vol. 2010. (ENG.). 176p. 90.00 *(978-0-7453-2995-6(0))*; pap. 30.00 *(978-0-7453-2994-9(2))* Pluto Pr. GBR. Dist: Macmillan.
Mishkin. The Economics of Money, Banking, & Fin. 2006. pap. 15.95 *(978-1-4288-0484-5(6))* Cram101 Inc.
Mishkin, Frederic S. The Economics of Money, Banking & Financial Markets. 3rd rev. ed. 2012. (ENG.). 736p. (C). 206.67 ***(978-0-13-274137-8(7)***, Prentice Hall) Prentice Hall PTR.
—The Economics of Money, Banking, & Financial Markets. 8th alt. ed. 2006. (Addison-Wesley Series in Economics). (Illus.). 768p. *(978-0-321-42177-7(9))*; 832p. *(978-0-321-28726-7(6))* Addison-Wesley Longman, Inc.
—Economics of Money, Banking & Financial Markets. 9th ed. 2009. (ENG., Illus.). 756p. (C). 206.67 *(978-0-321-59979-7(9)*, Prentice Hall) Prentice Hall PTR.
—The Economics of Money, Banking, & Financial Markets. 10th rev. ed. 2012 (ENG., Illus.). 720p. (C). 206.67 ***(978-0-13-277024-8(5)***, Prentice Hall) Prentice Hall PTR.
—The Economics of Money, Banking & Financial Markets: The Business School, Student Value Edition. 3rd ed. 2012. (ENG.). 752p. (C). ring bd. 134.33 ***(978-0-13-274144-6(X)***, Prentice Hall) Prentice Hall PTR.
—Economics of Money, Banking, & Financial Markets Business School Edition & MyEconLab Student Access Code Card. 2nd ed. 2010. (ENG.). (C). 213.33 *(978-0-13-247919-6(2)*, Prentice Hall) Prentice Hall PTR.
—The Economics of Money, Banking, & Financial Markets, Business School Edition plus MyEconLab 1-semester Student Access Kit. 2nd ed. 2009. (ENG.). 768p. (C). 180.00 *(978-0-321-59891-2(1))* Addison Wesley Higher Education.
—Economics of Money, Banking, & Financial Markets, the & MyEconLab Student Access Code Card. 9th ed. 2010. (ENG.). (C). 213.33 *(978-0-13-247918-9(4)*, Prentice Hall) Prentice Hall PTR.
Mishkin, Frederic S. Economics of Money, Banking & Financial Markets, the, Student Value Edition. 10th ed. 2012. (ENG.). 752p. (C). ring bd. 134.33 ***(978-0-13-276364-6(8)***, Prentice Hall) Prentice Hall PTR.
Mishra, Anubhav Anand. Customer Satisfaction & Retail Banking. 2011. 76p. pap. ***(978-3-8443-9423-8(0))*** Lambert Academic Publishing.
Mlynarski, Feliks. Gold & Central Banks. 2011. 164p. 41.95 ***(978-1-258-02526-7(4))*** Literary Licensing, LLC.
Moh, Feng-Yuan & Lin, Bing-Huei. Risk Issues on Banking Industry in Taiwan & Mainland Chin. 2011. 64p. pap. ***(978-3-8443-2715-1(0))*** Lambert Academic Publishing.
Molyneux, Philip, ed. Bank Performance, Risk & Firm Financing. 2011. (Palgrave Macmillan Studies in Banking & Financial Institutions Ser.). (ENG., Illus.). 296p. 105.00 *(978-0-230-31335-4(3))* Palgrave Macmillan.
—Bank Strategy, Governance & Ratings. 2011. (Palgrave Macmillan Studies in Banking & Financial Institutions Ser.). (ENG., Illus.). 280p. 100.00 *(978-0-230-31334-7(5))* Palgrave Macmillan.
Money & Banking Instructor's Manual. 2008. (ENG., Illus.). 500p. (C). cd-rom 75.00 *(978-0-89982-611-0(3))* American Bankers Assn.
Morrey, Jeffrey & Guyton, Alexander. Liquidity, Interest Rates & Banking. 2009. pap. 129.00 *(978-1-60692-775-5(2))* Nova Science Pubs., Inc.
Mouatt, Simon & Adams, Carl, eds. Corporate & Social Transformation of Money & Banking: Breaking the Serfdom. 2010. (Palgrave Macmillan Studies in Banking & Financial Institutions Ser.). (ENG., Illus.). 256p. 105.00 *(978-0-230-27594-2(X))* Palgrave Macmillan.
Muhammad, Aleem. Foreign Direct Investment in Pakistan. 2010. 48p. pap. *(978-3-8383-1994-0(X))* Lambert Academic Publishing.
Munchau, Wolfgang. The Meltdown Years: The Unfolding of the Global Economic Crisis. 2009. (ENG., Illus.). 256p. 29.95 *(978-0-07-163478-6(9)*, 0071634789) McGraw-Hill Cos., The.
Naeem, Hummayoun. A Tqm Model for Commercial Branch Banking Operations. 2011. 108p. pap. ***(978-3-8454-0044-0(7))*** Lambert Academic Publishing.
Nishiyama, Yasuo, ed. Monetary Policy: Roles, Forecasting & Effects. 2012. ***(978-1-61942-181-3(X))*** Nova Science Pubs., Inc.
Northern California Urban Development. FutureProfits: Empowering Youth to Make Wise Decisions about Life & Money. 2010. 344p. pap. 24.95 *(978-1-4502-5272-0(9))* iUniverse, Inc.
Northrop, Mildred B. Control Policies of the Reichsbank, 1924-1933. (Columbia University, Studies in the Social Sciences: No. 436). reprint ed. 32.50 *(978-0-404-51436-5(7))* AMS Pr., Inc.
Nyholm, Ken, et al, eds. Portfolio & Risk Management for Central Banks & Sovereign Wealth Funds. 2011. (ENG., Illus.). 256p. 105.00 *(978-0-230-27353-5(X))* Palgrave Macmillan.
Olivieri, Annamaria & Pitacco, Ermanno. Introduction to Insurance Mathematics: Technical & Financial Features of Risk Transfers. 2011. (ENG., Illus.). xv, 475p. pap. 74.95 *(978-3-642-16028-8(X)*, 364216028X) Springer.
Olutan, Roseline Oluwatoyin. Practical Approach to Bank Lending. 2011. 256p. pap. 18.79 ***(978-1-4567-8771-4(3))*** AuthorHouse.
Omarini, Anna. Private Banking & Wealth Management. 2010. 52p. pap. *(978-3-639-14845-9(2))* VDM Verlag Dr. Mueller e.K.
Onaran, Yalman. Zombie Banks: How Broken Banks & Debtor Nations Are Crippling the Global Economy. 2011. (Bloomberg Ser.: 160). (ENG., Illus.). 184p. 34.95 ***(978-1-118-09452-5(2)***, Bloomberg Pr.) Wiley, John & Sons, Inc.
Organisation for Economic Co-Operation and Development. Bank Profitability: Financial Statements of Banks; Oecd Banking Statistics 2000-2009. 2011. (Illus.). 647p. pap. 10.00 ***(978-92-64-08986-0(1))*** Organization for Economic Cooperation & Development.
—Oecd Banking Statistics: Methodological Country Notes 2010. 2011. (Illus.). 198p. pap. 84.00 ***(978-92-64-08989-1(6))*** Organization for Economic Cooperation & Development.
Organisation for Economic Co-operation and Development Staff. Bank Profitability: Methodological Country Notes. 2008. (Illus.). 176p. pap. 63.00 *(978-92-64-04157-8(5))* Organization for Economic Cooperation & Development.
—Building Transparent Tax Compliance by Banks. 2009. (Illus.). 135p. pap. 63.00 *(978-92-64-06782-0(5))* Organization for Economic Cooperation & Development.
—Oecd Tax Policy Studies N. 15 Encouraging Savings Through Tax-Preferred Accounts. 2007. (OECD Tax Policy Studies: No. 15). (Illus.). 126p. pap. *(978-92-64-03135-7(9))* Organization for Economic Cooperation & Development.
Ostrowick, John. Biting off More Than You Can Chew. 2008. 103p. pap. 16.95 *(978-1-4092-1385-7(4))* Lulu Enterprises Inc.
Paulet, Elisabeth, ed. Financial Markets & the Banking Sector: Roles & Responsibilities in a Global World, 1 vol. 2009. (Financial History Ser.). (ENG., Illus.). 256p. 99.00 *(978-1-85196-652-3(8))* Pickering & Chatto Pubs., Ltd GBR. Dist: Ashgate Publishing Co.
Pelzer, Peter. Risk Risk Management & Regulation in the Banking Industry. 2012. (Routledge International Studies in Money & Banking Ser.). (ENG., Illus.). 256p. (C). 130.00 ***(978-0-415-50850-6(9))*** Routledge.
Poll, Edward. The Successful Lawyer-Banker Relationship: A LawBiz Managment Special Report. 2006. 84p. per. 29.00 *(978-0-9654948-7-8(X))* Poll, Edward & Assocs., Inc.
Pond, Keith. Retail Banking. 3rd rev. ed. 2007. (Illus.). 184p. per. 29.95 *(978-0-85297-777-4(8))* Financial World Publishing GBR. Dist: Stylus Publishing, LLC.
—Retail Banking. 2009. 206p. pap. 29.95 *(978-1-906403-54-6(6))* Lessons Professional Publishing GBR. Dist: Stylus Publishing, LLC.
Price, Bonamy. Currency & Banking by Bonamy Price. 2006. 196p. per. 18.99 *(978-1-4255-1578-2(9))* MPublishing.
Principles of Banking. 10th rev. ed. 2010. (ENG., Illus.). 368p. (C). pap. 99.00 *(978-0-89982-646-2(6))* American Bankers Assn.
Quagliariello, Mario, ed. Stress-testing the Banking System: Methodologies & Applications. 2009. (ENG., Illus.). 354p. 139.00 *(978-0-521-76730-9(X))* Cambridge Univ. Pr.
Raguet, Condy. A Treatise on Currency & Banking. 2009. 230p. pap. *(978-0-217-34075-5(X))*; 220p. pap. *(978-1-4590-1795-5(1))* Books LLC.
—A Treatise on Currency & Banking. 2008. 338p. 46.95 *(978-1-4372-4960-6(4))*; pap. 31.95 *(978-1-4371-2202-2(7))* Kessinger Publishing, LLC.
Rambure, Dominique & Nacamuli, Alec. Payment Systems: From the Salt Mines to the Board Room. 2008. (ENG., Illus.). 256p. 105.00 *(978-0-230-20250-4(0))* Palgrave Macmillan.
Rezaee, Zabihollah & Menon, Ram. Financial Services Firms: Governance, Regulations, Valuations, Mergers, & Acquisitions. 3rd ed. 2011. (Wiley Corporate F&a Ser.: 14). (ENG., Illus.). 582p. 125.00 *(978-0-470-60447-2(6)*, Wiley) Wiley, John & Sons, Inc.
Ritter, Lawrence S. Principles of Money, Banking, & Financial Markets & MyEconLab Student Access Code Card. 12th ed. 2010. (ENG.). (C). 213.33 *(978-0-13-247921-9(4)*, Prentice Hall) Prentice Hall PTR.
Ritter, Lawrence S., et al. Principles of Money, Banking & Financial Markets. 12th rev. ed. 2008. (ENG., Illus.). 656p. (C). 206.67 *(978-0-321-33919-5(3)*, Prentice Hall) Prentice Hall PTR.
—Study Guide for Principles of Money, Banking & Financial Markets. 12th ed. 2008. (ENG.). 408p. (C). pap. 46.67 *(978-0-321-56741-3(2))* Addison Wesley.
Rosas, Guillermo. Curbing Bailouts: Bank Crises & Democratic Accountability in Comparative Perspective. 2009. (New Comparative Politics Ser.). (ENG., Illus.). 224p. 65.00 *(978-0-472-11713-0(0))* Univ. of Michigan Pr.
Rosenfeld, James. The Selected Works of George J. Benston, Volume 2: Accounting & Finance, 1 vol. 2010. (ENG., Illus.). 448p. 99.00 *(978-0-19-538902-9(6))* Oxford Univ. Pr., Inc.
Routledge Library Editions: Banking & Finance, 38 vols. 2012. (ENG.). 9850p. 4025.00 ***(978-0-415-52086-7(X))*** Routledge.
Russell, Ellen D. New Deal Banking Reforms & Keynesian Welfare State Capitalism. 2007. (New Political Economy Ser.). (ENG.). 158p. 125.00 *(978-0-415-95661-1(7))* Routledge.
Saddleback Educational Publishing, ed. Budgeting & Banking Math. 2011. (Lifeskills Math Ser.). (ENG.). 110p. (gr. 6-12). pap., tchr. ed. 21.95 *(978-1-61651-407-5(8))* Saddleback Educational Publishing.
Sakamoto, Takayuki. Economic Policy & Performance in Industrial Democracies: Party Governments, Central Banks, & the Fiscal-Monetary Policy Mix. 2008. (Routledge Frontiers of Political Economy Ser.). (ENG., Illus.). 368p. (C). 180.00 *(978-0-415-77414-7(4))* Routledge.
Saleh, Nashwa. An Anatomy of the Financial Crisis: Blowing Tumbleweed. 2010. (Anthem Studies in Development & Globalization Ser.). (ENG., Illus.). 208p. pap. 24.95 *(978-0-85728-961-2(6))* Anthem Pr. GBR. Dist: Books International, Inc.
—An Anatomy of the Financial Crisis: Blowing Tumbleweed: When Institutions Are Too Big to Frame!: What Lessons Can We Learn & Are We Capable of Learning Them? 2010. E-Book *(978-0-85728-668-0(4))*; (Illus.). xvi, 191p. E-Book *(978-0-85728-992-6(6))* Anthem Pr.
Santos, Alejandro, ed. Paraguay: Addressing the Stagnation & Instability Trap. 2009. 316p. pap. 25.00 *(978-1-58906-852-0(1))* International Monetary Fund.
Sarma, V. Nityananda. Banking & Financial Systems. 2011. 554p. pap. ***(978-81-7596-637-6(8))*** Cambridge Univ. Pr. India Pvt. Ltd.

Schmidt, Reinhard H. Microfinance, Kommerzialisierung und Ethik. 2009. (Wissenschaftliche Gesellschaft an der Johann Wolfgang Goethe-Universitat Frankfurt am Main - Sitzungsberichte (WGF-S) Ser.). (GER.). 41p. (C). pap. 27.00 (978-3-515-09299-9(4)) Steiner, Franz Verlag Wiesbaden GmbH DEU. Dist: Brown, David Bk. Co., The.

Schoon, Natalie. Islamic Asset Management. 2011. (Edinburgh Guides to Islamic Finance Ser.). (ENG., Illus.). 184p. (gr. 17). 120.00 (978-0-7486-3995-3(0)) Edinburgh Univ. Pr. GBR. Dist: Columbia Univ. Pr.

Schweiberer, Christian. Customer Equity: CE als ergänzendes Steuerungsmittel zur wertorientierten Unternehmensführung am Beispiel einer Bank - Möglichkeiten und Grenzen. 2010. 252p. pap. (978-3-639-24032-0(4)) VDM Verlag Dr. Mueller e.K.

Shevchenko, Pavel V. Modelling Operational Risk Using Bayesian Inference. 2011. (ENG., Illus.). xvii, 302p. 89.95 (978-3-642-15922-0(2), 3642159222) Springer.

Simmons, Margaret L. ACH Transactions Risk Management. 2007. (978-1-55827-446-4(4)) Sheshunoff Information Services.

Sinclair, Timothy J. J. & Rethel, Lena. The Problem with Banks. 2012. (ENG.). 160p. 107.95 (978-1-84813-939-8(X)) Zed Bks., Ltd. GBR. Dist: Macmillan.

—The Problem with Banks. 2012. (ENG.). 160p. pap. 19.95 (978-1-84813-938-1(1)) Zed Bks., Ltd. GBR. Dist: Macmillan.

Sinn, Hans-Werner. Casino Capitalism: How the Financial Crisis Came about & What Needs to be Done Now. 2010. (ENG., Illus.). 304p. 34.95 (978-0-19-958827-5(9)) Oxford Univ. Pr., Inc.

Skinner, Chris. The Future of Banking in a Globalised World. 2007. (Wiley Finance Ser.). (ENG., Illus.). 210p. 75.00 (978-0-470-51034-6(X), Wiley) Wiley, John & Sons, Inc.

Snider, David & Howard, Chris. Money Makers: Inside the New World of Finance & Business. 2010. (ENG.). 256p. 28.00 (978-0-230-61401-7(9)) Palgrave Macmillan.

Spitzeck, Heiko, et al, eds. Banking with Integrity: The Winners of the Financial Crisis? 2012. (Humanism in Business Ser.). (ENG., Illus.). 232p. 90.00 (978-0-230-28995-6(9)) Palgrave Macmillan.

Steele, Robert. Fico Is a Four Letter Word. 2008. 264p. 24.99 (978-1-4389-3382-5(7)); pap. 19.99 (978-1-4389-3383-2(5)) AuthorHouse.

Stolz, Stéphanie. Bank Capital & Risk-Taking. 2007. (Kieler Studien - Kiel Studies). (Illus.). xiv, 150p. (C). 139.00 (978-3-540-48544-5(9), 3540485449) Springer.

Stowell, David. An Introduction to Investment Banks, Hedge Funds, & Private Equity: The New Paradigm. 2010. (ENG.). 592p. (C). 82.95 (978-0-12-374503-3(9), Academic Pr.) Elsevier Science & Technology Bks.

Sylla, Richard, et al, eds. The State, the Financial System & Economic Modernization. 2007. (ENG., Illus.). 312p. pap. 63.00 (978-0-521-03798-3(0)) Cambridge Univ. Pr.

Szekely, Gyorgy. The Essence of Money & Banking - Penzugyer Es Bankuzletek. 327p. pap. (978-963-224-667-3(5)) Akademiai Kiado.

Tabb, William K. The Restructuring of Capitalism in Our Time. 2011. (ENG.). 352p. (gr. 17). 35.00 (978-0-231-15842-8(4)) Columbia Univ. Pr.

Tabi, Agbor. Management & the Adoption of New Technologies in Retail Banking. 2010. 108p. pap. (978-3-8383-7414-7(2)) Lambert Academic Publishing.

Tadesse, Solomon. Comparative Analysis of International Financial Systems. 2009. (ENG.). 288p. 74.95 (978-0-230-60082-9(4)) Palgrave Macmillan.

TheStreet.com Ratings Staff & Weiss Ratings Inc. Staff, eds. TheStreet. com Ratings Guide to Bank Fees & Services Charges. 2010. pap. 359.00 (978-1-59237-609-4(6)) Grey Hse. Publishing.

Thuong, Tran Van & Kreng, Victor B. Knowledge Management Exploring the Effects of Organizational Culture, Training on Knowledge Transfer, & Job Performance in the Banking Sector in Vi. 2008. 68p. pap. (978-3-639-10980-1(5)) VDM Verlag Dr. Mueller e.K.

Tomohara, Akinori & Sherlock, Molly. Financial Crisis in the Global Bubble Economy. 2011. (Global Recession - Causes, Impacts & Remedies Ser.). 187p. pap. 59.00 (978-1-61470-597-0(6)) Nova Science Pubs., Inc.

Tomohara, Akinori & Sherlock, Molly, eds. Financial Crisis in the Global Bubble Economy. 2011. (Global Recession - Causes, Impacts & Remedies Ser.). 187p. 59.00 (978-1-61668-339-9(2)) Nova Science Pubs., Inc.

Tucker, George. The Theory of Money & Banks Investigated. 2009. 424p. 41.99 (978-1-117-38439-9(X)); pap. 34.75 (978-1-117-38440-5(3)) BiblioBazaar.

—The Theory of Money & Banks Investigated. 2009. 224p. pap. (978-0-217-10927-7(6)) Books LLC.

—The Theory of Money & Banks Investigated. 2008. 424p. 51.95 (978-1-4374-4302-8(8)); pap. 36.95 (978-1-4373-4081-5(4)) Kessinger Publishing, LLC.

Urrutia, Eugenio Rivera. Competition Policies in Emerging Economies: Lessons & Challenges from Central America & Mexico. Schatan, Claudia, ed. 2008. (ENG., Illus.). xii, 244p. 109.00 (978-0-387-78432-8(2), 0387784322) Springer.

Vilanculos, Flatiel Fabião. Assessment of the Use of Ict in the Financial Sector. 2010. 176p. pap. (978-3-8383-0680-3(5)) Lambert Academic Publishing.

Ward, Martha Coonfield & Edelstein, Monica. A World Full of Women. 5th ed. 2008. (ENG., Illus.). 304p. (C). per. 74.80 (978-0-205-58455-0(1)) Allyn & Bacon, Inc.

Weber, Meier, et al. The Ultra High Net Worth Banker's. 2009. (ENG., Illus.). 200p. instr.'s hndbk. ed. 180.00 (978-1-905641-75-8(3)) Harriman Hse. Publishing GBR. Dist: Ingram Pub. Services.

Weber, Olaf & Remer, Sven. Social Banks & the Future of Sustainable Finance. 2011. (Routledge International Studies in Money & Banking Ser.). (ENG., Illus.). 256p. (C). 130.00 (978-0-415-58329-9(2)) Routledge.

Webster, Noah. Miscellaneous Papers on Political & Commercial Subjects. 2009. 178p. pap. 23.13 (978-1-150-92546-7(9)) General Bks. LLC.

Weiss Ratings, ed. Weiss Ratings Guide to Banks & Thrifts. 2010. pap. 249.00 (978-1-59237-774-9(2)) Grey Hse. Publishing.

Westerfield, Ray B. Banking Principles & Practice. 2010. 312p. 36.99 (978-1-140-18146-0(7)); pap. 29.75 (978-1-140-18147-7(5)) BiblioBazaar.

White, Horace. Money & Banking Illustrated by American History. 2009. (Illus.). 298p. pap. 23.37 (978-1-150-08198-9(8)) General Bks. LLC.

Whitney, Caroline. Experiments in Credit Control. (Columbia University, Studies in the Social Sciences: No. 400). reprint ed. 31.50 (978-0-404-51400-6(6)) AMS Pr., Inc.

Wilson, J. S. G. Banking Policy & Structure (RLE Banking & Finance) A Comparative Analysis, Volume 34. 2012. (ENG.). 480p. 150.00 (978-0-415-53852-7(1)) Routledge.

Wilson, John O. S. Wilson: Banking, 5 vols. 2011. (Illus.). (978-0-415-61552-5(6)); (978-0-415-61550-1(X)); (978-0-415-61551-8(8)); (978-0-415-61547-1(X)); (978-0-415-61549-5(6)) Routledge.

Wilson, John O. S., ed. Banking, 5 vols. 2011. (Critical Concepts in Finance Ser.). (ENG., Illus.). 2192p. (C). 1495.00 (978-0-415-61546-4(1)) Routledge.

Wood, Geoffrey E., et al, eds. Monetary & Banking History. 2011. (Routledge International Studies in Money & Banking Ser.). (ENG., Illus.). 352p. (C). 140.00 (978-0-415-45146-8(9)) Routledge.

Wood, Geoffrey E. & Mayes, David G., eds. The Structure of Financial Regulation. 2007. (Routledge International Studies in Money & Banking Ser.). (Illus.). 439p. 170.00 (978-0-415-41380-0(X)) Routledge.

Wübker, Georg & Benz, Men-Andri. Power Pricing dans le monde des Banques: En sortant de la Crise. 2009. (FRE.). 254p. pap. (978-3-0343-0033-9(6)) Lang, Peter.

Young, Mary Alice. Banking Secrecy & Offshore Financial Centres: Money laundering & offshore Banking. 2012. (Routledge Research in Finance & Banking Law Ser.). (ENG.). 256p. (C). 135.00 (978-0-415-52632-6(9)) Routledge.

Zeitlberger, Jnrgen. Sustainability in the Banking Sector: The Capacity of Sustainable Banking to Enter the Mainstream. 2008. 104p. pap. (978-3-639-10326-7(2)) VDM Verlag Dr. Mueller e.K.

Zhao, Minli. Incorporation of Environmental Risks into Corporate Financing. 2008. 212p. pap. (978-3-639-03808-8(8)) VDM Verlag Dr. Mueller e.K.

BANKS AND BANKING—ACCOUNTING

Apathy, Peter, et al, eds. Österreichisches Bankvertragsrecht 1: Geschäftsbeziehung. 2nd ed. 2006. (Springers Handbücher der Rechtswissenschaft Ser.). XXIV, 391p. 99.95 (978-3-211-36962-3(7), 3211369627) Springer.

—Österreichisches Bankvertragsrecht 6: Kapitalmarkt. 2nd ed. 2007. (Springers Handbücher der Rechtswissenschaft Ser.). XXIII, 419p. 89.00 (978-3-211-37040-7(4), 3211370404) Springer.

Blasi, Ronald W. 2000 Bank Tax Guide. Bond, Kris, ed. 1000p. pap. 195.00 (978-0-8080-0487-5(5)) Toolkit Media Group.

Chakrabarti, Rajesh & De, Sankar. Capital Markets in India. 2010. (Response Bks.). (Illus.). 420p. (C). pap. 34.95 (978-81-321-0500-8(1), B05008P) SAGE Pubns., Inc.

Freedman, Jeri. First Bank Account & First Investments Smarts. 2009. 77.70 (978-1-4358-5547-2(7)); pap. 12.95 (978-1-4358-5546-5(9)); (Illus.). 64p. (J). (gr. 7-12). lib. bdg. 29.25 (978-1-4358-5270-9(2)) Rosen Publishing Group, Inc., The.

Nosko, Andrej. Securitization Within Economic Sector. 2008. 76p. pap. (978-3-639-01503-4(7)) VDM Verlag Dr. Mueller e.K.

Ojo, Marianne. The Role of the External Auditor in Bank Regulation & Supervision. 2008. 380p. pap. (978-3-639-08746-8(1)) VDM Verlag Dr. Mueller e.K.

Public Policy Issues Raised by the Report of the Lehman Bankruptcy Examiner: Hearing Before the Committee on Financial Services, U.S. House of Representatives, One Hundred Eleventh Congress, Second Session, April 20, 2010. 2010. (Illus.). iv, 228p. (978-0-16-086777-4(0), 552-070-41698-6) United States Government Printing Office.

Stedman, Kim. Economic Vision: The Foundation of Personal Financial Freedom. 2010. 200p. 29.99 (978-1-4500-7171-0(6)) Xlibris Corp.

BANKS AND BANKING—AUTOMATION

Bank Card Industry: Survey Report 1996. Date not set. (Annual Ser.). (C). 875.00 (978-0-89982-007-1(7)) American Bankers Assn.

Buzzell, David. Bank Card Business (1996) Date not set. 52.00 (978-0-89982-447-5(1)) American Bankers Assn.

The Complete Guide to Your Personal Finances Online: Step-by-Step Instructions to Take Control of Your Financial Future Using the Internet. 2011. (ENG.). 288p. pap. 24.95 (978-1-60138-297-9(9)) Atlantic Publishing Co.

Jatana, Rimpi & Uppal, R. K., eds. E-banking in India: Challenges & Opportunities. 2007. 276p. (C). 37.50 (978-81-7708-137-4(3)) New Century Publications IND. Dist: International Specialized Bk. Services.

Ravi, Vadlamani. Advances in Banking Technology & Management: Impacts of ICT & CRM. 2007. (Premier Reference Source Ser.). (Illus.). 380p. 180.00 (978-1-59904-675-4(X)) IGI Global.

Sarlak, Mohammad Ali, ed. E-Banking & Emerging Multidisciplinary Processes: Social, Economical & Organizational Models. 2010. 350p. 180.00 (978-1-61520-635-3(3)) IGI Global.

Shah, Mahmood & Clarke, Steve. E-Banking Management: Issues, Solutions, & Strategies. 2009. (Illus.). 310p. 165.00 (978-1-60566-252-7(6)) IGI Global.

BANKS AND BANKING—BRANCH BANKS

Claessens, Roger & Wiertz, Philippe. Bank Branch Management. 2006. (978-2-87974-069-0(X)) Promoculture sarl.

Southworth, Shirley Donald. Branch Banking in the United States. 2007. pap. 28.95 (978-1-4067-5584-8(2)) Southworth Pr.

BANKS AND BANKING—CORRESPONDENT BANKS

see Correspondent Banks

BANKS AND BANKING—CORRUPT PRACTICES

see also Bank Fraud

Ali, Tariq. A Banker for All Seasons: Bank of Crooks & Cheats Incorporated. 2007. (ENG., Illus.). 264p. 24.95 (978-1-905422-65-4(2)) Seagull Bks. GBR. Dist: Chicago Distribution Ctr.

Chatain, Pierre-Laurent. Preventing Money Laundering & Terrorism Financing: A Practical Guide for Bank Supervisors. 2009. (ENG., Illus.). 304p. pap. 39.95 (978-0-8213-7912-7(7), 9780821379127) World Bank Pubns.

European Bank for Reconstruction & Development (EBRD), London: A Report to Members of the Committee on Foreign Relations, United States Senate, One Hundred Ninth Congress, Second Session, June 16, 2006. 2007. (S. Prt Ser.: Vols. 109-75). v, 25p. (978-0-16-077836-0(0), 552-070-35282-1) United States Government Printing Office.

Gup, Benton E. Money Laundering, Financing Terrorism & Suspicious Activities. 2006. 199p. (C). 140.00 (978-1-60021-387-8(1)) Nova Science Pubs., Inc.

Hudson, Michael W. The Monster: How a Gang of Predatory Lenders & Wall Street Bankers Fleeced America - And Spawned a Global Crisis. 2010. (ENG.). 384p. 26.00 (978-0-8050-9046-8(0), Times Bks.) Holt, Henry & Co.

Livesey, Bruce. Thieves of Bay Street: How Banks, Brokerages & the Wealthy Steal Billions a Year from Canadians. 2012. (ENG.). 320p. 27.50 (978-0-307-35963-6(8), Random Hse CAN) Random Hse. of Canada, Ltd. CAN. Dist: Random Hse., Inc.

Milne, Alistair. The Fall of the House of Credit: What Went Wrong in Banking & What can be Done to Repair the Damage? 2009. (ENG., Illus.). 380p. 30.00 (978-0-521-76214-4(6)) Cambridge Univ. Pr.

Multilateral Development Banks: Promoting Effectiveness & Fighting Corruption: Hearing Before the Committee on Foreign Relations, United States Senate, One Hundred Ninth Congress, Second Session, March 28, 2006. 2007. iii, 53p. (978-0-16-078934-2(6), 552-070-36061-1) United States Government Printing Office.

Ritholtz, Barry. Bailout Nation: How Greed & Easy Money Corrupted Wall Street & Shook the World Economy. 2009. 288p. 24.95 (978-0-07-160905-0(9), 0071609059) McGraw-Hill Cos., The.

—Bailout Nation: How Greed & Easy Money Corrupted Wall Street & Shook the World Economy. rev. ed. 2010. (ENG., Illus.). 332p. pap. 16.95 (978-0-470-59632-6(5), Wiley) Wiley, John & Sons, Inc.

Ritholtz, Barry & Task, Aaron. Bailout Nation: How Greed & Easy Money Corrupted Wall Street & Shook the World Economy. 2009. (ENG., Illus.). 332p. 24.95 (978-0-470-52038-3(6), Wiley) Wiley, John & Sons, Inc.

Stephenson, J. r. Broken Promises, Betrayals & Barefaced Lies. 2008. 144p. pap. (978-0-9558557-0-2(5)) ShieldCrest.

Storbeck, Olaf. Die Jahrhundertkrise: Über Finanzalchemisten, das Versagen der Notenbanken und John Maynard Keynes. 2009. (GER.). xi, 194p. pap. (978-3-7910-2919-1(3)) Metzler'sche, J. B. Verlagsbuchhandlung & Carl Ernst Poeschel GmbH.

Suspicious Activity & Currency Transaction Reports: Balancing Law Enforcement Utility & Regulatory Requirements: Hearing Before the Subcommittee on Oversight & Investigations of the Committee on Financial Services, U.S. House of Representatives, One Hundred Tenth Congress, First Session, May 10, 2007. 2007. v, 141p. (978-0-16-079492-6(7), 552-070-36485-4) United States Government Printing Office.

Tax Haven Banks & U.S. Tax Compliance: Hearings Before the Permanent Subcommittee on Investigations of the Committee on Homeland Security & Governmental Affairs, United States Senate of the One Hundred Tenth Congress, Second Session, July 17 & 25, 2008. 2008. (GER & ENG., Illus.). xii, 1202p. (978-0-16-082529-3(6), 552-070-38564-9) United States Government Printing Office.

Trehan, Jyoti. Crime & Money Laundering: The Indian Perspective. 2011. (Illus.). 268p. pap. 75.00 (978-0-19-567306-7(9)) Oxford Univ. Pr., Inc.

Uebergang, Colin. Banker's Lies, Crimes & Suicides. 2010. 268p. pap. (978-1-921578-40-3(8)) BookPal.

Vickers, Raymond. Panic in the Loop: Chicago's Banking Crisis of 1932. 2011. (ENG.). 348p. 80.00 (978-0-7391-6640-6(9)) Lexington Bks.

Vickers, Raymond B. Panic in Paradise: Florida's Banking Crash Of 1926. 2007. (Illus.). 336p. per. 36.00 (978-0-8173-5414-5(X)) Univ. of Alabama Pr.

Vickers, Raymond B. Panic in the Loop: Chicago's Banking Crisis of 1932. 2011. (978-0-7391-6642-0(5)) Lexington Bks.

BANKS AND BANKING—DATA PROCESSING

Bechhoefer, Ina S., ed. & intro. Guide to Real Estate & Mortgage Banking Software. 9th ed. Date not set. 1200p. (978-0-917935-19-0(5)) Real Estate Solutions, Inc.

Kehl, James E. Code Section 199 Compliance & Planning Manual. 2008. 400p. pap. 249.00 (978-0-8080-1876-6(0)) Toolkit Media Group.

Konopatzki, Volker. Funktionsauslagerung bei Kreditinstituten: Gesellschaftsrechtlicher und bankenaufsichtsrechtlicher Rahmen. 2008. (Frankfurter wirtschaftsrechtliche Studien Ser.). 362p. pap. 81.95 (978-3-631-56142-3(3)) Lang, Peter GmbH, Europaischer Verlag der Wissenschaften DEU. Dist: Lang, Peter.

Odoke, Wilfred. Mobile Banking Adoption in the Western Europe. 2011. 96p. pap. (978-3-8433-9091-0(6)) Lambert Academic Publishing.

Welch, Brian. Electronic Banking & Treasury Security. 2nd ed. (Association of Corporate Treasurers Ser.). 192p. (978-1-85573-336-7(6)) Woodhead Publishing Ltd.

BANKS AND BANKING—DEREGULATION

Doti, Lynne Pierson. Banking in an Unregulated Environment (RLE Banking & Finance) California, 1878-1905, Volume 27. 2012. (ENG.). 184p. 100.00 (978-0-415-53223-5(X)) Routledge.

Martinez-Diaz, Leonardo. Globalizing in Hard Times: The Politics of Banking-Sector Opening in the Emerging World. 2009. (Cornell Studies in Political Economy Ser.). (Illus.). 232p. 45.00 (978-0-8014-4755-6(0)) Cornell Univ. Pr.

Mullineux, Andy. Uk Banking after Deregulation, Volume 23. 2012. (ENG.). 192p. 100.00 (978-0-415-52672-2(8)) Routledge.

Park, Sangkyun. Contagion of Bank Failures (Rle Banking & Finance), Volume 26. 2012. (ENG.). 216p. 115.00 (978-0-415-52875-7(5)) Routledge.

BANKS AND BANKING—DICTIONARIES

Banks, Erik. Dictionary of Finance, Investment & Banking. 2010. (ENG., Illus.). 560p. 45.00 (978-0-230-23829-9(7)) Palgrave Macmillan.

Bellisco, Hernandez H. English-Spanish Dictionary of Banking & Stock Exchange. (SPA.). 170p. 35.95 (978-84-85198-02-3(6)) i. b. d., Ltd.

—Spanish-English Dictionary of Banking & Stock Exchange. (SPA.). 165p. 37.50 (978-84-85198-05-4(0)) i. b. d., Ltd.

Fitch, Thomas P. Dictionary of Banking Terms. 6th rev. ed. 2012. (Barron's Business Dictionaries Ser.). (ENG.). 544p. pap. 14.99 (978-0-7641-4756-2(0)) Barron's Educational Series, Inc.

Garza Bores, Jaime. Diccionario Tecnico de Terminologia Comercial Cantable y Bancaria. (SPA.). 19.95 (978-0-7859-0707-7(6), S-25235) French & European Pubns., Inc.

Law, Jonathan & Smullen, John, eds. A Dictionary of Finance & Banking. 4th ed. 2008. (Oxford Paperback Reference Ser.). (ENG., Illus.). 464p. pap. 18.99 (978-0-19-922974-1(0)) Oxford Univ. Pr., Inc.

Levow, David E. Banking & Financial Services: Glossary of Terms. 6th rev. ed. Date not set. 120p. spiral bd. 11.95 (978-0-9661656-1-6(6)) Levow Information Systems.

Pc. Electronic Dictionary of Banking & Finance Cd-rom. cd-rom (978-1-901659-35-1(6), T&AD Poyser) A & C Black.

Plunkett, Jack W. Plunkett's Banking, Mortgages & Credit Industry Almanac 2008: Banking, Mortgages & Credit Industry Market Research, Statistics, Trends & Leading Companies. annuals Plunkett, Jack W., ed. 2007. 465p. pap. 299.99 incl. cd-rom (978-1-59392-098-2(9)) Plunkett Research, Ltd.

Research Wing Of New Century Publications, ed. Dictionary of Banking & Finance. 2008. 248p. 33.50 (978-81-7708-166-4(7)) New Century Publications IND. Dist: International Specialized Bk. Services.

Russell, Jane & Whitacker Staff. Dictionary of Banking & Finance: Over 9,000 Terms Clearly Defined. 4th ed. 2010. (ENG., Illus.). 400p. pap. 14.95 (978-1-4081-2806-0(3)) A & C Black GBR. Dist: Macmillan.

BANKS AND BANKING—DIRECTORIES

Giudice, John J. Buttonwood's Global Custody Yearbook, 2006 the Industry Forum: Twelfth Annual Survey. 12th ed. 2006. 295.00 (978-1-891008-26-9(9)) Buttonwood International Group.

Grey House Publishing, creator. TheStreet. com Ratings' Guide to Banks & Thrifts: A Quarterly Compilation of Financial Institutions Ratings & Analyses. 2008. (Street. com Guide to Banks & Thrifts Ser.). (Illus.). 382p. per. 249.00 (978-1-59237-274-4(0)) Grey Hse. Publishing.

Mars-Proietti, Laura. TheStreet. com Ratings' Guide to Banks & Thrifts. 2008. (Street. com Guide to Banks & Thrifts Ser.). pap. 249.00 (978-1-59237-313-0(5)) Grey Hse. Publishing.

Mars-Proietti, Laura, ed. TheStreet. com Ratings Guide to Banks & Thrifts: 2008. 2008. pap. 249.00 (978-1-59237-312-3(7)); pap. 249.00 (978-1-59237-311-6(9)) Grey Hse. Publishing.

—TheStreet. com Ratings Guide to Banks & Thrifts: 2009. 2009. pap. 249.00 (978-1-59237-449-6(2)); pap. 249.00 (978-1-59237-448-9(4)) Grey Hse. Publishing.

Plunkett, Jack W. Plunkett's Banking, Mortgages & Credit Industry Almanac 2007: Banking, Mortgages & Credit Industry Market Research, Statistics, Trends & Leading Companies. Plunkett, Jack W., ed. 2006. 459p. pap. 279.99 incl. cd-rom (978-1-59392-078-4(4)) Plunkett Research, Ltd.

—Plunkett's Banking, Mortgages & Credit Industry Almanac 2007 (E-Book) Banking, Mortgages & Credit Industry Market Research, Statistics, Trends & Leading Companies. Plunkett, Jack W., ed. 2006. 491p. E-Book 499.99 incl. cd-rom (978-1-59392-420-1(8)) Plunkett Research, Ltd.

—Plunkett's Banking, Mortgages & Securities Industry Almanac 2008: Banking, Mortgages & Credit Industry Market Research, Statistics, Trends & Leading Companies. annuals Plunkett, Jack W., ed. 2007. 476p. E-Book 299.99 incl. cd-rom (978-1-59392-441-6(0)) Plunkett Research, Ltd.

Presley, John R., ed. Directory of Islamic Financial Institutions, Volume 29. 2012. (ENG.). 368p. 130.00 (978-0-415-52794-1(5)) Routledge.

Thestreet Com Ratings. The Street. com Ratings' Guide to Banks & Thrifts: A Quarterly Compilation of Financial Institutions Ratings & Analyses. 2007. (Street. com Guide to Banks & Thrifts Ser.). (Illus.). 386p. per. 249.00 (978-1-59237-245-4(7)) Grey Hse. Publishing.

TheStreet.com Ratings, ed. TheStreet. com Ratings Guide to Banks & Thrifts. 2010. pap. 249.00 (978-1-59237-504-2(9)) 2010. pap. 249.00

(978-1-59237-503-5(0)) 2009. pap. 249.00 (978-1-59237-502-8(2)) Grey Hse. Publishing.
—TheStreet. com Ratings Guide to Banks & Thrifts: Fall 2009. 2009. pap. 249.00 (978-1-59237-450-2(6)) Grey Hse. Publishing.
Weiss Ratings, ed. Weiss Ratings Guide to Banks & Thrifts. 2011. pap. 249.00 (978-1-59237-777-0(7)); pap. 249.00 (978-1-59237-776-3(9)); pap. 249.00 (978-1-59237-775-6(0)) Grey Hse. Publishing.
Weiss Ratings Inc, creator. The Street. com Ratings' Guide to Banks & Thrifts: A Quarterly Compilation of Financial Institutions Ratings & Analyses. 64th ed. 2006. (Street. com Guide to Banks & Thrifts Ser.). (Illus.). 390p. per. 249.00 (978-1-58773-261-4(0)) TheStreet.com Ratings, Inc.
Weiss Ratings Inc. Staff, ed. TheStreet. com Ratings Guide to Banks & Thrifts. 2010. pap. 249.00 (978-1-59237-505-9(7)) Grey Hse. Publishing.
Women's World Banking Staff. The Women's World Banking Atlas of Global Trade, 1989-1990 Edition. 352p. (Orig.). pap. 25.00 (978-0-9624822-0-5(X)) Women's World Banking.

BANKS AND BANKING—EMPLOYEES
see Bank Employees

BANKS AND BANKING—EXAMINATIONS
see Bank Examination

BANKS AND BANKING—FRAUD
see Bank Freud

BANKS AND BANKING—GOVERNMENT GUARANTY OF DEPOSITS
see Deposit Insurance

BANKS AND BANKING—HISTORY

Ackrill, Margaret. Barclays. 2008. (ENG.). 504p. pap. 63.00 (978-0-521-04100-3(7)) Cambridge Univ. Pr.
Austin, Peter E. Baring Brothers & the Birth of Modern Finance, 1 vol. 2007. (Financial History Ser.). (ENG.). 288p. 99.00 (978-1-85196-922-7(5)) Pickering & Chatto Pubs., Ltd. GBR. Dist: Ashgate Publishing Co.
Bremer, Cornelius D. American Bank Failures. (Columbia University, Studies in the Social Sciences: No. 412). reprint ed. 20.00 (978-0-404-51412-9(X)) AMS Pr., Inc.
Brown, John Crosby. A Hundred Years of Merchant Banking. 2009. 246p. pap. (978-0-217-34141-7(1)) Books LLC.
—A Hundred Years of Merchant Banking: A History of Brown Brothers & Company, Brown, Shipley & Company & the Allied Firms. Alexander Brown & Sons, 2010. 528p. pap. 40.75 (978-1-146-61706-2(2)) BiblioBazaar.
—A Hundred Years of Merchant Banking, a History of Brown Brothers & Company, Brown, Shipley [and] Company & the Allied Firms, Alexander. 2010. 204p. pap. 28.76 (978-1-152-32583-8(3)) General Bks. LLC.
Caprio, Gerard, Jr. & Vittas, Dimitri, eds. Reforming Financial Systems: Historical Implications for Policy. 2007. (ENG.). 236p. pap. 53.00 (978-0-521-03281-0(4)) Cambridge Univ. Pr.
Carli, Guido & Barucci, Piero. Scritti e Discorsi Di Guido Carli. 2008. (ITA & ENG.). (978-88-339-2027-6(5)); (978-88-339-1954-6(4)); (978-88-339-1955-3(2)); (978-88-339-1953-9(6)) Bollati Boringhieri.
Carlson, Avery Luvere. A Banking History of Texas 1835-1929. Haas, Michelle M., ed. 2nd rev. ed. 2007. 112p. 42.95 (978-0-9767799-1-9(9)) Copano Bay Pr.
Cashill, Jack. Popes & Bankers: A Cultural History of Credit & Debt, from Aristotle to AIG, 0 vols. 2010. 272p. pap. 14.99 (978-1-59555-273-0(1)) Nelson, Thomas Inc.
Cassis, Youssef. Capitals of Capital: A History of International Financial Centres, 1780-2005. Collier, Jacqueline, tr. from FRE. 2006. (ENG.). 400p. 49.00 (978-0-521-84535-9(1)) Cambridge Univ. Pr.
Chankowski, V., et al, eds. Pistoi dia ten technen. Bankers, Loans & Archives in the Ancient World: Studies in Honour of Raymond Bogaert. 2008. (Studia Hellenistica Ser.). (FRE.). 482p. (C). pap. 122.00 (978-90-429-1996-9(5)) Peeters Pubs. & Booksellers BEL. Dist: Brown, David Bk. Co., The.
Chapman, Stanley. The Rise of Merchant Banking. 2009. 288p. 39.95 (978-0-415-48948-5(2)) Routledge.
Chernow, Ron. The House of Morgan: An American Banking Dynasty & the Rise of Modern Finance. 2010. (ENG., Illus.). 848p. pap. 22.00 (978-0-8021-4465-2(9), Grove Pr.) Grove/Atlantic, Inc.
Cohan, William D. The Last Tycoons: The Secret History of Lazard Frères & Co. 2007. (ENG.). 752p. 29.95 (978-0-385-51451-4(4), Doubleday) Doubleday Religious Publishing Group, The.
Consiglio, John, et al. Banking & Finance in the Mediterranean: A Historical Perspective. 2012. (Studies in Banking & Financial History Ser.). (Illus.). 352p. 124.95 **(978-1-4094-2984-5(9))** Ashgate Publishing Co.
Corey, Lewis. House of Morgan. reprint ed. 72.50 (978-0-404-01728-6(2)) AMS Pr., Inc.
Cottrell, Philip L., et al, eds. Centres & Peripheries in Banking: The Historical Development of Financial Markets. 2007. (Studies in Banking & Financial History Ser.). (Illus.). 342p. 134.95 (978-0-7546-6121-4(0)) Ashgate Publishing Co.
De Roover, Raymond. The Medici Bank: Its Organization, Management, Operations, & Decline. 2008. 140p. pap. 12.00 (978-1-59740-381-8(4)) ACLS Humanities E-Book.
—The Rise & Decline of the Medici Bank, 1397-1494. 2008. 552p. pap. 54.00 (978-1-59740-373-3(3)) ACLS Humanities E-Book.
Dunbar, Charles F. Chapters on the Theory & History of Banking. Sprague, O. M. W., ed. 2010. 268p. pap. 22.36 (978-1-163-90133-5(4)) 2008. 266p. 42.95 (978-0-548-92439-6(2)) 2007. (ENG.). 268p. per. 27.95 (978-0-548-58411-8(7)) Kessinger Publishing, LLC.
Farrell, Greg. Crash of the Titans: Greed, Hubris, the Fall of Merrill Lynch, & the near-Collapse of Bank of America. 2011. (ENG.). 512p. pap. 17.00 (978-0-307-71787-0(9), Crown Business) Crown Publishing Group.
Farrell, Joseph P. Babylon's Banksters: The Alchemy of Deep Physics, High Finance & Ancient Religion. 2010. (ENG., Illus.). 340p. pap. 19.95 (978-1-932595-79-6(1)) Feral Hse.
Gay, Suzanne Marie. Moneylenders of Late Medieval Kyoto. 2009. (ENG.). 301p. pap. 24.00 (978-1-4379-6974-0(7)) DIANE Publishing Co.
Goldthwaite, Richard A. The Economy of Renaissance Florence. 2011. (ENG., Illus.). 672p. (gr. 17). pap. 35.00 (978-1-4214-0059-4(6)) Johns Hopkins Univ. Pr.
Gorton, Gary. Slapped by the Invisible Hand: The Panic of 2007, 1 vol. 2010. (Fma Survey Ser.). (ENG., Illus.). 240p. 34.95 (978-0-19-973415-3(1)) Oxford Univ. Pr., Inc.
Green, Edwin. Debtors to their Profession (RLE Banking & Finance) A History of the Institute of Bankers 1879-1979, Volume 15. 2012. (ENG., Illus.). 272p. 115.00 **(978-0-415-53896-1(3))** Routledge.
Grossman, Richard S. Unsettled Account: The Evolution of Banking in the Industrialized World since 1800. 2010. (Princeton Economic History of the Western World Ser.). (ENG., Illus.). 400p. (C). 39.50 (978-0-691-13905-0(9)) Princeton Univ. Pr.
Guarino, Giuseppe, et al. Scritti e Discorsi Di Guido Carli. 2008. (ITA & ENG.). (978-88-339-2028-3(3)) Bollati Boringhieri.
Guillen, Mauro F. & Tschoegl, Adrian. Building a Global Bank: The Transformation of Banco Santander. 2008. (ENG., Illus.). 280p. (C). 39.95 (978-0-591-13125-2(2)) Princeton Univ. Pr.
Hoggson, Noble Foster. Banking Through the Ages: From the Romans to the Medicis, from the Dutch to the Rothschilds. 2007. 132p. per. 19.95 (978-1-60206-199-6(8)) Cosimo, Inc.
James, Harold. The Nazi Dictatorship & the Deutsche Bank. 2007. (ENG.). 300p. (C). pap. 32.99 (978-0-521-04365-6(4)) Cambridge Univ. Pr.
Kirshner, Jonathan. Appeasing Bankers: Financial Caution on the Road to War. 2007. (Princeton Studies in International History & Politics). (Illus.). (ENG.). 248p. (C). per. 29.95 (978-0-691-13461-1(8)); 233p. 72.00 (978-0-691-13144-3(9)) Princeton Univ. Pr.
Mason, Paul. Meltdown: The End of the Age of Greed. 2nd ed. 2010. (ENG.). 288p. pap. 14.95 (978-1-84467-653-8(6), 844653) Verso Bks. GBR. Dist: Norton, W. W. & Co., Inc.
Melford Pearson. Scourge of Cords. 2009. 292p. pap. 21.48 (978-1-4269-1788-2(0)) Trafford Publishing.
Meltzer, Allan H. A History of the Federal Reserve, 1970-1986, Vol. 2, Bk. 2. 2010. (ENG., Illus.). 616p. 75.00 (978-0-226-51994-4(5)) Univ. of Chicago Pr.
Moulton, R. K. Legislative & Documentary History of the Banks of the United States from the Time of Establishing the Bank of North America, 1781, to October 1834: With Notes & Comments. 2007. 232p. 95.00 (978-1-58477-873-8(3)) Lawbook Exchange, Ltd., The.
Parsons, Francis. A History of Banking in Connecticut. 32p. reprint ed. lib. bdg. 88.00 (978-0-7222-0491-7(4)) Library Reprints, Inc.
Poliakov, Leon. Jewish Bankers & the Holy See, Volume 28. 2012. (ENG.). 296p. 115.00 **(978-0-415-52327-1(3))** Routledge.
Scott, William A. Money & Banking. 2007. (ENG.). 420p. per. (978-1-4067-3857-5(3)) Read Bks.
Teichova, Alice, et al, eds. Banking, Trade & Industry: Europe, America & Asia from the Thirteenth to the Twentieth Century. 2011. (ENG.). 444p. pap. 55.00 (978-0-521-18887-6(3)) Cambridge Univ. Pr.

BANKS AND BANKING—INSURANCE
see Bank Insurance

BANKS AND BANKING—INSURANCE BUSINESS
Here are entered works on insurance business activities conducted by banks. Works on the insurance coverage of general banking activities are entered under Insurance, Bank.

Augustinos, Theodore P. & Emmanuel, John N. Bank Insurance Sales Methods: Requirements, Restrictions & Guidelines - Southern States. 510p. pap. 389.00 (978-0-8080-0604-6(5)) Toolkit Media Group.
Fiordelisi, Franco & Ricci, Ornella, eds. Bancassurance in Europe: Past, Present & Future. 2011. (Palgrave Macmillan Studies in Banking & Financial Institutions Ser.). (ENG., Illus.). 248p. 100.00 **(978-0-230-27155-5(3))** Palgrave Macmillan.
Khorshid. Islamic Insurance. 2007. 248p. 39.95 (978-0-415-44450-7(0)) Routledge.

BANKS AND BANKING—INVESTMENTS
see Bank Investments

BANKS AND BANKING—LAW AND LEGISLATION
see Banking Law

BANKS AND BANKING—MANAGEMENT
see Bank Management

BANKS AND BANKING—MARKETING
see Bank Marketing

BANKS AND BANKING—PUBLIC RELATIONS

Hill, Vernon. Fans, Not Customers: How Commerce Bank Created a Super-Growth Business in a No-Growth Industry. 2007. 256p. (gr. 12). 24.95 (978-1-59184-173-9(9), Portfolio (Hardcover)) Penguin Group (USA) Inc.

BANKS AND BANKING—RECORDS AND CORRESPONDENCE

A Current Assessment of Money Laundering & Terrorist Financing Threats & Countermeasures: Hearings Before the Committee on Banking, Housing, & Urban Affairs, United States Senate, One Hundred Ninth Congress, Second Session, on a Current Assessment of Money Laundering & Terrorist Financing Threats & Countermeasures, April 4, 2006. 2007. iii, 77p. (978-0-16-080171-6(0), 552-070-36908-2) United States Government Printing Office.
Ekstrom, Leif. The Bank Secrecy Act: Information Sharing & Security Efforts. 2010. (Banking & Banking Developments Ser.). 89.00 (978-1-60741-983-9(1)) Nova Science Pubs., Inc.
Hardy, Peter D. Criminal Tax, Money Laundering, & Bank Secrecy ACT Litigation. 2010. (Illus.). xl, 1671p. (978-1-57018-856-5(4)) Bureau of National Affairs, Inc., (BNA), The.
Jones, Yvonne D. Bank Secrecy Act: Opportunities Exist for Fincen & the Banking Regulators to Further Strengthen the Framework for Consistent BSA Oversight. 2006. (Illus.). 127p. (C). pap. 35.00 (978-1-4223-0792-2(1)) DIANE Publishing Co.
Klein, Lilian B. Bank Secrecy ACT: Background, Statute, & Interpretation. 2006. 161p. 69.00 (978-1-60021-472-1(X)) Nova Science Pubs., Inc.
—Bank Secrecy Act/Anti-Money Laundering. 2008. vi, 118p. pap. 50.00 (978-1-60456-624-6(8)) Nova Science Pubs., Inc.
Leuter, Anne. The Bank Secrecy ACT & Anti-Money Laundering Examination Manual. 2010. (Financial Institutions & Services Ser.). 298p. 195.00 (978-1-60876-162-3(2)) Nova Science Pubs., Inc.
Leuter, Anne, ed. The Bank Secrecy Act & Anti-Money Laundering Examination Manual. 2010. (Financial Institutions & Services Ser.). 175.50 (978-1-61728-227-0(8)) Nova Science Pubs., Inc.
Neate, F. W. Neate & Godfrey: Bank Confidentiality. Griffiths, Gwendoline & Godfrey, Gwendoline, eds. 5th rev. ed. 2011. 1004p. 395.00 (978-1-84766-694-9(9), Bloomsbury Professional) Bloomsbury Publishing Plc GBR. Dist: International Specialized Bk. Services.
Steiner, Howard. Sar Investigations - the Complete Bsa/Aml Desktop Reference. 2008. 304p. 99.96 (978-0-615-21438-2(X)) ImpactAML-INX3 Financial Pr.
Steiner, Howard & Marini, Stephen. Independent Review for MSBs - the Complete BSA/AML Audit Workbook. 2009. 165p. pap. 119.95 (978-0-615-23992-7(7)) ImpactAML-INX3 Financial Pr.
Steiner, Howard & Marini, Stephen L. Independent Review for Banks - the Complete BSA/AML Audit Workbook. 2008. 377p. pap. 129.96 (978-0-615-23790-9(8)) ImpactAML-INX3 Financial Pr.
Torp, Jeffrey. BSA/Anti-Money Laundering Question & Answer Book. 2007. (978-1-55827-442-6(1)) Sheshunoff Information Services.
Torp, Jeffrey & Hyde, Lorraine. Identity Theft Prevention Program. 2007. (Illus.). (978-1-55827-962-9(8)) Sheshunoff Information Services.

BANKS AND BANKING—SECURITY MEASURES

Chibaya Mbuya, John. Bank Securities Management. 2010. 108p. pap. (978-3-8383-8542-6(X)) Lambert Academic Publishing.
Cross, Richard F. & Gillette, Clayton P. Self-Paced Security & Fraud Training for Banks. (978-1-55827-386-3(7)) Sheshunoff Information Services.
Ekstrom, Leif. The Bank Secrecy Act: Information Sharing & Security Efforts. 2010. (Banking & Banking Developments Ser.). 89.00 (978-1-60741-983-9(1)) Nova Science Pubs., Inc.
Foxx, George. Financial Dram: Some intriguing accounts & rudiments of those who have experienced or could relate to the dramatic effect of for the love of Money. 2009. 420p. pap. 20.49 (978-1-4490-4349-0(6)) AuthorHouse.
Giudice, John J. Buttonwood's Global Custody Yearbook, 2006 the Industry Forum: Twelfth Annual Survey. 12th ed. 2006. 295.00 (978-1-891008-26-9(9)) Buttonwood International Group.
McDaniel, Herman. Bank Robbers Now Use Computers. 2007. 260p. per. 17.95 (978-1-4327-0450-6(8)) Outskirts Pr., Inc.
Shams, Heba & Butler, Mark. A Banker's Compliance Guide to Preventing Money Laundering & Terrorist Financing. 2011. (978-0-8213-8571-5(2)) World Bank Pubns.
Welch, Brian. Electronic Banking & Treasury Security. 2nd ed. (Association of Corporate Treasurers Ser.). 192p. (978-1-85573-336-7(6)) Woodhead Publishing Ltd.

BANKS AND BANKING—SERVICE CHARGES

Abele, Hanns, et al. Kartenzahlungen im Euro-Zahlungsraum. 2007. (Illus.). XVI, 163p. 89.95 (978-3-7908-1907-6(7), 3790819077) Physica-Verlag DEU. Dist: Springer.
Bank Fees: Creeping up & Up. 2008. 90p. pap. 39.00 (978-1-60692-039-8(1)) Nova Science Pubs., Inc.
A Comparison of the Deposit & Loan Pricing Behavior of Credit Unions & Commercial Banks. 2006. per. 125.00 net. (978-1-932795-07-3(3)) Filene Research Institute, Inc.
H.R. 2382, the Credit Card Interchange Fees ACT of 2009; & H.R. 3639, the Expedited Card Reform for Consumers ACT of 2009: Hearing Before the Committee on Financial Services, House of Representatives, One Hundred Eleventh Congress, First Session, October 8, 2009. 2010. (Illus.). iv, 282p. (978-0-16-085864-2(X), 552-070-41076-7) United States Government Printing Office.
H.R. 627, the Credit Cardholders' Bill of Rights ACT of 2009; & H.R. 1456, the Consumer Overdraft Protection Fair Practices ACT of 2009: Hearing Before the Subcommittee on Financial Institutions & Consumer Credit of the Committee on Financial Services, U.S. House of Representatives, One Hundred Eleventh Congress, First Session, March 19, 2009. 2009. (Illus.). v, 229p. (978-0-16-083948-1(3), 552-070-39637-3) United States Government Printing Office.
Loeper, David B. Stop the Retirement Rip-Off: How to Keep More of Your Money for Retirement. 2nd ed. 2011. (ENG., Illus.). 222p. pap. 19.95 **(978-1-118-13304-0(8)**, Wiley) Wiley, John & Sons, Inc.
Overdraft Protection: Fair Practices for Consumers: Field Hearing Before the Subcommittee on Financial Institutions & Consumer Credit of the Committee on Financial Services, U.S. House of Representatives, One Hundred Tenth Congress, First Session, July 11, 2007. 2007. (Illus.). v, 104p. (978-0-16-079968-6(6), 552-070-36793-4) United States Government Printing Office.
Oversight of Federal Payment of Interchange Fees: How to Save Taxpayer Dollars: Hearing Before a Subcommittee of the Committee on Appropriations, United States Senate, One Hundred Eleventh Congress, Second Session: Special Hearing, June 16, 2010, Washington, DC. 2011. iv, 72p. **(978-0-16-087992-0(2)**, 552-070-42402-4) United States Government Printing Office.
Weiss Ratings, ed. Weiss Ratings Guide to Bank Fees & Services Charges. 2011. pap. 359.00 (978-1-59237-812-8(9)) Grey Hse. Publishing.

BANKS AND BANKING—STATE SUPERVISION
see also Banks and Banking, Central

Allison, Herbert M. Hearing with Herbert M. Allison, Jr., Assistant Secretary of the Treasury for Financial Stability: Hearing Before the Congressional Oversight Panel, One Hundred Eleventh Congress, First Session, October 22, 2009. 2009. (Illus.). iii, 56p. (978-0-16-085051-6(7), 552-070-40408-2) United States Government Printing Office.
Blömer, Ulrike. Grenzüberschreitende Sachverhalte im Bankenaufsichtsrecht. 2010. (Frankfurter wirtschaftsrechtliche Studien Ser.). (GER.). 276p. 79.95 (978-3-631-60413-7(0)) Lang, Peter GmbH, Europaischer Verlag der Wissenschaften DEU. Dist: Lang, Peter.
Busch, Andreas. Banking Regulation & Globalization. 2012. (ENG.). 304p. pap. 45.00 **(978-0-19-965557-1(X))** Oxford Univ. Pr., Inc.
CCH Incorporated. Wall Street Reform & Consumer Protection Act Of 2010: Law, Explanation & Analysis. 2010. 1623p. pap. 129.00 (978-0-8080-2164-3(3), CCH) Wolters Kluwer Tax & Accounting.
Crowley, Robert W., ed. Unique Treatment of GMAC under TARP. 2010. (Financial Institutions & Services Ser.). (Illus.). ix, 176p. 115.00 (978-1-61728-305-5(3)) Nova Science Pubs., Inc.
Dewatripont, Mathias & Tirole, Jean. The Prudential Regulation of Banks. 2009. (Walras-Pareto Lectures). (ENG.). 272p. (gr. 17). pap. 30.00 (978-0-262-51386-9(2)) MIT Pr.
Dewatripont, Mathias, et al. Balancing the Banks: Global Lessons from the Financial Crisis. Tribe, Keith, tr. from FRE. 2010. (ENG., Illus.). 160p. (C). 30.00 (978-0-691-14523-5(7)) Princeton Univ. Pr.
Does the Dodd-Frank ACT End "Too Big to Fail?" Hearing Before the Subcommittee on Financial Institutions & Consumer Credit of the Committee on Financial Services, U.S. House of Representatives, One Hundred Twelfth Congress, First Session, June 14, 2011. 2011. v, 103p. **(978-0-16-089633-0(9)**, 552-070-43522-1) United States Government Printing Office.
The End of Excess: Hearing Before the Subcommittee on Oversight & Investigations of the Committee on Financial Services, U.S. House of Representatives, One Hundred Eleventh Congress, Second Session. 2010. (Illus.). **(978-0-16-087020-0(8)**, 552-070-41879-2 (pt.1)) United States Government Printing Office.
Examining the Link Between Fed Bank Supervision & Monetary Policy: Hearing Before the Committee on Financial Services, U.S. House of Representatives, One Hundred Eleventh Congress, Second Session, March 17, 2010. 2010. iii, 129p. (978-0-16-086419-3(4), 552-070-41480-1) United States Government Printing Office.
Financial Regulatory Reform: Protecting Taxpayers & the Economy: Hearing Before the Joint Economic Committee, Congress of the United States, One Hundred Eleventh Congress, First Session, November 19, 2009. 2010. ii, 57p. (978-0-16-085972-4(7), 552-070-41163-1) United States Government Printing Office.
Frach, Lotte. Finanzmarktregulierung in Deutschland. 2010. (GER., Illus.). 267p. pap. (978-3-8329-5759-9(6)) Nomos Verlagsgesellschaft.
Goodhart, Charles. The Basel Committee on Banking Supervision: A History of the Early Years, 1974-1997. 2011. (ENG., Illus.). 624p. 150.00 (978-1-107-00723-9(2)) Cambridge Univ. Pr.
Goodhart, Charles A.E. The Regulatory Response to the Financial Crisis. 2009. (Illus.). 168p. 119.00 (978-1-84844-451-5(6)) Elgar, Edward Publishing, Inc.
Hendrickson, Jill M. Regulation & Instability in U. S. Commercial Banking: A History of Crises. 2011. (Palgrave Macmillan Studies in Banking & Financial Institutions Ser.). (ENG., Illus.). 320p. 110.00 (978-0-230-28066-3(8)) Palgrave Macmillan.
Huang, Yi. Yin Hang Jian Guan Fa Lü Yan Jiu: Legal Thoughts on Banking Regulation. 2009. (CHI., Illus.). 10p. (978-7-5036-9700-5(8)) Law Publishing Hse., The.
International Monetary Fund, Monetary and Financial Systems Dept Staff, contrib. by. Working Together. 2007. pap. (978-1-58906-487-4(9), International Monetary Fund.

B

Konopatzki, Volker. Funktionsauslagerung bei Kreditinstituten: Gesellschaftsrechtlicher und bankenaufsichtsrechtlicher Rahmen. 2008. (Frankfurter wirtschaftsrechtliche Studien Ser.). 362p. pap. 81.95 *(978-3-631-56142-3(3))* Lang, Peter GmbH, Europaischer Verlag der Wissenschaften DEU. Dist: Lang, Peter.

Lessons Learned in Risk Management Oversight at Federal Financial Regulators: Hearing Before the Subcommittee on Securities, Insurance, & Investment of the Committee on Banking, Housing, & Urban Affairs, United States Senate, One Hundred Eleventh Congress, First Session, on Discussing the Role of Federal Financial Regulators in the Financial Crisis in the United States & Reforming Regulation to Ensure a Strong Financial System, March 18, 2009. 2009. iii, 177p. *(978-0-16-084674-8(9)*, 552-070-40167-9) United States Government Printing Office.

Malloy, Michael P. Principles of Bank Regulation. 3rd rev. ed. 2011. 592p. pap. 46.00 ***(978-0-314-19456-5(8))*** West Publishing Co., College & Schl. Div.

Masciandaro, Donato & Quintyn, Marc, eds. Designing Financial Supervision Institutions: Independence, Accountability & Governance. 2007. 528p. 201.00 *(978-1-84720-216-1(0))* Elgar, Edward Publishing, Inc.

McKinley, Vern. Financing Failure: A Century of Bailouts. 2012. (ENG.). 384p. 29.95 ***(978-1-59813-053-9(6))*** Independent Institute, The.

—Financing Failure: A History of Bailouts. 2012. (ENG.). 384p. pap. 19.95 ***(978-1-59813-049-2(8))*** Independent Institute, The.

Moyer, Stephen E., ed. Financial Regulatory Reform. 2010. (Global Recession - Causes, Impacts & Remedies Ser.). 180p. pap. 89.00 *(978-1-60741-567-1(4))* Nova Science Pubs., Inc.

Onwunta, Akwum. Contributions to Credit Portfolio Modeling & Optimization. 2011. (Schriften zur empirischen Wirtschaftsforschung Ser.). 120p. 35.95 *(978-3-631-61171-5(4))* Lang, Peter GmbH, Europaischer Verlag der Wissenschaften DEU. Dist: Lang, Peter.

Parker, David C. & International Monetary Fund. Closing a Failed Bank: Resolution Practices & Procedures. 2011. (Illus.). 244p. pap. ***(978-1-61635-027-7(X))*** International Monetary Fund.

Peláez, Carlos A. & Peláez, Carlos M. Regulation of Banks & Finance: Theory & Policy after the Credit Crisis. 2009. (ENG., Illus.). 288p. 121.00 *(978-0-230-23903-6(X))* Palgrave Macmillan.

Peláez, Carlos M. & Peláez, Carlos A. Financial Regulation after the Global Recession. 2009. (ENG., Illus.). 208p. 100.00 *(978-0-230-23902-9(1))* Palgrave Macmillan.

Prohibiting Certain High-Risk Investment Activities by Banks & Bank Holding Companies: Hearing Before the Committee on Banking, Housing, & Urban Affairs, United States Senate, One Hundred Eleventh Congress, Second Session, on Examining Recent Restrictions Placed on Commercial Banks & Bank Holding Companies' High-Risk Investment Activities, February 2, 2010. 2010. iii, 71p. ***(978-0-16-087802-2(0)***, 552-070-42306-1) United States Government Printing Office.

Putten, Maartje van. Policing the Banks: Accountability Mechanisms for the Financial Sector. 2008. (ENG.). 520p. (C). *(978-0-7735-3401-8(6))* McGill-Queen's Univ. Pr.

Quintyn, Marc & Taylor, Michael W. Should Financial Sector Regulators Be Independent? (CHI.). *(978-1-58906-313-6(9)*, EIICA032); (ARA.). *(978-1-58906-312-9(0)*, EIIAA032); (SPA.). *(978-1-58906-311-2(2)*, EIISA032); (FRE.). *(978-1-58906-310-5(4)*, EIIFA032); (RUS.). *(978-1-58906-314-3(7)*, EIIRA032) International Monetary Fund.

Rochet, Jean-Charles. Why Are There So Many Banking Crises? The Politics & Policy of Bank Regulation. 2008. (ENG., Illus.). 336p. (C). 65.00 *(978-0-691-13146-7(5))* Princeton Univ. Pr.

The State of the Banking Industry: Hearing Before the Committee on Banking, Housing, & Urban Affairs, United States Senate, One Hundred Tenth Congress, Second Session, on the State of the Banking Industry. 2010. (Illus.). *(978-0-16-085662-4(0)*, 552-070-40899-1 (pt.1)); *(978-0-16-085685-3(X)*, 552-070-40899-1 (pt.1)) United States Government Printing Office.

Stern, Gary H. & Feldman, Ron J. Too Big to Fail: The Hazards of Bank Bailouts. 2009. (ENG.). 230p. pap. 22.95 *(978-0-8157-0304-4(X))* Brookings Institution Pr.

Strengthening & Streamlining Prudential Bank Supervision: Hearing Before the Committee on Banking, Housing, & Urban Affairs, United States Senate, One Hundred Eleventh Congress, First Session, on Strengthening & Streamlining Prudential Bank Supervision to Better Provide the Safety, Soundness, & Stability of the Financial Markets, August 4 & September 29, 2009. 2010. ii, 182p. ***(978-0-16-086103-1(9)***, 552-070-41213-1) United States Government Printing Office.

van Putten, Maartje. Policing the Banks: Accountability Mechanisms for the Financial Sector. 2008. (ENG.). 520p. (C). pap. *(978-0-7735-3402-5(4))* McGill-Queen's Univ. Pr.

Williamson, Philip B., ed. Insolvency Issues & the FDIC. 2010. (Financial Institutions & Services Ser.). 177p. 115.00 *(978-1-60876-801-1(5))* Nova Science Pubs., Inc.

BANKS AND BANKING—TECHNOLOGICAL INNOVATIONS

Banking Technology Competition Handbook: Companies-Products-Services. 125p. (Orig.). pap. 695.00 *(978-0-7605-1868-7(8))* Rector Pr., Ltd.

Batchelor, Simon, et al. M-Banking: An African Financial Revolution. 2010. (ENG.). 130p. pap. 29.95 *(978-90-5727-063-5(3))* International Bks. NLD. Dist: Independent Pubs. Group.

Khiaonarong, Tanai & Liebena, Jonathan. Banking on Innovation: Modernisation of Payment Systems. 2009. (Contributions to Economics Ser.). (ENG., Illus.). xviii, 190p. 129.00 *(978-3-7908-2332-5(5)*, 3790823325) Physica-Verlag DEU. Dist: Springer.

King, Brett. Bank 2. 0: How Customer Behaviour & Technology Will Change the Future of Financial Services, 1 vol. 2011. (ENG., Illus.). 360p. 39.99 *(978-981-4302-07-4(4))* Marshall Cavendish International (Asia) Private Ltd. SGP. Dist: Marshall Cavendish Corp.

Morris, Tim. Innovations in Banking, Volume 22. 2012. (ENG.). 152p. 100.00 ***(978-0-415-52667-8(1))*** Routledge.

Ravi, Vadlamani. Advances in Banking Technology & Management: Impacts of ICT & CRM. 2007. (Premier Reference Source Ser.). (Illus.). 380p. 180.00 *(978-1-59904-675-4(X))* IGI Global.

Rouse, Nick. Bankers' Lending Techniques. 3rd rev. ed. 2010. 300p. pap. 35.00 *(978-1-906403-00-3(7))* Lessons Professional Publishing GBR. Dist: Stylus Publishing, LLC.

Uppal, R., ed. Banking Services & Information Technology: The Indian Experience. 2008. 215p. 32.75 *(978-81-7708-176-3(4))* New Century Publications IND. Dist: International Specialized Bk. Services.

—Banking with Technology. 2008. 218p. 33.75 *(978-81-7708-151-0(9))* New Century Publications IND. Dist: International Specialized Bk. Services.

BANKS AND BANKING—TRUST DEPARTMENTS

see Trust Companies

BANKS AND BANKING—VOCATIONAL GUIDANCE

Careers in Financial Markets 2006-07: Your guide to finding a job in securities & Banking. 2006. per. 19.95 *(978-0-9788560-0-7(7))* eFinancialCareers.

Fitch, Thomas. Career Opportunities in Banking, Finance, & Insurance. 2nd rev. ed. 2007. (Career Opportunities Ser.). 288p. per. 18.95 *(978-0-8160-6474-8(1))*; (C). (gr. 9). 49.50 *(978-0-8160-6473-1(3))* Facts On File, Inc. (Ferguson Publishing Co.).

Haider, Saba. Vault Career Guide to Investment Banking, 2nd Edition: European Edition. 2009. 176p. pap. 34.95 *(978-1-58131-692-6(5))* Vault.com.

Reeves, Diane Lindsey & Hansen, W. A. Career Ideas for Teens in Finance. 2012. 45.00 ***(978-0-8160-8273-5(1)***, Ferguson Publishing Co.) Facts On File, Inc.

BANKS AND BANKING—AFRICA

Abafita, Jemal. Microfinance & Loan Repayment. 2009. 88p. pap. *(978-3-639-17359-8(7))* VDM Verlag Dr. Mueller e.K.

Agyei, Samuel Kwaku. Capital Structure & Performance of Banks in Ghan. 2011. 112p. pap. ***(978-3-8454-0311-3(X))*** Lambert Academic Publishing.

Alayande, Ben & Apati, Seth. The Nigerian Banking Sector Reforms: Power & Politics. 2012. (Palgrave Macmillan Studies in Banking & Financial Institutions Ser.). (ENG., Illus.). 224p. 90.00 *(978-0-230-27841-7(8))* Palgrave Macmillan.

Aregawi Weldegiorgis, Kibrom & Kibrom, Aregawi Weldegiorgis. Customer Satisfaction & Service Loyalty in Banking Industry: The Case of Wegagen Bank, Mekelle Branch, Mekelle, Ethiopia. 2011. 108p. pap. ***(978-3-639-32342-9(4))*** VDM Verlag Dr. Mueller e.K.

Asnakech, Getnet. Establishing Sound Corporate Governance Regime Ethiopia Private Banks. 2011. 116p. pap. ***(978-3-639-33303-9(9))*** VDM Verlag Dr. Mueller e.K.

Batchelor, Simon, et al. M-Banking: An African Financial Revolution. 2010. (ENG.). 130p. pap. 29.95 *(978-90-5727-063-5(3))* International Bks. NLD. Dist: Independent Pubs. Group.

Chirimubwe, Ranga Gilbert. Service Quality Dimensions in the Retail Banking Sector of Zimbabwe. 2011. 108p. pap. ***(978-3-8443-0633-0(1))*** Lambert Academic Publishing.

Cobham, David & Dibeh, Ghassan, eds. Monetary Policy & Central Banking in the Middle East & North Africa. 2012. (Routledge Political Economy of the Middle East & North Africa Ser.). (ENG., Illus.). 272p. (C). pap. 42.95 ***(978-0-415-54173-2(5))*** Routledge.

Donzo, Fonsia M. Banking Supervision in Liberi: How Adequate & Effective? 2011. 124p. pap. ***(978-3-8443-0872-3(5))*** Lambert Academic Publishing.

Enguah, Samuel Edusah. Information Technology a Partner for Customer Satisfaction in Banking. 2011. 92p. pap. ***(978-3-8454-1093-7(0))*** Lambert Academic Publishing.

Fadoju, Babatunde. Effects of Globalization on Bank Operations & Management. 2011. 92p. pap. ***(978-3-8454-0098-3(6))*** Lambert Academic Publishing.

Folami, Olakunle Michael. Crime in the Banking Sector & the Nation's Economy. 2011. 140p. pap. ***(978-3-8433-9320-1(6))*** Lambert Academic Publishing.

Garuba, Anthony. Credit Administration. 2011. 60p. pap. ***(978-3-8443-8258-7(5))*** Lambert Academic Publishing.

Gatsi, John G. & K. AKOTO, Richard. Debt Policy & Profitability of Commercial Banks in Ghan. 2010. 84p. pap. *(978-3-8383-9499-2(2))* Lambert Academic Publishing.

Goldface-Irokalibe, I. Law of Banking Nigeria. 2007. 376p. pap. *(978-978-023-225-2(7))* Malthouse Press Ltd, Nigeria NGA. Dist: Michigan State Univ. Pr.

Hicks, Tyler G., compiled by. Mideast & North African Banks & Financial Institutions. 17th ed. 2007. pap. 15.00 *(978-1-56150-839-6(X))* International Wealth Success, Inc.

Honohan, Patrick & Beck, Thorsten. Making Finance Work for Africa. 2007. (Stand Alones Ser.). (ENG., Illus.). 260p. pap. 29.95 incl. cd-rom *(978-0-8213-6909-8(1)*, 9780821369098) World Bank Pubns.

Lucy, Titus. Non-Performing Loans Management Practices & Financial Performance: A Case of Kenyan Commercial Banks. 2011. 108p. pap. ***(978-3-639-33919-2(3))*** VDM Verlag Dr. Mueller e.K.

Lukman, Raimi. Challenges of Restructuring on Human Resources Management in Nigeria: A Case Study of the Nigerian Banking Industry. 2011. 112p. pap. ***(978-3-639-32536-2(2))*** VDM Verlag Dr. Mueller e.K.

Nampewo, Dorothy. Determinants of Interest Rate Spreads in Uganda's Banking Sector. 2011. 72p. pap. ***(978-3-8443-2459-4(3))*** Lambert Academic Publishing.

Newman, Lucy. Employee Performance Management Practices Within Banks in Nigeri. 2011. 192p. pap. ***(978-3-8443-2854-7(8))*** Lambert Academic Publishing.

Nukpezah, Daniel & Nyumuyo, Cephas. What Drives Customer Loyalty & Profitability? 2010. 84p. pap. *(978-3-8383-7127-6(5))* Lambert Academic Publishing.

Oyungerel, Padsuren. Online Banking - the Effect of Prior Experience on Online Banking Acceptance in Mongolia. 2008. 112p. pap. *(978-3-639-00539-4(2))* VDM Verlag Dr. Mueller e.K.

Tesso, Dereje Worku. Evaluation of Credit Management. 2010. 92p. pap. *(978-3-639-16614-9(0))* VDM Verlag Dr. Mueller e.K.

The World Bank. Financial Access & Stability: A Road Map for the Middle East & North Africa. 2011. (MENA Development Report). (ENG., Illus.). 364p. pap. 40.00 ***(978-0-8213-8835-8(5)***, 9780821388358) World Bank Pubns.

Tikum, Bertrand Mbah. Implementing Online Banking System. 2010. 96p. pap. *(978-3-8383-7365-2(0))* Lambert Academic Publishing.

World Bank Staff, contrib. by. Financial Access & Stability: A Roadmap for the Middle East & North Africa. 2011. (Illus.). xxvi, 334p. ***(978-0-8213-8856-3(8))*** World Bank Pubns.

BANKS AND BANKING—ASIA

Abd Kadir, Hazlina. Banks Efficiency: A data envelopment Analysis. 2010. 120p. pap. *(978-3-8383-1964-3(8))* Lambert Academic Publishing.

Abdul Samad, Eleena Masnee. Demand Conditions for Islamic Home Financing in Malaysi. 2011. 336p. pap. ***(978-3-8443-0797-9(4))*** Lambert Academic Publishing.

Ahmad, Abu Umar Faruq. Developments in Islamic Banking Practice: The Experience of Bangladesh. 2010. 228p. pap. 25.95 *(978-1-59942-828-4(8))* Universal Pubs.

Asif, Saeed & Burki, Abid A. Productivity & Economies in Pakistan's Commercial Banking Sector: Productivity in Pakistani Banks. 2011. 72p. pap. ***(978-3-639-30288-2(5))*** VDM Verlag Dr. Mueller e.K.

Aslam, M. Farhan, et al. Islamic Banking in Pakistan. 2011. 96p. pap. ***(978-3-8454-0206-2(7))*** Lambert Academic Publishing.

Aspatore Books Staff, compiled by. Banking & Finance Client Strategies in Asia, 2010 Ed: Leading Lawyers on Understanding the Impact of Global Banking Reform, Navigating Regional Banking Laws, & Meeting the Needs of Today's Clients (Inside the Minds) 2010. (Illus.). 316p. pap. 100.00 *(978-0-314-26821-1(9))* Aspatore Bks.

Awal, Russel. Financial Exclusion & Microcredit. 2011. 64p. pap. ***(978-3-8443-2811-0(4))*** Lambert Academic Publishing.

BIA. Key Banking, Financial, & Insurance Companies of Asia. 6th rev. ed. 2006. 180p. (J). pap. 219.00 *(978-1-4187-4375-8(5))* Business Information Agency.

Clark, Heather A. When There Was No Money: Building ACLEDA Bank in Cambodia's Evolving Financial Sector. 2010. (ENG., Illus.). xx, 257p. pap. 74.95 *(978-3-642-06693-1(3)*, 3642066933) Springer.

Cohen, Robert. Turning Around a Bank in Korea, a Business & Cultural Challenge. 2008. 232p. pap. 29.78 *(978-0-557-03772-8(7))* Lulu Enterprises Inc.

Cook, Malcolm. Banking Reform in Southeast Asia. 2011. (ENG., Illus.). 176p. pap. 42.95 ***(978-0-415-67388-4(7))*** Routledge.

Cook, Malcolm. Banking Reform in Southeast Asia: The Region's Decisive Decade. 2008. (Routledge Studies in the Growth Economies of Asia Ser.). (Illus.). 176p. 150.00 *(978-0-415-41319-0(2))* Routledge.

Elaydi, Raed. In Search of Proof: Finding the Barefoot Banker in the Tea Hills. 2010. (C). pap. 7.00 *(978-1-61674-519-6(3))* Davidson, William Institute At The Univ. of Michigan, The.

Engel, Susan. The World Bank & the Post-Washington Consensus in Vietnam & Indonesia: Inheritance of Loss. 2009. (Routledge Studies in Asia's Transformations Ser.). (ENG., Illus.). 238p. 130.00 *(978-0-415-54743-7(1))* Routledge.

et al., compiled by. Banking & Finance Client Strategies in Asia: Leading Lawyers on Educating Clients, Understanding Key Rules & Regulations, & Navigating Recent Cases & Developments, Inside the Minds. 2009. 696p. pap. 125.00 *(978-0-314-90824-7(2))* Aspatore Bks.

Feldman, Gerald D. & Hertner, Peter. Finance & Modernization: A Transnational & Transcontinental Perspective for the Nineteenth & Twentieth Centuries. 2008. (Studies in Banking & Financial History Ser.). (Illus.). 320p. 134.95 *(978-0-7546-6271-6(3))* Ashgate Publishing Co.

Ferrari, Aurora. Increasing Access to Rural Finance in Bangladesh: The Forgotten Missing Middle. 2007. (Directions in Development Ser.). (ENG., Illus.). 156p. per. 20.00 *(978-0-8213-7333-0(1)*, 9780821373330) World Bank Pubns.

Grössinger, Klaus. Islamic Banking in South East Asi. 2010. 124p. pap. *(978-3-639-24500-4(8))* VDM Verlag Dr. Mueller e.K.

Hoflich, Peter & Asian Banker Staff. Asia's Banking CEOs: The Future of Finance in the Asia. 2008. (ENG., Illus.). 250p. 42.00 *(978-0-470-82359-0(3)*, Wiley) Wiley, John & Sons, Inc.

Hossain, A. Central Banking & Monetary Policy in the Asia-Pacific. 2009. (Illus.). 368p. 173.00 *(978-1-84720-372-4(8))* Elgar, Edward Publishing, Inc.

Howse, Joseph. Silk Road, Silver Lining. 2008. 204p. pap. *(978-3-639-07134-4(4))* VDM Verlag Dr. Mueller e.K.

Huang, Juan. Competition, Concentration & Efficiency of Commercial Banks in South Korea, Mainland China & Taiwan, 5 vols., Vol. 5. 2011. (Enrich Series on China's Economic Issues Ser.). (ENG.). 216p. 88.00 *(978-981-4298-26-1(3))* Enrich Professional Publishing (S)., Ltd. SGP. Dist: Independent Pubs. Group.

Jahan, Nusrat. Evaluation of Satisfaction of Employees with Performance Appraisal. 2010. 76p. pap. *(978-3-639-25796-0(0))* VDM Verlag Dr. Mueller e.K.

Khan, Mohammad Mansoor & Bhatti, M. Ishaq. Developments in Islamic Banking: The Case of Pakistan. 2008. (Palgrave Macmillan Studies in Banking & Financial Institutions Ser.). (ENG., Illus.). 256p. 109.00 *(978-1-4039-9877-4(9))* Palgrave Macmillan.

Leeamornsiri, Joseph Nantawut. Hrd Competency Used During the Mergers. 2009. 228p. pap. *(978-3-639-20816-0(1))* VDM Verlag Dr. Mueller e.K.

Long, Borareaksmey. Relationship Marketing in the Banking Industry. 2011. (Illus.). 80p. pap. ***(978-3-8433-8052-2(X))*** Lambert Academic Publishing.

Meenai, S. A. & Ansari, Javed A. Money & Banking in Pakistan. 6th ed. 2010. (ENG., Illus.). 320p. pap. 24.95 *(978-0-19-547809-9(6))* Oxford Univ. Pr., Inc.

Munusamy, Jayaraman, et al. Channel Innovation in Commercial Banking Sector. 2011. 80p. pap. ***(978-3-8443-9590-7(3))*** Lambert Academic Publishing.

—Service Channel Transformation in Retail Banking. 2011. 92p. pap. ***(978-3-8443-9960-8(7))*** Lambert Academic Publishing.

Nanava, Rusudan. Islamic Banking & Financial Products. 2009. 88p. pap. *(978-3-639-13926-6(7))* VDM Verlag Dr. Mueller e.K.

Peck Ling, Tee. Bond Market Development in Emerging Asian Economies. 2009. 124p. pap. *(978-3-639-17304-8(X))* VDM Verlag Dr. Mueller e.K.

Phuntsho, Dorji. Supervision of Banks to Minimize Non Performing Loans. 2011. 88p. pap. ***(978-3-8433-9077-4(0))*** Lambert Academic Publishing.

Saha, Anup Kumar. Financial Performance Analysis in the Banking Sector of Bangladesh. 2011. 112p. pap. ***(978-3-8443-2315-3(5))*** Lambert Academic Publishing.

Salam, Muhammad Abdus. The Role of Micro-Credit in Institutionalization of Development. 2011. 112p. pap. ***(978-3-8454-0685-5(2))*** Lambert Academic Publishing.

Saleem, Zohra & Rashid, Kashif. Customer Satisfaction in Mobile Banking Industry of Pakistan. 2011. 148p. pap. ***(978-3-8454-0249-9(0))*** Lambert Academic Publishing.

Sampa, Saha, et al. Job Satisfaction of Bank Employees in Bangladesh: An Analysis of Satisfaction Factors. 2011. 160p. pap. ***(978-3-639-30241-7(9))*** VDM Verlag Dr. Mueller e.K.

Satyanath, Shanker. Globalization, Politics, & Financial Turmoil: Asia's Banking Crisis. 2009. (Political Economy of Institutions & Decisions Ser.). (ENG., Illus.). 176p. pap. 26.99 *(978-0-521-10743-3(1))* Cambridge Univ. Pr.

Shah, Bahadar & Khan, Bakhtiar. Privatization of Banking Sector in Pakistan. 2010. 48p. pap. *(978-3-639-22146-6(X))* VDM Verlag Dr. Mueller e.K.

Shaharuddin, Amir. Mudarabah in Islamic Banking. 2011. 212p. pap. ***(978-3-8443-2252-1(3))*** Lambert Academic Publishing.

Shandre M Thangavelu, et al, eds. Real & Financial Aspect of Economic Integration in East Asia. 2012. (Routledge Studies in the Modern World Economy Ser.). (ENG., Illus.). 248p. (C). 152.00 *(978-0-415-68643-3(1))* Routledge.

Sophastienphong, Klatchai & Kulathunga, Anoma. Getting Finance in South Asia 2009: Indicators & Analysis of the Commercial Banking Sector. 2008. (Getting Finance in South Asia Ser.). (ENG., Illus.). 176p. pap. 45.00 *(978-0-8213-7571-6(7)*, 9780821375716) World Bank Pubns.

—Getting Finance in South Asia 2010: Indicators & Analysis of the Commercial Banking Sector - Managing the Impact of the Global Financial Crisis & Economic Slowdown. 2010. (Getting Finance in South Asia Ser.). (ENG., Illus.). 352p. pap. 45.00 incl. cd-rom *(978-0-8213-8057-4(5)*, 9780821380574) World Bank Pubns.

Starr, Peter. Citibank: A Century in Asia. 2007. (ENG., Illus.). 216p. 39.95 *(978-981-4068-29-1(2)*, Didier Millet,Csi) Continental Sales, Inc.

Terada-Hagiwara, Akiko & Pasadilla, Gloria. Experience of Asian Asset Management Companies: Do They Increase Moral Hazard? — Evidence from Thailand. 2007. (Illus.). 28p. (C). reprint ed. pap. 15.00 *(978-1-4223-1388-6(3))* DIANE Publishing Co.

Trinh Quang, Anh. Banking Supervision Moves Ahead in the New Er. 2010. 164p. pap. *(978-3-8383-7445-1(2))* Lambert Academic Publishing.

Venardos, Angelo M. Islamic Banking & Finance in South-East Asia: Its Development & Future. (Asia-Pacific Business Ser.). 2nd ed. 2006. 238p. pap. 48.00 *(978-981-256-888-5(3))* 3rd ed. 2011. 264p. pap. 48.00 ***(978-981-4350-42-6(7))*** World Scientific Publishing Co., Inc.

Yaseen, Asif. Fostering Innovations for Banking the Unbanked: Models & Mechanics. 2011. 96p. pap. ***(978-3-8443-2713-7(4))*** Lambert Academic Publishing.

BANKS AND BANKING—AUSTRALIA

Bain, Jim. A Financial Tale of Two Cities: Sydney & Melbourne's Remarkable Contest for Commercial Supremacy. 2007. (ENG., Illus.). 336p. per. 35.95 *(978-0-86840-963-4(4)*, UNSW Press) NewSouth Publishing AUS. Dist: Independent Pubs. Group.

Poulos, Patricia. 'Payback' & 'The Devil Called' The Sequel: 'Elders' & 'The Real Story' 2009. (Illus.). 211p. pap. *(978-0-9807439-0-6(7))* Poulos, Patricia Books.

BANKS AND BANKING—BELGIUM

BIA. Key Banking, Financial, & Insurance Companies of Belgium. 6th rev. ed. 2006. 300p. (J). pap. 259.00 *(978-1-4187-4381-9(X))* Business Information Agency.

BANKS AND BANKING—BRAZIL

Paula, Luiz Fernando de. Financial Liberalization & Economic Performance: Brazil at the Crossroads. 2010. *(978-0-203-83521-0(2))* Routledge.

von Mettenheim, Kurt E. Federal Banking in Brazil: Policies & Competitive Advantages, 1 vol. 2010. (Financial History Ser.). (ENG., Illus.). 240p. 99.00 *(978-1-84893-065-0(8))* Pickering & Chatto Pubs., Ltd. GBR. Dist: Ashgate Publishing Co.

BANKS AND BANKING—CANADA

Buckland, Jerry. Hard Choices: Financial Exclusion, Fringe Banks, & Poverty in Urban Canada. 2012. (ENG., Illus.). 288p. pap. ***(978-1-4426-1252-5(5))*** Univ. of Toronto Pr.

Canadian Forms & Precedents: Banking & Finance, 4 vols., Set. ring bd. 595.00 *(978-0-409-89842-2(2),* CN, MICHIE) LEXIS Publishing.

Livesey, Bruce. Thieves of Bay Street: How Banks, Brokerages & the Wealthy Steal Billions a Year from Canadians. 2012. (ENG.). 320p. 27.50 ***(978-0-307-35963-6(8),*** Random Hse CAN) Random Hse. of Canada, Ltd. CAN. Dist: Random Hse., Inc.

Powell, James. Bank of Canada of James Elliot Coyne: Challenges, Confrontation, & Change. 2009. (ENG., Illus.). 200p. (C). *(978-0-7735-3599-2(3))* McGill-Queen's Univ. Pr.

Ravindra, Dave. Understanding Credit. 2011. 160p. pap. 24.95 ***(978-1-4269-6429-9(3))*** Trafford Publishing.

Smart, Graham. Writing the Economy: Activity, Genre & Technology in the World of Banking. 2006. (Studies in Language & Communication Ser.). (ENG., Illus.). 256p. (C). 100.00 *(978-1-84553-066-2(7))* Equinox Publishing Ltd. GBR. Dist: ISD.

—Writing the Economy: Activity, Genre, & Technology in the World of Banking. 2006. (Studies in Language & Communication (Equinox) Ser.). (ENG., Illus.). 256p. (C). per. 29.95 *(978-1-84553-067-9(5))* Equinox Publishing Ltd. GBR. Dist: ISD.

University of Toronto Press. Money on the Margins. 2009. (ENG.). *(978-1-4426-4033-7(2))* Univ. of Toronto Pr.

BANKS AND BANKING—CARIBBEAN AREA

Armstrong, Eric. A History of Money & Banking in Barbados, 1627-1973. 2010. (Illus.). 150p. pap. *(978-976-640-239-6(6))* Univ. of the West Indies Pr.

Monteith, Kathleen E. A. Depression to Decolonization: Barclays Bank (DCO) in the West Indies, 1926-1962. 2008. (Illus.). 355p. pap. *(978-976-640-198-6(5))* Univ. of the West Indies Pr.

United Nations. New Directions for Development Banking in the Caribbean: Financing to Take Advantage of Unlimited Supplies of Labour Skills & Entrepreneurship. 2007. (Financiamiento del Desarrollo Ser.). (ENG.). 84p. pap. 10.00 *(978-92-1-121645-5(1))* United Nations Pubns.

BANKS AND BANKING—CHINA

Arayama, Yuko & Mourdoukoutas, Panos, eds. Rise & Fall of Abacus Banking in Japan & China. 2008. (Illus.). 208p. pap. 45.99 *(978-1-59311-268-4(8))* Information Age Publishing, Inc.

Avery, Martha, et al, eds. China's Emerging Financial Markets: Challenges & Global Impact. 2009. (Wiley Finance Ser.: 782). (ENG., Illus.). 400p. 170.00 *(978-0-470-82249-4(X),* Wiley) Wiley, John & Sons, Inc.

Chen, George. Banking on the Bund: The Untold Stories of Foreign Banks in China. 2011. (ENG.). 256p. 29.95 *(978-0-470-82599-0(5),* Wiley) Wiley, John & Sons, Inc.

Cheng, Linsun. Banking in Modern China: Entrepreneurs, Professional Managers, & the Development of Chinese Banks, 1897-1937. 2007. (Cambridge Modern China Ser.). (ENG.). 296p. pap. 58.00 *(978-0-521-03276-6(8))* Cambridge Univ. Pr.

China Knowledge Press, creator. Financial Services in China: The Past, Present & Future of a Changing Industry. 2007. (Illus.). 547p. pap. 90.00 *(978-981-4163-26-2(0),* CKP3260) China Knowledge Press Pte Ltd SGP. Dist: Independent Pubs. Group.

Cousin, Violaine. Banking in China. 2nd rev. ed. 2011. (ENG., Illus.). 352p. 105.00 *(978-0-230-27269-9(X))* Palgrave Macmillan.

Cousin, Volaine. Banking in China. Molyneux, Philip, ed. 2007. (Palgrave Macmillan Studies in Banking & Financial Institutions Ser.). (ENG.). 288p. 110.00 *(978-0-230-00695-9(7))* Palgrave Macmillan.

Discus, Eeske Tabea. China 's Banking Sector: Non-performing Loan Challenge and Impact of WTO Entry on Domestic Banks. 2008. 92p. pap. *(978-3-3364-5231-1(6))* VDM Verlag Dr. Mueller e.K.

Genberg, Hans & Hui, Cho-Hoi, eds. The Banking Sector in Hong Kong: Competition, Efficiency, Performance & Risk. 2008. (ENG., Illus.). 256p. 109.00 *(978-0-230-20266-5(7))* Palgrave Macmillan.

Goodstadt, Leo F. Profits, Politics & Panics: Hong Kong's Banks & the Making of a Miracle Economy, 1935-1985. 2007. (ENG., Illus.). 326p. (gr. 17). 45.00 *(978-962-209-896-1(7))* Hong Kong Univ. Pr. HKG. Dist: Columbia Univ. Pr.

Hkib. Fundamentals of Accounting & Law in Banking. 2011. 256p. pap. 50.50 *(978-0-470-82659-1(2),* Wiley) Wiley, John & Sons, Inc.

Huang, Juan. Competition, Concentration & Efficiency of Commercial Banks in South Korea, Mainland China & Taiwan, 5 vols., Vol. 5. 2011. (Enrich Series on China's Economic Issues Ser.). (ENG.). 216p. 88.00 *(978-981-4298-26-1(3))* Enrich Professional Publishing (S)., Ltd. SGP. Dist: Independent Pubs. Group.

Kuhn, Robert Lawrence & Yang, Li. China's Banking & Financial Markets: The Internal Research Report of the Chinese Government. 2007. (ENG., Illus.). 500p. 170.00 *(978-0-470-82219-7(8),* Wiley) Wiley, John & Sons, Inc.

Lu, Qing. Long-Term Commitment, Trust & the Rise of Foreign Banks in China. 2007. (Chandos Asian Studies). (ENG., Illus.). 284p. 110.00 *(978-1-84334-321-9(5),* Chandos Publishing) Woodhead Publishing Ltd. GBR. Dist: Ingram Pub. Services.

Meng, Chen. Multinational Banking in China: Theory & Practice. 2009. (New Horizons in International Business Ser.). 192p. 119.00 *(978-1-84542-589-0(8))* Elgar, Edward Publishing, Inc.

Nolan, Jane. Western Bankers in China. 2012. (Routledge Contemporary China Ser.). (ENG.). (C). 150.00 ***(978-0-415-58464-7(7))*** Routledge.

Peng, Yuanyuan. The Chinese Banking Industry: Lessons from History for Today's Challenges. (Routledge Studies on the Chinese Economy Ser.). (ENG., Illus.). 216p. (C). 2012. pap. 42.95 ***(978-0-415-54230-2(8))*** 2007. 158.00 *(978-0-415-42347-2(3))* Routledge.

Poon, Irene Hon-Fun. Human Resources Management Changes in Chin. 2010. 224p. pap. *(978-3-8383-4439-3(1))* Lambert Academic Publishing.

Roland, Christian. Banking Sector Liberalization in India: Evaluation of Reforms & Comparative Perspectives on China. (Contributions to Economics Ser.). (Illus.). xvi, 299p. 2010. (ENG.). pap. 139.00 *(978-3-7908-2538-1(7),* 3790825387) 2008. 139.00 *(978-3-7908-1981-6(6))* Physica-Verlag DEU. Dist: Springer.

Schmidt, Bjö B. The Dynamics of M & A Strategy: Mastering the Outbound M & A Wave of Chinese Banks. 2010. (Europäische Hochschulschriften. Reihe 5: Volks- und Betriebswirtschaft Ser.). 358p. pap. 86.95 *(978-3-631-60093-1(3))* Lang, Peter GmbH, Europaischer Verlag der Wissenschaften DEU. Dist: Lang, Peter.

Zhou. Banking Laws in China: Theory & Practice. 2007. *(978-90-411-2519-4(1))* Kluwer Law International.

BANKS AND BANKING—EGYPT

Abdel Aziz, Hadia H. Factors Affecting Customers' Decisions to Buy New Retail Banking Services: Their Implications on the New Service Development Process. 2008. (Schriften zur Unternehmensplanung Ser.). 246p. pap. 61.95 *(978-3-631-57783-7(4))* Lang, Peter GmbH, Europaischer Verlag der Wissenschaften DEU. Dist: Lang, Peter.

ElBannan, Mona & Elbannan, Mona. Framework for Bank Governance. 2011. 72p. pap. ***(978-3-8454-1571-0(1))*** Lambert Academic Publishing.

Tamer, Elshamouby. Managing Complexity of Customer-Service Provider Relationships: Lessons from the Egyptian Banking Industry. 2011. 268p. pap. ***(978-3-639-34225-3(9))*** VDM Verlag Dr. Mueller e.K.

BANKS AND BANKING—DEVELOPING COUNTRIES

Betrowe, Killian N. Bank Lending, Banking, & Financial Developments. 2008. 120.00 *(978-1-60456-491-4(1))* Nova Science Pubs., Inc.

Bongini, Paola, et al. Emerging Banking Systems. Bongini, Paola et al, eds. 2009. (ENG., Illus.). 208p. (C). 110.00 *(978-0-230-57434-2(3))* Palgrave Macmillan.

Cuevas, Carlos E. & Fischer, Klaus P. Cooperative Financial Institutions: Issues in Governance, Regulation, & Supervision. 2006. (World Bank Working Papers: 82). (ENG., Illus.). 70p. per. 10.00 *(978-0-8213-6684-4(X),* 9780821366844) World Bank Pubns.

Demirguc-Kunt, Asli, et al. Finance for All? Policies & Pitfalls in Expanding Access. 2007. (Policy Research Reports). (ENG., Illus.). 264p. pap. 45.00 *(978-0-8213-7291-3(2),* 9780821372913) World Bank Pubns.

Ensign, Margee M. Images & Behaviour of Private Bank Lending to Developing Countries. 2011. (ENG.). 128p. 90.00 *(978-0-415-59279-6(8))* Routledge

Huang, Wei-Xin. Institutional Banking for Emerging Markets: Principles & Practice. 2007. (Wiley Finance Ser.). (ENG.). 274p. 90.00 *(978-0-470-03076-9(3),* Wiley) Wiley, John & Sons, Inc.

Mallick, Indrajit & Marjit, Sugata. Financial Intermediation in a Less Developed Economy: The History of the United Bank of India. 2008. 328p. (C). 49.95 *(978-0-7619-3656-5(4),* B36565C) SAGE Pubns., Inc.

Martinez-Diaz, Leonardo. Globalizing in Hard Times: The Politics of Banking-Sector Opening in the Emerging World. 2009. (Cornell Studies in Political Economy Ser.). (Illus.). 232p. 45.00 *(978-0-8014-4755-6(0))* Cornell Univ. Pr.

World Bank Staff, contrib. by. Banking the Poor: Measuring Banking Access in 54 Economies. 2008. (ENG.). 150p. pap. 29.95 *(978-0-8213-7754-3(X),* 9780821377543) World Bank Pubns.

BANKS AND BANKING—EUROPE

Abele, Hanns, et al. Kartenzahlungen im Euro-Zahlungsraum. 2007. (Illus.). XVI, 163p. 89.95 *(978-3-7908-1907-6(7),* 3790819077) Physica-Verlag DEU. Dist: Springer.

Aliber, Robert Z. & Zoega, Gylfi, eds. Preludes to the Icelandic Financial Crisis. 2011. (ENG., Illus.). 320p. 110.00 *(978-0-230-27692-5(X))* Palgrave Macmillan.

Andersen, Thomas. Bank Mergers & Acquisitions in Central Eastern Europe. 2011. 112p. pap. ***(978-3-8443-1148-8(3))*** Lambert Academic Publishing.

Aslund, Anders. The Last Shall Be the First: East European Financial Crisis. 2010. (Illus.). pap. 21.95 *(978-0-88132-521-8(X))* Peterson Institute for International Economics.

Ayadi, Rym. Assessing Performancce Banking M & As E. 2007. (ENG., Illus.). 84p. pap. 30.00 *(978-92-9079-732-6(0))* Ctr. for European Policy Studies BEL. Dist: Brookings Institution Pr.

Ayadi, Rym, et al. Business Models in European Banking: A Pre-And Post-Crisis Screening. 2011. (ENG.). 104p. pap. 30.00 ***(978-94-6138-120-0(4))*** Ctr. for European Policy Studies BEL. Dist: Brookings Institution Pr.

Ayadi, Rym, et al. Investigating Diversity in the Banking Sector in Europe: Key Developments, Performance & Role of Cooperative Banks. 2011. (ENG.). 168p. pap. 30.00 *(978-94-6138-042-5(9))* Ctr. for European Policy Studies BEL. Dist: Brookings Institution Pr.

Aydin, Burcu. Credit Growth & Banking Structure. 2009. 112p. pap. *(978-3-639-12950-2(4))* VDM Verlag Dr. Mueller e.K.

Baranyai, Eszter. Liquidity Risk Management with Special Interest to the Hungarian Banking Sector. 2008. 80p. pap. *(978-3-639-11047-0(1))* VDM Verlag Dr. Mueller e.K.

Barisitz & Barisitz, Stephan. Banking in Central & Eastern Europe 1980-2006: A Comprehensive Analysis of Banking Sector Transformation in the Former Soviet Union, Czechoslovakia, East Germany, Yugoslavia, Belarus, Bulgaria, Croatia, the Czech Republic, Hungary, Kazakhstan, Poland, Romania, the Russian Federation, Serbia & Montenegro, Slovakia, Ukraine & Uzbekistan. 2007. (Routledge International Studies in Money & Banking Ser.). (Illus.). 224p. 160.00 *(978-0-415-42881-1(5))* Routledge.

Beccalli, Elena. IT & European Bank Performance. 2007. (ENG., Illus.). 264p. 116.00 *(978-0-230-00694-2(9))* Palgrave Macmillan.

BIA. Essential Banking & Financial Companies of Western Europe. 6th rev. ed. 2006. 500p. (J). pap. 249.00 *(978-1-4187-4378-9(X))* Business Information Agency.

—Key Banking, Financial, & Insurance Companies of Austria. 6th rev. ed. 2006. 200p. (J). pap. 249.00 *(978-1-4187-4380-2(1))* Business Information Agency.

—Key Banking, Financial, & Insurance Companies of Denmark. 6th rev. ed. 2006. 450p. (J). pap. 219.00 *(978-1-4187-4382-6(8))* Business Information Agency.

—Key Banking, Financial, & Insurance Companies of Portugal. 6th rev. ed. 2006. 250p. (J). pap. 219.00 *(978-1-4187-4386-4(0))* Business Information Agency.

—Key Banking, Financial, Insurance, & Real Estate Companies of the Netherlands. 6th rev. ed. 2006. 400p. (J). pap. 249.00 *(978-1-4187-4389-5(5))* Business Information Agency.

—Major Banking, Financial, & Insurance Companies of Eastern Europe: Banks, Financial & Insurance Companies. 6th rev. ed. 2006. 400p. (J). pap. 249.00 *(978-1-4187-4376-5(3))* Business Information Agency.

Borissova, Boriana. Divergence of Risk Measures Across Different Market Conditions. 2011. 56p. pap. ***(978-3-8443-1824-1(0))*** Lambert Academic Publishing.

Brown, Brendan. Euro Crash: The Implications of Monetary Failure in Europe. 2010. (ENG.). 208p. 95.00 *(978-0-230-22910-5(7))* Palgrave Macmillan.

Bundegaard, Christian, ed. Middelfart Sparekasse. 2011. (ENG & DAN.). 203p. pap. *(978-87-993680-1-3(3))* Actar Birkhauser Distribution.

Carlberg, Michael. Dynamic Policy Interactions in a Monetary Union. 2011. (ENG.). xii, 347p. 189.00 *(978-3-642-18227-3(5),* 3642182275) Springer.

CEPR. Monitoring the European Central Bank, Vol. 6. 2008. (ENG.). 64p. pap. 45.00 *(978-1-898128-86-1(3))* Ctr. for Economic Policy Research GBR. Dist: Brookings Institution Pr.

Coats, Warren. One Currency for Bosnia: Creating the Central Bank of Bosnia & Herzegovina. 2007. (Illus.). 368p. 42.50 *(978-0-915463-99-2(7))* Jameson Bks., Inc.

Cottrell & Cassis. Private Banking in Europe. 2009. (Studies in Banking & Financial History Ser.). (Illus.). 328p. 134.95 *(978-1-85928-432-2(9))* Ashgate Publishing Co.

Dailida, Dmitry. The Banking System in Belarus. 2009. 284p. pap. *(978-3-639-14983-8(1))* VDM Verlag Dr. Mueller e.K.

Diamondopoulos, John. Ecb Transparency. 2010. 124p. pap. *(978-3-8383-4388-4(3))* Lambert Academic Publishing.

Dimova Manchevska, Aleksandra. Sustainable Banking in Macedoni. 2010. 104p. pap. *(978-3-639-26463-0(0))* VDM Verlag Dr. Mueller e.K.

Dixon, Robert. Banking in Europe (Rle Banking & Finance), Volume 10. 2012. (ENG.). 160p. 100.00 ***(978-0-415-53022-4(9))*** Routledge.

Du Plessis, Suemari. Ethnic & Male/Female Diversity & the Performance of European Banks. 2009. 88p. pap. *(978-3-639-19282-7(6))* VDM Verlag Dr. Mueller e.K.

Dyson, Kenneth & Marcussen, Martin, eds. Central Banks in the Age of the Euro: Europeanization, Convergence, & Power. 2009. (ENG., Illus.). 384p. 125.00 *(978-0-19-921823-3(4))* Oxford Univ. Pr., Inc.

Dyson, Kenneth & Quaglia, Lucia. European Economic Governance & Policies: Volume I: Commentary on Key Historical & Institutional Documents, 2 vols. 2011. (ENG., Illus.). 806p. 160.00 *(978-0-19-959451-1(1))* Oxford Univ. Pr., Inc.

Eight European Central Banks, Volume 38. 2012. (ENG.). 336p. 130.00 ***(978-0-415-52333-2(8))*** Routledge.

European Bank for Reconstruction & Development (EBRD), London: A Report to Members of the Committee on Foreign Relations, United States Senate, One Hundred Ninth Congress, Second Session, June 16, 2006. 2007. (S. Prt Ser.: Vols. 109-75). v, 25p. *(978-0-16-077836-0(0),* 552-070-35282-1) United States Government Printing Office.

Feldman, Gerald D. & Hertner, Peter. Finance & Modernization: A Transnational & Transcontinental Perspective for the Nineteenth & Twentieth Centuries. 2008. (Studies in Banking & Financial History Ser.). (Illus.). 320p. 134.95 *(978-0-7546-6271-6(3))* Ashgate Publishing Co.

Fethi, Meryem Duygun. Financial Services: Efficiency & Risk Management. 2012. (Studies in Financial Optimization & Risk Management - Ser.). 252p. 140.00 ***(978-1-62100-560-5(7))*** Nova Science Pubs., Inc.

Fiordelisi, Franco & Ricci, Ornella, eds. Bancassurance in Europe: Past, Present & Future. 2011. (Palgrave Macmillan Studies in Banking & Financial Institutions Ser.). (ENG., Illus.). 248p. 100.00 ***(978-0-230-27155-5(3))*** Palgrave Macmillan.

Fischelmayer, Michaela. Work-Life-Balance: Maßnahmen und Auswirkungen im österreichischen Bankensektor. 2010. 128p. pap. *(978-3-639-23856-3(7))* VDM Verlag Dr. Mueller e.K.

Flyvbjaer, Silas Mygind & Komum, Thomas. Executive Compensation in the Danish Bank Sector. 2011. 100p. pap. ***(978-3-8443-2466-2(6))*** Lambert Academic Publishing.

Gabor, Daniela. Central Banking & Financialization: A Romanian Account of how Eastern Europe became Subprime. 2010. (Studies in Economic Transition Ser.). (ENG., Illus.). 256p. 105.00 *(978-0-230-27615-4(6))* Palgrave Macmillan.

Garcia Alcubilla, Raquel & Ruiz del Pozo, Javier. Credit Rating Agencies on the Watch List: Analysis of European Regulation. 2012. (ENG., Illus.). 320p. 99.00 ***(978-0-19-960886-7(5))*** Oxford Univ. Pr., Inc.

Gkoutzinis, Apostolos Ath. Internet Banking & the Law in Europe: Regulation, Financial Integration & Electronic Commerce. 2006. (ENG., Illus.). 402p. 139.00 *(978-0-521-86071-0(7))* Cambridge Univ. Pr.

Goodhart, Charles, et al. Managing the Liquidity & Credit Crunch: Monitoring the European Central Bank. 2012. (ENG.). 64p. pap. 45.00 *(978-0-9557009-8-9(1))* Ctr. for Economic Policy Research GBR. Dist: Brookings Institution Pr.

Haan, Jakob de & Berger, Helge, eds. The European Central Bank at Ten. 2010. (ENG., Illus.). xii, 196p. 139.00 *(978-3-642-14236-9(2),* 3642142362) Springer.

Hamori, Shigeyuki & Hamori, Naoko. Introduction of the Euro & the Monetary Policy of the European Central Bank. 2009. 111.00 *(978-981-283-843-8(0))* World Scientific Publishing Co., Inc.

Herrmann, Heinz. Designing Central Banks. Mayes, David & Wood, Geoffrey E., eds. 2009. (Routledge International Studies in Money & Banking Ser.). (ENG., Illus.). 272p. (C). 160.00 *(978-0-415-47616-4(X))* Routledge.

Howells, Peter & Bain, Keith. The Economics of Money, Banking & Finance: A European Text. 4th ed. 2008. (Illus.). 656p. pap. 112.50 *(978-0-273-71039-4(7))* Financial Times/Prentice Hall.

Jonsson, Asgeir. Why Iceland? How One of the World's Smallest Countries Became the Meltdown's Biggest Casualty. 2009. (ENG.). 224p. 22.95 *(978-0-07-163284-3(0),* 0071632840) McGraw-Hill Cos., The.

Kedow, Alexander. Testing for Euro Dominance in Central & Eastern Europe. 2011. 64p. pap. ***(978-3-8443-1765-7(1))*** Lambert Academic Publishing.

Kaltenthaler, Karl. Policy-Making in the European Central Bank: The Masters of Europe's Money. 2006. (Governance in Europe Ser.). (ENG., Illus.). 204p. 92.00 *(978-0-7425-5366-8(3))* Rowman & Littlefield Publishers, Inc.

—Policymaking in the European Central Bank: The Masters of Europe's Money. 2006. (Governance in Europe Ser.). (ENG., Illus.). 204p. per. 37.95 *(978-0-7425-5367-5(1))* Rowman & Littlefield Publishers, Inc.

Khan, M. Fahim & Porzio, Mario, eds. Islamic Banking & Finance in the European Union: A Challenge. 2010. (Studies in Islamic Finance, Accounting & Governance Ser.). (Illus.). 256p. 115.00 *(978-1-84980-017-4(0))* Elgar, Edward Publishing, Inc.

Kleimeier, Stefanie & Sander, Harald. Integrating Europe's Retail Banking Market: Where Do We Stand? 2007. (ENG., Illus.). 112p. pap. 30.00 *(978-92-9079-734-0(7))* Ctr. for European Policy Studies BEL. Dist: Brookings Institution Pr.

Krizek, Tomas. Analysis of Banking Sector in Selected Countries of South-East Europe. 2010. 100p. pap. *(978-3-8383-6293-9(4))* Lambert Academic Publishing.

Kroner, Niels. A Blueprint for Better Banking: Svenska Handelsbanken & a proven model for more stable & profitable Banking. 2011. (ENG.). 218p. pap. 60.00 ***(978-0-85719-097-0(0))*** Harriman Hse. Publishing GBR. Dist: Ingram Pub. Services.

Lewenhak, Sheila. The Role of the European Investment Bank (RLE Banking & Finance), Volume 20. 2012. (ENG.). 312p. 130.00 ***(978-0-415-53936-4(6))*** Routledge.

Matousek, Roman. Banking & Financial Markets in Central & Eastern Europe: 20 Years of Transition. 2010. (Palgrave Macmillan Studies in Banking & Financial Institutions Ser.). (ENG., Illus.). 304p. 110.00 *(978-0-230-23168-9(3))* Palgrave Macmillan.

Matthäus-Maier, Ingrid & Pischke, J. D. von, eds. The Development of the Financial Sector in Southeast Europe: Innovative Approaches in Volatile Environments. 2010. (ENG., Illus.). xviii, 245p. pap. 89.95 *(978-3-642-05792-2(6),* 3642057926) Springer.

Mitra, Pradeep K., et al. Turmoil at Twenty: Recession, Recovery, & Reform in Central & Eastern Europe & the Former Soviet Union. 2009. (Eastern Europe & Central Asia Flagship Ser.). (ENG., Illus.). 276p. pap. 28.00 *(978-0-8213-8113-7(X),* 9780821381137) World Bank Pubns.

Mu-Icek, Pavel. Credit Risk Monitoring in the Czech Banking Sector. 2011. 80p. pap. ***(978-3-8443-1772-5(4))*** Lambert Academic Publishing.

Naoko & Hamori, Shigeyuki. Introduction of the Euro & the Monetary Policy of the European Central Bank. 2009. (Illus.). 220p. 85.00 *(978-981-283-842-1(2))* World Scientific Publishing Co., Inc.

Neyer, Ulrike. The Design of the Eurosystem's Monetary Policy Instruments. 2007. (Contributions to Economics Ser.). (Illus.). x, 179p. 139.00 *(978-3-7908-1977-9(8))* Physica-Verlag DEU. Dist: Springer.

Nilsen, Henrik. Corporate Social Responsibility in Banking. 2011. 88p. pap. ***(978-3-8443-0227-1(1))*** Lambert Academic Publishing.

Odoke, Wilfred. Mobile Banking Adoption in the Western Europe. 2011. 96p. pap. ***(978-3-8433-9091-0(6))*** Lambert Academic Publishing.

Okhiria, Solomon. Internet Banking in Sweden. 2009. 64p. pap. *(978-3-639-16933-1(6))* VDM Verlag Dr. Mueller e.K.

B

Olgu, Özlem & Kara, Alper. European Banking: Enlargement, Structural Changes & Recent Developments. 2011. (Palgrave Macmillan Studies in Banking & Financial Institutions Ser.). (ENG., Illus.). 336p. 100.00 *(978-0-230-23171-9(3))* Palgrave Macmillan.

Pastré, Olivier. The New Banking Economics. Pastre, Olivier et al, eds. 2007. 208p. (C). 119.00 *(978-1-84720-273-4(X))* Elgar, Edward Publishing, Inc.

Quaglia, Lucia. Central Banking Governance in the European Union. 2010. (ENG., Illus.). 204p. pap. 39.95 *(978-0-415-58665-8(8))* Routledge.

—Governing Financial Services in the European Union: Banking, Securities & Post-Trading. 2010. (Routledge/UACES Contemporary European Studies). (ENG., Illus.). 210p. (C). 128.00 *(978-0-415-56418-2(2)*, Routledge) Taylor & Francis Group GBR. Dist: Taylor & Francis Group.

Ruozi, Roberto & Anderloni, Luisa, eds. Banking Privatisation in Europe: The Process & the Consequences on Strategies & Organisational Structures. 2010. (ENG., Illus.). xiv, 340p. pap. 149.00 *(978-3-642-08505-5(9)*, 3642085059) Springer.

Schnyder, A. European Banking & Insurance Law. 2009. 500p. 224.00 *(978-90-5095-708-3(0))* Intersentia Uitgevers N.V. BEL. Dist: International Specialized Bk. Services.

Sinclair, Pat. Scandinavian Classic Baking, 1 vol. 2011. (ENG., Illus.). 96p. 16.95 *(978-1-58980-897-3(5))* Pelican Publishing Co., Inc.

Smit, Jeroen. The Perfect Prey: The Fall of Abn Amro, or What Went Wrong in the Banking Industry. 2010. (ENG., Illus.). 480p. pap. 23.95 *(978-1-84916-268-5(9))* Quercus GBR. Dist: Independent Pubs. Group.

Stuerz, Waldemar. Banking System Risk in the United States of America & Europe. 2011. 96p. pap. ***(978-3-8443-0839-6(3))*** Lambert Academic Publishing.

Valkó, Júlia. E-banking & Its Difficulties in Hungary: Why e-banking services were not as prosperous as expected? 2008. 56p. pap. *(978-3-639-09646-0(0))* VDM Verlag Dr. Mueller e.K.

Van De Vijver Staff. Financial & Banking: Regulation in Netherlands. 2011. xvi, 194p. *(978-90-411-2863-8(8))* Wolters Kluwer Law & Business.

Wymeersch, Eddy, ed. Further Perspectives in Financial Integration in Europe: Reports presented at the Brussels meeting of the International Faculty for Corporate Market Law & Securities Regulations 26 - 30 April 1993. (ENG.). XVI, 281p. 374.00 ***(978-3-11-177848-8(7))*** De Gruyter, Walter Inc.

BANKS AND BANKING—EUROPEAN ECONOMIC COMMUNITY COUNTRIES

Boscia, Vittorio, et al, eds. Cooperative Banking in Europe: Case Studies. 2010. (Palgrave Macmillan Studies in Banking & Financial Institutions Ser.). (ENG., Illus.). 272p. 105.00 *(978-0-230-57677-3(X))* Palgrave Macmillan.

Canzoneri, Matthew B., et al, eds. Establishing a Central Bank: Issues in Europe & Lessons from the U. S. 2008. (ENG., Illus.). 328p. pap. 42.00 *(978-0-521-07069-0(4))* Cambridge Univ. Pr.

Quaglia, Lucia. Central Banking Governance in the European Union: A Comparative Analysis. 2008. (Routledge/UACES Contemporary European Studies). (Illus.). 208p. 135.00 *(978-0-415-42751-7(7))* Routledge.

Skinner, Chris, ed. The Future of Investing in Europe's Markets after MiFID. 2007. (Wiley Finance Ser.). (ENG., Illus.). 292p. 75.00 *(978-0-470-51038-4(2)*, Wiley) Wiley, John & Sons, Inc.

BANKS AND BANKING—FORMER SOVIET REPUBLICS

De Haas, Ralph. Banking Sector Development in Transition Countries - the Impact of Multinational Banks. 2007. 248p. per. *(978-3-8364-2720-3(6))* VDM Verlag Dr. Mueller e.K.

Tacis Technical Dissemination Project Staff & European Commission Staff, contrib. by. Banks & SMEs: Towards a Mutually Successful Co-operation: A Guide for SME Entrepreneurs. (Illus.). 46p. *(978-92-828-1546-5(3))* European Commission BEL. Dist: Balogh International, Inc.

BANKS AND BANKING—FRANCE

BIA. Key Banking, Financial, & Insurance Companies of France. 6th rev. ed. 2006. 320p. (J). pap. 259.00 *(978-1-4187-4383-3(6))* Business Information Agency.

Bonin, Hubert. Banque et Bourgeoisies: La Société bordelaise de CIC (1880-2005) 2010. (FRE., Illus.). 434p. pap. 70.95 *(978-90-5201-603-0(8))* PIE - Peter Lang BEL. Dist: Lang, Peter.

Cohan, William D. The Last Tycoons: The Secret History of Lazard Frères & Co. 2007. (ENG.). 752p. 29.95 *(978-0-385-51451-4(4)*, Doubleday) Doubleday Religious Publishing Group, The.

—The Last Tycoons: The Secret History of Lazard Frères & Co. 2008. (ENG.). 752p. pap. 17.00 *(978-0-7679-1979-1(3)*, Anchor) Knopf Doubleday Publishing Group.

Jacoud, Gilles. Political Economy & Industrialism: Banks in Saint-Simonian Economic Thought. 2010. (Routledge Studies in the History of Economics Ser.). (ENG.). 224p. (C). 150.00 *(978-0-415-48266-0(6)*, Routledge) Taylor & Francis Group GBR. Dist: Taylor & Francis Group.

BANKS AND BANKING—GERMANY

Art Works. 2011. (ENG., Illus.). 256p. pap. 55.00 ***(978-3-7757-2777-8(9))*** Hatje Cantz Verlag GmbH & Co KG DEU. Dist: D.A.P./Distributed Art Pubs.

BIA. Key Banking, Financial, & Insurance Companies of Germany. 6th rev. ed. 2006. 350p. (J). pap. 249.00 *(978-1-4187-4384-0(4))* Business Information Agency.

Dietrich, Benjamin H. German Banking Structure, Pricing & Competition: Implications & International Policy Perspectives. 2009. 246p. 72.95 *(978-3-631-59022-5(9))* Lang, Peter GmbH, Europaischer Verlag der Wissenschaften DEU. Dist: Lang, Peter.

Frach, Lotte. Finanzmarktregulierung in Deutschland. 2010. (GER., Illus.). 267p. pap. *(978-3-8329-5759-9(6))* Nomos Verlagsgesellschaft.

Francke, Hans-Hermann & Hudson, Michael. Banking & Finance in West Germany (Rle Banking & Finance), Volume 14. 2012. (ENG.). 184p. 100.00 ***(978-0-415-52858-0(5))*** Routledge.

Hein, Manfred. Die Banken. *(978-3-411-10511-3(9))* Bibliographisches Institut & F. A. Brockhaus AG DEU. Dist: i. b. d., Ltd.

Janssen, Sven. British & German Banking Strategies. 2009. (Palgrave Macmillan Studies in Banking & Financial Institutions Ser.). (ENG., Illus.). 256p. (C). 116.00 *(978-0-230-22048-5(7))* Palgrave Macmillan.

Kobrak, Christopher. Banking on Global Markets: Deutsche Bank & the United States, 1870 to the Present. 2007. (Cambridge Studies in the Emergence of Global Enterprise Ser.). (ENG., Illus.). 504p. 50.00 *(978-0-521-86325-4(2))* Cambridge Univ. Pr.

Konopatzki, Volker. Funktionsauslagerung bei Kreditinstituten: Gesellschaftsrechtlicher und bankenaufsichtsrechtlicher Rahmen. 2008. (Frankfurter wirtschaftsrechtliche Studien Ser.). 362p. pap. 81.95 *(978-3-631-56142-3(3))* Lang, Peter GmbH, Europaischer Verlag der Wissenschaften DEU. Dist: Lang, Peter.

Lücke, Tobias. Bankaufsichtsrechtliche Anerkennung Interner Kreditportfoliomodelle. 2011. (Europäische Hochschulschriften. Reihe 5: Volks- und Betriebswirtschaft Ser.). (GER.). 317p. pap. 83.95 ***(978-3-631-61810-3(7))*** Lang, Peter GmbH, Europaischer Verlag der Wissenschaften DEU. Dist: Lang, Peter.

Raddao, Nino. Potenzialorientierte Kundensegmentierung zur Optimierung des Leistungsportfolios in der Firmenkundenbank: Konzeption und Implementierung einer efficient customization am Beispiel von Genossenschaftsbanken. 2008. (Beiträge zum Controlling Ser.). (GRE.). 142p. pap. 39.95 *(978-3-631-58354-8(0))* Lang, Peter GmbH, Europaischer Verlag der Wissenschaften DEU. Dist: Lang, Peter.

Redenbach, Sven. The German Banking Sector. 2008. 60p. per. *(978-3-8364-6377-5(6))* VDM Verlag Dr. Mueller e.K.

Reichling, Tilman. Der staatliche Zugriff auf Bankkundendaten im Strafverfahren: Die Kontenabfrage als strafprozessuale Ermittlungsmaßnahme, mögliche Folgemaßnahmen und verfassungsrechtliche Legitimationsprobleme. 2009. (Grundlagen Gesamte Strafrechtswissenschaft Ser.). (GER.). 196p. 64.95 *(978-3-631-59949-5(8))* Lang, Peter GmbH, Europaischer Verlag der Wissenschaften DEU. Dist: Lang, Peter.

Schuster, Leo & Widmer, Alex W., eds. Wege aus der Banken- und Börsenkrise. 2006. (GER & ENG., Illus.). X, 527p. 89.95 *(978-3-540-21106-8(3)*, 3540211063) Springer.

Theis, Manfred. Die Rating-Erstellung der Sparkassen: Eine problemorientierte Analyse der Rating-Erstellung im Kontext individueller Entscheidungspräferenzen. 2009. (Europäische Hochschulschriften. Reihe 5: Volks- und Betriebswirtschaft Ser.). (GER.). 260p. pap. 72.95 *(978-3-631-58626-6(4))* Lang, Peter GmbH, Europaischer Verlag der Wissenschaften DEU. Dist: Lang, Peter.

Toussaint, Guido. Das Recht des Zahlungsverkehrs im Überblick: Praxishandbuch. 2009. (De Gruyter Handbuch Ser.).Tr. of Payment Law. (GER.). XXIII, 254p. 70.00 *(978-3-89949-532-4(2))* De Gruyter, Walter Inc.

Toussaint, Guido. Das Recht des Zahlungsverkehrs Im Ãœberblick. 2009. (De Gruyter Handbuch Ser.).Tr. of Payment Law. (GER.). XXIII, 254p. 112.00 ***(978-3-11-173447-7(1))*** De Gruyter, Walter Inc.

Weber, Danny. Das Handels- und Bankhaus Frege & Comp. in Leipzig (1739-1816) 2008. (Beitrage zur Wirtschafts- und Sozialgeschichte (BWSG) Ser.). (GER., Illus.). 430p. (C). pap. 109.00 *(978-3-515-09290-6(0))* Steiner, Franz Verlag Wiesbaden GmbH DEU. Dist: Brown, David Bk. Co., The.

BANKS AND BANKING—GREAT BRITAIN

Ackrill, Margaret. Barclays. 2008. (ENG.). 504p. pap. 63.00 *(978-0-521-04100-3(7))* Cambridge Univ. Pr.

Austin, Peter E. Baring Brothers & the Birth of Modern Finance, 1 vol. 2007. (Financial History Ser.). (ENG.). 288p. 99.00 *(978-1-85196-922-7(5))* Pickering & Chatto Pubs., Ltd. GBR. Dist: Ashgate Publishing Co.

Awal, Russel. Financial Exclusion & Microcredit. 2011. 64p. pap. ***(978-3-8443-2811-0(4))*** Lambert Academic Publishing.

Bagehot, Walter. Lombard Street. 2008. 196p. 22.99 *(978-0-554-31317-7(0))*; 25.99 *(978-0-554-22014-7(8))* BiblioBazaar.

—Lombard Street. 2007. (ENG.). 196p. per. 13.45 *(978-1-60424-204-1(3)*, Book Jungle) Standard Pubns., Inc.

—Lombard Street: A Description of the Money Market. 2011. (Cambridge Library Collection - History Ser.). (ENG.). 372p. pap. 29.99 ***(978-1-108-03581-1(7))*** Cambridge Univ. Pr.

—Lombard Street: A Description of the Money Market. 2007. (ENG.). 404p. 33.95 *(978-1-60206-953-4(0))* Cosimo, Inc.

—Lombard Street: A Description of the Money Market. 2009. 160p. pap. 9.45 *(978-1-60459-710-3(0))* Wilder Pubns., Ltd.

—Lombard Street: A description of the money Market. 2006. (ENG.). 204p. pap. 20.99 *(978-1-4264-1465-7(X))* BiblioBazaar.

—Lombard Street: A Description of the Money Market. l.t. ed. 2006. 194p. pap. 21.99 *(978-1-4264-1481-7(1))* BiblioBazaar.

—Lombard Street - a Description of the Money Market. 2009. 176p. pap. 12.99 *(978-1-59547-577-0(X))* NuVision Pubns., LLC.

Balogh, T. Studies in Financial Organization. 2011. (National Institute of Economic & Social Research Economic & Social Studies). (ENG.). 344p. pap. 28.99 *(978-1-107-64901-9(3))* Cambridge Univ. Pr.

BIA. Key Banking, Financial, & Insurance Companies of the United Kingdom. 6th rev. ed. 2006. 400p. (J). pap. 249.00 *(978-1-4187-4387-1(9))* Business Information Agency.

Brown, John Crosby. A Hundred Years of Merchant Banking. 2009. 246p. pap. *(978-0-217-34141-7(1))* Books LLC.

—A Hundred Years of Merchant Banking: A History of Brown Brothers & Company, Brown, Shipley & Company & the Allied Firms. Alexander Brown & Sons, 2010. 528p. pap. 40.75 *(978-1-146-61706-2(2))* BiblioBazaar.

—A Hundred Years of Merchant Banking, a History of Brown Brothers & Company, Brown, Shipley [and] Company & the Allied Firms, Alexander. 2010. 204p. pap. 28.76 *(978-1-152-32583-8(3))* General Bks. LLC.

Brubaker, Ralph, et al, eds. A Debtor World: Interdisciplinary Perspectives on Debt. 2012. 320p. 85.00 ***(978-0-19-987372-2(0))*** Oxford Univ. Pr., Inc.

Capie, Forrest. The Bank of England, from the 1950s to 1979. 2010. (Studies in Macroeconomic History Ser.). (ENG., Illus.). 920p. (C). 150.00 *(978-0-521-19282-8(X))* Cambridge Univ. Pr.

Cassis, Youssef. City Bankers, 1890-1914. Rocques, Margaret, tr. from FRE. 2009. (ENG., Illus.). 368p. pap. 38.99 *(978-0-521-10521-7(8))* Cambridge Univ. Pr.

City Girl Staff & S., Suzana. Confessions of a City Girl: The Devil Wears Pinstripes. 2010. (ENG.). 282p. pap. 14.95 *(978-0-7535-1981-3(X))* Virgin Bks. Ltd. GBR. Dist: Independent Pubs. Group.

Collins, Michael. Money & Banking in the Uk, Volume 6. 2012. (ENG.). 656p. 180.00 ***(978-0-415-52796-5(1))*** Routledge.

Consumer Focus. Banking Services & the Consumer, Volume 37. 2012. (ENG.). 264p. 115.00 ***(978-0-415-52666-1(3))*** Routledge.

Dawes, Margaret & Selwyn, Nesta. Women Who Made Money: Women Partners in British Private Banks 1752-1906. 2010. 192p. 24.77 *(978-1-4269-3726-2(1))*; pap. 14.77 *(978-1-4269-3725-5(3))* Trafford Publishing.

Drummond, Helga. The Dynamics of Organizational Collapse: The Case of Barings Bank. 2012. (Routledge International Studies in Money & Banking Ser.). (ENG.). 160p. (C). pap. 42.95 ***(978-0-415-54270-8(7))*** Routledge.

Elliott, Geoffrey. The Mystery of Overend & Gurney: A Financial Scandal in Victorian London. 2007. (Illus.). 266p. *(978-0-413-77573-3(9))* Methuen Publishing Ltd.

Fforde, John. The Bank of England & Public Policy, 1941-1958. 2011. (ENG.). 883p. pap. 76.00 *(978-0-521-29452-2(5))* Cambridge Univ. Pr.

Hennessy, Elizabeth. A Domestic History of the Bank of England, 1930-1960. 2008. (ENG.). 472p. pap. 58.00 *(978-0-521-07358-5(8))* Cambridge Univ. Pr.

Horesh, Niv & Horesh, N. Shanghai's Bund & Beyond: British Banks, Banknote Issuance, & Monetary Policy in China, 1842-1937. 2009. (Yale Series in Economic & Financial History Ser.). (ENG., Illus.). 256p. 48.00 *(978-0-300-14356-0(7))* Yale Univ. Pr.

Housby, Elaine. Islamic Financial Services in the United Kingdom. 2011. (Edinburgh Guides to Islamic Finance Ser.). (ENG.). 184p. (gr. 17). 120.00 *(978-0-7486-3997-7(7))*; pap. 40.00 *(978-0-7486-3998-4(5))* Edinburgh Univ. Pr. GBR. Dist: Columbia Univ. Pr.

Janssen, Sven. British & German Banking Strategies. 2009. (Palgrave Macmillan Studies in Banking & Financial Institutions Ser.). (ENG., Illus.). 256p. (C). 116.00 *(978-0-230-22048-5(7))* Palgrave Macmillan.

Kaplan, Herbert. Nathan Mayer Rothschild & the Creation of a Dynasty: The Critical Years 1806-1816. 2010. (ENG.). 224p. pap. 21.95 *(978-0-8047-7361-4(0))* Stanford Univ. Pr.

Marks, Jon. Check Your English Vocabulary for Banking & Finance: All You Need to Improve Your Vocabulary. 2nd rev. ed. 2007. (Check Your Vocabulary Ser.). (ENG.). 80p. pap. 14.95 *(978-0-7136-8250-2(7))* A & C Black GBR. Dist: Macmillan.

Mullineux, Andy. Uk Banking after Deregulation, Volume 23. 2012. (ENG.). 192p. 100.00 ***(978-0-415-52672-2(8))*** Routledge.

Nishimura, Shizuya. The Decline of Inland Bills of Exchange in the London Money Market, 1855-1913. 2010. (ENG.). 144p. pap. 27.99 *(978-0-521-13147-6(2))* Cambridge Univ. Pr.

Richards, Richard D. The Early History of Banking in England (Rle Banking & Finance), Volume 30. 2012. (ENG.). 344p. 130.00 ***(978-0-415-52878-8(X))*** Routledge.

Robinson, Leland R. Foreign Credit Facilities in the United Kingdom. (Columbia University, Studies in the Social Sciences: No. 244). reprint ed. 20.00 *(978-0-404-51244-6(5))* AMS Pr., Inc.

Roselli, Alessandro & Gola, Carlo. The UK Banking System & Its Regulatory & Supervisory Framework. 2009. (ENG., Illus.). 224p. 116.00 *(978-0-230-54282-2(4))* Palgrave Macmillan.

Singleton, Susan. Retention of Title. 2010. (Thorogood Reports). 100p. pap. 240.00 *(978-1-85418-703-1(1))* Thorogood GBR. Dist: Stylus Publishing, LLC.

Stephenson, J. r. Broken Promises, Betrayals & Barefaced Lies. 2008. 144p. pap. *(978-0-9558557-0-2(5))* ShieldCrest.

Tait, Jeremy. The Obedient Banker: From Bombay to Beverly Hills (A revealing insight into the unusual life of a colonial Banker) 2011. (Illus.). 236p. pap. 28.06 *(978-1-4567-7139-3(6))* AuthorHouse.

Tearle, David. Barings Bank, William Bingham & the Rise of the American Nation: A Transatlantic Relationship from the Revolutionary War through the Louisiana Purchase. 2009. (ENG., Illus.). 248p. pap. 45.00 *(978-0-7864-4437-3(1))* McFarland & Co., Inc. Pubs.

Tritton, Alan. Half-Closed Door. 2008. 572p. 39.95 *(978-1-84624-271-7(1))* Book Guild, Ltd. GBR. Dist: Trans-Atlantic Pubns., Inc.

Walters, Brian. The Fall of Northern Rock an Insiders Story of Britains Biggest Banking Disaster. 2008. (ENG.). 176p. pap. 16.95 *(978-1-905641-80-2(X))* Harriman Hse. Publishing GBR. Dist: Ingram Pub. Services.

Withers, Hartley. The Meaning of Money. 2009. 172p. pap. *(978-0-217-80317-5(2))* Books LLC.

—The Meaning of Money. 2007. (ENG.). 320p. 45.95 *(978-0-548-09645-1(7))* Kessinger Publishing, LLC.

Wood, Joanne. Bankrupt 130 Of 2006. 2009. 220p. pap. 14.49 *(978-1-4389-3362-7(2))* AuthorHouse.

BANKS AND BANKING—GREECE

Mastrojianni, Evmorfia. 'service Quality Determinants in the Greek Banking System' 2011. 84p. pap. ***(978-3-8443-2026-8(1))*** Lambert Academic Publishing.

Vasiliadis, Labros. The International Expansion of Greece's Largest Banks - the International Expansion of Greece's Largest Banks: Entry Methods & International Marketi. 2009. 152p. pap. *(978-3-639-11588-8(0))* VDM Verlag Dr. Mueller e.K.

BANKS AND BANKING—INDIA

Agrawal, Meenu, ed. Regional Rural Banks (RRBs) in India. 2009. 254p. 39.75 *(978-81-7708-223-4(X))* New Century Publications IND. Dist: International Specialized Bk. Services.

Ahmed, J. U. Asset Quality & Non-Performing Assets of Commercial Banks. 2008. (Illus.). 234p. 43.50 *(978-81-7533-146-4(1))* M. D. Pubns. Pvt, Ltd. IND. Dist: Coronet Bks.

Akhan, Jafor. Non-Banking Financial Companies (NBFCs) in India: Functioning & Reforms. 2010. 224p. 35.50 *(978-81-7708-229-6(9))* New Century Publications IND. Dist: International Specialized Bk. Services.

Arora, Rashmi Umesh. Bank Credit & Development. 2009. 304p. pap. *(978-3-639-13948-8(8))* VDM Verlag Dr. Mueller e.K.

Banerjee, G. D., et al. Towards Financial Inclusion in India. 2011. 600p. (C). 40.00 ***(978-81-321-0584-8(2)***, B05848C) SAGE Pubns., Inc.

Basak, Amit. Co-Operative Banks in India: Functioning & Reforms. 2010. 203p. 29.75 *(978-81-7708-250-0(7))* New Century Publications IND. Dist: International Specialized Bk. Services.

Bhasin, Niti. Banking & Financial Markets in India: 1947 to 2007. 2007. 552p. (C). 74.50 *(978-81-7708-136-7(5))* New Century Publications IND. Dist: International Specialized Bk. Services.

—Monetary, Banking & Financial Developments in India: 1947-48 To 2009-10. 2009. 604p. 122.50 *(978-81-7708-206-7(X))* New Century Publications IND. Dist: International Specialized Bk. Services.

Bhati, Shyam. Role of Trust in Bank Lending. 2011. 308p. pap. ***(978-3-8443-2504-1(2))*** Lambert Academic Publishing.

Bhattacharya, Hrishikes. Banking Strategy, Credit Appraisal, & Lending Decisions: A Risk-Return Framework. 2nd ed. 2011. (ENG., Illus.). 632p. pap. 50.00 ***(978-0-19-807410-6(7))*** Oxford Univ. Pr., Inc.

Chakrabarti, Manas. Rural Banking in India. 2011. (Illus.). 200p. 34.50 *(978-81-7708-262-3(0))* New Century Publications IND. Dist: International Specialized Bk. Services.

Chatterjee, Anup. Monetary & Credit Management in India. 2010. 273p. 42.50 *(978-81-7708-234-0(5))* New Century Publications IND. Dist: International Specialized Bk. Services.

Clement, Sudhahar. Loyalty in Indian Services Sector: A Relationship Model in Retail Banking. 2011. 248p. pap. ***(978-3-639-31613-1(4))*** VDM Verlag Dr. Mueller e.K.

Dange, Vishwesh. Evolution of Warana Beyond the Lucky Gold Star Group. 2011. 84p. pap. ***(978-3-8443-8714-8(5))*** Lambert Academic Publishing.

Das, Khanindra Ch. Risk Behaviour of Commercial Banks under Reform. 2010. 140p. pap. *(978-3-639-24478-6(8))* VDM Verlag Dr. Mueller e.K.

Dash, Priyadarshi. Universal Banking in Indi. 2010. 132p. pap. *(978-3-8383-5053-0(7))* Lambert Academic Publishing.

Desta, Tesfatsion Sahlu. Customer Service Satisfaction. 2010. 100p. pap. *(978-3-639-26631-3(5))* VDM Verlag Dr. Mueller e.K.

Dumpeti, Harikanth. Computerisation in Indian Banks. 2010. 240p. pap. *(978-3-8383-7511-3(4))* Lambert Academic Publishing.

Goswami, Bhaskar, et al. The Banking Sector in Indi. 2011. 92p. pap. ***(978-3-8443-3304-6(5))*** Lambert Academic Publishing.

Gupta, Shivani. Financial Appraisal & Comparative Analysis of Icici Bank Ltd & Sbi. 2011. 180p. pap. ***(978-3-8443-3359-6(2))*** Lambert Academic Publishing.

Guruswamy, Devabathini. Determinants of Profitability & Productivity Analysis: A Case Study with Reference to State Bank of India & Its Associates. 2011. 100p. pap. ***(978-3-639-32609-3(1))*** VDM Verlag Dr. Mueller e.K.

Jatana, Rimpi & Uppal, R. K., eds. E-banking in India: Challenges & Opportunities. 2007. 276p. (C). 37.50 *(978-81-7708-137-4(3))* New Century Publications IND. Dist: International Specialized Bk. Services.

Jawed Akhtar, S. M. Banking System in India: Reforms & Performance Evaluation. 2011. 236p. 36.50 ***(978-81-7708-283-8(3))*** New Century Publications IND. Dist: International Specialized Bk. Services.

Joseph, Anto. Factors Affecting Financial Inclusion in Rural Areas. 2011. 56p. pap. ***(978-3-8454-1481-2(2))*** Lambert Academic Publishing.

Joshi, Vasant C. e-Finance: The Future Is Here. 2nd ed. 2010. (Response Bks.). (Illus.). 212p. (C). pap. 24.95 *(978-81-321-0245-8(2)*, B02458P) SAGE Pubns., Inc.

Joshi, Vinay V. & Joshi, Vasant C. Managing Indian Banks: The Challenges Ahead. 3rd ed. 2009. (Response Bks.). (Illus.). 364p. (C). pap. 39.95 *(978-81-7829-852-8(X)*, B98528P) SAGE Pubns., Inc.

Kaur, Rimpi & Uppal, R. K. Banking Sector Reforms in India: A Review of Post-1991 Developments. 2006. 228p. 29.50 *(978-81-7708-119-0(5))* New Century Publications IND. Dist: International Specialized Bk. Services.

Kavitha, N. & Ramachandran, A. Funds Management in Commercial Banks: Indian Perspectives: Managing Asset Liability in Banking Scenario. 2011. 232p. pap. **(978-3-639-32735-9(7))** VDM Verlag Dr. Mueller e.K.

Keynes, John. Indian Currency & Finance. 2006. pap. 19.95 *(978-1-59605-740-1(8),* Cosimo Classics) Cosimo, Inc.

Keynes, John Maynard. Indian Currency & Finance. 272p. 2008. 42.95 *(978-1-4365-5882-2(4))* 2007. (ENG.). per. 27.95 *(978-0-548-76351-3(8))* Kessinger Publishing, LLC.

—Indian Currency & Finance. 2008. 276p. *(978-1-4437-3911-5(1),* Obscure Pr.) Read Bks.

Khandelwal, Anil K. Dare to Lead: The Transformation of Bank of Baroda - A CEO's Personal Account of Historic Changes in a Large Corporation. 2011. (Response Bks.). (Illus.). 480p. (C). 50.00 *(978-81-321-0628-9(8),* B06289C) SAGE Pubns., Inc.

Kochhar, Sameer, et al, eds. Financial Inclusion. 2009. (ENG.). 196p. 49.95 *(978-81-7188-744-6(9))* Academic Foundation IND. Dist: Independent Pubs. Group.

Kothari, Rajesh. Financial Services in India: Concept & Application. 2010. (Sage Texts). (Illus.). 360p. (C). pap. 25.95 *(978-81-321-0507-7(9),* B05077P) SAGE Pubns., Inc.

Kunjukunju, Benson. Commercial Banks in India: Growth, Challenges & Strategies. 2008. 342p. 48.75 *(978-81-7708-150-3(0))* New Century Publications IND. Dist: International Specialized Bk. Services.

Mandal, Anandadeep & Biresh K. Sahoo. Performance Evaluation of Banks in Indi: Post Transition Period. 2011. 76p. pap. **(978-3-8443-0293-6(X))** Lambert Academic Publishing.

Mishra, Bishnupriya & Uppal, R., eds. Modern Banking in India: Dimensions & Risks. 2009. 262p. 39.50 *(978-81-7708-212-8(4))* New Century Publications IND. Dist: International Specialized Bk. Services.

Misra, Biswa Swarup. Regional Rural Banks in Indi. 2010. 84p. pap. *(978-3-639-22352-1(7))* VDM Verlag Dr. Mueller e.K.

Mohan, Rakesh. Monetary Policy in a Globalized Economy: A Practitioner's View. (ENG., Illus.). 2011. 348p. pap. 29.95 **(978-0-19-807493-9(X))** 2009. 512p. 59.95 *(978-0-19-569735-3(9))* Oxford Univ. Pr., Inc.

Moore, Tomoe. India's Emerging Financial Market: A Flow of Funds Model. (Illus.). 208p. 2012. (ENG.). (C). pap. 42.95 **(978-0-415-53319-5(8))** 2007. 170.00 *(978-0-415-43409-6(2))* Routledge.

Ray, Partha. Commercial Banks & Monetary Policy in India. 2008. (ENG.). 250p. 59.95 *(978-81-7188-635-7(3))* Academic Foundation IND. Dist: Independent Pubs. Group.

Roland, Christian. Banking Sector Liberalization in India: Evaluation of Reforms & Comparative Perspectives on China. (Contributions to Economics Ser.). (Illus.). xvi, 299p. 2010. (ENG.). pap. 139.00 *(978-3-7908-2538-1(7),* 3790825387) 2008. 139.00 *(978-3-7908-1981-6(6))* Physica-Verlag DEU. Dist: Springer.

Shah, Ajay, et al. India's Financial Markets: An Insider's Guide to How the Markets Work. 2008. (Elsevier & IIT Stuart Center for Financial Markets Press Ser.). (ENG., Illus.). 264p. 80.95 *(978-0-12-374251-3(X),* Elsevier Science) Elsevier Science & Technology Bks.

Shanthi, Gopinath. Performance Evaluation of Foreign Banks Operating in India: Introduction, Review, Profile of Foreign Banks India, Analysis of Growth, Profitability, Productivity & Solvency & Findings, Suggestions. 2011. 256p. pap. **(978-3-639-33710-5(7))** VDM Verlag Dr. Mueller e.K.

Suthrum, Praveen & Krishnan, M. S. ICICI Bank (B) Going Global - Going Rural! 2010. (C). pap. 20.00 *(978-1-61674-187-7(2))* Davidson, William Institute At The Univ. of Michigan, The.

Tapiawala, Medha. Banking Reforms & Productivity in India. 2010. 240p. 36.50 *(978-81-7708-248-7(5))* New Century Publications IND. Dist: International Specialized Bk. Services.

Tarapore, S. S. Financial Policies & Everyday Life: The Indian Context. 2011. (ENG.). 306p. 59.95 *(978-81-7188-806-1(2))* Academic Foundation IND. Dist: Independent Pubs. Group.

Thingalaya, N. K., et al. Financial Inclusion & Beyond: Issues & Challenges. 2011. (ENG.). 160p. 39.95 *(978-81-7188-835-1(6))* Academic Foundation IND. Dist: Independent Pubs. Group.

Tiwari, Brajesh Kumar. Changing Scenario of Indian Banking Industry. 2011. 80p. pap. **(978-3-8443-3085-4(2))** Lambert Academic Publishing.

Trehan, Jyoti. Crime & Money Laundering: The Indian Perspective. 2011. (Illus.). 268p. pap. 75.00 **(978-0-19-567306-7(9))** Oxford Univ. Pr., Inc.

Uppal, R. Indian Banking in the Globalised World. 2008. 261p. 35.50 *(978-81-7708-174-9(8))* New Century Publications IND. Dist: International Specialized Bk. Services.

Uppal, R., ed. Banking Services & Information Technology: The Indian Experience. 2006. 215p. 32.75 *(978-81-7708-176-3(4))* New Century Publications IND. Dist: International Specialized Bk. Services.

—Financial Sector of India: Emerging Challenges. 2008. 233p. 39.25 *(978-81-7708-188-6(8))* New Century Publications IND. Dist: International Specialized Bk. Services.

Verma, Rajanikant. Managing Attitudinal Changes. 2011. 296p. pap. **(978-3-8443-1407-6(5))** Lambert Academic Publishing.

Vijayakumar, A., ed. Banking, Micro Finance & Self-help Groups (SHGs) in India. 2009. 333p. 46.50 *(978-81-7708-209-8(4))* New Century Publications IND. Dist: International Specialized Bk. Services.

BANKS AND BANKING—IRELAND

Byrne, Hugh & McEntagart, Louis. The National Asset Management Agency Act 2009: Annotations & Commentary: A Guide to Irish Law. 2010. 546p. pap. 160.00 *(978-1-84766-504-1(7),* Bloomsbury Professional) Bloomsbury Publishing Plc GBR. Dist: International Specialized Bk. Services.

Healy, Killian. From Heroes to Villains: Are Bankers Our New Dirty Workers? 2011. 152p. pap. **(978-3-8454-0061-7(7))** Lambert Academic Publishing.

Rouse, Paul & Duncan, Mark. Handling Change: A History of the Irish Bank Officials' Association. 2012. (ENG., Illus.). 300p. 34.95 **(978-1-84889-141-8(5))** Collins Pr., The IRL. Dist: Dufour Editions, Inc.

BANKS AND BANKING—ISLAMIC COUNTRIES

Abdul-Rahman, Yahia. The Art of Islamic Banking & Finance: Tools & Techniques for Community-Based Banking. 2010. (Wiley Finance Ser.: 504). (ENG., Illus.). 432p. 70.00 *(978-0-470-44993-6(4),* Wiley) Wiley, John & Sons, Inc.

Ahmad, Khaliq & Gulamali Rustam, Mohammed. Islamic Bank Customers. 2011. 100p. pap. **(978-3-8443-2374-0(0))** Lambert Academic Publishing.

Ahmed, Habib. Product Development in Islamic Banks. 2011. (Edinburgh Guides to Islamic Finance Ser.). (ENG., Illus.). 184p. (gr. 17). 120.00 *(978-0-7486-3951-9(9));* pap. 40.00 *(978-0-7486-3952-6(7))* Edinburgh Univ. Pr. GBR. Dist: Columbia Univ. Pr.

al-Bashir Muhammad al-Amine, Muhammad. Global Sukuk & Islamic Securitization Market: Financial Engineering & Product Innovation. 2011. (Brill's Arab & Islamic Laws Ser.). (Illus.). 463p. **(978-90-04-20267-2(6))** BRILL.

Al Manaseer, Mousa. Bank Profitability. 2009. 260p. pap. *(978-3-639-17148-8(9))* VDM Verlag Dr. Mueller e.K.

Al-Roubaie, Amer & Alvi, Shafiq. Islamic Banking & Finance V1, 4 vols. 2010. (Illus.). 400p. *(978-0-415-48874-7(5))* Routledge.

—Islamic Banking & Finance V2, 4 vols. 2010. (Illus.). 400p. *(978-0-415-48873-0(7))* Routledge.

—Islamic Banking & Finance V3, 4 vols. 2010. (Illus.). 400p. *(978-0-415-48872-3(9))* Routledge.

—Islamic Banking & Finance V4, 4 vols. 2010. (Illus.). 400p. *(978-0-415-48871-6(0))* Routledge.

Ayub, Muhammad. Understanding Islamic Finance. 2008. (Wiley Finance Ser.: 458). (ENG., Illus.). 542p. 60.00 *(978-0-470-03069-1(0),* Wiley) Wiley, John & Sons, Inc.

D. Pfeiffer and R. Stewart Staff & Schoon, Natalie. Islamic Banking & Finance Schoon, Natalie, ed. 2009. (Illus.). 203p. 187.50 *(978-1-904905-11-0(0))* Spiramus Pr. GBR. Dist: International Specialized Bk. Services.

El-Khalifa Mohamed, Mahmoud A. History of Islamic Banks. 2010. 188p. pap. *(978-3-639-21780-3(2))* VDM Verlag Dr. Mueller e.K.

El Tiby Ahmed, Amr Mohamed. Islamic Banking: How to Manage Risk & Improve Profitability. 2011. (Wiley Finance Ser.: 640). (ENG., Illus.). 211p. 70.00 *(978-0-470-88023-4(6),* Wiley) Wiley, John & Sons, Inc.

Farid, Fara Madehah Ahmad. Shariah Compliant Private Equity & Islamic Venture Capital. 2012. (Edinburgh Guides to Islamic Finance Ser.). (ENG., Illus.). 184p. (gr. 17). pap. 40.00 **(978-0-7486-4048-5(7))** Edinburgh Univ. Pr. GBR. Dist: Columbia Univ. Pr.

—Shariah-Compliant Private Equity & Islamic Venture Capital. 2012. (Edinburgh Guides to Islamic Finance Ser.). (ENG., Illus.). 184p. (gr. 17). 120.00 **(978-0-7486-4047-8(9))** Edinburgh Univ. Pr. GBR. Dist: Columbia Univ. Pr.

Grössinger, Klaus. Islamic Banking in South East Asi. 2010. 124p. pap. *(978-3-639-24500-4(8))* VDM Verlag Dr. Mueller e.K.

Hanif, Muhammad. Islamic Financing: Shift from Debt to Equity. 2010. 160p. pap. *(978-3-639-25301-6(9))* VDM Verlag Dr. Mueller e.K.

Haron, Sudin & Nursofiza, Wan. Islamic Finance & Banking System. 2009. (ENG.). 400p. 79.95 *(978-983-3850-61-7(8),* 9833850618) McGraw-Hill Cos., The.

Hassan, M. Kabir & Lewis, Mervyn K., eds. Handbook of Islamic Banking. 2009. (Elgar Original Reference Ser.). 464p. pap. 74.00 *(978-1-84844-473-7(7))* Elgar, Edward Publishing, Inc.

International Trade Centre. Islamic Banking: A Guide for Small & Medium-sized Enterprises. 2010. (ENG.). 112p. pap. 70.00 *(978-92-9137-375-8(3))* United Nations Pubns.

Iqbal, Munawar. A Guide to Islamic Finance. 2007. (Risk Executive Reports). pap. *(978-1-904339-85-4(9))* Risk Bks.

Iqbal, Zamir & Greuning, Hennie van. Risk Analysis for Islamic Banks. 2007. (Stand Alones Ser.). (ENG., Illus.). 328p. per. 50.00 *(978-0-8213-7141-1(X),* 9780821371411) World Bank Pubns.

Jackson-Moore, Elisabeth. The International Handbook of Islamic Banking & Finance. 2009. 270p. 50.00 *(978-1-906403-31-7(7))* Lessons Professional Publishing GBR. Dist: Stylus Publishing, LLC.

Kettell. Introduction to Islamic Banking & Finance. 2010. (Illus.). 100p. pap. 45.00 *(978-0-9558351-0-0(0))* Harriman Hse. Publishing GBR. Dist: Ingram Pub. Services.

Kettell, Brian. Frequently Asked Questions in Islamic Finance. 2010. (Wiley Finance Ser.). (ENG., Illus.). 334p. pap. 34.95 *(978-0-470-74860-2(5),* Wiley) Wiley, John & Sons, Inc.

—Islamic Finance in a Nutshell: A Guide for Non-Specialists. 2010. (Wiley Finance Ser.). (ENG., Illus.). 360p. pap., instr.'s gde. ed. 27.95 *(978-0-470-74861-9(3),* Wiley) Wiley, John & Sons, Inc.

Kettell, Brian B. Case Studies in Islamic Banking & Finance. 2011. (Wiley Finance Ser.: 550). (ENG., Illus.). 192p. pap. 65.00 *(978-0-470-97801-6(5),* Wiley) Wiley, John & Sons, Inc.

—Introduction to Islamic Banking & Finance. 2011. (Wiley Finance Ser.: 551). (ENG., Illus.). 192p. pap. 60.00 *(978-0-470-97804-7(X),* Wiley) Wiley, John & Sons, Inc.

—The Islamic Banking & Finance Workbook: Step-by-Step Exercises to Help You Master the Fundamentals of Islamic Banking & Finance. 2011. (Wiley Finance Ser.: 552). (ENG., Illus.). 152p. pap. 50.00 *(978-0-470-97805-4(8),* Wiley) Wiley, John & Sons, Inc.

Khandelwal, Sunil Kumar, et al. Financial Risk Management for Islamic Banking & Finance. 2008. (Finance & Capital Markets Ser.). (ENG., Illus.). 300p. 247.00 *(978-0-230-55381-1(8))* Palgrave Macmillan.

Kohli, Harinder S. & Ahmed, Jaseem, eds. Islamic Finance: Writings of V. Sundararajan. 2011. (Illus.). 320p. (C). 40.00 **(978-81-321-0706-4(3),** B07064C) SAGE Pubns., Inc.

Maatallah, Prof. Magid. Islamic Finance. 2011. 512p. pap. **(978-3-8443-2176-0(4))** Lambert Academic Publishing.

Mahlknecht, Michael & Hassan, Kabir. Islamic Capital Markets: Products & Strategies. 2011. (Wiley Finance Ser.: 558). (ENG., Illus.). 480p. 75.00 *(978-0-470-68957-8(9),* Wiley) Wiley, John & Sons, Inc.

Masood, Omar. Islamic Banking & Finance: Definitive Texts & Cases. 2011. (Economics of the Middle East Ser.). (ENG., Illus.). 304p. 125.00 **(978-0-230-33839-5(9))** Palgrave Macmillan.

Mastan, A. H. Islamic Finance & Banking. 2010. 311p. 59.50 *(978-81-7533-305-5(7))* M. D. Pubns. Pvt, Ltd. IND. Dist: Coronet Bks.

Millar, Roderick & Anwar, Habiba. Islamic Finance: A Guide for International Business & Investment. 2008. (ENG., Illus.). xviii, 216p. pap. 115.00 *(978-1-84673-078-8(3),* GMB Publishing Ltd.) Blue Ibex Ltd. GBR. Dist: Ingram Pub. Services.

Natalie Schoon Staff. Determining the Value of Banks: Residual Income Models & the Valuation of Conventional & Islamic Banks. 2009. (Illus.). 160p. 187.50 *(978-1-904905-82-0(X))* Spiramus Pr. GBR. Dist: International Specialized Bk. Services.

Sattar, Abdul. Risk Management in Islamic Banking. 2011. 96p. pap. **(978-3-8454-0716-6(6))** Lambert Academic Publishing.

Schoon, Natalie. Islamic Asset Management: An Asset Class on Its Own? 2011. (Edinburgh Guides to Islamic Finance Ser.). (ENG., Illus.). 184p. (gr. 17). pap. 40.00 *(978-0-7486-3996-0(9))* Edinburgh Univ. Pr. GBR. Dist: Columbia Univ. Pr.

—Islamic Banking & Finance. 2010. (Illus.). 222p. pap. 75.00 *(978-1-904905-83-7(8))* Spiramus Pr. GBR. Dist: International Specialized Bk. Services.

Toutounchian, Iraj & Hassan, M. Kabir. Islamic Money & Banking: Integrating Money in Capital Theory. 2009. (Wiley Finance Ser.: 788). (ENG., Illus.). 350p. 95.00 *(978-0-470-82319-4(4),* Wiley) Wiley, John & Sons, Inc.

Venardos, Angelo M. Current Issues in Islamic Banking & Finance: Resilience & Stability in the Present System. 2010. 300p. 68.00 *(978-981-283-392-1(7))* World Scientific Publishing Co., Inc.

—Islamic Banking & Finance in South-East Asia: Its Development & Future. (Asia-Pacific Business Ser.). 2nd ed. 2006. 238p. pap. 48.00 *(978-981-256-888-5(3))* 3rd ed. 2011. 264p. pap. 48.00 **(978-981-4350-42-6(7))** World Scientific Publishing Co., Inc.

Visser, Hans. Islamic Finance: Principles & Practice. 200p. 2011. (Illus.). pap. 29.95 *(978-1-84980-882-8(1))* 2009. 119.00 *(978-1-84542-525-8(1))* Elgar, Edward Publishing, Inc.

Wilson, Rodney, ed. Islamic Financial Markets (Rle Banking & Finance). Volume 35. 2012. (ENG.). 256p. 115.00 **(978-0-415-53019-4(9))** Routledge.

BANKS AND BANKING—ISRAEL

Maman, Daniel & Rosenhek, Zeev. The Israeli Central Bank: Political Economy, Global Logics & Local Actors. 2011. (Routledge Studies in Middle Eastern Economies Ser.). (ENG., Illus.). 192p. (C). 125.00 *(978-0-415-57328-3(9))* Routledge.

BANKS AND BANKING—ITALY

BIA. Key Banking, Financial, & Insurance Companies of Italy. 6th rev. ed. 2006. 400p. (J). pap. 249.00 *(978-1-4187-4385-7(2))* Business Information Agency.

Carli, Guido & Barucci, Piero. Scritti e Discorsi Di Guido Carli. 2008. (ITA & ENG.). *(978-88-339-2027-6(5)); (978-88-339-1953-9(6)); (978-88-339-1955-3(2),; (978-88-339-1954-6(4))* Bollati Boringhieri.

De Roover, Raymond. The Medici Bank: Its Organization, Management, Operations, & Decline. 2008. 140p. pap. 12.00 *(978-1-59740-381-8(4))* ACLS Humanities E-Book.

—The Medici Bank: Its Organization, Management, Operations, & Decline. 2011. 128p. 40.95 **(978-1-258-01015-7(1))** Literary Licensing, LLC.

De Roover, Raymond. The Rise & Decline of the Medici Bank, 1397-1494. 2008. 552p. pap. 54.00 *(978-1-59740-373-3(3))* ACLS Humanities E-Book.

Di Quirico, Roberto. Building on Borrowed Bricks. 2008. 224p. pap. *(978-88-8398-051-0(4))* European Pr. Academic Publishing.

Goldthwaite, Richard A. The Economy of Renaissance Florence. 2011. (ENG., Illus.). 672p. (gr. 17). pap. 35.00 *(978-1-4214-0059-4(6))* Johns Hopkins Univ. Pr.

Guarino, Giuseppe, et al. Scritti e Discorsi Di Guido Carli. 2008. (ITA & ENG.). *(978-88-339-2028-3(3))* Bollati Boringhieri.

Perrone, Marco. Corporate Governance & Internal Control System of Banks. 2011. 116p. pap. **(978-3-8443-8505-2(3))** Lambert Academic Publishing.

Poliakov, Leon. Jewish Bankers & the Holy See, Volume 28. 2012. (ENG.). 296p. 115.00 **(978-0-415-52327-1(3))** Routledge.

Silipo, Damiano. The Banks & the Italian Economy. Silipo, Damiano Bruno, ed. 2009. (ENG., Illus.). viii, 243p. 129.00 *(978-3-7908-2111-6(X),* 379082111X) Physica-Verlag DEU. Dist: Springer.

Silipo, Damiano Bruno, ed. The Banks & the Italian Economy. 2010. (ENG., Illus.). viii, 243p. pap. 129.00 **(978-3-7908-2574-9(3),** 3790825743) Physica-Verlag DEU. Dist: Springer.

BANKS AND BANKING—JAPAN

Amyx, Jennifer A. Japan's Financial Crisis: Institutional Rigidity & Reluctant Change. 2006. (ENG., Illus.). 392p. (C). per. 31.95 *(978-0-691-12868-9(5))* Princeton Univ. Pr.

Areyama, Yuko & Mourdoukoutas, Panos, eds. Rise & Fall of Abacus Banking in Japan & China. 2008. (Illus.). 208p. pap. 45.99 *(978-1-59311-268-4(8))* Information Age Publishing, Inc.

Azad, A. S. M. Sohel. Measuring Efficiency of Japanese Banks. 2010. 116p. pap. *(978-3-8383-5020-2(0))* Lambert Academic Publishing.

Gay, Suzanne Marie. Moneylenders of Late Medieval Kyoto. 2009. (ENG.). 301p. pap. 24.00 *(978-1-4379-6974-0(7))* DIANE Publishing Co.

Hamada, Koichi, et al, eds. Japan's Bubble, Deflation, & Long-Term Stagnation. 2010. (ENG., Illus.). 440p. (gr. 17). 42.00 *(978-0-262-01489-2(0))* MIT Pr.

Misawa. Current Business & Legal Issues in Japan's Banking & Finance Industry. 2006. (Illus.). xii, 451p. 82.00 *(978-981-256-859-5(X))* World Scientific Publishing Co., Inc.

Misawa, Mitsuru. Current Business & Legal Issues in Japan's Banking & Finance Industry. 2nd ed. 2010. 530p. 85.00 *(978-981-4291-01-9(3))* World Scientific Publishing Co., Inc.

Suzuki, Yasushi. Japan's Financial Slump: Collapse of the Monitoring System under Institutional & Transition Failures. 2011. (ENG., Illus.). 240p. 100.00 *(978-0-230-29034-1(5))* Palgrave Macmillan.

Tait, Jeremy. The Obedient Banker: From Bombay to Beverly Hills (A revealing insight into the unusual life of a colonial Banker) 2011. (Illus.). 236p. pap. 28.06 *(978-1-4567-7139-3(6))* AuthorHouse.

Tsutsui, William M. Banking Policy in Japan: American Efforts at Reform During the Occupation. 2010. (ENG.). 176p. 100.00 *(978-0-415-58525-5(2),* Routledge) Taylor & Francis Group GBR. Dist: Taylor & Francis Group.

BANKS AND BANKING—LATIN AMERICA

Diaz-Bonilla, Eugenio & del Campo, Victoria. A Long & Winding Road: The Creation of the Inter American Development Bank. 2011. 154p. pap. 9.16 **(978-1-257-08999-4(4))** Lulu Enterprises Inc.

Leveraging Remittances for Families & Communities: Hearing Before the Subcommittee on the Western Hemisphere of the Committee on Foreign Affairs, House of Representatives, One Hundred Tenth Congress, First Session, October 2, 2007. 2007. (Illus.). iii, 57p. *(978-0-16-079726-2(8),* 552-070-36652-1) United States Government Printing Office.

United Nations. Latin America: The Missing Financial Crisis. 2010. (Studies & Perspectives Ser.). (ENG.). 40p. pap. 10.00 *(978-92-1-121705-6(9))* United Nations Pubns.

Vento, Gianfranco A. Banking in Latin America: After the Great Financial Crisis. 2013. (Palgrave Macmillan Studies in Banking & Financial Institutions Ser.). (ENG.). 224p. 105.00 *(978-0-230-24017-9(8))* Palgrave Macmillan.

BANKS AND BANKING—MEXICO

Gomez Mont, Maria Teresa. Manuel Gómez Morin, 1915-1939: La Raíz y la Simiente de un Proyecto Nacional. 2009. (Vida y Pensamiento de México Ser.). (SPA., Illus.). 998p. 57.99 *(978-968-16-8600-0(4))* Fondo de Cultura Económica.

—Manuel Gomez Morin, 1915-1939: La Raiz y la Simiente de un Proyecto Nacional. 2009. (Vida y Pensamiento de Mexico Ser.). (SPA., Illus.). 998p. pap. 49.99 *(978-968-16-8336-8(6))* Fondo de Cultura Economica USA.

Marois, Thomas. States, Banks & Crisis: Emerging Finance Capitalism in Mexico & Turkey. 2012. 288p. 110.00 **(978-0-85793-857-2(6))** Elgar, Edward Publishing, Inc.

Schatan, Claudia & Rivera, Eugenio. Competition Policies in Emerging Economies: Lessons & Challenges from Central America & Mexico. 2008. (Illus.). xii, 238p. pap. 15.00 *(978-0-387-78434-2(9))* Springer.

Sigmond, Karen B. Mexican Banking Laws. 2008. 192p. pap. *(978-3-639-08230-2(3))* VDM Verlag Dr. Mueller e.K.

BANKS AND BANKING—MIDDLE EAST

Al-Muharrami, Saeed. Market Structure & Performance. 2010. 120p. pap. *(978-3-639-28598-7(0))* VDM Verlag Dr. Mueller e.K.

Altunbas, Yener, et al. Turkish Banking: Banking under Political Instability & Chronic High Inflation. Molyneux, Philip, ed. 2009. (Palgrave Macmillan Studies in Banking & Financial Institutions Ser.). (ENG., Illus.). 224p. 110.00 *(978-1-4039-9711-1(X))* Palgrave Macmillan.

Çetin, Tamer & Oguz, Fuat. Regulation & Competition in the Turkish Banking & Financial Markets. 2012. (Financial Institutions & Services Ser.). 263p. 140.00 **(978-1-61324-990-1(X))** Nova Science Pubs., Inc.

Cobham, David & Dibeh, Ghassan, eds. Monetary Policy & Central Banking in the Middle East & North Africa. 2012. (Routledge Political Economy of the Middle East & North Africa Ser.). (ENG., Illus.). 272p. (C). pap. 42.95 **(978-0-415-54173-2(5))** Routledge.

Cottrell, Philip L. East Meets West-Banking Commerce & Investment in the Ottoman Empire. 2008. (Studies in Banking & Financial History Ser.). (Illus.). 214p. 124.95 *(978-0-7546-6443-7(0))* Ashgate Publishing Co.

Gnitekin-Karakas, Derya. Global Integration of Turkish Finance Capital. 2009. 96p. pap. *(978-3-8364-8068-0(9))* VDM Verlag Dr. Mueller e.K.

B

Hicks, Tyler G., compiled by. Mideast & North African Banks & Financial Institutions. 17th ed. 2007. pap. 15.00 *(978-1-56150-839-6(X))* International Wealth Success, Inc.

Lale, Berkoz & Emre, Tepe. The Intra-Metropolitan Location of Banks in Istanbul: Location of Banks. 2011. 64p. pap. ***(978-3-639-34366-3(2))*** VDM Verlag Dr. Mueller e.K.

Soral, Bartu. Banking Crises & Bankruptcy for Profit in Turkey. 2008. 96p. pap. *(978-3-639-06085-0(7))* VDM Verlag Dr. Mueller e.K.

The World Bank. Financial Access & Stability: A Road Map for the Middle East & North Africa. 2011. (MENA Development Report). (ENG., Illus.). 364p. pap. 40.00 ***(978-0-8213-8835-8(5)***, 9780821388358) World Bank Pubns.

World Bank Staff, contrib. by. Financial Access & Stability: A Roadmap for the Middle East & North Africa. 2011. (Illus.). xxvi, 334p. ***(978-0-8213-8856-3(8))*** World Bank Pubns.

Zedan Salem, Mohammad & H. Kheirelsid, Musa. Advertising Efficiency & Effectiveness in the Palestinian Banking Sector. 2011. 344p. pap. ***(978-3-8443-0680-4(3))*** Lambert Academic Publishing.

BANKS AND BANKING—NEW ZEALAND

Adjei-Frimpong, Kofi & W. Tripe, David. Causality Between Bank Net Interest Margins & Operating Expenses. 2010. 60p. pap. *(978-3-8383-5235-0(1))* Lambert Academic Publishing.

Jesson, Bruce. Only Their Purpose is Mad: The Money Men Take over NZ. 226p. 18.00 *(978-0-86469-343-3(5))* Dunmore Pr. NZL. Dist: United Nations Pubns.

BANKS AND BANKING—RUSSIA (FEDERATION)

BIA. Key Banking, Finance, Insurance, & Real Estate Companies of Russia. 6th rev. ed. 2006. 478p. (J). pap. 249.00 *(978-1-4187-4532-5(4))* Business Information Agency.

Kulikov, A. G. & Makhanova, T. A. Faktoring V Rossii. 2010. (RUS.). 151p. *(978-5-7729-0499-2(X))* Rossijskaja akademija gosudarstvennoj sluzby pri Prezidente Rossijskoj Federacii.

Melloni, Nicola. Market Without Economy the 1998 Russian Financial Crisis. 2007. 160p. per. *(978-3-89821-407-0(9))* ibidem-Verlag.

Panibratov, A. IU. Russian Multinationals: From Regional Supremacy to Global Lead. 2012. xii, 226p. E-Book ***(978-0-203-13037-7(5))*** Routledge.

Panibratov, Andrei. Russian Multinationals. 2012. (Routledge Contemporary Russia & Eastern Europe Ser.). (ENG., Illus.). 240p. (C). 155.00 *(978-0-415-61588-4(7))* Routledge.

Penkin, A. F. Denezhno-Kreditnaia Sistema Rossii I Osnovy Ee Regulirovaniia: Uchebnoe Posobie. 2010. (RUS.). 170p. *(978-5-7729-0495-4(7))* Rossijskaja akademija gosudarstvennoj sluzby pri Prezidente Rossijskoj Federacii.

BANKS AND BANKING—SOUTH AFRICA

Alagbaoso, Manessah. Strategy Communication Effectiveness in South African Banks. 2011. 188p. pap. ***(978-3-8383-5932-8(1))*** Lambert Academic Publishing.

Chibaya Mbuya, John. The Rise & Fall of South Africa's Fifth Largest Bank. 2010. 168p. pap. *(978-3-8383-7369-0(3))* Lambert Academic Publishing.

Mkhize, Nkuli. Challenges & Trends of the South African Private Equity Industry. 2011. 112p. pap. ***(978-3-8443-0329-2(4))*** Lambert Academic Publishing.

Sowelem, R. A. Towards Financial Independence in a Developing Economy: An Analysis of the Monetary Experience of the Federation of Rhodesia & Nyasaland, 1952-1963. 2011. (ENG.). 336p. 115.00 *(978-0-415-59372-4(7))* Routledge.

BANKS AND BANKING—SWITZERLAND

Barber, Hoyt. Secrets of Swiss Banking: An Owner's Manual to Quietly Building a Fortune. 2008. (ENG.). 272p. 39.95 *(978-0-470-13671-3(5)*, Wiley) Wiley, John & Sons, Inc.

BIA. Key Banking, Financial, Insurance, & Real Estate Companies in Switzerland: Key Banks, Financial, Insurance & Real Estate Companies. 6th rev. ed. 2006. 400p. (J). pap. 249.00 *(978-1-4187-4388-8(7))* Business Information Agency.

Guldimann, Beat. Inside Swiss Banking. 2010. 238p. pap. 29.99 *(978-0-557-16584-1(9))* Lulu Enterprises Inc.

Orland, Leonard. A Final Accounting: Holocaust Survivors & Swiss Banks. 2010. 644p. 60.00 *(978-1-59460-769-1(9))* Carolina Academic Pr.

Tax Haven Banks & U.S. Tax Compliance: Hearings Before the Permanent Subcommittee on Investigations of the Committee on Homeland Security & Governmental Affairs, United States Senate of the One Hundred Tenth Congress, Second Session, July 17 & 25, 2008. 2008. (GER & ENG., Illus.). xii, 1202p. *(978-0-16-082529-3(6)*, 552-070-38564-9) United States Government Printing Office.

BANKS AND BANKING—SYRIA

Khashab, Basel. The Role of Information Technology in the Innovation Process. 2011. 120p. pap. ***(978-3-8443-9727-7(2))*** Lambert Academic Publishing.

BANKS AND BANKING—UNITED STATES

Aicpa. AICPA Audit & Accounting Guide Depositories & Lending Institutions. 2007. pap. 86.25 *(978-0-87051-662-7(0))* American Institute of Certified Public Accountants.

Allen, Thomas Coley. Reconstruction of America's Monetary & Banking System: A Return to Constitutional Money. 2009. 320p. pap. *(978-0-9656663-6-7(0))* Allen, T. C. Co.

Allison, Herbert M. Hearing with Herbert M. Allison, Jr., Assistant Secretary of the Treasury for Financial Stability: Hearing Before the Congressional Oversight Panel, One Hundred Eleventh Congress, First Session, October 22, 2009. 2009. (Illus.). iii, 56p. *(978-0-16-085051-6(7)*, 552-070-40408-2) United States Government Printing Office.

—Herb Allison, Assistant Secretary of the Treasury for Financial Stability: Hearing Before the Congressional Oversight Panel, One Hundred Eleventh Congress, First Session, Hearing Held in Washington, D.C., June 24, 2009. 2009. iii, 49p. *(978-0-16-084493-5(2)*, 552-070-40016-8) United States Government Printing Office.

Alternatives for Promoting Liquidity in the Commercial Real Estate Markets, Supporting Small Businesses, & Increasing Job Growth: Hearing Before the Committee on Financial Services, U.S. House of Representatives, One Hundred Eleventh Congress, Second Session, July 29, 2010. 2010. (Illus.). iii, 96p. ***(978-0-16-087402-4(5)***, 552-070-42095-9) United States Government Printing Office.

American Bankers Association. Banking Today: Handbook. 2007. (Illus.). 134p. (C). pap. 79.00 *(978-0-89982-604-2(0))* American Bankers Assn.

—Banking Today: Leader's Guide. 2007. 108p. (C). pap. 55.00 *(978-0-89982-605-9(9))* American Bankers Assn.

America's Community Bankers Staff, contrib. by. America's Community Bankers: Celebrating 115 Years of Leadership Through the Decades. 2007. *(978-0-9791229-8-9(8))* America's Community Bankers.

Aspatore Books Staff, compiled by. Trends in Consumer Bankruptcy Filings: Leading Lawyers on Understanding the Current Bankruptcy Landscape, Navigating the Filing Process, & Educating Clients (Inside the Minds) 2010. 188p. pap. 75.00 *(978-0-314-27344-4(1))* Aspatore Bks.

Aspelin, Carl D., ed. Financial Institutions in Turmoil. 2010. (Banking & Banking Developments Ser.). (Illus.). ix, 202p. 69.00 *(978-1-60692-044-2(8))* Nova Science Pubs., Inc.

Augustinos, Theodore P. & Emmanuel, John N. Bank Insurance Sales Methods: Requirements, Restrictions & Guidelines - Southern States. 510p. pap. 389.00 *(978-0-8080-0604-6(5))* Toolkit Media Group.

Bank Fees: Creeping up & Up. 2008. 90p. pap. 39.00 *(978-1-60692-039-8(1))* Nova Science Pubs., Inc.

Banking & Finance Law Client Strategies: Leading Lawyers on Understanding the Client's Goals, Working with Regulators, & Developing a Transactional Strategy in a Changing Marketplace (Inside the Minds) 2009. (Inside the Minds Ser.). 184p. pap. 80.00 *(978-0-314-90421-8(2))* Aspatore Bks.

Banking & Finance Litigation Strategies: Leading Lawyers on Working with Clients, Managing Documentation, & Negotiating Settlements (Inside the Minds) 2009. 120p. pap. 90.00 *(978-0-314-20736-4(8))* Aspatore Bks.

Banking Industry Perspectives on the Obama Administration's Financial Regulatory Reform Proposals: Hearing Before the Committee on Financial Services, U.S. House of Representatives, One Hundred Eleventh Congress, First Session, July 15, 2009. 2010. (Illus.). iii, 247p. *(978-0-16-085239-8(0)*, 552-070-40581-0) United States Government Printing Office.

Banks in Real Estate: A Review of the Office of the Comptroller of the Currency's December 2005 Rulings: Hearing Before the Subcommittee on Government Management, Finance, & Accountability of the Committee on Government Reform, House of Representatives, One Hundred Ninth Congress, Second Session, September 27, 2006. 2008. (Illus.). iii, 80p. *(978-0-16-082309-1(9)*, 552-070-38373-5) United States Government Printing Office.

Bernstein, Peter L. A Primer on Money, Banking, & Gold. 2008. (Peter L. Bernstein's Finance Classics Ser.: 1). (ENG.). 272p. pap. 19.95 *(978-0-470-28758-3(6)*, Wiley) Wiley, John & Sons, Inc.

Blasi J.D. LL. M., Ronald W. U. S. Master Bank Tax Guide 2009. 2008. 944p. pap. 275.00 *(978-0-8080-1919-0(8))* Toolkit Media Group.

Blasi, Ronald W. U. S. Master Bank Tax Guide. 2007th rev. ed. 2006. 928p. per. 225.00 *(978-0-8080-1577-2(X)*, 0-5874-400) Toolkit Media Group.

Bradford, Frederick A. Money & Banking. 2011. 942p. 79.95 ***(978-1-258-08661-9(1))*** Literary Licensing, LLC.

Brandeis, Louis Dembitz. Other People's Money: And How the Bankers Use It. 2009. *(978-1-57898-739-9(3))*; pap. *(978-1-57898-738-2(5))* Martino Publishing.

Broome, Lissa L. & Markham, Jerry W. Regulation of Bank Financial Service Activities: Cases & Materials. 4th ed. 2011. xxxvi, 1043p. ***(978-0-314-26616-3(X))*** West Publishing Co., College & Schl. Div.

Brown, John Crosby. A Hundred Years of Merchant Banking. 2009. 246p. pap. *(978-0-217-34141-7(1))* Books LLC.

—A Hundred Years of Merchant Banking: A History of Brown Brothers & Company, Brown, Shipley & Company & the Allied Firms. Alexander Brown & Sons. 2010. 528p. pap. 40.75 *(978-1-146-61706-2(2))* BiblioBazaar.

—A Hundred Years of Merchant Banking, a History of Brown Brothers & Company, Brown, Shipley [and] Company & the Allied Firms, Alexander. 2010. 204p. pap. 28.76 *(978-1-152-32583-8(3))* General Bks. LLC.

Buchbinder, David L. & Cooper, Robert J. Basic Bankruptcy Law for Paralegals. 2009. (Illus.). xxi, 361p. pap. *(978-0-7355-7240-9(2)*, Aspen Pubs.) Wolters Kluwer Law & Business.

Calomiris, Charles W. U. S. Bank Deregulation in Historical Perspective. 2006. (ENG., Illus.). 392p. pap. 53.00 *(978-0-521-02838-7(8))* Cambridge Univ. Pr.

Canzoneri, Matthew B., et al, eds. Establishing a Central Bank: Issues in Europe & Lessons from the U. S. 2008. (ENG., Illus.). 328p. pap. 42.00 *(978-0-521-07069-0(4))* Cambridge Univ. Pr.

Cappello, A. Barry. Lender Liability: 4th Edition. 2009. 800p. 195.00 *(978-1-57823-249-9(X))* Juris Publishing, Inc.

Carey, Leon. Scammers among Us Beware: Scammers & Frauds. 2009. 60p. pap. 9.95 *(978-1-60693-983-3(1)*, Eloquent Bks.) AEG Literary Publishing Services, Inc.

Carlson, Avery Luvere. A Banking History of Texas 1835-1929. Haas, Michelle M., ed. 2nd rev. ed. 2007. 112p. 42.95 *(978-0-9767799-1-9(9))* Copano Bay Pr.

Carrubba, Paul A. & Fisher, Dan M. Remote Deposit Capture: Practical Considerations. 2007. 43p. *(978-1-55827-737-3(4))* Sheshunoff Information Services.

Center for Financial Training. Banking Systems. 2nd ed. 2010. 400p. pap. *(978-1-4390-4206-9(3))* Cengage South-Western.

Cheatham, Anne J. Guide to Check 21 Implementation & Operations. *(978-1-55827-950-6(4))* Alex eSolutions, Inc.

Chernow, Ron. The House of Morgan: An American Banking Dynasty & the Rise of Modern Finance. 2010. (ENG., Illus.). 848p. pap. 22.00 *(978-0-8021-4465-2(9)*, Grove Pr.) Grove/Atlantic, Inc.

Cohan, William D. House of Cards: A Tale of Hubris & Wretched Excess on Wall Street. (ENG.). 2010. 608p. pap. 16.95 *(978-0-7679-3089-5(4)*, Anchor) 2009. 480p. 27.95 *(978-0-385-52826-9(4)*, Doubleday) Knopf Doubleday Publishing Group.

—House of Cards: A Tale of Hubris & Wretched Excess on Wall Street. l.t. ed. 2009. 819p. 32.95 *(978-1-4104-1835-7(9))* Thorndike Pr.

—The Last Tycoons: The Secret History of Lazard Frères & Co. 2008. (ENG.). 752p. pap. 17.00 *(978-0-7679-1979-1(3)*, Anchor) Knopf Doubleday Publishing Group.

Community & Consumer Advocates' Perspectives on the Obama Administration's Financial Regulatory Reform Proposals: Hearing Before the Committee on Financial Services, U.S. House of Representatives, One Hundred Eleventh Congress, First Session, July 16, 2009. 2009. (Illus.). iii, 211p. *(978-0-16-084937-4(3)*, 552-070-40328-1) United States Government Printing Office.

The Condition of Financial Institutions: Examining the Failure & Seizure of an American Bank: Hearing Before the Subcommittee on Financial Institutions & Consumer Credit of the Committee on Financial Services, U.S. House of Representatives, One Hundred Eleventh Congress, Second Session, January 21, 2010. 2010. v, 174p. *(978-0-16-086342-4(2)*, 552-070-41426-6) United States Government Printing Office.

Congressional Oversight Panel August Oversight Report: The Continued Risk of Troubled Assets. 2009. (Illus.). iii, 113p. *(978-0-16-084121-7(6)*, 552-070-39728-1) United States Government Printing Office.

Congressional Oversight Panel February Oversight Report: Valuing Treasury's Acquisitions. 2009. iii, 45p. *(978-0-16-082982-6(8)*, 552-070-38884-2) United States Government Printing Office.

Congressional Oversight Panel July Oversight Report: Small Banks in the Capital Purchase Program. 2010. (Illus.). iii, 103p. *(978-0-16-086306-6(6)*, 552-070-41393-6) United States Government Printing Office.

Congressional Oversight Panel June Oversight Report: Stress Testing & Shoring up Bank Capital. 2009. (Illus.). iii, 142p. *(978-0-16-083525-4(9)*, 552-070-39248-3) United States Government Printing Office.

The Consideration of Regulatory Relief Proposals: Hearing Before the Committee on Banking, Housing, & Urban Affairs, United States Senate, One Hundred Ninth Congress, First Session, on Proposals to Reduce Unnecessary Regulatory Burden on Depository Institutions Insured by the Federal Deposit Insurance Corporation, June 21, 2005. 2007. (Illus.). iv, 226p. *(978-0-16-079109-3(X)*, 552-070-36206-1) United States Government Printing Office.

Conway, J. North. King of Heists: The Sensational Bank Robbery of 1878 That Shocked America. 2010. (ENG., Illus.). 240p. pap. 14.95 *(978-1-59921-995-0(6)*, Lyons Pr.) Globe Pequot Pr., The.

Cram101 Textbook Reviews & Cram101 Textbook Reviews. Outlines & Highlights for Financial Markets & Institutions by Frederic S Mishkin. 2011. 676p. pap. 41.95 ***(978-1-61830-406-3(2))*** Cram101 Inc.

Cram101 Textbook Reviews Staff. Outlines & Highlights for Financial Institutions, Markets, & Money by Kidwell, Isbn: 0471697575. 2007. 160p. pap. 12.95 *(978-1-4288-5691-2(9))* Cram101 Inc.

—Outlines & Highlights for Financial Markets & Institutions by Mishkin & Eakins, Isbn: 0321116372. 2009. 340p. pap. 33.95 *(978-1-4288-3936-6(4))* Cram101 Inc.

Crowley, Robert W., ed. Unique Treatment of GMAC under TARP. 2010. (Financial Institutions & Services Ser.). (Illus.). ix, 176p. 115.00 *(978-1-61728-305-5(3))* Nova Science Pubs., Inc.

Davies, Howard. The Financial Crisis: Who Is to Blame? 2010. (ENG.). 240p. 69.95 *(978-0-7456-5163-7(1))*; pap. 19.95 *(978-0-7456-5164-4(X))* Polity Pr. GBR. Dist: Wiley, John & Sons, Inc.

Dawes, Charles Gates. Essays & Speeches. 427p. reprint ed. 98.00 *(978-0-7222-7442-2(4))* Library Reprints, Inc.

Dentzer, Jr. The Depository Trust Company: DTC's Formative Years & Creation of the Depository Trust & Clearing Corporation (DTCC) 2008. 100p. pap. 18.95 *(978-0-9800508-5-1(5))* YBK Pubs., Inc.

Dewatripont, Mathias & Tirole, Jean. The Prudential Regulation of Banks. 2009. (Walras-Pareto Lectures). (ENG.). 272p. (gr. 17). pap. 30.00 *(978-0-262-51386-9(2))* MIT Pr.

Dinkelspiel, Frances. Towers of Gold: How One Jewish Immigrant Named Isaias Hellman Created California. 2010. (ENG., Illus.). 400p. pap. 16.99 *(978-0-312-35527-2(0)*, St. Martin's Griffin) St. Martin's Pr.

Does the Dodd-Frank ACT End "Too Big to Fail?" Hearing Before the Subcommittee on Financial Institutions & Consumer Credit of the Committee on Financial Services, U.S. House of Representatives, One Hundred Twelfth Congress, First Session, June 14, 2011. 2011. v, 103p. ***(978-0-16-089633-0(9)***, 552-070-43522-1) United States Government Printing Office.

Dombroski, Thomas & Dombroski, Ronald. How America Was Financed: The True Story of Northeastern Pennsylvania's Contribution to the Financial & Economic Greatness of the United States of America. 2011. 274p. pap. 20.95 ***(978-1-4620-1800-0(9))*** iUniverse, Inc.

Doti, Lynne Pierson. Banking in an Unregulated Environment (RLE Banking & Finance) California, 1878-1905, Volume 27. 2012. (ENG.). 184p. 100.00 ***(978-0-415-53223-5(X))*** Routledge.

Duffus, James. The Old Bank: The Rochester Savings Bank & Its Presidents & Trustees from 1831 To 1983. 2010. (ENG., Illus.). 110p. pap. 19.95 *(978-1-933360-41-6(0)*, RIT Pr.) Rochester Institute of Technology, Cary Graphic Arts Pr.

Earp, Charles Albert & Gup, Benton E. Banking & Financial Institutions: A Guide for Directors, Investors, & Borrowers. 2011. (Wiley Finance Ser.: 615). (ENG., Illus.). 357p. 95.00 *(978-0-470-87947-4(5)*, Wiley) Wiley, John & Sons, Inc.

Ekstrom, Leif. The Bank Secrecy Act: Information Sharing & Security Efforts. 2010. (Banking & Banking Developments Ser.). 89.00 *(978-1-60741-983-9(1))* Nova Science Pubs., Inc.

Elsom, John R. Lightning over the Treasury Building: An Expose of Our Banking & Currency Monstrosity, America's Most Reprehensible & un-American Racket. 2011. 112p. 39.95 ***(978-1-258-00420-0(8))*** Literary Licensing, LLC.

The End of Excess: Hearing Before the Subcommittee on Oversight & Investigations of the Committee on Financial Services, U.S. House of Representatives, One Hundred Eleventh Congress, Second Session. 2010. (Illus.). ***(978-0-16-087020-0(8)***, 552-070-41879-2 (pt.1)) United States Government Printing Office.

Ennis, Huberto M. & Weinberg, John A. Interest on Reserves & Daylight Credit: A Reprint from the Federal Reserve Bank of Richmond Economic Quarterly. 2007. (Illus.). 31p. (C). pap. 15.00 *(978-1-4223-1737-2(4))* DIANE Publishing Co.

Ex-Im Bank Oversight: The Role of Trade Finance in Doubling Exports over Five Years: Joint Hearing Before the Subcommittee on Oversight & Investigations & the Subcommittee on International Monetary Policy & Trade of the Committee on Financial Services, U.S. House of Representatives, One Hundred Eleventh Congress, Second Session, September 29, 2010. 2010. v, 86p. ***(978-0-16-087699-8(0)***, 552-070-42251-0) United States Government Printing Office.

Examining the Link Between Fed Bank Supervision & Monetary Policy: Hearing Before the Committee on Financial Services, U.S. House of Representatives, One Hundred Eleventh Congress, Second Session, March 17, 2010. 2010. iii, 129p. *(978-0-16-086419-3(4)*, 552-070-41480-1) United States Government Printing Office.

Examining the State of the Banking Industry: Hearing Before the Subcommittee on Financial Institutions of the Committee on Banking, Housing, & Urban Affairs, United States Senate, One Hundred Eleventh Congress, First Session, on the Current Conditions of Key Financial Institutions & Examining the Continuing Challenges These Institutions Face, October 14, 2009. 2010. (Illus.). iii, 176p. *(978-0-16-086423-0(2)*, 552-070-41484-3) United States Government Printing Office.

Ezon. E-Z Rules for the Bankruptcy Code. 2009. (Illus.). xi, 383p. pap., stu. ed. 31.95 *(978-0-7355-7197-6(X))* Wolters Kluwer Law & Business.

Farrell, Greg. Crash of the Titans: Greed, Hubris, the Fall of Merrill Lynch, & the near-Collapse of Bank of America. 2011. (ENG.). 512p. pap. 17.00 *(978-0-307-71787-0(9)*, Crown Business) Crown Publishing Group.

Federal Regulator Perspectives on Financial Regulatory Reform Proposals: Hearing Before the Committee on Financial Services, U.S. House of Representatives, One Hundred Eleventh Congress, First Session, September 23, 2009. 2010. iii, 184p. *(978-0-16-085682-2(5)*, 552-070-40914-9) United States Government Printing Office.

Feinberg, Richard E. Subsidizing Success: The Export-Import Bank in the U. S. Economy. 2009. (ENG.). 204p. pap. 31.99 *(978-0-521-10466-1(1))* Cambridge Univ. Pr.

Financial Regulatory Reform: Protecting Taxpayers & the Economy: Hearing Before the Joint Economic Committee, Congress of the United States, One Hundred Eleventh Congress, First Session, November 19, 2009. 2010. iii, 57p. *(978-0-16-085972-4(7)*, 552-070-41163-1) United States Government Printing Office.

Fisher, June Breton. When Money Was in Fashion: Henry Goldman, Goldman Sachs, & the Founding of Wall Street. 2010. (ENG., Illus.). 288p. 27.00 *(978-0-230-61750-6(6))* Palgrave Macmillan.

Fishman, Shmulik. Fiction of Value. 2010. 78p. pap. 6.12 *(978-0-557-38852-3(X))* Lulu Enterprises Inc.

Fuller, Robert Lynn. Phantom of Fear: The Banking Panic Of 1933. 2011. (ENG.). 287p. pap. 49.95 ***(978-0-7864-6510-1(7))*** McFarland & Co., Inc. Pubs.

Gilbert, Mark. Complicit: How Greed & Collusion Made the Credit Crisis Unstoppable. 2010. (Bloomberg Ser.: 19). (ENG., Illus.). 192p. 24.95 *(978-1-57660-346-8(6)*, Bloomberg Pr.) Wiley, John & Sons, Inc.

Gorton, Gary. Slapped by the Invisible Hand: The Panic of 2007, 1 vol. 2010. (Fma Survey Ser.). (ENG., Illus.). 240p. 34.95 *(978-0-19-973415-3(1))* Oxford Univ. Pr., Inc.

Gray, Warren P. The Development of Banking in Tennessee. 2007. 136p. per. 39.95 *(978-0-9791702-6-3(5))* Capricorn Hse. Publishing.

Greenbaum, Stuart I. & Thakor, Anjan V. Contemporary Financial Intermediation. 2nd rev. ed. 2007. (Academic Press Advanced Finance Ser.). (ENG., Illus.). 672p. 103.00 *(978-0-12-299053-3(6)*, Academic Pr.) Elsevier Science & Technology Bks.

Greenberg, Alan C. (Ace). The Rise & Fall of Bear Stearns. 2010. (ENG., Illus.). 224p. 26.00 *(978-1-4165-6288-7(5))* Simon & Schuster.

Grey House Publishing, creator. TheStreet. com Ratings' Guide to Banks & Thrifts: A Quarterly Compilation of Financial Institutions Ratings & Analyses. 2008. (Street. com Guide to Banks & Thrifts Ser.). (Illus.). 382p. per. 249.00 *(978-1-59237-274-4(0))* Grey Hse. Publishing.

Griffin, G. Edward. The Creature from Jekyll Island: A Second Look at the Federal Reserve. 5th ed. 2010. pap. 24.50 *(978-0-912986-45-6(X))* American Media.

Griffiss, Bartow. The New York Call Money Market / by Bartow Griffiss. 2006. 140p. per. 16.99 *(978-1-4255-0997-2(5))* MPublishing.

Grind, Kirsten. The Lost Bank: The Story of Washington Mutual — The Biggest Bank Failure in American History. 2012. pap. ***(978-1-4516-1793-1(3))*** Simon & Schuster.

—The Lost Bank: The Story of Washington Mutual-The Biggest Bank Failure in American History. 2012. (ENG.). 400p. 27.00 ***(978-1-4516-1792-4(5))*** Simon & Schuster.

Gup, B. E. & Gup, Benton E. Handbook for Directors of Financial Institutions. 2008. (Elgar Original Reference Ser.). (Illus.). 200p. (C). 173.00 *(978-1-84720-469-1(4))* Elgar, Edward Publishing, Inc.

Haider, Saba. Vault Career Guide to Investment Banking, 2nd Edition: European Edition. 2009. 176p. pap. 34.95 *(978-1-58131-692-6(5))* Vault.com.

Harris, Ethan S. Ben Bernanke's Fed: The Federal Reserve after Greenspan. 2008. (ENG., Illus.). 237p. 26.95 *(978-1-4221-2584-7(X))* Harvard Business Review Pr.

Hawkins, Charles Albert. Economic Slavery or Freedom: Business Depressions, Their Cause & Cure. 2011. 140p. 40.95 ***(978-1-258-00765-2(7))*** Literary Licensing, LLC.

Hendrickson, Jill M. Regulation & Instability in U. S. Commercial Banking: A History of Crises. 2011. (Palgrave Macmillan Studies in Banking & Financial Institutions Ser.). (ENG., Illus.). 320p. 110.00 *(978-0-230-28066-3(8))* Palgrave Macmillan.

Hester, Donald D. The Evolution of Monetary Policy & Banking in the US. (ENG., Illus.). viii, 206p. 2010. pap. 129.00 *(978-3-642-09651-8(4),* 3642096514) 2008. 129.00 *(978-3-540-77793-9(8),* 3540777938) Springer.

Hill, Vernon. Fans, Not Customers: How Commerce Bank Created a Super-Growth Business in a No-Growth Industry. 2007. 256p. (gr. 12). 24.95 *(978-1-59184-173-9(9),* Portfolio (Hardcover)) Penguin Group (USA) Inc.

Hoffmann, Susan & Cassell, Mark K. Mission Expansion in the Federal Home Loan Bank System. 2010. (ENG., Illus.). 208p. pap. 24.95 *(978-1-4384-3342-4(5))* State Univ. of New York Pr.

Hoffmann, Susan M. & Cassell, Mark K. Mission Expansion in the Federal Home Loan Bank System. 2010. (ENG., Illus.). 208p. 75.00 *(978-1-4384-3341-7(7))* State Univ. of New York Pr.

Horvat, David K. The Export-Import Bank. 2011. (Trade Issues, Policies & Laws Ser.). (Illus.). viii, 183p. 115.00 *(978-1-61761-892-5(6))* Nova Science Pubs., Inc.

Hudson, Michael W. The Monster: How a Gang of Predatory Lenders & Wall Street Bankers Fleeced America - And Spawned a Global Crisis. 2010. (ENG.). 384p. 26.00 *(978-0-8050-9046-8(0),* Times Bks.) Holt, Henry & Co.

Hunt, James L. Relationship Banker: Eugene W. Stetson, Wall Street, & American Business, 1916-1959. 2009. (Illus.). 400p. 35.00 *(978-0-86554-915-9(X))* Mercer Univ. Pr.

Improving Federal Consumer Protection in Financial Services: Consumer & Industry Perspectives: Hearing Before the Committee on Financial Services, U.S. House of Representatives, One Hundred Tenth Congress, First Session, July 25, 2007. 2007. iii, 118p. *(978-0-16-079705-7(5),* 552-070-36641-5) United States Government Printing Office.

Improving Financial Literacy in the United States: Hearing Before the Committee on Banking, Housing, & Urban Affairs, United States Senate, One Hundred Ninth Congress, Second Session, on the Need to Improve Americans' Financial Literacy & Education to Ensure All Americans Have Tools & Resources to Make Sound Financial Decisions, May 23, 2006. 2009. iii, 67p. *(978-0-16-083073-0(7),* 552-070-38967-9) United States Government Printing Office.

INCORPORATED, CCH. Practical Guide to Bank Compliance. 2007. pap. *(978-0-8080-1738-7(1))* Wolters Kluwer Law & Business.

International Monetary Fund Staff. Macroeconomic Implications of Financial Dollarization: The Case of Uruguay. Piñon, Marco et al, eds. 2008. (Illus.). 80p. pap. *(978-1-58906-727-1(4))* International Monetary Fund.

Isaac, William M. Senseless Panic: How Washington Failed America. 2010. (ENG.). 190p. 24.95 *(978-0-470-64036-4(7),* Wiley) Wiley, John & Sons, Inc.

Johnson, Simon & Kwak, James. 13 Bankers: The Wall Street Takeover & the Next Financial Meltdown. (Vintage Ser.). (ENG.). 2011. 336p. pap. 15.95 *(978-0-307-47660-9(X),* Vintage) 2010. (Illus.). 320p. 26.95 *(978-0-307-37905-4(1),* Pantheon) Knopf Doubleday Publishing Group.

Kansas Bankers Association Staff. The Story of Banking in Kansas: Commemorating the Fiftieth Anniversary of the Organization of the Kansas Bankers Association, 1887-1937. (Illus.). 103p. reprint ed. lib. bdg. 88.00 *(978-0-7222-0602-7(X))* Library Reprints, Inc.

Kelly, Kate. Street Fighters: The Last 72 Hours of Bear Sterns, the Toughest Firm on Wall Street. 2010. (ENG.). 256p. (gr. 12-18). 16.00 *(978-1-59184-318-4(9),* Portfolio Trade) Penguin Group (USA) Inc.

Keyes, Emerson Willard. A History of Savings Banks in the United States from Their Inception in 1816 down to 1874 with Discussions of Their Theory, Practical Workings & In. 2006. 496p. per. 29.99 *(978-1-4255-5600-6(0))* MPublishing.

Kidwell, David S., et al. Financial Institutions, Markets, & Money. 11th ed. 2011. (CourseSmart Ser.). (ENG.). 736p. (C). 168.95 *(978-0-470-56108-9(4),* Wiley) Wiley, John & Sons, Inc.

Kiewe, Amos. FDR's First Fireside Chat: Public Confidence & the Banking Crisis. 2007. (Library of Presidential Rhetoric Ser.). (ENG., Illus.). 166p. pap. 16.95 *(978-1-58544-607-0(6))*; pap. 32.95 *(978-1-58544-597-4(5))* Texas A&M Univ. Pr.

Killenbeck, Mark Robert. McCulloch V. Maryland: Securing a Nation. 2006. (Landmark Law Cases & American Society Ser.). 227p. 35.00 *(978-0-7006-1472-1(9))* Univ. Pr. of Kansas.

—M'Culloch V. Maryland: Securing a Nation. 2006. (Landmark Law Cases & American Society Ser.). 227p. pap. 16.95 *(978-0-7006-1473-8(7))* Univ. Pr. of Kansas.

Kimbrell, Jody D. Bankers: the Only Profession That Drove Jesus to Violence: A True Story of Lies, Deceit, & Deception. 2011. pap. 9.99 *(978-1-61739-164-4(6))* Tate Publishing & Enterprises, LLC.

Klein, Lilian B. Bank Secrecy ACT: Background, Statute, & Interpretation. 2006. 161p. 69.00 *(978-1-60021-472-1(X))* Nova Science Pubs., Inc.

Kuhlmann, Arkadi & Philp, Bruce. The Orange Code: How ING Direct Succeeded by Being a Rebel with a Cause. 2010. (ENG.). 272p. pap. 14.95 *(978-0-470-53879-1(1),* Wiley) Wiley, John & Sons, Inc.

Lendman, Stephen. How Wall Street Fleeces America: Privatized Banking, Government Collusion & Class War. 2011. (ENG.). 216p. pap. 16.95 ***(978-0-9833539-4-2(8))*** Clarity Pr., Inc.

Lessons Learned in Risk Management Oversight at Federal Financial Regulators: Hearing Before the Subcommittee on Securities, Insurance, & Investment of the Committee on Banking, Housing, & Urban Affairs, United States Senate, One Hundred Eleventh Congress, First Session, on Discussing the Role of Federal Financial Regulators in the Financial Crisis in the United States & Reforming Regulation to Ensure a Strong Financial System, March 18, 2009. 2009. iii, 177p. *(978-0-16-084674-8(9),* 552-070-40167-9) United States Government Printing Office.

Leuter, Anne, ed. The Bank Secrecy Act & Anti-Money Laundering Examination Manual. 2010. (Financial Institutions & Services Ser.). 175.50 *(978-1-61728-227-0(8))* Nova Science Pubs., Inc.

Lindbergh, Charles A., Jr. Why Is Your Country at War & What Happens to You after the War & Related Subjects. 220p. reprint ed. lib. bdg. 98.00 *(978-0-7222-4763-1(X))* Library Reprints, Inc.

Loeper, David B. Stop the Retirement Rip-Off: How to Keep More of Your Money for Retirement. 2nd ed. 2011. (ENG., Illus.). 222p. pap. 19.95 ***(978-1-118-13304-0(8),*** Wiley) Wiley, John & Sons, Inc.

Loucks, Henry Langford. The Great Conspiracy of the House of Morgan & How to Defeat It. 2007. (ENG.). 310p. 45.95 *(978-0-548-15601-8(8))*; 312p. per. 30.95 *(978-1-4304-5055-9(X))* Kessinger Publishing, LLC.

Lumley, Darwyn H. Breaking the Banks in Motor City: The Auto Industry, the 1933 Detroit Banking Crisis & the Start of the New Deal. 2009. (ENG., Illus.). 202p. pap. 35.00 *(978-0-7864-4417-5(7))* McFarland & Co., Inc. Pubs.

Macey & Carnell, Richard Scott. The Law of Banking & Financial Institutions. 4th rev. ed. 2008. xxxii, 796p. 152.00 *(978-0-7355-5285-2(1),* Aspen Pubs.) Wolters Kluwer Law & Business.

Malloy, Michael P. Banking Law & Regulation. 2nd ed. 2011. ***(978-0-7355-5276-0(2))***; ***(978-0-7355-5275-3(4))***; ***(978-0-7355-5274-6(6))*** Wolters Kluwer Law & Business. (Aspen Pubs.).

—Principles of Bank Regulation. 3rd rev. ed. 2011. 592p. pap. 46.00 ***(978-0-314-19456-5(8))*** West Publishing Co., College & Schl. Div.

Marrs, Jim. The Trillion-Dollar Conspiracy: How the New World Order, Man-Made Diseases, & Zombie Banks Are Destroying America. 2011. (ENG.). 464p. pap. 15.99 *(978-0-06-197069-6(7),* William Morrow Paperbacks) HarperCollins Pubs.

Mars-Proietti, Laura. TheStreet. com Ratings' Guide to Banks & Thrifts. 2008. (Street. com Guide to Banks & Thrifts Ser.). pap. 249.00 *(978-1-59237-313-0(5))* Grey Hse. Publishing.

Mars-Proietti, Laura, ed. TheStreet. com Ratings Guide to Banks & Thrifts: 2008. 2008. pap. 249.00 *(978-1-59237-312-3(7))*; pap. 249.00 *(978-1-59237-311-6(9))* Grey Hse. Publishing.

—TheStreet. com Ratings Guide to Banks & Thrifts: 2009. 2009. pap. 249.00 *(978-1-59237-449-6(2))*; pap. 249.00 *(978-1-59237-448-9(4))* Grey Hse. Publishing.

Mayo, Mike. Exile on Wall Street: One Analyst's Fight to Save the Big Banks from Themselves. 2011. (ENG.). 208p. 29.95 ***(978-1-118-11546-6(5),*** Wiley) Wiley, John & Sons, Inc.

McCleskey, Scott. When Free Markets Fail: Saving the Market When It Can't Save Itself. 2010. (ENG.). 198p. 39.95 *(978-0-470-60336-9(4),* Wiley) Wiley, John & Sons, Inc.

McCulley, Richard T. Banks & Politics During the Progressive Era (Rle Banking & Finance), Volume 21. 2012. (ENG.). 360p. 130.00 ***(978-0-415-52854-2(2))*** Routledge.

Mihm, Stephen. A Nation of Counterfeiters: Capitalists, con Men, & the Making of the United States. (Illus.). 480p. 2009. pap. 21.00 *(978-0-674-03244-6(6))* 2007. 29.95 *(978-0-674-02657-5(8))* Harvard Univ. Pr.

Miller, Harry E. Banking Theories in the United States Before 1860. 2011. 252p. 46.95 ***(978-1-258-08326-7(4))*** Literary Licensing, LLC.

Milligan, Jack. The Guidebook to Effective Bank Board Committees. 2nd ed. 2006. 125.00 *(978-0-9785771-1-7(6))* America's Community Bankers.

Minar, Jan. Effective Us-Czech Stock Portfolio Allocation. 2010. 108p. pap. *(978-3-8383-5768-3(X))* Lambert Academic Publishing.

Mishkin & Eakins, Stanley G. Financial Markets & Institutions. 6th ed. 2008. (ENG., Illus.). 752p. (C). 220.00 *(978-0-321-37421-9(5))* Addison Wesley.

—Financial Markets & Institutions. 4th ed. 2006. pap. 16.95 *(978-1-4288-1114-0(1))* Cram101 Inc.

—Financial Markets & Institutions. 6th ed. 2009. (Illus.). 752p. pap. *(978-0-321-55211-2(3))* Prentice Hall PTR.

Mishkin, Frederic S. & Eakins, Stanley. Study Guide for Financial Markets & Institutions. 7th rev. ed. 2011. (ENG.). 360p. (C). pap. 46.67 *(978-0-13-213692-1(9),* Prentice Hall) Prentice Hall PTR.

Morris, Robert. The Banks of New York, Their Dealers, the Clearing-House, & the Panic of 1857 by J S Gibbons. 2006. 472p. per. 29.99 *(978-1-4255-5200-8(5))* MPublishing.

Moulton, R. K. Legislative & Documentary History of the Banks of the United States from the Time of Establishing the Bank of North America, 1781, to October 1834: With Notes & Comments. 2007. 232p. 95.00 *(978-1-58477-873-8(3))* Lawbook Exchange, Ltd., The.

Moyer, Stephen E., ed. Financial Regulatory Reform. 2010. (Global Recession - Causes, Impacts & Remedies Ser.). 180p. 89.00 *(978-1-60741-567-1(4))* Nova Science Pubs., Inc.

Mullins, Eustace Clarence. The Federal Reserve Conspiracy. 2011. 148p. 40.95 ***(978-1-258-10258-6(7))*** Literary Licensing, LLC.

—A Study of the Federal Reserve. 2011. 142p. 40.95 ***(978-1-258-00963-2(3))*** Literary Licensing, LLC.

—A Study of the Federal Reserve. 2009. *(978-1-57898-801-3(2))*; pap. *(978-1-57898-802-0(0))* Martino Publishing.

Mullins, Eustace Clarence & Mullins, Eustace. A Study of the Federal Reserve & Its Secrets. 2010. 158p. pap. 11.99 *(978-1-61720-073-1(5))* Wilder Pubns., Ltd.

Nadler, Marcus & Bogen, Jules. The Banking Crisis, Volume 24. 2012. (ENG.). 224p. 115.00 ***(978-0-415-52812-2(7))*** Routledge.

Nevins, Allan. History of the Bank of New York & Trust Company, 1784 to 1934 / Allan Nevins. 2011. 236p. pap. 20.99 ***(978-1-4181-8753-8(4))*** MPublishing.

New York University Stern School of Business Staff. Restoring Financial Stability: How to Repair a Failed System. Acharya, Viral & Richardson, Matthew, eds. 2009. (Wiley Finance Ser.: 542). (ENG., Illus.). 416p. 49.95 *(978-0-470-49934-4(6),* Wiley) Wiley, John & Sons, Inc.

Nominations of James S. Simpson, Robert M. Couch, Christopher A. Padilla, & Bijan Rafiekian: Hearing Before the Committee on Banking, Housing, & Urban Affairs, United States Senate, One Hundred Ninth Congress, Second Session, on Nominations of James S. Simpson, of New York, to Be Federal Transit Administrator, U.S. Department of Transportation: Robert M. Couch, of Alabama, to Be President, Government National Mortgage Association (Ginnie Mae): Christopher A. Padilla, of the District of. 2007. iii, 85p. *(978-0-16-079028-7(X),* 552-070-36138-3) United States Government Printing Office.

Noon, Kevin F. & Ward, Judith A. Green Wealth. 2007. (ENG., Illus.). 1p. pap. 18.95 *(978-0-7570-0282-3(X))* Square One Pubs.

Nordskog, Andrae B. Spiking the Gold: Or Who Caused the Depression & the Way Out. 2011. 128p. 40.95 ***(978-1-258-01011-9(9))*** Literary Licensing, LLC.

Ojo, Olu. Diversification & Performance Relationship in Nigerian Banks. 2011. 116p. pap. ***(978-3-8443-2774-8(6))*** Lambert Academic Publishing.

Olmstead, Alan L. & Olmstead

, Alan L. New York City Mutual Savings Banks, 1819-1861. 2011. (ENG.). 250p. pap. 40.00 ***(978-0-8078-9743-0(4))*** Univ. of North Carolina Pr.

Oversight of Federal Payment of Interchange Fees: How to Save Taxpayer Dollars: Hearing Before a Subcommittee of the Committee on Appropriations, United States Senate, One Hundred Eleventh Congress, Second Session: Special Hearing, June 16, 2010, Washington, DC. 2011. iv, 72p. ***(978-0-16-087992-0(2),*** 552-070-42402-4) United States Government Printing Office.

Paoe, R. Daniel. Limitations on the Business of Banking (RLE Banking & Finance) An Analysis of Expanded Securities, Insurance & Real Estate Activities, Volume 25. 2012. (ENG.). 176p. 100.00 ***(978-0-415-53932-6(3))*** Routledge.

Payi, Melchior. The Chicago Credit Market: Organization & Institutional Structure. 2011. 464p. 57.95 ***(978-1-258-04703-0(9))*** Literary Licensing, LLC.

Park, Sangkyun. Contagion of Bank Failures (Rle Banking & Finance), Volume 26. 2012. (ENG.). 216p. 115.00 ***(978-0-415-52875-7(5))*** Routledge.

Parsons, Francis. A History of Banking in Connecticut. 32p. reprint ed. lib. bdg. 88.00 *(978-0-7222-0491-7(4))* Library Reprints, Inc.

Paul, Ron. End the Fed. 2010. (ENG.). 224p. pap. 14.99 *(978-0-446-54917-2(7))* Grand Central Publishing.

Petersen, Mark A., et al. Subprime Banking Models. 2010. (Banking & Banking Developments Ser.). 129.00 *(978-1-61728-694-0(X))* Nova Science Pubs., Inc.

Phillips, Chester Arthur, et al. Banking & the Business Cycle: A Study of the Great Depression in the United States. 2011. 290p. 48.95 ***(978-1-258-03718-5(1))*** Literary Licensing, LLC.

Plunkett, Jack W. Plunkett's Banking, Mortgages & Credit Industry Almanac 2008: Banking, Mortgages & Credit Industry Market Research, Statistics, Trends & Leading Companies. annuals Plunkett, Jack W., ed. 2007. 465p. pap. 299.99 incl. cd-rom *(978-1-59392-098-2(9))* Plunkett Research, Ltd.

—Plunkett's Banking, Mortgages & Securities Industry Almanac 2008: Banking, Mortgages & Credit Industry Market Research, Statistics, Trends & Leading Companies. annuals Plunkett, Jack W., ed. 2007. 476p. E-Book 299.99 incl. cd-rom *(978-1-59392-441-6(0))* Plunkett Research, Ltd.

Prohibiting Certain High-Risk Investment Activities by Banks & Bank Holding Companies: Hearing Before the Committee on Banking, Housing, & Urban Affairs, United States Senate, One Hundred Eleventh Congress, Second Session, on Examining Recent Restrictions Placed on Commercial Banks & Bank Holding Companies' High-Risk Investment Activities, February 2, 2010. 2010. iii, 71p. ***(978-0-16-087802-2(0),*** 552-070-42306-1) United States Government Printing Office.

Promoting Bank Liquidity & Lending Through Deposit Insurance, Hope for Homeowners, & Other Enhancements: Hearing Before the Committee on Financial Services, U.S. House of Representatives, One Hundred Eleventh Congress, First Session, February 3, 2009. 2009. (Illus.). iii, 204p. *(978-0-16-083583-4(6),* 552-070-39301-3) United States Government Printing Office.

Public Policy Issues Raised by the Report of the Lehman Bankruptcy Examiner: Hearing Before the Committee on Financial Services, U.S. House of Representatives, One Hundred Eleventh Congress, Second Session, April 20, 2010. 2010. (Illus.). iv, 228p. *(978-0-16-086777-4(0),* 552-070-41698-6) United States Government Printing Office.

Rappaport, Jordan. Guide to Aggregate House Price Measures: A Reprint from the Federal Reserve Bank of Kansas City Economic Review. 2007. (Illus.). 30p. (C). pap. 15.00 *(978-1-4223-1742-6(0))* DIANE Publishing Co.

Regulatory Restructuring & Reform of the Financial System: Hearing Before the Committee on Financial Services, U.S. House of Representatives, One Hundred Tenth Congress, Second Session, October 21, 2008. 2009. iv, 266p. *(978-0-16-082948-2(8),* 552-070-38860-5) United States Government Printing Office.

Ritholtz, Barry. Bailout Nation: How Greed & Easy Money Corrupted Wall Street & Shook the World Economy. rev. ed. 2010. (ENG., Illus.). 332p. pap. 16.95 *(978-0-470-59632-6(5),* Wiley) Wiley, John & Sons, Inc.

Rothacker, Rick. Banktown: The Rise & Struggles of Charlotte's Big Banks. 2010. (Illus.). 336p. 26.95 *(978-0-89587-381-1(8))* Blair, John F. Pub.

Rubin, Julia Sass. Financing Low-Income Communities: Models, Obstacles, & Future Directions. 2007. (Illus.). 328p. *(978-0-87154-711-8(2))* Russell Sage Foundation.

Russell, Ellen. New Deal Banking Reforms & Keynesian Welfare State Capitalism. 2012. (New Political Economy Ser.). (ENG.). 158p. pap. 42.95 ***(978-0-415-54181-7(6))*** Routledge.

Scheer, Robert. The Great American Stickup: How Reagan Republicans & Clinton Democrats Enriched Wall Street While Mugging Main Street. 2010. (ENG.). 304p. (gr. 9). pap. 15.95 *(978-1-56858-434-8(2))* Basic Bks.

Scott, Hal S. Scott's International Finance, Transactions, Policy, & Regulation. 18th rev. ed. 2011. 1392p. 180.00 ***(978-1-59941-975-6(0),*** Foundation Pr.) West.

Shrader, Alan & Davis, Raymond P. Leading for Growth: How Umpqua Bank Got Cool & Created a Culture of Greatness. 2007. (J-B US Non-Franchise Leadership Ser.: 37). (ENG., Illus.). 240p. 27.95 *(978-0-7879-8607-0(0),* Jossey-Bass) Wiley, John & Sons, Inc.

Smithers, Andrew. Wall Street Revalued: Imperfect Markets & Inept Central Bankers. 2009. (ENG., Illus.). 256p. 27.95 *(978-0-470-75005-6(7),* Wiley) Wiley, John & Sons, Inc.

Sperry, Paul. The Great American Bank Robbery: The Cost & Causes of the New Depression: How Race-Based Lending & Other Multi-Cultural Schemes Make Us All Poorer, 0 vols. 2011. (Illus.). 320p. pap. 14.99 *(978-1-59555-270-9(7))* Nelson, Thomas Inc.

The State of Community Banking: Opportunities & Challenges: Hearing Before the Subcommittee on Financial Institutions & Consumer Protection of the Committee on Banking, Housing, & Urban Affairs, United States Senate, One Hundred Twelfth Congress, First Session, on Examining the Current Economic & Regulatory Environment Facing Community Banks, April 6, 2011. 2011. (Illus.). iii, 101p. ***(978-0-16-089779-5(3),*** 552-070-43631-6) United States Government Printing Office.

The State of the Banking Industry: Hearing Before the Committee on Banking, Housing, & Urban Affairs, United States Senate, One Hundred Tenth Congress, Second Session, on the State of the Banking Industry. 2010. (Illus.). *(978-0-16-085662-4(0),* 552-070-40899-1 (pt.1)); *(978-0-16-085685-3(X),* 552-070-40899-1 (pt.1)) United States Government Printing Office.

Steiner, Howard. Sar Investigations - the Complete Bsa/Aml Desktop Reference. 2008. 304p. 99.96 *(978-0-615-21438-2(X))* ImpactAML-INX3 Financial Pr.

Steiner, Howard & Marini, Stephen L. Independent Review for Banks - the Complete BSA/AML Audit Workbook. 2008. 377p. pap. 129.96 *(978-0-615-23790-9(8))* ImpactAML-INX3 Financial Pr.

Street Com Ratings Inc, creator. TheStreet. com Ratings Guide to Banks & Thrifts: A Quarterly Compilation of Financial Institutions Ratings & Analyses, Summer 2007. 66th ed. 2007. (Street. com Guide to Banks & Thrifts Ser.). (Illus.). 388p. per. 249.00 *(978-1-58773-329-1(3))* TheStreet.com Ratings, Inc.

Strengthening & Streamlining Prudential Bank Supervision: Hearing Before the Committee on Banking, Housing, & Urban Affairs, United States Senate, One Hundred Eleventh Congress, First Session, on Strengthening & Streamlining Prudential Bank Supervision to Better Provide the Safety, Soundness, & Stability of the Financial Markets, August 4 & September 29, 2009. 2010. ii, 182p. ***(978-0-16-086103-1(9),*** 552-070-41213-1) United States Government Printing Office.

Sturz, Waldemar. Banking System Risk in the United States of America & Europe. 2011. 96p. pap. ***(978-3-8443-0839-6(3))*** Lambert Academic Publishing.

Thestreet Com Ratings. The Street. com Ratings' Guide to Banks & Thrifts: A Quarterly Compilation of Financial Institutions Ratings & Analyses. 2007.

B

(Street. com Guide to Banks & Thrifts Ser.). (Illus.). 386p. per. 249.00 *(978-1-59237-245-4(7))* Grey Hse. Publishing.

TheStreet. com Ratings Guide to Banks & Thrifts: A Quarterly Compilation of Financial Institution Ratings & Analyses. 65th ed. 2007. pap. 249.00 *(978-1-58773-328-4(5))* TheStreet.com Ratings, Inc.

TheStreet. com Ratings Guide to Banks & Thrifts: A Quarterly Compilation of Financial Institutions Ratings & Analyses. 2007. 67th ed. pap. 249.00 *(978-1-58773-330-7(7))* 68th ed. pap. 249.00 *(978-1-58773-331-4(5))* TheStreet.com Ratings, Inc.

TheStreet.com Ratings, ed. TheStreet. com Ratings Guide to Banks & Thrifts. 2010. pap. 249.00 *(978-1-59237-504-2(9))* 2010. pap. 249.00 *(978-1-59237-503-5(0))* 2009. pap. 249.00 *(978-1-59237-502-8(2))* Grey Hse. Publishing.

—TheStreet. com Ratings Guide to Banks & Thrifts: Fall 2009. 2009. pap. 249.00 *(978-1-59237-450-2(6))* Grey Hse. Publishing.

TheStreet.com Ratings Staff & Weiss Ratings Inc. Staff, eds. TheStreet. com Ratings Guide to Credit Unions. 2011. pap. 249.00 *(978-1-59237-669-8(X))* Grey Hse. Publishing.

Too Big Has Failed: Learning from Midwest Banks & Credit Unions: Field Hearing Before the Subcommittee on Oversight & Investigations of the Committee on Financial Services, U.S. House of Representatives, One Hundred Eleventh Congress, Second Session, August 23, 2010. 2010. (Illus.). v, 91p. ***(978-0-16-087502-1(1)***, 552-070-42190-4) United States Government Printing Office.

Torp, Jeffrey. BSA/Anti-Money Laundering Question & Answer Book. 2007. *(978-1-55827-442-6(1))* Sheshunoff Information Services.

Torp, Jeffrey & Hyde, Lorraine. Identity Theft Prevention Program. 2007. (Illus.). *(978-1-55827-962-9(8))* Sheshunoff Information Services.

Treasury Dept. (U.S.), compiled by. The Department of the Treasury Blueprint for a Modernized Financial Regulatory Structure. 2008. (ENG.). 212p. pap. 24.00 *(978-0-16-080645-2(3)*, Treasury Dept.) United States Government Printing Office.

Troubled Asset Relief Program: Hearing Before the Subcommittee on Oversight of the Committee on Ways & Means, U.S. House of Representatives, One Hundred Eleventh Congress, First Session, March 19, 2009. 2009. (Illus.). iii, 70p. *(978-0-16-083739-5(1)*, 552-070-39441-9) United States Government Printing Office.

United States, Congress House Committee on Financial Services Subcommittee on Financial Institutions and Consumer Credit Staff, contrib. by. Improving Financial Literacy: Working Together to Develop Private Sector Coordination & Solutions: Hearing Before the Subcommittee on Financial Institutions & Consumer Credit of the Committee on Financial Services, U.S. House of Representatives, One Hundred Ninth Congress, Second Session, September 28, 2006. 2007. (Illus.). v, 177p. *(978-0-16-078632-7(0)*, 552-070-35876-5) United States Government Printing Office.

Van Overtveldt, Johan. Bernanke's Test: Ben Bernanke, Alan Greenspan, & the Drama of the Central Banker. 2010. (ENG.). 300p. pap. 19.95 *(978-1-932841-57-0(2))* Agate Publishing, Inc.

Vickers, Raymond B. Panic in Paradise: Florida's Banking Crash Of 1926. 2007. (Illus.). 336p. per. 36.00 *(978-0-8173-5414-5(X))* Univ. of Alabama Pr.

Waldthaler, Mattheus. Rating von strukturierten Produkten: Eine kritische Betrachtung der Rolle der Ratingagenturen im Rahmen der Subprime-Krise. 2009. 92p. pap. *(978-3-639-19287-2(7))* VDM Verlag Dr. Mueller e.K.

Ward, Vicky. The Devil's Casino: Friendship, Betrayal, & the High-Stakes Games Played Inside Lehman Brothers. 2011. (ENG., Illus.). 270p. pap. 16.95 *(978-1-118-01149-2(X)*, Wiley) Wiley, John & Sons, Inc.

Watson, Mark M. How Accurate are Real-Time Estimates of Output Trends & Gaps? A Reprint from the Federal Reserve Bank of Richmond Economic Quarterly. 2007. (Illus.). 18p. (C). pap. 15.00 *(978-1-4223-1736-5(6))* DIANE Publishing Co.

Weiss Ratings, ed. TheStreet. com Ratings Guide to Credit Unions. 2011. pap. 249.00 *(978-1-59237-671-1(1))*; pap. 249.00 *(978-1-59237-670-4(3))* Grey Hse. Publishing.

—Weiss Ratings Guide to Banks & Thrifts. 2011. pap. 249.00 *(978-1-59237-777-0(7))*; pap. 249.00 *(978-1-59237-776-3(9))*; pap. 249.00 *(978-1-59237-775-6(0))* Grey Hse. Publishing.

Weiss Ratings Inc, creator. The Street. com Ratings' Guide to Banks & Thrifts: A Quarterly Compilation of Financial Institutions Ratings & Analyses. 64th ed. 2006. (Street. com Guide to Banks & Thrifts Ser.). (Illus.). 390p. per. 249.00 *(978-1-58773-261-4(0))* TheStreet.com Ratings, Inc.

Weiss Ratings Inc. Staff, ed. TheStreet. com Ratings Guide to Banks & Thrifts. 2010. pap. 249.00 *(978-1-59237-505-9(7))* Grey Hse. Publishing.

Wells Fargo Historical Services Staff, contrib. by. Time Well Kept: Selections from the Wells Fargo Corporate Archives. 2011. *(978-1-57864-665-4(0))* Donning Co. Pubs.

Werner, Morris Robert. Little Napoleons & Dummy Directors: Being the Narrative of the Bank of United States. 2009. (ENG.). 224p. pap. 14.95 *(978-1-59416-095-0(3))* Westholme Publishing.

West. Bankruptcy Code Rules & Official Forms, June 2009 Law School Edition. 2009. 1188p. pap. 42.00 *(978-0-314-19145-8(3)*, West Legalworks) West.

Whidbee, David A., et al. Financial Institutions, Markets, & Money. 10th ed. 2008. (ENG., Illus.). 704p. (C). 219.95 *(978-0-470-17161-5(8)*, Wiley) Wiley, John & Sons, Inc.

Williamson, Philip B., ed. Insolvency Issues & the FDIC. 2010. (Financial Institutions & Services Ser.). 177p. 115.00 *(978-1-60876-801-1(5))* Nova Science Pubs., Inc.

Wood, John H. A History of Central Banking in Great Britain & the United States. 2008. (Studies in Macroeconomic History Ser.). (ENG., Illus.). 458p. pap. 36.99 *(978-0-521-74131-6(9))* Cambridge Univ. Pr.

The 15th Replenishment of the International Development Association (IDA) & the 11th Replenishment of the African Development Fund (AfDF) Hearing Before the Committee on Financial Services, U.S. House of Representatives, One Hundred Tenth Congress, Second Session, June 18, 2008. 2008. iii, 111p. *(978-0-16-081944-5(X)*, 552-070-38117-1) United States Government Printing Office.

BANKS AND BANKING, CENTRAL

see also Monetary Policy

also names of individual central banks and central banking systems e.g. Bank of England, Federal Reserve Banks

Abel, Caroline. Central Bank Independence in a Small Open Economy. 2009. 76p. pap. *(978-3-639-21975-3(9))* VDM Verlag Dr. Mueller e.K.

Ahamed, Liaquat. Lords of Finance: The Bankers Who Broke the World. 2009. (ENG.). 576p. (gr. 12-18). 18.00 *(978-0-14-311680-6(0)*, Penguin (Non-Classics)); (Illus.). 32.95 *(978-1-59420-182-0(X)*, Penguin Pr. HC, The) Penguin Group (USA) Inc.

Altig, David E. & Smith, Bruce D., eds. Evolution & Procedures in Central Banking. 2011. (ENG.). 334p. pap. 39.99 *(978-0-521-15828-2(1))* Cambridge Univ. Pr.

Antonella Anna, Porcelluzzi. Walter Bagehot & the Open Money Supply Approach to Monetary Theory. 2009. 268p. pap. *(978-3-639-02000-7(6))* VDM Verlag Dr. Mueller e.K.

Apel. Central Banking Systems Compared. 2007. pap. 43.95 *(978-0-415-45922-8(2))* Routledge.

Axilrod, Stephen H. Inside the Fed: Monetary Policy & Its Management, Martin Through Greenspan to Bernanke. 2nd rev. ed. 2011. (ENG., Illus.). 240p. (gr. 17). 24.95 *(978-0-262-01562-2(5))* MIT Pr.

Bakker, Age F. P., et al. Central Bank Reserve Management: New Trends, from Liquidity to Return. 2007. (Illus.). 272p. (C). 127.00 *(978-1-84542-957-7(5))* Elgar, Edward Publishing, Inc.

Berkelaar, Arjan Bastiaan, et al, eds. Interest Rate Models, Asset Allocation & Quantitative Techniques for Central Banks & Sovereign Wealth Funds. 2010. (ENG., Illus.). 432p. 116.00 *(978-0-230-24012-4(7))* Palgrave Macmillan.

Bindseil, Ulrich, et al, eds. Risk Management for Central Banks & Other Public Investors. (ENG.). 2011. 542p. pap. 65.00 ***(978-1-107-40356-7(1))*** 2009. (Illus.). 540p. 158.00 *(978-0-521-51856-7(3))* Cambridge Univ. Pr.

Blejer, Mario. The Capital Needs of Central Banks. Milton, Susan & Sinclair, Peter J. N., eds. 2010. (Routledge International Studies in Money & Banking Ser.). (ENG., Illus.). 224p. (C). 130.00 *(978-0-415-55328-5(8)*, Routledge) Taylor & Francis Group GBR. Dist: Taylor & Francis Group.

Borio, Claudio, et al, eds. The Past & Future of Central Bank Cooperation. (Studies in Macroeconomic History Ser.). (ENG.). 260p. 2011. pap. 35.99 *(978-0-521-18757-2(5))* 2008. (Illus.). 85.00 *(978-0-521-87779-4(2))* Cambridge Univ. Pr.

Brown, Brendan. Euro Crash: The Exit from Monetary Failure in Europe. 2nd rev. ed. 2012. (ENG., Illus.). 224p. pap. 30.00 ***(978-0-230-36849-1(2))*** Palgrave Macmillan.

Brown, Brendan. Euro Crash: The Implications of Monetary Failure in Europe. 2010. (ENG.). 208p. 95.00 *(978-0-230-22910-5(7))* Palgrave Macmillan.

Canzoneri, Matthew B., et al, eds. Establishing a Central Bank: Issues in Europe & Lessons from the U. S. 2008. (ENG., Illus.). 328p. pap. 42.00 *(978-0-521-07069-0(4))* Cambridge Univ. Pr.

Capie, Forrest. The Bank of England, from the 1950s to 1979. 2010. (Studies in Macroeconomic History Ser.). (ENG., Illus.). 920p. (C). 150.00 *(978-0-521-19282-8(X))* Cambridge Univ. Pr.

Capie, Forrest, et al. The Future of Central Banking: The Tercentenary Symposium of the Bank of England. 2008. (ENG., Illus.). 380p. (C). pap. 53.00 *(978-0-521-06546-7(1))* Cambridge Univ. Pr.

Cappello, Marlon & Rizzo, Cristian. Central Banking & Globalization. 2010. (Global Economic Studies). 189p. 145.00 *(978-1-60876-056-5(1))* Nova Science Pubs., Inc.

Carlberg, Michael. Dynamic Policy Interactions in a Monetary Union. 2011. (ENG.). xii, 347p. 189.00 *(978-3-642-18227-3(5)*, 3642182275) Springer.

Carli, Guido & Barucci, Piero. Scritti e Discorsi Di Guido Carli. 2008. (ITA & ENG.). *(978-88-339-1953-9(6))*; *(978-88-339-1955-3(2))*; *(978-88-339-1954-6(4))*; *(978-88-339-2027-6(5))* Bollati Boringhieri.

Chang, Kelly H. Appointing Central Bankers: The Politics of Monetary Policy in the United States & the European Monetary Union. 2006. (Political Economy of Institutions & Decisions Ser.). (ENG., Illus.). 176p. pap. 38.99 *(978-0-521-02984-1(8))* Cambridge Univ. Pr.

Cooper, George. The Origin of Financial Crises: Central Banks, Credit Bubbles, & the Efficient Market Fallacy. 2008. (Vintage Ser.). (ENG.). 208p. pap. 13.95 *(978-0-307-47345-5(7))* Knopf Doubleday Publishing Group.

Das, Rituparna. Monetary History of Indi. 2010. 140p. pap. *(978-3-639-26947-5(0))* VDM Verlag Dr. Mueller e.K.

Davies, Howard & Green, David. Banking on the Future: The Fall & Rise of Central Banking. 2010. (ENG., Illus.). 320p. (C). 45.00 *(978-0-691-13864-0(8))* Princeton Univ. Pr.

de Restre, Lucia Montoya Cadavid. El Debate Sobre la Banca Central Independiente: El Caso Colombiano. 2007. (SPA.). 176p. pap. 17.00 *(978-958-710-261-1(4))* Universidad Externado de Colombia COL. Dist: Siglo del Hombre.

Dyson, Kenneth & Marcussen, Martin, eds. Central Banks in the Age of the Euro: Europeanization, Convergence, & Power. 2009. (ENG., Illus.). 384p. 125.00 *(978-0-19-921823-3(4))* Oxford Univ. Pr., Inc.

Dyson, Kenneth & Quaglia, Lucia. European Economic Governance & Policies: Volume I: Commentary on Key Historical & Institutional Documents, 2 vols. 2011. (ENG., Illus.). 806p. 160.00 *(978-0-19-959451-1(1))* Oxford Univ. Pr., Inc.

Eijffinger, Sylvester C. W. & Masciandaro, Donato, eds. Handbook of Central Banking, Financial Regulation & Supervision: After the Financial Crisis. 2012. (Elgar Original Reference Ser.). (Illus.). 672p. 295.00 ***(978-1-84980-313-7(7))*** Elgar, Edward Publishing, Inc.

Epstein, Gerald A. & Yeldan, A. Erinc, eds. Beyond Inflation Targeting: Assessing the Impacts & Policy Alternatives. 2010. (Illus.). 336p. pap. 53.00 *(978-1-84844-804-9(X))* Elgar, Edward Publishing, Inc.

Fforde, John. The Bank of England & Public Policy, 1941-1958. 2011. (ENG.). 883p. pap. 76.00 *(978-0-521-29452-2(5))* Cambridge Univ. Pr.

Franzese, Robert, et al, eds. Institutional Conflicts & Complementarities: Monetary Policy & Wage Bargaining Institutions in EMU. 2010. (ENG.). 290p. pap. 149.00 *(978-1-4419-5380-3(9)*, 1441953809) Springer.

Gabor, Daniela. Central Banking & Financialization: A Romanian Account of how Eastern Europe became Subprime. 2010. (Studies in Economic Transition Ser.). (ENG., Illus.). 256p. 105.00 *(978-0-230-27615-4(6))* Palgrave Macmillan.

Garcia-Herrero, Alicia. Central Bank: Financial Stability & Financial Development. 2010. 204p. pap. *(978-3-8383-2263-6(0))* Lambert Academic Publishing.

Giannini, Curzio. The Age of Central Banks. 2011. 336p. 135.00 ***(978-0-85793-213-6(6))*** Elgar, Edward Publishing, Inc.

Gono, G. Zimbabwe's Casino Economy: Extraordinary Measures for Extraordinary Challenges. 2008. (Illus.). 256p. pap. *(978-0-7974-3679-4(0))* Zimbabwe Publishing House Ltd, Zimbabwe ZWE. Dist: Michigan State Univ. Pr.

Guarino, Giuseppe, et al. Scritti e Discorsi Di Guido Carli. 2008. (ITA & ENG.). *(978-88-339-2028-3(3))* Bollati Boringhieri.

Haldane, Andrew G., et al, eds. The Future of Payment Systems. 2007. (Routledge International Studies in Money & Banking Ser.). (Illus.). 288p. 170.00 *(978-0-415-43860-5(8))* Routledge.

Hall, Rodney Bruce. Central Banking As Global Governance: Constructing Financial Credibility. 2008. (Cambridge Studies in International Relations). (ENG., Illus.). 278p. 90.00 *(978-0-521-89861-4(7))*; pap. 36.00 *(978-0-521-72721-1(9))* Cambridge Univ. Pr.

Harris, Ethan S. Ben Bernanke's Fed: The Federal Reserve after Greenspan. 2008. (ENG., Illus.). 237p. 26.95 *(978-1-4221-2584-7(X))* Harvard Business Review Pr.

Hennessy, Elizabeth. A Domestic History of the Bank of England, 1930-1960. 2008. (ENG.). 472p. pap. 58.00 *(978-0-521-07358-5(8))* Cambridge Univ. Pr.

Herrmann, Heinz. Designing Central Banks. Mayes, David & Wood, Geoffrey E., eds. 2009. (Routledge International Studies in Money & Banking Ser.). (ENG., Illus.). 272p. (C). 160.00 *(978-0-415-47616-4(X))* Routledge.

Herrmann, Heinz, ed. Monetary Policy over Fifty Years: Experiences & Lessons. 2009. (Routledge International Studies in Money & Banking Ser.). (ENG., Illus.). 176p. (C). 120.00 *(978-0-415-47847-2(2))* Routledge.

Hetzel, Robert L. The Monetary Policy of the Federal Reserve: A History. 2008. (Studies in Macroeconomic History Ser.). (ENG., Illus.). 408p. 57.00 *(978-0-521-88132-6(3))* Cambridge Univ. Pr.

Hossain, A. Central Banking & Monetary Policy in the Asia-Pacific. 2009. (Illus.). 368p. 173.00 *(978-1-84720-372-4(8))* Elgar, Edward Publishing, Inc.

Irving, Jacqueline, et al. Migrant Remittance Flows: Findings from a Global Survey of Central Banks. 2010. (World Bank Working Papers: 194). (ENG., Illus.). 84p. pap. 15.00 *(978-0-8213-8360-5(4)*, 9780821383605) World Bank Pubns.

Killenbeck, Mark Robert. McCulloch V. Maryland: Securing a Nation. 2006. (Landmark Law Cases & American Society Ser.). 227p. 35.00 *(978-0-7006-1472-1(9))* Univ. Pr. of Kansas.

—M'Culloch V. Maryland: Securing a Nation. 2006. (Landmark Law Cases & American Society Ser.). 227p. per. 16.95 *(978-0-7006-1473-8(7))* Univ. Pr. of Kansas.

Kleimeier, Stefanie & Sander, Harald. Integrating Europe's Retail Banking Market: Where Do We Stand? 2007. (ENG., Illus.). 112p. pap. 30.00 *(978-92-9079-734-0(7))* Ctr. for European Policy Studies BEL. Dist: Brookings Institution Pr.

Kudkinski, Jim. The Tarnished Fed: Behind Closed Doors: Forty Years of Successes, Failures, Mystique, & Humor. 2010. 250p. pap. 16.95 *(978-0-533-16318-2(8))* Vantage Pr., Inc.

Lastra. Central Banking & Banking Regulation. 2nd rev. ed. 2011. *(978-90-411-2480-7(2))* Kluwer Law International.

Lastra, Rosa Maria. Legal Foundations of International Monetary Stability. 2006. (ENG.). 600p. 291.50 *(978-0-19-926934-1(3))* Oxford Univ. Pr., Inc.

Laurens, Bernard J., et al, eds. Central Bank Independence, Accountability, & Transparency: A Global Perspective. 2009. (ENG., Illus.). 256p. 105.00 *(978-0-230-20107-1(5))* Palgrave Macmillan.

Lehmbecker, Philipp. The Quality of Eligible Collateral, Central Bank Losses & Monetary Stability: An Empirical Analysis. 2008. (Europäische Hochschulschriften. Reihe 5: Volks- und Betriebswirtschaft Ser.). 272p. pap. 65.95 *(978-3-631-58076-9(2))* Lang, Peter GmbH, Europaischer Verlag der Wissenschaften DEU. Dist: Lang, Peter.

Maman, Daniel & Rosenhek, Zeev. The Israeli Central Bank: Political Economy, Global Logics & Local Actors. 2011. (Routledge Studies in Middle Eastern Economies Ser.). (ENG., Illus.). 192p. (C). 125.00 *(978-0-415-57328-3(9))* Routledge.

Manning, Mark, et al, eds. The Economics of Large-Value Payments & Settlement: Theory & Policy Issues for Central Banks. 2009. (ENG., Illus.). 216p. 120.00 *(978-0-19-957111-6(2))* Oxford Univ. Pr., Inc.

Masciandaro, Donato & Quintyn, Marc, eds. Designing Financial Supervision Institutions: Independence, Accountability & Governance. 2007. 528p. 201.00 *(978-1-84720-216-1(0))* Elgar, Edward Publishing, Inc.

Mayes, David & Wood, Geoffrey E., eds. Designing Central Banks. 2011. (ENG., Illus.). 272p. (C). pap. 42.95 ***(978-0-415-69654-8(2))*** Routledge.

Mayes, David G. & Toporowski, Jan, eds. Open Market Operations & Financial Markets. 2007. (Routledge International Studies in Money & Banking Ser.). (Illus.). 353p. 180.00 *(978-0-415-41775-4(9))* Routledge.

Maziad, Samar. Monetary Frameworks in Emerging Markets. 2010. 260p. pap. *(978-3-8383-4660-1(2))* Lambert Academic Publishing.

Mehrling, Perry. The New Lombard Street: How the Fed Became the Dealer of Last Resort. 2010. (ENG., Illus.). 184p. (C). 29.95 *(978-0-691-14398-9(6))* Princeton Univ. Pr.

Muchlinski, Elke. Central Banks & Coded Language: Risks & Benefits. 2011. (ENG., Illus.). 272p. 100.00 *(978-0-230-23228-0(0))* Palgrave Macmillan.

Mullins, Eustace Clarence. A Study of the Federal Reserve. 2011. 142p. 40.95 ***(978-1-258-00963-2(3))*** Literary Licensing, LLC.

—A Study of the Federal Reserve. 2009. *(978-1-57898-801-3(2))*; pap. *(978-1-57898-802-0(0))* Martino Publishing.

Officer. Pricing Theory, Financing of International Organizations & Monetary History. 2007. (Illus.). 336p. 160.00 *(978-0-415-77065-1(3))* Routledge.

Ozgercin, Kevin V. The Bank for International Settlements: The Politics of Global Financial Supervision in the Age of High Finance. 2013. (Global Institutions Ser.). (ENG., Illus.). 196p. 118.00 *(978-0-415-77929-6(4))* Routledge.

Paul, Ron. End the Fed. (ENG.). 2010. 224p. pap. 14.99 *(978-0-446-54917-2(7))* 2009. 224p. 21.99 *(978-0-446-54919-6(3))* 2009. 336p. pap. 21.00 *(978-0-446-55997-3(0))* Grand Central Publishing.

Picker, Anne Dolganos. International Economic Indicators & Central Banks. 2007. (Wiley Finance Ser.: 392). (ENG., Illus.). 295p. 70.00 *(978-0-471-75113-7(8)*, Wiley) Wiley, John & Sons, Inc.

Quaglia, Lucia. Central Banking Governance in the European Union. 2010. (ENG., Illus.). 204p. pap. 39.95 *(978-0-415-58665-8(8))* Routledge.

—Central Banking Governance in the European Union: A Comparative Analysis. 2008. (Routledge/UACES Contemporary European Studies). (Illus.). 208p. 135.00 *(978-0-415-42751-7(7))* Routledge.

Quintyn, Marc & Taylor, Michael W. Should Financial Sector Regulators Be Independent? (FRE.). *(978-1-58906-310-5(4)*, EIIFA032); (ARA.). *(978-1-58906-312-9(0)*, EIIAA032); (RUS.). *(978-1-58906-314-3(7)*, EIIRA032); (CHI.). *(978-1-58906-313-6(9)*, EIICA032); (SPA.). *(978-1-58906-311-2(2)*, EIISA032) International Monetary Fund.

Redrado, Martín. No Reserve: The Limit of Absolute Power, 0 vols. unabr. ed. 2011. (ENG.). 288p. pap. 13.95 *(978-1-935597-23-0(X)*, 9781935597230) Amazon Publishing.

Sakamoto, Takayuki. Economic Policy & Performance in Industrial Democracies: Party Governments, Central Banks & the Fiscal-Monetary Policy Mix. 2009. 334p. pap. 39.95 *(978-0-415-57227-9(4))* Routledge.

Santomero, Anthony M., et al, eds. Challenges for Central Banking. 2010. (ENG.). 288p. pap. 139.00 *(978-1-4419-4891-5(0)*, 1441948910) Springer.

Siklos, Pierre L. The Changing Face of Central Banking: Evolutionary Trends since World War II. 2006. (Studies in Macroeconomic History Ser.). (ENG.). 372p. pap. 74.00 *(978-0-521-03449-4(3))* Cambridge Univ. Pr.

Siklos, Pierre L., et al, eds. Challenges in Central Banking: The Current Institutional Environment & Forces Affecting Monetary Policy. 2010. (ENG., Illus.). 416p. 90.00 *(978-0-521-19929-2(8))* Cambridge Univ. Pr.

Singleton, John. Central Banking in the 20th Century. 2010. (ENG., Illus.). 350p. 99.00 *(978-0-521-89909-3(5))* Cambridge Univ. Pr.

Smithers, Andrew. Wall Street Revalued: Imperfect Markets & Inept Central Bankers. 2009. (ENG., Illus.). 256p. 27.95 *(978-0-470-75005-6(7)*, Wiley) Wiley, John & Sons, Inc.

Spahn, Heinz-Peter. From Gold to Euro: On Monetary Theory & the History of Currency Systems. 2010. (Illus.). x, 220p. pap. 149.00 *(978-3-642-07483-7(9)*, 3642074839) Springer.

Stubblebine, Michael A. Interest Rate Targeting, Inflation, & the Fisher Effect - an Empirical Test of the Real Interest Rate in Germany, 1970-200. 2008. 76p. pet. *(978-3-8364-3859-9(3))* VDM Verlag Dr. Mueller e.K.

Toporowski, J. Financial Markets & Financial Fragility, 2 vols. 2010. (Elgar Mini Ser.). (Illus.). 1008p. 490.00 *(978-1-84844-097-5(9))* Elgar, Edward Publishing, Inc.

Touffut, Jean-Philippe, ed. Central Banks As Economic Institutions. 2008. (Cournot Centre for Economic Studies). (Illus.). 232p. 120.00 *(978-1-84844-108-8(8))*; pap. 50.00 *(978-1-84844-109-5(6))* Elgar, Edward Publishing, Inc.

Tshiani, Noël K. Building Credible Central Banks: Policy Lessons for Emerging Economies. 2008. (ENG., Illus.). 192p. 109.00 *(978-0-230-21882-6(2))* Palgrave Macmillan.

Tymoigne, Éric. Central Banking, Asset Prices & Financial Fragility. 2010. pap. 42.50 *(978-0-415-78119-0(1))* Routledge.

Tymoigne, Éric. Central Banking, Asset Prices & Financial Stability. 2009. (Routledge International Studies in Money & Banking Ser.). (Illus.). XIV, 322p. 160.00 *(978-0-415-77399-7(7))* Routledge.

Van Overtveldt, Johan. Bernanke's Test: Ben Bernanke, Alan Greenspan, & the Drama of the Central Banker. 2010. (ENG.). 300p. pap. 19.95 *(978-1-932841-51-0(2))* Agate Publishing, Inc.

von Mettenheim, Kurt E. Federal Banking in Brazil: Policies & Competitive Advantages, 1 vol. 2010. (Financial History Ser.). (ENG., Illus.). 240p. 99.00 *(978-1-84893-065-0(8))* Pickering & Chatto Pubs., Ltd. GBR. Dist: Ashgate Publishing Co.

Wessel, David. In Fed We Trust: Ben Bernanke's War on the Great Panic. 2010. 352p. pap. 16.00 *(978-0-307-45969-5(1)*, Three Rivers Pr.) 2009. (ENG.). 336p. 26.99 *(978-0-307-45968-8(3)*, Crown Business) Crown Publishing Group.

Wiedmann, Marcel. Money, Stock Prices & Central Banks: A Cointegrated VAR Analysis. 2011. (Contributions to Economics Ser.). (ENG., Illus.). xvi, 430p. 189.00 *(978-3-7908-2646-3(4)*, 3790826464) Physica-Verlag DEU. Dist: Springer.

Wood, John H. A History of Central Banking in Great Britain & the United States. 2008. (Studies in Macroeconomic History Ser.). (ENG., Illus.). 458p. pap. 36.99 *(978-0-521-74131-6(9))* Cambridge Univ. Pr.

BANKS AND BANKING, COOPERATIVE

see also Agricultural Cooperative Credit Associations; Credit Unions

Ayadi, Rym, et al. Investigating Diversity in the Banking Sector in Europe: Key Developments, Performance & Role of Cooperative Banks. 2011. (ENG.). 168p. pap. 30.00 *(978-94-6138-042-5(9))* Ctr. for European Policy Studies BEL. Dist: Brookings Institution Pr.

Basak, Amit. Co-Operative Banks in India: Functioning & Reforms. 2010. 203p. 29.75 *(978-81-7708-250-0(7))* New Century Publications IND. Dist: International Specialized Bk. Services.

Boscia, Vittorio, et al, eds. Cooperative Banking in Europe: Case Studies. 2010. (Palgrave Macmillan Studies in Banking & Financial Institutions Ser.). (ENG., Illus.). 272p. 105.00 *(978-0-230-57677-3(X))* Palgrave Macmillan.

Chisse', Hassane, et al, eds. The World Bank Legal Review: International Financial Institutions & Global Legal Governance. 2011. (Law, Justice, & Development Ser.: 3). (ENG.). 424p. pap. 35.00 ***(978-0-8213-8863-1(0)***, 9780821388631) World Bank Pubns.

Cuevas, Carlos E. & Fischer, Klaus P. Cooperative Financial Institutions: Issues in Governance, Regulation, & Supervision. 2006. (World Bank Working Papers: 82). (ENG., Illus.). 70p. per. 10.00 *(978-0-8213-6684-4(X)*, 9780821366844) World Bank Pubns.

Garyfalia, Kolyvaki. Developing a Csr Program for a Regional Cooperative Bank: Basics, Concepts, Methods. 2011. 60p. pap. ***(978-3-639-34288-8(7))*** VDM Verlag Dr. Mueller e.K.

Goglio, Silvio & Alexopoulos, Yiorgos, eds. Financial Cooperatives & Local Development. 2012. (Routledge Studies in Development Economics Ser.). (ENG., Illus.). 224p. (C). 135.00 ***(978-0-415-69837-5(5))*** Routledge.

McWhorter Sember, Brette. The Complete Credit Repair Kit. 2nd ed. 2008. (ENG.). 448p. cd-rom 19.95 *(978-1-57248-681-2(3)*, Sphinx Publishing) Sourcebooks, Inc.

Michael, Justin Nelson. Non Performing Assets in C0-0perative Banks. 2011. 264p. pap. ***(978-3-8443-9681-2(0))*** Lambert Academic Publishing.

Molyneux, Philip, et al. Co-Operative Banking - Innovations & Developments. 2009. (Palgrave Macmillan Studies in Banking & Financial Institutions Ser.). (ENG.). 224p. 110.00 *(978-1-4039-9669-5(5))* Palgrave Macmillan.

Sinclair, Timothy J. The New Masters of Capital: American Bond Rating Agencies & the Politics of Creditworthiness. 2008. (Cornell Studies in Political Economy). (Illus.). 200p. pap. 21.00 *(978-0-8014-7491-0(4))* Cornell Univ. Pr.

Tucker, Donald S. Evolution of People's Banks. (Columbia University, Studies in the Social Sciences: No. 231). reprint ed. 29.50 *(978-0-404-51231-6(3))* AMS Pr., Inc.

Vélez-Ibáñez, Carlos G. An Impossible Living in a Transborder World: Culture, Confianza, & Economy of Mexican-Origin Populations. 2010. (ENG., Illus.). 264p. pap. 24.95 *(978-0-8165-2635-2(4))* Univ. of Arizona Pr.

BANKS AND BANKING, FOREIGN

Abd Kadir, Hazlina. Banks Efficiency: A data envelopment Analysis. 2010. 120p. pap. *(978-3-8383-1964-3(8))* Lambert Academic Publishing.

Chen, George. Banking on the Bund: The Untold Stories of Foreign Banks in China. 2011. (ENG.). 256p. 29.95 *(978-0-470-82599-0(5)*, Wiley) Wiley, John & Sons, Inc.

Gruson, Michael & Reisner, Ralph. Regulation of Foreign Banks, Vol. 1. 4th rev. ed. 2007. 142.00 *(978-0-327-16435-7(2))* LexisNexis Matthew Bender.

Le Cheminant, Keith. Colonial & Foreign Banking Systems (RLE Banking & Finance), Volume 19. 2012. (ENG.). 248p. 115.00 ***(978-0-415-53941-8(2))*** Routledge.

Lu, Qing. Long-Term Commitment, Trust & the Rise of Foreign Banks in China. 2007. (Chandos Asian Studies). (ENG., Illus.). 284p. 110.00 *(978-1-84334-321-9(5)*, Chandos Publishing) Woodhead Publishing Ltd. GBR. Dist: Ingram Pub. Services.

Martinez-Diaz, Leonardo. Globalizing in Hard Times: The Politics of Banking-Sector Opening in the Emerging World. 2009. (Cornell Studies in Political Economy Ser.). (Illus.). 232p. 45.00 *(978-0-8014-4755-6(0))* Cornell Univ. Pr.

McCann, Hilton. Offshore Finance. (ENG., Illus.). 2009. 564p. pap. 67.00 *(978-0-521-12359-4(3))* 2006. 562p. 144.00 *(978-0-521-86233-2(7))* Cambridge Univ. Pr.

Richmond Law & Tax Ltd., ed. Financial Services Regulators in Offshore Financial Centres. 2nd rev ed. 2006. 250p. pap. *(978-1-904501-75-6(3))* Richmond Law & Tax Ltd.

Shanthi, Gopinath. Performance Evaluation of Foreign Banks Operating in India: Introduction, Review, Profile of Foreign Banks India, Analysis of Growth, Profitability, Productivity & Solvency & Findings, Suggestions. 2011. 256p. pap. ***(978-3-639-33710-5(7))*** VDM Verlag Dr. Mueller e.K.

Shaxson, Nicholas. Treasure Islands: Uncovering the Damage of Offshore Banking & Tax Havens. 2011. (ENG.). 272p. 27.00 *(978-0-230-10501-0(7))* Palgrave Macmillan.

Tyndale, Walter. Fundamentals of Offshore Banking: How to Open Accounts Almost Anywhere. 2009. 127p. pap. 19.95 *(978-0-557-06326-0(4))* Lulu Enterprises Inc.

Vlcek, William. Offshore Finance & Small States: Sovereignty, Size & Money. 2008. (ENG., Illus.). 216p. 89.00 *(978-0-230-52220-6(3))* Palgrave Macmillan.

BANKS AND BANKING, FOREIGN—UNITED STATES

Brookins, Wade D. Tax Haven Banks. 2009. (Financial Institutions & Services Ser.). 89.00 *(978-1-60692-283-5(1))* Nova Science Pubs., Inc.

Greene, Edward F. U.S. Regulation of the International Securities & Derivative Markets. 9th ed. 2009. *(978-0-7355-6817-4(0)); (978-0-7355-6818-1(9))* Wolters Kluwer Law & Business. (Aspen Pubs.).

Gruson, Michael & Reisner, Ralph. Regulation of Foreign Banks, & Affiliates in the United States. 5th ed. 2008. *(978-1-4224-2882-5(6))* LexisNexis Matthew Bender.

Kobrak, Christopher. Banking on Global Markets: Deutsche Bank & the United States, 1870 to the Present. 2007. (Cambridge Studies in the Emergence of Global Enterprise Ser.). (ENG., Illus.). 504p. 50.00 *(978-0-521-86325-4(2))* Cambridge Univ. Pr.

Malloy. International Banking, Second Edition, 2007-2008 Supplement. 2007. 242p. per. 25.00 *(978-1-59460-466-9(5))* Carolina Academic Pr.

Tax Haven Banks & U.S. Tax Compliance: Hearings Before the Permanent Subcommittee on Investigations of the Committee on Homeland Security & Governmental Affairs, United States Senate of the One Hundred Tenth Congress, Second Session, July 17 & 25, 2008. 2008. (GER & ENG., Illus.). xii, 1202p. *(978-0-16-082529-3(6)*, 552-070-38564-9) United States Government Printing Office.

BANKS AND BANKING, GROUP

see Bank Holding Companies

BANKS AND BANKING, INDUSTRIAL

see Loans, Personal

BANKS AND BANKING, INTERNATIONAL

see also Financial Institutions, International

Alioski, Asim. The Integration of Islamic Finance into the Western Financial Markets. 2010. 120p. pap. *(978-3-639-23800-6(1))* VDM Verlag Dr. Mueller e.K.

Anderloni, Luisa, et al, eds. Financial Innovation in Retail & Corporate Banking. 2009. (New Horizons in Money & Finance Ser.). (Illus.). 352p. 155.00 *(978-1-84844-040-1(5))* Elgar, Edward Publishing, Inc.

Aspatore Books Staff, compiled by. Banking & Finance Client Strategies in Asia, 2010 Ed: Leading Lawyers on Understanding the Impact of Global Banking Reform, Navigating Regional Banking Laws, & Meeting the Needs of Today's Clients (Inside the Minds) 2010. (Illus.). 316p. pap. 100.00 *(978-0-314-26821-1(9))* Aspatore Bks.

Aubin. International Bank Guarantees Handbook. 2010. *(978-90-411-3133-1(7))* Wolters Kluwer Law & Business.

Bragg, Steven M. Treasury Management: The Practitioner's Guide. 2010. (Wiley Corporate F&a Ser.: 6). (ENG., Illus.). 304p. 78.95 *(978-0-470-49708-1(4)*, Wiley) Wiley, John & Sons, Inc.

Bufford, Samuel L. United States International Insolvency Law 2008-2009. 2009. (ENG.). 400p. 275.00 *(978-0-19-534078-5(7))* Oxford Univ. Pr., Inc.

Capie, Forrest & Wood, Geoffrey. Lender of Last Resort. 2007. (Routledge International Studies in Money & Banking Ser.). XXIV, 504p. 200.00 *(978-0-415-32333-8(9)*, RU42233) Routledge.

Capie, Forrest & Wood, Geoffrey E., eds. The Lender of Last Resort. 2008. XXIV, 504p. pap. 43.95 *(978-0-415-46495-6(1))* Routledge.

Caprio, Gerard, Jr., et al, eds. Cross-Border Banking: Regulatory Challenges. 2006. (World Scientific Studies in International Economics). (Illus.). 477p. 150.00 *(978-981-256-829-8(8))* World Scientific Publishing Co., Inc.

Chorafas, Dimitris N. Basel III, the Devil & Global Banking. 2011. (Palgrave Macmillan Studies in Banking & Financial Institutions Ser.). (ENG., Illus.). 304p. 100.00 ***(978-0-230-35377-0(0))*** Palgrave Macmillan.

Corbett, Jeffrey H. & Kish, Patrick J. Behind the Offshore Veil. 2009. 216p. 28.95 *(978-1-4401-4661-9(6))*; pap. 18.95 *(978-1-4401-4663-3(2))* iUniverse, Inc.

Cottrell, Philip L., et al, eds. Centres & Peripheries in Banking: The Historical Development of Financial Markets. 2007. (Studies in Banking & Financial History Ser.). (Illus.). 342p. 134.95 *(978-0-7546-6121-4(0))* Ashgate Publishing Co.

Coulbeck, Neil S. The Multinational Banking Industry (RLE Banking & Finance), Volume 9. 2012. (ENG.). 424p. 150.00 ***(978-0-415-53876-3(9))*** Routledge.

Cram101 Textbook Reviews Staff. Outlines & Highlights for Bank Management & Financial Services by Peter, Isbn: 007304623x. 2008. 192p. pap. 13.95 *(978-1-4288-5950-0(0))* Cram101 Inc.

—Outlines & Highlights for International Financial Management by Jeff Madura, Isbn: 9780324593471. 2009. 140p. pap. 28.95 *(978-1-4288-2981-7(4))* Cram101 Inc.

De Haas, Ralph. Banking Sector Development in Transition Countries - the Impact of Multinational Banks. 2007. 248p. per. *(978-3-8364-2720-3(6))* VDM Verlag Dr. Mueller e.K.

Di Quirico, Roberto. Building on Borrowed Bricks. 2008. 224p. pap. *(978-88-8398-051-0(4))* European Pr. Academic Publishing.

Dover a Staff & Ishikawa, Tetsuya. How I Caused the Credit Crunch. 2010. (ENG., Illus.). 366p. pap. 12.95 ***(978-1-84831-067-4(6))*** Totem Bks. GBR. Dist: Consortium Bk. Sales & Distribution.

Dragomir, Larisa. European Prudential Banking Regulation & Supervision: The Legal Dimension. 2012. (ENG.). 422p. pap. 44.95 ***(978-0-415-63147-1(5))*** Routledge.

Eatwell, John. Global Finance at Risk: The Case for International Regulation. 2008. (ENG.). 258p. 23.00 *(978-1-4379-5172-1(4))* DIANE Publishing Co.

Elson, Anthony. Governing Global Finance: The Evolution & Reform of the International Financial Architecture. 2011. (ENG., Illus.). 288p. 100.00 *(978-0-230-10378-8(2))* Palgrave Macmillan.

et al., compiled by. Banking & Finance Client Strategies in Asia: Leading Lawyers on Educating Clients, Understanding Key Rules & Regulations, & Navigating Recent Cases & Developments, Inside the Minds. 2009. 696p. pap. 125.00 *(978-0-314-90824-7(2))* Aspatore Bks.

Fatemi, Khosrow & Salvatore, Dominick, eds. Foreign Exchange Issues, Capital Markets & International Banking in the 1990s (RLE Banking & Finance), Volume 13. 2012. (ENG.). 296p. 115.00 ***(978-0-415-53880-0(7))*** Routledge.

Fohlin, Caroline. Finance Capitalism & Germany's Rise to Industrial Power. 2007. (Studies in Macroeconomic History Ser.). (ENG., Illus.). 406p. 110.00 *(978-0-521-81020-3(5))* Cambridge Univ. Pr.

Gleeson, Simon. International Regulation of Banking: Basel II, Capital & Risk Requirements. 2010. (ENG., Illus.). 350p. 395.00 *(978-0-19-921534-8(0))* Oxford Univ. Pr., Inc.

Gregoriou, Greg N. & Gregoriou. Operational Risk Toward Basel III: Best Practices & Issues in Modeling, Management, & Regulation. 2009. (Wiley Finance Ser.: 481). (ENG., Illus.). 497p. 95.00 *(978-0-470-39014-6(X)*, Wiley) Wiley, John & Sons, Inc.

Haynes, Andrew. The Law Relating to International Banking. 2010. (Illus.). 558p. pap. 170.30 *(978-1-84766-679-6(5)*, Bloomsbury Professional) Bloomsbury Publishing Plc GBR. Dist: International Specialized Bk. Services.

Heffernan, Shelagh. Sovereign Risk Analysis (RLE Banking & Finance), Volume 17. 2012. (ENG.). 200p. 115.00 ***(978-0-415-53855-8(6))*** Routledge.

Henkes-Wabro, Rike Claudia. Gewinnabgrenzung bei Bankbetriebsstätten im Internationalen Steuerrecht. 2009. (Trierer Studien zum Internationalen Steuerrecht Ser.). (GER.). 246p. 72.95 *(978-3-631-59421-6(6))* Lang, Peter GmbH, Europäischer Verlag der Wissenschaften DEU. Dist: Lang, Peter.

Hieronymi, Otto & Vautravers, Alexandre, eds. Globalization & the Reform of the International Banking & Monetary System. 2009. (ENG., Illus.). 256p. 116.00 *(978-0-230-23530-4(1))* Palgrave Macmillan.

Holton, Robert. Global Finance. 2012. (Shortcuts Ser.). (ENG., Illus.). 128p. (C). 100.00 *(978-0-415-61916-5(5))*; pap. 19.95 *(978-0-415-61917-2(3))* Routledge.

Horesh, Niv & Horesh, N. Shanghai's Bund & Beyond: British Banks, Banknote Issuance, & Monetary Policy in China, 1842-1937. 2009. (Yale Series in Economic & Financial History Ser.). (ENG., Illus.). 256p. 48.00 *(978-0-300-14356-0(7))* Yale Univ. Pr.

Ibrahim, Daniel. The Internationalization of Banking. 2010. 140p. pap. *(978-3-639-27009-9(6))* VDM Verlag Dr. Mueller e.K.

Jones, Geoffrey, ed. Banks as Multinationals (RLE Banking & Finance), Volume 18. 2012. (ENG.). 320p. 130.00 ***(978-0-415-53271-6(X))*** Routledge.

Kaufman, George G., et al, eds. International Financial Instability: Global Banking & National Regulation. 2008. (World Scientific Studies in International Economics). (Illus.). 479p. 150.00 *(978-981-270-763-5(8))* World Scientific Publishing Co., Inc.

Kim, Suk-Joong & McKenzie, Michael, eds. International Banking in the New Era: Post-crisis Challenges. 2010. (International Finance Review Ser.). (Illus.). 485p. *(978-1-84950-912-1(3))* Emerald Group Publishing Ltd.

Lastra, Rosa. Cross-Border Bank Insolvency. 2011. (ENG., Illus.). 592p. 250.00 *(978-0-19-957707-1(2))* Oxford Univ. Pr., Inc.

Lewis, Cleona. International Accounts. (Brookings Institution Reprint Ser.). reprint ed. lib. bdg. 32.50 *(978-0-697-00163-4(5))* Irvington Pubs.

Madura, Jeff. International Financial Management. 9th ed. (Illus.). 2008. xxv, 673p. *(978-0-324-56820-2(7))* 2007. (ENG., 704p. (C). 217.95 *(978-0-324-56819-6(3))* Cengage South-Western.

—International Financial Management, Abridged Edition. 10th ed. 2010. (ENG.). 560p. (C). pap. 168.95 *(978-0-538-48221-9(4))* Cengage South-Western.

Martinez-Diaz, Leonardo. Globalizing in Hard Times: The Politics of Banking-Sector Opening in the Emerging World. 2009. (Cornell Studies in Political Economy Ser.). (Illus.). 232p. 45.00 *(978-0-8014-4755-6(0))* Cornell Univ. Pr.

McGill, Ross. Investment Withholding Tax: Best Practice & Strategies for Intermediaries & Investors. 2009. (ENG., Illus.). 320p. 236.00 *(978-0-230-22162-8(9))* Palgrave Macmillan.

Meng, Chen. Multinational Banking in China: Theory & Practice. 2009. (New Horizons in International Business Ser.). 192p. 119.00 *(978-1-84542-589-0(8))* Elgar, Edward Publishing, Inc.

Molyneux, Philip. Frontiers of Banks in a Global Economy. Molyneux, Philip & Vallelado, Eleuterio, eds. 2008. (Palgrave Macmillan Studies in Banking & Financial Institutions Ser.). (ENG., Illus.). 320p. 131.00 *(978-0-230-52568-9(7))* Palgrave Macmillan.

Moore, David B. The World Bank: Development, Poverty, Hegemony. Moore, David, ed. 2007. 595p. (C). pap. 49.95 ***(978-1-86914-100-4(8))*** University of Kwazulu-Natal Press ZAF. Dist: International Specialized Bk. Services.

Morriss, Andrew P. Offshore Financial Centers & Regulatory Competition. 2010. (ENG.). 200p. (C). (gr. 13-17). 49.95 *(978-0-8447-4324-0(0)*, AEI Pr.) American Enterprise Institute for Public Policy Research.

Multilateral Development Banks: Promoting Effectiveness & Fighting Corruption: Hearing Before the Committee on Foreign Relations, United States Senate, One Hundred Ninth Congress, Second Session, March 28, 2006. 2007. iii, 53p. *(978-0-16-078934-2(6)*, 552-070-36061-1) United States Government Printing Office.

Norbin, Charles. Reconsidering Banking Regulation & the Legal Framework. 2011. 244p. pap. ***(978-3-8443-1493-9(8))*** Lambert Academic Publishing.

Ocampo, Jose Antonio, ed. Regional Financial Cooperation. 2006. (ENG., Illus.). 375p. per. 36.95 *(978-0-8157-6419-9(7))* Brookings Institution Pr.

Organisation for Economic Co-operation and Development Staff. Bank Profitability: Financial Statements of Banks, 1996-2005. 2008. (Illus.). 596p. pap. 63.00 *(978-92-64-04154-7(0))* Organization for Economic Cooperation & Development.

Ozdemir, Bogie & Miu, Peter. Basel II Implementation: A Guide to Developing & Validating a Compliant, Internal Risk Rating System. 2008. (ENG., Illus.). 480p. 125.00 *(978-0-07-159130-0(3)*, 0071591303) McGraw-Hill Cos., The.

Ozgercin, Kevin V. The Bank for International Settlements: The Politics of Global Financial Supervision in the Age of High Finance. 2013. (Global Institutions Ser.). (ENG., Illus.). 196p. 118.00 *(978-0-415-77929-6(4))* Routledge.

Paast, Greg. Vultures' Picnic: In Pursuit of Petroleum Pigs, Power Pirates, & High-Finance Carnivores. 2013. (ENG., Illus.). 416p. (gr. 12). pap. 17.00 ***(978-0-452-29864-4(4)***, Plume) Penguin Group (USA) Inc.

Proctor, Charles. The Law & Practice of International Banking. 2010. (ENG.). 1100p. 425.00 *(978-0-19-929186-1(1))* Oxford Univ. Pr., Inc.

Purten, Maartje van. Policing the Banks: Accountability Mechanisms for the Financial Sector. 2008. (ENG.). 520p. (C) *(978-0-7735-3401-8(6))* McGill-Queen's Univ. Pr.

Rhodes, William. Banker to the World: Leadership Lessons from the Front Line of Global Finance. 2011. (ENG.). 288p. 25.00 *(978-0-07-170425-0(6)*, 0071704256) McGraw-Hill Cos., The.

Rhodes, William R. Banker to the World: Leadership Lessons from the Front Lines of Global Finance. 2011. xxiii, 249p. E-Book ***(978-0-07-170424-3(8))*** McGraw-Hill Cos., The.

Richmond Law & Tax Ltd., ed. Financial Services Regulators in Offshore Financial Centres. 2nd rev. ed. 2006. 250p. pap. *(978-1-904501-75-6(3))* Richmond Law & Tax Ltd.

Rose & Hudgins. Bank Management & Financial Services. 9th ed. 2012. (ENG., Illus.). 768p. (C). 215.33 ***(978-0-07-803467-1(1)***, 0078034671) McGraw-Hill Cos., The.

Rose, Peter S. & Hudgins, Sylvia Conway. Bank Management & Financial Services. 7th ed. 2006. (McGraw-Hill/Irwin Series in Finance, Insurance, & Real Estate). (Illus.). 752p. (C). 145.94 *(978-0-07-304623-5(X)*, 9780073046235) McGraw-Hill Cos., The.

—Bank Management & Financial Services. 8th ed. 2009. (ENG., Illus.). 768p. (C). 215.33 *(978-0-07-338243-2(4)*, 0073382434, McGraw-Hill/Irwin) McGraw-Hill Higher Education.

Saunders, Anthony. Financial Institutions, in & Out of Crisis: Reflections by Anthony Saunders. 2011. ***(978-981-4374-02-6(4))***; 644p. *50.00 ***(978-981-4374-01-9(6))*** World Scientific Publishing Co., Inc.

Scott, Hal S. International Finance: Transactions, Policy, & Regulation. 14th rev. ed. 2007. (University Casebook Ser.). 993p. 124.00 *(978-1-59941-263-4(2)*, Foundation Pr.) West.

—International Finance, Transactions, Policy, & Regulation, 16th Edition. 16th rev. ed. 2009. (University Casebook Ser.). 1186p. 149.00 *(978-1-59941-719-6(7)*, Foundation Pr.) West.

—Scott International Finance: Transactions, Policy & Regulation. 15th rev. ed. 2008. (University Casebook Ser.). 1115p. 135.00 *(978-1-59941-547-5(X)*, Foundation Pr.) West.

Scott, Hal S. Scott's International Finance, Transactions, Policy, & Regulation. 18th rev. ed. 2011. 1392p. 180.00 ***(978-1-59941-975-6(0)***, Foundation Pr.) West.

Sharman, J. C. The Money Laundry: Regulating Criminal Finance in the Global Economy. 2011. (Cornell Studies in Political Economy Ser.). (Illus.). 224p. 29.95 ***(978-0-8014-5018-1(7))*** Cornell Univ. Pr.

Slager, Alfred. The Internationalization of Banks: Patterns, Strategies & Performance. 2006. (ENG., Illus.). 240p. 116.00 *(978-1-4039-9874-3(4))* Palgrave Macmillan.

Smith, Roy C., et al. Global Banking, 1 vol. 3rd ed. 2012. (ENG., Illus.). 456p. 65.00 *(978-0-19-533593-4(7))* Oxford Univ. Pr., Inc.

Snowden, P. N. Emerging Risk in International Banking (RLE Banking & Finance) Origins of Financial Vulnerability in The 1980s, Volume 31. 2012. (ENG.). 160p. 100.00 ***(978-0-415-52942-6(5))*** Routledge.

Stephenson, J. r. Broken Promises, Betrayals & Barefaced Lies. 2008. 144p. pap. *(978-0-9558557-0-2(5))* ShieldCrest.

Tarullo, Daniel & Tarullo, Daniel K. Banking on Basel: The Future of International Financial Regulation. 2008. (Illus.). 256p. (C). pap. 26.95 *(978-0-88132-423-5(X))* Peterson Institute for International Economics.

Taylor, Michael W. & Schooner, Heidi Mandanis. Global Bank Regulation: Principles & Policies. 2009. (ENG., Illus.). 352p. 82.95 *(978-0-12-641003-7(8)*, Academic Pr.) Elsevier Science & Technology Bks.

Toniolo, Gianni. Central Bank Cooperation at the Bank for International Settlements, 1930-1973. 2007. (Studies in Macroeconomic History Ser.). (ENG., Illus.). 768p. pap. 79.00 *(978-0-521-04370-0(0))* Cambridge Univ. Pr.

van Putten, Maartje. Policing the Banks: Accountability Mechanisms for the Financial Sector. 2008. (ENG.). 520p. (C). pap. *(978-0-7735-3402-5(4))* McGill-Queen's Univ. Pr.

Vlcek, William. Offshore Finance & Small States: Sovereignty, Size & Money. 2008. (ENG., Illus.). 216p. 89.00 *(978-0-230-52220-6(3))* Palgrave Macmillan.

Weston, Rae. Domestic & Multinational Banking (RLE Banking & Finance) The Effects of Monetary Policy, Volume 33. 2012. (ENG.). 416p. 150.00 ***(978-0-415-53853-4(X))*** Routledge.

BANKS AND BANKING, INVESTMENT
see Investment Banking

BANMANI (AFRICAN PEOPLE)
see Bambara (African People)

BANNATYNE CLUB, EDINBURGH

Bannatyne Club Staff. Lists of Members & the Rules. (Bannatyne Club, Edinburgh Publications: No. 116). reprint ed. 39.50 *(978-0-404-52874-4(0))* AMS Pr., Inc.

—Publications of the Bannatyne Club, Set, Nos. 1-120 & 8 Extra Vols. reprint ed. *(978-0-404-52700-6(0))* AMS Pr., Inc.

Maidment, James. Notices Relative to the Bannatyne Club. (Bannatyne Club, Edinburgh Publications). reprint ed. 37.50 *(978-0-404-52887-4(2))* AMS Pr., Inc.

BANNED BOOKS
see Prohibited Books

BANNEKER, BENJAMIN, 1731-1806

Allen, Will W. & Murray, Daniel A. Banneker: The Afro-American Astronomer. Date not set. pap. 15.95 *(978-0-88143-145-2(1))* Ayer Co. Pubs., Inc.

BANNERS

Hughes, Beatrice. Quilted Star & Logo Banner: For Organizations & Individuals with a Big Ten Affiliation & Anyone Interested in Making an Eleven-Point Star Where Each Point has Two Colors. Mervau, Katherine & Pratt, Sally, eds. 2009. (Illus.). 86p. spiral bd. 21.95 *(978-0-615-27065-4(4))* Full-Circle-Pubns.

Lose, Patrick. Poster Quilts with Patrick Lose. 2009. (ENG., Illus.). 48p. pap. 27.95 *(978-1-57120-653-4(1))* C & T Publishing.

Polk, Patrick Arthur. Haitian Vodou Flags. 2010. (Folk Art & Artists Ser.). (ENG.). 72p. (C). pap. 30.00 *(978-1-61703-017-8(1))* Univ. Pr. of Mississippi.

Znamensky, Pierre & Gallice, Guy. Sous les Plis du Drapeau Rouge. 2010. (FRE., Illus.). 348p. *(978-2-8126-0142-2(6))* Editions du Rouergue.

BANNISTER, ROGER, 1929-

Bale, John & Howe, David. The Four-Minute Mile: Historical & Cultural Interpretations of a Sporting Barrier. 2007. 168p. 140.00 *(978-0-415-40015-2(5))* Routledge.

Denison, Jim. Bannister & Beyond: The Mystique of the Four-Minute Mile. 2008. (ENG.). 256p. pap. 14.00 *(978-1-891369-81-0(4))* Breakaway Bks.

BANNOCK INDIANS
see Indians of North America—Northwest, Pacific

BANQUETS
see Dinners and Dining

BANTU LANGUAGES
see also Chewa Dialect; Ekoi Languages; Ganda Language; Kikuyu Language; Kongo Language; Kuanyama Language; Lingala Language; Mbo Language (Cameroon); Nyanja Language; Nyankole Language; Shona Language; Sotho-Tswana Languages; Swahili Language; Yao Language

Botne, Robert Dale Olson & Schafer, Loveness. The Chindali Language of Malawi. 2008. viii, 323p. *(978-1-60618-911-5(5))*; *(978-1-60618-910-8(7))* American Philosophical Society.

Campbell-Dunn, G. J. K. Maori: The African Evidence. 2007. 135p. *(978-1-877211-64-5(8))* Penny Farthing Press.

Chacha, Leonard M. Verbal Tone in Kuri. 2011. 340p. pap. ***(978-3-8443-9303-3(X))*** Lambert Academic Publishing.

De Cat, Cecile & Demuth, Katherine, eds. The Bantu-Romance Connection: A Comparative Investigation of Syntactic Structure. 2008. (Linguistik Aktuell/Linguistics Today Ser.: Vol. 131). 350p. (C). *(978-90-272-5514-3(8))* Benjamins, John Publishing Co.

Euro Talk. Talk Now! Sesotho. 2008. 29.99 *(978-1-84352-376-5(0))* TOPICS Entertainment.

—Talk Now! Setswana. 2008. 29.99 *(978-1-84352-334-5(5))* TOPICS Entertainment.

Icon Group International, Inc. Staff, compiled by. Webster's Bemba - English Thesaurus Dictionary. 2008. 64p. ring bd. 28.95 incl. audio compact disk *(978-0-497-83437-1(5))* Icon Group International, Inc.

—Webster's Bende - English Thesaurus Dictionary. 2008. 73p. ring bd. 28.95 incl. audio compact disk *(978-0-497-83439-5(1))* Icon Group International, Inc.

—Webster's Gusii - English Thesaurus Dictionary. 2008. 107p. ring bd. 28.95 incl. audio compact disk *(978-0-497-83507-1(X))* Icon Group International, Inc.

—Webster's Kiseri - English Thesaurus Dictionary. 2008. 109p. ring bd. 28.95 incl. audio compact disk *(978-0-497-83555-2(X))* Icon Group International, Inc.

—Webster's Kiseri Unn - English Thesaurus Dictionary. 2008. 81p. ring bd. 28.95 incl. audio compact disk *(978-0-497-83554-5(1))* Icon Group International, Inc.

—Webster's Kisi - English Thesaurus Dictionary. 2008. 125p. ring bd. 28.95 incl. audio compact disk *(978-0-497-83556-9(8))* Icon Group International, Inc.

—Webster's Kisuundi - English Thesaurus Dictionary. 2008. 73p. ring bd. 28.95 incl. audio compact disk *(978-0-497-83557-6(6))* Icon Group International, Inc.

—Webster's Lema Unn - English Thesaurus Dictionary. 2008. 79p. ring bd. 28.95 incl. audio compact disk *(978-0-497-83575-0(4))* Icon Group International, Inc.

—Webster's Meruimenti - English Thesaurus Dictionary. 2008. 113p. ring bd. 28.95 incl. audio compact disk *(978-0-497-83612-2(2))* Icon Group International, Inc.

—Webster's Merutig - English Thesaurus Dictionary. 2008. 95p. ring bd. 28.95 incl. audio compact disk *(978-0-497-83613-9(0))* Icon Group International, Inc.

—Webster's Mkwaya - English Thesaurus Dictionary. 2008. 115p. ring bd. 28.95 incl. audio compact disk *(978-0-497-83618-4(1))* Icon Group International, Inc.

—Webster's Mpoto - English Thesaurus Dictionary. 2008. 114p. ring bd. 28.95 incl. audio compact disk *(978-0-497-83623-8(8))* Icon Group International, Inc.

—Webster's Munyarwand - English Thesaurus Dictionary. 2008. 65p. ring bd. 28.95 incl. audio compact disk *(978-0-497-83625-2(4))* Icon Group International, Inc.

—Webster's Ndari - English Thesaurus Dictionary. 2008. 125p. ring bd. 28.95 incl. audio compact disk *(978-0-497-83633-7(5))* Icon Group International, Inc.

—Webster's Ntuzu - English Thesaurus Dictionary. 2008. 97p. ring bd. 28.95 incl. audio compact disk *(978-0-497-83642-9(4))* Icon Group International, Inc.

—Webster's Nyamwezi - English Thesaurus Dictionary. 2008. 115p. ring bd. 28.95 incl. audio compact disk *(978-0-497-83645-0(9))* Icon Group International, Inc.

—Webster's Nyaturucha - English Thesaurus Dictionary. 2008. 84p. ring bd. 28.95 incl. audio compact disk *(978-0-497-83647-4(5))* Icon Group International, Inc.

—Webster's Nyaturuwil - English Thesaurus Dictionary. 2008. 120p. ring bd. 28.95 incl. audio compact disk *(978-0-497-83648-1(3))* Icon Group International, Inc.

—Webster's Nyoro - English Thesaurus Dictionary. 2008. 123p. ring bd. 28.95 incl. audio compact disk *(978-0-497-83651-1(3))* Icon Group International, Inc.

—Webster's Rundi - English Thesaurus Dictionary. 2008. 109p. ring bd. 28.95 incl. audio compact disk *(978-0-497-83689-4(0))* Icon Group International, Inc.

—Webster's Rungwa - English Thesaurus Dictionary. 2008. 142p. ring bd. 28.95 incl. audio compact disk *(978-0-497-83690-0(4))* Icon Group International, Inc.

—Webster's Rwanda - English Thesaurus Dictionary. 2008. 57p. ring bd. 28.95 incl. audio compact disk *(978-0-497-83692-4(0))* Icon Group International, Inc.

—Webster's Samialugwe - English Thesaurus Dictionary. 2008. 110p. ring bd. 28.95 incl. audio compact disk *(978-0-497-83694-8(7))* Icon Group International, Inc.

—Webster's Shubi - English Thesaurus Dictionary. 2008. 126p. ring bd. 28.95 incl. audio compact disk *(978-0-497-83706-8(4))* Icon Group International, Inc.

—Webster's Soga - English Thesaurus Dictionary. 2008. 131p. ring bd. 28.95 incl. audio compact disk *(978-0-497-83712-9(9))* Icon Group International, Inc.

—Webster's Sukuma - English Thesaurus Dictionary. 2008. 116p. ring bd. 28.95 incl. audio compact disk *(978-0-497-83721-1(8))* Icon Group International, Inc.

—Webster's Swati - English Thesaurus Dictionary. 2008. 58p. ring bd. 28.95 incl. audio compact disk *(978-0-497-83726-6(9))* Icon Group International, Inc.

—Webster's Taabwa - English Thesaurus Dictionary. 2008. 88p. ring bd. 28.95 incl. audio compact disk *(978-0-497-83728-0(5))* Icon Group International, Inc.

—Webster's Temi - English Thesaurus Dictionary. 2008. 84p. ring bd. 28.95 incl. audio compact disk *(978-0-497-83737-2(4))* Icon Group International, Inc.

—Webster's Vunjo - English Thesaurus Dictionary. 2008. 69p. ring bd. 28.95 incl. audio compact disk *(978-0-497-83758-7(7))* Icon Group International, Inc.

—Webster's Wanda - English Thesaurus Dictionary. 2008. 71p. ring bd. 28.95 incl. audio compact disk *(978-0-497-83761-7(7))* Icon Group International, Inc.

—Webster's Wanji - English Thesaurus Dictionary. 2008. 74p. ring bd. 28.95 incl. audio compact disk *(978-0-497-83762-4(5))* Icon Group International, Inc.

—Webster's Xhosa - English Thesaurus Dictionary. 2008. 72p. ring bd. 28.95 incl. audio compact disk *(978-0-497-83765-5(X))* Icon Group International, Inc.

—Webster's Zanaki - English Thesaurus Dictionary. 2008. 88p. ring bd. 28.95 incl. audio compact disk *(978-0-497-83771-6(4))* Icon Group International, Inc.

—Webster's Zinza - English Thesaurus Dictionary. 2008. 96p. ring bd. 28.95 incl. audio compact disk *(978-0-497-83775-4(7))* Icon Group International, Inc.

—Webster's Zulu - English Thesaurus Dictionary. 2008. 193p. ring bd. 28.95 incl. audio compact disk *(978-0-497-83776-1(5))* Icon Group International, Inc.

—The 2009-2014 World Outlook for Electric Insect Killers. 2008. 198p. ring bd. 28.95 incl. audio compact disk *(978-0-497-83535-4(5))* Icon Group International, Inc.

Kayigema, Jacques Lwaboshi. Loanword Allocation in Kinyarwand. 2011. 204p. pap. ***(978-3-8443-8016-3(7))*** Lambert Academic Publishing.

Kondala, Shadreck & Mambwe, Kelvin. Natulande IciBemba: Let's Speak Bemba: (A First-Year Textbook) 2011. (BEM & ENG.). pap. ***(978-1-59703-021-2(X))*** Global Academic Publishing.

Nurse, Derek. Tense & Aspect in Bantu. 2008. (ENG., Illus.). 512p. 165.00 *(978-0-19-923929-0(0))* Oxford Univ. Pr., Inc.

Sibanda, Galen. Morphophonology. 2010. 336p. pap. *(978-3-8383-8537-2(3))* Lambert Academic Publishing.

Van Otterloo, Karen. The Kifuliiru Language, Volume 1: Phonology, Tone, & Morphological Derivation, 2 vols., Vol. 1. 2011. (ENG.). 516p. pap. 52.99 ***(978-1-55671-261-6(8))*** SIL International.

Van Otterloo, Roger. The Kifuliiru Language, Volume 2: A Descriptive Grammar, 2, Volume 2. 2011. (ENG.). 616p. pap. 59.99 ***(978-1-55671-270-8(7))*** SIL International.

BANTU-SPEAKING PEOPLES
see also Beti (African People); Fingo (African People); Ganda (African People); Gusii (African People); Kikuyu (African People); Kongo (African People); Kuba (African People); Lozi (African People); Luyia (African People); Makonde (African People); Nguni (African People); Nyamwezi (African People); Pedi (African People); Shambala (African People); Shona (African People); Suku (African People); Swazi (African People); Tsonga (African People); Tumbuka (African People)

Chigwedere, A. S. The Roots of the Bantu. (Illus.). iv, 339p. *(978-0-7974-1852-3(0))* Southern African Research & Documentation Centre.

Duggan-Cronin, Alfred M. The Bantu Tribes of South Africa, 4 vols. in 12 pts., Set. reprint ed. 450.00 *(978-0-404-12050-4(4))* AMS Pr., Inc.

Eno, Mohamed A. The Bantu - Jareer Somali: Unearthing Apartheid in the Horn of Africa. 2008. 320p. pap. *(978-1-905068-95-1(6))* Adonis & Abbey Publishers Ltd.

—The Bantu - Jareer Somalis: The bantu - jareer Somalis. 2008. 320p. *(978-1-905068-94-4(8))* Adonis & Abbey Publishers Ltd.

Gunderson. Sukuma Labor Songs from Western Tanzania: 'We Never Sleep, We Dream of Farming' 2010. (African Sources for African History Ser.). (Illus.). 488p. pap. *(978-90-04-18468-8(6))* BRILL.

Hoyt, Alta Howard, ed. Bantu Folklore Tales of Long Ago. 2011. 114p. 39.95 ***(978-1-258-03533-4(2))*** Literary Licensing, LLC.

John, Roscoe. The Northern Bantu: An Account of Some Central African Tribes of the Uganda Protectorate. 2010. (Cambridge Library Collection - Travel & Exploration Ser.). (Illus.). 372p. pap. 29.99 *(978-1-108-01072-6(5))* Cambridge Univ. Pr.

Lynch, Patricia. Beloved Strangers - a Collaborative Exploration of Language & Culture. 2008. 296p. pap. *(978-3-639-01443-3(X))* VDM Verlag Dr. Mueller e.K.

Mawanzi Ndombe, César. Das symbolische Denken als Schlüssel zum Verständnis der Negro-afrikanischen (Bantu-)Weltanschauung: Eine religionsphilosophische Deutung im Anschluss an die Kulturphilosophie Ernst Cassirers. 2008. (Europäische Hochschulschriften. Reihe 23: Theologie Ser.). (GRE & GER.). 420p. pap. 99.95 *(978-3-631-58531-3(4))* Lang, Peter GmbH, Europaischer Verlag der Wissenschaften DEU. Dist: Lang, Peter.

Monga Wa Matanga, Paulin. Membralité écologique des êtres dans la théologie chrétienne et dans la pensée Bantoue: Fondement d'une éthique de la Tempérance. 2010. (Europäische Hochschulschriften. Reihe 23: Theologie Ser.). (FRE.). 456p. pap. 105.95 *(978-3-631-60170-9(0))* Lang, Peter GmbH, Europaischer Verlag der Wissenschaften DEU. Dist: Lang, Peter.

Ribot, Isabelle. A Study through Skull Morphology on the Diversity of Holocene African Populations in a Historical Perspective. 2011. (Bar S Ser.). (ENG., Illus.). 217p. (C). pap. 107.50 ***(978-1-4073-0773-2(8))*** British Archaeological Reports Ltd. GBR. Dist: Brown, David Bk. Co., The.

Willoughby, W. C. Nature Worship & Taboo: Further Studies in the Soul of the Bantu 1932. 2007. (ENG.). 304p. 43.95 *(978-0-548-05382-9(0))* Kessinger Publishing, LLC.

BANTUS
see Bantu-Speaking Peoples; Blacks—South Africa

BAPTISM
see also Baptisteries; Fonts; Infant Baptism

Ajibola, Babatunde Ezekiel. Introduction to christian living:a baptismal & membership class Tutorial. 2008. 111p. pap. 20.95 *(978-1-4092-4955-9(7))* Lulu Enterprises Inc.

Alfani, Guido. Fathers & Godfathers: Spiritual Kinship in Early-Modern Italy. 2009. (Catholic Christendom, 1300-1700 Ser.). (Illus.). 288p. 124.95 *(978-0-7546-6737-7(5))* Ashgate Publishing Co.

Baker, H. A. Visions Beyond the Veil: Visions of Heaven, Angels, Satan, Hell, & the End of the Age. 2006. 190p. per. 9.99 *(978-0-88368-786-4(0))* Whitaker Hse.

Baptism. 4.50 *(978-0-687-09462-2(3))*; 4.50 *(978-0-687-05797-9(3))* Abingdon Pr.

Baptism-1 Peter. 7.50 *(978-0-8054-5910-4(3))* B&H Publishing Group.

Barsom, Murad & Samuel, Mor Athanasius Yeshue, trs. The Sacrament of Holy Baptism. 2011. (SYR.). 115.00 *(978-1-61143-958-8(2))* Gorgias Pr., LLC.

Barth, Karl. The Teaching of the Church Regarding Baptism. Payne, Ernest A., tr. 2006. 64p. pap. 9.00 *(978-1-59752-799-6(8))*, Wipf and Stock) Wipf & Stock Pubs.

Barton, George Aaron. The Origin of the Thought Pattern Which Survives in Baptism: American Oriental Society, V56, No. 2, June 1936. Brown, W. Norman & Shryock, John K., eds. 2011. 16p. pap. 35.95 ***(978-1-258-06552-2(5))*** Literary Licensing, LLC.

Bauer, A. D. Buried with Christ: The Sacrament of Baptism. 2012. (Illus.). 250p. per. 14.99 *(978-0-9658798-1-1(X))* Square Halo Bks.

Bays, Patricia. Baptism. (Anglican Learning Centres Ser.). pap. 15.95 *(978-1-55126-329-8(7)*, 1671) Forward Movement Pubns.

Beasley-Murray, G. R. Baptism in the New Testament. 2006. 432p. pap. 34.00 *(978-1-59752-859-7(5)*, Wipf and Stock) Wipf & Stock Pubs.

Berger, Albrecht, ed. Life & Works of Saint Gregentios, Archbishop of Taphar: Introduction, Critical Edition & Translation with a Contribution by Gianfranco Fiaccadori. 2006. (Millennium-Studien / Millennium Studies). (ENG & GRE.). IX, 915p. 189.00 *(978-3-11-018445-7(1))* De Gruyter, Walter Inc.

Best, Thomas F. Baptism Today: Understanding, Practice, Ecumenical Implications. 2008. (Faith & Order Paper Ser.). 416p. (C). pap. 39.95 *(978-0-8146-6221-2(8))* Liturgical Pr.

Best, Thomas F. & Grdzelidze, Tamara, eds. BEM At 25: Critical Insights into a Continuing Legacy. 2007. 318p. pap. 20.00 *(978-2-8254-1517-7(0))* World Council of Churches/Conseil Oecumenique des Eglises CHE. Dist: International Specialized Bk. Services.

Bliss, John. Letters on Christian Baptism, As the Initiating Ordinance into the Real Kingdom of Christ. 2006. 244p. per. 26.00 *(978-1-57978-638-0(3))* Baptist Standard Bearer, Inc.

Bloomer, George. More of Him. 2006. 224p. 12.99 *(978-0-88368-790-1(9))* Whitaker Hse.

Blue, Ken. Alien Emersions. 2007. per. *(978-1-60208-045-4(3))* FBC Pubns. & Printing.

Book of Discipline 1996 Macintosh Software. 19.95 *(978-0-687-10614-1(1))* Abingdon Pr.

Boora, Kulwant Singh. Baptism in the Name of Jesus (Acts 2: 38) from Jerusalem to Great Britain. 2011. 120p. pap. 25.00 *(978-1-4567-2083-4(X))* AuthorHouse.

Boora, Kulwant Singh. The Roman Catholic Church & Its Recognition of the Validity of Baptism in the Name of Jesus (Acts 2: 38) from 100 A. D. to 500 A. D. 2011. 112p. pap. 20.00 ***(978-1-4634-2906-5(1))*** AuthorHouse.

Borreson, Glenn L. Water for Your Soul. 2008. 110p. pap. 10.95 *(978-0-7414-4437-0(2))* Infinity Publishing.

Bowman, Peg. At Home with the Sacraments: Baptism. 48p. pap. 3.95 *(978-0-89622-478-0(3)*, C-49) Twenty-Third Pubns./Bayard.

Bradshaw, Paul, ed. Essays in Early Eastern Initiation. 2009. 88.00 *(978-1-60724-363-2(6))* Gorgias Pr., LLC.

Bridge, Donald & Phypers, David. The Water That Divides: Two Views on Baptism Explored. 2008. (ENG.). 240p. per. 14.99 *(978-1-84550-308-6(2))* Christian Focus Pubns. GBR. Dist: STL Distribution North America.

Bridston, Keith. One Lord, One Baptism: Studies in Ministry & Worship. 2011. 80p. 37.95 ***(978-1-258-03449-8(2))*** Literary Licensing, LLC.

Briggs, John H. Y. Pulpit & People. 2009. (Studies in Baptist History & Thought Ser.). 220p. pap. 25.00 *(978-1-60899-164-8(4)*, Wipf and Stock) Wipf & Stock Pubs.

Brock, Sebastian. The Holy Spirit in the Syrian Baptismal Tradition. 2008. (Gorgias Liturgical Studies: 4). 58.00 *(978-1-59333-844-2(9))* Gorgias Pr., LLC.

Brown, Kenneth Irving. And Be Baptized: A Minister's Handbook on Baptism. 2011. 94p. 38.95 ***(978-1-258-02796-4(8))*** Literary Licensing, LLC.

Bryant, Delmar De Forest. The Meaning of Baptism. 2006. pap. 9.95 *(978-1-4286-7519-3(1))* Kessinger Publishing, LLC.

Bunyan, John. Baptism & Church Communion. 26p. pap. 2.99 *(978-0-9652883-3-0(1))* Audubon Pr. & Christian Bk. Service.

Burke, Suzanne. Living the Promises of Baptism: 101 Ideas for Parents. 2010. (Illus.). 79p. ***(978-1-4514-0131-8(0))*** Augsburg Fortress, Pubs.

Burrage, Henry. Act of Baptism in the History of the Chr. 2006. 268p. per. 28.00 *(978-1-57978-418-8(6))* Baptist Standard Bearer, Inc.

Byzantine Catholic Church. The Order of Baptism & Confirmation According to the Byzantine Rite of the Catholic Church. 2011. 32p. 35.95 ***(978-1-258-05197-6(4))*** Literary Licensing, LLC.

Carrillo, Salvador. Y Fueron Llenos del Espiritu Santo. 192p. 8.95 *(978-958-607-876-4(0))* Sociedad de San Pablo COL. Dist: St Pauls/Alba Hse. Pubs.

Carson, Alexander. Baptism in Its Mode & Subjects. 2006. 556p. per. 50.00 *(978-1-57978-787-5(8))* Baptist Standard Bearer, Inc.

—Baptism in Its Mode & Subjects. 2009. 552p. 37.99 *(978-1-115-80387-8(5))*; pap. 41.75 *(978-1-115-80389-2(1))*; 37.99 *(978-1-113-59362-7(8))*; pap. 41.75 *(978-1-113-59361-0(X))*; pap. 42.75 *(978-1-113-60750-8(5))* BiblioBazaar.

—Baptism in Its Mode & Subjects. 2009. 532p. pap. *(978-0-217-44360-9(5))* Books LLC.

—Baptism in Its Mode & Subjects. 2008. 556p. pap. 42.95 *(978-1-4367-8546-4(4))* Kessinger Publishing, LLC.

Carter, Kenneth H. & Carter, Kenneth H., Jr. Baptism Services, Sermons, & Prayers. 2006. (Just in Time! Ser.). 86p. per. 12.00 *(978-0-687-33383-7(0))* Abingdon Pr.

Cathcart, William. Baptism of the Ages & of the Nations. 2006. 248p. per. 27.00 *(978-1-57978-406-5(2))* Baptist Standard Bearer, Inc.

Celebration of Baptism. 7.25 *(978-0-687-04750-5(1))* Abingdon Pr.

Certificates of Baptism. 12.99 *(978-0-7847-0818-7(5))* Standard Publishing.

Christian, John. Immersion the Act of Christian Baptism. 2006. 272p. per. 28.00 *(978-1-57978-416-4(X))* Baptist Standard Bearer, Inc.

[Christian Pamphlets. 2006. 392p. per. 26.99 *(978-1-4255-4422-5(3))* MPublishing.

Çiçek, Julius Yeshu, ed. The Sacraments of Holy Baptism & Marriage. 2010. (SYR.). 117.68 *(978-1-61143-210-7(3))* Gorgias Pr., LLC.

Çiçek, Julius Yeshu & Gorgis, Amill, eds. The Sacraments of Holy Baptism, Marriage, & Burial of the Dead. Fritsch, Volker, tr. 2010. (SYR.). 126.68 *(978-1-61143-211-4(1))* Gorgias Pr., LLC.

Cleverly, Charlie. The Passion That Shapes Nations: Catching Hold of the Courage of Martyrs from Paul to the Present. 2006. (ENG.). 176p. per. 12.99 *(978-1-84291-213-3(5))* Kingsway Pubns. GBR. Dist: STL Distribution North America.

Come, Follow Me: Discipleship Booklet with Baptism Certificate. 16p. 3.49 *(978-0-7847-0781-4(2)*, 01170) Standard Publishing.

Conant, T. J. The Meaning & Use of Baptizein: Philologically & Historically Investigated, for the American Bible Union. 2006. 172p. pap. 20.00 *(978-1-59752-707-1(6)*, Wipf and Stock) Wipf & Stock Pubs.

Conner, Kevin. Understanding the New Birth & the Baptism of the Holy Spirit. 64p. pap. *(978-1-85240-261-7(X))* Sovereign World, Ltd.

Cross, Anthony R. & Thompson, Philip E., eds. Baptist Sacramentalism 2. 2009. (Studies in Baptist History & Thought Ser.). 308p. pap. 36.00 *(978-1-60608-601-8(4)*, Wipf and Stock) Wipf & Stock Pubs.

Cunningham, Tommy. The Preacher. 2011. 112p. pap. 10.68 ***(978-1-4567-5648-2(6))*** AuthorHouse.

Dalby, Mark. Infant Communion. 2009. 88.00 *(978-1-60724-405-9(5))* Gorgias Pr., LLC.

Das, A. Andrew. Baptized into God's Family Second Edition: The Doctrine of Infant Baptism for Today. 2008. 152p. (Orig.). pap. *(978-0-8100-0409-2(7)*, 15N0543) Northwestern Publishing Hse.

Day, Juliette. Baptism in Early Byzantine Palestine 325-451. 2009. 88.00 *(978-1-60724-393-9(8))* Gorgias Pr., LLC.

—The Baptismal Liturgy of Jerusalem: 4th & 5th Century Evidence from Palestine, Syria, & Egypt. 2007. (Liturgy, Worship & Society Ser.). 166p. 89.95 *(978-0-7546-5751-4(5))* Ashgate Publishing Co.

de Waal, Esther. Seeking Life: Benedictine Wisdom for the Baptized. 2009. 160p. 19.95 *(978-0-8146-1880-6(4)*, Liturgical Pr. Bks.) Liturgical Pr.

DeHaes, Maarten U. Baptism: In the Christian Community. 32p. pap. 7.95 *(978-0-86315-026-5(8)*, 1065) Floris Bks. GBR. Dist: SteinerBooks, Inc.

Dockery, David S. Southern Baptist Consensus & Renewal: A Biblical, Historical, & Theological Proposal. 2008. (ENG.). 256p. pap. 9.99 *(978-0-8054-4740-8(7)*, B&H Academic) B&H Publishing Group.

Dragas, George Dion. The Holy Sacraments of Baptism, Chrismation & Holy Communion: The Five Mystagogical Catechisms of St. Cyril of Jerusalem. 2008. 140p. pap 11.95 *(978-1-933275-24-6(3)*, Orthodox Research Institute) Cocheco Falls Publishing.

Draper, James T., Jr. & Perry, John. Lifeway Legacy: A Personal History of Lifeway Christian Resources & the Sunday School Board of the Southern Baptist Convention. 2006. (ENG., Illus.). 464p. 29.99 *(978-0-8054-3170-4(5)*, B&H Bks.) B&H Publishing Group.

Drury, Keith. Experiencing Baptism & Communion. 2007. (D Ser.). (Illus.). 64p. per. 7.99 *(978-0-89827-368-7(4))* Wesleyan Publishing Hse.

Duncan, Lorida. Touching Lives. 2008. 288p. 25.99 *(978-1-60477-880-9(6))* Xulon Pr., Inc.

Duncan, William Cecil. A Brief History of the Baptists & Their Distinctive Principles & Practices, from the Beginning of the Gospel to the Present Time Part: Fr. 2006. 288p. per. 23.99 *(978-1-4255-2647-4(0))* MPublishing.

Duncan, William Cecil. History of the Early Baptists: From the Beginning of the Gospel to the Rise of Affusion As Baptism, & of Infant Baptism, 28 A. D. -250 A. D. with An. 2006. 280p. per. 23.99 *(978-1-4255-2547-7(4))* MPublishing.

Dundee, John G. Letters. Smythe, George, ed. (Bannatyne Club, Edinburgh Publications: No. 15). reprint ed. 34.50 *(978-0-404-52715-0(9))* AMS Pr., Inc.

Echle, Harry A. The Terminology of the Sacrament of Regeneration According to Clement of Alexandri. 2011. 60p. 36.95 ***(978-1-258-05583-7(X))*** Literary Licensing, LLC.

England, Stephen Jackson. The One Baptism: Baptism & Christian Unity, with Special Reference to Disciples of Christ. 2011. 94p. 38.95 ***(978-1-258-05571-4(6))*** Literary Licensing, LLC.

Fauss, Oliver F. Baptism in God's Plan. 2011. 44p. 35.95 ***(978-1-258-02089-7(0))*** Literary Licensing, LLC.

Ferguson, Everett. Baptism in the Early Church: History, Theology, & Liturgy in the First Five Centuries. 2009. (Illus.). 984p. 60.00 *(978-0-8028-2748-7(9))* Eerdmans, William B. Publishing Co.

Ferres, Michael. Civil War. 2007. 436p. per. 21.99 *(978-1-60477-204-3(2))* Xulon Pr., Inc.

Fesko, J. V. Word, Water, & Spirit: A Reformed perspective on Baptism. 2010. *(978-1-60178-101-7(6))* Reformation Heritage Bks.

Finley, Mark. Ten Days in the Upper Room. 2011. pap. 9.99 ***(978-0-8163-2487-3(5))*** Pacific Pr. Publishing Assn.

Flory, John S. Literary Activity of the German Baptist Brethren in the Eighteenth Century. 2007. (ENG.). 348p. 46.95 *(978-0-548-04297-7(7))* Kessinger Publishing, LLC.

Ford, Michael. The bible of the Adversary. 2009. 335p. 43.95 *(978-0-557-04429-0(4))* Lulu Enterprises Inc.

Fowler, Stanley K. More Than a Symbol: The British Baptist Recovery of Baptismal Sacramentalism. 2007. (Studies in Baptist History & Thought: Ser.). 309p. pap. 31.00 *(978-1-59752-733-0(5)*, Wipf and Stock) Wipf & Stock Pubs.

Franquiz, Bob. Watermark: An Explanation of Baptism. 2007. 52p. per. 5.99 *(978-0-9772047-2-4(3))* Fuel Media Group, Inc.

Gadol, Kohen Ben. Last Sounding of Shofar. 2010. pap. 24.95 *(978-0-7414-6126-1(9))* Infinity Publishing.

Galbreath, Paul. Leading Through the Water. 2011. *(978-1-56699-413-2(6))* Alban Institute, Inc.

Gibbs, George. A Defense of the Baptists or the Baptism of Believers by Immersion: 2007. (ENG.). 444p. per. 36.95 *(978-1-4304-4612-5(9))* Kessinger Publishing, LLC

Gibler, Linda. From the Beginning to Baptism: Scientific & Sacred Stories of Water, Oil, & Fire. 2010. 19.95 *(978-0-8146-5673-0(0))* Liturgical Pr.

Gill, John. Gospel Baptism. 2006. 672p. per. 58.00 *(978-1-57978-036-4(9))* Baptist Standard Bearer, Inc.

Gortner, J. Narver, et al. Water, Baptism, & the Trinity. 2011. 62p. 36.95 ***(978-1-258-05906-4(1))*** Literary Licensing, LLC.

Gouldson, Phil. We Ought to Explain: Practical Notes for New Churchgoers. 2009. 56p. pap. *(978-1-84748-559-5(6))* Athena Pr.

Graves, J. TriLemma or Death by Three Horns. 2006. 172p. per. 21.00 *(978-1-57978-512-3(3))* Baptist Standard Bearer, Inc.

Graves, J. R. What Is Conscience: Have You A Good Conscience. 2011. 60p. 36.95 ***(978-1-258-09680-9(3))*** Literary Licensing, LLC.

Green, Michael. Baptism: Its Purpose, Practice & Power. 144p. (Orig.). pap. 9.99 *(978-0-340-74542-7(8)*, Hodder & Stoughton) Hodder General Publishing Div. GBR. Dist: Trafalgar Square Publishing.

Gustitus, Paul. The Father's Promise: Questions & Answers about the Baptism of the Holy Spirit. 2007. 80p. pap. 9.99 *(978-0-9778614-5-3(7))* Partnership Pubns.

Haitch, Russell. From Exorcism to Ecstasy: Eight Views of Baptism. 2007. (ENG.). 160p. pap. 25.00 *(978-0-664-23000-5(8))* Westminster John Knox Pr.

Hardy, Willie. My Enemy Is a Coward: Fighting an Enemy That You Can't See. 2010. 116p. (ENG.). 22.19 *(978-1-4269-2934-2(X))*; pap. 12.19 *(978-1-4269-2933-5(1))* Trafford Publishing.

Harinck, Cornelis. We with Our Children. 2006. pap. 16.00 *(978-1-892777-92-8(4)*, Reformation Heritage Bks.

Hayden, Clarence B. Baptism in Relation to the Atonement. 2011. 98p. 38.95 ***(978-1-258-07137-0(1))*** Literary Licensing, LLC.

Haykin, Michael A. G., ed. At the Pure Fountain of Thy Word: Andrew Fuller as an Apologist. 2007. (Studies in Baptist History & Thought: Ser.). 315p. pap. 32.00 *(978-1-59752-797-2(1)*, Wipf and Stock) Wipf & Stock Pubs.

Heath, Gordon L. & Dvorak, James D., eds. Baptism: Historical, Theological, & Pastoral Perspectives. 2011. (McMaster Theological Studies). 290p. pap. 32.00 *(978-1-60899-186-1(4)*, Pickwick Pubns.) Wipf & Stock Pubs.

Hellholm, David, et al, eds. Ablution, Initiation, & Baptism: Late Antiquity, Early Judaism, & Early Christianity. (Beihefte zur Zeitschrift fur die neutestamentliche Wissenschaft und die Kunde der älteren Kirche Ser.). (ENG & GER., Illus.). 2011. XCVI, 2024p. 587.00 ***(978-3-11-214250-9(0))*** 2010. 1860p. 391.00 *(978-3-11-024751-0(8))* De Gruyter, Walter Inc.

Henry, Matthew. Family Religion: Principles for Raising a Godly Family. 2008. (ENG.). 272p. pap. 14.99 *(978-1-84550-313-0(9)*, Christian Heritage) Christian Focus Pubns. GBR. Dist: STL Distribution North America.

Hill, John W. Making Disciples: Serving Those Who Are Entering the Christian Life. 144p. spiral bd. 14.95 *(978-1-895457-02-5(5)*, 129) Hoskin Group CAN. Dist: Forward Movement Pubns.

Hiscox, Edward. The Baptist Short Method. 2008. 223p. pap. 18.50 *(978-0-557-00806-3(9))* Lulu Enterprises Inc.

Hodges, William. Baptism Tested by Scripture & History. 2009. 234p. pap. *(978-0-217-17976-8(2))*; 210p. pap. *(978-0-217-72591-0(0))* Books LLC.

—Baptism Tested by Scripture & History. 2006. 432p. per. 26.99 *(978-1-4255-4712-7(5))* MPublishing.

Hodges, William A. M. Baptism Tested by Scripture & History. 2007. (ENG.). 420p. 49.95 *(978-0-548-10188-9(4))* Kessinger Publishing, LLC.

Hoeksema, Herman. Baptized into Christ: The Heidelberg Catechism, the Triple Knowledge, V6. 2011. 178p. 42.95 ***(978-1-258-04323-0(8))*** Literary Licensing, LLC.

Holland, Kevin S. Why Be Fundamental. 2011. 140p. pap. 11.70 ***(978-1-4567-3629-3(9))*** AuthorHouse.

Houchen, Hoyt H. & Tatum, Ray. The Houchen-Tatum Debate, Four Subjects: Establishment of the Church, Baptism, Apostasy, Pre-Millennialism. 2011. 218p. 44.95 ***(978-1-258-04858-7(2))*** Literary Licensing, LLC.

Hunter, Harold D. Spirit Baptism: A Pentecostal Alternative. 2009. 248p. pap. 27.00 *(978-1-55635-930-9(6)*, Wipf and Stock) Wipf & Stock Pubs.

Hwata, Benny. Pentecostalism in Apostolic Faith Mission. 2011. 172p. pap. ***(978-3-8443-8884-8(2))*** Lambert Academic Publishing.

Iams, F. Before the FootLights. 2006. 276p. per. 29.00 *(978-1-57978-634-2(C))* Baptist Standard Bearer, Inc.

Intervarsity Press. Baptism: Three Views. Wright, David F., ed. 2009. (Spectrum Multiview Book Ser.). (ENG.). 200p. pap. 16.00 *(978-0-8308-3856-1(2)*, IVP Acad.) InterVarsity Pr.

James, Bill. Baptism & Church Membership. 2006. 27p. pap. *(978-0-9527913-3-1(1))* Reformation Today Trust.

James Pott Publisher. The Ministration of Holy Baptism: From the Book of Common Prayer. 2011. 20p. 35.95 ***(978-1-258-06182-1(1))*** Literary Licensing, LLC.

Jan Brind Staff. Baptism, Confirmation & Liturgiesfor the Journey. 2010. (Creative Ideas for Pastoral Liturgy Ser.). (ENG., Illus.). 224p. pap. 30.99 *(978-1-85311-950-7(4)*, Canterbury Pr. Norwich) Hymns Ancient & Modern Ltd GBR. Dist: Westminster John Knox Pr.

Jenkins, Lucy Howe. Letters to My Godchild. Hamlen, Caroline Schuyler Jenkins, ed. 2011. 82p. 37.95 ***(978-1-258-08891-0(6))*** Literary Licensing, LLC.

Jewett, Milo P. The Mode & Subjects of Baptism. 2007. (ENG.). 122p. 35.95 *(978-0-548-04476-6(7))* Kessinger Publishing, LLC.

Johnson, Elder Don & Johnson, Evangelist Charlene P. How Were You Baptized? The continued work of Evangelist Ann M. Sewell. 2010. 168p. pap. 12.99 *(978-1-4490-4611-8(8))* AuthorHouse.

Joseph, Msgr. Theo. My Glorious Journey: From Baptism Priestly Ministry. 2011. 88p. 24.99 ***(978-1-4628-6123-1(7))***; pap. 15.99 ***(978-1-4628-6122-4(9))*** Xlibris Corp.

Judson, Adoniram. Adoniram Judson on Christian Baptism. Date not set. pap. *(978-0-9652883-6-1(6))* Audubon Pr. & Christian Bk. Service.

Kendzia, Mary Carol. Catholic Update Guide to Baptism. 2011. x, 53p. ***(978-1-61636-063-4(1))*** Franciscan Media.

Kennedy, Crammond. Close Communion, or Open Communion? an Experience & an Argument. 2006. 176p. per. 18.99 *(978-1-4255-1434-1(0))* MPublishing.

Kirtley, James. Design of Baptism Viewed in Its Doctrina. 2006. 232p. per. 25.00 *(978-1-57978-518-5(2))* Baptist Standard Bearer, Inc.

Kujawa-Holbrook, Sheryl A. & Thompsett, Fredrica Harris. Born of Water, Born of Spirit: Supporting the Ministry of the Baptized in Small Congregations. 2010. *(978-1-56699-400-2(4))* Alban Institute, Inc.

Lahay, Ben J. Deep Creek Jamin Java Devotions. 2010. 768p. pap. 31.99 *(978-1-60957-562-5(8))* Xulon Pr., Inc.

Lavik, John R. Baptism & Faith: With Particular Attention to the Nature & Functions of Faith in Relation to Baptism. 2011. 72p. 36.95 ***(978-1-258-06538-6(X))*** Literary Licensing, LLC.

Lawoyin, Oyeronke Alake. Idi-Ab. 2007. 328p. per. 17.99 *(978-1-60477-072-8(4))* Xulon Pr., Inc.

Leithart, Peter J. The Baptized Body. 2007. (ENG.). 136p. pap. 15.00 *(978-1-59128-048-4(6))* Canon Pr.

Levington, John. Scripture Baptism Defended, & Anabaptist Notions Proved to Be Anti-Scriptural Novelties. 2006. 160p. per. 18.99 *(978-1-4255-1180-7(5))*, MPublishing.

Lindquist, Frank J. The Truth about the Trinity & Baptism in Jesus' Name Only. 2011. 46p. 35.95 ***(978-1-258-05618-6(6))*** Literary Licensing, LLC.

Mahon, Maeve. Baptism. 2009. (ENG., Illus.). 80p. pap. 14.95 *(978-1-84730-088-1(X))* Veritas Pubns. IRL. Dist: Dufour Editions, Inc.

Maidment, Pete. Reconnecting with Confirmation. 2010. (ENG.). pap. 21.99 *(978-0-7151-4208-0(9))* Church Hse. Publishing GBR. Dist: Westminster John Knox Pr.

Marty, Martin E. Baptism: A User's Guide. 2008. (Exploring Christian Faith Ser.). 176p. pap. 14.99 *(978-0-8066-8049-1(0)*, Augsburg Bks.) Augsburg Fortress, Pubs.

Maus, Tom A. Empowered for Mission: Through the Baptism of the Holy Spirit. 2010. 78p. pap. 10.95 *(978-1-4327-5577-5(3))* Outskirts Pr., Inc.

Mayo, Carl. Understanding Water Baptism in the Name of Jesus Christ, 1 vol. 2010. 52p. pap. 16.95 *(978-1-4512-9581-8(2))* PublishAmerica, Inc.

Mcallister, Joseph B. Emergency Baptism: Especially for Nurses, Physicians & Clerics. 2011. 48p. 35.95 ***(978-1-258-01964-8(7))*** Literary Licensing, LLC.

Meister, John W. What Baptism Means. 2011. 124p. 40.95 ***(978-1-258-05868-5(5))*** Literary Licensing, LLC.

Mell, P. Baptism in Its Mode & Subjects. 2006. 332p. per. 33.00 *(978-1-57978-420-1(8))* Baptist Standard Bearer, Inc.

Memories of My Baptism, Girl. 8.95 *(978-1-57734-237-3(2)*, 01113372) Covenant Communications, Inc.

Mick, Lawrence E. Baptism. 2007. (Understanding the Sacraments Ser.). (Illus.). 23p. pap. 2.00 *(978-0-8146-3188-1(6)*, Liturgical Pr. Bks.) Liturgical Pr.

Mikoski, Gordon S. Baptism & Christian Identity: Teaching in the Triune Name. 2009. 280p. pap. 30.00 *(978-0-8028-2460-8(9))* Eerdmans, William B. Publishing Co.

Montague, George T. Holy Spirit, Make Your Home in Me: Biblical Meditations on Receiving the Gift of the Spirit. 2008. 205p. per. 12.95 *(978-1-59325-129-4(9))* Word Among Us Pr.

Moody, Christopher. American Baptismal Sacramentalism? 2009. 288p. pap. *(978-3-639-15622-5(6))* VDM Verlag Dr. Mueller e.K.

Moody, Dwight Lyman. Secret Power. 2009. 74p. pap. *(978-1-151-49630-0(5))* Books LLC.

Morneau, Bishop Robert F. & Grzeca, Deacon Mike. Together in the Spirit: Celebrating & Living the Sacrament of Confirmation. 2010. 128p. 4.95 *(978-1-59471-230-2(1))* Ave Maria Pr.

Murk, William H. Four Kinds of Water Baptism. 2011. 116p. 39.95 ***(978-1-258-02131-3(5))*** Literary Licensing, LLC.

Murray, John. Christian Baptism. 2011. 100p. 39.95 ***(978-1-258-09825-4(3))*** Literary Licensing, LLC.

National Baptist Brotherhood 2003. *(978-1-58942-113-4(2))* R.H. Boyd Publishing Corp.

Nee, Watchman. Mensajes para Creyentes Nuevos, en Casete: El Bautismo. (ESP.). *(978-0-7363-1146-5(7))* Living Stream Ministry.

Nettles, Tom J., et al. Understanding Four Views on Baptism, 1 vol. 2007. (Counterpoints: Church Life Ser.). (ENG.). 224p. pap. 14.99 *(978-0-310-26267-1(4))* Zondervan.

Neusner, Jacob, ed. A History of the Mishnaic Law of Purities Pt. 1, Chs. 1-11: Kelim. 2006. (Studies in Judaism in Late Antiquity: Ser.). (Illus.). 306p. pap. 30.00 *(978-1-59752-925-9(7)*, Wipf and Stock) Wipf & Stock Pubs.

—A History of the Mishnaic Law of Purities Pt. 2: Kelim - Chapters Twelve Through Thirty. 2006. (Studies in Judaism in Late Antiquity: Ser.). (Illus.). 350p. pap. 34.00 *(978-1-59752-926-6(5)*, Wipf and Stock) Wipf & Stock Pubs.

—A History of the Mishnaic Law of Purities Pt. 3: Kelim - Literary & Historical Problems. 2006. (Studies in Judaism in Late Antiquity: Ser.). 431p. pap. 42.00 *(978-1-59752-927-3(3)*, Wipf and Stock) Wipf & Stock Pubs.

Newman, Larry Vern. The Ultimate Evidence: Rethinking the Evidence Issues for Spirit-Baptism. 2008. 170p. pap. 20.00 *(978-1-60608-093-1(8))* Wipf & Stock Pubs.

Osterhaven, M. Eugene. The Meaning of Baptism. 2011. 48p. 35.95 ***(978-1-258-05308-6(X))*** Literary Licensing, LLC.

—What Is Christian Baptism. 2011. 62p. 36.95 ***(978-1-258-09673-3(X))*** Literary Licensing, LLC.

Packer, J. I. Growing in Christ. 2007. 288p. pap. 17.99 *(978-1-58134-852-1(5))* Crossway.

Paolucci, Antonio. The Baptistry of San Giovanni: Florence, 2 vols. Settis, Salvatore & Bussi, Rolando, eds. (Illus.). 1056p. 450.00 *(978-0-8076-1368-9(1))* Braziller, George Inc.

Peterson, John. The Real Truth about Baptism in Jesus' Name. 2011. 32p. 35.95 ***(978-1-258-04943-0(0))*** Literary Licensing, LLC.

Pendleton, J. Distinctive Principles of Baptists. 2006. 256p. per. 27.00 *(978-1-57978-544-4(1))* Baptist Standard Bearer, Inc.

Power, David, notes. Irenaeus of Lyons on Baptism & Eucharist. 2009. 88.00 *(978-1-60724-372-4(5))* Gorgias Pr., LLC.

Pratt, Richard L., Jr. Why Do We Baptize Our Children? (Profession of Faith, Baptism, Church Membership Ser.). 16.99 *(978-1-930773-09-7(9)*, 155315) Third Millennium Ministries.

Puhalo, Lazar. Baptism & Economy. Date not set. 28p. pap. 3.50 *(978-1-879038-65-3(X)*, 9035) Synaxis Pr.

—Infant Baptism. Date not set. 42p. pap. 3.50 *(978-1-879038-58-5(7)*, 9028) Synaxis Pr.

Radcliffe, Timothy. Take the Plunge: Living Baptism & Confirmation. 2012. (ENG.). 320p. pap. 16.95 ***(978-1-4411-1848-6(9)***, Burns & Oates) Continuum International Publishing Group, Ltd. GBR. Dist: National Bk. Network.

Ramcharan-Maharajh, Bissessamath. The Hindu Concept of God. 2011. 46p. pap. 16.95 ***(978-1-4626-4259-5(4))*** PublishAmerica, Inc.

Reichert, Richard. To Live in Christ-Baptism: Growing in Daily Spirituality. 2007. 64p. pap. *(978-0-8091-9677-7(8)*, 9677-7) Paulist Pr.

Riggs, John W. Baptism in the Reformed Tradition: A Historical & Practical Theology. 2009. pap. *(978-0-664-23682-3(0))* Westminster John Knox Pr.

Ritual para Bautismo de Ninos (Rite of Baptism for Children) (SPA.). 176p. 29.95 *(978-968-7693-12-5(6))* Obra Nacional de la Buena Prensa, A.C. MEX. Dist: St Pauls/Alba Hse. Pubs.

Robinson, Lucille. Inspirations of the Holy Spirit. 2010. pap. 11.99 *(978-1-61579-777-6(7))* Xulon Pr., Inc.

Robinson, Robert. The History of Baptism. 2009. (Amer Philosophy, Religion Ser.). (ENG.). 576p. pap. 33.95 *(978-1-4290-1930-9(1))* Applewood Bks.

Rojcewicz, Rebekah. Baptism Is a Beginning: Bilingual Reproducible Handouts for Infant Baptism Preparation = el Bautismo Es en Comienzo: Hojas Bilingües Fotocopiables para la Preparación Del Bautismo de Niños. 2009. (ENG & SPA., Illus.). xvii, 78p. pap. ***(978-1-56854-498-4(7))*** Good Shepherd Pubns.

Rouse, Ted. Bible Proof: Every Real Christian Needs the Real Baptism with the Holy Ghost & Power. 2009. 260p. pap. 16.99 *(978-1-60791-936-0(2))* Xulon Pr., Inc.

Sante, Luc, et al, texts. Take Me to the Water. 2009. (ENG., Illus.). 96p. 39.95 *(978-0-9817342-1-7(9))* Dust-to-Digital.

Schlabach, Gerald W. On Baptism: Mennonite-Catholic Theological Colloquium, 2001-2002. 14.40 *(978-1-894710-47-3(9))* Pandora Pr. CAN. Dist: Herald Pr.

Schreiner, Thomas R. & Wright, Shawn, eds. Believer's Baptism: Sign of the New Covenant in Christ. annot. ed. 2007. (New American Commentary Studies in Bible & Theology Ser.). (ENG.). 364p. 19.99 *(978-0-8054-3249-7(3)*, B&H Academic) B&H Publishing Group.

Shirreff, William. Lectures on Baptism with A Preface by C. 2006. 280p. per. 29.00 *(978-1-57978-501-7(8))* Baptist Standard Bearer, Inc.

Smith, F. LaGard. The Cultural Church. pap. 12.50 *(978-0-89093-131-3(0))* Twentieth Century Christian Bks.

Smith, Ralph Allan. The Baptism of Jesus the Christ. 2010. (Illus.). 246p. pap. 27.00 *(978-1-60899-198-3(9))* Wipf & Stock Pubs.

So You Want to Know about Baptism? 2.50 *(978-0-570-09988-8(9)*, 16-6046) Concordia Publishing Hse.

Souto Copeiro. Fe y Bautismo: Faith & Baptism. (SPA., Illus.). 120p. *(978-84-7228-449-4(2)*, 220407) Clie, Editorial.

Speray, Steven. Baptism of Desire or Blood (A Defense in Brief Ad Majorem Dei Gloriam) 2010. 138p. pap. 19.99 *(978-0-578-03408-9(5))* Confiteor.

Spierling, Karen E. Infant Baptism in Reformation Geneva: The Shaping of a Community, 1536-1564. 2009. (ENG.). 256p. pap. 40.00 *(978-0-664-23341-9(4))* Westminster John Knox Pr.

Spinks, Bryan D. Reformation & Modern Rituals & Theologies of Baptism: From Luther to Contemporary Practices. 2006. (Liturgy, Worship, & Society Ser.). (Illus.). 266p. pap. 29.95 *(978-0-7546-5697-5(7))* Ashgate Publishing Co.

Sproul, R. C. What Is Baptism? 2011. ***(978-1-56769-260-0(5))*** Reformation Pubs.

Stauffer, S. Anita. On Baptismal Fonts: Ancient & Modern. 2009. 88.00 *(978-1-60724-381-6(4))* Gorgias Pr., LLC.

Stevens, Jesse Columbus. Does Baptism Save? 2011. 78p. 37.95 ***(978-1-258-01961-7(2))*** Literary Licensing, LLC.

Stout, Tracey Mark. A Fellowship of Baptism: Karl Barth's Ecclesiology in Light of His Understanding of Baptism. 2010. (Princeton Theological Monographs). 208p. pap. 23.00 *(978-1-60608-995-8(1)*, Pickwick Pubns.) Wipf & Stock Pubs.

Stovel, Charles. Christian Discipleship & Baptism. 2006. 568p. per. 51.00 *(978-1-57978-644-1(8))* Baptist Standard Bearer, Inc.

Stuhlman, Byron. The Initiatory Process in the Byzantine Tradition. 2009. 95.00 *(978-1-60724-430-1(6))* Gorgias Pr., LLC.

Thompson, David M. Baptism, Church & Society in Modern Britain: From the Evangelical Revival to Baptism, Eucharist & Ministry. 2007. (Studies in Christian History & Thought: Ser.). 228p. pap. 25.00 *(978-1-59752-795-8(5)*, Wipf and Stock) Wipf & Stock Pubs.

Toon, Peter. Mystical Washing & Spiritual Regeneration: Infant Baptism & the Renewal of the Anglican Way in America. 2007. pap. 7.50 *(978-1-879793-11-8(3))* Preservation Pr. of the Prayer Bk. Society USA.

Torrey, R. A. The Baptism with the Holy Spirit. 2009. (ENG.). 68p. pap. 16.75 *(978-1-117-69746-8(0))* BiblioBazaar.

—The Baptism with the Holy Spirit. 2010. 82p. 26.36 *(978-1-163-92945-7(8))*; 32.95 *(978-1-161-60739-0(0))* Kessinger Publishing, LLC.

United Methodist Church (U.S.) Staff, contrib. by. Book of Discipline 1996 Windows Software. 19.95 *(978-0-687-01933-5(8))* Abingdon Pr.

—Book of Discipline 88. 9.95 *(978-0-687-03697-4(6))* Abingdon Pr.

Vaagnes, Morris. Baptism: God's Activity of Grace. 2007. 134p. per. 15.00 *(978-1-933794-01-3(1))* Kirk Hse. Pubs.

Varghese, Baby. Baptism & Chrismation in the Syriac Tradition. 2011. pap. 31.10 ***(978-1-4632-0049-7(8))*** Gorgias Pr., LLC.

B

Waldron, Joseph Francis. The Minister of Baptism: An Historical Conspectus & Commentary. 2011. 218p. 44.95 ***(978-1-258-05449-6(3))*** Literary Licensing, LLC.

Webster, Allen. The Thief on the Cross. 2007. 0.75 *(978-1-933808-62-8(4))* House to House Heart to Heart Publishing, Inc.

Whitaker, E. C. Documents of the Baptismal Liturgy. 30.00 *(978-0-687-85286-4(2))* Abingdon Pr.

Whiteley, Robert L. What it Means to be Born from Above. 2011. 104p. 17.99 ***(978-1-61379-618-4(8))***; pap. 10.99 ***(978-1-61379-617-7(X))*** Xulon Pr., Inc.

Willimon, William H. A Guide to Preaching & Leading Worship. 2008. (ENG.). 144p. pap. 18.00 *(978-0-664-23257-3(4))* Westminster John Knox Pr.

Wilson, Christop. Passage into Discipleship. 2009. 128p. pap. 12.99 *(978-0-8272-3008-8(7))* Chalice Pr.

Witczak, Michael G. The Sacrament of Baptism. 2011. E-Book ***(978-0-8146-3946-7(1))*** Liturgical Pr.

Withey, Donald, ed. Adult Initiation. 2009. 88.00 *(978-1-60724-365-6(2))* Gorgias Pr., LLC.

Wood, Susan K. One Baptism: Ecumenical Dimensions of the Doctrine of Baptism. 2009. xiv, 218p. pap. 29.95 *(978-0-8146-5306-7(5))* Liturgical Pr.

Woodworth, Anjea. Celebrating Baptism Rememberin. 2009. 24p. pap. 5.00 *(978-0-88177-575-4(4))* Discipleship Resources.

Wright, Jeff. Tour of Life. 2010. 64p. pap. 10.99 *(978-0-8272-3661-5(1))* Chalice Pr.

Yong-Doo, Kim. Baptize by Blazing Fire: Divine Expose of Heaven & Hell. 2009. (ENG.). 176p. pap. 12.99 *(978-1-59979-767-0(4)*, Creation Hse.) Charisma Media.

BAPTISM—BIBLICAL TEACHING

Adams, John Quincy. Baptists, the Only Thorough Religious Reformers. 2008. 208p. per. 12.00 *(978-1-57978-600-7(6))* Baptist Standard Bearer, Inc.

Brownson, James V. The Promise of Baptism: An Introduction to Baptism in Scripture & the Reformed Tradition. 2006. 223p. per. 16.00 *(978-0-8028-3307-5(1))* Eerdmans, William B. Publishing Co.

Burdette, Dallas R. Biblical Preaching & Teaching: Jesus & Our Privileges. 2009. 476p. 36.99 *(978-1-61579-085-2(3))*; pap. 24.99 *(978-1-61579-084-5(5))* Xulon Pr., Inc.

Byars, Ronald P. The Sacraments in Biblical Perspective: Interpretation: Resources for the Use of Scripture in the Church. 2011. (Interpretation Ser.). (ENG.). 392p. 40.00 *(978-0-664-23518-5(2))* Westminster John Knox Pr.

Chaney, James M. & Evans, Ronald. William the Baptist: A Classic Story of a Man's Journey to Understand Baptism. 2011. pap. ***(978-1-59638-218-3(X))*** P & R Publishing.

Cox, Jack. What Does the Bible Say about Baptism. 96p. 6.95 *(978-1-56794-229-3(6))* Star Bible & Tract Corp.

Daniel, Howard, Sr. Water Baptism: The Revelation of Truth. 2010. 68p. pap. 12.99 *(978-1-4520-4850-5(9))* AuthorHouse.

Fike, Barry. Mikveh: The Relationship of Jewish Ritual Immersion & Christian Baptism, 1 vol. 2009. 160p. pap. 24.95 *(978-1-60703-774-3(2))* PublishAmerica, Inc.

Garrett, Bart. The Mystery of Grace in the Baptism of Our Children. 2006. 24p. pap. 3.00 *(978-1-59752-848-1(X)*, Resource Pubns.) Wipf & Stock Pubs.

Gatumu, Kabiro wa. The Pauline Concept of Supernatural Powers: A Reading from the African Worldview. 2009. (Paternoster Biblical Monographs). 326p. pap. 38.00 *(978-1-60608-472-4(0)*, Wipf and Stock) Wipf & Stock Pubs.

Johnson, Joyce E. Endtime Powerful Revelation of Water Baptism. 2008. 68p. pap. 12.99 *(978-1-60647-908-7(3))* Xulon Pr., Inc.

McClary, Judy Mckenzie. The Troubled Waters of Infant Baptism. 2009. 144p. pap. 11.99 *(978-1-59979-170-8(6)*, Creation Hse.) Charisma Media.

Mittelstadt, Martin. Reading Luke-Acts in the Pentecostal Tradition: Reflections on the History & Status of Research. 2010. (ENG.). 232p. (C). pap. 14.95 *(978-0-9819651-7-8(2))* CPT Pr.

Philip, Joe S. Baptism: Should I Obey It? 2010. 64p. pap. *(978-1-926765-00-6(1))* Gospel Folio Pr.

Wedderburn, A. J. M. Baptism & Resurrection: Studies in Pauline Theology against its Graeco-Roman Background. 2011. 496p. pap. 55.00 *(978-1-61097-087-7(X)*, Wipf and Stock) Wipf & Stock Pubs.

Witherington, Ben, III. Troubled Waters: The Real New Testament Theology of Baptism. 2007. (ENG.). 153p. 29.95 *(978-1-60258-004-6(9))* Baylor Univ. Pr.

Witherington Iii, Ben. Troubled Waters. 2010. 138p. pap. 24.95 *(978-1-60258-193-7(2))* Baylor Univ. Pr.

BAPTISMAL FONTS

see Fonts

BAPTISMAL RECORDS

see Registers of Births, etc.

BAPTIST CHURCH

see Baptists

BAPTISTERIES

see also Fonts

Keeran, Daniel M. A Pictorial Directory of Ancient & Medieval Places of Baptism. 2009. (Illus.). *(978-0-9782671-0-0(9))* Counselor Publishing.

Mell, Ulrich. Christliche Hauskirche und Neues Testament: Die Ikonologie des Baptisteriums von Dura Europos und das Diatessaron Tatians. 2010. (Novum Testamentum et Orbis Antiquus/Studien zur Umwelt des Neuen Testaments (NTOA/StUNT) Ser.). (GER., Illus.). 340p. (C). 98.00 *(978-3-525-53394-9(2))* Vandenhoeck & Ruprecht GmbH & Co. KG DEU. Dist: ISD.

Shenfield, Larry. How Much of the Florence Baptistery Is a Surviving Roman Building? A Re-Evaluation of the Archaeological, Architectural & Artistic Evidence. 2008. (Bar S Ser.). (Illus.). 433p. (C). pap. 157.50 *(978-1-4073-0225-6(6))* British Archaeological Reports Ltd. GBR. Dist: Brown, David Bk. Co., The.

BAPTISTS

Here are entered works on Baptist denominations and associations treated collectively, works for which the individual Baptist denomination or association cannot be identified, and works on Baptists as a class of persons.

see also African American Baptists; Anabaptists; Mennonites; Separate Baptists; Seventh-Day Baptists; Southern Baptist Convention

Anderson, Maria Frances (Hill). The Baptists in Sweden by Mrs M F Anderson. 2006. 204p. per. 20.99 *(978-1-4255-1688-8(2))* MPublishing.

Anderson, Mark Curtis. Jesus Sound Explosion. 2007. (Association of Writers & Writing Programs Award for Creative Nonfiction Ser.). (ENG.). 288p. per. 19.95 *(978-0-8203-3012-9(4))* Univ. of Georgia Pr.

Backus, Isaac. A History of New England Vol. 2: With Particular Reference to the Denomination of Christians Called Baptists. 2006. 1144p. pap. 75.00 *(978-1-59752-708-8(4)*, Wipf and Stock) Wipf & Stock Pubs.

Baker, Robert Andrew, et al. History of the First Baptist Church of Charleston, South Carolina, 1682-2007. 325th ed. 2007. (Charleston Association Ser.). (Illus.). 652p. *(978-1-888514-28-5(0))* Particular Baptist Pr.

Barcellos, Richard C. & Martin, Robert P., eds. Reformed Baptist Theological Review Iv: 1. 2007. 140p. per. 12.00 *(978-0-9760039-9-1(6))* Reformed Baptist Academic Pr., Inc.

—Reformed Baptist Theological Review Iv: 2. 2007. 160p. per. 12.00 *(978-0-9802179-0-2(3))* Reformed Baptist Academic Pr., Inc.

Blount, Douglas & Wooddell, Joseph D., eds. The Baptist Faith & Message 2000: Critical Issues in America's Largest Protestant Denomination. 2007. (ENG.). 260p. 73.00 *(978-0-7425-5102-2(4))* Rowman & Littlefield Publishers, Inc.

Blount, Douglas K. & Wooddell, Joseph D., eds. The Baptist Faith & Message 2000: Critical Issues in America's Largest Protestant Denomination. 2007. (ENG.). 260p. per. 32.95 *(978-0-7425-5103-9(2))* Rowman & Littlefield Publishers, Inc.

Brackney, William H. The A to Z of the Baptists. 121st ed. 2009. (A to Z Guide Ser.: No. 121). (ENG.). 712p. pap. 34.45 *(978-0-8108-7158-8(0))* Scarecrow Pr., Inc.

—Historical Dictionary of the Baptists. 2nd ed. 2009. (Historical Dictionaries of Religions, Philosophies, & Movements Ser.). (ENG.). 712p. 142.00 *(978-0-8108-5622-6(0))* Scarecrow Pr., Inc.

Brewster, C. Ray. Branches from Jesse's Tree: Sketches from the Life & Times of Jesse Mercer. 2008. (Illus.). 263p. pap. *(978-1-934144-45-9(2))* Indigo.

Brewster, Gurdon. No Turning Back: My Summer with Daddy King. 2011. 248p. 16.00 *(978-1-57075-836-2(0))* Orbis Bks.

Briggs, J. H. Friend Jasper: The Chaparral Philosopher. 2007. (ENG.). 108p. 33.95 *(978-0-548-06099-5(1))* Kessinger Publishing, LLC.

Brownlow, William Gannaway. The Great Iron Wheel Examined; or, Its False Spokes Extracted, & an Exhibition of Elder Graves, Its Builder in a Series of Chapters by William G. 2006. 344p. per. 23.99 *(978-1-4255-3513-1(5))* MPublishing.

Butt, Kyle. What the Bible Says about the Baptist Church. 2007. ii, 87p. *(978-0-932859-82-2(8))* Apologetics Pr., Inc.

Butterworth, James & Marshall, Jane. Mokili in Congo: A Biography of William Millman. 2011. (Illus.). 348p. pap. 20.77 *(978-1-4567-7104-1(3))* AuthorHouse.

Cain, Hamilton. This Boy's Faith: Notes from a Southern Baptist Upbringing. 2011. 272p. 25.00 *(978-0-307-46394-4(X)*, Crown) Crown Publishing Group.

Campbell, Alexander. The Christian Baptist. 2010. 300p. pap. 28.75 *(978-1-146-75616-7(X))*; 302p. pap. 29.75 *(978-1-146-37536-8(0))*; 298p. pap. 28.75 *(978-1-146-36103-3(3))*; 300p. pap. 29.75 *(978-1-142-24270-1(6))*; 302p. pap. 29.75 *(978-1-143-13090-8(1))* BiblioBazaar.

—The Christian Baptist. 2009. 294p. pap. *(978-0-217-32773-2(7))* Books LLC.

—The Christian Baptist. 2010. 220p. pap. 21.32 *(978-1-154-43077-6(4))* 2010. 220p. pap. 21.32 *(978-1-154-43078-3(2))* 2010. (Illus.). 198p. pap. 20.21 *(978-1-154-32728-1(0))* 2009. (Illus.). 254p. pap. 22.44 *(978-1-150-49113-9(2))* 2009. 314p. pap. 23.37 *(978-0-217-57695-6(8))* General Bks. LLC.

Campbell, Alexander & Burnet, David Staats. The Christian Baptist. 2010. 684p. pap. 48.75 *(978-1-143-75448-7(4))* BiblioBazaar.

Chaney, James M. & Evans, Ronald. William the Baptist: A Classic Story of a Man's Journey to Understand Baptism. 2011. pap. ***(978-1-59638-218-3(X))*** P & R Publishing.

Chappell, Roland. Chapel Chimes: The Story of a Little Known Baptist Preacher. 2011. 156p. pap. 13.95 ***(978-1-61507-885-1(1))*** Cross Bks. Publishing.

Choi, Weonjin. An Appraisal of Korean Baptist Missions in Kazakhstan, Central Asia. 2008. 268p. pap. *(978-3-639-09879-2(X))* VDM Verlag Dr. Mueller e.K.

The Christian Index: History of the Baptist Denomination in Georgia. 887p. reprint ed. lib. bdg. 198.00 *(978-0-7222-0865-6(0))* Library Reprints, Inc.

Chute, Anthony. Father Mercer: The Story of a Baptist Statesman. 2011. 160p. pap. 20.00 *(978-0-88146-262-3(4))* Mercer Univ. Pr.

Cline, Jeanie. Great Is Thy Faithfulness. 146p. 2015. 22.99 ***(978-1-61379-876-8(8))*** 2011. pap. 14.99 ***(978-1-61379-875-1(X))*** Xulon Pr., Inc.

Dexter, Henry Martyn. As to Roger Williams, & His 'Banishment' from the Massachusetts Plantation; with a Few Further Words Concerning the Baptists, the Quakers, & Relig. 2006. 156p. per. 18.99 *(978-1-4255-1179-1(1))* MPublishing.

Dockery, David S. & Duke, Roger D., eds. John A. Broadus: A Living Legacy. 2008. (Studies in Baptist Life & Thought). (ENG.). 272p. pap. 19.99 *(978-0-8054-4738-5(5)*, B&H Academic) B&H Publishing Group.

Duncan, R. S. A History of the Baptists in Missouri. reprint ed. lib. bdg. 125.00 *(978-0-7222-0695-9(X))* Library Reprints, Inc.

Durso, Keith E. Thy Will Be Done: A Biography of George W. Truett. 2009. (Illus.). 388p. 35.00 *(978-0-88146-157-2(1))* Mercer Univ. Pr.

Everette, James E. A Heritage of Hope: A History of the First Baptist Church of Wilmington, North Carolina, 1808-2008. 2008. (Illus.). 256p. *(978-1-57843-054-3(2))* Mercer Univ. Pr.

The Fundamentalist Takeover in the Southern Baptist Convention: A Brief History. 2007. per. *(978-0-9747755-2-4(5))* Wilkes Publishing Co., Inc.

Gardner, W. Church Communion As Practiced by the Bap. 2006. 308p. per. 31.00 *(978-1-57978-500-0(X))* Baptist Standard Bearer, Inc.

Gaskin, J. M. & Perry, E. W. A Prophet in Ebony: The Life Story of E. W. Perry. 2011. 126p. 40.95 ***(978-1-258-02794-0(1))*** Literary Licensing, LLC.

Gibbs De Peza, Hazel Ann. My Faith - Spiritual Baptist Christian. 2007. 96p. per. 9.99 *(978-1-60266-509-5(5))* Xulon Pr., Inc.

Gilding, David. Spiritual Baptist: Is it a Christian Religion? 2010. pap. 9.95 *(978-0-7414-5866-7(7))* Infinity Publishing.

Ginsburg, Solomon L. A Wandering Jew in Brazil: An Autobiography of Solomon L. Ginsburg. 2007. (Illus.). 324p. per. 23.25 *(978-1-4251-0851-9(2))* Trafford Publishing.

Gourley, Bruce. Diverging Loyalties: Baptists in Middle Georgia during the Civil War. 2011. 304p. 35.00 *(978-0-88146-258-6(6))* Mercer Univ. Pr.

—Leading the Way for 200 Years: The Story of First Baptist Church of Huntsville, Alabama 1809-2009. 2009. 288p. *(978-1-57843-060-4(7))* Fields Publishing, Inc.

Grant, James Ralph. Letters to the Seven Churches & Other Sermons. James, E. S., ed. 2011. 112p. 39.95 ***(978-1-258-09276-4(X))*** Literary Licensing, LLC.

Graves, J. TriLemma or Death by Three Horns. 2006. 172p. per. 21.00 *(978-1-57978-512-3(3))* Baptist Standard Bearer, Inc.

Griffith, Stephen, compiled by. Ruth Bell Graham: Celebrating the Extraordinary Life, 0 vols. 2007. (Illus.). 208p. per. 12.99 *(978-0-8499-1986-2(X))* Nelson, Thomas Inc.

Gutiérrez, Ángel Luis. Herencia E Identidad: Historia, Principios, y Practicas Bautistas. Gutiérrez, Miriam Z. & Gutiérrez-Rodríguez, Juan Ángel, eds. 2009. (SPA.). 224p. pap. 18.00 *(978-0-8170-1557-2(4))* Judson Pr.

Hall, Robert. The Works of the Rev Robert Hall, a M , with a Memoir of His Life, by Dr Gregory; Reminiscences, by John Greene, Esq; & His Character As a Preach. 2006. 492p. per. 29.99 *(978-1-4255-5508-5(X))* MPublishing.

Harmon Sr., E. Ken. Growing God's Kingdom. 2008. 124p. pap. 10.99 *(978-1-60477-972-1(1))* Xulon Pr., Inc.

Hartzell, Eric S. A Lutheran Looks at Baptists. 2010. pap. *(978-0-8100-2109-9(9))* Northwestern Publishing Hse.

Haykin, Michael. A Cloud of Witnesses: Calvinistic Baptists in the 18th Century. 2006. (Et Perspectives Ser.). (Illus.). 96p. per. *(978-0-9500129-3-3(9))* Evangelical Times.

Haymes, Brian. On Being the Church: Revisionist Baptist Identity. 2009. (Studies in Baptist History & Thought Ser.). 236p. pap. 27.00 *(978-1-60608-598-1(0)*, Wipf and Stock) Wipf & Stock Pubs.

Haynes, David C. Baptist Denomination Its History Doctrin. 2006. pap. 26.99 *(978-1-4255-3750-0(2))* MPublishing.

Hield, Charles S. & Ralston, Russell F. Baptism for the Dead. 2011. 46p. 35.95 ***(978-1-258-04291-2(6))*** Literary Licensing, LLC.

Hiscox, Edward. The Baptist Short Method. 2008. 223p. pap. 18.50 *(978-0-557-00806-3(9))* Lulu Enterprises Inc.

—New Director for Baptist Churches. 2006. 624p. per. 44.00 *(978-1-57978-422-5(4))* Baptist Standard Bearer, Inc.

Holman, Bob. F.B. Meyer: "If I Had a Hundred Lives, They Should Be at Christ's Disposal" 2007. (ENG.). 208p. per. 13.99 *(978-1-84550-243-0(4))* Christian Focus Pubns. GBR. Dist: STL Distribution North America.

Isgrigg, Daniel D. Pilgrimage into Pentecost: The Pneumatological Legacy of Howard M. Ervin. 2008. 160p. 25.99 *(978-0-9785352-7-8(8))* Word & Spirit Pr.

J. Johnson, Rev. Lamont. Autonomous: 21st Century Look at the African-American Baptist Church. 2011. 226p. pap. 14.95 ***(978-0-9840955-6-8(X))*** Godzchild Inc.

Jewett, Milo P. The Mode & Subjects of Baptism. 2007. (ENG.). 122p. 35.95 *(978-0-548-04476-6(7))* Kessinger Publishing, LLC.

Johnson, Robert E. A Global Introduction to Baptist Churches. 2010. (Introduction to Religion Ser.). (ENG., Illus.). 415p. 90.00 *(978-0-521-87781-7(4))*; pap. 32.99 *(978-0-521-70170-9(8))* Cambridge Univ. Pr.

Jonas, W. Glenn, Jr., ed. The Baptist River: Essays on Many Tributaries of a Diverse Tradition. 2008. (Baptists Ser.). 288p. per. 24.00 *(978-0-88146-120-6(2))* Mercer Univ. Pr.

Jones, Keith G. The European Baptist Federation. 2009. (Studies in Baptist History & Thought Ser.). 338p. pap. 40.00 *(978-1-60899-163-1(6)*, Wipf and Stock) Wipf & Stock Pubs.

Larkin, Clarence. Why I Am a Baptist. 2007. (ENG.). 56p. per. 12.95 *(978-1-60206-767-7(8))* Cosimo, Inc.

Leonard, Bill. Baptist Questions, Baptist Answers: Exploring Christian Faith. 2009. (ENG.). 112p. pap. 13.00 *(978-0-664-23289-4(2))* Westminster John Knox Pr.

Long, Eddie. Este Es su Momento: Reclame su Territorio para el Reino. 2007. (SPA.). 191p. per. 10.99 *(978-0-88368-791-8(7))* Whitaker Hse.

Lorance, Cody C. Ethnographic Chicago: Considering College Students & Ethiopian & Tamilian Immigrants Missiologically. 2008. pap. 24.95 *(978-0-615-21862-5(8))* Chicago Metropolitan Baptist Assn.

Lumpkin, William Latane & Leonard, Bill. Baptist Confessions of Faith. 2011. pap. *(978-0-8170-1695-1(3))* Judson Pr.

Maddox, Marilyn H. Treasures of the Heart. 2011. 358p. 22.99 ***(978-1-59467-244-6(X))*** Xulon Pr., Inc.

Mallory, Pat. Into Each Life Some Rain Must Fall... but, God! 2010. 110p. pap. 11.99 *(978-1-60957-522-9(9))* Xulon Pr., Inc.

McClure, Joshua A. Can These Bones Live? The Miraculous story of what can happen to a church that follows God's Vision. 2006. 250p. 14.95 *(978-1-59886-472-4(6))* Tate Publishing & Enterprises, LLC.

McKinley, Jacqueline I. The 18th Century Baptist Church & Burial Ground at West Butts Street, Poole, Dorset. 2008. (Illus.). xiii, 168p. (C). 19.95 *(978-1-874350-45-3(0))* Trust for Wessex Archaeology Ltd. GBR. Dist: Brown, David Bk. Co., The.

McSwain, Larry. Loving Beyond Your Theology: The Life & Ministry of Jimmy Raymond Allen. 2010. (Baptists Ser.). (Illus.). 288p. 35.00 *(978-0-88146-205-0(5))* Mercer Univ. Pr.

Memorials of Baptist Martyrs with a Preliminary Historical Essay, by J Newton Brown. 2006. 336p. per. 23.99 *(978-1-4255-3386-1(8))* MPublishing.

Mettey, Wendell E. On Which Side of the Road Do the Flowers Grow? 2009. xiii, 146p. pap. *(978-1-57736-414-6(7))* Providence Hse Pubs.

Meyer, F. B. F. B. Meyer: A Biography. pap. 11.99 *(978-0-921390-01-5(7))* Ontario Christian Bks. CAN. Dist: CLC Pubns.

Morrell, Z. N. Flowers & Fruits from the Wilderness; or, Thirty-Six Years in Texas & Two Winters in Honduras, by Z N Morrell, an Old Texan. 2006. 400p. per. 26.99 *(978-1-4255-4213-9(1))* MPublishing.

Mullins, Edgar Young. Baptist Beliefs: E.Y. Mullins. 2009. pap. 12.00 *(978-0-8170-1569-5(8))* Judson Pr.

Nicholson, Gary. Building Momentum. 2010. (Illus.). 224p. *(978-1-4158-6883-6(2))* LifeWay Christian Resources.

Norris, J. Frank. Three Sermons: The Worldwide Sweep of Russian Bolshevism; Individual Immortality; the Holy Spirit in the Life of the Believer. 2011. 52p. 36.95 ***(978-1-258-06425-9(1))*** Literary Licensing, LLC.

Nunn, Charles, Jr. The Life & Times of a Baptist Nunn, 1 vols., bk. 1. 2010. (Illus.). 350p. 14.95 *(978-0-615-39028-4(5))* Nunn,, Charles B. Jr.

Nuttall, Clay. The Coming Conflict: The Separation of Church & State. 2011. 166p. pap. 13.99 ***(978-1-937129-07-1(1))*** Faithful Life Pubs.

Partin, James Gallaway. Advancing the Kingdom since 1884: A Pictorial History of the First Baptist Church of Nacogdoches, Texas. 2009. *(978-1-57864-596-1(4))* Donning Co. Pubs.

Peterson, Brenda. I Want to Be Left Behind: Finding Rapture Here on Earth. 2010. (ENG.). 288p. 25.00 *(978-0-306-81804-2(3))* Da Capo Pr., Inc.

Phillips, Marshall. He Leadeth Me. 2011. 80p. pap. 12.95 ***(978-1-4670-3528-6(9))*** AuthorHouse.

Pitts, Byron. Step Out on Nothing: How Faith & Family Helped Me Conquer Life's Challenges. 2010. (ENG., Illus.). 304p. pap. 14.99 *(978-0-312-57999-9(3)*, St. Martin's Griffin) St. Martin's Pr.

Power, John Carroll. The Rise & Progress of Sunday Schools a Biography of Robert Raikes & William Fox. 2006. 296p. per. 23.99 *(978-1-4255-2781-5(7))* MPublishing.

Prevost, Ronnie. A Distinctively Baptist Church. 2008. per. 16.00 *(978-1-57312-502-4(4))* Smyth & Helwys Publishing, Inc.

Price, John. Memoir of George Swan Fowler Christian Merchant. 2009. 120p. pap. 26.45 *(978-1-4446-2276-8(5))* Audubon Pr. & Christian Bk. Service.

Randall, Ian M., et al, eds. Baptist Identities: International Studies from the Seventeenth to the Twentieth Centuries. 2006. (Studies in Baptist History & Thought: Ser.). 389p. pap. 38.00 *(978-1-59752-833-7(1)*, Wipf and Stock) Wipf & Stock Pubs.

Rasbeary, James. From One Church Planter to Another: Helps for the Pioneer Church Planter. 2008. 108p. per. *(978-0-9800096-8-2(5))* Calvary Publishing.

Richard, Barcellos & Martin, Robert P., eds. Rbtr V: 1. 2008. 132p. pap. 12.00 *(978-0-9802179-3-3(8))* Reformed Baptist Academic Pr., Inc.

Roberts, Zach T. Baptist Stories of Emergence. 2009. pap. *(978-1-57312-551-2(2))* Smyth & Helwys Publishing, Inc.

Schultz, Jack M. The Seminole Baptist Churches of Oklahoma: Maintaining a Traditional Community. 2008. (Civilization of the American Indian Ser.). (ENG.). 276p. (C). pap. 24.95 *(978-0-8061-3980-7(3))* Univ. of Oklahoma Pr.

Shanks, John C., ed. From Chickens to Churches: The J. Earl Mead Story. 2011. 172p. 30.95 ***(978-1-61507-770-0(7))***; pap. 13.95 ***(978-1-61507-769-4(3))*** Cross Bks. Publishing.

Sherman, Cecil. By My Own Reckoning. 2008. (Illus.). 288p. 24.00 *(978-1-57312-506-2(7))* Smyth & Helwys Publishing, Inc.

Sitkoff, Harvard. King: Pilgrimage to the Mountaintop. 2009. (ENG., Illus.). 288p. pap. 15.00 *(978-0-8090-6349-9(2)*, Hill & Wang) Farrar, Straus & Giroux.

Slatton, Jim. W. H. Whitsitt: The Man & the Controversy. 2009. (Illus.). 400p. 40.00 *(978-0-88146-133-6(4))* Mercer Univ. Pr.

Smith, Shannon. From the Cross to the Springs: A History of Double Springs Baptist Church. 2010. 149p. pap. 14.99 *(978-0-557-16206-2(8))* Lulu Enterprises Inc.

Smith, Wallace R. Baptism Ahead. 2009. *(978-0-8170-1570-1(1))* Judson Pr.

Spencer, J. H. A History of Kentucky Baptists Set, 2 vols. reprint ed. lib. bdg. 250.00 *(978-0-7222-4925-3(X))* Library Reprints, Inc.

Spurgeon, Susannah & Theobald, Don. A Cluster of Camphire: Words of Cheer & Comfort to Sick & Sorrowful Souls. 2nd ed. 2009. (Illus.). x, 174p. *(978-1-888514-31-5(0))* Particular Baptist Pr.

Stimson, Hiram K. From the Stage Coach to the Pulpit, Being an Autobiographical Sketch, with Incidents & Anecdotes, of Elder H K Stimson, the Veteran Pioneer of West. 2006. 432p. per. 26.99 *(978-1-4255-4679-3(X))* MPublishing.

Stovel, Charles. Christian Discipleship & Baptism. 2006. 568p. per. 51.00 *(978-1-57978-644-1(8))* Baptist Standard Bearer, Inc.

Sutton, Jerry. The Baptist Reformation: The Conservative Resurgence in the Southern Baptist Convention. 29.99 *(978-0-8054-4091-1(7))* B&H Publishing Group.

Tackett, Brian. Inside the Ku Klux Klan: The Rise & Fall of a Grand Dragon. 2009. 136p. 21.49 *(978-1-4490-2896-1(9))* AuthorHouse.

Thompson, David M. Baptism, Church & Society in Modern Britain: From the Evangelical Revival to Baptism, Eucharist & Ministry. 2007. (Studies in Christian History & Thought Ser.). 228p. pap. 25.00 *(978-1-59752-795-8(5),* Wipf and Stock) Wipf & Stock Pubs.

Travis, Ron. Great Commission. 2010. 208p. 25.00 *(978-1-4520-8989-8(2));* pap. 18.00 *(978-1-4520-8988-1(4))* AuthorHouse.

Trifault, Jean-Jacques. Among Those Born of Women There Was None Greater than John. Neuwirth, Gabriela & Trifault, Mary L., eds. 2011. (Illus.). 111p. pap. 9.99 *(978-0-9797877-9-9(3))* Footsteps to Wisdom Publishing.

Wardin, Albert W. The Twelve Baptist Tribes in the United States: A Historical & Statistical Analysis. 2007. (Illus.). 168p. *(978-1-57843-038-3(0))* Mercer Univ. Pr.

Wayland, Francis. Notes on the Principles & Practices of Baptist Churches. 2009. 190p. pap. *(978-1-150-46649-6(9))* Books LLC.

—Notes on the Principles & Practices of Baptist Churches. 2006. (ENG.). 340p. per. 23.99 *(978-1-4255-3438-7(4))* MPublishing.

Welch, Gina. In the Land of Believers: An Outsider's Extraordinary Journey into the Heart of the Evangelical Church. 2011. (ENG.). 352p. pap. 16.00 *(978-0-312-68070-1(8))* Picador.

Whelan, Timothy D., ed. Baptist Autographs in the John Rylands University Library of Manchester, 1741 - 1845. 2009. (Illus.). 560p. 55.00 *(978-0-88146-144-2(X))* Mercer Univ. Pr.

White, James. Sketches of the Christian Life & Public Labors of William Miller, Gathered from His Memoir by the Late Sylvester Bliss, & from Other Sources. 2006. 420p. per. 26.99 *(978-1-4255-4580-2(7))* MPublishing.

Whitley, W. T., ed. The Works of John Smyth - 2009. 454p. pap. 34.00 *(978-1-57978-260-3(4));* 476p. pap. 36.00 *(978-1-57978-261-0(2))* Baptist Standard Bearer, Inc.

William Floyd Dopp. The Tale of Two Churches. 2009. 140p. 19.95 *(978-1-4269-1785-8(4));* pap. 9.95 *(978-1-4269-1785-1(6))* Trafford Publishing.

Williamson, John. Sin in the Assembly: A Guide for Local Baptist Church Discipline. 2007. 84p. per. 16.95 *(978-1-60441-178-2(3))* PublishAmerica, Inc.

Willis, Jan. Dreaming Me: Black, Baptist, & Buddhist - One Woman's Spiritual Journey. 2008. (ENG.). 330p. pap. 16.95 *(978-0-86171-548-0(9))* Wisdom Pubns.

Winters, Fred. Reflections on Wisdom & Folly. 2010. 108p. 28.95 *(978-1-61507-214-9(4));* pap. 11.95 *(978-1-61507-213-2(6))* Cross Bks. Publishing.

Woodward, Clyde H. Preacher Without a Pulpit, 1 vol. 2009. (ENG.). 118p. pap. 19.95 *(978-1-60836-665-1(0))* PublishAmerica, Inc.

BAPTISTS—CATECHISMS AND CREEDS

Murrell, Adam. The Young Baptist's Catechism: A Beginner's Guide to the Baptist Confession of Faith Of 1689. 2007. 52p. pap. 7.00 *(978-1-55635-261-4(1),* Resource Pubns.) Wipf & Stock Pubs.

Schaff, Philip. The Creeds of Christendom: The Evangelical Protestant Creeds - Volume III - Part I. 2007. 528p. 34.95 *(978-1-60206-911-4(5))* Cosimo, Inc.

—The Creeds of Christendom: The Evangelical Protestant Creeds - Volume III, Part I. 2007. 528p. per. 26.95 *(978-1-60206-892-6(5))* Cosimo, Inc.

—The Creeds of Christendom: The Evangelical Protestant Creeds - Volume III, Part II. 2007. 460p. 32.95 *(978-1-60206-912-1(3));* per. 24.95 *(978-1-60206-893-3(3))* Cosimo, Inc.

BAPTISTS—CLERGY

Brewster, Gurdon, et al. No Turning Back: My Summer with Daddy King. 2007. (Illus.). 233p. 18.00 *(978-1-57075-728-0(3))* Orbis Bks.

Campbell, Will D. & Goode, Richard C. Crashing the Idols: The Vocation of Will D. Campbell (and Any Other Christian for That Matter) 2010. 244p. pap. 27.00 *(978-1-60608-127-3(6))* Wipf & Stock Pubs.

Carson, Clayborne, et al. The Martin Luther King, Jr. Encyclopedia, 1 vol. 2008. (Illus.). 456p. 65.00 *(978-0-313-29440-2(2),* GR9440, Greenwood Pr.) Greenwood Publishing Group, Inc.

Carson, D. A. Memoirs of an Ordinary Pastor: The Life & Reflections of Tom Carson. 2008. 160p. pap. 15.99 *(978-1-4335-0199-9(6))* Crossway.

Curry, Michael G. Only God's Man: The Calling of a Pastor. 2010. 65p. pap. 9.95 *(978-1-4327-6303-9(2))* Outskirts Pr., Inc.

Dahlberg, Keith. Edwin T. Dahlberg: Pastor, Peacemaker, Prophet. 2nd ed. 2010. 192p. pap. 18.00 *(978-0-8170-1660-9(0))* Judson Pr.

EBONY Magazine Staff. Martin Luther King Jr. 1929-1968: An Ebony Picture Biography. 2007. (ENG., Illus.). 80p. pap. 14.95 *(978-0-87485-005-5(3))* Johnson Publishing Co., Inc.

Edwards, Matt. Behold the Faithfulness of God. 2008. 192p. pap. *(978-1-55452-323-8(0),* Guardian Bks.) Essence Publishing.

Falwell, Macel. Jerry Falwell: His Life & Legacy. 2008. (ENG., Illus.). 272p. 23.99 *(978-1-4165-8028-7(X),* Howard Bks.) Howard Books.

Goodwin, Daniel C. Into Deep Waters: Evangelical Spirituality & Maritime Calvinistic Baptist Ministers, 1790-1855. 2010. (McGill-Queen's Studies in the History of Religion Ser.). (ENG.). 336p. *(978-0-7735-3668-5(X))* McGill-Queen's Univ. Pr.

Gordon, A. J., et al. How Christ Came to Church: The Pastor's Dream A Spiritual Autobiography. Lt. ed. 2011. pap. 17.99 *(978-1-59415-394-5(9))* Cengage Gale.

Guild, Reuben Aldridge. Life, Times, & Correspondence of James Manning, & the Early History of Brown University by Reuben Aldridge Guild. 2006. 532p. per. 29.99 *(978-1-4255-5926-7(3))* MPublishing.

Hallock, E. F. Preacher Hallock: All the Promises - The Remarkably Inspiring Autobiography of One Who Believed in Life Direction Through Bible Promises. 2006. 118p. pap. 16.00 *(978-1-59752-694-4(0),* Wipf and Stock) Wipf & Stock Pubs.

Hankins, Barry. God's Rascal: J. Frank Norris & the Beginnings of Southern Fundamentalism. 2010. (Religion in the South Ser.). (ENG.). 232p. pap. 30.00 *(978-0-8131-2611-1(8))* Univ. Pr. of Kentucky.

Hudson, Dottie L. He Still Stands Tall: The Life of Roland Q. Leavell, 1 vol. 2008. (ENG., Illus.). 176p. 19.95 *(978-1-58980-513-2(5))* Pelican Publishing Co., Inc.

Jackson, Troy. Becoming King: Martin Luther King Jr. & the Making of a National Leader. 2008. (Civil Rights & the Struggle for Black Equality in the Twentieth Century Ser.). (ENG., Illus.). 248p. 50.00 *(978-0-8131-2520-6(0))* Univ. Pr. of Kentucky.

James, Sydney V. John Clarke & His Legacies. 2008. pap. 23.95 *(978-0-271-02815-6(7))* Pennsylvania State Univ. Pr.

King, Martin Luther, Jr. Daddy King: My Life. 2007. (Illus.). 224p. pap. 16.95 *(978-1-58818-150-3(2))* Gibbs Smith, Publisher.

King, Martin Luther. Mlk: A Celebration in Word & Image. Adelman, Bob, ed. 2011. (ENG., Illus.). 64p. 15.00 *(978-0-8070-0316-9(6))* Beacon Pr.

Patterson, Horace, Sr. Unbroken & Unbound: A Life Dedicated to God, Justice, & the South. 2007. 208p. pap. 19.95 *(978-1-60306-030-1(8))* NewSouth, Inc.

Pink, Arthur Waddington. A W Pink's Studies in the Scriptures - 1932-33. 2008. 588p. pap. 33.99 *(978-1-58960-235-9(8))* Sovereign Grace Pubs., Inc.

Riker, D. B. A Catholic Reformed Theologian: Federalism & Baptism in the Thought of Benjamin Keach, 1640 - 1704. 2010. (Studies in Baptist History & Thought Ser.). 278p. pap. 32.00 *(978-1-60899-451-9(1),* Wipf and Stock) Wipf & Stock Pubs.

Rinaldi, Frank W. The Tribe of Dan: The New Connexion of General Baptists 1770-1891: A Study in the Transition from Revival Movement to Established Denomination. 2009. (Studies in Baptist History & Thought Ser.). 306p. pap. 33.00 *(978-1-60608-476-2(3),* Wipf and Stock) Wipf & Stock Pubs.

Schumacher, Andreas. August Rauschenbusch, 1816-1899: Ein Pioneer der Deutschen Baptisten in Nordamerika. 2010. (GER.). 241p. pap. 53.95 *(978-3-0343-0153-4(7))* Lang, Peter AG GBR. Dist: Lang, Peter.

Spurgeon, Charles. Essential Works of Charles Spurgeon. Partner, Daniel, ed. 2009. (ENG.). 1408p. 24.99 *(978-1-60260-387-5(1),* Barbour Bks.) Barbour Publishing, Inc.

Spurgeon, Charles H. The New Park Street Pulpit & Metropolitan Tabernacle Pulpit, 1855-1917 Vols. 1-63, Set. reprint ed. 2009. 1505.00 *(978-1-56186-004-3(2))* Pilgrim Pubns.

Stokes, David R. The Shooting Salvationist: J. Frank Norris & the Murder Trial That Captivated America. 2011. (ENG., Illus.). 384p. 27.00 *(978-1-58642-186-1(7))* Steerforth Pr.

Struecker, Jeff. Road to Unafraid, 0 vols. 2009. 224p. pap. 13.99 *(978-1-59555-332-4(0))* Nelson, Thomas Inc.

Taylor, James Barnett. Virginia Baptist Ministers. 2009. 314p. pap. *(978-0-217-80552-0(3));* 312p. pap. *(978-0-217-41568-2(7))* Books LLC.

—Virginia Baptist Ministers. 2006. 516p. per. 29.99 *(978-1-4255-5786-7(4))* MPublishing.

Tomlinson, Glenn. From Scotland to Canada: The Life of Pioneer Missionary Alexander Stewart. 2008. 336p. pap. 24.99 *(978-1-894400-29-9(1))* Sola Scriptura.

Winters, Michael Sean. God's Right Hand: How Jerry Falwell Made God a Republican & Baptized the American Right. 2012. (ENG.). 384p. 28.99 *(978-0-06-197067-2(0),* HarperOne) HarperCollins Pubs.

Wolever, Terry, ed. The Life & Works of Joseph Kinghorn, 3 vols., Vol 3. 2010 (Illus.). 590p. 29.00 *(978-1-888514-34-6(5))* Particular Baptist Pr.

BAPTISTS—DOCTRINES

Adams, John Quincy. Baptists, the Only Thorough Religious Reformers; by John Quincy Adams. 2006. 184p. per. 18.99 *(978-1-4255-1435-8(9))* MPublishing.

Allen, David L. & Lemke, Steve W., eds. Whosoever Will: A Biblical-Theological Critique of Five-Point Calvinism. 2010. (ENG.). 320p. pap. 24.99 *(978-0-8054-6416-0(6),* B&H Academic) B&H Publishing Group.

Backus, Isaac. The Doctrine of Sovereign Grace Opened & Vindicated from Holy Scripture. 2009. 158p. pap. 15.00 *(978-1-59925-208-7(2))* Solid Ground Christian Bks.

Barr, Beth Allison, et al, eds. The Acts of the Apostles: Four Centuries of Baptist Interpretation. 2009. (ENG.). 1000p. 99.95 *(978-1-60258-186-9(X))* Baylor Univ. Pr.

Batson, Howard. Jesus Is Lord: Exploring the Meaning of Jesus' Lordship. 2006. 128p. pap. *(978-1-931060-85-1(1))* Baptistway.

Belchen, Richard P. & Mattia, Anthony. Seventeenth Century Baptist Confessions of Faith. 56p. pap. 5.95 *(978-0-925703-23-1(0))* Crown Pubns., Inc.

Booth, Abraham. Defense for the Baptists. 2006. 348p. per. 34.00 *(978-1-57978-367-9(8))* Baptist Standard Bearer, Inc.

—Paedobaptism Examined. 2006. Vol. 1. 492p. per. 44.00 *(978-1-57978-373-0(2))* Vol. 2. (ENG.). 480p. per. 44.00 *(978-1-57978-374-7(0))* Vol. 3. (ENG.). 480p. per. 46.00 *(978-1-57978-375-4(9))* Baptist Standard Bearer, Inc.

—Paedobaptism Examined. 2009. 270p. pap. *(978-0-217-26838-7(2))* Books LLC.

Boyce, James P. Abstract of Systematic Theology. 2006. (ENG.). 534p. 29.95 *(978-0-9785711-1-5(8))* Founders Pr.

Brackney, William H. A Capsule History of Baptist Principles. 2009. 112p. pap. *(978-1-57843-058-1(5))* Mercer Univ. Pr.

Breed, Geoffrey R. Calvinism & Communion in Victorian England: Studies in Nineteenth-Century Strict-Communion Baptist Ecclesiology: Comprising the Minutes of the London Association of Strict Baptist Ministers & Churches, 1846-1855 & the Ramsgate Chapel Case, 1862. 2008. (Illus.). xii, 646p. *(978-1-888514-29-2(9))* Particular Baptist Pr.

Broughton, Virginia W. & Carter, Tomeiko Ashford. Virginia Broughton: The Life & Writings of a National Baptist Missionary. 2010. *(978-1-57233-696-4(X))* Univ. of Tennessee Pr.

Brown, L. Duane & Brown, Daniel R. Biblical Basis for Baptists. 2009. 103p. pap. 9.99 *(978-0-9821408-8-6(6))* Faithful Life Pubs.

Canipe, Lee. A Baptist Democracy: Separating God & Caesar in the Land of the Free. 2011. (Illus.). 192p. pap. 27.00 *(978-0-88146-239-5(X))* Mercer Univ. Pr.

Carroll, B. Ecclesia the Church. 2006. 180p. per. 21.00 *(978-1-57978-325-9(2))* Baptist Standard Bearer, Inc.

Carson, Alexander. Ecclesiastical Polity of the New Testame. 2006. 596p. per. 53.00 *(978-1-57978-847-6(5))* Baptist Standard Bearer, Inc.

Christian, John. Close Communion or Baptism As A Prerequi. 2006. 268p. per. 28.00 *(978-1-57978-414-0(3))* Baptist Standard Bearer, Inc.

Collins, Hercules. Devoted to the Service of the Temple: Piety, Persecution, & Ministry in the Writings of Hercules Collins. Haykin, Michael A. G. & Weaver, Steve, eds. 2007. per. *(978-1-60178-022-5(2))* Reformation Heritage Bks.

Cook, Henry. The Why of Our Faith. 2007. 96p. per. *(978-1-4067-8816-7(3),* Pomona Pr.) Read Bks.

Cross, Anthony R. & Thompson, Philip E., eds. Baptist Sacramentalism. 2007. (Studies in Baptist History & Thought Ser.). 314p. pap. 31.00 *(978-1-59752-743-9(2),* Wipf and Stock) Wipf & Stock Pubs.

—Baptist Sacramentalism 2. 2009. (Studies in Baptist History & Thought Ser.). 308p. pap. 36.00 *(978-1-60608-601-8(4),* Wipf and Stock) Wipf & Stock Pubs.

Dare, Helen & Woodman, Simon. The Plainly Revealed Word of God? Baptist Hermeneutics in Theory & Practice. 2011. 256p. pap. 40.00 *(978-0-88146-237-1(3))* Mercer Univ. Pr.

Dockery, David S. Southern Baptist Consensus & Renewal: A Biblical, Historical, & Theological Proposal. 2008. (ENG.). 256p. pap. 9.99 *(978-0-8054-4740-8(7),* B&H Academic) B&H Publishing Group.

Early, Joe, Jr. The Life & Writings of Thomas Helwys. 2009. 400p. 45.00 *(978-0-88146-146-6(6))* Mercer Univ. Pr.

Fiddes, Paul S. Tracks & Traces: Baptist Identity in Church & Theology. 2007. (Studies in Baptist History & Thought Ser.). 342p. pap. 34.00 *(978-1-59752-729-3(7),* Wipf and Stock) Wipf & Stock Pubs.

Fowler, Stanley K. More Than a Symbol: The British Baptist Recovery of Baptismal Sacramentalism. 2007. (Studies in Baptist History & Thought Ser.). 309p. pap. 31.00 *(978-1-59752-733-0(5),* Wipf and Stock) Wipf & Stock Pubs.

Free Baptists. conference. A Treatise on the Faith of the Free-Will Baptists: With an Appendix, Containing A Summary of their Usages in Church Government. Written under the Dire. 2006. 180p. per. 18.99 *(978-1-4255-1436-5(7))* MPublishing.

Garrett, James Leo. Baptist Theology: A Four-Century Study. 2009. xxvii, 743p. *(978-0-88146-129-9(6))* Mercer Univ. Pr.

George, Timothy & Mason, Eric F., eds. Theology in the Service of the Church: Essays Presented to Fisher H. Humphreys. 2008. 320p. 35.00 *(978-0-88146-114-5(8))* Mercer Univ. Pr.

Gill, John. Gospel Baptism. 2006. 672p. per. 58.00 *(978-1-57978-036-4(9))* Baptist Standard Bearer, Inc.

Hacker, John D. Church of Christ Viewed in the Midst of. 2006. pap. 33.95 *(978-1-4286-5348-1(1))* Kessinger Publishing, LLC.

Hammett, John, et al. Restoring Integrity in Baptist Churches, 1 vol. Yarnell, Malcolm B., III et al, eds. 2007. 272p. pap. 18.99 *(978-0-8254-4113-4(7))* Kregel Pubns.

Harmon, Steven R. Towards Baptist Catholicity: Essays on Tradition & the Baptist Vision. 2006. (Studies in Baptist History & Thought Ser.). (ENG.). 301p. (C). pap. 39.99 *(978-1-84227-362-3(0),* Paternoster) Authentic Media.

—Towards Baptist Catholicity: Essays on Tradition & the Baptist Vision. 2006. (Studies in Baptist History & Thought Ser.). 322p. pap. 35.00 *(978-1-59752-832-0(3),* Wipf and Stock) Wipf & Stock Pubs.

Harzell, Eric S. A Lutheran Looks at Baptists. 2010. pap. *(978-0-8100-2109-5(9))* Northwestern Publishing Hse.

Hiscox, Edward Thurston. The Baptist Church Directory: A Guide to the Doctrines & Discipline, officers & ordinances, Principles & Practices of Baptist Churches. 2006. 280p. per. 23.99 *(978-1-4255-2541-5(5))* MPublishing.

Holmes, Stephen R. Baptist Theology. 2012. (Doing Theology Ser.). (ENG.). 192p. 80.00 *(978-0-567-65097-9(9));* pap. 24.95 *(978-0-567-00031-6(1))* Continuum International Publishing Group, Ltd. GBR. (T&T Clark Int'l). Dist: National Bk. Network.

Houchen, Hoyt H. & Tatum, Ray. The Houchen-Tatum Debate, Four Subjects Establishment of the Church, Baptism, Apostasy, Pre-Millennialism. 2011. 218p. 44.95 *(978-1-258-04858-7(2))* Literary Licensing, LLC.

Howell, R. Terms of Communion at the Lords Table. 2006. 288p. per. 30.00 *(978-1-57978-505-5(0))* Baptist Standard Bearer, Inc.

Jones, T. G. The Baptists, Their Origin, Continuity, Principles, Spirit, Polity, Position, & Influence. 2006. 228p. per. 20.99 *(978-1-4255-1921-6(0))* MPublishing.

Kinghorn, Joseph. Defense of Baptism A Term of Communion A. 2006. 244p. per. 26.00 *(978-1-57978-632-8(4))* Baptist Standard Bearer, Inc.

Knight, Allan & Schroeder, Gordon H. New Life: Six Studies for New Baptists. 3rd rev. ed. 2009. 72p. pap. 7.00 *(978-0-8170-1563-3(9))* Judson Pr.

Leonard, Bill. Being Baptist: Exploring Christian Identity Then & Now. 2012. (ENG.). 1019p. (C). 99.95 *(978-1-60258-298-9(X))* Baylor Univ. Pr.

Leonard, Bill J. The Challenge of Being Baptist: Owning a Scandalous Past & an Uncertain Future. 2010. (ENG.). 162p. pap. 24.95 *(978-1-60258-306-1(4))* Baylor Univ. Pr.

Mell, P. Corrective Church Discipline with A Deve. 2006. 152p. per. 19.00 *(978-1-57978-640-3(5))* Baptist Standard Bearer, Inc.

Monday, Travis. Basic Baptist Beliefs. 2008. 95p. pap. 13.95 *(978-1-4357-3784-6(9))* Lulu Enterprises Inc.

Moody, Dale. Apostasy. 7.00 *(978-0-687-82119-8(3))* Abingdon Pr.

Moody, J. Distinguishing Doctrines of Baptists. 2006. 232p. per. 25.00 *(978-1-57978-525-3(5))* Baptist Standard Bearer, Inc.

Murrell, Adam. The Young Baptist's Catechism: A Beginner's Guide to the Baptist Confession of Faith Of 1689. 2007. 52p. pap. 7.00 *(978-1-55635-261-4(1),* Resource Pubns.) Wipf & Stock Pubs.

Nelson, Ed. Growing in Grace. 2007. per. 9.95 *(978-0-9791856-0-1(2),* Nelson, Ed Evangelistic Assn.

Neufeld, Alfred. What We Believe Together, 1 vol. 2007. (ENG.). 160p. pap. 9.95 *(978-1-56148-626-7(4))* Good Bks.

Pattison, Robert E. An Exposition of the Epistle to the Ephesians. 2011. (ENG.). 264p. 25.00 *(978-1-888514-38-4(8))* Particular Baptist Pr.

Pearle, Bob. The Vanishing Church: Searching for Significance in the 21st Century. 2009. 148p. pap. 14.95 *(978-1-934749-39-5(7),* 800-747-0738) Hannibal Bks.

Pirson, William, Jr. Baptists & Religious Liberty: The Freedom Road. 2007. 160p. pap. 6.95 *(978-1-934731-00-0(5))* Baptistway.

Rainer, Thom S., et al. Vibrant Church: Becoming a Healthy Church in the 21st Century. 2008. 160p. pap. 7.95 *(978-1-4158-6541-5(8))* LifeWay Christian Resources.

Richards, William. The Writings of the Radical Welsh Baptist Minister William Richards (1749-1818) Oddy, John, ed. & anno. by. 2008. 504p. 139.95 *(978-0-7734-5037-0(8))* Mellen, Edwin Pr., The.

Robinson, H. Wheeler. Baptist Principles. 2007. 84p. per. *(978-1-4067-8814-3(7),* Pomona Pr.) Read Bks.

Rogers, George Truett & Wolever, Terry. The Life, Journal & Works of David Jones, 1736-1820: Pastor of Baptist Churches in New Jersey & Pennsylvania & Chaplain in the American Army. 2007. (Philadelphia Association Series). (Illus.). vi, 639p. *(978-1-888514-27-8(2))* Particular Baptist Pr.

Santiago, J. Manny. Para Ser Bautistas: Lecciones para nuevos Miembros. 2009.Tr. of Being Baptist: Lessons for New Members. (ENG & SPA.). 144p. pap. 15.00 *(978-0-8170-1556-5(6))* Judson Pr.

Shaw, Susan M. God Speaks to Us, Too: Southern Baptist Women on Church, Home, & Society. 2008. (ENG., Illus.). 322p. 40.00 *(978-0-8131-2476-6(X))* Univ. Pr. of Kentucky.

Smith, A. J. & Smith, A. J. The Making of the 1963 Baptist Faith & Message. 2008. 266p. pap. 29.00 *(978-1-55635-426-7(6),* Wipf and Stock) Wipf & Stock Pubs.

Stringer, Phil. The Faithful Baptist Witness. 2011. 274p. pap. 12.00 *(978-0-9822230-6-2(4))* Old Paths Pubns., Inc., The.

Strong, Augustus Hopkins. Systematic Theology. 2009. 1200p. pap. 55.00 *(978-0-8170-1624-1(4))* Judson Pr.

Suggs, Terrell D. My Journey in Grace. 2008. v, 164p. *(978-0-9785711-0-8(X))* Founders Pr.

Thurman, Howard. Howard Thurman: Essential Writings. 2006. (Modern Spiritual Masters Ser.). 174p. per. 18.00 *(978-1-57075-670-2(8))* Orbis Bks.

Thurman, Howard, et al. The Papers of Howard Washington Thurman. 2009. 59.95 *(978-1-57003-804-4(X))* Univ. of South Carolina Pr.

Waite, D. A. Does the Critical Text Contain Doctrinal Errors? 2009. 58p. pap. 8.00 *(978-1-56848-065-7(2))* Old Paths Pubns., Inc., The.

Waldron, Samuel. A Modern Exposition of the 1689 Baptist Confession of Faith. *(978-0-85234-441-5(4))* Evangelical Pr.

Wayland, Francis. Notes on the Principles & Practices of. 2006. 352p. per. 34.00 *(978-1-57978-546-8(8))* Baptist Standard Bearer, Inc.

Weaver, C. Douglas, ed. The Axioms of Religion. 2010. 224p. pap. 32.00 *(978-0-88146-164-0(4))* Mercer Univ. Pr.

What Is a Southern Baptist? Key Denominational Distinctives. 2008. 28p. pap. 5.00 *(978-0-9776250-1-7(X))* Mount Pisgah Publishing Co.

White, Thomas. Selected Writings of James Madison Pendl. 2006. (ENG.). 488p. per. 40.00 *(978-1-57978-048-7(2));* 468p. per. 40.00 *(978-1-57978-046-3(6));* (ENG.). 460p. per. 40.00 *(978-1-57978-047-0(4))* Baptist Standard Bearer, Inc.

Wilson, Mark. William Owen Carver's Controversies in the Baptist South. 2010. (Baptists Ser.). 256p. 45.00 *(978-0-88146-202-9(0))* Mercer Univ. Pr.

Younce, Max Douglas. Salvation & the Public Invitation. 2007. 105p. spiral bd. 8.00 *(978-0-9815225-5-5(6))* Younce, Max.

BAPTISTS—EDUCATION

Carter, James E. The Gospel of Mark: Jesus' Works & Words. 2007. 154p. pap. (978-1-931060-98-1(3)) Baptistway.

Godsey, R. Kirby, et al. The Baptist Summit at Mercer University: 19-20 January 2006, Three Addresses. 2006. xvii, 77p. pap. (978-0-88146-061-2(3)) Mercer Univ. Pr.

Lassiter, Perry. The Gospel of Luke: Good News of Great Joy. 2009. 188p. pap. (978-1-934731-39-0(0)) Baptistway.

Reasons, Allen. The Gospel of Luke: Good News of Great Joy. 2009. 212p. pap. (978-1-934731-41-3(2)) Baptistway.

Schmeltekopf, Donald D. & Vitanza, Dianna M. The Future of Baptist Higher Education. 2007. (Illus.). 280p. per. 34.95 (978-1-932792-27-0(9)) Baylor Univ. Pr.

Smith, Wallace P. & Smith, Wallace R. Baptism Ahead: A Road Map for Young Disciples. 2009. 128p. (J). pap. 15.00 (978-0-8170-1551-0(5)) Judson Pr.

Ward, Roger & Gushee, David P., eds. The Scholarly Vocation & the Baptist Academy: Essays on the Future of Baptist Higher Education. 2008. 304p. pap. 30.00 (978-0-88146-104-6(0)) Mercer Univ. Pr.

Williams, Michael E. Ephesians, Philippians, Colossians: Living with Faithfulness & Joy. 2008. 158p. pap. (978-1-934731-16-1(1)) Baptistway.

BAPTISTS—GOVERNMENT

Asquith, Glenn H. The Work of the Church Officer. 2009. 116p. pap. 10.00 (978-0-8170-1639-5(2)) Judson Pr.

Crowell, William. The Church Member's Manual, of Ecclesiastical Principles, Doctrine, & Discipline: Presenting A Systematic View of the Structure, Polity, Doctrines, 2006. 288p. per. 23.99 (978-1-4255-2600-9(4)) MPublishing.

Hiscox, Edward Thurston. The Baptist Church Directory: A Guide to the Doctrines & Discipline, officers & ordinances, Principles & Practices of Baptist Churches. 2006. 280p. per. 23.99 (978-1-4255-2541-5(5)) MPublishing.

Reynolds, J. Church Polity or the Kingdom of Christ I. 2006. 264p. per. 28.00 (978-1-57978-519-2(0)) Baptist Standard Bearer, Inc.

BAPTISTS—HISTORIOGRAPHY

Cutting, Sewall S. Historical Vindications: A Discourse on the Province & Uses of Baptist History. 2006. 244p. per. 20.99 (978-1-4255-2065-6(0)) MPublishing.

BAPTISTS—HISTORY

Aalders, Cynthia Y. To Express the Ineffable: The Hymns & Spirituality of Anne Steele. 2009. (Studies in Baptist History & Thought Ser.). 234p. pap. 26.00 (978-1-60608-600-1(6), Wipf and Stock) Wipf & Stock Pubs.

Baptist History Celebration Steering Committee Staff, contrib. by. Baptist History Celebration - 2007: A Symposium on Our History, Theology, & Hymnody: Convened As a Tercentenary Anniversary Tribute to the Founding of the Philadelphia Baptist Association in 1707, Held at the First Baptist Church of Charleston, South Carolina on August 1-3, 2007. 2008. (Illus.). xviii, 590p. (978-1-888514-30-8(2)) Particular Baptist Pr.

Bebbington, David W. Baptists through the Centuries: A History of a Global People. 2010. (ENG., Illus.). 320p. (C). pap. 39.95 (978-1-60258-204-0(1)) Baylor Univ. Pr.

Belchen, Richard P. & Mattia, Anthony. Seventeenth Century Baptist Confessions of Faith. 56p. pap. 5.95 (978-0-925703-23-1(0)) Crown Pubns., Inc.

Benedict, David. Fifty Years among the Baptists by David Benedict. 2006. 448p. per. 26.99 (978-1-4255-4891-9(1)) MPublishing.

Bisagno, John R. Inside Information: Resolving Controversies in Baptist Churches Worship Wars, Calvinism, Elder Rule. 2010. 128p. 28.95 (978-1-61507-263-7(2)); pap. 11.95 (978-1-61507-262-0(4)) Cross Bks. Publishing.

Brackney, William H. Baptists in North America: An Historical Perspective. 2006. (Religious Life in America Ser.). (ENG.). 312p. 116.95 (978-1-4051-1865-1(2)); pap. 47.95 (978-1-4051-1864-4(4)) Wiley, John & Sons, Inc. (Wiley-Blackwell).

—A Capsule History of Baptist Principles. 2009. 112p. pap. (978-1-57843-058-1(5)) Mercer Univ. Pr.

—Congregation & Campus: A History of Baptists of North America in Higher Education. 2008. 500p. 49.00 (978-0-88146-130-5(X)) Mercer Univ. Pr.

Briggs, John H. Y., ed. A Dictionary of European Baptist Life & Thought. 2009. (Studies in Baptist History & Thought Ser.). 566p. pap. 69.00 (978-1-60899-165-5(2), Wipf and Stock) Wipf & Stock Pubs.

Brown, Louise Fargo. The Political Activities of the Baptists & Fifth Monarchy Men in England During the Interregnum. 2008. 280p. pap. 27.00 (978-1-59740-380-1(6)) ACLS Humanities E-Book.

—The Political Activities of the Baptists & Fifth Monarchy Men in England During the Interregnum. 2009. 260p. 24.99 (978-1-103-79362-4(4)); 260p. pap. 18.99 (978-1-103-79353-2(5)); 272p. 24.99 (978-1-103-45371-9(8)); 272p. pap. 18.99 (978-1-103-45369-6(6)) BiblioBazaar.

—The Political Activities of the Baptists & Fifth Monarchy Men in England During the Interregnum. 2008. 270p. 42.95 (978-1-4365-2022-5(3)) 2007. (ENG.). 272p. per. 27.95 (978-0-548-71183-5(6)) Kessinger Publishing, LLC.

Brown, Theron. A the Canton Baptist Memorial, Being a Historical Discourse Delivered Before the Baptist Church in Canton, Mass , at the Celebration of Their Fiftieth. 2006. 164p. per. 18.99 (978-1-4255-1277-4(1)) MPublishing.

Bustin, Dennis C. Paradox & Perseverance: Hanserd Knollys, Particular Baptist Pioneer in Seventeenth-Century England. 2006. (Studies in Baptist History & Thought Ser.). (Illus.). 416p. pap. 42.00 (978-1-59752-874-0(9), Wipf and Stock) Wipf & Stock Pubs.

Cantrell, Rufus Cantrell. History, Heritage, & Memories Abbotts Creek Missionary Baptist Church, High Point, North Carolina 1756-2006. 2008. (Illus.). 448p. (978-1-57843-051-2(8)) Fields Publishing, Inc.

Cox, Ethlene Boone. Following in His Train. 2007. (ENG.). 238p. 41.95 (978-0-548-06078-0(9)) Kessinger Publishing, LLC.

Cramp, John Mockett. Baptist History: From the Foundation of the Christian Church to the Close of the Eighteenth Century. 2006. 604p. per. 34.99 (978-1-4255-6485-8(2)) MPublishing.

Cutting, Sewall S. Historical Vindications: A Discourse on the Province & Uses of Baptist History. 2006. 244p. per. 20.99 (978-1-4255-2065-6(0)) MPublishing.

Davis, Alton Arthur. The Baptist Story: Sermons on the Trail of Blood. 2011. 178p. 42.95 (978-1-258-04542-5(7)) Literary Licensing, LLC.

Duncan, Carol B. This Spot of Ground: Spiritual Baptists in Toronto. 2008. (ENG.). 304p. 85.00 (978-1-55458-017-0(X)) Wilfrid Laurier Univ. Pr. CAN. Dist: Univ. of Toronto Pr.

Duncan, Edward J. Baptism in the Demonstrations of Aphraat. 2006. pap. 22.95 (978-1-4286-5880-6(7)) Kessinger Publishing, LLC.

Duncan, William Cecil. A Brief History of the Baptists & Their Distinctive Principles & Practices, from the Beginning of the Gospel to the Present Time Part: Fr. 2006. 288p. per. 23.99 (978-1-4255-2647-4(0)) MPublishing.

Duncan, William Cecil. History of the Early Baptists: From the Beginning of the Gospel to the Rise of Affusion As Baptism, & of infant Baptism, 28 A. D. -250 A. D. with An. 2006. 280p. per. 23.99 (978-1-4255-2547-7(4)) MPublishing.

Durso, Keith E. No Armor for the Back: Baptist Prison Writings, 1600s-1700s. 2007. 292p. 39.00 (978-0-88146-091-9(5)); per. 23.00 (978-0-88146-096-4(6)) Mercer Univ. Pr.

Early, Joe, Jr. The Life & Writings of Thomas Helwys. 2009. 400p. 45.00 (978-0-88146-146-6(6)) Mercer Univ. Pr.

Early, Joe. Readings in Baptist History: Four Centuries of Selected Documents. 2008. (ENG.). 288p. (C). pap. 19.99 (978-0-8054-4674-6(5), B&H Academic) B&H Publishing Group.

East Liberty Baptist Association: 1962-2010. 2010. (ENG., Illus.). 385p. 20.00 (978-0-615-39140-3(0)) East Liberty Baptist Assn.

Fish, Henry Clay. The Price of Soul Liberty & Who Paid It. 2008. 116p. per. 11.00 (978-1-57978-602-1(2)) Baptist Standard Bearer, Inc.

Garrett, James Leo. Baptist Theology: A Four-Century Study. 2009. xxvii, 743p. (978-0-88146-129-9(6)) Mercer Univ. Pr.

George, Timothy. Treasures from the Baptist Heritage. 19.99 (978-0-8054-2066-1(5)) B&H Publishing Group.

Gwaltney, L. L. Heralds of Freedom. 2007. (ENG.). 142p. 35.95 (978-0-548-06169-5(6)) Kessinger Publishing, LLC.

Harmon, Steven R. Towards Baptist Catholicity: Essays on Tradition & the Baptist Vision. 2006. (Studies in Baptist History & Thought Ser.). (ENG.). 301p. (C). pap. 39.99 (978-1-84227-362-3(0), Paternoster) Authentic Media.

—Towards Baptist Catholicity: Essays on Tradition & the Baptist Vision. 2006. (Studies in Baptist History & Thought Ser.). 322p. pap. 35.00 (978-1-59752-832-0(3), Wipf and Stock) Wipf & Stock Pubs.

Hedges, Brian. Christ Formed in You: The Power of the Gospel for Personal Change. 2010. (ENG.). pap. 15.95 (978-0-9824387-7-0(X)) Shepherd Pr. Inc.

Holliday, John F. & Holliday, Richard D. Muskoka Miracles: 80th Anniversary. 2010. 288p. pap. 20.95 (978-1-4502-5224-9(9)) iUniverse, Inc.

Holsinger, H. R. History of the Tunkers & the Brethren Church. 2007. (Illus.). 826p. pap. 25.00 net. (978-1-60121-000-5(0)) Graphe Pr.

Jones, Keith G., ed. Counter-Cultural Communities: Baptistic Life in Twentieth-Century Europe. 2008. (Studies in Baptist History & Thought Ser.). 402p. pap. 46.00 (978-1-60608-316-1(3), Wipf and Stock) Wipf & Stock Pubs.

Jones, T. G. The Baptists, Their Origin, Continuity, Principles, Spirit, Polity, Position, & Influence. 2006. 228p. per. 20.99 (978-1-4255-1921-6(0)) MPublishing.

Kell, Carl L., ed. Exiled: Voices of the Southern Baptist Convention Holy War. 2007. (Illus.). 240p. per. 22.50 (978-1-57233-590-5(4)) Univ. of Tennessee Pr.

Kemp, George. Dabbling in Religion: A Case Study of Baptists Living in the United States. 2008. 346p. 49.95 (978-1-4357-1647-6(7)) Lulu Enterprises Inc.

Kish, G. Alexander. The Origins of the Baptist Movement among the Hungarians: A History of the Baptists in the Kingdom of Hungary from, 1846 to 1893. 2011. (ENG.). X, 490p. (978-90-04-21136-0(5)) BRILL.

Kreitzer, Larry J. ÓSeditious Sectaryes: The Baptist Conventiclers of Oxford 1641Ð1691. 2008. (Studies in Baptist History & Thought Ser.). 1130p. pap. 115.00 (978-1-55635-320-8(0), Wipf and Stock) Wipf & Stock Pubs.

Leonard, Bill J. Baptists in America. 2007. (Columbia Contemporary American Religion Ser.). (ENG., Illus.). 336p. (gr. 17). pap. 28.00 (978-0-231-12703-5(0)) Columbia Univ. Pr.

Lindman, Janet Moore. Bodies of Belief: Baptist Community in Early America. (Early American Studies). (Illus.). 280p. (C). 2011. pap. 22.50 (978-0-8122-2182-4(6)) 2008. 39.95 (978-0-8122-4114-3(2)) Univ. of Pennsylvania Pr.

Lumpkin, William L. Baptist Foundations in the South: Tracing Through the Separates the Influence of the Great Awakening, 1754-1787. 2006. 176p. pap. 21.00 (978-1-59752-705-7(X), Wipf and Stock) Wipf & Stock Pubs.

Manley, Ken R. From Woolloomooloo to 'eternity' A History of Australian Baptists, 2 vols. 2006. (Illus.). xxviii, 856p. 44.99 (978-1-84227-404-0(X), Paternoster) Authentic Media.

—Redeeming Love Proclaim: John Rippon & the Baptists. 2007. (Studies in Baptist History & Thought Ser.). 374p. pap. 37.00 (978-1-59752-774-3(2), Wipf and Stock) Wipf & Stock Pubs.

McCall, Emmanuel. When All God's Children Get Together: A Memoir of Race & Baptists. 2007. 144p. pap. 18.00 (978-0-88146-065-0(6)) Mercer Univ. Pr.

Mills, Randy K. Christ Tasted Death for Every Man: The Story of America's Frontier General Baptist. Date not set. (978-0-9642674-2-8(X)) Stinson Pr.

Moody, Dale. Apostasy. 7.00 (978-0-687-82119-8(3)) Abingdon Pr.

Naylor, Peter. Calvinism, Communion & the Baptists: A Study of English Calvinistic Baptists from the Late 1600s to the Early 1800s. 2007. (Studies in Baptist History & Thought Ser.). 306p. pap. 31.00 (978-1-59752-740-8(8), Wipf and Stock) Wipf & Stock Pubs.

Nettles, Tom. The Baptists: Key People in Forming a Baptist Identity, 3 vols. 2007. (Baptists: Key People Involved in Forming a Baptist Identity Ser.). (ENG., Illus.). 464p. 29.99 (978-1-84550-211-9(6), Mentor) Christian Focus Pubns. GBR. Dist: STL Distribution North America.

Nooks, James. You Answer the Call or You Die: The Women Preach in the Black Baptist Church. 2007. 232p. per. 24.95 (978-1-4137-4347-0(1)) PublishAmerica, Inc.

Orchard, G. H. A Concise History of Foreign Baptists: Taken from the New Testament, the First Fathers, Early Writers, & Historians of All Ages; Chronologically Arr. 2006. 412p. per. 26.99 (978-1-4255-4453-9(3)) MPublishing.

Pilli, Toivo. Dance or Die: The Shaping of Estonian Baptist Identity under Communism. 2009. (Studies in Baptist History & Thought Ser.). 312p. pap. 36.00 (978-1-60608-599-8(9), Wipf and Stock) Wipf & Stock Pubs.

Pullen, Bruce Reed. Profiles in Faith: Discovering Baptist Beginnings. 2006. 123p. pap. 11.95 (978-0-7414-3438-8(5)) Infinity Publishing.

Ragwan, Rodney. Vision in Progress: The Missionary Enterprise of the Baptist Association of South Africa. 2011. 156p. pap. 18.00 (978-1-60899-557-8(7), Resource Pubns.) Wipf & Stock Pubs.

Ray, Thomas. Daniel & Abraham Marshall: Pioneer Baptist Evangelists to the South. 2006. (Illus.). 340p. 28.50 (978-1-888514-04-9(3)) Particular Baptist Pr.

Renfree, Harry A. Heritage & Horizon: The Baptist Story in Canada. 2007. (Illus.). 408p. pap. 46.00 (978-1-55635-138-9(0), Wipf and Stock) Wipf & Stock Pubs.

Richardson, Miles. Being-in-Christ & Putting Death in Its Place: An Anthropologist's Account of Christian Performance in Spanish America & the American South. 2006. (Illus.). 414p. per. 19.95 (978-0-8071-3204-3(7)) Louisiana State Univ. Pr.

Sandifer, Kevin. Baptist History in Retrospect. 2007. (Illus.). 160p. per. 16.95 (978-0-910653-80-0(1)) Red River Pr.

Sandifer, Kevin W. A Fellowship of Love, History of First Baptist Church of Blanchard, Louisiana. Tippett, Donald C., ed. rev. ed. 2009. (Illus.). 112p. 2.00 (978-0-910653-31-2(3), 8124P, Red River Pr.) Red River Pr.

Scully, Randolph Ferguson. Religion & the Making of Nat Turner's Virginia: Baptist Community & Conflict, 1740-1840. 2008. (American South Ser.). (ENG.). 320p. (gr. 17). 42.50 (978-0-8139-2738-1(2)) Univ. Pr. of Virginia.

Semple, Robert B. A History of the Rise & Progress of the Baptists in Virginia. 2008. (Illus.). 543p. pap. 46.00 (978-1-60608-027-6(X)) Wipf & Stock Pubs.

Semple, Robert B. & Beale, G. W. A History of the Rise & Progress of the Baptists in Virginia. (Illus.). 536p. reprint ed. lib. bdg. 98.00 (978-0-7222-0970-7(3)) Library Reprints, Inc.

Shurden, Walter B. & Williams, Michael E., Sr., eds. Turning Points in Baptist History: A Festschrift in Honor of Harry Leon Mcbeth. 2008. 332p. 45.00 (978-0-88146-135-0(0)) Mercer Univ. Pr.

Spangler, Jewel L. Virginians Reborn: Anglican Monopoly, Evangelical Dissent, & the Rise of the Baptists in the Late Eighteenth Century. 2008. (ENG., Illus.). 288p. (gr. 17). 45.00 (978-0-8139-2679-7(3)) Univ. Pr. of Virginia.

Sparkman, G. Temp. Saying No to Power: FOOTNOTE to 1980s SOUTHERN BAPTIST TUMULT. 2008. 220p. pap. 21.95 (978-1-4357-0666-8(8)) Lulu Enterprises Inc.

Stott, William T. Indiana Baptist History, 1798-1908. (Illus.). 381p. reprint ed. lib. bdg. 98.00 (978-0-7222-0822-9(7)) Library Reprints, Inc.

Stringer, Phil. The Faithful Baptist Witness. 2011. 274p. pap. 12.00 (978-0-9822230-6-2(4)) Old Paths Pubns., Inc., The.

Sutton, Jerry. The Baptist Reformation: The Conservative Resurgence in the Southern Baptist Convention. 29.99 (978-0-8054-4091-1(7)) B&H Publishing Group.

—A Matter of Conviction: A History of Southern Baptist Engagement with the Culture. 2008. (ENG., Illus.). 532p. 24.99 (978-0-8054-4755-2(5), B&H Bks.) B&H Publishing Group.

Talbot, Brian. The Search for a Common Identity: The Origins of the Baptist Union of Scotland, 1800-1870. 2007. (Studies in Baptist History & Thought Ser.). (Illus.). 437p. pap. 45.00 (978-1-59752-762-0(9), Wipf and Stock) Wipf & Stock Pubs.

Tharp, Jr. Standing Out of Sight: A History of Denominational Statistics in the Southern Baptist Convention 1882-2009. 2010. 160p. pap. 13.95 (978-1-61507-328-3(0)) Cross Bks. Publishing.

Thompson, Philip E. & Cross, Anthony R., eds. Recycling the Past or Researching History? Studies in Baptist Historiography & Myths. 2007. (Studies in Baptist History & Thought Ser.). 372p. pap. 37.00 (978-1-59752-785-9(8)) Wipf & Stock Pubs.

To God Be the Glory: Central Baptist Church, Douglasville, Georgia, 1907-2007. 2007. (Illus.). 216p. (978-1-57843-037-6(2)) Fields Publishing, Inc.

Townsend, Leah. South Carolina Baptists, 1670-1805. 391p. reprint ed. lib. bdg. 98.00 (978-0-7222-0535-8(X)) Library Reprints, Inc.

Vedder, Henry C. A Short History of the Baptists. 2009. 250p. 28.99 (978-1-110-59776-5(2)); pap. 25.75 (978-1-110-59773-4(8)) BiblioBazaar.

Weaver, C. Douglas. In Search of the New Testament Church: The Baptist Story. 2008. (Baptists Ser.). 304p. 45.00 (978-0-88146-106-0(7)); 296p. pap. 23.00 (978-0-88146-105-3(9)) Mercer Univ. Pr.

Wolever, Terry, et al. A Noble Company, Volume 2: Biographical Essays on Notable Particular-Regular Baptists in America. Wolever, Terry, ed. 2011. (Illus.). 581p. 34.00 (978-1-888514-37-7(X)) Particular Baptist Pr.

Zander, Viktor. Identity & Marginality among New Australians: Religion & Ethnicity in Victoria's Slavic Baptist Community. (Religion & Society Ser.). (ENG.). XVI, 327p. 225.00 (978-3-11-188443-1(0)) De Gruyter, Walter Inc.

BAPTISTS—HYMNS

Aalders, Cynthia Y. To Express the Ineffable: The Hymns & Spirituality of Anne Steele. 2009. (Studies in Baptist History & Thought Ser.). 234p. pap. 26.00 (978-1-60608-600-1(6), Wipf and Stock) Wipf & Stock Pubs.

Burrage, Henry S. Baptist Hymn Writers & Their Hymns. 2007. (ENG.). 704p. 65.95 (978-0-548-08979-8(5)) Kessinger Publishing, LLC.

Free Baptists. Sacred Melodies for Conference & Prayer Meetings, & for Social & Private Devotion. 2006. 260p. per. 23.99 (978-1-4255-2239-1(4)) MPublishing.

Fuller, Richard. The Baptist Praise Book. 2006. 468p. per. 29.99 (978-1-4255-5191-9(2)) MPublishing.

Fuller, Richard, et al. The Baptist Praise Book. 2008. 464p. 52.95 (978-1-4372-7244-4(4)); 462p. pap. 37.95 (978-1-4371-4663-9(5)) Kessinger Publishing, LLC.

Music, David W. & Richardson, Paul A. I Will Sing the Wondrous Story: A History of Baptist Hymnody in North America. 2007. 560p. 45.00 (978-0-86554-948-7(6)) Mercer Univ. Pr.

BAPTISTS—LITURGY

Carter, Kenneth H. & Carter, Kenneth H., Jr. Baptism Services, Sermons, & Prayers. 2006. (Just in Time! Ser.). 86p. per. 12.00 (978-0-687-33383-7(0)) Abingdon Pr.

Renihan, James M. Edification & Beauty: The Practical Ecclesiology of the English Particular Baptists, 1675Ð1705. 2009. (Studies in Baptist History & Thought Ser.). 232p. pap. 26.00 (978-1-60608-481-6(X), Wipf and Stock) Wipf & Stock Pubs.

BAPTISTS—MISSIONS

Appleby, John. I Can Plod... William Carey & the Early Years of the First Baptist Missionary Society. 2008. (Illus.). 309p. (978-0-946462-74-2(7)) Evangelical Pr.

Broughton, Virginia W. & Carter, Tomeiko Ashford. Virginia Broughton: The Life & Writings of a National Baptist Missionary. 2010. (978-1-57233-696-4(X)) Univ. of Tennessee Pr.

Bulzan, Ovidiu. Church Architecture & Baptist Missions in Transylvania, 1871 -1918. 2010. 180p. pap. (978-3-8383-1351-1(8)) Lambert Academic Publishing.

Carlton, R. Bruce. Strategy Coordinator: Changing the Course of Southern Baptist Missions. 2011. (Regnum Studies in Mission Ser.). 304p. pap. 33.00 (978-1-61097-436-3(0), Wipf and Stock) Wipf & Stock Pubs.

Chang, Derek. Citizens of a Christian Nation: Evangelical Missions & the Problem of Race in the Nineteenth Century. (Politics & Culture in Modern America Ser.). 248p. (C). 2012. pap. 24.95 (978-0-8122-2206-7(7)) 2010. (Illus.). 39.95 (978-0-8122-4218-8(1)) Univ. of Pennsylvania Pr.

Coleman, Inabelle Graves & Kelly, Willie Hayes. One of Us: The Story of the Life of Willie Hayes Kelly. 2011. 140p. 40.95 (978-1-258-09344-0(8)) Literary Licensing, LLC.

Cox, Ethlene Boone. Following in His Train. 2007. (ENG.). 238p. 41.95 (978-0-548-06078-0(9)) Kessinger Publishing, LLC.

Dennison, Wally. For the Love of God's Kids. 2007. (ENG.). 384p. per. (978-1-55452-110-4(6)) Essence Publishing.

Evans, Dorothy. He Led All the Way. 2007. 276p. per. 15.99 (978-1-60266-644-3(X)) Xulon Pr., Inc.

Fletcher, Jesse C. Bill Wallace of Chin. 2009. 256p. pap. 16.99 (978-1-61507-013-8(3)) Cross Bks. Publishing.

Gaines, Jane Ellen. Every Day with Jesus: A Missionary's Daily Life in West Africa: As Seen in the Memoirs & Letters of Jane Ellen Gaines, Missionary to Nigeria from 1967 to 1993. 2008. (Illus.). 160p. (978-1-57843-050-5(X)) Fields Publishing, Inc.

Kerr, Gordon. The Continuing Conflict - the Story of the One Hundred & Fifty-Fourth Year of the Baptist Missionary Society. 2007. 76p. per. (978-1-4067-8854-9(6), Pomona Pr.) Read Bks.

Kish, G. Alexander. The Origins of the Baptist Movement among the Hungarians: A History of the Baptists in the Kingdom of Hungary from, 1846 to 1893. 2011. (ENG.). X, 490p. (978-90-04-21136-0(5)) BRILL.

Levy, Edgar Mortimer. History of the Newark Baptist City Mission from Its Origin in 1851 to Its Seventeenth Anniversary In 1868. 2006. 148p. per. 16.99 (978-1-4255-1061-9(2)) MPublishing.

Marshman, John Clark. The Life & Labours of Carey, Marshman, & Ward: The Serampore Missionaries. 2010. (Cambridge Library Collection - Religion Ser.). (ENG.). 408p. pap. 31.99 (978-1-108-00826-6(7)) Cambridge Univ. Pr.

McCoy, Isaac. History of Baptist Indian Missions. 2009. (Native American Ser.). (ENG.). 624p. pap. 35.95 (978-1-4290-2253-8(1)) Applewood Bks.

—History of Baptist Indian Missions. 2009. 490p. pap. (978-1-217-00458-9(X)) Books LLC.

McCoy, Isaac & Wyeth, W. N. The Autobiography of Isaac Mccoy: Recounting his early life, conversion, marriage, & ministry in Indiana 1784-1816. 2011. (Illus.). 474p. 28.00 (978-1-888514-39-1(6)) Particular Baptist Pr.

Olson, Bruce. Bruchko & the Motilone Miracle: How Bruce Olson Brought a Stone Age Tribe into the 21st Century. 2006. (ENG., Illus.). 240p. pap. 14.99 (978-1-59185-795-2(3), Charisma Hse.) Charisma Media.

—Bruchko y el Milagro de los Motilone. 2007. (ENG & SPA., Illus.). 217p. 9.99 *(978-1-59979-048-0(3)*, Casa Creacion) Charisma Media.
Parker, F. Calvin. The Good Book Is Better Than It Used to Be: Eighty Years with the Bible. 2009. 198p. 26.95 *(978-1-4401-6010-3(4))*; pap. 16.95 *(978-1-4401-6012-7(0))* iUniverse, Inc.
Randall, Ian M. & Cross, Anthony R., eds. Baptists & Mission: Papers from the Fourth International Conference on Baptist Studies. 2008. (Studies in Baptist History & Thought Ser.). 362p. pap. 43.00 *(978-1-55635-869-2(5))* Wipf & Stock Pubs.
Rankin, Jerry. The Challenge to Great Commission Obedience: Motivational Messages for Contemporary Missionaries. 2006. (ENG.). 226p. per. 14.99 *(978-0-8054-4521-3(8)*, B&H Bks.) B&H Publishing Group.
Ray, T. B. Brazilian Sketches. 2008. 124p. 21.95 *(978-1-4218-9463-8(7))*; pap. 14.95 *(978-1-4218-9363-1(0))* 1st World Publishing, Inc. (1st World Library - Literary Society).
—Brazilian Sketches. 2007. (ENG.). 92p. per. *(978-1-4065-3760-4(8))* Dodo Pr.
—Brazilian Sketches. 2007. (ENG.). 96p. per. *(978-1-4068-3758-2(X))* Echo Library.
Rowden, Rebecca. Baptists in Israel: The Letters of Paul & Marjorie Rowden, 1952-1957. 2010. (Illus.). 424p. pap. *(978-1-57843-075-8(5))* Fields Publishing, Inc.
Stone, Richard Henry. In Africa's Forest & Jungle: Six Years among the Yorubas. Florey, Betty Finklea, ed. & intro. by. 2nd ed. 2009. (Religion & American Culture Ser.). (ENG., Illus.). 402p. pap. 35.00 *(978-0-8173-5567-8(7))* Univ. of Alabama Pr.
Tooze, George, ed. The Life & Letters of Emily Chubbuck Judson: January 1848 - September 1851. 2010. (Baptists Ser.). 700p. 60.00 *(978-0-88146-189-3(X))* Mercer Univ. Pr.
Tyson, Joan. A Missionary Journey Remembering His Marvelous Works. 2009. pap. *(978-1-61623-895-7(X))* Independent Pub.
Varberg, Richard. Why Didn't You Come Sooner? Stories from My Life As a Missionary in the Philippines. 2008. pap. *(978-0-87808-004-5(X))* Carey, William Library Pubs.
The White Foreigners from over the Water: The Story of the American Mission to the Burmese & the Karens. 2006. 336p. per. 23.99 *(978-1-4255-3367-0(1))* MPublishing.

BAPTISTS—RELATIONS—CATHOLIC CHURCH

Durso, Keith E. No Armor for the Back: Baptist Prison Writings, 1600s-1700s. 2007. 292p. 39.00 *(978-0-88146-091-9(5))*; per. 23.00 *(978-0-88146-096-4(6))* Mercer Univ. Pr.
Gandolfo, Lucian. Soul Baptism. 2006. (ENG.). 21.99 *(978-1-60034-931-7(5))*; pap. 13.99 *(978-1-60034-930-0(7))* Xulon Pr., Inc.

BAPTISTS—SERMONS

Ahlfeld, D. Friedrich. Sermons on the Catechism V4: The Sacraments & the Word. Richards, J. W., tr. 2011. 324p. 50.95 ***(978-1-258-03949-3(4))*** Literary Licensing, LLC.
Anderson, Dean. A Sacred Trust: Sermons on the Distinctive Beliefs of Baptists. 2010. 172p. 29.99 *(978-1-61507-132-6(6))*; pap. 14.99 *(978-1-61507-068-8(0))* Cross Bks. Publishing.
Ayer, William Ward. Seven Saved Sinners, or How God Saves Men. 2007. 132p. (ENG.). 24.95 *(978-1-4344-9468-9(3))*; per. 14.95 *(978-1-4344-9467-2(5))* Wildside Pr., LLC.
Bass, Paul William. In Jesus' Names. 2010. 102p. pap. 12.95 *(978-1-58107-178-8(7))* New Forums Pr.
Belcher, Joseph. The Baptist Pulpit of the United States. 2006. 496p. per. 29.99 *(978-1-4255-5526-9(8))* MPublishing.
Carroll, B. H., et al. Sermons & Life Sketch of B H Carroll. 2011. 130p. 40.95 ***(978-1-258-05413-7(2))*** Literary Licensing, LLC.
Caylor, John. The Great I Am's of Jesus. 2011. 86p. 37.95 ***(978-1-258-05726-8(3))*** Literary Licensing, LLC.
Christian Art Gifts, creator. John 3:16. 2008. 400p. pap. *(978-1-77036-010-5(7))* Christian Art Pubs.
Crosby, Terence Peter. C H Spurgeon's Sermons Beyond, Volume 63: An Authentic Supplement to the Metropolitan Tabernacle Pulpit. 2009. (C. H. Spurgeon Sermons Beyond Ser.). 640p. *(978-1-84625-145-0(1))* DayOne Pubns.
Crosby, Terence Peter, compiled by. 365 days with C H Spurgeon Vol 4: Further extracts from the writings of Charles Haddon Spurgeon, 6 vols. 2007. (356 days With Ser.). (Illus.). 462p. 20.00 *(978-1-84625-090-3(0))* DayOne Pubns. GBR. Dist: STL Distribution North America.
Denmark, Annie Dove. White Echoes. 2007. (ENG.). 224p. 39.95 *(978-0-548-07352-0(X))* Kessinger Publishing, LLC.
Dever, Mark. What Does God Want of Us Anyway? A Quick Overview of the Whole Bible. 2010. pap. *(978-1-4335-1416-6(8))*; 128p. 12.99 *(978-1-4335-1415-9(X))* Crossway.
Durso, Pamela R. This Is What a Preacher Looks Like: Sermons by Baptist Women. 2010. pap. *(978-1-57312-554-3(7))* Smyth & Helwys Publishing, Inc.
Forcey, Clark J. Crossing the Spiritual Divide. 2011. 90p. 38.95 ***(978-1-258-06222-4(4))*** Literary Licensing, LLC.
Fox, Arthur. Holy Fires for Unholy Days. 2007. (ENG.). 236p. 41.95 *(978-0-548-06189-3(0))* Kessinger Publishing, LLC.
Freeman, Curtis W. A Company of Women Preachers: Baptist Prophetesses in Seventeenth-Century England. 2011. (ENG.). 400p. 69.95 *(978-1-60258-318-4(8))* Baylor Univ. Pr.
Giddens, Howard P. Why Be a Christian? The Sermons of Howard P. Giddens. Ruffin, Michael L., ed. 2007. (Illus.). 191p. *(978-0-88146-081-0(8))* Mercer Univ. Pr.
Hull, William E. Harbingers of Hope: Claiming God's Promises in Today's World. 2007. (Hull Legacy Ser.). (ENG.). 320p. 29.95 *(978-1-931985-16-1(2))* Samford Univ. Pr.
Kemp, Richard A. Faith & Immortality: Selected Sermons. 2011. 78p. 37.95 ***(978-1-258-04332-2(7))*** Literary Licensing, LLC.
King, Martin Luther. Strength to Love: Gift Edition. 2010. 192p. pap. 20.00 *(978-0-8006-9740-2(5)*, Fortress Pr.) Augsburg Fortress, Pubs.
Massey, Karen, ed. And Your Daughters Shall Prophesy: Sermons by Women in Baptist Life. 2012. (Baptists Ser.). (ENG.). 240p. pap. 25.00 ***(978-0-88146-285-2(3))*** Mercer Univ. Pr.
Meyer, F. B. The Christ Life for Your Life. 2007. per. *(978-1-60208-049-2(6))* FBC Pubns. & Printing.
Michael, McMullen & Haykin, Michael A. G., eds. The Complete Works of Andrew Fuller (1754-1815) 2011. (Complete Works of Andrew Fuller 17541815 Ser.). (ENG.). 120p. pap. 19.99 *(978-1-84227-480-4(5)*, Paternoster) Authentic Media.
Norris, J. Frank. Sermons by J Frank Norris. 2011. 44p. 35.95 ***(978-1-258-03950-9(8))*** Literary Licensing, LLC.
Platt, Wilfred C., Jr., et al, eds. Jesse Mercer's Pulpit: Preaching in a Community of Faith & Learning. 2006. 168p. per. 20.00 *(978-0-88146-043-8(5))* Mercer Univ. Pr.
Pollard, Frank. Someone Once Said: The Preaching Ministry of Frank Pollard. 2008. *(978-0-914520-48-1(2))* Insight Pr.
Smith, J. Alfred, Sr. Speak until Justice Wakes: Prophetic Reflections from J. Alfred Smith Sr. Kilgore, Jini M., ed. 2006. 88p. per. 11.00 *(978-0-8170-1501-5(9))* Judson Pr.
Sorenson, Stephen W., ed. The Best of F. B. Meyer: 120 Daily Devotions to Nurture Your Spirit & Refresh Your Soul. 2006. (Honor Classics Ser.). 192p. 14.99 *(978-1-56292-581-9(4)*, 1562925814) Cook, David C.
Spurgeon, C. H. Sermons of Rev C H Spurgeon of London. 2007. (ENG.). 454p. 52.95 *(978-0-548-15674-2(3))*; 456p. per. 37.95 *(978-1-4304-5143-3(2))* Kessinger Publishing, LLC.
Spurgeon, C. H. (Charles Haddon). The Modern Whitfield Sermons of the Rev C H Spurgeon, of London; with an Introduction & Sketch of His Life, by E L Magoon. 2006. 360p. per. 26.99 *(978-1-4255-3806-4(1))* MPublishing.
Spurgeon, Charles. Essential Works of Charles Spurgeon. Partner, Daniel, ed. 2009. (ENG.). 1408p. 24.99 *(978-1-60260-387-5(1)*, Barbour Bks.) Barbour Publishing, Inc.
Spurgeon, Charles H. The New Park Street Pulpit, Vol. 3. 2007. 2856p. 60.00 *(978-0-8010-1298-3(8))* Baker Bks.
—The New Park Street Pulpit & Metropolitan Tabernacle Pulpit, 1855-1917 Vols. 1-63, Set. reprint ed. 1505.00 *(978-1-56186-004-3(2))* Pilgrim Pubns.
—Sermons on Men of the Bible. 2008. xv, 375p. *(978-1-59856-466-2(8))* Hendrickson Pubs. Marketing, LLC.
—Spurgeon's Sermons on Prayer. 2007. 509p. 14.97 *(978-1-59856-217-0(7))* Hendrickson Pubs. Marketing, LLC.
Spurgeon, Charles H. & Spurgeon, C. H. Sermons on Men of the Bible. 2008. 350p. *(978-1-59856-302-3(5))* Hendrickson Pubs. Marketing, LLC.
Spurgeon, Charles Haddon & Spurgeon, Charles H. Spurgeon's Sermons: 1855 - with full scriptural Index. 2011. 696p. pap. ***(978-1-84902-445-7(6))*** Benediction Classics.
—Spurgeon's Sermons: 1856 - with full scriptural Index. 2011. 684p. pap. ***(978-1-84902-442-6(1))*** Benediction Classics.
Straton, Hillyer Hawthorne. Preaching the Miracles of Jesus: The Meaning of Christ's Miracles & Their Sermon Values for Today. 2011. 222p. 44.95 ***(978-1-258-08523-0(2))*** Literary Licensing, LLC.
Thayer, James Henry. Blue Galilee. 2007. (ENG.). 142p. 35.95 *(978-0-548-05860-2(1))* Kessinger Publishing, LLC.
Wayland, Francis. Salvation by Christ a Series of Discourses on Some of the Most Important Doctrines of the Gospel. 2006. 412p. per. 26.99 *(978-1-4255-4449-2(5))* MPublishing.
Yeaple, Whitney S. K. Your Money & Your Life. 2007. (ENG.). 158p. 36.95 *(978-0-548-07400-8(3))* Kessinger Publishing, LLC.

BAPTISTS, AFRICAN AMERICAN

see African American Baptists

BAR

see Lawyers

BAR ASSOCIATIONS

Anderson, John. MPRE Ultimate Exam Prep. 2007. per. 29.95 *(978-0-9791306-2-5(X))* Mclaren Legal Pubs. LLC.
Beck, William. The Kane County Bar Association. 2008. *(978-1-57864-533-6(6))* Donning Co. Pubs.
Cavanagh, Robert F. From the Colonies to Today: Over Three Centuries of Law & Lawyers in New Haven. 2007. vii, 56p. pap. *(978-0-615-16483-0(8))* New Haven County Bar Assn.
Lampson, Marc. From Profanity Hill, King County Bar Association's Story. 29.95 *(978-0-935503-10-4(2)*, Documentary Book Publishers Corp.) Sasquatch Bks.
McTaggart, Michael F. & Holly, Suzanne Hill. History of the Delaware Bar from 1995 Through 2010. 2011. (Illus.). xix, 615p. ***(978-1-4224-9092-1(0))*** LexisNexis Matthew Bender.
Robertson, Edwin David. Brethren & Sisters of the Bar: A Centennial History of the New York County Lawyers' Association. 2008. (ENG., Illus.). 432p. 32.00 *(978-0-8232-2907-9(6))* Fordham Univ. Pr.
Sengkhounmany, Chay. The Lawyers Club of Atlanta. 2010. *(978-0-88146-181-7(4))* Mercer Univ. Pr.

BAR ASSOCIATIONS—GREAT BRITAIN

see also Inns of Court
Rider, Clare & Horsler, Val, eds. The Inner Temple: A Community of Communities. 2008. (ENG., Illus.). 192p. 85.00 *(978-1-903942-66-6(7)*, Third Millenium Pub Ltd) Antique Collectors' Club GBR. Dist: National Bk. Network.

BAR CODING

Hansen, Wolf-Ruediger & Gillert, Frank. RFID for the Optimization of Business Processes. 2008. (ENG., Illus.). 298p. 90.00 *(978-0-470-72422-4(6)*, Wiley) Wiley, John & Sons, Inc.
Michael, Katina & Michael, M. G. Innovative Automatic Identification & Location-Based Services: From Bar Codes to Chip Implants. 2009. (Premier Reference Source Ser.). (Illus.). 544p. 165.00 *(978-1-59904-795-9(0)*, Information Science Publishing) IGI Global.
Winter, Mick. Scan Me: Everybody's Guide to the Magical World of QR Codes — Barcodes, Mobile Devices & Hyperlinking the Real to the Virtual. 2011. (Illus.). 142p. ***(978-0-9659000-3-4(7))*** Westsong Publishing.
Wray, Bruce. ISBT 128 an Introduction to Bar Coding. 2nd ed. 2007. *(978-1-933243-04-7(X))* ICCBBA Inc.
2007 IEEE Workshop on Automatic Identification Advanced Technologies. 2007. pap. 206.00 *(978-1-4244-1299-0(4)*, 07EX1818) IEEE.

BAR EXAMINATIONS

American Bar Association, Section of Legal Education and Admissions to the Bar Staff, contrib. by. American Bar Association Law School Bar Prep Program Directory, 2008-2009. 2008. 61p. pap. *(978-1-60442-334-1(X))* American Bar Assn.
Bar Exam Writing Template Book. 2008. ring bd. 575.00 *(978-0-9753472-5-6(X))* Bar None Review.
Bar None Review California Essay Book, Vols. 1-2. 2008. ring bd. 199.95 *(978-0-9753472-4-9(1))* Bar None Review.
Barham, Charles Nicolas. Bar Examination Papers, Questions & Answers, 1901-2009. 148p. pap. 19.99 *(978-1-150-20821-8(X))* General Bks. LLC.
—Bar Examination Papers, Questions & Answers, 1901-; Containing the Questions with Full Outline Answers of All the Papers Set At. 2010. (Illus.). 232p. pap. 21.42 *(978-1-153-91992-0(3))*; 244p. pap. 22.26 *(978-1-154-23724-5(9))*; 224p. pap. 20.96 *(978-1-153-89351-0(7))* General Bks. LLC.
Blond & Shah, Tania N. Multistate Bar Exam. 5th ed. 2009. pap., stu. ed. 49.95 *(978-0-7355-7795-4(1))* Wolters Kluwer Law & Business.
Celebration Bar Review, LLC, L. L. C. California Essay Questions Book. 2012. (ENG.). 398p. pap. 94.95 *(978-1-4536-7582-3(5))* CreateSpace.
—California First Year Exam Outline Book. 2012. (ENG.). 326p. pap. 49.95 *(978-1-4536-9224-0(X))* CreateSpace.
—California Outline Book: Vol. 2. 2012. (ENG.). 356p. pap. 49.95 *(978-1-4536-7222-8(2))* CreateSpace.
—California Performance Exams Book. 2012. (ENG.). 418p. pap. 49.95 *(978-1-4536-7619-6(8))* CreateSpace.
—Florida Multiple Choice Questions Book. 2012. (ENG.). 322p. pap. 49.95 *(978-1-4536-8250-0(3))* CreateSpace.
—NY Multiple Choice Questions Book. 2010. (ENG.). 194p. pap. 49.95 *(978-1-4536-8513-6(8))* CreateSpace.
Civil Procedure Essay Writer. 2008. ring bd. 29.95 *(978-0-9747208-1-4(X))* Bar None Review.
Community Property Essay Writer. 2008. ring bd. 29.95 *(978-0-9747208-9-0(5))* Bar None Review.
Constitutional Law Essay Writer. 2008. ring bd. 29.95 *(978-0-9747208-2-1(8))* Bar None Review.
Contracts Essay Writer. 2008. ring bd. 29.95 *(978-0-9747208-3-8(6))* Bar None Review.
Corporations Essay Writer. 2008. ring bd. 29.95 *(978-0-9747208-8-3(7))* Bar None Review.
Criminal Law Essay Writer. 2008. ring bd. 29.95 *(978-0-9747208-5-2(2))* Bar None Review.
Criminal Procedure Essay Writer. 2008. ring bd. 29.95 *(978-0-9747208-4-5(4))* Bar None Review.
Danaher, Franklin Martin. Bar Examinations & Courses of Law Study. 2009. 318p. pap. 21.51 *(978-1-150-20825-6(2))* General Bks. LLC.
—Bar Examinations & Courses of Law Study, Containing the Statutes & Rules of Court Regulating Admission to the Bar in New York State And. 2010. (ENG.). 336p. pap. 31.75 *(978-1-176-34720-5(9))* BiblioBazaar.
Elkin, Keith. MBE: Beginning Your Campaign to Pass the Bar Exam. 2011. xv, 180p. pap. ***(978-0-7355-0996-2(4))*** Kluwer Law International.
Emanuel, Steven. Bar in A Box 2009. 2009. pap., stu. ed. 295.00 *(978-0-7355-9028-1(1)*, Aspen Pubs.) Wolters Kluwer Law & Business.
—Mbe Bootcamp: Constitutional Law. 2010. pap., stu. ed. *(978-0-7355-9738-9(3)*, Aspen Pubs.) Wolters Kluwer Law & Business.
—Mbe Bootcamp: Contracts. 2010. pap., stu. ed. *(978-0-7355-9736-5(7)*, Aspen Pubs.) Wolters Kluwer Law & Business.
—Mbe Bootcamp: Criminal Law & Procedure. 2010. pap., stu. ed. *(978-0-7355-9734-1(0)*, Aspen Pubs.) Wolters Kluwer Law & Business.
—Mbe Bootcamp: Emanuel Confidential. 2010. pap., stu. ed. *(978-0-7355-9747-1(2)*, Aspen Pubs.) Wolters Kluwer Law & Business.
—Mbe Bootcamp: Emanuels Essentials Vol 1: Contr Crim Law Pro Torts. 2010. pap., stu. ed. *(978-0-7355-9742-6(1)*, Aspen Pubs.) Wolters Kluwer Law & Business.
—Mbe Bootcamp: Emanuels Essentials Vol 2: Evid Real Prop Const Law. 2010. pap., stu. ed. *(978-0-7355-9743-3(X)*, Aspen Pubs.) Wolters Kluwer Law & Business.
—Mbe Bootcamp: Evidence. 2010. pap., stu. ed. *(978-0-7355-9740-2(5)*, Aspen Pubs.) Wolters Kluwer Law & Business.
—Mbe Bootcamp: Introduction to the Mbe & Mbe Bootcamp. 2010. pap., stu. ed. *(978-0-7355-9748-8(0)*, Aspen Pubs.) Wolters Kluwer Law & Business.
—Mbe Bootcamp: Property. 2010. pap., stu. ed. *(978-0-7355-9739-6(1)*, Aspen Pubs.) Wolters Kluwer Law & Business.
—Mbe Bootcamp: Self Assessment Test. 2010. pap., stu. ed. *(978-0-7355-9741-9(3)*, Aspen Pubs.) Wolters Kluwer Law & Business.
—Mbe Bootcamp: Simulated Mbe: Am Session. 2010. pap., stu. ed. *(978-0-7355-9744-0(8)*, Aspen Pubs.) Wolters Kluwer Law & Business.
—Mbe Bootcamp: Simulated Mbe: Pm Session. 2010. pap., stu. ed. *(978-0-7355-9745-7(6)*, Aspen Pubs.) Wolters Kluwer Law & Business.
—Mbe Bootcamp: Simulated Mbe: Questions & Answers. 2010. pap., stu. ed. *(978-0-7355-9746-4(4)*, Aspen Pubs.) Wolters Kluwer Law & Business.
—Mbe Bootcamp: Torts. 2010. pap., stu. ed. *(978-0-7355-9737-2(5)*, Aspen Pubs.) Wolters Kluwer Law & Business.
—Mbe Bootcamp Set. 2010. pap., stu. ed. *(978-0-7355-9735-8(9)*, Aspen Pubs.) Wolters Kluwer Law & Business.
—MPRE Audio Review. 2009. 39.95 *(978-0-7355-9439-5(2)*, Aspen Pubs.) Wolters Kluwer Law & Business.
—Strategies & Tactics for the MBE Volume Ii. 2009. pap., stu. ed. 49.95 *(978-0-7355-9408-1(2)*, Aspen Pubs.) Wolters Kluwer Law & Business.
Emanuel, Steven & Finz, Steven. Strategies & Tactics for Finz Multistate Method 2009. 2010. pap., stu. ed. 69.95 *(978-0-7355-7898-2(2))* Wolters Kluwer Law & Business.
Emanuel, Steven L. Emanuel Confidential for the MBE. 2009. pap., stu. ed. 19.95 *(978-0-7355-9409-8(0)*, Aspen Pubs.) Wolters Kluwer Law & Business.
—Emanuel Confidential for the MBE Audio Review. 2009. 19.95 *(978-0-7355-9410-4(4)*, Aspen Pubs.) Wolters Kluwer Law & Business.
—MBE Course, Pack. 2009. pap., stu. ed. 195.00 *(978-0-7355-9404-3(X)*, Aspen Pubs.) Wolters Kluwer Law & Business.
Enrico, Peter. MBE Bar Review. 2008. per. 29.95 *(978-0-9816785-0-4(5))* Mclaren Legal Pubs. LLC.
Evidence Essay Writer. 2008. ring bd. 29.95 *(978-0-9747208-7-6(9))* Bar None Review.
Friedland, Steven. Friedland's Exam Pro Bar Prep Workbook. 2010. (Exam Pro Ser.). 256p. pap. 35.00 *(978-0-314-20514-8(4)*, West Legalworks) West.
Glazier, Holly. Michigan Bar Exam Essay Deconstruction. 2012. (Illus.). xii, 943p. pap. ***(978-0-7355-0995-5(6))*** Wolters Kluwer Law & Business.
Kaplan PMBR Staff. MBE Review Flashcards. 2nd ed. 2009. (ENG.). 356p. 100.00 *(978-1-60714-104-4(3))* Kaplan Publishing.
La Puma, Rosemary. If I Don't Pass the Bar I'll Die: 73 Ways to Keep Stress & Worry from Affecting Your Performance on the Bar Exam. 2008. pap., stu. ed. 25.95 *(978-0-7355-7842-5(7))* Wolters Kluwer Law & Business.
MBE Exam Secrets Test Prep Staff, ed. Multistate Bar Exam Flashcard Study System: MBE Test Practice Questions & Review for the Multistate Bar Examination. 2011. (C). 105.99 *(978-1-61072-181-3(0))* Mometrix Media LLC.
—Multistate Bar Exam Secrets Study Guide: MBE Test Review for the Multistate Bar Examination. 2011. (C). pap. 105.99 *(978-1-61072-180-6(2))* Mometrix Media LLC.
Mclaren Legal Publishers. MBE Multistate Bar Examination. 2007. cd-rom 159.95 *(978-0-9791306-3-2(8))* Mclaren Legal Pubs. LLC.
—MBE Multistate Bar Examination: 800 Questions, Version 2.0 2007. cd-rom 79.95 *(978-0-9791306-4-9(6))* Mclaren Legal Pubs. LLC.
McLaren Legal Publishers LLC. Multistate Bar Review. 2008. cd-rom 49.95 *(978-0-9816785-1-1(3))* Mclaren Legal Pubs. LLC.
Nardiello, Jaimee & Grodin, Alyssa. The Bar Exam Survival Guide: The Insider's Handbook for Passing the Bar Exam. 2008. pap. *(978-0-9713017-8-8(6))* Professional Publishing.
Ncreuil, Chad. The Arizona Bar Exam: Pass It Now. 2010. 136p. pap. 18.00 *(978-1-59460-822-3(9))* 2nd ed. 2011. 140p. pap. 19.00 ***(978-1-61163-078-7(9))*** Carolina Academic Pr.
—The Zen of Passing the Bar Exam. 2010. 134p. pap. 18.00 *(978-1-59460-934-3(9))* Carolina Academic Pr.
Performance Test Maximizer Book. 2008. ring bd. 295.00 *(978-0-9753472-7-0(6))* Bar None Review.
Professional Responsibility Essay Writer. 2008. ring bd. 29.95 *(978-0-9753472-0-1(9))* Bar None Review.
Property Essay Writer. 2008. ring bd. 29.95 *(978-0-9747208-0-7(1))* Bar None Review.
Putney, Albert H. Bar Examination Review. 2009. 334p. pap. *(978-1-150-43115-9(6))* Books LLC.
—Bar Examination Review. 2010. 270p. pap. 34.89 *(978-1-154-63534-8(1))* General Bks. LLC.
Remedies Essay Writer. 2008. ring bd. 29.95 *(978-0-9753472-2-5(5))* Bar None Review.
Rigos. Mpre Review 3E W/ Cd. 2010. pap., stu. ed. 49.95 *(978-0-7355-9788-4(X)*, Aspen Pubs.) Wolters Kluwer Law & Business.
—Multistate Bar Exam 2009. 2010. Vol. 1. pap., stu. ed. *(978-0-7355-7838-8(9))* Vol. 2. pap., stu. ed. *(978-0-7355-7839-5(7))* Wolters Kluwer Law & Business.

Rigos & Shah, Tania N. What Not to Write: Ma Bar Exam Essay Book. 2008. pap., stu. ed. 29.95 *(978-0-7355-7834-0(6))* Wolters Kluwer Law & Business.

Rigos, James J. Ca Multistate Set: Mbe, Cpt, Cee. 2010. pap., stu. ed. 249.95 *(978-0-7355-9733-4(2),* Aspen Pubs.) Wolters Kluwer Law & Business.

—Multistate Bar Exam Review, 2 vols., Set. 2010. pap., stu. ed. 199.95 *(978-0-7355-8350-4(1))* Wolters Kluwer Law & Business.

—Multistate Set: Mbe, Mpt, Mee. 2010. pap., stu. ed. 249.95 *(978-0-7355-9732-7(4),* Aspen Pubs.) Wolters Kluwer Law & Business.

Saccuzzo, Dennis P. & Johnson, Nancy E. Bar Secrets: California Civil Procedure: Substantive Law & Model Essays. 2007. (Bar Secrets Ser.). xii, 51p. pap. *(978-1-933089-25-6(3))* Applications of Psychology of Law, Inc.

Sales Essay Writer. 2008. ring bd. 29.95 *(978-0-9753472-1-8(7))* Bar None Review.

Shah. What Not to Write: Fl Bar Exam Essay Book. pap., stu. ed. *(978-0-7355-9406-7(6),* Aspen Pubs.) Wolters Kluwer Law & Business.

Shah, Tania N. What Not to Write: Ca Real Essays, Real Performance Tests, Real Scores. 2010. pap., stu. ed. 34.95 *(978-0-7355-9405-0(8),* Aspen Pubs.) Wolters Kluwer Law & Business.

—What Not to Write: Ny Bar Exam Essay Book. 2009. pap., stu. ed. 29.95 *(978-0-7355-8813-4(9))* Wolters Kluwer Law & Business.

Stevenson, Wayne. Environmental Law. 2010. stu. ed. *(978-0-7355-7978-1(4))* Wolters Kluwer Law & Business.

Talamo, John J. Mastering the Multistate Bar Exam: Test-Taking Strategies for Scoring High on the Multistate Bar Exam. 2nd ed. 2007. (ENG.). 160p. per. 24.95 *(978-1-57248-596-9(5),* Sphinx Publishing) Sourcebooks, Inc.

Thompson, Ronald S. Attacking the Standardized Exam: The Art of Mastering Multiple Choice Standardized Tests. 2011. 112p. 24.99 ***(978-1-4634-2206-6(7))***; pap. 15.99 ***(978-1-4634-2207-3(5))*** AuthorHouse.

Torts Essay Writer. 2008. ring bd. 29.95 *(978-0-9747208-6-9(0))* Bar None Review.

Walton & Emanuel, Steven L. Strategies & Tactics for MBE 2008. 2009. pap., stu. ed. 69.95 *(978-0-7355-7063-4(9),* Aspen Pubs.) Wolters Kluwer Law & Business.

Wills & Trusts Essay Writer. 2008. ring bd. 29.95 *(978-0-9753472-3-2(3))* Bar None Review.

BAR MITZVAH

see also Confirmation (Jewish Rite)

Axelrod, Matt. Surviving Your Bar/Bat Mitzvah: The Ultimate Insider's Guide. 2012. (ENG.). 200p. pap. 16.95 ***(978-0-7657-0887-8(6),*** Aronson, Jason) Rowman & Littlefield Publishers, Inc.

Greenberg, Gail Anthony. Mitzvah Chic: How to Host a Meaningful, Fun, Drop Dead Gorgeous Bar or Bat Mitzvah. 2006. (ENG., Illus.). 240p. pap. 18.00 *(978-0-7432-8492-9(5),* Touchstone) Touchstone.

Kaplan-Mayer, Gabrielle. The Bar/Bat Mitzvah Planner: Everything You Need to Organize & Plan a Meaningful Ceremony & a Joyous Celebration. 2007. (Illus.). 192p. 21.95 *(978-1-56906-987-5(5),* BTM-987) Sellers Publishing, Inc.

Rappaport, Jill. Mazel Tov: Celebrities' Bar & Bat Mitzvah Memories. 2007. (ENG., Illus.). 176p. 25.00 *(978-0-7432-8787-6(8))* Simon & Schuster.

Siddur Lev Hadash: Bar Bat Mituah Siddur. 10.95 *(978-0-88125-625-3(0))* Ktav Publishing Hse., Inc.

Tobias, Pete. Never Mind the Bullocks: A Twenty-First Century Exploration of the Torah for bar-/bat-mitzvah Students. 2009. 168p. pap. 13.99 *(978-1-4389-2529-5(8))* AuthorHouse.

BARAKA, IMAMU AMIRI, 1934-

Anadolu-Okur, Nilgun. Contemporary African American Theater: Afrocentricity in the Works of Larry Neal, Amiri Baraka, & Charles Fuller. 2010. (ENG.). 236p. pap. 39.95 *(978-0-415-88324-5(5))* Routledge.

Baraka, Amiri, pseud. Razor. 2011. (ENG.). 300p. pap. 19.95 *(978-0-88378-300-9(2))* Third World Press.

Muyumba, Walton M. The Shadow & the Act: Black Intellectual Practice, Jazz Improvisation, & Philosophical Pragmatism. 2009. (ENG.). 232p. 48.00 *(978-0-226-55423-5(6))*; pap. 18.00 *(978-0-226-55424-2(4))* Univ. of Chicago Pr.

Schultz, Kathy Lou. The Afro-Modernist Epic & Literary History: Tolson, Hughes, Baraka. 2013. (Modern & Contemporary Poetry & Poetics Ser.). (ENG., Illus.). 256p. 80.00 ***(978-0-230-33873-9(9))*** Palgrave Macmillan.

BARBADOS

Barrow, Errol W. Speeches. Haniff, Yussuff, ed. (Illus.). 200p. 10.95 *(978-1-870518-70-3(5))* Penguin Group (USA) Inc.

Beckles, Hilary. A History of Barbados: From Amerindian Settlement to Nation-State. 2nd rev. ed. 2006. (ENG., Illus.). 334p. pap. 31.00 *(978-0-521-67849-0(8))* Cambridge Univ. Pr.

Cameron, Sarah. Barbados. 2nd ed. 2006. (Pocket Guides). (ENG., Illus.). 224p. per. 12.95 *(978-1-904777-58-8(9))* Footprint Handbooks GBR. Dist: Globe Pequot Pr., The.

Dangerfield, George. The Era of Good Feelings. 2008. 552p. pap. 54.00 *(978-1-59740-425-9(X))* ACLS Humanities E-Book.

Davis, Kortright. Cross & Crown in Barbados: Caribbean Political Religion in the Late 19th Century. 2011. 196p. pap. 22.00 *(978-1-61097-061-7(6),* Wipf and Stock) Wipf & Stock Pubs.

Govan, Chloe. Rihanna: Rebel Flower. 2012. (ENG., Illus.). 192p. pap. 15.95 ***(978-1-78038-127-5(1))*** Omnibus Pr.

Hartland, Michael. Great Guns of Barbados. 2009. (Illus.). 80p. 72.50 *(978-976-9515-35-2(3))* Miller Publishing Co. BRB. Dist: Trans-Atlantic Pubns., Inc.

Johnson, Stewart. Reading to Barbados & Back: Echoes of British History - the Tudor Family of Haynes of Reading. 2011. (ENG., Illus.). 450p. 42.50 ***(978-1-84624-611-1(3))*** Book Guild, Ltd. GBR. Dist: Trans-Atlantic Pubns., Inc.

Laurie, P. Barbadian Rum Shop: The Other Watering Hole. 2nd ed. 2011. 144p. pap. 29.95 *(978-0-230-02713-8(X),* Macmillan) Pan Macmillan GBR. Dist: Macmillan.

Laurie, Peter. Barbados: Caribbean Street Food. 2010. (ENG.). 112p. pap. 15.00 *(978-1-4050-8427-7(8))* Macmillan Caribbean GBR. Dist: Interlink Publishing Group, Inc.

Ligon, Richard. True & Exact History of the Island of Barbados. Kupperman, Karen Ordahl, ed. & intro. by. 2011. 201p. (C). pap. 15.95 *(978-1-60384-620-2(4))*; lib. bdg. 48.00 *(978-1-60384-621-9(2))* Hackett Publishing Co., Inc.

Locken, E. Travel Journal Barbados. 2010. 192p. pap. 19.99 *(978-0-557-43268-4(5))* Lulu Enterprises Inc.

—Travel Journal Hastings - Barbados. 2010. 192p. pap. 19.99 *(978-0-557-42161-9(6))* Lulu Enterprises Inc.

—Travel Journal St. Joseph - Barbados. 2010. 192p. pap. 19.99 *(978-0-557-42199-2(3))* Lulu Enterprises Inc.

—Travel Journal St Lawrence - Barbados. 2010. 192p. pap. 19.99 *(978-0-557-42186-2(1))* Lulu Enterprises Inc.

—Travel Journal St Peter - Barbados. 2010. 192p. pap. 19.99 *(978-0-557-42194-7(2))* Lulu Enterprises Inc.

—Travel Journal St Philip - Barbados. 2010. 192p. pap. 19.99 *(978-0-557-42200-5(0))* Lulu Enterprises Inc.

Murray, David A. B. Flaming Souls: Homosexuality, Homophobia, & Social Change in Barbados. 2012. (ENG.). 160p. pap. ***(978-1-4426-1300-3(9))***; ***(978-1-4426-4448-9(6))*** Univ. of Toronto Pr.

Oliver, Sarah. Rihanna? The Only Girl in the World. 2012. (ENG., Illus.). 280p. pap. 12.95 ***(978-1-84358-423-0(9))*** Blake, John Publishing, Ltd. GBR. Dist: Independent Pubs. Group.

Philpott, Don & Landmarks Staff. Barbados. 2nd rev. ed. 2008. (Illus.). 144p. pap. 13.99 *(978-1-84306-369-8(7))* Landmark Publishing Ltd. GBR. Dist: Hunter Publishing, Inc.

Prince, Danforth & Porter, Darwin. Jamaica. 6th ed. 2010. (Frommer's Complete Guides: 820). (ENG., Illus.). 288p. pap. 17.99 *(978-0-470-61444-0(7),* Frommers) Wiley, John & Sons, Inc.

Shales, Melissa. Barbados Travel Pack, 3rd. 3rd ed. 2011. (Globetrotter Travel Packs Ser.). (ENG., Illus.). 128p. 14.95 *(978-1-84773-851-6(6),* Globetrotter) New Holland Pubs., Ltd. GBR. Dist: Globe Pequot Pr., The.

Stow, Lee. AAA Essential Barbados, 5th Edition. 5th ed. 2011. (ENG.). 160p. pap. 11.95 *(978-1-59508-412-5(6))* AAA.

Thomas Cook Publishing. Barbados Pocket Guide, 2nd: Compact & practical pocket guides for sun seekers & city Breakers. 2nd ed. 2011. (Thomas Cook Pocket Guides). (ENG., Illus.). 128p. pap. 9.95 *(978-1-84848-451-1(8))* Cook, Thomas Publishing GBR. Dist: Globe Pequot Pr., The.

Thome, James A. & Kimball, J. Horace. Emancipation in the West Indies: A Six Months' Tour in Antigua, Barbados, & Jamaica, in the Year 1837. 2010. (Cambridge Library Collection - History Ser.). (Illus.). 498p. pap. 35.99 *(978-1-108-01670-4(7))* Cambridge Univ. Pr.

BARBARIAN INVASIONS OF ROME

see Rome—History—Germanic Invasions, 3rd-6th Centuries

BARBARIGO, ANDREA

Lane, Frederic C. Andrea Barbarigo, Merchant of Venice, 1418-1449. (Johns Hopkins University. Studies in the Social Sciences, Thirtieth Ser.: 1). reprint ed. 37.50 *(978-0-404-61300-6(4))* AMS Pr., Inc.

BARBAROSSA, D. 1546

Bradford, Ernle. The Sultan's Admiral: Barbarossa - Pirate & Empire Builder. 2009. (ENG., Illus.). 248p. pap. 15.95 *(978-1-84511-793-1(X),* Tauris Parke Paperbacks) I. B. Tauris & Co., Ltd. GBR. Dist: Macmillan.

BARBAROSSA, HOLY ROMAN EMPEROR, CA. 1123-1190

see Frederick I, Holy Roman Emperor, ca. 1123-1190

BARBARY CORSAIRS

see Pirates

BARBARY STATES

see Africa, North

BARBAULD, MRS. (ANNA LETITIA), 1743-1825

Barbauld, (Anna Letitia). Memoir, Letters, & a Selection from the Poems & Prose Writings of Anna L Titia Barbauld. 2006. 372p. per. 26.99 *(978-1-4255-3922-1(X))*; 484p. per. 29.99 *(978-1-4255-5367-8(2))* MPublishing.

Looser, Devoney. Women Writers & Old Age in Great Britain, 1750-1850. 2008. (ENG., Illus.). 252p. (gr. 17). 57.00 *(978-0-8018-8705-5(4))* Johns Hopkins Univ. Pr.

McCarthy, William. Anna Letitia Barbauld: Voice of the Enlightenment. 2008. (ENG., Illus.). 792p. (gr. 17). 62.00 *(978-0-8018-9016-1(0))* Johns Hopkins Univ. Pr.

Watkins, Daniel P. Anna Letitia Barbauld & Eighteenth-Century Visionary Poetics. 2012. (ENG., Illus.). 264p. (gr. 17). 60.00 ***(978-1-4214-0458-5(3))*** Johns Hopkins Univ. Pr.

BARBECUE COOKING

see Barbecuing

BARBECUING

Adam, Cornelia. Barbacoa (Barbecue) 6.95 *(978-84-89675-35-3(X))* Zendrera Zariquiey, Editorial ESP. Dist: AIMS International Bks., Inc.

Adler, Karen & Fertig, Judith. BBQ Bash: The Be-All, End-All Party Guide, from Barefoot to Black Tie. 2008. (ENG., Illus.). 256p. per. 16.95 *(978-1-55832-349-0(X))* Harvard Common Pr.

—300 Big & Bold Barbecue & Grilling Recipes. 2009. (ENG., Illus.). 440p. pap. 24.95 *(978-0-7788-0212-9(4))* Rose, Robert Inc. CAN. Dist: Firefly Bks., Ltd.

Adler, Karen & Fertig, Judith M. BBQ Bash: The Be-All, End-All Party Guide, from Barefoot to Black Tie. 2008. (ENG., Illus.). 256p. 29.95 *(978-1-55832-348-3(1))* Harvard Common Pr.

—25 Essentials: Techniques for Grilling Fish. 2010. (25 Essentials Ser.). (ENG.). 128p. spiral bd. 12.95 *(978-1-55832-669-9(3))* Harvard Common Pr.

—25 Essentials: Techniques for Planking. 2010. (25 Essentials Ser.). (ENG.). 128p. spiral bd. 12.95 *(978-1-55832-668-2(5))* Harvard Common Pr.

Adler, Karen & Wells, Carolyn. Pig Out on Kansas City Barbecue. Date not set. (Illus.). 96p. (Orig.). pap. 9.95 *(978-0-925175-21-2(8))* Pig Out Pubns., Inc.

August Home Publishing Co. Cuisine Tonight Grilling. 2008. 9.95 *(978-0-9801046-1-5(0))* August Home Publishing Co.

Australian Women's Weekly Staff. Barbecue. Coleman, Mary, ed. (Illus.). 64p. pap. 5.95 *(978-1-86396-093-9(7))* ACP Publishing Pty, Ltd. AUS. Dist: Graphic Arts Ctr. Publishing Co.

—The Barbecue Cookbook. Blacker, Maryanne, ed. (Illus.). 120p. pap. 12.95 *(978-0-949128-43-0(0))* ACP Publishing Pty, Ltd. AUS. Dist: Graphic Arts Ctr. Publishing Co.

—Barbecued Seafood. Clark, Pamela, ed. (Illus.). 64p. pap. 5.95 *(978-1-86396-245-2(X))* ACP Publishing Pty, Ltd. AUS. Dist: Graphic Arts Ctr. Publishing Co.

—Great Barbecue Food. (Illus.). 248p. (Orig.). pap. 34.95 *(978-1-86396-262-9(X))* ACP Publishing Pty, Ltd. AUS. Dist: Graphic Arts Ctr. Publishing Co.

Baker, Laverne. Food for the Soul. 2007. pap. 13.00 *(978-0-8059-8635-8(9))* Dorrance Publishing Co., Inc.

Barbecue. Date not set. 96p. spiral bd. 6.98 *(978-1-4054-0628-4(3))*; 224p. *(978-1-4054-9242-3(2))* Parragon, Inc.

Bartlett, Ben. BBQ Manual: Great Grilling Made Simple. 2012. (Owners Workshop Manual Ser.). (ENG., Illus.). 176p. 29.95 ***(978-0-85733-116-8(7),*** 0857331167) Haynes Publishing PLC GBR. Dist: MBI Distribution Services/Quayside Distribution.

Bernard, Françoise. La Cuisine: Everyday French Home Cooking. Sigal, Jane, tr. & frwd. by. 2010. (Illus.). 648p. 45.00 *(978-0-8478-3501-0(4))* Rizzoli International Pubns., Inc.

Better Homes and Gardens Books Staff. Better Homes & Gardens Grillin' & Chillin' Wal Mart Edition. 2011. (Better Homes & Gardens Cooking Ser.). 192p. pap. 5.00 *(978-1-118-07463-3(7),* Wiley) Wiley, John & Sons, Inc.

—Better Homes & Gardens Grilling Family Dinners Wp. 2011. 240p. *(978-1-57215-692-0(9))* Wiley, John & Sons, Inc.

—Better Homes & Gardens Grilling Family Dinners Wp PB. 2011. 240p. pap. *(978-1-57215-693-7(7))* Wiley, John & Sons, Inc.

—Better Homes & Gardens New Grilling Book (Wal Mart 3-Ring) 2nd ed. 2011. (Better Homes & Gardens Cooking Ser.). 424p. pap. 8.00 *(978-1-118-07213-4(8),* Wiley) Wiley, John & Sons, Inc.

—Grill It! Secrets to Delicious Flame-Kissed Food. 2011. 192p. pap. 5.00 *(978-1-118-07464-0(5))*; (ENG., Illus.). 372p. pap. 24.95 *(978-0-470-93277-3(5))* Wiley, John & Sons, Inc. (Wiley).

—5-Ingredient Grilling. Saari, Jessica, ed. 2007. (Better Homes & Gardens Cooking Ser.). (ENG., Illus.). 256p. pap. 14.95 *(978-0-696-23161-2(1),* Wiley) Wiley, John & Sons, Inc.

Better Homes and Gardens Editors. Grill It! Secrets to Delicious Flame-Kissed Food. 2nd ed. 2011. 192p. pap. 14.95 *(978-1-118-09804-2(8),* Wiley) Wiley, John & Sons, Inc.

Biuso, Julie & McLean, Aaron. Sizzle, Sensational Barbecue Food from New Zealand. 2008. 160p. 19.95 *(978-0-615-16951-4(1))* Biuso, Julie Publications.

Black, Rick. Grillin' Like a Villain: The Complete Grilling & Barbecuing Cookbook. 2006. (ENG.). 206p. per. 16.95 *(978-0-8117-3325-0(4))* Stackpole Bks.

Brothers, Lee A. The Three Elements of Barbeque: Easy Steps for Barbeque Success. 2009. (Illus.). 23p. pap. 17.95 *(978-1-4327-4058-0(X))* Outskirts Pr., Inc.

Browne, Rick. The Big Book of Barbecue Side Dishes. 2009. 160p. pap. 16.95 *(978-1-4162-0535-7(7))* Sellers Publishing, Inc.

—The Grillin' Wild Cookbook: Innovative Recipes for Hunters, Fishermen, & Outdoor Enthusiasts. 2012. (ENG., Illus.). 224p. pap. 21.95 ***(978-0-7627-7379-4(0),*** Lyons Pr.) Globe Pequot Pr., The.

—Grilling for All Seasons: 95+ Recipes to Fire up Year-Round Grilling. 2009. (Illus.). 160p. pap. 18.95 *(978-1-4162-0782-5(1))* Sellers Publishing, Inc.

—The Ultimate Guide to Grilling: How to Grill Just about Anything. 2011. (Ultimate Guides). (ENG., Illus.). 320p. pap. 14.95 *(978-1-61608-067-9(1),* 608067) Skyhorse Publishing Co., Inc.

—1,001 Best Grilling Recipes: Delicious, Easy-to-Make Recipes from Around the World. 2011. (1,001 Ser.). (ENG.). 720p. pap. 20.95 *(978-1-57284-116-1(8))* Surrey Bks.

Butel, Jane. Finger Lickin', Rib Stickin', Great Tastin', Hot & Spicy Barbecue. (Illus.). 83.40 *(978-1-56305-486-0(8),* 9483) Workman Publishing Co., Inc.

Canadian Living Staff & Chase, Andrew. Canadian Living: The Barbecue Collection - The Best Barbecue Recipes from Our Kitchen to Your Backyard. 2010. (Illus.). 552p. pap. 29.95 *(978-0-9809924-9-6(4))* Transcontinental Bks. CAN. Dist: Random Hse., Inc.

Canadian Living Test Kitchen Staff & Chase, Andrew. The Barbecue Collection. rev. ed. 2012. (ENG., Illus.). 552p. pap. 32.95 ***(978-0-9877474-0-2(1))*** Transcontinental Bks. CAN. Dist: Random Hse., Inc.

Carrabba's Italian Grill Staff. Carrabba's Italian Grill Cookbook: Recipes from Around Our Family Table. 2011. (ENG.). 160p. pap. 19.99 ***(978-1-118-19733-2(X),*** Wiley) Wiley, John & Sons, Inc.

Castro, Lourdes. Latin Grilling: Recipes to Share, from Patagonian Asado to Yucatecan Barbecue & More. 2011. (Illus.). 192p. pap. 22.00 *(978-1-60774-004-9(4))* Ten Speed Pr.

Chesman, Andrea. The New Vegetarian Grill: 250 Flame-Kissed Recipes for Fresh, Inspired Meals. rev. ed. 2008. (ENG., Illus.). 352p. per. 16.95 *(978-1-55832-362-9(7))* Harvard Common Pr.

Clercq, Peter de & Viegels, Kris. Just Grilling. 2008. (ENG., Illus.). 160p. pap. *(978-90-209-7751-6(2),* Lannoo Pubs. (Acc)) Antique Collectors' Club.

Coleman, Mary, ed. The Essential Barbecue Cookbook. (Illus.). 128p. pap. 12.95 *(978-1-86396-105-9(4))* ACP Publishing Pty, Ltd. AUS. Dist: Graphic Arts Ctr. Publishing Co.

Cookbook Resources, ed. 1001 Easy Inexpensive Grilling Recipes. 2011. (ENG.). 400p. pap. *(978-1-59769-111-6(9))* Cookbook Resources, LLC.

Cooking Light Magazine Editors, ed. Cooking Light Way to Cook: Grilling - The Complete Visual Guide to Healthy Grilling. 2012. (ENG., Illus.). 320p. pap. 24.95 *(978-0-8487-3593-7(5))* Oxmoor Hse., Inc.

Cooking Light Magazine Staff. Grilling. Averett, Heather, ed. rev. ed. 2007. (Cooking Light. cook's ESSENTIAL RECIPE COLLECTION). (ENG., Illus.). 144p. 17.95 *(978-0-8487-3157-1(3))* Oxmoor Hse., Inc.

Cook's Country Magazine Editors. Best Grilling Recipes: More Than 100 Regional Favorites Tested & Perfected for the Outdoor Cook. 2009. (ENG.). 256p. 29.95 *(978-1-933615-42-4(7))* America's Test Kitchen.

Cook's Illustrated Magazine Editors, ed. Grilling & Barbecue: A Practical Guide for the Outdoor Cook. (ENG., Illus.). 432p. 35.00 *(978-0-936184-86-9(8))* America's Test Kitchen.

Cooper, William & Williams-Sonoma Staff. Williams-Sonoma on the Grill: New Recipes & Adventures with Fire & Smoke. 2009. (ENG., Illus.). 256p. 34.95 *(978-0-8487-3269-1(3))* Oxmoor Hse., Inc.

Creative Homeowner Press Editors. Char-Broil America Grills! Flavorful Recipes That Will Fire up Your Appetite. 2010. (Grilling Ser.). (ENG., Illus.). 304p. (gr. 5). pap. 24.95 *(978-1-58011-502-5(0))* Creative Homeowner.

Creative Homeowner Press Staff. Char-Broil's Canada Grills! 2011. (Grilling Ser.). (ENG., Illus.). 304p. (gr. 5). pap. 24.95 ***(978-1-58011-525-4(X))*** Creative Homeowner.

Cumbay, Traci. BBQ Sauces, Rubs & Marinades for Dummies. 2008. (ENG., Illus.). 264p. per. 14.99 *(978-0-470-19914-5(8),* For Dummies) Wiley, John & Sons, Inc.

Cuthbert, Pippa, et al. Big Book of BBQ. New Holland Australia Staff, ed. 2012. (ENG., Illus.). 304p. 14.95 *(978-1-84773-552-2(5))* New Holland Pubs., Ltd. GBR. Dist: Sterling Publishing Co., Inc.

Davis, Ardie & Kirk, Paul. America's Best BBQ: 100 Recipes from America's Best Smokehouses, Pits, Shacks, Rib Joints, Roadhouses, & Restaurants. 2009. (ENG.). 240p. pap. 19.99 *(978-0-7407-7811-7(0))* Andrews McMeel Publishing.

Davis, Ardie A. & Kirk, Paul. America's Best Ribs: Tips & Recipes for Easy, Lip-Smacking, Pull-off-the-Bone, Pass-the-Sauce, Championship-Quality BBQ Ribs at Home. 2012. (ENG.). 160p. pap. 19.99 ***(978-1-4494-1413-9(3))*** Andrews McMeel Publishing.

Day, Jason & Chronister, Aaron. BBQ Makes Everything Better. (ENG.). 256p. 2011. pap. 16.00 *(978-1-4391-6831-8(8))* 2010. 30.00 *(978-1-4391-6830-1(X))* Scribner. (Scribner).

Delicious Barbecue. 2008. 96p. *(978-1-4075-3518-0(8))* Parragon, Inc.

DeMers, John. Follow the Smoke: 14,783 Miles of Great Texas Barbecue. 2008. (ENG.). 255p. pap. 19.95 *(978-1-933979-22-9(4))* Bright Sky Pr.

Devon, Bob. The Complete Wood Pellet Barbeque Cookbook: The Ultimate Guide & Recipe Book for Wood Pellet Grills. 2012. (ENG.). 192p. pap. ***(978-0-7570-0337-0(0))*** Square One Pubs.

Dobson, Ross. Grillhouse: Gastropub at Home. 2011. (ENG., Illus.). 224p. 27.50 *(978-0-7627-7378-7(2),* 1334235, Lyons Pr.) Globe Pequot Pr., The.

Dooley, Bryan & Bay, Leslie. Stories & Recipes from Bryan's Black Mountain Barbecue. 2011. (ENG., Illus.). 112p. pap. 21.95 ***(978-0-615-55400-6(8))*** Bryan's Black Mountain Barbecue.

Engelhardt, Elizabeth S. D. Republic of Barbecue: Stories Beyond the Brisket. 2009. (ENG., Illus.). 255p. pap. 21.95 *(978-0-292-71998-9(1))* Univ. of Texas Pr.

Evans, Pete. My Grill: Outdoor Cooking Australian Style. 2011. (ENG.). 256p. 30.00 *(978-1-61628-116-8(2))* Weldon Owen, Inc.

Favorite Brand Name Recipes Editors, ed. The Barbecue Bible: Your All-in-One Guide to Successful Grilling. 2010. 320p. 16.98 *(978-1-4508-1091-3(8))* Publications International, Ltd.

—Western BBQ. 2010. 128p. spiral bd. 10.98 *(978-1-60553-458-9(7))*; spiral bd. 10.98 *(978-0-7853-2146-0(2))* Publications International, Ltd. (PIL Kids).

Feller, Thomas. Barbecue Box. 2009. (ENG., Illus.). 160p. 24.99 *(978-0-600-61965-9(6),* Hamlyn) Octopus Publishing Group GBR. Dist: Hachette Bk. Group.

Fishman, Stanley A. Tender Grassfed Barbecue: Traditional, Primal & Paleo. 2011. 244p. pap. 24.95 ***(978-0-9823429-1-6(8))*** Alanstar Games.

Flay, Bobby. Bobby Flay's Boy Meets Grill: With More Than 125 Bold New Recipes. 2007. 288p. 32.50 *(978-1-4013-0365-5(X))* Hyperion Pr.

Flay, Bobby, et al. Bobby Flay's Grill It! 2008. (ENG., Illus.). 288p. 35.00 *(978-0-307-35142-5(4),* Clarkson Potter) Crown Publishing Group.
Foreman, George & Kellinger, Kathryn. George Foreman's Indoor Grilling Made Easy: More than 100 Simple, Healthy Ways to Feed Family & Friends. 2006. (Illus.). 230p. reprint ed. 20.00 *(978-1-4223-5474-2(1))* DIANE Publishing Co.
Fox Chapel Publishing Staff, ed. Grilling Gone Wild: Zesty Recipes for Meats, Mains, Marinades & More. 2012. (ENG., Illus.). 152p. pap. 14.95 ***(978-1-56523-725-4(0))*** Fox Chapel Publishing Co., Inc.
France, Christine. Classic Barbecue & Grill: 100 Step-by-Step Recipes in 400 Photographs. 2009. (ENG., Illus.). 160p. pap. 19.99 *(978-1-84476-663-5(2))* Anness Publishing GBR. Dist: National Bk. Network.
Gelin, David Howard. BBQ Joints: Stories & Secret Recipes from the Barbeque Belt. 1 vol. 2008. (ENG., Illus.). 160p. pap. 15.99 *(978-1-4236-0218-7(8))* Gibbs Smith, Publisher.
Good Housekeeping Editors, ed. Good Housekeeping Grilling: More than 275 Perfect Year-Round Recipes. 2011. (ENG., Illus.). 304p. 24.95 *(978-1-58816-714-9(3))* Hearst Communications, Inc.
Good Housekeeping Staff. Good Housekeeping Everyday Grilling. 2007. (Illus.). 192p. 6.98 *(978-1-58816-581-7(7))* Hearst Communications, Inc.
Griffith, Dotty. Celebrating Barbecue: The Ultimate Guide to America's 4 Regional Styles. 2011. (ENG.). 192p. pap. 13.99 *(978-1-4516-2764-0(5))* Simon & Schuster.
Hackett, Jolinda. Cookouts Veggie Style! 225 Backyard Favorites - Full of Flavor, Free of Meat. 2011. (ENG.). 240p. pap. 17.95 *(978-1-4405-1240-7(X))* Adams Media Corp.
Hamlyn. Barbecue: A Pyramid Cooking Paperback. 2010. (ENG., Illus.). 128p. pap. 9.95 *(978-0-600-62032-7(8),* Hamlyn) Octopus Publishing Group GBR. Dist: Hachette Bk. Group.
Harrisson, John, et al. Omaha Steaks the Great American Grilling Book: From the Best Burgers to Terrific T-Bones. 2008. (ENG., Illus.). 176p. 24.95 *(978-1-60320-020-2(7))* Time Home Entertainment, Inc.
Hayes, Shannon. The Farmer & the Grill: A Guide to Grilling, Barbecuing & Spit-Roasting Grassfed Meat... & for Saving the Planet, One Bite at a Time. 2008. (ENG., Illus.). 164p. pap. 21.95 *(978-0-9794391-0-0(8))* Left to Write Pr.
Hensler, George W. Startin' the Fire: Everything You Need to Know about Starting a Competition BBQ Team, (Except the Recipes) 2010. pap. *(978-1-890689-14-8(9),* Rio Grande Bks.) LPD Pr.
Howard, Margaret. All Fired Up! Outdoor & Indoor Grilling. 2nd rev. ed. 2010. (ENG., Illus.). 256p. pap. 24.95 *(978-1-55407-597-3(1))* Firefly Bks., Ltd.
Hughes, Chris. FAT BOY's GUIDE to GRILLING. 2006. 24.99 *(978-1-60034-839-6(4));* pap. 14.99 *(978-1-60034-838-9(6))* Xulon Pr., Inc.
Husbands, Andy, et al. Wicked Good Barbecue: Fearless Recipes from Two Damn Yankees Who Have Won the Biggest, Baddest BBQ Competitions in the World. 2012. (ENG., Illus.). 224p. pap. 21.99 ***(978-1-59233-499-5(7),*** 1592334997) Quayside.
Jesseph, Bonnie. Man Your Grill: Cookin' & Grillin' with Beer! 2007. (Illus.). vi, 210p. *(978-1-57156-480-8(7))* Hearts 'N Tummies Cookbook Co.
Joachim, David. A Man, a Can, a Grill Shipper. *(978-1-57954-934-3(9))* Rodale Pr., Inc.
—A Man, a Can, a Grill Tray. 2010. ***(978-1-57954-933-6(0))*** Rodale Pr., Inc.
Jollands, Beverley. Barbecues 400: Burgers, Kebabs, Fish-Steaks, Vegetarian Dishes & Tempting Salads, Desserts & Accompaniments, Demonstrated Step by Step Withmore Than 1500 Vibrant Photographs. 2008. (ENG., Illus.). 512p. 29.99 *(978-0-7548-1860-1(8))* Anness Publishing GBR. Dist: National Bk. Network.
Jung, Richard, photos by. Kabobs & Other Light Grills. 2010. (ENG., Illus.). 64p. *(978-1-84597-974-4(5))* Ryland Peters & Small.
Kahn, Lisa. Char-Broil's Everybody Grills! Creative Homeowner Press Editors, ed. 2008. (Grilling Ser.). (ENG., Illus.). 304p. (gr. 5). pap. 24.95 *(978-1-58011-208-6(0))* Creative Homeowner.
Karlin, Mary. Wood-Fired Cooking: Techniques & Recipes for the Grill, Backyard Oven, Fireplace, & Campfire. 2009. (ENG., Illus.). 208p. 27.99 *(978-1-58008-945-6(3))* Ten Speed Pr.
Karmel, Elizabeth & Karmel. Soaked, Slathered, & Seasoned: A Complete Guide to Flavoring Food for the Grill. 2009. (ENG., Illus.). 352p. pap. 19.95 *(978-0-470-18648-0(8),* Wiley) Wiley, John & Sons, Inc.
Kelley, Bill. Smokin' Willie's Guide to Great Grillin' The Best Family Recipes in the Known Universe! Insider Tips on Sauces, Spice Rubs, & Music to Listen to While You're Cookin' 2009. (Illus.). 106p. *(978-0-615-23303-1(1))* Wild Bill's Food, Inc.
Kinne, Anne. Coast to Coast BBQ: America's Best Recipes 2008. 2008. 178p. pap. 18.00 *(978-0-9798494-4-2(6),* Ithaca Pr.) Authors & Artists Publishers of New York, Inc.
Kirk, Paul. Simple Smoking: Over 80 Recipes for the Home-Smoking Enthusiast. 2011. (ENG., Illus.). 112p. pap. 12.95 *(978-1-61608-317-5(4),* 608317) Skyhorse Publishing Co., Inc.
—500 Barbecue Dishes: The Only Barbecue Compendium You'll Ever Need. 2008. (500 (Sellers Publishing) Ser.). (Illus.). 288p. 15.95 *(978-1-4162-0509-8(8))* Sellers Publishing, Inc.
Knight, Chris. More Grilled to Perfection: Recipes from License to Grill. 2007. (ENG., Illus.). 256p. pap. 24.95 *(978-1-55278-640-6(4))* McArthur & Co. CAN. Dist: National Bk. Network.
Knight, Chris & Smith, Tyler J. Grilled to Perfection: Recipes from License to Grill. 2006. (ENG., Illus.). 232p. pap. 24.95 *(978-1-55278-568-3(8))* McArthur & Co. CAN. Dist: National Bk. Network.
Kochilas, Diane. Mediterranean Grilling: More Than 100 Recipes from Across the Mediterranean. 2007. (Illus.). 208p. 29.95 *(978-0-06-055639-6(0),* Morrow, William Cookbooks) HarperCollins Pubs.
Krasner, Deborah. The New Outdoor Kitchen: Cooking up a Kitchen for the Way You Live & Play. 2009. (ENG., Illus.). 232p. pap. 19.95 *(978-1-60085-009-7(X))* Taunton Pr., Inc.
Lagasse, Emeril. Emeril at the Grill: A Cookbook for All Seasons. 2009. pap. 24.99 *(978-0-06-179115-4(6),* HarperStudio) HarperCollins Pubs.
Lampe, Ray. Dr. BBQ's Big-Time Barbecue Road Trip! 2007. (ENG., Illus.). 272p. pap. 16.95 *(978-0-312-34958-5(0),* St. Martin's Griffin) St. Martin's Pr.
—Ribs, Chops, Steaks & Wings: Irresistible Recipes for the Grill, Stovetop, & Oven. 2010. (ENG., Illus.). 132p. 19.95 *(978-0-8118-6826-6(5))* Chronicle Bks. LLC.
Lampe, Ray. Slow Fire: The Beginner's Guide to Barbecue. 2012. (ENG., Illus.). 176p. 22.95 ***(978-1-4521-0303-7(8))*** Chronicle Bks. LLC.
Lang, Adam Perry. BBQ 25. 2010. (ENG., Illus.). 68p. 19.99 *(978-0-06-199023-6(X),* Morrow, William Cookbooks) HarperCollins Pubs.
Lang, Adam Perry. Charred & Scruffed. 2012. (ENG.). 280p. pap. 24.95 ***(978-1-57965-465-8(7),*** 1579654657) Artisan.
Lang, Adam Perry, et al. Serious Barbecue: Smoke, Char, Baste, & Brush Your Way to Great Outdoor Cooking. 2009. (ENG.). 400p. 35.00 *(978-1-4013-2306-6(5))* Hyperion Pr.
Larsen, Linda Johnson. Grilling Basics: A Step-by-Step Guide to Delicious Recipes. 2009. (Knack: Make It Easy Ser.). (ENG., Illus.). 256p. pap. 19.95 *(978-1-59921-508-2(X),* Knack) Globe Pequot Pr., The.
Lawson, Jane & Broadfoot, Vanessa. BBQ Food for Friends. (Barbecue Cookbooks Ser.) (Illus.). 192p. 24.95 *(978-1-55285-481-5(7),* Walrus Bks.) Whitecap Bks., Ltd. CAN. Dist: Graphic Arts Ctr. Publishing Co.
Lebowitz, Josh & Pesantez, Eva. Brother Jimmy's BBQ: More than 100 Recipes for Pork, Beef, Chicken, & the Essential Southern Sides. 2012. (Illus.). 256p. pap. 24.95 ***(978-1-58479-954-2(4))*** Stewart, Tabori & Chang.
Lee, Sandra. Semi-Homemade Grilling 2. 2008. (ENG., Illus.). 237p. pap. 19.95 *(978-0-696-23828-4(4),* Wiley) Wiley, John & Sons, Inc.
Lilly, Chris. Big Bob Gibson's BBQ Book: Recipes & Secrets from a Legendary Barbecue Joint. 2009. (ENG., Illus.). 256p. pap. 24.99 *(978-0-307-40811-2(6))* Crown Publishing Group.
Lobel, Stanley, et al. Lobel's Prime Time Grilling: Recipes & Tips from America's #1 Butchers. 2nd rev. ed. 2007. (ENG., Illus.). 298p. 27.95 *(978-0-471-75682-8(2),* Wiley) Wiley, John & Sons, Inc.
Mariani, John, et al. Grilling. 3rd ed. 2009. (ENG., Illus.). 392p. pap. 21.99 *(978-0-470-42129-1(0),* For Dummies) Wiley, John & Sons, Inc.
Mastering the Grill Pb (BOMC) 2007. pap. 24.95 *(978-91-0-024964-9(5))* Chronicle Bks. LLC.
McGinley, Brendan. The Man's Book of the BBQ: A Celebration of Full-on, Flame-on Macho Cooking. 2011. (ENG., Illus.). 128p. 9.99 *(978-1-84601-391-7(7),* Hamlyn) Octopus Publishing Group GBR. Dist: Hachette Bk. Group.
McSpadden, Wyatt. Texas BBQ. 2009. (ENG., Illus.). 160p. 39.95 *(978-0-292-71858-6(6))* Univ. of Texas Pr.
Meals in Minutes - Everyday Grilling: Quick, Easy & Delicious. 2011. (ENG.). 112p. pap. 9.99 *(978-1-61628-153-3(7))* Weldon Owen, Inc.
Mixon, Myron & Alexander, Kelly. Smokin' with Myron Mixon: Recipes Made Simple, from the Winningest Man in Barbecue. 2011. (ENG., Illus.). 192p. pap. 22.00 *(978-0-345-52853-7(0),* Ballantine Bks.) Random House Publishing Group.
Moss, Robert F. Barbecue: The History of an American Institution. 2010. (ENG.). 288p. 26.00 *(978-0-8173-1718-8(X))* Univ. of Alabama Pr.
Mugnaini, Andrea & Thess, John. The Art of Wood-Fired Cooking. 1 vol. 2010. (ENG., Illus.). 192p. pap. 19.99 *(978-1-4236-0653-6(1))* Gibbs Smith, Publisher.
Mumm, Debbie, illus. Debbie Mumm 3 Books In 1: Old-Fashioned Cookies Cookbook, Country Casseroles Cookbook, Grilling & More Cookbook. 2007. (3 Books In 1 Ser.). 12.98 *(978-1-4127-2878-2(9))* Publications International, Ltd.
Neely, Patrick, et al. Down Home with the Neelys: A Southern Family Cookbook. 2009. (ENG., Illus.). 288p. 28.95 *(978-0-307-26994-2(9),* Knopf) Knopf Doubleday Publishing Group.
Niehaus, Carmen. You Let's Braai. 2011. 208p. pap. 35.00 *(978-0-7981-5105-4(6))* NB Pubs. Ltd. ZAF. Dist: International Publishers Marketing.
Oliver, Sandra. Saltwater Foodways Companion Cookbook. 2008. (Maritime Ser.). (ENG.). 228p. 19.95 *(978-0-939511-24-2(X))* Mystic Seaport Museum, Inc.
Olivier, Suzannah & Farrow, Joanna. Juicing, Smoothies & Blended Drinks: Fresh & flamboyant drinks to quench your Thirst. 2011. (ENG., Illus.). 256p. 24.99 ***(978-0-7548-2417-6(9))*** Anness Publishing GBR. Dist: National Bk. Network.
Palomino, Rafael & Chronicle Books Staff. Latin Grill: Sultry & Simple Food for Red-Hot Dinners & Parties. 2010. (ENG., Illus.). 160p. pap. 19.95 *(978-0-8118-6660-6(2))* Chronicle Bks. LLC.
Phillips, Jeff. Smoking Meat: The Essential Guide to Real Barbecue, 1 vol. 2012. (ENG.). 208p. pap. 29.95 *(978-1-77050-038-9(3))* Whitecap Bks., Ltd. CAN. Dist: Midpoint Trade Bks., Inc.
Pickford, Louise. 200 BBQ Recipes: Hamlyn All Color. 2009. (ENG.). 240p. pap. 7.99 *(978-0-600-61944-4(3),* Hamlyn) Octopus Publishing Group GBR. Dist: Hachette Bk. Group.
Powers, Remus & Davis, Ardie. 25 Essentials: Techniques for Grilling. 2009. (25 Essentials Ser.). (ENG.). 128p. spiral bd. 12.95 *(978-1-55832-392-6(9))* Harvard Common Pr.
Publications International Staff, contrib. by. Kingsford & More: Simple 1-2-3. 2007. (Illus.). 160p. spiral bd. 15.98 *(978-1-4127-2626-9(3))* Publications International, Ltd.
Publications International Staff, creator. Favorite Brand Name: Grilling. 2007. (Favorite Brand Name Cookbook Ser.). (Illus.). 383p. 15.98 *(978-1-4127-2879-9(7))* Publications International, Ltd.
Publications International Staff, ed. Incredibly Easy Grilling. 2007. (Illus.). 160p. spiral bd. *(978-1-4127-2547-7(X))* Publications International, Ltd.
Purviance, Jamie. Weber's Charcoal Grilling: Art of Cooking with Live Fire. rev. ed. 2007. (ENG., Illus.). 256p. pap. 19.95 *(978-0-376-02047-5(4),* Sunset Bks./Sunset Publishing Corp.) Oxmoor Hse., Inc.
—Weber's Real Grilling. 2007. (Illus.). 304p. reprint ed. pap. 25.00 *(978-1-4223-6680-6(4))* DIANE Publishing Co.
—Weber's Smoke: A Guide to Smoke Cooking for Everyone & Any Grill. 2012. (ENG., Illus.). 192p. pap. 21.95 ***(978-0-376-02067-3(9))*** Oxmoor Hse., Inc.
—Weber's Time to Grill: Get In. Get Out. Get Grilling. 2011. (ENG., Illus.). 304p. pap. 24.95 *(978-0-376-02060-4(1))* Oxmoor Hse., Inc.
—Weber's Way to Grill: The Step-by-Step Guide to Expert Grilling. 2009. (ENG., Illus.). 320p. pap. 24.95 *(978-0-376-02059-8(8),* Sunset Bks./Sunset Publishing Corp.) Oxmoor Hse., Inc.
Quester, "B" "B". Pop's Mops & Sops - Barbecue & Sauces from Around the World. 2009. 203p. pap. 24.95 *(978-0-557-21016-9(X))* Lulu Enterprises Inc.
Raichlen, Steven. The Barbecue! Bible: Over 500 Recipes! 10th anniv. annot. ed. 2008. (ENG., Illus.). 556p. pap. 22.95 *(978-0-7611-4943-9(0),* 0761149430); 576p. 35.00 *(978-0-7611-4944-6(9),* 0761149449) Workman Publishing Co., Inc.
—Best Ribs Ever: 100 Killer Recipes. 2012. (ENG., Illus.). 320p. pap. 13.95 ***(978-0-7611-6894-2(X),*** 076116894X) Workman Publishing Co., Inc.
Raichlen, Steven. Planet Barbecue! 309 Recipes, 60 Countries. 2010. (ENG., Illus.). 656p. pap. 22.95 *(978-0-7611-4801-2(9),* 0761148019) Workman Publishing Co., Inc.
Rainford, Rob. Rob Rainford's Born to Grill: Over 100 Recipes from My Backyard to Yours. 2012. (ENG., Illus.). 288p. pap. 27.95 ***(978-0-449-01563-6(7))*** Random Hse., Inc.
Rajah, Carol Selva. Barbecues. 2009. (Illus.). 80p. pap. *(978-981-261-564-0(4))* Marshall Cavendish.
Ralph, Gary, ed. Modern Grilling: More Than 300 Recipes & Menus for Grilling Year Round. 2007. (ENG., Illus.). 288p. pap. 24.99 *(978-1-59253-328-2(0),* 1592533280, Quarry Books) Quayside.
Reader, Ted. The Art of Plank Grilling: Licked by Fire, Kissed by Smoke. rev. ed. 2007. (ENG., Illus.). 144p. pap. 19.95 *(978-1-55263-779-1(4))* Key Porter Bks. CAN. Dist: Perseus-PGW.
—Beerlicious: The Art of Grillin' & Chillin' 2012. (ENG., Illus.). 320p. pap. 27.99 ***(978-0-7710-7367-0(4),*** McClelland & Stewart) McClelland & Stewart CAN. Dist: Random Hse., Inc.
—Everyday Gourmet Grilling: Inspired Recipes. 2009. (ENG., Illus.). 296p. pap. 25.00 *(978-1-55470-151-3(1))* Key Porter Bks. CAN. Dist: Perseus-PGW.
—Napoleon's Everyday Gourmet Burgers. 2010. (ENG., Illus.). 320p. pap. 25.00 *(978-1-55470-261-9(5))* Key Porter Bks. CAN. Dist: Perseus-PGW.
—Napoleon's Everyday Gourmet Grilling. 2008. (ENG., Illus.). 296p. 35.00 *(978-1-55470-003-5(5))* Key Porter Bks. CAN. Dist: Perseus-PGW.
—Napoleon's Everyday Gourmet Plank Grilling. 2010. (ENG., Illus.). 240p. pap. 25.00 *(978-1-55470-272-5(0))* Key Porter Bks. CAN. Dist: Perseus-PGW.
—Napoleon's Everyday Plank Grilling. 2009. (ENG., Illus.). 296p. 40.00 *(978-1-55470-150-6(3))* Key Porter Bks. CAN. Dist: Perseus-PGW.
Reed, John Shelton & Reed, Dale Volberg. Holy Smoke: The Big Book of North Carolina Barbecue. 2008. (ENG., Illus.). 328p. 32.00 *(978-0-8078-3243-1(X))* Univ. of North Carolina Pr.
Reinhardt, Julie. She-Smoke: A Backyard Barbecue Book. 2009. (ENG., Illus.). 304p. pap. 16.95 *(978-1-58005-284-9(3))* Seal Pr.
Rodgers, Rick & Kingsford Charcoal Staff. Kingsford Complete Grilling Cookbook. 2007. (ENG., Illus.). 266p. per. 19.95 *(978-0-470-07914-0(2),* Wiley) Wiley, John & Sons, Inc.
Rodgers, Rick, et al. Grilling. Chuck, Williams, ed. rev. ed. 2007. (Food Made Fast Ser.). (ENG., Illus.). 112p. 17.95 *(978-0-8487-3145-8(X))* Oxmoor Hse., Inc.
Rosenfeld, Tony. Sear, Sauce, & Serve: Mastering High-Heat, High-Flavor Cooking. 2011. (ENG.). 240p. pap. 20.00 *(978-0-7624-3872-3(X))* Running Pr. Bk. Pubs.
Ryland Peters & Small Staff, ed. Easy Grilling. 2011. (ENG., Illus.). 240p. *(978-1-84975-111-7(0))* Ryland Peters & Small.
Schlesinger, Chris & Dorling Kindersley Publishing Staff. Grill It! 2010. (ENG., Illus.). 352p. pap. 18.95 *(978-0-7566-6548-7(5))* Dorling Kindersley Publishing, Inc.
Schimm, John. Grilling - Vegan Style! 125 Fired up Recipes to Turn Every Bite into a Backyard BBQ. 2012. (ENG.). 256p. pap. 20.00 ***(978-0-7382-1572-3(4))*** Da Capo Pr., Inc.
Schloss, Andrew & Joachim, David. Fire It Up: More Than 400 Recipes for Grilling Everything. 2011. (ENG., Illus.). 416p. pap. 24.95 *(978-0-8118-6505-0(3))* Chronicle Bks. LLC.
Shewchuk, Ronnie. Barbecue Secrets: The Very Best Recipes, Tips & Tricks from a Barbecue Champion. deluxe ed. 2010. (ENG., Illus.). 496p. pap. 29.95 *(978-1-55285-949-0(5))* Whitecap Bks., Ltd. CAN. Dist: Midpoint Trade Bks., Inc.
Sinnes, A. Cort. 25 Essentials: Techniques for Gas Grilling. 2012. (25 Essentials Ser.). (ENG., Illus.). 128p. spiral bd. 12.95 *(978-1-55832-734-4(7))* Harvard Common Pr.
Siu, George & Heffelfinger, Park. Memphis Blues Barbeque House: The Cookbook Bringin' Southern BBQ Home. 2010. (ENG., Illus.). 192p. pap. 29.95 *(978-1-55285-914-8(2))* Whitecap Bks., Ltd. CAN. Dist: Midpoint Trade Bks., Inc.
Skaria, Alex. Asian Barbecue Book: From Teriyaki to Tandoori. 2011. (ENG., Illus.). 176p. pap. 19.95 *(978-0-8048-4168-9(3))* Tuttle Publishing.
Sloan-McIntosh, Kathleen. 100 Best Grilling Recipes: BBQ Food from Around the World. 2007. (ENG., Illus.). 192p. pap. 19.95 *(978-0-7788-0159-7(4))* Rose, Robert Inc. CAN. Dist: Firefly Bks., Ltd.
Smoliak, Brad. Canadian Barbecue Cookbook. 2008. (ENG.). 160p. pap. *(978-1-55105-600-5(3))* Lone Pine Publishing.
Snoor, Robert. The Sport of Grilling. 2007. 348p. per. 23.99 *(978-1-4343-1569-4(X))* AuthorHouse.
Solomon, Charmaine. The Basic Basics Barbecue Handbook. 2008. (BASIC BASICS Ser.). 192p. pap. 19.95 *(978-1-904010-59-3(8))* Grub Street GBR. Dist: Casemate Pubs. & Bk. Distributors, LLC.
Southern Living Editors. Southern Living Secrets of the South's Best Barbecue. Lorberau, Jane E. & Brennan, Rebecca, eds. rev. ed. 2007. (ENG., Illus.). 336p. pap. 24.95 *(978-0-8487-3153-3(0))* Oxmoor Hse., Inc.
Southern Living Magazine Editors. The Big Book of BBQ: Recipes & Revelations from the Barbecue Belt. 2010. (ENG., Illus.). 288p. pap. 24.95 *(978-0-8487-3332-2(0))* Oxmoor Hse., Inc.
St. John, Robert. New South Grilling: Fresh & Exciting Recipes from the Third Coast. 2008. (Illus.). 272p. 29.95 *(978-1-4013-0837-7(6))* Hyperion Pr.
Stage, John & Radke, Nancy. Dinosaur Bar-B-Que: An American Roadhouse. 2009. (ENG., Illus.). 192p. pap. 19.99 *(978-1-58008-971-5(2))* Ten Speed Pr.
Staten, Vince & Johnson, Greg. Real Barbecue: The Classic Barbecue Guide to the Best Joints Across the USA — with Recipes, Porklore, & More! 2007. (ENG., Illus.). 336p. per. 16.95 *(978-0-7627-4442-8(1))* Globe Pequot Pr., The.
Sunset Books Staff. The Sunset Grill: 125 Tasty Recipes for Casual Get-Togethers & Easy Weeknight Cookouts. Sunset Magazine Editors, ed. 2008. (ENG., Illus.). 256p. per. 21.95 *(978-0-376-02722-1(3),* Sunset Bks./Sunset Publishing Corp.) Oxmoor Hse., Inc.
Table, Sur La. Everyday Grilling: 50 Recipes from Appetizers to Desserts. 2011. (ENG.). 144p. 15.00 *(978-1-4494-0058-3(2))* Andrews McMeel Publishing.
Taste of Home Magazine Editors & Reader's Digest Editors. Parties, Potlucks, & Barbecues: 368 Recipes for Casual Gatherings. 2008. (ENG.). (gr. 12). pap. 15.95 *(978-0-89821-697-4(4))* Reader's Digest Assn., Inc., The.
Taste of Home Staff. Backyard Grilling. 2007. (ENG.). 256p. (gr. 12). pap. 15.95 *(978-0-89821-557-1(9))* Reader's Digest Assn., Inc., The.
—Taste of Home: Grill It! - 300 Recipes & Secrets for Flame-Broiled Success. 2010. (ENG.). 256p. (gr. 12). 15.95 *(978-0-89821-766-7(0))* Reader's Digest Assn., Inc., The.
The Editors of Good Housekeeping. Good Housekeeping Grill It! Mouthwatering Recipes for Unbeatable Barbeque. 2012. (ENG., Illus.). 160p. spiral bd. 14.95 ***(978-1-58816-939-6(1))*** Hearst Communications, Inc.
Thompson, Fred. Barbecue Nation: 350 Hot-off-the-Grill, Tried-and-True Recipes from America's Backyard. 2007. (ENG., Illus.). 348p. per. 18.95 *(978-1-56158-814-5(8),* Taunton) Taunton Pr., Inc.
—Grillin' with Gas: 150 Mouthwatering Recipes for Great Grilled Food. 2009. (ENG., Illus.). 305p. pap. 19.95 *(978-1-60085-031-8(6))* Taunton Pr., Inc.
—Williams-Sonoma Grill Master: The Ultimate Arsenal of Back-to-Basics Recipes for the Grill. 2011. (ENG.). 224p. pap. 24.95 *(978-1-61628-059-8(X))* Weldon Owen, Inc.
Tubby, Linda. 180 Barbecues. Cutler, Jan, ed. 2006. (ENG., Illus.). 256p. 29.99 *(978-0-7548-1678-2(8))* Anness Publishing GBR. Dist: National Bk. Network.
Tunnicliff, Nigel & Weatherell, Kate. Burgers, Wraps & Kebabs. 2008. (ENG., Illus.). 64p. 11.95 *(978-1-904573-71-5(1))* Absolute Pr. GBR. Dist: Independent Pubs. Group.
Venable, W.D. Venable's Book of Grillology: For the beginner or novice Griller. 2007. 48p. per. 12.95 *(978-1-4327-1342-3(6))* Outskirts Pr., Inc.
Veteto, James R. & Maclin, Edward M., eds. The Slaw & the Slow Cooked: Culture & Barbecue in the Mid-South. 2012. (ENG., Illus.). 232p. 59.95 *(978-0-8265-1801-9(X));* pap. 27.95 *(978-0-8265-1802-6(8))* Vanderbilt Univ. Pr.
Walsh, Robb. The Tex-Mex Grill & Backyard Barbacoa Cookbook. 2010. (ENG., Illus.). 256p. pap. 18.99 *(978-0-7679-3073-4(8))* Broadway Bks.
Warnes, Andrew. Savage Barbecue: Race, Culture, & the Invention of America's First Food. 2008. (ENG., Illus.). 224p. pap. 19.95 *(978-0-8203-3109-6(0));* lib. bdg. 59.95 *(978-0-8203-2896-6(0))* Univ. of Georgia Pr.
Weeknight Grilling. 2007. 9.99 *(978-0-9789378-7-4(2))* August Home Publishing Co.
Weinstein, Bruce & Scarbrough, Mark. Grill Thrills! Recipes & Inspiration for Creative Grilling. 2007. (Illus.). 176p. per. 14.95 *(978-1-58159-317-4(1),* Shady Oak Pr.) North American Media Group.
Wells, Carolyn, et al. The Kansas City Barbeque Society Cookbook. 25th anniv. ed. 2010. (ENG.). 336p. 24.99 *(978-0-7407-9010-2(2))* Andrews McMeel Publishing.
Williams, Chuck & Williams-Sonoma Staff. Grilling & Roasting. 2007. (Best of the Lifestyles Ser.). (ENG.). 304p. 24.95 *(978-0-8487-3167-0(0))* Oxmoor Hse., Inc.
Wilinsky, Helen. Jerk from Jamaica: Barbecue Caribbean Style. 2007. (ENG., Illus.). 192p. pap. 18.99 *(978-1-58008-842-8(2))* Ten Speed Pr.

B

Witzel, Michael Karl. Barbecue Road Trip: Recipes, Restaurants, & Pitmasters from America's Great Barbecue Regions. 2008. (ENG., Illus.). 192p. 30.00 *(978-0-7603-2752-4(1)*, 0760327521, Voyageur Pr) MBI Publishing Co. LLC.

Wiviott, Gary & Rush, Colleen. Low & Slow: Master the Art of Barbecue in 5 Easy Lessons. 2009. (ENG.). 256p. pap. 19.95 *(978-0-7624-3609-5(3))* Running Pr. Bk. Pubs.

Zien, Sam. Sam the Cooking Guy: Just Grill This! 2011. (ENG., Illus.). 272p. pap. 19.95 *(978-0-470-46793-0(2)*, Wiley) Wiley, John & Sons, Inc.

Zinczenko, David & Goulding, Matt. Grill This, Not That! Backyard Survival Guide. 2012. (ENG., Illus.). 368p. pap. 19.99 ***(978-1-60961-822-3(X))*** Rodale Pr., Inc.

BARBED WIRE

Liu, Joanne. Barbed Wire. 2009. 0208p. pap. 14.00 *(978-0-87842-557-0(8))* Mountain Pr. Publishing Co., Inc.

McCallum, Henry D. Barbed Wire in Texas: Southwestern Historical Quarterly V61, No. 2, October 1957. Carroll, H. Bailey & Ransom, Harry H., eds. 2011. 28p. 35.95 ***(978-1-258-05523-3(6))*** Literary Licensing, LLC.

Netz, Reviel. Barbed Wire: An Ecology of Modernity. 2009. (ENG., Illus.). 288p. pap. 24.95 *(978-0-8195-6959-2(3))* Wesleyan Univ. Pr.

BARBEQUING

see Barbecuing

BARBER, JEDEDIAH, 1787-1876

Howe, Herbert B. Jedediah Barber, 1787-1876: A Footnote to the History of the Military Tract of Central New York. reprint ed. 20.00 *(978-0-404-03356-9(3))* AMS Pr., Inc.

BARBER, SAMUEL, 1910-1981

Barber, Samuel. Ten Selected Songs: High Voice. 2008. (ENG.). 32p. pap. 19.95 incl. audio compact disk *(978-1-4234-3893-9(0)*, 1423438930, G Schirmer, Inc.) Leonard, Hal Corp.

—Ten Selected Songs: Low Voice. 2008. (ENG.). 32p. pap. 19.95 incl. audio compact disk *(978-1-4234-3894-6(9)*, 1423438949, G Schirmer, Inc.) Leonard, Hal Corp.

Dickinson, Peter. Samuel Barber Remembered: A Centenary Tribute. 2010. (Eastman Studies in Music Ser.: Volume 74). (Illus.). 214p. 49.95 *(978-1-58046-350-8(9))* Univ. of Rochester Pr.

Flachs, David, ed. Samuel Barber - Commemorative March: Piano Trio First Edition. 2010. (ENG.). 12p. pap. 12.99 *(978-1-61774-263-7(5)*, 1617742635, G Schirmer, Inc.) Leonard, Hal Corp.

Heyman, Barbara B. Samuel Barber: A Thematic Catalogue of the Complete Works, 1 vol. 2012. (ENG.). 608p. 99.00 *(978-0-19-974464-0(5))* Oxford Univ. Pr., Inc.

Wentzel, Wayne. Samuel Barber: A Research & Information Guide. 2nd rev. ed. 2010. 448p. 150.00 *(978-0-415-87558-5(7)*, Routledge) Taylor & Francis Group GBR. Dist: Taylor & Francis Group.

Wentzel, Wayne C. Samuel Barber. 2nd ed. 2010. xii, 466p. instr.'s gde. ed. 150.00 incl. cd-rom *(978-0-203-86003-8(9))* Routledge.

Wentzel, Wayne C. Samuel Barber: A Research & Information Guide. 2nd ed. 2010. xii, 466p. ***(978-0-415-85758-1(9))*** Routledge.

BARBER, RED, 1908-1992

Barber, Rowland. Rhubarb in the Catbird Seat. 27.95 *(978-0-8488-1565-3(3))* Amereon LTD.

BARBERS

Andrews, William. At the Sign of the Barber's Pole: Studies in Hirsute History. 2009. 140p. 21.99 *(978-0-559-91457-7(1))*; pap. 15.99 *(978-0-559-91455-3(5))* BiblioBazaar.

The Barber of Charleston: Life Lessons from the Depression. 2009. (Illus.). 180p. pap. 10.00 *(978-1-935272-01-4(2))* Southern Lion Bks.

Bensie, Dennis Milam. Shorn: Toys to Men. 2011. 268p. pap. 17.95 *(978-1-60381-092-0(7)*, Coffeetown Pr.) Coffeetown Enterprises, Inc.

Bristol, Douglas Walter, Jr. Knights of the Razor: Black Barbers in Slavery & Freedom. 2009. (ENG., Illus.). 232p. (gr. 17). 52.00 *(978-0-8018-9283-7(X))* Johns Hopkins Univ. Pr.

Chip. 50% Cut & 50% What Makes the Successful Barber: A Barber's True Story. 2008. 108p. pap. 19.95 *(978-1-60474-994-6(6))* PublishAmerica, Inc.

Lowther, Hastie. Willie E. Lowther: The Journey of My Life. 2007. (Illus.). 328p. per. 24.95 net. *(978-0-9742773-6-3(3))* Soleil Pr.

Mathis, Nathaniel. Portrait of a Professional. 2011. 216p. pap. 19.99 ***(978-1-4628-9454-3(2))*** Xlibris Corp.

Milady. Exam Review for Milady's Standard Professional Barbering. 5th ed. 2010. (ENG.). 192p. (C). pap. 39.95 *(978-1-4354-9712-2(0)*, Milady Publishing Co.) Delmar Cengage Learning.

—Exam Review, Spanish, for Milady's Standard Professional Barbering. 5th ed. 2010. (ENG.). 192p. (C). pap. 50.50 *(978-1-4354-9706-1(6)*, Milady Publishing Co.) Delmar Cengage Learning.

—Milady's Standard Professional Barbering, Spanish Edition. 5th ed. 2010. (ENG.). 848p. (C). pap. 131.50 *(978-1-4354-9708-5(2)*, Milady Publishing Co.) Delmar Cengage Learning.

—Student CD for Milady's Standard Professional Barbering. 5th ed. 2010. (ENG.). (C). 54.95 *(978-1-4354-9709-2(0)*, Milady Publishing Co.) Delmar Cengage Learning.

—Student Workbook for Milady's Standard Professional Barbering. 5th ed. 2010. (ENG.). 224p. (C). pap. 57.50 *(978-1-4354-9713-9(9)*, Milady Publishing Co.) Delmar Cengage Learning.

—Student Workbook, Spanish, for Milady's Standard Professional Barbering. 5th ed. 2010. (ENG.). 224p. (C). pap. 69.50 *(978-1-4354-9707-8(4)*, Milady Publishing Co.) Delmar Cengage Learning.

Milady Publishing Company Staff. Milady's Standard Professional Barbering Interactive Games CD-ROM. 5th ed. 2010. (ENG.). (C). 78.50 *(978-1-111-31333-3(4)*, Milady Publishing Co.) Delmar Cengage Learning.

Mueller, Gerry M. M. C. The Life of a Barber the Dos & Taboos: The Biography of John Tenuta. 2011. 102p. 24.99 ***(978-1-4628-9473-4(9))***; pap. 15.99 ***(978-1-4628-9472-7(0))*** Xlibris Corp.

Rothman, Irving, ed. The Barber in Modern Jewish Culture: A Genre of People, Places, & Things, with Illustrations. 2008. (Illus.). 680p. 149.95 *(978-0-7734-5072-1(6))* Mellen, Edwin Pr., The.

Willie E. Lowther: From Locust Grove to Harlem: the Journey of My Life. 2008. (Illus.). 328p. 36.95 *(978-0-9742773-8-7(X))* Soleil Pr.

Wright, Curtis. Behind the Chair: Rantings of a Burnt Out Stylist. 2009. 79p. pap. 14.95 *(978-1-4327-4239-3(6))* Outskirts Pr., Inc.

BARBERSHOPS

see also Barbers

Mayoral, Avelino R. Wacky Barbershop Cartoons. 2010. 101p. pap. 19.52 *(978-0-557-52724-3(4))* Lulu Enterprises Inc.

Nunley, Vorris. Keepin' It Hushed: The Barbershop & African American Hush Harbor Rhetoric. 2010. pap. 24.95 *(978-0-8143-3348-8(6))* Wayne State Univ. Pr.

Weiss, Brad. Street Dreams & Hip Hop Barbershops: Global Fantasy in Urban Tanzania. 2009. (Tracking Globalization Ser.). (ENG., Illus.). 280p. 65.00 *(978-0-253-32594-5(3)*, 0253325943); pap. 24.95 *(978-0-253-22075-2(0)*, 0253220750) Indiana Univ. Pr.

Weller, Simon & Walker, Garth. South African Township Barbershops & Salons. 2011. (ENG., Illus.). 128p. 27.95 *(978-1-935613-04-6(9))* Batty, Mark Pub., LLC.

BARBIE DOLLS

Augustyniak, J. Michael. Barbie Doll Around the World, 1964-2007. rev. ed. 2007. (ENG., Illus.). 368p. 29.95 *(978-1-57432-530-0(2)*, 1574325302) Collector Bks.

D'Amato, Jennie. Barbie: All Dolled Up - Celebrating 50 Years of Barbie. 2009. (ENG., Illus.). 128p. 29.95 *(978-0-7624-3686-6(7)*, Running Pr.) Running Pr. Bk. Pubs.

Day, Dennis. Barbie Dollhouse Plans Book One. 2008. 204p. pap. 39.95 *(978-1-4357-1344-4(3))* Lulu Enterprises Inc.

Deutsch, Stefanie & Dorfmann, Bettina. Barbie - The First 30 Years: 1959 Through 1989 & Beyond. 3rd ed. 2008. (ENG., Illus.). 384p. 29.95 *(978-1-57432-595-9(7)*, 1574325957) Collector Bks.

Gerber, Robin. Barbie & Ruth: The Story of the World's Most Famous Doll & the Woman Who Created Her. (ENG.). 288p. 2010. pap. 14.99 *(978-0-06-134132-8(0)*, Harper Paperbacks) 2009. (Illus.). 24.99 *(978-0-06-134131-1(2)*, Collins) HarperCollins Pubs.

Holder, Sandi. Barbie: A Rare Beauty. 2010. (ENG., Illus.). 224p. 30.00 *(978-1-4402-1279-6(1))* Krause Pubns.

James, Hillary Shilkitus. The Complete & Unauthorized Guide to Vintage Barbie(r) Dolls with Barbie(r) & Skipper(r) Fashions & the Whole Family of Barbie(r) Dolls. 2011. (Illus.). 160p. *(978-0-7643-3813-7(7)*, Schiffer Publishing Ltd) Schiffer Publishing, Ltd.

McDonough, Yona Zeldis. Barbie. (ENG., 2010. Illus.). 128p. 45.00 *(978-2-7594-0473-5(0))* 2008. 695.00 *(978-2-7594-0311-0(4))* Assouline FRA. Dist: Perseus Distribution.

Verbeten, Sharon. Barbie Doll. 2nd ed. 2009. (ENG., Illus.). 512p. pap. 12.99 *(978-0-89689-700-7(1))* Krause Pubns.

BARBITURATES

Henn, Debra & DeEugenio, Deborah. Barbiturates. Triggle, David J., ed. 2007. (Drugs Ser.). (Illus.). 112p. (YA). (gr. 9-12). lib. bdg. 30.00 *(978-0-7910-8548-6(1))* Facts On File, Inc.

BARBIZON SCHOOL

Finckh, Gerhard & Birthälmer, Antje. Abenteuer Barbizon. 2007. (Illus.). 299p. *(978-3-89202-066-0(3))* Von der Heydt-Museum der Stadt Wuppertal.

BARBUDA

Anderson, Brian & Anderson, Ellen. Antigua & Barbuda. 2nd rev. ed. (Illus.). 96p. pap. 11.95 *(978-1-84306-061-1(2))* Hunter Publishing, Inc.

Buhle, Paul. Tim Hector: A Caribbean Radical's Story. 2006. (ENG., Illus.). 272p. 32.00 *(978-1-57806-851-7(7))* Univ. Pr. of Mississippi.

Icon Group International, Inc. Staff, compiled by. The 2006 Economic & Product Market Databook for Codrington, Antigua & Barbuda. 2006. 618p. ring bd. 95.00 *(978-0-497-80388-9(7))* Icon Group International, Inc.

BARCELONA (SPAIN)

Aracil Martí, Rafael, et al. Diari D'una Postguerra: La Vanguardia Española (1939-1946) 2010. (Recerca I Pensament Ser.: Vol. 58). (CAT.). 229p. *(978-84-92542-39-0(X))* Afers, Editorial, S.L.

Bonet i Armengol, Jordi, et al. La Sagrada Familia de Gaudí: El Templo Expiatorio Desde Sus Orígenes Hasta Hoy. 2010. (ENG & SPA., Illus.). 303p. *(978-84-9785-684-3(8))* Lunwerg Editores, S.A.

Dalmau, Antoni. El Cas Rull: Viure Del Terror a la Ciutat de les Bombes (1901-1908) 2008. (CAT., Illus.). 411p. *(978-84-664-0897-4(5))* Columna Edicions.

De Sola Morales, Manuel. Ten Lessons on Barcelona: Urbanistic Episodes That Have Made the Modern City. 2008.Tr. of Diez Lecciones Sobre Barcelona: Los Episodios Urbanísticos Que Han Hecho la Ciudad Moderna. (Illus.). 584p. pap. *(978-84-96842-24-3(X))* Actar Birkhauser Distribution.

Fodor's. Fodor's Barcelona, 4th Edition: With Highlights of Catalonia & Bilbao. 2012. (Full-color Travel Guide Ser.). (ENG.). 408p. pap. 19.99 ***(978-0-307-92917-4(5)***, Fodor's) Fodor's Travel Pubns.

Martínez Fiol, David & Martínez Fiol, David. La Setmana Tràgica. 2009. (CAT., Illus.). 165p. *(978-84-9809-068-0(7))* Portic Editorial.

Robinson, William H., et al. Barcelona & Modernity: Picasso, Gaudi, Miro, Dali. 2006. (ENG., Illus.). 524p. 65.00 *(978-0-300-12106-3(7))* Yale Univ. Pr.

Sala, Teresa-M. Barcelona 1900. 2007. (Illus.). 196p. 57.95 *(978-0-8014-4657-3(0))* Cornell Univ. Pr.

Sprague, Paula A. El Europeo: (Barcelona, 1823-1824): Prensa, Modernidad y Universalismo. 2009. (SPA.). pap. 175.00 *(978-84-8489-430-8(4))* Iberoamericana Vervuert Publishing Corp.

Tejero, Elisabet & Torrabadella, Laura. Vidas Al Descubierto: Historias de Vida de Los "Sin Techo" 2010. (SPA., Illus.). 215p. *(978-84-9888-214-8(1))* Icaria.

Theros, Xavier. La Sisena Flota a Barcelona: Quan Els Nord-Americans Enväien la Rambla. 2010. (CAT., Illus.). 454p. *(978-84-96735-49-1(4))* La Campana, Edicions, S.L.

BARCELONA (SPAIN)—DESCRIPTION AND TRAVEL

AA Publishing Staff & Hayes, Lucie. Barcelona. 2009. (Great Walks Ser.). (ENG., Illus.). 176p. pap. 15.99 *(978-0-470-45373-5(7)*, Frommers) Wiley, John & Sons, Inc.

AAD Barcelona. 2011. 192p. pap. 12.95 *(978-3-8327-9465-1(4))* teNeues Publishing Co.

Asensio, Francisco. Barcelona Style. (SPA., Illus.). 200p. *(978-84-89439-57-3(5))* A. Asppan, S.L. Distribuidora Internacional de Libros y Revistas.

Barcelona. (Illus.). 144p. per. 14.95 *(978-88-7009-846-4(X))* Casa Editrice Bonechi ITA. Dist: CPG Publishing, Inc.

Barcelona. (Illus.). pap. *(978-3-8283-0055-2(3))* Hallwag Verlag GmbH DEU. Dist: Rand McNally.

Barcelona City Guide - Insight Guides. 7th ed. 2012. (City Guide Ser.). (Illus.). 320p. pap. 19.99 ***(978-1-78005-055-3(0))*** APA Publications Services SGP. Dist: Ingram Pub. Services.

Barcelona48. 2007. 44.95 *(978-0-9792639-0-3(5))* Orange Cup Media.

Benson, Andrew & Fisher, Teresa. AAA Spiral Barcelona, 4th Edition. 4th ed. 2010. (ENG.). 214p. spiral bd. 17.95 *(978-1-59508-390-6(1))* AAA.

Bofill, Roser, ed. Barcelona: Arquitectura Floral/Floral Architecture. Santamaria, Elia, tr. 2007. (ENG., Illus.). 144p. 85.00 *(978-90-5856-223-4(9)*, Stichting Kunstboak (Acc)) Antique Collectors' Club GBR. Dist: National Bk. Network.

Bourmer, Achim & Nahm, Peter M. Barcelona Baedeker Guide. 2012. (Baedeker Guides Ser.). (ENG., Illus.). 256p. pap. 20.00 ***(978-3-8297-6541-1(X))*** Marco Polo Travel Publishing GBR. Dist: Innovative Logistics.

Brown, Jules. The Rough Guide to Barcelona. 9th ed. 2012. (Rough Guide To... Ser.). (ENG., Illus.). 366p. 19.99 *(978-1-4053-8697-5(5))* Rough Guides, Ltd. GBR. Dist: Dorling Kindersley Publishing, Inc.

Brown, Jules & Rough Guides Staff. Pocket Rough Guide to Barcelona. 2010. (Rough Guide Pocket Guides). (ENG., Illus.). 192p. 12.99 *(978-1-84836-600-8(0))* Rough Guides, Ltd. GBR. Dist: Dorling Kindersley Publishing, Inc.

Bryant, Sue. Barcelona Travel Pack, 6th. 6th ed. 2010. (Globetrotter Travel Packs Ser.). (ENG., Illus.). 128p. 14.95 *(978-1-84773-622-2(X)*, Globetrotter) New Holland Pubs., Ltd. GBR. Dist: Globe Pequot Pr., The.

—The Best of Barcelona. 2nd ed. 2008. (Globetrotter Best of Ser.). (ENG., Illus.). 96p. pap. 8.95 *(978-1-84773-021-3(3))* New Holland Pubs., Ltd. GBR. Dist: Globe Pequot Pr., The.

Chronicle Books Staff & Andrews, Sarah. Barcelona: 50 Adventures on Foot. 2007. (City Walks Ser.: CITY). (ENG.). 50p. 14.95 *(978-0-8118-5911-0(8))* Chronicle Bks. LLC.

Cool Barcelona. 2011. 192p. pap. 12.95 *(978-3-8327-9495-8(6))* teNeues Publishing Co.

Explorer Publishing & Distribution. Barcelona Mini Explorer. rev. ed. 2008. (ENG.). 200p. pap. 11.95 *(978-9948-03-445-2(7))* Explorer Publishing UAE. Dist: Globe Pequot Pr., The.

Facaros, Dana & Pauls, Michael. Barcelona & Catalonia. 2009. (Illus.). 320p. pap. *(978-1-86011-421-2(0))* Cadogan Guides GBR. Dist: Globe Pequot Pr., The.

—Barcelona & Catalonia. 2009. (ENG., Illus.). 352p. pap. 21.95 *(978-1-56656-768-8(8))* Interlink Publishing Group, Inc.

Farino, Teresa & Lockwood, Michael. Costa Brava & Barcelona. (Illus.). 136p. pap. 14.95 *(978-1-85691-222-8(1))* Sunflower Bks. (UK) GBR. Dist: Hunter Publishing, Inc.

Fisher, Teresa. AAA Essential Barcelona, 4th Edition. 5th ed. 2011. (ENG.). 192p. pap. 11.95 *(978-1-59508-413-2(4))* AAA.

Fodor's Travel Publications, Inc. Staff. Barcelona: With Highlights of Catalonia & Bilbao. 3rd ed. 2010. (Full-Color Gold Guides). (ENG., Illus.). 416p. pap. 19.99 *(978-1-4000-0423-2(3)*, Fodor's) Fodor's Travel Pubns.

—Fodor's Barcelona's 25 Best, 6th Edition. 2010. (25 Best Ser.). (ENG.). 128p. pap. 11.99 *(978-1-4000-0538-3(8)*, Fodor's) Fodor's Travel Pubns.

Gallagher, Mary-Ann, et al. Eyewitness Travel Guides - Barcelona & Catalonia. 2011. (Eyewitness Travel Guides). (ENG.). 208p. 20.00 *(978-0-7566-6936-2(7))* Dorling Kindersley Publishing, Inc.

Gd, Insight. Barcelona. 6th rev. ed. 2010. (City Guide Ser.). (ENG., Illus.). 320p. pap. 19.99 *(978-981-282-158-4(9))* APA Publications Services SGP. Dist: Ingram Pub. Services.

Gd, Insight & Thomas Cook Publishing Staff. Barcelona. 3rd ed. 2010. (Thomas Cook Pocket Guides). (ENG., Illus.). 160p. pap. 9.95 *(978-1-84848-284-5(1))* Cook, Thomas Publishing GBR. Dist: Globe Pequot Pr., The.

Golden Book on Barcelona. (Illus.). 96p. pap. *(978-88-7009-865-5(6))* Casa Editrice Bonechi.

Hachette Staff. A Great Weekend in Barcelona. (Great Weekend Ser.). (Illus.). 144p. 9.95 *(978-1-84202-005-0(6))* Cassell Guides GBR. Dist: Sterling Publishing Co., Inc.

Ham, Anthony. Barcelona. 3rd rev. ed. 2012. (Encounter Ser.). (ENG., Illus.). 192p. pap. 12.99 ***(978-1-74179-716-9(0))*** Lonely Planet Pubns.

Harvard Student Agencies, Inc. Let's Go Barcelona: The Student Travel Guide. 2010. (Let's Go Ser.). (ENG., Illus.). 256p. pap. 17.95 *(978-1-59880-307-5(7)*, Let's Go) Avalon Travel Publishing.

Harvard Student Agencies Inc. Staff & Avalon Travel Publishing Staff. Let's Go Madrid & Barcelona: The Student Travel Guide. 2010. (Let's Go Ser.). (ENG., Illus.). 240p. pap. 14.95 *(978-1-59880-714-1(5)*, Let's Go) Avalon Travel Publishing.

Hayes, Lucie. Barcelona. 2nd ed. 2008. (ENG., Illus.). 152p. pap. 9.95 *(978-1-905131-24-2(0))* Blue Guides Ltd. GBR. Dist: Norton, W. W. & Co., Inc.

Horn, Petra. Barcelona: The Rhytmus of Catalunya. 2007. (ENG., Illus.). 124p. 50.00 *(978-3-937406-92-3(1)*, Earbooks) edel classics GmbH DEU. Dist: AtlasBooks Distribution.

Hughes, Robert. Barcelona the Great Enchantress. 2007. (Directions Ser.). (ENG., Illus.). 192p. per. 12.95 *(978-1-4262-0131-8(1)*, National Geographic) National Geographic Society.

Ingrosso, Chiara. Barcelona: City, Architecture, Society, 1975-2015. 2011. (ENG., Illus.). 192p. pap. 45.00 *(978-88-572-0056-9(6))* Skira Editore ITA. Dist: Random Hse., Inc.

Insight Guides, creator. Insight Guides Barcelona Step by Step. 2008. (Step by Step Ser.). (ENG., Illus.). 128p. pap. 14.95 *(978-981-258-841-8(8))* APA Publications Services SGP. Dist: Ingram Pub. Services.

Knopf Guides. Knopf MapGuide: Barcelona. 2007. (ENG.). pap. 10.95 *(978-0-307-26386-5(X)*, Knopf) Knopf Doubleday Publishing Group.

Lonely Planet Staff & Simonis, Damien. Barcelona. 7th rev. ed. 2010. (City Guide Ser.). (ENG., Illus.). 300p. pap. 19.99 *(978-1-74179-593-6(1))* Lonely Planet Pubns.

Maggi, A. 22 Days in Barcelona. 2009. (ENG.). 180p. 69.00 *(978-88-6302-015-1(9)*, Art Stock Bks. Ltd/Csi) Continental Sales, Inc.

Marco Polo. Barcelona Marco Polo Guide. 2012. (Marco Polo Guides Ser.). (ENG., Illus.). 148p. pap. 9.99 ***(978-3-8297-0652-0(9))*** Marco Polo Travel Publishing GBR. Dist: Innovative Logistics.

Michelin Must Sees. Michelin Must Sees Barcelona. 2010. (Must See Guides/Michelin Ser.). (ENG., Illus.). 160p. pap. 12.99 *(978-1-907099-00-7(X))* Michelin Travel & Lifestyle.

Moix, Llatzer & Moix Puig, Llàtzer. Barcelona Guide & Map, 1 vol. 2011. (ENG.). 64p. pap. 16.00 *(978-84-8478-484-5(3))* Triangle Postals, S.L. ESP. Dist: Innovative Logistics.

MONOCO BOOKS, compiled by. Inguide. 2011. (ENG., Illus.). 256p. 14.95 *(978-3-89944-775-0(1)*, Monaco Bks.) Verlag Wolfgang Kunth GmbH & Co. KG DEU. Dist: Innovative Logistics.

Montalban, Manuel Vazquez & Vivas Ortiz, Pere. Barcelona, 1 vol. 2011. (ENG, CAT, FRE, GER & SPA., Illus.). 280p. 53.00 *(978-84-8478-204-9(2))* Triangle Postals, S.L. ESP. Dist: Innovative Logistics.

Montes, Christina. Barcelona by Night. (Illus.). 128p. *(978-84-89439-72-6(9))* A. Asppan, S.L. Distribuidora Internacional de Libros y Revistas.

Oliva, Héctor & Oliva Camps, Héctor. Veinte Historias de la Barcelona Americana: — Y una Pregunta Descarada. 2008. (SPA., Illus.). 180p. *(978-84-92437-05-4(7))* Base, Editorial.

Permanyer, L. & Venteo, Daniel. Barcelona en Diagonal: Una Crònica Gràfica. 2010. (CAT., Illus.). 151p. *(978-84-8330-626-0(3))* Viena Serveis Editorial.

Pla, Ricard & Vivas, Pere. Close up Barcelona, 1 vol. 2012. (ENG.). 152p. pap. 15.00 *(978-84-8478-481-4(9))* Triangle Postals, S.L. ESP. Dist: Innovative Logistics.

—Close up Batlló, 1 vol. 2012. (ENG.). 152p. pap. 15.00 *(978-84-8478-479-1(7))* Triangle Postals, S.L. ESP. Dist: Innovative Logistics.

—Close up Gaudí, 1 vol. 2012. (ENG.). 152p. pap. 15.00 *(978-84-8478-480-7(0))* Triangle Postals, S.L. ESP. Dist: Innovative Logistics.

PopOut Products. Barcelona Inside Out. 2010. (Illus.). 64p. 10.95 *(978-1-84587-804-7(3))* Globe Pequot Pr., The.

Ross, Alice, et al. Barcelona: The Complete Residents' Guide. rev. ed. 2008. (Explorer (Explorer Publishing) Ser.). (ENG., Illus.). 452p. pap. 24.95 *(978-9948-03-380-6(9))* Explorer Publishing UAE. Dist: Globe Pequot Pr., The.

Sainsbury, Brendan & Simonis, Damien. Lonely Planet Discover Barcelona. 2011. (City Guide Ser.). (ENG., Illus.). 272p. pap. 19.99 *(978-1-74220-280-8(2))* Lonely Planet Pubns.

Schlecht, Neil Edward. Frommer's Barcelona Day by Day. 2nd ed. 2010. (Frommer's Day by Day - Pocket Ser.: 135). (ENG., Illus.). 192p. pap. 13.99 *(978-0-470-62780-8(8)*, Frommers) Wiley, John & Sons, Inc.

Simonis, Damien. Barcelona. 3rd rev. ed. 2009. (ENG., Illus.). 272p. 22.95 *(978-1-4262-0395-4(0)*, National Geographic) National Geographic Society.

Simonis, Damien & Lonely Planet Staff. Barcelona. 2nd rev. ed. 2009. (Encounter Ser.). (ENG., Illus.). 208p. pap. 12.99 *(978-1-74179-161-7(8))* Lonely Planet Pubns.

Sorensen, AnneLise & Chandler, Ryan. Top 10 Barcelona. 2012. (Eyewitness top 10 travel Guide Ser.). (ENG.). 160p. 14.00 *(978-0-7566-8450-1(1))* Dorling Kindersley Publishing, Inc.

Steves, Rick. Rick Steves' Snapshot Barcelona. 2009. (Rick Steves Snapshot Ser.). (ENG.). 108p. pap. 8.95 *(978-1-59880-488-1(X))* Avalon Travel Publishing.

Stone, Peter. Frommer's Barcelona. 4th ed. 2011. (Frommer's Complete Guides: 992). (ENG., Illus.). 352p. pap. 17.99 *(978-0-470-71124-8(8),* Frommers) Wiley, John & Sons, Inc.

Taschen, Angelika, ed. Barcelona: Restaurants & More. 2007. (Illus.). 192p. pap. 14.99 *(978-90-00-00053-1(X))* TASCHEN DEU. Dist: Ingram Pub. Services.

—Barcelona Restaurants & More. 2008. (ENG., Illus.). 190p. pap. 14.99 *(978-3-8365-0053-1(1))* TASCHEN DEU. Dist: Ingram Pub. Services.

—Barcelona, Shops & More. 2008. (ENG., Illus.). 191p. pap. 14.99 *(978-3-8365-0055-5(8))* TASCHEN DEU. Dist: Ingram Pub. Services.

teNeues, creator. Cool Barcelona. 2009. 224p. pap. 12.95 *(978-3-8327-9202-2(3))* teNeues Publishing Co.

Thomas Cook Publishing Staff. Traveller Guides Barcelona. 4th ed. 2011. (Travellers - Thomas Cook Ser.). (ENG., Illus.). 192p. pap. 16.95 *(978-1-84848-339-2(2))* Cook, Thomas Publishing GBR. Dist: Globe Pequot Pr., The.

Time Out Guides Staff. Time Out Barcelona. 14th ed. 2011. (Time Out Guides). (ENG., Illus.). 352p. pap. 19.95 *(978-1-84670-218-1(6))* Time Out Guides Ltd. GBR. Dist: Perseus-PGW.

Time Out Guides Staff, ed. Time Out Shortlist Barcelona 2012. 2011. (Time Out Shortlist Ser.). (ENG., Illus.). 192p. pap. 12.95 *(978-1-84670-235-8(6))* Time Out Guides Ltd. GBR. Dist: Perseus-PGW.

Vivas Ortiz, Pere. The Basilica of the Sagrada Familia, 1 vol. 2011. (ENG.). 240p. pap. 16.95 *(978-84-8478-511-8(4))* Triangle Postals, S.L. ESP. Dist: Innovative Logistics.

VV., AA., et al. Guia Popout - Barcelona. Compass Map. ed. 2008. 15.95 *(978-84-670-2677-1(4))* Espasa Calpe, S.A. ESP. Dist: Planeta Publishing Corp.

VV Staff. Barcelona y Gaudi: La Ruta Del Modernismo. (SPA.). 200p. *(978-84-36241-13-8(0))* A. Asppan, S.L. Distribuidora Internacional de Libros y Revistas.

Wales, Suzanne. Night+Day Barcelona. 2009. (Cool Cities Series from Pulse Guides). (Illus.). 236p. pap. 17.95 *(978-1-934724-17-0(3))* Davis, A. S. Media Group.

Wallpaper Magazine Editors, ed. Wallpaper City Guide - Barcelona. 2011. (ENG.). 128p. pap. 9.95 ***(978-0-7148-6279-8(7))*** Phaidon Pr., Inc.

BARCODING

see Bar Coding

BARDOT, BRIGITTE, 1934-

Baroni, Maurizio & D'Ubaldo, Marco. Brigitte Bardot: A Collection of Rare Photos & Original Posters & Music from the Complete Filmography of the Devine. 2009. (Amarkord Ser.). (ENG., Illus.). 129p. 17.95 *(978-88-96042-08-3(9))* Mediane ITA. Dist: Ingram Pub. Services.

Singer, Barnett. Brigitte Bardot: A Biography. 2006. (ENG., Illus.). 208p. 55.00 *(978-0-7864-2515-0(6))* McFarland & Co., Inc. Pubs.

BARDS AND BARDISM

see also Meistersinger; Minnesingers; Minstrels; Scalds and Scaldic Poetry; Troubadours; Trouveres

Delyth, Jen. Celtic Folk Soul: Art, Myth & Symbol. 2008. (Illus.). 228p. 35.00 *(978-1-60237-116-3(4))* Amber Lotus Publishing.

Manwaring, Kevan. Turning the Wheel. 2011. (ENG.). 313p. pap. 26.95 ***(978-1-84694-766-7(9))*** Hunt, John Publishing Ltd. GBR. Dist: National Bk. Network.

Manwaring, Kevan. The Way of Awen. 2010. (ENG.). 480p. pap. 29.95 *(978-1-84694-311-9(6))* Hunt, John Publishing Ltd. GBR. Dist: National Bk. Network.

O'Grady, Standish. Early Bardic Literature, Ireland. 2009. 92p. pap. 18.75 *(978-1-113-11166-1(6))* BiblioBazaar.

—Early Bardic Literature, Ireland. 2009. 284p. pap. *(978-0-217-77932-6(8))* Books LLC.

—Early Bardic Literature, Ireland. 2007. (ENG.). 56p. per. *(978-1-4065-3183-1(9))* Dodo Pr.

O'Riordan, Michelle. Irish Bardic Poetry & Rhetorical Reality. 2007. 482p. 49.00 *(978-1-85918-414-1(6))* Cork Univ. Pr. IRL. Dist: Stylus Publishing, LLC.

BAREFOOT, BEAUREGARD

Lucas, Kemba Jarena. The Barefoot Journey: Unrestricted to Fulfill Purpose. 2009. 158p. pap. 22.95 *(978-0-557-00688-5(0))* Lulu Enterprises Inc.

BARERE DE VIEUZAC, BERTRAND, 1755-1841

Gershoy, Leo. Bertrand Barere: A Reluctant Terrorist. 2011. 480p. 58.95 ***(978-1-258-06780-9(3))*** Literary Licensing, LLC.

BARGAINING

see Collective Bargaining; Negotiation

BARGELLO

see Canvas Embroidery

BARGES

Browne, Marie. Narrow Margins. 2009. (ENG.). 306p. pap. 11.95 ***(978-1-907016-00-4(7))*** Accent Pr. Ltd. GBR. Dist: SCB Distributors.

—Narrow Minds. 2012. (ENG.). 320p. 11.95 ***(978-1-908086-95-2(5),*** Xcite Bk.) Accent Pr. Ltd. GBR. Dist: SCB Distributors.

Conder, Tony. Canal Narrowboats & Barges. 2008. (Shire Library). (ENG., Illus.). 56p. pap. 12.95 *(978-0-7478-0587-8(3))* Shire Pubns., Ltd. GBR. Dist: Random Hse., Inc.

Langdon, David. A History of New Zealand Scows & their Trades. 2009. (ENG., Illus.). 336p. *(978-1-877197-36-9(X))* Captain Teach Pr.

BARIATRIC SURGERY

see Obesity—Surgery

BARING-GOULD, SABINE, 1834-1924

Rogal, Samuel J., ed. The Music & Poetry of Onward, Christian Soldiers (1864) & Sabine Baring-Gould (1834-1924) A Sung Prayer of the Protestant Tradition. 2009. 60p. 39.95 *(978-0-7734-3873-6(4))* Mellen, Edwin Pr., The.

BARINGS BANK

Drummond, Helga. The Dynamics of Organizational Collapse: The Case of Barings Bank. (Routledge International Studies in Money & Banking Ser.). 2012. (ENG.). 160p. (C). pap. 42.95 ***(978-0-415-54270-8(7))*** 2007. XVI, 144p. 143.00 *(978-0-415-39961-6(0))* Routledge.

BARIUM TITANATE

Rout, Sanjeeb Kumar. Structural & Dielectric Study of Barium Titanate Zirconate System. 2010. 196p. pap. *(978-3-8383-8678-2(7))* Lambert Academic Publishing.

BARK

see also Wood

McCurry, Chris & Chase, Nan. Bark House Style: Sustainable Designs from Nature, 1 vol. 2008. (ENG., Illus.). 152p. 30.00 *(978-1-4236-0214-9(5))* Gibbs Smith, Publisher.

Pollet, Cedric. Bark: An Intimate Look at the World's Trees. 2010. (ENG., Illus.). 192p. 45.00 *(978-0-7112-3137-5(0))* Lincoln, Frances Ltd. GBR. Dist: Perseus-PGW.

Vaucher, Hugues. Tree Bark: A Color Guide. 2010. (ENG.). 262p. pap. 59.95 *(978-1-60469-248-8(0),* 1604692480) Timber Pr., Inc.

Wojtech, Michael. Bark: A Field Guide to Trees of the Northeast. 2011. (Illus.). 280p. pap. 24.95 *(978-1-58465-852-8(5))* Univ. Pr. of New England.

BARK PAINTING—AUSTRALIA

Michael, Linda, ed. They are Meditating: Bark Paintings from the MCA's Arnott's Collection. 2008. (Illus.). 200p. pap. *(978-1-921034-23-7(8))* Museum of Contemporary Art - Sydney.

BARKER, GEORGE GRANVILLE, 1913-

Barker, Christopher. The Arms of the Infinite: Elizabeth Smart & George Barker. 2010. (Illus.). 258p. (C). pap. 29.95 *(978-1-55458-270-9(9))* Wilfrid Laurier Univ. Pr. CAN. Dist: Univ. of Toronto Pr.

BARKER, JAMES NELSON, 1784-1858

Musser, Paul H. James Nelson Barker, 1784-1858: With a Reprint of His Comedy, Tears & Smiles. reprint ed. 29.50 *(978-0-404-04546-3(4))* AMS Pr., Inc.

BARKLEY, ALBEN WILLIAM, 1877-1956

Libbey, James K. Dear Alben: Mr. Barkley of Kentucky. 2009. (Kentucky Bicentennial Bookshelf Ser.). (ENG.). pap. 25.00 *(978-0-8131-9289-5(7))* Univ. Pr. of Kentucky.

BARLAAM AND JOASAPH

Colin, G. La version ethiopienne de Barlaam et Josaphat (Baralam Wayewasef) 2008. 231p. (C). pap. 44.00 *(978-90-429-2064-4(5))* Peeters Pubs. & Booksellers BEL. Dist: Brown, David Bk. Co., The.

St. John of Damascus. Barlaam & Ioasaph. 2006. (ENG.). 240p. pap. 20.99 *(978-1-4264-0075-9(6));* 232p. pap. 15.99 *(978-1-4264-0204-3(X))* BiblioBazaar.

BARLACH, ERNST, 1870-1938

Anderson, Lisa Marie. German Expressionism & the Messianism of a Generation. 2011. (ENG., Illus.). 212p. pap. 63.00 ***(978-90-420-3352-8(5))*** Rodopi.

Beutin, Heidi & Beutin, Wolfgang, eds. Ernst Barlach (1870-1938) Sein Leben, sein Schaffen, seine Verfolgung in der NS-Diktatur. 2009. (Bremer Beiträge zur Literatur- und Ideengeschichte Ser.). (GER.). 298p. pap. 64.95 *(978-3-631-58817-8(8))* Lang, Peter GmbH, Europaischer Verlag der Wissenschaften DEU. Dist: Lang, Peter.

Paret, Peter. An Artist against the Third Reich: Ernst Barlach, 1933-1938. 2007. (ENG., Illus.). 248p. pap. 28.99 *(978-0-521-03570-5(8))* Cambridge Univ. Pr.

Paret, Peter & Thieme, Helga. Myth & Modernity: Barlach's Drawings on the Nibelungen. 2012. (ENG.). 116p. 45.00 ***(978-0-85745-346-4(7))*** Berghahn Bks., Inc.

BARLEY

Brennan, Charles, ed. Barley: Genetics, Composition, Structure & Uses. 2008. (Illus.). 416p. *(978-1-4051-2371-6(0),* Wiley-Blackwell) Wiley, John & Sons, Ltd.

Din, Ahmad, et al. Barley ß-Glucan: Functional Beverage for Chronic Diseases Management. 2011. 160p. pap. ***(978-3-8443-0782-5(6))*** Lambert Academic Publishing.

Elfson, Steven B., ed. Barley: Production, Cultivation & Uses. 2011. (Agriculture Issues & Policies Ser.). (Illus.). 353p. 129.00 *(978-1-61209-745-9(6))* Nova Science Pubs., Inc.

Jones, Huw D. & Shewry, P. R. Transgenic Wheat, Barley & Oats: Production & Characterization Protocols. 2008. (Methods in Molecular Biology Ser.). (Illus.). x, 349p. 129.00 *(978-1-58829-961-1(9))* Humana Pr.

Morrissey, Kate L. Biological & chemical induction of systemic resistance in the barley powdery mildew Pathosystem. 2007. (Schriften des Forschungszentrums Jülich: 73). 138p. pap. *(978-3-89336-475-6(7))* Forschungszentrum Julich GmbH - Zentralbibliothek, Verlag.

Newman, Rosemary K. & Newman, C. Walter. Barley for Food & Health: Science, Technology, & Products. 2008. (ENG., Illus.). 246p. 111.00 *(978-0-470-10249-7(7),* Wiley-Interscience) Wiley, John & Sons, Inc.

Parnas, Tali. Evidence for Incipient Sympatric Speciation in Wild Barley at Ec. 2009. 96p. pap. *(978-3-639-15501-3(7))* VDM Verlag Dr. Mueller e.K.

Ullrich, Steven E. Barley: Production, Improvement, & Uses. 2011. (World Agriculture Ser.: 14). (ENG., Illus.). 640p. 269.95 *(978-0-8138-0123-0(0),* Wiley-Blackwell) Wiley, John & Sons, Inc.

Zhang, Guoping & Li, Chengdao, eds. Genetics & Improvement of Barley Malt Quality. 2009. (Advanced Topics in Science & Technology in China Ser.). (ENG., Illus.). xiv, 296p. 259.00 *(978-3-642-01278-5(7),* 3642012787) Springer.

BARLOW, JOEL, 1754-1812

Baldwin, A. C. Joel Barlow by Rev a C Baldwin. 2011. 28p. pap. 11.99 ***(978-1-4181-9304-1(6))*** MPublishing.

Buel, Richard. Joel Barlow: American Citizen in a Revolutionary World. 2011. (ENG., Illus.). 448p. (gr. 17). 34.95 *(978-0-8018-9769-6(6))* Johns Hopkins Univ. Pr.

Hill, Peter P. Joel Barlow, American Diplomat & Nation Builder. 2012. (Illus.). 272p. 34.95 *(978-1-59797-682-4(2))* Potomac Bks., Inc.

—Joel Barlow, American Diplomat & Nation Builder. 2012. ***(978-1-59797-772-2(1))*** Potomac Bks., Inc., Pubs.

Howard, Leon. The Connecticut Wits. reprint ed. 40.00 *(978-0-404-20125-8(3))* AMS Pr., Inc.

BARMAIDS

see Bartenders

BARNABAS, APOSTLE, SAINT

Dale, Robert. Barnabas: A Good Man, Full of Faith. 2007. (People in the Bible Ser.). 93p. pap. 9.00 *(978-1-84625-088-0(9))* DayOne Pubns. GBR. Dist: STL Distribution North America.

Fukuda, Mitsuo. Mentoring Like Barnabas. Cozens, Simon, tr. 2011.Tr. of バルナバのように人を育てる. 90p. pap. ***(978-0-9565943-9-6(5))*** Wide Margin Bks. GBR. Dist: Gardners Bks. Ltd.

Snyder, Jackson. The Epistle of Barnabas: Revised Greek with Hebraic-English Translation. 2010. 108p. pap. 15.95 *(978-0-557-16576-6(8))* Lulu Enterprises Inc.

Yasin, Ibn. The Authenticity of the Gospel of Barnabas. 2011. 130p. 29.99 ***(978-1-4568-5453-9(4))***; pap. 19.99 ***(978-1-4568-5452-2(6))*** Xlibris Corp.

BARNACLES

Southward, A. J. Barnacles: Synopses of the British Fauna No. 57. 2008. (Illus.). 148p. pap. *(978-1-85153-270-4(6))* Backhuys Pubs.

BARNARD, HENRY, 1811-1900

Thursfield, Richard E. Henry Barnard's American Journal of Education. (Johns Hopkins University. Studies in the Social Sciences, Thirtieth Ser.: 1). reprint ed. 37.50 *(978-0-404-61303-7(9))* AMS Pr., Inc.

BARNARDO, THOMAS JOHN, 1845-1905

Burnier-Smith, Dennis. Thomas John Barnardo, His Life, Homes & Orphanages: A Short History. 2010. (Illus.). 76p. pap. 11.49 *(978-1-4490-9042-5(7))* AuthorHouse.

BARNES, ALBERT, 1798-1879

Landis, Robert W. (Robert Wharton). Bethlehem Church & Its Pastor. 2006. 228p. per. 20.99 *(978-1-4255-1895-0(8))* MPublishing.

Ross, F. A. (Frederick Augustus). Slavery Ordained of God by Rev Fred a Ross. 2006. 196p. per. 18.99 *(978-1-4255-1536-2(3))* MPublishing.

BARNES, ALBERT COOMBS, 1873-1951

Dolkart, Judith F., et al. Masterworks - The Barnes Foundation. 2012. (ENG., Illus.). 374p. 40.00 ***(978-0-8478-3806-6(4),*** Skira) Rizzoli International Pubns., Inc.

BARNES, DJUNA, 1892-1982

Azzarello, Robert. Queer Environmentality: Ecology, Evolution, & Sexuality in American Literature. 2012. 160p. 89.95 ***(978-1-4094-2664-6(5))*** Ashgate Publishing Co.

Becnel, Kim. The Rise of Corporate Publishing & Its Effects on Authorship in Early Twentieth-Century America. 2007. (Literary Criticism & Cultural Theory Ser.). 149p. 131.00 *(978-0-415-95555-3(6))* Routledge.

Caselli, Daniela. Djuna Barnes's Bewildering Corpus: Unreadable Simplicity. 2009. (Illus.). 300p. 124.95 *(978-0-7546-5200-7(9))* Ashgate Publishing Co.

Fatejskova, Mon, et al. The Gender Dynamics of Modernism: Tracing Nightwood. 2009. (Studies in Major Literary Authors Ser.). (ENG.). 240p. (C). 125.00 *(978-0-415-99626-6(0))* Routledge.

Goodspeed-Chadwick, Julie. Modernist Women Writers & War: Trauma & the Female Body in Djuna Barnes, H.D., & Gertrude Stein. 2011. 184p. 35.00 *(978-0-8071-3681-2(6))* Louisiana State Univ. Pr.

Goody, Alex. Modernist Articulations: A Cultural Study of Djuna Barnes, Mina Loy & Gertrude Stein. 2007. (ENG., Illus.). 256p. 84.00 *(978-0-230-50049-5(8))* Palgrave Macmillan.

Grobbel, Michaela. Enacting Past & Present: The Memory Theaters of Djuna Barnes, Ingeborg Bachmann, & Marguerite Duras. 2009. (ENG.). 222p. pap. 28.50 *(978-0-7391-3488-7(4))* Lexington Bks.

Madden, Ed. Tiresian Poetics: Modernism, Sexuality, Voice, 1888-2001. 2008. 408p. (C). 80.00 *(978-0-8386-3937-5(2))* Fairleigh Dickinson Univ. Pr.

Martin, Ann. Red Riding Hood & the Wolf in Bed: Modernism's Fairy Tales. 2007. (ENG.). 240p. pap. *(978-0-8020-9571-8(2))* Univ. of Toronto Pr.

Schiesari, Juliana. Polymorphous Domesticities: Pets, Bodies, & Desire in Four Modern Writers. 2012. (FlashPoints Ser.). (ENG.). 152p. pap. 39.95 ***(978-0-520-27084-8(3))*** Univ. of California Pr.

Svrljuga, Zeljka. Hysteria & Melancholy as Literary Style in the Works of Charlotte Perkins Gilman, Kate Chopin, Zelda Fitzgerald, & Djuna Barnes. 2011. (Illus.). 260p. 129.95 *(978-0-7734-1517-1(3))* Mellen, Edwin Pr., The.

Taylor, Julie. Djuna Barnes & Affective Modernism. 2012. (ENG., Illus.). 240p. (gr. 17). 105.00 ***(978-0-7486-4675-3(2))*** Edinburgh Univ. Pr. GBR. Dist: Columbia Univ. Pr.

Trubowitz, Lara. Civil Antisemitism, Modernism, & British Culture, 1902-1939. 2012. (ENG., Illus.). 280p. 90.00 ***(978-0-230-39166-6(4))*** Palgrave Macmillan.

Warren, Diane. Djuna Barnes' Consuming Fictions. 2008. 206p. 99.95 *(978-0-7546-3920-6(7))* Ashgate Publishing Co.

BARNES FAMILY

Barnes, Jr. Carefree: A Memoir of My Father & Family. 2008. 160p. pap. 14.95 *(978-0-595-49117-9(0))* iUniverse, Inc.

Barnes, Roger Elkins. Those Who Came Before: A Family History of Malcolm Harold Barnes & Kathryn Elkins Longmire. 2009. (Illus.). xxix, 413p. *(978-0-89725-862-3(2),* Penobscot Pr.) Picton Pr.

Hewitt, F. Whalley. Barnes & Yale Families. fac. ed. 115p. reprint ed. pap. 22.00 *(978-0-7404-1459-6(3))* Higginson Bk. Co.

BARNES FOUNDATION

Berenato, Carolyn. John Dewey's Educational Philosophy & the Barnes Foundation. 2010. 152p. pap. *(978-3-8383-4974-9(1))* Lambert Academic Publishing.

Dolkart, Judith F., et al. Masterworks - The Barnes Foundation. 2012. (ENG., Illus.). 374p. 40.00 ***(978-0-8478-3806-6(4),*** Skira) Rizzoli International Pubns., Inc.

Renoir, Auguste, et al. Renoir in the Barnes Foundation. 2012. (ENG., Illus.). 392p. 75.00 ***(978-0-300-15100-8(4))*** Yale Univ. Pr.

Wattenmaker, Richard J. American Paintings & Works on Paper in the Barnes Foundation. 2010. (Illus.). 404p. 75.00 *(978-0-300-15877-9(7))* Yale Univ. Pr.

BARNET, WILL, 1911-

Barnet, Will, illus. Will Barnet: A Sketchbook, 1932-1934. 2009. (ENG.). 90p. 49.95 *(978-0-8076-1597-3(8),* 761597) Braziller, George Inc.

BARNEY, JOSHUA, 1759-1818

Barney, Mary, abr. A Biographical Memoir. 2009. (Military History Ser.). (ENG.). 348p. pap. 22.95 *(978-1-4290-2115-9(2))* Applewood Bks.

Shomette, Donald G. Flotilla: The Patuxent Naval Campaign in the War of 1812. 2009. (Johns Hopkins Books on the War Of 1812 Ser.). (ENG., Illus.). 520p. (gr. 17). 38.00 *(978-0-8018-9122-9(1))* Johns Hopkins Univ. Pr.

BARNFIELD, RICHARD, 1574-1627

Daugherty, Leo. Shakespeare, Richard Barnfield, & the Sixth Earl of Derby. 2010. *(978-1-60497-712-7(4))* Cambria Pr.

BARNS

see also Stables

Apps, Jerry. Barns of Wisconsin. 3rd rev. ed. 2010. (Places along the Way Ser.). (ENG., Illus.). 224p. 29.95 *(978-0-87020-453-1(X))* Wisconsin Historical Society.

Barn Raising: Stories of a Vanishing American Legacy. 2008. (Illus.). pap. 11.95 *(978-0-9792974-1-0(9))* Essential Communications.

Co, Atlantic Publishing. The Complete Guide to Building Classic Barns, Fences, Storage Sheds, Animal Pens, Outbuildings, Greenhouses, Farm Equipment, & Tools: A Step-by-Step Guide to Building Everything You Might Need on a Small Farm. 2012. (ENG.). 288p. pap. 29.95 *(978-1-60138-372-3(X))* Atlantic Publishing Co.

Creative Homeowner Press Editors, ed. Barns, Sheds & Outbuildings. 3rd ed. 2010. (Home Improvement Ser.). (ENG., Illus.). 288p. (gr. 5). pap. 19.95 *(978-1-58011-483-7(0))* Creative Homeowner.

Creative Publishing International Editors. Sheds, Barns & Outbuildings: Includes Garages, Gazebos, Shelters & More. 2010. (Black & Decker Complete Photo Guide Ser.). (ENG., Illus.). 448p. pap. 24.99 *(978-1-58923-522-9(3),* 1589235223) Quayside.

Dillon, Joan. Barns of Cape Cod. 2007. (Illus.). 176p. 39.95 *(978-0-7643-2564-9(7))* Schiffer Publishing, Ltd.

Donaldson, Stephen R. Barns of the Berkshires. 2009. (Illus.). 112p. bds. 24.99 *(978-0-7643-3223-4(6))* Schiffer Publishing, Ltd.

Falk, C. Barns of New York. 2012. pap. ***(978-0-8014-7780-5(8))*** Cornell Univ. Pr.

Falk, Cynthia G. Barns of New York: Rural Architecture of the Empire State. 2012. (ENG.). 304p. pap. 27.95 ***(978-0-8014-4884-3(0))*** Cornell Univ. Pr.

Giagnocavo, Alan, ed. Barns: A Close-Up Look. 2011. (Built in America Ser.). (ENG., Illus.). 128p. pap. 19.95 *(978-1-56523-562-5(2))* Fox Chapel Publishing Co., Inc.

Halsted, Byron, ed. Barns & Outbuildings: And How to Build Them. 2nd ed. 2008. (Illus.). 235p. pap. 14.95 *(978-1-59921-371-2(0),* Lyons Pr.) Globe Pequot Pr., The.

Halsted, Byron D., ed. Barns & Outbuildings: And How to Construct Them. 2011. (ENG., Illus.). 240p. pap. 9.95 *(978-1-61608-195-9(3),* 608195) Skyhorse Publishing Co., Inc.

—Barns, Sheds & Outbuildings: A Practical Guide. 2007. (Dover Books on Woodworking & Carving Ser.). (ENG., Illus.). 240p. per. 11.95 *(978-0-486-45125-1(9))* Dover Pubns., Inc.

Hankins, Caneta Skelley & Gavin, Michael Thomas. Barns of Tennessee. 2009. (Illus.). 152p. *(978-1-57864-545-9(X))* Donning Co. Pubs.

Harrison, Terry. North Carolina Barn: In Watercolour. 2010. (Paint It Ser.). (Illus.). 16p. pap. *(978-1-84448-565-9(X))* Search Pr., Ltd.
Hazeltine, Luella. Barns Around Iowa: A Sampling of Iowa's Round Barns. Schense, Deb, ed. & photos by by. 2008. (Illus.). 128p. pap. 14.95 *(978-1-932043-44-0(6))* Penfield Bks.
Jiusto, Chere & Brown, Christine W. Hand Raised: The Barns of Montana. (ENG., Illus.). 320p. 2012. pap. 27.95 *(978-0-9801292-0-5(6))* 2011. 39.95 *(978-0-9759196-9-9(5))* Montana Historical Society Pr.
Johnson, Evelyn. Barns of Old Mission Peninsula & Their Stories. 2007. per. *(978-0-9790834-1-9(9),* BMS) Book Marketing Solutions, LLC.
—Barns of Old Mission Peninsula & Their Stories. 2007. (Illus.). 224p. (C). pap. 35.00 *(978-0-944311-21-9(0))* Michigan State Univ. Museum.
Kanfer, Larry. Barns of Illinois. 2009. (ENG., Illus.). 128p. 39.95 *(978-0-252-03274-5(8))* Univ. of Illinois Pr.
Leffingwell, Randy. The American Barn. 2009. (ENG.). 192p. 12.99 *(978-0-7858-2586-9(X),* 078582586X, Crestline) MBI Publishing Co. LLC.
Moffett, Marian & Wodehouse, Lawrence. East Tennessee Cantilever Barns. (Illus.). 160p. 18.00 *(978-1-57233-270-6(0))* Univ. of Tennessee Pr.
Mohr, Marsha Williamson. Indiana Barns. 2010. (ENG., Illus.). 152p. 29.95 *(978-0-253-35568-3(0),* 0253355680, Quarry Bks.) Indiana Univ. Pr.
Old House & Barn Resource Directory: Second Edition. 2nd ed. 2007. *(978-0-9643014-1-2(5))* New Hampshire Preservation Alliance.
Parron, Suzi & Groves, Donna Sue. Barn Quilts & the American Quilt Trail Movement. 2012. (ENG., Illus.). 240p. pap. 29.95 ***(978-0-8040-1138-9(9))*** Swallow Pr.
Rooney, E. Ashley. Barn Again: Restored & New Barns for the 21st Century. 2010. (Illus.). 176p. 34.99 *(978-0-7643-3431-3(X))* Schiffer Publishing, Ltd.
—Old Barns, New Homes: A Showcase of Architectural Conversions. 2007. (Illus.). 175p. 34.95 *(978-0-7643-2132-0(3))* Schiffer Publishing, Ltd.
Rural Builder Editors. The Complete Horse Barn Builder. 2009. (ENG.). cd-rom 17.99 *(978-1-4402-0819-5(0))* Krause Pubns.
Whipple, Paul. Barn Stories: Mostly True Stories Told by Barns. 2007. (Illus.). 106p. per. *(978-0-9796143-0-9(9))* Amos Communications, Inc.

BARNUM, P. T. (PHINEAS TAYLOR), 1810-1891
Barnum, P. T. Barnums Own Story. Browne, Waldo R., ed. 2008. (Illus.). 38.00 *(978-0-8446-4001-3(8))* Smith, Peter Pub., Inc.
—The Life of P T Barnum. 2007. 412p. 29.95 *(978-1-60206-958-9(1))* Cosimo, Inc.
Benton, Joel. A Unique Story of a Marvellous Career. Life of Hon. Phineas T. Barnum. 2006. (ENG.). 362p. pap. 26.99 *(978-1-4264-0345-3(3));* 372p. pap. 25.99 *(978-1-4264-0294-4(5))* BiblioBazaar.
Reiss, Benjamin. The Showman & the Slave: Race, Death, & Memory in Barnum's America. 2010. (Illus.). 288p. pap. 19.95 *(978-0-674-05564-3(0))* Harvard Univ. Pr.

BAROJA, PIO, 1872-1956
Rosales, Emilio. Baroja: La Novela Como Laberinto. 2012. (Hispanic Studies: Culture & Ideas Ser.). (SPA.). 155p. pap. 53.95 ***(978-3-0343-0774-1(8))*** Lang, Peter AG GBR. Dist: Lang, Peter.
Saz Parkinson, Carlos Roberto. Positively Negative: Pio Baroja, the Essayist. 2011. 276p. pap. 26.95 ***(978-1-58871-192-2(7),*** Juan de la Cuesta-Hispanic Monographs) LinguaText, Ltd.
Sosa-Velasco, Alfredo J. Médicos escritores en España, 1885-1955: Santiago Ramón y Cajal, Pío Baroja, Gregorio Marañón y Antonio Vallejo Nágera. 2010. (Monografías A Ser.: Volume 286). (SPA.). 230p. 99.00 *(978-1-85566-218-6(3,* Tamesis Bks.) Boydell & Brewer, Ltd. GBR. Dist: Boydell & Brewer, Inc.

BARONS' WAR, 1263-1267
see Great Britain—History—Barons' War, 1263-1267

BAROQUE ARCHITECTURE
see Architecture, Baroque

BAROQUE ART
see Art, Baroque

BAROQUE CIVILIZATION
see Civilization, Baroque

BAROQUE LITERATURE
see also Euphuism
Braungart, Wolfgang, ed. Manier und Manierismus. (Untersuchungen zur deutschen Literaturgeschichte Ser.).Tr. of Manner & Mannerism. (GER.). IX, 358p. 165.00 ***(978-3-11-183615-7(0))*** De Gruyter, Walter Inc.
Eybl, Franz M. & Wirtz, Irmgard M., eds. Delectatio: Unterhaltung und Vergnügen zwischen Grimmelshausen und Schnabel. 2008. (Beihefte zu Simpliciana Ser.). (GER., Illus.). 233p. pap. *(978-3-03911-734-5(3))* Lang, Peter.
Johnson, Christopher D. Hyperboles: The Rhetoric of Excess in Baroque Literature & Thought. 2010. (Harvard Studies in Comparative Literature Ser.). (Illus.). 695p. 45.00 *(978-0-674-05331-1(1));* pap. 27.95 *(978-0-674-05333-5(8))* Harvard Univ. Pr.
Treffinger, David. Adaption als Werktreue: Die opera seria des 18. Jahrhunderts vor modernem Publikum - Inszenierungsprobleme und szenische Lösungen. 2010. 92p. pap. *(978-3-639-14619-6(0))* VDM Verlag Dr. Mueller e.K.
Warnke, Frank. European Metaphysical Poetry. 2011. 328p. 50.95 ***(978-1-258-02521-2(3))*** Literary Licensing, LLC.

BAROQUE LITERATURE—HISTORY AND CRITICISM
Aurnhammer, Achim. Torquato Tasso im deutschen Barock. (Frahe Neuzeit Ser.). (GER.). X, 405p. 210.00 ***(978-3-11-218808-8(X))*** De Gruyter, Walter Inc.
Belmonte, Javier Jiménez. Las Obras en Verso Del Principe de Esquilache: Amateurismo y Conciencia Literaria. 2007. (Monografías A Ser.: Volume 242). 264p. 90.00 *(978-1-85566-149-3(7),* Tamesis Bks.) Boydell & Brewer, Ltd. GBR. Dist: Boydell & Brewer, Inc.
Beverley, John. Essays on the Literary Baroque in Spain & Spanish America. 2008. (Monografías A Ser.: Volume 265). (SPA & ENG.). 202p. 90.00 *(978-1-85566-175-2(6),* Tamesis Bks.) Boydell & Brewer, Ltd. GBR. Dist: Boydell & Brewer, Inc.
Castillo, David. Baroque Horrors: Roots of the Fantastic in the Age of Curiosities. 2011. (ENG.). 200p. (C). pap. 24.95 ***(978-0-472-03491-8(X))*** Univ. of Michigan Pr.
Doms, Misia Sophia. Die Viel-Einheit des Seelenraums in der deutschsprachigen barocken Lyrik. 2010. (Frühe Neuzeit Ser.).Tr. of Unity & Diversity of the Inner World in German Baroque Poetry. (GER.). VI, 437p. 105.00 *(978-3-11-023092-5(5))* De Gruyter, Walter Inc.
Egginton, William. The Theater of Truth: The Ideology of (Neo)Baroque Aesthetics. 2009. (ENG.). 184p. 55.00 *(978-0-8047-6954-9(0))* Stanford Univ. Pr.
Knapp, Éva & Taskés, Gábor. Emblematics in Hungary: A study of the history of symbolic representation in Renaissance & Baroque Literature. (Frahe Neuzeit Ser.). (ENG.). VII, 402p. 180.00 ***(978-3-11-182725-4(9))*** De Gruyter, Walter Inc.
Lambert, Gregg. On the (New) Baroque. 2009. (ENG.). 274p. pap. 26.00 *(978-1-888570-97-7(0))* Davies Group Pubs., The.
Lohenstein, Daniel Casper von, et al. Sämtliche Werke: Historisch-Kritische Ausgabe. 2008. (GER., Illus.). XII, 902p. 503.00 *(978-3-11-020377-6(4));* VI, 366p. 266.00 *(978-3-11-020465-0(7))* De Gruyter, Walter Inc.
Newman, Jane O. Benjamin's Library: Modernity, Nation, & the Baroque. 2011. (Signale: Modern German Letters, Cultures, & Thought Ser.). 272p. pap. 35.00 *(978-0-8014-7659-4(3))* Cornell Univ. Pr.
Parker, Blanford. The Triumph of Augustan Poetics: English Literary Culture from Butler to Johnson. 2006. (Cambridge Studies in Eighteenth-Century English Literature & Thought Ser.). (ENG.). 276p. pap. 53.00 *(978-0-521-02867-7(1))* Cambridge Univ. Pr.
Quintero, Maria Cristina. Gendering the Crown in the Spanish Baroque Comedia. 2012. (New Hispanisms: Cultural & Literary Studies). (Illus.). 230p. 99.95 ***(978-1-4094-3963-9(1))*** Ashgate Publishing Co.
Roaten, Darnell H. Wolfflins Principles in Spanish Drama 15. 2006. pap. 24.95 *(978-1-4286-5447-1(X))* Kessinger Publishing, LLC.
Wagman, Frederick Herbert. Magic & Natural Science in German Baroque Literature. Fife, Robert Herndon, ed. 2011. 188p. 42.95 ***(978-1-258-03358-3(5))*** Literary Licensing, LLC.

BAROQUE MUSIC
see Music, Baroque

BAROQUE PAINTING
see Painting, Baroque

BAROQUE SCULPTURE
see Sculpture, Baroque

BAROTSE (AFRICAN PEOPLE)
see Lozi (African People)

BAROTSELAND (NORTHERN RHODESIA)
see Western Province (Zambia)

BARRACUDA AUTOMOBILE
Grist, Peter. Dodge Challenger Plymouth Barracuda: Chrysler's Potent Pony Cars. 2009. (ENG., Illus.). 196p. 59.95 *(978-1-84584-105-8(0),* 1845841050) Veloce Publishing Ltd. GBR. Dist: MBI Distribution Services/Quayside Distribution.
Schild, Jim. Challenger & Barracuda, 1970-74. 2010. (Collector's Originality Guide Ser.). (ENG., Illus.). 128p. pap. 24.99 *(978-0-7603-3788-2(8),* 0760337888, Motorbooks) MBI Publishing Co. LLC.
Shields, Samuel. Source Books: Plymouth Barracuda & Dodge Challenger, Vol. 1. 144p. pap. 8.98 *(978-0-934780-19-3(6))* MBI Publishing Co. LLC.

BARRELS
Kilby, Ken. Coopers & Coopering. 2008. (Shire Library). (ENG., Illus.). 56p. pap. 12.95 *(978-0-7478-0584-7(9))* Shire Pubns., Ltd. GBR. Dist: Random Hse., Inc.

BARREN FIG TREE (PARABLE)
see Jesus Christ—Parables

BARRES, MAURICE, 1862-1923
Curtis, Michael. Three Against the Third Republic: Sorel, Barrès & Maurras. 2010. (ENG.). 343p. pap. 39.95 *(978-1-4128-1430-0(8))* Transaction Pubs.
González Cuevas, Pedro Carlos. Conservadurismo Heterodoxo: Tres Vías Ante Las Derechas Españolas: Maurice Barrès, José Ortega y Gasset y Gonzalo Fernández de la Mora. 2009. (SPA.). 224p. *(978-84-9742-878-1(1))* Biblioteca Nueva, Editorial, S.L.

BARRIE, J. M. (JAMES MATTHEW), 1860-1937
Dudgeon, Piers. Neverland: J. M. Barrie, the du Mauriers, & the Dark Side of Peter Pan. (ENG., Illus.). 352p. 2011. pap. 15.95 *(978-1-60598-191-8(5),* 605191) 2009. 26.95 *(978-1-60598-063-8(3),* 605063) Pegasus Bks.
Hanson, Bruce K. Peter Pan on Stage & Screen, 1904-2010. 2nd rev. ed. 2011. (ENG., Illus.). 417p. pap. 45.00 *(978-0-7864-4778-7(8))* McFarland & Co., Inc. Pubs.
Jack, R.D.S. Myths & the Mythmaker: A Literary Account of J. M. Barrie's Formative Years. 2010. (Illus.). 341p. pap. 95.00 *(978-90-420-3218-7(9))* Rodopi.
—The Road to the Never Land: A Reassessment of J M Barrie's Dramatic Art. 2010. 306p. pap. *(978-1-84622-032-6(7))* Humming Earth.
Kavey, Allison. Second Star to the Right: Peter Pan in the Popular Imagination. Friedman, Lester D., ed. 2008. (ENG., Illus.). xii, 277p. (C). pap. 25.95 *(978-0-8135-4437-3(8))* Rutgers Univ. Pr.
Kavey, Allison & Friedman, Lester D. Second Star to the Right: Peter Pan in the Popular Imagination. 2008. (ENG., Illus.). 288p. (C). 68.00 *(978-0-8135-4436-6(X))* Rutgers Univ. Pr.
Moult, Thomas. Barrie. 240p. 2008. 41.95 *(978-1-4366-8202-2(9))* 2007. (ENG.). per. 26.95 *(978-1-4325-7786-5(7))* Kessinger Publishing, LLC.
NASH, Andrew. Kailyard & Scottish Literature. 2007. (SCROLL Ser.: 8). 272p. per. 73.00 *(978-90-420-2203-4(5))* Rodopi.
Telfer, Kevin. Peter Pan's First XI: The Story of J. M. Barrie's Cricket Team. 2010. (ENG., Illus.). 336p. pap. 22.95 *(978-0-340-91965-1(5));* 27.95 *(978-0-340-91945-3(0))* Hodder General Publishing Div. GBR. (Hodder & Stoughton). Dist: Independent Pubs. Group.
Young, Timothy G. My Heart in Company: The Work of J. M. Barrie & the Birth of Peter Pan. 2007. (Illus.). 89p. per. 20.00 *(978-0-300-13403-2(7))* Yale Univ. Pr.

BARRIE, MARGARET OGILVY
Barrie, J. M. Margaret Ogilvy. 2007. (ENG.). 112p. 25.95 *(978-1-4218-3865-6(6),* 1st World Library - Literary Society) 1st World Publishing, Inc.
—Margaret Ogilvy. 2009. 218p. 32.99 *(978-1-116-05359-3(4))* 2009. 218p. 28.99 *(978-1-116-05360-9(8))* 2009. 218p. pap. 24.75 *(978-1-116-05361-6(6))* 2009. 218p. pap. 23.75 *(978-1-116-05362-3(4))* 2009. 218p. 28.99 *(978-1-110-50736-8(4))* 2009. 218p. pap. 23.75 *(978-1-110-50731-3(3))* 2009. 220p. 23.99 *(978-1-103-39025-0(2))* 2009. 220p. pap. 17.99 *(978-1-103-39024-3(4))* 2008. 220p. 24.99 *(978-0-559-52513-1(3))* 2008. 220p. pap. 23.75 *(978-0-559-52509-4(5))* BiblioBazaar.
—Margaret Ogilvy. 2009. 70p. pap. *(978-0-217-86376-6(0))* Books LLC.
—Margaret Ogilvy. reprint ed. lib. bdg. 98.00 *(978-0-7426-2514-3(1));* lib. bdg. 48.00 *(978-0-7426-1081-1(0))* Classic Bks.
—Margaret Ogilvy. 2006. (ENG.). pap. *(978-1-4065-0948-9(5))* Dodo Pr.
—Margaret Ogilvy. 2007. (ENG.). 80p. per. *(978-1-4068-3707-0(5))* Echo Library.

BARRIER-FREE DESIGN
see also subdivision Barrier-Free Design under types of buildings, structures, and facilities
Bridge, Catherine. Computational Case-Based Redesign for People with Ability Impairment. 2008. 316p. pap. *(978-3-639-04874-2(1))* VDM Verlag Dr. Mueller e.K.
Builder#039;s Book Inc, creator. California Accessibility Reference Manual Code & Checklist 4th Edition: CARM 4th Edition Is Based on 2010 California Building Code. 4th ed. 2011. (ENG., Illus.). spiral bd. 79.95 incl. cd-rom ***(978-1-889892-88-7(2))*** Builder's Bk., Inc. Bookstore/Pubs.
Burgstahler, Sheryl & Cory, Rebecca. Universal Design in Higher Education: From Principles to Practice. 2008. (Illus.). xii, 308p. *(978-1-891792-91-5(1),* Harvard Education Pr.) Harvard Education Publishing Group (HEPG).
Erlandson, Robert F. Universal & Accessible Design for Products, Services, & Processes. 2007. (ENG., Illus.). 288p. 97.95 *(978-0-8493-7493-7(6),* CRC Press) Taylor & Francis Group GBR. Dist: Taylor & Francis Group.
Evan Terry Associates, ed. Pocket Guide to the ADA: Americans with Disabilities Act Accessibility Guidelines for Buildings & Facilities. 3rd rev. ed. 2006. (ENG., Illus.). 198p. pap. 30.00 *(978-0-470-10870-3(3),* Wiley) Wiley, John & Sons, Inc.
Felker, Ervin C., ed. HUD Housing Programs for Persons with Disabilities. 2009. pap. 43.00 *(978-1-60741-113-0(X))* Nova Science Pubs., Inc.
Fischer, Joachim & Meuser, Philipp. Accessible Architecture: Construction & Design Manual, 1 vol. 2009. (ENG., Illus.). 327p. 99.95 *(978-3-938666-97-5(8))* DOM Pubs. DEU. Dist: Innovative Logistics.
Gibbens, Michael. Caldag 2009. 2009. spiral bd. 79.95 *(978-1-58001-783-1(5))* International Code Council.
Hartman, Bridget, et al. Americans with Disabilities Act: A Self-Guided Training Course for Historic Preservation Commissions. 2007. (ESK.). *(978-0-89133-425-5(4))* National Trust for Historic Preservation.
Heckel, Pamela. Putting People. 2010. 168p. pap. *(978-3-8383-4527-7(4))* Lambert Academic Publishing.
Heiss, Oliver. Barrier-Free Design: Principles Planning, Examples. 2010. (Detail Practice Ser.). (Illus.). 112p. pap. 54.95 *(978-3-0346-0577-9(3))* Birkhauser Verlag AG CHE. Dist: Actar Birkhauser Distribution.
ICC. Minnesota State Accessibility Code: Chapter 1341. 2007. pap. 45.00 *(978-1-58001-648-3(0))* International Code Council.
—2006 Accessibility Study Companion. 2008. 460p. pap. 54.00 *(978-1-58001-698-8(7))* International Code Council.
—2009 Accessibility Study Companion. 2009. pap. 54.00 *(978-1-58001-863-0(7))* International Code Council.
The Inclusive Home Design ACT: Hearing Before the Subcommittee on Housing & Community Opportunity of the Committee on Financial Services, U.S. House of Representatives, One Hundred Eleventh Congress, Second Session, September 29, 2010. 2010. (Illus.). v, 69p. ***(978-0-16-087675-2(3),*** 552-070-42227-7) United States Government Printing Office.
International Code Council, (International Code Council (ICC)) & Marinelli, Dominic. Code Source Accessibility: Codes, Standards, & Guidelines. 2011. (ENG.). 64p. spiral bd. 25.95 *(978-1-111-03724-6(8))* Delmar Cengage Learning.
International Code Council Staff. ICC A117. 1-2009 Accessible & Usable Buildings & Facilities. 2011. (ENG.). 136p. pap. 43.95 *(978-1-58001-918-7(8))* International Code Council.
Jordan, James E. Indiana State-Specific Accessibility Codes: A Simplified Approach to Accessibility. 2009. per. 60.00 *(978-1-932730-34-0(6))* Jordan Publishing.
—Indiana State-Specific Accessibility Codes on CD-ROM: A Simplified Approach to Accessibility. 2009. cd-rom 70.00 *(978-1-932730-35-7(4))* Jordan Publishing.
—Indiana State-Specific Accessibility Codes w/CD-ROM Set: A Simplified Approach to Accessibility. 2009. per. 100.00 incl. cd-rom *(978-1-932730-36-4(2))* Jordan Publishing.
—Michigan State-Specific Accessibility Codes: A Simplified Approach to Accessibility. 2008. per. 60.00 *(978-1-932730-16-6(8))* Jordan Publishing.
—Minnesota State-Specific Accessibility Codes w/CD-ROM Set: A Simplified Approach to Accessibility. 2009. per. 100.00 incl. cd-rom *(978-0-9740995-7-6(0))* Jordan Publishing.
—Texas Accessibility Standards (TAS) w/CD-ROM Set: Design Codes for Buildings & Facilities. 2010. (ENG.). per. 80.00 incl. cd-rom *(978-0-9740995-3-8(8))* Jordan Publishing.
Preiser, Wolfgang & Smith, Korydon H. Universal Design Handbook, 2E. 2nd rev. ed. 2010. (ENG., Illus.). 496p. 150.00 *(978-0-07-162923-2(8),* 0071629238) McGraw-Hill Professional Publishing.
Ryan, Deborah A. NFPA Pocket Guide to the ADA & ABA. 2008. (Illus.). xix, 316p. pap. *(978-0-87765-825-2(0))* National Fire Protection Assn.
State of California. 2008 California Access Compliance Reference Manual: Statutes, Regulation, Policies, Interpretation of Regulations (IRs) & Official Comments (Checklists) 2008. (Illus.). 583p. spiral bd. 49.95 *(978-0-9666265-4-4(0))* That Technical Bookstore, Inc.
Thornburg, Doug & International Code Council Staff. Accessibility Pocketbook 2009 2009. (ENG.). 310p. pap. 28.00 *(978-1-58001-864-7(5))* International Code Council.
Thorpe, Stephen. Wheelchair Housing Design Guide. 2nd rev. ed. 2010. (ENG., Illus.). 132p. pap. 65.00 ***(978-1-86081-897-4(8))*** Building Research Establishment GBR. Dist: Taylor & Francis Group.
Vavik, Tom, ed. Inclusive Buildings, Products & Services: Challenges in Universal Design. 2009. 289p. pap. 119.00 *(978-82-519-2344-6(1))* Tapir Forlag NOR. Dist: International Specialized Bk. Services.
Woodward, Jay & Paarlberg, Kim. Significant Changes to the 2008 Accessibility Standard: Covering 2009 & 2012 International Building Code & the ICC A117. 1 2009 Edition/1st Edition. 2010. (ENG.). 192p. pap. 34.95 *(978-1-4354-9898-3(4))* Delmar Cengage Learning.

BARRIER-FREE DESIGN FOR OLDER PEOPLE
AIA Staff. Design for Aging Review 9: The American Institute of Architects. 2008. (ENG., Illus.). 240p. 60.00 *(978-1-86470-245-3(1))* Images Publishing Group AUS. Dist: National Bk. Network.
American Institute of Architects Staff. Design for Aging Review 10: AIA Design for Aging Knowledge Community. 2011. (ENG., Illus.). 264p. 60.00 *(978-1-86470-391-7(1))* Images Publishing Group AUS. Dist: National Bk. Network.
Anderzhon, Jeffrey W., et al. Design for Aging: International Case Studies of Building & Program. 2012. (Wiley Series in Healthcare & Senior Living Design Ser.: 10). (ENG., Illus.). 320p. 85.00 ***(978-0-470-94672-5(5),*** Wiley) Wiley, John & Sons, Inc.
Buhalis, Dimitrios, et al. Best Practice in Accessible Tourism: Inclusion, Disability, Ageing Population & Tourism. 2012. (Aspects of Tourism Ser.). (ENG., Illus.). 408p. 179.95 ***(978-1-84541-253-1(2));*** pap. 59.95 ***(978-1-84541-252-4(4))*** Channel View Pubns., Ltd. GBR. Dist: Univ. of Toronto Pr.
Cisneros, Henry, et al, eds. Independent for Life: Homes & Neighborhoods for an Aging America. 2012. (ENG., Illus.). 336p. 45.00 ***(978-0-292-73791-4(2));*** pap. 24.95 ***(978-0-292-73792-1(0))*** Univ. of Texas Pr.
Hodge, Gerald. The Geography of Aging: Preparing Communities for the Surge in Seniors. 2008. (ENG., Illus.). 336p. (C). *(978-0-7735-3429-2(6))* McGill-Queen's Univ. Pr.
Öztop, Hülya & Erkal, Sibel. Housing Design & Safety for the Elderly. 2010. *(978-1-61728-844-9(6))* Nova Science Pubs., Inc.

BARRISTERS
see Lawyers

BARROW, CLYDE, 1909-1934
Guinn, Jeff. Go down Together: The True, Untold Story of Bonnie & Clyde. (ENG., Illus.). 480p. 2010. pap. 16.99 *(978-1-4165-5707-4(5))* 2009. 27.00 *(978-1-4165-5706-7(7))* Simon & Schuster.
—Go down Together: The True, Untold Story of Bonnie & Clyde. l.t. ed. 2009. 707p. 30.95 *(978-1-4104-1819-7(7))* Thorndike Pr.
Hendley, Nate. Bonnie & Clyde: A Biography, 1 vol. 2007. (Greenwood Biographies Ser.). (Illus.). 160p. 35.00 *(978-0-313-33871-7(X),* GR3871, Greenwood Pr.) Greenwood Publishing Group, Inc.
Parker, Emma & Cowan, Nell B. True Story of Bonnie & Clyde. Date not set. lib. bdg. 18.95 *(978-0-8488-2154-8(8))* Amereon LTD.
Schneider, Paul. Bonnie & Clyde: The Lives Behind the Legend. 2010. (ENG., Illus.). 400p. pap. 17.00 *(978-0-8050-9235-6(8),* Holt Paperback) St. Martin's Pr.
—Bonnie & Clyde: The True Story Behind the Myth. 2009. *(978-0-8050-8627-0(7))* Holt, Henry & Co.

BARROW, JOHN, SIR, 1764-1848

Barrow, John. An Auto-Biographical Memoir of Sir John Barrow, Bart, Late of the Admiralty: Including Reflections, Observations, & Reminiscences at Home & Abroad, from Early Life to Advanced Age. 2009. (Cambridge Library Collection - History Ser.). 536p. pap. 39.99 *(978-1-108-00470-1(9))* Cambridge Univ. Pr.

BARROWS

see Mounds

BARRY, JOHN, 1745-1803

John Barry - The Definitive Collection. 13.95 *(978-1-85909-915-5(7)*, Warner Bros. Pubns.) Alfred Publishing Co., Inc.

McGrath, Tim. John Barry: An American Hero in the Age of Sail. 2011. (ENG., Illus.). 656p. pap. 22.50 ***(978-1-59416-153-7(4))*** Westholme Publishing.

McGrath, Timothy. John Barry: An American Hero in the Age of Sail. 2010. (ENG., Illus.). 704p. 35.00 *(978-1-59416-104-9(6))* Westholme Publishing.

BARRY, PHILIP, 1896-1949

Anderson, Donald R. Shadowed Cocktails: The Plays of Philip Barry from Paris Bound to the Philadelphia Story. 2010. 238p. pap. 45.00 *(978-0-8093-2991-5(3))* Southern Illinois Univ. Pr.

BARRYMORE, JOHN, 1882-1942

Mank, Gregory William. Hollywood's Hellfire Club: The Misadventures of John Barrymore, W. C. Fields, Errol Flynn & the Bundy Drive Boys. 2007. (ENG., Illus.). 280p. per. 22.95 *(978-1-932595-24-6(4))* Feral Hse.

BARS (DRINKING ESTABLISHMENTS)

see also Hotels

Bunting, Chris. Drinking Japan: A Guide to Japan's Best Drinks & Drinking Establishments. 2011. (ENG., Illus.). 288p. pap. 24.95 *(978-4-8053-1054-0(5))* Tuttle Publishing.

Deliyannis, Melina, ed. A Pocketful of Bars. 2007. (ENG., Illus.). 256p. 19.95 *(978-1-86470-223-6(1)*, Images Publishing Dist Ac) Antique Collectors' Club GBR. Dist: National Bk. Network.

Food and Wine Magazine Editors. Food & Wine Cocktails 2011: An Indispensable Mix of Excellent Cocktails & Food to Go with Them, Plus the Ultimate Guide to the Top Bars & Lounges around the Country. 2011. (ENG., Illus.). 224p. pap. 14.95 *(978-1-60320-882-6(8))* Time Home Entertainment, Inc.

Graham, Kathryn & Homel, Ross. Raising the Bar: Preventing Aggression in & Around Bars, Pubs & Clubs. 2008. (Crime Science Ser.). (ENG.). 316p. (C). 125.00 *(978-1-84392-318-3(1))* Willan Publishing GBR. Dist: Taylor & Francis Group.

Herriott, Luke. 1,000 Restaurant Bar & Cafe Graphics: From Signage to Logos & Everything in Between. 2007. (1000 Ser.). (ENG., Illus.). 320p. per. 40.00 *(978-1-59253-332-9(9)*, 1592533329) Quayside.

Holiday, Ivan Doc. The Cooler's Grimoire: The Comprehensive Instructional Guide to Nightclub & Bar Security. 2008. 344p. pap. 39.95 *(978-1-4327-2641-6(2))* Outskirts Pr., Inc.

Holl & Schweber, John & Nate. Indiana Breweries. 2011. (Breweries Ser.). (ENG.). 144p. pap. 16.95 *(978-0-8117-0661-2(3))* Stackpole Bks.

Horwitz, Carolyn & Iannacci, Anthony, eds. The Place Itself: Selected Work of Bar Architects. 2009. (ENG., Illus.). 114p. 40.00 *(978-0-9823190-3-1(7))* Architecture Interiors Pr., Inc.

Krauel, Jacobo. Clubs & Bars Design. 2011. (ENG., Illus.). 240p. 49.00 *(978-84-92796-45-5(4))* Links International (Leading International Key Services Barcelona, S.A.) ESP. Dist: National Bk. Network.

Krols, Birgit. Extreme Bars, 1 vol. 2008. (ENG, DUT & FRE., Illus.). 192p. 39.95 *(978-90-76886-65-4(0))* Tectum B.V.B.A. BEL. Dist: Innovative Logistics.

—Extreme Locations, 1 vol. 2011. (DUT, FRE & ENG., Illus.). 500p. pap. 39.95 *(978-90-79761-68-5(0))* Tectum B.V.B.A. BEL. Dist: Innovative Logistics.

Lanier, Pamela. The Complete Guide to Bed & Breakfasts, Inns & Guesthouses International. 28th rev. ed. 2011. (ENG.). 664p. pap. 19.95 *(978-0-9843766-8-1(2))* Lanier Publishing International.

Laurie, P. Barbadian Rum Shop: The Other Watering Hole. 2nd ed. 2011. 144p. pap. 29.95 *(978-0-230-02713-8(X)*, Macmillan) Pan Macmillan GBR. Dist: Macmillan.

Li, Chunmei, ed. Hotel Restaurants & Bars. 2011. (ENG.). 272p. 50.00 ***(978-988-15-0690-0(5))*** Design Media Publishing Ltd. HKG. Dist: BookMasters Distribution Services (BDS).

McFarland, Ben & Sandham, Tom. Good Beer Guide West Coast USA: Including Las Vegas, Alaska & Hawaii. 2008. (Good Beer Guides). (ENG., Illus.). 320p. pap. 27.95 *(978-1-85249-244-1(9))* Camra Bks. GBR. Dist: Independent Pubs. Group.

Paley, Vitaly, et al. The Paley's Place Cookbook: Recipes & Stories from the Pacific Northwest. 2008. (ENG., Illus.). 240p. 35.00 *(978-1-58008-830-5(9))* Ten Speed Pr.

Petersen.a. Cafe Lehmitz. 2009. (GER & ENG., Illus.). 56p. 39.95 *(978-3-8296-0072-9(0))* Schirmer/Mosel Verlag GmbH DEU. Dist: Prestel Publishing.

Reeder, Ann. Heritage Pub Walks in the Isle of Man. 2011. 116p. pap. 14.09 ***(978-1-4567-7824-8(2))*** AuthorHouse.

Spenceley, Angela. Don't Drink the Water. 2007. pap. 19.99 *(978-0-9702168-2-3(3))* Coconut Pr., LLC.

Willems, Marlous, compiled by. Behind Bars: Design for Cafes & Bars. 2007. (ENG., Illus.). 344p. *(978-3-89955-300-0(4))* Die Gestalten Verlag DEU. Dist: Prestel Publishing.

Zagat Survey Staff. 2011/12 New York City Nightlife. 2011. (ZAGAT Nightlife Guides). (ENG.). 288p. pap. 14.95 *(978-1-60478-357-5(5))* Zagat Survey.

Zagat Survey Staff, ed. Boxed/New York City Weekend Edition. 2011. pap. 20.95 ***(978-1-60478-461-9(X))*** Zagat Survey.

BARS (DRINKING ESTABLISHMENTS)—DECORATION

Brandwood, Geoff, et al. Licensed to Sell: the History & Heritage of the Public House. 2nd ed. 2011. (ENG., Illus.). 200p. (C). pap. 33.00 *(978-1-84802-065-6(6))* English Heritage GBR. Dist: Brown, David Bk. Co., The.

DAAB Media Staff, compiled by. Bar Design, 1 vol. 2008. (ENG, GER, FRE, SPA & ITA., Illus.). 399p. 37.95 *(978-3-937718-55-2(9))* DAAB Media GmbH DEU. Dist: Innovative Logistics.

Grafe, Christoph & Bollerey, Franziska, eds. Cafes & Bars: The Architecture of Public Display. 2007. (Interior Architecture Ser.). (Illus.). 213p. per. 53.95 *(978-0-415-36328-0(4))* Routledge.

Grafe, Christoph & Lohmann. Cafes & Bars. 2007. (Interior Architecture Ser.). (ENG., Illus.). 224p. 165.00 *(978-0-415-36327-3(6))* Routledge.

Inglis, Kim & Kawana, Masano. Asian Bar & Restaurant Design. 2007. (ENG., Illus.). 256p. 44.95 *(978-0-7946-0407-3(2)*, PeriplusEdition) Tuttle Publishing.

Nepilly, Ellen. Hip Lounging Japan. 2008. (Illus.). 192p. *(978-981-245-490-4(X))* Page One Publishing.

Ryder, Bethan. New Bar & Club Design: A Century of Surface Design. 2007. (ENG., Illus.). 192p. pap. 35.00 *(978-0-7892-0860-6(1))* Abbeville Pr., Inc.

San Pietro, Silvio, et al. New Bars, Cafes & Pubs in Italy. 2008. (Best Interiors Selection Ser.). (ITA & ENG., Illus.). 216p. *(978-88-7685-158-2(5)*, Edizioni L'archivolto (Acc)) Antique Collectors' Club.

Teitelbaum, James. Tiki Road Trip: A Guide to Tiki Culture in North America. 2nd ed. 2007. (ENG., Illus.). 312p. per. 16.95 *(978-1-59580-019-0(0))* Santa Monica Pr.

Triviño, Santi. Small Bars. Trivino, Santi et al, eds. 2010. (Architectural Details Ser.). (ENG., Illus.). 256p. 57.50 *(978-84-96823-32-7(6))* Instituto Monsa de Ediciones, S.A. ESP. Dist: Trans-Atlantic Pubns., Inc.

Vidiella, Lex Sñchez & Quartino, Daniela Santos. New Bars & Restaurants 2. 2010. (ENG., Illus.). 336p. 50.00 *(978-0-06-196881-5(1)*, Collins Design) HarperCollins Pubs.

Watson, Howard. The Design Mix: Bars, Cocktails & Style. 2006. (ENG., Illus.). 164p. 35.00 *(978-0-470-02633-5(2)*, Academy Pr.) Wiley, John & Sons, Inc.

—Exclusive Bar Design - Hotels' & Members' Clubs. 2006. 224p. pap. 40.00 *(978-0-470-01148-5(3))* Wiley, John & Sons, Inc.

BARS (DRINKING ESTABLISHMENTS)—HISTORY

Arkell, Peter & Pentelow, Mike. A Pub Crawl Through History: The Ultimate Boozers' Who's Who. 2010. (Illus.). 368p. pap. *(978-1-85756-701-4(3))* Janus Publishing Co.

Brown, Pete. Three Sheets to the Wind: One Man's Quest for the Meaning of Beer. 2008. (ENG.). 480p. 14.95 *(978-0-330-44247-3(3))* Macmillan Pubs., Ltd. GBR. Dist: Independent Pubs. Group.

Tames, Richard. The Victorian Public House. 2008. (Shire Library). (Illus.). 40p. pap. 11.95 *(978-0-7478-0573-1(3))* Shire Pubns., Ltd. GBR. Dist: Random Hse., Inc.

Thorburn, Gordon. Pocket Guide to Pubs & their History. 2011. (Illus.). 192p. pap. 19.95 *(978-1-84468-093-1(2))* Pen & Sword Bks. Ltd. GBR. Dist: Casemate Pubs. & Bk. Distributors, LLC.

BARS (DRINKING ESTABLISHMENTS)—MANAGEMENT

Ahern, Michael. How to Stop Bartender Theft & Turn a Profit in the Bar Business. 2007. 84p. pap. 13.95 *(978-1-4303-2388-4(4))* Lulu Enterprises Inc.

Alonzo, Roy. The Upstart Guide to Owning & Managing a Bar or Tavern. 2nd rev. ed. 2006. (ENG., Illus.). 304p. pap. 20.95 *(978-1-4195-3553-6(6)*, 1255570) Kaplan Publishing.

Barratt, Robin. Respect & Reputation. 2010. 250p. 25.95 *(978-1-906358-81-5(8))* Apex Publishing Ltd., Essex GBR. Dist: APG Sales & Distribution Services.

Cassavoy, Liane. Start Your Own Bar & Club: Sports Bars, Night Clubs, Neighborhood Bars, Wine Bars, & More. 3rd ed. 2009. (ENG.). 240p. pap. 17.95 *(978-1-59918-349-7(8)*, 1599183498) Entrepreneur Pr. dba Entrepreneur Media, Inc.

Educational Foundation (National Restaurant Association) Staff, contrib. by. Servsafe Alcohol: Fundamentals of Responsible Alcohol Service. 2nd ed. 2009. (Illus.). *(978-1-58280-258-9(0))* Educational Foundation of the National Restaurant Assn.

Elliott, Mark S. How to Run a Successful Pub: The Comprehensive Guide to Finding a Pub & Making It Profitable. 2nd ed. 2010. (ENG.). 345p. pap. 34.00 *(978-1-84528-425-1(9))* How To Books GBR. Dist: Parkwest Pubns., Inc.

Foley, Ray & Dismore, Heather. Running a Bar for Dummies. 2007. (ENG., Illus.). 360p. per. 21.99 *(978-0-470-04919-8(7)*, For Dummies) Wiley, John & Sons, Inc.

Freeth, Adam W. Bartending: A Professional's Guide to the Industry. 2012. (ENG., Illus.). 192p. pap. 14.95 ***(978-1-78009-002-3(1))*** New Holland Pubs., Ltd. GBR. Dist: Sterling Publishing Co., Inc.

Grand, Larry. No More Risky Business: A Guide to Writing Bar Policies for Keeping Customers Safe & Reducing Liability. 2009. ***(978-0-88868-739-5(7))*** Centre for Addiction & Mental Health.

Hynes, Edward M., et al. Guide to Restaurants & Bars, 2 vols. Incl. Vol. 1. ring bd. 156.00 *(978-0-7646-0285-6(3))*; Vol. 2. ring bd. 156.00 *(978-0-7646-0286-3(1))*; 1997. 156.00 *(978-0-7646-0284-9(5))* Practitioners Publishing Co.

Johns, Steven, et al. The Complete Idiot's Guide to Starting & Running a Bar. 2008. (Complete Idiot's Guide Ser.). (ENG., Illus.). 336p. (gr. 12-18). 18.95 *(978-1-59257-696-8(6)*, Alpha Bks.) Penguin Group (USA) Inc.

National Restaurant Association Solutions Staff. ServSafe Alcohol: Fundamentals of Responsible Alcohol Service. 2nd ed. 2010. (ENG.). (C). pap. 29.13 *(978-0-13-210066-3(5)*, Prentice Hall) Prentice Hall PTR.

—ServSafe Alcohol: Fundamentals of Responsible Alcohol Service, Spanish Edition with Exam Answer Sheet. 2nd ed. 2010. (ENG.). (C). pap. 28.00 *(978-0-13-148058-2(8)*, Prentice Hall) Prentice Hall PTR.

National Restaurant Association Staff. Louisiana ServSafe Alcohol: Fundamentals of Responsible Alcohol Service. 2nd ed. 2010. (ENG.). (C). pap. 29.13 *(978-0-13-139275-5(1)*, Prentice Hall) Prentice Hall PTR.

—ServSafe Starters Spanish 5th Edition Update Employee Guide. 5th ed. 2010. (ENG.). (C). pap. 6.13 *(978-0-13-216334-7(9)*, Prentice Hall) Prentice Hall PTR.

BARS (DRINKING ESTABLISHMENTS)—SOCIAL ASPECTS

Awolin, Mareike. Bar-Room Violence. 2008. 116p. pap. *(978-3-639-07571-7(4))* VDM Verlag Dr. Mueller e.K.

Barich, Bill. A Pint of Plain: Tradition, Change & the Fate of the Irish Pub. 2009. (ENG., Illus.). 256p. 25.00 *(978-0-8027-1701-6(2))* Walker & Co.

—A Pint of Plain: Tradition, Change, & the Fate of the Irish Pub. 2010. (ENG.). 256p. pap. 15.00 *(978-0-8027-1062-8(X))* Walker & Co.

Brennan, Thomas E. Public Drinking in the Early Modern World: Voices from the Tavern, 1500-1800, 4 vols. 2011. (ENG., Illus.). 2048p. 625.00 *(978-1-85196-284-6(0))* Pickering & Chatto Pubs., Ltd. GBR. Dist: Ashgate Publishing Co.

Brown, Pete. Three Sheets to the Wind: One Man's Quest for the Meaning of Beer. 2008. (ENG.). 480p. 14.95 *(978-0-330-44247-3(3))* Macmillan Pubs., Ltd. GBR. Dist: Independent Pubs. Group.

Couch, Julianne. Jukeboxes & Jackalopes: A Wyoming Bar Journey. 2007. pap. 19.95 *(978-1-932636-34-5(X))* Pronghorn Pr.

Kumin, Beat. Drinking Matters: Public Houses & Social Exchange in Early Modern Central Europe. 2007. (Early Modern History Ser.). (ENG., Illus.). 320p. 110.00 *(978-0-230-55408-5(3))* Palgrave Macmillan.

BARS (DRINKING ESTABLISHMENTS)—ASIA

Inglis, Kim & Kawana, Masano. Asian Bar & Restaurant Design. 2007. (ENG., Illus.). 256p. 44.95 *(978-0-7946-0407-3(2)*, PeriplusEdition) Tuttle Publishing.

Robinson, Mark. Izakaya: The Japanese Pub Cookbook, 1 vol. 2008. (ENG., Illus.). 160p. 25.00 *(978-4-7700-3065-8(7))* Kodansha America, Inc.

Santema, Bartele. Bule Gila Tales of A Dutch Barman in Jak. 2006. 160p. per. *(978-979-3780-04-7(5))* Equinox Publishing.

Xie, Yeal. Lobby & Lounge. 2011. (ENG., Illus.). 272p. 50.00 *(978-988-19739-8-6(8))* Design Media Publishing Ltd. HKG. Dist: BookMasters Distribution Services (BDS).

BARS (DRINKING ESTABLISHMENTS)—AUSTRALIA

Thiessen, Tamara. Cafe Life Sydney: A Guide to the Neighborhood Cafés of Australia's Harbor City. 2011. (ENG., Illus.). 168p. pap. 20.00 *(978-1-56656-826-5(9)*, Interlink Bks.) Interlink Publishing Group, Inc.

BARS (DRINKING ESTABLISHMENTS)—CANADA

Brownstein, Bill. Montreal 24: Twenty-Four Hours in the Life of a City. 2009. (ENG., Illus.). 160p. pap. 18.95 *(978-1-55065-244-4(3))* Vehicule Pr. CAN. Dist: Independent Pubs. Group.

Grand, Larry. No More Risky Business: A Guide to Writing Bar Policies for Keeping Customers Safe & Reducing Liability. 2009. ***(978-0-88868-739-5(7))*** Centre for Addiction & Mental Health.

Lee, John. Drinking Vancouver: 100+ Bars in the City & Beyond, 1 vol. 2009. (ENG.). 160p. pap. *(978-1-894898-96-6(6))* TouchWood Editions.

Musgrave, Sarah. Montreal Resto a Go-Go: 200 Cheap & Fun Places to Eat & Drink in Montreal. 2007. (ENG., Illus.). 248p. per. 14.95 *(978-1-55065-218-5(4))* Vehicule Pr. CAN. Dist: Independent Pubs. Group.

BARS (DRINKING ESTABLISHMENTS)—EUROPE

Fitch, Noel Riley. The Grand Literary Cafes of Europe. 2007. (ENG., Illus.). 160p. 39.95 *(978-1-84537-114-2(3))* New Holland Pubs., Ltd. GBR. Dist: National Bk. Network.

Hawthorne, Larry. The Beer Drinker's Guide to Munich. 6th ed. 2008. (ENG., Illus.). 240p. pap. 16.95 *(978-0-9628555-3-5(7))* Freizeit Pubs.

Kumin, Beat. Drinking Matters: Public Houses & Social Exchange in Early Modern Central Europe. 2007. (Early Modern History Ser.). (ENG., Illus.). 320p. 110.00 *(978-0-230-55408-5(3))* Palgrave Macmillan.

Rail, Evan. Prague & Czech Republic. 2008. (ENG., Illus.). 224p. pap. 25.95 *(978-1-85249-233-5(3))* Camra Bks. GBR. Dist: Independent Pubs. Group.

Webb, Tim. Belgium. 6th ed. 2009. (ENG., Illus.). 352p. pap. 23.95 *(978-1-85249-261-8(9))* Camra Bks. GBR. Dist: Independent Pubs. Group.

BARS (DRINKING ESTABLISHMENTS)—FRANCE

Jegu, Pierrick. The Best Wine Bars & Shops of Paris: Fifty Charming & Notable Cavistes. Conrade, Anita & Cox, David W., trs. from FRE. 2008. (ENG., Illus.). 176p. pap. 16.95 *(978-1-892145-63-5(4))* Little Bookroom.

MacElhone, Isabelle. Harry's Bar. 2012. (ENG., Illus.). 128p. 29.95 ***(978-1-58479-974-0(9))*** Stewart, Tabori & Chang.

Time Out Guides Staff, creator. Time Out Paris Eating & Drinking. 8th ed. 2006. (Time Out Guides). (ENG., Illus.). 336p. per. 19.95 *(978-1-904978-95-4(9))* Time Out Guides Ltd. GBR. Dist: Perseus-PGW.

BARS (DRINKING ESTABLISHMENTS)—GREAT BRITAIN

AA Publishing Staff. Britain's Best Pubs 2011. 6th ed. 2011. (Britain's Best Ser.). (ENG., Illus.). 350p. pap. 14.95 *(978-0-7495-6789-7(9))* Automobile Assn. GBR. Dist: Independent Pubs. Group.

—Pubs 2010. 5th ed. 2010. (Britain's Best Ser.). (ENG., Illus.). 350p. pap. 14.95 *(978-0-7495-6466-7(0))* Automobile Assn. GBR. Dist: Independent Pubs. Group.

Aird, Alisdair & Stapley, Fiona. The Good Pub Guide 2011. 2010. (ENG., Illus.). 1056p. pap. 24.95 *(978-0-09-193026-4(X))* Ebury Publishing GBR. Dist: Independent Pubs. Group.

Aird, Alisdair & Stapley, Fiona. The Good Pub Guide 2012. 2011. (ENG., Illus.). 1120p. pap. 29.95 ***(978-0-09-193027-1(8))*** Ebury Publishing GBR. Dist: Independent Pubs. Group.

Brandon, David. Discovering Pub Names & Signs. 2010. (Shire Discovering Ser.). (ENG., Illus.). 80p. pap. 13.95 *(978-0-7478-0757-5(4))* Shire Pubns., Ltd. GBR. Dist: Random Hse., Inc.

—London Pubs. 2010. (Illus.). 128p. pap. 22.95 *(978-1-84868-227-6(1))* Amberley Publishing GBR. Dist: Casemate Pubs. & Bk. Distributors, LLC.

Brandon, David & Brooke, Alan. Haunted London Pubs. 2009. (Haunted Ser.). (ENG., Illus.). 96p. pap. 24.95 *(978-0-7524-4760-5(2))* History Pr. Ltd.,The GBR. Dist: Independent Pubs. Group.

Brandwood, Geoff, et al. Licensed to Sell: the History & Heritage of the Public House. 2nd ed. 2011. (ENG., Illus.). 200p. (C). pap. 36.00 *(978-1-84802-085-6(6))* English Heritage GBR. Dist: Brown, David Bk. Co., The.

Brandwood, Geoffrey K. & Jephcote, Jane. Londons Heritage Pubs. 2008. (Illus.). 208p. pap. 32.50 *(978-1-85249-247-2(3))* Campaign for Real Ale Ltd. GBR. Dist: Trans-Atlantic Pubns., Inc.

Bruning, Ted. London by Pub. 2009. (ENG., Illus.). 288p. pap. 24.95 *(978-1-84732-508-2(4))* Carlton Bks., Ltd. GBR. Dist: Independent Pubs. Group.

Butler, Gordon & Butler, Fetzer. Fancyapint? in London: The Comprehensive Guide to Drinking in the Capital. 2nd ed. 2009. (ENG., Illus.). 440p. pap. 15.95 *(978-1-84454-707-4(8))* Blake, John Publishing, Ltd. GBR. Dist: Independent Pubs. Group.

Cuthbertson, Anne. Pubs & Inns of Britain 2010. 2010. (Family Holiday Guides). (Illus.). 296p. pap. 18.95 *(978-1-85055-421-9(8))* FHG Pubns. Ltd. GBR. Dist: Midpoint Trade Bks., Inc.

de Moor, Des. The CAMRA Guide to London's Best Beer, Pubs & Bars. 2011. (ENG., Illus.). 196p. pap. 19.95 *(978-1-85249-285-4(6))* Camra Bks. GBR. Dist: Independent Pubs. Group.

Garnston, David. Yorkshire's Real Heritage Pubs. 2010. (ENG., Illus.). 80p. pap. 9.95 *(978-1-85249-277-9(5))* Camra Bks. GBR. Dist: Independent Pubs. Group.

Hadfield, Philip M. Bar Wars: Contesting the Night in Contemporary British Cities. 2007. (Clarendon Studies in Criminology Ser.). (ENG.). 344p. 55.00 *(978-0-19-929786-3(X))*; 139.95 *(978-0-19-929785-6(1))* Oxford Univ. Pr., Inc.

Hampson, Tim. 101 Beer Days Out. 2012. (ENG., Illus.). 184p. pap. 19.95 ***(978-1-85249-288-5(0))*** Camra Bks. GBR. Dist: Independent Pubs. Group.

Hancock, David & Sawday, Alastair. Pubs & Inns of England & Wales. (Special Places to Stay Ser.). (ENG., Illus.). 8th ed. 2011. 528p. pap. 23.95 *(978-1-906136-52-9(1))* 9th ed. 2012. 544p. pap. 23.95 ***(978-1-906136-57-4(2))*** Sawday, Alastair Publishing Co. Ltd. GBR. Dist: Globe Pequot Pr., The.

Haydon, Peter & Hampson, Tim. London's Best Pubs. 2nd ed. 2012. (ENG., Illus.). 224p. pap. 19.95 ***(978-1-84773-919-3(9))*** New Holland Pubs., Ltd. GBR. Dist: Sterling Publishing Co., Inc.

Jennings, Paul. The Local: A History of the English Pub. 2011. (ENG., Illus.). 288p. pap. 27.95 *(978-0-7524-5939-4(2))* History Pr. Ltd.,The GBR. Dist: Independent Pubs. Group.

Kemp, Carol. Memories of an East End Publican. 2009. 184p. pap. 14.49 *(978-1-4389-6953-4(8))* AuthorHouse.

Knowlden, Martin. AA 50 Cycles to Country Pubs. 2006. (Walking Bks.). (ENG., Illus.). 208p. pap. 19.95 *(978-0-7495-4812-4(6))* Automobile Assn. GBR. Dist: Independent Pubs. Group.

—AA Britain's Favourite Pub Walks & Cycle Rides. 2006. (Walking Bks.). (ENG., Illus.). 256p. pap. 19.95 *(978-0-7495-4846-9(0))* Automobile Assn. GBR. Dist: Independent Pubs. Group.

Manchester, Colin, et al. Alcohol & Entertainment Licensing Law. 2nd rev. ed. 2008. (Illus.). 975p. pap. 99.95 *(978-0-415-42290-1(6)*, Routledge Cavendish) Taylor & Francis Group GBR. Dist: Taylor & Francis Group.

McHugh, Evan. Pint-Sized Ireland: In Search of the Perfect Guinness. 2008. (ENG., Illus.). 288p. pap. 14.99 *(978-0-312-37758-8(4)*, St. Martin's Griffin) St. Martin's Pr.

Michelin Travel & Lifestyle. Michelin Eating Out in Pubs 2012: Great Britain & Ireland Good Food in Informal Surroundings. 8th ed. 2012. (ENG., Illus.). 616p. pap. 22.95 ***(978-2-06-716617-2(4))*** Michelin Travel & Lifestyle.

Mitchell, J. S. Belly up to the Bar: Dining with New York City's Celebrity Chefs Without Reservation(s) 2008. (ENG., Illus.). 223p. pap. 14.95 *(978-1-58182-636-4(2))* Turner Publishing Co.

Moody, Paul & Turner, Robin. The Search for the Perfect Pub. 2010. (ENG., Illus.). 288p. 28.95 *(978-1-4091-1267-9(5))* Orion Publishing Group, Ltd. GBR. Dist: Independent Pubs. Group.

Norman, Sara. 2004 London Nightlife. rev. ed. (ENG.). 192p. pap. 12.95 *(978-1-57006-537-8(3))* Zagat Survey.

Nowak, Susan & Adam, Jill. Good Pub Food: A Guide to Britain's Best 600 Pubs for Real Food & Real Ale. 6th ed. 2008. (ENG., Illus.). 380p. pap. 29.95 *(978-1-85249-214-4(7))* Camra Bks. GBR. Dist: Independent Pubs. Group.

B

Pascoe, Chris. Death, Destruction & a Packet of Peanuts: A Rollicking Pub Crawl Through Four Years of the English Civil War. 2009. (ENG., Illus.). 240p. 15.95 (978-1-906032-62-3(9)) Anova Bks. GBR. Dist: Independent Pubs. Group.
Pitts, Chris. 'Last Orders' Life as a Pub Landlord. 2007. (Illus.). 224p. per. (978-1-84748-029-3(2)) Athena Pr.
Protz, Roger. Good Beer Guide 2010. 2010. (ENG., Illus.). 880p. pap. 24.95 (978-1-85249-266-3(X)) Camra Bks. GBR. Dist: Independent Pubs. Group.
—Good Beer Guide 2011. 2011. (ENG., Illus.). 888p. pap. 24.95 (978-1-85249-272-4(4)) Camra Bks. GBR. Dist: Independent Pubs. Group.
Protz, Roger, ed. Good Beer Guide 2008. 2007. (ENG., Illus.). 880p. pap. 29.95 (978-1-85249-231-1(7)) Camra Bks. GBR. Dist: Independent Pubs. Group.
—Good Beer Guide 2009. 2008. (ENG., Illus.). 880p. pap. 24.95 (978-1-85249-249-6(X)) Camra Bks. GBR. Dist: Independent Pubs. Group.
Protz, Roger, ed. Good Beer Guide 2012: The Complete Guide to the UK's Best Pubs. 2011. (ENG., Illus.). 888p. pap. 24.95 **(978-1-85249-286-1(4))** Camra Bks. GBR. Dist: Independent Pubs. Group.
Recommended Inns & Pubs of Britain: Accommodation, Food & Traditional Good Cheer, with Details of Family & Pet Friendly Pubs. 2007. (Illus.). 160p. pap. 10.95 (978-1-85055-398-4(X)) FHG Pubns. Ltd. GBR. Dist: Ingram Pub. Services.
Rock, Hugh. Pub Beer Mugs & Glasses. 2008. (Shire Library). (ENG., Illus.). 56p. per. 12.95 (978-0-7478-0656-1(X)) Shire Pubns., Ltd. GBR. Dist: Random Hse., Inc.
Rowe, David. Flintshire Pubs. 2010. (ENG., Illus.). 160p. pap. 29.95 (978-0-7509-5095-4(1)) History Pr. Ltd., The GBR. Dist: Independent Pubs. Group.
Shelley, Henry C. Inns & Taverns of Old London. 2010. 488p. pap. 38.75 (978-1-144-57521-0(4)) 2008. 232p. 24.99 (978-0-554-33045-7(8)) 2008. 232p. 27.99 (978-0-554-23742-8(3)) 2007. (ENG.). 208p. pap. 20.99 (978-1-4264-4975-8(5)) 2007. 230p. pap. 22.99 (978-1-4264-5276-5(4)) BiblioBazaar.
—Inns & Taverns of Old London. 2008. (ENG.). 184p. per. (978-1-4065-6968-1(2)) Dodo Pr.
—Inns & Taverns of Old London. 2010. 128p. pap. 21.79 (978-1-153-63093-1(1)) General Bks. LLC.
—Inns & Taverns of Old London. 2010. 170p. pap. 17.56 (978-1-162-66823-9(7)); 29.56 **(978-1-169-27311-5(4))**; 36.95 (978-1-161-43688-4(X)) Kessinger Publishing, LLC.
Shoesmith, Ron & Eisel, John. Herefordshire Pubs. 2010. (ENG., Illus.). 128p. pap. 24.95 (978-0-7524-4466-6(2)) History Pr. Ltd., The GBR. Dist: Independent Pubs. Group.
Simpson, Jacqueline. Green Men & White Swans: The Folklore of British Pub Names. 2011. (ENG., Illus.). 288p. pap. 14.95 (978-0-09-952017-7(6)) Random Hse. GBR. Dist: Independent Pubs. Group.
Steel, Bob. Lake District Pub Walks. 2011. (ENG., Illus.). 160p. pap. 15.95 **(978-1-85249-271-7(6))** Camra Bks. GBR. Dist: Independent Pubs. Group.
—London Pub Walks. 2008. (ENG., Illus.). 160p. pap. 16.95 (978-1-85249-216-8(3)) Camra Bks. GBR. Dist: Independent Pubs. Group.
—Peak District Pub Walks. 2008. (Illus.). 176p. pap. 23.95 (978-1-85249-246-5(5), Macmillan) Pan Macmillan GBR. Dist: Trans-Atlantic Pubns., Inc.
Steel, Bob. South East Pub Walks. 2012. (ENG.). 160p. pap. 15.95 **(978-1-85249-287-8(2))** Camra Bks. GBR. Dist: Independent Pubs. Group.
Taylor, Arthur. Played at the Pub: The Pub Games of Britain. 2009. (Played in Britain Ser.). (ENG., Illus.). 184p. pap. 29.95 (978-1-905624-97-3(2)) English Heritage GBR. Dist: Brown, David Bk. Co., The.
Tierney-Jones, Adrian. Great British Pubs. 2012. (ENG., Illus.). 296p. pap. 23.95 **(978-1-85249-265-6(1))** Camra Bks. GBR. Dist: Independent Pubs. Group.
Time Out Guides Staff, ed. Time Out London's Best Bars. 12th ed. 2010. (ENG., Illus.). 288p. pap. 19.95 (978-1-905042-46-3(9)) Time Out Guides Ltd. GBR. Dist: Perseus-PGW.
—Time Out London's Best Bars & Pubs. 2012. (ENG., Illus.). 256p. pap. 19.95 (978-1-905042-61-6(2)) Time Out Guides Ltd. GBR. Dist: Perseus-PGW.
—Time Out London's Best Restaurants. 2012. (ENG., Illus.). 288p. pap. 19.95 (978-1-905042-63-0(9)) Time Out Guides Ltd. GBR. Dist: Perseus-PGW.
—Time Out London's Best Restaurants 2011. 2011. (ENG., Illus.). 432p. pap. 20.00 (978-1-905042-47-0(7)) Time Out Guides Ltd. GBR. Dist: Perseus-PGW.
Zagat Survey Staff, contrib. by. London Night Out Pack 2004. (ENG., Illus.). 384p. 21.90 (978-1-57006-578-1(0)) Zagat Survey.

BARS (DRINKING ESTABLISHMENTS)—IRELAND

Barich, Bill. A Pint of Plain: Tradition, Change & the Fate of the Irish Pub. 2009. (ENG., Illus.). 256p. 25.00 (978-0-8027-1701-6(2)) Walker & Co.
—A Pint of Plain: Tradition, Change, & the Fate of the Irish Pub. 2010. (ENG.). 256p. pap. 15.00 (978-0-8027-1062-8(X)) Walker & Co.
Campbell, Georgi. Georgina Campbells Ireland 07. 2006. (Illus.). 512p. 19.95 (978-1-903164-23-5(0)) Georgina Campbell's Guides Ltd. IRL. Dist: Interlink Publishing Group, Inc.
Campbell, Georgina. Georgina Campbell's Ireland: The Guide 2009. 2008. (ENG., Illus.). 626p. pap. 20.00 (978-1-903164-28-0(1)) Georgina Campbell's Guides Ltd. IRL. Dist: Interlink Publishing Group, Inc.
—Georgina Campbell's Ireland: the Guide: All the Best Places to Eat, Drink & Stay. 10th ed. 2007. (Georgina Campbell's Ireland Ser.). (ENG., Illus.). 456p. pap. 20.00 (978-1-903164-26-6(5)) Georgina Campbell's Guides Ltd. IRL. Dist: Interlink Publishing Group, Inc.
Connolly, Robert E. The Rise & Fall of the Irish Pub. 2010. (ENG., Illus.). 224p. pap. 26.95 (978-1-905785-78-0(X)) Liffey Pr., The IRL. Dist: Dufour Editions, Inc.
Fennell, James, photos by. The Irish Pub. 2008. (ENG., Illus.). 192p. 40.00 (978-0-500-51428-3(3), 551428) Thames & Hudson.
Jones, Bob & Jones, Anne. Ireland's Small Greens: Golf, Pubs, Lodging & Attractions. 2007. (Illus.). 328p. per. 18.95 (978-0-9799555-0-1(5)) Jones, Bob.

BARS (DRINKING ESTABLISHMENTS)—ITALY

Essa, Shannon & Edenbaum, Ruth. Chow! Venice: Savoring the Food & Wine of la Serenissima - A Guide to Restaurants & Bars in Venice. 2nd rev. exp. ed. 2007. (ENG., Illus.). 194p. per. 19.95 (978-1-934259-00-9(4)) Wine Appreciation Guild, Ltd.
San Pietro, Silvio, et al. New Bars, Cafes & Pubs in Italy. 2008. (Best Interiors Selection Ser.). (ITA & ENG., Illus.). 216p. (978-88-7685-158-2(5), Edizioni L'archivolto (Acc)) Antique Collectors' Club.
Wolff, Joe. Café Life Venice: A Guidebook to the Cafés & Bacari of la Serenissima. 2008. (Illus.). 176p. pap. 20.00 (978-1-56656-718-3(1), Interlink Bks.) Interlink Publishing Group, Inc.

BARS (DRINKING ESTABLISHMENTS)—SCOTLAND

Steel, Bob. Edinburgh Pub Walks. 2010. (ENG., Illus.). 160p. pap. 15.95 (978-1-85249-274-8(0)) Camra Bks. GBR. Dist: Independent Pubs. Group.

BARS (DRINKING ESTABLISHMENTS)—SOUTH AMERICA

Kogan, Gabriela. The Authentic Bars, Cafes & Restaurants of Buenos Aires. 2008. (ENG., Illus.). 144p. pap. 14.95 (978-1-892145-55-0(3)) Little Bookroom.

BARS (DRINKING ESTABLISHMENTS)—UNITED STATES

Armon, Rick. Ohio Breweries, 1 vol. 2011. (Breweries Ser.). (ENG., Illus.). 192p. pap. 19.95 (978-0-8117-0868-5(3)) Stackpole Bks.
Arnold, Jim & Lamis, Ingrid. Wine Clubs of Sonoma County: A Guide to the Pleasures & Perks of Belonging, 1 vol. 2007. (ENG., Illus.). 232p. pap. 22.95 (978-1-58980-432-6(5)) Pelican Publishing Co., Inc.
Baum, Gary & Corsello, Bill, eds. Zagat Los Angeles Nightlife. rev. ed. 2007. (Zagat Survey: Los Angeles Nightlife Ser.). (ENG.). 188p. per. 14.95 (978-1-57006-877-5(1)) Zagat Survey.
Bixby, Drew. Denver's Best Dive Bars: Drinking & Diving in the Mile-High City. 2009. (Best Dive Bars Ser.). (ENG.). 160p. pap. 12.95 (978-0-9815040-9-4(4), Gamble Guides) Ig Publishing, Inc.
BlackBook Jet Set Guide 2008. 2007. pap. 10.95 (978-1-932942-37-8(8)) Black Bk. Media Corp.
Bolden-Bowers, Stacey. The Clubs of La: A Guide Inside Fantastic Spots for Clubbing, Pubbing, & Chilling. Crump, A. K. & TasteTV, eds. 2011. (ENG., Illus.). 160p. pap. 16.95 (978-0-9822200-4-7(9)) TCB-Cafe Publishing.
Boothby, William T. Cocktail Boothby's American Bartender: The New Anchor Distilling Edition. Burkhart, David, ed. & frwd. by. Maytag, Fritz, frwd. 2009. (Illus.). 152p. pap. 14.95 (978-0-9822473-3-4(8)) Anchor Distilling Co.
Bounds, Gwendolyn. Little Chapel on the River: A Pub, a Town & the Search for What Matters Most. 2006. (Illus.). 320p. per. 13.95 (978-0-06-056407-0(5), William Morrow Paperbacks) HarperCollins Pubs.
Bryson, Lew. Pennsylvania Breweries. 4th ed. 2010. (Breweries Ser.). (ENG., Illus.). 304p. pap. 19.95 (978-0-8117-3641-1(5)) Stackpole Bks.
Bryson, Lew & Haynie, Mark. New Jersey Breweries. 2008. (Breweries Ser.). (ENG., Illus.). 148p. pap. 16.95 (978-0-8117-3504-9(4)) Stackpole Bks.
Cook, Alex V. Louisiana Saturday Night: Looking for a Good Time in South Louisiana's Juke Joints, Honky-Tonks, & Dance Halls. 2012. (Illus.). 256p. pap. 24.95 **(978-0-8071-4456-5(8))** Louisiana State Univ. Pr.
Cordwell, Colin, et al. Tales from the Red Lion. Weagly, John & Dubnick, Andrea, eds. 2007. per. 13.00 (978-0-9779856-2-3(8)) Twilight Tales, Inc.
Corey, Carl. Tavern League: Portraits of Wisconsin Bars. 2011. (ENG., Illus.). 136p. 29.95 (978-0-87020-478-4(5)) Wisconsin Historical Society.
Couch, Julianne. Jukeboxes & Jackalopes: A Wyoming Bar Journey. 2007. pap. 19.95 (978-1-932636-34-5(X)) Pronghorn Pr.
Daniels, Elise Ann. Boise. 2006. (It's Just Lunch Guide to Dating Ser.). 114p. per. 9.95 (978-1-933174-53-2(6)) 10 Finger Pr.
David, Tracey, ed. Thirsty? New York City: The Lowdown on Where the Real People Drink! 2009. 256p. pap. 14.95 (978-1-893329-34-8(8), Glove Box Guides) Hungry City Guides.
Draeger, Jim & Speltz, Mark. Bottoms Up: A Toast to Wisconsin's Historic Bars & Breweries. 2012. (Places along the Way Ser.). (ENG., Illus.). 272p. 29.95 **(978-0-87020-498-2(X))** Wisconsin Historical Society.
Eddings, Bryce. Missouri Breweries. 2012. (Breweries Ser.). (ENG., Illus.). 160p. pap. 19.95 (978-0-8117-0662-9(1)) Stackpole Bks.
Fellows, Will & Branson, Helen P. Gay Bar: The Fabulous, True Story of a Daring Woman & Her Boys in the 1950s. 2010. (Illus.). 186p. 26.95 (978-0-299-24850-5(X)) Univ. of Wisconsin Pr.
Gagliardi, Marcia. San Francisco: Find the Right Spot for Every Occasion. 2010. (ENG., Illus.). 240p. pap. 16.00 (978-1-58008-128-3(2)) Ten Speed Pr.
Gathje, Curt, ed. Zagat New York City Nightlife. rev. ed. 2007. (Zagat Ser.). (ENG., Illus.). 272p. pap. 14.95 (978-1-57006-874-4(7)) Zagat Survey.
Grazian, David. On the Make: The Hustle of Urban Nightlife. 2011. (ENG.). 296p. pap. 18.00 (978-0-226-30672-8(0)) Univ. of Chicago Pr.
Groves, Melody. Hoist a Cold One! Historic Bars of the Southwest. 2011. (ENG., Illus.). 144p. pap. 24.95 (978-0-8263-4668-1(5)) Univ. of New Mexico Pr.
Guerrero, Raul. Raul Guerrero: The Whaling Bar: la Jolla. 2007. (Illus.). 10.00 (978-0-9744804-7-3(9), Athenaeum Music & Arts Library) Library Assn. of La Jolla.
Haber, Mel. Bedtime Stories of the Legendary Ingleside Inn in Palm Springs. 2010. 248p. pap. 19.95 (978-1-59393-533-7(1)) BearManor Media.
Harburg, Ernest, et al. Liberty, Equality, Consensus, & All That Jazz at the Del Rio Bar. 2009. (978-1-932399-23-3(2)) Huron River Pr.
Harris, Dow. Savannah Tavern Tales & Pubs Review. 2007. (Illus.). 223p. pap. 16.95 (978-0-7643-2530-4(2)) Schiffer Publishing, Ltd.
Lanier, Pamela. The Complete Guide to Bed & Breakfasts, Inns & Guesthouses: In the United States, Canada, & Worldwide. 24th ed. 2007. (Complete Guide to Bed & Breakfasts, Inns & Guesthouses Ser.). (Illus.). 897p. per. 16.95 (978-1-58008-846-6(5)) Ten Speed Pr.
Lecaro, Lina. Los Angeles's Best Dive Bars: Drinking & Diving in the City of Angels. 2010. (Best Dive Bars Ser.). (ENG.). 176p. pap. 12.95 (978-1-935439-15-8(4), Gamble Guides) Ig Publishing, Inc.
Lomax, John Nova. Houston's Best Dive Bars: Drinking & Diving in the Bayou City. 2010. (Best Dive Bars Ser.). (ENG.). 176p. pap. 12.95 (978-1-935439-16-5(2), Gamble Guides) Ig Publishing, Inc.
Lovell, Jacquie & Mathews, Tom. Wine Bar Reveries - 2006: Wine Bars, Restaurants & Wine Shops in Ventura, Camarillo & Oxnard. 2006. (Illus.). 108p. pap. 14.95 (978-1-59800-450-2(6)) Outskirts Pr., Inc.
Lyons, Terry W. Bar Hopping Thru Americ. 2010. 256p. pap. 17.95 (978-0-9827442-4-6(2)) Fiction Publishing, Inc.
Macchione, Mikko. Napoleon House. 2006. (Illus.). 118p. 39.95 (978-0-9709336-6-9(5)) Vissi d'Arte Bks.
Macchione, Mikko. Napoleon House, 1 vol. 2011. (ENG., Illus.). 118p. 25.00 **(978-1-4556-1544-5(7))** Pelican Publishing Co., Inc.
Mary Jane Mahan. Love at the Pub: An Insider's Guide to Craftsmanship, Conversation, & Community at the Brick Store Pub. 2009. 224p. pap. 18.95 (978-1-4401-7035-5(5)) iUniverse, Inc.
McCaffety, Kerri. Obituary Cocktail: The Great Saloons of New Orleans, 1 vol. 2011. (ENG.). 144p. 35.00 **(978-1-4556-1584-1(6))** Pelican Publishing Co., Inc.
McManus, Brian. Philadelphia's Best Dive Bars: Drinking & Diving in the City of Brotherly Love. 2011. (Best Dive Bars Ser.). (ENG., Illus.). 168p. pap. 12.95 **(978-1-935439-20-2(0)**, Gamble Guides) Ig Publishing, Inc.
Mobil Travel Guide. Lodgings for Less. 2008. (ENG.). 214p. pap. 15.95 (978-1-936010-09-7(7)) Five Star Travel Corp., The.
Moehringer, J. R. The Tender Bar: A Memoir. 2006. (ENG.). 432p. pap. 14.99 (978-0-7868-8876-4(8)) Hyperion Pr.
Monahan, Sherry. Tombstone's Treasure: Silver Mines & Golden Saloons. 2007. (ENG., Illus.). 215p. pap. 17.95 (978-0-8263-4176-1(4)) Univ. of New Mexico Pr.
O'Neil, Luke. Boston's Best Dive Dars: Drinking & Diving in Beantown. 2011. (Best Dive Bars Ser.). (ENG., Illus.). 176p. pap. 12.95 **(978-1-935439-25-7(1)**, Gamble Guides) Ig Publishing, Inc.
Ottley, James. Atlanta History for Cocktail Parties. 2009. 89p. pap. 12.00 (978-0-557-04658-4(0)) Lulu Enterprises Inc.
Reid, Dale. The Shamrock: A neighborhood Waterhole. 2009. 248p. 24.99 (978-1-4389-5607-7(X)); pap. 17.95 (978-1-4389-5608-4(8)) AuthorHouse.
Ross, Victoria Jennings. Detroit's Historic Drinking Establishments. 2008. (IOA Ser.). (ENG., Illus.). 128p. pap. 21.99 (978-0-7385-6191-2(6)) Arcadia Publishing.
Ruschmann, Paul & Nasiatka, Maryanne. Michigan Breweries. 2006. (Breweries Ser.). (ENG., Illus.). 265p. per. 16.95 (978-0-8117-3299-4(1)) Stackpole Bks.
Russell, Don. Joe Sixpack's Philly Beer Guide: A Reporter's Notes on the Best Beer-Drinking City in America. 2008. (Illus.). 223p. per. 14.95 (978-1-933822-10-5(4)) Camino Bks., Inc.
Shecky's New York Bar, Club, & Lounge Guide 2007. 2007. 11.95 (978-1-931449-30-4(9)) Shecky's Publishing.
Shepard, Robin. Minnesota's Best Breweries & Brewpubs: Searching for the Perfect Pint. 2011. E-Book (978-0-299-28243-1(0)); (ENG., Illus.). 336p. pap. 24.95 (978-0-299-28244-8(9)) Univ. of Wisconsin Pr.
Singh, Alpana. Alpana Pours: About Being a Woman, Loving Wine & Having Great Relationships. 2006. (Illus.). 220p. per. 17.95 (978-0-89733-546-1(5)) Academy Chicago Pubs., Ltd.
Sismondo, Christine. America Walks into a Bar: A Spirited History of Taverns & Saloons, Speakeasies & Grog Shops, 1 vol. 2011. (ENG., Illus.). 320p. 24.95 (978-0-19-973495-5(X)) Oxford Univ. Pr., Inc.
Spude, Catherine Holder. Sin & Grace: A Historical Novel of the Skagway, Alaska Sporting Wars. 2007. (Illus.). 220p. pap. 16.95 (978-0-945284-08-6(X)) Lynn Canal Publishing.
Trends in the Hotel Industry USA Edition - 2007. 2007. per. 325.00 (978-0-9763664-9-2(5)) PKF Hospitality Research.
Tsutsumi, Cheryl Chee. The Hawaii Beer Book: Bars, Breweries & Beer Cuisine. 2007. (Illus.). 184p. spiral bd. 15.95 (978-0-9796769-2-5(4)) Watermark Publishing, LLC.
Viola, Kristin, ed. Thirsty? Los Angeles: The Lowdown on Where the Real People Drink! 2009. 224p. pap. 14.95 (978-1-893329-46-1(1), Glove Box Guides) Hungry City Guides.
Wells, Ken. Travels with Barley: A Journey Through Beer Culture in America. 2008. (ENG.). 304p. 24.00 (978-1-4379-5130-1(9)) DIANE Publishing Co.
Westhoff, Ben. New York City's Best Dive Bars: Drinking & Diving in the Big Apple. 2010. (Best Dive Bars Ser.). (ENG.). 180p. pap. 12.95 **(978-1-935439-19-6(7)**, Gamble Guides) Ig Publishing, Inc.
Williams, Jillian, ed. Thirsty? San Francisco: The Lowdown on Where the Real People Drink! 2009. 224p. pap. 14.95 (978-1-893329-58-4(5), Glove Box Guides) Hungry City Guides.
Wissing, Douglas A. Indiana: One Pint at a Time: A Traveler's Guide to Indiana's Brewpubs. 2010. (978-0-87195-283-7(1)) Indiana Historical Society.
Zagat Survey Staff. Food Lover's Guide 2011/12. 2011. (ZAGAT Guides). (ENG.). 352p. pap. 14.95 (978-1-60478-362-9(1)) Zagat Survey.
—Los Angeles Nightlife 2004. (ENG.). 192p. pap. 12.95 (978-1-57006-522-4(5)) Zagat Survey.
—New York City Nightlife 2008/09. Gathje, Curt, ed. 2008. (ENG., Illus.). 208p. pap. 14.95 (978-1-57006-977-2(8)) Zagat Survey.
—New York City Nightlife 2009/10. 2008. (ENG.). 50p. pap. 14.95 (978-1-60478-159-5(9)) Zagat Survey.
—San Francisco Nightlife 2009-10. 2008. (ENG.). 80p. pap. 6.95 (978-1-60478-157-1(2)) Zagat Survey.
—2008/09 Chicago ZAGAT. com & Book Pack. 2008. (ENG.). 34.90 (978-1-57006-987-1(5)) Zagat Survey.
—2008/09 Chicago ZAGAT to Go Pack. 2008. (ENG.). 34.90 (978-1-57006-988-8(3)) Zagat Survey.
Zagat Survey Staff, creator. Zagat America's Top Restaurants Special Edition Dining Journal. 2007. (ENG.). 574p. 25.95 (978-1-57006-910-9(7)) Zagat Survey.
—Zagat. com & Book Pack. 2008. (ENG., Illus.). 268p. 29.95 (978-1-57006-985-7(9)) Zagat Survey.
—Zagat New York City Pack. 2007. (ENG.). 320p. pap. 45.80 (978-1-57006-922-2(0)) Zagat Survey.
—Zagat New York City Restaurants Special Edition Dining Journal. 2007. (Zagat Survey: New York City Restaurants Ser.). (ENG.). 526p. pap. 25.95 (978-1-57006-909-3(3)) Zagat Survey.
Zagat Survey Staff, ed. New York City 2009, Pack. 2008. (ENG.). 320p. pap. 46.80 (978-1-60478-037-6(1)) Zagat Survey.
Zwicker, Roxie J. Haunted Pubs of New England: Raising Spirits of the Past. 2007. (ENG., Illus.). 125p. pap., per. 19.99 (978-1-59629-281-9(4)) History Pr., The.

BARS (ENGINEERING)

see also Girders; Springs (Mechanism)

American Society of Mechanical Engineers Staff, ed. Nail Puller Bars: Safety Requirements. 16p. 28.00 (978-0-7918-2493-1(4)) ASME Pr.
Shum, Wai. Vibration Modes of Steady Whirling Rods & Dynamic Roatating Annuli. 2009. 148p. pap. (978-3-639-19108-0(0)) VDM Verlag Dr. Mueller e.K.
Svetlitsky, Valery A. Dynamics of Rods. Evseev, E. & Ramodanova, K., trs. 2010. (Foundations of Engineering Mechanics Ser.). (Illus.). xii, 448p. pap. 239.00 (978-3-642-06352-7(7), 3642063527) Springer.
Technology Research Editors, ed. Drawing of Wire & Rod, 2007 Ed. 2007. pap. 128.50 (978-1-60030-441-5(9), Search-In-Print) CSA Journal Division.
Types of Mechanical Splices for Reinforcing Bars. 2007. per. (978-0-87031-239-7(1)) American Concrete Institute.

BARTENDERS

Bums, August "Sonny". Seven Swinging Years. 2006. v, 98p. 14.00 (978-0-8059-7110-1(6)) Dorrance Publishing Co., Inc.
Charming, Cheryl. Miss Charming's Guide for Hip Bartenders & Wayout Wannabes: Your Ultimate One-Stop Bar & Cocktail Resource. 2006. (ENG., Illus.). 224p. per. 14.95 (978-1-4022-0804-1(9)) Sourcebooks, Inc.
Edwards, Sam. In the Last Days of the Empire: Watching the Sixties Go by on Greenwich Village Time, A Bartender's Tale. 2010. 118p. pap. 14.94 (978-0-557-48568-0(1)) Lulu Enterprises Inc.
Johnson, Bob. The Disgusting Practice of Bartender Theft - Revealed, Analyzed & Solved, Vol. 1. Gauthier, Catherine, ed. 2007. 130p. pap. 49.00 (978-1-928605-08-9(7)) B M S Publishing Co.
KICHISE, K. A. T. S. U. I. C. H. I. Chief's tales of a comical Bartender. 2007. 98p. pap. 18.95 (978-1-4303-2833-9(9)) Lulu Enterprises Inc.
Mendile, Thecla & Mwageni, Prof. E. A. Correlates of Sexual Behaviour among Barmaids in Morogoro Municipality. 2010. 100p. pap. (978-3-639-26032-8(5)) VDM Verlag Dr. Mueller e.K.
Trueman, Jonathan. One for the Ditch. 2009. 80p. pap. 11.49 (978-1-4490-1719-4(3)) AuthorHouse.

BARTENDING

see also Bartenders

Ahern, Michael. How to Stop Bartender Theft & Turn a Profit in the Bar Business. 2007. 84p. pap. 13.95 (978-1-4303-2388-4(4)) Lulu Enterprises Inc.
The Bartender's Guide. 2008. 384p. (978-1-4075-3397-1(5)) Parragon, Inc.
Black Dog and Leventhal Publishers Staff. The New York Bartender's Guide. (Illus.). 9.98 (978-1-884822-13-1(4)) Black Dog & Leventhal Pubs., Inc.
Boothby, Wm T., compiled by. The World's Drinks & How to Mix Them: Standard Authority. 2009. ix, 143p. **(978-1-60311-189-8(1))** Mud Puddle, Inc.
Boston. Mr. Boston: Official Bartender's Guide. 75th ed. 2012. (Frommer's Portable Ser.: 263). (ENG., Illus.). 336p. pap. 9.99 **(978-0-470-88233-7(6)**, Wiley) Wiley, John & Sons, Inc.
—Mr. Boston Official Bartender's Guide. Pogash, Jonathan & Rodgers, Rick, eds. 75th anniv. ed. 2011. (ENG., Illus.). 376p. 14.99 **(978-0-470-88234-4(4)**, Wiley) Wiley, John & Sons, Inc.
Boston. Mr. Boston Platinum Edition: 1,500 Recipes, Tools, & Techniques for the Master Mixologist. Giglio, Anthony, ed. 2006. (ENG., Illus.). 328p. 19.95 (978-0-471-97302-7(5), Wiley) Wiley, John & Sons, Inc.
Boston's. Mr. Boston: Official Bartender's Guide. Giglio, Anthony & Meehan, Jim, eds. 67th ed. 2008. (ENG., Illus.). 336p. instr.'s gde. ed. 14.95 (978-0-470-39065-8(4), Wiley) Wiley, John & Sons, Inc.
Broom, Dave. The Complete Bartender's Guide: Expert Advice on Equipment, Bar Craft, Cocktails & the World of Alcoholic Drinks. 2011. (ENG., Illus.). 400p.

24.95 *(978-1-84732-643-0(9))* Carlton Bks., Ltd. GBR. Dist: Independent Pubs. Group.

Calabrese, Salvatore. Cocktails by Flavor: Over 340 Recipes to Tempt the Taste Buds. 2008. (ENG., Illus.). 224p. spiral bd. 14.95 *(978-1-4027-5305-3(5))* Sterling Publishing Co., Inc.

Charming, Cheryl. Bartender's Book: 750 Recipes for Classic & Mixed Drinks, Trendy Shots, & Non-alcoholic Alternatives. 2nd ed. 2007. (ENG.). 320p. pap. 9.95 *(978-1-59869-590-8(8))* Adams Media Corp.

—The Everything Bartender's Book: Your complete guide to cocktails, martinis, mixed drinks, & More! 3rd ed. 2010. (ENG.). 416p. pap. 10.95 *(978-1-4405-0383-2(4))* Adams Media Corp.

—Just Tropical Drinks: A Little Book of Liquid Paradise. 2010. 128p. pap. 9.95 *(978-1-59921-899-1(2))* Globe Pequot Pr., The.

Charming, Cheryl & Resnick, Jane Parker. The Everything Bartender's Book: Your Complete Guide to Cocktails, Martinis, Mixed Drinks, & More! 3rd ed. 2010. (Illus.). xv, 399p. ***(978-1-4405-0384-9(2))*** Adams Media Corp.

Cunningham, Stephen K. The Bartender's Black Book. 8th exp. ed. 2006. 264p. spiral bd. 12.95 *(978-1-891267-31-4(0))* Wine Appreciation Guild, Ltd.

Cunningham, Stephen Kittredge. The Bartender's Black Book. 10th ed. 2011. (ENG.). 176p. pap. 12.95 ***(978-1-935879-99-2(5))*** Wine Appreciation Guild, Ltd.

Elwins, Dannie. How to Become the Best Bartender Around Town. 2009. 48p. pap. 16.99 *(978-0-557-15443-2(X))* Lulu Enterprises Inc.

Fino, Rocky. Will Mix for Sex: Twenty-One Classic Cocktails to Set the Mood. 2006. (Illus.). 55p. spiral bd. 11.95 *(978-1-932173-78-9(1))* Stephens Pr. LLC.

Foley, Ray. Bartender Magazine's Ultimate Bartender's Guide: More Than 1,300 Recipes from the World's Best Bartenders, Plus Everything Your Need to Set up & Serve. 2007. (ENG.). 416p. 19.95 *(978-1-4022-0915-4(0))* Sourcebooks, Inc.

—Bartending. 4th ed. 2010. (ENG., Illus.). 394p. pap. 16.99 *(978-0-470-63312-0(3),* For Dummies) Wiley, John & Sons, Inc.

Foley, Ray, ed. The Bar Guide. 2006. (Illus.). 335p. *(978-1-74089-561-3(4))* Weldon Owen Pty. Ltd.

Food and Wine Magazine Editors. Food & Wine Cocktails 2011: An Indispensable Mix of Excellent Cocktails & Food to Go with Them, Plus the Ultimate Guide to the Top Bars & Lounges around the Country. 2011. (ENG., Illus.). 224p. pap. 14.95 *(978-1-60320-882-6(8))* Time Home Entertainment, Inc.

Freeth, Adam W. Bartending: A Professional's Guide to the Industry. 2012. (ENG., Illus.). 192p. pap. 14.95 ***(978-1-78009-002-3(1))*** New Holland Pubs., Ltd. GBR. Dist: Sterling Publishing Co., Inc.

Hemingway, Edward, Ilus. Hemingway & Bailey's Bartending Guide to Great American Writers. 2006. (ENG.). 100p. 15.95 *(978-1-55512-482-0(0),* 1565124820) Algonquin Bks. of Chapel Hill.

Johnson, Harry. The New & Improved Illustrated Bartenders' Manual, or, How to Mix Drinks of the Present Style: Containing Valuable Instructions & Hints by the Author in Reference to the Management of a Bar, a Hotel, & a Restaurant: Also, a Large List of Mixed Drinks, Including American, British, French, German, Italian, Russian, Spanish, Etc., with Illustrations & a Comprehensive Description of Bar Utensils, Wines, Liquors, Ales, Mixtures, Etc., Etc. 2008. (Illus.). 268p. ***(978-1-60311-167-6(0))*** Mud Puddle, Inc.

Julyan, Brian K. Sales & Service for the Wine Professional. 3rd ed. 2008. (Illus.). 357p. pap. *(978-1-84480-789-5(4))* Cengage Learning.

Kappeler, George J. Modern American Drinks: How to Mix & Serve All Kinds of Cups & Drinks. 2009. (Illus.). x, 120p. ***(978-1-60311-185-0(9))*** Mud Puddle, Inc.

Knorr, Paul. Big Bad-Ass Book of Cocktails: 1,500 Recipes to Mix It Up! Running Press Staff, ed. 2010. (ENG.). 672p. pap. 14.95 *(978-0-7624-3839-6(8),* Running Pr.) Running Pr. Bk. Pubs.

—Candy Shots: 150 Decadent, Delicious Drinks for Your Sweet Tooth. 2011. (ENG., Illus.). 160p. pap. 12.95 *(978-1-4027-7125-5(8))* Sterling Publishing Co., Inc.

—Shots. Playboy Magazine Editors, ed. 2010. (ENG., Illus.). 776p. pap. 14.95 *(978-1-4027-6954-2(7),* Sterling Innovation) Sterling Publishing Co., Inc.

—10,000 Drinks: 27 Years' Worth of Cocktails! Recipes & Tips for 10,000 Alcoholic & Nonalcoholic Mixed Drinks, Eye-Openers, Party Starters, Pick-Me-Ups, & Thirst-Quenching Libations. 2007. (ENG., Illus.). 1120p. 19.95 *(978-1-4027-4287-3(8))* Sterling Publishing Co., Inc.

Lologanes, John Peter & Schmid, Albert W. A. The Beverage Manager's Guide to Wines, Beers & Spirits. 3rd rev. ed. 2011. (ENG.). 360p. (C). pap. 97.33 ***(978-0-13-270672-8(5),*** Prentice Hall) Prentice Hall PTR.

Macelhone, Harry. Harry's Abc of Mixing Cocktails. 4th ed. 2011. (ENG., Illus.). 128p. 14.95 *(978-0-285-63891-4(2))* Souvenir Pr. Ltd. GBR. Dist: Independent Pubs. Group.

Marcus, Lori. Bartending Inside-Out: The Guide to Profession, Profit, & Fun. 3rd ed. 2008. (ENG., Illus.). 160p. per. 14.95 *(978-0-9642019-7-2(6))* Cadillac Pr.

Masson, Jeff & Boehm, Greg. The Big Bartender's Book. 2009. (Illus.). 480p. pap. ***(978-1-60311-186-7(7))*** Mud Puddle, Inc.

Meehan, Jim & Gall, Chris. The PDT Cocktail Book: The Complete Bartender's Guide from the Celebrated Speakeasy. 2011. (ENG., Illus.). 368p. 24.95 *(978-1-4027-7923-7(2),* Sterling Epicure) Sterling Publishing Co., Inc.

Morrell, Thomas. Bartending Basics: A Complete Beginner's Guide. 2008. 196p. pap. 19.95 *(978-1-4357-3636-8(2))* Lulu Enterprises Inc.

Nibbe, Dale A. & BarCharts Inc., Staff. Bartender's Guide to Cocktails. 2007. (Quick Study Ser.). (ENG.). 6p. 5.95 *(978-1-4232-0323-0(2))* Barcharts, Inc.

O'Neill, Patrick. Cellermanship. 5th ed. 2011. (ENG., Illus.). 152p. pap. 13.95 *(978-1-85249-276-6(3))* Camra Bks. GBR. Dist: Independent Pubs. Group.

Reed, Ben. Ben Reed's Bartender's Guide. 2006. (ENG., Illus.). 144p. *(978-1-84597-233-2(3))* Ryland Peters & Small.

Regan, Gary. Gaz Regan's Annual Manual for Bartenders 2011. 2011. 368p. pap. ***(978-1-907434-19-8(4))*** Mixellany, Ltd.

—Gaz Regan's Annual Manual for Bartenders, 2011 [Chatham Edition]. 2011. 368p. pap. ***(978-1-907434-24-2(0))*** Mixellany, Ltd.

Regan, Gaz. The Bartender's Gin Compendium. 2009. 372p. 30.99 *(978-1-4415-4688-3(X));* pap. 23.99 *(978-1-4415-4687-6(1))* Xlibris Corp.

Schmid, Albert W. A. Hospitality Manager's Guide to Wines, Beers, & Spirits. 2nd ed. 2007. (ENG., Illus.). 320p. (C). 110.80 *(978-0-13-205968-8(1),* Prentice Hall) Prentice Hall PTR.

Spenceley, Angela. Don't Drink the Water. 2007. pap. 19.99 *(978-0-9702168-2-3(3))* Coconut Pr., LLC.

Steward, Julie & Hesse, Olivia. The Geek's Guide to Bartending: Don't Be a Dummy! Get Twice As Smart for Half the Price! 2007. (Geek's Guides Ser.). (ENG., Illus.). 172p. pap. *(978-1-57587-261-2(7))* Crane Hill Pubs.

United Kingdom Bartenders' Guild Staff, creator. The International Guide to Drinks. 2007. (ENG., Illus.). 256p. 19.95 *(978-0-09-191202-4(4),* Ebury Pr.) Ebury Publishing GBR. Dist: Independent Pubs. Group.

Waller, James. Drinkology: The Art & Science of the Cocktail. rev. ed. 2010. (ENG., Illus.). 372p. 22.50 *(978-1-58479-828-6(9))* Stewart, Tabori & Chang.

Waters, John K. Bartender's Guide: An A to Z Companion to All Your Favorite Drinks. 2008. (ENG.). 528p. pap. 14.95 *(978-1-59869-764-3(1))* Adams Media Corp.

Waters, John Kevin, ed. Bartender's Guide. 2006. 528p. pap. 14.95 *(978-1-59869-113-9(9))* Adams Media Corp.

Zavatto, Amy. Bartending. 2nd rev. ed. 2010. (Complete Idiot's Guide Ser.). (ENG.). 416p. (gr. 12). 16.95 *(978-1-61564-044-7(4),* Alpha Bks.) Penguin Group (USA) Inc.

BARTER

see also Trading Posts

Collom, Ed, et al. Equal Time Equal Value: Community Currencies & Time Banking in the Us. 2012. (Illus.). 224p. 99.95 ***(978-1-4094-4904-1(1))*** Ashgate Publishing Co.

Evans, Mike. Persistence of the Gift: Tongan Tradition in Transnational Context. 2009. (ENG.). 222p. (C). pap. 42.95 *(978-1-55458-214-3(8))* Wilfrid Laurier Univ. Pr. CAN. Dist: Univ. of Toronto Pr.

Hoffman, Karen & Dalin, Shera. The Art of Barter: How to Trade for Almost Anything. 2010. (ENG.). 240p. pap. 12.95 *(978-1-60239-953-2(0),* 239953) Skyhorse Publishing Co., Inc.

Lyons, Deborah J. Dangerous Gifts: Gender & Exchange in Ancient Greece. 2012. E-Book ***(978-0-292-73554-5(5));*** (ENG., Illus.). 192p. 55.00 ***(978-0-292-72967-4(7))*** Univ. of Texas Pr.

MacDonald, Kyle. One Red Paperclip: Or How an Ordinary Man Achieved His Dream with the Help of a Simple Office Supply. 2007. (ENG., Illus.). 320p. pap. 13.95 *(978-0-307-35316-0(8),* Three Rivers Pr.) Crown Publishing Group.

Malinowski, Bronislaw. Argonauts of the Western Pacific. 2007. (ENG., Illus.). 632p. per. *(978-1-4067-5256-4(8))* Read Bks.

Thomason-Carroll, Kristi L. Young Adults' Guide to the History of Money. 2007. (Illus.). 77p. pap. 8.95 *(978-0-9723714-0-7(0))* Business Bks., LLC.

BARTH, HEINRICH, 1821-1865

Kemper, Steve. A Labyrinth of Kingdoms: 10,000 Miles Through Islamic Africa. 2012. (ENG., Illus.). 432p. 28.95 ***(978-0-393-07966-1(X),*** 7966) Norton, W. W. & Co., Inc.

BARTH, JOHN, 1930-

Clavier, Berndt. John Barth & Postmodernism: Spatiality, Travel, Montage. 2006. (Studies on Themes & Motifs in Literature: Vol. 83). (Illus.). 376p. (C). 81.95 *(978-0-8204-6385-8(X))* Lang, Peter Publishing, Inc.

Grausam, Daniel. On Endings: American Postmodern Fiction & the Cold War. 2011. viii, 196p. E-Book *(978-0-8139-3166-1(5));* (ENG.). 208p. (C). (gr. 13-17). pap. 22.50 *(978-0-8139-3162-3(2));* (ENG.). 208p. (gr. 17). 49.50 *(978-0-8139-3161-6(4))* Univ. Pr. of Virginia.

Punday, Daniel. Five Strands of Fictionality: The Institutional Construction of Contemporary American Fiction. 2010. (ENG.). 288p. 44.95 *(978-0-8142-1114-4(3));* cd-rom 14.95 *(978-0-8142-9212-9(7))* Ohio State Univ. Pr.

BARTH, KARL, 1886-1968

Allen, Michael R. Karl Barth's Church Dogmatics: An Introduction & Reader. 2012. (ENG.). 256p. 120.00 ***(978-0-567-00356-0(6));*** pap. 34.95 ***(978-0-567-15219-0(7))*** Continuum International Publishing Group, Ltd. GBR. (T&T Clark Int'l). Dist: National Bk. Network.

Anthony, Neal J. Cross Narratives. 2010. (Princeton Theological Monographs). (Illus.). 322p. pap. 35.00 *(978-1-60608-654-4(5),* Pickwick Pubns.) Wipf & Stock Pubs.

Asprey, Christopher. Eschatological Presence in Karl Barth's Göttingen Theology. 2010. (ENG.). 256p. 99.00 *(978-0-19-958470-3(2))* Oxford Univ. Pr., Inc.

Barth, Karl. Karl Barth's Table Talk. Godsey, John D., ed. 2011. 110p. 39.95 ***(978-1-258-08879-8(7))*** Literary Licensing, LLC.

Boesel, Chris. Risking Proclamation, Respecting Difference: Christian Faith, Imperialistic Discourse, & Abraham. 2007. 306p. pap. 33.00 *(978-1-55635-523-3(8))* Wipf & Stock Pubs.

Bradbury, Rosalene. Cross Theology: The Classical Theologia Crucis & Karl Barth's Modern Theology of the Cross. 2012. (ENG.). 338p. pap. 45.00 ***(978-0-227-68030-8(8))*** Clarke, James Co., Ltd. GBR. Dist: Brown, David Bk. Co., The.

—Cross Theology: The Classical Theologia Crucis & Karl Barth's Modern Theology of the Cross. 2010. 338p. pap. 37.00 *(978-1-60899-479-3(1),* Pickwick Pubns.) Wipf & Stock Pubs.

Brazier, P. H. Barth & Dostoevsky: A Study of the Influence of the Russian Writer Fyodor Mikhailovich Dostoevsky on the Development of the Swiss Theologian Karl Barth, 1915-1922. 2008. (Paternoster Theological Monographs). (Illus.). 290p. pap. 34.00 *(978-1-55635-868-5(7))* Wipf & Stock Pubs.

Busch, Eberhard. Barth. 2008. (Abingdon Pillars of Theology Ser.). 95p. pap. 13.00 *(978-0-687-49246-6(7))* Abingdon Pr.

—Meine Zeit mit Karl Barth: Tagebuch 1965-1968. 2011. (GER.). 760p. (C). 35.00 *(978-3-525-56001-3(X))* Vandenhoeck & Ruprecht GmbH & Co. KG DEU. Dist: ISD.

Busch, Eberhard, et al. The Great Passion: An Introduction to Karl Barth's Theology. 2010. x, 392p. pap. 30.00 *(978-0-8028-6654-7(9))* Eerdmans, William B. Publishing Co.

Camfield, F. W., ed. Reformation Old & New. 2009. 220p. pap. 24.00 *(978-1-60608-768-8(1),* Wipf and Stock) Wipf & Stock Pubs.

Chestnutt, Glenn A. Challenging the Stereotype: The Theology of Karl Barth as a Resource for Inter-religious Encounter in a European Context. 2010. (Religions & Discourse Ser.). 280p. pap. 58.95 *(978-3-0343-0184-8(7))* Lang, Peter AG GBR. Dist: Lang, Peter.

Chung, Paul S. Karl Barth: God's Word in Action. 2008. 520p. pap. 55.00 *(978-1-55635-527-1(0))* Wipf & Stock Pubs.

Chung, Sung Wook, ed. Karl Barth & Evangelical Theology: Convergences & Divergences. 2008. 302p. (C). pap. 32.00 *(978-0-8010-3127-4(3))* Baker Academic.

Clark, Tony. Divine Revelation & Human Practice: Responsive & Imaginative Participation. 2010. (ENG., Illus.). 242p. (C). pap. 43.00 *(978-0-227-17313-8(9))* Clarke, James Co., Ltd. GBR. Dist: Brown, David Bk. Co., The.

—Divine Revelation & Human Practice: Responsive & Imaginative Participation. 2007. 244p. pap. 27.00 *(978-1-55635-516-5(5))* Wipf & Stock Pubs.

Collins Winn, Christian T. Jesus Is Victor! The Significance of the Blumhardts for the Theology of Karl Barth. 2008. (Princeton Theological Monographs). 330p. pap. 36.00 *(978-1-55635-180-8(1),* Pickwick Pubns.) Wipf & Stock Pubs.

Colwell, John. Actuality & Provisionality: Eternity & Election in the Theology of Karl Barth. 2011. 330p. pap. 36.00 ***(978-1-61097-125-6(6),*** Wipf and Stock) Wipf & Stock Pubs.

Cortez. Embodied Souls, Ensouled Bodies: An Exercise in Christological Anthropology & Its Significance for the Mind/Body Debate. 2008. (T&T Clark Studies in Systematic Theology Ser.). (ENG.). 256p. 130.00 *(978-0-567-03368-0(6),* T&T Clark Int'l) Continuum International Publishing Group, Ltd. GBR. Dist: National Bk. Network.

Cortez, Marc. Embodied Souls, Ensouled Bodies: An Exercise in Christological Anthropology & Its Significance for the Mind/Body Debate. 2011. (ENG.). 250p. pap. 44.95 ***(978-0-567-26021-5(6),*** T&T Clark Int'l) Continuum International Publishing Group, Ltd. GBR. Dist: National Bk. Network.

Dawson, R. Dale. The Resurrection in Karl Barth. 2007. (Barth Studies). 256p. 114.95 *(978-0-7546-5555-8(5))* Ashgate Publishing Co.

Dempsey, Michael T. Trinity & Election in Contemporary Theology. 2011. pap. 38.00 *(978-0-8028-6494-9(5))* Eerdmans, William B. Publishing Co.

Demut, André. Evangelium und Gesetz: Eine systematisch-theologische Reflexion zu Karl Barths Predigtwerk. 2008. (Theologische Bibliothek Töpelmann Ser.). Tr. of Gospel & Law. Systematic Theological Reflections on Karl Barth's Sermons. (GER.). XIII, 382p. 147.00 *(978-3-11-020446-9(0))* De Gruyter, Walter Inc.

Fairweather, Alan. The Word As Truth. 2009. 164p. pap. 19.00 *(978-1-60608-767-1(3),* Wipf and Stock) Wipf & Stock Pubs.

Ford, David F. Barth & God's Story: Biblical Narrative & the Theological Method of Karl Barth in the Church Dogmatics. 2008. 194p. pap. 23.00 *(978-1-60608-056-6(3))* Wipf & Stock Pubs.

Franke, John R. Barth for Armchair Theologians. 2006. (Armchair Theologians Ser.). (ENG., Illus.). 183p. per. 17.00 *(978-0-664-22734-0(1))* Westminster John Knox Pr.

Gibson, David & Gibson. Engaging with Barth: Contemporary Evangelical Critiques. Strange, Daniel, ed. 2009. (ENG.). 408p. pap. 39.95 *(978-0-567-44296-3(9),* T&T Clark Int'l) Continuum International Publishing Group, Ltd. GBR. Dist: National Bk. Network.

Gignilliat, Mark S. Karl Barth & the Fifth Gospel: Barth's Theological Exegesis of Isaiah. 2009. (Barth Studies). 182p. 99.95 *(978-0-7546-5856-6(2))* Ashgate Publishing Co.

Gockel, Matthias. Barth & Schleiermacher on the Doctrine of Election: A Systematic-Theological Comparison. 2007. (ENG.). 240p. 99.00 *(978-0-19-920322-2(9))* Oxford Univ. Pr., Inc.

Greggs, Tom. Theology against Religion: Constructive Dialogues with Bonhoeffer & Barth. 2011. (ENG.). 256p. 130.00 *(978-0-567-46279-4(X));* pap. 34.95 *(978-0-567-10423-6(0))* Continuum International Publishing Group, Ltd. GBR. (T&T Clark Int'l). Dist: National Bk. Network.

Gunton, Colin E. The Barth Lectures. Brazier, Paul, ed. 2007. (ENG., Illus.). 320p. 150.00 *(978-0-567-03139-6(X),* T&T Clark Int'l) Continuum International Publishing Group, Ltd. GBR. Dist: National Bk. Network.

Gunton, Colin E. & Gunton. The Barth Lectures. Brazier, Paul, ed. 2007. (ENG., Illus.). 320p. 49.95 *(978-0-567-03140-2(3),* T&T Clark Int'l) Continuum International Publishing Group, Ltd. GBR. Dist: National Bk. Network.

Guretzki, David. Karl Barth on the Filioque. 2009. (Barth Studies). 226p. 99.95 *(978-0-7546-6704-9(9))* Ashgate Publishing Co.

Habets, Myk & Tolliday, Phillip, eds. Trinitarian Theology after Barth. 2010. (Princeton Theological Monographs). 418p. pap. 46.00 *(978-1-60899-490-8(2),* Pickwick Pubns.) Wipf & Stock Pubs.

Haddorff, David. Christian Ethics as Witness. 2011. (ENG.). 494p. pap. 58.00 *(978-0-227-17374-9(0))* Clarke, James Co., Ltd. GBR. Dist: Brown, David Bk. Co., The.

—Christian Ethics as Witness: Barth's Ethics for A World at Risk. 2010. 494p. pap. 54.00 *(978-1-60899-282-9(9),* Cascade Bks.) Wipf & Stock Pubs.

Hinlicky, Paul R. Paths Not Taken: Fates of Theology from Luther to Leibniz. 2009. (ENG.). 400p. pap. 50.00 *(978-0-8028-4571-9(1))* Eerdmans, William B. Publishing Co.

Hocking, Jeffrey S. & Stanley, Jon. Freedom Unlimited: Liberty, Autonomy, & Response-Ability in the Open Theism of Clark Pinnock. 2010. 140p. pap. 17.00 *(978-1-60899-469-4(4),* Wipf and Stock) Wipf & Stock Pubs.

Holmes, Christopher R. J. Revisiting the Doctrine of the Divine Attributes: In Dialogue with Karl Barth, Eberhard Juengel & Wolf Kroetke. 2007. (Issues in Systematic Theology Ser.: Vol. 15). 266p. (C). 70.95 *(978-0-8204-8696-3(5))* Lang, Peter Publishing, Inc.

Holtmann, Stefan. Karl Barth als Theologe der Neuzeit: Studien zur kritischen Deutung seiner Theologie. 2007. (Forschungen Zur Systematischen und Okumenischen Theologie Ser.). (GER.). 444p. (C). 111.00 *(978-3-525-56346-5(9))* Vandenhoeck & Ruprecht GmbH & Co. KG DEU. Dist: ISD.

Hunsinger, George. Thy Word Is Truth: Barth on Scripture. 2012. pap. ***(978-0-8028-6674-5(3))*** Eerdmans, William B. Publishing Co.

Johnson, Adam J. God's Being in Reconciliation: The Theological Basis of the Unity & Diversity of the Atonement in the Theology of Karl Barth. 2012. (ENG.). 240p. 120.00 ***(978-0-567-63833-5(2),*** T&T Clark Int'l) Continuum International Publishing Group, Ltd. GBR. Dist: National Bk. Network.

Johnson, Keith L. Karl Barth & the Analogia Entis. 2011. (T&T Clark Studies in Systematic Theology Ser.). (ENG.). 256p. pap. 44.95 ***(978-0-567-34463-2(0),*** T&T Clark Int'l) Continuum International Publishing Group, Ltd. GBR. Dist: National Bk. Network.

Jones, Paul Dafydd. The Humanity of Christ: Christology in Karl Barth's Church Dogmatics. 2011. (ENG.). 304p. pap. 44.95 ***(978-0-567-01200-5(X),*** T&T Clark Int'l) Continuum International Publishing Group, Ltd. GBR. Dist: National Bk. Network.

Jones, Paul Dafydd & Jones, Paul D. The Humanity of Christ: Christology in Karl Barth's Church Dogmatics. 2008. (ENG.). 304p. 130.00 *(978-0-567-03321-5(X),* T&T Clark Int'l) Continuum International Publishing Group, Ltd. GBR. Dist: National Bk. Network.

Käfer, Anne. Inkarnation und Schöpfung: Schöpfungstheologische Voraussetzungen und Implikationen der Christologie bei Luther, Schleiermacher und Karl Barth. 2010. (Theologische Bibliothek Töpelmann Ser.). (GER.). XVI, 388p. 126.00 *(978-3-11-022633-1(2))* De Gruyter, Walter Inc.

Kennedy, Darren. Providence & Personalism: Karl Barth in Conversation with Austin Farrerm John Macmurray & Vincent Brümmer. 2011. (Illus.). 328p. pap. 68.95 ***(978-3-0343-0735-2(7))*** Lang, Peter AG GBR. Dist: Lang, Peter.

Kerr, Nathan R. Christ, History & Apocalyptic: The Politics of Christian Mission. 2008. (Theopolitical Visions Ser.). 222p. pap. 28.00 *(978-1-60608-199-0(3))* Wipf & Stock Pubs.

Kim, Eunsoo. Time, Eternity, & the Trinity: A Trinitarian Analogical Understanding of Time & Eternity. 2010. 376p. pap. 41.00 *(978-1-60608-968-2(4),* Pickwick Pubns.) Wipf & Stock Pubs.

Leiner, Martin & Trowitzsch, Michael. Karl Barths Theologie als europäisches Ereignis. 2008. (GER.). 436p. (C). pap. 41.00 *(978-3-525-56964-1(5))* Vandenhoeck & Ruprecht GmbH & Co. KG DEU. Dist: ISD.

Lewis, John P. Karl Barth in North America: The Influence of Karl Barth in the Making of a New North American Evangelicalism. 2009. 244p. pap. 27.00 *(978-1-60608-083-2(0),* Resource Pubns.) Wipf & Stock Pubs.

Macken, John. The Autonomy Theme in the Church Dogmatics: Karl Barth & his Critics. 2008. (ENG.). 244p. (C). pap. 34.99 *(978-0-521-07237-3(9))* Cambridge Univ. Pr.

Marga, Amy. Karl Barth's Dialogue with Catholicism in Göttingen & Münster: Its Significance for His Doctrine of God. 2010. 200p. 157.50 *(978-3-16-150148-7(9))* Mohr Siebeck GmbH & Co. KG DEU. Dist: Coronet Bks.

Marquardt, Friedrich-Wilhelm. Theological Audacities: Selected Essays. Pangritz, Andreas, ed. Chung, Paul S., ed. & tr. by. from GER. McCord, Don, tr. from GER. 2010. (Princeton Theological Monographs). 278p. pap. 31.00 *(978-1-60608-943-9(9),* Pickwick Pubns.) Wipf & Stock Pubs.

Matczak, Sebastian A. Karl Barth on God: The Knowledge of the Divine Existence. 2011. 358p. 51.95 ***(978-1-258-08969-6(6))*** Literary Licensing, LLC.

McCormack, Bruce & Dahlke, Benjamin. Karl Barth, Catholic Renewal & Vatican II. 2012. (ENG.). 208p. 110.00 ***(978-0-567-60593-1(0),*** T&T Clark Int'l) Continuum International Publishing Group, Ltd. GBR. Dist: National Bk. Network.

McCormack, Bruce & Neven, Gerrit, eds. The Reality of Faith in Theology: Studies on Karl Barth Princeton-Kampen Consultation 2005. 2007. 280p. pap. 62.95 *(978-0-8204-8928-5(X))* Lang, Peter Publishing, Inc.

McCormack, Bruce L. Orthodox & Modern: Studies in the Theology of Karl Barth. 2008. 320p. (C). pap. 35.00 *(978-0-8010-3582-1(1))* Baker Academic.

B

McCormack, Bruce L. & Anderson, Clifford B. Karl Barth & American Evangelicalism: Friends or Foes? 2011. pap. 38.00 (978-0-8028-6656-1(5)) Eerdmans, William B. Publishing Co.
McKenny, Gerald. The Analogy of Grace: Karl Barth's Moral Theology. 2010. (ENG.). 320p. 120.00 (978-0-19-958267-9(X)) Oxford Univ. Pr., Inc.
Migliore, Daniel L. Commanding Grace: Studies in Karl Barth's Ethics. 2010. pap. 30.00 (978-0-8028-6570-0(4)) Eerdmans, William B. Publishing Co.
Migliore, Daniel L., et al. Theology As Conversation: The Significance of Dialogue in Historical & Contemporary Theology: A Festschrift for Daniel L. Migliore. 2009. (Illus.). 388p. 50.00 (978-0-8028-4859-8(1)) Eerdmans, William B. Publishing Co.
Mikkelsen, Hans Vium. Reconciled Humanity: Karl Barth in Dialogue. 2010. pap. 30.00 (978-0-8028-6363-8(9)) Eerdmans, William B. Publishing Co.
Miller, Daniel. Animal Ethics & Theology: The Lens of the Good Samaritan. 2011. (Routledge Studies in Religion Ser.). (ENG., Illus.). 250p. (C). 125.00 (978-0-415-80875-0(8)) Routledge.
Morgan, D. Densil. Barth Reception in Britain. 2010. (ENG.). 320p. 120.00 (978-0-567-03186-0(1), T&T Clark Int'l) Continuum International Publishing Group, Ltd. GBR. Dist: National Bk. Network.
Morgan, Densil. The Spck Introduction to Karl Barth. 2010. 128p. pap. **(978-0-281-06045-0(2))** SPCK Publishing.
Morgan, Densil D. Barth Reception in Britain. 2012. (ENG.). 320p. (gr. 17). pap. 55.00 **(978-0-567-52710-3(7)**, T&T Clark Int'l) Continuum International Publishing Group, Ltd. GBR. Dist: National Bk. Network.
Neder, Adam. Participation in Christ: An Entry into Karl Barth's Church Dogmatics. 2009. (Columbia Series in Reformed Theology Ser.). (ENG.). 160p. 25.00 (978-0-664-23460-7(7)) Westminster John Knox Pr.
Nimmo, Paul T. Being in Action: The Theological Shape of Barth's Ethical Vision. 2011. (ENG.). 214p. pap. 39.95 (978-0-567-09919-8(9), T&T Clark Int'l) Continuum International Publishing Group, Ltd. GBR. Dist: National Bk. Network.
Nimmo, Paul T. & Nimmo. Being in Action: The Theological Shape of Barth's Ethical Vision. 2007. (ENG.). 224p. 156.00 (978-0-567-03149-5(7), T&T Clark Int'l) Continuum International Publishing Group, Ltd. GBR. Dist: National Bk. Network.
Oakes, Kenneth. Karl Barth on Theology & Philosophy. 2012. (ENG.). 304p. 125.00 **(978-0-19-966116-9(2))** Oxford Univ. Pr., Inc.
—Reading Karl Barth: A Companion to Karl Barth's Epistle to the Romans. 2011. 180p. pap. 21.00 **(978-1-61097-016-7(0)**, Cascade Bks.) Wipf & Stock Pubs.
Oh & Oh, Peter S. Karl Barth's Trinitarian Theology: A Study in Karl Barth's Analogical Use of the Trinitarian Relation. 2007. (ENG.). 192p. 165.00 (978-0-567-03119-8(5), T&T Clark Int'l) Continuum International Publishing Group, Ltd. GBR. Dist: National Bk. Network.
Põ, et al. Doxologische Entzogenheit: Die fundamentaltheologische Bedeutung des Gebets bei Karl Barth. 2009. (Theologische Bibliothek Töpelmann Ser.).Tr. of Doxological Hiddenness. the Fundamental Theological Significance of Prayer in Karl Barth's Work. (GER.). 333p. 126.00 (978-3-11-020972-3(1)) De Gruyter, Walter Inc.
Pokrifka, Todd. Redescribing God: The Roles of Scripture, Tradition, & Reason in Karl Barth's Doctrines of Divine Unity, Constancy, & Eternity. 2010. (Princeton Theological Monographs). 328p. pap. 36.00 (978-1-60608-198-3(5), Pickwick Pubns.) Wipf & Stock Pubs.
Price, Robert B. Letters of the Divine Word: The Perfections of God in Karl Barth's Church Dogmatics. 2011. (T&T Clark Studies in Systematic Theology Ser.). (ENG.). 224p. 130.00 (978-0-567-07543-7(5), T&T Clark Int'l) Continuum International Publishing Group, Ltd. GBR. Dist: National Bk. Network.
Resch, Dustin. Barth's Interpretation of the Virgin Birth: A Sign of Mystery. 2012. (Barth Studies). 240p. 89.95 **(978-1-4094-4117-5(2))** Ashgate Publishing Co.
Robinson, Dominic. Understanding the 'Imago Dei' The Thought of Barth Balthasar & Moltmann. 2011. 202p. 99.95 (978-0-7546-6770-4(7)) Ashgate Publishing Co.
Rose, Matthew. Ethics with Barth: God, Metaphysics & Morals. 2010. (Barth Studies). 234p. 89.95 (978-1-4094-0623-5(7)) Ashgate Publishing Co.
Rumscheidt, Martin. Revelation & Theology: An Analysis of the BarthÐHarnack Correspondence Of 1923. 2011. 230p. pap. 25.00 **(978-1-61097-547-6(2)**, Wipf and Stock) Wipf & Stock Pubs.
Sheveland, John. Piety & Responsbility: Patterns of Unity in Karl Rahner Karl Bath & Vedanta Deshika. 2011. (New Critical Thinking in Religion, Theology & Biblical Studies). 224p. 89.95 (978-1-4094-0905-2(8)) Ashgate Publishing Co.
Slemmons, Timothy Matthew. Groans of the Spirit: Homiletical Dialectics in an Age of Confusion. 2010. (Princeton Theological Monographs). 160p. pap. 18.00 (978-1-60608-904-0(8), Pickwick Pubns.) Wipf & Stock Pubs.
Stanley, Timothy. Protestant Metaphysics after Karl Barth & Martin Heidegger. 2010. 296p. pap. 33.00 (978-1-60899-691-9(3), Cascade Bks.) Wipf & Stock Pubs.
Stout, Tracey Mark. A Fellowship of Baptism: Karl Barth's Ecclesiology in Light of His Understanding of Baptism. 2010. (Princeton Theological Monographs). 208p. pap. 23.00 (978-1-60608-995-8(1), Pickwick Pubns.) Wipf & Stock Pubs.
Sykes, S. W., ed. Karl Barth. 2009. (ENG.). 184p. pap. 31.99 (978-0-521-09721-5(5)) Cambridge Univ. Pr.
Thompson, John. Christ in Perspective: Christological Perspectives in the Theology of Karl Barth. 2012. viii, 202p. **(978-0-7152-0372-9(X))** Saint Andrew Pr., Ltd.
Tolliday, Phillip. Trinitarian Theology after Barth. Habets, Myk, ed. 2012. (ENG.). 418p. pap. 55.00 **(978-0-227-68032-2(4))** Clarke, James Co., Ltd. GBR. Dist: Brown, David Bk. Co., The.
Torrance, Alan. Persons in Communion: Trinitarian Description & Human Participation. 2010. (ENG.). 400p. 44.95 (978-0-567-28322-1(4), T&T Clark Int'l) Continuum International Publishing Group, Ltd. GBR. Dist: National Bk. Network.
Trowitzsch, Michael. Karl Barth heute. 2007. (GER.). 565p. (C). 62.00 (978-3-525-57123-1(2)) Vandenhoeck & Ruprecht GmbH & Co. KG DEU. Dist: ISD.
Van Til, Cornelius. Barth's Christology: International Library of Philosophy & Theology, Biblical & Theological Studies. Kik, Marcellus J., ed. 2011. 28p. 35.95 **(978-1-258-07287-2(4))** Literary Licensing, LLC.
Waap, Thorsten. Gottebenbildlichkeit und Identität: Zum Verhältnis von theologischer Anthropologie und Humanwissenschaft bei Karl Barth und Wolfhart Pannenberg. Forschungen zur systematischen und ökumenischen Theologie 121. 2008. (Forschungen Zur Systematischen und Okumenischen Theologie Ser.). (GER.). 575p. (C). 137.00 (978-3-525-56949-8(1)) Vandenhoeck & Ruprecht GmbH & Co. KG DEU. Dist: ISD.
Watson, Gordon. The Trinity & Creation in Karl Barth. 2009. (ENG.). 210p. (C). pap. 15.00 (978-1-921511-52-3(4)) ATF Pr. AUS. Dist: Brown, David Bk. Co., The.
Webster, John Bainbridge. Barth's Ethics of Reconciliation. 2007. (ENG.). 252p. pap. 51.00 (978-0-521-04411-0(1)) Cambridge Univ. Pr.
White, Thomas Joseph. The Analogy of Being: Invention of the Antichrist or the Wisdom of God? 2010. 448p. pap. 48.00 (978-0-8028-6533-5(X)) Eerdmans, William B. Publishing Co.
Wigley, Stephen & Wigley, Stephen D. Karl Barth & Hans Urs Von Balthasar: A Critical Engagement. 2007. (ENG.). 192p. 145.00 (978-0-567-03191-4(8), T&T Clark Int'l) Continuum International Publishing Group, Ltd. GBR. Dist: National Bk. Network.
Williams, Rowan. A Silent Action: Engagements with Thomas Merton. 2011. (ENG., Illus.). 112p. 19.95 **(978-1-891785-78-8(8))** Fons Vitae of Kentucky, Inc.
Wood, Donald. Barth's Theology of Interpretation. 2007. (Barth Studies). 204p. 99.95 (978-0-7546-5457-5(5)) Ashgate Publishing Co.
Yang, Chan-Ho. Begründung der Ethik bei Barth und Elert. 2008. (Europäische Hochschulschriften. Reihe 23: Theologie Ser.). 286p. pap. 74.95 (978-3-631-58215-2(3)) Lang, Peter GmbH, Europaischer Verlag der Wissenschaften DEU. Dist: Lang, Peter.

BARTHELME, DONALD, 1931-1989

Daugherty, Tracy. Hiding Man. 2010. (ENG., Illus.). 592p. pap. 20.00 (978-0-312-42930-0(4)) Picador.
Ladyga, Zuzanna. Rethinking Postmodern Subjectivity: Emmanuel Levinas & the Ethics of Referentiality in the Work of Donald Barthelme. 2009. (Anglo-amerikanische Studien - Anglo-American Studies). 192p. pap. 56.95 (978-3-631-59109-3(8)) Lang, Peter GmbH, Europaischer Verlag der Wissenschaften DEU. Dist: Lang, Peter.

BARTHES, ROLAND, 1915-1980

Badmington, Neil. Roland Barthes, 4 vols. 2010. (Critical Evaluations in Cultural Theory Ser.). (ENG., Illus.). 1324p. 1130.00 (978-0-415-47257-9(1)) Routledge.
Barthes, Roland. The Grain of the Voice: Interviews 1962-1980. Coverdale, Linda, tr. from FRE. 2009. (ENG., Illus.). 384p. pap. 24.95 (978-0-8101-2640-4(0)) Northwestern Univ. Pr.
—Mourning Diary, 1 vol. Howard, Richard, tr. & afterword by by. 2012. (ENG., Illus.). 272p. pap. 15.00 **(978-0-374-53311-3(3)**, Hill & Wang) Farrar, Straus & Giroux.
—Roland Barthes. Howard, Richard, tr. 2010. (ENG., Illus.). 208p. pap. 15.00 (978-0-374-25146-8(0), Hill & Wang) Farrar, Straus & Giroux.
Barthes, Roland. Travels in China. 2012. (ENG.). 240p. 19.95 **(978-0-7456-5080-7(5))** Polity Pr. GBR. Dist: Wiley, John & Sons, Inc.
Barthes, Roland & Léger, Nathalie. Mourning Diary. Howard, Richard, tr. from FRE. & afterword by by. 2010. (ENG., Illus.). 272p. 25.00 (978-0-8090-6233-1(X), Hill & Wang) Farrar, Straus & Giroux.
Brisolin, Viola. Power & Subjectivity in the Late Work of Roland Barthes & Pier Paolo Pasolini. 2011. (European Connections Ser.). 297p. pap. 61.95 **(978-3-0343-0231-9(2))** Lang, Peter AG GBR. Dist: Lang, Peter.
Burke, Seán & Burke, Sean. The Death & Return of the Author: Criticism & Subjectivity in Barthes, Foucault, & Derrida. 3rd ed. 2010. (ENG.). 312p. (gr. 17). pap. 37.50 (978-0-7486-3711-9(7)) Edinburgh Univ. Pr. GBR. Dist: Columbia Univ. Pr.
de Villiers, Nicholas. Opacity & the Closet: Queer Tactics in Foucault, Barthes, & Warhol. 2012. (Illus.). 224p. 75.00 **(978-0-8166-7570-8(8))**; pap. 25.00 **(978-0-8166-7571-5(6))** Univ. of Minnesota Pr.
Hill, Leslie. Radical Indecision: Barthes, Blanchot, Derrida, & the Future of Criticism. 2010. (ENG.). 512p. pap. 45.00 (978-0-268-03107-7(X)) Univ. of Notre Dame Pr.
Jürgen, Pieters & Pint, Kris, eds. Roland Barthes Retroactively Vol. 31, No. 1: Reading the Collège de France Lectures, Volume 31, Issue 1. 2009. (Paragraph Special Issues Ser.). (FRE & ENG.). 122p. (gr. 17). 40.00 (978-0-7486-3692-1(7)) Edinburgh Univ. Pr. GBR. Dist: Columbia Univ. Pr.
Lombardo, Patrizia. The Three Paradoxes of Roland Barthes. 2010. (ENG.). 184p. pap. 22.95 (978-0-8203-3493-6(6)) Univ. of Georgia Pr.
Mavor, Carol. Black & Blue: The Bruised Passion of Camera Lucida, la Jetée, Sans Soleil, & Hiroshima Mon Amour. 2012. (ENG.). 200p. pap. 24.95 **(978-0-8223-5271-6(0))**; (Illus.). 89.95 **(978-0-8223-5252-5(4))** Duke Univ. Pr.
Mavor, Carol. Reading Boyishly: Roland Barthes, J. M. Barrie, Jacques Henri Lartigue, Marcel Proust, & D. W. Winnicott. 2008. (ENG., Illus.). 536p. 99.95 (978-0-8223-3886-4(6)); pap. 29.95 (978-0-8223-3962-5(5)) Duke Univ. Pr.
McQuillan, Martin. Roland Barthes: Or the Profession of Cultural Studies. Wolfreys, Julian, ed. 2011. (Transitions Ser.). (ENG., Illus.). 256p. 100.00 (978-0-333-91457-1(0)); pap. 34.00 (978-0-333-91458-8(9)) Palgrave Macmillan.
Murray, Kevin. The Judgement of Paris. 192p. (Orig.). mass mkt. 19.95 (978-1-86373-055-6(9)) Allen & Unwin AUS. Dist: Paul & Co. Pubs. Consortium, Inc.
Noudelmann, François. The Philosopher's Touch: Sartre, Nietzsche, & Barthes at the Piano. Reilly, Brian, tr. from FRE. 2011. (European Perspectives: a Series in Social Thought & Cultural Criticism Ser.). (ENG.). 176p. (gr. 17). 26.50 **(978-0-231-15394-2(5))** Columbia Univ. Pr.
Olin, Margaret. Touching Photographs. 2012. (ENG., Illus.). 288p. pap. 35.00 (978-0-226-62646-8(6)) Univ. of Chicago Pr.
Pint, Kris. The Perverse Art of Reading. Gemerchak, Christopher M., tr. from FRE. 2010. 294p. pap. 80.00 (978-90-420-3092-3(5)) Rodopi.
Robbe-Grillet, Alain. Why I Love Barthes. 2011. (ENG.). 80p. 44.95 (978-0-7456-5078-4(3)); pap. 12.95 (978-0-7456-5079-1(1)) Polity Pr. GBR. Dist: Wiley, John & Sons, Inc.
Thody, Philip Malcolm Waller & Piero. Introducing Barthes. 2011. (Introducing Ser.). (ENG., Illus.). 176p. pap. 9.95 **(978-1-84831-204-3(0))** Totem Bks. GBR. Dist: Consortium Bk. Sales & Distribution.
Yacavone, Kathrin. Benjamin, Barthes & the Singularity of Photography. 2012. (ENG., Illus.). 272p. 110.00 (978-1-4411-1808-0(X)) Continuum International Publishing Group, Ltd. GBR. Dist: National Bk. Network.

BARTHIANISM

see Dialectical Theology

BARTHOLDI, FREDERIC AUGUSTE, 1834-1904

Berenson, Edward. The Statue of Liberty: A Transatlantic Story. 2012. (Icons of America Ser.). (ENG., Illus.). 248p. 25.00 **(978-0-300-14950-0(6))** Yale Univ. Pr.
Khan, Yasmin Sabina. Enlightening the World: The Creation of the Statue of Liberty. 2010. (Illus.). 240p. 24.95 (978-0-8014-4851-5(4)) Cornell Univ. Pr.

BARTHOLOMEW FAIR

Morley, Henry. Memoirs of Bartholomew Fair. 2008. 452p. 52.95 (978-1-4366-6475-2(6)); pap. 37.95 (978-0-548-90244-8(5)) Kessinger Publishing, LLC.

BARTLESVILLE (OKLA.)

Perkins, Scott W. Building Bartlesville: 1945-2000. 2008. (Images of America Ser.). (ENG., Illus.). 128p. pap. 21.99 (978-0-7385-5051-0(5)) Arcadia Publishing.

BARTLETT, ROBERT ABRAM, 1875-1946

Bartlett, Robert A. The Log of Bob Bartlett: The True Story of Forty Years of Seafaring & Exploration. 420p. 2008. 49.95 (978-1-4366-8253-4(3)) 2007. (ENG.). per. 34.95 (978-1-4325-4612-0(0)) Kessinger Publishing, LLC.

BARTOK, BELA, 1881-1945

Antokoletz, Elliot. Bela Bartok: A Research & Information Guide. 2nd rev. ed. 2011. (Routledge Music Bibliographies Ser.). (ENG.). 500p. 150.00 (978-0-415-99523-8(X)) Routledge.
Bartok, Peter, ed. Bartok's Viola Concerto Facsimile. 2009. (ENG.). 94p. 79.00 (978-0-9641961-0-0(7), 0964196107) Bartok Records & Pubns.
Brown, Julie. Bartok & the Grotesque: Studies in Modernity, the Body & Contradiction in Music. 2007. (Royal Musical Association Monographs Ser.). (Illus.). 192p. 99.95 (978-0-7546-5777-4(9)) Ashgate Publishing Co.
Chalmers, Kenneth. Béla Bartok. rev. ed. 2008. (ENG., Illus.). 240p. (Orig.). pap. 14.95 (978-0-7148-4770-2(4)) Phaidon Pr. Ltd. GBR. Dist: Hachette Bk. Group.
Dreps, Krystoffer. Béla Bartók im Jazz: Zur Bedeutung des Komponisten im Schaffen von Richie Beirach und Woody Shaw. 2010. 128p. pap. (978-3-639-25417-4(1)) VDM Verlag Dr. Mueller e.K.
Fosler-Lussier, Danielle. Music Divided: Bartok's Legacy in Cold War Culture. 2007. (California Studies in 20th-Century Music). (Illus.). 229p. 40.00 (978-0-520-24965-3(8)) Univ. of California Pr.
Gillies, Malcolm. Bartók: His Life & Works. 2009. (Master Musicians Ser.). (ENG., Illus.). 288p. 29.95 (978-0-19-513400-1(1)) Oxford Univ. Pr., Inc.
Kühnel, Jürgen, et al. Katastrophe, Sühne, Erlösung: Der Tod Im (Musik-)Theater: Vorträge des Salzburger Symposions 2008. 2010. (GER., Illus.). 751p. pap. (978-3-902537-19-5(1)) Muller-Speiser, Ursula.
Schneider, David E. Bartok, Hungary, & the Renewal of Tradition: Case Studies in the Intersection of Modernity & Nationality. 2006. (California Studies in 20th-Century Music: Vol. 5). (Illus.). 308p. 60.00 (978-0-520-24503-7(2)) Univ. of California Pr.
Sipos-Ori, Robert. A Performer's Guide to Bartok's Ten Easy Pieces & Allegro Barbaro. 2010. 80p. pap. (978-3-8383-1702-1(5)) Lambert Academic Publishing.

BARTOLOMEO, FRA, 1472-1517

Scott, Leader. Fra Bartolommeo. 2011. 182p. pap. 22.75 **(978-1-246-35127-9(7))** 2010. (ENG.). 188p. pap. 22.75 (978-1-171-67571-6(2)) 2010. 184p. pap. 22.75 (978-1-148-37495-6(7)) 2010. 178p. pap. 22.75 (978-1-143-74089-3(0)) 2010. 178p. pap. 22.75 (978-1-141-48325-9(4)) 2008. 136p. 24.99 (978-0-554-28015-8(9)) 2008. 136p. 21.99 (978-0-554-37318-8(1)) 2007. (ENG.). 124p. per. 18.99 (978-1-4346-4517-3(7)) 2007. (ENG.). 134p. per. 19.99 (978-1-4346-4518-0(5)) BiblioBazaar.
—Fra Bartolommeo. Shipp, Horace & Kendrick, Flora, eds. 2008. 108p. pap. (978-1-4099-4034-0(9)) Dodo Pr.
—Fra Bartolommeo. 2010. (Illus.). 70p. pap. 20.00 (978-1-153-62295-0(5)) 2009. 102p. pap. 16.96 (978-1-151-51068-6(8)) General Bks. LLC.
—Fra Bartolommeo. 2010. 96p. pap. (978-1-4076-4243-7(X)) HardPr.
—Fra Bartolommeo. 2010. 146p. 30.36 **(978-1-163-47963-6(2))** 2010. 146p. pap. 18.36 **(978-1-163-08265-2(1))** 2007. (ENG.). 144p. 35.95 (978-0-548-17545-3(4)) 2007. (ENG.). 144p. per. 20.95 (978-1-4304-7467-8(X)) Kessinger Publishing, LLC.

BARTOLUS DE SAXOFERRATO, 1314-1357

Sheedy, Anna T. Bartolus on Social Conditions in the Fourteenth Century. (Columbia University, Studies in the Social Sciences: No. 495). reprint ed. 31.50 (978-0-404-51495-2(2)) AMS Pr., Inc.

BARTON, CLARA, 1821-1912

Barton, Clara. The Story of My Childhood. 2010. 144p. pap. 21.75 (978-1-141-35084-1(X)) BiblioBazaar.
—The Story of My Childhood. 2008. 144p. 35.95 (978-1-4373-7245-8(7)); pap. 20.95 (978-1-4372-8284-9(9)) Kessinger Publishing, LLC.
Barton, William E. Life of Clara Barton, 2 vols. reprint ed. 78.50 (978-0-404-00730-0(9)) AMS Pr., Inc.
Conner, Jane Hollenbeck. Sinners, Saints, & Soldiers in Civil War Stafford. 2009. (Illus.). iv, 115p. pap. (978-0-9708370-1-1(1)) Parker Publishing, LLC.
Hallett, Christine & Lynaugh, Joan E. Celebrating Nurses: A Visual History. 2010. (ENG.). 192p. 24.99 (978-0-7641-6286-2(1)) Barron's Educational Series, Inc.
Marko, Eva. Clara Barton. 2006. (ENG.). 240p. (C). pap. 13.95 (978-1-4240-0532-1(9)) Cengage Heinle.

BARTRAM, WILLIAM, 1739-1823

Bartram, William. Bartram's Living Legacy: The Travels & the Nature of the South. Dallmeyer, Dorinda G., ed. 2010. (Illus.). 464p. 55.00 (978-0-88146-209-8(8)); pap. 28.00 (978-0-88146-222-7(5)) Mercer Univ. Pr.
—Travels through North & South Carolina, Georgia, East & West Florida, the Cherokee Country, the Extensive Territories of the Muscogulges or Creek Confederacy, & the Country of the Chactaws. 2011. (Cambridge Library Collection - Travel & Exploration Ser.). (ENG., Illus.). 580p. pap. 43.00 **(978-1-108-03266-7(4))** Cambridge Univ. Pr.
Bartram, William. William Bartram, the Search for Nature's Design: Selected Art, Letters, & Unpublished Writings. Hallock, Thomas & Hoffmann, Nancy E., eds. 2010. (Wormsloe Foundation Nature Book Ser.). (ENG., Illus.). 520p. 49.95 (978-0-8203-2877-5(4)) Univ. of Georgia Pr.
Braund, Kathryn E. Holland & Porter, Charlotte M., eds. Fields of Vision: Essays on the Travels of William Bartram, 1739-1823. 2nd ed. 2010. (ENG., Illus.). 296p. 50.00 (978-0-8173-1682-2(5)); pap. 29.95 (978-0-8173-5571-5(5)) Univ. of Alabama Pr.
Cashin, Edward J. William Bartram & the American Revolution on the Southern Frontier. (Illus.). 336p. pap. 24.95 (978-1-57003-685-9(3)) Univ. of South Carolina Pr.
Dion, Mark & Courtney, Julie. Travels of William Bartram Reconsidered. 2010. (Illus.). 111p. 35.00 (978-0-615-25748-8(8)) Bartram, John Assn.
Kautz, Jim. Footprints Across the South: Bartram's Trail Revisited. 2006. (Illus.). 304p. pap. 18.95 (978-1-933483-07-8(5)) Kennesaw State Univ. Pr.
Magee, Judith. The Art & Science of William Bartram. 2007. (ENG., Illus.). 276p. 45.00 (978-0-271-02914-6(5)) Pennsylvania State Univ. Pr.
Schafer, Daniel L. William Bartram & the Ghost Plantations of British East Florida. 2010. (ENG., Illus.). 144p. 24.95 (978-0-8130-3527-7(9)) Univ. Pr. of Florida.
Telfair Museum of Art. Philip Juras: the Southern Frontier: Landscapes Inspired by Bartram's Travels. 2011. (ENG., Illus.). 128p. 24.95 (978-0-933075-14-6(6)) Telfair Museum of Art.

BARUCH, BERNARD M. (BERNARD MANNES), 1870-1965

Rosenbloom, Morris V. Peace Through Strength Bernard Baruch an. 2006. pap. 30.95 (978-1-4286-5503-4(4)) Kessinger Publishing, LLC.

BARUTSE (AFRICAN PEOPLE)

see Lozi (African People)

BARYONS

see also Hyperons; Neutrons; Protons

Al & Anisovich, A. V. Mesons & Baryons: Systematization & Methods of Analysis. 2008. (Illus.). xxii, 580p. 175.00 (978-981-281-825-6(1)) World Scientific Publishing Co., Inc.
Davies, Jonathan I. & Disney, Michael J., eds. Dark Galaxies & Lost Baryons. 2008. (Proceedings of the International Astronomical Union Symposia & Colloquia Ser.). (ENG., Illus.). 420p. 127.00 (978-0-521-87466-3(1)) Cambridge Univ. Pr.
Hosaka, Atsushi, et al, eds. International Conference on the Structure of Baryons (Baryons '10) 2011. (AIP Conference Proceedings / High Energy Physics Ser.). (ENG.). 672p. pap. 201.00 **(978-0-7354-0952-1(8)**, 0735409528, AIP Pr.) Springer.
Thoma, Ulrike, et al, eds. Proceedings of the 11th Workshop on the Physics of Excited Nucleons. 2008. (Illus.). 279p. 269.00 (978-3-540-85143-1(7)) Springer.
Weigel, Herbert. Chiral Soliton Models for Baryons. (Lecture Notes in Physics Ser.). (Illus.). x, 274p. 2010. pap. 99.00 (978-3-642-09470-5(8), 3642094708) 2007. (ENG., 99.00 (978-3-540-75435-0(0), 3540754350) Springer.

BAS-RELIEF

see also Sculpture

Abadie, D. Dubuffet As Architect. 2011. (ENG., Illus.). 168p. pap. (978-2-7541-0543-9(3)) Yale Univ. Pr.

Lurson, Benoit. Osiris, Ramses, Thot et le Nil: Les Chapelles Secondaires des Temples de Derr et Ouadi Es-Seboua. 2007. (Orientalia Lovaniensia Analecta Ser.). (ENG., Illus.). 234p. (C). 109.00 (978-90-429-1891-7(8)) Peeters Pubs. & Booksellers BEL. Dist: Brown, David Bk. Co., The.

BASAL GANGLIA

see also Tardive Dyskinesia

Balleine, Bernard, et al, eds. Reward & Decision Making in Corticobasal Ganglia Networks. 2007. (Annals of the New York Academy of Sciences Ser.: Vol. 1105). (ENG., Illus.). 300p. pap. 159.95 (978-1-57331-674-3(1), Wiley-Blackwell) Wiley, John & Sons, Inc.

Cram101 Textbook Reviews & Cram101 Textbook Reviews. Outlines & Highlights for Subcortical Structures & Cognition: Implications for Neuropsychological Assessment by Leonard F. Koziol. 2011. 62p. pap. 27.95 (978-1-61830-425-1(7)) Cram101 Inc.

De Oliveira, João Ricardo Mendes, ed. Managing Idiopathic Basal Ganglia Calcification (Fahr's Disease) 2011. (Neuroscience Research Progress Ser.). (Illus.). 110p. pap. 47.00 (978-1-61324-583-5(1)) Nova Science Pubs., Inc.

Groenewegen, Henk J. The Basal Ganglia IX. Groenewegen, Henk J. et al, eds. 2009. (Advances in Behavioral Biology Ser.). (ENG., Illus.). xiii, 262p. 359.00 (978-1-4419-0339-6(9), 1441903399) Springer.

LU, XIAO-HONG, ed. Novel Approaches to Studying Basal Ganglia & Related Neuropsychiatric Disorders. 2009. (ENG., Illus.). xi, 196p. 198.00 (978-0-12-374894-2(1), Academic Pr.) Elsevier Science & Technology Bks.

Miller, Robert. A Theory of the Basal Ganglia & Their Disorders. 2007. (Conceptual Advances in Brain Research Ser.). (ENG., Illus.). 312p. 179.95 (978-1-4200-5897-0(5), CRC Press) Taylor & Francis Group GBR. Dist: Taylor & Francis Group.

Moretti, Rita, et al. Basal Ganglia & Thalamus: Their Role in Cognition & Behavior. 2009. 89.00 (978-1-60692-198-2(3)) Nova Science Pubs., Inc.

Seth, Anil, et al, eds. Modelling Natural Action Selection. 2011. (ENG., Illus.). 560p. 140.00 (978-1-107-00049-0(1)) Cambridge Univ. Pr.

Steiner, Heinz & Tseng, Kuei Y., eds. Handbook of Basal Ganglia Structure & Function. 2010. (Handbook of Behavioral Neuroscience Ser.: 20). (ENG., Illus.). 704p. 210.00 (978-0-12-374767-9(8), Academic Pr.) Elsevier Science & Technology Bks.

Stokes, Timothy B. What Freud Didn't Know: A Three-Step Practice for Emotional Well-Being Through Neuroscience & Psychology. 2009. (ENG., Illus.). 224p. 24.95 (978-0-8135-4640-7(0)) Rutgers Univ. Pr.

Tepper, J. M., et al, eds. GABA & the Basal Ganglia: From Molecules to Systems. 2007. (Progress in Brain Research Ser.). (ENG., Illus.). 350p. 268.00 (978-0-444-52184-2(4), Elsevier Science) Elsevier Science & Technology Bks.

Whalen, Paul J. & Phelps, Elizabeth A. The Human Amygdala. Whalen, Paul J. & Phelps, Elizabeth A., eds. 2009. (ENG., Illus.). 429p. 80.00 (978-1-60623-033-6(6)) Guilford Pubns., Inc.

BASALT

Macdougall, J. D., ed. Continental Flood Basalts. 2010. (Petrology & Structural Geology Ser.). 356p. pap. 249.00 (978-90-481-8458-3(4), 9048184584) Springer.

Massimo, C., et al, eds. Petrological Evolution of the European Lithospheric Mantle. 2010. (Illus.). 256p. (978-1-86239-304-2(4)) Geological Society Publishing Hse.

West, Janet P. Basalt: Types, Petrology & Uses. 2011. (Earth Sciences in the 21st Century Ser.). (Illus.). 242p. 129.00 (978-1-61209-635-3(2)) Nova Science Pubs., Inc.

BASARWA (AFRICAN PEOPLE)

see San (African People)

BASCO LANGUAGE

see Batan Language

BASE-EXCHANGE

see Ion Exchange

BASE-PLATES

see Plates, Iron and Steel

BASEBALL

see also All-American Girls Professional Baseball League; American League of Professional Baseball Clubs; Batting (Baseball); Catching (Baseball); Fantasy Baseball (Game); Little League Baseball; Minor League Baseball; National Baseball Hall of Fame and Museum; National League of Professional Baseball Clubs; Negro Leagues; Pitching (Baseball); Rotisserie League Baseball (Game); Softball; Spring Training (Baseball); World Series (Baseball)

Altchek, David W., et al. Sports Medicine of Baseball. 2012. (ENG.). 512p. 225.00 (978-1-60547-744-2(3)) Lippincott Williams & Wilkins.

Anson, Adrian C. A Ball Player's Career. (Illus.). reprint ed. lib. bdg. 98.00 (978-0-7222-4769-1(3)) Library Reprints, Inc.

—A Ball Player's Career. 2008. 424p. pap. (978-1-4097-8554-5(8)) Read Bks.

Augustyn, Adam. The Britannica Guide to Baseball. 2011. (Illus.). xvii, 269p. lib. bdg. 46.75 (978-1-61530-521-6(1)) Rosen Publishing Group, Inc., The.

Austin, Chesley H. So Swift: Season, Series, Bells & Belt. 2011. 348p. pap. 18.99 (978-1-61379-354-1(5)) Xulon Pr., Inc.

Baseball Bluebook College Edition, 1. 2007. spiral bd. 55.00 (978-0-9788368-0-1(4)) Baseball Bluebook, The.

Baseball Prospectus. Baseball Prospectus 2012. 3rd ed. 2012. (ENG.). 576p. pap. 24.95 (978-0-470-62207-0(5), Wiley) Wiley, John & Sons, Inc.

Baseball Prospectus Staff. Baseball Prospectus 2011. Goldman, Steven, ed. 2nd ed. 2011. (ENG.). 600p. pap. 24.95 (978-0-470-62206-3(7), Wiley) Wiley, John & Sons, Inc.

The Baseball Research Journal, 1977. 144p. 4.00 (978-0-910137-04-1(8)) Society for American Baseball Research.

Belliotti, Raymond Angelo. Watching Baseball, Seeing Philosophy: The Great Thinkers at Play on the Diamond. 2008. (ENG.). 198p. pap. 35.00 (978-0-7864-3303-2(5)) McFarland & Co., Inc. Pubs.

Bernstein, Ross. The Code: Baseball's Unwritten Rules & It's Ignore-at-Your-Own-Risk Code of Conduct. 2008. (ENG.). 272p. 22.95 (978-1-60078-010-3(5)) Triumph Bks.

Berra, Yogi. The Yogi Book: I Really Didn't Say Everything I Said! pap. 89.50 (978-0-7611-1316-4(9), 21316) Workman Publishing Co., Inc.

Bohnert, Suzy Beamer. Game-Day Goddess: Learning Baseball's Lingo. 2009. (Illus.). (978-1-60702-942-7(1)) Independent Pub.

Bray, Ken. How to Score. 2008. (ENG., Illus.). 256p. pap. 15.95 (978-1-86207-988-5(9)) Granta Bks. GBR. Dist: Independent Pubs. Group.

Briley, Ron. The Baseball Film in Postwar America: A Critical Study, 1948-1962. 2011. (ENG., Illus.). 220p. pap. 40.00 (978-0-7864-6123-3(3)) McFarland & Co., Inc. Pubs.

Brush, Daniel J., et al. Major League Baseball: An Interactive Guide to the World of Sports. 2008. (Sports by the Numbers Ser.). (Illus.). 240p. pap. 16.95 (978-1-932714-40-1(5)) Savas Beatie.

Burns, Brian, et al. Baseball Step-By-Step. 2009. (Skills in Motion Ser.). (ENG., Illus.). 96p. (YA). (gr. 4-7). 31.95 (978-1-4358-3361-6(9)) Rosen Publishing Group, Inc., The

Canseco, Jose. Vindicated: Big Names, Big Liars, & the Battle to Save Baseball. 2009. (ENG., Illus.). 272p. pap. 15.00 (978-1-4165-9351-5(9)) Gallery Pr., The IRL. Dist: Simon & Schuster, Inc.

Cheng, Jerry. Jerry's Dugout, an Original & Innovative Fan-Wear. 2010. 120p. pap. (978-3-639-22589-1(9)) VDM Verlag Dr. Mueller e.K.

Collins, Sean L. In Pursuit of the College Baseball Scholarship: From a Coach's Perspective. 2008. 108p. pap. 12.95 (978-0-595-48636-6(3)) iUniverse, Inc.

Costa, Gabriel B., et al. Understanding Sabermetrics: An Introduction to the Science of Baseball Statistics. 2007. (ENG., Illus.). 190p. per. 29.95 (978-0-7864-3388-9(4)) McFarland & Co., Inc. Pubs.

Cross, Rod. Physics of Baseball & Softball. 2011. (ENG., Illus.). xi, 324p. 169.00 (978-1-4419-8112-7(8), 1441981128) Springer.

Cryan, Mark. Cradle of the Game: Baseball & Ballparks in North Carolina. 2008. 400p. pap. 18.95 (978-0-9752706-3-9(X)) August Pubns.

Currie, James S. The Kingdom of God Is Like ... Baseball: A Metaphor for Jesus's Kingdom Parables. 2011. 124p. pap. 15.00 (978-1-60899-246-1(2), Cascade Bks.) Wipf & Stock Pubs.

Davies, Ric. Opening Day. 2011. 304p. (978-1-77067-056-3(4)); pap. (978-1-77067-057-0(2)) FriesenPress.

Deaver, Philip F., ed. Scoring from Second: Writers on Baseball. 2007. (ENG., Illus.). 355p. pap. 21.95 (978-0-8032-5991-1(3), A Bison Original) Univ. of Nebraska Pr.

Dempsey, John Mark. Sports-Talk Radio in America: Its Context & Culture. 2006. (ENG., Illus.). 238p. 108.00 (978-0-7890-2589-0(2)); per. 50.50 (978-0-7890-2590-6(6)) Routledge.

Dickson, Paul. The Joy of Keeping Score: How Scoring the Game Has Influenced & Enhanced the History of Baseball. 2007. (ENG., Illus.). 128p. 14.95 (978-0-8027-1570-8(2)) Walker & Co.

Dickson, Paul, ed. Baseball Is- Defining the National Pastime. 2011. (Dover Baseball Ser.). (ENG.). 256p. pap. 9.95 (978-0-486-48209-5(X)) Dover Pubns., Inc.

DiMaggio, Joe. Baseball for Everyone. 196p. 2008. 37.95 (978-1-4367-1514-0(8)) 2007. (ENG.). per. 22.95 (978-1-4325-5612-9(6)) Kessinger Publishing, LLC.

Doumit, Peter G. More of... What I Know about Baseball Is What I Know about Life. 2011. pap. 24.99 (978-1-61663-824-5(9)) Tate Publishing & Enterprises, LLC.

Epting, Chris. Roadside Baseball: The Locations of America's Baseball Landmarks. 2nd ed. 2009. (ENG., Illus.). 312p. pap. 16.95 (978-1-59580-041-1(7)) Santa Monica Pr.

Fantography LLC & Strasberg, Andy. Baseball Fantography: A Celebration in Snapshots & Stories from the Fans. 2012. (ENG., Illus.). 192p. 19.95 (978-1-4197-0213-6(0), Abrams Image) Abrams.

Finnigan, Sean. Baseball: Nonfiction Silver. 2008. (Nonfiction Collection). (ENG.). 16p. (J). pap. 5.75 (978-1-58453-355-9(2)) Pioneer Valley Educational Pr., Inc.

Freijo, Tom D. Not in Our House! A Decade of Home Court Advantage in American Sports. 2009. 214p. pap. 17.95 (978-0-9824108-0-6(8)) Sports Lit.

Garagiola, Joe. Just Play Ball. (ENG.). 256p. 2009. pap. 14.95 (978-0-87358-952-9(1)) 2007. 21.95 (978-0-87358-923-9(8)) Cooper Square Publishing Llc.

Garrow, Robert M. The Only Game in Town: A Century of North Country Town-Team Baseball, 1860-1960. 2009. (Illus.). 214p. pap. 22.00 (978-0-9795741-2-2(9)) Bloated Toe Publishing.

Gentile, Derek. Splitters, Squeezes & Steals: The Plays, Strategies & Rules of Baseball. 2009. (ENG., Illus.). 256p. 29.95 (978-1-57912-788-6(6), 1579127886) Black Dog & Leventhal Pubs., Inc.

Giamatti, A. Bartlett & Meacham, Jon. Take Time for Paradise: Americans & Their Games. 2011. (ENG.). 128p. 15.00 (978-1-60819-224-3(5)) Bloomsbury Publishing.

Gmelch, George, tr. Baseball Without Borders: The International Pastime. 2006. (ENG., Illus.). 326p. pap. 19.95 (978-0-8032-7125-8(5), Bison Bks.) Univ. of Nebraska Pr.

Gmelch, George & Weiner, J. J. In the Ballpark: The Working Lives of Baseball People. 2006. (ENG., Illus.). 1p. pap. 17.95 (978-0-8032-7127-2(1), Bison Bks.) Univ. of Nebraska Pr.

Gola, Mark. Baseball's Sixth Tool: Playing the Mental Game to Get the Competitive Edge. 2008. (ENG., Illus.). 192p. per. 18.95 (978-0-07-154515-0(8), 0071545158) McGraw-Hill Cos., The.

—The Five-Tool Player: Become the Total Package That Pro & College Baseball Scouts Want. 2007. (ENG., Illus.). 224p. per. 18.95 (978-0-07-147621-8(0), 0071476210) McGraw-Hill Cos., The.

Goldis, Al, et al. How to Make Pro Baseball Scouts Notice You: An Insider's Guide to Big League Scouting. 2009. (ENG., Illus.). 144p. pap. 12.95 (978-1-60239-684-5(1), 239684) Skyhorse Publishing Co., Inc.

Grohe, William. Carpets, Beards, & Baseball Signs. 2008. 312p. pap. (978-3-8364-3764-6(3)) VDM Verlag Dr. Mueller e.K.

Gullo, Jim. Trading Manny: How a Father & Son Learned to Love Baseball Again. 2012. (ENG.). 272p. 23.00 (978-0-306-82017-5(X)) Da Capo Pr., Inc.

Ham, Eldon L. Broadcasting Baseball: A History of the National Pastime on Radio & Television. 2011. (ENG., Illus.). 280p. pap. 39.95 (978-0-7864-4644-5(7)) McFarland & Co., Inc. Pubs.

Hample, Zack. Watching Baseball Smarter: A Professional Fan's Guide for Beginners, Semi-Experts, & Deeply Serious Geeks. 2007. (Vintage Ser.). (ENG., Illus.). 272p. pap. 14.00 (978-0-307-28032-9(2), Vintage) Knopf Doubleday Publishing Group.

Hays, Paul A. Apathetic Neglect, Fiscal Carelessness: The Huntsville Stars' Attendance Dilemma. 2012. pap. 12.95 (978-0-7414-7070-6(5)) Infinity Publishing.

Hirsch, Sheldon & Hirsch, Alan. The Beauty of Short Hops: How Chance & Circumstance Confound the Moneyball Approach to Baseball. 2011. (ENG., Illus.). 212p. pap. 29.95 (978-0-7864-6288-9(4)) McFarland & Co., Inc. Pubs.

Hogan, Lawrence. The Forgotten History of America's Negro Leagues, 1 vol. 2011. (Illus.). 204p. 48.00 (978-0-313-37984-0(X), A2038C, Praeger Pubs.) Greenwood Publishing Group, Inc.

Jacobs, Joe & Schmetzer, Mark J. The Comeback Kids: Cincinnati Reds 2010 Championship Season. 2010. (ENG., Illus.). 160p. pap. 22.95 (978-1-57860-493-7(1)) Clerisy Pr.

Jaffe, Chris. Evaluating Baseball's Managers: A History & Analysis of Performance in the Major Leagues, 1876-2008. 2010. (ENG.). 333p. pap. 39.95 (978-0-7864-3920-1(3)) McFarland & Co., Inc. Pubs.

James, Bill. The Bill James Gold Mine. 2008. 317p. per. 21.95 (978-0-87946-320-5(1)) ACTA Pubns.

Jones, Tom. Working at the Ballpark: The Fascinating Lives of Baseball People from Peanut Vendors & Broadcasters to Players & Managers. 2008. (Illus.). 361p. pap. 17.95 (978-1-60239-226-7(9)) Skyhorse Publishing Co., Inc.

Jordan, David M. Closing 'Em Down: Final Games at Thirteen Classic Ballparks. 2010. (ENG., Illus.). 224p. pap. 29.95 (978-0-7864-4968-2(3)) McFarland & Co., Inc. Pubs.

Jozsa, Frank P., Jr. Baseball in Crisis: Spiraling Costs, Bad Behavior, Uncertain Future. 2008. (ENG., Illus.). 215p. pap. 35.00 (978-0-7864-3331-5(0)) McFarland & Co., Inc. Pubs.

Jurinko, Andy. Soul of the Game: An Illustrated Celebration of the National League, 1946-1960. 2008. (ENG.). 224p. (978-1-894963-55-8(5)) Sport Media Publishing.

Kalas, Larry. Strength Down the Middle. (978-0-9675109-0-3(2)) Mereken Land & Production Co.

Karzen, Jeff. Homer: A Smalltown Baseball Odyssey. 2008. pap. 14.95 (978-0-9752706-5-3(6)) August Pubns.

Kates, Ronald E. & Tormey, Warren, eds. Baseball/Literature/Culture: Essays, 2006-2007. 2008. (Baseball in Literature & American Culture Conference Ser.). (ENG., Illus.). 210p. per. 45.00 (978-0-7864-3680-4(8)) McFarland & Co., Inc. Pubs.

—Baseball/Literature/Culture: Essays, 2008-2009. 2010. (Baseball in Literature & American Culture Conference Ser.). (ENG., Illus.). 243p. pap. 39.95 (978-0-7864-3681-1(6)) McFarland & Co., Inc. Pubs.

King, Larry. Why I Love Baseball. 2007. (ENG.). 160p. 19.00 (978-1-4223-9071-9(3)) DIANE Publishing Co.

Kloser, David. Stepping up to the Plate: 2nd Inning. 2007. (Illus.). 121p. per. 9.95 (978-0-9664806-6-5(X)) Love Your Life.

Kuehl, Karl, et al. Mental Toughness: Baseball's Winning Edge. 2006. (ENG., Illus.). 304p. per. 15.95 (978-1-56663-723-7(6)) Dee, Ivan R. Pub.

Kulegian, John. The Making of a Professional Baseball Player: What Every Prospect & Parent Should Know. 2008. 84p. pap. 16.95 (978-1-60563-697-9(5)) PublishAmerica, Inc.

La Russa, Tony. Unti la Russa. 2012. (ENG.). 304p. 27.99 (978-0-06-220738-8(5), Morrow, William & Co.) HarperCollins Pubs.

League Baseball & Williams, Pete. Baseball: How to Play the Game - The Official Playing & Coaching Manual of Major League Baseball. 2011. (Illus.). 320p. pap. 29.95 (978-0-7893-2218-0(8)) Universe Publishing.

Leahy, John. Living a King's Life, 1 vol. 2010. 200p. pap. 24.95 (978-1-4512-1403-1(0)) PublishAmerica, Inc.

Lebowitz, Paul. Paul Lebowitz's 2009 Baseball Guide: A Complete Guide to the 2009 Baseball Season. 2009. 264p. pap. 19.95 (978-1-4401-2817-2(0)) iUniverse, Inc.

Loeffler, Paul. Underdogs to Wonderdogs: Fresno State's Road to Omaha & the College World Series Championship. 2009. (ENG., Illus.). 168p. 34.95 (978-1-933502-27-4(4)) Linden Publishing Co., Inc.

Major League Baseball Most Feared Hitters. 2006. (J). 3.99 (978-0-9776476-1-3(7)) Major League Baseball.

Mann, Michael Francis. Baseball's Rare Triple Crown. 2011. 230p. 29.99 (978-1-4653-5225-5(2)); pap. 19.99 (978-1-4653-5224-8(4)) Xlibris Corp.

Mason, Tom. Maple Street Press Guide to New England Ballparks: From Maine to Fenway to the Cape ... & Everything in Between. 2007. (Illus.). 250p. per. 22.95 (978-0-9777436-4-3(0)) Maple Street Press LLC.

McManus, J. R. Baseball by the Numbers: Baseball Hall of Fame. 2010. 328p. pap. 30.95 (978-1-4502-0823-9(1)) iUniverse, Inc.

Meigs, Tom. Baseball in Long Beach. 2008. (Images of Baseball Ser.). (ENG., Illus.). 128p. pap. 19.99 (978-0-7385-5823-3(0)) Arcadia Publishing.

Mendez De Hall, Patricia. Corriendo Las Bases en Améric: ¡11Consejos delEstilo de Vidaydela Administración del Dineropara Beisbolistas Latinosque vienen a los Estados Unidos! 2011. 188p. pap. 17.95 (978-1-4575-0337-5(9)) Dog Ear Publishing, LLC.

Miller, E. Ethelbert. The 5th Inning. 2012. (Busboys & Poets Ser.). (ENG., Illus.). 176p. pap. 15.95 (978-1-60486-521-9(0)) PM Pr.

Minan, John H. & Cole, Kevin. The Little White Book of Baseball Law. 12th ed. 2010. (ENG.). 248p. pap. 19.95 (978-1-60442-100-2(2)) American Bar Assn.

Mollenkopf, Jim. One Summer Day in America: July 13 1954. 2010. 160p. 19.95 (978-0-9665910-6-4(2)) Lake of the Cat Publishing.

Nathan, David H., compiled by. The McFarland Baseball Quotations Dictionary. 3rd rev. ed. 2011. (ENG., Illus.). 350p. pap. 45.00 (978-0-7864-4790-9(7)) McFarland & Co., Inc. Pubs.

ONeal, Mark. What Happened to Little League Baseball in the Inner-City? 2007. 56p. per. 9.95 (978-1-4327-0046-1(4)) Outskirts Pr., Inc.

Panas, Lee. Beyond Batting Average. 2010. 152p. pap. 14.00 (978-0-557-31224-5(8)) Lulu Enterprises Inc.

Paul Lebowitz. Paul Lebowitz's 2010 Baseball Guide: A complete guide to the 2010 baseball Season. 2010. 364p. pap. 23.95 (978-1-4502-2148-1(3)) iUniverse, Inc.

Pesky, Johnny & Mullen, Maureen. Diary of a Red Sox Season, 2007. 2008. (ENG., Illus.). 192p. 19.95 (978-1-60078-068-4(7)) Triumph Bks.

Pfaff, Kelly J. & Piering, Peder N. The Mental Road to the Major Leagues: A Guide for Rising Ballplayers. 2012. (ENG.). 201p. pap. 29.95 (978-0-7864-6563-7(8)) McFarland & Co., Inc. Pubs.

Pierce, Gregory F. Augustine, ed. How Bill James Changed Our View of the Game of Baseball. 2007. 139p. 19.95 (978-0-87946-317-5(1)) ACTA Pubns.

Pomfrey, Ron. Baseball in Richmond. 2008. (Images of Baseball Ser.). (ENG., Illus.). 128p. pap. 21.99 (978-0-7385-5395-5(6)) Arcadia Publishing.

Posnanski, Joe. The Soul of Baseball: A Road Trip Through Buck O'Neil's America. (ENG.). 2008. 304p. pap. 13.99 (978-0-06-085404-1(9), William Morrow Paperbacks) 2007. 256p. 24.95 (978-0-06-085403-4(0), Morrow, William & Co.) HarperCollins Pubs.

Queen, Margaret. Baseball Wisdom from the Old Timers. 2010. (Illus.). 144p. per. 6.95 (978-1-882959-59-4(0)) Foxglove Pr.

Rahn, Larry. Baseball. 2008. 108p. 21.95 (978-1-4389-2391-8(0)); pap. 12.95 (978-1-4389-2390-1(2)) AuthorHouse.

Ranney, David. Secrets of the Mental Game of Baseball. 2009. pap. 47.00 (978-1-61623-321-1(4)); pap. 47.00 (978-1-61623-322-8(2)) Independent Pub.

Ray, David. Diamond Gems: Life Lessons between the Lines. 2008. 240p. pap. 15.99 (978-1-60647-855-4(9)) Xulon Pr., Inc.

Remy, Jerry. Watching Baseball: Discovering the Game Within the Game. 4th ed. 2008. (ENG., Illus.). 424p. pap. 14.95 (978-0-7627-4801-3(X), Lyons Pr.) Globe Pequot Pr., The.

Robinson, Guy. Chicago Bears: 100 Hard-Hitting Questions on Your Chicago Bears. 2008. (ENG.). 48p. pap. 5.95 (978-1-4022-1460-8(X)) Sourcebooks, Inc.

—Do You Know Baseball? Test Your Expertise with These Fastball Questions (and a Few Curves) about the Games Hurlers, Sluggers, STATS & Most Memorable Moments. 2007. (ENG.). 48p. pap. 5.95 (978-1-4022-1231-4(3)) Sourcebooks, Inc.

Rothman, Stanley. Sandlot Stats: Learning Statistics with Baseball. 2012. (978-1-4214-0602-2(0)); pap. (978-1-4214-0601-5(2)) Johns Hopkins Univ. Pr.

Rubin, Louis, ed. The Baseball Fanatic: The Best Things Ever Said about the Greatest Game Ever Invented. 2006. (Fanatic Ser.). (ENG., Illus.). 560p. per. 12.95 (978-1-59228-092-6(7), Lyons Pr.) Globe Pequot Pr., The.

Rudd Cycleback, David. Judging the Authenticity of Early Baseball Cards. 2008. 87p. pap. 16.53 (978-0-615-19651-0(9)) Cycleback Pr.

Schmidt, Mike & Waggoner, Glen. Clearing the Bases: Juiced Players, Monster Salaries, Sham Records, & a Hall of Famer's Search for the Soul of Baseball. 2007. (Illus.). 216p. pap. 13.95 (978-0-06-085500-0(2)) HarperCollins Pubs.

Selko, Jamie. Minor League All-Star Teams, 1922-1962: Rosters, Statistics & Commentary. 2007. (ENG., Illus.). 584p. per. 39.95 (978-0-7864-2652-2(7)) McFarland & Co., Inc. Pubs.

Shanburn, Eric. Basketball & Baseball Games: For the Driveway, Field or the Alleyway. 2008. 96p. pap. 11.98 (978-1-4343-8912-1(X)) AuthorHouse.

Shannon. Best of Spitball. 22.95 (978-0-8488-1563-9(7)) Amereon LTD.

B

Singletary, Wes. The Right Time: John Henry "Pop" Lloyd & Black Baseball. 2011. (ENG., Illus.). 234p. pap. 29.95 *(978-0-7864-3572-2(0))* McFarland & Co., Inc. Pubs.

Span, Emma. 90% of the Game Is Half Mental: And Other Tales from the Edge of Baseball Fandom. 2010. 192p. pap. 15.00 *(978-0-345-50175-2(6))*, Villard Bks.) Random House Publishing Group.

Sporting News Staff. Baseball Guide 2007 Edition: The Ultimate Baseball Almanac. 2007. (ENG.). 648p. pap. 18.95 *(978-0-89204-867-0(0))* Sporting News Publishing Co.

Sports Illustrated Editors. Sports Illustrated the Baseball Book. Fleder, Rob, ed. 2006. (ENG., Illus.). 294p. 29.95 *(978-1-933405-23-0(6))* Time Home Entertainment, Inc.

Sports Publishing Inc, creator. Boston Red Sox: 2007 World Series Champions. 2007. (World Series Champions Ser.). (Illus.). 128p. 19.95 *(978-1-59670-213-4(3))*; 125p. per. 14.95 *(978-1-59670-214-1(1))* Sports Publishing, LLC.

Sports Publishing LLC, creator. 2008 World Series (Al) 2008. (Illus.). 128p. 14.95 *(978-1-59670-331-5(8))*; pap. 19.95 *(978-1-59670-330-8(X))* Sports Publishing, LLC.

—2008 World Series (NL) 2008. (Illus.). 128p. 14.95 *(978-1-59670-333-9(4))*; pap. 19.95 *(978-1-59670-332-2(6))* Sports Publishing, LLC.

Stavans, Ilan, ed. Béisbol, 1 vol. 2012. (Ilan Stavans Library of Latino Civilization Ser.). 135p. 55.00 *(978-0-313-37513-2(5)*, GR7513) Greenwood Publishing Group, Inc.

Sutton, Joseph. The Year the Giants Won the Series: A Journal of the 2010 World Series Champions. 2011. (Illus.). 97p. pap. 9.95 ***(978-0-9825598-4-0(4))*** Mad Dog Publishing.

Szarka, Tommy. Abner's Curse: A Diary of Essays from a Baseball Itinerant. 2007. (ENG.). 176p. per. 24.95 *(978-1-4241-6984-9(4))* PublishAmerica, Inc.

Tango, Tom, et al. The Book: Playing the Percentages in Baseball. 2007. 386p. per. 21.95 *(978-1-59797-129-4(4))* Potomac Bks., Inc.

Taylor, Peter. Brit at the Ballpark: An Englishman's Baseball Tour of All 50 States. 2011. (ENG., Illus.). 215p. pap. 25.00 *(978-0-7864-6460-9(7))* McFarland & Co., Inc. Pubs.

Thorn, John. Baseball in the Garden of Eden: The Secret History of the Early Game. 2012. (ENG., Illus.). 384p. pap. 16.00 ***(978-0-7432-9404-1(1))*** Simon & Schuster.

Thornton, Patrick K. Legal Decisions That Shaped Modern Baseball. 2012. (ENG., Illus.). pap. 39.95 *(978-0-7864-3780-1(4))* McFarland & Co., Inc. Pubs.

Tominaga, Lance. Catch the Dream: The Story of Hawaii Winter Baseball. 2006. (Illus.). 191p. per. 19.95 *(978-0-9779143-4-0(8))* Watermark Publishing, LLC.

Tully, Gregory J. Nine College Nines: A Closeup View of Campus Baseball Programs Today. 2009. (ENG.). 224p. pap. 35.00 *(978-0-7864-4128-0(3))* McFarland & Co., Inc. Pubs.

Turbow, Jason & Duca, Michael. The Baseball Codes: Beanballs, Sign Stealing & Bench-Clearing Brawls - The Unwritten Rules of America's Pastime. 2010. (ENG.). 304p. 25.00 *(978-0-375-42469-4(5)*, Pantheon) Knopf Doubleday Publishing Group.

—Baseball Codes: Beanballs, Sign Stealing, & Bench-Clearing Brawls - The Unwritten Rules of America's Pastime. 2011. (ENG.). 304p. pap. 15.00 *(978-0-307-27862-3(X)*, Anchor) Knopf Doubleday Publishing Group.

Tygiel, Jules. Baseball's Great Experiment: Jackie Robinson & His Legacy. 25th ed. 2008. (ENG., Illus.). 448p. per. 19.95 *(978-0-19-533928-4(2))* Oxford Univ. Pr., Inc.

Vandyke, Candy L. Adventures of A Baseball Fan: Baseball Diamonds Are This Girl's Best Friend. 2010. 264p. 24.99 *(978-1-4520-2334-2(4))*; pap. 14.99 *(978-1-4520-2333-5(6))* AuthorHouse.

Vincent, David. Home Run's Most Wanted: The Top 10 Book of Monumental Dingers, Prodigious Swingers, & Everything Long-Ball. 2009. (Most Wanted Ser.). 288p. pap. 13.95 *(978-1-59797-192-8(8))* Potomac Bks., Inc.

Wheelock, Sean D. Buck O'Neil: A Baseball Legend. Date not set. lib. bdg. 18.95 *(978-0-8488-1687-2(0))* Amereon LTD.

Whitten, Wiley. Champions of Naught Six: The Story of the 1906 Cleburne Railroaders. 2010. 300p. pap. 19.00 *(978-0-557-46955-0(4))* Lulu Enterprises Inc.

Williams, Bernie, et al. Rhythms of the Game: The Link Between Musical & Athletic Performance. 2011. (ENG.). 208p. 24.99 *(978-1-4234-9947-3(6)*, 1423499476) Leonard, Hal Corp.

Williams, Tim. Psalmball. 2011. 190p. pap. 14.99 ***(978-1-61379-037-3(6))*** Xulon Pr., Inc.

Winfield, Dave. Dropping the Ball: Baseball's Troubles & How We Can & Must Solve Them. 2010. (ENG.). 224p. pap. 16.95 *(978-1-4391-7049-6(5)*, Scribner) Scribner.

—Making the Play: How to Get the Best of Baseball Back. 2008. (ENG.). 240p. pap. 14.00 *(978-1-4165-3450-1(4)*, Scribner) Scribner.

Wolff. What's a Nice Harvard Boy Like You. 24.95 *(978-0-8488-1545-5(9))* Amereon LTD.

Wollett, Don. Getting on Base: Unionism in Baseball. 2008. 156p. pap. 14.95 *(978-0-595-50412-1(4))* iUniverse, Inc.

Wubbena, Dennis. The Baseball Bluebook (2008 College Edition) 2008 College Baseball Guide & Scouting Register. 2008. 550p. per. 65.00 *(978-0-9788368-2-5(0))* Baseball Bluebook, The.

Zumsteg, Derek. The Cheater's Guide to Baseball. 2007. (ENG., Illus.). 288p. pap. 16.95 *(978-0-618-55113-2(1))* Houghton Mifflin Harcourt Trade & Reference Pubs.

1978. 116p. 4.00 Society for American Baseball Research.

BASEBALL—ANECDOTES

Adomites, Paul. Extra Innings Baseball: All-Star Stories, Stats, Lore & Legends. Publications International Staff, ed. 2009. (Illus.). 320p. 10.98 *(978-1-4127-5323-4(6))* Publications International, Ltd.

Adomites, Paul, et al. Armchair Reader Grand Slam Baseball. 2007. (Armchair Reader Ser.). (Illus.). 468p. per. 15.95 *(978-1-4127-1562-1(8))* Publications International, Ltd.

Allen, Maury. Yankees World Series Memories. 2008. (Illus.). 175p. 19.95 *(978-1-59670-228-8(1))* Sports Publishing, LLC.

Arnold, Kirby. Tales from the Seattle Mariners Dugout. 2007. (Illus.). 188p. 19.95 *(978-1-58261-831-9(3))* Sports Publishing, LLC.

Ballou, Bill. Behind the Green Monster: Red Sox Myths, Legends, & Lore. 2009. (ENG.). 224p. pap. 16.95 *(978-1-60078-191-9(8))* Triumph Bks.

Bement, James. Baseball, Battle, & a Bride: (an Okie in World War II) 2009. 172p. pap. 16.06 *(978-1-4269-2047-9(4))* Trafford Publishing.

Billingsley, Craig. I Love Baseball. 2010. 112p. pap. 22.00 *(978-0-9845519-0-3(5))* Big River Distribution.

Blauner, Andrew & Gutkind, Lee, eds. Anatomy of Baseball. 2008. (Sport in American Life Ser.). (ENG.). 232p. 22.50 *(978-0-87074-522-5(0))* Southern Methodist Univ. Pr.

Bradley, Mickey & Gordon, Dan. Field of Screams: Haunted Tales from the Baseball Diamond, the Locker Room, & Beyond. 2010. (ENG.). 288p. pap. 14.95 *(978-1-59921-856-4(9)*, Lyons Pr.) Globe Pequot Pr., The.

Cafardo, Nick. 100 Things Red Sox Fans Should Know & Do Before They Die. (100 Things... Fans Should Know Ser.). (ENG.). 2011. 240p. pap. 14.95 *(978-1-60078-632-7(4))* 2008. (Illus.). 192p. 19.95 *(978-1-60078-053-0(9))* Triumph Bks.

Champions Speak Out on Baseball: Quotes on Faith, Guts, Determination, & Humor. 2007. (ENG., Illus.). per. 7.99 *(978-1-932458-26-8(3))* Bronze Bow Publishing.

Chandler, Bob. Bob Chandler's Tales from the San Diego Padres. 2007. (Illus.). 179p. per. 15.95 *(978-1-59670-224-0(9))* Sports Publishing, LLC.

DeMarco, Tony. Tales from the Colorado Rockies. 2008. (Tales Ser.). (Illus.). 176p. 19.95 *(978-1-59670-232-5(X))* Sports Publishing, LLC.

Ebling, Jack. Tales from the Detroit Tigers. 2007. (Illus.). 200p. 19.95 *(978-1-59670-193-9(5))* Sports Publishing, LLC.

Feller, Bob & Rocks, Burton. Bob Feller's Little Blue Book of Baseball Wisdom. 2009. (ENG.). 176p. 22.95 *(978-1-60078-219-0(1))* Triumph Bks.

Freedman, Lew & Pierce, Billy. "Then Ozzie Said to Harold..." The Best Chicago White Sox Stories Ever Told. 2008. (Best Sports Stories Ever Told Ser.). (ENG., Illus.). 239p. 22.95 *(978-1-60078-063-9(6))* Triumph Bks.

Garrido, Augie. Life Is Yours to Win: Lessons Forged from the Purpose, Passion, & Magic of Baseball. (ENG.). 272p. 2012. pap. 15.00 *(978-1-4391-8694-7(4))* 2011. 23.00 *(978-1-4391-8693-0(6))* Touchstone. (Touchstone).

Gibson, Bob, et al. Sixty Feet, Six Inches: A Hall of Fame Pitcher & a Hall of Fame Hitter Talk about How the Game Is Played. 2011. (ENG.). 288p. pap. 15.95 *(978-0-7679-3110-6(6)*, Anchor) Knopf Doubleday Publishing Group.

Horvitz, Peter S. & Horvitz, Joachim. The New Big Book of Jewish Baseball: An Illustrated Encyclopedia & Anecdotal History. 2007. 350p. pap. 24.95 *(978-1-56171-821-4(1))* SPI Bks.

Hrbek, Kent. Kent Hrbek's Tales from the Minnesota Twins Dugout. 2008. (Tales Ser.). (Illus.). 185p. pap. 15.95 *(978-1-59670-293-6(1))* Sports Publishing, LLC.

Klein, Clayton. A Well-Kept Secret: From the Glory Years of the Detroit Tigers. 2007. (Illus.). 104p. 25.00 *(978-0-923568-81-8(6))* Wilderness Adventure Bks.

Kurkjian, Tim. Is This a Great Game, or What? From A-Rod's Heart to Zim's Head — -My 25 Years in Baseball. 2008. (ENG.). 288p. pap. 14.95 *(978-0-312-36224-9(2)*, St. Martin's Griffin) St. Martin's Pr.

Leitch, Will. Are We Winning? Fathers & Sons in the New Golden Age of Baseball. 2010. 304p. 24.99 *(978-1-4013-2370-7(7))* Hyperion Pr.

Manning, Sean, ed. Top of the Order: 25 Writers Pick Their Favorite Baseball Player of All Time. 2010. (ENG.). 240p. pap. 15.95 *(978-0-306-81855-4(8))* Da Capo Pr., Inc.

McCarver, Tim, et al. Tim McCarver's Diamond Gems: Favorite Baseball Stories from the Legends of the Game. 2008. (ENG.). 224p. 24.95 *(978-0-07-154594-5(8)*, 0071545948) McGraw-Hill Cos., The.

O'Brien, Tim. Baseball Oddities & Trivia. 2008. (Illus.). 119p. pap. 10.88 *(978-1-893951-29-7(4))* Ripley Entertainment, Inc.

Pepe, Phil. Magic Moments Yankees: Celebrating the Most Successful Franchise in Sports History. 2008. (ENG., Illus.). 176p. 27.95 *(978-1-57243-863-7(0))* Triumph Bks.

Pepe, Phil & Staub, Rusty. Few & Chosen Mets: Defining Mets Greatness Across the Eras. 2009. (Few & Chosen Ser.). (ENG.). 208p. 24.95 *(978-1-60078-153-7(5))* Triumph Bks.

Peters, Nick. Tales from the San Francisco Giants Dugout: A Collection of the Greatest Giants Stories Ever Told. 2011. (Tales from the Team Ser.). (ENG., Illus.). 256p. 19.95 *(978-1-61321-029-1(9)*, 613029) Skyhorse Publishing Co., Inc.

Plimpton, George. Out of My League: The Classic Hilarious Account of an Amateur's Ordeal in Professional Baseball. 2010. (ENG.). 128p. pap. 14.95 *(978-1-59921-808-3(9)*, Lyons Pr.) Globe Pequot Pr., The.

Publications International Staff. Armchair Reader Grand Slam Baseball. 2007. 464p. pap. 15.98 *(978-1-4127-1417-4(6))* Publications International, Ltd.

Rielly, Edward J., ed. Baseball in the Classroom: Essays on Teaching the National Pastime. 2006. (ENG., Illus.). 196p. per. 29.95 *(978-0-7864-2779-6(5))* McFarland & Co., Inc. Pubs.

Robinson, Craig. Flip Flop Fly Ball: An Infographic Baseball Adventure. 2011. (ENG., Illus.). 160p. 25.00 *(978-1-60819-269-4(5))* Bloomsbury Publishing.

Roe, Preacher & Preslar, Sarah. When Baseball Was Still A Game: Truths, Legends, Tales & Photos from Preacher Roe. 2006. (Illus.). 150p. (YA). per. 29.95 *(978-0-9772004-0-5(X))* Catalyst Apex Publishing.

Rowe, Martin & Lomke, Evander. Right off the Bat: Baseball, Cricket, Literature, & Life. 2011. (ENG., Illus.). 220p. pap. 16.95 ***(978-1-58988-069-6(2))*** Dry, Paul Bks., Inc.

Ruth, George H. Babe Ruth's Own Book of Baseball. Date not set. 323p. 24.95 *(978-0-8488-2385-6(0))* Amereon LTD.

Ryness, Gar & Dewart, Caleb. Batting Stance Guy: A Love Letter to Baseball. 2010. (ENG., Illus.). 256p. pap. 18.00 *(978-1-4391-8113-3(6)*, Scribner) Scribner.

Schwartz, Paul. Tales from the New York Giants Sideline: A Collection of the Greatest Giants Stories Ever Told. 2011. (Tales from the Team Ser.). (ENG., Illus.). 224p. 19.95 *(978-1-61321-032-1(9)*, 613032) Skyhorse Publishing Co., Inc.

Silverman, Matthew. 100 Things Mets Fans Should Know & Do Before They Die. 2010. (100 Things... Fans Should Know Ser.). (ENG.). 272p. pap. 14.95 *(978-1-60078-424-8(0))* Triumph Bks.

Slusser, Susan. Tales from the Oakland Athletics. 2008. (Tales Ser.). (Illus.). 192p. 19.95 *(978-1-59670-207-3(9))* Sports Publishing, LLC.

Smith, Curt. A Talk in the Park: Nine Decades of Baseball Tales from the Broadcast Booth. 2011. 320p. 27.50 *(978-1-59797-670-1(9))* Potomac Bks., Inc.

Souder, Mark, ed. Homeruns & Jackpots: Baseball in Nevada. 2009. (Illus.). pap. 11.95 *(978-0-615-27995-4(3))* Writer.

Stone, Steve. Said in Stone: Your Game, My Way. 2011. (ENG.). 256p. 22.95 *(978-1-60078-538-2(7))* Triumph Bks.

Vincent, Fay. The Last Commissioner: A Baseball Valentine. 2007. (ENG., Illus.). 336p. pap. 22.95 *(978-1-4165-7801-7(3))* Simon & Schuster.

Weber, Bruce. As They See 'Em: A Fan's Travels in the Land of Umpires. 2010. (ENG.). 368p. pap. 16.00 *(978-0-7432-9413-3(0)*, Scribner) Scribner.

Wilkinson, Jack. Atlanta Braves. 2007. (Game of My Life Ser.). (Illus.). 216p. 24.95 *(978-1-59670-099-4(8))* Sports Publishing, LLC.

Young, Geoff. Ducksnorts 2008 Baseball Annual. 2008. 208p. pap. 18.95 *(978-1-4357-1103-7(3))* Lulu Enterprises Inc.

BASEBALL—BIBLIOGRAPHY

Grobani, Anton. Guide to Baseball Literature. Date not set. 380p. 26.95 *(978-0-8488-2444-0(X))* Amereon LTD.

BASEBALL—BIOGRAPHY

see also Baseball Players

also names of baseball players, e.g. Ruth, Babe, 1895-1948

Abbott, Jim & Brown, Tim. Imperfect: An Improbable Life. 2012. (ENG., Illus.). 304p. 26.00 ***(978-0-345-52325-9(3)****, Ballantine Bks.) Random House Publishing Group.

Abrams, Dennis. Albert Pujols. 2008. (Baseball Superstars Ser.). (Illus.). 144p. (YA). (gr. 7-12). lib. bdg. 30.00 *(978-0-7910-9600-0(9))* Facts On File, Inc.

Achorn, Edward. Fifty-Nine in '84: Old Hoss Radbourn, Barehanded Baseball, & the Greatest Season a Pitcher Ever Had. 2011. 400p. pap. 15.99 *(978-0-06-182587-3(5)*, Harper Paperbacks) HarperCollins Pubs.

—Fifty-Nine in '84: Old Hoss Radbourn, Barehanded Baseball, & the Greatest Season a Pitcher Ever Had. 2010. 384p. 25.99 *(978-0-06-182586-6(7))* Smithsonian Institution Pr.

Ackmann, Martha. Curveball: The Remarkable Story of Toni Stone the First Woman to Play Professional Baseball in the Negro League. 2010. (ENG., Illus.). 288p. 24.95 *(978-1-55652-796-8(9)*, Hill, Lawrence Bks.) Chicago Review Pr., Inc.

Acosta, Yolanda & Schweighardt, Joan. Acosta. 2010. (ENG., Illus.). 360p. pap. 22.95 *(978-1-84694-333-1(7))* O Bks. John Hunt.

Adams, Walter Ryan. To Be the King of Diamonds. 2011. 108p. 23.00 *(978-1-4269-5636-2(3))*; pap. 13.00 *(978-1-4269-5635-5(5))* Trafford Publishing.

Alexander, Charles C. Spoke: A Biography of Tris Speaker. Rogers, C. Paul, ed. 2007. (Sport in American Life Ser.). (ENG.). 384p. 25.95 *(978-0-87074-517-1(4))* Southern Methodist Univ. Pr.

Alfredo Munoz Cortez. Legacy of the Father. 2010. 120p. pap. 12.95 *(978-1-4502-0017-2(6))* iUniverse, Inc.

Allen, Maury & Walker, Susan. Dixie Walker of the Dodgers: The People's Choice. 2nd ed. 2010. (Alabama Fire Ant Ser.). (ENG., Illus.). 288p. pap. 22.50 *(978-0-8173-5599-9(5))* Univ. of Alabama Pr.

Anderson, Ron. Long Taters: A Baseball Biography of George Boomer Scott. 2011. (ENG.). 308p. pap. 29.95 *(978-0-7864-4976-7(4))* McFarland & Co., Inc. Pubs.

Anton, Todd. No Greater Love: Life Lessons from the Men Who Saved Baseball. 2007. (ENG., Illus.). 320p. per. 18.95 *(978-1-57940-144-3(9))* Rounder Bks.

Armour, Mark L. Joe Cronin: A Life in Baseball. 2010. (ENG., Illus.). 432p. 31.95 *(978-0-8032-2530-5(X))* Univ. of Nebraska Pr.

Aronoff, Jason. Going, Going ... Caught! Baseball's Great Outfield Catches as Described by Those Who Saw Them, 1887-1964. 2009. (ENG., Illus.). 276p. pap. 39.95 *(978-0-7864-4113-6(5))* McFarland & Co., Inc. Pubs.

Bacchia, John. Augie: Stalag Luft Vi to the Major Leagues. 2011. 260p. 29.95 ***(978-1-4620-0725-7(2))***; pap. 19.95 ***(978-1-4620-0724-0(4))*** iUniverse, Inc.

Bailey, Peter. Justin Morneau: All-Star Ball Star. 2008. (ENG., Illus.). 128p. (J). pap. 12.95 *(978-1-55168-326-3(1))* Key Porter Bks. CAN. Dist: Perseus-PGW.

Bailey, Tom. Satchel Paige: Baseball's Greatest Pitcher. 2009. (Illus.). 100p. *(978-1-59421-046-4(2))* Seacoast Publishing, Inc.

Baltov, Jr. Baseball Is Americ: A Child of Baseball. 2009. 516p. 30.99 *(978-1-4490-2839-8(X))*; pap. 20.95 *(978-1-4490-2838-1(1))* AuthorHouse.

Barber-Starkey, Joe & Johnson, James W. Double No-Hit: Johnny Vander Meer's Historic Night under the Lights. 2012. (ENG., Illus.). 216p. pap. 15.95 ***(978-0-8032-7139-5(5))*** Univ. of Nebraska Pr.

Baseball America Editors, ed. 2011 National Baseball Hall of Fame Register: The Definitive Guide to the Baseball Hall of Fame Members. 2012. (ENG.). 534p. pap. 21.95 *(978-1-932391-36-7(3))* Baseball America, Inc.

Baseball Prospectus Staff. Extra Innings: More Baseball Between the Numbers from the Team at Baseball Prospectus. Goldman, Steven, ed. 2012. (ENG.). 464p. (gr. 9). 27.99 ***(978-0-465-02403-2(3))*** Basic Bks.

Berg, Steve. Target Field: The New Home of the Minnesota Twins. 2010. (ENG., Illus.). 224p. 40.00 *(978-0-7603-3965-7(1)*, 0760339651, MVP Bks.) MBI Publishing Co. LLC.

Berney, Louis. Game of My Life: Baltimore Orioles: Memorable Stories of Orioles Baseball. 2008. (Game of My Life Ser.). (Illus.). 256p. 24.95 *(978-1-59670-272-1(9))* Sports Publishing, LLC.

Berra, Yogi. Ten Rings: My Championship Seasons. 2008. (ENG.). 223p. pap. 14.00 *(978-1-4379-5180-6(5))* DIANE Publishing Co.

—You Can Observe a Lot by Watching: What I've Learned about Teamwork from the Yankees & Life. 2009. (ENG., Illus.). 240p. pap. 14.95 *(978-0-470-45404-6(0)*, Wiley) Wiley, John & Sons, Inc.

Berra, Yogi & Kaplan, Dave. Ten Rings: My Championship Seasons. 2006. (Illus.). 223p. reprint ed. 25.00 *(978-1-4223-5145-1(9))* DIANE Publishing Co.

Bissinger, Buzz. 3 Nights in August: Strategy, Heartbreak, & Joy Inside the Mind of a Manager. 2008. (Playaway Adult Fiction Ser.). 54.99 *(978-1-60640-938-1(7))* Findaway World, LLC.

Booth, Douglas, et al. The Fastest Thirty Ballgames: A Ballpark Chasers World Record Story. 2011. 272p. pap. 19.99 ***(978-1-4520-8679-8(6))*** AuthorHouse.

Borries, Philip Von. American Gladiator: The Life & Times of Pete Browning. 2007. 184p. pap. 14.95 *(978-1-60145-272-6(1))* Booklocker.com, Inc.

Bortolotti, Dan. Baseball Now! 2nd ed. 2011. (ENG., Illus.). 160p. pap. 24.95 *(978-1-55407-826-4(1))* Firefly Bks., Ltd.

Boyd, Dennis & Shalin, Mike. They Call Me Oil Can: My Life in Baseball. 2012. (ENG.). 240p. 25.95 ***(978-1-60078-682-2(0))*** Triumph Bks.

Branca, Ralph. A Moment in Time: An American Story of Baseball, Heartbreak, & Grace. 2011. (ENG.). 256p. 25.00 *(978-1-4516-3687-1(3)*, Scribner) Scribner.

Breslin, Jimmy. Branch Rickey. 2011. (Penguin Lives Ser.). (ENG.). 160p. (gr. 12). 19.95 *(978-0-670-02249-6(7)*, Viking Adult) Penguin Group (USA) Inc.

Breslin, Jimmy. Branch Rickey: A Life. 2012. (Penguin Lives Ser.). (ENG.). 160p. (gr. 12). 14.00 ***(978-0-14-312047-6(6)****, Penguin (Non-Classics)) Penguin Group (USA) Inc.

Brucato, Thomas W. Baseball Skippers & Their Crews: The History of Every Manager & Coach in the Major Leagues, 1871-2006. 2007. 39.95 *(978-1-878282-50-7(6))* St. Johann Pr.

Bucci, Steve & Brown, David W. Drinking Coffee with a Fork: The Story of Steve Carlton & the '72 Phillies. 2011. *(978-1-933822-25-9(2))*; (Illus.). xiii, 198p. ***(978-1-933822-32-7(5))*** Camino Bks., Inc.

Buscema, David. Game of My Life New York Yankees: 20 Stories of Yankees Baseball. 2008. (Game of My Life Ser.). (Illus.). 264p. per. 16.95 *(978-1-59670-296-7(6))* Sports Publishing, LLC.

Byrd, Paul. Free Byrd: The Power of a Liberated Life. 2011. (ENG., Illus.). 240p. pap. 15.99 *(978-1-4516-4147-9(8)*, Howard Bks.) Howard Books.

Caillault, Jean-Pierre, compiled by. The Complete New York Clipper Baseball Biographies: More Than 800 Sketches of Players, Managers, Owners, Umpires, Reporters & Others, 1859-1903, 2 vols. 2009. (ENG., Illus.). 758p. pap. 59.95 *(978-0-7864-3373-5(6))* McFarland & Co., Inc. Pubs.

Carew, Rod & Berkow, Ira. Carew. 2010. (Fesler-Lampert Minnesota Heritage Ser.). (ENG., Illus.). 268p. pap. 18.95 *(978-0-8166-7009-3(9))* Univ. of Minnesota Pr.

Carey, Pamela. Minor League Mom: A Mother's Journey Through the Red Sox Farm Teams. 2009. 336p. pap. 16.95 *(978-1-891724-17-6(7)*, Barking Cat Bks.) New River Pr.

Carroll, Jeff. Sam Rice: A Biography of the Washington Senators Hall of Famer. 2007. (ENG., Illus.). 252p. pap. 29.95 *(978-0-7864-3119-9(5))* McFarland & Co., Inc. Pubs.

Castro, Tony. Mickey Mantle: America's Prodigal Son. 2008. (Illus.). per. 9.95 *(978-1-59797-171-3(5))* Potomac Bks., Inc.

Center, Bill. Game of My Life: San Diego Padres: Memorable Stories of Padres Baseball. 2008. (Game of My Life Ser.). (Illus.). 256p. 24.95 *(978-1-59670-274-5(5))* Sports Publishing, LLC.

Chafets, Zev. Cooperstown Confidential: Heroes, Rogues, & the Inside Story of the Baseball Hall of Fame. (ENG.). 256p. 2010. pap. 15.00 *(978-1-60819-210-6(5))* 2009. (Illus.). 25.00 *(978-1-59691-545-9(5))* Bloomsbury Publishing.

Charyn, Jerome. Joe Dimaggio: The Long Vigil. (Icons of America Ser.). 192p. 2012. (ENG.). pap. 15.00 ***(978-0-300-18147-0(7))*** 2011. 24.00 *(978-0-300-12328-9(0))* Yale Univ. Pr.

Chicago Cubs Staff. Ron Santo: Always a Cub. 2011. 29.95 ***(978-1-60078-635-8(9))*** Triumph Bks.

Clavin, Tom & Peary, Danny. Gil Hodges: The Brooklyn Bums, the Miracle Mets, & the Extraordinary Life of a Baseball Legend. 2012. (ENG.). 320p. (gr. 12). 26.95 **(978-0-451-23586-2(X)**, N A L Hardcover) Penguin Group (USA) Inc.

Cobb, Ty. My Twenty Years in Baseball. Cobb, William R., ed. 2009. (Dover Baseball Ser.). (ENG.). 160p. pap. 8.95 *(978-0-486-47183-9(7))* Dover Pubns., Inc.

Cohen, Robert W. The 50 Greatest Players in New York Yankees History. 2012. (ENG., Illus.). 322p. 45.00 **(978-0-8108-8393-2(7))** Scarecrow Pr., Inc.

Cole, Justin. Inside the Batter's Box: Life Lessons about Leadership from America's Pastime & the World's Greatest Navy. 2007. 196p. per. 16.95 *(978-1-4120-8945-6(X))* Trafford Publishing.

Coleman, Jerry. An American Journey: My Life on the Field, in the Air, & on the Air. 2008. (ENG., Illus.). 224p. 24.95 *(978-1-60078-064-6(4))* Triumph Bks.

Collins, Sean L. In Pursuit of the College Baseball Scholarship: From a Coach's Perspective. 2003. 108p. 22.95 *(978-0-595-48769-1(6))* iUniverse, Inc.

Cook, William A. August Garry Herrmann: A Baseball Biography. 2007. (ENG., Illus.). 303p. per. 35.00 *(978-0-7864-3073-4(7))* McFarland & Co., Inc. Pubs.

Cook, William A. Big Klu: The Baseball Life of Ted Kluszewski. 2012. (ENG.). pap. 29.95 **(978-0-7864-6999-4(4))** McFarland & Co., Inc. Pubs.

Cooper, Brian E. Ray Schalk: A Baseball Biography. 2009. (ENG., Illus.). 338p. pap. 29.95 *(978-0-7864-4148-8(8))* McFarland & Co., Inc. Pubs.

Corbett, Warren. The Wizard of Waxahachie: Paul Richards & the End of Baseball as We Knew It. 2009. (Sport in American Life Ser.). (ENG., Illus.). 352p. 24.95 *(978-0-87074-555-0(5))* Southern Methodist Univ. Pr.

Corcoran, Dennis. Induction Day at Cooperstown: A History of the Baseball Hall of Fame Ceremony. 2010. (ENG., Illus.). 282p. pap. 39.95 *(978-0-7864-4415-8(9))* McFarland & Co., Inc. Pubs.

Coste, Chris. The 33-Year-Old Rookie: My 13-Year Journey from the Minor Leagues to the World Series. 2009. (ENG., Illus.). 272p. pap. 15.00 *(978-0-345-50703-7(7))*, Ballantine Bks.) Random House Publishing Group.

Crisafulli, Dave 'Agam'. Good Enough: An Autobiography of a Major Minor Local Athlete, 1 vol. 2009. 287p. pap. 27.95 *(978-1-60749-235-1(0))* PublishAmerica, Inc.

Dabscheck, Braham. Reading Baseball: Books, Biographies, & the Business of the Game. 2011. 238p. pap. 16.95 *(978-1-935412-24-3(8))* Fitness Information Technology, Inc.

D'Aloisio, Michael G. 5 C Hero: The Joel Stephens Story. 2009. 220p. 24.99 *(978-1-4490-5419-9(6))*; pap. 14.95 *(978-1-4490-5418-2(8))* AuthorHouse.

D'Antonio, Michael. Forever Blue: The True Story of Walter O'Malley, Baseball's Most Controversial Owner & the Dodgers of Brooklyn & Los Angeles. 2010. (ENG.). 400p. (gr. 12-18). 16.00 *(978-1-59448-441-4(4)*, Riverhead Trade (Paperbacks)) Penguin Group (USA) Inc.

Darling, Ron. The Complete Game: Reflections on Baseball & the Art of Pitching. 2010. (Vintage Ser.). (ENG.). 288p. pap. 15.00 *(978-0-307-39058-5(6)*, Vintage) Knopf Doubleday Publishing Group.

Darraj, Susan Muaddi & Maaddi, Rob. Randy Johnson. 2007. (Baseball Superstars Ser.). (Illus.). 128p. (YA). (gr. 7-12). lib. bdg. 30.00 *(978-0-7910-9441-9(3))* Facts On File, Inc.

DeCosta, John F. The Eastside Kid: Passion of a Gamer. 2011. 352p. 29.92 *(978-1-4269-5469-6(7))*; pap. 19.92 *(978-1-4269-5470-2(0))* Trafford Publishing.

DeVito, Carlo. Yogi: The Life & Times of an American Original. 2008. (ENG., Illus.). 400p. 25.95 *(978-1-57243-945-0(9))* Triumph Bks.

Dickey, R. A. & Coffey, Wayne. Wherever I Wind Up: My Quest for Truth, Authenticity & the Perfect Knuckleball. 2012. (ENG., Illus.). 352p. (gr. 12). 26.95 **(978-0-399-15815-5(4)**, Blue Rider Pr.) Penguin Group (USA) Inc.

Dickson, Paul. The Bill Veeck: Baseball's Greatest Maverick. 2012. (ENG., Illus.). 448p. 28.00 **(978-0-8027-1778-8(0)**, 226189) Walker & Co.

Dixon, Phil S. Wilber Bullet Rogan & the Kansas City Monarchs. 2010. (ENG., Illus.). 227p. pap. 39.95 *(978-0-7864-4425-0(8))* McFarland & Co., Inc. Pubs.

Dorfman, H. A. Copying in Down: An Anecdotal Memoir. 2009. (ENG.). 190p. pap. 29.99 *(978-0-7618-4755-7(3))* Hamilton Bks.

Dragseth, P. J. Major League Baseball Scouts: A Biographical Dictionary. 2011. (ENG., Illus.). 335p. pap. 75.00 *(978-0-7864-4360-4(X))* McFarland & Co., Inc. Pubs.

Dragseth, P. J., ed. Eye for Talent: Interviews with Veteran Baseball Scouts. 2009. (ENG., Illus.). 251p. pap. 39.95 *(978-0-7864-4361-1(8))* McFarland & Co., Inc. Pubs.

Duke, L. H. Billy & the Boys: The Shellman Wildcasts' run to the 1956 Georgia Class C High School Baseball Championship. 2009. 340p. pap. 17.95 *(978-1-60594-258-2(8)*, Llumina Pr.) Aeon Publishing Inc.

Durocher, Leo & Linn, Ed. Nice Guys Finish Last. 2009. (ENG., Illus.). 456p. pap. 18.00 *(978-0-226-17388-7(7))* Univ. of Chicago Pr.

Ephross, Peter & Abramowitz, Martin. Jewish Major Leaguers in Their Own Words: Oral Histories of 23 Players. 2012. (ENG.). 227p. pap. 35.00 **(978-0-7864-6507-1(7))** McFarland & Co., Inc. Pubs.

Erardi, John & Luckhaupt, Joel. The Wire-to-Wire Reds: Sweet Lou, Nasty Boys, & the Wild Run to a World Championship. 2010. (ENG.). 200p. pap. 24.95 *(978-1-57860-465-4(6))* Clerisy Pr.

Esquivel, Guille & Pérez, Mayrely. Out of the Park. 2009. 151p. pap. 12.95 *(978-0-557-07775-5(3))* Lulu Enterprises Inc.

Faber, Charles F. Major League Careers Cut Short: Leading Players Gone By 30. 2010. (ENG., Illus.). 298p. pap. 39.95 *(978-0-7864-4743-5(5))* McFarland & Co., Inc. Pubs.

Fast, Darcy. The Missing Cub. 2007. (ENG.). 240p. 24.99 *(978-1-60477-514-3(9))* Xulon Pr., Inc.

Fast, Darcy & Kravetz, Jonathan. The Missing Cub. 2007. 240p. per. 14.99 *(978-1-60477-277-7(8))* Xulon Pr., Inc.

Feinstein, John. Living on the Black: Two Pitchers, Two Teams, One Season to Remember. 2009. (ENG., Illus.). 560p. pap. 15.99 *(978-0-316-11392-2(1)*, Back Bay Bks.) Little Brown & Co.

Feller, Bob & Rocks, Burton. Bob Feller's Little Blue Book of Baseball Wisdom. 2009. (ENG.). 176p. 22.95 *(978-1-60078-219-0(1))* Triumph Bks.

Fleitz, David L. Shoeless: The Life & Times of Joe Jackson. l.t. alt. ed. 2007. (ENG., Illus.). 455p. per. 39.95 *(978-0-7864-3312-4(4))* McFarland & Co., Inc. Pubs.

Fornatale, Pete & Biegel, Brian. Miracle Ball: My Hunt for the Shot Heard 'Round the World. 2010. (ENG.). 256p. pap. 15.00 *(978-0-307-45269-6(7)*, Three Rivers Pr.) Crown Publishing Group.

Frankie, Chris. Nailed. 2010. 256p. 24.95 *(978-1-60078-433-0(X))* Triumph Bks.

Frascella, John. Theology: How a Boy Wonder Led the Red Sox to the Promised Land. 2009. (ENG.). 208p. pap. 14.95 *(978-0-9814536-9-9(4)*, Cambridge House Pr.) Sterling & Ross Pubs.

Freedman, Lew. Game of My Life: White Sox: Memorable Stories of Chicago White Sox Baseball. 2008. (Game of My Life Ser.). (Illus.). 221p. 24.95 *(978-1-59670-291-2(5))* Sports Publishing, LLC.

Friedlander, Brett & Reising, Robert. Chasing Moonlight: The True Story of Field of Dreams' Doc Graham. 2009. (Illus.). 208p. 19.95 *(978-0-89587-369-9(9))* Blair, John F. Pub.

Galarraga, Armando, et al. Nobody's Perfect: Two Men, One Call, & a Game for Baseball History. 2011. (ENG., Illus.). 240p. 24.00 *(978-0-8021-1988-9(3)*, Atlantic Monthly Pr.) Grove/Atlantic, Inc.

Garrido, Augie. Life Is Yours to Win: Lessons Forged from the Purpose, Passion, & Magic of Baseball. (ENG.). 272p. 2012. pap. 15.00 *(978-1-4391-8694-7(4))* 2011. 23.00 *(978-1-4391-8693-0(6))* Touchstone. (Touchstone).

Garvey, Steve. My Bat Boy Days: Lessons I Learned from the Boys of Summer. 2011. (ENG., Illus.). 160p. pap. 11.99 *(978-1-4165-4825-6(4)*, Scribner) Scribner.

Glanville, Doug M. The Game from Where I Stand: A Ballplayer's Inside View. 2010. (ENG.). 304p. 25.00 *(978-0-8050-9159-5(9)*, Times Bks.) Holt, Henry & Co.

Goldman, Steven. Forging Genius: The Making of Casey Stengel. 2007. (Illus.). 316p. per. 16.95 *(978-1-57488-874-4(9))* Potomac Bks., Inc.

Golenbock, Peter. George: The Poor Little Rich Boy Who Built the Yankee Empire. 2009. (ENG., Illus.). 384p. 26.95 *(978-0-470-39219-5(3)*, Wiley) Wiley, John & Sons, Inc.

Gomez, Vernona & Goldstone, Lawrence. Lefty: An American Odyssey. 2012. (ENG., Illus.). 416p. 28.00 **(978-0-345-52648-9(1)**, Ballantine Bks.) Random House Publishing Group.

Gordon, Bob. Game of My Life: Philadelphia Phillies: Memorable Stories of Phillies Baseball. 2008. (Game of My Life Ser.). (Illus.). 223p. 24.95 *(978-1-59670-257-8(5))* Sports Publishing, LLC.

Gordon, Dan & Bradley, Mickey. Haunted Baseball: Ghosts, Curses, Legends, & Eerie Events. 2007. (Haunted Ser.). (ENG., Illus.). 288p. per. 14.95 *(978-1-59921-022-3(3)*, Lyons Pr.) Globe Pequot Pr., The.

Gorman, Lou. High & Inside: My Life in the Front Offices of Baseball. 2007. (ENG., Illus.). 280p. per. 29.95 *(978-0-7864-3163-2(6))* McFarland & Co., Inc. Pubs.

Gorman, Robert. In Your Face - In Your Heart: The Story of Joe Cronin. 2007. pap. 14.95 *(978-0-9792287-0-4(0))* Baldwin Bks.

Gose, Elijah Jude. Ryan Howard: Power Hitter. 2010. (Inspiring Lives Ser.). (ENG.). 32p. (gr. 5-8). pap. 10.50 *(978-1-4339-3653-1(4))* Stevens, Gareth Publishing LLLP.

Granderson, Curtis. All You Can Be: Learning & Growing Through Sports. 2011. (All You Can Be Ser.). (ENG., Illus.). 48p. (J). (gr. 2-4). 16.95 **(978-1-60078-626-6(X))** Triumph Bks.

Green, G. Michael & Launius, Roger D. Charlie Finley: The Outrageous Story of Baseball's Super Showman. 2010. (ENG., Illus.). 368p. 27.00 *(978-0-8027-1745-0(4))* Walker & Co.

Green, Shawn. The Way of Baseball: Finding Stillness at 95 Mph. 2011. (ENG., Illus.). 224p. 24.00 *(978-1-4391-9119-4(0))* Simon & Schuster.

Greenberg, Hank. Story of My Life. 2009. (ENG.). 320p. pap. 16.95 *(978-1-56663-837-1(2))* Dee, Ivan R. Pub.

Gulas, Greg, Sr., told to. My Memories as a Brooklyn Dodger: By George Shotgun Shuba, as told to Greg Gulas. 2007. (Illus.). 230p. per. 20.00 *(978-0-615-15274-5(0))* George Shotgun Shuba Family Enterprise.

Gutteridge, Don, et al. From the Gas House Gang to the Go-Go Sox: My 50-Plus Years in Big League Baseball. 2007. 404p. 25.00 *(978-0-9779841-5-2(X))* Pepperpot Prodns, Inc.

Hamel, Randall B. Baseball's Unknown Angel, 1 vol. 2009. 281p. pap. 27.95 *(978-1-4489-7363-7(5))* PublishAmerica, Inc.

Hampton, Wilborn. Babe Ruth: A Twentieth-Century Life. 2009. (Up Close Ser.). (ENG.). 208p. (YA). (gr. 6-18). 16.99 *(978-0-670-06305-5(3)*, Viking Juvenile) Penguin Group (USA) Inc.

Harris, Rick. Rhode Island Baseball: The Early Years. 2008. pap. 19.99 *(978-1-59629-496-7(5))* History Pr., The.

Herzog, Whitey & Pitts, Jonathan. You're Missin' a Great Game: From Casey to Ozzie, the Magic of Baseball & How to Get It Back. 2007. (ENG., Illus.). 320p. pap. 21.95 *(978-1-4165-5205-5(7))* Simon & Schuster.

Hirsch, James S. Willie Mays: The Life, the Legend. (ENG.). 640p. 2011. pap. 18.00 *(978-1-4165-4791-4(6))* 2010. (Illus.). 30.00 *(978-1-4165-4790-7(8))* Scribner. (Scribner).

Holley, Michael. Red Sox Rule: Terry Francona & Boston's Rise to Dominance. 2009. (ENG.). 256p. pap. 15.99 *(978-0-06-145855-2(4))* HarperCollins Pubs.

Honig, Donald. The Fifth Season: Tales of My Life in Baseball. 2009. (ENG.). 296p. 26.95 *(978-1-56663-810-4(0))* Dee, Ivan R. Pub.

Hoose, Phillip. Perfect, Once Removed: When Baseball Was All the World to Me. 2008. (ENG., Illus.). 176p. per. 10.95 *(978-0-8027-1627-9(X))* Walker & Co.

Hunn, Rick. Eddie Collins: A Baseball Biography. 2008. (ENG., Illus.). 376p. per. 35.00 *(978-0-7864-3287-5(X))* McFarland & Co., Inc. Pubs.

James, LeBron & Bissinger, Buzz. LeBron's Dream Team: How Five Friends Made History. 2010. (ENG.). 272p. (gr. 12). 15.00 *(978-0-14-311822-0(6)*, Penguin (Non-Classics)) Penguin Group (USA) Inc.

Jenkinson, Bill. Baseball's Ultimate Power: Ranking the All-Time Greatest Distance Home Run Hitters. 2010. (ENG., Illus.). 352p. pap. 17.95 *(978-1-59921-544-0(6)*, Lyons Pr.) Globe Pequot Pr., The.

Kansas City Athletics Coaches: Whitey Herzog, Jimmy Dykes, Walker Cooper, Johnny Mize, Johnny Sain, Gabby Hartnett, Luke Appling. 2010. 106p. pap. 19.99 *(978-1-155-46024-6(3))* General Bks. LLC.

Kansas City Athletics Field Personnel: Kansas City Athletics Managers, Kansas City Athletics Players, Reggie Jackson, Satchel Paige. 2010. 746p. pap. 14.14 *(978-1-157-86307-6(8))* General Bks. LLC.

Kaplan, Jim. The Greatest Game Ever Pitched: Juan Marichal, Warren Spahn, & the Pitching Duel of the Century. 2011. (ENG.). 256p. 24.95 *(978-1-60078-341-8(4))* Triumph Bks.

Kashatus, William C. Money Pitcher: Chief Bender & the Tragedy of Indian Assimilation. 2011. (Keystone Book Ser.). (ENG.). 216p. pap. 24.95 **(978-0-271-02851-4(3))** Pennsylvania State Univ. Pr.

Katz, Jesse. The Opposite Field: A Memoir. 2010. (ENG.). 352p. pap. 15.00 *(978-0-307-40712-2(8)*, Three Rivers Pr.) Crown Publishing Group.

Kernan, Kevin. Girardi: No Ordinary Joe. 2012. (ENG.). 256p. 25.95 **(978-1-60078-582-5(4))** Triumph Bks.

Kerr, Roy. Buck Ewing: A Baseball Biography. 2012. (ENG.). 272p. pap. 29.95 **(978-0-7864-6948-2(X))** McFarland & Co., Inc. Pubs.

—Roger Connor: Home Run King of 19th Century Baseball. 2011. (ENG., Illus.). 212p. pap. 29.95 *(978-0-7864-5958-2(1))* McFarland & Co., Inc. Pubs.

—Sliding Billy Hamilton: The Life & Times of Baseball's First Great Leadoff Hitter. 2009. (ENG., Illus.). 216p. pap. 29.95 *(978-0-7864-4639-1(0))* McFarland & Co., Inc. Pubs.

King, Nelson J. Happiness Is Like a Cur Dog: The Thirty-Year Journey of a Major League Baseball Pitcher & Broadcaster. 2009. (ENG.). 300p. 26.00 *(978-1-4490-2548-9(X))*; pap. 15.60 *(978-1-4490-2547-2(1))* AuthorHouse.

Kirkpatrick, Rob. Cecil Travis of the Washington Senators: The War-Torn Career of an All-Star Shortstop. 2009. (ENG., Illus.). 200p. pap. 14.95 *(978-0-8032-2475-9(3)*, Bison Bks.) Univ. of Nebraska Pr.

Kole, Alex S. Captain Wonder, Lou Gehrig, & Me. 2008. (ENG., Illus.). 352p. pap. 15.00 *(978-0-9792371-6-4(5))* Keene Publishing.

Kuntz, Jerry. Baseball Fiends & Flying Machines: The Many Lives & Outrageous Times of George & Alfred Lawson. 2009. (ENG., Illus.). 238p. pap. 29.95 *(978-0-7864-4375-8(8))* McFarland & Co., Inc. Pubs.

Kurlansky, Mark. Hank Greenberg: The Hero Who Didn't Want to Be One. 2011. (Jewish Lives Ser.). (Illus.). 192p. 25.00 *(978-0-300-13660-9(9))* Yale Univ. Pr.

La Russa, Tony. One Last Strike LP: Fifty Years in Baseball, Ten & Half Games Back, & One Final Championship Season. l.t. ed. 2012. (ENG.). 432p. pap. 26.99 **(978-0-06-220771-5(7)**, HarperLuxe) HarperCollins Pubs.

Larsen, Don & Shaw, Mark. The Perfect Yankee: The Incredible Story of the Greatest Miracle in Baseball History. 2012. (ENG., Illus.). 256p. pap. 14.95 **(978-1-61321-077-2(9)**, 613077) Skyhorse Publishing Co., Inc.

Leach, Matthew. Game of My Life: St. Louis Cardinals: Memorable Stories of Cardinals Baseball. 2008. (Game of My Life Ser.). (Illus.). 206p. 24.95 *(978-1-59670-273-8(7))* Sports Publishing, LLC.

Leavengood, Ted. Clark Griffith: The Old Fox of Washington Baseball. 2011. (ENG., Illus.). 321p. pap. 29.95 *(978-0-7864-6386-2(4))* McFarland & Co., Inc. Pubs.

Leavy, Jane. The Last Boy: Mickey Mantle & the End of America's Childhood. (P.S. Ser.). 2011. (ENG.). 480p. pap. 16.99 *(978-0-06-088353-9(7)*, HarperPerennial) 2010. (ENG.). 400p. 27.99 *(978-0-06-088352-2(9))* 2010. 784p. pap. 27.99 *(978-0-06-177488-1(X)*, HarperLuxe) HarperCollins Pubs.

Levitt, Daniel R. Ed Barrow: The Bulldog Who Built the Yankees' First Dynasty. 2010. (ENG.). 456p. pap. 21.95 *(978-0-8032-2981-5(X)*, Bison Bks.) Univ. of Nebraska Pr.

Levitt, Daniel R. & Levitt, Dan. Ed Barrow: The Bulldog Who Built the Yankees' First Dynasty. 2008. (ENG., Illus.). 496p. 29.95 *(978-0-8032-2974-7(7))* Univ. of Nebraska Pr.

Lewin, Josh. Ballgame! A Decade Covering the Texas Rangers from the Best Seat in the House. 2012. (ENG.). 240p. 24.95 **(978-1-60078-659-4(6))** Triumph Bks.

Lewis, T. J. A View from the Mound; My Father's Life in Baseball. 2009. 232p. pap. 19.99 *(978-1-4357-1486-1(5))* Lulu Enterprises Inc.

Litwhiler, Daniel. Danny Litwhiler: Living the Baseball Dream. 2006. (Illus.). 312p. 47.00 *(978-1-59213-524-0(2))* Temple Univ. Pr.

Llc, Books, ed. Kansas City Athletics Executives: Charlie Finley, Hank Peters, Jim Schaaf. 2010. 24p. pap. 14.14 *(978-1-158-25628-0(0))* General Bks. LLC.

—Kansas City Athletics Managers: Joe Gordon, Haywood Sullivan, Alvin Dark, Hank Bauer, Lou Boudreau, Bob Elliott, Luke Appling, Harry Craft. 2010. 62p. pap. 19.99 *(978-1-155-46025-3(1))* General Bks. LLC.

—Kansas City Athletics Scouts: Whitey Herzog, Lena Blackburne, Bubber Jonnard, Jimmy Adair, Bill Posedel. 2010. 24p. pap. 14.14 *(978-1-158-26302-8(3))* General Bks. LLC.

Lowenfish, Lee. Branch Rickey: Baseball's Ferocious Gentleman. 2009. (ENG., Illus.). 728p. pap. 24.95 *(978-0-8032-2453-7(2)*, Bison Bks.) Univ. of Nebraska Pr.

Lucas, L. J. Then & Now. 2009. 243p. pap. 17.95 *(978-1-4327-3899-0(2))* Outskirts Pr., Inc.

Lynch, Michael T., Jr. Harry Frazee, Ban Johnson & the Feud That Nearly Destroyed the American League. 2008. (ENG., Illus.). 282p. pap. 29.95 *(978-0-7864-3330-8(2))* McFarland & Co., Inc. Pubs.

Macht, Norman L. Connie Mack: The Turbulent & Triumphant Years, 1915-1931. 2012. (ENG., Illus.). 720p. 39.95 **(978-0-8032-2039-3(1))** Univ. of Nebraska Pr.

Macht, Norman L. & Macht, Norman. Connie Mack & the Early Years of Baseball. 2007. (ENG., Illus.). 742p. 39.95 *(978-0-8032-3263-1(2))* Univ. of Nebraska Pr.

Machuca, Mel & Shepherd, Will. An Inning at a Time: An American Legion Baseball National Championship Story. 2011. 218p. pap. 16.95 *(978-1-59299-553-0(5))* Inkwater Pr.

Mack, Connie. My 66 Years in the Big Leagues. Date not set. lib. bdg. 21.95 *(978-0-8488-1587-5(4))* Amereon LTD.

—My 66 Years in the Big Leagues. 2009. (Dover Baseball Ser.). (ENG.). 288p. pap. 12.95 *(978-0-486-47184-6(5))* Dover Pubns., Inc.

Madden, Bill. Steinbrenner: The Last Lion of Baseball. 2011. (ENG.). 512p. pap. 16.99 *(978-0-06-169032-7(5))* 2010. (ENG., Illus.). 480p. 26.99 *(978-0-06-169031-0(7))* 2010. 782p. pap. 26.99 *(978-0-06-197956-9(2)*, HarperLuxe) HarperCollins Pubs.

Mahler, Jonathan. The Bronx Is Burning: 1977, Baseball, Politics, & the Battle for the Soul of a City. 2nd movie tie-in ed. 2007. (ENG., Illus.). 376p. pap. 15.00 *(978-0-312-42702-3(6))* Picador.

Maraniss, David. Clemente: The Passion & Grace of Baseball's Last Hero. 2007. (ENG., Illus.). 416p. pap. 15.00 *(978-0-7432-9999-2(X))* Simon & Schuster.

Marichal, Juan. Juan Marichal: My Journey from the Dominican Republic to Cooperstown. 2011. (ENG., Illus.). 288p. 25.00 *(978-0-7603-4059-2(5)*, 0760340595, MVP Bks.) MBI Publishing Co. LLC.

Markusen, Bruce. The Team That Changed Baseball: Roberto Clemente & the 1971 Pittsburgh Pirates. 2009. (ENG., Illus.). 240p. pap. 14.95 *(978-1-59416-089-9(9))* Westholme Publishing.

Martin, Jay. Live All You Can: Alexander Joy Cartwright & the Invention of Modern Baseball. 2009. (ENG., Illus.). 168p. (gr. 17). 22.95 *(978-0-231-14794-1(5))* Columbia Univ. Pr.

Matthews, Gary & Pepe, Phil. Few & Chosen Phillies: Defining Phillies Greatness Across the Eras. 2012. (Few & Chosen Ser.). (ENG.). 224p. 25.95 **(978-1-60078-658-7(8))** Triumph Bks.

McCormack, Shaun. Cool Papa Bell. 2009. (Baseball Hall of Famers of the Negro Leagues Ser.). 112p. (gr. 5-8). 63.90 *(978-1-61511-522-8(6)*, Rosen Central) Rosen Publishing Group, Inc., The.

McCrotty, Will. Lessons with a Bat & Ball. 2011. 84p. pap. 19.95 **(978-1-4560-2314-0(4))** PublishAmerica, Inc.

McDonald, Brian. Indian Summer: The Forgotten Story of Louis Sockalexis, the First Native American in Major League Baseball. 2006. 244p. reprint ed. 22.00 *(978-1-4223-5326-4(5))* DIANE Publishing Co.

McGough, Matthew. Bat Boy: Coming of Age with the New York Yankees. 2007. (ENG.). 288p. pap. 12.95 *(978-0-307-27864-7(6)*, Anchor) Knopf Doubleday Publishing Group.

McGwire, Jay. Mark & Me: Mark McGwire & the Truth Behind Baseball's Worst-Kept Secret. 2010. (ENG.). 208p. 24.95 *(978-1-60078-308-1(2))* Triumph Bks.

McKelvey, G. Richard. Lost in the Sun: The Comebacks & Comedowns of Major League Ballplayers. 2007. (ENG., Illus.). 219p. per. 32.00 *(978-0-7864-3218-9(7))* McFarland & Co., Inc. Pubs.

McKenna, Brian. Clark Griffith: Baseball's Statesman. 2010. 373p. pap. 26.97 *(978-0-557-47295-6(4))* Lulu Enterprises Inc.

McNeil, William F. Red Sox Nation Guide to the Players. 2008. (ENG.). 240p. pap. 9.95 *(978-1-55553-699-2(9)*, Northeastern University Pr.) Univ. Pr. of New England.

—Red Sox Roll Call: 200 Memorable Players, 1901-2010. 2012. (ENG., Illus.). 240p. pap. 45.00 *(978-0-7864-6471-5(2))* McFarland & Co., Inc. Pubs.

Mercurio, John A. & Samson, David. How to Be Funny Wen You Owe Money: The Ultimate Guide to Driving Bill Collectors & Creditors. 2007. (ENG.). 144p. pap. 10.95 *(978-1-56171-216-8(7))* SPI Bks.

Merritt, Paul. A Trophy Without a Face. 2010. 86p. pap. 10.00 *(978-1-935271-38-3(5))* Published by Westview, Inc.

Merritt, Roy B. The Perfect Game. 2008. 108p. pap. 14.95 *(978-1-4357-0945-4(4))* Lulu Enterprises Inc.

Miller, Ernestine. Babe Book: Baseball's Greatest Legend Remembered. 2007. (Illus.). 211p. reprint ed. 20.00 *(978-1-4223-9003-0(9))* DIANE Publishing Co.

Miller, Randy. Harry the K: The Remarkable Life of Harry Kalas. 2010. (ENG., Illus.). 336p. 24.95 *(978-0-7624-3896-9(7)*, Running Pr.) Running Pr. Bk. Pubs.

MLB Publishing. The Treasures of Major League Baseball. 2010. (ENG., Illus.). 64p. 35.00 *(978-1-84442-323-1(9))* Carlton Bks., Ltd. GBR. Dist: Sterling Publishing Co., Inc.

Moffi, Larry. The Conscience of the Game: Baseball's Commissioners from Landis to Selig. 2006. (ENG.). 228p. pap. 24.95 *(978-0-8032-8322-0(9)*, Bison Bks.) Univ. of Nebraska Pr.

Moncreiff, Robert P. Bart Giamatti: A Profile. 2007. (ENG., Illus.). 256p. 35.00 *(978-0-300-12187-2(3))* Yale Univ. Pr.

Moore, Gary W. Playing with the Enemy: A Baseball Prodigy, a World at War, & a Field of Broken Dreams. 2006. (Illus.). 299p. 29.95 (978-1-932714-24-1(3)) Savas Beatie.

Morris, Peter. Level Playing Fields: How the Groundskeeping Murphy Brothers Shaped Baseball. 2007. (ENG., Illus.). 216p. 24.95 (978-0-8032-1110-0(4)) Univ. of Nebraska Pr.

Morrissey, Rick. Ozzie's School of Management: Lessons from the Dugout, the Clubhouse, & the Doghouse. 2012. (ENG., Illus.). 288p. 26.00 **(978-0-8050-9500-5(4)**, Times Bks.) Holt, Henry & Co.

Motley, Bob. Ruling over Monarchs, Giants & Stars: Umpiring in the Negro Leagues & Beyond. 2007. (Illus.). 217p. per. 16.95 (978-1-59670-236-3(2)) Sports Publishing, LLC.

Motley, Bob, et al. Ruling over Monarchs, Giants, & Stars: True Tales of Breaking Barriers, Umpiring Baseball Legends, & Wild Adventures in the Negro Leagues. 2012. (ENG., Illus.). 240p. 24.95 **(978-1-61321-059-8(0)**, 613059) Skyhorse Publishing Co., Inc.

Mowday, Bruce & Donahue, Jim. Richie Ashburn: Why the Hall Not? And the Amazing Journey to Cooperstown. 2011. (Illus.). 288p. 19.95 (978-1-56980-450-6(8)) Barricade Bks., Inc.

Murnau, Thad. When the Grass Turns Green: Cherished Baseball Memories of a North Carolina Sports Writer. 2010. pap. 19.95 (978-1-59712-407-2(9)) Catawba Publishing Co.

Nagel, Kyle. Game of My Life Cincinnati Reds: Memorable Stories of Reds Baseball. 2008. (Game of My Life Ser.). (Illus.). 256p. 24.95 (978-1-59670-329-2(6)) Sports Publishing, LLC.

Nemec, David, ed. Major League Baseball Profiles, 1871-1900, 2-volume Set, 2 vols. 2011. (ENG., Illus.). 1264p. pap. 69.95 **(978-0-8032-3533-5(X)**, Bison Bks.) Univ. of Nebraska Pr.

—Major League Baseball Profiles, 1871-1900, Volume 1: The Ballplayers Who Built the Game, 2 vols. 2011. (ENG., Illus.). 688p. pap. 39.95 (978-0-8032-3024-8(9), Bison Bks.) Univ. of Nebraska Pr.

—Major League Baseball Profiles, 1871-1900, Volume 2: The Hall of Famers & Memorable Personalities Who Shaped the Game, 2 vols. 2011. (ENG., Illus.). 576p. pap. 39.95 (978-0-8032-3532-8(1), Bison Bks.) Univ. of Nebraska Pr.

New York Times Staff. Derek Jeter: From the pages of the New York Times. Kepner, Tyler, ed. 2011. (ENG., Illus.). 224p. 29.95 (978-0-8109-9656-4(1)) Abrams.

Nucciarone, Monica. Alexander Cartwright: The Life Behind the Baseball Legend. 2009. (ENG., Illus.). 326p. 27.95 (978-0-8032-3353-9(1)) Univ. of Nebraska Pr.

O'Connor, Ian. The Captain: The Journey of Derek Jeter. 2011. (ENG., Illus.). 416p. 26.00 (978-0-547-32793-8(5)) Houghton Mifflin Harcourt Trade & Reference Pubs.

Parker, Clifton Blue. Bucketfoot Al: The Baseball Life of Al Simmons. 2011. (ENG., Illus.). 251p. pap. 29.95 (978-0-7864-6143-1(8)) McFarland & Co., Inc. Pubs.

Pearlman, Jeff. The Rocket That Fell to Earth: Roger Clemens & the Rage for Baseball Immortality. 2010. (ENG.). 368p. pap. 14.99 (978-0-06-172482-4(3), Harper Paperbacks) HarperCollins Pubs.

Pederson, Charles E. Jackie Robinson: Baseball Great & Civil Rights Activist. 2009. (Essential Lives Set 3 Ser.). (Illus.). 112p. (YA). (gr. 7-12). 34.22 (978-1-60453-526-6(1)) ABDO Publishing Co.

Pepe, Phil. The Ballad of Billy & George: The Tempestuous Baseball Marriage of Billy Martin & George Steinbrenner. 2010. (ENG., Illus.). 272p. pap. 14.95 (978-0-7627-7066-3(X), Lyons Pr.) Globe Pequot Pr., The.

Perry, Dayn. Reggie Jackson: The Life & Thunderous Career of Baseball's Mr. October. 2011. (ENG.). 336p. pap. 16.99 (978-0-06-156237-2(8)) 2010. (Illus.). 336p. 25.99 (978-0-06-156238-9(6), Morrow, William & Co.) 2010. 476p. pap. 25.99 (978-0-06-194571-7(4), HarperLuxe) HarperCollins Pubs.

Peterson, Richard. Growing up with Clemente. 2009. (Illus.). 128p. pap. 18.00 (978-0-87338-982-2(4)) Kent State Univ. Pr.

Plaschke, Bill. I Live for This! Baseball's Last True Believer. 2007. (ENG., Illus.). 256p. 25.00 (978-0-618-65387-4(2)) Houghton Mifflin Harcourt Trade & Reference Pubs.

—I Live for This: Baseball's Last True Believer. 2009. (ENG., Illus.). 256p. pap. 14.95 (978-0-547-23788-6(X), Mariner Bks.) Houghton Mifflin Harcourt Trade & Reference Pubs.

Poekel, Charlie. Babe & the Kid: The Legendary Story of Babe Ruth & Johnny Sylvester. 2007. (Sports History Ser.). (ENG., Illus.). 160p. pap. 19.99 (978-1-59629-267-3(9)) History Pr., The.

Price, S. L. Heart of the Game: Life, Death, & Mercy in Minor League America. 2010. (ENG.). 336p. pap. 14.99 (978-0-06-167131-9(2)) 2009. 320p. 24.99 (978-0-06-167130-2(4)) HarperCollins Pubs. (Ecco).

Proia, Paul. Just a Big Kid: The Life & Times of Rube Waddell. 2007. 420p. pap. 29.95 (978-1-4241-6862-0(7)) PublishAmerica, Inc.

Rains, Rob. Tony la Russa: Man on a Mission. (ENG.). 320p. 2011. pap. 15.95 (978-1-60078-557-3(3)) 2009. 24.95 (978-1-60078-169-8(1)) Triumph Bks.

Randolph, Willie & Coffey, Wayne. Rising Son: Mets, Yankees, & My Journey to the Big Leagues. 2010. 336p. 25.99 (978-0-06-145077-8(4), Harper Entertainment) HarperCollins Pubs.

Reilly, Dan. The Original Mr Met Remembers: When the Miracle Began. 2007. 140p. (ENG.). 23.95 (978-0-595-70082-0(9)); per. 13.95 (978-0-595-46260-5(X)) iUniverse, Inc.

Reilly, Rick. Hate Mail from Cheerleaders: And Other Adventures from the Life of Reilly. 2007. (ENG., Illus.). 318p. 25.95 (978-1-933821-12-2(4)) Time Home Entertainment, Inc.

Reis, Ronald A. Ted Williams. 2008. (Baseball Superstars Ser.). (Illus.). 136p. (gr. 6-12). lib. bdg. 30.00 (978-0-7910-9545-4(2), Chelsea Hse.) Facts On File, Inc.

Remy, Jerry & Sandler, Corey. Jerry Remy's Red Sox Heroes. 2010. (Illus.). 288p. pap. 12.95 (978-1-59921-970-7(0)) Globe Pequot Pr., The.

Rhodes, Jean & Boburg, Shawn. Becoming Manny: Inside the Life of Baseball's Most Enigmatic Slugger. 2011. (ENG.). 320p. pap. 19.99 (978-1-4165-7707-2(6), Scribner) Scribner.

Rieger, Thomas E. Living It-A Baseball Memoir. 2011. 152p. pap. 24.95 **(978-1-4512-8091-3(2))** PublishAmerica, Inc.

Ritter, Lawrence S. The Glory of Their Times: The Story of the Early Days of Baseball Told by the Men Who Played It. 2010. (ENG.). 384p. pap. 14.99 (978-0-06-199471-5(5), HarperPerennial) HarperCollins Pubs.

Roberts, Selena. A-Rod: The Many Lives of Alex Rodriguez. 2010. 272p. pap. 15.99 (978-0-06-179165-9(2), Harper Paperbacks) HarperCollins Pubs.

Roensch, Greg. Rickey Henderson. 2008. (Baseball Superstars Ser.). (Illus.). 120p. (YA). (gr. 7-12). lib. bdg. 30.00 (978-0-7910-9601-7(7)) Facts On File, Inc.

Rogers, Phil. Ernie Banks: Mr. Cub & the Summer Of '69. 2011. (ENG.). 272p. 24.95 (978-1-60078-519-1(0)) Triumph Bks.

Rosenfeld, Harvey. Iron Man: The Cal Ripken, Jr. Story. 2007. 344p. per. 22.95 (978-0-595-46138-7(7), Backinprint.com) iUniverse, Inc.

Roth, B. A. Derek Jeter: A Yankee Hero. 2009. (All Aboard Reading Ser.). (ENG.). 48p. (J). (gr. 1-3). pap. 3.99 (978-0-448-45040-7(2), Grosset & Dunlap) Penguin Group (USA) Inc.

Rumor in Town: A Grandson's Promise to Right a Wrong. 2007. (Illus.). 300p. 24.95 (978-0-9795834-0-7(3)) Woodlyn Lane.

Ruth, Babe. Playing the Game: My Early Years in Baseball. Cobb, William R., ed. 2011. (Dover Baseball Ser.). (ENG., Illus.). 128p. pap. 8.95 (978-0-486-47694-0(4)) Dover Pubns., Inc.

Ryan, Kenneth F. Tossing Heat: The Ken Ryan Story. 2007. 132p. per. 19.95 (978-1-4241-8015-8(5)) PublishAmerica, Inc.

Sacco, Anthony J. Echoes in the Wind: A Biography of Guy Vitale, East Boston High School Sports Great. 2007. 560p. per. 32.95 (978-0-595-45522-5(0)) iUniverse, Inc.

Salmon, Tim & Goldman, Rob. Always an Angel: Playing the Game with Fire & Faith. 2010. (Always A Ser.). (ENG., Illus.). 240p. 19.95 (978-1-60078-343-2(0)) Triumph Bks.

Schacht, Mike. Clowning Through Baseball. 24.95 (978-0-8488-1574-5(2)) Amereon LTD.

Schiff, Andrew J. The Father of Baseball: A Biography of Henry Chadwick. 2008. (ENG., Illus.). 268p. per. 29.95 (978-0-7864-3216-5(0)) McFarland & Co., Inc. Pubs.

Schoendienst, Red & Rains, Rob. Red: A Baseball Life. 2007. (Illus.). 252p. pap. 16.95 (978-1-59670-219-6(2)) Sports Publishing, LLC.

Schraff, Anne E. Jackie Robinson: An American Hero. 2008. (Townsend Library). 138p. (J). (978-1-59194-102-6(4)) Townsend Pr. - Sunday Schl. Publishing Board.

Schuerholz, John & Guest, Larry. Built to Win: Inside Stories & Leadership Strategies from Baseball's Winningest General Manager. 2007. (ENG., Illus.). 288p. per. 20.99 (978-0-446-69653-1(6)) Grand Central Publishing.

Selzer, Steven Michael. Meet the Real Joe Black: An Inspiring Life - Baseball, Teaching, Business, Giving. 2010. 172p. 25.95 (978-1-4401-7120-8(3)); (ENG.). pap. 15.95 (978-1-4401-7119-2(X)) iUniverse, Inc.

Shafer, Ronald G. When the Dodgers Were Bridegrooms: Gunner Mcgunnigle & Brooklyn's Back-to-Back Pennants of 1889 And 1890. 2011. (ENG., Illus.). 212p. pap. 29.95 (978-0-7864-5899-8(2)) McFarland & Co., Inc. Pubs.

Shannon, Mike. Willie Mays: Art in the Outfield. 2nd ed. 2007. (ENG., Illus.). 89p. 29.95 (978-0-8173-1540-5(3)) Univ. of Alabama Pr.

Shannon, Mike & Hannig, Scott D. Hutch: Baseball's Fred Hutchinson & a Legacy of Courage. 2011. (ENG., Illus.). 224p. pap. 24.95 (978-0-7864-4625-4(0)) McFarland & Co., Inc. Pubs.

Skipper, James K. Baseball Nicknames: A Dictionary of Origins & Meanings. alt. ed. 2011. (ENG.). 398p. pap. 29.95 **(978-0-7864-6717-4(7))** McFarland & Co., Inc. Pubs.

Skipper, John C. A Biographical Dictionary of Major League Baseball Managers. alt. ed. 2011. (ENG., Illus.). 380p. pap. 45.00 (978-0-7864-4703-9(6)) McFarland & Co., Inc. Pubs.

Smiles, Jack. Big Ed Walsh: The Life & Times of a Spitballing Hall of Famer. 2007. (ENG., Illus.). 238p. per. 29.95 (978-0-7864-3278-3(0)) McFarland & Co., Inc. Pubs.

—Bucky Harris: A Biography of Baseball's Boy Wonder. 2011. (ENG., Illus.). 320p. pap. 29.95 (978-0-7864-4160-0(7)) McFarland & Co., Inc. Pubs.

Smith, Curt. A Talk in the Park: Nine Decades of Baseball Tales from the Broadcast Booth. 2011. 320p. 27.50 (978-1-59797-670-1(9)) Potomac Bks., Inc.

Smith, Daryl Raymond. Making the Big Red Machine: Bob Howsam & the Cincinnati Reds of The 1970s. 2009. (ENG., Illus.). 360p. pap. 35.00 (978-0-7864-3980-5(7)) McFarland & Co., Inc. Pubs.

Sporting News, creator. Cardinal Nation. 4th ed. 2006. (ENG., Illus.). 256p. 29.95 (978-0-89204-888-5(3)) Sporting News Publishing Co.

Sports Illustrated Editors. Sports Illustrated the Baseball Book Expanded Edition. 2011. (ENG., Illus.). 326p. 29.95 (978-1-60320-208-4(0)) Time Home Entertainment, Inc.

Staples, Bill. Kenichi Zenimura, Japanese American Baseball Pioneer. 2011. (ENG., Illus.). 282p. pap. 40.00 (978-0-7864-6134-9(9)) McFarland & Co., Inc. Pubs.

Staples, Billy, et al. Before the Glory: 20 Baseball Heroes Talk about Growing up & Turning Hard Times into Home Runs. 2007. (ENG., Illus.). 384p. pap. 16.95 (978-0-7573-0626-6(8)) Health Communications, Inc.

Stevens, Big Ed. The Other Side of the Jackie Robinson Story. 2010. pap. 15.99 (978-1-60799-112-0(8)) Tate Publishing & Enterprises, LLC.

Steverson, Bryan. Amazing Baseball Heroes: Inspirational Negro League Stories. 2011. (Illus.). xxii, 248p. **(978-1-932604-81-8(2))** Tennessee Valley Publishing.

Stewart, Wayne. Baseball Dads: The Game's Greatest Players Reflect on Their Fathers & the Game They Love. 2012. (ENG., Illus.). 160p. 19.95 **(978-1-61608-583-4(5)**, 608583) Skyhorse Publishing Co., Inc.

Stewart, Wayne. Stan the Man: The Life & Times of Stan Musial TBC. 2010. (ENG.). 256p. 24.95 (978-1-60078-322-7(8)) Triumph Bks.

Stinson, Mitchell Conrad. Edd Roush: A Biography of the Cincinnati Reds Star. 2010. (ENG., Illus.). 256p. pap. 29.95 (978-0-7864-4407-6(X)) McFarland & Co., Inc. Pubs.

Stottlemyre, Mel & Harper, John. Pride & Pinstripes: The Yankees, Mets, & Surviving Life's Challenges. 2008. (ENG.). 304p. pap. 13.95 (978-0-06-117409-4(2)) HarperCollins Pubs.

Strawberry, Darryl. Straw: Finding My Way. 2010. (ENG.). 256p. pap. 13.99 (978-0-06-170421-5(0), Ecco) HarperCollins Pubs.

Swearingen, Randall. A Great Teammate: The Legend of Mickey Mantle. 2007. (Illus.). 232p. per. 16.95 (978-1-59670-194-6(3)) Sports Publishing, LLC.

Swift, Tom. Chief Bender's Burden: The Silent Struggle of a Baseball Star. 2010. (ENG.). 352p. pap. 19.95 (978-0-8032-1498-9(7), Bison Bks.) Univ. of Nebraska Pr.

Thomson, Cindy & Brown, Scott. Three Finger: The Mordecai Brown Story. 2006. (ENG., Illus.). 264p. 26.95 (978-0-8032-4448-1(7)) Univ. of Nebraska Pr.

Thornton, AndrZcaron; & Janssen, Al. Triumph Born of Tragedy: The Story of Romance & Courage in the Life of AndrZcaron; Thornton: As Told to Al Janssen. 2011. 156p. pap. 18.00 (978-1-60899-408-3(2), Resource Pubns.) Wipf & Stock Pubs.

Tipre, Vincent. The Tennis Baseball League. 148p. 2011. pap. 12.95 **(978-1-4575-0346-7(8))** 2008. 26.95 (978-1-59858-676-3(9)) Dog Ear Publishing, LLC.

Torre, Joe & Verducci, Tom. The Yankee Years. (ENG., Illus.). 2010. 528p. pap. 16.95 (978-0-7679-3042-0(8), Anchor) 2009. 512p. 26.95 (978-0-385-52740-8(3), Doubleday) Knopf Doubleday Publishing Group.

—The Yankee Years. l.t. ed. 2009. (ENG.). 768p. pap. 26.95 (978-0-7393-2832-3(8)) Random Hse. Large Print.

Travers, Steven. The Last Icon: Tom Seaver & His Times. 2011. (ENG., Illus.). 312p. 24.95 (978-1-58979-660-7(8)); **(978-1-58979-661-4(6))** Taylor Trade Publishing.

Trimble, Delphine. Baseball Caps & Soda Pop Cans. 2011. pap. 8.99 **(978-1-61777-663-2(7))** Tate Publishing & Enterprises, LLC.

Trocchia, Scott. The 2006 Yankees: The Frustration of a Nation, A Fan's Perspective. 2009. 80p. pap. 10.95 (978-1-4401-7857-3(7)) iUniverse, Inc.

Veeck, Bill. The Hustler's Handbook. 2009. (ENG.). 352p. (J). (gr. -1-12). pap. 15.95 (978-1-56663-827-2(5)) Dee, Ivan R. Pub.

Verducci, Tom & Torre, Joe. Mis Años con los Yankees. Baranda, Martha, tr. from ENG. 2010. (SPA.). 592p. pap. 16.95 (978-0-307-47667-8(7), Vintage) Knopf Doubleday Publishing Group.

Vincent, Fay. The Last Commissioner: A Baseball Valentine. 2007. (ENG., Illus.). 336p. pap. 22.95 (978-1-4165-7801-7(3)) Simon & Schuster.

Volkmer, Jon. Roberto Clemente: The Story of a Champion. 2008. 135p. pap. (978-1-59194-103-3(2)) Townsend Pr. - Sunday Schl. Publishing Board.

Wakefield, Tim. Knuckler: My Life with Baseball's Most Confounding Pitch. (ENG., Illus.). 2012. 304p. pap. 14.95 **(978-0-547-75034-7(X)**, Mariner Bks.) 2011. 288p. 26.00 (978-0-547-51769-8(6)) Houghton Mifflin Harcourt Trade & Reference Pubs.

Waldo, Ronald T. Fred Clarke: A Biography of the Baseball Hall of Fame Player-Manager. 2010. (ENG., Illus.). 252p. pap. 29.95 (978-0-7864-5933-9(6)) McFarland & Co., Inc. Pubs.

Waldo, Ronald T. Hazen Kiki Cuyler: A Baseball Biography. 2012. (ENG.). pap. 29.95 **(978-0-7864-6885-0(8))** McFarland & Co., Inc. Pubs.

Weber, Bruce. As They See 'Em: A Fan's Travels in the Land of Umpires. 2010. (ENG.). 368p. pap. 16.00 (978-0-7432-9413-3(0), Scribner) Scribner.

Wee, K. P. No Runs, No Wins, No Glory: A Look Back at Tom Candiotti's Frustrating 1993 Season. 2009. 77p. pap. 16.50 (978-1-4357-4297-0(4)) Lulu Enterprises Inc.

—1991: the Red Sox, Baseball, & Hockey Memories. 2008. 139p. pap. 18.95 (978-1-4357-1375-8(3)) Lulu Enterprises Inc.

Weiss, Bill. The 100 Greatest Minor League Baseball Teams. 2006. (ENG.). 528p. per. 21.95 (978-1-59800-268-3(6)) Outskirts Pr., Inc.

Weiss, Stuart L. The Curt Flood Story: The Man Behind the Myth. 2007. (Sports & American Culture Ser.). (ENG., Illus.). 272p. (gr. 9). 34.95 (978-0-8262-1740-0(0)) Univ. of Missouri Pr.

Wheelock, Sean D. Buck O'Neil: A Baseball Legend. Date not set. pap. 10.95 (978-0-8488-1688-9(9)) Amereon LTD.

White, Bill. Uppity: My Untold Story about the Games People Play. 2012. (ENG., Illus.). 320p. pap. 15.99 **(978-0-446-55526-5(6))** Grand Central Publishing.

White, Roy & Berger, Darrell. "Then Roy Said to Mickey..." The Best Yankees Stories Ever Told. 2009. (Best Sports Stories Ever Told Ser.). (ENG.). 224p. 22.95 (978-1-60078-091-2(1)) Triumph Bks.

Whiting, Robert. The Meaning of Ichiro: The New Wave from Japan & the Transformation of Our National Pastime. 2006. (Illus.). 318p. reprint ed. 26.00 (978-1-4223-5632-6(9)) DIANE Publishing Co.

Wieren, Pete Van & Wilkinson, Jack. Of Mikes & Men: A Lifetime of Braves Baseball. 2010. (ENG.). 224p. 24.95 (978-1-60078-359-3(7)) Triumph Bks.

Wilker, Josh. Cardboard Gods. 2011. (ENG.). 243p. pap. 15.95 (978-1-61620-069-5(3), 1616200693) Algonquin Bks. of Chapel Hill.

—Cardboard Gods: An All-American Tale Told Through Baseball Cards. 2010. (ENG.). 208p. 24.95 (978-1-934734-16-2(0)) Seven Footer Pr.

Williams, Billy & Mitchell, Fred. Billy Williams: My Sweet-Swinging Lifetime with the Cubs. 2008. (ENG., Illus.). 256p. 24.95 (978-1-60078-050-9(4)) Triumph Bks.

Williams, Douglas. Always a Yankee. 2009. 202p. pap. 15.95 (978-0-7414-5762-2(8)) Infinity Publishing.

Williams, Mitch & Berger, Darrell. Straight Talk from Wild Thing. 2010. (ENG.). 208p. 19.95 (978-1-60078-306-7(6)) Triumph Bks.

Wilson, Doug. Fred Hutchinson & the 1964 Cincinnati Reds. 2010. (ENG., Illus.). 226p. pap. 29.95 (978-0-7864-5942-1(5)) McFarland & Co., Inc. Pubs.

Wolfe, R. Ron Santo: A Perfect 10. 2011. 264p. 24.95 **(978-0-9846278-2-0(0))** Lone Wolfe Pr.

Woods, Bob. Yankee Greats. 2012. (Illus.). 224p. 19.95 **(978-1-4197-0272-3(6))** Stewart, Tabori & Chang.

Wynn, Jimmy & McCurdy, Bill. Toy Cannon: The Autobiography of Baseball's Jimmy Wynn. 2010. (ENG., Illus.). 236p. pap. 29.95 (978-0-7864-5856-1(9)) McFarland & Co., Inc. Pubs.

Zemial, Gus, et al. Ozark Ike: Memories of Fence Buster Gus Zernial. 2007. 218p. 25.00 (978-0-9779841-6-9(8)) Pepperpot Prodns, Inc.

Zimbalist, Andrew. In the Best Interests of Baseball: The Revolutionary Reign of Bud Selig. 2007. (ENG., Illus.). 272p. per. 14.95 (978-0-470-12824-4(0), Wiley) Wiley, John & Sons, Inc.

Zminda, Don, et al, eds. Go-Go to Glory: The 1959 Chicago White Sox. 2009. (Illus.). 247p. pap. 19.95 (978-0-87946-386-1(4)) ACTA Pubns.

BASEBALL—CLUBS

see Baseball Teams

BASEBALL—COACHING

Acosta, Yolanda & Schweighardt, Joan. Acosta. 2010. (ENG., Illus.). 360p. pap. 22.95 (978-1-84694-333-1(7)) O Bks.,John Hunt.

American Baseball Coaches Association Staff. Practice Perfect Baseball. Bob, Bennett, ed. 2009. (Illus.). 256p. pap. 19.95 (978-0-7360-8713-1(3)) Human Kinetics Pubs.

American Sport Education Program Staff. Coaching Youth Baseball. 4th rev. ed. 2007. (ENG., Illus.). 192p. per. 16.95 (978-0-7360-6526-9(1)) Human Kinetics Pubs.

Arbogast, Gary. Baseball for Coaches: Techniques, Drills & Plans for Children & Young Adolescents. 2006. (Illus.). 85p. per. 13.95 (978-0-89641-432-7(9)) American Pr.

Barksdale, Xan. Catching-101: The Complete Guide for Baseball Catchers. 2011. 164p. 36.99 **(978-1-4634-3960-6(1))**; pap. 27.99 **(978-1-4634-3961-3(X))** AuthorHouse.

Bennett, Bob. Catching Fundamentals & Techniques. 2nd ed. 2007. (Coaches Choice Ser.). (Illus.). 111p. pap. 24.95 (978-1-58518-054-7(8)) Coaches Choice.

—Playing Like Champions: A Baseball Coach's Guide. 2011. (Illus.). 166p. (978-1-60679-125-7(7)) Coaches Choice.

—101 Pitching Drills (Second Edition) 2010. pap. 19.95 (978-1-60679-127-1(3)) Coaches Choice.

Brainard, Doug. Threw These Eyes. 2010. 48p. pap. 9.99 (978-1-60860-507-1(8), Eloquent Bks.) AEG Literary Publishing Services, Inc.

Caillault, Jean-Pierre, compiled by. The Complete New York Clipper Baseball Biographies: More Than 800 Sketches of Players, Managers, Owners, Umpires, Reporters & Others, 1859-1903, 2 vols. 2009. (ENG., Illus.). 758p. pap. 59.95 (978-0-7864-3373-5(6)) McFarland & Co., Inc. Pubs.

Carroll, Beverly, et al. How to Coach Youth Baseball: A Step-by-Step Appproach to Teaching Basic Skills. 2007. (ENG., Illus.). 160p. pap. 14.95 (978-1-59921-051-3(7), Lyons Pr.) Globe Pequot Pr., The.

Conradi, Candace. Diamond Moms: A Mother's Guide to Raising a Baseball Player. 2006. (Coaches Choice Ser.). (Illus.). 183p. per. 19.95 (978-1-58518-948-9(0)) Coaches Choice.

Curran, Mike & Newhan, Ross. Coaching Baseball Successfully. 2007. (ENG., Illus.). 208p. per. 19.95 (978-0-7360-6520-7(2)) Human Kinetics Pubs.

Czerwinski, Kevin T. Coaching Youth Baseball: Tips on Building a Winning Team. 2010. (Knack: Make It Easy Ser.). (ENG., Illus.). 256p. pap. 19.95 (978-1-59921-863-2(1), Knack) Globe Pequot Pr., The.

Duke, L. H. Billy & the Boys: The Shellman Wildcasts' run to the 1956 Georgia Class C High School Baseball Championship. 2009. 340p. pap. 17.95 (978-1-60594-258-2(8), Llumina Pr.) Aeon Publishing Inc.

Farney, Steven Michael. It's Time to Play! Jack Gardner, Basketball & Kansas State University. 2007. (Illus.). 140p. 24.95 (978-1-58597-435-1(8)) Leathers Publishing.

Garrido, Augie. Life Is Yours to Win: Lessons Forged from the Purpose, Passion, & Magic of Baseball. (ENG.). 272p. 2012. pap. 15.00 (978-1-4391-8694-7(4)) 2011. 23.00 (978-1-4391-8693-0(6)) Touchstone. (Touchstone).

Gildner, Gary. Warsaw Sparks: A Memoir. 2008. (ENG., Illus.). 256p. pap. 15.95 (978-0-8032-1756-0(0), Bison Bks.) Univ. of Nebraska Pr.

House, Tom. Fastball Fitness: The Art & Science of Training to Throw with Real Velocity. 2007. (Illus.). 142p. per. 19.95 (978-1-58518-037-0(8)) Coaches Choice.

Illiano, Scott. Our Time: A High School Baseball Coach's Journey. 2011. 288p. 30.95 (978-1-4620-2757-6(1)); pap. 20.95 **(978-1-4620-2756-9(3))** iUniverse, Inc.

Keller, Daniel. Coaching the Beginning Pitcher: How to Teach Pitching Safely & Effectively. 2009. 275p. pap. (978-0-9818895-2-8(2)) Lifeletics.

—Survival Guide for Coaching Youth Baseball. 2011. (Illus.). 176p. pap. 15.95 (978-0-7360-8773-5(7)) Human Kinetics Pubs.

Lewis, Michael. Coach: Lessons on the Game of Life. 2008. (ENG., Illus.). 96p. pap. 11.95 (978-0-393-33113-4(X), 33113) Norton, W. W. & Co., Inc.

Long, Kevin & Waggoner, Glen. Cage Rat: Lessons from a Life in Baseball by the Yankees Hitting Coach. 2012. (ENG.). 288p. pap. 15.99 **(978-0-06-199501-9(0),** Ecco) HarperCollins Pubs.

McIntosh, Ned. Little Leagues Drills & Strategies: Imaginative Practice Drills to Improve Skills & Attitude. 3rd ed. 2008. (ENG., Illus.). 192p. per. 14.95 (978-0-07-154801-4(7), 0071548017) McGraw-Hill Cos., The.

—Managing Little League Baseball. 3rd ed. 2008. (ENG., Illus.). 192p. per. 14.95 (978-0-07-154803-8(3), 0071548033) McGraw-Hill Cos., The.

Merritt, Roy B. The Perfect Game. 2008. 108p. pap. 14.95 (978-1-4357-0945-4(4)) Lulu Enterprises Inc.

Mongero, Trent. Winning Baseball for Beginner to Intermediate Play. 2011. (Coach's Companion Ser.). (ENG., Illus.). 256p. 19.95 (978-1-4027-5809-9(1)) Sterling Publishing Co., Inc.

National Alliance for Youth Sports Staff. Coaching Baseball for Dummies. 2007. (ENG., Illus.). 384p. per. 19.99 (978-0-470-08960-6(1), For Dummies) Wiley, John & Sons, Inc.

O'Connell, Tom. Play Ball: 100 Baseball Practice Games. 2009. (ENG., Illus.). 240p. pap. 18.95 (978-0-7360-8157-3(7)) Human Kinetics Pubs.

Ourvan, Jeff. How to Coach Youth Baseball So Every Kid Wins. 2012. (ENG., Illus.). 176p. pap. 14.95 **(978-1-61608-357-1(3),** 608357) Skyhorse Publishing Co., Inc.

Perconte, Jack. The Making of a Hitter: A Proven & Practical Step-by-Step Baseball Guide. 2009. (ENG.). 200p. pap. 19.95 (978-0-9793562-1-6(0)) Second Base Publishing.

Ripken, Cal, Jr., et al. Coaching Youth Baseball the Ripken Way. 2006. (ENG., Illus.). 264p. pap. 16.95 (978-0-7360-6782-9(5)) Human Kinetics Pubs.

Scala, Dom. One on One Baseball: The Fundamentals of the Game & How to Keep It Simple for Easy Instruction. 2009. (ENG., Illus.). 176p. pap. 16.95 (978-0-07-148843-3(X), 007148843X) McGraw-Hill Cos., The.

Solivan, Ernest. Mastering the Mental Side of Hitting. 2007. 104p. pap. 29.95 (978-0-615-17358-0(6)) Aries International (U.B.T.O.).

Stuper, John. 100 Things Every Baseball Coach Should Know: Helpful Tips Garnered from a lifetime in Baseball. 2009. 68p. pap. 9.95 (978-1-4401-3540-8(1)) iUniverse, Inc.

Swope, Bob. Youth Baseball & Softball Drills, Plays, & Situations Handbook. 2007. (Illus.). 108p. (J). per. 16.95 (978-0-9772817-8-7(7)) Jacobob Pr., LLC.

The National Alliance for Youth Sports. Coaching Basketball for Dummies. 2007. (ENG., Illus.). 384p. per. 19.99 (978-0-470-14976-8(0), For Dummies) Wiley, John & Sons, Inc.

Thome, J. D. 10 Commandments of Baseball. Norris, Lawrence Michael, ed. 2009. pap. 20.00 (978-0-9819342-0-4(X)) Sporting Chance Press, Inc. .

W. McLauchlan, author James, Jr. SO, YOU WANT to COACH? A how to book for parents Essential information for coaching grade school Children. 2010. 136p. pap. 14.00 (978-0-557-52655-0(8)) Lulu Enterprises Inc.

Weinstein, Jerry & Alston, Tom. Baseball Coach's Survival Guide: Practical Techniques & Materials for Building an Effective Program & a Winning Team. 2006. (Illus.). 351p. reprint ed. pap. 33.00 (978-1-4223-5564-0(0)) DIANE Publishing Co.

Weintraub, Aaron. Coaches' Guide to Winning the Mental Game. 2009. (Illus.). 197p. pap. 24.95 incl. DVD (978-1-60679-060-1(9)) Coaches Choice.

BASEBALL—COLLECTIBLES

see also Baseball Cards

Albert, Mike. 10 Good Reasons Why Pete Rose Belongs in Baseball. 2011. 68p. pap. 19.95 **(978-1-4626-4101-7(6))** PublishAmerica, Inc.

Fleischer, Brian, ed. Beckett Almanac of Baseball Cards & Coll-#16. 2011. 1344p. pap. 44.95 (978-1-930692-96-1(X)) Beckett Media LLP.

Jamieson, Dave. Mint Condition: How Baseball Cards Became an American Obsession. 2011. (ENG., Illus.). 288p. pap. 15.95 (978-0-8021-4532-1(9), Grove Pr.) Grove/Atlantic, Inc.

Katz, Harry, et al. Baseball Americana: Treasures from the Library of Congress. 2011. (ENG., Illus.). 288p. pap. 21.99 (978-0-06-162546-6(9), Harper Paperbacks) HarperCollins Pubs.

—Baseball Americana: Treasures from the Library of Congress. 2009. (Illus.). 256p. 29.99 (978-0-06-162545-9(0)) Smithsonian Institution Pr.

O'Connell, T. S. & Canale, Larry. Mickey Mantle - Memories & Memorabilia. 2011. (ENG.). 224p. pap. 26.99 (978-1-4402-1543-8(X)) Krause Pubns.

Shannon, Mike. Baseball Books: A Collector's Guide. 2007. (ENG.). 257p. per. 29.95 (978-0-7864-3139-7(3)) McFarland & Co., Inc. Pubs.

Wong, Stephen. Smithsonian Baseball: Inside the World's Finest Private Collections. 2007. (ENG.). 296p. pap. 21.99 (978-0-06-112121-0(5), HarperPerennial) HarperCollins Pubs.

Zachofsky, Dan. Collecting Baseball Memorabilia: A Handbook. 2nd rev. ed. 2009. (ENG., Illus.). 212p. pap. 29.95 (978-0-7864-4166-2(6)) McFarland & Co., Inc. Pubs.

BASEBALL—DICTIONARIES

Blabac, Eric. Encyclopedia of Baseball Statistics: From A to ZR. 2010. 504p. pap. 41.95 (978-1-4502-6552-2(9)) iUniverse, Inc.

Dickson, Paul. The Dickson Baseball Dictionary. 3rd ed. (ENG., Illus.). 2011. 974p. pap. 24.95 (978-0-393-34008-2(2), 34008) 2009. 1008p. 49.95 (978-0-393-06681-4(9), 6681) Norton, W. W. & Co., Inc.

Freedman, Lew. African American Pioneers of Baseball: A Biographical Encyclopedia, 1 vol. 2007. (Illus.). 320p. 75.00 (978-0-313-33851-9(5), GR3851, Greenwood Pr.) Greenwood Publishing Group, Inc.

Friedrich, Marty. The Iron Men of Baseball: Major League Leaders in Consecutive Games Played, 1876-2005. 2006. (ENG., Illus.). 291p. per. 35.00 (978-0-7864-2431-3(1)) McFarland & Co., Inc. Pubs.

Kiser, Brett. Baseball's War Roster: A Biographical Dictionary of Major & Negro League Players Who Served, 1861 to the Present. 2012. (ENG.). 284p. pap. 55.00 **(978-0-7864-6679-5(0))** McFarland & Co., Inc. Pubs.

Skipper, John C. A Biographical Dictionary of Major League Baseball Managers. alt. ed. 2011. (ENG., Illus.). 380p. pap. 45.00 (978-0-7864-4703-9(6)) McFarland & Co., Inc. Pubs.

BASEBALL—ECONOMIC ASPECTS

Bradbury, J. C. The Baseball Economist: The Real Game Exposed. 2008. (ENG., Illus.). 352p. (gr. 12-18). 16.00 (978-0-452-28902-4(5), Plume) Penguin Group (USA) Inc.

Bradbury, J. C. Hot Stove Economics: Understanding Baseball's Second Season. 2011. (Illus.). xx, 260p. E-Book **(978-1-4419-6269-0(7),** Copernicus) Springer.

Gennaro, Vince. Diamond Dollars: The Economics of Winning in Baseball. 2007. (Illus.). 250p. 24.95 (978-0-9777436-3-6(2)) Maple Street Press LLC.

Gould, William B. Bargaining with Baseball: Labor Relations in an Age of Prosperous Turmoil. 2011. (ENG., Illus.). 326p. pap. 39.95 (978-0-7864-6515-6(8)) McFarland & Co., Inc. Pubs.

Jozsa, Frank P. Major League Baseball Expansions & Relocations: A History, 1876-2008. 2010. (ENG., Illus.). 218p. pap. 39.95 (978-0-7864-4388-8(X)) McFarland & Co., Inc. Pubs.

Keri, Jonah. The Extra 2% How Wall Street Strategies Took a Major League Baseball Team from Worst to First. 2011. (ENG., Illus.). 272p. 26.00 (978-0-345-51765-4(2)) ESPN Enterprises.

Klein, Alan M. Growing the Game: The Globalization of Major League Baseball. 2008. (ENG.). 288p. per. 18.00 (978-0-300-13639-5(0)) Yale Univ. Pr.

Lewis, Michael. Moneyball: The Art of Winning an Unfair Game. movie tie-in ed. 2011. (Movie Tie-in Editions Ser.). (ENG.). 317p. pap. 15.95 (978-0-393-33839-3(8), 33839) Norton, W. W. & Co., Inc.

Lewis, Robert F. Smart Ball: Marketing the Myth & Managing the Reality of Major League Baseball. 2011. (ENG.). 176p. pap. 30.00 **(978-1-61703-208-0(5))** Univ. Pr. of Mississippi.

Lewis, Robert F., 2nd. Smart Ball: Marketing the Myth & Managing the Reality of Major League Baseball. 2009. (ENG.). 176p. 50.00 (978-1-60473-207-8(5)) Univ. Pr. of Mississippi.

Lowenfish, Lee. The Imperfect Diamond: A History of Baseball's Labor Wars. rev. ed. 2010. (ENG., Illus.). 352p. pap. 18.95 (978-0-8032-3360-7(4), Bison Bks.) Univ. of Nebraska Pr.

Medcalfe, Simon. Incentives in Baseball. 2008. 64p. pap. (978-3-639-00447-2(7)) VDM Verlag Dr. Mueller e.K.

Surdam, David George. The Ball Game Biz: An Introduction to the Economics of Professional Team Sports. 2010. (ENG., Illus.). 204p. pap. 29.95 (978-0-7864-6057-1(1)) McFarland & Co., Inc. Pubs.

—Wins, Losses, & Empty Seats: How Baseball Outlasted the Great Depression. 2011. (ENG., Illus.). 448p. 45.00 (978-0-8032-3482-6(1)) Univ. of Nebraska Pr.

Zimbalist, Andrew. Baseball & Billions. abr. ed. 15.95 incl. audio (978-1-56703-024-2(6)) High-Top Publishing.

BASEBALL—FANS

see Baseball Fans

BASEBALL—FICTION

see Baseball Stories

BASEBALL—HISTORY

Abrams, Roger I. The Dark Side of the Diamond: Gambling, Violence, Drugs & Alcoholism in the National Pastime. 2008. (ENG., Illus.). 208p. 24.95 (978-1-57940-156-6(2)) Rounder Bks.

Achorn, Edward. Fifty-Nine in '84: Old Hoss Radbourn, Barehanded Baseball, & the Greatest Season a Pitcher Ever Had. 2011. 400p. pap. 15.99 (978-0-06-182587-3(5), Harper Paperbacks) HarperCollins Pubs.

—Fifty-Nine in '84: Old Hoss Radbourn, Barehanded Baseball, & the Greatest Season a Pitcher Ever Had. 2010. 384p. 25.99 (978-0-06-182586-6(7)) Smithsonian Institution Pr.

Acocella, Nick. All-Stars All-Star Baseball Book. 24.95 (978-0-8488-1571-4(8)) Amereon LTD.

Adams, Timothy E. Still Not Forgiven. 2009. 196p. pap. 16.95 (978-1-4401-5770-7(7)) iUniverse, Inc.

Ahrens, Art. Chicago Cubs: Tinker to Evers to Chance. 2007. (Images of Baseball Ser.). (ENG., Illus.). 128p. per. 19.99 (978-0-7385-5130-2(9)) Arcadia Publishing.

Aiello, Thomas. The Kings of Casino Park: Black Baseball in the Lost Season of 1932. 2011. (ENG., Illus.). 264p. 39.95 (978-0-8173-1742-3(2)) Univ. of Alabama Pr.

Akin, William E. West Virginia Baseball: A History, 1865-2000. 2006. (ENG., Illus.). 239p. per. 29.95 (978-0-7864-2570-9(9)) McFarland & Co., Inc. Pubs.

Alexander, Charles C. Turbulent Seasons: Baseball In 1890-1891. 2011. (Sport in American Life Ser.). (Illus.). 272p. 24.95 (978-0-87074-572-0(7)) Southern Methodist Univ. Pr.

Allen, Lee. Hot Stove League. 24.95 (978-0-8488-1494-6(0)) Amereon LTD.

Allen, Maury. Yankees World Series Memories. 2008. (Illus.). 175p. 19.95 (978-1-59670-228-8(1)) Sports Publishing, LLC.

Anderson, Michael. Baseball & Its Greatest Players. 2011. lib. bdg. 31.70 (978-1-61530-510-0(6)) Rosen Publishing Group, Inc., The.

Anderson, Wayne. The Chicago Black Sox Trial: A Primary Source Account. 2009. (Great Trials of the Twentieth Century Ser.). 64p. (gr. 5-8). 58.50 (978-1-61513-213-3(9)) Rosen Publishing Group, Inc., The.

Andrews, Tom & Wolfe, Rich. For Milwaukee Brewers Fans Only! 2011. (ENG., Illus.). 256p. 24.95 (978-0-9846278-0-6(4)) Clerisy Pr.

Antos, Jason D. Shea Stadium. 2007. (Images of Sports Ser.). (Illus.). 127p. per. 19.99 (978-0-7385-5456-3(1)) Arcadia Publishing.

Arcidiacono, David. Major League Baseball in Gilded Age Connecticut: The Rise & Fall of the Middletown, New Haven & Hartford Clubs. 2009. (ENG., Illus.). 268p. pap. 35.00 (978-0-7864-3677-4(8)) McFarland & Co., Inc. Pubs.

Aronoff, Jason. Going, Going ... Caught! Baseball's Great Outfield Catches as Described by Those Who Saw Them, 1887-1964. 2009. (ENG., Illus.). 276p. pap. 39.95 (978-0-7864-4113-6(5)) McFarland & Co., Inc. Pubs.

Asinof, Eliot. Eight Men Out. 29.95 (978-0-8488-1567-7(X)) Amereon LTD.

Balderrama, Francisco E. & Santillan, Richard A. Mexican American Baseball in Los Angeles. 2011. (Images of Baseball Ser.). (Illus.). 128p. pap. 21.99 (978-0-7385-8180-4(1)) Arcadia Publishing.

Ballard, Chris. One Shot at Forever: A Small Town, an Unlikely Coach, & a Magical Baseball Season. 2012. (ENG.). 272p. 24.99 **(978-1-4013-2438-4(X))** Hyperion Pr.

Ballew, Bill. A History of Professional Baseball in Asheville. 2007. (Illus.). 126p. pap., per. 19.99 (978-1-59629-176-8(1)) History Pr., The.

Baltov, Jr. Baseball Is Americ: A Child of Baseball. 2009. 516p. 30.99 (978-1-4490-2839-8(X)); pap. 20.95 (978-1-4490-2838-1(1)) AuthorHouse.

Baltov, Victor Alexander. Baseball Is America: Origins & History: the Good, the Bad, & the Ugly. 2010. 412p. 28.95 (978-1-4520-0485-3(4)); pap. 19.95 (978-1-4520-0486-0(2)) AuthorHouse.

Barber. 1947: When All Hell Broke Loose. 31.95 (978-0-8488-1564-6(5)) Amereon LTD.

Barber-Starkey, Joe & Johnson, James W. Double No-Hit: Johnny Vander Meer's Historic Night under the Lights. 2012. (ENG., Illus.). 216p. pap. 15.95 **(978-0-8032-7139-5(5))** Univ. of Nebraska Pr.

Barra, Allen. Brushbacks & Knockdowns: The Greatest Baseball Debates of Two Centuries. Date not set. mass mkt. (978-0-312-99389-4(7), St. Martin's Paperbacks) St. Martin's Pr.

—Clearing the Bases: The Greatest Baseball Debates of the Last Century. 2008. (ENG., Illus.). 288p. pap. 16.95 (978-0-8032-1763-8(3), Bison Bks.) Univ. of Nebraska Pr.

Barry, Dan. Bottom of the 33rd: Hope, Redemption, & Baseball's Longest Game. (ENG., 2012. Illus.). 288p. pap. 14.99 (978-0-06-201449-8(8), HarperPerennial) 2011. 288p. 26.99 (978-0-06-201448-1(X)) 2011. 432p. pap. 26.99 (978-0-06-206503-2(3), HarperLuxe) HarperCollins Pubs.

Barthel, Thomas. Baseball Barnstorming & Exhibition Games, 1901-1962: A History of off-Season Major League Play. 2007. (ENG., Illus.). 283p. per. 29.95 (978-0-7864-2811-3(2)) McFarland & Co., Inc. Pubs.

Bartolick, John. Rise & Fall. 2009. 282p. pap. 24.98 (978-0-578-01632-0(X)) Bartolick, John.

Beach, Jerry. Fighting Words: The Media, the Red Sox & How Boston Finally Won It All. 2009. (ENG.). 280p. 24.95 (978-1-57940-121-4(X)) Rounder Bks.

Bedingfield, Gary. Baseball's Dead of World War II: A Roster of Professional Players Who Died in Service. 2009. (ENG., Illus.). 272p. pap. 39.95 (978-0-7864-4454-0(1)) McFarland & Co., Inc. Pubs.

Benson, John. Baseball Wisdom: What the Game Teaches Us. 2006. lib. bdg. 17.95 (978-1-880876-60-2(4)) Diamond Library.

Berney, Louis. Game of My Life: Baltimore Orioles: Memorable Stories of Orioles Baseball. 2008. (Game of My Life Ser.). (Illus.). 256p. 24.95 (978-1-59670-272-1(9)) Sports Publishing, LLC.

Beverage, Richard. The Los Angeles Angels of the Pacific Coast League: A History, 1903-1957. 2011. (ENG.). 260p. pap. 40.00 **(978-0-7864-6520-0(4))** McFarland & Co., Inc. Pubs.

Bevis, Charlie. Doubleheaders: A Major League History. 2010. (ENG., Illus.). 238p. pap. 29.95 (978-0-7864-4214-0(X)) McFarland & Co., Inc. Pubs.

Bielawa, Michael & Bielawa, Janice. Baseball in Baton Rouge. 2007. (Images of Baseball Ser.). (ENG., Illus.). 128p. per. 19.99 (978-0-7385-4223-2(7)) Arcadia Publishing.

Billheimer, John. Baseball & the Blame Game: Scapegoating in the Major Leagues. 2007. (ENG., Illus.). 228p. per. 35.00 (978-0-7864-2906-6(2)) McFarland & Co., Inc. Pubs.

Bjarkman, Peter C. A History of Cuban Baseball, 1864-2006. 2007. (ENG., Illus.). 496p. 49.95 (978-0-7864-2829-8(5)) McFarland & Co., Inc. Pubs.

Blue, Max. Philadelphia's Phillies: Baseball Thrills in Three Centuries. 2011. 372p. pap. 29.95 **(978-1-4560-2364-5(0))** PublishAmerica, Inc.

Boston, Talmage. Baseball & the Baby Boomer: A History, Commentary, & Memoir. 2009. (ENG., Illus.). 288p. 24.95 (978-1-933979-26-7(7)) Bright Sky Pr.

Bradley, Richard. The Greatest Game: The Day That Bucky, Yaz, Reggie, Pudge, & Company Played the Most Memorable Game in Baseball's Most Intense Rivalry. 2009. (ENG.). 304p. pap. 19.99 (978-1-4165-3439-6(3), Free Pr.) Free Pr.

Bresnahan, Jim, ed. Play It Again: Baseball Experts on What Might Have Been. 2006. (ENG., Illus.). 258p. per. 29.95 (978-0-7864-2546-4(6), McFarland & Co., Inc. Pubs.

Brown, Warren. The Chicago White Sox. 2007. (Writing Sports Ser.). (Illus.). 258p. per. 18.00 (978-0-87338-895-5(X)) Kent State Univ. Pr.

Bruns, Roger A. Negro Leagues Baseball, 1 vol. 2012. (Landmarks of the American Mosaic Ser.). 278p. 58.00 **(978-0-313-38648-0(X),** A3091C) Greenwood Publishing Group, Inc. The.

Bryant, Howard. The Last Hero: A Life of Henry Aaron. (ENG.). 2011. 640p. pap. 16.95 (978-0-307-27992-7(8), Anchor) 2010. (Illus.). 624p. 29.95 (978-0-375-42485-4(7), Pantheon) Knopf Doubleday Publishing Group.

Burke, Larry, et al. Change Up: An Oral History of 8 Key Events That Shaped Modern Baseball. 2008. (ENG., Illus.). 304p. 24.95 (978-1-59486-189-5(7)) Rodale Pr., Inc.

Burman, Howard. Gentlemen at the Bat: A Fictional Oral History of the New York Knickerbockers & the Early Days of Base Ball. 2010. (ENG.). 364p. pap. 25.00 (978-0-7864-4720-6(6)) McFarland & Co., Inc. Pubs.

Buscema, David. Game of My Life New York Yankees: 20 Stories of Yankees Baseball. 2008. (Game of My Life Ser.). (Illus.). 264p. per. 16.95 (978-1-59670-296-7(6)) Sports Publishing, LLC.

Butwin, Richard. Pinstripe Blues. 2007. 316p. 36.95 (978-1-4327-0936-5(4)); (ENG.). per. 23.95 (978-1-4327-1573-1(9)) Outskirts Pr., Inc.

Cantor, George. The Good, the Bad, & the Ugly: Detroit Tigers: Heart-Pounding, Jaw-Dropping, & Gut-Wrenching Moments from Detroit Tigers History. 2008. (Good, the Bad, & the Ugly Ser.). (ENG., Illus.). 192p. 19.95 (978-1-60078-052-3(0)) Triumph Bks.

Carroll, Brian. When to Stop the Cheering? The Black Press, the Black Community, & the Integration of Professional Baseball. 2009. 276p. 39.95 (978-0-415-80602-2(X)) Routledge.

Caruso, Gary. Marietta College Baseball: The Story of the 'Etta Express. 2012. 256p. pap. 21.99 **(978-1-60949-464-3(4))** History Pr., The.

Cash, Jon David. Before They Were Cardinals: Major League Baseball in Nineteenth-Century St. Louis. 2011. (SPORTS & AMERICAN CULTURE Ser.). (ENG., Illus.). 296p. (gr. 8). pap. 24.95 (978-0-8262-1935-0(7)) Univ. of Missouri Pr.

Cassuto, Leonard & Partridge, Stephen, eds. The Cambridge Companion to Baseball. 2011. (ENG., Illus.). 280p. 82.00 (978-0-521-76182-6(4)); pap. 24.99 (978-0-521-14575-6(9)) Cambridge Univ. Pr.

Castillo, Luis & Cane, William. Clubhouse Confidential: A Yankee Bat Boy's Insider Tale of Wild Nights, Gambling, & Good Times with Modern Baseball's Greatest Team. (ENG.). 2012. 320p. pap. 14.99 **(978-1-250-01748-2(3),** St. Martin's Griffin) 2011. (Illus.). 304p. 25.99 **(978-0-312-64542-7(2))** St. Martin's Pr.

Castle, George. Sweet Lou & the Cubs: A Year Inside the Dugout. 2009. (ENG., Illus.). 320p. pap. 16.95 (978-1-59921-526-6(8), Lyons Pr.) Globe Pequot Pr., The.

Center, Bill. Game of My Life: San Diego Padres: Memorable Stories of Padres Baseball. 2008. (Game of My Life Ser.). (Illus.). 256p. 24.95 (978-1-59670-274-5(5)) Sports Publishing, LLC.

Chafets, Zev. Cooperstown Confidential: Heroes, Rogues, & the Inside Story of the Baseball Hall of Fame. (ENG.). 256p. 2010. pap. 15.00 (978-1-60819-210-6(5)) 2009. (Illus.). 25.00 (978-1-59691-545-9(5)) Bloomsbury Publishing.

Chetwynd, Josh. Baseball in Europe: A Country by Country History. 2008. (ENG., Illus.). 344p. pap. 35.00 (978-0-7864-3724-5(3)) McFarland & Co., Inc. Pubs.

Chetwynd, Josh & Belton, Brian A. British Baseball & the West Ham Club: History of a 1930s Professional Team in East London. 2006. (ENG., Illus.). 272p. per. 29.95 (978-0-7864-2594-5(6)) McFarland & Co., Inc. Pubs.

Chuck, Bill & Kaplan, Jim. Walkoffs, Last Licks, & Final Outs: Baseball's Grand (and Not-So-Grand) Finales. 2007. (Illus.). 213p. pap. 14.95 (978-0-87946-342-7(2)) ACTA Pubns.

Cleaver, Kelly D. Sorry Kid, I Don't Much Feel Like Playing Today. 2011. 284p. 27.95 **(978-1-4620-1720-1(7))**; pap. 17.95 **(978-1-4620-1719-5(3))** iUniverse, Inc.

Coffin, Tristram Potter. The Mudville Heritage: Baseball in Folklore & Fiction. 2010. (ENG.). 188p. (gr. 6). pap. 15.00 (978-1-935073-09-3(5)) Creative Management Partners, LLC.

Cohen, Dan. Play Ball, Mr. President: A Century of Baseballs Signed by U. S. Presidents. 2008. (ENG.). 48p. pap. 19.99 (978-1-60194-020-9(3), Elevate) Advantage Media Group.

Cohen, Robert. Mvp. 2010. (ENG.). 400p. pap. 17.95 (978-1-58042-266-6(7)) Cardoza Publishing.

Cohen, Robert W. Baseball's Hall of Fame-or Hall of Shame? 2009. (ENG.). 400p. pap. 17.95 (978-1-58042-232-1(2)) Cardoza Publishing.

Cohen, Stanley. A Magic Summer: The Amazin' Story of the 1969 New York Mets. 40th ed. 2009. (ENG., Illus.). 320p. pap. 14.95 (978-1-60239-679-1(5), 239679) Skyhorse Publishing Co., Inc.

Colon-Delgado, Jorge. Santurce Cangrejeros 1954-1955: La maquinaria Perfecta. 2007. pap. (978-1-59608-304-2(2)) Biblio Services, Inc.

CONGDON, L. E. E. Baseball & Memory: Winning, Losing, & the Remembrance of Things Past. 2011. (Illus.). 192p. 25.00 (978-1-58731-063-8(5)) St. Augustine's Pr., Inc.

Craft, Jerry & Sullivan, Kathleen. Our White Boy. 2010. (Sport in the American West Ser.). (Illus.). 272p. 29.95 (978-0-89672-674-1(6)) Texas Tech Univ. Pr.

B

Crasnick, Jerry. Decades: 1950-1959. 2010. (Illus.). 160p. (978-1-58159-471-3(2)) North American Media Group.
—Decades: 2000-2009. 2009. (Illus.). 160p. (978-1-58159-437-9(2)) North American Media Group.
Crater, Paul. Baseball in Atlanta. 2007. (Images of Baseball Ser.). (ENG., Illus.). 128p. per. 21.99 (978-0-7385-4380-2(2)) Arcadia Publishing.
Crissey, Harrington E., Jr. Teenagers, Graybeards & 4-F's. Incl. Vol. 2. American League. (Illus.). 179p. 1982. pap. 11.00 (978-0-9608878-1-1(4)); pap. (978-0-9608878-2-8(2)) Crissey, Harrington E.
Crosby, Bonnie & D'Agostino, Dennis. Through a Blue Lens: The Brooklyn Dodger Photographs of Barney Stein, 1939-1957. 2007. (ENG., Illus.). 176p. 27.95 (978-1-57243-952-8(1)) Triumph Bks.
Dabscheck, Braham. Reading Baseball: Books, Biographies, & the Business of the Game. 2011. 238p. pap. 16.95 (978-1-935412-24-3(8)) Fitness Information Technology, Inc.
Darby, William. Deconstructing Major League Baseball, 1991-2004: How Statistics Illuminate Individual & Team Performances. 2006. (ENG., Illus.). 516p. per. 49.95 (978-0-7864-2537-2(7)) McFarland & Co., Inc. Pubs.
Darnell, Tim. The Crackers: Early Days of Atlanta Baseball. 2006. (Illus.). 224p. reprint ed. pap. 16.95 (978-1-58818-101-5(4)) Hill Street Pr., LLC.
Dater, Adrian. 100 Things Rockies Fans Should Know & Do Before They Die. 2009. (100 Things... Fans Should Know Ser.). (ENG.). 256p. pap. 14.95 (978-1-60078-161-2(6)) Triumph Bks.
De Quesada, A. M. Spring Training in Clearwater: A History of Major & Minor League Baseball in Clearwater, Florida. 2007. pap. 19.99 (978-1-59629-214-7(8)) History Pr., The.
Debono, Paul. The Indianapolis ABCs: History of a Premier Team in the Negro Leagues. alt. ed. 2007. (ENG., Illus.). 239p. per. 35.00 (978-0-7864-3092-5(3)) McFarland & Co., Inc. Pubs.
DeMarco, Tony. Tales from the Colorado Rockies. 2008. (Tales Ser.). (Illus.). 176p. 19.95 (978-1-59670-232-5(X)) Sports Publishing, LLC.
Desrochers, Dan, ed. The 1967 Impossible Dream Red Sox: Pandemonium on the Field. 2007. (ENG., Illus.). 340p. per. 19.95 (978-1-57940-141-2(4)) Rounder Bks.
Deveney, Sean. The Original Curse: Did the Cubs Throw the 1918 World Series to Babe Ruth's Red Sox & Incite the Black Sox Scandal? 2009. (ENG.). 256p. 24.95 (978-0-07-162997-3(1), 0071629971) McGraw-Hill Cos., The.
Diamond Dates. 2006. per. 16.95 (978-0-9789000-0-7(6)) G R Publishing.
Dierker, Larry. My Team: Choosing My Dream Team from My Forty Years in Baseball. 2007. (ENG., Illus.). 288p. pap. 13.00 (978-0-7432-7514-9(4)) Simon & Schuster.
Doutrich, Paul E. The Cardinals & the Yankees 1926: A Classic Season & St. Louis in Seven. 2010. (ENG., Illus.). 204p. pap. 29.95 (978-0-7864-4657-5(9)) McFarland & Co., Inc. Pubs.
Dragseth, P. J. Major League Baseball Scouts: A Biographical Dictionary. 2011. (ENG., Illus.). 335p. pap. 75.00 (978-0-7864-4360-4(X)) McFarland & Co., Inc. Pubs.
Durocher, Leo & Linn, Ed. Nice Guys Finish Last. 2009. (ENG., Illus.). 456p. pap. 18.00 (978-0-226-17388-7(7)) Univ. of Chicago Pr.
Ebling, Jack. Tales from the Detroit Tigers. 2007. (Illus.). 200p. 19.95 (978-1-59670-193-9(5)) Sports Publishing, LLC.
Egan, James M., Jr. Base Ball on the Western Reserve: The Early Game in Cleveland & Northeast Ohio, Year by Year & Town by Town, 1865-1900. 2008. (ENG., Illus.). 338p. pap. 29.95 (978-0-7864-3067-3(2)) McFarland & Co., Inc. Pubs.
Eig, Jonathan. Opening Day: The Story of Jackie Robinson's First Season. 2008. (ENG., Illus.). 336p. pap. 15.00 (978-0-7432-9461-4(0)) Simon & Schuster.
Elias, Robert. The Empire Strikes Out: How Baseball Sold U. S. Foreign Policy & Promoted the American Way Abroad. 2010. (ENG., Illus.). 448p. 27.95 (978-1-59558-195-2(2)) New Pr., The.
Encyclopaedia Britannica, Inc., compiled by. Take Me Out to the Ballgame. 2008. 49.95 (978-1-59339-622-0(8)) Encyclopaedia Britannica, Inc.
Enders, Eric. Baseball's Greatest Games: The Most Suspenseful, Exciting & Unforgettable Contests in Major League Baseball History. 2008. (Illus.). 160p. (978-1-58159-403-4(8)) North American Media Group.
Ephross, Peter & Abramowitz, Martin. Jewish Major Leaguers in Their Own Words: Oral Histories of 23 Players. 2012. (ENG.). 227p. pap. 35.00 (978-0-7864-6507-1(7)) McFarland & Co., Inc. Pubs.
Epstein, Dan. Big Hair & Plastic Grass: A Funky Ride Through Baseball & America in the Swinging '70s. 2010. (ENG., Illus.). 352p. 25.99 (978-0-312-60754-8(7), Dunne, Thomas Bks.) St. Martin's Pr.
Epting, Chris. Baseball in Orange County. 2012. (Images of America Ser.). (ENG., Illus.). 128p. pap. 21.99 (978-0-7385-9328-9(1)) Arcadia Publishing.
Epting, Chris & Hano, Arnold. The Early Polo Grounds. 2009. (Images of Sports Ser.). (ENG., Illus.). 128p. pap. 21.99 (978-0-7385-6287-2(4)) Arcadia Publishing.
Faber, Charles F. Major League Careers Cut Short: Leading Players Gone By 30. 2010. (ENG., Illus.). 298p. pap. 39.95 (978-0-7864-4743-5(5)) McFarland & Co., Inc. Pubs.
Faris, David. Baseball Homestand: the National Pastime: Experience the Excitement of Attending the 81 Home Games of A National League Baseball Team. 2011. 192p. 24.59 (978-1-4567-2376-7(6)); pap. 14.03 (978-1-4567-2381-1(2)) AuthorHouse.
—Understanding Baseball: An examination of the history, teams, economics & basic plays, & a review of the 2007 season, lead to a better Understand. 2008. 388p. 23.95 (978-1-4327-2706-2(0)); pap. 20.95 (978-1-4327-2630-0(7)) Outskirts Pr., Inc.
Farkas, Neil. My Time with the Catcher Spy, Morris Moe Berg. 2010. (ENG.). 112p. pap. 49.95 (978-0-557-72260-0(8)) Lulu Enterprises Inc.
Felber, Bill. A Game of Brawl: The Orioles, the Beaneaters, & the Battle for the 1897 Pennant. 2007. (ENG., Illus.). 320p. 24.95 (978-0-8032-1136-0(8)) Univ. of Nebraska Pr.
—Under Pallor, under Shadow: The 1920 American League Pennant Race That Rattled & Rebuilt Baseball. 2011. (ENG.). 304p. 26.95 (978-0-8032-3471-0(6)) Univ. of Nebraska Pr.
Feldmann, Doug. The 1976 Cincinnati Reds: Last Hurrah for the Big Red Machine. 2008. (ENG., Illus.). 276p. pap. 35.00 (978-0-7864-3854-9(1)) McFarland & Co., Inc. Pubs.
Fidler, Merrie A. The Origins & History of the All-American Girls Professional Baseball League. alt. ed. 2010. (ENG., Illus.). 400p. pap. 39.95 (978-0-7864-6089-2(X)) McFarland & Co., Inc. Pubs.
Figueredo, Jorge S. Who's Who in Cuban Baseball, 1878-1961. alt. ed. 2007. (ENG., Illus.). 422p. per. 55.00 (978-0-7864-3030-7(3)) McFarland & Co., Inc. Pubs.
Fink, Rob. Playing in Shadows: Texas & Negro League Baseball. 2010. (Sport in the American West Ser.). (ENG., Illus.). 224p. 29.95 (978-0-89672-701-4(7)) Texas Tech Univ. Pr.
Fitts, Robert K. Banzai Babe Ruth: Baseball, Espionage, & Assassination During the 1934 Tour of Japan. 2012. (ENG., Illus.). 340p. 34.95 (978-0-8032-2984-6(4)) Univ. of Nebraska Pr.
Fleder, Rob. Damn Yankees: Twenty-Four Major League Writers on the World's Most Loved (And Hated) Team. 2012. (ENG.). 320p. 27.99 (978-0-06-205962-8(9), Ecco) HarperCollins Pubs.
Fleitz, David L. The Irish in Baseball: An Early History. 2009. (ENG., Illus.). 200p. pap. 39.95 (978-0-7864-3419-0(8)) McFarland & Co., Inc. Pubs.
—Silver Bats & Automobiles: The Hotly Competitive, Sometimes Ignoble Pursuit of the Major League Batting Championship. 2011. (ENG., Illus.). 222p. pap. 29.95 (978-0-7864-5879-0(8)) McFarland & Co., Inc. Pubs.
Fornatale, Pete & Biegel, Brian. Miracle Ball: My Hunt for the Shot Heard 'Round the World. 2010. (ENG.). 256p. pap. 15.00 (978-0-307-45269-6(7), Three Rivers Pr.) Crown Publishing Group.
Fox, Bucky. The Orioles Fan's Little Book of Wisdom. 2008. (ENG.). 112p. pap. 7.95 (978-1-58979-346-0(3)) Taylor Trade Publishing.
Franks, Joel S. Asian Pacific Americans & Baseball: A History. 2008. (ENG., Illus.). 224p. pap. 29.95 (978-0-7864-3291-2(8)) McFarland & Co., Inc. Pubs.
Franks, Joel S. The Barnstorming Hawaiian Travelers: A Multiethnic Baseball Team Tours the Mainland, 1912-1916. 2012. (ENG.). 262p. pap. 29.95 (978-0-7864-6566-8(2)) McFarland & Co., Inc. Pubs.
Freedman, Lew. The Day All the Stars Came Out: Major League Baseball's First All-Star Game 1933. 2010. (ENG., Illus.). 231p. pap. 29.95 (978-0-7864-4708-4(7)) McFarland & Co., Inc. Pubs.
—Game of My Life: White Sox: Memorable Stories of Chicago White Sox Baseball. 2008. (Game of My Life Ser.). (Illus.). 221p. 24.95 (978-1-59670-291-2(5)) Sports Publishing, LLC.
—Going Yard: The Everything Home Run Book. 2011. (ENG.). 272p. pap. 16.95 (978-1-60078-535-1(2)) Triumph Bks.
—Hard-Luck Harvey Haddix & the Greatest Game Ever Lost. 2009. (ENG., Illus.). 218p. pap. 29.95 (978-0-7864-4124-2(0)) McFarland & Co., Inc. Pubs.
Freedman, Lew & Pierce, Billy. "Then Ozzie Said to Harold..." The Best Chicago White Sox Stories Ever Told. 2008. (Best Sports Stories Ever Told Ser.). (ENG., Illus.). 239p. 22.95 (978-1-60078-063-9(6)) Triumph Bks.
Friedrich, Marty. The Iron Men of Baseball: Major League Leaders in Consecutive Games Played, 1876-2005. 2006. (ENG., Illus.). 291p. per. 35.00 (978-0-7864-2431-3(1)) McFarland & Co., Inc. Pubs.
Frommer, Harvey. Yankee Century & Beyond. 2007. 464p. pap. 17.00 (978-1-4022-1002-0(7)) Sourcebooks, Inc.
Frost, Mark. Game Six: The Triumph of America's Pastime. 416p. 2010. (ENG.). pap. 15.99 (978-1-4013-1026-4(5)) 2009. 26.99 (978-1-4013-2310-3(3)) Hyperion Pr.
Fussman, Cal. After Jackie: Pride, Prejudice, & Baseball's Forgotten Heroes: an Oral History. 2007. (ENG., Illus.). 256p. 24.95 (978-1-933060-18-7(2), ESPN Bks.) ESPN Enterprises.
Galarraga, Armando, et al. Nobody's Perfect: Two Men, One Call, & a Game for Baseball History. 2011. (ENG., Illus.). 240p. 24.00 (978-0-8021-1988-9(3), Atlantic Monthly Pr.) Grove/Atlantic, Inc.
Gay, Timothy M. Satch, Dizzy, & Rapid Robert: The Wild Saga of Interracial Baseball Before Jackie Robinson. (ENG., Illus.). 368p. 2011. pap. 15.00 (978-1-4165-4799-0(1)) 2010. 26.00 (978-1-4165-4798-3(3)) Simon & Schuster.
Gedda, George. Dominican Connection: Talent from the Tropics Changes Face of National Pastime. 2009. 160p. pap. 12.95 (978-1-60693-023-6(0), Eloquent Bks.) AEG Literary Publishing Services, Inc.
Genovese, Daniel L. The Old Ball Ground: Volume 2: Town Teams & Bush Leaguers. 2007. 323p. pap. 17.95 (978-0-7414-3874-4(7)) Infinity Publishing.
Getz, Mike. The Giants Win the Series! Headlines & Highlights Of 1954. 2011. 268p. 25.00 (978-1-4567-2817-5(2)); pap. 15.00 (978-1-4567-2818-2(0)) AuthorHouse.
Giles, Bill. Pouring Six Beers at a Time: And Other Stories from a Lifetime in Baseball. 2007. (ENG., Illus.). 336p. 24.95 (978-1-57243-931-3(9)) Triumph Bks.
Giles, Bill & Myers, Doug. Pouring Six Beers at a Time. 2009. (ENG.). 386p. pap. 14.95 (978-1-60078-256-5(6)) Triumph Bks.
Gillette, Gary, et al. Big League Ballparks: The Complete Illustrated History. 2009. (ENG., Illus.). 512p. 29.98 (978-1-4351-1452-4(3)) Barnes & Noble, Inc.
Gisclair, S. Derby. Baseball at Tulane University. 2007. (Images of Baseball Ser.). (ENG., Illus.). 128p. per. 19.99 (978-0-7385-4208-9(3)) Arcadia Publishing.
Godfrey, Buck. The Team Nobody Would Play. 2008. 84p. pap. 12.99 (978-0-8059-7764-6(3)) Dorrance Publishing Co., Inc.
Goldblatt, Andrew. Major League Umpires' Performance, 2007-2010: A Comprehensive Statistical Review. 2011. (ENG., Illus.). 206p. pap. 39.95 (978-0-7864-6058-8(X)) McFarland & Co., Inc. Pubs.
Goldman, Steven, et al. It Ain't over 'Til It's Over: The Baseball Prospectus Pennant Race Book. (ENG., Illus.). 480p. (gr. 9). 2008. per. 15.95 (978-0-465-00285-6(4)) 2007. 25.95 (978-0-465-00284-9(6)) Basic Bks.
Goldstein, Warren. Playing for Keeps: A History of Early Baseball. 20th rev. ed. 2009. 200p. pap. 18.95 (978-0-8014-7508-5(2)) Cornell Univ. Pr.
Gonzales, Mark. The Good, the Bad, & the Ugly: Chicago White Sox - Heart Pounding, Jaw Dropping, & Gut-Wrenching Moments from Chicago White Sox Hist. 2009. (Good, the Bad, & the Ugly Ser.). (ENG.). 224p. pap. 14.95 (978-1-60078-203-9(5)) Triumph Bks.
Goode, Chris. California Baseball: from the Pioneers to the Glory Years. 2009. 390p. pap. 20.00 (978-0-557-08760-0(0)) Lulu Enterprises Inc.
Goodman, Michael E. The Story of the Cincinnati Reds. 2007. (Baseball, the Great American Game Ser.). (Illus.). 48p. (YA). (gr. 4-7). lib. bdg. 32.80 (978-1-58341-484-2(3)) Creative Co., The.
Gordon, Bob. Game of My Life: Philadelphia Phillies: Memorable Stories of Phillies Baseball. 2008. (Game of My Life Ser.). (Illus.). 223p. 24.95 (978-1-59670-257-8(5)) Sports Publishing, LLC.
Graf, Gary. And God Said, Tee It Up! Amusing & Thought-Provoking Parallels Between the Bible & Golf. 2009. (Illus.). 206p. pap. 14.95 (978-0-87946-385-4(6)) ACTA Pubns.
Gramling, Chad. Baseball in Fort Wayne. 2007. (Images of Baseball Ser.). (ENG., Illus.). 128p. per. 19.99 (978-0-7385-4129-7(X)) Arcadia Publishing.
Green, Ron, Jr. 101 Reasons to Love the Yankees: And 10 Reasons to Hate the Red Sox. rev. ed. 2008. (ENG., Illus.). 120p. 15.95 (978-1-58479-715-9(0)) Stewart, Tabori & Chang.
Guest, Christopher. The Philadelphia Phillies: An Extraordinary Tradition. Gummer, Scott, ed. 2010. (ENG., Illus.). 244p. 50.00 (978-1-933784-86-1(5), Insight Editions) Palace Publishing Group, LP.
Gutlon, Jerry M. It Was Never about the Babe: The Red Sox, Racism, Mismanagement, & the Curse of the Bambino. 2009. (ENG., Illus.). 336p. 24.95 (978-1-60239-349-3(4), 239349) Skyhorse Publishing Co., Inc.
Gutman, Bill. What If the Babe Had Kept His Red Sox? And Other Fascinating Alternate Histories from the World of Sports. 2008. 290p. pap. 14.95 (978-1-60239-629-6(9)) Skyhorse Publishing Co., Inc.
Hample, Zack. The Baseball: Stunts, Scandals, & Secrets Beneath the Stitches. 2011. (Vintage Ser.). (Illus.). 368p. pap. 14.95 (978-0-307-47545-9(X), Vintage) Knopf Doubleday Publishing Group.
Hancock, Ryne. Candy Bars & Fly Balls. 2008. 194p. pap. 24.95 (978-1-4241-7882-7(7)) PublishAmerica, Inc.
Hanley, John & DeLuca, Chris. Classic Cubs: A Tribute to the Men & Magic of Wrigley Field. 2008. (ENG., Illus.). 186p. 24.95 (978-1-58182-637-1(0)) Turner Publishing Co.
Harris, Rick. Brown University Baseball: A Legacy of the Game. 2012. 160p. pap. 19.99 (978-1-60949-501-5(2)) History Pr., The.
Harris, Rick. Rhode Island Baseball: The Early Years. 2008. pap. 19.99 (978-1-59629-496-7(5)) History Pr., The.
Harrison, Don. Connecticut Baseball: The Best of the Nutmeg State. 2008. pap. 19.99 (978-1-59629-552-0(X)) History Pr., The.
Heaphy, Leslie A. & May, Mel Anthony, eds. Encyclopedia of Women & Baseball. 2006. (Women's Studies). (ENG., Illus.). 448p. 75.00 (978-0-7864-2100-8(2)) McFarland & Co., Inc. Pubs.
Helpingstine, Daniel. The Cubs & the White Sox: A Baseball Rivalry, 1900 to the Present. 2010. (ENG., Illus.). 267p. pap. 29.95 (978-0-7864-4669-8(2)) McFarland & Co., Inc. Pubs.
Herron, Gary. Baseball in Albuquerque. 2011. (Images of Baseball Ser.). (Illus.). 128p. pap. 21.99 (978-0-7385-7964-1(5)) Arcadia Publishing.
Hinrichs, Kit & Hirasuna, Delphine. 100 Baseball Icons: From the National Baseball Hall of Fame & Museum Archive. 2008. (ENG., Illus.). 112p. 19.95 (978-1-58008-916-6(X)) Ten Speed Pr.
Hise, Beth. Swinging Away: How Cricket & Baseball Connect. 2010. (ENG., Illus.). 192p. pap. 35.00 (978-1-85759-644-1(7)) Scala, Editions FRA. Dist: National Bk. Network.
Hogan, Kenneth. Batting 10th for the Yankees: Recollections of 30 Yankees You May Not Remember. 2010. (Illus.). 296p. pap. 24.99 (978-1-4490-7188-2(0)) AuthorHouse.
Hogan, Lawrence D., et al. Shades of Glory: The Negro Leagues & the Story of African-American Baseball. 2007. (ENG., Illus.). 448p. per. 15.95 (978-1-4262-0033-5(1), National Geographic) National Geographic Society.
Housel, David. Glory Days Auburn: The Greatest Victories in Tigers History. 2008. (Illus.). 192p. 14.95 (978-1-59670-212-7(5)) Sports Publishing, LLC.
Hrbek, Kent. Kent Hrbek's Tales from the Minnesota Twins Dugout. 2008. (Tales Ser.). (Illus.). 185p. pap. 15.95 (978-1-59670-293-6(1)) Sports Publishing, LLC.
Hummel, Rick. Commish & the Cardinals: The Most Memorable Games, As Covered by Hall of Famer Rick Hummel for the St. Louis Post-Dispatch. Smith, Mike, ed. 2007. 224p. per. 21.95 (978-0-9661397-9-2(8)) St. Louis Post-Dispatch.
Humphreys, Michael A. Wizardry: Baseball's All-Time Greatest Fielders Revealed, 1 vol. 2011. (ENG., Illus.). 432p. pap. 19.95 (978-0-19-539776-5(2)) Oxford Univ. Pr., Inc.
Irvin, Monte & Pepe, Phil. Few & Chosen: Defining Negro Leagues Greatness. 2007. (Few & Chosen Ser.). (ENG., Illus.). 240p. 25.95 (978-1-57243-855-2(X)) Triumph Bks.
Istorico, Ray. Greatness in Waiting: An Illustrated History of the Early New York Yankees, 1903-1919. 2008. (ENG., Illus.). 240p. 55.00 (978-0-7864-3211-0(X)) McFarland & Co., Inc. Pubs.
Jacobson, Steve. Carrying Jackie's Torch: The Players Who Integrated Baseball - And America. 2007. (ENG., Illus.). 288p. 24.95 (978-1-55652-639-8(3), Hill, Lawrence Bks.) Chicago Review Pr., Inc.
Jacover, Jerry. Merkle's Curse: Why the Chicago Cubs Have Not Won a World Series Since 1908. 2008. 386p. pap. 19.99 (978-1-60462-935-4(5)) Tate Publishing & Enterprises, LLC.
Jenkinson, Bill. The Year Babe Ruth Hit 104 Home Runs: Recrowning Baseball's Greatest Slugger. 2007. (ENG., Illus.). 432p. per. 16.95 (978-0-7867-1906-8(0)) Da Capo Pr., Inc.
Jennison, Christopher & Jurinko, Andy. Golden Boys: Baseball Portraits, 1946-1960. 2012. (ENG., Illus.). 288p. 50.00 (978-1-61608-450-9(2), 608450) Skyhorse Publishing Co., Inc.
Jewell, Anne. Baseball in Louisville. 2006. (Images of Baseball Ser.). (ENG., Illus.). 128p. per. 21.99 (978-0-7385-4241-6(5)) Arcadia Publishing.
Johanson, Matt. San Francisco Giants. 2007. (Game of My Life Ser.). (Illus.). 229p. 24.95 (978-1-59670-177-9(3)) Sports Publishing, LLC.
Johnson, Richard. Field of Our Fathers: An Illustrated History of Fenway Park, 1912-2012. 2011. (ENG.). 320p. 35.00 (978-1-60078-423-1(2)) Triumph Bks.
Jozsa, Frank P. Major League Baseball Expansions & Relocations: A History, 1876-2008. 2010. (ENG., Illus.). 218p. pap. 39.95 (978-0-7864-4388-8(X)) McFarland & Co., Inc, Pubs.
Kahn, Roger. The Boys of Summer. 2011. 14.42 (978-0-7848-3571-5(3), Everbind) Marco Bk. Co.
Kashatus, William C. Almost a Dynasty: The Rise & Fall of the 1980 Phillies. 2008. (Illus.). 392p. 37.50 (978-0-8122-4036-8(7)) Univ. of Pennsylvania Pr.
Katz, Harry, et al. Baseball Americana: Treasures from the Library of Congress. 2011. (ENG., Illus.). 288p. pap. 21.99 (978-0-06-162546-6(9), Harper Paperbacks) HarperCollins Pubs.
—Baseball Americana: Treasures from the Library of Congress. 2009. (Illus.). 256p. 29.99 (978-0-06-162545-9(0)) Smithsonian Institution Pr.
Katz, Jeff. The Kansas City A's & the Wrong Half of the Yankees: How the Yankees Controlled Two of the Eight American League Franchises During the 1950's. 2007. (Illus.). 250p. 24.95 (978-0-9777436-5-0(9)) Maple Street Press LLC.
Kernan, Kevin. Amazing! Celebrating the Mets' Miracle 2006 Season. 2006. (ENG., Illus.). 127p. per. 14.95 (978-1-57243-966-5(1)) Triumph Bks.
King, David & Pickard, Chuck. Lone Stars of the Diamond: A Guide to Texans in Major League Baseball Since 1895. 2007. (Illus.). 390p. per. 24.95 (978-1-931823-44-9(8)) Halcyon Pr., Ltd.
Kirsch, George B. Baseball & Cricket: The Creation of American Team Sports, 1838-72. 2007. (Sport & Society Ser.). (Illus.). 304p. per. 26.00 (978-0-252-07445-5(9)) Univ. of Illinois Pr.
—Baseball in Blue & Gray: The National Pastime During the Civil War. 2007. (ENG., Illus.). 168p. per. 17.95 (978-0-691-13043-9(4)) Princeton Univ. Pr.
Klein, Clayton. A Well-Kept Secret: From the Glory Years of the Detroit Tigers. 2007. (Illus.). 104p. 25.00 (978-0-923568-81-8(6)) Wilderness Adventure Bks.
Klima, John. Willie's Boys: The 1948 Birmingham Black Barons, the Last Negro League World Series, & the Making of a Baseball Legend. 2009. (ENG., Illus.). 320p. 25.95 (978-0-470-40013-5(7), Wiley) Wiley, John & Sons, Inc.
Knight, Jonathan. Classic Tribe: The 50 Greatest Games in Cleveland Indians History. 2009. (Illus.). 248p. pap. (978-1-60635-017-1(X)) Kent State Univ. Pr.
Kreidler, Mark. Six Good Innings: How One Small Town Became a Little League Giant. 2008. 256p. 24.95 (978-0-06-147357-9(X)) HarperCollins Pubs.
Kreis, James. 1954 — A Baseball Season. 2011. 672p. 40.91 (978-1-4520-1857-7(X)); pap. 29.04 (978-1-4520-1856-0(1)) AuthorHouse.
Kurlansky, Mark. The Eastern Stars: How Baseball Changed the Dominican Town of San Pedro de Macoris. 2011. (ENG.). 352p. (gr. 12). 16.00 (978-1-59448-505-3(4), Riverhead Trade (Paperbacks)) Penguin Group (USA) Inc.
Kyle, Donald G. & Fairbanks, Robert B., eds. Baseball in America & America in Baseball. 2008. (Walter Prescott Webb Memorial Lectures). (ENG., Illus.). 252p. 29.95 (978-1-60344-023-3(2)) Texas A&M Univ. Pr.
Lamster, Mark. Spalding's World Tour: The Epic Adventure That Took Baseball Around the Globe - And Made It America's Game. 2007. (ENG., Illus.). 320p. per. 14.95 (978-1-58648-433-0(8)) PublicAffairs.
Lanctot, Neil. Negro League Baseball: The Rise & Ruin of a Black Institution. 2008. (Illus.). 512p. (C). pap. 24.95 (978-0-8122-2027-8(7)) Univ. of Pennsylvania Pr.
Lantos, James & Lantos, Jim, eds. Boston Baseball. 2009. (ENG., Illus.). 56p. pap. 9.95 (978-1-4290-9704-8(3)) Applewood Bks.
Leach, Matthew. Game of My Life: St. Louis Cardinals: Memorable Stories of Cardinals Baseball. 2008. (Game of My Life Ser.). (Illus.). 206p. 24.95 (978-1-59670-273-8(7)) Sports Publishing, LLC.
Leach, Matthew. Game of My Life St. Louis Cardinals: Memorable Stories of Cardinals Baseball. 2011. (Game of My Life Ser.). (ENG., Illus.). 224p. 19.95 (978-1-61321-072-7(8), 613072) Skyhorse Publishing Co., Inc.

Lebovitz, Hal. Ask Hal: Answers to Fans' Most Interesting Questions about Baseball Rules, from a Hall-of-Fame Sportswriter. 2007. (Illus.). 181p. per. 14.95 *(978-1-59851-034-8(7))* Gray and Company, Publishers.
Lester, Larry. Baseball's First Colored World Series: The 1924 Meeting of the Hilldale Giants & Kansas City Monarchs. 2006. (ENG., Illus.). 261p. 45.00 *(978-0-7864-2617-1(9))* McFarland & Co., Inc. Pubs.
Leventhal, Josh. Baseball Yesterday & Today. rev. ed. 2006. (ENG., Illus.). 144p. 24.95 *(978-0-7603-2646-6(0),* 0760326460, Voyageur Pr) MBI Publishing Co. LLC.
Levitt, Daniel R. The Battle That Forged Modern Baseball: The Federal League Challenge & Its Legacy. 2012. ***(978-1-56663-905-7(0))***; (ENG., Illus.). 336p. 39.95 ***(978-1-56663-869-2(0))*** Dee, Ivan R. Pub.
Lieb, Fred & Baumgartner, Stan. The Philadelphia Phillies. 2009. 260p. pap. *(978-1-60635-012-6(9))* Kent State Univ. Pr.
Lilliefors, Jim. Ball Cap Nation: A Journey Through the World of America's National Hat. 2009. (ENG., Illus.). 256p. pap. 15.95 *(978-1-57860-340-4(4))* Clerisy Pr.
Longest, A. Knoefel. Standing Room Only. 2009. (ENG.). 373p. pap. 9.99 *(978-0-9823672-0-9(1))* Bartlett Park.
Louisa, Angelo J. & Cotello, David, eds. Mysteries from Baseball's Past: Investigations of Nine Unsettled Questions. 2010. (ENG., Illus.). 205p. pap. 29.95 *(978-0-7864-4554-7(8))* McFarland & Co., Inc. Pubs.
Lowenfish, Lee. The Imperfect Diamond: A History of Baseball's Labor Wars. rev. ed. 2010. (ENG., Illus.). 352p. pap. 18.95 *(978-0-8032-3360-7(4),* Bison Bks.) Univ. of Nebraska Pr.
Lowry, Philip J. Baseball's Longest Games: A Comprehensive Worldwide Record Book. 2010. (ENG., Illus.). 370p. pap. 35.00 *(978-0-7864-4263-8(8))* McFarland & Co., Inc. Pubs.
Luke, Robert A. The Baltimore Elite Giants: Sport & Society in the Age of Negro League Baseball. 2009. (ENG., Illus.). 208p. 30.95 *(978-0-8018-9116-8(7))* Johns Hopkins Univ. Pr.
Lupton, Webster. A Place to Play. 2007. 384p. pap. 15.95 *(978-1-886057-07-4(9))* Warren Publishing, Inc.
Lynch, Michael T., Jr. Harry Frazee, Ban Johnson & the Feud That Nearly Destroyed the American League. 2008. (ENG., Illus.). 282p. pap. 29.95 *(978-0-7864-3330-8(2))* McFarland & Co., Inc. Pubs.
Macht, Norman L. & Macht, Norman. Connie Mack & the Early Years of Baseball. 2007. (ENG., Illus.). 742p. 39.95 *(978-0-8032-3263-1(2))* Univ. of Nebraska Pr.
Machuca, Mel & Shepherd, Will. An Inning at a Time: An American Legion Baseball National Championship Story. 2011. 218p. pap. 16.95 *(978-1-59299-553-0(5))* Inkwater Pr.
Mack, Bob. Bird Hunting in Brooklyn: Ebbets Field, the Dodgers & the 1949 National League Pennant Race. 2008. 479p. pap. 23.95 *(978-1-4357-1190-7(4))* Lulu Enterprises Inc.
Madden, W. C. & Stewart, Patrick J. The College World Series: A Baseball History, 1947-2003. alt. ed. 2011. (ENG., Illus.). 316p. pap. 39.95 *(978-0-7864-6103-5(9))* McFarland & Co., Inc. Pubs.
Magee, David & Shirley, Philip. Sweet Spot: 125 Years of Baseball & the Louisville Slugger. 2009. (ENG.). 176p. 27.95 *(978-1-60078-175-6(4))* Triumph Bks.
Markusen, Bruce. The Team That Changed Baseball: Roberto Clemente & the 1971 Pittsburgh Pirates. 2009. (ENG., Illus.). 240p. pap. 14.95 *(978-1-59416-089-9(9))* Westholme Publishing.
Maroon, Thomas, et al. Akron-Canton Baseball Heritage. 2007. (Images of Baseball Ser.). (ENG., Illus.). 128p. per. 19.99 *(978-0-7385-5113-5(9))* Arcadia Publishing.
Martin, Alfred M. & Martin, Alfred T. The Negro Leagues in New Jersey: A History. 2008. (ENG., Illus.). 280p. pap. 35.00 *(978-0-7864-3900-3(9))* McFarland & Co., Inc. Pubs.
Martin, Jay. Live All You Can: Alexander Joy Cartwright & the Invention of Modern Baseball. 2009. (ENG., Illus.). 168p. (gr. 17). 22.95 *(978-0-231-14794-1(5))* Columbia Univ. Pr.
Martini, Stephen. The Chattanooga Lookouts & 100 Seasons of Scenic City Baseball. 2010. 284p. pap. 17.00 *(978-0-557-27927-2(5))* Lulu Enterprises Inc.
Martino, Andy, et al. The Mets. 50th anniv. ed. 2011. (ENG., Illus.). 320p. 40.00 *(978-1-58479-914-6(5))* Stewart, Tabori & Chang.
Martirano, Ron. Baseball: The Players, the World Series, the Records. 2008. (ENG., Illus.). 238p. pap. 12.95 *(978-1-60433-011-3(2))* Cider Mill Pr. Bk. Pubs., LLC.
Marzano, Rudy. New York Baseball in 1951: The Dodgers, the Giants, the Yankees & the Telescope. 2011. (ENG., Illus.). 208p. pap. 29.95 *(978-0-7864-4830-2(X))* McFarland & Co., Inc. Pubs.
Matthews, George R. When the Cubs Won It All: The 1908 Championship Season. 2009. (ENG., Illus.). 234p. pap. 29.95 *(978-0-7864-3495-4(3))* McFarland & Co., Inc. Pubs.
Maulhardt, Jeffrey Wayne. Baseball in Ventura County. 2007. (Images of Baseball Ser.). (ENG., Illus.). 128p. per. 19.99 *(978-0-7385-4739-8(5))* Arcadia Publishing.
McCabe, Neal & McCabe, Constance. Baseball's Golden Age: The Photographs of Charles M. Conlon. 2011. (ENG., Illus.). 198p. 35.00 ***(978-1-4197-0197-9(5))*** Abrams.
McCollough, Christopher Jon. Media Framing of the Steroids Scandal in Major League Baseball - Negative Framing, the Fallen Hero, & Emerging Frames in Coverage. 2008. 88p. pap. *(978-3-639-01345-0(X))* VDM Verlag Dr. Mueller e.K.
McConnell, John. Cooperstown by the Numbers: An Analysis of Baseball Hall of Fame Elections. 2010. (ENG., Illus.). 252p. pap. 29.95 *(978-0-7864-4737-4(0))* McFarland & Co., Inc. Pubs.
McGee, Ryan. The Road to Omaha: Hits, Hopes, & History at the College World Series. 2010. (ENG., Illus.). 336p. pap. 15.99 *(978-0-312-62802-4(1),* St. Martin's Griffin) St. Martin's Pr.
McGuiggan, Amy Whorf. Take Me Out to the Ball Game: The Story of the Sensational Baseball Song. 2009. (ENG., Illus.). 160p. 24.95 *(978-0-8032-1891-8(5))* Univ. of Nebraska Pr.
McKelvey, G. Richard. Mexican Raiders in the Major Leagues: The Pasquel Brothers vs. Organized Baseball 1946. 2006. (ENG., Illus.). 211p. per. 29.95 *(978-0-7864-2563-1(6))* McFarland & Co., Inc. Pubs.
McKenna, Brian. Baseball History Research 101. 2010. 93p. pap. 16.97 *(978-0-557-49475-0(3))* Lulu Enterprises Inc.
—Early Exits: The Premature Endings of Baseball Careers. 2006. (ENG.). 304p. per. 50.00 *(978-0-8108-5858-9(4))* Scarecrow Pr., Inc.
McNeil, William F. All-Stars for All Time: A Sabermetric Ranking of the Major League Best, 1876-2007. 2008. (ENG., Illus.). 243p. pap. 39.95 *(978-0-7864-3500-5(3))* McFarland & Co., Inc. Pubs.
—Black Baseball Out of Season: Pay for Play Outside of the Negro Leagues. alt. ed. 2012. (ENG., Illus.). 244p. pap. 25.00 ***(978-0-7864-6924-6(2))*** McFarland & Co., Inc. Pubs.
McNeil, William F. The California Winter League: America's First Integrated Professional Baseball League. alt. ed. 2008. (ENG.). 335p. pap. 29.95 *(978-0-7864-3881-5(9))* McFarland & Co., Inc. Pubs.
Mead, William B. Even the Browns: Baseball During World War II. 2010. (Dover Baseball Ser.). (ENG.). 272p. pap. 12.95 *(978-0-486-47462-5(3))* Dover Pubns., Inc.
Mendell, Brooks C. Beaverball: A (Winning) Season with the M. I. T. Baseball Team. 2009. 206p. pap. 13.95 *(978-1-59330-586-4(9))* Aventine Pr.
Mills, Dorothy Seymour. Chasing Baseball: Our Obsession with Its History, Numbers, People & Places. 2010. (ENG., Illus.). 266p. pap. 39.95 *(978-0-7864-4289-8(1))* McFarland & Co., Inc. Pubs.
MLB Publishing. The Treasures of Major League Baseball. 2010. (ENG., Illus.). 64p. 35.00 *(978-1-84442-323-1(9))* Carlton Bks., Ltd. GBR. Dist: Sterling Publishing Co., Inc.
Moffi, Larry. This Side of Cooperstown: An Oral History of Major League Baseball in The 1950s. 2010. (Dover Baseball Ser.). (ENG.). 288p. pap. 12.95 *(978-0-486-47273-7(6))* Dover Pubns., Inc.
Morales, Bill. Farewell to the Last Golden Era: The Yankees, the Pirates & the 1960 Baseball Season. 2011. (ENG., Illus.). 230p. pap. 29.95 *(978-0-7864-6327-5(9))* McFarland & Co., Inc. Pubs.
Morris, Peter. But Didn't We Have Fun? An Informal History of Baseball's Pioneer Era, 1843-1870. 2008. (ENG., Illus.). 304p. 27.50 *(978-1-56663-748-0(1))* Dee, Ivan R. Pub.
—Catcher: How the Man Behind the Plate Became an American Folk Hero. 2010. (ENG.). 400p. pap. 18.95 *(978-1-56663-870-8(4))* Dee, Ivan R. Pub.
—A Game of Inches: The Stories Behind the Innovations That Shaped Baseball: the Game Behind the Scenes. 2006. (ENG.). 416p. 28.95 *(978-1-56663-705-3(8))* Dee, Ivan R. Pub.
—Level Playing Fields: How the Groundskeeping Murphy Brothers Shaped Baseball. 2007. (ENG., Illus.). 216p. 24.95 *(978-0-8032-1110-0(4))* Univ. of Nebraska Pr.
Motley, Bob. Ruling over Monarchs, Giants & Stars: Umpiring in the Negro Leagues & Beyond. 2007. (Illus.). 217p. per. 16.95 *(978-1-59670-236-3(2))* Sports Publishing, LLC.
Motley, Bob, et al. Ruling over Monarchs, Giants, & Stars: True Tales of Breaking Barriers, Umpiring Baseball Legends, & Wild Adventures in the Negro Leagues. 2012. (ENG., Illus.). 240p. 24.95 ***(978-1-61321-059-8(0),*** 613059) Skyhorse Publishing Co., Inc.
Mullen, Maureen. Yogi Was up with a Guy on Third... Hall of Famers Recall Their Favorite Baseball Games Ever. 2009. (ENG.). 272p. 19.95 *(978-1-60078-162-9(4))* Triumph Bks.
Murphy, Cait N. Crazy '08: How a Cast of Cranks, Rogues, Boneheads, & Magnates Created the Greatest Year in Baseball History. 2008. (ENG., Illus.). 400p. pap. 14.95 *(978-0-06-088938-8(1),* HarperPerennial) HarperCollins Pubs.
—Crazy '08: How a Cast of Cranks, Rogues, Boneheads, & Magnates Created the Greatest Year in Baseball History. 2007. (Illus.). 384p. 24.95 *(978-0-06-088937-1(3))* Smithsonian Institution Pr.
Murphy, R. Scott. Ducks on the Pond. 2011. 162p. 36.50 ***(978-1-257-09518-6(8))***; pap. 19.50 ***(978-1-257-09519-3(6))*** Lulu Enterprises Inc.
Museum of the City of New York Staff. The Glory Days: New York Baseball 1947-1957. Thorn, John, ed. 2007. (ENG., Illus.). 224p. 34.95 *(978-0-06-134404-6(4))* HarperCollins Pubs.
—The Glory Days: New York Baseball, 1947-1957. 2008. (ENG.). 224p. pap. 19.95 *(978-0-06-134405-3(2),* HarperPerennial) HarperCollins Pubs.
Nagel, Kyle. Game of My Life Cincinnati Reds: Memorable Stories of Reds Baseball. 2008. (Game of My Life Ser.). (Illus.). 256p. 24.95 *(978-1-59670-329-2(6))* Sports Publishing, LLC.
Naiman, Joe. The School with All the Catchers. 2012. pap. 19.95 ***(978-0-7414-6850-5(6))*** Infinity Publishing.
Nathanson, Mitchell. A People's History of Baseball. 2012. xiv, 275p. E-Book ***(978-0-252-09392-0(5))***; (ENG., Illus.). 272p. 29.95 ***(978-0-252-03680-4(8))*** Univ. of Illinois Pr.
Nemec, David, ed. Major League Baseball Profiles, 1871-1900, 2-volume Set, 2 vols. 2011. (ENG., Illus.). 1264p. pap. 69.95 ***(978-0-8032-3533-5(X),*** Bison Bks.) Univ. of Nebraska Pr.
—Major League Baseball Profiles, 1871-1900, Volume 1: The Ballplayers Who Built the Game, 2 vols. 2011. (ENG., Illus.). 688p. pap. 39.95 *(978-0-8032-3024-8(9),* Bison Bks.) Univ. of Nebraska Pr.
—Major League Baseball Profiles, 1871-1900, Volume 2: The Hall of Famers & Memorable Personalities Who Shaped the Game, 2 vols. 2011. (ENG., Illus.). 576p. pap. 39.95 *(978-0-8032-3532-8(1),* Bison Bks.) Univ. of Nebraska Pr.
Nemec, David & Flatow, Scott. Great Baseball Feats, Facts, & Firsts. 2010th ed. 2010. (ENG.). 464p. (gr. 12-18). 7.99 *(978-0-451-22955-7(X),* Signet) Penguin Group (USA) Inc.
—This Day in Baseball: A Day-By-Day Record of the Events That Shaped the Game. 2008. (ENG.). 336p. pap. 15.95 *(978-1-58979-380-4(3))* Taylor Trade Publishing.
Nemec, David & Zeman, Dave. The Baseball Rookies Encyclopedia. 2006. 386p. reprint ed. pap. 25.00 *(978-1-4223-5288-5(9))* DIANE Publishing Co.
Nemec, David, et al. The Baseball Chronicle: Year-by-Year History of Major League Baseball. 2007. (Illus.). 704p. 24.98 *(978-1-4127-1590-4(3))* Publications International, Ltd.
—Great Baseball Feats, Facts & Firsts 2011. 2011. (ENG.). 480p. (gr. 12). 7.99 *(978-0-451-23296-0(8),* Signet) Penguin Group (USA) Inc.
New York Post Staff & Triumph Books Staff. The Amazins: Celebrating 50 Years of New York Mets History. 2011. (ENG.). 176p. pap. 24.95 ***(978-1-60078-611-2(1))*** Triumph Bks.
Nipper, Skip. Baseball in Nashville. 2007. (Images of Baseball Ser.). (ENG., Illus.). 128p. per. 21.99 *(978-0-7385-4391-8(8))* Arcadia Publishing.
Nordell, John, Jr. Brooklyn Dodgers: The Last Great Pennant Drive 1957. 2nd ed. 2007. (Illus.). 120p. per. 14.95 *(978-0-9795045-4-9(6))* Tribute Bks.
Nowlin, Bill. Lefty, Double-X, & the Kid: The 1939 Red Sox, a Team in Transition. 2009. (ENG.). 210p. pap. 18.95 *(978-1-57940-162-7(7))* Rounder Bks.
—Red Sox Threads: Odds & Ends from Red Sox History. 2008. (ENG.). 600p. pap. 18.95 *(978-1-57940-157-3(0))* Rounder Bks.
—Spahn, Sain, & Teddy Ballgame: Boston's (almost) Perfect Baseball Summer Of 1948. 2008. (ENG.). 24p. pap. 19.95 *(978-1-57940-160-3(0))* Rounder Bks.
Nowlin, Bill, et al, eds. When Boston Still Had the Babe: The 1918 World Series Champion Red Sox. 2008. (ENG., Illus.). 288p. pap. 18.95 *(978-1-57940-159-7(7))* Rounder Bks.
Nowlin, Bill & Prime, Jim. Amazing Tales from the Boston Red Sox Dugout: A Collection of the Greatest Red Sox Stories Ever Told. 2012. (Tales from the Team Ser.). (ENG., Illus.). 320p. 24.95 ***(978-1-61321-023-9(X)*** 613023) Skyhorse Publishing Co., Inc.
Nucciarone, Monica. Alexander Cartwright: The Life Behind the Baseball Legend. 2009. (ENG., Illus.). 326p. 27.95 *(978-0-8032-3353-9(1))* Univ. of Nebraska Pr.
Nurse, Ammie L. Baseball's All-Star Game Reference Guide 1933-2007: 78 Games in 74 Years. 2007. 500p. per. 43.95 *(978-1-58736-740-3(8))* Wheatmark.
Ogden, W. Russell. The Freedom Book: Choosing Your Future. 2011. 332p. pap. 22.95 ***(978-1-4497-2165-7(6),*** WestBow Pr.) Author Solutions, Inc.
Oliphant, Tom. The Greatest Moment. mass mkt. *(978-0-312-99116-6(9),* St. Martin's Paperbacks) St. Martin's Pr.
Olney, Buster. The Last Night of the Yankee Dynasty: The Game, the Team, & the Cost of Greatness. 2008. (ENG.). 432p. pap. 14.99 *(978-0-06-167287-3(4),* HarperPerennial) HarperCollins Pubs.
On The Pine Publishing. Everybody on, Nobody Out: Hope & possibility in the New YOrk Collegiate Baseball League. 2010. 12.95 *(978-0-615-37532-8(4))* On the Pine Publishing.
Oser, Khyber, et al. Cardboard Gems: A Century of Baseball Cards & Their Stories, 1869-1969. 2008. (ENG., Illus.). 192p. 35.00 *(978-0-9716097-2-3(1),* Mastro Auctions (Acc)) Antique Collectors' Club GBR. Dist: National Bk. Network.
Pahigian, Josh. 101 Baseball Places to See Before You Strike Out. 2010. (ENG.). 240p. pap. 18.95 *(978-1-59921-884-7(4),* Lyons Pr.) Globe Pequot Pr., The.
Pajot, Dennis. The Rise of Milwaukee Baseball: The Cream City from Midwestern Outpost to the Major Leagues, 1859-1901. 2009. (ENG., Illus.). 362p. pap. 45.00 *(978-0-7864-3951-5(3))* McFarland & Co., Inc. Pubs.
Patten, William & McSpadden, J. Walker. The Book of Baseball 1911: Our National Pastime from Its Earliest Days. 2010. (Dover Baseball Ser.). (ENG., Illus.). 160p. 30.00 *(978-0-486-47957-6(9))* Dover Pubns., Inc.
Paxton, Harry T. The Whiz Kids: The Story of the Fightin' Phillies. 2011. 182p. 42.95 ***(978-1-258-05793-0(X))*** Literary Licensing, LLC.
Payne, Robert B. Let There Be Light: A History of Night Baseball 1880-2008. 2010. 196p. pap. 51.98 *(978-1-4490-5359-8(9))* AuthorHouse.
Pederson, Charles E. Jackie Robinson: Baseball Great & Civil Rights Activist. 2009. (Essential Lives Set 3 Ser.). (Illus.). 112p. (YA). (gr. 7-12). 34.22 *(978-1-60453-526-6(1))* ABDO Publishing Co.
Pepe, Phil. The Ballad of Billy & George: The Tempestuous Baseball Marriage of Billy Martin & George Steinbrenner. 2008. (ENG., Illus.). 272p. 24.95 *(978-1-59921-282-1(X),* Lyons Pr.) Globe Pequot Pr., The.
—1961: The Inside Story of the Maris-Mantle Home Run Chase. 2011. (ENG.). 288p. 20.00 *(978-1-60078-390-6(2))* Triumph Bks.
Pepe, Phil & Staub, Rusty. Few & Chosen Mets: Defining Mets Greatness Across the Eras. 2009. (Few & Chosen Ser.). (ENG.). 208p. 24.95 *(978-1-60078-153-7(5))* Triumph Bks.
Peraza, Marino Martinez. Por Amor a la Pelota: Historia del Beisbol Cubano. 2008. (Coleccion Cuba y Sus Jueces Ser.). 434p. pap. 35.00 *(978-1-59388-152-8(5))* Ediciones Universal.
Peterson, Armand & Tomashek, Tom. Town Ball: The Glory Days of Minnesota Amateur Baseball. 2006. (Illus.). 400p. 39.95 *(978-0-8166-4675-3(9))* Univ. of Minnesota Pr.
Peterson, Richard, ed. The St. Louis Baseball Reader. 2006. (Sports & American Culture Ser.). (ENG., Illus.). 456p. (gr. 9). 34.95 *(978-0-8262-1687-8(0))* Univ. of Missouri Pr.
Peterson, Robert. Only the Ball was White. 25.95 *(978-0-8488-1124-2(0))* Amereon LTD.
—Only the Ball Was White: A History of Legendary Black Players & All-Black Professional Teams. 2008. (ENG.). 406p. pap. 19.00 *(978-1-4379-6451-6(6))* DIANE Publishing Co.
Peterson, Todd. Early Black Baseball in Minnesota: The St. Paul Gophers, Minneapolis Keystones & Other Barnstorming Teams of the Deadball Era. 2010. (ENG., Illus.). 313p. pap. 39.95 *(978-0-7864-3816-7(9))* McFarland & Co., Inc. Pubs.
Petrocelli, Rico & Scoggins, Charles. Rico Petrocelli's Tales from the Impossible Dream. 2008. (Tales Ser.). (Illus.). 192p. per. 15.95 *(978-1-59670-292-9(3))* Sports Publishing, LLC.
Pieratt, Marty Ford. First Black Red: The Story of Chuck Harmon, the First African American to Play for the Cincinnati Reds. 2010. 208p. (ENG.). 24.99 *(978-1-4520-1995-6(9))*; pap. 18.00 *(978-1-4520-1994-9(0))* AuthorHouse.
Posnanski, Joe. The Machine: A Hot Team, a Legendary Season, & a Heart-Stopping. 2010. (ENG.). 336p. pap. 14.99 *(978-0-06-158255-4(7),* William Morrow Paperbacks) HarperCollins Pubs.
—The Machine: A Hot Team, a Legendary Season, & a Heart-Stopping World Series - The Story of the 1975 Cincinnati Reds. 2009. (ENG.). 320p. 25.99 *(978-0-06-158256-1(5),* Morrow, William & Co.) HarperCollins Pubs.
Potter, Steve. 2008 Philadelphia Phillies - a Poetic Season: The Story As Told from a Fan's Perspective. 2008. 408p. 28.99 *(978-1-4389-3855-4(1))*; pap. 18.99 *(978-1-4389-3854-7(3))* AuthorHouse.
Powell, Larry. Black Barons of Birmingham: The South's Greatest Negro League Team & Its Players. 2009. (ENG., Illus.). 226p. pap. 29.95 *(978-0-7864-3806-8(1))* McFarland & Co., Inc. Pubs.
Prager, Joshua. The Echoing Green: The Untold Story of Bobby Thomson, Ralph Branca & the Shot Heard Round the World. 2008. (Vintage Ser.). (ENG., Illus.). 544p. pap. 15.95 *(978-0-375-71307-1(7),* Vintage) Knopf Doubleday Publishing Group.
Publications International Staff, ed. Yesterday & Today: Ballparks. 2010. 160p 18.98 *(978-1-4508-1087-6(X))* Publications International, Ltd.
Rader, Benjamin G. Baseball: A History of America's Game. 3rd ed. 2008. (Illinois History of Sports Ser.). (ENG., Illus.). 328p. pap. 20.95 *(978-0-252-07550-6(1))* Univ. of Illinois Pr.
Raley, Dan. Pitchers of Beer: The Story of the Seattle Rainiers. (ENG.). 352p. 2012. pap. 19.95 ***(978-0-8032-4085-8(6),*** Bison Bks.) 2011. (Illus.). 26.95 *(978-0-8032-2847-4(3))* Univ. of Nebraska Pr.
Randall, Ed. Baseball for the Utterly Confused. 2010. (Utterly Confused Ser.). (ENG., Illus.). 240p. pap. 17.95 *(978-0-07-163474-8(6),* 0071634746) McGraw-Hill Cos., The.
Reilly, Dan. The Original Mr Met Remembers: When the Miracle Began. 2007. 140p. (ENG.). 23.95 *(978-0-595-70082-0(9))*; per. 13.95 *(978-0-595-46260-5(X))* iUniverse, Inc.
Remy, Jerry & Sandler, Corey. Red Sox Heroes: The Remdawg's All-Time Favorite Red Sox, Great Moments, & Top Teams. 2009. (ENG., Illus.). 288p. 24.95 *(978-1-59921-406-1(7),* Lyons Pr.) Globe Pequot Pr., The.
Rhodes, Greg, compiled by. Cincinnati Reds Hall of Fame Highlights: Memorable Moments in Team History as Heard on the Reds Radio Network. 2007. (ENG., Illus.). 256p. (Orig.). per. 16.99 *(978-1-57860-300-8(5))* Clerisy Pr.
Rhodes, Greg & Erardi, John. Crosley Field: The Illustrated History of a Classic Ballpark. 2009. (ENG., Illus.). 218p. pap. 25.00 *(978-1-57860-384-8(6))* Clerisy Pr.
Richter, Andrew J. Baseball with an Opinion. 2007. 284p. per. 16.95 *(978-1-59824-503-5(1))* E-BookTime LLC.
Riesgo, Nikco & Cohen, Russ. Strike Three! - A Player's Journey through the Infamous Baseball Strike Of 1994. 2010. 100p. pap. 19.94 *(978-0-557-24643-4(1))* Lulu Enterprises Inc.
Ritter, Lawrence S. The Glory of Their Times: The Story of the Early Days of Baseball Told by the Men Who Played It. abr. ed. 2009. (Playaway Adult Nonfiction Ser.). (ENG.). 44.99 *(978-1-60812-723-8(0))* Findaway World, LLC.
Robinson, Guy. Do You Know the New York Yankees? Test Your Expertise with These Fastball Questions (and a Few Curves) about Your Favorite Team's Hurlers, Sluggers, Stats & Most Memorable Moments. 2008. (ENG.). 48p. pap. 5.95 *(978-1-4022-1420-2(0))* Sourcebooks, Inc.
Robinson, Ray. The Home Run Heard 'Round the World: The Dramatic Story of the 1951 Giants-Dodgers Pennant Race. 2011. (Dover Baseball Ser.). (ENG.). 256p. pap. 12.95 *(978-0-486-48058-9(5))* Dover Pubns., Inc.
Rogosin, Donn. Invisible Men: Life in Baseball's Negro Leagues. 2007. (ENG., Illus.). 302p. pap. 24.95 *(978-0-8032-5969-0(7),* Bison Bks.) Univ. of Nebraska Pr.
Rose, George. One Hit Wonders. 2009. 216p. pap. 15.95 *(978-0-557-05395-7(1))* Lulu Enterprises Inc.
—One Win Wonders. 2009. 357p. pap. 18.94 *(978-0-557-04723-9(4))* Lulu Enterprises Inc.
Rosen, Charley. The Emerald Diamond: How the Irish Transformed America's Greatest Pastime. 2012. (ENG.). 288p. 25.99 ***(978-0-06-208988-5(9))*** HarperCollins Pubs.

B

Rosengren, John. Hammerin' Hank, George Almighty & the Say Hey Kid: The Year That Changed Baseball Forever. 2008. (ENG., Illus.). 352p. pap. 19.99 *(978-1-4022-0956-7(8))* Sourcebooks, Inc.

Ruck, Rob. Raceball: How the Major Leagues Colonized the Black & Latin Game. 2011. (ENG., Illus.). 288p. 25.95 *(978-0-8070-4805-4(4))* Beacon Pr.

Ryczek, William J. The Amazin' Mets, 1962-1969. 2007. (ENG., Illus.). 289p. per. 29.95 *(978-0-7864-3214-1(4))* McFarland & Co., Inc. Pubs.

—Baseball's First Inning: A History of the National Pastime Through the Civil War. 2009. (ENG., Illus.). 269p. pap. 29.95 *(978-0-7864-4194-5(1))* McFarland & Co., Inc. Pubs.

—When Johnny Came Sliding Home: The Post-Civil War Baseball Boom, 1865-1870. alt. ed. 2006. (ENG., Illus.). 323p. per. 29.95 *(978-0-7864-2757-4(4))* McFarland & Co., Inc. Pubs.

—The Yankees in the Early 1960s. 2007. (ENG., Illus.). 267p. per. 29.95 *(978-0-7864-2996-7(8))* McFarland & Co., Inc. Pubs.

Sandalow, Mark & Sutton, Jim. Ballparks: A Panoramic History. 2006. (Illus.). 256p. reprint ed. 45.00 *(978-1-4223-5188-8(2))* DIANE Publishing Co.

Santillan, Richard A., et al. Mexican American Baseball in the Inland Empire. 2012. (Images of Baseball Ser.). (ENG., Illus.). 128p. pap. 21.99 ***(978-0-7385-9316-6(8))*** Arcadia Publishing.

Sargent, Jim & Gorman, Robert M. The South Bend Blue Sox: A History of the All-American Girls Professional Baseball League Team & Its Players, 1943-1954. 2011. (ENG.). 302p. pap. 39.95 ***(978-0-7864-4647-6(1))*** McFarland & Co., Inc. Pubs.

Savitt, Robert P. The Blue Ridge League. 2011. (Images of Baseball Ser.). (Illus.). 128p. pap. 21.99 *(978-0-7385-8239-9(5))* Arcadia Publishing.

Scheibe, John. On the Road with Jim Murray: Baseball & the Summer Of '79. 2007. 21.95 *(978-0-9793709-0-8(6))* Encino Media Group.

Schwarz, Alan. The Numbers Game: Baseball's Lifelong Fascination with Statistics. Date not set. mass mkt. *(978-0-312-99375-7(7)*, St. Martin's Paperbacks) St. Martin's Pr.

—Once upon a Game: Baseball's Greatest Memories. 2007. (ENG., Illus.). 152p. 19.95 *(978-0-618-73127-5(X))* Houghton Mifflin Harcourt Trade & Reference Pubs.

Scott, Bill. 63-1: The Greatest Season in the History of Baseball, 1 vol. 2010. 94p. pap. 19.95 *(978-1-4512-8996-1(0))* PublishAmerica, Inc.

Selter, Ronald M. Ballparks of the Deadball Era: A Comprehensive Study of Their Dimensions, Configurations & Effects on Batting, 1901-1919. (ENG., 198p. 2008. Illus.). 45.00 *(978-0-7864-3561-6(5))* 2011. pap. 25.00 *(978-0-7864-6625-2(1))* McFarland & Co., Inc. Pubs.

Setterquist, Charles. Town Team Baseball in Riley County During the 1930's, 1940's, & 1950's. 2008. (Illus.). viii, 72p. *(978-0-9677686-8-7(3))* Riley County Historical Society.

Shalin, Neil. Yankees Triviology: Fascinating Facts from the Bleacher Seats. 2011. (Triviology: Fascinating Facts Ser.). (ENG.). 128p. pap. 9.95 ***(978-1-60078-624-2(3))*** Triumph Bks.

Shapiro, Michael. Bottom of the Ninth: Branch Rickey, Casey Stengel, & the Daring Scheme to Save Baseball from Itself. 2010. (ENG.). 320p. pap. 16.00 *(978-0-8050-9236-3(6)*, Holt Paperback) St. Martin's Pr.

Shaughnessy, Dan. Reversing the Curse: Inside the 2004 Boston Red Sox. 2008. (ENG.). 260p. 23.00 *(978-1-4379-5137-0(6))* DIANE Publishing Co.

Shiffert, John. Base Ball in Philadelphia: A History of the Early Game, 1831-1900. 2006. (ENG., Illus.). 288p. pap. 35.00 *(978-0-7864-2795-6(7))* McFarland & Co., Inc. Pubs.

—The Breaks Even Out & Midnight Comes Quickly for Cinderella. 2009. 289p. pap. 27.95 *(978-1-60813-699-5(X))* PublishAmerica, Inc.

Silvia, Tony. Baseball over the Air: The National Pastime on the Radio & in the Imagination. 2007. (ENG., Illus.). 230p. per. 39.95 *(978-0-7864-3066-6(4))* McFarland & Co., Inc. Pubs.

—Fathers & Sons in Baseball Broadcasting: The Carays, Brennamans, Bucks & Kalases. 2009. (ENG., Illus.). 214p. pap. 35.00 *(978-0-7864-3815-0(0))* McFarland & Co., Inc. Pubs.

Simmons, Bill. Now I Can Die in Peace: How the Sports Guy Found Salvation Thanks to the World Champion (Twice!) Red Sox. 2009. (ENG.). 464p. pap. 16.00 *(978-1-933060-72-9(7)*, Ballantine Bks.) Random House Publishing Group.

Simon, Scott. Jackie Robinson & the Integration of Baseball. 2007. (ENG.). 176p. per. 12.95 *(978-0-470-17041-0(7)*, Wiley) Wiley, John & Sons, Inc.

Simons, William M., ed. The Cooperstown Symposium on Baseball & American Culture, 2009-2010. 2011. (Cooperstown Symposium Ser.). (ENG., Illus.). 270p. pap. 38.00 *(978-0-7864-3570-8(4))* McFarland & Co., Inc. Pubs.

Simpson, John A. The Greatest Game Ever Played in Dixie: The Nashville Vols, Their 1908 Season, & the Championship Game. 2007. (ENG., Illus.). 292p. per. 29.95 *(978-0-7864-3050-5(8))* McFarland & Co., Inc. Pubs.

Slusser, Susan. Tales from the Oakland Athletics. 2008. (Tales Ser.). (Illus.). 192p. 19.95 *(978-1-59670-207-3(9))* Sports Publishing, LLC.

Smith, Burge Carmon. The 1945 Detroit Tigers: Nine Old Men & One Young Left Arm Win It All. 2010. (ENG., Illus.). 303p. pap. 29.95 *(978-0-7864-4196-9(8))* McFarland & Co., Inc. Pubs.

Smith, Daryl Raymond. Making the Big Red Machine: Bob Howsam & the Cincinnati Reds of The 1970s. 2009. (ENG., Illus.). 360p. pap. 35.00 *(978-0-7864-3980-5(7))* McFarland & Co., Inc. Pubs.

Smith, Patrick. Extra Innings: The Joy & the Pains of over-30 Baseball. 2007. (ENG., Illus.). 204p. per. 29.95 *(978-0-7864-2909-7(7))* McFarland & Co., Inc. Pubs.

Snelling, Dennis. The Greatest Minor League: A History of the Pacific Coast League, 1903-1957. 2011. (ENG.). 380p. 45.00 ***(978-0-7864-6524-8(7))*** McFarland & Co., Inc. Pubs.

Society for American Baseball Research (SABR). The Baseball Research Journal (BRJ), Volume 37. 2009. (ENG., Illus.). 132p. pap. 14.95 *(978-1-933599-10-6(3))* Society for American Baseball Research.

—The Baseball Research Journal (BRJ), Volume 38. 2009. (ENG., Illus.). 142p. pap. 14.95 *(978-1-933599-13-7(8))* Society for American Baseball Research.

—The Baseball Research Journal (BRJ), Volume 38 #2. 2010. (ENG.). pap. 14.95 *(978-1-933599-15-1(4))* Society for American Baseball Research.

—The Baseball Research Journal (BRJ), Volume 39 #1. 2010. (ENG.). pap. 14.95 *(978-1-933599-17-5(0))* Society for American Baseball Research.

—Baseball Research Journal (BRJ), Volume 39 #2. 2011. (ENG.). pap. 14.95 *(978-1-933599-18-2(9))* Society for American Baseball Research.

—Baseball Research Journal (BRJ), Volume 40 #1. 2011. (ENG.). 128p. pap. 14.95 ***(978-1-933599-19-9(7))*** Society for American Baseball Research.

—The National Pastime, Baseball in the Peach State 2010. 2010. (ENG.). 156p. pap. 14.95 *(978-1-933599-16-8(2))* Society for American Baseball Research.

—The National Pastime, Endless Seasons 2011: Baseball in Southern California. 2011. (ENG.). pap. 14.95 ***(978-1-933599-20-5(0))*** Society for American Baseball Research.

—The National Pastime, Volume 28: A Review of Baseball History. 2008. (ENG.). 144p. pap. 14.95 *(978-1-933599-09-0(X))* Society for American Baseball Research.

—The National Pastime, Volume 29: Monumental Baseball. 2009. (ENG.). 128p. pap. 14.95 *(978-1-933599-14-4(6))* Society for American Baseball Research.

Society for American Baseball Research Staff. The Baseball Research Journal. (ENG.). Vol. 35. 2007. 126p. pap. 14.95 *(978-1-933599-04-5(9))* Vol. 36. 2008. (Illus.). 128p. pap. 14.95 *(978-1-933599-07-6(3))* Society for American Baseball Research.

—The National Pastime Vol. 27: A Review of Baseball History. 2007. (ENG.). 144p. pap. 14.95 *(978-1-933599-05-2(7))* Society for American Baseball Research.

Soos, Troy. Before the Curse: The Glory Days of New England Baseball, 1858-1918. rev. ed. 2006. (ENG., Illus.). 226p. per. 35.00 *(978-0-7864-2625-6(X))* McFarland & Co., Inc. Pubs.

Spalding, Greg. Pittsburgh Major League Baseball's Five-Star City. 2006. pap. 19.95 *(978-1-59571-170-0(8))* Word Association Pubs.

Spatz, Lyle & Steinberg, Steve. 1921: The Yankees, the Giants, & the Battle for Baseball Supremacy in New York. (ENG.). 2012. 544p. pap. 24.95 ***(978-0-8032-3999-9(8))*** 2010. (Illus.). 538p. 31.95 *(978-0-8032-2060-7(X))* Univ. of Nebraska Pr.

Spink, J. G. Taylor. Judge Landis Twenty-Five Years Baseball. 25.95 *(978-0-8488-1576-9(9))* Amereon LTD.

Sports Illustrated Editors. Sports Illustrated the Baseball Book Expanded Edition. 2011. (ENG., Illus.). 326p. 29.95 *(978-1-60320-208-4(0))* Time Home Entertainment, Inc.

Stallard, Mark & Triumph Books Staff. Echoes of Cincinnati Reds Baseball: The Greatest Stories Ever Told. 2007. (Echoes Of Ser.). (ENG., Illus.). 224p. 19.95 *(978-1-57243-946-7(7))* Triumph Bks.

Stang, Mark. Phillies Photos: 100 Years of Philadelphia Phillies Images. 2008. (Illus.). 208p. 34.95 *(978-1-933197-58-6(7))* Orange Frazer Pr.

Starkey, John D. Cleveland Baseball Vol. II: Players, Teams & Records from 1901-1996. Date not set. (Illus.). 92p. (Orig.). pap. 14.95 *(978-0-9651583-0-5(6))* Timewise Pubs.

Stone, Steve. Said in Stone: Your Game, My Way. 2011. (ENG.). 256p. 22.95 *(978-1-60078-538-2(7))* Triumph Bks.

Stout, D. J. The Amazing Tale of Mr. Herbert & His Fabulous Alpine Cowboys Baseball Club: An Illustrated History of the Best Little Semi-Pro Baseball Team in Texas. 2010. (ENG., Illus.). 240p. 34.95 *(978-0-292-72334-4(2))* Univ. of Texas Pr.

Stout, Glenn. The Cubs: The Complete Story of Chicago Cubs Baseball. 2007. (ENG., Illus.). 480p. 40.00 *(978-0-618-59500-6(7))* Houghton Mifflin Harcourt Publishing Co.

Stowers, Carlton. Oh Brother, How They Played the Game: The Story of Texas' Greatest All-Brothers Baseball Team. 2007. (Texas Heritage Ser.). (ENG., Illus.). 80p. 14.95 *(978-1-933337-13-5(3))* State Hse. Pr.

Stuart, Jeff. Blue Mondays: The Long Goodbye of the Montreal Expos. 2008. 136p. pap. 24.95 *(978-1-60474-295-4(X))* PublishAmerica, Inc.

Sugar, Bert Randolph. The Baseball Hall of Fame: A Living History of America's Greatest Game. 2009. (ENG.). 272p. 35.00 *(978-0-7624-3024-6(9)*, Running Pr.) Running Pr. Bk. Pubs.

Sullivan, Brad, ed. Batting Four Thousand: Baseball in the Western Reserve. 2008. (ENG.). 112p. pap. 14.95 *(978-1-933599-08-3(1))* Society for American Baseball Research.

Sullivan, Dean A., ed. Final Innings: A Documentary History of Baseball, 1972-2008. 2010. (ENG., Illus.). 376p. pap. 29.95 *(978-0-8032-5965-2(4)*, Bison Bks.) Univ. of Nebraska Pr.

Sumner, Jim L. Separating the Men from the Boys: The First Half-Century of the Carolina League. 260p. reprint ed. 98.00 *(978-0-7222-2652-0(7))* Library Reprints, Inc.

Surdam, David George. Wins, Losses, & Empty Seats: How Baseball Outlasted the Great Depression. 2011. (ENG., Illus.). 448p. 45.00 *(978-0-8032-3482-6(1))* Univ. of Nebraska Pr.

Sutter, L. M. Ball, Bat & Bitumen: A History of Coalfield Baseball in the Appalachian South. 2008. (Contributions to Southern Appalachian Studies). (ENG., Illus.). 212p. pap. 35.00 *(978-0-7864-3594-4(1))* McFarland & Co., Inc. Pubs.

—New Mexico Baseball: Miners, Outlaws, Indians & Isotopes, 1880 to the Present. 2010. (ENG., Illus.). 251p. pap. 38.00 *(978-0-7864-4122-8(4))* McFarland & Co., Inc. Pubs.

Swaine, Rick. The Integration of Major League Baseball: A Team by Team History. (ENG., Illus.). 279p. 2009. 49.95 *(978-0-7864-3903-4(3))* 2012. pap. 25.00 ***(978-0-7864-6935-2(8))*** McFarland & Co., Inc. Pubs.

Swanton, Barry & Mah, Jay-Dell. Black Baseball Players in Canada: A Biographical Dictionary, 1881-1960. 2009. (ENG., Illus.). 212p. pap. 39.95 *(978-0-7864-4468-7(1))* McFarland & Co., Inc. Pubs.

Szalontai, James. Teenager on First, Geezer at Bat, 4-F on Deck: Major League Baseball In 1945. 2009. (ENG., Illus.). 334p. pap. 35.00 *(978-0-7864-3794-8(4))* McFarland & Co., Inc. Pubs.

Szalontai, James D. Small Ball in the Big Leagues: A History of Stealing, Bunting, Walking & Otherwise Scratching for Runs. 2010. (ENG., Illus.). 311p. pap. 39.95 *(978-0-7864-3793-1(6))* McFarland & Co., Inc. Pubs.

Thorn, John. Baseball in the Garden of Eden: The Secret History of the Early Game. 2011. (ENG., Illus.). 384p. 26.00 *(978-0-7432-9403-4(3))* Simon & Schuster.

Thornley, Stew, ed. Minnesotans in Baseball. 2009. pap. 25.95 *(978-1-932472-80-6(0))* Nodin Pr.

Tiemann, Bob, ed. Mound City Memories: Baseball in St. Louis. 2007. (ENG., Illus.). 120p. per. 14.95 *(978-1-933599-06-9(5))* Society for American Baseball Research.

Tootle, James R. Vintage Base Ball: Recapturing the National Pastime. 2011. (ENG., Illus.). 396p. pap. 39.95 *(978-0-7864-3599-9(2))* McFarland & Co., Inc. Pubs.

Travers, Steven. Angels Essential: Everything You Need to Know to Be a Real Fan! 2007. (Essential: Everything You Need to Know to Be a Real Fan Ser.). (ENG., Illus.). 224p. 19.95 *(978-1-57243-943-6(2))* Triumph Bks.

—A's Essential: Everything You Need to Know to Be a Real Fan! 2007. (Essential: Everything You Need to Know to Be a Real Fan Ser.). (ENG., Illus.). 240p. 19.95 *(978-1-57243-926-9(2))* Triumph Bks.

—The Good, the Bad, & the Ugly - Los Angeles Lakers: Heart-Pounding, Jaw-Dropping, & Gut-Wrenching Moments from Los Angeles Lakers History. 2007. (Good, the Bad, & the Ugly Ser.). (ENG., Illus.). 224p. pap. 19.95 *(978-1-60078-004-2(0))* Triumph Bks.

—A Tale of Three Cities: The 1962 Baseball Season in New York, Los Angeles, & San Francisco. 2009. 274p. 29.95 *(978-1-59797-431-8(5))* Potomac Bks., Inc.

Treto Cisneros, Pedro. The Mexican League / la Liga Mexicana: Comprehensive Player Statistics, 1937-2001 bilingual edition / Estadisticas Comprensivas de los Jugadores, 1937-2001 edicion Bilingue. alt. ed. 2011. (ENG & SPA., Illus.). 512p. pap. 45.00 *(978-0-7864-6120-2(9))* McFarland & Co., Inc. Pubs.

Tully, Gregory J. Nine College Nines: A Closeup View of Campus Baseball Programs Today. 2009. (ENG.). 224p. pap. 35.00 *(978-0-7864-4128-0(3))* McFarland & Co., Inc. Pubs.

Tygiel, Jules. Baseball's Great Experiment: Jackie Robinson & His Legacy. 25th ed. 2008. (ENG., Illus.). 448p. per. 19.95 *(978-0-19-533928-4(2))* Oxford Univ. Pr., Inc.

Vaccaro, Mike. 194 - The Greatest Year in Sports: Two Baseball Legends, Two Boxing Champs, & the Unstoppable Thoroughbred Who Made History in the Shadow of War. 2008. (ENG.). 320p. pap. 17.00 *(978-0-7679-2416-0(9))* Broadway Bks.

Valenti, Dan. Under a Grapefruit Sun: Red Sox Spring Training a Quarter Century Ago. 2007. (ENG., Illus.). 144p. 27.95 *(978-1-57940-122-1(8))* Rounder Bks.

Van Hyning, Thomas E. The Santurce Crabbers: Sixty Seasons of Puerto Rican Winter League Baseball. alt. ed. 2008. (ENG., Illus.). 279p. pap. 29.95 *(978-0-7864-3895-2(9))* McFarland & Co., Inc. Pubs.

Vecsey, George. Baseball: A History of America's Favorite Game. 2008. (Modern Library Chronicles Ser.). (ENG., Illus.). 272p. per. 14.00 *(978-0-8129-7870-4(6))* Random House Publishing Group.

Veeck, Bill. The Hustler's Handbook. 2009. (ENG.). 352p. (J). (gr. -1-12). pap. 15.95 *(978-1-56663-827-2(5))* Dee, Ivan R. Pub.

Vincent, David. Home Run: The Definitive History of Baseball's Ultimate Weapon. (Illus.). 304p. 2008. pap. 17.95 *(978-1-59797-036-5(0))* 2007. 26.95 *(978-1-59797-035-8(2))* Potomac Bks., Inc.

Vincent, Fay. It's What's Inside the Lines That Counts: Baseball Stars of the 1970s & 1980s Talk about the Game They Loved. (ENG., Illus.). 336p. 2011. pap. 15.00 *(978-1-4391-5922-4(X))* 2010. 25.00 *(978-1-4391-5921-7(1))* Simon & Schuster.

—The Only Game in Town: Baseball Stars of the 1930s & 1940s Talk about the Game They Loved. 2007. (ENG., Illus.). 256p. pap. 14.00 *(978-0-7432-7318-3(4))* Simon & Schuster.

—We Would Have Played for Nothing: Baseball Stars of the 1950s & 1960s Talk about the Game They Loved. 2008. (ENG., Illus.). 336p. 25.00 *(978-1-4165-5342-7(8))* Simon & Schuster.

Von Borries, Philip. The Louisville Baseball Almanac. 2010. (Sports History Ser.). (ENG., Illus.). 256p. pap. 24.99 *(978-1-59629-994-8(0))* History Pr., The.

Waldenbooks Publishing Company Staff. Norwegian Book of Knowledge. (Illus.). pap. 2.25 *(978-0-681-35056-4(3))* Waldenbooks, Inc.

Walker, James R. & Bellamy, Robert V., Jr. Center Field Shot: A History of Baseball on Television. 2008. (ENG., Illus.). 402p. pap. 24.95 *(978-0-8032-4825-0(3)*, Bison Bks.) Univ. of Nebraska Pr.

Wallace, Joseph. Baseball 365 Days: An Official Publication from the Archives of Major League Baseball. 2008. (ENG., Illus.). 744p. 32.50 *(978-0-8109-9524-6(7))* Abrams.

Warburton, Paul. Signature Seasons: Fifteen Baseball Legends at Their Most Memorable, 1908-1949. 2010. (ENG., Illus.). 264p. pap. 29.95 *(978-0-7864-4655-1(2))* McFarland & Co., Inc. Pubs.

Ward, Geoffrey C. Baseball: An Illustrated History. 2010. (ENG., Illus.). 592p. 75.00 *(978-0-307-27349-9(0)*, Knopf) Knopf Doubleday Publishing Group.

Ward, Geoffrey C., et al. Baseball: An Illustrated History. 2010. (ENG., Illus.). 592p. pap. 39.95 *(978-0-375-71197-8(X)*, Knopf) Knopf Doubleday Publishing Group.

Waters, Roger Lee. Soaring Like an Eagle the Courtney Moses Story. 2010. 260p. pap. 19.95 *(978-1-4502-5766-4(6))* iUniverse, Inc.

Watkins, Clarence. Baseball in Birmingham. 2010. (Images of Baseball Ser.). (ENG., Illus.). 128p. pap. 21.99 *(978-0-7385-6686-3(1))* Arcadia Publishing.

Watkins, Clarence. Baseball in Memphis. 2012. (Images of Baseball Ser.). (ENG., Illus.). 128p. pap. 21.99 ***(978-0-7385-9108-7(4))*** Arcadia Publishing.

Watts, Carl E. The Men That Cooperstown Forgot. 2008. 348p. pap. 29.95 *(978-1-60563-598-9(7))* PublishAmerica, Inc.

Wee, K. P. Baseball Pitchers: the Most Overrated & Underrated in the Last 20 Years (1988-2007) 2008. 124p. pap. 17.95 *(978-1-4357-1994-1(8))* Lulu Enterprises Inc.

Weintraub, Robert. The House That Ruth Built: A New Stadium, the First Yankees Championship, & the Redemption Of 1923. 2011. (ENG., Illus.). 432p. 26.99 *(978-0-316-08607-3(X))* Little Brown & Co.

Weisberger, Bernard A. When Chicago Ruled Baseball: The Cubs-White Sox World Series of 1906. 2007. (ENG., Illus.). 240p. per. 14.95 *(978-0-06-059237-0(0)*, William Morrow Paperbacks) HarperCollins Pubs.

Weisman, Jon. 100 Things Dodgers Fans Should Know & Do Before They Die. 2009. (100 Things... Fans Should Know Ser.). (ENG.). 320p. pap. 14.95 *(978-1-60078-166-7(7))* Triumph Bks.

Wendel, Tim. High Heat: The Secret History of the Fastball & the Improbable Search for the Fastest Pitcher of All Time. 2010. (ENG., Illus.). 288p. 25.00 *(978-0-306-81848-6(5))* Da Capo Pr., Inc.

Wendel, Tim. Summer of '68: The Season That Changed Baseball — And America — Forever. 2012. (ENG.). 304p. 25.00 ***(978-0-306-82018-2(8))*** Da Capo Pr., Inc.

Wendel, Tim & Villegas, Jose Luis. Far from Home: Latino Baseball Players in America. 2008. (ENG., Illus.). 160p. 28.00 *(978-1-4262-0216-2(4))* National Geographic Society.

White, Bill. Uppity: My Untold Story about the Games People Play. (ENG., Illus.). 320p. 2012. pap. 15.99 ***(978-0-446-55526-5(6))*** 2011. 26.99 *(978-0-446-55525-8(8))* Grand Central Publishing.

White, Roy & Berger, Darrell. "Then Roy Said to Mickey... " The Best Yankees Stories Ever Told. 2009. (Best Sports Stories Ever Told Ser.). (ENG.). 224p. 22.95 *(978-1-60078-091-2(1))* Triumph Bks.

White, Sol. Sol White's Official Baseball Guide. 16.95 *(978-0-8488-1588-2(2))* Amereon LTD.

Wiggins, Robert Peyton. The Federal League of Base Ball Clubs: The History of an Outlaw Major League, 1914-1915. (ENG., Illus.). 368p. 2008. 49.95 *(978-0-7864-3835-8(5))* 2011. pap. 40.00 ***(978-0-7864-6939-0(0))*** McFarland & Co., Inc. Pubs.

Wilbert, Warren N. The Arrival of the American League: Ban Johnson & the 1901 Challenge to National League Monopoly. 2007. (ENG., Illus.). 240p. per. 29.95 *(978-0-7864-3013-0(3))* McFarland & Co., Inc. Pubs.

—Opening Pitch: Professional Baseball's Inaugural Season. 2007. (ENG., Illus.). 192p. per. 40.00 *(978-0-8108-6020-9(1))* Scarecrow Pr., Inc.

Wilker, Josh. Cardboard Gods. 2011. (ENG.). 243p. pap. 15.95 *(978-1-61620-069-5(3)*, 1616200693) Algonquin Bks. of Chapel Hill.

Wilkinson, Jack. 100 Things Braves Fans Should Know & Do Before They Die. 2011. (100 Things... Fans Should Know Ser.). (ENG.). 296p. pap. 14.95 *(978-1-60078-555-9(7))* Triumph Bks.

Will, George F. Men at Work: The Craft of Baseball. 2010. (ENG.). 400p. pap. 14.99 *(978-0-06-199981-9(4)*, Harper Paperbacks) HarperCollins Pubs.

Wiseman, John B., ed. Joy in Mudville: Essays on Baseball & American Life. 2009. (ENG., Illus.). 252p. pap. 39.95 *(978-0-7864-4228-7(X))* McFarland & Co., Inc. Pubs.

Wright, Marshall D. The Eastern League in Baseball Set: A Statistical History, 1923-2005, 2 vols. 2006. (ENG., Illus.). 817p. pap. 75.00 *(978-0-7864-2794-9(9))* McFarland & Co., Inc. Pubs.

Zardetto, Ray. '30: Major League Baseball's Year of the Batter. 2008. (ENG., Illus.). 239p. pap. 35.00 *(978-0-7864-3666-8(2))* McFarland & Co., Inc. Pubs.

Zeiler, Thomas W. Ambassadors in Pinstripes: The Spalding World Baseball Tour & the Birth of the American Empire. 2006. (ENG., Illus.). 232p. 92.00 *(978-0-7425-5168-8(7))*; per. 30.95 *(978-0-7425-5169-5(5))* Rowman & Littlefield Publishers, Inc.

Ziegel, Vic. Summer in the City: New York Baseball 1947-1957. Guglberger, Claus, ed. 2006. (ENG., Illus.). 192p. 17.98 *(978-0-8109-8257-4(9))* Abrams.

Zimniuch, Fran. Going, Going, Gone! The Art of the Trade in Major League Baseball. 2008. (ENG., Illus.). 240p. pap. 16.95 *(978-1-58979-334-7(X))* Taylor Trade Publishing.

Zinn, Paul G. & Zinn, John G. The Major League Pennant Races of 1916: The Most Maddening Baseball Melee in History. 2009. (ENG., Illus.). 319p. pap. 32.00 *(978-0-7864-3630-9(1))* McFarland & Co., Inc. Pubs.

BASEBALL—JUVENILE LITERATURE

Glaser, Jason. Outfielders. 2011. (Play Ball: Baseball Ser.). (Illus.). 48p. (J). (gr. 4-8). pap. 14.05 *(978-1-4339-4492-5(8))* Stevens, Gareth Publishing LLLP.

—Pitchers. 2011. (Play Ball: Baseball Ser.). (Illus.). 48p. (J). (gr. 4-8). pap. 14.05 *(978-1-4339-4496-3(0))* Stevens, Gareth Publishing LLLP.

BASEBALL—MANAGEMENT

Courey, Fred. I Are What I Are Because... 2007. (Illus.). 80p. pap. *(978-1-57579-366-5(0))* Pine Hill Pr., Inc.

Frascella, John. Theology: How a Boy Wonder Led the Red Sox to the Promised Land. 2009. (ENG.). 208p. pap. 14.95 *(978-0-9814536-9-9(4)*, Cambridge House Pr.) Sterling & Ross Pubs.

Gorman, Robert. In Your Face - in Your Heart: The Story of Joe Cronin. 2007. pap. 14.95 *(978-0-9792287-0-4(0))* Baldwin Bks.

Lewis, Robert F. Smart Ball: Marketing the Myth & Managing the Reality of Major League Baseball. 2011. (ENG.). 176p. pap. 30.00 ***(978-1-61703-208-0(5))*** Univ. Pr. of Mississippi.

Lewis, Robert F., 2nd. Smart Ball: Marketing the Myth & Managing the Reality of Major League Baseball. 2009. (ENG.). 176p. 50.00 *(978-1-60473-207-8(5))* Univ. Pr. of Mississippi.

Masters, Todd. The 1972 Detroit Tigers: Billy Martin & the Half-Game Champs. 2010. (ENG., Illus.). 279p. pap. 29.95 *(978-0-7864-4820-3(2))* McFarland & Co., Inc. Pubs.

Morrissey, Rick. Ozzie's School of Management: Lessons from the Dugout, the Clubhouse, & the Doghouse. 2012. (ENG., Illus.). 288p. 26.00 ***(978-0-8050-9500-5(4)***, Times Bks.) Holt, Henry & Co.

Olney, Buster. The Last Night of the Yankee Dynasty: The Game, the Team, & the Cost of Greatness. 2008. (ENG.). 432p. pap. 14.99 *(978-0-06-167287-3(4)*, HarperPerennial) HarperCollins Pubs.

Pluto, Terry. Dealing: The Cleveland Indians' New Ballgame: How a Small-Market Team Reinvented Itself as a Major League Contender. 2nd ed. 2008. (ENG., Illus.). 248p. pap. 14.95 *(978-1-59851-049-2(5))* Gray and Company, Publishers.

Ruggiero, John. Frontiers in Major League Baseball: Nonparametric Analysis of Performance Using Data Envelopment Analysis. 2010. (Sports Economics, Management & Policy Ser.). (ENG., Illus.). xv, 139p. 119.00 *(978-1-4419-0830-8(7)*, 1441908307) Springer.

Shannon, Mike & Hannig, Scott D. Hutch: Baseball's Fred Hutchinson & a Legacy of Courage. 2011. (ENG., Illus.). 224p. pap. 24.95 *(978-0-7864-4625-4(0))* McFarland & Co., Inc. Pubs.

Waldo, Ronald T. Fred Clarke: A Biography of the Baseball Hall of Fame Player-Manager. 2010. (ENG., Illus.). 252p. pap. 29.95 *(978-0-7864-5933-9(6))* McFarland & Co., Inc. Pubs.

Zimbalist, Andrew. In the Best Interests of Baseball: The Revolutionary Reign of Bud Selig. 2007. (ENG., Illus.). 272p. per. 14.95 *(978-0-470-12824-4(0)*, Wiley) Wiley, John & Sons, Inc.

BASEBALL—MISCELLANEA

Bathroom Readers' Institute Staff. Uncle John's Bathroom Reader Takes a Swing at Baseball. 2008. (Uncle John's Bathroom Reader Ser.). (ENG.). 288p. pap. 12.95 *(978-1-59223-882-8(3)*, Portable Pr.) Advantage Pubs. Group.

Burnson, John, et al. The Graphical Player 2008: The Next Step in Sabermetric Research. 5th rev. ed. 2007. (Illus.). 212p. per. 21.95 *(978-1-891566-53-0(9))* Shandler Enterprises, LLC.

Cafardo, Nick. 100 Things Red Sox Fans Should Know & Do Before They Die. 2008. (100 Things... Fans Should Know Ser.). (ENG., Illus.). 192p. 19.95 *(978-1-60078-053-0(9))* Triumph Bks.

Costa, Gabriel B., et al. Understanding Sabermetrics: An Introduction to the Science of Baseball Statistics. 2007. (ENG., Illus.). 190p. per. 29.95 *(978-0-7864-3388-9(4))* McFarland & Co., Inc. Pubs.

Dickson, Paul. Baseball's Greatest Quotations: An Illustrated Treasury of Baseball Quotations & Historical Lore. rev. ed. 2008. (ENG., Illus.). 672p. pap. 19.95 *(978-0-06-126060-5(6))* HarperCollins Pubs.

—The Unwritten Rules of Baseball: The Etiquette, Conventional Wisdom, & Axiomatic Codes of Our National Pastime. 2009. (ENG.). 256p. 14.99 *(978-0-06-156105-4(3))* HarperCollins Pubs.

Dromgoole, Glenn & Christopher, Phil. Parables from the Diamond: Meditations for Men on Baseball & Life. 2009. (ENG., Illus.). 96p. pap. 9.95 *(978-1-933979-27-4(5))* Bright Sky Pr.

Green, David. 101 Reasons to Love the Tigers. 2009. (ENG., Illus.). 120p. 15.95 *(978-1-58479-756-2(8))* Stewart, Tabori & Chang.

Green, Ron, Jr. 101 Reasons to Love the Phillies. 2008. (ENG., Illus.). 120p. 15.95 *(978-1-58479-755-5(X))* Stewart, Tabori & Chang.

Hardy, James D., Jr. Baseball & the Mythic Moment: How We Remember the National Game. 2007. (ENG., Illus.). 219p. per. 35.00 *(978-0-7864-2650-8(0))* McFarland & Co., Inc. Pubs.

Kahn, Roger. Beyond the Boys of Summer: The Very Best of Roger Kahn. 2006. (ENG.). 400p. per. 16.95 *(978-0-07-148119-9(2)*, 0071481192) McGraw-Hill Cos., The.

Kuenster, Robert. The Baseball Entertainer. 2009. (ENG.). 96p. pap. 8.95 *(978-1-56663-820-3(8))* Dee, Ivan R. Pub.

—Baseball Entertainer, No. 2. 2010. (ENG.). 96p. pap. 8.95 *(978-1-56663-863-0(1))* Dee, Ivan R. Pub.

Kyle, Donald G. & Fairbanks, Robert B., eds. Baseball in America & America in Baseball. 2008. (Walter Prescott Webb Memorial Lectures). (ENG., Illus.). 252p. 29.95 *(978-1-60344-023-3(2))* Texas A&M Univ. Pr.

Lebovitz, Hal. Ask Hal: Answers to Fans' Most Interesting Questions about Baseball Rules, from a Hall-of-Fame Sportswriter. 2007. (Illus.). 181p. per. 14.95 *(978-1-59851-034-8(7))* Gray and Company, Publishers.

Lennox, Doug. Now You Know Baseball. 2010. (Now You Know Ser.). (ENG., Illus.). 200p. pap. 19.99 *(978-1-55488-713-2(5))* Dundurn CAN. Dist: Ingram Pub. Services.

Lyons, Steve & Rocks, Burton. The Psycho 100: Baseball's Most Outrageous Moments. 2009. (ENG.). 240p. pap. 14.95 *(978-1-60078-167-4(5))* Triumph Bks.

Martirano, Ron. Baseball: The Players, the World Series, the Records. 2011. (Little Seedling Edition Ser.). (ENG.). 128p. 4.95 *(978-1-60433-231-5(X))* Cider Mill Pr. Bk. Pubs., LLC.

McKenna, Brian. Early Exits: The Premature Endings of Baseball Careers. 2006. (ENG.). 304p. per. 50.00 *(978-0-8108-5858-9(4))* Scarecrow Pr., Inc.

Milano, Alyssa. Safe at Home: Confessions of a Baseball Fanatic. 2010. (ENG.). 272p. pap. 15.99 *(978-0-06-162511-4(6))* HarperCollins Pubs.

Miles, Jerry. Holy Cow! 2008. 90p. (J). pap. 10.00 *(978-1-935043-02-7(1))* Stephens Pr. LLC.

Morris, Peter. Game of Inches. 2010. (ENG.). 664p. pap. 26.95 *(978-1-56663-853-1(4))* Dee, Ivan R. Pub.

—A Game of Inches: The Stories Behind the Innovations That Shaped Baseball: the Game Behind the Scenes. 2006. (ENG.). 416p. 28.95 *(978-1-56663-705-3(8))* Dee, Ivan R. Pub.

Morse, Michael A. All-New Baseball Brainteasers: 60 Major League Puzzles. 2007. (ENG., Illus.). 160p. per. 6.95 *(978-1-4027-3101-3(9))* Sterling Publishing Co., Inc.

Nathan, David H. The Mcfarland Baseball Quotations Dictionary. alt. ed. 2007. (ENG.). 304p. per. 39.95 *(978-0-7864-3756-6(1))* McFarland & Co., Inc. Pubs.

Neyer, Rob. Rob Neyer's Big Book of Baseball Legends: The Truth, the Lies, & Everything Else. 2008. (ENG., Illus.). 352p. pap. 16.00 *(978-0-7432-8490-5(9)*, Touchstone) Touchstone.

O'Brien, Tim. Baseball Oddities & Trivia. 2008. (Illus.). 119p. pap. 10.88 *(978-1-893951-29-7(4))* Ripley Entertainment, Inc.

Pahigian, Josh. The Seventh Inning Stretch: Baseball's Most Essential & Inane Debates. 2010. (ENG., Illus.). 304p. pap. 18.95 *(978-1-59921-805-2(4)*, Lyons Pr.) Globe Pequot Pr., The.

Poulton, J. Alexander. Weird Facts about Baseball. 2009. (ENG.). 216p. pap. *(978-1-897277-28-7(8)*, OverTime Bks.) Editions de la Montagne Verte, Inc. CAN. Dist: Lone Pine Publishing.

Publications International Staff. Armchair Reader Grand Slam Baseball. 2007. 464p. pap. 15.98 *(978-1-4127-1417-4(6))* Publications International, Ltd.

Quigley, Brendan Emmett. Go Phillies! Crossword Puzzle Book: 25 All-New Baseball Trivia Puzzles. 2009. (ENG., Illus.). 64p. pap. 7.95 *(978-1-60433-085-4(6))* Cider Mill Pr. Bk. Pubs., LLC.

Roe, Preacher & Preslar, Sarah. When Baseball Was Still A Game: Truths, Legends, Tales & Photos from Preacher Roe. 2006. (Illus.). 150p. (YA). per. 29.95 *(978-0-9772004-0-5(X))* Catalyst Apex Publishing.

Ross, Ken. A Mathematician at the Ballpark: Odds & Probabilities for Baseball Fans. 2007. (ENG., Illus.). 224p. (gr. 12). per. 16.00 *(978-0-452-28782-2(0)*, Plume) Penguin Group (USA) Inc.

Schlossberg, Dan. Baseball Gold: Mining Nuggets from Our National Pastime. 2007. (ENG., Illus.). 416p. per. 14.95 *(978-1-57243-958-0(0))* Triumph Bks.

Schnakenberg, Robert. The Underground Baseball Encyclopedia: Baseball Stuff You Never Needed to Know & Can Certainly Live Without. 2010. (ENG.). 288p. pap. 14.95 *(978-1-60078-331-9(7))* Triumph Bks.

Schwarz, Alan. Once upon a Game: Baseball's Greatest Memories. 2007. (ENG., Illus.). 152p. 19.95 *(978-0-618-73127-5(X))* Houghton Mifflin Harcourt Trade & Reference Pubs.

Shalin, Neil. Mets Triviology: Fascinating Facts from the Bleacher Seats. 2011. (Triviology: Fascinating Facts Ser.). (ENG.). 128p. pap. 9.95 ***(978-1-60078-625-9(1))*** Triumph Bks.

—Red Sox Triviology: Fascinating Facts from the Bleacher Seats. 2011. (Triviology: Fascinating Facts Ser.). (ENG.). 128p. pap. 9.95 ***(978-1-60078-623-5(5))*** Triumph Bks.

Shatzkin, Mike & Idea Logical Company Staff. Little Giant Encyclopedia: Baseball Quizzes. 2009. (ENG.). 512p. pap. 9.95 *(978-1-4027-6418-9(9)*, Sterling Innovation) Sterling Publishing Co., Inc.

Shaughnessy, Dan. Senior Year: A Father, a Son, & High School Baseball. 2008. (ENG., Illus.). 240p. pap. 13.95 *(978-0-547-05382-0(7)*, Mariner Bks.) Houghton Mifflin Harcourt Trade & Reference Pubs.

Silverman, Matthew. Baseball Miscellany: Everything You Always Wanted to Know about Baseball. 2011. (Books of Miscellany Ser.). (ENG., Illus.). 192p. 14.95 *(978-1-61608-196-6(1)*, 608196) Skyhorse Publishing Co., Inc.

Society for American Baseball Research. The SABR Baseball List & Record Book: Baseball's Most Fascinating Records & Unusual Statistics. Spatz, Lyle, ed. 2007. (ENG., Illus.). 496p. pap. 17.95 *(978-1-4165-3245-3(5)*, Scribner) Scribner.

Stewart, Wayne. Name That Ballplayer: The Ultimate Baseball Whodunnit? Quiz Book. 2009. (ENG.). 160p. pap. 8.95 *(978-1-60239-319-6(2)*, 239319) Skyhorse Publishing Co., Inc.

—You're the Umpire: 139 Scenarios to Test Your Baseball Knowledge. 2010. (ENG., Illus.). 224p. pap. 8.95 *(978-1-60239-793-4(7)*, 239793) Skyhorse Publishing Co., Inc.

Stewart, Wayne, ed. The Gigantic Book of Baseball Quotations. 2007. 787p. 24.95 *(978-1-60239-072-0(X))* Skyhorse Publishing Co., Inc.

Von Borries, Philip. Ameridi (american Diamonds) An American Baseball Reader. 2008. 192p. pap. 15.95 *(978-1-60145-411-9(2))* Booklocker.com, Inc.

Wiles, Tim, et al. Baseball's Greatest Hit: The Story of Take Me Out to the Ball Game. 2008. (ENG., Illus.). 222p. 29.95 incl. audio compact disk *(978-1-4234-3188-6(X)*, 142343188X) Leonard, Hal Corp.

Wisnia, Saul. The Wit & Wisdom of Baseball. 2007. (Illus.). 168p. 9.98 *(978-1-4127-1975-9(5))* Publications International, Ltd.

BASEBALL—PICTORIAL WORKS

Antos, Jason D. Shea Stadium. 2007. (Images of Sports Ser.). (Illus.). 127p. per. 19.99 *(978-0-7385-5456-3(1))* Arcadia Publishing.

Balderrama, Francisco E. & Santillan, Richard A. Mexican American Baseball in Los Angeles. 2011. (Images of Baseball Ser.). (Illus.). 128p. pap. 21.99 *(978-0-7385-8180-4(1))* Arcadia Publishing.

Blau, Marc H. Baseball in Tacoma-Pierce County. 2011. (Images of Baseball Ser.). (Illus.). 128p. pap. 21.99 *(978-0-7385-8194-1(1))* Arcadia Publishing.

Breckin, Dennis & Reusse, Patrick. Minnesota Twins: The Complete Illustrated History. 2010. (ENG., Illus.). 192p. 30.00 *(978-0-7603-3684-7(9)*, 0760336849, MVP Bks.) MBI Publishing Co. LLC.

Brian Harold Lee Foreword by Skip Jennings & Skip Jennings. Baseball in Savannah. 2012. (Images of Baseball Ser.). (ENG., Illus.). 128p. pap. 21.99 ***(978-0-7385-9126-1(2))*** Arcadia Publishing.

Chambers, Timothy C., ed. Ballparks Across America: E-Mails from a Fan on the Road, Volume 3. 2008. (Illus.). 314p. pap. 19.95 *(978-0-9793604-3-5(9))* Jones, James.

Crosby, Bonnie & D'Agostino, Dennis. Through a Blue Lens: The Brooklyn Dodger Photographs of Barney Stein, 1939-1957. 2007. (ENG., Illus.). 176p. 27.95 *(978-1-57243-952-8(1))* Triumph Bks.

Finoli, David. Baseball in Altoona: From the Mountain City to the Curve. 2008. (Images of Baseball Ser.). (ENG., Illus.). 128p. per. 19.99 *(978-0-7385-5537-9(1))* Arcadia Publishing.

Flynn, Tom. Baseball in Baltimore. 2008. (Images of Baseball Ser.). (ENG., Illus.). 128p. per. 21.99 *(978-0-7385-5325-2(5))* Arcadia Publishing.

Getz, Mike. The Giants Win the Series! Headlines & Highlights Of 1954. 2011. 268p. 25.00 *(978-1-4567-2817-5(2))*; pap. 15.00 *(978-1-4567-2818-2(0))* AuthorHouse.

Hart, Michael, photos by. Biggio: The Final Game. 2008. (ENG., Illus.). 108p. 24.95 *(978-1-933979-28-1(3))* Bright Sky Pr.

Herron, Gary. Baseball in Albuquerque. 2011. (Images of Baseball Ser.). (Illus.). 128p. pap. 21.99 *(978-0-7385-7964-1(5))* Arcadia Publishing.

Hinrichs, Kit & Hirasuna, Delphine. 100 Baseball Icons: From the National Baseball Hall of Fame & Museum Archive. 2008. (ENG., Illus.). 112p. 19.95 *(978-1-58008-916-6(X))* Ten Speed Pr.

Iooss, Walter, Jr. & Anderson, Dave. Classic Baseball: The Photographs of Walter Iooss Jr. 2006. (ENG., Illus.). 210p. 17.98 *(978-0-8109-8250-5(1))* Abrams.

Kearney, Seamus & Rosen, Dick. The Philadelphia Phillies. 2011. (Images of Baseball Ser.). (Illus.). 128p. pap. 21.99 *(978-0-7385-7420-2(1))* Arcadia Publishing.

Kroll, Eric, ed. Neil Leifer: Ballet in the Dirt: Baseball Photography of the 1960s & 70s. 2007. (ENG., Illus.). 302p. 1000.00 *(978-3-8228-2207-4(8))* TASCHEN DEU. Dist: Ingram Pub. Services.

Lantos, James. Boston Baseball. Lantos, James & Lantos, Jim, eds. 2009. (Applewood's Pictorial America Ser.). (ENG.). 56p. pap. 9.95 *(978-1-60889-009-5(0))* Applewood Bks.

Leifer, Neil. Ballet in the Dirt: The Golden Age of Baseball. Volk, Annick & Kroll, Eric, eds. 2008. (ENG & GER., Illus.). 293p. 39.99 *(978-3-8228-4550-9(7))* TASCHEN DEU. Dist: Ingram Pub. Services.

Leventhal, Josh. Take Me Out to the Ballpark Revised & Updated: An Illustrated Tour of Baseball Parks Past & Present Featuring Every Major League Park, Plus Minor League & Negro League Parks. 2011. (ENG., Illus.). 144p. pap. 17.95 *(978-1-57912-866-1(1)*, 1579128661) Black Dog & Leventhal Pubs., Inc.

Levinthal, David. Baseball. 2006. (Illus.). 144p. 50.00 *(978-0-9779008-0-0(0))* Empire Editions.

Levinthal, David, photos by. Baseball. 2009. (ENG., Illus.). 144p. 50.00 *(978-1-57687-468-4(0)*, powerHouse Bks.) powerHouse Cultural Entertainment, Inc.

Martino, Andy, et al. The Mets. 50th anniv. ed. 2011. (ENG., Illus.). 320p. 40.00 *(978-1-58479-914-6(5))* Stewart, Tabori & Chang.

Maulhardt, Jeffrey Wayne. Baseball in Ventura County. 2007. (Images of Baseball Ser.). (ENG., Illus.). 128p. per. 19.99 *(978-0-7385-4739-8(5))* Arcadia Publishing.

Maxwell, Joshua R. & McCann, Kevin D. Kitty League. 2012. (Images of Baseball Ser.). (ENG., Illus.). 128p. pap. 21.99 ***(978-0-7385-9372-2(9))*** Arcadia Publishing.

McCabe, Neal & McCabe, Constance. Baseball's Golden Age: The Photographs of Charles M. Conlon. 2011. (ENG., Illus.). 198p. 35.00 ***(978-1-4197-0197-9(5))*** Abrams.

McCabe, Neal, et al. The Big Show: Charles M. Conlon's Golden Age Baseball Photographs. 2011. (ENG., Illus.). 224p. 35.00 *(978-1-4197-0069-9(3))* Abrams.

Outland, John W. Baseball Visions of the Roaring Twenties: A Fan's Photographs of More Than 400 Players & Ballparks of the Era. 2009. (ENG., Illus.). 492p. pap. 45.00 *(978-0-7864-4123-5(2))* McFarland & Co., Inc. Pubs.

Publications International Staff. Bk Brick Cooperstown. 2010. 320p. 12.98 *(978-1-4127-1383-2(8)*, PIL Kids) Publications International, Ltd.

Sports Publishing Inc. Staff, ed. The Rockies: 2007 Season. 2007. 128p. pap. 14.95 *(978-1-59670-346-9(6))* Sports Publishing, LLC.

Stang, Mark. Phillies Photos: 100 Years of Philadelphia Phillies Images. 2008. (Illus.). 208p. 34.95 *(978-1-933197-58-6(7))* Orange Frazer Pr.

Stout, D. J. The Amazing Tale of Mr. Herbert & His Fabulous Alpine Cowboys Baseball Club: An Illustrated History of the Best Little Semi-Pro Baseball Team in Texas. 2010. (ENG., Illus.). 240p. 34.95 *(978-0-292-72334-4(2))* Univ. of Texas Pr.

Vitti, Jim. Brooklyn Dodgers in Cuba. 2011. (Images of Baseball Ser.). (Illus.). 128p. pap. 21.99 *(978-0-7385-7427-1(9))* Arcadia Publishing.

Wallace, Joseph. Baseball 365 Days: An Official Publication from the Archives of Major League Baseball. 2008. (ENG., Illus.). 744p. 32.50 *(978-0-8109-9524-6(7))* Abrams.

Ward, Geoffrey C. Baseball: An Illustrated History. 2010. (ENG., Illus.). 592p. 75.00 *(978-0-307-27349-9(0)*, Knopf) Knopf Doubleday Publishing Group.

Ward, Geoffrey C., et al. Baseball: An Illustrated History. 2010. (ENG., Illus.). 592p. pap. 39.95 *(978-0-375-71197-8(X)*, Knopf) Knopf Doubleday Publishing Group.

Wendel, Tim & Villegas, Jose Luis. Far from Home: Latino Baseball Players in America. 2008. (ENG., Illus.). 160p. 28.00 *(978-1-4262-0216-2(4))* National Geographic Society.

BASEBALL—POLITICAL ASPECTS

Briley, Ron, ed. The Politics of Baseball: Essays on the Pastime & Power at Home & Abroad. 2010. (ENG., Illus.). 256p. pap. 39.95 *(978-0-7864-4129-7(1))* McFarland & Co., Inc. Pubs.

Guthrie-Shimizu, Sayuri. Transpacific Field of Dreams: How Baseball Linked the United States & Japan in Peace & War. 2012. (ENG., Illus.). 336p. 39.95 ***(978-0-8078-3562-3(5))*** Univ. of North Carolina Pr.

BASEBALL—RECORDS

Barry, Dan. Bottom of the 33rd: Hope, Redemption, & Baseball's Longest Game. (ENG., 2012. Illus.). 288p. pap. 14.99 *(978-0-06-201449-8(6)*, HarperPerennial) 2011. 288p. 26.99 *(978-0-06-201448-1(X))* 2011. 432p. pap. 26.99 *(978-0-06-206503-2(3)*, HarperLuxe) HarperCollins Pubs.

Brucato, Thomas W. Baseball Skippers & Their Crews: The History of Every Manager & Coach in the Major Leagues, 1871-2006. 2007. 39.95 *(978-1-878282-50-7(6))* St. Johann Pr.

Fischer, David. The Ultimate Yankees Record Book: A Complete Guide to the Most Unusual, Unbelievable, & Unbreakable Records in Yankees History. 2011. (ENG.). 213p. pap. 14.95 *(978-1-60078-520-7(4))* Triumph Bks.

Johnson, Daniel E. Japanese Baseball: A Statistical Handbook. alt. ed. 2006. (ENG.). 365p. per. 45.00 *(978-0-7864-2841-0(4))* McFarland & Co., Inc. Pubs.

Kelly, Robert E. Baseball's Offensive Greats of the Deadball Era: Best Producers Rated by Position, 1901-1919. 2009. (ENG.). 220p. pap. 45.00 *(978-0-7864-4125-9(9))* McFarland & Co., Inc. Pubs.

Kennedy, Kostya. 56: Joe Dimaggio & the Last Magic Number in Sports. 2011. (ENG., Illus.). 368p. 26.95 *(978-1-60320-177-3(7))* Time Home Entertainment, Inc.

Lewin, Josh. You Never Forget Your First: Ballplayers Recall Their Big League Debuts. 2007. (Illus.). 256p. per. 16.95 *(978-1-59797-065-5(4))* Potomac Bks., Inc.

Martirano, Ron. Baseball: The Players, the World Series, the Records. 2008. (ENG., Illus.). 238p. pap. 12.95 *(978-1-60433-011-3(2))* Cider Mill Pr. Bk. Pubs., LLC.

Nemec, David & Flatow, Scott. Great Baseball Feats, Facts, & Firsts. 2010th ed. 2010. (ENG.). 464p. (gr. 12-18). 7.99 *(978-0-451-22955-7(X)*, Signet) Penguin Group (USA) Inc.

Nemec, David, et al. Great Baseball Feats, Facts & Firsts 2011. 2011. (ENG.). 480p. (gr. 12). 7.99 *(978-0-451-23296-0(8)*, Signet) Penguin Group (USA) Inc.

Nurse, Ammie L. Baseball's All-Star Game Reference Guide 1933-2007: 78 Games in 74 Years. 2007. 500p. per. 43.95 *(978-1-58736-740-3(8))* Wheatmark.

Pepe, Phil. 1961: The Inside Story of the Maris-Mantle Home Run Chase. 2011. (ENG.). 288p. 20.00 *(978-1-60078-390-6(2))* Triumph Bks.

Siwoff, Seymour, ed. Elias Book of Baseball Records: 2008 Edition. 2008. 420p. 21.95 net. *(978-0-917050-10-7(X))* Elias Sports Bureau, Inc.

Society for American Baseball Research. The SABR Baseball List & Record Book: Baseball's Most Fascinating Records & Unusual Statistics. Spatz, Lyle, ed. 2007. (ENG., Illus.). 496p. pap. 17.95 *(978-1-4165-3245-3(5)*, Scribner) Scribner.

Sporting News, creator. Cardinal Nation. 4th ed. 2006. (ENG., Illus.). 256p. 29.95 *(978-0-89204-888-5(3))* Sporting News Publishing Co.

Sporting News Staff. The Complete Baseball Record & Fact Book: 2007 Edition. 2007. (ENG.). 424p. pap. 22.95 *(978-0-89204-865-6(4))* Sporting News Publishing Co.

Sports Illustrated Staff & Kennedy, Kostya. 56: Joe Dimaggio & the Last Magic Number in Sports. 2012. (ENG.). 368p. pap., pap. 16.95 ***(978-1-60320-913-7(1))*** Time Home Entertainment, Inc.

Swaine, Rick. The Integration of Major League Baseball: A Team by Team History. alt. ed. 2012. (ENG., Illus.). 279p. pap. 25.00 ***(978-0-7864-6935-2(8))*** McFarland & Co., Inc. Pubs.

Wubbena, Dennis. The Baseball Bluebook (2008 College Edition) 2008 College Baseball Guide & Scouting Register. 2008. 550p. per. 65.00 *(978-0-9788368-2-5(0))* Baseball Bluebook, The.

—The Baseball Bluebook (2008 Professional Edition) 2008 Professional Edition. 2008. 500p. per. 65.00 *(978-0-9788368-3-2(9))* Baseball Bluebook, The.

BASEBALL—RULES

Demetriou, George. College Baseball Rules: An In-Depth Analysis of NCAA Baseball Rules. 2009. 239p. pap. 19.95 *(978-1-58208-122-9(0))* Referee Enterprises, Inc.

Formosa, Dan & Hamburger, Paul. Baseball. 2nd ed. 2008. (Baseball Field Guide: an in-Depth Illustrated Guide to The Ser.). (ENG., Illus.). 128p. pap. 14.00 (978-0-306-81653-6(9)) Da Capo Pr., Inc.

Hopkins, B. Elliot, ed. NFHS High School Baseball Rules Simplified & Illustrated. 2009. (Illus.). 180p. pap. 7.95 (978-1-58208-121-2(2)) Referee Enterprises, Inc.

Lebovitz, Hal. Ask Hal: Answers to Fans' Most Interesting Questions about Baseball Rules, from a Hall-of-Fame Sportswriter. 2007. (Illus.). 181p. per. 14.95 (978-1-59851-034-8(7)) Gray and Company, Publishers.

Rowe, Martin & Lomke, Evander. Right off the Bat: Baseball, Cricket, Literature, & Life. 2011. (ENG., Illus.). 220p. pap. 16.95 **(978-1-58988-069-6(2))** Dry, Paul Bks., Inc.

Silva, Diedre & Koney, Jackie. The Savvy Girls of Summer: Every Woman's Guide to Understanding & Enjoying Baseball. 2007. 320p. 24.95 (978-1-60239-122-2(X)) Skyhorse Publishing Co., Inc.

Sporting News Staff. Official Baseball Rules 2007 Edition. League Baseball Staff, ed. 2007. (ENG.). 104p. pap. 7.95 (978-0-89204-868-7(9)) Andrews McMeel Publishing.

Triumph Books Staff, ed. 2011 Official Rules of Major League Baseball. 2011. (Official Rules Ser.). (ENG.). 240p. pap. 9.95 (978-1-60078-551-1(4)) Triumph Bks.

Turbow, Jason & Duca, Michael. The Baseball Codes: Beanballs, Sign Stealing & Bench-Clearing Brawls - The Unwritten Rules of America's Pastime. 2010. (ENG.). 304p. 25.00 (978-0-375-42469-4(5), Pantheon) Knopf Doubleday Publishing Group.

—Baseball Codes: Beanballs, Sign Stealing, & Bench-Clearing Brawls - The Unwritten Rules of America's Pastime. 2011. (ENG.). 304p. pap. 15.00 (978-0-307-27862-3(X), Anchor) Knopf Doubleday Publishing Group.

BASEBALL—SOCIAL ASPECTS

Alpert, Rebecca T. Out of Left Field: Jews & Black Baseball. 2011. (ENG., Illus.). 256p. 27.95 (978-0-19-539900-4(5)) Oxford Univ. Pr., Inc.

Benson, John. Baseball Wisdom: What the Game Teaches Us. 2006. lib. bdg. 17.95 (978-1-880876-60-2(4)) Diamond Library.

Borer, Michael Ian. Faithful to Fenway: Believing in Boston, Baseball, & America's Most Beloved Ballpark. 2008. (ENG., Illus.). 288p. pap. 19.95 (978-0-8147-9977-2(9)) New York Univ. Pr.

Briley, Ron, ed. The Politics of Baseball: Essays on the Pastime & Power at Home & Abroad. 2010. (ENG., Illus.). 256p. pap. 39.95 (978-0-7864-4129-7(1)) McFarland & Co., Inc. Pubs.

Butterworth, Michael L. Baseball & Rhetorics of Purity: The National Pastime & American Identity During the War on Terror. 2010. xi, 233p. (978-0-8173-8397-8(2)); (ENG.). 248p. 45.00 (978-0-8173-1710-2(4)) Univ. of Alabama Pr.

Carter, Thomas F. The Quality of Home Runs: The Passion, Politics, & Language of Cuban Baseball. 2008. (ENG., Illus.). 256p. (C). pap. 23.95 (978-0-8223-4276-2(6)) Duke Univ. Pr.

—The Quality of Home Runs: The Passion, Politics, & Language of Cuban Baseball. 2008. (ENG., Illus.). 256p. (C). 79.95 (978-0-8223-4253-3(7)) Duke Univ. Pr.

Cassuto, Leonard & Partridge, Stephen, eds. The Cambridge Companion to Baseball. 2011. (ENG., Illus.). 280p. 82.00 (978-0-521-76182-6(4)); pap. 24.99 (978-0-521-14575-6(9)) Cambridge Univ. Pr.

Castle, George. When the Game Changed: An Oral History of Baseball's True Golden Age, 1969-1979. 2010. (ENG., Illus.). 336p. 24.95 (978-1-59921-933-2(6), Lyons Pr.) Globe Pequot Pr., The.

CONGDON, L. E. E. Baseball & Memory: Winning, Losing, & the Remembrance of Things Past. 2011. (Illus.). 192p. 25.00 (978-1-58731-063-8(5)) St. Augustine's Pr., Inc.

Dupuis, Kelley. Three Flies Up: My Father, Baseball & Me. 2008. 392p. pap. 15.95 (978-1-4327-2155-8(0)) Outskirts Pr., Inc.

Epstein, Dan. Big Hair & Plastic Grass: A Funky Ride Through Baseball & America in the Swinging '70s. 2010. (ENG., Illus.). 352p. 25.99 (978-0-312-60754-8(7), Dunne, Thomas Bks.) St. Martin's Pr.

Forney, Craig. The Holy Trinity of American Sports: Civil Religion in Football, Baseball, & Basketball. 2010. (Sports & Religion Ser.). 224p. pap. 25.00 (978-0-88146-173-2(3)) Mercer Univ. Pr.

Frost, Mark. Game Six: The Triumph of America's Pastime. 416p. 2010. (ENG.). pap. 15.99 (978-1-4013-1026-4(5)) 2009. 26.99 (978-1-4013-2310-3(3)) Hyperion Pr.

Hample, Zack. The Baseball: Stunts, Scandals, & Secrets Beneath the Stitches. 2011. (Vintage Ser.). (Illus.). 368p. pap. 14.95 (978-0-307-47545-9(X), Vintage) Knopf Doubleday Publishing Group.

Jamail, Milton H. Full Count: Inside Cuban Baseball. 2008. (ENG.). 180p. pap. 20.00 (978-1-4223-9277-5(5)) DIANE Publishing Co.

Koney, Jackie & Silva, Deidre. It Takes More Than Balls: The Savvy Girls' Guide to Understanding & Enjoying Baseball. 2008. (ENG.). 266p. pap. 14.95 (978-1-60239-631-9(0), 239631) Skyhorse Publishing Co., Inc.

Lamb, Chris. Conspiracy of Silence: Sportswriters & the Long Campaign to Desegregate Baseball. 2012. (ENG.). 416p. 39.95 **(978-0-8032-1076-9(0))** Univ. of Nebraska Pr.

Lemay, Edward A. Getting on Base: The Vi-Jon Team & the American Dream One Hundred Years & More with the Brunner Family. 2010. (Illus.). 240p. (978-1-57864-585-5(9)) Donning Co. Pubs.

Lockwood, Kathleen. Major League Bride: An Inside Look at Life Outside the Ballpark. 2010. (ENG., Illus.). 230p. pap. 29.95 (978-0-7864-4560-8(2)) McFarland & Co., Inc. Pubs.

Lynch, Frank. Orioles Rise from the Ashes: Baltimore's Journey to the Majors. 2006. (ENG.). 88p. per. 16.95 (978-1-4241-6034-1(0)) PublishAmerica, Inc.

Mills, Dorothy Seymour. Chasing Baseball: Our Obsession with Its History, Numbers, People & Places. 2010. (ENG., Illus.). 266p. pap. 39.95 (978-0-7864-4289-8(1)) McFarland & Co., Inc. Pubs.

Nathanson, Mitchell. A People's History of Baseball. 2012. xiv, 275p. E-Book **(978-0-252-09392-0(5))**; (ENG., Illus.). 272p. 29.95 **(978-0-252-03680-4(8))** Univ. of Illinois Pr.

Powers-Beck, Jeffrey. The American Indian Integration of Baseball. 2009. (ENG.). 304p. pap. 19.95 (978-0-8032-2509-1(1)) Univ. of Nebraska Pr.

Reynolds, Bill. '78: The Boston Red Sox, a Historic Game, & a Divided City. 2010. (ENG.). 320p. (gr. 12-18). 15.00 (978-0-451-22922-9(3), N A L Trade) Penguin Group (USA) Inc.

Ring, Jennifer. Stolen Bases: Why American Girls Don't Play Baseball. 2009. (ENG., Illus.). 216p. 25.95 (978-0-252-03282-0(9)) Univ. of Illinois Pr.

Ruck, Rob. Raceball: How the Major Leagues Colonized the Black & Latin Game. (ENG., Illus.). 288p. 2012. pap. 18.00 **(978-0-8070-4807-8(0))** 2011. 25.95 (978-0-8070-4805-4(4)) Beacon Pr.

Ryczek, William J. Baseball's First Inning: A History of the National Pastime Through the Civil War. 2009. (ENG., Illus.). 269p. pap. 29.95 (978-0-7864-4194-5(1)) McFarland & Co., Inc. Pubs.

Simons, William M., ed. The Cooperstown Symposium on Baseball & American Culture, 2005-2006. 2007. (Cooperstown Symposium on Baseball & American Culture Ser.). (ENG., Illus.). 299p. per. 45.00 (978-0-7864-3212-7(8)) McFarland & Co., Inc. Pubs.

—The Cooperstown Symposium on Baseball & American Culture, 2009-2010. 2011. (Cooperstown Symposium Ser.). (ENG., Illus.). 270p. pap. 38.00 (978-0-7864-3570-8(4)) McFarland & Co., Inc. Pubs.

Wiseman, John B., ed. Joy in Mudville: Essays on Baseball & American Life. 2009. (ENG., Illus.). 252p. pap. 39.95 (978-0-7864-4228-7(X)) McFarland & Co., Inc. Pubs.

BASEBALL—TRAINING

Alejo, Bob, et al. Double Play: Training & Nutrition Advice from the World's Experts in Baseball, 1 vol. 2008. (ENG., Illus.). 128p. pap. 14.95 (978-1-59120-180-9(2)) Basic Health Pubns., Inc.

American Baseball Coaches Association. Gold Glove Baseball. 2006. (ENG., Illus.). 264p. per. 19.95 (978-0-7360-6263-3(7)) Human Kinetics Pubs.

Baker, Dirk. Baseball Drills for Young People: More Than 180 Games & Activities for Preschool to High School Players. 2nd rev. ed. 2008. (ENG., Illus.). 195p. pap. 24.95 (978-0-7864-3725-2(1)) McFarland & Co., Inc. Pubs.

Baseball Speed Training: The complete guide to improving your baseball Speed. 2007. per. 18.95 (978-0-9779098-1-0(6)) Everglades Publishing.

Bennett, Bob. Catching Fundamentals & Techniques. 2nd ed. 2007. (Coaches Choice Ser.). (Illus.). 111p. pap. 24.95 (978-1-58518-054-7(8)) Coaches Choice.

House, Tom. Fastball Fitness: The Art & Science of Training to Throw with Real Velocity. 2007. (Illus.). 142p. per. 19.95 (978-1-58518-037-0(8)) Coaches Choice.

Knouse, Tim. Amazing Baseball Tips: A Guide to Youth Baseball & Softball for Beginner Coaches, Players, & Parents. 2009. 112p. pap. 17.95 (978-1-4389-5737-1(8)) AuthorHouse.

Maher, Charlie. The Complete Mental Game of Baseball: Taking Charge of the Process, on & off the Field. 2011. 272p. 25.95 **(978-1-4634-0220-4(1))**; pap. 19.95 **(978-1-4634-0221-1(X))** AuthorHouse.

Mongero, Trent. Winning Baseball for Beginner to Intermediate Play. 2011. (Coach's Companion Ser.). (ENG., Illus.). 256p. 19.95 (978-1-4027-5808-9(1)) Sterling Publishing Co., Inc.

Okihiro, Michael M. Coach Manju Nitta's Baseball Secrets. 2011. 116p. pap. 12.37 **(978-1-4567-6219-3(2))** AuthorHouse.

Ripken, Cal, Jr., et al. Coaching Youth Baseball the Ripken Way. 2006. (ENG., Illus.). 264p. pap. 16.95 (978-0-7360-6782-9(5)) Human Kinetics Pubs.

Society for American Baseball Research (SABR). Baseball Research Journal (BRJ), Volume 40 #2. 2011. (ENG.). 128p. pap. 14.95 **(978-1-933599-21-2(9))** Society for American Baseball Research.

Stack Media Staff. Baseball Training: For the Athlete, By the Athlete. 2010. (ENG.). 176p. pap. 16.95 (978-1-60078-366-1(X)) Triumph Bks.

Swope, Bob. Youth Baseball & Softball Drills, Plays, & Situations Handbook. 2007. (Illus.). 108p. (J). per. 16.95 (978-0-9772817-8-7(7)) Jacobob Pr., LLC.

Tamborra, Steve. Complete Conditioning for Baseball. 2007. (ENG., Illus.). 272p. 24.95 (978-0-7360-6243-5(2)) Human Kinetics Pubs.

Taussig, Donald. Baseball: The Balanced Hand Method of Hitting. 2008. 72p. pap. 17.95 (978-1-4327-3075-8(4)) Outskirts Pr., Inc.

BASEBALL—UMPIRING

Caillault, Jean-Pierre, compiled by. The Complete New York Clipper Baseball Biographies: More Than 800 Sketches of Players, Managers, Owners, Umpires, Reporters & Others, 1859-1903, 2 vols. 2009. (ENG., Illus.). 758p. pap. 59.95 (978-0-7864-3373-5(6)) McFarland & Co., Inc. Pubs.

Goldblatt, Andrew. Major League Umpires' Performance, 2007-2010: A Comprehensive Statistical Review. 2011. (ENG., Illus.). 206p. pap. 39.95 (978-0-7864-6058-8(X)) McFarland & Co., Inc. Pubs.

Motley, Bob, et al. Ruling over Monarchs, Giants, & Stars: True Tales of Breaking Barriers, Umpiring Baseball Legends, & Wild Adventures in the Negro Leagues. 2012. (ENG., Illus.). 240p. 24.95 **(978-1-61321-059-8(0)**, 613059) Skyhorse Publishing Co., Inc.

Schafer, Michael. Life Behind the Mask: Memoir of a Youth Baseball Umpire. 2011. (ENG., Illus.). 184p. pap. 19.99 (978-0-7864-5945-2(X)) McFarland & Co., Inc. Pubs.

Stewart, Wayne. You're the Umpire: 139 Scenarios to Test Your Baseball Knowledge. 2010. (ENG., Illus.). 224p. pap. 8.95 (978-1-60239-793-4(7), 239793) Skyhorse Publishing Co., Inc.

Weber, Bruce. As They See 'Em: A Fan's Travels in the Land of Umpires. 2010. (ENG.). 368p. pap. 16.00 (978-0-7432-9413-3(0), Scribner) Scribner.

BASEBALL—YEARBOOKS

Borawski, Brian, et al, contrib. by. The Hardball Times Baseball Annual. 2006. (Hardball Times Baseball Annual Ser.). (Illus.). 350p. per. 19.95 (978-0-87946-312-0(0)) ACTA Pubns.

Lebowitz, Paul. Paul Lebowitz's 2011 Baseball Guide: A Complete Guide to the 2011 Baseball Season. 2011. 400p. pap. 25.95 (978-1-4620-0231-3(5)) iUniverse, Inc.

Spaulding. Spaulding's Official Baseball Guide, 1894. 21.95 (978-0-8488-1539-4(4)) Amereon LTD.

Tsao, Bryan, et al, eds. The Hardball Times Baseball Annual. 2007. (Hardball Times Baseball Annual Ser.). (Illus.). 366p. per. 19.95 (978-0-87946-341-0(4)) ACTA Pubns.

Zesch, Steve, ed. 2009 Cardinals All Star Game Yearbook. 2009. 200p. pap. 15.00 (978-0-9823575-5-2(9)) Big River Distribution.

BASEBALL—ASIA

Yu, Junwei. Playing in Isolation: A History of Baseball in Taiwan. 2007. (ENG., Illus.). 249p. 26.95 (978-0-8032-1140-7(6)) Univ. of Nebraska Pr.

BASEBALL—EUROPE

Chetwynd, Josh. Baseball in Europe: A Country by Country History. 2008. (ENG., Illus.). 344p. pap. 35.00 (978-0-7864-3724-5(3)) McFarland & Co., Inc. Pubs.

Chetwynd, Josh & Belton, Brian A. British Baseball & the West Ham Club: History of a 1930s Professional Team in East London. 2006. (ENG., Illus.). 272p. per. 29.95 (978-0-7864-2594-5(6)) McFarland & Co., Inc. Pubs.

BASEBALL—JAPAN

Fitts, Robert K. Wally Yonamine: The Man Who Changed Japanese Baseball. 2008. (ENG., Illus.). 368p. 26.95 (978-0-8032-1381-4(6)) Univ. of Nebraska Pr.

Johnson, Daniel E. Japanese Baseball: A Statistical Handbook. alt. ed. 2006. (ENG.). 365p. per. 45.00 (978-0-7864-2841-0(4)) McFarland & Co., Inc. Pubs.

Whiting, Robert. You Gotta Have Wa. 2nd ed. 2009. (Vintage Ser.). (ENG., Illus.). 416p. pap. 15.95 (978-0-307-45597-0(1)) Knopf, Alfred A. Inc.

BASEBALL—LATIN AMERICA

Bjarkman, Peter C. A History of Cuban Baseball, 1864-2006. 2007. (ENG., Illus.). 496p. 49.95 (978-0-7864-2829-8(5)) McFarland & Co., Inc. Pubs.

Carter, Thomas F. The Quality of Home Runs: The Passion, Politics, & Language of Cuban Baseball. 2008. (ENG., Illus.). 256p. (C). pap. 23.95 (978-0-8223-4276-2(6)) Duke Univ. Pr.

—The Quality of Home Runs: The Passion, Politics, & Language of Cuban Baseball. 2008. (ENG., Illus.). 256p. (C). 79.95 (978-0-8223-4253-3(7)) Duke Univ. Pr.

Figueredo, Jorge S. Who's Who in Cuban Baseball, 1878-1961. alt. ed. 2007. (ENG., Illus.). 422p. per. 55.00 (978-0-7864-3030-7(3)) McFarland & Co., Inc. Pubs.

Hernández, Lou. The Rise of the Latin American Baseball Leagues, 1947-1961: Cuba, the Dominican Republic, Mexico, Nicaragua, Panama, Puerto Rico & Venezuela. 2011. (ENG., Illus.). 412p. pap. 49.95 (978-0-7864-6384-8(8)) McFarland & Co., Inc. Pubs.

Jamail, Milton H. Full Count: Inside Cuban Baseball. 2008. (ENG.). 180p. pap. 20.00 (978-1-4223-9277-5(5)) DIANE Publishing Co.

—Venezuelan Bust, Baseball Boom: Andrés Reiner & Scouting on the New Frontier. 2008. (ENG., Illus.). 284p. pap. 19.95 (978-0-8032-1571-9(1), Bison Bks.) Univ. of Nebraska Pr.

Kurlansky, Mark. The Eastern Stars: How Baseball Changed the Dominican Town of San Pedro de Macoris. 2011. (ENG.). 352p. (gr. 12). 16.00 (978-1-59448-505-3(4), Riverhead Trade (Paperbacks)) Penguin Group (USA) Inc.

McKelvey, G. Richard. Mexican Raiders in the Major Leagues: The Pasquel Brothers vs. Organized Baseball 1946. 2006. (ENG., Illus.). 211p. per. 29.95 (978-0-7864-2563-1(6)) McFarland & Co., Inc. Pubs.

Nieto, Severo. Early U. S. Blackball Teams in Cuba: Box Scores, Rosters & Statistics from the Files of Cuba's Foremost Baseball Researcher. 2008. (Latino & Latin American Studies). (ENG., Illus.). 240p. per. 35.00 (978-0-7864-1928-9(8)) McFarland & Co., Inc. Pubs.

Virtue, John. South of the Color Barrier: How Jorge Pasquel & the Mexican League Pushed Baseball Toward Racial Integration. 2007. (ENG., Illus.). 239p. per. 29.95 (978-0-7864-3293-6(4)) McFarland & Co., Inc. Pubs.

Vitti, Jim. Brooklyn Dodgers in Cuba. 2011. (Images of Baseball Ser.). (Illus.). 128p. pap. 21.99 (978-0-7385-7427-1(9)) Arcadia Publishing.

BASEBALL CARDS

Beels, Eugene. Beels Baseball Rookie Cards 2007. 2007. vi, 517p. (978-0-8059-8471-2(2), Red Lead Pr.) Dorrance Publishing Co., Inc.

Clemens, Joe. 2010 Baseball Card Price Guide. 24th ed. 2010. (ENG.). 1376p. pap. 22.99 (978-1-4402-1336-6(4)) Krause Pubns.

Fleischer, Brian, ed. Beckett Baseball Card Price Gd-#33. 2011. 800p. pap. 34.95 (978-1-930692-95-4(1)) Beckett Media LLP.

Gall, John. Sayonara Home Run! The Art of the Japanese Baseball Card. 2008. (ENG.). 191p. pap. 19.00 (978-1-4223-9446-5(8)) DIANE Publishing Co.

Hanaway, Ken. Un-Commons: COLLECTING TREASURES 1950's EDITION with 1948 And 49. 2010. 164p. pap. 13.99 (978-1-4490-6358-0(6)) AuthorHouse.

Jamieson, Dave. Mint Condition: How Baseball Cards Became an American Obsession. (ENG., Illus.). 2011. 288p. pap. 15.95 (978-0-8021-4532-1(9), Grove Pr.) 2010. 320p. 25.00 (978-0-8021-1939-1(5), Atlantic Monthly Pr.) Grove/Atlantic, Inc.

Lemke, Bob. Standard Catalog of Vintage Baseball Cards. 21st ed. 2011. (ENG.). 696p. pap. 29.99 (978-1-4402-2378-5(5)) Krause Pubns.

—2011 Standard Catalog of Baseball Cards. 2010. (ENG.). 1848p. pap. 44.99 (978-1-4402-1371-7(2)) Krause Pubns.

Official Baseball Card Cross-Reference Guide, 1989-1990. 128p. 5.95 (978-0-88128-367-9(3)) Martin-Smith Publishing, Inc.

O'Keeffe, Michael & Thompson, Teri. The Card: Collectors, Con Men, & the True Story of History's Most Desired Baseball Card. 2008. 272p. pap. 14.95 (978-0-06-112393-1(5)) HarperCollins Pubs.

Oser, Khyber, et al. Cardboard Gems: A Century of Baseball Cards & Their Stories, 1869-1969. 2008. (ENG., Illus.). 192p. 35.00 (978-0-9716097-2-3(1), Mastro Auctions (Acc)) Antique Collectors' Club GBR. Dist: National Bk. Network.

Wilker, Josh. Cardboard Gods. 2011. (ENG.). 243p. pap. 15.95 (978-1-61620-069-5(3), 1616200693) Algonquin Bks. of Chapel Hill.

—Cardboard Gods: An All-American Tale Told Through Baseball Cards. 2010. (ENG.). 208p. 24.95 (978-1-934734-16-2(0)) Seven Footer Pr.

Woods, Bob. Yankee Greats. 2012. (Illus.). 224p. 19.95 **(978-1-4197-0272-3(6))** Stewart, Tabori & Chang.

Zappala, Tom & Zappala, Ellen. The T206 Collection: The Players & Their Stories. 2010. (ENG., Illus.). 224p. 38.00 (978-1-931807-94-4(9)) Randall, Peter E. Pub.

BASEBALL CLUBS

see Baseball Teams

BASEBALL COACHING

see Baseball—Coaching

BASEBALL FANS

Andrews, Tom & Wolfe, Rich. For Milwaukee Braves Fans Only! 2011. (ENG., Illus.). 256p. 24.95 (978-0-9846278-0-6(4)) Clerisy Pr.

Brand, Dana. Last Days of Shea: Delight & Despair in the Life of a Mets Fan. 2009. (ENG.). 280p. pap. 16.95 (978-1-58979-457-3(5)) Taylor Trade Publishing.

Chambers, Timothy, ed. Ballparks Across America: E-Mails from a Fan on the Road, Volume 1. 2007. 19.95 (978-0-9793604-1-1(2)) Jones, James.

—Ballparks Across America: E-Mails from a Fan on the Road, Volume 2. 2007. 19.95 (978-0-9793604-2-8(0)) Jones, James.

Chambers, Timothy C., ed. Ballparks Across America: E-Mails from a Fan on the Road, Volume 3. 2008. (Illus.). 314p. pap. 19.95 (978-0-9793604-3-5(9)) Jones, James.

Gordon, Dan, ed. Your Brain on Cubs: Inside the Heads of Players & Fans. 2008. (Illus.). 150p. 19.95 (978-1-932594-28-7(0)) Dana Pr., The.

Heller, Jane. Confessions of a She-Fan: The Course of True Love with the New York Yankees. 2009. (ENG.). 272p. 24.95 (978-1-59486-898-6(0)) Rodale Pr., Inc.

Jones, James K. Ballparks Across America: E-Mails from a Fan on the Road. 2007. lib. bdg. 32.95 (978-0-9793604-0-4(4)) Jones, James.

Karpin, Howie. Yankees Essential: Everything You Need to Know to Be a Real Fan! 2007. (Essential (Triumph) Ser.). (ENG., Illus.). 224p. 19.95 (978-1-57243-817-0(7)) Triumph Bks.

Koney, Jackie & Silva, Deidre. It Takes More Than Balls: The Savvy Girls' Guide to Understanding & Enjoying Baseball. 2008. (ENG.). 266p. pap. 14.95 (978-1-60239-631-9(0), 239631) Skyhorse Publishing Co., Inc.

Loverro, Thom. Orioles Essential: Everything You Need to Know to Be a Real Fan! 2007. (Essential (Triumph) Ser.). (ENG., Illus.). 208p. 19.95 (978-1-57243-832-3(0)) Triumph Bks.

Megdal, Howard. Taking the Field: A Fan's Quest to Run the Team He Loves. 2011. (ENG.). 256p. 25.00 (978-1-60819-579-4(1)) Bloomsbury Publishing.

Milano, Alyssa. Safe at Home: Confessions of a Baseball Fanatic. 2010. (ENG.). 272p. pap. 15.99 (978-0-06-162511-4(6)) HarperCollins Pubs.

Mnookin, Seth. Feeding the Monster: How Money, Smarts, & Nerve Took a Team to the Top. 2007. (ENG., Illus.). 464p. pap. 15.00 (978-0-7432-8682-4(0)) Simon & Schuster.

Poland, Hugh. Intentional Walk: More Devotions for Baseball Fans. 2009. 160p. pap. 14.00 (978-0-8170-1543-5(4)) Judson Pr.

Richter, Andrew J. Baseball with an Opinion. 2007. 284p. per. 16.95 (978-1-59824-503-5(1)) E-BookTime LLC.

Roeper, Richard. Sox & the City: A Fan's Love Affair with the White Sox from the Heartbreak of '67 to the Wizards of Oz. (ENG., Illus.). 240p. 2007. per. 14.95 (978-1-55652-679-4(2)) 2006. 19.95 (978-1-55652-650-3(4)) Chicago Review Pr., Inc.

Santelli, Robert & Santelli, Jenna. The Baseball Fan's Bucket List: 162 Things You Must Do, See, Get, & Experience Before You Die. 2010. (ENG.). 288p. pap. 15.95 (978-0-7624-3855-6(X), Running Pr.) Running Pr. Bk. Pubs.

Warner, Charles R. The Team America Loves to Hate: Why Baseball Fans Despise the New York Yankees, 1 vol. 2009. 148p. 34.95 (978-0-313-35704-6(8), C35704, Praeger Pubs.) Greenwood Publishing Group, Inc.

Wasif, Andy. Green Monster University: Creating Die-Hard Red Sox Fans Since 1901. 2008. (Illus.). 116p. per. 16.95 *(978-0-9796722-2-4(8))* Dirty Water Publishing.

Wasif, Andy & D'Elia, Rick. How to Talk to a Yankee Fan. 2nd rev. ed. 2007. (ENG., Illus.). 230p. per. 16.95 *(978-0-9796722-0-0(1))* Dirty Water Publishing.

BASEBALL FIELDS

Antos, Jason D. Shea Stadium. 2007. (Images of Sports Ser.). (Illus.). 127p. per. 19.99 *(978-0-7385-5456-3(1))* Arcadia Publishing.

Barra, Allen. Rickwood Field: A Century in America's Oldest Ballpark. 2010. (ENG., Illus.). 367p. 27.95 *(978-0-393-06933-4(8),* 6933) Norton, W. W. & Co., Inc.

Belth, Alex, ed. Lasting Yankee Stadium Memories: 45 Unforgettable Tales from the House That Ruth Built. 2010. (ENG., Illus.). 256p. 19.95 *(978-1-60239-979-2(4),* 239979) Skyhorse Publishing Co., Inc.

Benson, Michael. Ballparks of North America: A Comprehensive Historical Reference to Baseball Grounds, Yards & Stadiums, 1845 To 1988. alt. ed. 2009. (ENG., Illus.). 505p. pap. 39.95 *(978-0-7864-4421-2(5))* McFarland & Co., Inc. Pubs.

Borer, Michael Ian. Faithful to Fenway: Believing in Boston, Baseball, & America's Most Beloved Ballpark. 2008. (ENG., Illus.). 288p. pap. 19.95 *(978-0-8147-9977-2(9))* New York Univ. Pr.

Brand, Dana. Last Days of Shea: Delight & Despair in the Life of a Mets Fan. 2009. (ENG.). 280p. pap. 16.95 *(978-1-58979-457-3(5))* Taylor Trade Publishing.

Chambers, Timothy, ed. Ballparks Across America: E-Mails from a Fan on the Road, Volume 1. 2007. 19.95 *(978-0-9793604-1-1(2))* Jones, James.

—Ballparks Across America: E-Mails from a Fan on the Road, Volume 2. 2007. 19.95 *(978-0-9793604-2-8(0))* Jones, James.

Chambers, Timothy C., ed. Ballparks Across America: E-Mails from a Fan on the Road, Volume 3. 2008. (Illus.). 314p. pap. 19.95 *(978-0-9793604-3-5(9))* Jones, James.

Cicotello, David & Louisa, Angelo J., eds. Forbes Field: Essays & Memories of the Pirate's Historic Ballpark, 1909-1971. 2007. (McFarland Historic Ballparks Ser.). (ENG., Illus.). 254p. per. 39.95 *(978-0-7864-2754-3(X))* McFarland & Co., Inc. Pubs.

Cryan, Mark. Cradle of the Game: Baseball & Ballparks in North Carolina. 2008. 400p. pap. 18.95 *(978-0-9752706-3-9(X))* August Pubns.

Curtis, Stan. Covering All the Bases: One Fan's Quest to Visit Every Major League Ballpark. 2010. *(978-1-889274-38-6(0))* Posterity Pr.

Fischer, David. A Yankee Stadium Scrapbook: A Lifetime of Memories. 2008. (ENG., Illus.). 140p. 24.95 *(978-0-7624-3322-3(1),* Running Pr.) Running Pr. Bk. Pubs.

Fox, Jeff. Yankee Stadium: A Fan Says Good-bye: the Final Game. 2009. (ENG., Illus.). 80p. pap. 23.95 *(978-0-9823656-0-1(8))* Veridico Publishing LLC.

Frommer, Harvey. Remembering Fenway Park: An Oral & Narrative History of the Home of the Boston Red Sox. 2011. (ENG., Illus.). 240p. 45.00 *(978-1-58479-852-1(1))* Stewart, Tabori & Chang.

—Remembering Yankee Stadium: An Oral & Narrative History of the House That Ruth Built. 2008. (ENG., Illus.). 240p. 45.00 *(978-1-58479-716-6(9))* Stewart, Tabori & Chang.

Gaming the Tax Code: Public Subsidies, Private Profits, & Big League Sports in New York: Hearing Before the Subcommittee on Domestic Policy of the Committee on Oversight & Government Reform, House of Representatives, One Hundred Tenth Congress, Second Session, September 18, 2008. 2009. iii, 104p. *(978-0-16-083321-2(3),* 552-070-39146-1) United States Government Printing Office.

Gaming the Tax Code: The New York Yankees & the City of New York Respond to Questions about the New Yankee Stadium: Hearing Before the Subcommittee on Domestic Policy of the Committee on Oversight & Government Reform, House of Representatives, One Hundred Tenth Congress, Second Session, October 24, 2008. 2009. iii, 89p. *(978-0-16-083343-4(4),* 552-070-39167-3) United States Government Printing Office.

Gmelch, George & Weiner, J. J. In the Ballpark: The Working Lives of Baseball People. 2006. (ENG., Illus.). 1p. pap. 17.95 *(978-0-8032-7127-2(1),* Bison Bks.) Univ. of Nebraska Pr.

Hawcock, David & League Baseball Organisation Staff. Wrigley Field. 2010. (ENG., Illus.). 16p. 25.00 *(978-0-7893-2016-2(9))* Universe Publishing.

Hays, Paul A. Apathetic Neglect, Fiscal Carelessness: The Huntsville Stars' Attendance Dilemma. 2012. pap. 12.95 ***(978-0-7414-7070-6(5))*** Infinity Publishing.

Hermayln, Gary & Greene, Anthony C. Yankee Stadium: 1923-2008. 2009. (Images of Sports Ser.). (ENG., Illus.). 128p. pap. 21.99 *(978-0-7385-6596-5(2))* Arcadia Publishing.

Hernandez, Keith & Silverman, Matthew. Shea Good-Bye: The Untold Inside Story of the Historic 2008 Season. 2009. (ENG.). 256p. 19.95 *(978-1-60078-170-4(5))* Triumph Bks.

Institute of Transportation Engineers Staff, contrib. by. Public Transit Access to Major League Ballparks: An ITE Informational Report. 2007. *(978-1-933452-29-6(3))* Institute of Transportation Engineers.

Jones, James K. Ballparks Across America: E-Mails from a Fan on the Road. 2007. lib. bdg. 32.95 *(978-0-9793604-0-4(4))* Jones, James.

Jones, Tom. Working at the Ballpark: The Fascinating Lives of Baseball People from Peanut Vendors & Broadcasters to Players & Managers. 2008. (Illus.). 361p. pap. 17.95 *(978-1-60239-226-7(9))* Skyhorse Publishing Co., Inc.

Jordan, David M. Closing 'Em Down: Final Games at Thirteen Classic Ballparks. 2010. (ENG., Illus.). 224p. pap. 29.95 *(978-0-7864-4968-2(3))* McFarland & Co., Inc. Pubs.

Klekowski, James J. 1990 So Long Old Comiskey Park. 2006. 25.00 *(978-0-9714950-2-9(5),* 10000) Ellis Avenue Studios.

Krantz, Les. Yankee Stadium: A Tribute - 85 Years of Memories, 1923-2008. 2008. (ENG., Illus.). 176p. 29.95 *(978-0-06-143860-8(X))* HarperCollins Pubs.

Leventhal, Josh. Take Me Out to the Ballpark Revised & Updated: An Illustrated Tour of Baseball Parks Past & Present Featuring Every Major League Park, Plus Minor League & Negro League Parks. 2011. (ENG., Illus.). 144p. pap. 17.95 *(978-1-57912-866-1(1),* 1579128661) Black Dog & Leventhal Pubs., Inc.

Malan, Douglas S. Muzzy Field: Tales from a Forgotten Ballpark. 2009. 320p. pap. 18.95 *(978-1-935278-84-9(3),* iUniverse Star) iUniverse, Inc.

McGee, Bob. The Greatest Ballpark Ever: Ebbets Field & the Story of the Brooklyn Dodgers. 2006. (ENG., Illus.). 358p. per. 19.95 *(978-0-8135-3601-9(4))* Rutgers Univ. Pr.

Morris, Peter. Level Playing Fields: How the Groundskeeping Murphy Brothers Shaped Baseball. 2007. (ENG., Illus.). 216p. 24.95 *(978-0-8032-1110-0(4))* Univ. of Nebraska Pr.

Muschett, Jim, ed. Citi Field: Major League Baseball. 2009. (ENG., Illus.). 16p. 25.00 *(978-0-7893-9956-4(3))* Universe Publishing.

Nichole, Schrafft & Nichole, Schrafft. A Field Guide to Washington, D. C. 2009. (Illus.). 64p. (J). pap. 16.95 *(978-1-885435-97-2(5))* Twin Lights Pubs., Inc.

Nowlin, Bill & Prime, Jim. Fenway Park at 100: Baseball's Hometown. 2012. (ENG., Illus.). 176p. 29.95 ***(978-1-61321-001-7(9),*** 613001) Skyhorse Publishing Co., Inc.

Outland, John W. Baseball Visions of the Roaring Twenties: A Fan's Photographs of More Than 400 Players & Ballparks of the Era. 2009. (ENG., Illus.). 492p. pap. 45.00 *(978-0-7864-4123-5(2))* McFarland & Co., Inc. Pubs.

Pahigian, Josh. The Ultimate Minor League Baseball Road-Trip: A Fan's Guide to AAA, AA, A, & Independent League Stadiums. 2007. (ENG., Illus.). 480p. pap. 24.95 *(978-1-59921-024-7(X),* Lyons Pr.) Globe Pequot Pr., The.

—101 Baseball Places to See Before You Strike Out. 2010. (ENG.). 240p. pap. 18.95 *(978-1-59921-884-7(4),* Lyons Pr.) Globe Pequot Pr., The.

Pitoniak, Scott. Memories of Yankee Stadium. 2008. (ENG., Illus.). 224p. 19.95 *(978-1-60078-056-1(3))* Triumph Bks.

Publications International Staff, ed. Yesterday & Today: Ballparks. 2010. 160p. 18.98 *(978-1-4508-1087-6(X))* Publications International, Ltd.

Rhodes, Greg & Erardi, John. Crosley Field: The Illustrated History of a Classic Ballpark. 2009. (ENG., Illus.). 218p. pap. 25.00 *(978-1-57860-384-8(6))* Clerisy Pr.

Robinson, Craig. Flip Flop Fly Ball: An Infographic Baseball Adventure. 2011. (ENG., Illus.). 160p. 25.00 *(978-1-60819-269-4(5))* Bloomsbury Publishing.

Sandalow, Mark & Sutton, Jim. Ballparks: A Panoramic History. 2006. (Illus.). 256p. reprint ed. 45.00 *(978-1-4223-5188-8(2))* DIANE Publishing Co.

Selter, Ronald M. Ballparks of the Deadball Era: A Comprehensive Study of Their Dimensions, Configurations & Effects on Batting, 1901-1919. (ENG., 198p. 2008. Illus.). 45.00 *(978-0-7864-3561-6(5))* 2011. pap. 25.00 *(978-0-7864-6625-2(1))* McFarland & Co., Inc. Pubs.

Shabram, Patrick L. Shabram's Guide to California's Professional Ballparks. 2007. 11.95 *(978-0-9795107-0-0(8))* BAEB Publishing.

Shannon, Bill & Hooker, Richard. Ballparks. 51.95 *(978-0-8488-1561-5(0))* Amereon LTD.

Shaughnessy, Dan. Fenway, Expanded & Updated: A Biography in Words & Pictures. 2007. (ENG., Illus.). 192p. 29.95 *(978-0-618-73736-9(7))* Houghton Mifflin Harcourt Trade & Reference Pubs.

Smith, Mike. Busch Stadium - the First Season. 2006. 34.95 *(978-0-9661397-4-7(7));* im. lthr. 79.95 *(978-0-9661397-5-4(5))* St. Louis Post-Dispatch.

Stout, Glenn. Fenway 1912: The Birth of a Ballpark, a Championship Season, & Fenway's Remarkable First Year. (ENG.). 416p. 2012. pap. 14.95 ***(978-0-547-84457-2(3),*** Mariner Bks.) 2011. (Illus.). 26.00 *(978-0-547-19562-9(1))* Houghton Mifflin Harcourt Trade & Reference Pubs.

Vancil, Mark. Yankee Stadium. 2009. (ENG.). 240p. pap. 25.00 *(978-1-4391-5598-1(4))* Gallery Pr., The IRL. Dist: Simon & Schuster, Inc.

Wadsworth Schrafft, Nichole. A Field Guide to Fenway Park. 2nd ed. 2009. (Illus.). 64p. (J). pap. 16.95 *(978-1-885435-99-6(1))* Twin Lights Pubs., Inc.

Wise Guide, creator. Wise Guide at&T Park: The Fan Navigator to San Francisco. 2008. (Wise Guides). (Illus.). 80p. per. 9.99 *(978-0-9768772-8-8(7))* Wise Guides, LLC.

BASEBALL FOR CHILDREN

see also Little League Baseball

African Americans Reviving Baseball in Inner Cities. 2008. pap. 19.99 *(978-0-9703463-9-1(5))* All American Small Business Exporters Assn. (AASBEA).

Edgerton, Leslie. Perfect Game USA & the Future of Baseball: How the Remaking of Youth Scouting Affects the National Pastime. 2008. (ENG., Illus.). 202p. pap. 35.00 *(978-0-7864-3408-4(2))* McFarland & Co., Inc. Pubs.

Keller, Daniel. Survival Guide for Coaching Youth Baseball. 2011. (Illus.). 176p. pap. 15.95 *(978-0-7360-8773-5(7))* Human Kinetics Pubs.

Norwood, Andy. 30 Life Lessons My Boys Learned from Baseball, 1 vol. 2010. (ENG., Illus.). 136p. 14.95 *(978-1-58980-794-5(4))* Pelican Publishing Co., Inc.

Ourvan, Jeff. How to Coach Youth Baseball So Every Kid Wins. 2012. (ENG., Illus.). 176p. pap. 14.95 ***(978-1-61608-357-1(3),*** 608357) Skyhorse Publishing Co., Inc.

Scarlett, W. George, et al. The Baseball Starter: A Handbook for Coaching Children & Teens. 2009. (ENG., Illus.). 160p. pap. 24.95 *(978-0-7864-3858-7(4))* McFarland & Co., Inc. Pubs.

BASEBALL HALL OF FAME

see National Baseball Hall of Fame and Museum

BASEBALL PLAYERS

Abbott, Jim & Brown, Tim. Imperfect: An Improbable Life. 2012. (ENG., Illus.). 304p. 26.00 ***(978-0-345-52325-9(3),*** Ballantine Bks.) Random House Publishing Group.

Abrams, Dennis. Albert Pujols. 2008. (Baseball Superstars Ser.). (Illus.). 144p. (gr. 6-12). per. 11.95 *(978-0-7910-9847-9(8),* Checkmark Bks.); (YA). (gr. 7-12). lib. bdg. 30.00 *(978-0-7910-9600-0(9))* Facts On File, Inc.

Abrams, Roger I. The Dark Side of the Diamond: Gambling, Violence, Drugs & Alcoholism in the National Pastime. 2008. (ENG., Illus.). 208p. 24.95 *(978-1-57940-156-6(2))* Rounder Bks.

Achorn, Edward. Fifty-Nine in '84: Old Hoss Radbourn, Barehanded Baseball, & the Greatest Season a Pitcher Ever Had. 2011. 400p. pap. 15.99 *(978-0-06-182587-3(5),* Harper Paperbacks) HarperCollins Pubs.

—Fifty-Nine in '84: Old Hoss Radbourn, Barehanded Baseball, & the Greatest Season a Pitcher Ever Had. 2010. 384p. 25.99 *(978-0-06-182586-6(7))* Smithsonian Institution Pr.

Ackmann, Martha. Curveball: The Remarkable Story of Toni Stone the First Woman to Play Professional Baseball in the Negro League. 2010. (ENG., Illus.). 288p. 24.95 *(978-1-55652-796-8(9),* Hill, Lawrence Bks.) Chicago Review Pr., Inc.

Aikens, Willie Mays & Jordan, Gregory. Willie Mays Aikens: Safe at Home. 2012. (ENG.). 224p. 25.95 ***(978-1-60078-696-9(0))*** Triumph Bks.

Alexander, Charles C. Spoke: A Biography of Tris Speaker. Rogers, C. Paul, ed. 2007. (Sport in American Life Ser.). (ENG.). 384p. 25.95 *(978-0-87074-517-1(4))* Southern Methodist Univ. Pr.

Allen, Maury & Walker, Susan. Dixie Walker of the Dodgers: The People's Choice. 2nd ed. 2010. (Alabama Fire Ant Ser.). (ENG., Illus.). 288p. pap. 22.50 *(978-0-8173-5599-9(5))* Univ. of Alabama Pr.

Anderson, Michael. Baseball & Its Greatest Players. 2011. lib. bdg. 31.70 *(978-1-61530-510-0(6))* Rosen Publishing Group, Inc., The.

Anson, Adrian C. A Ball Player's Career - Cap Anson. 31.95 *(978-0-8488-1540-0(8))* Amereon LTD.

Anson, C. Adrian. A Ball Player's Career. 2007. 264p. 43.99 *(978-1-4280-7494-1(5));* (ENG.). per. 37.99 *(978-1-4280-7497-2(X))* IndyPublish.com.

Appel, Marty. Munson: The Life & Death of a Yankee Captain. 2010. (ENG.). 430p. pap. 16.00 *(978-0-7679-2755-0(9),* Anchor) Knopf Doubleday Publishing Group.

Araton, Harvey. Driving Mr. Yogi: Yogi Berra, Ron Guidry, & Baseball's Greatest Gift. 2012. (ENG., Illus.). 240p. 26.00 ***(978-0-547-74672-2(5))*** Houghton Mifflin Harcourt Trade & Reference Pubs.

—Driving Mr. Yogi: Yogi Berra, Ron Guidry, & Baseball's Greatest Gift. lt. ed. 2012. (ENG.). 32.99 ***(978-1-4104-4733-3(2))*** Thorndike Pr.

Aronoff, Jason. Going, Going ... Caught! Baseball's Great Outfield Catches as Described by Those Who Saw Them, 1887-1964. 2009. (ENG., Illus.). 276p. pap. 39.95 *(978-0-7864-4113-6(5))* McFarland & Co., Inc. Pubs.

Bailey, Peter. Justin Morneau: All-Star Ball Star. 2008. (ENG., Illus.). 128p. (J). pap. 12.95 *(978-1-55168-326-3(1))* Key Porter Bks. CAN. Dist: Perseus-PGW.

Bailey, Tom. Satchel Paige: Baseball's Greatest Pitcher. 2009. (Illus.). 100p. *(978-1-59421-046-4(2))* Seacoast Publishing, Inc.

Baldassaro, Lawrence & DiMaggio, Dom. Beyond Dimaggio: Italian Americans in Baseball. 2011. (ENG., Illus.). 520p. 34.95 *(978-0-8032-1705-8(6))* Univ. of Nebraska Pr.

Balderrama, Francisco E. & Santillan, Richard A. Mexican American Baseball in Los Angeles. 2011. (Images of Baseball Ser.). (Illus.). 128p. pap. 21.99 *(978-0-7385-8180-4(1))* Arcadia Publishing.

Baltov, Victor Alexander. Baseball Is America: Origins & History: the Good, the Bad, & the Ugly. 2010. 412p. 28.95 *(978-1-4520-0485-3(4));* pap. 19.95 *(978-1-4520-0486-0(2))* AuthorHouse.

Barber-Starkey, Joe & Johnson, James W. Double No-Hit: Johnny Vander Meer's Historic Night under the Lights. 2012. (ENG., Illus.). 216p. pap. 15.95 ***(978-0-8032-7139-5(5))*** Univ. of Nebraska Pr.

Baseball Prospectus. Baseball Prospectus 2012. 3rd ed. 2012. (ENG.). 576p. pap. 24.95 ***(978-0-470-62207-0(5),*** Wiley) Wiley, John & Sons, Inc.

Baseball Prospectus Staff. Baseball Prospectus 2011. Goldman, Steven, ed. 2nd ed. 2011. (ENG.). 600p. pap. 24.95 *(978-0-470-62206-3(7),* Wiley) Wiley, John & Sons, Inc.

Batesel, Paul. Major League Baseball Players Of 1916: A Biographical Dictionary. 2007. (ENG., Illus.). 215p. per. 45.00 *(978-0-7864-2782-6(5))* McFarland & Co., Inc. Pubs.

Bedingfield, Gary. Baseball's Dead of World War II: A Roster of Professional Players Who Died in Service. 2009. (ENG., Illus.). 272p. pap. 39.95 *(978-0-7864-4454-0(1))* McFarland & Co., Inc. Pubs.

Benson, John. Baseball Wisdom: What the Game Teaches Us. 2006. lib. bdg. 17.95 *(978-1-880876-60-2(4))* Diamond Library.

Berkow, Ira. The Corporal Was a Pitcher: The Courage of Lou Brissie. 2009. (ENG.). 272p. 24.95 *(978-1-60078-104-9(7))* Triumph Bks.

Berney, Louis. Tales from the Orioles Dugout. 2007. (Illus.). 202p. per. 15.95 *(978-1-59670-223-3(0))* Sports Publishing, LLC.

Bernstein, Ross. The Code: Baseball's Unwritten Rules & It's Ignore-at-Your-Own-Risk Code of Conduct. 2008. (ENG.). 272p. 22.95 *(978-1-60078-010-3(5))* Triumph Bks.

Berra, Yogi. The Yogi Book: I Really Didn't Say Everything I Said! pap. 89.50 *(978-0-7611-1316-4(9),* 21316) Workman Publishing Co., Inc.

—The Yogi Book: "I Really Didn't Say Everything I Said" 2010. (ENG., Illus.). 175p. pap. 8.95 *(978-0-7611-5443-3(4),* 0761154434) Workman Publishing Co., Inc.

—You Can Observe a Lot by Watching: What I've Learned about Teamwork from the Yankees & Life. (ENG., Illus.). 240p. 2009. pap. 14.95 *(978-0-470-45404-6(0))* 2008. 24.95 *(978-0-470-07992-8(4))* Wiley, John & Sons, Inc. (Wiley).

Billheimer, John. Baseball & the Blame Game: Scapegoating in the Major Leagues. 2007. (ENG., Illus.). 228p. per. 35.00 *(978-0-7864-2906-6(2))* McFarland & Co., Inc. Pubs.

Billingsley, Craig. I Love Baseball. 2010. 112p. pap. 22.00 *(978-0-9845519-0-3(5))* Big River Distribution.

Blaisdell, Lowell L. Carl Hubbell: A Biography of the Screwball King. 2010. (ENG., Illus.). 220p. pap. 29.95 *(978-0-7864-4465-6(7))* McFarland & Co., Inc. Pubs.

Blomberg, Rob. Designated Hebrew: The Ron Blomberg Story. 2012. (ENG., Illus.). 192p. 19.95 ***(978-1-61321-055-0(8),*** 613055) Skyhorse Publishing Co., Inc.

Borries, Philip Von. American Gladiator: The Life & Times of Pete Browning. 2007. 184p. pap. 14.95 *(978-1-60145-272-6(1))* Booklocker.com, Inc.

Bortolotti, Dan. Baseball Now! 2nd ed. 2011. (ENG., Illus.). 160p. pap. 24.95 *(978-1-55407-826-4(1))* Firefly Bks., Ltd.

Boxerman, Burton A. & Boxerman, Benita W. Jews & Baseball Vol. 1: Entering the American Mainstream, 1871-1948, 2 vols. 2006. (ENG., Illus.). 232p. 45.00 *(978-0-7864-2828-1(7))* McFarland & Co., Inc. Pubs.

—Jews & Baseball Vol. 2: The Post-Greenberg Years, 1949-2008, 2 vols. 2010. (ENG., Illus.). 340p. 45.00 *(978-0-7864-3357-5(4))* McFarland & Co., Inc. Pubs.

Boyd, Dennis & Shalin, Mike. They Call Me Oil Can: My Life in Baseball. 2012. (ENG.). 240p. 25.95 ***(978-1-60078-682-2(0))*** Triumph Bks.

Bradley, Mickey & Gordon, Dan. Field of Screams: Haunted Tales from the Baseball Diamond, the Locker Room, & Beyond. 2010. (ENG.). 288p. pap. 14.95 *(978-1-59921-856-4(9),* Lyons Pr.) Globe Pequot Pr., The.

Branca, Ralph. A Moment in Time: An American Story of Baseball, Heartbreak, & Grace. 2011. (ENG.). 256p. 25.00 *(978-1-4516-3687-1(3),* Scribner) Scribner.

Brown, Danny. Shooting the Pistol: Courtside Photos of Pete Maravich at LSU. 2008. (Illus.). 108p. 23.00 *(978-0-8071-3327-9(2))* Louisiana State Univ. Pr.

Browne, Ian. Dice-K: The First Season of the Red Sox $100 Million Man. 2008. (ENG., Illus.). 240p. per. 16.95 *(978-1-59921-347-7(8),* Lyons Pr.) Globe Pequot Pr., The.

Bryant, Howard. The Last Hero: A Life of Henry Aaron. (ENG.). 2011. 640p. pap. 16.95 *(978-0-307-27992-7(8),* Anchor) 2010. (Illus.). 624p. 29.95 *(978-0-375-42485-4(7),* Pantheon) Knopf Doubleday Publishing Group.

Bucci, Steve & Brown, David W. Drinking Coffee with a Fork: The Story of Steve Carlton & the '72 Phillies. 2011. *(978-1-933822-25-9(2));* (Illus.). xiii, 198p. ***(978-1-933822-32-7(5))*** Camino Bks., Inc.

Burgos, Adrian, Jr. Playing America's Game: Baseball, Latinos, & the Color Line. 2007. (American Crossroads Ser.). (Illus.). 384p. 60.00 *(978-0-520-23646-2(7));* 362p. per. 25.95 *(978-0-520-25143-4(1))* Univ. of California Pr.

Burke, Larry, et al. Change Up: An Oral History of 8 Key Events That Shaped Modern Baseball. 2008. (ENG., Illus.). 304p. 24.95 *(978-1-59486-189-5(7))* Rodale Pr., Inc.

Butwin, Richard. Pinstripe Blues. 2007. 316p. 36.95 *(978-1-4327-0936-5(4));* (ENG.). per. 23.95 *(978-1-4327-1573-1(9))* Outskirts Pr., Inc.

Byrd, Paul. Free Byrd: The Power of a Liberated Life. 2011. (ENG., Illus.). 240p. pap. 15.99 *(978-1-4516-4147-9(8),* Howard Bks.) Howard Books.

Caillault, Jean-Pierre, compiled by. The Complete New York Clipper Baseball Biographies: More Than 800 Sketches of Players, Managers, Owners, Umpires, Reporters & Others, 1859-1903, 2 vols. 2009. (ENG., Illus.). 758p. pap. 59.95 *(978-0-7864-3373-5(6))* McFarland & Co., Inc. Pubs.

Canseco, Jose. Vindicated: Big Names, Big Liars, & the Battle to Save Baseball. 2009. (ENG., Illus.). 272p. pap. 15.00 *(978-1-4165-9351-5(9))* Gallery Pr., The IRL. Dist: Simon & Schuster, Inc.

Carew, Rod & Berkow, Ira. Carew. 2010. (Fesler-Lampert Minnesota Heritage Ser.). (ENG., Illus.). 268p. pap. 18.95 *(978-0-8166-7009-3(9))* Univ. of Minnesota Pr.

Carroll, Jeff. Sam Rice: A Biography of the Washington Senators Hall of Famer. 2007. (ENG., Illus.). 252p. pap. 29.95 *(978-0-7864-3119-9(9))* McFarland & Co., Inc. Pubs.

Carter, Gary & Pepe, Phil. Still a Kid at Heart: My Life in Baseball & Beyond. 2008. (ENG., Illus.). 256p. 24.95 *(978-1-60078-054-7(7))* Triumph Bks.

Castro, Tony. Mickey Mantle: America's Prodigal Son. 2008. (Illus.). per. 9.95 *(978-1-59797-171-3(5))* Potomac Bks., Inc.

Charyn, Jerome. Joe Dimaggio: The Long Vigil. (Icons of America Ser.). 192p. 2012. (ENG.). pap. 15.00 ***(978-0-300-18147-0(7))*** 2011. 24.00 *(978-0-300-12328-9(0))* Yale Univ. Pr.

Chicago American Giants Players: Rube Foster, Ted Radcliffe, Bill Monroe, John Henry Lloyd, Pete Hill, Bill Foster, Oscar Charleston. 2010. 80p. pap. 19.99 *(978-1-155-54632-2(6))* General Bks. LLC.

B

Chicago Cubs Staff. Ron Santo: Always a Cub. 2011. 29.95 (978-1-60078-635-8(9)) Triumph Bks.
Clavin, Tom & Peary, Danny. Gil Hodges: The Brooklyn Bums, the Miracle Mets, & the Extraordinary Life of a Baseball Legend. 2012. (ENG.). 320p. (gr. 12). 26.95 (978-0-451-23586-2(X), N A L Hardcover) Penguin Group (USA) Inc.
Clavin, Tom & Peary, Danny. Roger Maris: Baseball's Reluctant Hero. (ENG., Illus.). 2011. 448p. pap. 15.99 (978-1-4165-8929-7(5)) 2010. 432p. 26.99 (978-1-4165-8928-0(7)) Touchstone. (Touchstone).
Clemans, Charles. Harpo, War Survivor, Basketball Wizard: How one courageous young Mexican American faced impossible Odds... twice. 2009. 108p. pap. 11.95 (978-1-60494-227-9(4)) Wheatmark.
Cobb, Ty. My Twenty Years in Baseball. Cobb, William R., ed. 2009. (Dover Baseball Ser.). (ENG.). 160p. pap. 8.95 (978-0-486-47183-9(7)) Dover Pubns., Inc.
Cohen, Marilyn. No Girls in the Clubhouse: The Exclusion of Women from Baseball. 2009. (ENG., Illus.). 228p. pap. 35.00 (978-0-7864-4018-4(X)) McFarland & Co., Inc. Pubs.
Cohen, Robert. Mvp. 2010. (ENG.). 400p. pap. 17.95 (978-1-58042-266-6(7)) Cardoza Publishing.
Coleman, Jerry. An American Journey: My Life on the Field, in the Air, & on the Air. 2008. (ENG., Illus.). 224p. 24.95 (978-1-60078-064-6(4)) Triumph Bks.
Conley, Kathryn L. One of A Kind: The Gene Conley Story. 2007. 336p. pap. 18.99 (978-1-59755-049-9(3), 7000, Advantage Biography) Advantage Bks.
Cook, William A. Big Klu: The Baseball Life of Ted Kluszewski. 2012. (ENG.). pap. 29.95 (978-0-7864-6999-4(4)) McFarland & Co., Inc. Pubs.
Cooper, Brian E. Ray Schalk: A Baseball Biography. 2009. (ENG., Illus.). 338p. pap. 29.95 (978-0-7864-4148-8(8)) McFarland & Co., Inc. Pubs.
—Red Faber: A Biography of the Hall of Fame Spitball Pitcher. 2006. (ENG., Illus.). 279p. per. 29.95 (978-0-7864-2721-5(3)) McFarland & Co., Inc. Pubs.
Cooper, Richard E. Hickory Bob: the Bob Harmon Story: From Missouri Orphan to the Major Leagues to Louisiana Millionaire, Bob Harmon Touched All the Bases. the True Story of a Dead Ball Era Star. 2007. (Illus.). 90p. 22.95 (978-1-58597-428-3(5)) Leathers Publishing.
Corbett, Warren. The Wizard of Waxahachie: Paul Richards & the End of Baseball as We Knew It. 2009. (Sport in American Life Ser.). (ENG., Illus.). 352p. 24.95 (978-0-87074-556-0(5)) Southern Methodist Univ. Pr.
Corcoran, Dennis. Induction Day at Cooperstown: A History of the Baseball Hall of Fame Ceremony. 2010. (ENG., Illus.). 282p. pap. 39.95 (978-0-7864-4416-8(9)) McFarland & Co., Inc. Pubs.
Coste, Chris. The 33-Year-Old Rookie: How I Finally Made It to the Big Leagues after Eleven Years in the Minors. 2008. (Playaway Adult Nonfiction Ser.). 59.99 (978-1-60640-949-7(2)) Findaway World, LLC.
—The 33-Year-Old Rookie: My 13-Year Journey from the Minor Leagues to the World Series. 2009. (ENG., Illus.). 272p. pap. 15.00 (978-0-345-50703-7(7), Ballantine Bks.) Random House Publishing Group.
Cottrell, Robert C. Two Pioneers: How Hank Greenberg & Jackie Robinson Transformed Baseball — and America. 2012. 280p. 27.50 (978-1-59797-842-2(6)) Potomac Bks., Inc.
Coverdale, Miles, Jr. Whitey Ford: A Biography. 2006. (ENG., Illus.). 249p. per. 29.95 (978-0-7864-2514-3(8)) McFarland & Co., Inc. Pubs.
Craft, Jerry & Sullivan, Kathleen. Our White Boy. 2010. (Sport in the American West Ser.). (Illus.). 272p. 29.95 (978-0-89672-674-1(6)) Texas Tech Univ. Pr.
Cramer, Richard Ben. What Do You Think of Ted Williams Now? A Remembrance. 2011. (ENG.). 128p. pap. 10.99 (978-1-4516-4340-4(3)) Simon & Schuster.
Crasnick, Jerry. Decades: 1950-1959. 2010. (Illus.). 160p. (978-1-58159-471-3(2)) North American Media Group.
—Decades: 2000-2009. 2009. (Illus.). 160p. (978-1-58159-437-9(2)) North American Media Group.
Crissey, Harrington E., Jr. Teenagers, Graybeards & 4-F's. Incl. Vol. 2. American League. (Illus.). 179p. 1982. pap. 11.00 (978-0-9608878-1-1(4)); pap. (978-0-9608878-2-8(2)) Crissey, Harrington E.
D'Aloisio, Michael G. 5 C Hero: The Joel Stephens Story. 2009. 220p. 24.99 (978-1-4490-5419-9(6)); pap. 14.95 (978-1-4490-5418-2(8)) AuthorHouse.
Darling, Ron. The Complete Game: Reflections on Baseball & the Art of Pitching. 2010. (Vintage Ser.). (ENG.). 288p. pap. 15.00 (978-0-307-39058-5(6), Vintage) Knopf Doubleday Publishing Group.
Darraj, Susan Muaddi & Maaddi, Rob. Randy Johnson. 2007. (Baseball Superstars Ser.). (Illus.). 128p. (YA). (gr. 7-12). lib. bdg. 30.00 (978-0-7910-9441-9(3)) Facts On File, Inc.
—Roberto Clemente. 2008. (Great Hispanic Heritage Ser.). (Illus.). 120p. (gr. 6-12). 35.00 (978-0-7910-9691-8(2), Chelsea Hse.) Facts On File, Inc.
Davis, Pepper Paire. Dirt in the Skirt. 2009. (Illus.). 515p. (978-1-4490-4378-0(X)) AuthorHouse.
DeVito, Carlo. Yogi: The Life & Times of an American Original. 2008. (ENG., Illus.). 400p. 25.95 (978-1-57243-945-0(9)) Triumph Bks.
Dickey, R. A. & Coffey, Wayne. Wherever I Wind Up: My Quest for Truth, Authenticity & the Perfect Knuckleball. 2012. (ENG., Illus.). 352p. (gr. 12). 26.95 (978-0-399-15815-5(4), Blue Rider Pr.) Penguin Group (USA) Inc.
Dierker, Larry. My Team: Choosing My Dream Team from My Forty Years in Baseball. 2007. (ENG., Illus.). 288p. pap. 13.00 (978-0-7432-7514-9(4)) Simon & Schuster.
Dixon, Phil S. John 'Buck' O'Neil. 2009. 224p. 29.99 (978-1-4389-5059-4(4)); pap. 19.99 (978-1-4389-5060-0(8)) AuthorHouse.
—Wilber Bullet Rogan & the Kansas City Monarchs. 2010. (ENG., Illus.). 227p. pap. 39.95 (978-0-7864-4425-0(8)) McFarland & Co., Inc. Pubs.
Dobrow, Marty. Knocking on Heaven's Door: Six Minor Leaguers in Search of the Baseball Dream. 2010. (Illus.). 360p. pap. 24.95 (978-1-55849-843-3(5)); lib. bdg. 80.00 (978-1-55849-842-6(7)) Univ. of Massachusetts Pr.
Doumit, Peter G. What I Know about Baseball Is What I Know about Life. 2007. (Illus.). 179p. per. 12.99 (978-1-60247-164-1(9)) Tate Publishing & Enterprises, LLC.
Doxsie, Don. Iron Man Mcginnity: A Baseball Biography. 2009. (ENG., Illus.). 224p. pap. 29.95 (978-0-7864-4203-4(4)) McFarland & Co., Inc. Pubs.
Eig, Jonathan. Opening Day: The Story of Jackie Robinson's First Season. 2008. (ENG., Illus.). 336p. pap. 15.00 (978-0-7432-9461-4(0)) Simon & Schuster.
Ephross, Peter & Abramowitz, Martin. Jewish Major Leaguers in Their Own Words: Oral Histories of 23 Players. 2012. (ENG.). 227p. pap. 35.00 (978-0-7864-6507-1(7)) McFarland & Co., Inc. Pubs.
Epstein, Dan. Big Hair & Plastic Grass: A Funky Ride Through Baseball & America in the Swinging '70s. 2010. (ENG., Illus.). 352p. 25.99 (978-0-312-60754-8(7), Dunne, Thomas Bks.) St. Martin's Pr.
Erwin, Phil. Pitching Aces, '99. Date not set. spiral bd. 19.95 (978-0-9663525-3-5(X)) Parrish Pubns.
Faber, Charles F. Baseball Ratings: The All-Time Best Players at Each Position, 1876 to the Present. 3rd rev. ed. 2008. (ENG., Illus.). 301p. per. 45.00 (978-0-7864-3414-5(7)) McFarland & Co., Inc. Pubs.
—Major League Careers Cut Short: Leading Players Gone By 30. 2010. (ENG., Illus.). 298p. pap. 39.95 (978-0-7864-4743-5(5)) McFarland & Co., Inc. Pubs.
Farkas, Neil. My Time with the Catcher Spy, Morris Moe Berg. 2010. (ENG.). 112p. pap. 49.95 (978-0-557-72260-0(8)) Lulu Enterprises Inc.
Feinstein, John. Living on the Black: Two Pitchers, Two Teams, One Season to Remember. l.t. ed. 2008. (ENG.). 800p. pap. 35.99 (978-0-316-02762-5(6)) Little Brown & Co.
Feldmann, Doug. Gibson's Last Stand: The Rise, Fall, & near Misses of the St. Louis Cardinals, 1969-1975. 2011. (SPORTS & AMERICAN CULTURE Ser.). (ENG., Illus.). 256p. (gr. 8). 29.95 (978-0-8262-1950-3(0)) Univ. of Missouri Pr.
Feller, Bob & Rocks, Burton. Bob Feller's Little Blue Book of Baseball Wisdom. 2009. (ENG.). 176p. 22.95 (978-1-60078-219-0(1)) Triumph Bks.
Ferguson, Marvin P. The Unknown Baseball Player. 2006. 283p. per. 14.99 (978-1-882286-01-0(4)) Parker Publishing.
Ferrell, Kerrie & Anderson, William M. Rick Ferrell, Knuckleball Catcher: A Hall of Famer's Life Behind the Plate & in the Front Office. 2010. (ENG., Illus.). 304p. pap. 29.95 (978-0-7864-4796-1(6)) McFarland & Co., Inc. Pubs.
Figueredo, Jorge S. Who's Who in Cuban Baseball, 1878-1961. alt. ed. 2007. (ENG., Illus.). 422p. per. 55.00 (978-0-7864-3030-7(3)) McFarland & Co., Inc. Pubs.
Fink, Rob. Playing in Shadows: Texas & Negro League Baseball. 2010. (Sport in the American West Ser.). (ENG., Illus.). 224p. 29.95 (978-0-89672-701-4(7)) Texas Tech Univ. Pr.
Fitts, Robert K. Wally Yonamine: The Man Who Changed Japanese Baseball. 2008. (ENG., Illus.). 368p. 26.95 (978-0-8032-1381-4(6)) Univ. of Nebraska Pr.
Fleitz, David L. Silver Bats & Automobiles: The Hotly Competitive, Sometimes Ignoble Pursuit of the Major League Batting Championship. 2011. (ENG., Illus.). 222p. pap. 29.95 (978-0-7864-5879-0(8)) McFarland & Co., Inc. Pubs.
Forr, James & Proctor, David. Pie Traynor: A Baseball Biography. 2010. (ENG., Illus.). 275p. pap. 29.95 (978-0-7864-4385-7(5)) McFarland & Co., Inc. Pubs.
Francis, Aidan. Prince Fielder: Home-Run King. 2010. (Inspiring Lives Ser.). (ENG.). 32p. (gr. 5-8). pap. 10.50 (978-1-4339-3650-0(X)) Stevens, Gareth Publishing LLLP.
Franks, Joel S. Asian Pacific Americans & Baseball: A History. 2008. (ENG., Illus.). 224p. pap. 29.95 (978-0-7864-3291-2(8)) McFarland & Co., Inc. Pubs.
Freedman, Lew. African American Pioneers of Baseball: A Biographical Encyclopedia, 1 vol. 2007. (Illus.). 320p. 75.00 (978-0-313-33851-9(5), GR3851, Greenwood Pr.) Greenwood Publishing Group, Inc.
—Early Wynn, the Go-Go White Sox & the 1959 World Series. 2009. (ENG., Illus.). 223p. pap. 29.95 (978-0-7864-4442-7(8)) McFarland & Co., Inc. Pubs.
—Going Yard: The Everything Home Run Book. 2011. (ENG.). 272p. pap. 16.95 (978-1-60078-535-1(2)) Triumph Bks.
—Hard-Luck Harvey Haddix & the Greatest Game Ever Lost. 2009. (ENG., Illus.). 218p. pap. 29.95 (978-0-7864-4124-2(0)) McFarland & Co., Inc. Pubs.
—Latino Baseball Legends: An Encyclopedia, 1 vol. 2010. (Illus.). 359p. 85.00 (978-0-313-37867-6(3), GR7867); E-Book (978-0-313-37868-3(1), Greenwood Pr.) Greenwood Publishing Group, Inc.
—Roberto Clemente: Baseball Star & Humanitarian. 2011. (Legendary Athletes Ser.). (Illus.). 112p. (YA). (gr. 7-12). 34.22 (978-1-61714-754-8(0)) ABDO Publishing Co.
Friedlander, Brett & Reising, Robert. Chasing Moonlight: The True Story of Field of Dreams' Doc Graham. 2009. (Illus.). 208p. 19.95 (978-0-89587-369-9(9)) Blair, John F. Pub.
Friedrich, Marty. The Iron Men of Baseball: Major League Leaders in Consecutive Games Played, 1876-2005. 2006. (ENG., Illus.). 291p. per. 35.00 (978-0-7864-2431-3(1)) McFarland & Co., Inc. Pubs.
Frommer, Harvey. Five O'Clock Lightning: Babe Ruth, Lou Gehrig & the Greatest Baseball Team in History, the 1927 New York Yankees. 2007. (ENG., Illus.). 272p. 24.95 (978-0-471-77812-7(5), Wiley) Wiley, John & Sons, Inc.
Galarraga, Armando, et al. Nobody's Perfect: Two Men, One Call, & a Game for Baseball History. 2011. (ENG., Illus.). 240p. 24.00 (978-0-8021-1988-9(3), Atlantic Monthly Pr.) Grove/Atlantic, Inc.
Garvey, Steve. My Bat Boy Days: Lessons I Learned from the Boys of Summer. 2011. (ENG., Illus.). 160p. pap. 11.99 (978-1-4165-4825-6(4), Scribner) Scribner.
Gay, Timothy M. Tris Speaker: The Rough-and-Tumble Life of a Baseball Legend. 2007. (ENG., Illus.). 344p. pap. 16.95 (978-1-59921-111-4(4), Lyons Pr.) Globe Pequot Pr., The.
Giglio, James N. Musial: From Stash to Stan the Man. 2007. (Missouri Biography Ser.). (ENG., Illus.). 368p. (gr. 9). per. 24.95 (978-0-8262-1735-6(4)) Univ. of Missouri Pr.
Gittleman, Sol. Reynolds, Raschi & Lopat: New York's Big Three & the Great Yankee Dynasty of, 1949-1953. (ENG., Illus.). 2007. 240p. per. 29.95 (978-0-7864-3055-0(9)) 2009. 360p. pap. 39.95 (978-0-7864-3936-2(X)) McFarland & Co., Inc. Pubs.
Glanville, Doug. The Game from Where I Stand: From Batting Practice to the Clubhouse to the Best Breakfast on the Road, an Inside View of a Ballplayer's Life. 2011. (ENG.). 304p. pap. 14.99 (978-0-312-57309-6(X), St. Martin's Griffin) St. Martin's Pr.
Glanville, Doug M. The Game from Where I Stand: A Ballplayer's Inside View. 2010. (ENG.). 304p. 25.00 (978-0-8050-9159-5(9), Times Bks.) Holt, Henry & Co.
Gmelch, George. Inside Pitch: Life in Professional Baseball. 2006. (ENG., Illus.). 1p. pap. 17.95 (978-0-8032-7128-9(X), Bison Bks.) Univ. of Nebraska Pr.
Gomez, Vernona & Goldstone, Lawrence. Lefty: An American Odyssey. 2012. (ENG., Illus.). 416p. 28.00 (978-0-345-52648-9(1), Ballantine Bks.) Random House Publishing Group.
Goode, Jon & Goode, Laurie. Pitching with the Papelbons. 2007. pap. 19.95 (978-1-60461-804-4(3)) Independent Pub.
Gordon, Dan, ed. Your Brain on Cubs: Inside the Heads of Players & Fans. 2008. (Illus.). 150p. 19.95 (978-1-932594-28-7(0)) Dana Pr., The.
Gorman, Robert M. & Weeks, David. Death at the Ballpark: A Comprehensive Study of Game-Related Fatalities of Players, Other Personnel & Spectators in Amateur & Professional Baseball, 1862-2007. 2008. (ENG., Illus.). 264p. 45.00 (978-0-7864-3435-0(X)) McFarland & Co., Inc. Pubs.
Gose, Elijah Jude. Ryan Howard: Power Hitter. 2010. (Inspiring Lives Ser.). (ENG.). 32p. (gr. 5-8). pap. 10.50 (978-1-4339-3653-1(4)) Stevens, Gareth Publishing LLLP.
Goudsouzian, Aram. King of the Court: Bill Russell & the Basketball Revolution. 2011. (Illus.). 448p. pap. 19.95 (978-0-520-26979-8(9)) Univ. of California Pr.
Gould, William B. Bargaining with Baseball: Labor Relations in an Age of Prosperous Turmoil. 2011. (ENG., Illus.). 326p. pap. 39.95 (978-0-7864-6515-6(8)) McFarland & Co., Inc. Pubs.
Grant, Jim "Mudcat", et al. The Black Aces: Baseball's only african-american twenty-game Winners. 2007. (ENG.). 492p. 34.95 (978-1-59330-488-1(9)); 496p. per. 23.95 (978-1-59330-487-4(0)) Aventine Pr.
Green, Guy, et al. The Nebraska Indians & Fun & Frolic with an Indian Baseball Team: Two Accounts of Baseball Barnstorming at the Turn of the Twentieth Century. 2010. (Mcfarland Historical Baseball Library). (ENG., Illus.). 242p. pap. 33.00 (978-0-7864-4359-8(6)) McFarland & Co., Inc. Pubs.
Green, Shawn. The Way of Baseball: Finding Stillness at 95 Mph. 2011. (ENG., Illus.). 224p. 24.00 (978-1-4391-9119-4(0)) Simon & Schuster.
Greenberg, Hank. Story of My Life. 2009. (ENG.). 320p. pap. 16.95 (978-1-56663-837-1(2)) Dee, Ivan R. Pub.
Greenberg, Robert A. Swish Nicholson: A Biography of Wartime Baseball's Leading Slugger. 2007. (ENG., Illus.). 272p. per. 29.95 (978-0-7864-3274-5(8)) McFarland & Co., Inc. Pubs.
Gullo, Jim. Trading Manny: How a Father & Son Learned to Love Baseball Again. 2012. (ENG.). 272p. 23.00 (978-0-306-82017-5(X)) Da Capo Pr., Inc.
Hamilton, Josh. Beyond Belief: Finding the Strength to Come Back. 2010. (ENG.). 288p. pap. 14.99 (978-1-59995-160-7(6)) FaithWords.
Hampton, Wilborn. Babe Ruth: A Twentieth-Century Life. 2009. (Up Close Ser.). (ENG.). 208p. (YA). (gr. 6-18). 16.99 (978-0-670-06305-5(3), Viking Juvenile) Penguin Group (USA) Inc.
Harrelson, Bud & Pepe, Phil. Turning Two: My Journey to the Top of the World & Back with the New York Mets. 2012. (ENG., Illus.). 288p. 25.99 (978-0-312-66240-0(8), Dunne, Thomas Bks.) St. Martin's Pr.
Harris, Rick. Rhode Island Baseball: The Early Years. 2008. pap. 19.99 (978-1-59629-496-7(5)) History Pr., The.
Hart, Michael, photos by. Biggio: The Final Game. 2008. (ENG., Illus.). 108p. 24.95 (978-1-933979-28-1(3)) Bright Sky Pr.
Hartley, Robert L. Bits of Bob: Tales from the Muskingum River. 2008. 136p. 23.95 (978-0-595-51489-2(8)); pap. 13.95 (978-0-595-52546-1(6)) iUniverse, Inc.
Hayhurst, Dick. Out of My League A Rookies Survival in the Bigs. 2013. (ENG.). 1p. pap. 14.95 (978-0-8065-3486-2(9), Citadel Pr.) Kensington Publishing Corp.
Hayhurst, Dirk. The Bullpen Gospels: Major League Dreams of a Minor League Veteran. 2010. (ENG.). 240p. pap. 14.95 (978-0-8065-3143-4(6), Citadel Pr.) Kensington Publishing Corp.
Hayhurst, Dirk. Out of My League. 2012. (ENG.). 340p. 24.95 (978-0-8065-3485-5(0), Citadel Pr.) Kensington Publishing Corp.
Heaphy, Leslie A., ed. Satchel Paige & Company: Essays on the Kansas City Monarchs, Their Greatest Star & the Negro Leagues. 2007. (Jerry Malloy Conference Ser.). (ENG., Illus.). 308p. per. 35.00 (978-0-7864-3075-8(3)) McFarland & Co., Inc. Pubs.
Herman, Bruce. New York Mets: Yesterday & Today. 2009. 12.95 (978-1-60553-371-1(8)) Publications International, Ltd.
Herskowitz, Mickey. Mickey Mantle: Stories & Memorabilia from a Lifetime with the Mick. 2006. (ENG., Illus.). 176p. 37.50 (978-1-58479-547-6(6)) Stewart, Tabori & Chang.
Herzog, Whitey & Pitts, Jonathan. You're Missin' a Great Game: From Casey to Ozzie, the Magic of Baseball & How to Get It Back. 2007. (ENG., Illus.). 320p. pap. 21.95 (978-1-4165-5205-5(7)) Simon & Schuster.
Higgins, Billy D. The Barling Darling: Hal Smith in American Baseball. 2009. (Illus.). 246p. pap. 19.95 (978-1-935106-09-8(0)) Butler Ctr. for Arkansas Studies.
Hirsch, James S. Willie Mays: The Life, the Legend. (ENG.). 640p. 2011. pap. 18.00 (978-1-4165-4791-4(6)) 2010. (Illus.). 30.00 (978-1-4165-4790-7(8)) Scribner. (Scribner).
Hoard, Greg. Joe: Rounding Third & Heading for Home. 2007. (Illus.). 287p. per. 22.00 (978-1-933197-46-3(3)) Orange Frazer Pr.
Hogan, Kenneth. Batting 10th for the Yankees: Recollections of 30 Yankees You May Not Remember. 2010. (Illus.). 296p. pap. 24.99 (978-1-4490-7188-2(0)) AuthorHouse.
Horvitz, Peter S. & Horvitz, Joachim. The New Big Book of Jewish Baseball: An Illustrated Encyclopedia & Anecdotal History. 2007. 350p. pap. 24.95 (978-1-56171-821-4(1)) SPI Bks.
Hubbard, Donald. The Heavenly Twins of Boston Baseball: A Dual Biography of Hugh Duffy & Tommy McCarthy. 2008. (ENG., Illus.). 252p. pap. 29.95 (978-0-7864-3455-8(4)) McFarland & Co., Inc. Pubs.
Humphreys, Michael A. Wizardry: Baseball's All-Time Greatest Fielders Revealed, 1 vol. 2011. (ENG., Illus.). 432p. pap. 19.95 (978-0-19-539776-5(2)) Oxford Univ. Pr., Inc.
Isaacson, Melissa. Sweet Lou: Lou Piniella a Life in Baseball. 2009. (ENG.). 224p. 24.95 (978-1-60078-201-5(9)) Triumph Bks.
Jacobson, Steve. Carrying Jackie's Torch: The Players Who Integrated Baseball - And America. 2007. (ENG., Illus.). 288p. 24.95 (978-1-55652-639-8(3), Hill, Lawrence Bks.) Chicago Review Pr., Inc.
—Carrying Jackie's Torch: The Players Who Integrated Baseball-And America. 2009. (ENG., Illus.). 288p. pap. 14.95 (978-1-55652-791-3(8), Hill, Lawrence Bks.) Chicago Review Pr., Inc.
Janczak, Joseph. The Rocket: Baseball Legend Roger Clemens. 2007. (Illus.). 320p. 26.95 (978-1-59797-088-4(3)) Potomac Bks., Inc.
Jenkins, Fergie & Freedman, Lew. Fergie: My Life from the Cubs to Cooperstown. 2009. (ENG.). 224p. 24.95 (978-1-60078-171-1(3)) Triumph Bks.
Jenkinson, Bill. Baseball's Ultimate Power: Ranking the All-Time Greatest Distance Home Run Hitters. 2010. (ENG., Illus.). 352p. pap. 17.95 (978-1-59921-544-0(6), Lyons Pr.) Globe Pequot Pr., The.
Jennison, Christopher & Jurinko, Andy. Golden Boys: Baseball Portraits, 1946-1960. 2012. (ENG., Illus.). 288p. 50.00 (978-1-61608-450-9(2), 608450) Skyhorse Publishing Co., Inc.
Johnson, Jim. "Dummy" Hanson. 2008. pap. 22.95 (978-1-59298-256-1(5)) Beaver's Pond Pr., Inc.
Johnson, Steve. Chicago Cubs Yesterday & Today. 2008. (ENG., Illus.). 144p. 26.95 (978-0-7603-3246-7(0), 0760332460, MVP Bks.) MBI Publishing Co. LLC.
Jones, David, ed. Deadball Stars of the American League: The Society for American Baseball Research. 2007. (ENG., Illus.). 416p. per. 24.95 (978-1-57488-982-6(6)) Potomac Bks., Inc.
Jones, Ryan. King James: The Buying & Selling of LeBron James. Date not set. (978-0-312-32228-1(3)) St. Martin's Pr.
Joyner, Ronnie & Bozman, Bill. He Hits! He Steals! He's Bob Dillinger! 2006. 183p. 25.00 (978-0-9779841-4-5(1)) Pepperpot Prodns, Inc.
Kann, Bob. Joyce Westerman: Baseball Hero. 2012. (Badger Biographies Ser.). (ENG., Illus.). 120p. (J). pap. 12.95 (978-0-87020-486-9(6)) Wisconsin Historical Society.
Kansas City Athletics Players: Reggie Jackson, Satchel Paige, Enos Slaughter, Billy Martin, Héctor López, Dick Williams, Tony la Russa. 2010. 798p. pap. 24.02 (978-1-155-74552-7(3)) General Bks. LLC.
Kaplan, Jim. The Greatest Game Ever Pitched: Juan Marichal, Warren Spahn, & the Pitching Duel of the Century. 2011. (ENG.). 256p. 24.95 (978-1-60078-341-8(4)) Triumph Bks.
Kashatus, William C. Money Pitcher: Chief Bender & the Tragedy of Indian Assimilation. 2011. (Keystone Book Ser.). (ENG.). 216p. pap. 24.95 (978-0-271-02851-4(3)) Pennsylvania State Univ. Pr.
Kaufman, Louis, et al. Moe Berg: Athlete, Scholar, Spy. Date not set. lib. bdg. 29.95 (978-0-8488-1387-1(1)) Amereon LTD.
Kelley, Brent. I Will Never Forget: Interviews with 39 Former Negro League Players. alt. ed. 2010. (ENG., Illus.). 199p. pap. 45.00 (978-0-7864-4694-0(3)) McFarland & Co., Inc. Pubs.
—The Negro Leagues Revisited: Conversations with 66 More Baseball Heroes. alt. ed. 2010. (ENG., Illus.). 399p. pap. 45.00 (978-0-7864-4695-7(1)) McFarland & Co., Inc. Pubs.
Kelly, Robert E. Baseball's Offensive Greats of the Deadball Era: Best Producers Rated by Position, 1901-1919. 2009. (ENG.). 220p. pap. 45.00 (978-0-7864-4125-9(9)) McFarland & Co., Inc. Pubs.
Kerr, Roy. Buck Ewing: A Baseball Biography. 2012. (ENG.). 272p. pap. 29.95 (978-0-7864-6948-2(X)) McFarland & Co., Inc. Pubs.
Kerr, Roy. Sliding Billy Hamilton: The Life & Times of Baseball's First Great Leadoff Hitter. 2009. (ENG., Illus.). 216p. pap. 29.95 (978-0-7864-4639-1(0)) McFarland & Co., Inc. Pubs.
Khan, Abraham Iqbal. Curt Flood in the Media: Baseball, Race, & the Demise of the Activist Athlete. 2012. (Race, Rhetoric, & Media Ser.). (ENG.). 224p. 55.00 (978-1-61703-138-0(0)) Univ. Pr. of Mississippi.

King, Nelson J. Happiness Is Like a Cur Dog: The Thirty-Year Journey of a Major League Baseball Pitcher & Broadcaster. 2009. (ENG.). 300p. 26.00 (978-1-4490-2548-9(X)); pap. 15.60 (978-1-4490-2547-2(1)) AuthorHouse.

Kirkpatrick, Rob. Cecil Travis of the Washington Senators: The War-Torn Career of an All-Star Shortstop. 2009. (ENG., Illus.). 200p. pap. 14.95 (978-0-8032-2475-9(3), Bison Bks.) Univ. of Nebraska Pr.

Kirst, Sean. Moonfixer. 2009. 152p. 29.95 (978-0-8156-0946-9(9)) Syracuse Univ. Pr.

Kiser, Brett. Baseball's War Roster: A Biographical Dictionary of Major & Negro League Players Who Served, 1861 to the Present. 2012. (ENG.). 284p. pap. 55.00 (978-0-7864-6679-5(0)) McFarland & Co., Inc. Pubs.

Kubiszyn, Lucy Stallworth. A Star Fell on Alabama the Jack Kubiszyn Story. 2009. pap. (978-1-61623-911-4(5)) Independent Pub.

Kurlansky, Mark. The Eastern Stars: How Baseball Changed the Dominican Town of San Pedro de Macoris. 2011. (ENG.). 352p. (gr. 12). 16.00 (978-1-59448-505-3(4), Riverhead Trade (Paperbacks)) Penguin Group (USA) Inc.

—Hank Greenberg: The Hero Who Didn't Want to Be One. 2011. (Jewish Lives Ser.). (Illus.). 192p. 25.00 (978-0-300-13660-9(9)) Yale Univ. Pr.

Lambert, Mike. Eastern Shore League. 2010. (Images of Baseball Ser.). (ENG., Illus.). 128p. pap. 21.99 (978-0-7385-6699-3(3)) Arcadia Publishing.

Lanctot, Neil. Campy: The Two Lives of Roy Campanella. 2011. (ENG., Illus.). 528p. 28.00 (978-1-4165-4704-4(5)) Simon & Schuster.

Leavengood, Ted. Clark Griffith: The Old Fox of Washington Baseball. 2011. (ENG., Illus.). 321p. pap. 29.95 (978-0-7864-6386-2(4)) McFarland & Co., Inc. Pubs.

Leavy, Jane. The Last Boy: Mickey Mantle & the End of America's Childhood. (P. S. Ser.). 2011. (ENG.). 480p. pap. 16.99 (978-0-06-088353-9(7), HarperPerennial) 2010. (ENG.). 400p. 27.99 (978-0-06-088352-2(9)) 2010. 784p. pap. 27.99 (978-0-06-177488-1(X), HarperLuxe) HarperCollins Pubs.

—Sandy Koufax: A Lefty's Legacy. 2010. (P. S. Ser.). (ENG.). 352p. pap. 14.99 (978-0-06-177900-8(8), HarperPerennial) HarperCollins Pubs.

Lee, Bill. Baseball Eccentrics: The Most Entertaining, Outrageous, & Unforgettable Characters in the Game. 2007. (ENG., Illus.). 240p. 22.95 (978-1-57243-953-5(X)) Triumph Bks.

—The Baseball Necrology: The Post-Baseball Lives & Deaths of More Than 7,600 Major League Players & Others. alt. ed. 2009. (ENG.). 525p. pap. 45.00 (978-0-7864-4239-3(5)) McFarland & Co., Inc. Pubs.

Letarte, Richard. That One Glorious Season: Baseball Players with One Spectacular Year, 1950-1961. 2006. (ENG., Illus.). 370p. per. 16.95 (978-1-931807-51-7(5)) Randall, Peter E. Pub.

Lewin, Josh. You Never Forget Your First: Ballplayers Recall Their Big League Debuts. 2007. (Illus.). 256p. per. 16.95 (978-1-59797-065-5(4)) Potomac Bks., Inc.

Lewis, Michael. Moneyball: The Art of Winning an Unfair Game. movie tie-in ed. 2011. (Movie Tie-in Editions Ser.). (ENG.). 317p. pap. 15.95 (978-0-393-33839-3(8), 33839) Norton, W. W. & Co., Inc.

Lewis, T. J. A View from the Mound; My Father's Life in Baseball. 2009. 232p. pap. 19.99 (978-1-4357-1486-1(5)) Lulu Enterprises Inc.

Liederman, Bill & Allen, Maury. Our Mickey: Cherished Memories of an American Icon. 2007. (ENG., Illus.). 192p. per. 12.95 (978-1-57243-967-2(X)) Triumph Bks.

Linge, Mary Kay. Jackie Robinson: A Biography, 1 vol. 2007. (Greenwood Biographies Ser.). (Illus.). 192p. 35.00 (978-0-313-33828-1(0), GR3828, Greenwood Pr.) Greenwood Publishing Group, Inc.

Liscio, Stephanie M. Integrating Cleveland Baseball: Media Activism, the Integration of the Indians & the Demise of the Negro League Buckeyes. 2010. (ENG., Illus.). 235p. pap. 29.95 (978-0-7864-3690-3(5)) McFarland & Co., Inc. Pubs.

Litwhiler, Daniel. Danny Litwhiler: Living the Baseball Dream. 2006. (Illus.). 312p. 47.00 (978-1-59213-524-0(2)) Temple Univ. Pr.

Lockwood, Kathleen. Major League Bride: An Inside Look at Life Outside the Ballpark. 2010. (ENG., Illus.). 230p. pap. 29.95 (978-0-7864-4560-8(2)) McFarland & Co., Inc. Pubs.

Lopez, Javy & Caruso, Gary. Behind the Plate: A Catcher's View of the Braves Dynasty. 2012. (ENG.). 208p. 25.95 (978-1-60078-653-2(7)) Triumph Bks.

Loria, Julie & Writers House LLC. Diamond Dishes: From the Kitchens of Baseball's Biggest Stars. 2011. (ENG., Illus.). 192p. 24.95 (978-0-7627-6962-9(9), Lyons Pr.) Globe Pequot Pr., The.

Luke, Bob. Willie Wells. 2007. (ENG., Illus.). 208p. pap. 19.95 (978-0-292-71751-0(2)) Univ. of Texas Pr.

Maaddi, Rob. Mike Schmidt: The Phillies' Legendary Slugger. 2010. (ENG.). 256p. 24.95 (978-1-60078-318-0(X)) Triumph Bks.

Mack, Bob. Bird Hunting in Brooklyn: Ebbets Field, the Dodgers & the 1949 National League Pennant Race. 2008. 479p. pap. 23.95 (978-1-4357-1190-7(4)) Lulu Enterprises Inc.

Mackey, R. Scott. Barbary Baseball: The Pacific Coast League of The 1920s. alt. ed. 2011. (ENG., Illus.). 237p. pap. 29.95 (978-0-7864-6709-9(6)) McFarland & Co., Inc. Pubs.

Maher, Charlie. The Complete Mental Game of Baseball: Taking Charge of the Process, on & off the Field. 2011. 272p. 25.95 (978-1-4634-0220-4(1)); pap. 19.95 (978-1-4634-0221-1(X)) AuthorHouse.

Maimon, Alan. Shane Victorino: The Flyin' Hawaiian. 2011. (ENG.). 230p. 24.95 (978-1-60078-542-9(5)) Triumph Bks.

Marichal, Juan. Juan Marichal: My Journey from the Dominican Republic to Cooperstown. 2011. (ENG., Illus.). 288p. 25.00 (978-0-7603-4059-2(5), 0760340595, MVP Bks.) MBI Publishing Co. LLC.

Martin, Alfred M. & Martin, Alfred T. The Negro Leagues in New Jersey: A History. 2008. (ENG., Illus.). 280p. pap. 35.00 (978-0-7864-3900-3(9)) McFarland & Co., Inc. Pubs.

Matthews, Gary & Pepe, Phil. Few & Chosen Phillies: Defining Phillies Greatness Across the Eras. 2012. (Few & Chosen Ser.). (ENG.). 224p. 25.95 (978-1-60078-658-7(8)) Triumph Bks.

McCabe, Neal, et al. The Big Show: Charles M. Conlon's Golden Age Baseball Photographs. 2011. (ENG., Illus.). 224p. 35.00 (978-1-4197-0069-9(3)) Abrams.

McCarthy, Matt. Odd Man Out: A Year on the Mound with a Minor League Misfit. 2010. (ENG.). 304p. (gr. 12-18). 16.00 (978-0-14-311681-3(9), Penguin (Non-Classics)) Penguin Group (USA) Inc.

McCarver, Tim, et al. Tim McCarver's Diamond Gems: Favorite Baseball Stories from the Legends of the Game. 2008. (ENG.). 224p. 24.95 (978-0-07-154594-5(8), 0071545948) McGraw-Hill Cos., The.

McCormack, Shaun. Cool Papa Bell. 2009. (Baseball Hall of Famers of the Negro Leagues Ser.). 112p. (gr. 5-8). 63.90 (978-1-61511-522-8(6), Rosen Central) Rosen Publishing Group, Inc., The.

McGwire, Jay. Mark & Me: Mark McGwire & the Truth Behind Baseball's Worst-Kept Secret. 2010. (ENG.). 208p. 24.95 (978-1-60078-308-1(2)) Triumph Bks.

McKelvey, G. Richard. Mexican Raiders in the Major Leagues: The Pasquel Brothers vs. Organized Baseball 1946. 2006. (ENG., Illus.). 211p. per. 29.95 (978-0-7864-2563-1(6)) McFarland & Co., Inc. Pubs.

McKenna, Brian. Early Exits: The Premature Endings of Baseball Careers. 2006. (ENG.). 304p. per. 50.00 (978-0-8108-5858-9(4)) Scarecrow Pr., Inc.

McKinney, Deric, et al. 2011 Minor League Baseball Analyst. 6th ed. 2011. (ENG., Illus.). 136p. pap. 19.95 (978-1-60078-550-4(6)) Triumph Bks.

McLain, Denny & Zaret, Eli. I Told You I Wasn't Perfect. 2007. (ENG., Illus.). 416p. 24.95 (978-1-57243-957-3(2)) Triumph Bks.

McNeil, William F. Black Baseball Out of Season: Pay for Play Outside of the Negro Leagues. alt. ed. 2012. (ENG., Illus.). 244p. pap. 25.00 (978-0-7864-6924-6(2)) McFarland & Co., Inc. Pubs.

McNeil, William F. Red Sox Nation Guide to the Players. 2008. (ENG.). 240p. pap. 9.95 (978-1-55553-699-2(9), Northeastern University Pr.) Univ. Pr. of New England.

Medcalfe, Simon. Incentives in Baseball. 2008. 64p. pap. (978-3-639-00447-2(7)) VDM Verlag Dr. Mueller e.K.

Meigs, Tom. Baseball in Long Beach. 2008. (Images of Baseball Ser.). (ENG., Illus.). 128p. pap. 19.99 (978-0-7385-5823-3(0)) Arcadia Publishing.

Merlino, Doug. The Hustle: One Team & Ten Lives in Black & White. 2010. (ENG., Illus.). 320p. 26.00 (978-1-60819-215-1(6)) Bloomsbury Publishing.

Metzger, Mike. My Lifelong Relationship with Larry Bowa. 2008. 84p. pap. 10.49 (978-1-4389-0189-3(5)) AuthorHouse.

Mickelson, Ed. Out of the Park: Memoir of a Minor League Baseball All-Star. 2007. (ENG., Illus.). 240p. per. 29.95 (978-0-7864-2889-2(9)) McFarland & Co., Inc. Pubs.

Miller, Ernestine. Babe Book: Baseball's Greatest Legend Remembered. 2007. (Illus.). 211p. reprint ed. 20.00 (978-1-4223-9003-0(9)) DIANE Publishing Co.

Milwaukee Brewers Baseball Club, Publicity Department Staff. Robin Yount: The Legend Lives On. (Illus.). 80p. 19.00 (978-0-9634967-0-6(0)) Milwaukee Brewers Baseball Club.

Minneapolis Star Tribune Staff. Joe Mauer. 2010. (ENG.). 128p. pap. 14.95 (978-1-60078-503-0(4)) Triumph Bks.

The Mitchell Report: The Illegal Use of Steroids in Major League Baseball: Hearing Before the Committee on Oversight & Government Reform, House of Representatives, One Hundred Tenth Congress, Second Session, January 15, 2008. 2010. iii, 155p. (978-0-16-085840-6(2), 552-070-41052-0) United States Government Printing Office.

Moffi, Larry. This Side of Cooperstown: An Oral History of Major League Baseball in The 1950s. 2010. (Dover Baseball Ser.). (ENG.). 288p. pap. 12.95 (978-0-486-47273-7(6)) Dover Pubns., Inc.

Moffi, Larry & Kronstadt, Jonathan. Crossing the Line: Black Major Leaguers, 1947-1959. 2006. (ENG.). 1p. pap. 15.95 (978-0-8032-8316-9(4), Bison Bks.) Univ. of Nebraska Pr.

Mongero, Trent. Winning Baseball for Beginner to Intermediate Play 2011. (Coach's Companion Ser.). (ENG., Illus.). 256p. 19.95 (978-1-4027-5808-9(1)) Sterling Publishing Co., Inc.

Moore, Gary W. Playing with the Enemy: A Baseball Prodigy, World War II, & the Long Journey Home. 2008. (ENG., Illus.). 336p. (gr. 12-18). 16.00 (978-0-14-311388-1(7), Penguin (Non-Classics)) Penguin Group (USA) Inc.

Moore, Joseph Thomas. Larry Doby: The Struggle of the American League's First Black Player. 2012. (Dover Baseball Ser.). (ENG., Illus.). 256p. pap. 12.95 (978-0-486-48337-5(1)) Dover Pubns., Inc.

Morris, Andrew D. Colonial Project, National Game: A History of Baseball in Taiwan. 2010. (Asia Pacific Modern Ser.). (ENG., Illus.). 304p. 49.95 (978-0-520-26279-9(4)) Univ. of California Pr.

Motley, Bob, et al. Ruling over Monarchs, Giants, & Stars: True Tales of Breaking Barriers, Umpiring Baseball Legends, & Wild Adventures in the Negro Leagues. 2012. (ENG., Illus.). 240p. 24.95 (978-1-61321-059-8(0), 613059) Skyhorse Publishing Co., Inc.

Mowday, Bruce & Donahue, Jim. Richie Ashburn: Why the Hall Not? And the Amazing Journey to Cooperstown. 2011. (Illus.). 288p. 19.95 (978-1-56980-450-6(8)) Barricade Bks., Inc.

Mullen, Maureen. Yogi Was up with a Guy on Third... Hall of Famers Recall Their Favorite Baseball Games Ever. 2009. (ENG.). 272p. 19.95 (978-1-60078-162-9(4)) Triumph Bks.

Mumau, Thad. When the Grass Turns Green: Cherished Baseball Memories of a North Carolina Sports Writer. 2010. pap. 19.95 (978-1-59712-407-2(9)) Catawba Publishing Co.

Murcer, Bobby & Waggoner, Glen. Yankee for Life: My 40-Year Journey in Pinstripes. 2009. (ENG.). 320p. pap. 14.99 (978-0-06-147342-5(1), Harper Paperbacks) HarperCollins Pubs.

Nathan, David H., compiled by. The McFarland Baseball Quotations Dictionary. 3rd rev. ed. 2011. (ENG., Illus.). 350p. pap. 45.00 (978-0-7864-4790-9(7)) McFarland & Co., Inc. Pubs.

Nemec, David, ed. Major League Baseball Profiles, 1871-1900, 2-volume Set, 2 vols. 2011. (ENG., Illus.). 1264p. pap. 69.95 (978-0-8032-3533-5(X), Bison Bks.) Univ. of Nebraska Pr.

—Major League Baseball Profiles, 1871-1900, Volume 1: The Ballplayers Who Built the Game, 2 vols. 2011. (ENG., Illus.). 688p. pap. 39.95 (978-0-8032-3024-8(9), Bison Bks.) Univ. of Nebraska Pr.

—Major League Baseball Profiles, 1871-1900, Volume 2: The Hall of Famers & Memorable Personalities Who Shaped the Game, 2 vols. 2011. (ENG., Illus.). 576p. pap. 39.95 (978-0-8032-3532-8(1), Bison Bks.) Univ. of Nebraska Pr.

Nemec, David, et al. The Baseball Chronicle: Year-by-Year History of Major League Baseball. 2007. (Illus.). 704p. 24.98 (978-1-4127-1590-4(3)) Publications International, Ltd.

New York Times Staff. Derek Jeter: From the pages of the New York Times. Kepner, Tyler, ed. 2011. (ENG., Illus.). 224p. 29.95 (978-0-8109-9656-4(1)) Abrams.

Nowlin, Bill & Prime, Jim. Amazing Tales from the Boston Red Sox Dugout: A Collection of the Greatest Red Sox Stories Ever Told. 2012. (Tales from the Team Ser.). (ENG., Illus.). 320p. 24.95 (978-1-61321-023-9(X), 613023) Skyhorse Publishing Co., Inc.

O'Connell, Brian. Johnny Damon. 2008. (Baseball Superstars Ser.). 128p. (YA). (gr. 7-12). 30.00 (978-0-7910-9646-8(7)); (Illus.). (gr. 6-12). pap. 11.95 (978-0-7910-9845-5(1), Checkmark Bks.) Facts On File, Inc.

O'Connor, Ian. The Captain: The Journey of Derek Jeter. (ENG., Illus.). 2012. 448p. pap. 14.95 (978-0-547-74760-6(8), Mariner Bks.) 2011. 416p. 26.00 (978-0-547-32793-8(5)) Houghton Mifflin Harcourt Trade & Reference Pubs.

O'Neal, Dick 'Lefty'. Dreaming of the Majors - Living in the Bush: A Life's Journey Through the Negro League with His Guardian Angels. 2009. 136p. pap. 14.99 (978-1-4141-1243-5(2)) Pleasant Word.

ONeal, Mark. What Happened to Little League Baseball in the Inner-City? 2007. 56p. per. 9.95 (978-1-4327-0046-1(4)) Outskirts Pr., Inc.

O'Rourke, Jack. A Wise New Yorker. 2011. pap. 16.95 (978-0-533-16367-0(6)) Vantage Pr., Inc.

Ortiz, David & Massaroti, Tony. Big Papi: My Story of Big Dreams & Big Hits. 2008. (ENG., Illus.). 288p. pap. 14.95 (978-0-312-38344-2(4), St. Martin's Griffin) St. Martin's Pr.

Outland, John W. Baseball Visions of the Roaring Twenties: A Fan's Photographs of More Than 400 Players & Ballparks of the Era. 2009. (ENG., Illus.). 492p. pap. 45.00 (978-0-7864-4123-5(2)) McFarland & Co., Inc. Pubs.

Pajot, Dennis. Baseball's Heartland War, 1902-1903: The Western League & American Association Vie for Turf, Players & Profits. 2011. (ENG., Illus.). 224p. pap. 29.95 (978-0-7864-6337-4(6)) McFarland & Co., Inc. Pubs.

Pallotta, Rip. One Day in Mudville: A look at some of the most unique baseball games of all Time. 2007. 220p. per. 14.49 (978-1-4259-7899-0(1)) AuthorHouse.

Paper, Lew. Perfect: Don Larsen's Miraculous World Series Game & the Men Who Made It Happen. 2010. (ENG.). 432p. (gr. 12). 15.00 (978-0-451-23123-9(6), N A L Trade) Penguin Group (USA) Inc.

Parker, Clifton Blue. Bucketfoot Al: The Baseball Life of Al Simmons. 2011. (ENG., Illus.). 251p. pap. 29.95 (978-0-7864-6143-1(8)) McFarland & Co., Inc. Pubs.

Pearlman, Jeff. Love Me, Hate Me: Barry Bonds & the Making of an Antihero. 2007. (ENG., Illus.). 384p. pap. 14.99 (978-0-06-079753-9(3)) HarperCollins Pubs.

—The Rocket That Fell to Earth: Roger Clemens & the Rage for Baseball Immortality. 2010. (ENG.). 368p. pap. 14.99 (978-0-06-172482-4(3), Harper Paperbacks) HarperCollins Pubs.

Pederson, Charles E. Jackie Robinson: Baseball Great & Civil Rights Activist. 2009. (Essential Lives Set 3 Ser.). (Illus.). 112p. (YA). (gr. 7-12). 34.22 (978-1-60453-526-6(1)) ABDO Publishing Co.

Pedroia, Dustin. Born to Play: My Life in the Game. 2010. (ENG., Illus.). 272p. pap. 16.00 (978-1-4391-5776-3(6)) Gallery Pr., The IRL. Dist: Simon & Schuster, Inc.

Pepe, Phil. Magic Moments Yankees: Celebrating the Most Successful Franchise in Sports History. 2008. (ENG., Illus.). 176p. 27.95 (978-1-57243-863-7(0)) Triumph Bks.

Perry, Dayn. Reggie Jackson: The Life & Thunderous Career of Baseball's Mr. October. 2011. (ENG.). 336p. pap. 16.99 (978-0-06-156237-2(8)) 2010. (Illus.). 336p. 25.99 (978-0-06-156238-9(6), Morrow, William & Co.) 2010. 476p. pap. 25.99 (978-0-06-194571-7(4), HarperLuxe) HarperCollins Pubs.

Peterson, Fritz. Mickey Mantle Is Going to Heaven. 2009. 227p. 24.95 (978-1-4327-4673-5(1)); (ENG.). pap. 19.95 (978-1-4327-4384-0(8)) Outskirts Pr., Inc.

Peterson, Robert. Only the Ball was White. 25.95 (978-0-8488-1124-2(0)) Amereon LTD.

—Only the Ball Was White: A History of Legendary Black Players & All-Black Professional Teams. 2008. (ENG.). 406p. pap. 19.00 (978-1-4379-6451-6(6)) DIANE Publishing Co.

Peterson, Todd. Early Black Baseball in Minnesota: The St. Paul Gophers, Minneapolis Keystones & Other Barnstorming Teams of the Deadball Era. 2010. (ENG., Illus.). 313p. pap. 39.95 (978-0-7864-3816-7(9)) McFarland & Co., Inc. Pubs.

Poekel, Charlie. Babe & the Kid: The Legendary Story of Babe Ruth & Johnny Sylvester. 2007. (Sports History Ser.). (ENG., Illus.). 160p. pap. 19.99 (978-1-59629-267-3(9)) History Pr., The.

Poolos, J. Hank Aaron. 2008. (Baseball Superstars Ser.). (Illus.). 128p. (gr. 6-12). pap. 11.95 (978-0-7910-9844-8(3), Checkmark Bks.) Facts On File, Inc.

Porter, David L. Michael Jordan: A Biography, 1 vol. 2007. (Greenwood Biographies Ser.). (Illus.). 208p. 35.00 (978-0-313-33767-3(5), GR3767, Greenwood Pr.) Greenwood Publishing Group, Inc.

Posnanski, Joe. The Soul of Baseball: A Road Trip Through Buck O'Neil's America. (ENG.). 2008. 304p. pap. 13.99 (978-0-06-085404-1(9), William Morrow Paperbacks) 2007. 256p. 24.95 (978-0-06-085403-4(0), Morrow, William & Co.) HarperCollins Pubs.

Pribble, Aaron. Pitching in the Promised Land: A Story of the First & Only Season in the Israel Baseball League. 2011. (ENG., Illus.). 280p. 24.95 (978-0-8032-3472-7(4)) Univ. of Nebraska Pr.

Proia, Paul. Just a Big Kid: The Life & Times of Rube Waddell. 2007. 420p. pap. 29.95 (978-1-4241-6862-0(7)) PublishAmerica, Inc.

Publications International Staff. Bk Brick Cooperstown. 2010. 320p. 12.98 (978-1-4127-1383-2(8), PIL Kids) Publications International, Ltd.

Reed, Ted. Carl Furillo, Brooklyn Dodgers All-Star. 2010. (ENG., Illus.). 210p. pap. 29.95 (978-0-7864-4709-1(5)) McFarland & Co., Inc. Pubs.

Regalado, Samuel O. Viva Baseball! Latin Major Leaguers & Their Special Hunger. 3rd ed. 2008. (Sport & Society Ser.). (Illus.). 288p. pap. 20.95 (978-0-252-07367-0(3)) Univ. of Illinois Pr.

Reis, Ronald A. Mickey Mantle. 2008. (Baseball Superstars Ser.). 136p. (gr. 6-12). 30.00 (978-0-7910-9546-1(0), Chelsea Hse.) Facts On File, Inc.

—Ted Williams. 2008. (Baseball Superstars Ser.). (Illus.). 136p. (gr. 6-12). lib. bdg. 30.00 (978-0-7910-9545-4(2), Chelsea Hse.) Facts On File, Inc.

Remy, Jerry & Sandler, Corey. Jerry Remy's Red Sox Heroes. 2010. (Illus.). 288p. pap. 12.95 (978-1-59921-970-7(0)) Globe Pequot Pr., The.

—Red Sox Heroes: The Remdawg's All-Time Favorite Red Sox, Great Moments, & Top Teams. 2009. (ENG., Illus.). 288p. 24.95 (978-1-59921-406-1(7), Lyons Pr.) Globe Pequot Pr., The.

Rhodes, Jean & Boburg, Shawn. Becoming Manny: Inside the Life of Baseball's Most Enigmatic Slugger. 2011. (ENG.). 320p. pap. 19.99 (978-1-4165-7707-2(6), Scribner) Scribner.

Riesgo, Nikco & Cohen, Russ. Strike Three! - A Player's Journey through the Infamous Baseball Strike Of 1994. 2010. 100p. pap. 19.94 (978-0-557-24643-4(1)) Lulu Enterprises Inc.

Ripken, Cal, Jr. & Phillips, Donald T. Get in the Game: 8 Elements of Perseverance That Make the Difference. 2008. (ENG.). 272p. (gr. 12-18). 15.00 (978-1-59240-280-9(1), Gotham) Penguin Group (USA) Inc.

Ritter, Lawrence S. The Glory of Their Times: The Story of the Early Days of Baseball Told by the Men Who Played It. abr. ed. 2009. (Playaway Adult Nonfiction Ser.). (ENG.). 44.99 (978-1-60812-723-8(0)) Findaway World, LLC.

—The Glory of Their Times: The Story of the Early Days of Baseball Told by the Men Who Played It. 2010. (ENG.). 384p. pap. 14.99 (978-0-06-199471-5(5), HarperPerennial) HarperCollins Pubs.

Roberts, Selena. A-Rod: The Many Lives of Alex Rodriguez. 2010. 272p. pap. 15.99 (978-0-06-179165-9(2), Harper Paperbacks) HarperCollins Pubs.

Robinson, Eddie & Rogers, C. Paul. Lucky Me: My Sixty-Five Years in Baseball. 2011. (Sport in American Life Ser.). (Illus.). 264p. 23.95 (978-0-87074-566-9(2)) Southern Methodist Univ. Pr.

Roensch, Greg. Rickey Henderson. 2008. (Baseball Superstars Ser.). (Illus.). 120p. (YA). (gr. 7-12). lib. bdg. 30.00 (978-0-7910-9601-7(7)) Facts On File, Inc.

Rosen, Charley. Bullpen Diaries: Mariano Rivera, Bronx Dreams, Pinstripe Legends, & the Future of the New York Yankees. 2011. (ENG.). 288p. 25.99 (978-0-06-200598-4(7)) HarperCollins Pubs.

Ruth, Babe. Playing the Game: My Early Years in Baseball. Cobb, William R., ed. 2011. (Dover Baseball Ser.). (ENG., Illus.). 128p. pap. 8.95 (978-0-486-47694-0(4)) Dover Pubns., Inc.

Ryan, Kenneth F. Tossing Heat: The Ken Ryan Story. 2007. 132p. per. 19.95 (978-1-4241-8015-8(5)) PublishAmerica, Inc.

Salmon, Tim & Goldman, Rob. Always an Angel: Playing the Game with Fire & Faith. 2010. (Always A Ser.). (ENG., Illus.). 240p. 19.95 (978-1-60078-343-2(0)) Triumph Bks.

Sarnoff, Gary A. The Wrecking Crew Of '33: The Washington Senators' Last Pennant. 2009. (ENG., Illus.). 245p. pap. 29.95 (978-0-7864-4291-1(3)) McFarland & Co., Inc. Pubs.

Schacht, Al. My Own Particular Screwball: An Informal Autobiography. Keyes, Ed, ed. 2011. 256p. 47.95 (978-1-258-10411-5(3)) Literary Licensing, LLC.

Schmidt, Mike & Waggoner, Glen. Clearing the Bases: Juiced Players, Monster Salaries, Sham Records, & a Hall of Famer's Search for the Soul of Baseball. 2007. (Illus.). 216p. pap. 13.95 (978-0-06-085500-0(2)) HarperCollins Pubs.

Schneider, Russell. Whatever Happened to Super Joe? Catching up with 45 Good Old Guys from the Bad Old Days of the Cleveland Indians. 2006. (Illus.). 208p. pap. 14.95 (978-1-59851-027-0(4)) Gray and Company, Publishers.

Schwarz, Alan. Rising Stars: The 10 Best Young Players in Baseball. 2009. (Sports Illustrated for Kids Bks). 176p. (gr. 7-12). 63.90 (978-1-60853-150-9(3)) Rosen Publishing Group, Inc., The.

B

Scoggins, Chaz. Game of My Life Boston Red Sox: Memorable Stories of Red Sox Baseball. 2008. (Game of My Life Ser.). (Illus.). 236p. per. 16.95 (978-1-59670-295-0(8)) Sports Publishing, LLC.

Seidel, Jeff. Baseball's Iron Man: Cal Ripken JR. a Tribute. 2007. (Illus.). 175p. per. 14.95 (978-1-59670-172-4(2)) Sports Publishing, LLC.

Shalin, Mike. Donnie Baseball: The Definitive Biography of Don Mattingly. 2011. (ENG.). 224p. 24.95 (978-1-60078-536-8(0)) Triumph Bks.

Shannon, Mike. Willie Mays: Art in the Outfield. 2nd ed. 2007. (ENG., Illus.). 89p. 29.95 (978-0-8173-1540-5(3)) Univ. of Alabama Pr.

Singletary, Wes. The Right Time: John Henry "Pop" Lloyd & Black Baseball. 2011. (ENG., Illus.). 234p. pap. 29.95 (978-0-7864-3572-2(0)) McFarland & Co., Inc. Pubs.

Skipper, James K. Baseball Nicknames: A Dictionary of Origins & Meanings. alt. ed. 2011. (ENG.). 398p. pap. 29.95 **(978-0-7864-6717-4(7))** McFarland & Co., Inc. Pubs.

Skipper, John C. Charlie Gehringer: A Biography of the Hall of Fame Tigers Second Baseman. 2008. (ENG., Illus.). 209p. pap. 29.95 (978-0-7864-3574-6(7)) McFarland & Co., Inc. Pubs.

—Dazzy Vance: A Biography of the Brooklyn Dodger Hall of Famer. 2007. (ENG., Illus.). 218p. per. 29.95 (978-0-7864-2985-1(2)) McFarland & Co., Inc. Pubs.

Skirboll, Aaron. The Pittsburgh Cocaine Seven: How a Ragtag Group of Fans Took the Fall for Major League Baseball. 2010. (ENG., Illus.). 288p. 22.95 (978-1-56976-288-2(0)) Chicago Review Pr., Inc.

Smiles, Jack. Bucky Harris: A Biography of Baseball's Boy Wonder. 2011. (ENG., Illus.). 320p. pap. 29.95 (978-0-7864-4160-0(7)) McFarland & Co., Inc. Pubs.

Smith, Curt. Pull up a Chair: The Vin Scully Story. 2009. 296p. 29.95 (978-1-59797-424-0(2)) Potomac Bks., Inc.

Smith, Patrick. Extra Innings: The Joy & the Pains of over-30 Baseball. 2007. (ENG., Illus.). 204p. per. 29.95 (978-0-7864-2909-7(7)) McFarland & Co., Inc. Pubs.

Snyder, Brad. A Well-Paid Slave: Curt Flood's Fight for Free Agency in Professional Sports. 2007. (ENG.). 480p. (gr. 12-18). 16.00 (978-0-452-28891-1(6), Plume) Penguin Group (USA) Inc.

Society for American Baseball Research (SABR). The National Pastime, Endless Seasons 2011: Baseball in Southern California. 2011. (ENG.). pap. 14.95 **(978-1-933599-20-5(0))** Society for American Baseball Research.

Society for American Baseball Research (SABR). The National Pastime, Volume 29: Monumental Baseball. 2009. (ENG.). 128p. pap. 14.95 (978-1-933599-14-4(6)) Society for American Baseball Research.

Sokolove, Michael. The Ticket Out: Darryl Strawberry & the Boys of Crenshaw. 2006. 291p. reprint ed. 25.00 (978-1-4223-5763-7(5)) DIANE Publishing Co.

Spatz, Lyle. Dixie Walker: A Life in Baseball. 2011. (ENG., Illus.). 273p. pap. 29.95 (978-0-7864-4633-9(1)) McFarland & Co., Inc. Pubs.

—Yankees Coming, Yankees Going: New York Yankee Player Transactions, 1903 Through 1999. alt. ed. 2009. (ENG.). 335p. pap. 35.00 (978-0-7864-4083-2(X)) McFarland & Co., Inc. Pubs.

Sporting News, creator. Cardinal Nation. 4th ed. 2006. (ENG., Illus.). 256p. 29.95 (978-0-89204-888-5(3)) Sporting News Publishing Co.

Sporting News Staff. Heroes of the Hall: Second Edition. 2007. (ENG.). 512p. 39.95 (978-0-89204-871-7(9)) Sporting News Publishing Co.

Springer, Jon & Silverman, Matthew. Mets by the Numbers: A Complete Team History of the Amazin' Mets by Uniform Number. 2008. (Illus.). 303p. per. 14.95 (978-1-60239-227-4(7)) Skyhorse Publishing Co., Inc.

St. Louis Post-Dispatch, compiled by. Stan Musial - Baseball's Perfect Knight. 2010. 176p. 34.95 (978-0-9842084-5-6(3)) St. Louis Post-Dispatch.

Stack Media Staff. Baseball Training: For the Athlete, By the Athlete. 2010. (ENG.). 176p. pap. 16.95 (978-1-60078-366-1(X)) Triumph Bks.

Stang, Mark. Athletics Album: A Photo History of the Philadelphia Athletics. 2006. (Illus.). 208p. (978-1-933197-24-1(2)) Orange Frazer Pr.

Stanton, Tom. Ty & the Babe: Baseball's Fiercest Rivals - A Surprising Friendship & the 1941 Has-Beens Golf Championship. 2008. (ENG., Illus.). 304p. pap. 15.99 (978-0-312-38224-7(3), St. Martin's Griffin) St. Martin's Pr.

Staples, Billy, et al. Before the Glory: 20 Baseball Heroes Talk about Growing up & Turning Hard Times into Home Runs. 2007. (ENG., Illus.). 384p. pap. 16.95 (978-0-7573-0626-6(8)) Health Communications, Inc.

Stavans, Ilan. Béisbol. 2012. E-Book **(978-0-313-37514-9(3)**, Greenwood Pr.) Greenwood Publishing Group, Inc.

Stevens, Big Ed. The Other Side of the Jackie Robinson Story. 2010. pap. 15.99 (978-1-60799-112-0(8)) Tate Publishing & Enterprises, LLC.

Stewart, Wayne. Alex Rodriguez: A Biography, 1 vol. 2007. (Greenwood Biographies Ser.). (Illus.). 184p. 35.00 (978-0-313-33975-2(9), GR3975, Greenwood Pr.) Greenwood Publishing Group, Inc.

—Babe Ruth: A Biography, 1 vol. 2006. (Baseball's All-Time Greatest Hitters Ser.). (Illus.). 200p. 35.00 (978-0-313-33596-9(6), GR3596, Greenwood Pr.) Greenwood Publishing Group, Inc.

—Baseball Dads: The Game's Greatest Players Reflect on Their Fathers & the Game They Love. 2012. (ENG., Illus.). 160p. 19.95 **(978-1-61608-583-4(5)**, 608583) Skyhorse Publishing Co., Inc.

Stewart, Wayne. Stan the Man: The Life & Times of Stan Musial TBC. 2010. (ENG.). 256p. 24.95 (978-1-60078-322-7(8)) Triumph Bks.

Stinson, Mitchell Conrad. Edd Roush: A Biography of the Cincinnati Reds Star. 2010. (ENG., Illus.). 256p. pap. 29.95 (978-0-7864-4407-6(X)) McFarland & Co., Inc. Pubs.

Stowers, Carlton. Oh Brother, How They Played the Game: The Story of Texas' Greatest All-Brothers Baseball Team. 2007. (Texas Heritage Ser.). (ENG., Illus.) 80p. 14.95 (978-1-933337-13-5(3)) State Hse. Pr.

Strawberry, Darryl. Straw: Finding My Way. 256p. 2010. (ENG.). pap. 13.99 (978-0-06-170421-5(0)) 2009. 26.99 (978-0-06-170420-8(2)) HarperCollins Pubs. (Ecco).

Swanton, Barry & Mah, Jay-Dell. Black Baseball Players in Canada: A Biographical Dictionary, 1881-1960. 2009. (ENG., Illus.). 212p. pap. 39.95 (978-0-7864-4468-7(1)) McFarland & Co., Inc. Pubs.

Swearingen, Randall. A Great Teammate: The Legend of Mickey Mantle. 2007. (Illus.). 232p. per. 16.95 (978-1-59670-194-6(3)) Sports Publishing, LLC.

Szalontai, James. Teenager on First, Geezer at Bat, 4-F on Deck: Major League Baseball in 1945. 2009. (ENG., Illus.). 334p. pap. 35.00 (978-0-7864-3794-8(4)) McFarland & Co., Inc. Pubs.

Szalontai, James D. Small Ball in the Big Leagues: A History of Stealing, Bunting, Walking & Otherwise Scratching for Runs. 2010. (ENG., Illus.). 311p. pap. 39.95 (978-0-7864-3793-1(6)) McFarland & Co., Inc. Pubs.

Tafoya, Dale. Bash Brothers: A Legacy Subpoenaed. 2008. (Illus.). 288p. 26.95 (978-1-59797-178-2(2)) Potomac Bks., Inc.

Theodore, John. Baseball's Natural: The Story of Eddie Waitkus. 2006. (ENG., Illus.). 140p. pap. 14.95 (978-0-8032-5958-4(1), Bison Bks.) Univ. of Nebraska Pr.

Thomson, Bobby & Pepe, Phil. Few & Chosen Giants: Defining Giants Greatness Across the Eras. 2007. (Few & Chosen Ser.). (ENG., Illus.). 256p. 25.95 (978-1-57243-854-5(1)) Triumph Bks.

Thomson, Cindy & Brown, Scott. Three Finger: The Mordecai Brown Story. 2008. (ENG., Illus.). 288p. pap. 17.95 (978-0-8032-1888-8(5), Bison Bks.) Univ. of Nebraska Pr.

Thornley, Stew, ed. Minnesotans in Baseball. 2009. pap. 25.95 (978-1-932472-80-6(0)) Nodin Pr.

Thornton AndrZcaron; & Janssen, Al. Triumph Born of Tragedy: The Story of Romance & Courage in the Life of AndrZcaron; Thornton: As Told to Al Janssen. 2011. 156p. pap. 18.00 (978-1-60899-408-3(2), Resource Pubns.) Wipf & Stock Pubs.

Tiemann, Bob, ed. Mound City Memories: Baseball in St. Louis. 2007. (ENG., Illus.). 120p. per. 14.95 (978-1-933599-06-9(5)) Society for American Baseball Research.

Tierney, John. Jack Coombs: A Life in Baseball. 2008. (ENG., Illus.). 214p. pap. 29.95 (978-0-7864-3959-1(9)) McFarland & Co., Inc. Pubs.

Travers, Steven. The Last Icon: Tom Seaver & His Times. 2011. (ENG., Illus.). 312p. 24.95 (978-1-58979-660-7(8)); **(978-1-58979-661-4(6))** Taylor Trade Publishing.

Treto Cisneros, Pedro. The Mexican League / la Liga Mexicana: Comprehensive Player Statistics, 1937-2001 bilingual edition / Estadisticas Comprensivas de los Jugadores, 1937-2001 edicion Bilingue. alt. ed. 2011. (ENG & SPA., Illus.). 512p. pap. 45.00 (978-0-7864-6120-2(9)) McFarland & Co., Inc. Pubs.

Trimble, Patrick. Media & the Creation of Babe Ruth. 2012. (Studies in American Popular History & Culture Ser.). (ENG.). 240p. 125.00 (978-0-415-99407-1(1)) Routledge.

Trimble, Richard M. He Touched 'em All: Wally Pontiff, Jr-an Abbreviated Life. 2007. (ENG.). 348p. per. 29.95 (978-1-4241-4870-7(7)) PublishAmerica, Inc.

Triumph Books Staff, et al. Albert Pujols: Simply The Best. 2009. (ENG.). 128p. pap. 14.95 (978-1-60078-351-7(1)) Triumph Bks.

Tully, Gregory J. Nine College Nines: A Closeup View of Campus Baseball Programs Today. 2009. (ENG.). 224p. pap. 35.00 (978-0-7864-4128-0(3)) McFarland & Co., Inc. Pubs.

Tye, Larry. Satchel: The Life & Times of an American Legend. 2010. (Illus.). 432p. pap. 16.00 (978-0-8129-7797-4(1), Random Hse. Trade Paperbacks) Random House Publishing Group.

Vecsey, George. Stan Musial: An American Life. (ENG., Illus.). 416p. 2012. pap. 16.00 **(978-0-345-51707-4(5))** 2011. 26.00 (978-0-345-51706-7(7)) ESPN Enterprises.

Vincent, Fay. It's What's Inside the Lines That Counts: Baseball Stars of the 1970s & 1980s Talk about the Game They Loved. (ENG., Illus.). 336p. 2011. pap. 15.00 (978-1-4391-5922-4(X)) 2010. 25.00 (978-1-4391-5921-7(1)) Simon & Schuster.

—The Only Game in Town: Baseball Stars of the 1930s & 1940s Talk about the Game They Loved. 2007. (ENG., Illus.). 256p. pap. 14.00 (978-0-7432-7318-3(4)) Simon & Schuster.

—We Would Have Played for Nothing: Baseball Stars of the 1950s & 1960s Talk about the Game They Loved. (ENG., Illus.). 336p. 2009. pap. 15.00 (978-1-4165-5343-4(6)) 2008. 25.00 (978-1-4165-5342-7(8)) Simon & Schuster.

Virtue, John. South of the Color Barrier: How Jorge Pasquel & the Mexican League Pushed Baseball Toward Racial Integration. 2007. (ENG., Illus.). 239p. per. 29.95 (978-0-7864-3293-6(4)) McFarland & Co., Inc. Pubs.

Von Borries, Philip. Ameridi (american Diamonds) An American Baseball Reader. 2008. 192p. pap. 15.95 (978-1-60145-411-9(2)) Booklocker.com, Inc.

Vorwald, Bob. What It Means to Be a Cub: The North Side's Greatest Players Talk about Cubs Baseball. 2010. (What It Means to Be Ser.). (ENG.). 320p. 24.95 (978-1-60078-277-0(9)) Triumph Bks.

—What It Means to Be a White Sox: The South Side's Greatest Players Talk about White Sox Baseball. 2010. (What It Means to Be Ser.). (ENG.). 336p. 24.95 (978-1-60078-278-7(7)) Triumph Bks.

Wafenheim, Kal. Clemente! 2006. (Illus.). 231p. reprint ed. pap. 16.00 (978-1-4223-5321-9(4)) DIANE Publishing Co.

Wagenheim, Kal. Clemente: The enduring Legacy. 2010. (Illus.). 268p. pap. 24.95 (978-1-55876-527-6(1)) Wiener, Markus Pubs., Inc.

Wakefield, Tim. Knuckler: My Life with Baseball's Most Confounding Pitch. 2011. (ENG., Illus.). 288p. 26.00 (978-0-547-51769-8(6)) Houghton Mifflin Harcourt Trade & Reference Pubs.

Waldo, Ronald T. Fred Clarke: A Biography of the Baseball Hall of Fame Player-Manager. 2010. (ENG., Illus.). 252p. pap. 29.95 (978-0-7864-5933-9(6)) McFarland & Co., Inc. Pubs.

Waldo, Ronald T. Hazen Kiki Cuyler: A Baseball Biography. 2012. (ENG.). pap. 29.95 **(978-0-7864-6885-0(8))** McFarland & Co., Inc. Pubs.

Warburton, Paul. Signature Seasons: Fifteen Baseball Legends at Their Most Memorable, 1908-1949. 2010. (ENG., Illus.). 264p. pap. 29.95 (978-0-7864-4655-1(2)) McFarland & Co., Inc. Pubs.

Ward, John Montgomery. Play Ball!: Everything You Need to Become the World's Best Baseball Player. 2008. 104p. pap. 9.95 (978-1-4357-3318-3(5)) Lulu Enterprises Inc.

Ward, Philip. The Interplanetary Pastime. 2010. 128p. pap. 9.95 (978-1-60844-363-5(9)) Dog Ear Publishing, LLC.

Weiss, Stuart L. The Curt Flood Story: The Man Behind the Myth. 2007. (Sports & American Culture Ser.). (ENG., Illus.). 272p. (gr. 9). 34.95 (978-0-8262-1740-0(0)) Univ. of Missouri Pr.

White, Bill. Uppity: My Untold Story about the Games People Play. (ENG., Illus.). 320p. 2012. pap. 15.99 **(978-0-446-55526-5(6))** 2011. 26.99 (978-0-446-55525-8(8)) Grand Central Publishing.

Whiting, Robert. The Meaning of Ichiro: The New Wave from Japan & the Transformation of Our National Pastime. 2006. (Illus.). 318p. reprint ed. 26.00 (978-1-4223-5632-6(9)) DIANE Publishing Co.

—You Gotta Have Wa. 2nd ed. 2009. (Vintage Ser.). (ENG., Illus.). 416p. pap. 15.95 (978-0-307-45597-0(1)) Knopf, Alfred A. Inc.

Whitten, Wiley. Champions of Naught Six: the Story of the 1906 Cleburne Railroaders. 2010. 300p. pap. 19.00 (978-0-557-46955-0(4)) Lulu Enterprises Inc.

Wiggins, Robert Peyton. Chief Bender: A Baseball Biography. 2009. (ENG., Illus.). 272p. pap. 29.95 (978-0-7864-4229-4(8)) McFarland & Co., Inc. Pubs.

—The Deacon & the Schoolmaster: Phillippe & Leever, Pittsburgh's Great Turn-of-the-Century Pitchers. 2011. (ENG., Illus.). 296p. pap. 35.00 (978-0-7864-5842-4(9)) McFarland & Co., Inc. Pubs.

Wilber, Rick. My Father's Game: Life, Death, Baseball. 2007. (ENG., Illus.). 214p. per. 29.95 (978-0-7864-2984-4(4)) McFarland & Co., Inc. Pubs.

Wilker, Josh. Cardboard Gods: An All-American Tale Told Through Baseball Cards. 2010. (ENG.). 208p. 24.95 (978-1-934734-16-2(0)) Seven Footer Pr.

Wilkinson, Jack. Atlanta Braves. 2007. (Game of My Life Ser.). (Illus.). 216p. 24.95 (978-1-59670-099-4(8)) Sports Publishing, LLC.

Williams, Billy & Mitchell, Fred. Billy Williams: My Sweet-Swinging Lifetime with the Cubs. 2008. (ENG., Illus.). 256p. 24.95 (978-1-60078-050-9(4)) Triumph Bks.

Williams, Douglas. Always a Yankee. 2009. 202p. pap. 15.95 (978-0-7414-5762-2(8)) Infinity Publishing.

Williams, Mitch & Berger, Darrell. Straight Talk from Wild Thing. 2010. (ENG.). 208p. 19.95 (978-1-60078-306-7(6)) Triumph Bks.

Williams, Pete. Inside the World Series: A Behind-The Scenes Look at the Fall Classic. 2009. (Illus.). 160p. **(978-1-58159-417-1(8))** North American Media Group.

Wise, Bill. Silent Star: The Story of Deaf Major Leaguer William Hoy. 2012. (Illus.). 40p. (J). 18.95 **(978-1-60060-411-9(0))** Lee & Low Bks., Inc.

Wolfe, R. Ron Santo: A Perfect 10. 2011. 264p. 24.95 **(978-0-9846278-2-0(0))** Lone Wolfe Pr.

Wong, Wylie & Johanson, Matt. San Francisco Giants: Where Have You Gone? 2007. (Illus.). 214p. per. 16.95 (978-1-59670-187-8(0)) Sports Publishing, LLC.

Wood, Gerald C. & Hazucha, Andrew, eds. Northsiders: Essays on the History & Culture of the Chicago Cubs. 2008. (ENG., Illus.). 229p. pap. 39.95 (978-0-7864-3623-1(9)) McFarland & Co., Inc. Pubs.

Wubbena, Dennis. The Baseball Bluebook (2008 College Edition) 2008 College Baseball Guide & Scouting Register. 2008. 550p. per. 65.00 (978-0-9788368-2-5(0)) Baseball Bluebook, The.

—The Baseball Bluebook (2008 Professional Edition) 2008 Professional Edition. 2008. 500p. per. 65.00 (978-0-9788368-3-2(9)) Baseball Bluebook, The.

Wynn, Jimmy & McCurdy, Bill. Toy Cannon: The Autobiography of Baseball's Jimmy Wynn. 2010. (ENG., Illus.). 236p. pap. 29.95 (978-0-7864-5856-1(9)) McFarland & Co., Inc. Pubs.

Yastrzemski, Carl. Yastrzemski. 2007. (Icons of Major League Baseball: Ser.). (ENG., Illus.). 246p. 34.95 (978-1-59071-089-0(4)) Rugged Land.

Zang, David W. Fleetwood Walker's Divided Heart. Zang, David W., ed. 2006. cd-rom 39.95 (978-0-9779883-4-1(1)) Legacy Audio Bks.

Zappala, Tom & Zappala, Ellen. The T206 Collection: The Players & Their Stories. 2010. (ENG., Illus.). 224p. 38.00 (978-1-931807-94-4(9)) Randall, Peter E. Pub.

Zemial, Gus, et al. Ozark Ike: Memories of Fence Buster Gus Zernial. 2007. 218p. 25.00 (978-0-9779841-6-9(8)) Pepperpot Prodns, Inc.

Zminiuch, Fran. Fireman: The Evolution of the Closer in Baseball. 2010. (ENG.). 288p. pap. 16.95 (978-1-60078-312-8(0)) Triumph Bks.

—Going, Going, Gone! The Art of the Trade in Major League Baseball. 2008. (ENG., Illus.). 240p. pap. 16.95 (978-1-58979-334-7(X)) Taylor Trade Publishing.

—Shortened Seasons: The Untimely Deaths of Major League Baseball's Stars & Journeymen. 2007. (ENG., Illus.). 240p. per. 16.95 (978-1-58979-363-7(3)) Taylor Trade Publishing.

BASEBALL PLAYERS—JUVENILE LITERATURE

Dunham, Montrew. Roberto Clemente; Young Ball Player. 2009. 8.32 (978-0-7848-2904-2(7), Everbind) Marco Bk. Co.

Glaser, Jason. Jackie Robinson: Baseball's Great Pioneer. 2007. (Graphic Biographies Ser.). (ENG.). 32p. (gr. 3-4). lib. bdg. 299.90 (978-1-4296-0867-1(6), Graphic Library) Capstone Pr., Inc.

BASEBALL PLAYERS—STATISTICS

Adomites, Paul, et al. Armchair Reader Grand Slam Baseball. 2007. (Armchair Reader Ser.). (Illus.). 468p. per. 15.95 (978-1-4127-1562-1(8)) Publications International, Ltd.

Barra, Allen. Clearing the Bases: The Greatest Baseball Debates of the Last Century. 2008. (ENG., Illus.). 288p. pap. 16.95 (978-0-8032-1763-8(3), Bison Bks.) Univ. of Nebraska Pr.

Baseball America, The Edi, ed. Baseball America 2011 Almanac: A Comprehensive Review of the 2010 Season. 2011. (ENG.). 468p. pap. 23.95 (978-1-932391-33-6(9)) Baseball America, Inc.

Baseball Prospectus Staff. Baseball Prospectus 2010. 2010. (ENG.). 672p. pap. 24.95 (978-0-470-55840-9(7), Wiley) Wiley, John & Sons, Inc.

Baseball Prospectus Staff. Extra Innings: More Baseball Between the Numbers from the Team at Baseball Prospectus. Goldman, Steven, ed. 2012. (ENG.). 464p. (gr. 9). 27.99 **(978-0-465-02403-2(3))** Basic Bks.

Baseball Prospectus Team of Experts. Baseball Prospectus 2007. 2007. (ENG.). 600p. pap. 17.95 (978-0-7611-4371-0(8)) Workman Publishing Co., Inc.

Baseball Prospectus Team of Experts Staff & Keri, Jonah. Baseball Between the Numbers: Why Everything You Know about the Game Is Wrong. 2007. (ENG., Illus.). 528p. (gr. 9). per. 17.95 (978-0-465-00547-5(0)) Basic Bks.

Batesel, Paul. Major League Baseball Players Of 1884: A Biographical Dictionary. 2010. (ENG., Illus.). 251p. pap. 39.95 (978-0-7864-5905-6(0)) McFarland & Co., Inc. Pubs.

Benson, John, ed. Benson Baseball Annual 2007. 2007. pap. 22.95 (978-1-880876-15-2(9)) Diamond Library.

Blabac, Eric. Encyclopedia of Baseball Statistics: From A to ZR. 2010. 504p. pap. 41.95 (978-1-4502-6552-2(9)) iUniverse, Inc.

Borawski, Brian, et al, contrib. by. The Hardball Times Baseball Annual. 2006. (Hardball Times Baseball Annual Ser.). (Illus.). 350p. per. 19.95 (978-0-87946-312-0(0)) ACTA Pubns.

Burnson, John. Graphical Player. 2008. 224p. pap. 21.95 (978-0-87946-372-4(4)) ACTA Pubns.

—The Graphical Player 2007. 2007. (Illus.). 205p. per. 21.95 (978-1-891566-52-3(0)) Shandler Enterprises, LLC.

Burnson, John, et al. The Graphical Player 2008: The Next Step in Sabermetric Research. 5th rev. ed. 2007. (Illus.). 212p. per. 21.95 (978-1-891566-53-0(9)) Shandler Enterprises, LLC.

Costa, Gabriel B., et al. Understanding Sabermetrics: An Introduction to the Science of Baseball Statistics. 2007. (ENG., Illus.). 190p. per. 29.95 (978-0-7864-3388-9(4)) McFarland & Co., Inc. Pubs.

Darby, William. Deconstructing Major League Baseball, 1991-2004: How Statistics Illuminate Individual & Team Performances. 2006. (ENG., Illus.). 516p. per. 49.95 (978-0-7864-2537-2(7)) McFarland & Co., Inc. Pubs.

Dewan, John. The Fielding Bible 2008. 2008. 320p. per. 21.95 (978-0-87946-343-4(0)) ACTA Pubns.

Diamond Dates. 2006. per. 16.95 (978-0-9789000-0-7(6)) G R Publishing.

Dierker, Larry. My Team: Choosing My Dream Team from My Forty Years in Baseball. 2007. (ENG., Illus.). 288p. pap. 13.00 (978-0-7432-7514-9(4)) Simon & Schuster.

Ezra, David. Asterisk: Home Runs, Steroids, & the Rush to Judgement. 2008. (ENG.). 256p. 24.95 (978-1-60078-062-2(8)) Triumph Bks.

Figueredo, Jorge S. Cuban Baseball: A Statistical History, 1878-1961. alt. ed. 2011. (ENG., Illus.). 552p. pap. 45.00 (978-0-7864-6425-8(9)) McFarland & Co., Inc. Pubs.

Fleitz, David L. More Ghosts in the Gallery: Another Sixteen Little-Known Greats at Cooperstown. 2007. (ENG., Illus.). 264p. per. 29.95 (978-0-7864-3133-5(4)) McFarland & Co., Inc. Pubs.

Guzzo, Glenn. The New Ballgame: Baseball Statistics for the Casual Fan. 2007. (Illus.). 167p. per. 14.95 (978-0-87946-318-2(X)) ACTA Pubns.

Hardball Times Writers. The Hardball Times Baseball Annual 2009. 2008. 352p. pap. 19.95 (978-0-87946-368-7(6)) ACTA Pubns.

—The Hardball Times Season Preview. 2009. 208p. pap. 17.95 (978-0-87946-370-0(8)) ACTA Pubns.

Humphreys, Michael A. Wizardry: Baseball's All-Time Greatest Fielders Revealed, 1 vol. 2011. (ENG., Illus.). 432p. pap. 19.95 (978-0-19-539776-5(2)) Oxford Univ. Pr., Inc.

James, Bill. The Bill James Handbook. 2007. (Illus.). 482p. per. 21.95 (978-0-87946-340-3(6)) ACTA Pubns.

—The Bill James Handbook 2010. 2009. 520p. pap. 23.95 (978-0-87946-407-3(0)) ACTA Pubns.

James, Bill & Baseball Info Solutions. The Bill James Handbook 2009. 2008. 448p. pap. 21.95 (978-0-87946-367-0(8)) ACTA Pubns.

Levitt, Daniel R. The Battle That Forged Modern Baseball: The Federal League Challenge & Its Legacy. 2012. **(978-1-56663-905-7(0))**; (ENG., Illus.). 336p. 39.95 **(978-1-56663-869-2(0))** Dee, Ivan R. Pub.

McKamey, Deric. Minor League Baseball Analyst. 2007. 127p. per. 19.95 (978-1-891566-72-1(5)) Shandler Enterprises, LLC.

—Minor League Baseball Analyst 2007. 2nd ed. 2007. (Illus.). 128p. per. 19.95 (978-1-891566-71-4(7)) Shandler Enterprises, LLC.

McNeil, William F. All-Stars for All Time: A Sabermetric Ranking of the Major League Best, 1876-2007. 2008. (ENG., Illus.). 243p. pap. 39.95 *(978-0-7864-3500-5(3))* McFarland & Co., Inc. Pubs.
Megdal, Howard. The Baseball Talmud: The Definitive Position-by-Position Ranking of Baseball's Chosen Players. 2009. (ENG.). 256p. 22.99 *(978-0-06-155843-6(5))* HarperCollins Pubs.
Nemec, David & Zeman, Dave. The Baseball Rookies Encyclopedia. 2006. 386p. reprint ed. pap. 25.00 *(978-1-4223-5288-5(9))* DIANE Publishing Co.
Peraza, Marino Martinez. Por Amor a la Pelota: Historia del Beisbol Cubano. 2008. (Coleccion Cuba y Sus Jueces Ser.). 434p. pap. 35.00 *(978-1-59388-152-8(5))* Ediciones Universal.
Plawecki, Mark J. How Could You Trade Billy Pierce? Essays & Analyses of MLB's Best Pitchers, 1901-2005. 2006. (Illus.). 302p. per. *(978-1-59571-129-8(5))* Word Association Pubs.
Russell, Scott. Too Much Time on His Hands: The Unauthorized Ultimate Statistical Guide of the World Champion Boston Red Sox. 2008. 146p. pap. 14.95 *(978-0-9796722-3-1(6))* Dirty Water Publishing.
Schwarz, Alan. The Numbers Game: Baseball's Lifelong Fascination with Statistics. Date not set. mass mkt. *(978-0-312-99375-7(7),* St. Martin's Paperbacks) St. Martin's Pr.
Shandler, Ron. Baseball Forecaster 2007. 21st ed. 2007. (Illus.). 252p. per. 24.95 *(978-1-891566-07-3(5))* Shandler Enterprises, LLC.
—Baseball Forecaster 2008. 22nd ed. 2007. (Illus.). 265p. per. 24.95 *(978-1-891566-08-0(3))* Shandler Enterprises, LLC.
Skipper, John C. A Biographical Dictionary of the Baseball Hall of Fame. 2nd rev. ed. 2008. (ENG., Illus.). 359p. 75.00 *(978-0-7864-3803-7(7))* McFarland & Co., Inc. Pubs.
Smith, Mike, ed. We Shocked the World: How the underdog St. Louis Cardinals won the 2006 World Series. 2006. pap. 19.95 *(978-0-9661397-7-8(1))* St. Louis Post-Dispatch.
Sporting News Staff. The Baseball Register & Fantasy Handbook 2007 Edition: Complete Guide to Major League Players & Prospects. 2007. (ENG.). 712p. pap. 22.95 *(978-0-89204-866-3(2))* Sporting News Publishing Co.
Stark, Jayson. The Stark Truth: The Most Overrated & Underrated Players in Baseball History. 2007. (ENG.). 224p. 24.95 *(978-1-57243-959-7(9))* Triumph Bks.
Taylor, Frederick E. The Runmakers: A New Way to Rate Baseball Players. 2011. (ENG.). 272p. 24.95 *(978-1-4214-0010-5(3))* Johns Hopkins Univ. Pr.
Tsao, Brian, et al, eds. The Hardball Times Season Preview. 2008. (Illus.). 238p. per. 17.95 *(978-0-87946-346-5(5))* ACTA Pubns.
Tsao, Bryan, et al, eds. The Hardball Times Baseball Annual. 2007. (Hardball Times Baseball Annual Ser.). (Illus.). 366p. per. 19.95 *(978-0-87946-341-0(4))* ACTA Pubns.
Weiss, Bill. The 100 Greatest Minor League Baseball Teams. 2006. (ENG.). 528p. per. 21.95 *(978-1-59800-268-3(6))* Outskirts Pr., Inc.
Wiggins, Robert Peyton. The Federal League of Base Ball Clubs: The History of an Outlaw Major League, 1914-1915. (ENG., Illus.). 368p. 2008. 49.95 *(978-0-7864-3835-8(5))* 2011. pap. 40.00 ***(978-0-7864-6939-0(0))*** McFarland & Co., Inc. Pubs.
Wright, Marshall D. The Eastern League in Baseball Set: A Statistical History, 1923-2005, 2 vols. 2006. (ENG., Illus.). 817p. pap. 75.00 *(978-0-7864-2794-9(9))* McFarland & Co., Inc. Pubs.

BASEBALL SPRING TRAINING
see Spring Training (Baseball)

BASEBALL STADIUMS
see Baseball Fields

BASEBALL STORIES

Adachi, Mitsuru. Cross Game, Vol. 3. 2011. (Cross Game Ser.). (ENG.). 376p. pap. 14.99 *(978-1-4215-3767-2(2))* Viz Media.
Alop, Alan & Noel, Doc. The Best Team Ever: A Novel of America, Chicago, & the 1907 Cubs. 2008. (Illus.). 503p. pap. 23.95 *(978-1-935098-02-7(0),* Bascom Hill Publishing Group, Ltd.) Hillcrest Publishing Group, Inc.
Aultman, Robert C. Myst, Titan & the Outcasts. 2008. 424p. 24.99 *(978-1-4389-1474-9(1))*; pap. 14.99 *(978-1-4389-1473-2(3))* AuthorHouse.
Carey, Mike. Heading for Home: A Baseball Odyssey. 2008. 132p. pap. 19.95 *(978-1-60703-081-2(0))* PublishAmerica, Inc.
Cecil, Trevor. Farewell to Greatness. 2011. 272p. pap. 27.95 ***(978-1-4560-7872-0(0))*** PublishAmerica, Inc.
Colbert, Norman V. An Autobiography Of: The Best Little League Baseball Player Ever! 2011. pap. 10.95 ***(978-0-7414-6662-4(7))*** Infinity Publishing.
Deford, Frank. Entitled: A Tale of Modern Baseball. 2008. (ENG.). 336p. per. 14.95 *(978-1-4022-1255-0(0),* Sourcebooks Landmark) Sourcebooks, Inc.
DeLillo, Don. Underworld. 2007. (ENG.). 832p. 55.00 *(978-1-4165-4864-5(5),* Scribner) Scribner.
Dodd, Pat. A Long Dirt Road. 2010. 56p. pap. 10.99 *(978-1-4490-3873-1(5))* AuthorHouse.
Duff, Gerald. Dirty Rice: A Season in the Evangeline League. 2012. pap. 20.00 ***(978-1-935754-13-8(0))*** Univ. of Louisiana at Lafayette Pr.
Farina, William. Eliot Asinof & the Truth of the Game: A Critical Study of the Baseball Writings. 2011. (ENG.). 250p. pap. 55.00 ***(978-0-7864-6302-2(3))*** McFarland & Co., Inc. Pubs.
Flexer, Bruce. Buhley Sparks, the Gift. 2009. 228p. 24.99 *(978-1-4389-5020-4(9))*; pap. 14.49 *(978-1-4389-5019-8(5))* AuthorHouse.
Flowers, Hugh A. Oklahoma Tomboy. 2007. (ENG.). 100p. per. 16.95 *(978-1-4241-6993-1(3))* PublishAmerica, Inc.
Gale, Robert L. Characters & Plots in the Fiction of Ring Lardner. 2008. (ENG.). 368p. pap. 55.00 *(978-0-7864-3688-0(3))* McFarland & Co., Inc. Pubs.
Gentry, Nancy. The Secret & the Sunday Rose. 2011. 158p. pap. 10.95 ***(978-0-9846244-4-7(9))*** O'More Publishing.
German, Norman. Switch-Pitchers. 2010. 274p. pap. 16.95 *(978-1-60452-040-8(X))* BluewaterPress, LLC.
Harrold, Anna Kaserman. The Giant Slayers: Book One of the Village of Crossroads Series. 2011. 108p. pap. 10.95 ***(978-1-4634-1054-4(9))*** AuthorHouse.
Irish, Hod. Casey 1888. 2007. 196p. per. 19.99 *(978-1-4257-8245-0(0))* Xlibris Corp.
Jody L. And Gabriel A. Lopez. From Sugar to Diamonds: Spanish/Mexican Baseball 1925-1969. 2009. 436p. pap. 32.95 *(978-1-4389-5252-9(X))* AuthorHouse.
Laz, Andrew. The Real World Series: And Another Year in the Bronx: Two Stories by Andrew Laz, 1 vol. 2009. 264p. pap. 27.95 *(978-1-60703-199-4(X))* PublishAmerica, Inc.
LeClair, James. The Glove. 2011. pap. 10.99 *(978-1-61739-598-7(6))* Tate Publishing & Enterprises, LLC.
Maeda, Shunshin. Ninja Baseball Kyuma!, 3 vols., Vol. 1. 2009. (Illus.). 200p. (J). pap. 7.99 *(978-1-897376-86-7(3))* URON Entertainment Corp. CAN. Dist: Diamond Bk. Distributors.
McCarty, Danny. The Fifty-Two-Year-Old Rookie. 2007. (ENG.). 180p. per. 24.95 *(978-1-4241-6744-9(2))* PublishAmerica, Inc.
McGill, William. Dream Team: A Novella & Other Stories of the Game. 2008. 234p. pap. 14.50 *(978-0-615-25998-7(7))* McGill, William J.
Michael, Sean. Bases Loaded: A Going for the Gold Novel. 2009. 252p. pap. 13.95 *(978-1-60370-734-3(4))* Torquere Pr.
Mitchell, Bob. Once upon a Fastball. 2009. (ENG.). 288p. 14.00 *(978-0-7582-2688-4(8))* Kensington Publishing Corp.
Mort, Terry. At Last! a Novel of Life, Love, Temptation & the Cubs. 2011. 216p. pap. 17.95 ***(978-1-61179-123-5(5))*** Fireship Pr.
MVP Books Staff, et al, eds. The Yankees Baseball Reader: A Collection of Writings on the Game's Greatest Dynasty. 2011. (ENG., Illus.). 352p. 25.00 *(978-0-7603-4061-5(7),* 0760340617, MVP Bks.) MBI Publishing Co. LLC.
Newell, James. Rookie Manager. 2007. 152p. per. 24.95 *(978-1-4241-7698-4(0))* PublishAmerica, Inc.
Perry, Thomas K. Just Joe: Baseball's Natural, As Told by His Wife. 2007. viii, 216p. pap. *(978-1-929763-30-6(1))* Pocol Pr.
Ribalow, M. Z. Peanuts & Crackerjacks: A Baseball Novel. 2011. (ENG.). 208p. pap. 25.00 ***(978-0-7864-6598-9(0))*** McFarland & Co., Inc. Pubs.
Rieger, Thomas E. Two for the Show. 2008. 123p. pap. 19.95 *(978-1-60672-764-5(8))* PublishAmerica, Inc.
Riley, G. D. Slow on the Clicker, 1 vol. 2009. 283p. pap. 27.95 *(978-1-60836-715-3(0))* PublishAmerica, Inc.
Schilling, Peter, Jr. The End of Baseball. 2008. (ENG.). 352p. 25.00 *(978-1-56663-782-4(1))* Dee, Ivan R. Pub.
Schraufnagel, Noel. The Baseball Novel: A History & Annotated Bibliography of Adult Fiction. 2008. (ENG.). 254p. pap. 39.95 *(978-0-7864-3557-9(7))* McFarland & Co., Inc. Pubs.
Seid, Mike. Chuckin' Chuck: The Astonishing Tale of Charles Manson Pitching in the Major Leagues. 296p. 2009. pap. 15.49 *(978-1-4389-6785-1(3))* 2008. pap. 22.99 *(978-1-4389-1100-7(9))* AuthorHouse.
Shalvis, Jill. Slow Heat. 2010. (ENG.). 336p. (gr. 12-18). 7.99 *(978-0-425-23366-5(9),* Berkley) Penguin Group (USA) Inc.
Shannon. Best of Spitball. 22.95 *(978-0-8488-1563-9(7))* Amereon LTD.
Shawn, Jim. When Everyone Loved the Game. 2008. 128p. pap. 10.95 *(978-0-9816505-3-1(8))* Beckham Pubns. Group, Inc.
Sheehan, Michael. One Fine Season. 2008. 236p. 24.99 *(978-1-4389-3228-6(6))*; pap. 14.99 *(978-1-4389-3225-5(1))* AuthorHouse.
Sherman, Wynn A. Double Plays to Dreams: The Road to the CIF Baseball Championship. 2009. 74p. pap. 16.95 *(978-1-60836-427-5(5))* PublishAmerica, Inc.
Smith, Mary-Ann Tirone & Smith, Jere. Dirty Water: A Red Sox Mystery. 2008. 256p. 22.95 *(978-0-9776240-2-7(1))* Hall of Fame Pr.
Sonstroem, Robert J. Diamond Rewards: A Tale of the Little Leagues. 2008. 242p. pap. 14.95 *(978-0-7414-4291-8(4))* Infinity Publishing.
Stanger, Jeff. Kansaska. 2008. pap. 13.95 *(978-0-9793574-0-4(3))* Blue Trolley Pr., LLC.
Staples, Billy & Herschlag, Rich. Billyball 2009: The Road to the Phillies-Yankees World Series. 2010. 204p. pap. 17.95 *(978-1-4502-5206-5(0))* iUniverse, Inc.
Staudohar, Paul D., ed. Baseball's Best Short Stories. 2012. (Sporting's Best Short Stories Ser.). (ENG.). 448p. pap. 18.95 ***(978-1-61374-376-8(9))*** Chicago Review Pr., Inc.
TAN. By the Creek. 2007. (ENG.). 356p. per. 29.95 *(978-1-4241-2215-8(5))* PublishAmerica, Inc.
Umpleby, Marshall F. Delayed Steal: Baseball Stories. 2007. 136p. (ENG.). 23.95 *(978-0-595-69476-1(4))*; per. 13.95 *(978-0-595-44010-8(X))* iUniverse, Inc.
Weintraub, Bob. Painting the Corners: A Collection of off-Center Baseball Stories, Vol. 1. 2012. (ENG.). 220p. pap. ***(978-1-927403-05-1(7))*** Iguana Bks.
Wilken, Kelly. Collective Bargaining: Taking Control Away from the Players! 2008. 184p. pap. 14.49 *(978-1-4343-8221-4(4))* AuthorHouse.

BASEBALL TEAMS
see also names of individual teams, e.g. New York Yankees (Baseball Team)

Andrews, Leonard E. The Village Nine. 2008. 532p. pap. 31.98 *(978-1-4357-1869-2(0))* Lulu Enterprises Inc.
Ap. photos by. Boston celtics NBA Champs 2010. 2010. 144p. (J). 14.95 *(978-0-9827138-0-8(0))* Sport-Publishing llc.
Bainbridge, Jim. The 70-Year Road Trip: The History of a PCL Franchise from Sacramento to Honolulu to Colorado Springs. 2007. (Illus.). xvii, 548p. *(978-1-932127-98-0(4))* Solution Tree.
Baseball America Editors, ed. Baseball America 2011 Directory: 2011 Baseball Reference, Schedules, Contacts, Phone Info & More. 2011. (ENG.). 312p. pap. 29.95 *(978-1-932391-35-0(5))* Baseball America, Inc.
The Baseball Bluebook Professional Edition, 1. 2007. spiral bd. 55.00 *(978-0-9788368-1-8(2))* Baseball Bluebook, The.
Baseball Prospectus. Baseball Prospectus 2012. 3rd ed. 2012. (ENG.). 576p. pap. 24.95 ***(978-0-470-62207-0(5),*** Wiley) Wiley, John & Sons, Inc.
Baseball Prospectus Staff. Baseball Prospectus 2011. Goldman, Steven, ed. 2nd ed. 2011. (ENG.). 600p. pap. 24.95 *(978-0-470-62206-3(7),* Wiley) Wiley, John & Sons, Inc.
Bradbury, J. C. Hot Stove Economics: Understanding Baseball's Second Season. 2010. (ENG., Illus.). xx, 260p. pap. 24.95 *(978-1-4419-6268-3(9),* 1441962689) Springer.
Bresnahan, Jim, ed. Play It Again: Baseball Experts on What Might Have Been. 2006. (ENG., Illus.). 258p. per. 29.95 *(978-0-7864-2546-4(6))* McFarland & Co., Inc. Pubs.
Brill, Bill. An Illustrated History of Duke Basketball: A Legacy of Achievement. 2012. (ENG., Illus.). 208p. 24.95 ***(978-1-61321-000-0(0),*** 613000) Skyhorse Publishing Co., Inc.
Bucci, Steve & Brown, David W. Drinking Coffee with a Fork: The Story of Steve Carlton & the '72 Phillies. 2011. *(978-1-933822-25-9(2))* Camino Bks., Inc.
Burman, Howard. Gentlemen at the Bat: A Fictional Oral History of the New York Knickerbockers & the Early Days of Base Ball. 2010. (ENG.). 364p. pap. 25.00 *(978-0-7864-4720-6(6))* McFarland & Co., Inc. Pubs.
Chastain, Bill. 100 Things Giants Fans Should Know & Do Before They Die. 2011. (100 Things... Fans Should Know Ser.). (ENG.). 240p. pap. 14.95 *(978-1-60078-556-6(5))* Triumph Bks.
Crasnick, Jerry. Decades: 1950-1959. 2010. (Illus.). 160p. ***(978-1-58159-471-3(2))*** North American Media Group.
—Decades: 2000-2009. 2009. (Illus.). 160p. ***(978-1-58159-437-9(2))*** North American Media Group.
Debono, Paul. The Chicago American Giants. alt. ed. 2011. (ENG.). 280p. pap. 35.00 *(978-0-7864-6608-5(1))* McFarland & Co., Inc. Pubs.
Deporter, Hoodoo. 2008. (Illus.). 176p. 24.99 *(978-0-9820512-0-7(4))* Rare Air, Ltd.
Dickson, Paul. The Bill Veeck: Baseball's Greatest Maverick. 2012. (ENG., Illus.). 448p. 28.00 ***(978-0-8027-1778-8(0),*** 226189) Walker & Co.
Dresser, Jannie, ed. 16th & Bryant: My Life & Education with the San Francisco Seals. 2007. (Illus.). 208p. pap. 19.95 *(978-0-9786517-4-9(X))* Synthesis Group, Inc.
Duke, L. H. Billy & the Boys: The Shellman Wildcasts' run to the 1956 Georgia Class C High School Baseball Championship. 2009. 340p. pap. 17.95 *(978-1-60594-258-2(8),* Llumina Pr.) Aeon Publishing Inc.
Enders, Eric. Baseball's Greatest Games: The Most Suspenseful, Exciting & Unforgettable Contests in Major League Baseball History. 2008. (Illus.). 160p. ***(978-1-58159-403-4(8))*** North American Media Group.
Farney, Steven Michael. It's Time to Play! Jack Gardner, Basketball & Kansas State University. 2007. (Illus.). 140p. 24.95 *(978-1-58597-435-1(8))* Leathers Publishing.
Figueredo, Jorge S. Cuban Baseball: A Statistical History, 1878-1961. alt. ed. 2011. (ENG., Illus.). 552p. pap. 45.00 *(978-0-7864-6425-8(9))* McFarland & Co., Inc. Pubs.
Gesker, Mike, et al. The Orioles Encyclopedia: A Half Century of History & Highlights. 2009. (ENG., Illus.). 896p. 56.00 *(978-0-8018-9114-4(0))* Johns Hopkins Univ. Pr.
Gildner, Gary. Warsaw Sparks: A Memoir. 2008. (ENG., Illus.). 256p. pap. 15.95 *(978-0-8032-1756-0(0),* Bison Bks.) Univ. of Nebraska Pr.
Golon, Bob. No Minor Accomplishment: The Revival of New Jersey Professional Baseball. 2008. (Rivergate Ser.). (ENG., Illus.). 232p. per. 19.95 *(978-0-8135-4274-4(X))* Rutgers Univ. Pr.
Green, Guy, et al. The Nebraska Indians & Fun & Frolic with an Indian Baseball Team: Two Accounts of Baseball Barnstorming at the Turn of the Twentieth Century. 2010. (Mcfarland Historical Baseball Library). (ENG., Illus.). 242p. pap. 33.00 *(978-0-7864-4359-8(6))* McFarland & Co., Inc. Pubs.
Gutteridge, Don, et al. From the Gas House Gang to the Go-Go Sox: My 50-Plus Years in Big League Baseball. 2007. 404p. 25.00 *(978-0-9779811-5-2(X))* Pepperpot Prodns, Inc.
Hagerty, Tim. Out of the Park Minor League Baseball Team Names: The the Story Behind the Oswego Starchboes, the Texarkana Caketmakers & 98 Other Wacky Team Names. 2012. (ENG.). 96p. pap. 12.95 *(978-1-60433-209-4(3))* Cider Mill Pr. Bk. Pubs., LLC.
Haney, Travis. Gamecock Glory: The University of South Carolina Baseball Team's Journey to the 2010 NCAA Championship. 2011. pap. 19.99 *(978-1-60949-254-0(4))* History Pr., The.
Harris, Rick. Rhode Island Baseball: The Early Years. 2008. pap. 19.99 *(978-1-59629-496-7(5))* History Pr., The.
Johnson, James W. The Dandy Dons: Bill Russell, K. C. Jones, Phil Woolpert, & One of College Basketball's Greatest & Most Innovative Teams. 2009. (ENG., Illus.). 284p. pap. 19.95 *(978-0-8032-1877-2(X),* Bison Bks.) Univ. of Nebraska Pr.
Jozsa, Frank P. Major League Baseball Expansions & Relocations: A History, 1876-2008. 2010. (ENG., Illus.). 218p. pap. 39.95 *(978-0-7864-4388-8(X))* McFarland & Co., Inc. Pubs.
Karzen, Jeff. Homer: A Smalltown Baseball Odyssey. 2008. pap. 14.95 *(978-0-9752706-5-3(6))* August Pubns.
Klima, John. Willie's Boys: The 1948 Birmingham Black Barons, the Last Negro League World Series, & the Making of a Baseball Legend. 2009. (ENG., Illus.). 320p. 25.95 *(978-0-470-40013-5(7),* Wiley) Wiley, John & Sons, Inc.
Knight, Jonathan. Classic Tribe: The 50 Greatest Games in Cleveland Indians History. 2009. (Illus.). 248p. pap. *(978-1-60635-017-1(X))* Kent State Univ. Pr.
Krantz, Les. Yankee Classics: World Series Magic from the Bronx Bombers, 1921 to Today. 2010. (ENG., Illus.). 176p. 30.00 *(978-0-7603-4019-6(6),* 0760340196, MVP Bks.) MBI Publishing Co. LLC.
Letarte, Richard. That One Glorious Season: Baseball Players with One Spectacular Year, 1950-1961. 2006. (ENG., Illus.). 370p. per. 16.95 *(978-1-931807-51-7(5))* Randall, Peter E. Pub.
Lowenfish, Lee. Branch Rickey: Baseball's Ferocious Gentleman. 2009. (ENG., Illus.). 728p. pap. 24.95 *(978-0-8032-2453-7(2),* Bison Bks.) Univ. of Nebraska Pr.
Luke, Bob. The Most Famous Woman in Baseball: Effa Manley & the Negro Leagues. 2011. (Illus.). 256p. 27.50 *(978-1-59797-546-9(X))* Potomac Bks., Inc.
Luke, Robert A. The Baltimore Elite Giants: Sport & Society in the Age of Negro League Baseball. 2009. (ENG., Illus.). 208p. 30.95 *(978-0-8018-9116-8(7))* Johns Hopkins Univ. Pr.
Macht, Norman L. Connie Mack: The Turbulent & Triumphant Years, 1915-1931. 2012. (ENG., Illus.). 720p. 39.95 ***(978-0-8032-2039-3(1))*** Univ. of Nebraska Pr.
Manning, Chris. One Team One Dream. 2008. 196p. pap. 14.99 *(978-0-9799884-7-9(0))* Blu Phi'er Publishing, LLC.
Martin, Alfred M. & Martin, Alfred T. The Negro Leagues in New Jersey: A History. 2008. (ENG., Illus.). 280p. pap. 35.00 *(978-0-7864-3900-3(9))* McFarland & Co., Inc. Pubs.
Martini, Stephen. The Chattanooga Lookouts & 100 Seasons of Scenic City Baseball. 2010. 284p. pap. 17.00 *(978-0-557-27927-2(5))* Lulu Enterprises Inc.
Muschett, Jim, ed. Citi Field: Major League Baseball. 2009. (ENG., Illus.). 16p. 25.00 *(978-0-7893-9956-4(3))* Universe Publishing.
Pajot, Dennis. The Rise of Milwaukee Baseball: The Cream City from Midwestern Outpost to the Major Leagues, 1859-1901. 2009. (ENG., Illus.). 362p. pap. 45.00 *(978-0-7864-3951-5(3))* McFarland & Co., Inc. Pubs.
Pepe, Phil. The Ballad of Billy & George: The Tempestuous Baseball Marriage of Billy Martin & George Steinbrenner. 2010. (ENG., Illus.). 272p. pap. 14.95 *(978-0-7627-7066-3(X),* Lyons Pr.) Globe Pequot Pr., The.
Peterson, Todd. Early Black Baseball in Minnesota: The St. Paul Gophers, Minneapolis Keystones & Other Barnstorming Teams of the Deadball Era. 2010. (ENG., Illus.). 313p. pap. 39.95 *(978-0-7864-3816-7(9))* McFarland & Co., Inc. Pubs.
Phillips, Doug. Baseball Summer: the Story of the 1937 Smiths Falls Beavers. 2008. 227p. pap. 16.95 *(978-0-557-01690-7(8))* Lulu Enterprises Inc.
Raley, Dan. Pitchers of Beer: The Story of the Seattle Rainiers. (ENG.). 352p. 2012. pap. 19.95 ***(978-0-8032-4085-8(6),*** Bison Bks.) 2011. (Illus.). 26.95 *(978-0-8032-2847-4(3))* Univ. of Nebraska Pr.
Robinson, George & Salzberg, Charles. On a Clear Day They Could See Seventh Place: Baseball's Worst Teams. 2010. (ENG., Illus.). 312p. pap. 17.95 *(978-0-8032-2988-4(7),* Bison Bks.) Univ. of Nebraska Pr.
Rose, George. One Hit Wonders. 2009. 216p. pap. 15.95 *(978-0-557-05395-7(1))* Lulu Enterprises Inc.
Society for American Baseball Research (SABR). The National Pastime, Endless Seasons 2011: Baseball in Southern California. 2011. (ENG.). pap. 14.95 ***(978-1-933599-20-5(0))*** Society for American Baseball Research.
Sotos, Wendy. The Portland Sea Dogs. 2008. (Images of Baseball Ser.). (Illus.). 127p. pap. 19.99 *(978-0-7385-5712-0(9))* Arcadia Publishing.
Stewart, Peter c. Early Professional Baseball in Hampton Roads: A History, 1884-1928. 2010. (ENG., Illus.). 264p. pap. 29.95 *(978-0-7864-4808-1(3))* McFarland & Co., Inc. Pubs.
Stout, D. J. The Amazing Tale of Mr. Herbert & His Fabulous Alpine Cowboys Baseball Club: An Illustrated History of the Best Little Semi-Pro Baseball Team in Texas. 2010. (ENG., Illus.). 240p. 34.95 *(978-0-292-72334-4(2))* Univ. of Texas Pr.
Sullivan, Floyd. Waiting for the Cubs: The 2008 Season, the Hundred-Year Slump & One Fan's Lifelong Vigil. 2010. (ENG., Illus.). 204p. pap. 29.95 *(978-0-7864-4902-6(0))* McFarland & Co., Inc. Pubs.
Swaine, Rick. The Integration of Major League Baseball: A Team by Team History. 2009. (ENG., Illus.). 279p. 49.95 *(978-0-7864-3903-4(3))* McFarland & Co., Inc. Pubs.
Tiemann, Bob, ed. Mound City Memories: Baseball in St. Louis. 2007. (ENG., Illus.). 120p. per. 14.95 *(978-1-933599-06-9(5))* Society for American Baseball Research.
Treto Cisneros, Pedro. The Mexican League / la Liga Mexicana: Comprehensive Player Statistics, 1937-2001 bilingual edition / Estadisticas Comprensivas de los Jugadores, 1937-2001 edicion Bilingue. alt. ed. 2011. (ENG & SPA., Illus.). 512p. pap. 45.00 *(978-0-7864-6120-2(9))* McFarland & Co., Inc. Pubs.

Van Hyning, Thomas E. The Santurce Crabbers: Sixty Seasons of Puerto Rican Winter League Baseball. alt. ed. 2008. (ENG., Illus.). 279p. pap. 29.95 *(978-0-7864-3895-2(9))* McFarland & Co., Inc. Pubs.

Wallace, Tom. The University of Kentucky Basketball Encyclopedia. 2012. (ENG., Illus.). 448p. pap. 24.95 ***(978-1-61321-018-5(3)***, 613018) Skyhorse Publishing Co., Inc.

BASEDOW'S DISEASE

see Graves' Disease

BASEL, COUNCIL OF, 1431-1449

Elbannan, Mona. Basel Accords Consequences. 2011. 80p. pap. ***(978-3-8443-8363-8(8))*** Lambert Academic Publishing.

Marepalli, Vamsi. Basel II -Progress of Implementation in Indian Commercial Banks. 2011. 128p. pap. ***(978-3-8443-8190-0(2))*** Lambert Academic Publishing.

BASEMENTS

Better Homes and Gardens Books Staff. Basement. Christian, Vicki, ed. 2007. (Do It Yourself Ser.). (ENG., Illus.). 216p. pap. 19.95 *(978-0-696-23458-3(0)*, Wiley) Wiley, John & Sons, Inc.

Creative Publishing International Editors. The Complete Guide to Finishing Basements: Step-by-Step Projects for Adding Living Space Without Adding On. 2009. (Black & Decker Complete Guide Ser.). (ENG., Illus.). 256p. pap. 24.99 *(978-1-58923-454-3(5)*, 1589234545) Quayside.

German, Roger. Remodeling a Basement. 2nd rev. ed. 2010. (Taunton's Build Like a Pro Ser.). (ENG., Illus.). 192p. pap. 19.95 *(978-1-60085-292-3(0))* Taunton Pr., Inc.

Jeswald, Peter. Basement Ideas That Work: Creative Design Solutions for Your Home. 2007. (Ideas That Work Ser.). (ENG., Illus.). 184p. pap. 19.95 *(978-1-56158-937-1(3)*, Taunton) Taunton Pr., Inc.

Kalyn, Wayne. Basements. 2nd ed. 2008. (Home Decorating Ser.). (ENG., Illus.). 208p. (gr. 5). pap. 19.95 *(978-1-58011-424-0(5))* Creative Homeowner.

King Jr., Willie E. Building Basements: The Definitive Book about Basements. 2011. 310p. 49.99 ***(978-1-60746-365-8(2))*** FastPrncil, Inc.

Nestor, Samantha & Feiring, Alice. Living with Wine: Passionate Collectors, Sophisticated Cellars, & Other Rooms for Entertaining, Enjoying, & Imbibing. 2009. (ENG., Illus.). 256p. 75.00 *(978-0-307-40789-4(6)*, Clarkson Potter) Crown Publishing Group.

Skinner, Tina. Wine Cellar Design. 2008. (Illus.). 256p. bds. 49.95 *(978-0-7643-2862-6(X))* Schiffer Publishing, Ltd.

Stanley Company Staff. Complete Basements. Johnston, Larry, ed. 2006. (ENG., Illus.). 240p. pap. 19.95 *(978-0-696-22742-4(8)*, Wiley) Wiley, John & Sons, Inc.

BASES (CHEMISTRY)

Carolina Biological Staff, compiled by. Discovering Acids & Bases. 2009. (Inquiries in Science Chemistry Ser.). *(978-1-4350-0410-8(8))* Carolina Biological Supply Co.

Ono, Yoshio & Hattori, Hideshi. Solid Base Catalysis. 2011. (Springer Series in Chemical Physics Ser.). (ENG., Illus.). 409p. 169.00 *(978-3-642-18338-6(7)*, 3642183387) Springer.

BASES, MILITARY

see Military Bases

BASHFULNESS

Adelman, Laurie. Don't Call Me Shy: Preparing Shy Children for a Lifetime of Social Success. 2007. 166p. per. 14.95 *(978-1-880292-32-7(7))* LangMarc Publishing.

Antony, Martin M. & Swinson, Richard P. The Shyness & Social Anxiety: Proven, Step-by-Step Techniques for Overcoming Your Fear. 2nd rev. ed. 2008. (New Harbinger Self-Help Workbook Ser.). (ENG.). 272p. pap., wbk. ed. 21.95 *(978-1-57224-553-2(0))* New Harbinger Pubns.

Axelby, Clayton P., ed. Social Phobia: Etiology, Diagnosis, & Treatment. 2009. 89.00 *(978-1-60692-159-3(2))* Nova Science Pubs., Inc.

Baker, Amy. Social Anxiety: Being Comfortable in Your Own Skin. 2011. (ENG.). 24p. 3.99 ***(978-1-936768-37-0(2))*** New Growth Pr.

Baker, Jim. Blushing Breakthrough: How to Stop Blushing & Conquer Social Anxiety. 2010. 123p. pap. 27.00 *(978-0-557-29688-0(9))* Lulu Enterprises Inc.

Brozovich, Richa & Chase, Linda. Say Goodbye to Being Shy: A Workbook to Help Kids Overcome Shyness. 2008. (Instant Help Ser.). 120p. pap. 16.95 *(978-1-931704-39-7(2))* Play2Grow.

Brozovich, Richard. Say Goodbye to Being Shy: A Workbook to Help Kids Overcome Shyness. 2008. (Instant Help Ser.). (ENG.). 120p. (J). pap. 24.95 *(978-1-57224-668-3(5))* Play2Grow.

Butler, Gillian. Overcoming Social Anxiety & Shyness: A Self-Help Guide Using Cognitive Behavioral Techniques. 2008. (Overcoming Ser.). (ENG., Illus.). 288p. pap. 15.95 *(978-0-465-00545-1(4))* Basic Bks.

Crozier, Ray. Coping with Shyness & Social Phobias: A Step-by-Step Guide Using CBT. 2009. (ENG.). 192p. pap. 14.95 *(978-1-85168-516-5(2))* Oneworld Pubns. GBR. Dist: National Bk. Network.

Crozier, W. Ray, ed. Shyness & Embarrassment: Perspectives from Social Psychology. 2010. (ENG.). 376p. pap. 35.99 *(978-0-521-17219-6(5))* Cambridge Univ. Pr.

Daly, John A. Avoiding Communication: Shyness, Reticence, & Communication Apprehension. 3rd ed. 2009. *(978-1-57273-688-7(7))*; *(978-1-57273-689-4(5))* Hampton Pr., Inc.

Dibartolo, Patricia Marten & Albano, Anne Marie. Cognitive-Behavioral Therapy for Social Phobia in Adolescents: Therapist Guide. 2007. (Treatments That Work Ser.). (ENG., Illus.). 208p. (C). pap. 42.95 *(978-0-19-530776-4(3))* Oxford Univ. Pr., Inc.

Flowers, Steve. The Mindful Path Through Shyness: How Mindfulness & Compassion Can Help Free You from Social Anxiety, Fear, & Avoidance. 2009. (ENG.). 208p. pap. 17.95 *(978-1-57224-650-8(2))* New Harbinger Pubns.

Gray, Christopher. From Shy to Social: The Shy Man's Guide to Personal & Dating Success. 2012. (ENG.). 214p. pap. ***(978-0-9868364-2-8(7))*** Sunbow Pr.

Hope, Debra A., et al. Managing Social Anxiety: A Cognitive-Behavioral Therapy Approach, 1 vol. 2nd ed. 2010. (Treatments That Work Ser.). (ENG., Illus.). 256p. wbk. ed. 27.95 *(978-0-19-533669-6(0))* Oxford Univ. Pr., Inc.

—Managing Social Anxiety: A Cognitive-behavioral Therapy Approach, Therapist Guide, 1 vol. 2nd ed. 2010. (Treatments That Work Ser.). (ENG., Illus.). 240p. 39.95 *(978-0-19-533668-9(2))* Oxford Univ. Pr., Inc.

Kearney, Christopher A. Silence Is Not Golden: Strategies for Helping the Shy Child, 1 vol. 2010. (ENG., Illus.). 144p. pap. 19.95 *(978-0-19-532662-8(8))* Oxford Univ. Pr., Inc.

Lane, Christopher. Shyness: How Normal Behavior Became a Sickness. 2008. (ENG., Illus.). 272p. pap. 18.00 *(978-0-300-14317-1(6))* Yale Univ. Pr.

Markway, Barbara G. & Markway, Gregory P. Nurturing the Shy Child: Practical Help for Raising Confident & Socially Skilled Kids & Teens. 2006. (ENG., Illus.). 240p. pap. 13.95 *(978-0-312-32978-5(4)*, St. Martin's Griffin) St. Martin's Pr.

Nourse, Caroline S. It's OK to Be Shy. 2006. 9.00 *(978-0-8059-8327-2(9))* Dorrance Publishing Co., Inc.

Rubin, Kenneth H. & Coplan, Robert J., eds. The Development of Shyness & Social Withdrawal. 2010. (Social, Emotional, & Personality Development in Context Ser.). (ENG.). 336p. 55.00 *(978-1-60623-522-5(2))* Guilford Pubns., Inc.

Scott, Susie. Shyness & Society: The Illusion of Competence. 2007. (ENG.). 242p. 100.00 *(978-1-4039-9603-9(2))* Palgrave Macmillan.

Shannon, Jennifer. The Shyness & Social Anxiety Workbook for Teens: CBT & ACT Skills to Help You Build Social Confidence. 2012. (ENG.). 136p. (J). pap. 16.95 ***(978-1-60882-187-7(0))*** Play2Grow.

Shockley, Talmer. The Love-Shy Survival Guide. 2009. (ENG.). 256p. pap. *(978-1-84310-897-9(6))* Kingsley, Jessica Ltd.

BASHKIRTSEFF, MARIE, 1860-1884

Bashirtseff, Marie. Marie Bashkirtseff the Journal of A Youn. 2006. pap. 37.95 *(978-1-4286-3607-1(2))* Kessinger Publishing, LLC.

Wilson, Sonia. Personal Effects: Reading the Journal of Marie Bashkirtseff. 2010. (Legenda Research Monographs in French Studies). (ENG.). 169p. (C). 89.50 *(978-1-906540-13-5(6))* European Humanities Research Ctr. GBR. Dist: Brown, David Bk. Co., The.

BASHO, MATSUO, 1644-1694

see Matsuo, Basho, 1664-1694

BASIC (COMPUTER PROGRAM LANGUAGE)

see also Microsoft QuickBASIC (Computer Program); Microsoft Visual BASIC (Computer Program)

Agarwal, Vidya Vrat & Huddleston, James. Beginning VB 2008 Databases. Hassell, Jonathan, ed. 2008. (Beginning Ser.). (ENG., Illus.). 409p. pap. 44.99 *(978-1-59059-947-1(0))* Apress L. P.

Bai, Ying. Practical Database Programming with Visual Basic. NET. 2008. (ENG., Illus.). 828p. (C). pap. 75.99 *(978-0-521-71235-4(1))* Cambridge Univ. Pr.

—Practical Database Programming with Visual Basic. NET. 2nd ed. 2012. (ENG.). 904p. pap. 99.95 ***(978-1-118-16205-7(6)***, Wiley-IEEE Pr.) Wiley, John & Sons, Inc.

Bai, Ying & Bhalla, Satish. Practical Database Programming with Visual Basic.NET. 2008. (ENG., Illus.). 828p. (C). 150.00 *(978-0-521-88518-8(3))* Cambridge Univ. Pr.

BASIC. (Society for Pure English Ser.). Garland Publishing, Inc.

Benitez, Roberto. Database Programming with OpenOffice. org Base & Basic. 2008. 352p. pap. 39.95 *(978-0-557-00758-5(5))* Lulu Enterprises Inc.

Birnbaum, Duane & Vine, Michael. Microsoft Excel VBA Programming for the Absolute Beginner. 3rd rev. ed. 2007. (ENG., Illus.). 544p. per. 29.99 *(978-1-59863-394-8(5))* Course Technology.

Black, Jeanne & Forker, Vickie. BASIC Programming 2: Lab Pack, Pt. 1. Schroeder, Bonnie & Dohney, Catherine, eds. (Illus.). 179.95 *(978-1-56177-080-9(9)*, L393-1); tchr. ed. 19.95 *(978-1-56177-082-3(5)*, T393-1) CES/Compu-Tech, Inc.

Boehm, Anne. Murach's Visual Basic 2005. 2006. (Murach: Training & Reference Ser.). (Illus.). 844p. per. 52.50 *(978-1-890774-38-7(3))* Murach, Mike & Assocs., Inc.

Bradley, Julia Case & Millspaugh, Anita. Programming in Visual Basic 2010. 2010. (ENG., Illus.). 704p. (C). pap. 122.67 *(978-0-07-351725-4(9)*, 0073517259) McGraw-Hill Higher Education.

Deitel and Associates Inc. Staff & Deitel, Paul. Simply Visual Basic 2008. 3rd ed. 2008. (ENG., Illus.). 896p. (C). pap. 137.20 *(978-0-13-605303-3(3)*, Prentice Hall) Prentice Hall PTR.

Deitel and Associates Inc. Staff & Deitel, Paul J. Visual Basic 2008 How to Program. 4th ed. 2008. (ENG.). 1600p. (C). pap. 133.00 *(978-0-13-605305-7(X))* Prentice Hall Higher Education.

Deitel, Paul & Deitel, Harvey. Simply Visual Basic 2010. 4th rev. ed. 2012. (ENG., Illus.). 840p. (C). pap. 122.00 ***(978-0-13-299060-8(1)***, Prentice Hall) Prentice Hall PTR.

Deitel, Paul & Deitel, Harvey. Visual Basic 2010 How to Program. 5th ed. 2010. (ENG., Illus.). 672p. (C). pap. 123.00 *(978-0-13-215213-6(4)*, Prentice Hall) Prentice Hall PTR.

Deitel, Paul J. & Deitel, Harvey M. Visual Basic 2010: How to Program. 5th ed. 2010. (Illus.). 672p. pap. *(978-0-13-254686-7(8))* Prentice Hall PTR.

Elizandro, David & Taha, Hamdy. Simulation of Industrial Systems. 2nd rev. ed. 2012. (ENG., Illus.). 503p. 129.95 ***(978-1-4398-7134-8(5)***, CRC Press) Taylor & Francis Group GBR. Dist: Taylor & Francis Group.

Evans, Carl M. Atari BASIC: Faster & Better. 300p. 19.95 *(978-0-936200-29-3(4))* Blue Cat.

Evjen, Bill, et al. Professional Visual Basic 2008. 2008. (ENG., Illus.). 1464p. pap. 59.99 *(978-0-470-19136-1(8)*, Wrox) Wiley, John & Sons, Inc.

Farrell, Joyce & Smith, Jo Ann. Visual Basic Programs to Accompany Programming Logic & Design. 3rd ed. 2010. (Logic & Design Ser.). (ENG., Illus.). 224p. pap. 44.95 *(978-0-538-74625-0(4))* Course Technology.

Floegel, Ekkehard. ZX-81 Timex: Programming in BASIC & Machine Language. 139p. 9.95 *(978-3-921682-98-2(3))* Blue Cat.

Fouché, Guy & Nash, Trey. Accelerated VB 2010. 2011. (ENG.). 450p. pap. 49.99 *(978-1-4302-2602-4(1))* Apress L. P.

Foxall, James. Visual Basic 2010, Kit. 2010. (Sams Teach Yourself — Hours Ser.). (ENG., Illus.). 528p. pap. 34.99 *(978-0-672-33113-8(6))* Sams.

Gaddis, Tony & Irvine, Kip. Starting Out with Visual Basic 2005. 3rd ed. 2006. pap. 16.60 incl. cd-rom *(978-0-321-49984-4(0))* Addison-Wesley Longman, Inc.

Gaddis, Tony & Irvine, Kip R. Starting Out with Visual Basic 2010. 5th ed. 2010. *(978-0-13-215565-6(6))* Addison-Wesley Longman, Inc.

Halvorson, Michael. Microsoft Visual Basic 2010 Step by Step. 2010. (ENG., Illus.). 576p. pap. 44.99 *(978-0-7356-2669-0(3))* Microsoft Pr.

Hamelin, Denis. Introduction to Programming Workbook. rev. ed. 2011. (ENG.). 294p. spiral bd. 42.28 *(978-0-7575-7965-3(5))* Kendall Hunt Publishing Co.

Herman, Todd, et al. Visual Basic 2005 Recipes: A Problem-Solution Approach. 2007. (Problem-Solution Approach Ser.). (ENG., Illus.). 664p. pap. 49.99 *(978-1-59059-852-8(0))* Apress L. P.

Hollis, Billy, et al. Professional Visual Basic 2010 & . NET 4. 2010. (ENG., Illus.). 1320p. pap. 59.99 *(978-0-470-50224-2(X)*, Wrox) Wiley, John & Sons, Inc.

Irvine, Kip & Gaddis, Tony. Advanced Visual Basic 2010. 5th rev. ed. 2011. (ENG., Illus.). 696p. (C). pap. 123.00 *(978-0-13-231674-3(9))* Addison Wesley.

Jones, Aubrey B. I Speak BASIC to My TI-99/4A: Teacher's Manual. 2011. *(978-0-8104-6163-5(3)*, Hayden) New Riders Publishing.

Journey Home. 3rd ed. pap., stu. ed. *(978-0-13-646448-2(2))* Prentice Hall (Schl. Div.).

Journey Home. 8.97 *(978-0-13-437493-2(2))* Prentice Hall PTR.

McGrath, Mike. Visual Basic. 3rd ed. 2011. (In Easy Steps Ser.). (ENG., Illus.). 192p. pap. 14.99 *(978-1-84078-409-1(1))* Computer Step GBR. Dist: Perseus-PGW.

McKeown, Jim. Programming in Visual Basic 2010: The Very Beginner's Guide. 2010. (ENG., Illus.). (C). 702p. 170.00 *(978-0-521-89653-5(3))*; 784p. pap. 80.00 *(978-0-521-72111-0(3))* Cambridge Univ. Pr.

Millspaugh, Anita & Bradley, Julia Case. Advanced Programming Using Visual Basic 2008. 4th ed. 2009. (ENG., Illus.). 672p. (C). pap. 125.00 *(978-0-07-351722-3(4)*, 0073517224) McGraw-Hill Higher Education.

Murach's Visual Basic 2008. 2008. (Murach: Training & Reference Ser.). (Illus.). 820p. per. 52.50 *(978-1-890774-45-5(6))* Murach, Mike & Assocs., Inc.

Petroutsos, Evangelos. Mastering Microsoft Visual Basic 2008. 2008. (ENG., Illus.). 1152p. per. 59.99 *(978-0-470-18742-5(5)*, Sybex) Wiley, John & Sons, Inc.

—Mastering Microsoft Visual Basic 2010. 2010. (ENG., Illus.). 1056p. pap. 59.99 *(978-0-470-53287-4(4)*, Sybex) Wiley, John & Sons, Inc.

Petroutsos, Evangelos, et al. Introduction to Programming Using Visual Basic. 2007. (ENG.). (C). pap. 71.81 *(978-0-470-17804-1(3)*, Wiley) Wiley, John & Sons, Inc.

Plenderleith, Jamie & Bunn, Steve. Microsoft Visual Studio 2008 Programming. 2009. (ENG., Illus.). 442p. pap. 49.99 *(978-0-07-160408-6(1)*, 0071604081) McGraw-Hill Osborne.

Press, William H., et al. Numerical Recipes: The Art of Scientific Computing. 3rd rev. ed. 2007. (ENG., Illus.). 1256p. (C). 159.00 incl. cd-rom *(978-0-521-88407-5(1))* Cambridge Univ. Pr.

Riordan, Rebecca M. Fluent Visual Basic. 2011. (ENG., Illus.). 888p. pap. 49.99 ***(978-0-672-33580-8(8))*** Sams.

Rowley, Thomas E. Atari BASIC: Learning by Using. 73p. 7.95 *(978-0-936200-35-4(9))* Blue Cat.

Rudman, Jack. Introduction to Computers with Basic Programming. (Dantes Subject Standardized Tests Ser.: Vol. 50). 49.95 *(978-0-8373-6550-3(3))* National Learning Corp.

Sanchez-Clark, Terry. Microsoft Visual Basic Interview Questio. 2007. pap. 29.95 *(978-1-933804-50-7(5))* Equity Pr.

Schneider, David I. Introduction to Programming Using Visual Basic 2010. 8th ed. 2010. (ENG.). 768p. (C). pap. 122.60 *(978-0-13-212856-8(X)*, Prentice Hall) Prentice Hall PTR.

Shelly, Gary & Hoisington, Corinne. Microsoft Visual Basic 2010: For Windows, Web, Office, & Database Applications - Comprehensive. 2010. (Shelly Cashman Ser.). (ENG.). 1048p. pap. 129.95 *(978-0-538-46847-3(5))* Course Technology.

Shelly, Gary B. & Hoisington, Corinne. Microsoft Visual Basic 2010: Windows Applications for Windows, Web, Office, & Database Applications - Complete. 2010. (Shelly Cashman Ser.). (ENG.). 768p. pap. 105.95 *(978-0-538-46848-0(3))* Course Technology.

—Microsoft Visual Basic 2010: Windows, Mobile, Web, Office, & Database Applications. 2010. (SAM 2010 Compatible Products Ser.). (ENG.). 520p. pap. 86.95 *(978-0-538-46845-9(9))* Course Technology.

Sheriff, Paul D. Fundamentals of Vb Net. 2008. 260p. pap. 24.95 *(978-0-9793748-4-5(7))* PDSA, Inc.

Sole, Alessandro Del. Visual Basic 2010 Unleashed. 2010. (Unleashed Ser.). (ENG., Illus.). 1272p. pap. 49.99 *(978-0-672-33100-8(4))* Sams.

Stephens, Rod. Stephens' Visual Basic Programming 24-Hour Trainer. 2011. (ENG., Illus.). 504p. pap. 39.99 *(978-0-470-94335-9(1)*, Wrox) Wiley, John & Sons, Inc.

Valdes-Perez, Fernando E. & Pallas-Areny, Ramon. Microcontrollers: Fundamentals & Applications with PIC. 2009. (ENG., Illus.). 300p. 102.95 *(978-1-4200-7767-4(8)*, CRC Press) Taylor & Francis Group GBR. Dist: Taylor & Francis Group.

Willis, Thearon & Newsome, Bryan. Beginning Microsoft Visual Basic 2008. 2008. (ENG., Illus.). 912p. pap. 44.99 *(978-0-470-19134-7(1)*, Wrox) Wiley, John & Sons, Inc.

—Beginning Visual Basic 2010. 2010. (ENG., Illus.). 720p. pap. 44.99 *(978-0-470-50222-8(3)*, Wrox) Wiley, John & Sons, Inc.

Zak, Diane. Microsoft Visual Basic 2008. 3rd ed. 2008. (Visual Studio Ser.). (ENG., Illus.). 784p. pap. 141.95 *(978-1-4239-0250-8(5))* Course Technology.

—Microsoft Visual Basic 2010: Reloaded. 4th ed. 2010. (SAM 2010 Compatible Products Ser.). (ENG., Illus.). 824p. (C). pap. 141.95 *(978-1-111-22179-9(0))* Course Technology.

—Programming with Microsoft Visual Basic 2010. 5th ed. 2011. (VB. Net Programming Ser.). (ENG.). 896p. pap. 142.95 *(978-1-111-52943-7(4))* Course Technology.

BASIC EDUCATION

Here are entered works on training to develop mastery of the basic subject areas in school programs. Works on training to develop minimum performance ability in practical skills essential to community development in socio-economically deprived areas and developing countries are entered under Fundamental Education.

see also Elementary Education of Adults

Cohen, Joel E. International Perspectives on the Goals of Universal Basic & Secondary Education. Cohen, Joel E. et al, eds. 2009. (Routledge Research in Education Ser.). (ENG., Illus.). 322p. 125.00 *(978-0-415-99766-9(6))* Routledge.

De, Anuradha, et al. Probe Revisited: A Report on Elementary Education in India. 2011. (ENG., Illus.). 200p. pap. 29.95 *(978-0-19-807157-0(4))* Oxford Univ. Pr., Inc.

Foley, E. & Coates, B. Homework for Grown-ups: Everything You Learned at School & Promptly Forgot. 2009. (ENG., Illus.). 368p. 19.99 *(978-0-7679-3238-7(2))* Broadway Bks.

Gabriel, Kathleen F. Teaching Unprepared Students: Strategies for Promoting Success & Retention in Higher Education. 2008. 160p. pap. 24.95 *(978-1-57922-230-7(7))*; (Illus.). 75.00 *(978-1-57922-229-1(3))* Stylus Publishing, LLC.

Key, Ellen Karolina Sofia. The Education of the Child. 2010. 48p. pap. *(978-1-4076-5512-3(4))* HardPr.

LearningExpress Staff. THEA: Texas Higher Education Assessment. 2nd rev. ed. 2010. (Complete Preparation Guides). (ENG.). 288p. pap. 19.95 *(978-1-57685-756-4(5))* LearningExpress, LLC.

McCune, Sandra J., et al. THEA: Texas Higher Education Assessment. 5th rev. ed. 2010. (ENG.). 624p. pap. 18.99 *(978-0-7641-4198-0(8))* Barron's Educational Series, Inc.

Miller, Bob. Bob Miller's Math for the Tabe. 2009. (GED & TABE Test Preparation Ser.). (ENG.). 272p. pap. 16.95 *(978-0-7386-0554-8(9))* Research & Education Assn.

Scholastic, Inc. Staff, contrib. by. Success with Basic Concepts. 2010. (Scholastic Success with Ser.). (ENG.). 48p. (gr. -1 — 1). pap. 5.99 *(978-0-545-20093-6(8)*, Teaching Resources) Scholastic, Inc.

Sellars, Maura. Using Students' Strengths to Support Learning Outcomes. 2008. 104p. pap. *(978-3-639-04847-6(4))* VDM Verlag Dr. Mueller e.K.

Shapiro, Edward S. Academic Skills Problems, Fourth Edition: Direct Assessment & Intervention. 4th ed. 2010. (ENG.). 447p. (gr. k-12). 55.00 *(978-1-60623-960-5(0))* Guilford Pubns., Inc.

—Academic Skills Problems Fourth Edition Workbook. 4th rev. ed. 2010. (ENG., Illus.). 190p. (gr. k-12). pap. 35.00 *(978-1-60918-021-8(6))* Guilford Pubns., Inc.

Shi, Ou. Zhongguo Ji Chu Jiao Yu 60 Nian: 1949-2009. 2009. (Illus.). 14p. *(978-7-5648-0039-0(9))* Hunan Normal University Publishing Hse.

TABE Exam Secrets Test Prep Staff, ed. TABE Practice Questions: TABE Practice Tests & Exam Review for the Test of Adult Basic Education. 2011. 34.99 *(978-1-61403-735-4(3))* Mometrix Media LLC.

Truscott, Robert Blake, et al. Texas Higher Education Assessment (THEA) 9th ed. 2011. (THEA Test Preparation Ser.). (ENG.). 656p. (C). pap. 19.95 *(978-0-7386-0966-9(8))* Research & Education Assn.

UNESCO Staff, creator. EFA Global Monitoring Report: Education for All by 2015: Will We Make It? 2007. (ENG., Illus.). 444p. pap. 45.00 *(978-0-19-953263-6(X))* Oxford Univ. Pr., Inc.

(UNESCO), United Nations Educational, Scientific and Cultural Organization. Education for All Global Monitoring Report 2010: Reaching the Marginalized. 2010. (ENG., Illus.). 528p. pap. 29.95 *(978-0-19-958498-7(2))* Oxford Univ. Pr., Inc.

United Nations Educational, Scientific, and Cultural Organization Staff. Education for All Global Monitoring Report 2009: Overcoming inequality- why governance Matters. 2009. (Education for All Global Monitoring Report). (Illus.). 500p. pap. 39.95 *(978-0-19-954419-6(0))* Oxford Univ. Pr., Inc.

Vegas, Emiliana & Petrow, Jenny. Raising Student Learning in Latin America: The Challenge for the 21st Century. 2007. (Latin American Development Forum Ser.). (ENG., Illus.). 262p. per. 30.00 *(978-0-8213-7082-7(0),* 9780821370827) World Bank Pubns.

Wang, Libing. Basic Education in China. 2009. *(978-1-931907-58-3(7))* Homa & Sekey Bks.

—Basic Education in China. 2010. (Illus.). xxiv, 150p. *(978-7-308-06918-2(4))* Zhejiang Univ. Pr.

Whitley Willis, Roslyn. Functional Skills: English Level 1. 2009. (Illus.). 206p. pap. *(978-1-904995-47-0(0))* Lexden Publishing Ltd.

BASIC ENGLISH

Merriam-Webster, Inc. Staff, ed. Merriam-Webster's Dictionary of Basic English. 2009. 800p. (gr. 7). 10.95 *(978-0-87779-731-9(5))* Merriam-Webster, Inc.

Rogers, Judy R. & Rogers, Glenn C. Patterns & Themes: A Basic English Reader. 4th ed. (Illus.). xvi, 236p. *(978-0-534-26192-4(2))* Wadsworth.

Taylor, Margaret W. The Basic English Handbook. Date not set. (Orig.). pap., tchr. ed. *(978-0-673-55905-0(X))* Tecohio Publishing Co.

BASIC LIFE SKILLS

see Life Skills

BASIC MUSIC THEORY

see Music Theory—Elementary Works

BASIC NEEDS

Here are entered works on human needs such as food, shelter, education, health, water, employment, etc. that provide a minimum quality of life.

see also Poverty; Quality of Life

Brighouse, Harry & Robeyns, Ingrid, eds. Measuring Justice: Primary Goods & Capabilities. 2010. (ENG.). 272p. 85.00 *(978-0-521-88451-8(9))*; 268p. pap. 31.00 *(978-0-521-71147-0(9))* Cambridge Univ. Pr.

Corning, Peter A. The Fair Society: The Science of Human Nature & the Pursuit of Social Justice. 2011. (ENG.). 256p. 27.50 *(978-0-226-11627-3(1))* Univ. of Chicago Pr.

Dorsey, Dale. The Basic Minimum: A Welfarist Approach. 2012. (ENG.). 236p. 95.00 ***(978-1-107-01711-5(4))*** Cambridge Univ. Pr.

Flanagan, Barbara. Flannagan's Smart Home: The 101 Essentials for Starting Out, Starting Over, Scaling Back. 2008. (ENG., Illus.). 216p. pap. 12.95 *(978-0-7611-4460-1(9),* 0761144609) Workman Publishing Co., Inc.

Ghai, Yash P. & Cottrell, Jill. The Millennium Declaration, Rights, & Constitutions. 2011. (ENG., Illus.). 240p. 100.00 *(978-0-19-806928-7(6))* Oxford Univ. Pr., Inc.

Gough, Ian & McGregor, J. Allister, eds. Wellbeing in Developing Countries: From Theory to Research. (ENG.). 424p. 2010. pap. 50.00 *(978-0-521-18080-1(5))* 2007. (Illus.). 118.00 *(978-0-521-85751-2(1))* Cambridge Univ. Pr.

Hamilton, Lawrence A. The Political Philosophy of Needs. 2007. (ENG.). 220p. per. 48.00 *(978-0-521-03404-3(3))* Cambridge Univ. Pr.

Hammond, Allen L. The Next 4 Billion: Market Size & Business Strategy at the Base of the Pyramid. 2007. (Illus.). 151p. pap. *(978-1-56973-625-8(1))* World Resources Institute.

Hertel, Shareen, et al. Economic Rights: Conceptual, Measurement, & Policy Issues. 2007. (ENG., Illus.). 420p. 99.99 *(978-0-521-87055-9(0))*; per. 38.00 *(978-0-521-69082-9(X))* Cambridge Univ. Pr.

Laquian, Aprodicio A., et al, eds. The Inclusive City: Infrastructure & Public Services for the Urban Poor in Asia. 2007. (ENG., Illus.). 368p. (gr. 17). 50.00 *(978-0-8018-8644-7(9))* Johns Hopkins Univ. Pr.

Liebenberg, Sandra. Socio - Economic Rights: Adjudication Under a Transformative Constitution. 2010. 565p. pap. 87.00 *(978-0-7021-8480-2(2))* Gaunt, Inc.

Smith, Stephen C. Ending Global Poverty: A Guide to What Works. 2008. (ENG., Illus.). 272p. pap. 27.00 *(978-0-230-60615-9(6))* Palgrave Macmillan.

Stewart, Frances. Defining Poverty in the Developing World. Stewart, Frances et al, eds. 2007. (ENG., Illus.). 256p. 100.00 *(978-0-230-51672-4(6))* Palgrave Macmillan.

Surles, Lawrence. How to Go up in a down Economy: ..... & have fun doing It. 2009. 120p. pap. 13.98 *(978-1-4389-6592-5(3))* AuthorHouse.

United Nations. Access to Basic Services for the Poor: The Importance of Good Governance. 2008. (Asia-Pacific MDG Study Ser.). (ENG.). 60p. pap. 17.00 *(978-92-1-120522-0(0))* United Nations Pubns.

United Nations. Paths to 2015 Mdg Priorities in Asia & the Pacific. 2011. (ENG.). 68p. pap. 12.00 ***(978-92-1-120618-0(9))*** United Nations Pubns.

United Nations Development Programme. Beyond the Midpoint: Achieving the Millennium Development Goals. 2010. 172p. pap. 35.00 *(978-92-1-126271-1(2))* United Nations Pubns.

United Nations University Staff. Human Insecurity in East Asia. Umegaki, Michio et al, eds. 2009. (ENG., Illus.). 308p. pap. 36.00 *(978-92-808-1164-3(9))* United Nations Univ. Pr. JPN. Dist: Brookings Institution Pr.

Young, Margot. Poverty: Rights, Social Citizenship, & Legal Activism. Young, Margot et al, eds. 2007. (Law & Society Ser.). (ENG.). 400p. 85.00 *(978-0-7748-1287-0(7))* UBC Pr. CAN. Dist: Univ. of Washington Pr.

Zuern, Elke. The Politics of Necessity: Community Organizing & Democracy in South Africa. 2011. (Critical Human Rights Ser.). (Illus.). 264p. pap. 29.95 *(978-0-299-25014-0(8))* Univ. of Wisconsin Pr.

BASIC RIGHTS

see Civil Rights; Human Rights

BASIDIOMYCETES

see also Mushrooms; Rusts (Fungi); Smuts

Boddy, Lynne, et al, eds. Ecology of Saprotrophic Basidiomycetes. 2007. (British Mycological Society Symposia Ser.: 28). (ENG., Illus.). 386p. 180.00 *(978-0-12-374185-1(8),* Academic Pr.) Elsevier Science & Technology Bks.

Frankland, J., et al, eds. Decomposer Basidiomycetes: Their Biology & Ecology. 2009. (British Mycological Society Symposia Ser.). (ENG.). 376p. pap. 63.00 *(978-0-521-10680-1(X))* Cambridge Univ. Pr.

Slippers, Bernard, et al, eds. The Sirex Woodwasp & its Fungal Symbiont: Research & Management of a Worldwide Invasive Pest. 2011. (ENG., Illus.). xii, 301p. 209.00 ***(978-94-007-1959-0(0),*** 9400719590) Springer.

BASIE, COUNT, 1906-1984

Basie, Count. Count Basie Classics: Jazz Play-along Volume 126, 1 vol. 2010. (ENG.). 88p. pap. 15.99 incl. audio compact disk *(978-1-4234-6868-4(6),* 1423468686) Leonard, Hal Corp.

BASIL, SAINT, BISHOP OF CAESAREA, CA. 329-379

Basilius. The Ascetic Works of Saint Basil. Clarke, W. K., tr. & intro. by. reprint ed. 57.50 *(978-0-404-18902-0(4))* AMS Pr., Inc.

Corona, Gabriella, ed. Aelfric's Life of Saint Basil the Great: Background & Context. 2006. (Anglo-Saxon Texts: Volume 5). 280p. 95.00 *(978-1-84384-095-4(2))* Boydell & Brewer, Inc.

DelCogliano, Mark. Basil of Caesarea's Anti-Eunomian Theory of Names: Christian Theology & Late-Antique Philosophy in the Fourth Century Trinitarian Controversy. 2010. (Vigiliae Christianae Supplements Ser.). (ENG.). XIV, 302p. *(978-90-04-18332-2(9))* BRILL.

Fenwick, John. Fourth Century Anaphoral Construction Techniques. 2009. 130.00 *(978-1-60724-353-3(9))* Gorgias Pr., LLC.

Hildebrand, Stephen M. The Trinitarian Theology of Basil of Caesarea: A Synthesis of Greek Thought & Biblical Truth. 2007. 254p. 59.95 *(978-0-8132-1473-3(4))* Catholic Univ. of America Pr.

Hübner, Reinhard M. Die Schrift des Apolinarius von Laodicea gegen Photin (Pseudo-Athanasius, Contra Sabellianos) und Basilius von Caesarea. (Patristische Texte und Studien Ser.). (GER., Illus.). VIII, 322p. 270.00 ***(978-3-11-180738-6(X))*** De Gruyter, Walter Inc.

Murphy, Margaret Gertrude. St Basil & Monasticism. 2011. 136p. 40.95 ***(978-1-258-04822-8(1))*** Literary Licensing, LLC.

Ngien, Dennis. Gifted Response: The Triune God as the Causative Agency of our Responsive Worship. 2008. (ENG.). 200p. 29.99 *(978-1-84227-610-5(7),* Paternoster) Authentic Media.

Prestige, George L. St. Basil the Great & Apollinaris of Laodicea. (Orthodoxies & Heresies in the Early Church Ser.). reprint ed. 32.50 *(978-0-404-62399-9(9))* AMS Pr., Inc.

Radde-Gallwitz, Andrew. Basil of Caesarea, Gregory of Nyssa, & the Transformation of Divine Simplicity. 2009. (Oxford Early Christian Studies). (ENG.). 272p. 100.00 *(978-0-19-957411-7(1))* Oxford Univ. Pr., Inc.

Schaff, Philip, ed. Nicene & Post-Nicene Fathers: Second Series, Volume VIII Basil. 2007. 448p. 31.95 *(978-1-60206-522-2(5))*; (ENG.). per. 21.95 *(978-1-60206-521-5(7))* Cosimo, Inc.

BASILICA DI SAN MARCO (VENICE, ITALY)

Fenlon, Iain. Piazza San Marco. 2009. (Wonders of the World Ser.). (Illus.). 256p. 19.95 *(978-0-674-02791-6(4))* Harvard Univ. Pr.

Huller, Stephan. The Real Messiah: The Throne of St. Mark & the True Origins of Christianity. 2009. (ENG.). 288p. 24.95 *(978-1-906787-12-7(3),* Watkins Publishing) Duncan Baird Pubs. GBR. Dist: Sterling Publishing Co., Inc.

Maguire, Henry & Nelson, Robert S., eds. San Marco, Byzantium, & the Myths of Venice. 2010. (Dumbarton Oaks Byzantine Symposia & Colloquia Ser.). (ENG., Illus.). 304p. 60.00 *(978-0-88402-360-9(5))* Dumbarton Oaks.

BASILICA DI SAN PIETRO IN VATICANO

Ebrecht, Ronald. Cavaillé-Coll's Monumental Organ Project for Saint Peter's, Rome: Bigger Than Them All. 2011. (ENG., Illus.). 238p. 70.00 ***(978-0-7391-6728-1(6))*** Lexington Bks.

—Cavaillé-Coll's Monumental Organ Project for Saint Peter's, Rome: Bigger Than Them All. 2011. E-Book ***(978-0-7391-7077-9(5))*** Lexington Bks.

Miller, Keith. St. Peter's. (Wonders of the World Ser.). (Illus.). 256p. 2012. pap. 14.95 ***(978-0-674-06395-2(3))*** 2007. 19.95 *(978-0-674-02689-6(6))* Harvard Univ. Pr.

Satzinger, Georg & Schutze, Sebastian, eds. St. Peter in Rom, 1506-2006: Akten der Internationalen Tagung 22.-25.02.2006 in Bonn. 2008. (GER., Illus.). 512p. (C). 218.00 *(978-3-7774-4155-9(4))* Hirmer Verlag GmbH DEU. Dist: Brown, David Bk. Co., The.

Scotti, R. A. Basilica: The Splendor & the Scandal: Building St. Peter's. 2007. (ENG., Illus.). 336p. (gr. 12-18). 16.00 *(978-0-452-28860-7(6),* Plume) Penguin Group (USA) Inc.

Tanner, M. Jerusalem on the Hill: Rome & the Vision of St. Peter's in the Renaissance. 2010. (Studies in Medieval & Early Renaissance Art History Ser.). (ENG., Illus.). 288p. (C). 174.00 *(978-1-905375-49-3(2))* Miller, Harvey Pubs. GBR. Dist: Brown, David Bk. Co., The.

Tronzo, William, ed. St. Peter's in the Vatican. 2008. (ENG., Illus.). 336p. (C). pap. 52.99 *(978-0-521-73210-9(7))* Cambridge Univ. Pr.

BASILICAS

Here are entered works on Christian churches built following the form of ancient Roman basilicas as well as Roman Catholic churches having certain liturgical privileges.

Palermo, P. & Pecis, P. La Musica Nella Basilica di Santa Maria Maggiore a Bergamo dal 1637 al 1810. 2011. (Studi Sulla Storia Della Musica in Lombardia). (ITA., Illus.). 526p. (C). 160.00 *(978-2-503-51033-0(7))* Brepols Pubs. BEL. Dist: Brown, David Bk. Co., The.

Regan, Brian. Gothic Pride: The Story of Building a Great Cathedral in Newark. 2012. (ENG.). 312p. 39.95 ***(978-0-8135-5288-0(5),*** Rivergate Bks.) Rutgers Univ. Pr.

BASILICATA (ITALY)

Lapadula, Erminia. The Chora of Metaponto 4: The Late Roman Farmhouse at San Biagio. 2012. (ENG., Illus.). 256p. 75.00 *(978-0-292-72877-6(8))* Univ. of Texas Pr.

BASILICATA (ITALY)—SOCIAL LIFE AND CUSTOMS

Bartalesi-Graf, Daniela. Voci dal Sud: A Journey to Southern Italy with Carlo Levi & His Christ Stopped at Eboli. 2010. (ENG & ITA., Illus.). 448p. (C). pap. 55.00 *(978-0-300-13744-6(3))* Yale Univ. Pr.

BASILIQUE SAINT-PIE X (LOURDES, FRANCE)

Lourdes. 2011. 24.95 *(978-1-58617-644-0(7))* Ignatius Pr.

BASING-POINT SYSTEM

Stocking, George W. Basing Point Pricing & Regional Development: A Case Study of the Iron & Steel Industry. 2011. (ENG.). 336p. pap. 40.00 ***(978-0-8078-6831-7(0))*** Univ. of North Carolina Pr.

BASKERVILLE, JOHN, 1706-1775

Gaskell, Philip. John Baskerville: A Bibliography. 2010. (ENG.). 108p. pap. 19.99 *(978-0-521-17072-7(9))* Cambridge Univ. Pr.

BASKET-BALL

see Basketball

BASKET MAKING

Adovasio, J. M. Basketry Technology: A Guide to Identification & Analysis. 2010. (Illus.). xxvi, 182p. ***(978-1-59874-662-4(6))*** Left Coast Pr., Inc.

Coats, Charlotte. Weaving an Oklahoma Cherokee Double Wall Basket. 2006. (Illus.). 32p. per. 17.99 *(978-0-9789657-1-6(X))* Coats, Charlotte.

—Weaving the Cherokee Lidded Double Weave Basket. 2006. (Illus.). 54p. per. 23.99 *(978-0-9789657-0-9(1))* Coats, Charlotte.

Crawford, B. J. The Weekend Crafter: Basketry: 17 Great Weekend Projects. 2011. (Weekend Crafter Ser.). (ENG., Illus.). 80p. pap. 9.95 *(978-1-4547-0179-8(X))* Lark Bks.

Franz, Linda & Hammond, Debra. Basic Basket Making: All the Skills & Tools You Need to Get Started. Franz, Linda, ed. 2008. (Stackpole Basics Ser.). (ENG., Illus.). 127p. spiral bd. 19.95 *(978-0-8117-3488-2(9))* Stackpole Bks.

Gerdes, Paulus. African Basketry: A Gallery of Twill-Plaited Designs & Patterns. 2008. 220p. pap. 19.95 *(978-1-4357-2625-3(1))* Lulu Enterprises Inc.

Harding, Stella & Waltener, Shane. Practical Basketry Techniques. 2012. (ENG., Illus.). 144p. pap. 29.95 ***(978-1-4081-3073-5(4))*** A & C Black GBR. Dist: Macmillan.

Kline, Jonathan. Black Ash Baskets: Tips, Tools & Techniques for Learning the Craft. 2011. (ENG., Illus.). 128p. pap. 24.95 *(978-0-8117-0529-5(3))* Stackpole Bks.

Lieberman, Justin. Justin Lieberman: Hopi Basket Weaving: Artistry in Natural Fibers, 1 vol. 2007. (ENG., Illus.). 116p. per. 35.00 *(978-0-9768533-6-7(1))* Zach Feuer Gallery.

MacDowell, Marsha & Myers, Kathleen S. Weaving History: A Basket Heritage Project. MacDowell, Marsha & Myers, Kathleen S., eds. 2007. (C). pap. 29.95 *(978-0-944311-24-0(5))* Michigan State Univ. Museum.

Mallow, Judy. Pine Needle Basketry: From Forest Floor to Finished Project. 2010. (ENG., Illus.). 112p. pap. 14.95 *(978-1-60059-603-2(7))* Lark Bks.

McGreevy, Susan Brown. Indian Basketry Artists of the Southwest: Deep Roots, New Growth. (Contemporary Indian Artists Ser.). (Illus.). 96p. pap. 11.95 *(978-0-933452-67-1(5))* School for Advanced Research Pr./SAR Pr.

Mukerji, Betty-Lou. Chinese Sewing Baskets. 2008. 212p. pap. 54.49 *(978-1-4389-1523-4(3))* AuthorHouse.

Schermer, Nancy. The Best Baskets in the World. 2011. 160p. pap. 26.00 *(978-1-936133-28-9(5),* Langdon Street Pr.) Hillcrest Publishing Group, Inc.

Sentance, Bryan. Basketry: A World Guide to Traditional Techniques. 2007. (ENG., Illus.). 216p. pap. 31.95 *(978-0-500-28670-8(1))* Thames & Hudson.

Shanks, Ralph C. California Indian Baskets: San Diego to Santa Barbara & Beyond to the San Joaquin Valley, Mountains & Deserts. Shanks, Lisa Woo, ed. 2010. (Indian Baskets of California & Oregon, vol. II Ser.). (ENG., Illus.). 168p. 39.95 *(978-0-930268-20-6(2))* Costano Bks.

Suddith, Billie Ruth. Basket Inspiration: For Makers & Collectors. 2010. (Illus.). 144p. 34.99 *(978-0-7643-3468-9(9))* Schiffer Publishing, Ltd.

Syler, Lyn. A Basketmaker's Odyssey: over, under, Around & Through: 24 Great Basket Patterns from Easy Beginner to More Challenging Advanced. 2007. (ENG., Illus.). 112p. pap. 23.95 *(978-0-9771941-1-7(6))* Word Weavers Ink.

White, Mary. How to Make Baskets. 2009. 70p. pap. *(978-1-151-72807-4(1))* Books LLC.

—How to Make Baskets. 248p. 2008. pap. *(978-1-4097-1787-4(9))* 2007. pap. *(978-1-4086-0544-8(9))* Read Bks.

—More Baskets & How to Make Them. 188p. 2008. 37.95 *(978-1-4366-7222-1(8))* 2007. (ENG.). per. 22.95 *(978-1-4325-9935-5(6))* Kessinger Publishing, LLC.

—More Baskets & How to Make Them. 2008. 188p. pap. *(978-1-4097-1136-0(6))* Read Bks.

White, Mary & Blanchan, Neltje. How to Make Baskets. 2008. 246p. 41.95 *(978-0-548-97927-3(8))* 2007. (ENG.). 248p. per. 26.95 *(978-0-548-65850-4(7))* Kessinger Publishing, LLC.

Wray, Jacilee, ed. From the Hands of a Weaver: Olympic Peninsula Basketry Through Time. 2012. (ENG., Illus.). 304p. 45.00 ***(978-0-8061-4245-6(6))*** Univ. of Oklahoma Pr.

Yarish, Vladimir, et al. Plaited Basketry with Birch Bark. 2009. (ENG., Illus.). 288p. 24.95 *(978-1-4027-4809-7(4))* Sterling Publishing Co., Inc.

BASKETBALL

see also National Basketball Association; Netball; Women Basketball Players also names of basketball teams, e.g. New York Knickerbockers (Basketball Team)

Araton, Harvey. Crashing the Borders: How Basketball Won the World & Lost Its Soul At. 2008. (ENG.). 224p. pap. 16.95 *(978-1-4391-0178-0(7),* Free Pr.) Free Pr.

Atkinson, Adrian, ed. Tar Heel Tip-Off 2007-2008: An Annual Guide to North Carolina Basketball. annuals 2007. 112p. per. 14.95 *(978-1-934186-15-2(5))* Maple Street Press LLC.

Bartholomew, Rafe. Pacific Rims: Beermen Ballin' in Flip-Flops & the Philippines' Unlikely Love Affair with Basketball. 2010. (ENG.). 400p. (gr. 12). 24.95 *(978-0-451-22999-1(1),* N A L Hardcover) Penguin Group (USA) Inc.

Boyd, Todd. Young, Black, Rich, & Famous: The Rise of the NBA, the Hip Hop Invasion, & the Transformation of American Culture. 2008. (ENG., Illus.). 224p. pap. 16.95 *(978-0-8032-1675-4(0),* Bison Bks.) Univ. of Nebraska Pr.

Brooks, Scott N. Black Men Can't Shoot. 2009. (Illus.). 248p. 22.00 *(978-0-226-07603-4(2))* Univ. of Chicago Pr.

Burns, Brian & Dunning, Mark. Skills in Motion: Basketball Step-By-Step. 2009. (Skills in Motion Ser.). (Illus.). 96p. (YA). (gr. 4-7). lib. bdg. 31.95 *(978-1-4358-3360-9(0))* Rosen Publishing Group, Inc., The.

Canfield, Jack L., et al. Inside Basketball: 101 Great Hoop Stories from Players, Coaches & Fans. 2009. (Chicken Soup for the Soul Ser.). (ENG.). 400p. pap. 14.95 *(978-1-935096-29-0(X))* Chicken Soup for the Soul Publishing, LLC.

Carter, Curtis W. The Road to the Nba. 2010. 336p. pap. 19.99 *(978-1-4535-3123-5(8))* Xlibris Corp.

Chen, Xiao-Xing. Three-Finger Zen: A Basketball Revolution. 2011. 176p. pap. 18.95 ***(978-1-4620-4717-8(3))*** iUniverse, Inc.

Clark, Micheal. Optimum Performance Training — Basketball. 2007. 224p. pap. 15.95 *(978-0-06-083979-6(1),* HC) HarperCollins Pubs.

Cremins, Bobby. Ultimate Offense: Winning Basketball Strategies & Plays from an NCAA Coach's Personal Playbook. 2008. (ENG., Illus.). 176p. pap. 18.95 *(978-0-07-147917-2(1),* 0071479171) McGraw-Hill Cos., The.

Crumbley, D. Larry & Campbell, Fred H. Dangerous Hoops: A Forensic Marketing Action Adventure. 2011. (Illus.). 248p. pap. 22.95 ***(978-0-8071-3911-0(4))*** Louisiana State Univ. Pr.

Davis, Calvin. Inner City Hoops: A History of Chicago Basketball. 2007. 132p. pap. 9.95 *(978-1-4327-0038-6(3))* Outskirts Pr., Inc.

Deters, Eric C. Pioneer Spirit: One High School's Rise from Tragedy to Glory. 2007. (Illus.). 328p. 24.95 *(978-0-9790025-0-2(8))* Acclaim Pr., Inc.

DeVenzio, Dick. Stuff Good Players Should Know: Intelligent Basketball from A to Z. 2nd ed. 2006. (Illus.). 293p. 29.95 *(978-1-933538-51-8(1))* Bridgeway Bks.

Dohrmann, George. Play Their Hearts Out: A Coach, His Star Recruit, & the Youth Basketball Machine. (ENG., Illus.). 2012. 448p. pap. 16.00 ***(978-0-345-50361-4(0))*** 2010. 432p. 26.00 *(978-0-345-50860-7(2))* Random House Publishing Group. (Ballantine Bks.).

Donaghy, Tim. Personal Foul: A First-Person Account of the Scandal that Rocked the NBA. 2010. (ENG.). 268p. pap. 14.95 *(978-0-615-36263-2(X))* Four Daughters.

Egan, John. The Vern Mikkelsen Story: The Original Power Forward. 2006. (Illus.). 184p. 19.95 *(978-1-932472-43-1(6))* Nodin Pr.

Farred, Grant. Phantom Calls: Race & the Globalization of the NBA. 2006. (Illus.). 100p. per. 12.95 *(978-0-9761475-3-4(X))* Prickly Paradigm Pr., LLC.

Filippi, Adam. Shoot Like the Pros: The Road to a Successful Shooting Technique. 2011. (ENG., Illus.). 164p. pap. 16.95 *(978-1-60078-546-7(8))* Triumph Bks.

Finnigan, Sean. Basketball: Nonfiction Brown. 2007. (Nonfiction Collection). (ENG.). 16p. (J). pap. 5.75 *(978-1-58453-360-3(9))* Pioneer Valley Educational Pr., Inc.

Fontanella, John J. The Physics of Basketball. 2006. (ENG., Illus.). 168p. 27.00 *(978-0-8018-8513-6(2))* Johns Hopkins Univ. Pr.

Francois, Francis B. Two Guys from Barnum, Iowa & How They Helped Save Basketball: A History of U. S. Patent 4, 534, 556: Paul D. Estlund & Ke. 2008. pap. *(978-0-615-18342-8(5))* Francois Pr.

Frazier, Walt. The Game Within the Game. 192p. 2006. 24.95 *(978-1-4013-0332-7(3))* 2007. per. 14.95 *(978-1-4013-0909-1(7))* Hyperion Pr.

Frazier, Walt & Berkow, Ira. Rockin' Steady: A Guide to Basketball & Cool. 2010. (ENG.). 144p. 24.95 *(978-1-60078-526-9(3))* Triumph Bks.

Frazier, Walt & Markowitz, Dan. The Game Within the Game. 2006. 192p. 24.95 *(978-1-4013-0253-5(X))* Hyperion Pr.

Fromm, Dave. Expatriate Games: My Season of Misadventures in Czech Semi-Pro Basketball. 2008. (ENG.). 288p. 24.95 *(978-1-60239-296-0(X),* 239296) Skyhorse Publishing Co., Inc.

Fullen, Larry. The Broncos Of 1945. 2010. 416p. (ENG.). 29.95 *(978-1-4490-7720-4(X))*; pap. 19.95 *(978-1-4490-7719-8(6))* AuthorHouse.

Furman, Andrew. My Los Angeles in Black & Almost White. 2010. (Illus.). 248p. 24.95 *(978-0-8156-0959-9(0))* Syracuse Univ. Pr.

Game 7: Inside the NBA's Ultimate Showdown. 2007. per. 18.95 *(978-0-9791299-0-2(7))* Woten, Bill.

B

Giannini, John. Court Sense: Winning Basketball's Mental Game. 2008. (ENG., Illus.). 256p. pap. 19.95 *(978-0-7360-4423-3(X))* Human Kinetics Pubs.
Glaser, Jason. Center. 2010. (Tip-off: Basketball Ser.). (ENG.). 48p. (gr. 4-8). pap. 14.05 *(978-1-4339-3972-3(X))*; lib. bdg. 31.95 *(978-1-4339-3971-6(1))* Stevens, Gareth Publishing LLLP.
—Shooting Guard. 2010. (Tip-off: Basketball Ser.). (ENG.). 48p. (gr. 4-8). pap. 14.05 *(978-1-4339-3981-5(9))*; lib. bdg. 31.95 *(978-1-4339-3980-8(0))* Stevens, Gareth Publishing LLLP.
—Small Forward. 2010. (Tip-off: Basketball Ser.). (ENG.). 48p. (gr. 4-8). pap. 14.05 *(978-1-4339-3984-6(3))*; lib. bdg. 31.95 *(978-1-4339-3983-9(5))* Stevens, Gareth Publishing LLLP.
Godwin, Koran. Everyone Hates a Ball Hog but They All Love a Scorer: The Complete Guide to Scoring Points on & off the Basketball Court. 2010. (ENG.). 152p. pap. 14.95 *(978-1-60037-712-9(2))* Morgan James Publishing.
Goldstein, Sidney. The Basketball Player's Bible: A Comprehensive & Systematic Guide to Playing. 2nd rev. ed. 2008. (Nitty-Gritty Basketball Ser.). (Illus.). 350p. pap. 24.95 *(978-1-884357-00-8(8))* Golden Aura Publishing.
Green Earth Publishers & Jones, Richard S. Doing Time. 2010. (C). 0.00 *(978-0-9821120-0-7(9))* Green Earth Pubs.
Griffin, Sean. Gaming the Game: Confessions of Jimmy Baba Battista — the Inside Story of the NBA Betting Scandal & the Gambler Who Made It All Happen. 2011. (ENG., Illus.). 320p. 24.95 *(978-1-56980-444-5(3))* Barricade Bks., Inc.
Halberstam, David. The Breaks of the Game. 2009. (ENG.). 416p. pap. 16.99 *(978-1-4013-0972-5(0))* Hyperion Pr.
Holland, David. When the Game Was Just a Game. 2008. 280p. pap. 27.95 *(978-1-60672-116-2(X))* PublishAmerica, Inc.
Hollinger, John. Pro Basketball Prospectus. 304p. pap. 21.95 *(978-1-57488-655-9(X))* Potomac Bks., Inc.
Hopla, Dave. Shooting the Basketball. 2011. pap. 24.95 *(978-0-7360-8737-7(0))* Human Kinetics Pubs.
Horsmann, Jannik. Mobile & E-Marketing in Professional Basketball. 2011. 104p. pap. ***(978-3-639-10441-7(2))*** VDM Verlag Dr. Mueller e.K.
Hudson, David L., Jr. Basketball Championships' Most Wanted: The Top 10 Book of March Mayhem, Playoff Performances, & Tournament Oddities. 2007. (Most Wanted Ser.). (Illus.). 272p. per. 13.95 *(978-1-59797-014-3(X))* Potomac Bks., Inc.
Jackson, Mannie & Nelson, Deborah. Boxcar Dreams to Boardroom Reality: Dream Planning. 2012. (ENG.). 206p. pap., wbk. ed. 29.95 ***(978-1-4537-6319-3(8))*** CreateSpace.
Jozsa, Frank P. The National Basketball Association: Business, Organization & Strategy. 2010. 280p. 58.00 *(978-981-4313-90-2(4))* World Scientific Publishing Co., Inc.
Kelly, Scott. Modeling Ncaa Men's Collegiate Basketball Recruiting As a Matching Market. 2008. 144p. pap. *(978-3-639-00324-6(1))* VDM Verlag Dr. Mueller e.K.
Kick The Ball, ed. Knickology Trivia Challenge: New York Knicks Basketball. 2nd rev. ed. 2007. (ENG.). 46p. per. 7.97 *(978-1-934372-10-4(2))* Kick The Ball.
King, Jason. Kansas Jayhawks: A Year to Remember: Inside the Greatest Season in KU Basketball History. 2008. 304p. 19.95 *(978-0-615-21303-3(0))* King, Jason.
Krzyzewski, Mike. The Gold Standard: Building a World-Class Team. 2010. (ENG.). 256p. pap. 15.99 *(978-0-446-54406-1(X)*, Business Plus) Grand Central Publishing.
Laney, Don W. Charley's Boys: St. Bernard College in the Sixties. 2010. 112p. 21.49 *(978-1-4520-2464-6(2))*; pap. 16.95 *(978-1-4520-2465-3(0))* AuthorHouse.
Leonard, David J. After Artest: The NBA & the Assault on Blackness. 2012. (ENG.). 288p. 85.00 ***(978-1-4384-4205-1(X))***; pap. 29.95 ***(978-1-4384-4206-8(8))*** State Univ. of New York Pr.
Lilly, Conor. A Feasibility Study for a Professional Basketball Franchise. 2011. 64p. pap. ***(978-3-8443-2646-8(4))*** Lambert Academic Publishing.
Litos, Michael. Cinderella: Inside the Rise of Mid-Major College Basketball. 2008. (Illus.). 279p. per. 14.95 *(978-1-4022-1252-9(6))* Sourcebooks, Inc.
, Love To Referee, Love To Referee. Love to referee recreational youth basketball officiating Handbook. 2009. 52p. pap. 10.98 *(978-0-557-06731-2(6))* Lulu Enterprises Inc.
MacMullan, Jackie & Auriemma, Geno. Geno: In Pursuit of Perfection. 2009. (ENG., Illus.). 352p. pap. 16.99 *(978-0-446-69477-3(0))* Grand Central Publishing.
Mad about U: Four Decades of Basketball at University Hall. 2006. per. 25.00 *(978-0-9748751-8-7(X))* Augusta Free Pr.
Manley, Martin. Basketball Heaven 1989. pap. 12.95 *(978-0-944877-01-2(X))* Facts Publishing Co.
May, Peter. The Last Banner: The Story of the 1985-86 Celtics & the NBA's Greatest Team of All Time. 2007. (ENG., Illus.). 304p. pap. 20.95 *(978-1-4165-5212-3(X))* Simon & Schuster.
McCallum, Jack. Seven Seconds or Less: My Season on the Bench with the Runnin' & Gunnin' Phoenix Suns. 2007. (ENG., Illus.). 320p. pap. 19.99 *(978-0-7432-9813-1(6)*, Touchstone) Touchstone.
McCormick, Brian. Cross over: the New Model of Youth Basketball Development. 2008. 207p. pap. 21.95 *(978-0-557-02588-6(5))* Lulu Enterprises Inc.
—Developing Basketball Intelligence. 2009. 92p. pap. 20.00 *(978-0-557-04335-4(2))* Lulu Enterprises Inc.
Mckenzie, Larry A. Basketball: So Much More Than Just A Game. 2011. 108p. 22.95 ***(978-1-4634-3752-7(8))***; pap. 15.95 ***(978-1-4634-3753-4(6))*** AuthorHouse.
McLaughlin, Thomas. Give & Go: Basketball As a Cultural Practice. 2008. 250p. 74.50 *(978-0-7914-7393-1(7))*; pap. 29.95 *(978-0-7914-7394-8(5))* State Univ. of New York Pr.
Meinelt, Keith. Fantasy Basketball: A Winning Playbook. 2009. 100p. pap. 17.95 *(978-1-4490-1138-3(1))* AuthorHouse.
Merlino, Doug. The Hustle: One Team & Ten Lives in Black & White. 2010. (ENG., Illus.). 320p. 26.00 *(978-1-60819-215-1(6))* Bloomsbury Publishing.
Montgomery, Jason. The Definitive Guide to the 1-1-3 Match-up Zone. 2007. 48p. pap. 14.95 *(978-0-615-14378-1(4))* Montgomery, Jason.
Montville, Leigh. Manute: The Center of Two Worlds. 2011. (ENG.). 240p. pap. 15.99 *(978-1-4516-2072-6(1))* Simon & Schuster.
Mosenson, Cecil. Work Hard-Never Give Up. 2010. 32p. pap. 14.95 *(978-1-60860-846-1(8)*, Eloquent Bks.) AEG Literary Publishing Services, Inc.
National Basketball Conditioning Coaches Association Staff. Complete Conditioning for Basketball. Foran, Bill & Pound, Robin, eds. 2007. (ENG., Illus.). 216p. 24.95 *(978-0-7360-5784-4(6))* Human Kinetics Pubs.
Newell, Pete & Nater, Swen. Pete Newell's Playing Big. 2007. (ENG., Illus.). 224p. 24.95 *(978-0-7360-6809-3(0))*; *(978-0-7360-6811-6(2))* Human Kinetics Pubs.
Orton, Kathy. Outside the Limelight: Basketball in the Ivy League. 2009. (ENG., Illus.). 240p. 24.95 *(978-0-8135-4616-2(8))* Rutgers Univ. Pr.
Oscar, Sophia & Robinson, Patrick. Mr. A. I. P: Taking it to the Hoop. 2011. 28p. (gr. -1). pap. 15.00 ***(978-1-4634-1407-8(2))*** AuthorHouse.
Peeler, Tim. When March Went Mad: A Celebration of NC State's 1982-83 National Championship. 2007. (Illus.). 295p. 24.95 *(978-1-59670-188-5(9))* Sports Publishing, LLC.
Phelps, Richard. Basketball for Dummies. 3rd ed. 2011. (ENG.). 432p. pap. 22.99 *(978-1-118-07374-2(6)*, For Dummies) Wiley, John & Sons, Inc.
Price, Robert G. The Ultimate Guide to Weight Training for Basketball. 4th ed. 2006. (Ultimate Guide to Weight Training for Sports Ser.). (Illus.). 168p. 16.95 *(978-1-932549-49-2(8))* Price World Publishing.
Raab, Scott. The Whore of Akron: One Man's Search for the Soul of Lebron James. 2011. (ENG.). 272p. 25.99 *(978-0-06-206636-7(6))* HarperCollins Pubs.
Radu, Alexandru. Basketball: A Guide to Skills, Techniques & Tactics. 2011. (ENG., Illus.). 160p. 29.95 *(978-1-84797-187-6(3))* Crowood Pr., Ltd. GBR. Dist: Independent Pubs. Group.
Resler, Bill. The Heart of the Team: Life Lessons on & off the Court. 2006. (ENG., Illus.). 256p. 23.95 *(978-1-57061-518-4(7))* Sasquatch Bks.
Reynolds, Bill. Rise of a Dynasty: The '57 Celtics, the First Banner, & the Dawning of a New America. 2011. (ENG.). 304p. (gr. 12). 15.00 *(978-0-451-23480-3(4)*, N A L Trade) Penguin Group (USA) Inc.
Rosen, Charley. The First Tip-Off: The Incredible Story of the Birth of the NBA. 2008. (ENG., Illus.). 288p. 24.95 *(978-0-07-148785-6(9)*, 0071487859) McGraw-Hill Cos., The.
Schleppi, John. Chicago's Showcase of Basketball: The World Tournament of Professional Basketball & the College All Star Classic. 2008. (ENG., Illus.). 228p. 45.00 *(978-1-878282-49-1(2))* St. Johann Pr.
Shanburn, Eric. Basketball & Baseball Games: For the Driveway, Field or the Alleyway. 2008. 96p. pap. 11.98 *(978-1-4343-8912-1(X))* AuthorHouse.
Shoals, Bethlehem, et al. The Macrophenomenal Pro Basketball Almanac: Styles, Stats, & Stars in Today's Game. 2008. (ENG., Illus.). 224p. 23.00 *(978-1-59691-561-9(7))* Bloomsbury Publishing.
Simmons, Bill. The Book of Basketball: The NBA According to the Sports Guy. 2010. (ENG., Illus.). 752p. pap. 18.00 *(978-0-345-52010-4(6))* ESPN Enterprises.
Solivan, Ernest. Mastering the Mental Side of Basketball. 2007. 110p. pap. 29.95 *(978-0-615-17233-0(4))* Aries International (U.B.T.O.).
Sports Illustrated Editors. Sports Illustrated the College Basketball Book. 2011. (ENG., Illus.). 256p. 29.95 *(978-1-60320-207-7(2))* Time Home Entertainment, Inc.
Sterman, Paul & Painter, Jill. Tales from the UCLA Bruins. 2007. (Illus.). 192p. 19.95 *(978-1-59670-216-5(8))* Sports Publishing, LLC.
Stodghill, Dick & Jackie. BEARCATS! - Muncie Central Basketball. 2008. 156p. pap. 11.95 *(978-1-4357-3511-8(0))* Lulu Enterprises Inc.
Swidey, Neil. The Assist: Hoops, Hope, & the Game of Their Lives. 2008. (ENG., Illus.). 392p. pap. 15.99 *(978-1-58648-666-2(7))* PublicAffairs.
The Herald-Times. This Is INDIANA: Tom Crean, the Team, & the Exciting Comeback of Hoosier Basketball. 2012. (ENG., Illus.). 128p. pap. 20.00 ***(978-0-253-00858-9(1)***, 0253008581) Indiana Univ. Pr.
Triumph Books Staff. Official 2010 NCAA Men's Basketball Records BK. 2009. (ENG.). 232p. pap. 17.95 *(978-1-60078-292-3(2))* Triumph Bks.
Voight, Mike. Mental Toughness Training for Basketball. 2010. (Illus.). 182p. 19.95 *(978-1-60679-108-0(7))* Coaches Choice.
Walls, Jerry L. & Bassham, Gregory. Basketball & Philosophy: Thinking Outside the Paint. 2008. (Philosophy of Popular Culture Ser.). (ENG.). 304p. per. 19.95 *(978-0-8131-9186-7(6))* Univ. Pr. of Kentucky.
Walls, Jerry L. & Bassham, Gregory, eds. Basketball & Philosophy: Thinking Outside the Paint. 2007. (Philosophy of Popular Culture Ser.). (ENG.). 304p. 50.00 *(978-0-8131-2435-3(2))* Univ. Pr. of Kentucky.
Wellington, Al & Miller, Randy. Oberlin Fever: A Championship Spirit in Black & White. 2011. (Illus.). 200p. pap. 29.00 ***(978-0-9770530-7-0(5))*** Miller, Randy.
Yardley, Jim. Brave Dragons: A Chinese Basketball Team, an American Coach, & Two Cultures Clashing. 2012. (ENG., Illus.). 320p. 26.95 ***(978-0-307-27221-8(4)***, Knopf) Knopf Doubleday Publishing Group.
YELLIN & K. C.JONES, Mark C. How to teach a kid to play Basketball. 2010. 121p. pap. 15.00 *(978-0-557-45735-9(1))* Lulu Enterprises Inc.
Zaremba, Alan Jay. The Madness of March: Bonding & Betting with the Boys in Las Vegas. 2009. (ENG.). 242p. pap. 19.95 *(978-0-8032-1383-8(2)*, Bison Bks.) Univ. of Nebraska Pr.
Zullo, Allen. March to Madness. 2007. (ENG., Illus.). 240p. per. 6.95 *(978-0-7624-2969-1(0))* Running Pr. Bk. Pubs.
2010 NCAA Men's Basketball Records. 2010. 164p. pap. 17.95 *(978-1-60078-420-0(8))* Triumph Bks.

BASKETBALL—BIOGRAPHY
see also Women Basketball Players

Alfieri, Gus. Lapchick: The Life of a Legendary Player & Coach in the Glory Days of Basketball. 2006. (ENG., Illus.). 344p. 22.95 *(978-1-59228-869-4(3)*, Lyons Pr.) Globe Pequot Pr., The.
Allred, Lance. Longshot: The Adventures of a Deaf Fundamentalist Mormon Kid & His Journey to the NBA. 2009. (ENG.). 272p. 25.99 *(978-0-06-171858-8(0)*, HarperOne) HarperCollins Pubs.
Arseneault, Paul & Assaf, Peter. Steve Nash, 1 vol. 2010. (ENG., Illus.). 80p. per. *(978-1-894974-25-7(5))* Heritage Hse.
Austin, Earl, Jr. The Phl in the Stl. 2009. 188p. pap. 19.95 *(978-0-9819913-0-6(0))* Prioritybooks Pubns.
Bagga, David. The Walk-on. 2009. 176p. 24.99 *(978-1-4490-3773-4(9))*; pap. 14.95 *(978-1-4490-3772-7(0))* AuthorHouse.
Ballard, Chris. The Art of a Beautiful Game: The Thinking Fan's Tour of the NBA. 2010. (ENG., Illus.). 256p. pap. 15.99 *(978-1-4391-1022-5(0))* Simon & Schuster.
Barbara Balter Kahn. Sam Balter: His Life & Times. 2010. 204p. pap. 17.95 *(978-1-4502-0459-0(7))* iUniverse, Inc.
Basketball Warfare: Life in the Big East. 2007. per. 20.00 *(978-0-9791552-0-8(7))* McNamara Publishing.
Berger, Ronald J. Hoop Dreams on Wheels: Disability & the Competitive Wheelchair Athlete. 2008. (Contemporary Sociological Perspectives Ser.). (Illus.). XIV, 170p. 34.95 *(978-0-415-96509-5(8))* Routledge.
Bird, Larry, et al. When the Game Was Ours. (ENG., Illus.). 2010. 368p. pap. 15.95 *(978-0-547-39458-9(6)*, Mariner Bks.) 2009. 352p. 26.00 *(978-0-547-22547-0(4))* Houghton Mifflin Harcourt Trade & Reference Pubs.
Blythe, Will. To Hate Like This Is to Be Happy Forever: A Thoroughly Obsessive, Intermittently Uplifting, & Occasionally Unbiased Account of the Duke-North Carolina Basketball Rivalry. 2007. (ENG.). 384p. per. 14.99 *(978-0-06-074024-5(8)*, HarperPerennial) HarperCollins Pubs.
Bowman, Bob. Wag: The Story of Texas Coaching Legend Floyd Wagstaff. 108p. 24.95 *(978-1-878096-33-3(8)*, Epigram Pr.) Best of East Texas Pubs.
Bradburd, Rus. Forty Minutes of Hell: The Extraordinary Life of Nolan Richardson. 2011. 352p. pap. 14.99 *(978-0-06-169047-1(3))* 2010. 336p. 24.99 *(978-0-06-169046-4(5))* HarperCollins Pubs. (Amistad).
—Paddy on the Hardwood: A Journey in Irish Hoops. (ENG., Illus.). 247p. 2009. pap. 19.95 *(978-0-8263-4027-6(X))* 2006. 24.95 *(978-0-8263-4026-9(1))* Univ. of New Mexico Pr.
Bradley, Bill. Life on the Run. 2009. (ENG.). 288p. pap. 29.95 *(978-1-4128-1274-0(7))* Transaction Pubs.
Brown M.S., Donald. Great Teams, Players, & Coaches: Stories about high school basketball from the state of Illinois. 2009. 156p. pap. 13.99 *(978-1-4389-3718-2(0))* AuthorHouse.
Buckner, Steve. Game of My Life: Kansas: Memorable Moments of Jayhawks Basketball. 2007. (Illus.). 239p. 24.95 *(978-1-58261-971-2(9))* Sports Publishing, LLC.
Buss, Jeanie & Springer, Steve. Laker Girl: From Pickfair to Playboy to the Prule & Gold. 2010. (ENG.). 256p. 24.95 *(978-1-60078-511-5(5))* Triumph Bks.
Carocci, Vincent P. Building Character Harry's Way: The value of sport & Harry Defrank's lifetime commitment to young Athletes. 2008. (ENG., Illus.). 208p. *(978-0-9774486-2-3(2))* Tuxedo Pr.
Christgau, John. Origins of the Jump Shot: Eight Men Who Shook the World of Basketball. 2007. (Illus.). 220p. pap. 15.00 *(978-1-4223-6621-9(9))* DIANE Publishing Co.
Christie, Doug & Christie, Jackie. No Ordinary Love: A True Story of Marriage & Basketball! 2007. 153p. 24.95 *(978-0-9794827-0-4(X))* Infinite Love Publishing.
Coach "B". Roundball at Phs. 2007. 324p. pap. 29.95 *(978-1-4241-8006-6(6))* PublishAmerica, Inc.
Coffey, Jeffery L. Coming Back: Matthew 6:34. 2010. 128p. 25.00 *(978-1-4520-1383-1(7))*; pap. 12.99 *(978-1-4520-1382-4(9))* AuthorHouse.
Conley, Kathryn L. One of A Kind: The Gene Conley Story. 2007. 336p. pap. 18.99 *(978-1-59755-049-9(3)*, 7000, Advantage Biography) Advantage Bks.
Day, Frederick J. Dream Team: Saints & Gentle Souls from the World of Sports. 2007. 392p. (ENG.). 35.95 *(978-0-595-70071-4(3))*; per. 25.95 *(978-0-595-45406-8(2))* iUniverse, Inc.
Delsohn, Steve & Heisler, Mark. Bob Knight: The Unauthorized Biography. 2006. (ENG., Illus.). 352p. pap. 21.99 *(978-0-7434-6267-9(X))* Pocket Books.
Drexler, Clyde & Eggers, Kerry. Clyde the Glide: My Life in Basketball. 2011. (ENG., Illus.). 432p. pap. 16.95 *(978-1-61321-042-0(6)*, 613042) Skyhorse Publishing Co., Inc.
Elder, Bill. All Guts & No Glory: An Alabama Coach's Memoir of Desegregating College Athletics. 2007. (Illus.). 143p. 23.95 *(978-1-58838-209-2(5)*, NewSouth Bks.) NewSouth, Inc.
Enberg, Dick, intro. Wooden: Basketball & Beyond: The Official UCLA Retrospective. 2011. (ENG., Illus.). 206p. 40.00 *(978-1-4197-0114-6(2)*, Skybox Pr.) Abrams.
—Wooden: Basketball & Beyond: The Official UCLA Retrospective. 2011. (ENG., Illus.). 256p. 250.00 *(978-1-4197-0115-3(0))* Skybox Pr./Abrams.
Farney, Steven Michael. It's Time to Play! Jack Gardner, Basketball & Kansas State University. 2007. (Illus.). 140p. 24.95 *(978-1-58597-435-1(8))* Leathers Publishing.
Feder, Fred. Free Throw Wizard. 2008. 92p. pap. 11.00 *(978-1-59755-167-0(8)*, Advantage Inspirational) Advantage Bks.
Federman, Wayne & Terrill, Marshall. Pete Maravich: The Authorized Biography of Pistol Pete. 2008. (ENG.). 480p. pap. 14.99 *(978-1-58997-535-4(9))* Tyndale Hse. Pubs.
Feinstein, John. A Season on the Brink: A Year with Bob Knight & the Indiana Hoosiers. 2011. (ENG.). 368p. pap. 16.00 *(978-1-4516-5025-9(6))* Simon & Schuster.
Fisher, Derek. Character Driven: Life, Lessons, & Basketball. 2012. (ENG., Illus.). 272p. pap. 14.99 ***(978-1-4516-7207-7(1)***, Howard Bks.) Howard Books.
—Character Driven: Life, Lessons, & Basketball. 2009. (ENG., Illus.). 272p. 24.99 *(978-1-4165-8053-9(0)*, Touchstone) Touchstone.
Franconeri, Steven. Need to Argue! Make A List: My List of All-Time Greatest Basketball Players. 2009. 356p. pap. 19.95 *(978-1-935097-34-1(2))* Hillcrest Publishing Group, Inc.
Freedman, Lew. Lebron James: A Biography. 2008. (Greenwood Biographies Ser.). (Illus.). 155p. 35.00 *(978-0-313-34361-2(6)*, GR4361, Greenwood Pr.) Greenwood Publishing Group, Inc.
Fromm, Dave. Away Games: My Season of Misadventures in Czech Semi-Pro Basketball. 2007. (Illus.). 320p. 24.95 *(978-1-60239-067-6(3))* Skyhorse Publishing Co., Inc.
Glaser, Jason. Dwyane Wade. 2011. (Today's Sports Greats Ser.). 32p. (gr. 4-6). pap. 10.50 *(978-1-4339-5864-9(3)*, Stevens, Gareth Learning Library); (YA). lib. bdg. 26.60 *(978-1-4339-5862-5(7))* Stevens, Gareth Publishing LLLP.
Glass, Keith. Taking Shots: Tall Tales, Bizarre Battles, & the Incredible Truth about the NBA. 2008. (ENG., Illus.). 304p. pap. 15.95 *(978-0-06-137390-9(7))* HarperCollins Pubs.
Goudsouzian, Aram. King of the Court: Bill Russell & the Basketball Revolution. (Illus.). 2011. 448p. pap. 19.95 *(978-0-520-26979-8(9))* 2010. 400p. 45.00 *(978-0-520-25887-7(8))* Univ. of California Pr.
Graham, Tom & Graham Cody, Rachel. Getting Open: The Unknown Story of Bill Garrett & the Integrat. 2011. (ENG.). 288p. pap. 18.99 *(978-1-4516-4317-6(9)*, Beyond Words/Atria Bks.) Atria Bks.
Grange, Michael. Basketball's Greatest Stars. 2010. (ENG., Illus.). 216p. 35.00 *(978-1-55407-637-6(4))* Firefly Bks., Ltd.
Grange, Michael & Embry, Wayne. Basketball's Greatest Stars. 2011. (ENG., Illus.). 216p. pap. 24.95 *(978-1-55407-979-7(9))* Firefly Bks., Ltd.
Greenhalgh, Paul J. Jr. In Search of Corky. 2008. 288p. 29.99 *(978-1-4363-5876-7(0))*; pap. 19.99 *(978-1-4363-5875-0(2))* Xlibris Corp.
Greg Grant And Martin Sumners. 94 Feet & Rising. 2009. 264p. 29.99 *(978-1-4415-4386-8(4))*; pap. 19.99 *(978-1-4415-4385-1(6))* Xlibris Corp.
Harris, Mike. Game of My Life Virginia Tech: Memorable Stories of Hokie Football & Basketball. 2006. (Game of My Life Ser.). (Illus.). 229p. 24.95 *(978-1-59670-004-8(1))* Sports Publishing, LLC.
Heisler, Mark. Kobe: And the New Lakers' Dynasty. 2009. (ENG.). 128p. pap. 14.95 *(978-1-60078-350-0(3))* Triumph Bks.
Herren, Chris & Reynolds, Bill. Basketball Junkie: A Memoir. 2011. (ENG., Illus.). 288p. 24.99 *(978-0-312-65672-0(6))* St. Martin's Pr.
Hey, William T. The Hawks Last Flight: Our Quest for a Championship. 2006. (Illus.). 199p. per. 16.95 *(978-1-60002-269-2(3)*, 4217) Mountain Valley Publishing, LLC.
Howard, Dwight & Denton, John. All You Can Be: Learning & Growing Through Sports. 2011. (All You Can Be Ser.). (ENG., Illus.). 48p. (J). (gr. 2-4). 16.95 ***(978-1-60078-414-9(3))*** Triumph Bks.
Hunt, Donald, et al. Chaney: Playing for a Legend. 2006. (ENG.). 224p. pap. 14.95 *(978-1-57243-913-9(0))* Triumph Bks.
Iooss, Walter, Jr., photos by. Rare Air: German Edition. 50.00 *(978-3-551-85019-5(4))* Carlsen Verlag DEU. Dist: Distribooks, Inc.
Jackson, Derek & Jackson, Chris. Eight Seconds Later... 2009. 81p. pap. 11.99 *(978-0-557-20156-3(X))* Lulu Enterprises Inc.
Jackson, Jackie & Agard, Carl. The Legend of Jumpin Jackie Jackson. 2008. 211p. pap. 19.95 *(978-0-9800518-3-4(5))* Adelphi Publishing & Media Group.
Jacobs, Barry. Across the Line: Profiles in Basketball Courage - Tales of the First Black Players in the ACC & Southeastern Conferences. 2007. (ENG., Illus.). 384p. 24.95 *(978-1-59921-042-1(8)*, Lyons Pr.) Globe Pequot Pr., The.
James, Mike. Fight for Your Dreams: Memoirs of NBA Star Mike James. 2010. 162p. pap. 14.95 *(978-0-615-33795-1(3))* Mike James Foundation.
Jenkins, Bruce. A Good Man: The Pete Newell Story. 2010. (ENG., Illus.). 352p. pap. 19.95 *(978-0-8032-2818-4(X)*, Bison Bks.) Univ. of Nebraska Pr.
Johnson, A. Mark. Basketball Slave: The Andy Johnson Harlem Globetrotter Story. 2010. 179p. pap. 19.95 *(978-0-615-17330-6(4))* Junior-Cam Publishing.
Jones, Ryan. King James: The Buying & Selling of LeBron James. Date not set. mass mkt. *(978-0-312-99376-4(5)*, St. Martin's Paperbacks) St. Martin's Pr.
Just for Fun: The Story of AAU Women's Basketball. 2008. 290p. pap. 19.95 *(978-1-55728-889-9(5))* Univ. of Arkansas Pr.
Katz, Milton S. Breaking Through: John B. McLendon, Basketball Legend & Civil Rights Pioneer. 2007. (Illus.). 256p. 32.50 *(978-1-55728-847-9(X))* Univ. of Arkansas Pr.

Keiderling, Kyle. Heart of a Lion: The Life, Death & Legacy of Hank Gathers. 2010. (Illus.). 402p. 29.95 *(978-0-9778996-8-5(3))* Morning Star Communications.
Kilbourne. Running with Zoé: A Conversation on the Meaning of Play, Games, & Sport. 2009. 194p. pap. 15.95 *(978-1-4490-0845-1(3))* AuthorHouse.
Knott, J. E. My Horse Can Outrun Your Horse. (Illus.). 400p. reprint ed. 16.00 *(978-0-9623471-3-9(2))* Mesa Publishing Corp.
Krider, Dave. Indiana High School Basketball's 20 Most Dominant Players. 2009. 272p. pap. 21.95 *(978-1-4389-7316-6(0))* 2007. (Illus.). 253p. per. 21.95 *(978-1-60008-028-9(6))*, Rooftop Publishing) AuthorHouse.
Kriegel, Mark. Pistol: The Life of Pete Maravich. 2008. (ENG., Illus.). 416p. pap. 15.00 *(978-0-7432-8498-1(4))*, Free Pr.) Free Pr.
Krzyzewski, Mike. The Gold Standard: Building a World-Class Team. 2009. (ENG.). 256p. 25.99 *(978-0-446-54407-8(8))*, Business Plus) Grand Central Publishing.
Lazenby, Roland. Jerry West: The Life & Legend of a Basketball Icon. 2010. (Illus.). 448p. 28.00 *(978-0-345-51083-9(6))*, Ballantine Bks.) Random House Publishing Group.
Lemon, Meadowlark & Stuart, Lee. Trust Your Next Shot: A Guide to a Life of Joy. 2010. 288p. 24.95 *(978-0-9841130-4-0(5))* Ascend Bks., LLC.
Life of Riley. abr. ed. 16.95 incl. audio *(978-1-56703-019-8(X))* High-Top Publishing.
Linde, Barbara M. LeBron James. 2010. (Today's Superstars Ser.). (ENG.). 48p. (gr. 5-8). pap. 14.05 *(978-1-4339-3996-9(7))*; lib. bdg. 31.95 *(978-1-4339-3995-2(9))* Stevens, Gareth Publishing LLLP.
Link, Coach Ron. Fearfully & Wonderfully Made. 2008. 152p. pap. 24.95 *(978-1-60441-622-0(X))* PublishAmerica, Inc.
Lucas, Adam. The Best Game Ever: How Frank Mcguire's '57 Tar Heels Beat Wilt & Revolutionized College Basketball. 2011. (ENG., Illus.). 256p. pap. 14.95 *(978-0-7627-7427-2(4))*, Lyons Pr.) Globe Pequot Pr., The.
Mallozzi, Vincent. Doc: The Rise & Rise of Julius Erving. 2009. (ENG., Illus.). 304p. 25.95 *(978-0-470-17018-2(2))*, Wiley) Wiley, John & Sons, Inc.
Marecek, Greg. The St. Louis Hawks: A Gallery of Images & Memorabilia. 2007. (Illus.). 144p. 39.95 *(978-1-933370-15-6(7))* Reedy Pr.
Martelli, Phil. Don't Call Me Coach: A Lesson Plan for Life. 2007. (Illus.). 207p. 24.95 *(978-1-933822-06-8(6))* Camino Bks., Inc.
May, Peter. The Big Three. 2007. (ENG., Illus.). 288p. pap. 19.95 *(978-1-4165-5207-9(3))* Simon & Schuster.
May, Reuben. Living through the Hoop: High School Basketball, Race, & the American Dream. 2009. (ENG.). 272p. pap. 22.00 *(978-0-8147-9596-5(X))* New York Univ. Pr.
May, Reuben A. Buford. Living Through the Hoop: High School Basketball, Race, & the American Dream. 2007. (ENG.). 272p. 60.00 *(978-0-8147-5729-1(4))* New York Univ. Pr.
Mayberry, Ron. Education 101: One Man's Journey to the Final Four. 2011. 272p. pap. 17.95 ***(978-1-4620-2963-1(9))*** iUniverse, Inc.
McCallum, Jack. Dream Team: How Michael, Magic, Larry, Charles, & the Greatest Team of All Time Conquered the World & Changed the Game of Basketball Forever. 2012. (ENG., Illus.). 384p. 28.00 ***(978-0-345-52048-7(3))***, Ballantine Bks.) Random House Publishing Group.
Mohatt, Everett J. Beyond Ceilings. 2007. 360p. per. 18.95 *(978-0-9774906-8-4(8))* Counterbalance Bks.
Morgan, David Lee, Jr. A Ring for the King. 2009. (ENG.). 128p. pap. 14.95 *(978-1-60078-327-2(9))* Triumph Bks.
Moscowitz, Raymond. Overtime: Small School, Giant Dream 20 Years Later. 2009. 188p. pap. 12.49 *(978-1-4490-2842-8(X))* AuthorHouse.
Mourning, Alonzo & Wetzel, Dan. Resilience. 2009. (ENG., Illus.). 272p. pap. 15.00 *(978-0-345-50750-1(9))*, Ballantine Bks.) Random House Publishing Group.
Oatman, R. S. Lindsay Whalen Story. 2010. 184p. pap. 19.95 *(978-1-935666-16-5(9))* Nodin Pr.
O'Hara, Michael E. University of Maryland Men's Basketball Games: A Complete Record, Fall 1953 Through Spring 2006. 2008. (ENG., Illus.). 450p. pap. 49.95 *(978-0-7864-3270-7(5))* McFarland & Co., Inc. Pubs.
Olney, Buster. How Lucky You Can Be: The Story of Coach Don Meyer. 2010. (ENG., Illus.). 240p. 25.00 *(978-0-345-52411-9(X))* ESPN Enterprises.
Olson, Lute & Fisher, David. Lute! The Seasons of My Life. 2007. (ENG., Illus.). 336p. pap. 16.95 *(978-0-312-35942-3(X))*, St. Martin's Griffin) St. Martin's Pr.
O'Neal, Shaquille. Shaq Uncut: My Story. 2011. (ENG., Illus.). 304p. 27.99 *(978-1-4555-0441-1(6))*; 432p. 29.99 *(978-1-4555-0725-2(3))* Grand Central Publishing.
Osier, Dan. Kobe Bryant. 2011. (Basketball's MVPs Ser.). (ENG.). 24p. (J). pap. 8.85 *(978-1-4488-2630-8(6))*, PowerKids Pr.); (gr. 3-6). lib. bdg. 21.25 *(978-1-4488-3135-7(0))* Rosen Publishing Group, Inc., The.
—Lebron James. 2011. (Basketball's MVPs / Jugadores más valiosos del baloncesto Ser.). (ENG & SPA.). 24p. (J). (gr. 3-6). lib. bdg. 21.25 *(978-1-4488-3134-0(2))* Rosen Publishing Group, Inc., The.
—Tim Duncan. 2011. (Basketball's MVPs / Jugadores más valiosos del baloncesto Ser.). 24p. (SPA & ENG.). (J). (gr. 3-6). lib. bdg. 21.25 *(978-1-4488-3139-5(3))*; (Illus.). pap. 8.85 *(978-1-4488-2638-4(1))*, PowerKids Pr.) Rosen Publishing Group, Inc., The.
Page M.S., Linda. Love, Pain & Passion the Heart of a Champion. 2010. (ENG.). 116p. pap. 19.95 *(978-1-4490-0891-8(7))* AuthorHouse.
Parr, Ann. Coach Tex Winter: Triangle Basketball. 2006. (Illus.). 160p. per. 26.95 *(978-1-933803-10-4(X))*, NDX Pr.) Child Sensitive Communication, LLC.
Peeler, Tim. NC State Basketball: 100 Years of Innovation. 2010. (ENG., Illus.). 256p. 30.00 *(978-0-8078-3447-3(5))* Univ. of North Carolina Pr.
Phelps, Richard "Digger". Undertaker's Son. 2010. (Illus.). 280p. pap. 12.95 *(978-1-59921-974-5(3))* Globe Pequot Pr., The.
Pitino, Rick. Rebound Rules: The Art of Success 2. 0. 2009. (Playaway Adult Nonfiction Ser.). 59.99 *(978-1-60847-575-9(1))* Findaway World, LLC.
Pitino, Rick & Forde, Pat. Rebound Rules: The Art of Success 2.0. 2010. 240p. pap. 16.99 *(978-0-06-168726-6(X))*, Harper Paperbacks) HarperCollins Pubs.
Pitoniak, Scott. Color Him Orange: The Jim Boeheim Story. 2011. (ENG.). 256p. 24.95 ***(978-1-60078-517-7(4))*** Triumph Bks.
Pluto, Terry & Windhorst, Brian. The Franchise: Lebron James & the Remaking of the Cleveland Cavaliers. 2007. (Illus.). 224p. 19.95 *(978-1-59851-028-7(2))* Gray and Company, Publishers.
Raab, Scott. The Whore of Akron: One Man's Search for the Soul of Lebron James. 2012. (ENG.). 272p. pap. 14.99 ***(978-0-06-206637-4(4))***, HarperPerennial) HarperCollins Pubs.
Roberts, N. H. & Richardson, C. A. Gene Bess College Basketball's Winningest Coach. 2006. 240p. pap. 24.95 *(978-0-9773198-7-9(3))* Acclaim Pr., Inc.
Robertson, Oscar P. The Big O: My Life, My Times, My Game. 2010. (ENG., Illus.). 376p. pap. 19.95 *(978-0-8032-3463-5(5))*, Bison Bks.) Univ. of Nebraska Pr.
Rodebush, Emmitt. The Accidental Millionaire: The Unusual Life of E. L. Rodebush. 2007. 60p. per. 9.95 *(978-0-595-34176-4(4))* iUniverse, Inc.
Rodman, Dennis. I Should Be Dead by Now. 2006. (Illus.). 224p. per. 16.95 *(978-1-59670-152-6(8))* Sports Publishing, LLC.
Rosen, Charley. Crazy Basketball: A Life in & Out of Bounds. 2011. (ENG.). 320p. 24.95 *(978-0-8032-1793-5(5))* Univ. of Nebraska Pr.
—Players & Pretenders: The Basketball Team That Couldn't Shoot Straight. 2007. (ENG., Illus.). 320p. pap. 18.95 *(978-0-8032-5964-5(5))*, Bison Bks.) Univ. of Nebraska Pr.

Ross, Alan. Lakers Glory: For the Love of Kobe, Magic, & Mikan. 2006. (ENG., Illus.). 256p. pap. 12.95 *(978-1-58182-554-1(4))* Turner Publishing Co.
Roth, John. The Encyclopedia of Duke Basketball. 2006. (ENG., Illus.). 456p. 39.95 *(978-0-8223-3904-5(8))* Duke Univ. Pr.
Russell, Bill & Steinberg, Alan. Red & Me: A Great Coach, a Life-Long Friend. 2009. (Illus.). 208p. 24.99 *(978-0-06-176614-5(3))*; (ENG.). 224p. pap. 24.99 *(978-0-06-177499-7(5))*, HarperLuxe) HarperCollins Pubs.
—Red & Me: My Coach, My Lifelong Friend. 2010. (ENG.). 224p. pap. 14.99 *(978-0-06-179206-9(3))*, Harper Paperbacks) HarperCollins Pubs.
Schumacher, Michael. Mr. Basketball: George Mikan, the Minneapolis Lakers, & the Birth of the NBA. 2008. (Illus.). 336p. pap. 18.95 *(978-0-8166-5675-2(4))* Univ. of Minnesota Pr.
Shelby, Don. The Season Never Ends: Wins, Losses, & the Wisdom of the Court. 2011. 188p. pap. 14.95 ***(978-1-935098-69-0(1))***, Bascom Hill Publishing Group, Ltd.) Hillcrest Publishing Group, Inc.
Shirley, Paul. Can I Keep My Jersey? 11 Teams, 5 Countries, & 4 Years in My Life as a Basketball Vagabond. 2008. (ENG., Illus.). 336p. pap. 15.00 *(978-0-345-49570-9(5))*, Ballantine Bks.) Random House Publishing Group.
Shrader, Charles A. Dreaming Small. 2010. pap. 17.95 *(978-0-7414-5951-0(5))* Infinity Publishing.
Smith, Constance Ridley. Coach Ridley's Basketball Glory: The Career of Cornelius Ridley at Pearl High School First Half 1960-1969. 2011. 244p. pap. 75.00 ***(978-1-4389-7252-7(0))*** AuthorHouse.
Sporting News Staff. Official NBA Guide 2007-08. 2007. (ENG.). 735p. pap. 18.95 *(978-0-89204-884-7(0))* Sporting News Publishing Co.
—Official NBA Register 2007-08. 2007. (ENG.). 472p. pap. 18.95 *(978-0-89204-885-4(9))* Sporting News Publishing Co.
Stokes, Whitworth. All the Way for Doc. 2010. (ENG.). 146p. 25.84 *(978-0-557-64016-4(4))*; 192p. pap. 20.00 *(978-0-557-16886-6(4))* Lulu Enterprises Inc.
Terrill, Marshall & Federman, Wayne. Maravich: The Short Life & Thriving Legacy of Pistol Pete. 2006. (ENG., Illus.). 384p. *(978-1-894963-52-7(0))* Sport Media Publishing.
Thorburn, Ryan. Cowboy Up: Kenny Sailors, the Jump Shot & Wyoming Basketball History. 2011. 158p. pap. 20.00 ***(978-0-9846523-0-3(2))***, Burning Daylight) Pearn & Assocs. Inc.
Thorburn, Ryan John. Lost Cowboys: The Story of Bud Daniel & Wyoming Baseball. Reich, Laurie Mansell, ed. 2010. 202p. pap. 18.00 *(978-0-9841683-2-3(X))*, Burning Daylight) Pearn & Assocs. Inc.
Titus, Mark. Don't Put Me in, Coach: My Incredible NCAA Journey from the End of the Bench to the End of the Bench. 2012. (ENG., Illus.). 272p. 24.95 ***(978-0-385-53510-6(4))***, Doubleday) Knopf Doubleday Publishing Group.
To Blake Sebring, By Lloy Ball As Told. The Biggest Mistake I Never Made: How an Indiana boy gave up basketball to become a world-class volleyball Player. 2008. 188p. pap. 17.50 *(978-1-4389-2907-1(2))* AuthorHouse.
Tomjanovich, Rudy & Falkoff, Robert. A Rocket at Heart: My Life & My Team. 2007. (ENG., Illus.). 304p. pap. 20.95 *(978-1-4165-5206-2(5))* Simon & Schuster.
Triumph Books Staff. Wade's World: The Flash That Ignites the Heat. 2006. (ENG., Illus.). 128p. per. 14.95 *(978-1-57243-948-1(3))* Triumph Bks.
Wade, Dwyane. A Father First: How My Life Became Bigger Than Basketball. 2012. (ENG.). 320p. 26.99 ***(978-0-06-213615-2(1))***, Morrow, William & Co.) HarperCollins Pubs.
Wallace, Robert K. Thirteen Women Strong: The Making of a Team. 2008. (ENG., Illus.). 352p. 29.95 *(978-0-8131-2515-2(4))* Univ. Pr. of Kentucky.
Walsh, Joseph. More Than A Championship. 2010. 153p. pap. 15.00 *(978-0-557-06889-0(4))* Lulu Enterprises Inc.
Waters, Mike. Game of My Life Syracuse. 2007. (Game of My Life Ser.). 256p. pap. 18.95 *(978-1-59670-235-6(4))* Sports Publishing, LLC.
Weiss, Dick. True Blue: A Tribute to Mike Krzyzewski's Career at Duke. 2nd ed. 2008. (Illus.). 16.95 *(978-1-59670-336-0(9))* Sports Publishing, LLC.
West, Jerry & Coleman, Jonathan. West by West: My Charmed, Tormented Life. (ENG., Illus.). 2012. 352p. pap. 16.99 ***(978-0-316-05350-1(3))***, Back Bay Bks.) 2011. 352p. 27.99 *(978-0-316-05349-5(X))* 2011. 464p. 29.99 *(978-0-316-19616-1(9))* Little Brown & Co.
Westcott, Rich. The Mogul: Eddie Gottlieb, Philadelphia Sports Legend & Pro Basketball Pioneer. 2008. (ENG., Illus.). 320p. 39.00 *(978-1-59213-655-1(9))* Temple Univ. Pr.
Western Horseman Staff. Legends Vol. 7: Outstanding Quarter Horse Stallions & Mares. Martindale, Cathy & Swan, Kathy, eds. 2006. (Legends Ser.). (ENG., Illus.). 256p. per. 23.95 *(978-0-911647-79-2(1))* Western Horseman.
Wilkens, Lenny. Unguarded: My Forty Years Surviving in the NBA. 2008. (ENG.). 302p. 25.00 *(978-1-4379-5246-9(1))* DIANE Publishing Co.
Williams, Roy. Hard Work: A Life on & off the Court. 2011. (ENG., Illus.). 336p. pap. 15.95 *(978-1-61620-107-4(X))*, 161620107X) Algonquin Bks. of Chapel Hill.
Williams, Roy & Crothers, Tim. Hard Work: My Life on & off the Court. 2009. (ENG.). 288p. 24.95 *(978-1-56512-959-7(8))*, 1565129598) Algonquin Bks. of Chapel Hill.
Wooden, John & Yaeger, Don. A Game Plan for Life: The Power of Mentoring. 2009. (ENG., Illus.). 208p. 25.00 *(978-1-59691-701-9(6))* Bloomsbury Publishing.
Wright, Luther & Hunter, Karen. A Perfect Fit. 2010. (ENG., Illus.). 208p. pap. 15.00 *(978-1-4165-7097-4(7))*, Gallery Books/Karen Hunter Publishing) Gallery Books/Karen Hunter Publishing.
Wu, Grace. Yao Ming: Chinese Biographies: Graded Readers = [Yao Ming: Lan Qiu de Ju Xing: Ren Wu Zhuan Ji: Zhong Wen Pin Yin Fu Zhu du Ben]. 2010. (CHI & ENG.). (C). pap. 15.95 *(978-0-88727-759-7(4))* Cheng & Tsui Co.
Wukovits, John, ed. Kobe Bryant. 2011. (People in the News Ser.). 128p. lib. bdg. 33.45 *(978-1-4205-0593-1(9))*, Lucent Bks.) Cengage Gale.
Yaeger, Don & Wooden, John. A Game Plan for Life: The Power of Mentoring. 2011. (ENG., Illus.). 40p. pap. 15.00 *(978-1-60819-268-7(7))* Bloomsbury Publishing.
Yorkey, Mike. Linspired: The Remarkable Rise of Jeremy Lin, 1 vol. 2012. (ENG.). 176p. pap. 12.99 ***(978-0-310-32068-5(2))*** Zondervan.

BASKETBALL—COACHING

Adkins, Clint, et al. Basketball Drills, Plays & Strategies: Comprehensive Resource for Coaches. 2007. (ENG., Illus.). 288p. per. 17.99 *(978-1-55870-810-5(3))*, Betterway Bks.) F&W Media, Inc.
Akali, Melissa W. & Welch Jr., Edward E. The Ultimate Guide in Becoming a Successful Assistant Coach and/or Team Parent: This handbook will provide Team Parents & Assistant Coaches with Guid. 2009. 154p. pap. 14.99 *(978-1-4389-8129-1(5))* AuthorHouse.
American Sport Education Program Staff. Coaching Basketball Technical & Tactical Skills. 2006. (ENG., Illus.). 272p. per. 24.95 *(978-0-7360-4705-0(0))* Human Kinetics Pubs.
—Coaching Youth Basketball. 4th rev. ed. 2006. (ENG., Illus.). 168p. per. 17.95 *(978-0-7360-6450-7(8))* Human Kinetics Pubs.
Battenberg, Terry D. Power Post Play: A Complete Guide to Developing Basketball's Big Men. 2007. (Illus.). 154p. per. 17.95 *(978-0-615-14520-4(5))* Fast Break Publishing.
Bishop, Ron. A Winning Legacy: An Autobiography. 2006. 20.00 *(978-0-9788748-3-4(8))* Synergistics International, Inc.

Bradburd, Rus. Forty Minutes of Hell: The Extraordinary Life of Nolan Richardson. 2011. 352p. pap. 14.99 *(978-0-06-169047-1(3))*, Amistad) HarperCollins Pubs.
Brown, Dale. Dale Brown's Handbook of Basketball Fundamentals & Drills. 2009. (ENG., Illus.). 109p. pap. 19.95 *(978-1-58518-357-9(1))* Coaches Choice.
Brown, James E. Maximum Performance Basketball: in-Season Workout Book for Players 7th Grade: 12th Grade. 2007. pap. 10.00 *(978-0-9801199-0-9(1))* Brown, James E. Pubs.
Caldwell, Howard. Tony Hinkle: Coach for All Seasons. 2010. (ENG., Illus.). 208p. pap. 21.95 *(978-0-253-22333-3(4))*, 0253223334) Indiana Univ. Pr.
Carocci, Vincent P. Building Character Harry's Way: The value of sport & Harry Defrank's lifetime commitment to young Athletes. 2008. (ENG., Illus.). 208p. *(978-0-9774486-2-3(2))* Tuxedo Pr.
Coach "B". Roundball at Phs. 2007. 324p. pap. 29.95 *(978-1-4241-8006-6(6))* PublishAmerica, Inc.
Coulter, Norman A. The and 6IXTH Man. 2011. 82p. pap. 10.99 ***(978-1-61379-065-6(1))*** Xulon Pr., Inc.
Crean, Tom & Pim, Ralph L. Coaching Team Basketball: Develop Winning Players with a Team-First Attitude. 2006. (ENG., Illus.). 224p. per. 18.95 *(978-0-07-146565-6(0))*, 0071465650) McGraw-Hill Cos., The.
Deveney, Sean. Win Like Lin: Finding Your Inner Linsanity on the Way to Breakout Success. 2012. (ENG.). 128p. pap. 9.99 ***(978-0-07-180399-1(8))***, 0071803998) McGraw-Hill Cos., The.
DeVenzio, Dick. Runnin' the Show: Basketball Leadership for Coaches & Players. 2nd ed. 2006. (Illus.). 152p. pap. 16.95 *(978-1-933538-53-2(8))* Bridgeway Bks.
—There's Only One Way to Win: Lessons from a Legend: Modern Success Principles from an Old-School Coach. 2nd ed. 2006. (Illus.). 185p. per. 16.95 *(978-1-933538-52-5(X))* Bridgeway Bks.
Dunphy, Fran & Hsieh, Lawrence. The Baffled Parent's Guide to Great Basketball Plays. 2009. (ENG., Illus.). 144p. pap. 16.95 *(978-0-07-150279-5(3))*, 0071502793, International Marine/Ragged Mountain Pr.) McGraw-Hill Professional Publishing.
Emma, Thomas. 101 Strength & Conditioning Exercises & Drills for Basketball. 2006. (Coaches Choice Ser.). (Illus.). 122p. per. 17.95 *(978-1-58518-968-7(5))* Coaches Choice.
Feinstein, John. A Season on the Brink: A Year with Bob Knight & the Indiana Hoosiers. 2011. (ENG.). 368p. pap. 16.00 *(978-1-4516-5025-9(6))* Simon & Schuster.
Formichella, Joe, told to. Staying Ahead of the Posse: The Ben Jobe Story. 2008. 25.00 *(978-1-57966-082-6(7))* River City Publishing.
Gandolfi, Giorgio. The Complete Book of Offensive Basketball Drills: Game-Changing Drills from Around the World. 2009. (ENG., Illus.). 272p. pap. 18.95 *(978-0-07-163586-8(6))*, 0071635866) McGraw-Hill Cos., The.
Goldstein, Sidney. The Basketball Coach's Bible: A Comprehensive & Systematic Guide to Coaching. 2nd rev. ed. 2008. (Nitty-Gritty Basketball Ser.). (Illus.). 414p. pap. 29.95 *(978-1-884357-99-2(7))* Golden Aura Publishing.
Harkins, Harry L., et al. Shuffle Offenses for Men's & Women's Basketball. 2008. (Art & Science of Coaching Ser.). (Illus.). 104p. pap. 17.95 *(978-1-58518-272-5(9))* Coaches Choice.
Hemminger, Andrew & Bensch, Dave. Destination Basketball: A Once in a Lifetime Adventure to Meet the Best Coaches in College Hoops. 2007. (Illus.). 226p. per. 18.95 *(978-0-615-15947-8(8))* Oak Town United LLC.
Hunt, Donald, et al. Chaney: Playing for a Legend. 2006. (ENG.). 224p. pap. 14.95 *(978-1-57243-913-9(0))* Triumph Bks.
Katz, Milton S. Breaking Through: John B. Mclendon, Basketball Legend & Civil Rights Pioneer. 2010. (Illus.). 280p. pap. 19.95 *(978-1-55728-951-3(4))* Univ. of Arkansas Pr.
Kimble, John. The Basketball Coaches' Complete Guide to Zone Offenses. 2007. (Illus.). pap. 21.95 *(978-1-58518-000-4(9))* Coaches Choice.
Klein, Leigh, ed. Five-Star Basketball Defense. 2010. 160p. pap. 16.95 *(978-1-930546-96-7(3))*, equilibrium bks.) Wish Publishing.
Knott, J. E. My Horse Can Outrun Your Horse. (Illus.). 400p. reprint ed. 16.00 *(978-0-9623471-3-9(2))* Mesa Publishing Corp.
Krause, Jerry & Brown, Bruce. NABC's Youth Basketball Coaching Handbook: Beyond the Backboard. 2006. (Illus.). 143p. per. 17.95 *(978-1-58518-890-1(5))* Coaches Choice.
Kruger, Lon & Allen, D. J. The Xs & Os of Success: A Playbook for Leaders in Business & Life. 2008. 270p. pap. 19.95 *(978-1-935043-03-4(X))* Stephens Pr. LLC.
Krzyzewski, Mike. The Gold Standard: Building a World-Class Team. 2009. (ENG.). 256p. 25.99 *(978-0-446-54407-8(8))*, Business Plus) Grand Central Publishing.
Krzyzewski, Mike & Spatola, Jamie K. Beyond Basketball: Coach K's Keywords for Success. 2007. (ENG.). 192p. per. 14.99 *(978-0-446-58187-5(9))*, Business Plus) Grand Central Publishing.
Lazenby, Roland. Mindgames: Phil Jackson's Long Strange Journey. 2007. (ENG.). 450p. pap. 21.95 *(978-0-8032-5998-0(0))*, Bison Bks.) Univ. of Nebraska Pr.
Life of Riley. abr. ed. 16.95 incl. audio *(978-1-56703-019-8(X))* High-Top Publishing.
Link, Coach Ron. Fearfully & Wonderfully Made. 2008. 152p. pap. 24.95 *(978-1-60441-622-0(X))* PublishAmerica, Inc.
McCarthy, John P., Jr. Coaching Youth Basketball: The Guide for Coaches, Parents & Athletes. 2nd rev. ed. 2006. (ENG., Illus.). 208p. pap. 14.99 *(978-1-55870-790-0(5))*, Betterway Bks.) F&W Media, Inc.
McCormick, Brian. 180 Shooter: 5 Steps to Shooting 90% from the Free Throw Line, 50% from the Field & 40% from the 3-Point Line. 2009. 116p. pap. 19.95 *(978-0-557-05861-7(9))* Lulu Enterprises Inc.
Media, Stack. Basketball Training. 2009. (ENG.). 176p. pap. 16.95 *(978-1-60078-281-7(7))* Triumph Bks.
Meyer, Don, et al. Basketball Skills & Drills. 3rd rev. ed. 2007. (ENG., Illus.). 272p. 24.95 *(978-0-7360-6707-2(8))* Human Kinetics Pubs.
Miniscalco, Keith & Kot, Greg. Survival Guide for Coaching Youth Basketball. 2008. (ENG., Illus.). 184p. pap. 15.95 *(978-0-7360-7383-7(3))* Human Kinetics Pubs.
Moscowitz, Raymond. Overtime: Small School, Giant Dream 20 Years Later. 2009. 188p. pap. 12.49 *(978-1-4490-2842-8(X))* AuthorHouse.
Mosenson, Cecil. It All Began with Wilt. 2008. 168p. 14.99 *(978-1-60604-055-3(3))* Tate Publishing & Enterprises, LLC.
Nater, Swen & Gallimore, R. You Haven't Taught Until They Have Learned. 2010. (ENG.). 176p. pap. 19.95 *(978-1-935412-08-3(6))* Fitness Information Technology, Inc.
National Basketball Coaches Association Staff. NBA Coaches Playbook: Techniques, Tactics, & Teaching Points. Gandolfi, Giorgio, ed. 2008. (ENG., Illus.). 368p. pap. 22.95 *(978-0-7360-6355-5(2))* Human Kinetics Pubs.
Nelson, Shawn. Basketball Coaches' Guide to Advanced Offensive Skill Development. 2008. 160p. pap. 24.95 incl. DVD *(978-1-60679-030-4(7))* Coaches Choice.
O'Halloran, Michael. Never Forget They're Kids - Ideas for Coaching Your Daughter's 4th - 8th grade basketball Team. 2007. 52p. pap. 17.95 *(978-0-615-15155-7(8))* Brilliant & Bright, Inc.
—Never Forget They're Kids - Ideas for Coaching Your Daughter's 4th-8th Grade Basketball Team: 2nd Edition. 2010. 128p. pap. 19.99 *(978-0-557-56867-3(6))* Lulu Enterprises Inc.

B

—The Well-Prepared Coach - 30 Youth Basketball Practice Plans. 2010. 87p. pap. 34.99 *(978-0-557-54764-7(4))* Lulu Enterprises Inc.
Olney, Buster. How Lucky You Can Be: The Story of Coach Don Meyer. 2010. (ENG., Illus.). 240p. 25.00 *(978-0-345-52411-9(X))* ESPN Enterprises.
Parr, Randall. Rare Eric: Basketball Fundamentals with A Twist. 2011. 324p. 28.95 *(978-1-4567-3599-9(3))*; pap. 17.95 *(978-1-4567-3600-2(0))* AuthorHouse.
Paye, Burrall & Paye, Patrick. The Complete Handbook of Advanced Multi-Purpose Offensive Basketball Drills. 2008. (Coaches Choice Ser.). (Illus.). 211p. per. 21.95 *(978-1-58518-068-4(8))* Coaches Choice.
Phillips, T. L. Fundamentals: Player Development Guide. 2008. 80p. pap. 32.49 *(978-1-4389-3983-4(3))* AuthorHouse.
—Fundamentals: Player Developmental Guide. 2009. 80p. pap. 32.49 *(978-1-4389-4861-4(1))* AuthorHouse.
Pitino, Rick. Rebound Rules: The Art of Success 2. 0. 2009. (Playaway Adult Nonfiction Ser.). 59.99 *(978-1-60847-575-9(1))* Findaway World, LLC.
Pitino, Rick & Forde, Pat. Rebound Rules: The Art of Success 2.0. 2010. 240p. pap. 16.99 *(978-0-06-168726-6(X)*, Harper Paperbacks) HarperCollins Pubs.
Powell, Norris A. And: So You Want to Be A Coach. 2011. 50p. 24.99 ***(978-1-4568-9884-7(1))***; pap. 15.99 ***(978-1-4568-9883-0(3))*** Xlibris Corp.
Prelesnik, Michael. A Study of Middle School Athletic Coaching Using the Competing Values Framework. 2008. 172p. pap. *(978-3-8364-8230-1(4))* VDM Verlag Dr. Mueller e.K.
Raising Big Smiling Basketball Kids: A Complete Roadmap for Every Parent & Coach. 2008. 29.95 *(978-1-932421-23-1(8))* Mansion Grove Hse.
Roberts, N. H. & Richardson, C. A. Gene Bess College Basketball's Winningest Coach. 2006. 240p. pap. 24.95 *(978-0-9773198-7-9(3))* Acclaim Pr., Inc.
Robinson, Craig. A Game of Character: A Family Journey from Chicago's Southside to the Ivy League & Beyond. 2011. (ENG.). 288p. (gr. 12). 16.00 *(978-1-59240-591-6(6)*, Gotham) Penguin Group (USA) Inc.
Russell, Bill & Steinberg, Alan. Red & Me: My Coach, My Lifelong Friend. 2010. (ENG.). 224p. pap. 14.99 *(978-0-06-179206-9(3)*, Harper Paperbacks) HarperCollins Pubs.
Saylor, Doug. Hooplife: The Basketball Player's Max-Potential Handbook. 2008. (Illus.). 110p. per. 19.95 *(978-1-58518-069-1(6))* Coaches Choice.
Sivils, Kevin. Game Strategies & Tactics for Basketball: Bench Coaching for Success. 2009. 124p. pap. 16.95 *(978-1-60844-045-0(1))* Dog Ear Publishing, LLC.
Somogyi, Kristen. Knack Coaching Youth Basketball: Step-by-Step Strategy, Mechanics & Drills for Consistent Success. 2010. (Knack: Make It Easy Ser.). (ENG., Illus.). 256p. pap. 19.95 *(978-1-59921-952-3(2)*, Knack) Globe Pequot Pr., The.
Spainhour, Dan. How to Run A Basketball Camp: A Guide to Directing a Successful Basketball Camp. 2007. 140p. pap. 19.95 *(978-0-615-14329-3(6))* Educational Coaching & Business Communications.
Swope, Bob. Youth Basketball Drills & Plays Handbook. 2007. (Illus.). 100p. (J). per. 16.95 *(978-0-9772817-6-3(0))* Jacobob Pr., LLC.
Tarkanian, Jerry. Runnin' Rebel: Shark Tales of Extra Benefits, Frank Sinatra, & Winning It All. 2006. (Illus.). 230p. per. 16.95 *(978-1-59670-155-7(2))* Sports Publishing, LLC.
Thomas, Jerry R., et al. Physical Education Methods for Elementary Teachers. 3rd ed. 2008. (ENG., Illus.). 472p. (gr. k-6). 68.00 *(978-0-7360-6704-1(3))* Human Kinetics Pubs.
W. McLauchlan, author James, Jr. SO, YOU WANT to COACH? A how to book for parents Essential information for coaching grade school Children. 2010. 136p. pap. 14.00 *(978-0-557-52655-0(8))* Lulu Enterprises Inc.
Walter Lee Prater. The Zone: The Philosophy of Championship Basketball. 2009. 100p. pap. 19.95 *(978-1-4389-3544-7(7))* AuthorHouse.
Weiss, Dick. True Blue: A Tribute to Mike Krzyzewski's Career at Duke. 2nd ed. 2008. (Illus.). 16.95 *(978-1-59670-336-0(9))* Sports Publishing, LLC.
Williams, Roy & Crothers, Tim. Hard Work: My Life on & off the Court. 2009. (ENG.). 288p. 24.95 *(978-1-56512-959-7(8)*, 1565129598) Algonquin Bks. of Chapel Hill.
Williams, Vicki. The Leadership Traits of Head Basketball Coach C Vivian Stringer. 2010. 228p. pap. *(978-3-8383-5074-5(X))* Lambert Academic Publishing.
Wissel, Hal. Basketball-3rd Edition: Steps to Success. 3rd ed. 2011. (Illus.). 368p. pap. 22.95 *(978-1-4504-1488-3(5))* Human Kinetics Pubs.
Wolden, Derek. BasketCases: How Youth Basketball Parents Can Lower Their Blood Pressure & Keep Their Sanity. 2008. (Illus.). 163p. pap. 20.00 *(978-1-59298-238-7(7))* Beaver's Pond Pr., Inc.
Women's Basketball Coaches Association Staff. WBCA Offensive Plays & Strategies. 2011. (ENG., Illus.). 280p. pap. 24.95 *(978-0-7360-8731-5(1))* Human Kinetics Pubs.
Women's Basketball Coaches Association Staff, creator. The Women's Basketball Drill Book. 2007. (ENG., Illus.). 336p. per. 19.95 *(978-0-7360-6846-8(5))* Human Kinetics Pubs.
Wooden, John & Jamison, Steve. The Wisdom of Wooden. 2010. (ENG.). 80p. 22.00 *(978-0-07-175116-2(5)*, 0071751165) McGraw-Hill Cos., The.
Wooden, John & Yaeger, Don. A Game Plan for Life: The Power of Mentoring. 2009. (ENG., Illus.). 208p. 25.00 *(978-1-59691-701-9(6))* Bloomsbury Publishing.
Yaeger, Don & Wooden, John. A Game Plan for Life: The Power of Mentoring. 2011. (ENG., Illus.). 40p. pap. 15.00 *(978-1-60819-268-7(7))* Bloomsbury Publishing.

BASKETBALL—HISTORY

Albers, Bucky. Tales from the Dayton Flyers Basketball. 2007. 192p. 19.95 *(978-1-59670-109-0(9))* Sports Publishing, LLC.
Anderson, Dave. University of Wisconsin Basketball. 2006. (Images of Sports Ser.). (Illus.). 127p. per. 19.99 *(978-0-7385-4121-1(4))* Arcadia Publishing.
Aron, Jaime & Cuban, Mark. Tales from the Dallas Mavericks Locker Room: A Collection of the Greatest Mavs Stories Ever Told. 2011. (Tales from the Team Ser.). (ENG., Illus.). 240p. 19.95 ***(978-1-61321-056-7(6)***, 613056) Skyhorse Publishing Co., Inc.
Atchison, Michael. True Sons: A Century of Missouri Tigers Basketball. 2006. (Illus.). 288p. *(978-1-57864-361-5(9))* Donning Co. Pubs.
Baker, Mark Allen. Basketball History in Syracuse: Hoops Roots. 2010. 192p. pap. 19.99 *(978-1-59629-983-2(5))* History Pr., The.
Ballard, Chris. The Art of a Beautiful Game: The Thinking Fan's Tour of the NBA. 2009. (ENG., Illus.). 240p. 26.00 *(978-1-4391-1021-8(2))* Simon & Schuster.
Bardo, Stephen. The Bardo Report. 2009. 256p. 24.95 *(978-1-60078-287-9(6))* Triumph Bks.
Bartholomew, Rafe. Pacific Rims: Beermen Ballin' in Flip-Flops & the Philippines' Unlikely Love Affair with Basketball. 2011. (ENG.). 400p. (gr. 12). 15.00 *(978-0-451-23322-6(0)*, N A L Trade) Penguin Group (USA) Inc.
Basloe, Frank J. & Rohman, D. Gordon. I Grew up with Basketball: Twenty Years of Barnstorming with Cage Greats of Yesterday. 2012. (ENG., Illus.). 256p. pap. 16.95 ***(978-0-8032-4023-0(6))*** Univ. of Nebraska Pr.
Bell, Taylor. Illinois: Legends of Illinois High School Basketball. 2006. (Glory Days Ser.). (Illus.). 181p. per. 14.95 *(978-1-58261-945-3(X))* Sports Publishing, LLC.
Bickley, Dan. Return of the Gold: The Journey of Jerry Colangelo & the Redeem Team. 2009. (ENG.). 216p. pap. 15.95 *(978-1-60037-637-5(1))* Morgan James Publishing.
Bird, Larry, et al. When the Game Was Ours. (ENG., Illus.). 2010. 368p. pap. 15.95 *(978-0-547-39458-9(6)*, Mariner Bks.) 2009. 352p. 26.00 *(978-0-547-22547-0(4))* Houghton Mifflin Harcourt Trade & Reference Pubs.
Black, Jimmy & Fowler, Scott. Jimmy Black's Tales from the Tar Heels. 2006. (Illus.). 192p. 19.95 *(978-1-58261-982-8(4))* Sports Publishing, LLC.
Bondy, Filip. Tip-Off: How the 1984 NBA Draft Changed Basketball Forever. 2008. (ENG.). 304p. pap. 16.95 *(978-0-306-81612-3(1))* Da Capo Pr., Inc.
Boston Celtics. 2008. 240p. pap. 16.95 *(978-1-932714-55-5(3))* Savas Beatie.
Bowling, Lewis. Duke Basketball: A Pictorial History. 2008. pap. 19.99 *(978-1-59629-467-7(1))* History Pr., The.
Bradburd, Rus. Paddy on the Hardwood: A Journey in Irish Hoops. (ENG., Illus.). 247p. 2009. pap. 19.95 *(978-0-8263-4027-6(X))* 2006. 24.95 *(978-0-8263-4026-9(1))* Univ. of New Mexico Pr.
Bradshaw, Dane. Vertical Leap: Inside the Rise of Tennessee Basketball. 2007. per. 19.95 *(978-1-932604-44-3(8))* Tennessee Valley Publishing.
Brush, Daniel. Sacramento Kings: An Interactive Guide to the World of Sports. 2009. (Sports by the Numbers Ser.). (Illus.). 220p. pap. 16.95 *(978-1-932714-69-2(3))* Savas Beatie.
Burdette, Dick. The Waterloo Wonders. 2008. pap. *(978-1-4389-0849-6(0))* AuthorHouse.
Cameron, T. C. Metro Detroit's High School Basketball Rivalries. 2009. 128p. pap. 21.99 *(978-0-7385-6014-4(6))* Arcadia Publishing.
Carp, Steve. Runnin' UNLV Rebels a Basketball Legacy. 2010. (Illus.). 131p. 24.95 *(978-1-932173-12-3(9))* Stephens Pr. LLC.
Carroll, Will. The Juice: The Real Story of Baseball's Drug Problems. 2006. (ENG.). 272p. per. 14.95 *(978-1-56663-720-6(1))* Dee, Ivan R. Pub.
Carter, Curtis W. The Road to the Nba. 2010. 336p. 29.99 *(978-1-4535-3124-2(6))* Xlibris Corp.
Ccny Beavers Basketball: Ccny Beavers Men's Basketball Coaches, Ccny Beavers Men's Basketball Players, Steve Lappas, Red Holzman, Norm Drucker. 2010. 32p. pap. 14.14 *(978-1-157-79179-9(4))* General Bks. LLC.
Chansky, Art. Blue Blood. Date not set. mass mkt. *(978-0-312-99669-7(1)*, St. Martin's Paperbacks) St. Martin's Pr.
—Blue Blood: Duke-Carolina: Inside the Most Storied Rivalry in College Hoops. 2006. (ENG., Illus.). 400p. pap. 15.99 *(978-0-312-32788-0(9)*, St. Martin's Paperbacks) St. Martin's Pr.
—Light Blue Reign: How a City Slicker, a Quiet Kansan, & a Mountain Man Built College Basketball's Longest-Lasting Dynasty. 2010. (ENG., Illus.). 400p. pap. 16.99 *(978-0-312-65016-2(7)*, St. Martin's Griffin) St. Martin's Pr.
Christgau, John. Origins of the Jump Shot: Eight Men Who Shook the World of Basketball. 2007. (Illus.). 220p. pap. 15.00 *(978-1-4223-6621-9(9))* DIANE Publishing Co.
—Tricksters in the Madhouse: Lakers vs. Globetrotters 1948. 2007. (ENG.). 232p. pap. 15.95 *(978-0-8032-1599-3(1)*, Bison Bks.) Univ. of Nebraska Pr.
Clark, Ryan. Game of My Life Kentucky Wildcats: Memorable Stories of Wildcats Basketball. 2nd ed. 2012. (Game of My Life Ser.). (ENG., Illus.). 256p. 24.95 *(978-1-61321-051-2(5)*, 613051) Skyhorse Publishing Co., Inc.
—Kentucky: Memorable Stories of Wildcat Basketball. 2007. (Game of My Life Ser.). (Illus.). 230p. 24.95 *(978-1-59670-119-9(6))* Sports Publishing, LLC.
Connelly, Michael P. Rebound! Basketball, Busing, Larry Bird, & the Rebirth of Boston. 2008. (ENG., Illus.). 304p. 25.00 *(978-0-7603-3501-7(X)*, 076033501X, MVP Bks.) MBI Publishing Co. LLC.
Cunningham, Carson. American Hoops: U. S. Men's Olympic Basketball from Berlin to Beijing. 2010. (ENG., Illus.). 528p. 40.00 *(978-0-8032-2293-9(9))* Univ. of Nebraska Pr.
Davis, Ken. University of Connecticut Basketball Vault. 2010. 144p. pap. 49.95 *(978-0-7948-2803-5(5))* Whitman Publishing LLC.
—University of Kansas Basketball Vault. 2008. 144p. pap. 49.95 *(978-0-7948-2440-2(4))* Whitman Publishing LLC.
Davis, Seth. When March Went Mad: The Game That Transformed Basketball. 2010. (ENG., Illus.). 352p. pap. 15.00 *(978-0-8050-9151-9(3)*, Holt Paperback) St. Martin's Pr.
Debbie, Jennings. Tennessee Lady Vol's Basketball Vault. 2008. 144p. pap. 49.95 *(978-0-7948-2437-2(4))* Whitman Publishing LLC.
Delmore, Joe. How Sweet It Was: And how the NBA can return to Greatness. 2011. 170p. 29.99 ***(978-1-4628-7763-8(X))***; pap. 19.99 ***(978-1-4628-7762-1(1))*** Xlibris Corp.
Denny, Dick. Glory Days Indiana: Legends of Indiana High School Basketball. 2006. (Illus.). 184p. per. 14.95 *(978-1-59670-062-8(9))* Sports Publishing, LLC.
Falkenstein, Max. A Good Place to Stop: 60 Seasons with Max & the Jayhawks. 2007. 256p. 24.95 *(978-0-9767330-2-7(1))* Power House.
Farney, Steven Michael. Club 50. 2009. 170p. 24.95 *(978-0-9786644-1-1(8))* Full Crescent Pubns.
—It's Time to Play! Jack Gardner, Basketball & Kansas State University. 2007. (Illus.). 140p. 24.95 *(978-1-58597-435-1(8))* Leathers Publishing.
Featherston, Al. Duke: Memorable Stories of Blue Devil Basketball. 2007. (Game of My Life Ser.). (Illus.). 230p. 24.95 *(978-1-59670-179-3(X))* Sports Publishing, LLC.
Feinstein, John. Last Dance: Behind the Scenes at the Final Four. 2007. (ENG., Illus.). 400p. per. 15.99 *(978-0-316-01425-0(7)*, Back Bay Bks.) Little Brown & Co.
Ferrin, Tres & Ferrin, Josh. Blitz Kids: The Cinderella Story of the 1944 University of Utah National Championship Basketball Team, 1 vol. 2012. (ENG.). 184p. pap. 14.99 ***(978-1-4236-2494-3(7))*** Gibbs Smith, Publisher.
Finkbeiner, Myron. Vanishing Hardwoods in Rural America. 2010. (ENG.). 172p. pap. 13.99 *(978-1-4490-5099-3(9))* AuthorHouse.
Fowler, Scott. Game of My Life UNC: Memorable Stories of Tar Heel Basketball. 2008. (Illus.). 256p. pap. 24.95 *(978-1-59670-031-4(9))* Sports Publishing, LLC.
Franconeri, Steven. Need to Argue! Make A List; My List of All-Time Greatest Basketball Players. 2009. 356p. pap. 19.95 *(978-1-935097-34-1(2))* Hillcrest Publishing Group, Inc.
Frisch, Aaron. Boston Celtics. 2008. (NBA Champions Ser.). (Illus.). 24p. (J). (gr. 4-7). lib. bdg. 24.25 *(978-1-58341-504-7(1)*, Creative Education) Creative Co., The.
—Chicago Bulls. 2008. (NBA Champions Ser.). (Illus.). 24p. (J). (gr. 1-4). lib. bdg. 24.25 *(978-1-58341-505-4(X))* Creative Co., The.
—Detroit Pistons. 2008. (NBA Champions Ser.). (Illus.). 24p. (J). (gr. 1-4). lib. bdg. 24.25 *(978-1-58341-506-1(8))* Creative Co., The.
—Houston Rockets. 2008. (NBA Champions Ser.). (Illus.). 24p. (J). (gr. 4-7). lib. bdg. 24.25 *(978-1-58341-507-8(6)*, Creative Education) Creative Co., The.
—Los Angeles Lakers. 2008. (NBA Champions Ser.). (Illus.). 24p. (J). (gr. 1-4). lib. bdg. 24.25 *(978-1-58341-508-5(4))* Creative Co., The.
—New York Knicks. 2008. (NBA Champions Ser.). (Illus.). 24p. (J). (gr. 4-7). lib. bdg. 24.25 *(978-1-58341-509-2(2)*, Creative Education) Creative Co., The.
—Philadelphia 76ers. 2008. (NBA Champions Ser.). (Illus.). 24p. (J). (gr. 4-7). lib. bdg. 24.25 *(978-1-58341-510-8(6)*, Creative Education) Creative Co., The.
—San Antonio Spurs. 2008. (NBA Champions Ser.). (Illus.). 24p. (J). (gr. 1-4). lib. bdg. 24.25 *(978-1-58341-511-5(4))* Creative Co., The.
Fulks, Matthew. Echoes of Kansas Football: The Greatest Stories Ever Told. 2006. (Echoes Of Ser.). (ENG., Illus.). 224p. 19.95 *(978-1-57243-868-2(1))* Triumph Bks.
Garrett, Thomas R. & Shampoe, Clay. Old Dominion University Men's Basketball. 2007. (Images of Sports Ser.). (Illus.). 127p. per. 19.99 *(978-0-7385-4292-8(X))* Arcadia Publishing.
Goudsouzian, Aram. King of the Court: Bill Russell & the Basketball Revolution. 2010. (Illus.). 400p. 45.00 *(978-0-520-25887-7(8))* Univ. of California Pr.
Graham, Tom & Graham Cody, Rachel. Getting Open: The Unknown Story of Bill Garrett & the Integrat. 2011. (ENG.). 288p. pap. 18.99 *(978-1-4516-4317-6(9)*, Beyond Words/Atria Bks.) Atria Bks.
Graham, Tom, et al. Getting Open: The Unknown Story of Bill Garrett & the Integration of College Basketball. 2008. (ENG., Illus.). 272p. pap. 14.95 *(978-0-253-22046-2(7)*, 0253220467) Indiana Univ. Pr.
Grasso, John. Historical Dictionary of Basketball. 2011. E-Book *(978-0-8108-7506-7(3))* 2010. (ENG.). 532p. 80.00 *(978-0-8108-6763-5(X))* Scarecrow Pr., Inc.
Griggs, Doug. March Gladness. 2008. 164p. 22.99 *(978-1-60647-852-3(4))*; pap. 14.99 *(978-1-60647-851-6(6))* Xulon Pr., Inc.
Gullan, Harold I. Jumping Through Hoops: Why Penn Wins. 2007. (Illus.). 168p. 29.95 *(978-1-933822-02-0(3))*; 136p. per. 16.95 *(978-1-933822-07-5(4))* Camino Bks., Inc.
Hall, M. Ann. The Grads Are Playing Tonight! The Story of the Edmonton Commercial Graduates Basketball Club. 2011. (ENG.). 360p. pap. 29.95 *(978-0-88864-602-6(X))* Univ. of Alberta Pr. CAN. Dist: Michigan State Univ. Pr., Chicago Distribution Ctr.
Hammes, L., et al. Hawkeye Greats, by the Numbers. 2010. 248p. pap. 19.99 *(978-1-4269-4303-4(2))* Trafford Publishing.
Hanneman, Dave. Wildcats: The Story of Miller City's Unbeaten State Championship Team Of 1950. 2007. 142p. per. 11.99 *(978-1-59886-557-8(9))* Tate Publishing & Enterprises, LLC.
Harrison, Don. Hoops in Connecticut: The Nutmeg State's Passion for Basketball. 2011. 128p. pap. 19.99 ***(978-1-60949-083-6(5))*** History Pr., The.
Hill, George E. The Season. 2007. 60p. pap. 9.95 *(978-1-4327-0023-2(5))* Outskirts Pr., Inc.
Hiner, Jason. Mac's Boys: Branch Mccracken & the Legendary 1953 Hurryin' Hoosiers. 2006. (ENG., Illus.). 360p. pap. 24.95 *(978-0-253-21814-8(4)*, 0253218144, Quarry Bks.) Indiana Univ. Pr.
Hugunin, Marc & Thornley, Stew. Minnesota Hoops: Basketball in the North Star State. 2006. (Illus.). 320p. 29.95 *(978-0-87351-574-0(9))* Minnesota Historical Society Pr.
Johnson, Gary K., compiled by. Official NCAA Men's Final Four Records Book. 2007. (NCAA Final Four: The Official Final Four Records Book Ser.). (Illus.). 249p. per. 15.95 *(978-1-57243-910-8(6))* Triumph Bks.
Jones, Luther, Jr. Thinking Basketball. 2008. 86p. pap. 10.00 *(978-0-8059-7637-3(X))* Dorrance Publishing Co., Inc.
Kelley, Harold. Legacies of Kentucky Mountain Basketball: Champions & Their Palaces of the Mid-1950's. 2011. ***(978-1-935001-75-1(2))*** Acclaim Pr., Inc.
Kelser, Greg & Grinczel, Steve. Greg Kelser's Tales from Michigan State. 2nd ed. 2008. (Illus.). 192p. pap. 15.95 *(978-1-59670-335-3(0))* Sports Publishing, LLC.
Kelser, Gregory & Grinczel, Steve. Greg Kelser's Tales from Michigan State Basketball. 2006. (Illus.). 179p. 19.95 *(978-1-59670-051-2(3))* Sports Publishing, LLC.
Kick The Ball. Tar Heelology Trivia Challenge: Basketball. 2006th ed. 2006. 6.97 *(978-0-9790396-4-5(9))* Kick The Ball.
Kick The Ball Staff. Blue Devilology Trivia Challenge: Duke Blue Devils Basketball. 3rd rev. ed. 2010. 96p. (YA). pap. 9.95 *(978-1-934372-91-3(9))* Kick The Ball.
King, Chris. Overtime Is Our Time! The Inside Story of the Maryland Terps' 2006 National Championship. 2007. (Illus.). 190p. 24.95 *(978-0-9788082-0-4(7))* Terrapin State Publishing, Inc.
Knight, Jonathan. Classic Cavs: The 50 Greatest Games in Cleveland Cavaliers History. 2009. pap. 18.95 *(978-1-60635-011-9(0))* Kent State Univ. Pr.
Kreiger, Scott. Four Sunny Saturdays: The story of the Canterbury Lady Cavaliers' 2008 State Championship Season. 2009. 236p. pap. 14.95 *(978-1-4389-8870-2(2))* AuthorHouse.
Krider, Dave, et al. Uncaged: The Rise of Greg Oden, Mike Conley, & the National Champion Lawrence North Wildcats. 2006. (Illus.). 205p. 22.95 *(978-1-59670-042-0(4))* Sports Publishing, LLC.
Kuska, Bob. Cinderella Ball: A Look Inside Small-College Basketball in West Virginia. 2008. (ENG., Illus.). 440p. pap. 19.95 *(978-0-8032-1392-0(1)*, Bison Bks.) Univ. of Nebraska Pr.
Lane, Jeffrey. Under the Boards: The Cultural Revolution in Basketball. 2007. (ENG., Illus.). 260p. pap. 21.95 *(978-0-8032-8053-3(X)*, Bison Bks.) Univ. of Nebraska Pr.
Laskowski, John. Tales from the Indiana Hoosiers Locker Room: A Collection of the Greatest Indiana Basketball Stories Ever Told. 2012. (Tales from the Team Ser.). (ENG., Illus.). 200p. 19.95 ***(978-1-61321-016-1(7)***, 613016) Skyhorse Publishing Co., Inc.
Lattin, David. Slam Dunk to Glory: The Amazing True Story of the 1966 NCAA Season & the Championship Game That Changed America Forever. 2007. (Illus.). 235p. per. 14.99 *(978-1-59379-117-9(8))* White Stone Bks.
Little, Bill. Texas Longhorns Men's Basketball. 2007. (Hoop Tales Ser.). (ENG., Illus.). 168p. per. 11.95 *(978-0-7627-4312-4(3))* Globe Pequot Pr., The.
Lucas, Adam. The Best Game Ever: How Frank Mcguire's '57 Tar Heels Beat Wilt & Revolutionized College Basketball. (ENG., Illus.). 2011. 256p. pap. 14.95 *(978-0-7627-7427-2(4))* 2006. 232p. 22.95 *(978-1-59228-982-0(7))* Globe Pequot Pr., The. (Lyons Pr.).
—Carolina Basketball: A Century of Excellence. 2010. (ENG., Illus.). 256p. 30.00 *(978-0-8078-3410-7(6))* Univ. of North Carolina Pr.
Lynn, Scott. Thornridge: The Perfect Season in Black & White. 2009. 316p. 27.95 *(978-1-4490-4090-1(X))*; pap. 22.95 *(978-1-4490-4089-5(6))* AuthorHouse.
Marantz, Steve. The Rhythm Boys of Central Omaha: High School Basketball at the '68 Racial Divide. 2011. (ENG., Illus.). 264p. pap. 17.95 *(978-0-8032-3434-5(1)*, Bison Bks.) Univ. of Nebraska Pr.
Martindale, Wight, Jr. & Martindale Jr., Wight. Inside the Cage: A Season at West 4th Street's Legendary Tournament. 2006. (ENG., Illus.). 288p. pap. 18.99 *(978-1-4169-1915-5(5))* Gallery Pr., The IRL. Dist: Simon & Schuster, Inc.
May, Peter. Top of the World: The Inside Story of the Boston Celtics' Amazing One-Year Turnaround to Become NBA Champions. 2009. (ENG., Illus.). 264p. pap. 14.95 *(978-0-306-81858-5(2))* Da Capo Pr., Inc.
McCallum, Jack. Dream Team: How Michael, Magic, Larry, Charles, & the Greatest Team of All Time Conquered the World & Changed the Game of Basketball Forever. 2012. (ENG., Illus.). 384p. 28.00 ***(978-0-345-52048-7(3)***, Ballantine Bks.) Random House Publishing Group.
McCullough, Brad, et al. Unstoppable Kansas Jayhawks Journey to the NCAA Title. 2008. 96p. pap. 19.95 *(978-1-933466-76-7(6))* Kansas City Star Bks.
Miller, Don. Ovetime Kids: The Untold Story of a Small-town Kentucky Basketball Team's Rise to the State Championship. 2011. (ENG.). 205p. pap. 19.95 *(978-1-59652-822-2(2))* Turner Publishing Co.
Natl Basketball Associatio. 2008. 240p. pap. 16.95 *(978-1-932714-54-8(5))* Savas Beatie.
NCAA 2010 Duke. 2010. 144p. pap. 19.95 *(978-0-9827138-1-5(9))* Sport-Publishing llc.
NCAA 2010 Spartans. 2010. 144p. pap. 19.95 *(978-0-9827138-2-2(7))* Sport-Publishing llc.
Neddenriep, Kyle. Historic Hoosier Gyms: Discovering Bygone Basketball Landmarks. 2010. 220p. 19.99 *(978-1-59629-946-7(0))* History Pr., The.

Neville, Susan S. Butler's Big Dance: The Team, the Tournament, & Basketball Fever. 2010. (ENG., Illus.). 128p. pap. 14.95 *(978-0-253-22312-8(1),* 0253223121) Indiana Univ. Pr.

Newspaper in Nursing City. 2007 NCAA Basketball Championship. 2007. (Illus.). 128p. 19.95 *(978-1-59670-199-1(4))*; pap. 14.95 *(978-1-59670-200-4(1))* Sports Publishing, LLC.

O'Hara, Michael E. Atlantic Coast Conference Men's Basketball Games: A Complete Record Through Spring 2006, 3 vols., Set. 2007. (ENG., Illus.). 2181p. 295.00 *(978-0-7864-2937-0(2))* McFarland & Co., Inc. Pubs.

—Clemson University Men's Basketball Games: A Complete Record, Fall 1953 Through Spring 2006. 2008. (ENG., Illus.). 430p. pap. 49.95 *(978-0-7864-3265-3(9))* McFarland & Co., Inc. Pubs.

—Duke University Men's Basketball Games: A Complete Record, Fall 1953 Through Spring 2006. 2008. (ENG., Illus.). 509p. per. 49.95 *(978-0-7864-3269-1(1))* McFarland & Co., Inc. Pubs.

—Georgia Tech Men's Basketball Games: A Complete Record, Fall 1979 Through Spring 2006. 2008. (ENG., Illus.). 281p. pap. 39.95 *(978-0-7864-3272-1(1))* McFarland & Co., Inc. Pubs.

—North Carolina State University Men's Basketball Games: A Complete Record, Fall 1953 Through Spring 2006. 2008. (ENG., Illus.). 456p. per. 49.95 *(978-0-7864-3267-7(5))* McFarland & Co., Inc. Pubs.

—University of North Carolina Men's Basketball Games: A Complete Record, Fall 1953 Through Spring 2006. 2008. (ENG., Illus.). 494p. per. 49.95 *(978-0-7864-3266-0(7))* McFarland & Co., Inc. Pubs.

—University of Virginia Men's Basketball Games: A Complete Record, Fall 1953 Through Spring 2006. 2008. (ENG., Illus.). 440p. pap. 49.95 *(978-0-7864-3271-4(3))* McFarland & Co., Inc. Pubs.

—Wake Forest University Mens Basketball Games: A Complete Record, Fall 1953 Through Spring 2006. 2008. (ENG.). 450p. pap. 49.95 *(978-0-7864-3268-4(3))* McFarland & Co., Inc. Pubs.

Oklahoma Baptist University. OBU Hoops: A History of Oklahoma Baptist University Bison & Lady Bison Basketball 1911-2007. 2007. (Illus.). 320p. 24.95 *(978-0-9762604-1-7(7))* Oklahoma Baptist Univ.

Peavy, Linda S. & Smith, Ursula. Full-Court Quest: The Girls from Fort Shaw Indian School Basketball Champions of the World. 2008. (ENG.). 496p. 29.95 *(978-0-8061-3973-9(0))* Univ. of Oklahoma Pr.

Pezzimenti, Vinny & Peters, Bill. From Behind the Bench: Inside the Basketball Scandal That Rocked St. Bonaventure. 2011. 204p. pap. 17.95 ***(978-1-4502-2565-6(9))*** iUniverse, Inc.

Pluto, Terry. Loose Balls: The Short, Wild Life of the American Basketball Association. 2007. (ENG., Illus.). 464p. pap. 16.00 *(978-1-4165-4061-8(X))* Simon & Schuster.

Pomerantz, Gary M. Wilt 1962: The Night of 100 Points & the Dawn of a New Era. 2008. (ENG.). 267p. 25.00 *(978-1-4379-5129-5(5))* DIANE Publishing Co.

Propst, Neil. Boys from Joes: A Colorado Basketball Legend. (Illus.). 200p. 16.95 *(978-0-87108-932-8(7))* Pruett Publishing Co.

Ragland, Shannon. Rupp Dreams. 2006. 16.95 *(978-0-9791222-0-0(1))* Set Shot Pr., The.

Rains, Rob. James Naismith: The Man Who Invented Basketball. 2011. 216p. pap. 21.95 ***(978-1-4399-0134-2(1))*** Temple Univ. Pr.

Rains, Rob & Carpenter, Hellen. James Naismith: The Man Who Invented Basketball. 2009. (ENG., Illus.). 216p. 35.00 *(978-1-4399-0133-5(3))* Temple Univ. Pr.

Rappoport, Ken & Wilner, Barry. The Big Dance: The Story of the NCAA Basketball Tournament. 2012. (ENG., Illus.). 304p. pap. 17.95 ***(978-1-58979-621-8(7))*** Taylor Trade Publishing.

Ratcliffe, Jerry. Tales from the Virginia Cavaliers Hardwood. 2007. 192p. 19.95 *(978-1-58261-743-5(0))* Sports Publishing, LLC.

Reagan, John. Georgetown Basketball Vault. 2010. 144p. pap. 49.95 *(978-0-7948-2813-4(2))* Whitman Publishing LLC.

Redden, Dave & Hall, Joe B. High School Basketball in Fayette County. 2008. (Images of Sports Ser.). (ENG., Illus.). 128p. pap. 19.99 *(978-0-7385-6735-5(1))* Arcadia Publishing.

Reynolds, Bill. Our Game: The Story of New England Basketball. 2007. 184p. pap. 16.95 *(978-0-9776240-0-3(5))* Hall of Fame Pr.

Rice, Russell. Kentucky University Basketball Vault. 2008. 144p. pap. 49.95 *(978-0-7948-2439-6(0))* Whitman Publishing LLC.

Rick, Brewer. University of North Carolina Basketball Vault. 2008. 144p. pap. 49.95 *(978-0-7948-2438-9(2))* Whitman Publishing LLC.

Rivera, Steve. Arizona Basketball Vault. 2010. 144p. pap. 49.95 *(978-0-7948-2812-7(4))* Whitman Publishing LLC.

—Tales from the Arizona Wildcats Hardwood. 2nd ed. 2008. (Illus.). 192p. pap. 15.95 *(978-1-59670-343-8(1))* Sports Publishing, LLC

Rosen, Charley. Pivotal Season How the 1971-1972 Los Angeles Lakers Changed Basketball. pap. *(978-0-312-32510-7(X)*, St. Martin's Paperbacks) St. Martin's Pr.

Schumacher, Michael. Mr. Basketball: George Mikan, the Minneapolis Lakers, & the Birth of the NBA. 2008. (Illus.). 336p. pap. 18.95 *(978-0-8166-5675-2(4))* Univ. of Minnesota Pr.

Shoals, Bethlehem, et al. The Undisputed Guide to Pro Basketball History. 2010. (ENG., Illus.). 224p. 25.00 *(978-1-60819-083-6(8))* Bloomsbury Publishing.

Shropshire, Mike. Sarah Palin & the Wasilla Warriors: The True Story of the Improbable 1982 Alaska State Basketball Championship. 2012. (ENG., Illus.). 288p. 25.99 ***(978-0-312-60424-0(6))*** St. Martin's Pr.

Sourcebooks, Inc. The Sports Challenge Arkansas Razorbacks. 2008. (ENG.). 96p. pap. 4.99 *(978-1-4022-1744-9(7))* Sourcebooks, Inc.

Sports Publishing Inc, creator. 2008 NCAA Basketball Championship. 2008. (NCAA Basketball Championship Ser.). (Illus.). 128p. 19.95 *(978-1-59670-309-4(1))*; pap. 14.95 *(978-1-59670-310-0(5))* Sports Publishing, LLC.

Stark, Douglas. The SPHAS: The Life & Times of Basketball's Greatest Jewish Team. 2011. (ENG., Illus.). 344p. 29.50 *(978-1-59213-533-9(8))* Temple Univ. Pr.

Stricklin, Scott. Echoes of Kentucky Basketball: The Greatest Stories Ever Told. 2006. (Echoes Of Ser.). (ENG., Illus.). 195p. 19.95 *(978-1-57243-887-3(8))* Triumph Bks.

Sumner, Jim. Tales from the Duke Blue Devils Hardwood. 2006. (Illus.). 184p. per. 14.95 *(978-1-59670-164-9(1))* Sports Publishing, LLC.

Sutton, Stan. Indiana Hoosiers: Memorable Stories of Hoosiers Basketball. 2008. (Game of My Life Ser.). (Illus.). 256p. 24.95 *(978-1-58261-886-9(0))* Sports Publishing, LLC.

Tarkanian, Jerry. Runnin' Rebel: Shark Tales of Extra Benefits, Frank Sinatra, & Winning It All. 2006. (Illus.). 230p. per. 16.95 *(978-1-59670-155-7(2))* Sports Publishing, LLC.

Taylor, John. The Rivalry: Bill Russell, Wilt Chamberlain, & the Golden Age of Basketball. annot. ed. 2006. (ENG.). 432p. pap. 17.00 *(978-0-8129-7030-2(6)*, Ballantine Bks.) Random House Publishing Group.

Titus, Mark. Don't Put Me In, Coach: My Incredible NCAA Journey from the End of the Bench to the End of the Bench. 2012. (ENG., Illus.). 272p. 24.95 ***(978-0-385-53510-6(4)***, Doubleday) Knopf Doubleday Publishing Group.

Tulumello, Mike. Tales from the Phoenix Suns. 2008. (Illus.). 192p. 19.95 *(978-1-59670-256-1(7))* Sports Publishing, LLC.

University of Kentucky Basketb. 2008. 200p. pap. 16.95 *(978-1-932714-56-2(1))* Savas Beatie.

University of Louisville Baske. 2008. 200p. pap. 16.95 *(978-1-932714-57-9(X))* Savas Beatie.

Wallace, Robert K. Thirteen Women Strong: The Making of a Team. 2008. (ENG., Illus.). 352p. 29.95 *(978-0-8131-2515-2(4))* Univ. Pr. of Kentucky.

Wallenberg, Dan. A New Vision: Thad Matta & the Rebirth of Buckeye Basketball. 2007. (ENG., Illus.). 128p. per. 14.95 *(978-1-60078-013-4(X))* Triumph Bks.

Warmsley, Titus. Don't Talk About It Be About It: Eight Lessons in All Star Achievement. 2008. pap. 22.00 *(978-1-60458-388-5(6))* Instant Pub.

Warner, Neil K. Under the Green Banners: The Story of a Season, the Season of a Lifetime. 2008. 220p. pap. 14.95 *(978-1-55517-754-6(9)*, 77549) Cedar Fort, Inc./CFI Distribution.

Waters, Mike. Game of My Life Syracuse. 2007. (Game of My Life Ser.). 256p. pap. 18.95 *(978-1-59670-235-6(4))* Sports Publishing, LLC.

—Syracuse Basketball Vault. 2009. (Illus.). 144p. pap. 29.95 *(978-0-7948-2788-5(8))* Whitman Publishing LLC.

West, Gary. The Kentucky Colonels of the American Basketball Association. 2011. ***(978-1-935001-82-9(5))*** Acclaim Pr., Inc.

Wiederer, Dan. Blue Streak: The Highs, Lows & Behind the Scenes Hijinks of a National Champion. 2010. 412p. 36.95 *(978-1-4502-1681-4(1))*; pap. 26.95 *(978-1-4502-1679-1(X))* iUniverse, Inc.

Wilner, Barry & Rappoport, Ken. The Big Dance: The Story of the NCAA Men's Basketball Tournament. 2012. ***(978-1-58979-622-5(5))*** Taylor Trade Publishing.

Wojciechowski, Gene. The Last Great Game: Duke vs. Kentucky & the 2. 1 Seconds That Changed Basketball. 2012. (ENG.). 320p. (gr. 12). 26.95 ***(978-0-399-15857-5(X)***, Blue Rider Pr.) Penguin Group (USA) Inc.

Woods, David. Underdawgs: How Brad Stevens & the Butler Bulldogs Marched Their Way to the Brink of College Basketball's National Championship. 2010. (ENG., Illus.). 288p. 24.00 *(978-1-4516-1057-4(2)*, Scribner) Scribner.

Yep, Kathleen. Outside the Paint: When Basketball Ruled at the Chinese Playground. 2009. (Asian American History & Culture Ser.). (ENG., Illus.). 216p. 21.95 *(978-1-59213-942-2(6))* Temple Univ. Pr.

BASKETBALL—JUVENILE LITERATURE

Woods, Mark & Owen, Ruth. Slam Dunk! Basketball Facts & Stats. 2011. (Top Score Math Ser.). (Illus.). 32p. (J). (gr. 3-6). lib. bdg. 26.60 *(978-1-4339-5017-9(0))* Stevens, Gareth Publishing LLLP.

BASKETBALL—PICTORIAL WORKS

Bowling, Lewis. Duke Basketball: A Pictorial History. 2008. pap. 19.99 *(978-1-59629-467-7(1))* History Pr., The.

Davis, Ken. University of Kansas Basketball Vault. 2008. 144p. pap. 49.95 *(978-0-7948-2440-2(4))* Whitman Publishing LLC.

Debbie, Jennings. Tennessee Lady Vol's Basketball Vault. 2008. 144p. pap. 49.95 *(978-0-7948-2437-2(4))* Whitman Publishing LLC.

Hareas, John & Fawaz, John. The Official NBA Finals 2005 Retrospective. 2006. 24.95 *(978-0-9770298-1-5(6))* ISC Pubns., Inc.

Lawrence Journal World, creator. An Incredible Year: Ku's Run to the 2008 NCAA Championship Title. 2008. (Illus.). 160p. pap. 24.95 *(978-0-9742513-6-3(4))* Sunflower Publishing.

Lucas, Adam, et al. One Fantastic Ride: The Inside Story of Carolina Basketball's 2009 Championship Season. 2009. (ENG., Illus.). 256p. 31.95 *(978-0-8078-3385-8(1))* Univ. of North Carolina Pr.

Rice, Russell. Kentucky University Basketball Vault. 2008. 144p. pap. 49.95 *(978-0-7948-2439-6(0))* Whitman Publishing LLC.

Rick, Brewer. University of North Carolina Basketball Vault. 2008. 144p. pap. 49.95 *(978-0-7948-2438-9(2))* Whitman Publishing LLC.

Sindaco, Angelo, photos by. Check This Out! 2007. (ENG., Illus.). 160p. pap. 35.00 *(978-88-88493-36-7(0))* Drago Arts & Communication ITA. Dist: SCB Distributors.

BASKETBALL CARDS

Hower, Keith, ed. Beckett Basketball Card Price Gd-#19. 2011. 480p. pap. 29.95 *(978-1-936681-98-3(6))* Beckett Media LLP.

BASKETBALL COACHING

see Basketball—Coaching

BASKETBALL FOR WOMEN

Baker, Christine A. Why She Plays: The World of Women's Basketball. 2008. (ENG., Illus.). 216p. pap. 17.95 *(978-0-8032-1633-4(5)*, Bison Bks.) Univ. of Nebraska Pr.

Bandy, Lana & Ratermann, Dale. The Ultimate Women's Basketball Trivia & Puzzle Book. 2008. (Illus.). 153p. per. 12.95 *(978-1-930546-90-5(4))* Wish Publishing.

Beran, Janice A. From Six-on-Six to Full Court Press: A Century of Iowa Girls' Basketball. 2008. (ENG., Illus.). 244p. per. 29.95 *(978-1-58729-525-3(X))* Univ. of Iowa Pr.

Bumgarner, Brittany. Marketing the Atlantic Coast Conference Women's Basketball Tournament. 2010. 76p. pap. *(978-3-8383-7985-2(3))* Lambert Academic Publishing.

Crabtree, Becky. Alaska Hoops: Tips & Tales from the Girls Locker Room. 2009. (Illus.). 100p. pap. 11.95 *(978-1-888215-11-3(9))* Fathom Publishing Co.

Gettelman, Elizabeth. Competitive Basketball for Girls. 2009. (SportsGirl Ser.). 64p. (gr. 5-8). 58.50 *(978-1-60853-191-2(0)*, Rosen Central) Rosen Publishing Group, Inc., The.

Goldberg, Jeff. Bird at the Buzzer: Uconn, Notre Dame, & a Women's Basketball Classic. 2011. (ENG., Illus.). 320p. 29.95 *(978-0-8032-2411-7(7))* Univ. of Nebraska Pr.

Grundy, Pamela & Shackelford, Susan. Shattering the Glass: The Remarkable History of Women's Basketball. 2007. (ENG., Illus.). 320p. per. 26.95 *(978-0-8078-5829-5(3))* Univ. of North Carolina Pr.

Lieberman, Nancy. Basketball for Women. 2nd ed. 2011. (ENG., Illus.). 272p. pap. 21.95 *(978-0-7360-9294-4(3))* Human Kinetics Pubs.

Miller, Faye Young & Coffey, Wayne R. Winning Basketball for Girls. 4th rev. ed. 2009. (Winning Sports for Girls Ser.). (Illus.). (gr. 6-12). 188p. 39.50 *(978-0-8160-7759-5(2))*; 192p. pap. 14.95 *(978-0-8160-7760-1(5))* Facts On File, Inc. (Checkmark Bks.).

O'Halloran, Michael. Never Forget They're Kids - Ideas for Coaching Your Daughter's 4th - 8th grade basketball Team. 2007. 52p. pap. 17.95 *(978-0-615-15155-7(8))* Brilliant & Bright, Inc.

Peavy, Linda S. & Smith, Ursula. Full-Court Quest: The Girls from Fort Shaw Indian School Basketball Champions of the World. 2008. (ENG.). 496p. 29.95 *(978-0-8061-3973-9(0))* Univ. of Oklahoma Pr.

Thomas, Mel. Heart of a Husky: Determination, Perseverance, & a Quest for a National Championship. 2009. (ENG.). 192p. pap. 19.95 *(978-1-57860-441-8(9))* Clerisy Pr.

Women's Basketball Coaches Association Staff. WBCA Offensive Plays & Strategies. 2011. (ENG., Illus.). 280p. pap. 24.95 *(978-0-7360-8731-5(1))* Human Kinetics Pubs.

Women's Basketball Coaches Association Staff, creator. The Women's Basketball Drill Book. 2007. (ENG., Illus.). 336p. per. 19.95 *(978-0-7360-6846-8(5))* Human Kinetics Pubs.

BASKETBALL OFFICIATING

Koester, Ken. Basketball Officiating Mechanics Illustrated: 2 & 3 Person High School Crews. 2009. (Right Spot at the Right Time Ser.). (Illus.). 196p. pap. 19.95 incl. cd-rom *(978-1-58208-119-9(0))* Referee Enterprises, Inc.

National Basketball Coaches Association Staff. NBA Coaches Playbook: Techniques, Tactics, & Teaching Points. Gandolfi, Giorgio, ed. 2008. (ENG., Illus.). 368p. pap. 22.95 *(978-0-7360-6355-5(2))* Human Kinetics Pubs.

BASKETBALL STORIES

Tulumello, Mike. Tales from the Phoenix Suns. 2008. (Illus.). 192p. 19.95 *(978-1-59670-256-1(7))* Sports Publishing, LLC.

BASKETS

see also Basket Making; Indian Baskets

Adovasio, J. M. Basketry Technology: A Guide to Identification & Analysis, Updated Edition. 2010. (ENG., Illus.). 200p. pap. 34.95 *(978-1-59874-557-3(3))* Left Coast Pr., Inc.

Chihuly, Dale & Taragin, Davira. Baskets. Portland Press Staff, ed. 2009. (Illus.). 112p. 14.95 *(978-1-57684-172-3(3))* Portland Pr., Inc.

Cotsen, Lloyd, et al. Japanese Bamboo Baskets: Masterworks of Form & Texture. (Illus.). 391p. 850.00 *(978-1-878529-59-6(5))* Art Media Resources, Inc.

Earle, Joe. New Bamboo: Contemporary Japanese Masters. 2008. (Illus.). 128p. 25.00 *(978-0-300-14141-2(6))* Japan Society Gallery.

Frazier, Shirley George. The Gift Basket Design Book: Everything You Need to Know to Create Beautiful, Professional-Looking Gift Baskets for All Occasions. 2nd ed. 2008. (Gift Basket Design Book: Everything You Need to Know to Create Ser.). (ENG., Illus.). 208p. pap. 17.95 *(978-0-7627-4436-7(7))* Globe Pequot Pr., The.

MacDowell, Marsha & Myers, Kathleen S. Weaving History: A Basket Heritage Project. MacDowell, Marsha & Myers, Kathleen S., eds. 2007. (C). pap. 29.95 *(978-0-944311-24-0(5))* Michigan State Univ. Museum.

Oguchi, Masami, et al. Japanese Bamboo Baskets: Meiji, Modern, & Contemporary, 1 vol. Frew, Gavin, tr. from JPN. 2007. (ENG., Illus.). 160p. 45.00 *(978-4-7700-3062-7(2))* Kodansha America, Inc.

Rindfuss, Jill, ed. The Bentley Collection Guide - Longaberger Collectors Guide: The book that helps you Insure, Sell & Collect Longaberger. 2006th ed. 2006. (Illus.). 235p. spiral bd. 21.95 incl. cd-rom *(978-0-9759815-1-1(X))* J. Phillip, Inc.

Sellato, Bernard. Plaited Arts from the Borneo Rainforest. 2011. 70.00 ***(978-0-8248-3619-1(7))*** Univ. of Hawaii Pr.

Sloan, Betsey & Sloan, E. Antler Art for Baskets & Gourds. 2011. (Illus.). 64p. 19.99 *(978-0-7643-3615-7(0))* Schiffer Publishing, Ltd.

Strong, Graham & Phoenix, Claire. Year-Round Containers, Baskets & Boxes. (Illus.). 208p. pap. *(978-1-55285-103-6(6))* Whitecap Bks., Ltd.

Woram, Catherine. Decorating Gift Baskets. 2008. (ENG., Illus.). 128p. pap. 19.95 *(978-1-906094-94-2(2))* CICO Bks. GBR. Dist: Ryland Peters & Small.

BASKETS, INDIAN

see Indian Baskets

BASQUE COUNTRY (FRANCE)

see Pays Basque (France)

BASQUE COUNTRY (SPAIN)

see País Vasco (Spain)

BASQUE PROVINCES (FRANCE)

see Pays Basque (France)

BASQUE PROVINCES (SPAIN)

see País Vasco (Spain)

BASQUE FOLKLORE

see Basques—Folklore

BASQUE LANGUAGE

Aberlaitz & De Oreyegui, P. Buenaventura. Diccionario Vasco-Castellano, Castellano-Vasco de Voces Comunes a Dos o Mas Dialectos del Euskera. (SPA.). 14.95 *(978-0-7859-0865-4(X)*, S3099) French & European Pubns., Inc.

Anderson, John M. An Essay Concerning Aspect: Some Considerations of a General Character Arising from the Abbé Darrigol's Analysis of the Basque Verb. (Janua Linguarum. Series Minor Ser.). (ENG.). 112p. 210.00 ***(978-3-11-180859-8(9))*** De Gruyter, Mouton DEU. Dist: de Gruyter, Walter GmbH & Co. KG.

Arregi, Karlos & Nevins, Andrew. Morphotactics: Basque Auxiliaries & the Structure of Spellout. 2012. (Studies in Natural Language & Linguistic Theory Ser.). (ENG., Illus.). xvi, 399p. 189.00 ***(978-94-007-3888-1(9)***, 9400738889) Springer.

Azkue, Resurreccion M. Diccionario Vasco-Espanol-Frances, 2 vols., Set. deluxe ed. (FRE & SPA.). 195.00 *(978-0-7859-0952-1(4)*, S12384) French & European Pubns., Inc.

Cenoz, Jasone. Towards Multilingual Education: Basque Educational Research from an International Perspective. 2009. (Bilingual Education & Bilingualism Ser.). (ENG., Illus.). 280p. 24.95 *(978-1-84769-192-7(7))*; 139.95 *(978-1-84769-193-4(5))* Multilingual Matters GBR. Dist: Univ. of Toronto Pr.

Cenoz, Jasone, ed. Teaching through Basque: Achievement & Challenges. 2008. (ENG., Illus.). 112p. 79.95 *(978-1-84769-070-8(X))* Multilingual Matters GBR. Dist: Univ. of Toronto Pr.

De Rijk, Rudolf P. G. Standard Basque: A Progressive Grammar. 2007. (Current Studies in Linguistics Ser.). (BAQ, SPA & ENG., Illus.). 1408p. (gr. 17). 100.00 *(978-0-262-04242-0(8))* MIT Pr.

Elderkin, George W. Zagreus in Ancient Basque Religion. 2011. 32p. 35.95 ***(978-1-258-08009-5(5))*** Literary Licensing, LLC.

Euro Talk. Talk Business Basque. 2008. 29.99 *(978-1-60077-200-9(5))* TOPICS Entertainment.

—Talk More Basque. 2008. 29.99 *(978-1-60077-216-0(1))* TOPICS Entertainment.

—Talk Now! Basque. 2008. 29.99 *(978-1-84352-365-9(5))* TOPICS Entertainment.

—Talk the Talk Basque. 2008. 29.99 *(978-1-60077-250-4(1))* TOPICS Entertainment.

Icon Group International, Inc. Staff, compiled by. Webster's Euskara - English Thesaurus Dictionary. 2008. 33p. ring bd. 28.95 incl. audio compact disk *(978-0-497-83488-3(X))* Icon Group International, Inc.

Jansen, Wim. Beginner's Basque. 2007. (Hippocrene Beginner's Ser.). (ENG.). 282p. 26.95 *(978-0-7818-1227-6(5))* Hippocrene Bks., Inc.

Kutscher, Silvia. Kausalität und Argumentrealisierung: Zur Konstruktionsvarianz bei Psychverben am Beispiel europäischer Sprachen. 2009. (Linguistische Arbeiten Ser.).Tr. of Causality & Argument Realisation. on the constructional variance of psychverbs using the example of European Languages. (GER.). XIV, 266p. 196.00 ***(978-3-11-173138-4(3))*** De Gruyter, Walter Inc.

Kutscher, Silvia. Kausalität und Argumentrealisierung: Zur Konstruktionsvarianz bei Psychverben am Beispiel Europäischer Sprachen. 2009. (Linguistische Arbeiten Ser.).Tr. of Causality & Argument Realisation. on the constructional variance of psychverbs using the example of European Languages. (GER.). XIV, 266p. pap. *(978-3-484-30528-1(2))* Verlag Max Niemeyer.

Michelena, Luis & Salaburu Etxeberria, Pello. Koldo Mitxelena: Selected Writings of a Basque Scholar. 2008. *(978-1-877802-80-5(8))*; pap. *(978-1-877802-81-2(6))* Ctr. for Basque Studies.

Morris, Mikel. CBS Morris Euskara-Ingelesa, English-Basque Compact Dictionary. 2010. (BAQ & ENG.). pap. *(978-1-877802-96-6(4))* Ctr. for Basque Studies.

Olaziregi, Mari Jose. Writers in Between Languages: Minority Literatures in the Global Scene. 2009. *(978-1-877802-90-4(5))* Ctr. for Basque Studies.

Orbea, Juan Madariaga. Anthology of Apologists & Detractors of the Basque Language. Fornoff, Frederick H. et al, trs. from SPA. 2006. (Basque Classics Ser.: No. 2). (Illus.). 703p. 39.95 *(978-1-877802-63-8(8))* Ctr. for Basque Studies.

White, Linda. Aurrera! A Textbook for Studying Basque, Volume 2. 2010. (Basque Ser.). (ENG., Illus.). 416p. (C). 60.00 *(978-0-87417-784-8(7))* Univ. of Nevada Pr.

—Aurrera! A Textbook for Studying Basque, Volumes 1 And 2. 2010. (Basque Ser.). 110.00 *(978-0-87417-799-2(5))* Univ. of Nevada Pr.

—Aurrera! Vol. 1. 2008. (Basque Ser.). (BAQ & ENG.). 456p. (C). 65.00 *(978-0-87417-726-8(X))* Univ. of Nevada Pr.

BASQUE LITERATURE

Lafarga, Francisco & Pegenaute, Luis, eds. Interacciones Entre las Literaturas Ibéricas. 2011. (Relaciones literarias en el Ambito Hispanico. Traduccion, Literatura y Cultura Ser.). (SPA & MUL., Illus.). 526p. pap. *(978-3-0343-0448-1(X))* Lang, Peter.

BASQUE LITERATURE—HISTORY AND CRITICISM

Kortazar, Jon, et al. Bernardo Atxaga: Basque Literature from the End of the Franco ERA to the Present. 2006. (SPA.). pap. *(978-1-877802-42-3(5))* Ctr. for Basque Studies.

Michelena, Luis & Salaburu Etxeberria, Pello. Koldo Mitxelena: Selected Writings of a Basque Scholar. 2008. *(978-1-877802-80-5(8))*; pap. *(978-1-877802-81-2(6))* Ctr. for Basque Studies.

Olaziregi, Mari Jose. Writers in Between Languages: Minority Literatures in the Global Scene. 2009. *(978-1-877802-90-4(5))* Ctr. for Basque Studies.

BASQUES

see also Celtiberi

Barandiarán, José Miguel de. Selected Writings of Jose Miguel de Barandiaran: Basque Prehistory & Ethnography. 2008. 39.95 *(978-1-877802-70-6(0))*; (Illus.). 288p. pap. 29.95 *(978-1-877802-69-0(7))* Ctr. for Basque Studies.

Bourne, Angela & Bourne, Angela K. The European Union & the Accommodation of Basque Difference in Spain. 2008. (Europe in Change Ser.). (ENG., Illus.). 192p. 89.00 *(978-0-7190-6750-1(2))* Manchester Univ. Pr. GBR. Dist: Macmillan.

Bray, Zoe. Living Boundaries: Frontiers & Identity in the Basque Country. 2nd ed. 2011. pap. ***(978-1-935709-17-6(8))*** Ctr. for Basque Studies.

Caro Baroja, Julio. The Basques. 2011. pap. *(978-1-935709-06-0(2))* 2009. *(978-1-877802-92-8(1))* Ctr. for Basque Studies.

Caro Baroja, Julio & Forstag, Robert. The Selected Essays of Julio Caro Baroja. 2011. ***(978-1-935709-16-9(X))***; pap. ***(978-1-935709-15-2(1))*** Ctr. for Basque Studies.

Davies, Hywel. Fleeing Franco: How Wales Gave Shelter to Refugee Children from the Basque Country During the Spanish Civil War. 2011. (Illus.). 169p. pap. 25.00 *(978-0-7083-2336-6(7))* Univ. of Wales Pr. GBR. Dist: Chicago Distribution Ctr.

Douglass, William A. Global Vasconia: Essays on the Basque Diaspora. 2006. (Basque Diaspora & Migration Ser.). 314p. 29.95 *(978-1-877802-67-6(0),* Center for Basque Studies) Univ. of Nevada Pr.

Douglass, William A. & Zulaika, Joseba. Basque Culture: Anthropological Perspectives. 2007. *(978-1-877802-66-9(2))* Ctr. for Basque Studies.

—Basque Culture: Anthropological Perspectives. 2007. (Basque Textbooks Ser.). (Illus.). 525p. per. 14.95 *(978-1-877802-64-5(6),* Center for Basque Studies) Univ. of Nevada Pr.

Heiberg, Marianne. The Making of the Basque Nation. 2007. (Cambridge Studies in Social & Cultural Anthropology Ser.). (ENG.). 284p. pap. 60.00 *(978-0-521-04028-0(0))* Cambridge Univ. Pr.

Hess, Andreas. Reluctant Modernization: Plebeian Culture & Moral Economy in the Basque Country. 2009. 207p. pap. 43.95 *(978-3-03911-908-0(7))* Lang, Peter AG GBR. Dist: Lang, Peter.

Urla, Jacqueline. Reclaiming Basque: Language, Nation, & Cultural Activism. 2012. (Basque Ser.). (Illus.). 292p. 45.00 ***(978-0-87417-875-3(4))***; E-Book ***(978-0-87417-880-7(0))*** Univ. of Nevada Pr.

BASQUES—FOLKLORE

Monteiro, Mariana. Legends & Popular Tales of the Basque People. 2009. 200p. 25.99 *(978-0-559-10930-0(X))*; 22.99 *(978-0-559-10942-3(3))*; pap. 23.75 *(978-0-559-10933-1(4))*; pap. 22.75 *(978-0-559-10938-6(5))* BiblioBazaar.

—Legends & Popular Tales of the Basque People. 2009. 134p. pap. *(978-1-150-67770-0(8))* Books LLC.

—Legends & Popular Tales of the Basque People. 2007. (ENG.). 292p. 43.95 *(978-0-548-10840-6(4))* Kessinger Publishing, LLC.

BASQUES—UNITED STATES

Fillmore, Colleen Asumendi. Basques of Boise. 2008. 100p. pap. *(978-3-639-03946-7(7))* VDM Verlag Dr. Mueller e.K.

Iberlin, Dollie. Buffalotarrak: An Anthology of the Basque People of Buffalo, Wyoming. 2011. (Orig.). pap. ***(978-1-935709-14-5(3))*** Ctr. for Basque Studies.

Kenyon, Quane & Cenarrusa, Pete T. Biskaia to Boise: The Memoirs of Pete T. Cenarrusa. 2009. pap. *(978-1-877802-91-1(3))* Ctr. for Basque Studies.

Laxalt, Robert. Sweet Promised Land. 50th annot. ed. 2007. (Basque Ser.). (ENG.). 207p. per. 18.00 *(978-0-87417-706-0(5))* Univ. of Nevada Pr.

Mallea-Olaetxe, J. Speaking Through the Aspens: Basque Tree Carvings in Nevada & California. 2008. (Basque Ser.). (ENG., Illus.). 256p. pap. 29.95 *(978-0-87417-762-6(6))* Univ. of Nevada Pr.

Mendieta, Eva. In Search of Catalina de Erauso: The National & Sexual Identity of the Lieutenant Nun. 2009. *(978-1-877802-87-4(5))* Ctr. for Basque Studies.

Zang, David W. Fleetwood Walker's Divided Heart. Zang, David W., ed. 2006. cd-rom 39.95 *(978-0-9779883-4-1(1))* Legacy Audio Bks.

BASQUIAT, JEAN MICHEL, 1961-1988

Basquiat, Jean-Michel. Jean-Michel Basquiat. 2010. (ENG., Illus.). 224p. 65.00 *(978-3-7757-2593-4(8))* Hatje Cantz Verlag GmbH & Co KG DEU. Dist: D.A.P./Distributed Art Pubs.

Basquiat, Jean-Michel, et al. Jean-Michel Basquiat. (Illus.). 664p. 350.00 *(978-2-911596-04-9(8))* Galerie Enrico Navarra FRA. Dist: D.A.P./Distributed Art Pubs.

Emmerling, Leonhard. Basquiat. 2011. (ENG., Illus.). 96p. 14.99 *(978-3-8365-2714-9(6))* TASCHEN DEU. Dist: Ingram Pub. Services.

Fretz, Eric. Jean-Michel Basquiat: A Biography, 1 vol. 2010. (Greenwood Biographies Ser.). (Illus.). 199p. 35.00 *(978-0-313-38056-3(2),* A2215C) Greenwood Publishing Group, Inc.

Mayer, Marc, ed. Basquiat. 2010. (ENG., Illus.). 224p. pap. 24.95 *(978-1-85894-519-4(4))* Merrell Pubs. Ltd. GBR. Dist: Perseus Distribution.

Mercurio, Gianni, ed. The Jean-Michel Basquiat Show. 2007. (ITA & ENG., Illus.). 324p. 85.00 *(978-88-7624-927-3(3))* Skira Editore ITA. Dist: Random Hse., Inc.

Nassau County Museum of Art Staff, contrib. by. Miro/DuBuffet/Basquiat. 2010. (Illus.). 24p. ***(978-0-9815644-7-0(X))*** Nassau County Museum of Art.

Sirmans, Franklin & Vassell, Nicola, eds. Jean-Michel Basquiat 1981: The Studio of the Street, 1 vol. 2007. (ENG., Illus.). 248p. 70.00 *(978-88-8158-625-7(8))* Charta ITA. Dist: D.A.P./Distributed Art Pubs.

Thompson, Margo. American Graffiti Art. 2009. (Temporis Ser.). (ENG., Illus.). 256p. 39.95 *(978-1-84484-561-3(3))* Parkstone International GBR. Dist: Ingram Pub. Services.

BASS, ELECTRIC

see Bass Guitar

BASS DRUM

see Drum

BASS FISHING

see also specific varieties of bass, e.g. Striped Bass

Barrett, Pete. Trolling for Striped Bass & Bluefish. 2007. (ENG., Illus.). 176p. per. 16.95 *(978-1-58080-145-4(5))* Burford Bks.

Burnley, Eric. The Ultimate Guide to Striped Bass Fishing: Where to Find Them, How to Catch Them. 2006. (ENG., Illus.). 176p. 22.95 *(978-1-59228-932-5(0),* Lyons Pr.) Globe Pequot Pr., The.

Clouser, Bob. Fly-Fishing for Smallmouth. 2007. (ENG., Illus.). 226p. 39.95 *(978-0-8117-0173-0(5))* Stackpole Bks.

Cooper, Pete, Jr. Redfish: All You Need to Know about Where, When & How to Catch Reds. 2008. (ENG., Illus.). 192p. pap. 15.95 *(978-0-88150-788-1(1),* 150788) Countryman Pr.

Cunningham, Albert Benjamin. Old Black Bass. 2007. (ENG.). 118p. 34.95 *(978-0-548-04208-3(X))* Kessinger Publishing, LLC.

Dirks, David. Fishing Bass Tournaments: Use the Secrets of the Pros to Compete Successfully. 2008. (ENG., Illus.). 128p. pap. 19.95 *(978-1-59921-423-8(7),* Lyons Pr.) Globe Pequot Pr., The.

Duke, Ken. The Bass Fishing Vault. 2010. 144p. pap. 49.95 *(978-0-7948-3261-2(X))* Whitman Publishing LLC.

Elwins, Dannie. How to Learn Bass Fishing & Catch Fish with Ease. 2009. 44p. pap. 16.99 *(978-0-557-15444-9(8))* Lulu Enterprises Inc.

Fivaz, Warrick Allan. The Quest. 2008. (Illus.). 108p. pap. *(978-0-9555562-5-8(2))* Esteemworld Pubns.

Hauge, Steven. Big Book of Bass: Strategies for Catching Largemouth & Smallmouth. 2008. (Freshwater Angler Ser.). (ENG., Illus.). 400p. pap. 29.99 *(978-1-58923-407-9(3),* 1589234073, Creative Publishing International) Quayside.

Holeman, Bill. The Bass Bum's Bonanza. 2007. 422p. 31.95 *(978-1-59824-517-2(1))*; per. 23.95 *(978-1-59824-516-5(3))* E-BookTime LLC.

Hoover, Chad. Kayak Bass Fishing. 2010. (Illus.). 224p. pap. *(978-1-896980-46-1(5))* Heliconia Pr., Inc.

—Kayak Bass Fishing: Largemouth, Smallmouth, Stripers. 2011. (ENG., Illus.). 224p. pap. 24.95 *(978-1-56523-639-4(4))* Fox Chapel Publishing Co., Inc.

Kinney, David. The Big One: An Island, an Obsession, & the Furious Pursuit of a Great Fish. 2010. (ENG., Illus.). 288p. pap. 14.95 *(978-0-8021-4476-8(4),* Grove Pr.) Grove/Atlantic, Inc.

Knie, Alberto, frwd. The Surfcaster's Guide to the Striper Coast. 2007. (ENG., Illus.). 224p. per. 16.95 *(978-1-58080-144-7(7))* Burford Bks.

Laney, Scot. The View from down Here Is Just Fine: Clay Dyer on Life, No Limbs, & Fishing. 2009. 140p. pap. 18.85 *(978-0-578-01237-7(5))* SMG Outdoors Publishing.

Montgomery, Robert U. Better Bass Fishing: Secrets from the Headwaters by á Bassmastér Senior Writer. 2009. (ENG., Illus.). 176p. pap. 21.95 *(978-0-88150-849-9(7),* 150849) Countryman Pr.

Muller, D. J. Striper Strategies: Surfcasting Methods for Catching Striped Bass. 2008. (ENG.). 192p. pap. 16.95 *(978-1-58080-152-2(8))* Burford Bks.

Pruet, David B. Bass Fishing 101: Your Guide to Largemouth Bass Fishing. 2009. 136p. pap. 14.50 *(978-1-4343-4578-3(5))* AuthorHouse.

Savik, Karen. Bass: Use the Secrets of the Pros to Catch More & Bigger Bass. 2008. (Pro Tactics Ser.). (ENG., Illus.). 136p. (gr. 7). pap. 19.95 *(978-1-59921-297-5(8),* Lyons Pr.) Globe Pequot Pr., The.

Sternberg, Dick. Bass! Proven Strategies, Skills & Secrets for Catching More & Bigger Largemouth Bass. 2007. (Illus.). 158p. per. 14.95 *(978-1-58159-318-1(X),* Shady Oak Pr.) North American Media Group.

White, Jim. Monster Shallow-Water Stripers: How to Catch the Largest Bass of Your Life. 2008. (ENG., Illus.). 289p. 24.95 *(978-0-9793460-9-5(6))* Headwater Bks.

Whitlock, Dave. L. L. Bean Fly Fishing for Bass Handbook. 2nd ed. 2007. (ENG., Illus.). 192p. pap. 19.95 *(978-1-59921-092-6(4),* Lyons Pr.) Globe Pequot Pr., The.

BASS GUITAR

Alfred Publishing Staff. Bass 101: A Contemporary Approach to Playing Bass, Book & DVD. 2008. (ENG.). 48p. pap. 19.95 *(978-0-7390-5695-0(6))* Alfred Publishing Co., Inc.

—Bass Guitar Poster: Poster. 2008. (ENG.). pap. 9.95 *(978-0-7390-5510-6(0))* Alfred Publishing Co., Inc.

—Deluxe Bass TAB Collection: Authentic Bass TAB. 2009. (ENG.). 148p. pap. 24.95 *(978-0-7390-5811-4(8))* Alfred Publishing Co., Inc.

—Electric Bass: The Ultimate Multimedia Instructor. 2009. (Play Ser.). (ENG.). 19.99 *(978-0-7390-6584-6(X))* Alfred Publishing Co., Inc.

—Epiphone Guitar & Bass Basics: Dvd. 2010. (ENG.). *(978-0-7579-2311-1(9))* Alfred Publishing Co., Inc.

—Flex-Ability Classics: Oboe/Guitar/Piano/Electric Bass. 2009. (Flex-Ability Ser.). (ENG.). 24p. pap. 6.95 *(978-0-7390-6030-8(9))* Alfred Publishing Co., Inc.

—Guitar World — Play Rock Bass! The Ultimate DVD Guide, DVD. 2009. (Guitar World Ser.). (ENG.). 14.95 *(978-0-7390-6454-2(1))* Alfred Publishing Co., Inc.

—Guitar World: How to Play Heavy Metal Bass! Dvd. 2011. (Guitar World Ser.). 14.99 ***(978-0-7390-8309-3(0))*** Alfred Publishing Co., Inc.

—Guitar World: How to Play the Best of Black Sabbath: Dvd. 2011. (Guitar World Ser.). 14.99 ***(978-0-7390-8310-9(4))*** Alfred Publishing Co., Inc.

—Jazz Band Collection for Jazz Ensemble: Bass. 2009. (Jazz Band Collection for Jazz Ensemble Ser.). (ENG.). 32p. pap. 9.95 *(978-0-7390-6678-2(1))* Alfred Publishing Co., Inc.

—Led Zeppelin Bass TAB Anthology: Authentic Bass TAB. 2009. (ENG.). 132p. pap. 21.95 *(978-0-7390-6258-6(1))* Alfred Publishing Co., Inc.

—Sound Innovations for Concert Band, Bk 2: A Revolutionary Method for Early-Intermediate Musicians (Electric Bass), Book, CD & DVD. 2011. (Sound Innovations Ser.). (ENG.). 48p. pap. 8.99 ***(978-0-7390-6759-8(1))*** Alfred Publishing Co., Inc.

—Ultimate Bass Play-along Foo Fighters: Authentic Bass TAB, Book & 2 Enhanced CDs. 2012. (Ultimate Play-Along Ser.). (ENG.). 64p. pap. 19.99 ***(978-0-7390-8700-8(2))*** Alfred Publishing Co., Inc.

—Ultimate Bass Play-along Radiohead: Authentic Bass TAB, Book & 2 Enhanced CDs. 2012. (Ultimate Play-Along Ser.). (ENG.). 56p. pap. 19.99 ***(978-0-7390-8656-8(1))*** Alfred Publishing Co., Inc.

—Ultimate Beginner Bass Basics: Steps One & Two, Book & CD. rev. ed. 2011. (Ultimate Beginner Ser.). (ENG.). 40p. pap. 12.99 ***(978-0-7390-8197-6(7))*** Alfred Publishing Co., Inc.

—Ultimate Beginner Electric Guitar Basics: Steps One & Two, Book & CD. rev. ed. 2011. (Ultimate Beginner Ser.). (ENG.). 40p. pap. 12.99 ***(978-0-7390-8198-3(5))*** Alfred Publishing Co., Inc.

—Young Jazz Collection for Jazz Ensemble: Bass. 2008. (Young Jazz Collection for Jazz Ensemble Ser.). (ENG.). 32p. pap. 9.95 *(978-0-7390-5543-4(7))* Alfred Publishing Co., Inc.

—21st Century Breakdown: Bass TAB. 2009. (ENG.). 112p. pap. 21.95 *(978-0-7390-6293-7(X))* Alfred Publishing Co., Inc.

Alfred Publishing Staff & Fieldy. Behind the Player — Fieldy: Dvd. 2008. (Artist for Artist Ser.). (ENG.). 9.99 *(978-0-7390-5625-7(5))* Alfred Publishing Co., Inc.

Alfred Publishing Staff & Overthrow, David. The Total Funk Bassist: A Fun & Comprehensive Overview of Funk Bass Playing, Book & CD. 2009. (Total Bassist Ser.). (ENG.). 128p. pap. 19.95 *(978-0-7390-6014-8(7))* Alfred Publishing Co., Inc.

Andrews, Lee, contrib. by. Mel Bay Presents Dobro Christmas Songbook, 1 vol. 2007. (ENG.). 32p. pap. 7.95 *(978-0-7866-7620-0(5))* Mel Bay Pubns., Inc.

Bacon, Tony & Moorhouse, Barry. The Bass Book: Every Bass Player's Favorite Book. rev. exp. ed. 2008. (ENG., Illus.). 176p. pap. 24.99 *(978-0-87930-924-4(5),* 0879309245, Backbeat Books) Leonard, Hal Corp.

Bailey, Steve. Fretless Bass: Book & DVD (Hard Case) 2008. (ENG.). 40p. pap. 19.95 *(978-0-7390-4079-9(0))* Alfred Publishing Co., Inc.

—Rock Bass. 2007. (ENG.). 56p. pap. 16.95 *(978-0-7390-4080-5(4))* Alfred Publishing Co., Inc.

Balmer, Paul. The Fender Bass Handbook: How to Buy, Maintain, Set up, Troubleshoot, & Modify Your Bass. 2010. (ENG., Illus.). 204p. 25.00 *(978-0-7603-3862-9(0),* 0760338620, Voyageur Pr) MBI Publishing Co. LLC.

Beatles, The & Lennon, John. Lennon & Mccartney: Pro Vocal Volume 19. 2010. (ENG.). 32p. pap. 14.99 incl. audio compact disk *(978-0-634-09975-5(2),* 0634099752) Leonard, Hal Corp.

Black Sabbath. Black Sabbath: Bass Play-along Volume 26. 2009. (ENG.). 56p. pap. 16.99 incl. audio compact disk *(978-1-4234-8213-0(1),* 1423482131) Leonard, Hal Corp.

Blasko. Behind the Player — Blasko: Dvd. 2008. (Artist for Artist Ser.). (ENG.). 9.99 *(978-0-7390-5516-8(X))* Alfred Publishing Co., Inc.

Boomer, Tim & Berry, Mick. The Bassist's Bible: How to Play Every Bass Style from Afro-Cuban to Zydeco. 2009. (Musician's Bible Ser.). (ENG., Illus.). 200p. pap. 32.95 *(978-1-884365-45-4(0))* See Sharp Pr.

Bradley, David. Compact Music Guides: Guitar for Bassists: Guitar for Bassists. 2009. 48p. pap. 6.95 *(978-0-8256-3691-2(4),* AM981761R, Amsco Music) Music Sales Corp.

Brown, Tyrone. Compositions for Bass, 1 vol. 2006. (ENG., Illus.). 40p. pap. 14.95 *(978-0-7866-7514-2(4),* 21118bcd) Mel Bay Pubns., Inc.

Capone, Phil. Learn to Play Bass Guitar. 2009. (Music Bibles Ser.). (ENG., Illus.). 256p. spiral bd. 16.99 *(978-0-7858-2480-0(4),* 0785824804, Chartwell) Book Sales, Inc.

Chiarelli, Robert. Dexterity Exercises for the Electric Bass. 2010. (ENG.). 120p. pap. 14.99 *(978-1-60378-195-4(1),* 1603781951) Cherry Lane Music Co.

Chiavaro, Mike. Picture Yourself Playing the Bass. 2008. (ENG., Illus.). 200p. pap. 34.99 *(978-1-59863-508-9(5))* Course Technology.

Collins, Bootsy. Bootsy Collins Legendary Licks: An Inside Look at the Bass Style of Bootsy Collins. 2011. (ENG.). 48p. pap. 17.99 incl. audio compact disk ***(978-1-60378-150-3(1)***, 1603781501) Cherry Lane Music Co.

Course Technology Staff. Picture Yourself Playing Bass. 2007. 34.99 *(978-1-59863-447-1(X))* Course Technology.

Dabczynski, Andrew H. & Phillips, Bob. Basic Fiddlers Philharmonic: Cello & Bass. 2007. (ENG., Illus.). 24p. pap. 6.95 *(978-0-7390-4862-7(7))* Alfred Publishing Co., Inc.

Dave Matthews Band. Learn to Play Bass with the Dave Matthews Band. 2011. (ENG.). pap. 15.99 incl. audio compact disk *(978-1-60378-030-8(0),* 1603780300) Cherry Lane Music Co.

Dethklok. Dethklok — Bass TAB Anthology: Authentic Bass TAB. 2011. 100p. pap. 22.99 *(978-0-7390-7609-5(4))* Alfred Publishing Co., Inc.

East, Nathan. Nathan East — Contemporary Bass: Dvd. 2008. (Alfred's Artist Ser.). (ENG.). 24.95 *(978-0-7390-5059-0(1))* Alfred Publishing Co., Inc.

Emmons, Tim. Odd Meter Bass: Playing Odd Time Signatures Made Easy. 2008. (ENG.). 88p. pap. 19.95 *(978-0-7390-4081-2(2))* Alfred Publishing Co., Inc.

Ensign, Marc D. Mel Bay's Slappin' A Complete Study of Slap Technique for Bass, 1 vol. 2007. (ENG., Illus.). 32p. pap. 19.95 *(978-0-7866-7676-7(0))* Mel Bay Pubns., Inc.

Eric Clapton: Bass Play-along Volume 29. 2011. (ENG.). 64p. pap. 14.99 incl. audio compact disk *(978-1-4234-8216-1(6),* 1423482166) Leonard, Hal Corp.

Eric Clapton: Fender Special Edition G-DEC Guitar Play-along Pack. 2011. (ENG.). 56p. pap. 29.99 incl. disk *(978-1-4584-0095-6(6),* 1458400956) Leonard, Hal Corp.

Friedland, Ed. Bass Licks: Over 200 Licks, Lines, & Grooves in Many Rhythmic Styles. 2009. (ENG.). 48p. pap. 14.99 incl. audio compact disk *(978-1-4234-5642-1(4),* 1423456424) Leonard, Hal Corp.

—Pentatonic Scales for Bass: Fingerings, Exercises & Proper Usage of the Essential Five-Note Scales. 2010. (ENG.). 64p. pap. 19.99 incl. audio compact disk *(978-1-4234-7796-9(0),* 1423477960) Leonard, Hal Corp.

Gallway, Bob. J. S. Bach for Electric Bass: Music * Instruction * Historical Analysis. 2010. (ENG.). 40p. pap. 12.99 incl. audio compact disk *(978-1-4234-9954-1(9),* 1423499549) Leonard, Hal Corp.

Gray, Paul. Behind the Player — Paul Gray: Dvd. 2008. (Artist for Artist Ser.). (ENG.). 9.99 *(978-0-7390-5522-9(4))* Alfred Publishing Co., Inc.

Green, Day. Green Day Ultimate Bass Play Along. 2007. (Ultimate Play-along Ser.). (ENG.). 44p. pap. 16.95 *(978-0-7390-4428-5(1))* Alfred Publishing Co., Inc.

Green, Eddie, et al. Ensemble Concepts for Band - Fundamental Level: Electric Bass. 2006. (ENG.). 16p. pap. 4.95 *(978-0-634-09463-7(7),* 0634094637) Leonard, Hal Corp.

Gruhn, George & Carter, Walter. Electric Guitars & Basses, 1 vol. 2nd ed. 2010. (ENG., Illus.). 272p. pap. 24.99 *(978-0-87930-974-9(1),* 0879309741, Backbeat Books) Leonard, Hal Corp.

Hal Leonard Corp., creator. Mainstream Rock: Bass Play-along Volume 15. 2010. (ENG.). 72p. pap. 14.99 incl. audio compact disk *(978-1-4234-1428-5(4),* 1423414284) Leonard, Hal Corp.

—Punk Classics: Bass Play-along Volume 12. 2010. (ENG.). 56p. pap. 12.99 incl. audio compact disk *(978-1-4234-1418-6(7),* 1423414187) Leonard, Hal Corp.

—Rock Bass Songs for Dummies. 2011. (ENG.). 256p. pap. 24.99 *(978-1-4234-9584-0(5),* 1423495845) Leonard, Hal Corp.

Hal Leonard Corporation Staff. Easy Songs: Bass Play-along Volume 34. 2010. (ENG.). 48p. pap. 12.99 incl. audio compact disk *(978-1-4234-9122-4(X),* 142349122X) Leonard, Hal Corp.

—Monster Book of Rock Bass Tab, 1 vol. 2010. (ENG.). 448p. pap. 24.99 *(978-1-60378-207-4(9),* 1603782079) Cherry Lane Music Co.

Hal Leonard Corporation Staff, creator. Christmas Favorites - Bass: Big Band Play-along Volume 5. 2008. (ENG.). 24p. pap. 14.95 incl. audio compact disk *(978-1-4234-5855-5(9),* 1423458559) Leonard, Hal Corp.

—Christmas Hits: Bass Play-along Volume 33. 2009. (ENG.). 24p. pap. 12.99 incl. audio compact disk *(978-1-4234-8258-1(1),* 1423482581) Leonard, Hal Corp.

—Christmas Songs for Bass: 24 Melodies Arranged for 4-String Electric Bass. 2007. (ENG.). 48p. per. 9.95 *(978-1-4234-3157-2(X),* 142343157X) Leonard, Hal Corp.

—Country: Bass Play-along Volume 11. 2008. (ENG.). 64p. pap. 12.95 incl. audio compact disk *(978-1-4234-1423-0(3),* 1423414233) Leonard, Hal Corp.

—Diction Coach - G. Schirmer Opera Anthology: Arias for Bass. 2008. (ENG.). 64p. pap. 19.99 incl. audio compact disk *(978-1-4234-1312-7(1),* 1423413121, G Schirmer, Inc.) Leonard, Hal Corp.

—FastTrack Bass Method Starter Pack: Includes Book/CD/DVD. 2009. (ENG.). 48p. pap. 14.99 incl. audio compact disk *(978-1-4234-9052-4(5),* 1423490525) Leonard, Hal Corp.

—Jazz Classics - Bass: Big Band Play-along Volume 4. 2008. (ENG.). 24p. pap. 14.95 incl. audio compact disk *(978-1-4234-4990-4(8),* 1423449908) Leonard, Hal Corp.

—Joy to the World - Bass Edition: Worship Band Play-along Volume 5. 2009. (ENG.). 48p. pap. 12.99 incl. audio compact disk *(978-1-4234-7085-4(0),* 1423470850) Leonard, Hal Corp.

—Latin - Bass: Big Band Play-along Volume 6. 2009. (ENG.). 24p. pap. 14.99 incl. audio compact disk *(978-1-4234-5880-7(X)*, 142345880X) Leonard, Hal Corp.
—Modern Rock: Bass Play-along Volume 14. 2009. (ENG.). 64p. pap. 14.99 incl. audio compact disk *(978-1-4234-1427-8(6)*, 1423414276) Leonard, Hal Corp.
—More Classic Rock Bass Lines. 2006. (ENG.). 248p. per. 17.95 *(978-1-57560-889-1(8)*, 1575608898) Cherry Lane Music Co.
—Pop Metal: Bass Play-along Volume 17. 2009. (ENG.). 72p. pap. 14.99 incl. audio compact disk *(978-1-4234-1443-8(8)*, 1423414438) Leonard, Hal Corp.
—Standards - Bass: Big Band Play-along Volume 7. 2009. (ENG.). 24p. pap. 14.99 incl. audio compact disk *(978-1-4234-5888-3(5)*, 1423458885) Leonard, Hal Corp.
—'80s Metal: Bass Play-along Volume 16. 2010. (ENG.). 80p. pap. 16.99 incl. audio compact disk *(978-1-4234-1439-1(X)*, 142341439X) Leonard, Hal Corp.
Hauser, Dominik. Bass Blueprints: Creating Bass Lines from Chord Symbols. 2009. (ENG.). 80p. pap. 18.99 incl. audio compact disk *(978-1-4234-3926-4(0)*, 1423439260, Musicians Institute Pr.) Leonard, Hal Corp.
—Chords for Bass: The Complete Guide to Understanding & Applying Chord Structures on the Bass Guitar. 2007. (ENG.). 80p. pap. 17.99 incl. audio compact disk *(978-1-4234-1198-7(6)*, 1423411986, Musicians Institute Pr.) Leonard, Hal Corp.
—Soloing for Bass: A Contemporary Approach to Improvising in Any Style. 2010. (ENG.). 96p. pap. 19.99 incl. audio compact disk *(978-1-4234-7643-6(3)*, 1423476433, Musicians Institute Pr.) Leonard, Hal Corp.
Hoffman, Steven. Learn to Play Bass with Metallica, Vol. 2. 2007. (ENG.). 72p. pap. 15.95 incl. audio compact disk *(978-1-57560-866-2(9)*, 1575608669) Cherry Lane Music Co.
Inez, Mike. Behind the Player — Mike Inez: Dvd. 2008. (Artist for Artist Ser.). (ENG.). 9.99 *(978-0-7390-5624-0(7))* Alfred Publishing Co., Inc.
Jisi, Chris. Bass Player Presents the Fretless Bass. 2008. (ENG., Illus.). 118p. pap. 19.95 *(978-0-87930-925-1(3)*, 0879309253, Backbeat Books) Leonard, Hal Corp.
John 5. Behind the Player — John 5: Dvd. 2008. (Artist for Artist Ser.). (ENG.). 9.99 *(978-0-7390-5517-5(8))* Alfred Publishing Co., Inc.
Johnson, Chad. All about Bass: A Fun & Simple Guide to Playing Bass. 2006. (All About Ser.). (ENG., Illus.). 208p. pap. 19.95 incl. audio compact disk *(978-1-4234-0817-8(9)*, 1423408179) Leonard, Hal Corp.
—Bass for Kids: A Beginner's Guide with Step-by-Step Instruction for Bass Guitar. 2010. (ENG.). 32p. pap. 12.99 incl. audio compact disk *(978-1-4234-9848-3(8)*, 1423498488) Leonard, Hal Corp.
Johnson, Todd. Todd Johnson Electric Bass Technique Builders. 2008. (Alfred's Artist Ser.). (ENG.). 48p. pap. 12.95 *(978-0-7390-5155-9(5))* Alfred Publishing Co., Inc.
—Todd Johnson Electric Bass Technique Builders: Book & DVD. 2008. (Alfred's Artist Ser.). (ENG.). 48p. pap. 39.95 *(978-0-7390-5157-3(1))* Alfred Publishing Co., Inc.
—The Todd Johnson Walking Bass Line Module System, Vol 1: Triad Modules. 2008. (Alfred's Artist Ser.). (ENG.). 40p. pap. 12.95 *(978-0-7390-5158-0(X))* Alfred Publishing Co., Inc.
—The Todd Johnson Walking Bass Line Module System. Vol 1: Triad Modules, Book & DVD. 2008. (Alfred's Artist Ser.). (ENG.). 40p. pap. 39.95 *(978-0-7390-5160-3(1))* Alfred Publishing Co., Inc.
—The Todd Johnson Walking Bass Line Module System, Vol 2: Scale Modules. 2008. (Alfred's Artist Ser.). (ENG.). 48p. pap. 12.95 *(978-0-7390-5161-0(X))* Alfred Publishing Co., Inc.
—The Todd Johnson Walking Bass Line Module System, Vol 2: Scale Modules, Book & DVD. 2008. (Alfred's Artist Ser.). (ENG.). 48p. pap. 39.95 *(978-0-7390-5163-4(6))* Alfred Publishing Co., Inc.
Journey. Ultimate Bass Play-along Journey: Book & 2 Enhanced CDs. 2011. (Ultimate Play-along Ser.). 48p. pap. 19.99 *(978-0-7390-7161-8(0))* Alfred Publishing Co., Inc.
Kershaw, Steve. Bass Guitar, Bk. 1. 2007. (New Tune a Day Ser.). (ENG., Illus.). 64p. pap. 9.95 incl. audio compact disk *(978-0-8256-3598-4(5)*, 0825635985, Boston Music) Music Sales Corp.
Kringel, Chris. The Bassist's Guide to Creativity: Expand Your Groove Potential, 1 vol. 2009. (ENG.). 72p. pap. 17.99 incl. audio compact disk *(978-1-4234-0556-6(0)*, 1423405560) Leonard, Hal Corp.
LaRue, Dave, contrib. by. Essential Bass Concepts. 2007. (Alfred's Artist Ser.). (ENG.). 24.95 *(978-0-7390-4967-9(4))* Alfred Publishing Co., Inc.
Led Zeppelin (Musical Group) Staff. Led Zeppelin I. 2007. (Alfred's Classic Album Editions Ser.). (ENG.). 72p. per. 16.95 *(978-0-7390-4818-4(X))* Alfred Publishing Co., Inc.
Leigh, Bill, ed. Bass Player Presents the Funky Bass Book. 2010. (ENG., Illus.). 256p. pap. 14.99 *(978-0-87930-994-7(6)*, 0879309946, Backbeat Books) Leonard, Hal Corp.
Lennon, John. Lennon & Mccartney: Bass Play-along Volume 13. 2009. (ENG.). 40p. pap. 14.99 incl. audio compact disk *(978-1-4234-1421-6(7)*, 1423414217) Leonard, Hal Corp.
Letsch, Glenn. Country Bass: A Guide to the Essential Styles & Techniques. 2007. (Hal Leonard Bass Method Ser.). (ENG.). 64p. pap. 14.95 incl. audio compact disk *(978-1-4234-0771-3(7)*, 1423407717) Leonard, Hal Corp.
—James Brown: A Step-by-Step Breakdown of the Styles & Techniques of James Brown's Bassists. 2009. (ENG.). 32p. pap. 19.99 incl. audio compact disk *(978-1-4234-5300-0(X)*, 142345300X) Leonard, Hal Corp.
—Stuff! Good Bass Players Should Know: An A-Z Guide to Getting Better. 2008. (Stuff! Ser.). (ENG.). 128p. pap. 19.95 incl. audio compact disk *(978-1-4234-3138-1(3)*, 1423431383) Leonard, Hal Corp.
Liebman, Jon. Bass Aerobics. 2011. (ENG.). 112p. pap. 17.99 incl. audio compact disk ***(978-1-4234-9563-5(2)***, 1423495632) Leonard, Hal Corp.
Liebman, Jon. Bass Grooves: The Ultimate Collection. 2009. (ENG.). 96p. pap. 19.99 incl. audio compact disk *(978-1-4234-4127-4(3)*, 1423441273) Leonard, Hal Corp.
Lopez, Victor. Flex-Ability More Pops: Oboe/Guitar/Piano/Electric Bass. 2008. (Flex-Ability Ser.). (ENG.). 24p. pap. 6.95 *(978-0-7390-5321-8(3))* Alfred Publishing Co., Inc.
Malone, Sean. Music Theory for Bassists: Everything You Ever Wanted to Know but Were Afraid to Ask. 2006. (ENG.). 64p. pap. 17.95 incl. audio compact disk *(978-0-634-05715-1(4)*, 0634057154) Leonard, Hal Corp.
Maloney, Christopher. Progressive Rock Bass: A Guide to Developing Progressive Concepts & Techniques. 2009. (ENG.). 80p. pap. 19.99 incl. audio compact disk *(978-1-4234-8091-4(0)*, 1423480910, Musicians Institute Pr.) Leonard, Hal Corp.
Manus, Ron & Hall, Steve. Alfred's Basic Bass Scales & Modes: The Easiest Way to Get the Essentials under Your Fingers. 2008. (Alfred's Basic Bass Guitar Library). (ENG.). 32p. pap. 8.95 *(978-0-7390-5584-7(4))* Alfred Publishing Co., Inc.
Manus, Ron & Hamsberger, L. C. Alfred's Basic Bass Method Bk. 1: The Most Popular Method for Learning How to Play. 2007. (Alfred's Basic Guitar Ser.). (ENG., Illus.). 64p. pap. 9.95 *(978-0-7390-4886-3(4))*; per. 6.99 *(978-0-7390-4885-6(6))* Alfred Publishing Co., Inc.
—Alfred's Basic Bass Method Bk. 2: The Most Popular Method for Learning How to Play. (Alfred's Basic Bass Guitar Library Ser.). (ENG.). 2008. 48p. pap. 6.95 *(978-0-7390-5393-5(0))* 2008. 48p. pap. 14.95 *(978-0-7390-5395-9(7))* 2007. 16.95 *(978-0-7390-4942-6(9))* Alfred Publishing Co., Inc.
—Alfreds Basic Bass Method 1: The Most Popular Method for Learning How to Play. 2007. (ENG.). pap. 19.95 *(978-0-7390-4887-0(2))* Alfred Publishing Co., Inc.
Manus, Ron, et al. Alfred's Basic Bass Method Complete: The Most Popular Method for Learning How to Play: for Individual or Class Instruction. 2008. (Alfred's Basic Bass Guitar Library). (ENG., Illus.). 136p. pap. 16.95 *(978-0-7390-5582-3(8))*; pap. 24.95 *(978-0-7390-5583-0(6))* Alfred Publishing Co., Inc.
Marley, Bob. Bob Marley, Vol. 35. 2011. (ENG.). 56p. pap. 14.99 inc. audio compact disk *(978-1-4234-9535-2(7)*, 1423495357) Leonard, Hal Corp.
Matheos, Chris. Mel Bay's Getting into Slap Bass, 1 vol. 2006. (Mel Bay's Getting Into... Ser.). (ENG., Illus.). 96p. pap. 17.95 *(978-0-7866-7372-8(9))* Mel Bay Pubns., Inc.
Matthews, Barry. Fender Bass for Britain: The History of the 1966 Slab-Bodied Precision Bass. 2009. (Illus.). 56p. pap. 23.99 *(978-1-4389-4662-7(7))* AuthorHouse.
McKagan, Duff. Behind the Player — Duff Mckagan: Dvd. 2008. (Artist for Artist Ser.). (ENG.). 9.99 *(978-0-7390-5623-3(9))* Alfred Publishing Co., Inc.
Mel Bay Publications Inc, creator. Mel Bay's Bass Chord Picture Book, 1 vol. 2006. (ENG., Illus.). 56p. pap. 12.95 *(978-0-7866-7667-5(1)*, 99920dp) Mel Bay Pubns., Inc.
Merrill, Robbie. Behind the Player — Robbie Merrill: Dvd. 2008. (Artist for Artist Ser.). (ENG.). 9.99 *(978-0-7390-5521-2(6))* Alfred Publishing Co., Inc.
Miller, Marcus. Marcus Miller - in Concert. 2008. (ENG.). 19.95 *(978-1-4234-4363-6(2)*, 1423443632) Leonard, Hal Corp.
Moore, Jeff. Yellowbird: For a Minimum of Five Steel Drums, Drumset, & Optional Bass Guitar, Conductor Score & Parts. 2011. (Alfred's Steel Drum Ensemble Ser.). 18p. pap. 17.99 ***(978-0-7390-8078-8(4))*** Alfred Publishing Co., Inc.
Mulford, Phil. Absolute Beginners Bass Guitar - Omnibus Edition: The Complete Absolute Beginners Method - All in One Book! 2010. (ENG.). 88p. pap. 19.99 incl. audio compact disk *(978-1-4234-9883-4(6)*, 1423498836) Music Sales Corp.
Nirvana. Nirvana: Bass Play-along Volume 25. 2009. (ENG.). 48p. pap. 14.99 incl. audio compact disk *(978-1-4234-8212-3(3)*, 1423482123) Leonard, Hal Corp.
Noel, Odile. Mel Bay Arpeges a la Basse en Images, 1 vol. 2007. (FRE & ENG., Illus.). 56p. pap. 6.95 *(978-0-7866-7735-1(X))* Mel Bay Pubns., Inc.
Overly, Mike. Bass 6 String Fretboard Flashcards: The Fastest Way to Learn 12 Pitches on 6 Strings. 2007. (Illus.). 126p. 24.95 *(978-0-9790177-0-4(X))* 12 Tone Music Publishing, LLC.
Overthrow, Dave. The Versatile Bassist: A Complete Course in a Variety of Musical Styles. 2008. (National Guitar Workshop Ser.). (ENG., Illus.). 96p. pap. 19.95 *(978-0-7390-4803-0(1))* Alfred Publishing Co., Inc.
Overthrow, David. Electric Bass Method Complete: Book, CD & DVD. 2010. (ENG.). 272p. pap. 29.99 *(978-0-7390-7399-5(0))* Alfred Publishing Co., Inc.
Palermo, Max. Chords & Scales in the Beginning: Created Especially for Bassists. 2007. (ENG.). 80p. per. 14.95 *(978-1-57424-224-9(5)*, 1574242245) Centerstream Publishing.
—Hip-Hop Grooves for Bass: 90 Full-Demo Tracks. 2007. (ENG.). 32p. pap. 14.95 incl. audio compact disk *(978-1-57424-225-6(3)*, 1574242253) Centerstream Publishing.
—Pentatonic Scales for Electric Bass: A Practical Approach to the Pentatonic World for the 4- And 5-String. 2009. (ENG.). 80p. pap. 19.95 *(978-1-57424-247-8(4)*, 1574242474) Centerstream Publishing.
—Ultimate Bass Exercises. 2006. (ENG.). 148p. pap. 19.95 *(978-1-57424-208-9(3)*, 1574242083) Centerstream Publishing.
Patitucci, John, contrib. by. Bass Day 97: John Patitucci. 2008. (Alfred's Artist Ser.). (ENG.). 19.95 *(978-0-7390-5407-9(4))* Alfred Publishing Co., Inc.
Pfeiffer, Patrick. Bass Guitar Exercises for Dummies. 2010. (ENG., Illus.). 216p. pap. 22.99 *(978-0-470-64722-6(1)*, For Dummies) Wiley, John & Sons, Inc.
—Bass Guitar for Dummies. 2nd ed. 2010. (ENG., Illus.). 360p. pap. 24.99 *(978-0-470-53961-3(5)*, For Dummies) Wiley, John & Sons, Inc.
Pinksterboer, Hugo. Electric Guitar & Bass Guitar: The Complete Guide. 3rd ed. 2008. (ENG., Illus.). 248p. pap. 14.95 *(978-1-4234-4274-5(1)*, 1423442741) Leonard, Hal Corp.
The Police: Bass Play-along Volume 20. 2010. (ENG.). 56p. pap. 14.99 incl. audio compact disk *(978-1-4234-4652-1(6)*, 1423446526) Leonard, Hal Corp.
Raskin, Joyce. Aching to Be. 2007. 208p. pap. 13.95 *(978-0-615-17221-7(0))* Number One Fan Pr.
Ray, Sharon. 5-String Bass: Taking Your Playing to New Lows. 2008. (ENG.). pap. 16.95 *(978-0-7390-5275-4(6))* Alfred Publishing Co., Inc.
Reid, John. Modern Electric Bass Method, Grade 1, 1 vol. 2008. (ENG., Illus.). 72p. pap. 14.95 *(978-0-7866-7759-7(7))* Mel Bay Pubns., Inc.
Richter, Stephan. Jazz Bass. (Progressive Ser.). 64p. pap. incl. audio compact disk *(978-1-86469-082-8(8)*, 256-114) Koala Music Publications.
Rogers, Lisa. The Lion Sleeps Tonight: For a Minimum of Five Steel Drums, Congas, Shaker, & Optional Bass Guitar, Conductor Score & Parts. 2011. (Alfred's Steel Drum Ensemble Ser.). (ENG.). 20p. pap. 17.99 ***(978-0-7390-8076-4(8))*** Alfred Publishing Co., Inc.
Rush. Ultimate Bass Play-along Rush: Authentic Bass TAB, Book & CD. 2009. (Ultimate Play-along Ser.). (ENG.). 56p. pap. 19.95 *(978-0-7390-5713-1(8))* Alfred Publishing Co., Inc.
Santerre, Joe. Fingerstyle Funk Bass Lines. Feist, Jonathan, ed. 2008. (ENG.). 50p. pap. 19.95 incl. audio compact disk *(978-0-87639-076-4(9)*, 0876390769, Berklee Pr.) Leonard, Hal Corp.
Sarzo, Rudy. Rock Bass Essentials: Dvd. 2008. (ENG.). 19.95 *(978-0-7390-5597-7(6))* Alfred Publishing Co., Inc.
Saunders, Tony & Sarzo, Rudy, told to. Learning Bass The Smart Way! 2007. (Icons of Rock (Smart Way) Ser.). (Illus.). 78p. pap. 24.95 *(978-0-9796928-2-6(2))* Too Smart Pubns.
Scharfglass, Matt. You Can Do It - Play Bass!, Pack. 2008. (ENG.). 96p. pap. 24.95 incl. audio compact disk *(978-0-8256-3579-3(9)*, 0825635799) Music Sales Corp.
Scheff, Jerry. Way Down: Playing Bass with Elvis, Dylan, the Doors & More - the Autobiography of Jerry Scheff. 2012. (ENG., Illus.). 256p. pap. 19.99 ***(978-1-61713-032-8(X)***, 161713032X, Backbeat Books) Leonard, Hal Corp.
Schmidt, Detlef. Fender Precision Basses: 1951-1954. 2010. (ENG., Illus.). 160p. 35.00 *(978-1-57424-254-6(7)*, 1574242547) Centerstream Publishing.
Scott, Laurie, et al, contrib. by. Learning Together: Sequential Repertoire for Solo Strings or String Ensemble (Bass), Book & CD. 2010. (ENG.). 36p. pap. 12.99 *(978-0-7390-6833-5(4))* Alfred Publishing Co., Inc.
Scott, Paul. The Bass Guitar: From Basics to Bassist. 2008. (Collins Need to Know? Ser.). (ENG., Illus.). 192p. pap. 19.95 *(978-0-00-726114-7(4))* HarperCollins Pubs. Ltd. GBR. Dist: Independent Pubs. Group.
Shaffer, James "Munky". Behind the Player — James Munky Shaffer: Dvd. 2008. (Artist for Artist Ser.). (ENG.). 9.99 *(978-0-7390-5518-2(6))* Alfred Publishing Co., Inc.
Sheehan, Billy. Bass Day 97 Featuring Billy Sheehan. 2008. (Alfred's Artist Ser.). (ENG.). 19.95 *(978-0-7390-5408-6(2))* Alfred Publishing Co., Inc.
Singleton, Alvin. Argoru Va for Bass Clarinet. 2009. (ENG.). 12p. pap. 15.95 *(978-1-4234-5710-7(2)*, 1423457102) Schott Music Corp.
Skold, Tim. Behind the Player — Tim Skold: Dvd. 2008. (Artist for Artist Ser.). (ENG.). 9.99 *(978-0-7390-5622-6(0))* Alfred Publishing Co., Inc.
Skynyrd, Lynyrd. Lynyrd Skynyrd - All-Time Greatest Hits. 2010. (ENG.). 114p. pap. 19.99 *(978-1-4234-5807-4(9)*, 1423458079) Leonard, Hal Corp.
Story, Michael. Movie Trios for All: Cello/Bass. 2009. (Instrumental Ensembles for All Ser.). (ENG.). 24p. pap. 7.95 *(978-0-7390-6324-8(3))* Alfred Publishing Co., Inc.
Tower of Power. Best of Tower of Power for Bass. 2008. (ENG.). 128p. pap. 19.95 *(978-1-60378-041-4(6)*, 1603780416) Cherry Lane Music Co.
Turner, Gary. How to Play Bass: For Beginners. 2008. 48p. pap. incl. audio compact disk *(978-1-86469-356-0(8))* Koala Music Publications.
Walton, Tracy & Alfred Publishing Staff. Bass Chord Encyclopedia: Over 30 Chords in Every Key. 2006. (ENG.). 96p. pap. 19.95 *(978-0-7390-3833-8(8))* Alfred Publishing Co., Inc.
Webster, Alex. Extreme Metal Bass: Essential Techniques, Concepts, & Applications for the Metal Bassist. 2011. (ENG.). 64p. pap. 17.99 incl. audio compact disk ***(978-1-4234-9715-8(5)***, 1423497155) Leonard, Hal Corp.
Weezer. Weezer: Bass Play-along Volume 24, 1 vol. 2009. (ENG.). 48p. pap. 14.99 incl. audio compact disk *(978-1-4234-6317-7(X)*, 142346317X) Leonard, Hal Corp.
The Who: Bass Play-along Volume 28. 2011. (ENG.). 72p. pap. 14.99 incl. audio compact disk ***(978-1-4234-8215-4(8)***, 1423482158) Leonard, Hal Corp.
Williams, Ryan & Hammond, Richard. Bass Guitar. 2006. (ENG., Illus.). 304p. per. 24.99 *(978-0-470-04850-4(6)*, Visual) Wiley, John & Sons, Inc.
Wooten, Victor, contrib. by. Super Bass Solo Technique. 2007. (Alfred's Artist Ser.). (ENG.). 29.95 *(978-0-7390-4272-4(6))* Alfred Publishing Co., Inc.

BASS VIOL

see Double Bass

BASSET HOUND

The Basset Hound - a Dog Anthology. 2007. 84p. per. *(978-1-4067-9116-7(4))* Read Bks.
Linzy, Jan & Pata, Sharae. Basset Hound Champions, 2000-2005. 2006. (Illus.). 161p. spiral bd. 46.95 *(978-1-55893-206-7(2))* Camino E.E. & Bk. Co.
Stahlkuppe, Joe. Basset Hounds: Everything about Purchase, Feeding, & Health Care. 2nd ed. 2008. (Complete Pet Owner's Manual Ser.). (ENG., Illus.). 96p. pap. 8.99 *(978-0-7641-3774-7(3))* Barron's Educational Series, Inc.
Wood, Deborah. The Shih Tzu. 2006. (Terra-Nova Ser.). (Illus.). 208p. 19.95 *(978-0-7938-3642-0(5))* TFH Pubns., Inc.

BASSET-HOUNDS

see Basset Hound

BASSOON

Alfred Publishing Staff. Flex-Ability Classics: Trombone/Baritone/Bassoon/Tuba. 2009. (Flex-Ability Ser.). (ENG.). 24p. pap. 6.95 *(978-0-7390-6037-7(6))* Alfred Publishing Co., Inc.
Alfred Publishing Staff. Sound Innovations for Concert Band, Bk 2: A Revolutionary Method for Early-Intermediate Musicians (Bassoon), Book, CD & DVD. 2011. (Sound Innovations Ser.). (ENG.). 48p. pap. 8.99 ***(978-0-7390-6746-8(X))*** Alfred Publishing Co., Inc.
Bartok, Bela. Stravinsky, Bartok & More Volume 8: Bassoon. 2007. (Orchestra Musician's CD-ROM Library). (ENG., Illus.). 8p. cd-rom 19.95 *(978-1-4234-3283-8(5)*, 1423432835) Leonard, Hal Corp.
Bulla, Stephen. The Sound of Gospel: BC Instruments (Bassoon, Euphonium, Trombone & Others) 2007. (ENG.). 24p. pap. 14.95 incl. audio compact disk *(978-90-431-2427-0(3)*, 9043124273) Leonard, Hal Corp.
Carson Turner, Barrie, ed. Bassoons for Christmas. 2008. (ENG.). 32p. pap. 24.95 incl. audio compact disk *(978-1-902455-74-7(6)*, 1902455746) Schott Music Corp.
Crider, Paula & Saunders, Jack. Essential Musicianship for Band - Masterwork Studies: Bassoon. 2007. (ENG.). 80p. pap. 14.95 incl. audio compact disk *(978-0-634-08858-2(0)*, 0634088580) Leonard, Hal Corp.
Curnow, James. The Beginning Band Collection: Trombone/Euphonium B. C. /Bassoon Part. 2007. 16p. pap. 4.95 *(978-90-431-2618-2(7)*, 9043126187) Leonard, Hal Corp.
Fowler, Andrew J. Directions for Singing - Contrabass. 2007. pap. 12.50 *(978-0-687-64427-8(5))* Abingdon Pr.
Froseth, James O. Do It! Play & Teach Woodwinds Bassoon Book & CD. 2007. 76p. (C). spiral bd. 19.95 *(978-1-57999-643-7(4)*, M590) G I A Pubns., Inc.
Green, Eddie, et al. Ensemble Concepts for Band - Fundamental Level: Bassoon. 2006. (ENG.). 16p. pap. 4.95 *(978-0-634-09450-7(5)*, 0634094505) Leonard, Hal Corp.
Hal Leonard Corporation Staff, creator. Concert Solos for the Young Player: Bassoon/Trombone/Euphonium. 2007. (ENG.). 48p. pap. 15.95 incl. audio compact disk *(978-90-431-2354-9(4)*, 9043123544) Leonard, Hal Corp.
—Tons of Tunes from the Classics: Bassoon/Trombone/Euphonium B. C. /T. C. 2007. (ENG.). 44p. pap. 12.95 incl. audio compact disk *(978-90-431-2583-3(0)*, 9043125830) Leonard, Hal Corp.
—10. Bach, Handel & More: The Orchestra Musician's CD-ROM Library - Bassoon. 2008. (ENG.). 8p. cd-rom 19.95 *(978-1-4234-3899-1(X)*, 142343899X) Leonard, Hal Corp.
Handel, George Frideric. Messiah at Christmas: Trombone/Euphonium BC/TC/Bassoon. 2007. (ENG.). 32p. pap. 12.95 incl. audio compact disk *(978-90-431-2596-3(2)*, 9043125932) Leonard, Hal Corp.
—Messiah at Easter: Trombone/ Euphonium BC/TC /Bassoon. 2007. 40p. pap. 12.95 *(978-90-431-2659-5(4)*, 9043126594) Leonard, Hal Corp.
Lipez, Victor. U. Play. Plus More Pops — Melody Plus Harmony (Solo — A, Duet — B/C/D, Trio — C, Quartet — D) with Optional Piano Accompaniment & Optional CD Accompaniment: Trombone/Baritone/Bassoon/Tuba. 2011. (U. Play. Plus Ser.). 24p. pap. 8.99 ***(978-0-7390-8124-2(1))*** Alfred Publishing Co., Inc.
Nelson, Eric. Mel Bay's Bassoon Fingering & Scale Chart, 1 vol. 2006. (ENG.). 4p. pap. 4.95 *(978-0-7866-7574-6(8)*, 20399) Mel Bay Pubns., Inc.
Paine, Henry T. Studies & Etudes Bassoon 3. 5.95 *(978-0-7692-2341-4(9)*, Warner Bros. Pubns.) Alfred Publishing Co., Inc.
Story, Michael. Movie Quartets for All: Trombone, Baritone B. C. , Bassoon, Tuba. 2009. (Instrumental Ensembles for All Ser.). (ENG.). 24p. pap. 7.95 *(978-0-7390-6333-0(2))* Alfred Publishing Co., Inc.
—Movie Trios for All: Trombone, Baritone B. C. , Bassoon, Tuba. 2009. (Instrumental Ensembles for All Ser.). (ENG.). 24p. pap. 7.95 *(978-0-7390-6321-7(9))* Alfred Publishing Co., Inc.
—Pop Quartets for All: Trombone, Baritone B. C. , Bassoon, Tuba. rev. ed. 2008. (Pop Instrumental Ensembles for All Ser.). (ENG.). 24p. pap. 6.95 *(978-0-7390-5457-4(0))* Alfred Publishing Co., Inc.
Wagner: Part 1 - Volume 11: The Orchestra Musician's CD-ROM Library - Bassoon. 2009. (ENG.). 8p. cd-rom 19.95 *(978-1-4234-8556-8(4)*, 1423485564) Leonard, Hal Corp.
Wagner: Part 2 - Volume 12: The Orchestra Musician's CD-ROM Library - Bassoon. 2009. (ENG.). 8p. cd-rom 19.95 *(978-1-4234-8570-4(X)*, 142348570X) Leonard, Hal Corp.
Waterhouse, William & Kopp, James B. The Bassoon. 2012. (Yale Musical Instrument Ser.). (ENG., Illus.). 352p. 40.00 *(978-0-300-11829-2(5))* Yale Univ. Pr.
Weissenborn, Julius. Method for Bassoon. Bettoney, Fred, ed. (Illus.). 159p. pap. 20.95 *(978-0-8258-0169-3(9)*, CU-96) Fischer, Carl LLC.

BASSOON MUSIC

Hal Leonard Corporation Staff, creator. Solos for the Bassoon. 2006. (ENG.). 23p. pap. 19.98 incl. audio compact disk *(978-1-59615-646-3(5)*, 1596156465) Music Minus One.

Phillips, Bob & Dabczynski, Andrew H. Basic Fiddlers Philharmonic Celtic Fiddle Tunes: Cello & Bass, Book & CD. 2010. (ENG.). 24p. pap. 12.95 *(978-0-7390-6241-8(7))* Alfred Publishing Co., Inc.

BASTARDY

see Illegitimacy

BASTIAT, FREDERIC, 1801-1850

Bastiat, Frederic. The Man & the Statesman: The Correspondence & Articles on Politics. 2011. (Collected Works of Frederic Bastiat Ser.). (ENG.). 600p. (C). (gr. 12). 30.00 *(978-0-86597-786-0(0))*; pap. 14.50 *(978-0-86597-787-7(9))* Liberty Fund, Inc.

Leroux, Robert. Political Economy & Liberalism in France. 2011. (Routledge Studies in the History of Economics Ser.). (ENG.). 208p. (C). 125.00 *(978-0-415-58055-7(2))* Routledge.

BASTOGNE, BATTLE OF, 1944-1945

see Ardennes, Battle of the, 1944-1945

BASUTO (AFRICAN PEOPLE)

see also Pedi (African People); Tswana (African People)

Eldredge, Elizabeth A. Power in Colonial Africa: Conflict & Discourse in Lesotho, 1870-1960. 2007. (Africa & the Diaspora Ser.). (ENG., Illus.). 264p. 65.00 *(978-0-299-22370-0(1))* Univ. of Wisconsin Pr.

Lehlohonolo, Phafoli. Language Techniques & Thematic Aspects of Basotho Accordion Music. 2011. 296p. pap. ***(978-3-8443-1338-3(9))*** Lambert Academic Publishing.

Moffett, Rodney. Sesotho Plant & Animal Names & Plants Used by the Basotho. 2010. (AFR & ENG.). xi, 306p. *(978-1-920383-08-4(5))* Sun Media.

Morojele, Pholoho Justice. Gender & Schooling in Lesotho Rural Communities. 2011. 332p. pap. ***(978-3-8443-3343-5(6))*** Lambert Academic Publishing.

Semenya, Dr David Kwena & Semenya, David Kwena. Biblical Counselling of Sotho Christians Believing in Witchcraft. 2011. 112p. pap. ***(978-3-8454-1653-3(X))*** Lambert Academic Publishing.

BASUTOLAND

see Lesotho

BAT

see Bats

BATAAN, BATTLE OF, PHILIPPINES, 1942

Resa, Jolinda Bull. Honor Them Always: For the Sacrifice of Their Youth at Bataan. 2011. 60p. pap. 14.95 ***(978-1-4327-7555-1(3))*** Outskirts Pr., Inc.

Sloan, Bill. Undefeated: America's Heroic Fight for Bataan & Corregidor. 2012. (ENG., Illus.). 416p. 28.00 ***(978-1-4391-9964-0(7))*** Simon & Schuster.

Young, Donald J. The Battle of Bataan: A Complete History. 2nd rev. ed. 2009. (ENG., Illus.). 296p. pap. 49.95 *(978-0-7864-4180-8(1))* McFarland & Co., Inc. Pubs.

—Final Hours in the Pacific: The Allied Surrenders of Wake Island, Bataan, Corregidor, Hong Kong & Singapore. 2011. (ENG., Illus.). 191p. pap. 38.00 *(978-0-7864-5938-4(7))* McFarland & Co., Inc. Pubs.

BATAILLE, GEORGES, 1897-1962

Ades, Dawn & Baker, Simon. Undercover Surrealism: Georges Bataille & Documents. 2006. (Illus.). 271p. pap. *(978-0-262-51197-1(5))*; (ENG., 272p. (gr. 17). pap. 40.00 *(978-0-262-01230-0(8))* MIT Pr.

Bataille, Georges. Guilty. 2011. (SUNY series in Contemporary French Thought Ser.). 256p. 85.00 *(978-1-4384-3461-2(8))*; pap. 29.95 *(978-1-4384-3462-9(6))* State Univ. of New York Pr.

Bataille, Georges & Leiris, Michel. Correspondence: Georges Bataille & Michel Leiris. Heron, Liz, tr. from FRE. 2008. (SB-The French List Ser.). (ENG.). 312p. 29.95 *(978-1-905422-67-8(9))* Seagull Bks. GBR. Dist: Chicago Distribution Ctr.

Biles, Jeremy. Ecce Monstrum: Georges Bataille & the Sacrifice of Form. 2nd ed. 2007. (ENG., Illus.). 372p. 75.00 *(978-0-8232-2778-5(2))* Fordham Univ. Pr.

French, Patrick. After Bataille: Sacrifice, Exposure, Community. 2007. (Legenda Main Ser.). (ENG.). 205p. (C). 79.50 *(978-1-904350-85-9(2))* European Humanities Research Ctr. GBR. Dist: Brown, David Bk. Co., The.

Gasché, Rodolphe & Végso, Roland. Phenomenology & Phantasmatology: On the Philosophy of Georges Bataille. 2012. (Cultural Memory in the Present Ser.). (ENG.). 368p. 85.00 ***(978-0-8047-7606-6(7))***; pap. 25.95 ***(978-0-8047-7607-3(5))*** Stanford Univ. Pr.

Kendall, Stuart. Georges Bataille. 2007. (Reaktion Books - Critical Lives Ser.). (ENG., Illus.). 192p. per. 16.95 *(978-1-86189-327-7(2))* Reaktion Bks., Ltd. GBR. Dist: Chicago Distribution Ctr.

Lala, Marie-Christine. Georges Bataille: Poète du Réel. 2010. (FRE.). 170p. pap. 48.95 *(978-3-03910-738-4(0))* Lang, Peter AG GBR. Dist: Lang, Peter.

Lozier, Claire. De L'abject et du Sublime: Georges Bataille, Jean Genet, Samuel Beckett. 2012. (Modern French Identities Ser.). (FRE.). 319p. pap. 74.95 ***(978-3-0343-0724-6(1))*** Lang, Peter AG GBR. Dist: Lang, Peter.

Mansfield, Nick. The God Who Deconstructs Himself: Sovereignty & Subjectivity Between Freud, Bataille, & Derrida. 4th ed. 2010. (Perspectives in Continental Philosophy Ser.). (ENG.). 144p. 70.00 *(978-0-8232-3241-3(7))*; pap. 29.00 *(978-0-8232-3242-0(5))* Fordham Univ. Pr.

Mitchell, Andrew J., ed. The Obsessions of Georges Bataille: Community & Communication. Winfree, Jason Kemp, tr. 2009. (SUNY series in Contemporary French Thought Ser.). (Illus.). 352p. 65.00 *(978-1-4384-2823-9(5))*; pap. 24.95 *(978-1-4384-2824-6(3))* State Univ. of New York Pr. (Suny Pr.).

Stoekl, Allan. Bataille's Peak: Energy, Religion, & Postsustainability. 2007. 280p. per. 20.00 *(978-0-8166-4819-1(0))*; (Illus.). 247p. 60.00 *(978-0-8166-4818-4(2))* Univ. of Minnesota Pr.

Surya, Michel. Georges Bataille: An Intellectual Biography. Fijalkowsk, Krzysztof & Richardson, Michael, trs. from FRE. 2010. (ENG., Illus.). 608p. pap. 29.95 *(978-1-85984-153-2(8)*, 859153) Verso Bks. GBR. Dist: Norton, W. W. & Co., Inc.

Sweedler, Milo. The Dismembered Community: Bataille, Blanchot, Leiris, & the Remains of Laure. 2009. *(978-0-87413-052-2(2))* Univ. of Delaware Pr.

Tauchert, Ashley. Against Transgression. 2008. (Critical Quarterly Book Ser.). (ENG., Illus.). 160p. pap. 34.95 *(978-1-4051-6989-9(3)*, Wiley-Blackwell) Wiley, John & Sons, Inc.

Winnubst, Shannon, ed. Reading Bataille Now. 2007. (ENG.). 304p. 65.00 *(978-0-253-34822-7(6)*, 0253348226); pap. 24.95 *(978-0-253-21882-7(9)*, 0253218829) Indiana Univ. Pr.

BATAN LANGUAGE

Icon Group International, Inc. Staff, compiled by. Webster's Ivatan - English Thesaurus Dictionary. 2008. 232p. ring bd. 28.95 incl. audio compact disk *(978-0-497-83529-3(0))* Icon Group International, Inc.

—The 2009-2014 World Outlook for Incandescent Hand Portable Flashlights & Flashlight Lanterns Excluding Rechargeable Battery-Operated Flashlights. 2008. 234p. ring bd. 28.95 incl. audio compact disk *(978-0-497-83527-9(4))* Icon Group International, Inc.

BATAVIA (INDONESIA)

see Jakarta (Indonesia)

BATCH PROCESSING IN ELECTRONIC DATA PROCESSING

see Electronic Data Processing—Batch Processing

BATES, DAISY, 1860-1951

Bates, Daisy. The Long Shadow of Little Rock. 2007. (ENG., Illus.). 260p. per. 18.95 *(978-1-55728-863-9(1))* Univ. of Arkansas Pr.

Bates, Daisy. The Long Shadow of Little Rock: A Memoir. 2011. 268p. 47.95 ***(978-1-258-09783-7(4))*** Literary Licensing, LLC.

Robinson, Deborah. Daisy Bates: In Her Own Words. Peyton, Dianne, ed. 2007. 240p. per. 50.00 *(978-0-9709263-2-6(4))* Robinson Omnimedia Publishing & Studios.

BATES, HENRY WALTER, 1825-1892

Bates, Henry. The Naturalist on the River Amazons. 2007. 376p. per. *(978-1-905748-56-3(6))*; 440p. per. *(978-1-905748-57-0(4))* Rediscovery Bks.

Bates, Henry Walter. The Naturalist on the River Amazon: A Record of Adventures, Habits of Animals, Sketches of Brazilian & Indian Life, & Aspects of Nature under the Equator, during Eleven Years of Travel. 3rd ed. 2009. (Cambridge Library Collection - Life Sciences Ser.). 412p. pap. 31.99 *(978-1-108-00163-2(7))* Cambridge Univ. Pr.

—The Naturalist on the River Amazons. 2007. (ENG., Illus.). 300p. *(978-1-4068-2507-7(7))*; per. *(978-1-4068-2502-2(6))* Echo Library.

BATES, HERBERT ERNEST, 1905-1974

Eads, Peter. H. E. Bates: A Bibliographical Study. 2007. (Illus.). 240p. 85.00 *(978-1-58456-215-3(3))* Oak Knoll Pr.

BATES, KATHARINE LEE, 1859-1929

Miele, Leonard. Voice of the Tide: The Cape Cod Heritage of Katharine Lee Bates. 2009. (Illus.). 112p. pap. 20.00 *(978-0-932027-13-9(X))* Spinner Pubns., Inc.

Rogal, Samuel J. America the Beautiful: A Sung Prayer of the Christian Tradition. 2012. (ENG.). 72p. 39.95 ***(978-0-7734-2605-4(1))*** Mellen, Edwin Pr., The.

BATES LABORATORY ASPIRATOR

see Separators (Machines)

BATH (ENGLAND)

Davenport, Peter, et al. Archaeology in Bath: Excavations at the New Royal Baths (the Spa), & Bellott's Hospital 1998-1999. 2007. (Oxford Archaeology Monograph Ser.). (Illus.). 182p. pap. 19.95 *(978-0-904220-45-2(1))* Oxford Archaeological Unit GBR. Dist: Brown, David Bk. Co., The.

Fergusson, Adam. The Sack of Bath. 2011. (Persephone Bks.). (ENG., Illus.). 77p. pap. ***(978-1-903155-83-7(5))*** Persephone Bks. Ltd.

Lansdown, Henry Venn. Recollections of the Late William Beckford. 2009. 56p. pap. *(978-1-4068-5135-9(3))* Echo Library.

BATH (ENGLAND)—HISTORY

Barbeau, A. Life & Letters at Bath in the Eighteenth Century. 2010. (ENG., Illus.). 320p. pap. 29.95 *(978-1-84588-602-8(X))* History Pr. Ltd.,The GBR. Dist: Independent Pubs. Group.

Bellenger, Dom Aidan, ed. Downside Abbey: An Architectural History. 2012. (ENG., Illus.). 224p. 75.00 *(978-1-85894-542-2(9))* Merrell Pubs. Ltd. GBR. Dist: Perseus Distribution.

Davis, Graham. Bath as Spa & Bath as Slum: The Social History of a Victorian City. 2010. (Illus.). xii, 344p. *(978-0-7734-3788-3(6))* Mellen, Edwin Pr., The.

Davis, Graham. History of Bath. 2012. (Illus.). 336p. 31.95 ***(978-1-85936-112-2(9))*** International Publishers Marketing.

Redvers-Higgins, Neville & Willis, Lynn. 'Finished Labour of a Thousand Hands' The archaeology of the Combe down Stone Mines, Bath, Somerset. 2011. (ENG., Illus.). 341p. (C). pap. 50.00 ***(978-0-904220-60-5(5))*** Oxford Archaeological Unit GBR. Dist: Brown, David Bk. Co., The.

BATH AND WELLS (DIOCESE)

Hunter, Joseph. Ecclesiastical Documents. 2009. 48p. pap. *(978-0-217-46574-8(9))*; 92p. pap. *(978-1-4590-6875-9(0))* Books LLC.

Hunter, Joseph, ed. Ecclesiastical Documents. (Camden Society, London, Publications, First Ser.: No. 8). reprint ed. 27.50 *(978-0-404-50108-2(7))* AMS Pr., Inc.

BATHING BEACHES

Misrach, Richard. On the Beach, 1 vol. 2007. (ENG., Illus.). 80p. 85.00 *(978-1-59711-048-8(5))* Aperture Foundation, Inc.

Phelts, Marsha Dean. An American Beach for African Americans. 2010. (ENG., Illus.). 200p. pap. 19.95 *(978-0-8130-3508-6(2))* Univ. Pr. of Florida.

Yegül, Fikret. Bathing in the Roman World. 2009. (ENG., Illus.). 300p. (C). pap. 29.99 *(978-0-521-54962-2(0))* Cambridge Univ. Pr.

BATHING SUITS

Alac, Patrik. Bikini. 2012. (Temporis Ser.). (ENG., Illus.). 256p. 39.95 *(978-1-84484-918-5(X))* Parkstone Pr. USA, Ltd.

Hsiao, Karen. Karen Hsiao: Rubber Duck. 2010. (ENG., Illus.). 128p. 35.00 *(978-0-9845210-0-5(3))* Baby Tattoo Bks.

Iooss, Walter. Heaven. 2010. (ENG., Illus.). 256p. 39.95 *(978-1-60320-116-2(5))* Time Home Entertainment, Inc.

Schoumann, Helene. Gottex: Swimwear Haute Couture. Jones, Paul, tr. from FRE. 2008. (Illus.). 79p. *(978-2-84323-872-7(2))* Assouline.

Sports Illustrated Editors. Portfolio. 2009. (ENG., Illus.). 192p. 29.95 *(978-1-60320-089-9(4))* Time Home Entertainment, Inc.

—Sports Illustrated Swimsuit Portfolio: Paradise Found, Vol. 3. Sports Illustrated Editors, ed. 2010. (ENG., Illus.). 192p. 29.95 *(978-1-60320-153-7(X))* Time Home Entertainment, Inc.

—Sports Illustrated Swimsuit Portfolio: Fantasy Islands. 2011. (ENG., Illus.). 176p. 34.95 *(978-1-60320-209-1(9))* Time Home Entertainment, Inc.

Sports Illustrated Editors, ed. Swimsuit: The Complete Portfolio. 2008. (ENG., Illus.). 176p. 29.95 *(978-1-60320-041-7(X))* Time Home Entertainment, Inc.

Vedrenne, Elisabeth. Bisazza: Contemporary Mosaics. 2006. (ENG., Illus.). 79p. 25.00 *(978-2-84323-870-3(6))* Assouline FRA. Dist: Perseus Distribution.

BATHROOMS

see also Toilets

American Society of Mechanical Engineers Staff, ed. Deck Mounted Bath/Shower Transfer Valves. 16p. 30.00 *(978-0-7918-2586-0(8))* ASME Pr.

Baeck, Philippe De. Neugestaltung von Küchen & Badezimmern, 1 vol. 2009. (DUT, FRE, GER & ENG., Illus.). 619p. pap. 24.95 *(978-94-6065-010-9(4))* booQs Publishers bvba BEL. Dist: Innovative Logistics.

Beta-Plus Publishing. Bathrooms: Home Series 4. 2009. (Home Ser.). (ENG., Illus.). 128p. pap. *(978-90-8944-035-8(6)*, Beta-Plus (Acc)) Antique Collectors' Club.

—Designer Bathrooms: Home Series 18. 2010. (Home Ser.). (ENG., Illus.). 128p. pap. *(978-90-8944-049-5(6)*, Beta-Plus (Acc)) Antique Collectors' Club.

Better Homes and Gardens Books Staff. Beautiful Baths. 2009. (Decorating Ser.). (ENG., Illus.). 192p. pap. 19.95 *(978-0-696-24241-0(9)*, Wiley) Wiley, John & Sons, Inc.

—Small Bath Solutions. 2010. (Better Homes & Gardens Decorating Ser.: 30). (ENG., Illus.). 192p. pap. 19.99 *(978-0-470-61295-8(9)*, Wiley) Wiley, John & Sons, Inc.

Better Homes and Gardens Books Staff, et al. Great Bath Ideas. 2009. (ENG., Illus.). 304p. pap. 21.99 *(978-0-470-49041-9(1)*, Wiley) Wiley, John & Sons, Inc.

Blair, Munroe. Bathroom Ceramics. 2008. (Shire Library). (ENG., Illus.). 40p. pap. 11.95 *(978-0-7478-0513-7(X))* Shire Pubns., Ltd. GBR. Dist: Random Hse., Inc.

Braun Editorial Staff. Relax! Best of Bath Design. 2008. (ENG., Illus.). 400p. pap. 19.95 *(978-3-938780-68-8(1)*, Braun Publish,Csi) Continental Sales, Inc.

Eroto, Carles. Charming Bathrooms. 2009. 300p. pap. 29.00 *(978-84-96969-83-4(5))* Links International (Leading International Key Services Barcelona, S.A.) ESP. Dist: National Bk. Network.

Compact Classics Staff. Compact Classics Leather, Vol. 1. 49.95 *(978-1-880184-15-8(X))* Scarab Bk. Ltd.

Conran, Terence. Bathrooms: Home Design, Decoration & Furnishing. 2010. (ENG., Illus.). 112p. 20.00 *(978-1-84091-551-8(X)*, Conran Octopus) Octopus Publishing Group GBR. Dist: Hachette Bk. Group.

Creative Homeowner Press Editors, creator. The Best of Signature Baths: Over 100 Luxurious Bathrooms from Top Designers. rev. ed. 2007. (Home Decorating Ser.). (ENG., Illus.). 240p. (gr. 5). pap. 19.95 *(978-1-58011-362-5(1))* Creative Homeowner.

Creative Homeowner Press Staff. Bathrooms: The Smart Approach to Design. 2011. (Home Decorating Ser.). (ENG., Illus.). 224p. (gr. 5). pap. 19.95 *(978-1-58011-474-5(1))* Creative Homeowner.

De Haan, Nathalie. Römische Privatbäder: Entwicklung, Verbreitung, Struktur und Sozialer Status. 2011. (GER., Illus.). 556p. 141.95 *(978-3-631-60069-6(0))* Lang, Peter GmbH, Europaischer Verlag der Wissenschaften DEU. Dist: Lang, Peter.

de Haro, Fernando & Fuentes, Omar. Bathrooms. 2006. (Smallbooks Ser.). (ENG., Illus.). 64p. pap. 3.49 *(978-970-9726-39-8(0))* AM Editores MEX. Dist: Perseus-PGW.

de Haro, Fernando & Fuentes, Omar, compiled by. Bathrooms. 2011. (Inside Ser.). (ENG., Illus.). 348p. pap. 14.95 ***(978-607-437-089-8(3))*** AM Editores MEX. Dist: Perseus-PGW.

Dorling Kindersley Publishing Staff. Step-by-Step Home. 2012. (ENG.). 400p. 40.00 *(978-0-7566-8976-6(7))* Dorling Kindersley Publishing, Inc.

Farris, Jerri. Kitchens & Baths for Today & Tomorrow: Ideas for Fabulous New Kitchens & Baths. 2008. (ENG., Illus.). 288p. pap. 24.95 *(978-1-58923-374-4(3)*, 1589233743, Creative Publishing International) Quayside.

Fine Homebuilding. Bathroom Remodeling. 2011. (For Pros by Pros Ser.). (ENG., Illus.). 240p. pap. 24.95 *(978-1-60085-363-0(3))* Taunton Pr., Inc.

Fisher Knott, Mary. Kitchen & Bath Design: A Guide to Planning Basics. 2011. (ENG., Illus.). 384p. pap. 55.00 *(978-0-470-39200-3(2)*, Wiley) Wiley, John & Sons, Inc.

Gibson, Scott. Bathroom: Creative Design Solutions for Your Home. 2007. (Ideas That Work Ser.). (ENG., Illus.). 218p. pap. 19.95 *(978-1-56158-836-7(9)*, Taunton) Taunton Pr., Inc.

Gibson, Scott. New Bathroom Ideas that Work. 2012. (Ideas That Work Ser.). (ENG., Illus.). 224p. pap. 19.95 ***(978-1-60085-357-9(9))*** Taunton Pr., Inc.

Hillstrom, Susan Boyle. Bathrooms: Products, Inspiration, Materials. 2nd ed. 2009. (Home Decorating Ser.). (ENG., Illus.). 224p. (gr. 5). pap. 19.95 *(978-1-58011-437-0(7))* Creative Homeowner.

Jaccarino, Pamela Lerner, ed. Leading Kitchen & Bath Designers. 2007. (Perfect Home Ser.). (ENG., Illus.). 296p. 39.95 *(978-0-9764713-3-2(7))* Sandow Media.

Kramer, Sibylle. Bath & Spa. 2008. (ENG., Illus.). 272p. 62.50 *(978-3-938780-39-8(8)*, Braun Publish,Csi) Continental Sales, Inc.

Lee, Vinny. Bathrooms. 2006. (ENG., Illus.). 192p. pap. *(978-1-84597-246-2(5))* Ryland Peters & Small.

—Bathrooms: Creative Ideas for Sanctuary Spaces. 2007. (Small Books Ser.). (ENG., Illus.). 128p. 19.95 *(978-1-903221-70-9(6))* Aurum Pr., Ltd. GBR. Dist: Independent Pubs. Group.

Listri, Massimo. Magnificent Baths: Private Indulgences from Baroque to Minimalist. 2012. (ENG., Illus.). 272p. 50.00 ***(978-0-8478-3650-5(9))*** Rizzoli International Pubns., Inc.

McLeod, Virginia. Detail in Contemporary Bathroom Design. 2009. (ENG., Illus.). 192p. 45.00 *(978-1-85669-590-9(5))* King, Laurence Publishing GBR. Dist: Hachette Bk. Group.

McMillan, Patricia Hart & McMillan, Katharine Kaye. Glass Tile Inspirations for Kitchens & Baths. 2006. 128p. pap. 19.95 *(978-0-7643-2509-0(4))* Schiffer Publishing, Ltd.

Meredith Books Staff. Bath Design Guide. 2008. (Do It Yourself Ser.). (ENG., Illus.). 216p. pap. 19.95 *(978-0-696-23606-8(0)*, Wiley) Wiley, John & Sons, Inc.

Meunier, Pascal, photos by. The Last Hammams of Cairo: A Disappearing Bathhouse Culture. 2009. (ENG., Illus.). 144p. 39.95 *(978-977-416-243-5(9))* American Univ. in Cairo Pr. EGY. Dist: Oxford Univ. Pr., Inc.

Moss, Richard. Bathroom Installations: A Complete Guide Planning, Managing & Completing Your Installation. 2007. (ENG., Illus.). 160p. 45.00 *(978-1-86126-919-5(6))* Crowood Pr., Ltd. GBR. Dist: Independent Pubs. Group.

Nestor, Samantha. The Luxury Bathroom: Extraordinary Spaces from the Simple to the Extravagant. 2008. (ENG., Illus.). 224p. 60.00 *(978-0-307-39370-8(4)*, Clarkson Potter) Crown Publishing Group.

Old House Magazine Staff. Easy Upgrades: Bathrooms - Smart Makeovers, Trusted Advice. 2010. (ENG., Illus.). 208p. pap. 22.95 *(978-0-8487-3394-0(0))* Oxmoor Hse., Inc.

Olson, Candice. Candice Olson Kitchens & Baths. 2011. (ENG., Illus.). 224p. pap. 19.99 *(978-0-470-88937-4(3)*, Wiley) Wiley, John & Sons, Inc.

Pauwels, Wim. Bathrooms & Bedrooms. Watkinson, Laura, tr. 2008. (ENG., Illus.). 204p. *(978-90-77213-88-9(0)*, Beta-Plus (Acc)) Antique Collectors' Club.

—Wellness at Home. 2011. (ENG., Illus.). 200p. 80.00 *(978-90-8944-093-8(3))* Beta-Plus Pubs. BEL. Dist: Antique Collectors' Club.

Pauwels, Wim. The 100 Best Bathrooms. 2012. (ENG., Illus.). 224p. 55.00 ***(978-90-8944-117-1(4))*** Beta-Plus Pubs. BEL. Dist: National Bk. Network.

Peterson, Chris & Creative Publishing Editors. The Complete Guide to Bathrooms: Remodeling on a Budget - Vanities & Cabinets - Plumbing & Fixtures - Showers, Sinks & Tubs. 3rd ed. 2010. (Black & Decker Complete Guide Ser.). (ENG., Illus.). 288p. pap. 24.99 *(978-1-58923-562-5(2)*, 1589235622) Quayside.

Powell, Jane. Bungalow Bathrooms, 1 vol. 2009. (ENG., Illus.). 176p. pap. 19.99 *(978-1-4236-0673-4(6))* Gibbs Smith, Publisher.

RBA. Cocinas y Baños. 96p. 17.95 *(978-84-7901-919-8(0))* RBA Libros, S.A. ESP. Dist: Santillana USA Publishing Co., Inc.

RS Means, creator. Kitchen & Bath Project Costs: Planning & Estimating Successful Projects. 2006. (Illus.). 182p. per. 29.95 *(978-0-87629-784-1(X))* Means, R.S. Co., Inc.

San Pietro, Silvio, et al. Bathrooms 2/Bagni 2. 2008. (ITA & ENG., Illus.). 208p. *(978-88-7685-168-1(2)*, Edizioni L'archivolto (Acc)) Antique Collectors' Club.

Skinner, Tina. The Spa Bath. 2008. (Illus.). 128p. pap. 19.95 *(978-0-7643-2953-1(7))* Schiffer Publishing, Ltd.

Soria, Sandra S. All New Bathroom Idea Book. 2009. (Taunton Home Idea Bks.). (ENG., Illus.). 224p. pap. 19.95 *(978-1-60085-086-8(3))* Taunton Pr., Inc.

Sunset Books Staff. Bathrooms: Inspiration - Expert Advice. 2008. (Sunset Design Guide Ser.). (ENG., Illus.). 224p. pap. 22.95 *(978-0-376-01343-9(5)*, Sunset Bks./Sunset Publishing Corp.) Oxmoor Hse., Inc.

Sunset Magazine Editors. Sunset Make It Your Own: Bathrooms: 50 Easy Weekend Projects. 2012. (ENG., Illus.). 160p. pap. 18.95 ***(978-0-376-01636-2(1))*** Oxmoor Hse., Inc.

teNeues. Bathroom Design. 2010. (ENG., Illus.). 224p. pap. 12.95 *(978-3-8327-9399-9(2))* teNeues Publishing Co.

Trulove, James Grayson. Luxury Bathrooms. 2008. (ENG., Illus.). 192p. 35.00 *(978-0-06-134828-0(7),* Collins Design) HarperCollins Pubs.

Vally, Norma. Norma Vally's Bathroom Fix-Ups: More Than 50 Projects for Every Skill Level. 2009. (Norma Vally Ser.: 1). (ENG., Illus.). 238p. pap. 24.99 *(978-0-470-25156-0(5),* Wiley) Wiley, John & Sons, Inc.

Wax, Amy & Leone, Catherine Warren. Can't Fail Color Schemes — Kitchen & Bath: How to Choose Color for Stone & Tile Surfaces, Cabinets & Walls. 2008. (Can't Fail Ser.). (ENG., Illus.). 304p. (gr. 5). pap. 19.95 *(978-1-58011-413-4(X))* Creative Homeowner.

Willis, David & Mack, Lorrie. Plan Your Bathroom: Hundreds of Design Combinations At-a-Glance. 2006. (ENG., Illus.). 256p. 24.95 *(978-0-06-113826-3(6),* Collins Design) HarperCollins Pubs.

Xie, Yeal. Guestroom & Bathroom. 2011. (ENG.). 272p. 50.00 *(978-988-19739-9-3(6))* Design Media Publishing Ltd. HKG. Dist: BookMasters Distribution Services (BDS).

BATHS

see also Hot Tubs; Hydrotherapy; Spa Pools

Ashenburg, Katherine. The Dirt on Clean: An Unsanitized History. 2008. (ENG., Illus.). 368p. pap. 24.00 *(978-0-374-53137-9(4),* North Point Pr.) Farrar, Straus & Giroux.

Aykut, Susan. Coming Clean: An Illustrated Visit to a Turkish Bath. 2007. (ENG., Illus.). 192p. (C). 120.00 *(978-1-876832-94-0(0))* Macmillan Art Publishing AUS. Dist: Brown, David Bk. Co., The.

De Haan, Nathalie. Römische Privatbäder: Entwicklung, Verbreitung, Struktur und Sozialer Status. 2011. (GER., Illus.). 556p. 141.95 *(978-3-631-60069-6(0))* Lang, Peter GmbH, Europäischer Verlag der Wissenschaften DEU. Dist: Lang, Peter.

Ergin, Nina, ed. Bathing Culture of Anatolian Civilizations: Architecture, History, & Imagination. 2011. (Ancient near Eastern Studies Supplement Ser.). (ENG.). 339p. (C). 122.00 *(978-90-429-2439-0(X))* Peeters Pubs. & Booksellers BEL. Dist: Brown, David Bk. Co., The.

Hardy, Dan. The Complete Spa Manual for Homeowners: A Step-by-Step Maintenance & Therapy Guide. 2010. (ENG., Illus.). 288p. per., instr.'s gde. ed. 24.95 *(978-1-60138-263-4(4))* Atlantic Publishing Co.

Huggard, William R. A Handbook of Climatic Treatment Including Balneology. 2008. pap. *(978-1-84830-054-5(9),* Wildhern Pr.) Echo Library.

Koren, Leonard. How to Take a Japanese Bath. 2nd rev. ed. 2006. (ENG., Illus.). 40p. (Orig.). per. 9.95 *(978-1-933330-08-2(2))* Stone Bridge Pr.

Kosso, Cynthia & Scott, Anne. The Nature & Function of Water, Baths, Bathing, & Hygiene from Antiquity Through the Renaissance. 2009. *(978-90-04-17357-6(9))* BRILL.

Lyons, Gloria Hander. Lavender Sensations: Fragrant Herbs for Home & Bath. 2007. (Illus.). 60p. pap. 7.95 *(978-0-9790618-8-2(1))* Blue Sage Pr.

Manderscheid, Hubertus, ed. Dulcissima Aequora: Wasserbewirtschaftung und Hydrotechnik der Terme Suburbane in Pompeii. 2009. (Babesch Supplementa Ser.). (GER.). 169p. (C). pap. 95.00 *(978-90-429-2220-4(6))* Peeters Pubs. & Booksellers BEL. Dist: Brown, David Bk. Co., The.

Mecchia, Paola & Soren, David, eds. An Ancient Roman Spa at Mezzomiglio: Chianciano Terme, Tuscany, 2 vols. 2010. (Bar S Ser.). (ITA & ENG., Illus.). 257p. (C). pap. 177.50 *(978-1-4073-0715-2(0))* British Archaeological Reports Ltd. GBR. Dist: Brown, David Bk. Co., The.

Meredith Books Staff, creator. Baths Designs for Living. 2006. (Designs for Living Ser.). (Illus.). 191p. per. 21.95 *(978-0-696-22880-3(7),* Home Depot Bks.) Meredith Bks.

Rader, Joanne, et al, eds. Bathing Without a Battle: Person-Directed Care of Individuals with Dementia. 2nd ed. 2008. (Springer Series on Geriatric Nursing). (Illus.). 182p. pap. 49.00 *(978-0-8261-0124-2(0))* Springer Publishing Co., Inc.

Rook, Tony. Roman Baths in Britain. 2008. (Archaeology Ser.: No. 69). (ENG., Illus.). 64p. pap. 13.95 *(978-0-7478-0157-3(6))* Shire Pubns., Ltd. GBR. Dist: Random Hse., Inc.

Santini, Nicky. Baby Shower. (SPA.). 7.98 *(978-970-643-084-7(9))* Selector, S.A. de C.V. MEX. Dist: AIMS International Bks., Inc.

Smith, Bruce. The Japanese Bath. 2012. (ENG., Illus.). 96p. pap. 16.99 *(978-1-4236-2587-2(0))* Gibbs Smith, Publisher.

Stavert, Elaine. Bath Bombs. 2009. (Cozy Ser.). (ENG., Illus.). 156p. pap. 14.95 *(978-1-86108-615-0(6))* Guild of Master Craftsman Pubns., Ltd. GBR. Dist: Sterling Publishing Co., Inc.

Williams, Jennette. The Bathers. 2009. (Center for Documentary Studies/Honickman First Book Prize in Photography Ser.). (ENG., Illus.). 72p. 39.95 *(978-0-8223-4623-4(0))* Duke Univ. Pr.

Yao, Haiyang. Zhong Yi Yao Yu Yang Sheng Da Quan. 2008. (CHI., Illus.). *(978-7-5013-3556-5(7))* Beijing Library Pr.

Yegül, Fikret. Bathing in the Roman World. 2009. (ENG., Illus.). 256p. (C). 92.00 *(978-0-521-84032-3(5))* Cambridge Univ. Pr.

BETSI (AFRICAN PEOPLE)

see Beti (African People)

BATIK

Achjadi, Judi. Glory of Batik: The Danar Hadi Collection. 2011. (ENG., Illus.). 336p. pap. 39.95 *(978-602-98697-0-5(1))* Tuttle Publishing.

Brown, Patricia L. Easy Batik Landscape Quilts. 2011. (ENG., Illus.). 80p. 24.95 *(978-1-60460-004-9(7),* 1604600047, American Quilter's Society) Collector Bks.

Elliott, Inger McCabe. Batik: Fabled Cloth of Java. 2010. (ENG., Illus.). 240p. pap. 29.95 *(978-0-7946-0668-8(7))* Tuttle Publishing.

Fleischmann-Heck, Isa, et al. Batik: 75 Selected Masterpieces: The Rudolf G. Smend Collection. 2007. (GER & ENG., Illus.). 176p. per. 45.00 *(978-0-8048-3895-5(X))* Tuttle Publishing.

Lin, Lee Chor. Batik: Creating an Identity. 2007. (ENG., Illus.). 144p. pap. 30.00 *(978-981-4155-91-5(8),* Didier Millet,Csi) Continental Sales, Inc.

Lu, Pu. Chinese Indigo Batik Designs. 2007. (Dover Pictorial Archive Ser.). (ENG., Illus.). 128p. per. 14.95 *(978-0-486-45560-0(2))* Dover Pubns., Inc.

Princess Mirah's Crafts Staff, contrib. by. Color Your World with Princess Mirah Batiks: With Princess Mirah Batiks. 2008. (ENG., Illus.). 64p. pap. 19.95 *(978-1-57120-563-6(2))* C & T Publishing.

Robinson, Rosi. Start to Batik. 2009. (Start to Ser.). (ENG., Illus.). 48p. (J). (gr. 4-7). pap. 10.95 *(978-1-84448-353-2(3))* Search Pr., Ltd. GBR. Dist: Independent Pubs. Group.

Ryan, Judith. Across the Desert: Aboriginal Batik from Central Australia. 2009. (ENG., Illus.). 168p. pap. 37.50 *(978-0-7241-0299-0(X))* National Gallery of Victoria AUS. Dist: National Bk. Network.

Shifrin, Laurie J. Batik Gems: 29 Dazzling Quilt Projects. 2009. (ENG., Illus.). 96p. pap. 27.95 *(978-1-57120-560-5(8))* C & T Publishing.

Van Dartel, Daan. Collectors Collected: Exploring Dutch Colonial Culture Through the Study of Batik. 2007. (Bulletins of the Royal Tropical Institute Ser.). (Illus.). 56p. per. 35.00 *(978-90-6832-163-0(3))* Royal Tropical Institute Pr. (KIT (Koninklijk Instituut voor de Tropen) NLD. Dist: Stylus Publishing, LLC.

Yunus, Noor Azlina. Malaysian Batik: Reinventing a Tradition. 2012. (ENG., Illus.). 176p. 34.95 *(978-0-8048-4264-8(7))* Tuttle Publishing.

BATILLE Y ORDONEZ, JOSE, 1856-1929

Vanger, Milton I. Uruguay¿s José Batlle y Ordoñez: The Determined Visionary, 1915-1917. 2009. (Illus.). 240p. *(978-1-58826-694-1(X))* Rienner, Lynne Pubs.

BATMAN (FICTITIOUS CHARACTER)

Beatty, Scott. The Batman Handbook: The Ultimate Training Manual. 2006. (Illus.). 191p. pap. 16.00 *(978-1-4223-5204-5(8))* DIANE Publishing Co.

Brooker, Will. Hunting the Dark Knight: Twenty-First Century Batman. 2012. (ENG., Illus.). 272p. 85.00 *(978-1-84885-279-2(7));* pap. 16.00 *(978-1-84885-280-8(0))* I. B. Tauris & Co., Ltd. GBR. Dist: Macmillan.

Durand, Kevin K. & Leigh, Mary K., eds. Riddle Me This, Batman! Essays on the Universe of the Dark Knight. 2011. (ENG., Illus.). 228p. pap. 40.00 *(978-0-7864-4629-2(3))* McFarland & Co., Inc. Pubs.

Greenberger, Robert. The Essential Batman Encyclopedia. 2008. (ENG., Illus.). 400p. pap. 29.95 *(978-0-345-50106-6(3),* Del Rey) Random House Publishing Group.

Greenberger, Robert & Manning, Matthew K. The Batman Vault: A Museum-in-a-Book with Rare Collectibles from the Batcave. 2009. (ENG.). 192p. 49.95 *(978-0-7624-3663-7(8))* Running Pr. Bk. Pubs.

Manning, Matthew K. The Batman Files. 2011. (ENG.). 308p. 100.00 *(978-1-4494-0822-0(2))* Andrews McMeel Publishing.

O'Neil, Dennis, ed. Batman Unauthorized: Vigilantes, Jokers, & Heroes in Gotham City. 2008. (Smart Pop Ser.). (ENG.). 219p. per. 17.95 *(978-1-933771-30-4(5))* BenBella Bks.

Rucka, Greg & Brubaker, Ed. Gotham Central Book 4: Corrigan. 2011. (ENG., Illus.). 224p. 29.99 *(978-1-4012-3003-6(2))* DC Comics.

Rucka, Greg, et al. Gotham Central. 2012. (ENG., Illus.). 224p. pap. 19.99 *(978-1-4012-3194-1(2))* DC Comics.

Urbaschek, Stephan, ed. Andreas Hofer: Andy Hope 1930. 2010. (ENG., Illus.). 192p. pap. 45.00 *(978-3-939894-13-1(3))* Goetz, Ingvild, Kunstverlag, GmbH DEU. Dist: D.A.P./Distributed Art Pubs.

White, Mark D. & Arp, Robert, eds. Batman & Philosophy: The Dark Knight of the Soul. 2008. (Blackwell Philosophy & Pop Culture Ser.: 2). (ENG.). 304p. pap. 17.95 *(978-0-470-27030-1(6),* Wiley) Wiley, John & Sons, Inc.

Zehr, E. Paul. Becoming Batman: The Possibility of a Superhero. 2008. (ENG., Illus.). 320p. 27.95 *(978-0-8018-9063-5(2))* Johns Hopkins Univ. Pr.

BATON ROUGE (LA.)

Aaron, Larry G. Historic Neighborhoods of Baton Rouge. 2010. (American Chronicles Ser.). (ENG., Illus.). 128p. pap. 19.99 *(978-1-59629-839-2(1))* History Pr., The.

Bielawa, Michael & Bielawa, Janice. Baseball in Baton Rouge. 2007. (Images of Baseball Ser.). (ENG., Illus.). 128p. per. 19.99 *(978-0-7385-4223-2(7))* Arcadia Publishing.

Campbell, Cynthia V. Baton Rouge. 2010. (Insiders' Guide Ser.). (ENG., Illus.). 176p. pap. 16.95 *(978-0-7627-5671-1(3),* Insiders' Guide) Globe Pequot Pr., The.

Frey, Fred C., photos by. Above Baton Rouge: A Pilot's View Then & Now. 2009. (Illus.). 168p. 39.95 *(978-0-8071-3438-2(4))* Louisiana State Univ. Pr.

Haase, Carol K. Louisiana's Old State Capitol, 1 vol. rev. ed. 2009. (ENG., Illus.). 136p. pap. 14.95 *(978-1-58980-615-3(8))* Pelican Publishing Co., Inc.

Hendry, Petra Munro, et al. Old South Baton Rouge: The Roots of Hope. 2009. 186p. pap. 30.00 *(978-1-887366-86-1(5))* Univ. of Louisiana at Lafayette Pr.

Martin, Mark E. Historic Photos of Baton Rouge. 2008. (Historic Photos Ser.). (ENG.). 206p. 39.95 *(978-1-59652-441-5(3))* Turner Publishing Co.

—Remembering Baton Rouge. 2010. (Remembering Ser.). (ENG., Illus.). 134p. pap. 16.95 *(978-1-59652-694-5(7))* Turner Publishing Co.

Moses, Jennifer Anne. Bagels & Grits: A Jew on the Bayou. 2007. (ENG.). 184p. 26.95 *(978-0-299-22440-0(6))* Univ. of Wisconsin Pr.

Rodrigue, Sylvia Frank & Phillips, Faye. Baton Rouge. 2008. (Images of America Ser.). (ENG., Illus.). 128p. pap. 21.99 *(978-0-7385-5406-8(5))* Arcadia Publishing.

Sykes, John. A Guide to Historic Downtown Baton Rouge. 2011. 128p. pap. 19.99 *(978-1-60949-182-6(3))* History Pr., The.

BATRACHIA

see Amphibians

BATS

Adams, Rick A. & Pedersen, Scott C., eds. Ontogeny, Functional Ecology, & Evolution of Bats. 2008. (ENG., Illus.). 408p. pap. 80.00 *(978-0-521-08735-3(X))* Cambridge Univ. Pr.

Allen, Harrison. Monograph of the Bats of North America. 2006. 116p. per. 16.99 *(978-1-4255-0767-1(0))* MPublishing.

Altringham, John D. Bats: From Evolution to Conservation. 2nd ed. 2011. (Illus.). 368p. 117.00 *(978-0-19-920711-4(9));* (ENG., 352p. pap. 58.50 *(978-0-19-920712-1(7))* Oxford Univ. Pr., Inc.

Ammerman, Loren K., et al. Bats of Texas. 2012. (W. L. Moody Jr. Natural History Ser.). (Illus.). 328p. pap. 35.00 *(978-1-60344-476-7(9))* Texas A&M Univ. Pr.

Anatomy. Bat Skeletal Growth: Molecular & Environmental Perspectives [Bibliography & Price Not Definite.]: Special Issue: Cells Tissues Organs 2008, Vol. 187, No. 1. Hermanson, J. W. & Farnum, C. E., eds. 2007. (Illus.). 88p. pap. *(978-3-8055-8421-0(0))* Karger, S. AG.

Barnard, Susan, ed. Bats in Captivity: Volume 2: Aspects of Rehabilitation. 2010. 484p. 89.95 *(978-1-934899-04-5(6));* (ENG.). pap. 67.95 *(978-1-934899-05-2(4))* ThinkBiotech, LLC. (Logos Pr.).

—Bats in Captivity: Volume 3: Diet & Feeding; Environment & Housing, 4, 3. 2011. 434p. (ENG.). 89.95 *(978-1-934899-06-9(2));* pap. 67.95 *(978-1-934899-07-6(0))* ThinkBiotech, LLC. (Logos Pr.).

Barnard, Susan M., ed. Bats in Captivity: Biological & Medical Aspects. 2009. 600p. 99.95 *(978-1-934899-02-1(X));* pap. 74.95 *(978-1-934899-03-8(8))* ThinkBiotech, LLC. (Logos Pr.).

Bat Conservation International Staff, creator. Educator's Activity Book about Bats. 2007. (ENG., Illus.). 64p. pap. 11.95 *(978-0-9638248-5-1(6))* Bat Conservation International, Inc.

Constantine, Denny G. Bat Rabies & Other Lyssavirus Infections. 2008. *(978-1-4113-2259-2(2))* United States Geological Survey.

Dietz, Markus. Thermoregulation & Foraging Strategies of the Trawling Bat Myotis Daubentonii. 2008. 132p. pap. *(978-3-639-03718-0(9))* VDM Verlag Dr. Mueller e.K.

Elangovan, V., et al. The Short-Nosed Fruit Bat: Development & Foraging Behaviour. 2010. 220p. pap. *(978-3-8383-7185-6(2))* Lambert Academic Publishing.

Fenton, M. Brock. Bats, 1 vol. rev. ed. 2012. (ENG., Illus.). 240p. pap. 18.95 *(978-1-55041-482-0(8))* Fitzhenry & Whiteside, Ltd. CAN. Dist: Ingram Pub. Services.

Fleming, Theodore H. & Racey, Paul A., eds. Island Bats: Evolution, Ecology, & Conservation. 2010. (ENG., Illus.). 560p. 65.00 *(978-0-226-25330-5(9))* Univ. of Chicago Pr.

Gone with the Wind: Impacts of Wind Turbines on Birds & Bats: Oversight Hearing Before the Subcommittee on Fisheries, Wildlife, & Oceans of the Committee on Natural Resources, U.S. House of Representatives, One Hundred Tenth Congress, First Session, Tuesday, May 1, 2007. 2007. iii, 82p. *(978-0-16-079595-4(8),* 552-070-36555-9) United States Government Printing Office.

Gray, Susan H. Gray Bat. 2007. (21st Century Skills Library: Road to Recovery Ser.). (ENG., Illus.). 32p. (gr. 4-8). lib. bdg. 28.50 *(978-1-60279-037-7(X),* 200080) Cherry Lake Publishing.

Gunnell, Gregg F. & Simmons, Nancy B., eds. Evolutionary History of Bats: Fossils, Molecules & Morphology. 2012. (Cambridge Studies in Morphology & Molecules: New Paradigms in Evolutionary Bio Ser.). (ENG., Illus.). 572p. 135.00 *(978-0-521-76824-5(1));* pap. 65.00 *(978-0-521-74526-0(8))* Cambridge Univ. Pr.

Harvey, Michael J., et al. Bats of the United States & Canada. 2011. (ENG., Illus.). 224p. pap. 24.95 *(978-1-4214-0191-1(6))* Johns Hopkins Univ. Pr.

Korad, Vishakha. Structural Organization of a Leaf-Nosed Bat. 2011. 408p. pap. *(978-3-8443-1631-5(0))* Lambert Academic Publishing.

Kunz, Thomas H. Field Guide to the Bats of North America. 224p. 2010. (ENG.). pap. 24.95 *(978-0-19-508072-8(6))* 2008. (Illus.). 49.50 *(978-0-19-508071-1(8))* Oxford Univ. Pr., Inc.

Kunz, Thomas H. & Parsons, Stuart, eds. Ecological & Behavioral Methods for the Study of Bats. 2nd ed. 2009. (ENG., Illus.). 920p. (gr. 17). 105.00 *(978-0-8018-9147-2(7))* Johns Hopkins Univ. Pr.

Lacki, Michael J., et al, eds. Bats in Forests: Conservation & Management. 2007. (ENG., Illus.). 352p. (gr. 17). 88.00 *(978-0-8018-8499-3(3))* Johns Hopkins Univ. Pr.

Lim, Burton K. Molecular Phylogenetics of New World Emballonurid Bats. 2010. 144p. pap. *(978-3-8383-0175-4(7))* Lambert Academic Publishing.

Mantill-Meluk, Hugo, et al. Phyllostomid Bats of Colombia: Annotated Checklist Distribution, & Biogeography, 56. 2009. (Illus.). 37p. pap. 9.95 net. *(978-1-929330-18-8(9))* Museum of Texas Tech Univ.

Marks, Cynthia S. & Marks, George E. Bats of Florida. 2006. (ENG., Illus.). 208p. per. 24.95 *(978-0-8130-2985-6(6))* Univ. Pr. of Florida.

Monadjem, Ara, et al. Bats of Central & Southern Africa: A Biogeographic & Taxonomic Synthesis. 2011. (ENG.). 400p. pap. 69.95 *(978-1-86814-508-9(5))* Witwatersrand Univ. Pr. Pubns. ZAF. Dist: Transaction Pubs.

Nogueira, Yeda L. Prevalence of Rabies Virus in Bats from Brazil Rain Forest. 2010. 84p. pap. *(978-3-639-27808-8(9))* VDM Verlag Dr. Mueller e.K.

Richardson, Phil. Bats. 2010. (ENG., Illus.). 128p. pap. 19.95 *(978-1-55407-803-5(2))* Firefly Bks., Ltd.

—Bats. (Illus.). 128p. 19.95 *(978-0-905483-41-2(3))* Whittet Bks., Ltd. GBR. Dist: Diamond Farm Bk. Pubs.

Schmidt-French, Barbara A. & Butler, Carol A. Do Bats Drink Blood? Fascinating Answers to Questions about Bats. 2009. (Illus.). x, 155p. *(978-0-8135-4587-5(0));* (ENG., 176p. pap. 21.95 *(978-0-8135-4588-2(9))* Rutgers Univ. Pr.

Schuchmann, Maike. Spatial Echo Suppression & Echo-Acoustic Object Normalization in Bats. 2008. 88p. pap. *(978-3-639-03447-9(3))* VDM Verlag Dr. Mueller e.K.

Vories, Kimery C., et al. Proceedings of Protecting Threatened Bats at Coal Mines: A Technical Interactive Forum: Held August 31-September 3, 2010, Ramada Plaza, South Charleston, West Virginia. 2011. *(978-1-885189-16-5(8))* Coal Research Ctr.

Wheeler, Jill C. Little Brown Bats. 2006. (Checkerboard Animal Library). (Illus.). 24p. (gr. k-6). 24.21 *(978-1-59679-325-5(2),* Checkerboard Library) ABDO Publishing Co.

White-Nose Syndrome: What's Killing Bats in the Northeast?: Joint Oversight Hearing Before the Subcommittee on Insular Affairs, Oceans, & Wildlife, Joint with the Subcommittee on National Parks, Forests, & Public Lands of the Committee on Natural Resources, U.S. House of Representatives, One Hundred Eleventh Congress, First Session, Thursday, June 4, 2009. 2009. (Illus.). v, 73p. *(978-0-16-084370-9(7),* 552-070-39913-5) United States Government Printing Office.

Zupan, Jakob L. & Mlakar, Sara L., eds. Bats: Biology, Behavior & Conservation. 2011. (Animal Science, Issues & Professions Ser.). (Illus.). 371p. 165.00 *(978-1-61209-749-7(9))* Nova Science Pubs., Inc.

BATS—JUVENILE LITERATURE

Markle, Sandra. Little Lost Bat. (J). (gr. 2-5). E-Book 6.99 *(978-1-60734-042-3(9))* Charlesbridge Publishing, Inc.

BATTERED CHILD SYNDROME

BarCharts, Inc. Child Abuse/Mandated Reporter Reference Guide. 2009. 4p. 1.57 *(978-1-4232-0149-6(3))* Barcharts, Inc.

Clements, Paul T. & Burgess, Ann W. Nursing Approach to the Evaluation of Child Maltreatment 2E. 2nd ed. 2012. (ENG., Illus.). pap. 75.00 *(978-1-878060-17-4(1))* STM Learning, Inc.

Frasier, Lori, et al. Abusive Head Trauma in Infants & Children; A Clinical Guide/Color Atlas: A Medical, Legal, & Forensic Reference. 2006. (Illus.). 630p. 175.00 *(978-1-878060-68-6(6))* STM Learning, Inc.

—Abusive Head Trauma in Infants & Children Guide/Atlas, & Supplementary CD-ROM: A Medical, Legal, & Forensic Reference. 2007. (ENG., Illus.). 630p. 275.00 incl. cd-rom *(978-1-878060-74-7(0))* STM Learning, Inc.

—Abusive Head Trauma Quick Reference: For Health Care, Social Service, & Law Enforcement Professionals. 2007. (ENG., Illus.). 355p. spiral bd. 52.00 *(978-1-878060-57-0(0))* STM Learning, Inc.

Frasier, Lori D. Abusive Head Trauma Pocket Atlas. 2012. (Illus.). pap. 60.00 *(978-1-878060-40-2(6))* STM Learning, Inc.

Frasier, Lori D., et al. Abusive Head Trauma in Infants & Children; Supplementary CD-ROM: A Medical, Legal, & Forensic Reference Supplementary CD-ROM, 1 disc. 2007. (ENG., Illus.). cd-rom 215.00 *(978-1-878060-64-8(3))* STM Learning, Inc.

Giardino, Angelo P., et al, eds. A Practical Guide to the Evaluation of Child Physical Abuse & Neglect. 2nd ed. 2010. (ENG., Illus.). xxxii, 400p. 159.00 *(978-1-4419-0701-1(7),* 1441907017) Springer.

Giardino, Angelo P. & Alexander, Randell. Child Abuse Quick Reference 2E: For Healthcare, Social Service, & Law Enforcement Professionals. 2nd rev. ed. 2006. (ENG., Illus.). 448p. spiral bd. 52.00 *(978-1-878060-60-0(0))* STM Learning, Inc.

Giardino, Angelo P., et al. Physical Abuse & Neglect: A Training Curriculum. 2008. (ENG., Illus.). 259p. spiral bd. 200.00 *(978-1-878060-79-2(1))* STM Learning, Inc.

Giardino, Eileen R. & Giardino, Angelo P. Nursing Approach to Child Maltreatment Curriculum: A Training Curriculum. 2012. (ENG., Illus.). spiral bd. 200.00 *(978-1-878060-72-3(4))* STM Learning, Inc.

BATTERED CHILDREN

see Abused Children

BATTERED WIVES

see Abused Wives

BATTERED WOMEN

see Abused Women

BATTERERS, MEN

see Abusive Men

BATTERIES

see Automobiles—Batteries; Electric Batteries; Lithium Cells; Solar Batteries; Space Vehicles—Batteries; Storage Batteries

BATTERIES, ELECTRIC

see Electric Batteries; Storage Batteries

BATTERIES, LITHIUM

see Lithium Cells

BATTERY (LAW)

see Assault and Battery

BATTERY INDUSTRY

Balderston, William. Philco: Autobiography of Progress. 2011. 32p. 35.95 *(978-1-258-09574-1(2))* Literary Licensing, LLC.

Battery & EV Industry Review 2005. 2006. per. 1950.00 *(978-1-59623-207-5(2))* BCC Research.

Munirruzzaman. Handling of Sludge in a Lead-Acid Battery Plant. 2010. 84p. pap. *(978-3-639-25007-7(9))* VDM Verlag Dr. Mueller e.K.

BATTING (BASEBALL)

Burda, Ted. Baseball's Hitting Secrets: How to Put a Round Baseball Bat on a Round Ball- Squarely. 2nd ed. 2009. 176p. pap. 18.95 *(978-1-892495-64-8(3))* Cycle Publishing/Van Der Plas Pubns.

Carew, Rod, et al. Rod Carew's Hit to Win: Batting Tips & Techniques from a Baseball Hall of Famer. 2012. (ENG., Illus.). 192p. pap. 22.99 *(978-0-7603-4266-4(0)*, 0760342660, MVP Bks.) MBI Publishing Co. LLC.

Fleitz, David L. Silver Bats & Automobiles: The Hotly Competitive, Sometimes Ignoble Pursuit of the Major League Batting Championship. 2011. (ENG., Illus.). 222p. pap. 29.95 *(978-0-7864-5879-0(8))* McFarland & Co., Inc. Pubs.

Gibson, Bob, et al. Sixty Feet, Six Inches: A Hall of Fame Pitcher & a Hall of Fame Hitter Talk about How the Game Is Played. 2011. (ENG.). 288p. pap. 15.95 *(978-0-7679-3110-6(6)*, Anchor) Knopf Doubleday Publishing Group.

Long, Kevin & Waggoner, Glen. Cage Rat: Lessons from a Life in Baseball by the Hitting Coach of the Yankees. 2011. (ENG.). 224p. 24.99 *(978-0-06-199499-9(5)*, Ecco) HarperCollins Pubs.

Perconte, Jack. The Making of a Hitter: A Proven & Practical Step-by-Step Baseball Guide. 2009. (ENG.). 200p. pap. 19.95 *(978-0-9793562-1-6(0))* Second Base Publishing.

Ryness, Gar & Dewart, Caleb. Batting Stance Guy: A Love Letter to Baseball. 2010. (ENG., Illus.). 256p. pap. 18.00 *(978-1-4391-8113-3(6)*, Scribner) Scribner.

Zardetto, Ray. '30: Major League Baseball's Year of the Batter. 2008. (ENG., Illus.). 239p. pap. 35.00 *(978-0-7864-3666-8(2))* McFarland & Co., Inc. Pubs.

BATTLE-CRIES

see also Slogans

Pearson, Andrew. The Slogans & Warcries of Scotland of Old. 2010. (ENG., Illus.). 250p. lib. bdg. *(978-0-9765609-4-4(1))* Wolfstar Graphics.

BATTLE DAMAGE REPAIR (WARSHIPS)

see Damage Control (Warships)

BATTLE OF BRITAIN, 1940

see Britain, Battle of, Great Britain, 1940

BATTLE OF THE ATLANTIC, 1939-1945

see World War, 1939-1945—Campaigns—Atlantic Ocean

BATTLEFIELD PHOTOGRAPHERS

see War Photographers

BATTLEFIELDS

see also subdivision Battlefields under individual wars, e.g. World War, 1914-1918—Battlefields; and names of individual Battlefields

Amber Books Staff, et al. Fighting Techniques of the Colonial Age: 1776 – 1914 Equipment, Combat Skills & Tactics. 2009. (ENG., Illus.). 256p. 29.95 *(978-0-312-59092-5(X)*, Dunne, Thomas Bks.) St. Martin's Pr.

Baynton-Williams, Ashley & Baynton-Williams, Miles. Maps of War. 2007. (Illus.). 223p. *(978-1-84724-207-5(3))* Quercus.

—Maps of War. 2011. (ENG., Illus.). 224p. 39.95 *(978-1-84724-206-8(5))* Quercus GBR. Dist: Independent Pubs. Group.

Bell, Graham. Yorkshire Battlefields: A Guide to the Great Conflicts on Yorkshire Soil, 937-1461. (Medieval Ser.). (Illus.). 144p. pap. 18.95 *(978-1-903425-12-1(3))* Pen & Sword Bks. Ltd. GBR. Dist: Casemate Pubs. & Bk. Distributors, LLC.

Bennett, Matthew. The Medieval World at War. Bennett, Matthew, ed. 2009. (ENG., Illus.). 272p. 55.00 *(978-0-500-25156-0(8)*, 525156) Thames & Hudson.

Benson, Michael. Ballparks of North America: A Comprehensive Historical Reference to Baseball Grounds, Yards & Stadiums, 1845 To 1988. alt. ed. 2009. (ENG., Illus.). 505p. pap. 39.95 *(978-0-7864-4421-2(5))* McFarland & Co., Inc. Pubs.

Bishop, Randy. Kentucky's Civil War Battlefields: A Guide to Their History & Preservation. 2012. E-Book *(978-1-4556-1608-4(7))*; (ENG., Illus.). 360p. 25.00 *(978-1-4556-1607-7(9))* Pelican Publishing Co., Inc.

Bishop, Randy. Mississippi's Civil War Battlefields: A Guide to Their History & Preservation, 1 vol. 2010. (ENG., Illus.). 384p. 25.00 *(978-1-58980-833-1(9))* Pelican Publishing Co., Inc.

Brown, Barry L., et al. Crossroads of Conflict: A Guide to Civil War Sites in Georgia. 2010. (ENG., Illus.). 304p. pap. 22.95 *(978-0-8203-3730-2(7))* Univ. of Georgia Pr.

Brown, Beth. Haunted Battlefields: Virginia's Civil War Ghosts. 2008. (Illus.). 160p. pap. 14.99 *(978-0-7643-3057-5(8))* Schiffer Publishing, Ltd.

Brown, Chris. Scottish Battlefields: 300 Battlefields That Shaped Scottish History. 2008. (ENG., Illus.). 336p. pap. 34.95 *(978-0-7524-3685-2(6))* History Pr. Ltd.,The GBR. Dist: Independent Pubs. Group.

Burley, Peter, et al. The Battles of St Albans. 2007. (Battleground: Wars of the Roses Ser.). (Illus.). 182p. per. 19.95 *(978-1-84415-569-9(2))* Pen & Sword Bks. Ltd. GBR. Dist: Casemate Pubs. & Bk. Distributors, LLC.

Burton, Brian K. The Peninsula & Seven Days: A Battlefield Guide. 2007. (This Hallowed Ground: Guides to Civil War Battlefields). (ENG., Illus.). 174p. pap. 21.95 *(978-0-8032-6246-1(9)*, Bison Bks.) Univ. of Nebraska Pr.

Bush, Bryan S. & Freese, Thomas. Haunted Battlefields of the South. 2010. (Illus.). 160p. pap. 14.99 *(978-0-7643-3385-9(2))* Schiffer Publishing, Ltd.

Cerew, Bruce. War Child. 2008. 320p. 28.49 *(978-1-4389-0538-9(6))*; pap. 19.99 *(978-1-4389-0537-2(8))* AuthorHouse.

Cooke, David. Battlefield Yorkshire: From the Romans to the English Civil War. 2006. (Illus.). 218p. 39.95 *(978-1-84415-424-1(6))* Pen & Sword Bks. Ltd. GBR. Dist: Casemate Pubs. & Bk. Distributors, LLC.

Cottrell, Steve. Haunted Ozark Battlefields: Civil War Ghost Stories & Brief Battle Histories, 1 vol. 2010. (ENG., Illus.). 116p. pap. 12.95 *(978-1-58980-877-5(0))* Pelican Publishing Co., Inc.

D'Arcy, David. Civil War Tours of the Low Country: Beaufort, Hilton Head, & Bluffton, South Carolina. 2008. (Illus.). 144p. pap. 16.95 *(978-0-7643-2790-2(9))* Schiffer Publishing, Ltd.

Doyle, P. & Bennett, Matthew R., eds. Fields of Battle: Terrain in Military History. 2010. (GeoJournal Library). 398p. pap. 289.00 *(978-90-481-5940-6(7)*, 9048159407) Springer.

Dukas, Neil Bernard. The Battle of Nu'uanu 1795: An Illustrated Pocket Guide to the O'ahu Battlefield. 2010. (ENG., Illus.). 104p. pap. 9.95 *(978-1-56647-922-6(3))* Mutual Publishing LLC.

Ethier, Eric & Aloisi, Rebecca. Insiders' Guide to Civil War Sites in the Eastern Theater. 3rd ed. 2008. (Insiders' Guide Ser.). (ENG., Illus.). 208p. pap. 15.95 *(978-0-7627-4182-3(1))* Globe Pequot Pr., The.

Gouin, John R. An Unforgettable Salute: Skirmishes, Battlefields, & Making Peace with My Father. 2010. 172p. 25.95 *(978-1-4502-3980-6(3))*; pap. 15.95 *(978-1-4502-3979-0(X))* iUniverse, Inc.

Hancock. High Wood. 2009. 208p. pap. 19.99 *(978-0-85052-650-9(7))* Pen & Sword Bks. Ltd. GBR. Dist: Casemate Pubs. & Bk. Distributors, LLC.

Heier, Vincent A. Little Bighorn. 2009. (Postcard History Ser.). (ENG., Illus.). 128p. pap. 21.99 *(978-0-7385-7007-5(9))* Arcadia Publishing.

Holmes, Richard & Marix Evans, Martin. A Guide to Battles: Decisive Conflicts in History. 2009. (Oxford Paperback Reference Ser.). (ENG., Illus.). 384p. pap. 18.95 *(978-0-19-280654-3(8))* Oxford Univ. Pr., Inc.

Holstein, Christina. Verdun: Fort Douaumont: Revised Edition. 2010. (Illus.). 192p. pap. 24.95 *(978-1-84884-345-5(3))* Pen & Sword Bks. Ltd. GBR. Dist: Casemate Pubs. & Bk. Distributors, LLC.

Middlebrook, Martin & Middlebrook, Mary. The Middlebrook Guide to the Somme Battlefields: A Comprehensive Coverage from Crecy to the Two World Wars. 2007. (Illus.). 383p. 50.00 *(978-1-84415-533-0(1))* Pen & Sword Bks. Ltd. GBR. Dist: Casemate Pubs. & Bk. Distributors, LLC.

Mueller, Robert J. Fields of War: Fifty Key Battlefields in France & Belgium. 2009. (Illus.). 467p. pap. 29.95 *(978-0-9823677-0-4(8))* French Battlefields.

Pascoe, Chris. Death, Destruction & a Packet of Peanuts: A Rollicking Pub Crawl Through Four Years of the English Civil War. 2009. (ENG., Illus.). 240p. 15.95 *(978-1-906032-62-3(9))* Anova Bks. GBR. Dist: Independent Pubs. Group.

Phillips, Thomas D. Battlefields of Nebraska. 2010. (ENG.). 300p. pap. 18.95 *(978-0-87004-471-7(0))* 2009. (Illus.). 295p. *(978-0-87004-710-7(8))* Caxton Pr.

Pollard, T. & Banks, I., eds. Bastions & Barbed Wire: Studies in the Archaeology of Conflict. 2009. 264p. *(978-90-04-17360-6(9))* BRILL.

Pollard, Tony, ed. Culloden: The History & Archaeology of the Last Clan Battle. 2009. (Illus.). 304p. 50.00 *(978-1-84884-020-1(9))* Pen & Sword Bks. Ltd. GBR. Dist: Casemate Pubs. & Bk. Distributors, LLC.

Pollard, Tony & Banks, Iain, eds. Scorched Earth: Studies in the Archaeology of Conflict. 2007. (Illus.). 330p. *(978-90-04-16448-2(0))* BRILL.

Rafuse, Ethan Sepp. Antietam, South Mountain, & Harpers Ferry: A Battlefield Guide. 2008. (This Hallowed Ground: Guides to Civil Wa Ser.). (ENG., Illus.). 282p. pap. 21.95 *(978-0-8032-3970-8(X)*, Bison Bks.) Univ. of Nebraska Pr.

Reclaiming the Beauty of the Battlefields. 2008. (Illus.). 48p. 74.95 *(978-0-9670928-2-9(5))*; (ENG., 50p. pap. 32.95 *(978-0-9670928-3-6(3))* Pecan Pr., The.

Robertson, James I. & Wills, Brian Steel. Civil War Sites in Virginia: A Tour Guide. 2nd rev. ed. 2011. (ENG., Illus.). 136p. pap. 12.95 *(978-0-8139-3111-1(8))* Univ. Pr. of Virginia.

Ryan, Chris, ed. Battlefield Tourism: History, Place & Interpretation. 2007. (ENG., Illus.). 316p. 106.00 *(978-0-08-045362-0(7))* Routledge.

Schofield, John. Aftermath: Readings in the Archaeology of Recent Conflict. 2010. (Illus.). 250p. pap. 39.95 *(978-0-387-09465-6(2)*, 0387094652) Springer.

Scott, Douglas, et al, eds. Fields of Conflict: Battlefield Archaeology from the Roman Empire to the Korean War, 2 vols. 2006. (Praeger Security International Ser.). (Illus.). 480p. 175.00 *(978-0-275-99315-3(9)*, C9315, Praeger Security International) Greenwood Publishing Group, Inc.

—Fields of Conflict: Battlefield Archaeology from the Roman Empire to the Korean War. 2009. (Illus.). 450p. pap. 24.95 *(978-1-59797-276-5(2))* Potomac Bks., Inc.

Smith, Timothy B. The Golden Age of Battlefield Preservation: The Decade of the 1890s & the Establishment of America's First Five Military Parks. 2008. (ENG., Illus.). 294p. 38.95 *(978-1-57233-622-3(6))* Univ. of Tennessee Pr.

Snow, Peter & Snow, Dan. 20th Century Battlefields. 2008. (ENG., Illus.). 368p. pap. 18.95 *(978-1-84607-286-4(7))* BBC Worldwide GBR. Dist: Independent Pubs. Group.

Starbuck, David R. The Archaeology of Forts & Battlefields. 2011. (American Experience in Archaeological Pespective Ser.). (ENG., Illus.). 128p. 69.95 *(978-0-8130-3689-2(5))* Univ. Pr. of Florida.

Sullivan, James R. Chickamauga & Chattanooga Battlefields. 2011. 72p. pap. 8.95 *(978-1-58218-778-5(9))* Digital Scanning, Inc.

Tully, Terry, compiled by. Stories of Faith & Courage from the Civil War: Battlefields & Blessings. 2006. 384p. pap. 16.99 *(978-0-89957-043-3(7))* AMG Pubs.

Vandkilde, Helle, ed. Globalisation, Battlefields, Economics: Three Inaugural Lectures in Archaeology. 2007. (ENG., Illus.). 54p. (C). pap. 20.00 *(978-87-7934-374-0(0))* Aarhus Universitetsforlag DNK. Dist: ISD.

White, Mel. Complete National Parks of the United States: Including Parks, Monuments, Battlefields, Historic Sites, Seashores, Recreation Areas, & Scenic Rivers. 2009. (Illus.). 527p. *(978-1-4262-0528-6(7))* National Geographic Society.

—National Geographic Complete National Parks of the United States. 2010. (ENG., Illus.). 528p. 40.00 *(978-1-4262-0527-9(9)*, National Geographic) National Geographic Society.

BATTLES

see also Battlefields; Imaginary Wars and Battles; Naval Battles

also names of battles, e.g. Gettysburg (Pa.), Battle of, 1863; also subdivisions Campaigns under names of wars, e.g. World War, 1914-1918—Campaigns; United States—History—Civil War, 1861-1865—Campaigns

Ardant Du Picq, Charles J. Battle Studies: Ancient & Modern Battle. Greely, John N. & Cotton, Robert C., trs. reprint ed. 27.00 *(978-0-404-20006-0(0))* AMS Pr., Inc.

Baynton-Williams, Ashley & Baynton-Williams, Miles. Maps of War. 2011. (ENG., Illus.). 224p. 39.95 *(978-1-84724-206-8(5))* Quercus GBR. Dist: Independent Pubs. Group.

Beattie, Judith, et al. The Battle of the Restigouche (La Bataille de la Ristigouche) 2nd ed. (Illus.). 48p. pap. *(978-0-660-16384-0(5))* Canadian Government Publishing.

Childs. Williamite Wars in Ireland (p) 2008. (ENG., Illus.). 464p. 34.95 *(978-1-84725-164-0(1)*, Hambledon Continuum) Continuum International Publishing Group, Ltd. GBR. Dist: National Bk. Network.

Clark, George B. Battle History of the United States Marine Corps, 1775-1945. 2010. (ENG., Illus.). 262p. 75.00 *(978-0-7864-4598-1(X))* McFarland & Co., Inc. Pubs.

Crane, Stephen. Great Battles of the World. 2007. (ENG.). 202p. 39.95 *(978-0-548-00742-6(X))* Kessinger Publishing, LLC.

Creasy, E. S. The Fifteen Decisive Battles from Marathon to Waterloo. 2007. 300p. 32.95 *(978-1-4344-8443-7(2))*; per. 19.95 *(978-1-4344-8442-0(4))* Wildside Pr., LLC.

Creasy, Edward Shepherd. Decisive Battles of the World. 2009. 532p. 36.99 *(978-1-113-67888-1(7))*; pap. 40.75 *(978-1-113-67886-7(0))*; pap. 39.75 *(978-1-113-67885-0(2))* BiblioBazaar.

—The Fifteen Decisive Battles of the World: From Marathon to Waterloo. 2008. (Dover Military History, Weapons, Armor Ser.). (ENG., Illus.). 400p. pap. 12.95 *(978-0-486-46170-0(X))* Dover Pubns., Inc.

Curry, John & Featherstone, Donald. Donald Featherstone's Battle Notes for Wargamers Solo Wargaming Edition. 2011. 172p. pap. 29.50 *(978-1-4467-3183-3(9))* Lulu Enterprises Inc.

Dawson, Henry, abr. Battles of the United States. 2009. (Military History Ser.). (ENG.). 584p. pap. 36.95 *(978-1-4290-2113-5(6))* Applewood Bks.

Dobbs, J. F. From Bunker Hill to Manila Bay. reprint ed. 150.00 *(978-0-7222-7693-8(1))* Library Reprints, Inc.

Dobbs, John F., ed. From Bunker Hill to Manila Bay. 2007. (ENG.). 366p. 48.95 *(978-0-548-03022-6(7))* Kessinger Publishing, LLC.

Dorling Kindersley Publishing Staff & Grant, R. G. Battle: A Visual Journey Through 5,000 Years of Combat. 2009. (ENG.). 360p. pap. 24.95 *(978-0-7566-5578-5(1))* Dorling Kindersley Publishing, Inc.

—Commanders: History's Greatest Military Leaders. 2010. (ENG., Illus.). 360p. 40.00 *(978-0-7566-6736-8(4))* Dorling Kindersley Publishing, Inc.

Fawcett, Bill. How to Lose a Battle: Foolish Plans & Great Military Blunders. 2006. (ENG., Illus.). 336p. pap. 13.99 *(978-0-06-076024-3(9))*, William Morrow Paperbacks) HarperCollins Pubs.

Finkel, David. The Good Soldiers. 2010. (ENG., Illus.). 336p. pap. 15.00 *(978-0-312-43002-3(7))* Picador.

Franks. Anthology of Tank Battles. Date not set. *(978-0-7653-0420-9(1))*; pap. *(978-0-7653-0421-6(X))* Doherty, Tom Assocs., LLC. (Forge Bks.).

Freeman, G. I. Currier & Ives Pictorial History of American Battle Scenes. Freeman, G. L., ed. 2011. 104p. 39.95 *(978-1-258-00187-2(X))* Literary Licensing, LLC.

Fuller, J. F. C. Decisive Battles of the U. S. A. , 1776-1918. 2007. (ENG., Illus.). 428p. per. 21.95 *(978-0-8032-6003-0(2)*, Bison Bks.) Univ. of Nebraska Pr.

Gramm, Kent. Battle: The Nature & Consequences of Civil War Combat. 2008. (ENG.). 184p. 32.50 *(978-0-8173-1622-8(1))*; xi, 147p. pap. *(978-0-8173-5482-4(4))* Univ. of Alabama Pr.

Grant, R. G., ed. 1001 Battles That Changed the Course of World History. 2011. (ENG., Illus.). 960p. 36.95 *(978-0-7893-2233-3(1))* Universe Publishing.

Hacht, Anne Marie & Hayes, Dwayne D. Gale Encyclopedia of World History Vol. 2: War, 2 vols. 2008. (Illus.). *(978-1-4144-3149-9(X))*; *(978-1-4144-3150-5(3))*; (ENG., 900p. 266.00 *(978-1-4144-3148-2(1))* Cengage Gale.

Harrington, Peter, frwd. Don Troiani's American Battles: The Art of the Nation at War, 1754-1865. 2006. (ENG., Illus.). 248p. 49.95 *(978-0-8117-3327-4(0))* Stackpole Bks.

Hathaway, Ella C. Battle of Big Hole. (Shorey Historical Ser.). 32p. reprint ed. pap. 10.00 *(978-0-8466-0138-8(9)*, S138) Shorey's Bookstore.

Hollick, Clive. The Battle of Benburb 1646. 2011. (ENG., Illus.). 352p. 39.95 *(978-1-85635-670-1(1))* Mercier Pr., Ltd., The IRL. Dist: Dufour Editions, Inc.

Hopkins, T. C. F. Empires, Wars, & Battles: The Middle East from Antiquity to the Rise of the New World. 2008. (ENG., Illus.). 256p. pap. 14.95 *(978-0-7653-0327-1(2)*, Forge Bks.) Doherty, Tom Assocs., LLC.

Jaques, Tony. Dictionary of Battles & Sieges: A Guide to 8,500 Battles from Antiquity through the Twenty-first Century, 3 vols. 2006. 1432p. 299.95 *(978-0-313-33536-5(2)*, GR3536, Greenwood Pr.) Greenwood Publishing Group, Inc.

Johnson, Rob. Outnumbered - Outgunned - Undeterred: Twenty Battles Against All Odds. 2011. (ENG., Illus.). 216p. 27.95 *(978-0-500-25187-4(8)*, 525187) Thames & Hudson.

Judd, Denis. Someone Has Blundered: Calamities of the British Army in the Victorian Age. 2007. (Phoenix Press Ser.). (ENG., Illus.). 208p. pap. 12.95 *(978-0-7538-2181-7(8)*, Phoenix) Orion Publishing Group, Ltd. GBR. Dist: Sterling Publishing Co., Inc.

Krefft, James J. Ten Battles: Decisive Conflicts You May Not Know about, but Should. 2008. 200p. pap. 19.95 *(978-0-9793510-6-8(5))* Ctr. for Third Age Leadership, LLC.

Kure, Mitsuo & Sharpe, Michael. Samurai Battles. 2009. (ENG.). 192p. 19.99 *(978-0-7858-2379-7(4)*, 0785823794, Chartwell) Book Sales, Inc.

Lewis, Jon E., ed. The Mammoth Book of Modern Battles. 2009. (ENG.). 512p. pap. 13.95 *(978-0-7624-3625-5(5))* Running Pr. Bk. Pubs.

Livesey, Anthony. Great Commanders & Their Battles. (Illus.). 200p. 14.99 *(978-0-7858-1668-3(2))* Book Sales, Inc.

Lloyd, Nick. Loos 1915: The Untold Story. Strachan, Hew, ed. 2006. (ENG., Illus.). 320p. 50.00 *(978-0-7524-3937-2(5))* History Pr. Ltd.,The GBR. Dist: Independent Pubs. Group.

Margulies, Martin. The Battle of Prestonpans 1745. 2007. (ENG., Illus.). 192p. pap. 37.95 *(978-0-7524-4035-4(7))* History Pr. Ltd.,The GBR. Dist: Independent Pubs. Group.

Marren, Peter. Battles of the Dark Ages. 2009. (Illus.). 224p. pap. 25.99 *(978-1-84415-884-3(5))* Pen & Sword Bks. Ltd. GBR. Dist: Casemate Pubs. & Bk. Distributors, LLC.

—Battles of the Dark Ages: British Battlefields Ad 410 To 1065. 2006. (Illus.). 210p. 39.95 *(978-1-84415-270-4(7))* Pen & Sword Bks. Ltd. GBR. Dist: Casemate Pubs. & Bk. Distributors, LLC.

Mars-Proietti, Laura & Grey House Publishing Staff, eds. Ground Warfare: an International Encyclopedia: 2008, 3 vols. 2nd rev. ed. 2011. 395.00 *(978-1-59237-294-2(5))* Grey Hse. Publishing.

Mauro, Charles V. The Civil War in Fairfax County: Civilians & Soldiers. 2006. (ENG., Illus.). 160p. pap. 21.99 *(978-1-59629-148-5(6))* History Pr., The.

McNab, Chris. World's Worst Military Disasters. (World's Worst: from Innovation to Disaster Ser.). 80p. 2009. (gr. 8-8). 61.20 *(978-1-60854-860-6(0))* 2008. (Illus.). 30.60 *(978-1-4042-1841-3(6))* Rosen Publishing Group, Inc., The.

Michno, Gregory & Michno, Susan. Circle the Wagons! Attacks on Wagon Trains in History & Hollywood Films. 2008. (ENG., Illus.). 246p. 55.00 *(978-0-7864-3997-3(1))* McFarland & Co., Inc. Pubs.

O'Brien, Cormac. Outnumbered: Incredible Stories of History's Most Surprising Battlefield Upsets. 2010. (ENG., Illus.). 304p. pap. 19.99 *(978-1-59233-405-6(9)*, 1592334059, Fair Winds Press) Quayside.

O'Shea, Stephen. Sea of Faith: Islam & Christianity in the Medieval Mediterranean World. 2007. (ENG., Illus.). 432p. per. 17.00 *(978-0-8027-1517-3(6))* Walker & Co.

Picq, Ardant du. Battle Studies. 2008. 256p. 28.99 *(978-0-554-22413-8(5))*; 25.99 *(978-0-554-31716-8(8))* BiblioBazaar.

—Battle Studies. Greely, John N., tr. 2007. (ENG.). 240p. pap. 20.99 *(978-1-4264-2276-8(8))* BiblioBazaar.

—Battle Studies. Greely, John N. & Cotton, Robert C., trs. l.t. ed. 2007. (ENG.). 254p. pap. 23.99 *(978-1-4264-2311-6(X))* BiblioBazaar.

Picq, Charles-Jean-Jacques-Jose. Battle Studies. Cotton, Robert C. & Greely, John N., trs. 2006. pap. *(978-1-4068-3097-2(6))* Echo Library.

Pollard, T. & Banks, I., eds. Bastions & Barbed Wire: Studies in the Archaeology of Conflict. 2009. 264p. *(978-90-04-17360-6(9))* BRILL.

Poyntz, Dermot. Plight of the Wild Geese. 2011. (ENG., Illus.). 50p. pap. *(978-0-9566558-4-4(X))* Moccu Pr.

—War of the Two Kings. 2011. (ENG., Illus.). 50p. pap. *(978-0-9566558-2-0(3))* Moccu Pr.

Pratt, Fletcher. Battles That Changed History. Date not set. 348p. 25.95 *(978-0-8488-2573-7(X))* Amereon LTD.

Prima Games Staff & Dawson, Bryan. Arcania Gothic 4: Prima Official Game Guide. 2010. (ENG.). 224p. pap. 19.99 *(978-0-307-47021-8(0)*, Prima Games) Random Hse. Information Group.

Quinn, Tom. Military's Strangest Campaigns & Characters: Extraordinary but True Stories. 2011. (Strangest Ser.). (ENG.). 256p. pap. 11.95 *(978-1-907554-13-1(0))* Anova Bks. GBR. Dist: Independent Pubs. Group.

Rashba, Gary. Holy Wars: 3000 Years of Battles in the Holy Land. 2011. (Illus.). 288p. 32.95 *(978-1-61200-008-4(8))* Casemate Pubs. & Bk. Distributors, LLC.

Riley, Jonathon. Decisive Battles: From Yorktown to Operation Desert Storm. 2010. (ENG., Illus.). 256p. 29.95 *(978-1-84725-250-0(8))* Continuum International Publishing Group, Ltd. GBR. Dist: National Bk. Network.

Sabin, Philip & Sabin. Lost Battles: Reconstructing the Great Clashes of the Ancient World. 2009. (ENG., Illus.). 320p. 27.95 *(978-0-8264-3015-1(5)*, Hambledon Continuum) Continuum International Publishing Group, Ltd. GBR. Dist: National Bk. Network.

Sadler, John & Serdiville, Rosie. The Great Siege of Newcastle 1644. 2011. (ENG., Illus.). 128p. pap. 23.95 *(978-0-7524-5989-9(9))* History Pr. Ltd.,The GBR. Dist: Independent Pubs. Group.

Snow, Peter & Snow, Dan. The World's Greatest Twentieth Century Battlefields. 2007. (ENG., Illus.). 288p. 36.95 *(978-0-563-52295-9(X)*, BBC Bks.) Ebury Publishing GBR. Dist: Independent Pubs. Group.

Tanner, Stephen. Epic Retreats: From 1776 to the Evacuation of Saigon. (Illus.). 346p. 9.99 *(978-0-7858-1403-0(5))* Book Sales, Inc.

Thompson, Michael. Granicus 334 BC: Alexander's First Persian Victory. 2007. (Campaign Ser.: Vol. 182). (ENG., Illus.). 96p. pap. 18.95 *(978-1-84603-099-4(4))* Osprey Publishing, Ltd. GBR. Dist: Random Hse., Inc.

Tucker, Spencer. Battles That Changed History: An Encyclopedia of World Conflict. 2010. E-Book *(978-1-59884-430-6(X))* ABC-CLIO, LLC.

Tucker, Spencer C. Battles that Changed History: An Encyclopedia of World Conflict. 2010. (Illus.). 655p. 95.00 *(978-1-59884-429-0(6)*, A2867C) ABC-CLIO, LLC.

Twentieth Century Fox Film Corporation. Avatar: The Visual Retelling In 3D. 2011. 168p. 22.99 *(978-0-06-204946-9(1))* HarperCollins Pubs.

Watson, Bruce. Desert Battles: From Napoleon to the Gulf War. 2007. (Stackpole Military History Ser.). (ENG., Illus.). 214p. per. 16.95 *(978-0-8117-3380-9(7))* Stackpole Bks.

Weir, William. Fatal Victories: From the Crusades to Bunker Hill to the Vietnam War: History's Most Tragic Military Triumphs & the High Cost of Victory. 2006. (ENG.). 1p. per. 14.95 *(978-1-933648-12-5(0))* Pegasus Bks.

—Secrets of Warfare: Exposing the Myths & Hidden History of Weapons & Battles. 2011. (ENG.). 1p. pap. 15.99 *(978-1-60163-155-8(3)*, New Page Bks.) Career Pr., Inc.

—Warfare: Exposing the Myths & Hidden History of Weapons & Battles. 2011. E-Book *(978-1-60163-671-3(7)*, New Page Bks.) Career Pr., Inc.

Wood, Larry. Civil War Springfield. 2011. 144p. pap. 19.99 ***(978-1-60949-308-0(7))*** History Pr., The.

Woolrych, Austin H. Battles of the English Civil War. 2011. 200p. 44.95 ***(978-1-258-00200-8(0))*** Literary Licensing, LLC.

Wyatt, Don J., ed. Battlefronts Real & Imagined: War, Border, & Identity in the Chinese Middle Period. 2008. (New Middle Ages Ser.). (ENG.). 324p. 100.00 *(978-1-4039-6084-9(4))* Palgrave Macmillan.

Zuehlke, Mark D. & Danie , C. Stuart. Canadian Military Atlas: Four Centuries of Conflict from New France to Kosovo, 1 vol. 2006. (ENG., Illus.). 240p. pap. 40.00 *(978-1-55365-209-0(6))* D&M Pubs. Inc. CAN. Dist: Perseus-PGW.

BATTLESHIPS

see Warships

BATUCO LANGUAGE

see Eudeve Language

BATUMBUKA (AFRICAN PEOPLE)

see Tumbuka (African People)

BATUTSI

see Tutsi (African People)

BAUCHANT, ANDRE, 1873-1958

Pierre, et al. Andre Bauchant: Catalogue Raisonne. 2009. (FRE & ENG., Illus.). 656p. 370.00 *(978-3-7165-1296-8(6))* Benteli Verlag CHE. Dist: Antique Collectors' Club.

BAUDELAIRE, CHARLES, 1821-1867

Abbott, Helen. Between Baudelaire & Mallarmé: Voice, Conversation & Music. 2009. (Illus.). 258p. 114.95 *(978-0-7546-6745-2(6))* Ashgate Publishing Co.

Aggeler, William F. Baudelaire Judged by Spanish Critics, 1857-1957. 2009. (ENG.). 132p. pap. 19.95 *(978-0-8203-3501-8(0))* Univ. of Georgia Pr.

Austin, Lloyd. Poetic Principles & Practice: Occasional Papers on Baudelaire, Mallarm_ & Val_ry. 2010. (ENG.). 372p. pap. 45.00 *(978-0-521-12861-2(7))* Cambridge Univ. Pr.

Bajorek, Jennifer. Counterfeit Capital: Poetic Labor & Revolutionary Irony. 2008. (ENG.). 160p. 50.00 *(978-0-8047-5824-6(7))* Stanford Univ. Pr.

Baudelaire, Charles. Les Fleurs du Mal et Le Spleen de Paris. pap. 13.95 *(978-2-7616-0992-0(1))* Beauchemin Editions CAN. Dist: Distribooks, Inc.

Benjamin, Walter. The Writer of Modern Life: Essays on Charles Baudelaire. Jennings, Michael W., ed. Eiland, Howard et al, trs. from GER. 2006. 320p. per. 20.00 *(978-0-674-02287-4(4)*, Belknap Pr.) Harvard Univ. Pr.

Burt, E. S. Regard for the Other: Autothanatography in Rousseau, de Quincey, Baudelaire, & Wilde. 2009. (ENG.). 288p. 80.00 *(978-0-8232-3090-7(2))*; pap. 30.00 *(978-0-8232-3091-4(0))* Fordham Univ. Pr.

Burton, Richard D. E. Baudelaire In 1859: A Study in the Sources of Poetic Creativity. 2009. (Cambridge Studies in French Ser.). (ENG.). 224p. pap. 33.99 *(978-0-521-11414-1(4))* Cambridge Univ. Pr.

Calasso, Roberto. La la Folie Baudelaire, 1 vol. McEwen, Alastair, tr. from ITA. 2012. (ENG., Illus.). 352p. 35.00 ***(978-0-374-18334-9(1))*** Farrar, Straus & Giroux.

Cargo, Robert T., ed. Concordance to Baudelaire's les Fleurs du Mal. 2011. (ENG.). 442p. pap. 50.00 ***(978-0-8078-7829-3(4))*** Univ. of North Carolina Pr.

Chesters, Graham. Baudelaire & the Poetics of Craft. 2010. (ENG.). 198p. pap. 19.99 *(978-0-521-15895-4(8))* Cambridge Univ. Pr.

Hemmings, F. W. J. Baudelaire the Damned: A Biography. 2012. 271p. pap. ***(978-1-4482-0515-8(8)***, 146214, Bloomsbury Reader) Bloomsbury Publishing Plc.

Holland, Eugene W. Baudelaire & Schizoanalysis: The Socio-Poetics of Modernism. 2006. (Cambridge Studies in French Ser.). (ENG.). 328p. pap. 69.00 *(978-0-521-03134-9(6))* Cambridge Univ. Pr.

Jamison, Anne. Poetics en Passant: Redefining the Relationship between Victorian & Modern Poetry. 2009. (Nineteenth-Century Major Lives & Letters Ser.). (ENG.). 272p. 89.00 *(978-0-230-61899-2(5))* Palgrave Macmillan.

Krueger, Cheryl. The Art of Procrastination: Baudelaire's Poetry in Prose. 2008. 156p. 39.00 *(978-0-87413-983-9(X))* Univ. of Delaware Pr.

Ligo, Larry L. Manet, Baudelaire & Photography Book 1, 2 vols. 2006. (Illus.). 472p. *(978-0-7734-5695-2(3))* Mellen, Edwin Pr., The.

—Manet, Baudelaire & Photography Book 2, 2 vols. 2006. (Illus.). 496p. *(978-0-7734-5697-6(X))* Mellen, Edwin Pr., The.

Lloyd, Rosemary. Baudelaire et Hoffmann: Affinités et Influences. 2010. (ENG.). 404p. pap. 31.99 *(978-0-521-15933-3(4))* Cambridge Univ. Pr.

—Charles Baudelaire. 2008. (Reaktion Books - Critical Lives Ser.). (ENG., Illus.). 192p. per. 16.95 *(978-1-86189-363-5(9))* Reaktion Bks., Ltd. GBR. Dist: Chicago Distribution Ctr.

Marchi, Dudley M. Contrary Affinities: Baudelaire, Emerson & the French-American Connection. 2011. xvii, 134p. (C). 68.95 *(978-1-4331-1442-7(9))* Lang, Peter Publishing, Inc.

McLees, Ainslie Armstrong. Baudelaire's Argot Plastique: Poetic Caricature & Modernism. 2010. (ENG., Illus.). 216p. pap. 24.95 *(978-0-8203-3486-8(3))* Univ. of Georgia Pr.

Meltzer, Françoise. Seeing Double: Baudelaire's Modernity. 2011. 280p. 45.00 *(978-0-226-51988-3(0))* Univ. of Chicago Pr.

Mills, Kathryn Olive. Formal Revolution in the Work of Baudelaire & Flaubert. 2012. (ENG.). 200p. (gr. 17). 65.00 ***(978-1-61149-394-8(3))*** Univ. of Delaware Pr.

Porche, Francois. Charles Baudelaire. Mavin, John, tr. 248p. 2008. 41.95 *(978-1-4366-8147-6(2))* 2007. (ENG.). per. 26.95 *(978-1-4325-6267-0(3))* Kessinger Publishing, LLC.

Pride, Jennifer. The Poetics of Black. 2009. 148p. pap. *(978-3-639-13271-7(8))* VDM Verlag Dr. Mueller e.K.

Rhodes, S. A. Cult of Beauty in Charles Baudelaire V1. 2006. pap. 28.95 *(978-1-4286-5372-6(4))* Kessinger Publishing, LLC.

—Cult of Beauty in Charles Baudelaire V2. 2006. pap. 31.95 *(978-1-4286-5373-3(2))* Kessinger Publishing, LLC.

Runyon, Randolph. Intratextual Baudelaire: The Sequential Fabric of the Fleurs du Mal & Spleen de Paris. 2010. (ENG.). 344p. 57.95 *(978-0-8142-1118-2(6))*; cd-rom 14.95 *(978-0-8142-9216-7(X))* Ohio State Univ. Pr.

Smith, Ann Kennedy. Painted Poetry: Colour in Baudelaire's Art Criticism. 2011. (Illus.). 248p. pap. 55.95 *(978-3-03911-094-0(2))* Lang, Peter AG GBR. Dist: Lang, Peter.

Turquet-Milnes, Gladys R. The Influence of Baudelaire in France & England. reprint ed. 41.50 *(978-0-404-16351-8(3))* AMS Pr., Inc.

Weisberg, Gabriel P. & Shaw, Jennifer L. Paris & the Countryside: Modern Life in Late 19th-Century France. 2006. (ENG., Illus.). 160p. 50.00 *(978-0-916857-43-1(3))* Portland Museum of Art.

BAUDRILLARD, JEAN, 1929-2007

Baudrillard, Jean. The Agony of Power. Hodges, Ames, tr. from FRE. 2010. (Semiotext(e) / Intervention Ser.). (ENG.). 128p. (gr. 17). pap. 12.95 *(978-1-58435-092-7(X))* Semiotexte/Smart Art.

—America. 2010. (ENG., Illus.). 160p. pap. 19.95 *(978-1-84467-682-8(X)*, 844682) Verso Bks. GBR. Dist: Norton, W. W. & Co., Inc.

—Forget Foucault. Beitchman, Philip et al, trs. from FRE. 2007. (Semiotext(e) / Foreign Agents Ser.). (ENG.). 128p. (gr. 17). per. 14.95 *(978-1-58435-041-5(5))* Semiotexte/Smart Art.

—Passwords. 2nd ed. 2011. (Radical Thinkers Ser.). (ENG.). 92p. pap. 15.95 *(978-1-84467-676-7(5)*, 844676) Verso Bks. GBR. Dist: Norton, W. W. & Co., Inc.

Bishop, Ryan, ed. Baudrillard Now: Current Perspectives in Baudrillard Studies. 2009. (ENG., Illus.). 200p. pap. 22.95 *(978-0-7456-4708-1(1))* Polity Pr. GBR. Dist: Wiley, John & Sons, Inc.

Clarke, David B. Jean Baudrillard: Fatal Theories. Doel, Marcus et al, eds. 2008. (International Library of Sociology Ser.). XVI, 208p. 150.00 *(978-0-415-46442-0(0))* Routledge.

Constable, Catherine. Adapting Philosophy: Jean Baudrillard & the Matrix Trilogy. 2009. (ENG.). 208p. 84.95 *(978-0-7190-7531-5(9))*; pap. 29.95 *(978-0-7190-7532-2(7))* Manchester Univ. Pr. GBR. Dist: Macmillan.

Dummies Press Staff. Baudrillard Now: Current Perspectives in Baudrillard Studies. Bishop, Ryan, ed. 2009. (ENG., Illus.). 200p. 64.95 *(978-0-7456-4707-4(3))* Polity Pr. GBR. Dist: Wiley, John & Sons, Inc.

Horrocks, Chris & Jevtic, Zoran. Introducing Baudrillard. 2011. (Introducing Ser.). (ENG., Illus.). 176p. pap. 9.95 ***(978-1-84831-207-4(5))*** Totem Bks. GBR. Dist: Consortium Bk. Sales & Distribution.

Kim Toffoletti Staff & Toffoletti, Kim. Baudrillard Reframed: Interpreting Key Thinkers for the Arts. 2011. (Contemporary Thinkers Reframed Ser.). (ENG., Illus.). 160p. pap. 25.00 *(978-1-84511-678-1(X))* I. B. Tauris & Co., Ltd. GBR. Dist: Macmillan.

Lane, Richard J. Jean Baudrillard. 2nd rev. ed. 2009. (Routledge Critical Thinkers Ser.). XVI, 176p. pap. 22.95 *(978-0-415-47448-1(5))*; 95.00 *(978-0-415-47447-4(7))* Routledge.

Pawlett, Willia. Jean Baudrillard: Against Banality. 2007. (Key Sociologists Ser.). 198p. per. 39.95 *(978-0-415-38645-6(4))* Routledge.

Pawlett, William. Jean Baudrillard: Against Banality. 2007. (Key Sociologists Ser.). 198p. 140.00 *(978-0-415-38644-9(6))* Routledge.

Redhead, Steve, ed. The Jean Baudrillard Reader. 2008. (European Perspectives: a Series in Social Thought & Cultural Criticism Ser.). (ENG.). 192p. (gr. 17). 85.00 *(978-0-231-14612-8(4))*; pap. 27.00 *(978-0-231-14613-5(2))* Columbia Univ. Pr.

Schuster, Marc. Practical Ambivalence: Don DeLillo, Jean Baudrillard, & the Consumer Conundrum. 2008. 232p. (C). 99.95 *(978-1-60497-504-8(0))* Cambria Pr.

Smith, Richard G., ed. The Baudrillard Dictionary. 2010. (ENG.). 257p. (gr. 17). 105.00 *(978-0-7486-3922-9(5))*; pap. 35.00 *(978-0-7486-3921-2(7))* Edinburgh Univ. Pr. GBR. Dist: Columbia Univ. Pr.

Woodward, Ashley. Nihilism in Postmodernity: Lyotard, Baudrillard, Vattimo. 2009. (ENG.). 332p. 28.00 *(978-1-934542-08-8(3))* Davies Group Pubs., The.

BAUHAUS

Bauhaus 1919-1933. *(978-3-7165-0600-4(1))* Benteli Verlag.

Baumann, Kirsten. Bauhaus Dessau: Architektur-Gestaltung-Idee, 1 vol. 2007. (ENG., Illus.). 144p. pap. 35.00 *(978-3-939633-11-2(9))* Jovis Verlag GmbH DEU. Dist: D.A.P./Distributed Art Pubs.

Bergdoll, Barry. Bauhaus 1919-1933: Workshops for Modernity. 2009. (ENG., Illus.). 328p. 75.00 *(978-0-87070-758-2(2))* Museum of Modern Art.

Buhr, Elke. Begegnung Bauhaus: Kurt Schmidt und Künstler der Avantgarde Von Kandinsky Bis Vasarely: Kunstsammlung Gera, 25. März Bis 28. Juni 2009. 2009. (Illus.). 159p. pap. *(978-3-910051-52-2(9))* Glaux Verlag Christine Jager KG.

Droste, Magdalena. The Bauhaus: 1919-1933: Reform & Avant-Garde. 2006. (GER & ENG., Illus.). 96p. pap. 9.99 *(978-3-8228-3649-1(4))* TASCHEN DEU. Dist: Ingram Pub. Services.

Droste, Magdalena & Archiv, Bauhaus. Bauhaus. Sonderausgabe. 2006. 256p. (ITA.). 12.99 *(978-3-8228-5202-6(3))*; (GER.). 12.99 *(978-3-8228-4999-6(5))*; (SPA.). 12.99 *(978-3-8228-5000-8(4))*; (FRE.). 12.99 *(978-3-8228-5001-5(2))*; (DUT.). 12.99 *(978-3-8228-5127-2(2))*; (POR.). 12.99 *(978-3-8228-5203-3(1))* Taschen America, LLC.

Fiedler, Jeannine. Bauhaus, 1 vol. Feierabend, Peter, ed. 2008. (ENG., Illus.). 640p. 59.95 *(978-3-8331-5436-2(5))* h.f.ullmann DEU. Dist: Innovative Logistics.

Fiedler, Jeannine, ed. Bauhaus. 2008. (Art & Architecture Ser.). (Illus.). 639p. 59.95 *(978-0-8416-0094-2(5))* American Map Corp.

Friedewald, Boris. Bauhaus: Living Art. 2009. (Illus.). 128p. pap. 14.95 *(978-3-7913-4200-9(2))* Prestel Publishing.

Gualdoni, Flaminio. Bauhaus. 2009. (Skira MINI Artbooks Ser.). (ENG., Illus.). 96p. pap. 8.99 *(978-88-572-0153-5(8))* Skira Editore ITA. Dist: Random Hse., Inc.

James, Kathleen. Bauhaus Culture: From Weimar to the Cold War. 2006. (Illus.). 272p. per. 27.50 *(978-0-8166-4688-3(0))* Univ. of Minnesota Pr.

Kennedy, Andrew. Bauhaus. 2009. (Todo Arte Ser.). (ENG.). 384p. pap. 19.00 *(978-84-9794-053-5(9))* Edimat Libros, S. A. ESP. Dist: Independent Pubs. Group.

Maciuika, John V. Before the Bauhaus: Architecture, Politics, & the German State, 1890-1920. 2008. (Modern Architecture & Cultural Identity Ser.). (ENG., Illus.). 402p. pap. 41.99 *(978-0-521-72822-5(3))* Cambridge Univ. Pr.

Muller, Ulrike. Bauhaus Women: Art, Handicraft, Design. 2009. (ENG., Illus.). 152p. 39.95 *(978-2-08-030120-8(9))* Flammarion et Cie FRA. Dist: Random Hse., Inc.

Neumüllers, Marie & Duhm, Burghard, contrib. by. Bauhaus.Bühne.Dessau: Szenenwechsel, 1 vol. 2006. (ENG & GER., Illus.). 272p. pap. 35.00 *(978-3-936314-81-6(0))* Jovis Verlag GmbH DEU. Dist: D.A.P./Distributed Art Pubs.

Oswalt, Philipp, ed. The Bauhaus Debate 1919-2009, 1 vol. 2010. (ENG., Illus.). 304p. pap. 30.00 *(978-3-7757-2488-3(5))* Hatje Cantz Verlag GmbH & Co KG DEU. Dist: D.A.P./Distributed Art Pubs.

Rüedi Ray, Katerina. Bauhaus Dream-House: Modernity & Globalization. 2010. (Architext Ser.). (ENG., Illus.). 240p. (C). pap. 49.95 *(978-0-415-47582-2(1))*; 165.00 *(978-0-415-47581-5(3))* Routledge.

Saletnik, Jeffrey & Schuldenfrei, Robin, eds. Bauhaus Construct: Fashioning Identity, Discourse & Modernism. 2009. (ENG., Illus.). 288p. (C). 165.00 *(978-0-415-77835-0(2))*; pap. 49.95 *(978-0-415-77836-7(0))* Routledge.

Schwarz, Dean & Schwarz, Geraldine, eds. Marguerite Wildenhain & the Bauhaus: An Eyewitness Anthology. 2nd ed. 2007. pap. 60.00 *(978-0-9761381-3-6(1))*; 75.00 *(978-0-9761381-2-9(3))* South Bear Pr.

Siebenbrodt, Michael, et al, texts. Bauhaus. 2009. (ENG., Illus.). 376p. 60.00 *(978-3-7757-2415-9(X))* Hatje Cantz Verlag GmbH & Co KG DEU. Dist: D.A.P./Distributed Art Pubs.

Siebenbrodt, Michael & Schöbe, Lutz. Bauhaus. 2009. (Temporis Ser.). (GER, FRE & ENG., Illus.). 256p. 39.95 *(978-1-85995-626-7(2))* Parkstone International GBR. Dist: Ingram Pub. Services.

Smock, William. Bauhaus Ideal: Then & Now. 2009. (ENG., Illus.). 150p. pap. 19.95 *(978-0-89733-590-4(2))* Academy Chicago Pubs., Ltd.

Stadler. Gunta Stolzl Bauhaus Master. 2009. *(978-3-7757-2417-3(6))* Museum of Modern Art.

Stolzl, Gunta & text. Gunta Stolzl: Bauhaus Master. 2009. (ENG., Illus.). 144p. 39.95 *(978-0-87070-773-5(6))* Museum of Modern Art.

Stölzl, Gunta, et al. Gunta Stölzl: Bauhaus-Meister. 2009. (Illus.). 123p. *(978-3-7757-2371-8(4))* Museum of Modern Art.

Strasser, Josef. 50 Bauhaus Icons You Should Know. 2009. (Illus.). 176p. pap. 19.95 *(978-3-7913-4196-5(0))* Prestel Publishing.

Trimingham, Melissa. The Theatre of the Bauhaus: The Modern & Postmodern Stage of Oskar Schlemmer. 2012. (ENG., Illus.). 214p. (C). pap. 39.95 ***(978-0-415-63417-5(2))*** Routledge.

Watkinson, Gordon. Bauhaus Twenty-21: An Ongoing Legacy. Vrachliotis, Georg, ed. 2009. 232p. 89.85 *(978-3-0346-0054-5(2))* Springer.

—Bauhaus Zwanzig - 21: Ideen für ein neues Jahrhundert. 2009. (GER., Illus.). 231p. *(978-3-0346-0055-2(0))* Birkhauser Verlag AG.

Weber, Nicholas Fox. The Bauhaus Group: Six Masters of Modernism. 2009. (ENG., Illus.). 544p. 40.00 *(978-0-307-26836-5(5)*, Knopf) Knopf Doubleday Publishing Group.

—The Bauhaus Group: Six Masters of Modernism. 2011. (ENG., Illus.). 544p. pap. 27.50 *(978-0-300-16984-3(1))* Yale Univ. Pr.

Weininger, Andor, et al. Andor Weininger: Works in the Busch-Reisinger Museum. 2006. (ENG., Illus.). 75p. pap. 10.00 *(978-1-891771-14-9(0)*, Harvard Art Museum (Acc)) Antique Collectors' Club GBR. Dist: National Bk. Network.

Wolfe, Tom. From Bauhaus to Our House. 2009. (ENG.). 128p. pap. 15.00 *(978-0-312-42914-0(2))* Picador.

Zinsmeiste, Annett. Update! 90 Jahre Bauhaus - und nun? 2011. (ENG & GER., Illus.). 176p. pap. 39.95 ***(978-3-86859-102-6(8))*** Jovis Verlag GmbH DEU. Dist: D.A.P./Distributed Art Pubs.

BAUM, L. FRANK (LYMAN FRANK), 1856-1919

Bienvenue, Paul R. The Book Collector's Guide to L. Frank Baum & Oz. 2009. (Illus.). 408p. 75.00 *(978-0-615-24725-0(3))* March Hare Bks.

Burger, Alissa. The Wizard of Oz as American Myth: A Critical Study of Six Versions of the Story, 1900-2007. 2012. (ENG., Illus.). 240p. pap. 35.00 ***(978-0-7864-6643-6(X))*** McFarland & Co., Inc. Pubs.

Durand, Kevin K. J. & Leigh, Mary K., eds. The Universe of Oz: Essays on Baum's Series & Its Progeny. 2010. (ENG., Illus.). 258p. pap. 35.00 *(978-0-7864-4628-5(5))* McFarland & Co., Inc. Pubs.

Greene, Douglas G., et al. Bibliographia Oziana. Date not set. 126p. 17.95 *(978-0-8488-2285-9(4))* Amereon LTD.

Levonian, Greg. Oz & Ends: Wisdom from the Emerald City. 2011. 70p. pap. 14.95 ***(978-1-59393-654-9(0))*** BearManor Media.

Loncraine, Rebecca. The Real Wizard of Oz: The Life & Times of L. Frank Baum. 2010. (ENG.). 352p. (gr. 12). 18.00 *(978-1-59240-558-9(4)*, Gotham) Penguin Group (USA) Inc.

Menten, Ted. Denslow's Wizard of Oz Illustrations CD-ROM & Book. 2010. (Dover Electronic Clip Art Ser.). (ENG., Illus.). 48p. pap. 19.95 *(978-0-486-99146-7(6))* Dover Pubns., Inc.

Schwartz, Evan I. Finding Oz: How L. Frank Baum Discovered the Great American Story. 2009. (ENG., Illus.). 400p. 28.00 *(978-0-547-05510-7(2))* Houghton Mifflin Harcourt Trade & Reference Pubs.

Snow, Jack. Who's Who in Oz: The Happiest Who's Who Ever Written. 2010. (ENG.). 292p. (J). pap. 28.95 *(978-1-59583-425-6(7)*, Green Tiger Pr.) Laughing Elephant.

Tuerk, Richard. Oz in Perspective: Magic & Myth in the L. Frank Baum Books. 2007. (ENG., Illus.). 241p. per. 35.00 *(978-0-7864-2899-1(6))* McFarland & Co., Inc. Pubs.

Walsh, Sheila. God Has a Dream for Your Life, 0 vols. 2009. 224p. pap. 14.99 *(978-1-4002-8035-3(4))* Nelson, Thomas Inc.

BAUMANN, GUSTAVE, 1881-1971

Traugott, Joseph. Gustave Baumann's Southwest. 2007. (Illus.). 80p. 24.95 *(978-0-7649-4178-8(X)*, A138) Pomegranate Communications, Inc.

BAUMEISTER, WILLI, 1889-1955

Ackermann, Marion. Im Rampenlicht - in the Limelight. 2008. 412p. 45.00 *(978-3-422-06775-2(2))* Deutscher Kunstverlag GmbH DEU. Dist: Independent Pubs. Group.

Beye, Peter & Baumeister, Felicitas. Willi Baumeister: Werkkatalog der Gemalde. (GER.). *(978-3-7757-0936-1(3))* Hatje Cantz Verlag GmbH & Co KG DEU. Dist: D.A.P./Distributed Art Pubs.

Presler, Gerd & Baumeister, Felicitas. Willi Baumeister. Werkverzeichnis der Skizzenbücher: catalogue raisonné of the sketchbooks. 2010. (ENG.). 300p. 37.00 *(978-3-422-06890-2(2)*, Art Stock Bks. Ltd/Csi) Continental Sales, Inc.

BAUXITE

Jitsangiam, Peerapong & Nikraz, Hamid. Utilisation of Bauxite Residue Sand in Construction Industry. 2010. 432p. pap. *(978-3-639-24746-6(9))* VDM Verlag Dr. Mueller e.K.

BAVARIA (GERMANY)

Bentley, James, et al. Bavaria Including Munich. 3rd ed. 2009. (Travellers - Thomas Cook Ser.). (ENG., Illus.). 192p. pap. 16.95 *(978-1-84848-001-8(6))* Cook, Thomas Publishing GBR. Dist: Globe Pequot Pr., The.

Canoy, Jose Raymund. The Discreet Charm of the Police State: The Landpolizei & the Transformation of Bavaria, 1945-1965. 2007. (Studies in Central European Histories: Vol. 41). 333p. *(978-90-04-15708-8(5))* BRILL.

Hansen, Kevan M. Map Guide to German Parish Registers - Kingdom of Bavaria I - Regierungsbezirk Unterfranken. 2007. lib. bdg. 65.00 *(978-1-933194-17-2(0))*; per. 34.95 *(978-1-933194-16-5(2)*, FR0027) Family Roots Publishing Co.

—Map Guide to German Parish Registers - Kingdom of Bavaria II - Regierungsbezirk Oberfranken. 2007. lib. bdg. 65.00 *(978-1-933194-19-6(7))*; per. 34.95 *(978-1-933194-18-9(9))* Family Roots Publishing Co.

—Map Guide to German Parish Registers - Kingdom of Bavaria III - Regierungsbezirk Mittelfranken. 2007. lib. bdg. 65.00 *(978-1-933194-21-9(9))*; per. 34.95 *(978-1-933194-20-2(0))* Family Roots Publishing Co.

—Map Guide to German Parish Registers - Kingdom of Bavaria IV - Regierungsbezirk Oberpfalz. 2007. lib. bdg. 65.00 *(978-1-933194-24-0(3))*; per. 34.95 *(978-1-933194-23-3(5))* Family Roots Publishing Co.

Steves, Rick. Rick Steves' Snapshot Munich, Bavaria & Salzburg. 2012. (Rick Steves Snapshot Ser.). (ENG., Illus.). 232p. pap. 11.99 *(978-1-59880-689-2(0))* Avalon Travel Publishing.

Thomas, Andrew L. A House Divided: Wittelsbach Confessional Court Cultures in the Holy Roman Empire, C. 1550-1650. 2010. (Illus.). 404p. *(978-90-04-18356-8(6))* BRILL.

BAVARIA (GERMANY)—DESCRIPTION AND TRAVEL

Bolt, Rodney. Bavaria. 4th ed. 2010. (Illus.). 254p. pap. 21.95 *(978-1-56656-812-8(9)*, Cadogan Guides (USA)) Interlink Publishing Group, Inc.

Dickens, David B. The Pleasures of Franconia. 2009. 434p. pap. 29.95 *(978-1-60703-355-4(0))* PublishAmerica, Inc.

Gregston, Brent. Bavaria & the Austrian Tyrol. 3rd ed. 2009. (Drive Around - Thomas Cook Ser.). (ENG., Illus.). 288p. pap. 26.95 *(978-1-84157-999-3(8))* Cook, Thomas Publishing GBR. Dist: Globe Pequot Pr., The.

Locken, E. Travel Journal the Bavarian Alps. 2010. 192p. pap. 19.99 *(978-0-557-34032-3(2))* Lulu Enterprises Inc.

Luthardt, Ernst-Otto. Fascinating Bavaria. 2011. (Fascinating Ser.). (ENG.). 96p. 14.95 *(978-3-88189-664-1(3))* Verlagshaus Wurzburg GmbH & Co. KG DEU. Dist: Independent Pubs. Group.

—Journey Through Bavaria. 2011. (Journey Through Ser.). (ENG., Illus.). 140p. 29.95 *(978-3-8003-4061-3(5))* Verlagshaus Wurzburg GmbH & Co. KG DEU. Dist: Independent Pubs. Group.

—Journey Through Upper Bavaria. 2011. (Journey Through Ser.). (ENG., Illus.). 140p. 29.95 *(978-3-8003-4082-8(8))* Verlagshaus Wurzburg GmbH & Co. KG DEU. Dist: Independent Pubs. Group.

Pfeiffer, Oliver. BAVARIA BLUES: Eine unkonventionelle Winterreise durch Bayern. 2011. 262p. pap. 28.90 ***(978-3-8423-2953-9(9))*** Bks. on Demand.

Schulte-Peevers, Andrea, et al. Munich, Bavaria & the Black Forest. 3rd rev. ed. 2008. (Lonely Planet Munich, Bavaria, & the Black Forest Ser.). (ENG., Illus.). 324p. pap. 19.99 *(978-1-74104-671-7(8))* Lonely Planet Pubns.

Trox, Trudie. Journey Through Lower Bavaria. 2011. (Journey Through Ser.). (Illus.). 128p. 24.95 *(978-3-8003-1793-6(1))* Verlagshaus Wurzburg GmbH & Co. KG DEU. Dist: Independent Pubs. Group.

BAVARIA (GERMANY)—HISTORY

Dickens, David B. The Pleasures of Franconia. 2009. 434p. pap. 29.95 *(978-1-60703-355-4(0))* PublishAmerica, Inc.

Dicker, Stefan. Landesbewusstsein und Zeitgeschehen: Studien Zur Bayerischen Chronistik des 15. Jahrhunderts. 2009. (GER., Illus.). 453p. *(978-3-412-20103-6(0))* Bohlau Verlag Gmbh & Cie.

Fistein, David. Social Revolutions in Small States. 2010. 380p. pap. *(978-3-639-27604-6(3))* VDM Verlag Dr. Mueller e.K.

Gaab, Jeffrey S. Munich: Hofbräuhaus & History: Beer, Culture, & Politics. 2006. (Illus.). 164p. (C). 61.95 *(978-0-8204-8606-2(X))* Lang, Peter Publishing, Inc.

Glaser, Hubert. Markus Heinsdorff. Design with Nature: Die Bambusbauten. The Bamboo Architecture, 2 vols. 2011. (GER., Illus.). 206p. 65.00 ***(978-3-7774-2791-1(8))*** Hirmer Verlag GmbH DEU. Dist: Chicago Distribution Ctr.

Hager, Angela. Ein Jahrzehnt der Hoffnungen: Reformgruppen in der bayerischen Landeskirche 1966-1976. 2010. (Arbeiten Zur Kirchlichen Zeitgeschichte Ser.). (GER.). 352p. (C). 98.00 *(978-3-525-55742-6(6))* Vandenhoeck & Ruprecht GmbH & Co. KG DEU. Dist: ISD.

Hammer, Carl I. From Ducatus to Regnum: Ruling Bavaria under the Merovingians & Early Carolingians. 2007. (Haute Moyen Age Ser.). (ENG., Illus.). 384p. (C). pap. 87.00 *(978-2-503-52582-2(2))* Brepols Pubs. BEL. Dist: ISD.

Mattern, Johannes. Bavaria & the Reich: The Conflict over the Law for the Protection of the Republic. (Johns Hopkins University. Studies in the Social Sciences, Thirtieth Ser.: 3). reprint ed. 27.50 *(978-0-404-61226-9(1))* AMS Pr., Inc.

Merkl, Peter H. Small Town & Village in Bavaria: The Passing of a Way of Life. 2012. E-Book ***(978-0-85745-348-8(3))*** Berghahn Bks., Inc.

—Small Towns & Villages in Bavaria: The Passing of a Way of Life. 2012. (ENG.). 288p. 90.00 ***(978-0-85745-347-1(5))*** Berghahn Bks., Inc.

Mixson, James D. Poverty's Proprietors: Ownership & Mortal Sin at the Origins of the Observant Movement. 2009. *(978-90-04-17405-4(2))* BRILL.

Mueller, Steven. The Wittelsbach Dynasty. 2007. (Illus.). 230p. per. 19.95 *(978-0-9702576-3-5(5))* Waldmann Pr.

Smith, William Bradford. Reformation & the German Territorial State: Upper Franconia, 1300-1630. 2008. (Changing Perspectives on Early Modern Europe Ser.: Volume 8). (Illus.). 298p. 85.00 *(978-1-58046-274-7(X))* Univ. of Rochester Pr.

BAVARIA (GERMANY)—POLITICS AND GOVERNMENT

Dicker, Stefan. Landesbewusstsein und Zeitgeschehen: Studien Zur Bayerischen Chronistik des 15. Jahrhunderts. 2009. (GER., Illus.). 453p. *(978-3-412-20103-6(0))* Bohlau Verlag Gmbh & Cie.

Hopp, Gerhard, et al. Die CSU: Strukturwandel, Modernisierung und Herausforderungen einer Volkspartei. 2010. (GER., Illus.). 590p. *(978-3-531-17275-0(1))* Westdeutscher Verlag GmbH.

Teutsch, Arthur. Ministerial Responsibility in Bavaria: Inaugural Dissertation. Heap, Denise Elaine, tr. 2011. 78p. pap. 18.00 ***(978-0-9822984-8-0(X))*** Exclamation! Pubs.

BAVARIAN MOTOR WORKS AUTOMOBILES

see BMW Automobiles

BAVILI (AFRICAN PEOPLE)

see Vili (African People)

BAXTER, RICHARD, 1615-1691

Beougher, Timothy K. Richard Baxter & Conversion: A Study of the Puritan Concept of Becoming a Christian. 2007. (ENG.). 240p. 17.99 *(978-1-84550-310-9(4)*, Mentor) Christian Focus Pubns. GBR. Dist: STL Distribution North America.

Black, J. William. Reformation Pastors: Richard Baxter & the Ideal of the Reformed Pastor. 2007. (Studies in Christian History & Thought: Ser.). 338p. pap. 34.00 *(978-1-59752-768-2(8)*, Wipf and Stock) Wipf & Stock Pubs.

Buchanan, Colin, intro. The Savoy Conference Revisited. 2009. 88.00 *(978-1-60724-403-5(9))* Gorgias Pr., LLC.

Cooper, Tim. John Owen Richard Baxter & the Formation of Nonconformity. 2011. 356p. 134.95 ***(978-0-7546-6361-4(2))*** Ashgate Publishing Co.

George, Edward Augustus. Seventeenth Century Men of Latitude: Forerunners of the New. 2007. (ENG.). 220p. per. 24.95 *(978-1-4304-4705-4(2))* Kessinger Publishing, LLC.

Richard, Baxter. The Practical Works of Richard Baxter with a Life of the Author & a Critical Examination of His Writings by William Orme (Volume: Christian. 2011. 594p. pap. ***(978-1-84902-569-0(X))*** Benediction Classics.

Tulloch, John. English Puritanism & Its Leaders: Cromwell, Milton, Baxter, Bunyan. 2008. 520p. pap. *(978-1-4086-6848-1(3))* Read Bks.

BAY OF PIGS INVASION

see Cuba—History—Invasion, 1961

BAY PSALM BOOK

Eames, Wilberforce. The Bay Psalm Book. 2009. 324p. 36.99 *(978-1-113-91079-0(8))*; (ENG.). 322p. pap. 29.75 *(978-1-113-91073-8(9)*, BiblioLife) BiblioBazaar.

BAYARD, JAMES ASHETON, 1767-1815

Borden, Morton. Federalism of James A. Bayard. (Columbia University, Studies in the Social Sciences: No. 584). reprint ed. 32.50 *(978-0-404-51584-3(3))* AMS Pr., Inc.

BAYARD, THOMAS FRANCIS, 1828-1898

Spooner, Lysander. No Treason. 2009. 98p. pap. *(978-1-4099-6127-7(3))* Dodo Pr.

BAYEREISCHE MOTOREN WERKE AUTOMOBILES

see BMW Automobiles

BAYES, THOMAS, D. 1761

Dale, Andrew I. Most Honourable Remembrance: The Life & Work of Thomas Bayes. 2012. (Sources & Studies in the History of Mathematics & Physical Sciences Ser.). (ENG., Illus.). xxiii, 667p. pap. 179.00 *(978-1-4419-1828-4(0)*, 1441918280) Springer.

BAYES' SOLUTION

see Bayesian Statistical Decision Theory

BAYESIAN STATISTICAL DECISION THEORY

Abbas, Nasir & Aslam, Muhammad. Paired Comparison Modeling with Bayesian Analysis. 2011. 180p. pap. ***(978-3-639-32658-1(X))*** VDM Verlag Dr. Mueller e.K.

Abdel-Aty, Yahia. Bayesian Prediction Intervals. 2010. 180p. pap. *(978-3-639-24593-6(8))* VDM Verlag Dr. Mueller e.K.

Aitkin, Murray. Statistical Inference: An Integrated Bayesian - Likelihood Approach. 2010. (Chapman & Hall/CRC Monographs on Statistics & Applied Probability Ser.). (ENG., Illus.). 254p. 94.95 *(978-1-4200-9343-8(6)*, Chapman & Hall/CRC) CRC Pr. LLC.

Albert, Jim. Bayesian Computation with R. (Use R Ser.). 2007. (Illus.). 267p. per. 54.95 *(978-0-387-71384-7(0))* 2nd ed. 2009. (ENG.). xii, 300p. pap. 59.95 *(978-0-387-92297-3(0)*, 0387922970) Springer.

Ando, Tomohiro. Bayesian Model Selection & Statistical Modeling. 2010. (Statistics: A Series of Textbooks & Monographs). (ENG., Illus.). 300p. 89.95 *(978-1-4398-3614-9(0)*, Chapman & Hall/CRC) CRC Pr. LLC.

Ardia, David. Financial Risk Management with Bayesian Estimation of Garch Models. 2008. (Lecture Notes in Economics & Mathematical Systems Ser.). pap. 139.00 *(978-3-540-78656-6(2))* Springer.

Artmann, Christian. The Value of Information Updating in New Product Development. 2009. (Lecture Notes in Economics & Mathematical Systems Ser.). (Illus.). xviii, 208p. pap. 119.00 *(978-3-540-93832-3(X))* Springer.

Å mídl, Václav & Quinn, Anthony. The Variational Bayes Method in Signal Processing. 2010. (Signals & Communication Technology Ser.). (Illus.). xx, 227p. pap. 99.00 *(978-3-642-06690-0(9)*, 3642066909) Springer.

Barber, David. Bayesian Reasoning & Machine Learning. 2012. (ENG., Illus.). 728p. (C). 90.00 ***(978-0-521-51814-7(8))*** Cambridge Univ. Pr.

Barber, David, et al, eds. Bayesian Time Series Models. 2011. (ENG., Illus.). 432p. 80.00 *(978-0-521-19676-5(0))* Cambridge Univ. Pr.

Bayesian Ideas & Data Analysis. 2011. 69.95 ***(978-1-4398-0355-4(2)***, CRC Press) Taylor & Francis Group GBR. Dist: Taylor & Francis Group.

Bayesian Methods for Data Analysis Third Edition. 2011. (C). 69.95 ***(978-1-58488-698-3(6)***, Chapman & Hall/CRC) CRC Pr. LLC.

Bayler, Gnnther. Penetrating Bayesian Spam Filters. 2008. 84p. pap. *(978-3-8364-5971-6(X))* VDM Verlag Dr. Mueller e.K.

Berger, James O. Statistical Decision Theory & Bayesian Analysis. 2nd ed. 2010. (Springer Series in Statistics Ser.). (Illus.). xvii, 624p. pap. 124.00 *(978-1-4419-3074-3(4)*, 1441930744) Springer.

Bernardo, Jose M., et al, eds. Bayesian Statistics 9. 2011. (ENG., Illus.). 720p. 198.50 ***(978-0-19-969458-7(3))*** Oxford Univ. Pr., Inc.

Bernardo, José M. & Smith, Adrian F. M. Bayesian Theory. 2nd rev. ed. 2007. (Wiley Series in Probability & Statistics Ser.). 640p. 110.00 *(978-0-470-02873-5(4))* Wiley, John & Sons, Inc.

Berry, Donald A., et al. Bayesian Adaptive Methods for Clinical Trials. 2010. (Chapman & Hall/CRC Biostatistics Ser.). (ENG., Illus.). 323p. 94.95 *(978-1-4398-2548-8(3)*, CRC Press) Taylor & Francis Group GBR. Dist: Taylor & Francis Group.

Bessière, Pierre. Probabilistic Reasoning & Decision Making in Sensory Motor Systems. 2008. (Springer Tracts in Advanced Robotics Ser.). (Illus.). xix, 373p. 179.00 *(978-3-540-79006-8(3))* Springer.

Bessière, Pierre, et al, eds. Probabilistic Reasoning & Decision Making in Sensory-Motor Systems. 2010. (Springer Tracts in Advanced Robotics Ser.). (Illus.). xx, 378p. pap. 179.00 *(978-3-642-09784-3(7)*, 3642097847) Springer.

Bessiere, Pierre, et al. Bayesian Programming. 2012. (ENG., Illus.). 350p. 89.95 ***(978-1-4398-8032-6(8)***, Chapman & Hall/CRC) CRC Pr. LLC.

Bijak, Jakub. Forecasting International Migration in Europe: the Bayesian Approach: The Bayesian Approach. 2010. (Springer Series on Demographic Methods & Population Analysis Ser.). (ENG., Illus.). xxiii, 308p. 139.00 *(978-90-481-8896-3(2)*, 9048188962) Springer.

Binmore, Ken. Rational Decisions. 2008. (Gorman Lectures). (ENG., Illus.). 216p. (C). 60.00 *(978-0-691-13074-3(4))* Princeton Univ. Pr.

Bolstad, William M. Introduction to Bayesian Statistics. 2nd rev. ed. 2007. (ENG., Illus.). 464p. 144.00 *(978-0-470-14115-1(8)*, Wiley-Interscience) Wiley, John & Sons, Inc.

—Understanding Computational Bayesian Statistics. 2009. (Wiley Series in Computational Statistics Ser.: 644). (ENG., Illus.). 336p. 127.00 *(978-0-470-04609-8(0)*, Wiley) Wiley, John & Sons, Inc.

Boreux, Jean-Jacques, et al. Pratique du Calcul Bayesien. 2010. (Statistique et Probabilites Appliquees Ser.). (FRE., Illus.). 333p. pap. 59.95 *(978-2-287-99666-5(4))* Springer.

Brimacombe Michael Staff. Bayesian Likelihood Methods in Ecology & Biology. 2009. (Statistics: A Series of Textbooks & Monographs). (Illus.). 79.95 *(978-1-58488-788-1(5)*, Chapman & Hall/CRC) CRC Pr. LLC.

Broemeling, Lyle D. Advanced Bayesian Methods for Medical Test Accuracy. 2011. (Chapman & Hall/CRC Biostatistics Ser.). (ENG., Illus.). 487p. 139.95 *(978-1-4398-3878-5(X)*, CRC Press) Taylor & Francis Group GBR. Dist: Taylor & Francis Group.

—Bayesian Biostatistics & Diagnostic Medicine. 2007. (ENG., Illus.). 216p. 94.95 *(978-1-58488-767-6(2)*, Chapman & Hall/CRC) CRC Pr. LLC.

—Bayesian Methods for Measures of Agreement. 2009. (Chapman & Hall/CRC Biostatistics Ser.). (ENG., Illus.). 340p. 92.95 *(978-1-4200-8341-5(4)*, Chapman & Hall/CRC) CRC Pr. LLC.

Brown, David. Rapid, Low Cost Modeling & Simulation. 2008. 288p. pap. *(978-3-639-07965-4(5))* VDM Verlag Dr. Mueller e.K.

Candy, James V. & Candy. Bayesian Signal Processing: Classical, Modern, & Particle Filtering Methods. 2009. (Adaptive & Learning Systems for Signal Processing, Communications & Control Ser.: 54). (ENG., Illus.). 472p. 152.00 *(978-0-470-18094-5(3)*, Wiley-Interscience) Wiley, John & Sons, Inc.

Carlin Bradley P Staff. Bayesian Methods for Data Analysis. 3rd rev. ed. 2008. (Chapman & Hall/CRC Texts in Statistical Science Ser.). (ENG., Illus.). 552p. (C). 72.95 *(978-1-58488-697-6(8)*, Chapman & Hall/CRC) CRC Pr. LLC.

Carrier, Richard C. Proving History: Bayes's Theorem & the Quest for the Historical Jesus. 2012. (ENG.). 390p. 28.00 ***(978-1-61614-559-0(5))*** Prometheus Bks., Pubs.

Catoni, Olivier. PAC-Bayesian Supervised Classifcation: The Thermodynamics of Statistical Learning. 2007. 163p. pap. 108.00 *(978-0-940600-72-0(2))* Institute of Mathematical Statistics.

Challa, Subhash, et al. Fundamentals of Object Tracking. 2011. (ENG., Illus.). 392p. 90.00 *(978-0-521-87628-5(1))* Cambridge Univ. Pr.

Chan, Hei. Sensitivity Analysis of Probabilistic Graphical Models. 2009. 164p. pap. *(978-3-639-13695-1(0))* VDM Verlag Dr. Mueller e.K.

Chen, Ming-Hui, et al, eds. Frontiers of Statistical Decision Making & Bayesian Analysis: In Honor of James O. Berger. 2010. (ENG.). xxiv, 636p. 79.95 *(978-1-4419-6943-9(8)*, 1441969438) Springer.

Cheng, Dunlei. Determining Bayesian Sample Size & Bayesian Optimal Model. 2010. 100p. pap. *(978-3-8383-1773-1(4))* Lambert Academic Publishing.

Chib, et al. Bayesian Econometrics. 2009. (Illus.). xii, 643p. 174.95 *(978-1-84855-308-8(0))* Emerald Group Publishing Ltd. GBR. Dist: Turpin Distribution Services Ltd.

Christakos, George. Modern Spatiotemporal Geostatistics. 2012. (Dover Earth Science Ser.). (ENG., Illus.). 304p. pap. 29.95 ***(978-0-486-48818-9(7))*** Dover Pubns., Inc.

Christensen, Ronald, et al. Bayesian Ideas & Data Analysis: An Introduction for Scientists & Statisticians. 2010. (Chapman & Hall/CRC Texts in Statistical Science Ser.). (ENG., Illus.). 516p. 72.95 *(978-1-4398-0354-7(4)*, CRC Press) Taylor & Francis Group GBR. Dist: Taylor & Francis Group.

Claeskens, Gerda & Hjort, Nils Lid. Model Selection & Model Averaging. 2008. (Cambridge Series in Statistical & Probabilistic Mathematics Ser.). (ENG., Illus.). 320p. 75.00 *(978-0-521-85225-8(0))* Cambridge Univ. Pr.

Congdon, Peter. Bayesian Statistical Modelling. 2nd rev. ed. 2007. (Wiley Series in Probability & Statistics Ser.: 670). (ENG., Illus.). 596p. 110.00 *(978-0-470-01875-0(5)*, Wiley) Wiley, John & Sons, Inc.

Congdon Peter D Staff. Bayesian Random Effect & Other Hierarchical Models: An Applied Perspective. 2010. (ENG., Illus.). 604p. 89.95 *(978-1-58488-720-1(6)*, Chapman & Hall/CRC) CRC Pr. LLC.

Corfield, D. & Williamson, J., eds. Foundations of Bayesianism. 2011. (Applied Logic Ser.). (ENG.). 428p. pap. 259.00 *(978-90-481-5920-8(2)*, 9048159202) Springer.

Cram101 Textbook Reviews. Outlines & Highlights for Bayesian Methods for Data Analysis by Bradley P Carlin. 2011. 248p. pap. 31.95 ***(978-1-61905-203-1(2))*** Cram101 Inc.

—Outlines & Highlights for Contemporary Bayesian & Frequentist Statistical Research Methods for Natural Resource Scientists by Howard B Stauffer. 2011. 108p. pap. 28.95 ***(978-1-61905-226-0(1))*** Cram101 Inc.

Cram101 Textbook Reviews & Cram101 Textbook Reviews. Outlines & Highlights for Coherent Stress Testing: A Bayesian Approach to the Analysis of Financial Risk by Riccardo Rebonato, ISBN. 2011. 78p. pap. 27.95 ***(978-1-4288-3117-9(7))*** Cram101 Inc.

Crisan, Dan & Rozovskii, Boris. The Oxford Handbook of Nonlinear Filtering. 2011. (ENG., Illus.). 1088p. 198.50 *(978-0-19-953290-2(7))* Oxford Univ. Pr., Inc.

D, Venkatesan, et al. Bayesian Inference for Structural Changes in Time Series Models. 2011. 120p. pap. ***(978-3-8443-1492-2(X))*** Lambert Academic Publishing.

Darwiche, Adnan. Modeling & Reasoning with Bayesian Networks. 2009. (ENG., Illus.). 560p. 99.00 *(978-0-521-88438-9(1))* Cambridge Univ. Pr.

D'Eaux, John. The Impact of Bayesian Technology on Networking. 2009. 140p. pap. *(978-3-639-15985-1(3))* VDM Verlag Dr. Mueller e.K.

del Castillo, Enrique, ed. Bayesian Process Monitoring, Control & Optimization. 2006. (ENG., Illus.). 352p. 102.95 *(978-1-58488-544-3(0)*, Chapman & Hall/CRC) CRC Pr. LLC.

Dey, Dipak K., et al. Bayesian Modeling in Bioinformatics. 2010. (Chapman & Hall/CRC Biostatistics Ser.). (ENG., Illus.). 466p. 89.95 *(978-1-4200-7017-0(7)*, Chapman & Hall/CRC) CRC Pr. LLC.

Do, Kim-Anh & Mueller, Peter R., eds. Bayesian Inference for Gene Expression & Proteomics. 2006. (ENG., Illus.). 456p. 103.00 *(978-0-521-86092-5(X))* Cambridge Univ. Pr.

Dong, Xiaojing. Hierarchical Bayesian Method in the Study of Individual Level Behavior- in the Context of Discrete Choice Modeling with Revealed & Stated Preference. 2007. 80p. per. *(978-3-8364-2353-3(7))* VDM Verlag Dr. Mueller e.K.

Doya, Kenji, et al, eds. Bayesian Brain: Probabilistic Approaches to Neural Coding. 2011. (Computational Neuroscience Ser.). (ENG., Illus.). 344p. (gr. 17). pap. 26.00 *(978-0-262-51601-3(2))* MIT Pr.

Eells, Ellery. Rational Decision & Causality. 2009. (Cambridge Studies in Philosophy Ser.). (ENG.). 248p. (C). pap. 36.00 *(978-0-521-11011-2(4))* Cambridge Univ. Pr.

Efron, Bradley. Large-Scale Inference: Empirical Bayes Methods for Estimation, Testing, & Prediction. 2010. (Institute of Mathematical Statistics Monographs). (ENG., Illus.). 276p. 70.00 *(978-0-521-19249-1(8))* Cambridge Univ. Pr.

Fahrmeir, Ludwig & Kneib, Thomas. Bayesian Smoothing & Regression for Longitudinal, Spatial & Event History Data. 2011. (ENG., Illus.). 536p. 98.50 *(978-0-19-953302-2(4))* Oxford Univ. Pr., Inc.

Fenton, Norman & Neil, Martin. Risk Assessment with Bayesian Networks. 2012. (ENG., Illus.). 600p. 79.95 ***(978-1-4398-0910-5(0)***, CRC Press) Taylor & Francis Group GBR. Dist: Taylor & Francis Group.

Ferrari, Clarissa. Circular Data Bayesian Modeling. 2010. 144p. pap. *(978-3-639-27999-3(9))* VDM Verlag Dr. Mueller e.K.

Ferreira, Marco A. R. & Lee, Herbert K. H. Multiscale Modeling: A Bayesian Perspective. (Springer Series in Statistics Ser.). 2010. xii, 252p. pap. 119.00 *(978-1-4419-2426-1(4)*, 1441924264) 2007. (Illus.). 245p. 119.00 *(978-0-387-70897-3(9))* Springer.

Festa, R. Optimum Inductive Methods: A Study in Inductive Probability, Bayesian Statistics, & Verisimilitude. 2010. (Synthese Library). 208p. pap. 189.00 *(978-90-481-4318-4(7)*, 9048143187) Springer.

Fox, Jean-Paul. Bayesian Item Response Modeling: Theory & Applications. 2010. (Statistics for Social & Behavioral Sciences Ser.). xiv, 313p. 79.95 *(978-1-4419-0741-7(6)*, 1441907416) Springer.

Fritsch, Arno. Bayesian Logic Regression for Snp Dat. 2008. 80p. pap. *(978-3-639-05130-8(0))* VDM Verlag Dr. Mueller e.K.

Frühwirth-Schnatter, Sylvia. Finite Mixture & Markov Switching Models. 2006. (Springer Series in Statistics). (Illus.). 492p. 109.00 *(978-0-387-32909-3(9)*, 0387329099) Springer.

Gelman, Andrew, et al. Bayesian Data Analysis. 3rd rev. ed. 2013. (Chapman & Hall/CRC Texts in Statistical Science Ser.). (ENG., Illus.). 800p. 69.95 *(978-1-4398-4095-5(4)*, Chapman & Hall/CRC) CRC Pr. LLC.

Geweke, John, et al, eds. The Oxford Handbook of Bayesian Econometrics. 2011. (Oxford Handbooks Ser.). (ENG., Illus.). 576p. 150.00 ***(978-0-19-955908-4(2))*** Oxford Univ. Pr., Inc.

Ghosh, J. K. & Ramamoorthi, R. V. Bayesian Nonparametrics. 2010. (Springer Series in Statistics Ser.). (Illus.). xii, 305p. pap. 119.00 *(978-1-4419-3044-6(2)*, 1441930442) Springer.

Ghosh, Jayanta K., et al. An Introduction to Bayesian Analysis: Theory & Methods. (Springer Texts in Statistics Ser.). 2010. xiv, 352p. pap. 109.00 *(978-1-4419-2303-5(9)*, 1441923039) 2006. (Illus.). 352p. 109.00 *(978-0-387-40084-6(2)*, 0387400842) Springer.

Gill, Jeff. Bayesian Methods: A Social & Behavioral Sciences Approach. 2nd rev. ed. 2007. (Statistics in the Social & Behavioral Sciences Ser.). (ENG., Illus.). 752p. (C). 81.95 *(978-1-58488-562-7(9)*, Chapman & Hall/CRC) CRC Pr. LLC.

Goggans, Paul M. & Chan, Chun-Yong, eds. Bayesian Inference & Maximum Entropy Methods in Scienec & Engineering: The 29th International Workshop on Bayesian Inference & Maximum Entropy Methods in Science &

Engineering. 2010. (AIP Conference Proceedings Ser.). 452p. 259.00 *(978-0-7354-0729-9(0),* 0735407290, AIP Pr.) Springer.

Gómez, José A., et al, eds. Advances in Bayesian Networks. 2010. (Studies in Fuzziness & Soft Computing Ser.). (ENG.). xii, 328p. pap. 179.00 *(978-3-642-05885-1(X),* 364205885X) Springer.

Greenberg, Edward. Introduction to Bayesian Econometrics. 2007. (ENG.). 224p. (C). 49.00 *(978-0-521-85871-7(2))* Cambridge Univ. Pr.

Gregory, Phil. Bayesian Logical Data Analysis for the Physical Sciences: A Comparative Approach with Mathematical Support. 2010. (ENG., Illus.). 486p. pap. 59.00 *(978-0-521-15012-5(4))* Cambridge Univ. Pr.

Guy, Tatiana Valentine, et al, eds. Decision Making with Imperfect Decision Makers. 2011. (Intelligent Systems Reference Library). (ENG., Illus.). xiv, 198p. 129.00 ***(978-3-642-24646-3(X)***, 364224646X) Springer.

Hamada, Michael S. Bayesian Reliability. 2008. (Springer Series in Statistics). 456p. 119.00 *(978-0-387-77948-5(5))* Springer.

Hamada, Michael S., et al. Bayesian Reliability. 2010. (Springer Series in Statistics Ser.). xvi, 437p. pap. 119.00 *(978-1-4419-2673-9(9),* 1441926739) Springer.

Hamelryck, Thomas, et al, eds. Bayesian Methods in Structural Bioinformatics. 2012. (Statistics for Biology & Health Ser.). (ENG., Illus.). xxii, 385p. 89.95 ***(978-3-642-27224-0(X)***, 364227224X) Springer.

Haug, Anton J. Bayesian Estimation & Tracking: A Practical Guide. 2012. (ENG., Illus.). 400p. 125.00 ***(978-0-470-62170-7(2)***, Wiley) Wiley, John & Sons, Inc.

Heidbreder, Glenn R., ed. Maximum Entropy & Bayesian Methods Santa Barbara, California, U. S. A. 1993. 2010. (Fundamental Theories of Physics Ser.). 428p. pap. 339.00 *(978-90-481-4407-5(8),* 9048144078) Springer.

Hjort, Nils Lid, et al, eds. Bayesian Nonparametrics. 2010. (Cambridge Series in Statistical & Probabilistic Mathematics Ser.). (ENG., Illus.). 312p. 65.00 *(978-0-521-51346-3(4))* Cambridge Univ. Pr.

Hobson, Michael P., et al, eds. Bayesian Methods in Cosmology. 2009. (ENG., Illus.). 316p. 65.00 *(978-0-521-88794-6(1))* Cambridge Univ. Pr.

Hoff, Peter D. A First Course in Bayesian Statistical Methods. 2009. (Statistics for Social & Behavioral Sciences Ser.). (ENG., Illus.). viii, 268p. 69.95 *(978-0-387-92299-7(7))* Springer.

Hoijtink, Herbert, et al, eds. Bayesian Evaluation of Informative Hypotheses. 2010. (Statistics for Social & Behavioral Sciences Ser.). xii, 361p. pap. 89.95 *(978-1-4419-1874-1(4),* 1441918744) Springer.

Holmes, Dawn E., ed. Innovations in Bayesian Networks: Theory & Applications. 2010. (Studies in Computational Intelligence Ser.). (Illus.). x, 322p. pap. 199.00 *(978-3-642-09875-8(4),* 3642098754) Springer.

Holmes, Dawn E. & Jain, Lakhmi C., eds. Innovations in Bayesian Networks: Theory & Applications. 2008. (Studies in Computational Intelligence Ser.). (Illus.). x, 322p. 199.00 *(978-3-540-85065-6(1))* Springer.

Horvath, B. Are Policy Variables Exogenous? The Econometric Implications of Learning while Maximizing. 2007. (Lecture Notes in Economics & Mathematical Systems Ser.). (Illus.). 180p. per. 52.95 *(978-3-540-54287-2(6))* Springer.

Howie, David. Interpreting Probability: Controversies & Developments in the Early Twentieth Century. 2007. (Cambridge Studies in Probability, Induction & Decision Theory Ser.). (ENG.). 276p. pap. 58.00 *(978-0-521-03754-9(9))* Cambridge Univ. Pr.

Husmeier, Dirk, et al, eds. Probabilistic Modeling in Bioinformatics & Medical Informatics. 2010. (Advanced Information & Knowledge Processing Ser.). (Illus.). xx, 508p. pap. 139.00 *(978-1-84996-912-3(4),* 1849969124) Springer.

Ibrahim, Joseph G., et al. Bayesian Survival Analysis. 2010. (Springer Series in Statistics Ser.). (Illus.). xiv, 479p. pap. 129.00 *(978-1-4419-2933-4(9),* 1441929339) Springer.

Idier, Jérôme, ed. Bayesian Approach to Inverse Problems. 2008. (Iste Ser.: 312). (ENG., Illus.). 392p. 184.00 *(978-1-84821-032-5(9),* Wiley-ISTE) Wiley, John & Sons, Inc.

Ishii, Shin, et al, eds. Bayesian Brain: Probabilistic Approaches to Neural Coding. 2006. (Computational Neuroscience Ser.). (ENG., Illus.). 344p. (gr. 17). 58.00 *(978-0-262-04238-3(X))* MIT Pr.

Jackman, Simon. Bayesian Analysis for the Social Sciences. 2009. (Wiley Series in Probability & Statistics Ser.: 845). (ENG., Illus.). 598p. 90.00 *(978-0-470-01154-6(8),* Wiley) Wiley, John & Sons, Inc.

Jazwinski, Andrew H. Stochastic Processes & Filtering Theory. 2007. (Dover Books on Electrical Engineering Ser.). (ENG., Illus.). 400p. per. 22.95 *(978-0-486-46274-5(9))* Dover Pubns., Inc.

Jensen, Finn B. & Graven-Nielsen, Thomas. Bayesian Networks & Decision Graphs. 2nd ed. 2010. (Information Science & Statistics Ser.). xvi, 448p. pap. 99.00 *(978-1-4419-2394-3(2),* 1441923942) Springer.

Jensen, Finn V. & Nielsen, Thomas. Bayesian Networks & Decision Graphs. 2nd rev. ed. 2007. (Information Science & Statistics Ser.). xvi, 448p. (C). 99.00 *(978-0-387-68281-5(3),* 0387682813) Springer.

Johnson, Valen E. & Rosner, Gary L. An Introduction to Bayesian Biostatistics. 2012. (Chapman & Hall/CRC Texts in Statistical Science Ser.). (ENG., Illus.). 400p. 79.95 *(978-1-4398-0008-9(1),* Chapman & Hall/CRC) CRC Pr. LLC.

Justice, James H. Maximum Entropy & Bayesian Methods in Applied Statistics: Proceedings of the Fourth Maximum Entropy Workshop University of Calgary 1984. 2009. (ENG.). 332p. pap. 61.00 *(978-0-521-09603-4(0))* Cambridge Univ. Pr.

Kadane, Joseph. Principles of Uncertainty. 2011. (Chapman & Hall/CRC Texts in Statistical Science Ser.). (ENG., Illus.). 503p. 89.95 *(978-1-4398-6161-5(7),* Chapman & Hall/CRC) CRC Pr. LLC.

Kanevski, Mikhail, ed. Advanced Mapping of Environmental Data: Geostatistics, Machine Learning, & Bayesian Maximum Entropy. 2008. (Iste Ser.: 340). (ENG., Illus.). 352p. 158.00 *(978-1-84821-060-8(4),* Wiley-ISTE) Wiley, John & Sons, Inc.

Kery, Marc & Schaub, Michael. Bayesian Population Analysis Using WinBUGS: A Hierarchical Perspective. 2011. (ENG.). 554p. pap. 69.95 ***(978-0-12-387020-9(8)***, Academic Pr.) Elsevier Science & Technology Bks.

Kjaeruff, Uffe B. & Madsen, Anders L. Bayesian Networks & Influence Diagrams: A Guide to Construction & Analysis. 2007. (Information Science & Statistics (Springer) Ser.). (Illus.). 318p. 109.00 *(978-0-387-74100-0(3))* Springer.

—Bayesian Networks & Influence Diagrams: A Guide to Construction & Analysis: A Guide to Construction & Analysis. 2010. (Information Science & Statistics Ser.). (Illus.). xviii, 318p. pap. 109.00 *(978-1-4419-2546-6(5),* 1441925465) Springer.

Klugman, Stuart A. Bayesian Statistics in Actuarial Science: With Emphasis on Credibility. 2010. (Huebner International Series on Risk, Insurance & Economic Security Ser.). (ENG.). 256p. pap. 219.00 *(978-90-481-5790-7(0),* 9048157900) Springer.

Knill, David C. & Richards, Whitman, eds. Perception as Bayesian Inference. 2008. (ENG., Illus.). 532p. pap. 100.00 *(978-0-521-06499-6(6))* Cambridge Univ. Pr.

Knuth, Kevin H. (Nasa Ames Research Center). Bayesian Inference & Maximum Entropy Methods in Science & Engineering. 2007. (AIP Conference Proceedings / Mathematical & Statistical Physics Ser.). 227.00 *(978-0-7354-0468-7(2),* American Institute of Physics.

Koch, Karl-Rudolf. Introduction to Bayesian Statistics. 2nd ed. (ENG., Illus.). xii, 250p. 2010. pap. 129.00 *(978-3-642-09183-4(0),* 3642091830) 2007. 129.00 *(978-3-540-72723-1(X),* 354072723X) Springer.

Koller, Daphne, et al. Probabilistic Graphical Models: Principles & Techniques. 2009. (Adaptive Computation & Machine Learning Ser.). (ENG., Illus.). 1280p. 99.00 *(978-0-262-01319-2(3))* MIT Pr.

Koop, Gary, et al. Bayesian Econometric Methods. 2007. (Econometric Exercises Ser.: Vol. 7). (ENG., Illus.). 380p. 107.00 *(978-0-521-85571-6(3))*; per. 53.00 *(978-0-521-67173-6(6))* Cambridge Univ. Pr.

Korb, Kevin B. & Nicholson, Ann E. Bayesian Artificial Intelligence. 2nd rev. ed. 2010. (Chapman & Hall/CRC Computer Science & Data Analysis Ser.). (ENG., Illus.). 491p. 94.95 *(978-1-4398-1591-5(7),* CRC Press) Taylor & Francis Group GBR. Dist: Taylor & Francis Group.

Koski, Timo & Noble, John. Bayesian Networks: An Introduction. 2009. (Wiley Series in Probability & Statistics Ser.). (ENG., Illus.). 366p. 95.00 *(978-0-470-74304-1(2),* Wiley) Wiley, John & Sons, Inc.

Kruschke, John K. Doing Bayesian Data Analysis: A Tutorial Introduction with R & Bugs. 2010. (ENG., Illus.). 672p. (C). 89.95 *(978-0-12-381485-2(5),* Academic Pr.) Elsevier Science & Technology Bks.

Lauwereyns, Jan. The Anatomy of Bias: How Neural Circuits Weigh the Options. (ENG., Illus.). 288p. (gr. 17). 2011. pap. 16.00 ***(978-0-262-51659-4(4))*** 2010. 30.00 *(978-0-262-12310-5(X))* MIT Pr.

Lawson, Andrew B. Bayesian Disease Mapping: Hierarchical Modeling in Spatial Epidemiology. 2008. (Chapman & Hall/CRC Interdisciplinary Statistics Ser.). (ENG., Illus.). 368p. 89.95 *(978-1-58488-840-6(7),* Chapman & Hall/CRC) CRC Pr. LLC.

Lawson, Andrew B. & Lesaffre, Emmanuel. Bayesian Methods in Biostatistics. 2012. (Statistics in Practice Ser.). (ENG.). 536p. 75.00 *(978-0-470-01823-1(2),* Wiley) Wiley, John & Sons, Inc.

Lee, Sik-Yum. Structural Equation Modeling: A Bayesian Approach. 2007. (Wiley Series in Probability & Statistics Ser.: 680). (ENG., Illus.). 458p. 130.00 *(978-0-470-02423-2(2),* Wiley) Wiley, John & Sons, Inc.

Lee, Sik-Yum & Song, Xin-Yuan. Basic & Advanced Structural Equation Models for Medical & Behavioural Sciences. 2012. (Wiley Series in Probability & Statistics Ser.). (ENG.). 376p. 105.00 ***(978-0-470-66952-5(7)***, Wiley) Wiley, John & Sons, Inc.

Liu, Haoyang. Applications of Bayesian Classifiers. 2008. 144p. pap. *(978-3-639-08895-3(6))* VDM Verlag Dr. Mueller e.K.

Lucas, Peter, et al, eds. Advances in Probabilistic Graphical Models. 2010. (Studies in Fuzziness & Soft Computing Ser.). (Illus.). x, 396p. pap. 189.00 *(978-3-642-08854-4(6),* 3642088546) Springer.

Lucas, Peter & José A., Gámez, eds. Advances in Probabilistic Graphical Models. 2007. (Studies in Fuzziness & Soft Computing Ser.). (Illus.). X, 396p. 189.00 *(978-3-540-68994-2(X),* 354068994X) Springer.

Lynch, Scott M. Introduction to Applied Bayesian Statistics & Estimation for Social Scientists. (Statistics for Social & Behavioral Sciences Ser.). (Illus.). xxviii, 364p. 2010. pap. 109.00 *(978-1-4419-2434-6(5),* 1441924345) 2007. (ENG., 109.00 *(978-0-387-71264-2(X),* 038771264X) Springer.

Mahler, Ronald P. S. Statistical Multisource-Multitarget Information Fusion. 2007. (Artech House Information Warfare Library). (Illus.). 856p. 165.00 *(978-1-59693-092-6(6))* Artech Hse., Inc.

Mallick, Bani K., et al. Bayesian Analysis of Gene Expression Data. 2009. (Statistics in Practice Ser.). (ENG., Illus.). 252p. 90.00 *(978-0-470-51766-6(2),* Wiley) Wiley, John & Sons, Inc.

Marin, Jean-Michel & Robert, Christian. Bayesian Core: A Practical Approach to Computational Bayesian Statistics: A Practical Approach to Computational Bayesian Statistics. 2010. (Springer Texts in Statistics Ser.). (Illus.). xiv, 258p. pap. 89.95 *(978-1-4419-2286-1(5),* 1441922865) Springer.

Marin, Jean-Michel & Robert, Christian P. Bayesian Core: A Practical Approach to Computational Bayesian Statistics. 2007. (Springer Texts in Statistics Ser.). (Illus.). 255p. 89.95 *(978-0-387-38979-0(2),* 0387389792) Springer.

McCarthy, Michael A. Bayesian Methods for Ecology. 2007. (ENG., Illus.). 310p. per. 56.00 *(978-0-521-61559-4(3))* Cambridge Univ. Pr.

McGrayne, Sharon Bertsch. The Theory That Would Not Die: How Bayes' Rule Cracked the Enigma Code, Hunted down Russian Submarines, & Emerged Triumphant from Two Centuries of Controversy. 2011. 336p. 27.50 *(978-0-300-16969-0(8))* Yale Univ. Pr.

Miller, Luke. Development of a Bayesian Real Options Framework. 2010. 192p. pap. *(978-3-639-28292-4(2))* VDM Verlag Dr. Mueller e.K.

Mishra, Satya N. & Upadhyay, S. K., eds. Modern Mathematical, Management & Statistical Sciences, V Vol. 55: Advances in Bayesian Theory & Application. 2007. 270p. 235.00 *(978-0-935950-59-5(1))* American Sciences Pr., Inc.

Mittal, Ankush. Bayesian Network Technologies: Applications & Graphical Models. 2007. (Illus.). 300p. 99.95 *(978-1-59904-141-4(3))* IGI Global.

Mockus, Jonas, et al. Bayesian Heuristic Approach to Discrete & Global Optimization: Algorithms, Visualization, Software, & Applications. 2010. (Nonconvex Optimization & Its Applications Ser.). 416p. pap. 359.00 *(978-1-4419-4767-3(1),* 1441947671) Springer.

Mohammad-Djafari, Ali. Bayesian Inference & Maximum Entropy Methods in Science & Engineering: Proceedings of the 30th International Workshop on Bayesian Inference & Maximum Entropy Methods in Science & Engineering. Mohammad-Djafari, Ali et al, eds. 2011. (AIP Conference Proceedings / Mathematical & Statistical Physics Ser.). 484p. 309.00 *(978-0-7354-0860-9(2),* 0735408602, AIP Pr.) Springer.

Mohammad-Djafari, Ali, ed. Bayesian Inference & Maximum Entropy Methods in Science & Engineering: 26th International Workshop on Bayesian Inference & Maximum Entropy Methods in Science & Engineering: Paris, France, 8-13 July 2006. 2006. (AIP Conference Proceedings / Mathematical & Statistical Physics Ser.). (Illus.). xvii, 589p. 273.00 *(978-0-7354-0371-0(6),* 0735403716) American Institute of Physics.

Mohammad-Djafari, Ali & Demoment, G., eds. Maximum Entropy & Bayesian Methods. 2010. (Fundamental Theories of Physics Ser.). (Illus.). 460p. pap. 429.00 *(978-90-481-4272-9(5),* 9048142725) Springer.

Moyé, Lemuel A. Elementary Bayesian Biostatics. 2007. 88.95 *(978-1-58488-725-6(7),* CRC Press) Taylor & Francis Group GBR. Dist: Taylor & Francis Group.

—Elementary Bayesian Biostatistics. 2007. (Chapman & Hall/CRC Biostatistics Ser.). (ENG., Illus.). 400p. (C). 92.95 *(978-1-58488-724-9(9),* Chapman & Hall/CRC) CRC Pr. LLC.

Naïm, Patrick, et al. Risk Quantification: Management, Diagnosis & Hedging. 2007. (Wiley Finance Ser.: 80). (ENG., Illus.). 286p. 99.00 *(978-0-470-01907-8(7),* Wiley) Wiley, John & Sons, Inc.

Ndanguza Rusatsi, Denis. Statistical Analysis of an Seir Epidemic Model. 2010. 84p. pap. *(978-3-8383-8487-0(3))* Lambert Academic Publishing.

Neapolitan, Richard E. Probabilistic Methods for Bioinformatics: With an Introduction to Bayesian Networks. 2009. (ENG., Illus.). 424p. 72.95 *(978-0-12-370476-4(6),* Morgan Kaufmann) Elsevier Science & Technology Bks.

Neapolitan, Richard E. & Jiang, Xia. Probabilistic Methods for Financial & Marketing Informatics. 2007. (ENG., Illus.). 432p. 79.95 *(978-0-12-370477-1(4),* Morgan Kaufmann) Elsevier Science & Technology Bks.

Ng, Kai Wang, et al. Bayesian Missing Data Problems: EM, Data Augmentation & Noniterative Computation. 2009. (Chapman & Hall/CRC Biostatistics Ser.). (ENG., Illus.). 344p. 89.95 *(978-1-4200-7749-0(X),* Chapman & Hall/CRC) CRC Pr. LLC.

Nikolaev, Nikolay & Iba, Hitoshi. Adaptive Learning of Polynomial Networks: Genetic Programming, Backpropagation & Bayesian Methods. 2010. (Genetic & Evolutionary Computation Ser.). (Illus.). xiv, 316p. pap. 95.00 *(978-1-4419-4060-5(X),* 144194060X) Springer.

Ntzoufras, Ioannis. Bayesian Modeling Using WinBUGS. 2009. (Wiley Series in Computational Statistics Ser.: 698). (ENG., Illus.). 520p. 140.00 *(978-0-470-14114-4(X),* Wiley) Wiley, John & Sons, Inc.

O'hara, Robert. Bayesian Analysis for the Life Sciences. 2008. 384p. *(978-0-470-02733-2(9),* Wiley-Blackwell) Wiley, John & Sons, Ltd.

O'neill Philip D Staff. Bayesian Inference for Infectious Disease Data. 2010. 79.95 *(978-1-58488-548-1(3),* Chapman & Hall/CRC) CRC Pr. LLC.

Pamminger, Christoph. Bayesian Clustering of Categorical Time Series. 2008. 176p. pap. *(978-3-8364-9805-0(7))* VDM Verlag Dr. Mueller e.K.

Parent Eric Staff & Parent, Eric. Bayesian Modeling of Ecological Data. 2012. (Chapman & Hall/CRC Applied Environmental Statistics Ser.: 8). (ENG., Illus.). 412p. 89.95 *(978-1-58488-919-9(5),* Chapman & Hall/CRC) CRC Pr. LLC.

Paruchuri, Praveen, et al. Keep the Adversary Guessing: Agent Security by Policy Randomization. 2008. 120p. pap. *(978-3-639-01925-4(3))* VDM Verlag Dr. Mueller e.K.

Pérez-Suárez, Marcos. Quantum Uncertainty Structures: A Bayesian Approach to Quantum Randomness. 2010. (Illus.). 200p. 129.00 *(978-1-4419-8260-5(4),* 1441982604) Springer.

Peterson, Martin. Non-Bayesian Decision Theory: Beliefs & Desires As Reasons for Action. 2008. (Theory & Decision Library A: Ser.). VIII, 170p. (C). 139.00 *(978-1-4020-8698-4(9),* 1402086989) Springer.

—Non-Bayesian Decision Theory: Beliefs & Desires as Reasons for Action. 2010. (Theory & Decision Library A: Ser.). viii, 170p. pap. 139.00 *(978-90-481-7957-2(2),* 9048179572) Springer.

Petris, Giovanni, et al. Dynamic Linear Models with R. 2009. (Use R Ser.). (ENG., Illus.). xii, 252p. pap. 79.95 *(978-0-387-77237-0(5),* 0387772375) Springer.

Petrov, Krassimir. A Bayesian Vector Autoregresive Model of the U S Dairy Industry. 2010. 176p. pap. *(978-3-8383-1893-6(5))* Lambert Academic Publishing.

Ponnuraja, Chinnaiyan & Venkatesan, Perumal. Bayesian Frailty Models. 2010. 156p. pap. *(978-3-8383-7526-7(2))* Lambert Academic Publishing.

Pourret, Olivier, et al, eds. Bayesian Networks: A Practical Guide to Applications. 2008. (Statistics in Practice Ser.). (ENG., Illus.). 446p. 110.00 *(978-0-470-06030-8(1),* Wiley) Wiley, John & Sons, Inc.

Puglielli, David. Galaxy Modelling Using Bayesian Statistics. 2010. 136p. pap. *(978-3-8383-1833-2(1))* Lambert Academic Publishing.

Rachev, Svetlozar T., et al. Bayesian Methods in Finance. 2008. (Frank J. Fabozzi Ser.: 153). (ENG., Illus.). 329p. 95.00 *(978-0-471-92083-0(5),* Wiley) Wiley, John & Sons, Inc.

Rahman, Azizur. Bayesian Predictive Inference for Some Linear Models under Student-T Errors. 2008. 88p. pap. *(978-3-639-04086-9(4))* VDM Verlag Dr. Mueller e.K.

Rao, C. R. & Dey, Dipak K. Essential Bayesian Models. 2010. (ENG.). 586p. 79.95 *(978-0-444-53732-4(5),* North Holland) Elsevier Science & Technology Bks.

Rebonato, Riccardo. Coherent Stress Testing: A Bayesian Approach to the Analysis of Financial Risk. 2010. (Wiley Finance Ser.). (ENG., Illus.). 238p. 75.00 *(978-0-470-66601-2(3),* Wiley) Wiley, John & Sons, Inc.

Robert, Christian P. The Bayesian Choice: From Decision-Theoretic Foundations to Computational Implementation. 2nd ed. 2007. (Springer Texts in Statistics Ser.). xxii, 602p. pap. 59.95 *(978-0-387-71598-8(3))* Springer.

Ruggeri, Fabrizio, et al. Bayesian Analysis of Stochastic Process Models. 2012. (Wiley Series in Probability & Statistics Ser.). (ENG.). 332p. 99.95 ***(978-0-470-74453-6(7)***, Wiley) Wiley, John & Sons, Inc.

Sadoddin, Amir. Bayesian Network Models For. 2010. 252p. pap. *(978-3-8383-5655-6(1))* Lambert Academic Publishing.

Samaniego, Francisco J. A Comparison of the Bayesian & Frequentist Approaches to Estimation. 2010. (Springer Series in Statistics Ser.). xii, 226p. 89.95 *(978-1-4419-5940-9(8),* 1441959408) Springer.

Sánchez-Cambronero, S., et al. Traffic Prediction Models. 2011. 240p. pap. ***(978-3-8443-2027-5(X))*** Lambert Academic Publishing.

Savchuk, Vladimir & Tsokos, Chris P. Bayesian Theory & Methods with Applications. 2011. (Atlantis Studies in Probability & Statistics Ser.). (ENG., Illus.). xiv, 317p. 74.95 ***(978-94-91216-13-8(9)***, 9491216139) Atlantis Pr. (Zeger Karssen) NLD. Dist: Springer.

Schena, Pietro. Model Choice or Hypotheses Testing? 2011. 100p. pap. ***(978-3-8443-3154-7(9))*** Lambert Academic Publishing.

Shami, Roland. Bayesian Analysis of a Structural Model with Switching Regime. 2010. 208p. pap. *(978-3-8383-6372-1(6))* Lambert Academic Publishing.

Sheng, Yanyan. Bayesian Irt Models with General & Specific Traits. 2008. 100p. per. *(978-3-8364-6436-9(5))* VDM Verlag Dr. Mueller e.K.

Simsekli, Umut. Bayesian Methods for Real-Time Pitch Tracking. 2011. 72p. pap. ***(978-3-8443-1251-5(X))*** Lambert Academic Publishing.

Singpurwalla, Nozer & Singpurwalla, Nozer D. Reliability & Risk: A Bayesian Perspective. 2006. (Wiley Series in Probability & Statistics Ser.: 637). (ENG., Illus.). 396p. 130.00 *(978-0-470-85502-7(9),* Wiley) Wiley, John & Sons, Inc.

Skilling, John, ed. Maximum Entropy & Bayesian Methods. 2010. (Fundamental Theories of Physics Ser.). 548p. pap. 409.00 *(978-90-481-4044-2(7),* 9048140447) Springer.

Smith, C. R., et al, eds. Maximum Entropy & Bayesian Methods. 2010. (Fundamental Theories of Physics Ser.). 480p. pap. 369.00 *(978-90-481-4220-0(2),* 9048142202) Springer.

Smith, C. R. & Grandy Jr., W. T., eds. Maximum Entropy & Bayesian Methods in Inverse Problems. 2010. (Fundamental Theories of Physics Ser.). 508p. pap. 279.00 *(978-90-481-8418-7(5),* 9048184185) Springer.

Smith, Jim Q. Bayesian Decision Analysis: Principles & Practice. 2010. (ENG., Illus.). 348p. (C). 65.00 *(978-0-521-76454-4(8))* Cambridge Univ. Pr.

Sobel, Jordan Howard. Taking Chances: Essays on Rational Choice. 2007. (Cambridge Studies in Probability, Induction & Decision Theory Ser.). (ENG.). 392p. pap. 82.00 *(978-0-521-03898-0(7))* Cambridge Univ. Pr.

Somersalo, Erkki & Calvetti, D. Introduction to Bayesian Scientific Computing: Subjective Computing. 2007. (Surveys & Tutorials in the Applied Mathematical Sciences Ser.: Vol. 2). 214p. pap. 44.95 *(978-0-387-73393-7(0))* Springer.

Sorensen, Daniel & Gianola, Daniel. Likelihood, Bayesian & MCMC Methods in Quantitative Genetics. (Statistics for Biology & Health Ser.). xvii, 740p. 2010. pap. 149.00 *(978-1-4419-2997-6(5),* 1441929975) 2007. (Illus.). 149.00 *(978-0-387-95440-0(6),* 0387954406) Springer.

Souza Lauretto, Marcelo de, et al, eds. Bayesian Interference & Maximum Entropy Methods in Science & Engineering: Proceedings of the 28th International Workshop. 2008. (AIP Conference Proceedings / Mathematical & Statistical Phsyics Ser.). 394p. 209.00 *(978-0-7354-0604-9(9))* American Institute of Physics.

Stauffer, Howard B. Contemporary Bayesian & Frequentist Statistical Research Methods for Natural Resource Scientists. 2007. (ENG., Illus.). 400p. 128.00 *(978-0-470-16504-1(9),* Wiley-Interscience) Wiley, John & Sons, Inc.

Taroni, Franco, et al. Data Analysis in Forensic Science: A Bayesian Decision Perspective. 2010. (Statistics in Practice Ser.). (ENG., Illus.). 388p. 95.00 *(978-0-470-99835-9(0),* Wiley) Wiley, John & Sons, Inc.

Thomas, Andrew. OpenBUGS: Constructing MCMC Software. 2007. (Wiley Series in Computational Statistics Ser.). 224p. *(978-0-470-51083-4(8),* Wiley-Blackwell) Wiley, John & Sons, Ltd.

Thomas Andrew Staff. Bayesian Analysis Using Bugs: A Practical Introduction. 2012. (Chapman & Hall/CRC Texts in Statistical Science Ser.). (ENG., Illus.).

B

320p. (C). pap. 39.95 *(978-1-58488-849-9(0),* Chapman & Hall/CRC) CRC Pr. LLC.
Trees, Harry L. Van & Bell, Kristine L., eds. Bayesian Bounds for Parameter Estimation & Nonlinear Filtering/Tracking. 2007. (ENG., Illus.). 951p. 137.95 *(978-0-470-12095-8(9),* Wiley-IEEE Pr.) Wiley, John & Sons, Inc.
Upadkhyay, S. K., et al, eds. Bayesian Statistics & Its Applications. 2007. (Illus.). 508p. 150.00 *(978-1-905740-00-0(X))* Anshan GBR. Dist: Publishers Storage & Shipping.
Utzka, Miroslawa. Bayesian Network Analysis Software. 2008. 116p. pap. *(978-3-639-01749-6(8))* VDM Verlag Dr. Mueller e.K.
Varadhan, Ravi & Frangakis, Constantine E. Design, Modelling, & Computation in Studies Addressing Etiology: Some Methodological Issues in Statistical Modelling of Public Health Studies. 2008. 160p. pap. *(978-3-639-09491-6(3))* VDM Verlag Dr. Mueller e.K.
West, Mike & O'Hagan, Anthony. The Oxford Handbook of Applied Bayesian Analysis. 2010. (Oxford Handbooks Ser.). (ENG., Illus.). 896p. 150.00 *(978-0-19-954890-3(0))* Oxford Univ. Pr., Inc.
Wikle, Christopher K. & Cressie, Noel A. C. Statistics for Spatio-Temporal Data. 2011. (Wiley Series in Probability & Statistics Ser.: 465). (ENG., Illus.). 624p. 89.95 *(978-0-471-69274-4(3),* Wiley) Wiley, John & Sons, Inc.
Williamson, Jon. In Defence of Objective Bayesianism. 2010. (ENG., Illus.). 200p. 85.00 *(978-0-19-922800-3(0))* Oxford Univ. Pr., Inc.
Woodward, Phil. Bayesian Analysis Made Simple: An Excel GUI for WinBUGS. 2011. (Chapman & Hall/CRC Biostatistics Ser.). (ENG., Illus.). 364p. 69.95 *(978-1-4398-3954-6(9),* Chapman & Hall/CRC) CRC Pr. LLC.
Woodworth, George G. Biostatistics: Intermediate Bayesian Inference. 2013. (Wiley Series in Probability & Statistics Ser.). (ENG., Illus.). 416p. 99.95 *(978-0-470-17942-0(2),* Wiley-Interscience) Wiley, John & Sons, Inc.
Xiang, Yang. Probabilistic Reasoning in Multiagent Systems: A Graphical Models Approach. 2010. (ENG., Illus.). 308p. pap. 39.99 *(978-0-521-15390-4(5))* Cambridge Univ. Pr.
Yildirim, Sinan. Bayesian Deconvolution of Sparse Processes. 2011. 104p. pap. ***(978-3-8443-2753-3(3))*** Lambert Academic Publishing.
Yuen, Ka-Veng. Bayesian Methods for Structural Dynamics & Civil Engineering. 2010. (ENG., Illus.). 320p. 140.00 *(978-0-470-82454-2(9),* Wiley) Wiley, John & Sons, Inc.
Zellner, Arnold. Information Processing & Bayesian Analysis. 2007. 416p. 89.95 *(978-0-471-48349-6(4),* Wiley-Interscience) Wiley, John & Sons, Inc.
Zuashkiani, Ali. Expert Knowledge Based Reliability Models. 2008. 184p. pap. *(978-3-639-02056-4(1))* VDM Verlag Dr. Mueller e.K.

BAYEUX TAPESTRY

Crafton, John Micheal. The Political Artistry of the Bayeux Tapestry: A Visual Epic of Norman Imperial Ambitions. 196p. 99.95 *(978-0-7734-5318-0(0))* Mellen, Edwin Pr., The.
Fowke, Frank Rede. The Bayeux Tapestry: A History & Description. 2009. 300p. 24.99 *(978-1-103-33481-0(6));* pap. 18.99 *(978-1-103-33478-0(6))* BiblioBazaar.
Foys, Martin K., et al, eds. The Bayeux Tapestry: New Interpretations. 2009. (Illus.). 248p. 90.00 *(978-1-84383-470-0(7),* Boydell Press) Boydell & Brewer, Ltd. GBR. Dist: Boydell & Brewer, Inc.
Hicks, Carola. The Bayeux Tapestry: The Life Story of a Masterpiece. 2008. (ENG., Illus.). 368p. pap. 18.95 *(978-0-09-945019-1(4))* Random Hse. GBR. Dist: Independent Pubs. Group.
Lewis, Michael J. The Real World of the Bayeux Tapestry. 2008. (ENG., Illus.). 192p. pap. 36.95 *(978-0-7524-3446-9(2))* History Pr. Ltd.,The GBR. Dist: Independent Pubs. Group.
Lewis, Michael J., et al, eds. New Research on the Bayeux Tapestry: The Proceedings of a Conference at the British Museum. 2011. (ENG., Illus.). 211p. (C). 90.00 *(978-1-84217-976-5(4))* Oxbow Bks., Ltd. GBR. Dist: Brown, David Bk. Co., The.
Lewis, Suzanne. The Rhetoric of Power in the Bayeux Tapestry. 2011. (Cambridge Studies in New Art History & Criticism Ser.). (ENG., Illus.). 186p. pap. 26.99 ***(978-1-107-40335-2(9))*** Cambridge Univ. Pr.
Messent, Jan. The Bayeux Tapestry Embroiderers' Story. 2011. (ENG., Illus.). 112p. pap. 29.95 *(978-1-84448-584-0(6))* Search Pr., Ltd. GBR. Dist: Independent Pubs. Group.
Owen-Crocker, Gale R., ed. King Harold II & the Bayeux Tapestry. 2011. (Pubns Manchester Centre for Anglo-Saxon Studies: Volume 3). (Illus.). 214p. pap. 29.95 *(978-1-84383-615-5(7),* Boydell Press) Boydell & Brewer, Ltd. GBR. Dist: Boydell & Brewer, Inc.
Wheeler, Candace. The Development of Embroidery in America. 2007. (Illus.). 232p. pap. 17.95 *(978-1-60355-068-0(2))* Juniper Grove.

BAYLE, PIERRE, 1647-1706

Bayle, Pierre. Correspondance de Pierre Bayle Volume IX: Janvier 1693 ¿ mars 1696, Lettres 902-1099. Bost, Hubert, ed. 2012. (FRE., Illus.). 779p. ***(978-0-7294-0984-1(8))*** Voltaire Foundation.
Bunge, Wiep van & Bots, Hans. Pierre Bayle (1647-1706), le Philosophe de Rotterdam: Philosophy, Religion, & Reception: Selected Papers of the Tercentenary Conference Held at Rotterdam, 7-8 December 2006. 2008. (Brill's Studies in Intellectual History: Vol. 167). (FRE & ENG.). 304p. (C). *(978-90-04-16536-6(3))* BRILL.
Labrousse, Elizabeth & McKenna, Antony, annos. Correspondance de Pierre Bayle Vol. 8: Janvier 1689 ¿ décembre 1692, Lettres 720-901. 2010. (FRE., Illus.). 836p. 210.00 *(978-0-7294-0983-4(X))* Voltaire Foundation GBR. Dist: Marston Bk. Services, Ltd.
Lerner, Ralph. Playing the Fool: Subversive Laughter in Troubled Times. 2009. (ENG.). 144p. 32.50 *(978-0-226-47315-4(5))* Univ. of Chicago Pr.
Ryan, Todd. Pierre Bayle's Cartesian Metaphysics. 2007. (Routledge Studies in Seventeenth Century Philosophy Ser.). 288p. 136.00 *(978-0-415-77018-7(1))* Routledge.
Ryan, Todd. Pierre Bayle's Cartesian Metaphysics: Rediscovering Early Modern Philosophy. 2012. (ENG.). 224p. (C). pap. 39.95 ***(978-0-415-53863-3(7))*** Routledge.

BAYLOR UNIVERSITY

Baylor University Press. Baylor: A Legacy of Spirit, Tradition, Beauty. 2008. (ENG.). 95p. 29.95 *(978-1-60258-191-3(6))* Baylor Univ. Pr.
Blodgett, Terrell. The Land, the Law, & the Lord: The Life of Pat Neff. 2007. (Illus.). 416p. 24.95 *(978-0-9761152-2-9(0))* Promised Land Bks.
CGuides Staff, ed. Baylor University: The Need to Know & Where to Go Guide to College Life. 2008. (Cguides Ser.). (Illus.). 112p. pap. 12.95 *(978-1-59186-801-9(7))* Cool Springs Pr.
Copeland, Todd. The Immortal Ten: The Definitive Account of the 1927 Tragedy & Its Legacy at Baylor University. 2007. (Illus.). 112p. per. 24.95 *(978-1-932792-90-4(2))* Baylor Univ. Pr.
Hankins, Barry & Schmeltekopf, Donald D. Baylor Beyond the Crossroads: An Interpretive History 1985-2005. 2006. pap. *(978-0-914108-06-1(9))* Baylor Univ. Pr.
Hankins, Barry G. & Schmeltekopf, Donald D., eds. The Baylor Project: Taking Christian Higher Education to the Next Level. 2007. 352p. 30.00 *(978-1-58731-062-1(7))* St. Augustine's Pr., Inc.
Raska, Ginny McNeill & Hill, Mary Lynn Gasaway, eds. The Uncompromising Diary of Sallie McNeill, 1858-1867. 2009. (Centennial Series of the Association of Former Students, Texas A&M University Ser.). (ENG., Illus.). 216p. 32.50 *(978-1-60344-087-5(9))* Texas A&M Univ. Pr.

BAYONETS

Angelo, Henry. Angelo's Bayonet Exercises 1857. 2009. 48p. pap. *(978-1-84734-830-2(0))* Naval & Military Pr., The.
Bayonets of Japan: A Comprehensive Reference on Japanese Bayonets. 2008. (Illus.). 480p. lib. bdg. 120.00 *(978-0-9801826-0-6(3))* RAYMAR, Inc.
Capwell, Tobias. The Illustrated Directory of Knives, Daggers & Bayonets: A Visual Encyclopedia of Edged Weapons from Around the World, Including Knives, Daggers, Bayonets, Machetes & Khanjars, with over 500 Illustrations. 2012. (ENG., Illus.). 160p. pap. 18.99 ***(978-1-84476-999-5(2))*** Anness Publishing GBR. Dist: National Bk. Network.
—The Illustrated Encyclopedia of Knives, Daggers & Bayonets: An Authoritative History & Visual Directory of Small Edged Weapons & Blades from Around the World, Shown in over 700 Stunning Colour Photographs. 2009. (ENG., Illus.). 256p. 35.00 *(978-0-7548-1890-8(X))* Anness Publishing GBR. Dist: National Bk. Network.
—Pictorial History of Knives, Daggers & Bayonets. 2011. (ENG., Illus.). 96p. pap. 16.99 *(978-1-84476-950-6(X))* Anness Publishing GBR. Dist: National Bk. Network.
Hutton, Alfred. Bayonet-Fencing & Sword-Practice 1882. 2009. 48p. pap. *(978-1-84734-865-4(3))* Naval & Military Pr., The.
—A Complete System of Fence for the Briti. 2007. 200p. per. *(978-1-84574-368-0(7))* Naval & Military Pr., The.
Lidstone, Squadron Leader R. A. L. Bloody Bayonets: The Complete Guide to Bayonet Fighting. 2009. (Illus.). 80p. pap. *(978-1-84734-818-0(1))* Naval & Military Pr., The.
Pattarozzi, Mack A. American Gladius: A Study of the M-9 Multi-Purpose Bayonet System. 2009. (Illus.). 224p. bds. 49.99 *(978-0-7643-3239-5(2))* Schiffer Publishing, Ltd.
Schmidt, Peter A. U. S. Military Flintlock Muskets & Their Bayonets: The Later Years, 1816 through the Civil War. 2007. (Illus.). 371p. 69.99 *(978-1-931464-27-7(8))* Mowbray, Andrew Inc., Pubs.
Sprague, Martina. A History of Edged Weapon Warfare. 2009. (ENG., Illus.). 528p. 39.95 *(978-1-59416-101-8(1))* Westholme Publishing.
Staff, The. Bayonet Training 1918. 2009. 52p. pap. *(978-1-84734-867-8(X))* Naval & Military Pr., The.
Twine, C. J. Bayonet Battle Training a Realistic & Practical Series of Exercises on the Use of the Training Stick & Dummy. 2009. 48p. pap. *(978-1-84734-811-1(4))* Naval & Military Pr., The.
The U. S. Krag Bayonets: History, Variations, Modifications. 2009. (Illus.). 332p. 109.95 *(978-0-9823021-0-1(X))* D&D Blade Research.

BAYREUTHER FESTSPIELE

Hilmes, Oliver. Cosima Wagner: The Lady of Bayreuth. Spencer, Stewart, tr. from GER. 2011. (Illus.). 400p. pap. 26.00 *(978-0-300-17090-0(4))* Yale Univ. Pr.
The Story of Bayreuth As Told in the Bayreuth Letters of Richard Wagner. 2009. 122p. pap. *(978-1-150-76327-4(2))* Books LLC.

BAYS

NZ Visitor Publications Ltd, creator. New Zealand: Bays & Beaches. 2006. (Illus.). 189p. 49.80 *(978-1-877339-15-8(6))* NZVP Bks. & Calendars Ltd. NZL. Dist: Perseus-PGW.

BAZIN, RENE, 1853-1932

Gelson, M. Aline. Analysis of the Realistic Elements in the Novels of Rene Bazin. (Catholic University of America, Studies in Romance Languages & Literatures: No. 23). reprint ed. 37.50 *(978-0-404-50323-9(3))* AMS Pr., Inc.

BBC

see British Broadcasting Corporation

BBQ COOKING

see Barbecuing

BCCI

see Bank of Credit and Commerce International

BE (THE WORD)

Verhaar, J. W., ed. The Verb 'Be' & Its Synonyms - Part V: Philosophical & Grammatical Studies Part V: Urdu/Turkish/Bengali/Amharic/Indonesian/Telugu/Estonian. 2010. (Foundation of Language Supplementary Ser.). 248p. pap. 139.00 *(978-90-481-8337-1(5),* 9048183375) Springer.

BEACH, SYLVIA, 1887-1962

Beach, Sylvia. The Letters of Sylvia Beach. Walsh, Keri, ed. 2010. (ENG., Illus.). 376p. (gr. 17). 29.95 *(978-0-231-14536-7(5))* Columbia Univ. Pr.
Beach, Sylvia. The Letters of Sylvia Beach. Walsh, Keri, ed. 2011. (ENG., Illus.). 376p. (gr. 17). pap. 19.95 ***(978-0-231-14537-4(3))*** Columbia Univ. Pr.

BEACH BIRDS

see Shore Birds

BEACH BOYS

Badman, Keith. The Beach Boys: The Definitive Diary of America's Greatest Band on Stage & in the Studio. 2006. (Illus.). 399p. reprint ed. pap. 30.00 *(978-1-4223-5811-5(9))* DIANE Publishing Co.
Beach Boys, contrib. by. The Beach Boys. 2007. (Paperback Songs Ser.). (ENG., Illus.). 160p. per. 7.95 *(978-0-634-06284-1(0),* 0634062840) Leonard, Hal Corp.
Dillon, Mark. Fifty Sides of the Beach Boys: The Songs That Tell Their Story. 2012. (ENG., Illus.). 360p. pap. 19.95 ***(978-1-77041-071-8(6))*** ECW Pr. CAN. Dist: Independent Pubs. Group.
Lloyd, Jack. Endless Summer: My life with the beach Boys. 2010. 238p. pap. 19.95 *(978-1-59393-113-1(1))* BearManor Media.
Schmidt, Manfred & Haschke, Christian. The Whole World: The Complete Beach Boys Single & EP Cover Collection. 2007. (Illus.). 300p. 39.95 *(978-3-931959-40-1(6))* Fossil-Verlag GmbH DEU. Dist: Gingko Pr., Inc.
Stebbins, Jon. The Beach Boys FAQ: All That's Left to Know about America's Band. 2011. (ENG., Illus.). 320p. pap. 19.99 *(978-0-87930-987-9(3),* 0879309873, Backbeat Books) Leonard, Hal Corp.
Stebbins, Jon, et al. The Lost Beach Boy: The True Story of Beach Boy David Marks, the Previously Unknown Founding Member. 2007. (ENG., Illus.). 288p. 34.95 *(978-1-85227-391-0(7))* Virgin Bks. Ltd. GBR. Dist: Independent Pubs. Group.

BEACH EROSION

see also Coast Changes; Shore Protection

Barnhardt, Walter A. & Schwab, William C. Coastal Change along the Shore of Northeastern South Carolina: The South Carolina Coastal Erosion Study. 2009. (Illus.). vi, 77p. *(978-1-4113-2538-8(9))* United States Geological Survey.
Kelley, Joseph T., et al. America's Most Vulnerable Coastal Communities. 2009. (Illus.). vi, 179p. pap. 65.00 *(978-0-8137-2460-7(0))* Geological Society of America, Inc.
Nordstrom, Karl F. Beach & Dune Restoration. 2008. (ENG., Illus.). 200p. 137.00 *(978-0-521-85346-0(X))* Cambridge Univ. Pr.
Sargent, William. Sea Level Rising. 2009. (Illus.). 224p. pap. 19.99 *(978-0-7643-3261-6(9))* Schiffer Publishing, Ltd.
Thorne, C., et al. Future Flooding & Coastal Erosion Risks. 2007. (Illus.). 350p. *(978-0-7277-3449-5(0))* Telford, Thomas Ltd.
Uda, Takaaki. Japan's Beach Erosion: Reality & Future Measures. 2010. (Illus.). 428p. 111.00 *(978-981-4277-12-9(6))* World Scientific Publishing Co., Inc.

Van Thiel De Vries, J. S. M., ed. Dune Erosion During Storm Surges. 2009. (Deltares Select Ser.). 220p. pap. 91.00 *(978-1-60750-041-4(8))* IOS Pr., Inc.

BEACH FAMILY

McKey, Leonard. The Beach Connection: A Man & Woman make a connection after meeting at the Beach. 2009. 116p. 21.49 *(978-1-4389-4535-4(3));* pap. 10.99 *(978-1-4389-2309-3(0))* AuthorHouse.

BEACH-LA-MAR JARGON

see Bislama Language

BEACHES

see also Bathing Beaches; Beach Erosion; Sand Dunes; Seashore

Allyn, David. The Q Guide to Gay Beaches. 2008. (Q Guide To... Ser.). (ENG., Illus.). 172p. per. 12.95 *(978-1-59350-041-2(6))* Alyson Pubns.
Ariza, Eduard. A System of Integral Quality Indicators As a Tool for Beach Management. 2008. 188p. pap. *(978-3-8364-7649-2(5))* VDM Verlag Dr. Mueller e.K.
Aubery, Patty, et al. Chicken Soup for the Beach Lover's Soul: Memories Made Beside a Bonfire, on the Boardwalk, & with Family & Friends in the Summer Sun. 2007. (Chicken Soup for the Soul Ser.). (ENG., Illus.). 384p. pap. 14.95 *(978-0-7573-0605-1(5))* Health Communications, Inc.
Ayers, R. Wayne & Ayers, Nancy. Tampa Bay's Beaches. 2008. (Then & Now Ser.). (ENG., Illus.). 96p. per. 19.99 *(978-0-7385-5338-2(7))* Arcadia Publishing.
Bisbort, Alan & Puterbaugh, Parke. California Beaches: The Best Places to Swim, Play, Eat, & Stay. 2009. (Moon Handbooks Ser.). (ENG., Illus.). 576p. pap. 21.95 *(978-1-56691-614-1(3))* Westview Pr.
Borhan, Pierre. The Sea: A Celebration in Photographs. 2011. (ENG., Illus.). 300p. pap. 34.95 *(978-2-08-020085-3(2))* Flammarion et Cie FRA. Dist: Random Hse., Inc.
Boyd, Michael. Naked Places. 4th ed. Date not set. 19.95 *(978-0-9656089-3-0(X))* Mercury Productions.
Brooks, Carellin. Wreck Beach. 2007. (Transmontanus Ser.). (ENG., Illus.). 96p. pap. *(978-1-55420-031-3(8))* New Star Bks., Ltd.
Burnham, Mary & Burnham, Bill. The Complete Florida Beach Guide. 2008. (Wild Florida Ser.). (ENG., Illus.). 256p. per. 19.95 *(978-0-8130-3221-4(0))* Univ. Pr. of Florida.
California Coastal Commission. Beaches & Parks from Monterey to Ventura: Experience the California Coast. 2007. (Experience the California Coast Ser.). (Illus.). 318p. pap. 26.95 *(978-0-520-24949-3(6))* Univ. of California Pr.
California Coastal Commission Staff. Beaches & Parks in Southern California: Counties Included - Los Angeles, Orange, San Diego. 2009. (Experience the California Coast Ser.). (ENG., Illus.). 352p. pap. 26.95 *(978-0-520-25852-5(5))* Univ. of California Pr.
Covert, Pat, text. The Beach: A Celebration of Life. 2007. (Illus.). 203p. *(978-1-58173-648-9(7))* Sweetwater Pr.
Cram101 Textbook Reviews Staff. Outlines & Highlights for Beaches & Coasts by Duncan Fitzgerald, Richard Davis Jr , Isbn: 9780632043088. 2009. 118p. pap. 28.95 *(978-1-4288-8104-4(2))* Cram101 Inc.
Dixon, Lee. Delaware & Maryland Beaches: 1905 - 1965. 2008. (Illus.). 176p. pap. 29.95 *(978-0-7643-2753-7(4))* Schiffer Publishing, Ltd.
Dombrowski, Theo. Secret Beaches of Greater Victoria: View Royal to Sidney, 1 vol. 2010. (ENG., Illus.). 256p. pap. *(978-1-894974-98-1(0))* Heritage Hse.
—Secret Beaches of Southern Vancouver Island: Qualicum to the Malahat, 1 vol. 2010. (ENG., Illus.). 256p. pap. *(978-1-894974-97-4(2))* Heritage Hse.
Flaherty, Liz. Action Literacy: Surf & Sand. 2008. 32p. pap. 10.95 *(978-0-86431-711-7(5))* ACER Pr. AUS. Dist: International Specialized Bk. Services.
Fodor's Travel Publications, Inc. Staff. 535 Best Beaches: In the U. S. , Caribbean, & Mexico. 2010. (Full-Color Gold Guides). (ENG., Illus.). 328p. pap. 18.99 *(978-1-4000-0505-5(1),* Fodor's) Fodor's Travel Pubns.
Fogle, Jean M. Salty Dogs. 2007. (ENG., Illus.). 112p. 14.99 *(978-0-470-16904-9(4),* Howell Bk. Hse.) Wiley, John & Sons, Inc.
Forbes, Andrew. DK Eyewitness Travel Guide: Thailand's Beaches & Islands: Thailand's Beaches & Islands. 2012. (Eyewitness travel Guide Ser.). (ENG.). 384p. pap. 25.00 ***(978-0-7566-8573-7(7))*** Dorling Kindersley Publishing, Inc.
Gelbert, Doug. Doggin' America's Beaches: A Traveler's Guide to Dog-Friendly Beaches (and those that Aren't) 2007. (Illus.). 124p. (ENG.). per. 12.95 *(978-0-9797074-5-2(5));* per. 12.95 *(978-0-9797074-4-5(7))* Cruden Bay Bks.
GElbert, Doug. Doggin' the Carolina Coasts: The 50 Best Places to Hike with Your Dog along the North Carolina & South Carolina Shores. 2007. (Illus.). 124p. per. 11.95 *(978-0-9795577-0-5(4))* Cruden Bay Bks.
Gelbert, Doug. Doggin' the Carolina Coasts: The 50 Best Places to Hike with Your Dog along the North Carolina & South Carolina Shores. 2007. (Illus.). 124p. per. 11.95 *(978-0-9795577-9-8(8))* Cruden Bay Bks.
Giovan, Tria, photos by. Tria Giovan: Sand Sea Sky: The Beaches of Sagaponack. 2012. (ENG., Illus.). 88p. 40.00 ***(978-88-6208-196-2(0))*** Damiani ITA. Dist: D.A.P./Distributed Art Pubs.
Griffiths, Tom. Safer Beaches: Planning, Design, & Operation. 2011. (ENG., Illus.). 152p. 49.00 ***(978-0-7360-8646-2(3))*** Human Kinetics Pubs.
Gruyaert, Harry, photos by. Edges. 2010. (ENG., Illus.). 104p. 100.00 *(978-90-5330-616-1(1))* Mets en Schilt Uitgevers NLD. Dist: Ingram Pub. Services.
Guthrie Ford, J. & Creighton, Mark. Port Aransas. 2011. (Images of America Ser.). (ENG., Illus.). 128p. pap. 21.99 *(978-0-7385-7960-3(2))* Arcadia Publishing.
Hardee, Lesta Sue & McDonald, Janice. Myrtle Beach Pavilion. 2010. (Images of America Ser.). (ENG., Illus.). 128p. pap. 21.99 *(978-0-7385-8601-4(3))* Arcadia Publishing.
Hobbs, Carl. The Beach Book: Science of the Shore. 2012. (ENG., Illus.). 192p. (gr. 17). pap. 19.50 ***(978-0-231-16055-1(0))*** Columbia Univ. Pr.
—The Beach Book - Science of the Shore. 2012. (ENG., Illus.). 192p. (gr. 17). 60.00 ***(978-0-231-16054-4(2))*** Columbia Univ. Pr.
Hoberman, Gerald, photos by. Miami & the Beaches. 2011. (ENG.). 304p. 34.95 ***(978-1-919939-82-7(2))*** Hoberman, Gerald Pubns. ZAF. Dist: Perseus Distribution.
Iselin, Josie & Chronicle Books Staff. Beach: A Book of Treasure. 2010. (ENG., Illus.). 144p. 24.95 *(978-0-8118-7155-6(X))* Chronicle Bks. LLC.
Killip, Chris. Seacoal, 1 vol. 2011. (ENG., Illus.). 112p. 48.00 *(978-3-86930-256-0(9))* Steidl, Gerhard Druckerei und Verlag DEU. Dist: Innovative Logistics.
Krestovnikoff, Miranda. Best British Beaches: Discover Over 100 Great Seaside Spots. 2009. (ENG., Illus.). 272p. pap. 22.95 *(978-1-86205-858-3(X))* Chrysalis Children's Bks. GBR. Dist: Independent Pubs. Group.
Lonely Planet Staff, et al. Thailand's Islands & Beaches. 7th ed. 2010. (Regional Guide Ser.). (ENG., Illus.). 468p. pap. 21.99 *(978-1-74179-413-7(7))* Lonely Planet Pubns.
Lucy, Gia. Beaches of San Diego. 2008. 178p. 29.50 *(978-0-9679452-2-4(4))* Vista Pacifica Publishing Co.
Marquez, Ernest. Santa Monica Beach: A Collector's Pictorial History. 2011. (Illus.). 207p. pap. 29.95 ***(978-1-883318-95-6(5))*** Angel City Pr.
McGuinness, Neil. The Beaches. 2010. (Illus.). 176p. 19.95 *(978-0-615-38519-8(2))* McGuinness Financial Corp.
McLachlan, Anton & Brown, A. C. The Ecology of Sandy Shores. 2nd ed. 2006. (ENG., Illus.). 392p. 99.95 *(978-0-12-372569-1(0),* Academic Pr.) Elsevier Science & Technology Bks.

Metusela, Christine & Waitt, Gordon. Tourism & Australian Beach Cultures: Revealing Bodies. 2012. (Tourism & Cultural Change Ser.). (ENG.). 200p. 129.95 ***(978-1-84541-286-9(9))***; pap. 39.95 ***(978-1-84541-285-2(0))*** Channel View Pubns., Ltd. GBR. Dist: Univ. of Toronto Pr.
Molloy, Johnny. Beach & Coastal Camping in Florida. 2nd ed. 2008. (ENG., Illus.). 208p. per. 16.95 *(978-0-8130-3223-8(7))* Univ. Pr. of Florida.
Morrall, June. Moss Beach. 2010. (Images of America Ser.). (ENG., Illus.). 128p. pap. 21.99 *(978-0-7385-8075-3(9))* Arcadia Publishing.
Neal, William J., et al. Atlantic Coast Beaches: A Guide to Ripples, Dunes, & Other Natural Features of the Seashore. 2007. (Illus.). 250p. per. 20.00 *(978-0-87842-534-1(9))* Mountain Pr. Publishing Co., Inc.
Nordstrom, Karl F. Estuarine Beaches: An Introduction to the Physical & Human Factors Affecting Use & Management of Beaches in Estuaries, Lagoons, Bays & Fjords. 2007. (Illus.). 252p. 296.00 *(978-1-85166-728-4(8))* Springer.
Nyega, Nyangubho, et al. Beach Management Units in Lake Victori. 2011. 88p. pap. ***(978-3-8443-9930-1(5))*** Lambert Academic Publishing.
NZ Visitor Publications Ltd, creator. New Zealand: Bays & Beaches. 2006. (Illus.). 189p. 49.80 *(978-1-877339-15-8(6))* NZVP Bks. & Calendars Ltd. NZL. Dist: Perseus-PGW.
Passaquindici, Stefano. Beaches: 100 Ultimate Escapes. Talarico, Sabrina, ed. 2011. (ENG., Illus.). 264p. 45.00 *(978-0-7893-2235-7(8))* Universe Publishing.
Pate, Jack. Florida's First Coast: A History in Images. 2008. pap. 19.99 *(978-1-59629-528-5(7))* History Pr., The.
Pilkey, Orrin H., et al. The World's Beaches: A Global Guide to the Science of the Shoreline. 2011. (ENG., Illus.). 302p. 70.00 *(978-0-520-26871-5(7))*; pap. 29.95 *(978-0-520-26872-2(5))* Univ. of California Pr.
Richardson, Howard. Regional Guide Thailand's Islands & Beaches. 2nd ed. 2012. (Regional Guides). (Illus.). 304p. pap. 18.99 ***(978-1-78005-040-9(2))*** APA Publications Services SGP. Dist: Ingram Pub. Services.
Ridout, Lucy, et al. Thailand's Beaches & Islands. 4th ed. 2009. (Rough Guide Travel Guides). (ENG., Illus.). 524p. 19.99 *(978-1-84836-091-4(6))* Rough Guides, Ltd. GBR. Dist: Dorling Kindersley Publishing, Inc.
Santa Cruz Seaside Company. The Santa Cruz Beach Boardwalk: A Century by the Sea. 2007. (ENG., Illus.). 176p. 28.95 *(978-1-58008-815-2(5))*; pap. 19.95 *(978-1-58008-814-5(7))* Ten Speed Pr.
Scholl, Steve. Beaches & Parks from San Francisco to Monterey: Counties Included - Marin, San Francisco, San Mateo, Santa Cruz, Monterey. 2012. (Experience the California Coast Ser.). (ENG.). 320p. pap. 29.95 ***(978-0-520-27157-9(2))*** Univ. of California Pr.
Spooner, Andrew. Thailand, Islands & Beaches: Full Colour Regional Travel Guide to Thailand, Islands & Beaches, Including Bangkok. 2010. (Footprint - Destination Guides). (ENG., Illus.). 288p. pap. 21.95 *(978-1-906098-84-1(0))* Footprint Handbooks GBR. Dist: Globe Pequot Pr., The.
Sweett, Lawrence J. New Smyrna Beach. 2006. (Images of America Ser.). (ENG., Illus.). 128p. per. 21.99 *(978-0-7385-4323-9(3))* Arcadia Publishing.
Thatcher, George. A Decade of Beach Walks. 2008. (Illus.). 239p. 12.00 *(978-1-934193-16-7(X))* Quail Ridge Pr., Inc.
Tigner, James. Colonial Beach, Virginia. 2008. (Illus.). 128p. pap. 24.99 *(978-0-7643-2806-4(5))* Schiffer Publishing, Ltd.
—Memories of Chesapeake Beach & North Beach, Maryland. 2007. (Illus.). 128p. pap. 24.95 *(978-0-7643-2768-1(2))* Schiffer Publishing, Ltd.
Time Out Guides Staff. Time Out Seaside: Discover Britain's Coastal Treasures. Graham, Hugh, ed. 2008. (Time Out Guides). (ENG., Illus.). 256p. pap. 26.95 *(978-1-84670-079-8(5))* Time Out Guides Ltd. GBR. Dist: Perseus-PGW.
Verne, photos by. Summertime: And the Living Is Easy. 2009. (ENG., Illus.). 176p. *(978-90-209-7884-1(5))*, Lannoo Pubs. (UK) Antique Collectors' Club.
Virginia Beach Public Library Staff, contrib. by. The Beach: A History of Virginia Beach, Virginia. 3rd ed. 2006. Orig. Title: The Beach A History of Virginia Beach, Virginia. (Illus.). xiv, 161p. pap. 8.95 *(978-0-9779570-0-2(4))* Virginia Beach Public Library, City of Virginia Be.
Walker, Julie A. Fun at the Beach. 2011. 32p. pap. 12.99 ***(978-1-4567-5926-1(4))*** AuthorHouse.
Wallpaper Magazine Editors. Beach, 5 vols., Set. 2008. (ENG., Illus.). pap. 49.75 *(978-0-7148-5590-5(1))* Phaidon Pr., Inc.
Williams, Allan & Micallef, Anton. Beach Management: Principles & Practice. 2011. (ENG., Illus.). 480p. pap. 59.95 *(978-1-84971-307-8(3))* Routledge.
Williams, Allan & Micallef, Anton, eds. Beach Management: Principles & Practice. 2009. (ENG., Illus.). 480p. 117.00 *(978-1-84407-435-8(8))* Routledge.
Williams, Lizzie. Kenya's Beaches Footprint Focus. 2011. (Footprint Focus Ser.). (ENG., Illus.). 144p. pap. 12.95 *(978-1-908206-29-9(2))* Footprint Handbooks GBR. Dist: Globe Pequot Pr., The.
Williams, Lorraine O'Donnell. Memories of the Beach: Reflections on a Toronto Childhood. 2010. (ENG., Illus.). 248p. pap. 26.99 *(978-1-55488-389-9(X))* Dundurn CAN. Dist: Ingram Pub. Services.
Witherington, Blair & Witherington, Dawn. Florida's Living Beaches: A Guide for the Curious Beachcomber. 2007. (ENG., Illus.). 326p. pap. 21.95 *(978-1-56164-386-3(6))* Pineapple Pr., Inc.
Witherington, Dawn & Witherington, Blair. Living Beaches of Georgia & the Carolinas. 2011. (ENG., Illus.). 352p. pap. 21.95 *(978-1-56164-490-2(0))* Pineapple Pr., Inc.

BEACONSFIELD, BENJAMIN DISRAELI, 1ST EARL OF, 1804-1881

see Disraeli, Benjamin, Earl of Beaconsfield, 1804-1881

BEADS

Adams, Kimberley. The Complete Book of Glass Beadmaking. 2010. (ENG., Illus.). 176p. pap. 19.95 *(978-1-60059-778-7(5))* Lark Bks.
Afshar, Ani. Beads & Strings Jewelry: A Step-by-Step Workshop. 2007. (Illus.). 48p. pap. 12.95 *(978-0-7643-2731-5(3))* Schiffer Publishing, Ltd.
—Beads & Wires Jewelry: A Step-by-Step Workshop. 2007. (Illus.). 48p. pap. 12.95 *(978-0-7643-2730-8(5))* Schiffer Publishing, Ltd.
Bead and Button Magazine Editors. Creative Beading Vol. 3: The Best Projects from a Year of Bead & Button Magazine. 3rd ed. 2008. (ENG.). 256p. 29.95 *(978-0-87116-262-5(8))* Kalmbach Publishing Co., Bks. Div.
Bead Review 3. 2008. 126p. pap. 21.00 *(978-0-9770831-5-2(2))* Pearson, Brad.
BeadStyle Magazine Editors. Easy Beading Vol. 4: Fast, Fashionable, Fun. 2008. (ENG., Illus.). 256p. 29.95 *(978-0-87116-263-2(6))* Kalmbach Publishing Co., Bks. Div.
BeadStyle Magazine Editors, compiled by. Easy Beading Vol. 5. 2009. (ENG., Illus.). 256p. 29.95 *(978-0-87116-288-5(1))* Kalmbach Publishing Co., Bks. Div.
—Easy Beading Vol. 7. 2011. (ENG., Illus.). 256p. 29.95 *(978-0-87116-420-9(5))* Kalmbach Publishing Co., Bks. Div.
Blackburn, Carol. Making Polymer Clay Beads: Step-by-Step Techniques for Creating Beautiful Ornamental Beads. 2007. (ENG., Illus.). 128p. pap. 24.95 *(978-1-59668-019-7(9))* Interweave Pr., LLC.
Blessing, Marlene & Hogsett, Jamie. Create Jewelry - Glass: Brilliant Designs to Make & Wear. 2009. (Create Jewelry Ser.). (ENG., Illus.). 120p. pap. 22.95 *(978-1-59668-067-8(9))* Interweave Pr., LLC.
Bogert, Kerry. Rustic Wrappings: Exploring Patina in Wire, Metal, & Glass Jewelry. 2012. (ENG., Illus.). 128p. pap. 22.95 ***(978-1-59668-549-9(2))*** Interweave Pr., LLC.
Bogert, Kerry. Totally Twisted: Innovative Wirework & Art Glass Jewelry. 2010. (ENG., Illus.). 144p. pap. 22.95 *(978-1-59668-168-2(3))* Interweave Pr., LLC.
Burger, Carolyn, et al. Websites for Beaders: The Bead-a-Holics Guide for Beads & Findings on the Web. 2007. 56p. per. 16.95 *(978-1-4327-1758-2(8))* Outskirts Pr., Inc.
Coles, Janet & Budwig, Robert. World Beads: An Exploration of Bead Traditions around the World, with 30 Projects to Create Your Own Jewelry. 2007. (Illus.). 159p. reprint ed. pap. 20.00 *(978-1-4223-6766-7(5))* DIANE Publishing Co.
Cooper, Candie. Metalworking 101 for Beaders: Create Custom Findings, Pendants & Projects. 2009. (ENG., Illus.). 128p. pap. 19.95 *(978-1-60059-332-1(1))* Lark Bks.
De Marco, Patricia. You Can Make Wire & Bead Jewelry. 2007. (Illus.). 96p. pap. 14.95 *(978-0-7643-2729-2(1))* Schiffer Publishing, Ltd.
Diffendaffer, Grant. Polymer Clay Beads: Techniques, Projects, Inspiration. (ENG., Illus.). 144p. 2011. pap. 19.95 *(978-1-60059-608-7(8))* 2008. 24.95 *(978-1-60059-024-5(1))* Lark Bks.
Dubin, Lois Sherr. The History of Beads: From 100,000 B. C. to the Present. rev. exp. ed. 2009. (ENG., Illus.). 396p. 75.00 *(978-0-8109-5174-7(6))* Abrams.
Eisen, Gustavus. The Characteristics of Eye Beads from the Earliest Times to the Present. 2009. pap. 19.36 *(978-1-60724-437-0(3))* Gorgias Pr., LLC.
Fitzgerald, Diane. Shaped Beadwork: Dimensional Jewelry with Peyote Stitch. 2009. (Beadweaving Master Class Ser.). (ENG., Illus.). 120p. 24.95 *(978-1-60059-277-5(5))* Lark Bks.
Hale, Julie, et al. Beadweaving: Major Works by Leading Artists. Hemachandra, Ray, ed. 2008. (Masters Ser.). (ENG., Illus.). 300p. pap. 24.95 *(978-1-60059-039-9(X))* Lark Bks.
Lark Books Staff, creator. Masters: Glass Beads: Major Works by Leading Artists. 2008. (Masters Ser.). (ENG., Illus.). 336p. pap. 24.95 *(978-1-57990-924-6(8))* Lark Bks.
McDougald, Crystal. Beading from Nature: Creating Jewelry with Stones from the Earth. 2007. (ENG., Illus.). 128p. spiral bd. 19.95 *(978-1-933027-21-0(5))* Sixth&Spring Bks.
Mehaffey, Louise. Glass Bead Inspirations: Ideas & Techniques for Lampworkers. 2012. (ENG., Illus.). 128p. pap. 19.95 ***(978-0-8117-0765-7(2))*** Stackpole Bks.
Mehaffey, Louise. Glass Beads: Tips, Tools, & Techniques for Learning the Craft. 2008. (Heritage Crafts Today Ser.). (ENG., Illus.). 132p. spiral bd. 26.95 *(978-0-8117-0376-5(2))* Stackpole Bks.
Nussinovitch, Amos. Polymer Macro- & Micro-Gel Beads: Fundamentals & Applications: Fundamentals & Applications. 2010. (ENG., Illus.). xxv, 303p. 209.00 *(978-1-4419-6617-9(X)*, 144196617X) Springer.
Owen, Cheryl. Precious Jewellery: 25 Jewellery Projects Using Precious & Semi-Precious Beads. 2010. (ENG., Illus.). 112p. pap. 19.95 *(978-1-84773-712-0(9))* New Holland Pubs., Ltd. GBR. Dist: Sterling Publishing Co., Inc.
Panini, Augusto. Middle Eastern & Venetian Glass Beads: Eighth to Twentieth Centuries. 2008. (ENG., Illus.). 312p. 100.00 *(978-88-6130-164-1(9))* Skira Editore ITA. Dist: Random Hse., Inc.
Ronat, Danny & Ronat, Hava. Making Handmade Lampwork Beads & Glass Jewelry: The Complete Guide to Making Handmade Lampwork Beads & Glass Jewelry. 2008. (ENG., Illus.). 128p. pap. 19.99 *(978-1-58923-391-1(3)*, 1589233913, Creative Publishing International) Quayside.
Simak, Evelyn & Dreibelbis, Carl. African Beads: Jewels of a Continent. Liechty, Jacob, ed. 2010. (Illus.). 216p. 69.95 *(978-0-9816267-2-7(6))* Africa Direct.
Simon, Barbara Becker. Metal Clay Beads: Techniques, Projects, Inspiration. 2009. (ENG., Illus.). 144p. 24.95 *(978-1-60059-025-2(X))* Lark Bks.
Van Brakel, Koos. The Beed Goes On: The Sample Card Collection with Trade Beads from the Company J. F. Sick & Co. in the Tropenmuseum, Amsterdam. 2007. (Illus.). 80p. 75.00 *(978-90-6832-487-7(X))* Royal Tropical Institute Pr. (KIT (Koninklijk Instituut voor de Tropen) NLD. Dist: Stylus Publishing, LLC.
Wang, Pauline. Making Metal Beads: Techniques, Projects, Inspiration. (ENG., Illus.). 160p. 2010. pap. 17.95 *(978-1-60059-609-4(6))* 2006. 24.95 *(978-1-57990-712-9(1))* Lark Bks.
Warhaftig, Jeri L. Creating Glass Beads: A New Workshop to Expand Your Beginner Skills & Develop Your Artistic Voice. 2011. (ENG., Illus.). 144p. 24.95 *(978-1-60059-582-0(0))* Lark Bks.
Warhaftig, Jeri L. & Warhaftig, Jeri. Glass Bead Workshop: Building Skills, Exploring Techniques, Finding Inspiration. 2008. (ENG., Illus.). 144p. 24.95 *(978-1-60059-123-5(X))* Lark Bks.
Wick, Kristal. Fabulous Fabric Beads: Create Custom Beads & Art Jewelry. 2008. (ENG., Illus.). 112p. pap. 22.95 *(978-1-59668-077-7(6))* Interweave Pr., LLC.
Wood, Dorothy & Wood, Ashley. Beading - 200 Q&A: Questions Answered on Everything from Basic Stitches to Finishing Touches. 2010. (ENG.). 224p. 18.99 *(978-0-7641-6359-3(0))* Barron's Educational Series, Inc.

BEADS—RELIGIOUS ASPECTS

Henry, Gray & Marriott, Susannah. Beads of Faith. (Illus.). 112p. 22.00 *(978-1-903258-47-7(2))* Carroll & Brown Pubs., Ltd. GBR. Dist: Trafalgar Square Publishing.
—Beads of Faith: Pathways to Meditation & Spirituality Using Rosaries, Prayer Beads, & Sacred Words. 2008. (ENG., Illus.). 112p. pap. 28.95 *(978-1-887752-95-4(1))* Fons Vitae of Kentucky, Inc.
Wiley, Eleanor. Changing Bead by Bead: Seeing Your Life as a Strand of Beads - A Present Moment Practice. 2009. 91p. pap. 12.95 *(978-1-4327-4823-4(8))* Outskirts Pr., Inc.
Winston, Kimberly. Bead One, Pray, Too: A Guide to Making & Using Prayer Beads. 2008. (Illus.). 182p. 28.00 *(978-0-8192-2276-3(3))*, Morehouse Publishing) Church Publishing, Inc.

BEADWORK

see also Indian Beadwork

Afshar, Ani. Flower Jewelry. 2008. (Illus.). 48p. pap. 12.95 *(978-0-7643-2855-8(7))* Schiffer Publishing, Ltd.
—Ribbon Jewelry. 2008. (Illus.). 48p. pap. 12.95 *(978-0-7643-2856-5(5))* Schiffer Publishing, Ltd.
Alden, Nancy. Simply Gemstones: Designs for Creating Beaded Gemstone Jewelry. 2009. (ENG., Illus.). 144p. pap. 22.95 *(978-0-307-45135-4(6))*, Potter Craft) Crown Publishing Group.
Atkins, Robin. Heart to Hands Bead Embroidery: Fresh Ideas & Techniques for Creating Art with Beads. 2008. (Illus.). 80p. pap. 24.00 *(978-0-9705538-9-8(7))* Tiger Pr.
Babcock, Jeff, illus. Wired Micro-Macramé Jewelry: Enhancing Fiber Designs with Wire. 2010. 66p. pap. 24.95 *(978-0-9773052-2-3(8))* Babcock, Joan.
BarCharts Inc., Staff, creator. Learning to Bead. 2006. (Quickstudy: Home Ser.). (ENG., Illus.). 6p. 5.95 *(978-1-4232-0281-3(3))* Barcharts, Inc.
Barrick, J. Devlin, ed. Wire-Wrapped & Beaded Jewelry. 2009. (ENG., Illus.). 128p. pap. 21.95 *(978-0-8117-3607-7(5))* Stackpole Bks.
Barta, Melinda A. Custom Cool Jewelry: Create 200+ Personalized Pendants, Charms, & Clasps. 2008. (ENG., Illus.). 144p. pap. 22.95 *(978-1-59668-074-6(1))* Interweave Pr., LLC.
Bateman, Sharon. Contemporary Loom Beading: A New Look at a Traditional Stitch. 2009. (ENG., Illus.). 144p. 24.95 *(978-1-60059-273-7(2))* Lark Bks.
Bead and Button Magazine Editors. Creative Beading Vol. 3: The Best Projects from a Year of Bead & Button Magazine. 3rd ed. 2008. (ENG.). 256p. 29.95 *(978-0-87116-262-5(8))* Kalmbach Publishing Co., Bks. Div.
—Seed Bead Savvy. rev. ed. 2006. (ENG., Illus.). 96p. pap. 19.95 *(978-0-87116-238-0(5))* Kalmbach Publishing Co., Bks. Div.
—Your Seed Bead Style: Accents, Embellishments, & Adornments. 2010. (ENG., Illus.). 88p. pap. 17.95 *(978-0-87116-284-7(9))* Kalmbach Publishing Co., Bks. Div.
Bead and Button Magazine Editors, compiled by. The Big Book of Beading Patterns: For Peyote Stitch, Square Stitch, Brick Stitch, & Loomwork Designs. 2010. (ENG., Illus.). 144p. pap. 21.95 *(978-0-87116-424-7(8))* Kalmbach Publishing Co., Bks. Div.
—Chic & Easy Beading, Vol. 3. 2009. (ENG., Illus.). 144p. pap. 21.95 *(978-0-87116-277-9(6))* Kalmbach Publishing Co., Bks. Div.
—Creative Beading Vol. 5: The Best Projects from a Year of Bear & Button Magazine. 2010. (ENG., Illus.). 256p. 29.95 *(978-0-87116-292-2(X))* Kalmbach Publishing Co., Bks. Div.
—Creative Beading Vol. 4. 2009. (ENG., Illus.). 265p. 29.95 *(978-0-87116-289-2(X))* Kalmbach Publishing Co., Bks. Div.
—Creative Beading Vol. 6. 2011. (ENG., Illus.). 256p. 29.95 *(978-0-87116-419-3(1))* Kalmbach Publishing Co., Bks. Div.
—Discover Beading. rev. ed. 2006. (ENG., Illus.). 96p. per. 19.95 *(978-0-87116-239-7(3))* Kalmbach Publishing Co., Bks. Div.
—Polymer Pizzazz: 25 Great Polymer Clay Jewelry Projects. 2006. (Best of Bead & Button Magazine Ser.). (ENG., Illus.). 96p. per. 19.95 *(978-0-87116-236-6(9))* Kalmbach Publishing Co., Bks. Div.
—Stitch Workshop: Basic Techniques, Advanced Results. 2011. (Stitch Workshop Ser.). (ENG., Illus.). 96p. pap. 17.95 *(978-0-87116-423-0(X))* Kalmbach Publishing Co., Bks. Div.
Bead and Button Magazine Editors, contrib. by. Stitch Workshop: Right-Angle Weave. 2011. (ENG., Illus.). 80p. pap. 17.95 *(978-0-87116-455-1(8))* Kalmbach Publishing Co., Bks. Div.
Bead Review 2. 2007. 21.00 *(978-0-9770831-3-8(6))* Pearson, Brad.
Bead Review 3. 2008. 126p. pap. 21.00 *(978-0-9770831-5-2(2))* Pearson, Brad.
The Beader's Guide to Survival Book: Techniques for Intrepid Beadlovers. 2006. (Beading Books Ser.: 14). (Illus.). 52p. pap., act. bk. ed. 11.95 *(978-1-889599-25-0(5))* Interstellar Publishing Co.
BeadStyle Magazine Editors. Easy Beading Vol. 4: Fast, Fashionable, Fun. 2008. (ENG., Illus.). 256p. 29.95 *(978-0-87116-263-2(6))* Kalmbach Publishing Co., Bks. Div.
—Easy Beading Vol. 6: Fast. Fashionable. Fun. 2010. (ENG., Illus.). 256p. 29.95 *(978-0-87116-291-5(1))* Kalmbach Publishing Co., Bks. Div.
BeadStyle Magazine Editors, compiled by. Beaded Ornaments for the Holidays & Beyond. 2009. (ENG., Illus.). 96p. pap. 19.95 *(978-0-87116-283-0(0))* Kalmbach Publishing Co., Bks. Div.
—Easy Beading Vol. 5. 2009. (ENG., Illus.). 256p. 29.95 *(978-0-87116-288-5(1))* Kalmbach Publishing Co., Bks. Div.
—Easy Beading Vol. 7. 2011. (ENG., Illus.). 256p. 29.95 *(978-0-87116-420-9(5))* Kalmbach Publishing Co., Bks. Div.
BeadStyle Magazine Editors, creator. Easy Beading, Vol. 3. 2007. (ENG., Illus.). 256p. 29.95 *(978-0-87116-241-0(5))* Kalmbach Publishing Co., Bks. Div.
—Jewelry in a Flash: Easy Earrings, Bracelets, & Necklaces in under One Hour. 2009. (ENG., Illus.). 96p. pap. 19.95 *(978-0-87116-268-7(7))* Kalmbach Publishing Co., Bks. Div.
Beal, Susan. Bead Simple: Essential Techniques for Making Jewelry Just the Way You Want It. 2008. (ENG., Illus.). 220p. pap. 19.95 *(978-1-56158-953-1(5))* Taunton Pr., Inc.
Bellingham, R. Quick & Easy Beadwork. 2008. (ENG., Illus.). 80p. pap. 12.95 *(978-1-84537-576-8(9))* New Holland Pubs., Ltd. GBR. Dist: Sterling Publishing Co., Inc.
Benson, Ann. Tapestry Bead Crochet: Projects & Techniques. 2010. (ENG., Illus.). 128p. 22.95 *(978-1-60059-337-6(2))* Lark Bks.
Berkebile, Janice & Stanley, Tracy. Making Wire & Bead Jewelry: Artful Wirework Techniques. 2012. (ENG., Illus.). 144p. pap. 24.95 ***(978-1-4547-0287-0(7))*** Lark Bks.
Birmingham, Helen. Beaded Felt Jewellery. 2008. (Twenty to Make Ser.). (ENG., Illus.). 48p. pap. 9.95 *(978-1-84448-315-0(0))* Search Pr., Ltd. GBR. Dist: Independent Pubs. Group.
Blessing, Marlene & Hogsett, Jamie. Create Jewelry - Crystals: Dazzling Designs to Make & Wear. 2007. (Create Jewelry Ser.). (ENG., Illus.). 128p. per. 22.95 *(978-1-59668-022-7(9))* Interweave Pr., LLC.
Boyd, Heidi. Simply Beaded Bliss: Adding Unique Elements to Classic Beaded Jewelry, Gifts & Cards. 2008. (ENG., Illus.). 144p. pap. 22.99 *(978-1-60061-095-0(1)*, North Light Bks.) F&W Media, Inc.
Brenner, Maya. Beaded Jewelry. 2012. (ENG.). 224p. 15.95 ***(978-0-7566-9394-7(2))*** Dorling Kindersley Publishing, Inc.
—Beaded Jewelry. 2007. 76p. (C). 33.33 *(978-0-13-208128-3(8))* Prentice Hall Higher Education.
Buckingham, Karin. The Absolute Beginners Guide: Stringing Beaded Jewelry. 2010. (Absolute Beginners Guide Ser.). (ENG., Illus.). 96p. pap. 21.95 *(978-0-87116-299-1(7))* Kalmbach Publishing Co., Bks. Div.
Buzaglo, Sigal. Creative Beaded Jewelry. 2011. (ENG., Illus.). 144p. pap. 19.95 *(978-1-936096-10-7(2))* Sixth&Spring Bks.
C&T Publishing. Stitch It New: Embroider, Bead & Adorn-Everything You Need to Get it Done! 2009. 20.00 *(978-1-57120-804-0(6))* C & T Publishing.
Campanella, Nicole. FlatWork: Beading techniques from old to New. Ridgeway, April, ed. 2008. pap. *(978-0-9767840-3-6(3))* Beadwright Nicole Campanella.
Campbell, Jean. The Art of Beaded Beads: Exploring Design, Color & Technique. 2010. (ENG., Illus.). 144p. pap. 17.95 *(978-1-60059-588-2(X))* Lark Bks.
—Beadwork Creates Jewelry: 40 Beaded Designs. 2007. (Beadwork Creates Ser.). (ENG., Illus.). 128p. pap. 18.95 *(978-1-59668-037-1(7))* Interweave Pr., LLC.
Carole Rodgers. The Beaded Bracelet: Beadweaving Techniques & Patterns for 20 Eye-Catching Projects. 2012. (ENG., Illus.). 128p. pap. 24.99 *(978-1-4403-1277-9(X)*, North Light Bks.) F&W Media, Inc.
Carpenter, Aimee. Endless Sparkle: 12 Crystal Components - Unlimited Jewelry Designs. 2011. (ENG., Illus.). 96p. pap. 19.95 *(978-0-87116-422-3(1))* Kalmbach Publishing Co., Bks. Div.
Case, Barbara. Making Jewellery with Gemstone Beads. 2007. (ENG., Illus.). 128p. pap. 19.99 *(978-0-7153-2594-0(9))* David & Charles Pubs. GBR. Dist: F&W Media, Inc.
Cheah, Hwei-Fe'N. Phoenix Rising: Cl. 2010. (Illus.). 400p. 78.00 *(978-9971-69-516-3(2))* National Univ. of Singapore Pr. SGP. Dist: Univ. of Hawaii Pr.
—Phoenix Rising: Pa. 2010. (Illus.). 400p. pap. 58.00 *(978-9971-69-468-5(9))* National Univ. of Singapore Pr. SGP. Dist: Univ. of Hawaii Pr.
Cheramy-Debray, Isabelle. Polymer Clay Beaded Jewellery: 35 Beautiful Designs. 2009. (ENG., Illus.). 48p. pap. 13.95 *(978-1-84448-400-3(9))* Search Pr., Ltd. GBR. Dist: Independent Pubs. Group.
Chiba, Nobuyo. The Beaded Dollhouse: Miniature Furniture & Accessories Made with Beads, 1 vol. Omae, Kaori & Saito, Yuki, eds. Ishiguro, Yoko, tr. 2007. (ENG., Illus.). 97p. per. 17.95 *(978-4-88996-212-3(3))* Japan Pubns. Trading Co. JPN. Dist: Oxford Univ. Pr., Inc.
Claydon, Jennifer, ed. Earring Chic: 35 Hand-Selected Projects. 2011. (ENG., Illus.). 144p. pap. 19.99 *(978-1-4403-1424-7(1)*, North Light Bks.) F&W Media, Inc.
Coles, Janet & Budwig, Robert. World Beads: An Exploration of Bead Traditions around the World, with 30 Projects to Create Your Own Jewelry. 2007. (Illus.). 159p. reprint ed. pap. 20.00 *(978-1-4223-6766-7(5))* DIANE Publishing Co.

B

Collingbourne's Bead Bags & Necklaces Book 29. 2007. 9.95 *(978-1-934268-14-8(3))* Bramcost Pubns., LLC.
Connor, Kaylee. Beaded Friendship Bracelets. 2007. (Illus.). 64p. *(978-1-59412-199-9(0))* Mud Puddle, Inc.
Cooper, Candie. Necklaceology: How to Make Chokers, Lariats, Ropes & More. 2012. (ENG., Illus.). 144p. pap. 24.95 ***(978-1-4547-0333-4(4))*** Lark Bks.
Cox, Patty. Native American Leather & Bead Crafting. 2008. (ENG., Illus.). 128p. pap. 14.95 *(978-1-4027-3519-6(7))* Sterling Publishing Co., Inc.
Crabtree, Caroline & Stallebrass, Pam. Beadwork: A World Guide. 2009. (ENG., Illus.). 208p. pap. 34.95 *(978-0-500-28801-6(1),* 528801) Thames & Hudson.
Crone, Lisa. A Bead in Time: 35 Jewelry Projects Inspired by Slices of Life. 2010. (ENG., Illus.). 128p. pap. 22.99 *(978-1-60061-310-4(1),* North Light Bks.) F&W Media, Inc.
Crowther-Smith, Alison. Shibori Knitted Felt. 2008. (ENG., Illus.). 112p. pap. 24.95 *(978-1-59668-085-2(7))* Interweave Pr., LLC.
Cypher, Carol Huber. Mastering Beadwork: A Comprehensive Guide to Off-Loom Techniques. 2007. (ENG., Illus.). 240p. 24.95 *(978-1-59668-013-5(X))* Interweave Pr., LLC.
Davis, Jane. Bracelets, Buttons & Brooches: 20 Projects Using Innovative Beading Techniques. 2007. (ENG., Illus.). 128p. pap. 22.99 *(978-0-89689-581-2(5))* Krause Pubns.
—Knitting with Beads: 30 Beautiful Sweaters, Scarves, Hats & Gloves. 2007. (ENG., Illus.). 128p. pap. 14.95 *(978-1-60059-135-8(3))* Lark Bks.
Deborah Schneebeli-Morrel. Handmade at Home: Button & Bead J. 2011. (ENG., Illus.). 96p. pap. 14.95 *(978-1-907563-74-4(1))* CICO Bks. GBR. Dist: Ryland Peters & Small.
DeCoster, Marcia. Beaded Opulence: Elegant Jewelry Projects with Right Angle Weave. 2009. (Beadweaving Master Class Ser.). (ENG., Illus.). 128p. 24.95 *(978-1-60059-292-8(9))* Lark Bks.
deGroot, Annika. Micro-Macrame: 30 Beaded Designs for Jewelry Using Crystals & Cords. 2009. (ENG., Illus.). 144p. pap. 19.95 *(978-0-312-38085-4(2),* St. Martin's Griffin) St. Martin's Pr.
Di Spirito, Maria. Designs for Beaded Jewellery Using Glass Beads. 2006. (ENG., Illus.). 64p. spiral bd. 15.95 *(978-1-84448-164-4(6))* Search Pr., Ltd. GBR. Dist: Independent Pubs. Group.
—Designs for Beaded Jewellery Using Natural Materials. 2006. (ENG., Illus.). 64p. spiral bd. 15.95 *(978-1-84448-163-7(8))* Search Pr., Ltd. GBR. Dist: Independent Pubs. Group.
Dickerson, Jane. Chain Style: 50 Contemporary Jewelry Designs. 2009. (ENG., Illus.). 128p. pap. 19.95 *(978-1-59668-150-7(0))* Interweave Pr., LLC.
Dickt, Donna DeAngelis. French Beaded Designs. 2006. (ENG., Illus.). 128p. pap. 14.95 *(978-1-4027-4048-0(4),* Chapelle) Sterling Publishing Co., Inc.
DiMarco, Deb. Off-Loom Woven Bead Necklaces. 2009. (Illus.). 128p. pap. 19.99 *(978-0-7643-3306-4(2))* Schiffer Publishing, Ltd.
Draeger, Anna Elizabeth. Crystal Brilliance: Making Designer Jewelry with Crystal Beads. 2010. (ENG., Illus.). 96p. pap. 21.95 *(978-0-87116-295-3(4))* Kalmbach Publishing Co., Bks. Div.
Dritz-Traum Co. Hiawatha Book of Beaded Bags — 1927 Vintage Beading Patterns for Jewelry & Knit/Crochet Purses (10th Edition) 2007. pap. 12.95 *(978-1-934268-12-4(7))* Bramcost Pubns., LLC.
—Hiawatha Book of Beaded Bags — 21 Vintage Beading Patterns for Jewelry & Knit/Crochet Purses from 1926 (9th Edition) 2007. pap. 12.95 *(978-1-934268-19-3(4))* Bramcost Pubns., LLC.
—How to Make the New Beaded Bags & Chains — - 25 Vintage Beading Patterns for Jewelry & Knit/Crochet Purses From 1924. 2007. pap. 12.95 *(978-1-934268-17-9(8))* Bramcost Pubns., LLC.
Dube, Hlengiwe. Zulu Beadwork: Talk with Beads. 2009. (Illus.). 112p. pap. 35.00 *(978-0-9816267-0-3(X))* Africa Direct.
Dumas, Ly. Pearls: The Pearl & the Queen. 2011. (FRE & ENG., Illus.). 180p. 60.00 *(978-2-35340-074-4(4))* Gourcuff Gradenigo FRA. Dist: National Bk. Network.
Dummies Press Staff, et al. Jewelry & Beading Designs for Dummies. 2008. (ENG., Illus.). 320p. pap. 19.99 *(978-0-470-29112-2(5),* For Dummies) Wiley, John & Sons, Inc.
Dupon, Olivier. The New Jewelers: Desirable Collectable Contemporary. 2012. (ENG., Illus.). 288p. 45.00 ***(978-0-500-51629-4(4),*** 551629) Thames & Hudson.
Durant, Judith. Knit One, Bead Too: Essential Techniques for Knitting with Beads. 2009. (ENG., Illus.). 160p. 18.95 *(978-1-60342-149-2(1),* 1603421491) Storey Publishing, LLC.
Durant, Judith & Campbell, Jean. Beadwork Inspired by Art: Art Nouveau Jewelry & Accessories. 2008. (Beading Works of Art Ser.). (ENG., Illus.). 96p. pap. 19.99 *(978-1-58923-388-1(3),* 1589233883, Creative Publishing International) Quayside.
—Impressionist: Jewelry & Accessories. 2008. (Beading Works of Art Ser.). (ENG., Illus.). 96p. pap. 19.99 *(978-1-58923-387-4(5),* 1589233875, Creative Publishing International) Quayside.
Eakin, Jamie Cloud. Dimensional Bead Embroidery: A Reference Guide of Techniques. 2011. (ENG., Illus.). 160p. 26.95 *(978-1-60059-796-1(3))* Lark Bks.
Ellsworth, Wendy. Beading-the Creative Spirit: Finding Your Sacred Center through the Art of Beadwork. 2009. 224p. 18.99 *(978-1-59473-267-6(1))* SkyLight Paths Publishing.
Fitzgerald, Diane. Diane Fitzgerald's Favorite Beading Projects: Designs from Stringing to Beadweaving. 2012. (ENG., Illus.). 128p. 27.95 ***(978-1-60059-922-4(2))*** Lark Bks.
—Shaped Beadwork: Dimensional Jewelry with Peyote Stitch. 2009. (Beadweaving Master Class Ser.). (ENG., Illus.). 120p. 24.95 *(978-1-60059-277-5(5))* Lark Bks.
—Zulu Inspired Beadwork: Weaving Techniques & Projects. 2007. (ENG., Illus.). 128p. pap. 24.95 *(978-1-59668-034-0(2))* Interweave Pr., LLC.
Fox, Danielle. Simply Modern Jewelry: Designs from the Editor of Stringing Magazine. 2008. (ENG., Illus.). 120p. pap. 21.95 *(978-1-59668-048-7(2))* Interweave Pr., LLC.
Ganderton, Lucinda. The Practical Illustrated Guide to Beading & Making Jewellery: A Complete Illustrated Guide to Traditional & Contemporary Techniques, Including 175 Creative Projects Shown Step by Step. 2007. (ENG., Illus.). 512p. 35.00 *(978-0-7548-1738-3(5))* Anness Publishing GBR. Dist: National Bk. Network.
Geary, Theresa Flores. The Illustrated Bead Bible: Terms, Tips & Techniques. 2008. (ENG., Illus.). 416p. 29.95 *(978-1-4027-2353-7(9))* Sterling Publishing Co., Inc.
Géraud, Marie. Beadweaving with Cabochons: 37 Stunning Jewelry Designs. 2010. (ENG., Illus.). 80p. 19.99 *(978-0-312-64377-5(2),* St. Martin's Griffin) St. Martin's Pr.
Gidez, Mabeline. I CAN Right Angle Weave: From Basic Stitch to Advanced Techniques, A Comprehensive Workbook for Beaders. 2012. (I Can Ser.). (ENG., Illus.). 128p. pap. 24.95 ***(978-1-4547-0366-2(0))*** Lark Bks.
Gilbert, Beverly. Beaded Colorways: Freeform Beadweaving Projects & Palettes. 2009. (ENG., Illus.). 128p. pap. 24.99 *(978-1-60061-318-0(7),* North Light Bks.) F&W Media, Inc.
Gilchrist, Paige. Beading: 20 Great Weekend Projects. 2011. (ENG., Illus.). 80p. pap. 9.95 *(978-1-60059-993-4(1))* Lark Bks.
Graham, Renata. Designing Bead & Wire Jewelry: Everything the Beginner Needs to Know. 2011. (ENG., Illus.). 144p. pap. 22.99 *(978-0-312-59137-3(3),* St. Martin's Griffin) St. Martin's Pr.
Haab, Sherri. Beaded Macrame Jewelry: Stylish Designs, Exciting New Materials. 2006. (ENG., Illus.). 96p. pap. 12.95 *(978-0-8230-2952-5(2))* Watson-Guptill Pubns., Inc.
Hale, Julie, et al. Beadweaving: Major Works by Leading Artists. Hemachandra, Ray, ed. 2008. (Masters Ser.). (ENG., Illus.). 300p. pap. 24.95 *(978-1-60059-039-9(X))* Lark Bks.
Harrison, Mary. Itty Bitty Beadys: Wire & Bead Characters for Earrings, Pins & Hair Clips! 2011. (Design Originals Ser.). (Illus.). 20p. pap. 6.99 ***(978-1-57421-152-8(8))*** Design Originals.
Haxell, Kate, ed. My Beading Journal. 2007. (ENG., Illus.). 144p. *(978-1-904991-99-1(8))* Ryland Peters & Small.
Heiberg, Joey. Dolly Mama Beads. 2008. (ENG., Illus.). 80p. pap. 21.95 *(978-1-56477-878-9(9))* Martingale & Co.
Hemachandra, Ray. Showcase 500 Beaded Jewelry: Photographs of Beautiful Contemporary Beadwork. 2012. (500 Ser.). (ENG., Illus.). 432p. pap. 27.95 ***(978-1-4547-0316-7(4))*** Lark Bks.
Herring, Ruth. Crochet for Beaders: 18 Stunning Jewelry Projects. 2007. (ENG., Illus.). 96p. per. 21.95 *(978-1-56477-824-6(X))* Martingale & Co.
—Knitted Beaded Jewelry: 16 Stylish Projects for Jewelry & Accessories. 2008. (ENG., Illus.). 96p. pap. 16.95 *(978-0-8117-3501-8(X))* Stackpole Bks.
Hershberg, Betsy. Betsy Beads: Creative Approaches for Knitters. Rowley, Elaine, ed. 2012. (ENG., Illus.). 192p. pap. 24.95 ***(978-1-933064-25-3(0),*** XRX Bks.) XRX, Inc.
Hewitt, Jema. First Beading: Projects for Novice Beaders. 2012. (First Crafts Ser.). (ENG., Illus.). 128p. pap. 12.95 ***(978-1-84340-613-6(6),*** Collins & Brown) Anova Bks. GBR. Dist: Sterling Publishing Co., Inc.
Heynen, Jennifer. Ceramic Bead Jewelry: 30 Fired & Inspired Projects. 2010. (ENG., Illus.). 128p. pap. 14.95 *(978-1-60059-690-2(8))* Lark Bks.
Hinson, Amanda & Murr-Hinson, Amanda Brooke. 100 Beaded Flowers, Charms & Trinkets: Perfect Little Designs to Use for Gifts, Jewelry, & Accessories. 2012. (ENG., Illus.). 128p. pap. 21.99 ***(978-0-312-59141-0(1),*** St. Martin's Griffin) St. Martin's Pr.
Hodgson, Nia Glain. Queen Bead's Creative Beading. 2008. (ENG., Illus.). 76p. (gr. 12-18). 18.00 *(978-0-14-300731-9(9),* Penguin Global) Penguin Group (USA) Inc.
Horn, Rona. Take the Next Step. Sprunger, Barb, ed. 2010. (ENG., Illus.). 64p. pap. 9.95 *(978-1-59635-307-7(4))* Annie's Publishing, LLC.
Houdeshell, Barbara & Maka Nah'i Wee Ya. Native American Beadwork Patterns. Knight, Denise, ed. 2008. (Illus.). 48p. pap. *(978-0-943604-64-0(8))* Eagles View Publishing.
Howren, Suzanne & Robertson, Beth. New Twists on Needlework Embellishment. 2007. (Illus.). 35p. spiral bd. 30.00 *(978-0-9663024-4-8(3))* Shear Creations, L.L.C.
Hurlbut, Joan L. Pristine's Beaded Beauties: Wolves, Bats & Other Critters of Travel, 1. 2006. (Illus.). 131p. per. 24.95 *(978-0-9760005-1-8(2))* Pristine's Publishing.
Hyman, Colette A. Dakota Women's Work: Creativity, Culture, & Exile. 2012. (ENG., Illus.). 240p. pap. 19.95 ***(978-0-87351-850-5(0))*** Minnesota Historical Society Pr.
Ito, Kumiko Mizuno. Beadweaving Brilliance 2: Make Beautiful Jewelry While Mastering Six Basic Beading Stitches, Special Bonus Section on Peyote Stitch, 1 vol. 2008. (ENG., Illus.). 88p. pap. 19.00 *(978-4-88996-231-4(X))* Japan Pubns. Trading Co. JPN. Dist: Oxford Univ. Pr., Inc.
Jackson, Barbara & Evans, Kristy. Bead by Bead: Reviving an Ancient African Tradition - The Monkeybiz Bead Project. 2008. (ENG.). 144p. pap. 28.95 *(978-1-77009-382-9(6))* Jacana Media ZAF. Dist: Independent Pubs. Group.
Jensen, Virginia. Cube Bead Stitching: Contemporary Jewelry Designs You Can Make. 2009. (ENG., Illus.). 96p. pap. 19.95 *(978-0-87116-281-6(4))* Kalmbach Publishing Co., Bks. Div.
Jones, Linda. Bead & Wire Jewelry for Special Occasions. 2007. (ENG., Illus.). 128p. pap. *(978-1-906094-01-0(2))* Ryland Peters & Small.
—The Complete Guide to Wire & Beaded Jewellery. 2009. (Illus.). 192p. pap. 24.95 *(978-1-906525-33-0(1))* CICO Bks. GBR. Dist: Ryland Peters & Small.
—Creating Beaded & Wire Earrings. 2011. (ENG., Illus.). 128p. pap. 19.95 *(978-1-907563-23-2(7))* CICO Bks. GBR. Dist: Ryland Peters & Small.
—Making Beautiful Bead & Wire Jewelry. 2010. (ENG., Illus.). 128p. pap. 19.95 *(978-1-907030-66-6(2))* CICO Bks. GBR. Dist: Ryland Peters & Small.
—Wire & Bead Celtic Jewelry: 35 Quick & Stylish Projects. 2007. (ENG., Illus.). 128p. pap. *(978-1-904991-56-4(4))* CICO Bks.
—Wire & Beaded Wedding Jewellry & Accessories. 2012. (ENG., Illus.). 128p. pap. 19.95 *(978-1-907563-84-3(9))* CICO Bks. GBR. Dist: Ryland Peters & Small.
Kalmbach Publishing Company, creator. Crochet with Beads III: 6 Projects. 2007. (Easy-Does-It Ser.). (Illus.). 18p. pap. 7.95 *(978-0-89024-687-0(4))* Kalmbach Publishing Co., Bks. Div.
—Easy Knotting. 2006. (Easy-Does-It Ser.). (Illus.). 19p. pap. *(978-0-89024-642-9(4))* Kalmbach Publishing Co., Bks. Div.
—Great Beaded Gifts. 2006. (Easy-Does-It Ser.). (Illus.). 19p. pap. *(978-0-89024-640-5(8))* Kalmbach Publishing Co., Bks. Div.
Kan, Lisa. Bead Romantique: Elegant Beadweaving Designs. 2008. (ENG., Illus.). 144p. pap. 24.95 *(978-1-59668-046-3(6))* Interweave Pr., LLC.
Kendall, Sharon Maxwell. Stitch A Beaded Garden (Leisure Arts #5407) 2011. (ENG.). 60p. pap. 14.95 ***(978-1-60900-123-0(0))*** Leisure Arts, Inc.
King, Kathy. Bead Quilled Jewelry: New Beadwork Designs with Square Stitch. 2010. (ENG., Illus.). 128p. pap. 19.99 *(978-1-58923-476-5(6),* 1589234766, Creative Publishing International) Quayside.
Kors, Margriet. Beaded Greeting Cards. (Illus.). 32p. pap. 9.95 *(978-90-5877-458-3(9),* 4589) Forte Uitgevers B.V. NLD. Dist: Search Pr. USA.
Kummli, Heidi & Serafini, Sherry. The Art of Bead Embroidery: Techniques, Designs, & Inspirations. 2007. (ENG., Illus.). 112p. per. 21.95 *(978-0-87116-243-4(1))* Kalmbach Publishing Co., Bks. Div.
Laithwaite, Heather. Dare to Bead. 2006. (ENG., Illus.). 128p. pap. 21.95 *(978-1-84448-203-0(0))* Search Pr., Ltd. GBR. Dist: Independent Pubs. Group.
Lareau, Viki. Marketing & Selling Your Handmade Jewelry: The Complete Guide to Turning Your Passion into Profit. 2006. (ENG., Illus.). 96p. pap. 21.95 *(978-1-59668-024-1(5))* Interweave Pr., LLC.
Lark Books. Simply Bead & Wire: 20 Jewelry Projects. 2011. (Simply Pamphlet Ser.). (ENG., Illus.). 64p. 9.95 *(978-1-4547-0024-1(6))* Lark Bks.
—Simply Charms: 20 Beading Projects. 2011. (Simply Pamphlet Ser.). (ENG., Illus.). 64p. 9.95 *(978-1-4547-0025-8(4))* Lark Bks.
—Simply Earrings: 20 Beading Projects. 2011. (Simply Pamphlet Ser.). (ENG., Illus.). 64p. 9.95 *(978-1-4547-0027-2(0))* Lark Bks.
—Simply Necklaces: 20 Beading Projects. 2011. (Simply Pamphlet Ser.). (ENG., Illus.). 64p. 9.95 *(978-1-4547-0026-5(2))* Lark Bks.
Lark Books Staff. Beading with Pearls: Beautiful Jewelry, Simple Techniques. Campell, Jean, ed. 2008. (Lark Jewelry Book Ser.). (ENG., Illus.). 128p. 24.95 *(978-1-60059-037-5(3),* 1281061) Lark Bks.
Lark Books Staff, creator. Masters: Glass Beads: Major Works by Leading Artists. 2008. (Masters Ser.). (ENG., Illus.). 336p. pap. 24.95 *(978-1-57990-924-6(8))* Lark Bks.
Leisure Arts, creator. Fast & Fabulous Fashion Jewelry. 2006. (ENG.). 32p. pap. 9.95 *(978-1-60140-130-4(2))* Leisure Arts, Inc.
Leonardo, Karen J. Creating Lampwork Beads for Jewelry. 2007. (ENG.). 144p. pap. 24.99 *(978-0-89689-549-2(1))* Krause Pubns.
Levaas, Laura. Beader's Stash: Designs from America's Favorite Bead Shops. 2006. (ENG., Illus.). 144p. pap. 21.95 *(978-1-931499-80-4(2))* Interweave Pr., LLC.
Lewis, Andrea R., ed. Bead International 2008 & Beyond Basketry: The Dairy Barn Arts Center. 2008. (ENG., Illus.). 152p. pap. 24.95 *(978-0-8214-1812-3(2))* Ohio Univ. Pr.
Lippert, Sabine. Sabine Lippert's Beaded Fantasies: 30 Romantic Jewelry Projects. 2012. (Beadweaving Master Class Ser.). (ENG., Illus.). 144p. 27.95 ***(978-1-4547-0246-7(X))*** Lark Bks.
Lockwood, Georgene. The Complete Idiot's Guide to Beading Basics. 2011. (Complete Idiot's Guide Ser.). (ENG.). 224p. (gr. 12). pap. 16.95 ***(978-1-61564-136-9(X),*** Alpha Bks.) Penguin Group (USA) Inc.
Marchand, Celine. Woven Crystal Beaded Jewellery. 2008. (ENG., Illus.). 80p. pap. 19.95 *(978-1-84448-277-1(4))* Search Pr., Ltd. GBR. Dist: Independent Pubs. Group.
May, Lana. Mixed Media Jewelry Techniques. 2010. (Illus.). 96p. pap. 12.99 *(978-0-7643-3429-0(8))* Schiffer Publishing, Ltd.
McCabe, Laura. Creating Crystal Jewelry with Swarovski: 65 Sparkling Designs with Crystal Beads & Stones. 2008. (ENG., Illus.). 128p. per. 24.95 *(978-1-58923-345-4(X),* 158923345X) Quayside.
—Embellished Beadweaving: Jewelry Lavished with Fringe, Fronds, Lacework & More. 2010. (Beadweaving Master Class Ser.). (ENG., Illus.). 144p. 24.95 *(978-1-60059-514-1(6))* Lark Bks.
McDougald, Crystal. Beading from Nature: Creating Jewelry with Stones from the Earth. 2007. (ENG., Illus.). 128p. spiral bd. 19.95 *(978-1-933027-21-0(5))* Sixth&Spring Bks.
McNeill, Suzanne. Tila Beads. 2011. (ENG.). 52p. pap. 16.99 ***(978-1-57421-402-4(0))*** Design Originals.
Meister, Maggie. Maggie Meister's Classical Elegance: 20 Beaded Jewelry Designs. 2011. (Beadweaving Master Class Ser.). (ENG., Illus.). 128p. 27.95 *(978-1-60059-691-9(6))* Lark Bks.
Meng, Kaari. French-Inspired Jewelry: Creating with Vintage Beads, Buttons & Baubles. 2007. (ENG., Illus.). 144p. 19.95 *(978-1-60059-096-2(9))* Lark Bks.
Meredith Corporation, compiled by. Easy Beading Project to Make, Wear & Share: Better Homes & Gardens. 2006. (ENG.). 64p. pap. 12.95 *(978-1-60140-171-7(X))* Leisure Arts, Inc.
Michaels, Chris Franchetti. Beading Visual Quick Tips. 2009. (Visual Quick Tips Ser.: 16). (ENG., Illus.). 224p. pap. 14.99 *(978-0-470-34383-8(4),* Visual) Wiley, John & Sons, Inc.
—Beadwork: Learning Off-Loom Beading Techniques One Stitch at a Time. 2009. (Teach Yourself VISUALLY Consumer Ser.). (ENG., Illus.). 256p. pap. 24.99 *(978-0-470-45466-4(0),* Visual) Wiley, John & Sons, Inc.
—Jewelry Making & Beading. 2007. (Teach Yourself VISUALLY Consumer Ser.). (ENG., Illus.). 304p. per. 24.99 *(978-0-470-10150-6(4),* Visual) Wiley, John & Sons, Inc.
Miech, Irina. Beautiful Wire Jewelry for Beaders 2. 2010. (ENG., Illus.). 112p. pap. 21.95 *(978-0-87116-418-6(3))* Kalmbach Publishing Co., Bks. Div.
Miech, Irina. Irina's Inspirations for Jewelry: From the Exotic to the Everyday. 2011. (ENG., Illus.). 112p. pap. 21.95 ***(978-0-87116-402-5(7))*** Kalmbach Publishing Co., Bks. Div.
Miller, Sharilyn. Wire Art Jewelry Workshop: Step-by-Step Techniques & Projects. 2011. (ENG., Illus.). 160p. 26.95 *(978-1-59668-408-9(9))* Interweave Pr., LLC.
Millodot, Suzen. Chinese, Celtic & Ornamental Knots. 2012. (ENG., Illus.). 192p. pap. 29.95 ***(978-1-84448-814-8(4))*** Search Pr., Ltd. GBR. Dist: Independent Pubs. Group.
Millodot, Suzen. Ornamental Knots for Beaded Jewellery. 2009. (ENG., Illus.). 80p. pap. 19.95 *(978-1-84448-248-1(0))* Search Pr., Ltd. GBR. Dist: Independent Pubs. Group.
Mitchell, Karen & Mitchell, Ann. Bead Jewelry 101, 2nd Edition: Master Basic Skills & Techniques Easily through Step-by-Step Instruction. 2011. (101 Ser.). (ENG., Illus.). 200p. spiral bd. 24.99 *(978-1-58923-665-3(3),* 1589236653) Quayside.
More Zulu Beadwork. (Contemporary Beadwork Ser.). 48p. 11.95 *(978-0-9646077-3-6(5))* Beautiful Beads Pr.
Momu, Nathalie. A Bounty of Bead & Wire Bracelets: 50 Fun, Fast Jewelry Projects. 2012. (Bounty of Bead & Wire Ser.). (ENG., Illus.). 144p. pap. 19.95 ***(978-1-4547-0407-2(1))*** Lark Bks.
—A Bounty of Bead & Wire Earrings: 50 Fun, Fast Jewelry Projects. 2011. (Bounty of Bead & Wire Ser.). (ENG., Illus.). 144p. pap. 19.95 *(978-1-4547-0018-0(1))* Lark Bks.
Momu, Nathalie. A Bounty of Bead & Wire Necklaces: 50 Fun, Fast Jewelry Projects. 2012. (Bounty of Bead & Wire Ser.). (ENG., Illus.). 160p. pap. 19.95 ***(978-1-4547-0289-4(3))*** Lark Bks.
Momu, Nathalie & Tourtillott, Suzanne J. E. Contemporary Bead & Wire Jewelry. 2010. (ENG., Illus.). 128p. pap. 14.95 *(978-1-60059-590-5(1))* Lark Bks.
Morris, Karen. The Beading Answer Book: Solutions to Every Problem You'll Ever Face - Answers to Every Question You'll Ever Ask. 2008. (ENG., Illus.). 432p. pap. 14.95 *(978-1-60342-034-1(7),* 1603420347) Storey Publishing, LLC.
Nelson-Smith, Rachel. Rachel Nelson-Smith's Bead Riffs: Jewelry Projects in Peyote & Right Angle Weave. 2011. (Beadweaving Master Class Ser.). (ENG., Illus.). 128p. 27.95 *(978-1-60059-783-1(1))* Lark Bks.
—Seed Bead Fusion: 18 Projects to Stitch, Wire, & String. 2009. (ENG., Illus.). 144p. pap. 24.95 *(978-1-59668-156-9(X))* Interweave Pr., LLC.
Nimri, Sonya. Beadalicious: 25 Fresh, Unforgettable Jewelry Projects for Beads Old & New. 2008. (ENG., Illus.). 128p. pap. 14.95 *(978-0-8230-9996-2(2))* Watson-Guptill Pubns., Inc.
Nishida, Midori & Design, C. R. K. The Beaded Edge: Inspired Designs for Crocheted Edgings & Trims. 2011. (ENG., Illus.). 88p. pap. 17.95 *(978-1-59668-300-6(7))* Interweave Pr., LLC.
Nozue, Sonoko. Japanese Beadwork with Sonoko Nozue: 25 Jewelry Designs from a Master Artist. 2012. (Beadweaving Master Class Ser.). (ENG., Illus.). 128p. 27.95 ***(978-1-4547-0278-8(8))*** Lark Bks.
Ogura, Yukiko. Bead Embroidery, 1 vol. Prener, Connie, tr. 2007. (ENG., Illus.). 40p. per. 14.95 *(978-4-88996-215-4(8))* Japan Pubns. Trading Co. JPN. Dist: Oxford Univ. Pr., Inc.
Olson-Phillips, Jane. Bead & Fiber Jewelry: Elegant Knotted Designs. 2008. (ENG., Illus.). 128p. pap. 17.95 *(978-1-60059-231-7(7))* Lark Bks.
Otterbein, Kim & Mabray, Angela. Polymer Clay: Master Basic Skills & Techniques Easily Through Step-by-Step Instruction. 2011. (101 Ser.). (ENG., Illus.). 192p. spiral bd. 24.99 *(978-1-58923-470-3(7),* 1589234707) Quayside.
Overlay Crochet Jewelry. 2006. 52p. 11.95 *(978-1-60140-088-8(8))* Leisure Arts, Inc.
Owen, Cheryl. Precious Jewellery: 25 Jewellery Projects Using Precious & Semi-Precious Beads. 2010. (ENG., Illus.). 112p. pap. 19.95 *(978-1-84773-712-0(9))* New Holland Pubs., Ltd. GBR. Dist: Sterling Publishing Co., Inc.
—101 Sparkling Necklaces. 2007. (ENG., Illus.). 128p. pap. 24.95 *(978-1-56477-782-9(0))* Martingale & Co.
Packham, Jo, ed. Friendship Bracelets All Grown Up. 2008. (ENG., Illus.). 64p. pap. 18.95 *(978-1-56477-846-8(0))* Martingale & Co.

Pankopf, Cindy Thomas. Beadmaille: Jewelry with Bead Weaving & Metal Rings. 2010. (ENG., Illus.). 128p. pap. 21.95 *(978-1-60059-495-3(6)*, 1312500) Lark Bks.

Pemberton, John, 3rd. African Beaded Art: Power & Adornment. 2008. (Illus.). 224p. pap. *(978-0-87391-058-3(3))* Smith College Pubns.

Peters, Anna. Beaded Daisy Chain Jewellery: 40 Designs to Make. 2007. (ENG., Illus.). 128p. pap. 14.95 *(978-1-86108-429-3(3))* Guild of Master Craftsman Pubns., Ltd. GBR. Dist: Sterling Publishing Co., Inc.

Peterson, Linda. Beading in No Time. 2010. (ENG., Illus.). 176p. pap. *(978-1-907030-26-0(3))* www.clickok.co.uk.

—How to Make Polymer Clay Beads: 35 Step-by-Step Projects Show How to Make Beautiful Beads & Jewelry. 2008. (ENG., Illus.). 128p. pap. 19.95 *(978-1-906094-44-7(6))* CICO Bks. GBR. Dist: Ryland Peters & Small.

Pettit, Juliette. Beads & Buttons. 2008. (Illus.). 96p. pap. 14.95 *(978-1-56906-988-2(3))* Sellers Publishing, Inc.

Picarello, Julie. Patterns in Polymer: Imprint & Accent Bead Techniques. 2011. (ENG., Illus.). 96p. pap. 21.95 *(978-0-87116-409-4(4))* Kalmbach Publishing Co., Bks. Div.

Plumlee, Scott David. Chain & Bead Jewelry: Soldering Connections. 2011. 80p. pap. 32.95 *(978-1-4520-7892-2(0))* AuthorHouse.

—Chain & Bead Jewelry Creative Connections: New Techniques for Wire-Wrapping & Bead-Setting. 2009. (Illus.). 160p. pap. 22.95 *(978-0-8230-2485-8(7))* Watson-Guptill Pubns., Inc.

—Chain & Bead Jewelry Geometric Connections: A New Angle on Creating Dimensional Earrings, Bracelets, & Necklaces. 2010. (ENG.). 160p. pap. 22.99 *(978-0-8230-3339-3(2))* Watson-Guptill Pubns., Inc.

—Handcrafting Chain & Bead Jewelry: Techniques for Creating Dimensional Necklaces & Bracelets. 2006. (ENG., Illus.). 128p. pap. 19.95 *(978-0-8230-2299-1(4))* Watson-Guptill Pubns., Inc.

Ponce, Patricia. Big Book of Crystal Beads: 70+ Bracelets, Earrings, Necklaces, & Rings. 2008. (ENG., Illus.). 176p. 24.95 *(978-1-58011-385-4(0))* Creative Homeowner.

Potter, Margot. The Impatient Beader Gets Inspired! A Crafty Chick's Guide to Instant Inspiration! 2006. (ENG., Illus.). 128p. pap. 19.99 *(978-1-58180-854-4(2)*, North Light Bks.) F&W Media, Inc.

—New Dimensions in Bead & Wire Jewelry: Unexpected Combinations, Unique Designs. 2011. (ENG., Illus.). 128p. pap. 24.99 *(978-1-4403-0924-3(8)*, North Light Bks.) F&W Media, Inc.

Potter, Margot, et al. Bead & Wire Jewelry Exposed: 50 Designer Projects Featuring Beadalon & Swarovski. 2009. (ENG., Illus.). 144p. pap. 22.99 *(978-1-60061-159-9(1)*, North Light Bks.) F&W Media, Inc.

—Bead Chic: 36 Stylish Jewelry Projects & Inspired Variations. 2010. (ENG., Illus.). 128p. pap. 22.99 *(978-1-4403-0315-9(0)*, North Light Bks.) F&W Media, Inc.

Power, Jean. 200 Beading Tips, Techniques & Trade Secrets: An Indispensable Compendium of Technical Know-How & Troubleshooting Tips. 2009. (200 Tips, Techniques & Trade Secrets Ser.). (ENG., Illus.). 160p. pap. 22.99 *(978-0-312-58747-5(3)*, St. Martin's Griffin) St. Martin's Pr.

Powers, Heather. Jewelry Designs from Nature: Woodlands, Gardens, Sea: Art Bead Jewelry Designs Inspired by Nature. 2011. (ENG., Illus.). 96p. pap. 19.95 *(978-0-87116-428-5(0))* Kalmbach Publishing Co., Bks. Div.

Preti, Julia S. Beaded Collars: 10 Decorative Neckpieces Built with Ladder Stitch. 2008. (ENG., Illus.). 112p. pap. 21.95 *(978-1-58923-381-2(6)*, 1589233816, Creative Publishing International) Quayside.

—Julia Preti's Big Book of Beadwork: 32 Projects for Adventurous Beaders. 2010. (ENG., Illus.). 320p. pap. 24.99 *(978-1-58923-527-4(4)*, 1589235274) Quayside.

—Little Bead Boxes: 12 Miniature Boxes Built with Beads. 2006. (ENG., Illus.). 112p. pap. 21.95 *(978-1-58923-291-4(7)*, 1589232917) Quayside.

Ray, Janie. Hemp It up with Beads! Bags, Bracelets, Buddies, Crosses. 2011. (Design Originals Ser.). (Illus.). 20p. pap. 8.50 ***(978-1-57421-147-4(1))*** Design Originals.

Reckles, Adele Rogers. Bead Crochet Snakes: History & Technique. 2007. (Illus.). 112p. pap. 22.95 *(978-0-9791649-0-3(7))* Reckless Beading Pr.

Rees, Nelli. Glass Bead Jewelry Projects. 2011. (ENG., Illus.). 176p. pap. 22.95 *(978-1-86108-815-4(9))* Guild of Master Craftsman Pubns., Ltd. GBR. Dist: Sterling Publishing Co., Inc.

Remmers, Wendy. Beaded Jewelry. 2007. (Make It in Minutes Ser.). (ENG., Illus.). 128p. spiral bd. 12.95 *(978-1-60059-032-0(2))* Lark Bks.

Rodgers, Carole. Beyond Beading Basics. 2009. (ENG., Illus.). 144p. pap. 24.99 *(978-0-89689-925-4(X))* Krause Pubns.

Rollason, Madeleine. Beginner's Guide to Bead Netting. 2007. (Beginner's Guide to Needlecrafts Ser.). (ENG., Illus.). 96p. pap. 19.95 *(978-1-84448-110-1(7))* Search Pr., Ltd. GBR. Dist: Independent Pubs. Group.

Ronat, Danny & Ronat, Hava. Making Handmade Lampwork Beads & Glass Jewelry: The Complete Guide to Making Handmade Lampwork Beads & Glass Jewelry. 2008. (ENG., Illus.). 128p. pap. 19.99 *(978-1-58923-391-1(3)*, 1589233913, Creative Publishing International) Quayside.

Roschyk, Maggie. Artistic Seed Bead Jewelry: Ideas & Techniques for Original Designs. 2011. (ENG., Illus.). 112p. pap. 21.95 ***(978-0-87116-429-2(9))*** Kalmbach Publishing Co., Bks. Div.

Ryan, M. T. More Glamorous Beaded Jewelry: Bracelets, Necklaces, Earrings, & Rings. 2008. (ENG., Illus.). 176p. pap. 19.95 *(978-1-58011-408-0(3))* Creative Homeowner.

Salamony, Sandra. 1000 Jewelry Inspirations: Beads, Baubles, Dangles, & Chains. 2011. (1000 Ser.). (ENG., Illus.). 440p. pap. 15.99 *(978-1-59253-710-5(3)*, 1592537103, Fair Winds Press) Quayside.

Samejima, Takako. Bead Fantasies IV: The Ultimate Collection of Beautiful, Easy-to-Make Jewelry, 1 vol. 2006. (Bead Fantasies Ser.). (ENG., Illus.). 80p. pap. 18.00 *(978-4-88996-204-8(2))* Japan Pubns. Trading Co. JPN. Dist: Oxford Univ. Pr., Inc.

Schneebeli-Morrell, Deborah. Vintage-Style Beaded Jewelry: 35 beautiful projects using new & old Materials. 2011. (ENG., Illus.). 128p. pap. 19.95 *(978-1-907563-10-2(5))* CICO Bks. GBR. Dist: Ryland Peters & Small.

Schneebeli-Morrell, Deborah & Piper, Rachel K. Big Bead Jewelry: 35 Beautiful Easy-to-Make Projects. 2006. (ENG., Illus.). 128p. pap. 19.99 *(978-1-58180-896-4(8)*, North Light Bks.) F&W Media, Inc.

Schneider, Zoe L. French Beaded Flowers - the Complete Guide. 2010. (ENG., Illus.). 256p. spiral bd. 29.99 *(978-1-4402-0369-5(5))* Krause Pubns.

Scott, Joyce J. Li'l Lies & Purty Thangs. 2010. pap. 0.00 *(978-1-4507-4147-7(9))* Independent Pub.

Serafini, Sherry. Sherry Serafini's Sensational Bead Embroidery: 25 Inspiring Jewelry Projects. 2011. (Beadweaving Master Class Ser.). (ENG., Illus.). 128p. 24.95 *(978-1-60059-672-8(X))* Lark Bks.

Serafini, Sherry, et al. Beading Across America: Jewelry Inspiration from Coast to Coast. 2011. (ENG., Illus.). 112p. pap. 21.95 *(978-0-87116-400-1(0))* Kalmbach Publishing Co., Bks. Div.

Sersich, Stephanie. Designing Jewelry with Glass Beads. 2008. (ENG., Illus.). 128p. pap. 22.95 *(978-1-59668-047-0(4))* Interweave Pr., LLC.

Sherman, Nicole Noelle. Making Designer Jewelry from Hardware, Gems, & Beads. 2008. (ENG., Illus.). 128p. pap. 24.99 *(978-1-59253-422-7(8)*, 1592534228, Quarry Books) Quayside.

Simak, Evelyn & Dreibelbis, Carl. African Beads: Jewels of a Continent. Liechty, Jacob, ed. 2010. (Illus.). 216p. 69.95 *(978-0-9816267-2-7(6))* Africa Direct.

Snelling, Kelly & Rae, Ruth. A Charming Exchange: 25 Jewelry Projects to Create & Share. 2008. (ENG., Illus.). 128p. pap. 22.99 *(978-1-60061-051-6(X)*, North Light Bks.) F&W Media, Inc.

Snyman, Fransie. Jewelry in a Jiffy: More Than 55 Quick & Easy Bead Projects. 2011. (ENG., Illus.). 144p. pap. 19.95 *(978-1-55407-936-0(5))* Firefly Bks., Ltd.

Southern, Sally. Sew Many Bags Sew Little Time: Over 30 Stylish Bags & Simple Accessories. 2008. (ENG., Illus.). 128p. pap. 22.99 *(978-0-7153-2649-7(X))* David & Charles Pubs. GBR. Dist: F&W Media, Inc.

Stegall, Carol. Beadwork with Seed Beads & Embellishments: Fabulous Bracelets, Necklaces, Brooches & More! 2011. (ENG., Illus.). 20p. pap. 7.99 ***(978-1-57421-886-2(7))*** Design Originals.

Sterbenz, Genevieve A. The Art of Beading: Essential Tools & Techniques Every Jewelry Maker Must Know. 2010. (ENG., Illus.). 384p. pap. 27.50 *(978-0-8118-7160-0(6))* Chronicle Bks. LLC.

Stone, Beth. More Seed Bead Stitching: Creative Variations on Traditional Techniques. 2009. (ENG., Illus.). 96p. pap. 19.95 *(978-0-87116-290-8(3))* Kalmbach Publishing Co., Bks. Div.

—Seed Bead Stitching: Creative Variations on Traditional Techniques. 2007. (ENG., Illus.). 96p. per. 19.95 *(978-0-87116-252-6(0))* Kalmbach Publishing Co., Bks. Div.

Stori, Mary. Embellishing with Felted Wool: 16 Projects with Applique, Beads, Buttons & Embroidery. 2008. (ENG., Illus.). 56p. pap. 19.95 *(978-1-57120-443-1(1))* C & T Publishing.

Sutton, Scott. Beadwork Techniques of the Native Americans. 2009. (Illus.). 96p. pap. 19.95 *(978-1-929572-11-3(5))* CCTP/Reddick Enterprises.

Switzer, Barb. Four Seasons of Beading. Sprunger, Barb, ed. 2009. (ENG., Illus.). 128p. pap. 15.95 *(978-1-59635-267-4(1)*, Annie's Attic, LLC) Annie's Publishing, LLC.

Taylor, Scarlet. Knit with Beads: Stunning Shawls & Wraps: Easy Techniques, 15 Beautiful Designs. 2007. (ENG., Illus.). 96p. pap. 14.95 *(978-0-8230-1675-4(7))* Watson-Guptill Pubns., Inc.

Taylor, Terry. A Very Beaded Christmas: 46 Projects that Glitter, Twinkle & Shine. 2009. (ENG., Illus.). 132p. pap. 17.95 *(978-1-60059-393-2(3)*, 1304883) Lark Bks.

The Timeless Cowrie. 2007. 10.00 *(978-0-9725066-3-2(2))* Bead Museum of Washington DC, The.

Vail, Juju. The Beader's Handbook: Beads - Tools - Materials - Techniques. 2007. (ENG., Illus.). 256p. pap. 29.95 *(978-1-56477-800-0(2))* Martingale & Co.

—I Love Beading: 25 Projects That Will Show You How to Bead Easily & Quickly. 2009. (ENG., Illus.). 128p. pap. 17.95 *(978-1-60529-931-0(6))* Rodale Pr., Inc.

Van Horn, Larkin Jean. Beading on Fabric: Encyclopedia of Bead Stitch Techniques. 2006. (ENG., Illus.). 120p. spiral bd. 21.95 *(978-1-59668-004-3(0))* Interweave Pr., LLC.

VanderPuy, Nancy. Knitting Beaded Purses: A Complete Guide to Creating Your Own. 2008. (Illus.). 64p. pap. 16.95 *(978-0-7643-2870-1(0))* Schiffer Publishing, Ltd.

Ventura, Carol. Bead & Felted Tapestry Crochet. 2006. (Illus.). 64p. 20.00 *(978-0-9721253-2-1(9))* Ventura, Carol.

Wagner, Connie. Beads & Agate Jewelry to Create Yourself. 2008. (Illus.). 64p. pap. 14.99 *(978-0-7643-2998-2(7))* Schiffer Publishing, Ltd.

Walker, Amanda. Bracelets. 2008. (Twenty to Make Ser.). (ENG., Illus.). 48p. pap. 9.95 *(978-1-84448-276-4(6))* Search Pr., Ltd. GBR. Dist: Independent Pubs. Group.

Wallace, Sandra. Beaders Color Mixing Directory: 200 Failsafe Color Schemes for Beautiful Beadwork. 2007. (ENG., Illus.). 128p. pap. 22.99 *(978-0-89689-480-8(0))* Krause Pubns.

Wang, Pauline. Making Metal Beads: Techniques, Projects, Inspiration. (ENG., Illus.). 160p. 2010. pap. 17.95 *(978-1-60059-609-4(6))* 2006. 24.95 *(978-1-57990-712-9(1))* Lark Bks.

Warhaftig, Jeri L. & Warhaftig, Jeri. Glass Bead Workshop: Building Skills, Exploring Techniques, Finding Inspiration. 2008. (ENG., Illus.). 144p. 24.95 *(978-1-60059-123-5(X))* Lark Bks.

Wedekind, Dustin. Getting Started with Seed Beads. 2012. (ENG., Illus.). 128p. pap. 14.95 ***(978-1-59668-975-6(7))*** Interweave Pr., LLC.

Weiss, Lesley. Stitching Beaded Jewelry: Everything You Need to Know to Get Started. 2010. (Absolute Beginners Guide Ser.). (ENG., Illus.). 96p. pap. 21.95 *(978-0-87116-412-4(4))* Kalmbach Publishing Co., Bks. Div.

Welsh, Kate Shoup. Not Your Mama's Beading: The Cool & Creative Way to String 'em Along. 2006. (ENG., Illus.). 256p. pap. 14.99 *(978-0-471-97380-5(7)*, Wiley) Wiley, John & Sons, Inc.

Weschler, Lawrence, et al, texts. Liza Lou. 2011. (ENG.). 264p. 60.00 *(978-0-8478-3461-7(1)*, Skira) Rizzoli International Pubns., Inc.

White, Terry. All Beaded up by Machine. 2008. (ENG., Illus.). 96p. 26.95 *(978-1-57432-969-8(3)*, 1574329693, American Quilter's Society) Collector Bks.

Whyte, Dylon. Beaded Chain Mail Jewelry: Timeless Techniques with a Twist. 2009. (ENG., Illus.). 144p. 24.95 *(978-1-60059-220-1(1))* Lark Bks.

Wiese, Kelly. Beaded Allure: Beadweaving Patterns for 25 Romantic Projects. 2010. (ENG., Illus.). 144p. pap. 24.99 *(978-1-60061-768-3(9)*, North Light Bks.) F&W Media, Inc.

Wigington, Melinda. How to Crochet Bead Tube Jewelry. 2011. (ENG., Illus.). 48p. pap. 14.95 *(978-1-59635-384-8(8))* Annie's Publishing, LLC.

Wildschut, William & Ewers, John C. Crow Indian Beadwork: A Descriptive & Historical Study. 2011. 108p. 39.95 ***(978-1-258-07150-9(9))*** Literary Licensing, LLC.

Wilson, Suzann Sladcik. Simple Beginnings: Beading - A Step-by-Step Guide for Creating Your Own Custom Jewelry. 2012. (Illus.). 96p. pap. 14.99 ***(978-1-57421-415-4(2))*** Design Originals.

Wiseman, Jill. Jill Wiseman's Beautiful Beaded Ropes: 24 Wearable Jewelry Projects in Multiple Stitches. 2012. (Beadweaving Master Class Ser.). (ENG., Illus.). 120p. 27.95 ***(978-1-4547-0356-3(3))*** Lark Bks.

Wood, Dorothy. The Bead Jewelry Bible. 2011. (ENG., Illus.). 144p. pap. 24.99 *(978-0-7153-3870-4(6))* David & Charles Pubs. GBR. Dist: F&W Media, Inc.

—Beaded Treasures. 2010. (ENG., Illus.). 128p. pap. 19.99 *(978-0-7153-3668-7(1))* David & Charles Pubs. GBR. Dist: F&W Media, Inc.

—The Beader's Bible. 2008. (ENG., Illus.). 160p. pap. 24.99 *(978-0-7153-2300-7(8))* David & Charles Pubs. GBR. Dist: F&W Media, Inc.

—Ultimate Necklace Maker. 2009. (ENG., Illus.). 128p. pap. 24.99 *(978-0-7153-3169-9(8))* David & Charles Pubs. GBR. Dist: F&W Media, Inc.

Wood, Dorothy & Wood, Ashley. Beading - 200 Q&A: Questions Answered on Everything from Basic Stitches to Finishing Touches. 2010. (ENG.). 224p. 18.99 *(978-0-7641-6359-3(0))* Barron's Educational Series, Inc.

Yates, Jean. Links: Inspired Bead & Wire Jewelry Creations. 2007. (ENG., Illus.). 128p. per. 22.99 *(978-1-60061-016-5(1)*, North Light Bks.) F&W Media, Inc.

You Made It Now Sell It: The Ultimate Guide to Selling Your Handmade Jewelry. 2007. 176p. pap. 19.99 *(978-0-9649887-0-5(4))* Pudgy Publishing.

Yu, Daphne. Pearl Projects for Beaders. 2010. (Illus.). 112p. pap. 24.99 *(978-0-7643-3552-5(9))* Schiffer Publishing, Ltd.

Zellers, Nancy. Bead Tube Jewelry: Peyote & brick stitch designs for 30+ necklaces, bracelets, & Earrings. 2011. (ENG., Illus.). 96p. pap. 19.95 *(978-0-87116-417-9(5))* Kalmbach Publishing Co., Bks. Div.

BEADWORK, INDIAN

see Indian Beadwork

BEAGLE, PETER S., 1939-

Beagle, Peter S. I See by My Outfit. 2007. (ENG.). 260p. per. 14.95 *(978-1-933572-07-9(8))* Centro Bks., LLC.

BEAGLE (DOG BREED)

Adamson, Eve. Beagles. 2009. *(978-0-7641-6228-2(4))*; (ENG., Illus.). 160p. 18.99 *(978-0-7641-9624-9(3))* Barron's Educational Series, Inc.

The Beagle - a Dog Anthology. 2007. 88p. per. *(978-1-4067-8780-1(9))* Read Bks.

DeVito, Dominique. Beagles, 1 vol. 2007. (Animal Planet Pet Care Library). (ENG., Illus.). 112p. 11.95 *(978-0-7938-3782-3(0))* TFH Pubns., Inc.

Dina Marie Marrazzo. Holiday Fun for Cody, Bailey & Lexy Rose. 2009. 44p. pap. 16.99 *(978-1-4389-7478-1(7))* AuthorHouse.

Dog Fancy Staff, compiled by. Beagle: Auswahl, Haltung, Erziehung, Beschäftigung. 2010. (Smart Owner's Guide Ser.). (ENG.). 176p. pap. 15.95 *(978-1-59378-777-6(4))*; (gr. 6). 17.95 *(978-1-59378-772-1(3))* Kennel Club Bks.

Domin, Tom & Domin, Velta. Breeding a Strain of Better Beagles. (Illus.). 112p. *(978-0-936369-50-1(7))* Son Rise Pubns.

Fields-Babineau, Miriam. Beagle, 1 vol. 2011. (ENG.). 144p. 15.95 *(978-0-7938-3722-9(7))* TFH Pubns., Inc.

Gewirtz, Elaine Waldorf. Beagle: Your Happy Healthy Pet. 2nd ed. 2008. (Happy Healthy Pet Ser.: 151). (ENG., Illus.). 144p. 16.99 *(978-0-470-39055-9(7)*, Howell Bk. Hse.) Wiley, John & Sons, Inc.

Kraeuter, Kristine. Training Your Beagle. 2nd rev. ed. 2011. (Training Your Dog Ser.). (Illus.). 184p. pap. 12.99 *(978-0-7641-4592-6(4))* Barron's Educational Series, Inc.

McCullough, Susan. Beagles for Dummies. 2006. (ENG., Illus.). 296p. per. 16.99 *(978-0-470-03961-8(2)*, For Dummies) Wiley, John & Sons, Inc.

Palazzi, Xavier. The Beagle Brain in Stereotaxic Coordinates. 2011. (ENG., Illus.). xvii, 119p. 189.00 *(978-1-4419-8371-8(6)*, 1441983716) Springer.

Pata, Sharae & Linzy, Jan. Beagle Champions, 1985-2005. 2006. (Illus.). 290p. spiral bd. 46.95 *(978-1-55893-200-5(3))* Camino E.E. & Bk. Co.

Pfaltz, Kay & Pfaltz, Sue. Beagle, 1 vol. 2011. (ENG., Illus.). 224p. 19.95 *(978-0-7938-3610-9(7))* TFH Pubns., Inc.

Schweitzer, Karen. The Beagle. 2010. *(978-1-932904-57-4(3))* Eldorado Ink.

BEAGLE EXPEDITION (1831-1836)

Australia, National Museum of. Charles Darwin: An Australian Selection. 2008. (ENG.). 144p. pap. 29.95 *(978-1-876944-72-8(2))* National Museum of Australia AUS. Dist: Independent Pubs. Group.

Brass, Daniel & Anderson, Katharine, eds. The Narrative of the Beagle Voyage, 1831-1836, 4 vols., Set. 2011. (Pickering Masters Ser.). (ENG., Illus.). 1616p. 625.00 *(978-1-85196-844-2(X))* Pickering & Chatto Pubs., Ltd. GBR. Dist: Ashgate Publishing Co.

Chancellor, Gordon & van Wyhe, John, eds. Charles Darwin's Notebooks from the Voyage of the Beagle. 2009. (ENG., Illus.). 650p. 155.00 *(978-0-521-51757-7(5))* Cambridge Univ. Pr.

Darwin, Charles. Geological Observations on the Volcanic Islands, Visited During the Voyage of H. M. S. Beagle: Together with Some Brief Notices on the Geology of Australia & the Cape of Good Hope. 2011. (Cambridge Library Collection - Earth Science Ser.). (ENG., Illus.). 192p. pap. 19.99 *(978-1-108-07233-5(X))* Cambridge Univ. Pr.

—Geological Observations on Volcanic Islands. 2008. (Illus.). 160p. per. *(978-1-4065-2000-2(4))* Dodo Pr.

—Journal of Researches into the Geology & Natural History of the Various Countries visited by H. M. S. Beagle. 2009. (Cambridge Library Collection - Life Sciences Ser.). 652p. pap. 37.99 ***(978-1-108-00210-3(2))*** Cambridge Univ. Pr.

—The Voyage of the Beagle. 2007. (ENG.). 546p. pap. 30.99 *(978-1-4346-8806-4(2))*; 616p. pap. 33.99 *(978-1-4346-8807-1(0))* BiblioBazaar.

—The Voyage of the Beagle. 2007. (ENG.). 316p. per. 11.99 *(978-1-4209-3020-7(6))* Digireads.com.

—The Voyage of the Beagle. 2008. (Illus.). 468p. per. *(978-1-4065-2001-9(2))* Dodo Pr.

—The Voyage of the Beagle. 2010. (Adventure Classics Ser.). (ENG., Illus.). 688p. 14.95 *(978-88-544-0176-1(5))* White Star ITA. Dist: Sterling Publishing Co., Inc.

—The Voyage of the Beagle Deluxe Edition. 2010. (ENG., Illus.). 550p. 35.00 *(978-88-544-0417-5(9))* White Star ITA. Dist: Random Hse., Inc.

Darwin, Charles, et al. The Works of Charles Darwin, Volumes 1-29 (complete Set), 29 vols. 2010. (ENG.). 248p. pap. 525.00 *(978-0-8147-2073-8(0))* New York Univ. Pr.

Fitz-Roy, Robert, et al. Narrative of the Surveying Voyages of His Majesty's Ships Adventure & Beagle, 3 vols. in 4 pts. reprint ed. 425.00 *(978-0-404-09900-8(9))* AMS Pr., Inc.

Keynes, Richard Darwin. The Beagle Record: Selections from the Original Pictorial Records & Written Accounts of the Voyage of H. M. S. Beagle. 2012. (ENG.). 424p. pap. 50.00 *(978-0-521-33855-4(7))* Cambridge Univ. Pr.

BEAGLES (DOGS)

see Beagle (Dog Breed)

BEALES, JOHN CHARLES

Brister, Louis E., ed. John Charles Beales's Rio Grande Colony: Letters by Eduard Ludecus, a German Colonist, to Freinds in Germany in 1833-1834, Recounting His Journey, Trials, & Observations in Early Texas. 2008. (ENG., Illus.). 250p. 29.95 *(978-0-87611-234-2(3))* Texas State Historical Assn.

Rister, Carl Coke & Richardson, R. N. Comanche Bondage: John Charles Beales's Settlement of la Villa de Dolores on Las Moras Creek in Southern Texas of The 1830's. 2011. 210p. 44.95 ***(978-1-258-06865-3(6))*** Literary Licensing, LLC.

BEAMS

see Girders

BEAMS, COMPOSITE

see Composite Construction

BEAMS, CONCRETE

see Concrete Beams

BEAMS, GAUSSIAN

see Gaussian Beams

BEAMS, ION

see Ion Bombardment

BEAMS, PARTICLE

see Particle Beams

BEAN, ROY, D. 1903

Sonnichsen, Charles L. Roy Bean: Law West of the Pecos. (Illus.). 14.95 *(978-0-8159-6715-6(2))* Devin-Adair Pubs., Inc.

BEAN FAMILY

Bean Jr., William J. Dark Force: The Terrifying & Tragic Story of the Bean Family. 2007. 169p. per. 24.95 *(978-0-9762139-1-8(5))* Meriones Publishing, LLC.

BEAN FAMILY (PLANTS)

see Legumes

B

BEANIE BABIES (TRADEMARK)

Wells, Rosie, ed. Rosie's Secondary Market Price Guide for Ty's Beanie Babies. 4th ed. (Illus.). 192p. pap. 10.95 *(978-1-886812-32-1(2))* Wells, Rosie Enterprises.

BEAR (SHIP)

Sandler, Martin W. The Impossible Rescue: The True Story of an Amazing Arctic Adventure. 2012. (ENG., Illus.). 176p. (J). (gr. 5-9). 22.99 ***(978-0-7636-5080-3(3))*** Candlewick Pr.

Taliaferro, John. In a Far Country: The True Story of a Mission, a Marriage, a Murder, & the Remarkable Reindeer Rescue of 1898. 2007. (ENG., Illus.). 424p. per. 15.95 *(978-1-58648-508-5(3))* PublicAffairs.

BEAR FLAG REVOLT, 1846

Bryant, Edwin. What I Saw in California. 2008. 228p. 27.99 *(978-0-554-24465-5(9))* 2007. 204p. pap. 20.99 *(978-1-4264-6558-1(0))* 2006. (ENG.). 226p. pap. 22.99 *(978-1-4264-6617-5(X))* BiblioBazaar.

—What I Saw in California. 2009. 380p. pap. *(978-0-217-65526-2(2))*; 382p. pap. *(978-0-217-14575-6(2))* Books LLC.

—What I Saw in California. 2008. 204p. pap. *(978-1-4099-3244-4(3))* Dodo Pr.

—What I Saw in California. 2008. (ENG.). 188p. pap. 13.95 *(978-1-4385-1024-8(1)*, Book Jungle) Standard Pubns., Inc.

Rogers, Fred B. Bear Flag Lieutenant: The Life of Henry L. Ford, 1822-1860. 2011. 104p. 39.95 ***(978-1-258-06926-1(1))*** Literary Licensing, LLC.

BEAR HUNTING

Holman, John P. Sheep & Bear Trails: A Hunter's Wanderings in Alaska & British Columbia. 2011. 272p. 47.95 ***(978-1-258-09857-5(1))*** Literary Licensing, LLC.

Jones, J. Y. Ask the Black Bear Guides. 2008. (ENG., Illus.). 227p. 24.95 *(978-1-57157-282-0(1))* Safari Pr., Inc.

Kelly, Allen. Bears I Have Met — and Others. 2007. (ENG.). 128p. pap. 18.99 *(978-1-4264-8554-1(9))*; 140p. pap. 19.99 *(978-1-4264-8611-1(1))* BiblioBazaar.

—Bears I Have Met — and Others. 2007. (Illus.). 136p. per. *(978-1-4065-1881-8(6))* Dodo Pr.

Lewis, Gary & Van Tassel, Lee. Black Bear Hunting: Expert Strategies for Success. 2007. (Complete Hunter Ser.). (ENG., Illus.). 128p. 21.95 *(978-1-58923-315-7(8)*, 1589233158, Creative Publishing International) Quayside.

Palmer, J. Frederick. Kodiak Bear Hunt: Stalking the Giant Bears of Alaska. 2011. 78p. 37.95 ***(978-1-258-09925-1(X))*** Literary Licensing, LLC.

Scorzafava, Dick. Radical Bear Hunter. 2007. (ENG., Illus.). 224p. per. 21.95 *(978-0-8117-3418-9(8))* Stackpole Bks.

Smith, Richard P. Black Bear Hunting. 2007. (ENG., Illus.). 384p. 32.95 *(978-0-8117-0269-0(3))* Stackpole Bks.

BEARD, CHARLES AUSTIN, 1874-1948

Brown, David S. Beyond the Frontier: The Midwestern Voice in American Historical Writing. 2009. (ENG., Illus.). 256p. 32.50 *(978-0-226-07651-5(2))* Univ. of Chicago Pr.

BEARD, DANIEL CARTER, 1850-1941

Beard, Daniel Carter. Hardly a Man Is Now Alive: The Autobiography of Dan Beard. 2011. 392p. 53.95 ***(978-1-258-00459-0(3))*** Literary Licensing, LLC.

Scott, David C. & Murphy, Brendan. The Scouting Party: Pioneering & Preservation, Progressivism & Preparedness in the Making of the Boy Scouts of America. 2010. (Illus.). 285p. *(978-0-9789836-3-5(7)*, Red Honor Pr.) PenlandScott Pubs.

BEARDED COLLIE

Au, Manfred. Bearded Dragons. 2009. (Complete Pet Owner's Manual Ser.). (ENG., Illus.). 64p. pap. 8.99 *(978-0-7641-4286-4(0))* Barron's Educational Series, Inc.

Laning, Charlotte. Bearded Collie. (SWE., Illus.). 188p. 40.00 *(978-0-9644628-1-6(8))* Laning, Charlotte.

BEARDEN, ROMARE, 1914-1988

Bearden, Romare. From Process to Print: Graphic Works by Romare Bearden. 2009. 136p. 35.00 *(978-0-7649-5148-0(3))* Pomegranate Communications, Inc.

—Romare Bearden: A Black Odyssey, 1 vol. 2008. (ENG., Illus.). 116p. 45.00 *(978-0-9774965-9-4(7))* DC Moore Gallery.

—Romare Bearden, American Modernist. Fine, Ruth & Francis, Jacqueline, eds. 2011. (Studies in the History of Art Ser.). (ENG., Illus.). 304p. 70.00 *(978-0-300-12161-2(X))* National Gallery of Art.

Bearden, Romare. Romare Bearden: Idea to Realization. 2011. (ENG., Illus.). 30p. pap. 20.00 ***(978-0-9826316-5-2(0))*** DC Moore Gallery.

Hanzal, Carla, et al. Romare Bearden: Southern Recollections. 2011. (ENG., Illus.). 144p. 44.95 *(978-1-904832-98-0(9))* Giles, D. Ltd. GBR. Dist: National Bk. Network.

Price, Sally & Price, Richard. Romare Bearden: The Caribbean Dimension. 2006. (Illus.). 192p. (C). 49.95 *(978-0-8122-3948-5(2))* Univ. of Pennsylvania Pr.

BEARDS

Belgie, O. S. Beards... And a Couple of Moustaches! 2010. (ENG., Illus.). 96p. 9.99 *(978-1-84601-360-7(7)*, Spruce) Octopus Publishing Group GBR. Dist: Hachette Bk. Group.

Johnston, Mark Albert. Beard Fetish in Early Modern England: Sex, Gender, & Registers of Value. 2011. (Women & Gender in the Early Modern World Ser.). (Illus.). 312p. 104.95 ***(978-1-4094-0542-9(7))*** Ashgate Publishing Co.

Martin, Chris. A Gentleman's Guide to Beard & Moustache Management. 2011. (ENG.). 160p. 14.95 ***(978-0-7524-5975-2(9))*** History Pr. Ltd.,The GBR. Dist: Independent Pubs. Group.

Peterkin, Allan & Burns, Nick. The Bearded Gentleman: The Style Guide to Shaving Face. 2010. (ENG., Illus.). 144p. pap. 14.95 *(978-1-55152-343-9(4))* Arsenal Pulp Pr. CAN. Dist: Consortium Bk. Sales & Distribution.

Rainwaters, Matthew. Beard. 2011. (ENG., Illus.). 120p. pap. 14.95 *(978-1-4521-0165-1(5))* Chronicle Bks. LLC.

BEARDSLEY, AUBREY, 1872-1898

Beardsley, Aubrey. Beardsley Illustrations. 2006. (Dover Electronic Clip Art Ser.). (ENG., Illus.). 64p. pap. 14.95 *(978-0-486-99770-4(7))* Dover Pubns., Inc.

—Last Letters of Aubrey Beardsley. 2009. 96p. pap. 14.14 *(978-1-151-70499-3(7))* General Bks. LLC.

—Last Letters of Aubrey Beardsley. 2009. 180p. 37.95 *(978-1-104-10177-0(7))*; pap. 22.95 *(978-1-104-09730-1(3))* Kessinger Publishing, LLC.

Games Design Workshop Staff. Blood & Iron. (Illus.). 224p. *(978-1-85585-000-2(1)*, Collins & Brown) Anova Bks.

Pease, Allison. Modernism, Mass Culture, & the Aesthetics of Obscenity. 2009. (ENG., Illus.). 264p. pap. 36.99 *(978-0-521-10095-3(X))* Cambridge Univ. Pr.

Ross, Robert Baldwin. Aubrey Beardsley. 2009. (Illus.). 62p. pap. *(978-0-217-33404-4(0))* Books LLC.

Ross, Robert Baldwin & Vallance, Aymer. Aubrey Beardsley. 2008. 144p. 35.95 *(978-1-4368-9941-3(9))*; pap. 20.95 *(978-1-4367-8332-3(1))* Kessinger Publishing, LLC.

Zatlin, Linda. Aubrey Beardsley: A Catalogue Raisonne. 2006. (ENG.). 80.00 *(978-0-300-11127-9(4))* Yale Univ. Pr.

BEARINGS (MACHINERY)

Here are entered all works relating to the supports used in engineering, more particularly in machinery, especially for the moving parts.

see also Ball-Bearings; Fluid-Film Bearings; Friction; Lubrication and Lubricants; Roller Bearings

Alahakoon, Sanath. Precise Digital Control of Active Magnetic Bearings. 2009. 100p. pap. *(978-3-639-16368-1(0))* VDM Verlag Dr. Mueller e.K.

American Society of Mechanical Engineers Staff, ed. Developments in Plain Bearings for the '90s. 72p. 58.00 *(978-0-85298-748-3(X))* Professional Engineering Publishing GBR. Dist: SAE Intl.

—Getting the Most from Your Bearings. (Illus.). vi, 69p. *(978-0-85298-504-5(5))* Professional Engineering Publishing.

—Rolling Element Bearings Towards the 21st Century. (Illus.). 60p. 78.00 *(978-0-85298-752-0(8))* Professional Engineering Publishing GBR. Dist: SAE Intl.

Andhare, Atul. Condition Monitoring of Rolling Element Bearings. 2010. 128p. pap. *(978-3-8383-5794-2(9))* Lambert Academic Publishing.

Chasalevris, Athanasios. Nonlinear Simulation of Defected Rotor-Bearing Systems. 2011. 300p. pap. ***(978-3-8443-8597-7(5))*** Lambert Academic Publishing.

Hannon, William M. & Braun, Minel J. THE GENERALIZED UNIVERSAL REYNOLDS EQUATION: for Variable Property Fluid-Film Lubrication & Variable Geometry Self-Acting Bearings. 2008. 424p. pap. *(978-3-639-01248-4(8))* VDM Verlag Dr. Mueller e.K.

Harris, Tedric A. & Kotzalas, Michael N. Advanced Concepts of Bearing Technology, 2 vols., Vol. 2. 5th rev. ed. 2006. (Rolling Bearing Analysis, Fifth Edtion Ser.). (ENG., Illus.). 368p. 149.95 *(978-0-8493-7182-0(1)*, CRC Press) Taylor & Francis Group GBR. Dist: Taylor & Francis Group.

Hooshang, Heshmat. Tribology of Interface Layers. 2010. (ENG., Illus.). 464p. 139.95 *(978-0-8247-5832-5(3)*, CRC Press) Taylor & Francis Group GBR. Dist: Taylor & Francis Group.

Khonsari, Michael M. & Booser, E. Richard. Applied Tribology: Bearing Design & Lubrication. 2nd ed. 2008. (Tribology in Practice Ser.: 14). (ENG., Illus.). 578p. 160.00 *(978-0-470-05711-7(4)*, Wiley) Wiley, John & Sons, Inc.

Rowe, W. Brian. Hydrostatic, Hybrid & Aerostatic Bearing Design. 2012. (ENG.). 352p. 140.00 ***(978-0-12-396994-1(8)***, Butterworth-Heinemann) Elsevier Science & Technology Bks.

Schrama, Richard C. Rolling Mills, Rolls & Bearing Maintenance. (Mechanics & Materials Science Ser.). 199.95 *(978-0-8493-8405-9(2))* CRC Pr. LLC.

Schweitzer, Gerhard & Maslen, Eric H., eds. Magnetic Bearings: Theory, Design, & Application to Rotating Machinery. 2009. (ENG., Illus.). xv, 535p. 139.00 *(978-3-642-00496-4(2)*, 3642004962) Springer.

Stephens, L. S., ed. 9th International Symposium on Magnetic Bearings 2004. 2007. 567p. pap. 156.00 *(978-1-60423-294-3(3))* Curran Assocs., Inc.

Sun, Guangyoung. Auxiliary Bearing Design Guides in Active Magnetic Bearing System. 2008. 244p. pap. *(978-3-639-08049-0(1))* VDM Verlag Dr. Mueller e.K.

Technology Research Editors, ed. Magnetic Bearings, 2007 Ed. 2007. pap. 128.50 *(978-1-60030-484-2(2)*, Search-In-Print) CSA Journal Division.

Tse, Peter W. & Leung, Jacko C. Advanced System for Automatically Detecting Faults Occurring in Bearings. 2010. (Engineering Tools, Techniques & Tables Ser.). (Illus.). viii, 80p. pap. 43.00 *(978-1-61728-953-8(1)*, Nova Novinka) Nova Science Pubs., Inc.

Yücel, Ugur. Stability of Rotor-Bearing-Seal Systems. 2009. 168p. pap. *(978-3-639-17527-1(1))* VDM Verlag Dr. Mueller e.K.

BEARS

see also Bear Hunting; Black Bear; Grizzly Bear; Polar Bear

Arnold, Sam. How I Learned to Talk with Bears. Date not set. (Illus.). 64p. (Orig.). pap. 7.50 *(978-0-914454-04-5(8))* Fur Pr., The.

Bargali, Harendra Singh. The Sloth Bear: Ecology, Conflict & Conservation. 2010. 144p. pap. *(978-3-8383-6137-6(7))* Lambert Academic Publishing.

Bears: Their Biology & Management, Set, Vols. 9 & 10. Date not set. (Illus.). pap. *(978-0-944740-07-1(3))* International Assn. for Bear Research & Management.

Breiter, Matthias. Bears: A Year in the Life. 2009. (ENG., Illus.). 176p. pap. 24.95 *(978-1-55407-461-7(4))* Firefly Bks., Ltd.

Brown, Gary. The Bear Almanac: A Comprehensive Guide to the Bears of the World. 2nd rev. ed. 2009. (ENG., Illus.). 352p. 29.95 *(978-1-59921-331-6(1)*, Lyons Pr.) Globe Pequot Pr., The.

Brunner, Bernd. Bears: A Brief History. Lantz, Lori, tr. from GER. 2008. (ENG., Illus.). 272p. pap. 15.00 *(978-0-300-14312-6(5))* Yale Univ. Pr.

Cummins, Bryan D. Bear Country: Predation, Politics, & the Changing Face of Pyrenean Pastoralism. 2008. 378p. pap. 42.00 *(978-1-59460-562-8(9))* Carolina Academic Pr.

De la Bédoyère, Camilla. Bears. 2010. (Discovery of Life Ser.). 48p. (YA). lib. bdg. 19.95 *(978-1-4222-1518-0(0))* Mason Crest Pubs.

Demerjian, Bonnie. Anan, Stream of Living Water. 2007. (ENG., Illus.). 70p. per. 13.95 *(978-0-9776792-1-8(7))* Stikine River Books.

Dolson, Sylvia. Bear-ology: Fascinating Bear Facts, Tales & Trivia. 2009. (Illus.). 192p. pap. 18.00 *(978-0-9773724-5-4(6))* PixyJack Pr., Inc.

Hirschi, Ron & Mangelsen, Thomas D. Our Three Bears. 2008. (ENG., Illus.). 32p. (J). (gr. 4-7). 16.95 *(978-1-59078-015-2(9))* Boyds Mills Pr.

Hopping, Nancy. Backyard Bears. 2011. pap. 18.95 ***(978-0-7414-6531-3(0))*** Infinity Publishing.

Hunter, Linda Jo. Lonesome for Bears: A Woman's Journey in the Tracks of the Wilderness. 2008. (ENG., Illus.). 144p. per. 19.95 *(978-1-59921-210-4(2)*, Lyons Pr.) Globe Pequot Pr., The.

Irimoto, Takashi. Ainu No Kumamatsuri. 2010. (JPN., Illus.). ii, 277p. *(978-4-639-02131-5(3))* Yuzankaku Shuppan.

Kaniut, Larry. Bear Tales for the Ages... From Alaska & Beyond. 2007. (ENG., Illus.). 256p. per. 14.95 *(978-0-88240-700-5(7)*, Alaska Northwest Bks.) Graphic Arts Ctr. Publishing Co.

Kelly, Allen. Bears I Have Met — and Others. 2007. (ENG.). 128p. pap. 18.99 *(978-1-4264-8554-1(9))*; 140p. pap. 19.99 *(978-1-4264-8611-1(1))* BiblioBazaar.

—Bears I Have Met — and Others. 2007. (Illus.). 136p. per. *(978-1-4065-1881-8(6))* Dodo Pr.

Krauss, Ruth. Bears. 2006. (Illus.). 20p. (J). (gr. k-4). 15.00 *(978-1-4223-5393-6(1))* DIANE Publishing Co.

Lang, Michale. Bears: Tracks Through Time, 1 vol. 2010. (ENG., Illus.). 128p. pap. *(978-1-897522-82-0(7))* Rocky Mountain Bks.

MacDonald, Jake. In Bear Country: Adventures among North America's Largest Predators. 2011. (Illus.). 272p. pap. 18.95 *(978-0-7627-7053-3(8)*, Lyons Pr.) Globe Pequot Pr., The.

Mann, Bill. Guide to Big Bear & Its Hidden Treasures. 2006. (Illus.). 100p. per. 19.95 *(978-0-9667947-5-5(3))* Shortfuse Publishing Co.

Mardaraj, Prakash & Kumar Dutta, Sushil. Human-Sloth Bear Conflict in Balasore Forest Division, Eastern Indi. 2011. 116p. pap. ***(978-3-8443-2956-8(0))*** Lambert Academic Publishing.

McCloskey, Erin. Bear Attacks. 2009. (ENG.). 224p. pap. 14.95 *(978-976-8200-56-3(1))* Lone Pine Publishing International Inc. BRB. Dist: Lone Pine Publishing USA.

—Bear Attacks in Canada. 2008. (ENG., Illus.). 224p. pap. *(978-1-55105-562-6(7))* Lone Pine Publishing.

Miller, Joaquin. True Bear Stories. 2010. 288p. pap. 28.75 *(978-1-172-31715-8(1))* BiblioBazaar.

—True Bear Stories. 2009. 96p. pap. *(978-1-151-40994-2(4))* Books LLC.

—True Bear Stories. 2010. 278p. 34.36 *(978-1-163-32569-8(4))* 2010. 278p. pap. 22.36 *(978-1-162-76395-8(7))* 2010. 178p. pap. 18.36 *(978-1-162-63396-1(4))* 2010. 178p. 37.95 *(978-1-161-41451-6(7))* 2007. (ENG.). 276p. 42.95 *(978-0-548-01360-1(8))* Kessinger Publishing, LLC.

Miller, Joaquin & Beringer, Pierre N. True Bear Stories. 2010. 318p. pap. 30.75 *(978-1-178-31035-1(3))* BiblioBazaar.

Momaday, N. Scott. In the Bear's House. 2010. (ENG., Illus.). 112p. 24.95 *(978-0-8263-4839-5(4))* Univ. of New Mexico Pr.

Morgan, Chris. Bears of the Last Frontier: The Adventure of a Lifetime among Alaska's Black, Grizzly, & Polar Bears. 2011. (ENG., Illus.). 224p. 35.00 *(978-1-58479-931-3(5))* Stewart, Tabori & Chang.

Orr, Aileen. Wojtek the Bear: Polish War Hero. (ENG., Illus.). 224p. 2012. pap. 17.99 ***(978-1-84158-972-5(1))*** 2010. 19.95 *(978-1-84158-845-2(8))* Birlinn, Ltd. GBR. Dist: Casemate Pubs. & Bk. Distributors, LLC.

Pacher, Martina, et al, eds. Early Pleistocene Bear Remains from Deutsch-Altenburg (Lower Austria)/ Die Altpleistozanen Baren von Deutsch-Altenburg (Niederosterreich) 2010. (MITTEILUNGEN der KOMMISSION FuR QUARTaRFORSCHUNG Ser.). (ENG & GER., Illus.). 139p. (C). 147.00 *(978-3-7001-6827-0(6))* Austrian Academy of Sciences Press AUT. Dist: Brown, David Bk. Co., The.

Pastoureau, Michel. The Bear: History of a Fallen King. Holoch, George, tr. from FRE. 2011. Orig. Title: L' ours: Histoire d'un roi Déchu. (ENG., Illus.). 384p. 29.95 *(978-0-674-04782-2(6)*, Belknap Pr.) Harvard Univ. Pr.

Poulsen, Else. Smiling Bears: A Zookeeper Explores the Behaviour & Emotional Life of Bears, 1 vol. 2009. (ENG.). 272p. 25.95 *(978-1-55365-387-5(4)*, Greystone Bks.) D&M Pubs. Inc. CAN. Dist: Perseus-PGW.

Sakurai, Ryo. Are Bears Our Friends or Enemies? 2011. 76p. pap. ***(978-3-8454-0386-1(1))*** Lambert Academic Publishing.

Scott, Keith Vincent. Coastal Bears. 2007. (Illus.). 80p. pap. 9.95 *(978-0-88839-626-6(0))* Hancock Hse. Pubs.

Smith, Howard. In the Company of Wild Bears: A Celebration of Backcountry Grizzlies & Black Bears. 2006. (ENG., Illus.). 248p. 22.95 *(978-1-59228-952-3(5)*, Lyons Pr.) Globe Pequot Pr., The.

Stringham, Stephen F. Bear Viewing in Alaska: Expert Techniques for a Great Adventure. 2007. (ENG., Illus.). 128p. per. 12.95 *(978-0-7627-3953-0(3)*, Falcon Guides) Globe Pequot Pr., The.

Van Daele, Larry, intro. Kodiak Kings. 2006. (Illus.). 128p. 27.95 *(978-1-932472-44-8(4))* Nodin Pr.

Van Tighem, Kevin. Bears, 1 vol. 2009. (SuperGuide Ser.). (ENG., Illus.). 160p. pap. *(978-1-897522-20-2(7))* Rocky Mountain Bks.

Ward, Peter L. Eric & the Mystical Bear. 2011. 152p. 23.14 *(978-1-4269-5500-6(6))*; pap. 13.14 *(978-1-4269-5501-3(4))* Trafford Publishing.

Weston, Chris. Brown Bears. 2010. (Wildlife Monographs). (ENG., Illus.). 96p. pap. 16.95 *(978-1-901268-50-8(0)*, 1901268500) Evans Mitchell Bks. GBR. Dist: MBI Distribution Services/Quayside Distribution.

Weston, Chris & Morgan, Robin. CliffHIStory: The Authorised Photographic Memoir. 2010. (ENG., Illus.). 192p. 39.95 *(978-1-901268-51-5(9)*, 1901268519) Evans Mitchell Bks. GBR. Dist: MBI Distribution Services/Quayside Distribution.

Wood, Daniel. Bears. rev. ed. 2010. (Wildlife Ser.). (ENG., Illus.). 112p. 14.95 *(978-1-55285-663-5(1))* Whitecap Bks., Ltd. CAN. Dist: Midpoint Trade Bks., Inc.

Zachry, Joel G. & Zachry, Kathy W. Bears We've Met: Short Stories of Close Encounters. 2010. 178p. 29.99 *(978-1-4520-0821-9(3))*; pap. 21.99 *(978-1-4520-0820-2(5))* AuthorHouse.

BEARS—FOLKLORE

see also Teddy Bears

Kailo, Kaarina, ed. Wo(men) & Bears: The Gifts of Nature, Culture & Gender Revisited. 2008. (ENG., Illus.). 387p. pap. 30.00 *(978-0-9782233-6-6(5))* Inanna Pubns. & Education, Inc. CAN. Dist: SPD-Small Pr. Distribution.

Pastoureau, Michel. The Bear: History of a Fallen King. Holoch, George, tr. from FRE. 2011. Orig. Title: L' ours: Histoire d'un roi Déchu. (ENG., Illus.). 384p. 29.95 *(978-0-674-04782-2(6)*, Belknap Pr.) Harvard Univ. Pr.

BEARTOOTH MOUNTAINS (MONT. AND WYO.)

Marcuson, Pat. Fishing the Beartooths: An Angler's Guide to More Than 400 Prime Fishing Spots. 2nd ed. 2008. (Fishing Ser.). (ENG., Illus.). 272p. pap. 18.95 *(978-0-7627-4227-1(5)*, Lyons Pr.) Globe Pequot Pr., The.

BEASTS

see Bestiaries; Domestic Animals; Zoology

BEAT GENERATION

Atkinson, Jay. Paradise Road: Jack Kerouac's Lost Highway & My Search for America. 2010. (ENG.). 272p. 25.95 *(978-0-470-23769-4(4)*, Wiley) Wiley, John & Sons, Inc.

Baker, Phil. William S. Burroughs. 2010. (Reaktion Books - Critical Lives Ser.). (ENG., Illus.). 192p. pap. 16.95 *(978-1-86189-663-6(8))* Reaktion Bks., Ltd. GBR. Dist: Chicago Distribution Ctr.

Ball, Gordon. East Hill Farm: Seasons with Allen Ginsberg. 2011. (ENG., Illus.). 416p. 28.50 *(978-1-58243-776-7(9)*, Counterpoint) Counterpoint LLC.

Bockris. The Last Beat. Date not set. *(978-0-312-30092-0(1))* St. Martin's Pr.

Boorman, Neil. Bonfire of the Brands: How I Learned to Live Without Labels. 2007. (Illus.). 256p. pap. *(978-1-84195-987-0(1))* Canongate Bks.

Campbell, James. Syncopations: Beats, New Yorkers, & Writers in the Dark. 2008. 251p. pap. 24.95 *(978-0-520-25237-0(3))* Univ. of California Pr.

Charters, Ann & Charters, Samuel Barclay. Brother-Souls: John Clellon Holmes, Jack Kerouac, & the Beat Generation. 2010. (ENG., Illus.). 464p. 35.00 *(978-1-60473-579-6(1))* Univ. Pr. of Mississippi.

Coupe, Laurence. Beat Sound, Beat Vision: The Beat Spirit & Popular Song. 2010. (ENG.). 232p. pap. 24.95 *(978-0-7190-7113-3(5))* Manchester Univ. Pr. GBR. Dist: Macmillan.

Creighton, David. Ecstasy of the Beats: On the Road to Understanding. 2007. (ENG., Illus.). 320p. pap. 26.99 *(978-1-55002-734-1(4))* Dundurn CAN. Dist: Ingram Pub. Services.

Dittman, Michael J. Masterpieces of Beat Literature, 1 vol. 2006. (Greenwood Introduces Literary Masterpieces Ser.). 136p. 49.95 *(978-0-313-33283-8(5)*, GR3283, Greenwood Pr.) Greenwood Publishing Group, Inc.

Elkholy, Sharin N., ed. The Philosophy of the Beats. 2012. (Philosophy of Popular Culture Ser.). (ENG.). 300p. 40.00 ***(978-0-8131-3580-9(X))*** Univ. Pr. of Kentucky.

Felver, Christopher. Beat. 2007. (Illus.). 208p. 29.95 *(978-0-86719-671-9(8))* Last Gasp of San Francisco.

Flota, Brian. A Survey of Multicultural San Francisco Bay Literature, 1955-1979: Ishnael Reed, Maxine Hong Kingston, Frank Chin & the Beat Generation. 2009. v, 326p. *(978-0-7734-3828-6(9))* Mellen, Edwin Pr., The.

Gair, Christopher. The Beat Generation: A Beginner's Guide. 2008. (Beginners Guide (Oneworld) Ser.). (ENG.). 192p. pap. 14.95 *(978-1-85168-542-4(1))* Oneworld Pubns. GBR. Dist: National Bk. Network.

Gertz, Stephen J. Dope Menace: The Sensational World of Drug Paperbacks, 1900-1975. 2008. (ENG., Illus.). 250p. pap. 24.95 *(978-1-932595-34-5(1))* Feral Hse.

Gewirtz, Isaac. Beatific Soul: Jack Kerouac on the Road. 2007. (ENG., Illus.). 208p. 35.00 *(978-1-85759-497-3(5))* Scala, Editions FRA. Dist: National Bk. Network.

Gifford, Barry & Lee, Lawrence. Jack's Book: An Oral Biography of Jack Kerouac. 2012. (ENG.). 368p. (gr. 12). pap. 16.00 ***(978-0-14-312188-6(X)**, Penguin (Non-Classics)) Penguin Group (USA) Inc.*

Gilmore, Mikal. Stories Done: Writings on the 1960s & Its Discontents. 2009. (ENG.). 400p. pap. 16.00 *(978-0-7432-8746-3(0), Free Pr.) Free Pr.*

Ginsberg, Allen S., et al. The Book of Martyrdom & Artifice: First Journals & Poems, 1937-1952. 2008. (ENG., Illus.). 544p. per. 17.50 *(978-0-306-81562-1(1)) Da Capo Pr., Inc.*

Grace, Nancy M. & Skerl, Jennie, eds. The Transnational Beat Generation. 2012. (ENG., Illus.). 294p. 95.00 ***(978-0-230-10840-0(7))**; pap. 27.00 **(978-0-230-10841-7(5))** Palgrave Macmillan.*

Grace, Nancy McCampbell, et al. Jack Kerouac & the Literary Imagination. 2007. (ENG.). 272p. 89.00 *(978-1-4039-6850-0(0)) Palgrave Macmillan.*

Greenough, Sarah. Beat Memories: The Photographs of Allen Ginsberg. 2010. (Illus.). 144p. 49.95 *(978-3-7913-5052-3(8)) Prestel Publishing.*

Hunt, Tim. Kerouac's Crooked Road: The Development of a Fiction. 2010. (ENG.). 308p. pap. 29.95 *(978-0-8093-2970-0(0)) Southern Illinois Univ. Pr.*

Johnson, Joyce. The Voice Is All: The Lonely Victory of Jack Kerouac. 2012. (ENG.). 512p. 32.95 ***(978-0-670-02510-7(0)**, Viking Adult) Penguin Group (USA) Inc.*

Kerouac, Jack. The Portable Jack Kerouac. Charters, Ann, ed. rev. ed. 2007. (ENG.). 656p. (gr. 12-18). 18.00 *(978-0-14-310506-0(X), Penguin Classics) Penguin Group (USA) Inc.*

Kerouac, Jack & Ginsberg, Allen S. Jack Kerouac & Allen Ginsberg: The Letters. Morgan, Bill & Stanford, David, eds. (ENG.). 528p. (gr. 12). 2011. 20.00 *(978-0-14-311954-8(0), Penguin (Non-Classics))* 2010. 35.00 *(978-0-670-02194-9(6), Viking Adult) Penguin Group (USA) Inc.*

Knight, Arthur & Knight, Kit. Kerouac & the Beats. Date not set. 288p. 23.95 *(978-0-8488-2347-4(8)) Amereon LTD.*

Lee, A. Robert. Modern American Counter Writing. 2011. (ENG.). 296p. pap. 39.95 ***(978-0-415-89650-4(9))** Routledge.*

Lee, A. Robert. Modern American Counter Writing: Beats, Outriders, Ethnics. 2010. (Literary Criticism & Cultural Theory Ser.). (ENG.). 308p. (C). 125.00 *(978-0-415-99811-6(5)) Routledge.*

Morgan, Bill. Beat Atlas: A State by State Guide to the Beat Generation. 2011. (ENG., Illus.). 225p. pap. 15.95 *(978-0-87286-512-9(6)) City Lights Bks.*

—I Celebrate Myself: The Somewhat Private Life of Allen Ginsberg. 2007. (ENG., Illus.). 720p. (gr. 12-18). 18.00 *(978-0-14-311249-5(X), Penguin (Non-Classics)) Penguin Group (USA) Inc.*

—The Typewriter Is Holy: The Complete, Uncensored History of the Beat Generation. 2011. (ENG., Illus.). 352p. pap. 15.95 *(978-1-58243-738-5(6), Counterpoint) Counterpoint LLC.*

Morgan, Bill & Morgan, William. The Typewriter Is Holy: The Complete, Uncensored History of the Beat Generation. 2010. (ENG., Illus.). 320p. 28.00 *(978-1-4165-9242-6(3), Free Pr.) Free Pr.*

Morgan, Ted. Literary Outlaw: The Life & Times of William S. Burroughs. 2012. (ENG.). 768p. pap. 24.95 ***(978-0-393-34260-4(3)**, 34260) Norton, W. W. & Co., Inc.*

Mortenson, Erik Ronald. Capturing the Beat Moment: Cultural Politics & the Poetics of Presence. 2010. E-Book *(978-0-8093-8613-0(5))*; (Illus.). 240p. pap. 35.00 *(978-0-8093-3013-3(X)) Southern Illinois Univ. Pr.*

Motier, Donald. Gerard: The Influence of Jack Kerouac's Brother on His Life & Writing. 1 vol. 2010. 66p. pap. 19.95 *(978-1-4489-5519-0(X)) PublishAmerica, Inc.*

Nicosia, Gerald & Santos, Anne Marie. One & Only: The Untold Story of on the Road. 2011. (ENG., Illus.). 242p. 22.95 *(978-1-936740-04-8(4), Viva Editions) Cleis Pr.*

Parry, Albert. Garrets & Pretenders: Bohemian Life in America from Poe to Kerouac. 2012. (New York City Ser.). (ENG.). 480p. pap. 16.95 ***(978-0-486-48605-5(2))** Dover Pubns., Inc.*

Pekar, Harvey & Buhle, Paul. The Beats: A Graphic History. 2010. (ENG., Illus.). 208p. pap. 15.95 *(978-0-8090-1649-5(4), Hill & Wang) Farrar, Straus & Giroux.*

Sandison, David & Vickers, Graham. Neal Cassady: The Fast Life of a Beat Hero. 2006. (ENG., Illus.). 368p. 24.95 *(978-1-55652-615-2(6)) Chicago Review Pr., Inc.*

Snyder, Gary & Ginsberg, Allen S. The Selected Letters of Allen Ginsberg & Gary Snyder. Morgan, Bill, ed. 2009. (ENG.). 336p. pap. 16.95 *(978-1-58243-533-6(2), Counterpoint Pr.) Basic Bks. GBR. Dist: Perseus-PGW.*

Soto, Michael. The Modernist Nation: Generation, Renaissance, & Twentieth-Century American Literature. 2007. (ENG.). 256p. per. 24.95 *(978-0-8173-5467-1(0)) Univ. of Alabama Pr.*

Sounes, Howard. Locked in the Arms of a Crazy Life. 2007. (Illus.). 202p. pap. *(978-1-84195-897-2(2)) Canongate Bks.*

Tietchen, Todd F. The Cubalogues. 2010. (ENG., Illus.). 192p. 29.95 *(978-0-8130-3520-8(1)) Univ. Pr. of Florida.*

Varner, Paul. Historical Dictionary of the Beat Movement. 2012. (Historical Dictionaries of Literature & the Arts Ser.). (ENG.). 400p. 95.00 ***(978-0-8108-7189-2(0))** Scarecrow Pr., Inc.*

Weaver, Helen. The Awakener: A Memoir of Jack Kerouac & the Fifties. 2009. (ENG.). 180p. pap. 16.95 *(978-0-87286-505-1(3)) City Lights Bks.*

BEATIFIC VISION

Marshall, Frank & Hatcher, Carole. Church Visioning. Date not set. pap. 11.25 *(978-1-56699-178-0(1), OD121) Alban Institute, Inc.*

BEATIFICATION

see also Canonization

La Rocque, Patrick de. John Paul II: Doubts about a Beatification. 2011. pap. ***(978-1-892331-91-5(8))** Angelus Pr.*

BEATING OF WIVES

see Wife Abuse

BEATITUDES

Baker, Heidi. Compelled by Love: How to Change the World Through the Simple Power of Love in Action. 2008. (ENG., Illus.). 176p. pap. 12.99 *(978-1-59979-351-1(2), Charisma Hse.) Charisma Media.*

Baker, John. Life's Healing Choices: Freedom from Your Hurts, Hang-Ups, & Habits. 2007. (ENG.). 288p. 19.99 *(978-1-4165-4395-4(3))*; (Illus.). x, 277p. pap. *(978-1-4165-7570-2(7)) Howard Books. (Howard Bks.).*

—Ocho Decisiones Sanadoras: Liberese de Sus Heridas, Complejos, y Habitos. 2008. (SPA.). 320p. pap. 14.99 *(978-1-4165-7828-4(5), Howard Bks.) Howard Books.*

Baker, John E. Life's Healing Choices Guided Journal: Freedom from Your Hurts, Hang-Ups, & Habits. 2008. (ENG.). 224p. 10.99 *(978-1-4165-5468-4(8), Howard Bks.) Howard Books.*

—Life's Healing Choices Small Group Study: Freedom from Your Hurts, Hang-Ups, & Habits. 2008. (ENG.). 128p. pap. 9.99 *(978-1-4165-7918-2(4), Howard Bks.) Howard Books.*

Baker, Robert C. Blessings in Disguise. 2008. (Insight Ser.). 48p. pap. 5.99 *(978-0-7586-1474-2(8)) Concordia Publishing Hse.*

Berrigan, Philip & Mcalister, Elizabeth. The Time's Discipline: The Beatitudes & Nuclear Resistance. 2010. (Catholic Worker Reprint Ser.). 324p. pap. 34.00 *(978-1-60899-057-3(5), Wipf and Stock) Wipf & Stock Pubs.*

Bransfield, J. Brian. Living the Beatitudes: A Journey to Life in Christ. 2011. 272p. pap. 14.95 ***(978-0-8198-4544-3(2))** Pauline Bks. & Media.*

Buck, Robert. The Book of Blessing: Speaking God's Word & Blessing into People's Lives. 2009. 19.99 *(978-1-60791-632-1(0))*; pap. 11.99 *(978-1-60791-631-4(2)) Xulon Pr., Inc.*

Cantalamessa, Raniero. Beatitudes: Eight Steps to Happiness. 2009. (ENG.). 146p. pap. 13.99 *(978-0-86716-922-5(2)) Franciscan Media.*

Carthusian, A. Way of Silent Love. 2006. 148p. per. *(978-0-85244-034-6(0)) Gracewing, Ltd.*

Clymer, Donald R. Meditations on the Beatitudes: Lessons from the Margins. 2011. ***(978-1-931038-85-0(6))** Cascadia Publishing Hse., LLC.*

Cook, Jeff. Seven: The Deadly Sins & the Beatitudes, 1 vol. 2008. (ENG.). 224p. pap. 12.99 *(978-0-310-27817-7(1)) Zondervan.*

Crum, George C. The Mount of Blessing; or, Lectures on the Beatitudes by Rev George C Crum Ed by Rev D W Clark. 2006. 240p. per. 20.99 *(978-1-4255-2020-5(0)) MPublishing.*

D'Avila-Latourrette, Victor-Antoine. Simply Living the Beatitudes. 2010. 144p. 15.99 *(978-0-7648-1885-1(6)) Liguori Pubns.*

de Blas, Alonso. The Beatitudes: Jesus Calls us above & beyond the Law. 2007. 3.95 *(978-0-9719921-2-2(6)) Tau Publishing.*

Dean, Jennifer Kennedy. Set Apart: A 6-Week Study of the Beatitudes. 2009. (ENG.). 176p. pap. 14.99 *(978-1-59669-263-3(4)) New Hope Pubs.*

Gibson, Kathleen K. How to Bee with Your Attitude the Beatitudes Matthew: 3-12 & the ARMOR of GOD Ephesians 6. 2009. 80p. pap. 10.99 *(978-1-61579-600-7(2)) Xulon Pr., Inc.*

Harling, Becky. Rewriting Your Emotional Script: Erase Old Messages, Embrace New Attitudes. 2008. (Growing in Christ Ser.). (ENG.). 240p. pap. 14.99 *(978-1-60006-188-2(5)) NavPress Publishing Group.*

Heard, Gerald. The Code of Christ: An Interpretation of the Beatitudes. 2008. (Gerald Heard Reprint Ser.). 202p. pap. 23.00 *(978-1-55635-173-0(9)) Wipf & Stock Pubs.*

Howard, Anne Sutherland. Claiming the Beatitudes: Nine Stories from a New Generation. 2009. *(978-1-56699-384-5(9)) Alban Institute, Inc.*

Howell, Timothy D. The Matthean Beatitudes in Their Jewish Origins: A Literary & Speech Act Analysis. 2011. (C). 89.95 ***(978-1-4331-1545-5(X))** Lang, Peter Publishing, Inc.*

John, J. The Happiness Secret: Finding True Contentment. 2011. (ENG.). 240p. pap. 13.95 *(978-0-340-97930-3(5), Hodder & Stoughton) Hodder General Publishing Div. GBR. Dist: Independent Pubs. Group.*

Kalas, J. Ellsworth. The Beatitudes from the Back Side. 2008. 122p. pap. 14.99 *(978-0-687-65084-2(4)) Abingdon Pr.*

Kalellis, Peter M. God's Power Within You: Attitudes for Living. 2010. 112p. pap. 12.95 *(978-0-8091-4655-0(X)) Paulist Pr.*

Kolbell, Erik. What Jesus Meant: The Beatitudes & a Meaningful Life. 2007. (ENG.). 140p. per. 15.00 *(978-0-664-23187-3(X)) Westminster John Knox Pr.*

Miller, J. R. & Miller, J. R. The Master's Blesseds, a Devotional Study of the Beatitudes. 2011. 68p. pap. 8.99 ***(978-1-61203-180-4(3))** Bottom of the Hill Publishing.*

Palmer, Robert Leslie. Truth in the Eight Towers. 2011. 172p. 30.95 ***(978-1-61507-844-8(4))**; pap. 13.95 **(978-1-61507-843-1(6))** Cross Bks. Publishing.*

Patterson, Dorothy Kelly. BeAttitudes for Women: Wisdom from Heaven for Life on Earth. 2008. 272p. pap. 29.00 *(978-1-60608-012-2(1)) Wipf & Stock Pubs.*

Pencook, Lawrence. Christ's Beatitudes. 2007. 124p. (ENG.). 18.99 *(978-1-60266-243-8(6))*; per. 10.99 *(978-1-60266-242-1(8)) Xulon Pr., Inc.*

Pinckaers, Servais. The Pursuit of HappinessNtilde;God's Way: Living the Beatitudes. Noble, Mary Thomas, tr. 2011. 214p. pap. 24.00 ***(978-1-61097-493-6(X)**, Wipf and Stock) Wipf & Stock Pubs.*

Pink, Arthur W. The Beatitudes. 2011. 62p. pap. 8.99 ***(978-1-61203-330-3(X))** Bottom of the Hill Publishing.*

Richard S. Hipps. The Focused Life: The Beatitudes for Everyday Living. 2009. 108p. 22.95 *(978-1-4401-8090-3(3))*; pap. 12.95 *(978-1-4401-8088-0(1)) iUniverse, Inc.*

Rose Publishing Staff. The Beatitudes. 2009. cd-rom 39.99 *(978-1-59636-321-2(5)) Rose Publishing.*

Smith, Charles Zachariah. The Divine Constitution. 2011. 152p. 41.95 ***(978-1-258-00846-8(7))** Literary Licensing, LLC.*

Stanford, Shane. The Eight Blessings: Rediscovering the Beatitudes. 2007. 147p. per. 12.00 *(978-0-687-64224-3(8)) Abingdon Pr.*

Stortz, Martha E. Blessed to Follow: The Beatitudes As a Compass for Discipleship. 2008. (Lutheran Voices Ser.). 112p. pap. 11.99 *(978-0-8066-8007-1(5), Augsburg Fortress) Augsburg Fortress, Pubs.*

Stott, John. The Beatitudes: Developing Spiritual Character. 2008. (John Stott Bible Studies). (ENG.). 63p. pap. 8.00 *(978-0-8308-2162-4(7), IVP Conn.) InterVarsity Pr.*

Wiens, Gary & Wiens, Marie. Reaching Your Power Potential: Authority on Earth as It Is in Heaven. 2006. 261p. per. 15.00 *(978-0-9786201-2-7(7)) BHM Publishing.*

—Reaching Your Power Potential HB: Authority on Earth as It Is in Heaven. 2006. 19.95 *(978-0-9786201-3-4(5)) BHM Publishing.*

Wiersbe, Warren W. Heirs of the King: Living the Beatitudes. 2007. (ENG.). 176p. per. 9.99 *(978-1-57293-215-9(5)) Discovery Hse. Pubs.*

BEATITUDES—MEDITATIONS

Drozdowski, Paul, illus. St. Seraphim's Beatitudes: Blessings for Our Path to Heaven Based on the Life of the Wonderworker of Sarov. 2008. 32p. (J). lib. bdg. 19.95 *(978-0-9786543-0-6(7)) St. Innocent Pr.*

Warren, Robert. Life Attitudes: A 5-Session Course on the Beatitudes. 2010. (ENG.). vi, 64p. pap. 7.99 *(978-0-7151-4233-2(X)) Church Hse. Publishing GBR. Dist: Westminster John Knox Pr.*

Webster, Douglas D. Beatitudes: Soundtrack for the Soul. 2009. 14.95 *(978-1-894667-91-3(3)) Clements Publishing.*

BEATITUDES—SERMONS

Calvin, John. Sermons on the Beatitudes. 2006. 114p. 13.99 *(978-0-85151-934-0(2)) Banner of Truth, The.*

Cole, Tom & Cole, Donna. Pure Heart: Restoration of the Heart Through the Beatitudes. 2008. 148p. pap. 13.99 *(978-1-60477-993-6(4)) Xulon Pr., Inc.*

Miaoulis, Nancy. Blessed Are Those Who Care for the Earth - Discerning an Ecological Consciousness in the Sermon on the Mount. 2008. 160p. pap. *(978-3-639-00158-7(3)) VDM Verlag Dr. Mueller e.K.*

Rose Publishing Staff. The Beatitudes: Jesus' Sermon on the Mount. 2008. 14p. 3.99 *(978-1-59636-193-5(X)) Rose Publishing.*

Webster, Douglas D. Beatitudes: Soundtrack for the Soul. 2009. 14.95 *(978-1-894667-91-3(3)) Clements Publishing.*

BEATLES

see also Harrison, George, 1943-2001; Lennon, John, 1940-1980; McCartney, Paul, 1942-; Starr, Ringo, 1940-

Badman, Keith. The Beatles off the Record. 2008. (ENG., Illus.). 496p. per. 24.95 *(978-1-84772-101-3(X), OP52118) Omnibus Pr.*

Beatles Staff. The Beatles - Magical Mystery Tour Memories. 2009. (ENG.). 19.95 *(978-1-4234-9044-9(4), 1423490444) Leonard, Hal Corp.*

—The Beatles - Rare & Unseen: The Unofficial Account of the Biggest Band in the World. 2009. (ENG.). 14.95 *(978-1-4234-9045-6(2), 1423490452) Leonard, Hal Corp.*

—The Beatles Antologia. 2006. (SPA & ENG., Illus.). 368p. pap. 59.95 *(978-84-656-1544-0(X)) Ediciones B ESP. Dist: Independent Pubs. Group.*

—Best of the Beatles: Flute. 2nd rev. ed. 2011. (ENG.). 96p. pap. 14.99 *(978-0-7935-2142-5(4), 0793521424) Leonard, Hal Corp.*

Beatles Staff & Sokolow, Fred. The Beatles for Banjo. 2009. (ENG.). 80p. pap. 14.99 *(978-1-4234-5653-7(X), 142345653X) Leonard, Hal Corp.*

Beatles Staff & Westfall, Bobby. The Beatles for Mandolin. 2010. (ENG.). 72p. pap. 14.99 *(978-1-4234-8404-2(5), 1423484045) Leonard, Hal Corp.*

Beatles, The. The Beatles for Ukulele. 2008. (ENG.). 72p. pap. 16.99 *(978-1-4234-3013-1(1), 1423430131) Leonard, Hal Corp.*

Beatles, The. The Beatles in Hong Kong. cd-rom 15.95 *(978-1-885959-47-8(8), JRCD7042) Jerden Records & Speechworks.*

—The Beatles Rock Band. 2010. (ENG.). 200p. pap. 27.99 *(978-1-4234-8851-4(2), 1423488512)*; 344p. pap. 34.99 *(978-1-4234-8855-2(5), 1423488555) Leonard, Hal Corp.*

Beatles, The. Rain: A Tribute to the Beatles on Broadway. 2010. (ENG.). 154p. pap. 19.99 *(978-1-61774-240-8(6), 1617742406) Leonard, Hal Corp.*

Beatles, The, contrib. by. The Best of the Beatles: Horn. 2006. (Best of the Beatles Ser.). (ENG., Illus.). 94p. pap. 12.95 *(978-1-4234-1050-8(5), 1423410505) Leonard, Hal Corp.*

—The Best of the Beatles: Oboe. 2006. (Best of the Beatles Ser.). (ENG., Illus.). 94p. pap. 12.95 *(978-1-4234-1183-3(8), 1423411838) Leonard, Hal Corp.*

—The Best of the Beatles: Tenor Sax. 2006. (Best of the Beatles Ser.). (ENG., Illus.). 96p. pap. 12.95 *(978-1-4234-1046-1(7), 1423410467) Leonard, Hal Corp.*

Beatles, the. 2008. (Images Ser.). 256p. *(978-1-4075-3949-2(3)) Parragon, Inc.*

Bedford, David. Liddypool - Birthplace of the Beatles: To Understand the Beatles, You Have to Understand Liverpool. 2011. (ENG., Illus.). 336p. pap. 39.95 ***(978-1-85443-248-3(6)**, 1854432486) Dalton Watson Fine Bks.*

Bellstorf, Arne. Baby's in Black: Astrid Kirchherr, Stuart Sutcliffe, & the Beatles in Hamburg. 2012. (ENG., Illus.). 208p. 24.99 ***(978-1-59643-771-5(5)**, First Second Bks.) Roaring Brook Pr.*

Belmo & Marsh, Garry. The Beatles Christmas Book: Everywhere It's Christmas. 2011. (ENG.). 228p. pap. 35.95 *(978-1-926592-25-1(5)) Collector's Guide Publishing, Inc. CAN. Dist: Independent Pubs. Group.*

Bench, Jeff & Tedman, Ray. The Beatles on Television. 2009. (Rex Collections). (ENG., Illus.). 176p. pap. 27.95 *(978-1-905287-88-8(7)) Reynolds & Hearn GBR. Dist: Independent Pubs. Group.*

Benson, Harry. The Beatles 1964-1966. 2012. (ENG., Illus.). 272p. 700.00 ***(978-3-8365-3315-7(4))** TASCHEN DEU. Dist: Ingram Pub. Services.*

Berman, Garry. We're Going to See the Beatles! An Oral History of Beatlemania as Told by the Fans Who Were There. 2008. (ENG., Illus.). 312p. pap. 16.95 *(978-1-59580-032-9(8)) Santa Monica Pr.*

Blaney, John. Beatles for Sale: How Everything They Touched Turned to Gold. 2008. (ENG., Illus.). 288p. pap. 19.95 *(978-1-906002-09-1(6), 1906002096, Jawbone) Outline Pr., Ltd. GBR. Dist: Leonard, Hal Corp.*

Bowen, Mark. McCartney Solo: See You Next Time. 2009. 302p. pap. 29.50 *(978-1-4092-9979-3(5)) Lulu Enterprises Inc.*

Browne, David. Fire & Rain: The Beatles, Simon & Garfunkel, James Taylor, CSNY, & the Lost Story of 1970. 2011. (ENG., Illus.). 392p. 26.00 *(978-0-306-81850-9(7)) Da Capo Pr., Inc.*

Browne, David. Fire & Rain: The Beatles, Simon & Garfunkel, James Taylor, CSNY, & the Lost Story Of 1970. 2012. (ENG.). 392p. pap. 16.00 ***(978-0-306-82072-4(2))** Da Capo Pr., Inc.*

Burrows, Terry. Treasures of the Beatles. 2009. (ENG., Illus.). 64p. 35.00 *(978-1-4027-7345-7(5)) Sterling Publishing Co., Inc.*

Carlson, Bill. The Beatles! A One-Night Stand in the Heartland: A Collection of Original Photographs from August 21 1965. 2007. (Illus.). 144p. 29.95 *(978-1-58182-590-9(0), Cumberland Hse.) Sourcebooks, Inc.*

Clough, Matthew H. & Fallows, Colin, eds. Astrid Kirchherr: A Retrospective. 2010. (ENG., Illus.). 208p. pap. 34.95 *(978-1-84631-477-3(1)) Liverpool Univ. Pr. GBR. Dist: Chicago Distribution Ctr.*

Courrier, Kevin. Artificial Paradise: The Dark Side of the Beatles' Utopian Dream. 1 vol. 2008. 360p. 39.95 *(978-0-313-34586-9(4), C34586, Praeger Pubs.) Greenwood Publishing Group, Inc.*

Courtney, Richard & Cassidy, George. Come Together: The Business Wisdom of the Beatles. 2011. (ENG.). 306p. 24.95 *(978-1-59652-808-6(7)) Turner Publishing Co.*

Creasy, Martin. Beatlemania! The Real Story of the Beatles UK Tours. 2011. (ENG., Illus.). 304p. pap. 25.95 *(978-1-84938-659-3(5)) Omnibus Pr.*

Davies, Hunter. The Beatles. 2010. (ENG., Illus.). 528p. pap. 17.95 *(978-0-393-33874-4(6), 33874) Norton, W. W. & Co., Inc.*

—The Beatles: Edicion Ilustrada y Actualizada de la Biografia Autorizada Mas Vendida. Trejo, Juan & Samara, Ersi, trs. 2006. (SPA., Illus.). 416p. pap. 40.00 *(978-84-666-2006-2(0)) Ediciones B ESP. Dist: Independent Pubs. Group.*

DeRogatis, Jim & Kot, Greg. The Beatles vs. The Rolling Stones: Sound Opinions on the Great Rock 'n' Roll Rivalry. 2010. (ENG., Illus.). 192p. 35.00 *(978-0-7603-3813-1(2), 0760338132, Voyageur Pr) MBI Publishing Co. LLC.*

Dickey, Jeff & Taylor, Alistair. With the Beatles. 2011. (ENG., Illus.). 248p. pap. 12.95 *(978-1-84358-349-3(6)) Blake, John Publishing, Ltd. GBR. Dist: Independent Pubs. Group.*

Doggett, Peter. You Never Give Me Your Money: The Beatles after the Breakup. (ENG.). 2011. 320p. pap. 15.99 *(978-0-06-177418-9(9), Harper Paperbacks)* 2010. 400p. 24.99 *(978-0-06-177446-1(4)) HarperCollins Pubs.*

Doggett, Peter & Humphries, Patrick. Beatles the Music & the Myth. 2010. (ENG., Illus.). 192p. pap. 14.95 *(978-1-84938-369-1(3)) Omnibus Pr.*

Dresser, Thomas. It Was 40 Years Ago Today. 2009. 200p. pap. 24.95 *(978-1-60610-420-0(9)) PublishAmerica, Inc.*

Egan, Sean, ed. The Mammoth Book of the Beatles. 2009. (ENG.). 512p. pap. 13.95 *(978-0-7624-3627-9(1)) Running Pr. Bk. Pubs.*

Eichenberger, Jim. Tuning into God the Beatles 1. 2007. (Tuning into God Ser.). 48p. pap. 7.99 *(978-0-7847-1994-7(2)) Standard Publishing.*

Emerick, Geoff & Massey, Howard. Here, There & Everywhere: My Life Recording the Music of the Beatles. 2007. (ENG.). 400p. (gr. 12-18). 17.00 *(978-1-59240-269-4(0), Gotham) Penguin Group (USA) Inc.*

Evans, Mike, ed. The Beatles: Paperback Writer - 40 Years of Classic Writing. 2nd ed. 2012. (ENG., Illus.). 392p. pap. 16.55 *(978-0-85965-465-4(6)) Plexus Publishing, Ltd. GBR. Dist: Perseus-PGW.*

Federal Bureau Of Investigation & Beatles, The. The Beatles: The FBI Files. 2007. 172p. per. 22.99 *(978-1-59986-256-9(5), Filibust) Filiquarian Publishing, LLC.*

Frontani, Michael R. The Beatles: Image & the Media. 2007. (ENG.). 286p. per. 30.00 *(978-1-57806-966-8(1)) Univ. Pr. of Mississippi.*

Geppetti, Marcello, photos by. The Beatles in Rome 1965. 2006. (ENG., Illus.). 44p. lib. bdg. 12.95 *(978-1-933149-12-7(4)) Manic D Pr.*

Gilmore, Mikal. The Winding Road: The Real Story Behind the Breakup of the Beatles. 2013. (ENG., Illus.). 288p. 26.00 *(978-1-4391-9078-4(X), Free Pr.) Free Pr.*

Gould, Jonathan. Can't Buy Me Love: The Beatles, Britain & America. 2008. (ENG., Illus.). 672p. pap. 15.95 *(978-0-307-35338-2(9), Three Rivers Pr.) Crown Publishing Group.*

Hal Leonard Corporation Staff. The Beatles Easy Fake Book, 1 vol. 2008. (ENG.). 224p. pap. 25.00 *(978-1-4234-5282-9(8), 1423452828) Leonard, Hal Corp.*

—Fab Four FAQ Deluxe Set: Fab Four FAQ & Fab Four FAQ 2. 0, the Solo Years, 1 vol. 2010. (ENG., Illus.). 800p. pap. 35.00 *(978-1-61713-001-4(X), 161713001X, Backbeat Books) Leonard, Hal Corp.*

Hal Leonard Corporation Staff, creator. The Best of the Beatles. 2nd rev. ed. 2006. (ENG., Illus.). 96p. pap. 14.99 (978-1-4234-1048-5(3), 1423410483) Leonard, Hal Corp.

—The Best of the Beatles - Violin. 2nd rev. ed. 2006. (ENG.). 96p. pap. 14.99 (978-1-4234-1047-8(5), 1423410475) Leonard, Hal Corp.

—The Best of the Beatles: Cello. 2nd rev. ed. 2006. (Best of the Beatles Ser.). (ENG.). 96p. pap. 14.99 (978-1-4234-1049-2(1), 1423410491) Leonard, Hal Corp.

Hall, Gary. Living Life Without Loving the Beatles: A Survivor's Guide. 2006. (ENG.). 176p. (C). per. 10.95 (978-1-84553-174-4(4)) Equinox Publishing Ltd. GBR. Dist: ISD.

Havers, Richard. The Beatles: The Days of Their Life. 2010. (ENG.). 320p. 19.99 (978-0-7858-2701-6(3), 0785827013, Chartwell) Book Sales, Inc.

Hayward, Mark. Beatles: On Camera, off Guard, 1963-1969. 2009. (ENG., Illus.). 208p. 40.00 (978-1-86205-867-5(9)) Chrysalis Children's Bks. GBR. Dist: Independent Pubs. Group.

Hewitt, Paolo. Fab Gear: The Beatles & Fashion. 2011. (ENG., Illus.). 240p. 45.00 (978-3-7913-4563-5(X)) Prestel Publishing.

Heylin, Clinton. The Act You've Known for All These Years. 2007. (Illus.). 416p. (978-1-84195-955-9(3)) Canongate Bks.

—The Act You've Known for All These Years: A Year in the Life of Sgt. Pepper & Friends. 2008. (ENG., Illus.). 336p. pap. (978-1-84767-105-9(5)) Canongate Bks.

Hickey, Andrew. The Beatles in Mono. 2010. 141p. pap. 29.50 (978-1-4461-8489-9(7)) Lulu Enterprises Inc.

Hill, Tim. John, Paul, George, & Ringo: the Definitive Illustrated Chronicle of the Beatles, 1960-1970: Rare Photographs, Collectible Ephemera, & Day-by-Day Timeline. 2007. (Illus.). 408p. 29.95 (978-1-4027-4223-1(1)) Sterling Publishing Co., Inc.

Hill, Tim & Clayton, Marie, eds. The Beatles Unseen Archives. 2009. 384p. (978-1-4075-6818-8(3)) Parragon Bk. Service Ltd.

Ingham, Chris & Rough Guides Staff. Beatles. 3rd ed. 2009. (ENG., Illus.). 336p. 18.99 (978-1-84836-525-4(X)) Rough Guides, Ltd. GBR. Dist: Dorling Kindersley Publishing, Inc.

Inglis, Ian. The Beatles in Hamburg. 2012. (Reaktion Books - Reverb Ser.). (Illus.). 224p. pap. 25.00 (978-1-86189-915-6(7)) Reaktion Bks., Ltd. GBR. Dist: Chicago Distribution Ctr.

Julien, Olivier. Sgt. Pepper & the Beatles: It Was Forty Years Ago Today. (Ashgate Popular & Folk Music Ser.). (Illus.). 208p. 2009. pap. 29.95 (978-0-7546-6708-7(1)) 2008. 99.95 (978-0-7546-6249-5(7)) Ashgate Publishing Co.

Kirchherr, Astrid & Scheler, Max, photos by. Yesterday: The Beatles Once upon a Time. 2007. (ENG., Illus.). 176p. 27.50 (978-0-86565-189-0(2)) Vendome Pr., The.

Kozinn, Allan. The Beatles: From the Cavern to the Rooftop. 2010. (ENG., Illus.). 244p. (Orig.). pap. 14.95 (978-0-7148-5946-0(X)) Phaidon Pr., Inc.

Lapham, Lewis. With the Beatles. 2009. (ENG.). 147p. pap. 13.00 (978-1-4379-6620-6(9)) DIANE Publishing Co.

Lefcowitz, Eric & Sethi, Anita, eds. Tomorrow Never Knows: The Beatles' Last Concert with Photographs by Jim Marshall. 2nd ed. 2010. (ENG., Illus.). 104p. pap. 12.95 (978-0-943249-04-9(X)) Retrofuture Products.

Leigh, Spencer. The Beatles in Hamburg: The Stories, the Scene & How It All Began. 2011. (ENG.). 128p. pap. 19.95 (978-1-56976-816-7(1)) Chicago Review Pr., Inc.

Lennon, Cynthia. John. 2006. (ENG., Illus.). 320p. per. 14.95 (978-0-307-33856-3(8), Three Rivers Pr.) Crown Publishing Group.

—John. Morales, Ivan, tr. 2007. (Illus.). 268p. pap. 26.95 (978-84-96222-74-8(8)) Ma Non Troppo ESP. Dist: Ediciones Urano S. A.

Lennon, John. Lennon & McCartney: Pro Vocal Series, Vol. 14. 2009. (ENG.). 32p. pap. 14.99 incl. audio compact disk (978-0-634-09956-4(6), 0634099566) Leonard, Hal Corp.

Lewisohn, Mark. The Complete Beatles Chronicle. 2006. (Illus.). 365p. pap. (978-0-600-61001-4(2), Hamlyn) Octopus Publishing Group.

—The Complete Beatles Chronicle: The Definitive Day-by-Day Guide to the Beatles' Entire Career. 2010. (ENG., Illus.). 368p. pap. 30.00 (978-1-56976-534-0(0)) Chicago Review Pr., Inc.

Life Magazine Editors. Life Remembering George Harrison: 10 Years Later. 2011. (ENG., Illus.). 112p. 17.95 (978-1-60320-243-5(9)) Time Home Entertainment, Inc.

Loker, Bradford E. History with the Beatles. 2009. 412p. pap. 24.95 (978-1-60844-039-9(7)) Dog Ear Publishing, LLC.

MacDonald, Ian. Revolution in the Head: The Beatles' Records & the Sixties. 3rd ed. 2007. (ENG.). 544p. pap. 16.95 (978-1-55652-733-3(0)) Chicago Review Pr., Inc.

MacFarlane, Thomas. The Beatles' Abbey Road Medley: Extended Forms in Popular Music. 2007. (ENG., Illus.). 218p. per. 41.00 (978-0-8108-6019-3(8)) Government Institutes.

Marion, Larry. The Lost Beatles Photographs: The Bob Bonis Archive, 1964-1966. 2011. (ENG., Illus.). 192p. 29.99 (978-0-06-196078-9(0)) HarperCollins Pubs.

Marsh, Dave. The Beatles' Second Album. 2007. (Rock of Ages Ser.). (ENG.). 160p. 16.95 (978-1-59486-426-1(8)) Rodale Pr., Inc.

Masini, Massimo. Thank You Boys: 50 Years with the Beatles. 2011. (ENG., Illus.). 120p. pap. 22.50 (978-88-96408-05-6(9)) Anniversary Bks. ITA. Dist: National Bk. Network.

McCullin, Don. A Day in the Life of the Beatles. 2010. (ENG., Illus.). 144p. 24.95 (978-0-8478-3611-6(8)) Rizzoli International Pubns., Inc.

Miles, Barry. Beatles: A Diary - An Intimate Day by Day History. 2009. (ENG.). 320p. pap. 24.95 (978-1-84772-082-5(X), OP52107) Omnibus Pr.

Millard, Andre. Beatlemania: Technology, Business, & Teen Culture in Cold War America. 2012. (Johns Hopkins Introductory Studies in the History of Technology Ser.). (ENG., Illus.). 240p. (C). (gr. 13-17). pap. 22.95 (978-1-4214-0525-4(3)) Johns Hopkins Univ. Pr.

Millard, André. Beatlemania: Technology, Business, & Teen Culture in Cold War America. 2012. (Johns Hopkins Introductory Studies in the History of Technology Ser.). (ENG., Illus.). 240p. (C). (gr. 13-17). 50.00 (978-1-4214-0524-7(5)) Johns Hopkins Univ. Pr.

Mulligan, Kate Siobhan. The Beatles: A Musical Biography. 2010. E-Book (978-0-313-37687-0(5), Greenwood Pr.); (Illus.). 177p. 35.00 (978-0-313-37686-3(7), GR7686) Greenwood Publishing Group, Inc.

Neill, Andy. The Beatles Across the Universe: John, Paul, George & Ringo on Tour & on Stage. 2010. (ENG., Illus.). 256p. 32.95 (978-1-84425-816-1(5), 1844258165) Haynes Publishing PLC GBR. Dist: MBI Distribution Services/Quayside Distribution.

Niezgoda, Joseph. Lennon Prophecy: A New Examination of the Death Clues of the Beatles. 2008. (ENG., Illus.). 240p. pap. 19.99 (978-0-942257-45-8(6)) New Chapter Pr., Inc.

O'Donnell, Jim. The Day John Met Paul: An Hour-By-Hour Account of How the Beatles Began. 2nd ed. 2006. (Illus.). 192p. 24.95 (978-0-415-97933-7(1)) Routledge.

Panenka, Stanley. Introducing ... the Beatles Record Price Guide. 2011. (Illus.). 232p. pap. 39.00 (978-0-932117-57-1(0)) Osborne Enterprises Publishing.

Pent, ed. Beatles Tapes III, Vol. 3. cd-rom 15.98 (978-1-885959-22-5(2), JRCD 7041) Jerden Records & Speechworks.

Pollock, Bruce. If You Like the Beatles... Here Are over 200 Bands, Films, Records & Other Oddities That You Will Love. 2011. (ENG., Illus.). 216p. pap. 14.99 (978-1-61713-018-2(4), 1617130184, Backbeat Books) Leonard, Hal Corp.

Reiter, Roland. The Beatles on Film: Analysis of Movies, Documentaries, Spoofs & Cartoons. 2008. (ENG.). 214p. pap. 39.95 (978-3-89942-885-8(4)) Transcript Verlag DEU. Dist: Transaction Pubs.

Rodriguez, Robert. Fab Four FAQ 2.0: The Beatles' Solo Years, 1970-1980. 2010. (ENG., Illus.). 510p. pap. 19.99 (978-0-87930-968-8(7), 0879309687, Backbeat Books) Leonard, Hal Corp.

Ryan, Kevin & Kehew, Brian. Kaleidescope Eyes: A Day in the Life of Sgt. Pepper. 2007. (Illus.). 241p. 495.00 (978-0-9785200-1-4(7)) Curvebender Publishing.

—Recording the Beatles: The Studio Equipment & Techniques Used to Create Their Classic Albums. 2006. (Illus.). 528p. (978-0-9785200-0-7(9)) Curvebender Publishing.

Sandercombe, W. Fraser. Beatle Books: From Genesis to Revolution. 2009. (ENG., Illus.). 432p. pap. 26.95 (978-1-926592-00-8(X)) Collector's Guide Publishing, Inc. CAN. Dist: Independent Pubs. Group.

—Beatlemania Forever: The Beatles Encyclopedia. 2008. (ENG.). 484p. pap. 27.95 (978-1-894959-78-0(7)) Collector's Guide Publishing, Inc. CAN. Dist: Independent Pubs. Group.

—The Beatles: Press Reports. 2007. (ENG., Illus.). 320p. per. 19.95 (978-1-894959-61-2(2)) Collector's Guide Publishing, Inc. CAN. Dist: Independent Pubs. Group.

Sawyers, June Skinner, ed. Read the Beatles: Classic & New Writings on the Beatles, Their Legacy, & Why They Still Matter. 2006. (ENG., Illus.). 416p. (gr. 12-18). 16.00 (978-0-14-303732-3(3), Penguin (Non-Classics)) Penguin Group (USA) Inc.

Schneider, Matthew. The Long & Winding Road from Blake to the Beatles. 2008. (Nineteenth-Century Major Lives & Letters Ser.). (ENG.). 240p. 89.00 (978-1-4039-8489-0(1)) Palgrave Macmillan.

Schwensen, Dave. Beatles in Cleveland: Memories, Facts & Photos about the Notorious 1964 & 1966 Concerts. 2007. (Illus.). 192p. pap. 19.95 (978-0-9791030-0-1(2)) North Shore Publishing.

Shea, Stuart & Rodriguez, Robert. Fab Four FAQ: Everything Left to Know about the Beatles — & More! 2007. (ENG., Illus.). 526p. per. 19.99 (978-1-4234-2138-2(8), 1423421388) Leonard, Hal Corp.

Snow, Mat. John Lennon. 2012. (978-0-7603-4360-9(8)) MBI Publishing Co. LLC.

Somacht, Denny & Sharp, Ken. Meet the Beatles . . . Again! Date not set. (Illus.). reprint ed. pap. 19.95 (978-0-9640672-0-2(X)) Musicom.

Sounes, Howard. Fab: An Intimate Life of Paul Mccartney. 2011. (ENG., Illus.). 624p. pap. 20.00 (978-0-306-82047-2(1)) Da Capo Pr., Inc.

Southall, Brian & Lennon, Julian. Beatles Memorabilia: The Julian Lennon Collection. 2011. (ENG., Illus.). 192p. 29.95 (978-1-84796-018-4(9), Goodman Pubs.) Carlton Bks., Ltd. GBR. Dist: Sterling Publishing Co., Inc.

Spignesi, Stephen J. & Lewis, Michael. 100 Best Beatles Songs: A Passionate Fan's Guide. 2009. (ENG., Illus.). 320p. pap. 14.95 (978-1-57912-842-5(4)) Black Dog & Leventhal Pubs., Inc.

Spitz, Bob. The Beatles: The Biography. 2006. (ENG., Illus.). 992p. per. 17.99 (978-0-316-01331-4(5), Back Bay Bks.) Little Brown & Co.

Spizer, Bruce. The Beatles Swan Song: She Loves You & Other Records. 2007. (Illus.). 280p. 50.00 (978-0-9662649-7-5(5)) 498 Productions, L.L.C.

Spizer, Bruce & Daniels, Frank. Beatles for Sale on Parlophone Records. 2011. 444p. 69.98 (978-0-9832957-0-9(0)) 498 Productions, L.L.C.

Starr, Ringo, pseud. Postcards from the Boys. 2008. (ENG.). 111p. 35.00 (978-1-4379-6375-5(7)) DIANE Publishing Co.

Tamutis, Vytautas, ed. Catalogue of Lithuanian Beetles (Insecta: Coleoptera) 2011. (ZooKeys Ser.). 494p. pap. 215.00 (978-954-642-600-0(8)) Pensoft Pubs. BGR. Dist: Coronet Bks.

Tedman, Ray & Bench, Jeff. The Beatles on Television. 2011. (ENG., Illus.). 176p. 19.95 (978-0-85768-571-1(6), Titan Bks.) Titan Bks. Ltd. GBR. Dist: Random Hse., Inc.

Tillinghast, Charles. How Capitol Got the Beatles: And Then What Happened. 2008. 104p. pap. 10.95 (978-1-4327-2924-0(1)) Outskirts Pr., Inc.

Toropov, Brandon. Wer war Eleanor Rigby? 909 Fragen & Antworten Rund um die Beatles. Biehl, Christiane, tr. (GER.). 460p. pap. (978-3-462-02661-0(5)) Kiepenheuer & Witsch GmbH & Company KG DEU. Dist: International Bk. Import Service, Inc.

Turner, Steve. The Beatles 1962-66: Stories Behind the Songs. 2011. (Stories Behind the Songs Ser.). (ENG., Illus.). 192p. 14.95 (978-1-84732-267-8(0)) Carlton Bks., Ltd. GBR. Dist: Sterling Publishing Co., Inc.

—The Beatles 1967-70: Stories Behind the Songs. 2011. (Stories Behind the Songs Ser.). (ENG., Illus.). 192p. 14.95 (978-1-84732-268-5(9)) Carlton Bks., Ltd. GBR. Dist: Sterling Publishing Co., Inc.

—The Gospel According to the Beatles. 2006. (Gospel according To... Ser.). (ENG., Illus.). 254p. 20.00 (978-0-664-22983-2(2)) Westminster John Knox Pr.

Unterberger, Richie. The Unreleased Beatles: Music & Film. 2006. (Music Ser.). (ENG., Illus.). 390p. pap. 34.95 (978-0-87930-892-6(3), 0879308923, Backbeat Books) Leonard, Hal Corp.

Womack, Kenneth, ed. The Cambridge Companion to the Beatles. 2009. (Cambridge Companions to Music Ser.). (ENG., Illus.). 344p. 94.00 (978-0-521-86965-2(X)); pap. 23.99 (978-0-521-68976-2(7)) Cambridge Univ. Pr.

Womack, Kenneth & Womack. Long & Winding Roads: The Evolving Artistry of the Beatles. 2007. (ENG.). 336p. 95.00 (978-0-8264-1745-9(0)); pap. 27.95 (978-0-8264-1746-6(9)) Continuum International Publishing Group, Ltd. GBR. Dist: National Bk. Network.

BEATLES—DISCOGRAPHY

Babiuk, Andy. Beatles Gear: All the Fab Four's Instruments from Stage to Studio. 2nd ed. 2010. (ENG., Illus.). 258p. 40.00 (978-0-87930-956-5(3), 0879309563, Backbeat Books) Leonard, Hal Corp.

Beatles Staff. The Beatles - the Capitol Albums, Volume 1, 1 vol. 2009. (ENG.). 224p. pap. 24.99 (978-1-4234-2994-4(X), 142342994X) Leonard, Hal Corp.

Cox, Perry & Daniels, Frank. Price Guide for the Beatles American Records. 6th ed. 2007. (Illus.). 330p. 50.00 (978-0-9662649-6-8(7)) 498 Productions, L.L.C.

Doggett, Peter & Humphries, Patrick. Beatles the Music & the Myth. 2010. (ENG., Illus.). 192p. pap. 14.95 (978-1-84938-369-1(3)) Omnibus Pr.

Donnelly, Stephen E. The Beatles Discography: The 60's. 2011. 164p. (ENG.). pap. 79.95 (978-1-4327-6979-6(0)); pap. 69.95 (978-1-4327-6924-6(3)) Outskirts Pr., Inc.

Engelhardt, Kristofer. Beatles Deeper Undercover. 2010. (ENG.). 376p. pap. 27.95 (978-1-926592-09-1(3)) Collector's Guide Publishing, Inc. CAN. Dist: Independent Pubs. Group.

Pieper, Jörg. The Solo Beatles Film & TV Chronicle 1971-1980. 2009. 330p. pap. 40.95 (978-1-4092-8301-0(1)) Lulu Enterprises Inc.

Winn, John C. Beatlegmania Volume Two. 2007. (Illus.). 112p. per. 30.00 (978-0-9728362-4-1(1)) Multiplus Bks.

—That Magic Feeling: The Beatles' Recorded Legacy, Volume Two, 1966-1970. 2009. (ENG.). 416p. pap. 28.00 (978-0-307-45239-9(5), Three Rivers Pr.) Crown Publishing Group.

—Way Beyond Compare Vol. 1: The Beatles' Recorded Legacy, 1957-1965. 2008. (ENG.). 416p. pap. 26.95 (978-0-307-45157-6(7), Three Rivers Pr.) Crown Publishing Group.

BEATNIKS

see Beat Generation

BEATON, CECIL, 1904-1984

Albrecht, Donald. Cecil Beaton: the New York Years: New York. 2011. (ENG., Illus.). 240p. 65.00 (978-0-8478-3565-2(0), Skira) Rizzoli International Pubns., Inc.

Brown, Susanna. Queen Elizabeth II: Portraits by Cecil Beaton. 2011. (ENG., Illus.). 128p. 35.00 (978-1-85177-654-2(0)) V & A Pubns. GBR. Dist: Hachette Bk. Group.

BEATRICE, CONSORT OF LODOVICO SFORZA IL MORO, DUKE OF MILAN, 1475-1497

Ryley, M. Beresford. Queens of the Renaissance. 2009. 372p. 38.99 (978-1-116-80850-6(1)); 33.99 (978-1-116-80851-3(X)); pap. 31.75 (978-1-116-80853-7(6)); pap. 32.75 (978-1-116-80852-0(8)) BiblioBazaar.

—Queens of the Renaissance. 2007. (ENG.). 412p. per. 34.95 (978-0-548-78699-4(2)) Kessinger Publishing, LLC.

BEATRICE, CONSORT OF PRINCE HENRY OF BATTENBERGG, 1857-1944

see Beatrice, Princess Henry Of Battenberg, 1857-1944

BEATRICE, PRINCESS HENRY OF BATTENBERG, 1857-1944

Dennison, Matthew. The Last Princess: The Devoted Life of Queen Victoria's Youngest Daughter. 2009. (ENG., Illus.). 320p. pap. 19.99 (978-0-312-56497-1(X), St. Martin's Griffin) St. Martin's Pr.

BEATTIE, ANN, 1947-

Trouard, Dawn, ed. Conversations with Ann Beattie. 2006. (ENG., Illus.). 190p. 50.00 (978-1-57806-922-4(X)); per. 22.00 (978-1-57806-923-1(8)) Univ. Pr. of Mississippi.

BEATTIE, JAMES, 1735-1803

Forbes, William. Account of the Life & Writings of Jame. 2006. pap. 40.95 (978-1-4286-3493-0(2)) Kessinger Publishing, LLC.

Sampson, Virginia. The Life & Works of James Beattie: A Philosopher Poet in the Age of Enlightenment. 2012. (Legenda Main Ser.). (ENG.). 200p. (C). 89.50 (978-1-906540-38-8(1)) European Humanities Research Ctr. GBR. Dist: Brown, David Bk. Co., The.

BEATTY, WARREN, 1937-

Biskind, Peter. Star: How Warren Beatty Seduced America. 2011. (ENG., Illus.). 640p. pap. 16.99 (978-0-7432-4659-0(4)) Simon & Schuster.

Finstad, Suzanne. Warren Beatty: A Private Man. 2006. (ENG., Illus.). 608p. pap. 15.95 (978-0-307-34529-5(7), Three Rivers Pr.) Crown Publishing Group.

BEAUCHAMP, ANN, 1786-1826

Schoenbachler, Matthew G. Murder & Madness: The Myth of the Kentucky Tragedy. 2011. (Topics in Kentucky History Ser.). (ENG., Illus.). 392p. pap. 25.00 (978-0-8131-3387-4(4)) Univ. Pr. of Kentucky.

BEAUCHAMP, JEREBOAM O., 1802-1826

Bruce, Dickson D. The Kentucky Tragedy: A Story of Conflict & Change in Antebellum America. 2006. (Illus.). 183p. 40.00 (978-0-8071-3173-2(3)) Louisiana State Univ. Pr.

Schoenbachler, Matthew G. Murder & Madness: The Myth of the Kentucky Tragedy. (Topics in Kentucky History Ser.). (ENG., Illus.). 392p. 2011. pap. 25.00 (978-0-8131-3387-4(4)) 2009. 40.00 (978-0-8131-2566-4(9)) Univ. Pr. of Kentucky.

BEAUFORT (S.C.)

Dimke, Sandy. Hands: At Work & Play in the Lowcountry of South Carolina. 2010. (Illus.). 29.95 (978-0-615-40307-6(7)) Dimke Photo Art.

Helsley, Alexia Jones. Wicked Beaufort. 2011. 128p. pap. 19.99 (978-1-60949-263-2(3)) History Pr., The.

Singleton, Gloria E. Beaufort Through the Ages. 2010. pap. 19.95 (978-0-7414-5665-6(6)) Infinity Publishing.

Spieler, Gerhard. Beaufort, South Carolina: Pages from the Past. 2008. (American Chronicles Ser.). (Illus.). 128p. pap. 19.99 (978-1-59629-428-8(0)) History Pr., The.

BEAUFORT COUNTY (N.C.)

Browning, Judkin. Shifting Loyalties: The Union Occupation of Eastern North Carolina. 2011. (ENG., Illus.). 256p. 37.50 (978-0-8078-3468-8(8)) Univ. of North Carolina Pr.

—The Southern Mind under Union Rule: The Diary of James Rumley, Beaufort, North Carolina, 1862-1865. 2009. (New Perspectives on the History of the South Ser.). (ENG., Illus.). 216p. 34.95 (978-0-8130-3407-2(8)) Univ. Pr. of Florida.

Paul, Mary C. & Paul, Grayden. Carteret County, North Carolina: History & Folklore. 2008. pap. 12.99 (978-1-59629-478-3(7)) History Pr., The.

Wilson, Mamre Marsh. A Story of North Carolina's Historic Beaufort. 2007. (Illus.). 126p. pap., per. 19.99 (978-1-59629-168-3(0)) History Pr., The.

Wrenn, Tony & Turberg, Edward, intros. Porchscapes, the Colors of Beaufort, NC: Three Centuries of History Woven Through Art & Words. 2009. (Illus.). 176p. (978-0-9659506-5-7(4)) Eastern Offset Publishing Co.

BEAUFORT COUNTY (S.C.)

Helsley, Alexia J. A Guide to Historic Beaufort, South Carolina. 2006. (Illus.). 139p. pap. 19.99 (978-1-59629-045-7(5)) History Pr., The.

Marscher, Fran. Remembering the Way it Was Vol. II: More Stores from Hilton Head, Bluffton & Daufuskie. 2007. 128p. pap. 19.99 (978-1-59629-138-6(9)) History Pr., The.

Marscher, Fran Heyward. Remembering the Way It Was at Beaufort, Sheldon & the Sea Islands. 2006. 126p. pap., per. 19.99 (978-1-59629-136-2(2)) History Pr., The.

BEAUMARCHAIS, PIERRE AUGUSTIN CARON DE, 1732-1799

Butler, Raymond Reagan. Figaro's Fleet: The French Gun-Runner & the American Rebels. 2009. (ENG., Illus.). 288p. 34.95 (978-1-84588-636-3(4)) History Pr. Ltd.,The GBR. Dist: Independent Pubs. Group.

Kite, Elizabeth Sarah. Beaumarchais & the War of American Independence. 2009. 340p. 32.99 (978-1-110-12266-0(7)) 2009. 340p. pap. 30.75 (978-1-110-12263-9(2)) 2009. 344p. 25.99 (978-1-103-11572-3(3)) 2009. 344p. pap. 19.99 (978-1-103-11569-3(3)) 2008. 340p. 28.99 (978-0-559-79346-2(4)) 2008. 340p. pap. 30.75 (978-0-559-79343-1(X)) 2008. 344p. 28.99 (978-0-559-22031-9(6)) 2008. 344p. pap. 31.75 (978-0-559-22029-6(4)) BiblioBazaar.

—Beaumarchais & the War of American Independence. 2009. 180p. pap. (978-1-4590-5482-0(2)); 220p. pap. (978-0-217-34409-8(7)) Books LLC.

—Beaumarchais & the War of American Independence, 2 vol., set. reprint ed. 250.00 (978-0-7222-7665-5(6)) Library Reprints, Inc.

Paul, Joel Richard. Unlikely Allies: How a Merchant, a Playwright, & a Spy Saved the American Revolution. 2010. (ENG.). 416p. (gr. 12). 16.00 (978-1-59448-487-2(2), Riverhead Trade (Paperbacks)) Penguin Group (USA) Inc.

Thomas, Hugh. Beaumarchais in Seville: An Intermezzo. 2009. (ENG., Illus.). 192p. pap. 15.00 (978-0-300-13633-3(1)) Yale Univ. Pr.

Unger, Harlow Giles. Improbable Patriot: The Secret History of Monsieur de Beaumarchais, the French Playwright Who Saved the American Revolution. 2011. (Illus.). 260p. 26.95 (978-1-58465-925-9(4)) Univ. Pr. of New England.

BEAUMONT, FRANCIS, 1584-1616

Beaumont, Francis. Dramatic Works, 10 vols. 2008. (ENG.). 708p. (C). pap. 84.00 *(978-0-521-06C52-3(4))* Cambridge Univ. Pr.

Beaumont, Francis & Fletcher, John. The Dramatic Works in the Beaumont & Fletcher Canon: Volume 9, 10 vols. Bowers, Fredson, ed. 2008. (Dramatic Works in the Beaumont & Fletcher Canon Ser.). (ENG.). 676p. (C). pap. 84.00 *(978-0-521-06050-9(8))* Cambridge Univ. Pr.

—Philaster: Or, Love Lies A-Bleeding. reprint ed. lib. bdg. 98.00 *(978-0-7426-2047-6(6))* Classic Bks.

Bowers, Fredson. The Dramatic Works in the Beaumont & Fletcher Canon: Volume 2, 10 vols. 2008. (ENG.). 704p. (C). pap. 84.00 *(978-0-521-06034-9(6))* Cambridge Univ. Pr.

Fletcher, John & Beaumont, Francis. The Dramatic Works in the Beaumont & Fletcher Canon: Volume 7, 10 vols. Bowers, Fredson, ed. 2008. (Dramatic Works in the Beaumont & Fletcher Canon Ser.). (ENG.). 752p. (C). pap. 84.00 *(978-0-521-06046-2(X))* Cambridge Univ. Pr.

—The Dramatic Works in the Beaumont & Fletcher Canon: Volume 8, 10 vols. Bowers, Fredson, ed. 2008. (Dramatic Works in the Beaumont & Fletcher Canon Ser.). (ENG.). 768p. (C). pap. 84.00 *(978-0-521-06048-6(6))* Cambridge Univ. Pr.

Gossett, Eric, et al. Philaster. Gossett, Suzanne, ed. 2009. (Arden Early Modern Drama Ser.). (ENG., Illus.). 296p. pap. 20.00 *(978-1-904271-73-4(1),* Arden Shakespeare) A & C Black GBR. Dist: Macmillan.

Thorndike, Ashley H. The Influence of Beaumont & Fletcher on Shakespeare. reprint ed. 29.50 *(978-0-404-06428-0(0))* AMS Pr., Inc.

—The Influence of Beaumont & Fletcher on Shakespeare. 2007. (ENG.). 184p. 37.95 *(978-0-548-03461-3(3))* Kessinger Publishing, LLC.

BEAUMONT, GUSTAVE DE, 1802-1866

Zunz, Olivier, ed. Alexis de Tocqueville & Gustave de Beaumont in America: Their Friendship & Their Travels. Goldhammer, Arthur, tr. from FRE. 2010. (ENG., Illus.). 744p. (gr. 17). 60.00 *(978-0-8139-3062-6(6))* Univ. Pr. of Virginia.

BEAUREGARD, PIERRE GUSTAVE TOUTANT, 1818-1893

Cunningham, O. Edward. Shiloh & the Western Campaign of 1862. 2009. (American Battle Ser.). (Illus.). 520p. pap. 22.95 *(978-1-932714-34-0(0))* Savas Beatie.

—Shiloh & the Western Campaign of 1862. Joiner, Gary D. & Smith, Timothy B., eds. 2007. (Illus.). 476p. 34.95 *(978-1-932714-27-2(8))* Savas Beatie.

Roman, Alfred. The Military Operations of Gen. Beauregard in the War Between the States 1861-1865, 2 vol., set. reprint ed. 250.00 *(978-0-7222-9272-3(4))* Library Reprints, Inc.

—The Military Operations of General Beauregard in the War Between the States 1861 to 1865, 2 vol., set. reprint ed. 250.00 *(978-0-7222-8045-4(9))* Library Reprints, Inc.

Wells, Bruce R. The Bermuda Hundred Campaign: The Creole & the Beast. 2011. 144p. pap. 19.99 ***(978-1-60949-314-1(1))*** History Pr., The.

BEAUTICIANS

see Beauty Operators

BEAUTIFICATION OF THE LANDSCAPE

see Landscape Protection

BEAUTIFUL, THE

see Aesthetics; Art—Philosophy

BEAUTY

see Aesthetics; Art—Philosophy; Beauty, Personal

BEAUTY, PERSONAL

Here are entered works on personal grooming and appearance. Works on the attractiveness of women as a philosophic or artistic concept are entered under Feminine Beauty (Aesthetics).

see also Beauty Culture; Beauty Shops; Body Piercing; Charm; Clothing and Dress; Cosmetics; Costume; Hair; Hairdressing; Hand; Manicuring; Perfumes; Skin; Teeth

Agius, Marie. The Art of Makeup. 2009. 92p. pap. 30.49 *(978-1-4490-1950-1(1))* AuthorHouse.

Akbari, Lisa. Every Woman's Guide to Beautiful Hair at Any Age: Learn What Can Be Done to Keep a Beautiful Head of Hair for a Lifetime. 2007. (ENG.). 160p. per. 13.95 *(978-1-4022-0877-5(4))* Sourcebooks, Inc.

Aldrich, Molly. How to Get the Perfect Brazilian Wax: A Step-by-Step Guide to Getting the Perfect Brazilian & Finding Your Inner Goddess. 2009. 76p. pap. 10.95 *(978-1-4401-2419-8(1))* iUniverse, Inc.

Antin, Jonathan. Blow Out. 2008. 256p. pap. 19.95 *(978-0-06-136924-7(1))* HarperCollins Pubs.

Antonaccio, Helena. What's Your Secret? How One Centerfold Stays Alluring & Fit Past the Age of Fifty. 2007. 164p. per. 14.95 *(978-0-595-41012-5(X))* iUniverse, Inc.

Ascroft, Eileen. The Magic Key to Charm: Instructions for a Delightful Life. 2009. (ENG., Illus.). 138p. 23.95 *(978-0-09-951823-5(6))* Random Hse. GBR. Dist: Independent Pubs. Group.

Aucoin, Kevyn. Mas Que Maquillaje. 2007. (SPA & ENG.). 178p. pap. 72.95 *(978-84-666-0060-6(4))* Ediciones B ESP. Dist: Independent Pubs. Group.

Baek, Ji. Rescue Your Nails: A Do-It-Yourself Guide to Perfect Fingers & Toes. 2008. (ENG., Illus.). 166p. pap. 12.95 *(978-0-7611-4377-2(7),* 0761143777) Workman Publishing Co., Inc.

Bailey, Eric J. Black America, Body Beautiful: How the African American Image Is Changing Fashion, Fitness, & Other Industries, 1 vol. 2008. 176p. 44.95 *(978-0-275-99595-9(X),* C9595, Praeger Pubs.) Greenwood Publishing Group, Inc.

Baker Hyde, Phoebe. The Beauty Experiment: How I Skipped the Lipstick, Cut My Hair, Forgot Fashion, & Faced the World Without Concealer for a Year ... & Made over My Life. 2012. (ENG.). 272p. pap. 16.00 *(978-0-7382-1465-8(5))* Da Capo Pr., Inc.

Ballestero, Shelly. Beauty by God: Inside-Out Secrets for Every Woman. 2009. (ENG., Illus.). 224p. pap. 15.99 *(978-0-8307-4684-2(6))* Gospel Light Pubns.

Baptista, Penny. Hair to Dye For: A Hair Colorist's Secrets Revealed. 2009. 68p. pap. 9.95 *(978-0-595-52483-9(4))* iUniverse, Inc.

Baratta, Maria. "Skinny" Revisited: Women, Beauty, & Anorexia. 2011. ***(978-0-87101-407-8(6),*** NASW Pr.) National Assn. of Social Workers/NASW Pr.

Barker, Nigel. Nigel Barker's Beauty Equation: Revealing a Better & More Beautiful You. 2010. (ENG., Illus.). 208p. pap. 19.95 *(978-0-8109-9642-7(1),* Abrams Image) Abrams.

Barnes, Scott. About Face: Amazing Transformations Using the Secrets of the Top Celebrity Makeup Artist. (ENG., Illus.). 240p. 2011. pap. 18.99 *(978-1-59233-488-9(1),* 1592334881) 2010. 24.99 *(978-1-59233-399-8(0),* 1592333990) Quayside.

Bartlett, Peter & Brunton, Paul A. Aesthetic Dentistry. (Illus.). 100p. 54.00 *(978-1-85097-077-4(7))* Quintessence Publishing Co., Inc.

Bashour, Mounir. Is an Objective Measuring System for Facial Attractiveness Possible? 2007. 292p. per. 25.95 *(978-1-58112-365-4(5),* Dissertation.com) Universal Pubs.

Becker, Kim & Becker, Mike. Hello Gorgeous! A Journey of Faith, Love & Hope. 2011. 208p. pap. 19.95 ***(978-0-9833586-4-0(8))*** Corby Books.

Beckham, Victoria. That Extra Half an Inch: Hair, Heels & Everything in Between. 2007. (Illus.). 384p. per. 19.99 *(978-0-06-154449-1(3))* HarperCollins Pubs.

Beer, Kenneth. Palm Beach Perfect Skin: The Quest for Ideal Skin Health & Beauty. 2010. (N/a Ser.). (Illus.). 192p. per. 14.95 *(978-0-9748997-3-2(9))* MDPublish.com.

Begoun, Paula. Belleza de Pies a Cabeza: La Guia Completa para Lograr su Look Ideal. 2006. (SPA & ENG., Illus.). 612p. pap. 24.95 *(978-1-59486-516-9(7))* Rodale Pr., Inc.

—The Original Beauty Bible: Unparalleled Information for Beautiful & Younger Skin at Any Age. 3rd rev. ed. 2009. (ENG.). 500p. pap. 22.95 *(978-1-877988-33-2(2))* Beginning Pr.

Begoun, Paula & Barron, Bryan. Don't Go to the Cosmetics Counter Without Me. 8th ed. 2009. (ENG.). 1100p. pap. 29.95 *(978-1-877988-34-9(0))* Beginning Pr.

Bell, Carrie & Helmes, Amy. The Bathtub Reader: An Amusing Miscellany for the Discerning Mademoiselle. 2008. (ENG., Illus.). 320p. pap. 14.95 *(978-1-60433-010-6(4))* Cider Mill Pr. Bk. Pubs., LLC.

Berry, Bonnie. Beauty Bias: Discrimination & Social Power, 1 vol. 2007. 176p. 39.95 *(978-0-275-99012-1(5),* C9012, Praeger Pubs.) Greenwood Publishing Group, Inc.

—The Power of Looks: Social Stratification of Physical Appearance. 2008. (Illus.). 154p. 99.95 *(978-0-7546-4758-4(7))* Ashgate Publishing Co.

Bharadwaj, Monisha. India's Beauty Secrets. 2008. (ENG., Illus.). 160p. pap. *(978-1-85626-778-6(4))* Cathie, Kyle Ltd. GBR. Dist: Independent Pubs. Group.

Bird, Linda, et al. Head-Turning, Eye-Popping, Jaw-Dropping Quick Fix Beauty Secrets. 2009. 129p. pap. 15.93 *(978-1-906821-20-3(8))* Infinite Ideas GBR. Dist: Sony Electronics.

Blanchard, Tamsin. Green Is the New Black: How to Change the World with Style. 2008. (Illus.). 288p. 24.95 *(978-0-06-171930-1(7))* HarperCollins Pubs.

Blissett, Bella. The 1000 Most Asked Questions about Beauty. 2009. (ENG., Illus.). 448p. pap. 9.99 *(978-1-84601-291-4(0))* M Q Pubns. GBR. Dist: Hachette Bk. Group.

Bloom, Natalie. Beauty in Bloom: A Collection of Beautiful Inspirations. 2009. (ENG., Illus.). 108p. 16.95 *(978-1-74175-529-9(8))* Allen & Unwin AUS. Dist: Independent Pubs. Group.

Blum, Esther. Eat, Drink, & Be Gorgeous: A Nutritionist's Guide to Living Well While Living It Up. 2007. (ENG., Illus.). 192p. 22.95 *(978-0-8118-5540-2(6))* Chronicle Bks. LLC.

—Secrets of Gorgeous: Hundreds of Ways to Live Well While Living It Up. 2008. (ENG.). 227p. 12.95 *(978-0-8118-6581-4(9))* Chronicle Bks. LLC.

Bogard, Hazel. The Beauty Shop World at A Glance: How to Keep Clients Forever How to Lose Clients Forever... . A Book Every Hair Stylist Should Have. 2011. 57p. pap. 12.95 ***(978-1-4327-7042-6(X))*** Outskirts Pr., Inc.

Borba, Scott-Vincent. Skintervention: The Personalized Solution for Healthier, Younger, & Flawless-Looking Skin. 2011. (ENG., Illus.). 240p. pap. 14.95 *(978-0-7573-1552-7(6))* Health Communications, Inc.

Borello, Lisa. Culture Versus Family - the Battle over Women's Bodies. 2008. 132p. per. *(978-3-8364-3578-9(0))* VDM Verlag Dr. Mueller e.K.

Borzillo-Vrenna, Carrie. Cherry Bomb: The Ultimate Guide to Becoming a Better Flirt, a Tougher Chick, & a Hotter Girlfriend — and to Living Life Like a Rock Star. 2008. (ENG.). 240p. 18.95 *(978-1-4169-6116-1(X))* Gallery Pr., The IRL. Dist: Simon & Schuster, Inc.

Bosniak, Stephen & Zilkha, Marian. Beautifeye. 2006. 224p. 29.95 *(978-0-9792240-0-3(4))* MDPublish.com.

Bosniak, Stephen, et al. Beautifeye. 2006. (Illus.). 224p. per. 16.95 *(978-0-9748997-5-6(5))* MDPublish.com.

Braendel, Shari. Good Girls Don't Have to Dress Bad: Every Woman, 1 vol. 2010. (ENG.). 192p. pap., pupil's gde. ed. 14.99 *(978-0-310-32601-4(X))* Zondervan.

Brandon, Ruth. Ugly Beauty: Helena Rubinstein, L'oréal, & the Blemished History of Looking Good. 2011. (Illus.). 304p. 26.99 *(978-0-06-174040-4(3))* HarperCollins Pubs.

Brandt, Frederic. 10 Minutes/10 Years: Your Definitive Guide to a Beautiful & Youthful. 2010. (ENG.). 288p. pap. 18.99 *(978-1-4391-9509-3(9),* Free Pr.) Free Pr.

Braverman, Eric R. Younger You: Unlock the Hidden Power of Your Brain to Look & Feel 15 Years Younger. 2007. 256p. 24.95 *(978-0-07-146613-4(4),* 9780071466134) McGraw-Hill Cos., The.

Brenner, Sandi. Beauty & the Budget. 2006. 160p. per. 13.95 *(978-1-58939-926-6(9))* Virtualbookworm.com Publishing, Inc.

Brewer, Gayle. Physical Attractiveness & Sexual Strategy Selection. 2009. 224p. pap. *(978-3-639-14167-2(9))* VDM Verlag Dr. Mueller e.K.

Bright, J. E. America's Next Top Model: Fierce Guide to Life - The Ultimate Source of Beauty, Fashion, & Model Behavior. 2009. (ENG., Illus.). 128p. pap. 24.95 *(978-0-7893-1859-6(8))* Universe Publishing.

—America's Next Top Model: Fierce Guide to Life: The Ultimate Source of Beauty, Fashion, & Model Behavior. 2010. (ENG., Illus.). 128p. pap. 9.98 *(978-0-7893-2098-8(3),* Rizzoli Universe Promotional Bks.) Rizzoli International Pubns., Inc.

Brinton, D. G. Personal Beauty Health & the Human Fo. 2006. 312p. per. *(978-1-4067-9577-6(1),* Pierides Pr.) Read Bks.

Brinton, Daniel Garrison & Napheys, George H. Personal Beauty: How to Cultivate & Preserve It in Accordance With. 2007. pap. 31.95 *(978-1-4304-5065-8(7))* Kessinger Publishing, LLC.

Brooks, Amanda. I Love Your Style: How to Define & Refine Your Personal Style. 2009. (ENG., Illus.). 288p. pap. 19.99 *(978-0-06-183312-0(6))* HarperCollins Pubs.

Brown, Bobbi. Bobbi Brown Living Beauty. 2009. (ENG.). 224p. pap. 19.99 *(978-0-446-58129-5(1))* Little Brown & Co.

—Bobbi Brown Makeup Manual: For Everyone from Beginner to Pro. (ENG., Illus.). 232p. 2011. pap. 19.99 *(978-0-446-58135-6(6))* 2008. 32.00 *(978-0-446-58134-9(8),* Springboard Pr.) Grand Central Publishing.

Brown, Bobbi. Bobbi Brown Pretty Powerful: Start-To-Finish Makeup Techniques, Fabulous Looks, & Empowering Lessons for Lasting Beauty. 2012. (ENG.). 288p. 29.95 ***(978-0-8118-7704-6(3))*** Chronicle Bks. LLC.

Brown, Bobbi & Paley, Rebecca. Bobbi Brown Beauty Rules: Fabulous Looks, Beauty Essentials, & Life Lessons for Loving Your Teens & Twenties. 2010. (ENG., Illus.). 288p. 24.95 *(978-0-8118-7468-7(0))* Chronicle Bks. LLC.

Buen Aspecto. 2010. (J). pap. 9.99 *(978-84-441-4512-9(2))* Everest Editora ESP. Dist: Lectorum Pubns., Inc.

Burckhardt, Svetlana. Confessions of a Brazilian Waxing Queen. 2011. 132p. 29.99 ***(978-1-4653-0001-0(5))***; pap. 19.99 ***(978-1-4653-0000-3(7))*** Xlibris Corp.

Burnes, Deborah. Look Great, Live Green: Choosing Bodycare Products That Are Safe for You, Safe for the Planet. 2009. (ENG.). 360p. pap. 16.95 *(978-0-89793-521-0(7))* Hunter Hse., Inc.

Burns, Leanna. Soul Beautiful, Naturally. 2007. 197p. per. 16.95 *(978-0-9794585-7-6(9))* Summerland Publishing.

Burres, Steven. Buying Beauty: The Eternal Commodity. 2009. 220p. pap. 16.99 *(978-1-4490-0801-7(1))* AuthorHouse.

Burt, Anne & Kline, Christina Baker, eds. About Face: Women Write about What They See When They Look in the Mirror. 2008. (ENG., Illus.). 256p. pap. 15.95 *(978-1-58005-246-7(0))* Westview Pr.

Cabuk, Lourdes Julian & Turske, Claudia. Yoga for a Beautiful Face: Easy Exercises to Help You Look Young Again. 2011. (ENG., Illus.). 144p. pap. 16.95 *(978-0-89793-526-5(8))* Hunter Hse., Inc.

Callard, Sarah. The Little Green Book of Beauty. 2009. (Little Green Bks.). (ENG., Illus.). 128p. pap. 12.95 *(978-1-84732-069-8(4))* Carlton Bks., Ltd. GBR. Dist: Sterling Publishing Co., Inc.

Campbell, Lady Colin. The Lady's Dressing Room 1892. 2006. (Illus.). 384p. 24.75 *(978-1-873590-62-1(8))* Old Hse. Bks. GBR. Dist: Parkwest Pubns., Inc.

Campen, Rebecca B. The Comprehensive Guide to Skin Care: From Acne to Wrinkles, What to Do (and Not Do) to Stay Healthy & Look Your Best, 1 vol. 2009. 250p. 34.95 *(978-0-313-37886-7(X),* C37886, Praeger Pubs.) Greenwood Publishing Group, Inc.

Campo, Riku. The Best in Beauty: An Ultimate Guide to Makeup & Skincare Techniques, Tools, & Products. 2010. (ENG., Illus.). 304p. pap. 24.99 *(978-1-4391-4825-9(2),* Beyond Words/Atria Bks.) Atria Bks.

Canton, Chamein. Down That Aisle in Style: A Wedding Guide for Full-Figured Women. 2006. (ENG., Illus.). 188p. 34.95 *(978-1-886249-13-4(X))* WindRiver Publishing, Inc.

Carmindy. Crazy Busy Beautiful: Beauty Secrets for Getting Gorgeous Fast. 2010. (ENG.). 336p. pap. 12.99 *(978-0-06-185202-2(3),* William Morrow Paperbacks) HarperCollins Pubs.

—Get Positively Beautiful: The Ultimate Guide to Looking & Feeling Gorgeous. 2010. (ENG., Illus.). 224p. pap. 15.39 *(978-1-59995-144-7(4))* Center St.

—The 5-Minute Face: The Quick & Easy Makeup Guide for Every Woman. 2009. (ENG., Illus.). 208p. pap. 16.99 *(978-0-06-137441-8(5),* William Morrow Paperbacks) HarperCollins Pubs.

Casinni, Fredo. Consejos de Belleza de las Estrellas.Tr. of Celebrity Beauty Tips. (SPA.). 9.98 *(978-970-643-314-5(7))* Selector, S.A. de C.V. MEX. Dist: AIMS International Bks., Inc.

Cecilia, Karen. The Lipstick Classified. 2009. 140p. pap. 14.95 *(978-0-557-15485-2(5))* Lulu Enterprises Inc.

Chairs-Brown, Tawana. Embracing Beauty: What Every Girl Should Know. 2010. 24p. 14.99 *(978-1-4520-4763-8(4))* AuthorHouse.

Champaneri, Bhavna. On Trend: Hairdressing/Beauty. 2011. 48p. pap. 47.01 *(978-1-4520-7252-4(3))* AuthorHouse.

Chang-Babaian, Taylor. Asian Faces: The Essential Beauty & Makeup Guide for Asian Women. 2007. (ENG., Illus.). 176p. (gr. 12-18). pap. 24.95 *(978-0-399-53314-3(1),* Perigee Trade) Penguin Group (USA) Inc.

—Style Eyes. 2010. (ENG.). 144p. (gr. 12). 17.95 *(978-0-399-53596-3(9),* Perigee Trade) Penguin Group (USA) Inc.

Charlton Fascitelli, Melanie & Charlton, Fascitelli M. Shop Your Closet: The Ultimate Guide to Organizing Your Closet with Style. 2008. (ENG., Illus.). 176p. pap. 19.95 *(978-0-06-134381-0(1),* Harper Paperbacks) HarperCollins Pubs.

Chibaya Mbuya, John & MONICA MAPHELA, Bulelwa. Grooming & Etiquette for Corporate Men & Women. 2010. 68p. pap. *(978-3-8383-7471-0(1))* Lambert Academic Publishing.

Chin, Cornel. Celebrity Body on a Budget. 2010. (Illus.). 224p. pap. 14.95 *(978-0-9724102-8-1(7))* Price World Publishing.

Christie, Jackie. Woman: A Practical Guide to Loving the Skin You're In. 2009. 148p. pap. 18.95 *(978-0-9794827-4-8(7))* Infinite Love Publishing.

Clark, Keisha. The Young Lady's Guide to Charm, Style & Femininity. 2007. 82p. per. 8.99 *(978-1-60247-290-7(4))* Tate Publishing & Enterprises, LLC.

Clarke, Laura Hurd. Facing Age: Women Growing Older in Anti-Aging Culture. 2010. ix, 165p. *(978-1-4422-0761-5(2))* Rowman & Littlefield Publishers, Inc.

Cohen, Juliet, et al. Vogue Beauty. 2009. (ENG., Illus.). 400p. pap. 24.95 *(978-1-55407-600-0(5))* Firefly Bks., Ltd.

Cojocaru, Steven. Glamour, Interrupted: How I Became the Best-Dressed Patient in Hollywood. 2008. 176p. 23.95 *(978-0-06-079136-0(5),* Morrow, William & Co.) HarperCollins Pubs.

Color Me Beautiful Organisation Staff. Color Me Beautiful Make up Manual. 2012. (ENG., Illus.). 128p. pap. 17.99 *(978-0-600-62331-1(9),* Hamlyn) Octopus Publishing Group GBR. Dist: Hachette Bk. Group.

Colour Me Beautiful. Be a Beautiful Bride: Walk down the Aisle in Style. 2010. (ENG.). 128p. pap. 17.99 *(978-0-600-62026-6(3),* Hamlyn) Octopus Publishing Group GBR. Dist: Hachette Bk. Group.

Condon, Lora. Spa Wars: The Ugly Truth about the Beauty Industry. 2011. 152p. 24.95 *(978-1-4502-8590-2(2))*; pap. 14.95 *(978-1-4502-8591-9(0))* iUniverse, Inc.

Conrad, Lauren, et al. Lauren Conrad Beauty. 2012. (ENG.). 288p. (J). (gr. 9). 21.99 ***(978-0-06-212845-4(0))*** HarperCollins Pubs.

Conway, Paula & Regan, Maureen. The Beauty Buyble: The Best Beauty Products of 2007. 2007. 144p. pap. 13.95 *(978-0-06-117208-3(1),* HC) HarperCollins Pubs.

Copeland, Michelle. The Beautiful Skin Workout: Eight Weeks to the Smoothest, Healthiest Skin of Your Life. 2007. (ENG., Illus.). 192p. pap. 16.99 *(978-0-312-37077-0(6),* St. Martin's Griffin) St. Martin's Pr.

Copperwaite, Paul. Suited & Booted. 2007. (ENG., Illus.). 64p. *(978-1-84597-506-7(5))* Ryland Peters & Small.

Cosmopolitan Editors, ed. Cosmo's Sexiest Beauty Secrets: The Ultimate Guide to Looking Gorgeous. 2010. (ENG., Illus.). 192p. pap. 16.95 *(978-1-58816-829-0(8))* Hearst Communications, Inc.

Couldridge, Greta, et al. Body Therapy & Facial Work: Electrical Treatments for Beauty Therapists. 4th rev. ed. 2012. (ENG.). 344p. pap. 47.95 *(978-1-4441-3745-3(X))* Hodder Arnold Pubs.

Courtin-Clarins, Olivier. The Courtin Concept: Six Keys to Great Skin at Any Age. 2007. (ENG., Illus.). 160p. per. 19.95 *(978-1-886039-86-5(0))* Addicus Bks.

Covey, Stephen R. Ageless Beauty: An Insider's Guide to Advanced Alternatives to Plastic Surgery. 2009. 150p. pap. 14.95 *(978-1-934937-96-9(7))* Mill City Pr., Inc.

Cox, Caroline. How to Be Adored: A Girl's Guide to Hollywood Glamour. 2010. (ENG.). 256p. 19.99 *(978-0-06-199291-9(7),* Collins Design) HarperCollins Pubs.

Cox, J. Belleza Natural con Productos Naturales: Elabora Tus Propios Productos de Belleza con Planetas y Flores Sin Salir de Casa. (SPA.). 264p. *(978-84-95456-03-8(6),* 87409) Ediciones Oniro S.A.

Cox, Lauren & Cox, Janice. EcoBeauty: Scrubs, Rubs, Masks, & Bath Bombs for You & Your Friends. 2009. (ENG., Illus.). 160p. pap. 19.99 *(978-1-58008-852-7(X))* Ten Speed Pr.

Craig, Ann. Encyclopedie de la Femme, 1: Les Secrets de la Beaute. (FRE.). 144p. 11.95 *(978-0-7859-0742-8(4),* M-6096) French & European Pubns., Inc.

Currie, Lachlan. Everybody's Guide to Cosmetic Plastic Surgery. 2008. 185p. pap. 31.50 *(978-0-9556809-0-8(5))* Gladiator Publishing GBR. Dist: Lulu Enterprises Inc.

Currin, Morag. Oncology Esthetics: A Practitioner's Guide. 2009. x, 461p. pap. ***(978-1-932633-49-8(9))*** Allured Business Media.

Cywinski, Sara. Kate Style Princess: The Fashion & Beauty Secrets of Britain's Most Glamorous Royal. 2011. (ENG., Illus.). 226p. 29.95 *(978-1-84358-393-6(3))* Blake, John Publishing, Ltd. GBR. Dist: Independent Pubs. Group.

Danekilde, Anne Sofie & Mandrup, Louise. Marketing Communications. 2011. 72p. pap. ***(978-3-8443-3093-9(3))*** Lambert Academic Publishing.

Davis, Erin. Graffiti: Learning to See the Art in Ourselves. 2008. (ENG., Illus.). 168p. pap. 13.99 *(978-0-8024-4585-3(3))* Moody Pubs.

B

Day, Doris J. & Forsyth, Sondra. Forget the Facelift: Turn Back the Clock with a Revolutionary Program for Ageless Skin. 2006. (ENG.). 304p. (gr. 12-18). 14.95 *(978-1-58333-261-0(8)*, Avery) Penguin Group (USA) Inc.

Dayal, Roshni. Natural Beauty Secrets from India: Easy, Economical, & Effective Head-to-Toe Home Remedies for a Beautiful You, Naturally. 2009. spiral bd. 13.99 *(978-1-60604-918-1(6))* Tate Publishing & Enterprises, LLC.

de la Fressange, Ines & Gachet, Sophie. Parisian Chic: A Style Guide by Ines de la Fressange. 2011. (ENG., Illus.). 240p. pap. 29.95 *(978-2-08-020073-0(9))* Flammarion et Cie FRA. Dist: Random Hse., Inc.

Dene, Debe. Now hair This! The Destruction of Black Hair. 2008. (Illus.). 141p. pap. 12.95 *(978-0-9801242-0-0(4))* Tell Pubns.

Diaz, Monica. 7 Days to Style. 2010. pap. 16.99 *(978-0-578-05625-8(9))* Style Matters Inc.

Dickinson, Janice. Everything about Me Is Fake... And I'm Perfect. 2006. (Illus.). 272p. pap. 14.95 *(978-0-06-055470-5(3))* HarperCollins Pubs.

Dion, Christine. High Performance Beauty: Makeup & Skin Care for Dance, Cheer, Show Choir, Pageants & Ice Skating. 2007. (ENG., Illus.). 128p. pap. 24.95 *(978-0-87127-303-1(9))* Princeton Bk. Co. Pubs.

Doonan, Simon. Eccentric Glamour: Creating an Insanely More Fabulous You. 2009. (ENG., Illus.). 304p. pap. 15.00 *(978-1-4165-3544-7(6))* Simon & Schuster.

Douglas, Kym & Pearlman, Cindy. The Beauty Cookbook: Over 200 Recipes to Make Your Kitchen Your Own Personal Spa — for Your Face, Your Body & Your Hair. 2010. 224p. pap. 14.99 *(978-1-61623-576-5(4))* Independent Pub.

—The Black Book of Hollywood Beauty Secrets. 2006. (ENG., Illus.). 256p. (gr. 12-18). 15.00 *(978-0-452-28765-5(0)*, Plume) Penguin Group (USA) Inc.

Downing, Sarah. Beauty & Cosmetics, 1550-1950. 2012. (Shire Library). (ENG., Illus.). 64p. pap. 12.95 ***(978-0-7478-0839-8(2))*** Shire Pubns., Ltd. GBR. Dist: Random Hse., Inc.

Drayer, Lisa. The Beauty Diet: Looking Great Has Never Been So Delicious. 2008. (ENG.). 288p. 22.95 *(978-0-07-154477-1(1)*, 0071544771) McGraw-Hill Cos., The.

Durand, Phebe. Spa Menu. 2008. 59p. pap. 32.50 *(978-1-4357-2307-8(4))* Lulu Enterprises Inc.

Dwivedi, Sharada & Holkar, Shalini Devi. Almond Eyes, Lotus Feet: Indian Traditions in Beauty & Health. 2007. (ENG., Illus.). 272p. 27.50 *(978-0-06-124653-1(0)*, Morrow, William & Co.) HarperCollins Pubs.

Dyhouse, Carol. Glamour: History, Women, Feminism. 2011. (ENG., Illus.). 238p. pap. 19.99 *(978-1-84813-861-2(X))* Zed Bks., Ltd. GBR. Dist: Macmillan.

—Glamour: Women, History, Feminism. 2010. (ENG., Illus.). 238p. 30.00 *(978-1-84813-407-2(X))* Zed Bks., Ltd. GBR. Dist: Macmillan.

Earle, Liz. Belleza Natural.Tr. of Liz Earle's Natural Beauty. (SPA.). 304p. 9.50 *(978-84-7927-162-6(0)*, RB9029) Robinbk., Ediciones S.L. ESP. Dist: Lectorum Pubns., Inc.

Edmonds, Alexander. Pretty Modern: Beauty, Sex, & Plastic Surgery in Brazil. 2010. (ENG., Illus.). 312p. 89.95 *(978-0-8223-4785-9(7))*; pap. 24.95 *(978-0-8223-4801-6(2))* Duke Univ. Pr.

Eiseman, Leatrice. More Alive with Color: Personal Colors — Personal Style. 2007. (Capital Lifestyles Ser.). (Illus.). 176p. pap. 10.00 *(978-1-933102-41-2(1))* Capital Bks., Inc.

Ellinwood, Ellae, et al. Earth Is Your Sweet Spot: Living Beautifully, a Woman's Guide. 2012. (ENG.). 128p. pap. 12.95 *(978-1-935952-03-9(X)*, Confluence Bks.) White Cloud Pr.

Ellis, Stella. Size Sexy: How to Look Good, Feel Good, & Be Happy - at Any Size. 2010. (ENG., Illus.). 216p. pap. 16.95 *(978-1-60550-355-4(X))* Adams Media Corp.

Emergency Nail Kit. (Mini Lifestyle Kits Ser.). 32p. *(978-1-84510-809-0(4))* Top That! Publishing PLC.

Epstein, Samuel S. & Fitzgerald, Randall. Healthy Beauty: Your Guide to Ingredients to Avoid & Products You Can Trust. 2010. (ENG.). 284p. pap. 16.95 *(978-1-935251-72-9(4))* BenBella Bks.

Essig, Laurie. American Plastic: Boob Jobs, Credit Cards, & Our Quest for Perfection. 2011. (ENG.). 248p. pap. 20.00 *(978-0-8070-0323-7(9))* Beacon Pr.

Fairley, Josephine & Stacey, Sarah. Feel Fab Forever: The Anti-Ageing Health & Beauty Bible. rev. ed. 2008. (ENG., Illus.). 256p. pap. *(978-1-85626-685-7(0))* Cathie, Kyle Ltd. GBR. Dist: Independent Pubs. Group.

Farley, Jenni Jwoww. The Rules According to Jwoww: Shore-Tested Secrets on Landing a Mint Guy, Staying Fresh to Death, & Kicking the Competition to the Curb. 2012. (ENG., Illus.). 224p. pap. 14.99 ***(978-0-06-208218-3(3)**, William Morrow Paperbacks)* HarperCollins Pubs.

Faxton, Carlita. Be Beautiful from Your Head to Your Feet. Date not set. 52p. (Orig.). pap. *(978-0-9636553-4-9(5))* Faxton, Carlita.

Fergason, Shannon. Simple Steps to a Beautiful Face. rev. ed. 2007. (ENG.). 64p. pap. 31.21 *(978-0-7575-4186-5(0))* Kendall Hunt Publishing Co.

Flaherty, Somer & Kollmer, Jen. Girl in a Fix: Quick Beauty Solutions (And Why They Work) 2007. (ENG., Illus.). 96p. (YA). (gr. 7-18). pap. 9.95 *(978-0-9772660-2-9(8))* Zest Bks.

Fletcher, Jefferson B. The Religion of Beauty in Woman, & Other Essays on Platonic Love in Poetry & Society. 205p. reprint ed. 98.00 *(978-0-7222-1765-8(X))* Library Reprints, Inc.

Floyd, Esme. 1001 Little Beauty Miracles: Secrets & Solutions from Head to Toe. 2012. (ENG., Illus.). 224p. pap. 14.95 ***(978-1-84732-952-3(7))*** Carlton Bks., Ltd. GBR. Dist: Independent Pubs. Group.

Floyd, Esme & Baxter-Wright, Emma. The Beauty Secrets Book: 2000 Head-to-Toe Tricks & Tips for Looking Gorgeous. 2011. (ENG., Illus.). 400p. pap. 16.95 *(978-1-84732-654-6(4))* Carlton Bks., Ltd. GBR. Dist: Sterling Publishing Co., Inc.

France, Kim & Linett, Andrea. The Lucky Guide to Mastering Any Style: How to Wear Iconic Looks & Make Them Your Own. 2008. (ENG.). 312p. (gr. 12-18). 30.00 *(978-1-59240-402-5(2)*, Gotham) Penguin Group (USA) Inc.

Franklin, Eric. Inner Focus, Outer Strength: Using Imagery & Exercise for Strength, Health & Beauty. 2006. (ENG., Illus.). 128p. per. 19.95 *(978-0-87127-288-1(1))* Princeton Bk. Co. Pubs.

Franklin, Regina. Designed by God: Honest Talk about Beauty, Modesty, & Self-Image. 2006. (ENG.). 128p. per. 9.99 *(978-1-57293-174-9(4))* Discovery Hse. Pubs.

Friedman, Paul, et al. Beautiful Skin Revealed: The Ultimate Guide to Better Skin. 2010. (ENG., Illus.). 176p. 59.95 *(978-0-9800398-2-5(7))* Sandow Media.

From the Editors of Marie Claire, ed. Gorgeous Face & Beautiful Body: A Guide to Total Skin Care. 2010. (ENG., Illus.). 192p. pap. 17.95 *(978-1-58816-667-8(8))* Hearst Communications, Inc.

Fuentes, Daisy. Unforgettable You: Master the Elements of Style, Spirituality, & True Beauty. 2012. (ENG., Illus.). 352p. pap. 21.99 *(978-1-4165-6303-7(2)*, Beyond Words/Atria Bks.) Atria Bks.

Gabriel, Julie. The Green Beauty Guide: Your Essential Resource to Organic & Natural Skin Care, Hair Care, Makeup, & Fragrances. 2008. (ENG.). 416p. pap. 16.95 *(978-0-7573-0747-8(7))* Health Communications, Inc.

Gallagher, Dawn. Nature's Beauty Secrets: Recipes for Beauty Treatments from the World's Best Spas. 2011. (ENG., Illus.). 192p. 35.00 *(978-0-7893-2211-1(0))* Universe Publishing.

Gantt, Morgan. How to Wear Your Hair: Hair Dos & Don'ts for Your Face Shape. 2010. 24.99 *(978-1-61566-908-0(6))* Tate Publishing & Enterprises, LLC.

Garcia, Nina. The Little Black Book of Style. 2007. (ENG., Illus.). 160p. 19.99 *(978-0-06-123490-3(7))* HarperCollins Pubs.

—The One Hundred: A Guide to the Pieces Every Stylish Woman Must Own. 2008. (ENG., Illus.). 304p. 21.99 *(978-0-06-166461-8(8))* HarperCollins Pubs.

Garcia, Oz. Redesigning 50: The No-Plastic-Surgery Guide to 21st-Century Age Defiance. 2008. (ENG.). 256p. 27.95 *(978-0-06-076047-2(8)*, Morrow, William & Co.) HarperCollins Pubs.

Garcia, Oz & Kolberg, Sharyn. Redesigning 50: The No Plastic Surgery Guide to 21st-Century Age Defiance. 2009. (Illus.). 256p. pap. 16.99 *(978-0-06-085976-3(8)*, Collins Living) HarperCollins Pubs.

Garrett, Ginger. Beauty Secrets of the Bible: The Ancient Arts of Beauty & Fragrance, 0 vols. 2007. 160p. per. 13.99 *(978-0-7852-2178-4(6))* Nelson, Thomas Inc.

Goddard-Clark, Lorri. The Hair Color Mix: More Than 150 Recipes for Salon-Perfect Color at Home. 2008. (ENG., Illus.). 320p. pap. 19.99 *(978-0-06-114790-6(7)*, Harper Paperbacks) HarperCollins Pubs.

Godfrey-June, Jean. Free Gift with Purchase: My Improbable Career in Magazines & Makeup. 2007. (ENG.). 272p. per. 12.95 *(978-0-307-23749-1(4)*, Three Rivers Pr.) Crown Publishing Group.

Goldstein, Nikki. GirlForce: Shine. 2009. (ENG., Illus.). 176p. (YA). (gr. 5-9). pap. 12.99 *(978-1-59990-355-2(5))* Bloomsbury Publishing.

Goroway, Patricia. Facial Fitness: Daily Exercise & Massage Techniques for a Healthier, Younger Looking You. 2006. *(978-0-7607-8094-7(3))* Barnes & Noble, Inc.

—Facial Fitness: Daily Exercises & Massage Techniques for a Healthier, Younger Looking You. 2011. (ENG., Illus.). 192p. pap. 14.95 *(978-1-4027-8046-2(X))* Sterling Publishing Co., Inc.

Green-Tarantelli, Holly. Goddess Glow. 2007. 56p. pap. 28.95 *(978-1-4303-2261-0(6))* Lulu Enterprises Inc.

Grimble, Frances, ed. The Ladys Stratagem: A Repository of 1820s Directions for the Toilet, Mantua-Making, Stay-Making, Millinery & Etiquette. 2009. (Illus.). 755p. pap. 75.00 *(978-0-9636517-7-8(3))* Lavolta Pr.

Gross, Kim Johnson. What to Wear for the Rest of Your Life: Ageless Secrets of Style. 2010. (ENG., Illus.). 288p. 24.99 *(978-0-446-53494-9(3)*, Springboard Pr.) Grand Central Publishing.

Gundle, Stephen. Glamour: A History. (ENG., Illus.). 2009. 496p. pap. 24.95 *(978-0-19-956978-6(9))* 2008. 320p. 45.00 *(978-0-19-921098-5(5))* Oxford Univ. Pr., Inc.

Gundle, Stephen & Castelli, Clino T. The Glamour System. 2006. (ENG.). 224p. 100.00 *(978-0-333-73380-6(0))* Palgrave Macmillan.

Hamermesh, Daniel S. Beauty Pays: Why Attractive People Are More Successful. 2011. (ENG., Illus.). 228p. 24.95 ***(978-0-691-14046-9(4))*** Princeton Univ. Pr.

Hamilton, Douglas, et al. Beverly Hills Beauty Secrets: A Prominent Dermatologist & Plastic Surgeon's Insider Guide to Facial Rejuvenation. 2009. (ENG., Illus.). 272p. 24.95 *(978-0-470-29403-1(5)*, Wiley) Wiley, John & Sons, Inc.

Hamlyn. Bikini Fit: A Pyramid Health Paperback. 2009. pap. 9.95 *(978-0-600-62155-3(3)*, Hamlyn) Octopus Publishing Group GBR. Dist: Hachette Bk. Group.

Haobsh, Nadine. Beauty Confidential: The No Preaching, No Lies, Advice-You'll-Actually-Use Guide to Looking Your Best. 2007. (Illus.). 304p. per. 13.99 *(978-0-06-112863-9(5)*, William Morrow Paperbacks) HarperCollins Pubs.

Harris, Lisa Delmedico. Beauty, Poise, & Righteousness: Walking as a King's Daughter. 2007. (YA). per. *(978-1-59872-794-4(X))* Instant Pub.

Harrison, Andrea & Scott, Joan. Spa: The Official Guide to Spa Therapy at Levels 2 And 3. 2006. (ENG., Illus.). 384p. (C). pap. 82.95 *(978-1-84480-312-5(0))* Cengage Learning GBR. Dist: CENGAGE Learning.

Hatzaki, Myrto. Beauty & the Male Body in Byzantium: Perceptions & Representations in Art & Text. 2009. (ENG., Illus.). 240p. 89.00 *(978-0-230-00715-4(5))* Palgrave Macmillan.

Hayes, Gail M. Daughters of the King. 260p. pap. *(978-1-886853-00-3(2))* Joshua Publishing.

Hemingway, Mariel. Healthy Living from the Inside Out: Every Woman's Guide to Real Beauty, Renewed Energy, & a Radiant Life. 2006. (ENG., Illus.). 224p. 26.95 *(978-0-06-089039-1(8)*, HarperOne) HarperCollins Pubs.

—Mariel Hemingway's Healthy Living from the Inside Out: Every Woman's Guide to Real Beauty, Renewed Energy, & a Radiant Life. 2007. (Illus.). 288p. per. 17.95 *(978-0-06-089040-7(1)*, HarperOne) HarperCollins Pubs.

Henderson, Veronique & Henshaw, Pat. Color Me Confident: Change Your Look - Change Your Life! 2008. (ENG., Illus.). 192p. pap. 17.99 *(978-0-600-61499-9(9)*, Hamlyn) Octopus Publishing Group GBR. Dist: Hachette Bk. Group.

—Color Me Younger: How to Look Younger & Feel Great! 2009. (ENG.). 160p. pap. 17.99 *(978-0-600-61961-1(3)*, Hamlyn) Octopus Publishing Group GBR. Dist: Hachette Bk. Group.

Hernandez, Gabriela. Classic Beauty: The History of Makeup. 2011. (Illus.). 256p. 49.99 ***(978-0-7643-3690-4(8)**,* Schiffer Publishing Ltd) Schiffer Publishing, Ltd.

Herron, Tara J. The Definitive Spa & Body Therapist's Handbook: The 5 Keys to Unlimited Energy, Balance & Bliss. 2008. (ENG., Illus.). 196p. pap. 24.95 *(978-1-84694-097-2(4))* Hunt, John Publishing Ltd. GBR. Dist: National Bk. Network.

Hill, Pamela. Advanced Face & Body Treatments for the Spa. 2007. (ENG.). 320p. (C). pap. 56.95 *(978-1-4018-8175-7(0)*, Milady Publishing Co.) Delmar Cengage Learning.

Hill, Pamela & Bickmore, Helen. Advanced Hair Removal. 2007. (ENG., Illus.). 360p. (C). per. 56.95 *(978-1-4018-8174-0(2)*, Milady Publishing Co.) Delmar Cengage Learning.

Holt, Victoria. Spiritual Facelift. 2011. 224p. pap. 15.95 ***(978-0-87604-625-8(1))*** A.R.E. Pr.

Home Spa. 2008. (Health Ser.). 64p. *(978-1-4075-4000-9(9))* Parragon, Inc.

Homer, Karen. Things a Woman Should Know about Beauty. 2012. (Things A Woman Should Know Ser.). (ENG., Illus.). 208p. 17.95 ***(978-1-85375-830-0(2))*** Prion GBR. Dist: Independent Pubs. Group.

Hope, Babe. Pretty Plus: How to Look Sexy, Sensational, & Successful, No Matter What You Weigh. 2010. (ENG., Illus.). 224p. pap. 14.95 *(978-0-88282-317-1(5))* New Horizon Pr. Pubs., Inc.

Hopkins, Christopher. Staging Your Comeback: A Complete Beauty Revival for Women Over 45. 2008. (ENG., Illus.). 344p. pap. 22.95 *(978-0-7573-0634-1(9))* Health Communications, Inc.

Hosford, Zia W. Face Value: Skin Care for Women over 35. rev. ed. (Illus.). reprint ed. pap. *(978-0-9628057-0-7(X))* Zia Cosmetics, Inc.

Hughes, Joanna. The Numbers Book: A Girl's Guide, 9 Rules to A Healthy, Happy & Beautiful Life. 2010. 116p. 24.99 *(978-1-4490-5120-4(0))* AuthorHouse.

Hunter, Emily, et al. Christian Charm Course (student) Today's Social Graces for Every Girl. 2009. 80p. (YA). pap. 9.99 *(978-0-7369-2576-1(7))* Harvest Hse. Pubs.

—Christian Charm Course (teacher) Today's Social Graces for Every Girl. 2009. 112p. pap. 12.99 *(978-0-7369-2577-8(5))* Harvest Hse. Pubs.

Hurd Clarke, Laura. Facing Age: Women Growing Older in Anti-Aging Culture. 2010. (Diversity & Aging Ser.). (ENG.). 176p. (C). (gr. 13-17). 75.00 *(978-1-4422-0759-2(0))*; pap. 22.95 *(978-1-4422-0760-8(4))* Rowman & Littlefield Publishers, Inc.

Ifould, Judith, et al. Beauty Therapy. 3rd rev. ed. 2011. (ENG.). 480p. pap. 37.95 *(978-1-4441-3543-5(0))* Hodder Arnold Pubs.

Ifould, Judith, et al. Level 3 Beauty Therapy for NVQ & VRQ Diploma. 2012. (ENG.). 512p. pap. 65.00 ***(978-1-4441-6835-8(5))*** Hodder Arnold Pubs.

Im, Hyong-Son, et al. Modon Kol, Ch'ijang Hada. 2008. (KOR., Illus.). 335p. *(978-89-8236-452-5(8))* National History Compilation Committee.

Iman. The Beauty of Color: The Ultimate Beauty Guide for Skin of Color. 2006. (ENG., Illus.). 176p. (gr. 12-18). 24.95 *(978-0-399-53284-9(6)*, Perigee Trade) Penguin Group (USA) Inc.

Indrani. Image Perfection: Define Who You Are to Get What You Want. 2011. 256p. 23.99 *(978-0-06-196910-2(9)*, HarperOne) HarperCollins Pubs.

Irwin, Brandith. The Surgery-Free Makeover: All You Need to Know for Great Skin & a Younger Face. 2008. (ENG., Illus.). 304p. 24.00 *(978-0-7382-1118-3(4))* Da Capo Pr., Inc.

Jacobsen, Pia. Pia... Me: A Fashion & Lifestyle Guide for Girls Who Aspire to be Their Best. 2010. 156p. 18.95 *(978-1-4269-2727-0(4))* Trafford Publishing.

Jaliman, Debra. Skin Rules: Trade Secrets from a Top New York Dermatologist. 2012. (ENG.). 208p. 22.99 ***(978-1-250-00095-8(5))*** St. Martin's Pr.

James, Kat. The Truth about Beauty: Transform Your Looks & Your Life from the Inside Out. 2nd ed. 2007. (ENG., Illus.). 432p. pap. 24.00 *(978-1-58270-195-6(4)*, Beyond Words/Atria Bks.) Atria Bks.

Janus. Looking Good. 2nd ed. pap. *(978-0-8224-4247-9(7)*, 4247) Globe Fearon Educational Publishing.

Jaoui, Sylvaine. For Girls Only: The Ultimate Guide to Being a Girl. Bussell, Andrea, ed. 2010. (Sunscreen Ser.). (ENG., Illus.). 112p. (YA). (gr. 7-11). pap. 10.95 *(978-0-8109-8432-5(6)*, Amulet Bks.) Abrams.

Jefferis, B. G. The Science of Eugenics. 2007. 352p. per. *(978-1-4068-3522-9(6))* Echo Library.

Jobity, Natalie. Frumpy to Fabulous: Your Ultimate Guide to Effortless Style. Revised Edition. rev. ed. 2010. (Illus.). 232p. pap. 18.95 *(978-0-9829297-0-4(6))* Elan Image Management LLC.

Johnson, Kalimah. Locs for Life: The Root to Well Being for African-American Women. 2008. 132p. pap. 12.00 *(978-1-4343-5721-2(X))* AuthorHouse.

Johnson, Lois Joy & Linter, Sandy. The Makeup Wakeup: Revitalizing Your Look at Any Age. 2011. (ENG.). 288p. pap. 23.00 *(978-0-7624-3935-5(1))* Running Pr. Bk. Pubs.

Jones, Caroline. 1001 Wys to Spend Less & Look Beautiful. 2010. (ENG., Illus.). 224p. pap. 9.95 *(978-1-84732-387-3(1))* Carlton Bks., Ltd. GBR. Dist: Sterling Publishing Co., Inc.

Jones, Kristle. LifeTips 101 Bridal Beauty Tips. 2007. 9.99 *(978-1-60275-026-5(2))* LifeTips.

Jones, Marlene. The Complete Guide to Creating Oils, Soaps, Creams, & Herbal Gels for Your Mind & Body: 101 Natural Body Care Recipes. 2010. 288p. pap. 24.95 *(978-1-60138-369-3(X))* Atlantic Publishing Co.

Jones, Robert. Makeup Makeovers: Weddings - Stunning Looks for the Entire Bridal Party. 2006. (ENG., Illus.). 136p. pap. 24.95 *(978-1-59233-231-1(5)*, 1592332315) Quayside.

—Makeup Makeovers Beauty Bible: Expert Secrets for Stunning Transformations. rev. exp. ed. 2011. (ENG., Illus.). 288p. spiral bd., spiral bd. 19.99 *(978-1-59233-473-5(3)*, 1592334733) Quayside.

Jones, Robert. Makeup Makeovers in 5, 10, 15, & 20 Minutes: Expert Secrets for Stunning Transformations. 2012. (ENG., Illus.). 320p. pap. 22.99 ***(978-1-59233-371-4(0)**,* 1592333710) Quayside.

Just Janet. Bitch: A New Statement on Beauty. 2009. 56p. pap. 23.99 *(978-1-4389-7253-4(9))* AuthorHouse.

—Bitch, Bang! Beautiful, Intuitive, Talented, Creative, & Happy! A New Statement on Beauty. 2009. 136p. pap. 11.99 *(978-1-4389-7716-4(6))* AuthorHouse.

Karolyi, Julia. C. H. A. R. m: How to Make Your World a More Beautiful Place. 2010. (ENG., Illus.). 191p. pap. 14.95 *(978-0-9822583-1-6(3))* Continental Shelf Publishing.

Katz, Erika. Bonding over Beauty. 2011. 240p. pap. 14.95 *(978-1-60832-098-1(7))* Greenleaf Book Group.

Keith, Juanita O. Your Radiant Body Series of Booklets. rev. ed. Date not set. 148p. pap. *(978-0-9628351-3-1(7))* Archer Creative Pr.

Kelly, Clinton. Freakin' Fabulous: How to Dress, Speak, Behave, Eat, Drink, Entertain, Decorate, & Generally Be Better Than Everyone Else. 2008. (ENG., Illus.). 256p. 26.00 *(978-1-4169-6149-9(6))* Gallery Pr., The IRL. Dist: Simon & Schuster, Inc.

Kenton, Leslie. Ultra Health. (Illus.). 320p. pap. 11.95 *(978-0-09-956660-1(5))* Random Hse. GBR. Dist: Trafalgar Square Publishing.

Keogh, Pamela. Are You a Jackie or a Marilyn? Timeless Lessons on Love, Power, & Style. (ENG.). 272p. (gr. 12). 2011. 16.00 *(978-1-59240-677-7(7))* 2010. 22.50 *(978-1-59240-569-5(X))* Penguin Group (USA) Inc. (Gotham).

Khachara, Star. The Holistic Beauty Book: Over 100 Natural Recipes for Gorgeous Healthy Skin. 2009. (ENG., Illus.). 176p. pap. 22.00 *(978-1-900322-27-0(7))* Green Bks. GBR. Dist: Chelsea Green Publishing.

Kidd, Jemma. Jemma Kidd Make-up Masterclass: Beauty Bible of Professional Techniques & Wearable Looks. 2009. (ENG., Illus.). 224p. 24.99 *(978-0-312-57371-3(5))* St. Martin's Pr.

Koda, Harold, pref. 100 Dresses: The Costume Institute - The Metropolitan Museum of Art. 2010. (Illus.). 232p. pap. 24.95 *(978-0-300-16655-2(9))* Yale Univ. Pr.

Koda, Harold & Yohannan, Kohle. The Model As Muse: Embodying Fashion. 2009. 35.00 *(978-1-58839-313-5(5))*; 50.00 *(978-1-58839-312-8(7))* Metropolitan Museum of Art, The.

Koopman, LeRoy. Salon de Belleza para el Oido: Beauty Care for the Ears. (SPA.). 80p. *(978-84-7228-613-9(4)*, 220786) Clie, Editorial.

—Salon de Belleza para las Manos: Beauty Care for the Hands. (SPA.). 112p. *(978-84-7228-507-1(3)*, 220789) Clie, Editorial.

—Salon de Belleza para los Ojos: Beauty Care for the Eyes. (SPA.). *(978-84-7228-395-4(X)*, 220791) Clie, Editorial.

—Salon de Belleza para los Pies: Beauty Care for the Feet. (SPA.). *(978-84-7228-557-6(X)*, 220785) Clie, Editorial.

Krupp, Charla. How Not to Look Old: Fast & Effortless Ways to Look 10 Years Younger, 10 Pounds Lighter, 10 Times Better. 2009. (ENG., Illus.). 232p. pap. 15.99 *(978-0-446-69997-6(7)*, Springboard Pr.) Grand Central Publishing.

—How Not to Look Old: Fast & Effortless Ways to Look 10 Years Younger, 10 Pounds Lighter, 10 Times Better. 2008. (ENG., Illus.). 232p. 25.99 *(978-0-446-58114-1(3))* Little Brown & Co.

—How to Never Look Fat Again: Over 1,000 Ways to Dress Thinner — Without Dieting! (ENG., Illus.). 264p. 2011. pap. 15.99 *(978-0-446-54746-8(8))* 2010. 26.99 *(978-0-446-54747-5(6)*, Springboard Pr.) Grand Central Publishing.

Kunin, Audrey & Gottlieb, Bill. The Dermadoctor Skinstruction Manual: The Smart Guide to Healthy, Beautiful Skin & Looking Good at Any Age. 2006. (Illus.). 397p. reprint ed. 25.00 *(978-1-4223-5748-4(1))* DIANE Publishing Co.

LaFlesh, Teri. Curly Like Me: How to Grow Your Hair Healthy, Long, & Strong. 2010. (ENG., Illus.). 288p. pap. 16.95 *(978-0-470-53642-1(X))* Wiley, John & Sons, Inc.

Lautin, Everett M., et al. You Don't Need Plastic Surgery: The Doctor's Guide to Youthful Looks with No Surgery, No Pain, No Downtime. 2006. 225p. reprint ed. 22.00 *(978-1-4223-5837-5(2))* DIANE Publishing Co.

Lerner, Dick. Dress Like the Big Fish: How to Achieve the Image You Want & the Success You Deserve. 2008. (ENG.). 210p. pap. 17.95 *(978-0-9793463-0-9(4))* Bel Air Fashions Pr.

Lester, Meera & Dean, Carolyn. 365 Ways to Look - & Feel - Younger: Everyday Tips to Reduce Wrinkles, Improve Memory, Boost Libido, Build Muscles, & More! 2009. (ENG.). 224p. pap. 8.95 *(978-1-4405-0222-4(6))* Adams Media Corp.

Levin, Jenny. Harper's Bazaar Great Style: Best Ways to Update Your Look. 2010. (ENG., Illus.). 240p. pap. 19.95 *(978-1-58816-800-9(X))* Hearst Communications, Inc.

—Harper's Bazaar Great Style: The Best Ways to Update Your Look. 2007. (ENG.). 240p. 24.95 *(978-1-58816-673-9(2))* Hearst Communications, Inc.

Liddell, Louise A. & Samuels, Carolee S. Clothes & Your Appearance. 9th ed. 2008. (ENG., Illus.). 600p. (gr. 7-12). 68.00 *(978-1-59070-685-5(4))* Goodheart-Willcox Pub.

Linamen, Karen. A Waist Is a Terrible Thing to Mind: Loving Your Body, Accepting Yourself, & Living Without Regret. 2010. (ENG.). 208p. pap. 13.99 *(978-1-4000-7401-3(0)*, WaterBrook Pr.) Doubleday Religious Publishing Group, The.

Linamen, Karen Scalf. A Waist Is a Terrible Thing to Mind: Loving Your Body, Accepting Yourself, & Living without Regret. Lt. ed. 2010. (ENG.). 288p. pap. 17.99 *(978-1-59415-326-6(4))* Cengage Gale.

Listowska Ma, Agata A. & NICHOLSON ASO, Mark A. Complementary Medicine, Beauty & Modeling. 2011. 462p. 34.99 ***(978-1-4568-8896-1(X))***; pap. 23.99 ***(978-1-4568-8895-4(1))*** Xlibris Corp.

Loehr, Gina. Choosing Beauty: A 30-Day Spiritual Makeover for Women. 2009. xi, 116p. pap. 12.99 *(978-0-86716-921-8(4))* Franciscan Media.

Look Better Naked! Food & Fitness Journal. 2010. pap. *(978-1-60961-042-5(3))* Rodale Pr., Inc.

Lubin, Judy. The Heart of Living Well: Six Principles for a Life of Health, Beauty & Balance. 2007. 180p. pap. 18.95 *(978-0-615-15139-7(6))* Heart & Style Bks.

Ludy, Leslie. The Lost Art of True Beauty: The Set-Apart Girl's Guide to Feminine Grace. 2010. 176p. pap. 10.99 *(978-0-7369-2290-6(3))* Harvest Hse. Pubs.

Luftman, Debra, et al. The Beauty Prescription: The Complete Formula for Looking & Feeling Beautiful. 2008. (ENG., Illus.). 304p. 24.95 *(978-0-07-154763-5(0)*, 0071547630) McGraw-Hill Cos., The.

Lustig, Andrea Pomerantz. How to Look Expensive: A Beauty Editor's Secrets to Getting Gorgeous without Breaking the Bank. 2012. (ENG.). 224p. (gr. 12). pap. 22.50 ***(978-1-59240-723-1(4)***, Gotham) Penguin Group (USA) Inc.

Madhok, Michelle. Wear This Now: Your Style Solution for Every Season & Any Occasion. 2012. (ENG.). 320p. pap. ***(978-0-373-89259-4(4))*** Harlequin Enterprises, Ltd.

Maggio, Carole. Ultimate Facercise: The Complete & Balanced Muscle-Toning Program for Renewed Vitality & a More Youthful Appearance. 2011. (ENG.). 128p. (gr. 12). 14.95 *(978-0-399-53667-0(1)*, Perigee Trade) Penguin Group (USA) Inc.

Maida, Marybeth & Kederer, Debbie. Beauty Pearls for Chemo Girls. 2009. (ENG.). 288p. pap. 14.95 *(978-0-8065-3118-2(5)*, Citadel Pr.) Kensington Publishing Corp.

Margolies, Eva & Jones, Stan. Seven Days to Sex Appeal: How to Be Sexier Without Surgery, Weight Loss, or Cleavage. 2008. (ENG., Illus.). 240p. pap. 18.99 *(978-0-7407-6069-3(6))* Andrews McMeel Publishing.

Marmur, Ellen. Simple Skin Beauty: Every Woman's Guide to a Lifetime of Healthy, Gorgeous Skin. (ENG., Illus.). 384p. 2010. pap. 15.00 *(978-1-4165-8697-5(0))* 2009. 27.00 *(978-1-4165-8696-8(2))* Atria Bks. (Beyond Words/Atria Bks.).

Marrone, Margo. The Organic Pharmacy: The Complete Guide to Natural Health & Beauty. 2009. (ENG., Illus.). 212p. pap. 22.95 *(978-1-84483-732-8(7))* Duncan Baird Pubs. GBR. Dist: Sterling Publishing Co., Inc.

Mars, Brigitte. Beauty by Nature. 2006. (ENG., Illus.). 192p. per. 18.95 *(978-1-57067-193-7(1)*, 1265704) Book Publishing Co.

Martin, Jill & Ravich, Dana. I Have Nothing to Wear! A Painless 12-Step Program to Declutter Your Life So You Never Have to Say This Again! 2011. (ENG., Illus.). 256p. 25.99 *(978-1-60529-077-5(7))* Rodale Pr., Inc.

Marwick, Arthur. A History of Human Beauty. 2007. (ENG., Illus.). 276p. per. 27.95 *(978-1-84725-050-6(5)*, Hambledon Continuum) Continuum International Publishing Group, Ltd. GBR. Dist: National Bk. Network.

Mason, Linda. Makeup for Ageless Beauty: More than 40 Colorful, Creative Looks for Women 40 & Over. 2011. (ENG., Illus.). 176p. pap. 19.99 *(978-0-8230-2479-7(2))* Watson-Guptill Pubns., Inc.

Mauceri, Rita & Rubin, Elycia. Curves Rule & Flat Is Fabulous: Sexy, Stylish Looks for Every Figure. 2009. (ENG.). 144p. 18.95 *(978-0-8065-2881-6(8)*, Citadel Pr.) Kensington Publishing Corp.

McCormack, Win, et al, eds. Tin House Special 50th Issue: Beauty. 2011. (ENG.). 220p. pap. 12.95 ***(978-0-9826507-5-2(2))*** Tin Hse. Bks., LLC.

McCoy, Lynn. How to Communicate Better with Your Hairdresser. 2010. 54p. pap. 14.99 *(978-0-557-06157-0(1))* Lulu Enterprises Inc.

McDuffie, Lora. Hygiene & Appearance: What Every Pre-Teen & Teenage Girl Should Know. 2009. 57p. pap. 16.95 *(978-1-60749-598-7(8))* PublishAmerica, Inc.

McGraw, Robin. What's Age Got to Do with It? Living Your Healthiest & Happiest Life. 0 vols. 2008. 240p. 24.99 *(978-1-4002-0214-0(0))*; pap. 14.99 ***(978-1-4002-8067-4(2))*** Nelson, Thomas Inc.

McQuade, Pamela. Spiritually Rich & Sexy. 2011. 206p. pap. 16.95 ***(978-1-935340-72-0(7))*** Worthy Shorts.

Milady. Exam Review for Milady Standard Cosmetology 2012. 2011. (ENG.). 176p. (C). pap. 33.95 ***(978-1-4390-5921-0(7))*** Delmar Cengage Learning.

—Spanish Translated Exam Review for Milady Standard Cosmetology 2012. 3rd ed. 2011. (ENG.). (C). pap. 43.95 ***(978-1-4390-5907-4(1)***, Milady Publishing Co.) Delmar Cengage Learning.

Milady Publishing Company Staff. Hair Coloring & Restoration. 2006. (ENG., Illus.). 120p. per. 54.50 *(978-1-4180-5090-0(3)*, Milady Publishing Co.) Delmar Cengage Learning.

—Haircutting & Styling. 2006. (ENG., Illus.). 120p. per. 54.50 *(978-1-4180-5089-4(X)*, Milady Publishing Co.) Delmar Cengage Learning.

—Milady U: Access Code. 2008. (ENG.). (C). 31.50 *(978-1-4354-1960-5(X)*, Milady Publishing Co.) Delmar Cengage Learning.

Miller, Alan S. & Kanazawa, Satoshi. Why Beautiful People Have More Daughters: From Dating, Shopping, & Praying to Going to War & Becoming a Billionaire- Two Evolutionary Psychologists Explain Why We Do What We Do. 2008. (ENG.). 272p. (gr. 12-18). 16.00 *(978-0-399-53453-9(9)*, Perigee Trade) Penguin Group (USA) Inc.

Miller, Laura. Beauty Up: Exploring Contemporary Japanese Body Aesthetics. 2006. (Illus.). 256p. 60.00 *(978-0-520-24508-2(3))*; per. 26.95 *(978-0-520-24509-9(1))* Univ. of California Pr.

Min, Janice. How to Look Hot in a Minivan: A Real Woman's Guide to Losing Weight, Looking Great, & Dressing Chic in the Age of the Celebrity Mom. 2012. (ENG., Illus.). 240p. 26.99 ***(978-0-312-65897-7(4))*** St. Martin's Pr.

Minassian, Jessie. The Big Sis Guide to Health & Beauty. 2007. 112p. (YA). per. 12.99 *(978-0-9795536-0-7(7))* Reflections Publishing.

Minguet, Josep Maria. Girls — New Look, Volume 1: In English & Spanish Texts. Camara, Eva M., ed. 2007. (International Hairdressing Ser.). (ENG.). 93p. 62.50 *(978-84-96823-06-8(7))* Instituto Monsa de Ediciones, S.A. ESP. Dist: Trans-Atlantic Pubns., Inc.

—Girls — New Look, Volume 2: In English & Spanish Texts. Camara, Eva M., ed. 2007. (International Hairdressing Ser.). (ENG.). 93p. 62.50 *(978-84-96823-07-5(5))* Instituto Monsa de Ediciones, S.A. ESP. Dist: Trans-Atlantic Pubns., Inc.

—Hairdo — New Look, Volume 1: In English & Spanish Texts. Camara, Eva M., ed. 2007. (International Hairdressing Ser.). (ENG.). 93p. 62.50 *(978-84-96823-04-4(0))* Instituto Monsa de Ediciones, S.A. ESP. Dist: Trans-Atlantic Pubns., Inc.

—Hairdo — New Look, Volume 2: In English & Spanish Texts. Camara, Eva M., ed. 2007. (International Hairdressing Ser.). (ENG.). 93p. 62.50 *(978-84-96823-05-1(9))* Instituto Monsa de Ediciones, S.A. ESP. Dist: Trans-Atlantic Pubns., Inc.

Minogue, Dannii. My Style. 2011. (ENG., Illus.). 256p. pap. 26.95 ***(978-0-85720-721-0(0))*** Simon & Schuster, Ltd. GBR. Dist: Independent Pubs. Group.

Miryala, Anirudha, et al. Ancient Indian Beauty Secrets: Anoo's Sisters. 2010. 80p. pap. 26.49 *(978-1-4490-4199-1(X))* AuthorHouse.

Mogilner, Victoria J. Ancient Secrets of Facial Rejuvenation: A Holistic, Nonsurgical Approach to Youth & Well-Being. 2006. (ENG., Illus.). 160p. per. 15.95 *(978-1-57731-552-0(9))* New World Library.

—Ancient Secrets of Facial Rejuvenation: A Holistic, Nonsurgical Approach to Youth & Well-Being. 2010. (ENG.). 158p. pap. 15.00 *(978-1-4379-7341-9(8))* DIANE Publishing Co.

Montefiore, Judith Cohen. The Jewish Manual: Or Practical Information in Jewish & Modern Cookery, with a Collection of Valuable Recipes & Hints Relating to the Toilette. 2007. (ENG.). 160p. pap. 19.99 *(978-1-4264-6012-8(0))*; 180p. pap. 21.99 *(978-1-4264-6083-8(X))* BiblioBazaar.

Moreno, Robyn. Practically Posh: The Smart Girls' Guide to a Glam Life. 2008. (ENG.). 256p. pap. 18.95 *(978-0-06-134946-1(1)*, Harper Paperbacks) HarperCollins Pubs.

Morgan, Jorj, et al. Gorgeous: The Sum of Your Glorious Parts: A Lifestyle Enhancement Guide. 2007. (ENG., Illus.). 432p. 28.95 *(978-1-58182-572-5(2))* Turner Publishing Co.

Morris, Rae. Makeup: The Ultimate Guide. 2008. (ENG.). 256p. pap. 29.95 *(978-1-74175-226-7(4))* Allen & Unwin AUS. Dist: Independent Pubs. Group.

Moses, Rebecca. A Life of Style: Fashion, Home, Entertaining. 2010. (ENG., Illus.). 208p. 35.00 *(978-1-58093-293-6(2))* Monacelli Pr., Inc.

Murad, Howard. The Water Secret: The Cellular Breakthrough to Look & Feel 10 Years Younger. 2010. (ENG., Illus.). 272p. pap. 18.95 *(978-0-470-55470-8(3)*, Wiley) Wiley, John & Sons, Inc.

My Beauty Box. Date not set. 64p. 5.98 *(978-1-4054-0403-7(5))* Parragon, Inc.

Nail Care Nightmares, the Truth Behind the Beauty: A Guide to Public Awareness. 2006. per. 24.95 net. *(978-0-9788243-7-2(7))* HEALMB Publishing.

Nanuwa, Raj. The Secret Beauty. 2010. (Illus.). 104p. pap. 33.49 *(978-1-4490-9887-2(8))* AuthorHouse.

Nars, Francois. Makeup Your Mind. 2011. (ENG., Illus.). 273p. 45.00 *(978-0-8478-3645-1(2))* Rizzoli International Pubns., Inc.

Nelson, Zed, photos by. Love Me. 2009. (ENG., Illus.). 192p. 45.00 *(978-88-6965-165-6(7))* Contrasto DUE ITA. Dist: Consortium Bk. Sales & Distribution.

Newton, Shawna. Grandma's Drugstore. 2008. 203p. pap. 24.50 *(978-0-557-01685-7(4))* Lulu Enterprises Inc.

Nolan, Coleen. Coleen Nolan's Beauty Secrets: From Drab to Fab in 15 Minutes. 2010. (ENG., Illus.). 224p. 27.95 ***(978-0-283-07112-6(5))*** Macmillan Pubs., Ltd. GBR. Dist: Independent Pubs. Group.

Nordmann, Lorraine. Beauty Basics: The Official Guide to Level 1. 2nd ed. 2007. (ENG., Illus.). 140p. (C). pap. 43.95 *(978-1-84480-694-2(4))* Cengage Learning GBR. Dist: CENGAGE Learning.

—Beauty Therapy: the Foundations: The Official Guide to NVQ/SVQ Level 2. 4th ed. 2007. (ENG., Illus.). 604p. (C). pap. 63.95 *(978-1-84480-695-9(2))* Cengage Learning GBR. Dist: CENGAGE Learning.

Norton, Sally, et al. The Ultimate Beauty Book: The Complete Professional Guide to Skin-Care, Make-Up, Haircare, Hairstyling, Fitness, Body Toning, Diet, Health & Vitality (Illus.). 256p. pap. *(978-0-681-03222-4(7))* Anness Publishing.

Nwankwo, Ebenezer A. Complexion, Cosmetics & the Christian. 2007. 78p. pap. 10.95 *(978-1-57258-466-2(1))* TEACH Services, Inc.

O'Connor, Siobhan & Spunt, Alexandra. No More Dirty Looks: The Truth about Your Beauty Products — And the Ultimate Guide to Safe & Clean Cosmetics. 2010. (ENG.). 304p. pap. 14.95 *(978-0-7382-1396-5(9))* Da Capo Pr., Inc.

Ogilvie, Madeleine. The Meaning Behind the Mask. 2009. 220p. pap. *(978-3-639-15353-8(7))* VDM Verlag Dr. Mueller e.K.

Ollivier, Debra. Entre Nous: A Woman's Guide to Finding Her Inner French Girl. mass mkt. *(978-0-312-98711-4(0)*, St. Martin's Paperbacks) St. Martin's Pr.

—What French Women Know: About Love, Sex, & Other Matters of the Heart & Mind. 2010. (ENG.). 272p. (gr. 12). 15.00 *(978-0-425-23648-2(X)*, Berkley Trade) Penguin Group (USA) Inc.

Ong, Coreenna. Nature's Spa: DIY Beauty Treatments, 1 vol. 2008. (ENG.). 152p. pap. 16.50 *(978-981-261-414-8(1))* Marshall Cavendish International (Asia) Private Ltd. SGP. Dist: Marshall Cavendish Corp.

Padilha, Janea & Frankel, Martha. Brazilian Sexy: Secrets to Living a Gorgeous & Confident Life. 2011. (ENG.). 144p. (gr. 12). 13.95 *(978-0-399-53650-2(7)*, Perigee Trade) Penguin Group (USA) Inc.

Palmer, Debbie & Kitchin, Jennifer. The Dermatologists' Prescription for a New You! 2011. 136p. 24.99 ***(978-1-4634-4740-3(X))*** AuthorHouse.

Parsons, Tina. The Beauty Chronicles - Sensorial Secrets for Redefining Human Perfection. 2011. (ENG.). 260p. pap. ***(978-1-907498-74-9(5))*** Lean Marketing Pr.

Patzer, Gordon. Looks: Why They Matter More Than You Ever Imagined. 8. 2008. (ENG.). 288p. 23.00 *(978-0-8144-8054-0(3))* Amacom.

Patzer, Gordon L. The Edwin Mellen Press: Lewiston Queenston Lampeter. 2006. (Illus.). 548p. 139.95 *(978-0-7734-5690-7(2))* Mellen, Edwin Pr., The.

Payne- Dennie, Candice. Pretty, Never Saved Me No Pain. 2010. 232p. (ENG.). 24.99 *(978-1-4520-5217-5(4))*; pap. 17.60 *(978-1-4520-5216-8(6))* AuthorHouse.

Pellicane, Arlene. 31 Days to a Younger You: No Surgery, No Diets, No Kidding. 2011. 192p. pap. 11.99 *(978-0-7369-2903-5(7))* Harvest Hse. Pubs.

Perrett, David. In Your Face: The New Science of Human Attraction. 2012. (MacSci Ser.). (ENG., Illus.). 320p. pap. 17.00 ***(978-0-230-34043-5(1))*** Palgrave Macmillan.

Perricone, Nicholas. Dr. Perricone's 7 Secrets to Beauty, Health, & Longevity: The Miracle of Cellular Rejuvenation. 2007. (ENG., Illus.). 352p. pap. 18.00 *(978-0-345-49245-3(3)*, Ballantine Bks.) Random House Publishing Group.

Persadsingh, Neil. The Hair in Black Women. 2008. 108p. pap. 11.99 *(978-1-60647-382-5(4))* Xulon Pr., Inc.

Phillips, Michelle. The Beauty Blueprint: 8 Steps to Building the Life & Look of Your Dreams. 2011. (ENG.). 288p. pap. 14.95 *(978-1-4019-3173-5(1))* Hay Hse., Inc.

Pierce, Stacia. The Image Course. pap. 249.00 *(978-1-886880-44-3(1))* Life Changers Publishing.

Port, Whitney & Berk, Sheryl. True Whit: Designing a Life of Style, Beauty, & Fun. 2011. (ENG.). 224p. 19.99 *(978-0-06-199686-3(6))* HarperCollins Pubs.

Power, Katherine & Kerr, Hillary. Who What Wear: Celebrity & Runway Style for Real Life. 2009. (ENG., Illus.). 160p. pap. 18.95 *(978-0-8109-8045-7(2)*, Abrams Image) Abrams.

Prasad, Amiya. The Fine Art of Looking Younger: A Leading Cosmetic Surgeon's Guide to Long Lasting Beauty. 2009. (Illus.). 240p. pap. 19.95 *(978-0-9792240-2-7(0))* MDPublish.com.

Prevention (Firm: Emmaus, Pa.) Staff, contrib. by. Health & Weight-Loss Breakthroughs 2011: Smart Strategies to Feel Young & Look Great. 2011. (Illus.). ix, 372p. ***(978-1-60529-171-0(4))*** Rodale Pr., Inc.

Price, Katie. Standing Out. (ENG., Illus.). 2010. 224p. pap. 23.95 *(978-1-84605-669-7(1))* 2009. 208p. 32.95 *(978-1-84605-668-0(3))* Random Hse. GBR. Dist: Independent Pubs. Group.

Promaulayko, Michele & Rhodes, Maura. Look Better Naked: The 6-Week Plan to Your Leanest, Hottest Body — Ever! 2010. (ENG., Illus.). 320p. 25.99 *(978-1-60529-463-6(2))* Rodale Pr., Inc.

—Look Better Naked: The 6-week plan to your leanest, hottest Body — ever! 2011. (ENG., Illus.). 320p. pap. 18.99 *(978-1-60961-051-7(2))* Rodale Pr., Inc.

Quirk, Jessica. What I Wore: Four Seasons, One Closet, Endless Recipes for Personal Style. 2011. (Illus.). 144p. pap. 18.00 *(978-0-345-52610-6(4)*, Ballantine Bks.) Random House Publishing Group.

Ramsey-Davis, Morae, et al. The Model Stimulus Plan: Resource Guide for Breaking into the Fashion, Commercial & Urban Modeling Industries, Joining a Union, Saving Money & Lockin. 2010. 296p. pap. 17.49 *(978-1-4490-1596-1(4))* AuthorHouse.

Ramsey, Valerie & Hummel, Heather. Gracefully: Looking & Being Your Best at Any Age. 2008. (ENG., Illus.). 304p. 24.95 *(978-0-07-154623-2(5)*, 0071546235) McGraw-Hill Cos., The.

Regan, Laura M. Winning the Battle Against Unwanted Hair Growth. 2006. pap. 19.95 *(978-0-9788341-0-4(0))* Divine Bks.

Reynolds, Katie. Style Me Vintage: Easy Step-By-Step Techniques for Creating Classic Looks. 2011. (ENG., Illus.). 112p. 15.95 ***(978-1-86205-918-4(7))*** Chrysalis Children's Bks. GBR. Dist: Independent Pubs. Group.

Reynolds, Star Jones. Shine: A Physical, Emotional, & Spiritual Journey to Finding Love. 2007. 256p. pap. 14.95 *(978-0-06-082421-1(2))* HarperCollins Pubs.

Rhode, Deborah L. Beauty Bias: The Injustice of Appearance in Life & Law, 1 vol. 2010. (ENG., Illus.). 272p. 24.95 *(978-0-19-537287-8(5))* Oxford Univ. Pr., Inc.

—The Beauty Bias: The Injustice of Appearance in Life & Law. 2011. (ENG., Illus.). 272p. pap. 17.95 *(978-0-19-979444-7(8))* Oxford Univ. Pr., Inc.

Richardson, Corinne. Dressing Nifty after Fifty: The Definitive Guide to a Simple, Stylish Wardrobe. Frank, Christine, ed. 2007. (Illus.). 188p. pap. 15.95 *(978-0-9786636-0-5(8))* Willcott & Corn Bks.

Ricke, M.D., PScott. The Little Book of Beauty: The Thinking Woman's Guide to Health & Beauty. 2009. 288p. pap. 14.95 *(978-0-9820403-0-0(X))* AMR Publishing Co., The.

Ringwald, Molly. Getting the Pretty Back: Friendship, Family, & Finding the Perfect Lipstick. 2011. (ENG.). 240p. pap. 16.99 *(978-0-06-180945-3(4))* HarperCollins Pubs.

Ripley, Jacqui. Celebrity Style Secrets: An Insider's Guide to Looking A-List. 2007. (Illus.). 230p. pap. 11.95 *(978-0-7499-2465-2(9))* Piatkus Bks. GBR. Dist: National Bk. Network.

—Getting Gorgeous. 2007. (ENG., Illus.). 64p. *(978-1-84597-508-1(1))* Ryland Peters & Small.

—The Ultimate Girls' Night In. 2008. (ENG., Illus.). 224p. 19.95 *(978-0-7499-2697-7(X))* Piatkus Bks. GBR. Dist: Independent Pubs. Group.

Robinson, Shaun. Exactly As I Am: Celebrated Women Share Candid Advice with Today's Girls on What It Takes to Believe in Yourself. 2009. (ENG.). 160p. 18.00 *(978-0-345-51195-9(6)*, Ballantine Bks.) Random House Publishing Group.

Robson, Pamela. Grown-up & Gorgeous in Your 40s. 2009. (ENG., Illus.). 144p. pap. 15.95 *(978-1-74166-801-8(8))* Random Hse. Australia AUS. Dist: Independent Pubs. Group.

—Grown-up & Gorgeous in Your 50s. 2009. (ENG., Illus.). 144p. pap. 15.95 *(978-1-74166-802-5(6))* Random Hse. Australia AUS. Dist: Independent Pubs. Group.

—Grown-up & Gorgeous in Your 60s. 2009. (ENG., Illus.). 144p. pap. 15.95 *(978-1-74166-803-2(4))* Random Hse. Australia AUS. Dist: Independent Pubs. Group.

Roizen, Michael F. & Oz, Mehmet C. You: Being Beautiful - The Owner's Manual to Inner & Outer Beauty. 2008. (ENG.). 432p. 26.99 *(978-1-4165-9985-2(1)*, Free Pr.) Free Pr.

Romano, Rafi, ed. The Art of the Smile: Integrating Prosthodontics, Orthodontics, Periodontics, Dental Technology, & Plastic Surgery in Esthetic Dental Treatment. (Illus.). 454p. 258.00 *(978-1-85097-096-5(3))* Quintessence Publishing Co., Inc.

Romanowski, Perry. The Beauty Aisle Insider: Top Cosmetic Scientists Answer Your Questions about the Lotions, Potions & Other Beauty Products You Use Every Day. 2012. (ENG.). 368p. mass mkt. ***(978-0-373-89266-2(7)***, 0373892667) Harlequin Enterprises, Ltd.

Romero, Ruth. Be the Rage at Any Age: Style Wisdom to Last a Lifetime. 2009. pap. *(978-1-61623-202-3(1))* Independent Pub.

Rose, Natalia. The Raw Food Life Force Energy: Enter a Totally New Stratosphere of Weight Loss, Beauty, & Health. 2006. 288p. 25.95 *(978-0-06-117618-0(4)*, Morrow, William & Co.) HarperCollins Pubs.

Ruder, Raisa, et al. Babushka's Beauty Secrets: Old World Tips for a Glamorous New You. 2010. (ENG., Illus.). 208p. 15.99 *(978-0-446-55586-9(X)*, Wellness Central) Grand Central Publishing.

RuPaul & Ginsberg, Merle. Workin' It! Rupaul's Guide to Life, Liberty, & the Pursuit of Style. 2010. (ENG., Illus.). 208p. 19.99 *(978-0-06-198583-6(X))* HarperCollins Pubs.

Russell, George. How to Create 1940s Hairstyles — Instructions & Illustrations for 17 Swing Era Styles. 2007. pap. 16.95 *(978-1-934268-30-8(5))* Bramcost Pubns., LLC.

Sachs, Robert & Sachs, Melanie. Ayurvedic Spa: Treatments for Large & Small Spas as Well as Home Care to Help Everyone Become Healthy, Happy, & Feel Inspired. 2007. (ENG., Illus.). 596p. pap. 29.95 *(978-0-940985-95-4(9))* Lotus Pr.

Saito, Kaori, ed. Beauty & Healthcare Package Design. 2009. (ENG., Illus.). 160p. 59.00 *(978-4-89444-729-5(0)*, PIE Bks.) Rizzoli International Pubns., Inc.

Salon Fundamentals Nails Student's Study Guide. 2007. spiral bd. *(978-0-9779961-9-3(0))* Pivot Point International, Inc.

Salon Fundamentals Nails Textbook. 2007. spiral bd. *(978-0-9779961-8-6(2))* Pivot Point International, Inc.

Samia Boctor. What If? ... a reflection on Hair. 2010. 64p. pap. 9.95 *(978-1-4502-0002-8(8))* iUniverse, Inc.

Schmaling, Susanne. Aging Skin. 2011. (ENG.). 304p. (C). pap. 56.95 *(978-1-4354-9614-9(0)*, Milady Publishing Co.) Delmar Cengage Learning.

Schoech, Samantha & Taggart, Lisa, eds. The Bigger the Better, the Tighter the Sweater: 21 Funny Women on Beauty, Body Image, & Other Hazards of Being Female. 2007. (ENG., Illus.). 256p. per. 14.95 *(978-1-58005-210-8(X))* Seal Pr.

Schweiger, Melissa. Sephora: The Ultimate Guide to Makeup, Skin, & Hair from the Beauty Authority. 2008. (ENG., Illus.). 208p. 27.95 *(978-0-06-146640-3(9)*, Morrow, William & Co.) HarperCollins Pubs.

Scrivo, Eva. Eva Scrivo on Beauty: The Tools, Techniques, & Insider Knowledge Every Woman Needs to Be Her Most Beautiful, Confident Self. 2011. (ENG., Illus.). 352p. 35.00 *(978-1-4391-6471-6(1)*, Beyond Words/Atria Bks.) Atria Bks.

Shich, Seth. A Philosophical Inquiry of Beauty. 2011. 60p. pap. ***(978-3-8443-0155-7(0))*** Lambert Academic Publishing.

Silvestry, Lydia. Lydia Silvestry's Beauty Secrets: Over 300 lifestyle tips, recommendations & Recipes. 2007. (Illus.). 256p. 24.95 *(978-0-9791183-9-5(5))* Gem Publishing LLC.

Slate, Shereese. At Hoome Hair Care Kit for the Every Day Woman. 2007. per. 0.01 net. *(978-1-60402-293-3(0))* Independent Pub.

Smithsonian Institution Staff. Beauty: Smithsonian Gift Books Series. 2006. 64p. *(978-1-59258-154-2(4))* Hylas Publishing.

Snodgrass, Bethanne. The Makeover Myth: The Real Story Behind Cosmetic Surgery, Injectables, Lasers, Gimmicks, & Hype, & What You Need to Know to Stay Safe. 2007. 304p. pap. 14.95 *(978-0-06-085719-6(6))* HarperCollins Pubs.

Snyder, Kimberly. The Beauty Detox Solution: Eat Your Way to Radiant Skin, Renewed Energy & the Body You've Always Wanted. 2011. (ENG.). 272p. pap. *(978-0-373-89232-7(2))* Harlequin Enterprises, Ltd.

Spencer, Kit. Pro Makeup: Salon Secrets of the Professionals. 2009. (ENG., Illus.). 256p. spiral bd. 29.95 *(978-1-55407-477-8(0))* Firefly Bks., Ltd.

Spencer, Mimi. 101 Things to Do Before You Diet: Because Looking Great Isn't Just about Losing Weight. 2009. (ENG.). 272p. 23.99 *(978-1-60529-848-1(4))* Rodale Pr., Inc.

Spokes, Liz. The A to Z of Modelling & Grooming. 2008. 115p. pap. 18.95 *(978-1-4092-4454-7(7))* Lulu Enterprises Inc.

Stacey, Sarah & Fairley, Jo. Green Beauty Bible. 2009. (ENG., Illus.). 224p. pap. 21.95 *(978-1-85626-851-6(9))* Cathie, Kyle Ltd. GBR. Dist: National Bk. Network.

Stacey, Sarah & Fairley, Josephine. The 21st Century Beauty Bible. (ENG., Illus.). 256p. pap. 29.95 *(978-1-55285-377-1(2))* Whitecap Bks., Ltd. CAN. Dist: Graphic Arts Ctr. Publishing Co.

Stanway, Penny. The Miracle of Apple Cider Vinegar: Practical Tips for Health, Home, & Beauty. 2010. (ENG.). 144p. pap. 12.95 *(978-1-907486-07-4(0)*, Watkins Publishing) Duncan Baird Pubs. GBR. Dist: Sterling Publishing Co., Inc.

Stavert, Elaine. Beauty Masks & Scrubs. 2011. (Cozy Ser.). (ENG., Illus.). 156p. pap. 14.95 *(978-1-86108-692-1(X))* Guild of Master Craftsman Pubns., Ltd. GBR. Dist: Sterling Publishing Co., Inc.

—Beauty Oils & Butters. 2011. (Cozy Ser.). (ENG., Illus.). 156p. pap. 14.95 *(978-1-86108-691-4(1))* Guild of Master Craftsman Pubns., Ltd. GBR. Dist: Sterling Publishing Co., Inc.

Steffen, Sylvester L. The Poetree Worldview: Leafing Through History - Book Three of the Justified Living Trilogy. 2010. 176p. 22.49 *(978-1-4520-4887-1(8))*; pap. 11.99 *(978-1-4520-4888-8(6))* AuthorHouse.

Sunnydale, Helena. The Complete Book of Beauty: A practical step-by-step guide to skincare, make-up, haircare, diet, body toning, fitness, health & vitality with over 1000 Photographs. 2010. (ENG., Illus.). 512p. pap. 24.99 *(978-1-84476-916-2(X))* Anness Publishing GBR. Dist: National Bk. Network.

Sutton, Denise H. Globalizing Ideal Beauty: How Female Copywriters of the J. Walter Thompson Advertising Agency Redefined Beauty for the Twentieth Century. 2009. (ENG., Illus.). 224p. 89.00 *(978-0-230-61174-0(5))* Palgrave Macmillan.

Tannis, Allison Joann. Feed Your Skin, Starve Your Wrinkles: Eat Your Way to Firmer, More Beautiful Skin with the 100 Best Anti-Aging Foods. 2009. (ENG., Illus.). 304p. pap. 24.99 *(978-1-59233-342-4(7)*, 1592333427, Fair Winds Press) Quayside.

Taschen, Angelika, ed. Aesthetic Surgery. 25th ed. 2008. (ENG., Illus.). 439p. 29.99 *(978-3-8365-0090-6(6))* TASCHEN DEU. Dist: Ingram Pub. Services.

Taussig, Michael. Beauty & the Beast. 2012. (ENG., Illus.). 192p. 55.00 ***(978-0-226-78985-9(3))***; pap. 18.00 ***(978-0-226-78986-6(1))*** Univ. of Chicago Pr.

Taylor, Mikki. Commander in Chic: Every Woman's Guide to Managing Her Style Like a First Lady. 2011. (ENG., Illus.). 192p. 26.99 *(978-1-4391-9672-4(9)*, Beyond Words/Atria Bks.) Atria Bks.

Taylor, Mikki. Commander-In-Chic: Every Woman's Guide to Managing Her Style Like a First Lady. 2011. pap. ***(978-1-4391-9673-1(7)***, Beyond Words/Atria Bks.) Atria Bks.

Taylor, Susan C. Dr. Susan Taylor's RX for Brown Skin: Your Prescription for Flawless Skin, Hair, & Nails. 2008. (ENG., Illus.). 304p. per. 14.95 *(978-0-06-157887-8(8)*, Amistad) HarperCollins Pubs.

Terri, Joy. The Make-up Book: Every Woman's Guide to the Art of Applying Make-up. 2011. (ENG., Illus.). 96p. pap. 12.95 *(978-1-84773-932-2(6))* New Holland Pubs., Ltd. GBR. Dist: Sterling Publishing Co., Inc.

Thompson, Paul, compiled by. Studio Hairstyling Course Workbook. 2008. *(978-0-9749500-9-9(2))* Make-up Designory.

Thorne, Phebe. Massage & a Facial Every 3,000 Miles: A Roadmap to Looking & Feeling Good. 2008. 68p. pap. 9.95 *(978-1-4401-1147-1(2))* iUniverse, Inc.

Tompkins, Rosalind Y. You Are Beautiful: Unlocking Beauty from Within. 2010. 114p. pap. 11.99 *(978-1-60911-363-6(2)*, Strategic Bk. Publishing) AEG Literary Publishing Services, Inc.

Tornambe, Robert. The Beauty Quotient Formula: How to Find Your Own Beauty Quotient to Look Your Best - No Matter What Your Age. 2010. (ENG.). 256p. 24.95 *(978-1-4019-2451-5(4))* Hay Hse., Inc.

Tornambe, Robert M. The Beauty Quotient Formula: How to Find Your Own Beauty Quotient to Look Your Best - No Matter What Your Age. 2011. (ENG.). 256p. pap. 14.95 *(978-1-4019-2452-2(2))* Hay Hse., Inc.

Tourles, Stephanie. Organic Body Care Recipes: 175 Homemade Herbal Formulas for Glowing Skin & a Vibrant Self. 2007. (ENG., Illus.). 384p. pap. 18.95 *(978-1-58017-676-7(3)*, 1580176763) Storey Publishing, LLC.

Trew, Sally W. & Gould, Zonella B. The Complete Idiot's Guide to Making Natural Beauty Products. 2010. (Complete Idiot's Guide Ser.). (ENG.). 304p. (gr. 12). 16.95 *(978-1-61564-023-2(1)*, Alpha Bks.) Penguin Group (USA) Inc.

Tuschen, Malou. Building a men's world: Eine qualitative Studie genderorientierter POS-Gestaltung am Beispiel von Männerkosmetik. 2010. 108p. pap. *(978-3-639-22487-0(6))* VDM Verlag Dr. Mueller e.K.

Tuttle, Cameron. Raising Eyebrows: Your Personal Guide to Fabulous Brows. 2012. (ENG.). 128p. 16.95 ***(978-1-4521-1133-9(2))*** Chronicle Bks. LLC.

Valvo, Carmen. Dressed to Perfection: The Art of Dressing for Your Red Carpet Moments. 2011. (ENG., Illus.). 176p. pap. 29.95 *(978-0-8478-3614-7(2))* Rizzoli International Pubns., Inc.

Valvo, Carmen Marc. Dressed to Perfection: The Art of Dressing for Your Red Carpet Moments. 2011. (ENG., Illus.). 176p. 50.00 *(978-0-8478-3541-6(3))* Rizzoli International Pubns., Inc.

van der Post, Lucia. Things I Wish My Mother Had Told Me: A Guide to Living with Impeccable Grace & Style. 2010. (ENG.). 400p. pap. 15.95 *(978-0-7382-1383-5(7))* Da Capo Pr., Inc.

Vetica, Robert. Good to Great Hair: Celebrity Hairstyling Techniques Made Simple. 2009. (ENG., Illus.). 272p. pap. 24.99 *(978-1-59233-357-8(5)*, 1592333575) Quayside.

Voak, Sally A. New You in Thirty Days. (Illus.). 154p. pap. 7.95 *(978-1-85479-189-4(3))* O'Mara, Michael Bks., Ltd. GBR. Dist: Trans-Atlantic Pubns., Inc.

Waldman, Christina. You Are Not Getting Older, You Are Getting Better. 2010. 80p. pap. 10.49 *(978-1-4490-9908-4(4))* AuthorHouse.

Walker, Susannah. Style & Status: Selling Beauty to African American Women, 1920-1975. 2007. (ENG., Illus.). 264p. 40.00 *(978-0-8131-2433-9(6))* Univ. Pr. of Kentucky.

Wallace, Barbara, et al. Beautiful Bride from Every Angle: Look Great in Every Photo... & in Life! 2011. (Illus.). 304p. 39.95 *(978-1-935108-00-9(X))* ZinGiBer Publishing.

Walrond, Karen. The Beauty of Different. 2010. (ENG.). 252p. 24.95 *(978-1-933979-96-0(8))* Bright Sky Pr.

Warren, Andrew. CondÉ Nast Johansens Luxury Sp. 2009. (Illus.). 115p. pap. 15.00 *(978-1-903665-50-3(7))* Conde Nast Johansens Ltd. GBR. Dist: Casemate Pubs. & Bk. Distributors, LLC.

Warren, Mary Sheehan. It's So You: Fitting Fashion to Your Life. 2006. (Illus.). 369p. 28.95 *(978-1-890626-67-9(8))* Spence Publishing Co.

Watson, Linda. Vogue Fashion: Over 100 years of Style by Decade & Designer, in association with Vogue. 2008. (ENG., Illus.). 408p. pap. 24.95 *(978-1-55407-437-2(1))* Firefly Bks., Ltd.

Watson, Rosie. Make-Up: The Complete Guide to Professional Results. 2007. (ENG., Illus.). 160p. 27.95 *(978-1-84537-720-5(6))* New Holland Pubs., Ltd. GBR. Dist: Sterling Publishing Co., Inc.

—New Holland Professional: Manicure & Pedicure: The Complete Guide to Professional Results. 2008. (New Holland Professional Ser.). (ENG., Illus.). 160p. 27.95 *(978-1-84537-977-3(2))* New Holland Pubs., Ltd. GBR. Dist: Sterling Publishing Co., Inc.

—Professional Make-Up: The Complete Guide to Professional Results. 2011. (ENG., Illus.). 160p. pap. 19.95 *(978-1-84773-591-1(6))* New Holland Pubs., Ltd. GBR. Dist: Sterling Publishing Co., Inc.

Weisberger, Rachelle. Biblical Beauty: ANCIENT SECRETS & MODERN SOLUTIONS. 2011. 26.95 *(978-0-9835585-0-7(7))*; (ENG.). pap. 18.95 *(978-0-9835585-1-4(5))* Anbern Pr.

Welch, Raquel. Raquel: Beyond the Cleavage. (ENG., Illus.). 2011. 304p. pap. 15.00 *(978-1-60286-136-7(6))* 2010. 288p. 26.95 *(978-1-60286-097-1(1)*, Weinstein Bks.) Perseus Bks. Group.

Wellman, Katharine. Beauty Begins at Home: How to Make & Use Cosmetics. 2011. 336p. 50.95 ***(978-1-258-06711-3(0))*** Literary Licensing, LLC.

Wells, Linda & Allure Magazine Staff. Allure: Confessions of a Beauty Editor. 2006. (ENG., Illus.). 192p. 24.99 *(978-0-8212-5779-1(X))* Bulfinch.

Werle, Simone. Fashionista: A Century of Style Icons. 2009. (Illus.). 176p. 29.95 *(978-3-7913-3936-8(2))* Prestel Publishing.

West, Beverly & Bergund, Jason. Pure Cute. 2009. (ENG.). 88p. 9.99 *(978-0-7407-7403-4(4))* Andrews McMeel Publishing.

White, Judith. Home Spa: Creating Your Own Spa Experience with Aromatherapy. 2006. (ENG., Illus.). 144p. per. 9.95 *(978-1-4019-1148-5(X))* Hay Hse., Inc.

Wohlenhaus, Kim, ed. Skin Health Information for Teens: Health Tips about Dermatological Concerns & Skin Cancer Risks Including Facts about Acne, Warts, Allergies, & Other Conditions & Lifestyle Choices, Such As Tanning, Tattooing, & Piercing, That Affect the Skin, Nails, Scalp, & Hair. 2nd rev. ed. 2009. (Teen Health Ser.). 418p. (YA). (gr. 8-18). 69.00 *(978-0-7808-1042-6(2))* Omnigraphics, Inc.

Wolfe, David. Eating for Beauty 3rd Edition. 3rd rev. ed. 2007. per. 24.95 *(978-0-9790648-2-1(1))* Sunfood Publishing/Maul Brothers Publishing.

Wood, Jo & Graham-Maw, Jane. Naturally: How to Look & Feel Healthy, Energetic & Radiant the Organic Way. 2007. (ENG., Illus.). 394p. 24.95 *(978-0-283-07041-9(2))* Macmillan Pubs., Ltd. GBR. Dist: Independent Pubs. Group.

Woodall, Trinny & Constantine, Susannah. Trinny & Susannah Take on America: What Your Clothes Say about You. 2006. (Illus.). 256p. per. 19.95 *(978-0-06-113744-0(8))* HarperCollins Pubs.

Woodruff, Sarah & Maroukian, Francine, told to. The Handbook of Style: Expert Fashion & Beauty Advice. 2006. (ENG., Illus.). 176p. pap. 16.95 *(978-1-59474-053-4(4))* Quirk Bks.

The Wrinkle Revolution: Every Woman's Guide to a Younger Looking Skin. 2008. (ENG., Illus.). 160p. pap. *(978-1-85626-771-7(7))* Cathie, Kyle Ltd. GBR. Dist: Independent Pubs. Group.

Wu, Jessica. Feed Your Face: Younger, Smoother Skin & a Beautiful Body in 28 Delicious Days. 2011. (ENG., Illus.). 384p. pap. 15.99 ***(978-1-250-00344-7(X)***, St. Martin's Griffin); 26.99 *(978-0-312-63077-5(8))* St. Martin's Pr.

Yabsley, Charmaine. Secrets of Staying Young: Natural Secrets to Combat the Effects of Aging & Enhnace Your Beauty. 2010. (ENG., Illus.). 144p. pap. 14.95 *(978-1-84483-911-7(7))* Duncan Baird Pubs. GBR. Dist: Sterling Publishing Co., Inc.

Yosh Jefferson, Dmd Magd Ibo Facd Ficd. Jefferson Cephalometric Analysis. 2010. 68p. pap. 18.26 *(978-1-4269-1747-9(3))* Trafford Publishing.

Zavasta, Tonya. Quantum Eating: The Ultimate Elixir of Youth. 2007. 456p. pap. 30.00 *(978-0-9742434-5-0(0))* BR Publishing LLC.

Zhang, Ping. A Comprehensive Handbook for Traditional Chinese Medicine Facial Rejuvenation. 2007. (Illus.). 304p. per. 29.95 *(978-1-59975-666-0(8))* Nefeli Corp.

Zhao, Xiaolan. Inner Beauty: Looking, Feeling & Being Your Best Through Traditional Chinese Healing. (ENG & CHI., Illus.). 320p. 2012. pap. 19.95 ***(978-0-307-35881-3(X)***, Vintage Canada) 2011. 27.95 *(978-0-307-35880-6(1)*, Random Hse CAN) Random Hse. of Canada, Ltd. CAN. Dist: Random Hse., Inc.

Zoe, Rachel & Apodaca, Rose. Style A to Zoe: The Art of Fashion, Beauty, & Everything Glamour. 2008. (ENG., Illus.). 192p. pap. 15.99 *(978-0-446-53586-1(9))* Grand Central Publishing.

Zyla, David. Color Your Style: How to Wear Your True Colors. 2011. (ENG.). 256p. (gr. 12). 15.00 *(978-0-452-29683-1(8)*, Plume) Penguin Group (USA) Inc.

BEAUTY CONTESTANTS

Dewey, Susan. Making Miss India Miss World: Constructing Gender, Power, & the Nation in Postliberalization India. 2008. (Gender & Globalization Ser.). (Illus.). 245p. 26.95 *(978-0-8156-3176-7(6))* Syracuse Univ. Pr.

Oliver, M. Cynthia. Queen of the Virgins: Pageantry & Black Womanhood in the Caribbean. 2009. (Caribbean Studies Ser.). (ENG., Illus.). 224p. 50.00 *(978-1-60473-242-9(3))* Univ. Pr. of Mississippi.

Prejean, Carrie. Still Standing: The Untold Story of My Fight Against Gossip, Hate, & Political Attacks. 2009. (ENG.). 256p. 27.95 *(978-1-59698-602-2(6))* Regnery Publishing, Inc., An Eagle Publishing Co.

Stevens, Jill. It's All Good: Whether as a military medic, marathon runner, or Miss America contestant, I take life in Stride. 2008. 288p. pap. 16.95 *(978-1-932898-93-4(X))* Spring Creek Bk. Co.

Tice, Karen Whitney. Queens of Academe: Beauty Pageantry, Student Bodies, & College Life, 1 vol. 2012. (ENG., Illus.). 264p. pap. 24.95 ***(978-0-19-984280-3(9))*** Oxford Univ. Pr., Inc.

BEAUTY CONTESTS

see also Miss America Pageant, Atlantic City, N.J.

Dewey, Susan. Making Miss India Miss World: Constructing Gender, Power, & the Nation in Postliberalization India. 2008. (Gender & Globalization Ser.). (Illus.). 245p. 26.95 *(978-0-8156-3176-7(6))* Syracuse Univ. Pr.

Dwyer, T. Ryle. The Rose of Tralee: Fifty Years A-Blooming. 2009. (ENG., Illus.). 128p. pap. 23.95 ***(978-1-84717-177-1(X))*** O'Brien Pr., Ltd., The IRL. Dist: Dufour Editions, Inc.

King-O'Riain, Rebecca Chiyoko. Pure Beauty: Judging Race in Japanese American Beauty Pageants. 2006. (Illus.). 280p. 60.00 *(978-0-8166-4789-7(5))*; per. 20.00 *(978-0-8166-4790-3(9))* Univ. of Minnesota Pr.

Majestic: A Pageant Girl's Guide to Winning. 2006. spiral bd. 29.99 *(978-0-9792002-0-5(2))* Nicely, Jessica.

Merino, Noël. Beauty Pageants. 2009. (At Issue Ser.). (Illus.). 128p. (J). (gr. 10-13). (ENG.). pap. 31.80 *(978-0-7377-4536-8(3))*; pap. 22.50 *(978-0-7377-4537-5(1))* Cengage Gale. (Greenhaven Pr., Inc.).

Oliver, M. Cynthia. Queen of the Virgins: Pageantry & Black Womanhood in the Caribbean. 2009. (Caribbean Studies Ser.). (ENG., Illus.). 224p. 50.00 *(978-1-60473-242-9(3))* Univ. Pr. of Mississippi.

Pearlman, Penny. Pretty Smart: Lessons from Our Miss Americas. 2008. 212p. 26.99 *(978-1-4389-3761-8(X))*; pap. 19.99 *(978-1-4389-3760-1(1))* AuthorHouse.

Savage, Candace. Beauty Queens: A Playful Category. 2006. (Illus.). 132p. reprint ed. pap. 25.00 *(978-1-4223-5810-8(0))* DIANE Publishing Co.

Tice, Karen Whitney. Queens of Academe: Beauty Pageantry, Student Bodies, & College Life, 1 vol. 2012. (ENG., Illus.). 264p. pap. 24.95 ***(978-0-19-984280-3(9))*** Oxford Univ. Pr., Inc.

BEAUTY CULTURE

see also Beauty, Personal; Beauty Operators; Cosmetics; Hairdressing

Alpert, Arlene, et al. Milady's Standard Cosmetology 2008. 2007. (ENG., Illus.). 960p. (C). per. 104.95 *(978-1-4180-4936-2(0)*, Milady Publishing Co.) Delmar Cengage Learning.

—Standard Cosmetology. 2007. (ENG., Illus.). 960p. (C). 110.50 *(978-1-4180-4935-5(2))* Delmar Cengage Learning.

Asadujjaman, Mohammad & Al-Amin, Abdullah. Handbook of Cosmetology. 2011. 88p. pap. ***(978-3-8443-8695-0(5))*** Lambert Academic Publishing.

Assouline. Vidal Sassoon. 2010. (ENG.). 164p. 50.00 *(978-2-7594-0484-1(6))* Assouline FRA. Dist: Perseus Distribution.

BarCharts, Inc. Cosmetology: Hair Color. 2011. 6p. 5.95 *(978-1-4232-1640-7(7))* Barcharts, Inc.

Barnes, Claire. The British Aestheticians Guide to Waxing the Twigs & Berries. 2011. 152p. pap. 16.99 ***(978-1-4634-3275-1(5))*** AuthorHouse.

Barnes, Julian & Milady Publishing Company Staff. Master Educator. 2nd ed. 2008. (ENG.). 176p. (C). pap. 48.50 *(978-1-4283-2154-0(3)*, Milady Publishing Co.) Delmar Cengage Learning.

Barnes, Letha & Milady Publishing Company Staff. Milady's Master Educator: Student Course Book. 2nd ed. 2008. (ENG.). 480p. (C). pap. 161.50 *(978-1-4283-2151-9(9)*, Milady Publishing Co.) Delmar Cengage Learning.

Barnes, Scott. About Face: Amazing Transformations Using the Secrets of the Top Celebrity Makeup Artist. (ENG., Illus.). 240p. 2011. pap. 18.99 *(978-1-59233-488-9(1)*, 1592334881) 2010. 24.99 *(978-1-59233-399-8(0)*, 1592333990) Quayside.

Bissoon, Lionel. The Cellulite Cure. 2006. (Illus.). 232p. 29.95 *(978-0-9764821-0-9(X))* Meso Pr.

Campo, Riku. The Best in Beauty: An Ultimate Guide to Makeup & Skincare Techniques, Tools, & Products. 2010. (ENG., Illus.). 304p. pap. 24.99 *(978-1-4391-4825-9(2)*, Beyond Words/Atria Bks.) Atria Bks.

Capellini, Steve. The Complete Spa Book for Massage Therapists. 2009. (ENG.). 288p. (C). pap., wbk. ed., pupil's gde. ed. 25.50 *(978-1-4180-0015-8(9)*, Milady Publishing Co.) Delmar Cengage Learning.

Cosmetologists State Board Exam Review for Use with Milady's Van Dean Manual. 7.50 *(978-1-56253-061-7(5)*, Milady Publishing Co.) Delmar Cengage Learning.

Cosmopolitan Editors, ed. Cosmo's Sexiest Beauty Secrets: The Ultimate Guide to Looking Gorgeous. 2010. (ENG., Illus.). 192p. pap. 16.95 *(978-1-58816-829-0(8))* Hearst Communications, Inc.

Couldridge, Greta, et al. Body Therapy & Facial Work: Electrical Treatments for Beauty Therapists. 4th rev. ed. 2012. (ENG.). 344p. pap. 47.95 *(978-1-4441-3745-3(X))* Hodder Arnold Pubs.

Culp, Judith & Campbell, Toni. Esthetician's Guide to Client Safety & Wellness. 2012. (ENG.). 288p. (C). spiral bd. 37.95 ***(978-1-4390-5745-2(1)***, Milady Publishing Co.) Delmar Cengage Learning.

Downing, Sarah. Beauty & Cosmetics, 1550-1950. 2012. (Shire Library). (ENG., Illus.). 64p. pap. 12.95 ***(978-0-7478-0839-8(2))*** Shire Pubns., Ltd. GBR. Dist: Random Hse., Inc.

Frangie, Catherine M. & Milady Publishing Company Staff. Standard Cosmetology 2008. 2007. (ENG.). 160p. (C). pap. 35.50 *(978-1-4180-4943-0(3)*, Milady Publishing Co.) Delmar Cengage Learning.

—Standard Cosmetology 2008: Situational Problems for Cosmetology Students. 2007. (ENG.). 304p. (C). pap. 39.95 *(978-1-4180-4944-7(1))* Delmar Cengage Learning.

Gavenas, Mary Lisa. Color Stories: Behind the Scenes of America's Billion-Dollar Beauty Industry. 2007. (ENG.). 224p. pap. 16.95 *(978-1-4165-7713-3(0))* Simon & Schuster.

—Color Stories: Behind the Scenes of America¿s Billion-Dollar Beauty Industry. 2007. 212p. reprint ed. 23.00 *(978-1-4223-6692-9(8))* DIANE Publishing Co.

Gerson, Joel. Milady's Standard Esthetics: Fundamentals. 10th ed. 2008. (ENG., Illus.). 672p. (C). 132.50 *(978-1-4283-1892-2(5)*, Milady Publishing Co.) Delmar Cengage Learning.

Gerson, Joel & Milady. Estética: Estándar. 10th ed. 2009. (ENG.). 140p. (C). pap. 55.50 *(978-1-4283-1896-0(8)*, Milady Publishing Co.) Delmar Cengage Learning.

—Esthetics: Standard Fundamentals. 10th ed. 2009. (ENG.). 176p. (C). pap., wbk. ed. 77.50 *(978-1-4283-1899-1(2)*, Milady Publishing Co.) Delmar Cengage Learning.

—Esthetics: Fundamentals. 10th ed. 2008. (ENG.). 144p. (C). pap. 48.50 *(978-1-4283-1895-3(X)*, Milady Publishing Co.) Delmar Cengage Learning.

—Standard Esthetics: Fundamentals. 10th ed. (ENG.). (C). 2009. 672p. 142.95 *(978-1-4283-1902-8(6))* 2008. 81.95 *(978-1-4283-1897-7(6))* Delmar Cengage Learning. (Milady Publishing Co.).

Gerson, Joel & Milady Publishing Company Staff. Standard Esthetics: Fundamentals. 10th ed. 2008. (ENG.). 176p. (C). pap., wbk. ed. 73.50 *(978-1-4283-1894-6(1)*, Milady Publishing Co.) Delmar Cengage Learning.

Gill, Tiffany. Beauty Shop Politics: African American Women's Activism in the Beauty Industry. 2010. (Women in American History Ser.). (ENG., Illus.). 208p. pap. 25.00 *(978-0-252-07696-1(6))* Univ. of Illinois Pr.

Grua, Antonella, ed. Italian Beauty. 2011. (ENG., Illus.). 224p. 95.00 *(978-88-370-7722-8(X))* Electa ITA. Dist: National Bk. Network.

Ifould, Judith, et al. Beauty Therapy. 3rd rev. ed. 2011. (ENG.). 480p. pap. 37.95 *(978-1-4441-3543-5(0))* Hodder Arnold Pubs.

Ifould, Judith, et al. Level 3 Beauty Therapy for NVQ & VRQ Diploma. 2012. (ENG.). 512p. pap. 65.00 ***(978-1-4441-6835-8(5))*** Hodder Arnold Pubs.

Kang, Miliann. The Managed Hand: Race, Gender, & the Body in Beauty Service Work. 2010. (ENG., Illus.). 275p. 60.00 *(978-0-520-26258-4(1))*; pap. 26.95 *(978-0-520-26260-7(3))* Univ. of California Pr.

LearningExpress Staff. Cosmetology Certification Exam. 4th rev. ed. 2009. (Complete Preparation Guides). (ENG.). 300p. pap. 22.95 *(978-1-57685-698-7(4))* LearningExpress, LLC.

Levesque, Kim Horton. Pampered in Paris: A Guide to the Best Spas, Salons & Beauty Boutiques. 2010. (ENG., Illus.). 232p. pap. 16.95 *(978-1-892145-86-4(3))* Little Bookroom.

Milady. Cosmetología: Estándar. 2009. (ENG.). 160p. (C). spiral bd. 37.95 *(978-1-4354-8420-7(7)*, Milady Publishing Co.) Delmar Cengage Learning.

—The Essential Companion for Milady Standard Cosmetology 2012. 3rd ed. 2011. (ENG.). 544p. (C). pap. 64.95 *(978-1-4390-5913-5(6)*, Milady Publishing Co.) Delmar Cengage Learning.

—The Essential Companion for Milady's Standard Cosmetology. 2011. (ENG.). 576p. (C). pap., pupil's gde. ed. 54.95 *(978-1-4390-5924-1(1)*, Milady Publishing Co.) Delmar Cengage Learning.

—Exam Review for Milady Standard Cosmetology 2012. 2011. (ENG.). 176p. (C). pap. 33.95 **(978-1-4390-5921-0(7))** Delmar Cengage Learning.
—Milady Standard Cosmetology 2012. 2011. (ENG.). 1120p. (C). 104.95 *(978-1-4390-5930-2(6))*; pap. 99.95 *(978-1-4390-5929-6(2))* Delmar Cengage Learning. (Milady Publishing Co.).
—Milady Standard Esthetics: Advanced. 2009. (ENG.). 880p. (C). 123.95 *(978-1-4283-1975-2(1),* Milady Publishing Co.) Delmar Cengage Learning.
—Milady's Standard Cosmetology 2012. 2011. (ENG.). 288p. (C). pap., wbk. ed. 44.95 *(978-1-4390-5923-4(3),* Milady Publishing Co.) Delmar Cengage Learning.
—Milady's Standard Esthetics: Advanced Step-by-Step Procedures. 2nd ed. 2012. (ENG.). 248p. (C). spiral bd. 34.50 **(978-1-133-01349-5(X),** Milady Publishing Co.) Delmar Cengage Learning.
—Milady's Standard Esthetics: Fundamentals, Step-by-Step Procedure. 11th ed. 2012. (ENG., Illus.). 208p. (C). spiral bd. 34.50 **(978-1-111-30709-7(1),** Milady Publishing Co.) Delmar Cengage Learning.
—Milady's Standard Esthetics Advanced Student Cd (School) 2009. (C). cd-rom 695.95 *(978-1-4354-1290-3(7),* Milady Publishing Co.) Delmar Cengage Learning.
—Milady's Standard Esthetics Fundamentals Student Cd (School) 2008. (C). cd-rom 695.95 *(978-1-4354-1289-7(3),* Milady Publishing Co.) Delmar Cengage Learning.
—Situational Problems for Milady Standard Cosmetology 2012. 2011. (ENG.). 304p. (C). pap. 37.95 **(978-1-4390-5920-3(9),** Milady Publishing Co.) Delmar Cengage Learning.
—Spanish Translated Milady Standard Cosmetology 2012. 2011. (ENG.). 1120p. (C). pap. 124.95 *(978-1-4390-5902-9(0),* Milady Publishing Co.) Delmar Cengage Learning.
—Spanish Translated Situational Problems for Milady Standard Cosmetology 2012. 2nd ed. 2011. (ENG.). 304p. (C). pap. 48.95 *(978-1-4390-5909-8(8),* Milady Publishing Co.) Delmar Cengage Learning.
—Standard Cosmetology. (ENG.). (C). 2007. 528p. pap. 57.50 *(978-1-4180-4940-9(9))* 2007. 224p. pap., wbk. ed. 47.50 *(978-1-4180-4942-3(5))* 2007. 272p. pap., wbk. ed. 47.50 *(978-1-4180-4941-6(7))* 2nd ed. 2008. 272p. pap. 57.50 *(978-1-4180-4953-9(0))* 2nd ed. 2008. 304p. pap. 51.50 *(978-1-4180-4954-6(9))* 2nd ed. 2008. 170p. pap. 46.50 *(978-1-4180-4955-3(7))* Delmar Cengage Learning. (Milady Publishing Co.).
—Standard Cosmetology 2012. 3rd ed. 2011. (ENG.). (C). 256p. pap., wbk. ed. 54.95 *(978-1-4390-5912-8(8))*; 288p. pap., wbk. ed. 54.95 *(978-1-4390-5910-4(1))* Delmar Cengage Learning. (Milady Publishing Co.).
Milady & Milady Publishing Company Staff. The Essential Companion for Milady's Standard Cosmetology 2008. 2nd ed. 2008. (SPA & ENG.). 528p. (C). pap., pupil's gde. ed. 68.50 *(978-1-4180-4951-5(4),* Milady Publishing Co.) Delmar Cengage Learning.
Milady & Salon Training Intl Staff. Business Fundamentals/Salon & Spa Professionals. 2006. (ENG.). 176p. (C). pap. 315.00 *(978-1-4283-0414-7(2))* Delmar Cengage Learning.
Milady, (Milady). Brazilian Waxing. 2011. (ENG.). 26.50 *(978-1-111-54134-7(5),* Milady Publishing Co.) Delmar Cengage Learning.
—Cosmetología. 2nd ed. 2008. (ENG.). 224p. (C). pap., wbk. ed. 57.50 *(978-1-4180-4952-2(2),* Milady Publishing Co.) Delmar Cengage Learning.
—The Edge by Milady, Vol. 1. 2008. (ENG.). 86p. (C). 53.50 *(978-1-4354-2001-4(2),* Milady Publishing Co.) Delmar Cengage Learning.
—Milady's Standard Esthetics. 2009. (ENG.). 272p. (C). pap., wbk. ed. 66.50 *(978-1-4283-1977-6(8),* Milady Publishing Co.) Delmar Cengage Learning.
—Milady's Standard Esthetics: Fundamentals. 10th ed. 2010. (ENG.). (C). 78.50 *(978-1-111-31335-7(0),* Milady Publishing Co.) Delmar Cengage Learning.
—Standard Cosmetology. (ENG.). (C). 2010. 78.50 *(978-1-111-12574-5(0))* 2nd ed. 2011. 1071.00 *(978-1-4390-5897-8(0))* Delmar Cengage Learning. (Milady Publishing Co.).
—Standard Cosmetology: Haircutting. 2008. (ENG., Illus.). 160p. (C). pap. 32.50 *(978-1-4354-0074-0(7),* Milady Publishing Co.) Delmar Cengage Learning.
—Standard Cosmetology 2012. 2011. (ENG.). (C). 77.95 *(978-1-4390-5919-7(5),* Milady Publishing Co.) Delmar Cengage Learning.
—Standard Esthetics. 2009. (ENG.). (C). 963.75 *(978-1-4354-1288-0(5),* Milady Publishing Co.) Delmar Cengage Learning.
—Standard Esthetics: Advanced Step-by-Step Procedures. 2009. (ENG.). 248p. (C). spiral bd. 34.50 *(978-1-4390-5911-1(X),* Milady Publishing Co.) Delmar Cengage Learning.
Milady Publishing Company Staff. Infection Control. 2010. (ENG.). (C). 31.50 *(978-1-111-31828-4(X),* Milady Publishing Co.) Delmar Cengage Learning.
—Milady's Standard Esthetics. 2009. (ENG.). (C). 62.95 *(978-1-4354-1286-6(9),* Milady Publishing Co.) Delmar Cengage Learning.
—SalonOvations Encyclopedia. Date not set. (Cosmetology Ser.). 49.95 *(978-1-56253-364-9(9),* Milady Publishing Co.) Delmar Cengage Learning.
—Standard Cosmetology 2008. 2nd ed. 2007. (SPA & ENG., Illus.). 960p. (C). per. 131.50 *(978-1-4180-4960-7(3))* Delmar Cengage Learning.
—Standard Esthetics: Fundamentals Step-by-Step Procedures. 2009. (ENG.). 144p. (C). spiral bd. 34.50 *(978-1-4390-5925-8(X),* Milady Publishing Co.) Delmar Cengage Learning.
Milady Publishing Company Staff & Gerson, Joel. Standard Esthetics: Advanced. 2009. (ENG.). 176p. (C). pap. 48.50 *(978-1-4283-1978-3(6),* Milady Publishing Co.) Delmar Cengage Learning.
Milady Standard Cosmetology 2012. 2011. (ENG.). (C). cd-rom 901.75 *(978-1-4390-5918-0(7),* Milady Publishing Co.) Delmar Cengage Learning.
Miller, Laura. Beauty Up: Exploring Contemporary Japanese Body Aesthetics. 2006. (Illus.). 256p. 60.00 *(978-0-520-24508-2(3))*; per. 26.95 *(978-0-520-24509-9(1))* Univ. of California Pr.
Nordmann, Lorraine. Beauty Basics: The Official Guide to Level 1. 2nd ed. 2007. (ENG., Illus.). 140p. (C). pap. 43.95 *(978-1-84480-694-2(4))* Cengage Learning GBR. Dist: CENGAGE Learning.
—Professional Beauty Therapy: The Official Guide to Level 3. 3rd ed. 2007. (ENG., Illus.). 650p. (C). pap. 74.95 *(978-1-84480-696-5(0))* Cengage Learning GBR. Dist: CENGAGE Learning.
Peiss, Kathy. Hope in a Jar: The Making of America's Beauty Culture. 2011. (Illus.). 352p. (C). pap. 17.95 *(978-0-8122-2167-1(2))* Univ. of Pennsylvania Pr.
Ririnui, Jana, et al. Makeup Is Art: Professional Techniques for Creating Original Looks. 2011. (ENG., Illus.). 224p. 34.95 *(978-1-84732-620-1(X))* Carlton Bks., Ltd. GBR. Dist: Sterling Publishing Co., Inc.
Royston, Angela. Skin Deep: The Business of Beauty. 2012. (Big-Buck Business Ser.). (Illus.). 48p. (gr. 6-8). pap. 14.05 **(978-1-4339-7764-0(8))**; lib. bdg. 31.95 **(978-1-4339-7763-3(X))** Stevens, Gareth Publishing LLLP.
Rudman, Jack. Cosmetology. Date not set. (Occupational Competency Examination Ser.). 49.95 *(978-0-8373-5763-8(2),* Passbooks) National Learning Corp.
Russo, Mario Luca. Rejuvenated Skin: Without Surgery. 2008. 68p. pap. *(978-1-873413-64-7(5))* Merit Publishing International, Inc.
Sadick. Cosmeceutical Science in Clinical Practice. 2010. (Series in Cosmetic & Laser Therapy Ser.). (ENG., Illus.). 120p. *(978-0-415-47114-5(1))* Informa Healthcare.
Samel, Arnold. The Cosmetologists Manual to Success. Jacobs, Temre, ed. (Illus.). 130p. pap. 14.95 *(978-0-9641106-0-1(1))* Samel, Arnold.
Success Dynamics Teacher's Guide. 2007. ring bd. *(978-0-9778242-5-0(X))* Certified Learning in Cosmetology, Inc.
Success Dynamics Textbook. 2007. spiral bd. *(978-0-9778242-4-3(1))* Certified Learning in Cosmetology, Inc.
Taussig, Michael. Beauty & the Beast. 2012. (ENG., Illus.). 192p. 55.00 **(978-0-226-78985-9(3))**; pap. 18.00 **(978-0-226-78986-6(1))** Univ. of Chicago Pr.
Thompson, Paul. Beauty Make-up Workbook. 2nd rev. ed. 2007. *(978-0-9749500-6-8(8))* Make-up Designory.
Thompson, Paul, compiled by. Beauty Make-up Artistry Course Workbook. 2nd ed. 2009. *(978-0-9802318-6-1(8))* Make-up Designory.
Walker, Susannah. Style & Status: Selling Beauty to African American Women, 1920-1975. 2007. (ENG., Illus.). 264p. 40.00 *(978-0-8131-2433-9(6))* Univ. Pr. of Kentucky.
Willett, Julie, ed. The American Beauty Industry Encyclopedia, 1 vol. 2010. (Illus.). 338p. 85.00 *(978-0-313-35949-1(0),* GR5949) Greenwood Publishing Group, Inc.
Wright, Curtis. Behind the Chair: Rantings of a Burnt Out Stylist. 2009. 79p. pap. 14.95 *(978-1-4327-4239-3(6))* Outskirts Pr., Inc.

BEAUTY CULTURE—VOCATIONAL GUIDANCE

Halloway, Lori. Shear Savvy: Secrets & Strategies for Successful Salon Apprenticeships. 2009. (Illus.). 122p. pap. 74.95 *(978-0-9822666-1-8(8))*; (ENG., cd-rom 14.95 *(978-0-9822666-4-9(2))* Willow Tree Pr.
Salon Success: A Learning Guide for Career Advancement Coursebook. 2009. spiral bd. *(978-1-934636-24-4(X))* 2006. spiral bd. *(978-0-9779961-3-1(1))* Pivot Point International, Inc.
Salon Success: A Learning Guide for Career Advancement Teacher's Support Material. 2009. ring bd. *(978-1-934636-26-8(6))* Pivot Point International, Inc.

BEAUTY OPERATORS

Allison Bridges. Trade Secrets of the Successful Hairstylist: The Successful Hairstylist's Proven Techniques for Making A LOT MORE MONEY While WORKING FEWER Hours! 2009. 76p. pap. 11.95 *(978-1-4401-7167-3(X))* iUniverse, Inc.
Blasco, Joe & Kehoe, Vincent J-R. The Professional Make-up Artist Volume II, Character Make-up: Motion Pictures * Television * Print & Theatre, 2 vols. 2009. (Illus.). 120p. 350.00 *(978-0-9771580-1-0(2))* Blasco, Joe.
Blasucci, Loa. All Health's Breaking Loose: Your personal boot camp guide to becoming your authentic, lean, naturally beautiful Self. 2010. 225p. pap. 19.95 *(978-1-4327-4455-7(0))* Outskirts Pr., Inc.
carter-Shabazz, Aginah. Choicez: How they impact our Lives. 2008. 176p. pap. 18.99 *(978-0-615-23027-6(X))* Sulermar-Aginah & Co., LLC.
Coffey, Tabatha. It's Not Really about the Hair: The Honest Truth about Life, Love, & the Business of Beauty. 2012. (ENG.). 224p. pap. 14.99 **(978-0-06-210395-6(4))** HarperCollins Pubs.
Frangie, Catherine M. & Milady Publishing Company Staff. Standard Cosmetology 2008. 2007. (ENG.). 160p. (C). pap. 35.50 *(978-1-4180-4943-0(3),* Milady Publishing Co.) Delmar Cengage Learning.
—Standard Cosmetology 2008: Situational Problems for Cosmetology Students. 2007. (ENG.). 304p. (C). pap. 39.95 *(978-1-4180-4944-7(1))* Delmar Cengage Learning.
Gerson, Joel & Milady. Esthetics: Standard Fundamentals. 10th ed. 2009. (ENG.). 176p. (C). pap., wbk. ed. 77.50 *(978-1-4283-1899-1(2),* Milady Publishing Co.) Delmar Cengage Learning.
Gilbert, Odile & Lindbergh, Peter, contrib. by. Odile Gilbert: Her Style, 1 vol. 2008. (ENG., Illus.). 261p. (gr. 13-18). 88.00 *(978-3-88243-925-0(4))* Steidl, Gerhard Druckerei und Verlag DEU. Dist: Innovative Logistics.
Halloway, Lori. Shear Savvy: Secrets & Strategies for Successful Salon Apprenticeships. 2009. (Illus.). 122p. pap. 74.95 *(978-0-9822666-1-8(8))*; (ENG., cd-rom 14.95 *(978-0-9822666-4-9(2))* Willow Tree Pr.
Herron, Tara J. The Definitive Spa & Body Therapist's Handbook: The 5 Keys to Unlimited Energy, Balance & Bliss. 2009. (Illus.). 196p. pap. 24.95 *(978-1-84694-097-2(4))* Hunt, John Publishing Ltd. GBR. Dist: National Bk. Network.
Hughes, Russell Paul. You'll Never Make a Hairdresser. 2010. 182p. pap. *(978-1-84991-202-0(5))* Chipmunkapublishing.
Inspire. No. 57. 57th ed. 2006. 34.95 *(978-0-9767959-5-7(7))*No. 58. 58th ed. 2006. 34.95 *(978-0-9767959-6-4(5))* Vol. 59. 2007. 34.95 *(978-0-9767959-7-1(3))* Creative Age Communications, Inc.
Inspire 60. 60th ed. 2007. 34.95 *(978-0-9767959-8-8(1))* Creative Age Communications, Inc.
Inspire Volume 61. 61st ed. 2007. 34.95 *(978-0-9767959-9-5(X))* Creative Age Communications, Inc.
LaFlesh, Teri. Curly Like Me: How to Grow Your Hair Healthy, Long, & Strong. 2010. (ENG., Illus.). 288p. pap. 16.95 *(978-0-470-53642-1(X),* Wiley) Wiley, John & Sons, Inc.
LearningExpress Staff. Cosmetology Certification Exam. 4th rev. ed. 2009. (Complete Preparation Guides). (ENG.). 300p. pap. 22.95 *(978-1-57685-698-7(4))* LearningExpress, LLC.
Mathis, Nathaniel. Portrait of a Professional. 2011. 216p. pap. 19.99 **(978-1-4628-9454-3(2))** Xlibris Corp.
Milady. The Essential Companion for Milady's Standard Cosmetology. 2011. (ENG.). 576p. (C). pap., pupil's gde. ed. 54.95 *(978-1-4390-5924-1(1),* Milady Publishing Co.) Delmar Cengage Learning.
—Exam Review for Milady Standard Cosmetology 2012. 2011. (ENG.). 176p. (C). pap. 33.95 **(978-1-4390-5921-0(7))** Delmar Cengage Learning.
—Retail Analysis & Coaching Tools for the Salon & Spa. 2011. (ENG.). (C). 221.50 **(978-1-111-54080-7(2),** Milady Publishing Co.) Delmar Cengage Learning.
—Spanish Translated Exam Review for Milady Standard Cosmetology 2012. 3rd ed. 2011. (ENG.). (C). pap. 43.95 **(978-1-4390-5907-4(1),** Milady Publishing Co.) Delmar Cengage Learning.
Milady. Standard Cosmetology. 2nd ed. 2008. (ENG.). (C). 304p. pap. 51.50 *(978-1-4180-4954-6(9))*; 170p. pap. 46.50 *(978-1-4180-4955-3(7))* Delmar Cengage Learning. (Milady Publishing Co.).
Milady, (Milady). Advanced Facial Machines. 2011. (ENG.). 26.50 *(978-1-111-54449-2(2)* Milady Publishing Co.) Delmar Cengage Learning.
Milady Publishing Company Staff. Custom Facials. 2011. (ENG.). 26.50 *(978-1-111-54447-8(6),* Milady Publishing Co.) Delmar Cengage Learning.
Miller, Mimi. Confessions of a Las Vegas Hairstylist. 2011. 152p. 29.99 **(978-1-4568-1462-5(1))**; pap. 19.99 **(978-1-4568-1461-8(3))** Xlibris Corp.
Mokotoff, Eric Charles. The Salon Industry Business Artist. 2010. 102p. pap. 19.99 *(978-0-557-18351-7(0))* Lulu Enterprises Inc.
Owens, Jetta Remonia & Walter, Debra. To Cripple A Butterfly: A Memoir. 2011. pap. 10.99 **(978-1-61777-512-3(6))** Tate Publishing & Enterprises, LLC.
Rae, Myrna. Beauty Shop Burnout. 1 vol. 2009. 78p. pap. 16.95 *(978-1-60672-744-7(3),* PublishAmerica, Inc.
Sanders-Peterson, Polly. Love Search. 2008. 136p. pap. 13.99 *(978-1-60477-702-4(8))* Xulon Pr., Inc.
Sassoon, Vidal. Vidal: The Autobiography. 2011. (ENG., Illus.). 360p. pap. 13.95 *(978-0-330-52129-1(2))*; 32.95 *(978-0-230-74689-3(6))* Macmillan Pubs., Ltd. GBR. Dist: Independent Pubs. Group.
Silk, Adrienne. Confessions from the Beauty Trade. 2007. 141p. pap. 12.95 *(978-0-7414-3709-9(0))* Infinity Publishing.
Smith, Steven. It Shouldn't Happen to a Hairdresser: Celebrity Tales from My Crimping Days. 2011. 256p. pap. 22.50 **(978-1-84624-631-9(8))** Book Guild, Ltd. GBR. Dist: Trans-Atlantic Pubns., Inc.
White, Carrie. Upper Cut: Highlights of My Hollywood Life. (ENG., Illus.). 400p. 2012. pap. 16.00 **(978-1-4391-9910-7(8))** 2011. 26.00 *(978-1-4391-9909-1(4))* Atria Bks. (Beyond Words/Atria Bks.).
Wingfield, Adia Harvey. Doing Business with Beauty: Black Women, Hair Salons, & the Racial Enclave Economy. 2008. (Perspectives on a Multiracial America Ser.). (ENG.). 176p. 70.00 *(978-0-7425-6116-8(X))* Rowman & Littlefield Publishers, Inc.
Wright, Curtis. Behind the Chair: Rantings of a Burnt Out Stylist. 2009. 79p. pap. 14.95 *(978-1-4327-4239-3(6))* Outskirts Pr., Inc.

BEAUTY PAGEANTS

see Beauty Contests

BEAUTY QUEENS

see Beauty Contestants

BEAUTY SHOPS

see also Beauty, Personal; Beauty Culture; Beauty Operators; Cosmetics

Allison Bridges. Trade Secrets of the Successful Hairstylist: The Successful Hairstylist's Proven Techniques for Making A LOT MORE MONEY While WORKING FEWER Hours! 2009. 76p. pap. 11.95 *(978-1-4401-7167-3(X))* iUniverse, Inc.
Berts, Jean-Michel, et al. Sulwhasoo. 2011. (ENG., Illus.). 80p. pap. 25.00 **(978-1-61428-012-5(6))** Assouline FRA. Dist: Perseus Distribution.
Corporation, Azur. X-Space No. 2. 2012. (ENG., Illus.). 444p. 115.00 **(978-4-903233-75-8(8))** Azur Corp. JPN. Dist: National Bk. Network.
Levesque, Kim Horton. Pampered in Paris: A Guide to the Best Spas, Salons & Beauty Boutiques. 2010. (ENG., Illus.). 232p. pap. 16.95 *(978-1-892145-86-4(3))* Little Bookroom.
Milady, (Milady). Successful Salon & Spa Management. 6th ed. 2011. (ENG.). 96p. (C). pap., wbk. ed. 52.50 *(978-1-4354-8247-0(6),* Milady Publishing Co.) Delmar Cengage Learning.
Milady Publishing Company Staff & Salon Training International Staff. Salon & Spa Management Tools. 2nd ed. 2007. (ENG.). 359p. (C). ring bd. 479.95 *(978-1-4283-5317-6(8),* Salon Training International) Delmar Cengage Learning.
Milady/Thomson Learning Staff, et al. Successful Salon & Spa Management. 6th ed. 2011. (ENG.). 224p. (C). pap. 68.50 *(978-1-4354-8246-3(8),* Milady Publishing Co.) Delmar Cengage Learning.
Rodriguez, Deborah. Kabul Beauty School. 2011. 14.72 *(978-0-7848-3406-0(7),* Everbind) Marco Bk. Co.
—Kabul Beauty School: An American Woman Goes Behind the Veil. Lt. ed. 2007. (Readers Circle Ser.). 351p. 32.95 *(978-1-60285-009-5(7))* Ctr. Point Large Print.
—Kabul Beauty School: An American Woman Goes Behind the Veil. 2008. (ENG.). 64.99 *(978-1-60640-750-9(3))* Findaway World, LLC.
Rodriguez, Deborah & Ohlson, Kristin. Kabul Beauty School: An American Woman Goes Behind the Veil. 2007. (ENG.). 320p. per. 14.95 *(978-0-8129-7673-1(8))* Random House Publishing Group.
Ruder, Raisa, et al. Babushka's Beauty Secrets: Old World Tips for a Glamorous New You. 2010. (ENG., Illus.). 208p. 15.99 *(978-0-446-55586-9(X),* Wellness Central) Grand Central Publishing.
Salon Success: A Learning Guide for Career Advancement Coursebook. 2009. spiral bd. *(978-1-934636-24-4(X))* 2006. spiral bd. *(978-0-9779961-3-1(1))* Pivot Point International, Inc.
Salon Success: A Learning Guide for Career Advancement Teacher's Support Material. 2009. ring bd. *(978-1-934636-26-8(6))* Pivot Point International, Inc.
Sandlin, Eileen Figure. Start Your Own Hair Salon & Day Spa. 2nd ed. 2010. (ENG., Illus.). 256p. pap. 17.95 *(978-1-59918-346-6(3),* 1599183463) Entrepreneur Pr. dba Entrepreneur Media, Inc.
Schmaling, Susanne. A Comprehensive Guide to Equipment. 2008. (ENG.). 432p. (C). pap. 56.95 *(978-1-4180-5078-8(4),* Milady Publishing Co.) Delmar Cengage Learning.
Shecky's Beauty Book NYC 2007. 2007. 12.95 *(978-1-931449-31-1(7))* Shecky's Publishing.
Sinclair Eakin, Julie. Salons & Spas: The Architecture of Beauty. 2007. (ENG., Illus.). 168p. pap. 30.00 *(978-1-59253-396-1(5),* 1592533965) Quayside.
Spalding, Robert. Death by Pedicure: The Dirty Secrets of Nail Salons. 2006. *(978-0-9711068-1-9(9))*; 2nd ed. *(978-0-9711068-2-6(7))* Chattanooga FuFu Factory.
Tsegay, Mahlet. Assessment of Customer Satisfaction in Women's Beauty Salon. 2010. 84p. pap. *(978-3-639-25205-7(5))* VDM Verlag Dr. Mueller e.K.
Willett, Julie, ed. The American Beauty Industry Encyclopedia, 1 vol. 2010. (Illus.). 338p. 85.00 *(978-0-313-35949-1(0),* GR5949) Greenwood Publishing Group, Inc.
Wingfield, Adia Harvey. Doing Business with Beauty: Black Women, Hair Salons, & the Racial Enclave Economy. 2008. (Perspectives on a Multiracial America Ser.). (ENG.). 176p. 70.00 *(978-0-7425-6116-8(X))* Rowman & Littlefield Publishers, Inc.
Woodbury, Susan. Salon Solutions: Salon marketing made easy without pulling your hair Out. 2010. 58p. pap. 15.99 *(978-1-4415-9535-5(X))* Xlibris Corp.
Wright, Curtis. Behind the Chair: Rantings of a Burnt Out Stylist. 2009. 79p. pap. 14.95 *(978-1-4327-4239-3(6))* Outskirts Pr., Inc.
Yousef-Sadeh, B. & Medcalf, Sally. Start & Run A Successful Beauty Salon: A Comprehensive Guide to Managing or Acquiring Your Own Salon. 2010. (ENG.). 258p. pap. 30.00 *(978-1-84528-376-6(7))* How To Books GBR. Dist: Parkwest Pubns., Inc.

BEAUVOIR, SIMONE DE, 1908-1986

Beauvoir, Simone de. Diary of a Philosophy Student: Volume 1, 1926-27. Le Bon de Beauvoir, Sylvie et al, eds. annot. ed. 2006. (Beauvoir Ser.). 392p. 42.00 *(978-0-252-03142-7(3))* Univ. of Illinois Pr.
—Faut-Il Bruler Sade? (Idees Ser.). (FRE.). 250p. pap. 8.95 *(978-2-07-035268-5(4))* Schoenhof's Foreign Bks., Inc.
—Journal de Guerre, Septembre, 1939-Janvier 1941. (Gallimard Ser.). (FRE.). pap. 32.95 *(978-2-07-071809-2(3))* Schoenhof's Foreign Bks., Inc.
—Letters to Sartre. Hoare, Quintin, tr. 2012. (ENG.). 544p. pap. 14.95 **(978-1-61145-498-7(0),** 611498, Arcade Publishing) Skyhorse Publishing Co., Inc.
—Memoires D'une Jeune Fille Rangee. 2008. (Collection Folio Ser.). (FRE.). 472p. per. *(978-2-07-035552-5(7))* Gallimard, Editions.
Beauvoir, Simone de. The Useless Mouths & Other Literary Writings. Simons, Margaret A. & Timmermann, Marybeth, eds. 2011. (Beauvoir Ser.). (ENG., Illus.). 424p. 50.00 **(978-0-252-03634-7(4))** Univ. of Illinois Pr.
Berghe, Christian Louis. Dictionnaire des idées dans l'oeuvre de Simone de Beauvoir. (Collection Dictionnaires des idées / Littérature Française Ser.). (FRE.). 290p. 135.00 **(978-3-11-102695-4(7))** De Gruyter, Mouton DEU. Dist: de Gruyter, Walter GmbH & Co. KG.
Cahill, Ann J. French Feminists Vol. 3: Critical Evaluations in Cultural Theory, 4 vols. Hansen, Jennifer, ed. 2007. 448p. *(978-0-415-39555-7(0))* Routledge.
Cahill, Ann J. & Hansen, Jennifer, eds. French Feminists Vol. 1: Critical Evaluations in Cultural Theory, 4 vols. 2007. 416p. *(978-0-415-39553-3(4))* Routledge.
—French Feminists Vol. 2: Critical Evaluations in Cultural Theory, 4 vols. 2007. 400p. *(978-0-415-39554-0(2))* Routledge.

Caust, Lesley. The Irreducible Other: The Second Sex Meets This Sex Which is Not One: Women, subjectivity, & ethics in Beauvoir & Irigaray. 2008. 224p. pap. *(978-3-639-08683-6(X))* VDM Verlag Dr. Mueller e.K.

Daigle, Christine & Golomb, Jacob J., eds. Beauvoir & Sartre: The Riddle of Influence. 2009. (ENG.). 296p. pap. 24.95 *(978-0-253-22037-0(8),* 0253220378) Indiana Univ. Pr.

de Beauvoir, Simone. Wartime Diary. Simons, Margaret A. et al, eds. Cordero, Anne Deing, tr. from FRE. 2008. (Beauvoir Ser.). (ENG.). 368p. 42.00 *(978-0-252-03377-3(9))* Univ. of Illinois Pr.

Deutscher, Penelope. The Philosophy of Simone de Beauvoir: Ambiguity, Conversion, Resistance. 2008. (Ideas in Context Ser.). (ENG.). 222p. (C). 83.00 *(978-0-521-88520-1(5))* Cambridge Univ. Pr.

Fullbrook, Edward & Fullbrook, Kate. Sex & Philosophy: Rethinking de Beauvoir & Sartre. 2008. (ENG.). 288p. 120.00 *(978-1-84706-065-5(X))*; pap. 49.95 *(978-1-84706-066-2(8))* Continuum International Publishing Group, Ltd. GBR. Dist: National Bk. Network.

Hansen. French Feminists V4, 4 vols. 2007. *(978-0-415-39556-4(9))* Routledge.

Hansen, Jennifer & Cahill, Ann J., eds. French Feminists: Critical Evaluations in Cultural Theory, 4 vols. 2007. (Critical Evaluations in Cultural Theory Ser.). 1672p. 1225.00 *(978-0-415-39552-6(6))* Routledge.

Holland, Alison. Excess & Transgression in Simone de Beauvoir's Fiction: The Discourse of Madness. 2009. 230p. 99.95 *(978-0-7546-5152-9(5))* Ashgate Publishing Co.

Kruks, Sonia. Simone de Beauvoir & the Politics of Ambiguity. 2012. (Studies in Feminist Philosophy Ser.). (ENG.). 240p. 99.00 ***(978-0-19-538144-3(0))***; pap. 29.95 ***(978-0-19-538143-6(2))*** Oxford Univ. Pr., Inc.

Lundgren-Gothlin, Eva. Sex & Existence. (Illus.). 240p. *(978-0-485-12124-7(7))* Continuum International Publishing Group, Ltd.

Mahon, Joseph. Simone de Beauvoir & Her Catholicism: An Essay on Her Ethical & Religious Meditations. 2007. 216p. pap. 29.95 *(978-1-903631-27-0(0))* Arlen Hse. IRL. Dist: Syracuse Univ. Pr.

Moi, Toril. Simone de Beauvoir: The Making of an Intellectual Woman. 2nd ed. (ENG.). 2009. 368p. pap. 29.95 *(978-0-19-923872-9(3))* 2008. 400p. 65.00 *(978-0-19-923871-2(5))* Oxford Univ. Pr., Inc.

Moser, Susanne. Freedom & Recognition in the Work of Simone de Beauvoir. 2008. (Philosophie, Phänomenologie und Hermeneutik der Werte. Reihe des Instituts für Axiologische Forschungen Ser.). 220p. pap. 56.95 *(978-3-631-50925-8(1))* Lang, Peter GmbH, Europaischer Verlag der Wissenschaften DEU. Dist: Lang, Peter.

Mussett, Shannon M. & Wilkerson, William S. Beauvoir & Western Thought from Plato to Butler. 2012. (ENG.). 272p. 80.00 ***(978-1-4384-4455-0(9))*** State Univ. of New York Pr.

O'Brien, Wendy & Embree, L., eds. The Existential Phenomenology of Simone de Beauvoir. 2010. (Contributions to Phenomenology Ser.). 272p. pap. 159.00 *(978-90-481-5732-7(3),* 9048157323) Springer.

Reineke, Sandra. Beauvoir & Her Sisters: The Politics of Women's Bodies in France. 2011. (ENG.). 128p. 45.00 *(978-0-252-03619-4(0))* Univ. of Illinois Pr.

Rowley, Hazel. Tête-à-Tête: The Tumultuous Lives & Loves of Simone de Beauvoir & Jean-Paul Sartre. 2008. (ENG.). 416p. pap. 16.00 *(978-1-4223-9557-8(X))* DIANE Publishing Co.

—Tête-à-Tête: The Tumultuous Lives & Loves of Simone de Beauvoir & Jean-Paul Sartre. 2006. (P. S. Ser.). (ENG., Illus.). 480p. per. 15.95 *(978-0-06-052060-1(4),* HarperPerennial) HarperCollins Pubs.

Sandford, Stella. How to Read Beauvoir. annot. ed. 2007. (How to Read Ser.). (ENG.). 128p. per. 11.95 *(978-0-393-32951-3(8),* 32951) Norton, W. W. & Co., Inc.

Seymour-Jones, Carole. A Dangerous Liaison: A Revelatory New Biography of Simone Debeauvoir & Jean-Paul Sartre. 2009. (ENG.). 576p. (gr. 12-18). 35.00 *(978-1-59020-268-5(6))* Overlook Pr., The.

Singh, Priyanka & Singh, Vipin K. What & Why They Are: A Peep into Feminism. 2010. 240p. pap. 21.49 *(978-1-4520-2772-2(2))* AuthorHouse.

Tidd, Ursula. Simone de Beauvoir. 2009. (Reaktion Books - Critical Lives Ser.). (ENG., Illus.). 192p. pap. 16.95 *(978-1-86189-434-2(1))* Reaktion Bks., Ltd. GBR. Dist: Chicago Distribution Ctr.

—Simone de Beauvoir, Gender & Testimony. 2006. (Cambridge Studies in French Ser.). (ENG.). 268p. pap. 50.00 *(978-0-521-03450-0(7))* Cambridge Univ. Pr.

Whitmarsh, Anne. Simone de Beauvoir & the Limits of Commitment. 2010. (ENG.). 228p. pap. 30.99 *(978-0-521-15530-4(4))* Cambridge Univ. Pr.

BEAUX

see Dandies

BEAVERBROOK, MAX AITKEN, BARON, 1879-1964

Poitras, Jacques. Beaverbrook: A Shattered Legacy. (ENG., 318p. 2007. Illus.). 30.00 *(978-0-86492-497-1(6))* 2nd ed. 2008. pap. 19.95 *(978-0-86492-522-0(0))* Goose Lane Editions CAN. Dist: Univ. of Toronto Pr.

BEAVERS

Almeida Monteiro, Gabriela. The Biodiesel Program & Sustainable Livelihoods. 2010. 80p. pap. *(978-3-8383-8770-3(8))* Lambert Academic Publishing.

Coles, Bryony. Beavers in Britain's Past. 2006. (WARP Occasional Paper Ser.: Vol. 19). (Illus.). 242p. per. 80.00 *(978-1-84217-226-1(3))* Oxbow Bks., Ltd. GBR. Dist: Brown, David Bk. Co., The.

Golden, Doug. When the Beaver Was the King. 2006. (ENG.). 100p. per. 9.95 *(978-0-7414-3270-4(6))* Infinity Publishing.

Kitchener, Andrew. Beavers. 2008. (ENG.). 144p. (J). 22.00 *(978-1-4223-9412-0(3))* DIANE Publishing Co.

Mills, Enos A. In Beaver World. 2007. (ENG.). 276p. 42.95 *(978-0-548-00752-5(7))* Kessinger Publishing, LLC.

Morgan, Lewis Henry. The American Beaver & His Works. 2009. 174p. pap. 19.99 *(978-0-217-94692-6(5))* General Bks. LLC.

Müller-Schwarze, Dietland. The Beaver: Its Life & Impact. 2nd rev. ed. 2011. (Illus.). 228p. 39.95 *(978-0-8014-5010-5(1),* Comstock Publishing Assocs.) Cornell Univ. Pr.

Owl, Grey. Pilgrims of the Wild. 2010. (ENG., Illus.). 256p. pap. 26.99 *(978-1-55488-734-7(8))* Dundurn CAN. Dist: Ingram Pub. Services.

Sandoz, Mari. The Beaver Men: Spearheads of Empire. 2nd ed. 2010. (ENG., Illus.). 368p. pap. 16.95 *(978-0-8032-2656-2(X),* Bison Bks.) Univ. of Nebraska Pr.

Sjoberg, Goran & Ball, John P., eds. Restoring the European Beaver: 50 Years of Experience. 2011. (Illus.). 280p. 167.50 ***(978-954-642-581-2(8))*** Pensoft Pubs. BGR. Dist: Coronet Bks.

Weymouth, Ellis L. Beavers, Rodents & Rodentia In Biology & Medicine with Index & Medical Analysis of New Research Information for All Nations. 2006. (Illus.). 160p. 69.95 *(978-0-7883-4338-4(6),* 07883-43386); pap. 59.95 *(978-0-7883-4339-1(4),* 07883-43394) ABBE Pubs. Assn. of Washington, D.C.

BEBOP (MUSIC)

see Jazz

BEC (ABBEY)

Constable, Giles. Three Treatises from Bec on the Nature of Monastic Life. Smith, Bernard S., tr. from LAT. 2008. (Medieval Academy Bks.). (ENG., Illus.). 208p. *(978-0-8020-9260-1(8))* Univ. of Toronto Pr.

BECCARIA, CESARE, MARCHESE DI, 1738-1794

Hostettler, John. Cesare Beccaria: The Genius of on Crimes & Punishments. 2011. 160p. pap. 44.95 *(978-1-904380-63-4(8))* Waterside Pr. GBR. Dist: International Specialized Bk. Services.

BECHE-DE-MER JARGON

see Bislama Language

BEC-HELLOUIN, FRANCE (BENEDICTINE ABBEY)

see Bec (Abbey)

BECHUANA (AFRICAN PEOPLE)

see Tswana (African People)

BECKER, CHARLES, 1870-1915

Dash, Mike. Satan's Circus: Murder, Vice, Police Corruption, & New York's Trial of the Century. 2008. (ENG., Illus.). 464p. pap. 16.00 *(978-1-4000-5472-5(9),* Three Rivers Pr.) Crown Publishing Group.

Keefe, Rose. The Starker: Big Jack Zelig, the Becker-Rosenthal Case, & the Advent of the Jewish Gangster. 2008. (ENG., Illus.). 320p. 24.95 *(978-1-58182-602-9(8))* Turner Publishing Co.

BECKETT, SAMUEL, 1906-1989

Ackerley, C. J. Demented Particulars: The Annotated Murphy. annot. ed. 2010. (ENG., Illus.). 260p. (gr. 17). pap. 35.00 *(978-0-7486-4150-5(5))* Edinburgh Univ. Pr. GBR. Dist: Columbia Univ. Pr.

Astro, Alan. Understanding Samuel Beckett. 2011. (ENG.). 248p. pap. 21.95 *(978-1-61117-004-7(4))* Univ. of South Carolina Pr.

Banier, Francois-Marie. Beckett, 1 vol. 2009. (ENG., Illus.). 88p. 25.00 *(978-3-86521-983-1(7))* Steidl, Gerhard Druckerei und Verlag DEU. Dist: Innovative Logistics.

Barfield. Beckett & Death, 2 vols. Feldman, Matthew & Tew, Philip, eds. 2009. (Continuum Literary Studies). (ENG., Illus.). 240p. 110.00 *(978-0-8264-9835-9(3))* Continuum International Publishing Group, Ltd. GBR. Dist: National Bk. Network.

Barry, Elizabeth. Beckett & Authority: The Uses of Cliché. 2006. (ENG.). 264p. 95.00 *(978-0-230-00833-5(X))* Palgrave Macmillan.

Beaujeu, Arnaud. Matière et lumière dans le théâtre de Samuel Beckett: Autour des Notions de Trivialité, de Spiritualité et D'autre-là. 2010. (Modern French Identities Ser.). (FRE.). 363p. pap. 74.95 *(978-3-0343-0206-7(1))* Lang, Peter AG GBR. Dist: Lang, Peter.

Beckett, Samuel. The Letters of Samuel Beckett, Vol. 1. Fehsenfeld, Martha Dow & Overbeck, Lois More, eds. 2009. (Letters of Samuel Beckett Ser.). (FRE, GER & ENG., Illus.). 882p. 55.00 *(978-0-521-86793-1(2))* Cambridge Univ. Pr.

Beckett, Samuel. The Letters of Samuel Beckett, 1941-1956, Vol. 2. Craig, George et al, eds. 2011. (Letters of Samuel Beckett Ser.). (ENG & FRE., Illus.). 886p. 50.00 ***(978-0-521-86794-8(0))*** Cambridge Univ. Pr.

Besbes, Khaled. The Semiotics of Beckett's Theatre: A Semiotic Study of the Complete Dramatic Works of Samuel Beckett. 2007. 328p. per. 29.95 *(978-1-58112-955-7(6))* Universal Pubs.

Bignell, Jonathan. Beckett on Screen: The Television Plays. (ENG.). 2012. 240p. pap. 29.95 ***(978-0-7190-6421-0(X))*** 2nd rev. ed. 2010. 208p. 74.95 *(978-0-7190-6420-3(1))* Manchester Univ. Pr. GBR. Dist: Macmillan.

Bixby, Patrick. Samuel Beckett & the Postcolonial Novel. 2009. (ENG., Illus.). 246p. 77.00 *(978-0-521-11388-5(1))* Cambridge Univ. Pr.

Bloom, Harold, ed. Waiting for Godot. 2nd rev. ed. 2008. (Modern Critical Interpretations Ser.). 184p. (C). (gr. 9). 45.00 *(978-0-7910-9793-9(5),* Chelsea Hse.) Facts On File, Inc.

Bohman-Kalaja, Kimberly. Reading Games: An Aesthetics of Play in Flann O'Brien, Samuel Beckett, & Georges Perec. 2007. (Dalkey Archive Scholarly Ser.). 238p. pap. 34.95 *(978-1-56478-473-5(8))* Dalkey Archive Pr.

Boulter, Jonathan & Boulter. Beckett. 2008. (Guides for the Perplexed Ser.). (ENG.). 200p. pap. 24.95 *(978-0-8264-8195-5(7))* Continuum International Publishing Group, Ltd. GBR. Dist: National Bk. Network.

—Beckett. 2008. (Guides for the Perplexed Ser.). (ENG.). 200p. 100.00 *(978-0-8264-9267-8(3))* Continuum International Publishing Group, Ltd. GBR. Dist: National Bk. Network.

Boxall, Peter. Since Beckett: Contemporary Writing in the Wake of Modernism. 2012. (ENG.). 256p. pap. 44.95 ***(978-1-4411-7813-8(9))*** Continuum International Publishing Group, Ltd. GBR. Dist: National Bk. Network.

Boxall, Peter C. & Boxall, Peter. Since Beckett: Contemporary Writing in the Wake of Modernism. 2009. (Continuum Literary Studies). (ENG., Illus.). 256p. 120.00 *(978-0-8264-9167-1(7))* Continuum International Publishing Group, Ltd. GBR. Dist: National Bk. Network.

Branigan, Kevin. Radio Beckett: Musicality in the Radio Plays of Samuel Beckett. 2008. 268p. pap. 68.95 *(978-3-03911-371-2(2))* Lang, Peter AG GBR. Dist: Lang, Peter.

Brater, Enoch. Ten Ways of Thinking about Samuel Beckett: The Falsetto of Reason. 2012. (Diaries, Letters & Essays Ser.). (ENG., Illus.). 208p. (C). pap. 25.95 ***(978-1-4081-3722-2(4),*** Methuen Drama) A & C Black GBR. Dist: Macmillan.

Brunet, Lynn. A Course of Severe & Arduous Trials: Bacon, Beckett & Spurious Freemasonry in Early Twentieth-Century Ireland. 2009. (Reimagining Ireland Ser.). (ENG.). 210p. pap. 46.95 *(978-3-03911-854-0(4))* Lang, Peter AG GBR. Dist: Lang, Peter.

Bryden, Mary & Topping, Margaret. Beckett's Proust/Deleuze's Proust. Bryden, Mary & Topping, Margaret, eds. 2009. (ENG., Illus.). 288p. 100.00 *(978-0-230-20141-5(5))* Palgrave Macmillan.

Byron, Mark S., ed. Samuel Beckett's Endgame. 2007. (Illus.). 304p. per. 84.00 *(978-90-420-2288-1(4))* Rodopi.

Carpenter, Charles A. Dramatic Works of Samuel Beckett: A Selective Bibliography of Publications about His Plays & Their Conceptual Foundations. 2011. (ENG.). 528p. 350.00 *(978-1-4411-8421-4(X))* Continuum International Publishing Group, Ltd. GBR. Dist: National Bk. Network.

Casanova, Pascale. Samuel Beckett: Anatomy of a Literary Revolution. Elliott, Gregory, tr. from FRE. 2007. (ENG.). 160p. 23.95 *(978-1-84467-112-0(7),* 844112) Verso Bks. GBR. Dist: Norton, W. W. & Co., Inc.

Caselli, Daniela. Beckett's Dantes: Intertextuality in the Fiction & Criticism. 2nd ed. 2009. (ENG.). 232p. 79.95 *(978-0-7190-7157-7(7))* Manchester Univ. Pr. GBR. Dist: Macmillan.

Caselli, Daniela, ed. Beckett & Nothing: Trying to Understand Beckett. (ENG., Illus.). 2012. 292p. pap. 29.95 ***(978-0-7190-8784-4(8))*** 2010. 240p. 79.95 *(978-0-7190-8019-7(3))* Manchester Univ. Pr. GBR. Dist: Macmillan.

Chan, Paul, ed. Paul Chan: Waiting for Godot in New Orleans: A Field Guide. 2010. (ENG., Illus.). 352p. 45.00 *(978-3-86560-809-3(4))* Creative Time.

Cixous, Hélène. Zero's Neighbour. Milesi, Laurent, tr. from FRE. 2010. (ENG.). 92p. 49.95 *(978-0-7456-4415-8(5))*; pap. 14.95 *(978-0-7456-4416-5(3))* Polity Pr. GBR. Dist: Wiley, John & Sons, Inc.

Connor, Steven. Samuel Beckett: Repetition, Theory, & Text. 2006. (ENG.). 260p. pap. 24.00 *(978-1-888570-88-5(1))* Davies Group Pubs., The.

Copeland, Hannah Case. Art & the artist in the works of Samuel Beckett. (De Proprietatibus Litterarum. Series Practica Ser.). (ENG.). 229p. 210.00 ***(978-3-11-198040-9(5))*** De Gruyter, Mouton DEU. Dist: de Gruyter, Walter GmbH & Co. KG.

De Vos, Laurens. Cruelty & Desire in the Modern Theater: Antonin Artaud, Sarah Kane, & Samuel Beckett. 2011. (ENG.). 256p. 75.00 *(978-1-61147-044-4(7))* 2010. *(978-0-8386-4263-4(2))* Fairleigh Dickinson Univ. Pr.

Dilks, Stephen. Samuel Beckett in the Literary Marketplace. 2011. (Illus.). 400p. *(978-0-8156-3254-2(1))* Syracuse Univ. Pr.

DOWD. Abstract Machines: Samuel Beckett & Philosophy after Deleuze & Guattari. 2007. (Faux Titre Ser.). 320p. per. 86.40 *(978-90-420-2206-5(X))* Rodopi.

Eliopulos, James. Samuel Beckett's dramatic Language. (De Proprietatibus Litterarum. Series Practica Ser.). (ENG.). 131p. 210.00 ***(978-3-11-198461-2(3))***; 135.00 ***(978-3-11-099116-1(0))*** De Gruyter, Mouton DEU. Dist: de Gruyter, Walter GmbH & Co. KG.

Engelberts, Matthijs, et al, eds. Where Never Before: Beckett's Poetics of Elsewhere. 2010. 258p. 75.00 *(978-90-420-2814-2(9))* Rodopi.

Engelberts, Matthijs & Kosters, Onno, eds. Verder: Beckett en de 21e Eeuw. 2008. (DUT., Illus.). 112p. pap. *(978-90-8964-066-6(5))* Amsterdam Univ. Pr.

Feldman, Matthew & Nixon, Mark. The International Reception of Samuel Beckett, 2 vols. Nixon, Mark, ed. 2009. (Continuum Reception Studies). (ENG.). 336p. 160.00 *(978-0-8264-9581-5(8))* Continuum International Publishing Group, Ltd. GBR. Dist: National Bk. Network.

Friedman, Alan Warren. Party Pieces: Oral Storytelling & Social Performance in Joyce & Beckett. 2007. (Illus.). 258p. 45.00 *(978-0-8156-3123-1(5))*; per. 22.95 *(978-0-8156-3148-4(0))* Syracuse Univ. Pr.

Gendron, Sarah. Repetition, Difference, & Knowledge in the Work of Samuel Beckett, Jacques Derrida, & Gilles Deleuze. 2008. (Studies in Literary Criticism & Theory Ser.). 208p. (C). 68.95 *(978-1-4331-0375-9(3))* Lang, Peter Publishing, Inc.

Gibson, Andrew. Samuel Beckett. 2009. (Reaktion Books - Critical Lives Ser.). (ENG., Illus.). 192p. pap. 16.95 *(978-1-86189-517-2(8))* Reaktion Bks., Ltd. GBR. Dist: Chicago Distribution Ctr.

Gontarski, S. E., ed. A Companion to Samuel Beckett. 2010. (Blackwell Companions to Literature & Culture Ser.: 119). (ENG., Illus.). 440p. 159.95 *(978-1-4051-5869-5(7),* Wiley-Blackwell) Wiley, John & Sons, Inc.

Harvey, Robert. Witnessness: Beckett, Dante, Levi & the Foundations of Responsibility. 2010. (ENG.). 176p. 100.00 *(978-1-4411-0072-6(5))*; pap. 29.95 *(978-1-4411-2424-1(1))* Continuum International Publishing Group, Ltd. GBR. Dist: National Bk. Network.

Hill, Leslie. Beckett's Fiction: In Different Words. 2009. (Cambridge Studies in French Ser.). (ENG.). 204p. pap. 33.99 *(978-0-521-11056-3(4))* Cambridge Univ. Pr.

Houppermans, Sjef, ed. Présence de Samuel Beckett / Presence of Samuel Beckett: Colloque de Cerisy. 2006. (Samuel Beckett Today/Aujourd'hui Ser.: 17). 533p. 139.00 *(978-90-420-2117-4(9))* Rodopi.

Hugh Kenner & Kenner, Hugh. Flaubert, Joyce y Beckett: Los Comediantes Estoicos. 2011. (SPA.). 150p. pap. 13.95 ***(978-607-16-0588-7(1))*** Fondo de Cultura Economica USA.

Jebb, Sharon. Writing God & the Self: Samuel Beckett & C. S. Lewis. 2011. (Distinguished Dissertations in Christian Theology Ser.). 292p. pap. 32.00 ***(978-1-60899-738-1(3),*** Pickwick Pubns.) Wipf & Stock Pubs.

Jeffers, Jennifer M. Beckett's Masculinity. 2009. (New Interpertations of Beckett in the Twenty-first Century Ser.). (ENG.). 216p. 84.00 *(978-0-230-61528-1(7))* Palgrave Macmillan.

Johns, Gregory. In the Dim Void: Samuel Beckett's Late Trilogy: Company. 4th ed. 2010. (European Writers Ser.). (Illus.). 132p. pap. *(978-1-86171-297-4(9))* Crescent Moon Publishing.

—In the Dim Void: See Oven. 3rd ed. 2010. (Illus.). 132p. 45.00 *(978-1-86171-260-8(X))* Crescent Moon Publishing GBR. Dist: Gardners Bks. Ltd.

Jones, David Houston. Samuel Beckett & Testimony. 2011. (ENG., Illus.). 216p. 80.00 *(978-0-230-27576-8(1))* Palgrave Macmillan.

Juliet, Charles. Conversations with Samuel Beckett & Bram van Velde. Nesme, Axel & Tucker, Janey, trs. from FRE. 2009. (French Literature Ser.). (ENG.). 192p. pap. 13.95 *(978-1-56478-531-2(9),* 478531) Dalkey Archive Pr.

Karic, Pol Popovic. Ironic Samuel Beckett: Samuel Beckett's Life & Drama: Waiting for Godot, Endgame, & Happy Days. 2006. (ENG.). 154p. per. 32.99 *(978-0-7618-3529-5(6))* Univ. Pr. of America, Inc.

Kennedy, Seán, ed. Beckett & Ireland. 2010. (ENG., Illus.). 236p. 89.00 *(978-0-521-11180-5(3))* Cambridge Univ. Pr.

Kennedy, Seán & Weiss, Katherine, eds. Samuel Beckett: History, Memory, Archive. 2009. (New Interpertations of Beckett in the Twenty-first Century Ser.). (ENG.). 236p. 89.00 *(978-0-230-61944-9(4))* Palgrave Macmillan.

Kim, Rina. Women & Ireland as Beckett's Lost Others: Beyond Mourning & Melancholia. 2010. (ENG., Illus.). 240p. 84.00 *(978-0-230-23047-7(4))* Palgrave Macmillan.

Lawley, Paul. Waiting for Godot: Character Studies. 2008. (Character Studies). (ENG.). 144p. 90.00 *(978-0-8264-9380-4(7))* Continuum International Publishing Group, Ltd. GBR. Dist: National Bk. Network.

Lawley, Paul & Lawley. Waiting for Godot. 2008. (Character Studies). (ENG.). 144p. 19.95 *(978-0-8264-9381-1(5))* Continuum International Publishing Group, Ltd. GBR. Dist: National Bk. Network.

Le Juez, Brigitte. Beckett Before Beckett: Samuel Beckett's Lectures on French Literature. Schwartz, Ros, tr. from FRE. 2010. (ENG.). 96p. pap. 10.95 *(978-0-285-63862-4(9))* Souvenir Pr. Ltd. GBR. Dist: Independent Pubs. Group.

Lozier, Claire. De L'abject et du Sublime: Georges Bataille, Jean Genet, Samuel Beckett. 2012. (Modern French Identities Ser.). (FRE.). 319p. pap. 74.95 ***(978-3-0343-0724-6(1))*** Lang, Peter AG GBR. Dist: Lang, Peter.

Lumsden, Alison & Ackerley, Chris. Obscure Locks, Simple Keys: The Annotated Watt. 2011. (ENG., Illus.). 300p. (gr. 17). pap. 35.00 *(978-0-7486-4151-2(3))* Edinburgh Univ. Pr. GBR. Dist: Columbia Univ. Pr.

MacKenzie, Gina Masucci. Theatre of the Real: Yeats, Beckett, & Sondheim. 2008. (ENG.). x, 173p. cd-rom 16.95 *(978-0-8142-9176-4(7))* Ohio State Univ. Pr.

—The Theatre of the Real: Yeats, Beckett, & Sondheim. 2008. (ENG.). 200p. 59.95 *(978-0-8142-1096-3(1))* Ohio State Univ. Pr.

Maude, Ulrika. Beckett & Phenomenology. Feldman, Matthew, ed. 2009. (Continuum Literary Studies). (ENG.). 226p. 120.00 *(978-0-8264-9714-7(4))* Continuum International Publishing Group, Ltd. GBR. Dist: National Bk. Network.

—Beckett, Technology & the Body. (ENG., Illus.). 222p. 2011. pap. 39.99 *(978-0-521-18150-1(X))* 2009. 83.00 *(978-0-521-51537-5(8))* Cambridge Univ. Pr.

McDonald, Ronan. The Cambridge Introduction to Samuel Beckett. 2007. (Cambridge Introductions to Literature Ser.). (ENG.). 152p. per. 26.00 *(978-0-521-54738-3(5))*; 150p. 75.00 *(978-0-521-83856-6(8))* Cambridge Univ. Pr.

McFadden, Catherine. Parallels in Beckett & Pinter. 2009. 56p. pap. *(978-3-639-16982-9(4))* VDM Verlag Dr. Mueller e.K.

McMullan. Performing Embodiment in Samuel Beckett. 2010. (Routledge Advances in Theatre & Performance Studies). (ENG.). 196p. (C). 125.00 *(978-0-415-38598-5(9))* Routledge.

McMullan, Anna. Performing Embodiment in Samuel Beckett's Drama. 2012. (ENG.). 186p. (C). pap. 39.95 ***(978-0-415-63420-5(2))*** Routledge.

McMullan, Anna & Wilmer, S. E. Reflections on Beckett: A Centenary Celebration. McMullan, Anna & Wilmer, S. E., eds. 2009. (Theater: Theory/Text/Performance Ser.). (ENG.). 256p. 70.00 *(978-0-472-11664-5(9))* Univ. of Michigan Pr.

Migernier, Eric. Beckett & French Theory: The Narration of Transgression. 2006. (Francophone Cultures & Literatures Ser.: Vol. 50). 154p. (C). 61.95 (978-0-8204-8649-9(3)) Lang, Peter Publishing, Inc.
Mooney, Sinead. A Tongue Not Mine: Beckett & Translation. 2011. (Oxford English Monographs). 288p. 110.00 (978-0-19-960825-6(3)) Oxford Univ. Pr., Inc.
Moorjani, Angela & Ben-Zvi, Linda. Beckett at 100: Revolving It All. 2008. (ENG., Illus.). 320p. pap. 29.95 (978-0-19-532548-5(6)) Oxford Univ. Pr., Inc.
Morin, Emilie. Samuel Beckett & the Problem of Irishness. 2009. (ENG.). 256p. 84.00 (978-0-230-21986-1(1)) Palgrave Macmillan.
Moss, Leonard. The Evolutionary Sequence in Tragedy & the Bible. 2009. (ENG.). 232p. pap. 24.00 (978-1-934542-04-0(0)) Davies Group Pubs., The.
Murphy, P. J. Beckett's Dedalus: Dialogical Engagements with Joyce in Beckett's Fiction. 2009. (ENG.). 336p. (978-0-8020-9796-5(0)) Univ. of Toronto Pr.
Murray, Christopher, ed. Samuel Beckett: 100 Years. 2007. 192p. pap. 13.95 (978-1-933648-42-2(2)) Pegasus Bks.
—Samuel Beckett: Playwright & Poet. 2009. (ENG.). 208p. pap. 14.95 (978-1-60598-002-7(1), 605002) Pegasus Bks.
National Gallery of Ireland Staff, creator. Samuel Beckett: A Passion for Painting. 2007. (ENG., Illus.). 128p. pap. 50.00 (978-1-904288-16-9(2)) Holberton, Paul Publishing GBR. Dist: Univ. of Washington Pr.
Nixon, Mark. Samuel Beckett's German Diaries 1936-1937. 2011. (Historicizing Modernism Ser.). (ENG., Illus.). 272p. 110.00 (978-1-4411-5258-9(X)) Continuum International Publishing Group, Ltd. GBR. Dist: National Bk. Network.
Nixon, Mark & Feldman, Matthew, eds. The International Reception of Samuel Beckett. 2011. (ENG.). 324p. pap. 49.95 **(978-1-4411-2318-3(0))** Continuum International Publishing Group, Ltd. GBR. Dist: National Bk. Network.
Nixon, Mark & van Hulle, Dirk, eds. Beckett & Germany, Vol. 19, No. 2. 2010. (ENG.). 128p. (gr. 17). pap. 30.00 (978-0-7486-4139-0(4)) Edinburgh Univ. Pr. GBR. Dist: Columbia Univ. Pr.
Oppo, Andrea. Philosophical Aesthetics & Samuel Beckett. 2008. 268p. pap. 66.95 (978-3-03911-824-3(2)) Lang, Peter AG GBR. Dist: Lang, Peter.
Pilling, John. Samuel Becketts More Pricks Than Kicks: In a Strait of Two Wills. 2011. (Historicizing Modernism Ser.). (ENG.). 288p. 120.00 (978-1-4411-5947-2(9)) Continuum International Publishing Group, Ltd. GBR. Dist: National Bk. Network.
Poole, Adrian. Joyce, Eliot, Auden, Beckett: Great Shakespeareans. 2012. (Great Shakespeareans Ser.). (ENG.). 248p. 140.00 (978-1-4411-8743-7(X)) Continuum International Publishing Group, Ltd. GBR. Dist: National Bk. Network.
Pothast, Ulrich. The Metaphysical Vision: Arthur Schopenhauer's Philosophy of Art & Life & Samuel Beckett's Own Way to Make Use of It. 2008. 260p. (C). 71.95 (978-1-4331-0286-8(2)) Lang, Peter Publishing, Inc.
Quayson, Ato. Aesthetic Nervousness: Disability & the Crisis of Representation. 2007. (ENG.). 264p. (gr. 17). 75.00 (978-0-231-13902-1(0)); pap. 26.50 (978-0-231-13903-8(9)) Columbia Univ. Pr.
Reid, James H. Proust, Beckett, & Narration. 2010. (ENG.). 204p. pap. 32.99 (978-0-521-14185-7(0)) Cambridge Univ. Pr.
Rose, Jacqueline. Proust among the Nations: From Dreyfus to the Middle East. 2012. (ENG., Illus.). 256p. 35.00 (978-0-226-72578-9(2)) Univ. of Chicago Pr.
Ross, Ciaran. Beckett's Art of Absence: Rethinking the Void. 2011. (ENG.). 248p. 80.00 (978-0-230-57518-9(8)) Palgrave Macmillan.
Salisbury, Laura. Samuel Beckett: Laughing Matters, Comic Timing. 2012. (ENG.). 256p. (gr. 17). 105.00 **(978-0-7486-4748-4(1))** Edinburgh Univ. Pr. GBR. Dist: Columbia Univ. Pr.
Schulz, Hans-Joachim. This hell of Stories: A Hegelian approach to the novels of Samuel Beckett. (De Proprietatibus Litterarum. Series Practica Ser.). (ENG.). 117p. 210.00 **(978-3-11-208470-0(5))**; 135.00 **(978-3-11-099169-7(1))** De Gruyter, Mouton DEU. Dist: de Gruyter, Walter GmbH & Co. KG.
Sheehan, Paul. Modernism, Narrative & Humanism. 2008. (ENG.). 256p. pap. 36.00 (978-0-521-09912-7(9)) Cambridge Univ. Pr.
Slade, Andrew. Lyotard, Beckett, Duras, & the Postmodern Sublime. (Currents in Comparative Romance Languages & Literatures Ser.: Vol. 146). (C). 58.95 (978-0-8204-7862-3(8)) Lang, Peter Publishing, Inc.
Smith, Russell & Smith. Beckett & Ethics. 2009. (Continuum Literary Studies). (ENG.). 193p. 130.00 (978-0-8264-9836-6(1)) Continuum International Publishing Group, Ltd. GBR. Dist: National Bk. Network.
Stewart, Paul. Sex & Aesthetics in Samuel Beckett's Work. 2011. (New Interpretations of Beckett in the Twenty-first Century Ser.). (ENG.). 238p. 85.00 (978-0-230-10881-3(4)) Palgrave Macmillan.
—Zone of Evaporation: Samuel Beckett's Disjunctions. 2006. (Faux Titre Ser.: 287). (ENG.). 212p. per. 55.00 (978-90-420-2077-1(6)) Rodopi.
Szafraniec, Asja. Beckett, Derrida, & the Event of Literature. 2007. (Cultural Memory in the Present Ser.). (ENG.). 264p. per. 24.95 (978-0-8047-5457-6(8)) Stanford Univ. Pr.
Szafraniec, Asja & De la Torre, Augusto. Beckett, Derrida, & the Event of Literature. 2007. (Cultural Memory in the Present Ser.). (ENG.). 264p. 65.00 (978-0-8047-5456-9(X)) Stanford Univ. Pr.
Szanto, George H. Narrative Consciousness: Structure & Perception in the Fiction of Kafka, Beckett, & Robbe-Grillet. 2012. (ENG.). 226p. pap. 25.00 **(978-0-292-74189-8(8))** Univ. of Texas Pr.
Tajiri, Yoshiki. Samuel Beckett & the Prosthetic Body: The Organs & Senses in Modernism. 2007. (ENG.). 240p. 84.00 (978-0-230-00817-5(8)) Palgrave Macmillan.
Taylor-Batty, Juliette & Taylor- Batty, Mark. Samuel Beckett's Waiting for Godot. 2009. (Modern Theatre Guides). (ENG.). 128p. 17.95 (978-0-8264-9594-5(X)) Continuum International Publishing Group, Ltd. GBR. Dist: National Bk. Network.
Taylor-Batty, Juliette, et al. Samuel Beckett's Waiting for Godot. 2009. (Modern Theatre Guides). (ENG.). 128p. 90.00 (978-0-8264-9593-8(1)) Continuum International Publishing Group, Ltd. GBR. Dist: National Bk. Network.
Tonning, Erik. Samuel Beckett's Abstract Drama: Works for Stage & Screen 1962-1985. 291p. pap. 70.95 (978-3-03911-022-3(5)) Lang, Peter CHE. Dist: Lang, Peter Publishing, Inc.
Uhlmann, Anthony. Beckett & Poststructuralism. 2008. (ENG.). 216p. pap. 31.00 (978-0-521-05243-6(2)) Cambridge Univ. Pr.
—Samuel Beckett & the Philosophical Image. (ENG.). 2009. 200p. pap. 31.00 (978-0-521-12012-8(8)) 2006. (Illus.). 198p. 101.00 (978-0-521-86520-3(4)) Cambridge Univ. Pr.
Van Hulle, Dirk. Manuscript Genetics, Joyce's Know-How, Beckett's Nohow. (Florida James Joyce Ser.). (ENG., Illus.). 2009. 256p. pap. 29.95 (978-0-8130-3414-0(0)) 2008. 272p. 59.95 (978-0-8130-3200-9(8)) Univ. Pr. of Florida.
Watt, Daniel. Fragmentary Futures: Blanchot, Beckett, Coetzee. 2nd ed. 2009. 180p. pap. (978-0-9556259-4-7(7)) Inkermen Pr.
Watt, Stephen. Beckett & Contemporary Irish Writing. 2012. (ENG.). 236p. pap. 35.00 **(978-1-107-40450-2(9))** Cambridge Univ. Pr.
Weagel, Deborah. Words & Music: Camus, Beckett, Cage, Gould. 2010. (American University Studies XX: Fine Arts Ser.). (Illus.). 176p. (C). 72.95 (978-1-4331-0836-5(4)) Lang, Peter Publishing, Inc.
West, Sarah. Say It: The Performative Voice in the Dramatic Works of Samuel Beckett. 2010. (Illus.). 277p. pap. 72.00 (978-90-420-3078-7(X)) Rodopi.
White, Kathryn. Beckett & Decay. 2009. (Continuum Literary Studies). (ENG.). 178p. 120.00 (978-1-84706-205-5(9)) Continuum International Publishing Group, Ltd. GBR. Dist: National Bk. Network.
Wynands, Sandra. Iconic Spaces: The Dark Theology of Samuel Beckett's Drama. 2007. (ENG.). 240p. per. 27.00 (978-0-268-04410-7(4)) Univ. of Notre Dame Pr.

BECKFORD, WILLIAM, 1760-1844

Beckford, William. Dreams, Waking Thoughts, & Incidents. 2009. 184p. pap. 7.99 (978-1-60450-684-6(9), Serenity Pubs.) Arc Manor.
—Dreams, Waking Thoughts, & Incidents. 2007. (ENG.). 220p. pap. 20.99 (978-1-4264-2269-0(5)); 234p. pap. 22.99 (978-1-4264-2304-8(7)) BiblioBazaar.
—Dreams, Waking Thoughts, & Incidents. 2009. (ENG.). 196p. pap. 13.95 (978-1-4385-2414-6(5), Book Jungle) Standard Pubns., Inc.
—Dreams, Waking Thoughts, & Incidents; in a Series of Letters from Various Parts of Europe. 2007. 204p. per. (978-1-4065-3710-9(1)) Dodo Pr.
—Recollections of an Excursion to the Monasteries of Alcobaça & Batalha. 2009. 86p. pap. 14.14 (978-0-217-74830-8(9)) General Bks. LLC.
Gotlieb, Howard. William Beckford of Fonthill: Writer, Traveler, Collector, Caliph, 1760-1844. 2011. 120p. 39.95 **(978-1-258-08573-5(9))** Literary Licensing, LLC.
Lansdown, Henry Venn. Recollections of the Late William Beckford. 2009. 56p. pap. (978-1-4068-5135-9(3)) Echo Library.
Millington, Jon. William Beckford: A Bibliography. 2008. (Illus.). 413p. 100.00 (978-0-9537836-3-2(4)) Beckford Society GBR. Dist: Oak Knoll Pr.

BECKMANN, MAX, 1884-1950

Beckmann, Max. Of Truths Impossible to Put in Words: Max Beckmann Contextualized. Long, Rose-Carol Washton & Makela, Maria Martha, eds. 2009. (Illus.). 436p. pap. 68.95 (978-3-03910-704-9(6)) Lang, Peter AG GBR. Dist: Lang, Peter.
Heller, Michael. Beckmann Variations & Other Poems. 2010. 80p. pap. 15.00 (978-1-84861-087-3(4)) Shearsman Bks. GBR. Dist: SPD-Small Pr. Distribution.
Peter, Nina & Mendes Burgi, Bernhard, eds. Max Beckmann: the Landscapes. 2011. (ENG., Illus.). 208p. 75.00 **(978-3-7757-3147-8(4))** Hatje Cantz Verlag GmbH & Co KG DEU. Dist: D.A.P./Distributed Art Pubs.
Spieler, Reinhard. T25 Beckmann. 2011. (25 Ser.). (ENG., Illus.). 200p. 19.99 **(978-3-8365-3253-2(0))** TASCHEN DEU. Dist: Ingram Pub. Services.
St. Louis City Art Museum Staff. Max Beckmann, 1948: Retrospective Exhibition Organized by City Art Museum of St. Louis. reprint ed. 55.00 (978-0-404-20225-5(X)) AMS Pr., Inc.
Wagner, Ernst. Max Beckmann - Apokalypse: Theorie & Praxis im Spaetwerk. (GER.). 304p. (978-3-496-01207-8(2)) Reimer, Dietrich.
Zeiller. Max Beckmann: Die Skizzenbücher. The Sketchbooks. 2011. (ENG., Illus.). 976p. 375.00 (978-3-7757-2274-2(2)) Hatje Cantz Verlag GmbH & Co KG DEU. Dist: D.A.P./Distributed Art Pubs.

BECQUER, GUSTAVO ADOLFO, 1836-1870

Peña, Pedro J. de la, et al. Mito y Realidad de Gustavo Adolfo Bécquer: Las Rimas. 2008. (Clásicos Tirant lo Blanch Ser.). (SPA.). 141p. (978-84-9876-265-5(0)) Tirant lo Blanch.

BED AND BREAKFAST ACCOMMODATIONS

Boissanneault, Dana. The Guests of Ittido Place Bed & Breakfast: A Year's Diary of Our Guests. 2010. 152p. pap. 15.16 (978-1-4269-2314-2(7)) Trafford Publishing.
Boyes, Roger. To Prussia with Love: Misadventures in Rural East Germany. 2012. (ENG.). 320p. pap. 13.95 **(978-1-84953-125-2(0))** Summerdale Pubs. GBR. Dist: Independent Pubs. Group.
Bursey, Michelle & Korgan, Carol. The Lighthouse Breakfast Cookbook: Recipes from Heceta Head Lighthouse Bed & Breakfast. 2009. (ENG., Illus.). 192p. 27.95 (978-0-88240-743-2(0), West Winds Pr.) Graphic Arts Ctr. Publishing Co.
Castillo, Joe. The Christian B&B Directory. 2006. 430p. pap. 12.95 (978-0-9770428-0-7(4)) William & Warren, Inc.
Fodor's Travel Publications, Inc. Staff. Green Travel. Hall, Beth, ed. 2008. (Fodor's Green Travel: the World's Best Eco-Lodges & Earth-Friendly Ser.). (Illus.). 328p. pap. 21.95 (978-1-4000-0753-0(4), Fodor's) Fodor's Travel Pubns.
Hammond, Richard & Sawday, Alastair. Green Places to Stay: From Beach Huts to Eco-Chic Hotels, All over the World. Hammond, Richard, ed. 2006. (Alastair Sawday's Special Places to Stay Ser.). (ENG., Illus.). 288p. pap. 21.95 (978-1-901970-77-7(9)) Globe Pequot Pr., The.
Lanier, Pamela. Bed & Breakfast Guide for Food Lovers. 2010. (ENG.). 160p. pap. 14.95 (978-0-9843766-6-7(6)) Lanier Publishing International.
—Bed & Breakfasts. 26th rev. ed. 2009. (ENG.). 800p. pap. 16.95 (978-1-58008-969-2(0)) Ten Speed Pr.
—The Complete Guide to Bed & Breakfasts, Inns & Guesthouses. 25th rev. ed. 2008. (Complete Guide to Bed & Breakfasts, Inns & Guesthouses Ser.). (ENG., Illus.). 895p. pap. 16.95 (978-1-58008-908-1(9)) Ten Speed Pr.
—The Complete Guide to Bed & Breakfasts, Inns & Guesthouses International. 28th rev. ed. 2011. (ENG.). 664p. pap. 19.95 (978-0-9843766-8-1(2)) Lanier Publishing International.
Lynch, Paul & Tucker, Hazel. Commercial Homes in Tourism: An international Perspective. Lynch, Paul & McIntosh, Alison J., eds. 2009. (Routledge Critical Studies in Tourism, Business & Management Ser.). (ENG., Illus.). 288p. (C). 133.00 (978-0-415-47018-6(8)) Routledge.

BED AND BREAKFAST ACCOMMODATIONS—MANAGEMENT

Daily Telegraph, creator. Starting & Running A B&B: A Practical Guide to Setting up & Managing a Successful Bed & Breakfast Business. 2nd ed. 2006. (Illus.). 316p. per. 26.00 (978-1-84528-156-4(X)) How To Books GBR. Dist: Parkwest Pubns., Inc.
Hunt, Deborah. How to Start & Run a BB in Franc. 2nd ed. 2009. (Illus.). 224p. 30.00 (978-1-84528-272-1(8)) How To Books GBR. Dist: Parkwest Pubns., Inc.
Jackman, Helen. Just Six Guests: How to Set up & Run a Small Bed & Breakfast. (Illus.). 2nd ed. 2006. 156p. per. 20.00 (978-1-84528-136-6(5)) 4th ed. 2010. (ENG., 169p. pap. 20.00 (978-1-84528-393-3(7)) How To Books GBR. Dist: Parkwest Pubns., Inc.
Miller, Edward. Full English: Or, How to Run a Rural Bed & Breakfast & Keep Your Sense of Humor! 2009. (ENG., Illus.). 176p. pap. 11.95 **(978-1-906122-15-7(6))** Unwin, Merlin Bks. GBR. Dist: SCB Distributors.
Milner, Christabel. Running a B & B: A Landlady's Guide: a Practical Guide for Anyone Planning to Set Up & Run a Small B & B in Their Home. 2007. (Illus.). 136p. pap. 20.00 (978-1-84528-269-1(8)) How To Books GBR. Dist: Parkwest Pubns., Inc.
Stankus, Jan. How to Open & Operate a Bed & Breakfast, 9th. 9th ed. 2011. (Home-Based Business Ser.). (ENG., Illus.). 392p. pap. 21.95 (978-0-7627-7200-1(X)) Globe Pequot Pr., The.
Taylor, Monica & Taylor, Richard. Start & Run a Bed & Breakfast. 4th ed. 2008. (ENG.). 224p. pap. 20.95 (978-1-55180-803-1(X)) Self-Counsel Pr., Inc. CAN. Dist: Midpoint Trade Bks., Inc.
White, Mary & White. Running a Bed & Breakfast for Dummies. 2009. (ENG.). 360p. pap. 21.99 (978-0-470-42682-1(9), For Dummies) Wiley, John & Sons, Inc.

BED AND BREAKFAST ACCOMMODATIONS—ALASKA

Crandall, Cass. Bed & Breakfast Alaska Style! 4th ed. (Illus.). 16.95 (978-0-9626071-5-8(0)) Kachemak Publishing.

BED AND BREAKFAST ACCOMMODATIONS—AUSTRALIA

Southern, Carl, ed. The Australian Bed & Breakfast 2010. 2009. (ENG., Illus.). 276p. pap. 16.95 (978-1-58980-793-8(6)) Pelican Publishing Co., Inc.
Southern, Carl, ed. The Australian Bed & Breakfast Book 2012. 2012. (Illus.). 288p. pap. 31.95 **(978-0-9758040-7-0(3))** Inn Australia AUS. Dist: Trans-Atlantic Pubns., Inc.

BED AND BREAKFAST ACCOMMODATIONS—CALIFORNIA

Brown, June Eveleigh. Karen Brown's California 2010: Exceptional Places to Stay & Itineraries. 2010. (ENG.). 272p. pap. 19.95 (978-1-933810-69-0(6)) Karen Brown's Guides.
Van Voorst, Joy. Tawanda's Bed & Breakfast. 2006. (ENG.). 180p. per. 16.95 (978-1-59800-749-7(1)) Outskirts Pr., Inc.

BED AND BREAKFAST ACCOMMODATIONS—CANADA

Hutchinson, Bobby. Blue Collar B & B. 2009. 172p. pap. 15.95 (978-1-934938-69-0(6), Langdon Street Pr.) Hillcrest Publishing Group, Inc.
Lanier, Pamela. The Complete Guide to Bed & Breakfasts, Inns & Guesthouses: In the United States, Canada, & Worldwide. 24th ed. 2007. (Complete Guide to Bed & Breakfasts, Inns & Guesthouses Ser.). (Illus.). 897p. per. 16.95 (978-1-58008-846-6(5)) Ten Speed Pr.
Moyer, Marybeth. The Canadian Bed & Breakfast Guide, 1 vol. 18th ed. 2006. (Canadian Bed & Breakfast Guide Ser.). (ENG., Illus.). 502p. per. 14.95 (978-1-55041-368-7(6)) Fitzhenry & Whiteside, Ltd. CAN. Dist: Ingram Pub. Services.
Sakach, Deborah Edwards. Bed & Breakfasts & Country Inns. (Bed & Breakfasts & Country Inns Ser.). (Illus.). 20th ed. 2008. 376p. pap. 24.95 (978-1-888050-05-9(5)) 21st ed. 2010. (ENG., 346p. pap. 24.95 (978-1-888050-21-9(7)) American Historic Inns.

BED AND BREAKFAST ACCOMMODATIONS—CARIBBEAN AREA

Groene, Janet. Personal Paradise: Caribbean. 2006. (ENG., Illus.). 224p. pap. 14.95 (978-1-59360-076-1(3)) Open Road Publishing.

BED AND BREAKFAST ACCOMMODATIONS—EUROPE

Bjorgen, Anne Marit. The Norway Bed & Breakfast Book, 1 vol. 2011. (NOR, GER & ENG., Illus.). 224p. pap. 17.95 (978-1-58980-973-4(4)) Pelican Publishing Co., Inc.
Plumridge, Lisa, ed. Croatia. 2007. (Alastair Sawday's Special Places to Stay Ser.). (ENG., Illus.). 288p. pap. 21.95 (978-1-901970-84-5(1)) Globe Pequot Pr., The.
Titus, Linda. Walking Inn to Inn: A Self-Guided Hike in the Swiss Hikes. 2007. (Illus.). 11p. per. 14.95 (978-0-9798060-0-1(3)) SwissHikes.com.

BED AND BREAKFAST ACCOMMODATIONS—FRANCE

AA Publishing Staff, contrib. by. Best B&Bs in France: Perfect Places for Bed & Breakfast. 2008. (AA Best Ser.). (ENG., Illus.). 208p. pap. 17.95 (978-0-7495-5574-0(2)) Automobile Assn. GBR. Dist: Independent Pubs. Group.
Fodor's Travel Publications, Inc. Staff. Fodor's Riviera Bed & Breakfast in France. 3rd ed. Date not set. pap. (978-0-679-03305-9(X)) Fodor's Travel Pubns.
Hunt, Deborah. How to Start & Run a BB in Franc. 2nd ed. 2009. (Illus.). 224p. 30.00 (978-1-84528-272-1(8)) How To Books GBR. Dist: Parkwest Pubns., Inc.
Juneau, Sam. A Chateau of One?'s Own. 2007. (ENG.). 320p. pap. 12.95 **(978-1-84024-641-4(3))** Summerdale Pubs. GBR. Dist: Independent Pubs. Group.
Sawday, Alastair. French Bed & Breakfast. 12th ed. 2011. (Special Places to Stay Ser.). (ENG., Illus.). 464p. pap. 23.95 (978-1-906136-40-6(8)) Sawday, Alastair Publishing Co. Ltd. GBR. Dist: Globe Pequot Pr., The.
Sawday, Alastair & Cooke-Yarborough, Ann. Go Slow France. 2010. (ENG., Illus.). 254p. pap. 26.95 (978-1-906136-35-2(1)) Sawday, Alastair Publishing Co. Ltd. GBR. Dist: Globe Pequot Pr., The.
Taylor, Jo. Running Gites & B&bs in France: A Survival Handbook. 2008. (ENG., Illus.). 320p. pap. 21.95 (978-1-905303-30-4(0)) Survival Bks., Ltd.
Thomas Cook Publishing Staff. Bed & Breakfast France 2009. 9th ed. 2009. (ENG., Illus.). 448p. pap. 26.95 (978-1-84848-011-7(3)) Cook, Thomas Publishing GBR. Dist: Globe Pequot Pr., The.

BED AND BREAKFAST ACCOMMODATIONS—GREAT BRITAIN

AA Publishing. AA Bed & Breakfast Guide 2012. 42nd ed. 2011. (AA Lifestyle Guides). (ENG., Illus.). 736p. pap. 24.95 **(978-0-7495-7069-9(5))** Automobile Assn. GBR. Dist: Independent Pubs. Group.
AA Publishing & AA Publishing Staff. Britain's Best Bed & Breakfast 2011. 7th ed. 2011. (Britain's Best Ser.). (ENG., Illus.). 530p. pap. 14.95 (978-0-7495-6787-3(2)) Automobile Assn. GBR. Dist: Independent Pubs. Group.
Alastair Sawday. British Bed & Breakfast. 16th ed. 2011. (Special Places to Stay Ser.). (ENG., Illus.). 464p. pap. 23.95 (978-1-906136-53-6(X)) Sawday, Alastair Publishing Co. Ltd. GBR. Dist: Globe Pequot Pr., The.
Bed & Breakfast Stops in Britain. 2007. (Illus.). 352p. pap. 13.95 (978-1-85055-402-8(1)) FHG Pubns. Ltd. GBR. Dist: Ingram Pub. Services.
Coast & Country Holidays in Britain: The Original Farm Holiday Guide. 2007. (Illus.). 320p. pap. 13.95 (978-1-85055-401-1(3)) Graphic Arts Ctr. Publishing Co.
Crosse, Nicola & Sawday, Alastair. Special Places to Stay in Britain for Garden Lovers. 6th ed. 2011. (Special Places to Stay Ser.). (ENG., Illus.). 232p. pap. 26.95 (978-1-906136-41-3(6)) Sawday, Alastair Publishing Co. Ltd. GBR. Dist: Globe Pequot Pr., The.
Daily Telegraph, creator. Starting & Running A B&B: A Practical Guide to Setting up & Managing a Successful Bed & Breakfast Business. 2nd ed. 2006. (Illus.). 316p. per. 26.00 (978-1-84528-156-4(X)) How To Books GBR. Dist: Parkwest Pubns., Inc.
Jackman, Helen. Just Six Guests: How to Set up & Run a Small Bed & Breakfast. (Illus.). 2nd ed. 2006. 156p. per. 20.00 (978-1-84528-136-6(5)) 4th ed. 2010. (ENG., 169p. pap. 20.00 (978-1-84528-393-3(7)) How To Books GBR. Dist: Parkwest Pubns., Inc.
—Just Six Guests 3e. 3rd ed. 2008. (Illus.). xiii, 166p. 20.00 (978-1-84528-279-0(5)) How To Books GBR. Dist: Parkwest Pubns., Inc.
Milner, Christabel. Running a B & B: A Landlady's Guide: a Practical Guide for Anyone Planning to Set Up & Run a Small B & B in Their Home. 2007. (Illus.). 136p. pap. 20.00 (978-1-84528-269-1(8)) How To Books GBR. Dist: Parkwest Pubns., Inc.
Moss, Linda. Organic Places to Stay in the UK. 2nd rev. ed. 2008. (ENG., Illus.). 304p. pap. 22.00 (978-1-900322-19-5(6)) Green Bks. GBR. Dist: Chelsea Green Publishing.
Plant, Ken. The Great British Bed & Breakfast. (Illus.). 544p. pap. 16.95 (978-1-902890-02-9(7)) KGP Publishing GBR. Dist: 7 Hills Bk. Distributors.
Sawday, Alastair. Alastair Sawdays British Bed Breakfast. Date not set. pap. (978-0-312-19603-5(2), St. Martin's Griffin) St. Martin's Pr.
—Scotland. 2009. (Special Places to Stay Ser.). (ENG., Illus.). 160p. pap. 17.95 (978-1-906136-14-7(9)) Sawday, Alastair Publishing Co. Ltd. GBR. Dist: Globe Pequot Pr., The.
—Special Places to Stay in Britain. Date not set. pap. (978-0-312-19611-0(3), St. Martin's Griffin) St. Martin's Pr.
Sawday, Alastair & Crosse, Nicola. Devon & Cornwall. 2008. (Special Places to Stay Ser.). (ENG., Illus.). 240p. pap. 21.95 (978-1-906136-01-7(7)) Sawday, Alastair Publishing Co. Ltd. GBR. Dist: Globe Pequot Pr., The.

B

Thomas, Roger. Wales Bed & Breakfast,1999. 108p. pap. 6.95 *(978-1-85013-086-4(8))* Jarrold Publishing GBR. Dist: 7 Hills Bk. Distributors.

VisitBritain Publishing. Bed & Breakfast 2009. 2008. (ENG., Illus.). 760p. pap. 19.95 *(978-0-7095-8447-6(4))* VisitBritain GBR. Dist: Globe Pequot Pr., The.

Weston, David & Weston, Louise. How to Start & Run A B & B: All You Need to Know to Make Money from Your Dream Property. 2006. (Illus.). 152p. per. 26.00 *(978-1-84528-111-3(X))* How To Books GBR. Dist: Parkwest Pubns., Inc.

—Start & Run a Bed & Breakfast: All you Need to Know to Make Money from your Dream Property. 2nd rev. ed. 2011. (ENG., Illus.). 174p. pap. 26.00 *(978-1-84528-443-5(7))* How To Books GBR. Dist: Parkwest Pubns., Inc.

BED AND BREAKFAST ACCOMMODATIONS—IRELAND

Crosse, Nicola. Ireland. Sawday, Alastair, ed. 7th ed. 2009. (Special Places to Stay Ser.). (ENG., Illus.). 320p. pap. 23.95 *(978-1-906136-08-6(4))* Sawday, Alastair Publishing Co. Ltd. GBR. Dist: Globe Pequot Pr., The.

Dillard, Elsie & Causin, Susan. The Irish Bed & Breakfast. 2008. (ENG., Illus.). 328p. pap. 19.95 *(978-1-58980-559-0(3))* Pelican Publishing Co., Inc.

BED AND BREAKFAST ACCOMMODATIONS—ITALY

Fort, Matthew. Eating up Italy: Voyages on a Vespa. 2006. (ENG., Illus.). 288p. per. 16.95 *(978-1-933572-02-4(7))* Centro Bks., LLC.

Oldfield, Florence & Sawday, Alastair. Italy: Special Places to Stay. 6th ed. 2010. (Special Places to Stay Ser.). (ENG., Illus.). 432p. pap. 23.95 *(978-1-906136-33-8(5))* Sawday, Alastair Publishing Co. Ltd. GBR. Dist: Globe Pequot Pr., The.

Paulist Press. Beds & Blessings in Italy: A Guide to Religious Hospitality. 2010. 424p. pap. 24.00 *(978-1-58768-062-5(9),* HiddenSpring) Paulist Pr.

BED AND BREAKFAST ACCOMMODATIONS—MIDDLE ATLANTIC STATES

Brown, Karen & Bullard Memorial Farm Association Staff. Mid-Atlantic 2010: Exceptional Places to Stay & Itineraries. 2010. (ENG.). 298p. pap. 19.95 *(978-1-933810-77-5(7))* Karen Brown's Guides.

Rizzoli, Carol Eron. The House at Royal Oak: Starting over & Rebuilding a Life One Room at a Time. 2010. (ENG., Illus.). 272p. 22.95 *(978-1-57912-840-1(8),* 1579128408) Black Dog & Leventhal Pubs., Inc.

BED AND BREAKFAST ACCOMMODATIONS—NEW ZEALAND

Cudby, Elliott. The New Zealand Bed & Breakfast 2008, 1 vol. 2007. (ENG., Illus.). 448p. pap. 21.95 *(978-1-58980-524-8(0))* Pelican Publishing Co., Inc.

BED AND BREAKFAST ACCOMMODATIONS—NORTHWEST, PACIFIC

Brown, Karen. Karen Brown's Pacific Northwest 2010. 2010. (ENG.). 234p. pap. 19.95 *(978-1-933810-81-2(5))* Karen Brown's Guides.

Kiely, Tracy. Murder at Longbourn: A Mystery. 2009. (ENG.). 320p. 24.99 *(978-0-312-53756-2(5),* Minotaur Bks.) St. Martin's Pr.

BED AND BREAKFAST ACCOMMODATIONS—SOUTHERN STATES

Hunt, Bruce. Florida's Finest Inns & Bed & Breakfasts. 2nd ed. 2009. (ENG.). 223p. pap. 14.95 *(978-1-56164-437-7(4))* Pineapple Pr., Inc.

Lanier, Pamela. Bed & Breakfast Getaways in the South. 2010. (ENG.). 160p. pap. 14.95 *(978-0-9843766-7-4(4))* Lanier Publishing International.

Stewart, Laura & Hupp, Susanne. Historic Homes of Florida. 2nd ed. 2008. (ENG.). 191p. pap. 18.95 *(978-1-56164-417-9(X))* Pineapple Pr., Inc.

BED AND BREAKFAST ACCOMMODATIONS—UNITED STATES

Lanier, Pamela. Bed & Breakfasts, Inns & Guesthouses International. 27th rev. ed. 2010. (ENG.). 664p. pap. 19.95 *(978-0-9843766-0-5(7))* Lanier Publishing International.

—Cinnamon Mornings & Savory Nights: Romantic Recipes from America's Inns. (ENG.). 2009. 160p. pap. 19.95 *(978-0-9840850-0-2(9))* 2008. (Illus.). 1p. pap. 19.95 *(978-1-58008-940-1(2))* Ten Speed Pr.

—The Complete Guide to Bed & Breakfasts, Inns & Guesthouses: In the United States, Canada, & Worldwide. 24th ed. 2007. (Complete Guide to Bed & Breakfasts, Inns & Guesthouses Ser.). (Illus.). 897p. per. 16.95 *(978-1-58008-846-6(5))* Ten Speed Pr.

Monahan, Tamra. Colorado's Best Bed & Breakfasts: 100 Unique Getaways. 2007. (ENG., Illus.). 240p. pap. 16.95 *(978-1-55591-623-7(6))* Fulcrum Publishing.

Morris, Roger & Ryan, Cathleen. The Brandywine Book of Food: Exploring the Culinary Landscape of the Brandywine Valley's Country Gardens, Bed-and-Breakfast Inns, Mushroom Barns, & Boutique Wineries. 2009. (ENG., Illus.). 160p. 34.95 *(978-1-58182-700-2(8),* Cumberland Hse.) Sourcebooks, Inc.

Panache Partners LLC., Staff. Distinguished Inns of North America: A Collection of the Finest Inns of Select Registry. 2008. (ENG., Illus.). 300p. 34.95 *(978-1-933415-42-0(8))* Panache Partners, LLC.

Plant, Ken. The Bed & Breakfast Directory. 4th ed. (Illus.). 608p. pap. 16.95 *(978-1-902890-03-6(5))* KGP Publishing GBR. Dist: 7 Hills Bk. Distributors.

Riley, Gail. Colorado Cravings: Recipes & Romance from the Highland Haven Creekside Inn. 2006. (ENG., Illus.). 35.00 *(978-0-9776906-1-9(X))* Blueline Publishing.

Robinson, Ed. Historic Inns of Southern West Virginia. 2007. (Images of America Ser.). (ENG., Illus.). 128p. per. 19.99 *(978-0-7385-5285-9(2))* Arcadia Publishing.

Sakach, Deborah. Bed & Breakfast & Country Inns. 14th ed. 21.95 *(978-1-888050-14-1(4))* American Historic Inns.

Sakach, Deborah Edwards. Bed & breakfasts & country inns. 2007. (Bed & Breakfasts & Country Inns Ser.). (Illus.). 396p. per. 24.95 *(978-1-888050-19-6(5))* American Historic Inns.

—Bed & Breakfasts & Country Inns. (Bed & Breakfasts & Country Inns Ser.). (Illus.). 20th ed. 2008. 376p. pap. 24.95 *(978-1-888050-05-9(5))* 21st ed. 2010. (ENG., 346p. pap. 24.95 *(978-1-888050-21-9(7))* American Historic Inns.

White, Mary & White. Running a Bed & Breakfast for Dummies. 2009. (ENG.). 360p. pap. 21.99 *(978-0-470-42682-1(9),* For Dummies) Wiley, John & Sons, Inc.

Zingaro Clark, Kathleen. Bucks County Inns & Taverns. 2008. (Images of America Ser.). (ENG., Illus.). 128p. pap. 21.99 *(978-0-7385-5798-4(6))* Arcadia Publishing.

BED REST

Halperin, Ofra. Perceived Stressors by High-Risk Pregnant Women on Bed Rest. 2010. 168p. pap. *(978-3-639-28541-3(7))* VDM Verlag Dr. Mueller e.K.

Isennock, Patricia D. Bedrest Before Baby: What's a Mother to Do? A Survival Handbook for High Risk Moms. 2nd ed. 112p. (Orig.). pap. 12.95 *(978-0-9632392-6-6(0))* Mustard Seed Pubns.

BED RUGS

see Coverlets

BED-WETTING

see Enuresis

BEDDING (HORTICULTURE)

see Gardening

BEDDOES, THOMAS, 1803-1849

Allard, James. Romanticism Medicine & the Poet's Body. 2007. (Nineteenth Century Ser.). 174p. 99.95 *(978-0-7546-5891-7(0))* Ashgate Publishing Co.

Beddoes, Thomas Lovell. The Letters of Thomas Lovell Beddoes. Gosse, Edmund, ed. 2007. (ENG.). 282p. 43.95 *(978-0-548-15650-6(6));* pap. 28.95 *(978-1-4304-5115-0(7))* Kessinger Publishing, LLC.

Berns, Ute. Science, Politics, & Friendship in the Works of Thomas Lovell Beddoes. 2011. (ENG.). 382p. 90.00 ***(978-1-61149-367-2(6))*** Univ. of Delaware Pr.

Bradshaw, Michael & Berns, Ute, eds. The Ashgate Research Companion to Thomas Lovell Beddoes. 2007. (Nineteenth Century Ser.). 292p. 149.95 *(978-0-7546-6009-5(5))* Ashgate Publishing Co.

BEDE, THE VENERABLE, SAINT, 673-735

Darby, Peter. Bede & the End of Time. 2012. (Studies in Early Medieval Britain Ser.). 276p. 124.95 ***(978-1-4094-3048-3(0))*** Ashgate Publishing Co.

DeGregorio, Scott, ed. The Cambridge Companion to Bede. 2010. (Cambridge Companions to Literature Ser.). (ENG., Illus.). (C). 304p. 95.00 *(978-0-521-51495-8(9));* 302p. pap. 32.99 *(978-0-521-73073-0(2))* Cambridge Univ. Pr.

Gunn, Vicky A. & Gunn, Vicky. Bede's Historiae: Genre, Rhetoric & the Construction of the Anglo-Saxon Church History. 2009. 256p. 90.00 *(978-1-84383-465-6(0),* Boydell Press) Boydell & Brewer, Ltd. GBR. Dist: Boydell & Brewer, Inc.

Harrison, Kenneth. The Framework of Anglo-Saxon History: To A. D. 900. 2010. (ENG.). 184p. pap. 19.99 *(978-0-521-14392-9(6))* Cambridge Univ. Pr.

Higham, N. J. Re-Reading Bede: The Ecclesiastical History in Context. 2006. (ENG., Illus.). 296p. (C). per. 40.95 *(978-0-415-35368-7(8))* Routledge.

—(Re-)Reading Bede: The Ecclesiastical History in Context. 2006. (Illus.). 279p. 140.00 *(978-0-415-35367-0(X))* Routledge.

Kendall, Calvin B., tr. from LAT. Bede - On Genesis. 2008. (Liverpool University Press - Translated Texts for Historians Ser.). (ENG.). 256p. pap. 29.95 *(978-1-84631-088-1(1))* Liverpool Univ. Pr. GBR. Dist: Chicago Distribution Ctr.

Kendall, Calvin B. & Wallis, Faith, trs. from LAT. Bede: On the Nature of Things & on Times. 2011. (Liverpool University Press - Translated Texts for Historians Ser.). (ENG., Illus.). 222p. 95.00 *(978-1-84631-495-7(X));* pap. 34.95 *(978-1-84631-496-4(8))* Liverpool Univ. Pr. GBR. Dist: Chicago Distribution Ctr.

Merrills, A. H. History & Geography in Late Antiquity. 2008. (Cambridge Studies in Medieval Life & Thought: Fourth Ser.). (ENG.). 408p. (C). pap. 53.00 *(978-0-521-07598-5(X))* Cambridge Univ. Pr.

Meyvaert, Paul. The Art of Words: Bede & Theodulf. 2008. (Variorum Collected Studies). (Illus.). 352p. 165.00 *(978-0-7546-5977-8(1))* Ashgate Publishing Co.

Novalija, Alen. Bede S Eclesiastical History. 2008. 60p. pap. *(978-3-639-07074-3(7))* VDM Verlag Dr. Mueller e.K.

Rowley, Sharon M. The Old English Version of Bede's Historia Ecclesiastica. 2011. (Anglo-Saxon Studies: Volume 16). (ANG & ENG., Illus.). 270p. 99.00 *(978-1-84384-273-6(4),* D. S. Brewer) Boydell & Brewer, Ltd. GBR. Dist: Boydell & Brewer, Inc.

Rumble, Alexander R., ed. Leaders of the Anglo-Saxon Church: From Bede to Stigand. 2012. (Pubns Manchester Centre for Anglo-Saxon Studies: Volume 12). (Illus.). 216p. 95.00 ***(978-1-84383-700-8(5),*** Boydell Press) Boydell & Brewer, Ltd. GBR. Dist: Boydell & Brewer, Inc.

Ward, Benedicta. The Venerable Bede. 2007. (Cistercian Studies). 156p. (Orig.). per. 13.46 *(978-0-87907-469-2(8))* Cistercian Pubns., Inc.

Wormald, Patrick. The Times of Bede: Studies in Early English Christian Society & Its Historian. Baxter, Stephen, ed. rev. ed. 2006. (ENG., Illus.). 312p. 99.95 *(978-0-631-16655-9(6),* Wiley-Blackwell) Wiley, John & Sons, Inc.

BEDFORD COUNTY (PA.)

Hite, Richard W. An Ordinary Story: Christopher Hite of Bedford, Pennsylvania & the Continental Army. 2010. (Illus.). 105p. ***(978-1-55856-525-8(6))*** Closson Pr.

McCulloush, Kevin & Meyers, Larry. 2011 Bedford County Data Book. McCulloush, Kevin, ed. 2011. (Illus.). 126p. pap. 45.00 *(978-1-58036-705-9(4))* Pennsylvania State Data Ctr.

Smith, Gerald H. Bedford County, Pennsylvania, Quarter Sessions, 1771-1801. 2010. (Illus.). iii, 351p. ***(978-0-7884-8485-8(0));*** pap. ***(978-0-7884-5253-6(3))*** Heritage Bks.

Von Lunen, S. & Smysor, J. R., compiled by. Gathered to Rest: Bedford County, Pennsylvania Civil War Veterans. 2007. 364p. pap. *(978-1-55856-489-3(6))* Closson Pr.

BEDFORD COUNTY (VA.)

Martin, Ben. Bedford County. 2008. (Images of America Ser.). (ENG., Illus.). 128p. pap. 19.99 *(978-0-7385-6727-3(2))* Arcadia Publishing.

BEDFORDSHIRE (ENGLAND)—HISTORY

Bunney, David. Bedford St Luke's: A Bit of Church History. 2010. (Illus.). 92p. pap. *(978-1-84748-694-3(0))* Athena Pr.

Luke, Mike & Preece, Tracy. Farm & Forge: Late Iron Age/Romano-British farmsteads at Marsh Leys, Kempston, Bedfordshire. 2011. (East anglian archaeology Monograph Ser.). (ENG., Illus.). 214p. (C). pap. 40.00 ***(978-0-9556546-3-3(7))*** East Anglian Archaeology GBR. Dist: Brown, David Bk. Co., The.

Malcolmson, Patricia & Malcolmson, Robert, eds. A Soldier in Bedfordshire, 1941-1942: The Diary of Private Denis Argent, Royal Engineers. 2009. (Publications Bedfordshire Hist Rec Soc Ser.: Volume 88). (Illus.). 238p. 45.00 *(978-0-85155-074-9(6))* Bedfordshire Historical Record Society GBR. Dist: Boydell & Brewer, Inc.

Smart, Richard, ed. The Bousfield Diaries: A Middle-Class Family in Late Victorian Bedford. 2009. (Publications Bedfordshire Hist Rec Soc Ser.: Volume 86). (Illus.). 282p. pap. 24.95 *(978-0-85155-075-6(4))* Bedfordshire Historical Record Society GBR. Dist: Boydell & Brewer, Inc.

Wood, Kenneth. Biggleswade & the Great War: Our Own Flesh & Blood. 2009. (ENG.). 160p. pap. 29.95 *(978-0-7524-4966-1(4))* History Pr. Ltd.,The GBR. Dist: Independent Pubs. Group.

BEDLINGTON TERRIERS

Glover, John. Bedlingtons in the Field. 2011. (ENG., Illus.). 192p. pap. 22.95 *(978-1-84689-097-0(7))* Quiller Publishing, Ltd. GBR. Dist: Stackpole Bks.

Pata, Sharae & Linzy, Jan. Bedlington Terrier Champions, 2000-2005. 2006. (Illus.). 142p. spiral bd. 46.95 *(978-1-55893-196-1(1))* Camino E.E. & Bk. Co.

BEDOUINS

Here are entered works on the nomadic Arabs. Comprehensive works on the Arabs as an ethnic group are entered under Arabs.

Adair, John. The Leadership of Muhammad. 2010. (ENG., Illus.). 148p. 19.95 *(978-0-7494-6076-1(8))* Kogan Page, Ltd. GBR. Dist: Ingram Pub. Services.

Aharoni, Reuven. The Pasha's Bedouin: Tribes & State in the Egypt of Mehemet Ali, 1805 - 1848. 2007. (Routledge Studies in Middle Eastern History). XI, 277p. 160.00 *(978-0-415-35036-5(0),* RU42455) Routledge.

Al-Krenawi, Alean & Graham, John R. Helping Professional Practice with Indigenous Peoples: The Bedouin-Arab Case. 2008. (ENG., Illus.). 220p. pap. 38.99 *(978-0-7618-4407-5(4))* Univ. Pr. of America, Inc.

Al-Krenawi, Alean, et al. Helping Professional Practice with Indigenous Peoples: The Bedouin-Arab Case. 2008. 89.00 *(978-1-60021-549-0(1))* Nova Science Pubs., Inc.

Amara, Ahmad, et al. Indigenous (In)justice: Law & Human Rights for Bedouin Arabs in the Naqab. 2012. ***(978-0-9796395-6-2(5))*** Human Rights Program at Harvard Law School.

Bailey, Clinton. Bedouin Law from Sinai & the Negev: Justice Without Government. 2009. (ENG., Illus.). 400p. 70.00 *(978-0-300-15324-8(4))* Yale Univ. Pr.

Blunt, Anne. Bedouin Tribes of the Euphrates. 2009. 312p. pap. *(978-0-217-34414-2(3));* 304p. pap. *(978-0-217-18130-3(9))* Books LLC.

—Bedouin Tribes of the Euphrates. 2010. 122p. pap. 21.14 *(978-1-152-62672-0(8))* General Bks. LLC.

Blunt, Anne & Blunt, Wilfrid Scawen. Bedouin Tribes of the Euphrates. 2010. 310p. pap. 29.75 *(978-1-177-94584-4(3))* BiblioBazaar.

Blunt, Lady Anne. Bedouin Tribes of the Euphrates. B., W. S., ed. 2007. (ENG.). 480p. 53.95 *(978-0-548-13620-1(3))* Kessinger Publishing, LLC.

—Bedouin Tribes of the Euphrates. 2006. pap. 38.95 *(978-1-4286-4766-4(X))* Kessinger Publishing, LLC.

—Bedouin Tribes of the Euphrates Vol I. 2006. 384p. per. *(978-1-4067-2908-5(6),* Hesperides Pr.) Read Bks.

Burckhardt, John Lewis. Notes on the Bedouins & Wahabys: Collected During His Travels in the East. Ouseley, William, ed. 2010. (Cambridge Library Collection - Travel & Exploration Ser.). (ENG., Illus.). 402p. pap. 31.99 *(978-1-108-02289-7(8))* Cambridge Univ. Pr.

Cole, Donald. Bedouins of the Empty Quarter. 2010. (ENG., Illus.). 202p. pap. 29.95 *(978-0-202-36357-8(0))* Aldine Transaction.

Dahan-Kalev, Henriette & Le Febvre, Emilie. Palestinian Activism in Israel: Bedouin Female Leadership in a Changing Middle East. 2012. (Middle East Today Ser.). (ENG., Illus.). 288p. 90.00 ***(978-0-230-10325-2(1))*** Palgrave Macmillan.

Dinero, Steven C. Settling for Less: The Planned Resettlement of Israel's Negev Bedouin. 2010. (SP Ser.). (Illus.). 248p. 70.00 *(978-1-84545-762-4(5))* Berghahn Bks., Inc.

Eloul, Rohn. Culture Change in a Bedouin Tribe: The 'arab Al-Hgerat, Lower Galilee, A. D. 1790-1977. 2010. (Illus.). 344p. 30.00 *(978-0-915703-73-9(4))* Univ. of Michigan, Museum of Anthropology, Pubns. Dept.

Ginat, Joseph. Bedouin Bisha'h Justice: Ordeal by Fire. 2009. (ENG., Illus.). 229p. 99.95 *(978-1-84519-269-3(9))* Sussex Academic Pr. GBR. Dist: International Specialized Bk. Services.

Hare, A. Paul. Desert Experience in Israel: Communities, Arts, Science, & Education in the Negev. 2009. (ARA & ENG., Illus.). 220p. pap. 33.99 *(978-0-7618-4840-0(1))* Univ. Pr. of America, Inc.

Hare, A. Paul & Kressel, Gideon M. The Desert Experience in Israel: Communities, Arts, Science, & Education in the Negev. 2009. (ARA., Illus.). viii, 211p. E-Book *(978-0-7618-4841-7(X))* Univ. Pr. of America, Inc.

Hill, Gray. With the Beduins: A Narrative of Journeys & Adventures in Unfrequented Parts of Syria. 2009. 318p. pap. 39.95 *(978-1-85964-219-1(5))* Garnet Publishing, Ltd. GBR. Dist: International Publishers Marketing.

Kennett, Austin. Bedouin Justice: Law & Custom among the Egyptian Bedouin. 2007. (Illus.). 176p. 175.00 *(978-0-415-43902-2(7))* Routledge.

—Bedouin Justice: Laws & Customs among the Egyptian Bedouin. 192p. 2008. 37.95 *(978-1-4366-7659-5(2))* 2007. (ENG.). per. 22.95 *(978-1-4325-8354-5(9))* Kessinger Publishing, LLC.

Kennett, Austin. Bedouin Justice: Laws & Customs Amongst the Egyptian Bedouin. 2011. (ENG., Illus.). 192p. pap. 19.99 ***(978-0-521-23083-4(7))*** Cambridge Univ. Pr.

Keohane, Alan. Bedouin: Nomads of the Desert. 2008. (ENG., Illus.). 176p. *(978-1-85626-791-5(1))* Cathie, Kyle Ltd. GBR. Dist: Independent Pubs. Group.

Keohane, Alan. Nomads of the Desert. 2011. (ENG., Illus.). 176p. pap. 26.95 ***(978-0-85783-027-2(9))*** Kyle Bks. GBR. Dist: National Bk. Network.

Lawrence, T. e. & Lawrence, T. E. Seven Pillars of Wisdom: A Triumph. 2011. 550p. 24.95 ***(978-1-61720-182-0(0));*** pap. 14.99 ***(978-1-61720-181-3(2))*** Wilder Pubns., Ltd.

Lawrence, T. e. & Lawrence, Thomas Edward. Seven Pillars of Wisdom: A Triumph. 2009. 540p. *(978-1-60796-062-1(1));* pap. *(978-1-60796-061-4(3))* Editorial Benei Noaj.

Lees, G. Robinson. The Witness of the Wilderness: The Bedawin of the Desert. 2007. 234p. 41.95 *(978-0-548-01032-7(3))* Kessinger Publishing, LLC.

Mandaville, James P. Bedouin Ethnobotany: Plant Concepts & Uses in a Desert Pastoral World. 2011. (ENG., Illus.). 352p. 55.00 *(978-0-8165-2900-1(0))* Univ. of Arizona Pr.

Papoutsakis, Nefeli. Desert Travel as a Form of Boasting: A Study of Dur-Rumma's Poetry. 2009. (Arabische Studien Ser.). (ENG.). 206p. (C). pap. 72.00 *(978-3-447-06112-4(X))* Harrassowitz, Otto Verlag DEU. Dist: ISD.

Peters, Emrys L. The Bedouin of Cyrenaica: Studies in Personal & Corporate Power. Goody, Jack & Marx, Emanuel, eds. 2007. (Cambridge Studies in Social & Cultural Anthropology Ser.). (ENG., Illus.). 336p. pap. 69.00 *(978-0-521-04046-4(9))* Cambridge Univ. Pr.

Van Geldermalsen, Marguerite. Married to a Bedouin. 2010. (ENG., Illus.). 288p. pap. 16.95 *(978-1-84408-220-9(2),* Virago Press) Little, Brown Bk. Group Ltd. GBR. Dist: Independent Pubs. Group.

BEDROOMS

Bader, Walter. Sleep Safe in a Toxic World: Your Guide to Identifying & Removing Hidden Toxins from Your Bedroom. 2011. (ENG.). 176p. pap. 14.00 ***(978-1-893910-90-4(3))*** Freedom Pr., Inc., The.

Beta-Plus Publishing. Bedrooms: Home Series 14. 2010. (Home Ser.). (ENG., Illus.). 128p. pap. *(978-90-8944-045-7(3),* Beta-Plus (Acc)) Antique Collectors' Club.

Better Homes and Gardens Books Staff. Beautiful Bedrooms. 2009. (Better Homes & Gardens Decorating Ser.: 22). (ENG., Illus.). 192p. pap. 19.99 *(978-0-470-48802-7(6),* Wiley) Wiley, John & Sons, Inc.

de Haro, Fernando. 100+ Bedrooms. 2011. (ENG., Illus.). 136p. pap. 11.95 *(978-607-437-054-6(0))* AM Editores MEX. Dist: Perseus-PGW.

de Haro, Fernando & Fuentes, Omar. Bedrooms. 2006. (Smallbooks Ser.). (ENG., Illus.). 64p. pap. 3.49 *(978-970-9726-57-2(9))* AM Editores MEX. Dist: Perseus-PGW.

de Haro, Fernando & Fuentes, Omar, compiled by. Inside: Bedrooms. 2011. (Inside Ser.). (ENG., Illus.). 348p. pap. 14.95 ***(978-607-437-092-8(3))*** AM Editores MEX. Dist: Perseus-PGW.

Gilliatt, Mary. Bedrooms: Creating & Decorating the Room of Your Dreams. 2007. (Small Books Ser.). (ENG., Illus.). 144p. 19.95 *(978-1-903221-92-1(7))* Aurum Pr., Ltd. GBR. Dist: Independent Pubs. Group.

James, Laura. Breafast in Bed. 2010. (ENG., Illus.). 160p. 19.95 *(978-1-906650-00-1(4))* Absolute Pr. GBR. Dist: Independent Pubs. Group.

Pauwels, Wim. Bathrooms & Bedrooms. Watkinson, Laura, tr. 2008. (ENG., Illus.). 204p. *(978-90-77213-88-9(0),* Beta-Plus (Acc)) Antique Collectors' Club.

RBA. Dormitorios. 96p. 17.95 *(978-84-7901-880-1(1))* RBA Libros, S.A. ESP. Dist: Santillana USA Publishing Co., Inc.

Torre, Francesca. Beautiful Bedrooms Around the World. 2008. (ENG., Illus.). 280p. 40.00 *(978-1-58479-725-8(8))* Stewart, Tabori & Chang.

Wills, Margaret Sabo. Pottery Barn Kids? Rooms: Simple Projects for Designing Child-Friendly Spaces in Your Home. 2011. (ENG.). 176p. pap. 16.95 *(978-1-61628-145-8(6))* Weldon Owen, Inc.

Zabihi, Karina & Jotisalikorn, Chami. Contemporary Asian Bedrooms. 2007. (Contemporary Asian Home Ser.). (ENG., Illus.). 128p. pap. 19.95 *(978-0-7946-0467-7(6),* PeriplusEdition) Tuttle Publishing.

BEDS AND BEDSTEADS

Better Homes and Gardens Books Staff. Bags, Pillows, & Pincushions: 35 Quick & Easy Projects. 2011. (Better Homes & Gardens Crafts Ser.: 21). (ENG., Illus.). 162p. pap. 16.99 *(978-0-470-88707-3(9),* Wiley) Wiley, John & Sons, Inc.

Davies, Val. State Beds & Throne Canopies: Care & Conservation. 2007. (ENG., Illus.). 148p. 95.00 *(978-1-873132-58-6(1))* Archetype Pubns. GBR. Dist: National Bk. Network.

Woodworker's Journal Editors. Benches, Chairs & Beds: Practical Projects from Shaker to Contemporary. 2007. (Best of Woodworker's Journal Ser.). (ENG.). 151p. pap. 19.95 *(978-1-56523-343-0(3))* Fox Chapel Publishing Co., Inc.

BEDSORES

Bader, Dan L., et al, eds. Pressure Ulcer Research: Current & Future Perspectives. 2010. (ENG., Illus.). xiv, 382p. pap. 189.00 *(978-3-642-06404-3(3),* 3642064043) Springer.

Brown, Pamela. Quick Reference to Wound Care. 3rd rev. ed. 2008. 238p. pap. 83.95 *(978-0-7637-5583-6(4))* Jones & Bartlett Learning, LLC.

Gebhardt, Krzysztof. Pressure Ulcer Prevention. 2009. (Wiley Series in Nursing Ser.). 160p. pap. *(978-0-470-01972-6(7),* Wiley-Blackwell) Wiley, John & Sons, Ltd.

Gefen, Amit, ed. Bioengineering Research of Chronic Wounds: A Multidisciplinary Study Approach. 2009. (Studies in Mechanobiology, Tissue Engineering & Biomaterials Ser.). (ENG., Illus.). x, 454p. 209.00 *(978-3-642-00533-6(0),* 3642005330) Springer.

Krapfl, Lee Ann. Specialists Speak Series: Pressure Ulcers: Prevention, Identification, & Treatment. rev. ed. 2008. (ENG.). 52p. (C). spiral bd. 39.95 *(978-1-58254-038-2(1))* Kendall Hunt Publishing Co.

Romanelli, Marco, et al, eds. Science & Practice of Pressure Ulcer Management. 2010. (ENG., Illus.). viii, 224p. pap. 149.00 *(978-1-84996-936-9(1),* 1849969361) Springer.

BEDSPREADS

see Coverlets

BEDUINS

see Bedouins

BEE

see Bees

BEE CULTURE

see also Bees; Honey; Honeybee

Allen, A. L. Sandeman. Bee-Keeping with Twenty Hives. 2011. (Illus.). 126p. pap. ***(978-1-904331-72-8(6))*** Travis & Emery Music Bookshop.

Baker, Gerard. Bees & Bee Keeping Explained. 2010. (ENG., Illus.). 64p. pap. 14.95 *(978-1-84674-200-2(5))* Countryside Bks. GBR. Dist: Brown, David Bk. Co., The.

Barth, Walter & Demuth, George S. Five Hundred Answers to Bee Questions: Pertaining to Bee Behavior, Colony Management, Products of Bees, & Handling & Marketing of Honey. 2011. 98p. 38.95 ***(978-1-258-02033-0(5))*** Literary Licensing, LLC.

Belknap, Cindy. The Complete Guide to Beekeeping for Fun & Profit: Everything You Need to Know Explained Simply. 2010. (ENG., Illus.). 288p. pap. 24.95 *(978-1-60138-362-4(2))* Atlantic Publishing Co.

Benjamin, Alison & McCallum, Brian. Keeping Bees & Making Honey. 2008. (ENG., Illus.). 128p. pap. 19.99 *(978-0-7153-2810-1(7))* David & Charles Pubs. GBR. Dist: F&W Media, Inc.

Berrevoets, Erik. Wisdom of the Bees: Principles for Biodynamic Beekeeping. 2009. (Illus.). 152p. pap. 18.00 *(978-0-88010-709-9(X))* SteinerBooks, Inc.

Blaylock, Iris T. & Richards, Terresa H., eds. Honey Bees: Colony Collapse Disorder & Pollinator Role in Ecosystems. 2008. (Illus.). vii, 282p. 129.00 *(978-1-60692-688-8(8))* Nova Science Pubs., Inc.

Bonney, Richard E. & Sanford, Malcolm T. Storey's Guide to Keeping Honey Bees: Honey Production, Pollination, Bee Health. 2010. (ENG., Illus.). 244p. pap. 19.95 *(978-1-60342-550-6(0),* 1603425500) Storey Publishing, LLC.

—Storey's Guide to Keeping Honey Bees: Honey Production, Pollination, Health. 2010. (ENG.). 256p. 29.95 *(978-1-60342-551-3(9),* 1603425519) Storey Publishing, LLC.

Brackney, Susan. Plan Bee: Everything You Ever Wanted to Know about the Hardest-Working Creatures on the Planet. 2010. (ENG.). 208p. (gr. 12). 13.95 *(978-0-399-53598-7(5),* Perigee Trade) Penguin Group (USA) Inc.

Brown, Kate. Honey Bees-Gde To Management. 2nd ed. (Illus.). 128p. pap. 22.99 *(978-1-86126-174-8(8))* Crowood Pr., Ltd. GBR. Dist: Trafalgar Square Publishing.

Brown, Ron. Beekeeping: A Seasonal Guide. 2011. (ENG.). 192p. 19.95 *(978-1-906368-97-3(0),* Batsford, B. T. Ltd.) Anova Bks. GBR. Dist: Sterling Publishing Co., Inc.

Buchmann, Stephen. Honey Bees: Letters from the Hive. 2010. (ENG.). 224p. (YA). (gr. 6-18). lib. bdg. 19.99 *(978-0-385-90683-8(8),* Delacorte Bks. for Young Readers) Random Hse. Children's Bks.

Chandler, P. J. The Barefoot Beekeeper. 2009. 111p. pap. 31.50 *(978-1-4092-7114-7(5))* Lulu Enterprises Inc.

Conrad, Ross & Conrad, Russ. Natural Beekeeping: Organic Approaches to Modern Apiculture. 2007. (ENG., Illus.). 240p. pap. 35.00 *(978-1-933392-08-0(8))* Chelsea Green Publishing.

Cramp, David. The Complete Step-by-Step Book of Beekeeping: A Practical Guide to Beekeeping, from Setting up a Colony to Hive Management & Harvesting the Honey, Shown in over 400 Photographs. 2012. (ENG., Illus.). 160p. 19.99 ***(978-0-7548-2348-3(2))*** Anness Publishing GBR. Dist: National Bk. Network.

Cramp, David. A Practical Manual of Beekeeping. 2009. (Illus.). 256p. 30.00 *(978-1-905862-23-5(7))* How To Books GBR. Dist: Parkwest Pubns., Inc.

Dadant, C. P. First Lessons in Beekeeping. 2008. 132p. *(978-1-4437-3750-0(X),* Home Farm Bks.) Read Bks.

Dadant, C. p. & Dadant, C. P. First Lessons in Beekeeping: Complete & Unabridged. 2010. (Illus.). 184p. pap. 9.99 *(978-1-61720-054-0(9))* Wilder Pubns., Ltd.

De Vito, Dominique. Beekeeping: A Primer on Starting & Keeping a Hive. 2012. (Illus.). 224p. ***(978-1-4027-7006-7(5))*** Sterling Publishing Co., Inc.

Delaplane, Keith S. First Lessons in Beekeeping. 2007. (Illus.). 166p. per. *(978-0-915698-12-7(9))* Dadant & Sons.

—Primeras Lecciones en Apicultura. Delaplane, Keith S., ed. 2007. (SPA.). pap. *(978-0-915698-13-4(7))* Dadant & Sons.

Dogterom, Margriet. Pollination with Mason Bees: A Gardener's Guide to Managing Mason Bees for Fruit Production. 2nd ed. 2009. 136p. pap. 16.95 *(978-0-9689357-3-6(7))* Beediverse CAN. Dist: AtlasBooks Distribution.

Dullas, William. Abc's of Beekeeping Problems & Problem Beekeepers. 2008. 248p. pap. 19.95 *(978-0-595-53382-4(5))* iUniverse, Inc.

Dummies Press Staff & Blackiston, Howland. Beekeeping for Dummies. 2nd ed. 2009. (ENG., Illus.). 392p. pap. 19.99 *(978-0-470-43065-1(6),* For Dummies) Wiley, John & Sons, Inc.

Ellis, Hattie. Sweetness & Light: The Mysterious History of the Honeybee. 2007. (ENG.). 243p. 23.00 *(978-1-4223-9096-2(9))* DIANE Publishing Co.

Elwins, Dannie. Beekeeping Techniques: How to Become A Beekeeper & Keep Bees. 2009. 32p. pap. 16.99 *(978-0-557-15521-7(5))* Lulu Enterprises Inc.

English, Ashley. Homemade Living: Keeping Bees with Ashley English: All You Need to Know to Tend Hives, Harvest Honey & More. 2011. (Homemade Living Ser.). (ENG., Illus.). 136p. 19.95 *(978-1-60059-626-1(6))* Lark Bks.

Flottum, Kim. The Backyard Beekeeper: An Absolute Beginner's Guide to Keeping Bees in Your Yard & Garden. rev. ed. 2010. (ENG., Illus.). 208p. pap. 24.99 *(978-1-59253-607-8(7),* 1592536077) Quayside.

—The Backyard Beekeeper's Honey Handbook: A Guide to Creating, Harvesting, & Cooking with Natural Honeys. 2009. (ENG., Illus.). 168p. pap., instr.'s hndbk. ed. 24.99 *(978-1-59253-474-6(0),* 1592534740, Quarry Books) Quayside.

—Better Beekeeping: The Ultimate Guide to Keeping Stronger Colonies & Healthier, More Productive Bees. 2011. (ENG., Illus.). 176p. pap. 24.99 *(978-1-59253-652-8(2),* 1592536522, Fair Winds Press) Quayside.

For Know-It-Alls Staff. Beekeeping for Know-It-Alls. 2008. pap. 9.99 *(978-1-59986-236-1(0),* For Know-It-Alls) Filiquarian Publishing, LLC.

Gary, Norman. Honey Bee Hobbyist: The Care & Keeping of Bees. 2010. (ENG.). 144p. (gr. 6). pap. 14.95 *(978-1-933958-94-1(4))* BowTie Pr.

Harbison, W. C. Bees & Bee-Keeping: A Plain, Practical Work; Resulting from Years of Experience & Close Observation in Extensive Apiaries, Both in Pennsylvania An. 2006. 308p. per. 23.99 *(978-1-4255-2885-0(6))* MPublishing.

—Bees & Bee-Keeping: a Plain, Practical Work. 2007. (ENG.). 308p. per. 28.95 *(978-1-4304-4524-1(6))* Kessinger Publishing, LLC.

Harissis, Haralampos V. & Harissis, Anastasios V. Apiculture in the Prehistoric Aegean: Minoan & Mycenaean Symbols Revisited. 2009. (ENG., Illus.). 101p. (C). pap. 100.00 *(978-1-4073-0454-0(2))* British Archaeological Reports Ltd. GBR. Dist: Brown, David Bk. Co., The.

Harris, W. H. The Honey-Bee - Its Nature, Homes & Products. 2009. 292p. pap. 29.45 *(978-1-4446-0114-5(8))* Research Pr.

Harris, William. The Honey-Bee: Nature, Homes, Products. 2008. (Gardening in America Ser.). (ENG.). 292p. pap. 19.95 *(978-1-4290-1358-1(3))* Applewood Bks.

Head, Vivian. The Beekeeping Handbook: A Practical Apiary Guide for the Yard, Garden, & Rooftop. 2012. (ENG., Illus.). 160p. pap. 12.95 ***(978-1-56523-681-3(5))*** Fox Chapel Publishing Co., Inc.

Howes, F. N. Plants & Beekeeping. 2007. (ENG.). 256p. per. *(978-1-4067-4523-8(5))* Read Bks.

Hughes, Craig. Urban Beekeeping: A Guide to Keeping Bees in the City. 2010. (ENG., Illus.). 210p. pap. 24.95 *(978-1-904871-69-9(0),* 1904871690) Good Life Pr., The GBR. Dist: MBI Distribution Services/Quayside Distribution.

Jackson, I. H. Bee-Keeping for Beginners. 2008. 136p. *(978-1-4437-3652-7(X),* Hesperides Pr.) Read Bks.

Jones, Richard A. & Sweeney-Lynch, Sharon. The Beekeeper's Bible: Bees, Honey, Recipes & Other Home Uses. 2011. (ENG., Illus.). 416p. 35.00 *(978-1-58479-913-4(8))* Stewart, Tabori & Chang.

Kritsky, Gene. The Quest for the Perfect Hive: A History of Innovation in Bee Culture. 2010. (ENG., Illus.). 224p. 24.95 *(978-0-19-538544-1(6))* Oxford Univ. Pr., Inc.

Langstroth, Lorenzo Lorraine. A Practical Treatise on the Hive & Honey-Bee. 2009. 250p. pap. *(978-0-217-34193-6(4));* 320p. pap. *(978-0-217-43271-9(9))* Books LLC.

—A Practical Treatise on the Hive & Honey-Bee. 2009. 324p. pap. 22.72 *(978-1-4590-1563-2(X))* General Bks. LLC.

—A Practical Treatise on the Hive & Honey-Bee. 2006. 460p. per. 29.99 *(978-1-4255-5127-8(0))* MPublishing.

Lawes, Geoffrey. The Victorian Beekeeping Revolution. 2011. 304p. pap. ***(978-1-904846-73-4(4))*** Northern Bee Bks.

MacFawn, David & Slade, Chris. Getting the Best from Your Bees. 2011. 153p. pap. 18.95 *(978-1-4327-6646-7(5))* Outskirts Pr., Inc.

Mader, Eric, et al. Managing Alternative Pollinators: A Handbook for Beekeepers, Growers, & Conservationists. 2009. *(978-1-933395-20-3(6))* Natural Resource, Agricultural, & Engineering Service.

Magill, Mark. The Way to Bee: Meditation & the Art of Beekeeping. 2011. (ENG.). 144p. 16.95 *(978-0-7627-7365-7(0),* Lyons Pr.) Globe Pequot Pr., The.

Marchese, C. Marina. Honeybee: Lessons from an Accidental Beekeeper. (ENG., Illus.). 256p. 2011. pap. 14.95 *(978-1-57912-873-9(4),* 1579128734) 2009. 22.95 *(978-1-57912-815-9(7),* 1579128157) Black Dog & Leventhal Pubs., Inc.

Miner, T. B. American Bee KeeperS Manual. 2006. pap. 26.99 *(978-1-4255-3754-8(5))* MPublishing.

Nordhaus, Hannah. The Beekeeper's Lament: How One Man & Half a Billion Honey Bees Help Feed America. 2011. (ENG., Illus.). 256p. pap. 14.99 *(978-0-06-187325-6(X),* HarperPerennial) HarperCollins Pubs.

Paudel, Laxman Prasad. Economics of Honey Production & Marketing in Chitwan, Nepal. 2011. 100p. pap. ***(978-3-8443-0889-1(X))*** Lambert Academic Publishing.

Peacock, Paul. Chickens, Ducks & Bees: A Beginner's Guide to Keeping Livestock in the Garden. 2011. (ENG., Illus.). 166p. pap. 20.00 *(978-1-905862-57-3(1))* How To Books GBR. Dist: Parkwest Pubns., Inc.

—Keeping Bees: A Complete Practical Guide, 1 vol. 2008. (ENG.). 144p. pap. 18.95 *(978-0-7938-0669-0(0))* TFH Pubns., Inc.

Phillips, E. F. Beekeeping as a Hobby. (Shorey Lost Arts Ser.). 40p. reprint ed. pap. 10.00 *(978-0-8466-6039-2(3),* U39) Shorey's Bookstore.

Phillips, Everett Franklin. Beekeeping. 2008. (Gardening in America Ser.). (ENG., Illus.). 496p. pap. 29.95 *(978-1-4290-1372-7(9))* Applewood Bks.

Pundyk, Grace. The Honey Trail: In Pursuit of Liquid Gold & Vanishing Bees. 2010. (ENG., Illus.). 352p. 27.99 *(978-0-312-62981-6(8))* St. Martin's Pr.

Ranabhat, Nar Bahadur. Bee-Keeping. 2010. 84p. pap. *(978-3-8383-8269-2(2))* Lambert Academic Publishing.

Rant, Phil. Backyard Beekeeping & Honey Production. 2011. (ENG., Illus.). 112p. 22.95 *(978-1-84797-268-2(3))* Crowood Pr., Ltd. GBR. Dist: Independent Pubs. Group.

Ryde, Joanna. Beekeeping: Self-Sufficiency. 2010. (Self-Sufficiency Ser.). (ENG., Illus.). 128p. 12.95 *(978-1-60239-958-7(1),* 239958) Skyhorse Publishing Co., Inc.

Sammataro, Diana & Avitabile, Alphonse. The Beekeeper's Handbook. 4th rev. ed. 2011. (Illus.). 272p. 65.00 *(978-0-8014-4981-9(2));* pap. 29.95 *(978-0-8014-7694-5(1))* Cornell Univ. Pr. (Comstock Publishing Assocs.).

Sammataro, Diana & Yoder, Jay, eds. Honey Bee Colony Health. 2011. (Contemporary Topics in Entomology Ser.). (ENG., Illus.). 320p. 99.95 ***(978-1-4398-7940-5(0),*** CRC Press) Taylor & Francis Group GBR. Dist: Taylor & Francis Group.

Sandeman Allen, Arthur Leonard. Bee-Keeping with Twenty Hives. 2008. (Illus.). 132p. *(978-1-904331-71-1(8))* Travis & Emery Music Bookshop.

Schacker, Michael. A Spring Without Bees: How Colony Collapse Disorder Has Endangered Our Food Supply. 2008. (ENG., Illus.). 304p. 24.95 *(978-1-59921-432-0(6),* Lyons Pr.) Globe Pequot Pr., The.

—A Spring without Bees: How Colony Collapse Disorder Has Endangered Our Food Supply. 2009. (ENG.). 304p. pap. 16.95 *(978-1-59921-600-3(0),* Lyons Pr.) Globe Pequot Pr., The.

Sekunda, Nicholas, ed. Ergasteria: Works Presented to John Ellis Jones on His 80th Birthday. 2011. (ENG., Illus.). 188p. (C). 50.00 *(978-83-929798-0-7(X))* Akanthina POL. Dist: Brown, David Bk. Co., The.

Smithers, Courtenay N. Backyard Beekeeping. 2nd rev. ed. 2011. 80p. pap. 19.95 ***(978-1-921719-19-6(2))*** Rosenberg Publishing Pty, Ltd. AUS. Dist: International Specialized Bk. Services.

Stiglitz, Dean & Herboldsheimer, Laurie. The Complete Idiot's Guide to Beekeeping. 2010. (Complete Idiot's Guide Ser.). (ENG., Illus.). 224p. (gr. 12). 14.95 *(978-1-61564-011-9(8),* Alpha Bks.) Penguin Group (USA) Inc.

Stuart, F. S. Bee-Keeping Practice. 2008. 232p. *(978-1-4437-3662-6(7),* Hesperides Pr.) Read Bks.

Trench, Nicki. Creating Your Backyard Farm. 2010. (Illus.). 192p. *(978-1-907030-11-6(5))* www.clickok.co.uk.

Turnbull, Bill. Confessions of a Bad Beekeeper: What Not to Do When Keeping Bees (with Apologies to My Own) 2011. (ENG., Illus.). 256p. pap. 13.95 *(978-1-61519-032-4(5),* 1615190325) Experiment LLC, The.

Vaughan, Mace, et al. Farming for Bees: Guidelines for Providing Native Bee Habitat on Farms. 2007. (Illus.). 44p. 15.00 *(978-0-9744475-1-3(X))* Xerces Society, The.

Waring, Adrain & Waring, Claire. Get Started in Beekeeping: A Teach Yourself Guide. 2nd ed. 2010. (Teach Yourself: Games/Hobbies/Sports Ser.). (ENG.). 208p. pap. 14.95 *(978-0-07-174015-9(5),* 0071740155) McGraw-Hill Cos., The.

Waring, Claire. Bee Manual: The Complete Step-by-Step Guide to Keeping Bees. 2011. (ENG., Illus.). 192p. 29.95 *(978-0-85733-057-4(8),* 0857330578) Haynes Publishing PLC GBR. Dist: MBI Distribution Services/Quayside Distribution.

Weiss, Karl. The Little Book of Bees. 2012. (Little Book Ser.). (ENG., Illus.). viii, 163p. pap. 21.95 *(978-1-4419-2922-8(3),* 1441929223) Springer.

Whitcombe, Harry J. & Douglas, John Scott. Bees Are My Business. 2011. 260p. 47.95 ***(978-1-258-01632-6(X))*** Literary Licensing, LLC.

Wilson, Bee. The Hive: The Story of the Honeybee & Us. 2008. 308p. 25.00 *(978-1-4379-5844-7(3))* DIANE Publishing Co.

—Hive: The Story of the Honeybee & Us. 2007. (ENG., Illus.). 320p. pap. 14.95 *(978-0-312-37124-1(1),* St. Martin's Griffin) St. Martin's Pr.

BEE POLLEN

Elkins MH, Rita. Bee Pollen, Royal Jelly & Propolis. 3rd ed. 2011. (Woodland Health Ser.). 36p. pap. 4.95 ***(978-1-58054-174-9(7))*** Woodland Publishing, Inc.

BEE PRODUCTS

see also Bee Pollen; Honey; Propolis

Broadhurst, C. Leigh. Health & Healing with Bee Products. 2007. (ENG.). 64p. mass mkt. 11.95 *(978-1-55312-031-5(0))* Books Alive.

Elkins MH, Rita. Bee Pollen, Royal Jelly & Propolis. 3rd ed. 2011. (Woodland Health Ser.). 36p. pap. 4.95 ***(978-1-58054-174-9(7))*** Woodland Publishing, Inc.

Havenhand, Gloria. Honey: Nature's Golden Healer. 2011. (ENG.). 160p. pap. 19.95 *(978-1-55407-915-5(2))* Firefly Bks., Ltd.

Jones, Richard A. & Sweeney-Lynch, Sharon. The Beekeeper's Bible: Bees, Honey, Recipes & Other Home Uses. 2011. (ENG., Illus.). 416p. 35.00 *(978-1-58479-918-4(8))* Stewart, Tabori & Chang.

Pundyk, Grace. The Honey Trail: In Pursuit of Liquid Gold & Vanishing Bees. 2010. (ENG., Illus.). 352p. 27.99 *(978-0-312-62981-6(8))* St. Martin's Pr.

Weiler, Michael. Bees & Honey: From Flower to Jar. 2006. (Illus.). 138p. per. *(978-0-86315-575-8(8))* Floris Bks.

BEECH AIRCRAFT CORPORATION

Ball, Larry A. Those Incomparable Bonanzas. 2008. (ENG., Illus.). 220p. 49.99 *(978-1-934980-25-5(0))* Cable Publishing.

BEECHAM, THOMAS, SIR, 1879-1961

Lucas, John. Thomas Beecham: An Obsession with Music. 2011. (Illus.). 416p. pap. 24.95 *(978-1-84383-626-1(2),* Boydell Press) Boydell & Brewer, Ltd. GBR. Dist: Boydell & Brewer, Inc.

BEECHCRAFT 17 (AIRPLANES)

Ball, Larry A. From Travel Air to Baron: How Beech Created a Classic. 2008. (ENG., Illus.). 504p. 49.99 *(978-1-934980-28-6(5))* Cable Publishing.

BEECHER, HENRY WARD, 1813-1887

Addison, Daniel Dulany. Clergy in American Life & Letters. 2006. pap. 34.95 *(978-1-4286-3782-5(6))* Kessinger Publishing, LLC.

Applegate, Debby. The Most Famous Man in America: The Biography of Henry Ward Beecher. 2007. (ENG., Illus.). 560p. pap. 16.95 *(978-0-385-51397-5(6),* Three Leaves) Doubleday Religious Publishing Group, The.

Beecher, Henry Ward. The Beecher Trial: A review of the evidence. Reprinted from the New York Times of July 3, 1875. with some revisions & Additions. 2011. 36p. pap. 11.99 ***(978-1-4181-9503-8(0))*** MPublishing.

Beecher, Henry Ward. Star Papers; or, Experiences of Art & Nature by Henry Ward Beecher. 2006. 364p. per. 26.99 *(978-1-4255-3773-9(1))* MPublishing.

Beecher, William C. & Scoville, Samuel. A Biography of Rev Henry Ward Beecher. 2007. (ENG.). 712p. 65.95 *(978-0-548-14944-7(5))* Kessinger Publishing, LLC.

Beecher, William C., et al. A Biography of Rev Henry Ward Beecher. 2007. (ENG.). 712p. per. 50.95 *(978-1-4304-4256-1(5))* Kessinger Publishing, LLC.

Doyle, John E. P. Plymouth Church & Its Pastor, B or, Henry Ward Beecher & His Accusers Compiled by J E Doyle. 2006. 592p. per. 32.99 *(978-1-4255-6375-2(9))* MPublishing.

BEECHER, LYMAN, 1775-1863

Beecher, Lyman. Autobiography, Correspondence, Etc., of Lyman Beecher, D. D. 2009. (Amer Philosophy, Religion Ser.). (ENG.). 608p. pap. 35.95 *(978-1-4290-1815-9(1));* 568p. pap. 33.95 *(978-1-4290-1805-0(4))* Applewood Bks.

—Autobiography, Correspondence, etc of Lyman Beecher V1. Beecher, Charles, ed. 2007. (ENG.). 568p. 58.95 *(978-0-548-11033-1(6))* Kessinger Publishing, LLC.

BEEF

Burch, Monte. The Complete Jerky Book: How to Dry, Cure, & Preserve Everything from Venison to Turkey. 2010. (ENG., Illus.). 160p. pap. 12.95 *(978-1-61608-040-2(X),* 608040) Skyhorse Publishing Co., Inc.

Committee on an Evaluation of the Food Safety Requirements of the Federal Purchase Ground Beef Program & National Research Council. An Evaluation of the Food Safety Requirements of the Federal Purchase Ground Beef Program. 2010. (ENG.). 44p. pap. 15.00 *(978-0-309-17709-2(X))* National Academies Pr.

Cram101 Textbook Reviews Staff. Outlines & Highlights for Beef Production & Management Decisions by Thomas G Field, Isbn: 9780131198388. 2009. 196p. pap. 30.95 *(978-1-4288-4034-8(6))* Cram101 Inc.

Fussell, Betty. Raising Steaks: The Life & Times of American Beef. 2009. (ENG., Illus.). 416p. pap. 15.95 *(978-0-547-24769-4(9),* Mariner Bks.) Houghton Mifflin Harcourt Trade & Reference Pubs.

Minnick, Fred. The Brand That Changed Beef: How Certified Angus Beef Became a Worldwide Icon of Quality: A Company Biography. 2010. *(978-1-59098-485-7(4))* Wooster Bk. Co., The.

Schatzker, Mark. Steak: One Man's Search for the World's Tastiest Piece of Beef. 2010. (ENG.). 304p. (gr. 12). 25.95 *(978-0-670-02181-9(4),* Viking Adult) Penguin Group (USA) Inc.

Underly, Kari. The Art of Beef Cutting: A Meat Professional's Guide to Butchering & Merchandising. 2011. (ENG., Illus.). 240p. 50.00 *(978-1-118-02957-2(7),* Wiley) Wiley, John & Sons, Inc.

VanOverbeke, Deborah L. Handbook of Beef Safety & Quality. 2007. (ENG., Illus.). 240p. (C). 81.95 *(978-1-56022-323-8(5)*, CRC Press) Taylor & Francis Group GBR. Dist: Taylor & Francis Group.

BEEF CATTLE

see also names of specific breeds of beef cattle

Baker, Fiona. Running a Small Beef Herd. 3rd ed. 2009. (Landlinks Press Ser.). 176p. pap. 44.00 *(978-0-643-09415-4(6))* CSIRO Publishing AUS. Dist: Stylus Publishing, LLC.

Blair, Robert. Nutrition & Feeding of Organic Cattle. 2011. (Illus.). 304p. 145.00 *(978-1-84593-758-4(9))* CABI GBR. Dist: Stylus Publishing, LLC.

Consumer Dummies Staff, et al. Raising Beef Cattle for Dummies. 2012. (ENG.). 360p. pap. 19.99 ***(978-0-470-93061-8(6)***, For Dummies) Wiley, John & Sons, Inc.

Cram101 Textbook Reviews Staff. Outlines & Highlights for Beef Production & Management Decisions by Thomas G Field, Isbn: 9780131198388. 2009. 196p. pap. 30.95 *(978-1-4288-4034-8(6))* Cram101 Inc.

Fussell, Betty. Raising Steaks: The Life & Times of American Beef. 2009. (ENG., Illus.). 416p. pap. 15.95 *(978-0-547-24769-4(9)*, Mariner Bks.) Houghton Mifflin Harcourt Trade & Reference Pubs.

Golden-Romero, Pat. Hotel Convention Sales, Services, & Operations. 2011. (ENG., Illus.). 336p. (C). per. 60.95 *(978-0-7506-7902-2(6))* Routledge.

Grist, Andrew. Bovine Meat Inspection: Anatomy, Physiology & Disease Conditions. 2nd ed. 2009. (ENG., Illus.). 188p. pap. 80.00 *(978-1-904761-83-9(6))* Nottingham Univ. Pr. GBR. Dist: Independent Pubs. Group.

Jones, D. D. Cow-Calf Production in the U.S. Corn Belt. 2011. ***(978-0-89373-107-6(2))*** MidWest Plan Service.

Kastner, Justin & Tenhouse, Blair. 150 Years of Kansas Beef. 2011. *(978-1-57864-685-2(5))* Donning Co. Pubs.

Laurence, Michael. Maternal Productivity in Beef Cattle. 2011. 328p. pap. ***(978-3-8454-0806-4(5))*** Lambert Academic Publishing.

Micheels, Eric. Market Orientation in Production Agriculture. 2010. 148p. pap. *(978-3-639-25674-1(3))* VDM Verlag Dr. Mueller e.K.

More O'Ferrall, G. J. Beef Production from Different Dairy Breeds & Dairy Beef Crosses. 2010. (Current Topics in Veterinary Medicine Ser.). 416p. pap. 389.00 *(978-90-481-8275-6(1)*, 9048182751) Springer.

Pala, Akin. Crossbreeding in Beef Cattle Using Terminal Sires. 2010. 112p. pap. *(978-3-639-23524-1(X))* VDM Verlag Dr. Mueller e.K.

Ratcliffe, Derek. Galloway & the Borders. 2007. (Collins New Naturalist Ser.). (ENG., Illus.). 384p. pap. 45.00 *(978-0-00-717402-7(0))* HarperCollins Pubs. Ltd. GBR. Dist: Independent Pubs. Group.

Thomas, Heather Smith. Storey's Guide to Raising Beef Cattle. 3rd ed. 2009. (ENG., Illus.). 340p. pap. 19.95 *(978-1-60342-454-7(7)*, 1603424547) Storey Publishing, LLC.

—Storey's Guide to Raising Beef Cattle. 3rd ed. 2009. (ENG., Illus.). 352p. 29.95 *(978-1-60342-455-4(5)*, 1603424555) Workman Publishing Co., Inc.

VanOverbeke, Deborah L. Handbook of Beef Safety & Quality. 2007. (ENG., Illus.). 240p. (C). 81.95 *(978-1-56022-323-8(5))*; per. 45.95 *(978-1-56022-324-5(3))* Taylor & Francis Group GBR. (CRC Press). Dist: Taylor & Francis Group.

BEEF INDUSTRY

Admassu, Samuel Amare. Demand for Beef Quality & Safety in Addis Ababa, Ethiopi. 2010. 100p. pap. *(978-3-8383-4615-1(7))* Lambert Academic Publishing.

Brocklebank, Andrea M., et al. The North American Beef Industry in Transition: New Consumer Demands & Supply Chain Responses. 2008. (C). 79.00 *(978-1-60456-121-0(1))* Nova Science Pubs., Inc.

Cram101 Textbook Reviews Staff. Outlines & Highlights for Beef Production & Management Decisions by Thomas G Field, Isbn: 9780131198388. 2009. 196p. pap. 30.95 *(978-1-4288-4034-8(6))* Cram101 Inc.

Ferrara, Alessandro. Global Beef Trade. 2009. (Agriculture Issues & Policies Ser.). 89.00 *(978-1-60741-121-5(0))* Nova Science Pubs., Inc.

Field, Thomas G., et al. Beef Production Management & Decisions. 5th rev. ed. 2006. (ENG., Illus.). 682p. per. 129.00 *(978-0-13-119838-8(6)*, Prentice Hall) Prentice Hall PTR.

Fussell, Betty. Raising Steaks: The Life & Times of American Beef. 2009. (ENG., Illus.). 416p. pap. 15.95 *(978-0-547-24769-4(9)*, Mariner Bks.) Houghton Mifflin Harcourt Trade & Reference Pubs.

Hanselka, Daniel. The Economic Impact of Country-of-Origin Labeling in the Us Beef Industry. 2008. 312p. per. *(978-3-8364-3806-3(2))* VDM Verlag Dr. Mueller e.K.

Hill, Rodney A. Feed Efficiency in the Beef Industry. 2012. (ENG.). 322p. 149.95 ***(978-0-470-95952-7(5)***, Wiley-Blackwell) Wiley, John & Sons, Inc.

The Importation of Canadian Beef That Comes from Animals Older Than 30 Months of Age: Field Hearing Before the Subcommittee on Interstate Commerce, Trade, & Tourism of the Committee on Commerce, Science, & Transportation, United States Senate, One Hundred Tenth Congress, First Session, February 21, 2007. 2007. (Illus.). iii, 48p. *(978-0-16-079375-2(0)*, 552-070-36405-6) United States Government Printing Office.

Kastner, Justin & Tenhouse, Blair. 150 Years of Kansas Beef. 2011. *(978-1-57864-685-2(5))* Donning Co. Pubs.

Kukucha, Christopher John & Luu, Joanne. Sacred Cow? Canada's Response to the BSE Crisis: Evaluating North American Integration, Science, & Questions of Intrusiveness & Autonomy. 2007. 48p. pap. *(978-1-882582-59-4(4))* Canadian-American Ctr.

Micheels, Eric. Market Orientation in Production Agriculture. 2010. 148p. pap. *(978-3-639-25674-1(3))* VDM Verlag Dr. Mueller e.K.

Sanchez, Mariela. Agri-Food Restructuring in the Australia Beef Industry. 2010. 220p. pap. *(978-3-8383-7212-9(3))* Lambert Academic Publishing.

Sarzeaud, Patrick, et al, eds. EU Beef Farming systems & CAP Regulations, Vol. 9. 2008. (Eaap-ts Ser.). (Illus.). 122p. pap. 57.00 *(978-90-8686-058-6(3))* Wageningen Academic Publishers NLD. Dist: Enfield Publishing & Distribution Co., Inc.

Tyler, Daniel. WD Farr: Cowboy in the Boardroom. 2011. (ENG., Illus.). 312p. 29.95 *(978-0-8061-4193-0(X))* Univ. of Oklahoma Pr.

VanOverbeke, Deborah L. Handbook of Beef Safety & Quality. 2007. (ENG., Illus.). 240p. (C). 81.95 *(978-1-56022-323-8(5))*; per. 45.95 *(978-1-56022-324-5(3))* Taylor & Francis Group GBR. (CRC Press). Dist: Taylor & Francis Group.

BEEKEEPING

see Bee Culture

BEER

see also Brewing; Cooking (Beer); Malt

Adams Media Corporation Staff. Bottom of the Glass Trivia Coasters - Beer. 2011. (ENG.). 50p. 12.95 *(978-1-4405-2904-7(3))* Adams Media Corp.

Alexander, John. A Guide to Craft Brewing. 2006. (ENG., Illus.). 160p. pap. 29.95 *(978-1-86126-899-0(8))* Crowood Pr., Ltd. GBR. Dist: Independent Pubs. Group.

Anheuser-Busch Publisher. How to Cook with Budweiser. 2011. 38p. 35.95 ***(978-1-258-07762-4(0))*** Literary Licensing, LLC.

Applebaum, Ben & DiSorbo, Dan. The Book of Beer Awesomeness: A Champion's Guide to Amazing Beer Activities, Party Skills, & More Than Fifty Drinking Games. 2012. (ENG., Illus.). 192p. pap. 15.95 ***(978-1-4521-0501-7(4))*** Chronicle Bks. LLC.

Bamforth, Charles. Beer: Tap into the Art & Science of Brewing. 3rd ed. 2009. (ENG., Illus.). 272p. 29.95 *(978-0-19-530542-5(6))* Oxford Univ. Pr., Inc.

Bamforth, Charles W. Beer Is Proof God Loves Us: Reaching for the Soul of Beer & Brewing. 2010. (FT Press Science Ser.). (ENG., Illus.). 304p. 25.99 *(978-0-13-706507-3(8))* FT Press.

—Grape vs. Grain: A Historical, Technological, & Social Comparison of Wine & Beer. 2008. (ENG., Illus.). 224p. 30.00 *(978-0-521-84937-1(3))* Cambridge Univ. Pr.

Beer Market Mexico: Companies-Products-Services. 200p. (Orig.). pap. 4995.00 *(978-0-7605-2162-5(X))* Rector Pr., Ltd.

Beer Market U. S. A. Companies-Products-Services. 345p. (Orig.). pap. 1595.00 *(978-0-7605-2161-8(1))* Rector Pr., Ltd.

Bernstein, Joshua M. Brewed Awakening: Behind the Beers & Brewers Leading the World's Craft Beer Revolution. 2011. (ENG., Illus.). 304p. 24.95 *(978-1-4027-7864-3(3)*, Sterling Epicure) Sterling Publishing Co., Inc.

Bostwick, William & Rymill, Jessi. Beer Craft: A Simple Guide to Making Great Beer. 2011. (ENG., Illus.). 176p. pap. 17.99 *(978-1-60529-133-8(1))* Rodale Pr., Inc.

Brown, Pete. Three Sheets to the Wind: One Man's Quest for the Meaning of Beer. 2008. (ENG.). 480p. 14.95 *(978-0-330-44247-3(3))* Macmillan Pubs., Ltd. GBR. Dist: Independent Pubs. Group.

Bryson, Lew & Haynie, Mark. New Jersey Breweries. 2008. (Breweries Ser.). (ENG., Illus.). 148p. pap. 16.95 *(978-0-8117-3504-9(4))* Stackpole Bks.

Calagione, Sam, et al. He Said Beer, She Said Wine: Impassioned Food Pairings to Debate & Enjoy - From Burgers to Brie & Beyond. 2009. (ENG.). 256p. (gr. 12). pap. 16.95 *(978-0-7566-5449-8(1))* Dorling Kindersley Publishing, Inc.

Cornell, Martyn. Amber, Gold & Black: The History of Britain's Great Beers. 2010. (ENG., Illus.). 240p. 24.95 *(978-0-7524-5567-9(2))* History Pr. Ltd.,The GBR. Dist: Independent Pubs. Group.

Coutts, Ian R. Brew North: How Canadians Made Beer & Beer Made Canada, 1 vol. 2010. (ENG., Illus.). 184p. pap. 19.95 *(978-1-55365-467-4(6)*, Greystone Bks.) D&M Pubs. Inc. CAN. Dist: Perseus-PGW.

Crocker, Ronnie. Houston Beer: A Heady History of Brewing in the Bayou City. 2012. 160p. pap. 19.99 ***(978-1-60949-537-4(3))*** History Pr., The.

Deaver, Paul. Market Share Instability. 2011. 80p. pap. ***(978-3-8443-0761-0(3))*** Lambert Academic Publishing.

DeBenedetti, Christian. The Great American Ale Trail: The Craft Beer Lover's Guide to the Best Watering Holes in the Nation. 2011. (ENG.). 368p. pap. 20.00 *(978-0-7624-4375-8(8))* Running Pr. Bk. Pubs.

Denny, Mark & Denny, M. Froth! The Science of Beer. 2009. (ENG., Illus.). 200p. 25.95 *(978-0-8018-9132-8(9))* Johns Hopkins Univ. Pr.

Dookeran, Mark. Ginger Beer. 2010. 124p. pap. *(978-3-639-24813-5(9))* VDM Verlag Dr. Mueller e.K.

Draeger, Jim & Speltz, Mark. Bottoms Up: A Toast to Wisconsin's Historic Bars & Breweries. 2012. (Places along the Way Ser.). (ENG., Illus.). 272p. 29.95 ***(978-0-87020-498-2(X))*** Wisconsin Historical Society.

Evans, Jeff. A Beer a Day: 366 Beers to Help You Through the Year. 2009. (ENG., Illus.). 384p. pap. 24.95 *(978-1-85249-235-9(X))* Camra Bks. GBR. Dist: Independent Pubs. Group.

—The Book of Beer Knowledge: Essential Wisdom for the Discerning Drinker. 2008. (ENG., Illus.). 160p. 19.95 *(978-1-85249-198-7(1))* Camra Bks. GBR. Dist: Independent Pubs. Group.

—The Book of Beer Knowledge: Essential Wisdom for the Discerning Drinker. 2011. (ENG., Illus.). 160p. pap. 12.95 ***(978-1-85249-292-2(9))*** Camra Bks. GBR. Dist: Independent Pubs. Group.

—Good Bottled Beer Guide. 7th ed. 2009. (ENG., Illus.). 320p. pap. 19.95 *(978-1-85249-262-5(7))* Camra Bks. GBR. Dist: Independent Pubs. Group.

—Good Bottled Beer Guide: The Camra Guide to Real Ale in a Bottle. 6th ed. 2008. (ENG., Illus.). 256p. 19.95 *(978-1-85249-226-7(0))* Camra Bks. GBR. Dist: Independent Pubs. Group.

Farías, Marta E., et al, eds. Microbial Interaction in Fermented Beverages. 2010. (Food Science & Technology Ser.). (Illus.). viii, 65p. pap. 43.00 *(978-1-60876-785-4(X))* Nova Science Pubs., Inc.

Gibson, Michael. The Sommelier Prep Course: An Introduction to the Wines, Beers, & Spirits of the World. 2010. (ENG., Illus.). 480p. pap. 35.00 *(978-0-470-28318-9(1)*, Wiley) Wiley, John & Sons, Inc.

Glassman, Bruce. San Diego's Top Brewers: Inside America's Craft Beer Capital. 2011. (Illus.). 208p. pap. 24.95 ***(978-0-9816222-3-1(2))*** Chefs Pr.

Griffiths, Iorwerth. Beer & Cider in Ireland: The Complete Guide. 2008. (ENG., Illus.). 174p. per. 21.95 *(978-1-905483-17-4(1))* Liberties Pr. IRL. Dist: Dufour Editions, Inc.

Hales, Steven D., ed. Beer & Philosophy: The Unexamined Beer Isn't Worth Drinking. 2007. (ENG., Illus.). 248p. per. 24.95 *(978-1-4051-5430-7(6)*, Wiley-Blackwell) Wiley, John & Sons, Inc.

Hampson, Tim. 101 Beer Days Out. 2012. (ENG., Illus.). 184p. pap. 19.95 ***(978-1-85249-288-5(0))*** Camra Bks. GBR. Dist: Independent Pubs. Group.

Hartley, Paul. Guinness: Celebrating 250 Remarkable Years. 2009. (ENG., Illus.). 128p. 12.99 *(978-0-600-62037-2(9)*, Hamlyn) Octopus Publishing Group GBR. Dist: Hachette Bk. Group.

Hawthorne, Larry. The Beer Drinker's Guide to Munich. 6th ed. 2008. (ENG., Illus.). 240p. pap. 16.95 *(978-0-9628555-3-5(7))* Freizeit Pubs.

Hieronymus, Stan. Brewing with Wheat: The "Wit' & Weizen" of World Wheat Beer Styles. 2010. (ENG.). 295p. pap. 17.95 *(978-0-937381-95-3(0))* Brewers Pubns.

Jackson, Michael. Great Beers of Belgium. 5th ed. 2007. (Illus.). 516p. 49.50 *(978-90-209-6598-8(0))* Lannoo N. V., Uitgeverij BEL. Dist: Antique Collectors' Club.

—Michael Jackson's Great Beers of Belgium, 6th Edition. 6th ed. 2008. (ENG.). 520p. pap. 36.95 *(978-0-937381-93-9(4))* Brewers Pubns.

Jackson, Michael & Dorling Kindersley Publishing Staff. Ultimate Beer. 2007. 160p. (C). 33.33 *(978-0-13-501762-3(9))* Prentice Hall Higher Education.

Jersey Brew: The Story of Beer in New Jersey. 2009. (Illus.). 160p. 19.95 *(978-0-9765233-1-4(0))* Lake Neepaulin Publishing.

Jesseph, Bonnie. Man Your Grill: Cookin' & Grillin' with Beer! 2007. (Illus.). vi, 210p. *(978-1-57166-480-8(7))* Hearts 'N Tummies Cookbook Co.

Keitel, Adolph. Government by the Brewers? 2007. (Illus.). 48p. per. *(978-1-4065-1869-6(7))* Dodo Pr.

—Government by the Brewers? 2010. 48p. pap. *(978-1-4076-5265-8(6))* HardPr.

Koch, Greg & Allyn, Matt. The Brewer's Apprentice: An Insider's Guide to the Art & Craft of Beer Brewing, Taught by the Masters. 2011. (Apprentice Ser.). (ENG., Illus.). 192p. pap. 24.99 *(978-1-59253-731-0(6)*, 1592537316) Quayside.

Koch, Greg, et al. The Craft of Stone Brewing Co: Liquid Lore, Epic Recipes, & Unabashed Arrogance. 2011. (ENG., Illus.). 208p. 25.00 *(978-1-60774-055-1(9))* Ten Speed Pr.

Kraven, Mark, et al. The College Survival Guide: Beer games, hangover remedies & much More! 2009. 85p. pap. 16.95 *(978-1-4327-4283-6(3))* Outskirts Pr., Inc.

Kuderka, Michael & Ench-Kuderka, Catherine A. Essential Reference of Domestic Brewers & Their Bottled Brands, 3rd Edition. 3rd ed. 2007. (Illus.). 574p. 60.00 *(978-0-9774800-1-2(1))* MC Basset, LLC.

Lawrence, Matt. Philosophy on Tap: Pint-Sized Puzzles for the Pub Philosopher. 2011. (ENG., Illus.). 264p. pap. 20.95 *(978-1-4443-3640-5(1)*, Wiley-Blackwell) Wiley, John & Sons, Inc.

Lebow, Jess. The Beer Devotional: A Daily Celebration of the World's Most Inspiring Beers. 2010. (ENG.). 384p. pap. 14.95 *(978-1-4405-0357-3(5))* Adams Media Corp.

Line, Dave. Brewing British-Style Beers: More Than 100 Thirst Quenching Pub Recipes to Brew at Home. 2012. (ENG., Illus.). 160p. pap. 14.95 ***(978-1-56523-689-9(0))*** Fox Chapel Publishing Co., Inc.

McFarland, Ben. World's Best Beers: One Thousand Craft Brews from Cask to Glass. 2009. (ENG., Illus.). 288p. 29.95 *(978-1-4027-6694-7(7)*, Sterling Innovation) Sterling Publishing Co., Inc.

McFarland, Ben & Sandham, Tom. Good Beer Guide West Coast USA: Including Las Vegas, Alaska & Hawaii. 2008. (Good Beer Guides). (ENG., Illus.). 320p. pap. 27.95 *(978-1-85249-244-1(9))* Camra Bks. GBR. Dist: Independent Pubs. Group.

Mittelman, Amy. Brewing Battles: The History of American Beer. 2007. 34.95 *(978-0-87586-573-7(9))*; (Illus.). pap. 22.95 *(978-0-87586-572-0(0))* Algora Publishing.

Monterosso, Gary. Artisan Beer: A Complete Guide to Savoring the World's Finest Beers. 2011. (ENG., Illus.). 160p. pap. 16.95 ***(978-1-58080-168-3(4))*** Burford Bks.

Morgan, Michael D. Over-the-Rhine: When Beer Was King. 2010. (Food & Drink Ser.). (ENG., Illus.). 184p. pap. 19.99 *(978-1-59629-914-6(2))* History Pr., The.

Morin, Brian & Beaumont, Stephen. The Beerbistro Cookbook. 2009. (ENG., Illus.). 296p. 40.00 *(978-1-55470-140-7(6))* Key Porter Bks. CAN. Dist: Perseus-PGW.

Mosher, Randy. Tasting Beer: An Insider's Guide to the World's Greatest Drink. 2009. (ENG., Illus.). 256p. pap. 16.95 *(978-1-60342-089-1(4)*, 1603420894) Storey Publishing, LLC.

Myers, Erik Lars. North Carolina Craft Brew & Breweries. 2012. (ENG., Illus.). 304p. pap. 16.95 ***(978-0-89587-571-6(3))*** Blair, John F. Pub.

Nachel, Marty. Beer for Dummies. 2nd ed. 2012. (ENG.). 360p. pap. 22.99 ***(978-1-118-12030-9(2)***, For Dummies) Wiley, John & Sons, Inc.

Narziß, Ludwig & Back, Werner. Die Bierbrauerei 2: Die Technologie der Würzebereitung, 2 vols. 8th ed. 2009. (GER., Illus.). 820p. *(978-3-527-32533-7(6)*, VCH) Wiley, John & Sons, Ltd.

Nelson, Max. The Barbarian's Beverage: A History of Beer in Ancient Europe. 2008. pap. 39.95 *(978-0-415-48692-7(0))* Routledge.

Neu, Denese. Chicago Beer: A High-Gravity History of Windy City Brewing. 2011. 128p. pap. 19.99 ***(978-1-60949-125-3(4))*** History Pr., The.

Oakes, Josh, ed. The Beer Guide: The Most Comprehensive Guide to Ales & Lagers Sold in America. 2006. per. 9.95 *(978-1-892588-16-6(1))* Great Texas Line Pr.

O'Brien, Christopher Mark. Fermenting Revolution: How to Drink Beer & Save the World. 2006. (ENG., Illus.). 288p. per. 18.95 *(978-0-86571-556-1(4)*, 0865715564) New Society Pubs., Ltd. CAN. Dist: Consortium Bk. Sales & Distribution.

Ogle, Maureen. Ambitious Brew: The Story of American Beer. 2007. (ENG., Illus.). 432p. pap. 21.95 *(978-0-15-603359-6(3)*, Mariner Bks.) Houghton Mifflin Harcourt Trade & Reference Pubs.

Palmer, John. How to Brew: Ingredients, Methods, Recipes & Equipment for Brewing Beer at Home. 400p. pap. 16.95 *(978-0-9710579-0-6(7))* Defenestrative Publishing, Co.

Pattyn, Joris & Webb, Tim. 100 Belgian Beers to Try Before You Die! 2010. (ENG., Illus.). 160p. pap. 24.95 *(978-1-85249-248-9(1))* Camra Bks. GBR. Dist: Independent Pubs. Group.

Penza, Robert C. Reflections of the Brewmaster. 2010. (Illus.). 175p. pap. 17.95 *(978-1-4327-5786-1(5))* Outskirts Pr., Inc.

Perozzi, Christina & Beaune, Hallie. The Naked Pint: An Unadulterated Guide to Craft Beer. (ENG.). 336p. (gr. 12). 2012. pap. 15.00 ***(978-0-399-16132-2(5))*** 2009. 22.00 *(978-0-399-53534-5(9))* Penguin Group (USA) Inc. (Perigee Trade).

Pettigrew, Timmons. Charleston Beer: A High-Gravity History of Lowcountry Brewing. 2011. 128p. pap. 19.99 ***(978-1-60949-244-1(7))*** History Pr., The.

Poling, Travis E. & Hightower, Paul W. Beer Across Texas: A Guide to the Brews & Brewmasters of the Lone Star State. 2009. (Illus.). 80p. pap. 12.95 *(978-1-893271-51-7(X))* Maverick Publishing Co.

Preedy, Victor R. Beer in Health & Disease Prevention. Preedy, Victor R., ed. 2008. (ENG., Illus.). 1248p. 200.00 *(978-0-12-373891-2(1)*, Academic Pr.) Elsevier Science & Technology Bks.

Protz, Roger. Good Beer Guide 2011. 2011. (ENG., Illus.). 888p. pap. 24.95 *(978-1-85249-272-4(4))* Camra Bks. GBR. Dist: Independent Pubs. Group.

—Life on the Hop: Memoirs from a Career in Beer. 2009. (ENG., Illus.). 240p. pap. 19.95 *(978-1-85249-256-4(2))* Camra Bks. GBR. Dist: Independent Pubs. Group.

—300 Beers to Try Before You Die! 2nd ed. 2010. (ENG., Illus.). 304p. pap. 24.95 *(978-1-85249-273-1(2))* Camra Bks. GBR. Dist: Independent Pubs. Group.

Protz, Roger, ed. Good Beer Guide 2008. 2007. (ENG., Illus.). 880p. pap. 29.95 *(978-1-85249-231-1(7))* Camra Bks. GBR. Dist: Independent Pubs. Group.

—Good Beer Guide 2009. 2008. (ENG., Illus.). 880p. pap. 24.95 *(978-1-85249-249-6(X))* Camra Bks. GBR. Dist: Independent Pubs. Group.

Protz, Roger, ed. Good Beer Guide 2012: The Complete Guide to the UK's Best Pubs. 2011. (ENG., Illus.). 888p. pap. 24.95 ***(978-1-85249-286-1(4))*** Camra Bks. GBR. Dist: Independent Pubs. Group.

Putman, Roger. Beers & Breweries of Britain. 2008. (Shire Library). (ENG., Illus.). 56p. pap. 12.95 *(978-0-7478-0606-6(3))* Shire Pubns., Ltd. GBR. Dist: Random Hse., Inc.

Rail, Evan. Prague & Czech Republic. 2008. (ENG., Illus.). 224p. pap. 25.95 *(978-1-85249-233-5(3))* Camra Bks. GBR. Dist: Independent Pubs. Group.

Reader, Ted. Beerlicious: The Art of Grillin' & Chillin' 2012. (ENG., Illus.). 320p. pap. 27.99 ***(978-0-7710-7367-0(4)***, McClelland & Stewart) McClelland & Stewart CAN. Dist: Random Hse., Inc.

Renfro, Mike. Shine On: 100 Years of Shiner Beer. 2009. (ENG., Illus.). 187p. pap. 24.95 *(978-1-933979-60-1(7))* Bright Sky Pr.

—Shine On, 1909-2009: 100 Years of Shiner Beer. 2008. (ENG.). 187p. 34.95 *(978-1-933979-20-5(8))* Bright Sky Pr.

Russell, Don. Christmas Beer: The Cheeriest, Tastiest, & Most Unusual Holiday Brews. 2008. (ENG., Illus.). 208p. 7.95 *(978-0-7893-1796-4(6))* Universe Publishing.

Salem, Frederick W. Beer: Its History & Its Economic Value as a National Beverage. 2007. (Illus.). 275p. reprint ed. 29.95 *(978-0-9662084-7-4(1))* BeerBooks.com.

Schiefenhövel, Wulf & Macbeth, Helen, eds. Liquid Bread: Beer & Brewing in Cross-Cultural Perspective. 2011. (AFN Ser.). 264p. 95.00 *(978-0-85745-215-3(0))* Berghahn Bks., Inc.

Shepard, Robin. Minnesota's Best Breweries & Brewpubs: Searching for the Perfect Pint. 2011. E-Book *(978-0-299-28243-1(0))*; (ENG., Illus.). 336p. pap. 24.95 *(978-0-299-28244-8(9))* Univ. of Wisconsin Pr.

Simpson, William & Downes, Andrew. Brewing Problems Solved. 2013. 320p. *(978-1-84569-196-7(2))* Woodhead Publishing Ltd.

Skilnik, Bob. Beer: A History of Brewing in Chicago. 2006. 416p. 24.95 *(978-1-56980-312-7(9))* Barricade Bks., Inc.

—Beer & Food: An American History. 2007. (ENG., Illus.). 280p. 24.95 *(978-0-9778086-1-8(0))* Jefferson Pr.

Stagliano, Kim. All I Can Handle: I'm No Mother Teresa - A Life Raising Three Daughters with Autism. 2010. (ENG., Illus.). 208p. 24.95 *(978-1-61608-069-3(8),* 608069) Skyhorse Publishing Co., Inc.

Stelzer, Howard & Stelzer, Ashley. Beer Cocktails: 50 Superbly Crafted Cocktails that Liven Up Your Lagers & Ales. 2012. (50 Ser.). (ENG., Illus.). 104p. 12.95 ***(978-1-55832-731-3(2))*** Harvard Common Pr.

Strong, Gordon. Brewing Better Beer: Master Lesson for Advanced Homebrewers. 2011. (ENG.). 336p. pap. 17.95 *(978-0-937381-98-4(5))* Brewers Pubns.

Swinnen, Johan F. M., ed. The Economics of Beer. 2011. (ENG., Illus.). 352p. 45.00 ***(978-0-19-969380-1(3))*** Oxford Univ. Pr., Inc.

Sykes, Walter J. The Principles & Practice of Brewing Beer & Ale. 2008. 532p. pap. 37.95 *(978-1-934939-23-9(4))* Wexford College Pr.

Szamatulski, Tess and Mark, et al. Clonebrews: Recipes for 200 Brand-Name Beers. 2nd ed. 2010. (ENG., Illus.). 439p. pap. 18.95 *(978-1-60342-539-1(X),* 160342539X) Storey Publishing, LLC.

Tamm, Elo. Beer Supply Agreements in Ec Competition Law. 2008. 76p. pap. *(978-3-639-04775-2(3))* VDM Verlag Dr. Mueller e.K.

Tierney-Jones, Adrian, ed. 1001 Beers You Must Taste Before You Die. 2010. (ENG., Illus.). 960p. 36.95 *(978-0-7893-2025-4(8))* Universe Publishing.

Tsutsumi, Cheryl Chee. The Hawaii Beer Book: Bars, Breweries & Beer Cuisine. 2007. (Illus.). 184p. spiral bd. 15.95 *(978-0-9796769-2-5(4))* Watermark Publishing, LLC.

Van Damme, Jaak. All Belgian Beers. 2nd rev. ed. 2012. (ENG, FRE & DUT., Illus.). 1568p. 47.50 ***(978-90-5856-377-4(4))*** Stichting Kunstboek Bvba BEL. Dist: Antique Collectors' Club.

Van Oudtshoorn, Nic. The Beerlovers' Bible & Homebar Handbook. (Illus.). 96p. pap. 7.95 *(978-1-873668-30-6(9))* Take That Bks. GBR. Dist: Trafalgar Square Publishing.

Vinken, Ben. Belgian Beer on the Menu. 2010. (ENG., Illus.). 160p. *(978-90-209-8741-6(0),* Lannoo Pubs. (Acc)) Antique Collectors' Club.

—Belgian Beers. 2009. (ENG., Illus.). 192p. 35.00 *(978-90-209-7920-6(5),* Lannoo Pubs. (Acc)) Antique Collectors' Club GBR. Dist: National Bk. Network.

Washawanny, Bill. Travels for Beer. 2007. 208p. per. 14.95 *(978-0-9796950-0-1(7))* Washawanny, William.

Webb, Tim. Belgium. 6th ed. 2009. (ENG., Illus.). 352p. pap. 23.95 *(978-1-85249-261-8(9))* Camra Bks. GBR. Dist: Independent Pubs. Group.

Wells, Ken. Travels with Barley: A Journey Through Beer Culture in America. 2008. (ENG.). 304p. 24.00 *(978-1-4379-5130-1(9))* DIANE Publishing Co.

Wenner, Lawrence A. & Jackson, Steven J. Sport, Beer, & Gender: Promotional Culture & Contemporary Social Life. 2008. (Popular Culture & Everyday Life Ser.). (C). 336p. 32.95 *(978-1-4331-0488-6(1));* 332p. 99.95 *(978-1-4331-0076-5(2))* Lang, Peter Publishing, Inc.

Wright, Chris. The Beer Journal. 2010. (ENG., Illus.). 272p. 12.95 *(978-1-61608-070-9(1),* 608070) Skyhorse Publishing Co., Inc.

Yaeger, Brian. Red, White, & Brew: An American Beer Odyssey. 2008. (ENG., Illus.). 272p. pap. 14.95 *(978-0-312-38314-5(2),* St. Martin's Griffin) St. Martin's Pr.

Yenne, Bill. Guinness: The 250-Year Quest for the Perfect Pint. 2007. (ENG., Illus.). 288p. 24.95 *(978-0-470-12052-1(5),* Wiley) Wiley, John & Sons, Inc.

BEERBOHM, MAX, SIR, 1872-1956

Beerbohm, Max. Letters to Reggie Turner. Hart-Davis, Rupert, ed. reprint ed. 39.50 *(978-0-404-18362-2(X))* AMS Pr., Inc.

—Works & More. 49.00 *(978-0-403-00144-6(7))* Scholarly Pr., Inc.

Lynch, Bohun. Max Beerbohm in Perspective. 2009. 94p. pap. 14.14 *(978-0-217-61532-7(5))* General Bks. LLC.

BEES

see also Africanized Honeybee; Bee Culture; Bee Products; Bumblebees; Honey; Honeybee

Baker, Gerard. Bees & Bee Keeping Explained. 2010. (ENG., Illus.). 64p. pap. 14.95 *(978-1-84674-200-2(5))* Countryside Bks. GBR. Dist: Brown, David Bk. Co., The.

Belknap, Cindy. The Complete Guide to Beekeeping for Fun & Profit: Everything You Need to Know Explained Simply. 2010. (ENG., Illus.). 288p. pap. 24.95 *(978-1-60138-362-4(2))* Atlantic Publishing Co.

Benjamin, Alison & McCallum, Brian. Keeping Bees & Making Honey. 2008. (ENG., Illus.). 128p. pap. 19.99 *(978-0-7153-2810-1(7))* David & Charles Pubs. GBR. Dist: F&W Media, Inc.

Bolesta, Murray. Bees, Butterflies & Blossoms of Southern Arizona, 3, Vol. 1. 2007. 72p. per. 19.95 *(978-0-9797842-0-0(4))* CactusHuggers Publishing Co.

Burroughs, John. Birds & Bees: Sharp Eyes & Other Papers. 2009. 196p. 22.99 *(978-1-103-08529-3(8));* pap. 16.99 *(978-1-103-08526-2(3))* BiblioBazaar.

—Birds & Bees: Sharp Eyes, & Other Papers. 2011. 198p. pap. 23.75 ***(978-1-245-39671-4(4))*** BiblioBazaar.

—Birds & Bees, Sharp Eyes & Other Papers. 2008. 136p. per. *(978-1-4065-9007-4(X))* Dodo Pr.

—Birds & Bees, Sharp Eyes & Other Papers. 2007. 104p. per. *(978-1-4068-2363-9(5))* Echo Library.

—Birds & Bees, Sharp Eyes & Other Papers. 2010. 90p. pap. 20.00 *(978-1-153-59228-4(2))* General Bks. LLC.

—Birds & Bees, Sharp Eyes & Other Papers. 2010. 114p. pap. 15.96 *(978-1-162-65557-4(7));* 27.96 ***(978-1-169-24726-0(1));*** 34.95 *(978-1-161-42422-5(9))* Kessinger Publishing, LLC.

—Birds & Bees Sharp Eyes & Other Papers. 2008. 164p. 22.99 *(978-0-554-37723-0(3));* 25.99 *(978-0-554-28420-0(0))* BiblioBazaar.

Burroughs, John & A Biographical Sketch. Birds & Bees Sharp Eyes & Other Papers. 2007. (ENG.). 162p. pap. 21.99 *(978-1-4346-5368-0(4));* 148p. pap. 18.99 *(978-1-4346-5367-3(6))* BiblioBazaar.

Dicks, Lynn V., et al. Bee Conservation: Evidence for the Effects of Interventions. 2010. 146p. *(978-1-907807-01-5(2));* pap. *(978-1-907807-00-8(4))* Pelagic Publishing Ltd.

Donovan, Barry. Fauna of New Zealand Number 57 Apoidea (Insecta: Hymenoptera) 2007.Tr. of Ko te Aitanga Pepeke o Aotearoa. (ENG & MAO., Illus.). 295p. per. *(978-0-478-09389-6(6))* Manaaki Whenua Pr. NZL. Dist: Balogh International, Inc.

Edwardes, Tickner. The Bee-Master of Warrilow. 2007. (ENG.). 108p. 34.95 *(978-0-548-12093-4(5))* Kessinger Publishing, LLC.

—The Lore of the Honey Bee. 2009. 210p. pap. 19.99 ***(978-1-4589-2869-6(1))*** General Bks. LLC.

Evans, Elizabeth Capaldi & Butler, Carol A. Why Do Bees Buzz? Fascinating Answers to Questions about Bees. 2010. (Rutgers Animal Q & A Ser.). (ENG., Illus.). 248p. pap. 21.95 *(978-0-8135-4721-3(0))* Rutgers Univ. Pr.

Fabre, J. Henri. Bramble-Bees & Others. Teixeira de Mattos, Alexander, tr. 2007. (ENG.). 220p. per. *(978-1-4065-1651-7(1))* Dodo Pr.

—Bramble-Bees & Others. 2010. 212p. pap. 19.96 *(978-1-162-65616-8(6));* 31.96 ***(978-1-169-28975-8(4))*** Kessinger Publishing, LLC.

—Bramble-bees & Others. 2009. (ENG.). 230p. pap. 15.95 *(978-1-4385-2674-4(1),* Book Jungle) Standard Pubns., Inc.

—The Mason-bees. 2009. (ENG.). 148p. pap. 11.45 *(978-1-4385-2640-9(7),* Book Jungle) Standard Pubns., Inc.

—The Mason-Bees. Teixeira de Mattos, Alexander, tr. 2007. (ENG.). 152p. per. *(978-1-4065-1654-8(6))* Dodo Pr.

—The Mason Bees. de Mattos, Alexander Teixeira, tr. 2011. 324p. 45.95 ***(978-1-169-83780-5(8))*** 2010. 324p. pap. 36.76 *(978-1-163-33087-6(6))* 2010. 324p. pap. 24.76 *(978-1-162-64132-4(0))* 2007. (ENG.). 322p. 45.95 *(978-0-548-01892-7(8))* Kessinger Publishing, LLC.

Fabre, Jean Henri. Bramble-Bees & Others. 2010. 466p. pap. 37.75 *(978-1-144-25863-2(4))* 2010. 470p. pap. 37.75 *(978-1-142-83113-4(2))* 2008. 464p. 31.99 *(978-0-559-37479-1(8))* 2008. 464p. pap. 36.75 *(978-0-559-37478-4(X))* 2008. 260p. 28.99 *(978-0-554-29400-1(1))* 2008. 260p. 25.99 *(978-0-554-38703-1(4))* BiblioBazaar.

—Bramble-Bees & Others. Mattos, Alexander Teixeira de, tr. 2007. (ENG.). 230p. per. 20.99 *(978-1-4346-7556-9(4));* 258p. per. 23.99 *(978-1-4346-7557-6(2))* BiblioBazaar.

—Bramble-Bees & Others. 2009. 184p. pap. *(978-0-217-44853-6(4))* Books LLC.

—The Mason-Bees. 2012. 330p. pap. 31.75 ***(978-1-277-20574-9(4))*** 2009. 326p. 28.99 *(978-1-113-81785-3(2))* 2009. 326p. 29.99 *(978-1-113-81786-0(0))* 2009. 326p. pap. 30.75 *(978-1-113-81782-2(8))* 2009. 326p. pap. 19.99 *(978-1-113-81780-8(1))* 2009. 324p. 25.99 *(978-0-559-93384-4(3))* 2009. 324p. pap. 19.99 *(978-0-559-93381-3(9))* 2008. 184p. 22.99 *(978-0-554-36490-2(5))* 2008. 184p. 25.99 *(978-0-554-27187-3(7))* 2007 (ENG.). 162p. pap. 19.99 *(978-1-4346-2632-5(6))* BiblioBazaar.

—The Mason-Bees. 2009. 120p. pap. *(978-1-150-18756-8(5))* Books LLC.

—The Mason-Bees. 2012. 334p. pap. ***(978-1-290-33865-3(5))*** HardPr.

—The Mason-bees. 2009. (ENG.). 324p. pap. 23.99 *(978-1-113-81776-1(3),* BiblioLife) BiblioBazaar.

—The Mason-Bees. Lt. ed. 2007. (ENG.). 180p. pap. 21.99 *(978-1-4346-2710-0(1))* BiblioBazaar.

Fabre, Jean-Henri & Fabre, J. Henri. Bramble-Bees & Others. 2010. 212p. 39.95 *(978-1-161-42481-2(4))* Kessinger Publishing, LLC.

Fabre, Jean-Henri & Fabre, Jean Henri. Bramble-Bees & Others. 2010. 466p. pap. 37.75 *(978-1-145-50082-2(X))* BiblioBazaar.

—Bramble-Bees & Others. 2010. 150p. pap. 23.74 *(978-1-153-59298-7(3))* General Bks. LLC.

—The Mason-Bees. 2010. (Illus.). 104p. pap. 20.00 *(978-1-153-71127-2(3))* General Bks. LLC.

Fabre, J.H. Bramble-Bees & Others. 2007. (ENG.). 168p. per. *(978-1-4068-6321-5(1))* Echo Library.

Frisch, Karl von. Dialects in the Language of the Bees: Scientific American, August 1962. 2011. 12p. pap. 35.95 ***(978-1-258-10399-6(0))*** Literary Licensing, LLC.

Gangloff-Kaufmann, Jody Lynn. Wasp & Bee Management: A Common-Sense Approach. 2011. ***(978-1-933395-22-7(2))*** Natural Resource, Agricultural, & Engineering Service.

Grissell, Eric. Bees, Wasps, & Ants: The Indispensable Role of Hymenoptera in Gardens. 2010. (ENG., Illus.). 336p. 27.95 *(978-0-88192-988-1(3),* 0881929883) Timber Pr., Inc.

Harbison, W. C. Bees & Bee-Keeping: a Plain, Practical Work. 2007. (ENG.). 308p. per. 28.95 *(978-1-4304-4524-1(6))* Kessinger Publishing, LLC.

Harris, William. The Honey-Bee: Nature, Homes, Products. 2008. (Gardening in America Ser.). (ENG.). 292p. pap. 19.95 *(978-1-4290-1358-1(3))* Applewood Bks.

Jones, Derek. Bird, Bee & Bug Houses: Simple Projects for Your Garden. 2011. (ENG., Illus.). 160p. pap. 17.95 *(978-1-86108-644-0(X))* Guild of Master Craftsman Pubns., Ltd. GBR. Dist: Sterling Publishing Co., Inc.

Kelley, Walter T. How to Keep Bees & Sell Honey. 2011. 114p. 39.95 ***(978-1-258-02589-2(2))*** Literary Licensing, LLC.

Lyon, D. Everett. How to Keep Bees for Profit. 2007. (ENG.). 356p. 46.95 *(978-0-548-09680-2(5))* Kessinger Publishing, LLC.

MacFawn, David & Slade, Chris. Getting the Best from Your Bees. 2011. 153p. pap. 18.95 *(978-1-4327-6646-7(5))* Outskirts Pr., Inc.

Mader, Eric, et al. Attracting Native Pollinators: The Xerces Society Guide to Conserving North American Bees & Butterflies & Their Habitat. 2011. (ENG., Illus.). 384p. pap. 29.95 *(978-1-60342-695-4(7),* 1603426957) Storey Publishing, LLC.

Maeterlinck, Maurice. The Life of the Bee. 2008. 148p. 24.99 *(978-0-554-22169-4(1))* 2008. 148p. 21.99 *(978-0-554-31472-3(X))* 2007. (ENG.). 154p. pap. 19.99 *(978-1-4264-1790-0(X))* 2007. (ENG.). 146p. pap. 19.99 *(978-1-4264-1848-8(5))* BiblioBazaar.

—The Life of the Bee. 2009. 116p. pap. *(978-0-217-12098-2(9));* 236p. pap. *(978-0-217-55547-0(0));* 122p. pap. *(978-0-217-12095-1(4))* Books LLC.

—The Life of the Bee. Sutro, Alfred, tr. 2008. 144p. pap. *(978-1-4065-9394-5(X))* Dodo Pr.

—The Life of the Bee. Sutro, Alfred, tr. from FRE. 2006. (Dover Books on Animals). (ENG., Illus.). 176p. per. 9.95 *(978-0-486-45143-5(7))* Dover Pubns., Inc.

—The Life of the Bee. 2008. 436p. *(978-1-4437-2367-1(3),* Hesperides Pr.); 432p. pap. *(978-1-4437-0756-5(2))* Read Bks.

—La Vie des Abeilles. 2009. (FRE.). 318p. 36.99 *(978-1-117-63546-0(5));* pap. 29.75 *(978-1-117-63547-7(3));* pap. 23.99 *(978-1-117-63548-4(1),* BiblioLife) BiblioBazaar.

Marchese, C. Marina. Honeybee: Lessons from an Accidental Beekeeper. 2011. (ENG., Illus.). 256p. pap. 14.95 *(978-1-57912-873-9(4),* 1579128734) Black Dog & Leventhal Pubs., Inc.

Michener, Charles D. The Bees of the World. 2nd ed. 2007. (ENG., Illus.). 992p. (gr. 17). 185.00 *(978-0-8018-8573-0(6))* Johns Hopkins Univ. Pr.

Morley, Margaret W. The Bee People. 2009. 134p. pap. 8.95 *(978-1-59915-318-6(1))* Yesterday's Classics.

O'Malley, Michael. The Wisdom of Bees: What the Hive Can Teach Business about Leadership, Efficiency, & Growth. 2010. (ENG., Illus.). 240p. (gr. 12). 22.95 *(978-1-59184-326-9(X),* Portfolio (Hardcover)) Penguin Group (USA) Inc.

Paetzel, Mary. Solitary Wasps & Bees: Their Hidden World in the Siskiyou Mountains. 2010. 174p. pap. 56.20 *(978-0-557-36970-6(3))* Lulu Enterprises Inc.

Quinby, M. Mysteries of Bee-Keeping Explained. 2008. (Illus.). 312p. pap. *(978-1-4099-0734-3(1))* Dodo Pr.

—Mysteries of Bee-Keeping Explained. 2010. (Illus.). 196p. pap. 28.11 *(978-1-153-78840-3(3))* General Bks. LLC.

—Mysteries of Beekeeping Explained. 2009. 272p. pap. 16.95 *(978-1-4357-4469-1(1))* Lulu Enterprises Inc.

Quinby, Moses. Mysteries of Bee-Keeping Explained. 2009. 198p. pap. 19.99 *(978-1-150-08318-1(2))* General Bks. LLC.

Savage, Candace. Bees: Nature's Little Wonders, 1 vol. (ENG., Illus.). 2011. 136p. pap. 16.95 *(978-1-55365-531-2(1))* 2008. 144p. 26.00 *(978-1-55365-321-9(1))* D&M Pubs. Inc. CAN. (Greystone Bks.). Dist: Perseus-PGW.

Stiglitz, Dean & Herboldsheimer, Laurie. The Complete Idiot's Guide to Beekeeping. 2010. (Complete Idiot's Guide Ser.). (ENG., Illus.). 224p. (gr. 12). 14.95 *(978-1-61564-011-9(8),* Alpha Bks.) Penguin Group (USA) Inc.

True, Margo & Sunset Magazine Editors. One-Block Feast: An Adventure in Food from Yard to Table. 2011. (Illus.). 272p. 24.99 *(978-1-58008-527-4(X))* Ten Speed Pr.

Vaughan, Mace, et al. Farming for Bees: Guidelines for Providing Native Bee Habitat on Farms. 2007. (Illus.). 44p. 15.00 *(978-0-9744475-1-3(X))* Xerces Society, The.

Weiler, Michael. Bees & Honey: From Flower to Jar. 2006. (Illus.). 138p. per. *(978-0-86315-575-8(8))* Floris Bks.

Weiss, Karl. The Little Book of Bees. 2012. (Little Book Ser.). (ENG., Illus.). viii, 163p. pap. 21.95 *(978-1-4419-2922-8(3),* 1441929223) Springer.

BEES—JUVENILE LITERATURE

Enslow, Brian. Counting Bees 1-2-3. 2011. (All About Counting Bugs 1-2-3 Ser.). (Illus.). 24p. (J). (gr. k-3). lib. bdg. 21.26 *(978-0-7660-3917-9(X))* Enslow Pubs., Inc.

Silverman, Buffy. Can You Tell a Bee from a Wasp? 2011. (Animal Look-Alikes Ser.). pap. 45.32 ***(978-0-7613-8382-6(4))*** Lerner Publishing Group.

BEES—POLLEN

see Bee Pollen

BEET

see Beets and Beet Sugar

BEETHOVEN, LUDWIG VAN, 1770-1827

Alfred Publishing, ed. Broadway Heroes & Villains Songbook. 2008. (ENG.). 224p. pap. 19.95 *(978-0-7390-5080-4(X))* Alfred Publishing Co., Inc.

Beethoven. 2010. (GER.). 130p. pap. 20.75 *(978-1-172-42859-5(X));* 100p. pap. 18.75 ***(978-1-172-52258-0(2))*** BiblioBazaar.

Beethoven. cd-rom 149.95 *(978-1-4213-0093-1(1))* Films Media Group.

Beethoven. 2008. pap. 16.95 *(978-1-4304-4203-5(4))* Kessinger Publishing, LLC.

Beethoven - Piano Concerto No. 3. 2008. (ENG.). 124p. pap. 17.99 incl. audio compact disk *(978-3-7957-6527-9(7),* 3795765277) Schott Musik International GmbH & Co. KG DEU. Dist: Leonard, Hal Corp.

Beethoven - Symphony No. 3, 'Eroica' 2008. (ENG.). 186p. pap. 17.99 incl. audio compact disk *(978-3-7957-6509-5(9),* 3795765099) Schott Musik International GmbH & Co. KG DEU. Dist: Leonard, Hal Corp.

Beethoven: The Man & the Artist. 2007. 80p. per. *(978-1-4068-1976-2(X))* Echo Library.

Beethoven: The Man & the Artist, as Revealed in His Own Words. 2009. 96p. pap. 18.75 *(978-0-559-08912-1(0));* pap. 18.75 *(978-0-559-08917-6(1))* BiblioBazaar.

Beethoven, Ludwig van. Beethoven, the Man & the Artist; As Revealed in His Own Words. 2009. 58p. pap. 7.34 *(978-0-217-78922-6(6))* General Bks. LLC.

Beethoven, Ludwig Van & Beethoven, Ludwig van. Beethoven, the Man & the Artist, As Revealed in His Own Words. 2010. (Illus.). 52p. pap. 20.00 *(978-1-153-59154-6(5))* General Bks. LLC.

Beethoven, Ludwig van & Kerst, Friedrich. Beethoven the Man & the Artist, As Revealed in His Own Words. 2010. (ENG.). 116p. pap. 19.75 *(978-1-171-73753-7(X))* BiblioBazaar.

Beethoven's Letters. 2010. 330p. pap. *(978-1-152-87168-7(4))* Books LLC.

Beethoven's Letters 1790-1826. 2009. 260p. 28.99 *(978-0-559-13446-3(0));* 212p. 24.99 *(978-0-559-12346-7(9));* 260p. 25.99 *(978-0-559-13454-8(1));* 212p. 27.99 *(978-0-559-12330-6(2));* 212p. pap. 23.75 *(978-0-559-12342-9(6));* 260p. pap. 23.99 *(978-0-559-13447-0(9));* 260p. pap. 25.75 *(978-0-559-13451-7(7));* 212p. pap. 24.75 *(978-0-559-12332-0(9))* BiblioBazaar.

Beikircher, Konrad. Beethoven - Sinfonie Nr. 9. 2007. (ENG., Illus.). 290p. 90.00 *(978-3-940004-32-1(4),* Earbooks) edel classics GmbH DEU. Dist: AtlasBooks Distribution.

Bellofatto, Luigi D. Alexander Wheelock Thayer, the Greatest Biographer of Ludwig Van Beethoven: A Study in Nineteenth-Century American Music Criticism. 2011. (ITA, GER & ENG., Illus.). x, 515p. 149.95 *(978-0-7734-1496-9(7))* Mellen, Edwin Pr., The.

Berge, P., et al, eds. Beethoven's Tempest Sonata: Perspectives of Analysis & Performance. 2009. (Analysis in context. leuven studies in Musicology Ser.). (ENG.). 341p. (C). 107.00 *(978-90-429-2289-1(3))* Peeters Pubs. & Booksellers BEL. Dist: Brown, David Bk. Co., The.

Broyles, Michael. Beethoven in America. 2011. (ENG., Illus.). 432p. 29.95 *(978-0-253-35704-5(7),* 0253357047) Indiana Univ. Pr.

Churgin, Bathia. Transcendent Mastery: Studies in the Music of Beethoven. 2008. (ENG.). 433p. 58.00 *(978-1-57647-122-7(5))* Pendragon Pr.

Cirone, Anthony J., ed. Timpani Master Class with Roland Kohloff: Beethoven Symphony No. 5. 2007. (ENG.). 28p. per. 14.95 *(978-1-57463-083-1(0),* 1574630830) Meredith Music Pubns.

Comini, Alessandra. The Changing Image of Beethoven: A Study in Mythmaking. 2008. 496p. pap. 50.00 *(978-0-86534-661-1(5))* Sunstone Pr.

Cooper, Barry. Beethoven. 2008. (Master Musicians Ser.). (ENG.). 464p. pap. 24.95 *(978-0-19-531331-4(3))* Oxford Univ. Pr., Inc.

Crowest, Frederick James. Beethoven. 2009. 348p. 32.99 *(978-1-110-10898-5(2));* pap. 31.75 *(978-1-110-10896-1(6))* BiblioBazaar.

D'Indy, Vincent. Beethoven: A Critical Biography. [Facsimile of First English Edition 1912]. 2009. (Illus.). 180p. pap. *(978-1-906857-76-9(8))* Travis & Emery Music Bookshop.

—Beethoven: Biographie Critique. [Facsimile 1911]. 2009. (FRE., Illus.). 178p. pap. *(978-1-906857-74-5(1))* Travis & Emery Music Bookshop.

D'Indy, Vincent. Beethoven Biographie Critique [Facsimile 1911]. 2011. 178p. ***(978-1-906857-73-8(3))*** Travis & Emery Music Bookshop.

Ellis, William Ashton, tr. Beethoven. 2008. 76p. pap. *(978-1-4099-3714-2(3))* Dodo Pr.

Elterlein, Ernst von. Beethoven's Pianoforte Sonatas Explained for the Lovers of the Musical Art. 2009. 56p. pap. *(978-0-217-72794-5(8))* Books LLC.

Greene, David B. The Imagining of Community in Works of Beethoven, Verdi, & Shostakovich: Musical Means for Envisioning Community. 2010. viii, 180p. *(978-0-7734-4665-6(6))* Mellen, Edwin Pr., The.

Greene, David B. The Theology of Handel's Messiah, Beethoven's Credo, & Verdi's Dies Irae: How Listening to Sung Theology Leads to the Contemplation of God. 2012. (ENG.). 128p. 129.95 ***(978-0-7734-2589-7(6))*** Mellen, Edwin Pr., The.

Grove, George. Beethoven & His Nine Symphonies. 2010. (ENG.). 420p. pap. 34.75 *(978-1-171-54227-8(5))* BiblioBazaar.

—Beethoven & His Nine Symphonies. 2010. 416p. 39.96 *(978-1-163-21401-5(9));* pap. 27.96 *(978-1-162-72798-1(5))* Kessinger Publishing, LLC.

—Beethoven & His Nine Symphonies. 2008. 420p. *(978-1-4437-3892-7(1),* Home Farm Bks.) Read Bks.

Guerrieri, Matthew. The First Four Notes: Beethoven's Fifth & the Human Imagination. 2012. (ENG.). 368p. 26.95 ***(978-0-307-59328-3(2),*** Knopf) Knopf Doubleday Publishing Group.

Hal Leonard Corporation Staff. Unlocking the Masters Set: Bach's Keyboard Music, Beethoven's Symphonies, & Brahms - A Listener's Guide. deluxe ed. 2010. (ENG.). 500p. pap. 55.00 incl. audio compact disk *(978-1-57467-192-6(8),* 1574671928, Amadeus Press) Leonard, Hal Corp.

Heartz, Daniel. Mozart, Haydn & Early Beethoven, 1781-1802. 2008. (ENG., Illus.). 800p. 75.00 *(978-0-393-06634-0(7),* 6634) Norton, W. W. & Co., Inc.

Hopkins, Antony. The Nine Symphonies of Beethoven. 2011. 302p. pap. ***(978-1-84955-029-1(8))*** Travis & Emery Music Bookshop.

Huchting, Detmar. Beethoven - Ein biografischer Bilderbogen. 2007. (ENG., Illus.). 120p. 60.00 *(978-3-940004-33-8(2),* Earbooks) edel classics GmbH DEU. Dist: AtlasBooks Distribution.

Hurwitz, David. Beethoven's Fifth & Seventh Symphonies: A Closer Look. 2008. (Magnum Opus Ser.). (ENG.). 144p. pap. 19.95 *(978-0-8264-2944-5(0))* Continuum International Publishing Group, Ltd. GBR. Dist: National Bk. Network.

Jander, Owen. Beethoven's "Orpheus" Concerto: The Fourth Piano Concerto in Its Cultural Context. 2009. *(978-1-57647-132-6(2))* Pendragon Pr.

B

Jennings, Pauline. Shakespeare & World Peace: With an Essay on Beethoven & World Brotherhood. 2011. 230p. 46.95 (978-1-258-03870-0(6)) Literary Licensing, LLC.

Jones, David Wyn. The Symphony in Beethoven's Vienna. 2006. (ENG., Illus.). 244p. 106.00 (978-0-521-86261-5(2)) Cambridge Univ. Pr.

Kahn, Robert S. Beethoven & the Grosse Fuge: Music, Meaning, & Beethoven's Most Difficult Work. 2010. (ENG., Illus.). 180p. (gr. 17). pap. 48.00 (978-0-8108-7418-3(0)) Scarecrow Pr., Inc.

Kerst, Friedrich. Beethoven, the Man & the Artist: As Revealed in His Own Words. 2010. 122p. pap. 19.75 (978-1-141-80293-7(7)) BiblioBazaar.

Kerst, Friedrich & Krehbiel, Henry Edward, eds. Beethoven: The Man & the Artist, as Revealed in His Own Words. 2007. 88p. per. (978-1-4065-3738-3(1)) Dodo Pr.

Kinderman, William. Beethoven. 2nd ed. 2009. (ENG., Illus.). 432p. 99.00 (978-0-19-532825-7(6)); pap. 35.00 (978-0-19-532836-3(1)) Oxford Univ. Pr., Inc.

Kivy, Peter. The Possessor & the Possessed: Handel, Mozart Beethoven & the Idea of Musical Genius. 2011. (Yale Series in the Philosophy & Theory Ser.). (ENG., Illus.). 304p. pap. 32.00 (978-0-300-18018-3(7)) Yale Univ. Pr.

Kobbé, Gustav. The Loves of Great Composers. 2008. (ENG.). 102p. pap. 18.75 (978-1-4375-0765-2(4)); 92p. pap. 18.75 (978-1-4375-0764-5(6)) BiblioBazaar.

—The Loves of Great Composers. 2007. (Illus.). 100p. per. (978-1-4065-2938-8(9)) Dodo Pr.

—The Loves of Great Composers. 2009. 238p. 41.95 (978-1-104-94773-6(0)); pap. 26.95 (978-1-104-91804-0(8)) Kessinger Publishing, LLC.

Larson, Andre, et al. Beethoven: Musical Treasures from the Age of Revolution & Romance. Date not set. (Illus.). 48p. pap. 17.95 (978-0-9633959-8-6(X)) Bowers Museum of Cultural Art.

Lederer, Victor. Beethoven's Chamber Music: Unlocking the Masters Series. 2012. (ENG.). 180p. pap. 22.99 incl. audio compact disk (978-1-57467-203-9(7), 1574672037, Amadeus Press) Leonard, Hal Corp.

Lederer, Victor. Beethoven's Piano Music - A Listener's Guide: Unlocking the Masters Series, No. 23. 2011. (ENG.). 166p. pap. 22.99 incl. audio compact disk (978-1-57467-194-0(4), 1574671944, Amadeus Press) Leonard, Hal Corp.

Lindley, Mark, et al. Beethovens Klaviervariationen Op. 34: Beethoven's Variations for Piano Opus 34. 2008. (GER & ENG., Illus.). 266p. pap. 49.95 incl. audio compact disk (978-3-7957-0575-6(4), 3795705754) Schott Music Corp.

Lockwood, Lewis, et al. Inside Beethoven's Quartets: History, Performance, Interpretation. 2008. (Illus.). 304p. 38.50 (978-0-674-02809-8(0)) Harvard Univ. Pr.

MacDonald, Hugh. Beethoven's Century: Essays on Composers & Themes. 2008. (Eastman Studies in Music Ser.: Volume 56). (Illus.). 272p. 80.00 (978-1-58046-275-4(8)) Univ. of Rochester Pr.

Mai, Francois Martin. Diagnosing Genius: The Life & Death of Beethoven. 2007. (ENG., Illus.). 288p. (C). (978-0-7735-3190-1(4)) McGill-Queen's Univ. Pr.

Mason, Daniel Gregory. Beethoven & His Forerunners. 2009. 118p. pap. 19.99 (978-1-150-65108-3(3)) General Bks. LLC.

Mellers, Wilfrid. Beethoven & the Voice of God. 468p. 2008. (978-1-904331-89-6(0)) 2007. (ENG.). per. (978-1-904331-23-0(8)) Travis & Emery Music Bookshop.

Morris, Edmund. Beethoven: The Universal Composer. 2010. (Eminent Lives Ser.). (ENG.). 256p. pap. 13.99 (978-0-06-075975-9(5), HarperPerennial) HarperCollins Pubs.

Muxfeldt, Kristina. Vanishing Sensibilities: Schubert, Beethoven, & Schumann, 1 vol. 2011. (ENG., Illus.). 288p. 39.95 (978-0-19-978242-0(3)) Oxford Univ. Pr., Inc.

Nohl, Louis. Life of Beethoven. Lalor, John J., tr. 2007. (ENG.). 204p. 39.95 (978-0-548-10844-4(7)) Kessinger Publishing, LLC.

—Life of Beethoven. 2008. 204p. pap. (978-1-4437-1242-2(6)) Read Bks.

Nohl, Ludwig. Life of Beethoven. 2009. 86p. pap. (978-1-151-35561-4(5)) Books LLC.

Orga, Ates. Beethoven. (SPA.). (978-84-95601-23-0(0)) Ma Non Troppo ESP. Dist: Lectorum Pubns., Inc.

Piano Concerto No. 5. 2008. (ENG.). 206p. pap. 19.99 incl. audio compact disk (978-3-7957-6520-0(X), 379576520X) Schott Musik International GmbH & Co. KG DEU. Dist: Leonard, Hal Corp.

Piddocke, Melanie. Beethoven & the Clarinet. 2011. 96p. pap. (978-3-8443-2106-7(3)) Lambert Academic Publishing.

Reid, Paul. The Beethoven Song Companion. 2008. (GER & ENG., Illus.). 352p. 95.00 (978-0-7190-7570-4(X)) Manchester Univ. Pr. GBR. Dist: Macmillan.

—Beethoven Song Companion. 2010. (ENG & GER., Illus.). 324p. pap. 30.00 (978-0-7190-7571-1(8)) Manchester Univ. Pr. GBR. Dist: Macmillan.

Rodriguez, Berta. Ludwig van Beethoven. 2007. (Grandes biografías Ser.). (SPA & ENG., Illus.). 192p. 8.95 (978-84-9764-565-2(0)) Edimat Libros, S. A. ESP. Dist: Independent Pubs. Group.

Rolland, Romain. Beethoven. 2009. 270p. 30.99 (978-1-110-59075-9(X)); pap. 26.75 (978-1-110-59072-8(5)) BiblioBazaar.

—Goethe & Beethoven. Pfister, G. A. & Kemp, E. S., trs. 332p. 2008. 45.95 (978-1-4366-8784-3(5)) 2007. (ENG.). per. 30.95 (978-1-4326-3009-6(1)) Kessinger Publishing, LLC.

Rucker, Andreas. Beethovens Klaviersatz: Technik und Stilistik, 2 vols. (Europaische Hochschulschriften Ser.: Vol. 219). (GER., Illus.). 1006p. 89.95 (978-3-631-39262-1(1)) Lang, Peter Publishing, Inc.

Rudall, H. A. Beethoven. 2009. (ENG.). 163p. 30.99 (978-1-117-30590-5(2)); pap. 20.75 (978-1-117-30591-2(0)) BiblioBazaar.

Rudolf, Max & Frager, Malcolm. Dear Max/Lieber Malcolm. Ellison, Paul, ed. 2010. (Illus.). xviii, 258p. pap. 54.00 (978-1-57647-184-5(5)) Pendragon Pr.

Sachs, Harvey. The Ninth: Beethoven & the World in 1824. 2011. (ENG., Illus.). 240p. pap. 15.00 (978-0-8129-6907-8(3), Random Hse. Trade Paperbacks) Random House Publishing Group.

—The Ninth: Beethoven & the World in 1824. 2010. (ENG., Illus.). 240p. 26.00 (978-1-4000-6077-1(X)) Random Hse., Inc.

Saloman, Ora Frishberg. Listening Well: On Beethoven, Berlioz, & Other Music Criticism in Paris, Boston, & New York, 1764-1890. 2009. (Illus.). 270p. (C). 75.95 (978-1-4331-0357-5(5)) Lang, Peter Publishing, Inc.

Sanborn, Pitts. Ludwig Van Beethoven. Peyser, Herbert F., ed. 2011. 70p. 36.95 (978-1-258-09277-1(8)) Literary Licensing, LLC.

Singer, Irving. Mozart & Beethoven: The Concept of Love in Their Operas. 2010. (Irving Singer Library). (ENG.). 176p. (gr. 17). pap. 25.00 (978-0-262-51364-7(1)) MIT Pr.

Skowroneck, Tilman. Beethoven the Pianist. 2010. (Musical Performance & Reception Ser.). (ENG., Illus.). 284p. 95.00 (978-0-521-11959-7(6)) Cambridge Univ. Pr.

Song, Moo Kyoung. The Evolution of Sonata-Form Design in Beethoven's Piano Sonatas. 2009. 370p. pap. (978-3-639-15639-3(0)) VDM Verlag Dr. Mueller e.K.

Steindorff, Ulrich L., tr. The Symphony of Life: Letters. reprint ed. 17.50 (978-0-404-12860-9(2)) AMS Pr., Inc.

Suchet, John. The Treasures of Beethoven. 2012. (ENG., Illus.). 64p. 29.95 (978-0-233-00354-2(1)) Andre Deutsch GBR. Dist: Sterling Publishing Co., Inc.

Symphony No. 5. 2008. (ENG.). 142p. pap. 14.99 incl. audio compact disk (978-3-7957-6515-6(3), 3795765153) Schott Musik International GmbH & Co. KG DEU. Dist: Leonard, Hal Corp.

Taub, Robert, ed. Beethoven Nos. 16-32, Vol. 2: Piano Sonatas. 2010. (ENG.). 372p. pap. 24.99 (978-1-4234-0393-7(2), 1423403932, G Schirmer, Inc.) Leonard, Hal Corp.

—Beethoven Nos. 16-32, Vol. 2, Set: Piano Sonatas. 2010. (ENG.). 8p. pap. 19.99 (978-1-4234-0395-1(9), 1423403959, G Schirmer, Inc.) Leonard, Hal Corp.

—Beethoven Vol. 1, Nos. 1-15: Piano Sonatas, 5 vols. 2010. (ENG.). 8p. pap. 19.99 (978-1-4234-0394-4(0), 1423403940, G Schirmer, Inc.) Leonard, Hal Corp.

—Beethoven - Piano Sonatas, Volume I - Book Only: Nos. 1-15. 2010. (ENG.). 312p. pap. 24.99 (978-1-4234-0392-0(4), 1423403924, G Schirmer, Inc.) Leonard, Hal Corp.

Taub, Robert & Hal Leonard Corporation Staff. Playing the Beethoven Piano Sonatas, 1 vol. 2009. (ENG.). 260p. pap. 19.99 (978-1-57467-178-0(2), 1574671782, Amadeus Press) Leonard, Hal Corp.

Thakar, Markand. Looking for the Harp Quartet: An Investigation into Musical Beauty. 2011. (Eastman Studies in Music Ser.: Volume 82). (Illus.). 227p. 49.95 (978-1-58046-346-1(0)) Univ. of Rochester Pr.

Tomo, Grandes de, ed. Los Grandes - Beethoven. 2007. 144p. pap. 5.95 (978-970-666-603-1(6)) Grupo Editorial Tomo, S.A. de C.V. MEX. Dist: Giron Bks.

Travis & Emery, notes. Beethoven. 2010. 84p. pap. (978-1-84955-085-7(9)) Travis & Emery Music Bookshop.

Tyson, Alan, ed. Beethoven Studies 3. 2009. (ENG.). 312p. pap. 46.00 (978-0-521-11166-9(8)) Cambridge Univ. Pr.

Velez, Jose Vincente Katarain, ed. Beethoven. 2007. (SPA., Illus.). 64p. (YA). (gr. 5-9). 14.95 (978-958-06-1042-7(8)) Oveja Negra, Editorial COL. Dist: Random Hse., Inc.

Walden, Edward. Beethoven's Immortal Beloved: Solving the Mystery. 2011. (Illus.). xxxviii, 145p. E-Book (978-0-8108-7774-0(0)); (ENG., 194p. (gr. 17). 49.95 (978-0-8108-7773-3(2)) Scarecrow Pr., Inc.

Wallace, Lady, tr. Beethoven's Letters 1790-1826. 2007. 456p. per. (978-1-4065-3737-6(3)) Dodo Pr.

Wallace, Robert K. Emily Bronte & Beethoven: Romantic Equilibrium in Fiction & Music. 2008. (ENG.). 248p. pap. 22.95 (978-0-8203-3295-6(X)) Univ. of Georgia Pr.

Watson, Angus. Beethoven's Chamber Music in Context. 2012. (Illus.). 318p. pap. 29.95 (978-1-84383-716-9(1), Boydell Press) Boydell & Brewer, Ltd. GBR. Dist: Boydell & Brewer, Inc.

Winkels, Ursula. Ludwig van Beethovens Mondschein-Sonate auf Welte-Mignon-Kunstlerrollen: Unter dem Aspekt der Dynamik und des Tempos. (Systemische Musikwissenschaft Ser.: Vol. 4). (GER., Illus.). 371 S.p. 43.95 (978-3-631-39743-5(7)) Lang, Peter Publishing, Inc.

Young, John Bell. Beethoven's Symphonies: A Guided Tour. 2008. (Unlocking the Masters Ser.). (ENG.). 224p. pap. 22.99 incl. audio compact disk (978-1-57467-169-8(3), 1574671693, Amadeus Press) Leonard, Hal Corp.

BEETJUANS (AFRICAN PEOPLE)

see Tswana (African People)

BEETLES

see also Ladybugs

Ahmed, Zia. Toxicity of Some Plant Materials Against Pulse Beetle: Callosobruchus Chinensis L. Attacking Chickpea under Storage. 2011. 112p. pap. (978-3-639-34285-7(2)) VDM Verlag Dr. Mueller e.K.

Bani Mfarrej, Manar & Naim Sharaf, Prof. Isolation, Identification & Manipulation of Almond Borer Pheromones. 2011. 88p. pap. (978-3-8443-2578-2(6)) Lambert Academic Publishing.

Barker, Shelley. Castiarina: Australia's Richest Jewel Beetle Genus. 2006. (Illus.). 348p. 75.00 (978-0-642-56843-4(X)) CSIRO Publishing AUS. Dist: Stylus Publishing, LLC.

Benkovskaya, Galina V. & Udalov, Maxim B. Colorado Potato Beetles Investigations in the South Urals. 2010. pap. 47.00 (978-1-61728-951-4(5)) Nova Science Pubs., Inc.

Bouchard, Patrice, ed. Family-Group Names in Coleoptera (Insecta) 2011. (ZooKeys Ser.). 972p. 287.50 (978-954-642-583-6(4)) Pensoft Pubs. BGR. Dist: Coronet Bks.

Bousquet, Yves. Illustrated Identification Guide to Adults & Larvae of Northeastern North American Ground Beetles (Coleoptera: Carabidae) 2010. (Illus.). 562p. 187.50 (978-954-642-522-5(2)) Pensoft Pubs. BGR. Dist: Coronet Bks.

Bright, Donald E., Jr. The Bark Beetles of Canada & Alaska: Coleoptera, Scolytidae. (Illus.). 241p. pap. (978-0-660-01320-6(7)) Canadian Government Publishing.

Buckland, Philip I. The Bugs Coleopteran Ecology Package. 2009. 244p. pap. (978-3-639-13530-5(X)) VDM Verlag Dr. Mueller e.K.

Buchard, Patrice, ed. Family-Group Names in Coleoptera (Insecta), 2 Volumes. 2011. (ZooKeys Ser.). 972p. pap. 245.00 (978-954-642-584-3(2)) Pensoft Pubs. BGR. Dist: Coronet Bks.

Buse, J., ed. Saproxylic Beetles: Their Role & Diversity in European Woodland & Tree Habitats. 2009. (Faunistica Ser.). (Illus.). 235p. pap. 115.00 (978-954-642-507-2(9)) Pensoft Pubs. BGR. Dist: Coronet Bks.

Ciegler, Janet. Leaf & Seed Beetles of South Carolina (Coleoptera: Biota of South Carolina, Volume 4. 2007. (Biota of South Carolina Ser.). (Illus.). 252p. per. 40.00 (978-0-9753471-8-8(7)) Clemson Univ. Public Service Publishing.

Desender, K., et al, eds. Carabid Beetles: Ecology & Evolution: Ecology & Evolution. 2010. (Series Entomologica Ser.). (Illus.). 492p. pap. 499.00 (978-90-481-4320-7(9), 9048143209) Springer.

Erwin, Terry L. Treatise on the Western Hemisphere Caraboidea (Coleoptera): Their Classification, Distributions, & Ways of Life: (Trachypachidae, Carabidae - Nebriiformes 1) 2007. 348p. 187.50 (978-954-642-298-9(3)) Pensoft Pubs. BGR. Dist: Coronet Bks.

Erwin, Terry L. & Pearson, David L. Treatise on the Western Hemisphere Caraboidea (Coleoptera). Their Classification, Distributions & Ways of Life. Volume II. Carabidae - Nebriiformes 2 - Cicindelitae. 2008. (Illus.). 402p. 210.00 (978-954-642-444-0(7)) Pensoft Pubs. BGR. Dist: Coronet Bks.

Evans, Arthur V. & Hogue, James N. Field Guide to Beetles of California. 2006. (California Natural History Guides Ser.: Vol. 88). (Illus.). 362p. 70.00 (978-0-520-24655-3(1)); pap. 24.95 (978-0-520-24657-7(8)) Univ. of California Pr.

Fabre, J.H. More Beetles. de Mattos, Alexander Teixeira, tr. 2007. (ENG.). 330p. 45.95 (978-0-548-01670-1(4)) Kessinger Publishing, LLC.

Fedorenko, Dmitri N. Evolution of the Beetle Hind Wing,with Special Reference to Folding: Insecta, Coleoptera. Golovatch, Sergei, ed. 2009. 336p. pap. 157.50 (978-954-642-494-5(3)) Pensoft Pubs. BGR. Dist: Coronet Bks.

Gerlach, Justin, ed. Coleoptera of the Seychelles Islands: (Illustrated) 2009. (Faunistica Ser.). (Illus.). 266p. pap. 139.50 (978-954-642-498-3(6)) Pensoft Pubs. BGR. Dist: Coronet Bks.

Gouix, N & Klimaszewski, J. Catalogue of Aleocharinae Rove Beetles of Canada & Alaska: (Coleoptera, Staphylinidae, Aleocharinae) 2007. (Faunistica Ser.: 65). (Illus.). 200p. (Orig.). pap. 117.50 (978-954-642-294-1(0)) Pensoft Pubs. BGR. Dist: Coronet Bks.

Hanley, Guy A., et al. Carrion Beetles of North Dakota: Including Descriptions & Identification Keys for the Entire North American Silphid Fauna. 2007. pap. (978-0-9619635-3-8(0)) Minot State Univ.

Jolivet, Pierre. Memoires Entomologiques: Paramemoires D'un Timarchophile. 2006. (FRE., Illus.). 346p. pap. 57.50 (978-954-642-264-4(9)) Pensoft Pubs. BGR. Dist: Coronet Bks.

Kaspin, Ruth, intro. Living Jewels 2: The Magical Design of Beetles. 2007. (Illus.). 111p. 45.00 (978-3-7913-3777-7(7)) Prestel Publishing.

Klimaszewski, Jan. Biodiversity, Biosystematics & Ecology of Canadian Coleoptera. Majka, Christopher G., ed. 2008. (ZooKeys Ser.). (Illus.). 402p. pap. 187.50 (978-954-642-451-8(X)) Pensoft Pubs. BGR. Dist: Coronet Bks.

Kotze, Johan, ed. Carabid Beetles as Bioindicatators: Biogeographical, Ecological & Environmental Studies. 2011. (ZooKeys Ser.). (Illus.). 573p. pap. 375.00 (978-954-642-590-4(7)) Pensoft Pubs. BGR. Dist: Coronet Bks.

Labeyrie, V. The Ecology of Bruchids Attacking Legumes (Pulses) 2010. (Series Entomologica Ser.). 252p. pap. 249.00 (978-90-481-8525-2(4), 9048185254) Springer.

Lake, P. Sam. Drought & Aquatic Ecosystems: Effects & Responses. 2011. (ENG., Illus.). 400p. 89.95 (978-1-4051-8560-8(0), Wiley-Blackwell) Wiley, John & Sons, Inc.

Leschen, Richard, et al, eds. Volume 2: Morphology & Systematics (Elateroidea, Bostrichiformia, Cucujiformia Partim) Morphology & Systematics (Elateroidea, Bostrichiformia, Cucujiformia Partim) 2010. (ENG., Illus.). XIII, 786p. 347.00 (978-3-11-019075-5(3)) De Gruyter, Walter Inc.

Leschen, Richard A. B., et al, eds. Volume 2: Morphology & Systematics (Elateroidea, Bostrichiformia, Cucujiformia Partim) Morphology & Systematics (Elateroidea, Bostrichiformia, Cucujiformia Partim) 2010. (ENG.). XIII, 786p. 517.00 (978-3-11-180737-9(1)) De Gruyter, Walter Inc.

Lingafelter, Steven. Illustrated Key to the Longhorned Woodboring Beetles of the Eastern United States. 2007. (Illus.). 206p. spiral bd. 65.00 (978-0-9726087-7-0(X)) Coleopterists Society, The.

Löbl, I. & Smetana, A., eds. Catalogue of Palaearctic Coleoptera Vol. 4: Elateroidea, Derodontoidea, Bostrichoidea, Lymexyloidea, Cleroidea & Cucujoidea. 2007. 935p. 216.00 (978-87-88757-67-5(6)) Apollo Bks. DNK. Dist: International Specialized Bk. Services.

Löbl, I. & Smetana, A., eds. Catalogue of Palaearctic Coleoptera Vol. 7: Curculionoidea I. 2011. 373p. 112.00 (978-87-88757-93-4(5)) Apollo Bks. DNK. Dist: International Specialized Bk. Services.

Löbl, I. & Smetana, A., eds. Catalogue of Palaearctic Coleoptera - Cerambycidae, Megalopodidae, Orsodacnidae, Bruchidae, & Chrysomelidae 5, Vol. 6. 2010. (Catalogue of Palaearctic Coleoptera Ser.: 5). 924p. 216.00 (978-87-88757-84-2(6)) Apollo Bks. DNK. Dist: International Specialized Bk. Services.

Löbl, Ivan & Smetana, Ales. Catalogue of Palaearctic Coleoptera. 2008. (Illus.). 140.00 (978-87-88757-71-2(4)) Apollo Bks. DNK. Dist: International Specialized Bk. Services.

Majka, Christopher G., ed. Biodiversity, Biosystematics, & Ecology of Canadian Coleoptera II: (Illustrated) 2009. (ZooKeys Ser.). (Illus.). 372p. pap. 162.50 (978-954-642-513-3(3)) Pensoft Pubs. BGR. Dist: Coronet Bks.

Mountain Pine Beetle: Strategies for Protecting the West: Joint Oversight Hearing Before the Subcommittee on Water & Power Joint with the Subcommittee on National Parks, Forests, & Public Lands of the Committee on Natural Resources, U.S. House of Representatives, One Hundred Eleventh Congress, First Session, Tuesday, June 16, 2009. 2009. (Illus.). vi, 124p. (978-0-16-085147-6(5), 552-070-40501-1) United States Government Printing Office.

New, T. R. Beetle Conservation. 2007. (Illus.). 94p. 99.00 (978-1-4020-5987-2(6)) Springer.

—Beetles in Conservation. 2010. (ENG., Illus.). 248p. 99.95 (978-1-4443-3259-9(7), Wiley-Blackwell) Wiley, John & Sons, Inc.

New, T. R., ed. Beetle Conservation. 2010. vi, 94p. pap. 99.00 (978-90-481-7496-6(1), 9048174961) Springer.

Nikiforuk, Andrew. Empire of the Beetle: How Human Folly & a Tiny Bug Are Killing North America's Great Forests. 2011. (ENG., Illus.). 240p. pap. 17.95 (978-1-55365-510-7(9), Greystone Bks.) D&M Pubs. Inc. CAN. Dist: Perseus-PGW.

Osella, Giuseppe & Bellò, Cesare. Revisione Di Minyops Schoenherr, 1823 e Faraminyops Nov. Gen. (Coleoptera, Curculionidae, Molytinae) 2010. (ITA., Illus.). 133p. (978-88-89230-11-4(8)) Museo Storia Naturale.

Oversight Hearing Concerning the Mountain Pine Beetle Epidemic in the Western United States: Hearing Before a Subcommittee of the Committee on Appropriations, United States Senate, One Hundred Tenth Congress, Second Session, Special Hearing, May 5, 2008, Eagle, CO. 2010. iii, 65p. (978-0-16-085055-4(X), 552-070-40412-1) United States Government Printing Office.

Petrillo, Holly A. Carabid Beetle Activity-Density & Diversity in Northern Hardwood Forests. 2008. 116p. pap. (978-3-8364-7426-9(3)) VDM Verlag Dr. Mueller e.K.

Preston-Mafham, Ken, et al. Complete Identifier Bugs, Beetles, Spiders, Snakes. 2010. (ENG.). 224p. 9.99 (978-0-7858-1852-6(9), 0785818529, Chartwell) Book Sales, Inc.

Redondo, V. M. Geometridae Ibericae. 2008. 670p. 172.00 (978-87-88757-69-9(2)) Apollo Bks. DNK. Dist: International Specialized Bk. Services.

Rucker, W. Coleoptera of Europe Vol. 1: Latridiidae, Merophysiidae & Casyceridae. Wagner, T., ed. 2012. 600p. 140.00 (978-87-88757-83-5(8)) Apollo Bks. DNK. Dist: International Specialized Bk. Services.

Rye, Edward Caldwell. British Beetles: An introduction to the study of our indigenous Coleoptera. 2010. (ENG., Illus.). 370p. pap. 32.75 (978-1-177-63078-8(8)) BiblioBazaar.

Simmons, Leigh. W & Ridsdill-Smith, T. James, eds. Ecology & Evolution of Dung Beetles. 2011. (ENG., Illus.). 368p. 124.95 (978-1-4443-3315-2(1), Wiley-Blackwell) Wiley, John & Sons, Inc.

United States, Government Accountability Office Staff, contrib. by. Invasive Forest Pests. 2006. (Illus.). 92p. 125.00 (978-1-60021-461-5(4)) Nova Science Pubs., Inc.

BEETON, MRS. (ISABELLA MARY), 1836-1865

Cohen, David. Mrs Beeton's Best Bits. 2007. (Illus.). 160p. (978-0-907633-21-1(8)) Psychology News Pr. Ltd.

BEETS AND BEET SUGAR

Donato, Ruben. Mexicans & Hispanos in Colorado Schools & Communities, 1920-1960. 2007. (Illus.). 180p. 55.00 (978-0-7914-6967-5(0)) State Univ. of New York Pr.

Fleischmann, Charles Louis. Memorial of Charles Louis Fleischmann on. 2006. pap. 15.95 (978-1-4286-5466-2(6)) Kessinger Publishing, LLC.

Grant E. B. Beet-Root Sugar & Cultivation of the Beet. 2008. 164p. 22.99 (978-0-554-51604-2(7)); 25.99 (978-0-554-51592-2(X)); pap. 21.75 (978-0-554-51594-6(6)); pap. 20.75 (978-0-554-51599-1(7)) BiblioBazaar.

—Beet-Root Sugar & Cultivation of the Beet. 2009. 98p. pap. (978-0-217-72791-4(3)) Books LLC.

—Beet-Root Sugar & Cultivation of the Beet. 2006. 160p. per. 18.99 (978-1-4255-1197-5(X)) MPublishing.

Hertsburg, Claus T. Sugar Beet Crops: Growth, Fertilization & Yield. 2009. (Agriculture Issues & Policies Ser.). 89.00 *(978-1-60741-491-9(0))* Nova Science Pubs., Inc.

Mandere, Nicodemus. Sugar Beet Cultivation in Keny. 2011. 60p. pap. ***(978-3-8443-2298-9(1))***; 72p. pap. ***(978-3-8433-9253-2(6))*** Lambert Academic Publishing.

Neelwarne, Bhagyalakshmi, ed. Red Beet Biotechnology: Food & Pharmaceutical Applications. 2012. (ENG., Illus.). xii, 448p. 209.00 ***(978-1-4614-3457-3(2)***, 1461434572) Springer.

Wang, Quanzeng. Biomethanol Conversion from Sugar Beet Pulp. 2008. 112p. pap. *(978-3-639-09120-5(5))* VDM Verlag Dr. Mueller e.K.

BEGGING
see also Tramps; Vagrancy

Adetunji, Micheal Adekola. Spatial Pattern of Street Begging in Nigeri. 2011. 88p. pap. ***(978-3-8454-0022-8(6))*** Lambert Academic Publishing.

Hermer, Joe. Policing Compassion: Begging, Law & Power in Public Spaces. Young, Richard, ed. 2013. (ENG.). 224p. 70.00 *(978-1-84113-269-3(1))* Hart Publishing Ltd. GBR. Dist: International Specialized Bk. Services.

Hitchcock. Down & Out in 18th-Century London. 2007. (ENG., Illus.). 360p. 29.95 *(978-1-85285-552-9(5)*, Hambledon Continuum) Continuum International Publishing Group, Ltd. GBR. Dist: National Bk. Network.

Mäkinen, Virpi & Pessi, Anne Birgitta. Kerjääminen Ellen Ja Tänään: Historiallisia, Oikeudellisia Ja Sosiaalipoliittisia Näkökulmia Kerjäämiseen. 2009. (FIN., Illus.). 307p. pap. *(978-951-768-251-0(4))* Vastapaino, Osuuskunta.

BEGHARDS
see also Beguines

Beguines & Beghards: Beghards & Beguines, Marguerite Porete, Heggbach Abbey, Heresy of the Free Spirit, the Mirror of Simple Souls. 2010. 64p. pap. 14.14 *(978-1-156-69537-1(6))* General Bks. LLC.

BEGINNING
see also Causation; Creation; Space and Time

Bojowald, Martin. Once Before Time: A Whole Story of the Universe. (Vintage Ser.). (ENG., Illus.). 320p. 2011. pap. 16.00 *(978-0-307-47455-1(0)*, Vintage) 2010. 27.95 *(978-0-307-27285-0(0)*, Knopf) Knopf Doubleday Publishing Group.

Frampton, Paul H. Did Time Begin? Will Time End? 2009. 116p. 32.00 *(978-981-4280-58-7(5))* World Scientific Publishing Co., Inc.

Frank, Adam. About Time: Cosmology & Culture at the Twilight of the Big Bang. 2011. (ENG.). 320p. 26.00 *(978-1-4391-6959-9(4)*, Free Pr.) Free Pr.

Haarsma, Deborah B. & Haarsma, Loren D. Origins: A Reformed Look at Creation, Design, & Evolution. 2007. *(978-1-59255-227-6(7))* Faith Alive Christian Resources.

—Origins: Christian Perspectives on Creation, Evolution, & Intelligent Design. 2nd ed. 2011. *(978-1-59255-573-4(X))* Faith Alive Christian Resources.

Krauss, Lawrence M. A Universe from Nothing: Why There Is Something Rather Than Nothing. 2012. (ENG., Illus.). 224p. 24.99 *(978-1-4516-2445-8(X)*, Free Pr.) Free Pr.

López, Ricardo O. The Origin of the Universe & Life: A Puzzle for Science & Theology. 2007. *(978-1-59835-043-2(9))* Cambridge BrickHouse, Inc.

Nagel, Thomas. Mind & Cosmos: Why the Materialist Neo-Darwinian Conception of Nature Is Almost Certainly False. 2012. (ENG.). 144p. 24.95 ***(978-0-19-991975-8(5))*** Oxford Univ. Pr., Inc.

O'Byrne, Anne. Natality & Finitude. 2010. (Studies in Continental Thought Ser.). (ENG., Illus.). 218p. 65.00 *(978-0-253-35531-7(1)*, 0253355311); pap. 22.95 *(978-0-253-22241-1(9)*, 0253222419) Indiana Univ. Pr.

BEGINNING TEACHERS
see First Year Teachers

BEGINNINGS (RHETORIC)
see Openings (Rhetoric)

BEGONIAS

Larter, Jack. Tuberous Begonias: An Essential Guide, 1 vol. 2011. (ENG., Illus.). 112p. 29.95 ***(978-1-84797-231-6(4))*** Crowood Pr., Ltd. GBR. Dist: Independent Pubs. Group.

Van Den Berg, Maaike, ed. Growing Tuberous Begonias. (Illus.). 40p. pap. *(978-0-646-25040-3(X))* Florilegium AUS. Dist: Vine Hse. Distribution.

BEGUINES
see also Beghards

Beguines & Beghards: Beghards & Beguines, Marguerite Porete, Heggbach Abbey, Heresy of the Free Spirit, the Mirror of Simple Souls. 2010. 64p. pap. 14.14 *(978-1-156-69537-1(6))* General Bks. LLC.

Brown, Jennifer. Three Women of Liege: A Critical Edition of & Commentary on the Middle English Lives of Elizabeth of Spalbeek, Christina Mirabilis, & Marie D'Oignies. 2009. (Medieval Women Texts & Contexts Ser.). (ENG & ENM.). 350p. (C). 123.00 *(978-2-503-52471-9(0))* Brepols Pubs. BEL. Dist: ISD.

Burnham, Louisa A. So Great a Light, So Great a Smoke: The Beguin Heretics of Languedoc. 2008. (Conjunctions of Religion & Power in the Medieval Past Ser.). (Illus.). 217p. 39.95 *(978-0-8014-4131-8(5))* Cornell Univ. Pr.

Huls, J. The Minne-Journey. Beatrice of Nazareth's 'Seuen Maniren van Minne'. Mystical Process & Mystagogical Process. 2012. (Fiery Arrow Ser.). (ENG.). 306p. (C). pap. 39.00 *(978-90-429-2189-4(7))* Peeters Pubs. & Booksellers BEL. Dist: Brown, David Bk. Co., The.

Mannaerts, P. Beghinae in cantu Instructae: Musical patrimony from Flemish beguinages (Middle Ages - Late 18th C.) 2010. (Epitome Musical Ser.). (ENG & LAT., Illus.). 296p. (C). pap. 80.00 ***(978-2-503-53015-4(X))*** Brepols Pubs. BEL. Dist: ISD.

von der Osten-Sacken, Vera. Jakob von Vitrys 'Vita Mariae Oigniacensis' Zu Herkunft und Eigenart der ersten Beginen. 2010. (Veroffentlichungen des Instituts fur Europaische Geschichte Mainz - Beihefte Abendlandische Religionsgeschichte Ser.). (GER.). 270p. (C). 68.00 *(978-3-525-10102-5(3))* Vandenhoeck & Ruprecht GmbH & Co. KG DEU. Dist: ISD.

BEHAN, BRENDAN, 1923-1964

Behan, Brendan. Borstal Boy. Meyer-Clason, Curt, tr. (GER.). 422p. pap. *(978-3-462-02544-6(9))* Kiepenheuer & Witsch GmbH & Company KG DEU. Dist: International Bk. Import Service, Inc.

BEHAVIOR
see Conduct of Life; Etiquette

BEHAVIOR (PSYCHOLOGY)
see Human Behavior

BEHAVIOR, ANIMAL
see Animal Behavior

BEHAVIOR, COMPARATIVE
see Psychology, Comparative

BEHAVIOR, COMPULSIVE
see Compulsive Behavior

BEHAVIOR, CONSUMER
see Consumer Behavior

BEHAVIOR, HELPING
see Helping Behavior

BEHAVIOR, NURTURING
see Nurturing Behavior

BEHAVIOR, OPERANT
see Operant Behavior

BEHAVIOR, STEREOTYPED (PSYCHIATRY)
see Stereotyped Behavior (Psychiatry)

BEHAVIOR, TYPE A
see Type A Behavior

BEHAVIOR, VERBAL
see Verbal Behavior

BEHAVIOR ASSESSMENT
see Behavioral Assessment

BEHAVIOR DISORDERS IN CHILDREN
see also Attention-Deficit Hyperactivity Disorder; Autism; Problem Children

Appelbaum, Maryln. How to Handle Hard-to-Handle Preschoolers: A Guide for Early Childhood Educators. 2009. (Illus.). 136p. pap. 24.95 *(978-1-4129-7003-7(2)*, B00720P) Corwin Pr.

—How to Handle the Hard-to-Handle Student, K-5. 2008. 136p. 66.95 *(978-1-4129-6438-8(5)*, B64385C); pap. 27.95 *(978-1-4129-6439-5(3)*, B64385P) Corwin Pr.

—The One-Stop Guide to Implementing RTI: Academic & Behavioral Interventions, K-12. 2008. (Illus.). 160p. 66.95 *(978-1-4129-6444-9(X)*, B64449C); pap. 27.95 *(978-1-4129-6445-6(8)*, B64449P) Corwin Pr.

Asher, Michael J., et al. The Behavior Problems Resource Kit: Forms & Procedures for Identification, Measurement, & Intervention. 2010. (Illus.). 248p. pap. 49.95 *(978-0-87822-633-7(8))* Research Pr.

Attaway, Kenny. Potholes in my Lawn: (175 & More Effective Group Activities for Troubled Adolescent & Teens) 2010. 264p. 31.99 *(978-1-4520-8802-0(0))*; pap. 18.49 *(978-1-4520-8801-3(2))* AuthorHouse.

Augustyn, Marilyn C., et al, eds. The Zuckerman Parker Handbook of Developmental & Behavioral Pediatrics for Primary Care. 3rd rev. ed. 2010. (ENG., Illus.). 560p. pap. 74.99 *(978-1-60831-914-5(8))* Lippincott Williams & Wilkins.

Austin, Vance L. & Sciarra, Daniel T. Children & Adolescents with Emotional & Behavioral Disorders. 2009. (ENG.). 504p. (C). pap. 123.60 *(978-0-205-50175-2(1)*, Prentice Hall) Prentice Hall PTR.

Baker, Jed. No More Meltdowns: Positive Strategies for Dealing with & Preventing Out-of-Control Behavior. 2008. (ENG.). 150p. pap. 14.95 *(978-1-932565-62-1(0))* Future Horizons, Inc.

Beidel, Deborah C. & Alfano, Candice. Child Anxiety Disorders: Research & Treatment. 2nd rev. ed. 2011. (ENG., Illus.). 544p. instr.'s gde. ed. 52.95 *(978-0-415-87373-4(8))* Routledge.

Beitchman, Joseph H., et al, eds. Language, Learning, & Behavior Disorders: Developmental, Biological, & Clinical Perspectives. 2006. (ENG., Illus.). 604p. pap. 116.00 *(978-0-521-03133-2(8))* Cambridge Univ. Pr.

Benaroch, Roy. Solving Health & Behavioral Problems from Birth Through Preschool: A Parent's Guide. 2007. (Praeger Series on Contemporary Health & Living Ser.). (Illus.). 208p. 44.95 *(978-0-275-99347-4(7)*, C9347, Praeger Pubs.) Greenwood Publishing Group, Inc.

Blythe, Sally Goddard, et al. Attention, Balance, & Coordination: The A. B. C. of Learning Success. 2009. (ENG., Illus.). 442p. pap. 74.95 *(978-0-470-51623-2(2)*, Wiley) Wiley, John & Sons, Inc.

Brock, Stephen E., et al. Identifying, Assessing, & Treating ADHD at School. 2009. (Developmental Psychopathology at School Ser.). (ENG.). xi, 168p. 149.00 *(978-1-4419-0500-0(6)*, 1441905006) Springer.

Bruce, Timothy J. & Jongsma, Arthur E. Evidence-Based Treatment Planning for Disruptive Child & Adolescent Behavior. 2011. (Evidence-Based Psychotherapy Treatment Planning Video Ser.: 36). (ENG.). 66p. pap., wbk. ed. 29.00 *(978-0-470-56850-7(X)*, Wiley) Wiley, John & Sons, Inc.

Burks, Harold F. Diagnosis & Remediation Practices for Troubled School Children. 2008. (ENG.). 350p. 145.00 *(978-1-57886-656-4(1))*; per. 69.95 *(978-1-57886-706-6(1))* Rowman & Littlefield Publishers, Inc.

Byrne, Brendan. Coping with Bullying in Schools. (Illus.). 96p. (Orig.). pap. *(978-0-304-33071-3(X)*, Burns & Oates) Continuum International Publishing Group, Ltd.

Chinn, Steve. Addressing the Unproductive Classroom Behaviours of Students with Special Needs. 2010. (ENG., Illus.). 128p. pap. *(978-1-84905-050-0(3))* Kingsley, Jessica Ltd.

Christie, Phil, et al. Understanding Pathological Demand Avoidance Syndrome in Children: A Guide for Parents, Teachers & Other Professionals. 2011. (ENG.). 192p. pap. ***(978-1-84905-074-6(0))*** Kingsley, Jessica Ltd.

Clarke, D. Aubrey's Journey. 2006. 274p. pap. 27.95 *(978-1-4241-1572-3(8))* PublishAmerica, Inc.

Cobert, Josiane. 100 Questions & Answers about Your Child's Obsessive Compulsive Disorder. 2009. (ENG.). 180p. pap. 22.95 *(978-0-7637-7154-6(6))* Jones & Bartlett Learning, LLC.

Cole, Ted, et al, eds. The Routledge International Handbook of Emotional & Behavioural Difficulties. 2012. (ENG., Illus.). 384p. (C). 190.00 *(978-0-415-58463-0(9))* Routledge.

Cook, Mary N. & with Invited Contributors. Transforming Behavior: Training Parents & Kids Together with CD-ROM. 2012. 384p. pap. 69.95 ***(978-1-59857-216-2(4))*** Brookes, Paul H. Publishing Co.

Copley, Anne. Challenging Behaviour: A Fresh Look at Promoting Positive Learning Behaviours. 2006. (ENG., Illus.). 112p. 39.95 *(978-1-85539-217-5(8)*, Network Continuum Education) Continuum International Publishing Group, Ltd. GBR. Dist: National Bk. Network.

Cram101 Textbook Reviews. Outlines & Highlights for Abnormal Child & Adolescent Psychology by Rita Wicks-Nelson, Allen C Israel, Isbn: 9780132359788. 2010. (Illus.). 166p. pap. 29.95 *(978-1-61698-739-8(1))* Cram101 Inc.

—Outlines & Highlights for Assessment of Childhood Disorders by Eric J Mash. 2011. 162p. pap. 29.95 ***(978-1-61905-143-0(5))*** Cram101 Inc.

—Outlines & Highlights for School-Based Interventions for Students with Behavior Problems by Julie Bowen. 2011. 58p. pap. 26.95 ***(978-1-61905-368-7(3))*** Cram101 Inc.

Cram101 Textbook Reviews & Cram101 Textbook Reviews. Outlines & Highlights for Antisocial Behavior in Schools: Evidence-Based Practices by Hill M. Walker. 2011. 78p. pap. 27.95 ***(978-1-61830-671-5(5))*** Cram101 Inc.

—Outlines & Highlights for Handbook of Positive Behavior Support by Wayne Sailor, Isbn: 9780387096315. 2011. 180p. pap. 29.95 ***(978-1-61461-047-2(9))*** Cram101 Inc.

—Outlines & Highlights for Oppositional Defiant Disorder & Conduct Disorder in Childhood by Walter Matthys, Isbn: 9780470682319. 2011. 66p. pap. 27.95 ***(978-1-61461-082-3(7))*** Cram101 Inc.

—Outlines & Highlights for Social Behavior & Skills in Children by Johnny L Matson. 2011. 208p. pap. 30.95 ***(978-1-61830-296-0(5))*** Cram101 Inc.

—Outlines & Highlights for Treatment of Childhood Disorders by Eric Mash, Isbn: 9781572309210. 2011. 528p. pap. 38.95 ***(978-1-61461-094-6(0))*** Cram101 Inc.

Cram101 Textbook Reviews Staff. Outlines & Highlights for Behavior Disorders of Childhood by Wicks-Nelson, Isbn: 0131539086. 2008. 96p. pap. 10.95 *(978-1-4288-5937-1(3))* Cram101 Inc.

—Outlines & Highlights for Child Psychopathology by Haugaard, Isbn: 9780073405506. 2008. 160p. pap. 12.95 *(978-1-4288-6013-1(4))* Cram101 Inc.

—Outlines & Highlights for Children & Adolescents with Emotional & Behavioral Disorders by VanCe L Austin, Isbn: 9780205501762. 2009. 118p. pap. 28.95 *(978-1-4288-8818-0(7))* Cram101 Inc.

Creed, Torrey A., et al. Cognitive Therapy for Adolescents in School Settings. 2011. (Guilford Practical Intervention in Schools Ser.). (ENG.). 173p. (gr. 6-12). pap. 35.00 *(978-1-60918-133-8(6))* Guilford Pubns., Inc.

Cross, Melanie. Children with Social, Emotional & Behavioural Difficulties & Communication Problems: There Is Always a Reason. 2nd rev. ed. 2011. (ENG., Illus.). 208p. pap. ***(978-1-84905-129-3(1))*** Kingsley, Jessica Ltd.

Culotta, Vincent P., et al. School Success for Kids with Emotional & Behavioral Disorders. 2010. (ENG.). 250p. pap. 16.95 *(978-1-59363-431-5(5))* Prufrock Pr.

Curtis, Steven E. Understanding Your Child's Puzzling Behavior: A Guide for Parents of Children with Behavioral, Social, & Learning Challenges. 2008. (Illus.). 160p. per. 14.95 *(978-0-9794982-0-6(1))* Lifrspan Pr.

Dodge, Kenneth A. & Rutter, Michael, eds. Gene-Environment Interactions in Developmental Psychopathology. 2011. (Duke Series in Child Develpment & Public Policy Ser.). (ENG.). 286p. 50.00 *(978-1-60623-518-8(4))* Guilford Pubns., Inc.

Durand, Mark V. & Hieneman, Meme. Helping Parents with Challenging Children: Positive Family Intervention. 2008. (Programs That Work Ser.). (ENG.). 144p. pap. 37.95 *(978-0-19-533298-8(9))* Oxford Univ. Pr., Inc.

Durand, V. Mark & Hieneman, Meme. Helping Parents with Challenging Children Positive Family Intervention Parent Workbook. 2008. (Programs That Work Ser.). (ENG.). 144p. pap. 27.95 *(978-0-19-533299-5(7))* Oxford Univ. Pr., Inc.

Durand, Vincent M. Optimistic Parenting: Hope & Help for You & Your Challenging Child. 2011. (Illus.). 336p. pap. 26.95 *(978-1-59857-052-6(8))* Brookes, Paul H. Publishing Co.

Easley, Jennifer & Glasser, Howard. Transforming the Difficult Child: True Stories of Triumph. 2008. 244p. pap. 24.95 *(978-0-9670507-9-9(0)*, Nurtured Heart Publications) Ctr. for the Difficult Child.

El-Sheikh, Mona, et al. Marital Conflict & Children's Externalizing Behavior: Interactions Between Parasympathetic & Sympathetic Nervous System Activity. 2009. (Monographs of the Society for Research in Child Development Ser.). (ENG., Illus.). 200p. pap. 39.95 *(978-1-4051-9942-1(3)*, Wiley-Blackwell) Wiley, John & Sons, Inc.

Ellis, Simon & Tod, Janet. Behaviour for Learning: Proactive Approaches to Behaviour Management. 2009. (ENG., Illus.). 310p. 150.00 *(978-0-415-49167-9(3))* Routledge.

Essa, Eva. What to Do When: Practical Guidance Strategies for Challenging Behaviors in the Preschool. 6th rev. ed. 2007. (ENG., Illus.). 448p. (C). pap. 68.95 *(978-1-4180-6716-8(4))* Delmar Cengage Learning.

Farrell, Michael. Educating Special Children. 2nd rev. ed. 2012. (ENG., Illus.). 344p. 180.00 ***(978-0-415-52369-1(9))***; pap. 51.95 ***(978-0-415-52370-7(2))*** Routledge.

—The Effective Teacher's Guide to Behavioural & Emotional Disord: Disruptive Behaviour Disorders, Anxiety Disorders, Depressive Disorders, & Attention Deficit Hyperactivity Disorder. 2nd rev. ed. 2011. (Effective Teacher's Guides). (ENG., Illus.). 136p. pap. 31.95 *(978-0-415-56568-4(5))* Routledge.

—The Effective Teacher's Guide to Behavioural & Emotional Disorders. 2nd rev. ed. 2011. (Effective Teacher's Guides). (ENG., Illus.). 136p. 112.00 *(978-0-415-56569-1(3))* Routledge.

Fattig, Michelle. A Prairie Day with Annie: Experience Attention Deficits Through the Eyes of a Child. 2007. (Illus.). 196p. (YA). (gr. 5-18). per. 14.99 *(978-0-9795805-1-2(X))* Flower by the Water Publishing.

Fern, Brad & Lutz, Tom. From Ashes to Gold: The Alchemy of Mentoring the Delinquent Boy. 2011. ***(978-1-59056-307-6(7))***; 203p. ***(978-1-59056-306-9(9))*** Lantern Bks.

Field, Andy, et al, eds. Child Anxiety Theory & Treatment: A Special Issue of Cognition & Emotion. 2009. (Special Issues of Cognition & Emotion Ser.). (ENG., Illus.). 176p. 79.95 *(978-1-84169-851-9(2)*, Psychology Press) Taylor & Francis Group GBR. Dist: Taylor & Francis Group.

Fine, Aubrey H. & Eisen, Cynthia J. Afternoons with Puppy: Inspirations from a Therapist & His Animals. 2007. (New Directions in the Human-Animal Bond Ser.). (Illus.). 201p. 24.95 *(978-1-55753-470-5(5))* Purdue Univ. Pr.

Foster, Evaline L. Implementation of a Social Skills Curriculum to Reduce Behavioral Problems of African American Boys in Elementary Classroom Settings. 2011. 92p. 24.99 ***(978-1-4628-5991-7(7))***; pap. 15.99 ***(978-1-4628-5990-0(9))*** Xlibris Corp.

Frank Barnhill. Mistaken for ADHD: How You Can Prevent Mislabeling Your Child as a Failure in Life in the Face of a Looming ADHD Misdiagnosis. 2010. 380p. pap. 24.95 *(978-1-4502-1428-5(2))* iUniverse, Inc.

Frick, Paul J., et al. Clinical Assessment of Child & Adolescent Personality & Behavior. 3rd ed. 2009. (ENG. Illus.). xi, 500p. 99.00 *(978-0-387-89642-7(2)*, 0387896422) Springer.

Friedman, Helen D. & Revera, Paulina K., eds. Abnormal Psychology: New Research. 2008. 89.00 *(978-1-60692-636-9(5))* Nova Science Pubs., Inc.

Gallico, Robin P., et al. Emotional & Behavioral Problems in Children with Learning Disabilities. 2nd ed. (Illus.). 192p. (Orig.). (C). pap. 2000.00 *(978-1-879105-73-7(X)*, A026, Singular) Delmar Cengage Learning.

Gold, Claudia M. Keeping Your Child in Mind: Overcoming Defiance, Tantrums, & Other Everyday Behavior Problems by Seeing the World Through Your Child's Eyes. 2011. (Merloyd Lawrence Book Ser.). (ENG.). 240p. pap. 15.00 *(978-0-7382-1485-6(X))* Da Capo Pr., Inc.

Greene, Ross W. The Explosive Child: A New Approach for Understanding & Parenting Easily Frustrated, Chronically Inflexible Children. 2010. (ENG.). 336p. pap. 14.99 *(978-0-06-190619-0(0)*, HarperPerennial) HarperCollins Pubs.

—Lost at School: Why Our Kids with Behavioral Challenges are Falling Through the Cracks & How We Can Help Them. (ENG.). 320p. 2009. pap. 16.00 *(978-1-4165-7227-5(9))* 2008. 26.00 *(978-1-4165-7226-8(0))* Scribner. (Scribner).

Greenspan, Stanley I. & Glovinsky, Cindy. Children & Babies with Mood Swings: New Insights for Parents & Professionals. 2007. (ENG.). 120p. pap. 24.95 *(978-0-9767758-5-0(9))* Interdisciplinary Council on Developmental & Learning Disorders.

Gullotta, Thomas P. & Blau, Gary. Handbook of Childhood Behavioral Issues: Evidence-Based Approaches to Prevention & Treatment. 2007. (ENG., Illus.). 432p. 125.00 *(978-0-415-95461-7(4))* Routledge.

Hirschland, Deborah. Collaborative Intervention in Early Childhood: Consulting with Parents & Teachers of 3- To 7-Year-Olds. 2008. (ENG., Illus.). 320p. 36.99 *(978-0-19-533120-2(6))* Oxford Univ. Pr., Inc.

Hobson, Peter N., et al, eds. Foundations for Self-Awareness: An Exploration Through Autism. 2006. (Monographs of the Society for Research in Child Development Ser.). (ENG., Illus.). 200p. pap. 38.95 *(978-1-4051-6722-2(X)*, Wiley-Blackwell) Wiley, John & Sons, Inc.

Hoffer, Abram. Healing Children's Attention & Behavior Disorders: Complementary Nutritional & Psychological Treatments. 2011. (Professional Edition Ser.). (ENG.). 368p. 49.95 ***(978-1-897025-41-3(6))*** Canadian College of Naturopathic Medicine Pr. CAN. Dist: SCB Distributors.

Howard, Mary. RTI from All Sides: What Every Teacher Needs to Know. 2009. 160p. pap. 23.13 *(978-0-325-02670-1(X)*, E02670) Heinemann.

Howell, Donna, ed. Bad Children Can Happen to Good Parents: A Survival Manual for Parents of Difficult Children. 2007. 157p. pap. 19.95 *(978-0-9792476-0-6(8))* VG Pr.

Hughes, Tammy L., et al. Identifying, Assessing, & Treating Conduct Disorder at School. 2010. (Developmental Psychopathology at School Ser.). x, 156p. pap. 59.95 *(978-1-4419-4499-3(0)*, 1441944990) Springer.

Hughes, William H. Raise Winning Kids Without a Fight: The Power of Personal Choice. 2009. (ENG., Illus.). 184p. 40.00 *(978-0-8018-9339-1(9))*; pap. 15.95 *(978-0-8018-9340-7(2))* Johns Hopkins Univ. Pr.

Johansen Psy.D., Thor M. Disruptive Kids: A Guide for Parents. 2008. 192p. pap. 18.95 *(978-1-4343-6293-3(0))* AuthorHouse.

Jongsma, Arthur E. & Bruce, Timothy J. Treatment Planning for Disruptive Child & Adolescent Behavior. 2011. (Evidence-Based Psychotherapy Treatment Planning Video Ser.: 7). (ENG.). mass mkt. 40.00 *(978-0-470-41789-8(7))*; (Illus.). 64p. pap., wbk. ed. 25.00 *(978-0-470-56858-3(5))*;Set. mass mkt., wbk. ed. 55.25 *(978-1-118-02894-0(5))* Wiley, John & Sons, Inc. (Wiley).

Kauffman, James. Working with Troubled Children. 2009. 158p. pap. 19.00 *(978-1-57861-678-7(6))* Attainment Co., Inc.

Kauffman, James M. & Landrum, Timothy J. Cases in Emotional & Behavioral Disorders of Children & Youth. 2nd ed. 2008. (ENG.). 128p. (C). pap. 20.80 *(978-0-13-500263-6(X))* Prentice Hall Higher Education.

—Cases in Emotional & Behavioral Disorders of Children & Youth. 3rd rev. ed. 2012. (ENG.). 112p. (C). pap. 20.80 ***(978-0-13-268466-8(7)***, Prentice Hall) Prentice Hall PTR.

—Characteristics of Emotional & Behavioral Disorders of Children & Youth. (ENG., Illus.). (C). 9th ed. 2008. 544p. 133.33 *(978-0-13-227514-9(7))* 10th rev. ed. 2012. 480p. 133.33 ***(978-0-13-265808-9(9))*** Prentice Hall PTR. (Prentice Hall).

Kauffman, James M. & Landrum, Timothy J. Characteristics of Emotional & Behavioral Disorders of Children & Youth, Student Value Edition. 10th ed. 2012. (ENG.). 528p. (C). ring bd. 86.67 ***(978-0-13-300789-3(8)***, Prentice Hall) Prentice Hall PTR.

Kazdin, Alan E. Parent Management Training: Treatment for Oppositional, Aggressive, & Antisocial Behavior in Children & Adolescents. 2008. (ENG., Illus.). 424p. pap. 29.95 *(978-0-19-538600-4(0))* Oxford Univ. Pr., Inc.

Kearney, Christopher A. Casebook in Child Behavior Disorders. 4th ed. 2009. (ENG.). 224p. (C). pap. 84.95 *(978-0-495-60441-9(0))* Wadsworth.

Kelso, Chandrika. Domestic Violence & Problem Behaviors among Children. 2009. 140p. pap. *(978-3-639-19213-1(3))* VDM Verlag Dr. Mueller e.K.

Kendall, Anne & DeGangi, Georgia A. Effective Parenting for the Hard-to-Manage Child: A Skills-Based Book. 2007. (ENG., Illus.). 304p. per. 24.95 *(978-0-415-95546-1(7))* Routledge.

Kerr, Mary M. & Nelson, C. Michael. Strategies for Addressing Behavior Problems in the Classroom. 6th ed. 2009. (ENG.). 448p. (C). pap. 120.80 *(978-0-13-604524-3(3)*, Prentice Hall) Prentice Hall PTR.

Kourkoutas, Elias E., ed. Behavioral Disorders in Children: Ecosystemic Psychodynamic Interventions within the Family & School Context. 2011. (Children's Issues, Laws & Programs Ser.). 140.00 ***(978-1-61470-718-9(9))*** Nova Science Pubs., Inc.

Kutaka-Kennedy, Joy. Inclusion in General Education Classes. 2009. 156p. pap. *(978-3-639-04139-2(9))* VDM Verlag Dr. Mueller e.K.

Kutscher, Martin L. & Kutscher, Martin. Kids with A Syndrome Mix of Adhd, Ld, As. 2nd ed. 2007. (ENG., Illus.). 24p. pap. *(978-1-84310-811-5(9))* Kingsley, Jessica Ltd.

Lane & Gresham & O'Shaughnessy & Cram101 Textbook Reviews Staff. Interventions for Children with or at Risk for Emotional & Behavioral Disorders. 2007. 104p. per. 10.95 *(978-1-4288-2018-0(3))* Cram101 Inc.

Lane, Kathleen Lynne, et al. Managing Challenging Behaviors in Schools: Research-Based Strategies That Work. 2010. (What Works for Special-Needs Learners Ser.). (ENG., Illus.). 255p. (gr. k-12). pap. 35.00 *(978-1-60623-951-3(1))* Guilford Pubns., Inc.

Larmar, Stephen. Early Intervention & Prevention of Conduct Problems in Children. 2011. 144p. pap. ***(978-3-8433-5394-6(8))*** Lambert Academic Publishing.

Laurence, Jennifer & McCallum, David. Inside the Child's Head: Histories of Childhood Behavioural Disorders. 2009. 136p. *(978-90-8790-701-3(X))*; pap. *(978-90-8790-700-6(1))* Sense Pubs.

Lavoie, Henri. Not Me Not Ever the Road Map of an Oppo. 2007. pap. 12.95 *(978-1-59800-996-5(6))* Outskirts Pr., Inc.

Leedom, Liane J. Just Like His Father? A Guide to Overcoming Your Child's Genetic Connection to Antisocial Behavior, Addiction & ADHD. 2006. per. 14.95 *(978-0-9778013-0-5(6))* Health & Well-Being Pubns., LLC.

Lochman, John E., et al. Coping Power: Child Group Facilitator's Guide, 2 vols. 2008. (Treatments That Work Ser.). (ENG.). 288p. (C). pap. 57.95 *(978-0-19-532787-8(X))* Oxford Univ. Pr., Inc.

Long, Rob. Intervention Toolbox: For Social, Emotional & Behavioural Difficulties. 2008. (Lucky Duck Bks.). 120p. pap. 51.00 *(978-1-4129-4605-6(0)*, B46050P) SAGE Pubns., Ltd. GBR. Dist: SAGE Pubns., Inc.

Luce, Stephen C. & Smith, Angela F. How to Support Children with Problem Behavior. 2007. viii, 50p. pap. 14.00 *(978-1-4164-0148-3(2))* PRO-ED, Inc.

Luiselli, James K., ed. The Handbook of High-Risk Challenging Behaviors in People with Intellectual & Developmental Disabilities. 2011. 320p. pap. 49.95 ***(978-1-59857-168-4(0))*** Brookes, Paul H. Publishing Co.

Manassis, Kathar & Manassis, Katharina. Cognitive Behavioral Therapy with Children: A Guide for the Community Practitioner. 2009. (ENG., Illus.). 288p. pap. 44.95 *(978-0-415-99670-9(8))* Routledge.

Martin, Conrad. Dyslexia: Reading, Learning & Behaviour. 2007. 320p. pap. *(978-0-470-01959-7(X)*, Wiley-Blackwell) Wiley, John & Sons, Ltd.

Mash, Eric J. & Barkley, Russell A., eds. Assessment of Childhood Disorders. 4th rev. ed. 2007. (ENG., Illus.). 866p. 90.00 *(978-1-59385-493-5(5))* Guilford Pubns., Inc.

Mastropieri, Margo A. & Scruggs, Thomas E., eds. Literacy & Learning. 2010. (Advances in Learning & Behavioral Disabilities Ser.). (Illus.). 336p. 134.95 *(978-1-84950-776-9(7))* Emerald Group Publishing Ltd. GBR. Dist: Turpin Distribution Services Ltd.

Mather, Nancy & Goldstein, Sam. Learning Disabilities & Challenging Behavior: A Guide to Intervention & Classroom Management. 2nd ed. 2008. (Illus.). 488p. pap. 56.95 *(978-1-55766-935-3(X))* Brookes, Paul H. Publishing Co.

Matson, Johnny L., ed. Social Behavior & Skills in Children. 2010. x, 334p. pap. 49.95 *(978-1-4419-8177-6(2)*, 1441981772) Springer.

Matthys, Walter & Lochman, John E. Oppositional Defiant Disorder & Conduct Disorder in Children. 2010. (ENG.). 278p. 110.95 *(978-0-470-68231-9(0))*; pap. 55.95 *(978-0-470-51088-9(9))* Wiley, John & Sons, Inc. (Wiley).

Mayer, Matthew J., et al, eds. Cognitive-Behavioral Interventions for Emotional & Behavioral Disorders: School-Based Practice. 2011. (ENG.). 420p. (gr. k-12). pap. 30.00 *(978-1-60918-481-0(5))* Guilford Pubns., Inc.

Melillo, Robert. Reconnected Kids: Help Your Child Achieve Physical, Mental, & Emotional Balance. 2011. (ENG.). 336p. (gr. 12). 15.95 *(978-0-399-53648-9(5)*, Perigee Trade) Penguin Group (USA) Inc.

Melillo, Robert & Leisman, Gerry. Neurobehavioral Disorders of Childhood: An Evolutionary Perspective. 2009. (ENG.). xii, 447p. pap. 59.95 *(978-1-4419-1232-9(0)*, 1441912320) Springer.

Morris, Richard. Handbook of Child & Adolescent Behavior Disorders. 2008. 89.95 *(978-0-8058-6110-5(6))*; 195.00 *(978-0-8058-6109-9(2))* Erlbaum, Lawrence Assocs., Inc.

Morris, Richard J. & Kratochwill, Thomas R., eds. The Practice of Child Therapy. 4th rev. ed. 2007. (Illus.). 587p. 210.00 *(978-0-8058-5328-5(6))*; per. 98.95 *(978-0-8058-5329-2(4))* Erlbaum, Lawrence Assocs., Inc.

Mullins, Celine. Time to See Adhd in a Whole New Light? 2010. 284p. pap. *(978-3-8383-5100-1(2))* Lambert Academic Publishing.

Murrihy, Rachael C., et al, eds. Clinical Handbook of Assessing & Treating Conduct Problems in Youth. 2010. (Illus.). xxiv, 544p. 179.00 *(978-1-4419-6295-9(6)*, 1441962956) Springer.

O'Brien, Gregory, ed. Behavioural Phenotypes in Clinical Practice. 2007. (Clinics in Developmental Medicine Ser.: No. 157). (ENG., Illus.). 256p. 87.95 *(978-1-898683-27-8(1))* Mac Keith Pr. GBR. Dist: Wiley, John & Sons, Inc.

Olfman, Sharna. No Child Left Different. 2008. (ENG.). 260p. pap. 27.95 *(978-1-57886-774-5(6))* Rowman & Littlefield Education.

Olson, Sheryl L. & Sameroff, Arnold J., eds. Biopsychosocial Regulatory Processes in the Development of Childhood Behavioral Problems. 2009. (ENG., Illus.). 352p. 99.00 *(978-0-521-84813-8(X))* Cambridge Univ. Pr.

Ong'era, Lynett. Managing Emotional & Behaviour Difficulties. 2011. 88p. pap. ***(978-3-639-33360-2(8))*** VDM Verlag Dr. Mueller e.K.

Papousek, Mechthild, et al. Disorders of Behavioral & Emotional Regulation in the First Years of Life: Early Risks & Intervention in the Developing Parent-Infant Relationships. 2007. *(978-1-934019-17-7(8))* Zero To Three Pr.

Patel, Dilip R., et al. Behavioral Pediatrics. 3rd Edition. Greydanus, Donald E., ed. 2008. 89.00 *(978-1-60692-702-1(7))* Nova Science Pubs., Inc.

Piacentini, John, et al. Cognitive-Behavioral Treatment of Childhood Ocd: It's Only a False Alarm Therapist Guide. 2007. (Treatments That Work Ser.). (ENG., Illus.). 144p. (C). pap., instr.'s gde. ed. 37.95 *(978-0-19-531051-1(9))* Oxford Univ. Pr., Inc.

Pierangelo, Roger & Giuliani, George. Classroom Management for Students with Emotional & Behavioral Disorders: A Step-by-Step Guide for Educators. 2008. 152p. pap. 28.95 *(978-1-4129-1787-2(5)*, B17875P) Corwin Pr.

Pierangelo, Roger & Giuliani, George A. Classroom Management for Students with Emotional & Behavioral Disorders: A Step-by-Step Guide for Educators. 2008. 152p. 68.95 *(978-1-4129-5426-6(6)*, B17875C) Corwin Pr.

Prescription Psychotropic Drug Use among Children in Foster Care: Hearing Before the Subcommittee on Income Security & Family Support of the Committee on Ways & Means, U.S. House of Representatives, One Hundred Tenth Congress, Second Session, May 8, 2008. 2009. (Illus.). iii, 89p. *(978-0-16-082699-3(3)*, 552-070-38716-1) United States Government Printing Office.

Probst, Barbara. When the Labels Don't Fit: A New Approach to Raising a Challenging Child. 2008. (ENG.). 288p. 13.95 *(978-0-307-39543-6(X)*, Three Rivers Pr.) Crown Publishing Group.

Quartier, Vincent. Du développement de la temporalité dans les hyperactivités de L'enfant. 2008. 307p. pap. *(978-3-03911-701-7(7))* Lang, Peter.

Reyes, Cassandra. Of Fists & Fangs. 2010. 132p. pap. *(978-3-639-24781-7(7))* VDM Verlag Dr. Mueller e.K.

Richardson, Amy, et al. Effects of Soldiers Deployment on Children. 2011. (Illus.). 176p. pap. 28.00 *(978-0-8330-5181-3(4))* Royal Pavilion, Art Gallery & Museums GBR. Dist: National Bk. Network.

Riffel, Laura A. Positive Behavior Support at the Tertiary Level: Red Zone Strategies. 2011. (Illus.). 216p. pap. 33.95 *(978-1-4129-8201-6(4)*, B82016P) Corwin Pr.

Riley, Douglas A. What Your Explosive Child Is Trying to Tell You: Discovering the Pathway from Symptoms to Solutions. 2008. (ENG.). 272p. pap. 14.95 *(978-0-618-70081-3(1))* Houghton Mifflin Harcourt Trade & Reference Pubs.

Rimland, Bernard. Dyslogic Syndrome: Why Millions of Kids Are 'Hyper', Attention-Disordered, Learning Disabled, Depressed, Aggressive, Defiant, or Violent- & What We Can Do about It. 2008. (ENG.). 24p. *(978-1-84310-877-1(1))* Kingsley, Jessica Ltd.

Roff, Hermione. Reflective Interpersonal Therapy for Children & Parents (RICAP) Mind That Child! A New Way of Helping Parents & Children with Extreme Conduct Disorder. 2008. (ENG., Illus.). 318p. 144.95 *(978-0-470-98648-6(4)*, Wiley) Wiley, John & Sons, Inc.

Rogers, Bill, ed. How to Manage Children's Challenging Behaviour. 2nd ed. 2009. (Illus.). 208p. 71.00 *(978-1-84860-684-5(2)*, B06842C); pap. 35.00 *(978-1-84860-685-2(0)*, B06842P) SAGE Pubns., Ltd. GBR. Dist: SAGE Pubns., Inc.

Rosenzweig, Julie/M & Brennan, Eileen M., eds. Work, Life, & the Mental Health System of Care: A Guide for Professionals Supporting Families of Children with Emotional or Behavioral Disorders, Vol. 8. 2008. (Systems of Care for Children's Mental Health Ser.). 384p. per. 34.95 *(978-1-55766-827-1(2))* Brookes, Paul H. Publishing Co.

Rutherford Jr., Robert B., et al, eds. Handbook of Research in Emotional & Behavioral Disorders. 2007. (ENG., Illus.). 622p. pap. 50.00 *(978-1-59385-471-3(4))* Guilford Pubns., Inc.

Sailor, Wayne, et al, eds. Handbook of Positive Behavior Support. 2010. (Issues in Clinical Child Psychology Ser.). xxvi, 850p. pap. 89.95 *(978-1-4419-8135-6(7)*, 1441981357) Springer.

Schaefer, Charles E. & Briesmeister, James M., eds. Handbook of Parent Training: Helping Parents Prevent & Solve Problem Behaviors. 3rd rev. ed. 2007. (ENG., Illus.). 576p. 95.00 *(978-0-471-78997-0(6)*, Wiley) Wiley, John & Sons, Inc.

Schusteff, Arlene, compiled by. Special Gifts: Women Writers on the Heartache, the Happiness & the Hope of Raising a Special Needs Child. 2007. 228p. per. 15.00 *(978-1-932279-59-7(8))* Wyatt-MacKenzie Publishing.

Shapiro, Lawrence E., et al. The Relaxation & Stress Reduction Workbook for Kids: Help for Children to Cope with Stress, Anxiety, & Transitions. 2009. (Instant Help Ser.). (ENG., Illus.). 144p. (J). pap. 16.95 *(978-1-57224-582-2(4))* New Harbinger Pubns.

Shaw, Steven R. & McCabe, Paul C. Psychiatric Disorders: Current Topics & Interventions for Educators. Shaw, Steven R. & McCabe, Paul C., eds. 2010. 184p. pap. 36.95 *(978-1-4129-6876-8(3)*, B68751P) Corwin Pr.

Sheen, Brian. Educate, Don't Medicate- the Clear Minded Non-Medication Solution for Children with ADD/ADHD Symptoms. 2008. 216p. pap. 22.14 *(978-1-4357-0167-0(4))* Lulu Enterprises Inc.

Shepherd, Terry L. Working with Students with Emotional & Behavior Disorders: Characteristics & Teaching Strategies. 2009. (ENG.). 312p. (C). pap. 56.60 *(978-0-13-229859-9(7)*, Prentice Hall) Prentice Hall PTR.

Shores, Cara. A Comprehensive RTI Model: Integrating Behavioral & Academic Interventions. 2009. (Illus.). 184p. pap. 34.95 *(978-1-4129-6295-7(1)*, B62940P) Corwin Pr.

Shores, Cara F., ed. A Comprehensive RTI Model: Integrating Behavioral & Academic Interventions. 2009. (Illus.). 184p. 78.95 *(978-1-4129-6294-0(3)*, B62940C) Corwin Pr.

Shriver, Mark D. & Allen, Keith D. Working with Parents of Noncompliant Children: A Guide to Evidence-Based Parent Training for Practitioners & Students. 2008. (School Psychology Book Ser.). (Illus.). 304p. 49.95 *(978-1-4338-0344-4(5))* American Psychological Assn.

Smith, Mack. Programs for Students with Emotional Disturbances. 2010. 112p. pap. *(978-3-639-22588-4(0))* VDM Verlag Dr. Mueller e.K.

Smith, Terry Jo. Teaching the Children We Fear. 2007. (Understanding Education & Policy Ser.). *(978-1-57273-672-6(0))*; *(978-1-57273-673-3(9))* Hampton Pr., Inc.

Sprague, Jeffrey R. RTI & Behavior: A Guide to Integrating Behavioral & Academic Supports. 2008. *(978-1-57834-102-3(7))* LRP Pubns.

Stattin, Håkan. Understanding Girls' Problem Behavior: How Girls' Delinquency Develops in the Context of Maturity & Health, Co-Occurring Problems, & Relationships. Kerr, Margaret et al, eds. 2011. (Hot Topics in Developmental Research - a Series of Three Edited Volumes Ser.: 5). (ENG., Illus.). 252p. 115.95 *(978-0-470-66632-6(3)*, Wiley-Blackwell) Wiley, John & Sons, Inc.

Storch, Eric, et al, eds. Handbook of Child & Adolescent Obsessive-Compulsive Disorder. 2007. (ENG., Illus.). 432p. 94.95 *(978-0-8058-6254-6(4))*; 136.95 *(978-0-8058-5766-5(4))* Routledge.

Surace, Sandra. What's Wrong with My Child? Navigating through the maze of diagnostic Information. 2010. 316p. (ENG.). 32.99 *(978-1-4520-1074-8(9))*; pap. 24.99 *(978-1-4520-1073-1(0))* AuthorHouse.

Sutton, James D. What Parents Need to Know about ODD, Revised: Up-to-Date Insights & Ideas for Managing Oppositional Disorder & Other Defiant Behaviors. l.t. rev. ed. 2006. (Illus.). 140p. per. 21.95 *(978-1-878878-73-1(5))* Friendly Oaks Pubns.

—60 Ways to Reach a Difficult & Defiant Child. l.t. ed. 2007. (Illus.). 108p. per. 21.50 *(978-1-878878-75-5(1))* Friendly Oaks Pubns.

Talan, Kenneth H. Help Your Child or Teen Get Back on Track: What Parents & Professionals Can Do for Childhood Emotional & Behavioral Problems. (ENG., 2007. Illus.). 256p. pap. *(978-1-84310-870-2(4))* 2nd ed. 2009. 288p. pap. *(978-1-84310-914-3(X))* Kingsley, Jessica Ltd.

Taylor, Michael Alan & Vaidya, Nutan Atre. Descriptive Psychopathology: The Signs & Symptoms of Behavioral Disorders. 2008. (ENG., Illus.). 498p. pap. 82.00 *(978-0-521-71391-7(9))* Cambridge Univ. Pr.

Telfer, J. Christopher's Story Part Ii. 2008. 156p. pap. *(978-1-84747-378-3(4))* Chipmunkapublishing.

Tremblay, Richard Ernest, et al. Development & Prevention of Behaviour Problems: From Genes to Social Policy. 2009. (ENG., Illus.). 280p. 79.95 *(978-1-84872-007-7(6)*, Psychology Press) Taylor & Francis Group GBR. Dist: Taylor & Francis Group.

Umeh, Kanayo. Understanding Adolescent Health Behaviour: A Decision Making Perspective. 2009. (ENG., Illus.). 318p. (C). pap. 49.99 *(978-0-521-69802-3(2))* Cambridge Univ. Pr.

Umeh, Kanayo & Umeh, Kanayo F. Understanding Adolescent Health Behaviour: A Decision Making Perspective. 2009. (ENG., Illus.). 318p. (C). 117.00 *(978-0-521-87526-4(9))* Cambridge Univ. Pr.

Wallace, Fiona. Just Stop... & Think! Helping Children Plan to Improve Their Own Behaviour. 2nd ed. 2007. (Lucky Duck Bks.). (Illus.). 104p. pap. 31.00 *(978-1-4129-2898-4(2)*, B28982P) SAGE Pubns., Ltd. GBR. Dist: SAGE Pubns., Inc.

Waller, Raymond J. The Educator's Guide to Solving Common Behavior Problems. 2008. (Illus.). 128p. 60.95 *(978-1-4129-5765-6(6)*, B57656C); pap. 24.95 *(978-1-4129-5766-3(4)*, B57656P) Corwin Pr.

Waller, Raymond Jefferson. The Teacher's Concise Guide to Functional Behavioral Assessment. Waller, Raymond Jefferson, ed. 2008. (Illus.). 136p. pap. 24.95 *(978-1-4129-6605-4(1)*, B66047P) Corwin Pr.

Waller, Raymond Jefferson, ed. The Teacher's Concise Guide to Functional Behavioral Assessment. 2008. (Illus.). 136p. 60.95 *(978-1-4129-6604-7(3)*, B66047C) Corwin Pr.

Webber, Jo & Plotts, Cynthia A. Emotional & Behavioral Disorders: Theory & Practice. 5th ed. 2007. (ENG., Illus.). 480p. (C). 138.00 *(978-0-205-41066-8(9))* Allyn & Bacon, Inc.

Wedge, Marilyn. Pills Are Not for Preschoolers: A Drug-Free Approach for Troubled Kids. 2012. (ENG.). 256p. pap. 15.95 ***(978-0-393-34316-8(2)***, 34316) Norton, W. W. & Co., Inc.

Wells, Karen, et al. Coping Power Set: Parent Group. 2008. (Treatments That Work Ser.). (ENG.). 128p. (C). pap., wbk. ed. 98.50 *(978-0-19-532796-0(9))* Oxford Univ. Pr., Inc.

Western Schools. Treating Explosive Kids: Behavioral Health Series. 2007. wbk. ed. 54.95 *(978-1-57801-205-3(8))* Western Schls.

—Treating Explosive Kids: Nursing Series. 2007. wbk. ed. 54.95 *(978-1-57801-204-6(X))* Western Schls.

Wicks-Nelson, Rita & Israel, Allen C. Abnormal Child & Adolescent Psychology. 7th ed. 2008. (ENG., Illus.). 576p. (C). 167.00 *(978-0-13-235978-8(2)*, Prentice Hall) Prentice Hall PTR.

Winfrey, Aida McClellan. H. Y. P. E. Healing Young People Thru Empowerment. 2009. (ENG., Illus.). 200p. pap. 14.95 *(978-1-934155-20-2(9))* African American Images.

Woliver, Robbie. Alphabet Kids - From ADD to Zellweger Syndrome: A Guide to Developmental, Neurobiological & Psychological Disorders for Parents & Professionals. 2008. (ENG.). 384p. *(978-1-84310-880-1(1))* Kingsley, Jessica Ltd.

Woods, Doug. Understanding Behavior Disorders: A Contemporary Behavioral Perspective. Kanter, Jonathan, ed. 2007. (Professional Ser.). (ENG., Illus.). 452p. per. 49.95 *(978-1-878978-61-5(6))* Context Pr.

Yokley, James. Social Responsibility Therapy for Adolescents & Young Adults: A Multicultural Treatment Manual for Harmful Behavior. 2008. (Illus.). (ENG.). 360p. 125.00 *(978-0-7890-3120-4(5))*; 376p. pap. 54.50 *(978-0-7890-3121-1(3))* Routledge.

Zimmerman, Barbara F. Why Can't They Just Behave? A Guide to Managing Student Behavior Disorders. 2nd ed. 2007. *(978-1-57834-093-4(4))* LRP Pubns.

BEHAVIOR EVOLUTION

see also Behavior Genetics

Adriaanse, C., ed. On Measuring & Explaining Neighbourhood Succes: A Behavioural Economic Approach. 2011. 200p. pap. 65.00 ***(978-1-60750-786-4(2))*** IOS Pr., Inc.

Alland, Alex. Evolution & Human Behaviour. 2nd ed. 2012. (ENG.). 368p. (C). pap. 42.95 ***(978-0-415-61200-5(4))*** Routledge.

Bailey, Scott, ed. The Evolution of Intelligence: Brain, Behavioral & Computational Approaches. (Brain, Behavior & Evolution Ser.: Vol. 59, No. 1-2). (Illus.). 100p. *(978-3-8055-7456-3(8))* Karger, S. AG.

Barrett, Deirdre. Supernormal Stimuli: How Primal Urges Overran Their Evolutionary Purpose. 2010. (ENG., Illus.). 216p. 24.95 *(978-0-393-06848-1(X)*, 6848) Norton, W. W. & Co., Inc.

Bowles, Samuel & Gintis, Herbert. A Cooperative Species - Human Reciprocity & Its Evolution. 2011. (ENG., Illus.). 288p. (C). 35.00 *(978-0-691-15125-0(3))* Princeton Univ. Pr.

Brown, Stephanie L., et al. Moving Beyond Self-Interest: Perspectives from Evolutionary Biology, Neuroscience, & the Social Sciences. 2011. (ENG., Illus.). 320p. 49.95 ***(978-0-19-538810-7(0))*** Oxford Univ. Pr., Inc.

Burghardt, Gordon M. The Genesis of Animal Play: Testing the Limits. 2006. (ENG., Illus.). 518p. (gr. 17). per. 32.00 *(978-0-262-52469-8(4))* MIT Pr.

Cartwright, John. Evolution & Human Behaviour: Darwinian Perspectives on Human Nature. 2nd ed. 2007. 384p. 89.95 *(978-0-333-98631-8(8))*; pap. 32.95 *(978-0-333-98632-5(6))* Palgrave Macmillan.

Ch'Ng, Kean Siang. The Evolutionary & Adaptive Economic Behavior. 2009. 192p. pap. *(978-3-639-17088-7(1))* VDM Verlag Dr. Mueller e.K.

Cram101 Textbook Reviews & Cram101 Textbook Reviews. Outlines & Highlights for Cognition, Evolution, & Behavior by Sara J Shettleworth. 2011. 154p. pap. 29.95 ***(978-1-61830-480-3(1))*** Cram101 Inc.

Dunbar, Robin. How Many Friends Does One Person Need? Dunbar's Number & Other Evolutionary Quirks. 2010. 312p. 27.95 *(978-0-674-05716-6(3))* Harvard Univ. Pr.

Frank, Steven A. Foundations of Social Evolution. 2006. (Illus.). 268p. reprint ed. pap. 20.00 *(978-1-4223-5884-9(4))* DIANE Publishing Co.

Fuentes, Agustin. Evolution of Human Behavior. 2008. (Illus.). 288p. (C). 84.95 *(978-0-19-533359-6(4))*; (ENG., pap. 44.95 *(978-0-19-533358-9(6))* Oxford Univ. Pr., Inc.

Fuentes, Agustin. Race, Monogamy, & Other Lies They Told You: Busting Myths about Human Nature. 2012. (ENG., Illus.). 304p. 27.50 ***(978-0-520-26971-2(3))*** Univ. of California Pr.

Hood, Kathryn E., et a., eds. Handbook of Developmental Science, Behavior, & Genetics. 2010. (ENG., Illus.). 776p. 204.95 *(978-1-4051-8782-4(4),* Wiley-Blackwell) Wiley, John & Sons, Inc.

Hrdy, Sarah Blaffer. Mothers & Others: The Evolutionary Origins of Mutual Understanding. 2011. (ENG., Illus.). 432p. pap. 19.95 *(978-0-674-06032-6(6),* Belknap Pr.) Harvard Univ. Pr.

Johnson, David Martel. Three Prehistoric Inventions That Shaped Us. 2011. xvi, 192p. (C). 76.95 *(978-1-4331-1090-0(3))* Lang, Peter Publishing, Inc.

Laland, Kevin N. & Brown, Gillian R. Sense & Nonsense: Evolutionary Perspectives on Human Behaviour. 2nd ed. 2011. (ENG., Illus.). 264p. pap. 39.95 *(978-0-19-958696-7(9))* Oxford Univ. Pr., Inc.

Leonard, Adam. Man by Nature: The Hidden Programming Controlling Human Behavior. 2009. (ENG.). 194p. pap. 14.95 *(978-0-615-28025-7(0))* Egress Publishing.

Neubauer, Raymond L. Evolution & the Emergent Self: The Rise of Complexity & Behavioral Versatility in Nature. 2011. (ENG., Illus.). 336p. (gr. 17). 32.50 ***(978-0-231-15070-5(9))*** Columbia Univ. Pr.

Pope, David J. Interrupting Behavioral Evolution: An Essay. 2006. xx, 76p. *(978-0-9779189-2-8(0))* Walden Hse. Publishing.

Spink, Amanda. Information Behavior: An Evolutionary Instinct. 2010. (Information Science & Knowledge Management Ser.). (ENG., Illus.). xi, 85p. 129.00 *(978-3-642-11496-0(2),* 3642114962) Springer.

Travis, Alice. Cognitive Evolution: The Biological Imprint of Applied Intelligence. 2007. 240p. per. 25.95 *(978-1-58112-981-6(5))* Universal Pubs.

Trivers, Robert. The Folly of Fools: The Logic of Deceit & Self-Deception in Human Life. 2011. (ENG.). 416p. (gr. 9). 28.00 *(978-0-465-02755-2(5))* Basic Bks.

Weiss, Alexander, et al. Personality & Temperament in Nonhuman Primates. 2011. (Illus.). xiv, 342p. E-Book ***(978-1-4614-0176-6(3))*** Springer.

BEHAVIOR GENETIC ANALYSIS
see Behavior Genetics

BEHAVIOR GENETICS
see also Behavior Evolution

Adriaanse, C., ed. On Measuring & Explaining Neighbourhood Succes: A Behavioural Economic Approach. 2011. 200p. pap. 65.00 ***(978-1-60750-785-4(2))*** IOS Pr., Inc.

Anholt, Robert R. H. & Mackay, Trudy F. C. Principles of Behavioral Genetics. 2009. (ENG., Illus.). x, 334p. (C). pap. 69.95 *(978-0-12-372575-2(5),* Academic Pr.) Elsevier Science & Technology Bks.

Assessing Interactions Among Social Committee. Genes, Behavior, & the Social Environment: Moving Beyond the Nature - Nurture Debate. Hernandez, Lyla M. & Blazer, Dan G., eds. 2006. (ENG., Illus.). 384p. pap. 42.00 *(978-0-309-10196-7(4))* National Academies Pr.

Avise, John C. Genetics in the Wild. 2010. (ENG., Illus.). 270p. pap. 24.95 *(978-1-58834-293-5(X))* Smithsonian Institution Pr.

Bailey, Jon & Burch, Mary. 25 Essential Skills & Strategies for Behavior Analysts: Expert Tips for Maximizing Consulting Effectiveness. 2009. (ENG., Illus.). 341p. (C). pap. 36.95 *(978-0-415-80068-6(4))* Routledge.

Carolina Biological Staff, compiled by. Behaving Like Animals. 2009. (Inquiries in Science Biology Ser.). *(978-1-4350-0372-9(1))*; tchr. ed., spiral bd. *(978-1-4350-0371-2(3))* Carolina Biological Supply Co.

Cooper, John O., et al. Applied Behavior Analysis. 2nd rev. ed. 2006. (ENG., Illus.). 800p. (C). 131.00 *(978-0-13-142113-4(1),* Prentice Hall) Prentice Hall PTR.

Cram101 Textbook Reviews. Outlines & Highlights for Behavioral Genetics by Robert Plomin, Gerald E Mcclearn, Peter Mcguffin, John C Defries, Isbn: 9781429205771 1429205776. 2011. 162p. pap. 29.95 ***(978-1-61812-486-9(2))*** Cram101 Inc.

Farahany, Nita. The Impact of Behavioral Sciences on Criminal Law. Farahany, Nita, ed. 2009. (ENG., Illus.). 250p. 65.00 *(978-0-19-534052-5(3))* Oxford Univ. Pr., Inc.

Flint, Jonathan, et al. How Genes Influence Behavior. 2010. (ENG., Illus.). 304p. 59.95 *(978-0-19-955990-9(2))* Oxford Univ. Pr., Inc.

Goldman, David. Our Genes, Our Choices: How genotype & gene interactions affect Behavior. 2012. (ENG.). 272p. pap. 74.95 ***(978-0-12-396952-1(2),*** Academic Pr.) Elsevier Science & Technology Bks.

Gorwood, Philip & Hamon, Michel D., eds. Psychopharmacogenetics. 2010. (ENG., Illus.). xvi, 566p. pap. 169.00 *(978-1-4419-4037-7(5),* 1441940375) Springer.

Heschl, Adolf. The Intelligent Genome: On the Origin of the Human Mind by Mutation & Selection. 2010. (ENG.). 362p. pap. 84.95 *(978-3-642-08648-9(9),* 3642086489) Springer.

Kim, Yong-Kyu, ed. Handbook of Behavior Genetics. 2010. (Illus.). xxiv, 560p. pap. 99.00 *(978-1-4419-6747-3(8),* 1441967478) Springer.

—Handbook of Behavioral Genetics. 2009. (ENG., Illus.). xxiv, 560p. 249.00 *(978-0-387-76726-0(6))* Springer.

Macdonald, Roderick A. Challenging Genetic Determinism: New Perspectives on the Gene in Its Multiple Environments. Maheu, Louis, ed. 2011. (ENG., Illus.). 328p. (C). *(978-0-7735-3780-4(5))* McGill-Queen's Univ. Pr.

Maheu, Louis & Macdonald, Roderick A. Challenging Genetic Determinism: New Perspectives on the Gene in Its Multiple Environments. 2011. (ENG., Illus.). 328p. (C). pap. *(978-0-7735-3813-9(5))* McGill-Queen's Univ. Pr.

Parens, Erik, et al, eds. Wrestling with Behavioral Genetics: Science, Ethics, & Public Conversation. 2008. (ENG., Illus.). 376p. (C). (gr. 13-17). pap. 25.00 *(978-0-8018-9091-8(8))* Johns Hopkins Univ. Pr.

Plomin, Robert, et al. Behavioral Genetics. 5th rev. ed. 2008. (ENG., Illus.). 560p. (C). 141.95 *(978-1-4292-0577-1(6))* Worth Pubs., Inc.

—Nature & Nurture during Infancy & Early Childhood. 2006. (ENG., Illus.). 360p. (C). pap. 48.00 *(978-0-521-03424-1(8))* Cambridge Univ. Pr.

Sesardic, Neven. Making Sense of Heritability. 2010. (Cambridge Studies in Philosophy & Biology Ser.). (ENG.). 282p. pap. 36.99 *(978-0-521-17333-9(7))* Cambridge Univ. Pr.

Shane, Scott. Born Entrepreneurs, Born Leaders: How Your Genes Affect Your Work Life. 1 vol. 2010. (ENG., Illus.). 304p. 29.95 *(978-0-19-537342-4(1))* Oxford Univ. Pr., Inc.

Shapiro, Bruce K. & Accardo, Pasquale J. Neurogenetic Syndromes: Behavioral Issues & Their Treatment. 2009. (Illus.). 328p. 59.95 *(978-1-59857-017-5(X))* Brookes, Paul H. Publishing Co.

Smoller, Jordan. The Other Side of Normal: How Biology Is Providing the Clues to Unlock the Secrets of Normal & Abnormal Behavior. 2012. (ENG.). 400p. 27.99 *(978-0-06-149219-8(1),* Morrow, William & Co.); 640p. pap. 27.99 *(978-0-06-206497-4(5),* HarperLuxe) HarperCollins Pubs.

Smoller, Jordan W. The Other Side of Normal: How Biology Is Providing the Clues to Unlock the Secrets of Normal & Abnormal Behavior. 2012. ***(978-0-06-149220-4(5),*** Morrow, William & Co.) HarperCollins Pubs.

Spuhler, J. N., ed. Genetic Diversity & Human Behavior. 2009. (ENG., Illus.). 321p. pap. 39.95 *(978-0-202-36308-0(2))* Aldine Transaction.

Yamamoto, Daisuke, ed. Genetics of Sexual Differentiation & Sexually Dimorphic Behaviors. 2007. (Advances in Genetics Ser.). (ENG., Illus.). 286p. 161.00 *(978-0-12-017660-1(2),* Academic Pr.) Elsevier Science & Technology Bks.

BEHAVIOR IN ORGANIZATIONS
see Organizational Behavior

BEHAVIOR MODIFICATION
see also Behavior Therapy; Brainwashing

Aditya, B. S. & Wilding, J. P. H. Obesity. 2011. (Atlas of Investigation & Management Ser.). (Illus.). 114p. ***(978-1-84692-027-1(2))*** Clinical Publishing Services.

Akin Little, Ang, et al, eds. Behavioral Interventions in Schools: Evidence-based Positive Strategies. 2009. (Illus.). 336p. 59.95 *(978-1-4338-0460-1(3))* American Psychological Assn.

Alberto, Paul A. & Troutman, Anne C. Applied Behavior Analysis for Teachers. (ENG., Illus.). (C). 8th ed. 2008. 504p. pap. 125.60 *(978-0-13-159289-6(0))* 9th rev. ed. 2012. 480p. pap. 125.60 ***(978-0-13-265597-2(7))*** Prentice Hall PTR. (Prentice Hall).

Algozzine, Bob. Responsible Classroom Management: A Schoolwide Plan. Queen, James Allen, ed. 2010. 152p. pap. 23.95 *(978-1-4129-7413-4(5),* B74134P) Corwin Pr.

Antony, Martin M. & Roemer, Lizabeth. Behavior Therapy. 2011. 188p. (C). pap. 24.95 *(978-1-4338-0984-2(2))* American Psychological Assn.

Antrobus, Laverne. Ain't Misbehavin' How to Understand Your Child's Behaviour & Get the Best from Them. 2007. (ENG.). 192p. pap. 33.50 *(978-0-273-71266-4(7))* Pearson Education, Ltd. GBR. Dist: Trans-Atlantic Pubns., Inc.

Arloski, Michael. Wellness Coaching for Lasting Lifestyle Change. 2007. 280p. pap. 29.95 *(978-1-57025-221-1(1))* Whole Person Assocs., Inc.

Baker, Jed. No More Meltdowns: Positive Strategies for Dealing with & Preventing Out-of-Control Behavior. 2008. (ENG.). 150p. pap. 14.95 *(978-1-932565-62-1(0))* Future Horizons, Inc.

Bambara, Linda M. & Knoster, Tim. Designing Positive Behavior Support Plans. 2nd ed. 2009. *(978-1-935304-03-6(8))* American Assn. on Intellectual & Developmental Disabilities.

Beckner, Rebecca, et al. Implementing Positive Behavior Support Systems in Early Childhood & Elementary Settings. Stormont, Melissa et al, eds. 2007. (Illus.). 152p. per. 27.95 *(978-1-4129-4056-6(7),* B40559P) Corwin Pr.

Bellack, Alan S., et al. Behavioral Treatment for Substance Abuse in People with Serious & Persistent Mental Illness: A Handbook for Mental Health Professionals. 2006. (ENG., Illus.). 288p. pap. 57.95 *(978-0-415-95283-5(2))* Routledge.

Bianchini, Terry. R U Listenin'? Help Defiant Young Men to Recognize Their True Potential. 2008. (Illus.). 159p. per. *(978-1-84310-616-6(7))* Kingsley, Jessica Ltd.

Blakeley, Karen. Leadership Blind Spots & What to Do about Them. 2007. (ENG., Illus.). 310p. 65.00 *(978-0-470-03193-3(X),* Jossey-Bass) Wiley, John & Sons, Inc.

Browne-Miller, Angela. Rewiring Your Self to Break Addictions & Habits: Overcoming Problem Patterns, 1 vol. 2009. (Illus.). 273p. 44.95 *(978-0-313-35388-8(3),* C35388, Praeger Pubs.) Greenwood Publishing Group, Inc.

Brownhill, Simon & Brownhill. Taking the Stress Out of Bad Behaviour: Behaviour Management of 3-11 Year Olds. 2007. (ENG., Illus.). 288p. 34.95 *(978-0-8264-9563-1(X))* Continuum International Publishing Group, Ltd. GBR. Dist: National Bk. Network.

Brownhill, Simon & Bullock, Emily E. A Quick Guide to Behaviour Management in the Early Years. 2011. (Illus.). 136p. 100.00 ***(978-0-85702-164-9(8),*** B21649C); pap. 33.00 ***(978-0-85702-165-6(6),*** B21649P) SAGE Pubns., Ltd. GBR. Dist: SAGE Pubns., Inc.

Brownhill, Simon, et al. 101 Essential Lists on Managing Behaviour in the Early Years. 2006. (101 Essential Lists Ser.). (ENG.). 128p. 35.95 *(978-0-8264-8989-0(3))* Continuum International Publishing Group, Ltd. GBR. Dist: National Bk. Network.

Brozovich, Richa & Chase, Linda. Say Goodbye to Being Shy: A Workbook to Help Kids Overcome Shyness. 2008. (Instant Help Ser.). 120p. pap. 16.95 *(978-1-931704-39-7(2))* Play2Grow.

Byron, Tanya. The House of Tiny Tearaways. 2006. (ENG., Illus.). 160p. (C). pap. *(978-0-563-52036-8(1))* Pearson Education Canada.

Campbell, Doug. Discipline Without Anger: A New Style of Classroom Management. 2012. (ENG.). 148p. 60.00 ***(978-1-61048-342-1(1))***; pap. 24.95 ***(978-1-61048-343-8(X))*** Rowman & Littlefield Education.

Campbell, Jack. Behavior Modification in the Classroom: Strategies for Teachers & Parents. 2009. 151p. pap. 17.95 *(978-1-4327-2980-6(2))* Outskirts Pr., Inc.

Canter, Lee. Lee Canter's Assertive Discipline: Positive Behavior Management for Today's Classroom. 4th ed. 2009. 176p. pap. 24.95 *(978-1-934009-15-4(6))*; lib. bdg. 44.95 *(978-1-935249-23-8(1))* Solution Tree Pr.

Caplan, Tom. The Needs ABC Therapeutic Model for Couples & Families. 2010. (ENG., Illus.). 264p. 125.00 *(978-0-415-87305-5(3))* Routledge.

—The Needs ABC Therapeutic Model for Couples & Families. 2010. (ENG., Illus.). 264p. pap. 32.95 *(978-0-415-87306-2(1),* Routledge) Taylor & Francis Group GBR. Dist: Taylor & Francis Group.

Cherry, Sally. Transforming Behaviour: Pro-Social Modelling in Practice. 2nd rev. ed. 2010. (Illus.). 256p. 44.95 *(978-1-84392-928-4(7))*; pap. 39.95 *(978-1-84392-927-7(9))* Willan Publishing GBR. Dist: Taylor & Francis Group.

Cheshire, Carol. Are You Having Fun? Doing all the Things You Want to Do? 2011. 48p. pap. 9.95 ***(978-1-4620-1798-0(3))*** iUniverse, Inc.

Cipani, Ennio. Functional Behavioral Assessment, Diagnosis, & Treatment: A Complete System for Education & Mental Health Settings. 2nd ed. 340p. pap. *(978-0-8261-0604-9(8))* Springer Publishing Co., Inc.

Cipani, Ennio & Schock, Keven M. Functional Behavioral Assessment, Diagnosis, & Treatment: A Complete System for Education & Mental Health Settings. (Illus.). 2007. 293p. per. 62.00 *(978-0-8261-0288-1(3))* 2nd ed. 2011. xv, 319p. E-Book ***(978-0-8261-0605-6(6))*** Springer Publishing Co., Inc.

Cole, Ted, et al, eds. The Routledge International Handbook of Emotional & Behavioural Difficulties. 2012. (ENG., Illus.). 384p. (C). 190.00 *(978-0-415-58463-0(9))* Routledge.

Colvin, Geoffrey. Defusing Disruptive Behavior in the Classroom. 2010. (Illus.). 168p. pap. 31.95 *(978-1-4129-8056-2(9),* B80562P) Corwin Pr.

Conyers, Beverly. Everything Changes: Help for Families of Newly Recovering Addicts. 2009. (ENG.). 168p. pap. 14.95 *(978-1-59285-697-8(7))* Hazelden Publishing & Educational Services.

Cooper, Barbara, et al. Social Success Workbook for Te. 2008. 136p. pap. 16.95 *(978-1-931704-43-4(0))* Play2Grow.

Copley, Anne. Challenging Behaviour: A Fresh Look at Promoting Positive Learning Behaviours. 2006. (ENG., Illus.). 112p. 39.95 *(978-1-85539-217-5(8),* Network Continuum Education) Continuum International Publishing Group, Ltd. GBR. Dist: National Bk. Network.

Cox, W. Miles & Klinger, Eric, eds. Handbook of Motivational Counseling: Goal-Based Approaches to Assessment & Intervention with Addiction & Other Problems. 2nd ed. 2011. (ENG., Illus.). 666p. 99.95 *(978-0-470-74926-5(1),* Wiley-Blackwell) Wiley, John & Sons, Inc.

Cram101 Textbook Reviews. Outlines & Highlights for Principles of Everyday Behavior Analysis by L Keith Miller. 2010. 222p. pap. 30.95 *(978-1-4288-5077-4(5))* Cram101 Inc.

—Outlines & Highlights for School-Based Interventions for Students with Behavior Problems by Julie Bowen. 2011. 58p. pap. 26.95 ***(978-1-61905-368-7(3))*** Cram101 Inc.

—Outlines & Highlights for Self-Directed Behavior by David L Watson, Roland G Tharp. 2011. 130p. pap. 28.95 ***(978-1-61654-124-8(5))*** Cram101 Inc.

Cram101 Textbook Reviews & Cram101 Textbook Reviews. Outlines & Highlights for Behavior Modification: What It Is & How to Do It by Garry Martin, ISBN. 2011. 102p. pap. 27.95 ***(978-1-61461-033-5(9))*** Cram101 Inc.

—Outlines & Highlights for First Course in Applied Behavior Analysis by Paul Chance, Isbn: 9781577664727. 2011. 62p. pap. 27.95 ***(978-1-61461-034-2(7))*** Cram101 Inc.

—Outlines & Highlights for Predicting & Changing Behavior: The Reasoned Action Approach by Martin Fishbein. 2011. 60p. pap. 26.95 ***(978-1-61830-478-0(X))*** Cram101 Inc.

Cram101 Textbook Reviews Staff. Outlines & Highlights for Learning & Behavior by Mazur, Isbn: 0131931636. 2008. 92p. pap. 10.95 *(978-1-4288-6048-3(7))* Cram101 Inc.

Crimmins, Daniel, et al. Positive Strategies for Students with Behavior Problems. 2007. (Illus.). 226p. per. 32.95 *(978-1-55766-878-3(7))* Brookes, Paul H. Publishing Co.

Crone, Deanne A., et al. Responding to Problem Behavior in Schools: The Behavior Education Program. 2nd ed. 2010. (Guilford Practical Intervention in Schools Ser.). (ENG., Illus.). 242p. (gr. -1-12). pap. 40.00 *(978-1-60623-600-0(8))* Guilford Pubns., Inc.

Danforth, Scot & Boyle, Joseph. Cases in Behavior Management. 2nd rev. ed. 2006. (ENG.). 176p. (C). per. 27.60 *(978-0-13-171591-2(7),* Prentice Hall) Prentice Hall PTR.

Daniels, Aubrey C. OOPS! 13 Management Practices That Waste Time & Money & What to Do Instead. 2009. 190p. 21.95 *(978-0-937100-17-2(X))* Performance Management Pubns.

Davis, Kim & Dixon, Susan D. When Actions Speak Louder Than Words: Understanding the Challenging Behaviors of Young Children & Students with Disabilities. 2009. pap. 29.95 *(978-1-934009-60-4(1))*; lib. bdg. 64.95 *(978-1-935249-13-9(4))* Solution Tree Pr.

Demetre, Danna. Change Your Habits, Change Your Life: A Proven Plan for Healthy Living. 2009. 352p. pap. 15.99 *(978-0-8007-3331-5(2))* Revell.

Denno, Dawn/M, et al. Addressing Challenging Behaviors in Early Childhood Settings: A Teacher's Guide. 2010. (Illus.). 256p. pap. 34.95 incl. cd-rom *(978-1-55766-984-1(8))* Brookes, Paul H. Publishing Co.

Denti, Louis G. Proactive Classroom Management, K-8: A Practical Guide to Empower Students & Teachers. 2012. 192p. pap. 33.95 ***(978-1-4522-0389-8(X),*** B0389P) Corwin Pr.

Derrington, Chris. 'Whole-Brain' Behaviour Management in the Classroom: Every Piece of the Puzzle. 2007. (Illus.). 232p. 135.00 *(978-0-415-41180-6(7))* Routledge.

Derrington, Chris & Goddard, Hilary. 'Whole-Brain' Behaviour Management in the Classroom: Every Piece of the Puzzle. 2007. (Illus.). 232p. 43.95 *(978-0-415-41181-3(5))* Routledge.

Diken, Ibrahim H. First Step to Success Early Intervention Program. 2010. 176p. pap. *(978-3-8383-5070-7(7))* Lambert Academic Publishing.

Dinnerstein, Pesi. A Cluttered Life: Searching for God, Serenity, & My Missing Keys. 2011. (ENG.). 312p. pap. 17.00 *(978-1-58005-310-5(6))* Seal Pr.

Dix, Paul. Taking Care of Behaviour. 2nd ed. 2010. (Illus.). 228p. pap. 42.50 *(978-1-4082-2554-7(9),* Longman) Pearson Education, Ltd. GBR. Dist: Trans-Atlantic Pubns., Inc.

—Taking Care of Behaviour: Practical Skills for Learning Support & Teaching Assistants. 2008. (Illus.). 192p. pap. incl. cd-rom *(978-1-4082-0374-3(X))* Pearson Education.

—Taking Care of Behaviour: Practical Skills for Learning Support & Teaching Assistants. 2007. (Illus.). 168p. pap. 62.50 incl. cd-rom *(978-1-4058-3275-5(4),* Longman) Pearson Education, Ltd. GBR. Dist: Trans-Atlantic Pubns., Inc.

Drifte, Collette. Encouraging Positive Behaviour in the Early Years: A Practical Guide. 2nd ed. 2008. (Illus.). 112p. 112.00 *(978-1-84787-374-3(X),* B73743C); pap. 52.00 *(978-1-84787-375-0(8),* B73743P) SAGE Pubns., Ltd. GBR. Dist: SAGE Pubns., Inc.

Dunnington, Kent J. Addiction & Virtue: Beyond the Models of Disease & Choice. 2011. (Strategic Initiatives in Evangelical Theology Ser.). (ENG.). 199p. pap. 30.00 *(978-0-8308-3901-8(1),* VP Acad.) InterVarsity Pr.

Durand, Mark V. & Hieneman, Meme. Helping Parents with Challenging Children: Positive Family Intervention. 2008. (Programs That Work Ser.). (ENG.). 144p. pap. 37.95 *(978-0-19-533298-3(9))* Oxford Univ. Pr., Inc.

Dyer, Warwick. Mercury's Child. 2008. 124p. pap. 37.95 *(978-1-60145-262-7(4))* Booklocker.com, Inc.

Ellis, Simon & Tod, Janet. Behaviour for Learning: Proactive Approaches to Behaviour Management. 2009. (ENG., Illus.). 310p. 150.00 *(978-0-415-49167-9(3))* Routledge.

Elven, Bo Hejlskov. No Fighting, No Biting, No Screaming: How to Make Behaving Positively Possible for People with Autism & Other Developmental Disabilities. 2010. (ENG., Illus.). 224p. pap. *(978-1-84905-126-2(7))* Kingsley, Jessica Ltd.

Farley, Janice J. Exploring the Stages of Change in Substance Abuse Behaviour - a Review of Substance Abusers at Two Inpatient Treatment Facilities in Barbados. 2008. 160p. pap. *(978-3-639-02396-1(X))* VDM Verlag Dr. Mueller e.K.

Fernley, Sheila. Ready to Use Professional Development: Focusing on Behavior Management. 2007. *(978-1-57834-077-4(2))* LRP Pubns.

Fields, Marjorie V., et al. Constructive Guidance & Discipline: Preschool & Primary Education. 5th ed. 2009. (ENG., Illus.). 416p. (C). pap. 82.80 *(978-0-13-603593-0(0),* Prentice Hall) Prentice Hall PTR.

—Constructive Guidance & Discipline: Preschool & Primary Education (with MyEducationLab) 5th ed. 2009. (ENG.). 432p. (C). pap. 89.47 *(978-0-13-610112-3(7),* Prentice Hall) Prentice Hall PTR.

Filter, Kevin J. & Alvarez, Michelle E. Functional Behavior Assessment: A Three-Tiered Prevention Model. 2011. (SSWAA Workshop Ser.). (ENG., Illus.). 192p. pap. 24.95 ***(978-0-19-976493-8(X))*** Oxford Univ. Pr., Inc.

Flicker, Eileen S. & Hoffman, Janet Andron. Guiding Children's Behavior: Developmental Discipline in the Classroom. 2006. (Early Childhood Education Ser.). (ENG., Illus.). 128p. pap. 21.95 *(978-0-8077-4713-1(0))* Teachers College Pr., Teachers College, Columbia Univ.

Flint, Richard. Behavior Never Lies. 2008. 181p. pap. 14.95 *(978-0-937851-33-3(7))* Flint Inc.

Flippen, Flip. The Flip Side: Break Free of the Behaviors That Hold You Back. 2008. (ENG.). 272p. pap. 14.99 *(978-0-446-58132-5(1))* Little Brown & Co.

Flynn, Brian, et al. Why Psychologists Need to Base Treatment Recommendations on Scientific Evidence: Methodologies for Intervening with Disruptive Adolescents. 2010. (Illus.). vii, 218p. *(978-0-7734-3775-3(4))* Mellen, Edwin Pr., The.

Foster, Stephen. The Project Mkultra Compendium: The CIA's Program of Research in Behavioral Modification. 2009. 621p. pap. 152.84 *(978-0-557-05084-0(7))* Lulu Enterprises Inc.

Fox, William M. Behavior Modeling Training for Developing Supervisory Skills: Instructor Manual (Pb) 2008. 76p. pap. 34.95 *(978-1-59311-981-2(X))* Information Age Publishing, Inc.

—Behavior Modeling Training for Developing Supervisory Skills: Trainee Manual. 2009. 52p. pap. *(978-1-60752-095-5(8))* Information Age Publishing, Inc.

B

French, Jeff, et al. Social Marketing Casebook. 2011. (Illus.). 280p. (C). 120.00 (978-0-85702-543-2(0), B25432C); pap. 45.00 (978-0-85702-544-9(9), B25432P) SAGE Pubns., Ltd. GBR. Dist: SAGE Pubns., Inc.

Ghenwa, El-Assi. The Effect of Barkley's Behavior Management Principles on Adhd Kids: A Case Study in an Inclusive Classroom. 2011. 76p. pap. (978-3-639-34053-2(1)) VDM Verlag Dr. Mueller e.K.

Glass, Cathy. Happy Kids: The Secrets to Raising Well-Behaved, Contented Children. 2010. (ENG.). 288p. (J). 12.95 (978-0-00-733925-9(9)) HarperCollins Pubs. Ltd. GBR. Dist: Independent Pubs. Group.

Glassman, Keri & Mahoney, Sarah. The Slim Calm Sexy Diet: 365 Proven Food Strategies for Mind/Body Bliss. 2012. (978-1-60961-749-3(5)); pap. (978-1-60961-859-9(9)) Rodale Pr., Inc.

—Slim Calm Sexy Diet: 365 Proven Food Strategies for Mind/Body Bliss. 2012. (ENG., Illus.). 288p. pap. 21.99 (978-1-60961-756-1(8)) Rodale Pr., Inc.

Goldstein, Sam & Brooks, Robert B. Understanding & Managing Children's Classroom Behavior: Creating Sustainable, Resilient Classrooms. 2nd rev. ed. 2007. (Wiley Series on Personality Processes Ser.: 207). (ENG., Illus.). 608p. 72.00 (978-0-471-74212-8(0), Wiley) Wiley, John & Sons, Inc.

Gray, Richard. About Addictions: Notes from Psychology, Neuroscience & NLP. 2008. 186p. pap. 19.99 (978-1-4357-5587-1(1)) Lulu Enterprises Inc.

Gregerson, Mary Banks, ed. Technology Innovations for Behavioral Education. 2011. (ENG., Illus.). xvii, 72p. 129.00 (978-1-4419-9391-5(6), 1441993916) Springer.

Grodner, Brian S. & Reid, David B. Permanent Habit Control: Practitioner's Guide to Using Hypnosis & Other Alternative Health Strategies. 2010. (Illus.). xvi, 306p. E-Book 60.00 (978-0-8261-0388-8(X)) Springer Publishing Co., Inc.

Hagenbach, Sandra. Teaching Children Responsible Behavior: A Complete Toolkit. 2010. (ENG., Illus.). 216p. (gr. k-12). 39.00 (978-0-7360-8431-4(2)) Human Kinetics Pubs.

Hamil, Sara & New Harbinger Publications Staff. My Feeling Better Workbook. 2008. 130p. pap. 16.95 (978-1-931704-38-0(4)) Play2Grow.

Handelman, Sapir. Thought Manipulation: The Use & Abuse of Psychological Trickery. 1 vol. 2009. (Illus.). 190p. 34.95 (978-0-313-35532-5(0), C35532, Praeger Pubs.) Greenwood Publishing Group, Inc.

Harris, Bryan & Goldberg, Cassandra. 75 Quick & Easy Solutions to Common Classroom Disruptions. 2012. (978-1-59667-209-3(9)) Eye On Education, Inc.

Hartnett, Richard G. Sobriety & Inspiration: Entrusting Ourselves to the Source of Our Healing & Creativity. 2008. (ENG.). 248p. pap. 19.95 (978-1-934937-07-5(X)) Mill City Pr., Inc.

Haydn, Terry. Managing Pupil Behaviour: Improving the classroom Atmosphere. 2nd rev. ed. 2012. (ENG., Illus.). 232p. (C). 160.00 (978-0-415-61431-3(7)); pap. 35.95 (978-0-415-61432-0(5)) Routledge.

Haynes, Stephen N., et al. Behavioral Assessment & Case Formulation. 2011. (ENG., Illus.). 394p. 90.00 (978-1-118-01864-4(8), Wiley) Wiley, John & Sons, Inc.

Henley, Martin, et al. Characteristics of & Strategies for Teaching Students with Mild Disabilities. 6th ed. 2008. (ENG., Illus.). 456p. (C). pap. 129.80 (978-0-205-60838-6(8)) Allyn & Bacon, Inc.

Heyen, Gina. Creating a Therapeutic Classroom: A Teacher's Guide to Meeting the Needs of All Students in the Classroom. 2007. 82p. per. 8.99 (978-1-60247-067-5(7)) Tate Publishing & Enterprises, LLC.

Hibbs, Stanley E. Consider It Done! Ten Prescriptions for Finishing What You Start. 2008. pap. 14.95 (978-1-897326-51-0(3)) Impact Pubns.

Hieneman, Meme, et al. Parenting with Positive Behavior Support: A Practical Guide to Resolving Your Child's Difficult Behavior. 2006. (Illus.). 206p. per. 22.95 (978-1-55766-865-3(5), 8655) Brookes, Paul H. Publishing Co.

Higgins, Stephen T., et al, eds. Contingency Management in Substance Abuse Treatment. 2007. (ENG., Illus.). 380p. 50.00 (978-1-59385-571-0(0)) Guilford Pubns., Inc.

Hilsen, Lindsay. A Step-by-Step Curriculum for Early Learners with Autism Spectrum Disorders. 2011. (ENG.). 384p. pap. (978-1-84905-874-2(1)) Kingsley, Jessica Ltd.

Holifield, Cassandra Allen. The A-B-C's of Response to Intervention & Behavior - Next Steps: A Practitioner's Guide to Implementation. 2008. 156p. pap. 34.95 (978-1-4327-3649-1(3)) Outskirts Pr., Inc.

Howarth, Roy & Howarth. 100 Ideas for Supporting Pupils with Social, Emotional & Behavioural Difficulties. 2008. (Continuum One Hundreds Ser.). (ENG.). 136p. 19.95 (978-0-8264-9661-4(X)) Continuum International Publishing Group, Ltd. GBR. Dist: National Bk. Network.

Hunt, Gilbert H., et al. Effective Teaching: Preparation & Implementation. 4th ed. 2009. 316p. 62.95 (978-0-398-07859-1(9)); pap. 42.95 (978-0-398-07860-7(2)) Thomas, Charles C. Pub., Ltd.

Hunter, William. Dream Greatness Be Unstoppable: Live Your Dream & Leave a Legacy. 2008. (ENG.). 184p. per. 14.95 (978-0-9792263-1-7(7)) William, Hunter.

Jackson, Lewis & Leon, Marjorie. Developing a Behavior Support Plan: A Manual for Teachers & Behavioral Specialists. 2nd ed. pap. 12.00 (978-1-884720-08-6(0)) PEAK Parent Ctr., Inc.

Janney, Rachel & Snell, Martha E. Behavioral Support. 2nd ed. 2008. (Teachers' Guides to Inclusive Practices Ser.). (Illus.). 192p. per. 26.95 (978-1-55766-911-7(2)) Brookes, Paul H. Publishing Co.

Johns, Beverley H. & Carr, Valerie G. Techniques for Managing Verbally & Physically Aggressive Students. 3rd ed. 2009. (ENG.). 194p. (C). pap. 39.95 (978-0-89108-342-9(1)) Love Publishing Co.

Kaiser, et al. Challenging Behavior in Young Children: Understanding, Preventing & Responding Effectively. 3rd ed. 2011. (ENG., Illus.). 368p. (C). pap. 39.99 (978-0-13-215912-8(0)) Allyn & Bacon, Inc.

Kaiser, Barbara, et al. Challenging Behavior in Elementary & Middle School. 2008. (ENG., Illus.). 384p. (C). pap. 49.00 (978-0-205-46099-1(2)) Allyn & Bacon, Inc.

Kapalka, George M. Eight Steps to Classroom Management Success: A Guide for Teachers of Challenging Students. Kapalka, George M., ed. 2009. 184p. 78.95 (978-1-4129-6943-7(3), B69437C) Corwin Pr.

Kazdin. Behavior Modification in Applied Settings. 3rd ed. Date not set. (Psychology Ser.). 350p. mass mkt. 23.00 net. (978-0-534-10621-8(8)) Brooks/Cole.

Kazdin, Alan E. Behavior Modification in Applied Settings. 6th ed. 2008. 512p. (C). pap. 63.95 (978-1-57766-582-3(1)) Waveland Pr., Inc.

Kearney, Albert J. Understanding Applied Behavior Analysis: An Introduction to ABA for Parents, Teachers, & Other Professionals. 2007. (Jkp Essentials Ser.). (ENG., Illus.). 112p. per. (978-1-84310-860-3(7)) Kingsley, Jessica Ltd.

Kernberg, Paulina F. Beyond the Reflection: The Role of the Mirror Paradigm in Clinical Practice. 2007. (ENG., Illus.). 232p. pap. 26.00 (978-1-59051-071-1(2)) Other Pr., LLC.

Kerr, Mary M. & Nelson, C. Michael. Strategies for Addressing Behavior Problems in the Classroom. 6th ed. 2009. (ENG.). 448p. (C). pap. 120.80 (978-0-13-604524-3(3), Prentice Hall) Prentice Hall PTR.

Khouri, Ed. Restarting with Ed Khouri: Workbook - Revised 2010. 2010. (YA). pap., wbk. ed. 24.95 (978-0-9674357-2-5(2)) Shepherd's Hse., Inc.

—Restarting with Ed Khouri: Workbook & Facilitator Guide. 2008. 190p. pap. 24.95 (978-0-9674357-3-2(0)) Shepherd's Hse., Inc.

Killinger, Barbara. Achieving Inner Balance in Anxious Times. 2011. (ENG.). 320p. (C). pap. (978-0-7735-3844-3(5)) McGill-Queen's Univ. Pr.

Killion, William K. Tackle Box: The Training Companion for the Functional Independence Skills Handbook or F. I. S. H. 2007. per. 29.95 (978-1-59872-750-0(8)) Instant Pub.

Klatt, D M. Grits, Rice, & Dustpan Biscuits. 2008. 184p. per. 13.99 (978-1-60477-331-6(6)) Xulon Pr., Inc.

Kotler, Philip & Lee, Nancy R. Social Marketing: Influencing Behaviors for Good. (Illus.). (C). 3rd ed. 2007. 456p. per. 70.95 (978-1-4129-5647-5(1), B56471P) 4th ed. 2011. 520p. pap. 70.00 (978-1-4129-8149-1(2), B81491P) SAGE Pubns., Inc.

Kottler, Jeffrey A. & Carlson, Jon. Creative Breakthroughs in Therapy: Tales of Transformation & Astonishment. 2009. (ENG., Illus.). 320p. pap. 45.00 (978-0-470-36240-2(5), Wiley) Wiley, John & Sons, Inc.

Kushner, Robert F., et al. Counseling Overweight Adults: The Lifestyle Patterns Approach & Toolkit. 2008. (978-0-88091-422-2(X)) Academy of Nutrition & Dietetics.

Lamb, James M. The Power to Change. 2007. 258p. pap. 18.95 (978-0-7414-4324-3(4)) Infinity Publishing.

Lamm, Brad. Just 10 LBS: Easy Steps to Weighing What You Want (Finally) 2011. (ENG.). 240p. 19.95 (978-1-4019-3179-7(0)) Hay Hse., Inc.

Lane, Kathleen Lynne, et al. Developing Schoolwide Programs to Prevent & Manage Problem Behaviors: A Step-by-Step Approach. 2009. (ENG., Illus.). 196p. (gr. k-12). pap. 35.00 (978-1-60623-032-9(8)) Guilford Pubns., Inc.

Leafgren, Sheri L. Reuben's Fall: A Rhizomatic Analysis of Disobedience in Kindergarten. (Int'l Inst Qualitative Methodology Serie Ser.). (ENG., Illus.). 288p. 2011. pap. 34.95 (978-1-59874-495-8(X)) 2009. lib. bdg. 69.00 (978-1-59874-494-1(1)) Left Coast Pr., Inc.

Leaman, Louisa & Leaman. The Dictionary of Disruption: A Practical Guide to Behaviour Management. 2007. (Practical Teaching Guides). (ENG.). 160p. 29.95 (978-0-8264-9466-5(8)) Continuum International Publishing Group, Ltd. GBR. Dist: National Bk. Network.

Lederer, Aaron. Taming the Wild Child: From Living Hell to Living Well. 2008. 176p. pap. 15.95 (978-1-4401-0142-7(6)) iUniverse, Inc.

Lee, Chris. Resolving Behaviour Problems in Your School: A Practical Guide for Teachers & Support Staff. 2007. 128p. 62.95 (978-1-4129-2413-9(8), B24138C); (Illus.). per. 30.00 (978-1-4129-2414-6(6), B24138P) SAGE Pubns., Ltd. GBR. Dist: SAGE Pubns., Inc.

Levine, James E. Learning from Behavior: How to Understand & Help Challenging Children in School. 1 vol. 2007. (Child Psychology & Mental Health Ser.). 168p. 44.95 (978-0-275-99040-4(0), C9040, Praeger Pubs.) Greenwood Publishing Group, Inc.

—Learning from Behavior: How to Understand & Help Challenging Children in School. 2009. (ENG.). 150p. pap. 27.95 (978-1-57886-804-9(1)) Rowman & Littlefield Publishers, Inc.

Lewis, Ramon. The Developmental Management Approach to Classroom Behaviour. 2008. 173p. pap. 39.95 (978-0-86431-647-9(X)) ACER Pr. AUS. Dist: International Specialized Bk. Services.

—Understanding Pupil Behaviour: Classroom management techniques for Teachers. 2009. 176p. pap. 33.95 (978-0-415-48353-7(0)) Taylor & Francis Group.

Lewis, Trevor. Behaviour Skills - A Parents & Support Workers Guide. 2008. 208p. pap. 24.95 (978-1-4092-1054-2(5)) Lulu Enterprises Inc.

Liggett, Tony. The Mental Diet. 2011. 124p. pap. 18.95 (978-0-89334-889-2(9)) Humanics Publishing Group.

Long, Rob. Rob Long's Omnibus Edition of Better Behaviour. 2007. (David Fulton / Nasen Ser.). 224p. 54.95 (978-1-84312-470-2(X)) Routledge.

Lutzer, Erwin W. Getting to No: How to Break a Stubborn Habit. 2007. (ENG.). 176p. per. 12.99 (978-0-7814-4514-6(0)) Cook, David C.

Mah, Ronald. Difficult Behavior in Early Childhood: Positive Discipline for PreK-3 Classrooms & Beyond. 2006. (Illus.). 176p. 72.95 (978-1-4129-3714-6(0), B37140C); pap. 31.95 (978-1-4129-3715-3(9), B37140P) Corwin Pr.

Marchand-Martella, Nancy E., et al. Comprehensive Behavior Management: Individualized, Classroom, & Schoolwide Approaches. 2nd ed. 2011. (Illus.). 456p. (C). pap. 79.00 (978-1-4129-8827-8(6), B88278P) SAGE Pubns., Inc.

Marcotte, Jerry & McMahon, Patrick. The Formation of a New Republic: A Photographic History of Boys Republic. 2007. (Illus.). 96p. (978-1-57864-461-2(5)) Donning Co. Pubs.

Martin, Garry & Pear, Joseph. Behavior Modification: What It Is & How to Do It. 9th ed. 2011. (Illus.). xvii, 462p. (978-0-205-83398-6(5)) Allyn & Bacon, Inc.

Martin, Garry L. & Pear, Joseph. Behavior Modification: What It Is & How to Do It. 9th ed. 2010. (ENG.). 480p. (C). pap. 146.20 (978-0-205-79272-6(3), Prentice Hall) Prentice Hall PTR.

Mayer, G. Roy, et al. Behavior Analysis for Lasting Change. 2nd ed. 2011. (C). 95.95 (978-1-59738-032-4(6)) Sloan Publishing.

Mazur, James E. Learning & Behavior. 7th rev. ed. 2013. (ENG.). 448p. (978-0-205-24644-1(3)) Pearson Bks.

McGrath, Helen & Edwards, Hazel. Difficult Personalities: A Practical Guide to Managing the Hurtful Behavior of Others (and Maybe Your Own) 2010. (ENG.). 304p. pap. 14.95 (978-1-61519-013-3(9), 1615190139) Experiment LLC, The.

McKenna, Paul. I Can Make You Thin: The Revolutionary System Used by More Than 6 Million People. 2012. (ENG., Illus.). 176p. 14.95 (978-1-4027-7554-3(7)) Sterling Publishing Co., Inc.

—I Can Make You Thin: The Revolutionary System Used by More Than 3 Million People. 2008. (ENG., Illus.). 176p. 22.95 (978-1-4027-6571-1(1)) Sterling Publishing Co., Inc.

Mennuti, Rosemary B., et al, eds. Cognitive-Behavioral Interventions in Educational Settings: A Handbook for Practice. 2nd rev. ed. 2012. (ENG., Illus.). 782p. 62.95 (978-0-415-80740-1(9)) Routledge.

Messurier, Mark Le. Teaching Tough Kids: Simple & Proven Strategies for Student Success. 2009. (ENG., Illus.). 240p. pap. 42.95 (978-0-415-46060-6(3)) Routledge.

Milland, Garehoff. Ouch! - Behavioural Safety Between the Sheets. 2008. 100p. pap. (978-1-905553-32-7(3)) BookPublishingWorld.

Miltenberger, Raymond G. Behavior Modification: Principles & Procedures. 5th ed. 2011. (ENG.). 688p. (C). pap. 186.95 (978-1-111-30611-3(7)) Wadsworth.

Mohammed, Abdel Rahim. Clinician's Guide Tobacco Cessation. 2009. 65p. pap. 29.95 (978-1-936176-02-1(5)) American Academy of Oral Medicine.

Morgan, Jill & Morgan. The Teaching Assistant's Guide to Managing Behaviour. 2007. (Teaching Assistant's Ser.). (ENG., Illus.). 152p. 35.95 (978-0-8264-9682-9(2)) Continuum International Publishing Group, Ltd. GBR. Dist: National Bk. Network.

Nelson, Tammy. Whats Eating You: A Workbook for Teens with Anorexia, Bulimia, & Other Eating Disorders. 2008. (Instant Help Ser.). 110p. pap. 14.95 (978-1-931704-44-1(9)) Play2Grow.

Nind, Melanie & Seale, Jane. Understanding & Promoting Access for People with Learning Difficulties: Seeing the opportunities & challenges of Risk. Nind, Melanie & Seale, Jane, eds. 2009. (ENG., Illus.). 190p. pap. 42.95 (978-0-415-47948-6(7)) Routledge.

Nissman, Blossom S. Teacher-Tested Classroom Management Strategies. 3rd ed. 2008. (What Every Student Should Know about... (WESSKA Series) Ser.). (ENG., Illus.). 176p. (C). pap. 7.80 (978-0-13-714915-5(8), Prentice Hall) Prentice Hall PTR.

Olive, Edna. PBF — Positive Behavior Facilitation: Understanding & Intervening in the Behavior of Youth. 2007. 136p. pap. 18.95 (978-0-87822-544-6(7)) Research Pr.

O'Regan, Fintan J. & O'Regan. Can't Learn, Won't Learn, Don't Care. 2007. (ENG., Illus.). 168p. 29.95 (978-0-8264-9024-7(7)) Continuum International Publishing Group, Ltd. GBR. Dist: National Bk. Network.

Otto, Michael, et al. Living with Bipolar Disorder: A Guide for Individuals & Families. 2008. (ENG., Illus.). 160p. per. 18.95 (978-0-19-532358-0(0)) Oxford Univ. Pr., Inc.

Palley, Sharon. Promoting Positive Behaviour: When Supporting People with a Learning Disability & People with Autism. 2012. (ENG., Illus.). 120p. pap. (978-0-85725-713-0(7)) Learning Matters Ltd.

Parry-Mitchell, Chris, ed. The Behaviour Management Toolkit: Avoiding Exclusion at School. 2012. (Lucky Duck Bks.). 136p. 140.00 (978-1-4462-1074-1(X), B10741C); pap. 53.00 (978-1-4462-1075-8(8), B10741P) SAGE Pubns., Ltd. GBR. Dist: SAGE Pubns., Inc.

Parsons, Richard D., ed. Thinking & Acting Like a Behavioral School Counselor. 2009. (Illus.). 176p. 72.95 (978-1-4129-6650-4(7), B66504C); pap. 31.95 (978-1-4129-6651-1(5), B66504P) Corwin Pr.

Perrow, Susan, ed. Healing Stories for Challenging Behaviour. 2008. (Early Years Ser.). (Illus.). 301p. (J). pap. (978-1-903458-78-5(1)) Hawthorn Pr.

Peterson, M V. 12 Step Workbook. 2007. 123p. per. 9.95 (978-1-885373-58-8(9)) Emerald Ink Publishing.

Piacentini, John, et al. It's Only a False Alarm: A Cognitive Behavioral Treatment Program Workbook. 2007. (Treatments That Work Ser.). (ENG., Illus.). 80p. pap. 17.95 (978-0-19-531052-8(7)) Oxford Univ. Pr., Inc.

Pierangelo, Roger & Giuliani, George A. Classroom Management Techniques for Students with ADHD: A Step-by-Step Guide for Educators. 2007. (Step-By-Step Guide for Educators Ser.). 120p. per. 27.95 (978-1-4129-1788-9(3), B17883P) Corwin Pr.

Porter, Louise. Behaviour in Schools. 2nd rev. ed. 2006. (Illus.). 368p. (C). pap. 68.00 (978-0-335-22001-4(0), 0335220010, Open University Pr.) McGraw-Hill Education GBR. Dist: McGraw-Hill Cos., The.

—Young Children's Behavior: Practical Approaches for Caregivers & Teachers. 3rd ed. 2008. 304p. pap. 34.95 (978-1-55766-956-8(2)) Brookes, Paul H. Publishing Co.

Porterfield, Jason. How to Beat Social Alienation. 2012. (Beating Bullying Ser.). (ENG., Illus.). 48p. (YA). (gr. 5-8). pap. 11.75 (978-1-4488-6821-6(1)); lib. bdg. 27.95 (978-1-4488-6812-4(2)) Rosen Publishing Group, Inc., The. (Rosen Central).

Pritchard, Robert & Ashwood, Elissa. Managing Motivation: A Manager's Guide to Diagnosing & Improving Motivation. 2008. (ENG., Illus.). 152p. 70.95 (978-1-84169-713-0(3), Routledge) Taylor & Francis Group GBR. Dist: Taylor & Francis Group.

Pudney, Warwick & Whitehouse, Eliane. Little Volcanoes: Helping Young Children & Their Parents to Deal with Anger. 2012. (Illus.). 176p. pap. (978-1-84905-217-7(4)) Kingsley, Jessica Ltd.

Raeburn, Susan & Maisel, Eric. Creative Recovery: A Complete Addiction Treatment Program That Uses Your Natural Creativity. 2008. (ENG., Illus.). 312p. pap. 16.95 (978-1-59030-544-7(2), Trumpeter) Shambhala Pubns., Inc.

Ravet, Jackie. Are We Listening? Making Sense of Classroom Behaviour with Pupils & Parents. 2007. (Illus.). 165p. per. 31.00 (978-1-85856-392-3(5)) Trentham Bks. Ltd. GBR. Dist: Stylus Publishing, LLC.

Reeves, Melissa A., et al. Comprehensive Planning for Safe Learning Environments: A School Professional's Guide to Integrating Physical & Psychological Safety: Prevention Through Recovery. 2009. (School-Based Practice in Action Ser.). (ENG., Illus.). 371p. pap. 34.95 (978-0-415-99835-2(2)) Routledge.

Riffel, Laura A. Target the Behavior: Not the Student. 2010. 115p. pap. 25.00 (978-0-557-29357-5(X)) Lulu Enterprises Inc.

Robertson, Donald. The Philosophy of Cognitive-Behavioural Therapy: Stoic Philosophy as Rational & Cognitive Psychotherapy. 2010. 316p. pap. 37.95 (978-1-85575-756-1(7)) Karnac Bks. GBR. Dist: Stylus Publishing, LLC.

Robinson, Maria. Understanding Behaviour & Development in Early Childhood: A Guide to Theory & Practice. 2010. (ENG.). 136p. (C). instr.'s gde. ed. 128.00 (978-0-415-56560-8(X)); pap., instr.'s gde. ed. 31.95 (978-0-415-56561-5(8)) Routledge.

Rogers, Bill. Behaviour Mangement: A Whole-School Approach. 2nd ed. (Illus.). 304p. pap. 39.95 (978-1-4129-3452-7(4), B34510PM); 2007. 105.00 (978-1-4129-3451-0(6), B34510C) SAGE Pubns., Ltd. GBR. Dist: SAGE Pubns., Inc.

—Classroom Behaviour: A Practical Guide to Effective Teaching, Behaviour Management & Colleague Support. 3rd ed. 2011. (Illus.). 280p. 104.00 (978-0-85702-166-3(4), B21663C); pap. 45.00 (978-0-85702-167-0(2), B21663P) SAGE Pubns., Ltd. GBR. Dist: SAGE Pubns., Inc.

—Cracking the Hard Class. 2nd ed. (Illus.). 224p. 106.00 (978-1-4129-2355-2(7), B23557C); pap. 33.95 (978-1-4129-2356-9(5), B23557P) SAGE Pubns., Ltd. GBR. Dist: SAGE Pubns., Inc.

Rogers, Bill, ed. How to Manage Children's Challenging Behaviour. 2nd ed. 2009. (Illus.). 208p. 71.00 (978-1-84860-684-5(2), B06842C); pap. 35.00 (978-1-84860-685-2(0), B06842P) SAGE Pubns., Ltd. GBR. Dist: SAGE Pubns., Inc.

Rollnick, Stephen, et al. Motivational Interviewing in Health Care: Helping Patients Change Behavior. 2007. (Applications of Motivational Interviewing Ser.). (ENG., Illus.). 210p. 55.00 (978-1-59385-613-7(X)); pap. 30.00 (978-1-59385-612-0(1)) Guilford Pubns., Inc.

Ryan, M. J. This Year I Will... How to Finally Change a Habit, Keep a Resolution, or Make a Dream Come True. 2006. (ENG.). 240p. 16.95 (978-0-7679-2008-7(2), Broadway) Broadway Bks.

Sarafino, Edward P. Applied Behavior Analysis: Principles & Procedures in Behavior Modification. 2011. (Wiley Desktop Editions Ser.). (ENG., Illus.). 472p. (C). pap. 147.95 (978-0-470-57152-1(7), Wiley) Wiley, John & Sons, Inc.

Scannell, Ma. Coaching for Behavior Change: A practical, easy to use 5-Step Method. 2008. 208p. 27.95 (978-0-595-50913-3(4)); pap. 17.95 (978-0-595-45899-8(8)) iUniverse, Inc.

Scannella, Anthony. Changing Student Behavior: Comprehensive Learning & Interventions for Correcting Kids. 2007. (ENG.). 92p. per. 19.95 (978-1-57886-708-0(8)) Rowman & Littlefield Publishers, Inc.

—Changing Student Behavior: Comprehensive Learning & Interventions for Correcting Kids - The Click Program. 2007. (ENG.). 92p. 49.95 (978-1-57886-707-3(X)) Rowman & Littlefield Education.

Scannella, Anthony & McCarthy, Sharon. Innovative Interventions for Today's Exceptional Children: Cultivating a Passion for Compassion. 2008. (ENG.). 94p. pap. 18.95 (978-1-57886-870-4(X)) Rowman & Littlefield Education.

Scheuermann, Brenda K. & Hall, Judy A. Positive Behavioral Supports for the Classroom. 2007. (ENG., Illus.). 544p. (C). per. 91.00 (978-0-13-113157-6(5), Prentice Hall) Prentice Hall PTR.

Schinke, Steven, ed. Behavioral Methods in Social Welfare: Helping Children, Adults, & Families in Community Settings. 2007. (Modern Applications of Social Work Ser.). (ENG., Illus.). 436p. pap. 39.95 (978-0-202-36214-4(0)) Aldine Transaction.

Schultz, Dana & Dubowitz, Tamara. Evaluation of the Arkansas Tobacco Settlement Program: Progress During 2006 And 2007. 2009. 242p. pap. 33.00 (978-0-8330-4626-0(8), tr-611) RAND Corp., The.

Schwartz, Jeffrey & Gladding, Rebecca. You Are Not Your Brain: The 4-Step Solution for Changing Bad Habits, Ending Unhealthy Thinking, & Taking

Control of Your Life. 2011. (ENG.). 368p. (gr. 12). 26.00 (978-1-58333-426-3(2), Avery) Penguin Group (USA) Inc.

Selig, Meg. Changepower! 37 Secrets to Habit Change Success. 2009. (ENG., Illus.). 281p. 19.95 (978-0-415-80066-2(8)) Routledge.

Seligman, Martin E. What You Can Change & What You Can't: The Complete Guide to Successful Self-Improvement. 2007. (Vintage Ser.). (ENG.). 336p. pap. 15.00 (978-1-4000-7840-0(7), Vintage) Knopf Doubleday Publishing Group.

Seven. Mind Strategies. 2010. 388p. 37.95 (978-0-595-51421-2(9)); pap. 27.95 (978-0-595-52606-2(3)) iUniverse, Inc.

Shapiro, Laweren. Stopping the Pain: A Workbook for Teens Who Self-Injure. 2008. (Instant Help Ser.). 142p. pap. 14.95 (978-1-931704-40-3(6)) Play2Grow.

Shapiro, Lawerence. Learning to Listen, Learning to Care: A Workbook to Help Kids Learn Self-Control & Empathy. 2008. (Instant Help Ser.). 130p. pap. 16.95 (978-1-931704-37-3(6)) Play2Grow.

Sheldon, Brian. Cognitive-Behavioural Therapy. 2nd rev. ed. 2011. Orig. Title: Behaviour Modification. (ENG., Illus.). 304p. (C). 140.00 (978-0-415-56436-6(0)); pap. 45.95 (978-0-415-56435-9(2)) Routledge.

Shelton, Fiona & Brownhill, Simon. Effective Behaviour Management in the Primary Classroom. (ENG., Illus.). 184p. (C). 2009. 117.00 (978-0-335-22540-8(3), 0335225403) 2008. pap. 40.00 (978-0-335-22541-5(1), 0335225411) McGraw-Hill Education GBR. Dist: McGraw-Hill Cos., The.

Shepherd, Terry L. Working with Students with Emotional & Behavior Disorders: Characteristics & Teaching Strategies. 2009. (ENG.). 312p. (C). pap. 56.60 (978-0-13-229859-9(7), Prentice Hall) Prentice Hall PTR.

Sherrer, Quin & Garlock, Ruthanne. Lord, Help Me Break This Habit: You Can Be Free from Doing the Things You Hate. 2009. 208p. pap. 13.99 (978-0-8007-9464-4(8)) Chosen Bks.

Shumaker, Sally A., et al. The Handbook of Health Behavior Change. 3rd ed. 2008. (Illus.). 896p. 85.00 (978-0-8261-1545-4(4)) Springer Publishing Co., Inc.

Sida-Nicholls, Kate. What if it happens in my Classroom? Developing skills for expert behaviour Management. 2012. (ENG.). 160p. (C). 155.00 (978-0-415-68713-3(6)); pap. 33.95 (978-0-415-68714-0(4)) Routledge.

Simmons, Linda L. The Everything Health Guide to Addiction & Recovery: Control Your Behavior & Build a Better Life. 2008. (ENG.). 320p. pap. 14.95 (978-1-59869-806-0(0)) Adams Media Corp.

Smith, Connie Jo. Behavioral Challenges in Early Childhood Settings. 2008. (Redleaf Quick Guides). (ENG.). 40p. spiral bd. 14.95 (978-1-933653-61-7(2)) Redleaf Pr.

Sousa, David A. How the Brain Influences Behavior: Management Strategies for Every Classroom. 2008. (Illus.). 264p. 90.95 (978-1-4129-5869-1(5), B58691C); pap. 41.95 (978-1-4129-5870-7(9), B58691P) Corwin Pr.

Sprick, Randy & Garrison, Mickey. Interventions: Evidence-Based Behavioral Strategies for Individual Students. 2nd rev. ed. 2008. 814p. cd-rom (978-1-59909-017-7(1)) Pacific Northwest Publishing, Inc.

Sprick, Randy, et al. Behavioral Response to Intervention: Creating a Continuum of Problem-Solving & Support. 2009. (Randy Sprick's Safe & Civil School Ser.). 352p. pap. incl. audio compact disk (978-1-59909-028-3(7)) Pacific Northwest Publishing, Inc.

Sprinson, John Scott & Berrick, Ken. Unconditional Care: Relationship-Based, Behavioral Intervention with Vulnerable Children & Families, 1 vol. 2010. (ENG.). 304p. pap. 31.99 (978-0-19-973303-3(1)) Oxford Univ. Pr., Inc.

St Clair, Joe. 100 Tips for Total Life Fulfilment: Live the life you have always wanted starting Today. 2009. 248p. pap. 14.49 (978-1-4389-5922-1(2)) AuthorHouse.

Sulzer-Azaroff, Beth. Applying Behavior Analysis Across the Autism Spectrum: A Guide for Practitioners. 2007. (C). pap. 30.00 net. (978-1-59738-009-6(1)) Sloan Publishing.

Sutton, James D. 60 Ways to Reach a Difficult & Defiant Child. I.t. ed. 2007. (Illus.). 108p. per. 21.50 (978-1-878878-75-5(1)) Friendly Oaks Pubns.

Suvan, Jean E. & Ramseier, Christoph, eds. Health Behavior Change in the Dental Practice. 2010. (ENG., Illus.). 196p. pap. 52.99 (978-0-8138-2106-1(1), Wiley-Blackwell) Wiley, John & Sons, Inc.

Swinson, Jeremy & Harrop, Alex. Positive Psychology for Teachers. 2012. (ENG., Illus.). 184p. (C). 155.00 (978-0-415-68676-1(8)); pap. 40.95 (978-0-415-68677-8(6)) Routledge.

Tan, Charlene. Teaching Without Indoctrination: Implications for Values Education. 2008. 132p. (978-90-8790-647-4(1)); pap. (978-90-8790-646-7(3)) Sense Pubs.

Tetteris, Belinda Christine. The Nitty-Gritty Classroom & Behavior Management Resource: Strategies, Reproducibles, & Tips for Teachers. 2006. (ENG., Illus.). 238p. per. 32.95 (978-1-57886-497-3(6)) Rowman & Littlefield Education.

Tharp, Roland G. Delta Theory & Psychosocial Systems: The Practice of Influence & Change. 2011. (ENG., Illus.). 206p. 90.00 **(978-1-107-01491-6(3))** Cambridge Univ. Pr.

Thew, Miranda & McKenna, Jim, eds. Lifestyle Management in Health & Social Care. 2008. (ENG., Illus.). 280p. pap. 66.99 (978-1-4051-7114-4(6), Wiley-Blackwell) Wiley, John & Sons, Inc.

Vargas, Julie & Vargas, Julie S. Behavior Analysis for Effective Teaching. 2009. (ENG., Illus.). 392p. 79.95 (978-0-415-99008-0(4)) Routledge.

Walker, David, ed. Taken to the Limit? Exploring the Boundaries of Government's Influence on People's Behaviour in 21st Century Britain. 2007. ("Political Quarterly" Special Issues Ser.). 208p. pap. 34.95 (978-1-4051-7631-6(8), Wiley-Blackwell) Wiley, John & Sons, Inc.

Wallace, Fiona. What Else Can I Do with You? Helping Children Improve Classroom Behaviour. 2nd ed. 2007. (Lucky Duck Bks.). (Illus.). 112p. pap. 31.00 (978-1-4129-2897-7(4), B28974P) SAGE Pubns., Ltd. GBR. Dist: SAGE Pubns., Inc.

Wallace, Fiona & Caesar, Diane. Not You Again! Helping Children Improve Playtime & Lunch-time Behaviour. 2nd ed. 2007. (Lucky Duck Bks.). (Illus.). 112p. pap. 31.00 (978-1-4129-2896-0(6), B28966P) SAGE Pubns., Ltd. GBR. Dist: SAGE Pubns., Inc.

Waller, Raymond Jefferson. The Teacher's Concise Guide to Functional Behavioral Assessment. Waller, Raymond Jefferson, ed. 2008. (Illus.). 136p. pap. 24.95 (978-1-4129-6605-4(1), B66047P) Corwin Pr.

Waller, Raymond Jefferson, ed. The Teacher's Concise Guide to Functional Behavioral Assessment. 2008. (Illus.). 136p. 60.95 (978-1-4129-6604-7(3), B66047C) Corwin Pr.

Walters, Jim & Frei, Shelly. Managing Classroom Behavior & Discipline. 2007. (Practical Strategies for Successful Classrooms Ser.). (ENG.). 224p. (gr. k-12). pap. 24.99 (978-1-4258-0378-0(4)) Shell Educational Publishing.

Wheeler, John J. & Richey, David Dean. Behavior Management: Principles & Practices of Positive Behavior Supports. 2nd ed. 2009. (ENG.). 416p. (C). pap. 90.40 (978-0-13-501071-6(3), Prentice Hall) Prentice Hall PTR.

Whitman, Thomas L. & DeWitt, Nicole. Key Learning Skills for Children with Autism Spectrum Disorders: A Blueprint for Life. 2011. (ENG.). 304p. (978-1-84905-864-3(4)) Kingsley, Jessica Ltd.

Wilhite, Jud. Throw It Down: Leaving Behind Behaviors & Dependencies That Hold You Back, 1 vol. 2010. (ENG.). 144p. 14.99 (978-0-310-32753-0(9)) Zondervan.

Young, Johnnie. 100 Completely New Ideas for Managing Behaviour. 2011. (Continuums One Hundreds Ser.). (ENG.). 136p. pap. 19.95 (978-1-4411-6908-2(3)) Continuum International Publishing Group, Ltd. GBR. Dist: National Bk. Network.

Zirpoli, Thomas J. Behavior Management: Positive Applications for Teachers. 6th rev. ed. 2010. (ENG.). 480p. (C). pap. 120.20 (978-0-13-706320-8(2), Prentice Hall) Prentice Hall PTR.

BEHAVIOR OF CHILDREN

see Child Rearing; Etiquette for Children and Teenagers

BEHAVIOR PROBLEMS IN CHILDREN

see Behavior Disorders in Children

BEHAVIOR THERAPY

see also Acceptance and Commitment Therapy; Rational-Emotive Psychotherapy

Agras, W. Stuart & Apple, Robin. Overcoming Your Eating Disorder: A Cognitive-Behavioral Therapy Approach for Bulimia Nervosa & Binge-Eating Disorder, Guided Self Help Workbook. 2007. (Treatments That Work Ser.). (ENG., Illus.). 112p. pap. 27.95 (978-0-19-533456-2(6)) Oxford Univ. Pr., Inc.

Albin, Jayme. Treating Fear of Flying Using Biofeedback & Virtual Reality. 2009. 56p. pap. (978-3-639-16521-0(7)) VDM Verlag Dr. Mueller e.K.

Alladin, Assen. Handbook of Cognitive Hypnotherapy for Depression: An Evidence-Based Approach. 2007. (Lippincott Williams & Wilkins Handbook Ser.). (Illus.). 240p. pap. 49.99 (978-0-7817-6604-3(4)) Lippincott Williams & Wilkins.

Alpert, Jonathan Edward & Bowman, Alisa. Be Fearless: Change Your Life in 28 Days. 2012. **(978-1-4555-1340-6(7))** Grand Central Publishing.

Anderson, Maureen. The Angry Adolescent: The Resiliencies & Forms of Forgiveness That Impact Teenage Anger Expression. 2008. 220p. pap. (978-3-639-06902-0(1)) VDM Verlag Dr. Mueller e.K.

Antai-Otong, Deborah. Psychiatric Nursing: Biological & Behavioral Concepts 2e. 2nd rev. ed. 2007. (ENG.). 1200p. (C). 165.95 (978-1-4180-3872-4(5)) Delmar Cengage Learning.

Antony, Martin M. & Roemer, Lizabeth. Behavior Therapy. 2011. 188p. (C). pap. 24.95 (978-1-4338-0984-2(2)) American Psychological Assn.

Ashby, Jeffrey S., et al. Active Interventions for Kids & Teens: Adding Adventure & Fun to Counseling! 2008. (978-1-55620-256-8(3)) American Counseling Assn.

Ban, Thomas. Conditioning Behavior & Psychiatry. 2008. (ENG.). 273p. pap. 29.95 (978-0-202-36235-9(3)) Aldine Transaction.

Barlow, David H., ed. Clinical Handbook of Psychological Disorders: A Step-by-Step Treatment Manual. 4th rev. ed. 2007. (ENG.). 722p. 85.00 (978-1-59385-572-7(9)) Guilford Pubns., Inc.

Battenhausen, Leo J. Defeating Depression: The Calm & Sense Way to Find Happiness & Satisfaction. 2011. (ENG.). 224p. pap. 14.95 (978-0-88282-324-9(8)) New Horizon Pr. Pubs., Inc.

Bellack, Alan S., et al. Behavioral Treatment for Substance Abuse in People with Serious & Persistent Mental Illness: A Handbook for Mental Health Professionals. 2006. (ENG., Illus.). 288p. pap. 57.95 (978-0-415-95283-5(2)) Routledge.

Bennett, Richard. Satin Susan vs. a Therapists' Ethics. 2008. 92p. pap. 10.49 (978-1-4389-0553-2(X)) AuthorHouse.

Bieling, Peter J., et al. Cognitive-Behavioral Therapy in Groups. 2006. (ENG., Illus.). 452p. 65.00 (978-1-59385-325-9(4)) Guilford Pubns., Inc.

Björgvinsson, Thröstur & Rosqvist, Johan. Cognitive-Behavioral Therapy for Depression: A Practical Guide to Management & Treatment. 2007. 240p. 85.00 (978-0-415-95339-9(1)) Routledge.

Blenkiron, Paul. Stories & Analogies in Cognitive Behaviour Therapy. 2010. (ENG., Illus.). 408p. 119.95 (978-0-470-05895-4(1)); pap. 59.95 (978-0-470-05896-1(X)) Wiley, John & Sons, Inc. (Wiley-Blackwell).

Bradshaw, John W. S., et al. Principles of Companion Animal Behaviour Therapy. 2nd rev. ed. 2007. (Illus.). 352p. pap. (978-0-632-06396-3(3), Wiley-Blackwell) Wiley, John & Sons, Ltd.

Brown, Julie F. The Skills System Instructor's Guide: An Emotion-Regulation Skills Curriculum for All Learning Abilities. 2011. 332p. pap. 31.95 **(978-1-4502-9548-2(7))** iUniverse, Inc.

Browning, Robert & Stover, Donald. Behavior Modification in Child Treatment: An Experimental & Clinical Approach. 2009. (ENG., Illus.). 428p. pap. 45.95 (978-0-202-36293-9(0)) Aldine Transaction.

Bruckisch, Rabea. Ressourcenorientierte Kunsttherapie mit Flüchtlingskindern: Ressourcenorientierte Arbeit mit Roma-Flüchtlingskindern im kunsttherapeutischen Setting einer Kunstwerkstatt. 2010. 100p. pap. (978-3-639-23605-7(X)) VDM Verlag Dr. Mueller e.K.

Butler, Gillian, et al. Cognitive-Behavioral Therapy for Anxiety Disorders: Mastering Clinical Challenges. 2010. (Guides to Individualized Evidence-Based Treatment Ser.). (ENG., Illus.). 224p. pap. 28.00 (978-1-60623-869-1(8)) Guilford Pubns., Inc.

Buttross, L. Susan. Understanding Attention Deficit Hyperactivity Disorder. 2007. (ENG., Illus.). 126p. 30.00 (978-1-57806-882-1(7)); per. 14.00 (978-1-57806-883-8(5)) Univ. Pr. of Mississippi.

Chantry, David. Talking ACT: Notes & Conversations on Acceptance & Commitment Therapy. 2007. (Professional Ser.). (ENG.). 342p. per. 44.95 (978-1-878978-58-5(6)) Context Pr.

Chapman, Alexander, et al. The Dialectical Behavior Therapy Skills Workbook for Anxiety: Breaking Free from Worry, Panic, PTSD, & Other Anxiety Symptoms. 2011. (ENG., Illus.). 240p. pap. 24.95 (978-1-57224-954-7(4)) New Harbinger Pubns.

Chisari, Fabio. The Match. 2010. 248p. pap. (978-3-8383-7057-6(0)) Lambert Academic Publishing.

Chorpita, Bruce F. Modular Cognitive-Behavioral Therapy for Childhood Anxiety Disorders. 2006. (Guides to Individualized Evidence-Based Treatment Ser.). (ENG., Illus.). 335p. (gr. 1-13). pap. 45.00 (978-1-59385-363-1(7)) Guilford Pubns., Inc.

Christensen, Riddoch. Dialectical Behavior Therapy Skills, 101 Mindfulness Exercises & Other Fun Activities for Children & Adolescents: A Learning Supplement. 2009. 160p. pap. 18.99 (978-1-4343-6825-6(4)) AuthorHouse.

Cipani, Ennio & Schock, Keven M. Functional Behavioral Assessment, Diagnosis, & Treatment: A Complete System for Education & Mental Health Settings. 2nd ed. 2011. (Illus.). xv, 319p. E-Book **(978-0-8261-0605-6(6))** Springer Publishing Co., Inc.

Clark, David A. Cognitive-Behavioral Therapy for OCD. 2006. (ENG., Illus.). 324p. pap. 35.00 (978-1-59385-375-4(0)) Guilford Pubns., Inc.

Contexo Media, creator. Illustrated Coding & Billing for Behavioral Health, Expert: A Comprehensive Specialty Guide. 2011. (Illus.). 186p. spiral bd. 199.95 (978-1-58383-722-1(1)) Contexo Media.

Cooper, Peter. Overcoming Bulimia Nervosa & Binge-Eating: A Self-Help Guide Using Cognitive Behavioral Techniques. 2010. (ENG.). 256p. pap. 14.95 (978-0-465-01267-1(1)) Basic Bks.

Cram101 Textbook Reviews & Cram101 Textbook Reviews. Outlines & Highlights for Handbook of Positive Behavior Support by Wayne Sailor, Isbn: 9780387096315. 2011. 180p. pap. 29.95 **(978-1-61461-047-2(9))** Cram101 Inc.

—Outlines & Highlights for Predicting & Changing Behavior: The Reasoned Action Approach by Martin Fishbein. 2011. 60p. pap. 26.95 **(978-1-61830-478-0(X))** Cram101 Inc.

—Outlines & Highlights for Treatment of Childhood Disorders by Eric Mash, Isbn: 9781572309210. 2011. 528p. pap. 38.95 **(978-1-61461-094-6(0))** Cram101 Inc.

Cram101 Textbook Reviews Staff. Outlines & Highlights for Motivational Interviewing: Preparing People for Change by William R. Miller, ISBN. 2009. 62p. pap. 27.95 (978-1-4288-8528-8(5)) Cram101 Inc.

Craske, Michelle G. Cognitive-Behavioral Therapy. 2009. x, 173p. pap. 24.95 (978-1-4338-0548-6(0)) American Psychological Assn.

Crisp, Bryan & Knox, David. Behavioral Family Therapy: An Evidenced Based Approach. 2008. 132p. pap. 25.00 (978-1-59460-627-4(7)) Carolina Academic Pr.

Dimeff, Linda A. & Koerner, Kelly, eds. Dialectical Behavior Therapy in Clinical Practice: Applications across Disorders & Settings. 2007. (ENG., Illus.). 363p. 50.00 (978-1-57230-974-6(1)) Guilford Pubns., Inc.

Disease Management Dimensions. (Illus.). 2007. 506p. ring bd. 725.00 (978-1-933402-78-9(4)) 2007. 506p. cd-rom 850.00 (978-1-933402-79-6(2)) 2006. 511p. cd-rom 672.00 (978-1-933402-40-6(7)) Healthcare Intelligence Network.

Dobson, Keith S., ed. The Handbook of Cognitive-Behavioral Therapies. 3rd ed. 2009. (ENG., Illus.). 481p. 65.00 (978-1-60623-437-2(4)) Guilford Pubns., Inc.

Donohue, Brad & Allen, Daniel N. Treating Adult Substance Abuse Using Family Behavior Therapy: A Step-by-Step Approach. 2011. (ENG., Illus.). 264p. pap. 55.00 (978-0-470-62193-6(1), Wiley) Wiley, John & Sons, Inc.

Donohue, Brad, et al. Treating Adolescent Substance Abuse Using Family Behavior Therapy: A Step-by-Step Approach. 2011. (ENG., Illus.). 288p. pap. 55.00 **(978-0-470-62192-9(3)**, Wiley) Wiley, John & Sons, Inc.

Dorpat, Theodore L. Crimes of Punishment: America's Culture of Violence. 2007. 35.00 (978-0-87586-564-5(X)); pap. 24.95 (978-0-87586-563-8(1)) Algora Publishing.

Douglas. Containment & Reciprocity: Integrating Psychoanalytic Theory & Child Development Research for Work with Children. 2007. (ENG., Illus.). 184p. (C). 34.95 (978-0-415-39698-1(0)) Routledge.

Douglas, Hazel. Containment & Reciprocity: Integrating Concepts for Work with Children. 2007. (ENG., Illus.). 184p. (C). 95.00 (978-0-415-39697-4(2)) Routledge.

Dryden, Windy. Rational Emotive Behaviour Therapy: Distinctive Features. 2008. (CBT Distinctive Features Ser.). (ENG., Illus.). 160p. (C). 95.00 (978-0-415-43085-2(2)); pap. 17.95 (978-0-415-43086-9(0)) Routledge.

—Understanding Emotional Problems: The REBT Perspective. 2009. (ENG., Illus.). 152p. (C). 95.00 (978-0-415-48196-0(1)); pap. 32.50 (978-0-415-48197-7(X)) Routledge.

Dryden, Windy & Branch, Rhena. The Fundamentals of Rational Emotive Behaviour Therapy: A Training Handbook. 2nd ed. 2008. (ENG., Illus.). 252p. 172.95 (978-0-470-31932-1(1)); pap. 55.95 (978-0-470-31931-4(3)) Wiley, John & Sons, Inc. (Wiley).

Durand, Mark V. & Hieneman, Meme. Helping Parents with Challenging Children: Positive Family Intervention. 2008. (Programs That Work Ser.). (ENG.). 144p. pap. 37.95 (978-0-19-533298-8(9)) Oxford Univ. Pr., Inc.

Durand, V. Mark & Hieneman, Meme. Helping Parents with Challenging Children Positive Family Intervention Parent Workbook. 2008. (Programs That Work Ser.). (ENG.). 144p. pap. 27.95 (978-0-19-533299-5(7)) Oxford Univ. Pr., Inc.

Edelstein, Michael R., et al. Therapy Breakthrough. 2012. (ENG.). 288p. pap. 29.95 (978-0-8126-9686-8(7)) Open Court Publishing Co.

Ellis, Albert & Ellis, Debbie Joffe. Rational Emotive Behavior Therapy. 2011. 160p. (C). pap. 24.95 (978-1-4338-0961-3(3)) American Psychological Assn.

Emmelkamp, Paul M. G. & Vedel, Ellen. Evidence-Based Treatment for Alcohol & Drug Abuse: A Practitioner's Guide to Theory, Methods, & Practice. 2006. (Practical Clinical Guidebooks). (ENG., Illus.). 304p. 94.95 (978-0-415-95285-9(9)); per. 32.35 (978-0-415-95286-6(7)) Routledge.

Etherington, Natasha. Gardening for Children with Autism Spectrum Disorders & Special Educational Needs: Engaging with Nature to Combat Anxiety, Promote Sensory Integration & Build Social Skills. 2012. (ENG., Illus.). 160p. pap. **(978-1-84905-278-8(6))** Kingsley, Jessica Ltd.

Fennell, Melanie. Overcoming Low Self-Esteem: A Self-Help Guide Using Cognitive Behavioral Techniques. 2009. (Overcoming Ser.). (ENG.). 288p. pap. 14.95 (978-0-465-01266-4(3)) Basic Bks.

Fitzer, Adrienne & Sturmey, Peter. Language & Autism: Applied Behavior Analysis, Evidence, & Practice. 2008. 40.00 (978-1-4164-0376-0(0)) PRO-ED, Inc.

Flick, Grad L. Understanding & Managing Emotional & Behavior Disorders in the Classroom. 2010. (ENG.). 528p. (C). pap. 77.40 (978-0-13-041713-8(0), Prentice Hall) Prentice Hall PTR.

Flora, Stephen Ray. Taking America off Drugs: Why Behavioral Therapy Is More Effective for Treating ADHD, OCD, Depression, & Other Psychological Problems. 2007. 184p. 53.50 (978-0-7914-7189-0(6)); per. 24.95 (978-0-7914-7190-6(X)) State Univ. of New York Pr.

Fruzzetti, Alan E. The Family Guide to Borderline Personality Disorder: Finding Peace in Your Family Using Dialectical Behavior Therapy. 2013. (ENG.). 224p. pap. 17.95 (978-1-60882-040-5(8)) New Harbinger Pubns.

—The High-Conflict Couple: A Dialectical Behavior Therapy Guide to Finding Peace, Intimacy, & Validation. 2006. (ENG., Illus.). 192p. pap. 16.95 (978-1-57224-450-4(X)) New Harbinger Pubns.

Gallagher-Thompson, Dolores, et al, eds. Handbook of Behavioral & Cognitive Therapies with Older Adults. 2007. (ENG., Illus.). xxxiv, 352p. 89.95 (978-0-387-72006-7(5), 0387720065) Springer.

Garrett. Effective Short-Term Counselling: Psychodynamic & Cbt Approaches in Primary Care. 2010. (Illus.). 240p. pap. 34.95 (978-1-85575-751-6(6)) Karnac Bks. GBR. Dist: Stylus Publishing, LLC.

Gaus, Valerie L. Cognitive-Behavioral Therapy for Adult Asperger Syndrome. 2007. (Guides to Individualized Evidence-Based Treatment Ser.). (ENG., Illus.). 244p. 35.00 (978-1-59385-497-3(8)) Guilford Pubns., Inc.

Glick, Barry & Gibbs, John C. Aggression Replacement Training, Third Edition, Revised & Expanded (Book & CD) A Comprehensive Intervention for Aggressive Youth. 2010. pap. 35.95 (978-0-87822-637-5(0)) Research Pr.

Goddard, Wendy. Life Changes: Managing Parents' & Children's Emotions: A Proven Programme Based on Mutual Respect Designed for Local Community Initiatives. 2009. 144p. spiral bd. 89.95 (978-1-905541-50-8(3)) Russell Hse. Publishing Ltd. GBR. Dist: International Specialized Bk Services.

Gordon Sheets, Melanie. Out-of-Control: A Dialectical Behavior Therapy (DBT) - Cognitive-Behavioral Therapy (CBT) Workbook for Getting Control of Our Emotions & Emotion-Driven Behavior (targeting drug / alcohol abuse, bipolar disorder, borderline personality disorder, depression, anger, cutting, & codependency Recovery) 2nd ed. 2010. (Illus.). 420p. pap. 39.99 (978-0-615-39276-9(8)) Recovery Works Pubns.

Graziano, Anthony, ed. Behavior Therapy with Children, Vol. 2. 2008. (ENG., Illus.). 669p. pap. 59.95 (978-0-202-36283-0(3)) Aldine Transaction.

Graziano, Anthony M. & Graziano, Anthony, eds. Behavior Therapy with Children, 2 vols. 2007. (ENG., Illus.). 470p. (gr. 11). pap. 34.95 **(978-0-202-30862-3(6))** Aldine Transaction.

Grove Deniz, Bethany, et al. Strategies for Success. 2011. 108p. pap. **(978-3-8443-0159-5(3))** Lambert Academic Publishing.

Hegerl, U., et al, contrib. by. Suizidale Krisen und Suizid: Risiken, Prävention und Intervention. (Verhaltenstherapie Ser.). (GER., Illus.). 72p. (978-3-8055-7939-1(X)) Karger, S. AG.

B

Hill, Robert, et al. Applied Cognitive & Behavioural Approaches to the Treatment of Addiction: A Practical Treatment Guide. 2010. (ENG., Illus.). 238p. pap. 52.95 *(978-0-470-51063-6(3),* Wiley) Wiley, John & Sons, Inc.

Hilsen, Lindsay. A Step-by-Step Curriculum for Early Learners with Autism Spectrum Disorders. 2011. (ENG.). 384p. pap. ***(978-1-84905-874-2(1))*** Kingsley, Jessica Ltd.

Hofmann, Stefan & Otto, Michael. Cognitive-Behavior Therapy of Social Phobia: Evidence-Based & Disorder-Specific Treatment Techniques. 2008. (Practical Clinical Guidebooks). (ENG., Illus.). 216p. 90.95 *(978-0-415-95402-0(9))* Routledge.

Hollaway, Keith J. New Research on Epilepsy & Behavior. 2006. (Illus.). 339p. 225.00 *(978-1-60021-381-6(2))* Nova Science Pubs., Inc.

Jena, S. P. K. Behaviour Therapy: Techniques, Research & Applications. 2008. (Illus.). 268p. (C). 59.95 *(978-0-7619-3624-4(6),* B36244C); xvii, 261p. *(978-81-7829-788-0(4))* SAGE Pubns., Inc.

Jespersen, Lori. From This Day On: Preserving Newfound Insight, Change & Growth in the Real-World. 2010. 216p. pap. 14.95 *(978-0-87516-847-0(7),* Devorss Pubns.) DeVorss & Co.

Kaluza, Gert. Gelassen und sicher im Stress: Das Stresskompetenz-Buch. Stress erkennen, verstehen, bewältigen. 3rd ed. 2007. (Illus.). XII, 184p. pap. 29.95 *(978-3-540-20489-3(X),* 354020489X) Springer.

Kanter, Jonathan W., et al, eds. The Practice of Functional Analytic Psychotherapy. (ENG., Illus.). 2012. 290p. pap. 59.95 ***(978-1-4614-3699-7(0),*** 1461436990) 2010. xvi, 272p. 129.00 *(978-1-4419-5829-7(0),* 1441958290) Springer.

Koerner, Kelly. Doing Dialectical Behavior Therapy: A Practical Guide. 2011. (Guides to Individualized Evidence-Based Treatment Ser.). (ENG., Illus.). 219p. 35.00 ***(978-1-4625-0232-5(6))*** Guilford Pubns., Inc.

Kohlenberg, Robert J. & Tsai, Mavis. Functional Analytic Psychotherapy: Creating Intense & Curative Therapeutic Relationships. 2007. (Illus.). 217p. per. 54.95 *(978-0-387-70854-6(5))* Springer.

Koplow, Lesley, ed. Unsmiling Faces: How Preschools Can Heal. 2nd rev. ed. 2007. (ENG., Illus.). 288p. 56.00 *(978-0-8077-4804-6(8))* Teachers College Pr., Teachers College, Columbia Univ.

Lam, Danny C. K. Cognitive Behaviour Therapy: A Practical Guide to Helping People Take Control. 2008. (ENG., Illus.). 256p. (C). 110.00 *(978-0-415-39811-4(8));* pap. 37.50 *(978-0-415-39812-1(6))* Routledge.

Lee, Stephen A. & Edget, Delaney M., eds. Cognitive Behavioral Therapy: Applications, Methods & Outcomes. 2012. ***(978-1-61942-655-9(2))*** Nova Science Pubs., Inc.

Legge, Deborah. The Healthy Boundaries Workbook: Using Dialectical Behavior Therapy Skills to Set & Maintain Better Boundaries. 2007. (Workbook Ser.). 200p. pap. 19.95 *(978-1-57224-479-5(8))* New Harbinger Pubns.

Levis, Donald, ed. Foundations of Behavioral Therapy. 2010. (ENG.). 262p. pap. 39.95 *(978-0-202-36369-1(4))* Aldine Transaction.

Levounis, Petros & Arnaout, Bachaar, eds. Handbook of Motivation & Change: A Practical Guide for Clinicians. 2010. (ENG., Illus.). 316p. pap. 54.00 *(978-1-58562-370-9(9))* American Psychiatric Publishing, Inc.

Lincoln, Michael J. Problematic Patterns Behavioral, Psychological & Psychiatric. 2007. 149.00 *(978-0-9772069-6-4(3))* Talking Hearts.

Luiselli, James K., et al, eds. Effective Practices for Children with Autism: Educational & Behavior Support Interventions that Work. 2008. (ENG., Illus.). 496p. (C). 67.95 *(978-0-19-531704-6(1))* Oxford Univ. Pr., Inc.

Maldonado, Guillermo. Overcoming Depression: Making the Best Out of the Difficult Situations in Our Lives. 2007. 68p. per. 7.99 *(978-1-59272-041-5(2))* GM Ministries.

Marlatt, G. Alan & Donovan, Dennis M., eds. Relapse Prevention: Maintenance Strategies in the Treatment of Addictive Behaviors. 2nd rev. ed. 2007. (ENG., Illus.). 416p. pap. 40.00 *(978-1-59385-641-0(5))* Guilford Pubns., Inc.

Martell, Christopher R., et al. Behavioral Activation for Depression: A Clinician's Guide. 2010. (ENG., Illus.). 220p. instr.'s gde. ed. 35.00 *(978-1-60623-515-7(X))* Guilford Pubns., Inc.

Mastropieri, Margo A. & Scruggs, Thomas E., eds. Literacy & Learning. 2010. (Advances in Learning & Behavioral Disabilities Ser.). (Illus.). 336p. 134.95 *(978-1-84950-776-9(7))* Emerald Group Publishing Ltd. GBR. Dist: Turpin Distribution Services Ltd.

Matson, Johnny L., ed. Applied Behavior Analysis for Children with Autism Spectrum Disorders. 2011. (ENG.). vii, 262p. pap. 49.95 *(978-1-4419-8132-5(2),* 1441981322) Springer.

—Social Behavior & Skills in Children. 2010. x, 334p. pap. 49.95 *(978-1-4419-8177-6(2),* 1441981772) Springer.

Matta, Christy. The Stress Response: How Dialectical Behavior Therapy Can Free You from Needless Anxiety, Worry, Anger, & Other Symptoms of Stress. 2012. (ENG.). 224p. pap. 17.95 ***(978-1-60882-130-3(7))*** New Harbinger Pubns.

Maultsby, Maxie C., Jr. & Vuorinen-Maultsby, Raili. Self Training Kit for Group Rational Behavior Therapy, 6 vols. 95.95 incl. audio *(978-0-932838-11-7(1))* Training Center for High Emotional IQ, LLC.

Mayville, Erik A. & Mulick, James A. Behavioral Foundations of Effective Autism Treatment. 2010. *(978-1-59738-031-7(8))* Sloan Publishing.

McCann-Beranger, Judith. A Caregiver's Guide to Alzheimer's & Related Diseases. 2008. (B& B Personal Wellness Ser.). (Illus.). 111p. pap. 10.00 *(978-1-933480-20-6(3))* Bunim and Bannigan Ltd.

Mckay, Matthew & Wood, Jeffrey. The Dialectical Behavior Therapy Diary: Monitoring Your Emotional Regulation Day by Day. 2011. (ENG.). 168p. pap. 15.95 *(978-1-57224-956-1(0))* New Harbinger Pubns.

McKay, Matthew, et al. The Dialectical Behavior Therapy Skills Workbook: Practical DBT Exercises for Learning Mindfulness, Interpersonal Effectiveness, Emotion Regulation, & Distress Tolerance. 2007. (Workbook Ser.). (ENG.). 248p. pap. 22.95 *(978-1-57224-513-6(1))* New Harbinger Pubns.

Mitcheson, Luke, et al. Applied Cognitive & Behavioural Approaches to the Treatment of Addiction: A Practical Treatment Guide. 2010. (ENG., Illus.). 238p. instr.'s gde. ed. 143.95 *(978-0-470-51062-9(5),* Wiley) Wiley, John & Sons, Inc.

Moonshine, Cathy. Acquiring Competency & Achieving Proficiency with Dialectical Behavior Therapy, Volume 1: The Clinician's Guidebook. 2008. (Illus.). 241p. pap. 29.99 *(978-0-9790218-4-8(7))* PESI Healthcare - PHC Publishing Group.

—Acquiring Competency & Achieving Proficiency with Dialectical Behavior Therapy, Volumes I & II: The Clinician's Guidebook/the Worksheets. 2008. pap. 49.99 *(978-0-01-533904-3(1))* PESI Healthcare - PHC Publishing Group.

Morris, Richard J. & Kratochwill, Thomas R., eds. The Practice of Child Therapy. 4th rev. ed. 2007. (Illus.). 587p. 210.00 *(978-0-8058-5328-5(6));* per. 98.95 *(978-0-8058-5329-2(4))* Erlbaum, Lawrence Assocs., Inc.

Neenan, Michael & Dryden, Windy. Working with Resistance in REBT. 2011. (ENG.). 240p. (C). 99.00 *(978-0-415-66479-0(9));* pap. 36.95 *(978-0-415-66750-0(X))* Routledge.

Nurius, Paula S., et al. Interviewing & Change Strategies for Helpers: Fundamental Skills & Cognitive Behavioral Interventions. 6th ed. 2008. (ENG., Illus.). 640p. (C). 165.95 *(978-0-495-41053-9(5))* Brooks/Cole.

Olatunji, Bunmi. Cognitive Behavioral Therapy: An Issue of Psychiatric Clinics. 2010. (Clinics: Internal Medicine Ser.: 33-3). (ENG.). 105.00 *(978-1-4377-2491-2(4),* Saunders) Elsevier - Health Sciences Div.

Ory, Nathan. Working with People with Challenging Behaviors: A Guide for Maintaining Positive Relationships. 2007. 294p. ring bd. 39.95 *(978-1-892696-38-0(X))* High Tide Pr.

Owen, Ian Rory. Talk, Action & Belief: How the intentionality model combines attachment-oriented psychodynamic therapy & cognitive behavioural Therapy. 2009. (Illus.). 460p. pap. 28.95 *(978-1-4401-0538-8(3))* iUniverse, Inc.

Pagoto, Sherry, ed. Psychological Co-Morbidities of Physical Illness: A Behavioral Medicine Perspective. 2011. (ENG., Illus.). xii, 468p. 179.00 *(978-1-4419-0030-2(6),* 1441900306) Springer.

Palca, Joe & Lichtman, Flora. Annoying: The Science of What Bugs Us. 2011. (ENG.). 272p. 25.95 *(978-0-470-63869-9(9),* Wiley) Wiley, John & Sons, Inc.

Pederson, Lane & Pederson, Cortney Sidwell. The Expanded DBT Skills Training Manual: For Self-Help & Individual & Group Therapy Settings. 2011. pap. ***(978-1-936128-12-9(8))*** PESI.

Perkins, Kenneth A., et al. Cognitive Behavior Therapy for Smoking Cessation. 2007. (Practical Clinical Guidebooks). (Illus.). 224p. 32.50 *(978-0-415-95463-1(0));* (ENG.). 125.00 *(978-0-415-95462-4(2))* Routledge.

Perlis, Michael L., et al, eds. Behavioral Treatments for Sleep Disorders: A Comprehensive Primer of Behavioral Sleep Medicine Interventions. 2010. (Practical Resources for the Mental Health Professional Ser.). (ENG.). 404p. 59.95 *(978-0-12-381522-4(3),* Academic Pr.) Elsevier Science & Technology Bks.

Petermann, Franz & Petermann, Ulrike. Behavior Therapy with Aggressive Childre & Adolescents: Studies in Adolescence & Family Research, Vol. 2. 2006. 135p. pap. *(978-0-8204-9887-4(4))* Lang, Peter AG.

Petry, Nancy M. Contingency Management for Substance Abuse. 2011. (ENG., Illus.). 334p. pap. 49.95 *(978-0-415-88289-7(3))* Routledge.

Prospect, LaMont. Control. 2007. 352p. 34.50 *(978-0-9795935-6-7(5));* 388p. pap. 22.50 *(978-0-9795935-5-0(7))* AEG Literary Publishing Services, Inc. (Eloquent Bks.).

Reed, Phil, ed. Behavioral Theories & Interventions for Autism. 2009. (Illus.). x, 351p. 79.00 *(978-1-60741-165-9(2))* Nova Science Pubs., Inc.

Riffel, Laura A. Writing A Behavioral Intervention Plan Using Functional Behavior Assessment Data. 2009. 90p. pap. 18.70 *(978-0-578-00796-0(7))* Behavior Doctor Seminars.

Robertson, Donald. The Philosophy of Cognitive-Behavioural Therapy: Stoic Philosophy as Rational & Cognitive Psychotherapy. 2010. 316p. pap. 37.95 *(978-1-85575-756-1(7))* Karnac Bks. GBR. Dist: Stylus Publishing, LLC.

Rollnick, Stephen, et al. Motivational Interviewing in Health Care: Helping Patients Change Behavior. 2007. (Applications of Motivational Interviewing Ser.). (ENG., Illus.). 210p. 55.00 *(978-1-59385-613-7(X));* pap. 30.00 *(978-1-59385-612-0(1))* Guilford Pubns., Inc.

Rombough, Barbara. A Living Loss: Surviving Separation from a Loved One. 2011. 164p. pap. 22.00 ***(978-1-4269-4113-9(7))*** Trafford Publishing.

Ronen, Tammie & Freeman, Arthur, eds. Cognitive Behavior Therapy in Clinical Social Work Practice. 2007. (Illus.). 615p. 70.00 *(978-0-8261-0215-7(8))* Springer Publishing Co., Inc.

Rosengren, David B. Building Motivational Interviewing Skills: A Practitioner Workbook. 2009. (Applications of Motivational Interviewin Ser.). (ENG., Illus.). 335p. pap. 45.00 *(978-1-60623-299-6(1))* Guilford Pubns., Inc.

Rossiter, Rachel. Dialectical Behaviour Therapists. 2009. 184p. pap. *(978-3-639-17358-1(9))* VDM Verlag Dr. Mueller e.K.

Ryland Peters and Small Staff, ed. Over 50 Ways to Leave Your Lover. 2009. (ENG., Illus.). 64p. 9.95 *(978-1-906094-89-8(6))* CICO Bks. GBR. Dist: Ryland Peters & Small.

Sailor, Wayne, et al, eds. Handbook of Positive Behavior Support. 2010. (Issues in Clinical Child Psychology Ser.). xxvi, 850p. pap. 89.95 *(978-1-4419-8135-6(7),* 1441981357) Springer.

Sapp, Marty. Psychodynamic, Affective, & Behavioral Theories to Psychotherapy. 2010. 242p. 55.95 *(978-0-398-07895-9(5));* pap. 35.95 *(978-0-398-07896-6(3))* Thomas, Charles C. Pub., Ltd.

Schaefer, Charles E. & Briesmeister, James M., eds. Handbook of Parent Training: Helping Parents Prevent & Solve Problem Behaviors. 3rd rev. ed. 2007. (ENG., Illus.). 576p. 95.00 *(978-0-471-78997-0(6),* Wiley) Wiley, John & Sons, Inc.

Schinke, Steven, ed. Behavioral Methods in Social Welfare: Helping Children, Adults, & Families in Community Settings. 2007. (Modern Applications of Social Work Ser.). (ENG., Illus.). 436p. pap. 39.95 *(978-0-202-36214-4(0))* Aldine Transaction.

Scott, Michael. Simply Effective Cognitive Behaviour Therapy: A Practitioner's Guide. 2009. (ENG., Illus.). 200p. (C). 95.00 *(978-0-415-46676-9(8));* pap. 34.95 *(978-0-415-46677-6(6))* Routledge.

Sheldon, Brian. Cognitive-Behavioural Therapy. 2nd rev. ed. 2011. Orig. Title: Behaviour Modification. (ENG., Illus.). 304p. (C). 140.00 *(978-0-415-56436-6(0));* pap. 45.95 *(978-0-415-56435-9(2))* Routledge.

Shumaker, Sally A., et al. The Handbook of Health Behavior Change. 3rd ed. 2008. (Illus.). 896p. 85.00 *(978-0-8261-1545-4(4))* Springer Publishing Co., Inc.

Shy, Shannon. It'll Be Okay: How I Kept Obsessive-Compulsive Disorder (OCD) from Ruining My Life. 2009. 112p. pap. 11.99 *(978-1-4389-5731-9(9))* AuthorHouse.

Spada. Cognitive Behavioural Therapy of Problem Drinking. 2010. (ENG., Illus.). 208p. (C). pap. 42.95 *(978-0-415-40876-9(8))* Routledge.

Spiegler, Michael D. & Guevremont, David C. Contemporary Behavior Therapy. 5th ed. 2009. (ENG.). 640p. (C). 228.95 *(978-0-495-50906-6(X))* Wadsworth.

Sprinson, John Scott & Berrick, Ken. Unconditional Care: Relationship-Based, Behavioral Intervention with Vulnerable Children & Families, 1 vol. 2010. (ENG.). 304p. pap. 31.99 *(978-0-19-973303-3(1))* Oxford Univ. Pr., Inc.

Thompson, Travis. Individualized Autism Intervention for Young Children: Blending Discrete Trial & Naturalistic Strategies. 2011. (Illus.). 208p. pap. 29.95 *(978-1-59857-173-8(7))* Brookes, Paul H. Publishing Co.

Tompkins, Michael A. & Hartl, Tamara L. Digging Out: Helping Your Loved One Manage Clutter, Hoarding, & Compulsive Acquiring. 2009. (ENG.). 208p. pap. 17.95 *(978-1-57224-594-5(8))* New Harbinger Pubns.

Torneke, Niklas. Learning RFT: An Introduction to Relational Frame Theory & Its Clinical Applications. 2010. (Professional Ser.). (ENG.). 288p. pap. 49.95 *(978-1-57224-906-6(4))* New Harbinger Pubns.

Tsai, Mavis, et al. Functional Analytic Psychotherapy. 2012. (CBT Distinctive Features Ser.). (ENG.). 168p. (C). pap. 19.99 *(978-0-415-60404-8(4))* Routledge.

—Functional Analytic Psychotherapy: Distinctive Features. 2012. (CBT Distinctive Features Ser.). (ENG.). 168p. (C). 100.00 *(978-0-415-60403-1(6))* Routledge.

—A Guide to Functional Analytic Psychotherapy: Awareness, Courage, Love, & Behaviorism. 2008. (ENG., Illus.). xvi, 240p. 59.95 *(978-0-387-09786-2(4),* 0387097864) Springer.

Tudor, Keith, ed. The Adult is Parent to the Child: Transactional Analysis with Children & Young People. 2008. 300p. pap. 69.95 *(978-1-905541-17-1(1))* Russell Hse. Publishing Ltd. GBR. Dist: International Specialized Bk. Services.

Tuten, L. Michelle & Jones, Hendree E. Reinforcement-Based Treatment for Substance Use Disorders: A Comprehensive Behavioral Approach. 2011. 256p. 69.95 ***(978-1-4338-1024-4(7))*** American Psychological Assn.

Twohig, Michael P. & Hayes, Steven C. ACT Verbatim for Depression & Anxiety: Annotated Transcripts for Learning Acceptance & Commitment Therapy. 2008. (Professional Ser.). (ENG., Illus.). 248p. pap. 39.95 *(978-1-57224-523-5(9))* New Harbinger Pubns.

Van Dijk, Sheri. Calming the Emotional Storm: Using Dialectical Behavior Therapy Skills to Manage Your Emotions & Balance Your Life. 2012. 174p. ***(978-1-60882-089-4(0));*** (ENG.). 184p. pap. 16.95 ***(978-1-60882-087-0(4))*** New Harbinger Pubns.

Van Dijk, Sheri & Guindon, Karma. The Bipolar Workbook for Teens: DBT Skills to Help You Control Mood Swings. 2010. (Instant Help Ser.). (ENG., Illus.). 160p. (J). (gr. 6-12). pap. 16.95 *(978-1-57224-696-6(0))* Play2Grow.

Van Gelder, Kiera. The Buddha & the Borderline: My Recovery from Borderline Personality Disorder through Dialectical Behavior Therapy, Buddhism, & Online Dating. 2010. (ENG.). 280p. pap. 17.95 *(978-1-57224-710-9(X))* New Harbinger Pubns.

Veale, David, et al. Overcoming Body Body Image Problems Including Body Dysmorphic Disorder: A Self-Help Guide Using Cognitive Behavioral Techniques. 2009. (Overcoming Ser.). (ENG.). 416p. pap. 16.95 *(978-0-465-01264-0(7))* Basic Bks.

Velten, Emmett Charlton & Penn, Patricia E. REBT for People with Co-Occurring Problems (COPs) Albert Ellis in the Wilds of Arizona. 2009. *(978-1-56887-123-3(6),* Professional Resource Pr.) Professional Resource Exchange, Inc.

Wernik, Uri. Chance Action & Therapy: The Playful Way of Changing. 2011. (Health & Human Development (Joav Merrick - Ser. Editor - National Institute of Child Health & Human Development, Ministry of Social Affairs, Jerusalem) Ser.). pap. 43.00 *(978-1-61122-987-5(1))* Nova Science Pubs., Inc.

Wilding, Christine & Palmer, Stephen. Beat Stress with CBT: A Teach Yourself Guide. 2012. (Teach Yourself: General Reference Ser.). (ENG.). 192p. pap. 15.00 ***(978-0-07-178531-0(0),*** 0071785310) McGraw-Hill Cos., The.

Williams, Randy & Williams, Betty. Effective Programs for the Treatment of Autism: Applied Behavior Analysis Models. 2010. (ENG.). 304p. 160.00 *(978-0-415-99931-1(6))* Routledge.

—Effective Programs for Treating Autism Spectrum Disorder: Applied Behavior Analysis Models. 2010. (ENG.). 304p. pap. 59.95 *(978-0-415-99932-8(4))* Routledge.

Willson, Rob, ed. Build a Better Life, 3 vols., Set. 2009. (ENG., Illus.). 1020p. pap. 44.99 *(978-0-470-74533-5(9),* For Dummies) Wiley, John & Sons, Inc.

Wilson, Kelly G., et al. Acceptance & Commitment Therapy for Eating Disorders: A Process-Focused Guide to Treating Anorexia & Bulimia. 2011. (Professional Ser.). (ENG., Illus.). 312p. 59.95 *(978-1-57224-733-8(9))* New Harbinger Pubns.

Woods, Douglas W. & Twohig, Michael P. Trichotillomania: An ACT-Enhanced Behavior Therapy Approach. 2008. (Treatments That Work Ser.). (ENG.). 144p. pap., instr.'s gde. ed. 37.95 *(978-0-19-533603-0(8))* Oxford Univ. Pr., Inc.

—Trichotillomania: An ACT-enhanced Behavior Therapy Approach Workbook. 2008. (Treatments That Work Ser.). (ENG., Illus.). 96p. pap. 24.95 *(978-0-19-533605-4(4))* Oxford Univ. Pr., Inc.

Wright, Jesse H., et al. High-Yield Cognitive-Behavior Therapy for Brief Sessions. 2010. (ENG., Illus.). pap., instr.'s gde. ed. 74.00 *(978-1-58562-362-4(8))* American Psychiatric Publishing, Inc.

Yokley, James. Social Responsibility Therapy for Adolescents & Young Adults: A Multicultural Treatment Manual for Harmful Behavior. 2008. (Illus.). (ENG.). 360p. 125.00 *(978-0-7890-3120-4(5));* 376p. pap. 54.50 *(978-0-7890-3121-1(3))* Routledge.

BEHAVIORAL ASSESSMENT

see also Behavior Modification

Akin Little, Ang, et al, eds. Behavioral Interventions in Schools: Evidence-based Positive Strategies. 2009. (Illus.). 336p. 59.95 *(978-1-4338-0460-1(3))* American Psychological Assn.

Allyn, Janet B. Writing to Clients & Referring Professionals about Psychological Assessment Results: A Handbook of Style & Grammar. 2012. (ENG., Illus.). 248p. (C). 125.00 *(978-0-415-89123-3(X));* pap. 36.95 *(978-0-415-89124-0(8))* Routledge.

Aspy, Ruth & Grossman, Barry. * Designing Comprehensive Interventions for High-Functioning Individuals with Autism Spectrum Disorders: The Ziggurat Model-Release 2. 0. 2011. 246p. pap. 59.00 ***(978-1-934575-96-3(8))*** Autism Asperger Publishing Co.

—UCC-HF Assessment Forms (contains 1 manual & 20 Forms) 2007. pap. 24.95 *(978-1-931282-39-0(0))* Autism Asperger Publishing Co.

—Underlying Characteristics Checklists (UCC) User Manual. 2011. 19.00 ***(978-1-934575-98-7(4))*** Autism Asperger Publishing Co.

—The Ziggurat Model ¿ A Framework for Designing Comprehensive Interventions for Individuals with High-Functioning Autism & Asperger Syndrome Updated & Expanded Edition. 2011. 340p. pap. 49.95 ***(978-1-934575-94-9(1))*** Autism Asperger Publishing Co.

Aspy, Ruth, et al. * Underlying Characteristics Checklist — Early Intervention (UCC-EI) 2011. 24.95 ***(978-1-934575-95-6(X))*** Autism Asperger Publishing Co.

Bailey, Jon & Burch, Mary. Ethics for Behavior Analysts. 2nd rev. exp. ed. 2011. (ENG., Illus.). 388p. 125.00 *(978-0-415-88029-9(7));* pap. 36.95 *(978-0-415-88030-5(0))* Routledge.

—25 Essential Skills & Strategies for Behavior Analysts: Expert Tips for Maximizing Consulting Effectiveness. 2009. (ENG., Illus.). 341p. (C). 125.00 *(978-0-415-80067-9(6));* pap. 36.95 *(978-0-415-80068-6(4))* Routledge.

Bannink, Fredrike P. 1001 Solution-Focused Questions. 2nd ed. 2010. (ENG., Illus.). 272p. pap. 24.95 *(978-0-393-70634-5(6),* 70634) Norton, W. W. & Co., Inc.

Bentzen, Warren R. Seeing Young Children: A Guide to Observing & Recording Behavior. 6th rev. ed. 2008. (ENG., Illus.). 528p. (C). per. 108.95 *(978-1-4180-7378-7(4))* Delmar Cengage Learning.

Browne, Kevin & Craig, Leam. Assessments in Forensic Practice: A Handbook. Beech, Anthony R., ed. 2010. (ENG.). 384p. pap. 49.95 *(978-0-470-01902-3(6))* Wiley, John & Sons, Inc.

Brutten, Gene & Vanryckeghem, Martine. Behavior Assessment Battery BCL-Behavior Checklist Reorder Set. 2006. pap. 19.95 *(978-1-59756-126-6(6))* Plural Publishing, Inc.

—Behavior Assessment Battery CAT-Communication Attitude Test Reorder Set. 2006. pap. 19.95 *(978-1-59756-123-5(1))* Plural Publishing, Inc.

—Behavior Assessment Battery SSC-ER-Speech Situation Checklist Reorder Set. 2006. pap. 29.95 *(978-1-59756-125-9(8))* Plural Publishing, Inc.

—Behavior Assessment Battery SSC-SD-Speech Situation Checklist Reorder Set. 2006. pap. 29.95 *(978-1-59756-127-3(4))* Plural Publishing, Inc.

Buccafusco, Jerry J., ed. Methods of Behavioral Analysis in Neuroscience. 2nd rev. ed. 2008. (Frontiers in Neuroscience Ser.). (ENG., Illus.). 360p. 157.95 *(978-1-4200-5234-3(9),* CRC Press) Taylor & Francis Group GBR. Dist: Taylor & Francis Group.

Cao, Longbing & Yu, Philip S., eds. Behavior Computing: Modeling, Analysis, Mining & Decision. 2012. (ENG., Illus.). xvi, 374p. 129.00 ***(978-1-4471-2968-4(7),*** 1447129687) Springer.

Chandler, Lynette K. & Dahlquist, Carol M. Functional Assessment. 2006. pap. 9.95 *(978-1-4288-1486-8(8))* Cram101 Inc.

Chorpita, Bruce F. Modular Cognitive-Behavioral Therapy for Childhood Anxiety Disorders. 2006. (Guides to Individualized Evidence-Based Treatment Ser.).

(ENG., Illus.). 335p. (gr. 1-13). pap. 45.00 *(978-1-59385-363-1(7))* Guilford Pubns., Inc.
Cipani, Ennio. Functional Behavioral Assessment, Diagnosis, & Treatment: A Complete System for Education & Mental Health Settings. 2nd ed. 340p. pap. *(978-0-8261-0604-9(8))* Springer Publishing Co., Inc.
Cipani, Ennio & Schock, Keven M. Functional Behavioral Assessment, Diagnosis, & Treatment: A Complete System for Education & Mental Health Settings. (Illus.). 2007. 293p. per. 62.00 *(978-0-8261-0288-1(3))* 2nd ed. 2011. xv, 319p. E-Book ***(978-0-8261-0605-6(6))*** Springer Publishing Co., Inc.
Cohen, David S. The Talent Edge: A Behavioral Approach to Hiring, Developing, & Keeping Top Performers. 2011. (ENG.). 232p. pap. 29.95 ***(978-1-118-20673-2(9)***, Wiley) Wiley, John & Sons, Inc.
Cohen, Libby G. & Spenciner, Loraine J. Assessment of Children & Youth with Special Needs. 4th ed. 2010. (ENG.). 432p. (C). pap. 129.80 *(978-0-13-705453-4(X)*, Prentice Hall) Prentice Hall PTR.
Cohen, Michael Henry. What You Accept Is What You Teach: Setting Standards for Employee Accountability. 2006. pap. *(978-1-886624-76-4(3))* Creative Health Care Management, Inc.
Committee on Behavioral and Social Science Research to Improve Intelligence Analysis for National Security & National Research Council. Intelligence Analysis: Behavioral & Social Scientific Foundations. Chauvin, Cherie & Fischhoff, Baruch, eds. 2011. (ENG.). 350p. pap. 70.00 *(978-0-309-17698-9(0))* National Academies Pr.
Corcoran, Jacqueline & Walsh, Joseph. Clinical Assessment & Diagnosis in Social Work Practice, 1 vol. 2nd ed. 2010. (ENG., Illus.). 528p. (C). 57.00 *(978-0-19-539886-1(6))* Oxford Univ. Pr., Inc.
Costantino, Giuseppe, et al. TEMAS (Tell-Me-A-Story) Assessment in Multicultural Societies. 2007. (ENG., Illus.). 512p. 68.95 *(978-0-8058-4451-1(1))* Routledge.
Cram101 Textbook Reviews. Outlines & Highlights for Understanding Human Behavior & the Social Environment by Charles Zastrow, Isbn: 9780495603740. 2011. 342p. pap. 33.95 ***(978-1-61698-529-5(1))*** Cram101 Inc.
Cram101 Textbook Reviews & Cram101 Textbook Reviews. Outlines & Facts101 for Handbook of Psychoeducational Assessment: A Practical HandbookA Volume in the EDUCATIONAL PSYCHOLOGY Series by Gary D. Phye. 2011. 122p. (C). pap. 28.95 ***(978-1-61830-266-3(3))*** Cram101 Inc.
—Outlines & Highlights for Family Assessment Handbook: An Introductory Practice Guide to Family Assessment by Barbara Thomlison, ISBN. 2011. 80p. pap. 27.95 ***(978-1-61461-005-2(3))*** Cram101 Inc.
—Outlines & Highlights for Human Behavior & the Social Environment: Shifting Paradigms in Essential Knowledge for Social Work Practice by Joe M. Schr. 2011. 210p. pap. 30.95 ***(978-1-61461-692-4(2))*** Cram101 Inc.
—Outlines & Highlights for Human Behavior in the MacRo Social Environment by Karen K Kirst-Ashman, Isbn: 9780495813651. 2011. 202p. pap. 30.95 ***(978-1-4288-8402-1(5))*** Cram101 Inc.
—Outlines & Highlights for Observational Measurement of Behavior by Paul Yoder. 2011. 58p. pap. 26.95 ***(978-1-61830-492-6(5))*** Cram101 Inc.
—Outlines & Highlights for Positive Behavioral Supports for the Classroom by Brenda K Scheuermann, Judy a Hall, Judy Hall, Isbn: 9780131131576. 2011. 72p. pap. 27.95 ***(978-1-61744-919-2(9))*** Cram101 Inc.
—Outlines & Highlights for Treatment of Childhood Disorders by Eric Mash, Isbn: 9781572309210. 2011. 528p. pap. 38.95 ***(978-1-61461-094-6(0))*** Cram101 Inc.
Cram101 Textbook Reviews Staff. Outlines & Highlights for Understanding Human Behavior & the Social Environment by Zastrow, Isbn: 049500622x. 2008. 196p. pap. 13.95 *(978-1-4288-6579-2(9))* Cram101 Inc.
Dawkins, Marian Stamp. Observing Animal Behaviour: Design & Analysis of Quantitive Controls. 2007. (ENG., Illus.). 176p. 150.00 *(978-0-19-856935-0(1))* Oxford Univ. Pr., Inc.
Dawson, Peg & Guare, Richard. Executive Skills in Children & Adolescents: A Practical Guide to Assessment & Intervention. 2nd ed. 2010. (Guilford Practical Intervention in Schools Ser.). (ENG., Illus.). 224p. (gr. k-12). pap. 40.00 *(978-1-60623-571-3(0))* Guilford Pubns., Inc.
Dunlap, Glen, et al. Prevent-Teach-Reinforce: The School-Based Model of Individualized Positive Behavior Support. 2009. 152p. pap. 49.95 net. *(978-1-59857-015-1(3))* Brookes, Paul H. Publishing Co.
Erford, Bradley T. Group Work: Processes & Applications. 2010. (ENG.). 480p. (C). 84.20 *(978-0-13-171410-6(4)*, Prentice Hall) Prentice Hall PTR.
Filter, Kevin J. & Alvarez, Michelle E. Functional Behavior Assessment: A Three-Tiered Prevention Model. 2011. (SSWAA Workshop Ser.). (ENG., Illus.). 192p. pap. 24.95 ***(978-0-19-976493-8(X))*** Oxford Univ. Pr., Inc.
Florence, Namulundah. Immigrant Teachers, American Students: Cultural Differences, Cultural Disconnections. 2010. (ENG., Illus.). 210p. 89.00 *(978-0-230-11049-6(5))* Palgrave Macmillan.
Gasberg, Beth A. Stop That (Seemingly) Senseless Behavior! FBA-based Interventions for People with Autism. 2008. 150p. pap. 19.95 *(978-1-890627-76-8(3))* Woodbine Hse.
George, Carol & West, Malcolm L. The Adult Attachment Projective Picture System: Attachment Theory & Assessment in Adults. 2012. (ENG.). 304p. 45.00 ***(978-1-4625-0425-1(6))*** Guilford Pubns., Inc.
Goldfinger, Karen & Pomerantz, Andrew M. Psychological Assessment & Report Writing. 2009. 160p. (C). pap. 53.00 *(978-1-4129-6096-0(7)*, B60960P) SAGE Pubns., Inc.
Grossman, Barry & Aspy, Ruth. The Ziggurat Model: A Framework for Designing Comprehensive Interventions for Individuals with High-Functioning Autism & Asperger Syndrome. 2007. pap. 49.95 *(978-1-931282-36-9(6))* Autism Asperger Publishing Co.
The Health Coach Collection, 4. 2007. (Illus.). 170p. ring bd. 320.60 *(978-1-933402-82-6(2))* Healthcare Intelligence Network.
Heward, Et Al. & Cram101 Textbook Reviews Staff. Focus on Behavior Analysis in Education. 2007. 136p. per. 11.95 *(978-1-4288-2062-3(0))* Cram101 Inc.
Hilsen, Lindsay. A Step-by-Step Curriculum for Early Learners with Autism Spectrum Disorders. 2011. (ENG.). 384p. pap. ***(978-1-84905-874-2(1))*** Kingsley, Jessica Ltd.
Hundert, Joel. Inclusion of Students with Autism: Using ABA-Based Supports in General Education. 2009. 51.00 *(978-1-4164-0390-6(6))* PRO-ED, Inc.
Hurlburt, Russell T. Comprehending Behavioral Statistics. 2nd ed. tchr. ed. *(978-0-534-35044-4(5))* Wadsworth.
Hutchings & Lane. Enhancing Parenting Skills. 2007. (Illus.). 352p. 120.00 *(978-0-415-33614-7(7))* Routledge.
Hutchings, Judy & Lane, Eleanor. Enhancing Parenting Skills. 2007. (Illus.). 352p. 35.95 *(978-0-415-33615-4(5))* Routledge.
Jordan, Cathleen & Franklin, Cynthia. Clinical Assessment for Social Workers 3E. 3rd ed. 2011. (ENG.). *(978-1-933478-80-7(2))* Lyceum Bks., Inc.
Kagan, Jerome, et al. Preservation of Two Infant Temperaments into Adolescence. 2007. (Monographs of the Society for Research in Child Development Ser.). (ENG., Illus.). 132p. pap. 42.95 *(978-1-4051-8011-5(0)*, Wiley-Blackwell) Wiley, John & Sons, Inc.
Kalueff, Allan V. & Cachat, Jonathan M. Zebrafish Neurobehavioral Protocols. 2011. (Illus.). xv, 206p. E-Book ***(978-1-60761-953-6(9))*** Humana Pr.
Kalueff, Allan V. & Cachat, Jonathan M., eds. Zebrafish Neurobehavioral Protocols. 2010. (Neuromethods Ser.). (Illus.). xv, 206p. 119.00 *(978-1-60761-952-9(0)*, 1607619520) Humana Pr.
Kassens, Alice Louise. Changing Perceptions & Waistlines- a Bayesian & Behavioral Approach. 2007. 168p. per. *(978-3-8364-2971-9(3))* VDM Verlag Dr. Mueller e.K.
Kayser, John. Psychological Evaluations & Case Plans: A Handbook for Referring Professionals. 2009. 320p. (C). pap. *(978-0-89108-334-4(0))* Love Publishing Co.
Killion, William K. Tackle Box: The Training Companion for the Functional Independence Skills Handbook or F. I. S. H. 2007. per. 29.95 *(978-1-59872-750-0(8))* Instant Pub.
Kushniruk, Andre W & Borycki, Elizabeth M., eds. Human, Social, & Organizational Aspects of Health Information Systems. 2008. (Premier Reference Source Ser.). (Illus.). 300+p. 180.00 *(978-1-59904-792-8(6)*, Medical Information Science Reference) IGI Global.
Lane, Kathleen Lynne, et al. Developing Schoolwide Programs to Prevent & Manage Problem Behaviors: A Step-by-Step Approach. 2009. (ENG., Illus.). 196p. (gr. k-12). pap. 35.00 *(978-1-60623-032-9(8))* Guilford Pubns., Inc.
Li, Yuelin & Baron, Jonathan. Behavioral Research Data Analysis with R. 2011. (Use R Ser.). (ENG., Illus.). xii, 245p. pap. 59.95 ***(978-1-4614-1237-3(4)***, 1461412374) Springer.
Losardo, Angela & Syverson, Angela Notari. Alternative Approaches to Assessing Young Children, Second Edition. 2nd ed. 2011. (Illus.). 272p. pap. 39.95 *(978-1-59857-087-8(0))* Brookes, Paul H. Publishing Co.
Mahendra, B. A Family Psychiatric Practice. 2010. (ENG.). 306p. pap. *(978-1-84661-224-4(1))* Jordan Publishing, Ltd.
Malt, Barbara & Wolff, Phillip, eds. Words & the Mind: How Words Capture Human Experience. 2010. (ENG., Illus.). 400p. 75.00 *(978-0-19-531112-9(4))* Oxford Univ. Pr., Inc.
Marlatt, G. Alan & Romaine, Deborah S. The Complete Idiot's Guide to Changing Old Habits for Good. 2008. (Complete Idiot's Guide Ser.). (ENG.). 336p. (gr. 12-18). 16.95 *(978-1-59257-780-4(6)*, Alpha Bks.) Penguin Group (USA) Inc.
Mash, Eric J. & Barkley, Russell A., eds. Assessment of Childhood Disorders. 4th ed. 2009. (ENG.). 866p. pap. 50.00 *(978-1-60623-615-4(6))* Guilford Pubns., Inc.
Matson, Johnny L., ed. Applied Behavior Analysis for Children with Autism Spectrum Disorders. 2011. (ENG.). vii, 262p. pap. 49.95 *(978-1-4419-8132-5(2)*, 1441981322) Springer.
—Social Behavior & Skills in Children. 2010. x, 334p. pap. 49.95 *(978-1-4419-8177-6(2)*, 1441981772) Springer.
Mercieca, Daniela. Beyond Conventional Boundaries: Uncertainty in Research & Practice with Children. 2011. 140p. ***(978-94-6091-489-8(6))***; pap. ***(978-94-6091-488-1(8))*** Sense Pubs.
Merrell, Kenneth W. Behavioral, Social, & Emotional Assessment of Children & Adolescents. 3rd rev. ed. 2007. (ENG., Illus.). 560p. 110.00 *(978-0-8058-5370-4(7))* Routledge.
—Home & Community Social Behavior Scales User's Guide. 2008. pap. *(978-1-55766-991-9(0))* Brookes, Paul H. Publishing Co.
Miller, Regina. Functional Behavior Assessment: 35 Ready-to-Use forms for assessing & addressing behavior Problems. 2007. 81p. per. 29.95 *(978-0-9798058-0-6(5))*; (ENG.). cd-rom 39.95 *(978-0-9798058-1-3(3))* Ram Bks., A.
Murrihy, Rachael C., et al, eds. Clinical Handbook of Assessing & Treating Conduct Problems in Youth. 2010. (Illus.). xxiv, 544p. 179.00 *(978-1-4419-6295-9(6)*, 1441962956) Springer.
Neukrug, Edward S. & Fawcett, R. Charles. Essentials of Testing & Assessment: A Practical Guide for Counselors, Social Workers, & Psychologists. 2nd ed. 2009. (PSY 660 Clinical Assessment & Decision Making Ser.). (ENG.). 336p. (C). pap. 124.95 *(978-0-495-60458-7(5))* Brooks/Cole.
Nilsen, Barbara Ann. Observation & Assessment. 4th ed. 2007. (ENG.). 228p. (C). pap. 24.95 *(978-1-4180-7279-7(6))* Wadsworth.
—Week by Week: Plans for Documenting Children's Development. 5th ed. 2010. (Whatrsquo;s New in Early Childhood Ser.). (ENG.). 432p. (C). pap. 126.95 *(978-0-495-81317-0(6))* Cengage South-Western.
—Week by Week: Plans for Documenting Children's Development, Reprint. 4th ed. 2009. (ENG.). 416p. (C). pap. 112.95 *(978-1-4390-4376-9(0))* Delmar Cengage Learning.
Nugent, J. Kevin, et al. Understanding Newborn Behavior & Early Relationships: The Newborn Behavioral Observations (NBO) System Handbook. 2007. (Illus.). 256p. pap. 57.95 *(978-1-55766-883-7(3))* Brookes, Paul H. Publishing Co.
Oakland, Thomas & Harrison, Patti L., eds. Adaptive Behavior Assessment System-II: Clinical Use & Interpretation. 2008. (Practical Resources for the Mental Health Professional Ser.). (ENG., Illus.). 432p. 61.95 *(978-0-12-373586-7(6)*, Academic Pr.) Elsevier Science & Technology Bks.
Olive, Edna. PBF — Positive Behavior Facilitation: Understanding & Intervening in the Behavior of Youth. 2007. 136p. pap. 18.95 *(978-0-87822-544-6(7))* Research Pr.
Overton, Terry. Assessing Learners with Special Needs: An Applied Approach. 7th rev. ed. 2011. (ENG., Illus.). 504p. (C). pap. 118.80 *(978-0-13-136710-4(2)*, Prentice Hall) Prentice Hall PTR.
Pelech, William. Dancing Towards Wholeness. 2010. 296p. pap. *(978-3-639-08331-6(8))* VDM Verlag Dr. Mueller e.K.
Prunckun, Hank. A Handbook of Scientific Methods of Inquiry for Intelligence Analysis. 2010. (Professional Intelligence Ser.). (ENG., Illus.). 248p. pap. 48.00 *(978-0-8108-6753-6(2))* Scarecrow Pr., Inc.
—Handbook of Scientific Methods of Inquiry for Intelligence Analysis. 2010. (Scarecrow Professional Intelligence Education Ser.). (ENG., Illus.). 248p. 74.00 *(978-0-8108-7191-5(2))* Scarecrow Pr., Inc.
Raber, Jacob. Animal Models of Behavioral Analysis. 2011. (Illus.). xv, 354p. E-Book ***(978-1-60761-883-6(4))*** Humana Pr.
Raber, Jacob, ed. Animal Models of Behavioral Analysis. 2010. (Neuromethods Ser.). (Illus.). xv, 354p. 139.00 *(978-1-60761-882-9(6)*, 1607618826) Humana Pr.
Rogers, Richard, ed. Clinical Assessment of Malingering & Deception. 3rd rev. ed. 2008. (ENG., Illus.). 526p. 70.00 *(978-1-59385-699-1(7))* Guilford Pubns., Inc.
Scheuermann, Brenda K. & Hall, Judy A. Positive Behavioral Supports for the Classroom. 2nd rev. ed. 2011. (ENG.). 528p. (C). pap. 94.20 *(978-0-13-214783-5(1)*, Prentice Hall) Prentice Hall PTR.
Schriver, Joe M. Human Behavior & the Social Environment: Shifting Paradigms in Essential Knowledge for Social Work Practice. 4th ed. 2006. pap. 10.95 *(978-1-4288-1724-1(7))* Cram101 Inc.
—Human Behavior & the Social Environment: Shifting Paradigms in Essential Knowledge for Social Work Practice. 5th ed. 2010. (ENG.). (C). 43.67 *(978-0-205-79218-4(9))*; 576p. 96.00 *(978-0-205-76995-7(0))*; (Illus.). 576p. pap. 131.33 *(978-0-205-52097-8(9))* Prentice Hall PTR. (Prentice Hall).
—Human Behavior & the Social Environment: Shifting Paradigms in Essential Knowledge for Social Work Practice, Books a la Carte Plus MySocialWorkLab. 5th ed. 2010. (ENG.). (C). ring bd. 90.47 *(978-0-205-00183-5(1)*, Prentice Hall) Prentice Hall PTR.
See, Letha A. Lee, ed. Human Behavior in the Social Environment from an African-American Perspective. 2nd ed. 2007. (Illus.). 782p. 175.00 *(978-0-7890-2831-0(X))*; per. 49.95 *(978-0-7890-2832-7(8))* Routledge.
Sheridan, Susan M. & Kratochwill, Thomas R. Conjoint Behavioral Consultation: Promoting Family-School Connections & Interventions. 2nd rev. ed. 2007. (ENG., Illus.). xvi, 224p. 59.95 *(978-0-387-71247-5(X)*, 038771247X) Springer.
Singh, Jay P., et al. Approaches to Behavior & Classroom Management: Integrating Discipline & Care. 2008. (Illus.). 320p. (C). pap. 68.00 *(978-1-4129-3744-3(2)*, B37442P) SAGE Pubns., Inc.
Smith, Tristram. Making Inclusion Work for Students with Autism Spectrum Disorders: An Evidence-Based Guide. 2011. (ENG., Illus.). 380p. (gr. k-12). pap. 40.00 *(978-1-60623-932-2(5))* Guilford Pubns., Inc.
Sparrow, Elizabeth P. & Kaufman, Alan S. Essentials of Conners Behavior Assessments. 2010. (Essentials of Psychological Assessment Ser.: 67). (ENG., Illus.). 416p. pap. 38.95 *(978-0-470-34633-4(7)*, Wiley) Wiley, John & Sons, Inc.
Sperry, Len, ed. Assessment of Couples & Families: Contemporary & Cutting-Edge Strategies. 2nd rev. ed. 2011. (Family Therapy & Counseling Ser.). (ENG., Illus.). 357p. 92.95 *(978-0-415-89406-7(9))*; pap. 39.95 *(978-0-415-89407-4(7))* Routledge.
Sulzer-Azaroff, Beth. Applying Behavior Analysis Across the Autism Spectrum: A Field Guide for New Practitioners. 2nd ed. 2011. ***(978-1-59738-036-2(9))*** Sloan Publishing.
Vanryckeghem, Martine & Brutten, Gene. KiddyCat Reorder Set: Communication Attitude Test for Preschool & Kindergarten Children who Stutter. 2006. pap. 69.95 *(978-1-59756-124-2(X))* Plural Publishing, Inc.
Vanryckeghem, Martine & Brutten, Gene J. The Behavior Assessment Battery for School-Aged Children Who Stutter. 2006. (ENG.). pap. 249.95 *(978-1-59756-114-3(2))* Plural Publishing, Inc.
Vargas, Julie & Vargas, Julie S. Behavior Analysis for Effective Teaching. 2009. (ENG., Illus.). 392p. 205.00 *(978-0-415-99007-3(6))* Routledge.
Vineyard, Catherine. Self-Concept in Children: The Relationship Between Self-Concept & Locus of Control, Sense of Inadequacy, & Self-Reliance. 2008. 64p. pap. *(978-3-639-01612-3(2))* VDM Verlag Dr. Mueller e.K.
Vrij, Aldert. Detecting Lies & Deceit: Pitfalls & Opportunities. 2nd ed. 2008. (Wiley Series in Psychology of Crime, Policing & Law Ser.). (ENG., Illus.). 502p. 184.95 *(978-0-470-51624-9(0))*; pap. 78.95 *(978-0-470-51625-6(9))* Wiley, John & Sons, Inc. (Wiley-Interscience).
Waller, Raymond Jefferson. The Teacher's Concise Guide to Functional Behavioral Assessment. Waller, Raymond Jefferson, ed. 2008. (Illus.). 136p. pap. 24.95 *(978-1-4129-6605-4(1)*, B66047P) Corwin Pr.
Waller, Raymond Jefferson, ed. The Teacher's Concise Guide to Functional Behavioral Assessment. 2008. (Illus.). 136p. 60.95 *(978-1-4129-6604-7(3)*, B66047C) Corwin Pr.
Walsh, Froma, ed. Normal Family Processes, Fourth Edition: Growing Diversity & Complexity. 4th rev. ed. 2011. (ENG., Illus.). 592p. 75.00 ***(978-1-4625-0255-4(5))*** Guilford Pubns., Inc.
Wheldall, Kevin, ed. The Behaviourist in the Classroom. 2012. (Routledge Library Editions: Education Ser.). (ENG.). 216p. 115.00 ***(978-0-415-67846-9(3))*** Routledge.
Williams, Jonathan J. & Hill, Peter D. A Handbook for the Assessment of Children's Behaviours. 2012. (ENG.). 622p. pap. 80.00 ***(978-1-119-97589-2(1)***, Wiley-Blackwell) Wiley, John & Sons, Inc.
Williams, Joseph. Who Do You See in the Mirror? Change Irresponsible Behavior in the Workplace to Responsible Behavior. 2009. 152p. 23.95 *(978-0-615-26855-2(2))* CSMS.
Williams, Randy & Williams, Betty. Effective Programs for the Treatment of Autism: Applied Behavior Analysis Models. 2010. (ENG.). 304p. 160.00 *(978-0-415-99931-1(6))* Routledge.
—Effective Programs for Treating Autism Spectrum Disorder: Applied Behavior Analysis Models. 2010. (ENG.). 304p. pap. 59.95 *(978-0-415-99932-8(4))* Routledge.
Wilson, Mark. Wandering Significance: An Essay on Conceptual Behaviour. 2008. (ENG.). 696p. pap. 60.00 *(978-0-19-953230-8(3))* Oxford Univ. Pr., Inc.
Zastrow, Charles & Kirst-Ashman, Karen K. Student Manual for Zastrow/Kirst-Ashman's Understanding Human Behavior & the Social Environment, 8th. 8th ed. 2009. (ENG.). 448p. (C). pap. 50.95 *(978-0-495-80590-8(4))* Brooks Cole.
—Understanding Human Behavior & the Social Environment. 8th ed. 2009. (Available Titles CengageNOW Ser.). (ENG.). 768p. (C). 151.95 *(978-0-495-60374-0(0))* Brooks Cole.
Zirpoli, Thomas J. Behavior Management: Positive Applications for Teachers. 6th rev. ed. 2010. (ENG.). 480p. (C). pap. 120.20 *(978-0-13-706320-8(2)*, Prentice Hall) Prentice Hall PTR.

BEHAVIORAL EVOLUTION
see Behavior Evolution

BEHAVIORAL GENETICS
see Behavior Genetics

BEHAVIORAL MODELS
see Human Behavior—Mathematical Models

BEHAVIORAL OPTOMETRY

Barry, Susan R. Fixing My Gaze: A Scientist's Journey into Seeing in Three Dimensions. 2010. (ENG., Illus.). 272p. (gr. 9). pap. 15.95 *(978-0-465-02073-7(9))* Basic Bks.
Peppes, Robert C. & Nordgren, Mary Jane. Stress - Point Learning: A Multisensory Approach to Processing Information. 2nd rev. ed. 2006. Orig. Title: A Multi Sensory Approach to Processing Information & Learning. (ENG.). 156p. pap. 39.95 *(978-0-929780-13-9(2))* Optometric Extension Program Fndtn.
Shapiro, Abraham & Esterson, Jack. Behaviors, Beliefs & Emotions: Doctor-Patient Relationships in Behavioral Optometry. 2007. (ENG.). 89p. pap. 25.00 *(978-0-929780-12-2(4))* Optometric Extension Program Fndtn.
Warshowsky, Joel H. How Behavioral Optometry Can Unlock Your Child's Potential: Identifying & Overcoming Blocks to Concentration, Self-Esteem & School Success with Vision Therapy. 2012. (ENG.). 160p. pap. ***(978-1-84905-881-0(4))*** Kingsley, Jessica Ltd.

BEHAVIORAL PHARMACOLOGY
see Psychopharmacology

BEHAVIORAL PSYCHOLOGY
see Psychophysiology

BEHAVIORAL PROBLEMS IN CHILDREN
see Behavior Disorders in Children

BEHAVIORAL SCIENCES
see Psychology; Social Sciences

BEHAVIORAL TOXICOLOGY

Berent, Stanley & Albers, James W. Neurobehavioral Toxicology Vol. 3: Neurological & Neuropsychological Perspectives, Central Nervous System, 3 vols. 2008. (Studies on Neuropsychology, Neurology & Cognition Ser.). (ENG., Illus.). 648p. 115.95 *(978-1-84169-494-8(0)*, Taylor & Francis) Taylor & Francis Group GBR. Dist: Taylor & Francis Group.
Rimland, Bernard. Dyslogic Syndrome: Why Millions of Kids Are 'Hyper', Attention-Disordered, Learning Disabled, Depressed, Aggressive, Defiant, or Violent- & What We Can Do about It. 2008. (ENG.). 24p. *(978-1-84310-877-1(1))* Kingsley, Jessica Ltd.

BEHAVIORISM (PSYCHOLOGY)
see also Behavior Modification; Conditioned Response

Bieling, Peter J., et al. Cognitive-Behavioral Therapy in Groups. 2006. (ENG., Illus.). 452p. 65.00 *(978-1-59385-325-9(4))* Guilford Pubns., Inc.

Cheney, Carl D. & Pierce, W. David. Behavior Analysis & Learning. 4th ed. 2008. (ENG., Illus.). 448p. 99.95 *(978-0-8058-6260-7(9)*, Psychology Press) Taylor & Francis Group GBR. Dist: Taylor & Francis Group.

Copello, Alex, et al. Social Behaviour & Network Therapy for Alcohol Problems. 2009. (ENG., Illus.). 176p. (C). 39.95 *(978-1-58391-803-6(5))* Routledge.

Cram101 Textbook Reviews Staff. Outlines & Highlights for Applied Behavior Analysis by John O Cooper, Isbn: 9780131421134. 2009. 130p. pap. 28.95 *(978-1-4288-9629-1(5))* Cram101 Inc.

—Outlines & Highlights for Behavior Analysis & Learning by W David Pierce, Isbn: 9780805862607. 2009. 134p. pap. 28.95 *(978-1-4288-7936-2(6))* Cram101 Inc.

—Outlines & Highlights for Human Learning by Ormrod, Isbn: 013232749x. 2008. 144p. pap. 11.95 *(978-1-4288-6223-4(4))* Cram101 Inc.

—Outlines & Highlights for Introduction to Learning & Behavior by Powell Isbn: 0534634516. 2008. 100p. pap. 10.95 *(978-1-4288-6047-6(9))* Cram101 Inc.

—Outlines & Highlights for Introduction to Learning & Behavior by Powell, Isbn: 9780495595281. 2009. 112p. pap. 28.95 *(978-1-4288-6733-8(3))* Cram101 Inc.

—Outlines & Highlights for the Principles of Learning & Behavior: Active Learning Edition by Michael P. Domjan, ISBN. 2009. 60p. pap. 26.95 *(978-1-4288-9015-2(7))* Cram101 Inc.

Dalbert, Claudia, ed. International Journal of Psychology, Volume 41: Behaviour Analysis Around the World. 2007. (Special Issues of the International Journal of Psychology Ser.). (ENG.). 156p. per. 74.50 *(978-1-84169-820-5(2)*, Psychology Press) Taylor & Francis Group GBR. Dist: Taylor & Francis Group.

De Waal, Frans B. M. Primates & Philosophers: How Morality Evolved. Macedo, Stephen & Ober, Josiah, eds. 2006. (University Center for Human Values Ser.). (Illus.). 209p. 22.95 *(978-0-691-12447-6(7))* Princeton Univ. Pr.

Domjan, Michael P. & Domjan, Michael. The Principles of Learning & Behavior: Active Learning Edition. 6th ed. 2009. (PSY 361 Learning Ser.). (ENG.). 696p. (C). pap. 195.95 *(978-0-495-60199-9(3))* Wadsworth.

Eisenman, Russell. Creativity, Mental Illness & Crime. rev. ed. 2008. (ENG.). 144p. pap. 39.35 *(978-0-7575-4223-7(9))* Kendall Hunt Publishing Co.

Eisenman, Russell. Creativity Mental Illness & Crime. 2nd rev. ed. 2012. (ENG.). 166p. pap. 37.00 ***(978-0-7575-9155-6(8))*** Kendall Hunt Publishing Co.

Hattwick, Richard E., ed. & intro. U. S. A. Aspects of Political & Social Life, Vol. XV. 75p. pap. 4.00 *(978-0-931497-27-8(2))* Western Illinois Univ., Ctr. for Business & Economic Research.

Hayden, Joanna. Introduction to Health Behavior Theory. 2008. 148p. pap. 72.95 *(978-0-7637-4383-3(6))* Jones & Bartlett Learning, LLC.

Hutchison, Elizabeth D., et al. Challenges of Living: A Multidimensional Working Model for Social Workers. 2007. (Illus.). 432p. (C). per. 53.00 *(978-1-4129-0899-3(X)*, B0899XP) SAGE Pubns., Inc.

Innis, Nancy K., ed. Reflections on Adaptive Behavior: Essays in Honor of J. E. R. Staddon. 2008. (ENG., Illus.). 408p. (gr. 17). 70.00 *(978-0-262-09044-5(9))*; pap. 35.00 *(978-0-262-59026-6(3))* MIT Pr.

Jones, James E. Exploring the Sixth Sense: An Introduction to Performance Mentalism. 2009. 107p. pap. 15.95 *(978-1-4327-4450-2(X))* Outskirts Pr., Inc.

Keehn, J. D. Master Builders of Modern Psychology: From Freud to Skinner. 2006. (Illus.). 202p. reprint ed. 45.00 *(978-1-4223-5640-1(X))* DIANE Publishing Co.

Kerr, Gordon. Contribution to the Theory of the Living. 2006. 212p. per. *(978-1-4067-1735-8(5)*, Hesperides Pr.) Read Bks.

Kimmel, Allan J. Ethical Issues in Behavioral Research: Basic & Applied Perspectives. 2nd rev. ed. 2007. (ENG., Illus.). pap. 74.95 *(978-1-4051-3439-2(9)*, Wiley-Blackwell) Wiley, John & Sons, Inc.

Leeming, Benjamin Christopher. Imagination: Mind's Dominant Power 1926. 2007. (ENG.). 300p. 43.95 *(978-0-548-05517-5(3))* Kessinger Publishing, LLC.

Lewis, Trevor. Behaviour Skills - A Parents & Support Workers Guide. 2008. 208p. pap. 24.95 *(978-1-4092-1054-2(5))* Lulu Enterprises Inc.

Maranell, Gary M., ed. Scaling: A Sourcebook for Behavioral Scientists. 2007. (ENG.). 455p. (gr. 11). pap. 39.95 *(978-0-202-36175-8(6))* Transaction Pubs.

Moore, John C. Conceptual Foundations of Radical Behaviorism. 2007. (C). pap. 33.00 net. *(978-1-59738-011-9(3))* Sloan Publishing.

Naour, Paul. E. O. Wilson & B. F. Skinner: A Dialogue Between Sociobiology & Radical Behaviorism. (Developments in Primatology: Progress & Prospects Ser.). (ENG., Illus.). xix, 138p. 2010. pap. 149.00 ***(978-1-4419-2795-8(6)**,* 1441927956) 2009. 149.00 *(978-0-387-89461-4(6))* Springer.

Nolan, Susan & Heinzen, Thomas. Statistics for the Behavioral Sciences. 2007. (ENG.). 736p. (C). 155.95 *(978-0-7167-5007-9(4))* Worth Pubs., Inc.

Nolan, Susan, et al. Statistics for the Behavioral Sciences. 2008. (ENG.). 350p. (C). pap., stu. ed. 28.95 *(978-1-4292-0635-8(7))* Worth Pubs., Inc.

Ormrod, Jeanne Ellis. Human Learning. 6th rev. ed. 2011. (ENG.). 624p. (C). 147.00 ***(978-0-13-259518-6(4)**,* Prentice Hall) Prentice Hall PTR.

Powell, Russell A., et al. Introduction to Learning & Behavior. 3rd ed. 2008. (ENG.). 576p. (C). pap. 150.95 *(978-0-495-59528-1(4))* Wadsworth.

Robertson, Donald. The Philosophy of Cognitive-Behavioural Therapy: Stoic Philosophy as Rational & Cognitive Psychotherapy. 2010. 316p. pap. 37.95 *(978-1-85575-756-1(7))* Karnac Bks. GBR. Dist: Stylus Publishing, LLC.

Rogers, Bill. Behavior Recovery. (Illus.). 127p. pap. *(978-0-86431-154-2(0))* ACER Pr.

Rogers, Carl Ransom & Skinner, B. F. A Dialogue on the Control of Human Behavior. Gladstein, Gerald, ed. unabr. ed. 30p. pap. 49.50 incl. audio *(978-0-88432-028-9(6)*, S29244) Norton, Jeffrey Pubs., Inc.

Rutherford, Alexandra. Beyond the Box: B. F. Skinner's Technology of Behavior from Laboratory to Life, 1950s-1970s. 2009. (ENG.). 224p. pap. *(978-0-8020-9618-0(2))*; (Illus.). *(978-0-8020-9774-3(X))* Univ. of Toronto Pr.

Sheldon, Brian. Cognitive-Behavioural Therapy. 2nd rev. ed. 2011. Orig. Title: Behaviour Modification. (ENG., Illus.). 304p. (C). 140.00 *(978-0-415-56436-6(0))*; pap. 45.95 *(978-0-415-56435-9(2))* Routledge.

Smith, T. L. Behavior & Its Causes: Philosophical Foundations of Operant Psychology. 2010. (Studies in Cognitive Systems Ser.). (Illus.). 288p. pap. 349.00 *(978-90-481-4393-1(4)*, 9048143934) Springer.

Stiehl, Charles W. The Origin of Human Characteristics & Behavior. (Enlightenment of Man Ser.). 128p. pap. 29.95 *(978-0-9701997-0-6(8)*, I) Scholars Library.

Strawson, Galen & Strawson, G. Mental Reality. 2nd ed. 2009. (Representation & Mind Ser.). (ENG., Illus.). 400p. (gr. 17). pap. 32.00 *(978-0-262-51310-4(2))* MIT Pr.

Thyer, B., ed. The Philosophical Legacy of Behaviorism. 2010. (Studies in Cognitive Systems Ser.). (Illus.). 288p. pap. 229.00 *(978-90-481-5231-5(3)*, 9048152313) Springer.

Toates, Frederick. Burrhus F. Skinner: The Shaping of Behaviour. 2009. (Mind Shapers Ser.). (ENG., Illus.). 150p. pap. 22.00 *(978-0-230-21866-6(0))* Palgrave Macmillan.

Tortoza, Carlos. Check Mate & Words Game: Postal Chess: Chess, Friendship & Philosophy! 2006. (ENG.). 200p. per. 18.95 *(978-1-59800-288-1(0))* Outskirts Pr., Inc.

Watson, David L. & Tharp, Roland G. Self-Directed Behavior. 9th ed. 2006. (PSY 103 Towards Self-Understanding Ser.). (ENG., Illus.). 368p. (C). per. 105.95 *(978-0-495-09324-4(6))* Wadsworth.

Woollard, John. Psychology in the Classroom: Behaviourism. 2010. (Illus.). 120p. (C). 140.00 *(978-0-415-49398-7(6))*; pap. 33.95 *(978-0-415-49399-4(4))* Taylor & Francis Group GBR. (Routledge). Dist: Taylor & Francis Group.

BEHCET'S DISEASE

Foster, C. Stephen, frwd. Essential Guide to Behcet's Disease. 2006. 198p. pap. 35.00 *(978-0-9658403-5-4(2))* Central Vision Pr.

Zouboulis, Christos, ed. Adamantiades-Behçet's Disease. 2010. (Advances in Experimental Medicine & Biology Ser.). 656p. pap. 259.00 *(978-1-4419-3403-1(0)*, 1441934030) Springer.

BEHISTUN INSCRIPTIONS

see Achaemenian Inscriptions; Old Persian Inscriptions

BEHN, APHRA, 1640-1689

Croft, Steven & Maybank, Diane, eds. Aphra Benn: The Rover. 2nd rev. ed. 2008. (Oxford Student Texts). (ENG., Illus.). 224p. (YA). 15.95 *(978-0-19-832573-4(8))* Oxford Univ. Pr., Inc.

Lewcock, Dawn. Aphra Behn Stages the Social Scene in the Restoration Theatre. 2008. (C). 104.95 *(978-1-60497-549-9(0))* Cambria Pr.

Stewart, Ann Marie. The Ravishing Restoration: Aphra Behn, Violence, & Comedy. 2010. (ENG.). 133p. 42.50 *(978-1-57591-134-2(5))* Susquehanna Univ. Pr.

Todd, Janet, ed. Aphra Behn Studies. 2009. (ENG.). 344p. pap. 42.00 *(978-0-521-11964-1(2))* Cambridge Univ. Pr.

Wiseman, S.J. & Wiseman, Susan. Aphra Behn. 2nd ed. 2006. (Writers & Their Work Ser.). (ENG.). 144p. (C). 26.00 *(978-0-7463-0965-0(1))* Northcote Hse. Publishers, Ltd. GBR. Dist: Brown, David Bk. Co., The.

BEIJING (CHINA)

Dorling Kindersley Publishing Staff. Beijing & Shanghai. 2011. (Eyewitness Travel Guides). (ENG.). 240p. 23.00 *(978-0-7566-6976-8(6))* Dorling Kindersley Publishing, Inc.

Holdsworth, May. The Palace of Established Happiness: Restoring a Garden in the Forbidden City. 2008. 223p. *(978-7-80047-331-9(7))* Forbidden City Publishing Hse.

Mooney, Paul & Hibbard, Peter. Beijing & Shanghai: China's Hottest Cities. 3rd ed. 2012. (Odyssey Illustrated Guides). (ENG., Illus.). 600p. pap. 27.95 *(978-962-217-797-0(2)*, 217797) Airphoto International/Odyssey HKG. Dist: Norton, W. W. & Co., Inc.

Obrist, Hans Ulrich, ed. & text. Battery City: A Post-Olympic Beijing Mini-Marathon. 2010. (ENG., Illus.). 138p. pap. 19.95 *(978-3-03764-096-8(0))* JRP Ringier Kunstverlag AG CHE. Dist: D.A.P./Distributed Art Pubs.

BEIJING (CHINA)—DESCRIPTION AND TRAVEL

CER Publishing, ed. Beijing Business Eats. 2007. 100p. pap. 19.95 *(978-988-17149-4-7(X))* China Economic Review Publishing HKG. Dist: Trans-Atlantic Pubns., Inc.

China Pictorial Staff. Strolling the Streets of Beijing. 2007. 110p. pap. 9.95 *(978-7-80220-063-0(6))* New World Pr. CHN. Dist: China Bks. & Periodicals, Inc.

De Baeck, Philippe. Destination Beijing, 1 vol. 2011. (ENG., Illus.). 300p. 35.00 *(978-90-79761-72-2(9))* Tectum B.V.B.A. BEL. Dist: Innovative Logistics.

Dutton, Michael, et al. Beijing Time. 2010. (Illus.). 288p. pap. 17.95 *(978-0-674-04734-1(6))* Harvard Univ. Pr.

Egle, Rene D. Hotel: Untold Stories II. 2009. 324p. 37.95 *(978-1-60594-192-9(1))*; pap. 17.95 *(978-1-60594-191-2(3))* Aeon Publishing Inc. (Llumina Pr.).

Finnegan, Gary. Beijing for Beginners: An Irishman in the People's Republic. 2009. (ENG., Illus.). 243p. pap. 27.95 *(978-1-905785-44-5(5))* Liffey Pr., The IRL. Dist: Dufour Editions, Inc.

Gaubil, Antoine. A Description of the Plan of Peking, the Capital of China. 2010. pap. 19.96 *(978-1-61143-308-1(8))* Gorgias Pr., LLC.

Hongwu, Peng, ed. +0086 Beijing Cool. 2009. (ENG & CHI., Illus.). 304p. pap. 19.95 *(978-988-18034-2-9(X))* Timezone 8 Ltd. HKG. Dist: D.A.P./Distributed Art Pubs.

Jia, Jun. Beijing Yihe Yuan: Summer Palace. 2009. (CHI., Illus.). 300p. *(978-7-302-19773-7(3))* Tsinghua Univ. Pr.

Locken, E. Beijing Hotels. 2010. 114p. pap. 19.99 *(978-0-557-42159-6(4))* Lulu Enterprises Inc.

—Travel Journal Beijing. 2010. 192p. pap. 19.99 *(978-0-557-41576-2(4))* Lulu Enterprises Inc.

Morris, Sarah. Sarah Morris: Beijing. 2010. (ENG., Illus.). 288p. 61.00 *(978-3-86560-646-4(6))* Verlag der Buchhandlung Walther Konig DEU. Dist: D.A.P./Distributed Art Pubs.

One Night in Beijing. 2007. 39.95 *(978-0-9773334-8-6(5))* True Run Advertising Co.

Pearson, Alexandra & Cavender, Lucy. Beijing: Portrait of a City. Pearson, Alexandra & Cavender, Lucy, eds. 2009. (ENG & CHI., Illus.). 172p. pap. 27.95 *(978-962-217-803-8(0)*, 217803) Airphoto International/Odyssey HKG. Dist: Norton, W. W. & Co., Inc.

Preston, William. Where Persimmon Was King. 2008. 204p. pap. 24.95 *(978-0-9802380-6-8(4))* Beckham Pubns. Group, Inc.

Raes, Fabien & Jambers, Paul. Beijing. 2009. (ENG., Illus.). 112p. *(978-90-5856-290-6(5)*, Stichting Kunstboak (Acc)) Antique Collectors' Club.

Ray, Mary-Ann, et al, texts. Caochangdi, Beijing Inside Out. 2009. (ENG., Illus.). 450p. pap. 24.95 *(978-988-17522-4-6(8))* Timezone 8 Ltd. HKG. Dist: D.A.P./Distributed Art Pubs.

Röh, Frederik & Schriever, Silja. A Day in Beijing. 2008. (GER & ENG., Illus.). 116p. 40.00 *(978-3-940004-40-6(5)*, Earbooks) edel classics GmbH DEU. Dist: AtlasBooks Distribution.

Santoro, Carlo & Greco, Claudio. Beijing: The New City. 2008. (ENG., Illus.). 272p. pap. 14.99 *(978-88-6130-302-7(1))* Skira Editore ITA. Dist: Random Hse., Inc.

Scocca, Tom. Beijing Welcomes You: Unveiling the Capital City of the Future. 2011. (ENG., Illus.). 384p. (gr. 12). 26.95 *(978-1-59448-784-2(7)*, Riverhead Bks. (Hardcover)) Penguin Group (USA) Inc.

Snijders, Patty, tr. Aram Tanis: Blowing Smoke & Seahorses. 2011. (ENG., Illus.). 104p. pap. 30.00 *(978-988-18907-2-6(1))* Timezone 8 Ltd. HKG. Dist: D.A.P./Distributed Art Pubs.

Tézenas, Ambroise, photos by. Beijing: Theatre of the People. 2007. (ENG., Illus.). 120p. 45.00 *(978-1-904587-36-1(4))* Lewis, Dewi Publishing GBR. Dist: Consortium Bk. Sales & Distribution.

Wang, Lansuo, text. Beijing's Siheyuan. 2007. (Illus.). 103p. 9.95 *(978-7-80220-066-1(0))* New World Pr. CHN. Dist: China Bks. & Periodicals, Inc.

Wilson, Jonathan. The Bus to Beijing. 2010. 324p. pap. 23.50 *(978-1-4452-9183-3(5))* Lulu Enterprises Inc.

Wong, Jan. Beijing Confidential: A Tale of Comrades Lost & Found. 2008. 336p. *(978-0-7322-8747-4(2))* HarperCollins Pubs. Australia.

Zhigang, Yang. Beijing's Imperial Palace: The Illustrated Guide to the Architecture, History, & Splendorof the Forbidden City. 2010. (ENG., Illus.). 152p. (gr. 12). pap. 19.95 *(978-1-60652-121-2(7))* Reader's Digest Assn., Inc., The.

Zhu, Hong & Yangquan, Li. Discover Beijing: The City's History & Culture Redefined, 1 vol. 2007. (Discover Ser.). (ENG., Illus.). 192p. pap. 16.50 *(978-981-261-364-6(1))* Marshall Cavendish International (Asia) Private Ltd. SGP. Dist: Marshall Cavendish Corp.

BEIJING (CHINA)—ECONOMIC CONDITIONS

Fleischer, Friederike. Suburban Beijing: Housing & Consumption in Contemporary China. 2010. (ENG., Illus.). 256p. 75.00 *(978-0-8166-4596-1(5))*; pap. 25.00 *(978-0-8166-6587-7(7))* Univ. of Minnesota Pr.

Li, Shaobing, text. Enjoy Tea in Beijing. 2007. (Illus.). 110p. 9.95 *(978-7-80220-062-3(8))* New World Pr. CHN. Dist: China Bks. & Periodicals, Inc.

Mangan, J. A. Beijing 2008: Preparing for Glory: Chinese Challenge in the 'Chinese Century' Jinxia, Dong, ed. 2009. 256p. pap. 40.00 *(978-0-415-48456-5(1))* Routledge.

BEIJING (CHINA)—GUIDEBOOKS

Beijing Excursion Guide. 2007. pap. 12.95 *(978-0-9773334-5-5(0))* True Run Advertising Co.

Best Days in Beijing. 2007. pap. 15.95 *(978-0-9773334-9-3(3))* True Run Advertising Co.

City Guides, LUXE. Beijing. 8th ed. 2012. (ENG.). 22p. 9.99 ***(978-988-8000-93-7(4))*** Luxe Asia Ltd. HKG. Dist: SCB Distributors.

—China Travel Set, 3 vols. 7th ed. 2012. (ENG.). 66p. 26.99 ***(978-988-8132-08-9(3))*** Luxe Asia Ltd. HKG. Dist: SCB Distributors.

Cohn, Don J. Beijing Walks: Exploring the Heritage. 2008. (Odyssey Illustrated Guides). (ENG., Illus.). 384p. pap. 24.95 *(978-962-217-762-8(X)*, 217762) Airphoto International/Odyssey HKG. Dist: Norton, W. W. & Co., Inc.

DAAB Media Staff, compiled by. Beijing, 1 vol. 2008. (ENG., Illus.). 238p. 59.95 *(978-3-86654-073-6(6))* DAAB Media Gmbh DEU. Dist: Innovative Logistics.

Gershman, Suzy. Suzy Gershman's Born to Shop Hong Kong, Shanghai & Beijing: The Ultimate Guide for People Who Love to Shop. 5th ed. 2010. (Born to Shop Ser.: 26). (ENG., Illus.). 336p. pap. 17.99 *(978-0-470-53769-5(8)*, Frommers) Wiley, John & Sons, Inc.

Humphreys, Andrew. Top 10 Beijing. 2011. (Eyewitness top 10 travel Guide Ser.). (ENG.). 128p. 14.00 *(978-0-7566-7046-7(2))* Dorling Kindersley Publishing, Inc.

Immersion Guides. Insider's Guide to Beijing: Fifth Edition. Barrett, Reid, ed. 2008. pap. 15.95 *(978-0-9801386-5-8(5)*, Immersion Guides) True Run Advertising Co.

Immersion Guides & Abrahamsen, Eric. Beijing by Foot. Jiang, Shelley, ed. 2008. pap. 15.95 *(978-0-9801386-2-7(0))* True Run Advertising Co.

The Insider's Guide to Beijing. 2007. pap. *(978-0-9773334-4-8(2))* 2006. pap. 15.95 *(978-0-9773334-1-7(8))* True Run Advertising Co.

Insight Guides. ICG Beijing. 6th ed. 2010. (City Guide Ser.). (ENG., Illus.). 304p. pap. 19.99 *(978-981-282-231-4(3))* APA Publications Services SGP. Dist: Ingram Pub. Services.

Jones, Kay. CultureShock! Beijing. 2007. (Illus.). 264p. pap. 15.95 *(978-981-261-118-5(5))* Marshall Cavendish International (Asia) Private Ltd. SGP. Dist: Marshall Cavendish Corp.

Lewis, Simon & Rough Guides Staff. The Rough Guide to Beijing. 4th ed. 2011. (ENG., Illus.). 200p. 19.99 *(978-1-84836-656-5(6))* Rough Guides, Ltd. GBR. Dist: Dorling Kindersley Publishing, Inc.

Lin-Liu, Jen. Frommer's Beijing Day by Day. 2nd ed. 2011. (Frommer's Day by Day - Pocket Ser.: 136). (ENG., Illus.). 192p. pap. 13.99 *(978-0-470-63006-8(X)*, Frommers) Wiley, John & Sons, Inc.

Lin-Liu, Jen & Pham, Sherisse. Beijing. 6th ed. 2010. (Frommer's Complete Guides: 738). (ENG., Illus.). 264p. pap. 18.99 *(978-0-470-52566-1(5)*, Frommers) Wiley, John & Sons, Inc.

—Frommer's Beijing Day by Day. 2007. (Frommer's Day by Day Ser.). (ENG., Illus.). 192p. pap. 12.99 *(978-0-470-22681-0(1)*, Frommers) Wiley, John & Sons, Inc.

Lonely Planet Staff & Eimer, Damian Harper. Beijing. 8th ed. 2010. (City Guide Ser.). (ENG., Illus.). 272p. pap. 19.99 *(978-1-74104-877-3(X))* Lonely Planet Pubns.

Lonely Planet Staff & Eimer, David. Beijing. 2nd rev. ed. 2010. (Encounter Ser.). (ENG., Illus.). 168p. pap. 12.99 *(978-1-74179-408-3(0))* Lonely Planet Pubns.

MapEasy Inc Staff. MapEasy's Guide to Beijing. 2006. 6.95 *(978-1-929038-03-9(8))* Mapeasy, Inc.

Mobil Travel Guide. Beijing City Guide. 2008. (ENG.). 176p. pap. 17.95 *(978-1-936010-07-3(0))* Five Star Travel Corp., The.

Mooney, Eileen Wen. Beijing Eats. Pillsbury, Adam & Yu, Jackie, eds. 2008. 200p. pap. *(978-0-9801386-3-4(9)*, Immersion Guides) True Run Advertising Co.

Moss, Chris & Time Out Guides Staff. Time Out Beijing. Moss, Chris, ed. 2007. (Time Out Guides). (ENG., Illus.). 320p. per. 19.95 *(978-1-904978-74-9(6))* Time Out Guides Ltd. GBR. Dist: Perseus-PGW.

Neville-Hadley, Peter. Beijing. 2nd ed. 2009. (Illus.). 480p. pap. 21.95 *(978-1-86011-393-2(1))* Cadogan Guides GBR. Dist: Globe Pequot Pr., The.

Pan, Anthony, et al. Beijing: A Survival Guide to Customs & Etiquette, 1 vol. 2008. (CultureShock! Ser.). (ENG., Illus.). 264p. pap. 15.95 *(978-0-7614-5475-5(6))* Marshall Cavendish Corp.

Pillsbury, Adam, ed. The Insider's Guide to Beijing: 2008. annuals 4th ed. 2007. pap. *(978-0-9801386-0-3(4)*, Immersion Guides) True Run Advertising Co.

Thomas Cook Publishing Staff. Beijing & Northern China. 2nd ed. 2010. (Travellers - Thomas Cook Ser.). (ENG., Illus.). 192p. pap. 16.95 *(978-1-84848-227-2(2))* Cook, Thomas Publishing GBR. Dist: Globe Pequot Pr., The.

VV., AA., et al. Beijing: Mit extra Cityplan. 2008. (City Guide Ser.). (SPA.). 192p. pap. 31.99 *(978-84-08-07718-3(X))* Lonely Planet Pubns.

Wallpaper Magazine Editors, ed. Beijing 2012 - Wallpaper City Guide. 2nd ed. 2011. (ENG., Illus.). 128p. pap., pap. 9.95 *(978-0-7148-6092-3(1))* Phaidon Pr., Inc.

BEIJING (CHINA)—HISTORY

Bai, Tiezheng. Lao Beiping de Gu Gu Dian Er. 2010. (CHI.). *(978-7-5306-5124-7(2))* Baihua Literature & Fine Arts Publishing Hse.

Barmé, Geremie R. The Forbidden City. 2008. (Wonders of the World Ser.). (Illus.). 288p. 19.95 *(978-0-674-02779-4(5))* Harvard Univ. Pr.

Boyd, Julia. A Dance with the Dragon. 2012. (ENG., Illus.). 288p. 29.00 ***(978-1-78076-052-0(3))*** I. B. Tauris & Co., Ltd. GBR. Dist: Macmillan.

Bredon, Juliet. Peking - a Historical & Intimate Description of Its Chief Places of Interest. 2008. 432p. pap. *(978-0-9680459-8-5(7))* Soul Care Publishing.

Brown, Frederick. From Tientsin to Peking with the Allied Forces. 2009. 62p. pap. *(978-1-151-31583-0(4))* Books LLC.

Chan, Hok-lam. Legends of the Building of Old Peking. 2008. (ENG., Illus.). 420p. 60.00 *(978-0-295-98782-8(0))* Univ. of Washington Pr.

Chen, Lianying. Wei Kai Fang de Zi Jin Cheng: Jiang Shu ni Suo Bu Zhi Dao de Zi Jin Cheng. 2010. (Illus.). *(978-7-5108-0253-9(9))* Jiuzhou Publishing Hse.

Clements, Jonathan. Beijing: The Biography of a City. 2008. (ENG., Illus.). 192p. 26.95 *(978-0-7509-4251-5(7))* History Pr. Ltd., The GBR. Dist: Independent Pubs. Group.

Danto, Arthur C. & Moeller, Hans-Georg. Legends of the Building of Old Peking. 2007. (ENG., Illus.). 450p. 55.00 *(978-962-996-313-2(2))* Chinese Univ. of Hong Kong, The HKG. Dist: Columbia Univ. Pr.

Fleischer, Friederike. Suburban Beijing: Housing & Consumption in Contemporary China. 2010. (ENG., Illus.). 256p. 75.00 *(978-0-8166-4596-1(5))*; pap. 25.00 *(978-0-8166-6587-7(7))* Univ. of Minnesota Pr.

French, Paul. Midnight in Peking: How the Murder of a Young Englishwoman Haunted the Last Days of Old China. 2012. (ENG., Illus.). 272p. (gr. 12). 26.00 ***(978-0-14-312100-8(6)**,* Penguin (Non-Classics)) Penguin Group (USA) Inc.

Fu, Hua. Beijing Xicheng Wen Hua Shi. 2007. (CHI., Illus.). 8p. *(978-7-5402-1923-9(8))* Beijing Yanshan Pr.

Gabbi, Giorgio. The Treasures of Beijing: Places & History. 2007. (Places & History Ser.). (ENG., Illus.). 136p. 24.95 *(978-88-544-0118-1(8)*, White Star) Rizzoli International Pubns., Inc.

Halper, Stefan. The Beijing Consensus: How China's Authoritarian Model Will Dominate the Twenty-First Century. 2010. (ENG.). 312p. (gr. 9). 28.95 *(978-0-465-01361-6(9))* Basic Bks.

Haw, Stephen. Beijing - A Concise History. 2008. (Routledge Studies in the Modern History of Asia Ser.). (ENG., Illus.). 224p. (C). pap. 44.95 *(978-0-415-39905-0(X))* Routledge.

Haw, Stephen G. Beijing. 2006. (Routledge Studies in the Modern History of Asia: Vol. 41). (Illus.). 212p. 160.00 *(978-0-415-39906-7(8))* Routledge.

Holdsworth, May & Courtauld, Caroline. Forbidden City: The Great Within. 2nd ed. 2008. (ENG.). 152p. pap. 24.95 *(978-962-217-792-5(1)*, 217792) Airphoto International/Odyssey HKG. Dist: Norton, W. W. & Co., Inc.

Johnston, Reginald Fleming. Twilight in the Forbidden City. 2007. 484p. per. *(978-1-84356-020-3(8))* Wallenberg, Simon Pr.

Li, Lillian M., et al. Beijing: From Imperial Capital to Olympic City. 2008. (ENG., Illus.). 368p. pap. 18.95 *(978-0-230-60527-5(3))* Palgrave Macmillan.

Martin, William A. P. The Siege in Peking: Inside the Legations During the Boxer Uprising by One of the Besieged. 2010. 124p. *(978-0-85706-076-1(7))*; pap. *(978-0-85706-075-4(9))* Leonaur Ltd.

Rennie, David Field. Peking & the Pekingese During the First Year of the British Embassy at Peking. 2009. 178p. pap. 19.99 *(978-1-150-00505-3(X))* General Bks. LLC.

Schwarcz, Vera. Place & Memory in the Singing Crane Garden. 2008. (Penn Studies in Landscape Architecture). (Illus.). 272p. (C). 65.00 *(978-0-8122-4100-6(2))* Univ. of Pennsylvania Pr.

Wang, Lansuo, text. Beijing's Siheyuan. 2007. (Illus.). 103p. 9.95 *(978-7-80220-066-1(0))* New World Pr. CHN. Dist: China Bks. & Periodicals, Inc.

Weale, B. L. Putnam. Indiscreet Letters from Peking. 2008. 384p. 31.99 *(978-0-554-26211-6(8))*; 29.99 *(978-0-554-35514-6(0))* BiblioBazaar.

—Indiscreet Letters from Peking: Being the Notes of an Eye-Witness... 2007. (ENG.). 342p. pap. 23.99 *(978-1-4346-0612-9(0))*; 382p. pap. 26.99 *(978-1-4346-0687-7(2))* BiblioBazaar.

Weale, B. L. Putnam, ed. Indiscreet Letters from Peking. 2007. (ENG.). 458p. 52.95 *(978-0-548-02089-0(2))* Kessinger Publishing, LLC.

West, James. Beijing Blur: A Head-Spinning Journey into Modern China. 2008. 230p. pap. 14.95 *(978-0-9788259-6-6(9))* Chilmark Pr., The.

White, Antony. The Forbidden City. 2006. (ENG., Illus.). 64p. pap., instr.'s gde. ed. *(978-962-86215-3-8(X))* London Editions (HK), Ltd.

Yue, Guo & Farrow, Clare. Music, Food & Love: A Memoir with Recipes. 2009. (ENG., Illus.). 272p. pap. 19.95 *(978-0-7499-2934-3(0))* Piatkus Bks. GBR. Dist: Independent Pubs. Group.

Zhu, Hong & Yangquan, Li. Discover Beijing: The City's History & Culture Redefined, 1 vol. 2007. (Discover Ser.). (ENG., Illus.). 192p. pap. 16.50 *(978-981-261-364-6(1))* Marshall Cavendish International (Asia) Private Ltd. SGP. Dist: Marshall Cavendish Corp.

BEIJING (CHINA)—POLITICS AND GOVERNMENT

Halper, Stefan. The Beijing Consensus: How China's Authoritarian Model Will Dominate the Twenty-First Century. 2010. (ENG.). 312p. (gr. 9). 28.95 *(978-0-465-01361-6(9))* Basic Bks.

Mangan, J. A. Beijing 2008: Preparing for Glory: Chinese Challenge in the 'Chinese Century' Jinxia, Dong, ed. 2009. 256p. pap. 40.00 *(978-0-415-48456-5(1))* Routledge.

Read, Benjamin Lelan. Roots of the State: Neighborhood Organization & Social Networks in Beijing & Taipei. 2012. (Contemporary Issues in Asia & Pacific Ser.). (ENG.). 376p. 80.00 ***(978-0-8047-7564-9(8))***; pap. 24.95 ***(978-0-8047-7565-6(6))*** Stanford Univ. Pr.

BEIJING (CHINA)—SOCIAL LIFE AND CUSTOMS

Aldrich, M. A. & Nikol, Lukas. The Perfumed Palace: Islam's Journey from Mecca to Peking. 2010. 288p. 60.00 *(978-1-85964-227-6(6))* Garnet Publishing, Ltd. GBR. Dist: International Publishers Marketing.

Boyd, Julia. A Dance with the Dragon. 2012. (ENG., Illus.). 288p. 29.00 ***(978-1-78076-052-0(3))*** I. B. Tauris & Co., Ltd. GBR. Dist: Macmillan.

Conley, Susan. The Foremost Good Fortune. (Vintage Ser.). (ENG., 2012. Illus.). 368p. pap. 15.00 ***(978-0-307-73986-5(4)***, Vintage) 2011. 288p. 25.95 *(978-0-307-59406-8(8)*, Knopf) Knopf Doubleday Publishing Group.

Hobson, Michael W. The Year I Smelled Like Milk: Stories from Beijing & Beyond. 2010. 248p. 32.97 *(978-0-557-21684-0(2))* Lulu Enterprises Inc.

Immersion Guides. Insider's Guide to Beijing: Fifth Edition. Barrett, Reid, ed. 2008. pap. 15.95 *(978-0-9801386-5-8(5)*, Immersion Guides) True Run Advertising Co.

Jones, Kay. CultureShock! Beijing. 2007. (Illus.). 264p. pap. 15.95 *(978-981-261-118-5(5))* Marshall Cavendish International (Asia) Private Ltd. SGP. Dist: Marshall Cavendish Corp.

Li, Shulan. Jing Wei Wen Hua Shi Lun. 2009. (CHI., Illus.). *(978-7-81119-325-1(6))* Capital Normal Univ. Pr.

Meyer, Michael. The Last Days of Old Beijing: Life in the Vanishing Backstreets of a City Transformed. 2009. (ENG., Illus.). 384p. pap. 16.00 *(978-0-8027-1750-4(0))* Walker & Co.

Morris, Sarah. Sarah Morris: Beijing. 2010. (ENG., Illus.). 288p. 61.00 *(978-3-86560-646-4(6))* Verlag der Buchhandlung Walther Konig DEU. Dist: D.A.P./Distributed Art Pubs.

Pan, Anthony, et al. Beijing: A Survival Guide to Customs & Etiquette, 1 vol. 2008. (CultureShock! Ser.). (ENG., Illus.). 264p. pap. 15.95 *(978-0-7614-5475-5(6))* Marshall Cavendish Corp.

Raes, Fabien & Jambers, Paul. Beijing. 2009. (ENG., Illus.). 112p. *(978-90-5856-290-6(5)*, Stichting Kunstboek (Acc)) Antique Collectors' Club.

Scocca, Tom. Beijing Welcomes You: Unveiling the Capital City of the Future. 2011. (ENG., Illus.). 384p. (gr. 12). 26.95 *(978-1-59448-784-2(7)*, Riverhead Bks. (Hardcover)) Penguin Group (USA) Inc.

Wei, Xin, text. World Cultural Heritage in Beijing: [Beijing de Shi Jie Wen Hua Yi Chan]. 2009. (Illus.). 143p. *(978-7-5104-0676-8(5))* New World Pr.

BEIJING (CHINA)—SOCIAL CONDITIONS

Boyd, Julia. A Dance with the Dragon. 2012. (ENG., Illus.). 288p. 29.00 ***(978-1-78076-052-0(3))*** I. B. Tauris & Co., Ltd. GBR. Dist: Macmillan.

Cheng, Weikun. City of Working Women: Life, Space, & Social Control in Early Twentieth-Century Beijing. 2011. *(978-1-55729-098-4(9))* Univ. of California, Institute of East Asian Studies.

Fleischer, Friederike. Suburban Beijing: Housing & Consumption in Contemporary China. 2010. (ENG., Illus.). 256p. 75.00 *(978-0-8166-4596-1(5))*; pap. 25.00 *(978-0-8166-6587-7(7))* Univ. of Minnesota Pr.

Wang, Jun & Li, Shaojun. The Rhetoric & Reality of Culture-Led Urban Regeneration: A Comparison of Beijing & Shanghai, China. 2011. (China in the 21st Century Ser.). 60p. pap. 43.00 *(978-1-61668-683-3(9))* Nova Science Pubs., Inc.

BEIJING DA XUE

Lanza, Fabio. Behind the Gate: Inventing Students in Beijing. 2010. (Studies of the Weatherhead East Asian Institute, Columbia University Ser.). (ENG., Illus.). 320p. (gr. 17). 50.00 *(978-0-231-15238-9(8))* Columbia Univ. Pr.

Peking University: High School of Peking University, Guanghua School of Management, Gregory B. Lee, Cai Yuanpei. 2010. 66p. pap. 14.14 *(978-1-157-38219-5(3))* General Bks. LLC.

Peking University Alumni: Michael Halliday, Mao Dun, Fan Changjiang, Jonny Blu, K. Natwar Singh, Bo Xilai, Zhang Chengzhi, Zhang Guotao, Dashan. 2010. 170p. pap. 19.99 *(978-1-155-63762-4(3))* General Bks. LLC.

Peking University Faculty: Mao Zedong, Hu Shih, Chen Duxiu, Lu Xun, Qian Xuantong, Fei Xiaotong, Lin Yutang, Jeffrey S. Lehman. 2010. 178p. pap. 19.99 *(978-1-155-63763-1(1))* General Bks. LLC.

BEIJING UNIVERSITY

see Beijing Da Xue

BEING

see Ontology

BEIRUT (LEBANON)

Abdelnour, Salma. Jasmine & Fire: A Bittersweet Year in Beirut. 2012. (ENG.). 336p. pap. 14.00 ***(978-0-307-88594-4(1))*** Broadway Bks.

Basilico, Gabriele. Beirut 1991 (2003) 2008. (ENG.). 172p. 65.00 *(978-88-6073-429-7(0))* Baldini Castoldi Dalai Editore ITA. Dist: Independent Pubs. Group.

Hall, Linda Jones. Roman Berytus: Beirut in Late Antiquity. 2008. 408p. pap. 39.95 *(978-0-415-48679-8(3))* Routledge.

Kassir, Samir. Beirut. DeBevoise, Malcolm, tr. from FRE. (ENG., Illus.). 2011. 656p. pap. 28.95 *(978-0-520-27126-5(2))* 2010. 650p. 39.95 *(978-0-520-25668-2(9))* Univ. of California Pr.

Khuri-Makdisi, Ilham. The Eastern Mediterranean & the Making of Global Radicalism, 1860-1914. 2010. (California World History Library). (ENG., Illus.). 296p. 50.00 *(978-0-520-26201-0(8))* Univ. of California Pr.

Lee, Jessica. Beirut Footprint Focus. 2011. (Footprint Focus Ser.). (ENG., Illus.). 96p. pap. 9.95 *(978-1-908206-11-4(X))* Footprint Handbooks GBR. Dist: Globe Pequot Pr., The.

Locken, E. Travel Journal Beirut. 2010. 192p. pap. 19.99 *(978-0-557-44411-3(X))* Lulu Enterprises Inc.

Mansel, Philip. Levant: Splendour & Catastrophe on the Mediterranean. 2011. (Illus.). 470p. 35.00 *(978-0-300-17264-5(8))* Yale Univ. Pr.

Sarkis, Hashim, et al. Two Squares: Martyrs Square, Beirut, & Sirkeci Square, Istanbul. Sarkis, Hashim, ed. 2006. (Aga Khan Program of the Graduate School of Design Ser.). (Illus.). 200p. per. 19.95 *(978-0-935617-89-4(2))* Harvard Univ., Graduate Schl. of Design.

Scianna, Ferdinando & Miracco, Renato. Giulio Rimondi: Beirut Nocturne. 2011. (ENG., Illus.). 88p. 37.95 *(978-88-8158-789-6(0))* Charta ITA. Dist: D.A.P./Distributed Art Pubs.

Thornhill, Teresa. The Curtain Maker of Beirut: Conversations with the Lebanese. 2011. (Illus.). 304p. 45.00 *(978-1-907784-01-9(2))* Berkshire Academic Pr., Ltd. GBR. Dist: International Specialized Bk. Services.

Ziadé, Lamia. Bye Bye Babylon: Beirut 1975-1979. Klang-Snaije, Olivia, tr. from FRE. 2011. pap. 24.95 ***(978-1-56656-877-7(3)***, Interlink Graphic) Interlink Publishing Group, Inc.

BEISSEL, CONRAD, 1690-1768

Lamech, Brother, abr. Chronicon Ephratense. 2009. (Amer Philosophy, Religion Ser.). (ENG.). 308p. pap. 20.95 *(978-1-4290-1933-0(6))* Applewood Bks.

BEJA (AFRICAN PEOPLE)

Fadlalla, Amal Hassan. Embodying Honor: Fertility, Foreignness, & Regeneration in Eastern Sudan. 2007. (Women in Africa & the Diaspora Ser.). *(978-0-299-22384-7(1))*; (Illus.). 232p. 55.00 *(978-0-299-22380-9(9))* Univ. of Wisconsin Pr.

Paul, A. A History of the Beja Tribes of the Sudan. 2011. (ENG.). 186p. pap. 33.99 ***(978-1-107-64686-5(3))*** Cambridge Univ. Pr.

BEKTASHI

Shankland, David. The Alevis in Turkey. 2007. 256p. 39.95 *(978-0-415-44436-1(5))* Routledge.

Trix, Frances. The Sufi Journey of Baba Rexheb. 2009. (Illus.). 240p. (C). 55.00 *(978-1-934536-12-4(1)*, Univ. of Pennsylvania Museum of Archaeology & Anthropology) Univ. Museum Pubns.

Yurekli, Zeynep. Architecture & Hagiography in the Ottoman Empire: The Politics of Bektashi Shrines in the Classical Age. 2012. (Illus.). 200p. ***(978-1-4094-1107-9(9))***; ***(978-1-4094-1106-2(0))*** Ashgate Publishing, Ltd.

BEKTASHITES

see Bektashi

BEL

see Baal (Deity)

BEL CANTO

Corte, Andrea Della, ed. Canto E Bel Canto P.F. Tosi: Opinioni De Cantori Antichi E Moderni 1723. reprint ed. 31.50 *(978-0-404-18823-8(0))* AMS Pr., Inc.

Duey, Philip A. Bel Canto in Its Golden Age - A Study of Its Teaching Concepts. 2007. (ENG.). 232p. per. *(978-1-4067-5437-7(4))* Read Bks.

Toft, Robert. Bel Canto: A Performer's Guide. 2012. ***(978-0-19-983231-6(5))***; pap. ***(978-0-19-983232-3(3))*** Oxford Univ. Pr., Inc.

BELAFONTE, HARRY, 1927-

Belafonte, Harry. My Song. 2012. (Vintage Ser.). (ENG., Illus.). 480p. pap. 16.00 ***(978-0-307-47342-4(2)***, Vintage) Knopf Doubleday Publishing Group.

Belafonte, Harry & Shnayerson, Michael. My Song: Die Autobiographie. 2011. (ENG., Illus.). 480p. 30.50 *(978-0-307-27226-3(5)*, Knopf) Knopf Doubleday Publishing Group.

—My Song: Die Autobiographie. lt. ed. 2011. (ENG.). 848p. pap. 31.00 *(978-0-7393-7838-0(4))* Random Hse. Large Print.

Shaw, Arnold. Belafonte: An Unauthorized Biography. 2011. 368p. 53.95 ***(978-1-258-06661-1(0))*** Literary Licensing, LLC.

BELARUS—BIOGRAPHY

Bennett, Brian. The Last Dictatorship in Europe: Belarus under Lukashenko. 2012. (Columbia/Hurst Ser.). (ENG.). 256p. (gr. 17). 35.00 ***(978-0-231-70280-5(9))*** Columbia Univ. Pr.

Boresky, Theodosia. Life of St Josaphat: Martyr of the Union. 2011. 388p. 53.95 ***(978-1-258-03017-9(9))*** Literary Licensing, LLC.

Chagall, Bella. Burning Lights. Guterman, Norbert, tr. 2011. 268p. 47.95 ***(978-1-258-02734-6(8))*** Literary Licensing, LLC.

Gimpelevich, Zina. Belarusian Jewish Writers of the Twentieth Century: Origin, History, Discourse, & Biographies. 2009. (BEL.). 195p. pap. 35.00 ***(978-1-59831-005-4(4))*** Southwestern College Academic Pr.

In the Struggle: Memoirs from Grodno & the Forests. 2009. 192p. pap. 15.95 ***(978-0-9814686-2-4(4))*** Holocaust Survivors' Memoirs Project.

Jackson, Carlton. Joseph Gavi — Young Hero of the Minsk Ghetto. 2010. *(978-1-935001-38-6(8))* Acclaim Pr., Inc.

Kolpanitzky, Kopel. Sentenced to Life: The Story of a Survivor of the Lahwah Ghetto. 2007. (Illus.). 287p. pap. 26.95 *(978-0-85303-695-1(0))* Vallentine Mitchell Pubs. GBR. Dist: International Specialized Bk. Services.

Radio Free Europe/Radio Liberty. One Day in the Life of a Political Prisoner. 2009.Tr. of One Day in the Life of a Political Prisoner. (BEL., Illus.). 358p. pap. *(978-0-929849-27-0(2))* Radio Free Europe/Radio Liberty, Inc.

Rafaeli, Esther Shapiro. The Modest Genius - Hebrew - Hc. 2009. 220p. 21.95 *(978-1-934440-78-0(7)*, Devora Publishing) Simcha Media Group.

Reznik, Lewis. A Boy's Holocaust. 2010. 120p. pap. 14.00 *(978-1-60844-634-6(4))* Dog Ear Publishing, LLC.

Shulman, Arkadii. Mestechko Marka Shagala: Ocherk. 2010. (RUS., Illus.). 115p. *(978-985-6887-83-6(6))* Medisont, Sumesnae TAA.

Vygodskaia, Anna Pavlovna. The Story of a Life: Memoirs of a Young Jewish Woman in the Russian Empire. Avrutin, Eugene M. & Greene, Robert H., eds. 2012. (ENG., Illus.). 150p. pap. 22.95 ***(978-0-87580-671-6(6))*** Northern Illinois Univ. Pr.

Vygodskaia, Anna Pavlovna, et al. The Story of a Life: Memoirs of a Young Jewish Woman in the Russian Empire. 2012. ***(978-1-60909-046-3(2))*** Northern Illinois Univ. Pr.

Wengeroff, Pauline. Memoirs of a Grandmother: Scenes from the Cultural History of the Jews of Russia in the Nineteenth Century, 2 vols. Magnus, Shulamit S., tr. from GER. 2010. (Stanford Studies in Jewish History & C Ser.). (ENG., Illus.). 384p. 55.00 *(978-0-8047-6879-5(X))* Stanford Univ. Pr.

BELARUS—DESCRIPTION AND TRAVEL

Locken, E. Travel Journal Belarus. 2010. 192p. pap. 19.99 *(978-0-557-43269-1(3))* Lulu Enterprises Inc.

BELARUS—ECONOMIC CONDITIONS

BIA. Essential Manufacturers of Belarus: Food, Textile, Clothing, & Chemical Companies. 6th rev. ed. 2006. 300p. (J). pap. 249.00 *(978-1-4187-4207-2(4))* Business Information Agency.

Gavrilenko, V. N. Mekhanizmy Ustoichivogo Razvitiia Innovatsionnykh Sotsialno-Ekonomicheskikh Sistem: Materialy V Mezhdunarodnoi Nauchno-Prakticheskoi Konferentsii, Bobruisk, 1 Aprelia 2010 Goda. 2010. (RUS.). 310p. *(978-985-484-687-3(3))* Belaruski dzjarzauny ekanamiciny universitet, Ustanova adukacyi.

Icon Group International, Inc. Staff, compiled by. The 2006 Economic & Product Market Databook for Baranovichi, Belarus. 2006. 618p. ring bd. 95.00 *(978-0-497-80140-3(X))* Icon Group International, Inc.

—The 2006 Economic & Product Market Databook for Borisov, Belarus. 2006. 618p. ring bd. 95.00 *(978-0-497-80227-1(9))* Icon Group International, Inc.

—The 2006 Economic & Product Market Databook for Brest, Belarus. 2006. 618p. ring bd. 95.00 *(978-0-497-80244-8(9))* Icon Group International, Inc.

—The 2006 Economic & Product Market Databook for Gomel, Belarus. 2006. 618p. ring bd. 95.00 *(978-0-497-80607-1(X))* Icon Group International, Inc.

—The 2006 Economic & Product Market Databook for Grodno, Belarus. 2006. 618p. ring bd. 95.00 *(978-0-497-80620-0(7))* Icon Group International, Inc.

—The 2006 Economic & Product Market Databook for Minsk, Belarus. 2006. 618p. ring bd. 95.00 *(978-0-497-81027-6(1))* Icon Group International, Inc.

—The 2006 Economic & Product Market Databook for Mogilyov, Belarus. 2006. 618p. ring bd. 95.00 *(978-0-497-81038-2(7))* Icon Group International, Inc.

—The 2006 Economic & Product Market Databook for Mozyr, Belarus. 2006. 618p. ring bd. 95.00 *(978-0-497-81067-2(0))* Icon Group International, Inc.

—The 2006 Economic & Product Market Databook for Orsha, Belarus. 2006. 618p. ring bd. 95.00 *(978-0-497-81168-6(5))* Icon Group International, Inc.

—The 2006 Economic & Product Market Databook for Pinsk, Belarus. 2006. 618p. ring bd. 95.00 *(978-0-497-81257-7(6))* Icon Group International, Inc.

—The 2006 Economic & Product Market Databook for Vitebsk, Belarus. 2006. 618p. ring bd. 95.00 *(978-0-497-81796-1(9))* Icon Group International, Inc.

Savchenko, Andrew. Belarus - A Perpetual Borderland. 2009. 252p. *(978-90-04-17448-1(6))* BRILL.

United Nations Staff. Investment Policy Review: Republic of Belarus. 2009. (ENG.). 124p. pap. 30.00 *(978-92-1-112780-5(7))* United Nations Pubns.

Yafimava, Katja. Post-Soviet Russian-Belarussian Relationships the Role of Gas Transit Pipelines. 2007. 148p. per. *(978-3-89821-655-5(1))* Ibidem-Verlag.

Yakavenka, Hanna. Transfer of International Knowledge. 2009. 296p. pap. *(978-3-639-13044-7(8))* VDM Verlag Dr. Mueller e.K.

BELARUS—FOREIGN RELATIONS

Danilovich, Alex. Russian-Belarusian Integration: Playing Games Behind the Kremlin Walls. 2006. (Post-Soviet Politics Ser.). (Illus.). 250p. 124.95 *(978-0-7546-4630-3(0))* Ashgate Publishing Co.

Schmidtke, Oliver & Yekelchyk, Serhy. Europe's Last Frontier? Belarus, Moldova, & Ukraine Between Russia & the European Union. 2008. (ENG., Illus.). 268p. 95.00 *(978-0-230-60372-1(6))* Palgrave Macmillan.

Silitski, Vitali & Moshes, Arkady. Political Trends in the New Eastern Europe: Belarus & Russia: Comradeship-in-Arms in Preempting Democracy, & Ukraine: Domestic Changes & Foreign Policy Reconfiguration. 2007. (U.S. & Russia Ser.). *(978-1-58487-294-8(2))* Strategic Studies Institute, U.S. Army War College Commandant (AWCC-DSI/Pubns.).

Yafimava, Katja. Post-Soviet Russian-Belarussian Relationships the Role of Gas Transit Pipelines. 2007. 148p. per. *(978-3-89821-655-5(1))* Ibidem-Verlag.

BELARUS—HISTORY

Anon. Passage de la Beresina26-27-28- et 29th Novembre 1812. 2011. 56p. pap. ***(978-1-84574-880-7(8))*** Naval & Military Pr., The.

Baranova, Olga. Nationalism, Anti-Bolshevism or the Will to Survive. 2010. 252p. pap. *(978-3-8383-4971-8(7))* Lambert Academic Publishing.

Brakel, Alexander. Zeitalter der Weltkriege 05. Unter Rotem Stern und Hakenkreuz: Branovicze 1939-1944: Das westliche Weißrussland unter sowjetischer und deutscher Besatzung. 2009. (Zeitalter der Weltkriege Ser.: Vol. 5). (Illus.). 426p. *(978-3-506-76784-4(4))* Schoningh, Ferdinand GmbH, Verlag.

Dunn, Walter S., Jr. Soviet Blitzkrieg: The Battle for White Russia 1944. 2008. (Stackpole Military History Ser.). (ENG., Illus.). 272p. per. 16.95 *(978-0-8117-3482-0(X))* Swan Hill Pr. GBR. Dist: Stackpole Bks.

Hourtoulle, François-Guy & Jouineau, André. Crossing the Berezina. 2011. (GREAT BATTLES of FIRST EMPIRE Ser.). (Illus.). 100p. 44.95 *(978-2-35250-044-5(3))* Histoire et Collections FRA. Dist: Casemate Pubs. & Bk. Distributors, LLC.

Parker, Stewart. The Last Soviet Republic. 2007. 249p. pap. 19.33 *(978-1-4251-3527-0(7))* Trafford Publishing.

Plavinski, Mikalai. Studies of the 10-13th Centuries Blade Weapons History in Belarus. 2010. 152p. pap. *(978-3-8383-4998-5(9))* Lambert Academic Publishing.

Rein. The Kings & the Pawns: Collaboration in Byelorussia During World War II. 2011. (WG Ser.). 458p. 110.00 *(978-1-84545-776-1(5))* Berghahn Bks., Inc.

Savchenko, Andrew. Belarus - A Perpetual Borderland. 2009. 252p. *(978-90-04-17448-1(6))* BRILL.

Shulman, Arkadii. Mestechko Marka Shagala: Ocherk. 2010. (RUS., Illus.). 115p. *(978-985-6887-83-6(6))* Medisont, Sumesnae TAA.

Silitski, Vitali. The A to Z of Belarus. 2010. (A to Z Guide Ser.). (ENG.). 470p. pap. 34.45 *(978-0-8108-7200-4(5))* Scarecrow Pr., Inc.

—Historical Dictionary of Belarus. 2nd ed. 2007. (Historical Dictionaries of Europe Ser.). (ENG.). 472p. 110.00 *(978-0-8108-5812-1(6))* Scarecrow Pr., Inc.

Staliūnas, Darius. Making Russians: Meaning & Practice of Russification in Lithuania & Belarus After 1863. 2007. (Illus.). 480p. 134.00 *(978-90-420-2267-6(1))* Rodopi.

Tec, Nechama. Defiance: The Bielski Partisans. 2008. (ENG., Illus.). 320p. pap. 14.95 *(978-0-19-537685-2(4))* Oxford Univ. Pr., Inc.

Wilson, Andrew. Belarus: The Last European Dictatorship. 2012. (ENG., Illus.). 256p. 35.00 *(978-0-300-13435-3(5))* Yale Univ. Pr.

BELARUS—POLITICS AND GOVERNMENT

Bennett, Brian. The Last Dictatorship in Europe: Belarus under Lukashenko. 2012. (Columbia/Hurst Ser.). (ENG.). 256p. (gr. 17). 35.00 ***(978-0-231-70280-5(9))*** Columbia Univ. Pr.

B

Drakahrust, Yuri. Accents of Freedom. 2009.Tr. of Accents of Freedom. (BEL., Illus.). 425p. pap. (978-0-929849-28-7(0)) Radio Free Europe/Radio Liberty, Inc.

Freedom Denied: Belarus on the Eve of the Election: Hearing Before the Commission on Security & Cooperation in Europe, One Hundred Ninth Congress, Second Session, March 9, 2006. 2007. iii, 65p. (978-0-16-079806-1(X), 552-070-36711-0) United States Government Printing Office.

Ioffe, Grigory. Understanding Belarus & How Western Foreign Policy Misses the Mark. 2008. (ENG., Illus.). 90.00 (978-0-7425-5558-7(5)) Rowman & Littlefield Publishers, Inc.

Parker, Stewart. The Last Soviet Republic. 2007. 249p. pap. 19.33 (978-1-4251-3527-0(7)) Trafford Publishing.

Radio Free Europe/Radio Liberty. One Day in the Life of a Political Prisoner. 2009.Tr. of One Day in the Life of a Political Prisoner. (BEL., Illus.). 358p. pap. (978-0-929849-27-0(2)) Radio Free Europe/Radio Liberty, Inc.

Savchenko, Andrew. Belarus - A Perpetual Borderland. 2009. 252p. (978-90-04-17448-1(6)) BRILL.

United Nations Staff. Investment Policy Review: Republic of Belarus. 2009. (ENG.). 124p. pap. 30.00 (978-92-1-112780-5(7)) United Nations Pubns.

Urban, Michael E. An Algebra of Soviet Power: Elite Circulation in the Belorussian Republic 1966-86. 2008. (Cambridge Russian, Soviet & Post-Soviet Studies). (ENG.). 200p. pap. 30.00 (978-0-521-05488-1(5)) Cambridge Univ. Pr.

Voloshina, T. O. & Malovitsina, O. O. Tamozhennyi Kodeks Tamozhennogo Soiuza: Tamozhennyi Kodeks Rossiiskoi Federatsii: Po Sostoianiiu Na 2010 G.: S Kommentariiami K Poslednim Izmeneniiam. 2010. (RUS.). 665p. (978-5-699-44275-1(8)) Eksmo-Press, Izdatel'skaja firma.

Wilson, Andrew. Belarus: The Last European Dictatorship. 2012. (ENG., Illus.). 256p. 35.00 (978-0-300-13435-3(5)) Yale Univ. Pr.

BELARUS—SOCIAL CONDITIONS

Chagall, Bella. Burning Lights. 2007. pap. (978-1-4067-5645-6(8)) Read Bks.

Epstein, Barbara. The Minsk Ghetto 1941-1943: Jewish Resistance & Soviet Internationalism. 2008. (Illus.). 376p. 45.00 (978-0-520-24242-5(4)) Univ. of California Pr.

Gavrilenko, V. N. Mekhanizmy Ustoichivogo Razvitiia Innovatsionnykh Sotsialno-Ekonomicheskikh Sistem: Materialy V Mezhdunarodnoi Nauchno-Prakticheskoi Konferentsii, Bobruisk, 1 Aprelia 2010 Goda. 2010. (RUS.). 310p. (978-985-484-687-3(3)) Belaruski dzjarzauny ekanamicny universitet, Ustanova adukacyi.

Ioffe, Grigory. Understanding Belarus & How Western Foreign Policy Misses the Mark. 2008. (ENG., Illus.). 90.00 (978-0-7425-5558-7(5)) Rowman & Littlefield Publishers, Inc.

Nadav, Mordechai. The Jews of Pinsk, 1506 to 1880. Rosman, Moshe & Mirsky, Mark, eds. 2007. (Stanford Studies in Jewish History & C Ser.). (ENG., Illus.). 656p. 75.00 (978-0-8047-4159-0(X)) Stanford Univ. Pr.

Surtees, Rebecca & International Organization for Migration. Trafficking of Men - A Trend Less Considered: The Case of Belarus & Ukraine. 2009. 124p. pap. 16.00 (978-92-1-103666-4(6)) International Organization for Migration (IOM) CHE. Dist: United Nations Pubns.

Wengeroff, Pauline. Memoirs of a Grandmother: Scenes from the Cultural History of the Jews of Russia in the Nineteenth Century, 2 vols. Magnus, Shulamit S., tr. from GER. 2010. (Stanford Studies in Jewish History & C Ser.). (ENG., Illus.). 384p. 55.00 (978-0-8047-6879-5(X)) Stanford Univ. Pr.

BELASCO, DAVID, 1859-1931

Belasco, David. The Theatre Through Its Stage Door. 2010. 310p. 36.99 (978-1-117-94611-5(8)); pap. 29.75 (978-1-117-94612-2(6)) BiblioBazaar.

—The Theatre Through Its Stage Door. 2009. 114p. pap. 19.99 (978-1-150-73508-0(2)) General Bks. LLC.

—The Theatre Through Its Stage Door. DeFoe, Louis V., ed. 312p. 2010. 36.76 (978-1-163-42455-1(2)) 2010. pap. 24.76 (978-1-162-95951-1(7)) 2007. (ENG.). 45.95 (978-0-548-11727-9(6)) Kessinger Publishing, LLC.

Belasco, David & De Foe, Louis Vincent. The Theatre Through Its Stage Door. 2010. (ENG.). 308p. pap. 29.75 (978-1-176-39514-5(9)) BiblioBazaar.

Timberlake, Craig. The Bishop of Broadway: The Life & Work of David Belasco. 2011. 512p. 60.95 (978-1-258-05236-2(9)) Literary Licensing, LLC.

Winter, William. The Life of David Belasco. reprint ed. Vol. 1. 530p. lib. bdg. 19.00 (978-0-8290-0502-8(1)) Vol. 2. 563p. lib. bdg. 19.00 (978-0-8290-0503-5(X)) Irvington Pubs.

BELAU ISLANDS

see Palau

BELEMNITES

Schulz, M. G., et al. Coniacian & Santonian Belemnite Faunas from Bornholm/Santonian to Maastrichtian Ammonites from Scania, Number 44. 2006. (Fossils & Strata Monograph Ser.: 44). (ENG.). 128p. pap. 54.95 (978-82-00-37695-8(8), Wiley-Blackwell) Wiley, John & Sons, Inc.

BELFAST (NORTHERN IRELAND)

Collins UK. Belfast. 2009. (ENG., Illus.). 48p. pap. 7.95 (978-0-00-725757-7(0)) HarperCollins Pubs. Ltd. GBR. Dist: Independent Pubs. Group.

Duncan, John. John Duncan: Bonfires, 1 vol. 2008. (ENG., Illus.). 72p. 40.00 (978-3-86521-726-4(5)) Steidl, Gerhard Druckerei und Verlag DEU. Dist: Innovative Logistics.

Harvey, David. Belfast Trolleybuses from Old Photographs. 2010. (Illus.). 192p. pap. 29.95 (978-1-84868-466-9(5)) Amberley Publishing GBR. Dist: Casemate Pubs. & Bk. Distributors, LLC.

Keenan, Brian. I'll Tell Me Ma: A Childhood Memoir. (ENG.). 312p. 2010. pap. 16.95 (978-0-09-942815-2(6)) 2009. 29.95 (978-0-224-06216-9(6)) Random Hse. GBR. Dist: Independent Pubs. Group.

Murphy, Liam D. Believing in Belfast: Charismatic Christianity after the Troubles. 2010. pap. (978-1-59460-728-8(1)) Carolina Academic Pr.

Yarwood, John. The Dublin-Belfast Development Corridor: Ireland's Mega-City Region? 2006. (Urban & Regional Planning & Development Ser.). (Illus.). 310p. 130.00 (978-0-7546-4702-7(1)) Ashgate Publishing Co.

BELFAST (NORTHERN IRELAND)—HISTORY

Benn, George & Stevenson, Siobhan. A History of the Town of Belfast: From the Earliest Times to the Close of the Eighteenth Century, 2 vols. 2009. (ENG., Illus.). 1017p. pap. 64.95 (978-0-85640-832-8(8)) Blackstaff Pr., Ltd. GBR. Dist: Dufour Editions, Inc.

Beranek, Iva. Belfast, a City with a Wounded Heart; Hope of Redemption. 2010. 52p. pap. (978-3-8383-4862-9(1)) Lambert Academic Publishing.

Bew, John. The Glory of Being Britons: Civic Unionism in Nineteenth-Century Belfast. 2009. 269p. 69.95 (978-0-7165-2974-3(2)) Irish Academic Pr. IRL. Dist: International Specialized Bk. Services.

Boal, Frederick W. & Royle, Stephen A., eds. Enduring City: Belfast in the Twentieth Century. 2007. (ENG., Illus.). 381p. 71.95 (978-0-85640-790-1(9)) Blackstaff Pr., The IRL. Dist: Dufour Editions, Inc.

Brannigan, Tim. Where Are You Really From? 2010. (ENG.). 208p. pap. 20.95 (978-0-85640-853-3(0)) Blackstaff Pr., Ltd. GBR. Dist: Dufour Editions, Inc.

Douds, Stephen. Belfast Blitz: The People's Story. 2011. (ENG., Illus.). 174p. pap. 26.95 (978-0-85640-863-2(8)) Blackstaff Pr., Ltd. GBR. Dist: Dufour Editions, Inc.

Doyle, Mark. Fighting Like the Devil for the Sake of God: Protestants, Catholics & the Origins of Violence in Victorian Belfast. 2010. (ENG., Illus.). 304p. 89.95 (978-0-7190-7952-8(7)); mass mkt. 32.95 (978-0-7190-7953-5(5)) Manchester Univ. Pr. GBR. Dist: Macmillan.

Gillespie, Raymond & Royle, Stephen A. Belfast C. 1600 to C. 1900. 2007. 19p. pap. 20.00 (978-1-904890-20-1(2)) Royal Irish Academy IRL. Dist: International Specialized Bk. Services.

Grayson, Richard S. Belfast Boys: How Unionists & Nationalists Fought & Died Together in the First World War. (ENG., Illus.). 272p. 2010. 19.95 (978-1-4411-0519-6(0)) 2009. 44.95 (978-1-84725-008-7(4)) Continuum International Publishing Group, Ltd. GBR. Dist: National Bk. Network.

Hamill, Heather. Hoods: Crime & Punishment in Belfast. 2010. (ENG., Illus.). 200p. (C). 29.95 (978-0-691-11963-2(5)) Princeton Univ. Pr.

Hepburn, A. C. Catholic Belfast & Nationalist Ireland in the Era of Joe Devlin, 1871-1934. 2008. (ENG., Illus.). 320p. 125.00 (978-0-19-929884-6(X)) Oxford Univ. Pr., Inc.

Locken, E. Travel Journal Belfast. 2010. 192p. pap. 19.99 (978-0-557-42185-5(3)) Lulu Enterprises Inc.

Lynch, John. Belfast Built Ships. 2012. (ENG., Illus.). 304p. pap. 34.95 (978-0-7524-6539-5(2)) History Pr. Ltd.,The GBR. Dist: Independent Pubs. Group.

McIntosh, Gillian. Belfast City Hall. 2006. (ENG., Illus.). 160p. 49.95 (978-0-85640-769-7(0)) Blackstaff Pr., Ltd. GBR. Dist: Dufour Editions, Inc.

Moore, Frank Frankfort. In Belfast by the Sea. Maume, Patrick, ed. 2007. (CIH Ser.). (ENG.). 208p. pap. 42.95 (978-1-904558-86-6(0)) Univ. College Dublin Pr. IRL. Dist: Dufour Editions, Inc.

Myers, Kevin. Watching the Door: Drinking up, Getting down & Cheating Death in 1970s Belfast. 2009. (ENG.). 288p. pap. 15.95 (978-1-59376-235-3(6), Soft Skull Pr.) Counterpoint LLC.

O'Regan, Raymond. Hidden Belfast: Benevolence, Blackguards & Balloon Heads. 2011. (ENG., Illus.). 253p. 31.95 (978-1-85635-683-1(3)) Mercier Pr., Ltd., The IRL. Dist: Dufour Editions, Inc.

O'Reilly, Des. Rivers of Belfast: A History. 2010. (Illus.). 253p. pap. (978-1-906578-75-6(3)) Colourpoint Bks.

Parkhill, Trevor & Pollock, Vivienne. A Century of Belfast: Events, People & Places over the 20th Century. 2011. (ENG., Illus.). 128p. pap. 15.95 (978-0-7509-5012-1(9)) History Pr. Ltd.,The GBR. Dist: Independent Pubs. Group.

Patrick Feenan. By Land, by Se. 2011. 180p. pap. (978-1-907011-19-1(6)) Esteemworld Pubns.

Pilson, James Adair, ed. History of the Rise & Progress of Belfast, & Annals of the County Antrim: From the Earliest Period till the Present Time (1846) 2009. (Illus.). 188p. pap. 22.95 (978-1-104-17968-7(7)) Kessinger Publishing, LLC.

Weatherall, Norman. South Belfast: History & Guide. 2008. (History & Guide Ser.). (ENG., Illus.). 128p. pap. 29.95 (978-1-84588-929-6(0)) History Pr. Ltd.,The GBR. Dist: Independent Pubs. Group.

BELFRIES

see Towers

BELGIAN ARCHITECTURE

see Architecture—Belgium

BELGIAN ART

see Art, Belgian

BELGIAN CONGO

see Congo (Democratic Republic)

BELGIAN LITERATURE

Goris, Jan-Albert & Gijsen, Marnix. Belgian Letters: A Short Survey of Creative Writing in the French & Dutch Languages in Belgium. 2011. 50p. 35.95 (978-1-258-01862-7(4)) Literary Licensing, LLC.

BELGIAN LITERATURE—HISTORY AND CRITICISM

Aubert, Nathalie, et al. La Belgique Entre Deux Siècles: Laboratoire de la Modernité, 1880-1914. (FRE & ENG., Illus.). 272p. pap. 63.95 (978-3-03910-528-1(0)) Lang, Peter Publishing, Inc.

Bainbrigge, Susan. Culture & Identity in Belgian Francophone Writing: Dialogue, Diversity & Displacement. 2008. (Modern French Identities Ser.). 230p. pap. 64.95 (978-3-03911-382-8(8)) Lang, Peter AG GBR. Dist: Lang, Peter.

Bainbrigge, Susan, et al. Francographies: Identité et Altérité Dans les Espaces Francophones Européens. 2010. (Belgian Francophone Library). (FRE.). 430p. (C). 93.95 (978-1-4331-0348-3(6)) Lang, Peter Publishing, Inc.

Fréché, Bibiane. Littérature et Société en Belgique Francophone (1944-1960) 2009. (FRE.). 381p. (978-2-87106-497-8(0)) Le Cri editions.

Goriely, Serge. Le Théâtre de René Kalisky: Tragique et ludique dans la représentation de L'histoire. 2008. (Comparatisme et Société / Comparatism & Society Ser.). (FRE.). 360p. pap. 55.95 (978-90-5201-447-0(7)) PIE - Peter Lang BEL. Dist: Lang, Peter.

Hennuy, Jean-Frédéric. Des Iconoclastes Heureux et Sans Complexe. (Belgian Francophone Library Ser.). 162p. (C). 61.95 (978-0-8204-7871-5(7)) Lang, Peter Publishing, Inc.

Huftier, Arnaud. Jean Ray: L'alchimie du Mystère. 2010. (FRE., Illus.). 768p. (C). pap. 90.00 (978-2-251-74243-4(3)) Societe d'edition Les Belles lettres FRA. Dist: ISD.

Silvestri, Agnese. Rene Kalisky, une Poetique de la Repetition. (FRE.). 415p. pap. 55.95 (978-90-5201-342-8(X)) Lang, Peter Publishing, Inc.

Terry, W. R. Seeing Marguerite in the Mirror: A Linguistic Analysis of Porete's Mirror of Simple Souls. 2011. (Studies in Spirituality Supplements Ser.). (ENG.). 169p. (C). pap. 64.00 (978-90-429-2322-5(9)) Peeters Pubs. & Booksellers BEL. Dist: Brown, David Bk. Co., The.

Vessels, Joel E. Drawing France: French Comics & the Republic. 2010. (ENG., Illus.). 304p. 50.00 (978-1-60473-444-7(2)) Univ. Pr. of Mississippi.

Warnar, Geert. Ruusbroec: Literature & Mysticism in the Fourteenth Century. Webb, Diane, tr. from DUT. 2007. (Brill's Studies in Intellectual History). 416p. (978-90-04-15869-6(3)) BRILL.

BELGIAN LITERATURE (FLEMISH)

see Flemish Literature

BELGIAN PAINTING

see Painting, Belgian

BELGIAN SCULPTURE

see Sculpture—Belgium

BELGIAN SHEEPDOG

Fleming, Deborah. The Complete Belgian Shepherd Dog Today. (Illus.). 96p. tchr. ed. 24.95 (978-1-86054-256-5(5), INT038) Ringpress Bks., Ltd. GBR. Dist: TFH Pubns., Inc.

Pollet, Robert. Belgian Sheepdog. Lee, Muriel P., ed. 2007. (Comprehensive Owners Guide Ser.). (ENG., Illus.). 158p. 19.95 (978-1-59378-267-2(5)) Kennel Club Bks.

BELGIAN SHEEPDOG, TERVUREN

see Belgian Tervuren

BELGIAN SHEPHERD DOG

see Belgian Sheepdog

BELGIAN TERVUREN

Pollet, Robert. Belgian Tervuren. Lee, Muriel P., ed. 2007. (Comprehensive Owners Guide Ser.). (ENG., Illus.). 155p. 19.95 (978-1-59378-652-6(2)) Kennel Club Bks.

BELGIANS

Jaenen, Cornelius J. Promoters, Planters & Pioneers: The Course & Context of Belgian Settlement in Western Canada. 2011. (West Ser.). (ENG., Illus.). 348p. pap. 41.95 (978-1-55238-258-5(3)) Univ. of Calgary Pr. CAN. Dist: Chicago Distribution Ctr.

BELGIANS—FOREIGN COUNTRIES

Van Ecke, Yolanda. Attachment & Immigrants: Emotional security among Dutch & Belgian Immigrants in California, U. S. A. 2007. (UvA Proefschriften Ser.). 124p. per. (978-90-5629-480-9(6), Leiden Univ. Pr.) Amsterdam Univ. Pr.

BELGIC CONFESSION

Gootjes, Nicolaas H. & Gootjes, Nicolaas Hendrik. The Belgic Confession: Its History & Sources. 2007. (Texts & Studies in Reformation & Post-Reformation Thought Ser.). (Illus.). 240p. (C). pap. 32.00 (978-0-8010-3235-6(0)) Baker Academic.

Hyde, Daniel. With Heart & Mouth: An Exposition of the Belgic Confession. 2008. 560p. 30.00 (978-0-9793677-5-5(1)) Reformed Fellowship, Inc.

BELGIUM

Organisation for Economic Co-operation and Development Staff, contrib. by. Belgium-Luxembourg Economic Union. 2011. (Illus.). 90p. pap. (978-92-64-11097-7(6)) Organization for Economic Cooperation & Development.

Tollet, A. Vilvoorde City, meer bepaald in de Far-West. Sociale huisvesting in Vlaams-Brabant. Met foto's van Piet Janssens. 2009. (Accenten uit de geschiedenis van Vlaams-Brabant Ser.). 167p. (C). pap. 29.00 (978-90-429-2287-7(7)) Peeters Pubs. & Booksellers BEL. Dist: Brown, David Bk. Co., The.

Van Goethem, Herman. Belgium & the Monarchy: From National Independence to National Disintegration. 2011. (Illus.). 258p. 42.95 (978-90-5487-698-4(0)) VUB Univ. Pr. BEL. Dist: Independent Pubs. Group.

BELGIUM—BIOGRAPHY

Assouline, Pierre. Hergé: The Man Who Created Tintin. Ruas, Charles, tr. from FRE. 2009. (ENG.). 288p. 24.95 (978-0-19-539759-8(2)) Oxford Univ. Pr., Inc.

Assouline, Pierre. Herge: The Man Who Created Tintin, 1 vol. Ruas, Charles, tr. from FRE. 2011. (ENG.). 288p. pap. 15.95 (978-0-19-983727-4(9)) Oxford Univ. Pr., Inc.

Bartolomé, Ana, et al. Autobiography & Other Writings. Donahue, Darcy, tr. from SPA. 2008. (Other Voice in Early Modern Europe Ser.). 196p. pap. 22.00 (978-0-226-14372-9(4)); 55.00 (978-0-226-14371-2(6)) Univ. of Chicago Pr.

Bizimana, John. Escape from Rwanda: A True Story of Faith, Hope, & Survival. 2010. (Illus.). 144p. 18.99 (978-1-60641-830-7(0)) Deseret Bk. Co.

Blake, Robin. Anthony Van Dyck. 2009. (ENG.). 480p. pap. 25.00 (978-1-56663-786-2(4)) Dee, Ivan R. Pub.

Blanckaert, Sandy. Will Tura. 2009. (DUT., Illus.). 364p. (978-90-8924-079-8(9)) Houtekiet, Uitgeverij.

Brahy, Gustave-Lambert. Confidential Recollections Revealed. Holden, James, tr. 2007. 240p. per. 19.95 (978-0-86690-570-1(7)) American Federation of Astrologers, Inc.

Clayson, Alan. Jacques Brel: La Vie Boheme. 2010. (ENG., Illus.). 300p. pap. 19.95 (978-1-84240-535-2(7)) Chrome Dreams GBR. Dist: Independent Pubs. Group.

Cooper, Jennifer. Humanity in the Mystery of God: The Theological Anthropology of Edward Schillebeeckx. 2011. (T&T Clark Studies in Systematic Theology Ser.). (ENG.). 230p. pap. 44.95 (978-0-567-03653-7(7), T&T Clark Int'l) Continuum International Publishing Group, Ltd. GBR. Dist: National Bk. Network.

Crombois, Jean F. Camille Gutt & Postwar International Finance, 1 vol. 2011. (Financial History Ser.: 18). (ENG., Illus.). 208p. 99.00 (978-1-84893-058-2(5)) Pickering & Chatto Pubs., Ltd. GBR. Dist: Ashgate Publishing Co.

D'Aygalliers, A. Wautier. The Mystic Current at the Heart of Scholasticism Represented by St. 2006. pap. 9.95 (978-1-4286-8236-8(8)) Kessinger Publishing, LLC.

—The Mystical School of St Victor. 2006. pap. 9.95 (978-1-4286-8235-1(X)) Kessinger Publishing, LLC.

—Ruysbroeck, the Church & the Sacraments. 2006. pap. 9.95 (978-1-4286-8234-4(1)) Kessinger Publishing, LLC.

De Maeseneer, Rita, et al, eds. El Hispanismo Omnipresente. 2010. (SPA.). 506p. pap. 50.00 (978-90-5487-562-8(3)) VUB Univ. Pr. BEL. Dist: Independent Pubs. Group.

Devreese, J. T. & Vanden Berghe, G. 'Magic Is No Magic' The Wonderful World of Simon Stevin. 2008. (Illus.). 352p. pap. 59.00 (978-1-84564-391-1(7)) WIT Pr GBR. Dist: WIT Pr.

Dufrasne, Dieudonné. Dom Anselme le Bail, 1913-1956, Abbot of Scourmont: A Monk, an Abbot, a Community. 2010. (978-0-87907-023-6(4)) Cistercian Pubns., Inc.

D'Ydewalle, Charles. Albert & the Belgians: Portrait of a King. 2007. (ENG.). 310p. 45.95 (978-0-548-05760-5(5)) Kessinger Publishing, LLC.

Fraiture, Eddy. Belgische uurwerken en hun makers AZ - Horloges et horlogers belges AZ. 2009. (DUT & FRE.). 638p. (C). pap. 85.00 (978-90-429-2251-8(6)) Peeters Pubs. & Booksellers BEL. Dist: Brown, David Bk. Co., The.

—Staande Klokken en Uurwerkmakers in Vlaanderen. 2006. (DUT & ENG., Illus.). 369p. (C). pap. 85.00 (978-90-429-1620-3(6)) Peeters Pubs. & Booksellers BEL. Dist: Brown, David Bk. Co., The.

Gruyaert, Harry, photos by. Harry Gruyaert: Story - TV Shots, 1 vol. 2008. (ENG., Illus.). 240p. pap. 50.00 (978-3-86521-375-4(8)) Steidl, Gerhard Druckerei und Verlag DEU. Dist: Innovative Logistics.

Imbert, Dorothee. Between Garden & City: Jean Canneel-Claes & Landscape Modernism. 2009. (ENG., Illus.). 360p. (C). 55.00 (978-0-8229-4370-9(0)) Univ. of Pittsburgh Pr.

Israel, Annette. Horsepower: A Memoir. 2008. 168p. pap. 15.95 (978-1-4401-0251-6(1), iUniverse Star) iUniverse, Inc.

Jacobsen, Anja Skaar. Between Bohr & Marx: Leon Rosenfeld in Physics & Ideology. 2011. 360p. 81.00 (978-981-4307-81-9(5)) World Scientific Publishing Co., Inc.

Kamagurka. The Holy Kama! 2012. (ENG., Illus.). 896p. 55.00 (978-90-5856-386-6(3)) Stichting Kunstboek Bvba BEL. Dist: National Bk. Network.

Lamster, Mark. Master of Shadows: The Secret Diplomatic Career of the Painter Peter Paul Rubens. 2010. (ENG.). 336p. pap. 17.00 (978-0-307-38735-6(6), Anchor) Knopf Doubleday Publishing Group.

Maes, Camillus P. The Life of Rev. Charles Nerinckx: With. 2006. pap. 48.95 (978-1-4286-5864-6(5)) Kessinger Publishing, LLC.

Martens, Wilfried. Europe: I Struggle, I Overcome: I Struggle, I Overcome. 2009. (ENG., Illus.). xvi, 276p. 59.95 (978-3-540-89288-5(5), 3540892885) Springer.

Moreau de Melen, Henri & Grosbois, Thierry. Mémoires, de Léopold III à la Corée. 2009. (FRE & ENG., Illus.). 479p. (978-2-87386-549-8(0)) Racine, Editions.

Mulder-Bakker, Anneke B. Mary of Oignies Mother of Salvation. 2007. (Medieval Women: Text & Contexts Ser.). (ENG., Illus.). 260p. (C). 102.00 (978-2-503-51703-2(X)) Brepols Pubs. BEL. Dist: ISD.

Nappo, Tommaso, ed. Index biographique Francais. 2d ed. (GER.). (978-3-11-197551-1(7)); (978-3-11-114550-1(6)) Saur, K. G. Verlag GmbH & Co.

Peeters, Benoit. Hergé, Son of Tintin. Kover, Tina A., tr. from FRE. 2011. (ENG., Illus.). 424p. 29.95 (978-1-4214-0454-7(0)) Johns Hopkins Univ. Pr.

Pontzeele, Didier. Krijgsgevangen: Belgische Officiers in Het Kasteel van Colditz 1940-1943. (DUT., Illus.). 192p. pap. 29.95 *(978-90-72547-91-0(8))* De Krijger BEL. Dist: Casemate Pubs. & Bk. Distributors, LLC.
Price, Michael. The Odds Are. 2011. (ENG.). 417p. pap. 22.95 ***(978-1-4327-7553-7(7))*** Outskirts Pr., Inc.
Prindiville, Raymond J. G. Damien, Martyr of Molokai. 2011. 26p. 35.95 ***(978-1-258-01593-0(5))*** Literary Licensing, LLC.
Reibel, Olivier. La Vie Secrète D'Hergé: Biographie Inattendue. 2010. (FRE.). 484p. *(978-2-84454-638-8(2))* Dervy, Editions.
Richards, Virginia Helen & Halpin, D. Thomas. Saint Damien of Molokai: Hero of Hawaii. 2009. (Illus.). 128p. (J). pap. 7.95 *(978-0-8198-7126-8(5))* Pauline Bks. & Media.
Rotsaert, M. & Segaert, B., eds. Markante Jezuieten uit de Lage Landen: Canisius, Verbiest, Lessius, Regout. 2007. (ENG.). 113p. (C). pap. 58.00 *(978-90-429-2003-3(3))* Peeters Pubs. & Booksellers BEL. Dist: Brown, David Bk. Co., The.
Schoof, Rene. Catalan's Conjecture. 2008. (Universitext Ser.). (Illus.). 152p. spiral bd. 49.95 *(978-1-84800-184-8(3))* Springer.
Stutje, Jan Willem. Ernest Mandel: A Rebel's Dream Deferred. Drucker, Peter & Beck, Christopher, trs. from DUT. 2009. (ENG., Illus.). 600p. 34.95 *(978-1-84467-316-2(2)*, 844316) Verso Bks. GBR. Dist: Norton, W. W. & Co., Inc.
Tectum, creator. A Rush of Blood to the Head: The Story of a Man Facing the Elements of Nature. 2006. (ENG, FRE & DUT., Illus.). 144p. *(978-90-76886-30-5(X))* Tectum B.V.B.A.

BELGIUM—COLONIES

Doyle, Arthur Conan. The Crime of the Congo. 2007. (ENG.). 132p. per. 10.95 *(978-1-60312-166-8(8))*; 24.95 *(978-1-60312-848-3(4))* Aegypan.
—The Crime of the Congo. reprint ed. lib. bdg. 98.00 *(978-0-7426-2721-5(7))* Classic Bks.
Morel, Edmund D. Red Rubber: The Story of the Rubber Slave Trade Flourishing on the Congo in the Year of Grace 1906. 213p. reprint ed. 98.00 *(978-0-7222-9823-7(4))* Library Reprints, Inc.
Schiller, Thomas Horne. History of the Rise & Progress of the Belgian Republic: Until The ... 2008. 245p. pap. 25.75 *(978-0-554-61226-3(7))* BiblioBazaar.
Stanard, Matthew G. Selling the Congo: A History of European Pro-Empire Propaganda & the Making of Belgian Imperialism. 2012. (ENG., Illus.). 408p. 65.00 *(978-0-8032-3777-3(4))* Univ. of Nebraska Pr.

BELGIUM—DESCRIPTION AND TRAVEL

Davison, Brenda. Floating Through Holland (and Belgium) 2008. 103p. pap. 13.95 *(978-1-4092-0162-5(7))* Lulu Enterprises Inc.
Debeerst, Philippe, photos by. Living in Great Style in Knokke-le Zoute: Beautiful homes in Belgium's most exclusive coastal City. 2011. (ENG., Illus.). 256p. 89.50 *(978-90-8881-030-5(3))* Exhibitions International BEL. Dist: Innovative Logistics.
Dennistoun, James, ed. Coltness Collections. (Maitland Club, Glasgow Publications: No. 58). reprint ed. 65.00 *(978-0-404-53047-1(8))* AMS Pr., Inc.
Locken, E. Travel Journal Belgium. 2010. 192p. pap. 19.99 *(978-0-557-43270-7(7))* Lulu Enterprises Inc.
MacDonald, Mandy. Belgium: Culture Smart! - A Quick Guide to Customs & Etiquette. 2006. (Culture Smart! A Quick Guide to Customs & Etiquette Ser.). (ENG., Illus.). 168p. pap. 9.95 *(978-1-85733-322-0(5))* Kuperard Pubs. GBR. Dist: Random Hse., Inc.
Morris, Joseph E. Beautiful Europe: Belgium. 2008. 48p. pap. *(978-1-4099-0398-7(2))* Dodo Pr.
Ornond, W. T. George. Peeps at Many Lands: Belgium. 2007. 68p. per. 87.99 *(978-1-4280-7633-4(6))* IndyPublish.com.
Paci, Delphine, et al. L'enfer Me Ment. 2007. (FRE., Illus.). 142p. *(978-2-916249-09-4(5))* Quo Vadis Pubns., Inc.
Ronsijn, W. De kadasterkaarten van Popp: Een sleutel tot uw lokale geschiedenis: Historische geografie van Aarschot, Asse, Halle en Tienen aan de hand van de kadasterkaarten van Popp. 2007. (Accenten uit de geschiedenis van Vlaams-Brabant Ser.). (ENG.). 148p. (C). pap. 40.00 *(978-90-429-2048-4(3))* Peeters Pubs. & Booksellers BEL. Dist: Brown, David Bk. Co., The.
Streuli, Beat, photos by. Beat Streuli: BXL. 2008. (FRE, GER & ENG., Illus.). 168p. 55.00 *(978-3-905829-79-2(7))* JRP Ringier Kunstverlag AG CHE. Dist: D.A.P./Distributed Art Pubs.
Travel, Michelin. Belgium & Luxembourg. 6th rev. ed. 2009. (Green Guide Ser.). (ENG., Illus.). 416p. pap. 21.99 *(978-1-906261-46-7(6))* Michelin Travel & Lifestyle.
Vanfleteren, Stephen & Vanfleteren, Stephan. Belgicum. 2008. (ENG., Illus.). 204p. *(978-90-209-7121-7(2)*, Lannoo Pubs. (Acc)) Antique Collectors' Club.
Wilssens, Marie-Anne. 365 Days - Antwerp. 2009. (DUT & ENG., Illus.). 744p. 65.00 *(978-90-209-7747-9(4))* Lannoo Pubs./Racine.

BELGIUM—ECONOMIC CONDITIONS

Belgium: Business Financing Handbook. (Illus.). 70p. (Orig.). pap. 295.00 *(978-0-7605-1181-7(0))* Rector Pr., Ltd.
Belgium: Commercial Law. 300p. (Orig.). pap. 295.00 *(978-0-7605-1228-9(0))* Rector Pr., Ltd.
BIA. Essential Belgian Manufacturers: Food, Textile, Clothing, & Chemical Companies. 6th rev. ed. 2006. 400p. (J). pap. 249.00 *(978-1-4187-4219-5(8))* Business Information Agency.
—Key Banking, Financial, & Insurance Companies of Belgium. 6th rev. ed. 2006. 300p. (J). pap. 259.00 *(978-1-4187-4381-9(X))* Business Information Agency.
Bucquoye, Moniek E. & Devos, Rika. Belgium Beyond Expectations: The Belgian EU Pavilion at World Expo Shanghai 2010. 2011. (ENG.). 144p. 48.95 *(978-90-5487-768-4(5))* VUB Univ. Pr. BEL. Dist: Independent Pubs. Group.
Doing Business in Belgium. Date not set. (Doing Business in Regions & Countries Around the World Ser.). *(978-1-882390-52-6(0))* Training Management Corp.
Dooms, Michael. Crafting the Integrative Value Proposition for Large Scale Transport Infrastructure Hubs: A Stakeholder Management Approach. 2011. (ENG.). 388p. pap. 35.95 *(978-90-5487-713-4(8))* VUB Univ. Pr. BEL. Dist: Independent Pubs. Group.
Elleboudt, Adrien S. The Limits of Consociationalism. 2008. 64p. pap. *(978-3-639-02271-1(8))* VDM Verlag Dr. Mueller e.K.
Hutton, Shennan. Women & Economic Activities in Late Medieval Ghent. 2011. (New Middle Ages Ser.). (ENG., Illus.). 256p. 85.00 *(978-0-230-10495-2(9))* Palgrave Macmillan.
Ibp, Usa. Belgium Industrial & Business Director. 2006. (Illus.). pap. 99.95 *(978-0-7397-9748-8(4))* International Business Pubns., USA.
Icon Group International, Inc. Staff, compiled by. The 2006 Economic & Product Market Databook for Aalst, Belgium. 2006. 605p. ring bd. 95.00 *(978-0-497-79936-6(7))* Icon Group International, Inc.
—The 2006 Economic & Product Market Databook for Antwerp, Belgium. 2006. 618p. ring bd. 95.00 *(978-0-497-80067-3(5))* Icon Group International, Inc.
—The 2006 Economic & Product Market Databook for Bruges, Belgium. 2006. 618p. ring bd. 95.00 *(978-0-497-80252-3(X))* Icon Group International, Inc.
—The 2006 Economic & Product Market Databook for Brussels, Belgium. 2006. 618p. ring bd. 95.00 *(978-0-497-80253-0(8))* Icon Group International, Inc.
—The 2006 Economic & Product Market Databook for Charleroi, Belgium. 2006. 618p. ring bd. 95.00 *(978-0-497-80341-4(0))* Icon Group International, Inc.
—The 2006 Economic & Product Market Databook for Ghent, Belgium. 2006. 618p. ring bd. 95.00 *(978-0-497-80596-8(0))* Icon Group International, Inc.
—The 2006 Economic & Product Market Databook for Kortrijk, Belgium. 2006. 618p. ring bd. 95.00 *(978-0-497-82013-8(7))* Icon Group International, Inc.
—The 2006 Economic & Product Market Databook for Leuven, Belgium. 2006. 618p. ring bd. 95.00 *(978-0-497-80848-8(X))* Icon Group International, Inc.
—The 2006 Economic & Product Market Databook for Liege, Belgium. 2006. 618p. ring bd. 95.00 *(978-0-497-80852-5(8))* Icon Group International, Inc.
—The 2006 Economic & Product Market Databook for Mechelen, Belgium. 2006. 618p. ring bd. 95.00 *(978-0-497-80999-7(0))* Icon Group International, Inc.
—The 2006 Economic & Product Market Databook for Mons, Belgium. 2006. 618p. ring bd. 95.00 *(978-0-497-81046-7(8))* Icon Group International, Inc.
—The 2006 Economic & Product Market Databook for Namur, Belgium. 2006. 618p. ring bd. 95.00 *(978-0-497-81092-4(1))* Icon Group International, Inc.
—The 2006 Economic & Product Market Databook for Oostende, Belgium. 2006. 618p. ring bd. 95.00 *(978-0-497-81163-1(4))* Icon Group International, Inc.
Limberger, Michael. Sixteenth-Century Antwerp & its Rural Surroundings: Social & Economic Change in the Hinterland of a Commerical Metropolis (ca. 1450-Ca. 1570) 2008. (Studies in European Urban History (1100-1800) Ser.). (ENG.). 284p. (C). pap. 94.00 *(978-2-503-52725-3(6))* Brepols Pubs. BEL. Dist: ISD.
Marius, Styczen. The Past, Present & the Future for Financial Centers in Belgium: A Comprehensive Case Study of the Tax & Business Environment for Financial Centers in Belgium. 2011. 112p. pap. ***(978-3-639-32483-9(8))*** VDM Verlag Dr. Mueller e.K.
Murray, James M. Bruges, Cradle of Capitalism, 1280-1390. 2009. (ENG., Illus.). 424p. (C). pap. 56.00 *(978-0-521-12053-1(5))* Cambridge Univ. Pr.
Oecd Publishing & Oecd Publishing. Études Économiques de L'Ocde: Belgique 2011. 2011. 166p. pap. 81.00 ***(978-92-64-09341-5(9))*** Organization for Economic Cooperation & Development.
Organisation For Economic Co-Operation And Development. Belgium. 2011. (Illus.). 147p. pap. 81.00 ***(978-92-64-09328-7(1))*** Organization for Economic Cooperation & Development.
Organisation for Economic Co-operation and Development Staff. Oecd Economic Surveys: Belgium - Volume 2007 Issue 3. 2007. pap. 68.00 *(978-92-64-03186-9(3))* Organization for Economic Cooperation & Development.
—Oecd Economic Surveys: Belgium 2009. 2009. 144p. pap. 63.00 *(978-92-64-05443-1(X))* Organization for Economic Cooperation & Development.
—Oecd Economic Surveys: Brazil 2009. 2009. 134p. pap. 63.00 *(978-92-64-05447-9(2))* Organization for Economic Cooperation & Development.
—OECD Economic Surveys: Luxembourg 2008. 2008. pap. 63.00 *(978-92-64-04397-8(7))* Organization for Economic Cooperation & Development.
Pieter, Demandt. The European Union Emissions Trading Scheme: The Economic Impact of Cap-and-Trade in Belgium. 2011. 80p. pap. ***(978-3-639-32988-9(0))*** VDM Verlag Dr. Mueller e.K.
Van der Wee, Herman & Verbreyt, Monique. A Small Nation in the Turmoil of the Second World War: Money, Finance & Occupation (Belgium, its Enemies, its Friends, 1939-1945) 2010. (Studies in Social & Economic History Ser.). (Illus.). 494p. 75.00 *(978-90-5867-759-4(1))* Leuven Univ. Pr. BEL. Dist: Cornell Univ. Pr.
Vanslembrouck, Isabel & Van Huylenbroeck, Guido. Landscape Amenities: Economic Assessment of Agricultural Landscapes. 2010. (Landscape Ser.). xv, 202p. pap. 159.00 *(978-90-481-6804-0(X)*, 904816804X) Springer.
Vanthemsche, Guy. Belgium & the Congo, 1885#x2013;1980. 2012. (ENG., Illus.). 304p. 99.00 ***(978-0-521-19421-1(0))*** Cambridge Univ. Pr.

BELGIUM—FOREIGN RELATIONS

Barroso, Jose Manuel. Flanders in EU 2020. 2012. (ENG.). 144p. pap. 30.00 ***(978-90-209-9849-8(8))*** Lannoo Pubs./Racine.
Lambrecht, Jeroen. Belgian Soldiers. 2010. 124p. pap. *(978-3-8383-5809-3(0))* Lambert Academic Publishing.
Lanneau, Catherine. L' inconnue Française: La France et les Belges Francophones (1944-1945) 2008. (Enjeux internationaux Ser.). (FRE.). 589p. pap. 83.95 *(978-90-5201-397-8(7))* PIE - Peter Lang BEL. Dist: Lang, Peter.
Marks, Sally. Innocent Abroad: Belgium at the Paris Peace Conference Of 1919. 2011. (ENG.). 480p. pap. 50.00 *(978-0-8078-9720-1(5))* Univ. of North Carolina Pr.
Vanthemsche, Guy. Belgium & the Congo, 1885#x2013;1980. 2012. (ENG., Illus.). 304p. 99.00 ***(978-0-521-19421-1(0))*** Cambridge Univ. Pr.

BELGIUM—GUIDEBOOKS

Cannon, Gwen, ed. Belgium: Grand Duchy of Luxembourg. 5th rev. ed. 2007. (Michelin Green Guide Belgium Ser.). (Illus.). 452p. 21.95 *(978-2-06-712326-7(2))* Michelin.
Ceulemans, Hadewijch. Belgium's Best Buildings. 2012. (ENG., Illus.). 160p. pap. 24.95 ***(978-94-6058-081-9(5)***, Uitgeverij Luster) Antique Collectors' Club GBR. Dist: National Bk. Network.
Copp, Terry & Bechthold, Mike. The Canadian Battlefields in Belgium, the Netherlands & Germany: A Visitor's Guide. 2010. (ENG., Illus.). 160p. (C). pap. 39.95 *(978-1-926804-02-6(3))* Wilfrid Laurier Univ. Pr. CAN. Dist: Univ. of Toronto Pr.
Dorling Kindersley Publishing Staff. Eyewitness Travel Guide - Belgium & Luxembourg. 2011. (Eyewitness Travel Guides). (ENG., Illus.). 352p. 25.00 *(978-0-7566-7014-6(4))* Dorling Kindersley Publishing, Inc.
—Eyewitness Travel Guides - Brussels Bruges Ghent Antwerp. 2011. (Eyewitness Travel Guides). (ENG., Illus.). 208p. 20.00 *(978-0-7566-6958-4(8))* Dorling Kindersley Publishing, Inc.
Dunford, Martin & Rough Guides Staff. Belgium & Luxembourg - Rough Guide. 5th ed. 2011. (ENG., Illus.). 448p. 22.99 *(978-1-84836-720-3(1))* Rough Guides, Ltd. GBR. Dist: Dorling Kindersley Publishing, Inc.
Elliot, Mark. Cultureshock Belgium, 1 vol. 2011. (ENG.). 240p. pap. 15.95 *(978-0-7614-5657-5(0))* Marshall Cavendish Corp.
Jackson, Michael. Great Beers of Belgium. 5th ed. 2007. (Illus.). 516p. 49.50 *(978-90-209-6598-8(0))* Lannoo N. V., Uitgeverij BEL. Dist: Antique Collectors' Club.
Jenkinson, Anna & Allegaert, Sophie. 10x Short Seaside Breaks on the Flanders Coast: Quality Hotels, Varied Sea Food & Trendy Shops. 2011. (ENG., Illus.). 204p. pap. 25.00 ***(978-90-209-9897-9(8))*** Lannoo Pubs./Racine.
Lonely Planet Staff & Elliott, Mark. Belgium & Luxembourg. 4th ed. 2010. (Country Guide Ser.). (ENG., Illus.). 312p. pap. 21.99 *(978-1-74104-989-3(X))* Lonely Planet Pubns.
Mueller, Robert J. Fields of War: Fifty Key Battlefields in France & Belgium. 2009. (Illus.). 467p. pap. 29.95 *(978-0-9823677-0-4(8))* French Battlefields.
Pattyn, Joris & Webb, Tim. 100 Belgian Beers to Try Before You Die! 2010. (ENG., Illus.). 160p. pap. 24.95 *(978-1-85249-248-9(1))* Camra Bks. GBR. Dist: Independent Pubs. Group.
Thomas Cook Publishing Staff. Traveller Guides Belgium. 5th ed. 2011. (Travellers - Thomas Cook Ser.). (ENG., Illus.). 192p. pap. 16.95 *(978-1-84848-340-8(6))* Cook, Thomas Publishing GBR. Dist: Globe Pequot Pr., The.
Thomson, Clare. Antwerp & Ghent. 2006. (Pocket Guides). (ENG., Illus.). 256p. pap. 12.95 *(978-1-904777-75-5(9))* Footprint Handbooks GBR. Dist: Globe Pequot Pr., The.
Thomson, Emma. Flanders: Northern Belgium: Brussels, Bruges & Beyond. 2012. (Bradt Travel Guide Ser.). (ENG., Illus.). 288p. pap. 23.99 ***(978-1-84162-377-1(6))*** Bradt Travel Guides GBR. Dist: Globe Pequot Pr., The.
Time Out Guides Staff. Time Out Shortlist Brussels. 2011. (Time Out Shortlist Ser.). (ENG., Illus.). 192p. pap. 12.95 *(978-1-84670-153-5(8))* Time Out Guides Ltd. GBR. Dist: Perseus-PGW.
Van Reck, Werner. CityLovers: People of Antwerp. 2010. (ENG., Illus.). 320p. pap. *(978-90-209-8479-8(9)*, Lannoo Pubs. (Acc)) Antique Collectors' Club.
Wallpaper Magazine Editors, ed. Wallpaper* City Guide Antwerp. 2008. (ENG., Illus.). 128p. pap. 9.95 *(978-0-7148-4893-8(X))* Phaidon Pr., Inc.
Webb, Tim. Belgium. 6th ed. 2009. (ENG., Illus.). 352p. pap. 23.95 *(978-1-85249-261-8(9))* Camra Bks. GBR. Dist: Independent Pubs. Group.

BELGIUM—HISTORY

Bearda, T., et al, eds. Campanae Lovanienses: Het klokkenpatrimonium van Groot-Leuven. 2008. (DUT.). 339p. (C). pap. 80.00 *(978-90-429-2185-6(4))* Peeters Pubs. & Booksellers BEL. Dist: Brown, David Bk. Co., The.
Begenat-Neuschäfer, Anne, ed. Die Deutschsprachige Gemeinschaft Belgiens: Eine Bestandsaufnahme. 2010. (Belgien im Fokus. Geschichte Sprachen Kulturen Ser.). (GER.). 318p. 57.95 *(978-3-631-59454-4(2))* Lang, Peter GmbH, Europaischer Verlag der Wissenschaften DEU. Dist: Lang, Peter.
Blom. History of the Low Countries. 2006. (Illus.). 384p. (C). 29.95 *(978-1-84545-272-8(0))* Berghahn Bks., Inc.
Bonnie, Rick. Cadastres, Misconceptions & Northern Gaul. 2009. (ENG.). 160p. (C). pap. 52.00 *(978-90-8890-024-2(8))* Sidestone Pr. NLD. Dist: Brown, David Bk. Co., The.
Braem, Lucien. Para! De Opleiding van een Belgisch Para-Commando in de Jaren Zestig. (Belgie Onder de Wapens Ser.: Vol. 10). (DUT., Illus.). 96p. pap. 18.95 *(978-90-72547-62-0(4))* De Krijger BEL. Dist: Casemate Pubs. & Bk. Distributors, LLC.
Brown, Andrew. Civic Ceremony & Religion in Medieval Bruges C. 1300-1520. 2011. (ENG., Illus.). 384p. 99.00 *(978-0-521-76445-2(9))* Cambridge Univ. Pr.
Cammaerts, Emile. Through the Iron Bars. 2009. (Illus.). 72p. pap. *(978-1-4099-6807-8(3))* Dodo Pr.
Celis, Peter. One Who Almost Made It Back: The Remarkable Story of One of World War Two's Unsung Heroes, Sqn Ldr Edward Teddy Blenkinsop, DFC, CdeG (Belge), RCAF. 2008. (Illus.). 224p. 42.95 *(978-1-906502-16-4(1))* Grub Street GBR. Dist: Casemate Pubs. & Bk. Distributors, LLC.
Ceunen, M. & Veldeman, P. Tegen brand Gewapend. 2007. (ENG.). 236p. (C). pap. 67.00 *(978-90-429-2050-7(5))* Peeters Pubs. & Booksellers BEL. Dist: Brown, David Bk. Co., The.
Chambry, Rene. The Truth about Louvain. 2010. 96p. 33.95 *(978-1-161-49169-2(4))* 2007. (ENG.). 108p. 33.95 *(978-0-548-04161-1(X))* Kessinger Publishing, LLC.
Champagne, Jacques. L' Artillerie Belge Tome 1: 1941-2001. (Belgique Sous les Armes Ser.: Tome 6). (FRE., Illus.). 80p. pap. 18.95 *(978-90-72547-71-2(3))* De Krijger BEL. Dist: Casemate Pubs. & Bk. Distributors, LLC.
—De Belgische Artillerie Deel 1: 1941-2000, Belgian Artillery. (Belgie Onder de Wapens Ser.: Vol. 12). (DUT., Illus.). 96p. pap. 18.95 *(978-90-72547-70-5(5))* De Krijger BEL. Dist: Casemate Pubs. & Bk. Distributors, LLC.
Conway, Martin. The Sorrows of Belgium: Liberation & Political Reconstruction, 1944-1947. 2012. (ENG., Illus.). 512p. 150.00 ***(978-0-19-969434-1(6))*** Oxford Univ. Pr., Inc.
De Decker, Cynrik & Roba, Jean-Louis. Doelwit Leuven: De Luchanvallen van 12 en 13 Mei 1944 en de Berging van een Halifax-Bommenwerper Bij Geraardsbergen. (DUT., Illus.). 224p. pap. 29.95 *(978-90-72547-61-3(6))* De Krijger BEL. Dist: Casemate Pubs. & Bk. Distributors, LLC.
—De Laatste Vlucht Van "Yvonne Proudbag" (Belgie in Oorlog Ser.: Vol. 7). (DUT., Illus.). 80p. pap. 18.95 *(978-90-72547-15-6(2))* De Krijger BEL. Dist: Casemate Pubs. & Bk. Distributors, LLC.
Demaret, Henri. AIFV In Dienst van de Belgische Landmacht. (Belgie Onder de Wapens Ser.: Vol. 4). (DUT., Illus.). 68p. pap. 18.95 *(978-90-72547-31-6(4))* De Krijger BEL. Dist: Casemate Pubs. & Bk. Distributors, LLC.
—Half-Tracks in Dienst Bij de Belgische Landmacht. (Belgie Onder de Wapens Ser.: Vol. 9). (DUT., Illus.). 84p. pap. 18.95 *(978-90-72547-52-1(7))* De Krijger BEL. Dist: Casemate Pubs. & Bk. Distributors, LLC.
—De ILTIS in Dienst van de Belgische Landmacht. (Belgie Onder de Wapens Ser.: Vol. 6). (DUT., Illus.). 80p. pap. 18.95 *(978-90-72547-42-2(X))* De Krijger BEL. Dist: Casemate Pubs. & Bk. Distributors, LLC.
Demaret, Henry. L' AIFV au Service de l'Armee Belge. (Belgique Sous les Armes Ser.: Tome 2). (FRE., Illus.). 68p. pap. 18.95 *(978-90-72547-32-3(2))* De Krijger BEL. Dist: Casemate Pubs. & Bk. Distributors, LLC.
Dombrecht, Omer. Dertien Bittere Jaren. (Herinneringen Ser.: Vol. 3). (DUT., Illus.). 160p. pap. 22.95 *(978-90-72547-85-9(3))* De Krijger BEL. Dist: Casemate Pubs. & Bk. Distributors, LLC.
Duerloo, Luc. Dynasty & Piety: Archduke Albert (1598-1621) & Habsburg Political Culture in an Age of Religious Wars. 2012. (Illus.). 589p. 144.95 ***(978-0-7546-6904-3(1))*** Ashgate Publishing Co.
Elliott, Sue & Fox, James. The Children Who Fought Hitler: A British Outpost in Europe. 2010. (ENG., Illus.). 320p. pap. 15.95 *(978-1-84854-087-3(6))* Murray, John GBR. Dist: Independent Pubs. Group.
Fox, James & Elliott, Sue. The Children Who Fought Hitler: A British Outpost in Europe. 2010. (ENG., Illus.). 320p. 32.95 *(978-1-84854-086-6(8))* Murray, John GBR. Dist: Independent Pubs. Group.
Fox, Renee C. In the Belgian Chateau: The Spirit & Culture of a European Society in an Age of Change. 2008. (American Ways Ser.). (ENG., Illus.). 288p. pap. 19.95 *(978-1-56663-712-1(0))* Dee, Ivan R. Pub.
Fraser, David. The Fragility of Law: Constitutional Patriotism & the Jews of Belgium, 1940-1945. 2009. 304p. 140.00 *(978-0-415-47761-1(1)*, Routledge Cavendish) Taylor & Francis Group GBR. Dist: Taylor & Francis Group.
Fraser, David. The Fragility of Law: Constitutional Patriotism & the Jews of Belgium, 1940ndash;1945. 2012. (ENG.). 304p. pap. 42.95 ***(978-0-415-54235-7(9)***, Routledge Cavendish) Taylor & Francis Group GBR. Dist: Taylor & Francis Group.
Fredericq, Paul. The Study of History in Holland & Belgium. Leonard, Henrietta, tr. 2010. 64p. 31.95 *(978-1-162-24578-9(2))*; pap. 16.95 *(978-1-120-93192-4(4))* Kessinger Publishing, LLC.
Gandilhon, Denis. Battle of Fontenoy. 2007. (Men & Battles 4 Ser.). (Illus.). 84p. pap. 19.95 *(978-2-35250-057-5(5))* Histoire et Collections FRA. Dist: Casemate Pubs. & Bk. Distributors, LLC.
Gibson, Hugh. A Diplomatic Diary. 2009. 204p. pap. 19.99 *(978-1-4432-8129-4(8))* General Bks. LLC.
—A Diplomatic Diary. 2008. 330p. 45.95 *(978-1-4366-4976-6(5))* 2008. 332p. pap. 30.95 *(978-0-548-85794-6(6))* 2007. (ENG.). 318p. 45.95 *(978-0-548-18007-5(5))* 2007. pap. 30.95 *(978-1-4304-8081-5(5))* Kessinger Publishing, LLC.
—A Journal from Our Legation in Belgium. 2008. (ENG.). 304p. pap. 28.75 *(978-1-4375-0921-2(5))*; 348p. pap. 32.75 *(978-1-4375-0922-9(3))* BiblioBazaar.
—A Journal from Our Legation in Belgium. 2009. 96p. pap. *(978-0-217-66966-5(2))*; pap. *(978-1-4432-6339-9(7))* Books LLC.
—A Journal from Our Legation in Belgium. 2007. (ENG., Illus.). 308p. per. *(978-1-4065-2800-8(5))* Dodo Pr.
—A Journal from Our Legation in Belgium. 2007. (ENG.). 450p. 52.95 *(978-0-548-03058-5(8))* Kessinger Publishing, LLC.

B

Gils, Robert. Vesting Antwerpen Deel 3: Schelde - En Redeverdediging 1938-1944. (Belgie Onder de Wapens Ser.: Vol. 13). (DUT., Illus.). 80p. pap. 18.95 (978-90-72547-72-9(1)) De Krijger BEL. Dist: Casemate Pubs. & Bk. Distributors, LLC.

—Vesting Antwerpen Deel 4: Bunkers en Bunkerstellingen 1914-1945. (Belgie Onder de Wapens Ser.: Vol. 19). (DUT., Illus.). 96p. pap. 18.95 (978-90-5868-027-3(4)) De Krijger BEL. Dist: Casemate Pubs. & Bk. Distributors, LLC.

Gonzáles de León, Fernando. The Road to Rocroi: Class, Culture, & Command in the Spanish Army of Flanders, 1567-1659. 2008. (History of Warfare Ser.). (Illus.). 448p. (978-90-04-17082-7(0)) BRILL.

Hannecart, Roch. Le dernier Carré: Les charbonniers belges, libres entrepreneurs face à la CECA (1950-1959) 2009. (Euroclio. Etudes et Documents / Studies & Documents Ser.). (FRE.). 392p. pap. 62.95 (978-90-5201-574-3(0)) PIE - Peter Lang BEL. Dist: Lang, Peter.

Jonckheere, K. Willem Key (1516-1568) Portrait of a Humanist Painter. 2011. (Pictura Nova Ser.). (ENG., Illus.). 345p. (C). 203.00 **(978-2-503-53678-1(6))** Brepols Pubs. BEL. Dist: ISD.

Jong, Leen de. The Royal Museum of Fine Arts: Antwerp - A History, 1810-2007. 2009. (ENG., Illus.). 256p. (978-90-5856-272-2(7), Stichting Kunstboak (Acc)) Antique Collectors' Club.

Kellogg, Vernon. Headquarters Nights: A Record of Conversations & Experiences at the Headquarters of the German Army in France & Belgium. 2011. 120p. pap. 13.50 **(978-1-906267-32-2(4))** Euston Grove Pr. GBR. Dist: Lightning Source, Inc.

Klinkenberg & Klinkenberg, Jean-Marie. Petites Mythologies Belges. (FRE.). 175p. (978-2-87449-073-6(3)) Les Impressions Nouvelles.

Kohler, Ludwig Von. The Administration of the Occupied Territories. Dittmar, W. R., tr. 2007. 260p. per. 39.95 (978-0-9791702-3-2(0)) Capricorn Hse. Publishing.

Kuipers, Sanneke. The Crisis Imperative: Crisis Rhetoric & Welfare State Reform in Belgium & the Netherlands in the Early 1990s. 2006. (Changing Welfare States Ser.). (Illus.). 232p. per. (978-90-5356-808-8(5), Leiden Univ. Pr.) Amsterdam Univ. Pr.

Lambrecht, Jeroen. Belgian Soldiers. 2010. 124p. pap. (978-3-8383-5809-3(0)) Lambert Academic Publishing.

Lampaert, Roger. De Inval. (Belgie in Oorlog Ser.: Vol. 8). (DUT., Illus.). 80p. pap. 18.95 (978-90-72547-16-3(0)) De Krijger BEL. Dist: Casemate Pubs. & Bk. Distributors, LLC.

—De Mijnenoorlog in Vlaanderen. (Belgie in Oorlog Ser.: Speciaal 3). (DUT., Illus.). 144p. pap. 29.95 (978-90-5868-002-0(9)) De Krijger BEL. Dist: Casemate Pubs. & Bk. Distributors, LLC.

—Van Pionier tot Luchtridder. (Belgie in Oorlog Ser.: Speciaal 1). (DUT., Illus.). 192p. pap. 29.95 (978-90-72547-46-0(2)) De Krijger BEL. Dist: Casemate Pubs. & Bk. Distributors, LLC.

Lights Out for Freedom. 2010. pap. 15.95 (978-0-7414-6047-9(5)) Infinity Publishing.

Lipkes, Jeff. Rehearsals: The German Army in Belgium, August 1914. 2008. (Illus.). 815p. pap. 55.95 (978-90-5867-596-5(3)) Leuven Univ. Pr. BEL. Dist: Cornell Univ. Pr.

—Rehearsals: The German Army in Belgium, August 1914. 2007. (ENG.). 815p. (C). pap. 75.00 (978-3-515-09159-6(9)) Steiner, Franz Verlag Wiesbaden GmbH DEU. Dist: Brown, David Bk. Co., The.

Marks, Sally. Belgium. 2010. (Makers of the Modern World Ser.). (ENG., Illus.). 224p. 19.95 (978-1-905791-81-1(X)) Haus Publishing GBR. Dist: Consortium Bk. Sales & Distribution.

McDonald, Robert K. The Hotton Report, 1. 2006. (Illus.). 168p. per. 13.95 (978-0-9665753-8-5(5)) Finbar Pr.

McManus, John C. Alamo in the Ardennes: The Untold Story of the American Soldiers Who Made the Defense of Bastogne Possible. 2007. (ENG., Illus.). 336p. 24.95 (978-0-471-73905-0(7), Wiley) Wiley, John & Sons, Inc.

Melion, Walter S. The Meditative Art: Studies in the Northern Devotional Print, 1550-1625. 2008. 90.00 (978-0-916101-60-2(6)) St. Joseph's Univ. Pr.

Mommaers, P. Jan van Ruusbroec: De mystieke vereniging met God. 2009. (DUT.). 234p. (C). pap. 35.00 (978-90-429-2045-3(9)) Peeters Pubs. & Booksellers BEL. Dist: Brown, David Bk. Co., The.

Morris, William. The Revolt of Ghent. 2011. (ENG.). 64p. pap. 7.95 **(978-1-926878-10-2(8))** Black Cat Pr. CAN. Dist: AK Pr. Distribution.

Nicholas, David. The Metamorphosis of a Medieval City: Ghent in the Age of the Arteveldes 1302-1390. 2008. 388p. pap. 38.00 (978-1-59740-503-4(5)) ACLS Humanities E-Book.

Olivier & Plot. Dinant 1940-1945. (Belgique en Guerre Ser.: Tome 3). (FRE., Illus.). 96p. pap. 18.95 (978-90-5868-030-3(4)) De Krijger BEL. Dist: Casemate Pubs. & Bk. Distributors, LLC.

Philippet, Henri. Et Mets ta Robe de Bal. (FRE., Illus.). Tome 1. 192p. pap. 29.95 (978-90-72547-64-4(0))Tome 2. 320p. pap. 29.95 (978-90-72547-78-1(0)) De Krijger BEL. Dist: Casemate Pubs. & Bk. Distributors, LLC.

Pontzeele. Goodnight Irene: Het Koreaans Oorlogsdagboek van Marcel Fichefet. (Herinneringen Ser.: Vol. 8). (DUT., Illus.). 192p. pap. 22.95 (978-90-5868-019-8(3)) De Krijger BEL. Dist: Casemate Pubs. & Bk. Distributors, LLC.

RÉMy, Desquennes. Normandy 1944, the Atlantic Wa. 2008. (Illus.). 32p. pap. 9.95 (978-2-915762-61-7(9)) OREP Edition & Communication FRA. Dist: Casemate Pubs. & Bk. Distributors, LLC.

Roba, Jean-Louis. Belgen in de RAF Deel 1: Jean Ester & Maurice Balasse. (Belgie in Oorlog Ser.: Vol. 20). (DUT., Illus.). 80p. pap. 18.95 (978-90-72547-79-8(9)) De Krijger BEL. Dist: Casemate Pubs. & Bk. Distributors, LLC.

—Belges dans la RAF Tome 1: Jean Ester & Maurice Balasse. (Belgique en Guerre Ser.: Tome 2). (FRE., Illus.). 80p. pap. 18.95 (978-90-72547-80-4(2)) De Krijger BEL. Dist: Casemate Pubs. & Bk. Distributors, LLC.

—Charleroi 1940-1945. (Belgique en Guerre Ser.: Tome 1). (FRE., Illus.). 96p. pap. 18.95 (978-90-72547-92-7(6)) De Krijger BEL. Dist: Casemate Pubs. & Bk. Distributors, LLC.

Roggemans, Marcel. History of Martinism & the F. U. D. O. S. I. 2009. 348p. pap. 30.95 (978-1-4092-8260-0(0)) Lulu Enterprises Inc.

Ronsijn, W. De kadasterkaarten van Popp: Een sleutel tot uw lokale geschiedenis: Historische geografie van Aarschot, Asse, Halle en Tienen aan de hand van de kadasterkaarten van Popp. 2007. (Accenten uit de geschiedenis van Vlaams-Brabant Ser.). (ENG.). 148p. (C). pap. 40.00 (978-90-429-2048-4(3)) Peeters Pubs. & Booksellers BEL. Dist: Brown, David Bk. Co., The.

Schiller, Thomas Horne. History of the Rise & Progress of the Belgian Republic: Until The ... 2008. 245p. pap. 25.75 (978-0-554-61226-3(7)) BiblioBazaar.

Schrijvers, Peter. Liberators: The Allies & Belgian Society, 1944-1945. 2009. (Studies in the Social & Cultural History of Modern Warfare Ser.). (ENG., Illus.). 358p. 109.00 (978-0-521-51482-8(7)); pap. 35.99 (978-0-521-73557-5(2)) Cambridge Univ. Pr.

Stallaerts, Robert. The A to Z of Belgium. 2010. (A to Z Guide Ser.). (ENG.). 354p. pap. 34.45 (978-0-8108-7201-1(3)) Scarecrow Pr., Inc.

—Historical Dictionary of Belgium. 2nd ed. 2006. (Historical Dictionaries of Europe Ser.). (ENG., Illus.). 352p. 99.00 (978-0-8108-5595-3(X)) Scarecrow Pr., Inc.

Stein, Robert & Pollmann, Judith. Networks, Regions & Nations: Shaping Identities in the Low Countries, 1300-1650. 2010. (Illus.). vi, 290p. (978-90-04-18024-6(9)) BRILL.

Taggart, George & Winchell, Wallace. A Yankee Major Invades Belgium: The Chronicle of a Merciful & Peaceful Mission. 2007. (ENG.). 238p. 41.95 (978-0-548-02643-4(2)) Kessinger Publishing, LLC.

Termote, Tomas. Verdwenen in de Noordzee. (Belgie in Oorlog Ser.: Speciaal 2). (DUT., Illus.). 160p. pap. 29.95 (978-90-72547-90-3(X)) De Krijger BEL. Dist: Casemate Pubs. & Bk. Distributors, LLC.

Thofner, Margit. Common Art: Urban Ceremonials in Antwerp & Brussels. 2007. (ENG., Illus.). 288p. 90.00 (978-90-400-8295-5(2)) Waanders B.V., Uitgeverij NLD. Dist: National Bk. Network.

Van der Stichelen, Katlijne, et al. A Romantic View: The Collection Rademakers, 1 vol. 2011. (ENG., Illus.). 144p. pap. 48.00 **(978-90-6153-351-1(1))** Exhibitions International BEL. Dist: Innovative Logistics.

Van der Wee, Herman & Verbreyt, Monique. A Small Nation in the Turmoil of the Second World War: Money, Finance & Occupation (Belgium, its Enemies, its Friends, 1939-1945) 2010. (Studies in Social & Economic History Ser.). (Illus.). 494p. 75.00 (978-90-5867-759-4(1)) Leuven Univ. Pr. BEL. Dist: Cornell Univ. Pr.

Van Geeteruyen, Alain. De Atlantische Muur Deel 1: De Bouwheren. (Belgie Onder de Wapens Ser.: Vol. 17). (DUT., Illus.). 80p. pap. 18.95 (978-90-5868-015-0(0)) De Krijger BEL. Dist: Casemate Pubs. & Bk. Distributors, LLC.

Van Raemdonck, Jasper. Het Belgisch Marinekorps: 1939-1945. (Belgie in Oorlog Ser.: Vol. 22). (DUT., Illus.). 72p. pap. 18.95 (978-90-72547-87-3(X)) De Krijger BEL. Dist: Casemate Pubs. & Bk. Distributors, LLC.

Vanhaute, Andre, anno. De Republic F-84F Thunderstreak in Dienst Bij de Belgische Luchtmacht. (Belgie Onder de Wapens Ser.: Vol. 8). (DUT., Illus.). 72p. pap. 18.95 (978-90-72547-41-5(1)) De Krijger BEL. Dist: Casemate Pubs. & Bk. Distributors, LLC.

Vansuyt, Michel & Van den Bogaert, Michel. De Militaire Begraafplaatsen Van W.O. I Deel 2: Boezinge, Brielen, Dikkebus, Elverdinge, Vlamertinge, Voormezele. (Belgie in Oorlog Ser.: Vol. 24). (DUT., Illus.). 80p. pap. 18.95 (978-90-72547-99-6(3)) De Krijger BEL. Dist: Casemate Pubs. & Bk. Distributors, LLC.

—De Militaire Begraafplaatsen Van W.O.I. Deel 3: Groot-Poperinge en Noord-Frankrijk. (Belgie in Oorlog Ser.: Vol. 25). (DUT., Illus.). 80p. pap. 18.95 (978-90-5868-001-3(0)) De Krijger BEL. Dist: Casemate Pubs. & Bk. Distributors, LLC.

Vinks, Jos. De Memoirs van Turksin. (DUT., Illus.). 192p. pap. 29.95 (978-90-72547-47-7(0)) De Krijger BEL. Dist: Casemate Pubs. & Bk. Distributors, LLC.

Vooght, Danielle De. The King Invites: Performing Power at a Courtly Dining Table (Belgium, 1831-1909) 2012. (Europe alimentaire / European Food Issues/ Europa alimentaria / L'Europa alimentare Ser.). (ENG.). 285p. pap. 54.95 **(978-90-5201-752-5(2))** PIE - Peter Lang BEL. Dist: Lang, Peter.

Weinstock, Malky. Angel of Orphans: The Story of R' Yona Tiefenbrunner & the Hundreds He Saved. 2009. (Illus.). 174p. **(978-1-56871-512-4(9))** Targum Pr., Inc.

Whiting, Charles. Decision at St Vith. 2008. (Spellmount Siegfried Line Ser.). (ENG., Illus.). 296p. pap. 23.95 (978-1-86227-398-6(7), Spellmount, Limited Pubs.) History Pr. Ltd.,The GBR. Dist: Independent Pubs. Group.

Whitlock, Brand. Belgium. 2009. 446p. pap. (978-0-217-72860-7(X)); 552p. pap. (978-0-217-18191-4(0)); 512p. pap. (978-0-217-68805-5(5)) Books LLC.

—Belgium. reprint ed. lib. bdg. 48.00 (978-0-7426-1342-3(9)) Classic Bks.

Wingham, Tom. Halifax Down! 2009. (Illus.). 224p. 39.95 (978-1-906502-39-3(0)) Grub Street GBR. Dist: Casemate Pubs. & Bk. Distributors, LLC.

BELGIUM—MAPS

Knoell, Donna L. & AA Publishing Staff. AA Glovebox Atlas France. 7th ed. 2010. (ENG., Illus.). 64p. spiral bd. 11.95 **(978-0-7495-6568-8(3))** Automobile Assn. GBR. Dist: Independent Pubs. Group.

Streetwise Maps Inc., des. & rev. Streetwise Brussels Map - Laminated City Street Map of Brussels, Belgium: Folding pocket size travel map with integrated metro map including tram lines & Stations. 2004th rev. ed. 2007. (Streetwise Ser.). (ENG.). 8.95 (978-1-886705-52-4(6)) Streetwise Maps, Inc.

BELGIUM—POLITICS AND GOVERNMENT

Baugnet, Lucy. Metamorphoses Identitaires. 2nd ed. (Illus.). 245p. 33.95 (978-90-5201-104-2(4)) College of Europe Pubns. Interuniversitaires Europeennes SC BEL. Dist: Lang, Peter Publishing, Inc.

Biscop, Sven, et al, eds. Belgium in the un Security Council: Reflections on the 2007-2008 Membership. 2009. 196p. pap. 82.75 (978-90-5095-930-8(X)) Intersentia Uitgevers N.V. BEL. Dist: International Specialized Bk. Services.

Bogaert, Dirk & Maes, Frank, eds. Who Rules the Coast? Policy Processes in Belgian MPAs & Beach Spatial Planning. 2008. 187p. pap. 50.00 (978-90-466-0174-7(9)) Maklu Uitgevers N.V. BEL. Dist: International Specialized Bk. Services.

Brans, Marleen. The Politics of Belgium: Institutions & policy under bipolar & centrifugal Federalism. De Winter, Lieven & Swenden, Wilfried, eds. 2009. (ENG., Illus.). 244p. 125.00 (978-0-415-48453-4(7)) Routledge.

Broomans, Petra, et al, eds. The Beloved Mothertongue: Ethnolinguistic Nationalism in Small Nations: Inventories & Reflections. 2008. (Groningen Studies in Cultural Change Ser.). (ENG.). 228p. (C). 70.00 (978-90-429-2150-4(1)) Peeters Pubs. & Booksellers BEL. Dist: Brown, David Bk. Co., The.

Cachet, Lex, et al. Governance of Security in the Netherlands & Belgium. 2008. 368p. pap. 55.00 (978-90-8974-016-8(3)) Eleven International Publishing NLD. Dist: International Specialized Bk. Services.

Cantillon, Bea, et al, eds. Social Federalism - The Creation of a Layered Welfare State: The Belgian Case. 2011. (Illus.). 302p. pap. 103.75 (978-94-000-0166-4(5)) Intersentia Uitgevers N.V. BEL. Dist: International Specialized Bk. Services.

Conway, Martin. The Sorrows of Belgium: Liberation & Political Reconstruction, 1944-1947. 2012. (ENG., Illus.). 512p. 150.00 **(978-0-19-969434-1(6))** Oxford Univ. Pr., Inc.

Craeybeckx, Jan, et al. Political History of Belgium: From 1830 Onwards. 2010. (ENG.). 516p. pap. 51.00 (978-90-5487-517-8(8)) VUB Univ. Pr. BEL. Dist: Independent Pubs. Group.

Delaite, Baudouin. Le Parlement Wallon. 2009. (FRE., Illus.). 171p. (978-2-87489-051-2(0)) Weyrich edition.

Delwit, Pascal. La Vie Politique en Belgique de 1830 à Nos Jours. 2009. (FRE., Illus.). 360p. pap. (978-2-8004-1447-8(2)) Editions de l'Universite de Bruxelles.

Deschouwer, Kris. The Politics of Belgium: Governing a Divided Society. 2009. (Comparative Government & Politics Ser.). (ENG., Illus.). 256p. 105.00 (978-0-230-21814-7(8)); pap. 37.00 (978-0-230-21815-4(6)) Palgrave Macmillan.

Fox, Renee C. In the Belgian Chateau: The Spirit & Culture of a European Society in an Age of Change. 2008. (American Ways Ser.). (ENG., Illus.). 288p. pap. 19.95 (978-1-56663-712-1(0)) Dee, Ivan R. Pub.

Gunst, P. Brussel en de Vlaamse Rand, een verhaal van migratie en Grenzen: Met een fotokatern van Michiel Hendryckx. 2008. (Accenten uit de geschiedenis van Vlaams-Brabant Ser.). (DUT.). 157p. (C). pap. 29.00 (978-90-429-2123-8(4)) Peeters Pubs. & Booksellers BEL. Dist: Brown, David Bk. Co., The.

Jaenen, Cornelius J. Promoters, Planters & Pioneers: The Course & Context of Belgian Settlement in Western Canada. 2011. (West Ser.). (ENG., Illus.). 348p. pap. 41.95 **(978-1-55238-258-5(3))** Univ. of Calgary Pr. CAN. Dist: Chicago Distribution Ctr.

Jones, Erik. Economic Adjustment & Political Transformation in Small States. 2008. (ENG., Illus.). 256p. 99.00 (978-0-19-920833-3(6)) Oxford Univ. Pr., Inc.

Kohler, Manfred. Language Politics in Belgium & the Flemish-Walloon Conflict. 2010. 164p. pap. (978-3-639-24024-5(3)) VDM Verlag Dr. Mueller e.K.

Kovzirdze, Tamara. Hierarchy & Interdependence in Multi-Level Structures: Foreign & European Relations of Belgian, German & Austrian Federated Entities. 2009. (ENG.). 291p. pap. 46.00 (978-90-5487-536-9(4)) VUB Univ. Pr. BEL. Dist: Independent Pubs. Group.

Lecours, André & Béland, Daniel. Nationalism & Social Policy: The Politics of Territorial Solidarity. Oxford University Press Staff, ed. 2008. (ENG.). 248p. 99.00 (978-0-19-954684-8(3)) Oxford Univ. Pr., Inc.

Martens, Wilfried. Europe: I Struggle, I Overcome: I Struggle, I Overcome. 2009. (ENG., Illus.). xvi, 276p. 59.95 (978-3-540-89288-5(5), 3540892885) Springer.

Moreau de Melen, Henri & Grosbois, Thierry. Mémoires, de Léopold III à la Corée. 2009. (FRE & ENG., Illus.). 479p. (978-2-87386-549-8(0)) Racine, Editions.

Murray, James M. Bruges, Cradle of Capitalism, 1280-1390. 2009. (ENG., Illus.). 424p. (C). pap. 56.00 (978-0-521-12053-1(5)) Cambridge Univ. Pr.

Roosevelt, Theodore. America & the World War. 2009. 300p. 24.99 (978-1-103-47685-5(8)); pap. 18.99 (978-1-103-47681-7(5)) BiblioBazaar.

—America & the World War. 2007. (ENG.). 296p. pap. 18.95 (978-1-60355-070-3(4)) Juniper Grove.

—America & the World War. 2007. (ENG.). 292p. 43.95 (978-0-548-36001-9(4)); per. 28.95 (978-0-548-30276-7(6)) Kessinger Publishing, LLC.

Schiller, Thomas Horne. History of the Rise & Progress of the Belgian Republic: Until The ... 2008. 245p. pap. 25.75 (978-0-554-61226-3(7)) BiblioBazaar.

Stevens, Fred, et al, eds. Europe: Constitutional Documents of Belgium, Luxembourg & the Netherlands 1789-1848; Verfassungsdokumente Belgiens, Luxemburgs und der Niederlande 1789-1848, 2 vols. rev. ed. 2008. (DUT, FRE & GER.). 681p. (978-3-598-35683-4(8)) Saur, K. G. Verlag GmbH & Co.

Vanthemsche, Guy. Belgium & the Congo, 1885#x2013;1980. 2012. (ENG., Illus.). 304p. 99.00 **(978-0-521-19421-1(0))** Cambridge Univ. Pr.

Vooght, Danielle De. The King Invites: Performing Power at a Courtly Dining Table (Belgium, 1831-1909) 2012. (Europe alimentaire / European Food Issues/ Europa alimentaria / L'Europa alimentare Ser.). (ENG.). 285p. pap. 54.95 **(978-90-5201-752-5(2))** PIE - Peter Lang BEL. Dist: Lang, Peter.

BELGIUM—SOCIAL CONDITIONS

Aubert, Nathalie & Fraiture, Pierre-Philippe. From Art Nouveau to Surrealism: Belgian Modernity in the Making. 2007. (Legenda Main Ser.). (Illus.). 207p. 79.50 (978-1-904350-64-4(X)) European Humanities Research Ctr. GBR. Dist: Brown, David Bk. Co., The.

Begenat-Neuschäfer, Anne, ed. Die Deutschsprachige Gemeinschaft Belgiens: Eine Bestandsaufnahme. 2010. (Belgien im Fokus. Geschichte Sprachen Kulturen Ser.). (GER.). 318p. 57.95 (978-3-631-59454-4(2)) Lang, Peter GmbH, Europaischer Verlag der Wissenschaften DEU. Dist: Lang, Peter.

Büttner, Nils. Herr P.P. Rubens: Von der Kunst, Berühmt Zu Werden. 2006. (Rekonstruktion der Künste Ser.). (GER., Illus.). 278p. (C). pap. 93.00 (978-3-525-47906-3(9)) Vandenhoeck & Ruprecht GmbH & Co. KG DEU. Dist: ISD.

Cantillon, Bea, et al, eds. Social Federalism - The Creation of a Layered Welfare State: The Belgian Case. 2011. (Illus.). 302p. pap. 103.75 (978-94-000-0166-4(5)) Intersentia Uitgevers N.V. BEL. Dist: International Specialized Bk. Services.

Easton, Marleen, et al, eds. Reflections on Reassurance Policing in the Low Countries. 2008. 228p. pap. 52.00 (978-90-5454-863-8(0)) Eleven International Publishing NLD. Dist: International Specialized Bk. Services.

Elliott, Mark & Cavendish, Marshall. CultureShock! Belgium, 1 vol. 2007. (Cultureshock Belgium: A Survival Guide to Customs & Etiquette Ser.). (ENG., Illus.). 32p. pap. 15.95 (978-0-7614-2487-1(3)) Marshall Cavendish Corp.

Fox, Renee C. In the Belgian Chateau: The Spirit & Culture of a European Society in an Age of Change. 2008. (American Ways Ser.). (ENG., Illus.). 288p. pap. 19.95 (978-1-56663-712-1(0)) Dee, Ivan R. Pub.

Hutton, Shennan. Women & Economic Activities in Late Medieval Ghent. 2011. (New Middle Ages Ser.). (ENG., Illus.). 256p. 85.00 (978-0-230-10495-2(9)) Palgrave Macmillan.

Limberger, Michael. Sixteenth-Century Antwerp & its Rural Surroundings: Social & Economic Change in the Hinterland of a Commerical Metropolis (ca. 1450-Ca. 1570) 2008. (Studies in European Urban History (1100-1800) Ser.). (ENG.). 284p. (C). pap. 94.00 (978-2-503-52725-3(6)) Brepols Pubs. BEL. Dist: ISD.

Marchal, Jules. Lord Leverhulme's Ghosts: Colonial Exploitation in the Congo. 2008. (ENG.). 256p. 29.95 (978-1-84467-239-4(5), 844239) Verso Bks. GBR. Dist: Norton, W. W. & Co., Inc.

Nieuwenhuyze, Inge Van & Nieuwenhuyze, Inge van. Getting by in Europe's Labour Markets. 2008. (IMISCOE Dissertations Ser.). pap. (978-90-8964-050-5(9)) Amsterdam Univ. Pr.

Selby, Scott Andrew & Campbell, Greg. Flawless: Inside the Largest Diamond Heist in History. 2012. (ENG.). 336p. pap. 14.95 **(978-1-4027-9755-2(9))** Sterling Publishing Co., Inc.

Winter, Anne. Migrants & Urban Change: Newcomers to Antwerp, 1760-1860, 1 vol. 2009. (Perspectives in Economic & Social History Ser.). (ENG., Illus.). 328p. 99.00 (978-1-85196-646-2(3)) Pickering & Chatto Pubs., Ltd. GBR. Dist: Ashgate Publishing Co.

BELGRADE (SERBIA)

Boogie, photos by. Belgrade Belongs to Me. 2008. (ENG.). 120p. 35.00 (978-1-57687-465-3(6)) powerHouse Cultural Entertainment, Inc.

Locken, E. Travel Journal Belgrade. 2010. 192p. pap. 19.99 (978-0-557-44420-5(9)) Lulu Enterprises Inc.

Norris, David. Belgrade: A Cultural History. 2008. (ENG.). 288p. pap. 16.95 (978-0-19-537609-8(9)) Oxford Univ. Pr., Inc.

Norris, David A. Belgrade A Cultural History. 2008. (ENG., Illus.). 288p. 74.00 (978-0-19-537608-1(0)) Oxford Univ. Pr., Inc.

BELIEF AND DOUBT

Here are entered works treating the subject from the philosophical standpoint. Works on religious belief are entered under the heading Faith.

see also Agnosticism; Error; Evidence; Faith; Irrationalism (Philosophy); Rationalism; Scruples; Skepticism; Truth

Alexander, Karyn. Mad at God. 2010. 266p. pap. 16.99 (978-1-60957-250-1(5)) Xulon Pr., Inc.

Allison, Jay. This I Believe: The Personal Philosophies of Remarkable Men & Women. Allison, Jay & Gediman, Dan, eds. 2007. (ENG., Illus.). 320p. pap. 15.00 (978-0-8050-8658-4(7), Holt Paperback) Holt, Henry & Co.

—This I Believe: The Personal Philosophies of Remarkable Men & Women. Allison, Jay & Gediman, Dan, eds. 2006. (ENG., Illus.). 304p. 25.00 (978-0-8050-8087-2(2)) Holt, Henry & Co.

Allison, Jay & Gediman, Dan. This I Believe II: More Personal Philosophies of Remarkable Men & Women. Gregory, John et al, eds. 2008. (ENG.). 288p. 23.00 (978-0-8050-8768-0(0)) Holt, Henry & Co.

—This I Believe II: The Personal Philosophies of Remarkable Men & Women. 2009. (ENG.). 288p. pap. 15.00 (978-0-8050-9089-5(4), Holt Paperback) Holt, Henry & Co.

Alston, William P. Beyond Justification: Dimensions of Epistemic Evaluation. 2006. 256p. per. 24.95 *(978-0-8014-7332-6(2),* ILR Pr.) Cornell Univ. Pr.

Anderson, Rick. God's Feet are in My Sandbox: Faith Chronicles of a Texas Death Row Chaplain. 201*. pap. 17.99 *(978-1-61739-810-0(1))* Tate Publishing & Enterprises, LLC.

Anderson, W. M. Action Literacy: I Believe In ... 2008. 32p. pap. 10.95 *(978-0-86431-735-3(2))* ACER Pr. AUS. Dist: International Specialized Bk. Services.

Appiah, Anthony. Assertion & Conditionals. 2008. (Cambridge Studies in Philosophy Ser.). (ENG.). 280p. pap. 38.99 *(978-0-521-07129-1(1))* Cambridge Univ. Pr.

Archer-Ellison Design. Choose to Believe: A Practical Guide to Living Your Dreams. 2008. 256p. pap. 17.95 *(978-0-9796726-4-4(3))* PowerKeys Publishing.

Baker, A.E. Prophets for an Age of Doubt. 2007. 248p. per. *(978-1-4067-8851-8(1),* Pomona Pr.) Read Bks.

Behrens, Mary Anne. The Church of Mary Anne: What I Believe. 2007. 76p. per. 9.95 *(978-0-595-47627-5(9))* iUniverse, Inc.

Bell, Jeff. When in Doubt, Make Belief: An OCD-Inspired Approach to Living with Uncertainty. 2009. (ENG.). 224p. pap. 14.95 *(978-1-57731-670-1(3))* New World Library.

Benjamin I., Phinnah. Yoked with Unbelief. 2008. 128p. pap. 14.99 *(978-1-60647-999-5(7))* Xulon Pr., Inc.

Berger, Peter & Zijcerveld, Anton. In Praise of Doubt: How to Have Convictions Without Becoming a Fanatic. 2010. (ENG.). 192p. pap. 13.99 *(978-0-06-177817-9(6),* HarperOne) HarperCollins Pubs.

Berger, Peter & Zijderveld, Anton C. In Praise of Doubt: How to Have Convictions Without Becoming a Fanatic. 2009. 192p. 23.99 *(978-0-06-177816-2(8),* HarperOne) HarperCollins Pubs.

Bicchieri, Cristina & Dalla Chiara, Maria Luisa, eds. Knowledge, Belief, & Strategic Interaction. 2008. (Cambridge Studies in Probability, Induction & Decision Theory Ser.). (ENG.). 432p. pap. 60.00 *(978-0-521-06126-1(1))* Cambridge Univ. Pr.

Bochman, Alexander. A Logical Theory of Nonmonotonic Inference & Belief Change. 2010. (Artificial Intelligence Ser.). (Illus.). xii, 434p. pap. 119.00 *(978-3-642-07516-2(9),* 3642075169) Springer.

Boër, Steven E. Thought-Contents: On the Ontology of Belief & the Semantics of Belief Attribution. 2010. (Philosophical Studies Ser.). xviii, 380p. pap. 219.00 *(978-90-481-7280-1(2),* 9048172802) Springer.

Braden, Gregg. The Spontaneous Healing of Belief: Shattering the Paradigm of False Limits. (ENG., Illus.). 2009. 215p. pap. 14.95 *(978-1-4019-1690-9(2))* 2008. 240p. 24.95 *(978-1-4019-1689-3(9))* Hay Hse., Inc.

Burt, David F. Y Como Creeran?Tr. of And How Shall They Believe? (SPA.). *(978-84-7645-203-5(9),* 223248) Clie, Editorial.

Caputo, John D. & Vattimo, Gianni. After the Death of God. Robbins, Jeffrey W., ed. 2007. (Insurrections: Critical Studies in Religion, Politics, & Culture Ser.). (ENG., Illus.). 216p. (gr. 17). 35.00 *(978-0-231-14124-6(6))* Columbia Univ. Pr.

Carrier, Leonard S. The Essential Tie Between Knowing & Believing: A Causal Account of Knowledge & Epistemic Reasons. 2011. 164p. 109.95 *(978-0-7734-1495-2(9))* Mellen, Edwin Pr., The.

Carse, James P. The Religious Case Against Belief. 2009. (ENG.). 240p. (gr. 12-18). 16.00 *(978-0-14-311544-1(8),* Penguin (Non-Classics)) Penguin Group (USA) Inc.

Casey, Suze. Belief Re-Patterning: The Amazing Technique for "Flipping the Switch" to Positive Thoughts. 2012. (ENG.). 256p. pap. 18.95 ***(978-1-4019-3556-6(7))*** Hay Hse., Inc.

Coley, Noel George. Darwin to Einstein. Date not set. ix, 358p. pap. 24.75 *(978-0-582-49159-5(2))* Addison-Wesley Longman, Ltd. GBR. Dist: Trans-Atlantic Pubns., Inc.

Collini, Stefan. That's Offensive! Criticism, Identity, Respect. 2011. (Manifestos for the 21st Century Ser.). (ENG.). 69p. 14.95 *(978-1-906497-79-8(6))* Seagull Bks. GBR. Dist: Chicago Distribution Ctr.

Concordia Publishing, creator. Overcoming Doubt. 2007. (Insight Ser.). 48p. pap. 5.99 *(978-0-7586-1465-0(9))* Concordia Publishing Hse.

Conor Cunningham Staff. Veritas: Belief & Metaphysics. 2011. pap. ***(978-0-334-04137-5(6),*** SCM Pr.) Hymns Ancient & Modern Ltd.

Conrad, Michael. The Center of My Life. 2007. 120p. per. 12.95 *(978-1-930301-90-0(1))* Learning Doctor, The.

Conrad, Michael Francis. How to Stop Assumicide: How Think Critically about What You Believe, Without Destroying Your Faith. 2008. 104p. pap. 9.95 *(978-1-930301-83-2(9))* Learning Doctor, The.

Cormack, Douglas. The Rational Trinity: Imagination, Belief & Knowledge. 2010. 460p. pap. *(978-0-7552-1196-8(0))* Authors OnLine, Ltd.

Cottingham, John. Why Believe? (ENG.). 208p. 2011. 17.95 *(978-1-4411-4305-1(X))* 2009. 24.95 *(978-0-8264-9636-2(9))* Continuum International Publishing Group, Ltd. GBR. Dist: National Bk. Network.

Cunningham, Conor & Candler, Peter M., Jr., eds. Beliefs & Metaphysics. 2007. (Veritas Ser.). 540p. *(978-0-334-04150-4(3))* Hymns Ancient & Modern Ltd.

Deacon, A. Theological Graffiti. 2011. 88p. pap. 12.95 *(978-0-533-16339-7(0))* Vantage Pr., Inc.

DeYoung, Curtiss Paul. Living Faith: How Faith Inspires Social Justice. annot. ed. 2007. 192p. per. 16.00 *(978-0-8006-3841-2(7),* Fortress Pr.) Augsburg Fortress, Pubs.

Dittrich, Andreas. Glauben, Wissen und Sagen: Studien zu Wissen und Wissenskritik im 'Zauberberg', in den 'Schlafwandlern' und im 'Mann ohne Eigenschaften' 2009. (Studien zur deutschen Literatur Ser.).Tr. of Believing, Knowing & Saying. Studies on Knowledge & Critique of Knowledge in the 'Magic mountainâ€(tm), â€˜the Sleepwalkersâ€(tm) & the â€˜the Man Without Qualitiesâ€(tm). (GER.). IX, 365p. 168.00 ***(978-3-11-173585-6(0))*** De Gruyter, Walter Inc.

—Glauben, Wissen und Sagen: Studien zu Wissen und Wissenskritik im 'Zauberberg', in den 'Schlafwandlern' und im 'Mann ohne Eigenschaften' 2009. (Studien zur deutschen Literatur Ser.).Tr. of Believing, Knowing & Saying. Studies on Knowledge & Critique of Knowledge in 'the Magic mountainâ€(tm), â€˜the Sleepwalkersâ€(tm) & the â€˜the Man Without Qualitiesâ€(tm). (GER.). IX, 365p. pap. *(978-3-484-18188-5(5))* Verlag Max Niemeyer.

Doherty, Catherine. In the Furnace of Doubts: Meditations - When You've Lost Your Way. 96p. pap. *(978-0-921440-80-2(4))* Madonna Hse. Pubns.

Dubucs, J. P., ed. Philosophy of Probability. 2010. (Philosophical Studies Ser.). 304p. pap. 289.00 *(978-90-481-4301-6(2),* 9048143012) Springer.

Dweck, Carol S. Mindset: The New Psychology of Success. 2007. (ENG., Illus.). 288p. pap. 16.00 *(978-0-345-47232-8(2),* Ballantine Bks.) Random House Publishing Group.

Eagle, Antony. Philosophy of Probability: Contemporary Readings: Contemporary Readings. 2009. (Routledge Contemporary Readings in Philosophy Ser.). (Illus.). 0p. 50.00 *(978-0-415-48387-2(5))* Routledge.

Eells, Ellery & Skyrms, Brian, eds. Probability & Conditionals: Belief Revision & Rational Decision. 2007. (Cambridge Studies in Probability, Induction & Decision Theory Ser.). (ENG., Illus.). 220p. per. 50.00 *(978-0-521-03933-8(9))* Cambridge Univ. Pr.

Feldman, Stanley & Marks, Vincent. Global Warming & Other Bollocks: The Truth about All Those Science Scare Stories. 2009. (ENG., Illus.). 338p. pap. 17.95 *(978-1-84454-718-0(3))* Blake, John Publishing, Ltd. GBR. Dist: Independent Pubs. Group.

Flanagan, Sabina. Doubt in an Age of Faith: Uncertainty in the Long Twelfth Century. 2009. (Disputatio Ser.). (ENG & LAT., Illus.). 216p. (C). 102.00 *(978-2-503-52745-2(5))* Brepols Pubs. BEL. Dist: ISD.

Flowers, Euletia. The Battle Is His: The Battle Was His to Begin & End. 2009. 141p. pap. 13.95 *(978-1-4327-3772-6(4))* Outskirts Pr., Inc.

Foley, Richard. When Is True Belief Knowledge? 2012. (Princeton Monographs in Philosophy Ser.). (ENG.). 162p. (C). 35.00 ***(978-0-691-15472-5(4))*** Princeton Univ. Pr.

Gerald Schmeling. Your God Spot: How the Brain Makes & the Mind Shapes All Forms of Faith. 2009. 172p. pap. 15.95 *(978-1-4389-3115-9(8))* AuthorHouse.

Giles, Terry. A Doubter's Guide to Heaven: Walking a Path from Doubt to Trust. 2007. (Illus.). 160p. per. 13.00 *(978-0-687-64214-4(0))* Abingdon Pr.

Green, Mitchell S. & Williams, John N., eds. Moore's Paradox: New Essays on Belief, Rationality, & the First Person. 2007. (ENG., Illus.). 272p. 85.00 *(978-0-19-928279-1(X))* Oxford Univ. Pr., Inc.

Hall, Manly P. How Belief in Rebirth Enriches Life. pap. 4.95 *(978-0-89314-318-3(9))* Philosophical Research Society, Inc.

Hancock, Wayne. It Matters What You Believe. 2010. 80p. pap. 10.99 *(978-1-61579-835-3(8))* Xulon Pr., Inc.

Harrison, Guy. 50 Popular Beliefs That People Think Are True. 2011. (ENG., Illus.). 350p. pap. 18.00 ***(978-1-61614-495-1(5))*** Prometheus Bks., Pubs.

Healy, Mary & Parry, Robin, eds. The Bible & Epistemology: Biblical Soundings on the Knowledge of God. 2007. (ENG.). 224p. 24.99 *(978-1-84227-540-5(2),* Paternoster) Authentic Media.

Heffernan, Margaret. Willful Blindness: Why We Ignore the Obvious at Our Peril. 2011. (ENG.). 304p. 26.00 *(978-0-8027-1998-0(8))* Walker & Co.

Helm, Paul. Belief Policies. 2007. (Cambridge Studies in Philosophy Ser.). (ENG.). 244p. (C). pap. 51.00 *(978-0-521-03872-0(3))* Cambridge Univ. Pr.

Hick, John. Between Faith & Doubt: Dialogues on Religion & Reason. 2010. (ENG.). 145p. 100.00 *(978-0-230-25166-3(8));* pap. 21.00 *(978-0-230-25167-0(6))* Palgrave Macmillan.

Hicks, David. Ritual & Belief: Readings in the Anthropology of Religion. 3rd ed. 2010. (ENG.). 496p. 99.00 *(978-0-7591-1155-4(3));* pap. 59.95 *(978-0-7591-1156-1(1))* AltaMira Pr.

Hood, Bruce, et al. Supersense: Why We Believe in the Unbelievable. 2009. (ENG., Illus.). 320p. 25.99 *(978-0-06-145264-2(5),* HarperOne) HarperCollins Pubs.

Hood, Bruce M. The Science of Superstition: How the Developing Brain Creates Supernatural Beliefs. 2010. (ENG.). 320p. pap. 14.99 *(978-0-06-145265-9(3),* HarperOne) HarperCollins Pubs.

Huber, Franz & Schmidt-Petri, Christoph. Degrees of Belief. 2009. (Synthese Library). (ENG.). x, 354p. 289.00 *(978-1-4020-9197-1(4))* Springer.

Huber, Franz & Schmidt-Petri, Christoph, eds. Degrees of Belief. 2009. (Synthese Library). x, 354p. pap. 27.95 *(978-90-481-3718-3(7),* 9048137187) Springer.

Humphrys, John. In God We Doubt: Confessions of a Failed Atheist. 2008. (ENG.). 368p. pap. 15.95 *(978-0-340-97673-9(X),* Hodder & Stoughton) Hodder General Publishing Div. GBR. Dist: Independent Pubs. Group.

Ingersoll, Janet & Torrence, Diana. Belief Change - the Book. 2009. 138p. pap. 20.90 *(978-0-557-08481-4(4))* Lulu Enterprises Inc.

James, William. The Will to Believe & Other Essays in Popular Philosophy. 2006. pap. 14.95 *(978-1-59605-891-0(9),* Cosimo Classics) Cosimo, Inc.

Jastrow, Joseph. The Psychology of Conviction. 2009. 224p. pap. 19.84 *(978-0-217-63685-8(3))* General Bks. LLC.

—The Psychology of Conviction. 2007. (ENG.). 408p. per. *(978-1-4067-4764-5(5))* Read Bks.

Jennings, William. God's Advocate, & the Trial of Faith versus Reason. 2009. 250p. pap. 29.95 *(978-0-9817141-0-3(2))* Pacific Southwest Consulting Group, Inc.

Jones, Todd. What People Believe When They Say That People Believe: Folk Sociology & the Nature of Group Intentions. 2010. (ENG.). 238p. 65.00 *(978-0-7391-4820-4(6))* Lexington Bks.

Jones, Todd E. What People Believe When They Say That People Believe: Folk Sociology & the Nature of Group Intentions. 2010. *(978-0-7391-4822-8(2))* Lexington Bks.

Jungmann De Castro, Rodrigo. Direct Reference & Belief Ascriptions. 2008. 140p. pap. *(978-3-8364-7*96-1(5))* VDM Verlag Dr. Mueller e.K.

Kenny, Anthony & Kenny. What I Believe. 2007. (ENG.). 184p. 19.95 *(978-0-8264-9616-4(4))* Continuum International Publishing Group, Ltd. GBR. Dist: National Bk. Network.

Keyes, Dick. Seeing Through Cynicism: A Reconsideration of the Power of Suspicion. 2006. (ENG., Illus.). 239p. per. 18.00 *(978-0-8308-3388-7(9),* IVP Bks.) InterVarsity Pr.

Koons, Robert C. Paradoxes of Belief & Strategic Rationality. 2009. (Cambridge Studies in Probability, Induction & Decision Theory Ser.). (ENG., Illus.). 192p. pap. 31.99 *(978-0-521-10059-5(3))* Cambridge Univ. Pr.

Kraft, James. The Epistemology of Religious Disagreement: A Better Understanding. 2012. (ENG., Illus.). 192p. 85.00 ***(978-0-230-11190-5(4))*** Palgrave Macmillan.

Kristeva, Julia. This Incredible Need to Believe. Brahic, Beverley Bie, tr. from ITA. 2011. (European Perspectives: a Series in Social Thought & Cultural Criticism Ser.). (ENG.). 136p. (gr. 17). pap. 14.95 ***(978-0-231-14785-9(6))*** Columbia Univ. Pr.

—This Incredible Need to Believe. 2009. *(978-82-311-4784-8(5))* Columbia Univ. Pr.

—This Incredible Need to Believe. Brahic, Beverley Bie, tr. from ITA. 2009. (European Perspectives: a Series in Social Thought & Cultural Criticism Ser.). (ENG.). 136p. (gr. 17). 19.95 *(978-0-231-14784-2(8))* Columbia Univ. Pr.

La Page, Will. Rethinking Park Protection: Treading the Uncommon Ground of Environmental Beliefs. 2012. 208p. 105.00 ***(978-1-84593-999-1(9));*** pap. 50.00 ***(978-1-78064-001-3(3))*** CABI GBR. Dist: Stylus Publishing, LLC.

Lamm, Norman. Faith & Doubt: Studies in Traditional Jewish Thought. 3rd ed. 2007. (C). *(978-0-88125-952-0(7))* Ktav Publishing Hse., Inc.

—Faith & Doubt: Studies in Traditional Jewish Thought. Date not set. pap. 11.95 *(978-0-88125-100-5(3))* Yeshiva Univ. Pr.

Lane, Christopher. The Age of Doubt: Tracing the Roots of Our Religious Uncertainty. 2011. (ENG., Illus.). 248p. 26.00 *(978-0-300-14192-4(0))* Yale Univ. Pr.

Larsen, Timothy. Crisis of Doubt: Honest Faith in Nineteenth-Century England. 2007. (ENG.). 336p. 135.00 *(978-0-19-928787-1(2))* Oxford Univ. Pr., Inc.

Laufer, Michael, et al. 106 Impossible Things Before Breakfast: Brain Boosting Techniques to Help You Achieve the Unachievable. 2010. (ENG.). 256p. pap. 14.95 *(978-1-4405-0626-0(4))* Adams Media Corp.

Lawrenz, Mel. I Want to Believe: Finding Your Way in an Age of Many Faiths. 2008. (ENG., Illus.). 256p. 16.99 *(978-0-8307-4452-7(5))* Gospel Light Pubns.

Ledwig, Marion. God's Rational Warriors: The Rationality of Faith Considered. 2008. (ENG.). 239p. 122.00 *(978-3-938793-87-9(2))* Ontos Verlag DEU. Dist: Transaction Pubs.

Levi, Isaac. The Fixation of Belief & Its Undoing: Changing Beliefs through Inquiry. 2009. (ENG.). 208p. (C). pap. 33.99 *(978-0-521-11029-7(7))* Cambridge Univ. Pr.

Levine, Andrew. In Bad Faith: What's Wrong with the Opium of the People. 2011. 224p. pap. 21.00 ***(978-1-61614-470-8(X))*** Prometheus Bks., Pubs.

Little, Paul E. Know What You Believe. 2008. (ENG.). 214p. per. 15.00 *(978-0-8308-3423-5(0),* IVP Bks.) InterVarsity Pr.

Loeb, Louis E. Reflection & the Stability of Belief: Essays on Descartes, Hume, & Reid, 1 vol. 2010. (ENG.). 384p. 99.00 *(978-0-19-536876-5(2));* pap. 39.95 *(978-0-19-536875-8(4))* Oxford Univ. Pr., Inc.

Loewen, Gregory V. How Can We Explain the Persistence of Irrational Beliefs? Essays in Social Anthropology. 2006. 248p. 109.95 *(978-0-7734-5508-5(6))* Mellen, Edwin Pr., The.

Loftus, John W. Why I Became an Atheist: A Former Preacher Rejects Christianity. 2008. (ENG.). 355p. pap. 19.98 *(978-1-59102-592-4(3))* Prometheus Bks., Pubs.

Lopez, Leanette. Breaking the Cycle of Self-Doubt. 2007. 272p. per. 15.99 *(978-1-60266-399-2(8))* Xulon Pr., Inc.

Lyall, Ian. I Believe (a mini-encyclopedia of Christian Belief. 2009. 72p. pap. 12.50 *(978-1-4092-6539-9(0))* Lulu Enterprises Inc.

Masangu, Alex. Are Miracles Reasonable Mysteries of Faith. 2008. 100p. pap. *(978-3-639-06202-1(7))* VDM Verlag Dr. Mueller e.K.

Matson, Wallace I. Grand Theories & Everyday Beliefs: Science, Philosophy, & Their Histories, 1 vol. 2011. (ENG., Illus.). 238p. 35.00 *(978-0-19-981269-1(1))* Oxford Univ. Pr., Inc.

Matthews, George. A Concrete Sign of Faith: Proof of the Existence of God. 2008. 108p. 22.95 *(978-0-595-48789-9(0));* pap. 12.95 *(978-0-595-48724-0(6))* iUniverse, Inc.

McCarthy, Paul. Ascension: Becoming an Ascended Master. 2011. 112p. 22.95 *(978-1-4502-7381-7(5));* pap. 12.95 *(978-1-4502-7380-0(7))* iUniverse, Inc.

McGrath, Alister E. Doubting: Growing Through the Uncertainties of Faith. 2006. (ENG., Illus.). 156p. per. 15.00 *(978-0-8308-3352-8(8),* IVP Bks.) InterVarsity Pr.

McMillin, Geraldean. 75 Years in the Wilderness: A Christian Agnostic's Search for Answers. 2008. 132p. pap. 12.95 *(978-1-59858-704-3(8))* Dog Ear Publishing, LLC.

Miller, Scott A. Theory of Mind: Beyond the Preschool Years. 2012. (ENG.). 264p. 94.95 *(978-1-84872-927-8(8));* pap. 45.95 *(978-1-84872-928-5(6))* Taylor & Francis Group GBR. (Psychology Press). Dist: Taylor & Francis Group.

Monsell, Carol L. Believe. 2009. 164p. pap. 14.99 *(978-1-61579-147-7(7))* Xulon Pr., Inc.

Murray, Andrew. Por Que No Crees? Why Do You Not Believe? (SPA.). *(978-84-7228-705-1(X),* 220709) Clie, Editorial.

Murray, Paul. I Loved Jesus in the Night: Teresa of Calcutta - A Secret Revealed. 2008. (ENG.). 120p. (gr. 13). 18.95 *(978-1-55725-579-2(2))* Paraclete Pr., Inc.

Murray, Steve. Reiki False Beliefs: Exposed for All: Misinformation Kept Secret by a Few Revealed. 2006. (Illus.). 208p. per. 24.95 *(978-0-9771609-6-9(3))* Body & Mind Productions, Inc.

Nathan, N. M. L. Evidence & Assurance. 2009. (Cambridge Studies in Philosophy Ser.). (ENG.). 204p. pap. 31.99 *(978-0-521-10793-8(8))* Cambridge Univ. Pr.

Oberhammer, Gerhard & Schmucker, Marcus, eds. Glaubensgewissheit und Wahrheit in religiöser Tradition: Arbeitsdokumentation eines Symposiums. 2008. (Beiträge zur Kultur- und Geistesgeschichte Asiens Ser.). (GER.). 349p. (C). pap. 79.00 *(978-3-7001-3735-1(4))* Austrian Academy of Sciences Press AUT. Dist: Brown, David Bk. Co., The.

Oldridge, Darren. Strange Histories. 2006. (ENG., Illus.). 216p. 27.95 *(978-0-415-40492-1(4))* Routledge.

Osho. Belief, Doubt, & Fanaticism: Is It Essential to Have Something to Believe In? 2012. (Osho Life Essentials Ser.). (ENG.). 224p. pap. 14.99 ***(978-0-312-59548-7(4),*** St. Martin's Griffin) St. Martin's Pr.

Pappas, Nicholas J. Belief & Integrity: Philosophical Dialogues. 2011. 240p. pap. 21.95 ***(978-0-87586-855-4(X));*** pap. 21.95 ***(978-0-87586-856-1(8))*** Algora Publishing.

—On Awareness: A Collection of Philosophical Dialogues. 2011. 202p. pap. 19.95 ***(978-0-87586-840-0(1));*** pap. 19.95 ***(978-0-87586-842-4(8));*** pap. 29.95 ***(978-0-87586-841-7(X))*** Algora Publishing.

Park, Robert L. Superstition: Belief in the Age of Science. 2008. (ENG.). 240p. (C). 24.95 *(978-0-691-13355-3(7))* Princeton Univ. Pr.

—Superstition: Belief in the Age of Science. 2010. (ENG.). 240p. pap. 16.95 *(978-0-691-14597-6(0))* Princeton Univ. Pr.

Peavy, Don E., Sr. What Must I Do... ? Bridging the Gap Between Being & Doing. rev. ed. 2008. (ENG.). 108p. pap. 43.27 *(978-0-7575-3315-0(9))* Kendall Hunt Publishing Co.

Phillips, D. Z. Whose God? Which Tradition? The Nature of Belief in God. 2008. 184p. 99.95 *(978-0-7546-6018-7(4),* Ashgate Publishing Co.

Pillow, William. Mind, Body, & Spirit: Challenges of Science & Faith. 2010. 312p. pap. 21.95 *(978-1-4502-3663-8(4))* iUniverse, Inc.

Piper, John. Battling Unbelief: Defeating Sin with Superior Pleasure. 2007. (ENG.). 128p. pap., stu. ed. 9.99 *(978-1-59052-920-1(0));* (Illus.). 176p. 16.99 *(978-1-59052-960-7(X))* Doubleday Religious Publishing Group, The. (Multnomah).

Ramsay, Hayden. Truth & Faith in Ethics. 2011. (St Andrews Ser.). (ENG.). 250p. 80.00 ***(978-1-84540-254-9(5));*** pap. 34.90 ***(978-1-84540-255-6(3))*** Imprint Academic GBR. Dist: Ingram Pub. Services.

Reidy, Maurice. The God I Believe in & Why. 2006. (ENG.). 200p. per. 27.95 *(978-1-85607-533-6(8))* Columba Pr. IRL. Dist: Dufour Editions, Inc.

Reisner, Andrew & Steglich-Petersen, Asbjorn, eds. Reasons for Belief. 2011. (ENG., Illus.). 284p. 90.00 *(978-1-107-00687-4(2))* Cambridge Univ. Pr.

Rodger, Peter. The OMG Chronicles: One Man's Quest to Discover What God Means to People All over the World. 2011. (ENG.). 256p. 17.95 *(978-1-4019-2845-2(5))* Hay Hse., Inc.

Ruiz, Don Miguel & Ruiz, Don Jose. The Fifth Agreement. 2011. (ENG.). 52p. 15.95 *(978-1-4019-2874-2(9))* Hay Hse., Inc.

—The Fifth Agreement: A Practical Guide to Self-Mastery. (ENG.). 2011. 248p. pap. 14.00 ***(978-1-878424-61-7(0))*** 2009. 264p. 19.95 *(978-1-878424-68-6(8))* Amber-Allen Publishing, Inc.

Sales, Leigh. On Doubt. 2010. (Little Books on Big Themes Ser.). (ENG.). 96p. 15.95 *(978-0-522-85604-0(7))* Melbourne Univ. Publishing AUS. Dist: Independent Pubs. Group.

Sangha, Laura. Angels & Belief in England, 1480-1700, 1 vol. 2012. (Religious Cultures in the Early Modern World Ser.). (ENG.). 288p. 99.00 *(978-1-84893-145-9(X))* Pickering & Chatto Pubs., Ltd. GBR. Dist: Ashgate Publishing Co.

Schellenberg, J. L. The Will to Imagine: A Justification of Skeptical Religion. 2009. 280p. 45.00 *(978-0-8014-4780-8(1))* Cornell Univ. Pr.

—The Wisdom to Doubt: A Justification of Religious Skepticism. 2007. (Illus.). 326p. 49.95 *(978-0-8014-4554-5(X))* Cornell Univ. Pr.

Schwarz, Hans. The God Who Is: The Christian God in a Pluralistic World. 2011. 288p. pap. 33.00 *(978-1-60899-434-2(1))* Cascade Bks.

Sherman, Angie. My Diary of Believing, 1 vol. 2009. 48p. pap. 16.95 *(978-1-60749-022-7(6))* PublishAmerica, Inc.

Shermer, Michael. The Believing Brain: From Ghosts & Gods to Politics & Conspiracies — -How We Construct Beliefs & Reinforce Them as Truths. 2011. (ENG., Illus.). 400p. 28.00 *(978-0-8050-9125-0(4),* Times Bks.) Holt, Henry & Co.

—The Believing Brain: From Ghosts & Gods to Politics & Conspiracies — -How We Construct Beliefs & Reinforce Them as Truths. 2012. (ENG.). 400p. pap. 15.99 ***(978-1-250-00880-0(8),*** St. Martin's Griffin) St. Martin's Pr.

Sim, Stuart. Empires of Belief: Why We Need More Scepticism & Doubt in the Twenty-First Century. 2007. (ENG., Illus.). 176p. (gr. 17). 29.00 *(978-0-7486-2326-6(4))* Edinburgh Univ. Pr. GBR. Dist: Columbia Univ. Pr.

B

Sinnott-Armstrong, Walter, et al, eds. Modality, Morality & Belief: Essays in Honor of Ruth Barcan Marcus. 2009. (ENG.). 292p. pap. 41.00 *(978-0-521-10057-1(7))* Cambridge Univ. Pr.

Smalley, Gary. Change Your Heart, Change Your Life: How Changing What You Believe Will Give You the Great Life You've Always Wanted. 2012. 256p. pap. 15.99 ***(978-0-8499-2993-9(8))*** Nelson, Thomas Inc.

Smalls, Archie J. Believe in God & Follow Your Dreams & Goals. 2010. 52p. pap. 15.99 *(978-1-4500-3605-4(8))* Xlibris Corp.

Specter, Michael. Denialism: How Irrational Thinking Harms the Planet & Threatens Our Lives. 2010. (ENG.). 320p. (gr. 12). 16.00 *(978-0-14-311831-2(5)*, Penguin (Non-Classics)) Penguin Group (USA) Inc.

Sposato, Jesse. Believe — And You'll Succeed: Positive Reminders for Success. 2008. (Illus.). 64p. ***(978-1-60311-155-3(7))*** Mud Puddle, Inc.

Sriraman, Bharath, ed. Beliefs & Mathematics: Festschrift in honor of Guenter Toerner's 60th Birthday (HC) 2007. (ENG & GER.). 272p. 73.99 *(978-1-59311-869-3(4))* Information Age Publishing, Inc.

—Beliefs & Mathematics: Festschrift in honor of Guenter Toerner's 60th Birthday (PB) 2007. (ENG & GER.). 272p. per. 39.99 *(978-1-59311-868-6(6))* Information Age Publishing, Inc.

Stepaniants, M. T. Knowledge & Belief in the Dialogue of Cultures. 2009. *(978-1-56518-262-2(6))* Council for Research in Values & Philosophy.

Strawson, Galen. Freedom & Belief. rev. ed. 2010. (ENG., Illus.). 320p. 99.00 *(978-0-19-924749-3(8))* Oxford Univ. Pr., Inc.

Sunday, Patricia Ann. Jimmy Swaggart: The Anointed Cherub That Covereth - A Catholic Diatribe. 2010. 216p. pap. 19.98 *(978-1-4490-2098-9(4))* AuthorHouse.

Taylor, Eldon. I Believe: When What You Believe Matters! 2012. (ENG., Illus.). 256p. 24.95 ***(978-1-4019-3127-8(8))*** Hay Hse., Inc.

Tennant, Neil. Changes of Mind: An Essay on Rational Belief Revision. 2012. (ENG., Illus.). 368p. 117.00 ***(978-0-19-965575-5(8))*** Oxford Univ. Pr., Inc.

Thompson, Damian. Counterknowledge: How We Surrendered to Conspiracy Theories, Quack Medicine, Bogus Science, & Fake History. 2008. (ENG.). 176p. 21.95 *(978-0-393-06769-9(6)*, 6769) Norton, W. W. & Co., Inc.

Toscano, Paul James. The Sacrament of Doubt. 2007. 168p. 21.95 *(978-1-56085-146-2(5))* Signature Bks., LLC.

Tutt, Alan. Choose to Believe: A Practical Guide to Living Your Dreams. 2008. 256p. 21.95 *(978-0-9796726-3-7(5))* PowerKeys Publishing.

Uyioghosa Clement Omoruyi. The False Cardinal Points. 2009. (Illus.). 224p. pap. 15.99 *(978-1-4389-6669-4(5))* AuthorHouse.

Vahid, Hamid. The Epistemology of Belief. 2008. (ENG.). 272p. 100.00 *(978-0-230-20146-0(6))* Palgrave Macmillan.

Vattimo, Gianni, et al. After the Death of God. Robbins, Jeffrey W., ed. 2009. (Insurrections: Critical Studies in Religion, Politics, & Culture Ser.). (ENG.). 216p. (gr. 17). pap. 18.50 *(978-0-231-14125-3(4))* Columbia Univ. Pr.

Vendera, Jaime. Mindset: Programming Your Mind for Success. 2008. (ENG., Illus.). 122p. pap. 24.95 *(978-0-9794911-0-3(7))* Vendera Publishing.

Vogt, Katja Maria. Belief & Truth: A Skeptic Reading of Plato. 2nd ed. 2012. (ENG., Illus.). 240p. 55.00 ***(978-0-19-991681-8(0))*** Oxford Univ. Pr., Inc.

White, Stephen R. A Space for Unknowing: The Place of Agnosis in Faith. 2007. (ENG.). 160p. per. 27.95 *(978-1-85607-544-2(3))* Columba Pr. IRL. Dist: Dufour Editions, Inc.

Wilkinson, Chris, et al. Conversations on Religion. Wilkinson, Chris & Gordon, Mick, eds. 2008. (ENG.). 240p. 24.95 *(978-0-8264-9909-7(0))* Continuum International Publishing Group, Ltd. GBR. Dist: National Bk. Network.

Williams, M. & Rott, Hans, eds. Frontiers in Belief Revision. 2010. (Applied Logic Ser.). 460p. pap. 249.00 *(978-90-481-5720-4(X)*, 904815720X) Springer.

Williams, Rowan. Tokens of Trust: An Introduction to Christian Belief. 2007. (Illus.). 192p. 16.95 *(978-1-85311-803-6(6))* Norwich Bks. & Music GBR. Dist: Westminster John Knox Pr.

Williams, Roy. God, Actually: Why God Probably Exists; Why Jesus Was Probably Divine; & Why the Rational Objections to Faith Are Unconvincing, 1 vol. 2009. 384p. pap. 18.99 *(978-0-8254-6315-0(7)*, Monarch Bks.) Lion Hudson PLC GBR. Dist: Kregel Pubns.

—God, Actually: Why God Probably Exists, Why Jesus Was Probably Divine, & Why the 'Rational' Objections to Religion Are Unconvincing. 2009. 384p. pap. 18.99 *(978-1-85424-920-3(7))* Lion Hudson PLC GBR. Dist: Independent Pubs. Group.

—God, Actually: Why God Probably Exists, Why Jesus Was Probably Divine, & Why the 'Rational' Objections to Religion are Unconvincing. 2009. (ENG.). 384p. pap. 18.99 *(978-0-7459-5391-5(3))* Lion Hudson PLC GBR. Dist: Independent Pubs. Group.

Wobbermin, Georg. Christian Belief in God: a German Criticism of German Materialistic. Robinson, Daniel Sommer, tr. 2007. (ENG.). 196p. per. 22.95 *(978-1-4304-4555-5(6))* Kessinger Publishing, LLC.

Wolpert, Lewis. Six Impossible Things Before Breakfast: The Evolutionary Origins of Belief. (ENG.). 256p. 2008. pap. 15.95 *(978-0-393-33203-2(9)*, 33203) 2007. 25.95 *(978-0-393-06449-0(2)*, 6449) Norton, W. W. & Co., Inc.

Wright, Edmond. Avatar-Philosophy (And -Religion) or Faitheism. 2011. (Societas Ser.). (ENG.). 96p. pap. 17.90 ***(978-1-84540-234-1(0))*** Imprint Academic GBR. Dist: Ingram Pub. Services.

Zerba, Michelle. Doubt & Skepticism in Antiquity & the Renaissance. 2012. (ENG.). 270p. 99.00 ***(978-1-107-02465-6(X))*** Cambridge Univ. Pr.

BELIEFS, DELUSIONAL

see Delusions

BELIEVERS' CHURCH

see Free Churches

BELINSKI, VISSARION GRIGONEVICH, 1811-1848

Randolph, John. The House in the Garden: The Bakunin Family & the Romance of Russian Idealism. 2007. (Illus.). 287p. 46.00 *(978-0-8014-4542-2(6))* Cornell Univ. Pr.

BELIZE

Carey Jones, N. S. The Pattern of a Dependent Economy: The National Income of British Honduras. 2011. (ENG.). 178p. pap. 19.99 ***(978-0-521-24201-1(0))*** Cambridge Univ. Pr.

Godden, C. H. Trespassers Forgiven: Memoirs of Imperial Service in an Age of Independence. 2009. (ENG., Illus.). 400p. 58.00 *(978-1-84511-780-1(8)*, Radcliffe Pr., The) I. B. Tauris & Co., Ltd. GBR. Dist: Macmillan.

Graham, Elizabeth. Maya Christians & Their Churches in Sixteenth-Century Belize. 2011. (Maya Studies). (ENG., Illus.). 416p. 79.95 *(978-0-8130-3666-3(6))* Univ. Pr. of Florida.

Haines, Helen. Intra-Site Obsidian Distribution & Consumption Patterns in Northern Belize & the North. 2012. (Bar S Ser.). (ENG., Illus.). 165p. (C). pap. 75.00 ***(978-1-4073-0909-5(9))*** British Archaeological Reports Ltd. GBR. Dist: Brown, David Bk. Co., The.

LeCount, Lisa J. & Yaeger, Jason, eds. Classic Maya Provincial Politics: Xunantunich & Its Hinterlands. 2010. (ENG., Illus.). 464p. 72.50 *(978-0-8165-2884-4(5))* Univ. of Arizona Pr.

Macpherson, Anne S. From Colony to Nation: Women Activists & the Gendering of Politics in Belize, 1912-1982. 2009. (Engendering Latin America Ser.). (ENG., Illus.). 408p. pap. 24.95 *(978-0-8032-2492-6(3))* Univ. of Nebraska Pr.

Murray, Sonia, compiled by. The First Parish Register of Belize, 1794-1810, & the First Four Censuses, 1816-1826. 2010. 292p. pap. 29.50 *(978-0-8063-5482-8(8))* Clearfield Co.

Murray, Sonia Bennett, compiled by. Second Parish Registers of Belize, 1813-1827; the First Newspaper: The Honduras Gazette, 1826-1827; the 1826 Census, pages 209-236; & the 1829 Censu. 2011. 326p. pap. 29.50 ***(978-0-8063-5526-9(3))*** Clearfield Co.

Mwakikagile, Godfrey. Belize & Its Identity: A Multicultural Perspective. 2010. 222p. pap. *(978-9987-16-020-4(4))* New Africa Pr.

Wainwright, Joel. Decolonizing Development: Colonial Power & the Maya. 2008. (Antipode Book Ser.). (ENG., Illus.). 328p. pap. 40.95 *(978-1-4051-5706-3(2))*; 94.95 *(978-1-4051-5705-6(4))* Wiley, John & Sons, Inc. (Wiley-Blackwell).

BELIZE—COMMERCE

Castillo, Philip. In the Footsteps of the Orange. 2010. 280p. pap. *(978-3-639-23036-9(1))* VDM Verlag Dr. Mueller e.K.

Icon Group International, Inc. Staff, compiled by. The 2006 Economic & Product Market Databook for Corozal, Belize. 2006. 618p. ring bd. 95.00 *(978-0-497-80412-1(3))* Icon Group International, Inc.

World Trade Organization Staff & Bernan Press Staff. Trade Policy Review - Belize 2010. 2011. (ENG.). 142p. pap. 75.00 *(978-1-59888-465-4(4))* Bernan Assocs.

BELIZE—DESCRIPTION AND TRAVEL

Berman, Joshua. Maya 2012: A Guide to Celebrations in Mexico, Guatemala, Belize & Honduras. 2011. (Moon Handbooks Ser.). (ENG., Illus.). 128p. pap. 7.99 *(978-1-61238-119-0(7))* Avalon Travel Publishing.

—Moon Belize. 2011. (Moon Handbooks Ser.). (ENG., Illus.). 360p. pap. 17.99 *(978-1-59880-852-0(4))* Avalon Travel Publishing.

—Moon Spotlight Belize Cayes: Including Belize City. 2011. (Moon Spotlight Ser.). (ENG., Illus.). 80p. pap. 8.99 *(978-1-59880-962-6(8))* Avalon Travel Publishing.

Church, Mike & Church, Terri. Traveler's Guide to Mexican Camping: Explore Mexico, Guatemala, & Belize with Your RV or Tent. 2009. (Traveler's Guide Ser.). (ENG.). 544p. pap. 21.95 *(978-0-9823101-0-6(2))* Rolling Homes Pr.

Cruising Guide to Belize & Mexico's Caribbean Coast, Including Guatemala's Rio Dulce: Third Edition. 3rd ed. 2007. per. 39.95 *(978-0-9755753-1-4(7))* Windmill Hill Bks.

Dhillon, Bob. Business & Retirement Guide to Belize: The Last Virgin Paradise. 2011. (ENG., Illus.). 128p. pap. 19.99 *(978-1-55488-957-0(X)*, Dundurn Pr.) Dundurn CAN. Dist: Ingram Pub. Services.

Diedrich, Amy. The Impacts of Tourism in Belize - an Assessment of the Impacts of Tourism Development in Six Coastal Communities in Belize, Central Americ. 2008. 184p. pap. *(978-3-8364-9013-9(7))* VDM Verlag Dr. Mueller e.K.

Eltringham, Peter & Rough Guides Staff. Belize. 5th ed. 2010. (ENG., Illus.). 312p. 19.99 *(978-1-84836-512-4(8))* Rough Guides, Ltd. GBR. Dist: Dorling Kindersley Publishing, Inc.

Fodor's Travel Publications, Inc. Staff. Belize: With el Petén. 5th ed. 2012. (Fodor's Gold Guides). (ENG.). 368p. pap. 18.99 ***(978-0-307-92833-7(0)***, Fodor's) Fodor's Travel Pubns.

Greenspan, Eliot. Frommer's Belize. 4th ed. 2011. (Frommer's Complete Guides: 909). (ENG., Illus.). 352p. pap. 19.99 *(978-0-470-88770-7(2)*, Frommers) Wiley, John & Sons, Inc.

Harvard Student Agencies, Inc. Let's Go Guatemala & Belize: The Student Travel Guide. 2009. (Let's Go Ser.). (ENG., Illus.). 304p. pap. 18.95 *(978-1-59880-297-9(6)*, Let's Go) Avalon Travel Publishing.

Insight Guides. Guatemala, Belize & Yucatan. 2nd ed. 2009. (Insight Guides). (ENG., Illus.). 384p. pap. 23.99 *(978-981-282-070-9(1))* APA Publications Services SGP. Dist: Ingram Pub. Services.

Joyness-Burgess, Kate. Belize - Great Destinations. 2010. (Explorer's Great Destinations Ser.). (ENG., Illus.). 368p. pap. 19.95 *(978-1-58157-129-5(1)*, 157129) Countryman Pr.

Locken, E. Travel Journal Belize. 2010. 192p. pap. 19.99 *(978-0-557-34230-3(9))* Lulu Enterprises Inc.

Morris, Charlie. Open Road's Best of Belize 2E. 2009. (ENG.). 256p. pap. 14.95 *(978-1-59360-125-6(5))* Open Road Publishing.

Rock, Tim & Lonely Planet Staff. Diving & Snorkeling Belize. 4th rev. ed. 2007. (Lonely Planet Diving & Snorkeling Guides). (ENG., Illus.). 144p. pap. 24.99 *(978-1-74059-531-5(9))* Lonely Planet Pubns.

Strom, Sharon Hartman & Weaver, Frederick Stirton. Confederates in the Tropics: Charles Swett's Travelogue. 2011. (ENG., Illus.). 176p. 55.00 *(978-1-60473-994-7(0))* Univ. Pr. of Mississippi.

Swett, Charles. A Trip to British Honduras, & to San Pedro, Republic of Honduras by Charles Swett. 2006. 132p. per. 16.99 *(978-1-4255-0902-6(9))* MPublishing.

Trejo, Jose. Valuing a Marine Protected Area in Belize. 2009. 72p. pap. *(978-3-639-19660-3(0))* VDM Verlag Dr. Mueller e.K.

Vorhees, Mara. Belize. 4th rev. ed. 2011. (Country Travel Guide Ser.). (ENG., Illus.). 320p. pap. 19.99 *(978-1-74179-465-6(X))* Lonely Planet Pubns.

BELK, WILLIAM HENRY, 1862-1952

Blythe, LeGette. William Henry Belk: Merchant of the South. 2011. (ENG.). 322p. pap. 40.00 *(978-0-8078-6510-1(9))* Univ. of North Carolina Pr.

BELL, ALEXANDER GRAHAM, 1847-1922

Biographiq. Alexander Graham Bell. 2008. pap. 9.99 *(978-1-59986-235-4(2)*, Biographiq) Filiquarian Publishing, LLC.

Gray, Charlotte. Reluctant Genius: Alexander Graham Bell & the Passion for Invention. 2011. (ENG., Illus.). 480p. pap. 14.95 *(978-1-61145-060-6(8)*, 611060, Arcade Publishing) Skyhorse Publishing Co., Inc.

Millard, Candice. Destiny of the Republic: A Tale of Madness, Medicine & the Murder of a President. 2011. (Playaway Adult Nonfiction Ser.). 59.99 ***(978-1-61657-787-2(8))*** Findaway World, LLC.

—Destiny of the Republic: A Tale of Madness, Medicine & the Murder of a President. (ENG.). 2012. 432p. pap. 16.00 ***(978-0-7679-2971-4(3)***, Anchor) 2011. (Illus.). 352p. 28.95 *(978-0-385-52626-5(1)*, Doubleday) Knopf Doubleday Publishing Group.

—Destiny of the Republic: A Tale of Madness, Medicine & the Murder of a President. l.t. ed. 2012. (ENG.). 597p. 32.99 ***(978-1-4104-4625-1(5))*** Thorndike Pr.

Osborne, Harold S. Biographical Memoir of Alexander Graham Bell, 1847-1922. 2011. 38p. 35.95 ***(978-1-258-01274-8(X))*** Literary Licensing, LLC.

Perez, Marco Antonio Gomez. Alexander Graham Bell: Mucho Mas Que un Inventor. 2010. (Los Grandes Ser.). (Illus.). 128p. pap. 5.95 *(978-970-666-916-2(7))* Grupo Editorial Tomo, S.A. de C.V. MEX. Dist: Giron Bks.

Pizer, Russell A. The Tangled Web of Patent #174465. 2009. 368p. 28.49 *(978-1-4389-8403-2(0))*; pap. 17.99 *(978-1-4389-8402-5(2))* AuthorHouse.

Shulman, Seth. The Telephone Gambit: Chasing Alexander Graham Bell's Secret. 2009. (ENG.). 256p. pap. 14.95 *(978-0-393-33368-8(X)*, 33368) Norton, W. W. & Co., Inc.

Towers, Walter Kellogg. Masters of Space: Morse, Thompson, Bell, Marconi, Carty. 2007. (ENG.). 154p. pap. 19.99 *(978-1-4264-6034-0(1))*; 168p. pap. 21.99 *(978-1-4264-6105-7(4))* BiblioBazaar.

Tulloch, Judith. The Bell Family in Baddeck: Alexander Graham Bell & Mabel Bell in Cape Breton. 2006. (ENG., Illus.). 96p. pap. *(978-0-88780-713-8(5))* Formac Publishing Co., Ltd.

—La Famille Bell à Baddeck: Alexander Graham Bell et Mabel Bell au Cap-Breton. Cantin, Monique, tr. from ENG. 2009. (FRE., Illus.). 96p. pap. *(978-0-88780-868-5(9))* Formac Publishing Co., Ltd.

BELL, G. K. A. (GEORGE KENNEDY ALLEN), 1883-1958

Bell, G. K. A., et al. Bishop George Bell: House of Lords Speeches & Correspondence with Rudolf Hess. 2009. 241p. pap. 49.95 *(978-3-03911-895-3(1))* Lang, Peter AG GBR. Dist: Lang, Peter.

Chandler, Andrew. The Church & Humanity: The Life & Work of George Bell, 1883-1958. 2012. 240p. 99.95 ***(978-1-4094-2557-1(6))***; 99.95 ***(978-1-4094-2556-4(8))*** Ashgate Publishing Co.

BELL, GERTRUDE LOWTHIAN, 1868-1926

Howell, Georgina. Gertrude Bell: Queen of the Desert, Shaper of Nations. 2008. (ENG., Illus.). 512p. pap. 16.00 *(978-0-374-53135-5(8))* Farrar, Straus & Giroux.

Winstone, H. V. Gertrude Bell. (Illus.). 348p. 12.95 *(978-0-224-01432-8(3))* Quartet Bks., Ltd. GBR. Dist: Charles River Bks.

BELL, JULIAN, 1908-1937

Stansky, Peter & Abrahams, William Miller. Julian Bell: From Bloomsbury to the Spanish Civil War. 2012. (ENG.). 328p. 45.00 ***(978-0-8047-7413-0(7))*** Stanford Univ. Pr.

BELL, MABEL GARDINER HUBBARD, 1857-1923

Tulloch, Judith. The Bell Family in Baddeck: Alexander Graham Bell & Mabel Bell in Cape Breton. 2006. (ENG., Illus.). 96p. pap. *(978-0-88780-713-8(5))* Formac Publishing Co., Ltd.

—La Famille Bell à Baddeck: Alexander Graham Bell et Mabel Bell au Cap-Breton. Cantin, Monique, tr. from ENG. 2009. (FRE., Illus.). 96p. pap. *(978-0-88780-868-5(9))* Formac Publishing Co., Ltd.

BELL, VANESSA, 1879-1961

Arnold, Anthea. Charleston Saved, 1979-1989. 2010. (ENG., Illus.). 144p. 39.95 *(978-0-7090-9018-2(8))* Hale, Robert Ltd. GBR. Dist: Independent Pubs. Group.

Bakos, Judit. Painting & Writing. 2009. (Illus.). 144p. pap. *(978-3-639-13500-8(8))* VDM Verlag Dr. Mueller e.K.

Spalding, Frances. Vanessa Bell. 2007. (ENG., Illus.). 320p. per. 24.95 *(978-0-7524-4033-0(0))* History Pr. Ltd.,The GBR. Dist: Independent Pubs. Group.

BELL RINGING

see Handbell Ringing

BELLAMY, EDWARD, 1850-1898

Beaumont, Matthew. The Spectre of Utopia: Utopian & Science Fictions at the Fin de Siècle. 2011. (Ralahine Utopian Studies). (ENG.). 307p. pap. 66.95 ***(978-3-0343-0725-3(X))*** Lang, Peter AG GBR. Dist: Lang, Peter.

Bellamy, Edward. Dr. Heidenhoff's Process. 2007. per. 6.99 *(978-0-9794154-4-9(6)*, TARK Classic Fiction) Arc Manor.

—Dr. Heidenhoff's Process. 2009. (ENG.). 141p. pap. 18.99 *(978-1-117-00946-9(7)*, BiblioLife) BiblioBazaar.

Geissler, Ludwig A. Looking Beyond. 2009. 60p. pap. 14.14 *(978-1-151-32058-2(7))* General Bks. LLC.

Morgan, Arthur E. Edward Bellamy. 500p. 2008. 53.95 *(978-1-4367-0676-6(9))* 2007. (ENG.). per. 38.95 *(978-1-4325-8555-6(X))* Kessinger Publishing, LLC.

—The Philosophy of Edward Bellamy. 108p. 2008. 34.95 *(978-1-4367-0781-7(1))* 2007. (ENG.). per. 19.95 *(978-1-4325-6395-0(5))* Kessinger Publishing, LLC.

BELLAMY, FRANCIS, 1855-1931

Bishop, Ronald. Taking on the Pledge of Allegiance: The News Media & Michael Newdow's Constitutional Challenge. 2007. 202p. 68.50 *(978-0-7914-7181-4(0))*; per. 29.95 *(978-0-7914-7182-1(9))* State Univ. of New York Pr.

Ellis, Richard J. To the Flag: The Unlikely History of the Pledge of Allegiance. 2007. (Illus.). 297p. per. 15.95 *(978-0-7006-1521-6(0))* Univ. Pr. of Kansas.

Murray, William J. The Pledge: One Nation under God. annot. ed. 2007. 192p. per. 14.99 *(978-0-89957-035-8(6))* AMG Pubs.

BELLARMINO, ROBERTO FRANCESCO ROMOLO, SAINT, 1542-1621

Schaff, David Schley. BellarmineJefferson Legend & the Decla. 2006. pap. 15.95 *(978-1-4286-5597-3(2))* Kessinger Publishing, LLC.

Tutino, Stefania. Empire of Souls: Robert Bellarmine & the Christian Commonwealth. 2010. (Oxford Studies in Historical Theology Ser.). (ENG.). 384p. 74.00 *(978-0-19-974053-6(4))* Oxford Univ. Pr., Inc.

BELLE-ALLIANCE, BATTLE OF, WATERLOO, BELGIUM, 1815

see Waterloo, Battle of, Waterloo, Belgium, 1815

BELLE EPOQUE ART

see Art Nouveau

BELLEAU WOOD, BATTLE OF, FRANCE, 1918

Axelrod, Alan. Miracle at Belleau Wood: The Birth of the Modern U. S. Marine Corps. (ENG., Illus.). 272p. 2010. pap. 16.95 *(978-0-7627-6130-2(X))* 2007. 24.95 *(978-1-59921-025-4(8))* Globe Pequot Pr., The. (Lyons Pr.).

Bonk, David. Chateau Thierry & Belleau Wood 1918: The AEF's Baptism of Fire on the Marne. 2007. (Campaign Ser.). (ENG., Illus.). 96p. pap. 19.95 *(978-1-84603-034-5(X))* Osprey Publishing, Ltd. GBR. Dist: Random Hse., Inc.

Camp, Dick. The Devil Dogs at Belleau Wood: U. S. Marines in World War I. 2008. (ENG., Illus.). 128p. pap. 19.95 *(978-0-7603-3189-7(8)*, 0760331898, Zenith Pr.) MBI Publishing Co. LLC.

BELLES-LETTRES

see Literature

BELLEVUE HOSPITAL

Holland, Julie. Weekends at Bellevue. 2010. 320p. pap. 16.00 *(978-0-553-38652-3(2))* Random House Publishing Group.

Monif, Gilles. Bellevue Diary: Lights Within the Shadows. 2011. 132p. pap. 13.95 ***(978-1-4620-0845-2(3))*** iUniverse, Inc.

Ofri, Danielle. Medicine in Translation: Journeys with My Patients, 1 vol. 2010. (ENG.). 256p. 24.95 *(978-0-8070-7320-9(2))* Beacon Pr.

BELLIGERENCY

Benton, Elbert Jay. International Law & Diplomacy of the Spanish-American War. 2010. 154p. pap. *(978-1-152-01509-8(5))* 2009. 184p. pap. *(978-0-217-85216-6(5))* Books LLC.

—International Law & Diplomacy of the Spanish-American War. 2009. 182p. pap. 19.99 *(978-0-217-85213-5(0))* General Bks. LLC.

Henriksen, Thomas H. America & the Rogue States. 2012. (American Foreign Policy in the 21st Century Ser.). (ENG., Illus.). 240p. 95.00 ***(978-1-137-00639-4(0))***; pap. 28.00 ***(978-1-137-01999-8(9))*** Palgrave Macmillan.

BELLIGERENT OCCUPATION

see Military Occupation

BELLINGHAM (WASH.)

Great Pacific Map Co. Staff. Map Bellingham/Whatcom. 2006. 5.95 *(978-0-938011-45-3(6))* Great Pacific Recreation Maps & Guides.

Holsather, Kent & Gannaway, Wesley L. Bellingham Then & Now: A Compilation of Articles & Photographs Covering the Development of the City of Bellingham from the Arrival of the First European Settlers to the Emergence

of the Modern City in 1904. 2008. (Illus.). iii, 223p. *(978-0-9729101-4-9(X))* Lonejack Mountain Pr.
Hunsby, George. Birth, Death, & Resurrection of Fairhaven. 2009. pap. 16.95 *(978-0-9842389-2-7(1))* Chuckanut Editions.
McQuaide, Mike. Insiders' Guide to Bellingham & Mount Baker. 2006. (Insiders' Guide Ser.). (ENG., Illus.). 224p. per. 17.95 *(978-0-7627-3845-8(6))* Globe Pequot Pr., The.
Mongo. GalbraithMt. com's Ultimate Galbraith Mt. Guide: The Guide to mountain biking Galbraith Mt. in Bellingham, WA. 6th ed. 2006. cd-rom *(978-0-9790642-2-7(8))* BF Communications Inc.
Turner, Mark. Bellingham Impressions. 2007. pap. 9.95 *(978-1-56037-466-4(7))* Farcountry Pr.

BELLINI, GIOVANNI, D. 1516

Batschmann, Oskar & Bätschmann, Oskar. Giovanni Bellini. 2008. (ENG., Illus.). 324p. 55.00 *(978-1-86189-357-4(4))* Reaktion Bks., Ltd. GBR. Dist: Chicago Distribution Ctr.
Bayer, Andrea & Rodeschini, Maria Cristina. Bellini, Titian, & Lotto: North Italian Paintings from the Accademia Carrara, Bergamo. 2012. (ENG., Illus.). 80p. pap. 19.95 ***(978-0-300-17956-9(1))*** Yale Univ. Pr.
Davis, Julia. Giovanni Bellini. 2nd ed. 2008. (Illus.). 124p. pap. ***(978-1-86171-164-9(6))*** Crescent Moon Publishing.
Fry, Roger. Giovanni Bellini. (Illus.). 112p. 19.95 *(978-1-883145-03-3(1))* Ursus Pr.
Gleyzon, François-Xavier. Shakespeare's Spiral: Tracing the Snail in King Lear & Renaissance Painting. 2010. (ENG., Illus.). 300p. pap. 41.99 *(978-0-7618-4137-1(7))* Univ. Pr. of America, Inc.
Hubbard, Elbert. Little Journeys to the Homes of Eminent Artists. 2009. 40p. pap. 12.99 *(978-1-110-79401-0(0))* BiblioBazaar.
—Little Journeys to the Homes of Eminent Artists. 2009. 48p. pap. *(978-0-217-50806-3(5))* Books LLC.
Humfrey, Peter, ed. The Cambridge Companion to Giovanni Bellini. 2008. (Cambridge Companions to the History of Art Ser.). (ENG., Illus.). 384p. (C). pap. 40.00 *(978-0-521-72855-3(X))* Cambridge Univ. Pr.

BELLINI, VINCENZO, 1801-1835

Willier, Stephen A. Vincenzo Bellini: A Guide to Research. 2nd ed. 2009. (ENG., Illus.). 280p. 150.00 *(978-0-415-99524-5(8))* Routledge.

BELLMER, HANS, 1902-1975

Webb, Peter. Death, Desire & the Doll: The Life & Art of Hans Bellmer. 2008. (Solar Art Directives Ser.). (Illus.). 208p. per. 29.95 *(978-0-9714578-6-7(7))* Solar Bks.

BELLOC, HILAIRE, 1870-1953

Copper, B. Across Sussex with Belloc. (Illus.). x, 148p. 17.95 *(978-0-7509-1022-4(4))* Sutton Publishing.

BELLOTTO, BERNARDO, 1721-1780

Pomyan, Krysztof, et al. Bernardo Bellotto: A Venetian Painter in Warsaw. 2008. (ENG., Illus.). 136p. 35.00 *(978-88-7439-123-3(4))* 5 Continents ITA. Dist: Hachette Bk. Group.

BELLOW, SAUL, 1915-2005

Assadi, Jamal. Acting, Rhetoric, & Interpretation in Selected Novels by F. Scott Fitzgerald & Saul Bellow. 2006. (C). 66.95 *(978-0-8204-6329-2(9))* Lang, Peter Publishing, Inc.
Bakker, J. Fiction As Survival Strategy: A Comparative Study of the Major Works of Ernest Hemingway & Saul Bellow. 2009. 220p. pap. 39.00 *(978-90-6203-924-1(3))* Rodopi.
Bellow, Saul. El Diciembre del Decano.Tr. of Dean's December. (SPA.). 8.95 *(978-84-01-38010-5(3))* Plaza & Janes Editories, S.A. ESP. Dist: AIMS International Bks., Inc.
—Saul Bellow: Letters. Taylor, Benjamin F., ed. 2010. (ENG., Illus.). 608p. (gr. 12). 35.00 *(978-0-670-02221-2(7)*, Viking Adult) Penguin Group (USA) Inc.
—Saul Bellow: Letters. Taylor, Benjamin F., ed. 2012. (ENG., Illus.). 622p. (gr. 12). 20.00 ***(978-0-14-312046-9(8)***, Penguin (Non-Classics)) Penguin Group (USA) Inc.
Bellow, Saul. To Jerusalem & Back. 2010. (ENG.). 234p. pap. 19.95 *(978-1-4128-1184-2(8))* Transaction Pubs.
Bradbury, Malcolm. Saul Bellow (Routledge Revivals) (ENG.). 2010. 110p. pap. 39.95 *(978-0-415-56802-9(1))* 2009. IV, 110p. 90.00 *(978-0-415-56245-4(7))* Routledge.
Chavkin, Allan Richard. Saul Bellow. 2011. ***(978-1-58765-824-2(0))*** Salem Pr., Inc.
Halldorson, Stephanie S. & Halldorson, Stephanie. The Hero in Contemporary American Fiction: The Works of Saul Bellow & Don Delillo. 2007. (American Literature Readings in the Twenty-First Century Ser.). (ENG.). 240p. 95.00 *(978-1-4039-8388-6(7))* Palgrave Macmillan.
Kociatiewicz, Justyna. Towards the Antibildungsroman: Saul Bellow & the Problem of the Genre. 2008. XIV, 156p. pap. 46.95 *(978-3-631-57574-1(2))* Lang, Peter Publishing, Inc.
Teranishi, Masayuki. Polyphony in Fiction: A Stylistic Analysis of Middlemarch, Nostromo, & Herzog. 2008. 328p. pap. 76.95 *(978-3-03911-363-7(1))* Lang, Peter AG GBR. Dist: Lang, Peter.

BELLOWS, GEORGE, 1882-1925

Bellows, George. George Bellows. 2012. ***(978-0-89468-374-9(8))*** National Gallery of Art.
Cash, Sarah, et al. George Bellows. Brock, Charles, ed. 2012. (Illus.). 336p. 60.00 ***(978-3-7913-5187-2(7))*** Prestel Publishing.
Conway, Robert. The Powerful Hand of George Bellows: Drawings from the Boston Public Library. 2007. (Illus.). 159p. per. 35.00 *(978-1-882507-17-7(7))* Trust for Museum Exhibitions.
Fagg, John. On the Cusp: Stephen Crane, George Bellows, & Modernism. 2nd ed. 2009. (Amer Lit Realism & Naturalism Ser.). (ENG., Illus.). 280p. 49.95 *(978-0-8173-1651-6(5))* Univ. of Alabama Pr.

BELLS

see also Carillons; Handbell Ringing

Bearda, T., et al, eds. Campanae Lovanienses: Het klokkenpatrimonium van Groot-Leuven. 2006. (DUT.). 339p. (C). pap. 80.00 *(978-90-429-2185-6(4))* Peeters Pubs. & Booksellers BEL. Dist: Brown, David Bk. Co., The.
Chelle, Paula. The Wind Chime. 2011. 48p. pap. 9.95 ***(978-1-4620-0822-3(4))*** iUniverse, Inc.
Graham, Sherry. The Silent Bell: A handbell Fantasy. 2007. 231p. pap. 14.00 net. *(978-0-9796022-0-7(3))* Starke & Dormi Publications.
Jennings, Trevor S. Bell Founding. 2009. (Shire Library). (ENG., Illus.). 32p. pap. 11.95 *(978-0-85263-911-5(2))* Shire Pubns., Ltd. GBR. Dist: Random Hse., Inc.
Llewellyn, J. Bells & Bell Founding. 20.00 *(978-0-87556-208-7(6))* Saifer, Albert Pub.
McKay, Chris. Big Ben: The Great Clock & the Bells at the Palace of Westminster. 2010. (ENG., Illus.). 296p. 75.00 *(978-0-19-958569-4(5))* Oxford Univ. Pr., Inc.
Sloane, Eric & Hatch, Eric. A Celebration of Bells. 2009. (ENG., Illus.). 144p. pap. 9.95 *(978-0-486-46826-6(7))* Dover Pubns., Inc.
Trinidad, A. A., Jr. Glass Bells from Around the World. 2010. (Illus.). 160p. 29.99 *(978-0-7643-3488-7(3))* Schiffer Publishing, Ltd.
Tyack, George S. A Book about Bells. 344p. 2010. pap. 25.56 *(978-1-163-78833-2(3))* 2007. 46.95 *(978-0-548-54736-6(X))* 2007. (ENG.). per. 31.95 *(978-0-548-47452-5(4))* Kessinger Publishing, LLC.

BELLY DANCE

Ali, Shalimar. Learn to Belly Dance Textbook & Certification Program: Dance Lessons & Choreographies for Students, Troupes, Performers & Dance Instructors. 2011. 216p. pap. 19.99 ***(978-1-4653-4658-2(9))*** Xlibris Corp.
Boiocchi, Pamela. Dolci Evasioni. 2010. (ITA.). 76p. pap. 14.50 *(978-1-4457-7559-3(X))* Lulu Enterprises Inc.
Burns, Martha. Belly Dance: Celebrating the Sacred Feminine. 2008. *(978-0-9801771-7-6(0))* Alta Vista Bks.
Dallal, Tamalyn & Harris, Richard. Belly Dancing for Fitness: The Ultimate Dance Workout to Unleash Your Creative Spirit. 2007. (Illus.). 144p. reprint ed. pap. 20.00 *(978-1-4223-9008-5(X))* DIANE Publishing Co.
Hayes, Kendra. Stomping Ground. 2009. 133p. pap. 12.00 *(978-0-557-20143-3(8))* Lulu Enterprises Inc.
Morad, Daleela. Belly Dance Wisdom: For Fitness, Pregnancy & a Divine Sexuality. 2006. 156p. pap. 15.95 *(978-1-60145-091-3(5))* Booklocker.com, Inc.
Ramona. Dynamic Belly Dance: The Joyful Journey of Dancemaking & Performing. 2007. (Illus.). 157p. *(978-0-615-13326-3(6))* American Bellydance Innovations.
Taaj, Taaj. Belly Dance Beyond Moves, Combos, & Choreography 82 Lesson Plans, Games, & Exercises to Make Your Classes Fun, Productive & Profitable. 2010. 122p. pap. 31.95 *(978-0-557-42672-0(3))* Lulu Enterprises Inc.
Woods, Jenna. The Dancing Cymbalist: How to Play Music with Finger Cymbals & Dance at the Same Time. 2007. (Illus.). 185p. per. 33.95 *(978-0-9778193-0-0(2))* Oyna Music in Motion Arts.

BELOIT (WIS.)

Goodwin, Anne. Stay For Lunch: A Story of Faith & Friendship. 2009. 94p. 14.95 *(978-0-9816499-0-0(4))* Pleasurable Pause Pr.

BELOIT COLLEGE

Kozak, Katie & Maehl, Sarah. Beloit College 2012: Off the Record. 2011. 188p. pap. 16.95 ***(978-1-4274-0344-5(9))*** College Prowler, Inc.

BELOUTCHI LANGUAGE

see Baluchi Language

BELSEN (CONCENTRATION CAMP)

see Bergen-Belsen (Concentration Camp)

BELT CONVEYORS

see Conveying Machinery

BELT DRIVES

Perneder, Raimund & Osborne, Ian. Handbook Timing Belts: Principles, Calculations, Applications. 2012. (ENG., Illus.). xii, 269p. 129.00 *(978-3-642-17754-5(9)*, 3642177549) Springer.

BELTS (CLOTHING)

Leisure Arts, creator. Fresh Fashion Accents to Crochet. 2006. (ENG.). 24p. pap. 8.95 *(978-1-60140-315-5(1))* Leisure Arts, Inc.

BELY, ANDREY, 1880-1934

Elsworth, J. D. Audrey Bely: A Critical Study of the Novels. 2009. (Cambridge Studies in Russian Literature Ser.). (ENG.). 272p. pap. 38.99 *(978-0-521-12455-3(7))* Cambridge Univ. Pr.
Matich, Olga, ed. Petersburg/Petersburg: Novel & City, 1900-1921. 2010. (Illus.). 320p. pap. 34.95 *(978-0-299-23604-5(8))* Univ. of Wisconsin Pr.
Steinberg, Ada. Word & Music in the Novels of Andrey Bely. 2009. (Cambridge Studies in Russian Literature Ser.). (ENG.). 328p. pap. 46.00 *(978-0-521-11566-7(3))* Cambridge Univ. Pr.

BELZONI, GIOVANNI BATTISTA, 1778-1823

Hume, Ivor Noël. Belzoni: The Giant Archaeologists Love to Hate. 2011. (ENG., Illus.). 320p. 34.95 *(978-0-8139-3140-1(1))* Univ. Pr. of Virginia.

BEMBO, PIETRO, 1470-1547

Bembo, Pietro. Petro Bembo History of Venice, Volume 3. 2009. (I Tatti Renaissance Library: 37). (LAT & ENG., Illus.). 416p. 29.95 *(978-0-674-02286-7(6))* Harvard Univ. Pr.

BEMIS'S HEIGHTS, BATTLE OF, N.Y., 1777

see Saratoga Campaign, 1777

BEN-GURION, DAVID, 1886-1973

Feldestein, Ariel. Ben-Gurion, Zionism & American Jewry: 1948 - 1963. 2009. 216p. pap. 39.95 *(978-0-415-57679-6(2))* Routledge.
Feldestein, Ariel Lionard. Ben-Gurion, Zionism & American Jewry: 1948 - 1963. 2006. (Israeli History, Politics & Society Ser.). 240p. (C). 150.00 *(978-0-415-37240-4(2))* Routledge.
Heller, Joseph. The Israel Palestine Puzzle: I. the Ben-Gurion Magnes Debates: Jewish State or Binational State; II. Israel's Borders in Historical Perspective: the Security-Demography Dilemma. 2008. 98p. pap. 18.00 *(978-1-58790-155-3(2))* Regent Pr.
Peres, Shimon & Landau, David. Ben-Gurion: A Political Life. 2011. (ENG., Illus.). 240p. 25.95 *(978-0-8052-4282-9(1)*, Schocken) Knopf Doubleday Publishing Group.

BENARES (INDIA)

see Varanasi (India)

BENCHLEY, ROBERT, 1889-1945

Benchley, Robert. Benchley Lost & Found. 20.95 *(978-0-89190-498-4(0))* Amereon LTD.
—Benchley Roundup. 25.95 *(978-0-8488-0915-7(7))* Amereon LTD.
—The Robert Benchley Omnibus. 26.95 *(978-0-8488-0069-7(9))* Amereon LTD.

BENCHMARKING (MANAGEMENT)

Ammons, David N. Municipal Benchmarks: Assessing Local Performance & Establishing Community Standards. 3rd ed. 2012. (ENG.). 536p. 119.95 ***(978-0-7656-2660-8(8))*** Sharpe, M.E. Inc.
Amstutz, Karen, et al. 2011 Healthcare Benchmarks Yearbook: Metrics, Measurements & Innovations. Donovan, Patricia & Papay, Jessica, eds. 2011. (Illus.). 480p. spiral bd. 447.00 ***(978-1-936186-66-2(7))*** Healthcare Intelligence Network.
Andersen, B(c)rn. Business Process Improvement Toolbox. 2nd ed. 2007. 69.00 *(978-0-87389-719-8(6))* ASQ Quality Pr.
Anderson, Frank J., et al. Leading a Learning Revolution: The Story Behind Defense Acquisition University's Reinvention of Training. 2008. (J-B US Non-Franchise Leadership Ser.: 4). (ENG., Illus.). 320p. 45.00 *(978-0-7879-8308-6(X)*, Pfeiffer) Wiley, John & Sons, Inc.
AWWA Staff. Benchmarking: 2006 Annual Survey Data & Analysis Report: Performance Indicators for Water & Wastewater Utilities. 2007. (Illus.). 81p. per. 159.00 *(978-1-58321-506-7(9))* American Water Works Assn.
Axson, David A. J. Best Practices in Planning & Performance Management: Radically Rethinking Management for a Volatile World. 3rd ed. 2010. (ENG., Illus.). 320p. 65.00 *(978-0-470-53979-8(8)*, Wiley) Wiley, John & Sons, Inc.
Barnard, Cynthia. Benchmarking Basics: A Resource Guide for Healthcare Managers. 2006. (Illus.). 183p. spiral bd. incl. cd-rom *(978-1-57839-865-2(7))* Opus Communications.
Basiletti, Mari. The Power of Collaboration. 2008. 140p. pap. *(978-3-639-07998-2(1))* VDM Verlag Dr. Mueller e.K.
Blazey, Mark L. Insights to Performance Excellence 2009-2010: An Inside Look at the 2009-2010 Baldrige Award Criteria. 2009. 364p. pap. 84.00 *(978-0-87389-755-6(2))* ASQ Quality Pr.
Bouckaert, Geert & Halligan, John. Managing Performance: International Comparisons. 2008. (Illus.). 440p. 195.00 *(978-0-415-42394-6(5))*; pap. 52.95 *(978-0-415-42395-3(3))* Routledge.
Breyfogle, Forrest W., 3rd & Breyfogle, Forrest W., III. The Integrated Enterprise Excellence System: An Enhanced, Unified Approach to Balanced Scorecards, Strategic Planning, & Business Improvement. 2008. (Illus.). 189p. per. 16.95 *(978-1-934454-11-4(7))* Bridgeway Bks.
Calloway, Joe. Becoming a Category of One: How Extraordinary Companies Transcend Commodity & Defy Comparison. 2nd ed. 2009. (ENG.). 272p. pap. 19.95 *(978-0-470-49635-0(5)*, Wiley) Wiley, John & Sons, Inc.
Camp, Robert C. Benchmarking: The Search for Industry Best Practices That Lead to Superior Performance. 2006. (ENG., Illus.). 320p. per. 41.95 *(978-1-56327-352-0(7))* Productivity Pr.
Castonguay, Julie. Benchmarking Carrots & Sticks: Developing a Model for the Evaluation of Work-Based Employment Programs. 2009. (UvA Proefschriften Ser.). 394p. pap. *(978-90-5629-575-2(6)*, Vossiupers UvA) Amsterdam Univ. Pr.
Cesta, Toni. 2011 Benchmarks in Healthcare Case Management: Responsibilities, Results & ROI. Donovan, Patricia & Papay, Jessica, eds. 2011. (Illus.). 40p. spiral bd. 139.00 ***(978-1-936186-76-1(4))*** Healthcare Intelligence Network.
Davis, Susan E. Design Firm Performance Benchmarks 2007. 2006. 52p. pap. 329.00 *(978-1-58673-205-9(6))* Institute of Management & Administration, IOMA.
Dzamba, Andy, ed. AP Benchmarks Executive Summary 2007. 2006. (Illus.). 32p. pap. 179.60 *(978-1-58673-202-8(1))* Institute of Management & Administration, IOMA.
—AP Department Benchmarks & Analysis 2007. 2006. (Illus.). 201p. pap. 495.00 *(978-1-58673-194-6(7))* Institute of Management & Administration, IOMA.
Feltenberger, Gregory S. & Gans, David N. Benchmarking Success: The Essential Guide for Group Practices. 2008. (Illus.). 276p. pap. 99.00 *(978-1-56829-289-2(9))* Medical Group Management Assn. (MGMA).
Finarelli, Hugo J., Jr. The Hospital Executive's Guide to Physician Staffing. 2009. (Illus.). 178p. pap. 129.00 *(978-1-60146-288-6(3))* Opus Communications.
Ford, Donis W., ed. Payroll Benchmarks & Analysis Report 2007. 2007. (Illus.). 193p. pap. 329.00 *(978-1-58673-206-6(4))* Institute of Management & Administration, IOMA.
Foundation for Ambulatory Surgery in America. 2007 ASC Financial Benchmarking Survey. 2007. spiral bd. 495.00 *(978-0-9719088-4-0(2))* ASC Assn.
Goonan, Kathleen Jennison. Journey to Excellence: Baldrige Health Care Leaders Speak Out. 2009. 56.00 *(978-0-87389-735-8(8))* ASQ Quality Pr.
Grobbel, Merle. Implementing Climate Change Measures in the EU: Key Success Factors. 2008. (Illus.). 430p. pap. 69.95 ***(978-3-531-16251-5(9)***, 3531162519) VS Verlag fur Sozialwissenschaften GmbH DEU. Dist: Springer.
Harris, Tim, ed. Improving the Budgeting Process: Benchmarks & Best Practices 2008. 2007. (Illus.). 81p. pap. 299.00 *(978-1-58673-240-0(4))* Institute of Management & Administration, IOMA.
Hatry, Harry P. Performance Measurement, Second Edition: Getting Results. 2nd ed. 2007. (Illus.). 342p. pap. 34.50 *(978-0-87766-734-6(9))* Urban Institute Pr.
Horner, Chris, ed. Credit & Collections Benchmarks & Analysis 2008. 2007. (Illus.). 135p. pap. 395.00 *(978-1-58673-244-8(7))* Institute of Management & Administration, IOMA.
Hubbell, Gary. Lessons from Benchmarking: Fast-Forwarding the Maturity of the Fundraising Operation. 2007. per. 0.01 net. *(978-1-60402-201-8(9))* Independent Pub.
Huwe, Ruth. Metrics 2. 0: Creating Scorecards for High-Performance Work Teams & Organizations, 1 vol. 2010. (Illus.). 349p. 44.95 *(978-0-313-38456-1(8)*, A2921C, Praeger Pubs.) Greenwood Publishing Group, Inc.
Jack, Lisa. Sustainable Change Through Benchmarking in Food & Farming. 2009. (Gower Sustainable Food Chains Ser.). (Illus.). 148p. 114.95 *(978-0-566-08835-3(5)*, Gower Publishing Co., Ltd.) Ashgate Publishing, Ltd. GBR. Dist: Ashgate Publishing Co.
Keehley, Patricia & Abercrombie, Neil. Benchmarking in the Public & Nonprofit Sectors: Best Practices for Achieving Performance Breakthroughs. 2nd ed. 2008. (ENG., Illus.). 256p. 55.00 *(978-0-7879-9831-8(1)*, Jossey-Bass) Wiley, John & Sons, Inc.
Leebov, Wendy, et al. Service Savvy Health Care: One Goal at a Time. 2007. (ENG.). 296p. per. 21.95 *(978-0-595-45697-0(9)*, Authors Choice Pr.) iUniverse, Inc.
Lin, Della M. Surgical Care Improvement Project: Improve Performance, Reduce Complications, & Comply with CMS. 2007. (Illus.). 138p. pap. 129.00 incl. cd-rom *(978-1-60146-030-1(9))* Opus Communications.
Mantri, Jibendu Kumar. Research Methodology on Data Envelopment Analysis (DEA) 2008. 380p. pap. 29.95 *(978-1-59942-950-2(0))* Universal Pubs.
McGill, Ross. Investment Withholding Tax: Best Practice & Strategies for Intermediaries & Investors. 2009. (ENG., Illus.). 320p. 236.00 *(978-0-230-22162-8(9))* Palgrave Macmillan.
Md Deros, Baba & Deros, Baba. Practical Benchmarking Implementation in Small & Medium Enterprises. 2010. 296p. pap. *(978-3-8383-1188-3(4))* Lambert Academic Publishing.
Merrill, Peter. Do It Right the Second Time: Benchmarking Best Practices in the Quality Change Process. 2nd ed. 2009. 44.00 *(978-0-87389-733-4(1))* ASQ Quality Pr.
Mohapatra, Sanjay. Benchmarking Productivity in It Projects. 2010. 348p. pap. *(978-3-639-25971-1(8))* VDM Verlag Dr. Mueller e.K.
Morrow, Rebecca, et al, eds. 2007 Guide to HR Benchmarks. 2006. (Illus.). 132p. pap. 329.00 *(978-1-58673-197-7(1))* Institute of Management & Administration, IOMA.
—2008 Guide to HR Benchmarks. 2008. (Illus.). 202p. pap. 459.00 *(978-1-58673-279-0(X))* Institute of Management & Administration, IOMA.
Mugisha, Silver. Utility Benchmarking & Regulation in Developing Countries: Practical Application of Performance Monitoring & Incentives. 2011. (Illus.). 200p. (C). pap. *(978-1-84339-257-6(7))* IWA Publishing.
Nambiar, Raghunath & Poess, Meikel. Performance Evaluation & Benchmarking: Transaction Processing Performance Council Technology Conference, TPCTC 2009, Lyon, France, August 24-28, 2009, Revised Selected Papers. 2009. (Lecture Notes in Computer Science / Programming & Software Engineering Ser.). xii, 267p. pap. 72.00 *(978-3-642-10423-7(1)*, 3642104231) Springer.
Nambiar, Raghunath & Poess, Meikel, eds. Performance Evaluation & Benchmarking: Second TPC Technology Conference, TPCTC 2010, Singapore, September 13-17, 2010. Revised Selected Papers. 2011. (Lecture Notes in Computer Science / Programming & Software Engineering Ser.). xvi, 233p. pap. 72.00 *(978-3-642-18205-1(4)*, 3642182054) Springer.
Niven, Paul R. Balanced Scorecard: Step-by-Step for Government & Nonprofit Agencies. 2nd ed. 2008. (ENG., Illus.). 384p. 57.95 *(978-0-470-18002-0(1)*, Wiley) Wiley, John & Sons, Inc.
Okonga Wabuyabo M., Brigitte. Benchmarking in the Kenyan & South African Electricity Sectors. 2011. 84p. pap. ***(978-3-8433-9219-8(6))*** Lambert Academic Publishing.
Ordys, Andrzej, et al, eds. Process Control Performance Assessment: From Theory to Implementation. (Advances in Industrial Control Ser.). (Illus.). xxii, 325p. 2010. pap. 199.00 *(978-1-84996-630-6(3)*, 1849966303) 2007. (C). 199.00 *(978-1-84628-623-0(9)*, 1846286239) Springer.

B

Ozcan, Yasar A. Health Care Benchmarking & Performance Evaluation: An Assessment using Data Envelopment Analysis (DEA) 2007. (International Series in Operations Research & Management Science Ser.). (Illus.). 248p. 149.00 *(978-0-387-75447-5(4))* Springer.

Paladino, Bob. Innovative Corporate Performance Management: Five Key Principles to Accelerate Results. 2010. (ENG., Illus.). 432p. 49.95 *(978-0-470-62773-0(5),* Wiley) Wiley, John & Sons, Inc.

Prybil, Lawrence. Governance in High-Performing Community Health Systems: A Report on Trustee & CEO Views. 2009. 58p. pap. 10.00 *(978-0-9815532-1-4(4))* Thornton, Grant LLP.

Scalzo, Bert, et al. Database Benchmarking: Practical Methods for Oracle & SQL Server. 2007. (IT In-Focus Ser.). (ENG., Illus.). 200p. pap. 39.95 *(978-0-9776715-3-3(4))* Rampant TechPress.

Seivold, Garett, ed. Security Compensation, Operations & Performance Benchmarks 2007. 2006. 204p. pap. 379.00 *(978-1-58673-207-3(2))* Institute of Management & Administration, IOMA.

Smith, Ralph F. Business Process Management & the Balanced Scorecard: Using Processes as Strategic Drivers. 2006. (ENG., Illus.). 240p. 63.50 *(978-0-470-04746-0(1),* Wiley) Wiley, John & Sons, Inc.

Sower, Victor E., et al. Benchmarking for Hospitals: Achieving Best-In-Class Performance Without Having to Reinvent the Wheel. 2007. pap. 58.00 *(978-0-87389-722-8(6))* ASQ Quality Pr.

Stapenhurst, Tim. The Benchmarking Book: A How-To Guide to Best Practice for Managers & Practitioners. 2009. (ENG., Illus.). 496p. pap. 56.95 *(978-0-7506-8905-2(6))* Routledge.

Strang, David. Learning by Example: Imitation & Innovation at a Global Bank. 2010. (ENG., Illus.). 304p. (C). 35.00 *(978-0-691-14218-0(1))* Princeton Univ. Pr.

Sutan, Wiraputra & Cheng, Min-Yuan. Benchmarking Based Process Re-Engineering for Construction Management. 2008. 124p. pap. *(978-3-639-00451-9(5))* VDM Verlag Dr. Mueller e.K.

Tannous, W. Kathy. Development & Application of Occupational Health & Safety Benchmarking Tool. 2008. 220p. pap. *(978-3-639-04987-9(X))* VDM Verlag Dr. Mueller e.K.

ten Raa, Thijs, et al. The Economics of Benchmarking: Measuring Performance for Competitive Advantage. 2008. (ENG., Illus.). 128p. pap. 43.00 *(978-0-230-22438-4(5))* Palgrave Macmillan.

Vieira, Marco. Dependability Benchmarking for Oltp Systems. 2010. 188p. pap. *(978-3-8383-0702-2(X))* Lambert Academic Publishing.

Watson, Gregory H. Strategic Benchmarking Reloaded with Six Sigma: Improving Your Company's Performance Using Global Best Practice. 2nd rev. ed. 2007. (ENG., Illus.). 360p. 45.00 *(978-0-470-06908-0(2),* Wiley) Wiley, John & Sons, Inc.

Wilson, et al. Benchmarking to Improve Coding Accuracy & Productivity. 2009. (Illus.). xvi, 136p. pap. *(978-1-58426-190-2(0),* Branch Line Video) American Health Information Management Assn.

Zhu, Joe. Quantitative Models for Performance Evaluation & Benchmarking. 2nd ed. 2008. (International Series in Operations Research & Management Science Ser.). (Illus.). xiv, 334p. 159.00 *(978-0-387-85981-1(0))* Springer.

Ziek, Peter J. & Schrecengost, Fred. Benchmarking Customer Satisfaction in the Help Desk Industry: A Help Desk Institute White Paper. Baltema, Patrick et al, eds. (Illus.). (Orig.). (C). pap. *(978-1-57125-001-8(8))* HDI.

Zuckerman, Alan M. Raising the Bar: Best Practices for Healthcare Strategic Planning. 2007. per. 50.00 *(978-0-9755973-7-8(X))* Society for Healthcare Strategy & Market Development.

100 Top Hospitals National Benchmarks for Success-2006 Study. 14th ed. 2007. per. 150.00 *(978-1-57372-360-2(6))* Solucient LLC.

BENDERLY, SAMSON, 1876-1944

Krasner, Jonathan B. The Benderly Boys & American Jewish Education. 2011. (Brandeis Series in American Jewish History, Culture & Life Ser.). (Illus.). 512p. (C). 95.00 *(978-1-58465-966-2(1));* (ENG., pap. 39.95 *(978-1-58465-983-9(1))* Univ. Pr. of New England. (Brandeis University Press).

BENDS (MEDICINE)

see Decompression Sickness

BENEDICT, SAINT, ABBOT OF MONTE CASSINO

Benedict XVI, pseud. Christ Our Hope: The Papal Addresses of the Apostolic Journey to the United States. 2008. (Illus.). 160p. 14.95 *(978-0-8091-0561-8(6),* 0561-6) Paulist Pr.

Benson, Robert. A Good Neighbor: Benedict's Guide to Community. 2009. (ENG.). 96p. (gr. 13). pap. 14.99 *(978-1-55725-582-2(2))* Paraclete Pr., Inc.

Böckmann, Aquinata & Burkhard, Marianne. Around the Monastic Table — RB 31-42: Growing in Mutual Service & Love. 2009. pap. 29.95 *(978-0-8146-1874-5(X))* Liturgical Pr.

Butler, Cuthbert. Benedictine Monachism: Studies in Benedictine Life & Rule. 2007. (ENG.). 394p. 49.95 *(978-0-548-17585-9(3))* Kessinger Publishing, LLC.

—Benedictine Monachism: Studies in Benedictine Life & Rule. 2007. pap. 34.95 *(978-1-4304-7514-9(5))* Kessinger Publishing, LLC.

Casey, Michael. Road to Eternal Life. 2011. 214p. pap. 19.95 ***(978-0-8146-3384-7(6))*** Liturgical Pr.

—The Road to Eternal Life: Reflections on the Prologue of Benedict's Rule. 2011. E-Book ***(978-0-8146-3954-2(2))*** Liturgical Pr.

Chittister, Joan. The Radical Christian Life: A Year with Saint Benedict. 2011. E-Book ***(978-0-8146-3955-9(0))***; 160p. pap. 15.95 ***(978-0-8146-3365-6(X))*** Liturgical Pr.

Chittister, Joan. The Rule of Benedict: A Spirituality for the 21st Century. 2010. (Spiritual Legacy Ser.). (ENG.). 192p. pap. 16.95 *(978-0-8245-2594-1(9))* Crossroad Publishing Co., The.

Coon, Lynda L. Dark Age Bodies: Gender & Monastic Practice in the Early Medieval West. 2010. (Middle Ages Ser.). (Illus.). 416p. (C). 65.00 *(978-0-8122-4269-0(6))* Univ. of Pennsylvania Pr.

de Vogüé, Adalbert. Saint Benedict: The Man & His Work. Malsbary, Gerald, tr. from FRE. 2006. (ENG.). 88p. pap. 18.00 *(978-1-879007-48-2(7))* Fordham Univ. Pr.

de Waal, Esther. Buscando A Dios: Tras las Huellas de San Benito. 2007. (Coleccion Nueva Alianza Ser.). 173p. pap. 24.00 *(978-84-301-1591-4(9))* Sigueme, Ediciones, S.A. ESP. Dist: Augsburg Fortress, Pubs.

—Seeking Life: Benedictine Wisdom for the Baptized. 2009. 160p. 19.95 *(978-0-8146-1880-6(4),* Liturgical Pr. Bks.) Liturgical Pr.

Delisi. What Makes a Cistercian Monk Chapter Talks on the Charisms of the Cistercian Order of the Strict Ob. 2010. pap. *(978-0-87907-022-9(6))* Cistercian Pubns., Inc.

Derkse, Wil. A Blessed Life: Benedictine Guidelines for Those Who Long for Good Days. 2009. 112p. 11.95 *(978-0-8146-1863-9(4))* Liturgical Pr.

Freeman, Laurence & Bishop, James. A Way in the Wilderness: A Commentary on the Rule of Benedict for the Physically & Spiritually Imprisoned. 2012. (ENG.). 248p. pap. 19.95 ***(978-1-4411-5115-5(X))*** Continuum International Publishing Group, Ltd. GBR. Dist: National Bk. Network.

Gobema, Regina. The Rule of Saint Benedict for Everyone. 2010. pap. *(978-1-56548-351-4(0))* New City Community Pr.

Gozier, André. 15 Days of Prayer with Saint Benedict. 2008. (15 Days of Prayer Ser.). 144p. pap. 12.95 *(978-1-56548-304-0(9))* New City Pr.

Gregory & Gardner, Edmund Garratt. The Dialogues of Saint Gregory the Great: Re-Edited with an Introduction & Notes. 2010. *(978-1-889758-94-7(9),* Evolution Publishing & Manufacturing) Arx Publishing.

Hay, Leslie A. Hospitality: The Heart of Spiritual Direction. 2006. (Spiritual Directors International Ser.). 128p. per. 19.00 *(978-0-8192-2181-0(3),* Morehouse Publishing) Church Publishing, Inc.

Holtz, Albert. Pilgrim Road: A Benedictine Journey Through Lent. 2006. (Illus.). 192p. per. 16.00 *(978-0-8192-2251-0(8),* Morehouse Publishing) Church Publishing, Inc.

Kardong, Terrence. Conversation with Saint Benedict: The Rule in Today's World. 2012. ***(978-0-8146-3419-6(2))*** Liturgical Pr.

Kardong, Terrence G. The Life of Saint Benedict by Gregory the Great: Translation & Commentary. 2009. 176p. pap. 16.95 *(978-0-8146-3262-8(9),* Liturgical Pr. Bks.) Liturgical Pr.

Masser, Achim. Lateinische und Althochdeutsche Glossierungen der Regula Benedicti im 8 und 9 Jahrhundert. 2008. 260p. pap. *(978-3-902571-86-1(1))* Books on Demand GmbH.

Newman, John Henry. Historical Sketches - The Church of the Fathers - St. Chrysostom - Theodoret - Mission of St. Benedict - Benedictine Schools. 2007. 500p. per. *(978-1-4086-0366-6(7))* Read Bks.

—Historical Sketches: The Church of the Fathers; St. Chrysostom; Theodoret; Mission of St. Benedict; Benedictine Schools (1873) 2008. 528p. 55.95 *(978-0-548-99791-8(8))* 2007. (ENG.). 532p. per. 40.95 *(978-0-548-64880-3(8))* Kessinger Publishing, LLC.

—Historical Sketches V2: The Church of the Fathers; St. Chrysostom; Theodoret; Mission of St. Benedict; Benedictine Schools (1912) 2008. 532p. 55.95 *(978-1-4365-4692-8(3))* 2007. 536p. per. 40.95 *(978-0-548-73880-1(7))* Kessinger Publishing, LLC.

O'Connell, Patrick F., ed. The Rule of Saint Benedict: Initiation into the Monastic Tradition 4. 2009. 310p. pap. 24.95 *(978-0-87907-019-9(6),* Cistercian Publications Bks.) Liturgical Pr.

Odo & Wickstrom, John B. The Life & Miracles of Saint Maurus: Disciple of Benedict, Apostle to France. 2008. (Illus.). 156p. pap. *(978-0-87907-323-7(3))* Cistercian Pubns., Inc.

Pennington, M. Basil. Listen with Your Heart: Spiritual Living with the Rule of Saint Benedict. 2007. (Voice from the Monastery Ser.). (ENG.). 207p. (gr. 13). per. 15.95 *(978-1-55725-548-8(2))* Paraclete Pr., Inc.

Saint Gregory the Great. The Life & Miracles of St Benedict. 2007. 116p. 24.95 *(978-1-60206-581-9(0));* per. 9.95 *(978-1-60206-580-2(2))* Cosimo, Inc.

Scheiba, Manuela. Gehorsam gegenüber dem Abt: Ein Beitrag zur Auslegungsgeschichte der Benediktus-Regel im 20. Jahrhundert. Regula Benedicti Studia, Traditio et Receptio 22. 2009. lxiv, 525p. *(978-3-8306-7336-1(1))* Eos Verlag.

Scott, Mark Alan. At Home with Saint Benedict: Monastery Talks. 2011. pap. 39.95 *(978-0-87907-027-4(7))* Cistercian Pubns., Inc.

Sorg, Rembert. Holy Work: Towards A Benedictine Theology of Manual Labor. 2011. 122p. 39.95 ***(978-1-258-02812-1(3))*** Literary Licensing, LLC.

—Towards a Benedictine Theology of Manual Labor. 2011. 126p. 40.95 ***(978-1-258-05845-6(6))*** Literary Licensing, LLC.

St Benedict on the Freeway [Palm Reader]. 10.00 *(978-0-687-02153-6(7))* Abingdon Pr.

Stock, Jon R., et al. Inhabiting the Church: Biblical Wisdom for a New Monasticism. 2006. (New Monastic Library: Resources for Radical Discipleship: Ser.). 140p. pap. 18.00 *(978-1-59752-990-7(7),* Cascade Bks.) Wipf & Stock Pubs.

Talbot, John Michael. Blessings of St Benedict. 2011. 112p. pap. 15.95 ***(978-0-8146-3385-4(4))*** Liturgical Pr.

—Blessings of St. Benedict. 2011. E-Book ***(978-0-8146-3386-1(2))*** Liturgical Pr.

Valters Paintner, Christine. The Artist's Rule: Nurturing Your Creative Soul with Monastic Wisdom. 2011. 192p. pap. 14.95 *(978-1-933495-29-3(4),* Sorin Bks.) Ave Maria Pr.

BENEDICT XVI, POPE, 1927-

Allen, John L., Jr. The Rise of Benedict XVI: The Inside Story of How the Pope Was Elected & Where He Will Take the Catholic Church. 2006. (ENG.). 272p. pap. 12.95 *(978-0-385-51321-0(6),* Image) Doubleday Religious Publishing Group, The.

—10 Things Pope Benedict XVI Wants You to Know. 2007. 45p. per. 2.95 *(978-0-7648-1672-7(1))* Liguori Pubns.

Anonymous. Against Ratzinger. Shugaar, Antony, tr. from ITA. 2008. (ENG.). 176p. pap. 14.95 *(978-1-58322-766-4(0))* Seven Stories Pr.

Aquilina, Mike. Companion Guide to Pope Benedict's The Fathers. 2008. 95p. pap. *(978-1-59276-542-3(4))* Our Sunday Visitor, Publishing Div.

Aquilina, Mike & Stubna, Kris D. Take Five: Meditations with Pope Benedict XVI. 2009. 176p. pap. 9.95 *(978-1-59276-554-6(8))* Our Sunday Visitor, Publishing Div.

Beller, Susan Provost. Pope John Paul II & Pope Benedict XVI: Keepers of the Faith. 2006. (Great Life Stories Ser.). (ENG., Illus.). 112p. (J). (gr. 6-8). lib. bdg. 30.50 *(978-0-531-13908-0(5))* Scholastic Library Publishing.

Benedict. Pope Benedict in America: The Full Texts of Papal Talks Given During His Apostolic Visit to the United States. 2008. 130p. 14.95 *(978-1-58617-293-0(X))* Ignatius Pr.

Benedict XVI, pseud. Benedict XVI: Spiritual Thoughts: In the First Year of His Papacy. 2007. 128p. pap. 9.95 *(978-1-57455-765-7(3))* United States Conference of Catholic Bishops.

—Coming Together in Joy: 99 Sayings by Benedict XVI. Liesenfeld, Stephen, ed. 2008. 99p. pap. 9.95 *(978-1-56548-274-6(3))* New City Pr.

—Following Christ. 2009. (Spiritual Thoughts Ser.). 132p. pap. 6.95 *(978-1-60137-056-3(3))* United States Conference of Catholic Bishops.

—Mary. 2008. (Spiritual Thoughts Ser.). 163p. pap. 9.95 *(978-1-60137-054-9(7))* United States Conference of Catholic Bishops.

—Papa Benedicto XVI: Caridad en la Verdad. Estenger, Vilma G., tr. 2009. (SPA.). 1p. 14.95 *(978-1-59276-458-7(4))* Our Sunday Visitor, Publishing Div.

—Pope Benedict XVI: Charity in Truth. 2009. 1p. 14.95 *(978-1-59276-457-0(6))* Our Sunday Visitor, Publishing Div.

—Pope Benedict XVI in the Holy Land. 2011. 176p. pap. *(978-0-8091-4672-7(X))* Paulist Pr.

—Study Guide for the Fathers. 2008. 60p. pap. 4.95 *(978-1-59276-448-8(7))* Our Sunday Visitor, Publishing Div.

Blanco Sarto, Pablo. Benedicto XVI: El Papa Alemán. 2010. (Planeta Testimonio Ser.). (SPA.). 606p. *(978-84-08-09619-1(2))* Planeta.

Brandmuller, Walter. Light & Shadows: Defending Church History amid Faith, Facts & Legends. 2009. 160p. pap. 16.95 *(978-1-58617-273-2(5))* Ignatius Pr.

Cameron, Peter John, ed. Benedictus: Day by Day with Pope Benedict XVI. 2006. (Illus.). 415p. 19.95 *(978-0-9676186-5-4(7))* Magnificat USA LLC.

Coco, Lucio. Preparing for Christmas with Pope Benedict Xvi. 2009. 0064p. pap. 2.50 *(978-1-59471-233-3(6))* Ave Maria Pr.

Collins, Michael. Pope Benedict XVI: The First Five Years. 2011. (ENG.). 236p. pap. 21.95 *(978-1-85607-707-1(1))* Columba Pr. IRL. Dist: Dufour Editions, Inc.

Collins Publishers Staff. God's New Man. 2006. 256p. *(978-0-8264-8274-7(0))* Continuum International Publishing Group, Ltd.

de Gaál, Emery. The Theology of Pope Benedict XVI: The Christocentric Shift. 2010. (ENG.). 386p. 100.00 *(978-0-230-10540-9(8))* Palgrave Macmillan.

Fox, Matthew. The Pope's War: Why Ratzinger's Secret Crusade Has Imperiled the Church & How It Can Be Saved. 2011. (ENG.). 304p. 22.95 *(978-1-4027-8629-7(8))* Sterling Publishing Co., Inc.

Gibson, David. The Rule of Benedict: Pope Benedict XVI & His Battle with the Modern World. 2007. (ENG.). 416p. pap. 14.95 *(978-0-06-116122-3(5),* HarperOne) HarperCollins Pubs.

Gregg, Samuel. Modern Papacy, 12 vols. Meadowcroft, John, ed. 2009. (Major Conservative & Libertarian Thinkers Ser.). (ENG.). 176p. 130.00 *(978-0-8264-3011-3(2))* Continuum International Publishing Group, Ltd. GBR. Dist: National Bk. Network.

Gribbin, Anselm J. Pope Benedict Xvi & the Liturgy. 2011. 252p. pap. ***(978-0-85244-755-0(8))*** Gracewing, Ltd.

Hahn, Scott W. Covenant & Communion: The Biblical Theology of Pope Benedict XVI. 2009. 160p. (C). 14.99 *(978-1-58743-269-9(2))* Brazos Pr.

Heim, Maximilian Heinrich. Joseph Ratzinger: Life in the Church & Living Theology: Fundamentals of Ecclesiology. Miller, Michael J., tr. from GER. 2007. 614p. 29.95 *(978-1-58617-149-0(6))* Ignatius Pr.

Ignatius Press Staff. Christ Our Hope: Pope Benedict XVI's Apostolic Visit to the United States. 2008. 145p. 21.95 *(978-1-58617-290-9(5))* Ignatius Pr.

Israely, Jeff & Giansanti, Gianni. Benedict XVI. 2006. (ENG., Illus.). 176p. 35.00 *(978-88-544-0162-4(5),* White Star) Rizzoli International Pubns., Inc.

Jankunas, Gediminas T. The Dictatorship of Relativism: Pope Benedict XVI's Response. 2011. *(978-0-8189-1316-7(9),* St. Pauls) St Pauls/Alba Hse. Pubs.

Koenig-Bricker, Woodeene, compiled by. A Study Guide to Living Charity in Truth: Pope Benedict's Encyclical on Social & Economic Justice. 2009. 64p. pap. 9.95 *(978-1-59276-578-2(5))* Our Sunday Visitor, Publishing Div.

Lam, Joseph & Lam Cong, Joseph Quy. Theologische Verwandtschaft: Augustinus Von Hippo und Joseph Ratzinger/Papst Benedikt XVI. 2009. (GER.). 268p. *(978-3-429-03077-3(3))* Echter Wuerzburg.

Liesenfeld, Stephen, ed. Coming Together in Joy: 99 Sayings by Benedict XVI. 2007. (99 Words to Live by Ser.). 99p. 14.95 *(978-1-56548-273-9(5))* New City Pr.

Ludemann, Gerd. Eyes That See Not: The Pope Looks at Jesus. 2008. 131p. per. 20.00 net. *(978-1-59815-006-3(5))* Polebridge Pr.

Maessen, Thorsten. Das Ökumeneverständnis Joseph Ratzingers. 2011. (Kirche, Konfession, Religion Ser.). (GER.). 407p. (C). 74.00 *(978-3-89971-798-3(8))* Vandenhoeck & Ruprecht GmbH & Co. KG DEU. Dist: ISD.

Marcelin-Rice, Kate, contrib. by. An Invitation to Faith: An A to Z Primer on the Thought of Pope Benedict XVI. 2007. 104p. 14.95 *(978-1-58617-213-8(1))* Ignatius Pr.

McKenna, Joanne. Letters to Priests: An Inspirational Journey of Faith. 2010. pap. 15.99 *(978-1-61663-875-7(3))* Tate Publishing & Enterprises, LLC.

McNeil, Brian, tr. from GER. Pope Benedict XVI: Servant of the Truth. 2006. (Illus.). 189p. 26.95 *(978-1-58617-151-3(8))* Ignatius Pr.

Melé, Domènec & Dierksmeier, Claus, eds. Reciprocity & the Logic of Gift: Business Challenges of the Encyclical Letter. 2012. (Humanism in Business Ser.). (ENG., Illus.). 280p. 95.00 ***(978-0-230-29682-4(3))*** Palgrave Macmillan.

Mills, Clifford W. Pope Benedict XVI. 2006. (Modern World Leaders Ser.). (Illus.). 104p. (YA). (gr. 7-12). lib. bdg. 30.00 *(978-0-7910-9228-6(3))* Facts On File, Inc.

Murphy, Joseph. Christ Our Joy: The Theological Vision of Pope Benedict XVI. 2008. 216p. 19.95 *(978-1-58617-182-7(8))* Ignatius Pr.

Nichols, Aidan & Ratzinger, Joseph. The Thought of Pope Benedict XVI: An Introduction to the Theology of Joseph Ratzinger. 2nd ed. 2007. (ENG.). 304p. 29.95 *(978-0-86012-421-4(5),* Burns & Oates) Continuum International Publishing Group, Ltd. GBR. Dist: National Bk. Network.

Pabst, Adrian. The Crisis of Global Capitalism: Pope Benedict XVIS Social Encyclical & the Future of Politic. 2012. (ENG.). 304p. (C). pap. 45.00 ***(978-0-227-68016-2(2))*** Clarke, James Co., Ltd. GBR. Dist: Brown, David Bk. Co., The.

Paddison, Angus & Pabst, Adrian. The Pope & Jesus of Nazareth: Christ, Scripture & the Church. Candler, Peter M. & Cunningham, Conor, eds. 2010. (Veritas Ser.). (ENG.). 288p. pap. 90.00 *(978-0-334-04321-8(2),* SCM Pr.) Hymns Ancient & Modern Ltd GBR. Dist: Westminster John Knox Pr.

Pursell, Brennan. Benedict of Bavaria: An Intimate Portrait of the Pope & His Homeland. 2008. (Illus.). 224p. 24.95 *(978-1-933271-17-0(5))* Circle Pr.

Quattrocchi, Angelo. Gay Popes & Homophobia. Clark, Romy Giuliani, tr. from ITA. 2010. (ENG., Illus.). 160p. pap. 16.95 *(978-1-84467-474-9(6),* 844474) Verso Bks. GBR. Dist: Norton, W. W. & Co., Inc.

Ratzinger, Joseph. Credo for Today: What Christians Believe. 2009. 225p. 19.95 *(978-1-58617-247-3(6))* Ignatius Pr.

Rausch, Thomas P. Pope Benedict XVI: An Introduction to His Theological Vision. 2009. viii, 195p. 22.95 *(978-0-8091-0556-4(X))* Paulist Pr.

Robertson, Geoffrey. The Case of the Pope: Vatican Accountability for Human Rights Abuse. 2010. (ENG., Illus.). 240p. pap. 9.99 *(978-0-241-95384-6(7),* Penguin Global) Penguin Group (USA) Inc.

Rose, Michael. Benedict XVI: The Man Who Was Ratzinger. 2008. (ENG.). 192p. 22.95 *(978-1-890626-63-1(5))* Spence Publishing Co.

Rourke, Thomas. The Social & Political Thought of Benedict XVI. 2010. (ENG.). 158p. 57.99 *(978-0-7391-4280-6(1))* Lexington Bks.

Rourke, Thomas R. The Social & Political Thought of Benedict XVI. 2011. (ENG.). 160p. pap. 24.95 *(978-0-7391-4281-3(X))* Lexington Bks.

Rowland, Tracey. Benedict XVI. 2010. (Guides for the Perplexed Ser.). (ENG.). 216p. 24.95 *(978-0-567-03437-3(2));* 80.00 *(978-0-567-03436-6(4))* Continuum International Publishing Group, Ltd. GBR. (T&T Clark Int'l). Dist: National Bk. Network.

Rowland, Tracey & Pell, George. Ratzinger's Faith: The Theology of Pope Benedict XVI. 2009. (ENG.). 232p. pap. 17.95 *(978-0-19-957034-8(5))* Oxford Univ. Pr., Inc.

Roy, Neil & Rutherford, Janet, eds. Benedict XVI & the Sacred Liturgy. 2010. 210p. 45.00 *(978-1-84682-254-4(8))* Four Courts Pr. IRL. Dist: International Specialized Bk. Services.

Rusch, William G., ed. The Pontificate of Benedict XVI: Its Premises & Promises. 2009. 192p. pap. 24.00 *(978-0-8028-4868-0(0))* Eerdmans, William B. Publishing Co.

Schall, James V. The Regensburg Lecture. 2007. 180p. 20.00 *(978-1-58731-695-1(1))* St. Augustine's Pr., Inc.

Seewald, Peter. Benedict XVI: An Intimate Portrait. 2008. 300p. 24.95 *(978-1-58617-190-2(9))* Ignatius Pr.

Shortt, Rupert. Benedict XVI: Commander of the Faith. 2006. (ENG., Illus.). 176p. per. 13.95 *(978-0-340-90905-8(6))* Hodder General Publishing Div. GBR. Dist: Independent Pubs. Group.

Thornton, John F. & Varenne, Susan B. Pope Benedict XVI: His Central Writings & Speeches. 2008. (ENG.). 512p. pap. 15.95 *(978-0-06-112884-4(8),* HarperOne) HarperCollins Pubs.

Twomey, D. Vincent. Pope Benedict XVI: The Conscience of Our Age: A Theological Portrait. 2007. 202p. 19.95 *(978-1-58617-170-4(4))* Ignatius Pr.

Twomey, Vincent. Benedict XVI & Beauty in Sacred Art & Architecture. Rutherford, Janet, ed. 2011. (Illus.). 224p. ***(978-1-84682-309-1(9))*** Four Courts Pr. IRL. Dist: International Specialized Bk. Services.

Twomey, Vincent & Rutherford, Janet Elaine. Benedict XVI & Beauty in Sacred Music. 2011. (Illus.). 224p. ***(978-1-84682-311-4(0))*** Four Courts Pr. IRL. Dist: International Specialized Bk. Services.

Walsh, Mary Ann, ed. Benedict XVI: Essays & Reflections on His Papacy. 2010. (ENG.). 224p. 29.95 *(978-1-58051-234-3(8)*, Sheed & Ward) Rowman & Littlefield Publishers, Inc.

Weigel, George. God's Choice: Pope Benedict XVI & the Future of the Catholic Church. annot. ed. 2006. 320p. pap. 16.95 *(978-0-06-093759-1(9)*, HarperPerennial) HarperCollins Pubs.

Welborn, Amy. Come Meet Jesus: An Invitation from Pope Benedict XVI. 2010. 160p. pap. 11.95 *(978-1-59325-167-3(X))* Word Among Us Pr.

—Enciclica Sobre la Esperanza. Estenger, Vilma G., tr. 2008. (Pope Benedict XVI Ser.). 1p. 14.95 *(978-1-59276-471-6(1))* Our Sunday Visitor, Publishing Div.

—Encyclical on Hope. 2008. (Pope Benedict XVI Ser.). 1p. 14.95 *(978-1-59276-407-5(X))* Our Sunday Visitor, Publishing Div.

BENEDICT, RUTH, 1887-1948

Benedict, Ruth. An Anthropologist at Work. 2011. (ENG., Illus.). 605p. pap. 39.95 *(978-1-4128-1950-6(8))* Transaction Pubs.

Roffman, Karin. From the Modernist Annex: American Women Writers in Museums & Libraries. 2nd ed. 2010. (ENG., Illus.). 272p. 44.50 *(978-0-8173-1698-3(1))* Univ. of Alabama Pr.

BENEDICTINES

Benedict of Nursia Staff & Venarde, Bruce L. The Rule of Saint Benedict. 2011. (Dumbarton Oaks Medieval Library). (LAT & ENG.). 304p. 29.95 *(978-0-674-05304-5(4))* Harvard Univ. Pr.

Benedict, Saint. Monastic Breviary Matins: According to the Holy Rule of Saint Benedict. 2007. 1297p. lib. bdg. 45.00 net. *(978-0-9777093-3-5(7))* Lancelot Andrewes Pr.

Blée, Fabrice, et al. The Third Desert: The Story of Monastic Interreligious Dialogue. 2011. 24.95 *(978-0-8146-3357-1(9))*; E-Book *(978-0-8146-3949-8(6))* Liturgical Pr.

Böckmann, Aquinata & Burkhard, Marianne. Around the Monastic Table — RB 31-42: Growing in Mutual Service & Love. 2009. pap. 29.95 *(978-0-8146-1874-5(X))* Liturgical Pr.

Brown, Virginia. Beneventan Discoveries: Collected Manuscript Catalogues, 1978¿2008. 2012. (Studies & Texts: 179). (ENG & LAT.). 300p. 90.00 ***(978-0-88844-179-9(7))*** Pontifical Institute of Mediaeval Studies, Dept. of Pubns. CAN. Dist: Univ. of Toronto Pr.

Butler, Cuthbert. Benedictine Monachism: Studies in Benedictine Life & Rule. 2007. (ENG.). 394p. 49.95 *(978-0-548-17585-9(3))* Kessinger Publishing, LLC.

—Benedictine Monachism: Studies in Benedictine Life & Rule. 2007. pap. 34.95 *(978-1-4304-7514-9(5))* Kessinger Publishing, LLC.

Casey, Michael. Road to Eternal Life. 2011. 214p. pap. 19.95 ***(978-0-8146-3384-7(6))*** Liturgical Pr.

—The Road to Eternal Life: Reflections on the Prologue of Benedict's Rule. 2011. E-Book ***(978-0-8146-3954-2(2))*** Liturgical Pr.

Chittister, Joan. Monasteries of the Heart: A Invitation to a Meaningful Life. 2011. (ENG.). 240p. 19.95 *(978-1-933346-34-2(5))* BlueBridge.

Constable, Giles. Three Treatises from Bec on the Nature of Monastic Life. Smith, Bernard S., tr. from LAT. 2008. (Medieval Academy Bks.). (ENG., Illus.). 208p. *(978-0-8020-9260-1(8))* Univ. of Toronto Pr.

de Waal, Esther. Seeking Life: Benedictine Wisdom for the Baptized. 2009. 160p. 19.95 *(978-0-8146-1880-6(4)*, Liturgical Pr. Bks.) Liturgical Pr.

Feiss, Hugh & Pepin, Ronald E. The Lives of Monastic Reformers: Robert of la Chaise-Dieu & Stephen of Obazine. 2010. 32.95 *(978-0-87907-322-0(5))* Liturgical Pr.

Forman, Mary. One Heart, One Soul, Many Communities: Proceedings of the 21st Annual Monastic Institute, School of Theology-Seminary, Saint John's University, Collegeville, Minnesota 56321, July 1-7, 2006. 2009. pap. 24.95 *(978-0-9740992-5-5(2))* Liturgical Pr.

Freeman, Laurence & Bishop, James. A Way in the Wilderness: A Commentary on the Rule of Benedict for the Physically & Spiritually Imprisoned. 2012. (ENG.). 248p. pap. 19.95 ***(978-1-4411-5115-5(X))*** Continuum International Publishing Group, Ltd. GBR. Dist: National Bk. Network.

Garborg, Rolf. The Family Blessing. 2009. (ENG.). 224p. 14.99 *(978-1-934770-62-7(0))* Ellie Claire & Summerside Pr.

Glassner, Christine. Neuzeitliche Handschriften aus dem Nachlass der Bruder Bernhard und Hieronymus Pez in der Bibliothek des Benediktinerstiftes Melk. 2008. (Denkschriften der Phil. -Hist. Klasse Ser.). 180p. (C). pap. 72.00 *(978-3-7001-6493-7(9))* Austrian Academy of Sciences Press AUT. Dist: Brown, David Bk. Co., The.

Gretsch, Mechthild. The Intellectual Foundations of the English Benedictine Reform. 2006. (Cambridge Studies in Anglo-Saxon England Ser.). (ENG.). 484p. pap. 61.00 *(978-0-521-03052-6(8))* Cambridge Univ. Pr.

Hall, Jeremy. Silence, Solitude, Simplicity: A Hermit's Love Affair with a Noisy, Crowded, & Complicated World. 2007. 181p. per. 14.95 *(978-0-8146-3185-0(1)*, Liturgical Pr. Bks.) Liturgical Pr.

Hilken, Charles. Memory & Community in Medieval Southern Italy: The History, Chapter Book, & Necrology of Santa Maria Del Gualdo Mazzocca. 2008. (Studies & Texts). (ENG.). 79.95 *(978-0-88844-157-7(6))* Pontifical Institute of Mediaeval Studies, Dept. of Pubns. CAN. Dist: Univ. of Toronto Pr.

Holtz, Albert. Pilgrim Road: A Benedictine Journey Through Lent. 2006. (Illus.). 192p. per. 16.00 *(978-0-8192-2251-0(8)*, Morehouse Publishing) Church Publishing, Inc.

—Walking in Valleys of Darkness: A Benedictine Journey through Troubled Times. 2011. 112p. pap. 12.00 *(978-0-8192-2739-3(0)*, Morehouse Publishing) Church Publishing, Inc.

—Walking in Valleys of Darkness: A Benedictine Journey Through Troubled Times. 2011. E-Book *(978-0-8192-2741-6(2)*, Morehouse Publishing) Church Publishing, Inc.

Jamison, Christopher. Finding Sanctuary: Monastic Steps for Everyday Life. 2006. (Illus.). 182p. 19.95 *(978-0-8146-3168-3(1))* Liturgical Pr.

Johns, Laurentia, ed. Touched by God: Ten Monastic Journeys. 2008. (ENG.). 248p. 24.95 *(978-0-86012-451-1(7)*, Burns & Oates) Continuum International Publishing Group, Ltd. GBR. Dist: National Bk. Network.

Kapsner, Oliver Leonard. A Benedictine Bibliography V1-2. 2011. 1170p. 87.95 ***(978-1-258-06401-3(4))*** Literary Licensing, LLC.

Kardong, Terrence G. The Life of Saint Benedict by Gregory the Great: Translation & Commentary. 2009. 176p. pap. 16.95 *(978-0-8146-3262-8(9)*, Liturgical Pr. Bks.) Liturgical Pr.

Kelly, S. E., ed. Charters of Peterborough Abbey. 2009. (ENG., Illus.). 320p. 125.00 *(978-0-19-726438-6(7))* Oxford Univ. Pr., Inc.

Kerr, Julie. Monastic Hospitality: The Benedictines in England, C. 1070-C. 1250. 2007. (Studies in the History of Medieval Religion Ser.: Volume 32). (Illus.). 260p. 99.00 *(978-1-84383-326-0(3)*, Boydell Press) Boydell & Brewer, Ltd. GBR. Dist: Boydell & Brewer, Inc.

Knowles, David. The Benedictines. 2011. 102p. 39.95 ***(978-1-258-04827-3(2))*** Literary Licensing, LLC.

Kownacki, Mary Lou. A Monk in the Inner City: The ABCs of a Spiritual Journey. 2008. 155p. pap. 18.00 *(978-1-57075-760-0(7))* Orbis Bks.

Leclercq, Jean & Merton, Thomas. Survival or Prophecy? The Correspondence of Jean Leclercq & Thomas Merton. 2008. 184p. pap. 21.95 *(978-0-87907-017-5(X))* Cistercian Pubns., Inc.

Mitchell, John. Lombard Legacy: Cultural Strategies & the Visual Arts in Early Medieval Italy. 2012. (ENG., Illus.). 644p. (C). 300.00 *(978-1-904597-34-6(3))* Pindar Pr. GBR. Dist: Brown, David Bk. Co., The.

Monks Of St. John's Abbey, ed. The Monastic Vesperal: A Companion to the Monastic Diurnal. 2011. 454p. 57.95 ***(978-1-258-05192-1(3))*** Literary Licensing, LLC.

Monks Of St. Vincent Archabbey. Manual for Benedictine Oblates. 2011. 150p. 41.95 ***(978-1-258-08997-9(1))*** Literary Licensing, LLC.

Monks of the Abbey of St. Peter of Solesmes Staff. Benedictiones Mensae. (LAT.). 16p. pap. 4.95 *(973-2-85274-058-7(3)*, 3018) Abbey of St. Peter of Solesmes, The FRA. Dist: Paraclete Pr., Inc.

Newman, John Henry. Historical Sketches - The Church of the Fathers - St. Chrysostom - Theodoret - Mission of St. Benedict - Benedictine Schools. 2007. 500p. per. *(978-1-4086-0366-6(7))* Read Bks.

—Historical Sketches: The Church of the Fathers; St. Chrysostom; Theodoret; Mission of St. Benedict; Benedictine Schools (1873) 2008. 528p. 55.95 *(978-0-548-99791-8(8))* 2007. (ENG.). 532p. per. 40.95 *(978-0-548-64880-3(8))* Kessinger Publishing, LLC.

—Historical Sketches V2: The Church of the Fathers; St. Chrysostom; Theodoret; Mission of St. Benedict; Benedictine Schools (1912) 2008. 532p. 55.95 *(978-1-4365-4692-8(3))* 2007. 536p. per. 40.95 *(978-0-548-73880-1(7))* Kessinger Publishing, LLC.

O Riain, Pádraig, ed. A Martyrology of Four Cities: Metz, Cologne, Dublin, Lund. 2009. (Henry Bradshaw Society Ser.: Volume 118). (LAT & ENG.). 310p. 60.00 *(978-1-870252-76-8(4))* Bradshaw, Henry Society GBR. Dist: Boydell & Brewer, Inc.

O'Connell, Patrick F., ed. The Rule of Saint Benedict: Initiation into the Monastic Tradition 4. 2009. 310p. pap. 24.95 *(978-0-87907-019-9(6)*, Cistercian Publications Bks.) Liturgical Pr.

O'Donohue, John. To Bless the Space Between Us: A Book of Blessings. 2008. (ENG.). 240p. 22.95 *(978-0-385-52227-4(4))* Knopf Doubleday Publishing Group.

Okholm, Dennis L. Monk Habits for Everyday People: Benedictine Spirituality for Protestants. 2007. 144p. per. 15.99 *(978-1-58743-185-2(8))* Brazos Pr.

Order Of St. Benedict. Rite of Monastic Profession: According to the Ritual of the American-Cassinese Congregation of the Order of St. Benedict. 2011. 38p. 35.95 ***(978-1-258-03584-6(7))*** Literary Licensing, LLC.

Pearce, Ernest Harold. The Monks of Westminster: Being a Register of the Brethren of the Convent from the Time of the Confessor to the Dissolution. 2010. (Cambridge Library Collection - History Ser.). (ENG.). 252p. pap. 22.99 *(978-1-108-01355-8(7))* Cambridge Univ. Pr.

Rees. Monks of England. xii, 258p. 29.95 *(978-0-281-05074-1(0))* International Publishers Marketing.

Saint Meinrad, The Monks of, ed. The Tradition of Catholic Prayer: The Monks of Saint Meinrad Archabbey. 2007. (Illus.). 304p. per. 24.95 *(978-0-8146-3184-3(3)*, Liturgical Pr. Bks.) Liturgical Pr.

Scheiba, Manuela. Gehorsam gegenüber dem Abt: Ein Beitrag zur Auslegungsgeschichte der Benediktus-Regel im 20. Jahrhundert. Regula Benedicti Studia, Traditio et Receptio 22. 2009. lxiv, 525p. *(978-3-8306-7336-1(1))* Eos Verlag.

Schwinn, Bonaventure. The American Benedictine Review, V2, No 1, Spring 1951: Ut in Omnibus Glorificetur Deus. Schwinn, Bonaventure et al, eds. 2011. 128p. 40.95 ***(978-1-258-06248-4(8))*** Literary Licensing, LLC.

—The American Benedictine Review, V2, No 2, Summer 1951: Ut in Omnibus Glorificetur Deus. Cummins, Patrick & Jurica, Edmund, eds. 2011. 130p. 40.95 ***(978-1-258-06257-6(7))*** Literary Licensing, LLC.

—The American Benedictine Review, V2, No 3, Autumn 1951: Ut in Omnibus Glorificetur Deus. Cummins, Patrick & Jurica, Edmund, eds. 2011. 98p. 38.95 ***(978-1-258-06258-3(5))*** Literary Licensing, LLC.

—The American Benedictine Review, V2, No 4, Winter 1951: Ut in Omnibus Glorificetur Deus. Cummins, Patrick & Jurica, Edmund, eds. 2011. 98p. 38.95 ***(978-1-258-06259-0(3))*** Literary Licensing, LLC.

Scott, Mark Alan. At Home with Saint Benedict: Monastery Talks. 2011. pap. 39.95 *(978-0-87907-027-4(7))* Cistercian Pubns., Inc.

Sorg, Rembert. Holy Work: Towards A Benedictine Theology of Manual Labor. 2011. 122p. 39.95 ***(978-1-258-02812-1(3))*** Literary Licensing, LLC.

—Towards a Benedictine Theology of Manual Labor. 2011. 126p. 40.95 ***(978-1-258-05845-6(6))*** Literary Licensing, LLC.

St. Benedict & Benedict. The Rule of St Benedict. White, Carolinne, ed. & tr. by. from LAT. 2008. (ENG.). 160p. (gr. 12-18). 13.00 *(978-0-14-044996-9(5)*, Penguin Classics) Penguin Group (USA) Inc.

St Benedict XVI. The Rule of St. Benedict. Gasquet, Cardinal, tr. from LAT. 2007. (Dover Books on Western Philosophy Ser.). (ENG., Illus.). 80p. per. 4.95 *(978-0-486-45796-3(6))* Dover Pubns., Inc.

St. Vincent Archabbey Publisher. Remembrance of Our Solemn Profession: The Benedictine Rite of Solemn Profession. 2011. 44p. 35.95 ***(978-1-258-01013-3(5))*** Literary Licensing, LLC.

Stock, Jon R., et al. Inhabiting the Church: Biblical Wisdom for a New Monasticism. 2006. (New Monastic Library: Resources for Radical Discipleship: Ser.). 140p. pap. 18.00 *(978-1-59752-990-7(7)*, Cascade Bks.) Wipf & Stock Pubs.

Swan, Laura. The Benedictine Tradition. Zagano, Phyllis, ed. 2007. (Spirituality in History Ser.). (Illus.). 176p. per. 15.95 *(978-0-8146-1914-8(2)*, Liturgical Pr. Bks.) Liturgical Pr.

Taunton, Ethelred L. English Black Monks of St Benedict V1 A. 2006. pap. 30.95 *(978-1-4286-5753-3(3))* Kessinger Publishing, LLC.

—The English Black Monks of St Benedict V2: a Sketch of Their History. 2006. (ENG.). 380p. per. 33.95 *(978-1-4286-5754-0(1))* Kessinger Publishing, LLC.

Wagner, Br. Francis de Sales, ed. Sacred Rhythms: The Monastic Way Every Day. 2011. (ENG., Illus.). 160p. pap. 14.95 ***(978-0-87029-466-2(0))*** Abbey Pr.

Wimmer, Boniface & Oetgen, Jerome. Boniface Wimmer: Letters of an American Abbot. 2008. pap. *(978-0-9773909-4-6(2))* St. Vincent Archabbey Pubns.

Wolf, Kirsten, ed. A Female Legendary from Iceland: Kirkjubæjarbók - AM 429 12mo in the Arnamagnæan Collection, Copenhagen. 2011. (ENG & ICE.). 147p. 76.00 *(978-87-635-3163-4(1))* Museum Tusculanum Pr. DNK. Dist: Chicago Distribution Ctr.

BENEDICTUS, SAINT, ABBOT OF MONTE CASSINO

see Benedict, Saint, Abbot of Monte Cassino

BENEFICES, ECCLESIASTICAL

see also Chantries

Boute, Bruno. Academic Interests & Catholic Confessionalisation: The Louvain Privileges of Nomination to Ecclesiastical Benefices. (Illus.). 686p. *(978-90-04-18417-6(1))* BRILL.

Putnam, James O. Speech of James O Putnam, of Buffalo, on the Bill, Providing for the Vesting of the Title of Church Property in Lay Trustees, Delivered in the Senate. 2011. 18p. pap. 11.99 ***(978-1-4181-8961-7(8))*** MPublishing.

BENEFICIAL INSECTS

see also individual and groups of beneficial insects, e.g. Bees; Silkworms

Agnello, A. Tree Fruit Field Guide to Insect, Mite, & Disease Pests & Natural Enemies of Eastern North America. 2006. (Illus.). xii, 238p. pap. *(978-1-933395-02-9(8))* Natural Resource, Agricultural, & Engineering Service.

Ekbom, B. S., et al, eds. Interchanges of Insects between Agricultural & Surrounding Landscapes. 2010. 256p. pap. 151.00 *(978-90-481-4027-5(7)*, 9048140277) Springer.

Hill, Dave. Insects of Economic Importance. Date not set. (Biology Ser.). pap. 60.50 *(978-0-04-445939-2(4))* CENGAGE Learning.

Hill, Dennis S. Agricultural Entomology. 2009. (ENG.). 636p. pap. 69.95 *(978-1-60469-101-6(8)*, 1604691018) Timber Pr., Inc.

Hodgson, Erin W. Gardening with Good Bugs. 2008. (ENG.). 128p. pap. 14.95 *(978-1-934393-01-7(0))* Silverleaf Pr.

Lamp, William O., et al. Handbook of Forage & Rangeland Insects. 2007. pap. 59.00 *(978-0-9776209-0-6(5))* Entomological Society of America.

Nardi, James B. Fireflies, Honey, & Silk. 2010. (ENG., Illus.). 248p. pap. 18.95 *(978-0-520-26807-4(5))* Univ. of California Pr.

Waldbauer, Gilbert. Fireflies, Honey, & Silk. 2009. (Illus.). 248p. 40.00 *(978-0-520-25883-9(5))* Univ. of California Pr.

Walliser, Jessica. Good Bug Bad Bug: Who's Who, What They Do, & How to Manage Them Organically. 2nd ed. 2011. (Illus.). 104p. 17.95 *(978-0-9819615-9-0(2))* St. Lynn's Pr.

BENEFIT FUNDS (TRADE UNION)

see Labor Union Welfare Funds

BENEFIT SOCIETIES

see Friendly Societies

BENEFITS, EMPLOYEE

see Employee Fringe Benefits

BENEFITS, FRINGE

see Employee Fringe Benefits

BENEFITS, UNJUSTIFIED

see Unjust Enrichment

BENELUX COUNTRIES

Here are entered works dealing collectively with Belgium, the Netherlands, and Luxemburg.

Alexander-Skipnes & Alexander-Skipnes, Ingrid. Cultural Exchange Between the Low Countries & Italy (1400-1600) 2007. (Museums at the Crossroads Ser.). (ENG., Illus.). 292p. (C). pap. 116.00 *(978-2-503-51838-1(9))* Brepols Pubs. BEL. Dist: ISD.

Arblaster, Paul. A History of the Low Countries. 2nd rev. ed. 2012. (Palgrave Essential Histories Ser.). (ENG., Illus.). 344p. (C). 80.00 ***(978-0-230-29309-0(3))***; pap. 27.00 ***(978-0-230-29310-6(7))*** Palgrave Macmillan.

Cruz, L. & Frijhoff, W. Th. M., eds. Myth in History, History in Myth: Proceedings of the Third International Conference of the Society for Netherlandic History (New York: June 5-6, 2006) 2009. (Brill's Studies in Intellectual History). 264p. *(978-90-04-17834-2(1))* BRILL.

De Mul/Boehmer. The Postcolonial Low Countries: Literature, Colonialism, & Multiculturalism. 2012. (ENG.). 264p. (gr. 17). 70.00 ***(978-0-7391-6428-0(7))*** Lexington Bks.

De Vries, Annette, ed. Cultural Mediators: Artists & Writers at the Crossroads of Tradition, Innovation & Reception in the Low Countries & Italy 1450-1650. 2008. (Groningen Studies in Cultural Change Ser.). (ENG.). 234p. (C). 66.00 *(978-90-429-2043-9(2))* Peeters Pubs. & Booksellers BEL. Dist: Brown, David Bk. Co., The.

Delsaerdt, P., et al, eds. The Quintessence of Lives: Intellectual Biographies in the Low Countries Presented to Jan Roegiers. 2010. (Bibliotheque de la Revue d'histoire Ecclesiastique Ser.). (DUT, ENG, FRE & GER.). 513p. (C). pap. 123.00 *(978-2-503-53210-3(1))* Brepols Pubs. BEL. Dist: ISD.

Easton, Marleen, et al, eds. Reflections on Reassurance Policing in the Low Countries. 2008. 228p. pap. 52.00 *(978-90-5454-863-8(0))* Eleven International Publishing NLD. Dist: International Specialized Bk. Services.

Gemert, Lia van & Marion, Olga van. Women's Writing from the Low Countries, 1200-1875: A Bilingual Anthology. Joldersma, Hermina et al, eds. 2011. (Amsterdam Anthologies Ser.). (Illus.). 624p. pap. *(978-90-8964-129-8(7))* Amsterdam Univ. Pr.

Lambert. The City, the Duke & Their Banker the Rapondi Family & the Formation of the Burgundian State 1384-1430. 2006. (Studies in European Urban History (1100-1800): Vol. 7). (ENG., Illus.). 215p. (C). pap. 94.00 *(978-2-503-52025-4(1))* Brepols Pubs. BEL. Dist: ISD.

van Bavel, Bas. Manors & Markets: Economy & Society in the Low Countries 500-1600. 2010. (ENG., Illus.). 512p. 140.00 *(978-0-19-927866-4(0))* Oxford Univ. Pr., Inc.

van der Heijden, Manon, et al, eds. Serving the Urban Community: The Rise of Public Facilities in the Low Countries. 2010. (ENG., Illus.). 286p. pap. 49.50 *(978-90-5260-350-6(2))* Aksant Academic Pubs. NLD. Dist: Amsterdam Univ. Pr.

BENELUX COUNTRIES—DESCRIPTION AND TRAVEL

McDonald, George. Frommer's Belgium, Holland & Luxembourg. 12th ed. 2011. (Frommer's Complete Guides: 905). (ENG., Illus.). 544p. pap. 22.99 *(978-0-470-88766-0(4)*, Frommers) Wiley, John & Sons, Inc.

Unverfehrt, Gerd & Dürer, Albrecht. Da Sah Ich Viel Köstliche Dinge: Albrecht Dürers Reise in Die Niederlande. 2007. (GER., Illus.). 261p. (C). pap. 51.00 *(978-3-525-47010-7(X))* Vandenhoeck & Ruprecht GmbH & Co. KG DEU. Dist: ISD.

BENEVOLENCE

see also Charity; Kindness; Poor

Charity & Lim, Arthur S. M. Did I Give Back Enough? 2009. 136p. 32.00 *(978-981-4289-86-3(8))* World Scientific Publishing Co., Inc.

Gilbert, Helen & Tiffin, Chris, eds. Burden or Benefit? Imperial Benevolence & Its Legacies. 2008. (Philanthropic & Nonprofit Studies). (ENG.). 240p. 60.00 *(978-0-253-35077-0(8)*, 0253350778); pap. 22.95 *(978-0-253-21960-2(4)*, 0253219604) Indiana Univ. Pr.

Gup, Ted. A Secret Gift: How One Man's Kindness - And a Trove of Letters - Revealed the Hidden History of the Great Depression. 2010. (ENG.). 368p. (gr. 12). 25.95 *(978-1-59420-270-4(2)*, Penguin Pr. HC, The) Penguin Group (USA) Inc.

—A Secret Gift: How One Man's Kindness — and a Trove of Letters — Revealed the Hidden History of the Great Depression. 2011. (ENG.). 384p. (gr. 12). 16.00 *(978-0-14-312000-1(X)*, Penguin (Non-Classics)) Penguin Group (USA) Inc.

Jamal, Azim & McKinnon, Harvey. The Power of Giving: How Giving Back Enriches Us All. 2009. (ENG.). 256p. (gr. 12-18). 13.95 *(978-1-58542-751-2(9)*, Tarcher) Penguin Group (USA) Inc.

Porter, Curtis & Deaver, Roy. Porter-Deaver Debate: Congregational Benevolence. 2007. pap. 15.95 *(978-1-58427-187-1(6))* Guardian of Truth Foundation.

Price, Patrick Hutcheson Jones & Price, Scott Todd. Looking for Goodwill. 2006. (ENG., Illus.). 326p. 30.00 *(978-1-57736-374-3(4))* Turner Publishing Co.

Sorek, Susan. Remembered for Good: A Jewish Benefaction System in Ancient Palestine. 2010. xii, 285p. ***(978-1-906055-69-1(6))*** Sheffield Phoenix Pr.

Stove, David. What's Wrong with Benevolence: Happiness, Private Property, & the Limits of Enlightenment. Irvine, Andrew, ed. 2011. (ENG.). 240p. 23.95 *(978-1-59403-523-4(7))* Encounter Bks.

BENEVOLENT INSTITUTIONS

see Almshouses; Asylums; Charities; Children—Institutional Care; Hospitals; Institutional Care; Mental Retardation Facilities; Public Welfare; Social Service

BENEZET, ANTHONY, 1713-1784

Brendlinger, Irv A. To Be Silent... Would Be Criminal: The Antislavery Influence & Writings of Anthony Benezet. 2006. (Revitalization: Explorations in World

B

Christian Movements Ser.: No. 20). (ENG., Illus.). 246p. per. 45.00 (978-0-8108-5765-0(0)) Scarecrow Pr., Inc.

Jackson, Maurice. Let This Voice Be Heard: Anthony Benezet, Father of Atlantic Abolitionism. (Illus.). 400p. (C). 2010. pap. 24.95 (978-0-8122-2126-8(5)) 2009. 55.00 (978-0-8122-4129-7(0)) Univ. of Pennsylvania Pr.

BENGAL (INDIA)

Bose, Sugata. Peasant Labour & Colonial Capital: Rural Bengal Since 1770. 2007. (New Cambridge History of India Ser.). (ENG., Illus.). 224p. pap. 50.00 (978-0-521-03322-0(5)) Cambridge Univ. Pr.

Dasgupta, Subrata. The Bengal Renaissance: Identity & Creativity from Rammohun Roy to Rabindranath Tagore. 2007. 280p. (978-81-7824-177-7(3)) Permanent Black.

Dodwell & Miles, compiled by. Alphabetical List of the Officers of the Indian Army 1760 to the Year 1834bengal. 2007. 308p. per. (978-1-84574-391-8(1)) Naval & Military Pr., The.

O'Malley, L. S. S. Bengal, Bihar, & Orissa Sikkim. 2011. (ENG.). 334p. pap. 28.99 (978-1-107-60064-5(2)) Cambridge Univ. Pr.

Sheppard, Samuel T., et al, eds. Bombay in the Days of Queen Anne, Being an Account of the Settlement Written by John Burnell. 2010. (Hakluyt Society, Second Ser.). 222p. 69.95 (978-1-4094-1439-1(6)) Hakluyt Society GBR. Dist: Ashgate Publishing Co.

BENGAL (INDIA)—ECONOMIC CONDITIONS

Biswas, Tapasi. Decentralized Production in West Bengal. 2009. 180p. pap. (978-3-639-06504-6(2)) VDM Verlag Dr. Mueller e.K.

Bose, Sugata. Agrarian Bengal: Economy, Social Structure & Politics, 1919-1947. 2007. (Cambridge South Asian Studies). (ENG.). 320p. pap. 45.00 (978-0-521-05362-4(5)) Cambridge Univ. Pr.

BENGAL (INDIA)—HISTORY

Anon. A State of the British Authority in Bengal under the Government of Mr Hastings. 2008. 64p. pap. 26.45 (978-1-4437-7913-5(X)) Barclay Pr., Inc.

Arephina, E. Esa Ema Samachula. Bangladesh Documents, 1971, 4 vols. (978-7-03-660000-8(4)) Science Pr.

Chatterji, Joya. The Spoils of Partition: Bengal & India, 1947-1967. (Cambridge Studies in Indian History & Society Ser.). (ENG.). 360p. 2011. pap. 45.00 (978-0-521-18806-7(7)) 2007. (Illus.). 98.00 (978-0-521-87536-3(6)) Cambridge Univ. Pr.

Diehl, Katharine S. Persian, Arabic, & Urdu Printing in Bengal from 1778. (Printers & Printing in the East Indies to 1850 Ser.: Vol. V). (978-0-89241-394-2(8)) Caratzas, Aristide D. Pub.

—Scholarship & Education in Bengal. (Printers & Printing in the East Indies to 1850 Ser.: Vol. VII). (978-0-89241-396-6(4)) Caratzas, Aristide D. Pub.

Gandhi, Gopalkrishna. A Frank Friendship: Gandhi & Bengal - A Descriptive Chronology. 2008. (ENG., Illus.). 616p. 69.95 (978-1-905422-63-0(6)) Seagull Bks. GBR. Dist: Chicago Distribution Ctr.

Gupta, Swarupa. Notions of Nationhood in Bengal: Perspectives on Samaj, C. 1867-1905. 2009. 410p. (978-90-04-17614-0(4)) BRILL.

Hatcher, Brian A. Bourgeois Hinduism, Or, the Faith of the Modern Vedantists: Rare Discourses from Early Colonial Bengal. 2007. (ENG., Illus.). 240p. 65.00 (978-0-19-532608-6(3)) Oxford Univ. Pr., Inc.

Hill, Samuel C. Bengal in Seventeen Fifty-Six to Seventeen Fifty-Seven: A Selection of Public & Private Papers Dealing with the Affairs of the British in Bengal During the Reign of Siraj-Udduala, 3 vols. reprint ed. 195.00 (978-0-404-03310-1(5)) AMS Pr., Inc.

Hunter, William Wilson. Famine Aspects of Bengal Districts. 2008. 216p. 39.95 (978-1-4369-2671-3(8)); pap. 24.95 (978-1-4368-4457-4(6)) Kessinger Publishing, LLC.

Kasyapa, Prasanta & Simha, Umesa Kumara. Bangala Ke Palavamsiya Rajaom Ka Itihasa: Eka Abhilekhiya Adhyayana. 2010. (HIN., Illus.). 224p. (978-93-80467-43-6(5)) Kala Prakashan.

Keneally, Thomas. Three Famines: Starvation & Politics. 2011. (ENG., Illus.). 336p. 27.99 (978-1-61039-065-1(2)) PublicAffairs.

Khan, Abdul Majed. The Transition in Bengal, 1756-75: A Study of Saiyid Muhammad Reza Khan. 2007. (Cambridge South Asian Studies). (ENG.). 400p. pap. 48.00 (978-0-521-04982-5(2)) Cambridge Univ. Pr.

Khan, Golam Sarwar. New Life, New Home: A Story of Retaining the Cultural Boundaries. 2009. 214p. pap. 30.00 (978-1-86335-623-7(1)) Common Ground Publishing Pty, Ltd.

Khan, Shahadat H. The Freedom of Intellect Movement (Buddhir Mukti Andolan) in Bengali Muslim Thought, 1926-1938. 2007. 484p. (978-0-7734-5423-1(3)) Mellen, Edwin Pr., The.

Marshall, P. J. Bengal: the British Bridgehead: Eastern India 1740-1828. 2006. (New Cambridge History of India Ser.). (ENG., Illus.). 216p. pap. 48.00 (978-0-521-02822-6(1)) Cambridge Univ. Pr.

Mukhopadhyay, Anindita. Behind the Mask: The Cultural Definition of the Legal Subject in Colonial Bengal (1715-1911) 2006. 316p. 55.00 (978-0-19-568083-6(9)) Oxford Univ. Pr., Inc.

Mukhopadhyay, Kali Mohan. Partition, Bengal & After: The Great Tragedy of India. 2007. 260p. (C). 32.00 (978-81-8405-034-9(8), Reference Pr.) Ess Ess Pubns. IND. Dist: International Specialized Bk. Services.

Ogborn, Miles. Indian Ink: Script & Print in the Making of the English East India Company. 2007. (ENG., Illus.). 288p. 42.50 (978-0-226-62041-1(7)) Univ. of Chicago Pr.

Openshaw, Jeanne. Writing the Self: The Life & Philosophy of a Bengali Baul Guru. 2010. (ENG., Illus.). 336p. 85.00 (978-0-19-806247-9(8)) Oxford Univ. Pr., Inc.

Pal, P. & Haque, E. Bengal: Sites & Sights. 2006. (Illus.). 152p. 66.00 (978-81-85026-59-6(9)) Marg Pubns. IND. Dist: National Bk. Network.

Purna Ch. Majum Staff. Musnud of Murshidabad. 2006. 408p. per. (978-1-4067-2420-2(3), Hesperides Pr.) Read Bks.

Ray, Sukhendu & Karlekar, Malavika. The Many Worlds of Sarala Devi & the Tagores & Sartorial Styles: A Diary. 2010. 228p. 70.00 (978-81-87358-31-2(9)) Berghahn Bks., Inc.

Sarkar, Tanika. Rebels, Wives, Saints: Designing Selves & Nations in Colonial Times. 2010. 356p. 29.00 (978-1-906497-29-3(X)) Seagull Bks. London Ltd. GBR. Dist: Chicago Distribution Ctr.

Talbot, Ian & Singh, Gurharpal. The Partition of India. 2009. (New Approaches to Asian History Ser.). (ENG., Illus.). 224p. (C). 88.99 (978-0-521-85661-4(2)); pap. 29.99 (978-0-521-67256-6(2)) Cambridge Univ. Pr.

Travers, Robert. Ideology & Empire in Eighteenth-Century India: The British in Bengal. 2007. (Cambridge Studies in Indian History & Society Ser.). (ENG., Illus.). 296p. pap. 35.00 (978-0-521-05003-6(0)) Cambridge Univ. Pr.

BENGAL (INDIA)—POLITICS AND GOVERNMENT

Bose, Sugata. Agrarian Bengal: Economy, Social Structure & Politics, 1919-1947. 2007. (Cambridge South Asian Studies). (ENG.). 320p. pap. 45.00 (978-0-521-05362-4(5)) Cambridge Univ. Pr.

Gandhi, Gopalkrishna. A Frank Friendship: Gandhi & Bengal - A Descriptive Chronology. 2008. (ENG., Illus.). 616p. 69.95 (978-1-905422-63-0(6)) Seagull Bks. GBR. Dist: Chicago Distribution Ctr.

Pande, Ishita. Medicine, Race & Liberalism in British Bengal: Symptoms of Empire. (ENG., Illus.). 272p. (C). 2012. pap. 42.95 **(978-0-415-62754-2(0))** 2009. 145.00 (978-0-415-77815-2(8)) Routledge.

Tagore, Rabindranath. The Home & the World. Surendranath Tagore, tr. 2007. (ENG.). 186p. pap. 19.99 (978-1-4264-2165-5(6)) BiblioBazaar.

—The Home & the World. Tagore, Surendranath, tr. 2007. (ENG.). 208p. per. (978-1-4065-4864-8(2)) Dodo Pr.

Travers, Robert. Ideology & Empire in Eighteenth-Century India: The British in Bengal. 2007. (Cambridge Studies in Indian History & Society Ser.). (ENG., Illus.). 296p. pap. 35.00 (978-0-521-05003-6(0)); 292p. 110.99 (978-0-521-86145-8(4)) Cambridge Univ. Pr.

Wilson, Jon E. The Domination of Strangers: Modern Governance in Eastern India, 1780-1835. 2011. (Cambridge Imperial & Post-Colonial Studies Ser.). (ENG., Illus.). 256p. pap. 31.00 (978-0-230-27915-5(5)) Palgrave Macmillan.

—The Domination of Strangers: Modern Governance in Eastern India, 1780-1835. Drayton, Richard & Vaughan, Megan, eds. 2008. (ENG., Illus.). 256p. 89.00 (978-0-230-57453-3(X)) Palgrave Macmillan.

BENGAL (INDIA)—RELIGION

Banerjee, Sumanta. Logic in a Popular Form: Essays on Popular Religion in Bengal. 2010. (ENG.). 233p. 35.00 (978-1-906497-55-2(9)) Seagull Bks. GBR. Dist: Chicago Distribution Ctr.

BENGAL (INDIA)—SOCIAL CONDITIONS

Bose, Sugata. Agrarian Bengal: Economy, Social Structure & Politics, 1919-1947. 2007. (Cambridge South Asian Studies). (ENG.). 320p. pap. 45.00 (978-0-521-05362-4(5)) Cambridge Univ. Pr.

Dasgupta, Prasenjit. Hari Bol: Evolution & Genesis of Funeral Music in Postcolonial Bengal. 2010. 116p. pap. (978-3-8383-7472-7(X)) Lambert Academic Publishing.

Gandhi, Gopalkrishna. A Frank Friendship: Gandhi & Bengal - A Descriptive Chronology. 2008. (ENG., Illus.). 616p. 69.95 (978-1-905422-63-0(6)) Seagull Bks. GBR. Dist: Chicago Distribution Ctr.

Janeja, Manpreet. Transactions in Taste: The Collaborative Lives of Everyday Bengali Food. 2009. (Illus.). 220p. 110.00 (978-0-415-55374-2(1), Routledge India) Taylor & Francis Group GBR. Dist: Taylor & Francis Group.

Khan, Golam Sarwar. New Life, New Home: A Story of Retaining the Cultural Boundaries. 2009. 214p. pap. 30.00 (978-1-86335-623-7(1)) Common Ground Publishing Pty, Ltd.

Pande, Ishita. Medicine, Race & Liberalism in British Bengal: Symptoms of Empire. 2009. (Routledge Studies in South Asian History Ser.). (ENG., Illus.). 272p. (C). 145.00 (978-0-415-77815-2(8)) Routledge.

BENGALI (SOUTH ASIAN PEOPLE)

Harder, Hans. Sufism & Saint Veneration in Contemporary Bangladesh. 2011. (Routledge Advances in South Asian Studies). (ENG., Illus.). 392p. (C). 148.00 (978-0-415-58170-7(2)) Routledge.

Mukharji, Projit Bihari. Nationalizing the Body: The Medical Market, Print & Daktari Medicine. (Anthem South Asian Studies). (ENG., Illus.). 368p. 2011. pap. 40.00 (978-0-85728-995-7(0)) 2009. 100.00 (978-1-84331-315-1(4)) Anthem Pr. GBR. Dist: Books International, Inc.

Zaman, Tasin. Food, Identity & Symbolic Metaphors in the Bengali-Canadian Community. 2010. 104p. pap. (978-3-8383-9063-5(6)) Lambert Academic Publishing.

BENGALI (SOUTH ASIAN PEOPLE)—FOLKLORE

Campbell, Alastair. Santal Folk Tales. (Folktale Ser.). reprint ed. 29.50 (978-0-404-16066-1(2)) AMS Pr., Inc.

McCulloch, W. Bengali Household Tales. (Folktale Ser.). reprint ed. 28.00 (978-0-404-16146-0(4)) AMS Pr., Inc.

BENGALI LANGUAGE

Bengali-English Dictionary, Modern. (BEN & ENG.). 29.95 (978-0-87557-109-6(3)) Saphrograph Corp.

Das, Shyamal. Essays in Linguistics. 2009. (978-81-8370-269-0(4), Library of Congress — New Delhi Overseas Office) Akansha Publishing House.

—Essays in Linguistics: Studies in Phonology, Syntax, & Sociolinguistics. 2009. xviii, 198p. (978-81-8370-184-6(1), Library of Congress — New Delhi Overseas Office) Akansha Publishing House.

Dash, Niladri. Corpus-Based Analysis of the Bengali Language. 2009. 252p. pap. (978-3-639-05774-4(0)) VDM Verlag Dr. Mueller e.K.

Dash, Niladri Sekhar. A Descriptive Study of the Modern Bengali Script. 2011. 312p. pap. **(978-3-8383-4448-5(0))** Lambert Academic Publishing.

Dil, Anwar S. & Dil, Afia. Bengali Language Movement & Creation of Bangladesh. 2011. (Illus.). 774p. **(978-984-20-0170-3(9))** Intercultural Forum.

Euro Talk. Talk Now! Bengali. 2008. 29.99 (978-1-84352-350-5(7)) TOPICS Entertainment.

Hanne-Ruth Thompson Staff. Bengali. 2010. (Comprehensive Grammars Ser.). (ENG., Illus.). 800p. 200.00 (978-0-415-41137-0(8)); pap. 110.00 (978-0-415-41139-4(4)) Routledge.

Hasan, A. A. Munir. Bengali-English English-Bengali Computer Science Glossary. 2009. (BEN & ENG.). iii, 90p. pap. (978-1-931546-57-7(6)) Dunwoody Pr.

Icon Group International, Inc. Staff, compiled by. Webster's Bengali - English Thesaurus Dictionary. 2008. 78p. ring bd. 28.95 incl. audio compact disk (978-0-497-83440-1(5)) Icon Group International, Inc.

Learn Bengali for English Speakers. (BEN & ENG.). pap. 20.95 (978-0-87557-005-1(4)) Saphrograph Corp.

Milles, Harriet. Bengali, 1 vol. 2012. (Languages of the World Ser.). (ENG & BEN.). 32p. (gr. 1-3). pap. 7.99 (978-1-4329-5843-5(7)); lib. bdg. 26.65 (978-1-4329-5835-0(6)) Heinemann-Raintree. (Heinemann First Library).

Mithun, Nasrin & Van der Wurff, Wim. Colloquial Bengali. 2009. (Colloquial Ser.). (BEN & ENG., Illus.). 288p. pap. 29.95 (978-0-415-26119-7(8)) Routledge.

Radice, William. Complete Bengali: A Teach Yourself Guide. 4th ed. 2011. (Teach Yourself Language Ser.). (ENG., Illus.). 448p. pap. 32.00 (978-0-07-176703-3(7), 0071767037) McGraw-Hill Cos., The.

—Complete Bengali with Two Audio CDs: A Teach Yourself Guide. 4th ed. 2011. (Teach Yourself Language Ser.). (ENG., Illus.). 448p. pap. 46.00 incl. audio compact disk, audio compact disk (978-0-07-176702-6(9), 0071767029) McGraw-Hill Cos., The.

Tagore, Rabindranath, et al. Selected Writings on Literature & Language. 2011. (ENG., Illus.). 432p. pap. 29.95 (978-0-19-806968-3(5)) Oxford Univ. Pr., Inc.

Thompson, Hanne-Ruth. Bengali (Bangla)-English/ English-Bengali (Bangla) Practical Dictionary. 2011. (BEN & ENG.). 224p. pap. **(978-0-7818-1270-2(4))** Hippocrene Bks., Inc.

—Bengali (Bangla)-English/English-Bengali (Bangla) Dictionary & Phrasebook. 2010. (BEN & ENG.). 248p. pap. (978-0-7818-1252-8(6)) Hippocrene Bks., Inc.

—Bengali Concise Dict. 2007. (ENG.). 400p. pap. 14.95 (978-0-7818-1195-8(3)) Hippocrene Bks., Inc.

VV., AA., et al. Lonely Planet Hindi, Urdu y Bengali: Para el Viajero. Vladisavljevic, Branislava, ed. 2007. (ENG., Illus.). 303p. per. 9.99 (978-84-08-06469-5(X)) Lonely Planet Pubns.

BENGALI LITERATURE

Bardhan, Kalpana. Anthology of Bengali Literature, 1941-1991, 2 vols., Vol. II. 2011. (ENG., Illus.). 552p. 50.00 (978-0-19-806461-9(6)) Oxford Univ. Pr., Inc.

—The Oxford India Anthology of Bengali Literature, 1861-1941, 2 vols., Vol. 1. 2011. (ENG., Illus.). 496p. 50.00 (978-0-19-806462-6(4)) Oxford Univ. Pr., Inc.

Mukharji, Projit Bihari. Nationalizing the Body: The Medical Market, Print & Daktari Medicine. (Anthem South Asian Studies). (ENG., Illus.). 368p. 2011. pap. 40.00 (978-0-85728-995-7(0)) 2009. 100.00 (978-1-84331-315-1(4)) Anthem Pr. GBR. Dist: Books International, Inc.

Sinha-Ray, Mondira. The Meditating Cat - Bengali Proverbs & Their Echoes in Far Cultures. 2011. 350p. pap. **(978-1-908341-24-2(6))** Paragon Publishing, Rothersthorpe.

BENGALI LITERATURE—HISTORY AND CRITICISM

Dhingra, Lavina & Cheung, Floyd, eds. Naming Jhumpa Lahiri: Canons & Controversies. 2012. (ENG., Illus.). 254p. (gr. 17). pap. 32.99 **(978-0-7391-7587-3(4))** Lexington Bks.

Mitra, Priti Kumar. The Dissent of Nazrul Islam: Poetry & History. 2009. (ENG., Illus.). 356p. 27.95 (978-0-19-806324-7(5)) Oxford Univ. Pr., Inc.

Pal, Pratapaditya, ed. Something Old, Something New: Rabindranath Tagore's 150th Birth Anniversary. 2011. (ENG.). 204p. 68.00 (978-93-80581-05-7(X)) Marg Pubns. IND. Dist: National Bk. Network.

BENIN

Bernan Press/ WTO Staff. Trade Policy Review: Benin, Burkina Faso, & Mali 2010. 2011. (ENG.). pap. 75.00 **(978-1-59888-459-3(X))** Bernan Assocs.

Bickford-Berzock, Kathleen. Benin: Royal Arts of a West African Kingdom. 2008. (ENG., Illus.). 36p. pap. 9.95 (978-0-300-13677-7(3)) Art Institute of Chicago.

Bindloss, Harold. In the Niger Country. 2009. 352p. pap. 32.75 (978-1-116-08160-2(1)); pap. 31.75 (978-1-116-08161-9(X)) BiblioBazaar.

—In the Niger Country. 2008. 352p. 46.95 (978-1-4369-7868-2(8)); pap. 31.95 (978-1-4368-8110-4(2)) Kessinger Publishing, LLC.

Claffey, Patrick. Christian Churches in Dahomey-Benin: A Study of Their Socio-Political Role. 2007. (Studies of Religion in Africa Ser.). (Illus.). 328p. (978-90-04-15572-5(4)) BRILL.

Locken, E. Travel Journal Benin. 2010. 192p. pap. 19.99 (978-0-557-43271-4(5)) Lulu Enterprises Inc.

BENIN (NIGERIA)

Plankensteiner, Barbara. Benin. 2010. (ENG., Illus.). 136p. pap. 34.95 (978-88-7439-410-4(1)) 5 Continents ITA. Dist: Hachette Bk. Group.

BENIN CITY (NIGERIA)

Gore Charles. Art, Performance & Ritual in Benin City. Peel, J. D. Y. et al, eds. 2008. (International African Library). (ENG., Illus.). 256p. (gr. 17). 100.00 (978-0-7486-3316-6(2)) Edinburgh Univ. Pr. GBR. Dist: Columbia Univ. Pr.

BENJAMIN (BIBLICAL FIGURE)

Jules, Jacqueline. Benjamin & the Silver Goblet. 2009. (Bible Ser.). (Illus.). 32p. (J). (gr. k-4). bds. 8.95 (978-0-8225-8758-3(0), Kar-Ben Publishing) Lerner Publishing Group.

BENJAMIN, J. P. (JUDAH PHILIP), 1811-1884

Butler, Pierce. Judah P. Benjamin. 2010. 474p. pap. 37.75 (978-1-148-60541-8(X)); 468p. pap. 37.75 (978-1-147-67657-0(7)); 478p. pap. 37.75 (978-1-144-05759-4(0)); 462p. pap. 36.75 (978-1-142-10476-4(1)) BiblioBazaar.

—Judah P. Benjamin. 2009. 254p. pap. (978-1-150-67183-8(1)) Books LLC.

—Judah P. Benjamin. 2007. 458p. 52.95 (978-0-548-15824-1(X)); 460p. per. 37.95 (978-1-4304-5324-6(9)) Kessinger Publishing, LLC.

—Judah P. Benjamin. (American Crisis Biographies Ser.). 459p. reprint ed. 98.00 (978-0-7222-8434-6(9)) Library Reprints, Inc.

—Judah P. Benjamin. 2007. 464p. per. (978-1-4086-0748-0(4)) Read Bks.

Kohler, Max J. Judah P Benjamin: Statesman & Jurist (1905) 2007. 32p. per. 15.95 (978-0-548-58227-5(0)) Kessinger Publishing, LLC.

Osterweis, Rollin. Judah P Benjamin - Statesman of the Lost Cause. 2007. 216p. per. (978-1-4067-2603-9(6)) Read Bks.

BENJAMIN, WALTER, 1892-1940

Adorno, Theodor W., ed. Current of Music. 2009. (ENG.). 480p. pap. 29.95 (978-0-7456-4286-4(1)) Polity Pr. GBR. Dist: Wiley, John & Sons, Inc.

—Current of Music: Elements of a Radio Theory. 2009. (ENG.). 480p. 79.95 (978-0-7456-4285-7(3)) Polity Pr. GBR. Dist: Wiley, John & Sons, Inc.

Bavidge, Jenny. Theorists of the City. 2009. (Routledge Critical Thinkers Ser.). 224p. 23.95 (978-0-415-33852-3(2)); 100.00 (978-0-415-33851-6(4)) Routledge.

Beasley-Murray, Tim & Beasley-murray, Tim. Mikhail Bakhtin & Walter Benjamin: Experience & Form. 2008. (ENG.). 256p. 100.00 (978-0-230-53535-0(6)) Palgrave Macmillan.

Benjamin, Andrew & Rice, Charles, eds. Walter Benjamin & the Architecture of Modernity. 2009. (Anamnesis Ser.). 226p. pap. 25.00 (978-0-9805440-2-2(5)) re.press AUS. Dist: Lightning Source, Inc.

Benjamin, Walter. Archive: Images, Texts, Signs. Marx, Ursula et al, eds. Leslie, Esther, tr. from GER. 2007. (ENG., Illus.). 311p. 27.95 (978-1-84467-196-0(8), 844196) Verso Bks. GBR. Dist: Norton, W. W. & Co., Inc.

—Walter Benjamin: Selected Writings, 1938-1940, 4 vols., Volume 4. Eiland, Howard & Jennings, Michael W., eds. Jephcott, Edmund, tr. from GER. 2006. (Illus.). 496p. per. 25.00 (978-0-674-02229-4(7), Belknap Pr.) Harvard Univ. Pr.

—The Work of Art in the Age of Its Technological Reproducibility, & Other Writings on Media. Jennings, Michael W. et al, eds. Jephcott, Edmund & Livingstone, Rodney, trs. from GER. 2008. (Illus.). 448p. pap. 18.95 (978-0-674-02445-8(1), Belknap Pr.) Harvard Univ. Pr.

Benjamin, Walter & Adorno, Gretel. Correspondence 1930-1940. Lonitz, Henri & Godde, Christoph, eds. Honban, Weiland, tr. from GER. 2008. (ENG., Illus.). 336p. 19.95 (978-0-7456-3669-6(1)) Polity Pr. GBR. Dist: Wiley, John & Sons, Inc.

Benjamin, Walter & Eiland, Howard. Early Writings (1910-1917) 2011. 320p. 27.95 (978-0-674-04993-2(4), Belknap Pr.) Harvard Univ. Pr.

Betancourt, Alex. Walter Benjamin & Sigmund Freud Between Theory & Politics. 2008. 180p. per. (978-3-8364-3854-4(2)) VDM Verlag Dr. Mueller e.K.

Boscagli, Maurizia & Duffy, Enda, eds. Joyce, Benjamin & Magical Urbanism. 2011. (Illus.). 254p. pap. 75.00 **(978-90-420-3425-9(4))** Rodopi.

Buse, Peter, et al. Benjamin's Arcades: An Unguided Tour. 2006. (Encounters: Cultural Histories Ser.). (ENG., Illus.). 224p. pap. 23.00 (978-0-7190-6989-5(0)) Manchester Univ. Pr. GBR. Dist: Macmillan.

Djerassi, Carl. Four Jews on Parnassus - A Conversation Vol. 1: Benjamin, Adorno, Scholem, Schönberg. 2008. (ENG., Illus.). 232p. (gr. 17). 29.50 (978-0-231-14654-8(X)) Columbia Univ. Pr.

Downing, Eric. After Images: Photography, Archaeology, & Psychoanalysis & the Tradition of Bildung. 2006. (Kritik: German Literary Theory & Cultural Studies). (Illus.). 372p. 54.95 (978-0-8143-3301-3(X)) Wayne State Univ. Pr.

Eagleton, Terry. Walter Benjamin: Or, Towards a Revolutionary Criticism. 2009. (Radical Thinkers Ser.). (ENG.). 204p. pap. 12.95 (978-1-84467-350-6(2), 844350) Verso Bks. GBR. Dist: Norton, W. W. & Co., Inc.

Elliott, Brian. Benjamin for Architects. 2011. (Thinkers for Architects Ser.). (ENG., Illus.). 160p. (C). 120.00 (978-0-415-55814-3(X)); pap. 28.95 (978-0-415-55815-0(8)) Taylor & Francis Group GBR. (Routledge). Dist: Taylor & Francis Group.

Fenves, Peter. The Messianic Reduction: Walter Benjamin & the Shape of Time. 2010. (Meridian: Crossing Aesthetics Ser.). (ENG.). 336p. 65.00 (978-0-8047-5787-4(9)); pap. 24.95 (978-0-8047-5788-1(7)) Stanford Univ. Pr.

Ferris, David S. Walter Benjamin. 2008. (Cambridge Introductions to Literature Ser.). (ENG.). 176p. (C). pap. 22.00 (978-0-521-68308-1(4)) Cambridge Univ. Pr.

Forrest, Tara. The Politics of Imagination: Benjamin, Kracauer, Kluge. 2008. (ENG.). 198p. pap. 34.95 (978-3-89942-681-6(9)) Transcript Verlag DEU. Dist: Transaction Pubs.

Friedlander, Eli. Walter Benjamin: A Philosophical Portrait. 2012. (ENG.). 304p. 39.95 (978-0-674-06169-9(1)) Harvard Univ. Pr.

Garber, Klaus. Rezeption und Rettung: Drei Studien zu Walter Benjamin. (Studien und Texte zur Sozialgeschichte der Literatur Ser.). (GER.). VI, 201p. 90.00 (978-3-11-185580-6(5)) De Gruyter, Walter Inc.

Goebel, Rolf J., ed. A Companion to the Works of Walter Benjamin. 2009. (Studies in German Literature Linguistics & Culture Ser.: Volume 44). (Illus.). 328p. 90.00 (978-1-57113-367-0(4)) Camden Hse.

Hansen, Miriam Bratu. Cinema & Experience: Siegfried Kracauer, Walter Benjamin, & Theodor W. Adorno. Dimendberg, Edward, ed. 2011. (Weimar & Now: German Cultural Criticism Ser.). (ENG.). 368p. 70.00 (978-0-520-26559-2(9)); pap. 29.95 (978-0-520-26560-8(2)) Univ. of California Pr.

Hanssen, Beatrice, ed. Walter Benjamin & the Arcades Project. 2006. (Walter Benjamin Studies). (ENG., Illus.). 256p. 44.95 (978-0-8264-6387-6(8)); 160.00 (978-0-8264-6386-9(X)) Continuum International Publishing Group, Ltd. GBR. Dist: National Bk. Network.

Hartoonian, Gevork. Walter Benjamin & Architecture. Hartoonian, Gevork, ed. 2009. (ENG., Illus.). 192p. 125.00 (978-0-415-48292-9(5)) Routledge.

Haustein, Katja. Regarding Lost Time: Photography, Identity & Affect in Proust, Benjamin, & Barthes. 2012. (Legenda Main Ser.). (ENG., Illus.). 206p. (C). 89.50 (978-1-907747-91-5(5)) European Humanities Research Ctr. GBR. Dist: Brown, David Bk. Co., The.

Idel, Moshe. Saturn's Jews: On Witches' Sabbat & Sabbateanism. 2011. 208p. E-Book (978-1-4411-3731-9(9)); E-Book (978-1-4411-0502-8(6)) Continuum International Publishing Group, Ltd.

—Saturn's Jews: On Witches' Sabbat & Sabbateanism. 2011. (Robert & Arlene Kogod Library Judaic Studies). (ENG.). 216p. 140.00 (978-1-4411-2144-8(7)); pap. 44.95 (978-0-8264-4453-0(9)) Continuum International Publishing Group, Ltd. GBR. Dist: National Bk. Network.

Jenckes, Kate. Reading Borges after Benjamin: Allegory, Afterlife, & the Writing of History. 2008. (SUNY Series in Latin American & Iberian Thought & Culture). 165p. per. 24.95 (978-0-7914-6990-3(5)) State Univ. of New York Pr.

Kambas, Chryssoula. Momentaufnahme der europäischen Intelligenz: Moderne, Exil und Kulturtransfer in Walter Benjamins Werk. 2009. (GER.). 362p. (978-3-930345-52-6(8)) Offizin Zurich Verlag, OZV.

Kaulen, Heinrich. Rettung und Destruktion: Untersuchungen zur Hermeneutik Walter Benjamins. (Studien zur deutschen Literatur Ser.). (GER.). VI, 283p. 210.00 (978-3-11-183860-1(9)) De Gruyter, Walter Inc.

Leslie, Esther. Walter Benjamin. 2008. (Reaktion Books - Critical Lives Ser.). (ENG., Illus.). 192p. per. 16.95 (978-1-86189-343-7(4)) Reaktion Bks., Ltd. GBR. Dist: Chicago Distribution Ctr.

Lupton, Julia Reinhard & Reinhard, Kenneth. After Oedipus: Shakespeare in Psychoanalysis. 2009. (ENG.). 310p. pap. 28.00 (978-1-888570-35-9(0)) Davies Group Pubs., The.

Martel, James. Divine Violence: Walter Benjamin & the Eschatology of Sovereignty. 2011. 224p. 35.00 (978-0-415-67157-6(4)) Routledge.

—Textual Conspiracies: Walter Benjamin, Idolatry, & Political Theory. 2011. (ENG.). 318p. 75.00 (978-0-472-11772-7(6)) Univ. of Michigan Pr.

Martel, James R. Divine Violence. 2011. (ENG.). 168p. 120.00 (978-0-415-67345-7(3)) Routledge.

Martel, James R. Textual Conspiracies: Walter Benjamin, Idolatry, & Political Theory. 2011. 314p. E-Book (978-0-472-02819-1(7)) Univ. of Michigan Pr.

Nebelin, Marian. Walter Benjamin und Die Besiegten: Theologie, Verlust, Geschichte. 2007. (GER.). xii, 152p. pap. (978-3-8300-3035-5(5)) Kovac, Dr. Josef Wissenschaftsverlag.

Newman, Jane O. Benjamin's Library: Modernity, Nation, & the Baroque. 2011. (Signale: Modern German Letters, Cultures, & Thought Ser.). 272p. pap. 35.00 (978-0-8014-7659-4(3)) Cornell Univ. Pr.

Nurmi-Schomers, Susan. Visionen dichterischen 'Mündigwerdens' Poetologische Perspektiven auf Robert Musil, Rainer Maria Rilke und Walter Benjamin. 2008. (Untersuchungen zur deutschen Literaturgeschichte Ser.).Tr. of Visions of Poetic Coming of Age: Poetological Perspectives on Robert Musil, Rainer Maria Rilke & Walter Benjamin. (GER.). VIII, 344p. pap. (978-3-484-32134-2(2)) Verlag Max Niemeyer.

Oliveira, Luiz Sérgio de & D'Angelo, Martha. Walter Benjamin: Arte e Experiência. 2010. (POR.). 327p. (978-85-228-0526-6(1)); (978-85-85936-79-2(7)) Universidade Federal Fluminense. Editora.

Ombrosi, Orietta. The Twilight of Reason: Benjamin, Adorno, Horkheimer & Levinas Tested by the Catastrophe. 2011. (Emunot: Jewish Philosophy & Kabbalah Ser.). (ENG.). 200p. 65.00 (978-1-936235-75-9(7)) Academic Studies Pr.

Palmier, Jean-Michel & Perrier, Florent. Walter Benjamin: Le Chiffonnier, L'ange et le Petit Bossu: Esthétique et Politique Chez Walter Benjamin. 2006. (FRE., Illus.). 916p. (C). pap. 59.00 (978-2-252-03591-7(9)) Klincksieck, Editions FRA. Dist: ISD.

Perloff, Marjorie. Unoriginal Genius: Poetry by Other Means in the New Century. (Illus.). 232p. 2012. (ENG.). pap. 17.50 (978-0-226-66062-2(1)) 2010. 32.50 (978-0-226-66061-5(3)) Univ. of Chicago Pr.

Polsky, Stephanie. Walter Benjamin's Transit: A Destructive Tour of Modernity. 2010. xxiii, 283p. (978-1-933146-73-7(7)) Academica Pr., LLC.

Purdy, Daniel. On the Ruins of Babel: Architectural Metaphor in German Thought. 2010. (Signale: Modern German Letters, Cultures, & Thought Ser.). 272p. pap. 35.00 (978-0-8014-7676-1(3)) Cornell Univ. Pr.

Pusca, Anca M., ed. Walter Benjamin & the Aesthetics of Change. 2010. (ENG., Illus.). 240p. 89.00 (978-0-230-58086-2(6)) Palgrave Macmillan.

Richter, Gerhard. Thought-Images: Frankfurt School Writers' Reflections from Damaged Life. 2007. (Cultural Memory in the Present Ser.). (ENG., Illus.). 256p. 65.00 (978-0-8047-5616-7(3)); per. 24.95 (978-0-8047-5617-4(1)) Stanford Univ. Pr.

Rosenthal, Lecia. Mourning Modernism: Literature, Catastrophe, & the Politics of Consolation. 2nd ed. 2011. (ENG., Illus.). 176p. 52.00 (978-0-8232-3397-7(9)) Fordham Univ. Pr.

Salzani, Carlo. Constellations of Reading: Walter Benjamin in Figures of Actuality. 2008. (Cultural History & Literary Imagination Ser.). 387p. pap. 92.95 (978-3-03911-860-1(9)) Lang, Peter AG GBR. Dist: Lang, Peter.

Schmitt, Carl. Hamlet or Hecuba: The Intrusion of the Time into the Play. Pan, David & Rust, Jennifer, trs. from GER. 2009. 120p. pap. 19.95 net. (978-0-914386-42-1(5)) Telos Pr., Ltd.

Schmitt, Carl & Draghici, Simona. Hamlet or Hecuba: The Interruption of Time into Play. 2006. 76p. pap. 9.95 (978-0-943045-25-2(8)) Plutarch Pr.

Scholem, Gershom & Dannhauser, Werner J. On Jews & Judaism in Crisis: Selected Essays. 2012. (ENG.). 306p. pap. 18.95 (978-1-58988-074-0(9)) Dry, Paul Bks., Inc.

Schöler, Uli. Die DDR und Wolfgang Abendroth, Wolfgang Abendroth und Die DDR: Kritik Einer Kampagne. 2009. (GER.). 128p. (978-3-930345-65-6(X)) Offizin Zurich Verlag, OZV.

Shelton, Allen. Dreamworlds of Alabama. 2007. pap. (978-0-8166-5035-4(7)); (Illus.). 240p. 22.95 (978-0-8166-5034-7(9)) Univ. of Minnesota Pr.

Spiropoulou, Angeliki. Virginia Woolf, Modernity & History: Constellations with Walter Benjamin. 2010. (ENG.). 240p. 84.00 (978-0-230-53758-3(8)) Palgrave Macmillan.

Steiner, Uwe. Walter Benjamin: An Introduction to His Work & Thought. Winkler, Michael, tr. from GER. (ENG.). 248p. 2012. pap. 20.00 (978-0-226-77222-6(5)) 2010. 35.00 (978-0-226-77221-9(7)) Univ. of Chicago Pr.

Stewart, Elizabeth. Catastrophe & Survival: Walter Benjamin & Psychoanalysis. 2009. (ENG., Illus.). 240p. 130.00 (978-1-4411-9632-3(3)) Continuum International Publishing Group, Ltd. GBR. Dist: National Bk. Network.

Stewart, Elizabeth. Catastrophe & Survival: Walter Benjamin & Psychoanalysis. 2012. (ENG., Illus.). 240p. pap. 39.95 (978-1-4411-1683-3(4)) Continuum International Publishing Group, Ltd. GBR. Dist: National Bk. Network.

Urbich, Jan. Darstellung bei Walter Benjamin: Die 'Erkenntniskritische Vorrede' im Kontext ästhetischer Darstellungstheorien der Moderne. 2011. (Studien zur deutschen Literatur Ser.).Tr. of Presentation in the Work of Walter Benjamin. (GER., Illus.). VII, 531p. 140.00 (978-3-11-026515-6(X)) De Gruyter, Walter Inc.

Visquerra Tischler, Serbio. Tiempo Y Emancipación. Mijail Bajtin Y Walter Benjamin En La Selva Lacandona., Vol. 3. 2008. (SPA.). 80p. pap. (978-99922-61-73-6(0)) F & G Editores.

Weber, Samuel. Benjamin's -Abilities. 2010. 376p. pap. 19.95 (978-0-674-04606-1(4)) Harvard Univ. Pr.

Wizisla, Erdmut. Walter Benjamin & Bertolt Brecht: The Story of a Friendship, 1924-1940. Shuttleworth, Christine, tr. from GER. 2009. (ENG., Illus.). 288p. 45.00 (978-0-300-13695-1(1)) Yale Univ. Pr.

Yacavone, Kathrin. Benjamin, Barthes & the Singularity of Photography. 2012. (ENG., Illus.). 272p. 110.00 (978-1-4411-1808-0(X)) Continuum International Publishing Group, Ltd. GBR. Dist: National Bk. Network.

Zathureczky, Kornél. The Messianic Disruption of Trinitarian Theology. 2009. (ENG.). 190p. 62.99 (978-0-7391-3150-3(8)) Lexington Bks.

BENN, GOTTFRIED, 1886-1956

Millington, Richard H. Snow from Broken Eyes: Cocaine in the Lives & Works of Three Expressionist Poets. 2011. (Australisch-Neuseeländische Studien zur deutschen Sprache und Literatur. Australian & New Zealand Studies in German Language & Literature Ser.). (ENG.). 341p. pap. (978-3-0343-1069-7(2)) Lang, Peter.

Travers, Martin. The Poetry of Gottfried Benn: Text & Selfhood. 2007. (Studies in Modern German Literature Ser.: Vol. 106). 428p. pap. 91.95 (978-3-03910-577-9(9)) Lang, Peter Publishing, Inc.

BENNET, ELIZABETH (FICTITIOUS CHARACTER)

Altman, Marsha, ed. The Road to Pemberley: An Anthology of New Pride & Prejudice Stories. 2011. (ENG.). 400p. pap. 14.95 (978-1-56975-934-9(0)) Ulysses Pr.

Bennett, John G. & Bennett, Elizabeth. Idiots in Paris: Diaries of J.G. Bennett & Elizabeth Bennett, 1949. 2008. (Illus.). 133p. pap. (978-1-881408-20-8(5)) Bennett Bks.

BENNETT, ARNOLD, 1867-1931

Bennett, Arnold. Arnold Bennett's Letters to His Nephew. 2007. (ENG.). 376p. 48.95 (978-0-548-11732-3(2)) Kessinger Publishing, LLC.

—Over There. 2008. 104p. pap. 6.99 (978-1-60450-327-2(0)) Arc Manor.

—Over There. 2009. 64p. pap. (978-1-4588-9495-3(9)) Books LLC.

—Over There. 2009. 68p. pap. 14.14 (978-0-217-26767-0(X)) General Bks. LLC.

—Over There: War Scenes on the Western Front. 2007. 76p. per. (978-1-4065-4798-6(0)) Dodo Pr.

Crozier-De Rosa, Sharon. The Middle Class Novels of Arnold Bennett & Marie Corelli: Realising the Ideals & Emotions of Late Victorian Women. 2010. 440p. 129.95 (978-0-7734-3739-5(8)) Mellen, Edwin Pr., The.

Flower, Newmas. Journals of Arnold Bennett. 2006. 324p. per. (978-1-4067-1047-2(4), Hesperides Pr.) Read Bks.

Gide, André. Correspondance avec Francis Jammes, 1893-1938. (FRE.). 6.95 (978-0-8288-9776-1(X), F10253) French & European Pubns., Inc.

Newman, Flower. Journals of Arnold Bennett. 2006. 336p. per. (978-1-4067-3208-5(7), Hesperides Pr.) Read Bks.

BENNETT, TONY, 1926-

Bennett, Tony. The Good Life: the Autobiography of Tony Bennett. 2007. (ENG.). 304p. pap. 23.95 (978-1-4165-7366-1(6), Beyond Words/Atria Bks.) Atria Bks.

—Tony Bennett: Music of the Stars Volume 1. 2010. (ENG.). 80p. pap. 14.99 (978-1-4234-9717-2(1), 1423497171) Leonard, Hal Corp.

—Unti Tony Bennett. 2012. (ENG.). 336p. 27.99 (978-0-06-220706-7(7)) HarperCollins Pubs.

—Unti Tony Bennett LP. l.t. ed. 2012. (ENG.). 336p. pap. 27.99 (978-0-06-220728-9(8), HarperLuxe) HarperCollins Pubs.

Bennett, Tony, contrib. by. Tony Bennett — Duets II: Piano/Vocal/Guitar. 2012. (ENG.). 116p. pap. 21.99 (978-0-7390-8747-3(9)) Alfred Publishing Co., Inc.

Evanier, David. All the Things You Are: The Life of Tony Bennett. l.t. ed. 2011. (Illus.). 567p. 31.99 (978-1-4104-4228-4(4)) Thorndike Pr.

—All the Things You Are: The Life of Tony Bennett. 2011. (ENG., Illus.). 352p. 26.95 (978-0-470-52065-9(5), Wiley) Wiley, John & Sons, Inc.

BENNINGTON COUNTY (VT.)

Smith, Richard B. The Revolutionary War in Bennington County: A History & Guide. 2008. pap. 19.99 (978-1-59629-444-8(2)) History Pr., The.

BENSERADE, ISAAC DE, 1613-1671

Burden, Michael & Thorp, Jennifer, eds. The Ballet de la Nuit: Rothschild B1/16/6. 2009. (ENG., Illus.). 360p. 86.00 (978-1-57647-143-2(8)) Pendragon Pr.

BENSON, ROBERT HUGH, 1871-1914

Benson, Arthur Christopher. Hugh: Memoirs of A Brother. 2007. 152p. per. (978-1-4065-4819-8(7)) Dodo Pr.

—Hugh: Memoirs of A Brother. 2007. (ENG.). 314p. 45.95 (978-0-548-25349-6(8)); 316p. per. 30.95 (978-1-4326-5660-7(0)) Kessinger Publishing, LLC.

—Hugh Memoirs of A Brother. 2006. 308p. per. (978-1-4067-1290-2(6), Hesperides Pr.) Read Bks.

BENSON (MINN.)

Lovoll, Odd S. Norwegians on the Prairie: Ethnicity & the Development of the Country Town. 2007. (ENG., Illus.). 344p. per. 22.95 (978-0-87351-603-7(6)) Minnesota Historical Society Pr.

BENTHAM, JEREMY, 1748-1832

Bentham, Jeremy. The Correspondence of Jeremy Bentham, 1752-1780, Vols. 1 & 2. (978-0-485-13200-7(1)) Continuum International Publishing Group, Ltd.

—Rationale of Punishment. 2008. (ENG.). 360p. pap. 12.98 (978-1-59102-627-3(X)) Prometheus Bks., Pubs.

Blake, Kathleen. The Pleasures of Benthamism: Victorian Literature, Utility, Political Economy. 2010. (ENG.). 288p. 95.00 (978-0-19-956326-5(8)) Oxford Univ. Pr., Inc.

Brunon-Ernst, Anne. Beyond Foucault: New Perspectives on Bentham's Panopticon. 2012. 200p. 124.95 (978-0-7546-6843-5(6)) Ashgate Publishing Co.

Brunon-Ernst, Anne. Utilitarian Biopolitics: Bentham, Foucault & Modern Power, 1 vol. 2012. (ENG.). 224p. 99.00 (978-1-84893-169-5(7)) Pickering & Chatto Pubs., Ltd. GBR. Dist: Ashgate Publishing Co.

Campos Boralevi, Lea. Bentham & the Oppressed. (European University Institute - Series C Ser.). (ENG.). XII, 448p. 195.00 (978-3-11-181062-1(3)) De Gruyter, Walter Inc.

Collings, David. Monstrous Society: Reciprocity, Discipline, & the Political Uncanny, C. 1780/1848. 2009. 61.50 (978-0-8387-5720-8(0)) Bucknell Univ. Pr.

Harrison, Ross. Bentham-arg Philosophers. 2008. (ENG.). 302p. 45.00 (978-0-415-48765-8(X)) Routledge.

Kayser, Elmer L. Grand Social Enterprise: A Study of Jeremy Bentham in His Relation to Liberal Nationalism. (Columbia University, Studies in the Social Sciences: No. 377). reprint ed. 20.00 (978-0-404-51377-1(8)) AMS Pr., Inc.

Leavis, F. R. Mill on Bentham & Coleridge. 2008. 180p. (978-1-4437-2590-3(0)) 2006. 176p. per. (978-1-4067-3728-8(3)) Read Bks. (Hesperides Pr.).

MacCunn, John. Six Radical Thinkers: Bentham, J. S. Mill, Cobden, Carlyle, Mazzini, T. H. Green. 2007. (ENG.). 274p. 42.95 (978-0-548-18676-3(6)); 276p. per. 27.95 (978-1-4304-9028-9(4)) Kessinger Publishing, LLC.

Parekh, Bhikhu, ed. Jeremy Bentham. 2010. (Routledge Revivals Ser.). (ENG.). 234p. 120.00 (978-0-415-69186-4(9)) Routledge.

Rosen, Frederick, ed. Bentham. 2007. (International Library of Essays in the History of Social & Political Thought Ser.). 622p. 350.00 (978-0-7546-2566-7(4)) Ashgate Publishing Co.

Schofield, Philip. The Spinning World: A Global History of Cotton Textiles, 1200-1850. 2009. (ENG.). 384p. pap. 50.00 (978-0-19-956336-4(5)) Oxford Univ. Pr., Inc.

—The Spinning World: A Global History of Cotton Textiles, 1200-1850. Parthasarathi, Prasannan & Riello, Giorgio, eds. 2006. (Pasold Studies in Textile History Ser.). (ENG.). 384p. 135.00 (978-0-19-820856-3(1)) Oxford Univ. Pr., Inc.

Schofield, Philip & Schofield, Philip. Bentham 2009. (Guides for the Perplexed Ser.). (ENG.). 192p. 27.95 (978-0-8264-9590-7(7)); 90.00 (978-0-8264-9589-1(3)) Continuum International Publishing Group, Ltd. GBR. Dist: National Bk. Network.

Sokol, Mary. Bentham Law & Marriage: A Utilitarian Code of Law in Historical Contexts. 2011. (ENG.). 208p. 120.00 (978-1-4411-3293-2(7)) Continuum International Publishing Group, Ltd. GBR. Dist: National Bk. Network.

Stephen, Leslie. The English Utilitarians. 2009. 532p. 36.99 (978-1-113-70514-3(0)) BiblioBazaar.

—The English Utilitarians. 2011. (Cambridge Library Collection - Philosophy Ser.). (ENG.). 536p. pap. 39.99 (978-1-108-04102-7(7)); 394p. pap. 31.99 (978-1-108-04101-0(9)) Cambridge Univ. Pr.

—The English Utilitarians. 2009. 260p. pap. (978-1-4099-5743-0(8)) 2008. 300p. pap. (978-1-4099-1829-5(7)) Dodo Pr.

Waldron, Jeremy. Nonsense upon Stilts. 2007. 304p. 26.95 (978-0-415-95678-9(1)); 95.00 (978-0-415-95679-6(X)) Routledge.

BENTHOS

Caskey, B. J., et al. Breakpoint Analysis & Assessment of Selected Stressor Variables on Benthic Macroinvertebrate & Fish Communities in Indiana Streams: Implications for Developing Nutrient Criteria. 2010. (Illus.). vi, 35p. (978-1-4113-2786-3(1)) United States Geological Survey.

Danovaro, Roberto. Methods for the Study of Deep-Sea Sediments, Their Functioning & Biodiversity. Danovaro, Roberto, ed. 2009. (ENG., Illus.). 458p. 144.95 (978-1-4398-1137-5(7), CRC Press) Taylor & Francis Group GBR. Dist: Taylor & Francis Group.

Giere, Olav. Meiobenthology: The Microscopic Motile Fauna of Aquatic Sediments. 2nd ed. 2008. (Illus.). 550p. 159.00 (978-3-540-68657-6(6), 3540686576) Springer.

Gray, John S. & Elliot, Michael. Ecology of Marine Sediments: From Science to Management. 2nd ed. 2009. (ENG., Illus.). 240p. pap. 65.00 (978-0-19-856902-2(5)) Oxford Univ. Pr., Inc.

Gray, John S. & Elliott, Michael. Ecology of Marine Sediments: From Science to Management. 2nd ed. 2009. (ENG., Illus.). 240p. 145.00 (978-0-19-856901-5(7)) Oxford Univ. Pr., Inc.

Harris, Peter T. & Baker, Elaine K., eds. Seafloor Geomorphology as Benthic Habitat: GeoHAB Atlas of Seafloor Geomorphic Features & Benthic Habitats. 2011. (ENG.). 936p. 130.00 (978-0-12-385140-6(8)) Elsevier Science & Technology Bks.

Kashuba, Roxolana. Multilevel Hierarchical Modeling of Benthic Macroinvertebrate Responses to Urbanization in Nine Metropolitan Regions Across the Conterminous United States. 2010. (Illus.). xi, 88p. (978-1-4113-2675-0(X)) United States Geological Survey.

Littler, Diane Scullion, et al. Submersed Plants of the Indian River Lagoon: A Floristic Inventory & Field Guide. 2008. (Illus.). 286p. (978-0-9678901-2-8(8)) Offshore Graphics, Inc.

Naser, Humood. Using MacRobenthos As a Tool in Ecological Impact Assessment. 2010. 264p. pap. (978-3-8383-4251-1(8)) Lambert Academic Publishing.

Widmark, J. G. V. Deep-Sea Benthic Foraminifera from Cretaceous-Paleogene Boundary Strata in the South Atlantic: Taxonomy & Paleoecology, Number 43. 2006. (Fossils & Strata Monograph Ser.: 43). (ENG.). 96p. pap. 44.95 (978-82-00-37667-5(2), Wiley-Blackwell) Wiley, John & Sons, Inc.

BENTINCK, GEORGE, LORD, 1802-1848

Disraeli, Benjamin. Lord George Bentinck. 2008. 148p. 24.99 (978-0-554-27607-6(0)); 21.99 (978-0-554-36910-5(9)) BiblioBazaar.

—Lord George Bentinck. 2007. 92p. per. (978-1-4068-6134-1(0)) Echo Library.

—Lord George Bentinck: A Political Biography. 2007. (ENG.). 130p. pap. 18.99 (978-1-4346-3582-2(1)); 144p. pap. 19.99 (978-1-4346-3583-9(X)) BiblioBazaar.

BENTINCK, WILLIAM HENRY CAVENDISH, LORD, 1774-1839

Rosselli, John. Lord William Bentinck & the British Occupation of Sicily, 1811-1814. 2008. (ENG.). 236p. pap. 34.99 (978-0-521-08877-0(1)) Cambridge Univ. Pr.

BENTLEY, RICHARD, 1662-1742

Bentley, Richard. The Correspondence of Richard Bentley, 2 vols. Monk, James Henry, ed. 2009. (Cambridge Library Collection - Cambridge Ser.). (ENG.). 220p. pap. 64.00 (978-1-108-00054-3(1)); 420p. pap. 31.99 (978-1-108-00056-7(8)); 468p. pap. 34.99 (978-1-108-00055-0(X)) Cambridge Univ. Pr.

Haugen, Kristine Louise. Richard Bentley: Poetry & Enlightenment. 2011. (Illus.). 352p. E-Book 39.95 (978-0-674-06100-2(4)); (ENG., 344p. 39.95 (978-0-674-05871-2(2)) Harvard Univ. Pr.

BENTLEY AUTOMOBILE

Bennett, Martin. Bentley Continental: Corniche & Azure, 1951-2002. 2nd rev. ed. 2010. (ENG., Illus.). 256p. 150.00 (978-1-84584-210-9(3), 1845842103) Veloce Publishing Ltd. GBR. Dist: MBI Distribution Services/Quayside Distribution.

—Bentley Continental, Corniche & Azure. (Illus.). 224p. lthr. (978-1-901295-16-0(8)) Veloce Publishing Ltd. GBR. Dist: MBI Distribution Services/Quayside Distribution.

—Bentley Continental, Corniche & Azure - 1951 to 1998. (Illus.). 224p. (978-1-901295-12-2(5)) Veloce Publishing Ltd. GBR. Dist: MBI Distribution Services/Quayside Distribution.

—Rolls-Royce & Bentley: The Crewe Years. 3rd ed. 2012. (ENG., Illus.). 480p. 120.00 (978-1-84425-481-1(X), 184425481X) Haynes Publishing PLC GBR. Dist: MBI Distribution Services/Quayside Distribution.

Bobbitt, Malcolm. Rolls-Royce Silver Shadow Bentley T-Series: Including Corniche, Camargue, Silver Shadow II & Bentley T2 - 1965 to 1995. 2008. (Essential Buyer's Guide Ser.). (ENG., Illus.). 64p. pap. 19.95

(978-1-84584-146-1(8), 1845841468) Veloce Publishing Ltd. GBR. Dist: MBI Distribution Services/Quayside Distribution.

—Silver Shadow & Bentley T-Series. rev. ed. (Illus.). 160p. lthr. *(978-1-901295-68-9(0))* Veloce Publishing Ltd. GBR. Dist: MBI Distribution Services/Quayside Distribution.

Dron, Tony & de Burton, Simon. The Bentley Brooklands. 2010. (ENG., Illus.). 208p. pap. 195.00 *(978-1-85894-549-1(6))* Merrell Pubs. Ltd. GBR. Dist: Perseus Distribution.

Nutland, Martyn. Bentley MKVI: Rolls-Royce Silver Wraith, Silver Dawn & Silver Cloud - Bentley R-Series & S-Series. 2007. (Classic Reprint Ser.). (ENG., Illus.). 176p. 69.95 *(978-1-84584-068-6(2)*, 1845840682) Veloce Publishing Ltd. GBR. Dist: MBI Distribution Services/Quayside Distribution.

Robson, Graham. Bentley: A Legend Reborn. 2nd ed. 2010. (Haynes Classic Makes Ser.). (ENG., Illus.). 184p. 34.95 *(978-1-84425-491-0(7)*, 1844254917) Haynes Publishing PLC GBR. Dist: MBI Distribution Services/Quayside Distribution.

Taylor, James. Bentley 3 Litre & 4 1/2 Litre. 2012. (In Detail Ser.). (ENG., Illus.). 160p. 64.95 *(978-1-906133-30-6(1)*, 1906133301) Herridge & Sons, Ltd. GBR. Dist: MBI Distribution Services/Quayside Distribution.

—Original Rolls-Royce & Bentley, 1946-65: The Restorer's Guide to the 'Standard' Saloons & Mainstream Coachbuilt Derivatives. 2008. (Original Ser.). (ENG., Illus.). 160p. 54.95 *(978-1-906133-06-1(9)*, 1906133069) Herridge & Sons, Ltd. GBR. Dist: MBI Distribution Services/Quayside Distribution.

Venables, David. Bentley: A Racing History. 2011. (ENG., Illus.). 304p. 59.95 *(978-0-85733-021-5(7)*, 0857330217) Haynes Publishing PLC GBR. Dist: MBI Distribution Services/Quayside Distribution.

BENTON, THOMAS HART, 1782-1858

Meigs, William M. The Life of Thomas Hart Benton. 2007. (ENG.). 548p. 57.95 *(978-0-548-36332-4(3))*; per. 42.95 *(978-0-548-30622-2(2))* Kessinger Publishing, LLC.

—The Life of Thomas Hart Benton. (Illus.). 535p. reprint ed. lib. bdg. 98.00 *(978-0-7222-0728-4(X))* Library Reprints, Inc.

Meigs, William Montgomery. The Life of Thomas Hart Benton. 2009. 350p. pap. 25.32 *(978-1-4589-2693-7(1))* General Bks. LLC.

—The Life of Thomas Hart Benton. 535p. reprint ed. 98.00 *(978-0-7222-8988-4(X))* Library Reprints, Inc.

Rogers, Joseph Morgan. Thomas H. Benton. (American Crisis Biographies Ser.). 361p. reprint ed. 98.00 *(978-0-7222-8989-1(8))*; 98.00 *(978-0-7222-8446-9(2))* Library Reprints, Inc.

Roosevelt, Theodore. The Life of Thomas Hart Benton. (American Statesmen Ser.). 372p. reprint ed. 98.00 *(978-0-7222-8990-7(1))* Library Reprints, Inc.

—Thomas H. Benton. 2009. (ENG.). 367p. pap. 25.99 *(978-1-117-02762-3(7)*, BiblioLife) BiblioBazaar.

—Thomas Hart Benton. 2010. 390p. pap. 33.75 *(978-1-142-99906-3(8))* 2010. 392p. pap. 33.75 *(978-1-142-82800-4(X))* 2010. 390p. pap. 33.75 *(978-1-142-96880-9(4))* 2010. 392p. pap. 33.75 *(978-1-142-98591-2(1))* 2008. 380p. pap. 29.99 *(978-0-559-32543-4(6))* 2008. 380p. pap. 32.75 *(978-0-559-32542-7(8))* BiblioBazaar.

—Thomas Hart Benton. 2009. 180p. pap. 19.99 *(978-1-4590-0705-5(0))* General Bks. LLC.

—Thomas Hart Benton. 372p. reprint ed. 98.00 *(978-0-7222-8504-6(3))* Library Reprints, Inc.

BENTON, THOMAS HART, 1889-1975

Adams, Henry. Tom & Jack: The Intertwined Lives of Thomas Hart Benton & Jackson Pollock. 2009. (ENG.). 416p. 35.00 *(978-1-59691-420-9(3))* Bloomsbury Publishing.

Berardi, Marianne & Adams, Henry. Discovering Margot Peet: The Artist & the Art World of Kansas City. 2008. *(978-1-889274-32-4(1))* Posterity Pr.

Mazow, Leo G. & Benton, Thomas Hart. Shallow Creek: Thomas Hart Benton & American Waterways. 2007. (Penn State Press Ser.). (ENG., Illus.). 60p. per. 24.95 *(978-0-911209-66-2(2))* Pennsylvania State Univ. Pr.

Mazow, Leo G. & Benton, Thomas Hart. Thomas Hart Benton & the American Sound. 2012. (ENG.). 200p. ***(978-0-271-05083-6(7))*** Pennsylvania State Univ. Pr.

Wolff, Justin. Thomas Hart Benton: A Life, 1 vol. 2012. (ENG., Illus.). 416p. 40.00 ***(978-0-374-19987-6(6))*** Farrar, Straus & Giroux.

BENTON FAMILY

Benton, Obie Folsom. Journey of a Pilgrim Family: The Bentons Come to America: With an Autobiography of Obie Folsom Benton. 2010. vi, 301p. ***(978-0-9741186-8-0(0))*** AAA-Writer's Inkhorn.

BENUE RIVER (CAMEROON AND NIGERIA)

Balfour Baikie, William. Narrative of an Exploring Voyage up the Rivers Kwo'Ra & Bi'Nue In 1854. 2007. 480p. per. *(978-1-905748-43-3(4))* Rediscovery Bks.

Crowther, Samuel. Journal of an Expedition up the Niger & Tshadda Rivers: Undertaken by Macgregor Laird, Esq. in Connection with the British Government, In 1854. 2010. (Cambridge Library Collection - Religion Ser.). (Illus.). 268p. pap. 23.99 *(978-1-108-01183-9(7))* Cambridge Univ. Pr.

BEN-YEHUDA, ELIEZER, 1858-1922

Kuzar, Ron. Hebrew & Zionism: A Discourse Analytic Cultural Study. (Language, Power & Social Process [LPSP] Ser.). (ENG.). XII, 324p. 84.00 ***(978-3-11-181137-6(9))***; 196.00 ***(978-3-11-187068-7(5))*** De Gruyter, Mouton DEU. Dist: de Gruyter, Walter GmbH & Co. KG.

Saposnik, Arieh Bruce. Becoming Hebrew: The Creation of a Jewish National Culture in Ottoman Palestine. 2008. (ENG., Illus.). 256p. 65.00 *(978-0-19-533121-9(4))* Oxford Univ. Pr., Inc.

Stavans, Ilan. Resurrecting Hebrew. 2008. (Jewish Encounters Ser.). (ENG.). 256p. 21.00 *(978-0-8052-4231-7(7)*, Schocken) Knopf Doubleday Publishing Group.

BENZENE

Tranfo, Giovanna. Benzene & its Derivatives: New Uses & Impacts on Environment & Human Health. 2011. (Materials Science & Technologies Ser.). 140.00 ***(978-1-62100-026-6(5))*** Nova Science Pubs., Inc.

BENZODIAZEPINES

Mercer, E. Robert. Worse Than Heroin. 2008. 201p. pap. 15.95 *(978-1-4357-1685-8(X))* Lulu Enterprises Inc.

Müller, Walter Erhard, et al. The Benzodiazepine Receptor: Drug Acceptor Only or a Physiologically Relevant Part of Our Central Nervous System? 2009. (Scientific Basis of Psychiatry Ser.). (ENG.). 196p. pap. 46.00 *(978-0-521-11527-8(2))* Cambridge Univ. Pr.

Otto, Michael W. & Pollack, Mark H. Stopping Anxiety Medication. 2nd ed. 2009. (Treatments That Work Ser.). (ENG.). 160p. pap., wbk. ed. 24.95 *(978-0-19-533855-3(3))*; (Illus.). 192p. pap., instr.'s gde. ed. 35.00 *(978-0-19-533854-6(5))* Oxford Univ. Pr., Inc.

Salamone, Salvatore J., ed. Benzodiazepines & GHB: Detection & Pharmacology. 2010. (Forensic Science & Medicine Ser.). (Illus.). 160p. pap. 139.00 *(978-1-61737-287-2(0)*, 1617372870) Humana Pr.

BEOWULF

Anderson, Earl R. Understanding Beowulf as an Indo-European Epic: A Study in Comparative Mythology. 2010. iv, 592p. *(978-0-7734-3755-5(X))* Mellen, Edwin Pr., The.

Anonymous. Beowulf. Raffel, Burton, tr. from ANG. & intro. by. 2008. (ENG.). 176p. (Orig.). (gr. 12-18). 4.95 *(978-0-451-53096-7(9)*, Signet Classics) Penguin Group (USA) Inc.

Beowulf. pap. *(978-0-7653-4045-0(3))*; *(978-0-7653-0140-6(7))* Doherty, Tom Assocs., LLC. (Forge Bks.).

Chambers, R. W. Beowulf: An Introduction to the Study of the Poem with a Discussion of the Stories of Offa & Finn. 3rd rev. ed. 2009. 648p. pap. 61.00 *(978-0-521-10062-5(3))* Cambridge Univ. Pr.

—Beowulf: An Introduction to the Study of the Poem, with A Discussion of the Stories of Offa & Finn (1921) 448p. 2008. 51.95 *(978-1-4365-9444-8(8))* 2007. per. 36.95 *(978-0-548-79379-4(4))* Kessinger Publishing, LLC.

Clemoes, Peter. Interactions of Thought & Language in Old English Poetry. 2006. (Cambridge Studies in Anglo-Saxon England Ser.). (ENG.). 544p. pap. 95.00 *(978-0-521-03516-3(3))* Cambridge Univ. Pr.

Drout, M. D. C. Beowulf & Critics-2Nd Rev Ed. Cb. 2nd rev. ed. 2011. xxv, 479p. ***(978-0-86698-450-8(X)***, Renaissance Society of America) MRTS.

Eickhoff, Lee Randy. Beowulf. rev. ed. Date not set. pap. *(978-0-7653-0141-3(5)*, Forge Bks.) Doherty, Tom Assocs., LLC.

Fulk, R. D., et al, eds. Klaeber's Beowulf. 4th ed. 2008. (ENG.). 704p. *(978-0-8020-9843-6(6))* Univ. of Toronto Pr.

George, Jodi-Anne. Beowulf. 2010. (Readers' Guides to Essential Criticism Ser.). (ENG.). 192p. 68.00 *(978-1-4039-9128-7(6))*; pap. 20.95 *(978-1-4039-9129-4(4))* Palgrave Macmillan.

Gwara, Scott. Heroic Identity in the World of Beowulf. 2008. (Medieval & Renaissance Authors & Texts Ser.). 412p. *(978-90-04-17170-1(3))* BRILL.

Hill, John M. The Narrative Pulse of Beowulf: Arrivals & Departures. (Toronto Old English Studies). (ENG.). 2009. 136p. pap. *(978-1-4426-1087-3(5))* 2008. 144p. *(978-0-8020-9329-5(9))* Univ. of Toronto Pr.

Kendall, Calvin B. The Metrical Grammar of Beowulf. 2006. (Cambridge Studies in Anglo-Saxon England Ser.). (ENG.). 336p. pap. 63.00 *(978-0-521-03121-9(4))* Cambridge Univ. Pr.

Magennis, Hugh. Images of Community in Old English Poetry. 2006. (Cambridge Studies in Anglo-Saxon England Ser.). (ENG.). 224p. pap. 42.00 *(978-0-521-03184-4(2))* Cambridge Univ. Pr.

—Translating Beowulf: Modern Versions in English Verse & Their Cultural Contexts. 2011. 254p. 90.00 *(978-1-84384-261-3(0)*, D. S. Brewer) Boydell & Brewer, Ltd. GBR. Dist: Boydell & Brewer, Inc.

Marshall, Henrietta Elizabeth. The Story of Beowulf. 2007. (Dover Children's Classics Ser.). (ENG.). 64p. per. 4.95 *(978-0-486-45449-8(5))* Dover Pubns., Inc.

McNamara, John, tr. & intro. Beowulf. 2007. (Barnes & Noble Classics Ser.). (ENG.). 176p. 7.95 *(978-1-59308-383-0(1))* Barnes & Noble, Inc.

Niles, John D. Beowulf & Lejre. 2006. (Illus.). xiv, 495p. (C). *(978-0-86698-368-6(6))* ACMRS.

Niles, John D., et al, eds. Klaeber's Beowulf. 4th ed. 2008. (Toronto Old English Studies). (Illus.). 704p. pap. *(978-0-8020-9567-1(4))* Univ. of Toronto Pr.

North, Richard. The Origins of Beowulf: From Vergil to Wiglaf. 2007. (Illus.). 400p. 150.00 *(978-0-19-920661-2(9))* Oxford Univ. Pr., Inc.

O'Donoghue, Heather, ed. Beowulf. Crossley-Holland, Kevin, tr. from ANG. 2008. (Oxford World's Classics Ser.). (ENG., Illus.). 176p. pap. 9.95 *(978-0-19-955529-1(X))* Oxford Univ. Pr., Inc.

Quasha, George. Monarch Notes on Beowulf. (C). 3.95 *(978-0-671-00550-4(2)*, Arco) Peterson's.

Ringler, Dick, tr. from ANG. & intro. Beowulf: A New Translation for Oral Delivery. 2007. 304p. pap. 9.95 *(978-0-87220-893-3(1))*; (Illus.). 27.95 *(978-0-87220-894-0(X))* Hackett Publishing Co., Inc.

Russom, Geoffrey. Beowulf & Old Germanic Metre. 2009. (Cambridge Studies in Anglo-Saxon England Ser.). (ENG.). 248p. pap. 34.99 *(978-0-521-09309-5(0))* Cambridge Univ. Pr.

Schulman, Jana K. & Szarmach, Paul E. Beowulf at Kalamazoo: Essays on Translation & Performance. 2012. ***(978-1-58044-152-0(1))*** Medieval Institute Pubns.

Slayton, Aumer. An Analysis of the Interpretations of the Finnsburg Documents. 2009. 40p. pap. 16.75 *(978-1-113-25429-0(7))* BiblioBazaar.

Stjerna, Knut. Essays on Questions Connected with the Old English Poem of Beowulf. Hall, J. R. Clark, tr. 2007. (ENG.). 316p. per. 30.95 *(978-0-548-79508-8(8))* Kessinger Publishing, LLC.

Stjerna, Knut Martin. Essays on Questions Connected with the Old English Poem of Beowulf. 2008. (ENG.). 320p. per. *(978-1-4086-6208-3(6))* Read Bks.

Vickrey, John F. Beowulf & the Illusion of History. 2009. 254p. 57.50 *(978-0-9801496-6-1(5))*; (ENG.). 1p. 57.50 *(978-1-61146-059-9(X))* Lehigh Univ. Pr.

Williamson, Craig. Beowulf & Other Old English Poems. 2011. (Middle Ages Ser.). (Illus.). 288p. (C). 45.00 *(978-0-8122-4345-1(5))* Univ. of Pennsylvania Pr.

BEOWULF—CONCORDANCES

Kiernan, Kevin & Iacob, Ionut Emil, eds. Electronic Beowulf. 3rd ed. 2011. (ENG., Illus.). stu. ed. 45.00 incl. cd-rom *(978-0-7123-5101-0(9))* British Library, The GBR. Dist: Chicago Distribution Ctr.

BEQUESTS

see Inheritance and Succession

BERBER LANGUAGES

see also Shilha Language

Euro Talk. Talk Now! Tamazight (Berber) 2008. 29.99 *(978-1-84352-397-0(3))* TOPICS Entertainment.

—Vocabulary Builder Tamazight. 2008. 24.99 *(978-1-84352-797-8(9))* TOPICS Entertainment.

Icon Group International, Inc. Staff, compiled by. Webster's Tamazight - English Thesaurus Dictionary. 2008. 35p. ring bd. 28.95 incl. audio compact disk *(978-0-497-83734-1(X))* Icon Group International, Inc.

Lafkioui, Mena & Brugnatelli, Vermondo. Berber in Contact: Linguistic & Sociolinguistic Perspectives = le Berbère en Contact: études en Linguistique et Sociolinguistique. 2008. (FRE & ENG., Illus.). 231p. *(978-3-89645-922-0(8))* Köppe, Rüdiger Verlag.

Mettouchi, A. & Philippson, G. Etudes de phonetique et de linguistique berberes. Hommage a Naima Louali (1961-2005) Chaker, S., ed. 2009. (Societe d'Etudes Linguistiques et Anthropologiques de France Ser.). 368p. (C). pap. 69.00 *(978-90-429-2246-4(X))* Peeters Pubs. & Booksellers BEL. Dist: Brown, David Bk. Co., The.

BERBERS

see also Celtiberi; Guanches; Hamites; Kabyles; Libyans; Tuaregs

Abrous, D. La Societe des Missionnaires d'Afrique a l'epreuve du mythe Berbere: Kabylie - Aures - Mzab. 2007. (Societe d'Etudes Linguistiques et Anthropologiques de France Ser.). (FRE.). 151p. (C). pap. 58.00 *(978-90-429-1959-4(0))* Peeters Pubs. & Booksellers BEL. Dist: Brown, David Bk. Co., The.

Bernasek, Lisa. Artistry of the Everyday: Beauty & Craftsmanship in Berber Art. 2008. (Peabody Museum Collections Ser.). (Illus.). 128p. pap. 21.95 *(978-0-87365-405-0(6))* Peabody Museum of Archaeology & Ethnology, Harvard Univ., Pubns. Dept.

Encyclopedie Berbere. Fasc. XXX. Maaziz - Matmata. 2010. (Encyclopedie Berbere Ser.). (FRE.). 261p. (C). pap. 44.00 ***(978-90-429-2367-6(9))*** Peeters Pubs. & Booksellers BEL. Dist: Brown, David Bk. Co., The.

Encyclopedie Berbere. Fasc. XXXI. Matmora-Mezrag. 2010. (Encyclopedie Berbere Ser.). (FRE.). 279p. (C). pap. 44.00 ***(978-90-429-2368-3(7))*** Peeters Pubs. & Booksellers BEL. Dist: Brown, David Bk. Co., The.

Encyclopedie Berbere. Fasc. XXXII. Mgild - Mzab. 2011. (Encyclopedie Berbere Ser.). (FRE., Illus.). 235p. (C). pap. 44.00 *(978-90-429-2369-0(5))* Peeters Pubs. & Booksellers BEL. Dist: Brown, David Bk. Co., The.

for Indigenous Affairs, International Work Group & Human and Peoples' Rights, African Commission on. Report of the African Commissions Working Group on Indigenous Populations / Communities: Research & Information Visit to Libya, August 2005. 2011. 100p. pap. 24.95 *(978-87-91563-67-6(4))* IWGIA DNK. Dist: Transaction Pubs.

Gellner, Ernest. Saints of the Atlas. 2008. 360p. pap. 34.00 *(978-1-59740-463-1(2))* ACLS Humanities E-Book.

How to Open & Operate a Financially Successful Herb & Herbal Plant Business: With Companion CD-ROM. 2011. (ENG.). 288p. pap. 39.95 *(978-1-60138-329-7(0))* Atlantic Publishing Co.

Ilahiane, Hsain. The A to Z of the Berbers (Imazighen) 2009. (A to Z Guide Ser.: No. 63). (ENG.). 358p. pap. 34.45 *(978-0-8108-6846-5(6))* Scarecrow Pr., Inc.

—Historical Dictionary of the Berbers (Imazighen) 2006. (Historical Dictionaries of Peoples & Cultures Ser.). (ENG., Illus.). 360p. 104.00 *(978-0-8108-5452-9(X))* Scarecrow Pr., Inc.

Maddy-Weitzman, Bruce. The Berber Identity Movement & the Challenge to North African States. 2011. (ENG., Illus.). 304p. 55.00 *(978-0-292-72587-4(6))* Univ. of Texas Pr.

Miller, Susan Gilson & Hoffman, Katherine E., eds. Berbers & Others: Beyond Tribe & Nation in the Maghrib. 2010. (Public Cultures of the Middle East & North Africa Ser.). (ENG., Illus.). 240p. 65.00 *(978-0-253-35480-8(3)*, 0253354803); pap. 24.95 *(978-0-253-22200-8(1)*, 0253222001) Indiana Univ. Pr.

Ouali, Hamid. Agreement, Pronominal Clitics & Negation in Tamazight Berber: A Unified Analysis. 2011. (Continuum Studies in Theoretical Linguistics Ser.). (BER & ENG., Illus.). 208p. 140.00 *(978-1-4411-0127-3(6))* Continuum International Publishing Group, Ltd. GBR. Dist: National Bk. Network.

Rabaté, Marie-Rose, et al. Costumes Berbères du Maroc: Décors Traditionnels. 2009.Tr. of Berber Costumes of Morocco - Traditional Patterns. (FRE & ENG., Illus.). 288p. 115.00 *(978-2-86770-185-6(6))* ACR Edition FRA. Dist: Antique Collectors' Club.

Roux, Arsène & Cooper, John. La Vie Berbère Par les Textes: Parlers du Sud-Ouest Marocain (Tachelhit) 2009. (BER, FRE, MUL & ENG.). xi, 223p. pap. *(978-3-89645-923-7(6))* Köppe, Rüdiger Verlag.

Travis, Georgia-Rose. Sugar Culture in Morocco, Particularly Within a Berber Community in Rastabouda. 2008. 124p. pap. *(978-3-639-01754-0(4))* VDM Verlag Dr. Mueller e.K.

BERCEO, GONZALO DE, 13TH CENT.

Lappin, Anthony John & Lappin, Anthony. Gonzalo de Berceo: The Poet & His Verses. 2008. (Monografías A Ser.: Volume 268). 278p. 130.00 *(978-1-85566-173-8(X)*, Tamesis Bks.) Boydell & Brewer, Ltd. GBR. Dist: Boydell & Brewer, Inc.

BERDIAEV, NIKOLAI ALEKSANDROVICH, 1874-1948

Berdiaev, Nikolai. Self-Knowledge: An Essay in Autobiography. 2009. pap. *(978-1-59731-258-5(4))* Perennis, Sophia.

Crone, Anna Lisa. Eros & Creativity in Russian Religious Renewal: The Philosophers & the Freudians. 2009. (Russian History & Culture Ser.). *(978-90-04-18005-5(2))* BRILL.

Mjor, Kåre Johan. Reformulating Russia: The Cultural & Intellectual Historiography of Russian First-Wave Émigré Writers. 2011. (Russian History & Culture Ser.). XII, 328p. *(978-90-04-19286-7(7))* BRILL.

Nicolaus, Georg. Individuation & the Person: A Critical Comparison. 2010. (ENG., Illus.). 240p. (C). pap. 39.95 *(978-0-415-49316-1(1))* Routledge.

—The Understanding of the Person in C. G. Jung's Psychology & The. 2010. (ENG., Illus.). 240p. (C). 99.00 *(978-0-415-49315-4(3))* Routledge.

Scaringi, Paul. Nikolai Berdiaev's Freedom to Create. 2010. 264p. pap. *(978-3-8383-3927-6(4))* Lambert Academic Publishing.

BEREAVEMENT

see also Consolation; Grief

Abercrombie, Barbara, ed. Cherished: 21 Writers on Animals They Have Loved & Lost. 2011. (ENG.). 240p. pap. 14.95 *(978-1-57731-957-3(5))* New World Library.

Adams, Amanda Rose. Heart Warriors: A Family Faces Congenital Heart Disease. 2012. (ENG.). 300p. pap. 16.95 ***(978-1-933016-80-1(9))*** Behler Pubns., LLC.

Aldrich, Sandra P. Will I Ever Be Whole Again? Surviving the Death of Someone You Love. 2006. (ENG.). 184p. per. 16.99 *(978-1-4141-0708-0(0))* Pleasant Word.

Aleshire, Liz. 101 Ways You Can Help. 2009. (ENG.). 224p. pap. 9.99 *(978-1-4022-1756-2(0))* Sourcebooks, Inc.

Amoroso, Angela. Surrounded by Angels. 2008. 112p. 22.95 *(978-0-595-48833-9(1))*; pap. 12.95 *(978-0-595-48779-0(3))* iUniverse, Inc.

Anderson, Allen & Anderson, Linda. Saying Goodbye to Your Angel Animals: Finding Comfort after Losing Your Pet. 2008. (ENG.). 176p. pap. 14.95 *(978-1-57731-626-8(6))* New World Library.

Andres, Judy A. The Valley of the Shadow of Death: A Mother's Journey Through the Dark Days of Grief... to a Brighter Tomorrow. 2006. 242p. pap. 15.95 *(978-0-7414-3455-5(5))* Infinity Publishing.

Anthony, Mark. Never Letting Go: Heal Grief with Help from the Other Side. 2011. (ENG.). 288p. pap. 15.95 *(978-0-7387-2721-9(0))* Llewellyn Pubns.

Appleby, Susan L. The Loss of the Most Precious Gift: The Life of a Son. 2007. 112p. 22.95 *(978-0-595-87320-3(0))*; per. 12.95 *(978-0-595-42653-9(0))* iUniverse, Inc.

Arthur, Kay. What Happens When We Die? Date not set. 96p. 9.99 *(978-0-7369-1072-9(7))* Harvest Hse. Pubs.

Atwood, Kate & Kelly, John. A Healing Place: Help Your Child Find Hope & Happiness after the Loss of a Loved One. 2009. (ENG.). 224p. (gr. 12-18). 14.95 *(978-0-399-53504-8(7)*, Perigee Trade) Penguin Group (USA) Inc.

Auberle, Sharon. Saturday Nights at the Crystal Ball. 2008. 60p. pap. 12.00 *(978-1-889460-21-5(4))* Cross+Roads Pr.

Auchard, Betty. Dancing in My Nightgown: The Rhythms of Widowhood. 2010. (Illus.). 140p. per. 16.95 *(978-1-932173-75-8(7))* Stephens Pr. LLC.

Austell, Darla. See You Later Alligator, after While Crocodile. 2008. 80p. pap. 10.99 *(978-1-60647-545-4(2))* Xulon Pr., Inc.

Balk, David E. Helping the Bereaved College Student. 2011. (Illus.). 216p. pap. ***(978-0-8261-0878-4(4))***; E-Book ***(978-0-8261-0879-1(2))*** Springer Publishing Co., Inc.

Balk, David E. & Corr, Charles A. Adolescent Encounters with Death, Bereavement, & Coping. 2009. (Illus.). 400p. 65.00 *(978-0-8261-1073-2(8))* Springer Publishing Co., Inc.

Barnett, Laura, ed. When Death Enters the Therapeutic Space: Existential Perspectives in Psychotherapy & Counselling. 2008. (ENG.). 256p. (C). 120.00 *(978-0-415-41654-2(X))*; pap. 37.50 *(978-0-415-41655-9(8))* Routledge.

Barnett-Streicher, Glenda. Finding the Me in Me: Do You Know the You in You? 2009. 108p. 21.49 *(978-1-4490-5297-3(5))*; pap. 10.99 *(978-1-4490-5298-0(3))* AuthorHouse.

Barthes, Roland. Mourning Diary, 1 vol. Howard, Richard, tr. & afterword by by. 2012. (ENG., Illus.). 272p. pap. 15.00 ***(978-0-374-53311-3(3)***, Hill & Wang) Farrar, Straus & Giroux.

Barthes, Roland & Léger Nathalie. Mourning Diary. Howard, Richard, tr. from FRE. & afterword by by. 2010. (ENG., Illus.). 272p. 25.00 (978-0-8090-6233-1(X), Hill & Wang) Farrar, Straus & Giroux.

Bartholomew, Caroline, et al, eds. Making Sense of Death, Dying & Bereavement: An Anthology. 2008. (Published in Association with the Open University Ser.). 224p. (C). 121.00 (978-1-84787-511-2(4), B75112C); (Illus.). pap. 55.00 (978-1-84787-512-9(2), B75112P) SAGE Pubns., Ltd. GBR. Dist: SAGE Pubns., Inc.

Baugher, Bob. Understanding Guilt During Bereavement. 2009th ed. 2009. (ENG.). 53p. (Orig.). pap. 10.00 (978-0-9635975-1-9(5)) Caring People Pr.

Bay, Jane. Love & Loss: A Story about Life, Death & Rebirth. 2006. 415p. pap. (978-1-57416-088-8(5)) Clear Light Pubs.

Beaulieu, Joyce. From a Mother's Heart. 2007. 132p. per. 19.95 (978-1-4241-9555-8(1)) PublishAmerica, Inc.

Bentley, Chris R. It's Not about the Funeral-What You Need to Know Before You Go. 2009. 160p. 23.25 (978-1-60693-660-3(3), Strategic Bk. Publishing) AEG Literary Publishing Services, Inc.

Berns, Nancy. Closure: A Tangled Story of Grief, Money, Politics, & Hope. 2011. (ENG.). 224p. 75.50 (978-1-4399-0576-0(2)); 228p. pap. 24.95 (978-1-4399-0577-7(0)) Temple Univ. Pr.

Bismal, Sehdev. Dream Interrupted. 2009. (Illus.). 208p. pap. 14.49 (978-1-4490-3679-9(1)) AuthorHouse.

Brauer, Anne Brooks. What Widow's Face. 2007. 96p. pap. 10.95 (978-0-7414-2194-4(1)) Infinity Publishing.

Bredenham, Douwieen. Living without Lies!: A True Story. 2011. 176p. pap. 20.95 (978-0-624-04832-9(2)) NB Pubs. Ltd. ZAF. Dist: International Publishers Marketing.

Brezina, Corona. Frequently Asked Questions about When a Friend Dies. 2009. (FAQ: Teen Life Ser.). 64p. (gr. 5-6). 58.50 (978-1-61512-592-0(2)) Rosen Publishing Group, Inc., The.

—When a Friend Dies. 2007. (FAQ Ser.). (Illus.). 64p. (YA). (gr. 7-12). lib. bdg. 29.25 (978-1-4042-1935-9(8)) Rosen Publishing Group, Inc., The.

Buckle, Jennifer. Parenting after the Death of a Child: A Practitioner's Guide. 2010. (Series in Death, Dying & Bereavement Ser.). (ENG., Illus.). 226p. 41.95 (978-0-415-99573-3(6)) Routledge.

Buckley, Kelly S. Gratitude in Grief: Finding Daily Joy & a Life of Purpose Following the Death of my Son. 2010. 340p. 28.49 (978-1-4490-6379-5(9)); pap. 17.99 (978-1-4490-6378-8(0)) AuthorHouse.

Bulka, Reuven P. Grieving - Personal Reflections. 2010. (ENG.). 144p. pap. 14.00 (978-0-88962-917-5(3)) Mosaic Pr.

Carlson, Richard & Carlson, Kristine. An Hour to Live, an Hour to Love: The True Story of the Best Gift Ever Given. 2007. (ENG.). 96p. 9.95 (978-1-4013-2257-1(3)) Hyperion Pr.

Casertano, Carol. Death Watch. 2011. 88p. pap. 14.95 (978-1-4327-6745-7(3)) Outskirts Pr., Inc.

Caughlin, Angela. Journaling Through Loss to Transformation: A Guided Approach to Understanding Grief. 2009. (ENG.). 176p. pap. 14.95 (978-1-933979-56-4(9)) Bright Sky Pr.

Chigier, E., ed. Grief & Bereavement, 3 vols. (978-965-294-022-3(4)) Freund Publishing Hse., Ltd.

Cimador (Roscigno), Diena M. Am I Going Crazy? 2011. pap. 10.95 (978-0-7414-6395-1(4)) Infinity Publishing.

Cohen, Michael E. Mike & Heather: A Young Widower's Short Story. 2009. 60p. pap. 10.49 (978-1-4389-8197-0(X)) AuthorHouse.

Collins, Judy. The Seven T's: Finding Hope & Healing in the Wake of Tragedy. 2007. (ENG.). 192p. (gr. 12-18). 14.95 (978-1-58542-495-5(1), Tarcher) Penguin Group (USA) Inc.

—The Seven T's: Finding Hope & Healing in the Wake of Tragedy. l.t. ed. 2007. 231p. 29.95 (978-0-7862-9845-7(6)) Thorndike Pr.

Connolly, Sally A. Never Better: All Things Considered. 2007. (Illus.). 148p. per. 16.95 (978-0-9772653-2-9(3)) Connolly Assocs.

Conrad, Michael. What Happens to You When You Lose a Pet? Spirituality for Pet Owners. 2007. 148p. per. 14.95 (978-1-930301-10-8(3)) Learning Doctor, The.

Cooke, Frances L. A Couple Still: A Personal Journey to Recovery & Independence after Bereavement. 2008. (Illus.). 103p. per. 9.95 (978-0-9761553-1-7(1)) Avventura Pr.

Copperfelt, Jillian. After Your Loved One Dies: Finding Hope & Strength to Carry On. 2009. 128p. pap. 12.49 (978-1-4389-4226-1(5)) AuthorHouse.

Côté-Arsenault, Denise & Freda, Margaret Comerford. Loss & Grief in the Childbearing Period. 2011. (978-0-86525-128-1(2)) March of Dimes Birth Defects Foundation.

Cram101 Textbook Reviews & Cram101 Textbook Reviews. Outlines & Highlights for Dying, Death, & Grief: Working with Adult Bereavement by Brenda Mallon, ISBN. 2011. 130p. pap. 28.95 (978-1-61461-073-1(8)) Cram101 Inc.

Cunningham, Alan Blain. I Walk Alone: Reflections of a Veterinarian. 2008. (Illus.). 124p. per. 15.95 (978-0-9777072-8-7(8), Agreka) Agreka Bks., LLC.

Curran, Marcia A. Widow Words: 100 Simple Pieces of Advice from Another Widow. 2007. 100p. 15.95 (978-1-889242-33-0(0)) VanderWyk & Burnham.

Davis, Iris. Chasing the Wind. 2007. 112p. 22.95 (978-0-595-91768-6(2)) iUniverse, Inc.

Davis, M. L. Pieces Putting Life Back Together after. 2006. 30.99 (978-1-4257-2584-6(8)) Xlibris Corp.

De Courcy, Catherine. Adventure in Grief. 2009. (ENG.). 255p. pap. 23.95 (978-1-905172-87-0(7)) Collins Pr., The IRL. Dist: Dufour Editions, Inc.

Deelstra, Jan. Blessings in the Mire. 2007. (ENG.). 264p. per. 15.95 (978-0-7414-3850-8(X)) Infinity Publishing.

Dickinson, George & Leming, Michael. Annual Editions: Dying, Death, & Bereavement 11/12. 12th ed. 2010. (Annual Editions Ser.). (ENG., Illus.). 208p. (C). pap. 44.00 (978-0-07-805078-7(2), 0078050782, McGraw-Hill/Dushkin) McGraw-Hill Higher Education.

Diehl, Charlene. Out of Grief, Singing. 2010. 176p. pap. 15.95 (978-1-897109-44-1(X)) Signature Editions CAN. Dist: Univ. of Toronto Pr.

Doka. Death Dying & Bereavement, 4 vols. 2006. (Illus.). 448p. (978-0-415-36916-9(9)); 496p. (978-0-415-36918-3(5)); 400p. (978-0-415-36917-6(7)) Routledge.

—Death Dying & Bereavement: Major Themes HealthSocial Welfare Vol1, 4 vols. 2006. (Illus.). 512p. (978-0-415-36915-2(0)) Routledge.

Draper, Tricia. Hope after Grief. 2010. 336p. 29.99 (978-1-4500-6015-8(3)); pap. 19.99 (978-1-4500-6014-1(5)) Xlibris Corp.

Dresser, Norine & Wasserman, Fredda. Saying Goodbye to Someone You Love: Your Emotional Journey Through End-of-Life & Grief. 2010. (ENG.). 202p. pap. 16.95 (978-1-932603-85-9(9)) Demos Medical Publishing, LLC.

Duke, Wendy. The Grace by Which We Stand. 2008. 132p. 29.99 (978-1-4363-7179-7(1)) Xlibris Corp.

Dunkel, Tamara. These Are My Final Wishes. 2007. 64p. per. 9.95 (978-1-4327-1275-4(6)) Outskirts Pr., Inc.

Dyregrov, Kari, et al. After the Suicide: Helping the Bereaved to Find a Path from Grief to Recovery. 2011. 176p. pap. (978-1-84905-211-5(5)) Kingsley, Jessica Ltd.

Ewing. Losing a Baby. 2007. 128p. pap. 13.95 (978-0-85969-928-0(5), Sheldon Press) SPCK Publishing GBR. Dist: Westminster John Knox Pr.

Exley, Richard. When You Lose Someone You Love: Comfort for Those Who Grieve, 1 vol. 2009. (ENG.). 128p. pap. 9.99 (978-1-4347-6480-5(X)) Cook, David C.

Fincher, Rhonda Roseland. Good Night Kendrick, I Love You: A Mother's Journal through Grief. 2011. 156p. pap. 13.95 (978-1-4269-5389-7(5)) Trafford Publishing.

Fitzpatrick G., Daniel. When Your Parent Dies. 2009. pap. 4.95 (978-0-87029-419-8(9)) Abbey Pr.

Flem, Lydia. The Final Reminder: How I Emptied My Parents' House. Powell, Elfreda, tr. from FRE. 2007. (ENG.). 128p. per. 17.95 (978-0-285-63782-5(7)) Souvenir Pr. Ltd. GBR. Dist: Independent Pubs. Group.

Froman, Paul Kent. After You Say Goodbye: When Someone You Love Dies of AIDS. 2007. 270p. reprint ed. pap. 11.00 (978-1-4223-6695-0(2)) DIANE Publishing Co.

Garbowski, Anthony J. & Shaw, Lorna J. Don't Walk Through the Mirror. 2007. per. 17.95 (978-1-888223-70-5(7)) McMillen Publishing.

Graviet, Xandra A. Angel in Disguise. 2006. pap. (978-1-928806-15-8(5)) Lightworker Pubns.

Grey, Robin. Bereavement, Loss & Learning Disabilities: A Guide for Professionals & Carers. 2010. (ENG.). 160p. pap. (978-1-84905-020-3(1)) Kingsley, Jessica Ltd.

Haddix-Fisher, Kimberly. Foreshadow. 2010. pap. 8.99 (978-1-61663-180-2(5)) Tate Publishing & Enterprises, LLC.

Hadley, Maggie. Coping with Suicide. 128p. (978-0-85969-871-9(8), Sheldon Press) SPCK Publishing.

Hansson, Robert O. & Stroebe, Margaret S. Bereavement in Late Life: Coping, Adaptation, & Developmental Influences. 2006. (Illus.). 219p. 49.95 (978-1-59147-472-2(8)) American Psychological Assn.

Harris, Paul Nigel & Crisman, Chris. Mothers in Charge: Faces of Courage. 2009. 96p. 35.00 (978-0-915180-43-1(X)) Harrowood Bks.

Harrison, Mary B. And You Will Know the World's Name: A Mother's Memoir. 2006. mass mkt. 15.95 (978-1-58597-393-4(9)) Leathers Publishing.

Hayward, Deborah Kay. Until Death Don't Us Part. 2011. (ENG.). 212p. pap. 22.95 (978-1-84694-371-3(X)) Hunt, John Publishing Ltd. GBR. Dist: National Bk. Network.

Hess, Shelly. Final Drive. 2011. 324p. pap. 16.99 (978-1-60844-994-1(7)) Dog Ear Publishing, LLC.

Holland, Ph.D, Debra, MS. The Essential Guide to Grief & Grieving. 2011. (ENG.). 336p. (gr. 12). 16.95 (978-1-61564-111-6(4), Alpha Bks.) Penguin Group (USA) Inc.

Holmberg, Lena. Palliative Home Care, Grief & Bereavement. 2008. 184p. pap. (978-3-8364-6541-0(8)) VDM Verlag Dr. Mueller e.K.

Hooyman, Nancy R. & Kramer, Betty J. Living Through Loss: Interventions Across the Life Span. 2008. (ENG.). 480p. (gr. 17). pap. 29.50 (978-0-231-12247-4(0)) Columbia Univ. Pr.

Horsley, Heidi & Horsley, Gloria Call. Teen Grief Relief: Parenting with Understanding, Support & Guidance. 2007. 87p. per. (978-1-56825-110-3(6)) Rainbow Bks., Inc.

Hoy, William G. Guiding People Through Grief: How to Start & Lead Bereavement Support Groups. 2007. per. 24.95 net. (978-0-9677235-4-9(X)) Compass Pr.

Jackson, P. N. Tommy Remembered (and Others) 2009. 236p. pap. 17.68 (978-1-4251-7526-9(0)) Trafford Publishing.

Jalland, Pat. Death in War & Peace: A History of Loss & Grief in England, 1914-1970. (ENG., Illus.). 336p. 2012. pap. 45.00 (978-0-19-965188-7(4)) 2010. 55.00 (978-0-19-926551-0(8)) Oxford Univ. Pr., Inc.

Johnston, Gail Perry & Rabideau, Jill Perry, eds. A Rumor of Angels: Quotations for Living, Dying & Letting Go. rev. ed. 2007. (ENG., Illus.). 176p. pap. 11.95 (978-0-9793345-0-4(0)) Cupola Pr.

Jones, Roger. Dealing with Death, Funerals, Wills & Bereavement: What to Do When Someone Dies. 2006. (Illus.). 160p. per. 20.00 (978-1-84528-119-9(5)) How To Books GBR. Dist: Parkwest Pubns., Inc.

Joyce, Jamerson. Will You Wipe My Tears? Helping others through Sorrow. 2008. 144p. per. 10.95 (978-0-9774754-5-2(X)) Spiritbuilding.

Kaczmarek, Sheryl. A Year Without Alex. 2008. 74p. pap. 16.95 (978-1-60563-698-6(3)) PublishAmerica, Inc.

Kauffman, Jeffrey, ed. The Shame of Death, Grief, & Trauma. 2010. (ENG., Illus.). 233p. 44.95 (978-0-415-99748-5(8)) Routledge.

Kay, Larene. Prayers from the River to the Mountains: Grief, Forgiveness, Peace, & Love. 2007. 100p. per. 12.95 (978-1-4327-0735-4(3)) Outskirts Pr., Inc.

Keenan, Paul A. Why We Love Them So: Surviving the Loss of an Animal Friend. 2009. 152p. 24.95 (978-1-4401-4338-0(2)); pap. 14.95 (978-1-4401-4340-3(4)) iUniverse, Inc.

Kelly, Marcy. From Sorrow to Dancing. 2008. 100p. per. 10.99 (978-1-60477-611-9(0)) Xulon Pr., Inc.

Kendall, Donna. Five Years & Yesterday. 2006. (ENG.). 128p. per. 19.95 (978-1-4241-3602-5(4)) PublishAmerica, Inc.

Kolb, Janice Gray. Cherishing: Poetry for Pilgrims Journeying On. 2007. (ENG., Illus.). 368p. pap. 19.95 (978-1-57733-205-3(9)) Blue Dolphin Publishing, Inc.

Konigsberg, Ruth Davis. The Truth about Grief: The Myth of Its Five Stages & the New Science of Loss. 2011. (ENG.). 272p. pap. 15.00 (978-1-4391-4834-1(1)) Simon & Schuster.

Kübler-Ross, Elisabeth. On Death & Dying: What the Dying Have to Teach Doctors, Nurses, Clergy & Their Own Families. 40th ed. 2008. (Illus.). 264p. pap. 37.95 (978-0-415-46399-7(8)) Routledge.

Kusman, Donna. Life after Death: A Memoir of Milestones. 2009. 52p. pap. (978-1-84923-964-6(9)) YouWriteOn.

Lane, Keith. Life on the Edge. 2010. (ENG.). 242p. pap. 14.95 (978-1-84454-931-3(3)) Blake, John Publishing, Ltd. GBR. Dist: Independent Pubs. Group.

Larson, Beth. Shirley's Garden. 2009. 64p. pap. 19.50 (978-1-60693-095-3(8), Eloquent Bks.) AEG Literary Publishing Services, Inc.

Lecomte, Dominique. La Maison du Mort. 2010. (FRE.). 202p. (978-2-213-60932-4(2)) Fayard, Artheme, Librairie.

Linton, Anna. Poetry & Parental Bereavement in Early Modern Lutheran Germany. 2008. (Oxford Modern Languages & Literature Monographs). (ENG., Illus.). 300p. 125.00 (978-0-19-923336-6(5)) Oxford Univ. Pr., Inc.

Mack, Stephanie Madoff. The End of Normal: A Wife's Anguish, a Widow's New Life. 2011. (ENG.). 304p. (gr. 12). 26.95 (978-0-399-15816-2(2), Blue Rider Pr.) Penguin Group (USA) Inc.

Mahoney, Beth. Grant Us Peace: Rosary Meditations for Those Who Mourn. 2008. (Holy Cross Family Ministry Ser.). 49p. pap. 4.95 (978-1-59471-164-0(X)) Ave Maria Pr.

Malkinson, Ruth. Cognitive Grief Therapy: Constructing a Rational Meaning to Life Following Loss. 2007. (ENG.). 288p. 35.00 (978-0-393-70439-6(4), 70439) Norton, W. W. & Co., Inc.

Mallon, Brenda. Dying, Death & Grief: Working with Adult Bereavement. 2008. 200p. (C). 109.00 (978-1-4129-3414-5(1), B34141C); pap. 51.00 (978-1-4129-3415-2(X), B34141P) SAGE Pubns., Ltd. GBR. Dist: SAGE Pubns., Inc.

Malone, D. Green: Surviving the Murder of Self. 2009. 172p. 25.95 (978-1-4401-8017-0(2)); pap. 15.95 (978-1-4401-8015-6(6)) iUniverse, Inc.

Maloney, RaeLynn & Wolfelt, Alan D. Caring for Donor Families: Before, During & After. 2nd ed. 2011. (ENG.). 160p. pap. 19.95 (978-1-61722-136-1(8)) Companion Pr.

Manning, Sean. The Things That Need Doing: A Memoir. 2010. (ENG.). 256p. pap. 15.00 (978-0-307-46324-1(9), Three Rivers Pr.) Crown Publishing Group.

Mast, Kathy. Tiny Hands, Little Feet: One Woman's Struggle with Grief & Heartache with the Loss of Her Baby. 2008. 52p. pap. 6.99 (978-1-933753-10-2(2)) Carlisle Pr.- Walnut Creek.

Mayer, Donald E. Letters to Peter: On the Journey from Grief to Wholeness. 2010. 194p. pap. 22.00 (978-1-60899-104-4(0), Cascade Bks.) Wipf & Stock Pubs.

Mayfield, Sue. First Steps Through Bereavement. 2011. (First Steps Ser.). (ENG.). 88p. pap. 9.95 (978-0-7459-5535-3(5)) Lion Hudson PLC GBR. Dist: Independent Pubs. Group.

McCann, Kathleen/Sheller. Dragon Grip: Journey into the grip of the Dragon. 2007. (Illus.). 273p. per. 14.95 (978-0-9800938-0-3(5)) McCann Communications.

McCarthy, Jane Ribbens. Young People's Experiences of Loss & Bereavement: Towards an Interdisciplinary Approach. 2006. 208p. (C). per. 63.00 (978-0-335-21664-2(1), 0335216641) McGraw-Hill Cos., The.

—Young People's Experiences of Loss & Bereavement: Towards an Interdisciplinary Approach. 2006. (ENG.). 208p. (C). 189.00 (978-0-335-21665-9(X), 033521665X, Open University Pr.) McGraw-Hill Education GBR. Dist: McGraw-Hill Cos., The.

Meaker, Mary. In Memory of My Two Daughters. 2007. 176p. per. 14.95 (978-1-59330-517-8(6)) Aventine Pr.

Metcalf, Doug. One: The Book. 2009. 228p. 24.99 (978-1-4389-6712-7(8)); pap. 16.95 (978-1-4389-6711-0(X)) AuthorHouse.

Meyers, Karen, et al. Death & Dying. 2nd rev. ed. 2009. (Truth about Ser.). (Illus.). 240p. (C). (gr. 9-18). 35.00 (978-0-8160-7631-4(6)) Facts On File, Inc.

Miller, Michael S. Maci's Place: The Loss of a Child Through a Father's Eyes. 2008. 158p. pap. 24.95 (978-1-60563-596-5(0)) PublishAmerica, Inc.

Mitchell, Margaret, ed. Remember Me: Socially Constructing Life after Death. 2007. (Illus.). 272p. 39.95 (978-0-415-95485-3(1)) Routledge.

Mohamed, Adam & Mohamed, Noorjehan. Journey into the Unknown. 2011. (ENG.). 152p. pap. 17.95 (978-1-920222-47-5(2)) STE Pubs. ZAF. Dist: Independent Pubs. Group.

Moss, Jane. Writing in Bereavement: A Creative Handbook. 2012. (ENG., Illus.). 240p. pap. (978-1-84905-212-2(3)) Kingsley, Jessica Ltd.

Namis, Mia. The Nicest Bitch You'll Ever Meet. 2011. 160p. pap. 24.95 (978-1-4626-2615-1(7)) PublishAmerica, Inc.

Neimeyer, Robert A., ed. Techniques in Grief Therapy: Creative Strategies for Counseling the Bereaved. 2012. (Series in Death, Dying, & Bereavement Ser.). (ENG., Illus.). 408p. pap. 44.95 (978-0-415-80725-8(5)) Routledge.

Njoroge, Penny Wanjiru. Healing Hope for Your Grief & Bereavement. 2010. 168p. pap. 13.95 (978-1-4497-0450-6(6), WestBow Pr.) Author Solutions, Inc.

Notman, Andrea. Remembering You: A practical guide for bereaved Parents. 2011. 108p. 24.99 (978-1-4653-0004-1(X)); pap. 15.99 (978-1-4653-0003-4(1)) Xlibris Corp.

Novak, Monica. The Good Grief Club: A True Story about the Power of Friendship & French Toast. 2008. 321p. per. 18.95 (978-0-9766340-5-8(8)) Inkwell Productions, LLC.

Oates, Joyce Carol. A Widow's Story: A Memoir. (ENG.). 2012. 320p. pap. 14.99 (978-0-06-202050-5(1)) 2011. 432p. 27.99 (978-0-06-201553-2(2)) HarperCollins Pubs. (Ecco).

—A Widow's Story: A Memoir. l.t. ed. 2011. 676p. 32.99 (978-1-4104-3692-4(6)) Thorndike Pr.

O'Brien, Mauryeen. Gentle Keeping: Prayers & Services for Remembering Departed Loved Ones Throughout the Year. 2008. 128p. pap. 7.95 (978-1-59471-130-5(5)) Ave Maria Pr.

Orfali, Robert. Grieving a Soulmate: The Love Story Behind till Death Do Us Part. 2011. 280p. pap. 14.95 (978-1-935400-66-9(9)) Mill City Pr., Inc.

Ortega, Holly. Parents for the First Time. Again. 2006. 59p. pap. 16.95 (978-1-4241-4985-8(1)) PublishAmerica, Inc.

Paget-Wilkes, Valerie. The Eggshell Path: A Story of Survival. 2007. 247p. per. 16.95 (978-0-9790950-9-2(3)) Seven Locks Pr.

Papadatou, Danai. In the Face of Death: Professionals Who Care for the Dying & the Bereaved. 2009. (Illus.). 320p. 55.00 (978-0-8261-0256-0(5)) Springer Publishing Co., Inc.

Parker, Faith. The Love of a Father. 2010. 108p. 28.95 (978-1-4497-0140-6(X), WestBow Pr.) Author Solutions, Inc.

Parkman, Francis. An Offering of Sympathy to Parents Bereaved of Their Children: And to Others under Affliction. 2010. 262p. pap. 26.75 (978-1-144-97695-6(2)) BiblioBazaar.

—An Offering of Sympathy to Parents Bereaved of Their Children: And to Others under Affliction. 2009. 86p. pap. 20.00 (978-0-217-77925-8(5)) General Bks. LLC.

—An Offering of Sympathy to Parents Bereaved of Their Children: And to Others under Affliction. 2010. 246p. 33.56 (978-1-164-73603-5(5)) 2010. 246p. pap. 21.56 (978-1-164-57462-0(0)) 2008. 248p. 41.95 (978-1-4369-3716-0(7)) 2008. 248p. pap. 26.95 (978-1-4367-7574-8(4)) Kessinger Publishing, LLC.

Partilla, John S. Grief Sucks. 2011. 60p. pap. 31.99 (978-1-4628-5968-9(2)) Xlibris Corp.

Pearson, Betty. I've Got Something to Tell You, but Don't Take It Personal!!! 2007. 128p. 23.95 (978-0-595-68780-0(5)); per. 13.95 (978-0-595-44074-0(6)) iUniverse, Inc.

Publications International Staff, ed. When You Lose Someone You Love. 2007. pap. 6.98 (978-1-4127-1527-0(X), Publications International, Ltd.

Reed, Kat. Begin Her. 2009. spiral bd. (978-1-61623-273-3(0)) Independent Pub.

Reiss, Johanna. A Hidden Life: A Memoir of August 1969. 2009. (ENG.). 217p. 24.95 (978-1-933633-55-8(7)) Melville Hse. Publishing.

Rember, Julie, ed. & intro. Saying Goodbye: To the People, Places & Things in Our Lives. 2010. (ENG.). 230p. pap. 13.95 (978-0-9825794-4-2(6)) Dream of Things.

Richetti, Frank. That's When Love Walks Out on You. 2011. 80p. 24.99 (978-1-4568-5520-8(4)); pap. 15.99 (978-1-4568-5519-2(0)) Xlibris Corp.

Robinson, Frank L. Alec's Legacy. 2006. 128p. pap. 13.95 (978-0-9788504-0-1(8)) ALR LLC.

Rohan, Christi & Rohan, Juli. Two Sisters' Journey: From Darkness into the Light. 2010. 258p. pap. 16.95 (978-1-4327-5024-4(0)) Outskirts Pr., Inc.

Rosenblatt, Roger. Kayak Morning: Reflections on Love, Grief, & Small Boats. 2012. (ENG.). 160p. pap. 13.99 (978-0-06-208403-3(8), Ecco) HarperCollins Pubs.

Rosenblatt, Roger. Making Toast: A Family Story. 2011. (ENG.). 128p. pap. 12.99 (978-0-06-182595-8(6)) 2010. 176p. 21.99 (978-0-06-182593-4(X)) HarperCollins Pubs. (Ecco).

—Making Toast: A Family Story. l.t. ed. 2010. 236p. 31.99 (978-1-4104-2861-5(3)) Thorndike Pr.

Roth, Marco. The Scientists: A Family Romance, 1 vol. 2012. (ENG.). 208p. 23.00 (978-0-374-21028-1(4)) Farrar, Straus & Giroux.

Ruff, Coralease Cox. Her Light Still Shines: A Beloved Daughter's Story & Her Mother's Grief Journey. 2008. 244p. 29.95 (978-0-595-50098-7(6)); pap. 19.95 (978-0-595-48468-3(9)) iUniverse, Inc.

Sattler, Verna. My Sweet Sam: A Widow's Journey thru Love & Loss. 2010. 54p. pap. 8.95 (978-1-4327-5993-3(0), Outskirts Pr., Inc.

Schafer, Yulee. Am I Supposed to Feel Like This? 2011. pap. 16.95 (978-1-59571-678-1(5)) Word Association Pubs.

Schreiber-Mosher, Judy. How to Cope with the Death of a Partner: Strategies for Surviving the Difficult Times Ahead & Maintaining Your Emotional Health. 2010. 32p. pap. 7.50 (978-0-9824023-2-0(5)) Soteria Pr.

—Tincture of Time: Living through Grief to Hope. 2010. 160p. pap. 14.00 *(978-0-9824023-0-6(9))* Soteria Pr.

Schwenker, Gretchen & Schwenker, Gretchen L. Every Tear Will Be Wiped Away: Prayers for Comfort in Times of Grief. 2011. ***(978-0-7648-2037-3(0))*** Liguori Pubns.

Scrutton, Steve. Bereavement & Grief: Supporting Older People Through Loss. (ENG.). 168p. *(978-0-340-60482-3(4),* Hodder Arnold) Hodder Education.

Seiden, Dorothy Rose. Love Lives On: A Survivor's Guide for Coping with the Loss of a Spouse. 2011. 88p. pap. 19.95 ***(978-1-4626-0739-6(X))*** PublishAmerica, Inc.

Shannon, Joyce Brennfleck, ed. Death & Dying Sourcebook. 2nd ed. 2006. (Health Reference Ser.). (Illus.). 653p. 87.00 *(978-0-7808-0871-3(1))* Omnigraphics, Inc.

Sheeler, Jim. Final Salute: A Story of Unfinished Lives. 2009. (ENG.). 288p. (gr. 12-18). 16.00 *(978-0-14-311545-8(6),* Penguin (Non-Classics)) Penguin Group (USA) Inc.

Simon, Joel K. Solution Focused Practice in End-Of-Life & Grief Counseling. 2009. 45.00 *(978-0-8261-0579-0(3))* Springer Publishing Co., Inc.

Simonis, Georgia. Death Matters. 2009. 196p. 24.99 *(978-1-4389-4058-8(0))*; pap. 14.49 *(978-1-4389-4059-5(9))* AuthorHouse.

Smith, Harold Ivan. Borrowed Narratives: Using Biographical & Historical Grief Narratives with the Bereaving. 2012. (ENG., Illus.). 299p. 39.95 *(978-0-415-89394-7(1))* Routledge.

Spargo, R. Clifton. Vigilant Memory: Emmanuel Lévinas, the Holocaust, & the Unjust Death. 2006. (ENG.). 328p. (gr. 17). 60.00 *(978-0-8018-8311-8(3))* Johns Hopkins Univ. Pr.

Sprague, Zander. Making Lemonade: Choosing A Positive Pathway after Losing your Sibling. 2008. 104p. pap. 9.95 *(978-0-9795030-0-9(0))* Paradiso Pr.

Stevens, Gwendolyn. Personality & Bereavement: Weaning a Life. 2007. 359p. pap. 18.95 *(978-0-7414-3959-8(X))* Infinity Publishing.

Straub, Larry G. Autumn Corridors. 2007. 144p. 19.95 ***(978-1-933538-68-6(6))*** Bridgeway Bks.

Swedenborg, Emanuel. Afterlife: A Guided Tour of Heaven & Its Wonders. Rose, Donald, ed. 2006. (ENG.). 142p. per. 12.95 *(978-0-87785-319-0(3),* 325-157) Swedenborg Foundation, Inc.

Taylor, Justine. Sharing the Pain. 2006. 87p. pap. 16.95 *(978-1-4241-4071-8(4))* PublishAmerica, Inc.

Taylor, Natalie. Signs of Life: A Memoir. 2012. (ENG.). 320p. pap. 15.00 ***(978-0-307-71750-4(X))*** Broadway Bks.

Thompson, Neil. Grief & its Challenges. 2012. (ENG., Illus.). 224p. (C). pap. 24.00 *(978-0-230-27756-4(X))* Palgrave Macmillan.

Tucholski-Mieczkowski, Kathryn. Lori's Gifts: A Mother's True Story of Love, Life, & Loss, 1 vol. 2009. 161p. pap. 24.95 *(978-1-60836-697-2(9))* PublishAmerica, Inc.

Van Essen, Mercedes O. Heal Your Grief, Accept Your Loss & Love Your Life Again. 2008. 80p. pap. 10.50 *(978-1-60693-078-6(8),* Eloquent Bks.) AEG Literary Publishing Services, Inc.

Veerman, Dave & Barton, Bruce. When Your Father Dies: How a Man Deals with the Loss of His Father, 0 vols. 2006. 224p. per. 13.99 *(978-0-7852-8830-5(9))* Nelson, Thomas Inc.

Walker, Lornie. Argyle Park A Memoir of My Sisters Suici. 2006. iv, 146p. pap. 15.95 *(978-1-4120-8573-1(X))* Trafford Publishing.

Watson, Linda. Facing Death: A Companion in Words & Images. 2009. (Illus.). 104p. pap. 24.95 *(978-1-932529-48-7(9))* Health Professions Pr.

Watts, Jacqueline. Death, Dying & Bereavement: Issues for Practice. 2010. 112p. pap. 26.95 *(978-1-906716-08-0(0))* Dunedin Academic Pr. GBR. Dist: International Specialized Bk. Services.

Weinstein, Jeremy. Working with Loss, Death & Bereavement: A Guide for Social Workers. 2007. 200p. (C). per. 49.00 *(978-1-4129-2391-0(3),* B23905P) SAGE Pubns., Ltd. GBR. Dist: SAGE Pubns., Inc.

Weinstein, Jeremy A. Working with Loss, Death & Bereavement: A Guide for Social Workers. 2007. 200p. (C). 99.95 *(978-1-4129-2390-3(5),* B23905C) SAGE Pubns., Ltd. GBR. Dist: SAGE Pubns., Inc.

Willis, Rick. The Carebridge. 2008. 156p. pap. 15.49 *(978-1-4343-9508-5(1))* AuthorHouse.

Wilmes, D M. Seven Days of Hospice: A Memoir. 2007. 116p. (ENG.). 22.95 *(978-0-595-70150-6(7))*; per. 12.95 *(978-0-595-46373-2(8))* iUniverse, Inc.

Wiltse, Duane. Gittin' Western: A True Adventure of Body, Mind, & Spirit. 2007. 228p. per. 14.95 *(978-1-60528-001-1(1),* iUniverse Star) iUniverse, Inc.

Wimpenny, Peter. Grief, Loss & Bereavement Care: An Evidence Based Approach for Health & Social Care. 2011. (ENG., Illus.). 288p. (C). 145.00 *(978-0-415-46750-6(0))* Routledge.

—Grief, Loss & Bereavement Care: An Evidence-Informed Approach for Health & Social Care. 2011. (ENG., Illus.). 288p. (C). 44.95 *(978-0-415-46751-3(9))* Routledge.

Wolfelt, Alan D. The Handbook for Companioning the Mourner: Eleven Essential Principles. 2009. (Companioning Ser.). (ENG.). 128p. 15.95 *(978-1-879651-61-6(0))* Companion Pr.

—Healing the Adult Sibling's Grieving Heart: 100 Practical Ideas after Your Brother or Sister Dies. 2008. (Healing Your Grieving Heart Ser.). (ENG.). 128p. pap. 11.95 *(978-1-879651-29-6(7))* Companion Pr.

—Healing Your Grieving Soul: 100 Spiritual Practices for Mourners. 2009. (Healing Your Grieving Heart Ser.). (ENG.). 128p. pap. 11.95 *(978-1-879651-57-9(2))* Companion Pr.

Wolfer, Terry A. & Runnion, Vicki M. Dying, Death, & Bereavement in Social Work Practice: Decision Cases for Advanced Practice. 2008. (End of Life Care: a Ser.). (ENG., Illus.). 280p. (gr. 17). 90.00 *(978-0-231-14174-1(2))* Columbia Univ. Pr.

—Dying, Death, & Bereavement in Social Work Practice: Decision Cases for Advanced Practice. 2008. (End of Life Care: a Ser.). (ENG.). 280p. (gr. 17). pap. 32.00 *(978-0-231-14175-8(0))* Columbia Univ. Pr.

Wolfson, Phil. Noe: A Father-Son Song of Love, Life, Illness, & Death. 2011. (ENG., Illus.). 360p. pap. 21.95 *(978-1-55643-971-1(7))* North Atlantic Bks.

Zwettler-Otte, Sylvia. The Melody of Separation: A Psychoanalytic Study of Separation Anxiety. 2011. 186p. pap. 57.95 ***(978-3-631-58938-0(7))*** Lang, Peter GmbH, Europaischer Verlag der Wissenschaften DEU. Dist: Lang, Peter.

BEREAVEMENT—PSYCHOLOGICAL ASPECTS

Abrams, Joy. What to Do? What to Say? There Has to Be Another Way. 2010. 114p. 29.99 *(978-1-4500-0554-8(3))*; pap. 19.99 *(978-1-4500-0553-1(5))* Xlibris Corp.

Abrams, Rebecca. When Parents Die: Learning to Live with the Loss of a Parent. 3rd rev. ed. 2013. (ENG.). 224p. 110.00 *(978-0-415-59011-2(6))*; pap. 32.95 *(978-0-415-59012-9(4))* Routledge.

Acton, Carol. Grief in Wartime: Private Pain, Public Discourse. 2007. (ENG., Illus.). 272p. 110.00 *(978-1-4039-4696-6(5))* Palgrave Macmillan.

Akhtar, Salman. Three Faces of Mourning: Melancholia, Manic Defense, & Moving On. 2006. (Margaret S. Mahler Ser.). (ENG.). 280p. pap. 39.99 *(978-0-7657-0516-7(8),* Aronson, Jason) Rowman & Littlefield Publishers, Inc.

Alapack, Richard. Sorrow's Profiles: Death, Grief & Crisis in the Family. 2010. 380p. pap. 41.95 *(978-1-85575-621-2(8))* Karnac Bks. GBR. Dist: Stylus Publishing, LLC.

Allen, Moira. Coping with Sorrow on the Loss of Your Pet. 2007. 160p. per. 16.95 *(978-1-59858-453-0(7))* Dog Ear Publishing, LLC.

Amatuzio, Janis. Forever Ours: Real Stories of Immortality & Living from a Forensic Pathologist. 2007. (ENG.). 224p. per. 14.95 *(978-1-57731-599-5(5))* New World Library.

Atlantic Publishing Group. How to Endure the Loss of a Child: A Parent's Guide to Mourning & Moving Forward. 2012. (ENG.). 288p. pap. 24.95 *(978-1-60138-571-0(4))* Atlantic Publishing Co.

Attig, Thomas. How We Grieve: Relearning the World, 1 vol. 2nd ed. 2010. (ENG.). 264p. pap. 26.95 *(978-0-19-539769-7(5))* Oxford Univ. Pr., Inc.

Axmann, Martha. She Won the Race: Footprints of Cancer. 2009. 212p. pap. 17.99 *(978-1-4141-1249-7(1))* Pleasant Word.

Ballard, Janice Holman & Ballard, Allison. The Longest Journey: Two Women's Parallel Stories of Grief & Healing. 2011. 259p. pap. 15.95 ***(978-1-4327-7381-6(X))*** Outskirts Pr., Inc.

Baltins, Andris A. Love Letters: Reflections on Living with Loss. 2007. 278p. per. 16.95 *(978-0-929636-70-2(8))* Syren Bk. Co.

Barber, Pam. Acceptance: A Grieving Mother Finds Peace... Nickols, Becky R., ed. 2007. 122p. per. 15.95 *(978-0-9796096-0-2(7))* J&J Publishing.

Beattie, Melody. The Grief Club: The Secret to Getting Through All Kinds of Change. 2006. (ENG.). 368p. pap. 14.95 *(978-1-59285-349-6(8))* Hazelden Publishing & Educational Services.

Beaulieu, Joyce. From a Father's Heart: (Heartfelt Sharings of the Loss of a Child) 2008. 154p. pap. 24.95 *(978-1-60610-699-0(6))* PublishAmerica, Inc.

Becker, Laura. Constructing Meaning Through Religious Coping. 2008. 84p. pap. *(978-3-8364-3715-8(5))* VDM Verlag Dr. Mueller e.K.

Beer, Susan. Move on Without Me: Secrets to a Positive Approach to Widowhood. 2010. (ENG.). 160p. 15.00 *(978-1-57826-336-3(0))* Hatherleigh Co., Ltd., The.

Berger, Susan A. The Five Ways We Grieve: Finding Your Personal Path to Healing after the Loss of a Loved One. 2011. (ENG.). 256p. pap. 17.95 *(978-1-59030-899-8(9),* Trumpeter) Shambhala Pubns., Inc.

Berman, Claire. When a Brother or Sister Dies: Looking Back, Moving Forward, 1 vol. 2009. 140p. 34.95 *(978-0-313-35528-8(2),* C35528, Praeger Pubs.) Greenwood Publishing Group, Inc.

Bialosky, Jill. History of a Suicide: My Sister's Unfinished Life. 2011. (ENG.). 272p. 24.00 *(978-1-4391-0193-3(0),* Beyond Words/Atria Bks.) Atria Bks.

Bisaccia, Fayegail Mandell. Dancing in My Mother's Slippers: A Journey of Grief & Healing. 2007. pap. 16.00 *(978-0-9789122-0-8(9))* Weaverbird Pr.

Blue-Salters, Melissa. His Death, My Angel. 2009. 40p. pap. 17.99 *(978-1-4389-8871-9(0))* AuthorHouse.

Bokanowski, Thierry, et al, eds. On Freud's Mourning & Melancholia. 2007. (IPA Contemporary Freud). 240p. (C). pap. 39.95 *(978-1-905888-06-1(6))* Karnac Bks. GBR. Dist: Stylus Publishing, LLC.

Bonanno, George A. The Other Side of Sadness: What the New Science of Bereavement Tells Us about Life after Loss. 2010. (ENG., Illus.). 240p. (gr. 9). pap. 15.95 *(978-0-465-02190-1(5))* Basic Bks.

Brodsky Resman, Jacalyn. You Left Us in A Lurch: A Siblings Journey to Healing over Loss of A Loved One. 2007. 111p. 29.97 *(978-1-4303-2868-1(1))* Lulu Enterprises Inc.

Brooks, Anne. Grieving Time: Year's Account of Recovery from Loss. 2006. 76p. per. 12.00 *(978-1-933480-07-7(6))* Bunim and Bannigan Ltd.

Brown, Elizabeth B. Surviving the Loss of a Child: Support for Grieving Parents, 1 vol. 2010. (ENG.). 176p. pap. 12.99 *(978-0-8007-3356-8(8))* Revell.

Caldwell, Frank. A Parent's Journey into Darkness: In Loving Tribute to Our Son, Eric. 2011. 64p. pap. 14.99 ***(978-1-4634-0080-4(2))*** AuthorHouse.

Campbell, Scott & Silverman, Phyllis R. Widower: When Men Are Left Alone. pap. 59.95 *(978-0-89503-286-7(4))* Baywood Publishing Co., Inc.

Carson, Jennifer. Letters to My Glory Baby. 2007. 188p. per. 13.99 *(978-1-60477-171-8(2))* Xulon Pr., Inc.

Carson, Stephanie A. Why My Child? A Clinical Guide for Helping Parents Survive the Sudden Death of a Child. 2009. 144p. pap. 11.99 *(978-1-60799-057-4(1))* Tate Publishing & Enterprises, LLC.

Catchings, Yvonne. Death: When it Happens — What to Do. 2007. 80p. per. 10.95 *(978-0-595-42504-4(6))* iUniverse, Inc.

Caughlin, Angela. The Only Way Through: A Journey of Loss, Transformation & Oneness. 2009. (ENG.). 160p. 19.95 *(978-1-933979-55-7(0))* Bright Sky Pr.

Centre for Addiction and Mental Health Staff, contrib. by. Hope & Healing after Suicide: A Practical Guide for People Who Have Lost Someone to Suicide in Ontario. 2011. ***(978-1-77052-346-3(4))*** Centre for Addiction & Mental Health.

Challenger, Mary. The Long Road: Coping with Depression Through Art. 2009. (Illus.). 70p. 21.95 *(978-1-84624-364-6(5))* Book Guild, Ltd. GBR. Dist: Trans-Atlantic Pubns., Inc.

Chesser, Barbara. Seven Steps for Handling Grief: Because You Care. 2009. 246p. pap. 24.95 *(978-0-86534-705-2(0))* Sunstone Pr.

Childress, Janet. Fishing in Heaven. 2008. 60p. per. 9.95 *(978-1-4327-1941-8(6))* Outskirts Pr., Inc.

Claussen, Cindy. Born to Fly: An Infant's Journey to God. 2007. (Illus.). per. 9.95 *(978-0-9650848-5-7(X))* ACTA Pubns.

Clyman, Seth. Touching the World of Angels: How My Daughter's Short Life Changed Mine. 2011. 168p. pap. 9.95 *(978-0-7573-1560-2(7))* Health Communications, Inc.

Collins, Chuck. Holding onto Love: Searching for Hope When a Child Dies. 2009. 212p. pap. 17.95 *(978-1-4401-2126-5(5))* iUniverse, Inc.

Connerton, Paul. The Spirit of Mourning: History, Memory & the Body. 2011. (ENG.). 190p. 85.00 ***(978-1-107-01139-7(6))***; pap. 28.99 ***(978-1-107-64883-8(1))*** Cambridge Univ. Pr.

Cope, Denys. Dying: A Natural Passage. 2008. 130p. pap. 14.95 *(978-0-9787506-5-7(9))* Three Whales Publishing LLC.

Corr, Charles A., et al. Death & Dying, Life & Living: With InfoTrac College Edition. 3rd ed. *(978-0-534-74506-6(7))* Wadsworth.

Coryell, Deborah Morris. Good Grief: Healing Through the Shadow of Loss. 10th ed. 2007. (ENG., Illus.). 1p. 18.95 *(978-1-59477-159-0(6),* Healing Arts Pr.) Inner Traditions International, Ltd.

Cram101 Textbook Reviews & Cram101 Textbook Reviews. Outlines & Highlights for Understanding Dying, Death, & Bereavement by Michael Leming, Isbn: 9780495810186. 2011. 138p. pap. 28.95 ***(978-1-61461-113-4(0))*** Cram101 Inc.

Cram101 Textbook Reviews Staff. Outlines & Highlights for Death & Dying: Life & Living by Corr ISBN. 2008. 192p. per. 13.95 *(978-1-4288-5761-2(3))* Cram101 Inc.

—Outlines & Highlights for Death & Dying, Life & Living by Charles a Corr, Isbn: 9780495506461. 2009. 100p. pap. 27.95 *(978-1-4288-9838-7(7))* Cram101 Inc.

—Outlines & Highlights for Death & Dying Understanding Dying, Death, & Bereavement by Leming, Isbn: 0534627366. 2008. 136p. per. 11.95 *(978-1-4288-5788-9(5))* Cram101 Inc.

Croft, George. Oh! So You Think You Know Dogs? 2006. (ENG.). 248p. per. 15.95 *(978-1-59800-897-5(8))* Outskirts Pr., Inc.

Cunningham, Alan Blain, compiled by. Rainbow Tears: Reflections of Pet Loss, Grief & Healing. 2009. (Illus.). 286p. ***(978-1-934243-05-3(1))*** Agreka Bks., LLC.

Daily, Art & Daily, Allison. Out of the Canyon: A True Story of Loss & Love. 2010. (ENG.). 288p. pap. 14.00 *(978-0-307-40941-6(4),* Three Rivers Pr.) Crown Publishing Group.

Deitch, Patricia. Living in the Presence of His Absence. 2008. 184p. pap. *(978-3-639-06404-9(6))* VDM Verlag Dr. Mueller e.K.

Deits, Bob. Life after Loss: A Practical Guide to Renewing Your Life after Experiencing Major Loss. 5th ed. 2009. (ENG.). 304p. pap. 15.95 *(978-0-7382-1346-0(2))* Da Capo Pr., Inc.

DeVita-Raeburn, Elizabeth. The Empty Room: Surviving the Loss of a Brother or Sister at Any Age. 2006. 229p. reprint ed. 23.00 *(978-1-4223-5484-1(9))* DIANE Publishing Co.

—The Empty Room: Understanding Sibling Loss. 2007. (ENG.). 240p. pap. 15.99 *(978-0-7432-0152-0(3),* Scribner) Scribner.

Dickinson, George & Leming, Michael. Annual Editions: Dying, Death, & Bereavement 12/13. 13th ed. 2011. (Annual Editions Ser.). (ENG., Illus.). 240p. (C). pap. 44.00 ***(978-0-07-805105-0(3)***, 0078051053, McGraw-Hill/Dushkin) McGraw-Hill Higher Education.

Dickinson, George, et al. Dying, Death, & Bereavement 09/10. 11th ed. 2009. (Annual Editions Ser.). (ENG., Illus.). 192p. (C). pap. 44.00 *(978-0-07-812767-0(X),* 007812767X, McGraw-Hill/Dushkin) McGraw-Hill Higher Education.

Dickinson, George E. Dying, Death & Bereavement. 7th ed. 2006. pap. 8.95 *(978-1-4288-1625-1(9))* Cram101 Inc.

Doka, Ken, ed. Death Dying & Bereavement, 4 vols. 2006. (Illus.). 1856p. 1305.00 *(978-0-415-36914-5(2))* Routledge.

Doka, Kenneth J. & Martin, Terry L. Grieving Beyond Gender: Understanding the Ways Men & Women Mourn. 2nd rev. ed. 2010. (Series in Death, Dying & Bereavement Ser.). (ENG.). 258p. pap. 34.95 *(978-0-415-99572-6(8))*; 95.95 *(978-0-415-99571-9(X))* Routledge.

Dunn, Michael. Time to Grieve: How to Come Through Bereavement to Recovery & Growth. 2nd rev. ed. 2006. 198p. per. 26.00 *(978-1-84528-081-9(4))* Parkwest Pubns., Inc.

Dyregrov, Kari & Dyregrov, Atle. Effective Grief & Bereavement Support: The Role of Family, Friends, Colleagues, Schools & Support Professionals. 2008. (ENG.). 272p. pap. *(978-1-84310-667-8(1))* Kingsley, Jessica Ltd.

Feldbaum, Rebecca Bram. What Should I Say, What Can I Do? How to Reach Out to Those You Love. 2008. (ENG., Illus.). 144p. 9.95 *(978-1-4165-5717-3(2))* Gallery Pr., The IRL. Dist: Simon & Schuster, Inc.

Ferrara, Yvette. Goodbye, My Love' A Guidebook for Endings. 2007. pap. 9.00 *(978-0-8059-8684-6(7))* Dorrance Publishing Co., Inc.

Fife, Bert. Free Bird Flies. 2009. (ENG., Illus.). 128p. pap. 14.95 *(978-0-9769934-3-8(0))* Voyages Pr., Inc.

Fiorini. On Freud's Mourning & Melancholia. 2nd rev. ed. 2009. 240p. pap. 34.95 *(978-1-85575-744-8(3))* Karnac Bks. GBR. Dist: Stylus Publishing, LLC.

Fishbane, Eitan P. Shadows in Winter: A Memoir of Love & Loss. 2011. ***(978-0-8156-0989-6(2))*** Syracuse Univ. Pr.

Fleming, David. Noah's Rainbow: A Father's Emotional Journey from the Death of His Son to the Birth of His Daughter. (Death & Bereavement Ser.). 212p. 39.95 *(978-0-89503-315-4(1))* Baywood Publishing Co., Inc.

Folger-Dineen, Eile. A Widow's Recovery: A Personal Journey. 2006. 143p. pap. 24.95 *(978-1-4241-4434-1(5))* PublishAmerica, Inc.

Forbes, Patricia. Healing Life's Broken Dreams , a Son's Tragedy, a Mother's Grief, a Miracle Recovery. 2009. 190p. 23.50 *(978-1-60693-641-2(7),* Eloquent Bks.) AEG Literary Publishing Services, Inc.

Gilbert, Allison. Always Too Soon: Voices of Support for Those Who Have Lost Both Parents. 2006. (ENG.). 200p. per. 14.95 *(978-1-58005-176-7(6))* Seal Pr.

Gordan, Sandra Kay & McKanders, Carolyn M. Nakia's Gift: A Mother's Journey from Misery to Ministry. 2009. 128p. pap. 14.99 *(978-1-933972-19-0(X))* PriorityONE Pubns.

Gossai, Hemchand. A Requiem for Neil. 2009. 124p. 24.95 *(978-1-60860-025-0(4),* Strategic Bk. Publishing) AEG Literary Publishing Services, Inc.

Graves, Dodie. Talking with Bereaved People: An Approach for Structured & Sensitive Communications. 2009. (ENG.). 192p. pap. *(978-1-84310-988-4(3))* Kingsley, Jessica Ltd.

Handler, Jessica & Jessica, Handler. Invisible Sisters: A Memoir. 2009. (ENG., Illus.). 272p. 24.95 *(978-1-58648-648-8(9))* PublicAffairs.

Hart, Jennifer. Marley Rides. 2007. (Illus.). 528p. pap. 20.00 *(978-0-9777632-2-1(6))* Lost Borders Pr.

Hartshorne, Edie. Light in Blue Shadows. 2007. 236p. pap. 14.95 *(978-0-9788699-0-8(7))* Ellsberg Bks.

Harvey, Greg. Grieving for Dummies. 2007. (ENG., Illus.). 358p. per. 19.99 *(978-0-470-06742-0(X),* For Dummies) Wiley, John & Sons, Inc.

Hawkins, Jennifer. The Gift Giver: A True Story. 2011. 254p. pap. 14.95 *(978-1-934572-80-1(2))* Emerald Bk. Co.

Hayton, A. Untwinned Perspectives on the Death of A. 2007. xii, 264p. pap. *(978-0-9525654-9-9(8))* Wren Pubns.

Healing the Hurt Spirit: Daily Affirmations for People Who Have Lost a Loved One to Suicide. 2006. pap. 15.95 *(978-0-9778244-0-3(3))* St. Dymphna Press.

Hoard, G. Richard. Alone among the Living: A Memoir of the Floyd Hoard Murder. 2007. (ENG.). 272p. per. 19.95 *(978-0-8203-3173-7(2))* Univ. of Georgia Pr.

Hood, Ann. Comfort: A Journey Through Grief. (ENG.). 192p. 2009. pap. 12.95 *(978-0-393-33659-7(X),* 33659) 2008. 19.95 *(978-0-393-06456-8(5),* 6456) Norton, W. W. & Co., Inc.

Humphrey, Geraldine M. & Zimpfer, David G. Counselling for Grief & Bereavement. 2nd ed. 2007. (Counselling in Practice Ser.). (Illus.). 192p. (C). 125.00 *(978-1-4129-3565-4(2),* B35652C); pap. 51.00 *(978-1-4129-3566-1(0),* B35652P) SAGE Pubns., Ltd. GBR. Dist: SAGE Pubns., Inc.

Janice, Perkins. How to Help a Child Cope with Grief: A Book for Adults Who Live & Work with Bereaved Children. 2007. (ENG., Illus.). 128p. per. 16.95 *(978-0-572-03309-5(5))* Foulsham, W. Co., Ltd. GBR. Dist: APG Sales & Distribution Services.

Jeffreys, J. Shep. Helping Grieving People - When Tears Are Not Enough: A Handbook for Care Providers. 2nd rev. ed. 2011. (Series in Death, Dying & Bereavement Ser.). (ENG., Illus.). 421p. pap. 44.95 *(978-0-415-87701-5(6))* Routledge.

Jordan, John R. & McIntosh, John L. Grief after Suicide: Understanding the Consequences & Caring for the Survivors. 2010. (Series in Death, Dying & Bereavement Ser.). (ENG., Illus.). 574p. 42.50 *(978-0-415-99355-5(5))* Routledge.

Karen Eden Herdman. Will I Ever Feel Happy Again? These Survivors of Suicide say Yes! 2009. 56p. pap. 9.95 *(978-1-4401-6343-2(X))* iUniverse, Inc.

Keeley, Maureen P. & Yingling, Julie M. Final Conversations: Helping the Living & the Dying Talk to Each Other. 2007. (Illus.). 234p. 24.95 *(978-1-889242-30-9(6))* VanderWyk & Burnham.

King, Alicia. Healing: The Essential Guide to Helping Others Overcome Grief & Loss. 2011. (ENG.). 178p. pap. 14.95 *(978-1-59652-816-1(8))* Turner Publishing Co.

—Sorry for Your Loss: What People Who Are Grieving Wish You Knew. 2010. (ENG.). 213p. pap. 9.99 *(978-1-59652-747-8(1))* Turner Publishing Co.

Koppelman, Kent L. Wrestling with the Angel: Literary Writings & Reflections on Death, Dying & Bereavement. 2010. 39.95 *(978-0-89503-392-5(5))* Baywood Publishing Co., Inc.

Kornfeld, Jody, et al. Death & Bereavement. 2012. (Teen Mental Health Ser.). (ENG., Illus.). 48p. (YA). (gr. 7-12). lib. bdg. 27.95 ***(978-1-4488-6892-6(0))*** Rosen Publishing Group, Inc., The.

Kosminsky, Phyllis. Getting Back to Life When Grief Won't Heal. 2006. (ENG.). 240p. per. 16.95 *(978-0-07-146472-7(7)*, 0071464727) McGraw-Hill Cos., The.

Kowalski, Gary. Goodbye, Friend: Healing Wisdom for Anyone Who Has Ever Lost a Pet. rev. ed. 2012. (ENG., Illus.). 184p. pap. 14.00 ***(978-1-60868-086-3(X))*** New World Library.

Kubler-Ross, Elisabeth, et al. On Grief & Grieving: Finding the Meaning of Grief Through the Five Stages of Loss. 2007. (ENG.). 256p. pap. 15.00 *(978-0-7432-6629-1(3)*, Scribner) Scribner.

Lake, Tony. Living with Grief. 2.99 *(978-0-687-85695-4(7))* Abingdon Pr.

—Living with Grief. 154p. *(978-0-85969-426-1(7)*, Sheldon Press) SPCK Publishing.

Landry, Julie. In Sickness & in Health: How to Keep Going When Death Interrupts Life. 2008. (ENG.). 68p. pap. 9.99 *(978-0-9762730-6-6(3))* Vision Publishing.

Lawrence, Don Harold. Glimpses into Grief. 2010. (Illus.). xviii, 300p. pap. ***(978-0-9827848-0-8(5))*** Monument Pr.

Leader, Darian. The New Black: Mourning, Melancholia, & Depression. 2009. (ENG., Illus.). 224p. pap. 16.00 *(978-1-55597-542-5(9))* Graywolf Pr.

Long, Cynthia L. Life after Suicide: Survival, Hope, & Healing. 2011. ***(978-0-7880-2666-9(6))*** CSS Publishing Co.

Lukas, Christopher & Seiden, Henry, eds. Silent Grief: Living in the Wake of Suicide. 2nd ed. 2007. (ENG.). 176p. per. *(978-1-84310-847-4(X))* Kingsley, Jessica Ltd.

Machin, Linda. Working with Loss & Grief: A New Model for Practitioners. 2008. (Illus.). 216p. (C). 102.00 *(978-1-4129-4667-4(0)*, B46674C); pap. 51.00 *(978-1-4129-4668-1(9)*, B46674P) SAGE Pubns., Ltd. GBR. Dist: SAGE Pubns., Inc.

Madill, Betty. One Step at a Time: Mourning a Child, 1 vol. (ENG., Illus.). 128p. 12.95 *(978-0-86315-338-9(0))* Floris Bks. GBR. Dist: SteinerBooks, Inc.

Magowan, Fiona. Melodies of Mourning: Music & Emotion in Northern Australia. 2007. (World Anthropology Ser.). (Illus.). 240p. 90.00 *(978-0-85255-993-2(3))*; pap. 34.95 *(978-0-85255-992-5(5))* Boydell & Brewer, Ltd. GBR. (Currey, James). Dist: Boydell & Brewer, Inc.

—Melodies of Mourning: Music & Emotion in Northern Australia. (Illus.). xvii, 222p. 65.00 *(978-1-930618-89-3(1))*; pap. 29.95 *(978-1-930618-90-9(5))* School for Advanced Research Pr./SAR Pr.

Marasco, Ron & Shuff, Brian. About Grief: Insights, Setbacks, Grace Notes, Taboos. 2010. (ENG.). 224p. 22.95 *(978-1-56663-858-6(5))* Dee, Ivan R. Pub.

Masi, Kimberly. Mending a Broken Heart: A Teenager's Guide Through the Loss of a Parent. 2008. 79p. pap. 16.95 *(978-1-60474-667-9(X))* PublishAmerica, Inc.

Matthews, Mignon. Mom No More: Coping with the Late-Life Loss of Adult Children - One Woman's Story. 2008. 200p. 29.95 *(978-1-933167-32-9(7))* Hatala Geroproducts.

Mayfield, Sue. Living with Bereavement. 2009. (ENG., Illus.). 128p. 14.95 *(978-0-7459-5295-6(X))* Lion Hudson PLC GBR. Dist: Independent Pubs. Group.

McCaffree, Ruthann Reim. Suddenly Single: A Guide for Rediscovering Life after Tragic Loss. 2011. 78p. pap. 12.95 ***(978-1-936183-66-1(8)***, Langdon Street Pr.) Hillcrest Publishing Group, Inc.

McKessar, Anna. Five Hours with Raj. 2010. 60p. pap. *(978-3-8383-4450-8(2))* Lambert Academic Publishing.

McNunn, Marty. A Group I Never Wanted to Join: Practical Advice & Stories of Hope & Recovery for Grieving People. 2006. 171p. per. 15.00 *(978-0-929636-67-2(8))* Syren Bk. Co.

Miller, Jeri Rae. Heartfelt: A Companion for Bereaved Parents. 2007. 62p. per. 10.00 *(978-1-879384-74-3(4))* Cypress Hse.

Mitchell, Ellen. Beyond Tears. Date not set. *(978-0-312-32828-3(1))*; mass mkt. *(978-0-312-99706-9(X)*, St. Martin's Paperbacks) St. Martin's Pr.

Mitchell, Ellen & Barkin, Carol. Beyond Tears: Living after Losing a Child. 2nd rev. ed. 2009. (ENG.). 208p. pap. 13.95 *(978-0-312-54519-2(3)*, St. Martin's Griffin) St. Martin's Pr.

Monkiewicz, Anthony. Men Don't Cry Between Hello & Good-Bye. 2011. 316p. 32.99 ***(978-1-4134-3392-0(8))***; pap. 22.99 ***(978-1-4134-3391-3(X))*** Xlibris Corp.

Monroe, Robin Prince. Devotions for the Brokenhearted: Hope for the Grieving. 2006. 155p. per. 12.99 *(978-1-59886-352-9(5))* Tate Publishing & Enterprises, LLC.

Moore, Sharee, ed. Stolen Angels: 25 Stories of Hope after Pregnancy or Infant Loss. 2006. per. 15.95 *(978-0-9789389-0-1(9))* Dynasty Pubs. LLC.

Morgan, John D., et al, eds. Death & Bereavement Around the World: Volume 5: Voluem 5: Reflective Essays, 5 vols. 2009. 296p. pap. 37.95 *(978-0-89503-239-3(2))* Baywood Publishing Co., Inc.

Moss, Bernard. Responding to Loss. 2010. 136p. spiral bd. 79.95 *(978-1-905541-58-4(9))* Russell Hse. Publishing Ltd. GBR. Dist: International Specialized Bk. Services.

Myers, Edward. When Will I Stop Hurting? Teens, Loss, & Grief. 2006. (It Happened to Me Ser.). (ENG., Illus.). 176p. pap. 20.00 *(978-0-8108-5758-2(8))* Scarecrow Pr., Inc.

Myers, Michael F. & Fine, Carla. Touched by Suicide: Hope & Healing after Loss. 2006. (ENG.). 304p. (gr. 12-18). 18.00 *(978-1-59240-228-1(3)*, Gotham) Penguin Group (USA) Inc.

Nadeau, Janice W. Clinical Implications of Family Meaning-Making in Bereavement: Making in Bereavement. 2009. 34.95 *(978-0-415-95626-0(9))* Routledge.

Neimeyer, Robert A. Grief & Bereavement in Contemporary Society: Bridging Research & Practice. 2011. (Series in Death, Dying & Bereavement Ser.). (ENG., Illus.). 472p. pap. 49.95 *(978-0-415-88481-5(0))* Routledge.

Neimeyer, Robert A., et al, eds. Grief & Bereavement in Contemporary Society: Bridging Research & Practice. 2011. (Series in Death, Dying & Bereavement Ser.). (ENG., Illus.). 472p. 130.00 *(978-0-415-88480-8(2))* Routledge.

Nicholson, Jane. Someone Traveling. 2011. 212p. 24.99 ***(978-1-4670-3478-4(9))***; pap. 14.99 ***(978-1-4670-3479-1(7))*** AuthorHouse.

Noel, Brook & Blair, Pamela. I Wasn't Ready to Say Goodbye (Revised, Updated & Expanded Edition) Surviving, Coping & Healing after the Sudden death of a Loved One. 2nd rev. ed. 2007. 312p. per. 14.95 *(978-1-932783-78-0(4))* Sourcebooks, Inc.

Noel, Brook & Blair, Pamela D. I Wasn't Ready to Say Goodbye: A Companion Workbook for Surviving, Coping, & Healing after the Sudden Death of a Loved One. 2nd ed. 2008. (ENG.). 224p. pap., wbk. ed. 22.99 *(978-1-4022-1239-0(9))* Sourcebooks, Inc.

—I Wasn't Ready to Say Goodbye: Surviving, Coping & Healing after the Sudden Death of a Loved One. 2008. (ENG.). 336p. pap. 15.99 *(978-1-4022-1221-5(6))* Sourcebooks, Inc.

Norman, Paulette. Waltz with Insanity: A Mother's Story about the Murder of Her Son & Her Process of Healing Through Faith. 2006. (Illus.). 216p. per. 14.95 *(978-1-933285-49-8(4))* Brown Bks. Publishing Group.

O'Byrne, Sandra. It Hurts When Someone You Love Dies. 2010. (ENG., Illus.). 48p. pap. *(978-1-84748-767-4(X))* Athena Pr.

O'Connor, Nancy. Letting Go with Love: The Grieving Process. rev. ed. 2007. 230p. per. *(978-0-9613714-8-7(X))* La Mariposa Pr.

Okun, Barbara & Nowinski, Joseph. Saying Goodbye: A Guide to Coping with a Loved One's Terminal Illness. 2012. (ENG.). 368p. (gr. 12). 16.00 ***(978-0-425-24518-7(7)***, Berkley Trade) Penguin Group (USA) Inc.

Okun, Barbara & Nowinski, Joseph. Saying Goodbye: How Families Can Find Renewal Through Loss. 2011. (ENG.). 336p. (gr. 12). 26.95 *(978-0-425-23322-1(7)*, Berkley Hardcover) Penguin Group (USA) Inc.

Olson, Susan. By Grief Transformed: Dreams & the Mourning Process. 2009. (ENG., Illus.). 240p. pap. 24.95 *(978-1-882670-77-2(9))* Spring Journal.

O'Shea, Jim. When a Child Dies: Footsteps of a Grieving Family. 2009. (ENG.). 144p. pap. 16.95 *(978-1-84730-178-2(2))* Veritas Pubns. IRL. Dist: Dufour Editions, Inc.

Palatnik, Lori & Palatnik, Yaakov. Remember My Soul: What to Do in Memory of a Loved One: A Path of Reflection & Inspiration for Shiva, the Stages of Jewish Mourning, & Beyond. 2008. 246p. pap. 23.99 *(978-1-60204-014-4(1))* K'hal Publishing.

Parkes, et al. Bereavement: Studies of Grief in Adult Life. 2nd rev. ed. 2009. (ENG., Illus.). 368p. 70.00 *(978-0-415-45118-5(3))* Routledge.

Parkes, Colin Murray. Love & Loss: The Roots of Grief & Its Complications. 2006. (ENG., Illus.). 448p. (C). 69.95 *(978-0-415-39041-5(9)*, RU0419) Routledge.

—Love & Loss: The Roots of Grief & its Complications. 2008. (ENG., Illus.). 448p. (C). pap. 34.95 *(978-0-415-47718-5(2))* Routledge.

Peckham, Joel. Resisting Elegy: On Grief & Recovery. 2012. (ENG.). 144p. 19.95 ***(978-0-89733-625-3(9))*** Academy Chicago Pubs., Ltd.

Perreault, Yvette. The Presence of Absence: The Effect of HIV Sero-Status on the Bereavement Experiences of Long-Term Survivors of Multiple AIDS-Related Losses. 2008. 228p. pap. *(978-3-8364-8340-7(8))* VDM Verlag Dr. Mueller e.K.

Petruso, Angelina. About Kyle: Life, Death & Beyond - A True Story. 2007. 201p. pap. 24.95 *(978-1-4241-9110-9(6))* PublishAmerica, Inc.

Pieterse, Anne. What If I Whispered Your Name? 2011. 96p. pap. 15.99 ***(978-1-4628-5741-8(8))*** Xlibris Corp.

Pomeroy, Elizabeth C. & Garcia, Renee Bradford. The Grief Assessment & Intervention Workbook: A Strengths Perspective. 2008. (Death & Dying/Grief & Loss Ser.). (ENG.). 272p. (C). pap. 52.95 *(978-0-495-00841-5(9))* Wadsworth.

Pope, Alan. From Child to Elder: Personal Transformation in Becoming an Orphan at Midlife. 2006. (American University Studies: Vol. 24). 294p. (C). 73.95 *(978-0-8204-7941-5(1))* Lang, Peter Publishing, Inc.

Reck, Julie. Facing Farewell: How & When to Decide on Euthanasia for Your Pet. 2012. ***(978-1-61781-076-3(2))*** Dogwise Publishing.

Redfern, Suzanne & Gilbert, Susan K. The Grieving Garden: Living with the Death of a Child - Twenty Two Parents Share Their Stories. 2008. 304p. 24.95 *(978-1-57174-569-9(6))*; (ENG., Illus.). per. 18.95 *(978-1-57174-581-1(5))* Hampton Roads Publishing Co., Inc.

Reynolds, Rita M. Blessing the Bridge: What Animals Teach Us about Death, Dying & Beyond. 2011. (ENG.). 206p. pap. 16.00 *(978-0-939165-59-9(7))* NewSage Pr., LLC.

Rogers, J. Earl, ed. The Art of Grief: The Use of Expressive Arts in a Grief Support Group. 2007. (Series in Death, Dying, & Bereavement). (ENG., Illus.). 224p. per. 34.95 *(978-0-415-95535-5(1))* Routledge.

Roiphe, Anne. Epilogue: A Memoir. (ENG.). 2009. 256p. pap. 14.99 *(978-0-06-125463-5(0)*, HarperPerennial) 2008. 288p. pap. 24.95 *(978-0-06-166857-9(5)*, HarperLuxe) HarperCollins Pubs.

Rubin, Simon Shimshon, et al. A Clinician's Guide to Working with the Bereaved. 2011. (Series in Death, Dying, & Bereavement Ser.). (ENG., Illus.). 282p. pap. 34.95 ***(978-0-415-88166-1(8))*** Routledge.

Rubin, Simon Shimshon, et al. Working with the Bereaved: Multiple Lenses on Loss & Mourning. 2011. (Series in Death, Dying & Bereavement Ser.). (ENG., Illus.). 282p. 130.00 *(978-0-415-88165-4(X))* Routledge.

Ryan, Jackie L. My Angel Damo: Walking Through Life after the Death of an Only Child, 1 vol. 2009. 57p. pap. 16.95 *(978-1-60703-078-2(0))* PublishAmerica, Inc.

Sauceda, Carol / T. My Journey with Grief: A Mother's Grief Revealed in Her Journals. 2009. 320p. pap. 22.00 *(978-1-58982-515-4(2)*, Millennial Mind Publishing) American Bk. Publishing Group.

Schaefer, Dan, et al. How Do We Tell the Children? 4th ed. 2010. (ENG.). 224p. pap. 16.95 *(978-1-55704-911-7(4)*, William Morrow Paperbacks) HarperCollins Pubs.

Schaefer, G. J. The Widower's Toolbox: Repairing Your Life after Losing Your Spouse. 2010. (ENG.). 224p. pap. 14.95 *(978-0-88282-345-4(0))* New Horizon Pr. Pubs., Inc.

Schrock, Julie Burget. Missing Max. 2011. 100p. pap. 13.00 ***(978-1-59755-263-1(0)***, Advantage Inspirational) Advantage Bks.

Schuette, Janice. Awakening by Departure. 2006. (ENG.). 84p. per. 16.95 *(978-1-4241-5231-5(3))* PublishAmerica, Inc.

Severin, Theresa. In the Wake of the Storm: Living Beyond the Tragedy of Flight 4184. 2008. (ENG.). 25.00 *(978-0-9796062-0-5(9))* North Cross Pr., Ltd.

Shabad, Peter. Despair & the Return of Hope: Echoes of Mourning in Psychotherapy. 2007. (ENG.). 352p. per. 39.99 *(978-0-7657-0581-5(8)*, Aronson, Jason) Rowman & Littlefield Publishers, Inc.

Shields, Marcella Harmon. Once upon a Time There Was a Little Girl: The healing power of fairy tales in the lives of seven Women. 2008. 304p. 31.95 *(978-0-595-71054-6(9))*; pap. 21.95 *(978-0-595-46106-6(9))* iUniverse, Inc.

Sidebotham, Peter & Fleming, Peter, eds. Unexpected Death in Childhood: A Handbook for Practitioners. 2008. (Wiley Child Protection & Policy Ser.: 16). (ENG.). 368p. 149.95 *(978-0-470-06095-7(6))*; pap. 57.95 *(978-0-470-06096-4(4))* Wiley, John & Sons, Inc. (Wiley-Interscience).

Simon, Leslie & Dranell, Jan Johnson. A Music I No Longer Heard: The Early Death of a Parent. 2010. (ENG.). 352p. pap. 21.99 *(978-1-4516-1364-3(4))* Simon & Schuster.

Smith, Claire Bidwell. The Rules of Inheritance. 2012. (ENG.). 304p. (gr. 12). 25.95 ***(978-1-59463-088-0(7)***, Hudson Street Pr.) Penguin Group (USA) Inc.

Smith, Penelope. Animals in Spirit: Our Faithful Companions' Transition to the Afterlife. 2008. (ENG.). 192p. pap. 14.00 *(978-1-58270-177-6(6)*, Beyond Words/Atria Bks.) Atria Bks.

Spencer, Violet. Life Out of Tragedy: One Woman's Path to Peace. 2009. pap. 10.99 *(978-1-60799-273-8(6))* Tate Publishing & Enterprises, LLC.

Stearns, Ann Kaiser. Living Through Personal Crisis. 2010. *(978-1-882883-57-5(X))* Idyll Arbor, Inc.

Stroebe, Margaret S. Handbook of Bereavement Research & Practice: Advances in Theory & Intervention. 2008. (Illus.). 624p. 69.95 *(978-1-4338-0351-2(8))* American Psychological Assn.

Stubbs, Tony. Death Without Fear: Comfort for Those Facing Death or Bereavement. 2008. 248p. per. 20.00 *(978-0-9789611-6-9(1))* Dandelion Bks.

Tangye. The Evening Gull. 212p. pap. 11.00 *(978-0-7515-0491-0(2))* Warner Futura GBR. Dist: Trafalgar Square Publishing.

Torckler, Gillian & Torckler, Darryl. Your Heart Will Sing Again: Comfort for Those Who Mourn. 2010. (ENG., Illus.). 72p. 9.99 *(978-0-7641-6364-7(7))* Barron's Educational Series, Inc.

Tracey, Anne. Surviving the Early Loss of a Mother: Daughters Speak. 2009. (ENG.). 160p. pap. 17.95 *(978-1-84730-130-7(4))* Veritas Pubns. IRL. Dist: Dufour Editions, Inc.

Tucci, Amy S. & Doka, Kenneth J., eds. Beyond Kübler-Ross: New Perspectives on Death, Dying & Grief. 2011. 250p. pap. 28.95 ***(978-1-893349-13-1(6))*** Hospice Foundation of America.

Tuzeo-Jarolmen, Joann. When a Family Pet Dies: A Parents' Guide to Dealing with Chidlren's Loss. 2006. (ENG.). 8p. per. *(978-1-84310-836-8(4))* Kingsley, Jessica Ltd.

Valentine, Christine. Bereavement Narratives: Continuing Bonds in the 21st Century. 2008. X, 198p. 45.95 *(978-0-415-45730-9(0))*; 160.00 *(978-0-415-45729-3(7))* Routledge.

Walter, Carolyn Ambler & McCoyd, Judith L. M. Grief & Loss Across the Lifespan: A Biopsychosocial Perspective. 2009. 373p. 55.00 *(978-0-8261-2757-0(6))* Springer Publishing Co., Inc.

Westra, Mary. After the Murder of My Son. 2010. pap. 14.95 *(978-0-87839-398-5(6))* North Star Pr. of St. Cloud.

Wheeler, Barbara Roberts. When a Spouse Dies. 2011. ***(978-1-59955-983-4(8))*** Cedar Fort, Inc./CFI Distribution.

White, Rob. Freud's Memory: Psychoanalysis, Mourning & the Stranger Self. 2008. (Language, Discourse, Society Ser.). (ENG.). 256p. 89.00 *(978-0-230-00264-7(1))* Palgrave Macmillan.

Williams, Sarah C. The Shaming of the Strong: The Challenge of an Unborn Life. 2007. (ENG.). 180p. per. *(978-1-57383-407-0(6)*, Regent College Publishing) Regent College Publishing.

Willock, Brent, et al, eds. On Death & Endings: Psychoanalysts' Reflections on Finality, Transformations & New Beginnings. 2007. (ENG., Illus.). 344p. (C). 115.00 *(978-0-415-39662-2(X))* Routledge.

—On Deaths & Endings: Psychoanalysts' Reflections on Finality, Transformations, & New Beginnings. 2007. (ENG., Illus.). 344p. (C). per. 42.50 *(978-0-415-39663-9(8))* Routledge.

Wolfelt, Alan D. The Mourner's Book of Hope. 2010. (Mourner's Book of Ser.). (ENG.). 192p. 15.95 *(978-1-879651-65-4(3))* Companion Pr.

—The Understanding Your Suicide Grief Journal: Exploring the Ten Essential Touchstones. 2009. (Understanding Your Grief Ser.). (ENG.). 136p. pap. 14.95 *(978-1-879651-59-3(9))* Companion Pr.

—The Wilderness of Suicide Grief: Finding Your Way. 2010. (Understanding Your Grief Ser.). (ENG.). 128p. 15.95 *(978-1-879651-68-5(8))* Companion Pr.

Wood, Sue & Fox, Peter. Dying: A Practical Guide for the Journey. 2009. 195p. pap. 11.95 *(978-1-77013-017-3(9))* Double Storey Bks. ZAF. Dist: International Publishers Marketing.

Woodward, Joan. The Lone Twin: Understanding Twin Bereavement & Loss. 2nd rev. ed. 2010. 187p. pap. 34.95 *(978-1-85343-200-2(8))* Free Assn. Bks. Ltd. GBR. Dist: International Specialized Bk. Services.

Yin. Why? When Both My Parents Took Their Lives. 2008. (Illus.). xi, 113p. *(978-981-08-1313-0(9))* Monsoon Bks. Pte. Ltd.

Zaugg, Sandra L. Surviving Grief: A Personal Journey. 2010. pap. 7.99 *(978-0-8163-2400-2(X))* Pacific Pr. Publishing Assn.

Zell, Shawn. The Right Word. 2008. (ENG.). 108p. pap. 11.95 *(978-0-533-15854-6(0))* Vantage Pr., Inc.

Zonnebelt-Smeenge, Susan J. & De Vries, Robert C. Traveling through Grief: Learning to Live Again after the Death of a Loved One. 2006. 160p. pap. 13.99 *(978-0-8010-6676-4(X))* Baker Bks.

Zuidervaart, Lambert. Dog-Kissed Tears: Songs of Friendship, Loss, & Healing. 2010. 88p. pap. 12.00 *(978-1-60899-700-8(6)*, Resource Pubns.) Wipf & Stock Pubs.

Zuniga, Michael A. & Zuniga, Micha'El A. A Special Vow: To Care for & Love Forever. 2009. 72p. pap. 10.99 *(978-1-61579-179-8(5))* Xulon Pr., Inc.

Zwelder. Seventy-Two Hours Spent in Paradise. 2011. 30p. pap. 16.95 ***(978-1-4560-9708-0(3))*** PublishAmerica, Inc.

BEREAVEMENT—RELIGIOUS ASPECTS

Adams, Nehemiah. Catharine. 2009. 194p. 37.95 *(978-1-104-68117-3(X))*; pap. 22.95 *(978-1-104-63083-6(4))* Kessinger Publishing, LLC.

Allison, Liz & Murphey, Cecil. Words of Comfort for Times of Loss: Help & Hope When You're Grieving. 2010. 64p. 10.99 *(978-0-7369-2429-0(9))* Harvest Hse. Pubs.

Anderson, Marlene. A Love So Great. 2007. 116p. per. 10.99 *(978-1-60266-660-3(1))* Xulon Pr., Inc.

Apple, Dennis L. Life after the Death of My Son: What I'm Learning. 2008. (ENG.). 192p. pap. 14.99 *(978-0-8341-2365-6(7)*, 083-412-3657) Beacon Hill Pr. of Kansas City.

Baker, Judy. Embracing Hope - a Grief Processing Journal. 2007. 64p. pap. 10.99 *(978-1-60495-001-4(3))* Grace Publishing.

Balas, Matilda (Millie). Lead Me, Guide Me: The Spiritual Rapture of Heaven. 2007. 110p. pap. 12.95 *(978-0-7414-3827-0(5))* Infinity Publishing.

Barrett, Elise Erikson. What Was Lost: A Christian Journey Through Miscarriage. 2010. (ENG., Illus.). 160p. pap. 17.00 *(978-0-664-23520-8(4))* Westminster John Knox Pr.

Bregman, Lucy, ed. Religion, Death, & Dying, 3 vols. 2009. 715p. 154.95 *(978-0-313-35173-0(2)*, C35173, Praeger Pubs.) Greenwood Publishing Group, Inc.

Brestin, Dee. The God of All Comfort: Finding Your Way into His Arms, 1 vol. 2009. (ENG.). 224p. pap. 16.99 *(978-0-310-29361-3(8))* Zondervan.

Breuer, Matthew. Thanatos. 2008. 200p. pap. 12.50 *(978-1-4357-4190-4(0))* Lulu Enterprises Inc.

Buckley, Christine. 21 Days of Harvest. 2008. 204p. pap. 14.99 *(978-1-60647-141-8(4))* Xulon Pr., Inc.

Bulen, Shirley. Forever Remembered: When Your Baby Is in Heaven. 2009. 100p. pap. 13.99 *(978-1-4343-8008-1(4))* AuthorHouse.

Bulka, Reuven P. Turning Grief into Gratitude: Reflections & Recommendations on Mourning & Condolence. 2007. (Illus.). 157p. per. 14.95 *(978-0-9732523-6-1(7))* Paper Spider CAN. Dist: AtlasBooks Distribution.

Butterfield, Edna. Golden Bubbles: Learning Through Loss: A Grandmother's Insight into Childhood Cancer. 2007. (Illus.). 96p. *(978-0-929540-64-1(6))* Publishing Designs, Inc.

Calloway-Miller, Brenda "Saw Jesus-". If You Want Your Life, You Have to Fight!!! The brenda saw jesus Story. 2009. 148p. pap. 14.95 *(978-1-4401-2292-7(X))* iUniverse, Inc.

Carter, Joyce Hau'oli. There Is No Veil: Aloha Is Eternal. 2009. 274p. pap. 14.95 *(978-1-4327-4161-7(6))* Outskirts Pr., Inc.

Charneski, Roberta M. & McElroy, Sylvia Rauzi. A Catholic Approach to Widowhood: A Journey with Mary. 2009. *(978-0-8189-1296-2(0)*, St. Pauls) St Pauls/Alba Hse. Pubs.

Christensen, Rachelle J. Lost Children: Coping with Miscarriage. 2010. (Illus.). xix, 75p. pap. 9.99 *(978-1-59955-248-4(5))* Cedar Fort, Inc./CFI Distribution.

Cole, Allan Hugh, Jr. Good Mourning: Getting Through Your Grief. 2008. (ENG.). 102p. pap. 13.00 *(978-0-664-23268-9(X))* Westminster John Knox Pr.

Cornish, Carol W. The Undistracted Widow: Living for God after Losing Your Husband. 2010. 208p. pap. 15.99 *(978-1-4335-1232-2(7))* Crossway.

Cox, Christy. Death of an Angel. 2009. 68p. pap. 10.99 *(978-1-60791-195-1(7))* Xulon Pr., Inc.

Croft, Brian & Newton, Phil A. Conduct Gospel-Centered Funerals: Applying the Gospel at the Unique Challenges of Death. 2011. (Ministering the Master's Way Ser.). 106p. pap. ***(978-1-84625-266-2(0))*** DayOne Pubns.

Cunningham, Marian Talley. The Faces of Grief: A Women's Bible Study. 2007. 105p. per. 6.95 *(978-1-59166-757-5(7))* BJU Pr.

Curtis, Kathy. Invisible Ink: The Journey Beyond Words. 2007. 63p. per. 14.95 *(978-0-9799645-0-3(4))* Curtis, Kathy.

Dodd, Terry. Life's Toughest Lessons Aren't Meant for Nothing. 2007. 312p. per. 17.99 *(978-1-60266-568-2(0))* Xulon Pr., Inc.

Doyle, Mary. Grieving with Mary: Finding Comfort & Healing in Devotion to the Mother of God. 2009. 160p. pap. 10.95 *(978-0-87946-397-7(X))* ACTA Pubns.

B

Du Bruyn, Barry. Rest in Pieces. 2007. 175p. pap. 22.95 *(978-1-84753-535-1(6))* Lulu Enterprises Inc.

Edmisten, Karen. Finding Hope after Miscarriage: A Companion in Grief & Healing, Hope, & Prayer. 2012. (ENG.). 144p. pap. 12.99 *(978-0-86716-997-3(4),* Servant Bks.) Franciscan Media.

Edwards, Syl. Heaven Bound: Know Where Your Saved Loved One Has Gone & Recovering from Other Losses in Life. 2010. pap. 14.99 *(978-1-61579-689-2(4))* Xulon Pr., Inc.

Eib, Lynn. When God & Grief Meet: True Stories of Comfort & Courage. 2009. (ENG.). 208p. pap. 12.99 *(978-1-4143-2174-5(0))* Tyndale Hse. Pubs.

Encounters at the Cross: Discover the Hope, Embrace the Power, Experience the Grace - Through Eyewitness Accounts of Those Who Were There. 2007. 208p. pap. 6.99 *(978-1-59379-111-7(9))* White Stone Bks.

Evans, Kathi. Our Baby, Our Love, Our Loss. 2007. (ENG.). 108p. per. 13.95 *(978-1-58736-730-4(0))* Wheatmark.

Fiegen, Kristine. Adrianna Rose-Precious Child of God. 2007. 168p. per. 13.99 *(978-1-60266-651-1(2))* Xulon Pr., Inc.

Flamming, Peter James. Healing the Heartbreak of Grief. 2010. 113p. pap. 12.00 *(978-1-4267-0221-1(3))* Abingdon Pr.

For Those Who Mourn. 0.45 *(978-0-687-85378-6(8))* Abingdon Pr.

Fowler, Gene. Ministry of Lament: Caring for the Bereaved. 2010. 160p. pap. 19.99 *(978-0-8272-2335-6(8))* Chalice Pr.

Fowler, John R. Dawning of the Age of Darkness: Coming to Grips with My Parents' Mortality. 2007. 85p. per. 9.99 *(978-1-59886-657-5(5))* Tate Publishing & Enterprises, LLC.

Frantz, Nadine Pence & Stimming, Mary T., eds. Hope Deferred: Heart-Healing Reflections on Reproductive Loss. 2010. 144p. pap. 18.00 *(978-1-60899-214-0(4),* Resource Pubns.) Wipf & Stock Pubs.

Friedman, Rabbi Dayle A. Jewish Pastoral Care: A Practical Handbook from Traditional & Contemporary Sources. 2nd ed. 2010. 528p. pap. 30.00 *(978-1-58023-427-6(5))* Jewish Lights Publishing.

Fry, Virgil M. Disrupted: Finding God in Illness & Loss. 2007. (Illus.). 127p. per. 12.99 *(978-0-89112-516-7(7),* Leafwood Pubs.) Abilene Christian Univ. Pr.

Geesey, Barbara. A Child's First Christmas in Heaven. 2009. 108p. 19.99 *(978-1-61579-199-6(X))* Xulon Pr., Inc.

Gewirtz, Matthew D. & Gewirtz, Matthew. The Gift of Grief: Finding Peace, Transformation, & Renewed Life after Great Sorrow. 2008. (ENG., Illus.). 160p. 14.95 *(978-1-58761-313-5(1),* Celestial Arts) Ten Speed Pr.

Gilion, Heather & Snell, Holly. Dancing on My Ashes: Learning to Love the One Who Gives & Takes Away. 2010. pap. 16.99 *(978-1-60799-871-6(8))* Tate Publishing & Enterprises, LLC.

Gilmour, Shannon. Persistent Grace. 2008. 55p. pap. 16.95 *(978-1-60441-890-3(7))* PublishAmerica, Inc.

Glynn, Marsha. Shattered Pieces of My Heart: A Mother's Story of Love, Loss, Faith, & Hope. 2007. 200p. (ENG.). 26.95 *(978-0-595-69812-7(3));* per. 16.95 *(978-0-595-44919-4(0))* iUniverse, Inc.

Gordon, Sandra Kay & McKanders, Carolyn M. Nakia's Gift: A Mother's Journey from Misery to Ministry. 2009. 128p. 15.99 *(978-1-933972-16-9(5))* PriorityONE Pubns.

Gore, Ralph. Grace Tried in the Fire. 2007. 84p. per. 9.99 *(978-1-60266-055-7(7))* Xulon Pr., Inc.

Graham. Dying to Live. 160p. pap. 11.99 *(978-0-340-73558-9(9),* Hodder & Stoughton) Hodder General Publishing Div. GBR. Dist: Trafalgar Square Publishing.

Greer, Ronald J. Markings on the Windowsill: A Book about Grief That's Really about Hope. 2006. 71p. per. 10.00 *(978-0-687-33363-9(6),* Dimensions For Living) Abingdon Pr.

Groft, Jan. As We Grieve: Discoveries of Grace in Sorrow. 2010. 184p. 15.95 *(978-0-9842306-0-0(2))* Graham Hse. Bks.

Guthrie, David & Guthrie, Nancy. When Your Family's Lost a Loved One: Finding Hope Together. 2008. (ENG.). 192p. pap. 13.99 *(978-1-58997-480-7(8))* Tyndale Hse. Pubs.

Hafen, Fran C. Joy Cometh in the Morning: A Story of Healing from the Loss of a Child. 2007. x, 201p. pap. *(978-1-59038-708-5(2))* Deseret Bk. Co.

Hahn, Eric. Held. 2011. 300p. pap. 18.99 *(978-1-61379-283-4(2))* Xulon Pr., Inc.

Ham, Ken. How Could a Loving God: Powerful Answers on Suffering. 2007. 198p. per. 12.99 *(978-0-89051-504-4(2))* Master Bks.

Hammell, Louise. That You May Know God Has a Purpose. 2008. 188p. pap. 14.99 *(978-1-60647-690-1(4))* Xulon Pr., Inc.

Harrelson, Bob. The Privilege of Pain: Help for Those Who Are Hurting. 2010. 164p. 30.95 *(978-1-61507-292-7(6));* pap. 13.95 *(978-1-61507-291-0(8))* Cross Bks. Publishing.

Haynes, Michael L. It Just Doesn't Make Sense. 2009. 108p. pap. 11.99 *(978-1-60791-829-5(3))* Xulon Pr., Inc.

Herndon, Larry. In the Cool of the Day. 2009. 306p. pap. 29.95 *(978-1-4241-9275-5(7))* PublishAmerica, Inc.

Hutchison, Joyce & Rupp, Joyce. Now That Youve Gone Home. 2009. 128p. pap. 10.95 *(978-1-59471-215-9(8))* Ave Maria Pr.

Isaac, Martha F. Reclaiming Our Citadel: Reflections on Widowhood. 2007. 88p. per. 10.95 *(978-0-595-42233-2(6))* iUniverse, Inc.

Jim Rule. Letting Go of Forever: When You Lose Someone You Love. 2010. 232p. pap. 18.95 *(978-1-4401-8988-3(9))* iUniverse, Inc.

Joel M. Mulholland. Ma Grandmere: At the Edge of Her Bed. 2009. 156p. 24.95 *(978-1-4401-8337-9(6));* pap. 14.95 *(978-1-4401-8334-8(1))* iUniverse, Inc.

Joiner, Judith P. Fly, Little Wing: The Healing of a Mother's Heart, 1 vol. 2009. 94p. pap. 16.95 *(978-1-60813-676-0(0))* PublishAmerica, Inc.

Jones, Richard. Words of Comfort from God & Others. 2007. 80p. per. 9.99 *(978-0-9793079-3-5(7))* Double-Edged Publishing, Inc.

Jones, Tonya Christine. God Said; Trust Me. 2008. 116p. pap. 9.99 *(978-0-9798890-1-1(4))* Encourage Pr.

Karlin, Wayne. Wandering Souls: Journeys with the Dead & the Living in Viet Nam. 2009. (ENG., Illus.). 376p. 25.95 *(978-1-56858-405-8(9),* Nation Bks.) Basic Bks.

Kaufmann, Larry T., et al. Why Do You Weep? Finding Consolation & Peace in Times of Grief. 2012. *(978-0-7648-2077-9(X))* Liguori Pubns.

Kiefert, Dwight. On Our Way Home: A True Story of a Family's Triumph over Tragedy. 2007. 77p. per. 8.99 *(978-1-59886-717-6(2))* Tate Publishing & Enterprises, LLC.

Killian, Wendy. To Have Loved. 2009. 116p. pap. 10.99 *(978-1-60799-032-1(6))* Tate Publishing & Enterprises, LLC.

Kinnaman, Scot A. Living with Dying: Blessings & Prayers for Those Who Grieve. 2012. *(978-0-7586-3404-7(8))* Concordia Publishing Hse.

Kitchell, Marjorie Holman. My Mother's Keeper: Through the Valley of the Shadow of Death. 2006. pap. 8.00 *(978-0-8059-7255-9(2))* Dorrance Publishing Co., Inc.

Koos, Lori. Grief to Grace. 2009. 200p. pap. 15.99 *(978-1-60791-499-0(9))* Xulon Pr., Inc.

Kreilkamp, PH.D., Ann. This Vast Being: A Voyage Through Grief & Exaltation. 2006. (Illus.). 238p. per. *(978-1-934023-20-4(5))* Tendre Pr.

Landry, Julie. In Sickness & in Health: How to Keep Going When Death Interrupts Life. 2008. (ENG.). 68p. pap. 9.99 *(978-0-9762730-6-6(3))* Vision Publishing.

Lasher, Cynthia Long. Death Is No Stranger: Helping Children Grieve. 2008. 93p. per. *(978-0-7880-2505-1(8))* CSS Publishing Co.

Lassiter, Wright L. Words of Comfort at Evening Time. 2011. 168p. 24.99 *(978-1-4269-7646-9(1));* pap. 14.99 *(978-1-4269-7645-2(3))* Trafford Publishing.

Lazar, Jean. Their Last PaintingStories of Life That. 2006. 104p. per. 11.95 *(978-0-595-39924-6(X))* iUniverse, Inc.

Leal, Martha V. DeLeon. Sweet Messenger. 2007. 106p. pap. 12.95 *(978-0-7414-3841-6(0))* Infinity Publishing.

Leary, David. The Beast Within! Destroyer of Souls! 2007. pap. 19.99 *(978-0-9790580-0-4(7))* Dave's Bks.

Leckey, Dolores R. Grieving with Grace: A Woman's Perspective. 2008. (Called to Holiness). 112p. pap. 11.95 *(978-0-86716-888-4(9))* Franciscan Media.

Licht, Chaim. In the Grip of Bereavement An. 2009. 272p. pap. 18.95 *(978-965-229-446-3(2))* Gefen Publishing Hse., Ltd ISR. Dist: Strauss Consultants.

Lucious, Eva M. The Light That Shines in Darkness. 2009. 136p. 22.99 *(978-1-60791-343-6(7));* pap. 14.99 *(978-1-60791-271-2(6))* Xulon Pr., Inc.

Luebering, Carol. Coping with Loss: Praying Your Way to Acceptance. 2009. 96p. pap. 9.95 *(978-0-86716-847-1(1))* Franciscan Media.

Mason, Thomas O. Transforming the Valley of Grief. 2009. 132p. pap. 14.99 *(978-1-60791-616-1(9))* Xulon Pr., Inc.

Mathis, Carl. Life Is What You Make It: Seven Steps to Moving Forward. 2010. 104p. pap. 9.99 *(978-1-61663-465-0(0))* Tate Publishing & Enterprises, LLC.

Mayer-Whittington, Nancy. For the Love of Angela. 2007. 93p. pap. *(978-0-9762284-7-9(5))* St. Catherine of Siena Pr.

Mayfield, James L. Amazing Grace in the Midst of Grief. 2011. 128p. pap. 16.00 *(978-1-60899-944-6(0),* Cascade Bks.) Wipf & Stock Pubs.

Mayfield, Sue. Living with Bereavement. 2009. (ENG., Illus.). 128p. 14.95 *(978-0-7459-5295-6(X))* Lion Hudson PLC GBR. Dist: Independent Pubs. Group.

Maynard, Jane Frances. Transfiguring Loss: Julian of Norwich As a Guide for Survivors of Traumatic Bereavement. 2006. *(978-0-8298-1601-3(1))* Pilgrim Pr., The/United Church Pr.

Mazzola, Lori E. The Lori Story. 2011. 74p. pap. 19.95 *(978-1-4560-0387-6(9))* PublishAmerica, Inc.

McKenzie, Lynn. Love Never Fails You... 2011. 118p. pap. 11.99 *(978-1-61379-810-2(5))* Xulon Pr., Inc.

Miedema, Rosemary. She Is Gone: A Mother's Search for Hope after the Tragic Loss of Her Daughter. 2010. pap. 11.99 *(978-1-61566-193-0(X))* Tate Publishing & Enterprises, LLC.

Miller, Carol L. Her Mansion Invisible: A Journey of Destruction. 2008. 84p. pap. 16.95 *(978-1-60563-970-3(2))* PublishAmerica, Inc.

Mize, Jean. Night of Anguish, Morning of Hope. 2011. 206p. 29.99 *(978-1-4568-7939-6(1));* pap. 19.99 *(978-1-4568-7938-9(3))* Xlibris Corp.

Moore, Mary G. Advent of Understanding: Facing the First Christmas after the Death of a Loved One. 2007. 93p. per. 5.95 *(978-1-933066-07-3(5),* Resurrection Pr.) Catholic Bk. Publishing Corp.

Morgan, John D., et al, eds. Death & Bereavement Around the World: Volume 5: Voluem 5: Reflective Essays, 5 vols. 2009. 296p. pap. 37.95 *(978-0-89503-239-3(2))* Baywood Publishing Co., Inc.

Moseley, Dan. Living with Loss. 2008. (Illus.). 126p. per. 14.95 *(978-1-60148-005-7(9))* Xyzzy Pr.

Neal Daggett, Nora A. When Tears Have Voice. 2009. 64p. pap. 10.99 *(978-1-60647-222-4(4))* Xulon Pr., Inc.

Nold, Deanna. The Best Is yet to Be! 2010. 48p. pap. 5.99 *(978-1-58169-348-5(6),* Axiom Pr.) Genesis Communications, Inc.

Obula, Rubby. Prisons, Sorcery & Homosexuality. 2009. 112p. pap. 11.99 *(978-1-60791-403-7(4))* Xulon Pr., Inc.

O'C. Davis, V. Experience the Miracles of Giving. 2008. 316p. pap. 17.99 *(978-1-60477-761-1(3))* Xulon Pr., Inc.

O'Connor, Brian P., et al. The Role of the Minister in Caring for the Dying Patient & the Bereaved. 19.95 *(978-0-405-12504-1(6))* Ayer Co. Pubs., Inc.

Osgood, Donald W. God's Silent Language: Hear His Silent Language in Unexpected Places. 2007. 160p. pap. 12.95 *(978-0-9701300-6-8(6))* Hitchhiker Bks.

Osgood, Judy. Meditations for the Bereaved. 2007. *(978-0-916895-06-8(8))* Gilgal Pubns.

Osko, Yvonne. The Unwelcome Journey. 2007. 132p. per. 13.99 *(978-1-60266-405-0(6))* Xulon Pr., Inc.

Owen. Living Through Bereavement. 2008. ix, 148p. pap. *(978-0-281-05934-8(9))* SPCK Publishing.

Palatnik, Lori & Palatnik, Yaakov. Remember My Soul: What to Do in Memory of a Loved One: A Path of Reflection & Inspiration for Shiva, the Stages of Jewish Mourning, & Beyond. 2008. 246p. pap. 23.99 *(978-1-60204-014-4(1))* K'hal Publishing.

Parsons, William B., et al, eds. Mourning Religion. 2008. (Studies in Religion & Culture Ser.). (ENG.). 288p. (C). (gr. 13-17). pap. 19.50 *(978-0-8139-2746-6(3));* (gr. 17). 55.00 *(978-0-8139-2745-9(5))* Univ. Pr. of Virginia.

Pennel, Joe E. Suffer Not Alone: A Guide to Helping Those Who Suffer. 2008. (ENG.). 128p. pap. 12.95 *(978-1-934314-37-1(4))* Common Thread Media, LLC.

Powlison, David. Grieving a Suicide: Help for the Aftershock. 2010. 24p. 3.99 *(978-1-935273-68-4(X))* New Growth Pr.

Rabey, Lois Mowday. Moments for Those Who Have Lost a Loved One. 2009. (ENG.). 155p. 15.00 *(978-1-4379-6811-8(2))* DIANE Publishing Co.

Rainey, Susan. Beyond the City Lights. 2007. pap. 13.97 *(978-1-934051-07-8(1))* Mystic Pubs.

Rice Jr., Carl. A Voice from Heaven, 1 vol. 2009. 61p. pap. 16.95 *(978-1-60703-905-1(2))* PublishAmerica, Inc.

Robinson, Haddon. Grief: Comfort for Those Who Grieve & Those Who Want to Help. 2009. (ENG.). 48p. pap. 7.99 *(978-1-57293-313-2(5))* Discovery Hse. Pubs.

Rogers, Joyce & Broadman and Holman Publishers Staff. Grace for the Widow: A Journey Through the Fog of Loss. 2009. (ENG.). 128p. pap. 10.99 *(978-0-8054-4846-7(2),* B&H Bks.) B&H Publishing Group.

Romanow, Beverly E. One Mother's Story. 2011. *(978-1-77069-270-1(3))* Word Alive Pr.

Rosemergy, Jim. Attaining the Unattainable: The Will of God. 2008. 136p. pap. 11.95 *(978-0-87516-830-2(2),* Devorss Pubns.) DeVorss & Co.

Rumsey, Ginny Fralick. Day My Life Changed Forever: A Young Widow's Perspective on Surviving the Loss of a Spouse. 2009. 56p. pap. 7.99 *(978-1-60696-966-3(8))* Tate Publishing & Enterprises, LLC.

Rupp, Joyce. May You Find Comfort: A Blessing for Times of Grieving. 2010. (Illus.). 32p. pap. 4.50 *(978-1-59471-244-9(1))* Ave Maria Pr.

Sauceda, Carol / T. My Journey with Grief: A Mother's Grief Revealed in Her Journals. 2009. 320p. pap. 22.00 *(978-1-58982-515-4(2),* Millennial Mind Publishing) American Bk. Publishing Group.

Schroedel, Jenny. Naming the Child: Hope-Filled Reflections on Miscarriage, Stillbirth, & Infant Death. 2009. (ENG.). 168p. (gr. 13). pap. 16.99 *(978-1-55725-585-3(7))* Paraclete Pr., Inc.

Schulte, Jane. My Mother, My Angel. 2008. 104p. pap. 19.95 *(978-1-60481-416-3(0))* Vesta Publishing.

Sheikh, Fazal, photos by. Moksha, 1 vol. 2008. (ENG., Illus.). 278p. 85.00 *(978-3-86521-125-5(9))* Steidl, Gerhard Druckerei und Verlag DEU. Dist: Innovative Logistics.

Silvera, Jennifer. Believe: A Young Widow's Journey Through Brokenness & Back, 1 vol. 2009. 224p. pap. 13.99 *(978-0-8254-3657-4(5))* Kregel Pubns.

Smith, Harold Ivan. A Long-Shadowed Grief: Suicide & Its Aftermath. 2007. (ENG.). 176p. per. 14.95 *(978-1-56101-281-7(5))* Cowley Pubns.

Smith, Marnie. The Unfolding of a Rose. 2009. 144p. 22.50 *(978-1-60860-058-8(0),* Strategic Bk. Publishing) AEG Literary Publishing Services, Inc.

Speck, Peter. Letting Go. 12.00 *(978-0-687-85670-1(1))* Abingdon Pr.

Springer, Rebecca Ruter. Heaven: My Dream of What Heaven Might Be Like. 2007. 106p. *(978-0-9765040-5-4(7))* Aylen Publishing.

Spurgeon, Susannah & Theobald, Don. A Cluster of Camphire: Words of Cheer & Comfort to Sick & Sorrowful Souls. 2nd ed. 2009. (Illus.). x, 174p. *(978-1-888514-31-5(0))* Particular Baptist Pr.

Stewart, Ed & McDowell, Josh. The Death of a Loved One. 2008. (My Friend Is Struggling With... Ser.). (ENG.). 64p. pap. 4.99 *(978-1-84550-355-0(4))* Christian Focus Pubns. GBR. Dist: STL Distribution North America.

Stickel, Leslie. Hope Defined: Learning to live with the loss of a loved one. Finding hope in all of the good things God has placed in your life. How I survived my moms suicide with God's Help. 2010. 140p. pap. 10.95 *(978-1-4327-5334-4(7))* Outskirts Pr., Inc.

Struthers, Marilyn F. Butterflies & Beyond: Preparing A Young Child to Cope with Grief or Loss. 2011. 44p. pap. 20.95 *(978-1-4497-1098-9(0),* WestBow Pr.) Author Solutions, Inc.

Tautges, Paul. Comfort Those Who Grieve: Ministering God's Grace in Times of Loss. 2009. (Ministering the Master's Way Ser.). 143p. pap. *(978-1-84625-155-9(9))* DayOne Pubns.

Valle, Ron & Mohs, Mary. Opening to Dying & Grieving: A Sacred Journey. 2006. (ENG., Illus.). 104p. per. *(978-0-936663-40-1(5))* Yes International Pubs.

Van Pelt, Sherry. Dear Conner, a Grandmother's Pain. 2007. 116p. per. 10.99 *(978-1-60266-806-5(X))* Xulon Pr., Inc.

Van Schaack, Mark. Comfort for Those Who Mourn. 2008. 116p. pap. 14.99 *(978-1-4389-2063-4(6))* AuthorHouse.

Vines, Thom & Vestal, John Michael. Tragedy & Trust: Can You Still Trust God after Losing a Child? 2011. 184p. 24.59 *(978-1-4567-2789-5(3));* pap. 14.03 *(978-1-4567-2791-8(5))* AuthorHouse.

Vorst, Moshe Yitzchak. Why? Reflections on the Loss of a Loved One. 52p. pap. 6.95 *(978-0-87306-525-2(5))* Feldheim Pubs.

Walsh, Susan. My Father, My Father. 2008. 56p. pap. 12.50 *(978-1-59858-715-9(3))* Dog Ear Publishing, LLC.

Werth, Jean. There's Someone in Your Kingdom, Lord. 2006. 156p. pap. 15.99 *(978-1-4141-0679-3(3))* Pleasant Word.

Whiting, Camille Call. For They Shall Be Comforted: Grieving the Loss of a Child. 2009. 100p. pap. *(978-1-59811-724-0(6),* Debolsillo) Covenant Communications, Inc.

Wilcox, S. Michael. Sunset: On the Passing of Those We Love. 2011. 135p. 16.99 *(978-1-60908-834-7(4))* Deseret Bk. Co.

Woodland, Desiree. I Still Believe. 2011. 146p. 29.99 *(978-1-4568-5357-0(0));* pap. 19.99 *(978-1-4568-5356-3(2))* Xlibris Corp.

Wray, Mary Ann. A Master Plan: A Young Man's Legacy - A Family's Journey. 2009. 152p. pap. 14.99 *(978-1-61579-272-6(4))* Xulon Pr., Inc.

Wright, H. Norman. Reflections of a Grieving Spouse: The Unexpected Journey from Loss to Renewed Hope. 2009. 208p. pap. 12.99 *(978-0-7369-2654-6(2))* Harvest Hse. Pubs.

Young, Annette. From Grief to Glory. 2007. 100p. per. 9.99 *(978-1-60477-197-8(6))* Xulon Pr., Inc.

Zimmerman, Dennis L. Healing Death: Finding Wholeness When a Cure Is No Longer Possible. 2007. 174p. per. *(978-0-8298-1760-7(3))* Pilgrim Pr., The/United Church Pr.

Zonnebelt-Smeenge, Susan J. & De Vries, Robert C. Traveling through Grief: Learning to Live Again after the Death of a Loved One. 2006. 160p. pap. 13.99 *(978-0-8010-6676-4(X))* Baker Bks.

BEREAVEMENT IN CHILDREN

Abrams, Rebecca. When Parents Die: Learning to Live with the Loss of a Parent. 3rd rev. ed. 2013. (ENG.). 224p. 110.00 *(978-0-415-59011-2(6));* pap. 32.95 *(978-0-415-59012-9(4))* Routledge.

Akhtar, Salman. Three Faces of Mourning: Melancholia, Manic Defense, & Moving On. 2006. (Margaret S. Mahler Ser.). (ENG.). 280p. pap. 39.99 *(978-0-7657-0516-7(8),* Aronson, Jason) Rowman & Littlefield Publishers, Inc.

Alexander, Susan G. Balloons to PawPaw. 2007. (ENG.). 68p. per. 10.99 *(978-1-4141-0777-6(3))* Pleasant Word.

Burns, Donna, ed. When Kids Are Grieving: Addressing Grief & Loss in School. 2010. 128p. pap. 27.95 *(978-1-4129-7490-5(9),* B74905P) Corwin Pr.

Chadwick, Ann. Responding to Loss & Grief in School: Guidance for Staff & School Teachers of Children Aged 4 To 11. 2011. (Illus.). 80p. pap. *(978-1-84905-246-7(8))* Kingsley, Jessica Ltd.

Chappell, Beverly. Children Helping Children with Grief: My Path to Founding the Dougy Center for Grieving Children & Their Families. 2007. (ENG., Illus.). 160p. per. 18.00 *(978-0-939165-54-4(6))* NewSage Pr., LLC.

Cleve, Elisabeth. A Big & a Little One Is Gone: Crisis Therapy with a Two-Year-Old Boy. 2008. (Illus.). 216p. (C). pap. 39.95 *(978-1-85575-541-3(6))* Karnac Bks. GBR. Dist: Stylus Publishing, LLC.

Corr, Charles A. & Balk, David E. Children's Encounters with Death, Bereavement, & Coping. 2010. (Illus.). 488p. 70.00 *(978-0-8261-3422-6(X))* Springer Publishing Co., Inc.

Dann, Patty. The Goldfish Went on Vacation: A Memoir of Loss (and Learning to Tell the Truth about It) 2007. (ENG.). 176p. per. 11.95 *(978-1-59030-564-5(7),* Trumpeter) Shambhala Pubns., Inc.

Doka, Kenneth J. & Tucci, Amy S., eds. Living with Grief: Children & Adolescents. 2008. 360p. pap. 24.95 *(978-1-893349-09-4(8))* Hospice Foundation of America.

Ferris, Lcsw-R. Balloons for Mary: A Children's Book about Grief & Coping with Death. 2009. 20p. pap. 14.95 *(978-1-4490-1604-3(9))* AuthorHouse.

Goldman, Linda. Great Answers to Difficult Questions about Death: What Children Need to Know. 2009. (ENG., Illus.). 96p. pap. *(978-1-84905-805-6(9))* Kingsley, Jessica Ltd.

Golding, Ellen & Leeuwenburgh, Erika. Why Did You Die?: Activities to Help Children Cope with Grief & Loss. 2008. (Instant Help Ser.). (ENG., Illus.). 136p. (J). per. 16.95 *(978-1-57224-604-1(9))* Play2Grow.

Janice, Perkins. How to Help a Child Cope with Grief: A Book for Adults Who Live & Work with Bereaved Children. 2007. (ENG., Illus.). 128p. per. 16.95 *(978-0-572-03309-5(5))* Foulsham, W. Co., Ltd. GBR. Dist: APG Sales & Distribution Services.

Kindred, Maggie. A Grief Unobserved: Helping parents & carers with early childhood Bereavement. 2012. (ENG.). 60p. pap. 13.99 *(978-1-907728-37-2(6))* Pneuma Springs Publishing GBR. Dist: Lightning Source, Inc.

Kubler-Ross, Elizabeth. On Life after Death, Revised. 2nd rev. ed. 2008. (ENG.). 96p. pap. 11.99 *(978-1-58761-318-0(2),* Celestial Arts) Ten Speed Pr.

Lasher, Cynthia Long. Death Is No Stranger: Helping Children Grieve. 2008. 93p. per. *(978-0-7880-2505-1(8))* CSS Publishing Co.

Mallon, Brenda. Working with Bereaved Children & Young People. 2010. 168p. (C). 104.00 *(978-1-84920-370-8(9),* B03708C); pap. 41.00 *(978-1-84920-371-5(7),* B03708P) SAGE Pubns., Ltd. GBR. Dist: SAGE Pubns., Inc.

Maritz, Jeanette. Until Death Do Us Part. 2010. 124p. pap. *(978-3-8383-6504-6(6))* Lambert Academic Publishing.

Markell, Kathryn A. & Markell, Marc A. The Children Who Lived: Using Harry Potter & Other Fictional Characters to Help Grieving Children & Adolescents. 2008. (ENG., Illus.). 208p. 39.95 *(978-0-415-95765-6(6))* Routledge.

Matthews, Mignon. Mom No More: Coping with the Late-Life Loss of Adult Children - One Woman's Story. 2008. 200p. 29.95 *(978-1-933167-32-9(7))* Hatala Geroproducts.

Monroe, Barbara & Kraus, Frances. Brief Interventions with Bereaved Children. 2nd ed. 2010. (ENG., Illus.). 264p. pap. 59.95 *(978-0-19-956164-3(8))* Oxford Univ. Pr., Inc.

Morrison, Delmont & Morrison, Shirley Linden. Memories of Loss & Dreams of Perfection: Unsuccessful Childhood Grieving & Adult Creativity. Sheikh, Anees A., ed. (Imagery & Human Development Ser.). 156p. 35.95 *(978-0-89503-309-3(7))* Baywood Publishing Co., Inc.

O'Shea, Jim. When a Child Dies: Footsteps of a Grieving Family. 2009. (ENG.). 144p. pap. 16.95 *(978-1-84730-078-2(2))* Veritas Pubns. IRL. Dist: Dufour Editions, Inc.

Pearlman, Michelle Y., et al. Grief in Childhood: Fundamentals of Treatment in Clinical Practice. 2010. *(978-1-4338-0753-4(X))*; (Illus.). 232p. 59.95 *(978-1-4338-0752-7(1))* American Psychological Assn.

Pomeroy, Elizabeth & Garcia, Renee. Children & Loss: A Practical Handbook for Professionals. 2010. pap. 0.00 *(978-1-933478-64-7(0))* Lyceum Bks., Inc.

Schonfeld, David J. & Quackenbush, Marcia. The Grieving Student: A Teacher's Guide. 2010. 208p. pap. 29.95 *(978-1-59857-116-5(8))* Brookes, Paul H. Publishing Co.

Silverman, Phyllis R. & Kelly, Madelyn. A Parent's Guide to Raising Grieving Children: Rebuilding Your Family after the Death of a Loved One. 2009. (ENG., Illus.). 272p. (YA). pap. 17.95 *(978-0-19-532884-4(1))* Oxford Univ. Pr., Inc.

Sjoqvist, Suzanna, ed. Still Here with Me: Teenagers & Children on Losing a Parent. Myers, Margaret, tr. from SWE. 2007. (ENG., Illus.). 16p. per. *(978-1-84310-501-5(2))* Kingsley, Jessica Ltd.

Sorensen, Julia. Overcoming Loss: Activities & Stories to Help Transform Children's Grief & Loss. 2008. (ENG., Illus.). 144p. pap. *(978-1-84310-646-3(9))* Kingsley, Jessica Ltd.

Strong, Judy. A Child's Grief: Surviving the Death of a Parent. 2009. 80p. pap. 16.95 *(978-1-59298-308-7(1))* Beaver's Pond Pr., Inc.

Turner, Mary. Talking with Children & Young People about Death & Dying. 2nd ed. 2006. (ENG., Illus.). 16p. per. *(978-1-84310-441-4(5))* Kingsley, Jessica Ltd.

Webb, Nancy Boyd, ed. Helping Bereaved Children: A Handbook for Practitioners. 3rd ed. 2010. (Social Work Practice with Children & Families Ser.). (ENG., Illus.). 408p. instr.'s hndbk. ed. 50.00 *(978-1-60623-597-3(4))* Guilford Pubns., Inc.

Webb, Nancy Boyd, ed. Helping Bereaved Children, Third Edition: A Handbook for Practitioners. 3rd rev. ed. 2011. (Social Work Practice with Children & Families Ser.). (ENG., Illus.). 408p. pap. 30.00 ***(978-1-4625-0451-0(5))*** Guilford Pubns., Inc.

Wolfelt, Alan D. Companioning the Bereaved Child: A Soulful Guide for Counselors & Caregivers. 2012. (Companioning Ser.). (ENG.). 176p. 29.95 ***(978-1-61722-158-3(9))*** Companion Pr.

35 Ways to Help a Grieving Child: Como Ayudar a un Niño a Sobrellevar una Muerte. 2007. pap. 9.95 *(978-1-890534-08-0(0))* Dougy Ctr.

BERENGARIUS, OF TOURS, 1000-1088

Lanfranc of Canterbury & Guitmund of Aversa. On the Body & Blood of the Lord & on the Truth of the Body & Blood of Christ in the Eucharist. Vaillancourt, Mark G., tr. from LAT. 2009. 248p. 39.95 *(978-0-8132-1678-2(8))* Catholic Univ. of America Pr.

BERENSON, BERNARD, 1865-1959

Berenson, Bernard. Rumor & Reflection. 2009. 478p. 52.95 *(978-1-104-84499-8(0))* 2007. (ENG.). 476p. per. 37.95 *(978-0-548-43796-4(3))* Kessinger Publishing, LLC.

Davenport-Hines, Richard, et al. Letters from Oxford: Hugh Trevor-Roper to Bernard Berenson. 2007. (ENG., Illus.). 368p. 45.95 *(978-0-297-85084-7(9))* Orion Publishing Group, Ltd. GBR. Dist: Independent Pubs. Group.

Mazaroff, Stanley. Henry Walters & Bernard Berenson: Collector & Connoisseur. 2010. (ENG., Illus.). 248p. (gr. 17). 40.00 *(978-0-8018-9512-8(X))* Johns Hopkins Univ. Pr.

Trevor-Roper, Hugh R. Letters from Oxford: Hugh Trevor-Roper to Bernard Berenson. Davenport-Hines, Richard, ed. 2007. (ENG., Illus.). 380p. per. 19.95 *(978-0-7538-2205-0(9)*, Phoenix) Orion Publishing Group, Ltd. GBR. Dist: Independent Pubs. Group.

BERG, ALBAN, 1885-1935

Adorno, Theodor W. Correspondence, 1925-1935. Lonitz, Henri, ed. Hoban, Wieland, tr. 2012. (ENG.). 168p. pap. 14.95 ***(978-0-7456-2336-8(0))*** Polity Pr. GBR. Dist: Wiley, John & Sons, Inc.

Floros, Constantin & Bernhardt-Kabisch, Ernest. Alban Berg & Hanna Fuchs: The Story of a Love in Letters. Bernhardt-Kabisch, Ernest, tr. from GER. 2007. (ENG., Illus.). 168p. 24.95 *(978-0-253-34966-8(4)*, 0253349664) Indiana Univ. Pr.

Hailey, C. Alban Berg & His World. 2010. (Bard Music Festival Ser.). (ENG., Illus.). 392p. (C). pap. 29.95 *(978-0-691-14856-4(2))* Princeton Univ. Pr.

Hailey, Christopher. Alban Berg & His World. 2010. (Bard Music Festival Ser.). (ENG., Illus.). 392p. (C). 75.00 *(978-0-691-14855-7(4))* Princeton Univ. Pr.

Hall, Patricia. Berg's Wozzeck, 1 vol. 2011. (Studies in Musical Genesis, Structure, & Interpretation Ser.). (ENG., Illus.). 256p. 74.00 *(978-0-19-534261-1(5))* Oxford Univ. Pr., Inc.

Simms, Bryan. Alban Berg. 2nd rev. ed. 2009. (Routledge Music Bibliographies Ser.). (ENG.). 336p. 150.00 *(978-0-415-99462-0(4))* Routledge.

BERG, MORRIS, 1902-1972

Farkas, Neil. My Time with the Catcher Spy, Morris Moe Berg. 2010. (ENG.). 112p. pap. 49.95 *(978-0-557-72260-0(8))* Lulu Enterprises Inc.

Kaufman, Louis, et al. Moe Berg: Athlete, Scholar, Spy. Date not set. lib. bdg. 29.95 *(978-0-8488-1387-1(1))* Amereon LTD.

BERGEN COUNTY (N.J.)

Hagstrom Map Co, creator. Bergen/Passaic/Rockland Counties, New Jersey Street Atlas. 4th ed. 2007. (Illus.). 125p. 24.95 *(978-1-59245-019-0(9))* Hagstrom Map Co., Inc.

Hagstrom Map Company Inc. Bergen County, NJ Pocket Map. 2007. *(978-1-59245-984-1(6))* Hagstrom Map Co., Inc.

Hagstrom Map Company Staff. Bergen/Passaic/Rockland Atlas Laminated. 2007. 128p. 49.95 *(978-1-59245-004-6(0))* Hagstrom Map Co., Inc.

Karels, Carol. The Revolutionary War in Bergen County: The Times That Tried Men's Souls. 2007. (Illus.). 191p. pap., per. 22.99 *(978-1-59629-358-8(6))* History Pr., The.

Larson, C. Kay & Trocano, Russell P. Leaving Santa Croce: The History of Maine Evergreen Nursery & the Costa Family in America, 1901-2008. 2008. (Illus.). 79p. *(978-0-578-00580-5(8))* Maine Evergreen Nursey, Inc.

Leiby, Adrian C. The Revolutionary War in Hackensack Valley: The Jersey Dutch & Neutral Ground, 1775-1783. 2011. 346p. 51.95 ***(978-1-258-09879-7(2))*** Literary Licensing, LLC.

Marchant, Barbara Z. Revolutionary Bergen County: The Road to Independence. 2009. 192p. pap. 21.99 *(978-1-59629-748-7(4))* History Pr., The.

BERGEN-BELSEN (CONCENTRATION CAMP)

Bardgett, Susanne. Belsen 1945: New Historical Perspective. 2006. (Illus.). 250p. (C). 69.50 *(978-0-85303-716-3(7))*; pap. 32.95 *(978-0-85303-717-0(5))* Vallentine Mitchell Pubs. GBR. Dist: International Specialized Bk. Services.

Baumann-Parkhurst, Marion. Searching Survivor & the Answer I Found. EDGE, Tracey, ed. 2007. 196p. pap. 14.95 *(978-0-9777251-5-1(4))* GenieHoldings.com, Inc.

Collis, Robert & Hogerzeil, Han. Straight On. 2010. (ENG., Illus.). 216p. 110.00 *(978-0-415-58076-2(5))* Routledge.

Goodman, Cecily. The Survivors: The Story of the Belsen Remnant. 2009. (Illus.). 113p. pap. 16.95 *(978-0-85303-821-4(X))* Vallentine Mitchell Pubs. GBR. Dist: International Specialized Bk. Services.

—The Survivors: The Story of the Belsen Remnant. 2009. (Illus.). 113p. 39.95 *(978-0-85303-831-3(7))* Vallentine Mitchell Pubs. GBR. Dist: International Specialized Bk. Services.

Herzberg, Abel J. Between Two Streams: A Diary from Bergen-Belsen. Santcross, Jack, tr. from DUT. 2008. (ENG.). 256p. pap. 16.95 *(978-1-84511-750-4(6)*, Tauris Parke Paperbacks) I. B. Tauris & Co., Ltd. GBR. Dist: Macmillan.

Lantos, Peter. Parallel Lines: A Journey from Childhood to Belsen. 2006. (ENG., Illus.). 246p. pap. 24.95 *(978-1-905147-20-5(1))* Arcadia Bks. Ltd. GBR. Dist: Dufour Editions, Inc.

Lévy-Hass, Hanna. Diary of Bergen-Belsen: 1944-1945. 2009. (ENG.). 220p. 20.00 *(978-1-931859-87-5(6))* Haymarket Bks.

Lob, Ladislaus. Rezsö Kasztner: The Daring Rescue of Hungarian Jews - A Survivor's Account. 2009. (ENG., Illus.). 338p. pap. 22.95 *(978-1-84595-008-8(9))* Random Hse. GBR. Dist: Independent Pubs. Group.

Pahor, Boris. Necropolis. Biggins, Michael, tr. from SLV. 2010. (Slovenian Literature Ser.). (ENG.). 208p. pap. 13.95 *(978-1-56478-611-1(0)*, 478611) Dalkey Archive Pr.

BERGMAN, INGMAR, 1918-2007

Bergman, Ingmar. Images: My Life in Film. Ruuth, Marianne, tr. from SWE. 2011. (ENG., Illus.). 456p. pap. 24.95 *(978-1-61145-041-5(1)*, 611041, Arcade Publishing) Skyhorse Publishing Co., Inc.

—The Magic Lantern: An Autobiography. Tate, Joan, tr. from SWE. 2007. (Illus.). 314p. per. 18.00 *(978-0-226-04382-1(7))* Univ. of Chicago Pr.

Coates, Paul. Screening the Face. 2012. (ENG., Illus.). 208p. 85.00 ***(978-0-230-29847-7(8))*** Palgrave Macmillan.

Donner, Jorn. The Personal Vision of Ingmar Bergman. (Biography Index Reprint Ser.). (Illus.). 276p. reprint ed. 22.25 *(978-0-8290-0832-6(2))* Irvington Pubs.

Hubner, Laura. The Films of Ingmar Bergman: Illusions of Light & Darkness. 2007. (ENG.). 256p. 100.00 *(978-0-230-00724-6(4))* Palgrave Macmillan.

Kawin, Bruce F. Mindscreen: Bergman, Godard, & First-Person Film. 2006. (Dalkey Archive Scholarly Ser.). (ENG., Illus.). 241p. per. 24.95 *(978-1-56478-461-2(4))* Dalkey Archive Pr.

Koskinen, Maaret. Ingmar Bergman Revisited: Performance, Cinema & the Arts. Koskinen, Maaret, ed. 2008. (ENG., Illus.). 256p. (gr. 17). pap. 28.00 *(978-1-905674-33-6(3))* Wallflower Pr. GBR. Dist: Columbia Univ. Pr.

—Ingmar Bergman's the Silence: Pictures in the Typewriter, Writings on the Screen. 2009. (Nordic Film Classics Ser.). (ENG., Illus.). 208p. (C). pap. 24.95 *(978-0-295-98943-3(2))* Univ. of Washington Pr.

Koskinen, Maaret, ed. Ingmar Bergman Revisited: Performance, Cinema & the Arts. 2008. (ENG., Illus.). 256p. (gr. 17). 85.00 *(978-1-905674-34-3(1))* Wallflower Pr. GBR. Dist: Columbia Univ. Pr.

Livingston, Paisley. Cinema, Philosophy, Bergman: On Film as Philosophy. (ENG., Illus.). 2012. 226p. pap. 35.00 ***(978-0-19-965514-4(6))*** 2009. 224p. 60.00 *(978-0-19-957017-1(5))* Oxford Univ. Pr., Inc.

Macnab, Geoffrey. Ingmar Bergman: The Life & Films of the Last Great European Director. 2009. (ENG., Illus.). 256p. 29.50 *(978-1-84885-046-0(8))* I. B. Tauris & Co., Ltd. GBR. Dist: Macmillan.

Mandelbaum, Jacques. Masters of Cinema: Ingmar Bergman. 2011. (ENG., Illus.). 104p. pap., pap. 9.95 *(978-2-86642-700-9(9))* Phaidon Pr., Inc.

Mastroianni, Roberto, ed. Through a Lens Darkly: Looking for Ingmar Bergman. 2012. (ENG., Illus.). 112p. 40.00 ***(978-88-6208-215-0(0))*** Damiani ITA. Dist: D.A.P./Distributed Art Pubs.

Shargel, Raphael, ed. Ingmar Bergman: Interviews. 2007. (ENG.). 204p. 50.00 *(978-1-57806-217-1(9))*; pap. 22.00 *(978-1-57806-218-8(7))* Univ. Pr. of Mississippi.

Singer, Irving & Singer, I. Ingmar Bergman, Cinematic Philosopher: Reflections on His Creativity. 2009. (Irving Singer Library). (ENG.) 256p. (gr. 17). pap. 13.95 *(978-0-262-51323-4(4))* MIT Pr.

Vermilye, Jerry. Ingmar Bergman: His Life & Films. alt. ed. 2006. (ENG., Illus.). 192p. per. 39.95 *(978-0-7864-2959-2(3))* McFarland & Co., Inc. Pubs.

BERGMAN, INGRID, 1915-1982

Chandler, Charlotte. Ingrid: Ingrid Bergman, a Personal Biography. 2008. (ENG., Illus.). 336p. per. 16.95 *(978-1-55783-735-6(X)*, 155783735X, Applause Theatre & Cinema) Leonard, Hal Corp.

Fernengel, Ingmar. Ängstlich und Gottverlassen: Woody Allen und Ingmar Bergman auf der Suche nach dem Sinn des Lebens. 2010. (GER.). 214p. 57.95 *(978-3-631-60467-0(X))* Lang, Peter GmbH, Europaischer Verlag der Wissenschaften DEU. Dist: Lang, Peter.

Gelley, Ora. Stardom & the Aesthetics of Neorealism: Ingrid Bergman in Rossellini's Italy. 2012. (Routledge Advances in Film Studies: 15). (ENG., Illus.). 222p. (C). 125.00 *(978-0-415-89003-8(9))* Routledge.

Kobal Collection, photos by. ICONS Film - Ingrid Bergmann. 2007. (Movie Icons Ser.). (FRE, GER & ENG., Illus.). 192p. per. 9.99 *(978-3-8228-2208-1(6))* TASCHEN DEU. Dist: Ingram Pub. Services.

Sorgi, Marcello. Le Amanti Del Vulcano: Bergman, Magnani, Rossellini: Un Triangolo Di Passioni Nell'Italia Del Dopoguerra. 2010. (ITA., Illus.). 202p. *(978-88-17-03999-4(3))* Rizzoli International Pubns., Inc.

Thomson, David. Ingrid Bergman. 2010. (ENG., Illus.). 128p. pap. 14.00 *(978-0-86547-934-0(8))* Faber & Faber, Inc.

BERGMANN, GUSTAV, 1906-1987

Addis, Laird, et al. Ontology & Analysis: Essays & Recollections about Gustav Bergmann. Addis, Laird et al, eds. 2007. (ENG.). 312p. 139.95 *(978-3-938793-69-5(4))* Ontos Verlag DEU. Dist: Transaction Pubs.

Egidi, Rosaria & Bonino, Guido, eds. Fostering the Ontological Turn: Gustav Bergmann (1906-1987) 2009. (ENG.). 274p. 122.00 *(978-3-86838-008-8(6))* Ontos Verlag DEU. Dist: Transaction Pubs.

BERGSON, HENRI, 1859-1941

Barnard, G. William. Living Consciousness: The Metaphysical Vision of Henri Bergson. 2011. 384p. 85.00 ***(978-1-4384-3957-0(1)***, Suny Pr.) State Univ. of New York Pr.

Blassnigg, Martha. Time, Memory, Consciousness & the Cinema Experience: Revisiting Ideas on Matter & Spirit. 2009. (Illus.). 256p. pap. 70.00 *(978-90-420-2640-7(5))* Rodopi.

Burwick, Frederick & Douglass, Paul, eds. The Crisis in Modernism: Bergson & the Vitalist Controversy. 2010. (ENG.). 424p. (C). pap. 45.00 *(978-0-521-13660-0(1))* Cambridge Univ. Pr.

Carr, Herbert. Henri Bergson: The Philosophy of Change. 2007. (ENG.). 108p. 33.95 *(978-0-548-05109-2(7))* Kessinger Publishing, LLC.

Cavarnos, Constantine. A Dialogue Between Bergson, Aristotle & Philologos. 2011. 58p. 36.95 ***(978-1-258-00862-8(9))*** Literary Licensing, LLC.

Chevalier, Jacques. Henri Bergson. Clare, Lilian A., tr. 376p. 2008. 48.95 *(978-1-4366-8143-8(X))* 2007. (ENG.). per. 33.95 *(978-1-4325-8299-9(2))* Kessinger Publishing, LLC.

Fraser, Benjamin. Encounters with Bergson(ism) in Spain: Reconciling Philosophy, Literature, Film & Urban Space. 2011. (North Carolina Studies in the Romance Languages & Literature Ser.). (ENG.). 384p. pap. 42.50 *(978-0-8078-9299-2(8))* Univ. of North Carolina Pr.

Glynn, Michael. Vladimir Nabokov: Bergsonian & Russian Formalist Influences in His Novels. 2007. (ENG.). 224p. 95.00 *(978-1-4039-7985-8(5))* Palgrave Macmillan.

Gunn, J. Alexander. Bergson & His Philosophy. 2008. 180p. 25.99 *(978-0-554-22292-9(2))* 2008. 180p. 22.99 *(978-0-554-31595-9(5))* 2007. (ENG.). 184p. pap. 19.99 *(978-1-4264-1973-7(2))* 2006. 178p. pap. 21.99 *(978-1-4264-2084-9(6))* BiblioBazaar.

Hill, Rebecca. The Interval: Relation & Becoming in Irigaray, Aristotle, & Bergson. 2012. (ENG.). 208p. 55.00 ***(978-0-8232-3724-1(9))*** Fordham Univ. Pr.

Howard, Damian. Being Human in Islam: The Impact of the Evolutionary Worldview. 2011. (Culture & Civilization in the Middle East Ser.). (ENG.). 240p. (C). 125.00 *(978-0-415-60358-3(4))* Routledge.

Kallen, Horace M. William James & Henri Bergson: A Study in Contrasting Theories of Life. 2007. (ENG.). 256p. 42.95 *(978-0-548-21922-5(2))*; 260p. per. 27.95 *(978-1-4325-3988-7(4))* Kessinger Publishing, LLC.

Kelly, Michael R., ed. Bergson & Phenomenology. 2010. (ENG.). 352p. 89.00 *(978-0-230-20238-2(1))* Palgrave Macmillan.

Lacey. Bergson-arg Philosophers. 2008. (ENG.). 400p. 45.00 *(978-0-415-48787-0(0))* Routledge.

Lefebvre, Alexandre. The Image of Law: Deleuze, Bergson, Spinoza. 2008. (Cultural Memory in the Present Ser.). (ENG.). 336p. 70.00 *(978-0-8047-5984-7(7))*; pap. 27.95 *(978-0-8047-5985-4(5))* Stanford Univ. Pr.

Lefebvre, Alexandre & White, Melanie eds. Bergson, Politics, & Religion. 2012. (ENG.). 352p. 94.95 ***(978-0-8223-5256-3(7))***; pap. 25.95 ***(978-0-8223-5275-4(3))*** Duke Univ. Pr.

Lim, Bliss Cua. Translating Time: Cinema, the Fantastic, & Temporal Critique. 2009. (ENG., Illus.). 360p. 94.95 *(978-0-8223-4499-5(8))*; pap. 25.95 *(978-0-8223-4510-7(2))* Duke Univ. Pr.

Maritain, Jacques. Bergsonian Philosophy & Thomism, Vol. 1. McInerny, Ralph, ed. Andison, J. Gordon & Andison, Mabelle L., trs. from FRE. 2nd ed. 2007. (Collected Works of Jacques Maritain). 392p. 40.00 *(978-0-268-02152-8(X))* Univ. of Notre Dame Pr.

Moulard-Leonard, Valentine. Bergson-Deleuze Encounters: Transcendental Experience & the Thought of the Virtual. (SUNY Series in Contemporary French Thought Ser.). (Illus.). 2009. 224p. pap. 23.95 *(978-0-7914-7532-4(8)*, Suny Pr.) 2008. x, 197p. (C). 65.00 *(978-0-7914-7531-7(X))* State Univ. of New York Pr.

Pilkington, A. E. Bergson & his Influence: A Reassessment. 2010. (ENG.). 262p. pap. 35.99 *(978-0-521-15788-9(9))* Cambridge Univ. Pr.

Quirk, Thomas. Bergson & American Culture: The Worlds of Willa Cather & Wallace Stevens. 2011. (ENG.). 318p. pap. 40.00 *(978-0-8078-9756-0(6))* Univ. of North Carolina Pr.

Roberts, James Deotis. Faith & Reason: A Comparative Study of Pascal, Bergson & James. 2011. 98p. 38.95 ***(978-1-258-02126-9(9))*** Literary Licensing, LLC.

Robinson, Keith & Robinson, Keith A. Deleuze, Whitehead, Bergson: Rhizomatic Connections. Robinson, Keith, ed. 2009. (ENG.). 256p. 89.00 *(978-0-230-51772-1(2))* Palgrave Macmillan.

Ruhe, Algot. Henri Bergson an Account of His Life and. 2006. pap. 27.95 *(978-1-4286-3946-1(2))* Kessinger Publishing, LLC.

Slegers, Rosa. Courageous Vulnerability: Ethics & Knowledge in Proust, Bergson, Marcel, & James. 2010. 230p. *(978-90-04-18188-5(1))* BRILL.

Slosson, Edwin E. Major Prophets of Today. 2007. 324p. 45.95 *(978-0-548-06360-6(5))* Kessinger Publishing, LLC.

Slosson, Edwin Emery. Major Prophets of To-Day. 2009. 328p. 25.99 *(978-1-103-47984-9(9))*; pap. 19.99 *(978-1-103-47981-8(4))* BiblioBazaar.

Solomon, Joseph. Bergson. 2010. (ENG.). 132p. pap. 20.75 *(978-1-177-55779-5(7))* 2010. (ENG.). 132p. pap. 20.75 *(978-1-176-21721-8(6))* 2010. (ENG.). 132p. pap. 20.75 *(978-1-176-42380-0(0))* 2010. 130p. 28.99 *(978-1-140-06016-1(3))* 2010. 130p. pap. 20.75 *(978-1-140-06017-8(1))* 2009. 130p. 24.99 *(978-1-110-64573-2(2))* 2009. 130p. pap. 19.75 *(978-1-110-64571-6(6))* 2009. (ENG.). 129p. pap. 18.99 *(978-1-110-64568-6(6)*, BiblioLife) 2009. (ENG.). 129p. pap. 19.99 *(978-1-110-64570-1(8)*, BiblioLife) BiblioBazaar.

—Bergson. 2010. 130p. pap. 16.76 *(978-1-164-08493-8(3))* 2008. 128p. 35.95 *(978-1-4365-7532-4(X))* 2007. (ENG.). 128p. per. 20.95 *(978-0-548-80418-6(4))* Kessinger Publishing, LLC.

Stephen, Karin. The Misuse of Mind. 2009. 50p. pap. *(978-0-217-80471-4(3))* Books LLC.

BERI-BERI

Williams, Robert R. Toward a Conquest of Beriberi. 2011. 368p. 53.95 ***(978-1-258-08568-1(2))*** Literary Licensing, LLC.

BERING, VITUS JONASSEN, 1681-1741

Goodhue, Cornelia. Journey into the Fog: The Story of Vitus Bering & the Bering Sea. 2011. 192p. 42.95 ***(978-1-258-03301-9(1))*** Literary Licensing, LLC.

Moller, Peter Ulf & Okhotina-Lind, N. A. Until Death Do Us Part: The Travels of Anna & Vitus Bering. 2007. (University of Alaska Press - Rasmuson Library Historic Translation Ser.). (GER & ENG., Illus.). 178p. 29.95 *(978-1-889963-94-5(1))* Univ. of Alaska Pr.

Urness, Carol L., et al, eds. The Journal of Midshipman Chaplin: A Record of Bering's First Kamchatka Expedition. 2010. (Beringiana Ser.). (ENG., Illus.). 320p. (C). 47.00 *(978-87-7934-314-6(7))* Aarhus Universitetsforlag DNK. Dist: ISD.

BERING SEA

Butler, B. F. Bering Sea Controversy. (Shorey Historical Ser.). 24p. reprint ed. pap. 10.00 *(978-0-8466-0035-0(8)*, S35) Shorey's Bookstore.

Fienup-Riordan, Ann & Rearden, Alice. Ellavut/Our Yup'ik World & Weather: Continuity & Change on the Bering Sea Coast, 1 vol. 2012. (ENG., Illus.). 416p. (C). pap. 45.00 ***(978-0-295-99161-0(5))*** Univ. of Washington Pr.

Fowler, Charles W. Systemic Management: Sustainable Human Interactions with Ecosystems & the Biosphere. (ENG., Illus.). 312p. 2010. pap. 55.00 *(978-0-19-956759-1(X))* 2009. 110.00 *(978-0-19-954096-9(9))* Oxford Univ. Pr., Inc.

Hillstrand, Johnathan, et al. Time Bandit: Two Brothers, the Bering Sea, & One of the World's Deadliest Jobs. 2009. (ENG., Illus.). 240p. pap. 16.00 *(978-0-345-50412-8(7)*, Ballantine Bks.) Random House Publishing Group.

Jorgensen, Elaina M. Field Guide to Squids & Octopods of the Eastern North Pacific & Bering Sea. 2011. (ENG., Illus.). 100p. pap. 25.00 *(978-1-56612-139-2(6))* Alaska Sea Grant College Program.

Thompson, Kalee. Deadliest Sea: The Untold Story Behind the Greatest Rescue in Coast Guard History. 2011. (ENG.). 336p. pap. 14.99 *(978-0-06-176630-5(5)*, Harper Paperbacks) HarperCollins Pubs.

Upton, Joe. Bering Sea Blues: A Crabber's Tale of Fear in the Icy North. 2011. (ENG., Illus.). 325p. (gr. 6). pap. 17.95 *(978-1-935347-11-8(X))* Epicenter Pr., Inc.

B

BERKELEY, BUSBY, 1895-1976

Spivak, Jeffrey. Buzz: The Life & Art of Busby Berkeley. 2010. (Screen Classics Ser.). (ENG., Illus.). 408p. 39.95 *(978-0-8131-2643-6(5))* Univ. Pr. of Kentucky.

BERKELEY, GEORGE, 1685-1753

Berkeley, George. Short Works of George Berkeley. 2008. 284p. 28.99 *(978-0-554-26830-9(2))* 2008. 284p. 25.99 *(978-0-554-36133-8(7))* 2007. (ENG.). 254p. pap. 21.99 *(978-1-4346-1956-3(7))* 2007. (ENG.). 282p. pap. 23.99 *(978-1-4346-1980-8(X))* BiblioBazaar.

—The Works of George Berkeley. 2009. 464p. 28.99 *(978-1-103-23368-7(8))* 2009. (Illus.). 464p. pap. 22.99 *(978-1-103-23365-6(3))* 2008. 420p. 27.99 *(978-0-559-88271-5(8))* 2008. 420p. pap. 21.99 *(978-0-559-88270-8(X))* BiblioBazaar.

Berkeley, George B., et al. George Berkeley: Three Dialogues Between Hylas & Philonous. 2006. (Longman Library of Primary Sources in Philosophy). (ENG.). 160p. (C). pap. 13.40 *(978-0-321-27613-1(2))* Longman Publishing Group.

Berman, David. Berkeley & Irish Philosophy. 2009. (Continuum Studies in British Philosophy Ser.). (ENG.). 248p. 44.95 *(978-1-4411-2635-1(X))* Continuum International Publishing Group, Ltd. GBR. Dist: National Bk. Network.

Bettcher, Talia Mae & Bettcher. Berkeley. 2009. (Guides for the Perplexed Ser.). (ENG., Illus.). 224p. 34.95 *(978-0-8264-8991-3(5))*; 100.00 *(978-0-8264-8990-6(7))* Continuum International Publishing Group, Ltd. GBR. Dist: National Bk. Network.

—Berkeley's Philosophy of Spirit: Consciousness, Ontology & the Elusive Subject. 2007. (Continuum Studies in British Philosophy). (ENG.). 182p. 140.00 *(978-0-8264-8643-1(6))* Continuum International Publishing Group, Ltd. GBR. Dist: National Bk. Network.

Breuninger, Scott. Recovering Bishop Berkeley: Virtue & Society in the Anglo-Irish Context. 2010. (Palgrave Studies in Cultural & Intellectual History Ser.). (ENG.). 256p. 89.00 *(978-0-230-10280-4(8))* Palgrave Macmillan.

Caffentzis, C. G. Exciting the Industry of Mankind George Berkeley's Philosophy of Money. 2010. (International Archives of the History of Ideas / archives internationales d'histoire des Idées Ser.). 462p. pap. 269.00 *(978-90-481-5453-1(7),* 9048154537) Springer.

Daniel, Stephen H. Reexamining Berkeley's Philosophy. 2007. (Toronto Studies in Philosophy). (ENG.). 224p. *(978-0-8020-9348-6(5))* Univ. of Toronto Pr.

Daniel, Stephen H., ed. New Interpretations of Berkeley's Thought. 2008. (JHP Books). (ENG.). 300p. 80.98 *(978-1-59102-557-3(5),* Humanity Bks.) Prometheus Bks., Pubs.

Dicker, Georges. Berkeley's Idealism: A Critical Examination, 1 vol. 2011. (ENG., Illus.). 480p. pap. 35.00 *(978-0-19-538145-0(9))* Oxford Univ. Pr., Inc.

Downing. Berkeley. 2010. 100.00 *(978-0-415-77320-1(2))*; pap. 26.95 *(978-0-415-77321-8(0))* Routledge.

Fields, Keota. Berkeley: Ideas, Immaterialism, & Objective Presence. 2011. (ENG.). 252p. 65.00 *(978-0-7391-4295-0(X))* Rowman & Littlefield Publishers, Inc.

—Berkeley: Ideas, Immaterialism, & Objective Presence. 2011. xi, 239p. E-Book *(978-0-7391-4297-4(6))* Rowman & Littlefield Publishers, Inc.

Fraser, Alexander Campbell. Selections from Berkeley with an Introduction & Notes. 2007. (ENG.). 454p. 52.95 *(978-0-548-01407-3(8))* Kessinger Publishing, LLC.

Garrett, Aaron & Garrett. Berkeley's Three Dialogues: A Reader's Guide. 2008. (Reader's Guides). (ENG.). 172p. 27.95 *(978-0-8264-9323-1(8))* Continuum International Publishing Group, Ltd. GBR. Dist: National Bk. Network.

Garrett, Reginald H. & Garrett, Aaron. Berkeleys Three Dialogues. 2008. (Reader's Guides). (ENG.). 172p. 100.00 *(978-0-8264-9662-1(8))* Continuum International Publishing Group, Ltd. GBR. Dist: National Bk. Network.

Gersh, Stephen & Moran, Dermot, eds. Eriugena, Berkeley, & the Idealist Tradition. 2006. 320p. per. 42.00 *(978-0-268-02969-2(5))* Univ. of Notre Dame Pr.

Johnston, G. A. The Development of Berkeley's Philosophy. 2007. (ENG.). 400p. per. *(978-1-4067-6258-7(X))* Read Bks.

Jones, Nick. Starting with Berkeley. 2009. (Starting with... Ser.). (ENG.). 200p. 19.95 *(978-1-84706-187-4(7))*; 95.00 *(978-1-84706-186-7(9))* Continuum International Publishing Group, Ltd. GBR. Dist: National Bk. Network.

Miller, Stephen G. The Berkeley Plato: From Neglected Relic to Ancient Treasure, an Archaeological Detective Story. 2009. (ENG., Illus.). 126p. 55.00 *(978-0-520-25833-4(9))* Univ. of California Pr.

Parigi, Silvia, ed. George Berkeley: Religion & Science in the Age of Enlightenment: Religion & Science in the Age of Enlightenment. 2010. (International Archives of the History of Ideas Archives Internationales d'histoire des Idées Ser.). (ENG.). xix, 204p. 139.00 *(978-90-481-9242-7(0),* 9048192420) Springer.

Pitcher. Berkeley-arg Philosophers. 2008. (ENG.). 272p. 45.00 *(978-0-415-48761-0(7))* Routledge.

Rand, Benjamin. Berkeley's American Sojourn. reprint ed. 32.50 *(978-0-404-59323-0(2))* AMS Pr., Inc.

Richmond, Alasdair. Berkeley's Principles of Human Knowledge. 2009. (Readers Guide Ser.). (ENG.). 208p. instr.'s gde. ed. 24.95 *(978-1-84706-029-7(3))* Continuum International Publishing Group, Ltd. GBR. Dist: National Bk. Network.

—Berkeley's 'Principles of Human Knowledge' 2009. (Readers Guide Ser.). (ENG.). 208p. 100.00 *(978-1-84706-028-0(5))* Continuum International Publishing Group, Ltd. GBR. Dist: National Bk. Network.

Roberts, John Russell. A Metaphysics for the Mob: The Philosophy of George Berkeley. 2007. (ENG.). 200p. 65.00 *(978-0-19-531393-2(3))* Oxford Univ. Pr., Inc.

Santos, Georgiou. Naturalising Berkeley's Unperceived Perceivable. 2011. (ENG.). 44p. pap. 8.95 *(978-1-907962-16-5(6),* Pichu Pr.) Cranmore Pubns. GBR. Dist: Lightning Source, Inc.

Stack, George J. Berkeley's analysis of Perception. (Studies in Philosophy Ser.). (ENG.). 165p. 210.00 ***(978-3-11-217853-9(X))***; 135.00 ***(978-3-11-131498-3(7))*** De Gruyter, Mouton DEU. Dist: de Gruyter, Walter GmbH & Co. KG.

Walmsley, Peter. The Rhetoric of Berkeley's Philosophy. 2006. (Cambridge Studies in Eighteenth-Century English Literature & Thought Ser.). (ENG., Illus.). 224p. pap. 50.00 *(978-0-521-02803-5(5))* Cambridge Univ. Pr.

BERKELEY (CALIF.)—HISTORY

Bowles, Gloria. Living Ideas: A Memoir of the Tumultuous Founding of Berkeley Women's Studies. 2009. (Illus.). 308p. pap. 20.00 *(978-0-615-32146-2(1))* Bowles, Gloria.

Markel, Wendy P. Berkeley. 2009. (Postcard History Ser.). (ENG., Illus.). 128p. pap. 21.99 *(978-0-7385-6942-0(9))* Arcadia Publishing.

Moremen, Grace E., ed. Student Life at the University of California, Berkeley During & after World War I: The Letters of Agnes Edwards Partin, 1917-1921. 2006. (Illus.). 562p. 139.95 *(978-0-7734-5797-3(6))* Mellen, Edwin Pr., The.

Richard, Schwartz & Schwartz, Richard. Eccentrics, Heroes, & Cutthroats of Old Berkeley. 2007. (Illus.). 244p. pap. 24.95 *(978-0-9678204-2-2(1))* RSB Bks.

Weinstein, Dave. It Came from Berkeley: How Berkeley Changed the World, 1 vol. 2008. (ENG., Illus.). 224p. 24.99 *(978-1-4236-0254-5(4))* Gibbs Smith, Publisher.

Wollenberg, Charles. Berkeley: A City in History. 2007. (Illus.). 224p. pap. 21.95 *(978-0-520-25307-0(8))* Univ. of California Pr.

BERKELEY FAMILY

Granger, Orman. The Triumph of Persistence, Determination & Preparation: If i could do it, you can Too. 2011. 158p. 29.99 ***(978-1-4653-6151-6(0))***; pap. 19.99 ***(978-1-4653-6150-9(2))*** Xlibris Corp.

BERKSHIRE (ENGLAND)

Crofts, John E. Shakespeare & the Post Horses: A New Study of the Merry Wives of Windsor. reprint ed. 27.50 *(978-0-404-01856-6(4))* AMS Pr., Inc.

BERKSHIRE (ENGLAND)—DESCRIPTION AND TRAVEL

Robinson, John Martin. Windsor Castle: Official Guidebook. 2006. (Illus.). 80 Pagesp. pap. 11.95 *(978-1-902163-34-5(6))* Royal Collection Enterprises Ltd. GBR. Dist: Antique Collectors' Club.

Tyack, Geoffrey, et al. Berkshire. 2010. (Pevsner Architectural Guides). (ENG., Illus.). 800p. 85.00 *(978-0-300-12662-4(X))* Yale Univ. Pr.

BERKSHIRE (ENGLAND)—HISTORY

Long, Roger. A Grim Almanac of Old Berkshire. 2010. (ENG., Illus.). 160p. pap. 27.95 *(978-0-7524-5677-5(6))* History Pr. Ltd., The GBR. Dist: Independent Pubs. Group.

Martin, Mary L. & Rooney, E. Ashley. Berkshires: Past & Present. 2009. (Illus.). 128p. pap. 24.99 *(978-0-7643-3133-6(7))* Schiffer Publishing, Ltd.

BERKSHIRE COUNTY (MASS.)

Gladden, Washington. From the Hub to the Hudson, with Sketches of Nature, History & Industry in Northwestern Massachusetts by Washington Gladden. 2006. 172p. per. 18.99 *(978-1-4255-1315-3(8))* MPublishing.

Leveille, Gary. Around Great Barrington. 2011. (Postcard History Ser.). (Illus.). 128p. pap. 21.99 *(978-0-7385-7476-9(7))* Arcadia Publishing.

BERKSHIRE COUNTY (MASS.)—DESCRIPTION AND TRAVEL

Bradley, Jim. Best Easy Day Hikes Berkshires. 2011. (Best Easy Day Hikes Ser.). (ENG., Illus.). 96p. pap. 9.95 *(978-0-7627-6057-2(5),* Falcon Guides) Globe Pequot Pr., The.

Donaldson, Stephen R. Barns of the Berkshires. 2009. (Illus.). 112p. bds. 24.99 *(978-0-7643-3223-4(6))* Schiffer Publishing, Ltd.

—The Berkshires. 2007. (Regional Photos Ser.). (ENG., Illus.). 128p. 29.95 *(978-1-933212-53-1(5))* Commonwealth Editions.

Gelbert, Doug. Doggin' the Berkshires: The 33 Best Places to Hike with Your Dog in Western Massachusetts. 2007. (Illus.). 92p. per. 9.95 *(978-0-9795577-6-7(3))* Cruden Bay Bks.

Laubach, Rene. AMC Best Day Hikes in the Berkshires: Four-Season Guide to 50 of the Best Trails in Western Massachusetts. 2009. (ENG., Illus.). 288p. pap. 18.95 *(978-1-934028-21-6(5))* Appalachian Mountain Club Bks.

McLaughlin, David John. Inside the Berkshires: Sixteen Journeys of Discovery. 2nd ed. 2008. (ENG.). 328p. per. 19.95 *(978-0-9763500-7-1(6))* Pentacle Pr.

Rooney, E. Ashley. Berkshire Ghosts: Legends & Lore. 2008. (Illus.). 176p. pap. 14.95 *(978-0-7643-2797-1(6))* Schiffer Publishing, Ltd.

[Smith, Joseph Edward Adams]. Taghconic; or Letters & Legends about Our Summer Home by Godfrey Greylock [Pseud.]. 2006. 232p. per. 20.99 *(978-1-4255-1935-3(0))* MPublishing.

BERLIN, IRVING, 1888-1989

Barrett, Mary Ellin. Irving Berlin: A Daughter's Memoir. 2009. (ENG.). 320p. pap. 21.95 *(978-1-4391-7096-0(7))* Simon & Schuster.

Magee, Jeffrey. Irving Berlin. 2009. (Yale Broadway Masters Ser.). (ENG.). 256p. 35.00 *(978-0-300-11185-9(1))* Yale Univ. Pr.

Magee, Jeffrey. Irving Berlin's American Musical Theater, 1 vol. 2012. (Broadway Legacies Ser.). (ENG., Illus.). 408p. 35.00 ***(978-0-19-539826-7(2))*** Oxford Univ. Pr., Inc.

Rosen, Jody. White Christmas: The Story of an American Song. 2006. 213p. reprint ed. 25.00 *(978-1-4223-5840-5(2))* DIANE Publishing Co.

—White Christmas: The Story of an American Song. 2007. (ENG., Illus.). 224p. pap. 16.95 *(978-0-7432-1876-4(0),* Scribner) Scribner.

Sears, Benjamin, ed. The Irving Berlin Reader, 1 vol. 2012. (Readers on American Musicians Ser.). (ENG., Illus.). 232p. 35.00 *(978-0-19-538374-4(5))* Oxford Univ. Pr., Inc.

BERLIN, ISAIAH, SIR, 1909-1997

Berlin, Isaiah. Conversations with Isaiah Berlin. 2nd ed. 2007. (ENG.). 224p. pap. 22.95 *(978-1-905559-03-9(8))* Halban Pubs. GBR. Dist: Independent Pubs. Group.

—Enlightening: Letters, 1946-1960. Hardy, Henry & Holmes, Jennifer, eds. 2011. (ENG.). 854p. pap. 29.95 *(978-1-84413-834-0(8))* Random Hse. GBR. Dist: Independent Pubs. Group.

—Enlightening, 1946-1960. Hardy, Henry & Holmes, Jennifer, eds. 2009. (ENG., Illus.). 930p. 50.00 *(978-0-7011-7889-5(2))* Random Hse. GBR. Dist: Independent Pubs. Group.

Crowder, George & Hardy, Henry, Jr., eds. The One & the Many: Reading Isaiah Berlin. 2007. (ENG.). 1p. 28.98 *(978-1-59102-448-4(X))* Prometheus Bks., Pubs.

Dubnov, Arie M. Isaiah Berlin: The Journey of a Jewish Liberal. 2012. (Palgrave Studies in Cultural & Intellectual History Ser.). (ENG., Illus.). 330p. 40.00 *(978-0-230-11070-0(3))* Palgrave Macmillan.

Hardy, Henry, ed. The Book of Isaiah: Personal Impressions of Isaiah Berlin. 2009. (Illus.). 368p. 45.00 *(978-1-84383-453-3(7),* Boydell Press) Boydell & Brewer, Ltd. GBR. Dist: Boydell & Brewer, Inc.

Walicki, Andrzej. Encounters with Isaiah Berlin: Story of an Intellectual Friendship. 2011. (Warschauer Studien zur Kultur- und Literaturwissenschaft Ser.). 228p. 64.95 ***(978-3-631-60633-9(8))*** Lang, Peter GmbH, Europaischer Verlag der Wissenschaften DEU. Dist: Lang, Peter.

BERLIN (GERMANY)

Cooper, Trevor. Who Goes There? A Challenge to Humanity. 2009. (Illus.). 124p. pap. 10.99 *(978-1-4389-8466-7(9))* AuthorHouse.

Ewers, Hans-Jürgen, et al, eds. The Future of the Metropolis: Berlin London Paris New York. Economic Aspects. (ENG., Illus.). XII, 484p. 270.00 ***(978-3-11-178311-6(1))*** De Gruyter, Walter Inc.

Laforgue, Jules. Berlin, la Cour et la Ville. reprint ed. 26.00 *(978-0-404-16325-9(4))* AMS Pr., Inc.

—Berlin, la Cour et la Ville. 2010. 292p. pap. 28.75 *(978-1-149-28403-2(X))* BiblioBazaar.

McGushin Sr, Ed. Reflections of a Cold War Warrior, 1 vol. 2009. 198p. pap. 24.95 *(978-1-60749-760-8(3))* PublishAmerica, Inc.

Sachsenroeder, Agnes. Berlin: A Survival Guide to Customs & Etiquette. 2009. 320p. pap. 15.95 *(978-0-7614-5681-0(3))* Marshall Cavendish Corp.

Speer, Albert. Spandau the Secret Diaries. Winston, Richard & Winston, Clara, trs. 2010. 566p. pap. 34.95 *(978-4-87187-879-1(1))* Ishi Pr. International.

Weszkalnys, Gisa. Berlin, Alexanderplatz: Transforming Place in a Unified Germany. 2010. (S&P Ser.). (Illus.). 224p. 60.00 *(978-1-84545-723-5(4))* Berghahn Bks., Inc.

BERLIN (GERMANY)—BAUHAUS

see Bauhaus

BERLIN (GERMANY)—DESCRIPTION AND TRAVEL

Adam, Hans Christian. Berlin. 2007. (FRE, GER & ENG., Illus.). 671p. 69.99 *(978-3-8228-1445-1(8))* TASCHEN DEU. Dist: Ingram Pub. Services.

Adler, Dieter & Adler, Anke. Berlin. 2009. (Small Panorama Ser.). (ENG., Illus.). 256p. 12.99 *(978-0-7858-2473-2(1),* 0785824731, Chartwell) Book Sales, Inc.

Agentur, Ostkreu, ed. 24h Berlin. 2010. (ENG., Illus.). 544p. pap. 45.00 *(978-3-86521-998-5(5))* Steidl, Gerhard Druckerei und Verlag DEU. Dist: D.A.P./Distributed Art Pubs.

Baedeker, Karl. Berlin & Its Environs. 2009. 228p. pap. *(978-1-151-73754-0(2))* Books LLC.

Baumann, Kirsten & Meuser, Natascha. Ambassadors' Residences, 1 vol. 2009. (ENG., Illus.). 352p. 74.95 *(978-3-938666-80-7(3))* DOM Pubs. DEU. Dist: Innovative Logistics.

Bedford-Eichler, Briand. Berlin von Hinten 2012. 2012. (GER & ENG., Illus.). 176p. pap. 20.99 ***(978-3-86787-362-8(3))*** Bruno Gmunder Verlag GmbH DEU. Dist: Bookazine Co., Inc.

Berlin, No. 11. pap. 3.50 *(978-1-894937-70-2(8))* Drawn & Quarterly Pubns. CAN. Dist: Chronicle Bks. LLC.

Berlin Citybook. 18.00 *(978-0-87431-365-9(1),* 20525) West End Games, Inc.

Berlin Now Paperback. 2011. 264p. pap. 39.95 *(978-3-8327-9478-1(6))* teNeues Publishing Co.

Berlin und Potsdam im Farbbild: Die neue und historische Hauptstadt. *(978-3-411-08371-8(9))* Bibliographisches Institut & F. A. Brockhaus AG DEU. Dist: i. b. d., Ltd.

Berlin und Potsdam im Farbbild: Die neue und historische Hauptstadt. (Illus.). pap. *(978-3-8283-0056-9(1))* Hallwag Verlag GmbH DEU. Dist: Rand McNally.

Berning, Maria, et al. Berliner Wohnquartiere: Ein Fuehrer durch 60 Siedlungen in Ost & West. 2nd ed. (GER., Illus.). xii, 397p. *(978-3-496-01112-5(2))* Reimer, Dietrich.

Brenner, Winfried & Werkbund, Deutscher. Bruno Taut: Meister des farbigen Bauens in Berlin. Deutscher Werkbund Berlin, ed. 2008. (Urban Planning & Construction Ser.). (GER & ENG., Illus.). 170p. pap. 29.95 *(978-3-935455-82-4(8),* Braun Publish,Csi) Continental Sales, Inc.

Brunhouse, Jay. Maverick Guide to Berlin, 1 vol. 3rd ed. 2007. (Maverick Guide Ser.). (ENG., Illus.). 432p. pap. 17.95 *(978-1-58980-301-5(9))* Pelican Publishing Co., Inc.

Bruno Gmunder, creator. Berlin Von Hinten. 2008. (Illus.). 176p. pap. *(978-3-86187-912-1(3))* Bruno Gmunder Verlag GmbH.

Christiani, Kerry. Frommer's Berlin Day by Day. 2nd ed. 2012. (Frommer's Day by Day - Pocket Ser.: 189). (ENG., Illus.). 192p. pap. 13.99 ***(978-1-119-99318-6(0),*** Frommers) Wiley, John & Sons, Inc.

Cohen, Tsafrir, et al. Berlin Von Hinten. 2007. (Gay Guides). (GER & ENG., Illus.). 75p. per. *(978-3-86187-862-9(3))* Bruno Gmunder Verlag GmbH.

Cool Berlin. 2011. 192p. pap. 12.95 *(978-3-8327-9486-6(7))* teNeues Publishing Co.

cursc24, citytravelreview. Berlin Inspired. 2009. 61p. pap. 29.50 *(978-1-4092-5996-1(X))* Lulu Enterprises Inc.

edel Entertainment. Berlin: A Personal view. 2008. (ENG., Illus.). 108p. 50.00 *(978-3-940004-34-5(0),* Earbooks) edel classics GmbH DEU. Dist: AtlasBooks Distribution.

Engel, Gerrit. Gerrit Engel: Berlin Architecture. 2008. (Illus.). 340p. *(978-3-8296-0392-8(4))* Schirmer/Mosel Verlag GmbH.

Epstein, Mitch. Berlin. 2011. (ENG., Illus.). 72p. 55.00 *(978-3-86930-224-9(0))* Steidl, Gerhard Druckerei und Verlag DEU. Dist: Innovative Logistics.

Flach, Alex, photos by. Berlin Calling. 2009. (Illus.). 112p. pap. 37.00 *(978-88-88493-37-4(9))* Drago Arts & Communication ITA. Dist: SCB Distributors.

Fodor's Travel Publications, Inc. Staff. Fodor's Berlin's 25 Best, 7th Edition. 2010. (25 Best Ser.). (ENG.). 128p. pap. 11.99 *(978-1-4000-0539-0(6),* Fodor's) Fodor's Travel Pubns.

Gaertringen, Hans G. von. Museumsinsel Berlin: Fünf Häuser und ihre Schätze. Bild- und Textredaktion: Hans Georg Hiller von Gaertringen. 2009. (ENG.). 72p. pap. 18.00 *(978-3-422-06879-7(1))* Deutscher Kunstverlag GmbH DEU. Dist: Independent Pubs. Group.

Glade, Clemens & Rehberg, Peter. Berlin von Hinten. Bedford, Briand, ed. 2011. (Illus.). 176p. pap. ***(978-3-86787-353-6(4))*** Bruno Gmunder Verlag GmbH.

Grobe, Jurgen. Urban Art Photography. 2008. (GER & ENG., Illus.). 216p. *(978-3-89955-205-8(9))* Die Gestalten Verlag.

Harvard Student Agencies, Inc. Let's Go Berlin, Prague & Budapest: The Student Travel Guide. 2010. (Let's Go Ser.). (ENG., Illus.). 280p. pap. 14.95 *(978-1-59880-712-7(9),* Let's Go) Avalon Travel Publishing.

James, Russell, text. Cool Guide Berlin. 2009. pap. 24.95 *(978-3-8327-9296-1(1))* teNeues Publishing Co.

Kiefer, Thomas. Berlin: Impressions Locations People. 2011. (ENG., Illus.). 416p. 14.95 *(978-3-03768-090-2(3),* Braun Publish,Csi) Continental Sales, Inc.

Klapsch, Thorsten, photos by. Berlin: Restaurants & More. 2007. (ENG., Illus.). 191p. 14.99 *(978-3-8365-0039-5(6))* TASCHEN DEU. Dist: Ingram Pub. Services.

—Berlin: Shops & More. 2007. (ENG., Illus.). 191p. 14.99 *(978-3-8365-0041-8(8))* TASCHEN DEU. Dist: Ingram Pub. Services.

Knobloch, Heinz. Stadtmitte Umsteigen: Berliner Phantasien. 5th ed. (GER., Illus.). 247p. *(978-3-371-00395-5(7))* Spiess, Voker Morgenbuch Verlag.

Knopf Guides Staff. Berlin - Knopf MapGuide. 2009. (Knopf MapGuide Ser.). (ENG., Illus.). 48p. pap. 10.95 *(978-0-375-71059-9(0),* Knopf) Knopf Doubleday Publishing Group.

Kopleck, M. Pastfinder: Berlin 1933-1945. 2008. pap. 12.90 *(978-3-86153-363-4(4))* Ch.Links Verlag DEU. Dist: Casemate Pubs. & Bk. Distributors, LLC.

—Pastfinder: Berlin 1945-1989. 2008. pap. 12.90 *(978-3-86153-411-2(8))* Ch.Links Verlag DEU. Dist: Casemate Pubs. & Bk. Distributors, LLC.

Kuhler, Michael. Fascinating Berlin. 2011. (Fascinating Ser.). (ENG.). 96p. 14.95 *(978-3-88189-682-5(1))* Verlagshaus Wurzburg GmbH & Co. KG DEU. Dist: Independent Pubs. Group.

—Horizon Berlin. 2011. (Premium Ser.). (ENG., Illus.). 224p. 69.95 *(978-3-8003-1950-3(0))* Verlagshaus Wurzburg GmbH & Co. KG DEU. Dist: Independent Pubs. Group.

Lehnert, Uta. Der Kaiser & die Siegesallee. (GER., Illus.). 414p. *(978-3-496-01189-7(0))* Reimer, Dietrich.

Locken, E. Travel Journal Berlin. 2010. 192p. pap. 19.99 *(978-0-557-41596-0(9))* Lulu Enterprises Inc.

Lonely Planet Staff & Schulte-Peevers, Andrea. Berlin. 2nd rev. ed. 2010. (Encounter Ser.). (ENG., Illus.). 200p. pap. 11.99 *(978-1-74179-289-8(4))* Lonely Planet Pubns.

—Lonely Planet Berlin, 26 vols. 7th rev. ed. 2011. (City Guide Ser.). (ENG., Illus.). 332p. pap. 19.99 *(978-1-74179-701-5(2))* Lonely Planet Pubns.

Luthardt, Ernst-Otto & Henkelmann, Jurgen. Journey through Berlin. 2007. (Journey Through Ser.). (Illus.). 124p. 24.95 *(978-3-8003-1552-9(1))* Verlagshaus Wurzburg GmbH & Co. KG DEU. Dist: Independent Pubs. Group.

Marco Polo. Berlin Marco Polo Guide. 2012. (Marco Polo Guides Ser.). (ENG., Illus.). 168p. pap. 9.99 ***(978-3-8297-0653-7(7))*** Marco Polo Travel Publishing GBR. Dist: Innovative Logistics.

Moleskine Staff. Moleskine City Notebook Berlin. 2008. (ENG.). 228p. 17.95 *(978-88-8370-616-5(1))* Moleskine ITA. Dist: Hachette Bk. Group.

MONACO BOOKS, compiled by. Berlin: Travelmag. 2011. (ENG., Illus.). 256p. 14.95 *(978-3-89944-671-5(2),* Monaco Bks.) Verlag Wolfgang Kunth GmbH & Co. KG DEU. Dist: Innovative Logistics.

Monaco Books, ed. Berlin: Fascinating Cities, 1 vol. 2010. (ENG., Illus.). 180p. 24.95 *(978-3-89944-539-8(2),* Monaco Bks.) Verlag Wolfgang Kunth GmbH & Co. KG DEU. Dist: Innovative Logistics.

Muir, Peter. Writing on the Wall: History, Memory, Aesthetics. 2010. (Illus.). 204p. 124.95 *(978-0-7546-6963-0(7))* Ashgate Publishing Co.

Neubauer, Helga & Vorbeck, Wolfgang. Berlin. 2007. (Panarama 360 Ser.). (Illus.). 104p. 59.95 *(978-1-877339-37-0(7))* NZVP Bks. & Calendars Ltd. NZL. Dist: Perseus-PGW.

Norton, Minerva Brace. In & Around Berlin. 2008. 156p. 22.99 *(978-0-554-39149-6(X))* 2008. 156p. 25.99 *(978-0-554-29846-7(5))* 2007. (ENG.). 138p. pap. 18.99 *(978-1-4346-8551-3(9))* 2007. (ENG.). 154p. pap. 21.99 *(978-1-4346-8552-0(7))* BiblioBazaar.

—In & Around Berlin. 2007. 132p. per. *(978-1-4065-4036-9(6))* Dodo Pr.

—In & Around Berlin. 2009. 100p. pap. *(978-1-4068-5235-6(X))* Echo Library.

NZ Visitor Publications Ltd, creator. Berlin. 2007. (Citypanoramas 360 Ser.). (Illus.). 32p. pap. 9.95 *(978-3-938446-60-7(9))* NZVP Books and Calendars GmbH. DEU. Dist: Perseus-PGW.

Omilanowska, Malgorzata. DK Eyewitness Travel Guide: Berlin: Berlin. 2012. (Eyewitness Travel Guides). (ENG.). 272p. pap. 25.00 *(978-0-7566-8406-8(4))* Dorling Kindersley Publishing, Inc.

Orel, Dennis & Tafel, Benjamin, photos by. Berliner Luft ²: Das Original. 2011. (ENG., Illus.). 256p. pap. 30.00 *(978-3-7757-2616-0(0))* Hatje Cantz Verlag GmbH & Co KG DEU. Dist: D.A.P./Distributed Art Pubs.

Plotkin, Abraham. An American in Hitler's Berlin: Abraham Plotkin's Diary, 1932-33. Collomp, Catherine et al, eds. 2009. (ENG., Illus.). 272p. 62.00 *(978-0-252-03361-2(2))* Univ. of Illinois Pr.

—An American in Hitler's Berlin: Abraham Plotkin's Diary 1932-33. Collomp, Catherine & Groppo, Bruno, eds. 2008. (ENG., Illus.). 272p. pap. 26.00 *(978-0-252-07559-9(5))* Univ. of Illinois Pr.

Ramsay, Maggie. Berlin: Monaco Books - Photo Guide. 1 vol. 2010. (ENG., Illus.). 228p. 19.95 *(978-3-89944-483-4(3)*, Monaco Bks.) Verlag Wolfgang Kunth GmbH & Co. KG DEU. Dist: Innovative Logistics.

Rave, Rolf. Modern Architecture in Berlin. 2009. (ENG., Illus.). 280p. pap. 49.90 *(978-3-936681-29-1(5))* Edition Axel Menges GmbH DEU. Dist: National Bk. Network.

Review, City Travel. Poor but Sexy: A Guide to Berlin. 2010. 102p. pap. 20.95 *(978-1-4461-6791-5(7))* Lulu Enterprises Inc.

Richards, Brian. Berlin. 2nd ed. 2008. (Globetrotter Travel Packs Ser.). (ENG., Illus.). 128p. pap. 14.95 *(978-1-84537-840-0(7))* New Holland Pubs., Ltd. GBR. Dist: Globe Pequot Pr., The.

—Globetrotter the Best of Berlin. 2007. (Globetrotter Best of Ser.). (ENG., Illus.). 96p. pap. 8.95 *(978-1-84537-552-2(1))* New Holland Pubs., Ltd. GBR. Dist: Globe Pequot Pr., The.

Richter, Jana, ed. The Tourist City Berlin: Tourism & Architecture. 2010. (ENG., Illus.). 368p. pap. 39.95 *(978-3-03768-058-2(X)*, Braun Publish,Csi) Continental Sales, Inc.

Rivaz, Dominique de. The Never Ending Wall. 2009. (ENG., Illus.). 288p. *(978-3-7165-1580-8(9)*, Benteli Verlags Ag Dist) Antique Collectors' Club.

Rough, Guides. Pocket Rough Guide Berlin. 2012. (Rough Guide Pocket Guides). (ENG., Illus.). 176p. 12.99 *(978-1-4053-8535-0(9))* Rough Guides, Ltd. GBR. Dist: Dorling Kindersley Publishing, Inc.

Schache, Wolfgang & Sconci, Maria Selene. An Italian Palazzo in Germany: The Embassy in Berlin. 2007. (ENG., Illus.). 124p. 70.00 *(978-88-422-1483-0(3))* Allemandi, Umberto & Co. GBR. Dist: Antique Collectors' Club.

Scheunemann, Juergen. Top 10 Berlin. 2012. (Eyewitness top 10 travel Guide Ser.). (ENG.). 192p. 14.00 *(978-0-7566-8451-8(X))* Dorling Kindersley Publishing, Inc.

Scheunemann, Jurgen. Berlin. 2009. (Step by Step Ser.). (ENG., Illus.). 128p. pap. 16.99 *(978-981-282-103-4(1))* APA Publications Services SGP. Dist: Ingram Pub. Services.

Schmidt, Michael. Berlin Nach 1945, 1 vol. 2008. (GER & ENG., Illus.). 144p. 55.00 *(978-3-86521-090-6(2))* Steidl, Gerhard Druckerei und Verlag DEU. Dist: Innovative Logistics.

Schulte-Peevers, Andrea. Berlin. 3rd rev. ed. 2012. (Encounter Ser.). (ENG., Illus.). 192p. pap. 12.99 ***(978-1-74179-855-5(8))*** Lonely Planet Pubns.

Sewcz, Maria. Inter Esse: Berlin, 1985-87, 1 vol. Schube, Inka, ed. 2011. (ENG., Illus.). 80p. 58.00 *(978-3-86521-788-2(5))* Steidl, Gerhard Druckerei und Verlag DEU. Dist: Innovative Logistics.

Siepen, Alois. Peeps at Great Cities - Berlin. 2007. 108p. per. 26.45 *(978-1-4067-4412-5(3))* Audubon Pr. & Christian Bk. Service.

Simonis, Damien. Berlin. 2006. (National Geographic Traveler Ser.). (ENG., Illus.). 272p. pap. 22.95 *(978-0-7922-6212-1(3)*, National Geographic) National Geographic Society.

Sinclair, Nicholas, photos by. Berlin: Imagining the Tri Chord. 2007. (ENG., Illus.). 80p. 49.95 *(978-1-905711-10-9(7))* Royal Academy of Arts GBR. Dist: Hachette Bk. Group.

Stappenbeck, Gisela, et al. Erlebtes Bauen: Ost-Berlin, 1959 Bis 1989, 1 vol. 2009. (RUS, FRE, GER & ENG., Illus.). 288p. 64.95 *(978-3-938666-37-1(4))* DOM Pubs. DEU. Dist: Innovative Logistics.

Steves, Rick. Rick Steves' Snapshot Berlin. 2012. (Rick Steves Snapshot Ser.). (ENG., Illus.). 208p. pap. 9.99 *(978-1-59880-690-8(4))* Avalon Travel Publishing.

Sullivan, Paul, photos by. A Hedonist's Guide to Berlin. 2nd ed. 2009. (Hedonist's Guide To... Ser.). (ENG., Illus.). 208p. im. lthr. 18.95 *(978-1-905428-30-4(8)*, HG2) Filmer Ltd. GBR. Dist: Perseus-PGW.

Taschen, Angelika, ed. TASCHEN's Berlin: Hotels, Restaurants & Shops. 2010. (FRE, GER & ENG., Illus.). 400p. 39.99 *(978-3-8365-1120-9(7))* TASCHEN DEU. Dist: Ingram Pub. Services.

Taschen, Angelika, ed. 4 Cities, 12 vols. 2011. (ENG, FRE & GER., Illus.). 1536p. pap. 59.99 ***(978-3-8365-3179-5(8))*** TASCHEN DEU. Dist: Ingram Pub. Services.

teNeues. AAD Berlin: Art Architecture Design. 2010. (Illus.). 168p. pap. 12.95 *(978-3-8327-9433-0(6))* teNeues Publishing Co.

—Cool Berlin. 2010. (Illus.). 224p. pap. 12.95 *(978-3-8327-9400-2(X))* teNeues Publishing Co.

Thomas Cook Publishing. Traveller Guides Berlin, 4th. 4th ed. 2011. (Travellers - Thomas Cook Ser.). (ENG., Illus.). 192p. pap. 16.95 *(978-1-84848-423-8(2))* Cook, Thomas Publishing GBR. Dist: Globe Pequot Pr., The.

Thomas Cook Publishing Staff. Berlin Pocket Guide. 3rd ed. 2010. (Thomas Cook Pocket Guides). (ENG., Illus.). 160p. pap. 9.95 *(978-1-84848-307-1(4))* Cook, Thomas Publishing GBR. Dist: Globe Pequot Pr., The.

—Out Around Berlin. 2nd ed. 2006. (Out Around - Thomas Cook Ser.). (ENG., Illus.). 160p. pap. 12.95 *(978-1-84157-663-3(8))* Cook, Thomas Publishing GBR. Dist: Globe Pequot Pr., The.

Time Out Guides Staff. Time Out Shortlist Berlin. 2nd ed. 2010. (Time Out Shortlist Ser.). (ENG., Illus.). 192p. pap. 12.95 *(978-1-84670-148-1(1))* Time Out Guides Ltd. GBR. Dist: Perseus-PGW.

Time Out Guides Staff, ed. Time Out Berlin. 9th ed. 2011. (Time Out Guides). (ENG., Illus.). 336p. pap. 19.95 ***(978-1-84670-249-5(6))*** Time Out Guides Ltd. GBR. Dist: Perseus-PGW.

Time Out Guides Staff, ed. Time Out Selecciones Berlin: Time Out Shortlist Berlin. 2010. (Selecciones Ser.). (SPA., Illus.). 192p. pap. 12.95 *(978-84-9801-460-0(3))* Time Out Guides Ltd. GBR. Dist: Perseus-PGW.

Uchimura, Kosuke, photos by. Kosuke Uchimura: Berlin & Tokyo, 1 vol. 2007. (JPN, GER & ENG., Illus.). 112p. 29.95 *(978-3-939633-05-1(4))* Jovis Verlag GmbH DEU. Dist: D.A.P./Distributed Art Pubs.

Ullmann, H. F., ed. Berlin. 2009. 480p. pap. 19.99 *(978-0-8416-1015-6(0))* American Map Corp.

Von Halasz, Joachim, ed. Hitler's Berlin - a Third Reich Tourist Guide. 2008. 56p. pap. *(978-1-905742-06-6(1))* Foxley Books.

Von Rauch, Friederike, photos by. Neues Museum. 2009. (ENG., Illus.). 96p. 45.00 *(978-3-7757-2376-3(5))* Hatje Cantz Verlag GmbH & Co KG DEU. Dist: D.A.P./Distributed Art Pubs.

von Taube, Dagmar, ed. Berlin Now. 2009. (GER & ENG., Illus.). 256p. 95.00 *(978-3-8327-9353-1(4))* teNeues Publishing Co.

Wallpaper Magazine Editors, ed. Berlin 2011 - Wallpaper City Guide. 3rd ed. 2011. (ENG., Illus.). 128p. pap. 9.95 *(978-0-7148-6087-9(5))* Phaidon Pr., Inc.

Wallpaper Magazine Editors, ed. Berlin 2012 - Wallpaper City Guide. 2011. (ENG.). 128p. pap. 9.95 ***(978-0-7148-6280-4(0))*** Phaidon Pr., Inc.

Williams, Christian & Rough Guides Staff. The Rough Guide to Berlin. 9th ed. 2011. (ENG., Illus.). 312p. 18.99 *(978-1-84836-627-5(2))* Rough Guides, Ltd. GBR. Dist: Dorling Kindersley Publishing, Inc.

Woerner, Martin, et al. Architekturführer Berlin. 6th ed. (GER., Illus.). 540p. *(978-3-496-01211-5(0))* Reimer, Dietrich.

Wolbergs, Benjamin. Urban Illustration: Street Art City Guide Berlin. 2007. (Illus.). 359p. pap. 29.95 *(978-1-58423-291-9(9))* Gingko Pr., Inc.

Yust, Larry, photos by. The Beautiful Walls: Photographic Elevations of Street Art in Los Angeles, Berlin, & Paris. 2010. (ENG., Illus.). 100p. 40.00 *(978-0-9778344-4-0(1))* Univ. of California, Los Angeles, Fowler Museum of Cultural History.

BERLIN (GERMANY)—GALLERIES AND MUSEUMS

Bitter, Jan, photos by. Daniel Libeskind: Jewish Museum Berlin: Museum Building Guides, 1 vol. 2011. (ENG., Illus.). 80p. pap. 25.00 ***(978-84-343-1292-0(1))*** Poligrafa, Ediciones, S. A. ESP. Dist: D.A.P./Distributed Art Pubs.

Musterttel Staff. The Neues Museum Berlin Conserving, Restoring, Rebuilding Within the World Heritage. 2009. (ENG.). 208p. 39.80 *(978-3-86502-207-3(3)*, Art Stock Bks. Ltd/Csi) Continental Sales, Inc.

Prestel. Berlinische Galerie,Berlin. pap. 14.95 *(978-3-7913-3205-5(8))* Prestel Publishing.

Wolf, Connie, et al. Daniel Libeskind & the Contemporary Jewish Museum: New Jewish Architecture from Berlin to San Francisco. 2008. (ENG., Illus.). 128p. 45.00 *(978-0-8478-3165-4(5))* Rizzoli International Pubns., Inc.

BERLIN (GERMANY)—HISTORY

Adam, Hans Christian. Berlin. 2007. (FRE, GER & ENG., Illus.). 671p. 69.99 *(978-3-8228-1445-1(8))* TASCHEN DEU. Dist: Ingram Pub. Services.

Barber, Stephen. The Walls of Berlin: Urban Surfaces - Art - Film. 2011. (Solar Books - Solar Art Directives Ser.). (Illus.). 189p. pap. 24.95 *(978-0-9820464-6-3(4))* Solar Bks.

Black, Monica. Death in Berlin: From Weimar to Divided Germany. 2010. (Publications of the German Historical Institute Ser.). (ENG., Illus.). 328p. 80.00 *(978-0-521-11851-4(4))* Cambridge Univ. Pr.

Bodenschatz, Harald. Berlin Urban Design, 1 vol. 2010. (ENG.). 140p. pap. 35.95 *(978-3-86922-105-2(4))* DOM Pubs. DEU. Dist: Innovative Logistics.

Boyd Whyte, Iain & Frisby, David, eds. Metropolis Berlin, 1880-1940. 2012. (Weimar & Now: German Cultural Criticism Ser.). (ENG.). 632p. 85.00 ***(978-0-520-27037-4(1))*** Univ. of California Pr.

Brennan, Sean. The Politics of Religion in Soviet Occupied Germany: The Case of Berlin-Brandenburg, 1945-1949. 2011. (ENG.). 256p. 70.00 ***(978-0-7391-5125-9(8))*** Lexington Bks.

—The Politics of Religion in Soviet-Occupied Germany: The Case of Berlin-Brandenburg, 1945-1949. 2011. ***(978-0-7391-5127-3(4))*** Lexington Bks.

Chesterton, G. K. The Barbarism of Berlin. 2008. 52p. pap. 9.99 *(978-1-59547-663-0(6))* NuVision Pubns., LLC.

Daum, Andreas & Mauch, Christof, eds. Berlin - Washington, 1800-2000: Capital Cities, Cultural Representation, & National Identities. 2011. (Publications of the German Historical Institute Ser.). (ENG.). 334p. pap. 33.99 *(978-1-107-40258-4(1))* Cambridge Univ. Pr.

Dewez, Luc & Faley, Michael P. High Noon over Haseluenne: The 100th Bombardment Group over Berlin, 2009 6,1944. 2009. (Illus.). 320p. bds. 69.99 *(978-0-7643-3237-1(6))* Schiffer Publishing, Ltd.

Dorr, Robert F. Mission to Berlin: The American Airmen Who Struck the Heart of Hitler's Reich. 2011. (ENG., Illus.). 336p. 28.00 *(978-0-7603-3898-8(1)*, 0760338981, Zenith Pr.) MBI Publishing Co. LLC.

Feiner, Shmuel, et al. Cultural Revolution in Berlin: Jews in the Age of Enlightenment. 2011. (Illus.). 104p. pap. 35.00 *(978-1-85124-291-7(0))* Bodleian Library GBR. Dist: Chicago Distribution Ctr.

Friedrich, Karin & Smart, Sara. The Cultivation of Monarchy in Brandenburg-Prussia & the Rise of Berlin, 1700-1701. 2010. (Illus.). 438p. 144.95 *(978-0-7546-0997-1(9))* Ashgate Publishing Co.

Funder, Anna. Stasiland: Stories from Behind the Berlin Wall. 2009. 320p. 24.95 *(978-84-92567-07-2(4))* Roca Editorial De Libros ESP. Dist: Ediciones Urano S. A.

Gordon, Mel. Voluptuous Panic: The Erotic World of Weimar Berlin. exp. ed. 2008. (ENG., Illus.). 300p. pap. 34.95 *(978-0-922915-96-5(2))* Feral Hse.

Graumann, Antje & Arndt, Nicole. Das Hansaviertel in Berlin: Bedeutung, Rezeption, Sanierung. 2007. (GER., Illus.). 238p. *(978-3-86568-287-1(1))* Imhof, Michael Verlag GmbH & Co. KG.

Hake, Sabine. Topographies of Class: Modern Architecture & Mass Society in Weimar Berlin. 2008. (Social History, Popular Culture, & Politics in Germany Ser.). (ENG., Illus.). 336p. (C). 90.00 *(978-0-472-07038-1(X))*; pap. 40.00 *(978-0-472-05038-3(9))* Univ. of Michigan Pr.

Harrington, Daniel F. Berlin on the Brink: The Blockade, the Airlift, & the Early Cold War. 2012. (ENG., Illus.). 504p. 40.00 ***(978-0-8131-3613-4(X))*** Univ. Pr. of Kentucky.

Hartung, Klaus. Berlin: A City for the Future. 2010. (ENG., Illus.). 352p. 50.00 *(978-88-544-0484-7(5))* White Star ITA. Dist: Random Hse., Inc.

Hertle, Hans-Hermann. Die Berliner Mauer / The Berlin Wall: Monument des Kalten Krieges -Monumente of the Cold War. 2008. (GER & ENG., Illus.). 334p. pap. 19.90 *(978-3-86153-463-1(0))* Ch.Links Verlag DEU. Dist: Casemate Pubs. & Bk. Distributors, LLC.

Imhof, Michael. Berlin: Gestern und heute / Yesterday & Today. 2011. (ENG.). 120p. 24.95 ***(978-3-86568-609-1(5))*** Imhof, Michael Verlag GmbH & Co. KG DEU. Dist: Independent Pubs. Group.

Katchourovskaja, Mareike. Die russische Öffentlichkeit im Berlin der Weimarer Republik. 2008. (Europäische Hochschulschriften. Reihe 3: Geschichte und Ihre Hilfswissenschaften Ser.). 112p. pap. 35.95 *(978-3-631-57670-0(6))* Lang, Peter GmbH, Europaischer Verlag der Wissenschaften DEU. Dist: Lang, Peter.

Knobloch, Heinz. Stadtmitte Umsteigen: Berliner Phantasien. 5th ed. (GER., Illus.). 247p. *(978-3-371-00395-5(7))* Spiess, Voker Morgenbuch Verlag.

Lewis, Ilse. Ilse's Berlin-I Was There-1926 To 1945. 2011. 124p. 24.95 ***(978-1-4634-0259-4(7))***; pap. 15.95 ***(978-1-4634-0261-7(9))*** AuthorHouse.

Middlebrook, Martin. The Bomber Battle for Berlin. 2010. (Illus.). 256p. 39.95 *(978-1-84884-224-3(4))* Pen & Sword Bks. Ltd. GBR. Dist: Casemate Pubs. & Bk. Distributors, LLC.

Moorhouse, Roger. Berlin at War: Life & Death in Hitler's Capital, 1939-1945. 2010. (Illus.). 448p. *(978-0-224-08071-2(7))* Basic Bks.

—Berlin at War: Life & Death in Hitler's Capital, 1939-45. (ENG.). (gr. 9). 2012. 480p. pap. 18.99 ***(978-0-465-02855-9(1))*** 2010. 464p. 29.95 *(978-0-465-00533-8(0))* Basic Bks.

Neiman, Susan. Slow Fire: Jewish Notes from Berlin. 2010. (ENG.). pap. 12.95 *(978-1-61027-031-1(2))* Quid Pro, LLC.

Palladini, Fiammetta. Die Berliner Hugenotten und der Fall Barbeyrac: Orthodoxe und 'Sozinianer' Im Refuge (1685-1720) 2011. (GER., Illus.). ***(978-90-04-20947-3(6))*** BRILL.

Perch, Brian. Encounter Berlin. 2011. 324p. 36.04 *(978-1-4567-7477-6(8))*; pap. 23.50 *(978-1-4520-5572-5(6))* AuthorHouse.

Plotkin, Abraham. An American in Hitler's Berlin: Abraham Plotkin's Diary, 1932-33. Collomp, Catherine et al, eds. 2009. (ENG., Illus.). 272p. 62.00 *(978-0-252-03361-2(2))* Univ. of Illinois Pr.

—An American in Hitler's Berlin: Abraham Plotkin's Diary 1932-33. Collomp, Catherine & Groppo, Bruno, eds. 2008. (ENG., Illus.). 272p. pap. 26.00 *(978-0-252-07559-9(5))* Univ. of Illinois Pr.

Prowe, Diethelm. Weltstadt in Krisen: Berlin 1949-1958. (Veröffentlichungen der Historischen Kommission zu Berlin Ser.). (GER.). X, 359p. 210.00 ***(978-3-11-176825-0(2))*** De Gruyter, Walter Inc.

Rosenfeld, Gavriel D. & Jaskot, Paul B., eds. Beyond Berlin: Twelve German Cities Confront the Nazi Past. 2008. (Social History, Popular Culture, & Politics in Germany Ser.). (ENG., Illus.). 336p. (C). 85.00 *(978-0-472-11611-9(8))* Univ. of Michigan Pr.

Rudolph, Katrin. Gilt die Taufe der Juden nicht, so erklären auch wir unsere Taufe für Ungültig... Zur Situation Berliner Christen jüdischer Herkunft im Nationalsozialismus. Rasseverfolgte, Evangelische Hilfsstelle für ehemals, ed. 2007. (GER.). 132p. pap. *(978-3-8325-1707-6(3))* Logos Verlag Berlin.

Sandes, Caroline A. Archaeology, Conservation & the City. 2010. (Bar S Ser.). (Illus.). 122p. (C). pap. 77.50 *(978-1-4073-0701-5(0))* British Archaeological Reports Ltd. GBR. Dist: Brown, David Bk. Co., The.

Schweizer, Hannah & Schweizer, Haro. Historische Karten und Ansichten von Berlin. 2010. 56p. pap. 19.99 *(978-0-8416-7237-6(7))* Langenscheidt Publishing Group.

—Historische Karten und Ansichten von Berlin, 1 vol. 2011. (ENG., Illus.). 56p. pap. 14.99 *(978-3-8331-5774-5(7))* h.f.ullmann DEU. Dist: Innovative Logistics.

Slayton, Robert A. Master of the Air: William Tunner & the Success of Military Airlift. 2010. (ENG., Illus.). 304p. 43.50 *(978-0-8173-1692-1(2))* Univ. of Alabama Pr.

Strecker, Kathleen. Mediaspree Berlin: ein ehemaliges Grenzgebiet im Werteparcours: Blicke auf wertschöpfungsorientierte Raumstrategien. 2010. 148p. pap. *(978-3-639-25845-5(2))* VDM Verlag Dr. Mueller e.K.

Studnitz, Hans-Georg von. While Berlin Burns. 2011. (Illus.). vii, 290p. 39.95 ***(978-1-84832-617-0(3)***, Frontline) Pen & Sword Bks. Ltd. GBR. Dist: Casemate Pubs. & Bk. Distributors, LLC.

't Groen, Adriaan in. De Wende en Humboldts Erfenis: De utopie Voorbij. 2009. (LUP Dissertaties Ser.). (DUT & GER.). 304p. pap. *(978-90-8728-069-7(6)*, Leiden Univ. Pr.) Amsterdam Univ. Pr.

Tissier, Tony Le & Le Tissier, Tony. Berlin Battlefield Guide: Third Reich & Cold War. 2008. (Illus.). 320p. 60.00 *(978-1-84415-766-2(0))* Pen & Sword Bks. Ltd. GBR. Dist: Casemate Pubs. & Bk. Distributors, LLC.

Von Halasz, Joachim, ed. Hitler's Berlin - a Third Reich Tourist Guide. 2008. 56p. pap. *(978-1-905742-06-6(1))* Foxley Books.

Wietzorek, Paul. Historic Berlin: Pictures tell the story. 2008. (ENG.). 192p. 14.95 *(978-3-86568-353-3(3)*, Art Stock Bks. Ltd/Csi) Continental Sales, Inc.

Zierenberg, Malte. Stadt der Schieber: Der Berliner Schwarzmarkt 1939 - 1950. Kritische Studien zur Geschichtswissenschaft Bd.179. 2008. (Kritische Studien Zur Geschichtswissenschaft Ser.). (GER., Illus.). 349p. (C). pap. 54.00 *(978-3-525-35111-6(9))* Vandenhoeck & Ruprecht GmbH & Co. KG DEU. Dist: ISD.

BERLIN (GERMANY)—HISTORY—1945-1990

see also Berlin (Germany)—International Status; Berlin, Battle of, Berlin, Germany, 1945; Berlin Wall, Berlin, Germany, 1961-1989

Broadbent, Philip & Hake, Sabine, eds. Berlin Divided City, 1945-1989. 2010. (CSG Ser.). (Illus.). 222p. 70.00 *(978-1-84545-755-6(2))* Berghahn Bks., Inc.

Canwell, Diane & Sutherland, Jon. The Berlin Airlift: The Salvation of a City. 1 vol. 2008. (ENG., Illus.). 256p. 24.95 *(978-1-58980-550-7(X))* Pelican Publishing Co., Inc.

Cherny, Andrei. The Candy Bombers: The Untold Story of the Berlin Aircraft & America's Finest Hour. 2009. (ENG.). 640p. (gr. 12-18). 18.00 *(978-0-425-22771-8(5)*, Berkley Trade) Penguin Group (USA) Inc.

Clarke, Bob. 10 Tons to Templeh of Berlin Airlift. 2007. (ENG., Illus.). 224p. pap. 34.95 *(978-0-7524-4092-7(6))* History Pr. Ltd.,The GBR. Dist: Independent Pubs. Group.

The Documentary History of the Truman Presidency Vol. 16: Cold War Confrontation - Truman, Stalin & the Berlin Airlift. Date not set. 185.00 *(978-1-55655-582-4(2))* ProQuest LLC.

Evans, Jennifer V. Life among the Ruins: Cityscape & Sexuality in Cold War Berlin. 2011. (Genders & Sexualities in History Ser.). (ENG., Illus.). 336p. 85.00 ***(978-0-230-20201-6(2))*** Palgrave Macmillan.

Finell, Karin. Good-Bye to the Mermaids: A Childhood Lost in Hitler's Berlin. 2006. (ENG., Illus.). 368p. (gr. 9). 29.95 *(978-0-8262-1690-8(0))* Univ. of Missouri Pr.

Flemming, Thomas. Berlin in the Cold War: The Battle for the Divided City. 2010. (Illus.). 78p. ***(978-1-935902-80-5(6))*** Berlinica Publishing LLC.

Goda, Norman J. W. Tales from Spandau: Nazi Criminals & the Cold War. 2008. (ENG., Illus.). 404p. (C). pap. 24.99 *(978-0-521-73062-4(7))* Cambridge Univ. Pr.

Hamilton, A. Stephen. Bloody Streets: The Soviet Assault on Berling, April 1945. 2007. (Illus.). 368p. 89.95 *(978-1-906033-12-5(9))* Helion & Co., Ltd. GBR. Dist: Casemate Pubs. & Bk. Distributors, LLC.

Jacobitz, Helmut, et al. We Were Berliners: From Weimar to the Wall. 2012. (ENG., Illus.). 192p. 32.95 ***(978-0-7524-6461-9(2))*** History Pr. Ltd.,The GBR. Dist: Independent Pubs. Group.

Latimer, C.A. My Struggle with Joseph Stalin. 2007. (Illus.). 264p. 37.95 *(978-1-84624-146-8(4))* Book Guild, Ltd. GBR. Dist: Trans-Atlantic Pubns., Inc.

Miller, Roger G. To Save a City: The Berlin Airlift, 1948-1949. 2008. (Military History Ser.: No. 68). (ENG.). 272p. pap. 22.50 *(978-1-60344-090-5(9))* Texas A&M Univ. Pr.

Reeves, Richard. Daring Young Men The Heroism & Triumph of the Berlin Airlift, June 1948- May 1949. 2010. (ENG., Illus.). 336p. 28.00 *(978-1-4165-4119-6(5))* Simon & Schuster.

—Daring Young Men: The Heroism & Triumph of the Berlin Airlift-June 1948-May 1949. 2011. (ENG., Illus.). 336p. pap. 16.00 *(978-1-4165-4120-2(9))* Simon & Schuster.

Roggenbuch, Frank. Das Berliner Grenzgängerproblem: Verflechtung und Systemkonkurrenz vor dem Mauerbau. 2008. (Veröffentlichungen der Historischen Kommission zu Berlin Ser.).Tr. of Problem of Berlin's Cross-Border Commuters. Integration & Systemic Competition before the Building of the Berlin Wall. (GER.). XIII, 481p. 189.00 *(978-3-11-020344-8(8))* De Gruyter, Walter Inc.

Salmon, Patrick, et al, eds. Berlin in Crisis, 1948-1990 Vol. 6: Documents on British Policy Overseas. 2009. (Whitehall Histories Ser.). (ENG., Illus.). 128p. (C). 150.00 *(978-0-415-44870-3(0))* Routledge.

Sieg, Heidimarie. After the Bombs: My Berlin: Memories of Post-World War II Berlin. 2011. 278p. pap. 15.95 ***(978-0-9843024-5-1(X)***, ABQ Pr.) ABQ Bks., Inc.

Stafford, David. Spies Beneath Berlin. 2006. (Illus.). 211p. reprint ed. pap. 16.00 *(978-1-4223-5379-0(6))* DIANE Publishing Co.
Steege, Paul. Black Market, Cold War: Everyday Life in Berlin, 1946-1949. (ENG.). 372p. 2008. pap. 35.00 *(978-0-521-74517-8(9))* 2007. (Illus.). 95.00 *(978-0-521-86496-1(8))* Cambridge Univ. Pr.
Verheyen, Dirk. United City, Divided Memories? Cold War Legacies in Contemporary Berlin. 2008. (ENG., Illus.). 320p. 83.99 *(978-0-7391-1839-9(0))* Lexington Bks.
—United City Divided Memories? Cold War Legacies in Contemporary Berlin. 2010. (ENG.). 320p. pap. 36.99 *(978-0-7391-1840-5(4))* Lexington Bks.

BERLIN (GERMANY)—HISTORY—1990-

Colomb, Claire. Staging the New Berlin. (Planning, History & Environment Ser.). (ENG., Illus.). 368p. (C). 2012. 155.00 *(978-0-415-59402-8(2))* 2011. pap. 53.95 ***(978-0-415-59403-5(0))*** Routledge.
Hakakian, Roya. Assassins of the Turquoise Palace. 2011. (ENG.). 320p. 25.00 *(978-0-8021-1911-7(5),* Grove Pr.) Grove/Atlantic, Inc.

BERLIN (GERMANY)—INTERNATIONAL STATUS

Colomb, Claire. Staging the New Berlin. (Planning, History & Environment Ser.). (ENG., Illus.). 368p. (C). 2012. 155.00 *(978-0-415-59402-8(2))* 2011. pap. 53.95 ***(978-0-415-59403-5(0))*** Routledge.
The Documentary History of the Truman Presidency Vol. 16: Cold War Confrontation - Truman, Stalin & the Berlin Airlift. Date not set. 185.00 *(978-1-55655-582-4(2))* ProQuest LLC.

BERLIN (GERMANY)—POLITICS AND GOVERNMENT

Chesterton, G. K. The Barbarism of Berlin. 2008. 52p. pap. 9.99 *(978-1-59547-663-0(6))* NuVision Pubns., LLC.
Friedrich, Thomas. Hitler's Berlin: Abused City. 2012. (ENG., Illus.). 480p. 40.00 ***(978-0-300-16670-5(2))*** Yale Univ. Pr.
Kosnick, Kira. Migrant Media: Turkish Broadcasting & Multicultural Politics in Berlin. 2007. (New Anthropologies of Europe Ser.). (ENG., Illus.). 256p. 60.00 *(978-0-253-34948-4(6),* 0253349486); pap. 22.95 *(978-0-253-21937-4(X),* 025321937X) Indiana Univ. Pr.
Swett, Pamela E. Neighbors & Enemies: The Culture of Radicalism in Berlin, 1929-1933. 2007. (ENG., Illus.). 360p. pap. 45.00 *(978-0-521-03997-0(5))* Cambridge Univ. Pr.
Timm, Annette F. The Politics of Fertility in Twentieth-Century Berlin. 2010. (ENG., Illus.). 374p. 95.00 *(978-0-521-19539-3(X))* Cambridge Univ. Pr.
Vorpahl, Frank. Die Berliner politischen Tageszeitungen in Nachmärz und Neuer Ära (1850-1862) Eine Pressehistorische Analyse im Kontext von Modernisierungskrise und Industrieller Revolution. 2011. (GER.). 202p. 61.95 *(978-3-631-60517-2(X))* Lang, Peter GmbH, Europaischer Verlag der Wissenschaften DEU. Dist: Lang, Peter.

BERLIN (GERMANY)—POLITICS AND GOVERNMENT—1945-1990

see also Berlin (Germany)—International Status; Berlin Wall, Berlin, Germany, 1961-1989

Buckley, William F., Jr. The Fall of the Berlin Wall. 20th ed. 2009. (Turning Points in History Ser.: 20). (ENG.). 240p. pap. 14.95 *(978-0-470-49668-8(1),* Wiley) Wiley, John & Sons, Inc.
Daum, Andreas. Kennedy in Berlin. 2007. (Publications of the German Historical Institute). (ENG., Illus.). 406p. (C). 79.99 *(978-0-521-85824-3(0))* Cambridge Univ. Pr.
Daum, Andreas W. Kennedy in Berlin. Geyer, Dona, tr. from GER. 2007. (Publications of the German Historical Institute). (ENG., Illus.). 316p. per. 27.00 *(978-0-521-67497-3(2))* Cambridge Univ. Pr.
Kempe, Frederick. Berlin 1961: Kennedy, Khrushchev, & the Most Dangerous Place on Earth. (ENG.). 608p. (gr. 12). 2012. 16.00 ***(978-0-425-24594-1(2),*** Berkley Trade) 2011. (Illus.). 29.95 *(978-0-399-15729-5(8),* Putnam Adult) Penguin Group (USA) Inc.
Roggenbuch, Frank. Das Berliner Grenzgängerproblem: Verflechtung und Systemkonkurrenz vor dem Mauerbau. 2008. (Veröffentlichungen der Historischen Kommission zu Berlin Ser.).Tr. of Problem of Berlin's Cross-Border Commuters. Integration & Systemic Competition before the Building of the Berlin Wall. (GER.). XIII, 481p. 189.00 *(978-3-11-020344-8(8))* De Gruyter, Walter Inc.
Taylor, Frederick. The Berlin Wall: A World Divided, 1961-1989. (Illus.). 2008. (ENG.). 528p. pap. 15.99 *(978-0-06-078614-4(0),* HarperPerennial) 2007. 512p. 27.95 *(978-0-06-078613-7(2))* HarperCollins Pubs.

BERLIN (GERMANY)—POLITICS AND GOVERNMENT—1990-

Beveridge, Ross. A Politics of Inevitability: The Privatisation of the Berlin Water Company, the Global City Discourse & Governance in 1990s Berlin. 2011. (ENG., Illus.). 234p. pap. 59.95 ***(978-3-531-18219-3(6),*** 3531182196) VS Verlag fur Sozialwissenschaften GmbH DEU. Dist: Springer.

BERLIN (GERMANY)—SOCIAL CONDITIONS

Adam, Hans Christian. Berlin. 2007. (FRE, GER & ENG., Illus.). 671p. 69.99 *(978-3-8228-1445-1(8))* TASCHEN DEU. Dist: Ingram Pub. Services.
Estraikh, Gennady & Krutikov, Mikhail, eds. Yiddish in Weimar Berlin: An Ivory Tower at the Crossroads of Diaspora Politics & Culture. 2010. (Legenda Studies in Yiddish Ser.). (ENG., Illus.). 286p. (C). 89.50 *(978-1-906540-70-8(5))* European Humanities Research Ctr. GBR. Dist: Brown, David Bk. Co., The.
Evans, Jennifer V. Life among the Ruins: Cityscape & Sexuality in Cold War Berlin. 2011. (Genders & Sexualities in History Ser.). (ENG., Illus.). 336p. 85.00 ***(978-0-230-20201-6(2))*** Palgrave Macmillan.
Huchzermeyer, Marie. Tenement Cities: From 19th Century Berlin to 21st Century Nairobi. 2011. (Illus.). xi, 275p. ***(978-1-59221-857-8(1));*** pap. ***(978-1-59221-858-5(X))*** Africa World Pr.
Klein, Hans Günter. Fanny Hensel. Briefe aus Paris an ihre Familie in Berlin: Nach den Quellen zum ersten Mal herausgegeben von Hans-Gunter Klein. 2007. (GER., Illus.). 120p. (C). 42.00 *(978-3-89500-480-3(4))* Reichert, Ludwig Dr. DEU. Dist: Brown, David Bk. Co., The.
Moorhouse, Roger. Berlin at War: Life & Death in Hitler's Capital, 1939-1945. 2010. (Illus.). 448p. *(978-0-224-08071-2(7))* Basic Bks.
Moorhouse, Roger. Berlin at War: Life & Death in Hitler's Capital, 1939-45. 2012. (ENG.). 480p. (gr. 9). pap. 18.99 ***(978-0-465-02855-9(1))*** Basic Bks.
Rajagopalan, Kavitha. Muslims of Metropolis: The Stories of Three Immigrant Families in the West. 2008. (ENG.). 304p. 25.95 *(978-0-8135-4344-4(4))* Rutgers Univ. Pr.
Roth, Joseph. Joseph Roth in Berlin: Ein Lesebuch fuer Spaziergaenger. Bienert, Michael, ed. (GER., Illus.). 419p. pap. *(978-3-462-02541-5(4))* Kiepenheuer & Witsch GmbH & Company KG DEU. Dist: International Bk. Import Service, Inc.
Stratigakos, Despina. A Women's Berlin: Building the Modern City. 2008. (Illus.). 256p. 75.00 *(978-0-8166-5322-5(4));* pap. 24.95 *(978-0-8166-5323-2(2))* Univ. of Minnesota Pr.
Ward, Janet. Post-Wall Berlin: Borders, Space & Identity. 2011. (ENG., Illus.). 404p. 100.00 *(978-0-230-27657-4(1))* Palgrave Macmillan.

BERLIN (GERMANY)—SOCIAL LIFE AND CUSTOMS

Black, Monica. Death in Berlin: From Weimar to Divided Germany. 2010. (Publications of the German Historical Institute Ser.). (ENG., Illus.). 328p. 80.00 *(978-0-521-11851-4(4))* Cambridge Univ. Pr.
Gordon, Mel. Voluptuous Panic: The Erotic World of Weimar Berlin. exp. ed. 2008. (ENG., Illus.). 300p. pap. 34.95 *(978-0-922915-96-5(2))* Feral Hse.
Hartmann, Brit & Kahane, Kitty. Berliner Typen: Mit Bildern und wahren Geschichten von Kitty Kahane und Brit Hartmann. 2010. (GER., Illus.). 127p. pap. *(978-3-89479-588-7(3))* Nicolaische Verlagsbuchhandlung.
Hartung, Klaus. Berlin: A City for the Future. 2010. (ENG., Illus.). 352p. 50.00 *(978-88-544-0484-7(5))* White Star ITA. Dist: Random Hse., Inc.
Roth, Joseph. Joseph Roth in Berlin: Ein Lesebuch fuer Spaziergaenger. Bienert, Michael, ed. (GER., Illus.). 419p. pap. *(978-3-462-02541-5(4))* Kiepenheuer & Witsch GmbH & Company KG DEU. Dist: International Bk. Import Service, Inc.
Sachsenroeder, Agnes. Berlin: A Survival Guide to Customs & Etiquette. 2009. 320p. pap. 15.95 *(978-0-7614-5681-0(3))* Marshall Cavendish Corp.
Scheiner, Joachim. Eine Stadt - Zwei Alltagswelten: Ein Beitrag zur Aktionsraumforschung & Wahrnehmungsgeographie im Vereinten Berlin. (GER., Illus.). xv, 334p. *(978-3-496-02702-7(9))* Reimer, Dietrich.
Uchimura, Kosuke, photos by. Kosuke Uchimura: Berlin & Tokyo, 1 vol. 2007. (JPN, GER & ENG., Illus.). 112p. 29.95 *(978-3-939633-05-1(4))* Jovis Verlag GmbH DEU. Dist: D.A.P./Distributed Art Pubs.

BERLIN, BATTLE OF, BERLIN, GERMANY, 1945

Anonymous. A Woman in Berlin: Eight Weeks in the Conquered City: A Diary. Boehm, Philip, tr. 2006. (ENG.). 288p. pap. 15.00 *(978-0-312-42611-8(9))* Picador.
Bartlett, Les & Jacobs, Peter. Bomb Aimer over Berlin: The Wartime Memoirs of les Bartlett. 2007. (Illus.). 224p. 39.95 *(978-1-84415-596-5(X))* Pen & Sword Bks. Ltd. GBR. Dist: Casemate Pubs. & Bk. Distributors, LLC.
Bernage, Georges. Berlin: L'agonie du Reich. 2010. (Illus.). 176p. 45.00 *(978-2-84048-262-8(2))* Editions Heimdal FRA. Dist: Casemate Pubs. & Bk. Distributors, LLC.
Le Tissier, Tony. The Battle of Berlin 1945. 2008. (ENG., Illus.). 288p. pap. 24.95 *(978-0-7524-4682-0(7))* History Pr. Ltd.,The GBR. Dist: Independent Pubs. Group.
—Zhukov at the Oder: The Decisive Battle for Berlin. 2009. (Military History Ser.). (ENG., Illus.). 384p. pap. 21.95 *(978-0-8117-3609-1(1))* Stackpole Bks.
—Zhukov at the Order: The Decisive Battle for Berlin. 2008. (ENG., Illus.). 288p. 37.95 *(978-0-7509-4838-8(8))* History Pr. Ltd.,The GBR. Dist: Independent Pubs. Group.
Mezhiritsky, Peter. Reading Marshal Zhukov: Stalin, Hitler & the Path to Barbarossa. 2011. (Illus.). 384p. 59.95 *(978-1-907677-25-0(9))* Helion & Co., Ltd. GBR. Dist: Casemate Pubs. & Bk. Distributors, LLC.
Middlebrook, Martin. The Bomber Battle for Berlin. 2010. (Illus.). 256p. 39.95 *(978-1-84884-224-3(4))* Pen & Sword Bks. Ltd. GBR. Dist: Casemate Pubs. & Bk. Distributors, LLC.
Ply'cyn, Alexander V. Penalty Strike: The Memoirs of a Red Army Penal Company Commander, 1943-45. 2008. (Stackpole Military History Ser.). (ENG., Illus.). 200p. pap. 18.95 *(978-0-8117-3599-5(0))* Stackpole Bks.
Tissier, Tony Le. Race for the Reichstag: The 1945 Battle for Berlin. 2010. (Illus.). 288p. pap. 29.95 *(978-1-84884-230-4(9))* Pen & Sword Bks. Ltd. GBR. Dist: Casemate Pubs. & Bk. Distributors, LLC.
Von Loringhoven, Bernd Freytag. In the Bunker with Hitler. 2008. (ENG.). 224p. pap. 14.95 *(978-1-60598-008-9(0),* 605008) Pegasus Bks.
Von Loringhoven, Bernd Freytag, et al. En el Bunker con Hitler. Irazazabal, Maria Pons, tr. 2007. 175p. 24.95 *(978-84-8432-856-8(2))* Critica Editorial ESP. Dist: Planeta Publishing Corp.

BERLIN QUESTION (1945-)

see Berlin (Germany)—History—1945-1990; Berlin (Germany)—Politics and Government—1945-1990

BERLIN WALL, BERLIN, GERMANY, 1961-1989

Ahonen, Pertti. Death at the Berlin Wall. 2011. (ENG.). 352p. 115.00 *(978-0-19-954630-5(4))* Oxford Univ. Pr., Inc.
brockman, beatrix. Vanderbilt Berlin Wall Project with ISBN. 2009. 95p. pap. 6.80 *(978-0-557-10819-0(5))* Lulu Enterprises Inc.
Buckley, William F., Jr. The Fall of the Berlin Wall. 20th ed. 2009. (Turning Points in History Ser.: 20). (ENG.). 240p. pap. 14.95 *(978-0-470-49668-8(1),* Wiley) Wiley, John & Sons, Inc.
Cooper, Trevor. Who Goes There? A Challenge to Humanity. 2009. (Illus.). 124p. pap. 10.99 *(978-1-4389-8466-7(9))* AuthorHouse.
Daum, Andreas. Kennedy in Berlin. 2007. (Publications of the German Historical Institute). (ENG., Illus.). 406p. (C). 79.99 *(978-0-521-85824-3(0))* Cambridge Univ. Pr.
Daum, Andreas W. Kennedy in Berlin. Geyer, Dona, tr. from GER. 2007. (Publications of the German Historical Institute). (ENG., Illus.). 316p. per. 27.00 *(978-0-521-67497-3(2))* Cambridge Univ. Pr.
Diewald, Martin, et al, eds. After the Fall of the Wall: Life Courses in the Transformation of East Germany. 2006. (Studies in Social Inequality). (ENG., Illus.). 408p. 70.00 *(978-0-8047-5208-4(7))* Stanford Univ. Pr.
Engel, Jeffrey A., ed. The Fall of the Berlin Wall: The Revolutionary Legacy Of 1989, 1 vol. (ENG., Illus.). 208p. 2011. pap. 19.95 *(978-0-19-983244-6(7))* 2009. 27.95 *(978-0-19-538910-4(7))* Oxford Univ. Pr., Inc.
Fuehr, Wieland. The Berlin Wall & Inner-German Border. 2009. (ENG.). 192p. pap. 19.95 *(978-3-86568-414-1(9),* Art Stock Bks. Ltd/Csi) Continental Sales, Inc.
Galloway, David & Jocks, Heinz-Norbert, texts. Stephan Kaluza: the Invisible Wall. 2010. (ENG., Illus.). 352p. 75.00 *(978-3-8321-9237-2(9))* DuMont DEU. Dist: D.A.P./Distributed Art Pubs.
Gerstenberger, Katharina. After the Berlin Wall: Germany & Beyond. Braziel, Jana Evans & Gerstenberger, Katharina, eds. 2011. (ENG., Illus.). 304p. 90.00 *(978-0-230-11192-9(0))* Palgrave Macmillan.
Hertle, Hans-Hermann. Die Berliner Mauer / The Berlin Wall: Monument des Kalten Krieges -Monumente of the Cold War. 2008. (GER & ENG., Illus.). 334p. pap. 19.90 *(978-3-86153-463-1(0))* Ch.Links Verlag DEU. Dist: Casemate Pubs. & Bk. Distributors, LLC.
Hilton, Christopher. The Wall: The People's Story. 2011. (ENG., Illus.). 480p. pap. 19.95 *(978-0-7524-5833-5(7))* History Pr. Ltd.,The GBR. Dist: Independent Pubs. Group.
Kempe, Frederick. Berlin 1961: Kennedy, Khrushchev, & the Most Dangerous Place on Earth. (ENG.). 608p. (gr. 12). 2012. 16.00 ***(978-0-425-24594-1(2),*** Berkley Trade) 2011. (Illus.). 29.95 *(978-0-399-15729-5(8),* Putnam Adult) Penguin Group (USA) Inc.
Lucas, Ulleno. Berlino: La Libertà Oltre il Muro = Berlin: Freedom Beyond the Wall. 2010. (ENG & ITA., Illus.). 112p. pap. 45.00 *(978-88-6302-029-8(9))* Alinari (IDEA) ITA. Dist: Antique Collectors' Club.
Ludwig, Corinne Frauke. Consensus Building. 2010. 88p. pap. *(978-3-639-25813-4(4))* VDM Verlag Dr. Mueller e.K.
Major, Patrick. Behind the Berlin Wall: East Germany & the Frontiers of Power. 2010. (ENG., Illus.). 352p. 99.00 *(978-0-19-924328-0(X))* Oxford Univ. Pr., Inc.
Manghani, Sunil. Image Critique & the Fall of the Berlin Wall. 2008. (ENG., Illus.). 272p. pap. 40.00 *(978-1-84150-190-1(5))* Intellect, Ltd. GBR. Dist: Chicago Distribution Ctr.
Mesch, Claudia. Modern Art at the Berlin Wall: Demarcating Culture in the Cold War Germanys. 2009. (ENG., Illus.). 384p. 100.00 *(978-1-84511-808-2(1),* Tauris Academic Studies) I. B. Tauris & Co., Ltd. GBR. Dist: Macmillan.
Millar, Peter. 1989 the Berlin Wall: My Part in Its Downfall. 2010. (ENG., Illus.). 220p. pap. 24.95 *(978-1-906413-47-7(9))* Arcadia Bks. Ltd. GBR. Dist: Dufour Editions, Inc.
Pleshakov, Constantine. There Is No Freedom Without Bread! 1989 & the Civil War That Brought down Communism. 2010. (ENG.). 304p. pap. 18.00 *(978-0-312-65533-4(9))* Picador.
Ratnesar, Romesh. Tear down This Wall: A City, a President, & the Speech That Ended the Cold War. 2010. (ENG., Illus.). 240p. pap. 16.00 *(978-1-4165-5691-6(5))* Simon & Schuster.
Rivaz, Dominique de. The Never Ending Wall. 2009. (ENG., Illus.). 288p. *(978-3-7165-1580-8(9),* Benteli Verlags Ag Dist) Antique Collectors' Club.
Roberts, Andrew, intro. Postcards from Checkpoint Charlie: Images of the Berlin Wall. 2009. (Bodleian Library - Postcards From Ser.). (Illus.). 112p. 20.00 *(978-1-85124-322-8(4))* Bodleian Library GBR. Dist: Chicago Distribution Ctr.
Roggenbuch, Frank. Das Berliner Grenzgängerproblem: Verflechtung und Systemkonkurrenz vor dem Mauerbau. 2008. (Veröffentlichungen der Historischen Kommission zu Berlin Ser.).Tr. of Problem of Berlin's Cross-Border Commuters. Integration & Systemic Competition before the Building of the Berlin Wall. (GER.). XIII, 481p. 189.00 *(978-3-11-020344-8(8))* De Gruyter, Walter Inc.
Rottman, Gordon L. The Berlin Wall: And the Inner-German Border 1961-89. 2008. (Fortress Ser.). (ENG., Illus.). 64p. pap. 18.95 *(978-1-84603-193-9(1))* Osprey Publishing, Ltd. GBR. Dist: Random Hse., Inc.
Silberman, Marc. The German Wall: Fallout in Europe. Silberman, Marc, ed. 2011. (Studies in European Culture & History Ser.). (ENG., Illus.). 274p. 90.00 *(978-0-230-11216-2(1))* Palgrave Macmillan.
Smyser, W. R. Kennedy & the Berlin Wall: A Hell of a Lot Better Than a War. (ENG.). 256p. 2010. pap. 17.95 *(978-0-7425-6091-8(0))* 2009. (Illus.). 39.95 *(978-0-7425-6090-1(2))* Rowman & Littlefield Publishers, Inc.
Taylor, Frederick. The Berlin Wall: A World Divided, 1961-1989. (Illus.). 2008. (ENG.). 528p. pap. 15.99 *(978-0-06-078614-4(0),* HarperPerennial) 2007. 512p. 27.95 *(978-0-06-078613-7(2))* HarperCollins Pubs.
Verheyen, Dirk. United City, Divided Memories? Cold War Legacies in Contemporary Berlin. 2008. (ENG., Illus.). 320p. 83.99 *(978-0-7391-1839-9(0))* Lexington Bks.
—United City Divided Memories? Cold War Legacies in Contemporary Berlin. 2010. (ENG.). 320p. pap. 36.99 *(978-0-7391-1840-5(4))* Lexington Bks.
Williamson, Richard. First Steps Toward Detente: American Diplomacy in the Berlin Crisis, 1958-1963. 2012. ***(978-0-7391-6880-6(0))*** Lexington Bks.

BERLIOZ, HECTOR, 1803-1869

Albright, Daniel. Berlioz, Verdi, Wagner, Britten: Great Shakespeareans. Albright, Daniel, ed. 2012. (Great Shakespeareans Ser.). (ENG.). 256p. 140.00 *(978-1-4411-7909-8(7))* Continuum International Publishing Group, Ltd. GBR. Dist: National Bk. Network.
Berlioz. Berlioz's Orchestration Treatise: A Translation & Commentary. Macdonald, Hugh, ed. 2007. (Cambridge Musical Texts & Monographs). (ENG., Illus.). 432p. pap. 87.00 *(978-0-521-03611-5(9))* Cambridge Univ. Pr.
Berlioz, Hector & Bernard, Daniel. Life & Letters of Berlioz. Dunstan, H. Mainwaring, tr. 2010. (Cambridge Library Collection - Music Ser.). (ENG.). 332p. pap. 28.99 *(978-1-108-02118-0(2));* 418p. pap. 31.99 *(978-1-108-02117-3(4))* Cambridge Univ. Pr.
Bloom, Peter, ed. Berlioz: Scenes from the Life & Work. 2008. (Eastman Studies in Music Ser.: Volume 52). (Illus.). 267p. 75.00 *(978-1-58046-209-9(X))* Univ. of Rochester Pr.
—Berlioz Studies. 2006. (Cambridge Composer Studies). (ENG., Illus.). 300p. pap. 61.00 *(978-0-521-02856-1(6))* Cambridge Univ. Pr.
Boult, Katharine F., tr. from FRE. The Life, As Written by Himself in His Letters & Memoirs. reprint ed. 37.50 *(978-0-404-12865-4(3))* AMS Pr., Inc.
Charlton, David & Ellis, Katharine, eds. The Musical Voyager: Berlioz in Europe. 2007. (Perspektiven der OPernforschung Ser.: Vol. 14). (Illus.). xviii, 320p. pap. *(978-0-8204-9942-0(0))* Lang, Peter AG.
Closson, Ernest, tr. Le Traite d'Orchestration d'Hector Berlioz. reprint ed. 34.50 *(978-0-404-13104-3(2))* AMS Pr., Inc.
The Conductor: The Theory of His Art. (Works of Hector Berlioz). reprint ed. lib. bdg. 59.00 *(978-0-7812-0737-9(1))* Reprint Services Co.
Currie, Norman. Robert Schumann, Hector Berlioz, & Their Publishers. 2009. 312p. pap. *(978-3-639-14092-7(3))* VDM Verlag Dr. Mueller e.K.
Hueffer, Francis. Half a Century of Music in England, 1837-1887: Essays Towards a History. 2009. (Cambridge Library Collection - Music Ser.). (ENG.). 260p. pap. 23.99 *(978-1-108-00472-5(5))* Cambridge Univ. Pr.
Mason, Daniel G. Romantic Composers. reprint ed. 29.50 *(978-0-404-04223-3(6))* AMS Pr., Inc.
Masson, Paul M. Berlioz. reprint ed. 29.50 *(978-0-404-13037-4(2))* AMS Pr., Inc.
Rodgers, Stephen. Form, Program, & Metaphor in the Music of Berlioz. 2009. (ENG., Illus.). 200p. 98.00 *(978-0-521-88404-4(7))* Cambridge Univ. Pr.
Rushton, Julian. The Musical Language of Berlioz. 2008. (Cambridge Studies in Music Ser.). (ENG.). 320p. pap. 42.00 *(978-0-521-08214-3(5))* Cambridge Univ. Pr.
Saloman, Ora Frishberg. Listening Well: On Beethoven, Berlioz, & Other Music Criticism in Paris, Boston, & New York, 1764-1890. 2009. (Illus.). 270p. (C). 75.95 *(978-1-4331-0357-5(5))* Lang, Peter Publishing, Inc.
Staatsoper Stuttgart & Zuber, Xavier, eds. Berlioz' Troyens und Halévys Juive im Spiegel der Grand Opéra. 2011. (GER., Illus.). 142p. (C). pap. 34.00 *(978-3-515-09859-5(3))* Steiner, Franz Verlag Wiesbaden GmbH DEU. Dist: Brown, David Bk. Co., The.

BERMUDA ISLANDS

Ayton, Mel. Assault on Law & Order in Bermuda, 1972-1973: The Assassination of Governor Sir Richard Sharples & the Related Killings. 2010. (ENG., Illus.). pap. 45.00 *(978-0-7864-4881-4(4))* McFarland & Co., Inc. Pubs.
Bernhard, Virginia. A Tale of Two Colonies: What Really Happened in Virginia & Bermuda? 2011. (ENG., Illus.). 232p. (gr. 7). 29.95 *(978-0-8262-1951-0(9))* Univ. of Missouri Pr.
Brown III, Marley R. & Fortenberry, Brent, eds. Bermuda: Celebrating 400 Years of History. 2011. (Post-Medieval Archaeology Ser.). (ENG.). 235p. (C). pap. 51.00 ***(978-1-907975-19-6(5))*** Maney Publishing GBR. Dist: Brown, David Bk. Co., The.
Glover, Lorri & Smith, Daniel Blake. The Shipwreck That Saved Jamestown: The Sea Venture Castaways & the Fate of America. 2009. (ENG., Illus.). 336p. pap. 16.99 *(978-0-8050-9025-3(8),* Holt Paperback) Holt, Henry & Co.
Icon Group International, Inc. Staff, compiled by. The 2006 Economic & Product Market Databook for Saint George, Bermuda. 2006. 618p. ring bd. 95.00 *(978-0-497-81225-6(8))* Icon Group International, Inc.
Jarvis, Michael. In the Eye of All Trade: Bermuda, Bermudians, & the Maritime Atlantic World, 1680-1783. 2010. (Published for the Omohundro Institute of Early American History & Culture, Williamsburg, Virginia Ser.). (ENG., Illus.). 688p. 65.00 *(978-0-8078-3321-6(5))* Univ. of North Carolina Pr.
Lefroy, J. Henry, ed. Historye of the Bermudaes or Summer Islands: Edited from a MS. in the Sloane Collection, British Museum. 2010. (Cambridge Library Collection - Travel & Exploration Ser.). (Illus.). 360p. pap. 29.99 *(978-1-108-01157-0(8))* Cambridge Univ. Pr.
Nausbaum, Donald. Bermuda. 2008. (ENG.). 184p. 50.00 *(978-1-4050-9487-0(7))* Macmillan Caribbean GBR. Dist: Interlink Publishing Group, Inc.
Spurling, Stanley. Sir Thomas Smythe: Governor of the East. 2006. pap. 16.95 *(978-1-4286-5802-8(5))* Kessinger Publishing, LLC.
Swan, Quito. Black Power in Bermuda: The Struggle for Decolonization. 2010. (Contemporary Black History Ser.). (ENG., Illus.). 262p. pap. 31.00 *(978-0-230-10958-2(6))* Palgrave Macmillan.

BERMUDA ISLANDS—DESCRIPTION AND TRAVEL

Baarvig, Haldor Marius Ingemann & Clark, Lis. $50 in My Pocket: I'm off to See America: An Historical Memoir. 2009. (Illus.). ix, 221p. E-Book *(978-1-4490-5563-6(6))* AuthorHouse.

Charles, Ron. Open Road's Best of Bermuda. 2009. (ENG.). 224p. pap. 14.95 *(978-1-59360-120-1(4))* Open Road Publishing.

Clark, Lis. $50 in My Pocket: I'm off to See America. 2009. 232p. 25.99 *(978-1-4490-5564-3(4))*; pap. 14.95 *(978-1-4490-5665-0(2))* AuthorHouse.

Fodor's Travel Publications, Inc. Staff. Bermuda. Moker, Molly, ed. 2008. (Pocket Guides). (ENG., Illus.). 192p. pap. 10.95 *(978-1-4000-0710-3(0)*, Fodor's) Fodor's Travel Pubns.

—Fodor's Bermuda 2012. 31st ed. 2011. (Fodor's Gold Guides). (ENG.). 240p. pap. 17.99 *(978-0-679-00957-3(4)*, Fodor's) Fodor's Travel Pubns.

Hawks, John K. Bermuda: A Complete Guide. 2009. (Great Destinations Ser.). 320p. pap. 18.95 *(978-1-58157-092-2(9))* Countryman Pr.

Howard, Blair. Adventure Guide to Bermuda. 3rd ed. (Hunter Publishing Adventure Guides). (Illus.). 240p. pap. 18.99 *(978-1-58843-392-3(7))* Hunter Publishing, Inc.

—Bermuda Adventure Guide. 4th rev. ed. 2008. (Illus.). 256p. pap. 16.99 *(978-1-58843-663-4(2))* Hunter Publishing, Inc.

Johansens, creator. Conde Nast Johansens the Americas: Atlantic, Caribbean & Pacific. 2007. (Recommended Hotels, Inns, Resorts, & Spas-the Americas, Atlantic, Caribbean & Pacific Ser.). (Illus.). 448p. per. 36.00 *(978-1-903665-36-7(1))* Conde Nast Johansens Ltd. GBR. Dist: Casemate Pubs. & Bk. Distributors, LLC.

Jones, Rosemary. Moon Bermuda. 2009. (Moon Handbooks). (ENG., Illus.). 360p. pap. 17.95 *(978-1-59880-178-1(3))* Avalon Travel Publishing.

Markle, Dave. Ruminations & Rumblings of A Rambling Sailor. 2011. 112p. pap. 12.00 ***(978-1-4634-1120-6(0))*** AuthorHouse.

Pearson, Amy K. Coastal Bermuda 10 Walks & 73 Plants... you'll see along the Way. 2008. (Illus.). 103p. pap. 19.95 *(978-0-615-20530-4(5))* BioQuill Publishing Co.

Philpott, Don. Landmark Visitors Guide Bermuda. 2nd rev. ed. 2007. (Landmark Visitors Guide Bermuda Ser.). (Illus.). 128p. per. 13.95 *(978-1-84306-102-1(3))* Hunter Publishing, Inc.

Porter, Darwin & Prince, Danforth. Frommer's Bermuda 2012. 7th ed. 2011. (Frommer's Complete Guides). (ENG., Illus.). 224p. pap. 18.99 *(978-1-118-00428-9(0)*, Frommers) Wiley, John & Sons, Inc.

Pory, John. John Pory's Lost Description of Plymouth Colony in the Earliest Days of the Pilgrim Fathers: Together with Contemporary Accounts of English Colonization Elsewhere in New England & in the Bermudas. 65p. reprint ed. 88.00 *(978-0-7222-6650-2(2))* Library Reprints, Inc.

Recommended Hotels/Inns in America 2007. 2007. (Illus.). 436p. pap. 35.00 *(978-1-903665-31-2(0))* Conde Nast Johansens Ltd. GBR. Dist: Casemate Pubs. & Bk. Distributors, LLC.

Warren, Andrew. Condé Nast Johansens the Americas Atlantic Caribbean & Pacific: Recommended Hotels Inns Resorts & Spas 2009. 2008. (Illus.). 452p. pap. 25.00 *(978-1-903665-42-8(6))* Conde Nast Johansens Ltd. GBR. Dist: Casemate Pubs. & Bk. Distributors, LLC.

BERMUDA TRIANGLE

Barnes, Tom. The Hurricane Hunters & Lost in the Bermuda Triangle. 2007. 132p. per. 12.95 *(978-0-595-45325-2(2))* iUniverse, Inc.

Iturralde, Robert. The Ufo Phenomenon & the Birth of the Jewish, Christian, & Muslim Religions. 2009. 332p. pap. 17.99 *(978-1-4389-7570-2(8))* AuthorHouse.

Johnson, George. Biblia y Triangulo Mortal Bermudas: Bible & the Bermuda Triangle. (SPA.). 208p. *(978-84-7228-470-8(0)*, 360075) Clie, Editorial.

Shumway, Vivian E. & Rosenberg, Aaron. Searching for the Bermuda Triangle. 2011. pap. 12.95 *(978-1-4488-4771-6(0)*, Rosen Central); 77.70 ***(978-1-4488-4779-2(6)**, Rosen Central)*; (YA). (gr. 5-9). lib. bdg. 30.60 *(978-1-4488-4759-4(1))* Rosen Publishing Group, Inc., The.

BERN (SWITZERLAND)—DESCRIPTION AND TRAVEL

Huber, Werner. Building Bern: A Guide to Contemporary Architecture, 1990-2010. 2010. (Verlag Scheidegger & Spiess-Edition Hochparterre at Scheidegger & Spiess Ser.). (Illus.). 240p. pap. 45.00 *(978-3-85881-722-8(8))* Scheidegger und Spiess AG, Verlag CHE. Dist: Antique Collectors' Club.

BERNADETTE, SAINT, 1844-1879

Ficocelli, Elizabeth. Lourdes: Font of Faith, Hope, & Charity. 2007. (Illus.). 181p. per. 16.95 *(978-0-8091-4486-0(7)*, 4486-0) Paulist Pr.

Harris, Ruth. Lourdes: Body & Spirit in the Secular Age. 2008. (ENG., Illus.). 496p. (gr. 12-18). 30.00 *(978-0-14-103848-3(9)*, Penguin Global) Penguin Group (USA) Inc.

Lasserre, Henry. Our Lady of Lourdes. 2007. (ENG.). 500p. 53.95 *(978-0-548-09711-3(9))* Kessinger Publishing, LLC.

O. Floinn, Criostoir. The One Who Saw Visions - Bernadette Soubirous. 2010. (Three French Saints Ser.). (ENG.). 139p. pap. 18.95 *(978-1-85607-659-3(8))* Columba Pr. IRL. Dist: Dufour Editions, Inc.

Perrier, Jacques. Lourdes Today & Tomorrow. 2008. (Contemporary Spirituality Ser.). 176p. pap. 14.95 *(978-1-56548-305-7(7))* New City Pr.

Taylor, Thérèse & Taylor. Bernadette of Lourdes: Her life, death & visions: new anniversary Edition. 2nd rev. ed. 2008. (ENG., Illus.). 372p. 19.95 *(978-0-8264-2085-5(0)*, Burns & Oates) Continuum International Publishing Group, Ltd. GBR. Dist: National Bk. Network.

Tricker, Greg. Bernadette of Lourdes: The Mystery of Mary & the Eternal Feminine. 2008. (Illus.). 144p. 40.00 *(978-1-903470-88-6(9))* Holberton, Paul Publishing GBR. Dist: Casemate Pubs. & Bk. Distributors, LLC.

BERNADOTTE, CARL JOHAN, 1763-1844

see Charles XIV John, King of Sweden and Norway, 1763-1844

BERNANOS, GEORGE, 1888-1948

Maubrey, Pierre. L Expression de la Passion Interieure dans le Style de Bernanos Romancier. (Catholic University of America, Studies in Romance Languages & Literatures: No. 59). (FRE.). reprint ed. 37.50 *(978-0-404-50359-8(4))* AMS Pr., Inc.

Tobin, Michael Robinson. Georges Bernanos: The Theological Source of His Art. 2007. (ENG.). 236p. (C). *(978-0-7735-3232-8(3))* McGill-Queen's Univ. Pr.

BERNARD, OF CLAIRVAUX, SAINT, 1090 OR 91-1153

Bernard of Clairvaux Staff. Honey & Salt: Selected Spiritual Writings of Bernard of Clairvaux. Thornton, John F. & Varenne, Susan B., eds. 2007. (Vintage Spiritual Classics Ser.). 496p. per. 13.95 *(978-0-375-72565-4(2)*, Vintage) Knopf Doubleday Publishing Group.

Bruun, Mette B. Parables: Bernard of Clairvaux's Mapping of Spiritual Topography. 2006. (Brill's Studies in Intellectual History: Vol. 148). 344p. *(978-90-04-15503-9(1))* BRILL.

Coulton, G. G. Two Saints: St Bernard & St Francis. 2012. (ENG., Illus.). 140p. pap. 24.00 ***(978-1-107-63323-0(0))*** Cambridge Univ. Pr.

Daniel, E. Randolph. Abbot Joachim of Fiore & Joachimism: Selected Articles. 2011. (Variorum Collected Studies). (Illus.). 374p. 154.95 *(978-1-4094-2401-7(4))* Ashgate Publishing Co.

France, James. Medieval Images of Saint Bernard of Clairvaux. 2007. (Cistercian Studies). (Illus.). 435p. pap. 49.95 incl. cd-rom *(978-0-87907-310-7(1)*, CS210P) Cistercian Pubns., Inc.

Greenia, Conrad & McCaffery, Hugh, eds. Bernard of Clairvaux: Miscellaneous Sermons (Sermones de diversis) 2007. pap. 24.99 *(978-0-87907-468-5(X))* Cistercian Pubns., Inc.

Greenia, Conrad & McCaffery, Hugh, trs. Bernard of Clairvaux: Sermones De Diversis/Occasional Sermons. 2007. (Cistercian Fathers Ser.). 240p. 23.99 *(978-0-87907-168-4(0))* Cistercian Pubns., Inc.

McCabe, Maureen F. I Am the Way: Stages of Prayer in Saint Bernard. 2012. ***(978-0-87907-028-1(5))***; E-Book ***(978-0-87907-476-0(0))*** Cistercian Pubns., Inc.

Ngien, Dennis. Gifted Response: The Triune God as the Causative Agency of our Responsive Worship. 2008. (ENG.). 200p. 29.99 *(978-1-84227-610-5(7)*, Paternoster) Authentic Media.

Posset, Branz & Posset, Franz. The Real Luther: A Friar at Erfurt & Wittenberg - Exploring Luther's Life with Melanchthon As Guide. 2011. pap. 39.99 *(978-0-7586-2685-1(1))* Concordia Publishing Hse.

Raymond, M. The Family that Overtook Christ: The amazing story of the family of Bernard of Clairvaux. 2008. 392p. (YA). pap. 22.95 *(978-1-933871-20-2(2))* IVE Pr.

BERNARD, CLAUDE, 1813-1878

Bergson, Henri. The Creative Mind: An Introduction to Metaphysics. Andison, Mabelle L., tr. from FRE. 2010. (Dover Books on Western Philosophy Ser.). (ENG.). 240p. per. 11.95 *(978-0-486-45439-9(8))* Dover Pubns., Inc.

Hirst, Paul Q. Durkheim, Bernard & Epistemology. 2010. (Routledge Library Editions: Emile Durkheim Ser.). (ENG.). 224p. 105.00 *(978-0-415-56349-9(6))* Routledge.

BERNARDIN DE SAINT-PIERRE, JACQUES HENRI, 1737-1814

Howells, R.J. Regressive Fictions. 2007. (Legenda Main Ser.). 200p. (C). 79.50 *(978-1-904350-86-6(0))* European Humanities Research Ctr. GBR. Dist: Brown, David Bk. Co., The.

BERNARDINO DA SIENA, SAINT, 1380-1444

Allies, Mary H. Three Catholic Reformers of the Fifteenth Century. 2010. (Illus.). 90p. pap. 14.84 *(978-1-154-87131-9(2))* General Bks. LLC.

BERNESE MOUNTAIN DOG

Kihn, Martin. Bad Dog: A Love Story. 2011. (ENG., Illus.). 224p. 23.95 *(978-0-307-37915-3(9)*, Pantheon) Knopf Doubleday Publishing Group.

Kihn, Martin. Bad Dog: (A Love Story) 2012. (Vintage Ser.). (ENG.). 224p. pap. 14.95 ***(978-0-307-47746-0(0)**, Vintage)* Knopf Doubleday Publishing Group.

Rehkopf, Linda. Bernese Mountain Dog. 2012. (Illus.). 141p. ***(978-0-7938-4184-4(4))*** TFH Pubns., Inc.

Riggsbee, Nikki. Bernese Mountain Dogs: Everything about Purchase, Care, Nutrition, Behavior & Training. 2nd rev. ed. 2007. (Complete Pet Owner's Manual Ser.). (ENG., Illus.). 96p. pap. 8.99 *(978-0-7641-3592-7(9))* Barron's Educational Series, Inc.

Swann, Barbara. The Complete Border Collie. (Illus.). 96p. tchr. ed. 24.95 *(978-0-948955-94-5(5)*, INT040) Ringpress Bks., Ltd. GBR. Dist: TFH Pubns., Inc.

BERNHARDT, SARAH, 1844-1923

Arthur, George. Sarah Bernhardt. 2008. 192p. *(978-1-4437-4068-5(3)*, Obscure Pr.) Read Bks.

Bernhardt, Lysiane S. Sarah Bernhardt, My Grandmother. Holland, Vyvyan, tr. reprint ed. 26.50 *(978-0-404-18365-3(4))* AMS Pr., Inc.

Bernhardt, Sarah. Memories of My Life: Being My Personal, Professional & Social. 2007. pap. 37.95 *(978-1-4304-8099-0(8))* Kessinger Publishing, LLC.

—My Double Life. 2008. 504p. 31.99 *(978-0-554-32246-3(X))*; 33.99 *(978-0-554-22945-4(5))* BiblioBazaar.

Gottlieb, Robert. Sarah: The Life of Sarah Bernhardt. 2010. (Jewish Lives Ser.). (ENG., Illus.). 256p. 25.00 *(978-0-300-14127-6(0))* Yale Univ. Pr.

Menefee, David W. Sarah Bernhardt in the Theatre of Films & Sound Recordings. alt. ed. 2008. (FRE & ENG., Illus.). 168p. pap. 35.00 *(978-0-7864-3882-2(7))* McFarland & Co., Inc. Pubs.

Row, Arthur William. Sarah the Divine: A Biography of Sarah Bernhardt. 2011. 190p. 42.95 ***(978-1-258-09640-3(4))*** Literary Licensing, LLC.

BERNHEIM, MOLLY

Bernheim, Molly. A Sky of My Own. 2011. 252p. 46.95 ***(978-1-258-01352-3(5))*** Literary Licensing, LLC.

BERNIER, JOSEPH ELZEAR, 1852-1936

Saint-Pierre, Marjolaine. Joseph-Elzar Bernier 1852-1934: Champion of Canadian Arctic Sovereignty. Barr, William, tr. from FRE. 2009. (ENG., Illus.). 372p. 70.00 *(978-0-9812405-4-1(2))*; pap. 37.95 *(978-0-9812405-1-0(8))* Baraka Bks. CAN. Dist: Independent Pubs. Group.

BERNINI, GIOVANNI LORENZO, 1598-1680

Avery, Charles. Bernini: Genius of the Baroque. 2006. (ENG., Illus.). 288p. pap. 44.95 *(978-0-500-28633-3(7))* Thames & Hudson.

Bacchi, Andrea. Bernini & the Birth of Baroque Portrait Sculpture. Hess, Catherine et al, eds. 2008. (Illus.). 336p. 70.00 *(978-0-89236-931-7(0))* Oxford Univ. Pr., Inc.

Brooks, Julian & Franklin, David. Bernini & the Birth of Baroque Portrait Sculpture. Bacchi, Andrea et al, eds. 2008. (Illus.). 336p. pap. 44.95 *(978-0-89236-932-4(9))* Oxford Univ. Pr., Inc.

Lehmann, Claudia. Un pien teatro di Meraviglie: Gian Lorenzo Bernini vor dem Hintergrund konzeptischer Emblematik. 2010. (Neue Berner Schriften zur Kunst Ser.). (GER, LAT, ITA & FRE., Illus.). 231p. pap. *(978-3-0343-0361-3(0))* Lang, Peter.

Levy, Evonne, et al, eds. Bernini's Biographies: Critical Essays. 2007. (ENG., Illus.). 376p. 65.00 *(978-0-271-02901-6(3))* Pennsylvania State Univ. Pr.

—Bernini's Biographies: Critical Essays. 2007. (ENG., Illus.). 376p. pap. 35.00 *(978-0-271-02902-3(1))* Pennsylvania State Univ. Pr.

McPhee, Sarah. Bernini's Beloved: A Portrait of Costanza Piccolomini. 2012. (ENG., Illus.). 280p. 45.00 ***(978-0-300-17527-1(2))*** Yale Univ. Pr.

BERNOULLI, JAKOB, 1654-1705

Tent, M. B. W. Leonhard Euler & the Bernoullis: Mathematicians from Basel. 2009. (ENG., Illus.). 296p. 29.95 *(978-1-56881-464-3(X))* AK Peters, Ltd.

BERNSTEIN, EDUARD, 1850-1932

Luxemburg, Rosa. Reform or Revolution & the Mass Strike. 2007. 148p. 32.95 *(978-0-9793363-3-1(3))* Ellis, Frederick.

BERNSTEIN, LEONARD, 1918-1990

Bernstein, Burton & Haws, Barbara B. Leonard Bernstein: American Original. 2008. (Illus.). 240p. 29.95 *(978-0-06-153786-8(1))* HarperCollins Pubs.

Bernstein, Leonard. Leonard Bernstein - Art Songs & Arias: Medium/Low Voice. 2007. (ENG.). 192p. pap. 21.99 *(978-1-4234-2860-2(9)*, 1423428609) Boosey & Hawkes, Inc.

Bloomaert, Jan. Bernstein & Poetics Revisited. 2008. (Professorial Lectures). (ENG., Illus.). 40p. (C). pap. 9.95 *(978-0-85473-791-8(X))* Institute of Education GBR. Dist: Stylus Publishing, LLC.

Gottlieb, Jack. Working with Bernstein: A Memoir. 2010. (ENG.). 372p. 24.99 *(978-1-57467-186-5(3)*, 1574671863, Amadeus Press) Leonard, Hal Corp.

Hurwitz, David. Bernstein's Orchestral Music - an Owner's Manual: Unlocking the Masters Series, No. 22. 2011. (ENG.). 136p. pap. 24.99 incl. audio compact disk *(978-1-57467-193-3(6)*, 1574671936, Amadeus Press) Leonard, Hal Corp.

Laird, Paul R. & Budds, Michael J. The Chichester Psalms of Leonard Bernstein. 2009. (Illus.). 255p. *(978-1-57647-152-4(7))* Pendragon Pr.

Oja, Carol J. Leonard Bernstein. 2009. (Yale Broadway Masters Ser.). 256p. 35.00 *(978-0-300-11508-6(3))* Yale Univ. Pr.

Seldes, Barry & Seldes, B. Leonard Bernstein: The Political Life of an American Musician. 2009. (ENG., Illus.). 288p. 35.00 *(978-0-520-25764-1(2))* Univ. of California Pr.

Sherman, Steve J. Leonard Bernstein at Work: His Final Years, 1984-1990. 2010. (ENG., Illus.). 192p. 34.99 *(978-1-57467-190-2(1)*, 1574671901, Amadeus Press) Leonard, Hal Corp.

Simeone, Nigel. Leonard Bernstein: West Side Story. 2009. (Landmarks in Music since 1950 Ser.). (Illus.). 192p. 64.95 *(978-0-7546-6484-0(8))* Ashgate Publishing Co.

Smith, Helen. There's A Place for Us: The Musical Theatre Works of Leonard Bernstein. 2011. (Illus.). 318p. 99.95 ***(978-1-4094-1169-7(9))*** Ashgate Publishing Co.

Walters, Richard, ed. Leonard Bernstein - Art Songs & Arias: High Voice. 2007. (ENG.). 152p. pap. 21.99 *(978-1-4234-2753-7(X)*, 142342753X) Boosey & Hawkes, Inc.

Wells, Elizabeth A. West Side Story: Cultural Perspectives on an American Musical. 2010. (ENG., Illus.). 326p. (gr. 17). 39.95 *(978-0-8108-7666-8(3))* Scarecrow Pr., Inc.

BERNSTEIN POLYNOMIALS

Gal, Sorin G. Approximation by Complex Bernstein & Convolution Type Operators, Vol. 8. 2009. (Series on Concrete & Applicable Mathematics: Vol. 8). 352p. 107.00 *(978-981-4282-42-0(1))* World Scientific Publishing Co., Inc.

—Shape-Preserving Approximation by Real & Complex Polynomials. 2008. xiii, 352p. E-Book *(978-0-8176-4703-2(1))* Birkhauser Verlag AG.

—Shape-Preserving Approximation by Real & Complex Polynomials. 2008. 344p. 89.95 *(978-0-8176-4702-5(3)*, 0817647023) Springer.

BERRA, LAWRENCE PETER, 1925-

see Berra, Yogi, 1925-

BERRA, YOGI, 1925-

Araton, Harvey. Driving Mr. Yogi: Yogi Berra, Ron Guidry, & Baseball's Greatest Gift. 2012. (ENG., Illus.). 240p. 26.00 ***(978-0-547-74672-2(5))*** Houghton Mifflin Harcourt Trade & Reference Pubs.

—Driving Mr. Yogi: Yogi Berra, Ron Guidry, & Baseball's Greatest Gift. l.t. ed. 2012. (ENG.). 32.99 ***(978-1-4104-4733-3(2))*** Thorndike Pr.

Barra, Allen. Yogi Berra: Eternal Yankee. (ENG.). 2010. 451p. pap. 16.95 *(978-0-393-33714-3(6)*, 33714) 2009. (Illus.). 480p. 27.95 *(978-0-393-06233-5(3)*, 6233) Norton, W. W. & Co., Inc.

—Yogi Berra: Eternal Yankee. l.t. ed. 2009. 747p. 31.50 ***(978-1-4104-1561-5(9))*** Thorndike Pr.

Berra, Yogi. Ten Rings: My Championship Seasons. 2008. (ENG.). 223p. pap. 14.00 *(978-1-4379-5180-6(5))* DIANE Publishing Co.

—The Yogi Book: I Really Didn't Say Everything I Said! pap. 89.50 *(978-0-7611-1316-4(9)*, 21316) Workman Publishing Co., Inc.

—The Yogi Book: "I Really Didn't Say Everything I Said" 2010. (ENG., Illus.). 175p. pap. 8.95 *(978-0-7611-5443-3(4)*, 0761154434) Workman Publishing Co., Inc.

—You Can Observe a Lot by Watching: What I've Learned about Teamwork from the Yankees & Life. (ENG., Illus.). 240p. 2009. pap. 14.95 *(978-0-470-45404-6(0))* 2008. 24.95 *(978-0-470-07992-8(4))* Wiley, John & Sons, Inc. (Wiley).

Berra, Yogi & Kaplan, Dave. Ten Rings: My Championship Seasons. 2006. (Illus.). 223p. reprint ed. 25.00 *(978-1-4223-5145-1(9))* DIANE Publishing Co.

DeVito, Carlo. Yogi: The Life & Times of an American Original. 2008. (ENG., Illus.). 400p. 25.95 *(978-1-57243-945-0(9))* Triumph Bks.

BERRIES

Bird, Richard & Whiteman, Kate. How to Grow Berries & Currants: A Practical Gardening Guide for Great Results, with Step-By-Step Techniques & 185 Colour Photographs. 2011. (ENG., Illus.). 64p. pap. 12.99 *(978-1-84476-944-5(5))* Anness Publishing GBR. Dist: National Bk. Network.

Folta, Kevin M. & Kole, Chittaranjan, eds. Genetics, Genomics & Breeding of Berries. 2011. (ENG., Illus.). 200p. 99.95 *(978-1-57808-707-5(4))* BIOS Scientific Publishers Ltd. GBR. Dist: Taylor & Francis Group.

Fuller, Andrew Samuel. The Small Fruit Culturist. 2008. (Gardening in America Ser.). (ENG.). 292p. pap. 18.95 *(978-1-4290-1317-8(6))* Applewood Bks.

—The Small Fruit Culturist. 2009. 304p. 25.99 *(978-1-103-72751-3(6))*; pap. 19.99 *(978-1-103-72750-6(8))* BiblioBazaar.

—The Small Fruit Culturist. 2008. 288p. 43.95 *(978-1-4366-0935-7(6))*; (ENG.). 292p. per. 28.95 *(978-0-548-81543-4(7))* Kessinger Publishing, LLC.

Gardezi, Syed Dilnawaz & Arif, Shazia. Comparisons of Few Important Bio-Chemicals from Sea Buckthorn. 2010. 76p. pap. *(978-3-8383-8337-8(0))* Lambert Academic Publishing.

Gault, Karen Szklany. The Complete Guide to Growing Your Own Fruits & Berries: Everything You Need to Know Explained Simply. 2010. 288p. pap. 24.95 *(978-1-60138-348-8(7))* Atlantic Publishing Co.

Haynes, Thomas & Thomas Haynes, Haynes. A Treatise on the Improved Culture of the Strawberry, Raspberry, & Gooseberry. 2009. (Gardening in America Ser.). (ENG.). 116p. pap. 10.95 *(978-1-4290-1343-7(5))* Applewood Bks.

Hester, Stephanie & Hester, Alex. The Huckleberry Cookbook. 2008. (ENG., Illus.). 128p. 14.95 *(978-0-7627-4795-5(1))* Three Forks Pr.

Hibler, Janie. Berry Bible: With 175 Recipes Using Cultivated & Wild, Fresh & Frozen Berries, 0 vols. unabr. ed. 2010. (ENG.). 352p. pap. 17.95 *(978-1-935597-12-4(4)*, 9781935597124) AmazonEncore.

Hills, William. Small Fruits. 2008. (Gardening in America Ser.). (ENG.). 140p. pap. 11.95 *(978-1-4290-1283-6(8))* Applewood Bks.

Hood, Karen Jean Matsko. Huckleberry Delights Cookbook: A Collection of Huckleberry Recipes. 2008. 320p. pap. 21.95 *(978-1-59649-386-5(0))* 2010. (ENG.). 326p. 29.95 *(978-1-59434-764-1(6))* Whispering Pine Pr. International, Inc.

Manning, Robert. The New England Fruit Book. Ives, John, ed. 2009. (Gardening in America Ser.). (ENG.). 144p. pap. 11.95 *(978-1-4290-1413-7(X))* Applewood Bks.

Matsko Hood, Karen Jean. Huckleberry Delights Cookbook: A Collection of Huckleberry Recipes. 2010. (ENG.). 326p. per. 19.95 *(978-1-59649-385-8(2))*; ring bd. 29.95 *(978-1-59210-507-6(6))*; pap. 29.95 *(978-1-59434-763-4(8))* Whispering Pine Pr. International, Inc.

Merritt, Christopher & Lynxwiler, J. Eric. Knott's Preserved: From Boysenberry to Theme Park: The History of Knott's Berry Farm. 2010. *(978-1-883318-77-2(7))*; *(978-1-883318-97-0(1))* Angel City Pr.

Nagel, Markus Peter. Wild berries in the Estonian food industry: Products, Importance, Potential. 2008. 80p. pap. *(978-3-639-10991-7(0))* VDM Verlag Dr. Mueller e.K.

Phillips, Michael. The Holistic Orchard: Tree Fruits & Berries the Biological Way. 2011. E-Book ***(978-1-60358-407-4(2))*** Chelsea Green Publishing.

Ramadan Hassanien, Mohamed Fawzy. Goldenberry: Golden Fruit of Golden Future. 2008. 100p. pap. *(978-3-8364-9489-2(2))* VDM Verlag Dr. Mueller e.K.

Roe, E. P. Success with Small Fruits. 2008. (ENG.). 292p. per. *(978-1-4065-6713-7(2))* Dodo Pr.

—Success with Small Fruits. 2007. (ENG.). 224p. per. *(978-1-4068-3990-6(6))* Echo Library.

Seeram, Navindra P. & Stoner, Gary D., eds. Berries & Cancer Prevention. 2010. (ENG., Illus.). xi, 313p. 189.00 *(978-1-4419-7553-9(5)*, 1441975535) Springer.

Shipman, Carol Ann. Alaska Berries Cookbook, Vol. 2. (Nature's Gourmet Ser.). (Illus.). 96p. pap. 10.95 *(978-0-88839-582-5(5))* Hancock Hse. Pubs.

Sukhorukikh, IU I. Lesnye Plodovye Vidy Severo-Zapadnogo Kavkaza: V Trekh Knigakh. 2010. (RUS., Illus.). *(978-5-9703-0267-5(8))* Kacestvo.

Tuberoso, Carlo. Berries: Properties, Consumption & Nutrition. 2012. (Food & Beverage Consumption & Health Ser.). 234p. 95.00 ***(978-1-61470-257-3(8))*** Nova Science Pubs., Inc.

Whealy, Kent. Fruit, Berry & Nut Inventory, 4th Edition: An Inventory of Nursery Catalogs & Websites Listing Fruit, Berry & Nut Varieties by Mail Order in the United States. 2009. (ENG., Illus.). 384p. 30.00 *(978-1-882424-62-7(X))* Seed Savers Exchange, Inc.

Whealy, Kent & Seed Saver's Exchange Staff. Fruit, Berry & Nut Inventory: An Inventory of Nursery Catalogs & Websites Listing Fruit, Berry & Nut Varieties by Mail Order in the United States. 4th ed. 2009. (ENG., Illus.). 384p. pap. 24.00 *(978-1-882424-61-0(1))* Seed Savers Exchange, Inc.

Zhao, Yanyun, ed. Berry Fruit: Value-Added Products for Health Promotion. 2007. (Food Science & Technology Ser.). (ENG., Illus.). 448p. 199.95 *(978-0-8493-5802-9(7)*, CRC Press) Taylor & Francis Group GBR. Dist: Taylor & Francis Group.

BERRIGAN, DANIEL, 1921-

Berrigan, Daniel. The Dark Night of Resistance. 2007. (Daniel Berrigan Reprint Ser.). 194p. pap. 22.00 *(978-1-55635-469-4(X))* Wipf & Stock Pubs.

—No Bars to Manhood: A Powerful, Personal Statement on Radical Confrontation with Contemporary Society. 2007. (Daniel Berrigan Reprint Ser.). 220p. pap. 24.00 *(978-1-55635-471-7(1))* Wipf & Stock Pubs.

—Portraits of Those I Love. 2007. (Daniel Berrigan Reprint Ser.). (Illus.). 164p. pap. 18.00 *(978-1-55635-472-4(X))* Wipf & Stock Pubs.

—To Dwell in Peace: An Autobiography. 2007. (Daniel Berrigan Reprint Ser.). 364p. pap. 40.00 *(978-1-55635-473-1(8))* Wipf & Stock Pubs.

Stringfellow, William & Towne, Anthony. Suspect Tenderness: The Ethics of the Berrigan Witness. 2006. (Dissent Trilogy: Ser.). 192p. pap. 22.00 *(978-1-59752-477-3(8)*, Wipf and Stock) Wipf & Stock Pubs.

BERRY, CHUCK, 1926-

Reff, Morten. Chuck Berry International Directory (Volume 3) 2012. (ENG., Illus.). 500p. pap. *(978-0-9547068-8-3(9))* Music Mentor Bks.

—Chuck Berry International Directory (Volume 4), Vol. 4. 2012. (ENG., Illus.). 500p. pap. *(978-0-9547068-9-0(7))* Music Mentor Bks.

BERRY, MARIE CAROLINE FERDINASIDE, LOUISE DE NAPLES, DUCHESSE DE, 1798-1870

Dermoncourt, Paul F. S. The Rebellious Duchess: The Adventures of the Duchess of Berri & Her Attempt to Overthrow French Monarchy. 2009. 180p. *(978-1-84677-642-7(2))*; pap. *(978-1-84677-641-0(4))* Leonaur Ltd.

Imbert de Saint-Amand. The Duchess of Berry & the Court of Charles X. 2007. 192p. per. *(978-1-4065-3409-2(9))* Dodo Pr.

BERRYMAN, JOHN, 1914-1972

COLEMAN, Philip & MCGOWAN, Philip, eds. After thirty Falls: New Essays on John Berryman. 2007. (DQR Studies In Literature: 38). 312p. 84.00 *(978-90-420-2219-5(1))* Rodopi.

Cooper, Brendan. Dark Airs: John Berryman & the Spiritual Politics of Cold War American Poetry. 2009. (Modern Poetry Ser.). 262p. 66.95 *(978-3-03911-861-8(7))* Lang, Peter AG GBR. Dist: Lang, Peter.

Rogers, Tom. 'God of Rescue' John Berryman & Christianity. 2011. 435p. pap. 82.95 *(978-3-03910-748-3(8))* Lang, Peter AG GBR. Dist: Lang, Peter.

BERTALANFFY, LUDWIG VON, 1901-1972

Pouvreau, David. The Dialectical Tragedy of the Concept of Wholeness: Ludwig von Bertalanffy's Biography Revisited. Schober, Elisabeth, tr. from FRE. 2009. (Exploring Unity Through Diversity Ser.). 240p. pap. 28.99 *(978-0-9817032-8-2(3))* Emergent Pubns.

BERTHOLD VON REGENSBURG, D. 1272

Czerwon, Ariane. Predigt gegen Ketzer: Studien zu den lateinischen Sermones Bertholds von Regensburg. 2011. (Spattmittelalter, Humanismus, Reformation Ser.). (GER.). 265p. 177.50 ***(978-3-16-150141-8(1))*** Mohr Siebeck GmbH & Co. KG DEU. Dist: Coronet Bks.

BERTILLON, ALPHONSE, 1853-1914

Ellenbogen. Reasoned & Unreasoned Images Cb. 2012. (ENG.). 240p. ***(978-0-271-05259-5(7))*** Pennsylvania State Univ. Pr.

BERTOIA, HARRY

Schiffer, Nancy N. Harry Bertoia Monoprints. 2011. (Illus.). 304p. 89.99 ***(978-0-7643-3850-2(1))*** Schiffer Publishing, Ltd.

BERYL

Ward, Fred, et al. Emeralds. 3rd ed. 2010. (Illus.). 64p. ***(978-1-887651-15-8(2))*** Gem Bk. Pubs.

BERYLLIUM

Adair, Rick. Beryllium. 2007. 52p. (gr. 4-7). pap. 26.50 *(978-1-4358-3780-5(0))* Rosen Publishing Group, Inc., The.

Brisson, Mike J. & Royal Society of Chemistry Staff. Beryllium: Environmental Analysis & Monitoring. Brisson, Mike J. & Ekechukwu, Amy A., eds. 2009. (ENG., Illus.). 214p. 141.00 ***(978-1-84755-903-6(4))*** Royal Society of Chemistry, The GBR. Dist: Ingram Pub. Services.

Committee on Beryllium Alloy Exposures, et al. Managing Health Effects of Beryllium Exposure. 2008. (ENG.). 186p. pap. 42.25 *(978-0-309-12532-1(4))* National Academies Pr.

National Research Council (U.S.), Committee on Beryllium Alloy Exposures Staff & National Research Council (U.S.), Committee on Toxicology Staff, contrib. by. Health Effects of Beryllium Exposure: A Literature Review. 2007. (ENG.). 118p. pap. 29.25 *(978-0-309-11167-6(6))* National Academies Pr.

Walsh, Kenneth A. Beryllium Chemisty & Processing. 2009. (Illus.). 400p. 235.00 *(978-0-87170-721-5(7))* ASM International.

BESANT, ANNIE WOOD, 1847-1933

Besant, Annie. Annie Besant's London Lectures of 1907. 2008. 128p. pap. 7.99 *(978-1-60450-183-4(9))* Arc Manor.

—Autobiographical Sketches. 2008. 168p. pap. 9.99 *(978-1-60450-181-0(2))* Arc Manor.

—Autobiographical Sketches. 2007. (ENG.). 172p. per. *(978-1-4065-5279-9(8))* Dodo Pr.

Besant, Annie W. Annie Besant: An Autobiography. 2007. 244p. pap. 20.99 *(978-1-4264-5795-1(2))*; (ENG.). 274p. pap. 23.99 *(978-1-4264-5855-2(X))* BiblioBazaar.

Besant, Annie Wood. Annie Besant: An Autobiography. 2011. (Cambridge Library Collection - Spiritualism & Esoteric Knowlege Ser.). (Illus.). 396p. pap. 31.99 *(978-1-108-02731-1(8))* Cambridge Univ. Pr.

—Autobiographical Sketches (Besant) 2007. (ENG.). 186p. pap. 19.99 *(978-1-4346-2206-8(1))*; 204p. pap. 22.99 *(978-1-4346-2266-2(5))* BiblioBazaar.

Schwarz, A. VadeMecum to Man V2 Whence How & Whith. 2006. pap. 16.95 *(978-1-4286-6346-6(0))* Kessinger Publishing, LLC.

BESNIER-BOECK DISEASE

see Sarcoidosis

BESSEL'S FUNCTIONS

see also Differential Equations; Harmonic Functions

Andrew Gray & G. B. Mathews. A Treatise on Bessel Functions & Their Applications to Physics. 2007. 304p. per. 14.95 *(978-1-60386-045-1(2)*, Merchant Bks.) Rough Draft Printing.

Grosswald E. Bessel Polynomials. 2008. (Lecture Notes in Mathematics Ser.). 200p. pap. 26.00 *(978-3-540-09104-2(1))* Springer.

Isaac Todhunter. An Elementary Treatise on Laplace's Functions, Lame's Functions & Bessel's Functions. 2007. 356p. per. 14.95 *(978-1-60386-070-3(3)*, Merchant Bks.) Rough Draft Printing.

Watson, G. N. A Treatise on the Theory of Bessel Functions, Vol. 4. reprint ed. lib. bdg. *(978-0-7222-3043-5(5))* Library Reprints, Inc.

—A Treatise on the Theory of Bessel Functions. 2008. 816p. pap. 25.00 *(978-1-60386-104-5(1)*, Merchant Bks.) Rough Draft Printing.

BESSEMER AND LAKE ERIE RAILROAD

Springirth, Kenneth C. Bessemer & Lake Erie Railroad. 2009. (Images of Rail Ser.). (Illus.). 128p. pap. 21.99 *(978-0-7385-6266-7(1))* Arcadia Publishing.

BEST, THOMAS, 1570-1639

Foster, William, ed. The Voyage of Thomas Best to the East Indies, 1612-14. 2010. (Hakluyt Society, Second Ser.). 372p. 69.95 *(978-1-4094-1442-1(6))* Hakluyt Society GBR. Dist: Ashgate Publishing Co.

BEST BOOKS

Here are entered lists of, and works about, recommended books.

see also Book Selection; Canon (Literature)

Aciman, Alexander & Rensin, Emmett L. Twitterature: The World's Greatest Books in Twenty Tweets or Less. 2009. (ENG.). 224p. (gr. 12). 12.00 *(978-0-14-311732-2(7)*, Penguin (Non-Classics)) Penguin Group (USA) Inc.

Barr, Catherine & Gillespie, John T. Best Books for Middle School & Junior High Readers, Grades 6-9, 1 vol. 2nd ed. 2009. (Children's & Young Adult Literature Reference Ser.). 1242p. 85.00 *(978-1-59158-573-2(2)*, LU8573) Libraries Unlimited, Inc.

Bartel, Julie & Holley, Pam Spencer. YALSA Annotated Booklists for Every Teen Reader: The Best from Experts at YALSA-BK. 2010. 250p. pap. 65.00 *(978-1-55570-658-6(4))* Neal-Schuman Pubs., Inc.

Basbanes, Nicholas A. Every Book Its Reader: The Power of the Printed Word to Stir the World. 2006. (ENG., Illus.). 400p. pap. 15.95 *(978-0-06-059324-7(5)*, HarperPerennial) HarperCollins Pubs.

Beha, Christopher. The Whole Five Feet: What the Great Books Taught Me about Life, Death, & Pretty Much Everthing Else. 2010. (ENG.). 272p. pap. 14.00 *(978-0-8021-4485-0(3)*, Grove Pr.) Grove/Atlantic, Inc.

Bennett, Arnold. Literary Taste: How to Form It. 2007. 84p. per. *(978-1-4065-4794-8(8))* Dodo Pr.

—Literary Taste — How to Form It: With detailed instructions for collecting a complete library of English Literature. 2010. (ENG.). 132p. pap. 20.75 *(978-1-178-03641-1(3))* BiblioBazaar.

—Literary Taste; How to Form It with Detailed Instructions for Collecting a Complete Library of English Literature. 2010. (Illus.). 50p. pap. 20.00 *(978-1-153-74417-1(1))* General Bks. LLC.

Bennett, Arnold & Swinnerton, Frank. Literary Taste; How to Form It, with Detailed Instructions for Collecting a Complete Library of English Literature. 2010. 138p. pap. 20.75 *(978-1-177-85195-4(4))* BiblioBazaar.

The Best Reading Hints on the Selection of Books; 2006. 264p. per. 23.99 *(978-1-4255-2335-0(8))* MPublishing.

Bowis, Duncan & Andrews, Stephen. 100 Must-Read Books for Men. 2008. (ENG., Illus.). 208p. 9.95 *(978-0-7136-8873-3(4))* A & C Black GBR. Dist: Macmillan.

Boxall, Peter, ed. 1001 Books You Must Read Before You Die: Revised & Updated Edition. 2010. (ENG., Illus.). 960p. 36.95 *(978-0-7893-2039-1(8))* Universe Publishing.

Broderick, Damien & Filippo, Paul Di. Science Fiction: the 101 Best Novels 1985-2010. 2012. (ENG.). 260p. pap. 14.99 ***(978-1-933065-39-7(7))*** Nonstop Pr.

Burroughs, William S. Mr. Burroughs Recommends. (Penguin Classics Ser.). 608p. pap. *(978-0-14-014044-6(1)*, Penguin Classics) Penguin Group (USA) Inc.

Burt, Daniel S., et al. What Do I Read Next? Volume 2: A Reader's Guide to Current Genre Fiction. 2007th rev. ed. 2007. (What Do I Read Next? Ser.: Vol. 2). (ENG.). 688p. 242.00 *(978-0-7876-9026-7(0))* Cengage Gale.

Carstensen, Angela. Outstanding Books for the College Bound: Titles & Programs for a New Generation. 2011. 192p. ***(978-0-8389-8570-0(X))*** American Library Assn.

Cords, Sarah Statz & Pearl, Nancy. Now Read This III: A Guide to Mainstream Fiction, 1 vol. 3rd rev. ed. 2010. (Genreflecting Advisory Ser.). 405p. 60.00 *(978-1-59158-570-1(8)*, LU5708) Libraries Unlimited, Inc.

Covert, Jack & Sattersten, Todd. The 100 Best Business Books of All Time: What They Say, Why They Matter, & How They Can Help You. (ENG., Illus.). (gr. 12). 2011. 368p. 16.00 *(978-1-59184-446-4(0)*, Portfolio Trade) 2009. 352p. 25.95 *(978-1-59184-240-8(9)*, Portfolio (Hardcover)) Penguin Group (USA) Inc.

De Bary, Wm Theodore. Finding Wisdom in East Asian Classics. 2011. (ENG., Illus.). 432p. (gr. 17). pap. 29.50 *(978-0-231-15397-3(X))* Columbia Univ. Pr.

de Bary, Wm. Theodore. Finding Wisdom in East Asian Classics. 2011. (ENG., Illus.). 432p. (gr. 17). 89.50 *(978-0-231-15396-6(1))* Columbia Univ. Pr.

Dirda, Michael. Book by Book: Notes on Reading & Life. 2007. (ENG.). 192p. pap. 14.99 *(978-0-8050-8338-5(3)*, Owl Bks.) Holt, Henry & Co.

Donaldson-Evans, Lance. One Hundred Great French Books: From the Middle Ages to the Present. 2010. (ENG.). 240p. pap. 15.95 *(978-1-933346-22-9(1))* BlueBridge.

Dunwell, Anna. Guide to the 400 Best Children's & Adult's Multicultural Books about Immigration & Moving. spiral bd. 42.95 *(978-1-891657-29-0(1)*, S2990) Lift Every Voice.

Edwards, Lee. Reading the Right Books: A Guide for the Intelligent Conservative. 2007. xv, 151p. pap. *(978-0-89195-127-8(X))* 2nd ed. 2009. xv, 163p. pap. *(978-0-89195-133-9(4))* Heritage Foundation.

Essential Guide to Spanish Reading for Children & Young Adults. 2009. 206p. pap. *(978-0-9821418-8-5(2))* TRIALTEA USA, LLC.

Feldman, Jessica R. & Stilling, Robert, eds. What Should I Read Next? 70 University of Virginia Professors Recommend Readings in History, Politics, Literature, Math, Science, Technology, the Arts, & More. 2008. (ENG., Illus.). 296p. pap. 19.50 *(978-0-8139-2736-7(6))* Univ. Pr. of Virginia.

Freeman, Judy. The WINNERS! Handbook: A Closer Look at Judy Freeman's Top-Rated Children's Books of 2006, 1 vol. 2007. 244p. per. 35.00 *(978-1-59158-510-7(4)*, LU5104) Libraries Unlimited, Inc.

—The Winners! Handbook: A Closer Look at Judy Freeman's Top-Rated Children's Books of 2007, 1 vol. 2008. 244p. pap. 35.00 *(978-1-59158-712-5(3)*, LU8712) Libraries Unlimited, Inc.

—The WINNERS! Handbook: A Closer Look at Judy Freeman's Top-Rated Children's Books Of 2008, 1 vol. 2008. (Illus.). 190p. pap. 35.00 *(978-1-59158-859-7(6)*, LU8859) Libraries Unlimited, Inc.

Gillespie, John & Barr, Catherine. Best Books for Children: Preschool Through Grade 6, 1 vol. 9th ed. 2010. (Children's & Young Adult Literature Reference Ser.). 1901p. 95.00 *(978-1-59158-575-6(9)*, LU8575) Libraries Unlimited, Inc.

Godfrey, Jason. Bibliographic: 100 Classic Graphic Design Books. 2009. (ENG., Illus.). 224p. 50.00 *(978-1-85669-592-3(1))* King, Laurence Publishing GBR. Dist: Hachette Bk. Group.

Govi, Fabrizio. I Classici Che Hanno Fatto L'Italia: Per un Nuovo Canone Bio Bibliografico Degli Autori. 2010. 415p. 95.00 *(978-88-96656-14-3(1))* Libreria Alberto Govi ITA. Dist: Oak Knoll Pr.

Greenfieldt, John. Fiction Core Collection. 16th ed. 2010. 1317p. 265.00 *(978-0-8242-1103-5(0))* Wilson, H.W.

Hesperides. Books to Read - a Classified & Annotated Catalogue Being a Guide for Young Readers. 2007. 600p. per. *(978-1-4067-5565-7(6)*, Hesperides Pr.) Read Bks.

Hysell, Shannon Graff, ed. Recommended Reference Books for Small & Medium-Sized Libraries & Media Centers 2009, 1 vol., Vol. 29. 29th rev. ed. 2009. (Recommended Reference Bks.). 332p. 70.00 *(978-1-59158-841-2(3)*, LU8841) Libraries Unlimited, Inc.

Jago, Carol. With Rigor for All, Second Edition: Meeting Common Core Standards for Reading Literature. 2nd ed. 2011. 168p. pap. 26.25 ***(978-0-325-04210-7(1)***, E04210) Heinemann.

Kenny, Des. Kenny's Choice: 101 Irish Books You Must Read. 2009. (ENG., Illus.). 332p. pap. 35.95 *(978-1-85607-967-9(8))* Currach Pr. IRL. Dist: Dufour Editions, Inc.

Kent, Henry Watson. Bibliographical Notes on One Hundred Books Famous in English Literature. 2009. 148p. pap. *(978-1-150-65057-4(5))* Books LLC.

Knight, Rachelle Rogers. Read, Remember, Recommend. 2010. (ENG.). 320p. pap. 15.99 *(978-1-4022-3718-8(9))* Sourcebooks, Inc.

—Read, Remember, Recommend for Teens: A Reading Journal for Young Adult Book Lovers. 2010. (ENG.). 352p. pap. 15.99 *(978-1-4022-3719-5(7))* Sourcebooks, Inc.

Koelling, Holly. Best Books for Young Adults. 3rd ed. 2007. (Illus.). 346p. per. 46.00 *(978-0-8389-3569-9(9))* American Library Assn.

Krim, Geri & Mittelman, Sandy, compiled by. Choices: A Core Collection for Young Reluctant Readers, Vol. 6. 2006. 237p. 50.00 *(978-0-934272-87-2(5))* Burke, John Gordon Pub., Inc.

Lange, Henrik. 90 Classic Books for People in a Hurry. 2009. (Illus.). 150p. pap. 9.95 *(978-91-85869-29-9(5))* Nicotext, Ltd. SWE. Dist: SCB Distributors.

Matthew, Kathryn I. & Lowe, Joy L. Neal-Schuman Guide to Recommended Children's Books & Media for Use with Every Elementary Subject. 2nd ed. 2010. 400p. 80.00 *(978-1-55570-688-3(6))* Neal-Schuman Pubs., Inc.

Murnighan, Jack. Beowulf on the Beach: What to Love & What to Skip in Literature's 50 Greatest Hits. 2009. (ENG.). 384p. pap. 15.00 *(978-0-307-40957-7(0)*, Three Rivers Pr.) Crown Publishing Group.

Newman, Sandra. The Western Lit Survival Kit: An Irreverent Guide to the Classics, from Homer to Faulkner. 2012. (ENG.). 304p. (gr. 12). 18.00 ***(978-1-59240-694-4(7)***, Gotham) Penguin Group (USA) Inc.

Nonamura. Books for Children & Youth in Nineteenth-Century America Series. 2008. 3300p. 1195.00 *(978-4-86166-044-3(0))* Synapse, Edition JPN. Dist: Taylor & Francis Group.

Oakley, Henry Augustus. Outline of a Course of English Reading, Based on That Prepared for the Mercantile Library Association of the City of New-York, by the Late Chancellor. 2006. 132p. per. 16.99 *(978-1-4255-0938-5(X))* MPublishing.

Oppenheim, Joanne F. & Oppenheim, Stephanie. Oppenheim Toy Portfolio: The Best Toys, Books, & DVDs for Kids. annuals 2006. (Oppenheim Toy Portfolio Ser.: 14). (Illus.). 228p. per. 10.00 *(978-0-9721050-6-4(9))* Oppenheim Toy Portfolio, Inc.

Pearl, Nancy. Book Lust to Go: Recommended Reading for Travelers, Vagabonds, & Dreamers. 2010. (ENG., Illus.). 320p. pap. 16.95 *(978-1-57061-650-1(7))* Sasquatch Bks.

Persky, Stan. Reading the 21st Century: Books of the Decade, 2000-2009. 2011. (ENG.). 264p. (C). ***(978-0-7735-3909-9(3))*** McGill-Queen's Univ. Pr.

Potter, Alonzo. Handbook for Readers & Students, Intended As a Help to Individuals, Associations, School Districts & Seminaries of Learning, in the Selection of W. 2006. 332p. per. 23.99 *(978-1-4255-3340-3(X))* MPublishing.

Pycroft, James. A Course of English Reading, Adapted to Every Taste & Capacity: With Literary Anecdotes. by the Rev. James Pycroft ... 2006. 356p. per. 26.99 *(978-1-4255-3600-8(X))* MPublishing.

Rennison, Nick. 100 Must-Read Life-Changing Books. 2008. (ENG.). 160p. pap. 9.95 *(978-0-7136-8872-6(6))* A & C Black GBR. Dist: Macmillan.

—100 Must-Read Prize Winning Novels: Discover Your Next Great Read... 2010. (ENG., Illus.). 192p. pap. 9.99 *(978-1-4081-2911-1(6))* A & C Black GBR. Dist: Macmillan.

Rigelhof, T. F. Hooked on Canadian Books: The Good, the Better, & the Best Canadian Novels since 1984. 2010. (ENG.). 336p. 32.00 *(978-1-897151-75-4(6))* Cormorant Bks. Inc. CAN. Dist: Univ. of Toronto Pr.

Rowley, Michael, ed. 100 Must-Read Graphic Novels. 2009. 320p. pap. 9.95 *(978-1-4081-0523-8(3))* A & C Black GBR. Dist: Consortium Bk. Sales & Distribution.

Shimada. Books on Children in 16th-18th Century Britain Series I. Engetsu, Yuko, ed. 2008. 1910p. 1040.00 *(978-4-902454-31-4(9))* Synapse, Edition JPN. Dist: Taylor & Francis Group.

Shorter, Clement King. Immortal Memories. 2008. 180p. 22.99 *(978-0-554-37307-2(6))* 2008. 180p. 25.99 *(978-0-554-28004-2(3))* 2007. 178p. pap. 21.99 *(978-1-4346-4494-7(4))* BiblioBazaar.

—Immortal Memories. 2009. 118p. pap. *(978-0-217-49313-0(0))*; pap. *(978-0-217-22994-4(8))* Books LLC.

—Immortal Memories. 2009. 148p. pap. *(978-1-4065-6998-8(4))* Dodo Pr.

Shriver, Lionel, frwd. The Book Club Bible: The Definitive Guide That Every Book Club Member Needs. 2008. (ENG.). 224p. pap. 15.95 *(978-1-84317-269-7(0))* O'Mara, Michael Bks., Ltd. GBR. Dist: Independent Pubs. Group.

Slater, J. Herbert. Library Manual. 2006. 128p. per. *(978-1-4067-1848-5(3)*, Hesperides Pr.) Read Bks.

Smith, F. Seymour. What Shall I Read Next? A Personal Selection of Twentieth Century English Books. 2010. (ENG.). 242p. pap. 22.99 *(978-0-521-15545-8(2))* Cambridge Univ. Pr.

Sutherland, John. Bestsellers: A Very Short Introduction. 2007. (Very Short Introductions Ser.). (ENG., Illus.). 144p. per. 11.95 *(978-0-19-921489-1(1))* Oxford Univ. Pr., Inc.

Thomson Gale, creator. What Do I Read Next?, Vol. 1. 2007th rev. ed. 2007. (What Do I Read Next? Ser.). (ENG.). 656p. 242.00 *(978-0-7876-9025-0(2))* Cengage Gale.

Tóibín, Colm & Callil, Carmen. A Brief Guide to the Modern Library. 2011. (ENG.). 320p. pap. 13.95 *(978-0-7624-4276-8(X))* Running Pr. Bk. Pubs.

Van Doren, Charles. The Joy of Reading: A Passionate Guide to 189 of the World's Best Authors & Their Works. 2008. (ENG.). 544p. 24.95 *(978-1-4022-1160-7(0))* Sourcebooks, Inc.

Walsh, George. 50 Plus One Great Books You Should Have Read (and probably Didn't) l.t. ed. 2009. 485p. 30.95 *(978-1-4104-1254-6(7))* Thorndike Pr.

Wheatley, Henry Benjamin. How to Form a Library. 2009. 256p. 24.99 *(978-1-103-31851-3(9))* 2009. 256p. pap. 18.99 *(978-1-103-31849-0(7))* 2008. 260p. 28.99 *(978-0-554-49788-4(3))* 2008. 240p. 28.99 *(978-0-554-63324-4(8))* 2008. 167p. 25.99 *(978-0-554-63333-6(7))* 2008. 260p. 25.99 *(978-0-554-49806-5(5))* 2008. 260p. pap. 25.75 *(978-0-554-49803-4(0))* 2008. 240p. pap. 26.75 *(978-0-554-63328-2(0))* 2008. 240p. pap. 25.75 *(978-0-554-63330-5(2))* 2008. 260p. pap. 26.75 *(978-0-554-49797-6(2))* BiblioBazaar.

—How to Form a Library. 2009. 94p. pap. *(978-0-217-93373-5(4))* Books LLC.

—How to Form a Library. 2010. (Cambridge Library Collection - Printing & Publishing History Ser.). 264p. pap. 23.99 *(978-1-108-02149-4(2))* Cambridge Univ. Pr.

Zbaracki, Matthew D. Best Books for Boys: A Resource for Educators, 1 vol. 2008. (Children's & Young Adult Literature Reference Ser.). (Illus.). 204p. 45.00 *(978-1-59158-599-2(6),* LU8599) Libraries Unlimited, Inc.

Zvirin, Stephanie. Read with Me: Best Books for Preschoolers. 2012. (ENG.). 184p. pap. 18.95 ***(978-1-937589-03-5(X),*** Huron Street Pr.) American Library Assn.

BEST BOOKS—BIBLIOGRAPHY

see Best Books

BEST SELLERS

Bloom, Clive. Bestsellers: Popular Fiction since 1900. 2nd ed. 2008. (ENG., Illus.). 352p. pap. 74.95 *(978-0-230-53689-0(1))* Palgrave Macmillan.

Bond, Jenny & Sheedy, Chris. Who the Hell Is Pansy O'Hara? The Fascinating Stories Behind 50 of the World's Best-Loved Books. 2008. (ENG.). 336p. (gr. 12-18). 13.00 *(978-0-14-311364-5(X),* Penguin (Non-Classics)) Penguin Group (USA) Inc.

Brown, Ellen Firsching & Wiley, John. Margaret Mitchell's Gone with the Wind: A Bestseller's Odyssey from Atlanta to Hollywood. 2011. (ENG., Illus.). 438p. 26.95 *(978-1-58979-567-9(9))* Taylor Trade Publishing.

Deery, Steve. How Customers Like to Buy: A Practical Guide to Understanding & Implementing the Key to Sales Success. rev. ed. 2010. (ENG.). 164p. pap. 19.95 *(978-1-61110-003-7(8))* Global Management Enterprises.

Hall, James W. Hit Lit: Cracking the Code of the Twentieth Century's Biggest Bestsellers. 2012. (ENG.). 336p. E-Book ***(978-0-679-60496-9(0));*** pap. 16.00 ***(978-0-8129-7095-1(0))*** Random House Publishing Group. (Random Hse. Trade Paperbacks)

Ilsley, Richard. Best Practice, USA: A Practical Primer for Every Manager to Implement Best Practice Models. rev. ed. 2010. (ENG.). 192p. pap. 21.95 *(978-1-61110-002-0(X))* Global Management Enterprises.

Jurilla, Patricia May B. Tagalog Bestsellers of the Twentieth Century: A History of the Book in the Philippines. (Illus.). xi, 264p. 50.00 *(978-971-550-563-5(5))* Ateneo de Manila Univ. Pr. PHL. Dist: Univ. of Hawaii Pr.

Ramone, Jenni & Cousins, Helen. The Richard & Judy Book Club Reader: Popular Texts & the Practices of Reading. 2011. 224p. 99.95 ***(978-1-4094-0133-9(2))*** Ashgate Publishing Co.

Sutherland, John. Bestsellers (Routledge Revivals) 2010. (Routledge Revivals Ser.). (ENG.). 282p. 115.00 *(978-0-415-61124-4(5))* Routledge.

Ueda, Yasuo. Hon Wa Yo ni Tsure: Besuto Sera Wa Ko Shite Umareta. 2009. (JPN., Illus.). 237p. *(978-4-88065-216-0(4))* Suiyo-Sha.

BEST SELLERS—BIBLIOGRAPHY

Bloom, Clive. Bestsellers: Popular Fiction Since 1900. 2nd ed. 2008. (ENG.). 352p. 110.00 *(978-0-230-53688-3(3))* Palgrave Macmillan.

BESTIALITY

Beirne, null & Beirne, Piers. Confronting Animal Abuse: Law, Criminology, & Human-Animal Relationships. 2009. (ENG., Illus.). 256p. 90.00 *(978-0-7425-4743-8(4));* pap. 33.00 *(978-0-7425-4744-5(2))* Rowman & Littlefield Publishers, Inc.

Cogliantry, Michael. Furverts. 2009. (ENG., Illus.). 24p. 12.95 *(978-0-8118-6847-1(8))* Chronicle Bks. LLC.

Podberscek, Anthony L. & Beetz, Andrea M., eds. Bestiality & Zoophilia: Sexual Relations with Animals. 2009. (ENG.). 1p. pap. 49.95 *(978-1-84788-354-4(0))* Berg Pubs. GBR. Dist: Macmillan.

Salisbury, Joyce. The Beast Within. 2nd rev. ed. 2010. (ENG., Illus.). 224p. (C). 130.00 *(978-0-415-78094-0(2));* pap. 34.95 *(978-0-415-78095-7(0))* Routledge.

BESTIARIES

Barber, Richard. Bestiary: Being an English Verison of the Bodleian Library, Oxford, MS Bodley 764. fac. ed. 2010. (Illus.). 206p. pap. 24.95 *(978-0-85115-753-5(X))* Boydell & Brewer, Inc.

Curley, Michael J., tr. from LAT. Physiologus: A Medieval Book of Nature Lore. 2009. (ENG., Illus.). 144p. pap. 17.00 *(978-0-226-12870-2(9))* Univ. of Chicago Pr.

de Hamel, Christpher, intro. Book of Beasts: A Facsimile of MS Bodley 764. fac. ed. 2010. (LAT & ENG., Illus.). 316p. (C). 250.00 *(978-1-85124-317-4(8))* Bodleian Library GBR. Dist: Brown, David Bk. Co., The.

Sedaris, David. Squirrel Seeks Chipmunk: A Modest Bestiary. 2011. (ENG., Illus.). 192p. pap. 13.99 *(978-0-316-03840-9(7),* Back Bay Bks.) Little Brown & Co.

—Squirrel Seeks Chipmunk: A Wicked Bestiary. 2010. (ENG., Illus.). 176p. 21.99 *(978-0-316-03839-3(3))* Little Brown & Co.

Tyler, Tom. Ciferae: A Bestiary in Five Fingers. 2012. (Posthumanities Ser.). (Illus.). 376p. 90.00 ***(978-0-8166-6543-3(5));*** pap. 30.00 ***(978-0-8166-6544-0(3))*** Univ. of Minnesota Pr.

BET ALFA SYNAGOGUE (HEFTSI BAH, ISRAEL)

Sukenik, Eleazar Lipa. The Ancient Synagogue of Beth Alpha. 2007. (Gorgias Classic Archaeological Reprints Ser.: 14). 180.00 *(978-1-59333-696-7(9))* Gorgias Pr., LLC.

BETA DECAY

Blank, Bertram, ed. The 4th International Conference on Proton Emitting Nuclei & Related Topics. 2012. (AIP Conference Proceedings / High Energy Physics Ser.). (ENG.). 232p. pap. 143.00 ***(978-0-7354-0983-5(8),*** 0735409838, AIP Pr.) Springer.

Civitarese, Osvaldo, et al, eds. Workshop on Calculation of Double-Beta-Decay Matrix Elements (MEDEX '11) 2012. (AIP Conference Proceedings / High Energy Physics Ser.: 1417). (ENG.). 174p. pap. 135.00 ***(978-0-7354-0994-1(3),*** 0735409943, AIP Pr.) Springer.

Civitarese, Osvaldo, et al, eds. Workshop on Circulation of Double-Beta-Decay-Matrix. 2009. (AIP Conference Proceedings Ser.). (ENG.). 170p. pap. 109.00 *(978-0-7354-0721-3(5),* 0735407215, AIP Pr.) Springer.

Ferreira, Lidia S. Proton Emitting Nuclei & Related Topics: International Conference-PROCON 2007. 2007. (AIP Conference Proceedings / High Energy Physics Ser.). 149.00 *(978-0-7354-0475-5(5))* American Institute of Physics.

ICRP. ICRP Publication 107: Nuclear Decay Data for Dosimetric Calculations. 2009. (International Commission on Radiological Protection Ser.). (ENG.). 96p. pap. 218.00 *(978-0-7020-3475-6(4),* Elsevier) Elsevier - Health Sciences Div.

Stekl, Ivan & Suhonen, Jouni, eds. Workshop on Calculation of Double-Beta-Decay Matrix Elements (Medex'07. 2007. (AIP Conference Proceedings / High Energy Physics Ser.). (Illus.). 106p. 69.00 *(978-0-7354-0456-4(9))* American Institute of Physics.

Sukhoruchkin, S. I. & Soroko, Z. N. Tables of Excitations of Proton-and Neutron-Rich Unstable Nuclei. 2008. (Landolt-Börnstein: Numerical Data & Functional Relationships in Science & Technology Ser.). xvi, 530p. 8759.00 *(978-3-540-75277-6(3))* Springer.

BETA ISRAEL

see Jews, Ethiopian

BETCHERRYGAH

see Budgerigar

BETHE, HANS ALBRECH, 1906-2005

Brown, Gerald E. & Lee, Chang-Hwan, eds. Hans Bethe & His Physics. 2006. (Illus.). 314p. pap. 52.00 *(978-981-256-610-2(4))* World Scientific Publishing Co., Inc.

Lee, Rachel. The Bethe-Peierls Correspondence. 2008. (C). 117.00 *(978-981-277-135-3(2))* World Scientific Publishing Co., Inc.

Schweber, Silvan S. In the Shadow of the Bomb: Oppenheimer, Bethe, & the Moral Responsibility of the Scientist. 2006. (Princeton Series in Physics). (ENG., Illus.). 288p. (C). per. 26.95 *(978-0-691-12785-9(9))* Princeton Univ. Pr.

Schweber, Silvan S. Nuclear Forces: The Making of the Physicist Hans Bethe. 2012. (ENG., Illus.). 608p. 35.00 ***(978-0-674-06587-1(5))*** Harvard Univ. Pr.

BETHEL (ME.)

Sowers, Gladys Bucher. Colonial Taxes East Hanover — Londonderry Township Lancaster County, Pennsylvania 1750-1783 (now Lebanon County) 2007. (Illus.). 128p. pap. 18.00 *(978-1-60126-028-4(8))* Masthof Pr.

BETHENCOURT, JEAN DE, 1360-425

Bontier, Pierre & Le Verrier, Jean. The Canarian: Or, Book of the Conquest & Conversion of the Canarians in the year 1402, by Messire Jean de Bethencourt, Kt. 2010. (Cambridge Library Collection- Hakluyt First Ser.). (Illus.). 302p. pap. 24.99 *(978-1-108-01139-6(X))* Cambridge Univ. Pr.

BETHLEHEM

Cox, Ronald B. The Journey to Bethlehem. 2011. 60p. pap. 9.95 ***(978-1-4620-4191-6(4))*** iUniverse, Inc.

Didion, Joan. Slouching Towards Bethlehem. 2008. (ENG.). 256p. pap. 15.00 *(978-0-374-53136-0(2))* Farrar, Straus & Giroux.

Humble, Myron. The Scribe & the Sword. 2009. 198p. pap. 20.92 *(978-0-557-08380-0(X))* Lulu Enterprises Inc.

Khamor, Levi. The Revelation of Bethlehem. 2011. 68p. 20.57 ***(978-1-4669-0077-6(6));*** pap. 10.57 ***(978-1-4669-0076-9(8))*** Trafford Publishing.

BETHLEHEM (PA.)

Engel, Katherine Carte. Religion & Profit: Moravians in Early America. (Early American Studies). (Illus.). 328p. (C). 2011. pap. 22.50 ***(978-0-8122-2185-5(0))*** 2009. 55.00 *(978-0-8122-4123-5(1))* Univ. of Pennsylvania Pr.

Larson, Paul S. Bach for a Hundred Years: A Social History of the Bach Choir of Bethlehem. 2011. (ENG.). 266p. 65.00 ***(978-1-61146-094-0(8))*** Lexington Bks.

Raniere, Kenneth F., et al. South Bethlehem. 2010. (Images of America Ser.). (Illus.). 128p. pap. 21.99 *(978-0-7385-7275-8(6))* Arcadia Publishing.

BETHLEHEM, STAR OF

see Star of Bethlehem

BETHUNE, MARY MCLEOD, 1875-1955

Long, Nancy Ann Zrinyi. The Life & Legacy of Mary Mcleod Bethune. 3rd ed. 2008. (ENG.). (C). pap. 19.20 *(978-0-558-05267-6(3))* Pearson Learning Solutions.

BETI (AFRICAN PEOPLE)

Quinn, Frederick. In Search of Salt: Changes in Beti (Cameroon) Society, 1880-1960. 2006. (Cameroon Studies: Vol. 6). (Illus.). 186p. 90.00 *(978-1-84545-006-9(X))* Berghahn Bks., Inc.

BETJEMAN, JOHN, 1906-1984

Betjeman, John. Betjeman's England. Games, Stephen, ed. 2009. (ENG., Illus.). 320p. 32.95 *(978-1-84854-091-0(4))* Murray, John GBR. Dist: Independent Pubs. Group.

—John Betjeman Letters: Volume One: 1926 To 1951, 2 vols. Lycett Green, Candida, ed. 2007. (Illus.). 584p. per. *(978-0-413-77595-5(X))* Methuen Publishing Ltd.

—John Betjeman Letters: Volume Two: 1951 To 1984, 2 vols. Lycett Green, Candida, ed. 2007. (Illus.). 616p. per. *(978-0-413-77596-2(8))* Methuen Publishing Ltd.

—Summoned by Bells: A Verse Autobiography. (Illus.). 115p. pap. 19.99 *(978-0-7195-6031-6(4))* Murray, John GBR. Dist: Trafalgar Square Publishing.

—Sweet Songs of Zion. 2008. (ENG.). 328p. pap. 17.95 *(978-0-340-96388-3(3),* Hodder & Stoughton) Hodder General Publishing Div. GBR. Dist: Independent Pubs. Group.

—Tennis Whites & Teacakes. 2008. (ENG.). 464p. pap. 17.95 *(978-0-7195-6904-3(4))* Murray, John GBR. Dist: Independent Pubs. Group.

Gardner, Kevin J. Betjeman: Writing the Public Life. 2010. (Making of the Christian Imagination Ser.). (ENG.). 254p. (C). 59.95 *(978-1-50258-254-5(8))* Baylor Univ. Pr.

Glancey, Jonathan & Betjeman, John. John Betjeman on Trains. 2007. (Illus.). 111p. *(978-0-413-77612-9(3))* Methuen Publishing Ltd.

Hillier, Bevis. John Betjeman: The Biography. 2006. (ENG., Illus.). 608p. pap. 32.50 *(978-0-7195-6443-7(3))* Murray, John GBR. Dist: Independent Pubs. Group.

Morse, Greg. John Betjeman. 2011. (Shire Library). (ENG., Illus.). 56p. pap. 12.95 *(978-0-7478-1051-3(6))* Shire Pubns., Ltd. GBR. Dist: Random Hse., Inc.

—John Betjeman: Reading the Victorians. 2nd rev. ed. 2012. (ENG.). 272p. pap. 34.95 ***(978-1-84519-534-2(5))*** Sussex Academic Pr. GBR. Dist: International Specialized Bk. Services.

Morse, Greg. John Betjeman - Reading the Victorians: Reading the Victorians. 2008. (ENG.). 254p. 75.00 *(978-1-84519-271-6(0))* Sussex Academic Pr. GBR. Dist: International Specialized Bk. Services.

Payton, Philip. John Betjeman & Cornwall: The Celebrated Cornish Nationalist. 2010. (Illus.). 258p. 95.00 *(978-0-85989-847-8(4));* 288p. pap. 30.00 *(978-0-85989-848-5(2))* Univ. of Exeter Pr. GBR. Dist: Chicago Distribution Ctr.

BETON

see Concrete

BETROTHAL

see also Courtship; Marriage; Marriage Customs and Rites; Mate Selection

Batshaw, Michael. 51 Things You Should Know Before You Get Engaged. 2009. (Good Things to Know Ser.). (ENG.). 137p. pap. 9.99 *(978-1-59652-548-1(7))* Turner Publishing Co.

David, Joseph. An Essay on Engagement & Marriage Contracts according to the Canons of the Roman Church & the Eastern Rites. 2010. pap. 26.32 *(978-1-61719-631-7(2))* Gorgias Pr., LLC.

Edwards, Brian H. & Edwards, Barbara. No Longer Two: A Christian Guide for Engagement & Marriage. 2009. (Family Focal Point Ser.). (Illus.). 191p. pap. *(978-1-84625-173-3(7))* DayOne Pubns.

Etienne, Elizabeth. The Art of Engagement Photography: Creative Techniques for Couples in Love. 2011. (Illus.). 160p. pap. 29.99 *(978-0-8174-0009-5(5),* Amphoto Bks.) Watson-Guptill Pubns., Inc.

Giraud, Claude. De la Trahison: Contribution à une Sociologie de L'engagement. 2010. (FRE.). 187p. *(978-2-296-13217-7(0))* Harmattan Pr.

Gudgel, Brent & Gudgel, David R. Before You Get Engaged, 0 vols. 2008. (Illus.). 240p. per. 14.99 *(978-0-8499-1918-3(5))* Nelson, Thomas Inc.

Hessel, Stéphane. Time for Outrage: Indignez-vous! 2011. (ENG.). 48p. 10.00 ***(978-1-4555-0972-0(8),*** Twelve) Grand Central Publishing.

Pallais, Don M., et al. Guide to Non-Traditional Engagements, 3 vols. Incl. Vol. 1. ring bd. *(978-0-7646-0086-9(9));* Vol. 2. ring bd. *(978-0-7646-0087-6(7));* Vol. 3. ring bd. *(978-0-7646-0088-3(5));* 1997. 150.00 *(978-0-7646-0085-2(0))* Practitioners Publishing Co.

Titus, Matt & Fadal, Tamsen. Why Hasn't He Proposed? Go from the First Date to Setting the Date. 2008. (ENG.). 224p. pap. 16.95 *(978-0-07-161496-2(6),* 0071614966) McGraw-Hill Cos., The.

BETTELHEIM, BRUNO, 1903-1990

Redford, Roberta Carly. Crazy: My Seven Years at Bruno Bettelheim's Orthogenic School. 2010. 364p. 30.33 *(978-1-4251-9176-4(2));* pap. 20.33 *(978-1-4251-9175-7(4))* Trafford Publishing.

BETTERMENT TAX

see Special Assessments

BETTERTON, THOMAS, 1635-1710

Lowe, Robert W. Eminent Actors Thomas Betterton. 2006. pap. 24.95 *(978-1-4286-4238-6(2))* Kessinger Publishing, LLC.

—Thomas Betterton. 2010. 206p. 32.99 *(978-1-117-94442-5(5));* pap. 24.75 *(978-1-117-94443-2(3))* BiblioBazaar.

Roberts, David. Thomas Betterton: The Greatest Actor of the Restoration Stage. 2010. (Illus.). 270p. 95.00 *(978-0-521-19584-3(5))* Cambridge Univ. Pr.

BETTING

see Gambling

BEUYS, JOSEPH, 1921-1986

Beuys, Joseph. Joseph Beuys: Das Ende des 20. Jahrhunderts/the End of the 20th Century. Willisch, Susanne & Heimberg, Bruno, eds. 2007. (GER & ENG., Illus.). 394p. 99.95 *(978-3-8296-0287-7(1))* Schirmer/Mosel Verlag GmbH DEU. Dist: Prestel Publishing.

—Joseph Beuys: The Border to Eurasia. (Illus.). 35.00 *(978-4-900398-15-3(2))* Watari-Um JPN. Dist: D.A.P./Distributed Art Pubs.

Beuys, Joseph, illus. Joseph Beuys: Sculpture & Drawing, 1 vol. 2008. (ENG.). 64p. 45.00 *(978-0-9773568-6-7(8))* Zwirner & Wirth.

Beuys, Joseph, et al. Beuys, Pourquoi Faites-Vous des Multiples? 2010. (FRE & ENG., Illus.). 96p. pap. 40.00 *(978-2-35340-030-0(2))* Gourcuff Gradenigo FRA. Dist: National Bk. Network.

Cooke, Lynne & Kelly, Karen, eds. Joseph Beuys: Arena - Where Would I Have Got If I Had Been Intelligent. (Illus.). 296p. *(978-3-89322-630-6(3))* D.A.P./Distributed Art Pubs.

De Dominizio Durini, Lucrezia. Beuys Voice. 2011. (Illus.). 960p. 125.00 ***(978-88-370-8567-4(2))*** Electa ITA. Dist: National Bk. Network.

de Duve, Thierry. Sewn in the Sweatshops of Marx: Beuys, Warhol, Klein, Duchamp. Krauss, Rosalind E., tr. 2012. 120p. pap. 22.50 ***(978-0-226-92238-6(3));*** (Illus.). 60.00 ***(978-0-226-92237-9(5))*** Univ. of Chicago Pr.

Dean, Tacita. Darmstädter Werkblock 1 vol. deluxe ed. 2009. (ENG., Illus.). 100p. pap. 100.00 *(978-3-86521-703-5(6))* Steidl, Gerhard Druckerei und Verlag DEU. Dist: Innovative Logistics.

Drechsler, Wolfgang & Leutgeb, Doris, texts. Joseph Beuys, 1 vol. 2007. (ENG., Illus.). 184p. pap. 30.00 *(978-3-938821-72-5(8))* Verlag fur Moderne Kunst DEU. Dist: D.A.P./Distributed Art Pubs.

Holland, Allison. Joseph Beuys & Rudolph Steiner: Imaginat. 2008. (ENG.). 104p. pap. 19.95 *(978-0-7241-0291-4(4))* National Gallery of Victoria AUS. Dist: National Bk. Network.

Lange, Barbara. Joseph Beuys - Richtkraefte einer neuen Gesellschaft: Der Mythos vom Kuenstler als Gesellschaftsreformer. (GER.). 293p. *(978-3-496-01205-4(6))* Reimer, Dietrich.

Mesch, Claudia & Michely, Viola, eds. Joseph Beuys: The Reader. 2007. (ENG., Illus.). 352p. (gr. 17). pap. 26.95 *(978-0-262-63351-2(5))* MIT Pr.

PaceWildenstein, prod. Joseph Beuys: Make the Secrets Productive. 2010. (Illus.). 120p. pap. 40.00 *(978-1-935410-03-4(2))* Pace Gallery, The.

Stüttgen, Johannes, et al, texts. Joseph Beuys: Parallel Processes. 2010. (Illus.). 432p. 75.00 *(978-3-8296-0482-6(3))* Schirmer/Mosel Verlag GmbH DEU. Dist: Prestel Publishing.

BEVAN, JOSEPH VALLENCE, 1798-1830

Coulter, E. Merton. Joseph Vallence Bevan: Georgia's First Official Historian. 2010. (ENG., Illus.). 182p. pap. 22.95 *(978-0-8203-3531-5(2))* Univ. of Georgia Pr.

BEVAN, ROBERT, 1865-1925

Stenlake, Frances. Robert Bevan: From Gauguin to Camden Town. 2008. (ENG., Illus.). 192p. 60.00 *(978-0-906290-92-7(9))* Unicorn Pr., London GBR. Dist: National Bk. Network.

BEVERAGE INDUSTRY

see also Bottling; Brewing Industry; Distilling Industries; Liquor Traffic; Soft Drink Industry; Wine and Wine Making

Allen, Gary & Albala, Ken. The Business of Food: Encyclopedia of the Food & Drink Industries, 1 vol. 2007. 456p. 85.00 *(978-0-313-33725-3(X),* GR3725, Greenwood Pr.) Greenwood Publishing Group, Inc.

Appleton, Jeremy. Acai Berry: Fruits of Paradise. 2007. (Woodland Health Ser.). (Illus.). 36p. pap. 4.95 *(978-1-58054-472-6(X))* Woodland Publishing, Inc.

Bacon, Christopher M., et al, eds. Confronting the Coffee Crisis: Fair Trade, Sustainable Livelihoods & Ecosystems in Mexico & Central America. 2008. (Food, Health, & the Environment Ser.). (ENG., Illus.). 408p. (gr. 17). 67.00 *(978-0-262-02633-8(3));* per. 30.00 *(978-0-262-52480-3(5))* MIT Pr.

Beverage Acquisitions Market U. S. A. 1994: Companies-Products-Services. 400p. (Orig.). pap. 2495.00 *(978-0-7605-2150-2(6))* Rector Pr., Ltd.

Beverage Container Market: Companies-Products-Services. 151p. (Orig.). pap. 2900.00 *(978-0-7605-2149-6(2))* Rector Pr., Ltd.

Beverage Corporations Environmental Report: Companies-Products-Services. 133p. (Orig.). pap. 1000.00 *(978-0-7605-2139-7(5))* Rector Pr., Ltd.

Beverage Market: Companies-Products-Services. 150p. (Orig.). pap. 2195.00 *(978-0-7605-2144-1(1));* pap. 2195.00 *(978-0-7605-2143-4(3))* Rector Pr., Ltd.

BIA. Key Russian Manufacturers & Suppliers of Beverages & Tobacco. 6th rev. ed. 2006. 436p. (J). pap. 249.00 *(978-1-4187-4502-8(2))* Business Information Agency.

Bilimoria, Karan & Bilimoria, Karan. Bottled for Business: The Less Gassy Guide to Entrepreneurship. 2007. (ENG., Illus.). 192p. per. 29.95 *(978-1-84112-726-2(4),* Capstone) Wiley, John & Sons, Inc.

Buxrud, Ulf. Rare Malts: Facts, Figures & Taste. 2007. (ENG., Illus.). 168p. 49.95 *(978-1-84689-007-9(1))* Quiller Pr., Ltd. GBR. Dist: Stackpole Bks.

Capparell, Stephanie. The Real Pepsi Challenge: How One Pioneering Company Broke Color Barriers in 1940s American Business. 2008. (ENG., Illus.). 384p. pap. 23.99 *(978-0-7432-6572-0(6),* Free Pr.) Free Pr.

Clark, Taylor. Starbucked: A Double Tall Tale of Caffeine, Commerce, & Culture. 2008. (ENG.). 320p. pap. 14.99 *(978-0-316-01403-8(6),* Back Bay Bks.) Little Brown & Co.

Cold Beverage Market: Companies-Products-Services. 292p. (Orig.). pap. 795.00 *(978-0-7605-2136-6(0))* Rector Pr., Ltd.

Doeg, Colin. Crisis Management in the Food & Drinks Industry: A Practical Approach: A Practical Approach. 2nd ed. 2010. (Practical Approaches to Food Control & Food Quality Ser.). (Illus.). xx, 263p. pap. 129.00 *(978-1-4419-3620-2(3),* 1441936203) Springer.

Euromonitor International Staff. Who Drinks What: Identifying International Drinks Consumption Trends. 2nd ed. 2011. 446p. (C). *(978-1-84264-540-6(4))* Euromonitor International PLC.

B

Fellner, Kim. Wrestling with Starbucks: Conscience, Capital, Cappuccino. 2008. (ENG.). 296p. 24.95 *(978-0-8135-4320-8(7))* Rutgers Univ. Pr.
Font, Mauricio A. Coffee & Transformation in So Paulo, Brazil. 2010. (ENG.). 394p. 85.00 *(978-0-7391-4750-4(1))* Lexington Bks.
Food & Beverage Market: Companies-Products-Services. 125p. (Orig.). pap. *(978-0-7605-2190-8(5))* Rector Pr., Ltd.
Fratamico, P., et al, eds. Biofilms in the Food & Beverage Industries. 2009. (ENG., Illus.). 600p. 249.95 *(978-1-4200-9484-8(X)*, CRC Press) Taylor & Francis Group GBR. Dist: Taylor & Francis Group.
—Biofilms in the Food & Beverage Industries. 2009. (Illus.). 576p. *(978-1-84569-477-7(5))* Woodhead Publishing Ltd.
Gjelten, Tom. Bacardi & the Long Fight for Cuba: The Biography of a Cause. 2009. (ENG.). 432p. (gr. 12-18). 17.00 *(978-0-14-311632-5(0)*, Penguin (Non-Classics)) Penguin Group (USA) Inc.
Glassman, Bruce. San Diego's Top Brewers: Inside America's Craft Beer Capital. 2011. (Illus.). 208p. pap. 24.95 ***(978-0-9816222-3-1(2))*** Chefs Pr.
Gottlieb, Richard. Food & Beverage Market Place: 2009, 3 vols. Mars-Proietti, Laura, ed. 8th rev. ed. 2008. 6000p. pap. 595.00 *(978-1-59237-361-1(5))* Grey Hse. Publishing.
Grey House Publishing, creator. Food & Beverage Market Place, Volume 1: Food & Beverage Manufacturers, Product Categories, Company Profiles. 7th ed. 2007. (Thomas Food & Beverage Market Place: V. 1 Food & Beverage Manufacturers Ser.). (Illus.). 1610p. per. 437.50 *(978-1-59237-199-0(X))* Grey Hse. Publishing.
—Food & Beverage Market Place, Volume 2: Equipment, Supplies & Services, Product Categories, Company Profiles. 7th ed. 2007. (Thomas Food & Beverage Market Place: V. 2 Equipment & Supply Companies, Transportation, Ser.). (Illus.). 1086p. per. 312.50 *(978-1-59237-200-3(7))* Grey Hse. Publishing.
—Food & Beverage Market Place, Volume 3: Brokers, Importers & Exporters, Transportation Firms, Warehouse Companies, Wholesalers & Distributors. 7th ed. 2007. (Thomas Food & Beverage Market Place: V. 3 Brokers, Importers, Exporters, Catalogs, Information Ser.). 1735p. per. 312.50 *(978-1-59237-201-0(5))* Grey Hse. Publishing.
Howlett, Leon. The Kentucky Bourbon Experience. 2011. ***(978-1-935001-81-2(7))*** Acclaim Pr., Inc.
Ionescu-Somers, Aileen & Steger, Ulrich. Business Logic for Sustainability: A Food & Beverage Industry Perspective. 2008. (ENG., Illus.). 288p. 100.00 *(978-0-230-55131-2(9))* Palgrave Macmillan.
Japanese Alcoholic Drinks Market. 146p. (Orig.). pap. 3495.00 *(978-0-7605-2176-2(X))* Rector Pr., Ltd.
Jolliffe, Lee, ed. Coffee Culture, Destinations & Tourism. 2010. (Illus.). x, 235p. E-Book *(978-1-84541-144-2(7))* Channel View Pubns., Ltd.
—Coffee Culture, Destinations & Tourism. 2010. (Tourism & Cultural Change Ser.). (ENG., Illus.). 248p. 44.95 *(978-1-84541-142-8(0))*; 149.95 *(978-1-84541-143-5(9))* Channel View Pubns., Ltd. GBR. Dist: Univ. of Toronto Pr.
Krishnamurthy, Ravichandran. Juice Market in Indi. 2010. 52p. pap. *(978-3-639-24449-6(4))* VDM Verlag Dr. Mueller e.K.
Lyon, S. Coffee & Community. 2010. 75.00 *(978-1-60732-056-2(8))*; pap. 32.50 *(978-1-60732-057-9(6))* Univ. Pr. of Colorado.
Lyon, Sarah. Coffee & Community: Maya Farmers & Fair-Trade Markets. 2011. (Illus.). ix, 266p. E-Book *(978-1-60732-058-6(4))* Univ. Pr. of Colorado.
Major Food & Drink Companies of the World. 13th ed. 2010. pap. 1250.00 *(978-1-86099-630-6(2))* Graham & Whiteside, Ltd. GBR. Dist: Cengage Gale.
Major Food & Drink Companies of the World 2007. 2007. 995.00 *(978-1-86099-500-2(4))* Graham & Whiteside, Ltd. GBR. Dist: Cengage Gale.
Malt Beverage Market. 100p. (Orig.). pap. 1295.00 *(978-0-7605-2169-4(7))* Rector Pr., Ltd.
Mars, Laura, ed. Food & Beverage Market Place, 3 vols., Set. 2011. pap. 595.00 *(978-1-59237-753-4(X))* 10th rev. ed. 2010. pap. 595.00 *(978-1-59237-577-6(4))* Grey Hse. Publishing.
—Food & Beverage Market Place: Volume 1 - Manufacturers, 3 vols. 10th rev. ed. 2010. pap. 350.00 *(978-1-59237-578-3(2))* Grey Hse. Publishing.
—Food & Beverage Market Place: Volume 2 - Suppliers, 3 vols. 10th rev. ed. 2010. pap. 250.00 *(978-1-59237-579-0(0))* Grey Hse. Publishing.
—Food & Beverage Market Place: Volume 3 - Brokers/Wholesalers/Importer, Etc, 3 vols. 10th rev. ed. 2010. pap. 250.00 *(978-1-59237-580-6(4))* Grey Hse. Publishing.
Mars-Proietti, Laura, ed. Food & Beverage Market Place. 9th rev. ed. 2009. 2000p. pap. 250.00 *(978-1-59237-426-7(3))* Grey Hse. Publishing.
—Food & Beverage Market Place: Brokers/Wholesalers/Importer, Etc. 2008. 2000p. pap. 250.00 *(978-1-59237-364-2(X))* Grey Hse. Publishing.
—Food & Beverage Market Place 2008. 7th ed. 2007. 4342p. pap. 595.00 *(978-1-59237-198-3(1))* Grey Hse. Publishing.
—Food & Beverage Market Place 2010, 3 vols. 9th rev. ed. 2009. 6000p. pap. 595.00 *(978-1-59237-423-6(9))* Grey Hse. Publishing.
Membrane Technology for Food & Beverage Processing. 2006. per. 4250.00 *(978-1-59623-208-2(0))* BCC Research.
New Strategist Editors. Who's Buying Alcoholic & Nonalcoholic Beverages. 3rd rev. ed. 2006. 124p. pap. 59.95 *(978-1-933588-11-7(X))* New Strategist Pubns., Inc.
New Strategist Publications, Incorporated Staff. Who's Buying Alcoholic & Nonalcoholic Beverages. 4th ed. 2007. (The Who's Buying Ser.). 119p. pap. 59.95 *(978-1-933588-54-4(3))* New Strategist Pubns., Inc.
Ohashi, Atsuko. Sekai Shisutemu to Chiiki Shakai: Nishi Jawa Ga Eta Mono Ushinatta Mono, 1700-1830. 2010. (JPN., Illus.). x, 474p. *(978-4-87698-942-3(7))* Kyoto Univ. Pr.
Organic Food & Beverage Market. 135p. (Orig.). pap. 1975.00 *(978-0-7605-2142-7(5))* Rector Pr., Ltd.
Panamerican Beverages Inc. 60p. (Orig.). pap. 595.00 *(978-0-7605-2179-3(4))* Rector Pr., Ltd.
Paquin, P. Functional & Specialty Beverage Technology. 2009. (Illus.). 384p. 249.95 *(978-1-4200-9987-4(6))* CRC Pr. LLC.
Paquin, P., ed. Functional & Speciality Beverage Technology. 2009. 512p. *(978-1-84569-342-8(6))* Woodhead Publishing Ltd.
Pepsico Inc. 60p. (Orig.). pap. 295.00 *(978-0-7605-2180-9(8))* Rector Pr., Ltd.
Rama, Ruth. Handbook of Innovation in the Food & Drink Industry. 2008. (ENG., Illus.). 428p. 159.95 *(978-1-56022-298-9(0)*, CRC Press) Taylor & Francis Group GBR. Dist: Taylor & Francis Group.
Rovell, Darren. First in Thirst: How Gatorade Turned the Science of Sweat into a Cultural Phenomenon. 2009. (ENG.). 243p. 22.00 *(978-1-4379-6598-8(9))* DIANE Publishing Co.
Schultz, Howard & Gordon, Joanne. Onward: How Starbucks Fought for Its Life Without Losing Its Soul. 2012. (ENG., Illus.). 384p. pap. 16.99 ***(978-1-60961-382-2(1))*** 2011. *(978-1-60961-165-1(9))* Rodale Pr., Inc.
Schultz, Howard & Gordon, Joanne. Onward: How Starbucks Fought for Its Life without Losing Its Soul. 2011. (ENG., Illus.). 384p. 25.99 *(978-1-60529-288-5(5))* Rodale Pr., Inc.
Tierney-Jones, Adrian, ed. 1001 Beers You Must Taste Before You Die. 2010. (ENG., Illus.). 960p. 36.95 *(978-0-7893-2025-4(8))* Universe Publishing.
Ukers, William H. All about Coffee. 2nd ed. 2007. (Illus.). 820p. 135.00 *(978-1-57898-630-9(3))* Martino Publishing.
Ukers, William H. & Ukers, William H. All about Coffee. 2010. 826p. pap. 38.50 *(978-1-57898-670-9(5))* Martino Publishing.
Wintgens, Jean Nicolas, ed. Coffee: Growing, Processing, Sustainable Production - A Guidebook for Growers, Processors, Traders, & Researchers. 2nd ed. 2009. (ENG., Illus.). 1040p. 440.00 *(978-3-527-32286-2(8)*, Wiley-VCH) Wiley John & Sons, Inc.
World Drinks Marketing Directory, 2 vols., Set. 6th rev. ed. 2010. 475.00 *(978-1-84264-515-4(3))* Euromonitor International PLC GBR. Dist: Cengage Gale.

BEVERAGES

see also Alcoholic Beverages; Bottling; Carbonated Beverages; Kombucha Tea also names of beverages, e.g. Cocoa, Coffee, Tea

Almada, Anthony L., ed. Sports, Fitness & Physique Foods & Beverages: Active Ingredients & Supplements. 2007. (Illus.). 304p. 99.99 *(978-0-8138-0237-4(7)*, Wiley-Blackwell) Wiley, John & Sons, Inc.
Appleton, Jeremy. Acai Berry: Fruits of Paradise. 2007. (Woodland Health Ser.). (Illus.). 36p. pap. 4.95 *(978-1-58054-472-6(X))* Woodland Publishing, Inc.
Bartone, John Charles. Cancer Disease for All Americans: Dr. Bartone Rule #2: Beverages Containing Carcinogens: Index, Reference & Medical Analysis of New Research Information. 2008. (Illus.). 160p. ring bd. 69.95 *(978-0-7883-3859-5(5))* ABBE Pubs. Assn. of Washington, D.C.
BCC Staff. Sugars & Sweeteners in Processed Foods & Beverages. 2007. per. 4250.00 *(978-1-59623-298-3(6))* BCC Research.
Blake, Susannah. Irresistible Smoothies & Shakes. 2012. (ENG., Illus.). 64p. 9.99 ***(978-0-7548-2174-8(9))*** Anness Publishing GBR. Dist: National Bk. Network.
Blake, Susannah. Smoothies & Shakes: 30 Heavenly Blends Shown in 100 Delicious Photographs. 2008. (ENG.). 64p. pap. 9.99 *(978-1-84476-469-3(9))* Anness Publishing GBR. Dist: National Bk. Network.
Boutenko, Victoria. Green for Life. 2010. (ENG., Illus.). 224p. pap. 16.95 *(978-1-55643-930-8(X))* North Atlantic Bks.
Brandon, Britt. The Everything Green Smoothies Book: Includes 300 Nutritious Recipes! 2011. (ENG.). 304p. pap. 15.95 *(978-1-4405-2564-3(1))* Adams Media Corp.
Brown, Derek & Searing, Dan. The Punch Bowl: 75 Recipes Spanning Four Centuries of Wanton Revelry. 2011. (ENG., Illus.). 192p. 14.95 *(978-1-4027-8582-5(8)*, Sterling Epicure) Sterling Publishing Co., Inc.
Bruning, Ted. Golden Fire: The Story of Cider. 2012. 202p. pap. ***(978-0-7552-1431-0(5))*** Authors OnLine, Ltd.
Capparell, Stephanie. The Real Pepsi Challenge: How One Pioneering Company Broke Color Barriers in 1940s American Business. 2008. (ENG., Illus.). 384p. pap. 23.99 *(978-0-7432-6572-0(6)*, Free Pr.) Free Pr.
Chace, Daniella. More Smoothies for Life: Satisfy, Energize, & Heal Your Body. 2007. (ENG., Illus.). 320p. per. 14.95 *(978-0-307-35136-4(X)*, Three Rivers Pr.) Crown Publishing Group.
Clarke, Oz & May, James. Drink to Britain. 2009. (ENG., Illus.). 192p. 32.95 *(978-1-86205-846-0(6))* Chrysalis Children's Bks. GBR. Dist: Independent Pubs. Group.
Colburn, Kerry. Good Drinks for Bad Days. 2009. (ENG., Illus.). 112p. 12.95 *(978-1-57061-621-1(3))* Sasquatch Bks.
Coles, Richard & Kirwan, Mark J. Food & Beverage Packaging Technology. 2nd ed. 2011. (ENG., Illus.). 344p. 209.95 ***(978-1-4051-8910-1(X)***, Wiley-Blackwell) Wiley, John & Sons, Inc.
Cookbook Resources, ed. Cool Smoothies. 2010. 176p. *(978-1-59769-042-3(2))* Cookbook Resources, LLC.
Cruz, Abe . Salud con Jugos. 2007. (Salud Ser.). (SPA.). 128p. pap. *(978-970-643-212-4(4))* Selector, S.A. de C.V.
Cuthbert, Pippa & Wilson, Lindsay Cameron. Jugo! Deliciosos Jugos para Disfrutar A Cualquier Hora del Dia. 2007. (Illus.). 176p. pap. 15.95 *(978-970-718-459-6(0)*, Degustis) Advanced Marketing, S. de R. L. de C. V. MEX. Dist: Perseus-PGW.
Dornenburg, Andrew & Page, Karen. What to Drink with What You Eat: The Definitive Guide to Pairing Food with Wine, Beer, Spirits, Coffee, Tea - Even Water - Based on Expert Advice from America's Best Sommeliers. 2006. (ENG., Illus.). 368p. 35.00 *(978-0-8212-5718-0(8))* Bulfinch.
Dow, Michael. Calorie Comparison Handbook for the Vast Majority of the World's Foods & some Beverages: An Interesting Supplement to the Pen & Paper Diet. 2009. 130p. 44.95 *(978-0-557-05291-2(2))* Lulu Enterprises Inc.
—Calorie Comparison Handbook for the Vast Majority of the World's Foods & some Beverages: an interesting supplement to the Pen & Paper Diet. 2009. 130p. pap. 24.95 *(978-0-557-05300-1(5))* Lulu Enterprises Inc.
Dubin, Rick & Van Cura, Kevin. Hottest Drinks of the 90's. Date not set. 68p. pap. 15.00 *(978-0-9672345-0-2(6))* Hottest Drinks 90'S.
Eding, June, ed. Cooking Well: Alcohol-Free Beverages - Over 150 Easy & Delicious All-Occasion Drink Recipes. 2010. (Cooking Well Ser.). (ENG., Illus.). 112p. pap. 12.50 *(978-1-57826-342-4(5))* Hatherleigh Co., Ltd., The.
Edwards, Graham & Edwards, Susan. The Dictionary of Drink: A Guide to Every Type of Beverage. 2008. (ENG., Illus.). 1456p. per. 17.99 *(978-0-7509-4245-4(2))* History Pr. Ltd.,The GBR. Dist: Independent Pubs. Group.
Euromonitor International, contrib. by. Who Drinks What? Indentifying International Drinks Consumption Trends. 2009. xi, 654p. *(978-1-84264-490-4(4))* Euromonitor International PLC.
Farmer, James T., III. Sip & Savor: Drinks for Party & Porch, 1 vol. 2012. (ENG., Illus.). 96p. 19.99 ***(978-1-4236-2484-4(X))*** Gibbs Smith, Publisher.
Food Consultants of Hawaii Staff. Take Home Recipes - Pupus & Drinks. pap. 3.50 *(978-0-681-02807-4(6))* Booklines Hawaii, Ltd.
Gage, Allan. Pitchers & Punches: 50 Crowd-Pleasing Drinks! 2010. (ENG., Illus.). 96p. pap. 9.95 *(978-1-55285-751-9(4))* Whitecap Bks., Ltd. CAN. Dist: Midpoint Trade Bks., Inc.
Gerson, Fany. Paletas: Authentic Recipes for Mexican Ice Pops, Shaved Ice & Aguas Frescas. 2011. (ENG., Illus.). 128p. 16.99 *(978-1-60774-035-3(4))* Ten Speed Pr.
Gobin, Anuradha. Leaving a Bittersweet Taste. 2011. 108p. pap. ***(978-3-8443-9059-9(6))*** Lambert Academic Publishing.
Gross, Paul M. Superfruits. 2009. (ENG.). 240p. pap. 16.95 *(978-0-07-163387-1(1)*, 0071633871) McGraw-Hill Cos., The.
Gusenoff, Alyssa. Margarita Mama: Mocktails for Moms-to-Be. 2008. (ENG., Illus.). 96p. 12.95 *(978-1-59474-215-6(4))* Quirk Bks.
Hamlyn. Juice Collection. 2009. (ENG.). pap. 14.99 *(978-0-600-62000-6(X)*, Hamlyn) Octopus Publishing Group GBR. Dist: Hachette Bk. Group.
Hamlyn & Nikoli. Juices & Smoothies: Over 200 Delicious Drinks for Health & Vitality. 2006. (ENG., Illus.). 176p. pap. 9.95 *(978-0-600-60843-1(3)*, 1222980, Hamlyn) Octopus Publishing Group GBR. Dist: Hachette Bk. Group.
Hamlyn All Color Staff. 200 Juices & Smoothies: Hamlyn All Color. 2010. (ENG., Illus.). 240p. pap. 7.99 *(978-0-600-62091-4(3)*, Hamlyn) Octopus Publishing Group GBR. Dist: Hachette Bk. Group.
Harris, Shell & Johnson, Elizabeth. Skinny Smoothies: 101 Delicious Drinks that Help You Detox & Lose Weight. 2012. (ENG., Illus.). 240p. pap. 16.00 ***(978-0-7382-1600-3(3))*** Da Capo Pr., Inc.
Hartley, Paul. The Horlicks Cookbook. 2010. (Storecupboard Ser.). (ENG., Illus.). 80p. 12.95 *(978-1-906650-31-5(4))* Absolute Pr. GBR. Dist: Independent Pubs. Group.
Hawaii's Best Tropical Food & Drinks. (Illus.). pap. 4.95 *(978-0-930492-44-1(7))* Hawaiian Service, Inc.
Heiss, Mary Lou, et al. Hot Drinks: Cider, Coffee, Tea, Hot Chocolate, Spiced Punch, Spirits. 2007. (ENG., Illus.). 112p. 16.95 *(978-1-58008-884-8(8))* Ten Speed Pr.
Henry, Mike. Caribbean Cocktails & Mixed Drinks: With Special Sandals Section. (Illus.). 101p. pap. *(978-976-610-209-8(0))* Creative Links.
Hensley, Jim, et al. Slurp: Drinks & Light Fare, All Day, All Night. 2008. (ENG., Illus.). 176p. pap. 16.99 *(978-0-7407-6990-0(1))* Andrews McMeel Publishing.
Hounhouigan, Joseph, ed. African Fermented Foods & Beverages. 2012. (Fermented Foods & Beverages Ser.). (ENG., Illus.). 584p. 179.95 ***(978-1-4398-4596-7(4)***, CRC Press) Taylor & Francis Group GBR. Dist: Taylor & Francis Group.
Hoving, Walter. The Definitive Drink Dictionary. 2007. 568p. per. 45.95 *(978-0-595-43833-4(4))* iUniverse, Inc.
Hui, Y. H., et al, eds. Handbook of Animal-Based Fermented Foods & Beverages. 2nd rev. ed. 2012. (ENG., Illus.). 814p. 199.95 ***(978-1-4398-5022-0(4)***, CRC Press) Taylor & Francis Group GBR. Dist: Taylor & Francis Group.
—Handbook of Plant-Based Fermented Foods & Beverages. 2nd rev ed. 2012. (ENG., Illus.). 821p. 199.95 ***(978-1-4398-4904-0(8)***, CRC Press) Taylor & Francis Group GBR. Dist: Taylor & Francis Group.
Hunking, Penny & Hunter, Fiona. Power Juices: 50 Energizing Juices & Smoothies. 2006. (ENG., Illus.). 192p. pap. 9.95 *(978-0-600-61422-7(0)*, Hamlyn) Octopus Publishing Group GBR. Dist: Hachette Bk. Group.
Innocent. Innocent: 57 & a Half Recipes from Our Kitchen to Yours. 2007. (ENG., Illus.). 192p. pap. 16.95 *(978-0-00-721376-4(X))* HarperCollins Pubs. Ltd. GBR. Dist: Independent Pubs. Group.
Kilcast, D., ed. Sensory Analysis for Food & Beverage Quality Control. 2010. (ENG., Illus.). 560p. 209.95 *(978-1-4398-3142-7(4)*, CRC Press) Taylor & Francis Group GBR. Dist: Taylor & Francis Group.
King, Alice. Fabulous Fizz: Choosing Champagne & Sparkling Wine for Every Occasion. 2006. (ENG., Illus.). 144p. pap. *(978-1-84597-289-9(9))* Ryland Peters & Small.
Klemm, Eben. The Cocktail Primer: All You Need to Know to Make the Perfect Drink. 2009. (ENG.). 128p. 19.99 *(978-0-7407-7816-2(1))* Andrews McMeel Publishing.
Lacour, Pierre. The Manufacture of Liquors, Wines, & Cordials, Without the Aid of Distillation. 2007. (Cooking in America Ser.). (ENG.). 316p. per. 19.95 *(978-1-4290-1039-9(8))* Applewood Bks.
Lee, Sandra. Easy Entertaining at Home: Cocktails, Finger Foods, & Creative Ideas for Year-Round Celebrations. 2011. (ENG.). 208p. pap. 14.99 ***(978-1-4013-1080-6(X))*** Hyperion Pr.
Manheim, Jason. The Healthy Green Drink Diet: Advice & Recipes to Energize, Alkalize, Lose Weight, & Feel Great. 2012. (ENG., Illus.). 176p. 14.95 ***(978-1-61608-473-8(1)***, 608473) Skyhorse Publishing Co., Inc.
Masum, A. K. M., et al. Utilization of Soymilk As Milk Replacer for Raising Calves. 2011. 108p. pap. ***(978-3-8443-8208-2(9))*** Lambert Academic Publishing.
Matthews, Rupert. Leicestershire Food & Drink. 2010. (ENG., Illus.). 128p. pap. 24.95 *(978-0-7524-4863-3(3))* History Pr. Ltd.,The GBR. Dist: Independent Pubs. Group.
Mazza, Giuseppe. Functional Beverages. 2009. 159.95 *(978-1-4200-6240-3(9))* CRC Pr. LLC.
McCulloch-Williams, Martha. Dishes & Beverages of the Old South. 2009. (Illus.). 146p. pap. *(978-1-4099-7830-5(3))* Dodo Pr.
—Dishes & Beverages of the Old South. 2008. 320p. 45.95 *(978-1-4369-6672-6(8))*; pap. 30.95 *(978-1-4368-2349-4(8))* Kessinger Publishing, LLC.
Meusburger, Magdalena. The Energy Drink Market in South Afric. 2009. 104p. pap. *(978-3-639-16236-3(6))* VDM Verlag Dr. Mueller e.K.
Mew, James. Drinks of the World. 2009. 148p. pap. 16.73 *(978-1-151-40932-4(4))* General Bks. LLC.
Mew, James & Ashton, John. Drinks of the World. 2009. 370p. 48.95 *(978-1-120-83039-5(7))*; pap. 33.95 *(978-1-120-61347-9(7))* Kessinger Publishing, LLC.
Meyerowitz, Steve. Power Juices, Super Drinks. 2010. (ENG.). 432p. 16.00 *(978-0-7582-6712-2(6))* Kensington Publishing Corp.
Miles, Kristine. The Green Smoothie Bible: 300 Delicious Recipes. 2012. (ENG.). 240p. pap. 14.95 *(978-1-56975-974-5(X))* Ulysses Pr.
Montgomery, Lisa. Liquid Raw: Over 125 Juices, Smoothies, Soups, & other Raw Beverages. Eding, June, ed. 2011. (Complete Book of Raw Food Ser.). (ENG.). 144p. pap. 16.50 *(978-1-57826-373-8(5))* Hatherleigh Co., Ltd., The.
Moore, Helen. On Uncle Sam's Water Wagon. 2007. (Cooking in America Ser.). (ENG.). 236p. per. 15.95 *(978-1-4290-1047-4(9))* Applewood Bks.
Moore, Victoria. How to Drink. 2009. (ENG.). 344p. 18.99 *(978-0-7407-8574-0(5))* Andrews McMeel Publishing.
Natural Beverages Health Guide. 700p. (Orig.). pap. 995.00 *(978-0-7605-2140-3(9))* Rector Pr., Ltd.
New Internationalist Publication Staff, creator. Desserts & Drinks from Around the World. 2006. (Chunky Cook Book: Supporting Fair Trade Ser.). (ENG., Illus.). 176p. pap. 11.95 *(978-1-904456-16-2(2))* New Internationalist Pubns., Ltd. GBR. Dist: Consortium Bk. Sales & Distribution.
O'Brien, Sarah. Wee Little Irish Drinking Companion. 2007. (Wee Little Ser.). (ENG.). 128p. 4.95 *(978-0-7624-2988-2(7)*, Running Pr. Minature Editions) Running Pr. Bk. Pubs.
Olivier, Susannah & Farrow, Joanna. Smoothies & Jucies: Delicious Drinks, Blends, Tonics, Shakes & Floats. 2008. (ENG., Illus.). 224p. 29.99 *(978-0-7548-1848-9(9))* Anness Publishing GBR. Dist: National Bk. Network.
Olivier, Suzannah. Juices & Smoothies: Over 160 Healthy, Refreshing & Irresistible Drinks & Blends. (Illus.). 256p. pap. *(978-0-681-37393-8(8))* Anness Publishing, Inc.
—75 Smoothies: How to Make Fabulous Fresh Fruit Drinks, Shakes & Floats with 290 Step-by-step Colour Photographs. 2009. (ENG., Illus.). 96p. pap. 8.99 *(978-1-84476-715-1(9))* Anness Publishing GBR. Dist: National Bk. Network.
Olivier, Suzannah & Farrow, Joanna. Juices & Smoothies. 2011. (ENG., Illus.). 264p. pap. 18.99 ***(978-1-78019-008-2(5))*** Anness Publishing GBR. Dist: National Bk. Network.
Paquin, P. Functional & Specialty Beverage Technology. 2009. (Illus.). 384p. 249.95 *(978-1-4200-9987-4(6))* CRC Pr. LLC.
Paquin, P., ed. Functional & Speciality Beverage Technology. 2009. 512p. *(978-1-84569-342-8(6))* Woodhead Publishing Ltd.
Petersen-Schepelern, Elsa. Cool Smoothies: Juices & Cocktails. 2007. (ENG., Illus.). 128p. pap. *(978-1-84597-389-6(5))* Ryland Peters & Small.
Pickford, Louise. Cool Drinks for Hot Days. 2009. (ENG., Illus.). 96p. *(978-1-84597-847-1(1))* Ryland Peters & Small.
—Hot Drinks: Indulgent Hot Chocolates, Great Coffees, Soothing Teas, Spiced Punches, & Other Warming Treats for Cold Days. 2008. (ENG., Illus.). 96p. *(978-1-84597-804-4(8))* Ryland Peters & Small.
—Smoothies: Over 100 Fabulous Blended Drinks from Breakfast Boosters to Indulgent Treats. 2008. (ENG., Illus.). 96p. *(978-1-84597-594-4(4))* CICO Bks.
Pie Books Staff. @Super Market: Package Designs. Takahashi, Kaoru, ed. 2010. (ENG., Illus.). 160p. 59.00 *(978-4-7562-4002-6(X)*, PIE Bks.) Rizzoli International Pubns., Inc.
Powers, Lindsay. The Teeny-Weeny Merry Martini, Set. Running Press Staff, ed. 2008. (ENG.). 32p. pap. 8.95 *(978-0-7624-3431-2(7))* Perseus Bks. Group.
Preston-Campbell, Brian. Cool Waters: 50 Refreshing, Healthy, Homemade Thirst Quenchers. 2009. (50 Ser.). (ENG.). 96p. 12.95 *(978-1-55832-384-1(8))* Harvard Common Pr.

Publications International Staff, ed. Rival Crock Pot. 2009. 256p. 14.98 *(978-1-4127-7663-3(8),* PIL Kids) Publications International, Ltd.

Quinion, Michael B. Cidermaking. 2009. (Shire Library: No. 95). (ENG., Illus.). 32p. pap. 11.95 *(978-0-85263-614-5(8))* Shire Pubns., Ltd. GBR. Dist: Random Hse., Inc.

Reed, Ben. Punch Parties: Pitchers, punches & refreshing cocktails to share with Friends. 2012. (ENG., Illus.). 128p. ***(978-1-84975-206-0(0))*** Ryland Peters & Small.

Reynolds, Virginia. The Little Pink Book of Frozen Drinks: And Other Party Classics. 2007. (Little Pink Books (Peter Pauper) Ser.). (Illus.). 176p. 9.95 *(978-1-59359-861-7(0))* Peter Pauper Pr. Inc.

Rosen, Darryl. Winning the Customer Loyalty Marathon: How to Achieve Sales & Service Excellence in the Beverage Business. 2009. 316p. pap. 19.99 *(978-1-4389-5424-0(7))* AuthorHouse.

Roskelley, Amy. 201 Healthy Smoothies & Juices for Kids. 2012. E-Book ***(978-1-4405-3612-0(0))*** Adams Media Corp.

—201 Healthy Smoothies & Juices for Kids: Fresh, Wholesome No-Sugar Added Drinks Your Child Will Love. 2012. (ENG.). 240p. pap. 15.95 ***(978-1-4405-3364-8(4))*** Adams Media Corp.

Ryland Peters & Small Staff, ed. Easy Smoothies & Juices. 2011. (ENG., Illus.). 240p. *(978-1-84975-109-4(9))* Ryland Peters & Small.

Savona, Natalie. The Big Book of Juices: More Than 400 Natural Blends for Health & Vitality Every Day. (ENG., Illus.). 728p. 2010. pap. 19.95 *(978-1-84483-973-5(7))* 2009. 24.95 *(978-1-84483-799-1(8))* Duncan Baird Pubs. GBR. Dist: Sterling Publishing Co., Inc.

—The Big Book of Juices & Smoothies: 365 Natural Blends for Health & Vitality Every Day. 2006. (ENG., Illus.). 192p. spiral bd. 19.95 *(978-1-84483-266-8(X))* Duncan Baird Pubs. GBR. Dist: Sterling Publishing Co., Inc.

Scardina, Pauline G. Fruit Juices: Properties, Consumption & Nutrition. 2009. (Food & Beverage Consumption & Health Ser.). 125.00 *(978-1-60741-505-3(4),* Nova Biomedical Bks.) Nova Science Pubs., Inc.

Schmidt, A. William. The Flowing Bowl. 2008. (Cooking in America Ser.). (ENG.). 304p. pap. 19.95 *(978-1-4290-1163-9(1))* Applewood Bks.

Science and Life Consultants Association Staff. Food, Beverages & Methylene Chloride (Dichloromethane) with Index & Medical Analysis of New Research Information for All Nations. 2007. (Illus.). 165p. 69.95 *(978-0-7883-4483-1(8),* 0-7883-4483-8) ABBE Pubs. Assn. of Washington, D.C.

Shomron, Leah & Borowski, Hanny. Smoothies, Smoothies & More Smoothies! (Illus.). 144p. 2011. 1695.00 *(978-1-936140-24-4(1))* 2010. (ENG., 18.95 *(978-1-936140-12-1(8),* Imagine Publishing) Charlesbridge Publishing, Inc.

Sibley, Barbara, et al. Antojitos: Festive & Flavorful Mexican Appetizers. 2009. (ENG., Illus.). 160p. 22.99 *(978-1-58008-929-6(1))* Ten Speed Pr.

Smith, R. E. F. & Christian, David. Bread & Salt: A Social & Economic History of Food & Drink in Russia. 2008. (ENG.). 412p. pap. 53.00 *(978-0-521-08963-0(8))* Cambridge Univ. Pr.

Steiner, Jean. Taste of Home Cool & Creamy: Smoothies, Ice Cream Treats, & More! 2008. (Illus.). 112p. *(978-0-89821-688-2(5))* Reiman Pubns., L.P.

Strauss, Bob. Minibar Mixology. 2006. (Illus.). 224p. 12.95 *(978-1-4027-2925-6(1))* Sterling Publishing Co., Inc.

Strong, Jeremy & Strong, Jeremy, eds. Educated Tastes: Food, Drink, & Connoisseur Culture. 2011. (At Table Ser.). (ENG.). 320p. pap. 35.00 *(978-0-8032-1935-9(0))* Univ. of Nebraska Pr.

Suzanne, Kristen. Kristen Suzanne's Easy Raw Vegan Smoothies, Juices, Elixirs, & Drinks: The Definitive Raw Fooder's Book of Beverage Recipes for Boosting Energy, Getting Healthy, Losing Weight, Having Fun, or Cutting Loose ... Including Wine Drinks! 2008. 96p. pap. *(978-0-9817556-7-0(4))* Green Butterfly Pr.

Sweetser, Wendy. Healthy Juices for Healthy Kids. 2010. (ENG., Illus.). 160p. pap. 12.95 *(978-1-84773-612-3(2))* New Holland Pubs., Ltd. GBR. Dist: Sterling Publishing Co., Inc.

Tamang, Jyoti Prakash. Fermented Foods & Beverages of the World. 2010. (ENG., Illus.). 460p. 159.95 *(978-1-4200-9495-4(5),* CRC Press) Taylor & Francis Group GBR. Dist: Taylor & Francis Group.

Terrington, William. Cooling Cups & Dainty Drinks. 2009. 126p. pap. *(978-1-4590-4310-7(3))* Books LLC.

Thompson, Fred. Hot Chocolate: 50 Heavenly Cups of Comfort. 2006. (50 Ser.). (ENG., Illus.). 96p. 12.95 *(978-1-55832-290-5(6))* Harvard Common Pr.

Tsutsumi, Cheryl Chee. 101 Great Tropical Drinks. 2008. (ENG., Illus.). 152p. pap. *(978-1-59700-583-8(5))* Island Heritage Publishing.

Turback, Michael. Coffee Drinks. 2008. (ENG., Illus.). 112p. 14.95 *(978-1-58008-926-5(7))* Ten Speed Pr.

Vale, Jason. The Funky Fresh Juice Book. 2011. (Illus.). 256p. ***(978-0-9547664-1-2(5))*** Crown Hse. Publishing.

Walton, Stuart & Jones, Bridget. Complete Cocktails & Party Food: Two Fabulous Cookbooks in One Special Gift Box. 2010. (ENG.). 528p. 30.00 *(978-0-7548-2015-4(7))* Anness Publishing GBR. Dist: National Bk. Network.

Whitcore, Robin. The Herbal Beverage Book: Simple & Delicious Recipes for the Whole Family. 2010. 111p. pap. 12.95 *(978-0-615-41960-2(7))* Practical Intuitive Media LLC.

Wilson, Ted & Temple, Norman J., eds. Beverages in Nutrition & Health. 2010. (Nutrition & Health Ser.). (Illus.). 456p. pap. 159.00 *(978-1-61737-402-9(4),* 1617374024) Humana Pr.

Womack, Raven. The Raven's Flight Book of Incense, Oils, Potions & Brews: A Friendly Guide to Magickal Products. 2007. (Illus.). 112p. pap. 10.95 *(978-0-9796168-1-5(6))* Pendraig Publishing.

Wood, Hayden. Groovy Drinks. 2010. 214p. pap. 29.95 *(978-2-552-85830-8(9))* Whitecap Bks., Ltd. CAN. Dist: Midpoint Trade Bks., Inc.

—Party Drinks. 2010. 208p. pap. 29.95 *(978-2-552-85838-4(4))* Whitecap Bks., Ltd. CAN. Dist: Midpoint Trade Bks., Inc.

Wright, Helen S. Old Time Recipes for Home Made Wines. 2007. 160p. per. 12.45 *(978-1-59462-480-3(1),* 516, Book Jungle) Standard Pubns., Inc.

Yabsley, Charmaine & Cross, Amanda. Miracle Juices: Over 50 Juices for a Healthy Life. 2007. (ENG., Illus.). 128p. pap. 9.95 *(978-0-600-61606-1(1),* Hamlyn) Octopus Publishing Group GBR. Dist: Hachette Bk. Group.

Zinczenko, David & Goulding, Matt. Drink This Not That! The No-Diet Weight Loss Solution. 2010. (ENG., Illus.). 336p. pap. 19.99 *(978-1-60529-539-8(6))* Rodale Pr., Inc.

BEVERLY HILLS (CALIF.)

Cook, Lisa Fineberg. Japan Took the J. A. P. Out of Me: The True Story of a Domesticated Princess. 2009. (ENG.). 288p. pap. 15.00 *(978-1-4391-1003-4(4),* Downtown Press) Downtown Pr.

Oldham, Mike. Greetings from Beverly Hills. 2007. (Illus.). 128p. pap. 24.95 *(978-0-7643-2628-8(7))* Schiffer Publishing, Ltd.

Wanamaker, Marc. Beverly Hills: 1930-2005. 2006. (Images of America Ser.). (ENG., Illus.). 128p. per. 21.99 *(978-0-7385-4669-9(3))* Arcadia Publishing.

Zager, Norma. Erin Brockovich & the Beverly Hills Greenscam, 1 vol. 2010. (ENG.). 272p. 21.00 *(978-1-58980-810-2(X))* Pelican Publishing Co., Inc.

BEWICK, THOMAS, 1753-1828

Bewick, Thomas. A Memoir of Thomas Bewick. 2008. 372p. 48.95 *(978-1-4369-8464-5(5));* pap. 33.95 ***(978-1-4367-4014-2(2))*** Kessinger Publishing, LLC.

Dobson, Austin. Thomas Bewick & His Pupils. 2010. 294p. pap. 28.75 *(978-1-141-70113-1(8));* 328p. pap. 31.75 *(978-1-142-20850-9(8))* BiblioBazaar.

—Thomas Bewick & His Pupils. 2009. 94p. pap. *(978-1-151-69009-8(0))* Books LLC.

—Thomas Bewick & His Pupils. 2008. 284p. 43.95 *(978-1-4365-5945-4(6))* 2007. (ENG.). 288p. per. 28.95 *(978-0-548-77194-5(4))* Kessinger Publishing, LLC.

Tattersfield, Nigel. The Complete Illustrative Work of Thomas Bewick. 2010. 245.00 *(978-1-58456-273-3(0))* Oak Knoll Pr.

Uglow, Jenny. Nature's Engraver: A Life of Thomas Bewick. 2007. (ENG., Illus.). 480p. 30.00 *(978-0-374-11236-3(3))* Farrar, Straus & Giroux.

—Nature's Engraver: A Life of Thomas Bewick. 2009. (ENG., Illus.). 480p. pap. 18.00 *(978-0-226-82391-1(1))* Univ. of Chicago Pr.

BEYLE, MARIE HENRI, 1783-1842

see Stendhal, 1783-1842

BEZE, THEODORE DE, 1519-1605

Bèze, Théodore de, et al. Correspondance de Théodore de Bèze. 2009. (Travaux d'Humanisme et Renaissance Ser.). (LAT & FRE., Illus.). 272p. (C). 164.00 *(978-2-600-01330-7(X))* Droz, Librairie CHE. Dist: Brown, David Bk. Co., The.

Dufour, A., et al. Theodore de Beze: Correspondance. Tome XXXI 1590. 2009. (Travaux d'Humanisme et Renaissance Ser.). (FRE & LAT., Illus.). 305p. (C). 217.00 *(978-2-600-01277-5(X))* Droz, Librairie CHE. Dist: Brown, David Bk. Co., The.

Krans, Jan. Beyond What Is Written: Erasmus & Beza as Conjectural Critics of the New Testament. 2006. (New Testament Tools & Studies: Vol. 35). (Illus.). 394p. *(978-90-04-15286-1(5))* BRILL.

Wright, Shawn D. Our Sovereign Refuge: The Pastoral Theology of Theodore Beza. 2007. (Studies in Christian History & Thought Ser.). 334p. pap. 34.00 *(978-1-59752-772-9(6))* Wipf & Stock Pubs.

BHAGAVADGITA

Abhinavagupta. Abhinavagupta's Commentary on the Bhagavad Gita: Gitartha-Samgraha. 2006. (SAN & ENG.). xxiv, 354p. 24.95 *(978-0-915801-93-0(0))* Rudra Pr.

Arnold, Edwin. Bhagavad-Git. Arnold, Sir Edwin, tr. 2011. 90p. pap. 6.49 ***(978-1-61720-337-4(8))*** Wilder Pubns., Ltd.

Beloved, Michael. Bhagavad Gita Explained: Bhagavad Gita in Its Own Time & Place. 2nd rev. ed. 2008. (ENG., Illus.). 596p. pap. 24.99 *(978-0-9793916-0-6(1))* Beloved, Michael.

—Bhagavad Gita Revealed. 2008. (ENG., Illus.). 310p. pap. 12.99 *(978-0-9793916-2-0(8))* Beloved, Michael.

Bhagavad Gita. 2008. 29.90 *(978-1-60591-002-4(3))* Titto Player, Inc.

Bhagavad-Gita. 2007. (ENG.). 72p. per. 9.99 *(978-1-59547-942-6(2))* NuVision Pubns., LLC.

Bhagavad-Gita Tal Como Es. (SPA.). 14.95 *(978-0-89213-173-0(X))* Bhaktivedanta Bk. Trust.

The Bhagavadgita: The Sanatsugatiya & the Anugita. 446p. reprint ed. 68.00 *(978-0-7222-9944-9(3))* Library Reprints, Inc.

Bhatnagar, Sant K. The Lord's Song Gita: Rendering the 700 divine Shlokas of the Holy Gita. 2009. 342p. pap. *(978-81-223-1032-0(X))* Mahal, Pustak Pubs., Booksellers & Order Suppliers.

Bodhananda, Swami. A Conversation with Lord Krishna: Five Spiritual Questions of Arjuna. 2007. pap. *(978-0-9785969-4-1(3))* Sambodh Society, Inc., The.

Browning, K. Notes & Index to the Bhagavad Gita 1916. 2007. (ENG.). 108p. 34.95 *(978-0-548-05640-0(4))* Kessinger Publishing, LLC.

Byrd, Charles Michael. The Bhagavad-Gita in Black & White: From Mulatto Pride to Krishna Consciousness. 2007. 218p. per. 16.95 *(978-0-939479-27-6(3),* Backintyme) Boxes & Arrows, Inc.

Chatterji, Mohini M. The Bhagavad Gita or the Lord's Lay with References to the Christian Scriptures. 2007. (ENG.). 310p. 45.95 *(978-0-548-04167-3(9))* Kessinger Publishing, LLC.

Cope, Stephen. The Great Work of Your Life: A Guide for the Journey to Your True Calling. 2012. (ENG.). 304p. 26.00 ***(978-0-553-80751-6(X))*** Random House Publishing Group.

Cornille, C. The Song Divine: Christian Commentaries on the Bhagavad Gita. 2006. (Christian Commentaries on Non-Christian Sacred Texts Ser.: Vol. 1). vi, 219p. *(978-90-429-1769-9(5))* Peeters Pubs. & Booksellers.

Cornille, Catherine, ed. Song Divine: Christian Commentaries on the Bhagavad Gita. 2006. (Christian Commentaries on Non-Christian Sacred Texts). 219p. pap. 40.00 *(978-0-8028-4016-5(7))* Eerdmans, William B. Publishing Co.

Dasi, Visakha. Harmony & the Bhagavad-Gita: Lessons from a Life-Changing Move to the Wilderness. 2011. (Illus.). 188p. pap. 14.95 *(978-0-9817273-5-6(2))* Torchlight Publishing.

Easwaran, Eknath. Essence of the Bhagavad Gita: A Contemporary Guide to Yoga, Meditation, & Indian Philosophy. 2011. (Wisdom of India Ser.). (ENG.). 225p. pap. 14.95 *(978-1-58638-068-7(0))* Nilgiri Pr.

Easwaran, Eknath, tr. from SAN. & intro. The Bhagavad Gita. 2nd ed. 2007. (Classic of Indian Spirituality Ser.). (ENG.). 296p. per. 10.95 *(978-1-58638-019-9(2))* Nilgiri Pr.

Feuerstein, Georg. The Bhagavad-Gita: A New Translation. Feuerstein, Brenda, tr. from SAN. 2011. (ENG.). 464p. 39.95 *(978-1-59030-893-6(X))* Shambhala Pubns., Inc.

Flood, Gavin. The Bhagavad Gita: A New Translation. Flood, Gavin & Martin, Charles, trs. from SAN. 2012. (ENG.). 224p. 25.95 ***(978-0-393-08165-7(6),*** 8165) Norton, W. W. & Co., Inc.

Fosse, Lars Martin. The Bhagavad Gita: The Original Sanskrit & an English Translation, 1 vol. 2007. 224p. per. 14.95 *(978-0-9716466-7-4(8));* 29.95 *(978-0-9716466-6-7(X))* YogaVidya.com.

Fowler, Jeaneane D. The Bhagavad Gita: A Text & Commentary for Students. 2012. (ENG.). 418p. 79.95 ***(978-1-84519-520-5(5),*** Sussex Academic Pr. GBR. Dist: International Specialized Bk. Services.

Fowler, Jeaneane D. & Fowler, Merv. The Bhagavad Gita: A Text & Commentary for Students. 2012. (ENG.). 418p. pap. 39.95 *(978-1-84519-346-1(6))* Sussex Academic Pr. GBR. Dist: International Specialized Bk. Services.

Framarin, Christopher G. Desire & Motivation in Indian Philosophy. 2009. (Routledge Hindu Studies Ser.). 208p. 170.00 *(978-0-415-46194-8(4))* Routledge.

Friedrich, Paul. The Gita Within Walden. 120p. 2009. pap. 19.95 *(978-0-7914-7618-5(9),* Suny Pr.) 2008. (C). 60.00 *(978-0-7914-7617-8(0))* State Univ. of New York Pr.

Gandhi, Mahatma. The Bhagavad Gita According to Gandhi. 2009. (ENG.). 248p. pap. 13.95 *(978-1-55643-800-4(1))* North Atlantic Bks.

Gandhi, Mohandas K. The Bhagavad Gita According to Gandhi. Desai, Mahadev, tr. 2011. 80p. pap. 9.99 ***(978-1-61720-333-6(5))*** Wilder Pubns., Ltd.

Gandhi, Mohandas K., et al. Three Translations of the Bhagavad Git. 2011. 224p. pap. 12.99 ***(978-1-61720-339-8(4))*** Wilder Pubns., Ltd.

Gowda, Nagappa. The Bhagavadgita in the Nationalist Discourse. 2011. (ENG.). 312p. 59.95 ***(978-0-19-807206-5(6))*** Oxford Univ. Pr., Inc.

Greene, Joshua. Gita Wisdom: Krishna's Teachings on the Yoga of Love. 2009. (Traditional Chants Ser.). (ENG.). 96p. pap. 14.95 *(978-1-60109-036-2(6))* Mandala Publishing.

Guru, Nataraja. The Bhagavad Gita: A Sublime Hymn of Dialectics. Teitsworth, Scott, ed. 2nd ed. 2008. 783p. *(978-81-246-0450-2(9))* D. K. Print World (P) Ltd.

Hawley, Jack. The Bhagavad Gita: A Walkthrough for Westerners. 2011. (ENG.). 224p. pap. 14.95 *(978-1-60868-014-6(2))* New World Library.

Herling, Bradley L. The German Gita: Hermeneutics & Discipline in the Early German Reception of Indian Thought. 2009. 360p. 39.95 *(978-0-415-87114-3(X))* Routledge.

Hudson, D. Dennis. Krishna's Mandala: Bhagavata Religion & Beyond. Hawley, John, ed. 2009. (ENG., Illus.). 384p. 74.00 *(978-0-19-806276-9(1))* Oxford Univ. Pr., Inc.

Johnson, W. J., tr. from SAN. The Bhagavad Gita. 2009. (Oxford World's Classics Ser.). (ENG.). 128p. 8.95 *(978-0-19-953812-6(3))* Oxford Univ. Pr., Inc.

Kalupahana, David J. A Path of Morals: Dhammapada: Text & Translation of the Dhammapada Together with an Introductory Essay Comparing the Dhammapada & the Bhagavadgita [i.e. Bhagavadgita], & Commentary on the Verses. 2008. (PLI & ENG.). xvii, 290p. pap. *(978-955-663-066-4(X),* Library of Congress — New Delhi Overseas Office) Buddhist Cultural Centre, The.

Kharb, Karan. Lead to Succeed: Success Secrets from the Bhagavad Gita. 2007. 214p. 29.95 *(978-81-8328-004-4(8))* Wisdom Tree IND. Dist: SCB Distributors.

Krishna, Hare. Secrets of Srimad Bhagavad Gita Revealed. 2010. 192p. pap. 18.00 *(978-0-557-60953-6(4))* Lulu Enterprises Inc.

Krishna, Lord. Srimad Bhagavad Gita. 2011. (Illus.). 544p. pap. 29.95 ***(978-4-87187-650-6(0))*** Ishi Pr. International.

Kriyananda, Swami. The Bhagavad Gita: According to Paramhansa Yogananda, Edited by his disciple, Swami Kriyananda. 2008. (ENG.). 110p. pap. 11.95 *(978-1-56589-232-3(1))* Crystal Clarity Pubs.

La Violette, Wesley, tr. The Bhagavad Gita an Immortal Song: An Interpretation of a Sacred Epic 1945. 2007. (ENG.). 206p. 39.95 *(978-0-548-05644-8(7))* Kessinger Publishing, LLC.

Life Bliss Foundation Staff. I am the Ultimate. 2006. pap. 24.99 *(978-1-934364-17-8(7))* Life Bliss Foundation.

—Krishna - the Cosmic Window. 2007. 19.99 *(978-1-934364-42-0(8))* Life Bliss Foundation.

—Live All Your Dimentions. 2007. 19.99 *(978-1-934364-39-0(8))* Life Bliss Foundation.

—Sincerety - Straight Way to Liberation. 2007. 19.99 *(978-1-934364-44-4(4))* Life Bliss Foundation.

Maitra, Keya & Kolak, Daniel. The Bhagavad Gita. 2007. (Longman Library of Primary Sources Ser.). 300p. (C). pap. 13.33 *(978-0-205-43963-8(2))* Longman Publishing.

Malinar, Angelika. The Bhagavadgita: Doctrines & Contexts. (ENG.). 2009. 312p. pap. 42.00 *(978-0-521-12211-5(2));* 2008. 308p. 105.00 *(978-0-521-88364-1(4))* Cambridge Univ. Pr.

McCrea, Ruth, illus. The Bhagavad-Git: A Book of Hindu Scriptures in the Form of A Dialogue Between Prince Arjuna & the God Krishna. 2011. 116p. 39.95 ***(978-1-258-10556-3(X))*** Literary Licensing, LLC.

Narla, V. A. The Truth about the Gita: A Closer Look at Hindu Scripture. 2010. (ENG.). 230p. pap. 18.00 *(978-1-61614-183-7(2))* Prometheus Bks., Pubs.

Nithyananda, Paramahamsa. Love Is Your Very Life: Discourse on Bhagavad Gita, Chapter - 12. 2006. 24.99 *(978-0-9790806-2-3(2))* Life Bliss Foundation.

Nithyananda, Swami. Beauty of Purposelessness. 2007. 24.99 *(978-1-934364-02-4(9))* Life Bliss Foundation.

—Path of Knowledge. 2007. 24.99 *(978-1-934364-03-1(7))* Life Bliss Foundation.

Oshos, Osho. Inner War & Peace: Timeless Solutions to Conflict from the Bhagavad Gita. 2006. (ENG.). 288p. pap. 16.95 *(978-1-84293-131-8(6),* Watkins Publishing) Duncan Baird Pubs. GBR. Dist: Sterling Publishing Co., Inc.

Paramahamsa, K. R. Ekam Sat. 2008. 232p. pap. 19.99 *(978-1-59095-873-5(X))* 2007. (ENG.). 220p. per. 24.99 *(978-1-59095-888-9(8))* TotalRecall Pubns., Inc.

Parameshananda, Swami. Eternal Answers. 2011. 268p. pap. 20.40 ***(978-1-4269-6347-6(5))*** Trafford Publishing.

Patton, Laurie L. & Anonymous. The Bhagavad Gita. Patton, Laurie L., tr. from SAN. 2008. (ENG.). 288p. (gr. 12-18). 13.00 *(978-0-14-044790-3(3),* Penguin Classics) Penguin Group (USA) Inc.

Piironen, Henry M. The Divine Krishna: Interpreting the Teachings in the Bhagavad Gita. 2010. 172p. pap., wbk. ed. 15.95 *(978-1-4502-1291-5(3))* iUniverse, Inc.

Prasad, Ramananda. The Bhagavad-Gita. 2008. 264p. pap. 19.49 *(978-0-557-01059-2(4))* Lulu Enterprises Inc.

Prem, Sri Krishna. The Yoga of the Bhagavad Gita. 2nd ed. 2008. (ENG.). 250p. pap. 13.95 *(978-1-59675-024-1(3))* Morning Light Pr.

Priya Devi Dasi, Madhava. Bhagavad-Gita In 3d: A Study Guide for the Bhagavad-Gita As It Is. 2008. 208p. pap. 14.95 *(978-1-4327-3726-9(0))* Outskirts Pr., Inc.

Ramacharaka, Yogi. Bhagavad Gita. reprint ed. 11.00 *(978-0-911662-10-8(3))* Yoga Pubn. Society.

—The Bhagavad Gita's Teachings on the Mystery Omnipresence - 2006. pap. 9.95 *(978-1-4304-1925-9(3))* Kessinger Publishing, LLC.

Ramaswami, Krishnaswami. The Bhagavad Gita: The Divine Message. 2006. (ENG.). 200p. per. 24.95 *(978-1-4241-1502-0(7))* PublishAmerica, Inc.

Rosen, Steven J. Krishna's Song: A New Look at the Bhagavad Gita, 1 vol. 2007. 192p. 49.95 *(978-0-313-34553-1(8),* C34553, Praeger Pubs.) Greenwood Publishing Group, Inc.

Ryder, Arthur William. Bhagavad-Gita. 2008. pap. 14.95 *(978-0-9767122-1-3(0))* Non-Ado Publishing.

Sahadeo, Ramnarine. Mohandas K Gandhi: Thoughts, Words, Deeds. 2011. 160p. 29.99 ***(978-1-4653-4283-6(4));*** pap. 19.99 ***(978-1-4653-4282-9(6))*** Xlibris Corp.

Sankaracharya, Sri. The Bhagavad Gita: With Text, Translation & Commentary by Sri Sankaracharya. Sastry, Alladi M., tr. from SAN. 534p. 21.95 *(978-0-910261-03-6(2));* pap. 17.95 *(978-0-910261-04-3(0))* Lotus Pr. (Arcana Publishing).

Sargeant, Winthrop. The Bhagavad Gita. Chapple, Christopher Key, ed. 25th ed. 2009. (Excelsior Editions Ser.). (SAN & ENG.). 774p. pap. 32.95 *(978-1-4384-2842-0(1));* 49.95 *(978-1-4384-2841-3(3))* State Univ. of New York Pr. (Suny Pr.).

Sarma, Deepak. Authority & Its Challenges in Hindu Texts, Translations, & Transnational Communities: Proceedings of Two of the Sessions at the Fourth DANAM Conference, Held on Site at the American Academy of Religion, Washington, DC, 17-19 November 2006. 2009. *(978-0-937194-52-2(2),* Deepak Heritage Bks.) Deepak, A Publishing.

Savitripriya, Swami. Bhagavad Gita: The Journey Through Life to Enlightenment. 200p. (Orig.). pap. 13.95 *(978-1-879722-03-3(8))* New Life Bks.

Schweig, Graham M. Bhagavad Gita: The Beloved Lord's Secret Love Song. 368p. 2010. (ENG.). pap. 13.99 *(978-0-06-199730-3(7))* 2007. (SAN & ENG.). 24.99 *(978-0-06-075425-9(7))* HarperCollins Pubs. (HarperOne).

Searle, January. Essays, Poems, Allegories & Fables with an Elucidation & Analysis of the Bhagvat Geeta 1851. 2007. (ENG.). 194p. 37.95 *(978-0-548-05642-4(0))* Kessinger Publishing, LLC.

Singh, Dharmdeo. Bhagavad Git. 2011. 282p. pap. 14.95 ***(978-1-60594-621-4(4),*** Llumina Pr.) Aeon Publishing Inc.

Singh, Udai Vir. Management Wisdom of Lord Krishna. 2008. (SAN & ENG.). 352p. 59.75 *(978-81-7708-160-2(8))* New Century Publications IND. Dist: International Specialized Bk. Services.

Steiner, Rudolf. The Bhagavad Gita & the West: The Esoteric Significance of the Bhagavad Gita & Its Relation to the Letters of St. Paul. Easwaran, Eknath, tr. from GER. 2009. (Collected Works of Rudolf Steiner: 142).Tr. of Die Bhagavad Gita und die Paulusbriefe — Die okkulten Grundlagen der Bhagavad Gita. 464p. pap. 35.00 *(978-0-88010-604-7(2))* SteinerBooks, Inc.

Sunil Kristi Krishnadas, Kristi Krishnad. Bhagavad Gita- the Spiritual Song. 2010. 276p. 31.00 *(978-1-4251-8003-4(5))* Trafford Publishing.

Sunil Kristi Krishnadas, Kristi Krishnad & Krishnadas, Sunil Kristi. Bhagavad Gita- the Spiritual Song. 2010. 276p. pap. 21.00 *(978-1-4251-8002-7(7))* Trafford Publishing.

Swami Chinmayananda, comment. The Holy Geeta. 1133p. 20.00 *(978-1-880687-19-2(4))* Chinmaya Pubns.

Swarupananda, Swami. Bhagavad Git. 2011. 66p. pap. 6.49 ***(978-1-61720-338-1(6))*** Wilder Pubns., Ltd.

Tadatmananda. Bhagavad Gita: A Lyrical Translation. Date not set. (Illus.). 140p. pap. 9.00 *(978-1-882325-16-0(8))* Arsha Vidya Gurukulam.

Teitsworth, Scott. Krishna in the Sky with Diamonds: The Bhagavad Gita As Psychedelic Guide. 2012. (ENG.). 1p. pap. ***(978-1-59477-441-6(2)***, Park Street Pr.) Inner Traditions International, Ltd.

Theodor, Ithamar. Exploring the Bhagavad Gita: Philosophy Structure & Meaning. 2010. 172p. 89.95 *(978-0-7546-6658-5(1))* Ashgate Publishing Co.

Thompson, George. Bhagaved Gita: A New Translation. 2008. (ENG., Illus.). 160p. pap. 11.00 *(978-0-86547-744-5(2)*, North Point Pr.) Farrar, Straus & Giroux.

Tirtha, Swami Sadashiva. Bhagavad Gita for Modern Times: Secrets to Attaining Inner Peace & Harmony. 2007. (ENG.). 217p. per. 17.95 *(978-0-9658042-6-4(7))* Sat Yuga Pr.

Tsoukalas, Steven. Bhagavadgita: Exegetical & Comparative Commentary with Sanskrit Text, Translation, Interlinear Transliteration with Parsing, Mini Lexicon & Text-Critical Notes (Vol III), 6 vols., Vol. 3. 2010. (SAN & ENG.). *(978-0-7734-1369-6(3))* Mellen, Edwin Pr., The.

—Bhagavadgita Vol. I: Exegetical & Commentary with Sanskrit Text, Translation, Interlinear Transliteration with Parsing, Mini Lexicon, & Text-Critical Notes, 2 vols. 2007. (SAN & ENG.). 440p. 129.95 *(978-0-7734-5290-9(7))* Mellen, Edwin Pr., The.

—Bhagavadgita Vol. II: Exegetical & Comparative Commentary with Sanskrit Text, Translation, Interlinear Transliteration with Parsing, Mini-Lexicon & Text-Critical Notes, 2 vols. 2007. (SAN & ENG.). 452p. *(978-0-7734-5291-6(5))* Mellen, Edwin Pr., The.

Turci, Rubens. Shraddha in the Bhagavad-G8ta- a Magnetic Needle Pointing Toward Brahmanirvan. 2008. 312p. pap. *(978-3-639-04703-5(6))* VDM Verlag Dr. Mueller e.K.

Veeraswamy Krishnaraj. Bhagavadgita in Sanskrit, Transliteration, & Translation: Word for word transliteration, Translation, & word Superscription. 2009. 368p. pap. 33.95 *(978-1-4401-7641-8(8))* iUniverse, Inc.

Walters, J. Donald. Rays of the One Light: Weekly Commentaries on the Bible & the Bhagavad Gita. 2nd ed. 2007. (ENG.). 143p. per. 17.95 *(978-1-56589-208-8(9))* Crystal Clarity Pubs.

Watkins, ed. The Bhagavad Gita: The Song Celestial with Introduction & Notes. Arnold, Edwin, tr. 2006. (Sacred Wisdom Ser.). (ENG., Illus.). 192p. 7.95 *(978-1-84293-124-0(5)*, Watkins Publishing) Duncan Baird Pubs. GBR. Dist: Sterling Publishing Co., Inc.

Wilkins, Charles. The Bhagvat-Geeta, or, Dialogues of Kreeshna & Arjoon; in Eighteen Lectures; with Notes Translated from the Original, in the Sanskreet by Charl. 2006. 136p. per. 16.99 *(978-1-4255-0958-3(4))* MPublishing.

Wood, Ernest & Sattwikagraganya, Shri. The Bhagavad Gita Explained. 2011. 242p. 46.95 ***(978-1-258-01073-7(9))*** Literary Licensing, LLC.

Yogananda, Paramhansa. The Essence of the Bhagavad Gita: Explained by Paramhansa Yogananda, as Remembered by His Disciple, Swami Kriyananda. 2nd rev. ed. 2008. (ENG.). 692p. per. 14.00 *(978-1-56589-226-2(7))* Crystal Clarity Pubs.

—God Talks with Arjuna: The Bhagavad Gita: Royal Science of God-Realization, 2 vols. (Illus.). 1224p. 28.00 *(978-0-87612-031-6(1))* Self-Realization Fellowship Pubs.

—Spiritual Relationships. 2007. (Wisdom of Yogananda Ser.: Vol. 3). (ENG., Illus.). 156p. per. 9.95 *(978-1-56589-224-8(0))* Crystal Clarity Pubs.

—The Yoga of the Bhagavad Gita: An Introduction to India's Universal Science of God-Realization. 2007. (Illus.). 180p. per. 14.00 *(978-0-87612-033-0(8))* Self-Realization Fellowship Pubs.

BHAGAVATAS

Tapasyananda. Srimad Bhagavata, 4 vols., Set. (ENG & SAN.). 84.00 *(978-0-87481-550-4(9))* Vedanta Pr.

Yogananda, Paramhansa. God Talks with Arjuna: The Bhagavad Gita: Royal Science of God-Realization, 2 vols., Set. (Illus.). 1224p. 52.00 *(978-0-87612-030-9(3))* Self-Realization Fellowship Pubs.

BHAGVATAS

see Bhagavatas

BHAGVATS

see Bhagavatas

BHAKTI

see also God—Worship and Love

Badarayana. The Vedanta-Sutras, 3 Vols. reprint ed. 204.00 *(978-0-7222-9956-2(7))* Library Reprints, Inc.

Gupta, Ravi M. The Caitanya Vaisnava Vedanta of Jiva Gosvami: When Knowledge Meets Devotion. 2007. (Routledge Hindu Studies). (Illus.). 225p. 160.00 *(978-0-415-40548-5(3))* Routledge.

Holdrege, Barbara A. Bhakti & Embodiment: Fashioning Divine Bodies & Devotional Bodies in Krsna Bhakti. 2012. (Routledge Hindu Studies Ser.). (ENG.). 256p. (C). 140.00 *(978-0-415-67070-8(5))* Routledge.

Hussain, Hamid. Sufism & Bhakti Movement, Eternal Relevance. 2007. xxi, 312p. *(978-81-7827-155-2(9))* Manak Pubns. Pvt., Ltd.

Kumar, Samrat Schmiem. Bhakti: The Yoga of Love - Trans-Rational Approaches to Peace Studies. 2011. 168p. 34.95 ***(978-3-643-50130-1(7))*** Lit Verlag DEU. Dist: Transaction Pubs.

McGregor, R. S., ed. Devotional Literature in South Asia: Current Research, 1985-1988. 2008. (University of Cambridge Oriental Publications). (ENG.). 340p. (C). pap. 39.99 *(978-0-521-05185-9(1))* Cambridge Univ. Pr.

Narada, -. Narada Bhakti Sutras. Bhuteshananda, Swami, tr. 212p. 6.95 *(978-81-7505-199-7(X))* Advaita Ashrama IND. Dist: Vedanta Pr.

Novetzke, Christian Lee. Religion & Public Memory: A Cultural History of Saint Namdev in India. (ENG., Illus.). 336p. (gr. 17). 2011. pap. 27.50 ***(978-0-231-14185-7(8))*** 2008. 55.00 *(978-0-231-14184-0(X))* Columbia Univ. Pr.

Pechilis, Karen. Interpreting Devotion: The Poetry & Legacy of a Female Bhakti Saint of India. 2011. (Routledge Hindu Studies Ser.). (ENG., Illus.). 272p. (C). 145.00 *(978-0-415-61586-0(0))* Routledge.

Ramanuja. VedantaSutras. 2006. pap. *(978-1-4068-0964-0(0))* Echo Library.

Schelling, Andrew. The Oxford Anthology of Bhakti Literature. 2011. (ENG.). 352p. 55.00 *(978-0-19-806912-6(X))* Oxford Univ. Pr., Inc.

Singh, R. Raj. Bhakti & Philosophy. (ENG.). 121p. 2007. per. 26.50 *(978-0-7391-2510-6(9))* 2006. 68.50 *(978-0-7391-1424-7(7))* Lexington Bks.

Tapasyananda, Swami. Bhakti Schools of Vedanta: Lives & Philosophies of Ramanuja, Nimbarka, Madhva, Vallabha & Caitanya. 2011. 408p. pap. 29.95 ***(978-4-87187-652-0(7))*** Ishi Pr. International.

BHAKTI-MARGA

see Bhakti

BHILAI (INDIA)

Majhi, Anita Srivastava. Tribal Culture, Continuity, & Change: A Study of Bhils in Rajasthan. 2010. (Illus.). xviii, 214p. *(978-81-8324-298-1(7)*, Library of Congress — New Delhi Overseas Office) Mittal Pubns.

BHOTANTA LANGUAGE

see Tibetan Language

BHUTAN

Ardussi, John A. & Pommaret, Françoise, eds. Proceedings of the Tenth Seminar of the IATS, 2003, Volume 5 Bhutan: Traditions & Changes. 2006. 175p. *(978-90-04-15551-0(1))* BRILL.

Aris, Michael. Bhutan: The Early History of a Himalayan Kingdom. (Illus.). xxxiv, 344p. 49.95 *(978-0-85668-082-3(6))*; pap. 32.50 *(978-0-85668-199-8(7))* Aris & Phillips GBR. Dist: Brown, David Bk. Co., The.

Icon Group International, Inc. Staff, compiled by. The 2006 Economic & Product Market Databook for Bumthang, Bhutan. 2006. 618p. ring bd. 95.00 *(978-0-497-80268-4(6))* Icon Group International, Inc.

Izu, Kenro. Bhutan, Sacred Within. 2008. (Illus.). 70p. *(978-1-59005-225-9(0))* Nazraeli Pr.

JohnWehrheim. Bhutan: Hidden Lands of Happiness. 2008. *(978-1-932476-32-3(6))* Serindia Pubns., Inc.

Leaming, Linda. Married to Bhutan: How One Woman Got Lost, Said 'I Do', & Found Bliss. 2011. (ENG.). 256p. pap. 14.95 *(978-1-4019-2846-9(3))* Hay Hse., Inc.

Ngawang, Gyaltshen K. Sustainable Solid Waste Management: Phuntsholing City, Bhutan. 2011. 116p. pap. ***(978-3-639-32678-9(4))*** VDM Verlag Dr. Mueller e.K.

Pommaret, Françoise. Bhutan: Himalayan Mountain Kingdom. 6th ed. 2009. (ENG., Illus.). 320p. pap. 23.95 *(978-962-217-810-6(3)*, 217810) Airphoto International/Odyssey HKG. Dist: Norton, W. W. & Co., Inc.

Rakesh, Raman. Weaker Sex Stronger Endeavour: Women in Economic Development of Bhutan. 2011. 124p. pap. ***(978-3-639-32942-1(2))*** VDM Verlag Dr. Mueller e.K.

Wangchuck, Ashi Dori Wangmo. Treasures of the Thunder Dragon: A Portrait of Bhutan. 2007. (ENG., Illus.). 224p. (gr. 12-18). 19.95 *(978-0-670-99901-9(6)*, Penguin Global) Penguin Group (USA) Inc.

BHUTAN—DESCRIPTION AND TRAVEL

Dorje, Gyurme. Bhutan. 2nd ed. 2010. (Footprint - Handbooks Ser.). (ENG., Illus.). 376p. 25.95 *(978-1-907263-08-8(X))* Footprint Handbooks GBR. Dist: Globe Pequot Pr., The.

Herman, Steven. Bhutan in Color 2007: A Himalayan Kingdom through the Lens of an American Journalist. 2008. (Illus.). 50p. 29.95 *(978-0-9655614-2-6(9)*, Nama Pr.) Nama Productions, Inc.

Jordans, Bart. Bhutan: A Trekker's Guide. 2nd rev. ed. 2010. (Illus.). 336p. pap. 24.95 *(978-1-85284-553-7(8))* Cicerone Pr. GBR. Dist: Midpoint Trade Bks., Inc.

Kassel, Wendy. Nepal & Bhutan. 2010. (Frommer's Complete Ser.). (ENG.). 416p. pap. 22.99 *(978-0-470-55320-6(0)*, Frommers) Wiley, John & Sons, Inc.

Leaming, Linda. Married to Bhutan: How One Woman Got Lost, Said 'I Do', & Found Bliss. 2011. (ENG.). 256p. pap. 14.95 *(978-1-4019-2846-9(3))* Hay Hse., Inc.

Limaye, Trishaala. A Pleasure Hunt to Bhutan. 2011. 68p. pap. 22.88 *(978-1-4520-9574-5(4))* AuthorHouse.

Lloyd, Libby & Van Koesveld, Robert. Bhutan Heartland: Travels in the Land of the Thunder Dragon. 2010. (ENG., Illus.). 208p. 43.95 *(978-1-921361-74-6(3))* Fremantle Pr. AUS. Dist: Independent Pubs. Group.

Locken, E. Travel Journal Bhutan. 2010. 192p. pap. 19.99 *(978-0-557-43272-1(3))* Lulu Enterprises Inc.

Matthieu, Ricard. Bhutan: The Land of Serenity. 2012. (ENG., Illus.). 232p. pap. 19.95 ***(978-0-500-29044-6(X)***, 529044) Thames & Hudson.

Mayhew, Bradley. Bhutan. 4th rev. ed. 2011. (Country Guide Ser.). (ENG., Illus.). 284p. pap. 26.99 *(978-1-74104-919-0(9))* Lonely Planet Pubns.

Napoli, Lisa. Radio Shangri-La: What I Discovered on My Accidental Journey to the Happiest Kingdom on Earth. 2012. (ENG.). 320p. pap. 15.00 ***(978-0-307-45303-7(0))*** Broadway Bks.

Napoli, Lisa. Radio Shangri-La: What I Learned in Bhutan, the Happiest Kingdom on Earth. 2011. 304p. 25.00 *(978-0-307-45302-0(2))* Crown Publishing Group.

Peck, Mary. Bhutan: Between Heaven & Earth. 2011. (ENG., Illus.). 144p. pap. 35.00 ***(978-0-615-49933-8(3))*** Merlin Pr. LLC.

Rosenthal, Chuck. Are We Not There Yet? Travels in Nepal, North India, & Bhutan. 2009. 184p. pap. 15.00 *(978-0-9823542-0-9(7))* What Bks.

Uitz, Martin. Hidden Bhutan: Entering the Kingdom of the Thunder Dragon. 2012. (Armchair Traveller Ser.). (ENG.). 101p. pap. 11.95 ***(978-1-907973-16-1(8))*** Haus Publishing GBR. Dist: Consortium Bk. Sales & Distribution.

White, J.Claude. Sikkim & Bhutan. 2007. 400p. 49.95 *(978-0-548-13982-0(2))* 2006. pap. 34.95 *(978-1-4286-5168-5(3))* Kessinger Publishing, LLC.

BHUTAN LANGUAGE

see Tibetan Language

BHUTTO, BENAZIR, 1953-2007

Anjum, Shakeel. Who Assassinated Benazir Bhutto. 2010. (Illus.). xvi, 290p. *(978-969-496-378-5(8))* Dost Publications.

Bhatia, Shyam. Goodbye Shahzadi: A Political Biography of Benazir Bhutto. 2008. (Illus.). 130p. *(978-81-7436-658-0(X))* Lotus Collection.

Bhutto, Benazir. Daughter of the East: An Autobiography. 2008. (ENG., Illus.). 464p. pap. 17.95 *(978-1-84739-085-1(4))* Simon & Schuster, Ltd. GBR. Dist: Independent Pubs. Group.

Bhutto, Benazir & Bhutto, Benazir. Daughter of Destiny: An Autobiography. 2008. (ENG.). 480p. pap. 15.95 *(978-0-06-167268-2(8)*, HarperPerennial) HarperCollins Pubs.

Di Martino, Carla. Le Pakistan, Islam et Modernité: Le Projet de Benazir Bhutto. 2010. (FRE.). 154p. pap. *(978-2-296-12852-1(1))* Editions L'Harmattan.

Farwell, James P. The Pakistan Cauldron: Conspiracy, Assassination & Instability. 2011. (Illus.). 360p. 29.95 ***(978-1-59797-982-5(1))*** Potomac Bks., Inc.

—The Pakistan Cauldron: Conspiracy, Assassination & Instability. 2011. (Illus.). xx, 331p. ***(978-1-59797-983-2(X))*** Potomac Bks., Inc., Pubs.

Raynaud, Eric. Benazir Bhutto: Jusqu'au Bout du Destin. 2008. (FRE.). 281p. *(978-2-7538-0307-7(2))* Alphee, Editions.

Senauth, Frank. The Last Call: Curse of the Bhutto's Name. 2008. 184p. pap. 15.50 *(978-1-4389-0024-7(4))* AuthorHouse.

Shakir, Shakir Husain, et al. Shahid Benazir Bhutto: Nasr. 2008. (URD.). 466p. *(978-969-472-189-7(X))* Pakistan Academy of Letters.

United States, Congress House Committee on Foreign Affairs Subcommittee on the Middle East and South Asia Staff, contrib. by. U.S.-Pakistan Relations: Assassination, Instability & the Future of U.S. Policy: Hearing Before the Subcommittee on the Middle East & South Asia of the Committee on Foreign Affairs, House of Representatives, One Hundred Tenth Congress, Second Session, January 16, 2008. 2008. iii, 77p. *(978-0-16-080746-6(8)*, 552-070-37350-1) United States Government Printing Office.

BHUTTO, ZULFIQUAR ALI, 1928-1979

Mir, Hamid. Bhutto Ki Siyasi Pesh Goiyan Aur Cautha Marshal La. 2nd ed. 2010. (URD., Illus.). 190p. *(978-969-8455-57-6(4))* Jumhoori Publications.

Yunus, Mohammed. Bhutto & the Breakup of Pakistan. 2012. (ENG.). 148p. 20.00 ***(978-0-19-906379-6(6))*** Oxford Univ. Pr., Inc.

BI-RACIAL CHILDREN

see Children of Interracial Marriage

BIACETYLENE

see Acetylene

BIALIK, HAYYIM NAHMAN, 1873-1934

Eisenberg, Azriel & Segal, Abraham. Presenting Bialik: A Study of His Life & Works. 2011. 114p. 39.95 ***(978-1-258-03815-1(3))*** Literary Licensing, LLC.

BIAS (LAW)

Levinson, Justin D. & Smith, Roger J., eds. Implicit Racial Bias Across the Law. 2012. (ENG.). 288p. 99.00 ***(978-1-107-01095-6(0))***; pap. 32.99 ***(978-1-107-64818-0(1))*** Cambridge Univ. Pr.

Luttrell, Sam. Bias Challenge in International Arbitration. 2009. xix, 296p. *(978-90-411-3191-1(4))* Kluwer Law International.

BIAS (PSYCHOLOGY)

see Prejudices

BIAS CRIMES

see Hate Crimes

BIAS IN JOURNALISM

see Journalism—Objectivity

BIAS IN MASS MEDIA

see Mass Media—Objectivity

BIAS IN TEXTBOOKS

see Textbook Bias

BIBLE—ANIMALS

see Nature in the Bible

BIBLE—ANTIQUITIES

see also Christian Antiquities; Jews—Antiquities; Palestine—Antiquities

also subdivision Antiquities under names of Biblical countries and cities

Aitken, James K., et al, eds. On Stone & Scroll: Essays in Honour of Graham Ivor Davies. 2011. (Beihefte zur Zeitschrift far die alttestamentliche Wissenschaft Ser.). (ENG., Illus.). XXVIII, 576p. 280.00 ***(978-3-11-175624-0(6))*** De Gruyter, Walter Inc.

Albl, Martin C. Biblical Life & Times. 2009. pap. 20.95 *(978-0-88489-898-6(9))* St. Mary's Pr.

Albright, William F. The Archaeology of Palestine & the Bible. 2007. (Gorgias Classic Archaeological Reprints Ser.: 12). 76.00 *(978-1-59333-665-3(9))* Gorgias Pr., LLC.

Albright, William Foxwell. Archaeology & the Religion of Israel. 2006. (Old Testament Library). (ENG.). 247p. per. 40.00 *(978-0-664-22742-5(2))* Westminster John Knox Pr.

Arav, Rami. Cities Through the Looking Glass: Essays on the History & Archaeology of Biblical Urbanism. 2008. 34.50 *(978-1-57506-142-9(2))* Eisenbrauns, Inc.

Arav, Rami, ed. Bethsaida: A City by the North Shore of the Sea of Galilee, 4 vols., Vol. 4. 2009. (ENG., Illus.). 362p. pap. 35.00 *(978-1-931112-84-0(3))* Truman State Univ. Pr.

Arav, Rami & Freund, Richard, eds. Bethsaida: A City by the North Shore of the Sea of Galilee, 4 vols., Vol. 4. 2009. (ENG., Illus.). 362p. 49.00 *(978-1-931112-83-3(5))* Truman State Univ. Pr.

Arnold, Patrick M. Gibeah: The Search for a Biblical City. 2009. (Library of Hebrew Bible/Old Testament Studies, the Ser.). (ENG.). 200p. 39.95 *(978-0-567-40212-7(6)*, T&T Clark) Continuum International Publishing Group, Ltd. GBR. Dist: National Bk. Network.

Athas, George. Tel Dan Inscription: A Reappraisal & a New Introduction. 2009. (Library of Hebrew Bible/Old Testament Studies, the Ser.). (ENG.). 352p. 60.00 *(978-0-567-20645-9(9)*, T&T Clark Int'l) Continuum International Publishing Group, Ltd. GBR. Dist: National Bk. Network.

Aufrecht, Walter E. Urbanism in Antiquity: From Mesopotamia to Crete. Gauley, Steven W. & Mirau, Neil A., eds. 2009. (Library of Hebrew Bible/Old Testament Studies, the Ser.). (ENG.). 296p. 49.95 *(978-0-567-41055-9(2)*, T&T Clark) Continuum International Publishing Group, Ltd. GBR. Dist: National Bk. Network.

Bakker, Pamela A. Pondering Four Controversial Sites in Biblical Archeology: Eden, Noah's Landing, Joseph's Main Granary, the Exodus Crossing Point with A New Mt. Horeb. 2007. 128p. pet. 10.95 *(978-1-4327-0403-2(6))* Outskirts Pr., Inc.

Benjamin, Don C. Stones & Stories: An Introduction to Archaeology & the Bible. 2009. 400p. (C). pap. 39.00 *(978-0-8006-2357-9(6)*, Fortress Pr.) Augsburg Fortress, Pubs.

Bible Expositor & Illuminator: Winter, 2006/2007. 2006. pap. *(978-1-59843-063-9(7))* Incorporated Trustees of the Gospel Worker Society, The.

Bible Expositor & Illuminator Vol. 4: Fall 2006. 2006. pap. *(978-1-59843-062-2(9))* Incorporated Trustees of the Gospel Worker Society, The.

Boscawen, W. St. Chad. Bible & the Monuments the Primitive He. 2006. pap. 25.95 *(978-1-4286-3630-9(7))* Kessinger Publishing, LLC.

Brug, John F. Bible Discovery Series: Using Archaeology to Study the Bible: Digging for Insights. 2010. pap. *(978-0-8100-2233-1(8))* Northwestern Publishing Hse.

Burge, Gary M., et al. New Testament in Antiquities, 1 vol. 2009. (ENG., Illus.). 496p. 49.99 *(978-0-310-24495-0(1))* Zondervan.

Burleigh, Nina. Unholy Business: A True Tale of Faith, Greed & Forgery in the Holy Land. 2008. (ENG.). 288p. 27.50 *(978-0-06-145845-3(7))* Smithsonian Institution Pr.

Burroughs, Dillon. The Jesus Family Tomb Controversy: How the Evidence Falls Short in the LOST TOMB of JESUS Documentary. 2007. 200p. per. 19.94 *(978-0-9788138-7-1(1))* Nimble Bks. LLC.

Charlesworth, James H., ed. Jesus & Archaeology. 2006. (Illus.). 740p. per. 50.00 *(978-0-8028-4880-2(X))* Eerdmans, William B. Publishing Co.

Clay, Albert T. Light on the Old Testament from Babel. 2007. (Ancient near East: Classic Studies: Ser.). (Illus.). 484p. pap. 44.00 *(978-1-59752-717-0(3)*, Wipf and Stock) Wipf & Stock Pubs.

Cline, Eric H. Biblical Archaeology. 2009. (Very Short Introductions Ser.). (ENG., Illus.). 144p. pap. 11.95 *(978-0-19-534263-5(1))* Oxford Univ. Pr., Inc.

Cohn, Yehudah. Tangled up in Text: Tefillin & the Ancient World. 2008. *(978-1-930675-56-8(9))* Brown Judaic Studies.

Connelly, Douglas. Amazing Discoveries That Unlock the Bible: A Visual Experience, 1 vol. 2008. (Zondervan Visual Reference Ser.). (ENG., Illus.). 96p. 12.99 *(978-0-310-25799-8(9))* Zondervan.

Currie, Robin & Hyslop, Stephen. The Letter & the Scroll: What Archaeology Tells Us about the Bible. 2009. (ENG., Illus.). 336p. 40.00 *(978-1-4262-0514-9(7)*, National Geographic) National Geographic Society.

Currie, Robin & Hyslop, Stephen G. The Letter & the Scroll: What Archaeology Tells Us about the Bible. 2009. (Illus.). 335p. *(978-1-4262-0469-2(8))* National Geographic Society.

Davies, Graham. The Schweich Lectures & Biblical Archaeology. 2011. (ENG., Illus.). 100p. 35.00 *(978-0-19-726487-4(5))* Oxford Univ. Pr., Inc.

Davies, Graham I., et al. On Stone & Scroll: Essays in Honour of Graham Ivor Davies. 2011. (Beihefte zur Zeitschrift für die alttestamentliche Wissenschaft Ser.). 182.00 ***(978-3-11-022805-2(X))*** De Gruyter, Walter Inc.

Davies, Philip R. Memories of Ancient Israel: An Introduction to Biblical History — -Ancient & Modern. 2008. (ENG.). 208p. pap. 25.00 (978-0-664-23288-7(4)) Westminster John Knox Pr.

Dever, William G. The Lives of Ordinary People: What the Bible & Archaeology Tell Us about Everyday Life in Ancient Israel. 2012. pap. (978-0-8028-6701-8(4)) Eerdmans, William B. Publishing Co.

Dever, William G., et al. Confronting the Past: Archaeological & Historical Essays on Ancient Israel in Honor of William G. Dever. 2006. (Illus.). 376p. 69.50 (978-1-57506-117-7(1)) Eisenbrauns, Inc.

DeVries, LaMoine F. Cities of the Biblical World: An Introduction to the Archaeology, Geography, & History of Biblical Sites. 2006. (Illus.). 420p. pap. 40.00 (978-1-55635-120-4(8), Wipf and Stock) Wipf & Stock Pubs.

Down, David. Unveiling the Kings of Israel: Revealing the Bible's Archaeological History. 2011. (Illus.). 170p. (978-0-89051-609-6(X)) Master Bks.

Drane, John. The World of the Bible. 2010. (ENG., Illus.). 256p. 34.95 (978-0-7459-5250-5(X)) Lion Hudson PLC GBR. Dist: Independent Pubs. Group.

Driver, S. R. Modern Research As Illustrating the Bible. 2008. 132p. pap. (978-1-4086-8808-3(5)) Read Bks.

Driver, Samuel R. Modern Research as Illustrating the Bible: The Schweich Lectures 1908. 2007. (Schweich Lectures of the British Academy Ser.). (Illus.). 104p. pap. 14.00 (978-1-55635-452-6(5), Wipf and Stock) Wipf & Stock Pubs.

Edwards, Rex. An Adventure into Discovery. 2010. (Illus.). 195p. pap. 13.95 (978-1-57258-613-0(3)) TEACH Services, Inc.

Fant, Clyde E., et al. Lost Treasures of the Bible: Understanding the Bible Through Archaeological Artifacts in World Museums. 2008. (Illus.). 528p. 28.00 (978-0-8028-2881-1(7)) Eerdmans, William B. Publishing Co.

Faust, Avraham. Israel's Ethnogenesis: Settlement, Interaction, Expansion & Resistance. (Approaches to Anthropological Archaeology Ser.). (ENG., Illus.). 288p. (C). 2008. pap. 45.00 (978-1-84553-456-1(5)) 2006. 125.00 (978-1-904768-98-2(9)) Equinox Publishing Ltd. GBR. Dist: ISD.

Feigh, Craig T. The Sure Way to Him. 2008. 216p. per. 14.99 (978-1-60477-781-9(8)) Xulon Pr., Inc.

Finkelstein, Israel & Silberman, Neil Asher. David & Solomon: In Search of the Bible's Sacred Kings & the Roots of the Western Tradition. 2007. (ENG., Illus.). 352p. pap. 22.95 (978-0-7432-4363-6(3), Free Pr.) Free Pr.

Finkelstein, Israel, et al. The Quest for the Historical Israel: Debating Archaeology & the History of Early Israel: Lectures Delivered at the Annual Colloquium of the Institute for Secular Humanistic Judaism, Detroit, October 2005. 2007. (978-90-401-5738-7(3)) BRILL.

—The Quest for the Historical Israel: Debating Archaeology & the History of Early Israel: Lectures Delivered at the Annual Colloquium of the Institute for Secular Humanistic Judaism, Detroit, October 2005. 2007. (Archaeology & Biblical Studies). 24.95 (978-1-58983-277-0(9)) Society of Biblical Literature.

Fischer, Richard James. Historical Genesis: From Adam to Abraham. 2008. (ENG., Illus.). 210p. 41.99 (978-0-7618-3806-7(6)); per. 19.99 (978-0-7618-3807-4(4)) Univ. Pr. of America, Inc.

Frendo, Anthony J. Pre-Exilic Israel, the Hebrew Bible, & Archaeology: Integrating Text & Artefact. 2011. (Library Hebrew Bible/Old Testament Studies). 144p. 120.00 (978-0-567-41563-9(5), T&T Clark Int'l) Continuum International Publishing Group, Ltd. GBR. Dist: National Bk. Network.

Freund, Richard A. Digging Through the Bible: Modern Archaeology & the Ancient Bible. (ENG., 352p. 2009. Illus.). pap. 18.95 (978-0-7425-4645-5(4)) 2008. 47.95 (978-0-7425-4644-8(6)) Rowman & Littlefield Publishers, Inc.

Fritz, Glen A. The Lost Sea of Exodus: A Modern Geographical Analysis. 2007. per. (978-1-59872-745-6(1)) Instant Pub.

Gaber, Pamela. Daily Life in Bible Times: What Archaeology Can Tell Us. 2007. (Illus.). 31p. (J). (gr. 4-7). per. 12.95 (978-1-59298-180-9(1)) Beaver's Pond Pr., Inc.

Gardiner, Philip. The Ark, the Shroud, & Mary: The Untold Truths about the Relics of the Bible. 2007. (ENG., Illus.). 1p. per. 17.99 (978-1-56414-924-4(2), 1266522) Career Pr., Inc.

Gibson, Shimon. The Final Days of Jesus: The Archaeological Evidence. 2010. (ENG.). 272p. pap. 15.99 (978-0-06-145849-1(X), HarperOne) 2009. 368p. pap. 27.99 (978-0-06-172000-0(3), HarperLuxe) HarperCollins Pubs.

Gibson, Simon. Flights Into Biblical Archaeol. 2008. (Illus.). 256p. 60.00 (978-965-90283-4-4(2)) Gefen Publishing Hse., Ltd ISR. Dist: Gefen Bks.

Graham, William Creighton & May, Herbert Gordon. Culture & Conscience: An Archaeological Study of the New Religious Past in Ancient Palestine. 2011. 386p. 53.95 (978-1-258-01724-8(5)) Literary Licensing, LLC.

Hagelia, Hallvard. The Dan Debate: The Tel Dan Inscription in Recent Research. 2009. ix, 161p. (978-1-906055-47-9(5)) Sheffield Phoenix Pr.

—Tel Dan Inscription: A Critical Investigation of Recent Research on Its Palaeography & Philology. 2006. (Studia Semantica Upsaliensia Ser.: No. 250). 250p. pap. 59.50 (978-91-554-6613-8(3)) Uppsala Universitet/Acta Universitatis Uppsaliensis SWE. Dist: Coronet Bks.

Hardy, E. The Unvarying East. 2009. 114.00 (978-1-60724-318-2(0)) Gorgias Pr., LLC.

Hess, Richard S., et al. Critical Issues in Early Israelite History. 2008. 324p. (C). 44.50 (978-1-57506-804-6(4)) Eisenbrauns, Inc.

Hilprecht, Hermann Vollrat, ed. The Excavations in Assyria & Babylonia. 2011. (Cambridge Library Collection - Archaeology Ser.). (Illus.). 688p. pap. 48.00 (978-1-108-02564-5(1)) Cambridge Univ. Pr.

Hoerth, Alfred J. Archaeology & the Old Testament. 2009. (Illus.). 448p. (C). pap. 45.00 (978-0-8010-3625-5(9)) Baker Academic.

Hoffmeier, James K. The Archaeology of the Bible. 2008. (ENG., Illus.). 192p. 29.95 (978-0-7459-5226-0(7)) Lion Hudson PLC GBR. Dist: Independent Pubs. Group.

Hurtado, Larry W. The Earliest Christian Artifacts: Manuscripts & Christian Origins. 2006. (Illus.). 248p. per. 20.00 (978-0-8028-2895-8(7)) Eerdmans, William B. Publishing Co.

Kaiser, Walter C. & Kaiser. Archaeological Study Bible, 1 vol. Kaiser, Jr., Walter C., Walter C & Garrett, Duane, eds. rev. ed. 2007. (ENG., Illus.). 2336p. lthr. 84.99 (978-0-310-93844-6(9)) Zondervan.

Kalantzis, George & Martin, Thomas F., eds. Studies on Patristic Texts & Archaeology: If these stones could speak... Essays in Honor of Dennis Edward Groh. 2009. (Illus.). 232p. 109.95 (978-0-7734-4853-7(5)) Mellen, Edwin Pr., The.

Keller, Werner. The Bible As History. 2008. 204p. (978-965-00-6016-9(2)) Editorial Benei Noaj.

Kogan, Leonid, ed. Babel und Bibel, 3. 2007. 59.50 (978-1-57506-134-4(1)) Eisenbrauns, Inc.

Kratz, Reinhard G. & Spieckermann, Hermann, eds. One God - One Cult - One Nation: Archaeological & Biblical Perspectives. (Beihefte zur Zeitschrift fur die alttestamentliche Wissenschaft Ser.). (Illus.). 2011. XX, 463p. 210.00 (978-3-11-174103-1(6)) 2010. (ENG., XIX, 463p. 140.00 (978-3-11-022357-6(0)) De Gruyter, Walter Inc.

Kuchler, Max & Schmidt, Karl Matthias, eds. Texte-Fakten-Artefakte: Beiträge zur Bedeutung der Archäologie für Die Neutestamentliche Forschung. 2006. (Novum Testamentum et Orbis Antiquus (Ntoa) Ser.: 59). (GER.). 242p. (C). 56.00 (978-3-525-53962-0(2)) Vandenhoeck & Ruprecht GmbH & Co. KG DEU. Dist: ISD.

Kyle, Melvin Grove. Excavating Kirjath-Sepher's Ten Cities: A Palestine Fortress from Abraham's Day to Nebuchadnezzar's. 2007. (Illus.). 204p. pap. 18.00 (978-1-55635-582-0(3)) Wipf & Stock Pubs.

Lees, G. Robinson. The Witness of the Wilderness: The Bedawin of the Desert. 2007. 234p. 41.95 (978-0-548-01032-7(3)) Kessinger Publishing, LLC.

Levy, Thomas E., ed. Historical Biblical Archaeology & the Future: The New Pragmatism. 2010. (ENG., Illus.). 392p. (C). pap. 39.95 (978-1-84553-258-1(9)); 125.00 (978-1-84553-257-4(0)) Equinox Publishing Ltd. GBR. Dist: ISD.

Luedke, Robert James, creator. The Collected Eye Witness Slipcased Set. 2010. (Eye Witness Ser.). (ENG.). 390p. pap. 44.99 (978-0-9758924-8-0(7)) Head Pr. Publishing.

—Eye Witness: Unknown God. 2010. (Eye Witness Ser.). (ENG.). 128p. pap. 13.99 (978-0-9758924-7-3(9)) Head Pr. Publishing.

MacRae, Allan. Biblical Archaeology. 2007. 80p. per. 7.99 (978-1-58960-368-4(0)) Sovereign Grace Pubs., Inc.

Magness, Jodi. The Archaeology of the Holy Land: From the Destruction of Solomon's Temple to the Muslim Conquest. 2012. (ENG., Illus.). 350p. (C). 99.00 (978-0-521-19535-5(7)); pap. 32.99 (978-0-521-12413-3(1)) Cambridge Univ. Pr.

Malena, Sarah & Miano, David. Milk & Honey: Essays on Ancient Israel & the Bible in Appreciation of the Judaic Studies Program at the University of California, San Diego. 2007. (Illus.). 44.50 (978-1-57506-127-6(9)) Eisenbrauns, Inc.

Matthews, Victor H. Manners & Customs in the Bible: An Illustrated Guide to Daily Life in Bible Times. 3rd ed. 2006. (Illus.). 256p. 17.97 (978-1-59856-059-6(X)) Hendrickson Pubs. Marketing, LLC.

—Studying the Ancient Israelites: A Guide to Sources & Methods. 2007. (Illus.). 240p. (C). pap. 25.00 (978-0-8010-3197-7(4)) Baker Academic.

Matthews, Victor Harold. Old Testament Parallels (New Revised & Expanded Third Edition) Laws & Stories from the Ancient near East. 3rd rev. exp. ed. 2007. (Illus.). 448p. per. 22.95 (978-0-8091-4435-8(2), 4435-2) Paulist Pr.

McLeroy, Leigh. Treasured: Knowing God by the Things He Keeps. 2009. (ENG.). 224p. 14.99 (978-1-4000-7481-5(9), WaterBrook Pr.) Doubleday Religious Publishing Group, The.

McRay, John. Archaeology & the New Testament. (978-0-687-01678-5(9)) Abingdon Pr.

—Archaeology & the New Testament. 2008. (Illus.). 432p. (C). (gr. 13). pap. 42.99 (978-0-8010-3608-8(9)) Baker Academic.

Meitlis, Itzhak. Excavating the Bible: New Archaeological Evidence for the Historical Reliability of Scripture. 2012. (978-0-935437-41-6(X)) Bartleby Pr.

Myers, E. A. The Ituraeans & the Roman near East: Reassessing the Sources. 2010. (Society for New Testament Studies Monograph Ser.). (ENG., Illus.). 232p. 100.00 (978-0-521-51887-1(3)) Cambridge Univ. Pr.

Parfitt, Tudor. The Lost Ark of the Covenant: Solving the 2,500-Year-Old Mystery of the Fabled Biblical Ark. 2009. 384p. pap. 14.99 (978-0-06-137104-2(1), HarperOne) HarperCollins Pubs.

Pritchard, J. B. The Ancient near East - an Anthology of Texts & Pictures. 2010. (ENG., Illus.). 664p. (C). 85.00 (978-0-691-14725-3(6)) Princeton Univ. Pr.

Pritchard, James B. Archaeology & the Old Testament. 2010. 280p. 34.36 (978-1-163-38627-9(8)) 2010. 282p. pap. 22.36 (978-1-162-92075-7(0)) 2007. (ENG.). 280p. 42.95 (978-0-548-07710-8(X)) Kessinger Publishing, LLC.

—Archaeology & the Old Testament. 2008. (Ancient near East: Classic Studies: Ser.). (Illus.). 280p. pap. 24.00 (978-1-60608-092-4(X)) Wipf & Stock Pubs.

Pritchard, James Bennett. The Ancient Near East: An Anthology of Texts & Pictures. 2010. (ENG., Illus.). 664p. (C). pap. 39.50 (978-0-691-14726-0(4)) Princeton Univ. Pr.

Reed, Jonathan L. The HarperCollins Visual Guide to the New Testament: What Archaeology Reveals about the First Christians. 2007. (ENG., Illus.). 176p. pap. 24.95 (978-0-06-084249-9(0), HarperOne) HarperCollins Pubs.

Savage, Carl E. Biblical Bethsaida: An Archaeological Study of the First Century. 2011. (Illus.). xv, 195p. (978-0-7391-3783-3(2)) Lexington Bks.

Schloen, J. David & Stager, Lawrence E. Exploring the Longue Durée: Essays in Honor of Lawrence E. Stager. 2009. 69.50 (978-1-57506-161-0(9)) Eisenbrauns, Inc.

Shanks, Hershel. Freeing the Dead Sea Scrolls: And Other Adventures of an Archaeology Outsider. 2010. (ENG., Illus.). 272p. 29.95 (978-1-4411-5217-6(2)) Continuum International Publishing Group, Ltd. GBR. Dist: National Bk. Network.

—Scholars on the Record: Insightful Interviews on Bible & Archaeology. 2009. (Illus.). 254p. (978-1-935335-23-8(5)) Biblical Archaeology Society.

Stripling, Scott. The Trowel & the Truth. 2007. 168p. per. 18.95 (978-1-931178-28-0(3)) Vision Publishing.

Wachsmann, Shelley. The Sea of Galilee Boat. 2009. (Ed Rachal Foundation Nautical Archaeology Ser.). (ENG.). 442p. pap. 23.00 (978-1-60344-113-1(1)) Texas A&M Univ. Pr.

Walker, Kenneth. Log of the Ark. 21.95 (978-0-8488-1214-0(X)) Amereon LTD.

Weidmann, Frederick W. Polycarp & John: The Harris Fragments & Their Challenge to the Literary Traditions. 2010. (ND Christianity & Judaism Antiqui Ser.). (ENG.). 206p. pap. 25.00 (978-0-268-03826-7(0)) Univ. of Notre Dame Pr.

Williams, Philip Lee. The Archaeological Evidence of Noah's Flood. 2011. (ENG., Illus.). 411p. 34.95 (978-0-9793102-2-5(9)) Christian Leaders & Scholars Pr.

Willis, Mike. Archaeology & the Bible. 2007. pap. 14.95 (978-1-58427-171-0(X)) Guardian of Truth Foundation.

Wineland, John D., et al, eds. My Father's World: Celebrating the Life of Reuben G. Bullard. 2011. 234p. pap. 26.00 (978-1-60608-870-8(X), Wipf and Stock) Wipf & Stock Pubs.

BIBLE—APPRECIATION

Bailey, Samuel W. Homage of Eminent Persons to the Book Comp by Samuel W Bailey. 2006. 132p. per. 16.99 (978-1-4255-0940-8(1)) MPublishing.

Deitz, Reginald W. What the Bible Can Mean for You. 2009. 110p. 34.95 (978-1-104-85492-8(9)) 2007. (ENG.). 108p. per. 19.95 (978-0-548-43889-3(7)) Kessinger Publishing, LLC.

Descubre tu Biblia.Tr. of Bible Book by Book. (SPA.). Bk. 1. pap., stu. ed., wbk. ed. 5.50 (978-0-311-11056-8(8))Bk. 2. pap., tchr. ed. 5.25 (978-0-311-11057-5(6))Bk. 2. pap., stu. ed., wbk. ed. 5.50 (978-0-311-11058-2(4))Bk. 3. pap., tchr. ed. 5.25 (978-0-311-11059-9(2))Bk. 3. pap., stu. ed., wbk. ed. 5.50 (978-0-311-11060-5(6)) Casa Bautista de Publicaciones.

Grampa Ed. Afraid to Read the Bible?, 1 vol. 2010. 48p. pap. 16.95 (978-1-4489-6222-8(6)) PublishAmerica, Inc.

Krehbiel, Dan E. The Power & Prestige of the Bible. Krehbiel, Dan E., ed. 2011. 20p. pap. 35.95 (978-1-258-00305-0(8)) Literary Licensing, LLC.

Song, C. S. In the Beginning Were Stories, Not Texts. 2012. (ENG.). 180p. (C). pap. 30.00 (978-0-227-68023-0(5)) Clarke, James Co., Ltd. GBR. Dist: Brown, David Bk. Co., The.

BIBLE—ARCHAEOLOGY

see Bible—Antiquities

BIBLE—ART

see Bible—Illustrations

BIBLE—ATLASES

see Bible—Geography—Maps

BIBLE—AUTHORITY

see Bible—Evidences, Authority, etc.

BIBLE—AUTHORSHIP

Coote, Robert B. The Interface of Orality & Writing: Hearing, Seeing, Writing in New Genres. Weissenrieder, Annette, ed. 2010. (Illus.). 452p. 257.50 (978-3-16-150445-7(3)) Mohr Siebeck GmbH & Co. KG DEU. Dist: Coronet Bks.

Curtis, Byron G. Up the Steep & Stony Road: The Book of Zechariah in Social-Location Trajectory Analysis. 2006. (Illus.). 330p. (978-90-04-15112-3(5)) BRILL.

—Up the Steep & Stony Road: The Book of Zechariah in Social-Location Trajectory Analysis. 2006. 44.95 (978-1-58983-238-1(8)) Society of Biblical Literature.

Donelson, Lewis R. Pseudepigraphy & Ethical Argument in the Pastoral Epistles. 2006. (Hermeneutische Untersuchungen zur Theologie Ser.: No. 22). 221p. pap. 72.50 (978-3-16-149082-8(7)) Mohr Siebeck GmbH & Co. KG DEU. Dist: Coronet Bks.

Ehrman, Bart D. Forged: Writing in the Name of God — Why the Bible's Authors Are Not Who We Think They Are. (ENG.). 2012. 256p. pap. 15.99 (978-0-06-201262-3(2)) 2011. 304p. 26.99 (978-0-06-201261-6(4)) HarperCollins Pubs. (HarperOne).

Ford, Clayton Howard. Who Really Wrote the Bible? 2010. pap. 15.99 (978-1-61566-224-1(3)) Tate Publishing & Enterprises, LLC.

Frey, Jörg, et al, eds. Pseudepigraphie und Verfasserfiktion in frühchristlichen Briefen: Pseudepigraphy & Author Fiction in Early Christian Letters. 2009. (GER.). XII, 902p. 275.00 (978-3-16-150042-8(3)) Mohr Siebeck GmbH & Co. KG DEU. Dist: Coronet Bks.

Hoppin, Ruth. La Carta de Priscila: Encontrando el Autor de la Epistola a Los Hebreos. 2009. (SPA.). pap. 15.00 (978-1-882897-99-5(4)) Lost Coast Pr.

Kavanagh, Preston. The Shaphan Group: The Fifteen Authors Who Shaped the Hebrew Bible. 2011. 154p. pap. 18.00 (978-1-60608-611-7(1), Pickwick Pubns.) Wipf & Stock Pubs.

Law, David R. Historical Critical Method: A Guide for the Perplexed. 2012. (ENG.). 344p. 90.00 (978-0-567-11130-2(X)); pap. 27.95 (978-0-567-40012-3(3)) Continuum International Publishing Group, Ltd. GBR. (T&T Clark Int'l). Dist: National Bk. Network.

Mazor, Yair. Who Wrought the Bible? Unveiling the Bible's Aesthetic Secrets. 2008. (ENG.). 232p. pap. 26.95 (978-0-299-22844-6(4)); (Illus.). 60.00 (978-0-299-22840-8(1)) Univ. of Wisconsin Pr.

Rothschild, Clare K. Hebrews As Pseudepigraphon: The History & Significance of the Pauline Attribution of Hebrews. 2009. (Illus.). xvii, 287p. (978-3-16-149826-8(7)) Mohr Siebeck GmbH & Co. KG.

Sturdy, J. V. M. Redrawing the Boundaries: The Date of Early Christian Literature. Knight, Jonathan, ed. 2008. (BibleWorld Ser.). (ENG.). 192p. (C). per. 34.95 (978-1-84553-302-1(X)) Equinox Publishing Ltd. GBR. Dist: ISD.

Sturdy, J. V. M. & Knight, Jonathan. Redrawing the Boundaries: The Date of Early Christian Literature. 2008. (BibleWorld Ser.). (ENG.). 192p. (C). 99.95 (978-1-84553-301-4(1)) Equinox Publishing Ltd. GBR. Dist: ISD.

BIBLE—BIBLIOGRAPHY

American Bible Society. Library. Catalogue of Books Contained in the Library of the American Bible Society. 2006. 120p. per. 16.99 (978-1-4255-0882-1(0)) MPublishing.

Bauer, David R. An Annotated Guide to Biblical Resources for Ministry. 2011. 336p. pap. 37.00 (978-1-61097-386-1(0), Wipf and Stock) Wipf & Stock Pubs.

Copinger, Walter Arthur. Incunabula Biblica, or, the First Half Century of the Latin Bible: Being a Bibliographical Account of the Various Editions of the Latin Bible Between 1450 & 1500: with an Appendix Containing a Chronological List of the Editions of the Sixteenth Century. 2007. (Illus.). 301p. 125.00 (978-1-57898-659-0(1)) Martino Publishing.

Cotton, Henry. Editions of the Bible & Parts Thereof in English. 2007. (ENG.). 452p. 52.95 (978-0-548-05189-4(5)) Kessinger Publishing, LLC.

Evans, John. A Guide to Biblical Commentaries & Reference Works: For students & Pastors. 9th ed. 2010. (ENG.). 378p. pap. 14.95 (978-0-9828715-6-0(2)) Doulos Resources.

Eys, W. J. van. Bibliographie des Bibles et des Nouveaux Testaments en Langue Française des XVme et XVIme Siecles. 2008. (FRE.). 85.00 (978-1-57898-716-0(4)) Martino Publishing.

Glynn, John J. & Glynn, John. Commentary & Reference Survey: A Comprehensive Guide to Biblical & Theological Resources, 1 vol. 10th ed. 2007. 384p. pap. 24.99 (978-0-8254-2737-4(1)) Kregel Pubns.

Hall, Isaac H. American Greek Testaments: A Critical Bibliography of the Greek New Testament, as Published in America. 2010. 84p. pap. 12.00 (978-1-60899-609-4(3)) Wipf & Stock Pubs.

Haththotuwa, Minoli. Just Say the Word. 2010. 186p. pap. 14.99 (978-1-60957-509-0(1)) Xulon Pr., Inc.

Hilliard, Jack M. Life, Death, & After. 2010. 148p. 22.99 (978-1-60957-394-2(3)) Xulon Pr., Inc.

Horne, Thomas Hartwell. Manual of Biblical Bibliography: Comprising a Catalogue ... of the Principal Editions & Versions of the Holy Scriptures: Together with Notices of the Principal Philosophers, Critics, & Interpreters of the Bible. 2006. (ENG.). 450p. 75.00 (978-1-57898-562-3(5)) Martino Publishing.

Humphrey, Hugh Minear. The Gospel of Mark: An Indexed Bibliography 1980-2005. 2006. 348p. 119.95 (978-0-7734-5553-5(1)) Mellen, Edwin Pr., The.

Loftie, W. J. A Century of Bibles: The Authorised Version from 1611 To 1711. 2010. (Cambridge Library Collection - Printing & Publishing History Ser.). 264p. pap. 23.99 (978-1-108-01094-8(6)) Cambridge Univ. Pr.

Longman, Tremper, III. Old Testament Commentary Survey. 4th ed. 2007. 160p. (C). pap. 16.00 (978-0-8010-3123-6(0)) Baker Academic.

Lubetski, Edith & Lubetski, Meir. The Book of Esther: A Classified Bibliography. 2008. xviii, 268p. (978-1-905048-33-5(5)) Sheffield Phoenix Pr.

Mills, Watson E., compiled by. Bibliographies for Biblical Research Vol. III: The Gospel of Luke. (New Testament Ser.). 416p. 169.95 (978-0-7734-2402-9(4)) Mellen, Edwin Pr., The.

O'Callaghan, E. B. A List of Editions of the Holy Scriptures & Parts Thereof Printed in America Previous to 1860. 2010. 490p. pap. 38.75 (978-1-142-63157-4(5)) BiblioBazaar.

O'Callaghan, E. B. A List of Editions of the Holy Scriptures & Parts Thereof Printed in America Previous to 1860: With Introduction & Bibliographical Notes. 2010. (ENG.). 492p. pap. 38.75 (978-1-177-58335-0(6)); 496p. pap. 38.75 (978-1-176-43086-0(6)) BiblioBazaar.

—A List of Editions of the Holy Scriptures & Parts Thereof Printed in America Previous to 1860: With Introduction & Bibliographical Notes. 2010. 356p. pap. 42.96 (978-1-152-38873-4(8)) 2009. 364p. pap. 43.71 (978-1-150-41968-3(7)) General Bks. LLC.

—A List of Editions of the Holy Scriptures & Parts Thereof Printed in America Previous to 1860: With Introduction & Bibliographical Notes. 2012. 498p. pap. (978-1-290-06812-3(7)) HardPr.

—A List of Editions of the Holy Scriptures & Parts Thereof Printed in America Previous to 1860: With Introduction & Bibliographical Notes. 2010. 484p. 43.16 (978-1-164-43645-4(7)) 2010. 486p. pap. 31.16 (978-1-163-91896-8(2)) 2008. 484p. 53.95 (978-0-548-94197-3(1)) 2007. (ENG.). 484p. per. 38.95 (978-0-548-57032-6(9)) Kessinger Publishing, LLC.

B

—A List of Editions of the Holy Scriptures & Parts Thereof Printed in America Previous to 1860: With Introduction & Bibliographical Notes. 2006. 480p. per. 29.99 *(978-1-4255-5429-3(6))* MPublishing.

O'Callaghan, E. B., et al. A List of Editions of the Holy Scriptures & Parts Thereof Printed in America Previous to 1860: With Introduction & Bibliographical Notes. 2010. 400p. pap. 34.75 ***(978-1-147-46492-4(8))*** BiblioBazaar.

Orme, William. Bibliotheca Biblica: A Select List of Books on Sacred Literature: With Notices, Biographical, Critical, & Bibliographical. 2009. pap. *(978-1-57898-750-4(4))* Martino Publishing.

—Bibliotheca Biblica: A Select List of Books on Sacred Literature: with Notices, Biographical, Critical, & Bibliographical. 2009. 65.00 *(978-1-57898-749-8(0))* Martino Publishing.

Reuss, Eduard. Bibliotheca Novi Testamenti Graeci: Cuius editiones ab initio typographiae ad nostram aetatem Impressas. 2007. (LAT.). 320p. 75.00 *(978-1-57898-661-3(3))* Martino Publishing.

Sandy, D. Brent, et al. Prophecy & Apocalyptic: An Annotated Bibliography. 2007. (IBR Bibliographies Ser.). 240p. (C). pap. 28.00 *(978-0-8010-2601-0(6))* Baker Academic.

Stuart, Douglas. Old Testament Exegesis, Fourth Edition: A Handbook for Students & Pastors. 4th ed. 2009. (ENG.). 224p. pap. 25.00 *(978-0-664-23344-0(9))* Westminster John Knox Pr.

Walther, Wilhelm. Die Deutsche Bibelubersetzung des Mittelalters. 766p. reprint ed. 148.00 *(978-0-7222-2136-5(3))* Library Reprints, Inc.

BIBLE—BIOGRAPHY

see also Apostles; Children in the Bible; Patriarchs (Bible); Prophets; Women in the Bible

also names of individuals mentioned in the Bible, e.g. Moses (Biblical Leader); Mary, Blessed Virgin, Saint

Adams, Charles. Women of the Bible. Kidder, Daniel P., ed. 2007. (ENG.). 224p. 39.95 *(978-0-548-38321-6(9))*; per. 24.95 *(978-0-548-32678-7(9))* Kessinger Publishing, LLC.

—Women of the Bible. 2006. 228p. per. 20.99 *(978-1-4255-1938-4(5))* MPublishing.

Ashburn Jr., Thomas. God's Greater Glory. 2008. 132p. pap. 14.99 *(978-1-60647-849-3(4))* Xulon Pr., Inc.

Baker, Robert C. Great Women of the Bible: Eve, Sarah, Rebekah, Leah, & Rachel. 2008. 48p. pap. 6.99 *(978-0-7586-1555-8(8))* Concordia Publishing Hse.

Bal, Mieke. Anti-Covenant: Counter-Reading Women's Lives in the Hebrew Bible. 2009. (Library of Hebrew Bible/Old Testament Studies, the Ser.). (ENG.). 39.95 *(978-0-567-46347-0(8)*, T&T Clark) Continuum International Publishing Group, Ltd. GBR. Dist: National Bk. Network.

Baldwin, George Colfax. Representative Women; from Eve, the Wife of the First, to Mary, the Mother of the Second Adam, by Geo C Baldwin. 2006. 368p. per. 26.99 *(978-1-4255-3858-3(4))* MPublishing.

BarCharts, Inc. Bible Characters - New Testament. 2010. (ENG.). 6p. 5.95 *(978-1-4232-1417-5(X))* Barcharts, Inc.

—Bible Characters-Old Testament. 2010. (ENG.). 6p. 5.95 *(978-1-4232-1418-2(8))* Barcharts, Inc.

Beharrell, T. G. (Thomas G.). A Complete Alphabetically Arranged Biblical Biography. 2006. 516p. per. 29.99 *(978-1-4255-5752-2(X))* MPublishing.

Bingham, Derick. Ruth: A foreigner Redeemed. 2008. 60p. pap. *(978-1-897117-72-9(8))* Gospel Folio Pr.

Binz, Stephen J. Abraham: Father of All Believers. 2011. (Ancient-Future Bible Study: Experience Scripture Through Lectio Divina Ser.). 192p. pap. 11.99 *(978-1-58743-277-4(3))* Brazos Pr.

Brown, John. Brown's Dictionary of Bible Characters. Stonier, Geoffrey, ed. 2007. (ENG.). 596p. 29.99 *(978-1-84550-266-9(3)*, Christian Heritage) Christian Focus Pubns. GBR. Dist: STL Distribution North America.

Butler, Kerrick Aubrey Robert, Jr. A Walk on the Beach with Abraham. 2006. per. 7.99 *(978-1-59872-675-6(7))* Instant Pub.

Case, Steve L. Caffeine & Chutzpah. 2009. *(978-0-8298-1844-4(8))* Pilgrim Pr., The/United Church Pr.

Chappell, Clovis G. More Sermons on Biblical Characters. 2008. 204p. 24.95 *(978-1-4344-7454-4(2))*; pap. 14.95 *(978-1-4344-7453-7(4))* Wildside Pr., LLC.

—Sermons on Biblical Characters. 2007. 108p. per. *(978-1-4068-4518-1(3))* Echo Library.

Coekin, Richard. A Few Good Men: Inspiring Biblical Heroes for Todays' Christian Men. 2010. 208p. pap. *(978-1-905564-59-0(7))* Good Bk. Co.

Cox, Francis Augustus. Female Scripture Biography. 2008. 340p. 29.99 *(978-0-554-23079-5(8))* 2008. 340p. 29.99 *(978-0-554-23080-1(1))* 2008. 340p. 28.99 *(978-0-554-32383-1(4))* 2008. 340p. 28.99 *(978-0-554-32382-4(6))* 2007. (ENG.). 482p. pap. 30.99 *(978-1-4264-3730-4(7))* Vol. 1. 2007. (ENG.). 302p. pap. 23.99 *(978-1-4264-3673-4(4))* Vol. 2. 2007. (ENG.). 302p. pap. 23.99 *(978-1-4264-3674-1(2))* BiblioBazaar.

—Female Scripture Biography. 2009. 316p. pap. *(978-1-4099-7000-2(0))* Dodo Pr.

—Female Scripture Biograpy. l.t. ed. 2007. (ENG.). 496p. pap. 30.99 *(978-1-4264-3731-1(5))* BiblioBazaar.

Dalley, Stephanie. Esther's Revenge at Susa: From Sennacherib to Ahasuerus. 2008. (ENG., Illus.). 280p. 110.00 *(978-0-19-921663-5(0))* Oxford Univ. Pr., Inc.

Evans, Tony. God's Unlikely Path to Success: How He Uses Less-Than-Perfect People. 2012. 192p. pap. 12.99 ***(978-0-7369-3998-0(9))*** Harvest Hse. Pubs.

Fink, John F. Biblical Women: Females in a Patriarchal Society. 2008. *(978-0-8189-1262-7(6)*, St. Pauls) St Pauls/Alba Hse. Pubs.

Fuller, Pastor Brett Everett. Relate Well: Properly Relating to Your World & the People Most Important to You. 2010. 612p. 44.95 *(978-1-4497-0158-1(2))*; pap. 38.95 *(978-1-4497-0157-4(4))* Author Solutions, Inc. (WestBow Pr.).

Gale, Stanley D. The Prayer of Jehoshaphat: Seeing Beyond Life's Storms. 2007. 143p. pap. *(978-1-59638-062-2(4))* P & R Publishing.

George, Jeannette Clift. Some Run with Feet of Clay. 127p. reprint ed. 8.95 *(978-0-9616513-1-2(8))* Manor of Grace.

Gilfillan, George. The Poets & Poetry of the Bible. 2007. (ENG.). 328p. 45.95 *(978-0-548-03855-0(4))* Kessinger Publishing, LLC.

Gooder, Paula. The Meaning Is in the Waiting: The Spirit of Advent. 2009. (ENG.). 144p. (gr. 13). pap. 14.99 *(978-1-55725-662-1(4))* Paraclete Pr., Inc.

Gordon, Charlotte. The Woman Who Named God: Abraham's Dilemma & the Birth of Three Faiths. 2009. (ENG., Illus.). 400p. 27.99 *(978-0-316-11474-5(X))* Little Brown & Co.

Great Women of the Bible: Mary, the Mother of Jesus: Women Who Served Jesus: Women Whom Jesus Helped: Women Who Helped the Apostles. 2008. (Small-Group Bible Study Ser.). 48p. pap. 6.99 *(978-0-7586-1558-9(2))* Concordia Publishing Hse.

Great Women of the Bible: The Wives of King David, Jezebel, the Shunammite Woman, Ester. 2008. (Small-Group Bible Study Ser.). 48p. pap. 6.99 *(978-0-7586-1557-2(4))* Concordia Publishing Hse.

Halsey, Leroy J. (Leroy Jones). Life Pictures from the Bible; 2006. 460p. per. 29.99 *(978-1-4255-5096-7(7))* MPublishing.

Headley, P. C. (Phineas Camp). Historical & Descriptive Sketches of the Women of the Bible, from Eve of the Old to the Marys of the New Testament, by P C Headley. 2006. 292p. per. 23.99 *(978-1-4255-2752-5(3))* MPublishing.

Heroes en la Biblia (Heroes in the Bible) Quarter 3, Level 2. (Caminando con Jesus (Walking with Jesus) Series A). (SPA.). tchr. ed. 3.50 *(978-0-570-05128-2(2)*, 16-2803) Concordia Publishing Hse.

Higgs, Liz Curtis. Slightly Bad Girls of the Bible: Flawed Women Loved by a Flawless God. l.t. ed. 2009. (ENG.). 480p. pap. 17.95 *(978-1-59415-244-3(6)*, Walker Large Print) Cengage Gale.

Hoge, William James. Blind Bartimeus; or, the Story of a Sightless Sinner, & His Great Physician. 2006. 264p. per. 23.99 *(978-1-4255-2339-8(0))* MPublishing.

Holman Reference Editorial Staff, creator. Holman Illustrated Pocket Bible Dictionary: Pocket Reference Edition. 2007. (Illus.). 395p. per. 9.99 *(978-1-58640-314-0(1)*, Holman Pubs.) B&H Publishing Group.

Howard Books Staff. Saints & Scoundrels of the Bible: The Good, the Bad, & the Downright Dastardly. 2008. (ENG., Illus.). 272p. pap. 17.99 *(978-1-4165-6677-9(5)*, Howard Bks.) Howard Books.

Jeffery, Peter. Meeting God: Past, Present & Future. 2007. 125p. pap. *(978-0-85234-671-6(9))* Evangelical Pr.

Lawler, Joy. Bible People - Women: Cokesbury. pap. 5.95 *(978-0-687-07385-6(5))* Abingdon Pr.

Losch, Richard R. All the People in the Bible: An A-Z Guide to the Saints, Scoundrels, & Other Characters in Scripture. 2008. 578p. pap. 26.00 *(978-0-8028-2454-7(4))* Eerdmans, William B. Publishing Co.

Lucado, Max. Cast of Characters: Common People in the Hands of an Uncommon God. l.t. ed. 2009. (ENG.). 393p. pap. 17.99 *(978-1-59415-294-8(2))* Cengage Gale.

—Cast of Characters: Common People in the Hands of an Uncommon God, 0 vols. 2010. 240p. pap. 15.99 *(978-0-8499-2155-1(4))* Nelson, Thomas Inc.

Mandel, David. The Ultimate Who's Who in the Bible: From Aaron to Zurishaddai. 2007. (Illus.). 716p. pap. 19.99 incl. cd-rom *(978-0-88270-372-5(2))* Bridge-Logos Foundation.

—Who's Who in the Jewish Bible. 2007. (ENG.). 550p. per. 30.00 *(978-0-8276-0863-4(2))* Jewish Pubn. Society.

Manser. Who's Who of the Bible. 2012. (ENG., Illus.). 304p. pap. 14.95 ***(978-0-7459-5518-6(5))*** Lion Hudson PLC GBR. Dist: Independent Pubs. Group.

Markham, Ray. Bit Part Players of the Bible: 30 Lesser-Known Characters on God's Stage. 2007. 232p. *(978-1-85345-445-5(1))* Crusade for World Revival.

Matthews, Leah. Facing Change. 2010. (Insights: Bible Studies for Growing Faith Ser.). 48p. pap. 7.00 *(978-1-60899-222-5(5)*, Wipf and Stock) Wipf & Stock Pubs.

McNeill, Robert E. Extraordinary Characters. 2009. xi, 140p. *(978-1-57921-969-7(1))* WinePress Publishing.

Milligan, George & Greenhough, G. Men of the Bible - Some Lesser-Known Ch. 2006. pap. *(978-1-4068-1265-7(X))* Echo Library.

Milligan, George, et al. Men of the Bible, Some Lesser Known Characters. 2011. 128p. pap. 12.99 ***(978-1-61203-258-0(3))*** Bottom of the Hill Publishing.

Morgan-Cole, Trudy. Daughters of Grace: Experiencing God Through Their Stories. 2008. 17.99 *(978-0-8280-2383-2(2))* Review & Herald Publishing Assn.

Moskal, Daniele. Many Are Called but Few Are Chosen Knowi. 2007. 73p. pap. 16.95 *(978-1-4241-1254-8(0))* PublishAmerica, Inc.

Owens, Virginia Stem. Daughters of Eve: Seeing Ourselves in Women of the Bible. 2007. (Navigators Reference Library). (ENG.). 256p. per. 13.99 *(978-1-60006-200-1(8))* NavPress Publishing Group.

Phillips, John. Exploring People of the Old Testament & New Testament Set, 4 vols. 2007. (John Phillips Bible Characters Ser.). 1328p. 89.99 *(978-0-8254-3372-6(X))* Kregel Pubns.

Poinsett, Brenda. Wonder Women of the Bible: Heroes of Yesterday Who Inspire Us Today. 2007. (ENG.). 224p. per. 14.99 *(978-1-59669-094-3(1))* New Hope Pubs.

Roberts, Howard W. In Search of Faith: Profiles of Biblical Seekers. 2010. 174p. pap. 20.00 *(978-1-60899-189-1(X)*, Wipf and Stock) Wipf & Stock Pubs.

Rogers, Heath. Minor Bible Characters. 2007. pap. 6.99 *(978-1-58427-190-1(6))* Guardian of Truth Foundation.

Schneider, Tammi J. Mothers of Promise: Women in the Book of Genesis. 2008. 240p. (C). pap. 24.00 *(978-0-8010-2949-3(X))* Baker Academic.

Sears, Robert. Bible Biography: Or the Lives & Characters of the Personages Recorded in Sacred Writings. 2007. (ENG.). 494p. 53.95 *(978-0-548-04743-9(X))* Kessinger Publishing, LLC.

Stoner, Marcia Joslin. Bible People of Faith: Learning about Bible People. 2007. (Learning about Bible People Ser.). (Illus.). 160p. 18.00 *(978-0-687-64238-0(8))* Abingdon Pr.

Sturdivant, Kevin D. Uncovering Church Cliques & Finding Faithful Friends. 2009. 168p. pap. 14.99 *(978-1-61579-126-2(4))* Xulon Pr., Inc.

Swindoll, Charles R. Great Days with the Great Lives, 0 vols. 2007. (Great Lives from God's Word Ser.). 384p. per. 14.99 *(978-0-8499-1888-9(X))* Nelson, Thomas Inc.

Talley, Allan J. Great People of the Bible Catechist Guide. 2010. (ENG.). (gr. 5-8). pap. 21.95 *(978-0-88489-869-6(5))* St. Mary's Pr.

THE WILDS Christian Association. Joseph. 2008. 96p. (J). spiral bd. 6.95 net. *(978-0-9815235-2-1(8))* WILDS Christian Assn., Inc., The.

Travis, Chris. Unnamed: Unsuspecting Heroes Singled Out by God. 2010. (ENG.). 144p. pap. 9.99 *(978-0-7847-7439-7(0))* Standard Publishing.

Travis, Chris & Karpenske, Nancy. Unnamed Group Member Discussion Guide: Unsuspecting Heroes Singled Out by God. 2010. (ENG.). 64p. pap. 6.99 *(978-0-7847-7440-3(4))* Standard Publishing.

Von Hagel, Thomas A. One Lord, One Faith, One Baptism: Christians Through the Centuries. 2006. (Illus.). 256p. per. 17.49 *(978-0-7586-0760-7(1))* Concordia Publishing Hse.

Water, Mark, ed. The Baker Encyclopedia of Bible People: A Comprehensive Whobs Who from Aaron to Zurishaddai. 2006. 492p. per. 16.99 *(978-0-8010-6604-7(2))* Baker Bks.

Weatherhead, Leslie D. Personalities of the Passion - a Devotional Study of Some of the Characters Who Played a Part in a Drama of Christ's Passion & Resurrection. 2008. 148p. *(978-1-4437-3271-0(0))* 2007. 144p. per. *(978-1-4067-8897-6(X))* Read Bks. (Pomona Pr.).

West, Sandy Lane. Heroes de la Biblia (Champions of the Bible) Conquistadores, Guerreros y Reyes (Settlers, Warriors & Kings) (Bible World Ser.: Vol. 2). (SPA.). 48p. 6.95 *(978-958-692-078-0(X))* Sociedad de San Pablo COL. Dist: St Pauls/Alba Hse. Pubs.

Wiersbe, Warren W. Life Sentences: Discover the Key Themes of 63 Bible Characters, 1 vol. 2007. (ENG.). 320p. pap. 14.99 *(978-0-310-27282-3(3))* Zondervan.

BIBLE—BIOGRAPHY—N. T.

Allen, Richard J. New Testament Who's Who: A Comprehensive Guide to the People in the New Testament. 2010. (Illus.). xvii, 221p. ***(978-1-60861-072-3(1))*** Covenant Communications, Inc.

Bieringer, R., et al. 2 Corinthians: A Bibliography. 2008. (Biblical Tools & Studies). (ENG.). 372p. (C). 113.00 *(978-90-429-2000-2(9))* Peeters Pubs. & Booksellers BEL. Dist: Brown, David Bk. Co., The.

Bruce, Alexander B. The Training of The. 2007. 572p. per. 19.95 *(978-1-60206-539-0(X))* Cosimo, Inc.

Bryan, Timothy. Bible People Prophets. pap. 5.95 *(978-0-687-07405-1(3))* Abingdon Pr.

Chilton, Bruce. Mary Magdalene: A Biography. 2006. (ENG.). 240p. pap. 15.00 *(978-0-385-51318-0(6)*, Image) Doubleday Religious Publishing Group, The.

Chisley, J. r. Going Deeper: Notes for the Serious Bible Student. 2011. 141p. pap. 24.95 *(978-0-9841991-8-1(7))* Beckham Pubns. Group, Inc.

Doyle-Nelson, Theresa. Saints of the Bible: Exploring Scripture with Holy Men & Women. 2009. 111p. pap. 9.95 *(978-1-59276-317-7(0))* Our Sunday Visitor, Publishing Div.

Grundvig, Arnold S. I Am Peter. 2011. pap. 9.99 *(978-1-59955-791-5(6))* Cedar Fort, Inc./CFI Distribution.

Hanks, Scott. Characters of the New Testament. 2007. 3.00 *(978-0-9794157-1-5(3))* Hanks, Scott.

Howson, John Saul. The Metaphors of St Paul & Companions of St Paul. 2008. 328p. 25.99 *(978-0-559-19011-7(5))*; pap. 29.75 *(978-0-559-19009-4(3))* BiblioBazaar.

—The Metaphors of St Paul & Companions of St Paul. 2007. (ENG.). 318p. 45.95 *(978-0-548-16767-0(2))*; 320p. per. 30.95 *(978-1-4304-6479-2(8))* Kessinger Publishing, LLC.

—The Metaphors of St Paul & Companions of St Paul. 2006. 312p. per. 23.99 *(978-1-4255-3296-3(9))* MPublishing.

Hyen, Susan. Imperfect Believers: Ambiguous Characters in the Gospel of John. 2009. (ENG.). 212p. pap. 25.00 *(978-0-664-23372-3(4))* Westminster John Knox Pr.

Kunn, Alvin Boyd. Mary Magdalene & Her Seven Devils. 2011. 26p. 35.95 ***(978-1-258-00593-1(X))*** Literary Licensing, LLC.

Maasen, Janis. Peter the Leader: How an Imperfect Man Became the Leader of the Church. 2009. (ENG.). 160p. pap. 12.99 *(978-1-59979-776-2(3)*, Creation Hse.) Charisma Media.

Magary, Alvin Edwin. Saints Without Halos. 2011. 176p. 42.95 ***(978-1-258-09411-9(8))*** Literary Licensing, LLC.

Metzner, Rainer. Die Prominenten Im Neuen Testament: Ein Prosopographischer Kommentar. 2008. (Novum Testamentum et Orbis Antiquus/Studien zur Umwelt des Neuen Testaments (NTOA/StUNT) Ser.). (GER.). 695p. (C). 117.00 *(978-3-525-53967-5(3))* Vandenhoeck & Ruprecht GmbH & Co. KG DEU. Dist: ISD.

Phillips, John. Exploring People of the New Testament, 1 vol. 2007. (John Phillips Bible Characters Ser.). 432p. 26.99 *(978-0-8254-3387-0(8))* Kregel Pubns.

Purnell, Puck. Through Mark's Eyes: A Portrait of Jesus Based on the Gospel of Mark. 2006. (Illus.). 144p. per. 12.00 *(978-0-687-33572-5(8))* Abingdon Pr.

Roehl, Tim. The Day that Changed Forever: Twenty One Life Changing Experiences at the Cross. 2010. (ENG.). 224p. pap. 14.99 *(978-0-8307-4803-7(2))* Gospel Light Pubns.

Schmeller, Thomas, ed. Historiographie und Biographie Im Neuen Testament und Seiner Umwelt. 2009. (Novum Testamentum et Orbis Antiquus/Studien zur Umwelt des Neuen Testaments (NTOA/StUNT) Ser.). (GER.). 208p. (C). 77.00 *(978-3-525-53968-2(1))* Vandenhoeck & Ruprecht GmbH & Co. KG DEU. Dist: ISD.

Segerhammar, Carl William. They Talked with God: Sermon Studies on New Testament Characters. 2011. 192p. 42.95 ***(978-1-258-06509-6(6))*** Literary Licensing, LLC.

Witherington, Ben, III. What Have They Done with Jesus? Beyond Strange Theories & Bad History — Why We Can Trust the Bible. 2007. (ENG.). 256p. pap. 14.95 *(978-0-06-112002-2(2)*, HarperOne) HarperCollins Pubs.

Yee, Tet-Lim N. Jews, Gentiles & Ethnic Reconciliation: Paul's Jewish identity & Ephesians. 2008. (Society for New Testament Studies Monograph Ser.). (ENG.). 328p. pap. 44.00 *(978-0-521-09146-6(2))* Cambridge Univ. Pr.

BIBLE—BIOGRAPHY—O. T.

Abbott, Dustin L. Hard Knocks & Life Lessons. 2009. 224p. pap. *(978-1-55452-376-4(1))* Essence Publishing.

Aguilar, Grace. The Women of Israel by Grace Aguilar. 2006. 280p. per. 23.99 *(978-1-4255-2563-7(6))* MPublishing.

—The Women of Israel or Characters & Sketches from the Holy Scriptures & Jewish History. 2007. (ENG.). 588p. 58.95 *(978-0-548-03518-4(0))* Kessinger Publishing, LLC.

Beauchamp, Paul. Fifty Biblical Portraits. 2011. (Illus.). 246p. pap. *(978-0-87462-789-3(3))* Marquette Univ. Pr.

Bellis, Alice Ogden. Helpmates, Harlots, & Heroes: Women's Stories in the Hebrew Bible. 2nd ed. 2007. (ENG.). 306p. per. 30.00 *(978-0-664-23028-9(8))* Westminster John Knox Pr.

Bryan, William Jennin. Famous Figures of the Old Testament. 2006. pap. 26.95 *(978-1-4286-5854-7(8))* Kessinger Publishing, LLC.

Bulter, John G. Daniel: The Man of Loyalty. 2007. 427p. *(978-1-889773-21-6(2))* LBC Pubns.

—Isaac: The Promised Son. 2008. 223p. *(978-1-889773-25-4(5))* LBC Pubns.

Chisley, J. r. Going Deeper: Notes for the Serious Bible Student. 2011. 141p. pap. 24.95 *(978-0-9841991-8-1(7))* Beckham Pubns. Group, Inc.

Cribb, Bryan & Block, Daniel. Speaking on the Brink of Sheol. 2010. 119.60 *(978-1-60724-671-8(6))* Gorgias Pr., LLC.

Crowther, Duane S. They Walked with God: Intimate Biographies of Patriarchs from the Book of Genesis. 2009. pap. 17.99 *(978-0-88290-968-4(1))* Cedar Fort, Inc./CFI Distribution.

Deeley, Mary & Deeley, Mary Katharine. Mothers, Lovers, Priests, Prophets, & Kings. 2010. xiii, 120p. pap. *(978-0-7648-1938-4(0))* Liguori Pubns.

Dennis, Trevor. Sarah Laughed: Women's Voices in the Old Testament. 208p. (Orig.). 14.00 *(978-0-281-04689-8(1))* SPCK Publishing GBR. Dist: Pilgrim Pr., The/United Church Pr.

Downey, Paul W. Trusting God When Life Is Hard: A Fresh Look at the Life of Jacob. 2009. *(978-1-59166-987-6(1))* BJU Pr.

Fox, Michael V. Character & Ideology in the Book of Esther: A New Postscript on a Decade of Esther Scholarship. 2nd ed. 2010. 344p. pap. 38.00 *(978-1-60899-495-3(3))* Wipf & Stock Pubs.

Garland, David E. & Garland, Diana R. Flawed Families of the Bible: How God's Grace Works Through Imperfect Relationships. 2007. 236p. (C). pap. 20.00 *(978-1-58743-155-5(6))* Brazos Pr.

Goe, Billy L. The Life of King David: I Samuel 16 thru I Kings 2. 2009. 80p. pap. 11.99 *(978-1-4343-5935-3(2))* AuthorHouse.

Gruber, Mayer. Grace Aguilar's Women of Israel. 2010. 188.96 *(978-1-61719-626-3(6))* Gorgias Pr., LLC.

Hanks, Scott. Characters of the Old Testament. 2007. 3.00 *(978-0-9794157-0-8(5))* Hanks, Scott.

Hercus, John. David. 2nd ed. 144p. pap. 8.99 *(978-1-900507-04-2(8))* Solway GBR. Dist: O. M. Literature.

Higgs, Liz Curtis. Slightly Bad Girls of the Bible: Flawed Women Loved by a Flawless God. 2007. (ENG.). 288p. pap. 13.99 *(978-1-4000-7212-5(3)*, WaterBrook Pr.) Doubleday Religious Publishing Group, The.

Hiltrands, Walter. Heilige Oder Hure? Die Rezeptionsgeschichte Von Juda und Tamar (Genesis 38) Von der Antike Bis Zur Reformationszeit. 2007. (Contributions to Biblical Exegesis & Theology Ser.). (GER & ENG.). 315p. (C). pap. 64.00 *(978-90-429-1914-3(0))* Peeters Pubs. & Booksellers BEL. Dist: Brown, David Bk. Co., The.

Kephart, Lore. Continuing Paths to Prayer: A Little Book of Old Testament Devotions. 2007. (Paths to Prayer Ser.). (Illus.). 114p. 19.95 *(978-1-57736-399-6(X))* Providence Hse Pubs.

Klingbeil, Chantal J. & Klingbeil, Gerald A. Illuminating the Shadow Figures in Scripture. 2010. 126p. pap. 12.99 *(978-0-8280-2509-6(6))* Review & Herald Publishing Assn.
Lee, Witness. Life Study of the Old Testament: Joshua-Malachi, 15 vols., Set. 10,000p. 220.00 *(978-0-7363-0351-4(0))* Living Stream Ministry.
Levine, Michelle J. Nahmanides on Genesis: The Art of Biblical Portraiture. 2009. *(978-1-930675-69-8(0))* Brown Univ.
Lichtenberger, Hermann & Mittmann-Richert, Ulrike. Biblical Figures in Deuterocanonical & Cognate Literature. 2009. (GER & ENG.). *(978-3-11-020368-4(5))* de Gruyter, Walter GmbH & Co. KG.
Lutzer, Erwin W. Keep Your Dream Alive. 141p. pap. 9.99 *(978-0-8307-3451-1(1),* Regal Bks.) Gospel Light Pubns.
Malan, S. C., intro. The Book of Adam & Eve. 2011. 113.12 *(978-1-61143-830-7(6))* Gorgias Pr., LLC.
Maurice, Frederick D. The Patriarchs & Lawgivers of the Old Testament. 2010. 360p. pap. 31.00 *(978-1-60899-712-1(X),* Wipf and Stock) Wipf & Stock Pubs.
Olson, Camille Fronk. Women of the Old Testament. 2009. 39.95 *(978-1-59038-791-7(0))* Deseret Bk. Co.
Phillips, John. Exploring People of the Old Testament, 1 vol. (John Phillips Bible Characters Ser.). (Illus.). Vol. 2. 2006. 288p. 22.99 *(978-0-8254-3385-6(1))* Vol. 3. 2007. 304p. 22.99 *(978-0-8254-3386-3(X))* Kregel Pubns.
Pinegar, Ed J. & Allen, Richard J. Old Testament Who's Who: A Comprehensive Guide to the People in the Old Testament & Pearl of Great Price. 2009. (Illus.). xiv, 190p. *(978-1-59811-850-6(1),* Nicholson) Covenant Communications, Inc.
Pinsky, Robert. The Life of David. 2008. (ENG.). 224p. pap. 12.95 *(978-0-8052-1153-5(5),* Schocken) Knopf Doubleday Publishing Group.
Rolphe, Anne. Water from the Well: Women of the Bible: Sarah, Rebekah, Rachel, & Leah. 2007. (P. S. Ser.). 304p. pap. 13.95 *(978-0-06-073797-9(2),* HarperPerennial) HarperCollins Pubs.
Salkin, Jeffrey K. Righteous Gentiles in the Hebrew Bible: Ancient Role Models for Sacred Relationships. 2008. 192p. pap. 18.99 *(978-1-58023-364-4(3))* Jewish Lights Publishing.
Segerhammar, Carl William. They Walked with God: Sermon Studies on the Old Testament Characters. 2011. 154p. 41.95 ***(978-1-258-05699-5(2))*** Literary Licensing, LLC.
Shanley, John P. David: A Biographical Sketch. 2007. 182p. pap. 12.95 *(978-0-7414-4084-6(9))* Infinity Publishing.
Spurgeon, Charles H. Sermons on Women of the Bible. 2008. 374p. 14.97 *(978-1-59856-641-3(5))* Hendrickson Pubs. Marketing, LLC.
Steinsaltz, Rabbi Adin. Biblical Images: Men & Women of the Book. 2010. 230p. 22.95 *(978-1-59264-294-6(2),* Maggid) Toby Pr. LLC, The.
Stuart, R. D. Heroes & Villains of the Bible: Old Testament. 2008. 360p. pap. 19.99 *(978-1-60266-668-9(7))* Xulon Pr., Inc.
Swindoll, Charles R. Elijah: A Man of Heroism & Humility. 0 vols. 2008. (Great Lives Ser.). 208p. pap. 14.99 *(978-1-4002-8032-2(X))* Nelson, Thomas Inc.
—Esther: A Woman of Strength & Dignity. 0 vols. 2008. (Great Lives Ser.). 224p. pap. 14.99 *(978-1-4002-0223-2(X))* Nelson, Thomas Inc.
—Great Lives: David: A Man of Passion & Destiny. 0 vols. 2008. 320p. pap. 14.99 *(978-1-4002-0224-9(8))* Nelson, Thomas Inc.
—Moses: A Man of Selfless Dedication. 0 vols. 2009. 400p. pap. 14.99 *(978-1-4002-0249-2(3))* Nelson, Thomas Inc.
Thomas, Matthew A. These Are the Generations: Identity, Covenant & the Toledot Formula. 2011. (Library Hebrew Bible/Old Testament Studies). (ENG.). 176p. 120.00 *(978-0-567-15141-4(7),* T&T Clark Int'l) Continuum International Publishing Group, Ltd. GBR. Dist: National Bk. Network.
Thompson, Michael. David: the Illustrated Novel, Vol 2. 2011. 128p. 29.50 ***(978-0-9845282-3-3(7))*** Shepherd King Publishing, LLC.
Weitzman, Steven. Solomon: The Lure of Wisdom. 2011. (Jewish Lives Ser.). (Illus.). 240p. 25.00 *(978-0-300-13718-7(4))* Yale Univ. Pr.
Wiebe, Dianna. Old Testament Overview: A Chronological Study of the Major Characters & Events of the Old Testament: Beginner. 2007. (Stick Figure Ser.). 104p. per. 18.95 *(978-1-59873-002-9(9));* (Illus.). 208p. per. 23.95 *(978-1-59873-000-5(2))* Grapevine Studies.
Wray, T. J. Good Girls, Bad Girls: The Enduring Lessons of Twelve Women of the Old Testament. 2008. (ENG.). 216p. 24.95 *(978-0-7425-6251-6(4))* Rowman & Littlefield Publishers, Inc.

BIBLE—BIRDS
see Nature in the Bible

BIBLE—BLACKS
see Blacks in the Bible

BIBLE—BOTANY
see Nature in the Bible

BIBLE—CANON

Alexander, Archibald. The Canon of the Old & New Testament Ascertained; 2006. 364p. per. 26.99 *(978-1-4255-3788-3(X))* MPublishing.
Alexander, Joseph Addison. Notes on New Testament Literature & Ecclesiastical History. 2007. 340p. 46.95 *(978-0-548-54684-0(3));* (ENG.). per. 31.95 *(978-0-548-47314-6(5))* Kessinger Publishing, LLC.
—Notes on New Testament Literature & Ecclesiastical History. 2006. 340p. per. 23.99 *(978-1-4255-3446-2(5))* MPublishing.
Allert, Craig D. A High View of Scripture? The Authority of the Bible & the Formation of the New Testament Canon. 2007. (Evangelical Ressourcement Ser.). 204p. (C). pap. 22.00 *(978-0-8010-2778-9(0))* Baker Academic.
Brewer, Julius A. The History of the New Testament Canon in the Syrian Church. 2010. pap. 24.40 *(978-1-61143-356-2(8))* Gorgias Pr., LLC.
Carr, David McLain. The Formation of the Hebrew Bible: A New Reconstruction, 1 vol. 2011. (ENG.). 544p. 74.00 *(978-0-19-974260-8(X))* Oxford Univ. Pr., Inc.
Childs, Brevard S. The Church's Guide for Reading Paul: The Canonical Shaping of the Pauline Corpus. 2008. 288p. pap. 28.00 *(978-0-8028-6278-5(0))* Eerdmans, William B. Publishing Co.
Cosin, John. The Works of the Right Reverend Father in God, John Cosin, Lord Bishop of Durham. vol. IV: Miscellaneous Works. 2008. 544p. pap. 41.00 *(978-1-60608-139-6(X),* Wipf and Stock) Wipf & Stock Pubs.
Davidson, Samuel. The Canon of the Bible: Its Formation, History, & Fluctuations. 2008. 296p. 25.99 *(978-0-559-55825-2(2));* pap. 27.75 *(978-0-559-55623-8(6))* BiblioBazaar.
—The Canon of the Bible: Its Formation, History, & Fluctuations. 3rd ed. 2008. 292p. pap. 25.00 *(978-1-55635-795-4(8))* Wipf & Stock Pubs.
Edwards, Brian H. Why Twenty Seven? How Can We Be Sure That We Have the Right Books in the New Testament? 2007. 253p. per. *(978-0-85234-650-1(6))* Evangelical Pr.
Evans, Craig A. & Zacharias, Daniel H., eds. Jewish & Christian Scripture as Artifact & Canon. 2011. (ENG.). 338p. pap. 55.00 ***(978-0-567-29329-9(7),*** T&T Clark Int'l) Continuum International Publishing Group, Ltd. GBR. Dist: National Bk. Network.
—'What Does the Scripture Say?' Studies in the Function of Scripture in Early Judaism & Christianity: The Synoptic Gospels, 2 vols. 2012. (Library of New Testament Studies). (ENG.). 288p. 120.00 ***(978-0-567-38350-1(4),*** T&T Clark Int'l) Continuum International Publishing Group, Ltd. GBR. Dist: National Bk. Network.
Foss, Brooke. El Canon Sagrada Escritura: The Canon of the Holy Scripture. (SPA.). *(978-84-7645-241-7(1),* 223275) Clie, Editorial.
Goodspeed, Edgar J. The Formation of the New Testament. 2011. 220p. 44.95 ***(978-1-258-04780-1(2))*** Literary Licensing, LLC.
—New Solutions of New Testament Problems. 2011. 138p. 40.95 ***(978-1-258-03442-9(5))*** Literary Licensing, LLC.
Harris, R. Laird. Inspiration & Canonicity of the Scriptures. 2008. 348p. pap. 38.00 *(978-1-55635-887-6(3))* Wipf & Stock Pubs.
Holland, David F. Sacred Borders: Continuing Revelation & Canonical Restraint in Early America. 2011. (Religion in America Ser.). (ENG., Illus.). 304p. 65.00 *(978-0-19-975361-1(X))* Oxford Univ. Pr., Inc.
Hovhanessian, Vahan S. The Canon of the Bible & the Apocrypha in the Churches of the East. 2011. (C). 64.95 ***(978-1-4331-1035-1(0))*** Lang, Peter Publishing, Inc.
Jasper, David. Readings in the Canon of Scripture. 2009. (David Jasper Reprint Ser.). 180p. pap. 21.00 *(978-1-60608-835-7(1),* Wipf and Stock) Wipf & Stock Pubs.
Judd, Frank F. & Strathearn, Gaye. How the New Testament Came to Be: 35th Annual Sidney B. Sperry Symposium. 2006. 432p. 24.95 *(978-1-59038-627-9(2))* Deseret Bk. Co.
Keeler, Bronson C. The Early Church Fathers Quoted As Scripture Books Which Are Now. 2006. pap. 12.95 *(978-1-4304-0182-7(6))* Kessinger Publishing, LLC.
McClelland, Alexander. A Brief Treatise on the Canon & Interpretation of the Holy Scriptures. 2006. 240p. per. 20.99 *(978-1-4255-2120-2(7))* MPublishing.
McDonald, Lee Martin. The Biblical Canon: Its Origin, Transmission, & Authority. 3rd ed. 2006. 546p. per. *(978-1-56563-925-6(1))* Hendrickson Pubs. Marketing, LLC.
—Forgotten Scriptures: The Selection & Rejection of Early Religious Writings. 2009. (ENG.). 304p. pap. 30.00 *(978-0-664-23357-0(0))* Westminster John Knox Pr.
—Formation of the Christian Biblical Canon. 13.00 *(978-0-687-13293-5(2))* Abingdon Pr.
—Origin of the Bible: A Guide for the Perplexed. 2011. (Guides for the Perplexed Ser.). (ENG.). 272p. 90.00 *(978-0-567-17802-2(1),* T&T Clark Int'l) Continuum International Publishing Group, Ltd. GBR. Dist: National Bk. Network.
McDonald, Lee Martin, et al. From Biblical Criticism to Biblical Faith: Essays in Honor of Lee Martin Mcdonald. 2007. 450p. 45.00 *(978-0-88146-052-0(4))* Mercer Univ. Pr.
McKendrick, Scot & Doyle, Kathleen. Bible Manuscripts: 1400 Years of Scribes & Scripture. 2007. (ENG., Illus.). 159p. 35.00 *(978-0-7123-4922-2(7))* British Library, The GBR. Dist: Chicago Distribution Ctr.
Moore, Edward Caldwell. The New Testament in the Christian Church. 2007. (ENG.). 380p. 48.95 *(978-0-548-02540-6(1))* Kessinger Publishing, LLC.
Nienhuis, David R. Not by Paul Alone: The Formation of the Catholic Epistle Collection & the Christian Canon. 2007. (Illus.). 285p. 44.95 *(978-1-932792-71-3(6))* Baylor Univ. Pr.
Porter, Stanley E. The Pauline Canon. 2009. 272p. pap. 32.95 *(978-1-58983-428-6(3))* Society of Biblical Literature.
Reuss, Eduard. History of the Canon of the Holy Scriptures in the Christian Church. Hunter, David, tr. 2007. 416p. pap. 35.00 *(978-1-55635-747-3(8))* Wipf & Stock Pubs.
Schroter, Jens. Von Jesus zum Neuen Testament. 2007. (Wissenschaftliche Untersuchungen Zum Neuen Testament Ser.: 204). 441p. (C). 157.50 *(978-3-16-149231-0(5))* Mohr Siebeck GmbH & Co. KG DEU. Dist: Coronet Bks.
Seitz, Christopher R. The Goodly Fellowship of the Prophets: The Achievement of Association in Canon Formation, 1 vol. 2009. (Acadia Studies in Bible & Theology Ser.). 144p. (C). pap. 20.00 *(978-0-8010-3883-9(9))* Baker Academic.
Stuart, Moses. Critical History & Defence of the Old Testament Canon. 2009. (Amer Philosophy, Religion Ser.). (ENG.). 460p. pap. 27.95 *(978-1-4290-1879-1(8))* Applewood Bks.
—Critical History & Defence of the Old Testament Canon. 2009. 400p. 31.99 *(978-1-115-70119-8(3));* 400p. pap. 29.99 *(978-1-115-70120-4(7));* 400p. pap. 20.99 *(978-1-115-70122-8(3));* 400p. pap. 26.99 *(978-1-115-70121-1(5));* 396p. 26.99 *(978-1-103-19682-1(0));* 396p. pap. 20.99 *(978-1-103-19680-7(4))* BiblioBazaar.
—Critical History & Defence of the Old Testament Canon. 2009. 322p. pap. *(978-0-217-92672-0(X))* Books LLC.
Theissen, Gerd. The New Testament: A Literary History. Maloney, Linda M., tr. from GER. 2011. 304p. (C). 49.00 *(978-0-8006-9785-3(5),* Fortress Pr.) Augsburg Fortress, Pubs.
Thomassen, Einar, ed. Canon & Canonicity: The Formation & Use of Scripture. 2010. 232p. 48.00 *(978-87-635-3027-9(9))* Museum Tusculanum Pr. DNK. Dist: Chicago Distribution Ctr.
Tov, Emanuel & Evans, Craig A., eds. Exploring the Origins of the Bible: Canon Formation in Historical, Literary, & Theological Perspective. 2008. (Acadia Studies in Bible & Theology Ser.). 272p. (C). pap. 28.00 *(978-0-8010-3242-4(3))* Baker Academic.
Watts, John D. W. How We Got Our Bible: Files from an Alttestamentler's Hard Drive. 2011. 246p. pap. 27.00 *(978-1-60899-394-9(9),* Wipf and Stock) Wipf & Stock Pubs.
Zaman, Luc. Bible & Canon: A Modern Historical Inquiry. 2008. (Studia Semitica Neerlandica Ser.). 736p. *(978-90-04-16743-8(9))* BRILL.

BIBLE—CATECHISMS
see also Bible Games and Puzzles

Aaberg, Dennis G. Topic Bible Studies Addressing Everyday Problems & Questions. 2009. 184p. pap. 16.99 *(978-1-61579-209-2(0))* Xulon Pr., Inc.
Austin, Michael. Lost Relation: Finding Humanity & God - After the Party. 2009. 168p. pap. 14.99 *(978-1-60791-978-0(8))* Xulon Pr., Inc.
Barbour Publishing, Inc. 365-Day Fun Bible Fact Book. 2010. (ENG.). 384p. pap. 9.99 *(978-1-60260-848-1(2),* Barbour Bks.) Barbour Publishing, Inc.
Barbour Publishing Staff. Bible Answers for the New Year. 2009. (Value Bks.). (ENG.). 160p. pap. 1.99 *(978-1-60260-384-4(7),* Barbour Bks.) Barbour Publishing, Inc.
Clark, George. The Bible Revisited II: Beyond the Bible. 2009. 129p. pap. 14.95 *(978-1-4327-3852-5(6))* Outskirts Pr., Inc.
Engelbrecht, Edward. One True God: Understanding Large Catechism II. 66. 2007. (Illus.). 150p. pap. 3.99 *(978-0-7586-1351-6(2))* Concordia Publishing Hse.
Fireside Catholic Publishing, creator. The New Catholic Answer Bible RCIA Program: A Scripture-Based Question & Answer Approach to Rite of Christian Initiation for Adults. 2008. 64p. pap. 19.95 *(978-1-55665-034-5(5))* Fireside Catholic Bibles.
Gullion, David S. The Last Christian: The Story of the Christ. 2009. 424p. pap. 20.49 *(978-1-4389-8237-3(2))* AuthorHouse.
Ham, Ken, ed. The New Answers Book: Over 25 Questions on Creation/Evolution & the Bible. 2007. (Illus.). 378p. per. 14.99 *(978-0-89051-509-9(3))* Master Bks.
Hanegraaff, Hank. The Bible Answer Book for Students. 0 vols. 2007. (Illus.). 256p. 14.99 *(978-1-4041-0450-1(X))* Nelson, Thomas Inc.
Hellen, John. The Bible Is No Fairy Tale! The Compelling Evidence Proving the Bible to be God's True & Inspired Word. 2009. 236p. pap. 12.99 *(978-1-60799-029-1(6))* Tate Publishing & Enterprises, LLC.
Huffnagle, Sylvia. Bible Living Quiz Book: 964 Q/A - Rated According to Difficulty. 2006. 393p. per. 20.95 *(978-1-59824-302-4(0))* E-BookTime LLC.
Hunt, Cecil. Who Killed Cain? A Quiz on Biblical, Religious & Allied Subjects (with Answers & Reference Index) 2007. 128p. per. *(978-1-4067-8809-9(0),* Pomona Pr.) Read Bks.
Hylton, Worrell. The Battle for Moses's Dead Body: Why Would the Two Most Powerful Created Being Fight over a Dead Body. 2009. 336p. pap. 18.99 *(978-1-60791-891-2(9))* Xulon Pr., Inc.
Lang, J. Stephen. The Good Book Bible Trivia: Over 4,300 Questions & Answers about the Bible. 2008. (Illus.). 354p. pap. *(978-1-4143-1974-2(6))* Tyndale Hse. Pubs.
Lennox, Doug. Now You Know the Bible. 2010. (Now You Know Ser.). (ENG.). 192p. pap. 19.99 *(978-1-55488-798-9(4))* Dundurn CAN. Dist: Ingram Pub. Services.
Livingstone Corporation Staff. 500 Questions & Answers from the Bible. Fackler, Mark, ed. 2006. (ENG., Illus.). 256p. per. 9.99 *(978-1-59789-473-9(7),* Barbour Bks.) Barbour Publishing, Inc.
Manser, Martin H. The Ultimate Bible Fact & Quiz Book. Chartwell Books Staff, ed. 2009. (ENG., Illus.). 384p. spiral bd. 9.99 *(978-0-7858-2161-8(9),* 0785821619, Chartwell) Book Sales, Inc.
Matlock, Roy A. The Bible Quiz: Sharpen Your Bible Skills. 2009. 168p. pap. 12.99 *(978-1-4389-6304-4(1))* AuthorHouse.
Packer, J. I. & Parrett, Gary A. Grounded in the Gospel: Building Believers the Old-Fashioned Way, 1 vol. 2010. (ENG.). 240p. pap. 16.99 *(978-0-8010-6838-6(X))* Baker Bks.
Platt, Christian. Banned Questions about the Bible. 2011. 176p. pap. 19.99 *(978-0-8272-0246-7(6))* Chalice Pr.
Pinnock, W. H. An Analysis of Scripture History with Examination Questions. 2007. 380p. 48.95 *(978-0-548-03427-9(3))* Kessinger Publishing, LLC.
Save, Ken & Save, Vickie. Fun Bible Q & A for Kids. 2010. (ENG.). 224p. pap. 3.99 *(978-1-60260-861-0(X),* Barbour Bks.) Barbour Publishing, Inc.
Shelton, Rick. John: 16. 2009. 160p. pap. 17.00 *(978-1-4389-8362-2(X))* AuthorHouse.
Spargimino, Larry. Digging Deeper: Questions & Answers on the Bible, the Christian Life, & the End Times. 2009. 256p. pap. 13.95 *(978-1-933641-29-4(0))* Bible Belt Pubns.
St. Maximus Staff. St. Maximus the Confessor's Questions & Doubts. Prassas, Despina D., tr. from FRE. 2009. (ENG.). 234p. 40.00 *(978-0-87580-413-2(6))* Northern Illinois Univ. Pr.
Waite, Th. D. The Superior Foundation of the King James Bible. 2008. 108p. pap. 12.00 *(978-1-56848-062-6(8))* Old Paths Pubns., Inc., The.
Wesley Lloyd Cann. The Origin of God: Little Book. 2009. 352p. 29.99 *(978-1-4389-2031-3(8));* pap. 19.99 *(978-1-4389-2032-0(6))* AuthorHouse.
Wessel, Dawn. Missing Pieces of the Bible: Lost Books Fill-In the Blanks REVISED EDITION. 2008. 168p. pap. 17.50 *(978-1-4357-1462-5(8))* Lulu Enterprises Inc.
Wheeler, Tompaul. Bible Readings: Straight Answers from the Bible. 2007. *(978-0-8280-1728-2(X))* Review & Herald Publishing Assn.
Williams, Clinton H. The Ultimate Truth about the Creation of Man: Answers to Hard Bible Questions. 2009. 80p. pap. 12.49 *(978-1-4490-1146-8(2))* AuthorHouse.

BIBLE—CHARACTERS
see Bible—Biography

BIBLE—CHILDREN
see Children in the Bible

BIBLE—CHRONOLOGY

Abeelen, Jack. The Jesus Chronicles. 2009. 768p. 39.99 *(978-1-57921-988-8(8))* WinePress Publishing.
Abrams, John A. Look at the Moon! the Revelation Chronology. 2007. 664p. per. 24.95 *(978-1-4327-0786-6(8))* Outskirts Pr., Inc.
Ashton, John & Down, David. Unwrapping the Pharaohs: How Egyptian Archaeology Confirms the Biblical Timeline. 2006. (Illus.). 218p. 34.99 *(978-0-89051-468-9(2))* Master Bks.
Barr, Adam T. Exploring the Story: A Reference Companion, 1 vol. 2011. (Story Ser.). (ENG.). 176p. pap. 19.99 *(978-0-310-32699-1(0))* Zondervan.
Bigelow, Christopher Kimball. The Timechart History of Mormonism: From Premortality to the Present. 2007. (Illus.). 31p. 17.99 *(978-1-903025-40-6(0))* Worth Pr. Ltd. GBR. Dist: Book Sales, Inc.
Blanchett, Elnora. Clarified New Testament Chronological. 2008. 356p. 43.00 *(978-1-4251-7253-4(9))* Trafford Publishing.
—Clarified New Testament, Traditional. 2008. 332p. 43.00 *(978-1-4251-7885-7(5))* Trafford Publishing.
Books of the Way. Old Testament History in Chronological Order. 2007. (YA). per. 36.95 *(978-0-9793995-6-5(4))* Bks. of the Way.
Borg, Marcus J. Evolution of the Word: Reading the New Testament in the Order It Was Written. 2012. (ENG.). 608p. 29.99 ***(978-0-06-208210-7(8),*** HarperOne) HarperCollins Pubs.
Bosanquet, S. R. Hindu Chronology & Antediluvian Histor. 2006. pap. 16.95 *(978-1-4286-6335-0(5))* Kessinger Publishing, LLC.
Boyer. Tabla Cronologica del Nuevo Testamento - Chronological Chart of the New Testament. (Tablas Cronologicas - Chronological Chart Ser.). (SPA.). *(978-1-56063-935-0(0))* Editorial Unilit.
—Tabla Cronologica del Periodo Intertestamentario - Chronological Chart of the Period Between the Testaments. (Tablas Cronologicas Ser.). (SPA.). *(978-1-56063-934-3(2))* Editorial Unilit.
Cadwallader, Alan H. & Trainor, Michael, eds. Colossae in Space & Time: Linking to an Ancient City. 2011. (Novum Testamentum et Orbis Antiquus/Studien zur Umwelt des Neuen Testaments (NTOA/StUNT) Ser.). (ENG., Illus.). 368p. (C). 168.00 *(978-3-525-53397-0(7))* Vandenhoeck & Ruprecht GmbH & Co. KG DEU. Dist: ISD.
Cohen, Tim. Messiah, History, & the Tribulation Period: Multi-Volume Set, 7 vols., Cohen, Tim, ed. rev. ed. 2006. (Illus.). pap. *(978-0-9662793-1-3(X),* BK-02) Prophecy House, Inc.
—Messiah, History, & the Tribulation Period Vol. 4: Biblical Chronology: the Young Creation. Cohen, Tim, ed. 2006. pap. *(978-0-9662793-5-1(2))* Prophecy House, Inc.
Cook, David C., 3rd. There! A Biblical Chronology. 2010. 170p. 38.95 *(978-0-557-27966-1(6))* Lulu Enterprises Inc.
Cook, David C., 3rd & Blaschak, Lois. There! A Biblical Chronicle. Canary, Margaret Cook & Cook, Bruce L., eds. 2006. pap. 14.95 *(978-0-9726996-6-2(X),* ThereO") Cook Communication.
Dixon, James W. Chronological Commentary of the Bible: A Guide for Understanding the Scriptures Vol. 1 And 2. 2011. 744p. pap. 45.00 *(978-1-4120-6520-7(8))* Trafford Publishing.
Finch, Paul R. The Passover Papers: Controversy, Myth, Fairy Tales & Nonsense! 2nd ed. 2008. xii, 340p. pap. *(978-0-9800739-3-5(6))* B-F Enterprises Inc.
Gouin, Walter Robert. Chronicles III: Moses 1490 Exodus, to Cyrus of Persia 485 Bce Chronological Hebrew History of Israel & Judah's Patriarchs, Judges, Kings, Prophets & Governors. 2011. 276p. 34.99 ***(978-1-4567-3870-9(4));*** pap. 22.00 ***(978-1-4567-3868-6(2))*** AuthorHouse.
Green, Richard. The Order of Things to Come. 2007. 84p. per. 16.95 *(978-1-60441-136-2(8))* PublishAmerica, Inc.
Halza, Miroslav. The Chronology of Revelation. 2006. pap. 13.99 *(978-1-60034-338-4(4))* Xulon Pr., Inc.

B

Hollandbeck, Beverly. Christian Chronicles: Bargersville First Christian. 2008. 640p. pap. 33.49 *(978-1-4343-9250-3(3))* AuthorHouse.
Hughes, Jeremy. Secrets of the Times: Myth & History in Biblical Chronology. 2009. (Library of Hebrew Bible/Old Testament Studies, the Ser.). (ENG.). 312p. 49.95 *(978-0-567-25414-6(3)*, T&T Clark) Continuum International Publishing Group, Ltd. GBR. Dist: National Bk. Network.
Keller, Werner. The Bible As History. 2008. 180p. pap. *(978-965-91241-5-2(5))* Editorial Benei Noaj.
Newton, Isaac. The Chronology of Ancient Kingdoms. 2007. (ENG.). 224p. per. *(978-1-4065-5032-0(9))* Dodo Pr.
—The Chronology of Ancient Kingdoms. 2007. 160p. per. *(978-1-4068-3453-6(X))* Echo Library.
—The Chronology of Ancient Kingdoms Amended. 2008. 308p. per. 16.99 *(978-1-59986-578-2(5))* Filiquarian Publishing, LLC.
Newton, Isaac, et al. Newton's Revised History of Ancient Kingdoms: A Complete Chronology. 2008. (Illus.). 205p. *(978-0-89051-556-3(5))* Master Bks.
Ozanne, Charles. The Believer's Guide to Bible Chronology: From Man's Beginning to the End of Acts. 2011. (Illus.). 256p. pap. 16.99 *(978-1-4389-4323-7(7))* AuthorHouse.
Rhodes, Ron. The End Times in Chronological Order. 2012. 240p. pap. 13.99 ***(978-0-7369-3778-8(1))*** Harvest Hse. Pubs.
Robinson, John A. T. The Priority of John. Coakley, J. F., ed. 2011. 460p. pap. 56.00 *(978-1-61097-102-7(7)*, Wipf and Stock) Wipf & Stock Pubs.
Robinson, John A. T. & Coakley, J. F. The Priority of John. 2012. 443p. ***(978-0-334-02273-2(8)***, SCM Pr.) Hymns Ancient & Modern Ltd.
Rose Publishing Staff. Then & Now Bible Maps Insert. 2008. (ENG., Illus.). 44p. 16.99 *(978-1-59636-293-2(6))* Rose Publishing.
Rose Publishing Staff, ed. Rose Book of Bible Charts, Vol. 2. 2008. (ENG.). 192p. 29.99 *(978-1-59636-275-8(8))* Rose Publishing.
Steinmann, Andrew. From Abraham to Paul: A Biblical Chronology. 2011. 79.99 ***(978-0-7586-2799-5(8))*** Concordia Publishing Hse.
Templeton, William M. The Chronology of the Revelation. Templeton, Bonita I., ed. 2006. spiral bd. 18.95 *(978-0-9787896-1-9(X))* ARARAT Pubs.
Thomas, John. Eureka, an Exposition of the Apocalypse V1. 2011. 470p. 57.95 ***(978-1-258-03729-1(7))*** Literary Licensing, LLC.
—Eureka, an Exposition of the Apocalypse V2. 2011. 754p. 71.95 ***(978-1-258-02428-4(4))*** Literary Licensing, LLC.
Thomas Nelson. The Chronological Guide to the Bible, 0 vols. 2010. 464p. pap. 24.99 *(978-1-4185-4175-0(3))* Nelson, Thomas Inc.
Thompson, Darren. Why the Bible Is Historically Accurate. 2nd ed. 2007. 101p. pap. 15.31 *(978-1-4303-1062-4(6))* Lulu Enterprises Inc.
Thurman, William C. Our Bible Chronology Established the Sealed Book of Daniel Opened. 2006. 256p. per. 23.99 *(978-1-4255-2238-4(6))* MPublishing.
Tyndale House Publishers Staff, creator. The One Year Chronological Bible. 2nd ed. 2007. (ENG.). 1728p. per. 19.99 *(978-1-4143-1408-2(6))* Tyndale Hse. Pubs.
Tyndale House Publishers Staff, prod. The One Year Chronological Bible NIV. 2007. (ENG.). 1728p. 24.99 *(978-1-4143-1409-9(4))* Tyndale Hse. Pubs.
—The One Year Chronological Bible NLT. 2007. (ENG.). 1728p. 24.99 *(978-1-4143-1407-5(8))* Tyndale Hse. Pubs.
Ussher, James. The Annals of the World. 2007. (Illus.). 960p. per. *(978-0-89051-510-5(7))* Master Bks.
Vilardi, Michael. The Time of His Coming: The Fictionalized Account of the Coming of Christ That Could Come True. 2006. pap. 16.99 *(978-1-58158-101-0(7)*, Serenity Bks.) McDougal Publishing Co.
Wallraff, Martin, ed. Iulius Africanus Chronographiae: The Extant Fragments. Adler, William, tr. from GEC. 2007. (Die Griechischen Christlichen Schriftsteller der Ersten Jahr Ser.). (GEC & ENG.). LXXXIX, 352p. 154.00 *(978-3-11-019493-7(7))* De Gruyter, Walter Inc.
Whitcomb. Tabla Cronologica de los Cinco Mundos - Chronological Chart of the Five Worlds. (Tablas Cronologicas - Chronological Chart Ser.). (SPA.). *(978-1-56063-929-6(6))* Editorial Unilit.
—Tabla Cronologica/Cautividad Babilonica I-II - Chart of Babylonia Captivity I-II. (Tablas Cronologicas - Chronological Chart Ser.). (SPA.). *(978-1-56063-933-6(4))* Editorial Unilit.
—Tabla de los Patriarcas y Jueces de A. T. - Chart of the O. T. Patriarchs & Judges. (Tablas Cronologicas - Chronological Chart Ser.). (SPA.). *(978-1-56063-931-2(8))* Editorial Unilit.
Wiebe, Dianna. Old Testament Overview: A Chronological Study of the Major Characters & Events of the Old Testament: Beginner. 2007. (Stick Figure Ser.). 104p. per. 18.95 *(978-1-59873-002-9(9))*; (Illus.). 208p. per. 23.95 *(978-1-59873-000-5(2))* Grapevine Studies.
Witcomb. Tabla de los Reyes/Profetas del A. T. - Chart of the O. T. Kings & Prophets. (Tablas Cronologicas Ser.). (SPA.). *(978-1-56063-932-9(6))* Editorial Unilit.

BIBLE—CODICES
see Bible—Manuscripts

BIBLE—COINS
see Bible—Numismatics

BIBLE—COLPORTAGE
see Bible—Publication and Distribution

BIBLE—COMMENTARIES
Here are entered only commentaries on the whole Bible. Commentaries on the New Testament, and portions of the New Testament, precede commentaries on the Old Testament, and portions of the Old Testament.
see also Scholia

Abbett, Gailen (Butch). Bible Truths Learned from Life. 2008. 256p. pap. 16.99 *(978-1-60647-953-7(9))* Xulon Pr., Inc.
Abingdon. What's in the Bible about God? What's in the Bible & Why Should I Care? 2008. (Why Is That in the Bible & Why Should I Care? Ser.). 80p. pap. 8.00 *(978-0-687-65363-8(0))* Abingdon Pr.
—What's in the Bible about Jesus? What's in the Bible & Why Should I Care? 2008. (Why Is That in the Bible & Why Should I Care? Ser.). 84p. pap. 8.00 *(978-0-687-65383-6(5))* Abingdon Pr.
—What's in the Bible about Us? What's in the Bible & Why Should I Care? 2008. (Why Is That in the Bible & Why Should I Care? Ser.). 82p. pap. 8.00 *(978-0-687-65373-7(8))* Abingdon Pr.
Abingdon Press. What's in the Bible about God, Jesus, & Us? Leader E-Tools. 2008. 16.00 *(978-0-687-65393-5(2))* Abingdon Pr.
—What's in the Bible & How Do I Use It? Real Help for Regular People. 2008. (Why Is That in the Bible & Why Should I Care? Ser.). 109p. pap. 10.00 *(978-0-687-65403-1(3))* Abingdon Pr.
Adult Bible Class: Winter, 2006/2007. 2006. pap. *(978-1-59843-071-4(8))* Incorporated Trustees of the Gospel Worker Society, The.
Adult Bible Class Vol. 4: Fall 2006. 2006. pap. *(978-1-59843-070-7(X))* Incorporated Trustees of the Gospel Worker Society, The.
Alcott, Amos Bronson. Conversations with Children on the Gospels. 2009. 326p. 32.99 *(978-1-115-64648-2(6))*; pap. 30.75 *(978-1-115-64650-5(8))* BiblioBazaar.
—Conversations with Children on the Gospels. 2010. 154p. pap. *(978-1-152-00391-0(7))* 2010. 166p. pap. *(978-1-152-00385-9(2))* 2009. 186p. pap. *(978-0-217-70106-8(0))* Books LLC.
Alexander, Joseph Addison. Isaiah Translated & Explained by Joseph Addison Alexander an Abridgment of the Author's Critical Commentary on Isaiah + 2006. (ENG.). 464p. per. 29.99 *(978-1-4255-5153-7(X))*; 404p. per. 26.99 *(978-1-4255-4331-0(6))* MPublishing.
Alexander Maclaren. Expositions of Holy Scripture Ezekiel Daniel & the Minor Prophets. St Matthew Chapters I to VIII. l.t. ed. 2007. (ENG.). 734p. pap. 35.99 *(978-1-4264-8979-2(X))* BiblioBazaar.
The Alien Presence Book Two: The Bloodline Project. 2008. (Illus.). 302p. per. 44.95 *(978-0-9707873-2-3(4))* Green Earth Research Pubns.
The Ancient Christian Commentary on Scripture, 7 vols., Set. Incl. James, 1-2 Peter, 1-3 John, Jude Vol. 11. Bray, Gerald L., ed. 318p. 2000. 50.00 *(978-0-8308-1496-1(5)*, IVP Acad.); Vol. 2. Mark: New Testament. Oden, Thomas C. & Hall, Christopher A., eds. 1998. 40.00 *(978-0-8308-1487-9(6)*, 1487); Vol. 3. Exodus, Leviticus, Numbers, Deuteronomy. Lienhard, Joseph T., ed. 414p. 2001. 50.00 *(978-0-8308-1473-2(6)*, IVP Acad.); Vol. 9. Colossians, 1-2 Thessalonians, 1-2 Timothy, Titus, Philemon. Gorday, Peter, ed. 380p. 2000. 50.00 *(978-0-8308-1494-7(9)*, IVP Acad.); Vols. 1-11. Genesis. Louth, Andrew, ed. 256p. 2001. 50.00 *(978-0-8308-1471-8(X)*, IVP Acad.); 17p. 680.00 *(978-0-8308-1470-1(1))* InterVarsity Pr.
Anders, Max. What You Need to Know about the Bible in 12 Lessons. 2011. 192p. pap. 12.99 *(978-1-4185-4631-1(3))* Nelson, Thomas Inc.
Apocalipsis. (SPA., Illus.). No. 1. 0.39 *(978-0-945792-37-6(9)*, 496120)No. 2. 0.39 *(978-0-945792-38-3(7)*, 496121)No. 3. 0.39 *(978-0-945792-77-2(8)*, 496122) Editorial Unilit.
Arnold, V. W. The Lord Our Comforter. 2007. 196p. per. 13.99 *(978-1-60266-636-8(9))* Xulon Pr., Inc.
Assad, Assad, tr. The Commentary of Saint Ephrem on Genesis with an Arabic Translation. 2010. (ARA.). 126.68 *(978-1-61143-548-1(X))* Gorgias Pr., LLC.
Asumang, Annang. Unlocking the Book of Hebrews: A Spatial Analysis of the Epistle to the Hebrews. 2008. (Illus.). 214p. pap. 24.00 *(978-1-55635-306-2(5))* Wipf & Stock Pubs.
Bacote, Vincent. Precepts for Living Personal Study Guide. 2008th ed. 2008. (Precepts for Living Ser.). 140p. pap. 7.95 *(978-1-60352-331-8(6))* UMI (Urban Ministries, Inc.).
Bacote, Vincent, ed. Precepts for Living 2009-2010 W/CD-ROM. 2009. (Precepts for Living Ser.). 504p. pap. 21.95 *(978-1-60352-685-2(4))* UMI (Urban Ministries, Inc.).
—Precepts for Living Annual Commentary 2008-2009. 11th rev. ed. 2008. (Precepts for Living Ser.). 512p. pap. 16.95 *(978-1-60352-329-5(4))* UMI (Urban Ministries, Inc.).
Ball-Kilbourne, Gary, ed. All Four Leader's Guides. (Genesis to Revelation Ser.). 65.00 *(978-0-687-03089-7(7))* Abingdon Pr.
Ballester, Gonzalo Torrente. Fragmentos de Apocalipsis. (Classicos Contemporaneos Comentados Ser.). (SPA., Illus.). 536p. 19.95 *(978-84-233-2733-1(7)*, DE7337) Ediciones Destino ESP. Dist: Continental Bk. Co., Inc.
Balthasar, Hans Urs Von. Credo: Meditations on the Apostles' Creed. 108p. *(978-0-567-29185-1(5)*, Burns & Oates) Continuum International Publishing Group, Ltd.
Bartholomew, Craig G. & Bartholomew. Canon & Biblical Interpretation, 1 vol., Vol. 7. Parry, Robin et al, eds. 2006. (Scripture & Hermeneutics Ser.: Vol. 7). (ENG., Illus.). 464p. 39.99 *(978-0-310-23417-3(4))* Zondervan.
Bartlett, F. Steward. Fundamental Misconceptions of Bible Basics A Search for Spiritual Truth & Moral Purity. 2008. 262p. pap. 15.98 *(978-0-615-25704-4(6))* Bartlett, F. Steward.
Belsky, Yisroel. Einei Yisroel: Shemos. 2007. 24.95 *(978-1-60091-000-5(9))* Israel Bookshop Pubns.
ben David, Eliyahu. Holy Order Restored: Or Bible Study of Angels, Eden, Tree of Life, Adam & Eve, Marriage, Family, Government, Lucifer as Satan, Sin, Cain, Abel, Nephilim, the First Patriarchs, Seth, Enoch, Methuselah, Last Days of the Pre-Flood World & Noah's Ark Informs the End Times Sons of God to Take Dominion. 2007. 140p. per. 15.80 *(978-0-9679471-1-2(1)*, Zarach) Bfree Publishing.
Berg, Michael. Secrets of the Bible: Teachings from Kabbalistic Masters. 2011. (ENG.). 320p. 34.95 *(978-1-57189-769-5(0))* Research Centre of Kabbalah.
—Secrets of the Zohar: Stories & Meditations to Awaken the Heart. 2007. (ENG., Illus.). 240p. 24.95 *(978-1-57189-577-6(9))* Research Centre of Kabbalah.
Berg, Yehuda, ed. Genesis: The Kabbalistic Bible, Volume One. 2008. (ENG & HEB.). 448p. 24.95 *(978-1-57189-606-3(6))* Research Centre of Kabbalah.
Bianco, D. & Merisio, P. I Am with You Always. (Illus.). 127p. pap. 15.00 *(978-0-88840-659-0(2))* Mediaspaul CAN. Dist: St Pauls/Alba Hse. Pubs.
Bible Expositor & Illuminator: Winter, 2006/2007. 2006. pap. *(978-1-59843-063-9(7))* Incorporated Trustees of the Gospel Worker Society, The.
Bible Expositor & Illuminator Vol. 4: Fall 2006. 2006. pap. *(978-1-59843-062-2(9))* Incorporated Trustees of the Gospel Worker Society, The.
Bible Foundations 101: Fast Tracking New Believers Handbook. 2007th ed. 2006. (POR & SPA.). pap. 17.95 *(978-0-9793173-0-4(5))* Montague, Jason.
Bible Study for New Korean Immigrants. 8.00 *(978-0-687-02147-5(2))* Abingdon Pr.
Binz, Stephen J. The Sacred Heart of Jesus. 2006. (Threshold Bible Study Ser.). 136p. pap. 12.95 *(978-1-58595-597-8(3))* Twenty-Third Pubns./Bayard.
Bischoff, Bernhard & Lapidge, Michael, eds. Biblical Commentaries from the Canterbury School of Theodore & Hadrian. 2007. (Cambridge Studies in Anglo-Saxon England Ser.). (ENG & LAT., Illus.). 628p. pap. 116.00 *(978-0-521-03347-3(0))* Cambridge Univ. Pr.
Blackaby, Henry, et al. Colossians/Philemon, 0 vols. 2008. (Encounters with God Ser.). 96p. pap. 9.99 *(978-1-4185-2649-8(5))* Nelson, Thomas Inc.
—Galatians, 0 vols. 2008. (Encounters with God Ser.). 96p. pap. 9.99 *(978-1-4185-2646-7(0))* Nelson, Thomas Inc.
—Philippians, 0 vols. 2008. (Encounters with God Ser.). 96p. pap. 9.99 *(978-1-4185-2648-1(7))* Nelson, Thomas Inc.
—2 Corinthians, 0 vols. 2008. (Encounters with God Ser.). 96p. pap. 9.99 *(978-1-4185-2645-0(2))* Nelson, Thomas Inc.
Boda, Mark J. 1 & 2 Chronicles. 2010. (Cornerstone Biblical Commentary Ser.: 5). (ENG.). 456p. 29.99 *(978-0-8423-3431-0(9))* Tyndale Hse. Pubs.
Boice, James Montgomery. The Boice Expositional Commentaries on CD-ROM. 2007. cd-rom 349.99 *(978-0-8010-0298-4(2))* Baker Bks.
Boyd's Commentary for 2002-2003. *(978-1-58942-122-6(1))* R.H. Boyd Publishing Corp.
Boyd's Commentary for the Sunday School. pap. *(978-1-58942-195-0(7))* R.H. Boyd Publishing Corp.
Boyett, Jason & Boyett. Pocket Guide to the Bible No. 1: A Little Book about the Big Book. 2009. (ENG., Illus.). 208p. pap. 12.95 *(978-0-470-37309-5(1)*, Jossey-Bass) Wiley, John & Sons, Inc.
Bruce, F. F. Zondervan Bible Commentary. 2008. (ENG.). 1616p. 44.99 *(978-0-310-26264-0(X))* Zondervan.
Brueggemann, Walter, et al. Texts for Preaching: A Lectionary Commentary Based on the NRSV Year A. 2007. (ENG.). cd-rom 80.00 *(978-0-664-23193-4(4))* Westminster John Knox Pr.
Bullinger, E. W. Chief Musician or Studies in the Psalms. 2006. pap. 23.95 *(978-1-60206-036-4(3)*, Cosimo Classics) Cosimo, Inc.
Bullinger, Ethelbert. Commentary on Revelation, or, the Apocalypse. 2007. 752p. 39.95 *(978-1-60206-948-0(4))* Cosimo, Inc.
Burroughs, Jeremiah. Exposition of the Prophecy of Hosea. 2006. pap. 50.00 *(978-1-892777-94-2(0))* Reformation Heritage Bks.
Butarbutar, Robinson. Paul & Conflict Resolution: An Exegetical Study of Paul's Apostolic Paradigm in 1 Corinthians 9. 2007. (Paternoster Biblical Monographs: Ser.). 312p. pap. 36.00 *(978-1-55635-479-3(7)*, Wipf and Stock) Wipf & Stock Pubs.
Butler, Stella V. F. Understanding the Word. 2009. (Library of Hebrew Bible/Old Testament Studies, the Ser.). (ENG.). 65.00 *(978-0-567-63134-3(6)*, T&T Clark) Continuum International Publishing Group, Ltd. GBR. Dist: National Bk. Network.
Byrd, Rabon, ed. If Any Man Be in Christ. 2007. 228p. 20.00 *(978-0-9796285-1-2(2))* International Fellowship of Covenant Ministries, The.
Caldwell, David. Parochial Lectures on the Psalms by Rev David Caldwell Psalms 1-50. 2006. 592p. per. 32.99 *(978-1-4255-6383-7(X))* MPublishing.
Calvin, John. Calvin's Commentaries, 1 vol. 500th ed. 2009. 250.00 *(978-0-8010-1331-7(3))* Baker Bks.
—Commentaries on the Catholic Epistles. Owen, John, tr. 2009. 488p. 53.95 *(978-1-104-11108-3(X))*; pap. 38.95 *(978-1-104-08552-0(6))* Kessinger Publishing, LLC.
Calvin, John & Owen, John. Commentaries on the Catholic Epistles. 2007. 492p. per. 24.95 *(978-1-60206-420-1(2))* Cosimo, Inc.
Campbell, Alexander. The Covenant Story of the Bible. 2009. 168p. pap. 19.00 *(978-1-60608-862-3(9)*, Wipf and Stock) Wipf & Stock Pubs.
Canclini, A. Comentario Biblico Continente Nuevo: 1 Corintios.Tr. of New Continent Bible Commentary: I Corinthians. (SPA.). pap. 5.99 *(978-0-7899-0160-6(9)*, 498646) Editorial Unilit.
Carl, Kimberley J. Pass It on, Pay It Forward: Sharing Our Love Any Way We Can! 2008. 84p. pap. 16.95 *(978-1-60672-555-9(6))* PublishAmerica, Inc.
Carson, D. A. God with Us. 2009. 166p. (Orig.). pap. 19.00 *(978-1-60608-666-7(9)*, Wipf and Stock) Wipf & Stock Pubs.
Cavalca, Flavio. Salmos De Los Ninos. 80p. 2.95 *(978-958-607-565-7(6))* Sociedad de San Pablo COL. Dist: St Pauls/Alba Hse. Pubs.
Christian Art Gifts, creator. Grace for Each Moment. 2008. (One-Minute Devotions Ser.). 400p. *(978-1-77036-007-5(7))* Christian Art Pubs.
Cloud, David W. The Book of Revelation. 2007. 465p. per. 19.95 *(978-1-58318-105-8(9))* Way of Life Literature.
Collins, Oral Edmond. The Final Prophecy of Jesus: An Introduction, Analysis & Commentary on the Book of Revelation. 2007. 610p. pap. 60.00 *(978-1-55635-260-7(3)*, Wipf and Stock) Wipf & Stock Pubs.
Comfort, Comfort, ed. Cornerstone Biblical Commentary: Vol 1. 2008. 550p. 34.99 *(978-1-84233-427-0(1))* Tyndale Hse. Pubs.
The Commentary That Makes You the Expert! Shelftalker. (Illus.). *(978-0-8400-4076-3(8))* B&H Publishing Group.
Communication Architects. The Most Essential Truth in the Bible: A concise summation of the ultimate purpose & principles of Life. 2008. 170p. per. 12.95 *(978-0-935597-07-3(7))* Communication Architects.
Concordia Self-Study: Bible Study. cd-rom 34.99 *(978-0-570-00532-2(9)*, 01-1938) Concordia Publishing Hse.
Conder, Claude. The First Bible. 2007. (ENG.). 256p. 42.95 *(978-0-548-05266-2(2))* Kessinger Publishing, LLC.
Constance, Mal'akya. All about Israel: The Bible & Religion from God's Perspective. 2012. (ENG., Illus.). 248p. pap. 14.95 ***(978-0-9787587-3-8(0))*** Tenacity Design & Publishing.
Coogan, Michael, et al, eds. New Oxford Annotated Bible with the Apocrypha. 4th annot. rev. ed. 2010. (ENG., Illus.). 2096p. pap. 35.00 *(978-0-19-528960-2(9))* Oxford Univ. Pr., Inc.
—The New Oxford Bible. 4th annot. rev. ed. 2010. (ENG., Illus.). xxiii, 1917p. 34.99 *(978-0-19-528954-1(4))* Oxford Univ. Pr., Inc.
Correll, Mark. Psalms, the Journey Begins. 2006. (ENG.). pap. 15.99 *(978-1-60034-792-4(4))*; pap. 17.99 *(978-1-60034-784-9(3))* Xulon Pr., Inc.
Coulter, Fred R. The Holy Bible in Its Original Order: A Faithful Version with Commentary, 1 Volume. Coulter, Fred R., tr. 2007. 1p. 55.95 *(978-0-9675479-6-1(2))* York Publishing Co.
Coulter, Fred R., tr. & comment. The Holy Bible in Its Original Order: A Faithful Version with Commentary, 1. 2007. 1p. lthr. 89.95 *(978-0-9675479-9-2(7))* York Publishing Co.
Courson, Jon. Jon Courson's Application Commentary on the Whole Bible for PDA. 2007. cd-rom 39.99 *(978-1-4185-2777-8(7))* Nelson, Thomas Inc.
Cousar, Charles B. Texts for Preaching: A Lectionary Commentary, Based on the NRSV. 2010. *(978-0-664-23687-8(1))* Westminster John Knox Pr.
Cross, Randy. Lent: Bound for Golgotha. 2006. 59p. pap., stu. ed. 6.00 *(978-0-687-33373-8(3))* Abingdon Pr.
Daniel, R. P. Outline of Booth's Chart of the Ages. pap. 3.25 *(978-0-88172-018-1(6))* Believers Bookshelf, Inc.
Daniel-Rops, Henri. What Is the Bible? 2007. Orig. Title: Qu'est ce que la Bible? 150p. per. 11.95 *(978-1-933184-24-1(8))* Sophia Institute Pr.
Danyans, Eugenio. Misterios Biblicos Al Descubierto: Biblical Mysteries Revealed. (SPA.). 192p. *(978-84-7228-270-4(8)*, 220604) Clie, Editorial.
Darby, J. N. Notes & Comments on Scripture, 7 vols., Set. 37.00 *(978-0-88172-068-6(2))* Believers Bookshelf, Inc.
—Notes & Jottings on Scripture. 7.95 *(978-0-88172-069-3(0))* Believers Bookshelf, Inc.
Davey, Stephen. Wisdom Commentary Series: Esther. 2012. 14.99 ***(978-0-9776641-3-9(9))*** Charity Hse. Pubs.
Davis, Avraham. Metsudah Midrash Tanchuma Slipcased Set: 8 Vol. 2007. (HEB & ENG.). 209.00 *(978-1-60091-029-6(7))* Israel Bookshop Pubns.
—Metsudah Midrash Tanchuma V: Vayikra. 2007. (HEB & ENG.). 24.95 *(978-1-60091-034-0(3))* Israel Bookshop Pubns.
del Sole, Ray. Success in Bardon's first Steps - A Commentary. 2010. 82p. pap. 16.95 *(978-1-4461-8013-6(1))* Lulu Enterprises Inc.
Delighting in Scripture. 12.00 *(978-0-687-02094-2(8))* Abingdon Pr.
Dellavolta, Norma. The Gospel According to Saint Michael the Archangel. 2007. 1*7p. pap. 14.50 *(978-1-84753-374-6(4))* Lulu Enterprises Inc.
Denard, Shannon. Birthing A Ministry of Intercession. 2006. per. 10.99 *(978-0-9789341-0-1(5))* Firehouse Pubns.
DeRycke, Larry I. A Bible Study. 2007. 144p. per. 24.95 *(978-1-4241-8119-3(4))* PublishAmerica, Inc.
Dixon, James W. Chronological Commentary of the Bible: A Guide for Understanding the Scriptures Vol. 1 And 2. 2011. 744p. pap. 45.00 *(978-1-4120-6520-7(8))* Trafford Publishing.
Duerling, Nan. Come to the Cross 2008: Scriptures for the Church Seasons. 2008. (Sftcs Ser.). 32p. pap. 7.00 *(978-0-687-64818-4(1))* Abingdon Pr.
Durham, Ron & DeGraffenried, Doug. The Higley Lesson Commentary, Vol. 68. Reagan, Wesley C., ed. l.t. ed. 52p. 12.99 *(978-1-886763-18-0(6))* Higley Publishing Corp.
—The Higley Lesson Commentary 2000-2001, Vol. 68. Reagan, Wesley C., ed. (Illus.). 52p. pap. 13.99 *(978-1-886763-16-6(X))* Higley Publishing Corp.
Durham, Ron & De Graffenried, Doug. The Higley Lesson Commentary 2000-2001, Vol. 68. Reagan, Wesley C., ed. (Illus.). 52p. 17.99 *(978-1-886763-17-3(8))* Higley Publishing Corp.
Eason, Charles. The Genevan Bible: Notes on Its Production & Distribution. 2nd ed. 56p. pap. 11.00 *(978-1-58329-002-6(8))* Lazarus Ministry Pr.
Eastman: Men of Power. *(978-0-687-24773-8(X))* Abingdon Pr.
Edlin, Handley. Commentary on the Revelation of Jesus Christ. 2007. 212p. per. 14.99 *(978-1-60266-196-7(0))* Xulon Pr., Inc.
Elmore, Joe. Highlighted for Life: The Bible Says. 2007. *(978-0-9799233-4-0(4))* Elmore, Joe.

The Essential IVP Reference Collection 3. 0. 2008. (ENG.). 1p. cd-rom 190.00 (978-0-8308-2447-2(2), IVP Acad.) InterVarsity Pr.

Essex, Barbara J. More Bad Girls of the Bible. 2009. xvi, 127p. (978-0-8298-1824-6(3)) Pilgrim Pr., The/United Church Pr.

Evans, John. A Guide to Biblical Commentaries & Reference Works: For students & Pastors. 9th ed. 2010. (ENG.). 378p. pap. 14.95 (978-0-9828715-6-0(2)) Doulos Resources.

Evans, Mary J. The Women's Study Bible 3114. Kroeger, Catherine Clark, ed. 2009. (ENG.). 2016p. 69.99 (978-0-19-529127-8(1)) Oxford Univ. Pr., Inc.

Eveson, Philip H. The Beauty of Holiness: The Book of Leviticus Simply Explained. 2007. (Welwyn Commentary Ser.). (Illus.). 416p. per. (978-0-85234-640-2(9)) Evangelical Pr.

Fernandez Jr., Greg. Spirituality: looking up to Heaven. 2010. 75p. pap. 7.99 (978-0-557-30672-5(8)) Lulu Enterprises Inc.

Fernandez, Margarita. Your Word Is A Lamp unto My Feet. 2007. 91p. 16.95 (978-1-4241-5562-0(2)) PublishAmerica, Inc.

Fifty-Two Weeks with the Bible. 6.00 (978-1-890569-30-3(5)) General Board of Global Ministries, The United Methodist Church.

Finch, Michael Keith. 100% Jesus. 2007. 168p. per. (978-0-9704382-2-5(2)) 100% Publishing and Industries.

Fortress Press Staff, et al. Hermeneia: A Critical & Historical Commentary on the Bible, 38 vols., Set. 2006. cd-rom 977.00 (978-0-8006-6199-1(0)) Augsburg Fortress, Pubs.

Fuller, David O., ed. Which Bible? rev. ed. 350p. reprint ed. pap. 11.95 (978-0-944355-24-4(2)) Institute for Biblical Textual Studies, The.

Garland. Expos Bib Com Rev Vol12 Ephesi/phi, 1 vol., Vol. 12. Garland, David E. & Longman, Tremper, III, eds. rev. ed. 2006. (Expositor's Bible Commentary Ser.). (ENG.). 656p. 39.99 (978-0-310-23503-3(0)) Zondervan.

Garland, et al. Luke-Acts, 1 vol., Vol. 10. rev. ed. 2007. (Expositor's Bible Commentary Ser.). (ENG.). 1104p. 49.99 (978-0-310-23500-2(6)) Zondervan.

Garland, David E. & Garland. Romans-Galatians, 1 vol., Vol. 11. Longman, Tremper, III, ed. rev. ed. 2008. (Expositor's Bible Commentary Ser.). (ENG.). 640p. 39.99 (978-0-310-23501-9(4)) Zondervan.

Garlington, Don. An Exposition of Galatians, Third Edition: A Reading from the New Perspective. 2007. 452p. pap. 50.00 (978-1-59752-779-8(3), Wipf and Stock) Wipf & Stock Pubs.

Garrett, Emlen. The Mark of a Christian. 2007. 192p. per. 13.99 (978-1-60266-119-6(7)) Xulon Pr., Inc.

Garza, Carlos Junco. Catholics & the Bible. 2007. 1.95 (978-0-8294-2487-4(3)) Loyola Pr.

Gatewood, Otis. Acts Commentary. 654p. 14.95 (978-1-56794-169-2(9), C-2508) Star Bible & Tract Corp.

—The Revelation... God Gave: A Commentary. 483p. pap. 14.95 (978-1-56794-170-8(2), C-2509) Star Bible & Tract Corp.

God's Holy Words. 2009. 128p. pap. 10.99 (978-1-4389-9660-8(8)) AuthorHouse.

Golitzin, Alexander. Jacob of Sarug's Homily on the Chariot that Prophet Ezekiel Saw: Complete Homilies of Jacob of Sarug: Fascicle 125. 2007. (Texts from Christian Late Antiquity: 3). per. 39.00 (978-1-59333-735-3(3)) Gorgias Pr., LLC.

Goodrich O.P., Kevin. Plugging into Real Worship. 2007. 220p. 24.99 (978-1-60266-149-3(9)) Xulon Pr., Inc.

Gothard, Bill. The Power of the House of God. 2007. (Illus.). 160p. (978-0-916888-39-8(8)) Institute in Basic Life Principles.

Graham, Billy. Answers to Life's Problems. 2009. pap. 0.00 (978-1-59328-229-5(X)) Graham, Billy Evangelistic Assn.

Haggai/Zechariah/Malachi. (People's Bible Commentary Ser.). 160p. 12.99 (978-0-7586-0438-5(6)) Concordia Publishing Hse.

Hahnenberg, Edward J. Understanding the Bible: A Layman's Guide to the Historical-Critical Method. 2008. 144p. per. 12.95 (978-1-59594-267-8(X)) WingSpan Publishing.

Hall, Howard W. Understanding God's First Earth. Bazzrea, Farah, ed. 2011. 122p. (YA). pap. 9.99 **(978-0-9818611-9-7(9))** Granny's Bks. Publishing Hse.

Hamilton, Mark W., et al. The Transforming Word: One-Volume Commentary on the Bible. 2009. (Illus.). viii, 1117p. 69.95 (978-0-89112-521-1(3)) Abilene Christian Univ. Pr.

Harkovy, Alexander. The Holy Scriptures Holy Bible Commentary. 32.50 (978-0-87559-195-7(7)) Shalom, P. Pubns., Inc.

Harnack, Adolf. Brüchstucke des Evangeliums und der Apokalypse des Petrus. 2010. (GER & GRE.). 92.48 (978-1-61719-288-3(0)) Gorgias Pr., LLC.

Harper, Tom. The Holy Kabal: Commonly Called the Somaic Bible. 2007. pap. 12.00 (978-0-8059-8740-9(1)) Dorrance Publishing Co., Inc.

Harrelson, Walter J. The New Interpreter's Study Bible. (Illus.). xxxi, 2298p. 45.00 (978-0-687-02295-3(9)) Abingdon Pr.

Hastings, James, ed. Index to the Great Texts of the Bible. 2009. pap. 37.70 (978-1-60724-283-3(4)) Gorgias Pr., LLC.

Heck, Susan J. With the Master in the School of Tested Faith. 2006. (Illus.). 372p. per. 25.99 (978-1-59886-559-2(5)) Tate Publishing & Enterprises, LLC.

Heizer, Jean. The I Love My Bible Commentary. 2007. 508p. per. 32.95 (978-1-4327-1283-9(7)) Outskirts Pr., Inc.

Henderson, E. The Book of the Twelve Minor Prophets, Translated from the Original Hebrew with a Commentary, Critical, Philological, & #, by E Henderson, # # Wi. 2006. 500p. per. 29.99 (978-1-4255-5580-1(2)) MPublishing.

Henry, Charles R. The Testaments of the Twelve Patriarchs. 247p. reprint ed. 68.00 (978-0-7222-9905-0(2)) Library Reprints, Inc.

Henry, Matthew. Comentario Matthew Henry: Historicos: Matthew Henry's Commentary, Historical Books, Vol. I. (SPA.). (978-84-7645-146-5(6), 223192) Clie, Editorial.

—Comentario Matthew Henry: Historicos: Matthew Henry's Commentary: Historical Books, Vol. II. (SPA.). 656p. (978-84-7645-147-2(4), 223193) Clie, Editorial.

—Comentario Matthew Henry: Santiago: Matthew Henry's Commentary. (SPA.). 592p. (978-84-7645-504-3(6), 223412) Clie, Editorial.

—The New Matthew Henry Commentary: The Classic Work with Updated Language, 1 vol. Manser, Martin H., ed. abr. ed. 2010. (ENG.). 2600p. 29.99 (978-0-310-25399-0(3)) Zondervan.

Hindson, Edward E., ed. Zondervan King James Version Commentary-Set, 1 vol. 2010. (ENG.). 74.99 (978-0-310-25682-3(8)) Zondervan.

Hodge, Charles. Conference Papers. 2009. 606p. pap. (978-0-217-69680-7(5)) Books LLC.

Hodges, George. How to Know the Bible. 2007. (ENG.). 366p. 48.95 (978-0-548-06204-3(8)) Kessinger Publishing, LLC.

Hole, Frank. Galatians to Philemon. 2007. 204p. (ENG.). (978-0-901860-48-4(4)); (Illus.). per. (978-0-901860-44-6(1)) Scripture Truth Pubns.

Holland, Carl. Revelation Simplified. 2007. 200p. per. 14.99 (978-1-60477-353-8(7)) Xulon Pr., Inc.

Holman Bible Editorial Staff. The Apologetics Study Bible. 2009. (Apologetics Bible Ser.). (ENG.). 2048p. im. lthr. 49.99 (978-1-58640-510-6(1), Holman Pubs.) B&H Publishing Group.

—The Apologetics Study Bible. 2009. (Apologetics Bible Ser.). (ENG.). 2048p. im. lthr. 49.99 (978-1-58640-509-0(8), Holman Pubs.) B&H Publishing Group.

Holmes, Rickie. The Mystery of Godliness — Revealed. 2007. 80p. per. 9.99 (978-1-60266-313-8(0)) Xulon Pr., Inc.

Hosea/Joel/Amos. (People's Bible Commentary Ser.). 288p. 14.99 (978-0-7586-0435-4(1)) Concordia Publishing Hse.

Howard, Abraham. Searching for Jesus. 2010. 280p. pap. 18.99 (978-1-60957-667-7(5)) Xulon Pr., Inc.

Howat, I. Light in the Middle of the Tunnel. 160p. 6.99 (978-1-85792-099-4(6)) Christian Focus Pubns. GBR. Dist: Spring Arbor Distributors, Inc.

Hughes, Bill. Studying Angels. 5.99 (978-0-89098-150-4(7)) Twentieth Century Christian Bks.

Hugley, Nadine. Reaching a New Generation of Believers: What Are You Using in Your Studies? 2009. 340p. pap. 18.99 (978-1-60791-491-4(3)) Xulon Pr., Inc.

Hunt, John, compiled by. Ultimate Bible Outline Book: Every Book of the Bible Made Simple. 2006. 1200p. 29.99 (978-0-89957-105-8(0)) AMG Pubs.

I & II Kings. (People's Bible Commentary Ser.). 328p. 15.99 (978-0-7586-0422-4(X)) Concordia Publishing Hse.

I & II Samuel. (People's Bible Commentary Ser.). 336p. 15.99 (978-0-7586-0414-9(9)) Concordia Publishing Hse.

I Chronicles. (People's Bible Commentary Ser.). 320p. 15.99 (978-0-7586-0423-1(8)) Concordia Publishing Hse.

Indermark, John. Come to the Cross 2008: Scriptures for the Church Seasons. 2008. 64p. pap., stu. ed. 7.00 (978-0-687-64808-5(4)) Abingdon Pr.

Interpreter's Bible: Carton Individual. Vol. 6. (978-0-687-96105-4(X)) Vol. 8. (978-0-687-96107-8(6)) Vol. 9. (978-0-687-96108-5(4)) Vol. 11. (978-0-687-96110-8(6)) Abingdon Pr.

Intervarsity Press. Exploring the Bible Series. 5p. 125.00 (978-0-8308-2550-9(9)) InterVarsity Pr.

The IVP New Testament Commentary, 15 vols., Set. Incl. Matthew. Keener, Craig S. 444p. 1997. 24.00 (978-0-8308-1801-3(4), 1801); Vol. 5. Acts. Larkin, William J., Jr. 422p. 1995. 24.00 (978-0-8308-1805-1(7), 1805); Vol. 8. 2 Corinthians. Belleville, Linda L. Robinson, Haddon W. et al, eds. 357p. 1996. 24.00 (978-0-8308-1808-2(1), 1808); Vol. 15. Hebrews. Stedman, Ray C. Robinson, Haddon W. et al, eds. 168p. 1992. 22.00 (978-0-8308-1815-0(4), 1815); Vol. 16. James. Stulac, George M. Osborne, Grant R., ed. 206p. 1993. 22.00 (978-0-8308-1816-7(2), 1816); Vol. 19. 1-3 John. Thompson, Marianne Meye. 168p. 1992. 22.00 (978-0-8308-1819-8(7), 1819);, IVP Acad. (IVP New Testament Commentary Ser.). 18p. (978-0-8308-1800-6(6), 1800) InterVarsity Pr.

Jefferson, Thomas. Jefferson Bible, or the Life & Morals of Jesus of Nazareth. 2010. 174p. pap. 5.95 (978-1-57898-878-5(0)) Martino Publishing.

Jenkyn, William. Exposition of the Epistle of Jude. 2006. 50.00 (978-1-59925-092-2(6)) Solid Ground Christian Bks.

Jerusalem: Old Testament New Testament & Contemporary. 21.48 incl. trans. (978-0-687-00168-2(4)) Abingdon Pr.

Jewish Publication Society Staff, ed. Five Megilloth & Jonah. 2008. (ENG.). 122p. pap. 12.95 (978-0-8276-0890-0(X)) Jewish Pubn. Society.

Johnson, James R. All Power to the Lamb. 2011. 580p. 40.99 **(978-1-61379-124-0(0))**; pap. 27.99 **(978-1-61379-123-3(2))** Xulon Pr., Inc.

Journey Through the Bible Colossians-Jude Student. 4.00 (978-0-687-05648-4(9)) Abingdon Pr.

Journey Through the Bible Korean Acts Student. 4.00 (978-0-687-06607-0(7)) Abingdon Pr.

Karni, Leona. In His Image. 2007. 112p. per. 10.99 (978-1-60266-849-2(3)) Xulon Pr., Inc.

Kealy, Sean P. A History or the Interpretation of the Gospel of Mark: Volume II: the Twentieth Century, 2 vols. 720p. 159.95 (978-0-7734-5117-9(X)) Mellen, Edwin Pr., The.

Kelly, William. In the Beginning & the Adamic Earth - an Exposition of Genesis I - Ii. 2007. 132p. per. (978-1-4067-8808-2(2), Pomona Pr.) Read Bks.

—Lectures on the Epistle of Jude. 2007. 212p. per. (978-1-4067-8817-4(1), Pomona Pr.) Read Bks.

Keyser, John Robert. Eternal Instant. 144p. pap. 8.95 (978-1-56794-141-8(9), C-2481) Star Bible & Tract Corp.

Kimhi, David. Commentary upon the Prophecies of Zechariah. McCaul, A., tr. 2007. 202p. pap. 22.00 (978-1-55635-329-1(4), Wipf and Stock) Wipf & Stock Pubs.

Know Your Bible Handbook. 2.00 (978-0-687-20924-8(2)) Abingdon Pr.

Kollamparampil, Thomas. Jacob of Sarug's Homily on Epiphany: Complete Homilies of Jacob of Sarug: Fascicle 8. 2007. (Texts from Christian Late Antiquity: 4). per. 39.00 (978-1-59333-736-0(1)) Gorgias Pr., LLC.

—Jacob of Sarug's Homily on Palm Sunday: Complete Homilies of Jacob of Sarug: Fascicle 18. 2007. (Texts from Christian Late Antiquity: 5). per. 29.00 (978-1-59333-737-7(X)) Gorgias Pr., LLC.

Kramer, Robert L. What The Bible Really Says About That...! A Contextual Study of Familiar Texts & Doctrines Generally Misinterpreted. 2008. 240p. pap. 14.99 (978-1-60647-023-7(X)) Xulon Pr., Inc.

Kump, William T. The Land, the Seed & the Blessing: A Chronological Biblical Compendium. 2006. (ENG.). 400p. 29.95 (978-1-60037-008-3(X)) Morgan James Publishing.

Kuyper, Abraham. Mujeres del Nuevo Testamento: Women of the New Testament. (SPA.). 80p. (978-84-7228-792-1(0), 220613) Clie, Editorial.

LaCocque, Andre. The Trial of Innocence: Adam, Eve, & the Yahwist. 2006. 324p. pap. 31.00 (978-1-59752-620-3(7), Cascade Bks.) Wipf & Stock Pubs.

Lamsa, George M. & Jones, Alice Faye. Idioms in the Bible Explained with Vignettes: A Key to the Holy Scriptures. 132p. 15.95 (978-0-9675989-8-7(2)) Aramaic Bible Society,The.

Lange, John Peter & Van Oosterzee, J. J. The Epistle General of James: An Exegetical & Doctrinal Commentary. Lange, John Peter & Schaff, Philip, eds. Mombert, J. Isidor, tr. 2007. (Lange's Commentary on the Holy Scripture: Ser.). 158p. pap. 18.00 (978-1-55635-399-4(5), Wipf and Stock) Wipf & Stock Pubs.

Law. Testament: From Adam to Apocalypse. 2006. (ENG., Illus.). 688p. 17.95 (978-0-8264-8160-3(4)) Continuum International Publishing Group, Ltd. GBR. Dist: National Bk. Network.

Layman Bible Book Commentary. 9.99 (978-0-7673-4969-7(5)) LifeWay Christian Resources.

Leanues, Paula, text. The Jeremiah Connection. 2006. lib. bdg. 12.95 (978-0-9789402-0-1(2)) Faith On The Earth.

Lechler, Gotthard Victor. The Acts of the Apostles: An Exegetical & Doctrinal Commentary. 2007. (Lange's Commentary on the Holy Scripture: Ser.). 480p. pap. 45.00 (978-1-55635-398-7(7), Wipf and Stock) Wipf & Stock Pubs.

Lee, Gregory Von. Lyrical Bible. 2011. 814p. 24.99 **(978-1-4568-7640-1(6))**; pap. 15.99 **(978-1-4568-7639-5(2))** Xlibris Corp.

Lee, Rebecca Carol. The Three Resurrections: Kabballistically Decoding the "Book of Revelations" 168p. pap. (978-0-9670103-0-4(6)) Lee, Rebecca.

Lee, Witness. Crucial Truths in the Holy Scriptures. 2008. pap. 8.75 (978-0-7363-3517-1(X)) Vol. 1. 2007. per. 9.50 (978-0-7363-3276-7(6)) Living Stream Ministry.

—The Fullness of God. 2008. per. 6.50 (978-0-7363-3535-5(8)) Living Stream Ministry.

Leeser, Isaac. The Holy Scriptures Holy Bible Commentary. 32.50 (978-0-87559-196-4(5)) Shalom, P. Pubns., Inc.

Life Publishers, prod. Bulgarian Full Life Study Bible. 2007. (BUL.). lthr. (978-0-7361-0361-9(9)) Life Pubs. International.

Lightfoot, John. From the Talmud & Hebraica. 2007. (ENG.). 460p. per. 23.95 (978-1-60206-408-9(3)); (ENG.). 320p. per. 19.95 (978-1-60206-409-6(1)); 388p. per. 21.95 (978-1-60206-406-5(7)); (ENG.). 484p. per. 23.95 (978-1-60206-407-2(5)) Cosimo, Inc.

Lockhart Sr., John. Iran Israel under Siege/the Refiner's Fire. 2007. 100p. per. 9.99 (978-1-60034-999-7(4)) Xulon Pr., Inc.

Longman, Tremper. One Chronicles Thru Job Vol. 4: Timeless Stories & Life Lessons. 2009. (QuickNotes Commentaries Ser.: Vol. 4.1). (ENG.). 240p. pap. 9.99 (978-1-59789-770-9(1), Barbour Bks.) Barbour Publishing, Inc.

Longman, Tremper, III & Garland, David E. The Exposition Bible Commentary, 1 vol., Vol. 2. rev. ed. 2012. (ENG.). 1360p. 49.99 (978-0-310-23494-4(8)) Zondervan.

Luman, J. W. The Door unto Fulness. 2007. 157p. 15.00 (978-0-9796285-3-5(9)) International Fellowship of Covenant Ministries, The.

—The Gospel. 2007. 129p. 15.00 (978-0-9796285-7-3(1)) International Fellowship of Covenant Ministries, The.

—The Liberating Secret of Christ. 2007. 120p. 12.00 (978-0-9796285-5-9(5)) International Fellowship of Covenant Ministries, The.

—The Reality of Being in Christ. 2007. 531p. 25.00 (978-0-9799888-0-6(2)) International Fellowship of Covenant Ministries, The.

MacDougald, Dan, Jr. Illuminacion del Arameo. Yosef, Ed ben, ed. 127p. 29.95 (978-0-9675989-5-6(8)) Aramaic Bible Society,The.

Maclaren, Alexander. Expositions of Holy Scripture. 2006. 640p. pap. 31.99 (978-1-4264-2138-9(9)) 2007. (ENG.). 678p. pap. 34.99 (978-1-4264-2206-5(7)) BiblioBazaar.

—Expositions of Holy Scripture. 2008. 580p. pap. (978-1-4065-4579-1(1)) Dodo Pr.

—Expositions of Holy Scripture: Second Kings Chapters VIII to End & Chronicles, Ezra, & Nehemiah. Esther, Job, Proverbs, & Ecclesiastes. 2007. (ENG.). 698p. pap. 32.99 (978-1-4264-2659-9(3)); 738p. pap. 35.99 (978-1-4264-2716-9(6)) BiblioBazaar.

Malik Le-Blanc, Abdul. The Bible Led Me to Islam. 82p. pap. (978-9960-9148-3-1(6)) Al-Attique Pubs., Inc.

Marshall, Jacqueline. Leah. 2007. 104p. per. 9.99 (978-1-60266-384-8(X)) Xulon Pr., Inc.

Masopust, William. A Mustard Seed of Wisdom. 2010. 152p. pap. 14.99 (978-0-557-30560-5(8)) Lulu Enterprises Inc.

Matt, Daniel, tr. from ARC. The Zohar, Vol. 4. 2007. (Zohar: Pritzker Edition Ser.). (ENG., Illus.). 592p. 55.00 (978-0-8047-5712-6(7)) Stanford Univ. Pr.

Maydell, Karl. Ephesus: Bible Study Commentary. 2010. 175p. pap. 18.95 (978-1-4327-5780-9(6)) Outskirts Pr., Inc.

—Total Triumph: Bible-Study-Commentary. 2009. 248p. pap. 20.95 (978-1-4327-4038-2(5)) Outskirts Pr., Inc.

Mayer, Stephen McRae. Before the Twinkling of an Eye, There Are the Ways of God. 2008. 364p. 32.99 (978-1-60477-900-4(4)); pap. 20.99 (978-1-60477-899-1(7)) Xulon Pr., Inc.

—Before the Twinkling of an Eye, There Is the Voice of God. 2008. 168p. 22.99 (978-1-60477-898-4(9)); pap. 14.99 (978-1-60477-897-7(0)) Xulon Pr., Inc.

Mayo, Mary. Understanding How to Put Heaven into Your Day & Kick Hell Out. 2007. 136p. per. 13.99 (978-1-60477-075-9(9)) Xulon Pr., Inc.

McLean, Julienne. Towards Mystical Union: A Modern Commentary on the mystical text the Interior Castle by St. Teresa of Avila. 319p. 19.95 (978-0-8189-0960-3(9)) St Pauls/Alba Hse. Pubs.

McMahon, T. A. & Oakland, Roger. Understand the Times: A Simplified Biblical Perspective. 171p. pap. 7.99 (978-0-936728-38-4(8)) Calvary Chapel Publishing.

McQuilkin, Robertson. Understanding & Applying the Bible. rev. expurg. ed. 2009. (ENG.). 384p. pap. 19.99 (978-0-8024-9092-6(1)) Moody Pubs.

Medes-Flohr, Paul. Love, Accusative & Dative: Reflections on Leviticus 19:18. 2007. (B. G. Rudolph Lectures in Judaic Studies). 23p. pap. 5.95 (978-0-8156-3143-9(X)) Syracuse Univ. Pr.

Mehringer, Phillip. The Be's of the Bible. 2007. 116p. (ENG.). 18.99 (978-1-60477-233-3(6)); per. 10.99 (978-1-60477-232-6(8)) Xulon Pr., Inc.

Merton, T. Leer la Biblia. (SPA.). 128p. 6.30 (978-84-89920-66-8(4), 86917) Ediciones Oniro S.A. ESP. Dist: Lectorum Pubns., Inc.

Miller, Todd. Trying to Lose My Self in Israel: What I Learned on God's Turf. 2007. 148p. per. 24.95 (978-1-4241-6843-9(0)) PublishAmerica, Inc.

Missler, Chuck. Learn the Bible in 24 Hours. 2011. 352p. pap. 19.99 (978-1-4185-4918-3(5)) Nelson, Thomas Inc.

Moloney, Francis J. The Living Voice of the Gospels. 2007. (Illus.). 344p. per. 19.95 (978-1-59856-065-7(4)) Hendrickson Pubs. Marketing, LLC.

Moore, Walter W. The Indispensable Book. 2007. (ENG.). 112p. 34.95 (978-0-548-02770-7(6)) Kessinger Publishing, LLC.

Morgan, G. Campbell. Exposition of the Whole Bible. 2010. (G. Campbell Morgan Reprint Ser.). (Illus.). 544p. pap. 59.00 (978-1-60899-292-8(6), Wipf and Stock) Wipf & Stock Pubs.

—Great Chapters of the Bible. 2010. (G. Campbell Morgan Reprint Ser.). 378p. pap. 40.00 (978-1-60899-301-7(9), Wipf and Stock) Wipf & Stock Pubs.

Morgan, J. Stephen, Jr. The Nephilim. 2007. (Illus.). 388p. per. 29.95 (978-0-9801841-0-5(X)) Draconigena.

Moule, Handley C. G. The Second Epistle to Timothy: Short Devotional Studies on the Dying Letter of St. Paul. 2007. 180p. pap. 18.00 (978-1-55635-252-2(2), Wipf and Stock) Wipf & Stock Pubs.

Neander, August. The Scriptural Expositions of Dr Augustus Neander, Complete in One Volume Tr from the German by Mrs H C Conant. 2006. 580p. per. 32.99 (978-1-4255-6328-8(7)) MPublishing.

Nelson Reference, creator. Everyday Access: Your Bible Concordance, 0 vols. 2007. (Everyday Ser.). (Illus.). 992p. 16.99 (978-1-4185-0564-6(1)) Nelson, Thomas Inc.

—Everyday Living: Bible Life & Times, 0 vols. 2007. (Everyday Ser.). (Illus.) 480p. 14.99 (978-1-4185-0566-0(8)) Nelson, Thomas Inc.

New Beacon Bible Commentary Library, Volume 1. 2009. pap. 109.50 (978-0-8341-2477-6(7), 9780834124776) Beacon Hill Pr. of Kansas City.

The New Interpreters Bible. 130.00 (978-0-687-01973-1(7)) Abingdon Pr.

New Interpreters Bible. Vol. 3. 110.00 incl. audio compact disk (978-0-687-01971-7(0)) Vol. 6. (978-0-687-09039-6(3)) Abingdon Pr.

New Interpreters Bible: Genuine Leather, Vol. 3. (978-0-687-09037-2(7)) Abingdon Pr.

Newsom, Carol A., et al, eds. Women's Bible Commentary, Third Edition: Newly Revised & Updated. 3rd ed. 2012. (ENG.). 704p. 50.00 **(978-0-664-23707-3(X))** Westminster John Knox Pr.

Newton, Richard. Bible Jewels: And Lessons Taught by Them for Children. 2007. 180p. per. 15.99 (978-1-59925-101-1(9)) Solid Ground Christian Bks.

Nicholes, Lou. John. 2010. (Illus.). 196p. pap. 14.99 (978-1-60957-231-0(9)) Xulon Pr., Inc.

Los Ninos de la Biblia. (SPA.). stu. ed. 9.00 (978-84-241-5410-3(X)) Torres, Eliseo & Sons.

Northwestern Publishing House Staff. Ready, Set, Gold! (Vacation Bible Study Ser.). (978-0-8100-1533-3(1)); (978-0-8100-1532-6(3)) Northwestern Publishing Hse.

Noyes, George R. A New Translation of Job, Ecclesiastes, & the Canticles, with Introductions, & Notes, Chietly Explanatory by George R Noyes. 2006. 356p. per. 26.99 (978-1-4255-3644-2(1)) MPublishing.

—A New Translation of the Book of Psalms & of the Proverb, with Introductions, & Notes, Chiefly Explanatory by George R Noyes. 2006. 424p. per. 26.99 (978-1-4255-4588-8(2)) MPublishing.

—A New Translation of the Book of Psalms & of the Proverbs, with Introductions, & Notes, Chiefly Explanatory by George R Noyes. 2006. 428p. per. 26.99 (978-1-4255-4659-5(5)) MPublishing.

—A New Translation of the Hebrew Prophets, with an Introduction & Notes. 2006. 364p. per. 26.99 *(978-1-4255-3789-0(8))*; (ENG.). 420p. per. 26.99 *(978-1-4255-4525-3(4))* MPublishing.
Nuss, Donald R. The Anatomies of God, the Bible, & Religion: Decoding the Old & New Testaments. 2010. 600p. 43.95 *(978-1-4502-5013-9(0))*; pap. 33.95 *(978-1-4502-5012-2(2))* iUniverse, Inc.
O'Bannon, Kathleen. Nutrition & Health in the Bible, 0 vols. Richards, Larry, ed. 2008. (Smart Guide to the Bible Ser.). (Illus.). 384p. pap. 14.99 *(978-1-4185-1003-9(3))* Nelson, Thomas Inc.
O'Day, Gail R. & Petersen, David L. Theological Bible Commentary. 2009. (ENG.). 504p. 50.00 *(978-0-664-22711-1(2))* Westminster John Knox Pr.
Ortiz, Pedro. Salmos: Oracion Del Pueblo De Dios. 256p. 10.95 *(978-958-607-873-3(6))* Sociedad de San Pablo COL. Dist: St Pauls/Alba Hse. Pubs.
Overview of the Bible. ldr.'s ed. (LifeLight Ser.). pap. 8.99 *(978-0-570-06875-4(4), 20-3200)* Concordia Publishing Hse.
Oxford, ed. The Old Scofield Study Bible. 2006. (ENG., Illus.). 1610p. 49.99 *(978-0-19-527479-0(2))* Oxford Univ. Pr., Inc.
Palasundram, Chellam Mary. 50 golden years of life with Jesus. 2008. pap. 11.99 *(978-1-60477-835-9(0))* Xulon Pr., Inc.
Park, Robert L. Reflections on Selected Scriptures: A Christian Layman's Informal Commentary. 2008. 664p. pap. 24.95 *(978-1-4327-0976-1(3))* Outskirts Pr., Inc.
Parris, Peter. The Truth of the Gospel. 2008. 192p. 21.99 *(978-1-60477-769-7(9))*; per. 13.99 *(978-1-60477-768-0(0))* Xulon Pr., Inc.
Partee, Milton. Discipleship Dynamics. 2009. 88p. pap. 14.95 *(978-1-4489-2579-7(7))* PublishAmerica, Inc.
Patterson, Richard D. & Hill, Andrew E. Minor Prophets: Hosea-Malachi. 2008. (Cornerstone Biblical Commentary Ser.: 10). (ENG.). 672p. 32.99 *(978-0-8423-3436-5(X))* Tyndale Hse. Pubs.
Perkins, Tyrone C. A Commentary on Acts. pap. 14.95 *(978-1-56794-176-0(1), C-2517)* Star Bible & Tract Corp.
Petersen, David L. The New Interpreter's Bible. 2010. 1068p. 75.00 *(978-0-687-33411-7(X))* Abingdon Pr.
—The New Interpreter's One-Volume Commentary on the Bible Kit with Study Bible. 2010. 75.00 *(978-1-4267-1217-3(0))* Abingdon Pr.
Peterson, David, ed. Where Wrath & Mercy Meet. 2007. (ENG.). 193p. pap. 16.99 *(978-1-84227-079-0(6)*, Paternoster) Authentic Media.
Petrosino, Arnold J. The Catholic Church vs. the Bible. 2008. 136p. pap. 14.99 *(978-1-60647-836-3(2))* Xulon Pr., Inc.
Pettinggill, William & Torrey, R. A. 1001 Bible Questions Answered. 2011. (ENG.). 496p. pap. 14.95 *(978-0-88486-479-0(0))* Bristol Park Bks.
Philipps, James. Turning Points: Unlocking the Treasures of the Church. 2006. pap. 12.95 *(978-1-58595-577-0(9))* Twenty-Third Pubns./Bayard.
Phillips, John. Exploring People of the Old Testament & New Testament Set, 4 vols. 2007. (John Phillips Bible Characters Ser.). 1328p. 89.99 *(978-0-8254-3372-6(X))* Kregel Pubns.
Phillips, Karynthia. Quiet Time Before all the other important Stuff Quiet Time Before all the other important Stuff: Exploring How to develop personal Bible Study. 2006. spiral bd. 12.95 *(978-0-9788690-0-7(1))* Echoes Christian Media, LLC.
Polter, Moshe Tzvi HaLevi. The Shevatim. 270p. 19.99 *(978-1-56871-340-3(1))* Targum Pr., Inc.
Porter, J. R. The Forgotten Bible: The Unknown Jesus, Visions of the Apocalypse, Prophets & Patriarchs. 2007. (ENG.). 288p. per. *(978-1-905857-01-2(2)*, Watkins Publishing) Duncan Baird Pubs. GBR. Dist: Sterling Publishing Co., Inc.
Preus, Robert D. & Rosin, Wilbert H., eds. A Contemporary Look at the Formula of Concord. 176p. 16.99 *(978-0-570-03326-4(8))* Concordia Publishing Hse.
Prince, Benny. Praying & Confessing Blessings from God's Word. 2008. 112p. per. 8.50 *(978-0-9801438-1-2(0))* Avid Readers Publishing Group.
Publishing, Barbour. The Bible Promise Book. 2006. (Bible Promise Bks.). (ENG.). 176p. pap. 1.99 *(978-1-59789-520-0(2))*; pap. 3.99 *(978-1-59789-514-9(8))* Barbour Publishing, Inc. (Barbour Bks.).
Puen, Ray. Is That in the Bible? Fascinating Insights & Discoveries from the Book of Books. 2010. 304p. pap. 18.99 *(978-1-61579-762-2(9))* Xulon Pr., Inc.
—Is That in the Bible? Fascinating Insights & Discoveries in the Book of Books. 2008. 96p. per. *(978-0-9795930-0-0(X))* Regency Pr.
Quiggle, James D. The Epistle of Jesus to the Church: A Commentary on the Revelation. 2008. 488p. pap. 54.00 *(978-1-55635-489-2(4))* Wipf & Stock Pubs.
Radmacher, Earl D., et al, eds. Nelson's Student Bible Commentary: Quick, Clear & Accessible Comments on the Whole Bible, 0 vols. 2008. 528p. pap. 19.99 *(978-0-7180-2495-6(8))* Nelson, Thomas Inc.
Ramsay, William M. The First Christian Century: Notes on Dr. Moffatt's Introduction to the Literature of the New Testament. 2007. (ENG.). 202p. 39.95 *(978-0-548-03655-6(1))* Kessinger Publishing, LLC.
Ravasi, Gianfranco. Salmos. 282p. 11.95 *(978-958-607-826-9(4))* Sociedad de San Pablo COL. Dist: St Pauls/Alba Hse. Pubs.
Reference Bible. 26.50 *(978-0-529-05314-5(4))* Nelson, Thomas Inc.
Ries, Raul. Doctrines: A Simplified Road Map of Biblical Truth. 176p. 2009. pap. 13.99 *(978-1-934820-08-7(3))* 2010. (YA). pap. 13.99 *(978-1-934820-15-5(6))* Somebody Loves You Media Group.
Roberts, Sam. Christian Economics. (Extensions Adult Elective Bible Study Ser.). 56p. pap. 10.00 *(978-1-57312-112-5(6))* Smyth & Helwys Publishing, Inc.
Robertson, Frederick W. Sermons on St Paul's Epistles to the Corinthians: Delivered at Trinity Chapel, Brighton. by the Late Rev. F. W. Robertson ... 2006. 444p. per. 26.99 *(978-1-4255-4890-2(3))* MPublishing.
Robinson, Gene. God Believes in Love: Straight Talk about Gay Marriage. 2012. (ENG.). 208p. 24.00 ***(978-0-307-95788-7(8)**, Knopf)* Knopf Doubleday Publishing Group.
Rochedieu, C. Comentario Practico - Sinopticos, Vol. I: Practical Comment. I - Synoptics. (SPA.). 224p. *(978-84-7228-569-9(3)*, 220125) Clie, Editorial.
Rogers, Donna M. Shattered Dreams - Wake up America Before It Is too Late! The Solution for a Nation in Crisis. 2009. 152p. pap. 14.99 *(978-1-60791-748-9(3))* Xulon Pr., Inc.
Rohrig, George. God's Glorious Church: Understanding the Purposes of God. 2011. 148p. 22.23 *(978-1-4567-1680-6(8))*; pap. 11.70 *(978-1-4567-1681-3(6))* AuthorHouse.
Roland, Wanleatha. Taking It to the Streets Witnessing Guidebook, 1 vol. 2010. 55p. pap. 16.95 *(978-1-4489-9424-3(1))* PublishAmerica, Inc.
Rose Publishing Staff. Where to Find Favorite Bible Verses. 2008. 14p. 3.99 *(978-1-59636-195-9(6))* Rose Publishing.
Rosenberg, Paul A. A Second Look at Eden. 2007. 50p. per. 9.95 *(978-0-9796011-4-9(2))* Vera Verba, Inc.
RSV Harper Study Bible Black Calfskin Leather RS347. 2007. (Illus.). 2150p. lthr. 80.00 *(978-0-521-53701-8(0))* Cambridge Univ. Pr.
Rudd, A. B. Epistolas Generales: Commentary to the General, 1 vol. 2008. (SPA.). 320p. pap. 12.99 *(978-84-7645-177-9(6)*, 223221) Clie, Editorial ESP. Dist: Zondervan.
Runes, Dagobert D. Bible for the Liberal. 2006. (ENG.). 392p. per. *(978-1-4067-1951-2(X)*, Hesperides Pr.) Read Bks.
Sailhamer, John. NIV Bible Study Commentary. abr. ed. 2011. (ENG.). 400p. pap. 14.99 *(978-0-310-33119-3(6))* Zondervan.
Sakenfeld, Katharine Doob. The New Interpreter's Dictionary of the Bible, 5 vols., Set. 2009. (Illus.). 400.00 *(978-0-687-33346-2(6))* Abingdon Pr.
—The New Interpreter's Dictionary of the Bible Vol. 5: S - Z, 5 vols. 2009. (New Interpreter's Dictionary of the Bible Ser.). (Illus.). 1075p. 79.99 *(978-0-687-33395-0(4))* Abingdon Pr.
Sakenfeld, Katharine Doob, ed. New Interpreter's Dictionary of the Bible Vol. 3, 5 vols., Vol. 3. 2008. (New Interpreter's Dictionary of the Bible Ser.). (Illus.). 936p. 79.99 *(978-0-687-33365-3(2))* Abingdon Pr.
—The New Interpreter's Dictionary of the Bible Vol. 4, 5 Vols. 2009. (New Interpreter's Dictionary of the Bible Ser.). (Illus.). 79.99 *(978-0-687-33375-2(X))* Abingdon Pr.
—The New Interpreter's Dictionary of the Bible - A-C Vol. 1, 5 vols. 2006. (New Interpreter's Dictionary of the Bible Ser.). (Illus.). 843p. pap. 79.99 *(978-0-687-05427-5(3))* Abingdon Pr.
Sakenfeld, Katharine Doob, et al, eds. The New Interpreter's Dictionary of the Bible Vol. 2: D-H, 5 vols. 2007. (New Interpreter's Dictionary of the Bible Ser.). (Illus.). 1012p. 79.99 *(978-0-687-33355-4(5))* Abingdon Pr.
Scheele, Charles. The Christian & the Struggle with Truth & the sin, salvation, & sanctification of the human Soul. 2006. per. 8.45 *(978-0-9779407-0-7(5))* Father's Pr., LLC.
Scully, Alladin. Exploring the Bible & Religion. 2008. 532p. pap. 34.95 *(978-1-60563-253-7(8))* PublishAmerica, Inc.
Set of Four Commentaries. (Gospel Commentary Ser.). 79.99 *(978-0-8024-5449-2(6))* Moody Pubs.
Shenton, Tim. Exploring the Bible: Habakkuk: An Expositional Commentary. 2007. (Exploring the Bible Ser.). 91p. per. 10.00 *(978-1-84625-055-2(2))* DayOne Pubns. GBR. Dist: STL Distribution North America.
Shipe, Ernest. Seven Words of Love: A Love Letter from Golgotha to Your Heart. 2010. 124p. pap. 13.95 *(978-1-4502-1305-9(7))* iUniverse, Inc.
Silber, David & Rashi. Pentateuch with Targum Onkelos & Rashi's Commentary: Torah - the Book of Genesis (Hebrew / English) 2007. (HEB.). 548p. per. *(978-956-291-394-2(5))* Editorial Benei Noaj.
Smith, F. G. What the Bible Teaches. 2008. per. 13.00 *(978-1-60416-155-7(8))* Reformation Pubs.
Smith, Hamilton. The Gospel of Mark. 2007. 144p. (ENG.). *(978-0-901860-70-5(0))*; per. *(978-0-901860-69-9(7))* Scripture Truth Pubns.
Smith, Jerome H., compiled by. Nelson's Cross-Reference Guide to the Bible: Illuminating God's Word Verse-by-Verse, 0 vols. 2007. 1522p. 29.99 *(978-1-4185-0459-5(9))* Nelson, Thomas Inc.
Smith, Lesley. The Glossa Ordinaria: The Making of a Medieval Bible Commentary. 2009. 288p. *(978-90-04-17785-7(X))* BRILL.
Soncino Books of the Bible, 14 vols., Set. 239.00 *(978-1-871055-70-2(9))* Soncino Pr.
Sopherim. reprint ed. 68.00 *(978-0-7222-9930-2(3))* Library Reprints, Inc.
Spitzer, Lee B. Jesus Christ from Cover to Cover: Tracing the Messianic Journey from Genesis to Revelation. 2006. per. 19.95 *(978-0-9709666-4-3(4)*, 1) Spiritual Journey Pr.
Standard Lesson Commentary: Casebound. 448p. 19.99 *(978-0-7847-1303-7(0))* Standard Publishing.
Standard Lesson Commentary: NIV Standard Lesson Commentary(r) Soft Cover. 448p. 17.99 incl. audio compact disk *(978-0-7847-1306-8(5))* Standard Publishing.
Standard Lesson Commentary: Soft Cover. 448p. 16.99 *(978-0-7847-1319-8(7))*; 14.99 *(978-0-7847-1304-4(9))*; 16.99 *(978-0-7847-1318-1(9))* Standard Publishing.
Standard Lesson Commentary: Standard Lesson Commentary(r) (KJV) Soft Cover. 448p. 17.99 incl. audio compact disk *(978-0-7847-1305-1(7))* Standard Publishing.
Standard Publishing Staff. KJV Standard Lesson Commentary. 2009. (ENG.). 456p. pap. 19.99 *(978-0-7847-2256-5(0))*; 456p. pap. 15.99 *(978-0-7847-2257-2(9))*; 520p. pap. 18.99 *(978-0-7847-2258-9(7))* Standard Publishing.
—NIV Standard Lesson Commentary. 2009. (ENG.). 448p. pap. 15.99 *(978-0-7847-2254-1(4))* Standard Publishing.
Stefaniw, Blossom. Mind, Text, & Commentary: Noetic Exegesis in Origen of Alexandria, Didymus the Blind, & Evagrius Ponticus. 2010. (Early Christianity in the Context of Antiquity Ser.). 418p. 98.95 *(978-3-631-60267-6(7))* Lang, Peter GmbH, Europaischer Verlag der Wissenschaften DEU. Dist: Lang, Peter.
Stob, William S. The Four Gospels: A Guide to Their Historical Background, Characteristic Differences, & Timeless Significance. 2007. (Illus.). 382p. per. 19.99 *(978-1-932307-75-7(3)*, Ambassador International) Emerald Hse. Group, Inc.
Strauss, Jeanette. From God's Hands to Your Land: Blessings. 2009. (Illus.). 73p. 9.00 *(978-0-9770180-3-1(2))* Glorious Creations.
Strba, Blazej. Take Off Your Sandals from Your Feet! An Exegetical Study of Josh 5, 13-15. 2008. 404p. pap. 82.95 *(978-3-631-57599-4(8))* Lang, Peter Publishing, Inc.
Strege, Merle D. Bible Backgrounds: Explanatory Notes on the Bible. 2006. (ENG.). 412p. 24.95 *(978-1-59317-144-5(7))* Warner Pr. Pubs.
Strelan, John G. Where Earth Meets Heaven: A Commentary on Revelation. 2007. (Illus.). 402p. pap. 44.00 *(978-1-55635-439-7(8))* Wipf & Stock Pubs.
Strong, James. Compact Reference Library Set. 2007. 2818p. pap. 34.99 *(978-0-7180-0729-4(8))* Nelson, Thomas Inc.
Sub FBS Advanced Bible Study Commentary. 21.95 *(978-0-633-05044-3(X))* LifeWay Christian Resources.
Sub FBS All Youth. ldr.'s ed. 18.95 *(978-0-633-05045-0(8))* LifeWay Christian Resources.
Sub FBS Life Truths Learner Guide. 9.95 *(978-0-633-05055-9(5))* LifeWay Christian Resources.
Sullivan, Dennis & Sullivan, Jessee. A Trilogy. 2006. (Illus.). 116p. pap. 14.95 *(978-0-932845-79-5(7))* Lowell Pr., The, Gallion Communications.
Swanson, Reuben J. Reflections on Biblical Themes by an Octogenarian. 2007. 210p. pap. 24.00 *(978-1-59752-877-1(3)*, Wipf and Stock) Wipf & Stock Pubs.
Swedenborg, Emanuel. Arcana C+Lestia the Heavenly Arcana Contained in the Holy Scriptures or Word of the Lord Unfolded Beginning with the Book of Genesis Together with Wo. 2006. (ENG.). 612p. per. 34.99 *(978-1-4255-6506-0(9))*; 576p. per. 32.99 *(978-1-4255-6282-3(5))* MPublishing.
Sweet, Elizabeth A., et al. At Home with the Word 2007. 2006. pap. 8.00 *(978-1-56854-566-0(5)*, AHW07); pap. 10.00 *(978-1-56854-567-7(3)*, AHW07L) Liturgy Training Pubns.
Swete, Henry Barclay. Apocalypse of St John. 2006. pap. 43.95 *(978-1-4286-4290-4(0))* Kessinger Publishing, LLC.
Taize. Seek & You Shall Find: Questions on the Christian Faith & the Bible. 2006. (ENG.). 176p. per. 15.95 *(978-1-57999-592-8(6))* G I A Pubns., Inc.
Tanach Simanim: Small. 2009. 1534p. 17.99 *(978-1-59826-331-2(5))* Feldheim Pubs.
Tanhuma, Rabbi. Kabbalistic Bible According to the Zohar. 2006. 108p. per. *(978-956-291-326-3(0))* Editorial Benei Noaj.
Thomas Nelson Publishing Staff. Reader Friendly Edition Bible. 2009. 14.99 *(978-0-7180-2701-8(9))*; pap. 10.00 *(978-1-4185-4272-6(5))* Nelson, Thomas Inc.
Thornborough, Tim & Archer, Trevor. Rock Solid - 12 Gospel Truths to Live By. 2010. 152p. pap. *(978-1-906334-68-0(4))* Good Bk. Co.
Tidball, Derek, ed. The Bible Speaks Today Bible Themes Series, 5 vols. (Bible Speaks Today: Bible Themes Ser.). 9p. pap. 151.00 *(978-0-8308-2400-7(6))* InterVarsity Pr.
Trench, Richard Chenevix. Commentary on the Epistles to the Seven Churches in Asia Revelation II III by Richard Chenevix Trench. 2006. 316p. per. 23.99 *(978-1-4255-3084-6(2))* MPublishing.
Tyndale House Publishers Staff, prod. NLT Desktop Concordance. 2008. (Tyndale Desktop Reference Ser.). (ENG.). 320p. pap. 14.99 *(978-1-4143-2200-1(3))* Tyndale Hse. Pubs.
Union & Communion or, Thoughts on the Song of Solomon. 2007. 96p. per. 8.95 *(978-1-60206-422-5(9))* Cosimo, Inc.
Van Gorder, Paul. Respuestas Preguntas Dificiles Biblia: Answer to Puzzling Bible Questions. (SPA.). 64p. *(978-84-7228-278-0(3)*, 220768) Clie, Editorial.
Vannoy, J. Robert. 1 & 2 Samuel. 2009. (Cornerstone Biblical Commentary Ser.: 4). (ENG.). 464p. 34.99 *(978-0-8423-3430-3(0))* Tyndale Hse. Pubs.
Vine, W. E. Christ, 0 vols. 2010. (Vine's Topical Commentaries Ser.). 256p. 29.99 *(978-1-4185-4309-9(8))* Nelson, Thomas Inc.
Vreeland, G. D. The Darker Side of Samuel, Saul & David. 2008. 392p. pap. 19.99 *(978-1-60647-329-0(8))* Xulon Pr., Inc.
Watkins, Ray. Proof the Bible Is True. 2006. 219p. pap. 14.95 *(978-0-7414-3371-8(0))* Infinity Publishing.
Welburn, Andrew. Myth of the Nativity: The Virgin Birth Re-Examined. 2007. 189p. 40.00 *(978-0-86315-543-7(X))* Floris Bks. GBR. Dist: SteinerBooks, Inc.
Wells, David C. What God Wants from You: Instruction from the Bible. 2006. 389p. per. 27.95 *(978-1-59886-370-3(3))* Tate Publishing & Enterprises, LLC.
Wells, Jan. Colossians. 2007. 160p. per. 15.99 *(978-1-60266-357-2(2))* Xulon Pr., Inc.
Wesleyan Publishing House, creator. Wesley Bible Lesson Commentary: For Teachers & Students. 2009. (Illus.). 398p. pap. 21.99 *(978-0-89827-414-1(1))* Wesleyan Publishing Hse.
Westbrook, Richard B. The Bible: Whence & What? 2007. (ENG.). 240p. 41.95 *(978-0-548-03936-6(4))* Kessinger Publishing, LLC.
Whidden, Theodore L. The Bible Plumb Line: Life of the Prophet Abraham, Sarah, & Noah's Flood. 2006. per. *(978-0-9786684-4-0(8))* Heritage Ink Christian Publishing Co., LLC.
—The Bible Plumb Line: Pharoahs of the Israelites. 2006. *(978-0-9786684-5-7(6))* Heritage Ink Christian Publishing Co., LLC.
Whitelaw, Robert. Blessed Hope. pap. 1.49 *(978-0-87377-096-5(X))* GAM Pubns.
—Death of Saint: Fact or Fiction? pap. 1.49 *(978-0-87377-101-6(X))* GAM Pubns.
—The Gospel Millennium & Obedience to Scripture. pap. 1.49 *(978-0-87377-104-7(4))* GAM Pubns.
Wiemers, Galyn. Hope for America's Last Generation. 2007. (Illus.). 258p. per. 14.95 *(978-0-9794382-0-2(9))* Last Hope Bks. & Pubns.
Wiersbe, Warren W. The Complete Old & New Testaments OT/NT, 2 vols., Set. 2007. (Wiersbe Bible Commentaries Ser.). (ENG.). 2624p. 89.99 *(978-0-7814-4541-2(8))* Cook, David C.
Williams, George. The Complete Bible Commentary, 1 vol. 2008. 1064p. pap. 38.99 *(978-0-8254-4104-2(8))* Kregel Pubns.
Williams, Matt, ed. The Last Days of Jesus Participant's Guide: Six in-Depth Studies Connecting the Bible to Life, 1 vol. 2009. (ENG.). 144p. pap. 9.99 *(978-0-310-29302-6(2))* Zondervan.
Wilson, Neil S. The One Year Life Lessons from the Bible. 2006. (ENG.). 384p. per. 14.99 *(978-1-4143-1195-1(8))* Tyndale Hse. Pubs.
Wingeier, Douglas E. Covenant: God's Living Covenant. 2006. (Great Themes of the Bible Ser.). (Illus.). 91p. per. 8.50 *(978-0-687-49130-8(4))* Abingdon Pr.
Winter, Naphtali. Purim Revealed: The Inside Story of Megillas Esther. 2007. 19.95 *(978-1-60091-016-6(5))* Israel Bookshop Pubns.
Wise, Janet. Free from Worry. 2010. (Women of the Word Bible Study Ser.). (ENG.). 112p. pap. 9.99 *(978-0-8307-5232-4(3))* Gospel Light Pubns.
Wood, Barry G. Bible Secrets Revealed. 2008. 184p. pap. 13.99 *(978-1-60477-861-8(X))* Xulon Pr., Inc.
Woods, Dorothy. PTP Peace Bible. 2008. (ENG.). 73p. pap. 8.95 *(978-0-533-15746-4(3))* Vantage Pr., Inc.
Wright, Charles Henry. Biblical Essays or Exegetical Studies on. 2006. pap. 28.95 *(978-1-4286-3616-3(1))* Kessinger Publishing, LLC.
Yandian, Bob. James Notes. Noble, Linda, ed. 222p. pap. *(978-1-885600-09-7(7))* Bob Yandian Ministries.
Yoccou, Raul C. Comentario Biblico Continente Nuevo: Hechos II.Tr. of New Continent Bible Commentary: Acts II. (SPA.). 5.99 *(978-1-56063-991-6(1)*, 498644) Editorial Unilit.
Young People's Bible Class: Fall 2006, Vol. 4. 2006. pap. *(978-1-59843-058-5(0))* Incorporated Trustees of the Gospel Worker Society, The.
Young People's Bible Class: Winter, 2006/2007. 2006. pap. *(978-1-59843-059-2(9))* Incorporated Trustees of the Gospel Worker Society, The.

BIBLE—COMMENTARIES—N. T.

Here are entered only commentaries on the New Testament as a whole.

Alexander, Loveday C. A. & Alexander. Acts in Its Ancient Literary Context Vol. 289: A Classicist Looks at the Acts of the Apostles. 2007. (Library of New Testament Studies, the Ser.). (ENG.). 304p. 60.00 *(978-0-567-08219-0(9)*, T&T Clark Int'l) Continuum International Publishing Group, Ltd. GBR. Dist: National Bk. Network.
Allen, Richard J. Unlocking the New Testament: A Side-By-Side Commentary. 2010. (Illus.). viii, 404p. ***(978-1-60861-119-5(1))*** Covenant Communications, Inc.
Aune, David E., ed. The Blackwell Companion to the New Testament. 2010. (Wiley-Blackwell Companions to Religion Ser.: 28). (ENG., Illus.). 712p. 204.95 *(978-1-4051-0825-6(8)*, Wiley-Blackwell) Wiley, John & Sons, Inc.
Bailey, Mark. Nelson's New Testament Survey, 0 vols. 2009. 704p. pap. 29.99 *(978-1-4185-3227-7(4))* Nelson, Thomas Inc.
Balch, David L. & Lamoreaux, Jason T., eds. Finding A Woman's Place: Essays in Honor of Carolyn Osiek. 2010. (Princeton Theological Monographs). (Illus.). 406p. pap. 45.00 *(978-1-60608-989-7(7)*, Pickwick Pubns.) Wipf & Stock Pubs.
Bar Hebraeus, Gregory. Barn of Mysteries. 2010. (SYR.). pap. 85.00 *(978-1-61719-918-9(4))* Gorgias Pr., LLC.
Barclay, William. The Daily Study Bible Series: New Testament Commentary. cd-rom 99.00 *(978-1-57822-080-9(7))* Loizeaux/Bible Companion Software.
Barclay, William. Jesus As They Saw Him: New Testament Interpretations of Jesus. 2012. 429p. pap. ***(978-0-334-00771-5(2)**, SCM Pr.)* Hymns Ancient & Modern Ltd.
Barker, Margaret. Gate of Heaven. 20.00 *(978-0-687-85409-7(1))* Abingdon Pr.
Barrett, C. K. New Testament Essays. 2010. 160p. pap. 18.00 *(978-1-60899-732-9(4)*, Wipf and Stock) Wipf & Stock Pubs.
Barth, Markus. The People of God. annot. ed. 2006. 102p. pap. 14.00 *(978-1-59752-852-8(8)*, Wipf and Stock) Wipf & Stock Pubs.
Barton, Stephen C. Spirituality of the Gospels. 176p. 15.00 *(978-0-281-04613-3(1))* SPCK Publishing GBR. Dist: Pilgrim Pr., The/United Church Pr.
Bauckham, Richard. Jesus & the God of Israel: God Crucified & Other Studies on the New Testament's Christology of Divine Identity. 2008. 336p. pap. 34.00 *(978-0-8028-4559-7(2))* Eerdmans, William B. Publishing Co.

Bayes, Jonathan F. The Weakness of the Law: God's Law & the Christian in New Testament Perspective. 2007. (Paternoster Biblical Monographs: Ser.). 274p. pap. 28.00 *(978-1-59752-745-3(9))*, Wipf and Stock) Wipf & Stock Pubs.
Bell, Randall. QuickMarks: New Testament. 2006. (Illus.). 6p. vinyl bd. 4.99 *(978-0-9765486-4-5(X))* Owners Manual Pr.
Bennema, Cornelis. The Power of Saving Wisdom: An Investigation of Spirit & Wisdom in Relation to the Soteriology of the Fourth Gospel. 2008. 328p. pap. 37.00 *(978-1-55635-737-4(0))* Wipf & Stock Pubs.
Berman, David M. Berman's Commentary on the Book of Romans: A Verse-by-Verse Study. 2007. 281p. per. 16.99 *(978-1-60247-317-1(X))* Tate Publishing & Enterprises, LLC.
Beza, Theodore, tr. Novum Testamentum Domini Nostri Jesu Christi. 2010. 296p. pap. 33.00 *(978-1-60899-606-3(9))* Wipf & Stock Pubs.
Bishop, Mary Ann. Servants of the Most High God. 2010. 208p. pap. 17.99 *(978-1-60957-516-8(4))* Xulon Pr., Inc.
Bleek, Friedrich. Introduction to the New Testament. 2009. 464p. 42.99 *(978-1-115-88617-8(7))*; 35.99 *(978-1-115-88618-5(5))* BiblioBazaar.
Blount, Brian K. True to Our Native Land: An African American New Testament Commentary. Felder, Cain Hope et al, eds. 2007. (Illus.). 586p. 35.00 *(978-0-8006-3421-6(7)*, Fortress Pr.) Augsburg Fortress, Pubs.
Bock, Darrell L., et al. Baker Exegetical Commentary on the New Testament, Vol. 1. 2006. (Baker Exegetical Commentary on the New Testament Ser.). (C). cd-rom 299.99 *(978-0-8010-0297-7(4))* Baker Academic.
Böhm, Martina. Rezeption und Funktion der Vätererzählungen Bei Philo Von Alexandria: Zum Zusammenhang Von Kontext, Hermeneutik und Exegese Im Frühen Judentum. (Beihefte zur Zeitschrift far die neutestamentliche Wissenschaft und die Kunde der älteren Kirche Ser.). (GER., Illus.). XIII, 502p. 314.00 ***(978-3-11-181185-7(9))*** De Gruyter, Walter Inc.
Boring, M. Eugene & Craddock, Fred B. The People's New Testament Commentary. 2010. (ENG.). 840p. pap. 30.00 *(978-0-664-23592-5(1))* Westminster John Knox Pr.
Brickey, Wayne E. 101 Powerful Promises from the New Testament. 2006. 240p. *(978-1-59038-625-5(6))* Deseret Bk. Co.
Bruce, Frederick Fyvie & Bruce, F. F. The Epistle of Paul to the Romans: An Introduction & Commentary. 2011. 290p. pap. 11.95 ***(978-1-61427-073-7(2))*** Martino Publishing.
Burroughs, Dillon. Misquotes in Misquoting Jesus: Why You Can Still Believe. 2006. 76p. per. 12.94 *(978-0-9777424-6-2(6))* Nimble Bks. LLC.
Burt, David F. Comentario Ampliado Del N. T Vol. 1: Commentary to the New Testament. (SPA.). *(978-84-7645-481-7(3)*, 223411) Clie, Editorial.
Buxbaum, J. G. The New Matthew Henry Commentary: On the Books of the Prophets Hosea & Joel. 2010. 320p. pap. 14.95 *(978-1-4327-5573-7(0))* Outskirts Pr., Inc.
Buxbaum, Jg. The New Matthew Henry Commentary: On the Letters of Paul to Galatia, Ephesus, & Phillipi. 2009. 348p. pap. 14.95 *(978-1-4327-5270-5(7))* Outskirts Pr., Inc.
Carson, D. A. New Testament Commentary Survey. 6th ed. 2007. 160p. (C). pap. 14.99 *(978-0-8010-3124-3(9))* Baker Academic.
Chace, Sharon R. An Artistic Approach to New Testament Literature. 2008. (ENG.). 212p. pap. 38.00 *(978-0-7188-9180-0(5))* Lutherworth Pr., The GBR. Dist: Brown, David Bk. Co., The.
—An Artistic Approach to New Testament Literature. 2008. (Illus.). 212p. pap. 23.00 *(978-1-55635-121-1(6))* Wipf & Stock Pubs.
Comfort, Philip W. & Comfort, John. New Testament Text & Translation Commentary. 2008. (ENG.). 944p. 39.99 *(978-1-4143-1034-3(X))* Tyndale Hse. Pubs.
Commentaries on the New Testament, 14 vols., Set. Incl. Acts. Boles, H. Leo. 14.99 *(978-0-89225-005-9(4))*; Corinthians I. Lipscomb, David & Shepherd, J. W. 14.99 *(978-0-89225-007-3(0))*; Corinthians II: Galatians. Lipscomb, David & Shepherd, J. W. 14.99 *(978-0-89225-008-0(9))*; Ephesians - Colossians. Shepherd, J. W. 14.99 *(978-0-89225-009-7(7))*; Hebrews. Milligan, Robert. 14.99 *(978-0-89225-011-0(9))*; James. Woods, Guy N. 14.99 *(978-0-89225-012-7(7))*; Luke. Boles, H. Leo. 14.99 *(978-0-89225-003-5(8))*; Mark. Dorris, C. E. 14.99 *(978-0-89225-002-8(X))*; Matthew. Boles, H. Leo. 14.99 *(978-0-89225-001-1(1))*; Peter I, II; John I, II, III; Jude. Woods, Guy N. 14.99 *(978-0-89225-013-4(5))*; Revelation. Hinds, John T. 14.99 *(978-0-89225-014-1(3))*; Romans. Lipscomb, David & Shepherd, J. W. 14.99 *(978-0-89225-006-6(2))*; Thessalonians I, II: Timothy I, II: Titus: Phelomon. Shepherd, J. W. 14.99 *(978-0-89225-010-3(0))*; 189.99 *(978-0-89225-000-4(3))* Gospel Advocate Co., Inc.
Cox, Clyde C. Apocalyptic Commentary: An Exposition of the Book of Revelation. 2011. 352p. 51.95 ***(978-1-258-08283-3(7))*** Literary Licensing, LLC.
Crumpler, Anne. Entering the New Testament. 2008. 112p. pap. 15.00 *(978-0-8358-9968-0(3))* Upper Room Bks.
DeConick, April D. & DeConick. The Original Gospel of Thomas in Translation: With a Commentary & New English Translation of the Complete Gospel. 2007. (Library of New Testament Studies). (ENG.). 376p. 65.00 *(978-0-567-04292-7(8)*, T&T Clark Int'l) Continuum International Publishing Group, Ltd. GBR. Dist: National Bk. Network.
DeMaris, Richard. The New Testament in its Ritual World. 2008. (Illus.). (ENG.). 160p. (C). 115.00 *(978-0-415-43825-4(X))*; X, 150p. pap. 37.95 *(978-0-415-43826-1(8))* Routledge.
Desilva. Invitation to the New Testament - VHS. *(978-0-687-49701-0(9))* Abingdon Pr.
Devotions. 2006. 3.29 *(978-0-7847-6067-3(5)*, 00201); 4.29 *(978-0-7847-6020-8(9)*, 00296) Standard Publishing.
Discover Colossians. (Discover Your Bible Ser.). (KOR.). pap., tchr. ed. 3.95 *(978-1-55883-188-9(6)*, 600205); pap., stu. ed. 2.75 *(978-1-55883-187-2(8)*, 600200) C R C World Literature Ministries/Libros Desafio.
Durken, Daniel, ed. The New Collegeville Bible Commentary: New Testament. 2009. (ENG.). 912p. pap. 29.95 *(978-0-8146-3260-4(2))* Liturgical Pr.
Eberts, Harry W. & Eberts, Paul R. The Early Jesus Movement & Its Parties: A New Way to Look at the New Testament. 2009. 144p. pap. 27.95 *(978-0-9824012-3-1(X))* YBK Pubs., Inc.
Eisele, Oril W. The Light of the New Testament. 2007. 468p. 29.95 *(978-1-58597-430-6(7))* Leathers Publishing.
Epp, Eldon Jay. Perspectives on New Testament Textual Criticism: Collected Essays, 1962-2004. 2008. 82.95 *(978-1-58983-395-2(6))* Society of Biblical Literature.
Fair, Ian, et al. Matthew & Mark Vol. 8: Good News for Everyone. 2007. (Bible Reference Library). (ENG.). 224p. per. 9.99 *(978-1-59789-774-7(4)*, Barbour Bks.) Barbour Publishing, Inc.
Farrar, F. W. The Messages of the Books Being Discourses & Notes on the Books of the New Testament. 2007. (ENG.). 552p. 57.95 *(978-0-548-02141-5(4))* Kessinger Publishing, LLC.
Fashbaugh, Earl. Snapshots: Sixty-Six Books of the Bible: A Devotional. 2011. 264p. pap. 13.99 ***(978-1-4269-6427-5(7))*** Trafford Publishing.
Fenton, John. More about Mark. 128p. 15.00 *(978-0-281-05452-7(5))* SPCK Publishing GBR. Dist: Pilgrim Pr., The/United Church Pr.
Fernandez, Steve. Free Justification: The Glorification of Christ in the Justification of a Sinner. 2008. (ENG.). 97p. per. 11.99 *(978-0-9772262-9-0(8))* Kress Christian Pubns.
Field, Frederick. Notes on the Translation of the New Testament. 2010. 216p. pap. 24.64 *(978-1-152-67887-3(6))* General Bks. LLC.
Finger, Reta Halteman. Of Widows & Meals: Communal Meals in the Book of Acts. 2007. (Illus.). 326p. per. 28.00 *(978-0-8028-3053-1(6))* Eerdmans, William B. Publishing Co.
Flynn, Cleta M. Searching for Mary among the Daughters of the King. 2008. 388p. pap. 25.95 *(978-1-4357-0578-4(5))* Lulu Enterprises Inc.
Fullmer, Paul & Smith, Robert H. Greek at a Glance: Summary Reference Sheets for Readers of New Testament Greek. 2007. 20p. pap. 3.00 *(978-1-55635-101-3(1)*, Wipf and Stock) Wipf & Stock Pubs.
Gardner, Quency. Is the Tithe a New Testament Requirement? 2008. 86p. pap. 9.99 *(978-1-60647-355-9(7))* Xulon Pr., Inc.
Gathercole, Simon J. The Preexistent Son: Recovering the Christologies of Matthew, Mark, & Luke. 2006. 344p. per. 32.00 *(978-0-8028-2901-6(5))* Eerdmans, William B. Publishing Co.
Gibson, Margaret Dunlop. The Commentaries of Isho'dad of Merv, Bishop of Hadatha (C. 850 A. D.) Volume 5: The Epistles of Paul the Apostle in Syriac. 2010. (Cambridge Library Collection - Religion Ser.). (Illus.). 106p. pap. 19.99 *(978-1-108-01905-7(6))* Cambridge Univ. Pr.
Giddens, Pastor/Missionary Donald Louis. The Four Gospels in One. 2007. 258p. pap. 26.50 *(978-1-4357-0197-7(6))* Lulu Enterprises Inc.
Goetz, W. Apocalipsis Ya.Tr. of Apocalypse Next. (SPA.) 8.99 *(978-0-7899-0502-4(7)*, 407845) Editorial Unilit.
Gomes, Robert. The Q Testament. 2007. 272p. per. 15.99 *(978-1-60266-958-1(9))* Xulon Pr., Inc.
Goodrich, Richard J., et al. Readers Greek New Testament, 1 vol. 2nd rev. ed. 2007. (ENG.). 592p. pap. 34.99 *(978-0-310-27378-3(1))* Zondervan.
Grant, Robert M. The Letter & the Spirit. 2009. 172p. pap. 20.00 *(978-1-55635-958-3(6)*, Wipf and Stock) Wipf & Stock Pubs.
Gundry, Robert H. Commentary on the New Testament. 2010. 1100p. (C). 49.99 *(978-0-8010-4647-6(5))* Baker Academic.
Gundry, Robert Horton. Commentary on the New Testament. 2010. 1100p. *(978-1-56563-933-1(2))* Hendrickson Pubs. Marketing, LLC.
Hahn, Scott, ed. Ignatius Catholic Study Bible New Testament. 2009. 700p. pap. 21.95 *(978-1-58617-250-3(6))* Ignatius Pr.
—Ignatius Catholic Study Bible: New Testament. 2010. 700p. lthr. 39.95 *(978-1-58617-485-9(1))* Ignatius Pr.
Hahn, Scott & Mitch, Curtis, eds. Ignatius Catholic Study Bible: New Testament. 2010. 700p. 31.95 *(978-1-58617-484-2(3))* Ignatius Pr.
Hale, Tom & Thorson, Steve. Applied New Testament Commentary: Applying God's Word to Your Life. 2007. (ENG.). 1024p. 34.99 *(978-0-7814-4865-9(4))* Cook, David C.
Haneke, Dianne Louise Myers. Guide to the Names of God. 2011. 264p. pap. 29.99 ***(978-1-4567-1716-2(2))*** AuthorHouse.
Hanks, Tom. The Subversive Gospel: A New Testament Commentary of Liberation. 2009. 288p. pap. 32.00 *(978-1-60608-400-7(3)*, Wipf and Stock) Wipf & Stock Pubs.
Hargreaves. Guide to Parables. (Illus.). 144p. 12.00 *(978-0-281-02730-9(7))* SPCK Publishing GBR. Dist: Pilgrim Pr., The/United Church Pr.
Harris, Murray J. Prepositions & Theology in the Greek New Testament, 1 vol. 2012. (ENG.). 192p. (C). 42.99 ***(978-0-310-49392-1(7))*** Zondervan.
Heffern, Andrew D. Apology & Polemic in the New Testament: The Bohlen Lectures 1915. 2007. (ENG.). 424p. 51.95 *(978-0-548-17948-2(4))*; per. 36.95 *(978-1-4304-8008-2(4))* Kessinger Publishing, LLC
Heidt, William G. The Book of the Apocalypse: New Testament Reading Guide, No. 14. 2011. 130p. 40.95 ***(978-1-258-04434-3(X))*** Literary Licensing, LLC.
Hendriksen, William. San Mateo. (Comentario al Nuevo Testamento Ser.). (SPA.). 1066p. pap. 25.00 *(978-1-55883-043-1(X)*, 6703-4400C) Libros Desafio.
Hill, Charles E. & Kruger, Michael J. The Early Text of the New Testament. 2012. (ENG.). 448p. 175.00 ***(978-0-19-956636-5(4))*** Oxford Univ. Pr., Inc.
Hoerber, Robert G. Introduccion al Nuevo Testamento.Tr. of Introduction to the New Testament. (SPA.). 258p. 11.99 *(978-0-7586-0323-4(1))* Concordia Publishing Hse.
—Lea y Comprenda (Reading the New Testament for Understanding) (SPA.). 222p. pap. 3.95 *(978-0-570-05114-5(2)*, 16-3011) Concordia Publishing Hse.
Hovey, Alvah. An American Commentary on the New Testament. 2010. 524p. pap. *(978-1-151-87699-7(2))*; 536p. pap. *(978-1-151-87693-5(3))* Books LLC.
Hovey, Alvah, ed. An American Commentary on the New Testament. 2009. 304p. 43.95 *(978-1-120-24200-6(2))*; pap. 28.95 *(978-1-120-14725-7(5))* Kessinger Publishing, LLC.
Hurtak, J. J. & Hurtak, D. E. The Gospel of Mary: A Text of Mary Magdalene with Commentary. 2008. (Illus.). 100p. pap. 10.00 *(978-1-892139-67-2(7))* Academy for Future Science.
Illuminated World Staff. Bible Illuminated: The Book, New Testament. 2008. 288p. pap. 35.00 *(978-91-976694-4-3(X))* Illuminated World SWE. Dist: Midpoint Trade Bks., Inc.
Intervarsity Press. Tyndale New Testament Commentaries, 20 vols., Set. 2009. (Tyndale Commentaries Complete Set Ser.). (ENG.). pap. 325.00 *(978-0-8308-4230-6(6)*, IVP Acad.) InterVarsity Pr.
Ironside, H. A. James & 1 & 2 Peter, 1 vol. 2008. (Ironside Expository Commentaries Ser.). 128p. 18.99 *(978-0-8254-2928-6(5))* Kregel Pubns.
Jackson, Wayne. A New Testament Commentary. 631p. 2011. (ENG.). pap. 49.95 ***(978-1-932723-10-6(2))*** 2nd ed. 2012. pap. 49.95 ***(978-1-932723-07-6(2))*** Christian Courier Pubns.
Jay. New Testament Greek. 32p. 5.00 *(978-0-281-00664-9(4))* SPCK Publishing GBR. Dist: Pilgrim Pr., The/United Church Pr.
Johnson, B. W. Johnson's Notes: The Peoples New Testament with Notes. 24.99 *(978-0-89225-141-4(7))* Gospel Advocate Co., Inc.
Johnson, Bruce. Come & Behold. 48p. mass mkt., stu. ed. 5.50 *(978-0-687-74170-0(X))* Abingdon Pr.
Keith, Chris. Jesus' Literacy: Education & the Teacher from Galilee. 2011. (Library of New Testament Studies). (ENG.). 242p. 100.00 *(978-0-567-11972-8(6)*, T&T Clark Int'l) Continuum International Publishing Group, Ltd. GBR. Dist: National Bk. Network.
Kennedy, Rick. Jesus, History & Mount Darwin: An Academic Excursion. 2008. (ENG.). 112p. pap. 33.00 *(978-0-7188-9189-3(9))* Lutherworth Pr., The GBR. Dist: Brown, David Bk. Co., The.
Kim, Sang-jin. The Miracle Narratives of the Bible. 2010. 368p. pap. *(978-3-639-27767-8(8))* VDM Verlag Dr. Mueller e.K.
Kraus, Thomas J. Ad Fontes: Original Manuscripts & Their Significance for Studying Early Christianity - Selected Essays. 2007. (Texts & Editions for New Testament Study Ser.). (MUL., Illus.). 304p. *(978-90-04-16182-5(1))* BRILL.
Lands of the Bible New Testament. 21.48 incl. trans. *(978-0-687-00167-5(6))* Abingdon Pr.
Lashua, Shereen K. Naked, Embarrassed, & Exposed? Then Put Something On. 2009. 208p. pap. 15.99 *(978-1-60791-909-4(5))* Xulon Pr., Inc.
Leadership Ministries Worldwide, creator. The Preachers Outline & Sermon Bible-KJV: Ezra, Nehemiah, Esther. 2007. (Preacher's Outline & Sermon Bible-KJV Ser.). 404p. per. 35.99 *(978-1-57407-201-3(3))* Leadership Ministries Worldwide.
Lee, Witness. The Conclusion of the New Testament, Messages 306-322. 2007. 139p. per. *(978-0-7363-3216-3(2))* Living Stream Ministry.
—The Conclusion of the New Testament, Messages 323-345. 2007. per. 9.50 *(978-0-7363-3284-2(7))* Living Stream Ministry.
—The Conclusion of the New Testament, Messages 346-366. 2008. per. 9.50 *(978-0-7363-3572-0(2))* Living Stream Ministry.
Levine, Amy-Jill. The Jewish Annotated New Testament, 1 vol. Brettler, Marc Z., ed. 2011. (ENG., Illus.). 700p. 35.00 *(978-0-19-529770-6(9))* Oxford Univ. Pr., Inc.
Lightfoot, J. B. Biblical Essays. 2010. 430p. 43.16 *(978-1-163-43613-4(5))* 2010. 480p. pap. 31.16 *(978-1-162-97361-4(1))* 2007. (ENG.). 480p. 53.95 *(978-0-548-12915-9(0))* 2006. (ENG.). pap. 38.95 *(978-1-4286-3941-6(1))* Kessinger Publishing, LLC.
Lincoln. The Gospel According to St. John. (Black's New Testament Commentaries Ser.). pap. *(978-0-7136-4116-5(9)*, Burns & Oates) Continuum International Publishing Group, Ltd.
Lindars, Barnabas & Smalley, Stephen S. Christ & Spirit in the New Testament: Studies in Honour of Charles Francis Digby Moule. 2008. (ENG.). 464p. pap. 48.00 *(978-0-521-10216-2(2))* Cambridge Univ. Pr.
Lorimer, William. The New Testament in Scots. Lorimer, Robin, ed. 2012. (ENG.). 328p. pap. 23.95 ***(978-0-85786-285-3(5))*** Canongate Bks. GBR. Dist: Independent Pubs. Group.
Lomes, Herman. Salvation Weekly: The Theological Activist. 2011. 180p. pap. 19.99 ***(978-1-4568-9788-8(8))*** Xlibris Corp.
Luther, Martin & Luther, Martin. The Essential Martin Luther Commentary Set: Romans, Galatians, & Peter & Jude, 3 vols. 2006. 914p. pap. 49.99 *(978-0-8254-3082-4(8)*, Kregel Classics) Kregel Pubns.
MacArthur, John. The MacArthur New Testament Commentary: Unleashing God's Truth, One Verse at a Time, 0 vols. 2007. (MacArthur New Testament Commentary Ser.). 992p. 24.99 *(978-1-4185-2743-3(2))* Nelson, Thomas Inc.
Mack, Wayne A. Maximum Impact: Living & Loving for God's Glory. 2010. pap. *(978-1-59638-204-6(X))* P & R Publishing.
Magiera, Janet M. Aramaic Peshitta New Testament Translation, 3 vols. 2009. (SYR & ENG.). ***(978-0-9679613-9-2(4)***, LWM Pubns.) Light of the Word Ministry.
Magiera, Janet M. & Magiera, Janet. Aramaic Peshitta New Testament Translation, 3 vols. 2009. (SYR & ENG.). ***(978-0-9679613-8-5(6))***; (SYR & ENG.). ***(978-0-9820085-0-8(3))***; 735p. ***(978-0-9820085-2-2(X))*** Light of the Word Ministry. (LWM Pubns.).
—Aramaic Peshitta New Testament Translation: Messianic Version. 2009. 603p. ***(978-0-9679613-6-1(X)***, LWM Pubns.) Light of the Word Ministry.
Magiera, Janet M., et al. Aramaic Peshitta New Testament Translation. 2008. 730p. ***(978-0-9820085-1-5(1)***, LWM Pubns.) Light of the Word Ministry.
Malahay D. D., Chris B. & Malahay D.D., Chris B. The Bible's Answers to the Sabbath Question. 2010. 108p. 27.49 *(978-1-4490-3288-3(5))*; pap. 18.99 *(978-1-4490-3287-6(7))* AuthorHouse.
Malone, Peter. The Same as Christ Jesus: Gospel & Type. (Illus.). 143p. 11.50 *(978-0-85439-592-7(X))* St. Paul Pubns. GBR. Dist: St Pauls/Alba Hse. Pubs.
Manning, T. Deering. Eye Witnesses of His Majesty. 2007. 256p. per. 15.99 *(978-1-60266-216-2(9))* Xulon Pr., Inc.
Martin, Russell. Understanding the Real Jesus. 2006. 277p. pap. 15.95 *(978-0-7414-3119-6(X))* Infinity Publishing.
Maselli, Christopher P. N. Miracles of Jesus. Szitas, Kathie, ed. 2008. (Fun Faith-Builders Ser.). (ENG.). 32p. (gr. 1-3). pap. 4.99 *(978-1-60022-519-2(5))* Carson-Dellosa Publishing, LLC.
Mason, John & Hurtgen, John. Reading the New Testament: Exercises for Beginning Readers of the Greek New Testament. 99.95 *(978-0-88946-791-0(9))* Mellen, Edwin Pr., The.
Maus, Tom A. Empowered for Mission: Through the Baptism of the Holy Spirit. 2010. 78p. pap. 10.95 *(978-1-4327-5577-5(3))* Outskirts Pr., Inc.
McIntosh, Diane. Spiritual Treasure Hunt. 2010. 188p. pap. 12.50 *(978-0-557-44049-8(1))* Lulu Enterprises Inc.
McKenzie, J. L., ed. New Testament for Spiritual Reading, 25 vols. Incl. Pt. 1. Revelation of St. John. pap. 4.95 Pt. 2. Revelation of St. John. pap. 4.95 Vol. 1, Pt. 1. Gospel According to St. Matthew. pap. 4.95 Vol. 2, Pt. 1. Gospel According to St. Matthew. pap. 4.95 Vol. 3, Pt. 1. Gospel According to St. Mark. pap. 4.95 Vol. 4, Pt. 2. Gospel According to St. Mark. pap. 4.95 *(978-0-8245-0337-6(6))*; Vol. 5, Pt. 1. Gospel According to St. Luke. pap. 4.95 Vol. 6, Pt. 2. Gospel According to St. Luke. pap. 4.95 Vol. 7, Pt. 1. Gospel According to St. John. pap. 4.95 Vol. 8, Pt. 2. Gospel According to St. John. 4.95 *(978-0-8164-1079-8(8))*; Vol. 9, Pt. 3. Gospel According to St. John. pap. 4.95 Vol. 10. Acts of the Apostles, Pt. 1. pap. Vol. 11. Acts of the Apostles, Pt. 2. pap. 4.95 Vol. 12. Epistle to the Romans. pap. 4.95 Vol. 13. First Epistle to the Corinthians. pap. 4.95 Vol. 14. Second Epistle to the Corinthians. pap. 4.95 *(978-0-8245-0347-5(3))*; Vol. 14. Second Epistle to the Corinthians. *(978-0-8245-0123-5(3))*; Vol. 15. Epistle to the Galatians. pap. 4.95 Vol. 16. Epistle to the Ephesians. pap. 4.95 Vol. 17. Epistle to the Philippians, Epistle to the Colossians. pap. 4.95 *(978-0-8164-1088-0(7))*; Vol. 18. First Epistle to the Thessalonians. Second Epistle to the Thessalonians. pap. 4.95 Vol. 19. First Epistle to Timothy. Second Epistle to Timothy. pap. 4.95 Vol. 20. Epistle to Titus. Epistle to Philemon. pap. 4.95 *(978-0-8245-0354-3(6))*; Vol. 20. Epistle to Titus. Epistle to Philemon. *(978-0-8245-0129-7(2))*; Vol. 21. Epistle to the Hebrews. Epistle to James. pap. 4.95 Vol. 22. First Epistle to Peter. Second Epistle to Peter. pap. 4.95 Vol. 23. Epistle to Jude, Three Epistles of John. pap. 4.95 123.75 o.p. *(978-0-8245-0135-8(7))* Crossroad Publishing Co., The.
Mesrobian, Armen Z. The Sermon on the Mount & the Sermon on the Plain. Mesrobian, Armen Z., ed. I.t. ed. 2007. (Illus.). 92p. (YA). pap. 9.95 *(978-0-9632735-5-0(8))* EPS Excel Publishing Services.
Metzger, Bruce M. A Textual Commentary on the Greek New Testament. 2nd ed. 2006. 696p. pap. 29.99 *(978-1-59856-164-7(2))* Hendrickson Pubs. Marketing, LLC.
Middleton, Paul & Middleton. Radical Martyrdom & Cosmic Conflict in Early Christianity. 2006. (Library of New Testament Studies: Vol. 307). (ENG.). 224p. 170.00 *(978-0-567-04164-7(6)*, T&T Clark Int'l) Continuum International Publishing Group, Ltd. GBR. Dist: National Bk. Network.
Miller, J. R. Devotional Hours with the Bible Volume Iv, from Solomon to Malachi. 2011. 178p. pap. 14.99 ***(978-1-61203-202-3(8))*** Bottom of the Hill Publishing.
Miller, Mark Heber. The Nazarene Commentary: 21st Century Version of the Christian Scriptures, 2, Vol. 1. 2007. 494p. per. 69.99 *(978-0-9798154-4-7(4))* Living Waters Publishing Co.
Moriya, Akio & Hata, Gohei. Pentateuchal Traditions in the Late Second Temple Period: Proceedings of the International Workshop in Tokyo August 28-31, 2007. 2012. (ENG.). ***(978-90-04-18453-4(8))*** BRILL.
Murphy, Harry. The Great Exchange. 2009. 104p. pap. 10.99 *(978-1-60791-501-0(4))* Xulon Pr., Inc.
Navarre Bible Editors. Introduction to the Bible: New Testament. 2012. (Illus.). 256p. pap. 14.95 *(978-1-84682-205-6(X))* Four Courts Pr. IRL. Dist: International Specialized Bk. Services.
Naylor, P. 2 Corinthians: Chapters 1-7, Vol. 2. 304p. 24.99 *(978-0-85234-516-0(X))* Evangelical Pr. GBR. Dist: Spring Arbor Distributors, Inc.
The New English Bible: The New Testament. 2009. (ENG.). 464p. pap. 29.99 *(978-0-521-10196-7(4))* Cambridge Univ. Pr.
New Testament, English. 5.99 *(978-0-89827-203-1(3)*, GMA403) Wesleyan Publishing Hse.
The New Testament of Our Lord & Savior Jesus Christ. 2009. 394p. pap. *(978-0-217-88356-6(7))* Books LLC.
Newton, Tim. The Forgotten Gospels: Life & Teachings of Jesus Supplementary to the New Testament. 2010. (ENG.). 224p. pap. 15.95 *(978-1-58243-633-3(9)*, Counterpoint) Counterpoint LLC.

Nicoll, W. Robertson. The Expositor's Greek Testament V5. Nicoll, W. Robertson, ed. 2011. 500p. 58.95 ***(978-1-258-05092-4(7))*** Literary Licensing, LLC.
No Room in the Inn. 0.60 *(978-0-687-28038-4(9))* Abingdon Pr.
Olivi, Pierre Jean. Commentary on the Gospel of Mark. 2011. 96p. ***(978-1-57659-234-2(0))*** Franciscan Institute Pubns.
Olshausen, Hermann. Biblical Commentary on the New Testament. 2009. 316p. pap. *(978-1-4588-2334-2(2))*; 542p. pap. *(978-0-217-31638-5(7))*; 508p. pap. *(978-0-217-31643-9(3))*; 592p. pap. *(978-0-217-44459-0(8))* Books LLC.
Omanson, Roger L. A Textual Guide to the Greek New Testament: An Adaptation of Bruce M. Metzger's Textual Commentary for the Needs of Translators. 2007. 553p. 49.95 *(978-1-59856-202-6(9))* Hendrickson Pubs. Marketing, LLC.
Palestine New Testament. 19.98 incl. trans. *(978-0-687-00164-4(1))* Abingdon Pr.
Palmer, E. The Greek Testament: Novum Testamentum Graece. 2007. 576p. per. *(978-1-84356-023-4(2))* Wallenberg, Simon Pr.
Phillips, John. Exploring People of the New Testament, 1 vol. 2007. (John Phillips Bible Characters Ser.). 432p. 26.99 *(978-0-8254-3387-0(8))* Kregel Pubns.
—An Expository Survey, 1 vol. 2009. (Exploring the Bible Book by Book Ser.). 320p. 25.99 *(978-0-8254-3566-9(8))* Kregel Pubns.
Pinkston, Ron. Our Father. 2009. 76p. pap. 10.99 *(978-0-9796620-2-7(8))* Selah Publishing Group, LLC.
Pouilly, Alfredo. Nuevo Viacrucis. 64p. 2.95 *(978-958-607-495-7(1))* Sociedad de San Pablo COL. Dist: St Pauls/Alba Hse. Pubs.
Pratt, Charles Edgar. Paganism in Christianity: A New Testament for Rational Believers. 2011. 256p. 47.95 ***(978-1-258-04190-8(1))*** Literary Licensing, LLC.
Precious Promises New Testament. 1.69 *(978-1-886097-11-7(9))* Stonehaven Pr.
Price, Robert M. The Pre-Nicene New Testament: Fifty-Four Formative Texts. 2006. 1235p. 49.95 *(978-1-56085-194-3(5))* Signature Bks., LLC.
Prince, Benny D. Tithing Promoters Big Lies. 2008. 164p. pap. 9.95 *(978-1-935105-05-3(1))* Avid Readers Publishing Group.
Ray, Charles. The Books of First & Second Timothy, Titus, & Philemon: Goals to Godliness. Couch, Mal & Hindson, Ed, eds. 2008. (21 St Century Biblical Commentary Ser.). (ENG., Illus.). 256p. 19.99 *(978-0-89957-826-2(8))* AMG Pubs.
Reuss, Eduard. Bibliotheca Novi Testamenti Graeci: Cuius editiones ab initio typographiae ad nostram aetatem Impressas. 2007. (LAT.). 320p. 75.00 *(978-1-57898-661-3(3))* Martino Publishing.
Robertson, A. T. Luke the Historian in the Light of Research. 2009. (ENG.). 268p. 34.99 *(978-1-117-06842-8(0))* BiblioBazaar.
—Luke the Historian in the Light of Research. 2008. 266p. 42.95 *(978-1-4365-5848-8(4))* 2007. (ENG.). 268p. per. 27.95 *(978-0-548-75183-1(8))* Kessinger Publishing, LLC.
—Luke the Historian in the Light of Research. 2008. 268p. pap. *(978-1-4086-8576-1(0))* Read Bks.
—The Minister & His Greek New Testament. 2008. 144p. pap. 14.00 *(978-1-59925-196-7(5))* Solid Ground Christian Bks.
—Types of Preachers in the New Testament. 2009. 128p. pap. *(978-1-150-19626-3(2))* Books LLC.
Rogers, Glenn. The Simplified New Testament Study Bible. 2010. 636p. pap. 45.00 *(978-0-9792072-9-7(0))* Mission & Ministry Resources.
Russell, Robert Lloyd. One Precious Pearl: God's Design for His Church. 2010. pap. 14.95 *(978-0-7414-6232-9(X))* Infinity Publishing.
Schweizer. Theological Introduction to New Testament. 192p. 19.95 *(978-0-281-04602-7(6))* International Publishers Marketing.
Scott, Eric. Simple Gospel. 2008. 220p. 24.99 *(978-1-60477-300-2(6))*; pap. 14.99 *(978-1-60477-299-9(9))* Xulon Pr., Inc.
Seubert, Augusto. Como Entender el Mensaje del Nuevo Testamento. (SPA.). 144p. 6.95 *(978-958-607-331-8(9))* Sociedad de San Pablo ESP. Dist: St Pauls/Alba Hse. Pubs.
Shelly, Rubel. New Testament: A Book-by-Book Study. pap. 13.99 *(978-0-89098-012-5(8))* Twentieth Century Christian Bks.
A Simple Little Book about Jesus. 2nd rev. ed. 2007. per. 10.00 *(978-0-9778902-2-4(8))* Augusta L Enterprises.
Sodeinde. Life Lessons from Our Favorite Scripture. 2007. pap. 14.99 *(978-1-60034-996-6(X))* Xulon Pr., Inc.
Standard Lesson Commentary: Soft Cover. 448p. 14.99 *(978-0-7847-1302-0(2))* Standard Publishing.
Stein, Robert H. Mark. 2008. (Baker Exegetical Commentary on the New Testament Ser.). (Illus.). 848p. (C). 54.99 *(978-0-8010-2682-9(2))* Baker Academic.
Stott, John, contrib. by. The Bible Speaks Today: New Testament. rev. ed. 2008. (Bible Speaks Today Ser.). (ENG.). cd-rom 115.00 *(978-0-8308-2449-6(9)*, IVP Acad.) InterVarsity Pr.
Stott, John, ed. The Bible Speaks Today Series - New Testament Set. (Bible Speaks Today Ser.). 22p. pap. 352.00 *(978-0-8308-8183-3(2))* InterVarsity Pr.
Strauss, Mark & Barnes, Peter. Acts Thru 2 Corinthians: What about Church? 2008. (Bible Reference Library). (ENG.). 240p. pap. 9.99 *(978-1-59789-776-1(0)*, Barbour Bks.) Barbour Publishing, Inc.
Stuckemeyer, Phillip. A Three-Fold Cord: God Bears Witness to His Salvation Plan for Mankind: The Death, Burial & Resurrection of Jesus Christ. 2011. 192p. pap. 17.00 *(978-1-4567-2796-3(6))* AuthorHouse.
Stulac, George M. James. 2010. (IVP New Testament Commentary Ser.: Volume 16). (ENG.). 206p. pap. 17.00 *(978-0-8308-4016-8(8)*, IVP Acad.) InterVarsity Pr.
Swaggart, Jimmy. The Expositor's New Testament - Spanish Edition. 2007. lthr. 39.95 *(978-1-934655-36-8(8))* Swaggart, Jimmy Ministries.
Swete, H. B. Akhmim Fragment of the Apocryphal Gospel. 2006. pap. 18.95 *(978-1-4286-3947-8(0))* Kessinger Publishing, LLC.
Thomas, Cecil K. Alexander Campbell & His New Version. 2011. 224p. pap. 19.00 ***(978-1-61097-563-6(4)***, Wipf and Stock) Wipf & Stock Pubs.
Thomas, James. Ruminating on the Psalms, Volume 1. 2010. 92p. pap. 14.96 *(978-0-557-49671-6(3))* Lulu Enterprises Inc.
Thomas Nelson. Personal Size Giant Print Reference Bible, NKJV Edition. 2010. im. lthr. 54.99 *(978-1-4185-4761-5(1))* Nelson, Thomas Inc.
Thomas Nelson Publishing Staff. The Voice New Testament, Designer Series, 0 vols. 2009. 480p. pap. 34.99 *(978-1-4185-4249-8(0))* Nelson, Thomas Inc.
—The Voice Reader's New Testament, 0 vols. 2009. 600p. pap. 9.99 *(978-1-4185-4215-3(6))* Nelson, Thomas Inc.
—Word Biblical Commentary, 59 vols. 2009. (Word Biblical Commentary Ser.). cd-rom 1199.99 *(978-1-4185-7145-0(8))* Nelson, Thomas Inc.
Thurston, Bonnie B. & Ryan, Judith M., eds. Philippians & Philemon. 2009. 304p. pap. 39.95 *(978-0-8146-5979-3(9))* Liturgical Pr.
Tomtania, Monica M. The End-Time Daughters of the King. 2008. 300p. per. 17.99 *(978-1-60477-387-3(1))* Xulon Pr., Inc.
Trapp, John. A Commentary of the New Testament. 2008. (Illus.). 800p. 69.99 *(978-1-59925-133-2(7))* Calvary Pr.
Tyndale House Publishers Staff, prod. Nuevo Testamento Vida Abundante. 2009.Tr. of Abundant Life Bible NT NLT. (SPA.). 288p. pap. 1.79 *(978-1-4143-2640-5(8)*, Tyndale Espanol) Tyndale Hse. Pubs.
Tyndale, William. Expositions & Notes on Sundry Portions of the Holy Scriptures. 2009. 184p. pap. *(978-0-217-71656-7(3))* Books LLC.
Upper Room Staff. Entering the New Testament. 2008. 96p. pap., wbk. ed. 10.00 *(978-0-8358-9967-3(5))* Upper Room Bks.
Vine, W. E. Prophecy, 0 vols. 2010. (Vine's Topical Commentaries Ser.). 256p. 29.99 *(978-1-4185-4308-2(X))* Nelson, Thomas Inc.
Voorhies, Barry K., et al. Tongues vs. Cessationism! The Great Debate Settled?! 2009. 228p. pap. 15.99 *(978-1-61579-265-8(1))* Xulon Pr., Inc.
Wade, Patricia A. Jesus & a Baby Boomer, 1 vol. 2010. 78p. pap. 19.95 *(978-1-4489-9108-2(0))* PublishAmerica, Inc.
Warrington, Keith. Jesus the Healer: Paradigm or Unique Phenomenon. 2006. (ENG.). 208p. pap. 29.99 *(978-0-85364-822-2(0)*, Paternoster) Authentic Media.
Westcott, Brooke Foss, intro. The Epistle to the Hebrews. 2010. 150.32 *(978-1-61719-680-5(0))* Gorgias Pr., LLC.
Westminster John Knox Press Staff. Interpretation, New Testament Series Set. Achtemeier, Paul J. & Mays, James Luther, eds. 2012. (ENG.). pap. 340.00 ***(978-0-664-23921-3(8))*** Westminster John Knox Pr.
—Interpretation, Old Testament Series Set. Mays, James Luther, ed. 2012. (ENG.). pap. 540.00 ***(978-0-664-23922-0(6))*** Westminster John Knox Pr.
Wettstein, Neuer. Texte Zum Neuen Testament Aus Griechentum und Hellenismus, Band I/1. 1: Texte Zum Markusevangelium. Schnelle, Udo, ed. 2008. (GER.). VIII, 879p. 217.00 *(978-3-11-020030-0(9))* De Gruyter, Walter Inc.
Wiersbe, Warren W. The Complete Old & New Testament, Vol. 2. 2007. (Wiersbe Bible Commentaries Ser.). (ENG.). 1088p. 44.99 *(978-0-7814-4539-9(6))* Cook, David C.
Wilkins, Michael J., contrib. by. Zondervan Illustrated Bible Background Commentary Library, 1 vol. 2007. (Zondervan Illustrated Bible Backgrounds Commentary Ser.). (ENG.). pap., pap., pap. 197.88 *(978-0-310-64981-6(1))* Zondervan.
Williamson, Roy. Not Least in the Kingdom. 128p. 10.00 *(978-0-281-05421-3(5))* SPCK Publishing GBR. Dist: Pilgrim Pr., The/United Church Pr.
—Open Return: Renewing Your Faith Through the Gospel Story. 144p. 9.00 *(978-0-281-05292-9(1))* SPCK Publishing GBR. Dist: Pilgrim Pr., The/United Church Pr.
Wilson, Andrew P. Transfigured: A Derridean Re-Reading of the Markan Transfiguration. 2007. (T & T Clark Library of Biblical Studies). (ENG.). 200p. 145.00 *(978-0-567-02601-9(9)*, T&T Clark Int'l) Continuum International Publishing Group, Ltd. GBR. Dist: National Bk. Network.
Witherington, Ben, III. Letters & Homilies for Jewish Christians: A Socio-Rhetorical Commentary on Hebrews, James & Jude. 2007. (Letters & Homilies for Hellenized Christians Ser.). (ENG., Illus.). 656p. 40.00 *(978-0-8308-2932-3(6)*, IVP Acad.) InterVarsity Pr.
World Bible Translation Center, creator. Arabic New Testament-FL-Easy to Read. 2007. 446p. pap. 7.50 *(978-977-6124-98-1(4))* World Bible Translation Ctr., Inc.
—Urdu New Testament-FL: Easy to Read. 2007. 312p. pap. 4.50 *(978-1-932438-70-3(X))* World Bible Translation Ctr., Inc.
World Bible Translation Center, tr. Arabic New Testament AR102: Easy-to-Read Version. 2007. 446p. pap. 7.50 *(978-1-932438-30-7(0))* World Bible Translation Ctr., Inc.
—Arabic New Testament AR103: Easy-to-Read Version. 2007. 446p. pap. 7.50 *(978-1-935189-00-8(X))* World Bible Translation Ctr., Inc.
—Myanmarese (Burmese) New Testament. 2008. (BUR., Illus.). 461p. pap. 7.50 *(978-1-935189-01-5(8))* World Bible Translation Ctr., Inc.
World Bible Translation Ctr, creator. Novo Testamento: Versao Facil de Ler. 2008. (Illus.). 392p. pap. 7.50 *(978-1-932438-34-5(3))* World Bible Translation Ctr., Inc.
Yarbrough, Robert W. 1-3 John. 2008. (Baker Exegetical Commentary on the New Testament Ser.). (Illus.). 464p. 39.99 *(978-0-8010-2687-4(3))* Baker Academic.
Yorke, H. Lefroy. Studies in the Epistle to the Philippian. 2007. 316p. per. *(978-1-4067-8888-4(0)*, Pomona Pr.) Read Bks.
Zondervan. A Survey of the New Testament: 5th Edition, 1 vol. 2012. (ENG.). (C). 49.99 ***(978-0-310-49475-1(3))*** Zondervan.
Zondervan. Zondervan King James Version Commentary — -New Testament, 1 vol. 2010. (ENG.). 39.99 *(978-0-310-68067-3(0))* Zondervan.
Zondervan Publishing Staff & Hindson, Edward E. Zondervan King James Version Commentary, 1 vol. Mitchell, Daniel Raymond, ed. 2010. (ENG.). 928p. 34.99 *(978-0-310-25150-7(8))* Zondervan.

BIBLE—COMMENTARIES—N. T. ACTS

Abbott, Lyman. The Acts of the Apostles. 2007. (ENG.). 264p. per. 27.95 *(978-1-4304-5495-3(4))* Kessinger Publishing, LLC.
—The Acts of the Apostles. 2006. 264p. per. 23.99 *(978-1-4255-2367-1(6))* MPublishing.
Act I. (LifeLight Bible Studies: Course 13). stu. ed. 0.55 incl. audio *(978-0-570-09285-8(X)*, 20-2307) Concordia Publishing Hse.
Acts. (People's Bible Commentary Ser.). 304p. 14.99 *(978-0-7586-0443-9(2))* Concordia Publishing Hse.
The Acts of the Apostles. 2009. 350p. 28.99 *(978-1-116-46263-0(X))*; pap. 32.75 *(978-1-116-46264-7(8))*; pap. 31.75 *(978-1-116-46265-4(6))* BiblioBazaar.
Alexander, Loveday. Acts: Daily Bible Commentary: A Guide for Reflection & Prayer. 2007. (Daily Bible Commentary Ser.). 195p. per. 12.95 *(978-1-59856-189-0(8))* Hendrickson Pubs. Marketing, LLC.
Alexanser, Joseph Addison. The Acts of the Apostles Explained by Joseph Addison Alexander; 2006. 504p. per. 29.99 *(978-1-4255-5628-0(0))* MPublishing.
American Bible Society Staff. The Acts of the Apostles Translated Out of the Original Greek. 2007. (ENG.). 114p. 34.95 *(978-0-548-01085-3(4))* Kessinger Publishing, LLC.
Arnold, Clinton E. Acts, 1 vol. 2007. (Zondervan Illustrated Bible Backgrounds Commentary Ser.). (ENG., Illus.). 304p. (gr. 13). pap. 19.99 *(978-0-310-27825-2(2))* Zondervan.
Baker Publishing Group Staff & Life Together Staff. Acts, 1 vol. 2009. (Deepening Life Together Ser.). 128p. pap. 8.99 *(978-0-8010-6842-3(8))* Baker Bks.
Barrier, Jeremy W. The Acts of Paul & Thecla: A Critical Introduction & Commentary. 2009. (GEC & ENG., Illus.). XX, 232p. pap. 117.50 *(978-3-16-149998-2(0))* Mohr Siebeck GmbH & Co. KG DEU. Dist: Coronet Bks.
Berrigan, Daniel. Whereon to Stand: The Acts of the Apostles & Ourselves. 2009. (Daniel Berrigan Reprint Ser.). 352p. (Orig.). pap. 39.00 *(978-1-60608-468-7(2)*, Wipf and Stock) Wipf & Stock Pubs.
Blomberg, Craig L. From Pentecost to Patmos: An Introduction to Acts Through Revelation. 2006. (ENG., Illus.). 592p. 39.99 *(978-0-8054-3248-0(5)*, B&H Academic) B&H Publishing Group.
Bock, Darrell L. Acts. 2007. (Baker Exegetical Commentary on the New Testament Ser.). (Illus.). 880p. (C). 54.99 *(978-0-8010-2668-3(7))* Baker Academic.
Brackett, Charlie. In the Steps of the Apostles: Devotional Messages from Acts of the Apostles. 2007. (Illus.). 368p. per. 16.95 *(978-0-9779577-7-4(2))* Clarion Word Publishing.
Brenk, Frederick E. With Unperfumed Voice: Studies in Plutarch, in Greek Literature, Religion & Philosophy, & in the New Testament Background. 2007. (Potsdamer Altertumswissenschaftliche Beitrage (PAwB) Ser.). (ENG., Illus.). 544p. (C). pap. 128.00 *(978-3-515-08929-6(2))* Steiner, Franz Verlag Wiesbaden GmbH DEU. Dist: Brown, David Bk. Co., The.
Burnside, W. F., ed. The Acts of the Apostles. 2010. (GRE.). pap. 54.64 *(978-1-61719-331-6(3))* Gorgias Pr., LLC.
Carroll, B. H. Coment. Carroll-Siete: Carroll's Comment-7: Facts. (SPA.). *(978-84-7645-133-5(4)*, 223179) Clie, Editorial.
Cavins, Jeff & Sarah, Christmyer. Adventures in Acts Study Set: The Spread of the Kingdom. 2007. (Great Adventure Ser.). 29.95 *(978-1-932927-74-0(3))* Ascension Pr.
Chance, J. Bradley. Annual Bible Study: Acts Teaching Guide. 2008. (Smyth & Helwys Bible Commentaries Ser.). (Illus.). 562p. 14.00 incl. cd-rom *(978-1-57312-080-7(4))* Smyth & Helwys Publishing, Inc.
Chester, Tim. Ruth: Poverty & Plenty: Four Studies for Individuals or Groups. 2010. (Good Book Guides). 32p. pap. *(978-1-905564-91-0(0))* Good Bk. Co.
Coneybeare, Frederick. On the Western Text of the Acts as Evidenced by Chrysostom. 2009. pap. 20.44 *(978-1-60724-608-4(2))* Gorgias Pr., LLC.
Conley, Frazier. Acts of the Apostles. 12.95 *(978-1-56794-251-4(2)*, C-3042) Star Bible & Tract Corp.
Cook, David. Teaching Acts: Unlocking the Book of Acts for the Bible Teacher. 2007. (ENG.). 304p. per. 10.99 *(978-1-84550-255-3(8))* Christian Focus Pubns. GBR. Dist: STL Distribution North America.
Dick, John. Lectures on the Acts of the Apostles. 2007. (ENG.). 408p. 49.95 *(978-0-548-22085-6(9))*; per. 34.95 *(978-1-4325-4177-4(3))* Kessinger Publishing, LLC.
Discover Acts. (Discover Your Bible Ser.). (KOR.). pap., stu. ed. 4.25 *(978-1-55883-218-3(1)*, 600170) C R C World Literature Ministries/Libros Desafio.
Freeman, Kaye. A Journey Through the Gospels & Acts. 2007. per. 11.99 net. *(978-1-60402-327-5(9))* Independent Pub.
Hackett, Horatio Balch. A Commentary on the Original Text of the Acts of the Apostles. 2006. 420p. per. 26.99 *(978-1-4255-4552-9(1))* MPublishing.
—A Commentary on the Original Text of the Acts of the Apostles by H B Hackett. 2006. 488p. per. 29.99 *(978-1-4255-5462-0(8))* MPublishing.
Hahn, Scott & Mitch, Curtis. Ignatius Catholic Study Bible: The Letters of St. James, St. Peter & St. Jude. 2008. (Ignatius Catholic Study Bible Ser.). 65p. pap. 9.95 *(978-1-58617-248-0(4))* Ignatius Pr.
Hargreaves. Guide to Acts. (Illus.). 272p. 15.00 *(978-0-281-04367-5(1))* SPCK Publishing GBR. Dist: Pilgrim Pr., The/United Church Pr.
Haya-Prats, Gonzalo. Empowered Believers: The Holy Spirit in the Book of Acts. Elbert, Paul, ed. Ellington, Scott A., tr. from FRE. 2010. 316p. pap. 35.00 *(978-1-60899-778-7(2)*, Cascade Bks.) Wipf & Stock Pubs.
Hemer, Colin J. The Book of Acts in the Setting of Hellenistic History. Gempf, Conrad H., ed. 2008. 482p. 59.50 *(978-0-931464-58-4(7))* Eisenbrauns, Inc.
Henry, Matthew. Comentario Matthew Henry: Hechos: Matthew Henry's Commentary of Acts. (SPA.). 488p. *(978-84-7645-348-3(5)*, 223358) Clie, Editorial.
Hort, Fenton John Anthony. The Acts of the Apostles: Being the Greek Text as Revised by Drs Westcott & Hort. Westcott, Brooke Foss & Page, Thomas Ethelbert, eds. 2010. (Cambridge Library Collection - Religion Ser.). (ENG.). 288p. pap. 23.99 *(978-1-108-00750-4(3))* Cambridge Univ. Pr.
Ironside, Henry A. & Ironside, H. A. Acts. 2007. (Ironside Expository Commentaries Ser.). 368p. 24.99 *(978-0-8254-2917-0(X))* Kregel Pubns.
Jacobus, Melancthon. Notes, Critical & Explanatory, on the Acts of the Apostles. 2007. 436p. per. 32.00 *(978-1-59925-016-8(0))* Solid Ground Christian Bks.
Jay. New Testament Greek. 360p. 22.00 *(978-0-281-02806-1(0))* SPCK Publishing GBR. Dist: Pilgrim Pr., The/United Church Pr.
Johnson, Luke Timothy. The Acts of the Apostles. Harrington, Daniel J., ed. 2006. (Sacra Pagina Ser.). 570p. per. 39.95 *(978-0-8146-5968-7(3)*, Liturgical Pr. Bks.) Liturgical Pr.
Johnson, Luke Timothy. Prophetic Jesus, Prophetic Church: The Challenge of Luke-Acts to Contemporary Christians. 2011. 206p. pap. 23.00 ***(978-0-8028-0390-0(3))*** Eerdmans, William B. Publishing Co.
Kiraz, George A. The Acts of Saint George & the Story of his Father: From the Syriac & Garshuni Versions. 2007. (Texts from Christian Late Antiquity: 7). (SYR & ARA.). per. 36.00 *(978-1-59333-784-1(1))* Gorgias Pr., LLC.
Larkin, William J., Jr. Acts. 2011. (IVP New Testament Commentary Ser.: Volume 5). (ENG.). 422p. pap. 20.00 ***(978-0-8308-4005-2(2)***, IVP Acad.) InterVarsity Pr.
Lavender, Earl. Acts of the Apostles: Jesus Alive in His Church. 2007. (Meditative Commentary Ser.). 223p. per. 13.99 *(978-0-89112-501-3(9)*, Leafwood Pubs.) Abilene Christian Univ. Pr.
Lucado, Max. Book of Acts: Christ's Church in the World, 0 vols. 2006. (Inspirational Bible Study; Life Lessons with Max Lucado Ser.). 128p. per. 9.99 *(978-1-4185-0945-3(0))* Nelson, Thomas Inc.
Maclaren, Alexander. Expositions of Holy Scripture: The Acts. 2007. (ENG.). 660p. pap. 32.99 *(978-1-4264-2926-2(6))* 2006. 724p. pap. 35.99 *(978-1-4264-2979-8(7))* BiblioBazaar.
Marshall, I. Howard. Acts. 2008. (Tyndale New Testament Commentaries Ser.: Volume 5). (ENG., Illus.). 447p. pap. 17.00 *(978-0-8308-4235-3(7)*, IVP Acad.) 2007. (Tyndale New Testament Commentaries Ser.). 427p. per. 15.00 *(978-0-8308-2984-2(9))* InterVarsity Pr.
Martin, Francis, ed. Acts. 2006. (Ancient Christian Commentary on Scripture Ser.: New Testament Volume 5). (ENG.). 394p. 50.00 *(978-0-8308-1490-9(6)*, IVP Acad.) InterVarsity Pr.
Meadows, James L. Acts. Vol. I. pap. 5.50 *(978-0-89098-393-5(3))* Vol. II. pap. 5.50 *(978-0-89098-394-2(1))* Twentieth Century Christian Bks.
Miller, J. r. & Miller, J. R. Paul's Message for Today. 2011. 126p. pap. 12.99 ***(978-1-61203-178-1(1))*** Bottom of the Hill Publishing.
Mitchell, Alison. Comings & Goings: Bible Discovery for Children. 2010. (XTB Ser.). 96p. (J). pap. *(978-1-873166-25-3(7))* Good Bk. Co.
Moore, Phil. Straight to the Heart of Acts: 60 Bite-Sized Insights, 1 vol. 2010. (Straight to the Heart Ser.). 272p. pap. 14.99 *(978-1-85424-989-0(4)*, Monarch Bks.) Lion Hudson PLC GBR. Dist: Kregel Pubns.
Page, Nick. The Big Story: What Actually Happens in the Bible. 2007. (ENG., Illus.). 128p. per. 14.99 *(978-1-85078-726-6(3))* Authentic Media.
Parsons, Mikeal C. Acts. 2008. (Paideia: Commentaries on the New Testament Ser.). (Illus.). 464p. (C). pap. 30.00 *(978-0-8010-3188-5(5))* Baker Academic.
Pervo, Richard I. Acts: A Commentary. Attridge, Harold W., ed. 2008. (Hermeneia Ser.). 800p. 85.00 *(978-0-8006-6045-1(5)*, Fortress Pr.) Augsburg Fortress, Pubs.
Peters, Rob. Evangel-Lies. 2007. 180p. per. 13.99 *(978-1-60266-051-9(4))* Xulon Pr., Inc.
Peterson, David G. The Acts of the Apostles. 2009. (Pillar New Testament Commentary Ser.). 846p. 65.00 *(978-0-8028-3731-8(X))* Eerdmans, William B. Publishing Co.
Ponessa, Joseph & Watson Manhardt, Laurie. Come & See: Acts & Letters. 2008. 218p. pap. 19.95 *(978-1-931018-51-7(0))* Emmaus Road Publishing.
RRaphael, Monir/ B., Sr. Coptic Language Analysis: The Book of the Acts of the Holy Apostles. 2007. (COP, ENG & ARA., Illus.). 320p. lib. bdg. 40.00 *(978-0-9760091-2-2(9)*, Coptic Language and History Bks.) Copts In.
Schnabel, Eckhard J. Acts, 1 vol. 2012. (ENG.). 1040p. 59.99 ***(978-0-310-24367-0(X))*** Zondervan.
Shauf, Scott. Theology as History, History as Theology: Paul in Ephesus in Acts 19 (Beihefte zur Zeitschrift far die neutestamentliche Wissenschaft und die Kunde der älteren Kirche Ser.). (ENG.). X, 377p. 255.00 ***(978-3-11-182501-4(9))*** De Gruyter, Walter Inc.
Sproul, R. C. Acts. 2010. (St. Andrew's Expository Commentary Ser.). 448p. 34.99 *(978-1-4335-2273-4(X))* Crossway.

St. Paul Coalition for Community Development Staff. The Epistles of Paul & Acts of the Apostles. Johnson, Suzanne E. & Waldrep, Mary Carolyn, eds. 2007. (Dover Thrift Editions Ser.). (ENG., Illus.). 208p. per. 3.50 *(978-0-486-46169-4(6))* Dover Pubns., Inc.

Tyndale House Publishers Staff, prod. Acts. 2008. (Life Application Bible Studies: NLT Ser.). (ENG.). 160p. pap. 7.99 *(978-1-4143-2562-0(2))* Tyndale Hse. Pubs.

Wagner, C. Peter. The Book of Acts: A Commentary. 3rd ed. 2008. (ENG.). 504p. pap. 22.99 *(978-0-8307-4595-1(5))* Gospel Light Pubns.

Walton, Steve, et al. Reading Acts Today. Walton, Steve et al, eds. 2011. (Library of New Testament Studies). (ENG.). 256p. 120.00 *(978-0-567-23813-9(X),* T&T Clark Int'l) Continuum International Publishing Group, Ltd. GBR. Dist: National Bk. Network.

Whedon's Commentary on Acts, Romans, Vol. 3. 25.99 *(978-0-88019-125-8(2))* Schmul Publishing Co., Inc.

White, Ellen G. The Acts of the Apostles. 2010. 642p. pap. 45.75 *(978-1-145-00130-5(0))* BiblioBazaar.

—The Acts of the Apostles in the Proclamation of the Gospel of Jesus Christ. 2009. 456p. pap. *(978-0-217-56901-9(3))* Books LLC.

—The Acts of the Apostles in the Proclamation of the Gospel of Jesus Christ. 2007. (ENG.). 628p. 60.95 *(978-0-548-02728-8(5))* Kessinger Publishing, LLC.

Wiersbe, Warren W. Acts - Put Your Faith Where the Action Is. 2010. (Wiersbe Bible Study Ser.). (ENG.). 144p. pap. 8.99 *(978-0-7814-0422-8(3))* Cook, David C.

—Be Daring (Acts 13-28) Put Your Faith Where the Action Is, 1 vol. 2009. (BE Ser. Commentary Ser.). (ENG.). 176p. pap. 12.99 *(978-1-4347-6742-4(6))* Cook, David C.

—Be Dynamic (Acts 1-12) Experience the Power of God's People, 1 vol. 2009. (BE Ser. Commentary Ser.). (ENG.). 192p. pap. 12.99 *(978-1-4347-6746-2(9))* Cook, David C.

Willimon, William H. Acts: Interpretation: A Bible Commentary for Teaching & Preaching. 2010. (Interpretation Ser.). (ENG.). 216p. pap. 25.00 *(978-0-664-23625-0(1))* Westminster John Knox Pr.

Wood, George O. Hechos del Espiritu Santo-Manual del Estudiante. McGhee, Quentin, ed. Segura, Sara & Segura, Maritza, trs. from ENG. 4th ed. 2011. Orig. Title: Acts of the Holy Spirit. (SPA., Illus.). spiral bd. 25.00 *(978-1-931984-44-7(1),* 4413-16S0) Faith & Action Team.

Wright, Jr. Acts for Everyone Part 1. 2008. *(978-0-281-05308-7(1))* Westminster John Knox Pr.

Wright, N. T. Acts for Everyone. 2008. (New Testament Commentary Ser.). (ENG., Illus.). Pt. 1. 212p. per. 16.00 *(978-0-664-22795-1(3))*Pt. 2. 268p. per. 16.00 *(978-0-664-22796-8(1))* Westminster John Knox Pr.

Yandian, Bob & Noble, Linda. Acts, Pt. 1. *(978-1-885600-12-7(7))* Bob Yandian Ministries.

Yoccou, Raul C. Comentario Biblico Continente Nuevo: Hechos I.Tr. of New Continent Bible Commentary: Acts I. (SPA.). 5.99 *(978-1-56063-989-3(X),* 498642) Editorial Unilit.

BIBLE—COMMENTARIES—N. T. CATHOLIC EPISTLES

Here are entered commentaries on the Catholic Epistles as a whole, as well as on one or more of the following Epistles: James, John, Jude, Peter.

Andrews, Jack A. Understanding James. 2007. 236p. per. 24.95 *(978-1-4241-7389-1(2))* PublishAmerica, Inc.

Arnold, Clinton E. Zondervan Illustrated Bible Backgrounds Commentary 1 2 Peter 1 2, 1 vol. 2007. (Zondervan Illustrated Bible Backgrounds Commentary Ser.). (ENG., Illus.). 144p. (gr. 13). pap. 14.99 *(978-0-310-27824-5(4))* Zondervan.

—Zondervan Illustrated Bible Backgrounds Commentary Hebrews James, 1 vol. 2007. (Zondervan Illustrated Bible Backgrounds Commentary Ser.). (ENG., Illus.). 144p. (gr. 13). pap. 14.99 *(978-0-310-27826-9(0))* Zondervan.

Augustine, Saint. Homilies on the First Epistle of John Part III: Tractatus in Epistolam Joannis Ad Parthos I/14. Doyle, Daniel E. & Martin, Thomas, eds. Ramsey, Boniface, tr. from LAT. 2008. (Works of Saint Augustine). 173p. lib. bdg. 27.00 *(978-1-56548-288-3(3))* New City Pr.

Baldwin, Clinton S. The So-Called Mixed Text: An Examination of the Non-Alexandrian & Non-Byzantine Text-Type in the Catholic Epistles. 2011. ***(978-1-4331-0755-9(4))*** Lang, Peter GmbH, Europaischer Verlag der Wissenschaften.

Barnes, Albert. Notes, Explanatory & Practical, on the General Epistles of James, Peter, John & Jude by Albert Barnes. 2006. 464p. per. 29.99 *(978-1-4255-5130-8(0))* MPublishing.

Bateman, Herbert W., IV & Bateman IV, Herbert W. A Workbook for Intermediate Greek: Grammar, Exegesis, & Commentary on 1-3 John, 1 vol. 2008. (Illus.). 614p. pap. 28.99 *(978-0-8254-2149-5(7))* Kregel Pubns.

Beeke, Joel. The Epistles of John. 2006. 250p. per. *(978-0-85234-633-4(6))* Evangelical Pr.

Blomberg, Craig, et al. Zondervan Esegetical Commentary on the New Testament James Vol 16, 1 vol. 2008. (Zondervan Exegetical Commentary on the New Testament Ser.: Vol. 16). (ENG.). 288p. 24.99 *(978-0-310-24402-8(1))* Zondervan.

Boice, James Montgomery. The Epistles of John. 2006. (Expositional Commentary Ser.). 192p. pap. 16.99 *(978-0-8010-6642-9(5))* Baker Bks.

Braune, Karl F. C. The Epistles General of John: An Exegetical & Doctrinal Commentary. Lange, John Peter & Schaff, Philip, eds. Mombert, J. Isidor, tr. 2007. (Lange's Commentary on the Holy Scripture: Ser.). 202p. pap. 22.00 *(978-1-55635-401-4(0),* Wipf and Stock) Wipf & Stock Pubs.

Burk, Dorsey, compiled by. Epistles. 2011. ***(978-0-7577-4218-7(1))*** Word Aflame Pr.

Butler, John G. Joshua to II Samuel. 830p. ***(978-1-889773-73-5(5))*** LBC Pubns.

Buxbaum, J. G. The Light Was in the World: The New Matthew Henry Commentary on the Gospel of John, Book 2, Chapters 7-12. 2008. 356p. pap. 15.95 *(978-1-4327-3371-1(0))* Outskirts Pr., Inc.

Caldwell, Chris. James: Gaining True Wisdom. 2011. ***(978-0-9823842-4-4(6))*** Smyth & Helwys Publishing, Inc.

Case, David & Holdren, David W. 1-2 Peter, 1-3 John, Jude: A Commentary for Bible Students. 2006. (Illus.). 383p. 18.99 *(978-0-89827-306-9(4))* Wesleyan Publishing Hse.

Conner, Kevin J. The Epistle of Jude: An Exposition. 127p. pap. *(978-0-949829-72-6(2))* Acacia Pr.

Cundall, Arthur Ernest, et al. Judges & Ruth. 2008. (Tyndale Old Testament Commentaries Ser.: Volume 7). (ENG., Illus.). 307p. pap. 16.00 *(978-0-8308-4207-0(1),* IVP Acad.) InterVarsity Pr.

Dana, H. E. The Epistles & Apocalypse of John: A Brief Commentary. 2011. 160p. 41.95 ***(978-1-258-05666-7(6))*** Literary Licensing, LLC.

Davids, Peter H. The Letters of 2 Peter & Jude. 2006. (Pillar New Testament Commentary Ser.). (Illus.). 348p. 34.00 *(978-0-8028-3726-4(3))* Eerdmans, William B. Publishing Co.

Delitzsch, Franz. Commentary on the Epistle to the Hebrews. 2010. 420p. pap. 34.75 *(978-1-171-91069-5(X))* 2010. (ENG.). 512p. pap. 39.75 *(978-1-176-58570-6(3))* 2009. 502p. 36.99 *(978-1-116-71257-5(1))* 2009. 502p. 43.99 *(978-1-116-71256-8(3))* 2009. 502p. pap. 39.75 *(978-1-116-71258-2(X))* 2009. 502p. pap. 38.75 *(978-1-116-71259-9(8))* 2009. (ENG.). 501p. pap. 31.99 *(978-1-116-71260-5(1),* BiblioLife) 2009. (ENG.). 501p. pap. 30.99 *(978-1-116-71261-2(X),* BiblioLife) BiblioBazaar.

—Commentary on the Epistle to the Hebrews. 2009. 323p. pap. *(978-1-151-17358-4(4))* Books LLC.

—Commentary on the Epistle to the Hebrews. 2010. 312p. pap. 33.10 *(978-1-151-98854-6(5));* 272p. pap. 35.16 *(978-1-152-52710-2(X))* General Bks. LLC.

DeVries, William C. James: Living on the Edge. I.t. ed. 5.25 *(978-1-56212-658-2(X),* 150091) Faith Alive Christian Resources.

Discover Jesus in John: Who He Is. (Discover Your Bible Ser.). (KOR.). pap., tchr. ed. 6.95 *(978-1-55883-216-9(5),* 600155); pap., stu. ed. 4.25 *(978-1-55883-213-8(0),* 600150) C R C World Literature Ministries/Libros Desafio.

Discover Jesus in John: Who He Is. (Discover Your Bible Ser.). pap., stu. ed. 4.25 *(978-1-56212-156-3(1),* 152340) Faith Alive Christian Resources.

Donelson, Lewis R. I & II Peter & Jude: A Commentary. 2010. (New Testament Library). (ENG.). 336p. 40.00 *(978-0-664-22138-6(6))* Westminster John Knox Pr.

Doriani, Daniel M. James. 2007. (Reformed Expository Commentary Ser.). 220p. 19.99 *(978-0-87552-785-7(X))* P & R Publishing.

Eaton, Michael. 1 Peter. (Preaching Through the Bible Ser.). 125p. pap. *(978-1-85240-245-7(8))* Sovereign World, Ltd.

Ellenburg, B. Dale & Morgan, Christopher W. James: Wisdom for the Community. 2008. (Focus on the Bible Ser.). (ENG.). 272p. pap. 14.99 *(978-1-84550-335-2(X))* Christian Focus Pubns. GBR. Dist: STL Distribution North America.

Elliott, John H. The Elect & the Holy: An Exegetical Examination of 1 Peter 2:4-10 & the Phrase Basileion Hierateuma. 2006. 274p. pap. 27.00 *(978-1-59752-410-0(7),* Wipf and Stock) Wipf & Stock Pubs.

Everett, Randel. The Letters of James & John: Real Faith. 2010. 136p. pap. *(978-1-934731-55-0(2))* Baptistway.

Farley, Lawrence. Universal Truth: The Catholic Epistles of James, Peter, Jude, & John. 2009. (Orthodox Bible Study Companion Ser.). 232p. pap. 15.95 *(978-1-888212-60-0(8))* Conciliar Pr.

Feldmeier, Reinhard. The First Letter of Peter: A Commentary on the Greek Text. 2008. 265p. pap. 34.95 *(978-1-60258-024-4(3))* Baylor Univ. Pr.

Fishcer, Mary Jane. Praying with Peter, Volume 2: Exciting Insights into the Words of First Peter. 2007. 132p. pap. 10.99 *(978-1-58169-239-6(0),* Gazelle Pr.) Genesis Communications, Inc.

Foster, Paul. The Gospel of Peter: Critical Edition, Introduction & Commentary. 2010. (Texts & Editions for New Testament Study Ser.). (Illus.). xvi, 555p. *(978-90-04-18094-9(X))* BRILL.

Fronmuller, G. F. C. The Epistles General of Peter & the Epistle General of Jude: An Exegetical & Doctrinal Commentary. Mombert, J. Isisdor, tr. 2007. (Lange's Commentary on the Holy Scripture: Ser.). 183p. pap. 20.00 *(978-1-55635-400-7(2),* Wipf and Stock) Wipf & Stock Pubs.

General Epistles. (People's Bible Commentary Ser.). 352p. 15.99 *(978-0-7586-0452-1(1))* Concordia Publishing Hse.

Giese, Curtis P. 2 Peter & Jude. 2012. ***(978-0-7586-0696-9(6))*** Concordia Publishing Hse.

Green, Gene L. Jude & 2 Peter. 2008. (Baker Exegetical Commentary on the New Testament Ser.). (Illus.). 448p. (C). 39.99 *(978-0-8010-2672-0(5))* Baker Academic.

Green, Joel B. 1 Peter. 2007. (T Wo Horizons New Testament Commentary Ser.). 331p. per. 20.00 *(978-0-8028-2553-7(2))* Eerdmans, William B. Publishing Co.

Green, Michael. 2 Peter & Jude, 1 vol. (ENG.). 2009. (Tyndale New Testament Commentaries Ser.: Volume 18). 221p. pap. 16.00 *(978-0-8308-4248-3(9),* IVP Acad.) 2007. (Tyndale New Testament Commentaries Ser.). 208p. per. 14.00 *(978-0-8308-2997-2(0))* InterVarsity Pr.

Greenlee, J. Harold. Exegetical Summary of James. 2nd ed. 2008. 214p. pap. 28.00 *(978-1-55671-195-4(6))* SIL International.

—Exegetical Summary of Jude. 2nd ed. 2008. 82p. pap. 15.00 *(978-1-55671-190-9(5))* SIL International.

Group Publishing, creator. 1 Peter: Standing Firm in Jesus. 2006. (Illus.). 95p. pap. 9.99 *(978-0-7644-3245-3(1),* Group) Group Publishing, Inc.

Harink, Douglas. 1 & 2 Peter, 1 vol. 2009. (ENG.). 240p. (C). 29.99 *(978-1-58743-097-8(5))* Brazos Pr.

Hartin, Patrick J. James: (Sacra Pagina Series) 2009. 336p. pap. 39.95 *(978-0-8146-5975-5(6))* Liturgical Pr.

Harvey, Robert & Towner, Philip H. 2 Peter & Jude. (IVP New Testament Commentary Ser.: Volume 18). (ENG.). 249p. 2011. pap. 17.00 ***(978-0-8308-4018-2(4))*** 2009. 20.00 *(978-0-8308-1818-1(9))* InterVarsity Pr. (IVP Acad.).

Hebreos, Santiago, 1 y 2 Pedro, Judas. (Comentario Biblico Mundo Hispano Ser.: Vol. 23).Tr. of Hebrews, James, 1 & 2 Peter, Jude. (SPA.). pap. 10.99 *(978-0-311-03123-8(4),* Editorial Mundo Hispano) Casa Bautista de Publicaciones.

Helm, David R. 1 & 2 Peter & Jude: Sharing Christ's Sufferings. Griffin, Ted, ed. 2008. (Preaching the Word Ser.). 416p. 29.99 *(978-1-58134-960-3(2))* Crossway.

Hiebert, D. Edmond. James. 2006. 348p. per. 17.99 *(978-0-88469-253-9(1))* BMH Bks.

—1 Peter. 2006. 369p. per. 17.99 *(978-0-88469-252-2(3))* BMH Bks.

Hodge, Charles. Commentary on the Epistle to the Romans. 2009. 456p. pap. *(978-1-150-43552-2(6))* Books LLC.

—Commentary on the Epistle to the Romans. 2006. pap. 38.99 *(978-1-4255-6898-6(X))* MPublishing.

—An Exposition of the First Epistle to the Corinthians. 400p. 2009. pap. 33.75 *(978-1-117-57885-9(2))* 2008. 29.99 *(978-0-559-83153-9(6))* 2008. pap. 33.75 *(978-0-559-83151-5(X))* BiblioBazaar.

—An Exposition of the First Epistle to the Corinthians. 2009. 282p. pap. 22.72 *(978-1-150-64122-0(3))* General Bks. LLC.

—An Exposition of the First Epistle to the Corinthians. 2008. 400p. 49.95 *(978-1-4369-9273-2(7));* pap. 34.95 *(978-1-4367-7292-1(3))* Kessinger Publishing, LLC.

Holloway, Gary. Letters of Peter, John & Jude: Living in Jesus. 2008. (Meditative Commentary Ser.). 96p. pap. 8.99 *(978-0-89112-557-0(4),* Leafwood Pubs.) Abilene Christian Univ. Pr.

—Meditative Commentary Series: Hebrews & James: Brother Jesus. 2007. (Meditative Commentary Ser.). 111p. pap. 11.99 *(978-0-89112-505-1(1),* Leafwood Pubs.) Abilene Christian Univ. Pr.

Hort, Fenton John Anthony, ed. The Epistle of St. James: The Greek Text with Introduction, Commentary as Far as Chapter IV, Verse 7, & Additional Notes. 2009. (Cambridge Library Collection - Religion Ser.). (ENG.). 164p. pap. 19.99 *(978-1-108-00753-5(8))* Cambridge Univ. Pr.

Hough, J. W. The Mode of Baptism; a Discourse Delivered in the First Congregational Church, of Jackson, Mich , April 18, 1869, & Repeated April 25 1869. 2011. 30p. pap. 11.99 ***(978-1-4181-9380-5(1))*** MPublishing

Hughes, R. Kent. Philippians: The Fellowship of the Gospel. 2007. (Preaching the Word Ser.). 240p. 24.99 *(978-1-58134-954-2(8))* Crossway.

Hultin, Jeremy. 2 Peter & Jude Hermeneia. 2019. (Hermeneia Ser.). *(978-0-8006-6103-8(6))* Augsburg Fortress, Pubs.

Ironside, H. A. James & 1 & 2 Peter, 1 vol. 2008. (Ironside Expository Commentaries Ser.). 128p. 18.99 *(978-0-8254-2928-6(5))* Kregel Pubns.

Jarman, Mark. Epistles. 2007. 112p. 21.95 *(978-978-193-251-9(1))* Sarabande Bks., Inc.

Jobes, Karen H. Letters to the Church: A Survey of Hebrews & the General Epistles, 1 vol. 2011. (ENG.). 448p. 44.99 *(978-0-310-26738-6(2))* Zondervan.

John Brown Of Edinburgh. Exposition of First Peter. 2008. 744p. pap. 46.99 *(978-1-58960-133-8(5))* Sovereign Grace Pubs., Inc.

Jowett, John Henry. The Epistles of Saint Peter. 2010. 122.24 *(978-1-61719-470-2(0))* Gorgias Pr., LLC.

Kelly, W. Lectures on the Epistle of Jude. 6.95 *(978-0-88172-101-0(8))* Believers Bookshelf, Inc.

Knight, George R. Exploring the Letters of John & Jude: A Devotional Commentary. 2009. 285p. pap. 17.99 *(978-0-8280-2444-0(8))* Review & Herald Publishing Assn.

Kostenberger, Andreas J. A Theology of John's Gospel & Letters: The Word, the Christ, the Son of God, 1 vol. 2009. (Biblical Theology of the New Testament Ser.). (ENG.). 656p. 39.99 *(978-0-310-26986-1(5))* Zondervan.

Lee, Witness. The Holy Word for Morning Revival: Crystallization-study of 1 & 2 Peter & Judy, Vol. 1. 2008. (ENG.). per. 5.50 *(978-0-7363-3618-5(4));* per. 5.50 *(978-0-7363-3617-8(6))* Living Stream Ministry.

—The Holy Word for Morning Revival: Crystallization-study of the Epistles of John, Vol. 1. 2007. per. 5.50 *(978-0-7363-3501-0(3))* Living Stream Ministry.

—The Holy Word for Morning Revival: Crystallization-Study of the Epistles of John, Vol. 2. 2007. per. 5.50 *(978-0-7363-3502-7(1))* Living Stream Ministry.

Lieu, Judith. I, II & III John: A Commentary. 2008. (New Testament Library). (ENG.). 336p. 50.00 *(978-0-664-22098-3(3))* Westminster John Knox Pr.

Lifetogether. James. 2011. (Deepening Life Together Ser.). (Illus.). 121p. pap. 8.99 *(978-0-8010-6869-0(X))* Baker Bks.

Lightner, Robert Paul. Solid Stepping Stones for the Christian's Journey. 2011. pap. *(978-1-60265-034-3(9))* Grace Acres Pr.

Lillie, John. Lectures on the First & Second Epistles of Peter. 2009. 552p. pap. 41.75 *(978-1-117-66878-9(9))* BiblioBazaar.

Lopez, Diane D. Por el amor de Dios: Guia de Estudio. 2010. (SPA.). pap. 3.00 ***(978-1-933663-44-9(8),*** WD/GBGM Bks.) General Board of Global Ministries, The United Methodist Church.

Lucado, Max. Book of James: Practical Wisdom, 0 vols. 2007. (Inspirational Bible Study; Life Lessons with Max Lucado Ser.). (Illus.). 128p. per. 9.99 *(978-1-4185-0956-9(6))* Nelson, Thomas Inc.

Marberry, Thomas, et al. 1, 2, 3 John & Revelation. 2010. vii, 503p. ***(978-0-89265-537-3(2))*** Randall Hse. Pubns.

Marshall, I. Howard. 1 Peter. 2011. (IVP New Testament Commentary Ser.: Volume 17). (ENG.). 184p. pap. 17.00 *(978-0-8308-4017-5(6),* IVP Acad.) InterVarsity Pr.

Martin, Harold S. Brethren New Testament Commentary - Galatians. Martin, Harold S., ed. 2008. (ENG.). 140p. 12.00 *(978-0-9777766-1-0(1))* Brethren Revival Fellowship.

McCartney, Dan G. James, 1 vol. 2009. (Baker Exegetical Commentary on the New Testament Ser.). (ENG., Illus.). 268p. (C). 39.99 *(978-0-8010-2676-8(8))* Baker Academic.

McCullar, Michael D. Annual Bible Study: James. 2011. ***(978-1-57312-604-5(7))*** Smyth & Helwys Publishing, Inc.

McDermond, Jay. Epistles of 1, 2, 3 John. 2011. pap. *(978-0-8361-9555-2(8))* Herald Pr.

McKnight, Scot. The Letter of James (NICNT) 2010. 536p. 55.00 *(978-0-8028-2627-5(X))* Eerdmans, William B. Publishing Co.

Mead, Patrick. Expository Nuggets from 1 Peter. 2008. 48p. pap. 8.95 *(978-0-615-20068-2(0))* Machaira Touch Ministries, Inc.

Meadows, James L. James, I & II Peter. pap. 5.50 *(978-0-89098-408-6(5))* Twentieth Century Christian Bks.

Moloney, Francis J. James to Jude: A Guide for Reflection & Prayer. 2007. (Daily Bible Commentary Ser.: Vol. 12). 170p. per. 12.95 *(978-1-59856-196-8(0))* Hendrickson Pubs. Marketing, LLC.

Moo, Douglas J. James, 1 vol. (ENG.). 2009. (Tyndale New Testament Commentaries Ser.: Volume 16). 196p. pap. 16.00 *(978-0-8308-4246-9(2),* IVP Acad.) 2007. (Tyndale New Testament Commentaries Ser.). 191p. per. 14.00 *(978-0-8308-2995-8(4))* InterVarsity Pr.

Mueller, Ekkehardt. The Letters of John. 2009. 6.97 *(978-0-8163-2333-3(X))* Pacific Pr. Publishing Assn.

Nash, Robert N. Embracing the Word of God. 2009. 63p. pap. *(978-0-9823842-6-8(2))* NextSunday Resources.

Painter, John. 1, 2, & 3 John (Sacra Pagina) 2008. 416p. pap. 29.95 *(978-0-8146-5973-1(X))* Liturgical Pr.

Pentecost, J. Dwight. The Joy of Fellowship: A Study of First John. 2007. 144p. pap. 10.99 *(978-0-8254-3468-6(8))* Kregel Pubns.

Perkins, Pheme. First & Second Peter, James, & Jude: Interpretation: A Bible Commentary for Teaching & Preaching. 2012. (Interpretation: A Bible Commentary for Teaching & Preaching Ser.). (ENG.). 218p. pap. 25.00 ***(978-0-664-23867-4(X))*** Westminster John Knox Pr.

Perkins, Tyrone C. A Commentary on James. pap. 9.95 *(978-1-56794-175-3(3),* C-2516) Star Bible & Tract Corp.

—A Commentary on the Epistles of John. 91p. pap. 9.95 *(978-1-56794-180-7(X),* C-2524) Star Bible & Tract Corp.

Plummer, A. Epistles of St. John. 2010. (ENG.). 254p. pap. 23.99 *(978-0-521-14111-6(7))* Cambridge Univ. Pr.

Plummer, Alfred. The General Epistles of Saint James & Saint Jude. 2010. 138.32 *(978-1-61719-402-3(6))* Gorgias Pr., LLC.

Qualls, Charles. Sessions with 1, 2, & 3 John & Jude: God's Abiding Words for an Active Faith. 2009. pap. *(978-1-57312-535-2(0))* Smyth & Helwys Publishing, Inc.

Rathmann, Rodney L. 1 Peter & 1 John. (LifeLight Bible Studies: Course 9). stu. ed. 0.55 incl. audio *(978-0-570-09277-3(9),* 20-2284) Concordia Publishing Hse.

Reese, Ruth Anne. 2 Peter & Jude. 2007. (Two Horizons New Testament Commentary Ser.). 232p. pap. 20.00 *(978-0-8028-2570-4(2))* Eerdmans, William B. Publishing Co.

Robinson, James McConkey. The Secrets of Judas: The Story of the Misunderstood Disciple & His Lost Gospel. 2007. (Illus.). 272p. per. 13.95 *(978-0-06-117064-5(X),* HarperOne) HarperCollins Pubs.

Rochedieu, C. Comentario Practico - Epistolas, Vol. III: Practical Comment. III - Epist. (SPA.). 264p. *(978-84-7228-567-5(7),* 220127) Clie, Editorial.

Saarinen, Risto. The Pastoral Epistles with Philemon & Jude. 2008. (Brazos Theological Commentary on the Bible Ser.). 272p. (C). 29.99 *(978-1-58743-154-8(8))* Brazos Pr.

Schoffstall, Robert O. Reflections on the Gospel of John: That You May Believe & on the First Epistle of John That You Ma. 2007. 123p. pap. 11.95 *(978-0-7414-3779-2(1))* Infinity Publishing.

Senior, Donald & Harrington, Daniel, eds. 1 Peter, Jude & 2 Peter (Sacra Pagina) 2008. 336p. pap. 29.95 *(978-0-8146-5976-2(4))* Liturgical Pr.

Shaw, Linda. James & 1 & 2 Peter: Lessons of Faith at Work. McCullough, Jeannie, ed. 2006. (Wisdom of the Word Ser.). (ENG.). 104p. spiral bd. 14.99 *(978-0-8341-2299-4(5),* 083-412-2995) Beacon Hill Pr. of Kansas City.

Shelly, Rubel. Something to Hold on To: Studies in First & Second Peter. pap., tchr. ed. 7.99 *(978-0-89098-087-3(X));* pap., stu. ed. 7.99 *(978-0-89098-026-2(8))* Twentieth Century Christian Bks.

—What Christian Living Is All About: Studies in James. pap. 7.99 *(978-0-89098-023-1(3))* Twentieth Century Christian Bks.

Smith, D. Moody. First, Second, & Third John: Interpretation - A Bible Commentary for Teaching & Preaching. 2012. (Interpretation: A Bible Commentary for

Teaching & Preaching Ser.). (ENG.). 174p. pap. 25.00 **(978-0-664-23871-1(8))** Westminster John Knox Pr.

Sproul, R. C. 1-2 Peter. 2011. (St. Andrew's Expositional Commentary Ser.). 304p. 27.99 *(978-1-4335-2289-5(6))* Crossway.

Strauss, Mark, et al. Hebrews Thru Revelation Vol. 12: Wisdom for Today-And Forever. 2008. (QuickNotes Commentaries Ser.: Vol. 12). (ENG.). 240p. pap. 9.99 *(978-1-59789-778-5(7)*, Barbour Bks.) Barbour Publishing, Inc.

Swindoll, Charles R. Insights on James, 1 & 2 Peter, 1 vol. 2010. (Swindoll's New Testament Insights Ser.). (ENG.). 336p. 25.99 *(978-0-310-28432-1(5))* Zondervan.

Thomas Nelson Publishing Staff. The Chronological Study Bible, 0 vols. 2009. 1728p. 74.99 *(978-1-4185-4251-1(2))* Nelson, Thomas Inc.

Thompson, Marianne Meye. 1-3 John. 2011. (IVP New Testament Commentary Ser.: Volume 19). (ENG.). 168p. pap. 16.00 **(978-0-8308-4019-9(2)**, IVP Acad.) InterVarsity Pr.

Tyndale House Publishers Staff, prod. James. 2008. (Life Application Bible Studies: NLT Ser.). (ENG.). 96p. pap. 7.99 *(978-1-4143-2560-6(6))* Tyndale Hse. Pubs.

Vinson, Richard Bolling, et al. 1 & 2 Peter: Jude. 2010. *(978-1-57312-565-9(2))* Smyth & Helwys Publishing, Inc.

Von Wahlde, Urban C. A Commentary on the Gospel & Letters of John, 3 vols. 2010. 752p. 60.00 *(978-0-8028-0991-9(X))* Eerdmans, William B. Publishing Co.

Walker, Neville Earl. Making Wise the Simple: Behaviors, Attitudes & Principles of the Body of Christ. 2007. 456p. per. 29.95 *(978-1-4120-9616-4(2))* Trafford Publishing.

Warden, Duane. 1 & 2 Peter & Jude. Cloer, Eddie, ed. 2009. 526p. 29.95 *(978-0-9818128-4-7(8))* Resource Pubns.

Waterbury, Deb. James on the Mount: A Bible Study on the Book of James & the Sermon on the Mount. 2008. pap. 13.99 *(978-1-60477-670-6(6))* Xulon Pr., Inc.

Westcott, Brooke Foss, intro. The Epistles of Saint John. 2010. pap. 67.72 *(978-1-61719-743-7(2))* Gorgias Pr., LLC.

Wiersbe, Warren W. Be Alert (2 Peter, 2 & 3 John, Jude) Beware of the Religious Impostors, 1 vol. 2010. (BE Series Commentary Ser.). (ENG.). 208p. pap. 12.99 *(978-1-4347-6504-8(0))* Cook, David C.

—Be Hopeful (1 Peter) How to Make the Best of Times Out of Your Worst of Times, 1 vol. 2009. (BE Ser. Commentary Ser.). (ENG.). 176p. pap. 12.99 *(978-1-4347-6743-1(4))* Cook, David C.

—Be Real (1 John) Turning from Hypocrisy to Truth, 1 vol. 2009. (BE Ser. Commentary Ser.). (ENG.). 192p. pap. 12.99 *(978-1-4347-6744-8(2))* Cook, David C.

—James: Growing up in Christ. 2007. (Wiersbe Bible Study Ser.). (ENG.). 128p. per. 8.99 *(978-0-7814-4571-9(X))* Cook, David C.

William Wake, Archbishop. The Forbidden Books - the Suppressed Gospels & Epistles of the Original New Testament - HARDBACK. 2007. 601p. 56.50 *(978-1-84799-915-3(8))* Lulu Enterprises Inc.

Witherington, Ben, III. Letters & Homilies for Hellenized Christians Vol. 1: A Socio-Rhetorical Commentary on Titus, 1-2 Timothy & 1-3 John. 2006. (Letters & Homilies for Hellenized Christians Ser.). (ENG.). 623p. 40.00 *(978-0-8308-2931-6(8)*, IVP Acad.) InterVarsity Pr.

—Letters & Homilies for Hellenized Christians Vol. 2: A Socio-Rhetorical Commentary on 1-2 Peter. 2008. (Letters & Homilies for Hellenized Christians Ser.). (ENG.). 432p. 35.00 *(978-0-8308-2933-0(4)*, IVP Acad.) InterVarsity Pr.

Woolever & González, Catherine Gunsalus. 1 & 2 Peter & Jude: A Theological Commentary on the Bible. 2011. (Belief: a Theological Commentary on the Bible Ser.). (ENG.). 272p. 30.00 *(978-0-664-23202-3(7))* Westminster John Knox Pr.

Zanchettin, Leo. The Church Moves Out: A Devotional Commentary on the Catholic Epistles. 2006. (New Testament Devotional Commentary Ser.). 184p. per. 16.00 *(978-1-59325-082-9(7))* Word Among Us Pr.

BIBLE—COMMENTARIES—N. T. COLOSSIANS

Allen, Earl E. The Book of Colossians. 2007. 85p. tchr. ed., spiral bd. *(978-1-878766-80-9(5))*; stu. ed., spiral bd. *(978-1-878766-81-6(3))* Miracle Pubns. International, Inc.

Arnold, Clinton E. Ephesians, Philippians, Colossians, Philemon, 1 vol. 2007. (Zondervan Illustrated Bible Backgrounds Commentary Ser.). (ENG., Illus.). 128p. (gr. 13). pap. 14.99 *(978-0-310-27827-6(9))* Zondervan.

Arthur, J. Philip, ed. Christ All-Sufficient: Colossians & Philemon Simply Explained. 2007. (Welwyn Commentary Ser.). (Illus.). 240p. per. *(978-0-85234-655-6(7))* Evangelical Pr.

Beet, J. Agar. Ephesians, Philippians, Colossians & Philemon. pap. 12.99 *(978-0-88019-058-9(2))* Schmul Publishing Co., Inc.

Beetham, Christopher. Echoes of Scripture in the Letter of Paul to the Colossians. 2008. (Biblical Interpretation Ser.). 362p. (C). *(978-90-04-17081-0(2))* BRILL.

Beetham, Christopher A. Echoes of Scripture in the Letter of Paul to the Colossians. 2010. *(978-1-58983-499-6(2))* Society of Biblical Literature.

Bird, Michael. Colossians & Philemon. Bird, Michael & Keener, Craig S., eds. 2009. (New Covenant Commentary Ser.). 192p. pap. 22.00 *(978-1-60608-131-0(4)*, Cascade Bks.) Wipf & Stock Pubs.

Bird, Michael F. Colossians & Philemon. 2011. (New Testament at Crossway College Ser.). (ENG.). 192p. pap. 30.25 *(978-0-7188-9237-1(2))* Lutherworth Pr., The GBR. Dist: Printondemand-worldwide.com.

Buffard, Percy J. Colosenses: Colossians. (SPA.). *(978-84-7645-258-5(6)*, 223321) Clie, Editorial.

Cassady, David. Colossians: Living the Faith Faithfully. 2009. pap. *(978-0-9823842-8-2(9))* NextSunday Resources.

Eadie, John. A Commentary on the Greek Text of the Epistle of Paul to the Colossians. 2009. 358p. 29.99 *(978-1-116-47293-6(7))*; pap. 31.75 *(978-1-116-47295-0(3))*; 38.99 *(978-1-116-47292-9(9))*; pap. 32.75 *(978-1-116-47294-3(5))* BiblioBazaar.

—A Commentary on the Greek Text of the Epistle of Paul to the Colossians. 2008. 372p. 48.95 *(978-1-4369-8458-4(0))*; pap. 33.95 *(978-1-4367-2174-5(1))* Kessinger Publishing, LLC.

Frank, Nicole. Der Kolosserbrief im Kontext des paulinischen Erbes: Eine intertextuelle Studie zur Auslegung und Fortschreibung der Paulustradition. 2009. (GER.). 423p. pap. 157.50 *(978-3-16-150118-0(7))* Mohr Siebeck GmbH & Co. KG DEU. Dist: Coronet Bks.

Galatians - Philippians - Colossians. ldr.'s ed. (LifeLight Ser.). pap. 7.50 *(978-0-570-07854-8(7)*, 20-3316) Concordia Publishing Hse.

George, Elizabeth. Embracing God's Grace: Colossians/Philemon. 2010. (Woman after God's Own Heart Ser.). 176p. pap. 8.99 *(978-0-7369-1246-4(0))* Harvest Hse. Pubs.

González, Justo L. Three Months with Paul. 2006. (Three Months With Ser.). 171p. per. 11.50 *(978-0-687-49539-9(3))* Abingdon Pr.

Guzik, David. Philippians & Colossians Commentary. 2008. 128p. pap. 12.99 *(978-1-56599-029-6(3))* Yahshua Publishing.

Hack, Keith. Colossians 3 Principle. 2006. pap. 9.99 *(978-1-60034-776-4(2))* Xulon Pr., Inc.

Hoehner, Harold W., et al. Ephesians, Philippians, 1-2 Thessalonians Colossians, Philemon. 2008. (Cornerstone Biblical Commentary Ser.: 16). (ENG.). 456p. 29.99 *(978-0-8423-8344-8(1))* Tyndale Hse. Pubs.

Houghton, John. The Letter to the Colossians: In Christ Alone. 2006. 72p. *(978-1-85345-405-9(2))* Crusade for World Revival.

Hughes, Bill. Studying Colossians. 5.99 *(978-0-89098-151-1(5))* Twentieth Century Christian Bks.

Ironside, Henry A. & Ironside, H. A. Philippians & Colossians. 2007. (Ironside Expository Commentaries Ser.). 216p. 19.99 *(978-0-8254-2920-0(X))* Kregel Pubns.

Lavender, Earl. Meditative Commentary Series: Ephesians, Philippians, Colossians, Philemon: Jesus above All. 2008. (Meditative Commentary Ser.). 144p. pap. 9.99 *(978-0-89112-561-7(2)*, Leafwood Pubs.) Abilene Christian Univ. Pr.

MacDonald, Margaret Y. Sacra Pagina: Colossians & Ephesians. 2008. 424p. pap. 34.95 *(978-0-8146-5978-6(0)*, Liturgical Pr. Bks.) Liturgical Pr.

Martin, Ralph P. Ephesians, Colossians, & Philemon: Interpretation: A Bible Commentary for Teaching & Preaching. 2012. (Interpretation: A Bible Commentary for Teaching & Preaching Ser.). (ENG.). 172p. pap. 25.00 **(978-0-664-23861-2(0))** Westminster John Knox Pr.

Maxwell, Marcus. Ephesians to Colossians & Philemon: A Guide for Reflection & Prayer. 2007. (Daily Bible Commentary Ser.). 277p. per. 12.95 *(978-1-59856-194-4(4))* Hendrickson Pubs. Marketing, LLC.

Meadows, James L. Colossians & Philemon. pap. 5.50 *(978-0-89098-399-7(2))* Twentieth Century Christian Bks.

Meynell, Mark. Colossians: Confident Christianity: Six Studies for Individuals or Groups. 2010. (Good Book Guides). 48p. (YA). pap. *(978-1-906334-24-6(2))* Good Bk. Co.

Moo, Douglas J. The Letters to the Colossians & to Philemon. 2008. (Pillar New Testament Commentary Ser.). 504p. 44.00 *(978-0-8028-3727-1(1))* Eerdmans, William B. Publishing Co.

Nielson, Kathleen Buswell. Colossians & Philemon: Contiue to Live in Him. 2007. (Living Word Bible Studies). 124p. spiral bd. *(978-1-59638-073-8(X))* P & R Publishing.

Storms, Sam. The Hope of Glory: 100 Daily Meditations on Colossians. 2008. 368p. pap. 17.99 *(978-1-58134-931-3(9))* Crossway.

Strauss, Mark, et al. Galatians Thru Philemon Vol. 11: Putting Faith into Practice. 2008. (QuickNotes Commentaries Ser.). (ENG.). 224p. pap. 9.99 *(978-1-59789-777-8(9)*, Barbour Bks.) Barbour Publishing, Inc.

Sumney, Jerry L. Colossians: A Commentary. 2008. (New Testament Library). (ENG.). 344p. 50.00 *(978-0-664-22142-3(4))* Westminster John Knox Pr.

Talbert, Charles H. Ephesians & Colossians. 2007. (Paideia: Commentaries on the New Testament Ser.). (Illus.). 320p. (C). pap. 30.00 *(978-0-8010-3128-1(1))* Baker Academic.

Taylor Williams, Debbie. If God Is in Control, Why Am I a Basket Case? Extraordinary Choices for a JoyFilled Life. rev. ed. 2011. (ENG.). 224p. pap. 14.99 **(978-1-59669-337-1(1))** New Hope Pubs.

Thurston, Bonnie Bowman. Reading Colossians, Ephesians, & 2 Thessalonians. 2008. *(978-1-57312-500-0(8))* Smyth & Helwys Publishing, Inc.

Tyndale House Publishers Staff, prod. Philippians & Colossians. 2009. (Life Application Bible Studies: NLT Ser.). (ENG.). 112p. pap. 7.99 *(978-1-4143-2645-0(9))* Tyndale Hse. Pubs.

Wall, Robert W. Colossians & Philemon. 2010. (IVP New Testament Commentary Ser.: Volume 12). (ENG.). 225p. pap. 18.00 *(978-0-8308-4012-0(5)*, IVP Acad.) InterVarsity Pr.

Westcott, Frederick Brooke. Colossians: A Letter to Asia. 2007. 210p. pap. 22.00 *(978-1-55635-169-3(0)*, Wipf and Stock) Wipf & Stock Pubs.

Wiersbe, Warren W. Be Complete: Become the Whole Person God Intends You to Be. 2008. (Be Ser.). (ENG.). 176p. pap. 12.99 *(978-1-4347-6780-6(9))* Cook, David C.

Wilson, Earle L., et al. Galatians, Philippians, Colossians: A Commentary for Bible Students. 2007. (Illus.). 352p. *(978-0-89827-307-6(2))* Wesleyan Publishing Hse.

Witherington, Ben, III. The Letters to Philemon, the Colossians, & the Ephesians: A Socio-Rhetorical Commentary on the Captivity Epistles. 2007. 382p. per. 38.00 *(978-0-8028-2488-2(9))* Eerdmans, William B. Publishing Co.

Wright, N. T. Colossians & Philemon, 1 vol. 2009. (N. T. Wright for Everyone Bible Study Guides). (ENG.). 62p. pap. 8.00 *(978-0-8308-2192-1(9)*, IVP Conn.) 2008. (Tyndale New Testament Commentaries Ser.: Volume 12). (ENG.). 199p. pap. 16.00 *(978-0-8308-4242-1(X)*, IVP Acad.) 2007. (Tyndale New Testament Commentaries Ser.). 192p. per. 14.00 *(978-0-8308-2991-0(1))* InterVarsity Pr.

BIBLE—COMMENTARIES—N. T. CORINTHIANS

Ambrosiaster. Commentaries on Romans & 1-2 Corinthians, 1 vol. 2009. (Ancient Christian Texts). (ENG.). 300p. 60.00 *(978-0-8308-2903-3(2)*, IVP Acad.) InterVarsity Pr.

Artz-Grabner, Peter. 1. Korinther: Papyrologische Kommentare zum Neuen Testament. 2006. (Papyrologische Kommentare zum Neuen Testament Ser.: Vol. 2). (GER.). 576p. (C). 144.00 *(978-3-525-51001-8(2))* Vandenhoeck & Ruprecht GmbH & Co. KG DEU. Dist: ISD.

Baker, William, et al. 1 & 2 Corinthians. 2009. (Cornerstone Biblical Commentary Ser.: 15). (ENG.). 400p. 29.99 *(978-0-8423-8343-1(3))* Tyndale Hse. Pubs.

Belchen, Richard P. Teaching Helps in II Corinthians. 38p. pap. 6.95 *(978-0-925703-15-6(X))* Crown Pubns., Inc.

Bensly, R. L. & Kennett, Robert H., eds. The Epistles of S. Clement to the Corinthians in Syriac. 2010. (SYR.). pap. 27.52 *(978-1-61143-610-5(9))* Gorgias Pr., LLC.

Bensly, Robert L. & Kennett, Robert H., eds. The Epistles of Saint Clement to the Corinthians. 2010. (SYR.). pap. 23.68 *(978-1-61143-406-4(8))* Gorgias Pr., LLC.

Best, Ernest. Second Corinthians: Interpretation: A Bible Commentary for Teaching & Preaching. 2012. (Interpretation: A Bible Commentary for Teaching & Preaching Ser.). (ENG.). 160p. pap. 25.00 **(978-0-664-23612-0(X))** Westminster John Knox Pr.

Bieringer, R., et al. 2 Corinthians: A Bibliography. 2008. (Biblical Tools & Studies). (ENG.). 372p. (C). 113.00 *(978-90-429-2000-2(9))* Peeters Pubs. & Booksellers BEL. Dist: Brown, David Bk. Co., The.

Blank, R. Spanish Commentry on 1st. Corinthians /Primera carta a los Corintos. 2010. 400p. 24.99 *(978-0-7586-2593-6(9))* Concordia Publishing Hse.

Bray, Gerald L., ed. 1-2 Corinthians. 2nd rev. ed. 2006. (Ancient Christian Commentary on Scripture Ser.: New Testament Volume 7). (ENG.). 372p. 50.00 *(978-0-8308-2492-2(8)*, IVP Acad.) InterVarsity Pr.

Canclini, A. Comentario Biblico Continente Nuevo: I Corintios.Tr. of New Continent Bible Commentary: I Corinthians. (SPA.). 276p. 9.99 *(978-0-7899-0159-0(5)*, 498645) Editorial Unilit.

Carroll, B. H. Comentario Carroll-Diez: Tes-Corintios: Carroll's Commentary 10: Corinthians. (SPA.). *(978-84-7645-219-6(5)*, 223265) Clie, Editorial.

Carson, D. A. A Model of Christian Maturity: An Exposition of 2 Corinthians 10-13. 2007. 192p. pap. 15.00 *(978-0-8010-6768-6(5))* Baker Bks.

Carter, Christopher L. The Great Sermon Tradition as a Fiscal Framework in 1 Corinthians: Towards a Pauline Theology of Material Possessions. 2010. (Library of New Testament Studies, the Ser.). (ENG.). 288p. 130.00 *(978-0-567-47304-2(X)*, T&T Clark Int'l) Continuum International Publishing Group, Ltd. GBR. Dist: National Bk. Network.

Carver, Frank G. NBBC, 2 Corinthians: A Commentary in the Wesleyan Tradition. 2009. (ENG.). 384p. pap. 34.99 *(978-0-8341-2396-0(7)*, 9780834123960) Beacon Hill Pr. of Kansas City.

Chrysostom, John. The Love Chapter: The Meaning of First Corinthians 13. 2009. (ENG.). 112p. (gr. 13). pap. 12.99 *(978-1-55725-668-3(3))* Paraclete Pr., Inc.

Ciampa, Roy E. The First Letter to the Corinthians (PNTC) 2010. 65.00 *(978-0-8028-3732-5(8))* Eerdmans, William B. Publishing Co.

Collins, Raymond F. First Corinthians. Harrington, Daniel J., ed. 2006. (Sacra Pagina Ser.). 703p. per. 39.95 *(978-0-8146-5970-0(5))* Liturgical Pr.

Crewdson, Robert Henry. Church Unity: And the Corinthian Correspondence. 2008. 96p. pap. 12.95 *(978-0-9820172-1-0(9))* Mariner Publishing.

Eaton, Michael. 1 Corinthians, 10-16. (Preaching Through the Bible Ser.). 125p. pap. *(978-1-85240-290-7(3))* Sovereign World, Ltd.

Fitzmyer, J. & Fitzmyer, Joseph A. First Corinthians: A New Translation with Introduction & Commentary. 2008. (Anchor Yale Bible Commentaries Ser.). (ENG., Illus.). 688p. 55.00 *(978-0-300-14044-6(4))* Yale Univ. Pr.

Fitzmyer, Joseph A. First Corinthians. 2007. 800p. 50.00 *(978-0-385-50166-8(8))* Knopf Doubleday Publishing Group.

Grogan, Geoffrey. 2 Corinthians: The Glories & Responsibilities of Christian Service. 2007. (Focus on the Bible Ser.). (ENG.). 336p. stu. ed., per. 15.99 *(978-1-84550-252-2(3))* Christian Focus Pubns. GBR. Dist: STL Distribution North America.

Guide to 1 Corinthians. 3.00 *(978-0-687-85450-9(4))* Abingdon Pr.

Hays, Richard B. First Corinthians: Interpretation: A Bible Commentary for Teaching & Preaching. 2011. (Interpretation Ser.). (ENG.). 320p. pap. 25.00 *(978-0-664-23440-9(2))* Westminster John Knox Pr.

Henry, Matthew. Comentario Matthew Henry: Dos Corintios: II Corintios. (SPA.). *(978-84-7645-368-1(X)*, 223357) Clie, Editorial.

Hodge, Charles. An Exposition of the First Epistle to the Corinthians by Charles Hodge. 2006. 408p. per. 26.99 *(978-1-4255-4362-4(6))* MPublishing.

—An Exposition of the Second Epistle to the Corinthians by Charles Hodge. 2006. 320p. per. 23.99 *(978-1-4255-3157-7(1))* MPublishing.

Hole, Frank. Romans & Corinthians. 2007. 176p. (ENG.). *(978-0-901860-47-7(6))*; (Illus.). per. *(978-0-901860-43-9(3))* Scripture Truth Pubns.

Johnson, Alan F. 1 Corinthians. 2010. (IVP New Testament Commentary Ser.: Volume 7). (ENG.). 343p. pap. 19.00 *(978-0-8308-4007-6(9)*, IVP Acad.) InterVarsity Pr.

Kelly, W. Notes on First Corinthians. 9.95 *(978-0-88172-094-5(1))* Believers Bookshelf, Inc.

Kent, Homer A., Jr. A Heart Opened Wide: Studies in 2 Corinthians. 2nd ed. 2006. (Kent Collection). (Illus.). 217p. per. 14.99 *(978-0-88469-086-3(5))* BMH Bks.

King, Richard, et al. 1 Corinthians, 0 vols. 2008. (Encounters with God Ser.). 96p. pap. 9.99 *(978-1-4185-2644-3(4))* Nelson, Thomas Inc.

Kruse, Colin G. 2 Corinthians. (ENG.). 2008. (Tyndale New Testament Commentaries Ser.: Volume 8). 217p. pap. 16.00 *(978-0-8308-4238-4(1)*, IVP Acad.) 2007. (Tyndale New Testament Commentaries Ser.). 224p. per. 14.00 *(978-0-8308-2987-3(3))* InterVarsity Pr.

Lavender, Earl. Meditative Commentary Series: 1 & 2 Corinthians: Jesus, Cross, Church. 2008. (Meditative Commentary Ser.). 143p. pap. 11.99 *(978-0-89112-560-0(4)*, Leafwood Pubs.) Abilene Christian Univ. Pr.

Lockwood, Gregory J. Concordia Popular Commentary: 1 Corinthians. 2010. 24.99 *(978-0-7586-2545-8(6))* Concordia Publishing Hse.

Lull, David J. 1 Corinthians. 2007. 169p. per. 24.99 *(978-0-8272-0530-7(9))* Chalice Pr.

Maclaren, Alexander. Expositions of Holy Scripture (to II Corinthians Chapt. V) Romans Corinthians (to II Corinthians Chap. V) 2007. 662p. pap. 32.99 *(978-1-4264-7094-3(0))*; (ENG.). 726p. pap. 35.99 *(978-1-4264-7170-4(X))* BiblioBazaar.

Martin, Ralph. 2 Corinthians Word Biblical Co. 2009. 352p. 49.99 *(978-1-4185-0773-2(3))* Nelson, Thomas Inc.

Milligan, William. The Resurrection of the Dead: An Exposition of 1 Corinthians XV. 2009. 246p. pap. 21.00 *(978-1-60608-438-0(0)*, Wipf and Stock) Wipf & Stock Pubs.

Minor, Mitzi. Second Corinthians. 2009. *(978-1-57312-538-3(5))* Smyth & Helwys Publishing, Inc.

Mitchell, Dan. Book of Second Corinthians: Grace under Siege. Hindson, Ed & Couch, Mal, eds. 2008. (21st Century Biblical Commentary Ser.). (ENG.). 256p. 19.99 *(978-0-89957-824-8(1))* AMG Pubs.

Moore, Phil. Straight to the Heart of 1 & 2 Corinthians: 60 Bite-Sized Insights, 1 vol. 2011. (Straight to the Heart Ser.). 272p. pap. 14.99 *(978-0-85721-002-9(5)*, Monarch Bks.) Lion Hudson PLC GBR. Dist: Kregel Pubns.

Morgan, G. Campbell. The Corinthian Letters of Paul: An Exposition on I & II Corinthians. 2010. (G. Campbell Morgan Reprint Ser.). 278p. pap. 30.00 *(978-1-60899-288-1(8))* Wipf & Stock Pubs.

Morris, Leon L. 1 Corinthians. 2008. (Tyndale New Testament Commentaries Ser.: Volume 7). (ENG.). 238p. pap. 16.00 *(978-0-8308-4237-7(3)*, IVP Acad.) InterVarsity Pr.

Murphy, Joseph. Love Is Freedom. 2010. 98p. pap. 8.50 *(978-1-57898-913-3(2))* Martino Publishing.

Murphy-O'Connor, Jerome. Keys to Second Corinthians: Revisiting the Major Issues. 2010. (ENG., Illus.). 224p. 110.00 *(978-0-19-959210-4(1))* Oxford Univ. Pr., Inc.

Nash, Scott. First Corinthians. 2009. *(978-1-57312-082-1(0))* Smyth & Helwys Publishing, Inc.

O'Connor, Jerome Murphy. 1 Corinthians: A Guide for Reflection & Prayer. 2007. (Daily Bible Commentary Ser.). 199p. per. 12.95 *(978-1-59856-191-3(X))* Hendrickson Pubs. Marketing, LLC.

Ortberg, John, et al. 2 Corinthians, 1 vol. 2008. (New Community Bible Study Ser.). (ENG.). 96p. pap. 7.99 *(978-0-310-28054-5(0))* Zondervan.

Perrotta, Kevin. 2 Corinthians: Power in Weakness. Perrotta, Kevin, ed. 2006. (Catholic Perspectives Ser.). (ENG.). 88p. per. 7.95 *(978-0-8294-2326-6(5))* Loyola Pr.

Powers, B. Ward. First Corinthians: an Exegetical & Explanatory Commentary: A Somewhat Traditional Interpretation Plus Contemporary Application. 2008. 482p. pap. 49.00 *(978-1-55635-933-0(0)*, Wipf and Stock) Wipf & Stock Pubs.

Prime, Derek. Under God's Smile: The Trinitarian Blessing of 2 Corinthians 13:14. 2008. (Reflections (DayOne) Ser.). (Illus.). 122p. pap. *(978-1-84625-059-0(5))* DayOne Pubns.

Roberts, Richard. The Gospel at Corinth. 2011. 172p. 42.95 **(978-1-258-08367-0(1))** Literary Licensing, LLC.

Roetzel, Calvin J. 2 Corinthians. 2007. (Abingdon New Testament Commentaries Ser.). 189p. per. 24.00 *(978-0-687-05677-4(2))* Abingdon Pr.

Scott, Latayne C. To Love Each Other: 1 Corinthians - 13 Studied by Love's Principles Personified. pap. 7.99 *(978-0-89098-116-0(7))* Twentieth Century Christian Bks.

Spencer, Aida Besancon. 2 Corinthians: A Guide for Reflection & Prayer. 2007. (Daily Bible Commentary Ser.). 231p. per. 12.95 *(978-1-59856-192-0(8))* Hendrickson Pubs. Marketing, LLC.

Spillman, James R. The Fire of God: The Gifts of the Spirit: Available & Active. 2nd ed. 2006. 281p. spiral bd. 29.95 *(978-0-9767811-4-1(X)*, True Potential) True Potential Publishing, Inc.

Stegman, Thomas D. Second Corinthians, 1 vol. 2009. (Catholic Commentary on Sacred Scripture Ser.). (ENG.). 336p. (C). pap. 19.99 *(978-0-8010-3583-8(X))* Baker Academic.

Storms, Sam. A Sincere & Pure Devotion to Christ: 100 Daily Meditations on 2 Corinthians. 2010. 240p. pap. 25.99 *(978-1-4335-1311-4(0))* Crossway.

Strachan, R. H. The Second Epistle of Paul to the Corinthians. 2008. 160p. pap. 14.00 *(978-1-60608-066-5(0))* Wipf & Stock Pubs.

Taiwo, Moses. Paul's Rhetoric in 1 Corinthians: 29b-30. 2008. 244p. pap. *(978-3-639-01048-0(5))* VDM Verlag Dr. Mueller e.K.

Thiselton, Anthony C. First Corinthians: A Shorter Exegetical & Pastoral Commentary. 2006. (Illus.). 325p. 30.00 *(978-0-8028-2682-4(2))* Eerdmans, William B. Publishing Co.

Vogel, Manuel. Commentatio mortis: 2Kor 5,1-1- auf dem Hintergrund antiker ars moriendi. 2006. (Forschungen Zur Religion und Literatur des Alten & Neuen Testament Ser.: Vol. 214). (GER.). 408p. (C). 119.00 *(978-3-525-53078-8(1))* Vandenhoeck & Ruprecht GmbH & Co. KG DEU. Dist: ISD.

Walls, Anne & Heseman, Dottie. 1 Corinthians. 2007. (ENG.). 144p. spiral bd. 23.99 *(978-1-932017-31-1(3))* Joy of Living Bible Studies.

Whedon's Commentary on First Corinthians, Vol. 4. 25.99 *(978-0-88019-126-5(0))* Schmul Publishing Co., Inc.

Wiersbe, Warren W. Be Encouraged (2 Corinthians) God Can Turn Your Trials into Triumphs, 1 vol. 2010. (BE Series Commentary Ser.). (ENG.). 176p. pap. 12.99 *(978-1-4347-6633-5(0))* Cook, David C.

—Be Wise (1 Corinthians) Discern the Difference Between Man's Knowledge & God's Wisdom, 1 vol. 2010. (BE Series Commentary Ser.). (ENG.). 192p. pap. 12.99 *(978-1-4347-6636-6(5))* Cook, David C.

Wolff, Christian. Der erste Brief des Paulus an die Korinther. 3rd rev. ed. 2011. (Theologischer Handkommentar zum Neuen Testament Ser.). (GER.). 450p. (C). 55.00 ***(978-3-374-01622-8(7))*** Evangelische Verlagsanstalt GmbH DEU. Dist: Brown, David Bk. Co., The.

—Der zweite Brief des Paulus an die Korinther. 3rd rev. ed. 2011. (Theologischer Handkommentar zum Neuen Testament Ser.). (GER.). 304p. (C). 61.00 ***(978-3-374-00857-5(7))*** Evangelische Verlagsanstalt GmbH DEU. Dist: Brown, David Bk. Co., The.

1 Corinthians. (LifeLight Bible Studies: Course 20). stu. ed. 5.50 *(978-0-570-09430-2(5)*, 20-2551); 6.50 *(978-0-570-09429-6(1)*, 20-2550) Concordia Publishing Hse.

2 Corinthians 5: 17 Bulletin, Regular Size. 4.50 *(978-0-687-04170-1(8))* Abingdon Pr.

BIBLE—COMMENTARIES—N. T. EPHESIANS

Allen, Earl E. The Book of Ephesians. 2007. 97p. tchr. ed., spiral bd. *(978-1-878766-72-4(4))*; stu. ed., spiral bd. *(978-1-878766-73-1(2))* Miracle Pubns. International, Inc.

Arnold, Clinton E. Ephesians, 1 vol. 2010. (Zondervan Exegetical Commentary on the New Testament Ser.). (ENG.). 544p. 36.99 *(978-0-310-24373-1(4))* Zondervan.

—Ephesians, Philippians, Colossians, Philemon, 1 vol. 2007. (Zondervan Illustrated Bible Backgrounds Commentary Ser.). (ENG., Illus.). 128p. (gr. 13). pap. 14.99 *(978-0-310-27827-6(9))* Zondervan.

Baker Publishing Group Staff & Life Together Staff. Ephesians, 1 vol. 2009. (Deepening Life Together Ser.). 96p. pap. 8.99 *(978-0-8010-6845-4(2))* Baker Bks.

Beet, J. Agar. Ephesians, Philippians, Colossians & Philemon. pap. 12.99 *(978-0-88019-058-9(2))* Schmul Publishing Co., Inc.

Brannon, M. Jeff. The Heavenlies in Ephesians: A Lexical, Exegetical, & Conceptual Analysis. 2012. (Library of New Testament Studies). (ENG.). 272p. 110.00 *(978-0-567-57741-2(4)*, T&T Clark Int'l) Continuum International Publishing Group, Ltd. GBR. Dist: National Bk. Network.

Braune, Karl. The Epistle of Paul to the Ephesians: An Exegetical & Doctrinal Commentary. Lange, John Peter & Schaff, Philip, eds. Riddle, M. B., tr. 2007. (Lange's Commentary on the Holy Scripture: Ser.). 236p. pap. 24.00 *(978-1-55635-410-6(X)*, Wipf and Stock) Wipf & Stock Pubs.

Callahan, Robert B. The Triune God Speaks to the Saints: An Expository Commentary Based upon PaulÕs Letter to the Ephesians. 2011. (Walking with Jesus Ser.). 294p. pap. 32.00 ***(978-1-60899-645-2(X)***, Resource Pubns.) Wipf & Stock Pubs.

Chapell, Bryan. Ephesians. 2009. *(978-1-59638-016-5(0))* P & R Publishing.

Chrysostom, John & Copeland, William John. Commentary on Galatians & Homilies on Ephesians. 2010. pap. 65.80 *(978-1-61143-364-7(9))* Gorgias Pr., LLC.

Cohick, Lynn H. Ephesians. 2011. (ENG.). pap. 32.00 *(978-0-7188-9239-5(9))* Lutherworth Pr., The GBR. Dist: Brown, David Bk. Co., The.

Cripe, Earl. Grace & Glory: A Commentary on Ephesians. 2009. 336p. 28.49 *(978-1-4490-4094-9(2))*; pap. 17.99 *(978-1-4490-4095-6(0))* AuthorHouse.

Custer, Stewart. In the Heavenlies: A Commentary on Ephesians. 2008. *(978-1-59166-831-2(X))* BJU Pr.

Eaton, Michael. Ephesians. (Preaching Through the Bible Ser.). 125p. pap. *(978-1-85240-310-2(1))* Sovereign World, Ltd.

Ephesians: A Map to Your Incredible. Date not set. pap. *(978-0-87162-502-1(4))* Warner Pr. Pubs.

Ephesians 1 & 2 Thessalonians. ldr.'s ed. (LifeLight Bible Studies: Course 18). 6.50 *(978-0-570-09423-4(2)*, 20-2540) Concordia Publishing Hse.

Foulkes, Francis. Ephesians, 1 vol. 2008. (Tyndale New Testament Commentaries Ser.: Volume 10). (ENG.). 187p. pap. 16.00 *(978-0-8308-4240-7(3)*, IVP Acad.) InterVarsity Pr.

Fowl, Stephen E. Ephesians: A Commentary. 2012. (New Testament Library). (ENG.). 280p. 40.00 ***(978-0-664-22125-6(4))*** Westminster John Knox Pr.

Galatians, Ephesians. (People's Bible Commentary Ser.). 222p. pap. 10.99 *(978-0-570-05324-8(2)*, 12-8050) Concordia Publishing Hse.

Gardner, Paul. Ephesians: Grace & Joy in Christ. 2007. (Focus on the Bible Commentaries Ser.). (ENG.). 192p. per. 14.99 *(978-1-84550-264-5(7))* Christian Focus Pubns. GBR. Dist: STL Distribution North America.

González, Justo L. Three Months with Paul. 2006. (Three Months With Ser.). 171p. per. 11.50 *(978-0-687-49539-9(3))* Abingdon Pr.

Guzik, David. Galatians & Ephesians Commentary. 2007. 220p. per. 12.99 *(978-1-56599-034-0(X))* Yahshua Publishing.

Hodge, Charles. A Commentary on the Epistle to the Ephesians by Charles Hodge. 2006. 412p. per. 26.99 *(978-1-4255-4384-6(7))* MPublishing.

Hoehner, Harold W., et al. Ephesians, Philippians, 1-2 Thessalonians Colossians, Philemon. 2008. (Cornerstone Biblical Commentary Ser.: 16). (ENG.). 456p. 29.99 *(978-0-8423-8344-8(1))* Tyndale Hse. Pubs.

Howell, Sarah L. Ephesians: Finding True Love. 2008. (Heart Stealers Bible Studies). (ENG.). 160p. (gr. 11). per. 12.99 *(978-0-89957-111-9(5))* AMG Pubs.

Ironside, Henry A. & Ironside, H. A. Ephesians. 2007. (Ironside Expository Commentaries Ser.). 192p. 19.99 *(978-0-8254-2918-7(8))* Kregel Pubns.

Julien, Tom. Inherited Wealth: Studies in Ephesians. 2006. 141p. per. 7.99 *(978-0-88469-034-4(2))* BMH Bks.

Lathrop, John P. Apostles, Prophets, Evangelists, Pastors, & Teachers Then & Now. 2008. 152p. pap. 13.99 *(978-1-60647-459-4(6))* Xulon Pr., Inc.

Lavender, Earl. Meditative Commentary Series: Ephesians, Philippians, Colossians, Philemon: Jesus above All. 2008. (Meditative Commentary Ser.). 144p. pap. 9.99 *(978-0-89112-561-7(2)*, Leafwood Pubs.) Abilene Christian Univ. Pr.

Liefeld, Walter L. Ephesians. 2010. (IVP New Testament Commentary Ser.: Volume 10). (ENG.). 178p. pap. 16.00 *(978-0-8308-4010-6(9)*, IVP Acad.) InterVarsity Pr.

Lockhart, Jay & Roper, David L. Ephesians & Philippians. 2009. (Truth for Today Commentary Ser.). 610p. 29.95 *(978-0-9818128-2-3(1))* Resource Pubns.

Longman, Tremper, III. The Expositor's Bible Commentary, 1 vol., Vol. 12. rev. ed. 2008. (Expositor's Bible Commentary Ser.). (ENG.). 864p. 39.99 *(978-0-310-26893-2(1))* Zondervan.

MacDonald, Margaret Y. Sacra Pagina: Colossians & Ephesians. 2008. 424p. pap. 34.95 *(978-0-8146-5978-6(0)*, Liturgical Pr. Bks.) Liturgical Pr.

Martin, Ralph P. Ephesians, Colossians, & Philemon: Interpretation: A Bible Commentary for Teaching & Preaching. 2012. (Interpretation: A Bible Commentary for Teaching & Preaching Ser.). (ENG.). 172p. pap. 25.00 ***(978-0-664-23861-2(0))*** Westminster John Knox Pr.

Masopust, William. The Letter to the Ephesians: A Commentary. 2008. 96p. pap. 12.00 *(978-0-615-23901-9(3))* Masopust, William.

Maxwell, Marcus. Ephesians to Colossians & Philemon: A Guide for Reflection & Prayer. 2007. (Daily Bible Commentary Ser.). 277p. per. 12.95 *(978-1-59856-194-4(4))* Hendrickson Pubs. Marketing, LLC.

Meadows, James L. Ephesians & Philippians. pap. 5.50 *(978-0-89098-398-0(4))* Twentieth Century Christian Bks.

Meyer, F. b. & Meyer, F. B. Devotional Commentary of Ephesians. 2011. 80p. pap. 9.99 ***(978-1-61203-265-8(6))*** Bottom of the Hill Publishing.

M'Ghee, Robert J. Expository Lectures on the Epistle to the Ephesians. 2006. 656p. per. 36.99 *(978-1-4255-6703-3(7))* MPublishing.

Paden, Gerald. Ephesians in Spanish. 2007. 144p. pap. 12.99 *(978-0-9796369-1-2(4))* Sunset Institute Pr.

Pattison, Robert E. An Exposition of the Epistle to the Ephesians. 2011. (ENG.). 264p. 25.00 ***(978-1-888514-38-4(8))*** Particular Baptist Pr.

Perkins, Tyrone C. A Commentary on the Books of Galatians, Ephesians, Philippians. 112p. pap. 9.95 *(978-1-56794-202-6(4)*, C-2555) Star Bible & Tract Corp.

Peterson, Eugene H. Practice Resurrection: A Conversation on Growing up in Christ. 2010. 272p. 24.00 *(978-0-8028-2955-9(4))* Eerdmans, William B. Publishing Co.

Phillips, Richard D. Saved by Grace: The Glory of Salvation in Ephesians 2. 2009. pap. *(978-1-59638-127-8(2))* P & R Publishing.

Phillips, Tanya D. A Journey Back to Eden: Life as God Designed It. 2010. 64p. pap. 15.99 *(978-1-4500-6039-4(0))* Xlibris Corp.

Scott, Byron J. The Mystery of God's Will: Living the Christian Life as Seen in Ephesians. 2007. 136p. per. 10.95 *(978-1-4327-0444-5(3))* Outskirts Pr., Inc.

Seiferth, Jackie. Discipline & Discovery Series: Exploring Ephesians: No Subtitle. 2008. 192p. pap. 13.99 *(978-1-60647-591-1(6))* Xulon Pr., Inc.

Slater, Thomas B. Ephesians. 2012. ***(978-1-57312-624-3(1))*** Smyth & Helwys Publishing, Inc.

Snodgrass, Klyne, et al. Ephesians, 1 vol. 2008. (Bringing the Bible to Life Ser.). (ENG.). 96p. pap. 7.99 *(978-0-310-27654-8(3))* Zondervan.

Stott, John. Ephesians: Building a Community in Christ. 2008. (John Stott Bible Studies). (ENG.). 64p. pap. 8.00 *(978-0-8308-2163-1(5)*, IVP Conn.) InterVarsity Pr.

Strauss, Lehman. Galatians & Ephesians. 2010. 248p. pap. *(978-1-926765-17-4(6))* Gospel Folio Pr.

Strauss, Mark, et al. Galatians Thru Philemon Vol. 11: Putting Faith into Practice. 2008. (QuickNotes Commentaries Ser.). (ENG.). 224p. pap. 9.99 *(978-1-59789-777-8(9)*, Barbour Bks.) Barbour Publishing, Inc.

Swindoll, Charles R. Insights on Galatians & Ephesians, 1 vol. 2012. (Swindoll's New Testament Insights Ser.). (ENG.). 400p. 25.99 ***(978-0-310-28443-7(0))*** Zondervan.

Talbert, Charles H. Ephesians & Colossians. 2007. (Paideia: Commentaries on the New Testament Ser.). (Illus.). 320p. (C). pap. 30.00 *(978-0-8010-3128-1(1))* Baker Academic.

Thurston, Bonnie Bowman. Reading Colossians, Ephesians, & 2 Thessalonians. 2008. *(978-1-57312-500-0(8))* Smyth & Helwys Publishing, Inc.

Tyndale House Publishers Staff, prod. Galatians & Ephesians. 2009. (Life Application Bible Studies: NLT Ser.). (ENG.). 120p. pap. 7.99 *(978-1-4143-2644-3(0))* Tyndale Hse. Pubs.

Verhey, Allen & Harvard, Joseph S. Ephesians: A Theological Commentary on the Bible. 2011. (Belief: a Theological Commentary on the Bible Ser.). (ENG., Illus.). 208p. 35.00 *(978-0-664-23266-5(3))* Westminster John Knox Pr.

Wickham, Pablo. La Biblia y Su Mensaje - Efesios: The Bible & Its Message - Ephesians. (SPA.). 160p. *(978-84-7228-689-4(4)*, 223176) Clie, Ecitorial.

Wiersbe, Warren W. Be Rich (Ephesians) Gaining the Things That Money Can't Buy 2009. (Be Series Commentary Ser.). (ENG.). 192p. pap. 12.99 *(978-1-4347-6732-5(9))* Cook, David C.

Williamson, Peter S. Ephesians, 1 vol. 2009. (Catholic Commentary on Sacred Scripture Ser.). (ENG.). 208p. (C). pap. 19.99 *(978-0-8010-3584-5(8))* Baker Academic.

Witherington, Ben, III. The Letters to Philemon, the Colossians, & the Ephesians: A Socio-Rhetorical Commentary on the Captivity Epistles. 2007. 382p. per. 38.00 *(978-0-8028-2488-2(9))* Eerdmans, William B. Publishing Co.

Witmer, John & Couch, Mal. The Books of Galatians & Ephesians: By Grace Through Faith. Hindson, Ed, ed. 2009. (Twenty-First Century Biblical Commentary Ser.). (ENG.). 256p. 19.99 *(978-0-89957-817-0(9))* AMG Pubs.

BIBLE—COMMENTARIES—N. T. EPISTLES OF JOHN

see Bible—Commentaries—N. T. Catholic Epistles

BIBLE—COMMENTARIES—N. T. EPISTLES OF PAUL

Aageson, James W. Paul, the Pastoral Epistles, & the Early Church. Porter, Stanley E., ed. 2008. (Library of Pauline Studies). 235p. per. *(978-1-59856-041-1(7))* Hendrickson Pubs. Marketing, LLC.

Adamczewski, Bartosz. Heirs of the Reunited Church: The History of the Pauline Mission in Paul's Letters, in the So-Called Pastoral Letters, & in the Pseudo-Titus Narrative of Acts. 2010. 178p. 57.95 *(978-3-631-60504-2(8))* Lang, Peter GmbH, Europaischer Verlag der Wissenschaften DEU. Dist: Lang, Peter.

Adeyemi, Femi. The New Covenant Torah in Jeremiah & the Law of Christ in Paul. 2006. (Studies in Biblical Literature: Vol. 94). (C). 81.95 *(978-0-8204-8137-1(8))* Lang, Peter Publishing, Inc.

Akenson, Donald H. Saint Saul: A Skeleton Key to the Historical Jesus. (ENG.). 360p. pap. *(978-0-7735-2395-1(2))* McGill-Queen's Univ. Pr.

Ambrosiaster & Intervarsity Press. Commentaries on Galatians — Philemon, 1 vol. 2009. (Ancient Christian Texts). (ENG.). 188p. 60.00 *(978-0-8308-2904-0(0)*, IVP Acad.) InterVarsity Pr.

Anderson Scott, Charles A. Christianity According to St Paul. 2009. (ENG.). 300p. pap. 38.99 *(978-0-521-10061-8(5))* Cambridge Univ. Pr.

Aquinas, Thomas. Commentaries on St. Paul's Epistles to Timothy, Titus, & Philemon. Baer, Chrysostom, tr. from LAT. 2008. 234p. (C). 60.00 *(978-1-58731-128-4(3))* St. Augustine's Pr., Inc.

—Commentaries on St. Paul's Epistles to Timothy, Titus, & Philemon. Baer, O.Praem., Chrysostom, tr. from LAT. 2008. 234p. pap. 28.00 *(978-1-58731-129-1(1))* St. Augustine's Pr., Inc.

Bandy, Owen. The Glory & the Covenants: The Old & New Covenants According to the Apostle Paul. 2009. (Illus.). 165p. pap. 14.95 *(978-1-4327-3624-8(8))* Outskirts Pr., Inc.

Bardwell, H. B. Pablo: Su Vida & Sus Epistolas: Paul: His Life & Epistles, 1 vol. 2008. (SPA.). 368p. pap. 14.99 *(978-84-7645-283-7(7)*, 223337) Clie, Editorial ESP. Dist: Zondervan.

Barnes, Albert. Romans Notes, Explanatory & Practical on the Epistle to the Romans by Albert Barnes. 2006. 332p. per. 23.99 *(978-1-4255-3304-5(3))* MPublishing.

Barnett, Albert Edward. The Letters of Paul. 2011. 160p. 41.95 ***(978-1-258-05057-3(9))*** Literary Licensing, LLC.

Barrett, C. K. Paul. (Outstanding Christian Thinkers Ser.). 180p. pap. *(978-0-8264-5611-3(1))* Continuum International Publishing Group, Ltd.

Bassler, Jouette M. Navigating Paul: An Introduction to Key Theological Concepts. 2006. (ENG.). 139p. per. 20.00 *(978-0-664-22741-8(4))* Westminster John Knox Pr.

Bohlen, Maren. Sanctorum Communio: Die Christen Als "Heilige" Bei Paulus. 2011. (Beihefte zur Zeitschrift far die neutestamentliche Wissenschaft und die Kunde der älteren Kirche Ser.). (GER.). XIV, 285p. 140.00 *(978-3-11-025948-3(6))* De Gruyter, Walter Inc.

Bordwine, James E. The Pauline Doctrine of Male Headship: The Apostle Versus Biblical Feminists. 2009. 334p. pap. 37.00 *(978-1-60608-568-4(9)*, Wipf and Stock) Wipf & Stock Pubs.

Brenk, Frederick E. With Unperfumed Voice: Studies in Plutarch, in Greek Literature, Religion & Philosophy, & in the New Testament Background. 2007. (Potsdamer Altertumswissenschaftliche Beitrage (PAwB) Ser.). (ENG., Illus.). 544p. (C). pap. 128.00 *(978-3-515-08929-6(2))* Steiner, Franz Verlag Wiesbaden GmbH DEU. Dist: Brown, David Bk. Co., The.

Breton, Stanislas. A Radical Philosophy of Saint Paul. Ballan, Joseph N., tr. from FRE. 2011. (Insurrections: Critical Studies in Religion, Politics, & Culture Ser.). (ENG.). 184p. (gr. 17). 84.50 ***(978-0-231-15104-7(7))***; pap. 26.50 ***(978-0-231-15105-4(5))*** Columbia Univ. Pr.

Breytenbach, Cilliers & Du Toit, David S., eds. Focusing on Paul: Persuasion & Theological Design in Romans & Galatians. 2007. (Beihefte Zur Zeitschrift Für Die Neutestamentliche Wissenschaft und Die Kunde der älteren Kirche Ser.). (ENG., Illus.). XIV, 443p. 154.00 *(978-3-11-019512-5(7))* De Gruyter, Walter Inc.

Breytenbach, Cilliers & du Toit, David S., eds. Focusing on Paul: Persuasion & Theological Design in Romans & Galatians. (Beihefte zur Zeitschrift far die neutestamentliche Wissenschaft und die Kunde der älteren Kirche Ser.). (ENG.). XIV, 443p. 255.00 ***(978-3-11-185305-5(5))*** De Gruyter, Walter Inc.

Brown, Emma Mitchell. Has God Said? Paul Affirms Women Ministers. Date not set. 284p. pap. 19.99 *(978-0-9742712-0-0(9))* EJMB Publishing Co.

Brown, John. Analytical Exposition of the Epistle of Paul to the Romans. 2009. 454p. pap. *(978-0-217-77623-3(X))* Books LLC.

Buckland, R. St Paul's First Epistle to the Thessalonians - A Devotional Commentary. 2007. 172p. per. *(978-1-4067-8873-0(2)*, Pomona Pr.) Read Bks.

Bullinger, Ethelbert. The Church Epistles: Romans to Thessalonians. 2007. 276p. per. 22.95 *(978-1-60206-047-0(9))* Cosimo, Inc.

Callahan, Robert B. Sin & Redemption: An Expository Commentary Based upon PaulÕs Letter to the Ephesians. 2011. (Walking with Jesus: Ser.). 290p. pap. 32.00 ***(978-1-60899-646-9(8)***, Resource Pubns.) Wipf & Stock Pubs.

Callan, Charles J. Epistles of St Paul V1 with Introduction. 2006. pap. 50.95 *(978-1-4286-4642-1(6))* Kessinger Publishing, LLC.

—Epistles of St Paul V2 with Introduction. 2006. pap. 38.95 *(978-1-4286-4643-8(4))* Kessinger Publishing, LLC.

Callan, Terrance. Dying & Rising with Christ: The Theology of Paul the Apostle. 2006. 187p. per. 19.95 *(978-0-8091-4395-5(X)*, 4395-x) Paulist Pr.

Calvin, John. Commentaries on the Epistles of Paul the Apostle to the Philippians, Colossians, & Thessalonians. Pringle, John, tr. 2008. 492p. 53.95 *(978-1-4370-0770-1(8))*; pap. 38.95 *(978-1-4368-1039-5(6))* Kessinger Publishing, LLC.

—Commentaries on the Epistles of Paul the Apostle to the Philippians, Colossians, & Thessalonians. 2007. 490p. pap. 35.00 *(978-1-55635-313-0(8)*, Wipf and Stock) Wipf & Stock Pubs.

Cameron, Peter John, ed. Praying with Saint Paul: Daily Reflections on the Letters of the Apostle Paul. 2008. 382p. pap. 12.95 *(978-0-9798086-2-3(6))* Magnificat USA LLC.

Caputo, John D. & Alcoff, Linda Martin, eds. St. Paul among the Philosophers. 2009. (Indiana Ser. in the Philosophy of Religion Ser.). (ENG.). 208p. 60.00 *(978-0-253-35317-7(3)*, 0253353173); pap. 22.95 *(978-0-253-22083-7(1)*, 0253220831) Indiana Univ. Pr.

Carrón Pérez, Julián, et al. Acontecimiento y Razón en San Pablo. 2010. (SPA.). 53p. *(978-84-9920-025-5(7))* Encuentro Ediciones, S.A.

Carter, Christopher L. The Great Sermon Tradition as a Fiscal Framework in 1 Corinthians: Towards a Pauline Theology of Material Possessions. 2010. (Library of New Testament Studies, the Ser.). (ENG.). 288p. 130.00 *(978-0-567-47304-2(X)*, T&T Clark Int'l) Continuum International Publishing Group, Ltd. GBR. Dist: National Bk. Network.

Cary, Phillip. Inner Grace: Augustine in the Traditions of Plato & Paul. 2008. (ENG.). 208p. 55.00 *(978-0-19-533648-1(8))* Oxford Univ. Pr., Inc.

Clarke, Andrew D. Called to Serve: A Pauline Theology of Leadership. 2008. (Library of New Testament Studies, the Ser.). (ENG.). 220p. 130.00 *(978-0-567-04560-7(9)*, T&T Clark Int'l) Continuum International Publishing Group, Ltd. GBR. Dist: National Bk. Network.

Collins, Ann. Teacher in Faith & Virtue: Lanfranc of Bec's Commentary on Saint Paul. 2007. (Commentaria Ser.). (Illus.). 219p. *(978-90-04-16347-8(6))* BRILL.

Commentarii in Epistolas D. Pauli. 2010. (LAT.). pap. 52.00 *(978-1-61143-296-1(0))* Gorgias Pr., LLC.

Cossette, Thomas L. Hebrew Prophecies of the Coming of Paul. 2008. 124p. pap. 11.99 *(978-1-60647-480-8(4))* Xulon Pr., Inc.

Cripe, Earl. Not Ashamed of the Gospel: A Commentary on the Epistle of St. Paul to the Church at Rome. 2009. 512p. pap. 20.49 *(978-1-4389-5924-5(9))* AuthorHouse.

David, Wilson. Paul's Letters to Timothy & the Church Today: Words of Admonition, Encouragement, & Warning. 2007. 128p. per. 6.25 *(978-0-9786002-7-3(4))* Wilson, David.

DeWitt, Norman Wentworth. Epicurus & His Philosophy. 2009. (ENG.). 400p. pap. 60.00 *(978-0-8166-5745-2(9))* Univ. of Minnesota Pr.

—St. Paul & Epicurus. 2009. (ENG.). 212p. pap. 50.00 *(978-0-8166-5746-9(7))* Univ. of Minnesota Pr.

Duncan, J. Ligon. Misunderstanding Paul? Responding to the New Perspectives. 2006. 112p. pap. 12.99 *(978-1-58134-720-3(0)*, Crossway Bibles) Crossway.

Eadie, John. A Commentary on the Greek Text of the Epistle of Paul to the Colossians. 2009. 358p. 29.99 *(978-1-116-47293-6(7))*; pap. 31.75 *(978-1-116-47295-0(3))*; 38.99 *(978-1-116-47292-9(9))*; pap. 32.75 *(978-1-116-47294-3(5))* BiblioBazaar.

—A Commentary on the Greek Text of the Epistle of Paul to the Colossians. 2008. 372p. 48.95 *(978-1-4369-8458-4(0))*; pap. 33.95 *(978-1-4367-2174-5(1))* Kessinger Publishing, LLC.

—A Commentary on the Greek Text of the Epistle of Paul to the Philippians. 2009. 340p. 25.99 *(978-1-103-52954-4(4))*; pap. 19.99 *(978-1-103-52950-6(1))* BiblioBazaar.

Erasmus, Desiderius & Hovingh, Pieter Frans. Vi-7 Ordinis Sexti Tomus Septimus: Annotationes in Epistolam Ad Romanos. 2011. (LAT, ENG & GRE., Illus.). XII, 420p. ***(978-90-04-20338-9(9))*** BRILL.

Fantin, Joseph D. The Lord of the Entire World: Lord Jesus, a Challenge to Lord Caesar? 2011. 354p. ***(978-1-907534-12-6(1))*** Sheffield Phoenix Pr.

Farley, Lawrence. Words of Fire: The Early Epistles of St. Paul to the Thessalonians & the Galatians. 2010. (Orthodox Bible Study Companion Ser.). 172p. pap. 15.95 *(978-1-936270-02-6(1))* Conciliar Pr.

Fee, Gordon D. Pauline Christology: An Exegetical-Theological Study. 2007. 707p. *(978-1-59856-035-0(2))* Hendrickson Pubs. Marketing, LLC.

Finlan, Stephen. The Apostle Paul & the Pauline Tradition. 2008. xiv, 229p. (C). pap. 29.95 *(978-0-8146-5271-8(9))* Liturgical Pr.

Furnish, Victor. Moral Teaching of Paul. 3rd ed. 2009. 176p. pap. 18.00 *(978-0-687-33293-9(1))* Abingdon Pr.

Garlington, Don. Studies in the New Perspective on Paul: Essays & Reviews. 2008. 400p. pap. 44.00 *(978-1-60608-004-7(0))* Wipf & Stock Pubs.

Gaventa, Beverly Roberts. Our Mother Saint Paul. 2007. (ENG.). 218p. per. 25.00 *(978-0-664-23149-1(7))* Westminster John Knox Pr.

Goodspeed, Edgar J. New Solutions of New Testament Problems. 2011. 138p. 40.95 ***(978-1-258-03442-9(5))*** Literary Licensing, LLC.

Groseclose, Win. The Preeminence of Christ: Reflections on Paul's Letter to the Colossians. 2008. 155p. pap. 14.08 *(978-1-4357-6023-3(9))* Lulu Enterprises Inc.

Hafemann, Scott J. Paul, Moses, & the History of Israel: The Letter/Spirit Contrast & the Argument from Scripture in 2 Corinthians 3. 2008. (Paternoster Biblical Monographs). 526p. pap. 64.00 *(978-1-59752-775-0(0))* Wipf & Stock Pubs.

Hankins, Mark. Paul's System of Truth: The Life & Teachings of the Apostle Paul. 2010. 256p. pap. 14.99 *(978-1-889981-23-9(0))* Harrison House Pubs.

Hatch, William Henry Paine. The Pauline Idea of Faith in Its Relation to Jewish & Hellenistic Religion. 2007. (ENG.). 108p. 34.95 *(978-0-548-03203-9(3))* Kessinger Publishing, LLC.

Hausser, Detlef. Christusbekenntnis und Jesusüberlieferung bei Paulus. 2006. (Wissenschaftliche Untersuchungen Zum Neuen Testament 2 Ser.: Vol. 210). 416p. (C). pap. 135.00 *(978-3-16-148962-4(4))* Mohr Siebeck GmbH & Co. KG DEU. Dist: Coronet Bks.

Hendricks, J. L. All the Bible Is Based on Just Three Verses. 2008. 116p. pap. 11.99 *(978-1-60647-731-1(5))* Xulon Pr., Inc.

Hering, Jean. The First Epistle of Saint Paul to the Corinthians. 2009. 210p. pap. 25.00 *(978-1-60608-414-4(3)*, Wipf and Stock) Wipf & Stock Pubs.

Hongze, Fang. An Aperçu of Paul's Letter to the Galatians. Noether, Roger, tr. 2011. 136p. 21.23 ***(978-1-4634-2975-1(4))***; pap. 10.68 ***(978-1-4634-2976-8(2))*** AuthorHouse.

Howard, James M. Paul, the Community, & Progressive Sanctification: An Exploration into Community-Based Transformation Within Pauline Theology. 2006. (Studies in Biblical Literature: Vol. 90). 238p. (C). 69.95 *(978-0-8204-7928-6(4))* Lang, Peter Publishing, Inc.

Howson, John Saul. The Metaphors of St Paul & Companions of St Paul. 2008. 328p. 25.99 *(978-0-559-19011-7(5))*; pap. 29.75 *(978-0-559-19009-4(3))* BiblioBazaar.

—The Metaphors of St Paul & Companions of St Paul. 2007. (ENG.). 318p. 45.95 *(978-0-548-16767-0(2))*; 320p. per. 30.95 *(978-1-4304-6479-2(8))* Kessinger Publishing, LLC.

—The Metaphors of St Paul & Companions of St Paul. 2006. 312p. per. 23.99 *(978-1-4255-3296-3(9))* MPublishing.

Huttunen, Niko. Paul & Epictetus on Law: A Comparison. 2009. (Library of New Testament Studies, the Ser.). (ENG.). 208p. 120.00 *(978-0-567-07439-3(0)*, T&T Clark Int'l) Continuum International Publishing Group, Ltd. GBR. Dist: National Bk. Network.

Inaam, Roshan. Follow Jesus or Follow Paul. 75p. pap. *(978-9960-777-06-1(5))* Al-Attique Pubs., Inc.

Jones, Joe & Jones, Wanda. Romans: How to Be Right with God. 2007. 108p. per. 16.95 *(978-1-4241-9343-1(5))* PublishAmerica, Inc.

Judge, E. A. & Scholer, David M. Social Distinctives of the Christians in the First Century: Pivotal Essays. 2008. 232p. pap. *(978-1-56563-880-8(8))* Hendrickson Pubs. Marketing, LLC.

Kerrigan, Michael P. Saint Paul the Apostle for Every Day: A Vision That Inspires, a Mission for Life. 2008. (Illus.). 128p. pap. 6.95 *(978-0-8091-4567-6(7))* Paulist Pr.

Kim, Seyoon. Christ & Caesar: The Gospel & the Roman Empire in the Writings of Paul & Luke. 2008. 240p. pap. 24.00 *(978-0-8028-6008-8(7))* Eerdmans, William B. Publishing Co.

Kim, Yung Suk. A Theological Introduction to PaulÕs Letters: Exploring a Threefold Theology of Paul. 2011. 162p. pap. 19.00 ***(978-1-60899-793-0(6)***, Cascade Bks.) Wipf & Stock Pubs.

Knox, Wilfred L. St Paul & the Church of the Gentiles. 2008. (ENG.). 276p. pap. 37.99 *(978-0-521-08979-1(4))* Cambridge Univ. Pr.

Kraus, Wolfgang, ed. Beiträge zur urchristlichen Theologiegeschichte. 2009. (Beihefte zur Zeitschrift far die neutestamentliche Wissenschaft und die Kunde der älteren Kirche Ser.).Tr. of Studies on the History of Early Christian Theology. (GER.). XVI, 560p. 280.00 ***(978-3-11-173599-3(0))*** De Gruyter, Walter Inc.

Kraus, Wolfgang, ed. Beiträge zur urchristlichen Theologiegeschichte. 2009. (Beihefte zur Zeitschrift für die neutestamentliche Wissenschaft und die Kunde der älteren Kirche Ser.).Tr. of Studies on the History of Early Christian Theology. (GER.). XVI, 560p. 182.00 *(978-3-11-021565-6(9))* De Gruyter, Walter Inc.

Lacy, G. H. Comentario Epistola a los Efesios: Paul's Letter to Ephesians. (SPA.). *(978-84-7645-077-2(X)*, 223139) Clie, Editorial.

Lavender, Earl. Meditative Commentary Series: Ephesians, Philippians, Colossians, Philemon: Jesus above All. 2008. (Meditative Commentary Ser.). 144p. pap. 9.99 *(978-0-89112-561-7(2)*, Leafwood Pubs.) Abilene Christian Univ. Pr.

Lenski, R. C. H. Saint Paul: A Brief Series of Evening Texts Made Ready for Pulpit Work. 2008. 247p. pap. 21.00 *(978-1-60608-281-2(7)*, Wipf and Stock) Wipf & Stock Pubs.

Lewis, Agnes Smith, ed. Acta Mythologica Apostolorum in Arabic: Transcribed from an Arabic MS in the Convent of Deyr-Es-Suriani, Egypt, & from MSS in the Convent of St Catherine, on Mount Sinai. 2010. (Cambridge Library Collection - Religion Ser.). (ARA., Illus.). 254p. pap. 23.99 *(978-1-108-01898-2(X))* Cambridge Univ. Pr.

Lifetogether. Paul. 2011. (Deepening Life Together Ser.). (Illus.). 89p. pap. 8.99 *(978-0-8010-6905-5(X))* Baker Bks.

Lin, Rong-Hua Jefferson. Is St. Paul a Jewish Deviant or Reformer of Judaism? The Clash of Jewish Identity & Christian Identity in the Asia Minor. 2009. 216p. 109.95 *(978-0-7734-4743-1(1))* Mellen, Edwin Pr., The.

Ludwig, Alison C. Abundant Life. 2007. 184p. pap. 19.96 *(978-0-615-16014-6(X))* Ludwig, Alison C.

Machen, J. Gresham. Origin of Pauls Religion. 2006. pap. 31.95 *(978-1-4286-4490-8(3))* Kessinger Publishing, LLC.

Manning, Lawrence J. Divine Letters from a Roman Prison: A Commentary on Paul's Prison Epistles. 2008. 295p. pap. 27.95 *(978-1-60563-005-2(5))* PublishAmerica, Inc.

Marguerat, D., ed. Reception of Paulinism in Acts - Reception du paulinisme dans les Actes des Apotres. 2009. (Bibliotheca Ephemeridum Theologicarum Lovaniensium Ser.). (ENG, FRE & GER.). 355p. (C). pap. 108.00 *(978-90-429-2241-9(9))* Peeters Pubs. & Booksellers BEL. Dist: Brown, David Bk. Co., The.

Martini, Carlo Maria. The Gospel According to St. Paul: Meditations on His Life & Letters. Daigle-Williamson, Marsha, tr. from SPA. 2008. 127p. pap. 10.95 *(978-1-59325-145-1(9))* Word Among Us Pr.

McCarthy, Dave. Called unto Liberty: A Commentary on the Apostle. 2007. 183p. per. *(978-0-9800096-5-1(0))* Calvary Publishing.

Meech, John L. Paul in Israel's Story: Self & Community at the Cross. 2006. (AAR Academy Ser.). (ENG.). 192p. 75.00 *(978-0-19-530694-1(5))* Oxford Univ. Pr., Inc.

Meyer, Jason C. The End of the Law: Mosaic Covenant in Pauline Theology, 1 vol. 2009. (ENG.). 352p. 19.99 *(978-0-8054-4842-9(X)*, B&H Academic) B&H Publishing Group.

Middleton, Paul, et al, eds. Paul, Grace & Freedom: Essays in Honour of John K. Riches. 2012. (ENG.). 234p. pap. 44.95 ***(978-0-567-38254-2(0)***, T&T Clark Int'l) Continuum International Publishing Group, Ltd. GBR. Dist: National Bk. Network.

Middleton, Paul & Middleton, Paul, Grace & Freedom: Essays in Honour of John K. Riches. Paddison, Angus & Wenell, Karen J., eds. 2009. (ENG.). 234p. 130.00 *(978-0-567-03318-5(X)*, T&T Clark Int'l) Continuum International Publishing Group, Ltd. GBR. Dist: National Bk. Network.

Miller, J. r. & Miller, J. R. Paul's Message for Today. 2011. 126p. pap. 12.99 ***(978-1-61203-178-1(1))*** Bottom of the Hill Publishing.

Miller, Kathy Collard. Paul & the Prison Epistles, 0 vols. Richards, Larry, ed. 2008. (Smart Guide to the Bible Ser.). 352p. pap. 14.99 *(978-1-4185-1007-7(6))* Nelson, Thomas Inc.

Muddiman, John & Barton, John. The Pauline Epistles. 2010. (ENG., Illus.). 344p. pap. 24.95 *(978-0-19-958026-2(X))* Oxford Univ. Pr., Inc.

Mueller, Daniel G. Paul's Word to Families. 2007. (Insight Ser.). 48p. pap. 5.99 *(978-0-7586-1463-6(2))* Concordia Publishing Hse.

Murphy-O'Connor, Jerome. St. Paul's Ephesus: Texts & Archaeology. 2008. (Michael Glazier Bks.). (Illus.). 289p. per. 29.95 *(978-0-8146-5259-6(X)*, Liturgical Pr. Bks.) Liturgical Pr.

Norton, Jonathan D. H. Contours in the Text: Textual Variation in the Writings of Paul Josephus & the Yahad. 2011. (Library of New Testament Studies). (ENG.). 224p. 120.00 *(978-0-567-22939-7(4)*, T&T Clark Int'l) Continuum International Publishing Group, Ltd. GBR. Dist: National Bk. Network.

Paul as the Original Christian Liberation Theologian. 14.00 *(978-0-687-09786-9(X))* Abingdon Pr.

Pauls Gospel. 18.00 *(978-0-687-09295-6(7))* Abingdon Pr.

Payne, Philip Barton & Payne, Philip B. Man & Woman, One in Christ: An Exegetical & Theological Study of Paul's Letters, 1 vol. 2009. (ENG.). 512p. pap. 29.99 *(978-0-310-21988-0(4))* Zondervan.

Peat, Timothy & Ashworth, Timothy. Paul's Necessary Sin: The Experience of Liberation. 2006. (Illus.). 272p. 114.95 *(978-0-7546-5499-5(0))* Ashgate Publishing Co.

Petersen, Norman R. Rediscovering Paul: Philemon & the Sociology of Paul's Narrative World. 2008. 320p. pap. 35.00 *(978-1-60608-113-6(6)*, Wipf and Stock) Wipf & Stock Pubs.

Pfleiderer, Otto. The Hibbert Lectures 1885: Lectures on the Influence of the Apostle Paul on the Development of Christianity 1885. Smith, J. Frederick, tr. 2007. (ENG.). 298p. 43.95 *(978-0-548-05653-0(6))* Kessinger Publishing, LLC.

Piper, John. The Future of Justification: A Response to N. T. Wright. 2007. 240p. pap. 17.99 *(978-1-58134-964-1(5))* Crossway.

Porter, Stanley E. Paul & His Opponents. 2009. 272p. pap. 32.95 *(978-1-58983-430-9(5))* Society of Biblical Literature.

—The Pauline Canon. 2009. 272p. pap. 32.95 *(978-1-58983-428-6(3))* Society of Biblical Literature.

Porter, Stanley E., ed. Paul & His Theology. 2006. (Pauline Studies: Vol. 3). 454p. *(978-90-04-15408-7(6))* BRILL.

Rabens, Volker. The Holy Spirit & Ethics in Paul: Transformation & Empowering for Religious-Ethical Life. 2010. (Illus.). 390p. pap. 137.50 *(978-3-16-149895-4(X))* Mohr Siebeck GmbH & Co. KG DEU. Dist: Coronet Bks.

Raisanen, Heikki. Paul & the Law (2nd Edition) 2010. 352p. pap. 39.00 *(978-1-60899-750-3(2)*, Wipf and Stock) Wipf & Stock Pubs.

Ratke, David C. The New Perspective on Paul: Perennial Questions & Contemporary Challenges. 2012. ***(978-1-932688-67-2(6))*** Kirk Hse. Pubs.

Roetzel, Calvin J. The Letters of Paul, Fifth Edition: Conversations in Context. 5th ed. 2009. (ENG.). 288p. pap. 30.00 *(978-0-664-23392-1(9))* Westminster John Knox Pr.

Rosner, Brian S. Greed as Idolatry: The Origin & Meaning of a Pauline Metaphor. 2007. 214p. per. 22.00 *(978-0-8028-3374-7(8))* Eerdmans, William B. Publishing Co.

RRaphael, Monir/ B., Sr. Coptic Language Analysis: The Book of the Acts of the Holy Apostles. 2007. (COP, ENG & ARA., Illus.). 320p. lib. bdg. 40.00 *(978-0-9760091-2-2(9)*, Coptic Language and History Bks.) Copts In.

RUDEN, Sarah. Paul among the People: The Apostle Reinterpreted & Reimagined in His Own Time. 2010. (ENG.). 240p. 25.00 *(978-0-375-42501-1(2)*, Pantheon) Knopf Doubleday Publishing Group.

Samra, James G. & Samra. Being Conformed to Christ in Community: A Study of Maturity, Maturation & the Local Church in the Undisputed Pauline Epistles. 2006. (Library of New Testament Studies: Vol. 320). (ENG.). 280p. 140.00 *(978-0-567-04354-2(1)*, T&T Clark Int'l) Continuum International Publishing Group, Ltd. GBR. Dist: National Bk. Network.

Sandnes, Karl Olav & Sandnes. The Challenge of Homer: School, Pagan Poets & Early Christianity. 2009. (Library of New Testament Studies, the Ser.). (ENG.). 336p. 150.00 *(978-0-567-42664-2(5)*, T&T Clark Int'l) Continuum International Publishing Group, Ltd. GBR. Dist: National Bk. Network.

Schmitz, Bertram. Paulus und der Koran. 2010. (GER.). 212p. (C). pap. 32.00 *(978-3-525-51007-0(1))* Vandenhoeck & Ruprecht GmbH & Co. KG DEU. Dist: ISD.

Scornaienchi, Lorenzo. Sarx und Soma bei Paulus: Der Mensch zwischen Destruktivität und Konstruktivität. 2008. (Novum Testamentum et Orbis Antiquus/Studien zur Umwelt des Neuen Testaments (NTOA/StUNT) Ser.). (GER.). 388p. (C). 98.00 *(978-3-525-53966-8(5))* Vandenhoeck & Ruprecht GmbH & Co. KG DEU. Dist: ISD.

Simmons, Albert C. I, Paul... God's Ambassador to the Gentiles. 2007. 356p. pap. 18.95 *(978-0-7414-4186-7(1))* Infinity Publishing.

St. Paul Coalition for Community Development Staff. The Epistles of Paul & Acts of the Apostles. Johnson, Suzanne E. & Waldrep, Mary Carolyn, eds. 2007. (Dover Thrift Editions Ser.). (ENG., Illus.). 208p. per. 3.50 *(978-0-486-46169-4(6))* Dover Pubns., Inc.

Stedman, Ray C. Letters to a Troubled Church: 1 & 2 Corinthians. 2007. (ENG.). 416p. per. 16.99 *(978-1-57293-255-5(4))* Discovery Hse. Pubs.

Steiner, Rudolf. The Bhagavad Gita & the West: The Esoteric Significance of the Bhagavad Gita & Its Relation to the Letters of St. Paul. Easwaran, Eknath, tr. from GER. 2009. (Collected Works of Rudolf Steiner: 142).Tr. of Die Bhagavad Gita und die Paulusbriefe — Die okkulten Grundlagen der Bhagavad Gita. 464p. pap. 35.00 *(978-0-88010-604-7(2))* SteinerBooks, Inc.

Still, Todd D. & Horrell, David G. After the First Urban Christians: The Social-Scientific Study of Pauline Christianity Twenty-Five Years Later. Still, Todd D. & Horrell, David G., eds. 2009. (ENG., Illus.). 192p. 120.00 *(978-0-567-42774-8(9))*; pap. 34.95 *(978-0-567-21967-1(4))* Continuum International Publishing Group, Ltd. GBR. (T&T Clark Int'l). Dist: National Bk. Network.

Tarrell, Charles. Testing the Gospel in the Book of Romans: The Letter to the Romans & the Supersession Controversy. 2011. 166p. pap. 19.99 ***(978-1-4653-4375-8(X))*** Xlibris Corp.

Theodore. The Commentaries on the Minor Epistles of Paul. 2011. (LAT, GEC & ENG.). XLIV, 840p. *(978-90-04-15740-8(9))* BRILL.

—The Commentaries on the Minor Epistles of Paul. 2010. (LAT, GEC & ENG.). xliv, 839p. *(978-1-58983-279-4(5))* Society of Biblical Literature.

Thompson, Frederick M. Devotions from the Epistle of Romans. 2007. 280p. per. 15.99 *(978-1-60266-375-6(0))* Xulon Pr., Inc.

Tobin, Thomas H. The Spirituality of Paul. 2008. (Illus.). 194p. pap. 22.00 *(978-1-55635-891-3(1))* Wipf & Stock Pubs.

Towns, Elmer L. Praying Paul's Letters. 2008. (Praying the Scriptures Ser.). 271p. per. 15.99 *(978-0-7684-2614-4(6))* Destiny Image Pubs.

Unaegbu, Alajemba R. Attitude for Living: Commentary on Paul's Epistle to the Philippians, an African Perspective. 2006. 298p. pap. 29.95 *(978-1-4241-0993-7(0))* PublishAmerica, Inc.

Vickers, Brian. Jesus' Blood & Righteousness: Paul's Theology of Imputation. 2006. 256p. pap. 14.99 *(978-1-58134-754-8(5))* Crossway.

Wedderburn, A. J. M. Baptism & Resurrection: Studies in Pauline Theology against its Graeco-Roman Background. 2011. 496p. pap. 55.00 *(978-1-61097-087-7(X)*, Wipf and Stock) Wipf & Stock Pubs.

Westerholm, Stephen, ed. The Blackwell Companion to Paul. 2011. (Wiley-Blackwell Companions to Religion Ser.: 59). (ENG., Illus.). 632p. 199.95 *(978-1-4051-8844-9(8)*, Wiley-Blackwell) Wiley, John & Sons, Inc.

Wiles, Gordon P. Paul's Intercessory Prayers: The Significance of the Intercessory Prayer Passages in the Letters of St Paul. 2007. (Society for New Testament Studies Monograph Ser.). (ENG.). 364p. pap. 45.00 *(978-0-521-04835-4(4))* Cambridge Univ. Pr.

Wills, Garry. What Paul Meant. 2007. (ENG.). 208p. (gr. 12-18). 14.00 *(978-0-14-311263-1(5)*, Penguin (Non-Classics)) Penguin Group (USA) Inc.

—What Paul Meant. l.t. ed. 2007. (Thorndike Inspirational Ser.). 245p. 30.95 *(978-0-7862-9009-3(9))* Thorndike Pr.

Wilson, Walter T. Pauline Parallels: A Comprehensive Guide. 2009. (ENG.). 544p. pap. 50.00 *(978-0-664-23120-0(9))* Westminster John Knox Pr.

Witherup, Ronald D. Stations of the Cross According to Saint Paul. 2008. (Illus.). 48p. pap. 9.95 *(978-0-8091-4574-4(X))* Paulist Pr.

Yinger, Kent L. The New Perspective on Paul: An Introduction. 2011. 120p. pap. 16.00 *(978-1-60899-463-2(5))* Cascade Bks.

—Paul, Judaism, & Judgment according to Deeds. 2007. (Society for New Testament Studies Monograph Ser.). (ENG., Illus.). 336p. pap. 69.00 *(978-0-521-03669-6(0))* Cambridge Univ. Pr.

Young, M. Joseph. About the Fruit. 2007. 80p. pap. 11.95 *(978-0-615-16379-6(3))* Young, Mark Joseph.

Zoccali, Christopher. Whom God Has Called. 2010. 236p. pap. 26.00 *(978-1-60899-517-2(8)*, Pickwick Pubns.) Wipf & Stock Pubs.

BIBLE—COMMENTARIES—N. T. GALATIANS

Arnaudova, Elena. Growing in the Fruit of the Holy Spirit: No Subtitle. 2008. 96p. pap. 9.99 *(978-1-60647-639-0(4))* Xulon Pr., Inc.

Arnold, Clinton E. Romans Galatians, 1 vol. 2007. (Zondervan Illustrated Bible Backgrounds Commentary Ser.). (ENG., Illus.). 160p. (gr. 13). pap. 14.99 *(978-0-310-27833-7(3))* Zondervan.

Bible. N.T. Galatians. English. Paraphra. Law & Grace: A paraphrase of the Epistle to the churches of Galatia, by William Morris ... 2011. 28p. pap. 11.99 ***(978-1-4181-9345-4(3))*** MPublishing.

Borchert, Gerald L. & Mohrlang, Roger. Romans, Galatians. 2007. (Cornerstone Biblical Commentary Ser.: 14). (ENG.). 356p. 29.99 *(978-0-8423-8342-4(5))* Tyndale Hse. Pubs.

Breytenbach, Cilliers & Du Toit, David S., eds. Focusing on Paul: Persuasion & Theological Design in Romans & Galatians. 2007. (Beihefte Zur Zeitschrift Für Die Neutestamentliche Wissenschaft und Die Kunde der älteren Kirche Ser.). (ENG., Illus.). XIV, 443p. 154.00 *(978-3-11-019512-5(7))* De Gruyter, Walter Inc.

Breytenbach, Cilliers & du Toit, David S., eds. Focusing on Paul: Persuasion & Theological Design in Romans & Galatians. (Beihefte zur Zeitschrift far die neutestamentliche Wissenschaft und die Kunde der älteren Kirche Ser.). (ENG.). XIV, 443p. 255.00 ***(978-3-11-185305-5(5))*** De Gruyter, Walter Inc.

Brown, John. An Exposition of the Epistle of Paul the Apostle to the Galatians. 2006. 492p. per. 29.99 *(978-1-4255-5494-1(6))* MPublishing.

Byrne, Brendan. Galatians & Romans. 2010. 16.95 *(978-0-8146-3324-3(2))*; viii, 189p. E-Book *(978-0-8146-3937-5(2))* Liturgical Pr.

Chrysostom, John & Copeland, William John. Commentary on Galatians & Homilies on Ephesians. 2010. pap. 65.80 *(978-1-61143-364-7(9))* Gorgias Pr., LLC.

Cole, R. Alan. Galatians. (ENG.). 2007. (Tyndale New Testament Commentaries Ser.). 240p. pap. 14.00 *(978-0-8308-2988-0(1))* 2nd ed. 2008. (Tyndale New Testament Commentaries Ser.: Volume 9). 242p. pap. 16.00 *(978-0-8308-4239-1(X)*, IVP Acad.) InterVarsity Pr.

Conrad, Jason. Conrad Commentaries: Galatians. 2008. 224p. pap. 20.95 *(978-1-4343-9196-4(5))* AuthorHouse.

Cousar, Charles B. Galatians: Interpretation: A Bible Commentary for Teaching & Preaching. 2012. (Interpretation: A Bible Commentary for Teaching & Preaching Ser.). (ENG.). 170p. pap. 25.00 ***(978-0-664-23872-8(6))*** Westminster John Knox Pr.

de Boer, Martinus C. Galatians: A Commentary. 2011. (New Testament Library). (ENG.). 488p. 50.00 *(978-0-664-22123-2(8))* Westminster John Knox Pr.

Ellicott, Charles. A Commentary, Critical & Grammatical, on St Paul's Epistle to the Galatians, with a Revised Translation by Charles J Ellicott & an Introduc. 2006. 196p. per. 18.99 *(978-1-4255-1611-6(4))* MPublishing.

Elliott, Susan M. Cutting Too Close for Comfort: Paul's Letter to the Galatians in Its Anatolian Cultic Context. 2008. (Library of New Testament Studies, the Ser.). (ENG.). 412p. 75.00 *(978-0-567-03435-9(6)*, T&T Clark Int'l) Continuum International Publishing Group, Ltd. GBR. Dist: National Bk. Network.

Fenton, John. Galatians, 1 & 2 Thessalonians: A Guide for Reflection & Prayer. 2007. (Daily Bible Commentary Ser.). 191p. per. 12.95 *(978-1-59856-193-7(6))* Hendrickson Pubs. Marketing, LLC.

Fladerer, Ludwig. Augustinus als Exeget: Zu seinen Kommentaren des Galaterbriefes und der Genesis. 2010. (Sitzungsberichte der Phil. -Hist. Klasse Ser.). (GER.). 261p. (C). pap. 80.00 *(978-3-7001-6647-4(8))* Austrian Academy of Sciences Press AUT. Dist: Brown, David Bk. Co., The.

Fortner, Donald S. Discovering Christ in Galatians. 2008. 352p. *(978-0-9548624-5-9(7))* Go Pubns.

Galatians - Philippians - Colossians. ldr.'s ed. (LifeLight Ser.). pap. 7.50 *(978-0-570-07854-8(7)*, 20-3316) Concordia Publishing Hse.

Galatians, Ephesians. (People's Bible Commentary Ser.). 222p. pap. 10.99 *(978-0-570-05324-8(2)*, 12-8050) Concordia Publishing Hse.

Guzik, David. Galatians & Ephesians Commentary. 2007. 220p. per. 12.99 *(978-1-56599-034-0(X))* Yahshua Publishing.

Hansen, G. Walter. Galatians. 2010. (IVP New Testament Commentary Ser.: Volume 9). (ENG.). 212p. pap. 18.00 *(978-0-8308-4009-0(5)*, IVP Acad.) InterVarsity Pr.

Harmon, Matthew S. She Must & Shall Go Free: Paul's Isaianic Gospel in Galatians. 2011. (Beihefte zur Zeitschrift far die neutestamentliche Wissenschaft und die Kunde der älteren Kirche Ser.). (ENG., Illus.). XI, 330p. 210.00 ***(978-3-11-174167-3(2))*** De Gruyter, Walter Inc.

Holloway, Gary. Romans & Galatians: The Spirit of Jesus. 2007. (Meditative Commentary Ser.). 136p. per. 11.99 *(978-0-89112-502-0(7)*, Leafwood Pubs.) Abilene Christian Univ. Pr.

Layne Sr., E. R. Power over the Flesh. 2007. 80p. per. 9.99 *(978-1-60266-635-1(0))* Xulon Pr., Inc.

Lightfoot, Joseph B. St. Paul's Epistle to the Galatians. 2009. 380p. pap. 32.00 *(978-1-55635-571-4(8)*, Wipf and Stock) Wipf & Stock Pubs.

Longman, Tremper, III. Romans - Galatians, 1 vol. rev. ed. 2010. (Expositor's Bible Commentary Ser.). (ENG.). 992p. 44.99 *(978-0-310-26892-5(3))* Zondervan.
Lund, Enrique. Comentario Epistola a los Galatas: Galatians-A Practical. (SPA.). *(978-84-7645-028-4(1)*, 223097) Clie, Editorial.
Luther, Martin. Commentary on Galatians. 2007. 26.98 *(978-1-4245-0792-4(8))* Treasures Media Inc.
—Commentary on the Epistle to the Galatians. 2008. 260p. 28.99 *(978-0-554-26402-8(1))* 2008. 260p. 25.99 *(978-0-554-35705-8(4))* 2007. (ENG.). 228p. pap. 20.99 *(978-1-4346-1012-6(8))* BiblioBazaar.
—Commentary on the Epistle to the Galatians. 2008. (ENG.). 224p. per. 13.95 *(978-1-60597-066-0(2)*, Book Jungle) Standard Pubns., Inc.
—Commentary on the Epistle to the Galatians. 2010. (Illus.). 146p. pap. 23.37 *(978-1-153-59662-6(8))* General Bks. LLC.
—A Commentary on the Epistle to the Galatians. 2010. 206p. pap. 19.96 *(978-1-162-65820-9(7))*; 31.96 ***(978-1-169-28746-4(8))***; 39.95 *(978-1-161-42585-4(X))* Kessinger Publishing, LLC.
—Commentary on the Epistle to the Galatians. l.t. ed. 2007. 256p. pap. 23.99 *(978-1-4346-1111-6(6))* BiblioBazaar.
Lyons, George. NBBC, Galatians: A Commentary in the Wesleyan Tradition. 2012. (ENG.). 400p. pap. 34.99 *(978-0-8341-2402-8(5)*, 9780834124028) Beacon Hill Pr. of Kansas City.
Matera, Frank J. Galatians. 2007. (Sacra Pagina Ser.). 263p. per. 29.95 *(978-0-8146-5972-4(1)*, Liturgical Pr. Bks.) Liturgical Pr.
Mauro, Philip. Our Liberty in Christ: A Study in Galatians. 2008. 206p. pap. 18.00 *(978-1-60608-358-1(9)*, Wipf and Stock) Wipf & Stock Pubs.
McKnight, Scot & Lee-Thorp, Karen. Galatians: Living in Freedom & Love, 1 vol. 2010. (Bringing the Bible to Life Ser.). (ENG.). 96p. pap. 7.99 *(978-0-310-32045-6(3))* Zondervan.
Meiser, Martin. Galater: Novum Testamentum Patristicum. 2007. (Novum Testamentum Patristicum Ser.). (GER.). 373p. (C). 123.00 *(978-3-525-53988-0(6))* Vandenhoeck & Ruprecht GmbH & Co. KG DEU. Dist: ISD.
Metzger, Bruce M. Apostolic Letters of Faith, Hope, & Love: Galatians, 1 Peter, & 1 John. 2006. 110p. pap. 15.00 *(978-1-59752-501-5(4)*, Cascade Bks.) Wipf & Stock Pubs.
Moule, Handley C. G. The Cross & the Spirit. 2009. 62p. pap. 9.00 *(978-1-60608-950-7(1)*, Wipf and Stock) Wipf & Stock Pubs.
Ortlund, Dane C. Zeal Without Knowledge: The Concept of Zeal in Romans 10, Galatians 1 & Philippians 3. 2012. (Library of New Testament Studies). (ENG.). 208p. 110.00 ***(978-0-567-53759-1(5)***, T&T Clark Int'l) Continuum International Publishing Group, Ltd. GBR. Dist: National Bk. Network.
Perkins, Tyrone C. A Commentary on the Books of Galatians, Ephesians, Philippians. 112p. pap. 9.95 *(978-1-56794-202-6(4)*, C-2555) Star Bible & Tract Corp.
Perrotta, Kevin. Six Weeks with the Bible: Free in Christ. 2006. (ENG.). 96p. pap. 7.95 *(978-0-8294-2007-4(X))* Loyola Pr.
Reed, Tony. Looking for Love in the Wrong Places. 2009. 48p. pap. 13.95 *(978-1-59858-928-3(8))* Dog Ear Publishing, LLC.
Scheck, Thomas & Jerome, St. St Jeromes Commentaries on Gal. 2010. (ENG.). 376p. pap. 40.00 *(978-0-268-04133-5(4))* Univ. of Notre Dame Pr.
Schmoller, Otto. The Epistle of Paul to the Galatians: An Exegetical & Doctrinal Commentary. Lange, John Peter & Schaff, Philip, eds. Starbuck, Charles C., tr. 2007. (Lange's Commentary on the Holy Scripture: Ser.). 162p. pap. 18.00 *(978-1-55635-409-0(6)*, Wipf and Stock) Wipf & Stock Pubs.
Schreiner, Thomas R. Galatians, 1 vol. 2010. (Zondervan Exegetical Commentary on the New Testament Ser.). (ENG.). 464p. 34.99 *(978-0-310-24372-4(6))* Zondervan.
Smith, Argile. Truth about Grace: Studies in Galatians. 2010. (Illus.). 97p. pap. ***(978-1-4158-6535-4(3))*** LifeWay Christian Resources.
St. Jerome. Commentary on Galatians. Cain, Andrew, tr. from LAT. 2010. 312p. 39.95 *(978-0-8132-0121-4(7))* Catholic Univ. of America Pr.
Strauss, Lehman. Galatians & Ephesians. 2010. 248p. pap. *(978-1-926765-17-4(6))* Gospel Folio Pr.
Strauss, Mark, et al. Galatians Thru Philemon Vol. 11: Putting Faith into Practice. 2008. (QuickNotes Commentaries Ser.). (ENG.). 224p. pap. 9.99 *(978-1-59789-777-8(9)*, Barbour Bks.) Barbour Publishing, Inc.
Swindoll, Charles R. Insights on Galatians & Ephesians, 1 vol. 2012. (Swindoll's New Testament Insights Ser.). (ENG.). 400p. 25.99 ***(978-0-310-28443-7(0))*** Zondervan.
Thielman, Frank. From Plight to Solution: A Jewish Framework for Understanding Paul's View of the Law in Galatians & Romans. 2008. (Supplements to Novum Testamentum (Wipf & Stock Publishers) Ser.). 170p. pap. 20.00 *(978-1-55635-639-1(0))* Wipf & Stock Pubs.
Thollander, Lance. Walking the Galatian Road: Moving from Law to Life. 2010. pap. 13.99 *(978-1-61663-096-6(5))* Tate Publishing & Enterprises, LLC.
Tyndale House Publishers Staff, prod. Galatians & Ephesians. 2009. (Life Application Bible Studies: NLT Ser.). (ENG.). 120p. pap. 7.99 *(978-1-4143-2644-3(0))* Tyndale Hse. Pubs.
Weidmann, Frederick W. Galatians. 2012. (Westminster Bible Companion Ser.). (ENG.). 144p. pap. 25.00 ***(978-0-664-25814-6(X))*** Westminster John Knox Pr.
Wiersbe, Warren W. Be Free (Galatians) Exchange Legalism for True Spirituality, 1 vol. 2009. (BE Ser. Commentary Ser.). (ENG.). 176p. pap. 12.99 *(978-1-4347-6747-9(7))* Cook, David C.
—The Wiersbe Bible Study Series: Galatians: Exchange Legalism for True Spirituality, 1 vol. 2010. (Wiersbe Bible Study Ser.). (ENG.). 128p. pap. 8.99 *(978-1-4347-6509-3(1))* Cook, David C.
Wilson, Earle L., et al. Galatians, Philippians, Colossians: A Commentary for Bible Students. 2007. (Illus.). 352p. *(978-0-89827-307-6(2))* Wesleyan Publishing Hse.
Witmer, John & Couch, Mal. The Books of Galatians & Ephesians: By Grace Through Faith. Hindson, Ed, ed. 2009. (Twenty-First Century Biblical Commentary Ser.). (ENG.). 256p. 19.99 *(978-0-89957-817-0(9))* AMG Pubs.
Young, M. Joseph. About the Fruit. 2007. 80p. pap. 11.95 *(978-0-615-16379-6(3))* Young, Mark Joseph.

BIBLE—COMMENTARIES—N. T. GOSPELS

Here are entered commentaries on the Gospels as a whole, as well as on the individual Gospels: Matthew, Mark, Luke, John.

Abbott, Lyman. An Illustrated Commentary on the Gospel According to Matthew for Family Use & Reference by Rev Lyman Abbott. 2006. (Illus.). 332p. per. 23.99 *(978-1-4255-3360-1(4))* MPublishing.
Abeelen, Jack. The Jesus Chronicles. 2009. 768p. 39.99 *(978-1-57921-988-8(8))* WinePress Publishing.
Abingdon. Gospels & the Early Church Runner's Reader: Matthew - Acts. 2008. 128p. pap. 6.00 *(978-0-687-33468-1(3))* Abingdon Pr.
Adelaar, Alexander. Siraya: Retrieving the Phonology, Grammar & Lexicon of a Dormant Formosan Language. 2012. (Trends in Linguistics. Documentation [TiLDOC] Ser.). (ENG., Illus.). XVI, 413p. (gr. 17). E-Book 280.00 ***(978-3-11-219171-2(4))*** De Gruyter, Mouton DEU. Dist: de Gruyter, Walter GmbH & Co. KG.
Alber, Erasmus. Evangelienharmonie. Horner, Petra, ed. 2009. (GER.). XV, 214p. 126.00 *(978-3-11-020910-5(1))* De Gruyter, Walter Inc.
Aldridge, Robert E. The First Gospel: The Aramaic Gospel Before Matthew, Mark, Luke, & John. 2011. 156p. 30.95 ***(978-1-4497-1430-7(7))***; pap. 13.95 ***(978-1-4497-1428-4(5))*** Author Solutions, Inc. (WestBow Pr.).
Alexander, Larry D. Home Bible Study Commentaries from the Gospel of John. 2008. 134p. pap. 16.95 *(978-0-615-20347-8(7))* Alexander, Larry D.
Alfaro, Juan I. Homilias Sobre Los Evangelios de Domingos. 2011. (SPA.). ***(978-0-8146-3962-7(3))*** Liturgical Pr.
Allen, Larry & Neeley, Linda. Translator's Notes on Luke 9-16. 2010. 570p. spiral bd. 60.00 *(978-1-55671-248-7(0))* SIL International.
Allen, Willoughby C. A Critical & Exegetical Commentary on the Gospel according to Saint Matthew. 2010. pap. 68.08 *(978-1-61719-741-3(6))* Gorgias Pr., LLC.
Alrabf, Nathanael Ben-Yehoshua. Jesus the Messiah According to the Gospels. 2007. 236p. (ENG.). 24.99 *(978-1-60477-161-9(5))*; per. 14.99 *(978-1-60477-160-2(7))* Xulon Pr., Inc.
Anderson, Paul N. The Christology of the Fourth Gospel. 2009. 448p. (Orig.). pap. 49.00 *(978-1-60608-629-2(4)*, Cascade Bks.) Wipf & Stock Pubs.
Anderson, William Angor. The Gospel of Matthew: A Scripture Study & Reflection. 2012. ***(978-0-7648-2120-2(2))*** Liguori Pubns.
Aquinas, Thomas. Catena Aurea: Commentary on the Four Gospels, Collected Out of the Works of the Fathers, Volume I Part 1 Gospel of St. Matthew. 2007. 424p. per. 24.95 *(978-1-60206-582-6(9))* Cosimo, Inc.
—Catena Aurea: Commentary on the Four Gospels, Collected Out of the Works of the Fathers, Volume I Part 2 Gospel of St. Matthew. 2007. 348p. per. 21.95 *(978-1-60206-583-3(7))* Cosimo, Inc.
—Catena Aurea: Commentary on the Four Gospels, Collected Out of the Works of the Fathers, Volume I Part 3 Gospel of St. Matthew. 2007. 264p. per. 21.95 *(978-1-60206-584-0(5))* Cosimo, Inc.
—Catena Aurea: Commentary on the Four Gospels, Collected Out of the Works of the Fathers, Volume II Gospel of St. Mark. 2007. 356p. per. 22.95 *(978-1-60206-585-7(3))* Cosimo, Inc.
—Catena Aurea: Commentary on the Four Gospels, Collected Out of the Works of the Fathers, Volume III Part 1, Gospel of St. Luke. 2007. 400p. per. 24.95 *(978-1-60206-586-4(1))* Cosimo, Inc.
—Catena Aurea: Commentary on the Four Gospels, Collected Out of the Works of the Fathers, Volume III Part 2, Gospel of St. Luke. 2007. 420p. per. 24.95 *(978-1-60206-587-1(X))* Cosimo, Inc.
—Catena Aurea: Commentary on the Four Gospels, Collected Out of the Works of the Fathers, Volume IV Part 1 Gospel of St. John. 2007. 380p. per. 23.95 *(978-1-60206-588-8(8))* Cosimo, Inc.
—Catena Aurea: Commentary on the Four Gospels, Collected Out of the Works of the Fathers, Volume IV Part 2, Gospel of St. John. 2007. 276p. per. 21.95 *(978-1-60206-589-5(6))* Cosimo, Inc.
—Commentary on the Gospel of John, 3 vols. Larcher, Fabian, tr. from LAT. 2010. 352p. 79.95 *(978-0-8132-1745-1(8))* Catholic Univ. of America Pr.
—Commentary on the Gospel of John, Chapters 1-5, 3 vols. Keating, Daniel & Levering, Matthew, eds. Larcher, Fabian & Weisheipl, James A., trs. from LAT. 2010. 352p. pap. 29.95 *(978-0-8132-1723-9(7))* Catholic Univ. of America Pr.
—Commentary on the Gospel of John, Chapters 13-21, 3 vols. Keating, Daniel & Levering, Matthew, eds. Larcher, Fabian & Weisheipl, James A., trs. from LAT. 2010. 288p. pap. 29.95 *(978-0-8132-1734-5(2))* Catholic Univ. of America Pr.
—Commentary on the Gospel of John, Chapters 6-12, 3 vols. Keating, Daniel & Levering, Matthew, eds. Larcher, Fabian & Weisheipl, James A., trs. from LAT. 2010. 288p. pap. 29.95 *(978-0-8132-1733-8(4))* Catholic Univ. of America Pr.
Arillotta, Richard. Possessing All in Christ. 2007. 456p. (ENG.). 35.99 *(978-1-60266-130-1(8))*; per. 23.99 *(978-1-60266-129-5(4))* Xulon Pr., Inc.
Arnold, Clinton. Zondervan Illustrated Bible Backgrounds Commentary Mark, 1 vol. 2007. (Zondervan Illustrated Bible Backgrounds Commentary Ser.). (ENG., Illus.). 128p. (gr. 13). pap. 14.99 *(978-0-310-27830-6(3))* Zondervan.
Arnold, Clinton E. John, 1 vol. 2007. (Zondervan Illustrated Bible Backgrounds Commentary Ser.). (ENG., Illus.). 240p. (gr. 13). pap. 19.99 *(978-0-310-27828-3(7))* Zondervan.
—Zondervan Illustrated Bible Backgrounds Commentary: 2 Peter 1 2, 1 vol. 2007. (Zondervan Illustrated Bible Backgrounds Commentary Ser.). (ENG., Illus.). 144p. (gr. 13). pap. 14.99 *(978-0-310-27824-5(4))* Zondervan.
Arrington, French L. The Spirit-Anointed Jesus: A Study of the Gospel of Luke. 2008. 427p. *(978-1-59684-317-2(9))* Pathway Pr.
Arthur, Kay & De Lacy, Pete. Experiencing the Miracles of Jesus: Mark. 2010. (New Inductive Study Ser.). 112p. pap. 8.99 *(978-0-7369-2513-6(9))* Harvest Hse. Pubs.
—The God Who Cares & Knows You. 2008. (New Inductive Study Ser.). (Illus.). 159p. per. 8.99 *(978-0-7369-2193-0(1))* Harvest Hse. Pubs.
B. Woodward. Magdalene: The Other St. Mary. 2009. 48p. pap. 19.49 *(978-1-4389-4380-0(6))* AuthorHouse.
Baert, B., et al. Noli me Tangere: Mary Magdalene: One Person, Many Images. 2006. (Documenta Libraria Ser.). (ENG., Illus.). 125p. (C). pap. 35.00 *(978-90-429-1807-8(1))* Peeters Pubs. & Booksellers BEL. Dist: Brown, David Bk. Co., The.
Baido-Essien, Christopher. Examining the Great Commission: A Call to Study. 2011. 384p. 31.50 ***(978-1-4670-3698-6(6))*** AuthorHouse.
Baidoo-Essien, Christopher. Examining the Great Commission: A Call to Study. 2011. 384p. pap. 24.95 ***(978-1-4670-3699-3(4))*** AuthorHouse.
Bailey, Kenneth E. Finding the Lost: Cultural Keys to Luke 15. (Concordia Scholarship Today Ser.). 184p. 17.99 *(978-0-570-04563-2(0)*, 12-4008) Concordia Publishing Hse.
Bajema, Edith. Discover Jesus in John: The Lives He Touched. (Discover Your Bible Ser.). pap., tchr. ed. 4.95 *(978-1-56212-617-9(2)*, 152335) Faith Alive Christian Resources.
Baker Publishing Group Staff & Life Together Staff. John, 1 vol. 2009. (Deepening Life Together Ser.). 128p. pap. 8.99 *(978-0-8010-6844-7(4))* Baker Bks.
Banks, William L. Now I See. 2011. pap. 10.95 ***(978-0-7414-6643-3(0))*** Infinity Publishing.
Bar Salibi, Dionysius & Bar Hebraeus, Gregory Abulfaraj. The Exposition of Dionysius Syrus: Written above 900 Years since on the Evangelist St. Mark. 2011. (LAT.). pap. 53.45 *(978-1-61143-924-3(8))* Gorgias Pr., LLC.
Barnstone, Willis, tr. from SEM. The Restored New Testament: A New Translation with Commentary, Including the Gnostic Gospels Thomas, Mary, & Judas. 2009. (ENG.). 1152p. 59.95 *(978-0-393-06493-3(X)*, 6493) Norton, W. W. & Co., Inc.
Barrett. Gospel According to St John, the Paperback. 2nd ed. 2009. (GEC & ENG.). xv, 638p. pap. *(978-0-281-06194-5(7))* SPCK Publishing.
Bartlett, David, et al. The New Proclamation Commentary on the Gospels. 2006. (New Proclamation Ser.). 320p. 35.00 *(978-0-8006-3752-1(6)*, Fortress Pr.) Augsburg Fortress, Pubs.
Bass, Michael R. Gospel of Grace. 2008. 204p. pap. 14.99 *(978-1-60477-857-1(1))* Xulon Pr., Inc.
Basser, Herbert. The Mind Behind the Gospels: A Commentary to Matthew 1-14. 2009. (Reference Library of Jewish Intellectual History Ser.). (ENG.). 396p. 69.00 *(978-1-934843-33-8(4))*; pap. 35.00 *(978-1-934843-34-5(2))* Academic Studies Pr.
Bauckham, Richard & Mosser, Carl. The Gospel of John & Christian Theology. Bauckham, Richard & Mosser, Carl, eds. 2008. 404p. per. 32.00 *(978-0-8028-2717-3(9))* Eerdmans, William B. Publishing Co.
Beals, Timothy J. The Red Letters: The Sayings & Teachings of Jesus. Beals, Timothy J., ed. 2009. 160p. tchr. ed. 16.99 *(978-1-4335-0140-1(6))* Crossway.
Beaton. St Matthew. 2013. (ENG.). 480p. 120.00 *(978-0-8264-5497-3(6))* Continuum International Publishing Group, Ltd. GBR. Dist: National Bk. Network.
Beaton, Richard. Isaiah's Christ in Matthew's Gospel. 2007. (Society for New Testament Studies Monograph Ser.). (ENG.). 260p. pap. 55.00 *(978-0-521-03610-8(0))* Cambridge Univ. Pr.
Beck, Brian E. Christian Character in the Gospel of Luke. 2009. 232p. pap. 26.00 *(978-1-60608-641-4(3)*, Wipf and Stock) Wipf & Stock Pubs.
Beck, Sanderson. The Good Message of Jesus the Christ: A Harmony, Synthesis, & Interpretation of the Gospels. Beck, Sanderson, ed. 2008. pap. 25.00 *(978-0-9792532-8-7(4))* World Peace Communications.
Bede. The Venerable Bede: On the Song of Songs & Selected Writings. 2011. pap. *(978-0-8091-4700-7(9))*; (Illus.). *(978-0-8091-0591-5(8))* Paulist Pr.
Bell, Thornton, Sr. The Kingdom of God Passport. 2007. 103p. pap. 14.95 *(978-0-615-16358-1(0))* Impact Now Ministries.
Bernhard, Andrew, et al. Other Early Christian Gospels: A Critical Edition of the Surviving Greek Manuscripts. 2007. (Library of New Testament Studies). (GEC & ENG., Illus.). 208p. 65.00 *(978-0-567-04568-3(4))* Continuum International Publishing Group, Ltd. GBR. Dist: National Bk. Network.
Bertolini, Rebecca & Bertolini, Dewey. The Book of Matthew, 0 vols. Richards, Larry, ed. 2008. (Smart Guide to the Bible Ser.). (Illus.). 384p. per. 14.99 *(978-1-4185-1006-0(8))* Nelson, Thomas Inc.
Binz, Stephen J. Los Relatos de la Pasion y Resurreccion de Jesus: Un Comentario. Icaza, Rosa Maria, tr. from ENG. 2007. (SPA.). 114p. per. 9.95 *(978-0-8146-2806-5(0)*, Liturgical Pr. Bks.) Liturgical Pr.
Blackwell, John. A Whole New World. 2006. (ENG.). 120p. per. 13.95 *(978-1-933596-95-2(3)*, 1933596953) Morgan James Publishing.
Blackwell, John. A Whole New World: The Gospel of Matthew. 2011. (ENG.). 156p. pap. 13.95 ***(978-1-60037-861-3(8))*** Morgan James Publishing.
Blanchett, Elnora. Clarified Gospels Intertwined. 2007. 152p. 29.00 *(978-1-4251-5139-3(6))* Trafford Publishing.
Blight, Richard C. An Exegetical Summary of Luke 1 - 11. 2006. 549p. pap. 45.00 *(978-1-55671-170-1(0))* SIL International.
—An Exegetical Summary of Luke 12 - 24. 2006. 581p. pap. 45.00 *(978-1-55671-171-8(9))* SIL International.
Blue, Ken & Swan, Alden. The Gospel Uncensored: How Only Grace Leads to Freedom. 2010. 220p. 33.95 *(978-1-4497-0455-1(7))*; pap. 17.95 *(978-1-4497-0454-4(9))* Author Solutions, Inc. (WestBow Pr.).
Bock, Darrell L. Luke. 2010. (IVP New Testament Commentary Ser.: Volume 3). (ENG.). 412p. pap. 20.00 *(978-0-8308-4003-8(6)*, IVP Acad.) InterVarsity Pr.
—Luke Vol. 2: 9:51-24:53. 2007. (Baker Exegetical Commentary on the New Testament Ser.: Vol. 3). 1,162p. (C). 59.99 *(978-0-8010-1052-1(7))* Baker Academic.
Bock, Emil. Three Years. 3rd rev. ed. 320p. pap. 30.00 *(978-0-86315-535-2(9))* Floris Bks. GBR. Dist: SteinerBooks, Inc.
Boice, James Montgomery. The Gospel of Matthew Vol. 1: The King & His Kingdom, Matthew 1-17. 2006. (Expositional Commentary Ser.). 368p. pap. 21.99 *(978-0-8010-6643-6(3))* Baker Bks.
—The Gospel of Matthew Vol. 2: The Triumph of the King, Matthew 18-28. 2006. (Expositional Commentary Ser.). 320p. pap. 21.99 *(978-0-8010-6644-3(1))* Baker Bks.
Boison, Kojo Tawiah. Judas Iscariot: The Devil & the Betrayal of Jesus Christ. 2008. 52p. pap. 9.00 *(978-0-8059-7723-3(6))* Dorrance Publishing Co., Inc.
The Book of the Gospels: The Saint John's Bible Edition. 2007. 526p. lthr. 695.00 *(978-0-8146-9064-2(5))*; (ENG.). 595.00 *(978-0-8146-9097-0(1))* Liturgical Pr. (Liturgical Pr. Bks.).
Bosetti, Elena. John: The Word of Light. 2009. 176p. pap. 14.95 *(978-0-8198-3990-9(6))* Pauline Bks. & Media.
Bowman, Dixie & Marsala, Kerry. I Do Believe, Help My Unbelief. 2007. 220p. per. 14.99 *(978-1-60477-325-5(1))* Xulon Pr., Inc.
Brackett, Charlie. We Have Seen the Lord: Devotional Messages from John's Gospel. 2007. (Illus.). 241p. per. 15.95 *(978-0-9779577-6-7(4))* Clarion Word Publishing.
Bradley, Marshell Carl. Matthew: Poet, Historian, Dialectician. 2007. (Studies in Biblical Literature Ser.: Vol. 103). 204p. (C). 67.95 *(978-0-8204-8855-4(0))* Lang, Peter Publishing, Inc.
Bradley, William E. Freedom: Compiled Study of the Gospel of John. 2011. 356p. 31.99 *(978-1-4520-2848-4(6))*; pap. 17.99 *(978-1-4520-2847-7(8))* AuthorHouse.
Brauninger, Dallas A. Preaching the Miracles. 2008. 142p. pap. *(978-0-7880-2576-1(7))* CSS Publishing Co.
Brewer, David. Milk & Meat Series: Over 1450 questions you can answer from the book of John. 2007. 120p. per. 10.99 *(978-1-60266-338-1(6))* Xulon Pr., Inc.
Bright, William Marshall. Matthew for the Sunday School Teacher. 2011. 166p. pap. 24.95 ***(978-1-4626-2264-1(X))*** PublishAmerica, Inc.
Briner, Bob & Pritchard, Ray. Leadership Lessons of Jesus: A Timeless Model for Today's Leaders. 2008. (ENG.). 240p. 14.99 *(978-0-8054-4520-6(X)*, B&H Bks.) B&H Publishing Group.
Broadhead, Edwin K. & Broadhead, Edwin Keith. Mark. 2nd ed. 2009. viii, 167p. pap. *(978-1-905048-95-3(5))* Sheffield Phoenix Pr.
Broadhead, Edwin Keith. Mark. 2nd ed. 2009. viii, 167p. *(978-1-905048-94-6(7))* Sheffield Phoenix Pr.
Brogdon, Joyce Sidey. Navigating Through the Gospel of Mark with Captain Bill Brogdon. 2008. 140p. pap. 13.99 *(978-1-60647-336-8(0))* Xulon Pr., Inc.
Brumbaugh, Judith A. Answers to Questions - Deuteronomy 24:4; Jeremiah 3:1; Matthew 5:32 & 19:9: Returning to an Original Mate; Marriage to an Unsaved Mate Followed by a Subsequent Marriage to a Christian; The "Exception Clause" rev. ed. 18p. pap. *(978-0-9624603-4-0(6))* Committee for the Restoration of the Family.
Bruner, Frederick Dale. Matthew: The Christbook, Matthew 1-12. 2007. pap. 30.00 *(978-0-8028-4506-1(1))* Eerdmans, William B. Publishing Co.
—Matthew: The Churchbook, Matthew 13-28, 2. 2007. pap. 40.00 *(978-0-8028-4507-8(X))* Eerdmans, William B. Publishing Co.
Bruno, Joseph. And Now There Is Light... 2007. 252p. pap. 18.95 *(978-0-615-13496-3(3))* Bruno, Joseph.
Buchanan, George Wesley. The Gospel of Matthew, Volume 1. 2006. 600p. pap. 56.00 *(978-1-59752-866-5(8)*, Wipf and Stock) Wipf & Stock Pubs.
—The Gospel of Matthew, Volume 2. 2006. 541p. pap. 47.00 *(978-1-59752-867-2(6)*, Wipf and Stock) Wipf & Stock Pubs.
Bullis, Marty A. The Miraculous Journey: Anticipating God in the Christmas Season. 2007. (ENG.). 144p. 14.99 *(978-0-8307-4278-3(6))* Gospel Light Pubns.
—The Passionate Journey. 2006. pap. *(978-0-8307-4392-6(8)*, Regal Bks.) Gospel Light Pubns.
Bunyan, John. The Pharisee & Publican. 2010. (Illus.). 92p. pap. 20.00 *(978-1-153-71613-0(5))* General Bks. LLC.
—The Pharisee & Publican. 2010. 124p. 28.76 ***(978-1-169-25176-2(5))***; pap. 16.76 ***(978-1-162-70448-7(9))*** Kessinger Publishing, LLC.
Bunyan, John Jr. & Bunyan, John. The Pharisee & Publican. 2010. 124p. 35.95 *(978-1-161-47312-4(2))* Kessinger Publishing, LLC.
Burridge, Richard A. John: A Guide for Reflection & Prayer. 2007. (Daily Bible Commentary Ser.). 248p. per. 12.95 *(978-1-59856-188-3(X))* Hendrickson Pubs. Marketing, LLC.
Buxbaum, J. G. It Is Finished Bk. 3: The New Matthew Henry Commentary on the Gospel of John, Chapters 13-21. 2009. 404p. pap. 15.95 *(978-1-4327-2973-8(X))* Outskirts Pr., Inc.
—The New Matthew Henry Commentary: On the Letter of Paul to the Romans. 2009. 496p. pap. 16.95 *(978-1-4327-3874-7(7))* Outskirts Pr., Inc.

Byrne, Brendan. A Costly Freedom: A Theological Reading of Mark's Gospel. 2008. (Illus.). xx, 283p. pap. 26.95 *(978-0-8146-1856-1(1))* Liturgical Pr.

C F Evans Staff. Saint Luke - Reissue. 2nd ed. 2011. xxxi, 933p. pap. ***(978-0-334-04209-9(7)***, SCM Pr.) Hymns Ancient & Modern Ltd.

Calvin, John. Commentary on a Harmony of the Evangelists V2: Matthew, Mark, & Luke. Pringle, William, tr. 2011. 456p. 57.95 ***(978-1-258-02053-8(X))*** Literary Licensing, LLC.

Cameron, Peter John. Praying with Saint Matthew's Gospel: Daily Reflections to Lead You Through the Word of God. 2010. 384p. pap. 12.95 *(978-1-936260-01-0(8))* Magnificat USA LLC.

Cameron, Ron. The Other Gospels. 2006. (ENG.). 192p. (C). reprint ed. pap. 40.00 *(978-0-7188-9174-9(0))* Lutherworth Pr., The GBR. Dist: Brown, David Bk. Co., The.

Campbell, Iain D. Matthew's Gospel. 2008. (Opening Up Ser.). (Illus.). 192p. pap. *(978-1-84625-116-0(8))* DayOne Pubns.

Cannon, Michael E. The Trials & Passion of Christ: An Expository & Analytical Commentary on John 18 And 19. 2011. 184p. pap. 21.00 *(978-1-60899-877-7(0)*, Resource Pubns.) Wipf & Stock Pubs.

Caradus, Sel. Matty & Matt: A Conversational Approach to MatthewÕs Gospel. 2011. 204p. pap. 23.00 ***(978-1-61097-432-5(8)***, Resource Pubns.) Wipf & Stock Pubs.

Card, Michael. Luke: the Gospel of Amazement. 2011. (Biblical Imagination Ser.). (ENG.). 272p. pap. 18.00 *(978-0-8308-3835-6(X)*, IVP Bks.) InterVarsity Pr.

Carlton, Matthew E. Translator's Reference Translation of the Gospel of Luke. 2008. 495p. pap. 39.00 *(978-1-55671-217-3(0))* SIL International.

Carrington, Philip. According to Mark: A Running Commentary on the Oldest Gospel. 2011. (ENG.). 398p. pap. 31.99 *(978-1-107-66168-4(4))* Cambridge Univ. Pr.

Carroll, B. H. Coment, Carroll-Cinco No. 1: Evangelios: Carroll's Comment-6: Gospels. (SPA.). *(978-84-7645-112-0(1)*, 223165) Clie, Editorial.

—Coment, Carroll-Cinco No. 2: Evangelios: Carroll's Comment-6: Gospels. (SPA.). *(978-84-7645-113-7(X)*, 223166) Clie, Editorial.

Carroll, John T. Luke: A Commentary. 2012. (New Testament Library). (ENG.). 560p. 50.00 ***(978-0-664-22106-5(8))*** Westminster John Knox Pr.

Chae, Young S. Jesus as the Eschatological Davidic Shepherd: Studies in the Old Testament, Second Temple Judaism, & in the Gospel of Matthew. (Wissenschaftliche Untersuchungen Zum Neuen Testament Ser.: Vol. 216). (GER.). 446p. pap. 115.00 *(978-3-16-148876-4(8))* Mohr Siebeck GmbH & Co. KG DEU. Dist: Eisenbrauns, Inc.

Chamblin, Knox. Matthew Volume 1 (1-13) A Mentor Commentary, 2 vols. 2010. (Mentor Commentary Ser.). (ENG.). 736p. 39.99 *(978-1-84550-364-2(3)*, Mentor) Christian Focus Pubns. GBR. Dist: STL Distribution North America.

Chester, Tim. Mark 1-8: the Coming King: Ten Studies for Individuals or Groups. 2010. (Good Book Guides). 96p. pap. *(978-1-904889-28-1(X))* Good Bk. Co.

—Mark 9-16: the Servant King: Seven Studies for Individuals or Groups. 2010. (Good Book Guides). 64p. pap. *(978-1-904889-51-9(4))* Good Bk. Co.

Chinese Gospel of Luke. 117p. pap. 1.25 *(978-962-293-645-4(8))* Hong Kong Bible Society (HK) HKG. Dist: American Bible Society.

Christianus & Huygens, R. B. C. Expositio Super Librum Generationis. 2008. (Corpus Christianorum Ser.: Vol. 224). (LAT & FRE.). 609p. *(978-2-503-05241-0(X))* Brepols Pubs.

Chung, Andrew B. Trust the Truth: Only the truth can cure the hunger Is starvation Delusion. 2009. 56p. pap. 9.95 *(978-1-4401-4766-1(3))* iUniverse, Inc.

Church Publishing Staff. The Gospels. rev. ed. 2007. 240p. lthr. 190.00 *(978-0-89869-552-6(X))* Church Publishing, Inc.

—The Gospels: For the Revised Common Lectionary Together with Holy Days & Special Occasions. rev. ed. 2007. 240p. 95.00 *(978-0-89869-553-3(8))* Church Publishing, Inc.

Clemmer, Edward Joseph. Gospel (on the Road to) Emmaus, 2 vols. 2011. 712p. 46.66 *(978-1-4567-7379-3(8))*; 656p. 46.66 *(978-1-4567-7429-5(8))*; 656p. pap. 31.68 *(978-1-4567-7430-1(1))* AuthorHouse.

Clowes, John. The Gospel According to Matthew. 2007. (ENG.). 474p. 52.95 *(978-0-548-02113-2(9))* Kessinger Publishing, LLC.

Cole, R. Alan. Mark. (ENG.). 340p. 2008. (Tyndale New Testament Commentaries Ser.: Volume 2). pap. 17.00 *(978-0-8308-4232-2(2)*, IVP Acad.) 2007. (Tyndale New Testament Commentaries Ser.). per. 14.00 *(978-0-8308-2981-1(4))* InterVarsity Pr.

Collins, Adela Yarbro & Attridge, Harold W. Mark: A Commentary. Attridge, Harold W., ed. 2007. (Hermeneia: A Critical & Historical Commentary on the Bible Ser.). 930p. 80.00 *(978-0-8006-6078-9(1)*, Fortress Pr.) Augsburg Fortress, Pubs.

Concordia Publishing House Staff. Meditations on the Gospels: According to His Word. 2009. 25.99 *(978-0-7586-1506-0(X))* Concordia Publishing Hse.

Confessing the Gospel. 49.99 *(978-0-570-04287-7(9))* Concordia Publishing Hse.

Cook, Grant Osmond, III. The Life of Christ: From the Joseph Smith Translation of the Four Gospels with Modern Scripture. 2006. 240p. 24.95 *(978-0-9787997-0-0(4))* Rockshire Publishing, LLC.

Cormier, Jay. Table Talk: Beginning the Sunday Conversation on the Gospel of Luke (Year C) 2009. (ENG.). 208p. pap. 16.95 *(978-1-56548-322-4(7))* New City Pr.

Corstjens, R., et al. The Vocabulary of Luke: An Alphabetical Presentation & a Survey of Characteristic & Noteworthy Words & Word Groups in Luke's Gospel. 2010. (Biblical Tools & Studies). 655p. (C). 122.00 *(978-90-429-2348-5(2))* Peeters Pubs. & Booksellers BEL. Dist: Brown, David Bk. Co., The.

Costa, Isaac da. The Four Witnesses. 2006. 504p. per. 29.99 *(978-1-4255-5603-7(5))* MPublishing.

Cox, Steven L. & Easley, Kendell H. HCSB Harmony of the Gospels. 2007. (ENG.). 400p. 24.99 *(978-0-8054-9444-0(8)*, Holman Pubs.) B&H Publishing Group.

Craddock, Fred B. Luke. 2009. (Interpretation, a Bible Commentary for Teaching & Preaching Ser.). (ENG.). 312p. pap. 25.00 *(978-0-664-23435-5(6))* Westminster John Knox Pr.

—Overhearing the Gospel: Preaching & Teaching the Faith to Persons Who Have Already Heard. 11.95 *(978-0-687-29937-9(3))* Abingdon Pr.

Crain, Sellers S., Jr. & Stewart, David. Matthew 14-28. 2011. (ENG.). 510p. 29.95 *(978-0-9818128-8-5(0))* Resource Pubns.

Crane, Steven A. Marveling with Mark. 2010. 370p. pap. 41.00 *(978-1-60899-339-0(6)*, Wipf and Stock) Wipf & Stock Pubs.

Crowley, Edna. God's Way of Love. 2007. 376p. per. 19.99 *(978-1-60477-408-5(8))* Xulon Pr., Inc.

Crowter, Phil. Preaching Mark: Talk Outlines for the Gospel of Mark. 2010. (Pray, Prepare, Preach Ser.). 160p. pap. *(978-1-906334-63-5(3))* Good Bk. Co.

Css Publishing Company, compiled by. Sermons on the Gospel Readings, Series III, Cycle C. 2009. (Illus.). 408p. pap. 37.95 *(978-0-7880-2621-8(6))* CSS Publishing.

Cueni, R. Robert. When Walls Shift & the Ceiling Collapses: Cycle C Sermons for Pentecost 3, Proper 23 Through Thanksgiving Based on the Gospel Texts. 2012. ***(978-0-7880-2677-5(1))*** CSS Publishing Co.

Culòs, Ermes. The Gospel of Matthew. 2008. 208p. pap. 21.50 *(978-1-4357-5259-7(7))* Lulu Enterprises Inc.

Culpepper, R. Alan. Mark. 2007. (Smyth & Helwys Bible Commentary Ser.). *(978-1-57312-077-7(4))* Smyth & Helwys Publishing, Inc.

Cundiff, Margaret. Travelling Light. 192p. 7.00 *(978-0-281-04570-9(4))* SPCK Publishing GBR. Dist: Pilgrim Pr., The/United Church Pr.

Custer, Stewart. The Divine Son of God: A Commentary on John. 2011. *(978-1-60682-186-2(5))* BJU Pr.

Dateno, Maria Grace & Trouvé, Marianne Lorraine. Ordinary Grace Weeks 1-17: Daily Gospel Reflections. 2011. pap. *(978-0-8198-5442-1(5))* Pauline Bks. & Media.

Davies, Margaret. Matthew. 2nd ed. 2009. 254p. *(978-1-906055-04-2(1))*; pap. *(978-1-906055-05-9(X))* Sheffield Phoenix Pr.

Day, Ashley. Exploring John's Gospel: A Devotional Commentary. 2009. 380p. 28.95 *(978-1-4389-6686-1(5))*; pap. 17.99 *(978-1-4389-6687-8(3))* AuthorHouse.

DiGiacomo, James. Sundays with Jesus: Reflections for the Year of Mark. 2008. 112p. pap. 7.95 *(978-0-8091-4503-4(0))* Paulist Pr.

Dillaway, Newton, ed. The Gospel of Emerson 1949. 2007. (ENG.). 108p. 33.95 *(978-0-548-05479-6(7))* Kessinger Publishing, LLC.

Dilling, David R. The Gospel of John. 2008. 273p. pap. 24.50 *(978-1-4357-2296-5(5))* Lulu Enterprises Inc.

Discover Jesus in John: Who He Is. (Discover Your Bible Ser.). pap., tchr. ed. 6.95 *(978-1-56212-618-6(0)*, 152345) Faith Alive Christian Resources.

Discover Jesus in John: Why He Came. (Discover Your Bible Ser.). pap., tchr. ed. 6.95 *(978-1-56212-619-3(9)*, 152355) Faith Alive Christian Resources.

Do, Maria Yen Thi. The Lucan Journey: A Study of Luke 9:28-36 & Acts 1:6-11 As an Architectural Pair. 2010. (Illus.). 357p. pap. *(978-3-0343-0092-6(1))* Lang, Peter.

Doriani, Daniel M. Matthew. 2008. *(978-0-87552-657-7(8))*; *(978-1-59638-132-2(9))* P & R Publishing.

—Matthew, Volume 1-2. 2008. (Reformed Expository Commentary Ser.). 59.99 *(978-1-59638-151-3(5))* P & R Publishing.

Doriani, Daniel M., et al. The Incarnation in the Gospels. 2008. v, 227p. *(978-1-59638-140-7(X))* P & R Publishing.

Douglas, Stauffer D. Freedom's Ring: Life, Liberty & the Pursuit of Salvation. 2008. (Illus.). 400p. 29.95 *(978-0-9677016-9-1(4))* McCowen Mills Pubs.

Dunderberg, Ismo. The Beloved Disciple in Conflict? Revisiting the Gospels of John & Thomas. 2006. (ENG.). 272p. 110.00 *(978-0-19-928496-2(2))* Oxford Univ. Pr., Inc.

Dunlap, Judith. Bringing Home the Gospel: The Year of Matthew: A Weekly Journal for Catholic Parents. 2007. 126p. per. 10.95 *(978-0-86716-780-1(7))* Franciscan Media.

Duran, Nicole & Okure, Teresa, eds. Mark: Texts @ Contexts. 2010. 288p. (C). 40.00 *(978-0-8006-5998-1(8)*, Fortress Pr.) Augsburg Fortress, Pubs.

Duren, Marty & Wright, Todd. Journeys: Transitioning Churches to Relevance. 2008. 192p. per. 14.99 *(978-0-9798053-1-8(7))* Missional Pr.

Dykes, Ray. Mark, Matthew & Luke As You've Never Seen Them Before: A Theoretical History of the Writing of the Synoptic Gospels. 2006. per. 9.25 *(978-0-9723884-2-9(7))* Pair'o'Docs Pr.

Easter-John 11. 7.50 *(978-0-8054-5924-1(3))* B&H Publishing Group.

Eaton, Michael. Luke, 12-24. (Preaching Through the Bible Ser.). 125p. pap. *(978-1-85240-283-9(0))* Sovereign World, Ltd.

—Mark. (Preaching Through the Bible Ser.). 125p. pap. *(978-1-85240-222-8(9))* Sovereign World, Ltd.

Eccles, Lance. Grammatical Commentary on the Syriac Gospel of Mark. 2007. (Gorgias Handbooks Ser.: 5). 65.00 *(978-1-59333-343-0(9))* Gorgias Pr., LLC.

Edersheim, Alfred. The Life & Times of Jesus the Messiah. 2010. 734p. pap. 50.75 *(978-1-143-78751-5(X))* 2010. 736p. pap. 51.75 *(978-1-143-39221-4(3))* 2010. 744p. pap. 52.75 *(978-1-143-56873-2(7))* 2009. 736p. pap. 50.75 *(978-1-116-30869-3(X))* 2009. 736p. 47.99 *(978-1-116-30866-2(5))* 2009. 736p. 40.99 *(978-1-116-30867-9(3))* 2009. 736p. pap. 51.75 *(978-1-116-30868-6(1))* BiblioBazaar.

—The Life & Times of Jesus the Messiah. 2010. 662p. pap. 32.98 *(978-1-153-40236-1(X))* 2009. 564p. pap. 32.98 *(978-1-151-53786-7(1))* General Bks. LLC.

Edmunds, James. Discussion on Revision of the Holy Oracles & upon the Objects, Aims, Motives the Constitution, Organization, Facilities & Capacities of the Americ. 2006. 224p. per. 20.99 *(978-1-4255-1880-6(X))* MPublishing.

Edwards, Sue. Luke: Finding Truth & Healing in Jesus' Words to Women, 1 vol. 2009. (Sue Edwards Inductive Bible Study Ser.). (ENG.). 96p. pap. 12.99 *(978-0-8254-2545-5(X))* Kregel Pubns.

Elder, Robert J. Sermons on the Gospel Readings. 2008. 408p. pap. *(978-0-7880-2544-0(9))* CSS Publishing Co.

Elowsky, Joel C., ed. John 11-21. 2007. (Ancient Christian Commentary on Scripture Ser.: New Testament Volume 4b). (ENG.). 480p. 50.00 *(978-0-8308-1099-4(4)*, IVP Acad.) InterVarsity Pr.

Elowsky, Joel C. & Oden, Thomas C., eds. John 1-10. 2007. (Ancient Christian Commentary on Scripture Ser.: New Testament Volume 4a). (ENG.). 421p. 50.00 *(978-0-8308-1489-3(2)*, IVP Acad.) InterVarsity Pr.

Entsminger, Gary Lee & Elliott, Susan Elizabeth. Remembering the Parables: Using the Art of Memory to remember Jesus' Parables. 2010. (Illus.). 160p. pap. 18.00 *(978-0-9821561-3-1(8))* Pinyon Publishing.

Evans, H. Walker. The Book of Mark, 0 vols. Richards, Larry, ed. 2007. (Smart Guide to the Bible Ser.). (Illus.). 352p. per. 14.99 *(978-1-4185-0994-1(9))* Nelson, Thomas Inc.

Evenhouse, Neva. Discover Mark. (Discover Your Bible Ser.). (KOR.). pap., stu. ed. 4.25 *(978-1-55883-202-2(5)*, 600120); Vol. 2. pap., stu. ed. 4.25 *(978-1-55883-203-9(3)*, 600130) C R C World Literature Ministries/Libros Desafio.

—Discover Mark, Vol. 2. (Discover Your Bible Ser.). pap., tchr. ed. 7.95 *(978-1-56212-616-2(4)*, 152165) Faith Alive Christian Resources.

Fabrizius, Karl F. Bible Stories for Daily Prayer: New Testament Stories Year III, the Gospel of Luke, 10 vols., Vol. 6. Bender, Peter C., ed. 2007. 209p. (J). ring bd. 20.00 *(978-0-9725687-8-4(6))* Concordia Catechetical Academy.

Farag, Lois M. St. Cyril of Alexandria, A New Testament Exegete: His Commentary on the Gospel of John. 2007. (Gorgias Dissertations in Early Christian Studies: 7). 88.00 *(978-1-59333-581-6(4))* Gorgias Pr., LLC.

Farley, Lawrence R. The Gospel of John: Beholding the Glory. 2006. (Orthodox Bible Study Companion Ser.). 376p. per. 19.95 *(978-1-888212-55-6(1))* Conciliar Pr.

Ferrini, Paul. The Gospel According to Jesus: A New Testament for Our Time. 2010. 398p. pap. 25.00 *(978-1-879159-82-2(1))* Heartways Pr.

Fogarty, Philip. Navigating the Gospels - John. 2010. (ENG.). 90p. pap. 19.95 *(978-1-85607-664-7(4))* Columba Pr. IRL. Dist: Dufour Editions, Inc.

—Navigating the Gospels - Luke. 2010. (ENG.). 136p. pap. 20.95 *(978-1-85607-663-0(6))* Columba Pr. IRL. Dist: Dufour Editions, Inc.

Fogarty, Philip & Collins, Gregory. Navigating the Gospels - Matthew. 2011. (ENG.). 128p. pap. 19.95 *(978-1-85607-665-4(2))* Columba Pr. IRL. Dist: Dufour Editions, Inc.

Foulkes, Francis. Guide to Matthews Gospel. (Illus.). 304p. 16.00 *(978-0-281-05173-1(9))* SPCK Publishing GBR. Dist: Pilgrim Pr., The/United Church Pr.

France, Dick. Mark: A Guide for Reflection & Prayer. 2007. (Daily Bible Commentary Ser.). 227p. per. 12.95 *(978-1-59856-186-9(3))* Hendrickson Pubs. Marketing, LLC.

France, R. T. The Gospel of Matthew. 2007. (New International Commentary on the New Testament). 1169p. 65.00 *(978-0-8028-2501-8(X))* Eerdmans, William B. Publishing Co.

—Matthew. 2007. (Tyndale New Testament Commentaries Ser.). (ENG.). 416p. per. 15.00 *(978-0-8308-2980-4(6))* InterVarsity Pr.

—Matthew: An Introduction & Commentary. 2008. (Tyndale New Testament Commentaries Ser.: Volume 1). (ENG.). 422p. pap. 17.00 *(978-0-8308-4231-5(4)*, IVP Acad.) InterVarsity Pr.

Franklin, Barbara Jean. Through Another Lens: Reflections on the Gospels, Year B. 2011. ***(978-0-7648-1989-6(5))*** Liguori Pubns.

Freeman, Kaye. A Journey Through the Gospels & Acts. 2007. per. 11.99 net. *(978-1-60402-327-5(9))* Independent Pub.

Gall, Mark. Jesus Mean & Wild: The Unexpected Love of an Untamable God. 2008. 208p. pap. 15.00 *(978-0-8010-7157-7(7))* Baker Bks.

Garland, David E. & Arnold, Clinton E. Luke, 1 vol. 2011. (Zondervan Exegetical Commentary on the New Testament Ser.). (ENG.). 400p. 49.99 ***(978-0-310-24359-5(9))*** Zondervan.

Garrett, Gregg & Turner, Matthew Paul. The Voice of Mark: Let Them Listen, 0 vols. 2008. (Illus.). 176p. per. 9.99 *(978-0-529-12350-3(9))* Nelson, Thomas Inc.

Gary, Burge & Lee-Thorp, Karen. John, 1 vol. 2008. (Bringing the Bible to Life Ser.). (ENG.). 144p. pap. 7.99 *(978-0-310-27651-7(9))* Zondervan.

Gates, Mitchell. Easy to Use Object Lessons. 2011. 232p. pap. 19.99 ***(978-1-4568-6671-6(0))*** Xlibris Corp.

Gench, Frances Taylor. Encounters with Jesus: Studies in the Gospel of John. 2007. (ENG.). 170p. per. 17.00 *(978-0-664-23006-7(7))* Westminster John Knox Pr.

Gibbs, Jeffrey A. Matthew 1:1-11:1: A Theological Exposition of Sacred Scripture. 2006. (Concordia Commentary Ser.). (ENG., Illus.). 547p. 42.99 *(978-0-7586-0318-0(5))* Concordia Publishing Hse.

—Matthew 11:2-20. 2010. (Concordia Commentary Ser.). 584p. 42.99 *(978-0-7586-1099-7(8))* Concordia Publishing Hse.

Goffin, Yuen H., ed. Rivers of Living Water: A\Visual Harmony of the Four Gospels. 2006. Orig. Title: The Four-Lane Gospel; A Visual Harmony. *(978-0-9791409-0-7(0))* Heavenly Bright, A Non-Profit Corp.

González, Justo L. Luke. 2010. (Belief Ser.). (ENG.). 376p. 35.00 *(978-0-664-23201-6(9))* Westminster John Knox Pr.

Gospel & Ethnic Traditions. 10.00 *(978-0-687-04827-4(3))* Abingdon Pr.

Gospel of John. 2007. 0.65 *(978-1-882536-92-4(4))* Bible League.

Grant, Frederick C. Earliest Gospel Studies of the Evangelic. 2006. pap. 27.95 *(978-1-4286-5309-2(0))* Kessinger Publishing, LLC.

Greene, Jerry. Outer Darkness: 70 AD - End of the Jewish World. 2007. 75p. per. 8.95 *(978-1-59824-469-4(8))* E-BookTime LLC.

Greenlees, Duncan. The Gospel of Hermes. 2006. (ENG.). 328p. per. 26.95 *(978-1-58509-006-8(9))* Book Tree, The.

—The Gospel of the Gnostics. 2006. (ENG.). 412p. 55.00 *(978-1-58509-501-8(X))*; per. 29.95 *(978-1-58509-007-5(7))* Book Tree, The.

Griffin, C. Jh. Lyrics on Matters Relating To: The Knowledge of Good & Evil. 2008. 260p. pap. 15.99 *(978-1-4389-1166-3(1))* AuthorHouse.

Griggs, Sr. Behold the King & His Kingdom! 2007. 160p. 21.99 *(978-1-60266-540-8(0))*; per. 13.99 *(978-1-60266-539-2(7))* Xulon Pr., Inc.

Groff, Randy & Neeley, Linda. Translator's Notes on Luke 1 - 8. 2009. 648p. spiral bd. 60.00 *(978-1-55671-228-9(6))* SIL International.

—Translator's Notes on Mark 1 - 8. 2008. 546p. spiral bd. 60.00 *(978-1-55671-214-2(6))* SIL International.

—Translator's Notes on Mark 9 - 16. 2008. 588p. spiral bd. 60.00 *(978-1-55671-215-9(4))* SIL International.

Guide to St Marks Gospel. 16.00 *(978-0-687-85453-0(9))* Abingdon Pr.

Gurtner, Daniel M. & Willitts, Joel. Jesus, Matthew's Gospel & Early Christianity: Studies in Memory of Graham N. Stanton. Gurtner, Daniel M. & Willitts, Joel, eds. Burridge, Richard A., ed. 2011. (Library of New Testament Studies). (ENG., Illus.). 240p. 120.00 *(978-0-567-50085-4(3)*, T&T Clark Int'l) Continuum International Publishing Group, Ltd. GBR. Dist: National Bk. Network.

Hahn, Roger L. Matthew: A Commentary for Bible Students. 2007. (Wesleyan Bible Commentary Ser.). 352p. 18.99 *(978-0-89827-308-3(0))* Wesleyan Publishing Hse.

Hare, Douglas R. A. & Hare, Douglas. Matthew. 2009. (Interpretation, a Bible Commentary for Teaching & Preaching Ser.). (ENG.). 352p. pap. 30.00 *(978-0-664-23433-1(X))* Westminster John Knox Pr.

Hargreaves. Guide to St Mark's Gospel. 4th ed. (Illus.). 336p. 12.00 *(978-0-281-04786-4(3))* SPCK Publishing GBR. Dist: Pilgrim Pr., The/United Church Pr.

Harrington, Daniel. Meeting St. Mark Today. 2011. (ENG.). 144p. pap. 12.95 *(978-0-8294-2915-2(8))* Loyola Pr.

Harrington, Daniel J. The Gospel of Matthew. 2007. (Sacra Pagina Ser.). 433p. per. 29.95 *(978-0-8146-5964-9(0)*, Liturgical Pr. Bks.) Liturgical Pr.

—Meeting St. Matthew Today: Understanding the Man, His Mission, & His Message. 2010. (ENG.). 144p. pap. 12.95 *(978-0-8294-2914-5(X))* Loyola Pr.

Harrington, Daniel J. Sj & Harrington, Daniel J. Meeting St. Luke Today. 2009. (ENG.). 144p. pap. 12.95 *(978-0-8294-2916-9(6))* Loyola Pr.

Harrington, Wilfrid. What Was Mark At: The Gospel of Mark: A Commentary. 2009. (ENG.). 170p. pap. 26.95 *(978-1-85607-634-0(2))* Columba Pr. IRL. Dist: Dufour Editions, Inc.

Hartman, Lars. Mark for the Nations. 2010. (Illus.). 704p. pap. 70.00 *(978-1-55635-894-4(6)*, Pickwick Pubns.) Wipf & Stock Pubs.

Hauerwas, Stanley M. Matthew. 2007. (Brazos Theological Commentary on the Bible Ser.). 272p. (C). 29.99 *(978-1-58743-095-4(9))* Brazos Pr.

Havner, Vance. Reflections on the Gospels. 2006. (ENG.). 227p. pap. 12.99 *(978-0-87508-783-2(3))* CLC Pubns.

Hawley, Wendell C., et al. The Gospel of John, 1-3 John. 2007. (Cornerstone Biblical Commentary Ser.: 13). (ENG.). 432p. 34.99 *(978-0-8423-8341-7(7))* Tyndale Hse. Pubs.

Hayes, Kate. The Journey of the Son. 2006. 54p. pap. *(978-1-84427-097-2(1))* Scripture Union.

Hayworth, Miguel. Hope 08 A Hidden Agenda. 2009. 500p. pap. 26.95 *(978-1-4092-5754-7(1))* Lulu Enterprises Inc.

Healy, Mary & Hahn, Scott. The Gospel of Mark. 2008. (Catholic Commentary on Sacred Scripture Ser.). (Illus.). 352p. (C). pap. 19.99 *(978-0-8010-3586-9(4))* Baker Academic.

Hedrick, Charles W. Unlocking the Secrets of the Gospel according to Thomas. 2010. 246p. pap. 27.00 *(978-1-55635-239-3(5)*, Cascade Bks.) Wipf & Stock Pubs.

Henderson, Betty. Divine Service: A Woman's Bible Study. 2010. viii, 152p. pap. *(978-1-60682-158-9(X))* BJU Pr.

Henry, Matthew. Coment, Matthew Henry: Mateo: Matthew Henry's Commentary: Matthew. (SPA.). *(978-84-7228-820-1(X)*, 222102) Clie, Editorial.

—Comentario Matthew Henry: Juan: Matthew Henry's Commentary: John. (SPA.). 592p. *(978-84-7228-918-5(4)*, 222104) Clie, Editorial.

—Comentario Matthew Henry: Marcos y Lucas: Matthew Henry's Commentary: Mark & Luke. (SPA.). 552p. *(978-84-7228-899-7(4)*, 222103) Clie, Editorial.

Herr, Ken. Luke: A Commentary for Bible Students. 2007. (Wesleyan Bible Commentary Ser.). 336p. 18.99 *(978-0-89827-343-4(9))* Wesleyan Publishing Hse.

Hilgeman, Matthew J. 1:1 with Jesus: A Month-Long Daily Devotional from the Gospel of Matthew, 1 vol. 2010. 110p. pap. 19.95 *(978-1-4489-4622-8(0))* PublishAmerica, Inc.

Hill, J. Hamlyn. A Dissertation on the Gospel Commentary of S. Ephraem the Syrian. 2010. 103.28 *(978-1-61719-321-7(6))* Gorgias Pr., LLC.

Hindson, Edward & Borland, James. The Gospel of Matthew: The King Is Coming. Couch, Mal, ed. 2007. (Twenty-First Century Biblical Commentary Ser.). (ENG.). 256p. (gr. 11). 19.99 *(978-0-89957-823-1(3))* AMG Pubs.
Hindson, Edward & Couch, Mal, eds. The Gospel of Luke: Christ, the Son of Man. 2006. (21 St Century Biblical Commentary Ser.). (ENG.). 256p. (gr. 11). 19.99 *(978-0-89957-822-4(5))* AMG Pubs.
Holland, Carl E. 18 Hours. 2008. 140p. per. 13.99 *(978-1-60477-551-8(3))* Xulon Pr., Inc.
Hood, Jason B. The Messiah, His Brothers, & the Nations (Matthew 1. 1-17) 2011. (Library of New Testament Studies). 208p. 110.00 *(978-0-567-43228-5(9),* T&T Clark Int'l) Continuum International Publishing Group, Ltd. GBR. Dist: National Bk. Network.
Hornik, Heidi J., et al. Illuminating Luke Vol. 3: The Passion & Resurrection Narratives in Italian Renaissance & Baroque Paintings, 3 vols. 2007. (ENG., Illus.). 184p. pap. 49.95 *(978-0-567-02696-5(5),* T&T Clark) Continuum International Publishing Group, Ltd. GBR. Dist: National Bk. Network.
Houck, Jr. The Apostle Peter. 2009. 208p. pap. 15.99 *(978-1-60791-569-0(3))* Xulon Pr., Inc.
Hunter, Warren. God Working with God: Understanding God's Reciprocal Nature as the Greatest Key to True Intimacy. 2006. 190p. per. 15.99 *(978-0-7684-2400-3(3))* Destiny Image Pubs.
Huntzinger, Jonathan David. John, 0 vols. Hayford, Jack W. & Seemuth, David P., eds. 2006. (Spirit-Filled Life New Testament Commentary Ser.). (Illus.). 322p. per. 16.99 *(978-0-7852-5254-2(1))* Nelson, Thomas Inc.
Hybels, Bill, et al. Luke, 1 vol. 2008. (New Community Bible Study Ser.). (ENG.). 96p. pap. 7.99 *(978-0-310-28056-9(7))* Zondervan.
Inauguration Gospel of John. 94p. *(978-1-880349-06-9(X))* Pocket Testament League, Inc.
Ingham, Michael. Mansions of the Spirit: The Gospel in a Multi-Faith World. 167p. pap. 10.95 *(978-1-55126-185-0(5),* 1447) Forward Movement Pubns.
Into the Word, into the World Resource Library-Disciple II. 100.00 *(978-0-687-75722-0(3))* Abingdon Pr.
Into the Word, into the World Video #1-Disciple II. 35.00 incl. VHS *(978-0-687-75768-8(1))* Abingdon Pr.
Into the Word, into the World Video #2-Disciple II. 35.00 incl. VHS *(978-0-687-75769-5(X))* Abingdon Pr.
Into the Word, into the World Video #3-Disciple II. 35.00 incl. VHS *(978-0-687-75770-1(3))* Abingdon Pr.
Into the Word, into the World Video #4-Disciple II. 35.00 incl. VHS *(978-0-687-75771-8(1))* Abingdon Pr.
Into the Word, into the World Videos Disciple. 150.00 incl. VHS *(978-0-687-75772-5(X))* Abingdon Pr.
Into the Word, into the World Videos Disciple II. 150.00 incl. VHS *(978-0-687-75723-7(1))* Abingdon Pr.
Ironside, Henry A. & Ironside, H. A. John. 2006. (Ironside Expository Commentaries Ser.). 504p. 29.99 *(978-0-8254-2915-6(3))* Kregel Pubns.
—Luke. 2007. (Ironside Expository Commentaries Ser.). 480p. 29.99 *(978-0-8254-2919-4(6))* Kregel Pubns.
Jacobs, Alan & Nersessian, Vrej N. The Essential Gnostic Gospels: Including the Gospel of Judas, the Gospel of Thomas & the Gospel of Mary. 2009. (ENG.). 320p. pap. 19.95 *(978-1-906787-33-2(6),* Watkins Publishing) Duncan Baird Pubs. GBR. Dist: Sterling Publishing Co., Inc.
Jacobus, Melancthon. Notes on the Gospels, Critical & Explanatory; Incorporating with the Notes, on a New Plan, the Most Approved Harmony of the Four Gospels by Melanct. 2006. 324p. per. 23.99 *(978-1-4255-3227-7(6))* MPublishing.
Jefferson, Thomas. The Thomas Jefferson Bible: The Life & Morals of Jesus of Nazareth. 2007. 164p. 19.99 *(978-1-59986-716-8(8))* Filiquarian Publishing, LLC.
Jeffery, Peter. The Secret Gospel of Mark Unveiled: Imagined Rituals of Sex, Death, & Madness in a Biblical Forgery. 2007. (ENG., Illus.). 352p. 45.00 *(978-0-300-11760-8(4))* Yale Univ. Pr.
Jerome & Scheck, Thomas P. Commentary on Matthew. 2008. 360p. 39.95 *(978-0-8132-0117-7(9))* Catholic Univ. of America Pr.
Jesus, A Likely Story: A non-theistic view of Christianity's central figure, gleaned from the Gospel of Matthew. 2006. per. 14.95 *(978-0-9788430-1-4(0))* Ultimate Bks.
Jesus in the Gospels Video # 2. 35.00 *(978-0-687-02752-1(7))* Abingdon Pr.
Jesus in the Gospels Video # 3. 35.00 *(978-0-687-02732-3(2))* Abingdon Pr.
Jesus in the Gospels Video # 4. 35.00 *(978-0-687-02702-6(0))* Abingdon Pr.
Jesus in the Gospels Video #1. 35.00 *(978-0-687-02762-0(4))* Abingdon Pr.
Johnson, Edythe J. Peace, Poise, Power: Meditations for Women Based on the Gospel of Luke. 2011. 438p. 56.95 ***(978-1-258-03473-3(5))*** Literary Licensing, LLC.
Johnson, Jeffrey D. The Gift: Christmas: Luke 1 And 2. 2007. 24p. pap. 3.00 *(978-1-55635-082-5(1),* Wipf and Stock) Wipf & Stock Pubs.
—Metamorphosis Factor: Contact with Heaven-The Reversal - Matthew 17, Mark 9, Luke 9. 2007. 24p. pap. 3.00 *(978-1-55635-075-7(9),* Wipf and Stock) Wipf & Stock Pubs.
Johnson, Lin. The Book of John, 0 vols. 2006. (Smart Guide to the Bible Ser.). (Illus.). 320p. per. 14.99 *(978-1-4185-0991-0(4))* Nelson, Thomas Inc.
Johnson, Luke Timothy. The Gospel of Luke: Sacra Pagina, Paperback. Harrington, Daniel J., ed. 2006. (Sacra Pagina Ser.). 468p. per. 29.95 *(978-0-8146-5966-3(7),* Liturgical Pr. Bks.) Liturgical Pr.
Johnson, Luke Timothy. Prophetic Jesus, Prophetic Church: The Challenge of Luke-Acts to Contemporary Christians. 2011. 206p. pap. 23.00 ***(978-0-8028-0390-0(3))*** Eerdmans, William B. Publishing Co.
Jones, Duane. Jesus Was a Middle Schooler Too. 2007. 84p. per. 9.99 *(978-1-60477-011-7(2))* Xulon Pr., Inc.
Jones, Lonetha. Who Touched Me? 2010. 47p. pap. 11.95 *(978-1-4327-5308-5(8))* Outskirts Pr., Inc.
Jordan, Rick. A Holy & Surprising Birth. 2009. pap. *(978-0-9823842-9-9(7))* NextSunday Resources.
Journey Through the Bible-John-Korean. 4.00 *(978-0-687-01982-3(6))* Abingdon Pr.
Journey Through the Bible Luke Korean. 4.00 *(978-0-687-01983-0(4))* Abingdon Pr.
Journey Through the Bible Mark Korean. 4.00 *(978-0-687-01984-7(2))* Abingdon Pr.
Journey Through the Bible Matthew Korean. 4.00 *(978-0-687-02062-1(X))* Abingdon Pr.
Kaniamparampil, Curian, ed. The Gospel of St. Matthew. 2010. 96.80 *(978-1-61143-564-1(1))* Gorgias Pr., LLC.
Kardec, Allan. El Evangelio Segun el Espiritismo.Tr. of Gospel According to Spiritism. (SPA.). pap. 8.98 *(978-968-15-0136-5(5))* Editores Mexicanos Unidos MEX. Dist: Lectorum Pubns., Inc.
Karris, Robert J. John: Stories of the Word & Faith. 2008. (NCP Biblical Commentaries Resources for Pastoral Ministry Ser.). 176p. pap. 15.95 *(978-1-56548-297-5(2))* New City Pr.
Kasomo, Daniel W. New Testament Studies. 2010. 148p. pap. *(978-3-8383-0404-5(7))* Lambert Academic Publishing.
Keene, Lorie Looney. Pull up a Chair: You, Me, & the Gospel of John. 2008. (ENG.). 192p. pap. 12.99 *(978-1-59669-202-2(2))* New Hope Pubs.
Keener, Craig S. The Gospel of John: A Commentary 2 Volume Set. 2010. 1696p. pap. 59.95 *(978-1-59856-537-9(0))* Hendrickson Pubs. Marketing, LLC.
—The Gospel of Matthew: A Socio-Rhetorical Commentary. 2009. 2000p. pap. 50.00 *(978-0-8028-6498-7(8))* Eerdmans, William B. Publishing Co.
Keener, Craig S. Matthew. 2011. (IVP New Testament Commentary Ser.: Volume 1). (ENG.). 444p. pap. 20.00 ***(978-0-8308-4001-4(X),*** IVP Acad.) InterVarsity Pr.
Kernaghan, Ronald J. Mark. 2010. (IVP New Testament Commentary Ser.: Volume 2). (ENG.). 351p. pap. 18.00 *(978-0-8308-4002-1(8),* IVP Acad.) InterVarsity Pr.
Killinger, John. Hidden Mark: Exploring Christianity's Heretical Gospel. 2010. 160p. pap. 18.00 *(978-0-88146-223-4(3))* Mercer Univ. Pr.
Kim, Seyoon. Christ & Caesar: The Gospel & the Roman Empire in the Writings of Paul & Luke. 2008. 240p. pap. 24.00 *(978-0-8028-6008-8(7))* Eerdmans, William B. Publishing Co.
Kleist, James A., tr. The Memoirs of St Peter: Or the Gospel According to St. Mark. 2011. 242p. 46.95 ***(978-1-258-09472-0(X))*** Literary Licensing, LLC.
Klutz, Todd. The Exorcism Stories in Luke-Acts: A Sociostylistic Reading. 2008. (Society for New Testament Studies Monograph Ser.). (ENG.). 312p. pap. 44.00 *(978-0-521-07605-0(6))* Cambridge Univ. Pr.
Kruse, Colin G. John. 2008. (Tyndale New Testament Commentaries Ser.: Volume 4). (ENG.). 389p. pap. 17.00 *(978-0-8308-4234-6(9),* IVP Acad.) 2007. (Tyndale New Testament Commentaries Ser.). 395p. per. 16.00 *(978-0-8308-2983-5(0))* InterVarsity Pr.
Kysar, Robert D. Invitation to John. ldr.'s ed. 2007. (Short-Term Disciple Bible Studies). 63p. pap. 13.65 *(978-0-687-64277-9(9))* Abingdon Pr.
—Short-Term Disciple Bible Study - Invitation to John Participant Book. 2007. (Short-Term Disciple Bible Studies). (Illus.). 141p. per. 11.50 *(978-0-687-64257-1(4))* Abingdon Pr.
LaChance, Albert. The Way of Christ: The Gospel of John through the Unitive Lens. 2009. (ENG.). 320p. pap. 16.95 *(978-1-55643-801-1(X))* North Atlantic Bks.
Lagnado, Edward. Zacchaeus: The Crippled Tree-climber. 2007. 272p. pap. *(978-1-84401-864-2(4))* Athena Pr.
Lamsa, George M. Gospel Light. 508p. 36.95 *(978-0-9675989-9-4(0))* Aramaic Bible Society,The.
Lange, John Peter. The Gospel According to John: An Exegetical & Doctrinal Commentary. Schaff, Philip, tr. 2007. (Lange's Commentary on the Holy Scripture: Ser.). 670p. pap. 55.00 *(978-1-55635-413-7(4),* Wipf and Stock) Wipf & Stock Pubs.
—The Gospel According to Mark: An Exegetical & Doctrinal Commentary. Shedd, William G. T., ed. 6th ed. 2007. (Lange's Commentary on the Holy Scripture: Ser.). 166p. pap. 18.00 *(978-1-55635-402-1(9),* Wipf and Stock) Wipf & Stock Pubs.
Larsen, Kasper Bro. Recognizing the Stranger: Recognition Scenes in the Gospel of John. 2008. (Biblical Interpretation Ser.). (Illus.). 256p. *(978-90-04-16690-5(4))* BRILL.
Lathrop, John P. Answer the Prayer of Jesus: A Call for Biblical Unity. 2011. (House of Prisca & Aquila Ser.). 128p. pap. 16.00 *(978-1-60899-392-5(2),* Wipf and Stock) Wipf & Stock Pubs.
Laurie, Greg. Living Out Your Faith Vol. 3: Messages from the Gospel of John. 2008. (ENG.). 288p. per. 11.95 *(978-0-9777103-2-4(7))* Kerygma Publishing.
—Strengthening Your Faith: Messages from the Gospel of John. 2008. (ENG.). 227p. per. 9.95 *(978-0-9762400-7-5(6))* Kerygma Publishing.
Lavender, Earl. Luke: Jesus Is Savior. 2007. (Meditative Commentary Ser.). 238p. per. 13.99 *(978-0-89112-500-6(0),* Leafwood Pubs.) Abilene Christian Univ. Pr.
—Meditative Commentary Series: Mark: Jesus Is God's Son. 2007. (Meditative Commentary Ser.). 143p. pap. 11.99 *(978-0-89112-551-8(5),* Leafwood Pubs.) Abilene Christian Univ. Pr.
Lawson, Keith. The Purpose of This Life: The Full Gospel. 2009. 116p. pap. 13.95 *(978-1-4327-2398-9(7))* Outskirts Pr., Inc.
Lee, Sang-Il. Jesus & Gospel Traditions in Bilingual Context: A Study in the Interdirectionality of Language. 2011. (Beihefte Zur Zeitschrift Für Die Neutestamentliche Wissenschaft und Die Kunde der älteren Kirche Ser.). (ENG.). XVIII, 522p. 168.00 ***(978-3-11-026617-7(2))*** De Gruyter, Walter Inc.
Lee, Witness. The Holy Word for Morning Reviva: Crystallization-study of the Gospel of Mark, Vol. 1. 2007. 111p. per. *(978-0-7363-3379-5(7))* Living Stream Ministry.
—The Holy Word for Morning Revival: Crystallization-study of the Gospel of Mark, 2. 2007. 119p. per. 5.50 *(978-0-7363-3380-1(0))* Living Stream Ministry.
Leston, Stephen, et al. Luke & John Vol. 9: Life That Lasts Forever. 2008. (Bible Reference Library). (ENG.). 224p. per. 9.99 *(978-1-59789-775-4(2),* Barbour Bks.) Barbour Publishing, Inc.
Lifetogether. Matthew. 2010. (Deepening Life Together Ser.). 24.99 *(978-0-8010-3052-9(8));* pap. 8.99 *(978-0-8010-6922-2(X))* Baker Bks.
Ling, Timothy J. M. The Judaean Poor & the Fourth Gospel. 2006. (Society for New Testament Studies Monograph Ser.). (ENG.). 264p. 104.00 *(978-0-521-85722-2(8))* Cambridge Univ. Pr.
Llull, Ramon & Pereira, Michela. Raimundi Lulli Opera Latina. 2008. (Corpus Christianorum Ser.: Vol. 224). (LAT, GER & FRE., Illus.). 609p. *(978-2-503-03000-5(9))* Brepols Pubs.
Loftus, Dudley. A Clear & Learned Explication of the History of Our Blessed Saviour Jesus Christ. 2011. pap. 43.85 *(978-1-61143-933-5(7))* Gorgias Pr., LLC.
Lotz, Anne Graham. Just Give Me Jesus. Lt. ed. 2009. (ENG.). 621p. pap. 17.99 *(978-1-59415-291-7(8))* Cengage Gale.
Low, Kenneth. Dark Knowledge. 2011. 328p. 37.00 *(978-1-4567-5566-9(8));* pap. 27.00 *(978-1-4567-5567-6(6))* AuthorHouse.
Lucado, Max. Book of John: When God Became Man, 0 vols. 2006. (Inspirational Bible Study; Life Lessons with Max Lucado Ser.). 128p. per. 9.99 *(978-1-4185-0944-6(2))* Nelson, Thomas Inc.
—Book of Luke: Jesus, the Son of Man, 0 vols. 2006. (Inspirational Bible Study; Life Lessons with Max Lucado Ser.). 128p. per. 9.99 *(978-1-4185-0943-9(4))* Nelson, Thomas Inc.
—Book of Mark: A Life-Changing Story, 0 vols. 2006. (Inspirational Bible Study; Life Lessons with Max Lucado Ser.). 128p. per. 9.99 *(978-1-4185-0942-2(6))* Nelson, Thomas Inc.
—A Gentle Thunder: Hearing God Through the Storm. 2012. 240p. pap. 15.99 ***(978-0-8499-4733-9(2))*** Nelson, Thomas Inc.
—A Gentle Thunder: Hearing God through the Storm, 0 vols. 2009. (Bestseller Collection). 256p. 9.99 *(978-0-8499-2148-3(1))* Nelson, Thomas Inc.
—El Trueno Apacible, 0 vols. 2008.Tr. of Gentle Thunder. (SPA.). 288p. pap. 16.99 *(978-1-60255-253-1(3))* Grupo Nelson.
—3:16: A Study for Small Groups, 0 vols. 2007. (ENG.). 128p. per. 9.99 *(978-1-4185-2923-9(0))* Nelson, Thomas Inc.
Lucas. (Comentario Biblico Mundo Hispano Ser.: Vol. 16).Tr. of Luke. (SPA.). pap. 10.99 *(978-0-311-03116-0(1),* Editorial Mundo Hispano) Casa Bautista de Publicaciones.
Luebbert, Richard W. Jesus for the 21st Century: The Unified Gospel. 2011. 288p. 25.99 *(978-1-4520-6711-7(2));* pap. 15.49 *(978-1-4520-6710-0(4))* AuthorHouse.
Luke. (People's Bible Commentary Ser.). 272p. 14.99 *(978-0-7586-0441-5(6))* Concordia Publishing Hse.
Lupieri, Edmondo F. A Commentary on the Apocalypse of John. Johnson, Maria Poggi & Kamesar, Adam, trs. from ITA. 2006. (Italian Texts & Studies on Religion & Society). (ENG & GEC., Illus.). 395p. per. *(978-0-8028-6073-6(7))* Eerdmans, William B. Publishing Co.
Luz, Ulrich. Matthew 1-7. Koester, Helmut, ed. Crouch, James E., tr. from GER. 2007. (Hermeneia Ser.). (Illus.). 472p. 75.00 *(978-0-8006-6099-4(4),* Fortress Pr.) Augsburg Fortress, Pubs.
Luzac's Semitic Text & Translation Series, 20 vols. in 18. reprint ed. *(978-0-404-11290-5(0))* AMS Pr., Inc.
Lyman, Mary Redington Ely. The Fourth Gospel & the Life of Today. 2007. (ENG.). 166p. 36.95 *(978-0-548-06901-1(8))* Kessinger Publishing, LLC.
MacArthur, John. John 12-21. 2008. (Macarthur New Testament Commentary Serie Ser.). (ENG.). 440p. 29.99 *(978-0-8024-0824-2(9))* Moody Pubs.
—1-3 John. 2007. (Macarthur New Testament Commentary Serie Ser.). (ENG.). 304p. 26.99 *(978-0-8024-0772-6(2))* Moody Pubs.
MacKenzie, R. Sheldon. The Master Teacher: Sermons from Mark. 2007. 170p. *(978-0-7880-2189-3(3),* Fairway Pr.) CSS Publishing Co.
Maclaren, Alexander. Expositions of Holy Scripture: St. John Chaps. XV to XXI. 2007. (ENG.). 324p. pap. 23.99 *(978-1-4264-2921-7(5));* 364p. pap. 26.99 *(978-1-4264-2974-3(6))* BiblioBazaar.
—Expositions of Holy Scripture: St. John Chapters I to XIV. 2007. (ENG.). 598p. pap. 30.99 *(978-1-4264-2562-2(7),);* 662p. pap. 34.99 *(978-1-4264-2603-2(8))* BiblioBazaar.
—Expositions of Holy Scripture: St. Luke. 2007. (ENG.). 652p. pap. 32.99 *(978-1-4264-3010-7(8));* 724p. pap. 35.99 *(978-1-4264-2957-6(6))* BiblioBazaar.
—Expositions of Holy Scripture: St. Mark. 2006. 514p. pap. 30.99 *(978-1-4264-2563-9(5))* 2007. (ENG.). 552p. pap. 32.99 *(978-1-4264-2604-9(6))* BiblioBazaar.
—Expositions of Holy Scripture: St. Matthew Chaps. IX to XXVIII. 2007. (ENG.). 616p. pap. 31.99 *(978-1-4264-2330-7(6));* 428p. pap. 28.99 *(978-1-4264-2378-9(0))* BiblioBazaar.
MacLear, G. F. The Gospel According to St Mark, with Maps, Notes & Introduction. 2011. 288p. pap. 30.45 ***(978-1-4460-7027-7(1))*** Research Pr.
Mahelona Sr., Vernon. The Allegory of the Gospel of Jesus Christ. 2007. 244p. per. 14.99 *(978-1-60034-641-5(3))* Xulon Pr., Inc.
Maltese, Tess. By Their Fruits Ye Shall Know Them Matthew: 20. 2007. 88p. per. 9.99 *(978-1-60477-347-7(2))* Xulon Pr., Inc.
Manzanga, Peter. A Background Study of Life & Light in John's Gospel. 2010. 144p. pap. *(978-3-639-26629-0(3))* VDM Verlag Dr. Mueller e.K.
Marcus, Joel. Mark 8-16. 2009. (Anchor Yale Bible Commentaries Ser.). (ENG., Illus.). 672p. 55.00 *(978-0-300-14116-0(5))* Yale Univ. Pr.
Maris McCrabb. Reflections on the Gospel of Matthew. 2010. 300p. 31.95 *(978-1-4502-0246-6(2));* pap. 21.95 *(978-1-4502-0244-2(6))* iUniverse, Inc.
Martin, George. Bringing the Gospel of Mark to Life: Insight & Inspiration. 2007. (Opening the Scriptures Ser.). 477p. per. 19.95 *(978-1-59325-121-5(1))* Word Among Us Pr.
—Bringing the Gospel of Matthew to Life: Insight & Inspiration. 2008. (Opening the Scriptures Ser.). (Illus.). 688p. pap. 29.95 *(978-1-59325-130-7(0))* Word Among Us Pr.
Martin, Harold S. Brethren New Testament Commentary - 1, 2, 3 John. 2007. (ENG.). 12.00 *(978-0-9777766-0-3(3))* Brethren Revival Fellowship.
—Brethren New Testament Commentary - Luke. 2007. (ENG.). 20.00 *(978-0-9745027-9-3(0))* Brethren Revival Fellowship.
Martin, James C., et al. A Visual Guide to Gospel Events: Fascinating Insights into Where They Happened & Why. 2010. 208p. 29.99 *(978-0-8010-1311-9(9))* Baker Bks.
Martin, John C. The Gospel According to Matthew. 2011. 420p. pap. 20.49 *(978-1-4567-3944-7(1))* AuthorHouse.
Matthew. (People's Bible Commentary Ser.). 456p. 16.99 *(978-0-7586-0439-2(4))* Concordia Publishing Hse.
Maydell, Karl. Ephesus: Bible Study Commentary. 2010. 175p. pap. 18.95 *(978-1-4327-5780-9(6))* Outskirts Pr., Inc.
McCullar, Michael D. & Letson, Rickey. Sessions with Mark: Following Jesus at Full Speed. 2008. pap. *(978-1-57312-517-8(2))* Smyth & Helwys Publishing, Inc.
McDonnell, Rea. From Glory to Glory: Spirit & Sacrament in the Writings of Paul & John. 2011. pap. *(978-1-56548-368-2(5))* New City Community Pr.
McGrath, Mark. A Forgotten Gospel: Rediscovering a Radical, Compassionate Approach to Evangelism. 2008. 80p. per. 12.99 *(978-0-9790362-0-0(8))* McGrath Communications Group.
McHugh, John. John 1-4: A Critical & Exegetical Commentary. 2009. (International Critical Commentary Ser.). (ENG.). 368p. 100.00 *(978-0-567-03158-7(6),* T&T Clark Int'l) Continuum International Publishing Group, Ltd. GBR. Dist: National Bk. Network.
McKenna, Megan. Luke: The Book of Blessings & Woes. 2009. (ENG.). 240p. pap. 19.95 *(978-1-56548-323-1(5))* New City Pr.
—Matthew: The Book of Mercy. 2007. 200p. per. 17.95 *(978-1-56548-279-1(4))* New City Pr.
McMurray, Carl. From Beneath the Altar. 2007. (Illus.). 252p. pap. 13.95 *(978-0-9774754-2-1(5))* Spiritbuilding.
McWhirter, Jocelyn. The Bridegroom Messiah & the People of God: Marriage in the Fourth Gospel. 2006. (Society for New Testament Studies Monograph Ser.). (ENG.). 192p. 117.00 *(978-0-521-86425-1(9))* Cambridge Univ. Pr.
Meadows, James. Matthew 24. pap. 1.99 *(978-0-89098-449-9(2))* Twentieth Century Christian Bks.
Meadows, James L. Luke. pap. 5.99 *(978-0-89098-391-1(7))* Twentieth Century Christian Bks.
—Mark. pap. 5.50 *(978-0-89098-390-4(9))* Twentieth Century Christian Bks.
—Matthew, Vol. I. pap. 5.50 *(978-0-89098-388-1(7))* Vol. II. pap. 5.50 *(978-0-89098-389-8(5))* Twentieth Century Christian Bks.
—Study of John. pap. 5.99 *(978-0-89098-392-8(5))* Twentieth Century Christian Bks.
A Medieval Christmas. 16.95 *(978-0-89870-991-9(1))* Ignatius Pr.
Mell, Ulrich. Christliche Hauskirche und Neues Testament: Die Ikonologie des Baptisteriums von Dura Europos und das Diatessaron Tatians. 2010. (Novum Testamentum et Orbis Antiquus/Studien zur Umwelt des Neuen Testaments (NTOA/StUNT) Ser.). (GER., Illus.). 340p. (C). 98.00 *(978-3-525-53394-9(2))* Vandenhoeck & Ruprecht GmbH & Co. KG DEU. Dist: ISD.
Mercier, Roberto. Evangelio Segun El Discipulo A Quien Jesus Amaba. Vol. 1. 744p. 26.95 *(978-958-607-721-7(7),* Vol. 2. 856p. 26.95 *(978-958-607-722-4(5))* Sociedad de San Pablo COL. Dist: St Pauls/Alba Hse. Pubs.
Metzger, Paul Louis. The Gospel of John: When Love Comes to Town. 2010. (Resonate Ser.). (ENG.). 304p. pap. 18.00 *(978-0-8308-3641-3(1),* IVP Bks.) InterVarsity Pr.
Michaels, J. Ramsey. The Gospel of John. 2010. 1152p. 65.00 *(978-0-8028-2302-1(5))* Eerdmans, William B. Publishing Co.
Mills, William C. A Light to the Gentiles: Reflections on the Gospel of Luke. 2008. 128p. pap. 13.95 *(978-1-933275-25-3(1),* Orthodox Research Institute) Cocheco Falls Publishing.
Mitchell, Alison. Why Did Jesus Come? 2010. 6p. (J). *(978-1-904889-75-5(1))* Good Bk. Co.
Moberg, Marlys Taege. The Heart of Jesus: Women in the Gospel of Luke. 2009. 52p. pap., wbk. ed. 5.99 *(978-0-7586-1661-6(9));* 48p. pap. 8.99 *(978-0-7586-1660-9(0))* Concordia Publishing Hse.

B

Moloney, Francis J. The Living Voice of the Gospel: The Gospels Today. 2006. (ENG.). 344p. (Orig.). pap. 23.95 *(978-1-84730-009-6(X))* Veritas Pubns. IRL. Dist: Dufour Editions, Inc.

Montague, George T. Companion God: A Cross-Cultural Commentary on the Gospel of Matthew. 2010. (Illus.). 368p. pap. 24.95 *(978-0-8091-4501-0(4))* Paulist Pr.

Moo, Douglas J. The Old Testament in the Gospel Passion Narratives. 2008. (Illus.). 480p. pap. 53.00 *(978-1-55635-757-2(5))* Wipf & Stock Pubs.

Moore, Michael S. WealthWatch: A Study of Socioeconomic Conflict in the Bible. 2011. 320p. pap. 35.00 ***(978-1-61097-296-3(1)***, Pickwick Pubns.) Wipf & Stock Pubs.

Moore, Phil. Straight to the Heart of John: 60 Bite-Sized Insights, 1 vol. 2012. (Straight to the Heart Ser.). 272p. pap. 14.99 ***(978-0-85721-253-5(2)***, Monarch Bks.) Lion Hudson PLC GBR. Dist: Kregel Pubns.

Moore, Phil. Straight to the Heart of Matthew: 60 Bite-Sized Insights, 1 vol. 2010. (Straight to the Heart Ser.). 272p. pap. 14.99 *(978-1-85424-988-3(6)*, Monarch Bks.) Lion Hudson PLC GBR. Dist: Kregel Pubns.

Mopsuestia, Theodore of. Commentary on the Gospel of John, 1 vol. Elowsky, Joel C., ed. Conti, Marco, tr. from SYR. 2010. (Ancient Christian Texts). (ENG.). 202p. 60.00 *(978-0-8308-2906-4(7)*, IVP Acad.) InterVarsity Pr.

Moretz, Jim. Mark: Lectio Divina for Youth. 2007. (Ancient Faith Ser.). (ENG.). 80p. per. 7.99 *(978-0-8341-5015-7(6)*, 083-415-0158) Beacon Hill Pr. of Kansas City.

Morgan, G. Campbell. The Gospel According to Luke. 2010. (G. Campbell Morgan Reprint Ser.). 284p. pap. 30.00 *(978-1-60899-299-7(3)*, Wipf and Stock) Wipf & Stock Pubs.

Morgan, Philip. Walk Again with Me. 2009. 87p. pap. 9.96 *(978-0-557-06363-5(9))* Lulu Enterprises Inc.

Morison, John Hopkins. Disquisitions & Notes on the Gospels Matthew by John H Morison. 2006. 548p. per. 29.99 *(978-1-4255-6077-5(6))* MPublishing.

Morris, Leon. Luke. 2007. (Tyndale New Testament Commentaries Ser.). (ENG.). 382p. per. 15.00 *(978-0-8308-2982-8(2))* InterVarsity Pr.

Morris, Leon L. Luke. 2008. (Tyndale New Testament Commentaries Ser.: Volume 3). (ENG., Illus.). 370p. pap. 17.00 *(978-0-8308-4233-9(0)*, IVP Acad.) InterVarsity Pr.

Moule, Handley C. G. The High Priestly Prayer: A Devotional Commentary on the Seventeenth Chapter of St. John. 2007. 222p. pap. 18.00 *(978-1-55635-455-7(X)*, Wipf and Stock) Wipf & Stock Pubs.

Muddiman, John & Barton, John. The Gospels. 2010. (ENG., Illus.). 358p. pap. 24.95 *(978-0-19-958025-5(1))* Oxford Univ. Pr., Inc.

Mullins, Michael. The Gospel of Luke: A Commentary. 2010. (ENG.). 544p. pap. 49.95 *(978-1-85607-691-3(1))* Columba Pr. IRL. Dist: Dufour Editions, Inc.

—The Gospel of Matthew: A Commentary. 2007. (ENG.). 661p. pap. 46.95 *(978-1-85607-591-6(5))* Columba Pr. IRL. Dist: Dufour Editions, Inc.

Myers, Charles D., Jr. & Griggs, Donald L. Mark's Gospel from Scratch: The New Testament for Beginners. 2010. (Bible from Scratch Ser.). (ENG.). 112p. pap. 13.00 *(978-0-664-23486-7(0))* Westminster John Knox Pr.

Christopher. 666 the Mark of America, Seat of the Beast - the Apostle John's New Testament Revelation Unfolded. 2006. 546p. pap. 20.99 *(978-0-9785264-2-9(2)*, Worldwide United Publishing) Pearl Publishing, LLC.

Christopher. 666 the Mark of America, Seat of the Beast - the Apostle John's New Testament Revelation Unfolded. ltd. ed. 2006. *(978-0-9785264-0-5(6))* Pearl Publishing, LLC.

Na, Christopher. 666 the Mark of America, Seat of the Beast - the Apostle John's New Testament Revelation Unfolded. 2006. (ENG.). 546p. pap. 28.99 *(978-0-9785264-1-2(4)*, Worldwide United Publishing) Pearl Publishing, LLC.

Nappa, Mike. Interactive Illustrations-the Gospels: For Every Preacher, Teacher, & Small Group Leader. 2010. (Interactive Illustrations Ser.). (ENG.). 160p. pap. 12.99 *(978-0-7847-2357-9(5))* Standard Publishing.

Nast, William. The Gospel Records: Their Genuineness, Authenticity, Historic Verity, & inspiration, with Some Preliminary Remarks on the Gospel History. by William. 2006. 380p. per. 26.99 *(978-1-4255-4009-8(0))* MPublishing.

National Geographic Society Staff, et al, eds. The Gospel of Judas. 2nd ed. 2008. (ENG., Illus.). 224p. pap. 12.95 *(978-1-4262-0048-9(X)*, National Geographic) National Geographic Society.

Nee, Watchman. Preguntas Vitales Sobre el Evangelio: Crucial Question on the Gospel. (SPA.). *(978-84-7645-235-6(7)*, 223258) Clie, Editorial.

Nelson Impact, creator. Matthew: The Kingdom of Heaven, 0 vols. 2006. (Nelson Impact Bible Study Guide Ser.). (Illus.). 128p. stu. ed., per. 9.99 *(978-1-4185-0866-1(7))* Nelson, Thomas Inc.

Nerses & Thomson, R. W. Nerses of Lambron. Commentary on the Revelation of Saint John: Translation of the Armenian Text, Notes & Introduction. 2007. (Hebrew University Armenian Studies Ser.). (ENG.). 225p. (C). pap. 63.00 *(978-90-429-1866-5(7))* Peeters Pubs. & Booksellers BEL. Dist: Brown, David Bk. Co., The.

Neumann, Nils. Lukas und Menippos: Hoheit und Niedrigkeit in Lk 1,1-2,40 und in der menippischen Literatur. Novum Testamentum et Orbis Antiquus/Studien zur Umwelt des Neuen Testaments (NTOA/StUNT) 68. 2008. (Novum Testamentum et Orbis Antiquus/Studien zur Umwelt des Neuen Testaments (NTOA/StUNT) Ser.). (GER., Illus.). 384p. (C). 98.00 *(978-3-525-53965-1(7))* Vandenhoeck & Ruprecht GmbH & Co. KG DEU. Dist: ISD.

Newbolt, W. C. E. The Gospel of Experience or the Witness of Human Life to the Truth of Revelation. 2007. (ENG.). 222p. 39.95 *(978-0-548-01581-0(3))* Kessinger Publishing, LLC.

Neyrey, Jerome H. The Gospel of John. 2006. (New Cambridge Bible Commentary Ser.). (ENG.). 374p. 85.00 *(978-0-521-82801-7(5))*; (Illus.). per. 28.00 *(978-0-521-53521-2(2))* Cambridge Univ. Pr.

Nyman, Monte S. New Testament Restoration Harmony: The Complete Guide to the Four Gospels. 2006. 411p. pap. 24.99 *(978-1-55517-979-3(7))* Cedar Fort, Inc./CFI Distribution.

Odia, Ruth. The Kingdom of God: A Children's First Daily Devotional. 2009. 484p. pap. 24.99 *(978-1-60791-672-7(X))* Xulon Pr., Inc.

O'Driscoll, Herbert. A Time for Good News: Reflections on the Gospel for People on the Go, Year B. 152p. pap. 15.95 *(978-0-921846-32-1(0)*, 1378) Anglican Bk. Ctr. CAN. Dist: Forward Movement Pubns.

—A Time for Good News: Reflections on the Gospel for People on the Go: Year A. 137p. pap. 15.95 *(978-0-921846-07-9(X)*, 1359) Anglican Bk. Ctr. CAN. Dist: Forward Movement Pubns.

—A Time for Good News: Reflections on the Gospel for People on the Go: Year C. 157p. pap. 15.95 *(978-0-921846-41-3(X)*, 1320) Anglican Bk. Ctr. CAN. Dist: Forward Movement Pubns.

Ogden, D. Kelly & Skinner, Andrew C. Verse by Verse, the Four Gospels. 2006. (Illus.). viii, 856p. *(978-1-59038-583-8(7))* Deseret Bk. Co.

Ogenaarekhua, Mary. Effective Prayers for Various Situations. 2007. 268p. per. 18.95 *(978-0-9774265-9-1(9))* To His Glory Publishing Co., Inc.

O'Grady, John F. The Gospel of Matthew: Question by Question. 2007. (Question by Question Ser.). 313p. per. 24.95 *(978-0-8091-4440-2(9)*, 4440-2) Paulist Pr.

Olubobokun, John A. The Parallel Chronological Gospels. 2011. 236p. pap. 24.99 ***(978-1-59755-262-2(3)***, Advantage Inspirational) Advantage Bks.

O'Malley, William J. On Your Mark: Reading Scripture Without a Teacher. 2011. 19.95 *(978-0-8146-3350-2(1))*; E-Book *(978-0-8146-3944-3(5))* Liturgical Pr.

Origen. The Commentary of Origen on S. John's Gospel. Brooke, Alan England, ed. 2011. (Cambridge Library Collection - Religion Ser.). (ENG.). 360p. pap. 29.99 *(978-1-108-02956-8(6))*; 362p. pap. 29.99 *(978-1-108-02955-1(8))* Cambridge Univ. Pr.

Orozco, Ellis, et al. The Gospel of Mark: Jesus' Works & Words: Adult Bible Study Guide. 2007. 148p. pap. *(978-1-931060-96-7(7))* Baptistway.

Osborne, Grant R. Matthew, 1 vol. Zondervan Publishing Staff & Arnold, Clinton E., eds. 2010. (Zondervan Exegetical Commentary on the New Testament Ser.). (ENG.). 1152p. 49.99 *(978-0-310-24357-1(2))* Zondervan.

Oxford University Press Staff, ed. The Armenian Gospel of the Infancy: With Three Early Versions of the Protevangelium of James. Terian, Abraham, tr. from ARM. 2008. (ENG.). 272p. 145.00 *(978-0-19-954156-0(6))* Oxford Univ. Pr., Inc.

Pace, Rose Mary. The Best Wine: The Master of the Feast Called the Bridegroom & Said to Him, Every Man at the Beginning Sets Out the Good Wine, & When the Guests Have Well Drunk, Then the Inferior, but You Have Kept the Best W. 2009. 320p. pap. 18.99 *(978-1-60791-758-8(0))* Xulon Pr., Inc.

Papadopoulos, Gerasimos & Chamberas, Peter A. The Gospel of St. John: A Commentary. 2010. (GRE & ENG.). *(978-1-935317-15-9(6))*; *(978-1-935317-14-2(8))*; (GRE & ENG.). 341p. pap. *(978-1-935317-06-7(7))* Holy Cross Orthodox Pr.

Park, Tae Soo. A Biblical Response to Open Theism. 2010. 208p. pap. *(978-3-639-23261-5(5))* VDM Verlag Dr. Mueller e.K.

Paterson, Ross. The Antioch Factor. 256p. *(978-1-85240-284-6(9))* Sovereign World, Ltd.

Payne Smith, Robert, intro. The Syriac Version of Cyril of Alexandria's Commentary on Luke. 2010. (SYR.). 140.00 *(978-1-60724-939-9(1))* Gorgias Pr., LLC.

Perkins, Tyrone C. A Commentary on the Gospel According to John. 144p. pap. 9.95 *(978-1-56794-211-8(3)*, C-2565) Star Bible & Tract Corp.

Peterson, Eugene H. A Year with Jesus: Daily Readings & Meditations. 2006. (ENG.). 432p. 19.95 *(978-0-06-111843-2(5)*, HarperOne) HarperCollins Pubs.

Pink, Arthur W. The Prophetic Parables of Matthew. 2011. 100p. pap. 12.99 ***(978-1-61203-314-3(8))*** Bottom of the Hill Publishing.

—Why Four Gospels? 2011. 114p. pap. 12.99 ***(978-1-61203-212-2(5))*** Bottom of the Hill Publishing.

—Why Four Gospels? 2010. 192p. pap. 17.00 *(978-1-60899-786-2(3)*, Wipf and Stock) Wipf & Stock Pubs.

Pink, Arthur Walkington. The Prophetic Parables of Matthew. 2011. 104p. 39.95 ***(978-1-258-05641-4(0))*** Literary Licensing, LLC.

Placher, William C. Mark. 2010. (Belief Ser.). (ENG.). 272p. 30.00 *(978-0-664-23209-2(4))* Westminster John Knox Pr.

Plisch, Uwe-Karsten. The Gospel of Thomas: Original Text with Commentary. Robinson, Gesine Schenke, tr. 2009. (Illus.). 281p. 69.95 *(978-1-59856-308-5(4))* Hendrickson Pubs. Marketing, LLC.

Plummer, Alfred. An Exegetical Commentary on the Gospel according to S. Matthew. 2010. pap. 74.80 *(978-1-61719-742-0(4))* Gorgias Pr., LLC.

Pokorný, Petr. Commentary on the Gospel of Thomas: From Interpretations to the Interpreted. 2009. (Jewish & Christian Text Ser.). (ENG.). 190p. 120.00 *(978-0-567-02744-3(9)*, T&T Clark Int'l) Continuum International Publishing Group, Ltd. GBR. Dist: National Bk. Network.

Polich, Laurie. John, 1 vol. 2006. (Studies on the Go Ser.). (ENG., Illus.). 128p. (gr. 13). pap. 9.99 *(978-0-310-27200-7(9))* Zondervan.

Pontifical Bibical Commssion Staff. Historicity of Gospels. 16p. pap. 1.95 *(978-0-8198-3344-0(4)*, 332-111) Pauline Bks. & Media.

Porter, J. R. & Porter, J.R. Jesucristo: Vida, Escenario, Doctrina, Interpretaciones, Jesus en el Arte. Gutierrez, Margarita, tr. 2009. (SPA.). 240p. pap. 15.95 *(978-84-8076-723-1(5))* Blume ESP. Dist: Independent Pubs. Group.

Powers, B. Ward. The Progressive Publication of Matthew, 1 vol. 2010. (ENG.). 624p. pap. 36.99 *(978-0-8054-4848-1(9)*, B&H Academic) B&H Publishing Group.

Practical Christianity Foundation, comment. Matthew: A King's Randsom. 2007. (Easy-to-Read Commentary Ser.). 668p. per. 12.99 *(978-1-60098-003-9(1))* Green Key Bks.

Price, Robert M. Night of the Living Savior. 2011. vii, 239p. pap. 21.95 *(978-1-57884-010-6(4))* American Atheist Pr.

Proctor, John. Matthew: Daily Bible Commentary: A Guide for Reflection & Prayer. 2007. (Daily Bible Commentary Ser.). 256p. per. 12.95 *(978-1-59856-185-2(5))* Hendrickson Pubs. Marketing, LLC.

Puosi, Eric E. I Am Love. 2007. 432p. per. 21.99 *(978-1-60477-409-2(6))* Xulon Pr., Inc.

Quesnel, Pasquier. The Gospels: With Moral Reflections on Each Verse. Vol. 2. 2006. 648p. per. 34.99 *(978-1-4255-6684-5(7))* MPublishing.

—The Gospels V1: with Moral Reflections on Each Verse. 2007. pap. 48.95 *(978-1-4304-5197-6(1))* Kessinger Publishing, LLC.

Reed, David. Parallel Gospels in Harmony - with Study Guide. 2009. 282p. pap. 18.98 *(978-0-557-07435-8(5))* Lulu Enterprises Inc.

Reich, Keith A. Figuring Jesus: The Power of Rhetorical Figures of Speech in the Gospel of Luke. 2011. 185p. *(978-90-04-20185-9(8))* BRILL.

Reid, John Howard. Essential Bible Wisdom: GOOD NEWS by John, the Beloved Disciple, & John, the Elder. 2008. 120p. pap. 9.50 *(978-1-4357-0397-1(9))* Lulu Enterprises Inc.

—Mark & John the First & Last Gospels. 2009. 178p. pap. 10.70 *(978-0-557-11921-9(9))* Lulu Enterprises Inc.

—More Bible Wisdom for Modern Times: Selections from the Early New Testament. 2008. 123p. pap. 9.50 *(978-1-4303-2597-0(6))* Lulu Enterprises Inc.

Riffe, Clinton. One Wind. 2011. 218p. pap. 15.99 ***(978-1-61379-312-1(X))*** Xulon Pr., Inc.

Risen, T. A. Gospel of Adam. 2007. 232p. per. 14.99 *(978-1-60266-280-3(0))* Xulon Pr., Inc.

Roberts, Paul William. Journey of the Magi: Travels in Search of the Birth of Jesus. 2nd ed. 2006. (ENG.). 400p. per. 19.95 *(978-1-84511-242-4(3)*, Tauris Parke Paperbacks) I. B. Tauris & Co., Ltd. GBR. Dist: Macmillan.

Robertson, A. T. The Divinity of Christ in the Gospel of John. 2010. 76p. pap. *(978-1-152-88765-7(3))* Books LLC.

Robertson, Irvine. Believe & Live: Studies in the Gospel of John, Chapters 1-7. 2011. 64p. 36.95 ***(978-1-258-08130-0(X))*** Literary Licensing, LLC.

Robinson, George W. The Overflowing Heart: Illustrations for the Gospel of Matthew. 2007. 59p. pap. 8.95 *(978-0-7414-4339-7(2))* Infinity Publishing.

Robinson, Maurice, et al. Perspectives on the Ending of Mark: Four Views. Black, David Alan, ed. 2008. (Perspectives Ser.). (ENG.). 160p. pap. 19.99 *(978-0-8054-4762-0(8)*, B&H Academic) B&H Publishing Group.

Rochedieu, C. Comentario Practico - Juan, Vol. II: Practical Comment.I - John. (SPA.). 192p. *(978-84-7228-570-5(7)*, 220126) Clie, Editorial.

Roland, Brother. Chapter: God's Instructions from Walk the Talk Ministries. 2008. 320p. pap. 17.99 *(978-1-4343-9760-7(2))* AuthorHouse.

Rundle, Elizabeth. Meeting Jesus. 2007. (Illus.). 72p. *(978-1-85345-442-4(7))* Crusade for World Revival.

Rushforth, Rebecca. St Margaret's Gospel-Book: The Favourite Book of an Eleventh-Century Queen of Scots. 2007. (ENG., Illus.). 120p. 45.00 *(978-1-85124-370-9(4))* Bodleian Library GBR. Dist: Chicago Distribution Ctr.

Rushton, Kathleen P. The Parable of the Woman in Childbirth of John 16: A Metaphor for the Death & Glorification of Jesus. 2011. 404p. 139.95 *(978-0-7734-1500-3(9))* Mellen, Edwin Pr., The.

Ryken, Philip Graham. Luke. 2009. *(978-1-59638-070-7(5))*; *(978-1-59638-152-0(3))* P & R Publishing.

Ryle, J. C. Expository Thoughts on the Gospels: Matthew & Mark. 2009. (ENG.). 385p. 38.99 *(978-1-117-40092-1(1))*; 443p. 41.99 *(978-1-117-40089-1(1))*; 443p. pap. 26.99 *(978-1-117-40091-4(3)*, BiblioLife); 443p. pap. 35.75 *(978-1-117-40090-7(5))*; 385p. pap. 32.75 *(978-1-117-40093-8(X))*; 385p. pap. 25.99 *(978-1-117-40094-5(8)*, BiblioLife) BiblioBazaar.

Saint Thomas, Aquinas. Catena Aurea: Catholic Clasics, 4 vols. 2010. 2832p. *(978-1-905574-50-6(9))* Baronius Pr. Ltd.

Salvetti, Neville. The Gospel of Jesus the Christ. 2010. 100p. pap. 15.99 *(978-1-4535-5470-8(X))* Xlibris Corp.

Sanchez, Bernardo. La Biblia y Su Mensaje - Marcos: The Bible & Its Message - Mark. (SPA.). *(978-84-7645-104-5(0)*, 223175) Clie, Editorial.

Saunders, Stanley P. Preaching the Gospel of Matthew: Proclaiming God's Presence. 2010. (ENG.). 312p. pap. 25.00 *(978-0-664-22920-7(4))* Westminster John Knox Pr.

Schlafer, David J. The Shattering Sound of Amazing Grace: Disquieting Tales from Saint John's Gospel. 2006. (ENG.). 112p. per. 12.95 *(978-1-56101-247-3(5))* Cowley Pubns.

Schoffstall, Robert O. Reflections on the Gospel of John: That You May Believe & on the First Epistle of John That You Ma. 2007. 123p. pap. 11.95 *(978-0-7414-3779-2(1))* Infinity Publishing.

Schonborn, Christoph Cardinal. Jesus, the Divine Physician: Reflections on the Gospel During the Year of Luke. Taylor, Henry, tr. from GER. 2008. 237p. pap. 16.95 *(978-1-58617-180-3(1))* Ignatius Pr.

Schuett, James. If Any of You Lack Wisdom: Why Am I Here? 2007. (Illus.). 36p. (YA). pap. 7.95 *(978-0-9800442-0-1(0))* Schuett, Jim Designs.

Sears, Edmund Hamilton. The Fourth Gospel, the Heart of Christ by Edmund H Sears. 2006. 564p. per. 32.99 *(978-1-4255-6194-9(2))* MPublishing.

Seubert, Augusto. Como Entender los Mensajes del Evangelio de Juan. (SPA.). 176p. 8.95 *(978-958-607-817-7(5))* Sociedad de San Pablo ESP. Dist: St Pauls/Alba Hse. Pubns.

Seymour, Jody. Marking the Gospel: A Devotional Commentary on the Gospel of Mark. 2011. 170p. pap. 20.00 ***(978-1-61097-340-3(2)***, Resource Pubns.) Wipf & Stock Pubs.

Shackleford, William A., Sr. The Sin That Will Keep Many Church Members Out of Heaven. 2009. 180p. 22.99 *(978-1-60791-173-9(6))*; pap. 14.99 *(978-1-60791-172-2(8))* Xulon Pr., Inc.

Shauf, Scott. Theology as History, History as Theology: Paul in Ephesus in Acts 19. (Beihefte zur Zeitschrift far die neutestamentliche Wissenschaft und die Kunde der älteren Kirche Ser.). (ENG.). X, 377p. 255.00 ***(978-3-11-182501-4(9))*** De Gruyter, Walter Inc.

Sheffield, Richard Louie. Preaching the Parables: Series IV, Cycle A: I Love to Tell the Story. 2007. 115p. per. 14.95 *(978-0-7880-2458-0(2))* CSS Publishing Co.

Shelton, Bob. Prophecy in Context. 2008. *(978-1-59166-851-0(4))* BJU Pr.

Shields, Ann. Deeper Conversion: Extraordinary Grace for Ordinary Times. 2008. 112p. per. 11.99 *(978-0-86716-811-2(0)*, Servant Bks.) Franciscan Media.

Showalter, M. V., ed. The Divine Biography of Jesus Christ: With Harmonic Index. 2011. 296p. 48.95 ***(978-1-258-09018-0(X))*** Literary Licensing, LLC.

Siegert, Folker. Das Johannesevangelium in seiner ursprünglichen Gestalt: Wiederherstellung und Kommentar. Schriften des Institutum Judaicum Delitzschianum, Band 7. 2008. (Schriften des Institutum Judaicum Delitzschianum Ser.). (GER.). 856p. (C). 204.00 *(978-3-525-50147-4(1))* Vandenhoeck & Ruprecht GmbH & Co. KG DEU. Dist: ISD.

Sim, John. God Revealed in John. 2011. 226p. 29.99 ***(978-1-4568-0796-2(X))***; pap. 19.99 ***(978-1-4568-0795-5(1))*** Xlibris Corp.

Simoson, A. B. Comentario Al Evangelio de Juan: The Gospel of John. (SPA.). 256p. *(978-84-7228-979-6(6)*, 223052) Clie, Editorial.

—Comentario Al Evangelio de Mateo: The Gospel of Matthew. (SPA.). *(978-84-7228-980-2(X)*, 223053) Clie, Editorial.

Sloyan, Gerard Stephen & Sloyan, Gerard. John. 2009. (Interpretation, a Bible Commentary for Teaching & Preaching Ser.). (ENG.). 360p. pap. 25.00 *(978-0-664-23436-2(4))* Westminster John Knox Pr.

Smalley, Stephen S. 1, 2, 3 John, 0 vols. rev. ed. 2009. (Word Biblical Commentary Ser.: Vol. 51). 350p. 49.99 *(978-1-4185-1424-2(1))* Nelson, Thomas Inc.

Smiga, George M. The Gospel of John Set Free: Preaching without Anti-Judaism. 2008. (Stimulus Bks.). (Illus.). 208p. pap. 14.95 *(978-0-8091-4457-0(3))* Paulist Pr.

Smith, Abner. The Gospel Harmony of Jesus Christ. 2009. 304p. 32.50 *(978-1-4251-9110-8(X))* Trafford Publishing.

Smith, Andrew Phillip. The Gnostics: History, Tradition, Scriptures, Influence. 2008. (ENG.). 256p. pap. 14.95 *(978-1-905857-78-4(0)*, Watkins Publishing) Duncan Baird Pubs. GBR. Dist: Sterling Publishing Co., Inc.

Smith, David. Mark: A Commentary for Bible Students. 2007. (Wesleyan Bible Commentary Ser.). (Illus.). 310p. 18.99 *(978-0-89827-344-1(7))* Wesleyan Publishing Hse.

Smith, Dudley. The Expository Commentary-Matthews. 2010. 413p. pap. 26.99 *(978-0-557-27856-5(2))* Lulu Enterprises Inc.

—Student's Concise Commentary: the Four Gospels. 2010. 510p. pap. 34.98 *(978-0-557-50981-2(5))* Lulu Enterprises Inc.

Smith, Mike. Gospel for Starters: Gospel According to Mark, translated with Commentary. 2009. (Illus.). 134p. pap. *(978-1-84748-681-3(9))* Athena Pr.

Smith, Robert H. Wounded Lord: Reading John Through the Eyes of Thomas: A Pastoral & Theological Commentary on the Fourth Gospel. Duensing, Donna, ed. 2009. 202p. pap. 24.00 *(978-1-60608-660-5(X))* Cascade Bks.

Spanuth, J., ed. The Scholia of Barhebraeus on the Gospel of Matthew. 2010. (SYR.). pap. 26.20 *(978-1-61719-600-3(2))* Gorgias Pr., LLC.

Spell, David. Miracles in Mark. 2009. 130p. pap. 16.00 *(978-1-60608-406-9(2)*, Resource Pubns.) Wipf & Stock Pubs.

Sproul, R. C. John. 2009. *(978-1-56769-185-6(4))* Reformation Pubs.

Sproul, R. C. Mark. 2011. ***(978-1-56769-265-5(6))*** Reformation Pubs.

St. John of the Cross. Ascent of Mt. Carmel. 2009. (ENG.). 180p. pap. 14.95 *(978-1-55725-640-9(3))* Paraclete Pr., Inc.

Stanko, John W. The Faith Files-Volume: The Gospels. 2008. 128p. pap. 10.99 *(978-1-58169-282-2(X))* Genesis Communications, Inc.

Stauffer, Claude T. Stay the Course & Stick with the True Gospel. 2009. 328p. pap. 18.99 *(978-1-60791-541-6(3))* Xulon Pr., Inc.

Stearns, Gail J. Open Your Eyes Toward Living More Deeply in the Present. 2010. 150p. pap. 19.00 *(978-1-60899-635-3(2)*, Wipf and Stock) Wipf & Stock Pubs.

Stedman, Ray C. & Collins, Nancy J. Gospel of Mark, Part 1: Chapters 1-8. 2007. (ENG.). 120p. spiral bd. 21.49 *(978-1-932017-34-2(8))* Joy of Living Bible Studies.

Steiner, Rudolf. Some Deeper Secrets of Human Development in the Light of the Gospel of St Matthew. 2011. 70p. 36.95 ***(978-1-258-00532-0(8))*** Literary Licensing, LLC.

Stevens, Noel & Stevens, Noel. The Gospel According to Gaius Scipio, the Roman: Revolutionary Archaeological Find Jesus Shows Nowhere in the Historical Record. 2007. 156p. per. 14.95 *(978-0-595-44334-5(6))* iUniverse, Inc.

Stevick, Daniel B. Jesus & His Own: A Commentary on John 13-17. 2010. 384p. pap. 38.00 *(978-0-8028-4865-9(6))* Eerdmans, William B. Publishing Co.

Stier, Ewald Rudolf. The Words of the Lord Jesus by Rudolf Stier Tr from the 2d Rev & Enl German Ed , by the Rev William B Pope. 2006. 516p. pap. 29.99 *(978-1-4255-5714-0(7))*; (ENG.). 452p. per. 26.99 *(978-1-4255-4947-3(0))*; (ENG.). 524p. per. 29.99 *(978-1-4255-5802-4(X))*; (ENG.). 520p. per. 29.99 *(978-1-4255-5801-7(1))*; (ENG.). 432p. per. 26.99 *(978-1-4255-4678-6(1))*;

(ENG.). 544p. per. 29.99 (978-1-4255-5988-5(3)); 492p. per. 29.99 (978-1-4255-5461-3(X)); (ENG.). 468p. per. 29.99 (978-1-4255-5173-5(4)); (ENG.). 512p. per. 29.99 (978-1-4255-5715-7(5)) MPublishing.

Study Manual Jesus in the Gospels. 30.00 (978-0-687-02692-0(X)) Abingdon Pr.

Subramanian, Dheena. Jesus, the Yogi. 2009. 84p. pap. (978-1-926582-07-8(1)) Insomniac Pr.

Swanson, Richard W. Provoking the Gospel of John: A Storyteller's Commentary, Years a, B, & C. 2010. (978-0-8298-1866-6(9)) Pilgrim Pr., The/United Church Pr.

Sweetland Dennis. Mark: From Death to Life. 2007. 214p. per. 16.95 (978-1-56548-266-1(2)) New City Pr.

Swete, Henry Barclay, intro. The Gospel according to St. Mark. 2010. 146.24 (978-1-61719-679-9(7)) Gorgias Pr., LLC.

Swindoll, Charles R. Insights on John, 1 vol. 2010. (Swindoll's New Testament Insights Ser.). (ENG.). 368p. 25.99 (978-0-310-28435-2(X)) Zondervan.

—Insights on Luke, 1 vol. 2012. (Swindoll's New Testament Insights Ser.). (ENG.). 640p. 25.99 (978-0-310-28431-4(7)) Zondervan.

Talbot, Elizabeth Viera. Luke: Salvation for All. 2011. pap. 1.99 (978-0-8163-2482-8(4)) Pacific Pr. Publishing Assn.

—Matthew: Prophecy Fulfilled. 2009. (Jesus 101: Introduction to the Real Jesus Ser.). 63p. pap. 1.99 (978-0-8163-2353-1(4)) Pacific Pr. Publishing Assn.

Thettayil, Benny & Thettayil, B. In Spirit & Truth: An Exegetical Study of John 4:19-26 & a Theological Investigation of the Replacement Theme in the Fourth Gospel y B. Thettayil. 2007. (Contributions to Biblical Exegesis & Theology Ser.). (ENG.). 522p. (C). pap. 60.00 (978-90-429-1887-0(X)) Peeters Pubs. & Booksellers BEL. Dist: Brown, David Bk. Co., The.

Thompson, Alan Carter. Meet the Real Jesus: A No-Spin Look at Jesus Through the Eyes of Matthew. 2011. (ENG.). 147p. pap. 9.95 **(978-1-4327-7802-6(1))** Outskirts Pr., Inc.

Thornborough, Tim. Why Did Jesus Come? (Access for All) 2010. 6p. (978-1-905564-61-3(9)) Good Bk. Co.

Thurber, Bill. A Moment of Truth. 2007. 336p. per. 17.99 (978-1-60477-034-6(1)) Xulon Pr., Inc.

—A Moment of Truth John: 16. 2007. 336p. 27.99 (978-1-60477-035-3(X)) Xulon Pr., Inc.

Tice, Rico & Cooper, Barry. Christianity Explored. 2010. (Christianity Explored Ser.). (SPA.). 60p. pap., pupil's gde. ed. (978-1-906334-58-1(7)); pap. (978-1-906334-59-8(5)) Good Bk. Co.

Tuohy, Timothy. The Gospel According to Timothy. 2008. 114p. pap. 7.98 (978-1-4357-3401-2(7)) Lulu Enterprises Inc.

Turner, David L. Matthew. 2008. (Baker Exegetical Commentary on the New Testament Ser.). 848p. (C). 54.99 (978-0-8010-2684-3(9)) Baker Academic.

Tyndale House Publishers Staff, prod. John. 2008. (Life Application Bible Studies: NLT Ser.). (ENG.). 144p. pap. 7.99 (978-1-4143-2561-3(4)) Tyndale Hse. Pubs.

—Luke. 2009. (Life Application Bible Studies: NLT Ser.). (ENG.). 160p. pap. 7.99 (978-1-4143-2649-8(1)) Tyndale Hse. Pubs.

—Matthew. 2009. (Life Application Bible Studies: NLT Ser.). (ENG.). 160p. pap. 7.99 (978-1-4143-2647-4(5)) Tyndale Hse. Pubs.

Tyndale, William. The Parable of the Wicked Mammon. 2010. 102p. pap. 34.95 (978-1-4092-2793-9(6)) Lulu Enterprises Inc.

Um, Stephen & Um. Theme of Temple Christology in John's Gospel. 2006. (Library of New Testament Studies: Vol. 312). (ENG.). 256p. 170.00 (978-0-567-04224-8(3), T&T Clark Int'l) Continuum International Publishing Group, Ltd. GBR. Dist: National Bk. Network.

Upchurch, Cackie & Yeary, Clifford, eds. Un Ano de Domingos: Reflexiones de los Evangelios 2007. Icaza, Rosa Maria, tr. 2006. 87p. per. 2.00 (978-0-8146-3113-3(4), Liturgical Pr. Bks.) Liturgical Pr.

Van Oosterzee, J. J. The Gospel According to Luke: An Exegetical & Doctrinal Commentary. Lange, John Peter, ed. & tr. by. Schaff, Philip, ed. Starbuck, Charles C., tr. 2007. (Lange's Commentary on the Holy Scripture Ser.). 406p. pap. 40.00 (978-1-55635-403-8(7)) Wipf & Stock Pubs.

Vernon, Alejandra, illus. The Lost Spiritual World. 2007. 239p. 39.95 (978-0-9745750-6-3(2)) Global Renaissance Society, LLC, The.

Videle, Arlene. Break the Seven Common Hindrances to Prayer. 2007. 172p. per. 13.99 (978-1-60266-739-6(X)) Xulon Pr., Inc.

Vinson, Richard Bolling. Luke. 2008. (978-1-57312-078-4(2)) Smyth & Helwys Publishing, Inc.

Von Wahlde, Urban C. A Commentary on the Gospel & Letters of John, 3 vols. 2010. 752p. 60.00 (978-0-8028-0991-9(X)) Eerdmans, William B. Publishing Co.

Wagener, Kenneth. The Gospel According to Paul. (Discipleship Ser.). pap., stu. ed. 3.99 (978-0-570-09467-8(4), 20-2389) Concordia Publishing Hse.

Wansbrough, Henry. The Lion & the Bull: The Gospels of Mark & Luke. (Illus.). 208p. pap. (978-0-232-52162-7(X)) South Asia Bks.

—Luke: A Guide for Reflection & Prayer. 2007. (Daily Bible Commentary Ser.). 215p. per. 12.95 (978-1-59856-187-6(1)) Hendrickson Pubs. Marketing, LLC.

Ward, Jean Elizabeth, Poet Laureate. The Forbidden Gospels & Epistles, Complete. 2008. 599p. pap. 39.99 (978-1-4357-3211-7(1)) Lulu Enterprises Inc.

Ware, George W. Jesus Christ, a Complete Harmony: Narrating the Four Gospels in Chronological Order. 14.95 (978-1-56794-228-6(8)) Star Bible & Tract Corp.

Weaver, James. Workbook for Lectors & Gospel Readers 2007, Canada: NRSV, Year C. 2006. pap. 13.00 (978-1-56854-572-1(X), CWL07) Liturgy Training Pubns.

—Workbook for Lectors & Gospel Readers 2007 USA: RNAB, Year C. 2006. pap. 13.00 (978-1-56854-571-4(1), WL07) Liturgy Training Pubns.

Weber, Charles. A Little Guidebook for the Servant-Leader. 2008. 64p. pap. 10.95 (978-1-4327-2700-0(1)) Outskirts Pr., Inc.

Welch, Louise Banner. Hidden for Centuries: The Key to the Original Gospel of Luke. 2009. 316p. 32.95 (978-1-4401-4351-9(X)); pap. 22.95 (978-1-4401-4349-6(8)) iUniverse, Inc.

Wellhausen, J. Das Evangelium Marci: Ubersetzt und Erklart von J. Wellhausen. 2009. 138p. pap. 12.00 (978-1-60608-678-0(2), Wipf and Stock) Wipf & Stock Pubs.

—Das Evangelium Matthaei: Ubersetzt und Erklart. 2009. 152p. pap. 13.00 (978-1-60608-677-3(4), Wipf and Stock) Wipf & Stock Pubs.

Wells, Samuel. Power & Passion: Six Characters in Search of Resurrection, 1 vol. 2006. (ENG.). 48p. (gr. 13). pap. 14.99 (978-0-310-27017-1(0)) Zondervan.

Wetterling, J. D. No One... When Jesus Says It, He Means It. 2006. (ENG.). 128p. pap. 11.99 (978-1-84550-153-2(5)) Christian Focus Pubns. GBR. Dist: STL Distribution North America.

Whedon's Commentary on Luke, Vol. 2. 25.99 (978-0-88019-124-1(4)) Schmul Publishing Co., Inc.

Whedon's Commentary on Matthew, Vol. 1. 25.99 (978-0-88019-123-4(6)) Schmul Publishing Co., Inc.

Whitacre, Rodney A. John. 2010. (IVP New Testament Commentary Ser.: Volume 4). (ENG.). 526p. pap. 20.00 (978-0-8308-4004-5(4), IVP Acad.) InterVarsity Pr.

Why Become Born Again? 2008. pap. (978-0-9789909-6-1(X)) True-Way Tracts.

Wiersbe, Warren W. Be Alive (John 1-12) Get to Know the Living Savior 2009. (Be Series Commentary Ser.). (ENG.). 208p. pap. 12.99 (978-1-4347-6736-3(1)) Cook, David C.

—Be Compassionate (Luke 1-13) Let the World Know That Jesus Cares, 1 vol. 2nd ed. 2010. (BE Series Commentary Ser.). (ENG.). 192p. pap. 12.99 (978-1-4347-6502-4(4)) Cook, David C.

—Be Courageous (Luke 14-24) Take Heart from Christ's Example, 1 vol. 2010. (BE Series Commentary Ser.). (ENG.). 176p. pap. 12.99 (978-1-4347-6499-7(0)) Cook, David C.

—Be Diligent (Mark) Serving Others as You Walk with the Master Servant, 1 vol. 2010. (BE Series Commentary Ser.). (ENG.). 192p. pap. 12.99 (978-1-4347-6631-1(4)) Cook, David C.

—Loyal: Following the King of Kings. 2008. (Be Ser.). (ENG.). 272p. pap. 12.99 (978-1-4347-6779-0(5)) Cook, David C.

—Transformados en Cristo: Juan 13-21. Hilliker, Gary, ed. 2008.Tr. of Be Transformed. (SPA.). 171p. pap. 6.99 (978-1-932607-21-5(8)) Editorial Bautista Independiente.

—Vivos en Cristo: Juan 1-12. Hilliker, Gary, ed. 2008.Tr. of Be Alive. (SPA.). 177p. pap. 6.99 (978-1-932607-20-8(X)) Editorial Bautista Independiente.

—The Wiersbe Bible Study Series: John: Get to Know the Living Savior, 1 vol. 2010. (Wiersbe Bible Study Ser.). (ENG.). 192p. pap. 8.99 (978-1-4347-6507-9(5)) Cook, David C.

—The Wiersbe Bible Study Series: Matthew: Following the King of Kings, 1 vol. 2010. (Wiersbe Bible Study Ser.). (ENG.). 160p. pap. 8.99 (978-1-4347-6512-3(1)) Cook, David C.

Wilhelm, Dawn Ottoni. Preaching the Gospel of Mark: Proclaiming the Power of God. 2008. (ENG.). 312p. pap. 25.00 (978-0-664-22921-4(2)) Westminster John Knox Pr.

Williams, Marcia D. Evangelizing the Nations in Your Micst. 2007. 52p. 10.95 (978-1-4303-1625-1(X)) Lulu Enterprises Inc.

Williamson, Lamar, Jr. Mark. 2009. (Interpretation, a Bible Commentary for Teaching & Preaching Ser.). (ENG.). 312p. pap. 25.00 (978-0-664-23434-8(8)) Westminster John Knox Pr.

Wilson, Alistair I. When Will These Things Happen? A Study of Jesus as Judge in Matthew 21Ð25. 2007. (Paternoster Biblical Monographs: Ser.). 312p. pap. 31.00 (978-1-59752-727-9(0), Wipf and Stock) Wipf & Stock Pubs.

Wilson, Carl W. The Fulfillment: A Look at the Person & Ministry of Jesus Christ in a Uniquely Arranged Harmony & Commentary of the Gospels. 2009. (Modern Girl's Bible Study Ser.). (ENG.). 464p. pap. 29.99 (978-1-60006-320-6(9)) NavPress Publishing Group.

Winner, Lauren F. The Voice of Matthew, 0 vols. 2007. (Voice Ser.). 208p. per. 9.99 (978-0-529-12349-7(5)) Nelson, Thomas Inc.

Woodley, Matt. The Gospel of Matthew: God with Us. 2011. (Resonate Ser.). (ENG.). 301p. pap. 18.00 **(978-0-8308-3642-0(X)**, IVP Bks.) InterVarsity Pr.

Wright, N. T. Lent for Everyone: Luke, Year C: A Daily Devotional. 2012. (ENG.). 144p. pap. 15.00 **(978-0-664-23895-7(5))** Westminster John Knox Pr.

Wright, N. T. Simply Jesus: A New Vision of Who He Was, What He Did, & Why He Matters. 2011. (ENG.). 256p. 24.99 (978-0-06-208439-2(9), HarperOne) HarperCollins Pubs.

Wurst, Gregor. The Gospel of Judas: Together with the Letter of Peter to Philip, James, & a Book of Allogenes from Codex Tchacos. Meyer, Marvin & Gaudard, Francois, trs. 2007. (COP & ENG., Illus.). 378p. 45.00 (978-1-4262-0191-2(5)) National Geographic Society.

Yarbrough, Robert W. John: With a New Preface & Bibliography. 2011. 216p. pap. 24.00 **(978-1-61097-395-3(X)**, Wipf and Stock) Wipf & Stock Pubs.

Younger, Carol Davis. The Gospel of Matthew: Hope in the Resurrected Christ: Adult Bible Study Guide. 2008. 137p. pap. (978-1-934731-20-8(X)) Baptistway.

6 short messages to the hip-hop generation from the word of God____. 2007. (YA). 7.00 (978-0-9792839-1-8(4)) Word Of God Ministry.

21 Days with Jesus. 2007. 1.00 (978-1-882536-91-7(6)) Bible League.

BIBLE—COMMENTARIES—N. T. HEBREWS

Alexander, Larry D. Home & Church Bible study commentaries from the Book of Hebrews. 2009. 86p. pap. 15.00 (978-0-578-03453-9(0)) Alexander, Larry D.

Allen, David L. Hebrews. 2010. (New American Commentary Studies in Bible & Theology Ser.: Vol. 35). (ENG.). 672p. 32.99 (978-0-8054-0135-6(0), B&H Academic) B&H Publishing Group.

Allen, David L. & Broadman and Holman Publishers Staff. Lukan Authorship of Hebrews, 1 vol. 2010. (New American Commentary Studies in Bible & Theology Ser.). (ENG.). 432p. 24.99 (978-0-8054-4714-9(8), B&H Academic) B&H Publishing Group.

Anderson, Robert. Types in Hebrews, 1 vol. 2008. (Sir Robert Anderson Library). 192p. pap. 11.99 (978-0-8254-2577-6(8), Kregel Classics) Kregel Pubns.

Aquinas, Thomas. Commentary on the Epistle to the Hebrews. Baer, Chrysostom & Praem, O., trs. from LAT. 2006. 348p. 85.00 (978-1-58731-126-0(7)) St. Augustine's Pr., Inc.

—Commentary on the Epistle to the Hebrews. Baer, Chrysostom, tr. from LAT. 2006. 348p. per. 35.00 (978-1-58731-127-7(5)) St. Augustine's Pr., Inc.

Arnold, Clinton E. Zondervan Illustrated Bible Backgrounds Commentary Hebrews James, 1 vol. 2007. (Zondervan Illustrated Bible Backgrounds Commentary Ser.). (ENG., Illus.). 144p. (gr. 13). pap. 14.99 (978-0-310-27826-9(0)) Zondervan.

Bauckham, Richard. The Epistle to the Hebrews & Christian Theology. Bauckham, Richard et al, eds. 2009. 480p. pap. 36.00 (978-0-8028-2588-9(5)) Eerdmans, William B. Publishing Co.

Belchen, Richard P. Teaching Helps in Hebrews. 56p. pap. 6.95 (978-0-925703-16-3(8)) Crown Pubns., Inc.

Bensly, Robert L., intro. The Harklean Version of the Epistle to the Hebrews, Chap. XI. 28-XIII. 25. 2010. pap. 23.44 (978-1-61719-601-0(0)) Gorgias Pr., LLC.

Bowley, James E. Introduction to Hebrew Bible: A Guided Tour of Israel's Sacred Library. 2007. (ENG., Illus.). 528p. (C). per. 78.80 (978-0-13-045357-0(9), Prentice Hall) Prentice Hall PTR.

Brown, John. Epistle to the Hebrews. 2008. 744p. pap. 46.99 (978-1-58960-564-0(0)) Sovereign Grace Pubs., Inc.

Buchanan, George Wesley. The Book of Hebrews: Its Challenge from Zion - Intertextal Bible Commentary. 2006. (Illus.). 528p. pap. 47.00 (978-1-59752-819-1(6), Wipf and Stock) Wipf & Stock Pubs.

Burnett, Joel S. Where Is God? Divine Absence in the Hebrew Bible. 2010. 192p. (C). 35.00 (978-0-8006-6297-4(0), Fortress Pr.) Augsburg Fortress, Pubs.

Butler, John G. Joshua to II Samuel. 830p. **(978-1-889773-73-5(5))** LBC Pubns.

Buzzard, Justin. Hebrews: Consider Jesus: 8 Studies for Individuals or Groups. 2010. (Good Book Guides). (Illus.). 94p. pap. (978-1-906334-42-0(0)) Good Bk. Co.

Calvin, John. Commentaries on the Epistle of Paul the Apostle to the Hebrews. 2009. 452p. 27.99 (978-1-103-03602-8(5)); pap. 21.99 (978-1-103-03598-4(3)) BiblioBazaar.

—Commentaries on the Epistle of Paul the Apostle to the Hebrews. 2007. 478p. pap. 35.00 (978-1-55635-221-8(2), Wipf and Stock) Wipf & Stock Pubs.

Conner, Kevin J. The Book of Hebrews: An Exposition. 523p. (978-0-949829-56-6(0)) Acacia Pr.

Cook, John. The Book of Hebrews: Christ Is Greater. 2009. (Twenty-First Century Biblical Commentary Ser.). (ENG.). 288p. 19.99 (978-0-89957-820-0(9)) AMG Pubs.

Cooper, Phyllis A. Questions God Asks in the Hebrew Scriptures. 2008. pap. 13.00 (978-0-8059-7929-9(8)) Dorrance Publishing Co., Inc.

C.V.L. Heroes of Faith. 2008. 352p. pap. 22.50 (978-1-4357-4733-3(X)) Lulu Enterprises Inc.

Demarco, Loris. Sweeter Than Honey. 2008. 212p. 25.99 (978-1-60647-402-0(2)); pap. 15.99 (978-1-60647-401-3(4)) Xulon Pr., Inc.

Ebrard, John H. A. Biblical Commentary on the Epistle to the Hebrews in Continuation of the Work of Olshausen. Fulton, John, tr. 2008. 437p. pap. 37.00 (978-1-55635-791-6(5), Wipf and Stock) Wipf & Stock Pubs.

Fortner, Donald S. Discovering Christ in Hebrews. 2007. (978-0-9548624-4-2(9)) Go Pubns.

France, Dick. Timothy, Titus, & Hebrews: A Guide for Reflection & Prayer. 2007. (Daily Bible Commentary Ser.). 2‘7p. per. 12.95 (978-1-59856-195-1(2)) Hendrickson Pubs. Marketing, LLC.

Fudge, Edward. Hebrews: Ancient Encouragement for Believers Today. 2009. 262p. pap. (978-0-89112-625-6(2), Leafwood Pubs.) Abilene Christian Univ. Pr.

Garrett, Gregg. The Voice of Hebrews: The Mystery of Mel-Kiz E-Dek, 0 vols. 2008. (Illus.). 144p. per. 9.99 (978-0-529-12353-4(3)) Nelson, Thomas Inc.

Gelardini, Gabriella. Verhartet Eure Herzen Nicht: Der Hebraer, eine Synagogenhomilie Zu Tischa Be-Aw. 2006. (Biblical Interpretation Ser.). (GER., Illus.). 470p. (978-90-04-15406-3(X)) BRILL.

George, Guthrie. Hebrews: Running the Race Before Us, 1 vol. 2008. (Bringing the Bible to Life Ser.). (ENG.). 128p. pap. 7.99 (978-0-310-27653-1(5)) Zondervan.

Girard, Robert C. The Book of Hebrews, 0 vols. Richards, Larry, ed. 2008. (Smart Guide to the Bible Ser.). 384p. pap. 14.99 (978-1-4185-1008-4(4)) Nelson, Thomas Inc.

God's Revised Will & the Rest of the Story. v, 338p. pap. 9.95 (978-0-9710207-1-9(X)) Focus on Faith Studies.

Godspeed Bible Greek/Hebrew 525 Software Edition. 29.95 (978-0-687-01071-4(3)) Abingdon Pr.

Gordon, Robert P. Hebrews. 2nd ed. 2008. (ENG.). 220p. (978-1-905048-90-8(4)); per. (978-1-905048-91-5(2)) Sheffield Phoenix Pr.

Greenlee, J. Harold. An Exegetical Summary of Hebrews. 2nd ed. 2008. (Exegetical Summary Ser.). 592p. pap. 49.00 (978-1-55671-209-8(X)) SIL International.

Guthrie, Donald. Hebrews. (ENG.). 281p. 2009. (Tyndale New Testament Commentaries Ser.: Volume 15). pap. 16.00 (978-0-8308-4245-2(4), IVP Acad.) 2007. (Tyndale New Testament Commentaries Ser.). per. 14.00 (978-0-8308-2994-1(6)) InterVarsity Pr.

Hacking, Philip H. Opening up Hebrews. 2006. (Opening up the Bible Ser.). (Illus.). 96p. per. 9.00 (978-1-84625-042-2(0)) DayOne Pubns. GBR. Dist: STL Distribution North America.

Hahn, Scott & Mitch, Curtis. Ignatius Catholic Study Bible: The Letter to the Hebrews. 2007. 60p. pap. 9.95 (978-1-58617-191-9(7)) Ignatius Pr.

Haldane, James A. An Exposition of the Epistle to the Hebrews. 2010. (Newport Commentary Ser.). (Illus.). 423p. 26.00 (978-1-888514-36-0(1)) Particular Baptist Pr.

Harkins, Keegan. A Better Plan for Us: A Study of the Book of Hebrews. 2011. 152p. pap. 24.95 **(978-1-4560-3943-1(1))** PublishAmerica, Inc.

Hartum, A. S. Tanach Cussuto Zahav (15 Volume Hebrew Bible Commentary) 2010. 4350p. 440.00 (978-965-7305-01-0(2)) Yavneh Publishing Hse. ISR. Dist: Gefen Bks.

Hebreos, Santiago, 1 y 2 Pedro, Judas. (Comentario Biblico Mundo Hispano Ser.: Vol. 23).Tr. of Hebrews, James, 1 & 2 Peter, Jude. (SPA.). pap. 10.99 (978-0-311-03123-8(4), Editorial Mundo Hispano) Casa Bautista de Publicaciones.

Hebrews. (People's Bible Commentary Ser.). 192p. 12.99 (978-0-7586-0451-4(3)); (LifeLight Bible Studies: Course 12). 6.50 (978-0-570-09282-7(5), 20-2301) Concordia Publishing Hse.

Holloway, Gary. Certain Hope: An Encouraging Word from Hebrews. 2007. 143p. per. 12.95 (978-0-89112-448-1(9)) Abilene Christian Univ. Pr.

—Meditative Commentary Series: Hebrews & James: Brother Jesus. 2007. (Meditative Commentary Ser.). 111p. pap. 11.99 (978-0-89112-505-1(1), Leafwood Pubs.) Abilene Christian Univ. Pr.

Ironside, H. A. Hebrews, 1 vol. 2008. (Ironside Expository Commentaries Ser.). 144p. 19.99 (978-0-8254-2921-7(8)) Kregel Pubns.

Jackson, Melissa. Comedy & Feminist Interpretation of the Hebrew Bible: A Subversive Collaboration. 2012. (ENG.). 288p. 125.00 **(978-0-19-965677-6(0))** Oxford Univ. Pr., Inc.

Jacobs, Donald R. Consider Jesus: Daily Reflections on the Book of Hebrews. 2006. 367p. 15.99 (978-0-8361-9348-0(2)); pap. 11.99 (978-0-8361-9347-3(4)) Herald Pr.

Jobes, Karen H. Letters to the Church: A Survey of Hebrews & the General Epistles, 1 vol. 2011. (ENG.). 448p. 44.99 (978-0-310-26738-6(2)) Zondervan.

Johnson, Earl S., Jr. Hebrews. 2008. (Interpretation Bible Studies). (ENG., Illus.). 80p. pap. 13.00 (978-0-664-23190-3(X)) Westminster John Knox Pr.

Joslin, Barry C. Hebrews, Christ & the Law: The Theology of the Mosaic Law in Hebrews 71 1018. 2008. (Paternoster Biblical Monographs). (ENG.). 353p. 49.99 (978-1-84227-530-6(5), Paternoster) Authentic Media.

—Hebrews, Christ, & the Law: The Theology of the Mosaic Law in Hebrews 7:1Ð10:18. 2009. (Paternoster Biblical Monographs). 354p. pap. 42.00 (978-1-60608-474-8(7), Wipf and Stock) Wipf & Stock Pubs.

Klein, John & Spears, Adam. Lost in Translation. 2007. 220p. per. 15.99 (978-1-58930-199-3(4)) Selah Publishing Group, LLC.

Laansma, Jon C., et al. 1 & 2 Timothy, Titus, Hebrews. 17th ed. 2009. (Cornerstone Biblical Commentary Ser.: 17). (ENG.). 492p. 29.99 (978-0-8423-8345-5(X)) Tyndale Hse. Pubs.

Long, D. Stephen. Hebrews: Belief: A Theological Commentary on the Bible. 2011. (Belief Ser.). (ENG.). 208p. 30.00 (978-0-664-23251-1(5)) Westminster John Knox Pr.

Lucado, Max. Book of Hebrews: Incomparable Christ, 0 vols. 2007. (Inspirational Bible Study; Life Lessons with Max Lucado Ser.). (Illus.). 128p. per. 9.99 (978-1-4185-0955-2(8)) Nelson, Thomas Inc.

Luman, J. W. The Time & Order of His Appearing. 2007. 210p. 15.00 (978-0-9799888-4-4(5)) International Fellowship of Covenant Ministries, The.

Marlowe, Stephen R. Bereishis the Holy Scriptures of Yeshu: The Messiah of Israel. 2010. 266p. pap. 16.99 (978-1-61579-734-9(3)) Xulon Pr., Inc.

Mason, Eric Farrel & McCruden, Kevin B. Reading the Epistle to the Hebrews: A Resource for Students. 2011. **(978-1-58983-609-9(X))**; **(978-1-58983-608-2(1))** Society of Biblical Literature.

Mcpherson, Bishop B. C. R. A. W. Real Alive Word. 2011. 285p. pap. 27.95 **(978-1-4327-6982-6(0))** Outskirts Pr., Inc.

Mitchell, Alan. Hebrews. 2009. 384p. pap. 29.95 (978-0-8146-5981-6(0), Liturgical Pr. Bks.) Liturgical Pr.

Morgan, G. Campbell. God's Last Word to Man: Studies in Hebrews. 2010. (G. Campbell Morgan Reprint Ser.). 162p. pap. 18.00 (978-1-60899-294-2(2), Wipf and Stock) Wipf & Stock Pubs.

Moule, Handley C. G. Messages from the Epistle to the Hebrews. 2008. 80p. pap. (978-1-4068-7473-0(6)) Echo Library.

—Messages from the Epistle to the Hebrews. 2007. 120p. pap. 12.00 (978-1-55635-456-4(8)) Wipf & Stock Pubs.

Nurmela, Risto. The Mouth of the Lord Has Spoken: Inner-Biblical Allusions in the Second & Third Isaiah. Nurmela, Risto, ed. 2006. (Studies in Judaism Ser.). (ENG.). 220p. pap. 34.99 (978-0-7618-3476-2(1)) Univ. Pr. of America, Inc.

O'Brien, Peter Thomas. The Letter to the Hebrews. 2010. xxxiii, 596p. *(978-1-84474-422-0(1))* Eerdmans, William B. Publishing Co.

O'Brien, Peter Thomas & Carson, D. A. The Letter to the Hebrews. 2010. xxxiii, 596p. 50.00 *(978-0-8028-3729-5(8))* Eerdmans, William B. Publishing Co.

Pace, Martel. Hebrews. 2007. (ENG.). 618p. 29.95 *(978-0-9760327-6-2(7))* Resource Pubns.

Perkins, Tyrone C. A Commentary on Hebrews. pap. 9.95 *(978-1-56794-174-6(5),* C-2515) Star Bible & Tract Corp.

Phillips, Richard D. Hebrews: Reformed Expositry Commentary. 2006. (Reformed Expository Commentary Ser.). 656p. 34.99 *(978-0-87552-784-0(1))* P & R Publishing.

Pink, Arthur W. An Exposition of Hebrews. 2011. 866p. pap. 34.99 ***(978-1-61203-348-8(2))*** Bottom of the Hill Publishing.

—An Exposition of Hebrews. 2009. 788p. pap. 25.99 *(978-1-60459-681-6(3))* Wilder Pubns., Ltd.

Poling, Edward. Hebrews: Beyond Christianity 101. 2008. 67p. pap. 7.95 *(978-0-87178-071-3(2),* FaithQuest) Brethren Pr.

Rochedieu, C. Comentario Practico - Hebreos, Vol. IV: Practical Comment. IV - Heb. - Rev. (SPA.). 208p. *(978-84-7228-568-2(5),* 220128) Clie, Editorial.

Seiss, Joseph Augustus. Lectures on Hebrews. 2008. 410p. pap. 35.00 *(978-1-55635-756-5(7))* Wipf & Stock Pubs.

Smith, Richard G. & Smith. The Fate of Justice & Righteousness During David's Reign: Narrative Ethics & Rereading the Court History According to 2 Samuel 8:15-20:26. 2009. (Library of Hebrew Bible/Old Testament Studies, the Ser.). (ENG.). 294p. 135.00 *(978-0-567-02684-2(1),* T&T Clark Int'l) Continuum International Publishing Group, Ltd. GBR. Dist: National Bk. Network.

Strauss, Mark, et al. Hebrews Thru Revelation Vol. 12: Wisdom for Today-And Forever. 2008. (QuickNotes Commentaries Ser.: Vol. 12). (ENG.). 240p. pap. 9.99 *(978-1-59789-778-5(7),* Barbour Bks.) Barbour Publishing, Inc.

Thompson, James W. Hebrews. 2008. (Paideia: Commentaries on the New Testament Ser.). (Illus.). 336p. (C). pap. 30.00 *(978-0-8010-3191-5(5))* Baker Academic.

Timmons, J. P. Hebrews: The Book of Better Things. 2008. (ENG.). 154p. pap. 11.95 *(978-1-56350-005-3(1))* C. C. I. Publishing.

Turner, Samuel H. The Epistle to the Hebrews, with Explanatory Notes: To Which Are Added A Condensed View of the Priesthood of Crist, & A Translation of the Epistle. 2006. 204p. per. 20.99 *(978-1-4255-1687-1(4))* MPublishing.

Tyndale House Publishers Staff, prod. Hebrews. 2008. (Life Application Bible Studies: NLT Ser.). (ENG.). 112p. pap. 7.99 *(978-1-4143-2564-4(9))* Tyndale Hse. Pubs.

VanBuren, Eve. Frenchie's Story: Cinderella to Compton. 2009. (ENG.). 199p. pap. 15.95 *(978-0-9766288-2-8(1),* 1003) Ketch Publishing.

Vander Beek, William. God's Word Is Dynamic. 2006. (ENG.). 135p. pap. *(978-1-55452-041-1(X))* Essence Publishing.

Vander Haagen, Elizabeth. Discover Hebrew. 2007. (Discover Your Bible Ser.). 78p. pap. 6.50 *(978-1-59255-288-7(9))* Faith Alive Christian Resources.

—Discover Hebrews. 2007. (Discover Your Bible Ser.). 52p. pap. 4.75 *(978-1-59255-287-0(0))* Faith Alive Christian Resources.

Wiersbe, Warren W. Hebrews: Live by Faith, Not by Sight. 2009. (WBS Ser.). (ENG.). 144p. pap. 8.99 *(978-0-7814-4566-5(3))* Cook, David C.

Wood, Charles R. The Heroes of the Faith, 1 vol. 2008. (Wood Sermon Outline Ser.). 64p. pap. 5.99 *(978-0-8254-4179-0(X))* Kregel Pubns.

BIBLE—COMMENTARIES—N. T. JAMES

see Bible—Commentaries—N. T. Catholic Epistles

BIBLE—COMMENTARIES—N. T. JOHN

see Bible—Commentaries—N. T. Gospels

BIBLE—COMMENTARIES—N. T. JUDE

see Bible—Commentaries—N. T. Catholic Epistles

BIBLE—COMMENTARIES—N. T. LUKE

see Bible—Commentaries—N. T. Gospels

BIBLE—COMMENTARIES—N. T. MARK

see Bible—Commentaries—N. T. Gospels

BIBLE—COMMENTARIES—N. T. MATTHEW

see Bible—Commentaries—N. T. Gospels

BIBLE—COMMENTARIES—N. T. PASTORAL EPISTLES

Here are entered commentaries on the Pastoral epistles as a whole as well as those on Titus or Timothy.

Aageson, James W. Paul, the Pastoral Epistles, & the Early Church. Porter, Stanley E., ed. 2008. (Library of Pauline Studies). 235p. per. *(978-1-59856-041-1(7))* Hendrickson Pubs. Marketing, LLC.

Aejmelaeus, Lars. The Nordic Paul: Finnish Approaches to Pauline Theology. Mustakallio, Antti, ed. 2008. (Library of New Testament Studies, the Ser.). (ENG.). 264p. 140.00 *(978-0-567-03310-9(4),* T&T Clark Int'l) Continuum International Publishing Group, Ltd. GBR. Dist: National Bk. Network.

Arnold, Clinton E. 1 & 2 Thessalonians, 1 & 2 Timothy, Titus , 1 vol. 2007. (Zondervan Illustrated Bible Backgrounds Commentary Ser.). (ENG., Illus.). 128p. (gr. 13). pap. 14.99 *(978-0-310-27823-8(6))* Zondervan.

Bean, Mark Ellis. Translator's Notes on 1 Timothy. 2008. 196p. spiral bd. 24.00 *(978-1-55671-212-8(X))* SIL International.

Blacoe, William Victor. Understanding the New Testament: 1 & 2 Timothy, Titus, & Philemon. 2011. 256p. pap. 19.99 *(978-1-59955-900-1(5))* Cedar Fort, Inc./CFI Distribution.

Bustamante, Roberto E. Carta de Pablo a Tito. 2008. (SPA., Illus.). 414p. 22.99 *(978-0-7586-1306-6(7))* Concordia Publishing Hse.

—Segunda Carta A Timoteo. 2007. 524p. 24.99 *(978-0-7586-1307-3(5))* Concordia Publishing Hse.

Bystrom, Raymond O. Living Today with an Eye for Eternity: Studies in the Pastoral Letters. 2007. 299p. *(978-1-894791-12-0(6))* Kindred Productions.

Calvin, John. Commentaries on the Epistles to Timothy, Titus, & Philemon. 2009. 400p. 26.99 *(978-0-559-90352-6(9));* pap. 20.99 *(978-0-559-90351-9(0))* BiblioBazaar.

—Commentaries on the Epistles to Timothy, Titus, & Philemon. Pringle, William, tr. 2009. 398p. 49.95 *(978-1-120-09247-2(7));* pap. 34.95 *(978-1-120-05550-7(4))* Kessinger Publishing, LLC.

—Commentaries on the Epistles to Timothy, Titus, & Philemon. Pringle, William, tr. 2007. (Calvin's Commentaries Ser.). 398p. pap. 25.00 *(978-1-55635-165-5(8),* Wipf and Stock) Wipf & Stock Pubs.

Campbell, David. Opening up Titus. 2007. (Opening up the Bible Ser.). 128p. 9.00 *(978-1-84625-079-8(X))* DayOne Pubns. GBR. Dist: STL Distribution North America.

David, Wilson. Paul's Letters to Timothy & the Church Today: Words of Admonition, Encouragement, & Warning. 2007. 128p. per. 6.25 *(978-0-9786002-7-3(4))* Wilson, David.

Easton, Burton Scott. The Pastoral Epistles - Introduction, Translation, Commentary & Word Studies. 2009. 248p. pap. 28.95 *(978-1-4446-2769-5(4))* Barclay Pr., Inc.

Eaton, Michael. 2 Timothy. (Preaching Through the Bible Ser.). 125p. pap. *(978-1-85240-265-5(2))* Sovereign World, Ltd.

Ellicott, Charles J. A Critical & Grammatical Commentary on the Pastoral Epistles. 2009. 292p. pap. 22.00 *(978-1-59925-230-8(9))* Solid Ground Christian Bks.

Farley, Lawrence. Shepherding the Flock: The Pastoral Epistles of Saint Paul the Apostle to Timothy & to Titus. 2008. (Orthodox Bible Study Companion Ser.). 144p. pap. 13.95 *(978-1-888212-56-3(X))* Conciliar Pr.

France, Dick. Timothy, Titus, & Hebrews: A Guide for Reflection & Prayer. 2007. (Daily Bible Commentary Ser.). 217p. per. 12.95 *(978-1-59856-195-1(2))* Hendrickson Pubs. Marketing, LLC.

Gloer, Hulitt. The Letters of Paul to Titus & Timothy. 2010. pap. *(978-1-57312-552-9(0))* Smyth & Helwys Publishing, Inc.

Greenlee, J. Harold. Exegetical Summary of Titus & Philemon. 2nd ed. 2008. 147p. pap. 24.00 *(978-1-55671-192-3(1))* SIL International.

Griend, Ronald Vander. 1 & 2 Timothy: Keeping the Faith. 5.25 *(978-1-56212-664-3(4),* 150150) Faith Alive Christian Resources.

Guthrie, Donald. The Pastoral Epistles, 1 vol. (ENG.). 2009. (Tyndale New Testament Commentaries Ser.: Volume 14). 251p. pap. 16.00 *(978-0-8308-4244-5(6),* IVP Acad.) 2007. (Tyndale New Testament Commentaries Ser.). 240p. per. 14.00 *(978-0-8308-2993-4(8))* InterVarsity Pr.

Holloway, Gary. 1 & 2 Thessalonians, 1 & 2 Timothy & Titus: Jesus Grows His Church: A Meditative Commentary on the New Testament. 2007. (Meditative Commentary Ser.). 119p. per. 11.99 *(978-0-89112-503-7(5),* Leafwood Pubs.) Abilene Christian Univ. Pr.

Hudson, Henry T. Henceforth a Crown: An Exposition of Second Timothy. 2009. 280p. pap. 20.95 *(978-1-4401-1990-3(2))* iUniverse, Inc.

I & II Timothy/Titus. (People's Bible Commentary Ser.). 232p. 13.99 *(978-0-7586-0450-7(5))* Concordia Publishing Hse.

Ironside, H. A. 1 & 2 Timothy, Titus, & Philemon. 2007. (Ironside Expository Commentaries Ser.). (Illus.). 192p. 19.99 *(978-0-8254-2922-4(6))* Kregel Pubns.

Kitchen, John. The Pastoral Epistles for Pastors. 2009. (ENG.). 624p. 39.99 *(978-1-934952-02-3(8))* Kress Christian Pubns.

Laansma, Jon C., et al. 1 & 2 Timothy, Titus, Hebrews. 17th ed. 2009. (Cornerstone Biblical Commentary Ser.: 17). (ENG.). 492p. 29.99 *(978-0-8423-8345-5(X))* Tyndale Hse. Pubs.

Lips, Herrmann von & von Lips, Hermann. Timotheus und Titus: Unterwegs für Paulus. 2010. (Biblische Gestalten Ser.). (GER.). 240p. (C). pap. 27.00 *(978-3-374-02621-0(4))* Evangelische Verlagsanstalt GmbH DEU. Dist: Brown, David Bk. Co., The.

Lively, Peggy. Above Reproach: A Study of 1 Timothy 3. 2008. 68p. pap. 11.99 *(978-1-60647-373-3(5))* Xulon Pr., Inc.

McCullar, Michael. Sessions with Timothy & Titus: Timeless Teachings for Leaders of Any Age. 2006. (Sessions Ser.). 105p. per. *(978-1-57312-468-3(0))* Smyth & Helwys Publishing, Inc.

Minor, Eugene E. Exegetical Summary of 2 Timothy. 2nd ed. 2008. 136p. pap. 22.00 *(978-1-55671-191-6(3))* SIL International.

Montague, George T. & Montague, George T. First & Second Timothy, Titus. 2008. (Catholic Commentary on Sacred Scripture Ser.). (Illus.). 272p. (C). pap. 19.99 *(978-0-8010-3581-4(3))* Baker Academic.

Mueller, A. C. & Rake, Tim. 1 & 2 Timothy/Titus. 2006. (God's Word for Today Ser.). 120p. pap. 8.99 *(978-0-7586-1355-4(5))* Concordia Publishing Hse.

Mutschler, Bernhard. Glaube in den Pastoralbriefen: Pistis als Mitte christlicher Existenz. 2010. (GER., Illus.). 487p. 237.50 *(978-3-16-150544-7(1))* Mohr Siebeck GmbH & Co. KG DEU. Dist: Coronet Bks.

Ngewa, Samuel. 1 & 2 Timothy & Titus, 1 vol. 2009. (Hippo / Africa Bible Commentary Ser.). (ENG.). 304p. pap. 21.99 *(978-9966-805-38-6(9))* Zondervan.

Oden, Thomas C. First & Second Timothy & Titus: Interpretation: A Bible Commentary for Teaching & Preaching. 2012. (Interpretation: A Bible Commentary for Teaching & Preaching Ser.). (ENG.). 206p. pap. 25.00 ***(978-0-664-23870-4(X))*** Westminster John Knox Pr.

Pastoral Epistles. Kregel Pubns.

Patterson, Paige. Living in Hope of Eternal Life: An Exposition of the Book of Titus. 2008. 56p. pap. 8.00 *(978-1-55635-486-1(X),* Wipf and Stock) Wipf & Stock Pubs.

Ryken, Philip Graham. 1 Timothy. 2007. (Reformed Expository Commentary Ser.). 312p. *(978-1-59638-049-3(7))* P & R Publishing.

Scheck, Thomas & Jerome, St. St Jeromes Commentaries on Gal. 2010. (ENG.). 376p. pap. 40.00 *(978-0-268-04133-5(4))* Univ. of Notre Dame Pr.

Stepp, Perry L. & Gloer, W. Hullitt. Reading Paul's Letters to Individuals: A Literary & Theological Commentary on Paul's Letters to Philemon, Titus, & Timothy. 2008. pap. 22.00 *(978-1-57312-519-2(9))* Smyth & Helwys Publishing, Inc.

Stevens, Woodie J. & Sailors, J. D. Every Paul Needs a Timothy: Blessings for Teachers & Small-Group Leaders. 2009. (ENG.). 64p. pap. 4.99 *(978-0-8341-2476-9(9),* 9780834124769) Beacon Hill Pr. of Kansas City.

Stott, John. 1 Timothy & Titus: Fighting the Good Fight. 2008. (John Stott Bible Studies). (ENG.). 64p. pap. 8.00 *(978-0-8308-2167-9(8),* IVP Conn.) InterVarsity Pr.

—2 Timothy: Standing Firm in Truth. 2008. (John Stott Bible Studies). (ENG.). 59p. pap. 8.00 *(978-0-8308-2168-6(6),* IVP Conn.) InterVarsity Pr.

Swindoll, Charles R. Swindoll's New Testament Insights on 1 & 2 Timothy, Titus, 1 vol. 2010. (Swindoll's New Testament Insights Ser.). (ENG.). 320p. 25.99 *(978-0-310-28433-8(3))* Zondervan.

Towner, Philip H. The Letters to Timothy & Titus. 2006. (New International Commentary on the New Testament). 886p. 58.00 *(978-0-8028-2513-1(3))* Eerdmans, William B. Publishing Co.

Tuohy, Timothy. The Gospel According to Timothy. 2008. 114p. pap. 7.98 *(978-1-4357-3401-2(7))* Lulu Enterprises Inc.

Twomey, Jay. The Pastoral Epistles Through the Centuries. 2009. (Blackwell Bible Commentaries Ser.: 14). (ENG., Illus.). 272p. 115.95 *(978-1-4051-2614-4(0),* Wiley-Blackwell) Wiley, John & Sons, Inc.

Walters, Dennis, contrib. by. The Letters of Saint Paul to the Thessalonians, Timothy, & Titus. 2nd ed. 2007. (Ignatius Catholic Study Bible Ser.). 63p. pap. 9.95 *(978-1-58617-162-9(3))* Ignatius Pr.

Ward, Jean Elizabeth, Poet Laureate. The Forbidden Gospels & Epistles, Complete. 2008. 599p. pap. 39.99 *(978-1-4357-3211-7(1))* Lulu Enterprises Inc.

Whedon's Commentary on Titus & Revelations, Vol. 5. 25.99 *(978-0-88019-127-2(9))* Schmul Publishing Co., Inc.

Wiersbe, Warren W. Be Faithful (1 & 2 Timothy, Titus, Philemon) It's Always Too Soon to Quit! 2009. (Be Series Commentary Ser.). (ENG.). 208p. pap. 12.99 *(978-1-4347-6734-9(5))* Cook, David C.

—The Wiersbe Bible Study Series: 1 & 2 Timothy, Titus, Philemon: It's Always Too Soon to Quit!, 1 vol. 2010. (Wiersbe Bible Study Ser.). (ENG.). 128p. pap. 8.99 *(978-1-4347-6510-9(5))* Cook, David C.

—1 & 2 Timothy, Titus, Philemon: It's Always Too Soon to Quit! 2010. 127p. *(978-0-7814-0375-7(8))* Kingsway Pubns.

Winkler, Jude. The Gospels Simply Explained. 2008. (Illus.). 208p. pap. 8.95 *(978-0-89942-714-0(6))* Catholic Bk. Publishing Corp.

Witherington, Ben, III. Letters & Homilies for Hellenized Christians Vol. 1: A Socio-Rhetorical Commentary on Titus, 1-2 Timothy & 1-3 John. 2006. (Letters & Homilies for Hellenized Christians Ser.). (ENG.). 623p. 40.00 *(978-0-8308-2931-6(8),* IVP Acad.) InterVarsity Pr.

—Letters & Homilies for Hellenized Christians Vol. 2: A Socio-Rhetorical Commentary on 1-2 Peter. 2008. (Letters & Homilies for Hellenized Christians Ser.). (ENG.). 432p. 35.00 *(978-0-8308-2933-0(4),* IVP Acad.) InterVarsity Pr.

Zehr, Paul M. 1 & 2 Timothy, Titus. 2010. pap. 24.99 *(978-0-8361-9492-0(6))* Herald Pr.

BIBLE—COMMENTARIES—N. T. PETER

see Bible—Commentaries—N. T. Catholic Epistles

BIBLE—COMMENTARIES—N. T. PHILEMON

Arnold, Clinton E. Ephesians, Philippians, Colossians, Philemon, 1 vol. 2007. (Zondervan Illustrated Bible Backgrounds Commentary Ser.). (ENG., Illus.). 128p. (gr. 13). pap. 14.99 *(978-0-310-27827-6(9))* Zondervan.

Arthur, J. Philip, ed. Christ All-Sufficient: Colossians & Philemon Simply Explained. 2007. (Welwyn Commentary Ser.). (Illus.). 240p. per. *(978-0-85234-655-6(7))* Evangelical Pr.

Beet, J. Agar. Ephesians, Philippians, Colossians & Philemon. pap. 12.99 *(978-0-88019-058-9(2))* Schmul Publishing Co., Inc.

Bird, Michael. Colossians & Philemon. Bird, Michael & Keener, Craig S., eds. 2009. (New Covenant Commentary Ser.). 192p. pap. 22.00 *(978-1-60608-131-0(4),* Cascade Bks.) Wipf & Stock Pubs.

Bird, Michael F. Colossians & Philemon. 2011. (New Testament at Crossway College Ser.). (ENG.). 192p. pap. 30.25 *(978-0-7188-9237-1(2))* Lutherworth Pr., The GBR. Dist: Printondemand-worldwide.com.

Blacoe, William Victor. Understanding the New Testament: 1 & 2 Timothy, Titus, & Philemon. 2011. 256p. pap. 19.99 *(978-1-59955-900-1(5))* Cedar Fort, Inc./CFI Distribution.

Cousar, Charles B. Philippians & Philemon: A Commentary. 2009. (New Testament Library). (ENG.). 120p. 30.00 *(978-0-664-22122-5(X))* Westminster John Knox Pr.

George, Elizabeth. Embracing God's Grace: Colossians/Philemon. 2010. (Woman after God's Own Heart Ser.). 176p. pap. 8.99 *(978-0-7369-1246-4(0))* Harvest Hse. Pubs.

González, Justo L. Three Months with Paul. 2006. (Three Months With Ser.). 171p. per. 11.50 *(978-0-687-49539-9(3))* Abingdon Pr.

Greenlee, J. Harold. Exegetical Summary of Titus & Philemon. 2nd ed. 2008. 147p. pap. 24.00 *(978-1-55671-192-3(1))* SIL International.

Ironside, H. A. 1 & 2 Timothy, Titus, & Philemon. 2007. (Ironside Expository Commentaries Ser.). (Illus.). 192p. 19.99 *(978-0-8254-2922-4(6))* Kregel Pubns.

Kreitzer, Larry J. Philemon. 2008. 212p. *(978-1-906055-29-5(7));* (Illus.). pap. *(978-1-906055-30-1(0))* Sheffield Phoenix Pr.

Lavender, Earl. Meditative Commentary Series: Ephesians, Philippians, Colossians, Philemon: Jesus above All. 2008. (Meditative Commentary Ser.). 144p. pap. 9.99 *(978-0-89112-561-7(2),* Leafwood Pubs.) Abilene Christian Univ. Pr.

Longman, Tremper, III. The Expositor's Bible Commentary, 1 vol., Vol. 12. rev. ed. 2008. (Expositor's Bible Commentary Ser.). (ENG.). 864p. 39.99 *(978-0-310-26893-2(1))* Zondervan.

Martin, Ralph P. Ephesians, Colossians, & Philemon: Interpretation: A Bible Commentary for Teaching & Preaching. 2012. (Interpretation: A Bible Commentary for Teaching & Preaching Ser.). (ENG.). 172p. pap. 25.00 ***(978-0-664-23861-2(0))*** Westminster John Knox Pr.

Maxwell, Marcus. Ephesians to Colossians & Philemon: A Guide for Reflection & Prayer. 2007. (Daily Bible Commentary Ser.). 277p. per. 12.95 *(978-1-59856-194-4(4))* Hendrickson Pubs. Marketing, LLC.

McInteer, Jim Bill. A Study of the Epistle to Philemon. pap., tchr. ed. 3.50 *(978-0-89098-467-3(0));* pap., stu. ed. 3.50 *(978-0-89098-466-6(2))* Twentieth Century Christian Bks.

Meadows, James L. Colossians & Philemon. pap. 5.50 *(978-0-89098-399-7(2))* Twentieth Century Christian Bks.

Moo, Douglas J. The Letters to the Colossians & to Philemon. 2008. (Pillar New Testament Commentary Ser.). 504p. 44.00 *(978-0-8028-3727-1(1))* Eerdmans, William B. Publishing Co.

Nielson, Kathleen Buswell. Colossians & Philemon: Contiue to Live in Him. 2007. (Living Word Bible Studies). 124p. spiral bd. *(978-1-59638-073-8(X))* P & R Publishing.

Reinmuth, Eckart. Der Brief des Paulus an Philemon. 2006. (Theologischer Handkommentar Zum Neuen Testament Ser.). (GER.). 63p. 33.00 *(978-3-374-02352-3(5))* Evangelische Verlagsanstalt GmbH DEU. Dist: Eisenbrauns, Inc.

Saarinen, Risto. The Pastoral Epistles with Philemon & Jude. 2008. (Brazos Theological Commentary on the Bible Ser.). 272p. (C). 29.99 *(978-1-58743-154-8(8))* Brazos Pr.

Scheck, Thomas & Jerome, St. St Jeromes Commentaries on Gal. 2010. (ENG.). 376p. pap. 40.00 *(978-0-268-04133-5(4))* Univ. of Notre Dame Pr.

Stepp, Perry L. & Gloer, W. Hullitt. Reading Paul's Letters to Individuals: A Literary & Theological Commentary on Paul's Letters to Philemon, Titus, & Timothy. 2008. pap. 22.00 *(978-1-57312-519-2(9))* Smyth & Helwys Publishing, Inc.

Still, Todd D. Philippians & Philemon. 2010. *(978-1-57312-084-5(7))* Smyth & Helwys Publishing, Inc.

Wall, Robert W. Colossians & Philemon. 2010. (IVP New Testament Commentary Ser.: Volume 12). (ENG.). 225p. pap. 18.00 *(978-0-8308-4012-0(5),* IVP Acad.) InterVarsity Pr.

Weidmann, Frederick W. Philippians, First & Second Thessalonians, & Philemon. 2012. (Westminster Bible Companion Ser.). (ENG.). 264p. pap. 25.00 ***(978-0-664-23852-0(1))*** Westminster John Knox Pr.

Wiersbe, Warren W. Be Faithful (1 & 2 Timothy, Titus, Philemon) It's Always Too Soon to Quit! 2009. (Be Series Commentary Ser.). (ENG.). 208p. pap. 12.99 *(978-1-4347-6734-9(5))* Cook, David C.

—The Wiersbe Bible Study Series: 1 & 2 Timothy, Titus, Philemon: It's Always Too Soon to Quit!, 1 vol. 2010. (Wiersbe Bible Study Ser.). (ENG.). 128p. pap. 8.99 *(978-1-4347-6510-9(5))* Cook, David C.

—1 & 2 Timothy, Titus, Philemon: It's Always Too Soon to Quit! 2010. 127p. *(978-0-7814-0375-7(8))* Kingsway Pubns.

Witherington, Ben, III. The Letters to Philemon, the Colossians, & the Ephesians: A Socio-Rhetorical Commentary on the Captivity Epistles. 2007. 382p. per. 38.00 *(978-0-8028-2488-2(9))* Eerdmans, William B. Publishing Co.

Wright, N. T. Colossians & Philemon, 1 vol. 2009. (N. T. Wright for Everyone Bible Study Guides). (ENG.). 62p. pap. 8.00 *(978-0-8308-2192-1(9),* IVP Conn.) 2008. (Tyndale New Testament Commentaries Ser.: Volume 12). (ENG.). 199p. pap. 16.00 *(978-0-8308-4242-1(X),* IVP Acad.) 2007. (Tyndale New Testament Commentaries Ser.). 192p. per. 14.00 *(978-0-8308-2991-0(1))* InterVarsity Pr.

BIBLE—COMMENTARIES—N. T. PHILIPPIANS

Allen, Earl E. The Book of Philippians. 2007. 72p. tchr. ed., spiral bd. *(978-1-878766-74-8(0));* stu. ed., spiral bd. *(978-1-878766-75-5(9))* Miracle Pubns. International, Inc.

Arnold, Clinton E. Ephesians, Philippians, Colossians, Philemon, 1 vol. 2007. (Zondervan Illustrated Bible Backgrounds Commentary Ser.). (ENG., Illus.). 128p. (gr. 13). pap. 14.99 *(978-0-310-27827-6(9))* Zondervan.

Baker Publishing Group Staff. A Walk Thru the Book of Philippians: Experience the Joy of the Lord, 1 vol. 2010. (Walk Thru the Bible Discussion Guides). (ENG.). 96p. pap. 7.99 *(978-0-8010-7177-5(1))* Baker Bks.

Beet, J. Agar. Ephesians, Philippians, Colossians & Philemon. pap. 12.99 *(978-0-88019-058-9(2))* Schmul Publishing Co., Inc.

Boice, James Montgomery. Philippians. 2006. (Expositional Commentary Ser.). 288p. pap. 20.99 *(978-0-8010-6645-0(X))* Baker Bks.

Braune, Karl. The Epistle of Paul to the Philippians & to Colossians: An Exegetical & Doctrinal Commentary. Lange, John Peter & Schaff, Philip, eds. Hackett, Horatio B. & Riddle, M. B., trs. 2007. (Lange's Commentary on the Holy Scripture: Ser.). 164p. pap. 17.00 *(978-1-55635-411-3(8),* Wipf and Stock) Wipf & Stock Pubs.

Collange, Jean-François. The Epistle of Saint Paul to the Philippians. Heathcote, A. W., tr. 2009. 168p. pap. 19.00 *(978-1-60608-644-5(8),* Wipf and Stock) Wipf & Stock Pubs.

Cousar, Charles B. Philippians & Philemon: A Commentary. 2009. (New Testament Library). (ENG.). 120p. 30.00 *(978-0-664-22122-5(X))* Westminster John Knox Pr.

Crowter, Phil. Preaching Philippians: Talk Outlines for the Book of Philippians. 2010. (Pray, Prepare, Preach Ser.). 64p. pap. *(978-1-906334-92-5(7))* Good Bk. Co.

Evenhouse, Neva. Discover Philippians. (Discover Your Bible Ser.). pap., tchr. ed. 3.50 *(978-1-56212-606-3(7),* 152185) Faith Alive Christian Resources.

Fee, Gordon D. Philippians. 2010. (IVP New Testament Commentary Ser.: Volume 11). (ENG.). 204p. pap. 17.00 *(978-0-8308-4011-3(7),* IVP Acad.) InterVarsity Pr.

Flemming, Dean E. NBBC, Philippians: A Commentary in the Wesleyan Tradition. 2009. (ENG.). 256p. pap. 25.99 *(978-0-8341-2411-0(4),* 9780834124110) Beacon Hill Pr. of Kansas City.

Freeman, Bill. The Christian Life Is a Supplied Life: A Study in the Book of Philippians. Date not set. 300p. (Orig.). pap. 7.50 *(978-0-914271-67-3(9))* Ministry Pubns.

Galatians - Philippians - Colossians. ldr.'s ed. (LifeLight Ser.). pap. 7.50 *(978-0-570-07854-8(7),* 20-3316) Concordia Publishing Hse.

González, Justo L. Three Months with Paul. 2006. (Three Months With Ser.). 171p. per. 11.50 *(978-0-687-49539-9(3))* Abingdon Pr.

Greenlee, J. Harold. Exegetical Summary of Philippians. 2nd ed. 2008. 252p. pap. 32.00 *(978-1-55671-199-2(9))* SIL International.

Guzik, David. Philippians & Colossians Commentary. 2008. 128p. pap. 12.99 *(978-1-56599-029-6(3))* Yahshua Publishing.

Halstead, Elizabeth Steele. Dwelling with Philippians: A Conversation with Scripture through Image & Word. 2011. (Illus.). 312p. 22.00 *(978-0-8028-6618-9(2))* Eerdmans, William B. Publishing Co.

Hansen, G. Walter. The Letter to the Philippians. 2009. (ENG.). 396p. 44.00 *(978-0-8028-3737-0(9))* Eerdmans, William B. Publishing Co.

Hoehner, Harold W., et al. Ephesians, Philippians, 1-2 Thessalonians Colossians, Philemon. 2008. (Cornerstone Biblical Commentary Ser.: 16). (ENG.). 456p. 29.99 *(978-0-8423-8344-8(1))* Tyndale Hse. Pubs.

Ironside, Henry A. & Ironside, H. A. Philippians & Colossians. 2007. (Ironside Expository Commentaries Ser.). 216p. 19.99 *(978-0-8254-2920-0(X))* Kregel Pubns.

Lavender, Earl. Meditative Commentary Series: Ephesians, Philippians, Colossians, Philemon: Jesus above All. 2008. (Meditative Commentary Ser.). 144p. pap. 9.99 *(978-0-89112-561-7(2),* Leafwood Pubs.) Abilene Christian Univ. Pr.

Lockhart, Jay & Roper, David L. Ephesians & Philippians. 2009. (Truth for Today Commentary Ser.). 610p. 29.95 *(978-0-9818128-2-3(1))* Resource Pubns.

Martin, Ralph P. Philippians. (ENG.). 187p. 2008. (Tyndale New Testament Commentaries Ser.: Volume 11). pap. 16.00 *(978-0-8308-4241-4(1),* IVP Acad.) 2007. (Tyndale New Testament Commentaries Ser.). per. 14.00 *(978-0-8308-2990-3(3))* InterVarsity Pr.

Maxwell, Marcus. Ephesians to Colossians & Philemon: A Guide for Reflection & Prayer. 2007. (Daily Bible Commentary Ser.). 277p. per. 12.95 *(978-1-59856-194-4(4))* Hendrickson Pubs. Marketing, LLC.

Meadows, James L. Ephesians & Philippians. pap. 5.50 *(978-0-89098-398-0(4))* Twentieth Century Christian Bks.

Newman, Jeff. Conflict under Control. 2007. 84p. *(978-1-59402-652-2(1))* Regular Baptist Pr.

Painter, Inalie. God Is... An in-depth Study of the Character of God. 2009. pap. 16.99 *(978-1-60799-473-2(9))* Tate Publishing & Enterprises, LLC.

Peale, Norman Vincent. Secret of Dynamic & Happy Living. 2011. 16p. pap. 35.95 *(978-1-258-00466-8(6))* Literary Licensing, LLC.

Perkins, Tyrone C. A Commentary on the Books of Galatians, Ephesians, Philippians. 112p. pap. 9.95 *(978-1-56794-202-6(4),* C-2555) Star Bible & Tract Corp.

Philippians/Colossians/Philemon. (People's Bible Commentary Ser.). 232p. 13.99 *(978-0-7586-0448-4(3))* Concordia Publishing Hse.

Prosser, Bo. Sessions with Philippians. 2011. pap. *(978-1-57312-579-6(2))* Smyth & Helwys Publishing, Inc.

Reumann & Reumann, John Henry Paul. Philippians. 2008. (Anchor Yale Bible Commentaries Ser.). (ENG.). 808p. (C). 65.00 *(978-0-300-14045-3(3))* Yale Univ. Pr.

Reumann, John. Philippians: A New Translation with Introduction & Commentary. 2008. 432p. 45.00 *(978-0-385-06309-8(1),* Anchor Bible) Doubleday Religious Publishing Group, The.

Shellenberger, Susie. The Secret Power of Joy: The Book of Philippians, 1 vol. 2012. (Faithgirlz! Bible Study Ser.). (ENG.). 128p. (J). pap. 8.99 *(978-0-310-72842-9(8))* Zonderkidz.

Still, Todd D. Philippians & Philemon. 2010. *(978-1-57312-084-5(7))* Smyth & Helwys Publishing, Inc.

Strauss, Mark, et al. Galatians Thru Philemon Vol. 11: Putting Faith into Practice. 2008. (QuickNotes Commentaries Ser.). (ENG.). 224p. pap. 9.99 *(978-1-59789-777-8(9),* Barbour Bks.) Barbour Publishing, Inc.

Taylor, Preston. Filipenses: Gozo en Cristo.Tr. of Phillipians: Joy in Christ. (SPA.). 222p. pap. 5.99 *(978-1-56063-240-5(2),* 490224) Editorial Unilit.

Tezeno, Timmy H. The Bible Trainer Series: Ruth & Philippians. 2008. pap. 11.00 *(978-0-8059-8590-0(5))* Dorrance Publishing Co., Inc.

Tyndale House Publishers Staff, prod. Philippians & Colossians. 2009. (Life Application Bible Studies: NLT Ser.). (ENG.). 112p. pap. 7.99 *(978-1-4143-2645-0(9))* Tyndale Hse. Pubs.

Weidmann, Frederick W. Philippians, First & Second Thessalonians, & Philemon. 2012. (Westminster Bible Companion Ser.). (ENG.). 264p. pap. 25.00 *(978-0-664-23852-0(1))* Westminster John Knox Pr.

Wheeler, Steve. Forget What? The Philippian Misconception. 2009. 262p. pap. 14.99 *(978-1-60696-426-2(7))* Tate Publishing & Enterprises, LLC.

Wilson, Earle L., et al. Galatians, Philippians, Colossians: A Commentary for Bible Students. 2007. (Illus.). 352p. *(978-0-89827-307-6(2))* Wesleyan Publishing Hse.

Witherington, Ben. Paul's Letter to the Philippians: A Socio-Rhetorical Commentary. 2011. 344p. pap. 38.00 ***(978-0-8028-0143-2(9))*** Eerdmans, William B. Publishing Co.

Zapata, R. Comentario Biblico Continente Nuevo: Filipenses.Tr. of New Continent Bible Commentary: Philippians. (SPA.). pap. 5.99 *(978-0-7899-0305-1(9),* 498654) Editorial Unilit.

BIBLE—COMMENTARIES—N. T. REVELATION

Abbott, Dustin. Revelation Unveiled. 2007. 365p. *(978-1-55452-144-9(0))* Essence Publishing.

Amos, Catherine. The Holy Spirit - She Is with Us: A Book of Revelation & Hope. 2011. 102p. 24.95 *(978-1-4327-6836-2(0));* (ENG.). pap. 16.95 *(978-1-4327-7001-3(2))* Outskirts Pr., Inc.

Anderson, Bobi. God Will Have the Last Word: A Study of the Revelation. 2011. 568p. pap. 38.95 ***(978-1-4497-2157-2(5),*** WestBow Pr.) Author Solutions, Inc.

Arnold, Clinton E. Revelation, 1 vol. 2007. (Zondervan Illustrated Bible Backgrounds Commentary Ser.). (ENG., Illus.). 160p. (gr. 13). pap. 16.99 *(978-0-310-27832-0(5))* Zondervan.

Bargo, Jason. Are We There Yet? A Guide to Revelation. 2009. pap. 16.99 *(978-1-60799-946-1(3))* Tate Publishing & Enterprises, LLC.

Barr, David L. Tales of the End: A Narrative Commentary on the Book of Revelation. 2011. xiii, 377p. ***(978-1-59815-033-9(2))*** Polebridge Pr.

Barrett, Telford. Revelation for Today. 2009. 224p. pap. 15.99 *(978-1-60791-090-9(X))* Xulon Pr., Inc.

Bauer, Thomas Johann. Das Tausendjahrige Messiasreich der Johannesoffenbarung: Eine Literarkritische Studie Zu Offb 19,11-21,8. 2007. (Beihefte Zur Zeitschrift Für Die Neutestamentliche Wissenschaft und Die Kunde der älteren Kirche Ser.). (GER., Illus.). XI, 442p. 154.00 *(978-3-11-019550-7(X))* De Gruyter, Walter Inc.

Beasley-Murray, G. R., ed. The Book of Revelation: Based on the Revised Standard Version. 2010. 352p. pap. 39.00 *(978-1-60899-566-0(6),* Wipf and Stock) Wipf & Stock Pubs.

Beauvais, Matt. Jesus Speaks Summer 2008: Piracy, Casting & the Ignominious Spirit. 2008. 164p. pap. 29.50 *(978-1-4389-2167-9(5))* AuthorHouse.

Berchie, Daniel. An Investigation into the Meaning & Identity. 2010. 216p. pap. *(978-3-639-27872-9(0))* VDM Verlag Dr. Mueller e.K.

Berry, Ronald G. The Power of the Beast: A Commentary on the Book of Revelation. 2010. 260p. 24.99 *(978-1-4520-7912-7(9));* pap. 16.99 *(978-1-4520-7913-4(7))* AuthorHouse.

Bertucci, Mary Lou, compiled by. Tiffany's Swedenborgian Angels: Stained Glass Windows Representing the Seven Churches from the Book of Revelation. 2011. (Illus.). 96p. pap. *(978-0-87785-339-8(8))* Swedenborg Foundation, Inc.

Bickle, Mike, notes. Book of Revelation NKJV. 2009. (Illus.). 139p. pap. 10.00 *(978-0-9823262-0-6(3))* Forerunner Books.

Blomberg, Craig L. From Pentecost to Patmos: An Introduction to Acts Through Revelation. 2006. (ENG., Illus.). 592p. 39.99 *(978-0-8054-3248-0(5),* B&H Academic) B&H Publishing Group.

Blount, Brian K. Revelation: A Commentary. 2009. (New Testament Library). (ENG.). 400p. 50.00 *(978-0-664-22121-8(1))* Westminster John Knox Pr.

Boersma, Hans. The Visions of Zechariah: Lighting the Darkness. lt. ed. 5.25 *(978-1-56212-654-4(7),* 150051) Faith Alive Christian Resources.

Boxall, Ian. The Revelation of Saint John. 2009. (Black's New Testament Commentary Ser.). (ENG., Illus.). 347p. pap. 24.95 *(978-1-59856-458-7(7))* Hendrickson Pubs. Marketing, LLC.

Brighton, Louis. Revelation-Reader's Edition. 2010. 512p. pap. 24.99 *(978-0-7586-1793-4(3))* Concordia Publishing Hse.

Briley, Terry. Meditative Commentary: Revelation: Jesus the Lamb. 2009. (Meditative Commentary Ser.). 122p. pap. 10.99 *(978-0-89112-559-4(0),* Leafwood Pubs.) Abilene Christian Univ. Pr.

Bullinger, Ethelbert. Commentary on Revelation: Or, the Apocalypse. 2007. 752p. per. 21.95 *(978-1-60206-112-5(2))* Cosimo, Inc.

Butler, John G. Joshua to II Samuel. 830p. ***(978-1-889773-73-5(5))*** LBC Pubns.

Caesarea, Andrew of. Commentary on the Apocalypse. 2011. (Fathers of the Chrch Ser.). 288p. 39.95 ***(978-0-8132-0123-8(3))*** Catholic Univ. of America Pr.

Carrington, Philip. The Meaning of the Revelation. 2008. 424p. pap. 36.00 *(978-1-55635-673-5(0),* Wipf and Stock) Wipf & Stock Pubs.

Castner, John. Investing for Armageddon. 2006. (ENG.). 92p. per. 16.95 *(978-1-4241-5595-8(9))* PublishAmerica, Inc.

Chambers, Joe. The Masterpiece: The Church in the Book of Revelation. 2007. 314p. 19.99 *(978-0-9779535-0-9(5))* 21st Century Pr.

Charlesworth, James H. The Good & Evil Serpent: How a Universal Symbol Became Christianized. 2010. (Anchor Yale Bible Reference Library). (Illus.). 744p. 45.00 *(978-0-300-14082-8(7))* Yale Univ. Pr.

Choice, Eloise T. Secularism & Scripture Reconciled, 1 vol. 2010. 525p. pap. 34.95 *(978-1-4489-6632-5(9))* PublishAmerica, Inc.

Christian, Shirley. TYPES & SHADOWS: Prophetic Pictures to Wholeness in Christ. 2006. pap. 15.99 *(978-1-59781-911-4(5))* Xulon Pr., Inc.

Corbin, Bruce. The Great Divine Consummation: An Exposition & Interpretation of the Book of Revelation. 2011. 116p. 39.95 ***(978-1-258-04847-1(7))*** Literary Licensing, LLC.

Crew, Denver. The Revelations of Jesus Christ. 2009. 152p. 22.49 *(978-1-4389-9908-1(9));* pap. 11.99 *(978-1-4389-9907-4(0))* AuthorHouse.

Culleton, James. A Key to the Apocalypse. 2011. 38p. 35.95 ***(978-1-258-01509-1(9))*** Literary Licensing, LLC.

Dalrymple, Rob. Revelation & the Two Witnesses: The Implications for Understanding JohnÕs Depiction of the People of God & His Hortatory Intent. 2011. 174p. pap. 20.00 ***(978-1-61097-138-6(8),*** Wipf and Stock) Wipf & Stock Pubs.

David Steele. Notes on the Apocalypse. lt. ed. 2007. (ENG.). 308p. pap. 24.99 *(978-1-4264-8080-5(6))* BiblioBazaar.

Davis, Peter J. The Book of Revelation & the Bible as Never Explained Before. 2010. pap. 20.99 *(978-1-61663-172-7(4))* Tate Publishing & Enterprises, LLC.

de Ruyter, Frank. Withdrawing the Veil: Sermons in Pakistan, Book 1, 1 vol. 2010. 96p. pap. 19.95 *(978-1-4489-4884-0(3))* PublishAmerica, Inc.

Dean, G. Davis, Jr. The Revelation of Jesus Christ: The Cross & the Crown of Our Savior & Lord. 2009. 312p. pap. 27.00 *(978-1-4349-9612-1(3),* RoseDog Bks.) Dorrance Publishing Co., Inc.

Delorme, Jean & Donegani, Isabelle. L'Apocalypse de Jean: Révélation Pour le Temps de la Violence et du Désir, 2 vols. 2010. (FRE.). *(978-2-204-08894-7(3)); (978-2-204-09170-1(7));* pap. *(978-2-204-09231-9(2))* Editions du Cerf.

DeRuvo, Fred. End of the Ages: A Study-Grow-Know Commentary: Revelation. 2011. (Illus.). 380p. (C). pap. 16.99 *(978-0-9774244-9-8(9))* Study-Grow-Know.

Diedricks, Louis. The Day of the Lord. 2010. 76p. pap. 13.95 *(978-1-936198-05-4(3))* Hillcrest Publishing Group, Inc.

Disciple IV Revelation Video. 60.00 *(978-0-687-09678-7(2))* Abingdon Pr.

Downall, Donn. Breaking the Code: Understanding the Book of Revelation. ldr.'s ed. 2006. 31p. pap. 12.00 *(978-0-687-49779-9(5))* Abingdon Pr.

Duck, Daymond R. The Book of Revelation, 0 vols. 2006. (Smart Guide to the Bible Ser.). (Illus.). 384p. per. 14.99 *(978-1-4185-0990-3(6))* Nelson, Thomas Inc.

Duren, James. The Overcomers: The Book of the Revelation of Jesus Christ. 2009. 344p. pap. 18.99 *(978-1-60791-620-8(7))* Xulon Pr., Inc.

Dymally, Billye. Revelation. 2006. 127p. pap. 11.95 *(978-0-7414-3510-1(1))* Infinity Publishing.

Eade, Alfred Thompson. The New Panorama Bible Study Course: Panorama Study No. 4 the Book of Revelation, No.4. deluxe ed. 2008. (Illus.). 33p. 24.99 *(978-0-9799734-3-7(0))* Oak Knoll Publishing.

EDWARDS, Larry D. The Mystery Revealed! A Commentary on the Book of Revelation in the Holy Bible. 2008. 480p. 35.99 *(978-1-60647-728-1(5));* pap. 23.99 *(978-1-60647-727-4(7))* Xulon Pr., Inc.

Emmanuel. Wisdom of God - the Little Scroll. 2007. 360p. (ENG.). 32.99 *(978-1-4257-5564-5(X));* per. 22.99 *(978-1-4257-5563-8(1))* Xlibris Corp.

Faber, George Stanley. Napoleon III: the Man of Prophecy or, the Revival of the French. 2007. pap. 19.95 *(978-1-4304-8264-2(8))* Kessinger Publishing, LLC.

Fair, Ian. Conquering with Christ. 2011. (ENG.). pap. ***(973-0-89112-294-4(X),*** ACU Pr.) Abilene Christian Univ. Pr.

Fee, Gordon D. Revelation. 2010. (New Covenant Commentary Ser.). 354p. pap. 39.00 *(978-1-60899-431-1(7),* Cascade Bks.) Wipf & Stock Pubs.

Fox, Emmet. The Four Horsemen of the Apocalypse. pap. 4.95 *(978-0-87516-763-3(2))* DeVorss & Co.

Franzmann, Martin H. A Revelation to John: A Commentary. 148p. 15.99 *(978-0-570-04430-7(8))* Concordia Publishing Hse.

Gardner, Paul. Revelation: The Compassion & Protection of Christ. 2008. (Focus on the Bible Commentaries Ser.). (ENG.). 320p. pap. 14.99 *(978-1-84550-344-4(9))* Christian Focus Pubns. GBR. Dist: STL Distribution North America.

Garland, Anthony/Charles. A Testimony of Jesus Christ: A Commentary on the Book of Revelation, 2. 2007. (Illus.). 566p. *(978-0-9788864-1-7(0));*2. 585p. *(978-0-9788864-2-4(9))* SpiritAndTruth.org.

Geisler, Norman L. & Howe, Thomas. The Big Book of Bible Difficulties: Clear & Concise Answers from Genesis to Revelation. 2008. 624p. pap. 29.99 *(978-0-8010-7158-4(5))* Baker Bks.

Glabach, Wilfried E. Reclaiming the Book of Revelation: A Suggestion of New Readings in the Local Church. 2007. (American University Studies: Vol. 259). xii, 212p. 70.95 *(978-0-8204-9504-0(2))* Lang, Peter Publishing, Inc.

Greer, Lisa Jo. The Preparation Realm of Heaven. 2009. 176p. pap. 14.99 *(978-1-61579-487-4(5))* Xulon Pr., Inc.

Guttesen, Poul F. Leaning into the Future: The Kingdom of God in the Theology of Jurgen Moltmann & the Book of Revelation. 2011. (ENG.). 278p. pap. 48.00 *(978-0-227-17352-7(X))* Clarke, James Co., Ltd. GBR. Dist: Brown, David Bk. Co., The.

Guy, Laurie & Fiddes, Paul S. Making Sense of the Book of Revelation. 2009. pap. *(978-1-57312-543-7(1))* Smyth & Helwys Publishing, Inc.

Hamilton, James M. Revelation: The Spirit Speaks to the Churches. 2012. (Preaching the Word Ser.). 464p. 34.99 *(978-1-4335-0541-6(X))* Crossway.

Hanson, Christopher Mark. A Scripture for Mankind: The Revelation of St. John the Divine. 2008. 256p. pap. 14.49 *(978-1-4343-8614-4(7))* AuthorHouse.

Harthern, Roy. Armageddon Ahead: An Easy to Understand Commentary on the Apocalypse. 2009. (ENG.). 160p. 12.95 *(978-0-9817608-5-8(6))* Lifebridge Bks.

Hartman, Gregory L. New Testament Imperativity: Because You Want to Be Close to God. 2010. 332p. pap. 22.95 *(978-1-4497-0148-2(5),* WestBow Pr.) Author Solutions, Inc.

Hartman, Roger. Unfolding the Mysteries of Revelation. 2008. 204p. pap. 14.99 *(978-1-60477-092-6(9))* Xulon Pr., Inc.

Hemenway, Harold. European History Foretold. 2007. 204p. per. 14.99 *(978-1-60266-796-9(9))* Xulon Pr., Inc.

Hille, Kirk. Deceived by Light: The Truth about the End Times. 96p. 14.99 *(978-0-7586-0040-0(2))* Concordia Publishing Hse.

Hobbs, Evangelist David. The Great Whore: The Apostate Church Unveiled, Identified, & Exposed. 2009. 232p. 29.99 *(978-1-4363-5313-7(0));* pap. 19.99 *(978-1-4363-5312-0(2))* Xlibris Corp.

Holland, Carl E. Shout It from the Housetops. 2008. 160p. per. 13.99 *(978-1-60477-604-1(8))* Xulon Pr., Inc.

Hort, Fenton John Anthony. The Apocalypse of St John, I-III: The Greek Text with Introduction, Commentary, & Additional Notes. 2010. (Cambridge Library Collection - Religion Ser.). (ENG.). 104p. pap. 19.99 *(978-1-108-00757-3(0))* Cambridge Univ. Pr.

Howard, Robert Glenn, ed. Network Apocalypse: Visions of the End in an Age of Internet Media. 2011. 248p. ***(978-1-907534-13-3(X))*** Sheffield Phoenix Pr.

Hunter Jr., Donald R. Revelations of Jesus Christ: Predetermined End. 2008. 152p. 24.99 *(978-1-4389-0687-4(0));* pap. 19.99 *(978-1-4389-0686-7(2))* AuthorHouse.

Jackson, Ph.D., James H., Jr. The Mystical Bible. 2009. 678p. pap. 44.50 *(978-1-4357-0609-5(9))* Lulu Enterprises Inc.

Jones, Patrick M., compiled by. Revelations from Revelation. 2008. (Illus.). 636p. pap. 31.95 *(978-1-57258-505-8(6))* TEACH Services, Inc.

Journey Through the Bible Revelation Student. 4.00 *(978-0-687-05617-0(9))* Abingdon Pr.

Joyner, Rick. Taking the Land Part 1. 2009. 170p. pap. 9.99 *(978-1-59933-826-2(2))* MorningStar Pubns., Inc.

Kanzlemar, Joseph. The End of the Age & Beyond: Opening the Book of Revelation to the Contemporary Church. 2nd rev. ed. 2007. (Illus.). 291p. *(978-0-9797786-5-0(4))* Bible Based Studies.

Kingdom Quotes Staff. The Beast of the Revelation: The Antichrist Network. pap. *(978-0-930179-22-9(6))* Johns Enterprises.

—Notes on the Seven Seals: (From the Book of Revelation) pap. *(978-0-930179-39-7(0))* Johns Enterprises.

—The Seven Plagues of the Revelation. pap. *(978-0-930179-35-9(8))* Johns Enterprises.

—The Seven Seals of the Revelation. pap. *(978-0-930179-20-5(X))* Johns Enterprises.

—The Seven Trumpets of the Revelation. pap. *(978-0-930179-36-6(6))* Johns Enterprises.

, Kir-b, Kir-b. Genesis Unraveled. 2010. 102p. pap. 10.99 *(978-0-557-53046-5(6))* Lulu Enterprises Inc.

Klein, John & Spears, Adam. The Book of Revelation Through Hebrew Eyes. 2009. 342p. pap. 18.99 *(978-1-58930-237-2(0))* Selah Publishing Group, LLC.

Knight, Jonathan. Revelation. 2011. 212p. ***(978-1-906055-06-6(8));*** pap. ***(978-1-906055-07-3(6))*** Sheffield Phoenix Pr.

Lamb, Jonathan & Chester, Tim. Revelation 2-3: A Message from Jesus to the Church Today. 2010. (Good Book Guides). 64p. pap. *(978-1-905564-68-2(6))* Good Bk. Co.

Larkin, Clarence. The Book of Revelation. 2006. pap. 13.95 *(978-1-59605-300-7(3),* Cosimo Classics) Cosimo, Inc.

—The Book of Revelation. 2007. (ENG.). 228p. per. 26.95 *(978-1-4209-2872-3(4))* Digireads.com.

Lee, Witness. The Vision of the Universal Woman & the Man-Child. 2007. per. 6.75 *(978-0-7363-3600-0(1))* Living Stream Ministry.

Lo-Bue. The Turin Fragments of Tyconius' Commentary on Revelation. 2009. (ENG.). 220p. pap. 31.99 *(978-0-521-10824-9(1))* Cambridge Univ. Pr.

Lucado, Max. Book of Revelation: Final Curtain Call, 0 vols. 2007. (Inspirational Bible Study; Life Lessons with Max Lucado Ser.). (Illus.). 128p. per. 9.99 *(978-1-4185-0958-3(2))* Nelson, Thomas Inc.

Lyall, Ian. All things made New. 2010. 50p. pap. 9.50 *(978-1-4461-5271-3(5))* Lulu Enterprises Inc.

Lynch, Dan. Glorification. 2007. per. 10.00 *(978-1-59712-125-5(8))* Catawba Publishing Co.

Lyons, George. Revelation: Lectio Divina for Youth. 2007. (Ancient Faith Ser.). (ENG.). 80p. per. 7.99 *(978-0-8341-5014-0(X),* 083-415-014X) Beacon Hill Pr. of Kansas City.

MacArthur, John F. Because the Time Is Near: John MacArthur Explains the Book of Revelation. 2007. (ENG., Illus.). 368p. per. 16.99 *(978-0-8024-0728-3(5))* Moody Pubs.

Mangina, Joseph L. Revelation. 2010. (Brazos Theological Commentary on the Bible Ser.). 272p. (C). 29.99 *(978-1-58743-112-8(2))* Brazos Pr.

Marberry, Thomas, et al. 1, 2, 3 John & Revelation. 2010. vii, 503p. ***(978-0-89265-537-3(2))*** Randall Hse. Pubns.

Martin, Timothy P. & Vaughn, Jeffrey L. Beyond Creation Science: New Covenant Creation from Genesis to Revelation. 2007. 527p. per. *(978-0-9799147-0-6(1))* Martin, Timothy.

Massegee, Charles. The Rise & Fall of the Antichrist: Islam, Allah, & the Antichrist in Prophecy. 2011. 450p. pap. 29.95 ***(978-1-4327-7335-9(6))*** Outskirts Pr., Inc.

B

Mathews, Susan Fournier. The Book of Revelation: Question by Question. 2009. (Question by Question Bible Study Commentary Ser.). 224p. pap. 19.95 (978-0-8091-4585-0(5)) Paulist Pr.

Mauro, Philip. The Patmos Visions: A Study of the Apocalypse. 2011. 584p. 63.95 **(978-1-258-05776-3(X))** Literary Licensing, LLC.

Maxwell, Marcus. Revelation: A Guide for Reflection & Prayer. 2007. (Daily Bible Commentary Ser.). 229p. per. 12.95 (978-1-59856-197-5(9)) Hendrickson Pubs. Marketing, LLC.

McGowan, Victor. The Revelation & the History of Christendom: Prophecy Fulfilled to the End of Our Time. 2011. 88p. pap. 9.95 (978-1-4502-7809-6(4)) iUniverse, Inc.

McIntyre, Rev. Frances. The Greatness of God Almighty. 2010. 120p. pap. 13.99 (978-1-4490-6942-1(8)) AuthorHouse.

Meadows, James L. Revelation. pap. 5.50 (978-0-89098-410-9(7)) Twentieth Century Christian Bks.

Metzger, Bruce M. Breaking the Code: Understanding the Book of Revelation. 2006. pap. 35.00 (978-0-687-49759-1(0)); 111p. per., wbk. ed. 11.00 (978-0-687-49200-8(9)) Abingdon Pr.

—Breaking the Code Kit: Understanding the Book of Revelation. 2006. pap. 50.00 (978-0-687-49769-0(8)) Abingdon Pr.

Michaels, J. Ramsey. Revelation. 2011. (IVP New Testament Commentary Ser.: Volume 20). (ENG.). 265p. pap. 18.00 (978-0-8308-4020-5(6), IVP Acad.) InterVarsity Pr.

Michailidis, Rev. Andreas. The Creed. 2011. 220p. pap. 15.99 **(978-1-61379-158-5(5))** Xulon Pr., Inc.

Moore, Marvin. Could It Really Happen? Revelation 13 in the Light of History & Current Events. 2007. 287p. 16.99 (978-0-8163-2185-8(X)) Pacific Pr. Publishing Assn.

Moore, Phil. Straight to the Heart of Revelation: 60 Bite-Sized Insights, 1 vol. 2010. (Straight to the Heart Ser.). 272p. pap. 14.99 (978-1-85424-990-6(8), Monarch Bks.) Lion Hudson PLC GBR. Dist: Kregel Pubns.

Morgan, G. Campbell. Mensaje de Apocalipsis a las Iglesias: Message of Revelation to the . . . (SPA.). 128p. (978-84-7228-822-5(6), 222348) Clie, Editorial.

Morris, Leon. Revelation. 2007. (Tyndale New Testament Commentaries Ser.). (ENG.). 256p. per. 14.00 (978-0-8308-2999-6(7)) InterVarsity Pr.

Morris, Leon L. & Morris, Leon. Revelation, 1 vol. 2009. (Tyndale New Testament Commentaries Ser.: Volume 20). (ENG.). 250p. pap. 16.00 (978-0-8308-4250-6(0), IVP Acad.) InterVarsity Pr.

Mulder, John. The Gems of Heaven. 2006. 59p. pap. 16.95 (978-1-4241-4607-9(0)) PublishAmerica, Inc.

Munson Jr, Rev Herbert Melville. Strange Work. 2010. 409p. pap. 21.95 (978-0-557-31890-2(4)) Lulu Enterprises Inc.

Newton, Isaac. Observations upon the Prophecies of Daniel & the Apocalypse of St John. 2008. 248p. per. 9.99 (978-1-59986-580-5(7)) Filiquarian Publishing, LLC.

Noel, Ted. A Primer on the Book of Revelation. 2009. 222p. pap. 24.00 (978-1-55635-532-5(7), Resource Pubns.) Wipf & Stock Pubs.

Oecumenius & Andrew of Caesarea. Greek Commentaries on Revelation. Oden, Thomas C., ed. Weinrich, William C., tr. from GEC. 2011. (Ancient Christian Texts). (ENG.). 212p. 60.00 (978-0-8308-2908-8(3), IVP Acad.) InterVarsity Pr.

Ogden, Arthur M. The Avenging of the Apostles & Prophets: A Commentary on Revelation. 470p. 19.95 (978-0-9646497-1-2(3)); 112p. pap., wbk. ed. 4.95 (978-0-9646497-2-9(1)) Ogden Pubns.

O'Kirwan, Cornelia. Behind the Psychic Curtain. 2007. 436p. per. 21.99 (978-1-60477-169-5(0)) Xulon Pr., Inc.

Parry, Jay & Parry, Donald. Understanding the BK of Revelation. 2007. 368p. pap. 16.95 (978-1-59038-762-7(7)) Deseret Bk. Co.

Patterson, Warnette B. The Book with the Seven Seals. 2010. 120p. pap. 15.98 (978-1-4269-3002-7(X)) Trafford Publishing.

Perkins, Tyrone C. A Commentary on the Book of Revelation. 240p. pap. 14.95 (978-1-56794-190-6(7), C-2538) Star Bible & Tract Corp.

Rainbow, Paul A. The Pith of the Apocalypse: Essential Message & Principles for Interpretation. 2008. 180p. pap. 21.00 (978-1-55635-914-9(4)) Wipf & Stock Pubs.

Ren, C. H. Two Beasts Rising: Book Two of the End Times Series. 2011. 220p. 33.95 (978-1-4497-1384-3(X)); pap. 17.95 (978-1-4497-1385-0(8)) Author Solutions, Inc. (WestBow Pr.).

Resseguie, James L. The Revelation of John: A Narrative Commentary, 1 vol. 2009. 288p. (C). pap. 26.00 (978-0-8010-3213-4(X)) Baker Academic.

Revelation. (People's Bible Commentary Ser.). 228p. pap. 10.99 (978-0-570-04986-9(5), 12-8048); (People's Bible Commentary Ser.). 240p. 13.99 (978-0-7586-0453-8(X)); (LifeLight Bible Studies: Course 15). stu. ed. 5.50 (978-0-570-09289-6(2), 20-2317); (LifeLight Bible Studies: Course 15). 6.50 (978-0-570-09288-9(4), 20-2316) Concordia Publishing Hse.

Revelation, the Book: A Commentary. 2007. 15.00 (978-0-9747893-4-7(8)) Robinson, Robert.

Richard, Pablo. Apocalypse: A PeopleÕs Commentary on the Book of Revelation. 2009. 192p. pap. 22.00 (978-1-60608-159-4(4), Wipf and Stock) Wipf & Stock Pubs.

Richardson, John, Jr. Revelation Unwrapped: Revealing the Blessing of John's Vision. 2010. 84p. pap. (978-0-9524894-2-9(2)) Good Bk. Co.

Roberts, Derrill L. The Revelation of Jesus Christ: A Commentary. 2010. 298p. pap. 17.95 (978-1-4327-4526-4(3)) Outskirts Pr., Inc.

Roberts, Gary M. A Quick Guide to the Book of Revelation. 2007. 155p. pap. 12.00 (978-1-4116-1560-1(3)) Lulu Enterprises Inc.

Robson, Edward A. Revelation: The Book of Blessing, vols. 12, Vol. 2. 2nd ed. 2011. (Illus.). 242p. pap. 14.00 **(978-0-9797742-3-2(3))** Robson, Edward A.

Roman, Frank. El Apocalipsis Al Descubierto: Revelation Unveiled. (SPA.). (978-84-7645-424-4(4), 223548) Clie, Editorial.

Ruotolo, Augustine. Revelation: A Layman's View. 2006. 156p. per. 10.95 (978-1-59824-378-9(0)) E-BookTime LLC.

Russell, Daniel. Preaching the Apocalypse. 2007. (ENG.). 256p. 42.95 (978-0-548-09202-6(8)) Kessinger Publishing, LLC.

Scokzek, Louis C. El Apocalipsis Al Dia: Revelation Updated. (SPA.). (978-84-7645-455-8(4), 223552) Clie, Editorial.

Sedinger, Ione L. The Good News of the Apocalypse: Dancing Your Way Through the Bible. 2010. 380p. 34.95 (978-1-4502-5474-8(8)); pap. 24.95 (978-1-4502-5473-1(X)) iUniverse, Inc.

Sellman, Paul. The Tree of Life: A Biblical Study of Immortality & New Creation. 2010. 238p. pap. 15.95 (978-1-4327-6232-2(X)) Outskirts Pr., Inc.

Seven Scrolls of Revelation. 2008. (978-0-9711779-0-1(2)) Wilderness Publishing Co.

Shua, Rafael. The Sand Table: A Tactical Approach to Revelation. 2009. 364p. pap. 20.99 (978-1-61579-134-7(5)) Xulon Pr., Inc.

Smith, Uriah. The United States in the Light of Prophe. 2006. pap. (978-1-84702-488-6(2)) Echo Library.

—The United States in the Light of Prophecy: An Exposition of Rev. 13:11-17. 2007. (ENG.). 116p. pap. 18.99 (978-1-4346-2683-7(0)); 124p. pap. 19.99 (978-1-4346-2688-2(1)) BiblioBazaar.

—The United States in the Light of Prophecy; Or, an Exposition of Rev. 13. 2006. 180p. per. 18.99 (978-1-4255-1387-0(5)) MPublishing.

Spore, Andrew. The Joy of Exile. 2010. 177p. pap. 20.00 (978-0-557-35310-1(6)) Lulu Enterprises Inc.

Steele, David. Notes on the Apocalypse. 2008. 312p. 29.99 (978-0-554-25024-3(1)); 28.99 (978-0-554-34327-3(4)) BiblioBazaar.

Steele, David & Henry, O. Notes on the Apocalypse. rev. ed. 2007. (ENG.). 276p. pap. 21.99 (978-1-4264-8023-2(7)) BiblioBazaar.

Stefanovic, Ranko. Revelation of Jesus Christ: Commentary on the Book of Revelation. 2009. (978-1-883925-66-6(5)); (ENG.). 686p. (C). 39.99 (978-1-883925-67-3(3)) Andrews Univ. Pr.

Steinle, C. Come Out of Her My People. 2007. 164p. pap. 9.96 (978-1-4303-0135-6(X)) Lulu Enterprises Inc.

Strauss, Mark, et al. Hebrews Thru Revelation Vol. 12: Wisdom for Today-And Forever. 2008. (QuickNotes Commentaries Ser.: Vol. 12). (ENG.). 240p. pap. 9.99 (978-1-59789-778-5(7), Barbour Bks.) Barbour Publishing, Inc.

Swaggart, Jimmy. Revelation of the Cross: Cross of Christ Series. 2007. pap. 20.00 (978-1-934655-33-7(3)) Swaggart, Jimmy Ministries.

Swedenborg, Emanuel. The Apocalypse Revealed, Wherein Are Disclosed the Areana There Foretold, Which Have Heretofore Remained Concealed Tr from the Latin of Emanuel Swed. 2006. 484p. per. 29.99 (978-1-4255-5332-6(X)); 480p. per. 29.99 (978-1-4255-5333-3(8)) MPublishing.

—Apocalypsis Revelata: In Qua Deteguntur Arcana Quae Ibi Praedicta Sunt, et Hactenus Recondita Latuerunt. 2007. (LAT.). (978-0-910557-67-2(5)) Academy of the New Church.

Swindoll, Charles R. Insights on Revelation. 2011. (978-0-310-33107-0(2)); (ENG.). 384p. 25.99 (978-0-310-28434-5(1)) Zondervan.

Tassell Jr., Ray Van. The Milk of His Word. 2009. 228p. pap. 15.99 (978-1-60791-401-3(8)) Xulon Pr., Inc.

Tavo, Felise & Tavo, F. Woman, Mother & Bride: An Exegetical Investigation into the 'Ecclesial' Notions of the Apocalypse. 2007. (Biblical Tools & Studies). (ENG.). 420p. (C). 114.00 (978-90-429-1814-6(4)) Peeters Pubs. & Booksellers BEL. Dist: Brown, David Bk. Co., The.

Taylor, Donald R. The Apocalypse: A Revelation of Jesus Christ. 304p. 16.95 (978-0-9650597-0-1(7)) WriteWay Publishing.

Templeton, William M. The Chronology of the Revelation. Templeton, Bonita I., ed. 2006. spiral bd. 18.95 (978-0-9787896-1-9(X)) ARARAT Pubs.

Thomas, John. Eureka, an Exposition of the Apocalypse V1. 2011. 470p. 57.95 **(978-1-258-03729-1(7))** Literary Licensing, LLC.

—Eureka, an Exposition of the Apocalypse V2. 2011. 754p. 71.95 **(978-1-258-02428-4(4))** Literary Licensing, LLC.

Townsend, Eileen. America's Role in Revelation. 2011. 80p. pap. 11.99 **(978-1-4567-9657-0(7))** AuthorHouse.

Tucker, Mike. Meeting Jesus in the Book of Revelation. 2007. (978-0-8163-2215-2(5)) Pacific Pr. Pubns.

Tyndale House Publishers Staff, prod. Revelation. 2009. (Life Application Bible Studies: NLT Ser.). (ENG.). 120p. pap. 7.99 (978-1-4143-2646-7(7)) Tyndale Hse. Pubs.

Urbano, Jesse. Revelations Revealed. 2010. (978-1-935001-49-2(3)) Acclaim Pr., Inc.

Van Popta, George. The Glorious Victory. 2011. 316p. pap. 20.00 **(978-1-4583-7138-6(7))** Lulu Enterprises Inc.

Vandaalen. Guide to Revelation. (Illus.). 256p. 13.00 (978-0-281-04193-0(8)) SPCK Publishing GBR. Dist: Pilgrim Pr., The/United Church Pr.

Vena, Osvaldo D. Apocalipsis. González, Justo L., ed. 2008. (Conozca Ser.). (SPA.). 160p. per. 15.00 (978-0-8066-8017-0(2)) Augsburg Fortress, Pubs.

Victorinus of Petovium, et al. Latin Commentaries on Revelation. 2011. (Ancient Christian Texts). (ENG.). 251p. 60.00 **(978-0-8308-2909-5(1)**, IVP Acad.) InterVarsity Pr.

Vincent, Robert L. & Vincent, Consuelo M. The Prophecy & Testament: The Book of True Revealing. 2006. (Illus.). 608p. per. 40.00 (978-1-4251-0020-9(1)) Trafford Publishing.

Wade, Theodore E., Jr. Revelation Explained: A detailed interpretative & devotional Commentary. 2008. (Illus.). 336p. pap. 17.95 (978-1-57258-464-8(5)) TEACH Services, Inc.

Wagner, Ernst. Max Beckmann - Apokalypse: Theorie & Praxis im Spaetwerk. (GER.). 304p. (978-3-496-01207-8(2)) Reimer, Dietrich.

Warner, Sandy. Words to Ponder - Softcover. 2008. 698p. pap. 39.00 (978-1-4357-2945-2(5)) Lulu Enterprises Inc.

Waterloo, Bob. Revelation: Verse by Verse. 2009. 168p. pap. 14.99 (978-1-60791-923-0(0)) Xulon Pr., Inc.

Whedon's Commentary on Titus & Revelations, Vol. 5. 25.99 (978-0-88019-127-2(9)) Schmul Publishing Co., Inc.

Wicks, Douglas M. Hearing from God: Instructions & Revelations from the King of Glory. 2011. 164p. pap. 16.99 **(978-1-4567-6001-4(7))** AuthorHouse.

Wiersbe, Warren W. Colossians: Become the Whole Person God Intends You to Be. 2009. (WBS Ser.). (ENG.). 128p. pap. 8.99 (978-0-7814-4567-2(1)) Cook, David C.

—Victorious: In Christ You Are an Overcomer. 2008. (Be Ser.). (ENG.). 192p. pap. 12.99 (978-1-4347-6782-0(5)) Cook, David C.

Wilcox. Who Shall Be Able To Stand? Finding Personal Meaningin the Book of Revelation. 2011. 352p. 19.99 (978-1-60908-700-5(3)) Deseret Bk. Co.

Williams, Michael E., ed. The Storyteller's Companion to the Bible Vol. 8: Daniel & Revelation. 2009. (Storyteller's Companion to the Bible Ser.). 208p. pap. 21.00 (978-0-687-02652-4(0)) Abingdon Pr.

Wilmshurst, Steve. The Final Word: Revelation Simply Explained. 2007. (Welwyn Commentary Ser.). 286p. pap. (978-0-85234-669-3(7)) Evangelical Pr.

Wilson, Bill. As It Is Written, So Shall It Be. 2010. 400p. 29.99 (978-1-4500-5464-5(1)); pap. 19.99 (978-1-4500-5463-8(3)) Xlibris Corp.

Woodman, Simon Patrick. The Book of Revelation. 2008. (Scm Core Text Ser.). (Illus.). 259p. pap. (978-0-334-04104-7(X)) Hymns Ancient & Modern Ltd.

Zanchettin, Leo, ed. Revelation: A Devotional Commentary. 2007. 165p. per. 15.00 (978-1-59325-106-2(8)) Word Among Us Pr.

BIBLE—COMMENTARIES—N. T. ROMANS

Abelard, Peter. Commentary on the Epistle to the Romans. Cartwright, Steven R., tr. from LAT. 2011. (ENG.). 440p. 49.95 (978-0-8132-1860-1(8)) Catholic Univ. of America Pr.

Abingdon Press, creator. Invitation to Romans. ldr.'s ed. 2006. (Disciple Bible Study Ser.). 40p. pap. 13.65 (978-0-687-49659-4(4)) Abingdon Pr.

Ambrosiaster. Commentaries on Romans & 1-2 Corinthians, 1 vol. 2009. (Ancient Christian Texts). (ENG.). 300p. 60.00 (978-0-8308-2903-3(2), IVP Acad.) InterVarsity Pr.

Arnold, Clinton E. Romans Galatians, 1 vol. 2007. (Zondervan Illustrated Bible Backgrounds Commentary Ser.). (ENG., Illus.). 160p. (gr. 13). pap. 14.99 (978-0-310-27833-7(3)) Zondervan.

Arthur, Kay & De Lacy, Pete. Experiencing the Real Power of Faith. 2011. (New Inductive Study Ser.). 120p. pap. 8.99 (978-0-7369-1273-0(8)) Harvest Hse. Pubs.

Barrett, C. K. Reading Through Romans. 2009. 94p. pap. 13.00 (978-1-60608-721-3(5), Wipf and Stock) Wipf & Stock Pubs.

Boguslawski, Steven C. Thomas Aquinas on the Jews: Insights into His Commentary on Romans 9-11. 2008. (Stimulus Bks.). 145p. per. 18.95 (978-0-8091-4233-0(3)) Paulist Pr.

Borchert, Gerald L. & Mohrlang, Roger. Romans, Galatians. 2007. (Cornerstone Biblical Commentary Ser.: 14). (ENG.). 356p. 29.99 (978-0-8423-8342-4(5)) Tyndale Hse. Pubs.

Bowen. Guide to Romans. (Illus.). 256p. 13.00 (978-0-281-04953-0(X)) SPCK Publishing GBR. Dist: Pilgrim Pr., The/United Church Pr.

Breytenbach, Cilliers & du Toit, David S., eds. Focusing on Paul: Persuasion & Theological Design in Romans & Galatians. (Beihefte zur Zeitschrift far die neutestamentliche Wissenschaft und die Kunde der älteren Kirche Ser.). (ENG.). XIV, 443p. 255.00 **(978-3-11-185305-5(5))** De Gruyter, Walter Inc.

Breytenbach, Cilliers & Du Toit, David S., eds. Focusing on Paul: Persuasion & Theological Design in Romans & Galatians. 2007. (Beihefte Zur Zeitschrift Für Die Neutestamentliche Wissenschaft und Die Kunde der älteren Kirche Ser.). (ENG., Illus.). XIV, 443p. 154.00 (978-3-11-019512-5(7)) De Gruyter, Walter Inc.

Brown, John. Analytical Exposition of the Epistle of Paul, the Apostle to the Romans. 2006. 664p. per. 36.99 (978-1-4255-6736-1(3)) MPublishing.

Bruce, F. F. Romans. 2008. (Tyndale New Testament Commentaries Ser.: Volume 6). (ENG.). 283p. pap. 16.00 (978-0-8308-4236-0(5), IVP Acad.) InterVarsity Pr.

Burns, J. Patout & Newman, Constantine. Romans: Interpreted by Early Christian Commentators. 2012. **(978-0-8028-2575-9(3))** Eerdmans, William B. Publishing Co.

Byrne, Brendan. Galatians & Romans. 2010. 16.95 (978-0-8146-3324-3(2)); viii, 189p. E-Book (978-0-8146-3937-5(2)) Liturgical Pr.

—Romans. Harrington, Daniel J., ed. 2007. (Sacra Pagina Ser.). 506p. per. 34.95 (978-0-8146-5969-4(1), Liturgical Pr. Bks.) Liturgical Pr.

Calvin, John. Commentaries on the Epistle of Paul to T. 2006. pap. 44.95 (978-1-4286-3720-7(6)) Kessinger Publishing, LLC.

Carter, Warren. The Roman Empire & the New Testament: An Essential Guide. 2006. (Abingdon Essential Guides Ser.). 148p. pap. 18.00 (978-0-687-34394-2(1)) Abingdon Pr.

Colet, John. An Exposition of St. Paul's Epistle to the Romans. 2007. 280p. pap. 24.00 (978-1-55635-577-6(7), Wipf and Stock) Wipf & Stock Pubs.

A Commentary on the Epistle to the Romans, with a translation & various Excursus. 2010. pap. 20.32 (978-1-61143-187-2(5)) Gorgias Pr., LLC.

Custer, Stewart. The Righteousness of God: A Commentary on Romans. 2007. 418p. (978-1-59166-688-2(0)) BJU Pr.

Dix, Morgan. An Exposition of the Epistle of Saint Paul to the Romans, According to the Analogy of the Catholic Faith by the Rev Morgan Dix. 2006. 184p. per. 18.99 (978-1-4255-1463-1(4)) MPublishing.

Dodson, Joseph R. The "Powers" of Personification: Rhetorical Purpose in the Book of Wisdom & the Letter to the Romans. 2008. (Beihefte zur Zeitschrift far die neutestamentliche Wissenschaft und die Kunde der älteren Kirche Ser.). (ENG.). XII, 264p. 147.00 (978-3-11-020976-1(4)) De Gruyter, Walter Inc.

Dunn, James D. G. Romans: A Guide for Reflection & Prayer. 2007. (Daily Bible Commentary Ser.). 189p. per. 12.95 (978-1-59856-190-6(1)) Hendrickson Pubs. Marketing, LLC.

Ehrensperger, Kathy & Ehrensperger. Reformation Readings of Romans. Holder, R. Ward, ed. 2008. (Romans Through History & Culture Ser.). (ENG.). 230p. pap. 39.95 (978-0-567-02714-6(7), T&T Clark Int'l) Continuum International Publishing Group, Ltd. GBR. Dist: National Bk. Network.

Eisenbaum, Pamela M. Invitation to Romans. 2006. (Disciple Bible Study Ser.). (Illus.). 101p. per. 11.50 (978-0-687-49649-5(7)) Abingdon Pr.

Franzmann, Martin H. Romans: A Commentary. 288p. 17.99 (978-0-570-04431-4(6), 12-3036) Concordia Publishing Hse.

Freeman, Richard E. The Heart of the Apostle: A Commentary on Romans 9-11. 2007. per. 12.00 (978-1-59872-809-5(1)) Instant Pub.

Grant, L. Comments on the Book of Romans. pap. 3.95 (978-0-88172-078-5(X)) Believers Bookshelf, Inc.

Greathouse, William M. Romans 1-8: A Commentary in the Wesleyan Tradition. 2008. (New Beacon Bible Commentary Ser.). (ENG.). 288p. pap. 29.99 (978-0-8341-2362-5(2), 083-412-3622) Beacon Hill Pr. of Kansas City.

—Romans 9-16: A Commentary in the Wesleyan Tradition. 2008. (New Beacon Bible Commentary Ser.). (ENG.). 288p. pap. 29.99 (978-0-8341-2363-2(0), 083-412-3630) Beacon Hill Pr. of Kansas City.

Hahne. Corruption & Redemption of Creation: Nature in Romans 8. 19-22 & Jewish Apocalyptic Literature. 2007. (Library of New Testament Studies, the Ser.). (ENG., Illus.). 286p. 170.00 (978-0-567-03055-9(5), T&T Clark Int'l) Continuum International Publishing Group, Ltd. GBR. Dist: National Bk. Network.

Hole, Frank. Romans & Corinthians. 2007. 176p. (ENG.). (978-0-901860-47-7(6)); (Illus.). per. (978-0-901860-43-9(3)) Scripture Truth Pubns.

Holland, Tom. Romans: the Divine Marriage: A Biblical Theological Commentary. 2011. 558p. pap. 56.00 **(978-1-60899-809-8(6)**, Pickwick Pubns.) Wipf & Stock Pubs.

Holloway, Gary. Romans & Galatians: The Spirit of Jesus. 2007. (Meditative Commentary Ser.). 136p. per. 11.99 (978-0-89112-502-0(7), Leafwood Pubs.) Abilene Christian Univ. Pr.

Hughes, Bill. Studying Romans. 5.99 (978-0-89098-149-8(3)) Twentieth Century Christian Bks.

Ingram, Chip. Living on the Edge: Dare to Experience True Spirituality. 2011. (ENG.). 304p. pap. 14.99 (978-1-4391-9052-4(6), Howard Bks.) Howard Books.

Jeon, Paul. Introducing Romans. 2011. 80p. pap. 11.00 **(978-1-61097-356-4(9)**, Wipf and Stock) Wipf & Stock Pubs.

Jewett, Robert. Romans: A Commentary. Epp, Eldon Jay, ed. 2006. (Hermeneia — A Critical & Historical Commentary on the Bible Ser.). 1250p. 90.00 (978-0-8006-6084-0(6), Fortress Pr.) Augsburg Fortress, Pubs.

Journey Through the Bible Romans-Phillipians Student Korean. 4.00 (978-0-687-05628-6(4)) Abingdon Pr.

Karen, Jobes & Moo, Thorp. Romans: Celebrating the Good News. 2008. (Bringing the Bible to Life Ser.). (ENG.). 144p. pap. 7.99 (978-0-310-27652-4(7)) Zondervan.

Keener, Craig S. Romans. 2011. (ENG.). 300p. pap. 40.50 (978-0-7188-9238-8(0)) Lutherworth Pr., The GBR. Dist: Printondemand-worldwide.com.

—Romans. Keener, Craig S. & Bird, Michael, eds. 2009. (New Covenant Commentary Ser.). 300p. pap. 32.00 (978-1-60608-156-3(X), Cascade Bks.) Wipf & Stock Pubs.

Knight, George R. Exploring Romans: A Devotional Commentary. 2010. 303p. pap. 19.99 (978-0-8280-2503-4(7)) Review & Herald Publishing Assn.

Knight, Robert. A Critical Commentary on the Epistle of St. Paul the Apostle to the Romans. 2009. 660p. pap. 56.00 (978-1-60608-686-5(3), Wipf and Stock) Wipf & Stock Pubs.

Kuske, David P. A Commentary on Romans 1-8. 2007. (GEC & ENG., Illus.). 460p. (978-0-8100-1979-9(5)) Northwestern Publishing Hse.

Longman, Tremper, III. Romans - Galatians, 1 vol. rev. ed. 2010. (Expositor's Bible Commentary Ser.). (ENG.). 992p. 44.99 (978-0-310-26892-5(3)) Zondervan.

Lucado, Max. Book of Romans: God's Big Picture, 0 vols. 2006. (Inspirational Bible Study; Life Lessons with Max Lucado Ser.). 128p. per. 9.99 (978-1-4185-0946-0(9)) Nelson, Thomas Inc.

Malone, A. Hodge. God's Eternal Power: The Epistle to the Romans in an Intensive Study. 2011. 228p. 46.95 **(978-1-258-02283-9(4))** Literary Licensing, LLC.

Martin, Gib. The Book of Romans, 0 vols. 2007. (Smart Guide to the Bible Ser.). (Illus.). 320p. per. 14.99 (978-1-4185-0992-7(2)) Nelson, Thomas Inc.

Meadows, James L. Romans. pap. 5.50 (978-0-89098-395-9(X)) Twentieth Century Christian Bks.
Melanchthon, Philipp & Kramer, Fred. Commentary on Romans. 2nd ed. 2010. 307p. (978-0-7586-2686-8(X)) Concordia Publishing Hse.
Michielin, Maico M. A Shorter Commentary on Romans by Karl Barth: With an Introductory Essay by Maico Michielin. 2007. (Barth Studies). 146p. 89.95 (978-0-7546-5757-6(4)) Ashgate Publishing Co.
Moore, Phil. Straight to the Heart of Romans: 60 Bite-Sized Insights, 1 vol. 2011. (Straight to the Heart Commentary Ser.). 272p. pap. 14.99 (978-0-85721-057-9(2), Monarch Bks.) Lion Hudson PLC GBR. Dist: Kregel Pubns.
Morgan, Robert J. The Promise: God Works All Things Together for Your Good, 1 vol. 2010. (ENG.). 240p. pap. 14.99 (978-0-8054-6482-5(4), B&H Bks.) B&H Publishing Group.
Morrison, James. A Critical Exposition of the Third Chapter of Paul's Epistle to the Romans. A Monograph. 2009. 444p. pap. 36.00 (978-1-60608-376-5(7), Wipf and Stock) Wipf & Stock Pubs.
Nygren, Anders, tr. Spanish Commentary on Romans / la epistola a los Romanos. 2010. 400p. 24.99 (978-0-7586-2549-6(9)) Concordia Publishing Hse.
Oakes, Kenneth. Reading Karl Barth: A Companion to Karl Barth's Epistle to the Romans. 2011. 180p. pap. 21.00 (978-1-61097-016-7(0), Cascade Bks.) Wipf & Stock Pubs.
Olyott, Stuart. This Way to Godliness: Romans 6, 7 And 8. 2006. 104p. per. (978-1-85049-217-7(4)) Bryntirion Pr.
Ortlund, Dane C. Zeal Without Knowledge: The Concept of Zeal in Romans 10, Galatians 1 & Philippians 3. 2012. (Library of New Testament Studies). (ENG.). 208p. 110.00 (978-0-567-53759-1(5), T&T Clark Int'l) Continuum International Publishing Group, Ltd. GBR. Dist: National Bk. Network.
Osborne, Grant R. Romans. 2010. (IVP New Testament Commentary Ser.: Volume 6). (ENG.). 447p. pap. 20.00 (978-0-8308-4006-9(0), IVP Acad.) InterVarsity Pr.
Pearl, Michael. Romans 1-8 Verse by Verse. 2009. (ENG.). 222p. pap. 8.95 (978-1-892112-08-6(6)) No Greater Joy Ministries, Inc.
Romans. (Lift & Look Ser.). 6p. spiral bd. (978-1-4054-9440-3(9)) Parragon, Inc.
Romans 1. (LifeLight Bible Studies: Course 5). stu. ed. 5.50 (978-0-570-09269-8(8), 20-2264) Concordia Publishing Hse.
Romans 2. (LifeLight Bible Studies: Course 6). stu. ed. 5.50 (978-0-570-09271-1(X), 20-2269); 6.50 (978-0-570-09270-4(1), 20-2268) Concordia Publishing Hse.
Royster, Dmitri. St. Paul's Epistle to the Romans: A Pastoral Commentary. 2008. 416p. pap. 22.00 (978-0-88141-321-2(6)) St. Vladimir's Seminary Pr.
Rutledge, Fleming. Not Ashamed of the Gospel: Sermons from Paul's Letter to the Romans. 2007. 411p. per. 19.00 (978-0-8028-2737-1(3)) Eerdmans, William B. Publishing Co.
Sabou, Sorin. Between Horror & Hope: Paul's Metaphorical Language of Death in Romans 6:1-11. 2007. (Paternoster Biblical Monographs: Ser.). 194p. pap. 22.00 (978-1-59752-766-8(1), Wipf and Stock) Wipf & Stock Pubs.
Sadiku, Matthew N. O. Romans: A Pentecostal Commentary. 2011. 288p. 30.95 (978-1-4620-4245-6(7)); pap. 20.95 (978-1-4620-4243-2(0)) iUniverse, Inc.
Scharlemann, John. Romans: An Introductory Course. (Journeys Through God's Word Ser.). pap., stu. ed. 8.99 (978-0-570-06888-4(6), 20-2816); pap. 8.99 (978-0-570-06889-1(4), 20-2817) Concordia Publishing Hse.
Scheck, Thomas P. Origen & the History of Justification: The Legacy of Origen's Commentary on Romans. 2008. (ENG.). 304p. 60.00 (978-0-268-04128-1(8)) Univ. of Notre Dame Pr.
Schenck, Kenneth. Paul: Soldier of Peace. 2011. 156p. (978-0-89827-440-0(0)) Wesleyan Publishing Hse.
Scott-Miller. The Gift. 2009. 68p. pap. 10.99 (978-1-60791-439-6(5)) Xulon Pr., Inc.
Shedd, William. Commentary on Romans. 2007. 452p. per. 30.00 (978-1-59925-100-4(0)) Solid Ground Christian Bks.
Smith, Hamilton. The Epistle to the Romans. 2008. 196p. pap. (978-0-901860-85-9(9)) Scripture Truth Pubns.
Somoza, J. Comentario Biblico Continente Nuevo: Romanos.Tr. of New Continent Commentary: Romans. (SPA.). 5.99 (978-0-7899-0278-8(8), 498648) Editorial Unilit.
Sproul, R. C. Jr. & Sproul, R. C. Romans. 2009. (St. Andrew's Expositional Commentary Ser.). 520p. 34.99 (978-1-4335-0685-7(8)) Crossway.
St. Helen's Bishopga. Romans: A Small Group Bible Study. 2008. (ENG.). 320p. pap. 12.99 (978-1-84550-362-8(7)) Christian Focus Pubns. GBR. Dist: STL Distribution North America.
Stuart, Moses. A Commentary on the Epistle to the Romans. 2009. 60p. pap. (978-0-217-90705-7(9)); pap. (978-0-217-42468-4(6)) Books LLC.
—A Commentary on the Epistle to the Romans. Robbins, D. C., ed. 2007. (ENG.). 552p. 57.95 (978-0-548-35271-7(2)); per. 42.95 (978-0-548-29520-5(4)) Kessinger Publishing, LLC.
Taylor, Vincent. The Epistle to the Romans. 2010. 100p. pap. 14.00 (978-1-60899-781-7(2), Wipf and Stock) Wipf & Stock Pubs.
Thielman, Frank. From Plight to Solution: A Jewish Framework for Understanding Paul's View of the Law in Galatians & Romans. 2008. (Supplements to Novum Testamentum (Wipf & Stock Publishers) Ser.). 170p. pap. 20.00 (978-1-55635-639-1(0)) Wipf & Stock Pubs.
Trebilco, Paul. The Early Christians in Ephesus from Paul to Ignatius. 2007. 826p. per. 85.00 (978-0-8028-0769-4(0)) Eerdmans, William B. Publishing Co.
Waetjen, Herman C. The Letter to the Romans: Salvation as Justice & the Deconstruction of Law. 2011. 418p. (978-1-907534-22-5(9)) Sheffield Phoenix Pr.
Whedon's Commentary on Acts, Romans, Vol. 3. 25.99 (978-0-88019-125-8(2)) Schmul Publishing Co., Inc.
Woodward, Michael S., intro. & notes. The Glossa Ordinaria on Romans: Medieval Texts in Translation. 2011. (978-1-58044-109-4(2)) Medieval Institute Pubns.
World Book, Inc Staff, creator. Romans. 2009. (Life Application Bible Studies: NLT Ser.). (ENG.). 112p. pap. 7.99 (978-1-4143-2563-7(0)) Tyndale Hse. Pubs.

BIBLE—COMMENTARIES—N. T. THESSALONIANS

Arnold, Clinton E. 1 & 2 Thessalonians, 1 vol. 2012. (ENG.). 384p. 32.99 (978-0-310-24396-0(3)) Zondervan.
Arnold, Clinton E. 1 & 2 Thessalonians, 1 & 2 Timothy, Titus , 1 vol. 2007. (Zondervan Illustrated Bible Backgrounds Commentary Ser.). (ENG., Illus.). 128p. (gr. 13). pap. 14.99 (978-0-310-27823-8(6)) Zondervan.
Beale, G. K. 1-2 Thessalonians. 2010. (IVP New Testament Commentary Ser.: Volume 13). (ENG.). 279p. pap. 18.00 (978-0-8308-4013-7(3), IVP Acad.) InterVarsity Pr.
Blight, Richard C. Exegetical Summary of 1 & 2 Thessalonians. 2nd ed. 2008. 259p. pap. 32.00 (978-1-55671-200-5(6)) SIL International.
Bridges, Linda McKinnish. 1 & 2 Thessalonians: Smyth & Helwys Bible Commentary. 2008. 45.00 (978-1-57312-083-8(9)) Smyth & Helwys Publishing, Inc.
Eaton, Michael. 1 & 2 Thessalonians. (Preaching Through the Bible Ser.). (Illus.). 125p. pap. (978-1-85240-180-1(X)) Sovereign World, Ltd.
Edwards, Earl D. 1 & 2 Thessalonians. 2008. (ENG.). 364p. 29.95 (978-0-9760327-5-5(9)) Resource Pubns.
Ephesians 1 & 2 Thessalonians. ldr.'s ed. (LifeLight Bible Studies: Course 18). 6.50 (978-0-570-09423-4(2), 20-2540) Concordia Publishing Hse.
Fee, Gordon D. The First & Second Letters to the Thessalonians. 2009. (ENG.). xxviii, 366p. 44.00 (978-0-8028-6362-1(0)) Eerdmans, William B. Publishing Co.
Fenton, John. Galatians, 1 & 2 Thessalonians: A Guide for Reflection & Prayer. 2007. (Daily Bible Commentary Ser.). 191p. per. 12.95 (978-1-59856-193-7(6)) Hendrickson Pubs. Marketing, LLC.
Furnish, Victor Paul. 1 Thessalonians, 2 Thessalonians. 2007. (Abingdon New Testament Commentaries Ser.). 208p. pap. 22.00 (978-0-687-05743-6(4)) Abingdon Pr.
Gaventa, Beverly Roberts. First & Second Thessalonians: Interpretation: A Bible Commentary for Teaching & Preaching. 2012. (Interpretation: A Bible Commentary for Teaching & Preaching Ser.). (ENG.). 154p. pap. 25.00 (978-0-664-23869-8(6)) Westminster John Knox Pr.
Grant Jr., James H. 1 & 2 Thessalonians: The Hope of Salvation. 2011. (Preaching the Word Ser.). 240p. 27.99 (978-1-4335-0544-7(4)) Crossway.
Hawkes-Teeples, Steven. The Liturgical Commentaries: St symeon of Thessalonika. 2011. (Studies & Texts). (ENG, GEC & GRE.). 310p. 90.00 (978-0-88844-168-3(1)) Pontifical Institute of Mediaeval Studies, Dept. of Pubns. CAN. Dist: Univ. of Toronto Pr.
Hiebert, D. Edmond. 1 & 2 Thessalonians. 2006. (Illus.). 415p. per. 19.99 (978-0-88469-250-8(7)) BMH Bks.
Hoehner, Harold W., et al. Ephesians, Philippians, 1-2 Thessalonians Colossians, Philemon. 2008. (Cornerstone Biblical Commentary Ser.: 16). (ENG.). 456p. 29.99 (978-0-8423-8344-8(1)) Tyndale Hse. Pubs.
Holloway, Gary. 1 & 2 Thessalonians, 1 & 2 Timothy & Titus: Jesus Grows His Church: A Meditative Commentary on the New Testament. 2007. (Meditative Commentary Ser.). 119p. per. 11.99 (978-0-89112-503-7(5), Leafwood Pubs.) Abilene Christian Univ. Pr.
I & II Thessalonians. (People's Bible Commentary Ser.). 128p. 11.99 (978-0-7586-0449-1(1)) Concordia Publishing Hse.
Killen, James L. What Can We Believe? Reflections on the Second Readings for Cycle a Proper 23 Through Thanksgiving. 2010. (978-0-7880-2631-7(3)) CSS Publishing Co.
Killion, Larry. The Thessalonian Doctrine. 2009. 112p. pap. 19.99 (978-1-4363-9929-6(7)) Xlibris Corp.
Knight, George R. Exploring Thessalonians: A Devotional Commentary. 2012. (978-0-8280-2643-7(2)) Review & Herald Publishing Assn.
Kreinecker, Christina. 2. Thessaloniker. 2010. (Papyrologische Kommentare zum Neuen Testament Ser.). (GER.). 240p. (C). 68.00 (978-3-525-51006-3(3)) Vandenhoeck & Ruprecht GmbH & Co. KG DEU. Dist: ISD.
Meadows, James L. 2 Thessalonians & 2 Timothy. pap. 5.50 (978-0-89098-413-0(1)) Twentieth Century Christian Bks.
Morris, Leon. 1 & 2 Thessalonians. 2007. (Tyndale New Testament Commentaries Ser.). (ENG.). 152p. per. 14.00 (978-0-8308-2992-7(X)) InterVarsity Pr.
Paulien, Jon. Letters to the Thessalonians. 2012. pap. (978-0-8163-2626-6(6)) Pacific Pr. Publishing Assn.
Richard, Earl J. First & Second Thessalonians. Harrington, Daniel J., ed. 2007. (Sacra Pagina Ser.). 415p. per. 29.95 (978-0-8146-5974-8(8), Liturgical Pr. Bks.) Liturgical Pr.
Steveson, Peter A. 1 & 2 Thessalonians. 2012. (978-1-60682-221-0(7)) BJU Pr.
Strauss, Mark, et al. Galatians Thru Philemon Vol. 11: Putting Faith into Practice. 2008. (QuickNotes Commentaries Ser.). (ENG.). 224p. pap. 9.99 (978-1-59789-777-8(9), Barbour Bks.) Barbour Publishing, Inc.
Terry, Kenneth E. A Model for All Believers: An Expositional Commentary on 1 Thessalonians. 2011. 196p. 33.95 (978-1-4497-2531-0(7)); pap. 17.95 (978-1-4497-2530-3(9)) Author Solutions, Inc. (WestBow Pr.).
Thiselton, Anthony C. 1 & 2 Thessalonians Through the Centuries. 2010. (Blackwell Bible Commentaries Ser.: 28). (ENG., Illus.). 336p. 119.95 (978-1-4051-9682-6(3), Wiley-Blackwell) Wiley, John & Sons, Inc.
Thurston, Bonnie Bowman. Reading Colossians, Ephesians, & 2 Thessalonians. 2008. (978-1-57312-500-0(8)) Smyth & Helwys Publishing, Inc.
Walters, Dennis, contrib. by. The Letters of Saint Paul to the Thessalonians, Timothy, & Titus. 2nd ed. 2007. (Ignatius Catholic Study Bible Ser.). 63p. pap. 9.95 (978-1-58617-162-9(3)) Ignatius Pr.
Weidmann, Frederick W. Philippians, First & Second Thessalonians, & Philemon. 2012. (Westminster Bible Companion Ser.). (ENG.). 264p. pap. 25.00 (978-0-664-23852-0(1)) Westminster John Knox Pr.
Wiersbe, Warren W. Be Ready (1 & 2 Thessalonians) Living in Light of Christ's Return, 1 vol. 2010. (BE Series Commentary Ser.). (ENG.). 192p. pap. 12.99 (978-1-4347-6501-7(6)) Cook, David C.
Witherington, Ben, III. 1 & 2 Thesssalonians: A Socio-Rhetorical Commentary. 2006. 286p. per. 30.00 (978-0-8028-2836-1(1)) Eerdmans, William B. Publishing Co.

BIBLE—COMMENTARIES—N. T. TIMOTHY

see Bible—Commentaries—N. T. Pastoral Epistles

BIBLE—COMMENTARIES—N. T. TITUS

see Bible—Commentaries—N. T. Pastoral Epistles

BIBLE—COMMENTARIES—O. T.

Here are entered only Commentaries on the Old Testament as a whole.

Alter, Robert. The Wisdom Books: Job, Proverbs, & Ecclesiastes - A Translation with Commentary. 2011. (ENG.). 394p. pap. 17.95 (978-0-393-34053-2(8), 34053) Norton, W. W. & Co., Inc.
Baker, David W., et al. Illustrated Bible Backgrounds Commentary: Old Testament, 1 vol. Walton, John H., ed. 2011. (Zondervan Illustrated Bible Backgrounds Commentary Ser.). (ENG.). 2928p. 249.95 (978-0-310-25572-7(4)) Zondervan.
Baker, Robert. Sinonimos Del Antiguo Testamento: Synonims of the Old Testament. (SPA.). (978-84-7645-144-1(X), 223191) Clie, Editorial.
Bar Hebraeus, Gregory. Barn of Mysteries. 2010. (SYR.). pap. 85.00 (978-1-61719-918-9(4)) Gorgias Pr., LLC.
Barker, Margaret. Old Testament. 80.00 (978-0-687-85932-0(8)) Abingdon Pr.
Beasley, Bob. 101 Portraits of Jesus in the Hebrew Scriptures. 2008. 208p. pap. 14.95 (978-0-9799731-4-7(7)) Living Stone Bks.
Bentley, Michael. David: Encountering the Man after God's Heart, 2 vols., Vol. 1. 2006. (Face 2 Face Ser.). 96p. per. 9.00 (978-1-84625-040-8(4)) DayOne Pubns. GBR. Dist: STL Distribution North America.
Blanchett, Elnora. Clarified Old Testament: Books of Ecclesiastes, Esther, Job, Jonah, Proverbs, Ruth, Solomon. 2008. 140p. 27.00 (978-1-4251-9043-9(X)) Trafford Publishing.
Boer, Roland & Carden, Michael. He Who Reads May Run: Essays in Honour of Edgar W. Conrad, Vol. 553. Boer, Roland & Carden, Michael, eds. Kelso, Julie, ed. 2012. (Library Hebrew Bible/Old Testament Studies). (ENG.). 304p. 150.00 (978-0-567-60217-6(6), T&T Clark Int'l) Continuum International Publishing Group, Ltd. GBR. Dist: National Bk. Network.
Books of the Old Testament. 3.00 (978-0-687-85473-8(3)) Abingdon Pr.
Burrows, D. Peter. Jonah, the Reluctant Missionary. 2008. 164p. pap. (978-0-85244-652-2(7)) Gracewing, Ltd.
Campbell, Antony F. God & Bible: Exploring Stories from Genesis to Job. 2008. 128p. per. 14.95 (978-0-8091-4520-1(0), 4520-1) Paulist Pr.
Carson, Samuel. The Long Road Home. 174p. 10.99 (978-1-84030-049-9(3)) Ambassador Productions, Ltd. IRL. Dist: Emerald Hse. Group, Inc.
Cary, Phillip. Jonah. 2008. (Brazos Theological Commentary on the Bible Ser.). 192p. (C). 29.99 (978-1-58743-137-1(8)) Brazos Pr.
Chalmers, Thomas. Sabbath Scripture Readings II - Spiritual Meditations from the Old Testament. 2008. 520p. pap. 35.00 (978-1-59925-192-9(2)) Solid Ground Christian Bks.
Clowney, Edmund P. How Jesus Transforms the Ten Commandments. annot. ed. 2007. 162p. per. 12.99 (978-1-59638-036-3(5)) P & R Publishing.
Courson, Jon. Jon Courson's Application Commentary: Old Testament, 0 vols. 2007. (Jon Courson's Application Commentary Ser.). 939p. 39.99 (978-1-4185-0147-1(6)) Nelson, Thomas Inc.
Crabtree, Sue. 4,000 Years in Thirteen Weeks: Back to Basics with the Old Testament. pap. 9.99 (978-0-89098-191-7(4)) Twentieth Century Christian Bks.
Darst, G. Albert. The Revelation of Jesus Christ in the Old Testament. 2010. 356p. 32.99 (978-1-60957-587-8(3)); pap. 20.99 (978-1-60957-586-1(5)) Xulon Pr., Inc.
Davis, Max. Success Secrets of the World's Most Cynical Man: A True Story, 0 vols. 2007. 128p. 12.99 (978-1-59145-564-6(2)) Nelson, Thomas Inc.
Delitzsch, Franz. A New Commentary on Genesis. 2008. 420p. 30.99 (978-0-559-35938-5(1)); pap. 33.75 (978-0-559-35937-8(3)) BiblioBazaar.
—A New Commentary on Genesis. 2009. 292p. pap. (978-0-217-43319-8(7)); 76p. pap. (978-0-217-16092-6(1)); 278p. pap. (978-0-217-16096-4(4)) Books LLC.
—Old Testament History of Redemption. 2009. 230p. 28.99 (978-1-110-47358-8(3)); pap. 24.75 (978-1-110-47355-7(9)) BiblioBazaar.
Devlin, Jennifer. Verses We Know by Heart: Discovering the Details of Familiar Old Testament Passages. 2008. 124p. per. 10.99 (978-0-89265-565-6(8)) Randall Hse. Pubns.
Distefano, Michel G. Inner-Midrashic Introductions & Their Influence on Introductions to Medieval Rabbinic Bible Commentaries. 2009. (Studia Judaica Ser.). (ENG.). XVI, 227p. 98.00 (978-3-11-021368-3(0)); 154.00 (978-3-11-173641-9(5)) De Gruyter, Walter Inc.
Duck, Daymond. Return from Exile, 0 vols. Richards, Larry, ed. 2008. (Smart Guide to the Bible Ser.). (Illus.). 364p. per. 14.99 (978-1-4185-1004-6(1)) Nelson, Thomas Inc.
Dutcher-Walls, Patricia. Family in Life & in Death: The Family in Ancient Israel - Sociological & Archaeological Perspectives. 2009. (Library Hebrew Bible/Old Testament Studies). (ENG., Illus.) 160p. 135.00 (978-0-567-02757-3(0), T&T Clark Int'l) Continuum International Publishing Group, Ltd. GBR. Dist: National Bk. Network.
Ebenhoe, Joseph R. The Prophecy Puzzle: Fitting Prophecy from the Whole Bible into the Book of Revelation. 2008. 252p. pap. 15.99 (978-1-60647-661-1(0)) Xulon Pr., Inc.
Endres, John. First & Second Chronicles. 2011. 136p. pap. 6.95 (978-0-8146-2844-7(3)) Liturgical Pr.
Ewald, Heinrich. Syntax of the Hebrew Language of the Old Testament. 2009. 248p. pap. (978-1-4588-5758-3(1)) Books LLC.
—Syntax of the Hebrew Language of the Old Testament. Kennedy, James, tr. 2009. 344p. 46.95 (978-1-104-57216-7(8)); pap. 31.95 (978-1-104-47380-8(1)) Kessinger Publishing, LLC.
Fashbaugh, Earl. Snapshots: Sixty-Six Books of the Bible: A Devotional. 2011. 264p. pap. 13.99 (978-1-4269-6427-5(7)) Trafford Publishing.
Forlaget Illuminated Sweden Staff, ed. Bible Illuminated: The Book, Old Testament. 2009. 528p. pap. 45.00 (978-91-976694-5-0(8)) Illuminated World SWE. Dist: Midpoint Trade Bks., Inc.
Friedman, D. S. The Search: A Guide for Finding Spirituality through Old Testament Scripture. 2007. (ENG.). 120p. per. 15.95 (978-1-58736-764-9(5)) Wheatmark.
Friedman, Sam. Joyous Torah Treasures. 2008. 450p. 34.95 (978-1-934440-51-3(5) Devora Publishing) Simcha Media Group.
—Joyous Torah Treasures: Vayikra, Bamidbar, Devorim. 2008. 225p. 18.95 (978-1-934440-21-6(3), Devora Publishing) Simcha Media Group.
Gamble, Richard C. The Whole Counsel of God Vol. 1: God's Mighty Acts in the Old Testament. 2006. 864p. pap. 39.99 (978-0-87552-191-6(6)) P & R Publishing.
Goldingay, John. Psalms 42-89, 3 vols., Vol. 2. 2007. (Baker Commentary on the Old Testament Wisdom & Psalms Ser.). (Illus.). 752p. (C). 49.99 (978-0-8010-2704-8(7)) Baker Academic.
Golightly Marshall, Brian Leonard. 2012 Mayan Calendar & the Great Pyramid Predicts the Earth Will Enter Paradise after It Crosses the Milky Way Equator In 2013. 2008. 496p. pap. 38.95 (978-1-4092-2041-1(9)) Lulu Enterprises Inc.
Goodman, Yitzch. Great Torah Lights from Great Torah Minds. 2008. 2000p. 79.95 (978-1-934440-31-5(0), Devora Publishing) Simcha Media Group.
—Great Torah Lights from Great Torah Minds: Bamidbar. 2008. 400p. 39.95 (978-1-934440-35-3(3), Devora Publishing) Simcha Media Group.
—Great Torah Lights from Great Torah Minds: Beraishis. 2008. 400p. 39.95 (978-1-934440-32-2(9), Devora Publishing) Simcha Media Group.
—Great Torah Lights from Great Torah Minds: Devorim. 2008. 400p. 39.95 (978-1-934440-36-0(1), Devora Publishing) Simcha Media Group.
—Great Torah Lights from Great Torah Minds: Shemos. 2008. 400p. 39.95 (978-1-934440-33-9(7), Devora Publishing) Simcha Media Group.
—Great Torah Lights from Great Torah Minds: Vayikra. 2008. 400p. 39.95 (978-1-934440-34-6(5), Devora Publishing) Simcha Media Group.
Grant, Edward F. Wisdom for the Good Life. 2011. 404p. 35.95 (978-1-4620-4149-7(3)) iUniverse, Inc.
Griffin, Winn. God's EPIC Adventure: Changing Our Culture by the Story We Live & Tell. 2007. 412p. pap. 29.99 (978-0-9799076-0-9(8)) Harmon Pr.
Gundry, Robert H. A Survey of the New Testament, 1 vol. 2007. (Zondervan Get an A! Ser.). (ENG.). 6p. 6.99 (978-0-310-27314-1(5)) Zondervan.
Hale, Tom & Thorson, Steve. The Applied Old Testament Commentary: Applying God's Word to Your Life. 2007. (ENG., Illus.). 1344p. 39.99 (978-0-7814-4864-2(6)) Cook, David C.
Haneke, Dianne Louise Myers. Guide to the Names of God. 2011. 264p. pap. 29.99 (978-1-4567-1716-2(2)) AuthorHouse.
Heller, Tzipporah. This Way Up. 256p. 25.99 (978-1-58330-416-7(9)) Feldheim Pubs.
Hill, Andrew E., et al. Survey of the Old Testament, 1 vol. ed. 2009. (ENG.). 777p. 49.99 (978-0-310-28095-8(8)) Zondervan.
Hinson. Books of Old Testament. (978-0-281-04565-5(8)) SPCK Publishing.
—Books of the Old Testament. 2nd ed. (Illus.). 224p. 14.00 (978-0-281-04564-8(X)) SPCK Publishing GBR. Dist: Pilgrim Pr., The/United Church Pr.
—History of Israel. 2nd ed. (Illus.). 256p. 12.00 (978-0-281-04472-6(4)) SPCK Publishing GBR. Dist: Pilgrim Pr., The/United Church Pr.
Holman Reference Editorial Staff. Holman Old Testament Commentary Series. 2009. (ENG.). 400p. 299.97 (978-0-8054-9523-2(1), Holman Reference) B&H Publishing Group.
Hubbard, David Allan. Joel & Amos. 2009. (Tyndale Old Testament Commentaries Ser.: Volume 25). (ENG.). 196p. pap. 16.00 (978-0-8308-4225-4(X), IVP Acad.) InterVarsity Pr.
Ingram, Chip. Holy Ambition: Turning God-Shaped Dreams into Reality. rev. ed. 2010. (ENG.). 192p. pap. 14.99 (978-0-8024-2983-4(1)) Moody Pubs.
The International Theological Commentaries on the Old Testament, 26 vols. pap. 200.00 (978-1-871828-45-0(7), Handsel Pr., Ltd. GBR. Dist: Continuum International Publishing Group, Inc.
Invitation to the Old Testament - VHS Tapes. (978-0-687-49711-9(6)) Abingdon Pr.

B

Ironside, H. A. Ezra, Nehemiah, & Esther, 1 vol. 2008. (Ironside Expository Commentaries Ser.). (Illus.). 224p. 19.99 (978-0-8254-2925-5(0)) Kregel Pubns.

Jenkins, Jacqueline. Cain, Ishmael, David.... 2007. 108p. per. 14.95 (978-0-9777060-6-8(0)) Asta Publications, LLC.

Jewish Publication Society, creator. Tanakh-FL: The Holy Scriptures. 2007. 1624p. 35.00 (978-0-8276-0855-9(1)) Jewish Pubn. Society.

Jewish Publication Society Staff, ed. Tanakh (Metallic Copper Leatherette Edition) 2007. 1664p. im. lthr. 35.00 (978-0-8276-0853-5(5)) Jewish Pubn. Society.

Kasomo, Daniel W. An Introduction to Old Testament Studies. 2010. 104p. pap. (978-3-8383-5236-7(X)) Lambert Academic Publishing.

Kim, Sang-jin. The Literary & the Theological Functions of Nt Miracle Narratives. 2010. 124p. pap. (978-3-639-09188-5(4)) VDM Verlag Dr. Mueller e.K.

—The Miracle Narratives of the Bible. 2010. 368p. pap. (978-3-639-27767-8(8)) VDM Verlag Dr. Mueller e.K.

Kuyper, Abraham. Mujeres del Antiguo Testamento: Women of the Old Testament. (SPA.). 144p. (978-84-7228-841-6(2), 220615) Clie, Editorial.

Lamb, David T. God Behaving Badly: Is the God of the Old Testament Angry, Sexist & Racist? 2011. (ENG.). 205p. pap. 15.00 (978-0-8308-3826-4(0), IVP Bks.) InterVarsity Pr.

Lands of the Bible Old Testament. 19.98 incl. trans. (978-0-687-00166-8(8)) Abingdon Pr.

Lapsley, Jacqueline E. Can These Bones Live? The Problem of the Moral Self in the Book of Ezekiel. (Beihefte zur Zeitschrift fur die alttestamentliche Wissenschaft Ser.). (ENG.). XI, 208p. 225.00 (**978-3-11-185762-6(X)**) De Gruyter, Walter Inc.

Lee, Samuel. A Lexicon, Hebrew Chaldee, & English. 2011. (HEB & ARA.). 163.16 (978-1-61143-828-4(4)) Gorgias Pr., LLC.

Lindsay, John W. & Steele, D. Whedon's Commentary on the Old Testament Vol. 2: Leviticus-Deuteronomy. 25.99 (978-0-88019-129-6(5)) Schmul Publishing Co., Inc.

Longman, Tremper. Deuteronomy Thru Ruth Vol. 2: The Importance of Obedience. 2009. (QuickNotes Commentaries Ser.). (ENG.). 240p. pap. 9.99 (978-1-59789-768-6(X), Barbour Bks.) Barbour Publishing, Inc.

Longman, Tremper, III. Old Testament Commentary Survey. 4th ed. 2007. 160p. (C). pap. 16.00 (978-0-8010-3123-6(0)) Baker Academic.

Maclaren, Alexander. Expositions of Holy Scripture: Deuteronomy, Joshua, Judges, Ruth, & First Book of Samuel, Second Samuel, First Kings, & Second Kings chapters I to VII. 2007. (ENG.). 760p. pap. 33.99 (978-1-4264-2702-2(6)) BiblioBazaar.

Maus, Tom A. Empowered for Mission: Through the Baptism of the Holy Spirit. 2010. 78p. pap. 10.95 (978-1-4327-5577-5(3)) Outskirts Pr., Inc.

May, Iva. Shepherd-Shaped: I Am My Beloved's & He Is Mine. 2007. 260p. per. 14.95 (978-0-929292-79-3(0), 800-747-0738) Hannibal Bks.

McIntosh, Diane. Spiritual Treasure Hunt. 2010. 188p. pap. 12.50 (978-0-557-44049-8(1)) Lulu Enterprises Inc.

Mehr, Bethany. The Hoax: Satan's Grand Deception, 1 vol. 2009. 173p. pap. 24.95 (978-1-60836-563-0(8)) PublishAmerica, Inc.

Meijers, Marja. Grace of Giving: Turning the Key to Enter & Experience Fullness of Life. 2011. pap. 10.99 (978-1-61739-078-4(X)) Tate Publishing & Enterprises, LLC.

Miletto, Gianfranco. Glauben und Wissen im Zeitalter der Reformation: Der salomonische Tempel bei Abraham ben David Portaleone (1542-1612) (Studia Judaica Ser.). (GER.). XII, 356p. 255.00 (**978-3-11-181858-0(6)**) De Gruyter, Walter Inc.

Miller, Waymon D. New Testament Elders. 126p. pap. 7.95 (978-1-56794-167-8(2), C-2506) Star Bible & Tract Corp.

Moule, Handley C. Antiguo Evangelio Para Una Nueva Era: The Old Gospel for a New Age. (SPA.). (978-84-7645-015-4(X), 223092) Clie, Editorial.

Muraoka, T. A Greek-Hebrew/Aramaic Two-way Index to the Septuagint. 2010. (ENG.). 394p. (C). 87.00 (978-90-429-2356-0(3)) Peeters Pubs. & Booksellers BEL. Dist: Brown, David Bk. Co., The.

N. Ben Zvi Enterprises Ltd., ed. Jerusalem Crown: Special Edition with Companion Volume in Presentation Case. lthr. (978-3-8055-7001-5(5)) Karger, S. AG.

—Jerusalem Crown: The Bible of the Hebrew University of Jerusalem Pentateuch, Prophets & Writings. (978-3-8055-7002-2(3)) Karger, S. AG.

Neff, Robert W. & Ramirez, Frank. Country Seer City Prophet: The Unpopular Messages of Micah & Isaiah. 2007. 66p. pap. 6.95 (978-0-87178-081-2(X)) Brethren Pr.

The New English Bible: The Old Testament, 2 vols. 2009. (ENG.). 1390p. pap. 65.00 (978-0-521-10197-4(2)) Cambridge Univ. Pr.

Newbegin, Terry L. Genesis: Your Journey Home. 2008. 692p. 59.95 (978-1-4251-8403-2(0)) Trafford Publishing.

Ogden, Graham. Qoheleth. 2007. (ENG.). 256p. (978-1-906055-08-0(4)); 2nd ed. per. (978-1-906055-09-7(2)) Sheffield Phoenix Pr.

Old Testament. 14.99 (978-0-7847-0740-1(5)) Standard Publishing.

Old Testament, English. 5.99 (978-0-89827-202-4(5), GMA402) Wesleyan Publishing Hse.

Orten, James D. Understanding the Old Testament: From Creation to Captivity. 366p. 14.95 (978-1-56794-238-5(5)) Star Bible & Tract Corp.

Palestine Contemporary. 19.98 incl. trans. (978-0-687-00165-1(X)) Abingdon Pr.

Phillips, John. Exploring People of the Old Testament, 1 vol. (John Phillips Bible Characters Ser.). (Illus.). Vol. 2. 2006. 288p. 22.99 (978-0-8254-3385-6(1)) Vol. 3. 2007. 304p. 22.99 (978-0-8254-3386-3(X)) Kregel Pubns.

—Exploring the Old Testament Book by Book: An Expository Survey, 1 vol. 2009. (Exploring the Bible Book by Book Ser.). 814p. 31.99 (978-0-8254-3373-3(8)) Kregel Pubns.

Pink, Arthur. Gleanings in Genesis. 2007. 552p. 29.99 (978-1-59986-741-0(9)) Filiquarian Publishing, LLC.

Pratt, Samuel Jackson. The Sublime & Beautiful of Scripture Being Essays on Select Passages of Sacred Composition. 2007. (ENG.). 258p. 42.95 (978-0-548-03659-4(4)) Kessinger Publishing, LLC.

Preacher's Outline & Sermon Bible, Daniel-Hosea (KJV) 2008. pap. 39.99 (978-1-57407-226-6(9)) Leadership Ministries Worldwide.

Preacher's Outline & Sermon Bible, Ezekiel (NIV) 2007. pap. 39.99 (978-1-57407-230-3(7)) Leadership Ministries Worldwide.

Preacher's Outline & Sermon Bible, Habakkuk-Malachi (KJV) 2009. pap. 39.99 (978-1-57407-241-9(2)) Leadership Ministries Worldwide.

Preacher's Outline & Sermon Bible, Joel-Nahum (NIV) 2009. pap. 39.99 (978-1-57407-239-6(0)) Leadership Ministries Worldwide.

Ramagge, Henry J. The Elusive Alien Has Been Here All Along. 2009. 328p. pap. 28.96 (978-1-4251-8854-2(0)) Trafford Publishing.

Reardon, Patrick Henry. Chronicles of History & Worship: Orthodox Christian Reflections on the Books of Chronicles. 2006. 185p. per. 14.95 (978-1-888212-83-9(7)) Conciliar Pr.

Ridges, David J., compiled by. Your Study of the Old Testament Made Easier: Part 3 - Selections from Ecclesiastes through Malachi. 2006. per. 24.99 (978-1-55517-957-1(6)) Cedar Fort, Inc./CFI Distribution.

Riell, Howard Michael. Enoch, Israel & Americ. 2008. 276p. pap. 14.95 (978-1-60264-217-1(6)) Virtualbookworm.com Publishing, Inc.

Sailhamer, John & Baker, David L. Two Testaments, One Bible: The Theological Relationship Between the Old & New Testaments. 3rd rev. ed. 2010. (ENG.). 362p. pap. 29.00 (978-0-8308-1421-3(3), IVP Acad.) InterVarsity Pr.

Satterthwaite, Philip E. & McConville, J. Gordon. Exploring the Old Testament Vol. 2: A Guide to the Historical Books. 2007. (Exploring the Old Testament Ser.). (ENG.). 311p. 30.00 (978-0-8308-2552-3(5), IVP Acad.) InterVarsity Pr.

Scherman, Nosson, et al, eds. Tanach: the Stone Edition. 2010. (ArtScroll (Mesorah) Ser.). (Illus.). 2079p. pap. 24.99 (978-1-4226-1003-9(9)) Mesorah Pubns., Ltd.

Shearman, David. 12 Dead Men Speak. 192p. pap. (978-1-85240-340-9(3)) Sovereign World, Ltd.

Smith-Christopher, Daniel & Gustafson, Janie. The Old Testament: Our Call to Faith & Justice. 2007. (Illus.). 288p. tchr. ed., per. 26.95 (978-0-87793-604-6(8)) Ave Maria Pr.

Spawn, Kevin L. As It Is Written & Other Citation Formulae in the Old Testament: Their Use, Development, Syntax, & Significance. (Beihefte zur Zeitschrift far die alttestamentliche Wissenschaft Ser.). (ENG.). XVII, 301p. 240.00 (**978-3-11-180437-8(2)**) De Gruyter, Walter Inc.

Standard Publishing Staff. 40 Instant Studies: Old Testament. Eichenberger, Jim, ed. 2009. (True to Life Ser.). (ENG.). 96p. (YA). pap. 9.99 (978-0-7847-2298-5(6)) Standard Publishing.

Stephenson, Maude A. A Commentary on the Five Scrolls: Song of Songs, Ruth, Lamentations, Ecclesiastes, Esther. 2011. 130p. 40.95 (**978-1-258-06019-0(1)**) Literary Licensing, LLC.

Swete, Henry Barclay & Ottley, Richard Rusden. An Introduction to the Old Testament in Greek. Thackeray, H. J., ed. 2011. (GRE & ENG.). 156.80 (978-1-61143-842-0(X)) Gorgias Pr., LLC.

Talbot, Dee Dee. In the Beginning...: Study Guide 1 for the Daily Bible in Chronological Order / Dee Dee Talbot. 2007. 202p. pap. 21.95 (978-1-4303-1754-8(X)) Lulu Enterprises Inc.

Tamberino, Tony. Scripture Session on the Old Testament. ldr.'s ed. 2006. 95p. per. 18.95 (978-0-88489-865-8(2)) St. Mary's Pr.

—Scripture Sessions on the Old Testament. 2006. 42p. per., wbk. ed. 7.25 (978-0-88489-864-1(4)) St. Mary's Pr.

Van Pelt, Miles V. Basics of Biblical Aramaic: Complete Grammar, Lexicon, & Annotated Text, 1 vol. 2011. (ENG.). 304p. pap. 44.99 (978-0-310-49391-4(9)) Zondervan.

Vaughan, Patrick H. The Meaning of Bāmâ in the Old Testament: A Study of Etymological, Textual & Archaeological Evidence. 2009. (Society for Old Testament Study Monographs). (ENG.). 108p. pap. 20.99 (978-0-521-10410-4(6)) Cambridge Univ. Pr.

Vidmar, Peter. QuickMarks: Old Testament. 2006. (Illus.). 6p. vinyl bd. 4.99 (978-0-9765486-3-8(1)) Owners Manual Pr.

Vogan, Charles. The Treasury of Christ - Volume 1 - Overview of the Old Testament. 2007. 192p. pap. 15.95 (978-0-615-15618-7(5)) Shenandoah Bible Ministries.

Weiss, Yosaif Asher. A Daily Dose of Torah: [Limud Yomi]: A Torah Theme for Every Day of Every Week from All Areas of Torah Literature, Collected for Daily Study: Series Two. 2008. (ArtScroll Ser.). (978-1-4226-0598-1(1)); (978-1-4226-0594-3(9)); (978-1-4226-0599-8(X)); (978-1-4226-0596-7(5)); (978-1-4226-0597-4(3)); (978-1-4226-0600-1(7)); (978-1-4226-0604-9(X)); (978-1-4226-0595-0(7)); (**978-1-4226-0606-3(6)**); (**978-1-4226-0605-6(8)**); (**978-1-4226-0603-2(1)**); (**978-1-4226-0602-5(3)**); (**978-1-4226-0601-8(5)**) Mesorah Pubns., Ltd.

Werlitz, Jürgen. Studien zur literarkritischen Methode: Gericht und Heil in Jesaja 7,1-17 Und 29,1-8. (Beihefte zur Zeitschrift für die alttestamentliche Wissenschaft Ser.). (GER., Illus.). X, 351p. 210.00 (**978-3-11-178455-7(X)**) De Gruyter, Walter Inc.

Whitley, Charles F. Koheleth: His Language & Thought. (Beihefte zur Zeitschrift far die alttestamentliche Wissenschaft Ser.). (ENG.). VIII, 199p. 196.00 (**978-3-11-179012-1(6)**) De Gruyter, Walter Inc.

WHYBRAY. The Intellectual Tradition in the Old Testament. (Beihefte zur Zeitschrift far die alttestamentliche Wissenschaft Ser.). (ENG.). XII, 158p. 210.00 (**978-3-11-176100-8(2)**) De Gruyter, Walter Inc.

Wiersbe, Warren W. The Complete Old & New Testaments OT/NT, Vol. 2. 2007. (Wiersbe Bible Commentaries Ser.). (ENG.). 1536p. 49.99 (978-0-7814-4540-5(X)) Cook, David C.

Williams, T. K. The Just Shall Live by Faith. Huntley, Yolanda, ed. 2010. 152p. pap. 12.95 (978-0-578-05053-9(6)) Vision Pubns.

Wiseman, Donald J. Tyndale Old Testament Commentaries. 2009. (Tyndale Commentaries Complete Set Ser.). (ENG.). pap. 448.00 (978-0-8308-4200-1(4), IVP Acad.) InterVarsity Pr.

, Word of Life Press, Word of Life Press. Japanese Living Bible New Testament. 2011. (JPN.). 656p. mass mkt. 32.20 (**978-4-8206-0289-7(6)**) Word of Life Press Ministries JPN. Dist: STL Distribution North America.

Yoder, Christine Roy. Wisdom as a Woman of Substance: A Socioeconomic Reading of Proverbs 1-9 And 31:10-31. (Beihefte zur Zeitschrift far die alttestamentliche Wissenschaft Ser.). (ENG.). XII, 165p. 150.00 (**978-3-11-188009-9(5)**) De Gruyter, Walter Inc.

Zondervan. Zondervan King James Version Commentary — -Old Testament, 1 vol. 2010. (ENG.). 49.99 (978-0-310-68068-0(9)) Zondervan.

Zondervan Publishing Staff. Zondervan King James Version Commentary-Old Testament, 1 vol. 2010. (ENG.). 1216p. 39.99 (978-0-310-25139-2(7)) Zondervan.

BIBLE—COMMENTARIES—O. T. AMOS

see Bible—Commentaries—O. T. Minor Prophets

BIBLE—COMMENTARIES—O. T. APOCRYPHA

Anon. The Apocrypha. 2007. 448p. per. (978-1-4067-8843-3(0), Pomona Pr.) Read Bks.

The Assumption of Moses. 42p. reprint ed. 68.00 (978-0-7222-9911-1(7)) Library Reprints, Inc.

Balla, Ibolya. Ben Sira on Family, Gender, & Sexuality. 2011. (Deuterocanonical & Cognate Literature Studies). (ENG., Illus.). X, 334p. 168.00 (**978-3-11-215017-7(1)**); 112.00 (**978-3-11-024746-6(1)**) De Gruyter, Walter Inc.

Bullard, Roger Aubrey & Hatton, Howard. A Handbook on Sirach. 2008. (978-0-8267-0203-6(1)) United Bible Societies.

—A Handbook on the Shorter Books of the Deuterocanon. 2006. (978-0-8267-0201-2(5)) United Bible Societies.

Callahan, Gertrude E. Through the Old Testament & the Apocryph. 2011. 328p. 50.95 (**978-1-258-05840-1(5)**) Literary Licensing, LLC.

Charles, R. The Apocalypse of Baruch. 2007. (ENG.). 258p. 42.95 (978-0-548-05183-2(6)) Kessinger Publishing, LLC.

Charles, R. H. The Book of Enoch. 2007. (ENG.). 136p. per. 9.95 (978-1-60206-568-0(3)) Cosimo, Inc.

—The Book of Enoch, Second Edition: 1 Enoch Translated from the Editor's Ethiopic Text (1912) 2011. 444p. pap. 38.00 (978-1-60608-824-1(6), Wipf and Stock) Wipf & Stock Pubs.

Charles, R. H., ed. The Book of the Secrets of Enoch. Morfill, W.R., tr. 2006. pap. 9.99 (978-1-59986-936-0(5)) Filiquarian Publishing, LLC.

Charles, R. H., tr. The Book of Enoch. 2007. (Dover Occult Ser.). (ENG., Illus.). 160p. per. 7.95 (978-0-486-45466-5(5)) Dover Pubns., Inc.

Coogan, Michael, et al, eds. Apocrypha. 4th annot. rev. ed. 2010. (ENG., Illus.). 2096p. 37.99 (978-0-19-528959-6(5)) Oxford Univ. Pr., Inc.

—Bible with the Apocrypha. 4th rev. annot. ed. 2010. (ENG., Illus.). 2096p. 90.00 (978-0-19-528952-7(8)) Oxford Univ. Pr., Inc.

de Lange, Nicholas, ed. Jewish Reception of Greek Bible Versions: Studies in Their Use in Late Antiquity & the Middle Ages. 2009. (Text & Studies in Medieval & Early Modern Judaism Ser.). (Illus.). 338p. 195.00 (978-3-16-149779-7(1)) Mohr Siebeck GmbH & Co. KG DEU. Dist: Coronet Bks.

Dodson, Joseph R. The "Powers" of Personification: Rhetorical Purpose in the Book of Wisdom & the Letter to the Romans. 2008. (Beihefte zur Zeitschrift far die neutestamentliche Wissenschaft und die Kunde der älteren Kirche Ser.). (ENG.). XII, 264p. 147.00 (978-3-11-020976-1(4)) De Gruyter, Walter Inc.

Duff, Archibald, ed. The First & Second Books of Esdras 1903. 2007. (ENG.). 192p. 37.95 (978-0-548-05583-0(1)) Kessinger Publishing, LLC.

Fitzmyer, Joseph A. Tobit. (Commentaries on Early Jewish Literature Ser.). (ENG.). XVIII, 374p. 210.00 (**978-3-11-180006-6(7)**) De Gruyter, Walter Inc.

Goodman, Martin, et al, eds. The Apocrypha. 2013. (ENG.). 352p. pap. 27.95 (**978-0-19-965081-1(0)**) Oxford Univ. Pr., Inc.

Horne, Charles F. The Great Rejected Books of the Biblical Apocrypha (the Sacred Books of Early Literature of the East), Vol. 14. 2007. per. 34.95 (978-1-4209-2943-0(7)) Digireads.com.

Kasole Ka-Mungu, Benjamin. Des ténèbres à la Lumière: La guérison dans le livre de Tobit. 2008. (Europäische Hochschulschriften. Reihe 23: Theologie Ser.). 376p. pap. 81.95 (978-3-631-57720-2(6)) Lang, Peter GmbH, Europaischer Verlag der Wissenschaften DEU. Dist: Lang, Peter.

Kearns, Conleth. The Expanded Text of Ecclesiasticus: Its Teaching on the Future Life as a Clue to its Origin. Beentjes, Pancratius C., ed. 2011. (Deuterocanonical & Cognate Literature Studies). (ENG., Illus.). VI, 333p. 210.00 (**978-3-11-219102-6(1)**) De Gruyter, Walter Inc.

Levi, Gerson B. Gnomic Literature in Bible & Apocrypha: With Special Reference to the Gnomic Fragments & Their Bearing on the Proverb Collections. 2007. 114p. pap. 10.00 (978-1-55635-648-3(X), Wipf and Stock) Wipf & Stock Pubs.

Newbold, William Romaine. Bar Daysan & the Odes of Solomon. 2007. (Analecta Gorgiana Ser.: 46). per. 24.00 (978-1-59333-860-2(0)) Gorgias Pr., LLC.

Nordline, John G. Religion & Resistance in Early Judaism Greek Reading in 1 Maccabees & Josephus. 2010. (GRE & ENG.). 384p. (C). pap. 29.99 (978-0-7586-2667-7(3)) Concordia Publishing Hse.

Oesterley, W. O. E. An Introduction to the Books of the Apocrypha. 2006. pap. 18.95 (978-1-933993-22-5(7)) Apocryphile Pr.

—An Introduction to the Books of the Apocrypha. 2011. 356p. pap. 42.00 (**978-1-61097-631-2(2)**, Wipf and Stock) Wipf & Stock Pubs.

Oesterley, W. O. E., ed. The Wisdom of Solomon 1917. 2007. (ENG.). 108p. 33.95 (978-0-548-05560-1(2)) Kessinger Publishing, LLC.

Oesterley, William O. E. The Wisdom of Solomon. 94p. reprint ed. 68.00 (978-0-7222-9914-2(1)) Library Reprints, Inc.

Patterson, Stephen J., et al. The Fifth Gospel: The Gospel of Thomas Comes of Age. 2011. (ENG.). 144p. pap. 19.95 (978-0-567-54906-8(2), T&T Clark Int'l) Continuum International Publishing Group, Ltd. GBR. Dist: National Bk. Network.

R. H. Charles. The Book of Jubilees. 2011. 364p. pap. 7.88 (**978-1-60386-413-8(X)**, Merchant Bks.) Rough Draft Printing.

Reardon, Patrick. Wise Lives: Orthodox Christian Reflections on the Wisdom of Sirach. 2009. 204p. pap. 16.95 (978-0-9822770-3-4(2)) Conciliar Pr.

Reiterer, Friedrich V., ed. Zählsynopse Zum Buch Ben Sira. (Fontes et Subsidia ad Bibliam Pertinentes Ser.). (GER., Illus.). XII, 247p. 180.00 (**978-3-11-186871-4(0)**) De Gruyter, Walter Inc.

Schwartz, Daniel R. 2 Maccabees. 2008. (Commentaries on Early Jewish Literature Ser.). (ENG.). X, 617p. 189.00 (978-3-11-019118-9(0)); 280.00 (**978-3-11-173871-0(X)**) De Gruyter, Walter Inc.

Surburg, Raymond F. Introduction to the Intertestamental Period. 176p. pap. 14.99 (978-0-570-03856-6(1)) Concordia Publishing Hse.

Translations of Early Documents: Palestinian Jewish Texts. reprint ed. 652.80 (978-0-7222-9900-5(1)) Library Reprints, Inc.

Ueberschaer, Frank. Weisheit aus der Begegnung: Bildung nach dem Buch Ben Sira. 2007. (Beihefte zur Zeitschrift für die alttestamentliche Wissenschaft Ser.).Tr. of Wisdom from Encounter. Education according to the Wisdom of Ben Sira (Ecclesiasticus). (GER.). X, 446p. 154.00 (978-3-11-020064-5(3)) De Gruyter, Walter Inc.

Voicu, Sever J., ed. Apocrypha. 2010. (Ancient Christian Commentary on Scripture Ser.: Old Testament Volume 15). (ENG.). 575p. 50.00 (978-0-8308-1485-5(X), IVP Acad.) InterVarsity Pr.

The Wisdom of Ben-Sira: Ecclesiasticus. 148p. reprint ed. 68.00 (978-0-7222-9902-9(8)) Library Reprints, Inc.

BIBLE—COMMENTARIES—O. T. CHRONICLES

see Bible—Commentaries—O. T. Historical Books

BIBLE—COMMENTARIES—O. T. DANIEL

see Bible—Commentaries—O. T. Prophets

BIBLE—COMMENTARIES—O. T. DEUTERONOMY

see Bible—Commentaries—O. T. Pentateuch

BIBLE—COMMENTARIES—O. T. ECCLESIASTES

see Bible—Commentaries—O. T. Poetical Books

BIBLE—COMMENTARIES—O. T. ESTHER

see Bible—Commentaries—O. T. Historical Books

BIBLE—COMMENTARIES—O. T. EXODUS

see Bible—Commentaries—O. T. Pentateuch

BIBLE—COMMENTARIES—O. T. EZEKIEL

see Bible—Commentaries—O. T. Prophets

BIBLE—COMMENTARIES—O. T. EZRA

see Bible—Commentaries—O. T. Historical Books

BIBLE—COMMENTARIES—O. T. FIVE SCROLLS

Ganin, Leela, illus. The Koren Illustrated Five Megillot: The Five Scrolls in Book Form, Hebrew/English. 2009. (HEB & ENG.). 184p. 29.95 (978-965-301-188-5(X), Koren Pubs.) Toby Pr. LLC, The.

Midrash Ha-Mevo'ar Institute. The Midrash Rabbah: Megillas Eichah. 25.99 (978-1-58330-274-3(3)) Feldheim Pubs.

Midrash Rabbah: Midrashim on the Pentateuch & the Five Scrolls with the Matnoth Kehunah Commentary, 2 vols., Set. deluxe ed. (ENG, HEB & YID.). 75.00 (978-0-87559-096-7(9)) Shalom, P. Pubns., Inc.

Neff, Robert W. & Ramirez, Frank. The Five Festal Scrolls. 2008. 86p. pap. 7.95 (978-0-87178-114-7(X), FaithQuest) Brethren Pr.

BIBLE—COMMENTARIES—O. T. GENESIS

see Bible—Commentaries—O. T. Pentateuch

BIBLE—COMMENTARIES—O. T. HABAKKUK

see Bible—Commentaries—O. T. Minor Prophets

BIBLE—COMMENTARIES—O. T. HAGGAI

see Bible—Commentaries—O. T. Minor Prophets

BIBLE—COMMENTARIES—O. T. HISTORICAL BOOKS

Abingdon Youth, creator. History Leg 2 Joshua - Esther. 2007. (Amazing Bible Race Ser.). cd-rom 30.00 (978-0-687-33398-1(9)) Abingdon Pr.

Abingdon Press, creator. History, Leg 2: Joshua-Esther. 2007. (Amazing Bible Race Ser.). (Illus.). 127p. per. 6.00 (978-0-687-33408-7(X)) Abingdon Pr.

Ackroyd, Peter R. Chronicler in His Age. 2009. (Library of Hebrew Bible/Old Testament Studies, the Ser.). (ENG.). 65.00 *(978-0-567-00132-0(6)*, T&T Clark) Continuum International Publishing Group, Ltd. GBR. Dist: National Bk. Network.
Andrews, Stephen J., et al. 1, 2 Samuel Vol. 6: Holman Old Testament Commentary. 2009. (Holman Old Testament Commentary Ser.). (ENG.). 400p. 19.99 *(978-0-8054-9466-2(9)*, Holman Reference) B&H Publishing Group.
Auld, A. Graeme. I & II Samuel: A Commentary. 2011. (Old Testament Library). (ENG.). 744p. pap. 75.00 *(978-0-664-22105-8(X))* Westminster John Knox Pr.
Baker Publishing Group Staff. A Walk Thru the Book of Esther: Courage in the Face of Crisis, 1 vol. 2010. (Walk Thru the Bible Discussion Guides). (ENG.). 96p. pap. 7.99 *(978-0-8010-7180-5(1))* Baker Bks.
—A Walk Thru the Life of Elijah: Standing Strong for Truth, 1 vol. 2010. (Walk Thru the Bible Discussion Guides). (ENG.). 64p. pap. 7.99 *(978-0-8010-7176-8(3))* Baker Bks.
Baldwin, Joyce G. 1 & 2 Samuel. 2008. (Tyndale Old Testament Commentaries Ser.: Volume 8). (ENG.). 240p. pap. 16.00 *(978-0-8308-4208-7(X)*, IVP Acad.) InterVarsity Pr.
Barber, Cyril J. Ezra & Esther: A Devotional Commentary. 2007. 196p. pap. 20.00 *(978-1-55635-598-1(X))* Wipf & Stock Pubs.
Bede & Bede. Bede: On Ezra & Nehemiah. DeGregorio, Scott, tr. from LAT. 2006. (Liverpool University Press - Translated Texts for Historians Ser.: 47). (ENG.). 208p. pap. 35.00 *(978-1-84631-001-0(6))* Liverpool Univ. Pr. GBR. Dist: Chicago Distribution Ctr.
Beecher, Willis J. The Dated Events of the Old Testament: Being a Presentation of Old Testament Chronology. 2007. (Illus.). 206p. pap. 20.00 *(978-1-55635-220-1(4)*, Wipf and Stock) Wipf & Stock Pubs.
Berrigan, Daniel. The Kings & Their Gods: The Pathology of Power. 2008. 202p. pap. 20.00 *(978-0-8028-6043-9(5))* Eerdmans, William B. Publishing Co.
Bertolini, Rebecca. Joshua, Judges & Ruth, 0 vols. Richards, Larry, ed. 2008. (Smart Guide to the Bible Ser.). (Illus.). 384p. per. 14.99 *(978-1-4185-1005-3(X))* Nelson, Thomas Inc.
Bodner, Keith. 1 Samuel: A Narrative Commentary. 2008. 352p. *(978-1-906055-10-3(6))* Sheffield Phoenix Pr.
Boice, James Montgomery. Joshua. 2006. (Expositional Commentary Ser.). 152p. pap. 17.00 *(978-0-8010-6646-7(8))* Baker Bks.
Bolin, Thomas. Ezrah Nehemiah. 2011. 136p. pap. 6.95 ***(978-0-8146-2845-4(1))*** Liturgical Pr.
Booher, Dianna. The Esther Effect, 0 vols. 2008. 144p. pap. 15.99 *(978-0-7852-9675-1(1))* Nelson, Thomas Inc.
Brandt, Brad & Kress, Eric. God in Everyday Life: The Book of Ruth for Expositors & Biblical Counselors. 2007. (ENG.). 187p. per. 14.99 *(978-0-9772262-5-2(5))* Kress Christian Pubns.
Branson, Robert. NBBC, Judges: A Commentary in the Wesleyan Tradition. 2009. (ENG.). 192p. pap. 25.99 *(978-0-8341-2407-3(6)*, 9780834124073) Beacon Hill Pr. of Kansas City.
Brestin, Dee. A Woman of Faith: Esther Overcoming the World's Influences. 2007. (Dee Brestins Ser.). (ENG., Illus.). 128p. per. 9.99 *(978-0-7814-4448-4(9))* Cook, David C.
—A Woman of Love: A Women's Journey Through Ruth. 2006. (Dee Brestins Ser.). (ENG., Illus.). 128p. per. 10.99 *(978-0-7814-4450-7(0))* Cook, David C.
Bristow, Mark D. Nehemiah's Gates. 2008. 136p. pap. 13.99 *(978-1-60647-470-9(7))* Xulon Pr., Inc.
Broca, Lilian, et al. The Hidden & the Revealed: The Queen Esther Mosaics of Lilian Broca. 2011. ***(978-965-229-560-6(4))*** Gefen Bks.
Brueggemann, Walter. First & Second Samuel: Interpretation: A Bible Commentary for Teaching & Preaching. 2012. (Interpretation: A Bible Commentary for Teaching & Preaching Ser.). (ENG.). 374p. pap. 25.00 ***(978-0-664-23868-1(8))*** Westminster John Knox Pr.
Bush, George H. W. Notes, Critical & Practical, on the Book of Joshua: Designed As A General Help to Biblical Reading & Instruction. by George Bush ... 2006. 232p. per. 20.99 *(978-1-4255-1970-4(9))* MPublishing.
—Notes, Critical & Practical, on the Book of Judges; Designed As a General Help to Biblical Reading & Instruction. 2006. 260p. per. 23.99 *(978-1-4255-2288-9(2))* MPublishing.
C. Paul Puckett. Liberalization & Apostasy of Americ. 2009. 72p. pap. 10.49 *(978-1-4389-9887-9(2))* AuthorHouse.
Carroll, B. H. Comentario Carroll-Tres: Numeros-Ruth: Carroll's Commentary 3: Numbers - Ruth. (SPA.). *(978-84-7645-132-8(6)*, 223178) Clie, Editorial.
Carruthers, Jo. Esther Through the Centuries. 2008. (Blackwell Bible Commentaries Ser.). (ENG., Illus.). 320p. 115.95 *(978-1-4051-3213-8(2)*, Wiley-Blackwell) Wiley, John & Sons, Inc.
Christian Art Gifts, creator. Joy Nehemiah 8:10. 2008. 400p. *(978-1-77036-013-6(1))* Christian Art Pubs.
Cooke, G. A. The Book of Judges & the Book of Ruth - Both with Extensive Notes. 2007. 284p. per. *(978-1-4067-8841-9(4)*, Pomona Pr) Read Bks.
Cundall, Arthur Ernest, et al. Judges & Ruth. 2008. (Tyndale Old Testament Commentaries Ser.: Volume 7). (ENG., Illus.). 307p. pap. 16.00 *(978-0-8308-4207-0(1)*, IVP Acad.) InterVarsity Pr.
Davis, Dale Ralph. I Kings: The Wisdom & the Folly. 2007. (Focus on the Bible Commentaries Ser.). (ENG.). 35p. per. 14.99 *(978-1-84550-251-5(5))* Christian Focus Pubns. GBR. Dist: STL Distribution North America.
—Judges: Such a Great Salvation. l.t. ed. 2007. (Focus on the Bible Commentaries Ser.). (ENG.). 240p. per. 15.99 *(978-1-84550-138-9(1))* Christian Focus Pubns. GBR. Dist: STL Distribution North America.
—2 Samuel: Out of Every Adversity. 2007. (Focus on the Bible Ser.). (ENG., Illus.). 336p. per. 15.99 *(978-1-84550-270-6(1))* Christian Focus Pubns. GBR. Dist: STL Distribution North America.
Davis, John J. Conquest & Crisis: Studies in Joshua, Judges & Ruth. rev. ed. 2008. (ENG., Illus.). 274p. pap. 17.99 *(978-0-88469-258-4(2))* BMH Bks.
Deane, William J. Samuel y Saul-Su Vida y Sus Tiempos: Life & Times of Samuel & Saul. (SPA.). *(978-84-7645-163-2(6)*, 223206) Clie, Editorial.
Debelak, Robert P. Jr. Hidden in Plain Sight: Esther & a Marginalised Hermeneutic. 2008. (ENG.). 156p. pap. 33.00 *(978-0-7188-9181-7(3))* Lutherworth Pr., The GBR. Dist: Brown, David Bk. Co., The.
Discover Esther. (Discover Your Bible Ser.). (KOR.). pap., tchr. ed. 3.95 *(978-1-55883-161-2(4)*, 600105); pap., stu. ed. 2.75 *(978-1-55883-160-5(6)*, 600100) C R C World Literature Ministries/Libros Desafio.
Eaton, Michael. Ezra - Nehemiah - Esther. (Preaching Through the Bible Ser.). 125p. pap. *(978-1-85240-313-3(6))* Sovereign World, Ltd.
—Joshua. (Preaching Through the Bible Ser.). 125p. pap. *(978-1-85240-264-8(4))* Sovereign World, Ltd.
—Judges & Ruth. (Preaching Through the Bible Ser.). 125p. pap. *(978-1-85240-291-4(1))* Sovereign World, Ltd.
—2 Kings. (Preaching Through the Bible Ser.). 125p. pap. *(978-1-85240-177-1(X))* Sovereign World, Ltd.
Edelman, Diana. The Origins of the 'Second' Temple: Persian Imperial Policy & the Rebuilding of Jerusalem. rev. ed. 2010. (BibleWorld Ser.). (ENG., Illus.). 458p. (C). per. 39.95 *(978-1-84553-017-4(9))* Equinox Publishing Ltd. GBR. Dist: ISD.
Ellsworth, Roger. Joshua. 2008. (Opening Up Ser.). (Illus.). 128p. pap. *(978-1-84625-118-4(4))* DayOne Pubns.
Eskenazi, Tamara Cohn & Frymer-Kensky, Tikvah. The JPS Bible Commentary: Ruth. 2011. (JPS Bible Commentary Ser.). (ENG & HEB.). 216p. 40.00 *(978-0-8276-0744-6(X))* Jewish Pubn. Society.
Essex, Barbara J. Misbehavin' Monarchs: Exploring Biblical Kings of Questionable Character. 2006. 187p. per. *(978-0-8298-1655-6(0))* Pilgrim Pr., The/United Church Pr.
Ezra/Nehemiah/Esther. (People's Bible Commentary Ser.). 208p. 12.99 *(978-0-7586-0425-5(4))* Concordia Publishing Hse.
Faley, Roland. Joshua Judges. 2011. 136p. pap. 6.95 ***(978-0-8146-2841-6(9))*** Liturgical Pr.
Farrar, F. W. The Second Book of Kings. 2009. 514p. 36.99 *(978-1-113-89023-8(1))*; 514p. 35.99 *(978-1-113-89024-5(X))*; (ENG.). 513p. pap. 30.99 *(978-1-113-89016-0(9)*, BiblioLife); 514p. pap. 30.99 *(978-1-113-89022-1(3))*; 514p. pap. 38.75 *(978-1-113-89021-4(5))* BiblioBazaar.
Ferguson, Sinclair. Faithful God. 2007. 157p. pap. 10.99 *(978-1-85049-216-0(6))* Bryntirion Pr. GBR. Dist: Spring Arbor Distributors, Inc.
Fernandez, Nancy. Samuel. (SPA.). 104p. *(978-84-7228-243-8(0)*, 220793) Clie, Editorial.
Firth, David G. 1 & 2 Samuel. 2009. (Apollos Old Testament Commentary Ser.: Volume 8). (ENG.). 614p. 40.00 *(978-0-8308-2508-0(8)*, IVP Acad.) InterVarsity Pr.
Fox, Michael V. Character & Ideology in the Book of Esther: A New Postscript on a Decade of Esther Scholarship. 2nd ed. 2010. 344p. pap. 38.00 *(978-1-60899-495-3(3))* Wipf & Stock Pubs.
Fruchtenbaum, Arnold G. Ariel's Bible Commentary: The Books of Judges & Ruth. 2007. *(978-0-97652-3-3(2))* Ariel Ministries, Inc.
Fuller, Thomas. A Comment on Ruth: And Notes upon Jonah. Nichols, William, ed. 2008. 219p. pap. 19.00 *(978-1-60608-032-0(6))* Wipf & Stock Pubs.
Furst, Renata. Rut, Esdras, Nehemias y Ester: Ruth, Ezra, Nehemiah & Esther. 2009. (Conozca su Biblia Ser.). 128p. pap. 15.00 *(978-0-8066-5778-3(2))* Augsburg Fortress, Pubs.
Fyall, Robert. The Message of Ezra & Haggai. 2010. (Bible Speaks Today Ser.). (ENG.). 190p. pap. 16.00 *(978-0-8308-2432-8(4)*, IVP Acad.) InterVarsity Pr.
Garrick, Gene. Stones of Rememberance. 2007. 144p. per. 13.99 *(978-1-60034-768-9(1))* Xulon Pr., Inc.
Goldingay, John. Ezra, Nehemiah, & Esther for Everyone. 2012. (Old Testament for Everyone Ser.). (ENG.). 256p. pap. 16.00 ***(978-0-664-23382-2(1))*** Westminster John Knox Pr.
—Joshua, Judges, & Ruth for Everyone. 2011. (Old Testament for Everyone Ser.). (ENG.). 256p. pap. 16.00 *(978-0-664-23378-5(3))* Westminster John Knox Pr.
—1 & 2 Chronicles for Everyone. 2012. (Old Testament for Everyone Ser.). (ENG.). 216p. pap. 15.00 ***(978-0-664-23381-5(3))*** Westminster John Knox Pr.
—1 & 2 Kings for Everyone. 2011. (Old Testament for Everyone Ser.). (ENG.). 216p. pap. 16.00 *(978-0-664-23380-8(5))* Westminster John Knox Pr.
—1 & 2 Samuel for Everyone. 2011. (Old Testament for Everyone Ser.). (ENG.). 256p. pap. 16.00 *(978-0-664-23379-2(1))* Westminster John Knox Pr.
Gordon, Debra. God Said! With King James Bible Verses 2010. 24p. 14.95 *(978-1-4269-4430-7(6))* Trafford Publishing.
Greig, Doris W. Esther. 2007. (ENG.). 56p. spiral bd. 10.99 *(978-1-932017-38-0(0))* Joy of Living Bible Studies.
Grossman, David. Lion's Honey: The Myth of Samson. Schoffman, Stuart, tr. 2007. (Myths Ser.). (ENG.). 168p. per. 13.00 *(978-1-84195-913-9(8))* Canongate Bks. GBR. Dist: Perseus-PGW.
—Lion's Honey: The Myth of Samson. Schoffman, Stuart, tr. unabr. l.t. ed. 2006. (Isis Hardcover Ser.). 152p. 35.50 *(978-0-7531-7716-7(1))* ISIS Large Print Bks. GBR. Dist: Ulverscroft Large Print Bks., Ltd.
Gunn, David. 1 & 2 Samuel. 2011. (Blackwell Bible Commentaries Ser.). 230p. pap. *(978-0-631-22204-0(9)*, Wiley-Blackwell) Wiley, John & Sons, Ltd.
Hawk, L. Daniel. Joshua In 3-D: A Commentary on Biblical Conquest & Manifest Destiny. 2010. 316p. pap. 35.00 *(978-1-60608-819-7(X))* Wipf & Stock Pubs.
Hawley, Charles Arthur. A Critical Examination of the Peshitta Version of the Book of Ezra. 2008. 80p. pap. 17.95 *(978-0-548-85862-2(4))* Kessinger Publishing, LLC.
Heijkoop, H. L. The Book of Ruth. 7.50 *(978-0-88172-086-0(0))*; pap. 4.50 *(978-0-88172-185-0(9))* Believers Bookshelf, Inc.
Heitzig, Lenya & Rose, Penny Pierce. Live Fearlessly: A Study in the Book of Joshua. 2008. (Fresh Life Ser.). (ENG., Illus.). 392p. pap. 17.99 *(978-1-4347-9941-8(7))* Cook, David C.
Hens-Piazza, Gina. Abingdon Old Testament Commentaries - 1 & 2 Kings. 2006. (Aotc Ser.). 407p. per. 40.00 *(978-0-687-49021-9(9))* Abingdon Pr.
Howard, David M., Jr. An Introduction to the Old Testament Historical Books. 2007. (ENG., Illus.). 456p. 34.99 *(978-0-8024-4155-3(6))* Moody Pubs.
Ibn Ezra, Abraham & Zedner, Joseph. Abraham Aben Ezra's Commentary on the Book of Esther. 2010. pap. 19.72 *(978-1-61143-297-8(9))* Gorgias Pr., LLC.
II Chronicles. (People's Bible Commentary Ser.). 448p. 16.99 *(978-0-7586-0424-8(6))* Concordia Publishing Hse.
Imoru, Nicholas. A Heart for God. 2007. 140p. per. *(978-0-9555562-4-1(4))* Esteemworld Pubns.
Japheth ben Ali & Wechsler, Michael G. The Arabic Translation & Commentary of Yefet Ben Eli the Karaite on the Book of Esther. 2008. (Études Sur le Judaïsme Médiéval Ser.: Vol. 36). (ENG.). 346p. *(978-90-04-16388-1(3))* BRILL.
Jarick, John. 1 Chronicles. 2007. 192p. *(978-1-905048-88-5(2))*; (ENG.). per. *(978-1-905048-89-2(0))* Sheffield Phoenix Pr.
—2 Chronicles. 2007. 216p. *(978-1-905048-96-0(3))*; (ENG.). per. *(978-1-905048-97-7(1))* Sheffield Phoenix Pr.
Jennings, F. C. Judges & Ruth. 9.95 *(978-0-88172-152-2(2))* Believers Bookshelf, Inc.
Jobes, Karen H. Esther: God Fulfills a Promise, 1 vol. 2008. (Bringing the Bible to Life Ser.). (ENG.). 112p. pap. 7.99 *(978-0-310-27649-4(7))* Zondervan.
Joshua. (People's Bible Commentary Ser.). 264p. 14.99 *(978-0-7586-0420-0(3))* Concordia Publishing Hse.
Joshua. deluxe ed. ring bd. 36.95 *(978-1-57407-154-2(8))* Leadership Ministries Worldwide.
Judges/Ruth. (People's Bible Commentary Ser.). 272p. 14.99 *(978-0-7586-0421-7(1))* Concordia Publishing Hse.
Kann, Alice G. Ezra: Collected Insights, Essays & Meditations. Date not set. 112p. 14.95 *(978-0-9654522-2-9(0))* Metapublishing.
Kidner, Derek. Ezra & Nehemiah. 2009. (Tyndale Old Testament Commentaries Ser.: Volume 12). (ENG.). 192p. pap. 16.00 *(978-0-8308-4212-4(8)*, IVP Acad.) InterVarsity Pr.
Kimhi, David & Berger, Yitzhak. The Commentary of Rabbi David Kimhi to Chronicles: A Translation with Introduction & Supercommentary by Yitzhak Berger. 2007. *(978-1-930675-47-6(X))* Brown Univ.
Klein, Ralph W. 1 Samuel: Second Edition, 0 vols. 2nd ed. 2009. (Word Biblical Commentary Ser.). 384p. 49.99 *(978-0-7180-2531-1(8))* Nelson, Thomas Inc.
Kohlmoos, Melanie. Ruth. 2009. (Altes testament deutsch neubearbeitungen - Leinen Ser.). (GER.). 85p. (C). 41.00 *(978-3-525-51244-9(9))* Vandenhoeck & Ruprecht GmbH & Co. KG DEU. Dist: ISD.
Kok, Joel. Judges: Doing as We See Fit. l.t. ed. 5.25 *(978-1-56212-653-7(9)*, 150041) Faith Alive Christian Resources.
Konkel, August H. One & Two Kings, 1 vol. 2006. (NIV Application Commentary Ser.). (ENG.). 704p. 36.99 *(978-0-310-21129-7(8))* Zondervan.
Kravitz, Leonard S. & Olitzky, Kerry M., comments. Esther: A Modern Commentary. 2010. *(978-0-8074-1139-1(6))* URJ Pr.
Laffey, Alice L. First & Second Kings. 2011. 136p. pap. 6.95 ***(978-0-8146-2843-0(5))*** Liturgical Pr.
Leithart, Peter J. 1 & 2 Kings. 2006. (Brazos Theological Commentary on the Bible Ser.). 304p. (C). 29.99 *(978-1-58743-125-8(4))* Brazos Pr.
Levering, Matthew. Ezra & Nehemiah. 2007. (Brazos Theological Commentary on the Bible Ser.). 240p. (C). 29.99 *(978-1-58743-161-6(0))* Brazos Pr.
Lewis, Tiffany. When Boaz Comes. 2008. 102p. (YA). pap. 15.00 *(978-0-9786088-8-0(7))* True Vine Publishing Co.
Lifetogether. Ruth. 2011. (Deepening Life Together Ser.). (Illus.). 87p. pap. 8.99 *(978-0-8010-6872-0(X))* Baker Bks.
Loken, Israel. Esther. 2007. 188p. per. 13.99 *(978-1-60477-438-2(X))* Xulon Pr., Inc.
—Ezr. 2007. 220p. per. 14.99 *(978-1-60477-442-9(8))* Xulon Pr., Inc.
Loken, Israel P. The Old Testament Historical Books: An Introduction. 2008. 452p. pap. 23.99 *(978-1-60647-238-5(0))* Xulon Pr., Inc.
Longman, Tremper. 1 Samuel Thru 2 Kings Vol. 3: Who Rules You? 2009. (QuickNotes Commentaries Ser.). (ENG.). 240p. pap. 9.99 *(978-1-59789-769-3(8)*, Barbour Bks.) Barbour Publishing, Inc.
Louer, Chris. Pursuing Your Passion. 2009. 84p. pap. 10.99 *(978-1-60791-495-2(6))* Xulon Pr., Inc.
Lowrie, John M. Esther & Her Times, in a Series of Lectures on the Book of Esther. 2006. 280p. per. 23.99 *(978-1-4255-2560-6(1))* MPublishing.
Magennis, Feidhlimidh. First & Second Samuel. 2011. 136p. pap. 6.95 ***(978-0-8146-2842-3(7))*** Liturgical Pr.
McCann, J. Clinton. Judges: Interpretation: A Bible Commentary for Teaching & Preaching. 2011. (Interpretation Ser.). (ENG.). 320p. pap. 25.00 *(978-0-664-23598-7(0))* Westminster John Knox Pr.
McConville, J. G. & Williams, Stephen N. Joshua. 2010. 272p. pap. 20.00 *(978-0-8028-2702-9(0))* Eerdmans, William B. Publishing Co.
Messianic life lessons from the book of Ruth: The gentiles witness to Israel. 2006. per. 14.00 *(978-0-9786568-0-5(6))* Word of Messiah Ministries.
Minter, Kelly. Hannah's One Wish: A Bible Study for Teen Girls. 2007. 120p. 10.95 *(978-1-4158-5254-5(5))* LifeWay Christian Resources.
Moore, Phil. Straight to the Heart of 1 & 2 Samuel: 60 Bite-Sized Insights, 1 vol. 2012. (Straight to the Heart Ser.). 272p. pap. 14.99 ***(978-0-85721-252-8(4)***, Monarch Bks.) Lion Hudson PLC GBR. Dist: Kregel Pubns.
Moore, Rickie Dale. God Saves: Lessons from the Elisha Stories. 2009. (Library of Hebrew Bible/Old Testament Studies, the Ser.). (ENG.). 169p. 29.95 *(978-0-567-15865-9(9)*, T&T Clark) Continuum International Publishing Group, Ltd. GBR. Dist: National Bk. Network.
Nee, Watchman. El Cantar de los Cantares: Song of Songs-Commentary. (SPA.). 192p. *(978-84-7228-156-1(6)*, 220137) Clie, Editorial.
Nelson, Richard D. First & Second Kings: Interpretation: A Bible Commentary for Teaching & Preaching. 2012. (Interpretation: A Bible Commentary for Teaching & Preaching Ser.). (ENG.). 284p. pap. 25.00 ***(978-0-664-23866-7(1))*** Westminster John Knox Pr.
Neusner, Jacob. Ezekiel in Talmud & Midrash. 2007. (Studies in Judaism Ser.). (ENG.). 412p. per. 55.99 *(978-0-7618-3694-0(2))* Univ. Pr. of America, Inc.
Nevertheless, God: A Study of Israel's Judges. 2010. (ENG.). 170p. pap. *(978-0-9844841-2-6(4))* Kohlbrecher, Sarah.
Newsome, James D. & Newsome, James, eds. A Synoptic Harmony of Samuel, Kings, & Chronicles: With Related Passages from Psalms, Isaiah, Jeremiah, & Ezra. 2006. 276p. pap. 28.00 *(978-1-59752-994-5(X)*, Wipf and Stock) Wipf & Stock Pubs.
Omanson, Roger L. & Ellington, John. A Handbook on 1-2 Kings. 2008. *(978-0-8267-0176-3(0))*; *(978-0-8267-0177-0(9))*; *(978-0-8267-0175-6(2))* United Bible Societies.
Origen. Homilies on Judges. Dively Lauro, Elizabeth, tr. from FRE. 2009. 144p. 29.95 *(978-0-8132-0119-1(5))* Catholic Univ. of America Pr.
Ortberg, John, et al. 1 & 2 Samuel: Growing a Heart for God, 1 vol. 2008. (New Community Bible Study Ser.). (ENG.). 96p. pap. 7.99 *(978-0-310-28049-1(4))* Zondervan.
Peckham, Colin N. Joshua: A Devotional Commentary. 2007. (Exploring the Bible Ser.). (Illus.). 235p. pap. 13.00 *(978-1-84625-093-4(5))* DayOne Pubns. GBR. Dist: STL Distribution North America.
Peipman, J. Darline. The Book of Ruth, Precept upon Precept. 2007. 348p. per. 17.99 *(978-1-60477-305-7(7))* Xulon Pr., Inc.
Petit, F. & Van Rompay, L. Sévère D'Antioche: Fragments grecs tirés des chaînes sur les derniers livres de l'Octateuque et sur les Règnes. 2006. (Traditio Exegetica Graeca Ser.). (SYR, FRE, GEC & ENG.). 214p. (C). 114.00 *(978-90-429-1725-5(3))* Peeters Pubs. & Booksellers BEL. Dist: Brown, David Bk. Co., The.
Piper, John. A Sweet & Bitter Providence: Sex, Race, & the Sovereignty of God. 2009. 160p. 17.99 *(978-1-4335-1437-1(0))* Crossway.
Pitkänen, Pekka. Joshua. 2010. (Apollos Old Testament Commentary Ser.: 6). (ENG., Illus.). 454p. 40.00 *(978-0-8308-2506-6(1)*, IVP Acad.) InterVarsity Pr.
Pollak, P. S. Marbin Besimho. 15.00 *(978-0-87559-083-7(7))*; pap. 10.00 *(978-0-87559-084-4(5))* Shalom, P. Pubns., Inc.
Pratt, Richard L. Mentor: 1 & 2 Chronicles. 2006. (Mentor Commentary Ser.). (ENG.). 736p. 39.99 *(978-1-84550-144-0(6)*, Mentor) Christian Focus Pubns. GBR. Dist: STL Distribution North America.
Provan, Iain W. Hezekiah & the Books of Kings: A Contribution to the Debate about the Composition of the Deuteronomistic History. (Beihefte zur Zeitschrift far die alttestamentliche Wissenschaft Ser.). (ENG.). XIII, 218p. 180.00 ***(978-3-11-187783-9(3))*** De Gruyter, Walter Inc.
Quayle, William A., ed. The Book of Ruth. 2007. (ENG.). 116p. 34.95 *(978-0-548-02762-2(5))* Kessinger Publishing, LLC.
Rata, Tiberius. Ezra/Nehemiah: A Mentor Commentary. 2011. (Mentor Commenatary Ser.). (ENG.). 288p. 24.99 *(978-1-84550-571-4(9)*, Mentor) Christian Focus Pubns. GBR. Dist: STL Distribution North America.
Reid, Debra. Esther. 2nd rev. ed. 2008. (Tyndale Old Testament Commentaries Ser.: Volume 13). (ENG.). 168p. pap. 16.00 *(978-0-8308-4213-1(6)*, IVP Acad.) InterVarsity Pr.
Ries, Xavier. The King Who Failed as a Parent. 2006. *(978-0-9773829-7-2(4))* Calvary Chapel Pasadena.
Rossier, H. Meditations on Joshua. 7.25 *(978-0-88172-119-5(0))* Believers Bookshelf, Inc.
Ruth: 2Kor 5,1-1- auf dem Hintergrund antiker ars moriendi. 2006. (Gottingen Septuagint Ser.). (GER & GRE.). 208p. (C). 108.00 *(978-3-525-53448-9(5))* Vandenhoeck & Ruprecht GmbH & Co. KG DEU. Dist: ISD.
Ryan, Roger. Judges. 2007. 236p. *(978-1-906055-23-3(8))*; (ENG.). per. *(978-1-906055-24-0(6))* Sheffield Phoenix Pr.
Ryken, Philip Graham. 1 Kings. 2011. ***(978-1-59638-208-4(2))*** P & R Publishing.
Schultz, Frederick William. The Book of Esther: An Exegetical & Doctrinal Commentary. Lange, John Peter & Schaff, Philip, eds. Strong, James, tr. 2007. (Lange's Commentary on the Holy Scripture: Ser.). 96p. pap. 18.00 *(978-1-55635-406-9(1)*, Wipf and Stock) Wipf & Stock Pubs.
—The Book of Ezra - The Book of Nehemiah: An Exegetical & Doctrinal Commentary. Briggs, Charles A., tr. 2007. (Lange's Commentary on the Holy Scripture: Ser.). 162p. pap. 18.00 *(978-1-55635-405-2(3)*, Wipf and Stock) Wipf & Stock Pubs.
Scott, W. A. Esther; 2006. 360p. per. 26.99 *(978-1-4255-3713-5(8))* MPublishing.

B

Selman, Martin J. 1 Chronicles. 2008. (Tyndale Old Testament Commentaries Ser.: Volume 10). (ENG.). 274p. pap. 16.00 *(978-0-8308-4210-0(1)*, IVP Acad.) InterVarsity Pr.
—2 Chronicles. 2008. (Tyndale Old Testament Commentaries Ser.: Volume 11). (ENG.). 292p. pap. 16.00 *(978-0-8308-4211-7(X)*, IVP Acad.) InterVarsity Pr.
Sparks, James T. The Chronicler's Genealogies: Towards an Understanding of 1 Chronicles, 1-9. 2008. (SBL - Academia Biblica Ser.). (Illus.). 402p. (C). *(978-90-04-15751-4(4))* BRILL.
—The Chronicler's Genealogies: Towards an Understanding of 1 Chronicles, 1-9. 2008. 404p. pap. 47.95 *(978-1-58983-365-4(1))* Society of Biblical Literature.
Stedman, Ray C. For Such a Time as This: Queen Esther's Secrets for Strategic Living. 2010. (ENG.). 160p. pap. 11.99 *(978-1-57293-378-1(X))* Discovery Hse. Pubs.
Steinmann, Andrew E. Ezra & Nehemiah. 2010. (Concordia Commentary Ser.). 42.99 *(978-0-7586-1596-1(5))* Concordia Publishing Hse.
Steveson, Peter A. Ezra, Nehemiah, & Esther. 2010. pap. *(978-1-60682-052-0(4))* BJU Pr.
Stith, D. Matthew. The Coups of Hazael & Jehu: Building an Historical Narrative. 2008. (Gorgias Dissertations in Biblical Studies: 3). 95.00 *(978-1-59333-833-6(3))* Gorgias Pr., LLC.
Storniolo, Ivo. Como Leer Los Libros De Los Reyes. 80p. 3.95 *(978-958-607-731-6(4))* Sociedad de San Pablo COL. Dist: St Pauls/Alba Hse. Pubs.
Sweeney, Marvin A. I & II Kings: A Commentary. 2007. (Old Testament Library). (ENG.). 476p. 50.00 *(978-0-664-22084-6(3))* Westminster John Knox Pr.
Talbert, Josh. The Book of Joshu. 2009. 116p. 21.49 *(978-1-4389-6796-7(9))*; pap. 10.99 *(978-1-4389-6679-3(2))* AuthorHouse.
Talbot, Dee Dee. Israel a Monarchy: Study Guide 2. 2007. (ENG.). 244p. per. 21.95 *(978-1-4303-1551-3(2))* Lulu Enterprises Inc.
—Prophets, Priests, & Kings: Study Guide 3. 2007. (ENG.). 220p. per. 21.94 *(978-1-4303-1553-7(9))* Lulu Enterprises Inc.
Tezeno, Timmy H. The Bible Trainer Series: Ruth & Philippians. 2008. pap. 11.00 *(978-0-8059-8590-0(5))* Dorrance Publishing Co., Inc.
Throntveit, Mark A. Ezra-Nehemiah: Interpretation: A Bible Commentary for Teaching & Preaching. 2012. (Interpretation: A Bible Commentary for Teaching & Preaching Ser.). (ENG.). 144p. pap. 25.00 ***(978-0-664-23864-3(5))*** Westminster John Knox Pr.
Towns, Elmer. Praying the Heart of David: Praying the Scriptures with Elmer Towns. 2009. (Praying the Scriptures with Elmer Towns Ser.). pap. 15.99 *(978-0-7684-3096-7(8))* Destiny Image Pubs.
Tsumura, David Toshio. The First Book of Samuel. 2007. (New International Commentary on the Old Testament Ser.). 698p. 50.00 *(978-0-8028-2359-5(9))* Eerdmans, William B. Publishing Co.
Tuell, Steven S. First & Second Chronicles: Interpretation: A Bible Commentary for Teaching & Preaching. 2012. (Interpretation: A Bible Commentary for Teaching & Preaching Ser.). (ENG.). 266p. pap. 25.00 ***(978-0-664-23865-0(3))*** Westminster John Knox Pr.
Van Wijk-Bos, Johanna W. H. Reading the Old Testament: Samuel. 2011. ***(978-1-57312-607-6(1))*** Smyth & Helwys Publishing, Inc.
Wahl, Harald-Martin. Das Buch Esther: Äcebersetzung und Kommentar. 2009.Tr. of Book of Esther. Translation & Commentary. (GER.). XII, 249p. 154.00 ***(978-3-11-173308-1(4))*** De Gruyter, Walter Inc.
Wahl, Harald Martin & Wahl, Harald-Martin. Das Buch Esther: Übersetzung und Kommentar. 2009.Tr. of Book of Esther. Translation & Commentary. (GER.). XII, 249p. 104.00 *(978-3-11-020504-6(1))* De Gruyter, Walter Inc.
Walton, John H., et al. Joshua, Judges, Ruth, 1 & 2 Samuel, 1 vol. 2009. (Zondervan Illustrated Bible Backgrounds Commentary Ser.). (ENG.). 624p. 49.99 *(978-0-310-25574-1(0))* Zondervan.
—1 & 2 Kings, 1 vol. 2009. (Zondervan Illustrated Bible Backgrounds Commentary Ser.). (ENG.). 560p. 49.99 *(978-0-310-25575-8(9))* Zondervan.
Wiersbe, Warren W. Be Available (Judges) Accepting the Challenge to Confront the Enemy. 2010. (ENG.). 208p. pap. 12.99 *(978-1-4347-0048-3(8))* Cook, David C.
—Be Determined (Nehemiah) Standing Firm in the Face of Opposition, 1 vol. 2009. (BE Ser. Commentary Ser.). (ENG.). 176p. pap. 12.99 *(978-1-4347-6745-5(0))* Cook, David C.
—Be Distinct (2 Kings & 2 Chronicles) Standing Firmly Against the World's Tides. 2010. (BE Series Commentary Ser.). (ENG.). 240p. pap. 12.99 *(978-1-4347-0051-3(8))* Cook, David C.
—Be Responsible (1 Kings) Being Good Stewards of God's Gifts. 2010. (BE Series Commentary Ser.). (ENG.). 240p. pap. 12.99 *(978-1-4347-0054-4(2))* Cook, David C.
—Be Restored: Trusting God to See Us Through. 2010. (BE Series Commentary Ser.). (ENG.). 240p. pap. 12.99 *(978-1-4347-0049-0(6))* Cook, David C.
—Be Strong (Joshua) Putting God's Power to Work in Your Life, 1 vol. 2010. (BE Series Commentary Ser.). (ENG.). 208p. pap. 12.99 *(978-1-4347-6637-3(3))* Cook, David C.
—Be Successful (1 Samuel) Attaining Wealth That Money Can't Buy, 1 vol. 2010. (BE Series Commentary Ser.). (ENG.). 224p. pap. 12.99 *(978-1-4347-6500-0(8))* Cook, David C.
Wiesemann, Falk. The Book of Esther: The Esther Scroll. 2011. ***(978-3-8365-1778-2(7))*** TASCHEN.
Wilch, John R. Ruth. 2006. (Concordia Commentary Ser.). (ENG., Illus.). 418p. 42.99 *(978-0-570-06388-9(4))* Concordia Publishing Hse.
Wiseman, Donald J. 1 & 2 Kings. 2008. (Tyndale Old Testament Commentaries Ser.: Volume 9). (ENG., Illus.). 339p. pap. 16.00 *(978-0-8308-4209-4(8))*, IVP Acad.) InterVarsity Pr.
Woodhouse, John. 1 Samuel: Looking for a Leader. 2008. (Preaching the Word Ser.). 672p. 34.99 *(978-1-58134-873-6(8))* Crossway.
Zockler, Otto. The Books of the Chronicles: An Exegetical & Doctrinal Commentary. Murphy, James G., ed. & tr. by. 2007. (Lange's Commentary on the Holy Scripture: Ser.). 278p. pap. 28.00 *(978-1-55635-404-5(5)*, Wipf and Stock) Wipf & Stock Pubs.

BIBLE—COMMENTARIES—O. T. HOSEA
see Bible—Commentaries—O. T. Minor Prophets

BIBLE—COMMENTARIES—O. T. ISAIAH
see Bible—Commentaries—O. T. Prophets

BIBLE—COMMENTARIES—O. T. JEREMIAH
see Bible—Commentaries—O. T. Prophets

BIBLE—COMMENTARIES—O. T. JOB
see Bible—Commentaries—O. T. Poetical Books

BIBLE—COMMENTARIES—O. T. JOEL
see Bible—Commentaries—O. T. Minor Prophets

BIBLE—COMMENTARIES—O. T. JONAH
see Bible—Commentaries—O. T. Minor Prophets

BIBLE—COMMENTARIES—O. T. JOSHUA
see Bible—Commentaries—O. T. Historical Books

BIBLE—COMMENTARIES—O. T. JUDGES
see Bible—Commentaries—O. T. Historical Books

BIBLE—COMMENTARIES—O. T. KINGS
see Bible—Commentaries—O. T. Historical Books

BIBLE—COMMENTARIES—O. T. LAMENTATIONS
see Bible—Commentaries—O. T. Prophets

BIBLE—COMMENTARIES—O. T. LEVITICUS
see Bible—Commentaries—O. T. Pentateuch

BIBLE—COMMENTARIES—O. T. MALACHI
see Bible—Commentaries—O. T. Minor Prophets

BIBLE—COMMENTARIES—O. T. MICAH
see Bible—Commentaries—O. T. Minor Prophets

BIBLE—COMMENTARIES—O. T. MINOR PROPHETS

Alban. Minor Prophets, Vol. 10. 25.00 *(978-0-8028-8044-4(4))* Eerdmans, William B. Publishing Co.
Alexander, T. Desmond, et al. Obadiah, Jonah & Micah. 2009. (Tyndale Old Testament Commentaries Ser.: Volume 26). (ENG.). 226p. pap. 16.00 *(978-0-8308-4226-1(8)*, IVP Acad.) InterVarsity Pr.
Andersen, Francis I. & Freedman, David Noel. Micah. 2006. (Anchor Yale Bible Commentaries Ser.). (ENG.). 664p. pap. 50.00 *(978-0-300-13972-3(1))* Yale Univ. Pr.
Arthur, Kay & de Lacy, Pete. Finding Hope When Life Seems Dark: Hosea/Micah/Nahum/Habakkuk/Zephaniah. 2006. (New Inductive Study Ser.). (Illus.). 108p. per. 8.99 *(978-0-7369-1825-1(6))* Harvest Hse. Pubs.
Baker, David W. Nahum, Habakkuk, & Zephaniah: An Introduction & Commentary. 2009. 120p. pap. *(978-1-84474-361-2(6)*, IVP Acad.) InterVarsity Pr.
Banger, Dene. The Spirit of Prophecy. 2009. 642p. pap. 23.99 *(978-1-4415-3012-7(6))* Xlibris Corp.
Barnwell, Katharine. Translator's Notes on Malachi. 2007. (Translator's Notes Ser.). 128p. spiral bd. 16.00 *(978-1-55671-172-5(7))* SIL International.
Belchen, Richard P. Teaching Helps in Malachi. 38p. pap. 6.95 *(978-0-925703-63-7(X))* Crown Pubns., Inc.
Birnbaum, Philip & Hal-Lewi, Yafet Ben Ali. The Arabic Commentary of Yefet Ben Ali the Karaite, on the Book of Hose. 2011. 316p. 50.95 ***(978-1-258-04233-2(9))*** Literary Licensing, LLC.
Christensen, Duane L. Nahum: A New Translation with Introduction & Commentary. 2009. (Anchor Yale Bible Commentaries Ser.). (Illus.). 464p. 65.00 *(978-0-300-14479-6(2))* Yale Univ. Pr.
Christian Art Gifts, creator. Habakkuk 3:18. 2008. 400p. *(978-1-77036-015-0(8))* Christian Art Pubs.
Crafer, T. W. The Books of Haggai & Zechariah. 2011. (ENG.). 134p. pap. 19.99 *(978-0-521-27943-7(7))* Cambridge Univ. Pr.
Davis, Tom. Zechariah: God Remembers the Plight of His People. 124p. pap. 9.95 *(978-1-931235-56-3(2))* Word of Life Fellowship, Inc.
Dearman, J. Andrew. The Book of Hosea. 2010. 45.00 *(978-0-8028-2539-1(7))* Eerdmans, William B. Publishing Co.
Discover Jonah. (Discover Your Bible Ser.). (KOR.). pap., tchr. ed. 3.95 *(978-1-55883-163-6(0)*, 600115); pap., stu. ed. 2.75 *(978-1-55883-162-9(2)*, 600110) C R C World Literature Ministries/Libros Desafio.
East, Sun Hui. Under God, Part One. 2006. 200p. per. 16.99 *(978-1-934388-12-9(2))* First Love Pr., Inc.
—Under God, Part Three. 2006. 200p. per. 16.99 *(978-1-934388-14-3(9))* First Love Pr., Inc.
—Under God, Part Two. 2006. 200p. per. 16.99 *(978-1-934388-13-6(0))* First Love Pr., Inc.
Eaton, Michael. Joel & Amos. (Preaching Through the Bible Ser.). 125p. pap. *(978-1-85240-243-3(1))* Sovereign World, Ltd.
Edelman, Diana. The Origins of the 'Second' Temple: Persian Imperial Policy & the Rebuilding of Jerusalem. rev. ed. 2010. (BibleWorld Ser.). (ENG., Illus.). 458p. (C). per. 39.95 *(978-1-84553-017-4(9))* Equinox Publishing Ltd. GBR. Dist: ISD.
Field, David. Obadiah: A Practical Commentary. 2008. (Exploring the Bible Ser.). (Illus.). 128p. pap. *(978-1-84625-146-7(X))* DayOne Pubns.
Finitsis, Antonios. Visions & Eschatology: A Socio-Historical Analysis of Zechariah 1-6. 2011. (Library of Second Temple Studies). 208p. 110.00 *(978-0-567-43098-4(7)*, T&T Clark Int'l) Continuum International Publishing Group, Ltd. GBR. Dist: National Bk. Network.
Fuller, Thomas. A Comment on Ruth: And Notes upon Jonah. Nichols, William, ed. 2008. 219p. pap. 19.00 *(978-1-60608-032-0(6))* Wipf & Stock Pubs.
Fyall, Robert. The Message of Ezra & Haggai. 2010. (Bible Speaks Today Ser.). (ENG.). 190p. pap. 16.00 *(978-0-8308-2432-8(4)*, IVP Acad.) InterVarsity Pr.
Goldingay, John & Scalise, Pamela J. Minor Prophets II. 2009. xiv, 392p. *(978-1-56563-228-8(1))*; *(978-1-84227-665-5(4))* Hendrickson Pubs. Marketing, LLC.
Gregory, Bryan R. Longing for God in an Age of Discouragement: The Gospel According to Zechariah. 2010. pap. *(978-1-59638-142-1(6))* P & R Publishing.
Greig, Doris W. Jonah. 2007. (ENG.). 40p. spiral bd. 8.49 *(978-1-932017-39-7(9))* Joy of Living Bible Studies.
Groseclose, Win. Faith in the Presence of Judgment: Reflections on the Laments & Song of Habakkuk. 2010. 116p. pap. 10.00 *(978-0-557-61045-7(1))* Lulu Enterprises Inc.
Hubbard, David Allan. Hosea, 1 vol. 2009. (Tyndale Old Testament Commentaries Ser.: Volume 24). (ENG.). 246p. pap. 16.00 *(978-0-8308-4224-7(1)*, IVP Acad.) InterVarsity Pr.
Jenson, Philip Peter & Jenson. Obadiah, Jonah, Micah: A Theological Commentary. 2008. (Library of Hebrew Bible/Old Testament Studies, the Ser.). (ENG.). 240p. 140.00 *(978-0-567-04222-4(7)*, T&T Clark Int'l) Continuum International Publishing Group, Ltd. GBR. Dist: National Bk. Network.
Kimchi, David B. Commentary of Rabbi David Kimchi on Hosea. Cohen, Harry, ed. (Columbia University, Oriental Studies: No. 20). reprint ed. 29.50 *(978-0-404-50510-3(4))* AMS Pr., Inc.
Klein, George L. Zechariah. Clendenen, Ray, ed. 2008. (New American Commentary Ser.: Vol. 21B). (Illus.). 464p. 29.99 *(978-0-8054-9494-5(4)*, Holman Reference) B&H Publishing Group.
Lamb, Jonathan. From Why to Worship: A Journey Through the Prophecy of Habakkuk. 2007. (ENG.). 144p. per. 14.99 *(978-1-85078-747-1(6))* Authentic Media.
Landy, Francis. Hosea. 2011. 230p. ***(978-1-905048-98-4(X))***; pap. ***(978-1-905048-99-1(8))*** Sheffield Phoenix Pr.
Lessing, R. Reed. Amos. 2009. (Concordia Commentary Ser.). 42.99 *(978-0-7586-1269-4(9))* Concordia Publishing Hse.
—Jonah. 2007. (Concordia Commentary Ser.). (Illus.). 451p. 42.99 *(978-0-7586-0273-2(1))* Concordia Publishing Hse.
Levy, David M. The Ruin & Restoration of Israel: A Study of Hosea, Amos, & Micah. 2008. (Illus.). 222p. pap. 10.95 *(978-0-915540-02-0(9))* Friends of Israel Gospel Ministry, Inc., The.
Limburg, James. Hosea — Micah: Interpretation: A Bible Commentary for Teaching & Preaching. 2011. (Interpretation Ser.). (ENG.). 320p. pap. 25.00 *(978-0-664-23610-6(3))* Westminster John Knox Pr.
Logsdon, S. Franklin. Malachi, or Will a Man Rob God? 2011. 130p. 40.95 ***(978-1-258-08428-8(7))*** Literary Licensing, LLC.
MacKay, J. L. Jonah, Micah & Nahum. (Focus on the Bible Commentaries Ser.). (Illus.). 207p. 11.99 *(978-1-85792-030-7(9))* Christian Focus Pubns. GBR. Dist: Spring Arbor Distributors, Inc.
MacKay, John L. Jonah, Micah, Nahum, Habakkuk, & Zephaniah: God's Just Demands. 2008. (Focus on the Bible Ser.). (ENG., Illus.). 420p. pap. 14.99 *(978-1-84550-345-1(7))* Christian Focus Pubns. GBR. Dist: STL Distribution North America.
Mackrell, Paul. Opening up Jonah. 2007. (Opening up the Bible Ser.). 112p. 9.00 *(978-1-84625-080-4(3))* DayOne Pubns. GBR. Dist: STL Distribution North America.
Mays, James Luther. Micah: A Commentary. 2007. (Old Testament Library). (ENG.). 180p. per. 30.00 *(978-0-664-23233-7(7))* Westminster John Knox Pr.
McComiskey, Thomas Edward, ed. The Minor Prophets: An Exegetical & Expository Commentary. 2009. 1456p. (C). 69.99 *(978-0-8010-3631-6(3))* Baker Academic.
Meadowcroft, Tim. Haggai. 2006. 276p. *(978-1-905048-59-5(9))*; per. *(978-1-905048-60-1(2))* Sheffield Phoenix Pr.
Miley, Dinah M. Worship Inspired from the Book of Malachi. 2008. 68p. pap. 9.99 *(978-1-60647-458-7(8))* Xulon Pr., Inc.
Minor Prophets. ldr.'s ed. (LifeLight Bible Studies: Course 19). 8.99 *(978-0-570-09425-8(9)*, 20-2545) Concordia Publishing Hse.
Morgan, G. Campbell. Profetas Menores: Minor Prophets. (SPA.). 112p. *(978-84-7228-837-9(4)*, 220726) Clie, Editorial.
Neusner, Jacob. Zephaniah, Haggai, Zechariah, & Malachi in Talmud & Midrash: A Source Book. 2007. (Studies in Judaism Ser.). (ENG.). 336p. per. 45.50 *(978-0-7618-3698-8(5))* Univ. Pr. of America, Inc.
Nogalski, James. The Book of the Twelve: Micah — Malachi. 2011. ***(978-1-57312-598-7(9))*** Smyth & Helwys Publishing, Inc.
—Hosea — Jonah. 2011. ***(978-1-57312-075-3(8))*** Smyth & Helwys Publishing, Inc.
Norden, Rudolph F. God's Answers to Modern Problems: A Study of Habakkuk. pap. 3.99 *(978-0-570-09311-4(2)*, 20-1087) Concordia Publishing Hse.
Patterson, Richard D. Hosea - an Exegetical Commentary. 2008. 160p. pap. 19.95 *(978-0-7375-0152-0(9))* Biblical Studies Pr.
Phillips, Richard D. Jonah & Micah. 2010. xiv, 381p. *(978-1-59638-114-8(0))* P & R Publishing.
—Zechariah. 2007. (Reformed Expository Commentary Ser.). 351p. 29.99 *(978-1-59638-028-8(4))* P & R Publishing.
Pusey, Edward B. The Minor Prophets. 2007. 508p. pap. 24.95 *(978-1-60206-636-6(1))* Cosimo, Inc.
Shenton, Tim. Exploring Haggai: An expositional Commentary. 2007. (Exploring the Bible Ser.). 8.00 *(978-1-84625-086-6(2))* DayOne Pubns. GBR. Dist: STL Distribution North America.
—Exploring Nahum & Obadiah: An expositional Commentary. 2007. (Exploring the Bible Ser.). 11.00 *(978-1-84625-087-3(0))* DayOne Pubns. GBR. Dist: STL Distribution North America.
Silva, Kittim. Predicando Sobre el Libro de Jonas: Preaching on the Book of Jonah. (SPA.). *(978-84-7645-411-4(2)*, 223478) Clie, Editorial.
Simpson, William. The Jonah Legend: A Suggestion of Interpretation. 2009. 204p. 22.99 *(978-1-103-69074-9(4))*; pap. 16.99 *(978-1-103-69070-1(1))* BiblioBazaar.
Smith, Dudley. The Expository Commentary: Hosea - Jonah. 2010. 126p. pap. 19.95 *(978-0-557-29282-0(4))* Lulu Enterprises Inc.
Smith, George Adam. The Book of Twelve Prophets v1: Commonly. 2006. pap. 37.95 *(978-1-4286-4827-2(5))* Kessinger Publishing, LLC.
Smith, James E. Postexilic Prophets. 2007. 356p. pap. 19.95 *(978-1-4357-0127-4(5))* Lulu Enterprises Inc.
Stephan, David G. Which, of the 31 Zechariahs, Is Which? A Way to Easily Identify Each of the 1443 Bible Characters Who Share Their Name with Others. 2006. (ENG.). 164p. per. 19.99 *(978-1-4141-0529-1(0))* Pleasant Word.
Tassell Jr., Ray Van. The Milk of His Word. 2009. 228p. pap. 15.99 *(978-1-60791-401-3(8))* Xulon Pr., Inc.
The Prophet Elijah. The Sixty-Seventh Book of the Holy Bible by Elijah the Prophet as God Promised from the Book of Malachi. 2010. 548p. 41.95 *(978-1-4502-4342-1(8))*; pap. 31.95 *(978-1-4502-4341-4(X))* iUniverse, Inc.
THE WILDS Christian Association. Jonah. 2009. (ENG.). 96p. (J). 5.95 net. *(978-0-9815235-3-6(0))* WILDS Christian Assn., Inc., The.
Theodoret. Commentary on the Twelve Prophets. 2006. pap. *(978-1-885652-76-8(3))* Holy Cross Orthodox Pr.
Timmer, Daniel C. A Gracious & Compassionate God: Mission, Salvation & Spirituality in the Book of Jonah. 2011. 201p. *(978-1-84474-499-2(X)*, Apollos) Inter-Varsity Pr.
—A Gracious & Compassionate God: Mission, Salvation & Spirituality in the Book of Jonah. 2011. (New Studies in Biblical Theology Ser.: Volume 26). (ENG.). 201p. pap. 22.00 *(978-0-8308-2627-8(0)*, IVP Acad.) InterVarsity Pr.
Tucker, W. Dennis & Tucker, W. Dennis, Jr. Jonah: A Handbook on the Hebrew Text. 2006. (Baylor Handbook on the Hebrew Bible Ser.). (ENG & HEB.). 175p. per. 24.95 *(978-1-932792-66-9(X))* Baylor Univ. Pr.
Waggoner, Jarl K. Prophets for Our Time: An Exposition of Obadiah & Jonah. 2009. 124p. pap. 15.00 *(978-1-60608-957-6(9))* Wipf & Stock Pubs.
Waltke, Bruce K. A Commentary on Micah. 2008. 480p. pap. 28.00 *(978-0-8028-6412-3(0))* 2007. 490p. 32.00 *(978-0-8028-4933-5(4))* Eerdmans, William B. Publishing Co.
Westerink, Jaap. Obadiah & Micah: The Prophets of God's Faithfulness. Kranendonk, David & Kranendonk, Elly, trs. from DUT. 2008.Tr. of Obadja en Micha: Profeten van de trouw van God. 134p. per. 10.00 *(978-1-60178-038-6(9))* Reformation Heritage Bks.
Wiersbe, Warren W. Be Amazed (Minor Prophets) Restoring an Attitude of Wonder & Worship, 1 vol. 2010. (BE Series Commentary Ser.). (ENG.). 224p. pap. 12.99 *(978-1-4347-6505-5(9))* Cook, David C.
—Be Concerned (Minor Prophets) Making a Difference in Your Lifetime. 2010. (BE Series Commentary Ser.). (ENG.). 192p. pap. 12.99 *(978-0-7814-0337-5(5))* Cook, David C.
—Be Heroic (Minor Prophets) Demonstrating Bravery by Your Walk. 2010. (ENG.). 208p. pap. 12.99 *(978-0-7814-0335-1(9))* Cook, David C.
Williams, Peter. Haggai. 2008. (Opening Up Ser.). (Illus.). 80p. pap. *(978-1-84625-144-3(3))* DayOne Pubns.

BIBLE—COMMENTARIES—O. T. NAHUM
see Bible—Commentaries—O. T. Minor Prophets

BIBLE—COMMENTARIES—O. T. NEHEMIAH
see Bible—Commentaries—O. T. Historical Books

BIBLE—COMMENTARIES—O. T. NUMBERS
see Bible—Commentaries—O. T. Pentateuch

BIBLE—COMMENTARIES—O. T. OBADIAH
see Bible—Commentaries—O. T. Minor Prophets

BIBLE—COMMENTARIES—O. T. PENTATEUCH

A. W. Pink. Gleanings in Genesis. 2011. 412p. pap. 8.89 ***(978-1-60386-421-3(0)***, Watchmaker Publishing) Wexford College Pr.
Abarbenel, Don I. Abarbenel Al Hatorah, 3 Vols, Set. (HEB.). 45.00 *(978-0-87559-078-3(0))* Shalom, P. Pubns., Inc.
Abingdon. Amazing Bible Race Director's Manual, Leg 1: Genesis-Deuteronomy. 2007. 16p. 30.00 *(978-0-687-46520-0(6))* Abingdon Pr.
Adelman, Rachel. The Return of the Repressed: Pirqe De-Rabbi Eliezer & the Pseudepigrapha. 2009. 368p. *(978-90-04-17049-0(9))* BRILL.
Aiken, Lisa & Michaels, Ira. Genesis: A Refreshing Look at Our Owner's Manual: the Untold Story. Lane, Rebecca, ed. 2007. 265p. *(978-0-9779629-1-4(1))* Rossi Pubns.

Alford, Henry. The Book of Genesis & Part of the Book of Exodus: A Revised Version with Marginal References & an Explanatory Commentary. 2008. 340p. pap. 29.00 *(978-1-60608-033-7(4))* Wipf & Stock Pubs.

Almond, Philip C. Adam & Eve in Seventeenth-Century Thought. 2008. (ENG.). 252p. pap. 36.00 *(978-0-521-09084-1(9))* Cambridge Univ. Pr.

Alter, Robert. Moses: A Translation with Commentary, 5 bks. 2008. (ENG.). 1120p. pap. 29.95 *(978-0-393-33393-0(0)*, 33393) Norton, W. W. & Co., Inc.

Anonimo. Biblia de Bosquejos y Sermones: Genesis 12-50, 1 vol. 2007. (Biblia/Bosque/Serm Ser.). (SPA.). 472p. pap. 27.99 *(978-0-8254-0726-0(5)*, Editorial Portavoz) Kregel Pubns.

Arnold, Bill & Arnold, Bill T. Genesis. 2008. (New Cambridge Bible Commentary Ser.). (ENG.). 432p. (C). pap. 27.99 *(978-0-521-00067-3(X))* Cambridge Univ. Pr.

Artson, Bradley Shavit. The Everyday Torah: Weekly Reflections & Inspirations. 2008. (ENG.). 384p. pap. 18.95 *(978-0-07-154619-5(7)*, 0071546197) McGraw-Hill Cos., The.

Avital, Moshe. Hamesha Me Yodayah. 2007. (HEB.). 212p. per. 18.00 *(978-965-7344-36-1(0))* Mazo Pubs.

Bailey, Randall C. The College Press NIV Commentary: Exodus. 2007. *(978-0-89900-877-6(1))* College Pr. Publishing Co., Inc.

Baker, David W., et al. Leviticus, Numbers, Deuteronomy. 2008. (Cornerstone Biblical Commentary Ser.: 2). (ENG.). 696p. 36.99 *(978-0-8423-3428-0(9))* Tyndale Hse. Pubs.

Baker Publishing Group Staff. A Walk Thru the Life of Abraham: Faith in God's Promises, 1 vol. 2010. (Walk Thru the Bible Discussion Guides). (ENG.). 96p. pap. 7.99 *(978-0-8010-7178-2(X))* Baker Bks.

Barhebraeus, Gregory Abulfaraj & Kerber, George. A Commentary to Deuteronomy. 2010. (SYR.). pap. 19.60 *(978-1-61143-503-0(X))* Gorgias Pr., LLC.

Barnwell, Katharine & Kuhn, Hanni. Translator's Notes on Genesis 1-11. 2007. 248p. spiral bd. 22.00 *(978-1-55671-173-2(5))* SIL International.

Barton, John & Muddiman, John. The Pentateuch. 2010. (ENG., Illus.). 280p. pap. 24.95 *(978-0-19-958024-8(3))* Oxford Univ. Pr., Inc.

Berg, Philip S. & Berg, Michael. The Sacred Zohar: The Secrets of the Bible: The Complete Original Aramaic Text. 2007. (HEB & ARC.). xxv, 1800p. *(978-1-57189-554-7(X))* Research Centre of Kabbalah.

Berg, Yehuda. Deuteronomy. 2010. (Kabbalistic Bible Ser.). (ENG.). 360p. 24.95 *(978-1-57189-627-8(9))* Research Centre of Kabbalah.

Berg, Yehuda, ed. The Kabbalistic Bible - Exodus: Technology for the Soul. 2009. (Kabbalistic Bible Ser.). (ENG & HEB.). 352p. 24.95 *(978-1-57189-614-8(7))* Research Centre of Kabbalah.

—Numbers. 2010. (Kabbalistic Bible Ser.). (ENG.). 392p. 24.95 *(978-1-57189-626-1(0))* Research Centre of Kabbalah.

Berrigan, Daniel. Exodus: Let My People Go. 2007. 182p. pap. 20.00 *(978-1-55635-105-1(4))* Wipf & Stock Pubs.

—No Gods but One. 2009. 192p. pap. 15.00 *(978-0-8028-6462-8(7))* Eerdmans, William B. Publishing Co.

Bigman, David. The Fire & the Cloud-Contemporary Reflections on the Weekly Torah Readingt. 2011. 176p. *(978-965-229-489-0(6))* Gefen Publishing Hse., Ltd.

Blake, William, et al. Genesis: William Blake's Last Illuminated Work. 2012. (ENG., Illus.). 100p. 80.00 ***(978-0-87328-247-5(7))*** Huntington Library Pr.

Blenkinsopp, Joseph. Creation, Un-Creation, Re-Creation: A Discursive Commentary on Genesis 1-11. 2011. (ENG.). 232p. 100.00 *(978-0-567-59101-2(8))*; pap. 29.95 *(978-0-567-37287-1(1))* Continuum International Publishing Group, Ltd. GBR. (T&T Clark Int'l). Dist: National Bk. Network.

Block, Daniel I. Deuteronomy, 1 vol. 2012. (NIV Application Commentary Ser.). (ENG.). 880p. 39.99 ***(978-0-310-21048-1(8))*** Zondervan.

Bobosh, Ted. Questioning God: A Look at Genesis 1-3. 2007. (ENG.). 210p. pap. 17.95 *(978-1-933654-11-9(2))* Light & Life Publishing Co.

Boehme, Jacob. Of the Creation of the Fifth Day. 2006. pap. 9.95 *(978-1-4286-7340-3(7))* Kessinger Publishing, LLC

Bonar, Horatius. Earth's Morning. 2006. 388p. per. 26.99 *(978-1-4255-4142-2(9))* MPublishing.

Bonchek, Avigdor. What's Bothering Rashi?, 5 vols. 107.99 *(978-1-58330-631-4(5))* Feldheim Pubs.

—What's Bothering Rashi? 1: Bereishis, 5 vols. (HEB & ENG., Illus.). 144p. 17.99 *(978-0-87306-849-9(1))* Feldheim Pubs.

—What's Bothering Rashi? 2: Shemos, 5 vols. (HEB & ENG., Illus.). 210p. 19.99 *(978-0-87306-906-9(4))* Feldheim Pubs.

—What's Bothering Rashi? 3: Vayikra, 5 vols. (HEB & ENG., Illus.). 198p. 20.99 *(978-1-58330-400-6(2))* Feldheim Pubs.

—What's Bothering Rashi? 5: Devarim, 5 vols. (HEB & ENG., Illus.). 252p. 23.99 *(978-1-58330-564-5(5))* Feldheim Pubs.

—What's Bothering Rashi? 6: Megillas Esther. 24.99 *(978-1-58330-735-9(4))* Feldheim Pubs.

Bosman, Leonard. The Book of Genesis Unveiled. 2007. (ENG.). 142p. 35.95 *(978-0-548-00560-6(5))* Kessinger Publishing, LLC.

Bowker, John. The Targums & Rabbinic Literature: An Introduction to Jewish Interpretations of Scripture. 2009. (ENG.). 408p. pap. 51.00 *(978-0-521-09771-0(1))* Cambridge Univ. Pr.

Boyce, Richard Nelson. Leviticus & Numbers. 2008. (Westminster Bible Companion Ser.). (ENG.). 282p. pap. 25.00 *(978-0-664-25525-1(6))* Westminster John Knox Pr.

Bradshaw, Jeffrey M. In the Beginning: Moses 1-6: 12 A Companion to JST Genisis. 2007. *(978-1-58958-100-5(8))* Kofford, Greg Books, Inc.

Brannock, Gary. The Final Blasphemy to the Face of an Angry God. 2011. 104p. 24.99 ***(978-1-4628-7831-4(8))***; pap. 15.99 ***(978-1-4628-7830-7(X))*** Xlibris Corp.

Brayford, Susan. Genesis. 2007. (Septuagint Commentary Ser.). 468p. lib. bdg. *(978-90-04-15552-7(X))* BRILL.

Brenner, Athalya. Genesis: Texts @ Contexts. Lee, Archie Chi Chung, ed. 2010. 368p. (C). 40.00 *(978-0-8006-5999-8(6)*, Fortress Pr.) Augsburg Fortress, Pubs.

Brinson Mdiv, John D. The Black Presence in the Biblical Exodus: The Exodus Revisited. 2008. 160p. per. 18.95 *(978-1-4327-2087-2(2))* Outskirts Pr., Inc.

Bruckner, James K. Exodus. 2008. (New International Biblical Commentary Ser.). 348p. per. *(978-1-56563-212-7(5))* Hendrickson Pubs. Marketing, LLC.

Brueggemann, Walter. Genesis. 2010. (Interpretation: A Bible Commentary Ser.). (ENG.). 400p. pap. 30.00 *(978-0-664-23437-9(2))* Westminster John Knox Pr.

Brumbaugh, Judith A. Answers to Questions - Deuteronomy 24:4; Jeremiah 3:1; Matthew 5:32 & 19:9: Returning to an Original Mate; Marriage to an Unsaved Mate Followed by a Subsequent Marriage to a Christian; The "Exception Clause" rev. ed. 18p. pap. *(978-0-9624603-4-0(6))* Committee for the Restoration of the Family.

Bush, Charles Peck. The Fugitive Slave Law: A sermon preached in the Fourth Congregational church, Norwich, Conn. , June 25th, 1854. by Rev. Charles P. Bush, pastor. Publi. 2011. 20p. pap. 11.99 ***(978-1-4181-9070-5(5))*** MPublishing.

Bush, George H. W. Notes, Critical & Practical, on the Book of Exodus. 2006. 304p. per. 23.99 *(978-1-4255-2874-4(0))*; per. 23.99 *(978-1-4255-2875-1(9))* MPublishing.

—Notes, Critical & Practical, on the Book of Exodus: Designed As A General Help to Biblical Reading & instruction. Vol. Ii by George Bush ... 2006. 304p. per. 23.99 *(978-1-4255-2876-8(7))* MPublishing.

—Notes, Critical & Practical, on the Book of Genesis; Designed As a General Help to Biblical Reading & Instruction. 2006. 380p. per. 26.99 *(978-1-4255-4010-4(4))*; 448p. per. 29.99 *(978-1-4255-5008-0(8))*; 448p. per. 26.99 *(978-1-4255-4948-0(9))*; 380p. per. 26.99 *(978-1-4255-4011-1(2))* MPublishing.

—Notes, Critical & Practical, on the Book of Leviticus: Designed As A General Help to Biblical Reading & instruction. by George Bush ... 2006. 292p. per. 23.99 *(978-1-4255-2716-7(7))*; 284p. per. 23.99 *(978-1-4255-2596-5(2))* MPublishing.

—Notes, Critical & Practical, on the Book of Numbers. 2006. 480p. per. 29.99 *(978-1-4255-5325-8(7))* MPublishing.

—Notes, Critical & Practical, on the Book of Numbers: Designed As A General Help to Biblical Reading & instruction by George Bush ... 2006. 480p. per. 29.99 *(978-1-4255-5329-6(X))* MPublishing.

Caduto, Michael J. Abraham's Bind & Other Bible Tales of Trickery, Folly, Mercy & Love. 2006. 208p. 19.99 *(978-1-59473-186-0(1))* SkyLight Paths Publishing.

Camus, Jean-Christopher & Dufranne, Michel, adapted by. The Bible: The Old Testament: Genesis Part One. 2010. (Illus.). *(978-1-935351-20-7(6))* Heavy Metal Magazine.

Carasik, Michael. The Commentators' Bible: Numbers. 2011. (Commentators' Bible Ser.). (ENG & HEB.). 360p. 75.00 *(978-0-8276-0921-1(3))* Jewish Pubn. Society.

Carasik, Michael, tr. & anno. The Commentators' Bible: Leviticus. 2009. (Commentators' Bible Ser.). (HEB & ENG.). 270p. 75.00 *(978-0-8276-0897-9(7))* Jewish Pubn. Society.

Carmichael, Calum. The Book of Numbers: A Critique of Genesis. 2012. (ENG.). 216p. 55.00 ***(978-0-300-17918-7(9))*** Yale Univ. Pr.

Carroll, B. H. Coment, Carroll-Dos: Exodo-Levitico: Carroll's Comment-2: Exodus - Leviticus. (SPA.). *(978-84-7645-111-3(3)*, 223164) Clie, Editorial.

—Coment, Carroll-Uno: Genesis: Carroll's Comment-1: Genesis. (SPA.). 480p. *(978-84-7645-110-6(5)*, 223163) Clie, Editorial.

—Comentario Carroll-Tres: Numeros-Ruth: Carroll's Commentary 3: Numbers - Ruth. (SPA.). *(978-84-7645-132-8(6)*, 223178) Clie, Editorial.

Charlesworth, James H. The Good & Evil Serpent: How a Universal Symbol Became Christianized. 2010. (Anchor Yale Bible Reference Library). (Illus.). 744p. 45.00 *(978-0-300-14082-8(7))* Yale Univ. Pr.

Chastain, James G. Breve Estudio Sobre el Pentateuco: Lectures on the Pentateuch. (SPA.). *(978-84-7645-062-8(1)*, 223120) Clie, Editorial.

Choi, Kyoungwon. An Analysis of Subject-Before-Finite-Verb Clauses: An Analysis of Subject-Before-Finite-Verb Clauses in the Book of Genesis Based on Traditional Grammarians. 2008. 136p. pap. *(978-3-639-10031-0(X))* VDM Verlag Dr. Mueller e.K.

Churchville, John Elliott. Leadership Lessons from Genesis. 2010. pap. 20.95 *(978-0-7414-5908-4(6))* Infinity Publishing.

Classical Jewish Commentaries. Torah: The Five Books of Moses. 2007. 568p. per. *(978-956-291-488-8(7))* Editorial Benei Noaj.

Cole, R. Alan. Exodus. 2008. (Tyndale Old Testament Commentaries Ser.: Volume 2). (ENG.). 249p. pap. 16.00 *(978-0-8308-4202-5(0)*, IVP Acad.) InterVarsity Pr.

Collier, M. W. The Good Book: Chapter 1 Book 1 Genesis 1-50. 2011. 194p. 29.99 ***(978-1-4628-8845-0(3))***; pap. 19.99 ***(978-1-4628-8844-3(5))*** Xlibris Corp.

Collins, C. John. Did Adam & Eve Really Exist? Who They Were & Why You Should Care. 2011. *(978-1-4335-2426-4(0))* Crossway.

Collins, Nancy J. Genesis. 2006. (ENG.). 225p. spiral bd. 37.99 *(978-1-932017-30-4(5))* Joy of Living Bible Studies.

Cook, Joan E. Genesis. 2010. 6.95 *(978-0-8146-2836-2(2))* Liturgical Pr.

Cousens, Gabriel. Torah as a Guide to Enlightenment. 2011. (ENG.). 692p. 72.00 *(978-1-58394-249-9(1))* North Atlantic Bks.

Crowther, Duane S. They Walked with God: Intimate Biographies of Patriarchs from the Book of Genesis. 2009. pap. 17.99 *(978-0-88290-968-4(1))* Cedar Fort, Inc./CFI Distribution.

Currid, John D. Numbers. 2009. (Ep Study Commentary Ser.). (Illus.). 479p. *(978-0-85234-705-8(7))* Evangelical Pr.

Cyril Of Alexandria. Commentary on the Book of Exodus: First Discourse. Zachariades-Holmberg, Evie, ed. 2010. 124p. pap. 14.95 *(978-1-933275-47-5(2)*, Orthodox Research Institute) Cocheco Falls Publishing.

Daley, Robert. Genesis: Chapter 1 - Chapter 11: A Clear Understanding. 2007. (Illus.). 118p. pap. 25.00 *(978-0-9800839-3-4(1))* Daley, Robert.

Davies, Philip R., et al. The Books of Moses: Opening the Books. 2012. (Books of Moses Ser.). (ENG., Illus.). 192p. (C). 95.00 *(978-1-84553-684-8(3))* Equinox Publishing Ltd. GBR. Dist: Brown, David Bk. Co., The.

—Opening the Books of Moses. 2012. (Books of Moses Ser.). (ENG., Illus.). 192p. (C). pap. 30.00 *(978-1-84553-685-5(1))* Equinox Publishing Ltd. GBR. Dist: Brown, David Bk. Co., The.

De La Torre, Miguel A. Genesis: Belief: A Theological Commentary on the Bible. 2011. (Belief Ser.). (ENG.). 272p. 35.00 *(978-0-664-23252-8(3))* Westminster John Knox Pr.

Dennis, Alan. Looking God in the Eye. 128p. 12.00 *(978-0-281-05003-1(1))* SPCK Publishing GBR. Dist: Pilgrim Pr., The/United Church Pr.

Deuteronomy. 2009. 74p. pap. *(978-0-217-82620-4(2))* Books LLC.

Deuteronomy. (People's Bible Commentary Ser.). 360p. 15.99 *(978-0-7586-0419-4(X))* Concordia Publishing Hse.

Dickson, Edward L. Genesis. 2008. 408p. pap. 22.99 *(978-1-60647-354-2(9))* Xulon Pr., Inc.

Dillmann, August. Die Genesis Erklärt. 2007. (Gorgias Occasional Historical Commentaries Ser.: 1). (GER.). 96.00 *(978-1-59333-676-9(4))* Gorgias Pr., LLC.

Discover Exodus 1-15: Out of Oppression. (Discover Your Bible Ser.). (KOR.). pap., tchr. ed. 6.95 *(978-1-55883-159-9(2)*, 600085); pap., stu. ed. 4.25 *(978-1-55883-158-2(4)*, 600080) C R C World Literature Ministries/Libros Desafio.

Discover Exodus 16-40: On the Way. (Discover Your Bible Ser.). (KOR.). pap., tchr. ed. 6.95 *(978-1-55883-165-0(7)*, 600095); pap., stu. ed. 4.25 *(978-1-55883-164-3(9)*, 600090) C R C World Literature Ministries/Libros Desafio.

Discover Genesis Vol. 1: Creation to Abraham. (Discover Your Bible Ser.). (KOR.). pap., stu. ed. 3.25 *(978-1-55883-152-0(5)*, 600050); pap., tchr. ed. 4.95 *(978-1-55883-155-1(X)*, 600055) C R C World Literature Ministries/Libros Desafio.

Discover Genesis Vol. 2: Abraham & Sarah. (Discover Your Bible Ser.). (KOR.). pap., stu. ed. 4.25 *(978-1-55883-153-7(3)*, 600060); pap., stu. ed. 6.95 *(978-1-55883-156-8(8)*, 600065) C R C World Literature Ministries/Libros Desafio.

Dobson. Guide to Exodus. 16.00 *(978-0-687-85446-2(6))* Abingdon Pr.

Dozeman, Thomas B. Exodus. 2009. (ENG.). 888p. pap. 55.00 *(978-0-8028-2617-6(2))* Eerdmans, William B. Publishing Co.

Drazin, Drazin & WAGNER, Stanley. Onkelos on the Torah. 2008. 376p. 35.00 *(978-965-229-425-8(X))* Gefen Publishing Hse., Ltd ISR. Dist: Gefen Bks.

Drazin, Israel. A Rational Approach to Judaism & Torah Commentary. 2007. 237p. 23.95 *(978-965-7108-91-8(8))* Urim Pubns. ISR. Dist: Coronet Bks.

Drazin, Israel & Wagner, Stanley. Onkelos on the Torah Understan. 2010. 480p. 35.00 *(978-965-229-473-9(X))* Gefen Publishing Hse., Ltd ISR. Dist: Strauss Consultants.

Driver, S. R. Book of Exodus Cambridge Bible for Schoo. 2006. pap. 42.95 *(978-1-4286-5114-2(4))* Kessinger Publishing, LLC.

Eaton, Michael. Genesis, 1-11. (Preaching Through the Bible Ser.). 125p. pap. *(978-1-85240-179-5(6))* Sovereign World, Ltd.

—Genesis, 12-23. (Preaching Through the Bible Ser.). 125p. pap. *(978-1-85240-244-0(X))* Sovereign World, Ltd.

—Genesis, 24-50. (Preaching Through the Bible Ser.). 125p. pap. *(978-1-85240-269-3(5))* Sovereign World, Ltd.

Edels, Samuel Eliezer ben Judah & Ginzburg, Eliezer ben Efrayim Mordekhai. Sefer Mesilat Ha-Maharsha: Likutim Al Seder Ha-Parashiyot Mi-Tokh Hidushe Agadot Maharsha Al Ha-Shas, Le-Vaer Ule-Laben Divre Hazal Al Pesuke Ha-Torah ... 2009. ***(978-1-4226-0990-3(1))***; 2nd ed. *(978-1-4226-0941-5(3))* Mesorah Pubns., Ltd.

Edgar, Swift, et al. The Pentateuch: Douay-Rheims Translation, Volume I. 2010. (Dumbarton Oaks Medieval Library). (LAT & ENG.). 1200p. 29.95 *(978-0-674-05534-6(9))* Harvard Univ. Pr.

Elkins, Rabbi Dov Peretz. Sidrah Sparks: Talking Torah at the Table with Your Family. 2010. 512p. (ENG.). 30.99 *(978-1-4490-9202-3(0))*; pap. 20.49 *(978-1-4490-9201-6(2))* AuthorHouse.

Elliott, James D. Pre-Adamite World Revealed in God's Word. 2011. 44p. pap. 21.99 ***(978-1-4628-7820-8(2))*** Xlibris Corp.

Errico, Rocco A. & Lamsa, George M. Aramaic Light on Genesis. 2007. pap. 21.95 *(978-0-9631292-2-2(8))* Nochra Foundation.

Eskenazi, Tamara Cohn. The Torah: A Women's Commentary. 2007. 1350p. 75.00 *(978-0-8074-1081-3(0))* URJ Pr.

Eslinger, Lyle. Into the Hands of the Living God. 2009. (Library of Hebrew Bible/Old Testament Studies, the Ser.). (ENG.). 271p. 44.95 *(978-0-567-31623-3(8)*, T&T Clark) Continuum International Publishing Group, Ltd. GBR. Dist: National Bk. Network.

Exodus 1. (LifeLight Bible Studies: Course 10). stu. ed. 5.50 *(978-0-570-09279-7(5)*, 20-2291) Concordia Publishing Hse.

Exodus 2. (LifeLight Bible Studies: Course 11). stu. ed. 13.95 incl. audio *(978-0-570-09281-0(7)*, 20-2296); 6.50 *(978-0-570-09280-3(9)*, 20-2295) Concordia Publishing Hse.

Ezrahiyan, Yedidiyah. Payam-I Zindagi: Tafsir-I Matalib-I Mundarij Dar Panj Kitab-I Tawrat-I Muqaddas. 2007. (PER & HEB.). 359p. *(978-1-59584-008-0(7))* Ketab Corp.

Fennema, Deb. Discover Genesis Vol. 2: Abraham & Sarah. (Discover Your Bible Ser.). pap., stu. ed. 4.95 *(978-1-56212-165-5(0)*, 152230) Faith Alive Christian Resources.

Fernando, Ajith. Deuteronomy: Loving Obedience to a Loving God. 2012. (Preaching the Word Ser.). 752p. 44.99 ***(978-1-4335-3100-2(3))*** Crossway.

Fladerer, Ludwig. Augustinus als Exeget: Zu seinen Kommentaren des Galaterbriefes und der Genesis. 2010. (Sitzungsberichte der Phil. -Hist. Klasse Ser.). (GER.). 261p. (C). pap. 80.00 *(978-3-7001-6647-4(8))* Austrian Academy of Sciences Press AUT. Dist: Brown, David Bk. Co., The.

Fretheim, Terence E. Exodus: Interpretation: A Bible Commentary for Teaching & Preaching. 2010. (Interpretation Ser.). (ENG.). 336p. pap. 30.00 *(978-0-664-23619-9(7))* Westminster John Knox Pr.

Friedländer, M. Essays on the Writings of Abraham Ibn Ezra. 2010. (HEB.). pap. 57.76 *(978-1-61143-303-6(7))* Gorgias Pr., LLC.

Friedman, David B. Bereshit, the Book of Beginnings. 2009. 190p. pap. 22.00 *(978-1-60608-734-3(7)*, Wipf and Stock) Wipf & Stock Pubs.

Fruchtenbaum, Arnold G. Ariel's Bible Commentary: The Book of Genesis. 2009. (Illus.). xxvi, 719p. *(978-1-935174-00-4(2))* Ariel Ministries, Inc.

Fuller, Andrew. Expository Discourses on the Book of Genesis. 2009. 624p. pap. 40.00 *(978-1-59925-213-1(9))* Solid Ground Christian Bks.

Gamliel, Chanoch. Rashi Ke-Farshan Ukhe-Balshan: Tefisot Tahbiriyot Be-Perush Rashi La-Torah. 2010. (HEB.). 258p. *(978-965-536-008-0(3))* Bialik Institute.

Gane, Roy. In the Shadow of the Shekinah: God's Journey with Us. 2009. 158p. pap. 11.99 *(978-0-8280-2421-1(9))* Review & Herald Publishing Assn.

Gardiner, G. David. We See. 2011. 78p. 24.99 ***(978-1-4535-9996-9(7))***; pap. 15.99 ***(978-1-4535-9995-2(9))*** Xlibris Corp.

Geisler, Norman L. & Howe, Thomas. The Big Book of Bible Difficulties: Clear & Concise Answers from Genesis to Revelation. 2008. 624p. pap. 29.99 *(978-0-8010-7158-4(5))* Baker Bks.

Genesis 1. (LifeLight Bible Studies: Course 3). stu. ed. 5.50 *(978-0-570-09299-5(X)*, 20-2226); 6.50 *(978-0-570-09298-8(1)*, 20-2225) Concordia Publishing Hse.

Genesis 1: 31 Bulletin, Regular Size. 4.50 *(978-0-687-04173-2(2))* Abingdon Pr.

Genesis 2. (LifeLight Bible Studies: Course 4). 5.50 incl. audio *(978-0-570-09262-9(0)*, 20-2259) 6.50 *(978-0-570-09261-2(2)*, 20-2258) Concordia Publishing Hse.

Gibson, Joyce L. The Book of Genesis, 0 vols. 2007. (Smart Guide to the Bible Ser.). (Illus.). 352p. per. 14.99 *(978-1-4185-0993-4(0))* Nelson, Thomas Inc.

Gill, John. An Exposition of Genesis. 2010. 836p. 32.00 *(978-1-888514-35-3(3))* Particular Baptist Pr.

Goldingay, John. Exodus & Leviticus for Everyone. 2010. (Old Testament for Everyone Ser.). (ENG.). 256p. pap. 16.00 *(978-0-664-23376-1(7))* Westminster John Knox Pr.

—Genesis for Everyone. 2010. (Old Testament for Everyone Ser.). (ENG.). 256p. Pt. 1, Chapters 1-16. pap. 16.00 *(978-0-664-23374-7(0))*Pt. 2, Chapters 17-50. pap. 16.00 *(978-0-664-23375-4(9))* Westminster John Knox Pr.

—Numbers & Deuteronomy for Everyone. 2010. (Old Testament for Everyone Ser.). (ENG.). 256p. pap. 16.00 *(978-0-664-23377-8(5))* Westminster John Knox Pr.

Goldstein, Elyse, ed. The Women's Torah Commentary: New Insights from Women Rabbis on the 45 Weekly Torah Portions. 2008. 496p. pap. 19.99 *(978-1-58023-370-5(8))* Jewish Lights Publishing.

Good, Edwin. Genesis 1-11: Tales of the Earliest World. 2011. (ENG.). 144p. 40.00 ***(978-0-8047-7496-3(X))***; pap. 15.95 ***(978-0-8047-7497-0(8))*** Stanford Univ. Pr.

Grace, Bob. Genesis & Biblical Science Revealed. 2011. 104p. 24.99 ***(978-1-4568-8622-6(3))***; pap. 15.99 ***(978-1-4568-8621-9(5))*** Xlibris Corp.

Gray, Brian Wayne. Leviticus Revealed. 2009. 72p. pap. 10.95 *(978-1-4401-5614-4(X))* iUniverse, Inc.

Green, Randy. Deuteronomy Book: Chapters 1-16. 2011. 520p. 43.95 ***(978-1-4627-0611-2(8))*** Cross Bks. Publishing.

—Deuteronomy Book I: Chapters 1-16. 2011. 520p. pap. 34.95 ***(978-1-4627-0610-5(X))*** Cross Bks. Publishing.

—Deuteronomy Book II: Chapters 17-34. 2011. 452p. 43.95 ***(978-1-4627-0613-6(4))***; pap. 34.95 ***(978-1-4627-0612-9(6))*** Cross Bks. Publishing.

Greidanus, Sidney. Preaching Christ from the Genesis: Foundations for Expository Sermons. 2007. 518p. per. 30.00 *(978-0-8028-2586-5(9))* Eerdmans, William B. Publishing Co.

Griffin, C. Jh. Lyrics on Matters Relating To: The Knowledge of Good & Evil. 2008. 260p. pap. 15.99 *(978-1-4389-1166-3(1))* AuthorHouse.

Guide to Deuteronomy lsg 32. 15.00 *(978-0-687-06637-7(9))* Abingdon Pr.

Guyon, Madame. The Mystical Sense of the Sacred Scriptures. 2008. 427p. pap. 36.00 *(978-1-55635-794-7(X)*, Wipf and Stock) Wipf & Stock Pubs.

B

Haberman, Daniel. The Hirsch Chumash: The Five Books of Torah. 2009. (HEB & ENG.). 880p. 34.99 *(978-1-58330-746-5(X))*; (ENG & HEB.). 34.99 *(978-1-58330-295-8(6))* Feldheim Pubs.

Halbrooks Vaughn, Nicole Love. Devotions from Genesis: It's Not Just Ancient History. 2010. pap. 13.99 *(978-1-61663-150-5(3))* Tate Publishing & Enterprises, LLC.

Hall, Brian P. The Genesis Effect: Personal & Organizational Transformations. 2006. (Illus.). 376p. (Orig.). pap. 36.00 *(978-1-59752-702-6(5)*, Resource Pubns.) Wipf & Stock Pubs.

Hamilton, Jeffrey. Genesis: A Study of the Beginning. 2009. 149p. pap. 12.84 *(978-0-557-07265-1(4))* Lulu Enterprises Inc.

Hammer, Reuven. Entering Torah Prefaces to The. 2009. 320p. 29.95 *(978-965-229-434-0(9))* Gefen Publishing Hse., Ltd ISR. Dist: Strauss Consultants.

Hammer, Shalom. The Family Rashi Book. 2010. 223p. *(978-1-934440-88-9(4)*, Devorah Publishing) Urim Pubns.

—The Family Rashi Book. 2010. (ENG.). 223p. pap. 19.95 *(978-1-936068-16-6(8)*, Devorah Publishing) Urim Pubns. ISR. Dist: Lambda Pubs., Inc.

Harman, Allan M. Deuteronomy: The Commands of a Covenant God. 2007. (Focus on the Bible Commentaries Ser.). (ENG.). 320p. per. 14.99 *(978-1-84550-268-3(X))* Christian Focus Pubns. GBR. Dist: STL Distribution North America.

Harper, Robert Francis. The Code of Hammurabi: King of Babylon about 2250 B. C. 2007. (Ancient Texts & Translations Ser.). (Illus.). 326p. pap. 28.00 *(978-1-55635-567-7(X))* Wipf & Stock Pubs.

Harrison, R. K. Leviticus. 2008. (Tyndale Old Testament Commentaries Ser.: Volume 3). (ENG., Illus.). 254p. pap. 16.00 *(978-0-8308-4203-2(9)*, IVP Acad.) InterVarsity Pr.

Hastings, James. The Great Texts of the Bible. 2009. 466p. pap. 37.75 *(978-1-116-37852-8(3))*; 42.99 *(978-1-116-37850-4(7))*; pap. 36.75 *(978-1-116-37853-5(1))* BiblioBazaar.

—The Great Texts of the Bible. 2010. 250p. pap. *(978-1-152-92969-2(0))* 2010. 312p. pap. *(978-1-152-05498-1(8))* 2010. 292p. pap. *(978-1-152-05494-3(5))* 2010. 306p. pap. *(978-1-152-05492-9(9))* 2010. 294p. pap. *(978-1-152-05488-2(0))* 2010. 266p. pap. *(978-1-152-05486-8(4))* 2010. 276p. pap. *(978-1-152-05496-7(1))* 2009. 350p. pap. *(978-1-150-29623-9(2))* Books LLC.

Henry, Matthew. Comentario Matthew Henry: Pentateuco: Matthew Henry's Commentary: Pentateuch. (SPA.). 944p. *(978-84-7228-815-7(3)*, 222101) Clie, Editorial.

Herzfeld, Shmuel. And Shmuel Invoked His Name: The Relevance of the Torah for Our Modern Lives. 2012. ***(978-965-229-558-3(2))*** Gefen Bks.

Hess, Richard S. Studies in the Personal Names of Genesis 1-11. 2009. pap. *(978-1-57506-160-3(0))* Eisenbrauns, Inc.

Hill, Bill. Moses: From the Burning Bush to the Promised Land. 2009. pap. *(978-0-9823842-7-5(0))* NextSunday Resources.

Hirsch, Samson R. The Hirsch Chumash: Bereishis. 2009. 901p. 34.99 *(978-1-58330-565-2(3))* Feldheim Pubs.

—The Hirsch Chumash: Complete Set. 2009. 159.99 *(978-1-59826-260-5(2))* Feldheim Pubs.

—The Hirsch Chumash: Devorim. 2009. 34.99 *(978-1-59826-261-2(0))* Feldheim Pubs.

Hirsch, Samson R. & Haberman, Daniel, trs. from HEB. The Hirsch Chumash: The Five Books of Torah. 2009. (ENG & HEB.). 49.99 *(978-1-58330-196-8(8))* Feldheim Pubs.

Hirsch, Samson Raphael. Timeless Torah: An Anthology of the Writings of Samson Raphael Hirsch. Breuer, Jacob, ed. 2011. 540p. 62.95 ***(978-1-258-05969-9(X))*** Literary Licensing, LLC.

Holborn, Alfred. The Pentateuch in the Light of Today Being a Simple Introduction to the Pentateuch on the Lines of the Higher Criticism. 2007. (ENG.). 124p. 35.95 *(978-0-548-02563-5(0))* Kessinger Publishing, LLC.

Hoppe, Hector, ed. Dios, Su Creacion, y Su Pueblo (God, His Creation & His People) Estudios Devocionales Sobre el Libro de Genesis. (SPA.). 64p. pap. 2.95 *(978-0-570-05013-1(8)*, 16-2550) Concordia Publishing Hse.

Into the Word, into the World Resource Library-Disciple II. 100.00 *(978-0-687-75722-0(3))* Abingdon Pr.

Into the Word, into the World Video #1-Disciple II. 35.00 incl. VHS *(978-0-687-75768-8(1))* Abingdon Pr.

Into the Word, into the World Video #2-Disciple II. 35.00 incl. VHS *(978-0-687-75769-5(X))* Abingdon Pr.

Into the Word, into the World Video #3-Disciple II. 35.00 incl. VHS *(978-0-687-75770-1(3))* Abingdon Pr.

Into the Word, into the World Video #4-Disciple II. 35.00 incl. VHS *(978-0-687-75771-8(1))* Abingdon Pr.

Into the Word, into the World Videos Disciple. 150.00 incl. VHS *(978-0-687-75772-5(X))* Abingdon Pr.

Into the Word, into the World Videos Disciple II. 150.00 incl. VHS *(978-0-687-75723-7(1))* Abingdon Pr.

Jacob, Benno, et al. The First Book of the Bible, Genesis. 2007. xvii, 358p. *(978-0-88125-960-5(8))* Ktav Publishing Hse., Inc.

Jacobus, Melancthon. Notes, Critical & Explanatory, on the Book of Genesis. 2006. 308p. per. 23.99 *(978-1-4255-2957-4(7))* MPublishing.

Jellie, W. The Preacher's Commentary on the Book of Leviticus. 2007. (ENG.). 646p. 63.95 *(978-0-548-03859-8(7))* Kessinger Publishing, LLC.

Jemas, Bill. Genesis Rejuvenated. 2009. 114p. pap. 20.00 *(978-1-935444-87-9(5))*; pap. 25.00 *(978-1-935444-95-4(6))* World Audience Pubs.

John, Walton. Genesis, 1 vol. 2008. (Bringing the Bible to Life Ser.). (ENG.). 160p. pap. 7.99 *(978-0-310-27648-7(9))* Zondervan.

Johnson, Jeffrey D. The Descent of God: The Ancient Message: Exodus 19, 20. 2007. 20p. pap. 3.00 *(978-1-55635-078-8(3)*, Wipf and Stock) Wipf & Stock Pubs.

Kahn, Rabbi Ari D. Echoes of Eden. 2011. 320p. pap. *(978-965-229-499-9(3))* Gefen Publishing Hse., Ltd.

Kalas, J. Ellsworth. Genesis. 2011. *(978-1-4266-7162-3(8))* Abingdon Pr.

—Immersion Bible Studies: Genesis. 2011. (Immersion Bible Studies). 112p. 9.00 *(978-1-4267-1623-2(0))* Abingdon Pr.

Kardec, Allan. El Genesis, los Milagros y las Predicciones.Tr. of Genesis, Miracles & Predictions. (SPA.). pap. *(978-968-15-0201-0(9))* Editores Mexicanos Unidos.

Kern, Steve. No Other Gods - the Biblical Creation Worldview. 2007. pap. 24.99 *(978-0-9778085-7-1(2))* Amerisearch, Inc.

Kidner, Derek. Genesis. 2008. (Tyndale Old Testament Commentaries Ser.: Volume 1). (ENG.). 236p. pap. 16.00 *(978-0-8308-4201-8(2)*, IVP Acad.) InterVarsity Pr.

Kim, Hoon. Creative Bible Lessons in Genesis, 1 vol. 2006. (Creative Bible Lessons Ser.). (ENG., Illus.). 144p. (gr. 13). pap. 16.99 *(978-0-310-27093-5(6))* Zondervan.

Kim, Sun-Jong. Se Reposer Pour la Terre, Se Reposer Pour Dieu: L'Année Sabbatique en Lv 25,1-7. 2012. (Beihefte zur Zeitschrift für die alttestamentliche Wissenschaft Ser.). (FRE.). 360p. (gr. 17). 140.00 ***(978-3-11-027557-5(0))*** De Gruyter, Walter Inc.

Kim, Yoon-Kyung. Augustine's Changing Interpretations of Genesis 1-3: From de Genesi contra Manichaeos to de Genesi ad Litteram. 2006. 208p. 109.95 *(978-0-7734-5670-9(8))* Mellen, Edwin Pr., The.

Kiuchi, Nobuyoshi. Leviticus. 2007. (Apollos Old Testament Commentary Ser.: Volume 3). (ENG.). 538p. 40.00 *(978-0-8308-2503-5(7)*, IVP Acad.) InterVarsity Pr.

Klaiber, Walter. On Creation: Religion & Science in Dialogue. 2011. 212p. pap. 35.00 *(978-0-687-46687-0(3))* Abingdon Pr.

Klarfeld, Marshall. ADAM the Missing Link. 2009. 80p. pap. 38.95 *(978-1-4251-9184-9(3))* Trafford Publishing.

Koedoot, Gerrit. Deuteronomy: Keeping the Promises. l.t. ed. 5.25 *(978-1-56212-650-6(4)*, 15011) Faith Alive Christian Resources.

Langermann, Y. Tzvi. Yemenite Midrash: Philosophical Commentaries on the Torah: an Anthology of Writings from the Golden Age of Judaism in the Yemen. 2010. (Sacred Literature Trust Ser.). (ENG.). 384p. pap. 29.95 *(978-0-300-16531-9(5))* Yale Univ. Pr.

Laura, Lieber. Yannai on Genesis: An Invitation to Piyyut. 2010. 500p. 59.50 *(978-0-87820-464-9(4))* Hebrew Union College Pr.

Leibowitz, Yeshayahu. Accepting the Yoke of Heaven: Commentary on the Weekly Torah Portion. Himelstein, Shmuel, tr. 2006. 203p. per. 15.95 *(978-965-7108-77-2(2))* Urim Pubns. ISR. Dist: Coronet Bks.

Lesser, Joshua, et al. Torah Queeries: Weekly Commentaries on the Hebrew Bible. Drinkwater, Gregg et al, eds. 2009. (ENG.). 368p. 30.00 *(978-0-8147-2012-7(9))* New York Univ. Pr.

Leviticus. (People's Bible Commentary Ser.). 256p. 13.99 *(978-0-7586-0417-0(3))* Concordia Publishing Hse.

Lewis, Philip A. Genesis for Today. 2011. 206p. pap. 19.99 ***(978-1-4568-7319-6(9))*** Xlibris Corp.

Lier, Gudrun. A Redaction History of the Pentateuchal Targums. 2010. 119.00 *(978-1-61719-181-7(7))* Gorgias Pr., LLC.

Lunsford, Joe. Leviticus 101: A closer look at one of the more difficult books in the Bible. 2007. 25.00 *(978-1-60416-033-8(0))*; pap. 20.00 *(978-1-60416-032-1(2))* Reformation Pubns.

MacDonald, Nathan, et al. Genesis & Christian Theology. 2012. pap. ***(978-0-8028-6725-4(1))*** Eerdmans, William B. Publishing Co.

Mackintosh, Charles H. Notes on the Book of Genesis. 2006. 324p. per. 23.99 *(978-1-4255-3222-2(5))* MPublishing.

Malbim, Meir Loeb ben Jehiel Michael & Weinbach, Mendel. The Essential Malbim: Flashes of Insight on Bereishis/Genesis. 2009. (HEB & ENG.). 365p. *(978-1-4226-0927-9(8))* Mesorah Pubns., Ltd.

Mansour, Eli & Silverberg, David. The Daily Halacha: A Compendium of Practical Halachot & Illuminating Insights from the Weekly Parasha. 2009. (Illus.). 411p. *(978-1-4226-0899-9(9))* Mesorah Pubns., Ltd.

Manthey, Jim. A Genesis Commentary. 2009. 262p. pap. 19.99 *(978-1-4415-3986-1(7))* Xlibris Corp.

Mathews, Kenneth A. Leviticus: Holy God, Holy People. 2009. (Preaching the Word Ser.). 288p. 32.99 *(978-1-4335-0628-4(9))* Crossway.

Matt, Daniel, tr. from ARC. The Zohar. (Zohar: Pritzker Edition Ser.). (ENG., Illus.). Vol. 5. 2009. 656p. 55.00 *(978-0-8047-6219-9(8))* Vol. 6. 2011. 472p. 55.00 ***(978-0-8047-7663-9(6))*** Stanford Univ. Pr.

Maxfield, John A. Luther's Lectures on Genesis & the Formation of Evangelical Identity. 2008. (Sixteenth Century Essays & Studies: 80). (Illus.). 264p. 54.00 *(978-1-931112-75-8(4))* Truman State Univ. Pr.

Mceleney, Neil J. The Law Given Through Moses: Introduction to the Pentateuch. 2011. 34p. 35.95 ***(978-1-258-09537-6(8))*** Literary Licensing, LLC.

McIntosh, Andy. Genesis for Today: The Relevance of the Creation/Evolution Debate to Today's Society. 4th ed. 2011. (Creation Points Ser.). (Illus.). 232p. pap. ***(978-1-84625-240-2(7))*** DayOne Pubns.

—Genesis for Today: The Relevance of the Creation/Evolution Debate to Today's Society. 3rd ed. 2006. (Illus.). 230p. per. 13.00 *(978-1-84625-051-4(X))* DayOne Pubns. GBR. Dist: STL Distribution North America.

McIntyre, Rev. Frances. The Greatness of God Almighty. 2010. 120p. pap. 13.99 *(978-1-4490-6942-1(8))* AuthorHouse.

McKeown, James. Genesis. 2008. (Two Horizons Old Testament Commentary Ser.). 398p. per. 25.00 *(978-0-8028-2705-0(5))* Eerdmans, William B. Publishing Co.

Mcmillion, Ky. Choose Life: Volume 1. 2011. 392p. 36.99 ***(978-1-4567-6500-2(0))***; pap. 19.99 ***(978-1-4567-6501-9(9))*** AuthorHouse.

Mesorah Heritage Foundation Staff, contrib. by. [Midrash Rabah]: The Midrash = Midrash Rabbah: With an Annotated, Interpretive Elucidation & Additional Insights. 2010. (HEB & ENG.). ***(978-1-4226-1056-5(X))*** Mesorah Pubns., Ltd.

Metzler, Karin, ed. Die Kommentierung des Buches Genesis 1.1. 2010.Tr. of Commentary on the Book of Genesis. (GER.). XXV, 341p. 126.00 *(978-3-11-019344-2(2))*; 196.00 ***(978-3-11-173586-3(9))*** De Gruyter, Walter Inc.

Meyer, Mark. A Comparative Dialectical Study of Genitive Constructions in Aramaic Translations of Exodus. 2010. 140.00 *(978-1-61143-002-8(X))* Gorgias Pr., LLC.

Midrash Ha-Mevo'ar Institute. The Midrash Rabbah: Esther & Ruth. (HEB & ENG.). 23.99 *(978-1-58330-610-9(2))*; 25.99 *(978-1-58330-522-5(X))* Feldheim Pubs.

—The Midrash Rabbah: Megillas Eichah. 25.99 *(978-1-58330-274-3(3))* Feldheim Pubs.

Midrash Rabbah: Midrashim on the Pentateuch & the Five Scrolls with the Matnoth Kehunah Commentary, 2 vols., Set. deluxe ed. (ENG, HEB & YID.). 75.00 *(978-0-87559-096-7(9))* Shalom, P. Pubns., Inc.

Miller, Chaim, compiled by. The Gutnick Edition Chumash - Synagogue Edition (the Five Books of Moses) With Rashi's Commentary, Targum Onkelos & Haftoras with a Commentary anthologized from Classic Rabbinic Texts & the works of the Lubavitcher Rebbe. 2006. 1600p. 59.99 *(978-1-934152-01-0(3))* KOL Menachem.

Miller, William T. The Book of Exodus: Question by Question. 2009. (Question by Question Bible Study Commentary Ser.). 352p. pap. 21.95 *(978-0-8091-4612-3(6))* Paulist Pr.

Moore, Phil. Straight to the Heart of Genesis: 60 Bite-Sized Insights, 1 vol. 2011. (Straight to the Heart Ser.). 272p. pap. 14.99 *(978-0-85721-001-2(7)*, Monarch Bks.) Lion Hudson PLC GBR. Dist: Kregel Pubns.

Moore, Phil. Straight to the Heart of Moses: 60 Bite-Sized Insights, 1 vol. 2011. (Straight to the Heart Commentary Ser.). 272p. pap. 14.99 ***(978-0-85721-056-2(4)***, Monarch Bks.) Lion Hudson PLC GBR. Dist: Kregel Pubns.

Morgenstern, Julian. The Book of the Covenant. 2007. 152p. pap. 17.00 *(978-1-55635-415-1(0)*, Wipf and Stock) Wipf & Stock Pubs.

Morrison, Chanan. Gold from the Land of Israel: A New Light on the Weekly Torah Portion from the Writings of Rabbi Abraham Isaac Hakohen Kook. 2007. 367p. 27.95 *(978-965-7108-92-5(6))* Urim Pubns. ISR. Dist: Coronet Bks.

Murphy, James G. A Critical & Exegetical Commentary on the Book of Exodus. 2009. (ENG.). 375p. 38.99 *(978-1-117-19293-2(8))*; pap. 32.75 *(978-1-117-19294-9(6))* BiblioBazaar.

Murphy, James Gracey. A Critical & Exegetical Commentary on the Book of Genesis with a New Translation by J G Murphy with a Preface by J P Thompson. 2006. 536p. per. 29.99 *(978-1-4255-5989-2(1))* MPublishing.

Navarre Bible Editors. The Navarre Bible: Exodus. 2010. (ENG., Illus.). 214p. pap. 14.95 *(978-1-84682-207-0(6))* Four Courts Pr. IRL. Dist: International Specialized Bk. Services.

—The Navarre Bible: Genesis. 2010. (Illus.). 240p. pap. 14.95 *(978-1-84682-206-3(8))* Four Courts Pr. IRL. Dist: International Specialized Bk. Services.

Nelson, Richard D. From Eden to Babel: An Adventure in Bible Study. 2006. xii, 148p. pap. 18.99 *(978-0-8272-1039-4(6))* Chalice Pr.

Nelson, W. David. Mekhilta de-Rabbi Shimon Bar Yohai: Edward E. Elson Classic. annot. ed. 2006. (Edward E. Elson Classic Ser.). (ENG & HEB.). 1100p. 75.00 *(978-0-8276-0799-6(7))* Jewish Pubn. Society.

Neusner & Chilton, Bruce D. Torah Revealed, Torah Fulfilled: Scriptural Laws in Formative Judaism & Earliest Christianity. 2008. (ENG.). 256p. 130.00 *(978-0-567-02739-9(2)*, T&T Clark Int'l) Continuum International Publishing Group, Ltd. GBR. Dist: National Bk. Network.

Nowell, Irene. Numbers. 2011. 6.95 *(978-0-8146-2839-3(7))* Liturgical Pr.

O'Donnell, Kevin, ed. Exodus. 2011. (Almighty Bible Ser.). (Illus.). 149p. (J). (gr. 4-7). pap. 17.99 ***(978-1-936081-65-3(2))*** Casscom Media.

—Genesis. 2011. (Almighty Bible Ser.). (Illus.). 147p. (J). (gr. 4-7). pap. 17.99 ***(978-1-936081-66-0(0))*** Casscom Media.

Olson, Dennis T. Numbers: Interpretation: A Bible Commentary for Teaching & Preaching. 2012. (Interpretation: A Bible Commentary for Teaching & Preaching Ser.). (ENG.). 210p. pap. 25.00 ***(978-0-664-23882-7(3))*** Westminster John Knox Pr.

Oppen, Menachem Moshe. A Twist of the Tongue, Vol. 2. (Illus.). 123p. 10.95 *(978-1-56062-009-9(9))*; pap. 7.95 *(978-1-56062-010-5(2))* C I S Communications, Inc.

Owens, J. Edward & Durken, Daniel. Deuteronomy. 2011. 6.95 *(978-0-8146-2840-9(0))* Liturgical Pr.

Owens, Jane. Torah Simply Spoken - Genesis. 2008. 468p. pap. 23.99 *(978-1-60647-393-1(X))* Xulon Pr., Inc.

Parker-Shigemura, Alexandria. The New World Order in Genesis 1-9: A Commentary. 2011. 552p. 42.95 ***(978-1-4620-1597-9(2))***; pap. 32.95 ***(978-1-4620-1596-2(4))*** iUniverse, Inc.

Parry, J. H., prod. Sefer Ha-Yashar or the Book of Jasher. unabr. ed. 2007. (ENG.). 280p. per. *(978-1-897352-30-4(1))* Providence University.

Patel, Sanjay C. & Patel, Sanjay. The Undeniable Evidence for God. 2008. (Illus.). ix, 528p. pap. ***(978-0-9822267-0-4(5))*** Purplewater Paperbacks LLC.

Petit, F. & Van Rompay, L. Sévère D'Antioche: Fragments grecs tirés des chaînes sur les derniers livres de l'Octateuque et sur les Règnes. 2006. (Traditio Exegetica Graeca Ser.). (SYR, FRE, GEC & ENG.). 214p. (C). 114.00 *(978-90-429-1725-5(3))* Peeters Pubs. & Booksellers BEL. Dist: Brown, David Bk. Co., The.

Petruccione, John F., rev. Theodoret of Cyrus: The Questions on the Octateuch, Volume 1 on Genesis & Exodus, 2 vols., Vol. 1. 2008. (Library of Early Christianity Ser.). (GEC & ENG.). 345p. per. 29.95 *(978-0-8132-1499-3(8))* Catholic Univ. of America Pr.

—Theodoret of Cyrus, Volume 2: The Questions on the Octateuch: on Leviticus, Numbers, Deuteronomy, Joshua, Judges, & Ruth, 2 vols., Vol. 2. 2008. (Library of Early Christianity Ser.). (GEC & ENG.). 431p. 44.95 *(978-0-8132-1500-6(5))* Catholic Univ. of America Pr.

Philo. Philo V9: Every Good Man Is Free; on the Contemplative Life; on the Eternity of the World; Flaccus; Hypothetica; on Providence. Colson, F. H., tr. 2011. 558p. 62.95 ***(978-1-258-03069-8(1))*** Literary Licensing, LLC.

Pink, Arthur. Gleanings in Exodus. 2011. 418p. pap. 19.99 ***(978-1-61203-104-0(8))*** Bottom of the Hill Publishing.

Pink, Arthur W. Gleanings in Genesis. 2011. 288p. pap. 16.99 ***(978-1-61203-213-9(3))*** Bottom of the Hill Publishing.

Pixler, Steve. The Creation & Fall of the Family: Studies on the Family from Genesis 1-5. 2007. 280p. per. 19.95 *(978-0-9796261-1-1(0))* Continuum Ministry Resources.

Pollak, P. S. Minhas Marheshes: Commentary on Genesis. (ENG & HEB.). 12.00 *(978-0-87559-101-8(9))* Shalom, P. Pubns., Inc.

Ponessa, Joseph & Manhardt, Laurie Watson. Moses & the Torah: Exodus, Leviticus, Numbers, Deuteronomy. 2007. (Come & See Catholic Bible Study Ser.). (Illus.). 220p. pe. 19.95 *(978-1-931018-45-6(6))* Emmaus Road Publishing.

Ponessa, Joseph L. & Manhardt, Laurie Watson. Come & See: Genesis. 2009. 220p. pap. 19.95 *(978-1-931018-50-0(2))* Emmaus Road Publishing.

Porter, Paul. The Creation Account Unsnagged. 2008. 108p. 18.99 *(978-1-60477-907-3(1))*; pap. 10.99 *(978-1-60477-906-6(3))* Xulon Pr., Inc.

Propp, William H. Exodus 19-40: A New Translation with Introduction & Commentary by William H. C. Propp. 2006. (Illus.). 896p. 50.00 *(978-0-385-24693-4(5)*, Anchor Bible) Doubleday Religious Publishing Group, The.

Propp, William H. C. Exodus, 19-40. 2006. (Anchor Yale Bible Commentaries Ser.). (ENG.). 865p. 65.00 *(978-0-300-13939-6(X))* Yale Univ. Pr.

Rabbi M. Silber. Pentateuch with Targum Onkelos & Rashi's Commentary: Torah the Book of Devarim, Volume V (Hebrew / English) 2011. 446p. pap. ***(978-1-60796-300-4(0))*** Editorial Benei Noaj.

Rabbi M. Silber & Rashi. Pentateuch with Targum Onkelos & Rashi's Commentary: Torah - the Book of Vayyiqra-Leviticus, Volume III (Hebrew / English) 2007. 448p. per. *(978-956-291-490-1(9))* Editorial Benei Noaj.

—Pentateuch with Targum Onkelos & Rashi's Commentary: Torah the Book of Bamidbar-Numbers, Volume IV (Hebrew / English) 2007. 448p. per. *(978-956-291-491-8(7))* Editorial Benei Noaj.

Radner, Ephraim. Leviticus. 2008. (Brazos Theological Commentary on the Bible Ser.). 320p. (C). 32.99 *(978-1-58743-099-2(1))* Brazos Pr.

Raphael, Wesley, Sr. Converting the Soul. 2010. 194p. pap. 10.76 *(978-0-557-23647-3(9))* Lulu Enterprises Inc.

Reardon, Patrick Henry. Creation & the Patriarchal Histories: Orthodox Christian Reflections on the Book of Genesis. 2008. (Biblical Commentary Ser.). 160p. pap. 13.95 *(978-1-888212-96-9(9))* Conciliar Pr.

Reno, R. R. Genesis, 1 vol. 2010. (Brazos Theological Commentary on the Bible Ser.). (ENG.). 304p. (C). 32.99 *(978-1-58743-091-6(6))* Brazos Pr.

Riskin, Shlomo. Torah Lights: A Biblical Commentary, Confronting Life, Love & Family. 2nd ed. 2009. 340p. 24.95 *(978-1-59264-272-4(1)*, Maggid) Toby Pr. LLC, The.

—Torah Lights: Defining a Nation. 2nd ed. 2009. 350p. 24.95 *(978-1-59264-273-1(X)*, Koren Pubns.) Toby Pr. LLC, The.

—Torah Lights: Sacrifice, Sanctity & Silence: Vayikra. 2nd ed. 2009. 350p. 24.95 *(978-1-59264-274-8(8)*, Maggid) Toby Pr. LLC, The.

—Torah Lights Volume II Exodus Defines the Birth of a Nation: The Goldberg Edition, Vol. 2. 2006. 320p. 27.95 *(978-965-7108-87-1(X))* Urim Pubns. ISR. Dist: Coronet Bks.

Robinson, Jerry. Family Book of Exodus. 2009. 78p. pap. 15.95 *(978-1-4327-1603-5(4))* Outskirts Pr., Inc.

Rogers, Marilyn T. The Book: The Love Story of Creation. 2008. 124p. 20.95 *(978-0-595-71972-3(4))*; pap. 10.95 *(978-0-595-48583-3(9))* iUniverse, Inc.

Roper, Coy D. Exodus. 2008. (Truth for Today Commentary Ser.). (Illus.). 710p. 29.95 *(978-0-9818128-1-6(3))* Resource Pubns.

Ross, Allen P., et al. Genesis, Exodus. 2008. (Cornerstone Biblical Commentary Ser.: 1). (ENG.). 576p. 34.99 *(978-0-8423-3427-3(0))* Tyndale Hse. Pubs.

Ross, Archie M. A Commentary on Genesis. 2008. 512p. pap. *(978-1-897117-32-3(9))* Gospel Folio Pr.

S., J., tr. Torah: The Five Books of Moses - the Interlinear Bible. 2007. 404p. *(978-956-291-437-6(2))* Editorial Benei Noaj.

Salathe, Harriet & Lawless, Agnes. Keys to God's Heart: Twelve Lessons on the Offerings, the Priests, & the Feasts: Unlocking Leviticus. 2006. (ENG.). 140p. per. 16.99 (978-1-4141-0744-8(7)) Pleasant Word.

Salkin, Jeffrey K. The Modern Men's Torah Commentary. 2009. 450p. 24.99 (978-1-58023-395-8(3)) Jewish Lights Publishing.

Salvesen, Alison. The Exodus Commentary of St Ephrem. 2010. pap. 20.20 (978-1-61719-808-3(0)) Gorgias Pr., LLC.

Scharfstein, Sol. Torah & Commentary: The Five Books of Moses: Translation, Rabbinic & Contemporary Commentary. 2008. (Illus.). 532p. 49.50 (978-0-88125-973-5(X)); pap. 35.00 (978-1-60280-020-5(0)) Ktav Publishing Hse., Inc.

Scharlemann, Jon. Genesis: An Introductory Course. (Journeys Through God's Word Ser.). pap., stu. ed. 8.99 (978-0-570-06869-3(X), 20-2812); pap. 8.99 (978-0-570-06870-9(3), 20-2813) Concordia Publishing Hse.

Sellman, Paul. The Tree of Life: A Biblical Study of Immortality & New Creation. 2010. 238p. pap. 15.95 (978-1-4327-6232-2(X)) Outskirts Pr., Inc.

Shama, Moshe. Recalling the Covenant: A Contemporary Commentary on the Five Books of the Torah. 2011. **(978-1-60280-184-4(3))** Ktav Publishing Hse., Inc.

Shneur Zalman & Gufin, Sheneur Zalman. Shiurim Ba-Hasidut: "Shaar Ha-Yihud Veha-Emunah", Perakim 1-12 Helek Sheni Be-Sefer Ha-Tanya. 2nd ed. 2010. (HEB.). 540p. **(978-965-91675-0-0(4))** Kehot Pubn. Society.

Sicker, Martin. The Theopolitical Discourses of Moses: The Book of Deuteronomy in Political Perspective (Book One) 2009. 428p. pap. 26.95 (978-1-4401-4513-1(X)) iUniverse, Inc.

Sivertsen, Barbara. The Parting of the Sea - How Volcanoes, Earthquakes, & Plagues Shaped the Story of Exodus. 2011. (ENG., Illus.). 264p. (C). pap. 22.95 (978-0-691-15021-5(4)) Princeton Univ. Pr.

Skinner, John. A Critical & Exegetical Commentary on Genesis. 2010. 156.44 (978-1-61719-681-2(9)) Gorgias Pr., LLC.

Smith, James E. Biblical Protology. 2007. 528p. pap. 26.95 (978-1-4303-2727-1(8)) Lulu Enterprises Inc.

Smith, Mark S. Exodus. 2011. 6.95 (978-0-8146-2837-9(0)) Liturgical Pr.

Smith, Russell Dan. Studies in the Bible for the Layman: Genesis. 2011. 505p. pap. 23.95 **(978-1-4327-7189-8(2))** Outskirts Pr., Inc.

Smith, Sholom. Shabbos with Rav Pam: The Rosh HaYeshivah's Inspiring Thoughts on the Weekly Torah Readings. 2007. (ArtScroll Ser.). xxv, 290p. (978-1-4226-0578-3(7)) Mesorah Pubns., Ltd.

Sokolow, Moshe. Studies in the Weekly Parashah Based on the Lessons of Nehama Leibowitz. 2008. 285p. 24.95 (978-965-524-004-7(5)) Urim Pubns. ISR. Dist: Lambda Pubs., Inc.

Spence, Anthony C. In the Beginning. 2009. (Illus.). 69p. pap. 10.95 (978-1-57258-568-3(4)) TEACH Services, Inc.

Stahl, Bill. The Bible's Story of Salvation: Book I. 2008. 392p. 35.95 (978-0-595-48918-3(4)); pap. 25.95 (978-0-595-48840-7(4)) iUniverse, Inc.

Stratton, Beverly J. Out of Eden: Reading, Rhetoric, & Ideology in Genesis 2-3. 2009. (Library of Hebrew Bible/Old Testament Studies, the Ser.). (ENG.). 292p. 49.95 (978-0-567-06911-5(7), T&T Clark) Continuum International Publishing Group, Ltd. GBR. Dist: National Bk. Network.

Striks, Aryeh, et al. Pinnacle of Creation: Torah Insights into Human Nature. 2007. (ArtScroll Ser.). (HEB & ENG.). 266p. (978-1-4226-0569-1(8)) Mesorah Pubns., Ltd.

Stubbs, David L. Numbers, 1 vol. 2009. (Brazos Theological Commentary on the Bible Ser.). 272p. (C). 29.99 (978-1-58743-140-1(8)) Brazos Pr.

Sugirtharajah, R. S., ed. Voices from the Margin: Interpreting the Bible in the Third World. 3rd rev. exp. ed. 2006. 506p. per. 35.00 (978-1-57075-686-3(4)) Orbis Bks.

Swaggart, Jimmy. Jimmy Swaggart Bible Commentary - Numbers through Deuteronomy. 2007. 40.00 (978-1-934655-35-1(X)) Swaggart, Jimmy Ministries.

Swedenborg, Emanuel. Arcana Coelestia. 2009. 724p. 40.99 (978-0-559-05680-2(X)); 680p. 39.99 (978-0-559-05320-7(7)); 680p. 35.99 (978-0-559-05334-4(7)); 636p. 38.99 (978-0-559-05373-3(8)); 712p. 40.99 (978-0-559-05384-9(3)); 636p. 34.99 (978-0-559-05386-3(X)); 712p. 36.99 (978-0-559-05399-3(1)); 716p. 40.99 (978-0-559-05556-0(0)); 716p. 36.99 (978-0-559-05569-0(2)); 656p. 39.99 (978-0-559-05601-7(X)); 732p. 40.99 (978-0-559-05602-4(8)); 656p. 35.99 (978-0-559-05517-8(6)); 732p. 36.99 (978-0-559-05618-5(4)); 712p. 40.99 (978-0-559-05574-1(5)); 712p. 36.99 (978-0-559-05687-1(7)); 688p. 39.99 (978-0-559-05590-1(7)); 724p. 36.99 (978-0-559-05693-2(1)); 688p. 35.99 (978-0-559-05701-4(6)); 684p. 39.99 (978-0-559-05719-9(9)); 684p. 35.99 (978-0-559-05734-2(2)); 364p. 31.99 (978-0-559-05936-0(1)); 364p. 29.99 (978-0-559-05946-9(9)); 680p. pap. 46.75 (978-0-559-05330-6(4)); 636p. pap. 45.75 (978-0-559-05377-1(0)); 636p. pap. 44.75 (978-0-559-05381-8(9)); 712p. pap. 49.75 (978-0-559-05388-7(6)); 712p. pap. 48.75 (978-0-559-05395-5(9)); 716p. pap. 49.75 (978-0-559-05559-1(5)); 716p. pap. 48.75 (978-0-559-05567-6(6)); 656p. pap. 46.75 (978-0-559-05604-8(4)); 732p. pap. 50.75 (978-0-559-05606-2(0)); 732p. pap. 49.75 (978-0-559-05612-3(5)); 656p. pap. 45.75 (978-0-559-05613-0(3)); 712p. pap. 49.75 (978-0-559-05677-2(X)); 712p. pap. 48.75 (978-0-559-05683-3(4)); 724p. pap. 50.75 (978-0-559-05685-7(0)); 724p. pap. 49.75 (978-0-559-05691-8(5)); 688p. pap. 48.75 (978-0-559-05692-5(3)); 688p. pap. 47.75 (978-0-559-05698-7(2)); 684p. pap. 47.75 (978-0-559-05724-3(5)); 684p. pap. 46.75 (978-0-559-05728-1(8)); 364p. pap. 32.75 (978-0-559-05941-4(8)); 364p. pap. 31.75 (978-0-559-05945-2(0)); 680p. pap. 47.75 (978-0-559-05326-9(6)) BiblioBazaar.

—Arcana Coelestia. 2009. 240p. pap. (978-1-4590-3452-5(X)); 184p. pap. (978-1-4590-3442-6(2)); 74p. pap. (978-0-217-43901-5(2)); 74p. pap. (978-0-217-43896-4(2)); 514p. pap. (978-0-217-43898-8(9)); 96p. pap. (978-0-217-43900-8(4)); 106p. pap. (978-0-217-68744-7(X)); 154p. pap. (978-0-217-68752-2(0)); 182p. pap. (978-0-217-68753-9(9)); 142p. pap. (978-0-217-17638-5(0)); 508p. pap. (978-0-217-17614-9(3)); 448p. pap. (978-0-217-17618-7(6)) Books LLC.

—Secrets of Heaven, Vol. 1. Cooper, Lisa Hyatt, tr. from LAT. 2010. (Nw century Edition Ser.). 552p. pap. 14.95 (978-0-87785-408-1(4)) Swedenborg Foundation, Inc.

Swedenborg, Emanuel & Smoley, Richard. A Disclosure of Secrets of Heaven Contained in Sacred Scripture, or, the Word of the Lord: Here First Those in Genesis, Together with Amazing Things Seen in the World of Spirits & in the Heaven of Angels, Vol. 1. Cooper, Lisa Hyatt, tr. from LAT. 2008. 759p. 49.00 (978-0-87785-486-9(6)) Swedenborg Foundation, Inc.

Swedenborg, Emanuel, et al. Secrets of Heaven, Vol. 1. Cooper, Lisa Hyatt, tr. from LAT. 2008. (Nw century Edition Ser.). 758p. pap. 15.00 (978-0-87785-504-0(8), 325-155) Swedenborg Foundation, Inc.

Tamari, Meir. Truths Desired by God. 2011. 352p. pap. (978-965-229-451-7(9)) Gefen Publishing Hse., Ltd.

Theodoret of Cyrus. The Questioms of the Octaeuch, 2 vols., Vol. 2. Hill, Robert C., ed. 2007. (GEC & ENG.). 448p. 24.95 (978-0-8132-1501-3(3)) Catholic Univ. of America Pr.

—The Questions on the Octateuch, 2 vols., Vol. 1. Hill, Robert H., ed. 2007. (GEC & ENG.). 480p. 49.95 (978-0-8132-1498-6(X)) Catholic Univ. of America Pr.

Thomas, W. Griffith. Genesis: Comentario Devocional: A Devotional Commentary. (SPA.). 416p. (978-84-7228-919-2(2), 220424) Clie, Editorial.

Tjjohnson. Chapter & Verse, Crosswords & Other Puzzles: Genesis Book Two. 2010. 112p. pap. 13.49 (978-1-4490-5129-7(4)) AuthorHouse.

Tomaschoff, Avner. Abarbanel on the Torah. 2010. 440p. (978-965-7118-05-4(0)) The Jewish Agency for Israel, Dept. of Jewish Education.

The Torah: A Modern Commentary, Travel Edition. 2007. pap. 30.00 (978-0-8074-0995-4(2), 381585) URJ Pr.

Towns, Elmer. Praying Genesis: Praying the Scriptures with Elmer Towns. 2008. pap. 15.99 (978-0-7684-2722-6(3)) Destiny Image Pubs.

Trajtmann, Uri & Rovner, Yoram, trs. La Torah: Los 5 Libros de Moises. 2008. 356p. pap. (978-0-9793119-4-9(2)) Editorial Benei Noaj.

Turner, Laurence A. Announcements of Plot in Genesis. 2008. 208p. pap. 23.00 (978-1-55635-733-6(8)) Wipf & Stock Pubs.

—Genesis. 2nd ed. 2009. viii, 234p. (978-1-906055-65-3(3)); pap. (978-1-906055-66-0(1)) Sheffield Phoenix Pr.

Vasholz, Robert I. Leviticus: A Mentor Commentary. 2007. (Mentor Ser.). (ENG.). 380p. 29.99 (978-1-84550-044-3(X), Mentor) Christian Focus Pubns. GBR. Dist: STL Distribution North America.

Voices of Torah. 2010. pap. (978-0-88123-159-5(2)) Central Conference of American Rabbis/CCAR Pr.

Voitila, Anssi, et al. Scripture in Transition: Essays on Septuagint, Hebrew Bible, & Dead Sea Scrolls in Honour of Raija Sollamo. Voitila, Anssi & Jokiranta, Jutta, eds. 2008. (Supplements to the Journal for the Study of Judaism Ser.). 700p. (978-90-04-16582-3(7)) BRILL.

Wagner, Stanley. Onkelos on the Torah. 2010. (HEB, ARC & ENG.). 340p. 35.00 (978-965-229-461-6(6)) Gefen Publishing Hse., Ltd ISR. Dist: Strauss Consultants.

Wagshul, Yitzchok Dovid, adapted by. Words of the Living G-D, Volume 1: The Book of Genesis. 2008. (Illus.). 375p. 24.95 (978-0-9792187-0-5(5)) Purity Pr., Inc.

Wainer, Ivan. The Ascension. 2010. 51p. pap. 11.95 (978-1-4327-5119-7(0)) Outskirts Pr., Inc.

Weimar, Peter. Die doppelte Thamar: Thomas Manns Novelle als Kommentar der Thamarerzählung des Genesisbuches. 2008. (GER.). x, 156p. (978-3-7887-2334-7(3)) Neukirchener Verlag.

Weinberg, Matis. Frameworks 3: Leviticus. 31.99 (978-1-892984-02-9(4)) Foundation for Jewish Pubns., Inc.

—Frameworks 4: Numbers. 31.99 (978-1-892984-03-6(2,) Foundation for Jewish Pubns., Inc.

Wenham, Gordon J. Numbers. 2008. (Tyndale Old Testament Commentaries Ser.: Volume 4). (ENG.). 192p. pap. 16.00 (978-0-8308-4204-9(7), IVP Acad.) InterVarsity Pr.

Wicks, Douglas M. Hearing from God: Instructions & Revelations from the King of Glory. 2011. 164p. pap. 16.99 **(978-1-4567-6001-4(7))** AuthorHouse.

Wiersbe, Warren W. Be Authentic (Genesis 25-50) Exhibiting Real Faith in the Real World, 1 vol. 2010. (BE Series Commentary Ser.). (ENG.). 224p. pap. 12.99 (978-1-4347-6630-4(6)) Cook, David C.

—Be Basic (Genesis 1-11) Believing the Simple Truth of God's Word, 1 vol. 2010. (BE Series Commentary Ser.). (ENG.). 192p. pap. 12.99 (978-1-4347-6635-9(7)) Cook, David C.

—Be Counted (Numbers) Living a Life That Counts for God, 1 vol. 2nd ed. 2010. (BE Series Commentary Ser.). (ENG.). 208p. pap. 12.99 (978-1-4347-6498-0(2)) Cook, David C.

—Be Delivered (Exodus) Finding Freedom by Following God, 1 vol. 2010. (BE Series Commentary Ser.). (ENG.). 240p. pap. 12.99 (978-1-4347-6503-1(2)) Cook, David C.

—Be Equipped (Deuteronomy) Acquiring the Tools for Spiritual Success. 2010. (BE Series Commentary Ser.). (ENG.). 272p. pap. 12.99 (978-1-4347-0052-0(6)) Cook, David C.

—Be Obedient (Genesis 12-25) Learning the Secret of Living by Faith, 1 vol. 2010. (BE Series Commentary Ser.). (ENG.). 176p. pap. 12.99 (978-1-4347-6632-8(2)) Cook, David C.

Willis, Timothy M. Leviticus. 2009. 241p. pap. 37.00 (978-1-4267-0017-0(2)) Abingdon Pr.

Winn-Lederer, Ilene. Between Heaven & Earth: An Illuminated Torah Commentary. 2009. 192p. 45.00 (978-0-7649-5098-8(3)) Pomegranate Communications, Inc.

Wolf's Anti-Homeric Theory, as applied to the Pentateuch. 2010. pap. 17.80 (978-1-61143-168-1(9)) Gorgias Pr., LLC.

Woods, Edward J. Deuteronomy. 2011. (Tyndale Old Testament Commentaries Ser.: 5). (ENG.). 333p. pap. 16.00 **(978-0-8308-4281-0(0)**, IVP Acad.) InterVarsity Pr.

Work, Telford. Deuteronomy, 1 vol. 2009. (Brazos Theological Commentary on the Bible Ser.). 336p. (C). 29.99 (978-1-58743-098-5(3)) Brazos Pr.

Yadler, Ben-Tsiyon. From the Maggidim of Yesteryear. 2008. (978-1-4226-0828-9(X)); (978-1-4226-0884-5(0)) Mesorah Pubns., Ltd.

Yah Chanan: The Beloved. (978-0-9631951-5-9(8)) Exegeses Bibles.

Zornberg, Avivah Gottlieb. The Beginning of Desire: Reflections on Genesis. 2011. (ENG.). 480p. pap. 19.95 (978-0-8052-1239-6(6), Schocken) Knopf Doubleday Publishing Group.

—The Particulars of Rapture: Reflections on Exodus. 2011. (ENG.). 592p. pap. 21.95 (978-0-8052-1237-2(X), Knopf) Knopf Doubleday Publishing Group.

BIBLE—COMMENTARIES—O. T. POETICAL BOOKS

Aitken, James. The Book of Job: A Handbook for Bible Classes & Private Students. 2007. 124p. per. (978-1-4067-8899-0(6), Pomona Pr.) Read Bks.

Alexander, J. A. The Psalms, Tr & Explained by J a Alexander + 2006. (ENG.). 356p. per. 26.99 (978-1-4255-3726-5(X)); 320p. per. 23.99 (978-1-4255-3156-0(3)); (ENG.). 456p. per. 29.99 (978-1-4255-5053-0(3)) MPublishing.

Alobaidi, Joseph, ed. Old Jewish Commentaries on the Song of Songs I: The Commentary of Yefet Ben Eli. 2010. 357p. pap. (978-3-0343-0452-8(8)) Lang, Peter.

Alter, Robert. The Book of Psalms: A Translation with Commentary. 2007. (ENG.). 560p. 35.00 (978-0-393-06226-7(0), 6226) Norton, W. W. & Co., Inc.

Alter, Robert, et al. The Book of Psalms: A Translation with Commentary. 2009. (ENG.). 560p. pap. 19.95 (978-0-393-33704-4(9), 33704) Norton, W. W. & Co., Inc.

Andersen, Francis I. Job, 1 vol. 2008. (Tyndale Old Testament Commentaries Ser.: Volume 14). (ENG., Illus.). 318p. pap. 16.00 (978-0-8308-4214-8(4), IVP Acad.) InterVarsity Pr.

Arthur, Kay & De Lacy, Pete. Praising God Through Prayer & Worship: Psalms. 2008. (New Inductive Study Ser.). 176p. pap. 9.99 (978-0-7369-2304-0(7)) Harvest Hse. Pubs.

Baker Publishing Group Staff. Moments of Peace from the Psalms. 2007. (Illus.). 384p. 13.99 (978-0-7642-0420-3(3)) Bethany Hse. Pubs.

Balentine, Samuel E. Job. 2006. (Smyth & Helwys Bible Commentary Ser.). (Illus.). 750p. incl. cd-rom (978-1-57312-067-8(7)) Smyth & Helwys Publishing, Inc.

Band, Debra. I Will Wake the Dawn: Illuminated Psalms. 2007. (ENG., Illus.). 128p. 75.00 (978-0-8276-0839-9(X)) Jewish Pubn. Society.

Banks, Zari. O Lord, Hear My Cry: A Book of Psalms Devotional. 2011. (ENG.). 74p. pap. 9.00 **(978-0-615-52426-9(5))** Smarty Pants Publishing.

Barbiero, Gianni. Song of Songs: A Close Reading. 2011. 450p. **(978-90-04-20325-9(7))** BRILL.

Barnes, Albert. Notes, Critical, Explanatory, & Practical, on the Book of Psalms. 2009. 424p. 34.99 (978-1-115-93448-0(1)); 41.99 (978-1-115-93447-3(3)); pap. 34.75 (978-1-115-93450-3(3)); pap. 35.75 (978-1-115-93449-7(X)) BiblioBazaar.

—Notes, Critical, Explanatory, & Practical, on the Book of Psalms. 2006. (ENG.). 428p. per. 26.99 (978-1-4255-4703-5(6)); (ENG.). 388p. per. 26.99 (978-1-4255-4163-7(1)); 356p. per. 26.99 (978-1-4255-3714-2(6)) MPublishing.

Bartholomew, Craig G. Ecclesiastes, 1 vol. 2009. (Baker Commentary on the Old Testament Wisdom & Psalms Ser.) 448p. (C). 42.99 (978-0-8010-2691-1(1)) Baker Academic.

Bede. The Venerable Bede: On the Song of Songs & Selected Writings. 2011. pap. (978-0-8091-4700-7(9)); (Illus.). (978-0-8091-0591-5(8)) Paulist Pr.

Beyerlin, Walter. Werden und Wesen des 107. Psalms. (Beihefte zur Zeitschrift far die alttestamentliche Wissenschaft Ser.). (GER.). XII, 120p. 210.00 **(978-3-11-177629-3(8))** De Gruyter, Walter Inc.

Bicksler, William H. Job's Spiritual Journey: The Believer & Rationalist with Questions of God & Man. 2009. 592p. pap. 29.99 (978-1-4389-2255-3(8)) AuthorHouse.

Biermann, Joel D. Psalms of the Messiah: A Man's Journey Through the Psalms. 2009. (Blessed Is the Man Ser.). (Illus.). 192p. pap. 9.99 (978-0-7586-1722-4(4)) Concordia Publishing Hse.

Blaising, Craig A. & Hardin, Carmen S., eds. Psalms 1-50, Vol. 7. 2008. (Ancient Christian Commentary on Scripture Ser.: Old Testament Volume 7). (ENG.). 486p. 50.00 (978-0-8308-1477-0(9), IVP Acad.) InterVarsity Pr.

Blake, William. Illustrations of the Book of Job. 2006. pap. 15.95 (978-1-4286-4375-8(3)) Kessinger Publishing, LLC.

Blank, Rodolfo. Salmos: Una Ventana Al Antiguo Testamento y Al Mesías. 2008. (Comentario Concordia Ser.). (SPA.). 695p. 24.99 (978-0-7586-0823-9(3)) Concordia Publishing Hse.

Bollhagen, James G. Ecclesiastes. 2011. (Concordia Commentary Ser.). 504p. 42.99 (978-0-570-06387-2(6)) Concordia Publishing Hse.

Bolton, Martha. Don't Jump to Conclusions Without a Bungee Cord. 210p. pap. 10.99 (978-0-8307-3414-6(7), Gospel Light) Gospel Light Pubns.

Bourgeault, Cynthia. Chanting the Psalms: A Practical Guide with Instructional CD. 2006. (Illus.). 240p. pap. 24.95 (978-1-59030-257-6(5), New Seeds Bks.) Shambhala Pubns., Inc.

Branon, Dave, et al. My Soul Thirsts for God: Reflections on the Psalms from Our Daily Bread. 2009. (ENG.). 208p. pap. 11.99 (978-1-57293-324-8(0)) Discovery Hse. Pubs.

Brestin, Dee. A Woman of Contentment: Ecclesiastes Insights into Life's Sorrows & Trials. 2007. (Dee Brestins Ser.). (ENG., Illus.). 160p. per. 10.99 (978-0-7814-4447-7(0)) Cook, David C.

Bridges, Charles. An Exposition of the Book of Proverbs V1. 2007. (ENG.). 496p. 53.95 (978-0-548-09683-3(X)) Kessinger Publishing, LLC.

Briggs, Charles August. Critical & Exegetical Commentary on Th. 2006. pap. 42.95 (978-1-4286-4167-9(X)) Kessinger Publishing, LLC.

Brookins, Larry A. Seven Things That God Hates & Seven Letters to Seven Churches. 2010. 232p. 24.99 (978-1-4520-4727-0(8)); pap. 19.99 (978-1-4520-4728-7(6)) AuthorHouse.

Brown, Michelle P. The Luttrell Psalter. fac. ed. 2006. (LAT & ENG., Illus.). 309p. (C). 675.00 (978-0-7123-4934-5(0)) British Library, The GBR. Dist: Chicago Distribution Ctr.

Brown, William P. Ecclesiastes: Interpretation: A Bible Commentary for Teaching & Preaching. 2011. (Interpretation Ser.). (ENG.). 160p. pap. 25.00 (978-0-664-23824-7(6)) Westminster John Knox Pr.

Bullinger, E. W. Book of Job Including the Oldest Lesson. 2006. pap. 17.95 (978-1-60206-020-3(7), Cosimo Classics) Cosimo, Inc.

—The Book of Job, Including the Oldest Lesson in the World. 2007. 216p. 26.95 (978-1-60206-784-4(8)) Cosimo, Inc.

—The Chief Musician or, Studies in the Psalms, & Their Titles. 2007. 332p. 29.95 (978-1-60206-785-1(6)) Cosimo, Inc.

Burchfiel, Kristi. Without Regrets: A Study of Ecclesiastes. 2010. pap. 12.99 (978-1-61566-500-6(5)) Tate Publishing & Enterprises, LLC.

Burns, Paul C. A Model for the Christian Life: Hilary of Poitiers' Commentary on the Psalms. 2012. **(978-0-8132-1987-5(6))** Catholic Univ. of America Pr.

Burt, David. 25 Sketches about Proverbs. 2006. (ENG.). 173p. per. 12.99 (978-0-85476-871-4(8)) Kingsway Pubns. GBR. Dist: STL Distribution North America.

Canclini, Arnoldo. Amada Mia, Amado Mio: Song of Songs - a Commentary. (SPA.). 112p. (978-84-7228-196-7(5), 220015) Clie, Editorial.

Candlish, Robert S. The Prayer of a Broken Heart: Expository Discourses on Psalm 51. 2011. 100p. pap. 12.00 **(978-1-59925-251-3(1))** Solid Ground Christian Bks.

Christianson, Eric S. Ecclesiastes Through the Centuries. (ENG.). 336p. 2012. pap. 44.95 **(978-0-470-67491-8(1))** 2007. (Illus.). 110.95 (978-0-631-22529-4(3)) Wiley, John & Sons, Inc. (Wiley-Blackwell).

Çiçek, Julius Yeshu. Three Memre about the Book of Ecclesiastes. 2010. (SYR.). 84.80 (978-1-61143-221-3(9)) Gorgias Pr., LLC.

Claire, Ellie, compiled by. Psalmos. 2011. (ENG & SPA.). 144p. 9.99 **(978-1-60936-473-1(2))** Ellie Claire & Summerside Pr.

Clarke, Thomas B. A Topical Treasury of Proverbs. 2009. 336p. pap. 19.95 (978-0-7375-0164-3(2)) Biblical Studies Pr.

Clarke, Thomas B., ed. A Topical Treasury of Proverbs. 2008. 336p. 29.95 (978-0-7375-0155-1(3)) Biblical Studies Pr.

Clements, R. Songs of Experience. 192p. 10.99 (978-1-85792-019-2(8)) Christian Focus Pubns. GBR. Dist: Spring Arbor Distributors, Inc.

Clines, David J. A. Job 21-37, 0 vols. 2006. (Word Biblical Commentary Ser.: Vol. 18). 560p. 49.99 (978-0-8499-0217-8(7)) Nelson, Thomas Inc.

—Job 38-42, 0 vols. 2011. (Word Biblical Commentary Ser.). 544p. 49.99 (978-0-7852-5267-2(3)) Nelson, Thomas Inc.

Cloud, David W. Proverbs: Wisdom of the Wise & Foolish. Date not set. pap. 19.95 (978-1-58318-007-5(9), WOL Proverbs) Way of Life Literature.

Conant, Thomas. The Psalms the Common Version Revised for the American Bible Union. 2006. 240p. per. 20.99 (978-1-4255-2036-6(7)) MPublishing.

Connelly, Douglas. The Book of Psalms, 0 vols. Richards, Larry, ed. 2008. (Smart Guide to the Bible Ser.). 416p. pap. 14.99 (978-1-4185-1010-7(6)) Nelson, Thomas Inc.

Conti, Marco, ed. 1-2 Kings, 1-2 Chronicles, Ezra, Nehemiah, Esther. 2008. (Ancient Christian Commentary on Scripture Ser.: Old Testament Volume 5). (ENG.). 480p. 50.00 (978-0-8308-1475-6(2), IVP Acad.) InterVarsity Pr.

Cooper, Kathryn. Dear Church. 2007. 88p. per. 16.95 (978-1-4241-7310-5(8)) PublishAmerica, Inc.

Cox, Harvey & Paulsell, Stephanie. Lamentations & the Song of Songs: A Theological Commentary on the Bible. 2012. (Belief: A Theological Commentary on the Bible Ser.). (ENG.). 304p. 30.00 **(978-0-664-23302-0(3))** Westminster John Knox Pr.

Crenshaw, James L. Reading Job. 2011. pap. (978-1-57312-574-1(1)) Smyth & Helwys Publishing, Inc.

Crotts, Stephen M. A Psalm for Every Sigh. 2008. (978-0-7880-2548-8(1)) CSS Publishing Co.

Darby, J. N. Reflexiones Sobre los Salmos: Lectures on the Psalms. (SPA.). (978-84-7645-029-1(X), 223100) Clie, Editorial.

Davis, Dale Ralph. The Way of the Righteous in the Muck of Life: Psalms 112. 2010. (ENG.). 144p. 10.99 *(978-1-84550-581-3(6))* Christian Focus Pubns. GBR. Dist: STL Distribution North America.

Daw, Carl P., Jr. & Hackett, Kevin R. Gradual Psalms: Advent Through the Day of Pentecost. 2007. (Illus.). 200p. spiral bd. 25.00 *(978-0-89869-558-8(9))* Church Publishing, Inc.

—Gradual Psalms: The Season after Pentecost. 2007. 272p. spiral bd. 30.00 *(978-0-89869-573-1(2))* Church Publishing, Inc.

Dawn, Marva J. My Soul Waits: Solace for the Lonely in the Psalms. 2007. (ENG.). 268p. per. 16.00 *(978-0-8308-3443-3(5)*, IVP Bks.) InterVarsity Pr.

De Valdes, Juan. Comentario a los Salmos: The Book of Psalms. (SPA.). 256p. *(978-84-7645-174-8(1)*, 223214) Clie, Editorial.

Delitzsch, Franz. Commentary on the Song of Songs & Ecclesiastes. Easton, M. G., tr. 2008. 454p. pap. 38.00 *(978-1-60608-191-4(8)*, Wipf and Stock) Wipf & Stock Pubs.

Donelan, Thomas. Filling the Empty Life. 2009. 40p. pap. 10.00 *(978-0-557-21424-2(6))* Lulu Enterprises Inc.

Dunn, Robert. Proverbs of Solomon Revisted. 2011. pap. 10.95 ***(978-0-7414-6574-0(4))*** Infinity Publishing.

Eaton, John. Psalms for Life: Hearing & Praying the Book of Psalms. 2007. (ENG.). 389p. per. 25.00 *(978-0-664-23116-3(0))* Westminster John Knox Pr.

Elgin, Vernon G. Seven Abominations with a Wrench: Proverbs 6:16-19. 2010. 132p. 21.49 *(978-1-4520-2511-7(8))*; pap. 10.99 *(978-1-4520-2510-0(X))* AuthorHouse.

Emmenegger, Gregor. Der Text des koptischen Psalters aus al-Mudil: Ein Beitrag zur Textgeschichte der Septuaginta und zur Textkritik koptischer Bibelhandschriften, mit der kritischen Neuausgabe des Papyrus 37 der British Library London (U) und des Papyrus 39 der Leipziger Universitätsbibliothek (2013) 2007. (Texte und Untersuchungen zur Geschichte der altchristlichen Literatur Ser.: Vol. 159). (GEC & GER., Illus.). XXVIII, 391p. 182.00 *(978-3-11-019948-2(3))* De Gruyter, Walter Inc.

Encina, David. Whosoever: Finding Christ in the Book of Proverbs. 2010. pap. 23.99 *(978-1-61663-015-7(9))* Tate Publishing & Enterprises, LLC.

Engelsma, David J. Prosperous Wicked & Plagued Saints: An Exposition of Psalm 73. 2007. (ENG.). 120p. pap. 10.95 *(978-0-916206-96-3(3))* Reformed Free Publishing Assn.

Ewald, Georg Heinrich. Commentary on the Psalms. Johnson, E., tr. 2007. 715p. pap. 60.00 *(978-1-55635-749-7(4)*, Wipf and Stock) Wipf & Stock Pubs.

An Exposition of the Psalms, 2 vols., Vol. 1. 2009. 670p. reprint ed. 32.50 net. *(978-1-888514-32-2(9))* Particular Baptist Pr.

Faughn, Adam. Be Wise God's Way. 2007. (YA). per. 9.00 *(978-0-9725894-3-7(0))* Riddle Creek Publishing.

Fesko, J. V. Where Wisdom Is Found: Christ in Ecclesiastes. 2010. pap. 10.00 *(978-1-60178-092-8(3))* Reformation Heritage Bks.

Fogg, Paul, illus. Psalm 23 for Little Hands & Hearts. 2010. 16p. pap. 5.95 *(978-0-9814878-4-7(X))* Little Hands Bk. Co., LLC.

Fox, Michael V. & Fox, M. V. Proverbs 10-31. 2009. (Anchor Yale Bible Commentaries Ser.). (ENG., Illus.). 752p. 60.00 *(978-0-300-14209-9(9))* Yale Univ. Pr.

Fredericks, Daniel C. & Estes, Daniel J. Ecclesiastes & the Song of Songs. 2010. (Apollos Old Testament Commentary Ser.). (ENG.). 472p. 40.00 *(978-0-8308-2515-8(0)*, IVP Acad.) InterVarsity Pr.

Furst, Renata. Rut, Esdras, Nehemias y Ester: Ruth, Ezra, Nehemiah & Esther. 2009. (Conozca su Biblia Ser.). 128p. pap. 15.00 *(978-0-8066-5778-3(2))* Augsburg Fortress, Pubs.

Futato, Mark D. & Schwab, George M. Psalms, Proverbs. 2009. (Cornerstone Biblical Commentary Ser.: 7). (ENG.). 684p. 36.99 *(978-0-8423-3433-4(5))* Tyndale Hse. Pubs.

Fyall, R. Travelling Hopefully. 128p. 10.00 *(978-0-281-04942-4(4))* SPCK Publishing GBR. Dist: Pilgrim Pr., The/United Church Pr.

Gaba, Latif Haki. The English Psalter. 2010. 182p. pap. 21.96 *(978-0-557-33774-3(7))* Lulu Enterprises Inc.

Gallagher, Steve. He Leads Me Beside Still Waters: A 12week Study Through the Choicest Psalms. 2009. (Walk Ser.). (ENG.). 144p. pap. 10.99 *(978-0-9800286-0-7(4))* Pure Life Ministries.

Garcia-Treto, Francisco. Salmos. 2008. (Conozca su Biblia Ser.). 168p. pap. 15.00 *(978-0-8066-8020-0(2))* Augsburg Fortress, Pubs.

Garman, Kelsey. Living the Word: A Devotional & Practical Commentary on Psalm 119. 2008. 356p. pap. 18.99 *(978-1-60791-225-5(2))* Xulon Pr., Inc.

Gillingham, Susan. Psalms Through the Centuries, Vol. 1. (Blackwell Bible Commentaries Ser.). (ENG.). 2012. 408p. pap. 39.95 ***(978-0-470-67490-1(3))*** 2008. (Illus.). 400p. 115.95 *(978-0-631-21855-5(6))* Wiley, John & Sons, Inc. (Wiley-Blackwell).

Ginsburg, Christian D. The Song of Songs. 2009. 202p. pap. 17.00 *(978-1-60608-749-7(5)*, Wipf and Stock) Wipf & Stock Pubs.

Givens, Don. Storms of Life. 2008. 164p. 22.99 *(978-1-60647-748-9(X))*; pap. 14.99 *(978-1-60647-747-2(1))* Xulon Pr., Inc.

Glavich, Mary Kathleen. The Catholic Companion to the Psalms. 2008. 160p. pap. 9.95 *(978-0-87946-364-9(3))* ACTA Pubns.

Glazer, Miriyam. Psalms of the Jewish Liturgy: A Guide to Their Beauty, Power, & Meaning. 2009. (ENG.). 260p. pap. 17.95 *(978-0-916219-41-3(0)*, Aviv Pr.) Rabbinical Assembly.

Goertzen, Gaylord. Blessed by God: Studies in the Book of Psalms. 118p. pap. 3.60 *(978-0-921788-75-1(4))* Kindred Productions.

Gold, Shefa. In the Fever of Love: An Illumination of the Song of Songs. 2009. 25.00 *(978-1-934730-25-6(4))*; 112p. pap. 14.95 *(978-1-934730-26-3(2))* Yehuda, Ben Pr.

Goldingay, John. Psalms, 3 vols. 2008. (Baker Commentary on the Old Testament Wisdom & Psalms Ser.). 2208p. (C). 135.00 *(978-0-8010-3607-1(0))* Baker Academic.

—Psalms 1-41, 3 vols., Vol. 1. 2006. (Baker Commentary on the Old Testament Wisdom & Psalms Ser.). (Illus.). 640p. (C). 49.99 *(978-0-8010-2703-1(9))* Baker Academic.

—Psalms, 90-150 Vol. 3, 3 vols., Vol. 3. 2008. (Baker Commentary on the Old Testament Wisdom & Psalms Ser.). (Illus.). 816p. (C). 49.99 *(978-0-8010-3143-4(5))* Baker Academic.

Gray, John, ed. Book of Job. 2010. 450p. ***(978-1-905048-02-1(5))*** Sheffield Phoenix Pr.

Griffiths, Paul J. Song of Songs. 2011. lviii, 182p. (C). 32.99 *(978-1-58743-135-7(1))* Brazos Pr.

Grigor. The Blessing of Blessings: Gregory of Narek's Commentary of the Song of Songs. Ervine, Roberta, tr. from ARM. 2008. (Cistercian Studies). 220p. per. *(978-0-87907-215-5(6))* Cistercian Pubns., Inc.

Grogan, Geoffrey W. Psalms. 2008. (Two Horizons Old Testament Commentary Ser.). 432p. pap. 25.00 *(978-0-8028-2706-7(3))* Eerdmans, William B. Publishing Co.

Gruber, Mayer I. Rashi's Commentary on Psalms. 2007. (Brill Reference Library of Judaism Ser.). (ENG.). 920p. per. 50.00 *(978-0-8276-0872-6(1))* Jewish Pubn. Society.

Hakham, Amos. Bible: Job: With the Jerusalem Commentary. 2009. 456p. 57.50 *(978-965-7265-08-6(8))* Mosad Harav Kook ISR. Dist: Coronet Bks.

Hales, Mick, photos by. The Book of Psalms. 2008. (ENG., Illus.). 368p. 17.95 *(978-0-8109-9527-7(1))* Abrams.

Hanks, Scott. Men & Women of Proverbs. 2nd ed. 2007. (Illus.). per. *(978-0-9799518-0-0(1))* Hanks, Scott.

Hargrove, Th. D. Triumph of the Soul. 2008. 178p. pap. 24.95 *(978-1-60474-751-5(X))* PublishAmerica, Inc.

Harper, Ayrion & Harper, Sharon. Don't Be Ashamed to Pray, 1 vol. 2010. 48p. pap. 16.95 *(978-1-4489-4666-2(2))* PublishAmerica, Inc.

Haupt, Paul. Ecclesiastes. 2009. pap. 21.64 *(978-1-60724-631-2(7))* Gorgias Pr., LLC.

Hayden, Valda. Through the Valley: A Stunning Revelation of the Good Shepherd's Care for His Flock. Comprehensively Outlined in Psalm 23. 2009. 116p. pap. 11.99 *(978-1-61579-106-4(X))* Xulon Pr., Inc.

Hayford, Jack W. Psalms/Proverbs, 0 vols. 2008. (Spirit-Filled Life Study Guide Ser.). 128p. pap. 9.99 *(978-1-4185-3329-8(7))* Nelson, Thomas Inc.

Heirich, Beverly Coney, compiled by. Mornings with Fulton Sheen: 120 Holy Hour Readings. 2007. 120p. per. 10.99 *(978-0-86716-842-6(0)*, Servant Bks.) Franciscan Media.

Hempe, Isaiah. E-Z Memory Book of Psalms. 2010. 272p. pap. 15.99 *(978-0-9840725-1-4(9))* Tzyon Pr.

Henry, Matthew. Comentario Matthew Henry Vol. I: Poeticos: Matthew Henry's Commentary: Matthew Henry. (SPA.). 512p. *(978-84-7645-222-6(5)*, 223269) Clie, Editorial.

Hickey, Marilyn. Psalms Classic. lib. bdg. 24.95 *(978-1-56441-039-9(0))* Hickey, Marilyn Ministries.

Holbert, John C. Preaching Job. 2011. 204p. pap. 22.00 ***(978-1-61097-278-9(3)***, Wipf and Stock) Wipf & Stock Pubs.

Hooks, Stephen M. Job. 2006. 485p. *(978-0-89900-886-8(0))* College Pr. Publishing Co., Inc.

Hossfeld, Frank Lothar & Zenger, Erich. Psalms 3: A Commentary on Psalms 101-150. 2011. (Hermeneia Ser.). 600p. 69.00 *(978-0-8006-0762-3(7)*, Fortress Pr.) Augsburg Fortress, Pubs.

Hughes, Selwyn & Sewter, Ian. 23rd Psalm. 2008. 72p. *(978-1-85345-449-3(4))* Crusade for World Revival.

Imoru, Nicholas. A Heart for God. 2007. 140p. per. *(978-0-9555562-4-1(4))* Esteemworld Pubns.

Ingram, Doug & Nodet, Etienne. Historical Jesus? Necessity & Limits of an Inquiry. Crowley, J. Edward, tr. from FRE. 2008. (Jewish & Christian Texts in Contexts & Related Studies Ser.). (ENG., Illus.). 256p. 150.00 *(978-0-567-02721-4(X)*, T&T Clark Int'l) Continuum International Publishing Group, Ltd. GBR. Dist: National Bk. Network.

Ironside, Henry A. & Ironside, H. A. Proverbs & Song of Solomon, 1 vol. 2006. (Ironside Expository Commentaries Ser.). 360p. 24.99 *(978-0-8254-2916-3(1))* Kregel Pubns.

Iskowitz, Yaakov Yosef, tr. from HEB. Tehillim Eis Ratzon. (HEB & ENG.). 200p. 15.99 *(978-1-58330-634-5(X))* Feldheim Pubs.

Janzen, J. Gerald. Job: Interpretation: A Bible Commentary for Teaching & Preaching. 2012. (Interpretation: A Bible Commentary for Teaching & Preaching Ser.). (ENG.). 288p. pap. 25.00 ***(978-0-664-23877-3(7))*** Westminster John Knox Pr.

Jastrow, Morris. The Book of Job: Its Origin, Growth & Interpretation. 2007. 368p. pap. 31.00 *(978-1-55635-617-9(X)*, Wipf and Stock) Wipf & Stock Pubs.

—A Gentle Cynic. 2009. 144p. pap. *(978-0-217-16144-2(8))* Books LLC.

Jenson, Robert W. Song of Songs: Interpretation: A Bible Commentary for Teaching & Preaching. 2012. (Interpretation: A Bible Commentary for Teaching & Preaching Ser.). (ENG.). 118p. pap. 25.00 ***(978-0-664-23886-5(6))*** Westminster John Knox Pr.

Jerome. St. Jerome: Commentary on Ecclesiastes. 2012. ***(978-1-61643-090-0(7))***; 272p. 39.95 ***(978-0-8091-0601-1(9))*** Paulist Pr. (Newman Pr., The).

John Chrysostom. St. John Chrysostom Commentary on Job. 2006. pap. *(978-1-885652-77-5(1))* Holy Cross Orthodox Pr.

—St. John Chrysostom Commentary on Proverbs & Commentary on Ecclesiastes. 2006. pap. *(978-1-885652-78-2(X))* Holy Cross Orthodox Pr.

Johnson, Vivian L. David in Distress: His Portrait Through the Historical Psalms. 2009. (Library of Hebrew Bible/Old Testament Studies, the Ser.). (ENG.). 176p. 120.00 *(978-0-567-02734-4(1)*, T&T Clark Int'l) Continuum International Publishing Group, Ltd. GBR. Dist: National Bk. Network.

Jones, Beth. 21 Days to a Satisfied Life: Encouraging Words for Fabulous Days. 2009. 96p. pap. 4.99 *(978-1-57794-966-4(8))* Harrison House Pubs.

Jones, Hywel R. Job. 2007. (Evangelical Press Study Commentary Ser.). 304p. *(978-0-85234-664-8(6))* Evangelical Pr.

Jones, Rev. C. B. Above & Beyond All Circumstances God Has a Unique Answer. 2010. 50p. pap. 15.99 *(978-1-4535-2738-2(9))* Xlibris Corp.

Jones, Sheila. My Bucket of Sand: And Other Spiritual Thoughts. 2010. 200p. pap. 13.00 *(978-1-57782-237-0(4))* Discipleship Pubns. International.

Keck, Ron & Colter, Ben. Song of Songs: The Epic Romance. 2007. (Illus.). 128p. 7.90 *(978-1-57494-340-5(5)*, Serendipity Hse.) LifeWay Christian Resources.

Keller, W. Phillip & Keller, W. P. A Shepherd Looks at Psalm 23, 1 vol. 2007. (ENG.). 128p. 15.99 *(978-0-310-27442-1(7))*; 144p. (gr. 13). mass mkt. 4.99 *(978-0-310-27441-4(9))*; 144p. (gr. 13). pap. 12.99 *(978-0-310-27443-8(5))* Zondervan.

Kendon, F. Thirty Six Psalms. 2009. (ENG.). 76p. pap. 20.99 *(978-0-521-10325-1(8))* Cambridge Univ. Pr.

Kidner, Derek. Proverbs, 1 vol. 2009. (Tyndale Old Testament Commentaries Ser.: Volume 17). (ENG.). 189p. pap. 16.00 *(978-0-8308-4217-9(9)*, IVP Acad.) InterVarsity Pr.

Kitchen, John. Praying Through: Finding Wholeness & Healing in the Prayers of David. 2007. (ENG.). 276p. pap. 13.99 *(978-0-87508-976-2(X))* CLC Pubns.

Kitchen, John A. Proverbs: A Mentor Commentary. 2006. (Mentor Commentary Ser.). (ENG.). 792p. 39.99 *(978-1-84550-059-7(8))* Christian Focus Pubns. GBR. Dist: STL Distribution North America.

Kniep Seth. Loving God's Word: 7 Strategies for Slaying Bible Apathy. 2007. 286p. *(978-0-9718306-9-1(X))* LifeSong Pubs.

Kriegshauser, Laurence. Praying the Psalms in Christ. 2009. (ND Reading the Scriptures Ser.). (ENG.). 376p. pap. 35.00 *(978-0-268-03320-0(X))* Univ. of Notre Dame Pr.

Kushner, Harold S. The Book of Job: When Bad Things Happened to a Good Person. 2012. (ENG.). 224p. 24.00 ***(978-0-8052-4292-8(9)***, Schocken) Knopf Doubleday Publishing Group.

Landy, Francis. Paradoxes of Paradise: Identity & Difference in the Song of Songs. 2nd ed. 2011. xiv, 305p. pap. ***(978-1-906055-41-7(6))*** Sheffield Phoenix Pr.

Lane, Eric. Proverbs: Everyday Wisdom for Everyone. 2007. (Focus on the Bible Commentaries Ser.). (ENG.). 432p. per. 14.99 *(978-1-84550-267-6(1))* Christian Focus Pubns. GBR. Dist: STL Distribution North America.

—Psalms 90-150: The Lord Reigns, 2 vols. 2006. (ENG.). 320p. per. 15.99 *(978-1-84550-202-7(7))* Christian Focus Pubns. GBR. Dist: STL Distribution North America.

—Psalms Chapters 1-89: The Lord Saves, 2 vols. 2006. (ENG.). 416p. per. 17.99 *(978-1-84550-180-8(2))* Christian Focus Pubns. GBR. Dist: STL Distribution North America.

Larosa, Frank. The Book of Proverbs in Plain English. 2011. 144p. 28.50 ***(978-1-4567-9635-8(6))***; pap. 19.98 ***(978-1-4567-9636-5(4))*** AuthorHouse.

Layne, W. P. Vanity for All Sanity for None. 2007. 84p. per. 9.99 *(978-1-60266-440-1(4))* Xulon Pr., Inc.

Let the Reedeemed of the Lord Say So. 6.00 incl. audio *(978-0-687-76226-2(X))* Abingdon Pr.

Levi, Israel. The Hebrew Text of the Book of Ecclesiasticus. 2007. (ENG.). 108p. 33.95 *(978-0-548-25716-6(7))*; 100p. per. 18.95 *(978-1-4326-6075-8(6))* Kessinger Publishing, LLC.

Levi, Israel, ed. The Hebrew Text of the Book of Ecclesiasticus. 2008. 100p. pap. 14.00 *(978-1-55635-718-3(4))* Wipf & Stock Pubs.

Lifetogether. Proverbs. 2010. (Deepening Life Together Ser.). 24.99 *(978-0-8010-3054-3(4))*; pap. 8.99 *(978-0-8010-6967-3(X))* Baker Bks.

—Psalms. 2011. (Deepening Life Together Ser.). (Illus.). 85p. pap. 8.99 *(978-0-8010-6855-3(X))* Baker Bks.

Limburg, James. Encountering Ecclesiastes: A Book for Our Time. 2006. (Illus.). 141p. per. 14.00 *(978-0-8028-3047-0(1))* Eerdmans, William B. Publishing Co.

Lioy, Dan. The Divine Sabotage: An Expositional Journey Through Ecclesiastes. 2008. 192p. pap. 22.00 *(978-1-55635-961-3(6))* Wipf & Stock Pubs.

Longman, Tremper, ed. Quicknotes Simplified Bible Commentary Vol. 5: Psalms thru Song of Solomon. 2010. (QuickNotes Commentaries Ser.). (ENG.). 208p. pap. 9.99 *(978-1-59789-771-6(X)*, Barbour Bks.) Barbour Publishing, Inc.

Louer, Chris. Staircase to Transformation. 2008. 72p. pap. 10.99 *(978-1-60647-880-6(X))* Xulon Pr., Inc.

Luther, Martin. Reading the Psalms with Luther: The Psalter for Individual & Family Devotions. 2007. (ENG.). 363p. 14.99 *(978-0-7586-1375-2(X))* Concordia Publishing Hse.

Maclaren, Alexander. Expositions of Holy Scripture- Psalms. 2007. 622p. pap. 31.99 *(978-1-4264-4987-1(9))* BiblioBazaar.

—Expositions of Holy Scripture, Psalms. Lt. ed. 2007. (ENG.). 688p. pap. 34.99 *(978-1-4264-5288-8(8))* BiblioBazaar.

Mangano, Mark J. Power & Grace: A Theology of the Psalms. 2010. 152p. pap. 17.00 *(978-1-60899-909-5(2)*, Wipf and Stock) Wipf & Stock Pubs.

Marquardt, Thomas. Psalms: The Timeline to Jesus Christ's Return. 2011. 76p. pap. 10.84 *(978-1-4269-6333-9(5))* Trafford Publishing.

Martínez, José M. Biblia y Su Mensaje - Salmos: Bible & Its Message - Psalms, Vol. 6. (SPA.). 176p. *(978-84-7645-410-7(4)*, 223547) Clie, Editorial.

Marwick, Lawrence, ed. The Arabic Commentary of Salmon Ben Yeruham, the Karaite, on the Book of Psalms Chapters 42-72. 2011. 128p. 40.95 ***(978-1-258-04500-5(1))*** Literary Licensing, LLC.

Masters, Sylvia P. Praise, Thanksgiving, Lament & More with the Psalms for Our Times Songs Now We Too Can Sing! 2008. 288p. pap. 16.99 *(978-1-60647-452-5(9))* Xulon Pr., Inc.

Mays, James Luther. Psalms: Interpretation: A Bible Commentary for Teaching & Preaching. 2011. (Interpretation Ser.). (ENG.). 480p. pap. 30.00 *(978-0-664-23439-3(9))* Westminster John Knox Pr.

McAlpine, Campbell. Wisdom from Above: God's Wisdom from the Book of Proverbs. 2007. 351p. pap. *(978-1-903725-94-8(1))* New Wine Pr.

McConica, James K. & Baker-Smith, Dominic. Expositions of the Psalms: Collected Works of Erasmus, Vol. 65. 2010. (Collected Works of Erasmus Ser.). (Illus.). 352p. *(978-0-8020-9979-2(3))* Univ. of Toronto Pr.

McCorkle, Dennis F. The Davidic Cipher: Unlocking the Music of the Psalms. 2009. 258p. 29.95 *(978-1-4327-4984-2(6))* Outskirts Pr., Inc.

Meadows, James L. Ecclesiastes. pap. 5.50 *(978-0-89098-386-7(0))* Twentieth Century Christian Bks.

Merrill, Nan C. Psalms for Praying: An Invitation to Wholeness. 10th anniv. ed. 2006. (ENG.). 320p. 32.95 *(978-0-8264-1905-7(4))* Continuum International Publishing Group, Ltd. GBR. Dist: National Bk. Network.

Merrill, Nan C. & Merrill. Psalms for Praying: An Invitation to Wholeness. 10th anniv. ed. 2006. (ENG.). 320p. pap. 22.95 *(978-0-8264-1906-4(2))* Continuum International Publishing Group, Ltd. GBR. Dist: National Bk. Network.

Meyer, F. B. Salmo del Pastor: The Shepherd's Psalm. (SPA.). 144p. *(978-84-7228-425-8(5)*, 220792) Clie, Editorial.

Meyer, F. B. Shepherd Psalm. 2011. 78p. pap. 9.99 ***(978-1-61203-267-2(2))*** Bottom of the Hill Publishing.

Mike Herron Music. Heart of A Psalmist: Worshipping Christ Through the Psalms. 2010. (Illus.). 412p. 19.95 *(978-0-615-38537-2(0))* LatterGlory International.

Miller, Douglas B. Ecclesiastes: Believers Church Bible Commentary Series, Vol. 23. 2010. (ENG.). 400p. pap. 24.99 *(978-0-8361-9491-3(8))* Herald Pr.

Morgan, G. Campbell. Notes on the Psalms. 2010. (G. Campbell Morgan Reprint Ser.). 288p. pap. 32.00 *(978-1-60899-303-1(5)*, Wipf and Stock) Wipf & Stock Pubs.

Murphy, Neal. The Psalms. 2008. 544p. 34.99 *(978-1-4363-7623-5(8))*; pap. 23.99 *(978-1-4363-7622-8(X))* Xlibris Corp.

My Cup Runneth Over. *(978-0-687-04952-3(0))* Abingdon Pr.

Nail, Marvin P. God's Encouraging Word. 2008. 248p. pap. 14.99 *(978-1-60647-524-9(X))* Xulon Pr., Inc.

Newbold, William Romaine. The Descent of Christ in the Odes of Solomon. 2007. per. 24.00 *(978-1-59333-866-4(X))* Gorgias Pr., LLC.

Oesterley, W. O. E. The Psalms in the Jewish Church. 2009. 280p. 30.99 *(978-1-110-58310-2(9))*; pap. 26.75 *(978-1-110-58309-6(5))* BiblioBazaar.

Ortlund Jr., Raymond C. Proverbs: Wisdom that Works. 2012. (Preaching the Word Ser.). 224p. 27.99 ***(978-1-58134-883-5(5))*** Crossway.

Orvis, David L., et al, eds. Psalms in the Early Modern World. 2011. (Illus.). 410p. 119.95 ***(978-1-4094-2282-2(8))*** Ashgate Publishing Co.

Overton, Janice M. Through the Word Today: A 365-Day Journey Through the Psalms & Proverbs. 2010. (Illus.). 384p. 14.95 *(978-0-615-39314-8(4))* Through the Word Today.

Owoc, Gregory. Let Wisdom Flow, the Entire Book of Proverbs in Poetic Verse: A Heart -Stirring Journey into the Truth That Lead to the Blessed Life. 2006. (Illus.). 352p. per. 19.99 *(978-0-9777696-5-0(8)*, LWF-992006) Virtue Publishing.

Parry, Arthur E. The Psalms for Today. 2006. 255p. pap. 27.95 *(978-1-4241-1759-8(3))* PublishAmerica, Inc.

Pearson, Carol Lynn. The Lord Is My Shepherd: Inspiration for Couples, 1 vol. 2009. (ENG.). 64p. 9.99 *(978-1-4236-0586-7(1))* Gibbs Smith, Publisher.

Pennington, M. Basil. Psalms: A Spiritual Commentary. 2008. (Illus.). 149p. pap. 16.99 *(978-1-59473-234-8(5))* SkyLight Paths Publishing.

—The Song of Songs: A Spiritual Commentary. 2007. (Illus.). 136p. per. 16.99 *(978-1-59473-235-5(3))* SkyLight Paths Publishing.

Perdue, Leo G. Proverbs: Interpretation: A Bible Commentary for Teaching & Preaching. 2012. (Interpretation: A Bible Commentary for Teaching & Preaching Ser.). (ENG.). 302p. pap. 25.00 ***(978-0-664-23884-1(X))*** Westminster John Knox Pr.

Phillips, Dan. God's Wisdom in Proverbs: Hearing God's Voice in Scripture. 2011. (ENG., Illus.). 405p. 24.99 ***(978-1-934952-14-6(1))*** Kress Christian Pubns.

Phillips, John. Exploring Proverbs, 2 vols., Set. 59.98 *(978-0-87213-579-6(9))* Loizeaux Brothers, Inc.

Powell, Bill. A Season with Solomon: Daily Devotions from the Book of Proverbs. 2009. (ENG.). 196p. pap. 16.95 *(978-1-60037-641-2(X))* Morgan James Publishing.

Psalm 19: 14 Bulletin, Large Size. 5.00 *(978-0-687-04011-7(6))* Abingdon Pr.

Psalm 23. 4.50 *(978-0-687-07619-2(6))* Abingdon Pr.

Ramirez, Frank. Proverbs, Ecclesiastes, Song of Solomon. 2012. 112p. 9.00 ***(978-1-4267-1631-7(1))*** Abingdon Pr.

Reitman, James. Unlocking Wisdom: Forming Agents of God in the House of Mourning - A Canonical-Linguistic Exposition of the Books of Job & Ecclesiastes. 2008. (ENG., Illus.). 384p. per. 19.99 *(978-0-9779535-5-4(6))* 21st Century Pr.

Rey, Jean-Sebastien & Joosten, Jan, eds. The Texts & Versions of the Book of Ben Sira: Transmission & Interpretation. 2011. (Supplements to the Journal for the Study of Judaism Ser.). (FRE.). X, 354p. (978-90-04-20692-2(2)) BRILL.
Rhodes, Schuyler. A Journey Through the Psalms: Reflections for Worried Hearts & Troubled Times: Preaching the Psalms, Cycles a, B, C. 2009. (978-0-7880-2527-0(5)) CSS Publishing Co.
Ries, Trudy & Scotti, Karen. Search My Heart, O God: Studies from the Book of Psalms. 2011. 122p. spiral bd. (978-0-9796332-4-9(9)) Calvary Chapel Pasadena.
Robinson, James T. Samuel Ibn Tibbon's Commentary on Ecclesiastes: The Book of the Soul of Man. 2007. (Texts & Studies in Medieval & Early Modern Judaism: 20). 670p. 267.50 (978-3-16-149067-5(3)) Mohr Siebeck GmbH & Co. KG DEU. Dist: Coronet Bks.
Roper, David. Psalm 23: The Song of a Passionate Heart. 2006. (ENG.). 176p. per. 9.99 (978-1-57293-200-5(7)) Discovery Hse. Pubs.
Roselli, Robert. The un-American Genocidal Complex. 2010. 132p. pap. 13.95 (978-1-4502-3547-1(6)) iUniverse, Inc.
Ross, Michael F. The Light of the Psalms: Deepening Your Faith with Every Psalm. 2006. (ENG.). 288p. per. 15.99 (978-1-84550-150-1(0)) Christian Focus Pubns. GBR. Dist: STL Distribution North America.
Ryken, Philip Graham, ed. Ecclesiastes: Why Everything Matters. 2010. (Preaching the Word Ser.). 320p. 33.99 (978-1-4335-1375-6(7)) Crossway.
Ryken, Philip Graham & Hughes, R. Kent. Ecclesiastes: Why Everything Matters. 2010. pap. (978-1-4335-1376-3(5)) Crossway.
S., J. Psalms Hebrew Text English Translation. 2006. 240p. per. (978-956-291-346-1(5)) Editorial Benel Noaj.
Salah, Daniel. Commentary on the Psalms. 2010. (SYR.). 143.60 (978-1-61143-245-9(6)) Gorgias Pr., LLC.
Salakpi, Alexander G. K. Social Alienation as a Consequence of Human Suffering in the Book of Job: A Study of Job 19: 13-22. 2010. 216p. pap. 17.95 (978-1-4502-4251-5(8)) iUniverse, Inc.
Sandling, Carly Martynia. Walking Through the Psalms of Life. 2008. 60p. pap. 9.99 (978-1-60477-256-2(5)) Xulon Pr., Inc.
Seals, Thomas. Proverbs: Wisdom for All Ages. 2007. 144p. per. 14.95 (978-1-58427-213-7(9)) Guardian of Truth Foundation.
Segal, Benjamin. Song of Songs: A Woman in Love. 2009. 204p. 30.00 (978-965-229-445-6(4)) Gefen Publishing Hse., Ltd ISR. Dist: Gefen Bks.
Selected Psalms. ldr's ed. (LifeLight Bible Studies: Course 25). pap. 8.99 (978-0-570-09722-8(3), 20-2755) Concordia Publishing Hse.
Shank, Carl. Upfront & Indepth: Deeper Devotional Studies on Psalm 119. 2010. 91p. pap. 8.95 (978-0-557-70770-6(6)) Lulu Enterprises Inc.
Shapiro, Rabbi Rami, tr. & anno. Ecclesiastes: Annotated & Explained. 2010. 192p. pap. 16.99 (978-1-59473-287-4(6)) SkyLight Paths Publishing.
Silva, Kittim. Predicando Sobre el Cantar de los Cantares: Preaching on the Song of Songs. (SPA.). (978-84-7645-288-2(8), 223364) Clie, Editorial.
Simmons, Brian, tr. The Most Amazing Song of All! A dynamic, equivalent translation of the Song of Songs from the Hebrew into modern English. 2011. pap. 9.00 (978-1-936578-03-0(4)) 5 Fold Media LLC.
Simpson, A. B. Los Salmos Mesianicos: Christ in the Psalms. (SPA.). 200p. (978-84-7228-953-6(2), 223022) Clie, Editorial.
Skevington, Andrea. Insights of the Psalms. 2007. (ENG., Illus.). 48p. 11.00 (978-0-7459-5217-8(8)) Lion Hudson PLC GBR. Dist: Independent Pubs. Group.
Smith, David. Precepts from the Psalms. 2010. 138p. pap. 12.99 (978-0-9845208-3-1(X)) Faithful Life Pubs.
Smith, Dudley. The Expository Commentary:Psalms. 2010. 516p. pap. 34.99 (978-0-557-31252-8(3)) Lulu Enterprises Inc.
Sorg, Rembert. God's Love Songs V1: An Essay on the Spirituality of the Psalms. 2011. 32p. 35.95 (978-1-258-02077-4(7)) Literary Licensing, LLC.
Speray, Steven. The Greatest Conspiracy Ever. 2009. 386p. pap. 26.99 (978-0-578-03574-1(X)) Confiteor.
Stedman, Ray L. Salmos de Esperanza & Fe: Folk Psalms of Faith. (SPA.). 288p. (978-84-7228-236-0(8), 220787) Clie, Editorial.
Steinhauser, Kenneth B., et al. Anonymi in Iob Commentarius. 2006. (Corpus Scriptorum Ecclesiasticorum Latinorum Ser.). (LAT & ENG.). 421p. (C). 97.50 (978-3-7001-3608-8(0)) Austrian Academy of Sciences Press AUT. Dist: Brown, David Bk. Co., The.
Steinke, Sean. Psalmanaul. 2007. 64p. per. 12.00 (978-1-59919-029-7(X)) Elim Publishing.
Steinmann, Andrew E. Proverbs. 2009. (Concordia Commentary Ser.). (Illus.). 719p. 42.99 (978-0-7586-0320-3(7)) Concordia Publishing Hse.
Strickman, Norman, tr. from HEB. Rabbi Abraham Ibn Ezra's Commentary on the First Book of Psalms. 2009. (Reference Library of Jewish Intellectual History Ser.). (ENG.). 324p. 48.00 (978-1-934843-30-7(X)) Academic Studies Pr.
—Rabbi Abraham Ibn Ezra's Commentary on the Second Book of Psalms: Chapters 42-72. 2009. (Reference Library of Jewish Intellectual History Ser.). (ENG.). 216p. 48.00 (978-1-934843-31-4(8)) Academic Studies Pr.
Stuart, Moses. A Commentary on the Book of Proverbs. 2008. 436p. 30.99 (978-0-554-42266-4(2)); 30.99 (978-0-554-42291-6(3)); 32.99 (978-0-554-42277-0(8)); 32.99 (978-0-554-42258-9(1)); pap. 35.75 (978-0-554-42280-0(8)); pap. 34.75 (978-0-554-42275-6(4)); pap. 35.75 (978-0-554-42262-6(X)); pap. 34.75 (978-0-554-42287-9(5)) BiblioBazaar.
—A Commentary on the Book of Proverbs. 2009. 310p. pap. (978-0-217-33520-1(9)) Books LLC.
—A Commentary on the Book of Proverbs. 2009. 144p. pap. 21.98 (978-1-4432-6119-7(X)) General Bks. LLC.
—A Commentary on the Book of Proverbs. 2007. 436p. 51.95 (978-0-548-55611-5(3)); (ENG.). per. 36.95 (978-0-548-50080-4(0)) Kessinger Publishing, LLC.
—A Commentary on the Book of Proverbs. 2006. 440p. per. 26.99 (978-1-4255-4770-7(2)) MPublishing.
Stuart, Moses & Robbins, Rensselaer David Chanceford. A Commentary on Ecclesiastes. 2009. 346p. 32.99 (978-1-115-25249-2(6)); pap. 31.75 (978-1-115-25245-4(3)) BiblioBazaar.
Sturtevant, Arnold H. Come with Me from Lebanon: A Study of the Song of Solomon. 2011. 276p. 27.48 (978-1-4269-7502-8(3)); pap. 17.48 (978-1-4269-7503-5(1)) Trafford Publishing.
Swaggart, Jimmy. Jimmy Swaggart Bible Commentary - Psalms. 2007. 650p. 40.00 (978-0-9769530-8-1(0)) Swaggart, Jimmy Ministries.
Talbert, Layton. Beyond Suffering: Discovering the Message of Job. 2007. (978-1-59166-620-2(1)) BJU Pr.
Tamez, Elsa. When the Horizons Close: Rereading Ecclesiastes. Wilde, Margaret, tr. 2006. 176p. pap. 21.00 (978-1-59752-855-9(2), Wipf and Stock) Wipf & Stock Pubs.
Tanner, Beth LaNeel. The Psalms for Today. 2008. (For Today Ser.). (ENG.). 128p. pap. 13.00 (978-0-664-22935-1(2)) Westminster John Knox Pr.
Teems, David. Discovering Your Spiritual Center: The Power of Psalm 119. 2011. (ENG.). pap. 14.99 (978-0-89112-296-8(6), Leafwood Heritage) Abilene Christian Univ. Pr.
The Messenger. Life, the Unspoken Walk. 2011. 116p. pap. 19.95 (978-1-4560-5711-4(1)) PublishAmerica, Inc.
Theodore. Commentary on Psalms 1-81. 2006. (LAT, ENG & GEC.). xxxviii, 1138p. (978-90-04-12722-7(4)) BRILL.
Thomas Nelson Publishing Staff. Comfort from the Word of Promise: Reassuring Passages from the Psalms, 0 vols. 2009. 64p. 14.99 (978-1-4041-8670-5(0)) Nelson, Thomas Inc.
Thomas Nelson Publishing Staff & Peters, Angie. The Life of Solomon, 0 vols. Richards, Larry, ed. 2009. (Smart Guide to the Bible Ser.). (Illus.). 384p. pap. 14.99 (978-1-4185-1012-1(2)) Nelson, Thomas Inc.
Thomas, W. James, Jr. Psalm 23. 2007. per. 12.99 (978-1-59872-921-4(7)) Instant Pub.
Townsend, John & Townsend, Susan. Ecclesiastes: A Course for Small Group Discipleship. 2009. 196p. pap. 16.99 (978-1-60791-534-8(0)) Xulon Pr., Inc.
Tripp, Paul David. A Shelter in the Time of Storm: Meditations on God & Trouble. 2009. 160p. pap. 12.99 (978-1-4335-0598-0(3)) Crossway.
Vasquez, James. The Psalms - in Verse. 2011. 320p. 37.95 (978-1-4497-1036-1(0)); pap. 22.95 (978-1-4497-1034-7(4)) Author Solutions, Inc. (WestBow Pr.).
Vila-Pozo. Comentario Cantar de los Cantares: Song of Solomon Commentary. (SPA.). (978-84-7228-686-3(X), 220226) Clie, Editorial.
Waldron, Bridget. The Psalms: Letters to God (KJV) 2010. 360p. pap. 29.99 (978-0-557-23643-5(6)) Lulu Enterprises Inc.
Waltner, James H. Psalms. 2006. (Believers Church Bible Commentary Ser.). (Illus.). 833p. per. 29.99 (978-0-8361-9337-4(7)) Herald Pr.
Watson, Rebecca S. Chaos Uncreated: A Reassessment of the Theme of Chaos in the Hebrew Bible. (Beihefte zur Zeitschrift fur die alttestamentliche Wissenschaft Ser.). (ENG.). XIX, 504p. 300.00 (978-3-11-180403-3(8)) De Gruyter, Walter Inc.
Wesselschmidt, Quentin F., ed. Psalms 51-150. 2007. (Ancient Christian Commentary on Scripture Ser.: Old Testament Volume 8). (ENG.). 523p. 50.00 (978-0-8308-1478-7(7), IVP Acad.) InterVarsity Pr.
Whitell, Evelyn. The Silence. 2011. 74p. 36.95 (978-1-258-05043-6(9)) Literary Licensing, LLC.
Whybray, R. N. Job. 2008. vi, 207p. (978-1-906055-02-8(5)); pap. (978-1-906055-03-5(3)) Sheffield Phoenix Pr.
Wiersbe, Warren W. Be Exultant (Psalms 90-150) Praising God for His Mighty Works 2009. (Be Series Commentary Ser.). (ENG.). 240p. pap. 12.99 (978-1-4347-6737-0(X)) Cook, David C.
—Be Patient (Job) Waiting on God in Difficult Times, 1 vol. 2009. (BE Ser. Commentary Ser.). (ENG.). 192p. pap. 12.99 (978-1-4347-6741-7(8)) Cook, David C.
—Be Satisfied (Ecclesiastes) Looking for the Answer to the Meaning of Life, 1 vol. 2010. (BE Series Commentary Ser.). (ENG.). 160p. pap. 12.99 (978-1-4347-6506-2(7)) Cook, David C.
—Be Skillful (Proverbs) God's Guidebook to Wise Living 2nd ed. 2009. (Be Series Commentary Ser.). (ENG.). 224p. pap. 12.99 (978-1-4347-6733-2(7)) Cook, David C.
—Be Worshipful (Psalms 1-89) Glorifying God for Who He Is, 1 vol. 2009. (Be Series Commentary Ser.). (ENG.). 288p. pap. 12.99 (978-1-4347-6739-4(6)) Cook, David C.
—Daniel: Determining to Go God's Direction. 2009. (WBS Ser.). (ENG.). 160p. pap. 8.99 (978-0-7814-4569-6(8)) Cook, David C.
—The Wiersbe Bible Study Series: Psalms: Glorifying God for Who He Is, 1 vol. 2010. (Wiersbe Bible Study Ser.). (ENG.). 176p. pap. 8.99 (978-1-4347-6487-4(7)) Cook, David C.
Williams, Allan. A Black Man's Worth. 2009. 320p. pap. 17.99 (978-1-4490-3003-2(3)) AuthorHouse.
Williams, Tim. Psalmball. 2011. 190p. pap. 14.99 (978-1-61379-037-3(6)) Xulon Pr., Inc.
Wilson, Gerald H., ed. Job. 2007. (New International Biblical Commentary Ser.). 494p. per. (978-1-56563-219-6(2)) Hendrickson Pubs. Marketing, LLC.
Winslow, Octavius. Soul-Depths & Soul-Heights: An Exposition of Psalm 130. 2006. 135p. per. 12.00 (978-0-85151-935-7(0)) Banner of Truth, The.
Wright, William Aldis, ed. The Hexaplar Psalter: Being the Book of Psalms in Six English Versions. 2008. 396p. pap. 34.00 (978-1-60608-013-9(X)) Wipf & Stock Pubs.
Yoder, Christine Elizabeth & Yoder, Christine Roy. Proverbs: Abingdon Old Testament Commentaries. 2009. (Aotc Ser.). 315p. pap. 40.00 (978-1-4267-0001-9(6)) Abingdon Pr.
Zigarelli, Michael. Management by Proverbs. 2008. 376p. 32.99 (978-1-60791-018-3(7)); pap. 20.99 (978-1-60791-017-6(9)) Xulon Pr., Inc.
Zimmerman, Joyce, ed. Living Liturgy for Cantors Year C 2010. 2009. 208p. pap. 9.95 (978-0-8146-3281-9(5), Liturgical Pr. Bks.) Liturgical Pr.

BIBLE—COMMENTARIES—O. T. PROPHETS

see also Bible—Commentaries—O. T. Minor Prophets

Allen, Leslie C. Jeremiah: A Commentary. 2008. (Old Testament Library). (ENG.). 656p. 60.00 (978-0-664-22223-9(4)) Westminster John Knox Pr.
Anderson, Robert. The Coming Prince: The Marvelous Prophecy of Daniel's Seventy Weeks Concerning the Antichrist. 2007. 312p. per. 10.75 (978-1-60206-230-6(7)) Cosimo, Inc.
Andre, G. Jeremiah, the Prophet. (Let's Discuss It Ser.). pap. 3.95 (978-0-88172-135-5(2)) Believers Bookshelf, Inc.
Arobateau, Red Jordan. Lamentations in the Cool of the Evening. 2007. 356p. pap. 25.00 (978-0-615-16611-7(3)) Red Jordan Pr.
Atkinson, Basil F. Ezekiel (Eleven Chapters for Soul Winners) pap. 1.99 (978-1-56632-004-7(6)) Revival Literature.
Avraham, Calev Ben. The Book of Daniel Unsealed: Prophecy: Past, Present & Future (the Hidden Secrets in the Book of Daniel) 2011. 224p. pap. 18.95 (978-1-4502-4526-5(9)) iUniverse, Inc.
Baker, David W. & Wenham, Gordon J., eds. Apollos Old Testament Commentary Series. 2p. 70.00 (978-0-8308-2500-4(2)) InterVarsity Pr.
Baldwin, Joyce G. Daniel. 2009. (Tyndale Old Testament Commentaries Ser.: Volume 23). (ENG.). 232p. pap. 16.00 (978-0-8308-4223-0(3), IVP Acad.) InterVarsity Pr.
Ball, C. J. Prophecies of Jeremiah with A Sketch of. 2006. pap. 36.95 (978-1-4286-4386-4(9)) Kessinger Publishing, LLC.
Ball, Charles James. The Prophecies of Jeremiah: With A Sketch of His Life & Times. 2011. 430p. 56.95 (978-1-258-05370-3(5)) Literary Licensing, LLC.
Barnes, Albert. Notes, Critical, Illustrative, & Practical, on the Book of Daniel, with an Introductory Dissertation. 2006. 500p. per. 29.99 (978-1-4255-5575-7(6)) MPublishing.
—Notes on Isaiah. 2010. pap. 160.64 (978-1-61719-330-9(5)); pap. 160.64 (978-1-61719-329-3(1)) Gorgias Pr., LLC.
Barnes, W. E. Isaiah. 2007. (ENG.). 214p. 39.95 (978-0-548-06253-1(6)) Kessinger Publishing, LLC.
Beaton, Richard. Isaiah's Christ in Matthew's Gospel. 2007. (Society for New Testament Studies Monograph Ser.). (ENG.). 260p. pap. 55.00 (978-0-521-03610-8(0)) Cambridge Univ. Pr.
Bennett, W. H. Book of Jeremiah Chapters Xxiii. 2006. pap. 34.95 (978-1-4286-4481-6(4)) Kessinger Publishing, LLC.
Berrigan, Daniel. Daniel: Under the Siege of the Divine. 2009. (Daniel Berrigan Reprint Ser.). 228p. pap. 25.00 (978-1-60608-467-0(4), Wipf and Stock) Wipf & Stock Pubs.
Blenkinsopp, Joseph. Ezekiel: Interpretation: A Bible Commentary for Teaching & Preaching. 2012. (Interpretation: A Bible Commentary for Teaching & Preaching Ser.). (ENG.). 254p. pap. 25.00 (978-0-664-23863-6(7)) Westminster John Knox Pr.
Boadt, Lawrence. Jeremiah 1-25. 2008. (Illus.). 246p. pap. 27.00 (978-1-60608-215-7(9)) Wipf & Stock Pubs.
—Jeremiah 26-52, Habakkuk, Zephaniah, Nahum. 2009. 288p. pap. 33.00 (978-1-60608-182-2(9)) Wipf & Stock Pubs.
Boice, James Montgomery. Daniel. 2006. (Expositional Commentary Ser.). 144p. pap. 16.99 (978-0-8010-6641-2(7)) Baker Bks.
Bowen, Nancy R. Ezekiel. 2010. 280p. pap. 35.00 (978-1-4267-0445-1(3)) Abingdon Pr.
Brown, Charles Rufus. The Book of the Prophet Jeremiah. 2007. (ENG.). 260p. 42.95 (978-0-548-07745-0(2)) Kessinger Publishing, LLC.
Bullock, Robert H. Hammer on the Rock: The Message of the Prophet Jeremiah. 2011. 66p. 36.95 (978-1-258-02805-3(0)) Literary Licensing, LLC.
Canadian Biotechnology Advisory Committee & Brueggemann, Walter. Like Fire in the Bones: Listening for the Prophetic Word in Jeremiah. Miller, Patrick D., ed. 2006. 272p. 35.00 (978-0-8006-3561-9(2), Fortress Pr.) Augsburg Fortress, Pubs.
Carroll, B. H. Comentario Carroll-Cinco: Daniel: Carroll's Commentary 5: Daniel. (SPA.). (978-84-7645-215-5(0), 223262) Clie, Editorial.
Carroll, Robert P. When Prophecy Failed: Reactions & Responses to Failure in the Old Testament Prophetic Traditions. 2011. 256p. (978-1-85931-045-8(1), SCM Pr.) Hymns Ancient & Modern Ltd.
Carvalho, Corrine L. The Book of Ezekiel: Question by Question. 2010. (Question by Question Bible Study Commentary Ser.). 224p. pap. (978-0-8091-4678-9(9)) Paulist Pr.
Christian Art Gifts, creator. Isaiah 40:31. 2009. (978-1-77036-164-5(2)) Christian Art Pubs.
—Isaiah 61. 2009. 160p. (978-1-77036-306-9(8)) Christian Art Pubs.
—Jeremiah 29:11. 2008. 400p. (978-1-77036-011-2(5)) Christian Art Pubs.
Clark, Wayne. Isaiah: a Prophet for Our Times: A Study of the Book of Isaiah. 2007. pap. 15.99 (978-1-60477-183-6(7)) Xulon Pr., Inc.
Cox, Harvey & Paulsell, Stephanie. Lamentations & the Song of Songs: A Theological Commentary on the Bible. 2012. (Belief: A Theological Commentary on the Bible Ser.). (ENG.). 304p. 30.00 (978-0-664-23302-0(3)) Westminster John Knox Pr.
Cyril. Commentary on Isaiah. 2008. pap. (978-1-885652-94-2(1)) Holy Cross Orthodox Pr.
Daniels-Jesus Christ Light of World. 0.45 (978-0-687-19965-5(4)) Abingdon Pr.
Davies, Philip R. Among the Prophets: Language, Image & Structure in the Prophetic Writings. Clines, David J. A., ed. 2009. (Library of Hebrew Bible/Old Testament Studies, the Ser.). (ENG.). 218p. 39.95 (978-1-4411-9648-4(X), T&T Clark) Continuum International Publishing Group, Ltd. GBR. Dist: National Bk. Network.
Davis, Dennis. The Apocrypha Timimg. 2010. pap. 8.95 (978-0-7414-6100-1(5)) Infinity Publishing.
Davis, Ellen F. Swallowing the Scroll: Textuality & the Dynamics of Discourse in Ezekiel's Prophecy. 2009. (Library of Hebrew Bible/Old Testament Studies, the Ser.). (ENG.). 184p. 29.95 (978-1-4411-4299-3(1), T&T Clark) Continuum International Publishing Group, Ltd. GBR. Dist: National Bk. Network.
de Sousa, Rodrigo F. Eschatology & Messianism in LXX Isaiah 1-12, Vol. 516. 2010. (Library of Hebrew Bible/Old Testament Studies). (ENG.). 204p. 120.00 (978-0-567-25819-9(X), T&T Clark Int'l) Continuum International Publishing Group, Ltd. GBR. Dist: National Bk. Network.
Deane, Dona. Honor Your Gifts. 2007. 232p. (ENG.). 24.99 (978-1-60477-153-4(4)); per. 14.99 (978-1-60477-152-7(6)) Xulon Pr., Inc.
Dempsey, Carol. Isaiah: God's Poet of Light. 2010. 224p. pap. 34.99 (978-0-8272-1630-3(0)) Chalice Pr.
Duguid, Iain M. Daniel. 2008. (Reformed Expository Commentary Ser.). 236p. (978-1-59638-068-4(3)) P & R Publishing.
Earl, Sue. A New Heart of Flesh & the New Spirit: A Perspective on Flesh & Spirit through Understanding Ezekiel. 2011. pap. 12.99 (978-1-61777-367-9(0)) Tate Publishing & Enterprises, LLC.
Edlin, Jim. NBBC, Daniel: A Commentary in the Wesleyan Tradition. 2009. (ENG.). 288p. pap. 29.99 (978-0-8341-2398-4(3), 9780834123984) Beacon Hill Pr. of Kansas City.
Ellington, Scott A. Risking Truth: Reshaping the World Through Prayers of Lament. 2008. (Princeton Theological Monographs). 214p. pap. 24.00 (978-1-55635-263-8(8), Pickwick Pubns.) Wipf & Stock Pubs.
Elliott, Mark W. & Oden, Thomas C., eds. Isaiah 40-66. 2007. (Ancient Christian Commentary on Scripture Ser.: Old Testament Volume 11). (ENG.). 380p. 50.00 (978-0-8308-1481-7(7), IVP Acad.) InterVarsity Pr.
Evans, John S. The Prophecies of Daniel. 2008. 280p. 25.99 (978-1-60477-904-2(7)) Xulon Pr., Inc.
—The Prophecies of Daniel 2. 2008. 280p. pap. 15.99 (978-1-60477-903-5(9)) Xulon Pr., Inc.
Ezekiel. (People's Bible Commentary Ser.). 288p. 14.99 (978-0-7586-0433-0(5)) Concordia Publishing Hse.
Finkelstein, Louis. The Commentary of David Kimhi on Isaiah: Edited, with his Unpublished Allegorical Commentary on Genesis. 2007. (Gorgias Occasional Historical Commentaries Ser.: 2). 107.00 (978-1-59333-675-2(6)) Gorgias Pr., LLC.
Ford, Desmond. How Long, O Lord? An Introduction to the Book of Daniel. 2010. 72p. pap. 10.95 (978-1-4502-2729-2(5)) iUniverse, Inc.
Fox, Emmet. The Lion's Den: Daniel 6. 3.00 (978-0-87516-746-6(2)) DeVorss & Co.
Friesen, Ivan D. Isaiah. 2009. pap. 29.99 (978-0-8361-9440-1(3)) Herald Pr.
Gindin, Thamar E. The Early Judaeo-Persian Tafsirs of Ezekiel: Text, Translation, Commentary. 2007. (Veroeffentlichungen zur Byzanzforschung Ser.). (ENG & AFR.). (C). 51.00 (978-3-7001-3961-4(6)); 78.00 (978-3-7001-3996-6(9)) Austrian Academy of Sciences Press AUT. Dist: Brown, David Bk. Co., The.
Gindin, Thamar Eiram. The Early Judaeo-Persian Tafsirs of Ezekiel: Text, Translation, Commentary. Vol. III: Commentary. 2011. (Veroffentlichungen zur Iranistik Ser.). (ENG.). 214p. (C). pap. 44.00 (978-3-7001-3997-3(7)) Austrian Academy of Sciences Press AUT. Dist: Brown, David Bk. Co., The.
Graves, Michael. Jerome's Hebrew Philology: A Study Based on his Commentary on Jeremiah. 2007. (Vigiliae Christianae Supplements Ser.). 236p. (978-90-04-16204-4(6)) BRILL.
Greig, Doris W. Daniel (Chapters 1-6) 2007. (ENG.). 56p. spiral bd. 10.99 (978-1-932017-37-3(2)) Joy of Living Bible Studies.
Guide to Isaiah 1 39. 3.00 (978-0-687-85448-6(2)) Abingdon Pr.
Guntrip, Elizabeth. The Apocalyptic Prince of Persi. 2008. 140p. pap. (978-3-639-05516-0(0)) VDM Verlag Dr. Mueller e.K.
Harrington, Maurice. Guide to Isaiah 40:66 (Illus.). 240p. 12.00 (978-0-281-03668-4(3)) SPCK Publishing GBR. Dist: Pilgrim Pr., The/United Church Pr.
Hammond, M. K. Balm in Gilead: Writings of Jeremiah. 2007. 156p. pap. 18.00 (978-1-55635-108-2(9), Resource Pubns.) Wipf & Stock Pubs.
Hanson, Paul D. Isaiah 40-66: Interpretation: A Bible Commentary for Teaching & Preaching. 2012. (Interpretation: A Bible Commentary for Teaching & Preaching Ser.). (ENG.). 266p. pap. 25.00 (978-0-664-23875-9(0)) Westminster John Knox Pr.
Harman, Allan M. A Study Commentary on Daniel. 2007. (Ep Study Commentary Ser.). (Illus.). 333p. (978-0-85234-649-5(2)) Evangelical Pr.
Harmon, Matthew S. She Must & Shall Go Free: Paul's Isaianic Gospel in Galatians. 2011. (Beihefte zur Zeitschrift fur die neutestamentliche

Wissenschaft und die Kunde der älteren Kirche Ser.). (ENG., Illus.). XI, 330p. 210.00 **(978-3-11-174167-3(2))** De Gruyter, Walter Inc.

Harrison, R. K. Jeremiah & Lamentations, 1 vol. 2009. (Tyndale Old Testament Commentaries Ser.: Volume 21). (ENG.). 246p. pap. 16.00 *(978-0-8308-4221-6(7),* IVP Acad.) InterVarsity Pr.

Hatcher, Min. Loraine. Book of Lamentations: Book Two of Jeremiah. 2007. 144p. per. 24.95 *(978-1-4241-1838-0(7))* PublishAmerica, Inc.

Hauser, Alan J. Recent Research on the Major Prophets. 2008. xiv, 388p. *(978-1-906055-13-4(0))* Sheffield Phoenix Pr.

Henry, Matthew. Comentario Matthew Henry: Ezeqias: Matthew Henry's Commentary: Ezekial. (SPA.). 560p. *(978-84-7645-457-2(0),* 223528) Clie, Editorial.

—Comentario Matthew Henry: Isaias A: Matthew Henry's Commentary: Isaiah. (SPA.). 640p. *(978-84-7645-420-6(1),* 223517) Clie, Editorial.

The Hidden Book of Zechariah Found & Translated: The Linear Bible Code: Reading the Text Backward. 2007. cd-rom 10.00 net. *(978-0-9773032-2-9(5))* Mahler Hse.

Hill, Robert C., tr. from GEC. Commentary on the Twelve Prophets, Volume 2: St. Cyril of Alexandria, Vol. 2. 2008. (Fathers of the Church Ser.). 432p. 44.95 *(978-0-8132-0116-0(0))* Catholic Univ. of America Pr.

Hollingshead, Paul, text. The Holy Remnant: An Exposition of the Book of Isaiah. 2008. 289p. pap. 8.90 *(978-0-7399-2390-0(0))* Rod & Staff Pubs., Inc.

Houghton, John. Isaiah 1-39: Prophet to the Nations, 1 vol. 2009. (Cover to Cover Bible Study Ser.). 72p. pap. *(978-1-85345-510-0(5))* Crusade for World Revival.

Howe, Thomas A. Daniel in the Preterists' Den: A Critical Look at Preterist Interpretations of Daniel. 2008. 742p. pap. 77.00 *(978-1-55635-273-7(5),* Wipf and Stock) Wipf & Stock Pubs.

Hrobon, Bohdan. Ethical Dimension of Cult in the Book of Isaiah. 2011. (Beihefte zur Zeitschrift far die alttestamentliche Wissenschaft Ser.). (ENG., Illus.). XIII, 256p. 196.00 **(978-3-11-215064-1(3))** De Gruyter, Walter Inc.

Hummel, Horace D. Ezekiel 21-48. 2008. (Concordia Commentary Ser.). 42.99 *(978-0-7586-1001-0(7))* Concordia Publishing Hse.

Hunt, Keith Malcolm. The Biblical Prophets for Today. 2011. 456p. pap. 38.95 *(978-1-4502-7613-9(X))* iUniverse, Inc.

Hunter, John C. Guide to Jeremiah. (Illus.). 256p. 13.00 *(978-0-281-04627-0(1))* SPCK Publishing GBR. Dist: Pilgrim Pr., The/United Church Pr.

Hutchings, Noah W. Daniel the Prophet: A Comprehensive Examination of the Prophecies Concerning the Historical & Future Gentile World Empires. 2007. (Illus.). 336p. pap. 12.95 *(978-1-933641-16-4(9))* Bible Belt Pubns.

Imoru, Nicholas. A Heart for God. 2007. 140p. per. *(978-0-9555562-4-1(4))* Esteemworld Pubns.

Ironside, H. A. Jeremiah & Lamentations, 1 vol. 2008. (Ironside Expository Commentaries Ser.). (Illus.). 240p. 21.99 *(978-0-8254-2926-2(9))* Kregel Pubns.

Isaiah. 2009. 64p. pap. *(978-0-217-84026-2(4))* Books LLC.

Isaiah, Vol. 7. 25.00 *(978-0-8028-8041-3(X))* Eerdmans, William B. Publishing Co.

Isaiah, Vol. 11. 6.99 Westminster John Knox Pr.

Isaiah 1. ldr.'s ed. (LifeLight Bible Studies: Course 16). 6.50 *(978-0-570-09376-3(7),* 20-2530) Concordia Publishing Hse.

Isaiah 2. (LifeLight Bible Studies: Course 17). stu. ed. 0.55 incl. audio *(978-0-570-09379-4(1),* 20-2536); 6.50 *(978-0-570-09378-7(3),* 20-2535) Concordia Publishing Hse.

Jackman, David. Teaching Isaiah: Unlocking Isaiah for the Bible Teacher. 2010. (Teaching the Bible Ser.). (ENG.). 320p. 14.99 *(978-1-84550-565-3(4))* Christian Focus Pubns. GBR. Dist: STL Distribution North America.

Jenson, Robert W. Ezekiel. 2009. 384p. (C). 32.99 *(978-1-58743-166-1(1))* Brazos Pr.

Jerome, St. Jerome's Commentary on Daniel. 2009. 189p. pap. 17.00 *(978-1-60608-375-8(9),* Wipf and Stock) Wipf & Stock Pubs.

Joachimsen, Kristin. Identities in Transition: The Pursuit of Isa. 52:13-53:12. 2011. XIV, 450p. *(978-90-04-20106-4(8))* BRILL.

Joyce, Paul M. Ezekiel: A Commentary. 2009. (Library of Hebrew Bible/Old Testament Studies, the Ser.). (ENG.). 328p. pap. 49.95 *(978-0-567-48361-4(4),* T&T Clark Int'l) Continuum International Publishing Group, Ltd. GBR. Dist: National Bk. Network.

Kay, Roy. The Ethiopian Prophecy in Black American Letters. 2011. (History of African-American Religions Ser.). (ENG., Illus.). 240p. 74.95 *(978-0-8130-3732-5(8))* Univ. Pr. of Florida.

Keesee, Dayton. Jeremiah 1-25. 2011. 534p. 29.95 **(978-0-9818128-9-2(9))** Resource Pubns.

—Jeremiah 26-52 & Lamentations. 2011. 594p. 29.95 **(978-0-9837098-0-0(7))** Resource Pubns.

Kelley, Page. Interpreting Isaiah: Study Guide. 6.00 *(978-0-687-82354-3(4))* Abingdon Pr.

Kitchen, John. Pathways to Peace: Facing the Future with Faith — Meditations from Isaiah 40. 2011. (Reflections (DayOne) Ser.). 122p. pap. **(978-1-84625-212-9(1))** DayOne Pubns.

Klein, Zo'. The Scroll of Anatiya. 2009. 190p. pap. 22.00 *(978-1-60608-543-1(3),* Resource Pubns.) Wipf & Stock Pubs.

Kravitz, Leonard S. & Olitzky, Kerry M., comments. Eichah: A Modern Commentary on the Book of Lamentations. 2008. *(978-0-8074-1061-5(6))* URJ Pr.

Kroeze, George. Ezekiel: Catching the Vision. l.t. ed. 5.25 Faith Alive Christian Resources.

Landman, Isaac. Stories of the Prophets. 2007. 172p. per. *(978-1-4068-1502-3(0))* Echo Library.

Lessing, R. Reed. Isaiah 40-55. 2011. 792p. 42.99 **(978-0-7586-0268-8(5))** Concordia Publishing Hse.

Li, Tarsee. The Verbal System of the Aramaic of Daniel: An Explanation in the Context of Grammaticalization. 2009. (Studies in the Aramaic Interpretation of Scripture). (ARC & ENG.). 215p. *(978-90-04-17514-3(8))* BRILL.

Longman, Tremper, ed. Quicknotes Simplified Bible Commentary Vol. 6: Isaiah thru Ezekiel. 2010. (QuickNotes Commentaries Ser.). (ENG.). 224p. pap. 9.99 *(978-1-59789-772-3(8),* Barbour Bks.) Barbour Publishing, Inc.

Longman, Tremper & Longman, Tremper, III. Jeremiah, Lamentations. 2008. (New International Biblical Commentary Ser.). 412p. pap. 16.95 *(978-1-56563-224-0(9))* Hendrickson Pubs. Marketing, LLC.

Longman, Tremper, III, et al. Daniel: Faith under Pressure, 1 vol. 2010. (Bringing the Bible to Life Ser.). (ENG.). 160p. pap. 7.99 *(978-0-310-32042-5(9))* Zondervan.

Mackay, John L. Lamentations. 2008. (Mentor Commentary Ser.). (ENG.). 240p. 29.99 *(978-1-84550-363-5(5),* Mentor) Christian Focus Pubns. GBR. Dist: STL Distribution North America.

Maclaren, Alexander. Expositions of Holy Scripture: Isaiah & Jeremiah. 2007. (ENG.). 642p. pap. 31.99 *(978-1-4264-2703-9(4));* 152p. pap. 21.99 *(978-1-4264-2760-2(3))* BiblioBazaar.

Mann, Thomas W. The Book of the Former Prophets. 2012. (ENG.). 456p. (C). pap. 60.00 **(978-0-227-68010-0(3))** Clarke, James Co., Ltd. GBR. Dist: Brown, David Bk. Co., The.

—The Book of the Former Prophets. 2011. 456p. pap. 50.00 **(978-1-60608-669-8(3),** Cascade Bks.) Wipf & Stock Pubs.

Mark D. Spencer. A Portrait of Intercession. 2010. 152p. 26.94 *(978-1-4269-2267-1(1))* Trafford Publishing.

McMurray, Carl. Esteemed of God: Studying Daniel the man & his prophecies of the time between the Testaments. 2007. 84p. pap. 7.70 *(978-0-9774754-3-8(3))* Spiritbuilding.

Meadowcroft, T. J. Aramaic Daniel & Greek Daniel: A Literary Comparison. 2009. (Library of Hebrew Bible/Old Testament Studies, the Ser.). (ENG.). 336p. 55.00 *(978-0-567-30693-7(3),* T&T Clark) Continuum International Publishing Group, Ltd. GBR. Dist: National Bk. Network.

Meier, Samuel A. Themes & Transformations in Old Testament Prophecy, 1 vol. 2009. (ENG.). 240p. pap. 23.00 *(978-0-8308-1768-9(9),* IVP Acad.) InterVarsity Pr.

Mellish, Norman. The Times of the Gentiles, a Study in Daniel. 2010. 216p. pap. *(978-1-926765-09-9(5))* Gospel Folio Pr.

Miscall, Peter. Isaiah. 2nd ed. 2006. 188p. *(978-1-905048-44-1(0));* per. *(978-1-905048-45-8(9))* Sheffield Phoenix Pr.

Motyer, J. Alec & InterVarsity Press Editors. Isaiah, 1 vol. 2009. (Tyndale Old Testament Commentaries Ser.: Volume 20). (ENG.). 461p. pap. 16.00 *(978-0-8308-4220-9(9),* IVP Acad.) InterVarsity Pr.

Muratori, John Louis & Muratori, John. Seven Women Shall Take Hold of One Man: God's Incredible Plan of Provision, Protection & Revival for the 21st Century Church. 2007. (ENG.). 144p. pap. 14.95 *(978-0-9704753-0-5(6))* Gatekeeper Publishing.

Nagelsbach, Carl Wilhelm Eduard. The Prophet Isaiah: Theologically & Homiletically Expounded. Lowrie, Samuel T. & Moore, Dunlop, trs. 2007. (Lange's Commentary on the Holy Scripture Ser.). 742p. pap. 65.00 *(978-1-55635-412-0(6))* Wipf & Stock Pubs.

Neusner, Jacob. Isaiah in Talmud & Midr: Part, 2 vols. 2007. (Studies in Judaism Ser.). (ENG.). 430p. pap. 57.99 *(978-0-7618-3695-7(0))* Univ. Pr. of America, Inc.

—Isaiah in Talmud & Misrash: A Source Book, Part B, 2 vols. 2007. (Studies in Judaism Ser.). (ENG.). 382p. per. 55.99 *(978-0-7618-3696-4(9))* Univ. Pr. of America, Inc.

Newton, Isaac. Observations upon the Prophecies of Daniel & the Apocalypse of St John. 2008. 248p. per. 9.99 *(978-1-59986-580-5(7))* Filiquarian Publishing, LLC.

Nixon Ph. D., Thomas C. The Prophecy of Daniel: Unsealed. 2008. 260p. pap. 15.99 *(978-1-4389-2061-0(X))* AuthorHouse.

Noel, Ted. A Primer on the Book of Daniel. 2008. 142p. pap. 18.00 *(978-1-55635-533-2(5),* Resource Pubns.) Wipf & Stock Pubs.

Nordberg, Bette. Jeremiah: A Bright Light in a Dark Season. 2008. (Following God Through the Bible Ser.). (ENG.). 160p. pap. 14.99 *(978-0-89957-030-3(5))* AMG Pubs.

Olley, John W. Ezekiel: A Commentary Based on Iezekiel in Codex Vaticanus. 2009. (Septuagint Commentary Ser.). 599p. *(978-90-04-17713-0(2))* BRILL.

Ortberg, John, et al. Daniel, 1 vol. 2008. (New Community Bible Study Ser.). (ENG.). 96p. pap. 7.99 *(978-0-310-28053-8(2))* Zondervan.

Ottley, R. R., ed. The Book of Isaiah According to the Septuagint (Codex Alexandrinus), 2 Volumes. 2011. 800p. pap. 68.00 *(978-1-61097-122-5(1),* Wipf and Stock) Wipf & Stock Pubs.

Pace, Sharon. Daniel. 2008. (Smyth & Helwys Bible Commentary Ser.). 55.00 *(978-1-57312-074-6(X))* Smyth & Helwys Publishing, Inc.

Parry, Donald & Parry, Jay. Understanding Isaiah. 2009. 672p. pap. 27.99 *(978-1-60641-081-3(4))* Deseret Bk. Co.

Paul, Shalom M. Isaiah 40-66: A Commentary. 2011. (HEB & ENG.). 672p. pap. 68.00 **(978-0-8028-2603-9(2))** Eerdmans, William B. Publishing Co.

The Preacher's Outline & Sermon Bible, Jeremiah 2, Lamentations, KJV: Jeremiah 2, Lamentations. 2006. pap. 39.99 *(978-1-57407-222-8(6))* Leadership Ministries Worldwide.

The Preacher's Outline & Sermon Bible, Jeremiah 2-Lamentations, KJV: Jeremiah 2, Lamentations. 2006. ring bd. 44.99 *(978-1-57407-223-5(4))* Leadership Ministries Worldwide.

Price, Walter. God Focus. 2009. 96p. pap. 11.99 *(978-1-61507-034-3(6))* Cross Bks. Publishing.

Pytlik, George. Daniel: God's Messenger to Our Times. 2010. 37.95 *(978-0-578-05455-1(8));* pap. 24.97 *(978-0-578-05376-9(4))* Illuminosity Pr.

Rhodes, Ron. Northern Storm Rising: Russia, Iran, & the Emerging End-Times Military Coalition Against Israel. 2008. 246p. per. 13.99 *(978-0-7369-2174-9(5))* Harvest Hse. Pubs.

Ridges, David J. Jeremiah Made Easier. 2010. 208p. pap. 19.99 *(978-1-59955-400-6(3))* Cedar Fort, Inc./CFI Distribution.

—Your Study of Isaiah Made Easier: In the Bible & Book of Mormon. 2nd ed. 2009. (Gospel Studies). 276p. pap. 17.99 *(978-1-59955-388-7(0))* Cedar Fort, Inc./CFI Distribution.

Robin, Parry. Lamentations (THOTC) 2010. 280p. pap. 22.00 *(978-0-8028-2714-2(4))* Eerdmans, William B. Publishing Co.

Rogers, Richard. Commentary on Isaiah. 2008. 288p. pap. 14.99 *(978-0-9796369-3-6(0))* Sunset Institute Pr.

Sabih, Joshua A. & Japheth ben Ali. Japheth Ben Ali's Book of Jeremiah: A Critical Edition & Linguistic Analysis of the Judaeo-Arabic Translation. 2009. (Copenhagen International Seminar Ser.). (HEB, ARA & ENG., Illus.). 520p. (C). 150.00 *(978-1-84553-338-0(0))* Equinox Publishing Ltd. GBR. Dist: ISD.

Salters, R. B. Lamentations (ICC) A Critical & Exegetical Commentary. 2011. (International Critical Commentary Ser.). (ENG.). 416p. 110.00 *(978-0-567-57651-4(5),* T&T Clark Int'l) Continuum International Publishing Group, Ltd. GBR. Dist: National Bk. Network.

Scherman, Nosson. Artscroll English Tanach-FL-Stone. 2011. (HEB.). 1416p. 26.99 **(978-1-4226-1064-0(0));** lthr. 59.99 **(978-1-4226-1086-2(1))** Mesorah Pubns., Ltd.

Schmidt, Werner H. Das Buch Jeremia: Kapitel 1 - 20. 2008. (Alte Testament Deutsch. ATD. Kartonierte Ausgabe Ser.). (GER.). 340p. (C). pap. 84.00 *(978-3-525-51243-2(0))* Vandenhoeck & Ruprecht GmbH & Co. KG DEU. Dist: ISD.

Schroder, Wilhelm Julius. The Book of the Prophet Ezekiel: An Exegetical & Doctrinal Commentary. Lange, John Peter & Schaff, Philip, eds. Fairbairn, Patrick & Findlay, William, trs. 2007. (Lange's Commentary on the Holy Scripture Ser.). 498p. pap. 45.00 *(978-1-55635-407-6(X))* Wipf & Stock Pubs.

The Sealed Book of Daniel Found & Translated: Revised Edition. 2007. Orig. Title: The Sealed Book of Daniel Revealed. cd-rom 12.95 net. *(978-0-9773032-1-2(7))* Mahler Hse.

Sedem Agbemafle. From Saul to You: The purpose of the Purposed... 2010. 212p. pap. 17.95 *(978-1-4502-1102-4(X))* iUniverse, Inc.

Seed, Hal. Future History: Understanding the Book of Daniel & End Times Prophecy. 2007. 206p. pap. *(978-0-9797878-0-5(7))* HalSeedBooks.

Sharp, Carolyn J. Old Testament Prophets for Today. 2009. (For Today Ser.). (ENG.). 128p. pap. 13.00 *(978-0-664-23178-1(0))* Westminster John Knox Pr.

Shelton, W. Brian. Martyrdom from Exegesis in Hippolytus: An Early Church Presbyter's Commentary on Daniel. 2008. (Studies in Christian History & Thought Ser.). 192p. pap. 22.00 *(978-1-60608-311-6(2),* Wipf and Stock) Wipf & Stock Pubs.

Sheum'un, Basileios. Commentary on the Six Wings of the Seraph as Spoken by the Prophet Isaiah. 2010. (SYR.). pap. 19.00 *(978-1-61719-925-7(2))* Gorgias Pr., LLC.

Smith, Gary V. Isaiah 1-39, Vol. 15A. 2007. (New American Commentary Ser.). 696p. 32.99 *(978-0-8054-0115-8(6))* B&H Publishing Group.

—The New American Commentary - Isaiah 40-66, 1 vol. 2009. (New American Commentary Ser.). (ENG.). 784p. 29.99 *(978-0-8054-0144-8(X),* B&H Academic) B&H Publishing Group.

Smith, James E. Ezekiel: A Christian Interpretation. 2008. 472p. pap. 23.95 *(978-1-4357-1725-1(2))* Lulu Enterprises Inc.

St Cyril of Alexandria. Commentary on the Twelve Prophets Volume 1. 2007. (Fathers of the Church Ser.). (Illus.). 317p. 39.95 *(978-0-8132-0115-3(2))* Catholic Univ. of America Pr.

Stefanovic, Zdravko. Aramaic of Daniel in the Light of Old Aramaic. 2009. (Library of Hebrew Bible/Old Testament Studies, the Ser.). (ENG.). 128p. 27.95 *(978-0-567-17443-7(3),* T&T Clark) Continuum International Publishing Group, Ltd. GBR. Dist: National Bk. Network.

—Daniel: Wisdom for the Wise: Commentary on the Book of Daniel. 2007. 34.99 *(978-0-8163-2212-1(0))* Pacific Pr. Publishing Assn.

Stevenson, Kenneth, et al, eds. Ezekiel, Daniel. 2008. (Ancient Christian Commentary on Scripture Ser.: Old Testament Volume 13). (ENG.). 396p. 50.00 *(978-0-8308-1483-1(3),* IVP Acad.) InterVarsity Pr.

Steveson, Peter A. Daniel. 2008. *(978-1-59166-855-8(7))* BJU Pr.

Strauss, Lehman. The Prophecies of Daniel. 2008. 384p. pap. 17.99 *(978-0-88469-089-4(X))* BMH Bks.

Stromberg, Jake. Introduction to the Study of Isaiah. 2011. (T&T Clark Approaches to Biblical Studies). 160p. (ENG.). 110.00 *(978-0-567-54394-3(3));* pap. 19.95 *(978-0-567-36330-5(9))* Continuum International Publishing Group, Ltd. GBR. (T&T Clark Int'l). Dist: National Bk. Network.

Stuart, Moses. A Commentary on the Book of Daniel by Moses Stuart. 2006. 512p. per. 29.99 *(978-1-4255-5691-4(4))* MPublishing.

Talbot, Dee Dee. Prophets, Priests, & Kings: Study Guide 3. 2007. (ENG.). 220p. per. 21.94 *(978-1-4303-1553-7(9))* Lulu Enterprises Inc.

Taylor, John B. Ezekiel, 1 vol. 2009. (Tyndale Old Testament Commentaries Ser.: Volume 22). (ENG., Illus.). 277p. pap. 16.00 *(978-0-8308-4222-3(5),* IVP Acad.) InterVarsity Pr.

Theocharous, Myrto. Lexical Dependence & Intertextual Allusion in the Septuagint of the Twelve Prophets: Studies in Hosea, Amos & Micah. 2012. (Library Hebrew Bible/Old Testament Studies). (ENG.). 256p. 130.00 **(978-0-567-10564-6(4),** T&T Clark Int'l) Continuum International Publishing Group, Ltd. GBR. Dist: National Bk. Network.

Theodoret of Cyrus. Theodoret of Cyrus: Commentary on Daniel. 2006. (Writings from the Greco-Roman World: No. 7). (ENG & GRE.). 340p. *(978-90-04-13051-7(9))* BRILL.

Thomas, John. Eureka, an Exposition of the Apocalypse V1. 2011. 470p. 57.95 **(978-1-258-03729-1(7))** Literary Licensing, LLC.

—Eureka, an Exposition of the Apocalypse V2. 2011. 754p. 71.95 **(978-1-258-02428-4(4))** Literary Licensing, LLC.

Trenow, Arturo. El Senor Salva (The Lord Saves) Estudios Devocionales Sobre Isaias 40-55. (SPA.). 32p. 2.00 *(978-0-570-09975-8(7),* 16-6035) Concordia Publishing Hse.

Tuell, Steven Shawn. Ezekiel. 2009. 420p. pap. *(978-1-56563-226-4(5))* Hendrickson Pubs. Marketing, LLC.

Tull, Patricia K. Isaiah 1-39. 2010. *(978-1-57312-071-5(5))* Smyth & Helwys Publishing, Inc.

Van der Kooij, A. & Van der Meer, M. N., eds. Old Greek of Isaiah: Issues & Perspectives. Papers read at the Conference on the Septuagint of Isaiah, held in Leiden 10-11 April 2008. 2010. (Contributions to Biblical Exegesis & Theology Ser.). (ENG.). 253p. (C). pap. 56.00 *(978-90-429-2351-5(2))* Peeters Pubs. & Booksellers BEL. Dist: Brown, David Bk. Co., The.

Varughese, Alex. Jeremiah 1-25: A Commentary in the Wesleyan Tradition. 2008. (New Beacon Bible Commentary Ser.). (ENG.). 320p. pap. 29.99 *(978-0-8341-2364-9(9),* 083-412-3649) Beacon Hill Pr. of Kansas City.

Varughese, Alex & Modine, Mitchel. NBBC, Jeremiah 26-52: A Commentary in the Wesleyan Tradition. 2010. (ENG.). 320p. pap. 29.99 *(978-0-8341-2406-6(8),* 9780834124066) Beacon Hill Pr. of Kansas City.

Walker, William. The Islands of Destiny. 2011. 248p. pap. 16.67 *(978-1-4269-6010-9(7))* Trafford Publishing.

Walton, John H., et al. Isaiah, Jeremiah, Lamentations, Ezekiel, Daniel, 1 vol. 2009. (Zondervan Illustrated Bible Backgrounds Commentary Ser.). (ENG.). 624p. 49.99 *(978-0-310-25576-5(7))* Zondervan.

Wanefsky, David. The Prophets Speak to Us Anew. 2011. 248p. 46.95 **(978-1-258-07705-1(1))** Literary Licensing, LLC.

Weaver, Terry. The Prophets. 2007. 304p. per. 19.95 *(978-1-59919-019-8(2))* Elim Publishing.

Wenthe, Dean O., ed. Jeremiah, Lamentations. 2009. (Ancient Christian Commentary on Scripture Ser.: Old Testament Volume 12). (ENG.). 373p. 50.00 *(978-0-8308-1482-4(5),* IVP Acad.) InterVarsity Pr.

Westermann, Klaus. Isaiah 40-66. 2012. xv, 429p. **(978-0-334-00730-2(5),** SCM Pr.) Hymns Ancient & Modern Ltd.

Wiersbe, Warren W. Be Decisive (Jeremiah) Taking a Stand for the Truth, 1 vol. 2nd ed. 2010. (BE Series Commentary Ser.). (ENG.). 240p. pap. 12.99 *(978-1-4347-6634-2(9))* Cook, David C.

—Be Reverent (Ezekiel) Bowing Before Our Awesome God. 2010. (BE Series Commentary Ser.). (ENG.). 256p. pap. 12.99 *(978-1-4347-0050-6(X))* Cook, David C.

—Resolute: Determining to Go God's Direction. 2008. (Be Ser.). (ENG.). 208p. pap. 12.99 *(978-1-4347-6781-3(7))* Cook, David C.

Wilken, Robert Louis, ed. & tr. from MUL. The Church's Bible: Isaiah: Interpreted by Early Christian & Medieval Commentators. 2007. (Church's Bible Ser.). 590p. 45.00 *(978-0-8028-2581-0(8))* Eerdmans, William B. Publishing Co.

Wilkins, Lauress. The Book of Lamentations & the Social World of Judah in the Neo-Babylonian Era. 2010. 110.00 *(978-1-60724-112-6(9))* Gorgias Pr., LLC.

Williamson, Hugh Godfrey Maturin & Williamson. Isaiah 1-5, 3 vols., Vol. 1. 2nd ed. 2006. (International Critical Commentary on the Holy Scriptures of the Old & New Testaments Ser.). (ENG.). 448p. 120.00 *(978-0-567-04451-8(3),* T&T Clark Int'l) Continuum International Publishing Group, Ltd. GBR. Dist: National Bk. Network.

Wood, Fred M. & McLaren, Ross H. Holman Old Testament Commentary - Jeremiah, Lamentations. Anders, Max, ed. 2006. (Holman Reference Ser.: Vol. 16). (ENG.). 383p. 19.99 *(978-0-8054-9474-7(X),* Holman Reference) B&H Publishing Group.

Young, Paul. A Glimmer of Light: Studies in the Book of Lamentations. 2010. 336p. pap. 17.99 *(978-1-4520-1686-3(0))* AuthorHouse.

Zöckler, Otto. The Books of the Prophet Daniel: An Exegetical & Doctrinal Commentary. Strong, James, ed. & tr. by. 2007. (Lange's Commentary on the Holy Scripture: Ser.). 274p. pap. 27.00 *(978-1-55635-408-3(8),* Wipf and Stock) Wipf & Stock Pubs.

BIBLE—COMMENTARIES—O. T. PROVERBS
see Bible—Commentaries—O. T. Poetical Books

BIBLE—COMMENTARIES—O. T. PSALMS
see Bible—Commentaries—O. T. Poetical Books

BIBLE—COMMENTARIES—O. T. RUTH
see Bible—Commentaries—O. T. Historical Books

BIBLE—COMMENTARIES—O. T. SAMUEL
see Bible—Commentaries—O. T. Historical Books

BIBLE—COMMENTARIES—O. T. SONG OF SOLOMON

see Bible—Commentaries—O. T. Poetical Books

BIBLE—COMMENTARIES—O. T. WISDOM LITERATURE

Alter, Robert. The Wisdom Books: Job, Proverbs, & Ecclesiastes - A Translation with Commentary. 2010. (ENG.). 416p. 35.00 *(978-0-393-06812-2(9)*, 6812) Norton, W. W. & Co., Inc.

Reid, John Howard. BIBLE WISDOM for MODERN TIMES: Selections from the Orthodox Old Testament. 2007. 119p. pap. 9.95 *(978-1-4303-0169-1(4))* Lulu Enterprises Inc.

The Social World of the Hebrew Sages. 18.00 *(978-0-687-34404-8(2))* Abingdon Pr.

BIBLE—COMMENTARIES—O. T. ZECHARIAH

see Bible—Commentaries—O. T. Minor Prophets

BIBLE—COMMENTARIES—O. T. ZEPHANIAH

see Bible—Commentaries—O. T. Minor Prophets

BIBLE—CONCORDANCES

Here are entered works which list the words of the Bible and give the passages where each word occurs. Works which list the ideas of the Bible and give the passages where the idea rather than the exact word occurs are entered under Bible—Indexes.

Abercrombie, Melvin. Does God Have a Penis? 2006. 276p. per. 20.00 *(978-1-4251-0115-2(1))* Trafford Publishing.

Felder, Cain Hope. The Original African Heritage Study Bible. 2007. (Illus.). 2200p. lm. lthr. 50.00 *(978-0-8170-1512-1(4))* Judson Pr.

Felder, Cain Hope, ed. Original African Heritage Study Bible-KJV. l.t. ed. 2007. (Illus.). 1893p. per. 34.00 *(978-0-8170-1511-4(6))* Judson Pr.

Green, Kevin. Zondervan All in One Bible Reference Guide. 2008. 675p. ***(978-0-310-61164-6(4))*** Zondervan.

Gurtner, Daniel M. Second Baruch: A Critical Edition of the Syriac Text: With Greek & Latin Fragments, English Translation, Introduction, & Concordances. 2011. (ENG.). 240p. pap. 44.95 ***(978-0-567-04616-1(8)***, T&T Clark Int'l) Continuum International Publishing Group, Ltd. GBR. Dist: National Bk. Network.

A Handy Concordance of the Septuagint: Giving Various Readings from Codices Vaticanus, Alexandrinus, Sinaiticus, & Ephraemi. 2008. 290p. pap. 25.00 *(978-1-55635-767-1(2)*, Wipf and Stock) Wipf & Stock Pubs.

Harris, Leila Ae. All of the Animals in the Bible: A topical index of All of the Animals in the Bible. 2009. 476p. 41.00 *(978-1-59755-199-1(6)*, 8046, Advantage Inspirational) Advantage Bks.

—All of the Animals in the Bible: A Topical Index of All of the Animals in the Bible. 2009. 476p. pap. 25.00 *(978-1-59755-206-6(2)*, Advantage Inspirational) Advantage Bks.

Hudson, Charles Frederic. A Critical Greek & English Concordance of the New Testament Prepared by Charles F Hudson under the Direction of Horace L Hastings Revised And. 2006. 528p. per. 29.99 *(978-1-4255-5869-7(0))* MPublishing.

Knight, George W., ed. KJV Super Giant Print Dictionary & Concordance. 2007. (ENG., Illus.). 1248p. 24.99 *(978-0-8054-9492-1(8)*, Holman Reference) B&H Publishing Group.

Kohlenberger III, John R. NIV Compact Concordance, 1 vol. 2009. (NIV Compact Ser.). 610p. pap. 6.99 *(978-0-310-28569-4(0))* Zondervan.

Kohlenberger, John R., III. TNIV Compact Concordance, 1 vol. 2008. (ENG.). 608p. 14.99 *(978-0-310-26503-0(7))* Zondervan.

Longman Publishing Staff. Mini-Concordancer 5.25. Date not set. pap. 29.00 *(978-0-582-03816-5(2))* Addison-Wesley Longman, Ltd. GBR. Dist: Trans-Atlantic Pubns., Inc.

Lyons, C. W. & Deliduka, Thomas, compiled by. The Catholic Bible Concordance: Revised Standard Version, Catholic Edition. 2009. xiv, 2173p. *(978-1-931018-49-4(9))* Emmaus Road Publishing.

Oxford, ed. English Standard Version Bible with Apocrypha. 2009. (ENG., Illus.). xiii, 1446p. 29.99 *(978-0-19-528910-7(2))* Oxford Univ. Pr., Inc.

Peterson, Eugene H. The Message Concordance: Including Phrase & Synonym Finder. 2009. (Secrets Ser.). (ENG.). 416p. pap. 12.99 *(978-1-60006-978-9(9))* Message Bks. AUS. Dist: NavPress Publishing Group.

Petter, Hugo. Concordancia Greco-Espanola N. T. Greek-Spanish Concordance. (SPA.). 676p. *(978-84-7228-263-6(5)*, 220189) Clie, Editorial.

Religious Tract and Book Society for Ireland, Dublin Staff. The Scripture Text Book. 2006. 288p. per. 23.99 *(978-1-4255-2624-5(1))* MPublishing.

Sloan, William H. Concordancia Completa Santa Biblia: Complete Concordance of the Bible. (SPA.). 1015p. *(978-84-7228-262-9(7)*, 220186) Clie, Editorial.

Snyder, C. Arnold & Peters, Galen, eds. Reading the Anabaptist Bible: Reflections for Every Day of the Year. 425p. 36.00 *(978-1-894710-25-1(8))* Pandora Pr. CAN. Dist: Herald Pr.

Strong, James. Compact Reference Library Set. 2007. 2818p. pap. 34.99 *(978-0-7180-0729-4(8))* Nelson, Thomas Inc.

—The New Strong's Exhaustive Concordance of the Bible, 0 vols. 2010. 1968p. 34.99 *(978-1-4185-4169-9(9))* Nelson, Thomas Inc.

—The New Strong's Exhaustive Concordance of the Bible, Supersaver, 0 vols. 2010. 1968p. 34.99 *(978-1-4185-4170-5(2))* Nelson, Thomas Inc.

—The New Strong's Expanded Exhaustive Concordance of the Bible, 0 vols. 2010. 2000p. 39.99 *(978-1-4185-4168-2(0))* Nelson, Thomas Inc.

—The New Strong's Expanded Exhaustive Concordance of the Bible, Supersaver, 0 vols. 2010. 2000p. 39.99 *(978-1-4185-4237-5(7))* Nelson, Thomas Inc.

—Strong's Exhaustive Concordance of the Bible. 2007. 1685p. 29.95 incl. cd-rom *(978-1-56563-359-9(8))* Hendrickson Pubs. Marketing, LLC.

—Strong's Exhaustive Concordance to the Bible. 2009. (Illus.). 1685p. 29.95 *(978-1-59856-378-8(5))* Hendrickson Pubs. Marketing, LLC.

Strong, James & Thomas Nelson Publishing Staff. The New Strong's Guide to Bible Words: An English Index to Hebrew & Greek Words, 0 vols. 2008. 304p. pap. 18.99 *(978-1-4185-3218-5(5))* Nelson, Thomas Inc.

Tuggy, Alfred. Concordancia Analitica: Greek-Spanish Analytical Concor., 1 vol. 2010. (SPA.). 1088p. 49.99 *(978-84-7228-991-8(5)*, 223058) Clie, Editorial ESP. Dist: Zondervan.

—Concordancia Preposiciones Griegas: Concordance of Greek Prepositions. (SPA.). 1392p. *(978-84-7228-928-4(1)*, 222235) Clie, Editorial.

Viking, creator. Psalms. 2006. (ENG.). 132p. (gr. 12-18). 20.00 *(978-0-670-02955-9(X)*, Penguin Global) Penguin Group (USA) Inc.

Wilson, William. The Bible Student's Guide to the More Correct Understanding of the Old Testament by Reference to the original Hebrew. 2011. (HEB.). 187.00 *(978-1-61143-942-7(6))* Gorgias Pr., LLC.

Wood, Barry G. Bible Secrets Revealed. 2008. 184p. pap. 13.99 *(978-1-60477-861-8(X))* Xulon Pr., Inc.

Wright, Charles H. H. The Bible Readers' Aids. 2007. 360p. 46.95 *(978-0-548-06795-6(3))* Kessinger Publishing, LLC.

Zondervan Publishing Staff. Concordance Dictionary Topical Bible, 1 vol. 2008. (ENG.). 688p. 19.99 *(978-0-310-28309-6(4))* Zondervan.

BIBLE—CONCORDANCES—DATA PROCESSING

Dickerson, Patrick L., des. Apollos Database for New Testament & Early Christianity. cd-rom 149.95 *(978-0-9793291-0-4(8))* Apollos Data Projects LLC.

BIBLE—COSMOLOGY

see Biblical Cosmology

BIBLE—CRITICISM, FORM

Buss, Martin J. The Changing Shape of Form Criticism: A Relational Approach. 2010. 356p. *(978-1-906055-54-7(8))* Sheffield Phoenix Pr.

Koopmans, William T. Joshua 24 as Poetic Narrative. 2009. (Library of Hebrew Bible/Old Testament Studies, the Ser.). (ENG.). 522p. 75.00 *(978-0-567-29387-9(4)*, T&T Clark) Continuum International Publishing Group, Ltd. GBR. Dist: National Bk. Network.

Mazor, Yair. Who Wrought the Bible? Unveiling the Bible's Aesthetic Secrets. 2008. (ENG.). 232p. pap. 26.95 *(978-0-299-22844-6(4))*; (Illus.). 60.00 *(978-0-299-22840-8(1))* Univ. of Wisconsin Pr.

Petter, Donna Lee. The Book of Ezekiel & Mesopotamian City Laments. 2011. (Orbis Biblicus et Orientalis Ser.). (GER & ENG.). 207p. (C). 75.00 *(978-3-525-54367-2(0))* Vandenhoeck & Ruprecht GmbH & Co. KG DEU. Dist: ISD.

BIBLE—CRITICISM, HIGHER

see Bible—Criticism, Interpretation, etc.; Bible—Introductions

BIBLE—CRITICISM, INTERPRETATION, ETC.

Here are entered critical works on the Bible as a whole. Works on the principals of Biblical criticism are entered under Bible—Hermeneutics.

see also Bible—Feminist Criticism; Bible As Literature; Sex in the Bible

Abraham, Joseph. Eve: Accused or Acquitted? An Analysis of Feminist Readings of the Creation Narrative Texts in Genesis 1-3. 2007. (Paternoster Biblical Monographs: Ser.). 312p. pap. 31.00 *(978-1-59752-767-5(X)*, Wipf and Stock) Wipf & Stock Pubs.

Adams, Jay E. Fifty Difficult Passages Explained. 2008. 107p. pap. 10.99 *(978-1-889032-64-1(6))* Timeless Texts, Inc.

Adler, Leo. The Biblical View of Man. Schwartz, Daniel R., tr. from GER. 2007. (Illus.). 114p. 21.95 *(978-965-7108-96-3(9))* Urim Pubns. ISR. Dist: Coronet Bks.

Alexander, Willie J. Entering the Promised Land. 2007. (Illus.). 190p. spiral bd. 24.95 *(978-0-9798779-0-2(3))* Entering The Promised Land.

Alison, James. Undergoing God: Dispatches from the Scene of a Break-in. 2006. (ENG.). 246p. pap. 19.95 *(978-0-8264-1928-6(3))* Continuum International Publishing Group, Ltd. GBR. Dist: National Bk. Network.

Allay, Shabir. Is Jesus God? The Bible Says No. 98p. *(978-9960-9148-8-6(7))* Al-Attique Pubs., Inc.

—What God Said about Eating Pork. 38p. pap. *(978-9960-777-02-3(2))* Al-Attique Pubs., Inc.

—101-Clear Contradictions in the Bible. 39p. pap. *(978-9960-9148-9-3(5))* Al-Attique Pubs., Inc.

Allen, Connie J. World Peace: The Return of Jesus Christ. 2010. 284p. 30.95 *(978-1-4502-4080-2(1))*; pap. 20.95 *(978-1-4502-4078-9(X))* iUniverse, Inc.

Allen, Matthew James. Convincing Evidence of God. 2008. 268p. pap. 27.95 *(978-1-60563-039-7(X))* PublishAmerica, Inc.

Anastaplo, George. The Bible: Respectful Readings. 2008. (ENG.). 410p. 94.50 *(978-0-7391-2498-7(6))*; pap. 36.99 *(978-0-7391-2499-4(4))* Lexington Bks.

Anderson, Cheryl. Ancient Laws & Contemporary Controversies: The Need for Inclusive Biblical Interpretation, 1 vol. 2009. (ENG.). 208p. 25.00 *(978-0-19-530550-0(7))* Oxford Univ. Pr., Inc.

Anderson, Kevin L. But God Raised Him from the Dead: The Theology of Jesus' Resurrection in Luke-Acts. 2007. (Paternoster Biblical Monographs: Ser.). 392p. pap. 47.00 *(978-1-55635-237-9(9)*, Wipf and Stock) Wipf & Stock Pubs.

Anderson, Robert. Daniel in the Critics' Den: A Defense of the Historicity of the Book of Daniel. 2007. 204p. per. 19.95 *(978-1-60206-198-9(X))* Cosimo, Inc.

Andrews, Reg. Timber: A Call to Personal & Corporate Renewal. 2007. 176p. per. *(978-1-55452-224-8(2))* Essence Publishing.

Ankerberg, John & Burroughs, Dillon. How Do We Know the Bible Is True?, 8, Bk 1. 2008. (Contender's Bible Study Ser.). (ENG.). 112p. (gr. 11). pap. 7.99 *(978-0-89957-779-1(2))* AMG Pubs.

—How Is Christianity Different from Other Religions?, 8, Bk 2. 2008. (Contender's Bible Study Ser.). (ENG.). 112p. (gr. 11). pap. 7.99 *(978-0-89957-780-7(6))* AMG Pubs.

Aparicio Rodríguez, Ángel. Salmos 107-150. 2008. (SPA.). 394p. *(978-84-330-2289-9(X))* De Brouwer, DDB, Desclee.

Ariarajah, S. Wesley. The Bible & People of Other Faiths. 2009. 86p. (Orig.). pap. 12.00 *(978-1-60608-908-8(0))* Wipf & Stock Pubs.

Armerding, Carl Edwin, et al. The Bible in World Christian Perspective: Studies in Honor of Carl Edwin Armerding. 2008. *(978-1-57383-432-2(7))* Regent College Publishing.

Armstrong, Dave. Bible Proofs for Catholic Truths: A Source Book for Apologists & Inquirers. 2009. xiv, 445p. pap. 15.95 *(978-1-933184-57-9(4))* Sophia Institute Pr.

Arnold, Matthew. God & the Bible: A Review of Objections to Literature & Dogma. 2007. (ENG.). 386p. 48.95 *(978-0-548-02716-5(1))* Kessinger Publishing, LLC.

—God & the Bible: A Review of Objections to "Literature & Dogma" reprint ed. lib. bdg. 98.00 *(978-0-7426-2171-8(5))* Classic Bks.

—Literature & Dogma: An Essay Towards a Better Apprehension of the Bible. reprint ed. lib. bdg. 98.00 *(978-0-7426-2170-1(7))* Classic Bks.

Astell, Ann W. & Goodhart, Sandor, eds. Sacrifice, Scripture, & Substitution: Readings in Ancient Judaism & Christianity. 2011. (ND Christianity & Judaism Anitqui Ser.). (ENG.). 424p. pap. 49.00 *(978-0-268-02038-5(8))* Univ. of Notre Dame Pr.

Attridge, Harold W. & VanderKam, James C. Presidential Voices: The Society of Biblical Literature in the Twentieth Century. 2006. xi, 350p. pap. 39.95 *(978-1-58983-259-6(0))* Society of Biblical Literature.

Aune, David E. Apocalypticism, Prophecy, & Magic in Early Christianity: Collected Essays. 2008. 496p. (C). pap. 50.00 *(978-0-8010-3594-4(5))* Baker Academic.

Ausloos, H. & Lemmelijn, B., eds. The Book of Life: Biblical Answers to Existential Questions. 2010. (Louvain Theological & Pastoral Monographs). (ENG.). 256p. (C). pap. 37.00 *(978-90-429-2296-9(6))* Peeters Pubs. & Booksellers BEL. Dist: Brown, David Bk. Co., The.

Ausloos, Hans. The Book of Life: Biblical Answers to Existential Questions. 2010. x, 256p. pap. 48.00 *(978-0-8028-6574-8(7))* Eerdmans, William B. Publishing Co.

Authorised Version of the English Bible 1611 5 Volume Set. 2010. (ENG.). 2954p. pap. 155.00 *(978-0-521-18478-6(9))* Cambridge Univ. Pr.

Authorised Version of the English Bible 1611: Volume 1, Genesis to Deuteronomy. 2010. (ENG.). 520p. pap. 34.99 *(978-0-521-17931-7(9))* Cambridge Univ. Pr.

Authorised Version of the English Bible 1611: Volume 2, Joshua to Esther. 2010. (ENG.). 642p. pap. 34.99 *(978-0-521-17933-1(5))* Cambridge Univ. Pr.

Authorised Version of the English Bible 1611: Volume 3, Job to Malachi. 2010. (ENG.). 800p. pap. 34.99 *(978-0-521-17935-5(1))* Cambridge Univ. Pr.

Authorised Version of the English Bible 1611: Volume 4, Apocrypha. 2010. (ENG.). 450p. pap. 34.99 *(978-0-521-17930-0(0))* Cambridge Univ. Pr.

Authorised Version of the English Bible 1611: Volume 5, the New Testament. 2010. (ENG.). 600p. pap. 34.99 *(978-0-521-17936-2(X))* Cambridge Univ. Pr.

Avalos, Hector. The End of Biblical Studies. 2007. (ENG.). 1p. 32.98 *(978-1-59102-536-8(2))* Prometheus Bks., Pubs.

Baban, Octavian D. On the Road Encounters in Luke-Acts: Hellenistic Mimesis & Luke's Theology of the Way. 2006. (Paternoster Biblical Monographs: Ser.). 366p. pap. 37.00 *(978-1-59752-993-0(0)*, Wipf and Stock) Wipf & Stock Pubs.

Bacon, Benjamin Wisne. Fourth Gospel in Research & Debate A S. 2006. pap. 42.95 *(978-1-4286-3631-5(5))* Kessinger Publishing, LLC.

Bailey, R. C. & Liew, T-s. B., eds. They Were All Together in One Place? Toward Minority Biblical Criticism. 2009. (SBL - Semeia Studies). 412p. *(978-90-04-15117-8(6))* BRILL.

Bailey, Randall C., et al. They Were All Together in One Place: Toward Minority Biblical Criticism. 2009. 412p. pap. 45.95 *(978-1-58983-245-9(0))* Society of Biblical Literature.

Baker, A.E. Prophets for an Age of Doubt. 2007. 248p. per. *(978-1-4067-8851-8(1)*, Pomona Pr.) Read Bks.

Baker, F. Joan. Metaphysical Bible Interpretation: Can It Change Our World? 2010. 60p. pap. *(978-3-639-26546-0(7))* VDM Verlag Dr. Mueller e.K.

Bar-Jonah, Nathanael. The Gospel According to Nathanael. 2008. 112p. pap. 10.99 *(978-1-4389-0814-4(8))* AuthorHouse.

Barbour, Clarence A. The Bible in the World of Today. 2009. 226p. pap. 25.75 *(978-1-116-07393-5(5))* BiblioBazaar.

Barnes, Margaret A. Biblical Essays: Writings to Touch the Heart String. Date not set. 100p. pap. *(978-1-891597-63-3(9)*, SDC Pr.) Mleecole Pub.

Barr, James & Barton, John. Bible & Interpretation: The Collected Essays of James Barr, 3 vols. 2012. (ENG.). 792p. 230.00 ***(978-0-19-969289-7(0))***; 696p. 230.00 ***(978-0-19-969290-3(4))*** Oxford Univ. Pr., Inc.

Barr, James, et al. Bible & Interpretation: The Collected Essays of James Barr, 3 vols. 2012. (ENG.). 736p. 230.00 ***(978-0-19-969288-0(2))*** Oxford Univ. Pr., Inc.

Barrett, Charles D. Funny Things Can Happen on Your Way Through the Bible: Scriptural Oddities & Odd Thoughts about Them in a Book of More Rhyme Than Reason. 2010. 354p. pap. 39.00 *(978-1-60899-393-2(0)*, Resource Pubns.) Wipf & Stock Pubs.

Barrows, E. P. Normas de Interpretacion Biblica: Principles of Bible Interpretation. *(978-84-7645-061-1(3)*, 223126) Clie, Editorial.

Barton. Invitation to the Bible. 176p. 13.00 *(978-0-281-05075-8(9))* SPCK Publishing GBR. Dist: Pilgrim Pr., The/United Church Pr.

Barton, John. The Nature of Biblical Criticism. 2007. (ENG.). 206p. per. 25.00 *(978-0-664-22587-2(X))* Westminster John Knox Pr.

Bates, Matthew W. The Hermeneutics of the Apostolic Proclamation: The Center of Paul's Method of Scriptural Interpretation. 2012. (ENG.). 415p. 69.95 ***(978-1-60258-328-3(5))*** Baylor Univ. Pr.

Bauer, David R. An Annotated Guide to Biblical Resources for Ministry. 2011. 336p. pap. 37.00 *(978-1-61097-356-1(0)*, Wipf and Stock) Wipf & Stock Pubs.

Beal, Timothy. The Rise & Fall of the Bible: The Unexpected History of an Accidental Book. (ENG.). 256p. 2012. pap. 15.95 ***(978-0-547-73734-8(3)***, Mariner Bks.) 2011. (Illus.). 25.00 *(978-0-15-101358-6(6))* Houghton Mifflin Harcourt Trade & Reference Pubs

Beam, Jack. The God Awful Truth about Heaven. 2008. 95p. 9.95 *(978-0-9796749-1-4(3))* Flanders Fields Pr.

Beardslee, William A., et al. Biblical Preaching on the Death of Jesus. Lull, David J., ed. 2007. 240p. pap. 26.00 *(978-1-55635-214-0(X)*, Wipf and Stock) Wipf & Stock Pubs.

Beck, John A., et al. A Visual Guide to Bible Events: Fascinating Insights into Where They Happened & Why. 2009. 272p. 39.99 *(978-0-8010-1285-3(6))* Baker Bks.

Beck, Kevin A. This Book Will Change Your World: How All Things Become New. 2009. pap. 16.95 *(978-1-934049-04-4(2))* Bimillennial Pr.

Beck, T. David. The Holy Spirit & the Renewal of All Things: Pneumatology in Paul & Jurgen Moltmann. 2007. (Princeton Theological Monographs). 278p. pap. 31.00 *(978-1-55635-102-0(X)*, Pickwick Pubns.) Wipf & Stock Pubs.

Bell, Rob & Golden, Don. Jesus Wants to Save Christians: A Manifesto for the Church in Exile. 2012. (ENG.). 240p. pap. 14.99 ***(978-0-06-212582-8(6)***, HarperOne) HarperCollins Pubs.

Bell, Rob, et al. Jesus Wants to Save Christians: A Manifesto for the Church in Exile, 1 vol. 2008. (ENG., Illus.). 224p. 19.99 *(978-0-310-27502-2(4))* Zondervan.

Benedict XVI, pseud. The Apostles: The Origin of the Church & Their Co-Workers. 2007. (Illus.). 174p. 14.95 *(978-1-59276-405-1(3))* Our Sunday Visitor, Publishing Div.

—Jesus, the Apostles & the Early Church. 2007. 163p. 19.95 *(978-1-58617-220-6(4))* Ignatius Pr.

Benedix, Beth Hawkins, ed. Subverting Scriptures: Critical Reflections on the Use of the Bible. 2009. (ENG.). 256p. 89.00 *(978-0-230-61069-9(2))* Palgrave Macmillan.

Bennett, Zoë & Gowler, David, eds. Radical Christian Voices & Practice: Essays in Honour of Christopher Rowland. 2012. (ENG.). 320p. 125.00 ***(978-0-19-959977-6(7))*** Oxford Univ. Pr., Inc.

Berg, Jacob Albert van den. Biblical Argument in Manichaean Missionary Practice: The Case of Adimantus & Augustine. 2009. (Nag Hammadi & Manichaean Studies). *(978-90-04-18034-5(6))* BRILL.

Bergant, Dianne. Scripture: History & Interpretation. 2008. (Engaging Theology: Catholic Perspectives Ser.). 174p. pap. 19.95 *(978-0-8146-5995-3(0)*, Liturgical Pr. Bks.) Liturgical Pr.

Bergen, Wesley. Voyages in Uncharted Waters Essays on Th. 2006. 248p. *(978-1-905048-57-1(2))* Sheffield Phoenix Pr.

Bergsma, William. We Have Also a More Sure Word of Prophecy 2 Peter: 19. 2007. 188p. (ENG.). 21.99 *(978-1-60266-064-9(6))*; per. 13.99 *(978-1-60266-063-2(8))* Xulon Pr., Inc.

Best, James O. The Lord Is My Shepherd. 2008. 136p. pap. 15.70 *(978-1-4343-9473-6(5))* AuthorHouse.

Beynon, Nigel & Sach, Andrew. Dig Deeper: Tools for Understanding God's Word. 2010. 160p. pap. 14.99 *(978-1-58134-971-9(8))* Crossway.

Biliarsky, Ivan & Paun, Radu G. The Biblical Models of Power & Law: Papers of the International Conference, Bucharest, New Europe College 2005 = les Modèles Bibliques du Pouvoir et du Droit: Actes du Colloque International, Bucarest, New Europe College 2005. 2008. (FRE, MUL, GER & ENG., Illus.). 309p. pap. 72.95 *(978-3-631-57240-5(9))* Lang, Peter GmbH, Europaischer Verlag der Wissenschaften DEU. Dist: Lang, Peter.

Birch, Bruce C., et al, eds. The Discipleship Study Bible: New Revised Standard Version, Including Apocrypha. 2008. (ENG.). 2200p. 40.00 *(978-0-664-22371-7(0))* Westminster John Knox Pr.

Bird, Michael & Pahl, Michael, eds. The Sacred Text. 2010. 114.00 *(978-1-60724-741-8(0))* Gorgias Pr., LLC.

Bird, Michael F. Saving Righteousness of God: Studies on Paul, Justification & the New Perspective. 2008. (Paternoster Biblical Monographs Ser.). (ENG.). 250p. pap. 39.99 *(978-1-84227-455-1(1)*, Paternoster) Authentic Media.

—The Saving Righteousness of God: Studies on Paul, Justification & the New Perspective. 2007. (Paternoster Biblical Monographs). 266p. pap. 30.00 *(978-1-55635-274-4(3)*, Wipf and Stock) Wipf & Stock Pubs.

Black, C. Clifton. The Eighth Day of Creation: An Anthology of Christian Scripture. 2008. 376p. 24.00 *(978-0-8028-6272-3(1))* Eerdmans, William B. Publishing Co.

Black, Fiona C. The Recycled Bible: Autobiography, Culture, & the Space Between. 2006. (SBL - Semeia Studies). (Illus.). 218p. *(978-90-04-13088-3(8))* BRILL.

Blue, Debbie. From Stone to Living Word: Letting the Bible Live Again. 2008. 224p. pap. 18.00 (978-1-58743-190-6(4)) Brazos Pr.

Bockmuehl, Carleton Paget, et al. Redemption & Resistance: The Messianic Hopes of Jews & Christians in Antiquity. 2009. (ENG.). 410p. 65.00 (978-0-567-03044-3(X), T&T Clark Int'l) Continuum International Publishing Group, Ltd. GBR. Dist: National Bk. Network.

Bockmuehl, Markus. Redemption & Resistance: The Messianic Hopes of Jews & Christians in Antiquity. Paget, James Carleton, ed. 2007. (ENG., Illus.). 410p. 160.00 (978-0-567-03043-6(1), T&T Clark Int'l) Continuum International Publishing Group, Ltd. GBR. Dist: National Bk. Network.

Boda, Mark, et al, eds. Seeking the Favor of God: Volume 2. 2007. 300p. per. 39.95 (978-1-58983-278-7(7)) Society of Biblical Literature.

Bodner, Keith. David Observed: A King in the Eyes of his Court. 2008. 212p. per. (978-1-906055-11-0(4)) Sheffield Phoenix Pr.

Boer, Roland. Criticism of Heaven: On Marxism & Theology. 2007. (Historical Materialism Book Ser.). 465p. (978-90-04-16111-5(2)) BRILL.

—Novel Histories: The Fiction of Biblical Criticism. 2006. (ENG.). 224p. per. 23.95 (978-1-58983-249-7(3)) Society of Biblical Literature.

—Rescuing the Bible. 2007. (Blackwell Manifestos Ser.). (ENG.). 184p. pap. 34.95 (978-1-4051-7020-8(4)); 99.95 (978-1-4051-7021-5(2)) Wiley, John & Sons, Inc. (Wiley-Blackwell).

Boer, Roland, ed. Secularism & Biblical Studies. 2010. (BibleWorld Ser.). (ENG.). 224p. (C). 34.95 (978-1-84553-375-5(5)); 99.95 (978-1-84553-374-8(7)) Equinox Publishing Ltd. GBR. Dist: ISD.

Boer, Roland & +kland, Jorunn, eds. Marxist Feminist Criticism of the Bible. 2008. 260p. (978-1-906055-35-6(1)) Sheffield Phoenix Pr.

Booker, Martin. Chapters in a Life: Written by God, Lived by All. 2011. 248p. 35.95 (978-1-4497-1096-5(4)); pap. 19.95 (978-1-4497-1095-8(6)) Author Solutions, Inc. (WestBow Pr.).

books to uplift youth. Questions about the Bible People Are Afraid to Ask - Revised: An Afrikan Spiritual Interpretation. 2007. pap. 11.95 (978-0-9740031-3-9(1)) Bks. To Uplift Youth.

Bornkamm, Gü, et al. Studien zum Matthäus-Evangelium. 2009. (GER.). xiii, 420p. (978-3-7887-2365-1(3)) Neukirchener Verlag.

Bosetti, Elena. Praying with Women of the Bible. 2009.Tr. of Donne nel popolo di Dio. 208p. pap. 12.95 (978-0-8198-5960-0(5)) Pauline Bks. & Media.

Braddock, Thomas. A Study Guide for Oswald Chambers' My Utmost for His Highest. 2006. 544p. per. 31.99 (978-1-4141-0527-7(4)) Pleasant Word.

Bragg, David. Pure Religion: A Study of James. 2007. 132p. pap. 8.99 (978-0-89225-559-7(5)) Gospel Advocate Co., Inc.

Bramlett, James. The Top Ten Mysteries of the Bible: Revealed & Explained. 2006. (ENG.). 156p. per. 24.95 (978-1-4241-4451-8(5)) PublishAmerica, Inc.

Brash, Donald James. The Indispensable Guide to God's Word. 2010. (978-0-8298-1829-1(4)) Pilgrim Pr., The/United Church Pr.

Breslauer, S. Daniel. Decoding Religion in the Bible: Learning to Recognize Diversity of Biblical Texts. 2006. (C). pap. 30.00 net. (978-1-59738-001-0(6)) Sloan Publishing.

Brett, Mark G. Decolonizing God: The Bible in the Tides of Empire. 2008. 237p. (978-1-906055-37-0(8)) Sheffield Phoenix Pr.

Brettler, Marc Zvi, et al. The Bible & the Believer: How to Read the Bible Critically & Religiously. 2012. (ENG., Illus.). 224p. 27.95 **(978-0-19-986300-6(8))** Oxford Univ. Pr., Inc.

Brewer, Homer. Exploding Myths of Biblical Interpretation. 2010. pap. 9.99 (978-1-61566-806-9(3)) Tate Publishing & Enterprises, LLC.

Briggs, Charles Augustus & Briggs, Charles A. The Higher Criticism of the Hexateuch. 2008. 271p. pap. 25.00 (978-1-60608-036-8(9)) Wipf & Stock Pubs.

Brown, James Baldwin. Misread Passages of Scripture. 2008. 139p. 21.99 (978-0-554-88266-6(3)); 245p. 24.99 (978-0-554-88258-1(2)); 203p. pap. 20.75 (978-0-554-88260-4(4)); 178p. pap. 19.75 (978-0-554-88263-5(9)) BiblioBazaar.

—Misread Passages of Scripture. 2008. 136p. 35.95 (978-1-4371-8270-5(4)); pap. 20.95 (978-1-4370-5125-4(1)) Kessinger Publishing, LLC.

—Misread Passages of Scripture. 2006. 144p. per. 16.99 (978-1-4255-1033-6(7)) MPublishing.

Brown, Kate. Word to Set You Free. 224p. pap. 8.95 (978-0-281-04806-9(1)) International Publishers Marketing.

Brown, Steve. Jesus Drank, Judas Repented & God Divorced His Bride. 2011. 146p. pap. 16.95 **(978-1-60005-201-9(0))** Happy About.

Brug, John F. Bible Discovery Series: Using Archaeology to Study the Bible: Digging for Insights. 2010. pap. (978-0-8100-2233-1(8)) Northwestern Publishing Hse.

Bull, Michael. Bible Matrix Ii: The Covenant Key. 2011. 320p. pap. 22.95 **(978-1-4497-2375-0(6)**, WestBow Pr.) Author Solutions, Inc.

Bullen, Donald A. A Man of One Book? John Wesley's Interpretation & Use of the Bible. 2007. (Studies in Evangelical History & Thought Ser.). 272p. pap. 31.00 (978-1-55635-490-8(8)) Wipf & Stock Pubs.

Bullinger, E. W. Number in Scripture. 2006. (ENG.). 26.95 (978-1-59605-957-3(5), Cosimo Classics) Cosimo, Inc.

Bullinger, E. w. & Bullinger, E. W. Number in Scripture: Its Supernatural Design & Spiritual Significance. 2011. 314p. pap. 10.75 **(978-1-61427-047-8(3))** Martino Publishing.

Bullinger, Ethelbert W. The Witness of the Stars. (ENG.). 300p. 2007. 43.95 (978-0-548-13851-9(6)) 2006. per. 28.95 (978-1-4286-5022-0(9)) Kessinger Publishing, LLC.

Burge, Gary M. The Bible & the Land, 1 vol. 2009. (Ancient Context, Ancient Faith Ser.). (ENG.). 112p. pap. 14.99 (978-0-310-28044-6(3)) Zondervan.

Burgon, Dean John William. Inspiration & Interpretation. 2008. pap. 29.00 (978-1-888328-04-2(5)) Old Paths Pubns., Inc., The.

Burke, Brad. ¿Por Qué Dios No Detiene el Mal? (Why Doesn't God Stop Evil) 2011. (SPA.). 172p. pap. 10.95 **(978-1-58802-447-3(4))** Editorial Patmos.

Burke, David G. Translation That Openeth the Window: Reflections on the History & Legacy of the King James Bible. 2009. (978-90-04-15741-5(7)) BRILL.

—Translation That Openeth the Window: Reflections on the History & Legacy of the King James Bible. 2009. 34.95 (978-1-58983-356-2(2)) Society of Biblical Literature.

Burr, William Henry. Self-Contradictions of the Bible. 2007. (ENG.). 78p. pap. 16.99 (978-1-4346-8038-9(X)); 88p. pap. 18.99 (978-1-4346-8039-6(8)) BiblioBazaar.

Burt, Robert A. In the Whirlwind: God & Humanity in Conflict. 2012. (ENG.). 400p. 29.95 **(978-0-674-06566-6(2))** Harvard Univ. Pr.

Burton, Keith Augustus. The Blessing of Africa: The Bible & African Christianity. 2007. (ENG.). 294p. per. 22.00 (978-0-8308-2762-6(5), IVP Acad.) InterVarsity Pr.

Buss, Martin J. The Changing Shape of Form Criticism: A Relational Approach. 2010. 356p. (978-1-906055-54-7(8)) Sheffield Phoenix Pr.

—The Concept of Form in the Twentieth Century. 2008. 284p. (978-1-906055-51-6(3)) Sheffield Phoenix Pr.

Bytheway, John. When Times Are Tough: 5 Scriptures That Will Help You Get Through Almost Anything. 2010. 176p. pap. 10.99 (978-1-60641-848-2(3)) Deseret Bk. Co.

Callahan, Allen Dwight. The Talking Book: African Americans & the Bible. 2008. (ENG.). 304p. per. 18.00 (978-0-300-13616-6(1)) Yale Univ. Pr.

Camp, Richard R. Constructions of Space I: Theory, Geography, & Narrative. Berquist, Jon L., ed. 2008. (Library of Hebrew Bible/Old Testament Studies, the Ser.). (ENG., Illus.). 176p. 130.00 (978-0-567-02707-8(4), T&T Clark Int'l) Continuum International Publishing Group, Ltd. GBR. Dist: National Bk. Network.

Can I Trust My Bible? 2008. pap. 15.00 (978-0-9771829-3-0(2)) Berean Pubns.

Caragounis, Chrys C. The Son of Man: Vision & Interpretation. 2011. 330p. pap. 37.00 **(978-1-61097-385-4(2)**, Wipf and Stock) Wipf & Stock Pubs.

Carmichael, Calum & Daube, David. The Deed & the Doer in the Bible: David Daube's Gifford Lectures, Vol. 1. 2007. (ENG.). 312p. pap. 34.95 (978-1-59947-134-1(5)) Templeton Pr.

Carpenter, J. Estlin. First Three Gospels Their Origin & Rel. 2006. pap. 36.95 (978-1-4286-6363-3(0)) Kessinger Publishing, LLC.

Carroll, Raymond Allen. The Road to Healing. 2008. 76p. per. 9.99 (978-1-60477-639-3(0)) Xulon Pr., Inc.

Carson, D. A. Collected Writings on Scripture. 2010. 336p. 27.99 (978-1-4335-1441-8(9)) Crossway.

Carver, Stephen. An Introduction to the Literature of the Bible. 2010. (C). pap. 25.00 (978-0-615-33004-4(5)) Carver, Stephen S.

Caspi, Mishael M. Unbinding the Binding of Isaac. 2006. (ENG.). 222p. pap. 37.99 (978-0-7618-3566-0(0)) Univ. Pr. of America, Inc.

Caspi, Mishael M. & Greene, John T. Parables & Fables as Distinctive Jewish Literary Genres: The Origins & Structure of Indirect Speech about God. 2012. 372p. 129.95 **(978-0-7734-2598-9(5))** Mellen, Edwin Pr., The.

Caspi, Mishael M. & Greene, John T., eds. How Jonah Is Interpreted in Judaism, Christianity, & Islam: Essays on the Authenticity & Influence of the Biblical Prophet. 2011. 372p. 129.95 **(978-0-7734-3931-3(5))** Mellen, Edwin Pr., The.

Catholic Religion Proved by the Protestant Bible. 2009. 29p. 1.00 **(978-1-892875-49-5(7))** New Hope Pubns.

Cavins, Jeff, et al. The Bible Timeline 4-Part Study: Study Materials. 2007. (Great Adventure Ser.). 44.95 (978-1-932645-98-9(5)) Ascension Pr.

Cayen, Daniel Theo. The Holy Bible: Great Truths/ Many Lies. 2008. 172p. pap. 12.95 (978-0-7414-4547-6(6)) Infinity Publishing.

Chalmers, R. Scott. The Struggle of Yahweh & El for Hosea's Israel. 2008. (HEB & ENG.). 288p. (978-1-905048-40-3(8)) Sheffield Phoenix Pr.

Chan, Zenobia C. Y. Silenced Women. 2009. 167p. 49.00 (978-1-60692-199-9(1)) Nova Science Pubs., Inc.

Channing, Steven. Religion vs Christianity. 2008. 388p. 31.99 (978-1-60647-022-0(1)) Xulon Pr., Inc.

—Religion vs Christianity: The Seven Women. 2008. 388p. pap. 19.99 (978-1-60647-021-3(3)) Xulon Pr., Inc.

Cheever, George Barrell. The Guilt of Slavery & the Crime of Slaveholding, Demonstrated from the Hebrew & Greek Scriptures by Rev George B Cheever. 2006. 484p. per. 29.99 (978-1-4255-5353-1(2)) MPublishing.

Cheever, Lloyd "Pentar". The Heart: Naked Truth, Right Before Our Eyes. 2006. pap. 10.00 (978-0-8059-7107-1(6)) Dorrance Publishing Co., Inc.

Christian, Donna. Revived by His Word. 2006. 10p. audio compact disk 10.00 (978-0-9672804-5-5(1)) Family Harvest Church.

Claiborne, Shane & Wilson-Hartgrove, Jonathan. Becoming the Answer to Our Prayers: Prayer for Ordinary Radicals. 2008. (ENG.). 125p. pap. 13.00 (978-0-8308-3622-2(5), IVP Bks.) InterVarsity Pr.

Clark, George. The Bible Revisited. 2007. 272p. 23.95 (978-1-4327-0530-5(X)); per. 12.95 (978-1-4327-0256-4(4)) Outskirts Pr., Inc.

Clasby, Nancy Tenfelde. God, the Bible, & Human Consciousness. 2008. (ENG.). 272p. 95.00 (978-0-230-60543-5(5)) Palgrave Macmillan.

Clever, Charles Huntley. The Wise Shall Understand. 2009. 204p. 25.99 (978-1-60791-307-8(0)); pap. 15.99 (978-1-60791-575-1(8)) Xulon Pr., Inc.

Cline, Eric H. From Eden to Exile: Unraveling Mysteries of the Bible. (ENG.). 256p. 2008. pap. 16.95 (978-1-4262-0208-7(3)) 2007. (Illus.). 26.00 (978-1-4262-0084-7(6), National Geographic) National Geographic Society.

Clines, David J. A. Bible in Three Dimensions: Essays in Celebration of Forty Years of Biblical Studies in the University of Sheffield. Porter, Stanley E. & Fowl, Stephen E., eds. 2009. (Library of Hebrew Bible/Old Testament Studies, the Ser.). (ENG.). 408p. 65.00 (978-0-567-26307-0(X), T&T Clark) Continuum International Publishing Group, Ltd. GBR. Dist: National Bk. Network.

Cloud, David W. Dressing for the Lord. 2007. (AFA.). 211p. per. 9.95 (978-1-58318-106-5(7)) Way of Life Literature.

Cohen, Ken. The Infiltration of Error in the Church: A Study which Identifies & Corrects, Through the Scriptures, Errors that have Crept into Christianity Over. 2008. 165p. pap. 13.95 (978-1-4327-2848-9(2)) Outskirts Pr., Inc.

Cohen, Norman J. Moses & the Journey to Leadership: Timeless Lessons of Effective Management from the Bible & Today's Leaders. 2008. pap. 18.99 (978-1-58023-351-4(1)) Jewish Lights Publishing.

Cohen, Tim. Messiah, History, & the Tribulation Period Vol. 4: Biblical Chronology: the Young Creation. Cohen, Tim, ed. 2006. pap. (978-0-9662793-5-1(2)) Prophecy House, Inc.

Collins, Christopher. Homeland Mythology: Biblical Narratives in American Culture. 2007. (ENG.). 264p. 29.95 (978-0-271-02993-1(5)) Pennsylvania State Univ. Pr.

Combs, William C., ed. Biblical & Theological Essays: Selections from the Detroit Baptist Seminary Journal, 1996-2000. 2010. 428p. pap. 24.99 (978-0-88469-263-8(9)) BMH Bks.

Conder, Tim & Rhodes, Daniel. Free for All: Rediscovering the Bible in Community. 2009. (Emersion). (Illus.). 256p. pap. 16.99 (978-0-8010-7147-8(X)) Baker Bks.

Coogan, Michael, et al, eds. The New Oxford Annotated Bible with Apocrypha. 4th rev. ed. 2010. (ENG., Illus.). 2416p. 95.00 (978-0-19-528957-2(9)) Oxford Univ. Pr., Inc.

Cook, Richard R. & Pao, David W., eds. After Imperialism: Christian Identity in China & the Global Evangelical Movement. 2012. (ENG.). 256p. pap. 35.00 **(978-0-7188-9257-9(7))** Lutterworth Pr., The GBR. Dist: Brown, David Bk. Co., The.

Coote, Robert & Gottwald, Norman, eds. To Break Every Yoke: Essays in Honor of Marvin L. Chaney. 2007. (Illus.). 396p. (978-1-906055-27-1(0)) Sheffield Phoenix Pr.

Coote, Robert B. The Interface of Orality & Writing: Hearing, Seeing, Writing in New Genres. Weissenrieder, Annette, ed. 2010. (Illus.). 452p. 257.50 (978-3-16-150445-7(3)) Mohr Siebeck GmbH & Co. KG DEU. Dist: Coronet Bks.

Copan, Paul & Linville, Mark. What Is Truth? 2007. (RZIM Critical Questions Discussion Guides). (ENG.). 75p. per. 8.00 (978-0-8308-3154-8(1), IVP Conn.) InterVarsity Pr.

Cord, John. Selfless Spirit, Selfish Ego: The Way to Everlasting Peace for Judaism, Christianity & Islam: A Biblical Tribute Inspired by Oprah Winfrey's Unprecedented, Worldwide Interactive Spiritual Event Featuring Eckhart Tolle. 2008. pap. (978-1-57733-229-9(6)) Blue Dolphin Publishing, Inc.

Corob, Lawrence W. The Order of the Code: hellip;Deciphering the Bible. 2007. (ENG.). 288p. per. 27.95 (978-1-4241-6436-3(2)) PublishAmerica, Inc.

Cox, James. Confronting Obstacles to Full Salvation on God's Terms. 2007. 116p. per. 10.99 (978-1-60266-203-2(7)) Xulon Pr., Inc.

Craffert, Pieter F. The Life of a Galilean Shaman: Jesus of Nazareth in Anthropological-Historical Perspective. 2007. (Matrix: the Bible in Mediterranean Context: Ser.). 470p. pap. 52.00 (978-1-55635-085-6(6)) Wipf & Stock Pubs.

Craughwell, Thomas J. Bad Kids of the Bible: And What They Can Teach Us. 2008. (ENG., Illus.). 304p. pap. 16.99 (978-1-59233-361-5(3), 1592333613) Quayside.

Cronometria: Consideraciones: Cronometry, Critic Considerations. (SPA.). (978-84-7645-204-2(7), 223327) Clie, Editorial.

Crook, Zeba & Harland, Philip, eds. Identity & Interaction in the Ancient Mediterranean: Jews, Christians & Others. Essays in Honour of Stephen G. Wilson. 2007. (Illus.). 312p. (978-1-906055-17-2(3)) Sheffield Phoenix Pr.

Cross, John R. All that the Prophets have Spoken. 2nd ed. 2007. (Illus.). per. (978-1-890082-53-6(8)) GoodSeed International.

—The Stranger on the Road to Emmaus. I.t. ed. 2009. pap. (978-1-890082-71-0(6)) 4th rev. ed. 2008. pap. (978-1-890082-54-3(6)) GoodSeed International.

Crossan, John Dominic. The Cross That Spoke: The Origins of the Passion Narrative. 2008. (Illus.). 454p. pap. 50.00 (978-1-55635-819-7(9)) Wipf & Stock Pubs.

Crouch, Earl. Do You Know? 2007. 192p. per. 24.95 (978-1-4241-7391-4(4)) PublishAmerica, Inc.

Cumming, John. Moses Right, & Bishop Colenso Wrong; Being Popular Lectures on the Pentateuch. 2006. 276p. per. 23.99 (978-1-4255-2493-7(1)) MPublishing.

Custer, Stewart. The Way of the Lord. 2009. (978-1-60682-035-3(4)) BJU Pr.

C.V.L. Some imperatives from the Bible. 2008. 228p. pap. 16.95 (978-1-4357-4735-7(6)) Lulu Enterprises Inc.

Daniel, R. P. Let's Play Bible Detective. 36p. pap. 2.95 (978-0-88172-017-4(8)) Believers Bookshelf, Inc.

Daniels, Thomas A. The Last 4 Visions of Daniel: Some Startling Revelations. 2007. (Illus.). 320p. per. 22.99 (978-1-59886-775-6(X)) Tate Publishing & Enterprises, LLC.

Darby, J. n. & Darby, J. N. Synopsis of the Books of the Bible. 2010. 608p. 45.99 (978-1-117-94899-7(4)); pap. 45.75 (978-1-117-94900-0(1)) BiblioBazaar.

Dardess, George. Do We Worship the Same God? Comparing the Bible & the Qur'an. 2006. 166p. per. 12.95 (978-0-86716-731-3(9)) Franciscan Media.

David, Clemens Joseph, ed. The Syriac Bible According to the Mosul Edition. 2010. (SYR.). 350.00 (978-1-60724-893-4(X)); 350.00 (978-1-60724-891-0(3)); 350.00 (978-1-60724-892-7(1)) Gorgias Pr., LLC.

Davidson, Don. The Eternal Perspective: Essays on the Truths of Christianity by a Former Skeptic. 2007. 191p. pap. 24.95 (978-1-4241-9941-9(7)) PublishAmerica, Inc.

Davies, John. Words Remembered, Texts Renewed: Essays in Honour of John F. A. Sawyer. Watson, Wilfred G. E. & Harvey, Graham, eds. 2009. (Library of Hebrew Bible/Old Testament Studies, the Ser.). (ENG.). 533p. 75.00 (978-0-567-63423-8(X), T&T Clark) Continuum International Publishing Group, Ltd. GBR. Dist: National Bk. Network.

Davila, Marcos. Walk in the Spirit. 2008. 178p. pap. 14.99 (978-1-4357-6035-6(2)) Lulu Enterprises Inc.

De Waal Dryden, J. Theology & Ethics in 1 Peter: Paraenetic Strategies for Christian Character Formation. 2006. (Wissenschaftliche Untersuchungen Zum Neuen Testament 2 Ser.: Vol. 209). 237p. (C). pap. 89.50 (978-3-16-148910-5(1)) Mohr Siebeck GmbH & Co. KG DEU. Dist: Coronet Bks.

De Young, James B. Burning down 'the Shack' How the 'Christian' bestseller Is deceiving Millions. 2010. 288p. pap. 15.95 (978-1-935071-84-6(X)) WND Bks, Inc.

Deadmond, Rick. The Betrothed Bride of Messiah. 2007. 408p. per. 21.99 (978-1-60266-151-6(0)) Xulon Pr., Inc.

Dempsey, Carol J. Reading the Bible, Transforming Conflict: Theology in Dialogue Series. 2011. 224p. pap. 26.00 (978-1-57075-914-7(6)) Orbis Bks.

Derry, Timothy J. & Stewart, Gary P. 101 Most Puzzling Bible Verses: Insight into Frequently Misunderstood Scriptures. 2006. 217p. per. 11.99 (978-0-7369-1775-9(6)) Harvest Hse. Pubs.

Dennison, John A. Jesus' Death & the Gathering of True Israel: The Johannine Appropriation of Restoration Theology in the Light of John 11.47-52. 2006. (Wissenschaftliche Untersuchungen Zum Neuen Testament 2 Ser.: No. 217). 429p. pap. 125.00 (978-3-16-148821-4(0)) Mohr Siebeck GmbH & Co. KG DEU. Dist: Coronet Bks.

Denny, Randal Earl. Wind in the Rigging: A Study of Acts 9-12 & Its Meaning for Today. 2007. 116p. pap. 14.00 (978-1-55635-385-7(5), Wipf and Stock) Wipf & Stock Pubs.

DeRouchie, Jason. A Call to Covenant Love: Text Grammar & Literary Structure in Deuteronomy 5¿11. 2007. 32.00 **(978-1-59333-674-5(8))** Gorgias Pr., LLC.

Dever, Mark. What Does God Want of Us Anyway? A Quick Overview of the Whole Bible. 2010. pap. (978-1-4335-1416-6(8)); 128p. 12.99 (978-1-4335-1415-9(X)) Crossway.

DeYoung, Curtiss Paul & Gafney, Wilda C., eds. The Peoples' Companion to the Bible. 2010. 320p. pap. 29.00 (978-0-8006-9702-0(2), Fortress Pr.) Augsburg Fortress, Pubs.

Dively Lauro, Elizabeth Ann. The Soul & Spirit of Scripture Within Origen's Exegesis. 2010. (978-1-58983-500-9(X)) Society of Biblical Literature.

Doane, Thomas. Bible Myths & Their Parallels in Other Religions. 2007. 624p. 39.95 (978-1-60206-951-0(4)); per. 28.95 (978-1-60206-203-0(X)) Cosimo, Inc.

Dobyns, William Ray. The Book in the Light of Its Books. 2007. (ENG.). 186p. 37.95 (978-0-548-06805-2(4)) Kessinger Publishing, LLC.

The Doctrine of the New Jerusalem Respecting the Sacred Scripture. 2007. (ENG.). 136p. 35.95 (978-0-548-05160-3(7)) Kessinger Publishing, LLC.

Dods, Marcus. The Bible: Its Origin & Nature. 2007. (ENG.). 258p. 42.95 (978-0-548-06793-2(7)) Kessinger Publishing, LLC.

Dohrmann, Natalie B. & Stern, David, eds. Jewish Biblical Interpretation & Cultural Exchange: Comparative Exegesis in Context. 2008. (Jewish Culture & Contexts Ser.). (Illus.). 352p. (C). 69.95 (978-0-8122-4074-0(X)) Univ. of Pennsylvania Pr.

Dole, George F. A Book about Us: The Bible & Stages of Our Lives. 2007. (ENG.). 96p. pap. 12.95 (978-0-87785-326-8(6)) Swedenborg Foundation, Inc.

Donelson, Lewis R. Pseudepigraphy & Ethical Argument in the Pastoral Epistles. 2006. (Hermeneutische Untersuchungen zur Theologie Ser.: No. 22). 221p. pap. 72.50 (978-3-16-149082-8(7)) Mohr Siebeck GmbH & Co. KG DEU. Dist: Coronet Bks.

Doudna, Greg. Showdown at Big Sandy: Youthful Creativity Confronts Bureaucratic Inertia at an Unconventional Bible College in East Texas, 1. 2006. 540p. per. 56.00 (978-0-9789838-0-2(7)) Scrollery, The.

Dove, Mary. The First English Bible: The Text & Context of the Wycliffite Versions. 2011. (Cambridge Studies in Medieval Literature Ser.). (ENG.). 334p. pap. 39.99 (978-0-521-17547-0(X)) Cambridge Univ. Pr.

Dowdle, John R. Ignore the Detours. 2012. **(978-1-55452-802-8(X))** Essence Publishing.

Dowell, Bob. Understanding the Bible: Head & Heart: Part Two: Matthew through Acts. 2011. 728p. pap. 30.99 (978-1-61215-454-1(9)) Xulon Pr., Inc.

Drews, Arthur. The Witnesses to the Historicity of Jesus. 2010. 190p. pap. 15.37 (978-1-152-12230-7(4)) General Bks. LLC.

Driver, Daniel R. Brevard Childs, Biblical Theologian: For the Church's One Bible. 2010. (Illus.). 330p. pap. 137.50 (978-3-16-150368-9(6)) Mohr Siebeck GmbH & Co. KG DEU. Dist: Coronet Bks.

Drolsum, T. Joyner. Unholy Writ: An Infidel's Critique of the Bible. 2011. 824p. pap. 36.95 **(978-1-4567-9575-7(9))** AuthorHouse.

Drosnin, Michael. El Nuevo Codigo Secreto de la Biblia. (SPA.). 336p. (978-84-08-05409-2(0)) GeoPlaneta, Editorial, S. A.

Drummonds, Audrey. Living in the Inheritance of God: As New Creations in Christ Jesus. 2009. 336p. pap. 22.95 (978-1-4401-3392-3(1)) iUniverse, Inc.

Du Chatelet, Emilie. Selected Philosophical & Scientific Writings. Zinsser, Judith P., ed. & tr. by. from FRE. Bour, Isabelle, tr. from FRE. 2009. (Other Voice in Early Modern Europe Ser.). (ENG., Illus.). 456p. 95.00 (978-0-226-16806-7(9)) Univ. of Chicago Pr.

—Selected Philosophical & Scientific Writings. Zinsser, Judith P., ed. & tr. by. from FRE. Bour, Isabelle, tr. from FRE. 2009. (Other Voice in Early Modern Europe Ser.). (ENG., Illus.). 456p. pap. 35.00 (978-0-226-16807-4(7)) Univ. of Chicago Pr.

Dudley, Donald. MidTrib Rapture: Are You Ready? Not Left Behind, Left to Testify! 2009. 211p. (ENG.). 27.95 (978-1-4327-3972-0(7)); pap. 14.95 (978-1-4327-3926-3(3)) Outskirts Pr., Inc.

Dunning, H. Ray. The Whole Christ for the Whole World: A Wesleyan Perspective on the Work of Christ. 2008. 142p. pap. 18.00 (978-1-55635-267-6(0)) Wipf & Stock Pubs.

Duvall, J. Scott, et al. Journey into God's Word: Your Guide to Understanding & Applying the Bible, 1 vol. abr. ed. 2008. (ENG., Illus.). 160p. (gr. 13). pap. 14.99 (978-0-310-27513-8(X)) Zondervan.

Dykstra, Laurel & Myers, Ched, eds. Liberating Biblical Study: Scholarship, Art, & Action in Honor of the Center & Library for the Bible & Social Justice. 2011. (Center & Library for the Bible & Social Justice Ser.). 278p. pap. 31.00 **(978-1-61097-401-1(8)**, Cascade Bks.) Wipf & Stock Pubs.

Easley, Kendell. Holman QuickSource Guide to Understanding the Bible. 2011. (ENG., Illus.). 408p. pap. 14.99 (978-0-8054-9550-8(9), Holman Reference) B&H Publishing Group.

Eby, Richard. Didn't You Read My Book? & Caught up into Paradise. 2008. pap. 15.99 (978-0-7684-2588-8(3)) Destiny Image Pubs.

Edgar, Swift, ed. The Vulgate Bible, Volume II: the Historical Books: Douay-Rheims Translation, Part A, Part A. 2011. (Dumbarton Oaks Medieval Library). (ENG & LAT.). 1168p. 29.95 (978-0-674-99667-0(4)) Harvard Univ. Pr.

—The Vulgate Bible, Volume II: the Historical Books: Douay-Rheims Translation, Part B, Part B. 2011. (Dumbarton Oaks Medieval Library). (ENG & LAT.). 816p. 29.95 (978-0-674-06077-7(6)) Harvard Univ. Pr.

Edwards, Chilperic. Old Testament. 2006. pap. 21.95 (978-1-4304-4167-0(4)) Kessinger Publishing, LLC.

Edwards, Larry. The Twelve Generations of the Creation! 2007. 424p. (ENG.). 33.99 (978-1-60034-914-0(5)); per. 21.99 (978-1-60034-913-3(7)) Xulon Pr., Inc.

Edwards, Richard M. Scriptural Perspicuity in the Early English Reformation in Historical Theology. 2008. (Studies in Biblical Literature Ser.). 48.95 (978-0-8204-7057-3(0)) Lang, Peter Publishing, Inc.

Edwards, Timothy. Exegesis in the Targum of Psalms: The Old, the New & the Rewritten. 2007. (Gorgias Dissertations in Biblical Studies: 1). 78.00 (978-1-59333-432-1(X)) Gorgias Pr., LLC.

Ehrlich, Carl S. & White, Marsha C., eds. Saul in Story & Tradition. 2006. (Forschungen Zum Alten Testament Ser.: Vol. 47). (Illus.). 358p. (C). 152.50 (978-3-16-148569-5(6)) Mohr Siebeck GmbH & Co. KG DEU. Dist: Coronet Bks.

Ehrman, Bart D. God's Problem: How the Bible Fails to Answer Our Most Important Question — Why We Suffer. 2009. (ENG.). 304p. pap. 16.99 (978-0-06-117392-9(4), HarperOne) 2008. 448p. per. 25.95 (978-0-06-147035-6(X), HarperLuxe) HarperCollins Pubs.

—Jesus, Interrupted: Revealing the Hidden Contradictions in the Bible (and Why We Don't Know about Them) 2009. (ENG.). 256p. 25.99 (978-0-06-117393-6(2), HarperOne) HarperCollins Pubs.

—Jesus, Interrupted: Revealing the Hidden Contradictions in the Bible (And Why We Don't Know about Them) 2010. (ENG.). 304p. pap. 15.99 (978-0-06-117394-3(0), HarperOne) HarperCollins Pubs.

—Jesus No Dijo Eso: Los Errores y Falsificaciones de la Biblia. Noriega, Luis, tr. 2007. (Illus.). 303p. 24.95 (978-84-8432-852-0(X)) Critica Editorial ESP. Dist: Planeta Publishing Corp.

Elbert, Paul, ed. Faces of Renewal: Studies in Honor of Stanley M. Horton. 2007. 320p. pap. 35.00 (978-1-55635-250-8(6), Wipf and Stock) Wipf & Stock Pubs.

Ellens, J., ed. Text & Community: Essays in Memory of Bruce M. Metzger, 2 vols. 2007. (Illus.). (ENG.). 244p. (978-1-906055-18-9(1)); 348p. (978-1-906055-15-8(7)) Sheffield Phoenix Pr.

Elliott, John Huxtable. Conflict, Community, & Honor: 1 Peter in Social-Scientific Perspective. 2007. (Cascade Companions: Ser.). 106p. pap. 14.00 (978-1-55635-234-8(4), Cascade Bks.) Wipf & Stock Pubs.

Ellul, Jacques. Good News for the Empty Pew: The Ultimate Story of Freedom & Love. Vanderburg, Willem H., ed. 2010. (ENG.). xxi, 247p. (978-1-4426-4220-1(3)) Univ. of Toronto Pr.

—On Freedom Love & Power: The Ultimate Story of Freedom & Love. Vanderburg, Willem H., ed. 2010. xxi, 247p. pap. (978-1-4426-1117-7(0)) Univ. of Toronto Pr.

Enns, Peter. Ecclesiastes. 2011. pap. 25.00 **(978-0-8028-6649-3(2))** Eerdmans, William B. Publishing Co.

Enrique, José & Chiu, Aguilar. Bible et Terre Sainte: Mélanges Marcel Beaudry. 2007. (POR, ITA, FRE, GER & SPA.). 574p. (C). 96.95 (978-0-8204-9720-4(7)) Lang, Peter Publishing, Inc.

Ephraim. Moses Didn't Write about Creation! 2007. 432p. per. 29.95 (978-1-4241-8220-6(4)) PublishAmerica, Inc.

Erickson, Al & Malloy, Patricia. Parents Arise! Grandparents Arise! Book. 2011. 212p. pap. 15.95 **(978-1-880292-39-6(4))** LangMarc Publishing.

Erickson, Alvin & Malloy, Patricia. Parents Arise! Grandparents Arise! Book 2 Ten Actions to Take to Safeguard Our Children. 2011. 230p. pap. 15.95 **(978-1-880292-40-2(8))** LangMarc Publishing.

Ernest, James D. The Bible in Athanasius of Alexandria. 2010. (978-1-58983-496-5(8)) Society of Biblical Literature.

Evans, Craig A. The World of Jesus & the Early Church: Identity & Interpretation in Early Communities of Faith. 2011. (Illus.). 260p. 29.95 **(978-1-59856-825-7(6))** Hendrickson Pubs. Marketing, LLC.

Evans, G. R. The Language & Logic of the Bible: The Road to Reformation. 2009. (ENG.). 220p. pap. 31.99 (978-0-521-09293-7(0)) Cambridge Univ. Pr.

Evans, Robert. Using the Bible: Studying the Text. (Exploring Faith Ser.). 160p. pap. (978-0-232-52344-7(4), 553883) Darton, Longman & Todd, Ltd.

Evans, Roderick L. The Mystery of the Thorn: A Study of Paul's Thorn in the Flesh. 2009. 60p. pap. 11.95 (978-1-60141-045-0(X), 80978) Kingdom Builders Publishing.

—Times of Refreshing: The Restoration of Mephibosheth. 2006. 25p. pap. 8.95 (978-1-60141-041-2(7), 60113) Kingdom Builders Publishing.

—The Word was Made Flesh: The Principles of Christ versus the Personality of Christ. 2011. 64p. pap. 10.95 (978-1-60141-093-1(X), 146053) Kingdom Builders Publishing.

Evans, Roderick L., comment. The Epistle of Titus: The Evans Practical Bible Commentary. 2009. (ENG.). 40p. pap. 11.95 (978-1-60141-094-8(8), 319445) Kingdom Builders Publishing.

Evans, Tony. Theology You Can Count On: Experiencing What the Bible Says about ... God the Father, God the Son, God the Holy Spirit, Angels, Salvation, the Church, the Bible, the Last Things. 2008. (ENG., Illus.). 1376p. 39.99 (978-0-8024-6653-2(2)) Moody Pubs.

Exploring God's Word: Church History. (Voyages Ser.). stu. ed. 8.98 (978-0-570-00296-3(6), 57-0721); tchr. ed., spiral bd. 32.95 (978-0-570-00297-0(4), 57-0722) Concordia Publishing Hse.

Exum, J. Cheryl & Nutu, Ela. Between the Text & the Canvas: The Bible & Art in Dialogue. Exum, J. Cheryl & Nutu, Ela, eds. 2007. (Illus.). 264p. (978-1-906055-19-6(X)) Sheffield Phoenix Pr.

Falkenberg, Lorence A. The Last Chapter. 2008. 176p. 21.99 (978-1-60647-220-0(8)); pap. 13.99 (978-1-60647-219-4(4)) Xulon Pr., Inc.

Fee, Gordon D. & Stuart, Douglas. How to Read the Bible Book by Book: A Guided Tour, 1 vol. 2009. (ENG.). 448p. pap. 6.99 (978-0-310-28573-1(9)) Zondervan.

Feffelfinger, Freddy. G-D Is a Flaming Liberal. 2009. 208p. pap. 21.49 (978-1-4343-4530-1(0)) AuthorHouse.

Fiorenza, Elisabeth Schüssler. Democratizing Biblical Studies: Toward an Emancipatory Educational Space. 2009. (ENG., Illus.). 232p. 25.00 (978-0-664-23362-4(7)) Westminster John Knox Pr.

Fitzgerald, Gray. The Bible Confronts the Bible: A More Wonderful Image of God Emerges. 2009. 150p. pap. 13.95 (978-1-934937-89-1(4)) Mill City Pr., Inc.

Fitzgerald, Troy. 20 Questions God Wants to Ask You: Life-Changing Encounters with the Divine. 2008. 14.99 (978-0-8163-2275-6(9)) Pacific Pr. Publishing Assn.

Fitzmyer, Joseph A. The Interpretation of Scripture: In Defense of the Historical-Critical Method. 2008. 176p. pap. 18.95 (978-0-8091-4504-1(9), 4504-1) Paulist Pr.

Fontaine, Carole R. With Eyes of Flesh: The Bible, Gender & Human Rights. 2008. (Illus.). 352p. (978-1-905048-54-0(8)); xxxii, 317p. pap. (978-1-905048-55-7(6)) Sheffield Phoenix Pr.

Force, J. E. & Popkin, R. H., eds. Newton & Religion: Context, Nature, & Influence. 2010. (International Archives of the History of Ideas / archives internationales d'histoire des Idées Ser.). 344p. pap. 229.00 (978-90-481-5235-3(6), 9048152356) Springer.

Ford, David F. & Pecknold, C. C., eds. The Promise of Scriptural Reasoning. 2007. (Directions in Modern Theology Ser.). (ENG., Illus.). 232p. per. 34.95 (978-1-4051-4630-2(3), Wiley-Blackwell) Wiley, John & Sons, Inc.

Ford, James. Rapture Blessed Hope or Human Hoax A Scr. 2007. 129p. 19.95 (978-1-4241-5020-5(5)) PublishAmerica, Inc.

Ford, William A. God, Pharaoh, & Moses: Explaining the Lord's Actions in the Exodus Plagues Narrative. 2007. (Paternoster Biblical Monographs: Ser.). 268p. pap. 31.00 (978-1-55635-321-5(9), Wipf and Stock) Wipf & Stock Pubs.

Fortress Press Staff, et al. Hermeneia: A Critical & Historical Commentary on the Bible, 38 vols., Set. 2006. cd-rom 977.00 (978-0-8006-6199-1(0)) Augsburg Fortress, Pubs.

Foster, Richard J. Life with God: Reading the Bible for Spiritual Transformation. 2010. (ENG.). 240p. pap. 14.99 (978-0-06-167174-6(6), HarperOne) HarperCollins Pubs.

Fountain, Samuel. Jesus, a Man for All Time. 2008. 280p. 27.50 (978-1-60693-091-5(5), Eloquent Bks.) AEG Literary Publishing Services, Inc.

Fowl, Stephen E. Engaging Scripture: A Model for Theological Interpretation. 2008. 228p. pap. 25.00 (978-1-60608-112-9(8)) Wipf & Stock Pubs.

—Theological Interpretation of Scripture. 2009. (Cascade Companions Ser.). 108p. pap. 13.00 (978-1-55635-241-6(7), Cascade Bks.) Wipf & Stock Pubs.

Fowl, Stephen E., et al. Reading Scripture with the Church: Toward a Hermeneutic for Theological Interpretation. 2006. 156p. (C). pap. 20.00 (978-0-8010-3173-1(7)) Baker Academic.

Frankforter, A. Daniel. Word of God, Words of Men: The Use & Abuse of Scripture. 2011. 444p. pap. 29.95 **(978-1-84694-534-2(8))** O Bks., John Hunt.

Freed, Edwin D. & Roberts, Jane F. The Bible Says So! From Simple Answers to Insightful Understanding. 2009. (BibleWorld Ser.). (ENG.). 320p. (C). 99.95 (978-1-84553-163-8(9)); pap. 29.95 (978-1-84553-164-5(7)) Equinox Publishing Ltd. GBR. Dist: ISD.

Frey, Jorg. Heil und Geschichte: Die Geschichtsbezogenheit des Heils und das Problem der Heilsgeschichte in der biblischen Tradition und in der theologischen Deutung. Krauter, Stefan & Lichtenberger, Hermann, eds. 2009. (GER.). 834p. 375.00 (978-3-16-150110-4(1)) Mohr Siebeck GmbH & Co. KG DEU. Dist: Coronet Bks.

Frishcosy, Unofficial Pastor Douglas E. Back Way into Heaven: Living for Life. 2008. 60p. pap. 16.95 (978-1-60474-978-6(4)) PublishAmerica, Inc.

Galvin, Garrett. Egypt as a Place of Refuge. 2011. (Forschungen zum Alten Testament Ser.). 230p. pap. 117.50 **(978-3-16-150816-5(5))** Mohr Siebeck GmbH & Co. KG DEU. Dist: Coronet Bks.

Garbini, Giovanni. Myth & History in the Bible. 2009. (Library of Hebrew Bible/Old Testament Studies, the Ser.). (ENG.). 192p. 39.95 (978-0-567-01839-7(3), T&T Clark) Continuum International Publishing Group, Ltd. GBR. Dist: National Bk. Network.

Gardner-Smith, P. Saint John & the Synoptic Gospels. 2011. (ENG.). 116p. pap. 19.99 (978-1-107-60126-0(6)) Cambridge Univ. Pr.

Gaw, Albert. The Eyes of the Heart. 2007. 208p. (ENG.). 24.99 (978-1-60266-980-2(5)); per. 14.99 (978-1-60266-979-6(1)) Xulon Pr., Inc.

Gench, Frances Taylor. Faithful Disagreement: Wrestling with Scripture in the Midst of Church Conflict. 2009. (ENG.). 176p. pap. 17.00 (978-0-664-23338-9(4)) Westminster John Knox Pr.

Genung, John F. Epic of the Inner Life Being the Book of. 2006. pap. 33.95 (978-1-4286-3451-0(7)) Kessinger Publishing, LLC.

Gerhard, Johann, et al. On the Nature of Theology & on Scripture. 2nd rev. ed. 2009. (Theological Commonplaces Ser.). xix, 606p. 54.99 (978-0-7586-1512-1(4)) Concordia Publishing Hse.

Ghosh, Kantik. The Wycliffite Heresy: Authority & the Interpretation of Texts. 2009. (Cambridge Studies in Medieval Literature Ser.). (ENG.). 316p. pap. 42.00 (978-0-521-10987-1(6)) Cambridge Univ. Pr.

Giles, Terry. A Doubter's Guide to the Bible. 2009. 156p. pap. 14.00 (978-0-687-65833-6(0)) Abingdon Pr.

Gingerich, Ray & Zimmerman, Earl, eds. Telling Our Stories: Personal Accounts of Engagement with Scripture. 2006. (Journeys with Scripture Ser.: 1). 288p. pap. 21.95 (978-1-931038-36-2(8)) Cascadia Publishing Hse., LLC.

Gladden, Washington. Who Wrote the Bible? 2008. 272p. 25.99 (978-0-554-33124-9(1)); 28.99 (978-0-554-23821-0(7)) BiblioBazaar.

—Who Wrote the Bible? 2009. 178p. pap. (978-0-217-97086-0(9)) Books LLC.

—Who Wrote the Bible? 2007. (ENG.). 220p. per. (978-1-4065-4495-4(7)) Dodo Pr.

—Who Wrote the Bible? 2007. (ENG.). 176p. per. (978-1-4068-6208-9(8)) Echo Library.

—Who Wrote the Bible? 2008. 292p. pap. 15.95 (978-1-4341-0161-7(4)) Editorium, The.

—Who Wrote the Bible? A Book for the People. 2010. 398p. pap. 33.75 (978-1-146-04116-4(0)) 2010. 382p. pap. 33.75 (978-1-142-18935-8(X)) 2007. (ENG.). 242p. pap. 20.99 (978-1-4264-5054-9(0)) BiblioBazaar.

—Who Wrote the Bible? A Book for the People. 2012. 402p. pap. **(978-1-290-18194-5(2))** 2010. 184p. pap. (978-1-4076-4082-2(8)) HardPr.

—Who Wrote the Bible? A Book for the People. 2010. (Illus.). 156p. pap. 24.30 (978-1-153-73322-9(6)) General Bks. LLC.

—Who Wrote the Bible? A book for the People. 2010. 396p. pap. 33.75 (978-1-177-09689-8(7)); 400p. pap. 34.75 **(978-1-149-58508-5(0))** BiblioBazaar.

—Who Wrote the Bible? A Book for the People. Lt. ed. 2007. (ENG.). 268p. pap. 23.99 (978-1-4264-5355-7(8)) BiblioBazaar.

Gladding, Sean. The Story of God, the Story of Us: Getting Lost & Found in the Bible. 2010. (ENG.). 251p. pap. 17.00 (978-0-8308-3632-1(2), IVP Bks.) InterVarsity Pr.

Glas, Gerrit, et al, eds. Hearing Visions & Seeing Voices: Psychological Aspects of Biblical Concepts & Personalities. 2007. (ENG., Illus.). xviii, 326p. 149.00 (978-1-4020-5938-4(8), 1402059388) Springer.

Glaspey, Terry. The One-Minute Bible Guide. 2008. 144p. pap. 6.99 (978-0-7369-2323-1(3)) Harvest Hse. Pubs.

Gnanaharan, R. The Lamb of God & the Seven-Sealed Scroll. 2007. 248p. per. 14.99 (978-1-60477-061-2(9)) Xulon Pr., Inc.

Goldsmith, Joel S. Spiritual Interpretation of Scripture. 2008. 124p. pap. (978-0-9793119-2-5(6)) Editorial Benei Noaj.

—Spiritual Interpretation of Scripture. 2010. 236p. pap. 7.50 (978-1-57898-958-4(2)) Martino Publishing.

Goodenough, Erwin R., et al. Five Essays on the Bible: Papers Read at the 1960 Annual Meeting of the American Council of Learned Societies. 2011. 90p. 38.95 **(978-1-258-01888-7(8))** Literary Licensing, LLC.

Goodrich O.P., Kevin. Plugging into God's Story. 2007. 220p. per. 14.99 (978-1-60266-148-6(0)) Xulon Pr., Inc.

Gordley, Matthew E. Colossian Hymn in Context: An Exegesis in Light of Jewish & Greco-Roman Hymnic & Epistolary Conventions. 2007. (Wissenschaftliche Untersuchungen Zum Neuen Testament 2 Ser.: 228). 301p. (Orig.). (C). pap. 99.50 (978-3-16-149255-6(2)) Mohr Siebeck GmbH & Co. KG DEU. Dist: Coronet Bks.

Gordon, Charlotte. The Woman Who Named God: Abraham's Dilemma & the Birth of Three Faiths. 2009. (ENG., Illus.). 400p. 27.99 (978-0-316-11474-5(X)) Little Brown & Co.

Gordon, S. D. Quiet Talks on John's Gospel. 2010. (Illus.). 110p. pap. 20.03 (978-1-153-68240-4(0)) General Bks. LLC.

—Quiet Talks on John's Gospel. 2010. 146p. pap. (978-1-4076-1420-5(7)) HardPr.

Gordon, S. d. 1859-1936. Quiet Talks on John's Gospel. 2010. 266p. pap. 27.75 (978-1-149-53234-6(4)) BiblioBazaar.

Gordon, Samuel Dickey. Quiet Talks on John's Gospel. 2008. 192p. 22.99 (978-0-554-34530-7(7)) 2008. 192p. 25.99 (978-0-554-25227-8(9)) 2007. (ENG.). 168p. pap. 19.99 (978-1-4264-8465-0(8)) 2007. (ENG.). 190p. pap. 21.99 (978-1-4264-8523-7(9)) BiblioBazaar.

Gorman, Michael J. Elements of Biblical Exegesis: A Basic Guide for Students & Ministers. rev. ed. 2008. 304p. (C). pap. 21.99 (978-0-8010-4640-7(8)) Baker Academic.

—Elements of Biblical Exegesis: A Basic Guide for Students & Ministers. 2009. 300p. pap. (978-1-59856-311-5(4)) Hendrickson Pubs. Marketing, LLC.

—Reading Paul. 2008. (Cascade Companions: Ser.). 206p. pap. 22.00 (978-1-55635-195-2(X)) Wipf & Stock Pubs.

Gorringe. Sign of Love. 112p. 16.95 (978-0-281-04996-7(3)) International Publishers Marketing.

Gossai, Hemchand. Barrenness & Blessing: Abraham, Sarah, & the Journey of Faith. 2007. 136p. pap. 17.00 (978-1-55635-292-8(1)) Wipf & Stock Pubs.

Gottwald. Bible & Liberation. 584p. 45.00 (978-0-281-04719-2(7)) International Publishers Marketing.

Grabner-Haider, Anton. Kulturgeschichte der Bibel. 2007. (GER.). 487p. (C). 54.00 (978-3-525-57309-9(X)) Vandenhoeck & Ruprecht GmbH & Co. KG DEU. Dist: ISD.

Graf, Gary. And God Said, It's Good! Amusing & Thought-Provoking Parallels Between the Bible & Football. 2007. (Illus.). 181p. 19.95 (978-0-7648-1578-2(4), Liguori/Triumph) Liguori Pubns.

—And God Said, Tee It Up! Amusing & Thought-Provoking Parallels Between the Bible & Golf. 2009. (Illus.). 206p. pap. 14.95 (978-0-87946-385-4(6)) ACTA Pubns.

Grafton, Anthony & Weinberg, Joanna. I Have Always Loved the Holy Tongue: Isaac Casaubon, the Jews, & a Forgotten Chapter in Renaissance Scholarship. 2011. (Carl Newell Jackson Lectures). (Illus.). 392p. 35.00 (978-0-674-04840-9(7), Belknap Pr.) Harvard Univ. Pr.

Grant, L. M. Wonderful Paradoxes of Scripture. pap. 0.95 (978-0-88172-171-3(9)) Believers Bookshelf, Inc.

Greeley, Andrew M. & Neusner, Jacob. Common Ground: A Priest & a Rabbi Read Scripture Together. 2008. (ENG.). 354p. (C). pap. (978-0-7735-3447-6(4)) McGill-Queen's Univ. Pr.

Greenlee, J. Harold. The Text of the New Testament: From Manuscript to Modern Edition. 2008. (Illus.). 144p. pap. (978-1-59856-240-8(1)) Hendrickson Pubs. Marketing, LLC.

Grove, Daisy E. The Mystery Teaching of the Bible. 2007. (ENG.). 128p. 35.95 (978-0-548-00665-8(2)) Kessinger Publishing, LLC.

Grubbs, Esther. And God Said. 2008. 232p. 32.42 (978-1-4303-1010-5(3)) Lulu Enterprises Inc.

—God Also Said. 2008. 320p. 35.87 (978-1-4303-0823-2(0)) Lulu Enterprises Inc.

Gruenwald, Ithamar. Rituals & Ritual Theory in Ancient Israel. 2010. (978-1-58983-498-9(4)) Society of Biblical Literature.

Gutierrez, M. L. The Bible Dilemm: Historical contradictions, misquoted statements, failed prophecies & oddities in the Bible. 2010. 424p. pap. 24.95 (978-1-60844-021-4(4)) Dog Ear Publishing, LLC.

Habel, Norman. An Inconvenient Text: Is Green Reading of the Bible Possible? 2012. (ENG.). 236p. (C). pap. 16.00 (978-1-921511-56-1(7)) ATF Pr. AUS. Dist: Brown, David Bk. Co., The.

Habel, Norman C. & Trudinger, Peter L. Exploring Ecological Hermeneutics. 2008. 200p. pap. 24.95 (978-1-58983-346-3(5)) Society of Biblical Literature.

Habel, Norman C. & Trudinger, Peter L., eds. Exploring Ecological Hermeneutics. 2008. (SBL - Symposium Ser.). 198p. (978-90-04-15745-3(X)) BRILL.

Hagedorn, Anselm, et al, eds. In Other Words: Essays on Social Science Methods & the New Testament in Honor of Jerome H. Neyrey. 2007. (Illus.). 280p. (978-1-905048-39-7(4)) Sheffield Phoenix Pr.

Hagedorn, Anselm C., ed. Perspectives on the Song of Songs / Perspektiven der Hoheliedauslegung. (Beihefte zur Zeitschrift fur die alttestamentliche Wissenschaft Ser.). (ENG & GER.). XXII, 373p. 255.00 **(978-3-11-187628-3(4))** De Gruyter, Walter Inc.

Hahn, Augustus. On the Grammatico-Historical Interpretation of the Scriptures. 2010. 83.36 (978-1-61143-455-2(6)) Gorgias Pr., LLC.

Hahn, Scott. A Pocket Guide to St. Paul. 2008. 94p. pap. 6.95 (978-1-59276-563-8(7)) Our Sunday Visitor, Publishing Div.

Hahn, Scott, compiled by. Spirit & Life: Essays on Interpreting the Bible in Ordinary Time. 2009. 162p. mass mkt. 15.95 (978-1-931018-53-1(7)) Emmaus Road Publishing.

Hahn, Scott, ed. Letter & Spirit for the Sake of Our Salvation: The Truth & Humility of God's Word, 6. 2011. 440p. pap. (978-1-931018-68-5(5)) Emmaus Road Publishing.

Hahn, Scott & Socias, James. Faith & Revelation: Knowing God Through Sacred Scripture. 2009. (978-1-936045-01-3(X)) Midwest Theological Forum.

Hahn, Scott W. & Scott, David, eds. Letter & Spirit, Volume 5: Liturgy & Empire: Faith in Exile & Political Theology. 2009. (Letter & Spirit Ser.). 286p. pap. 15.95 (978-1-931018-56-2(1)) Emmaus Road Publishing.

Hahnenberg, Edward J. Understanding the Bible: A Layman's Guide to the Historical-Critical Method. 2008. 144p. per. 12.95 (978-1-59594-267-8(X)) WingSpan Publishing.

Hairfield, Steven. Metaphysical Interpretation of the Bible. 2006. 808p. 39.95 (978-0-9720080-5-1(5)) InnerCircle Publishing.

B

Haley, John William. An Examination of the Alleged Discrepancies of the Bible by John W Haley with an Introduction by Alvah Hovey. 2006. 508p. per. 29.99 *(978-1-4255-5669-3(8))* MPublishing.

Hall, Joseph. Contemplations on the Historical Passages of the Old & New Testaments. 2009. 536p. pap. *(978-1-4590-7339-5(8))*; 510p. pap. *(978-0-217-77630-1(2))* Books LLC.

Hall, Joseph & Hamilton, James. Contemplations on the Historical Passages of the Old & New Testaments. 2007. (ENG.). 636p. 60.95 *(978-0-548-25760-9(4))*; 640p. per. 45.95 *(978-1-4326-6129-8(9))* Kessinger Publishing, LLC.

Hamer, Colin. Finding GodÕs Will. 2010. 168p. pap. 19.00 *(978-1-60899-878-4(9)*, Wipf and Stock) Wipf & Stock Pubs.

Hamilton, Mark W., et al. The Transforming Word: One-Volume Commentary on the Bible. 2009. (Illus.). viii, 1117p. 69.95 *(978-0-89112-521-1(3))* Abilene Christian Univ. Pr.

Hamlin, Hannibal & Jones, Norman W., eds. The King James Bible after Four Hundred Years: Literary, Linguistic, & Cultural Influences. 2010. (ENG., Illus.). 378p. 39.99 *(978-0-521-76827-6(6))* Cambridge Univ. Pr.

Han, Jin Hee. Daniel's Spiel: Apocalyptic Literacy in the Book of Daniel. 2007. (ENG.). 134p. per. 29.50 *(978-0-7618-3913-2(5))* Univ. Pr. of America, Inc.

Hanley, P. J. Israel Awakening: Why the Church Needs to Wake up Concerning Israel. 2008. 226p. per. 14.99 *(978-1-60247-889-3(9))* Tate Publishing & Enterprises, LLC.

Hanson, Paul D. Political Engagement as Biblical Mandate. 2009. 168p. pap. 19.00 *(978-1-55635-515-8(7)*, Cascade Bks.) Wipf & Stock Pubs.

Harper, Steven. Making Sense of the Doctrine & Covenants: A Guided Tour Through Modern Revelation. 2008. 608p. 34.95 *(978-1-59038-921-8(2))* Deseret Bk. Co.

HarperCollins Publishers Ltd. Staff, et al. King James Version Standard Christening Bible. gif. ed. 2006. (ENG., Illus.). 1104p. lthr. 27.50 *(978-0-00-716633-6(8))* HarperCollins Pubs. Ltd. GBR. Dist: Independent Pubs. Group.

Harrington, Wilfrid. John: Spiritual Theologian: The Jesus of John. 2nd rev. ed. 2007. (ENG.). 103p. pap. 21.95 *(978-1-85607-594-7(X))* Columba Pr. IRL. Dist: Dufour Editions, Inc.

Harris, Harriet A. Fundamentalism & the Bible. 2012. (Biblical Challenges in the Contemporary World Ser.). (ENG.). 256p. (C). 90.00 *(978-1-84553-151-5(5))*; pap. 24.95 *(978-1-84553-152-2(3))* Equinox Publishing Ltd. GBR. Dist: ISD.

Harwood, William, et al. The Protestant Bible Correctly Translated. 2009. 802p. 49.00 *(978-1-935444-29-9(8))* World Audience Pubs.

Hassan, Imad. Shajara Code Decoded. 2009. (Illus.). 546p. pap. 23.49 *(978-1-4490-0819-2(4))* AuthorHouse.

Healy, Mary & Parry, Robin, eds. The Bible & Epistemology: Biblical Soundings on the Knowledge of God. 2007. (ENG.). 224p. 24.99 *(978-1-84227-540-5(2)*, Paternoster) Authentic Media.

Hegeman, David Bruce. Plowing in Hope: Toward a Biblical Theology of Culture. 2nd ed. 2007. (ENG.). pap. 12.00 *(978-1-59128-049-1(4))* Canon Pr.

Heisner, John R. The Secrets of Hiram Abif: A Key to Understanding Masonic Symbolism, 1 vol. 2009. 329p. pap. 29.95 *(978-1-60836-847-1(5))* PublishAmerica, Inc.

Helmer, Christine & Higbe, Charlene T. The Multivalence of Biblical Texts & Theological Meanings. 2006. (SBL - Symposium Ser.). (Illus.). 199p. *(978-90-04-15110-9(9))* BRILL.

Henderson, Warren. In Search of God: A Quest for Truth. 2007. 320p. per. *(978-0-9795387-0-4(X))* Henderson, Warren.

Hengel, Martin. Theologische, historische und biographische Skizzen: Kleine Schriften VII. Thornton, Claus-Jargen, ed. 2010. (GER., Illus.). 805p. 397.50 *(978-3-16-150201-9(9))* Mohr Siebeck GmbH & Co. KG DEU. Dist: Coronet Bks.

Henze, Matthias. A Companion to Biblical Interpretation in Early Judaism. 2011. pap. 50.00 ***(978-0-8028-0388-7(1))*** Eerdmans, William B. Publishing Co.

Hermon, Peter. Lifting the Veil: A Plain Language Guide to the Bible. 2007. (ENG.). 500p. per. 53.00 *(978-0-7188-3063-2(6))* Lutterworth Pr., The GBR. Dist: Brown, David Bk. Co., The.

Hessayon, Ariel & Keene, Nicholas. Scripture & Scholarship in Early Modern England. 2006. (Illus.). 268p. 140.00 *(978-0-7546-3893-3(6))* Ashgate Publishing Co.

Hinnant, Greg. Gold Tried in the Fire: Tested Truths for Trying Times. 2008. (ENG.). 336p. pap. 14.99 *(978-1-59979-364-1(4)*, Creation Hse.) Charisma Media.

Hitchcock, Mark. The Late Great United States: What Bible Prophecy Reveals about America's Last Days. 2010. (ENG.). 208p. pap. 14.99 *(978-1-60142-141-8(9)*, Multnomah) Doubleday Religious Publishing Group, The.

Hodson, Geoffrey. The Hidden Wisdom in Christian Scriptures. 2011. 28p. 35.95 ***(978-1-258-00474-3(7))*** Literary Licensing, LLC.

Hole, Frank. Gospels & Acts. 2007. (Illus.). 392p. per. *(978-0-901860-42-2(5))* Scripture Truth Pubns.

Holladay, Carl R., et al. Scripture & Traditions: Essays on Early Judaism & Christianity in Honor of Carl R. Holladay. 2008. *(978-90-04-16747-6(1))* BRILL.

Holloway, Richard. How to Read the Bible. 2007. (How to Read Ser.). (ENG.). 144p. per. 11.95 *(978-0-393-32954-4(2)*, 32954) Norton, W. W. & Co., Inc.

Holmes, Ernest. The Bible in the Light of Religious Science. 2010. 222p. pap. 10.95 *(978-1-57898-908-9(6))* Martino Publishing.

—The Hidden Power of the Bible: What Science of Mind Reveals about the Bible & You. 2006. (ENG.). 240p. (gr. 12-18). 13.95 *(978-1-58542-511-2(7)*, Tarcher) Penguin Group (USA) Inc.

The Holy Bible: Containing the Old & New Testaments, Newly Translated Out of the Original Tongues, & with the Former Translations Diligently Compared & Revised. 2006. *(978-1-57898-647-7(8))* Martino Publishing.

Homan, Jacqueline S. Divine Right: The Truth Is a Lie. 2009. 456p. 27.95 *(978-0-9815679-4-5(0))* Elf Bks.

Horne, Thomas Hartwell. A Compendious Introduction to the Study of the Bible, Being an Analysis of an Introduction to the Critical Study & Knowledge of the Holy Scriptures. 2006. 424p. per. 26.99 *(978-1-4255-4589-5(0))* MPublishing.

—Manual of Biblical Bibliography: Comprising a Catalogue ... of the Principal Editions & Versions of the Holy Scriptures: Together with Notices of the Principal Philosophers, Critics, & Interpreters of the Bible. 2006. (ENG.). 450p. 75.00 *(978-1-57898-562-3(5))* Martino Publishing.

Horrell, David G. Ecological Hermeneutics: Biblical, Historical, & Theological Perspectives. Hunt, Cherryl et al, eds. 2010. (ENG., Illus.). 352p. 44.95 *(978-0-567-03304-8(X))*; 145.00 *(978-0-567-03303-1(1))* Continuum International Publishing Group, Ltd. GBR. (T&T Clark Int'l). Dist: National Bk. Network.

Houck, Tom. Between the Tackles. 2007. 160p. per. *(978-1-55452-199-9(8)*, Guardian Bks.) Essence Publishing.

Houston, Walter. Justice: The Biblical Challenge. 2010. (Biblical Challenges in the Contemporary World Ser.). (ENG.). 165p. (C). 95.00 *(978-1-84553-887-3(0))*; pap. 26.95 *(978-1-84553-888-0(9))* Equinox Publishing Ltd. GBR. Dist: ISD.

Hovde, Howard & Moore, Louis. Families of the Bible: How they Coped with Today's Problems. 2009. 126p. pap. 12.95 *(978-1-934749-53-1(2))* Hannibal Bks.

Hovorun, Serhiy. Will, Action & Freedom: Christological Controversies in the Seventh Century. 2008. (Medieval Mediterranean Ser.). 224p. *(978-90-04-16666-0(1))* BRILL.

Howard-Brook, Wes. Come Out My People: God's Call Out of Empire in the Bible & Beyond. 2010. 544p. pap. 30.00 *(978-1-57075-892-8(1))* Orbis Bks.

Hubbard, Norman. Left of Matthew: Exploring the Great Ideas of the Old Testament. 2007. (Exploring the Great Ideas Ser.). (ENG.). 144p. pap. 9.99 *(978-1-60006-052-6(8))* NavPress Publishing Group.

Huffstetler, Joel W. & Holladay, Carl R. Boundless Love: The Parable of the Prodigal Son & Reconciliation. 2008. (ENG.). 90p. pap. 26.50 *(978-0-7618-4091-6(5))* Univ. Pr. of America, Inc.

Hunsinger, George. Thy Word Is Truth: Barth on Scripture. 2012. pap. ***(978-0-8028-6674-5(3))*** Eerdmans, William B. Publishing Co.

Hurtado, Larry W. The Freer Biblical Manuscripts: Fresh Studies of an American Treasure Trove. 2006. (SBL - Text-Critical Studies). (Illus.). 308p. *(978-90-04-14679-2(2))* BRILL.

Hwang, Sung Chul. The Bible & Experience Conversion & Biblical Interpretation in the Revival Movements of Charles G Finney & Asahel Nettleton. 2008. 172p. pap. *(978-3-639-10715-9(2))* VDM Verlag Dr. Mueller e.K.

Hygh, Earl H. Oh, No! Not Another Book about the Bible. 2006. 44.00 *(978-0-8059-9066-9(6))* Dorrance Publishing Co., Inc.

Ian Young Robert Rezetko Staff. Linguistic Dating of Biblical Texts, 2 vols. 2008. (BibleWorld Ser.). (ENG.). 512p. (C). 195.00 *(978-1-84553-081-5(0))* Equinox Publishing Ltd. GBR. Dist: ISD.

Inch, Morris. Wonder of It All: Mystery & Meaning in Scripture. 2009. (ENG.). 168p. pap. 28.50 *(978-0-7618-4802-8(9))* Univ. Pr. of America, Inc.

Inch, Morris A. In Christ & on Track: The Essential Paul. 2007. (ENG.). 102p. pap. 26.50 *(978-0-7618-3965-1(8))* Univ. Pr. of America, Inc.

—The Wonder of It All: Mystery & Meaning in Scripture. 2009. vi, 158p. E-Book *(978-0-7618-4812-7(6))* Univ. Pr. of America, Inc.

Ingersoll, Robert G. About the Holy Bible. 2010. 78p. pap. 14.36 *(978-1-162-90428-3(3))*; 32.95 *(978-1-161-59307-5(1))* Kessinger Publishing, LLC.

Interpreters One Volume Commentary Indexed U. *(978-0-687-96132-0(7))* Abingdon Pr.

Ipsen, Avaren. Sex Working & the Bible. 2009. (BibleWorld Ser.). (ENG., Illus.). 248p. (C). 35.00 *(978-1-84553-333-5(X))*; 99.95 *(978-1-84553-332-8(1))* Equinox Publishing Ltd. GBR. Dist: ISD.

Isherwood, Lisa, ed. Patriarchs, Prophets & Other Villains. 2007. (Gender, Theology, & Spirituality Ser.). (ENG.). 248p. (C). 99.95 *(978-1-84553-130-0(2))*; per. 34.95 *(978-1-84553-131-7(0))* Equinox Publishing Ltd. GBR. Dist: ISD.

Israel, Hephzibah. Religious Transactions in Colonial South India: Language, Translation, & the Making of Protestant Identity. 2011. (Palgrave Studies in Cultural & Intellectual History Ser.). (ENG.). 286p. 85.00 *(978-0-230-10562-1(9))* Palgrave Macmillan.

Jackson, Earl. The Serpent Seed. 2009. 190p. pap. 15.94 *(978-0-557-04361-3(1))* Lulu Enterprises Inc.

Jackson, Kent J. The King James Bible & the Restoration. 2011. (Illus.). 304p. ***(978-0-8425-2802-3(4)***, Brigham Young Univ. Religious Studies Ctr.) Brigham Young Univ.

Jacobs, A. J. The Year of Living Biblically: One Man's Humble Quest to Follow the Bible as Literally as Possible. 2008. (ENG.). 416p. pap. 15.00 *(978-0-7432-9148-4(4))* Simon & Schuster.

—The Year of Living Biblically: One Man's Humble Quest to Follow the Bible as Literally as Possible. l.t. ed. 2008. (Thorndike Core Ser.). (Illus.). 597p. 31.95 *(978-1-4104-0507-4(9))* Thorndike Pr.

Jacobs, Steven, et al. Maven in Blue Jeans: A Festschrift in Honor of Zev Garber. 2009. (Illus.). 513p. pap. 59.95 *(978-1-55753-521-4(3))* Purdue Univ. Pr.

Jacobson, Diane L. Book of Faith Lenten Journey: Water Marks. 2011. ***(978-1-4514-0262-9(7))*** Augsburg Fortress, Pubs.

Jakes, T. D. The T. D. Jakes Relationship Bible: Life Lessons on Relationships from the Inspired Word of God. deluxe ed. 2011. (ENG., Illus.). 1584p. 75.00 ***(978-1-4516-6781-3(7)***, Beyond Words/Atria Bks.) Atria Bks.

Janssen, Martina, et al, eds. Fruhes Christentum und Religionsgeschichtliche Schule: Festschrift zum 65. Geburtstag von Gerd Ludemann. 2011. (Novum Testamentum et Orbis Antiquus/Studien zur Umwelt des Neuen Testaments (NTOA/StUNT) Ser.). (GER.). 218p. (C). 95.00 ***(978-3-525-53977-4(0))*** Vandenhoeck & Ruprecht GmbH & Co. KG DEU. Dist: ISD.

Jarick, John. Sacred Conjectures: The Context & Legacy of Robert Lowth & Jean Astruc. 2007. (T & T Clark Library of Biblical Studies). (ENG., Illus.). 280p. 140.00 *(978-0-567-02932-4(8)*, T&T Clark Int'l) Continuum International Publishing Group, Ltd. GBR. Dist: National Bk. Network.

Jasper, David. Readings in the Canon of Scripture. 2009. (David Jasper Reprint Ser.). 180p. pap. 21.00 *(978-1-60608-835-7(1)*, Wipf and Stock) Wipf & Stock Pubs.

Jefferson, Thomas. The Thomas Jefferson Bible: The Life & Morals of Jesus of Nazareth. 2007. pap. 7.99 *(978-1-59986-841-7(5)*, FQ Classics) Filiquarian Publishing, LLC.

Jefford, Clayton N. The Apostolic Fathers & the New Testament. 2006. 267p. per. 19.95 *(978-1-56563-425-1(X))* Hendrickson Pubs. Marketing, LLC.

Jenkins, Philip. Laying down the Sword: Why We Can't Ignore the Bible's Violent Verses. (ENG.). 256p. 2012. pap. 15.99 ***(978-0-06-199072-4(8))*** 2011. 26.99 *(978-0-06-199071-7(X))* HarperCollins Pubs. (HarperOne).

Jenkins, Simon. The Bible from Scratch. 2006. (Illus.). 259p. per. 16.75 *(978-0-88489-940-2(3))* St. Mary's Pr.

Jennings, Alvin. What the Bible Does Not Say. pap. 1.00 *(978-1-56794-250-7(4)*, D-3040) Star Bible & Tract Corp.

Jessa, Azra. Ramadhan & Eid-ul-Fitr. 2008. (ENG., Illus.). 16p. (J). (gr. -1). pap. 7.95 *(978-1-879402-20-1(3))* Tahrike Tarsile Quran, Inc.

Jones, Arvil. The Faith, the Cross, the Gospel, & the Worship of God. 2008. 356p. pap. 19.99 *(978-1-60647-297-2(6))* Xulon Pr., Inc.

Jukes, Andrew. Types of Genesis Briefly Considered As R. 2006. pap. 37.95 *(978-1-4286-3979-9(9))* Kessinger Publishing, LLC.

Kalas, J. Ellsworth. Easter from the Back Side. 2008. 91p. pap. 10.50 *(978-0-687-49079-0(0))* Abingdon Pr.

—A Hop, Skip, & a Jump Through the Bible. 2007. 141p. per. 14.95 *(978-0-687-64446-9(1))* Abingdon Pr.

Kaler, Michael. Flora Tells a Story: The Apocalypse of Paul & Its Contexts. Kaler, Michael, ed. 2008. (Studies in Christianity & Judaism Ser.). (ENG., Illus.). 276p. 85.00 *(978-1-55458-044-6(7))* Wilfrid Laurier Univ. Pr. CAN. Dist: Univ. of Toronto Pr.

Kalimi, Isaac. Biblical Interpretation in Judaism & Christianity. Haas, Peter J., ed. 2006. (Library of Hebrew Bible/Old Testament Studies: Vol. 439). (ENG.). 280p. 150.00 *(978-0-567-02682-8(5)*, T&T Clark Int'l) Continuum International Publishing Group, Ltd. GBR. Dist: National Bk. Network.

Kannengiesser, Charles, et al. The Reception & Interpretation of the Bible in Late Antiquity: Proceedings of the Montreal Colloquium in Honour of Charles Kannengiesser, 11-13 October 2006. 2008. (Bible in Ancient Christianity Ser.). (FRE & ENG., Illus.). 632p. *(978-90-04-16715-5(3))* BRILL.

Kasdan, Barney. God's Appointed Times-New Edition: A Practical Guide for Understanding & Celebrating the Biblical Holy Days. 2007. (Illus.). 145p. per. *(978-1-880226-35-3(9)*, Lederer Bks.) Messianic Jewish Pubs.

Kasole Ka-Mungu, Benjamin. Des ténèbres à la Lumière: La guérison dans le livre de Tobit. 2008. (Europäische Hochschulschriften. Reihe 23: Theologie Ser.). 376p. pap. 81.95 *(978-3-631-57720-2(6))* Lang, Peter GmbH, Europäischer Verlag der Wissenschaften DEU. Dist: Lang, Peter.

Keck, Leander E. New Interpreter's Bible, Vol. 7. *(978-0-687-03326-3(8))* Abingdon Pr.

Keech, Charles. The Christian Deception. 2008. 259p. pap. 15.95 *(978-0-7414-4737-1(1))* Infinity Publishing.

Kelsey, Catherine L. Schleiermacher's Preaching, Dogmatics, & Biblical Criticism: The Interpretation of Jesus Christ in the Gospel of John. 2007. (Princeton Theological Monographs). 200p. pap. 23.00 *(978-1-59752-905-1(2)*, Pickwick Pubns.) Wipf & Stock Pubs.

Kendall, R. T. The Parables of Jesus: A Guide to Understanding & Applying the Stories Jesus Told. 2008. 368p. pap. 24.00 *(978-0-8007-9458-3(3))* Chosen Bks.

Kenney, Garrett C. Mark's Gospel: Lectures & Lessons. 2007. (ENG.). 136p. pap. 29.50 *(978-0-7618-3709-1(4))* Univ. Pr. of America, Inc.

Kent, Paul. Know Your Bible: All 66 Books Explained & Applied. 2008. (Value Books Ser.). (ENG.). 96p. pap. 1.49 *(978-1-60260-015-7(5)*, Barbour Bks.) Barbour Publishing, Inc.

Kichline, Kathleen MacInnis. Sisters in Scripture: Exploring the Relationships of Biblical Women. 2009. 128p. pap. 16.95 *(978-0-8091-4580-5(4))* Paulist Pr.

Kidd, Colin. The Forging of Races: Race & Scripture in the Protestant Atlantic World, 1600-2000. 2006. (ENG.). 318p. 102.00 *(978-0-521-79324-7(6))*; per. 35.99 *(978-0-521-79729-0(2))* Cambridge Univ. Pr.

Kienzle, Beverly Mayne. Hildegard of Bingen & her Gospel Homilies: Speaking New Mysteries. 2009. (Medieval Women: Texts & Contexts Ser.). (ENG, GER & LAT., Illus.). 338p. (C). 123.00 *(978-2-503-51777-3(3))* Brepols Pubs. BEL. Dist: ISD.

Kim, Heerak Christian. Intricately Connected: Biblical Studies, Intertextuality, & Literary Genre. 2008. (ENG.). 112p. pap. 26.50 *(978-0-7618-4149-4(0))* Univ. Pr. of America, Inc.

Kim, Heerak Christian, ed. Biblical Studies in Motion: British Korean Scholarly Contributions. 2009. 50.00 *(978-1-59689-084-8(3))*; pap. 30.00 *(978-1-59689-085-5(1))* Hermit Kingdom Pr., The. (Hermit Kingdom Pr., The).

—Journeys in Biblical Studies: Academic Papers from SBL International 2008, New Zealand. 2008. 152p. pap. 27.00 *(978-1-59689-087-9(8)*, Hermit Kingdom Pr., The) Hermit Kingdom Pr., The.

Kim, Heerak Christian Kim, ed. Journeys in Biblical Studies: Academic Papers from SBL International 2008, New Zealand. 2008. 152p. 70.00 *(978-1-59689-146-3(7)*, Hermit Kingdom Pr., The) Hermit Kingdom Pr., The.

Kim, Jin-Myung. Holiness & Perfection: A Canonical Unfolding of Leviticus 19. 2011. (Illus.). 144p. pap. 59.95 *(978-3-0343-0580-8(X))* Lang, Peter.

Kim, Lloyd. Polemic in the Book of Hebrews: Anti-Judaism, Anti-Semitism, Supersessionism? 2006. (Princeton Theological Monographs). 236p. pap. 25.00 *(978-1-59752-839-9(0)*, Pickwick Pubns.) Wipf & Stock Pubs.

Kimber, Joyce A. Words from God's Word: Topical Words Beginning with A B C. 2008. 164p. pap. 13.95 *(978-1-4327-3304-9(4))* Outskirts Pr., Inc.

Kimelman, Reuven. The Moral Meaning of the Bible: The What, How, & Why of Biblical Ethics, 3 vols. Simmel, Sergiu, ed. (Illus.). Vol. II. 2007. 60p. per. 120.00 net. incl. audio compact disk *(978-0-9769330-3-8(9))* Vol.I. 2006. (ENG., 49p. per. 120.00 net. incl. audio compact disk *(978-0-9769330-2-1(0))* Our Learning Co. LLC.

King, Dr. Dorothy. The Seven Seals of Revelation. 2007. 336p. pap. 32.50 *(978-1-4116-4349-9(6))* Lulu Enterprises Inc.

King, Philip J. The Bible Is for Living: A Scholar's Spiritual Journey. 2008. *(978-0-9796357-9-3(9))* Biblical Archaeology Society.

Kingdom Quotes Staff. The Lord's Day. pap. *(978-0-930179-13-7(7))* Johns Enterprises.

Kissinger, Thomas / Mark. The Noble Berean: And they searched the scriptures daily, whether those things were So..., 5 volumes, Volume 1. 2007. 104p. pap. 12.95 *(978-0-9785134-1-2(X))* Straightway Publishing Co.

Kissinger, Thomas / Mark. The Noble Berean 2. 2008. pap. ***(978-0-9785134-2-9(8))*** Straightway Publishing Co.

Klein, William W. Handbook for Personal Bible Study: Enriching Your Experience with God's Word. 2008. (Navigators Reference Library). (ENG.). 448p. 19.99 *(978-1-60006-117-2(6))* NavPress Publishing Group.

Knighton, Douglas. Promises for the Battle. 2007. pap. 14.99 *(978-1-60034-932-4(3))* Xulon Pr., Inc.

Knudson, Albert C. Beacon Lights of Prophecy an Interpretat. 2006. pap. 28.95 *(978-1-4286-4308-6(7))* Kessinger Publishing, LLC.

Kobia, Samuel. Called to the One Hope: A New Ecumenical Epoch. 2006. (Risk Book Ser.: No. 114). 144p. (C). pap. 13.00 *(978-2-8254-1489-7(1))* World Council of Churches/Conseil Oecumenique des Eglises CHE. Dist: International Specialized Bk. Services.

Kohler, Frederick A. '1' God, Faith & Baptism-the Absolute Resolution. 2008. 316p. pap. 26.95 *(978-0-595-52595-9(4)*, iUniverse, Inc.) iUniverse, Inc.

Kooten, Geurt Hendrik van & Ruiten, J. Van. The Prestige of the Pagan Prophet Balaam in Judaism, Early Christianity & Islam. Kooten, George H. van & Ruiten, Jacques van, eds. 2008. (Themes in Biblical Narrative Ser.). 344p. *(978-90-04-16564-9(9))* BRILL.

Koutoupis, Petros. An Adopted Legacy: Neo-Assyrian Origin to Hebrew Lore. 2007. 176p. 29.95 *(978-1-60264-004-7(1))* Virtualbookworm.com Publishing, Inc.

Krü, et al. Das Lob des Schöpfers: Studien zur Sprache, Motivik und Theologie von Psalm 104. WMANT 124. 2010. (GER., Illus.). xii, 502p. *(978-3-7887-2379-8(3))* Neukirchener Verlag.

Krauter, Stefan. Studien zu Röm 13,1-7: Paulus und der politische Diskurs der neronischen Zeit. 2009. (GER.). XI, 354p. 197.50 *(978-3-16-150099-2(7))* Mohr Siebeck GmbH & Co. KG DEU. Dist: Coronet Bks.

Kuan, Jeffrey Kah-jin, ed. Ways of Being, Ways of Reading: Asian American Biblical Interpretation. 2007. 240p. per. 29.99 *(978-0-8272-4254-8(9))* Chalice Pr.

Kulus, Chester W. Those So-Called Errors: Debunking the Liberal, New Evangelical, & Fundamentalist Myth that You Should Not Hear, Receive, & Believe All the Numbers. 2009. 516p. pap. 27.95 *(978-0-9820608-9-6(0))* Old Paths Pubns., Inc., The.

Kuntaraf, Jonathan & Liwijaya-Kuntaraf, Kathleen H. God's Book of Wisdom: What's in It for Me? 2006. *(978-0-8280-2017-6(5))* Review & Herald Publishing Assn.

Kurtz, Dennis. Youth Engaging Scripture: Diving into the Sunday Gospels. 2007. cd-rom 17.75 *(978-0-88489-913-6(6))* St. Mary's Pr.

Kwak, Arie-Jan & Cliteur, Paul. Holy Writ: Interpretation in Law & Religion. 2009. (Applied Legal Philosophy Ser.). 218p. 124.95 *(978-0-7546-7896-0(2))* Ashgate Publishing Co.

Kyomya, Michael. Interpreting Scripture: Context, Harmony, & Application, 1 vol. 2010. (Hippo Ser.). (ENG.). 128p. pap., instr.'s gde. ed. 12.99 *(978-9966-00-308-9(8))* Zondervan.

L&L Publishing, creator. Let There Be Light. 2008. (Illus.). 126p. pap. 20.00 *(978-0-9799833-0-6(4))* L & L Publishing Co.

Lachmann, Rainer, et al. Elementare Bibeltexte: Exegetisch - systematisch - didaktisch. 2010. (Theologie fur lehrerinnen und Lehrer Ser.). (GER.). 479p. (C). pap. 41.00 *(978-3-525-61421-1(7))* Vandenhoeck & Ruprecht GmbH & Co. KG DEU. Dist: ISD.

Lancaster, Irene. Deconstructing the Bible. 2007. (Illus.). 256p. 39.95 *(978-0-415-44444-6(6))* Routledge.

Laney, J. Carl. Answers to Tough Questions: A Survey of Problem Passages & Issues from Every Book of the Bible. 2010. 352p. pap. 39.00 *(978-1-60899-840-1(1)*, Wipf and Stock) Wipf & Stock Pubs.

Langlois, Jim. Is It Okay to Pray in Tongues in Church? 2008. 124p. pap. 13.99 *(978-0-88144-290-8(9))* Yorkshire Publishing Group.

Lapsley, Jacqueline E. Can These Bones Live? The Problem of the Moral Self in the Book of Ezekiel. (Beihefte zur Zeitschrift far die alttestamentliche Wissenschaft Ser.). (ENG.). XI, 208p. 225.00 ***(978-3-11-185762-6(X))*** De Gruyter, Walter Inc.

Larsen, Ludwig. Key to the Bible & Heaven. 2007. 284p. pap. 19.95 *(978-1-60206-798-1(8)*, Cosimo Classics) Cosimo, Inc.

Lasley, Bernice White. Master key the final Decision. 2007. 396p. pap. 27.12 *(978-1-4303-2032-6(X))* Lulu Enterprises Inc.

Laufer, Nathan. The Genesis of Leadership: What the Bible Teaches Us about Visions, Values & Leading Change. 2008. 288p. pap. 18.99 *(978-1-58023-352-1(X))* Jewish Lights Publishing.

Laurie, Greg. Beyond: A Devotional. 2007. (ENG.). 320p. per. 14.99 *(978-1-59052-831-0(X)*, Multnomah) Doubleday Religious Publishing Group, The.

Law, David R. Historical Critical Method: A Guide for the Perplexed. 2012. (ENG.). 344p. 90.00 ***(978-0-567-11130-2(X))***; pap. 27.95 ***(978-0-567-40012-3(3))*** Continuum International Publishing Group, Ltd. GBR. (T&T Clark Int'l). Dist: National Bk. Network.

Lawrence, Kenneth. The Evolution Delusion. 2008. 244p. 24.99 *(978-1-60647-105-0(8))* Xulon Pr., Inc.

—The Evolution Delusion: How 21St Century Science & Logic Prove the Evolutionist Worldview Is a Giant Delusion. 2008. 244p. pap. 14.99 *(978-1-60647-103-6(1))* Xulon Pr., Inc.

Lawson, Steven J. Foundations of Grace: 1400 BC - Ad 100. 2006. (Long Line of Godly Men Ser.). 577p. *(978-1-56769-077-4(7)*, Jacqui Small) Ligonier Ministries.

Le Grys, Alan. Shaped by God's Story: making sense of the Bible. 2010. 169p. pap. 25.50 *(978-1-4461-4178-6(0))* Lulu Enterprises Inc.

Leach, Ted. Faith Questions - How Does the Bible Shape My Faith? A Study of Biblical Interpretation & Faith Development. 2006. (Faithquestions Ser.). 102p. per. 10.00 *(978-0-687-49739-3(6))* Abingdon Pr.

Leaming, Charles M. The Key to Fulfillment of Bible Prophecy. 2007. 175p. per. 9.95 *(978-1-59886-638-4(9))* Tate Publishing & Enterprises, LLC.

Leiter, David A. Peace in Isaiah. 2011. ***(978-0-87178-166-6(2))*** Brethren Pr.

Leithart, Peter J. & Barach, John, eds. The Glory of Kings: A Festschrift for James B. Jordan. 2011. 366p. pap. 40.00 ***(978-1-60899-680-3(8)***, Pickwick Pubns.) Wipf & Stock Pubs.

Leithart, Peter J. & Leithart, Peter. Deep Exegesis: The Mystery of Reading Scripture. 2009. (ENG.). 253p. pap. 29.95 *(978-1-60258-069-5(3))* Baylor Univ. Pr.

Leman, Derek. The World to Come. 2008. pap. 9.99 *(978-1-880226-04-9(9))* Messianic Jewish Pubs.

Leneman, Helen. The Performed Bible: The Story of Ruth in Opera & Oratorio. 2007. (Illus.). 276p. *(978-1-905048-56-4(4))* Sheffield Phoenix Pr.

Levin, Saul. Guide to the Bible: The Hebrew Scriptures (or Old Testament), Selected Apocryphal Books, the New Testament. 2009. (Global Academic Publishing Ser.). (ENG.). 592p. pap. 36.95 *(978-1-58684-276-5(5))* Global Academic Publishing.

Levine, Amy-Jill. The Misunderstood Jew: The Church & the Scandal of the Jewish Jesus. 2007. (ENG.). 256p. pap. 13.99 *(978-0-06-113778-5(2)*, HarperOne) HarperCollins Pubs.

Levingston, Harold. The Modern Words of God. 2008. 344p. pap. 29.95 *(978-1-60672-372-2(3))* PublishAmerica, Inc.

Levy, Steve. Bible Overview. 2008. (ENG.). pap. 11.99 *(978-1-84550-378-9(3))* Christian Focus Pubns. GBR. Dist: STL Distribution North America.

Lewis, Joseph. The Bible Unmasked. 2007. (ENG.). 248p. 41.95 *(978-0-548-28089-8(4))* Kessinger Publishing, LLC.

—The Bible Unmasked. 2007. (ENG.). 256p. pap. 19.95 *(978-1-61033-295-8(4)*, TGS Publishing) TGS.

—Theábible Unmasked. 2007. 164p. per. 19.99 *(978-1-59547-945-7(7))* NuVision Pubns., LLC.

Lewis, Tayler. The Bible & Science; or, the World-Problem. 2006. 352p. per. 23.99 *(978-1-4255-3549-0(6))* MPublishing.

—The Divine Human in the Scriptures. 2009. 142p. pap. *(978-0-217-38306-6(8))* Books LLC.

—The Divine Human in the Scriptures. 2007. (ENG.). 410p. 49.95 *(978-0-548-17927-7(1))*; 412p. per. 34.95 *(978-1-4304-7976-5(0))* Kessinger Publishing, LLC.

—The Divine Human in the Scriptures. 2006. 412p. per. 26.99 *(978-1-4255-4445-4(2))* MPublishing.

Lieb, Michael, et al. The Oxford Handbook of the Reception History of the Bible. 2011. (ENG., Illus.). 752p. 150.00 *(978-0-19-920454-0(3))* Oxford Univ. Pr., Inc.

Lioy, Dan. Evolutionary Creation in Biblical & Theological Perspective. 2011. (Studies in Biblical Literature Ser.). 336p. (C). 87.95 ***(978-1-4331-1624-7(3))*** Lang, Peter Publishing, Inc.

Lipton, Diana. Longing for Egypt & Other Unexpected Biblical Tales. 2008. x, 285p. *(978-1-906055-14-1(9))* Sheffield Phoenix Pr.

Llorca, Raymond. Radical Christ: A Biblical Criticism on God, Jesus & Christian Belief. 2009. 236p. 26.50 *(978-1-60860-622-1(8)*, Eloquent Bks.) AEG Literary Publishing Services, Inc.

Lorenzen, Thorwald. Toward a Culture of Freedom: Reflections on the Ten Commandments Today. 2008. (ENG., Illus.). 260p. pap. 38.00 *(978-0-7188-9193-0(7))* Lutherworth Pr., The GBR. Dist: Brown, David Bk. Co., The.

Lucci, Diego. Scripture & Deism: The Biblical Criticism of the Eighteenth-Century British Deists. 2008. 256p. pap. 58.95 *(978-3-03911-254-8(6))* Lang, Peter Publishing, Inc.

Luther, Martin. The Bible in Pictures. Fussel, Stephan, ed. 2009. (ENG., Illus.). 200p. 39.99 *(978-3-8365-1814-7(7))* TASCHEN DEU. Dist: Ingram Pub. Services.

Lutzer, Erwin W. Is God on America's Side? The Surprising Answer & How It Affects Our Future. 2009. (ENG.). 112p. pap. 6.99 *(978-0-8024-8952-4(4))* Moody Pubs.

Lyrics for Life: Selected Psalms. 2007. 128p. pap. *(978-1-59402-480-1(4))* Regular Baptist Pr.

Ma, Julie C. Mission Possible: The Biblical Strategy for Reaching the Lost. 2008. (Regnum Studies in Mission Ser.). 162p. pap. 19.00 *(978-1-59752-821-4(8))* Wipf & Stock Pubs.

Maccammon, Linda M. Liberating the Bible: A Guide for the Curious & Perplexed. 2008. 269p. 24.00 *(978-1-57075-775-4(5))* Orbis Bks.

Mack, Barbara Ann Mary. The Present Testament: Behold My Manifestation (Barbara) on Earth Today, Says the Lord! My Interpretation of the Holy Bible: God's Words Today! 2011. 740p. 54.55 ***(978-1-4634-0435-2(2))***; pap. 38.72 ***(978-1-4634-0436-9(0))*** AuthorHouse.

Madrid, Patrick. Does the Bible Really Say That? Discovering Catholic Teaching in Scripture. 2006. 186p. per. 13.99 *(978-0-86716-774-0(2)*, Servant Bks.) Franciscan Media.

—150 Bible Verses Every Catholic Should Know. 2008. pap. *(978-0-86716-902-7(8)*, Servant Bks.) Franciscan Media.

Magunagoicoechea, Juan P. Del Mito a la Literatura y la Biblia. 2008. (SPA.). *(978-1-59835-067-8(6))* Cambridge BrickHouse, Inc.

Make Disciples. l.t. ed. 5.00 *(978-0-687-05242-4(4))* Abingdon Pr.

Mangasarian, M. M. The Bible Unveiled. 2007. (ENG.). 270p. 42.95 *(978-0-548-03935-9(6))* Kessinger Publishing, LLC.

—The Neglected Book or the Bible Unveiled. 2007. (ENG.). 272p. 42.95 *(978-0-548-08371-0(1))* Kessinger Publishing, LLC.

Mangum, Todd & Sweetnam, Mark. The Scofield Bible: Its History & Impact on the Evangelical Church. 2009. (ENG.). 255p. pap. 16.99 *(978-1-60657-033-3(1)*, Paternoster) Authentic Media.

Manimas, John. The Primacy of Stewardship: The Handbook for Christians Who Believe in Democracy. 2nd ed. 2009. 168p. pap. 25.00 *(978-0-9821860-2-2(9))* JManimas Publishing.

Manser, Martin H., et al. Critical Companion to the Bible. 2009. (Critical Companion Ser.). (Illus.). 496p. (C). (gr. 9-18). 75.00 *(978-0-8160-7065-7(2))* Facts On File, Inc.

Manson, William. Jesus the Messiah - the Synoptic Tradition of the Revelation of God in Christ. 2007. 216p. per. *(978-1-4067-8824-2(4)*, Pomona Pr.) Read Bks.

March, W. Eugene. God's Tapestry: Reading the Bible in a World of Religious Diversity. 2009. (ENG.). 160p. pap. 15.00 *(978-0-664-23360-0(0))* Westminster John Knox Pr.

Marchadour, Alain, et al. The Land, the Bible, & History: Toward the Land That I Will Show You. 3rd ed. 2010. (Abrahamic Dialogues Ser.). (ENG.). 232p. pap. 26.00 *(978-0-8232-2660-3(3))* Fordham Univ. Pr.

Marguerat, D., et al, eds. L' intrigue dans le recit Biblique: Quatrieme colloque international du RRENAB, Universite Laval, Quebec, 29 mai-1er Juin 2008. 2010. (Bibliotheca Ephemeridum Theologicarum Lovaniensium Ser.). (FRE.). 479p. (C). pap. 99.00 *(978-90-429-2328-7(8))* Peeters Pubs. & Booksellers BEL. Dist: Brown, David Bk. Co., The.

Marshall, David, ed. Communicating the Word: Revelation, Translation, & Interpretation in Christianity & Islam. 2011. (Illus.). 208p. pap. 24.95 *(978-1-58901-784-9(6))* Georgetown Univ. Pr.

Marshall, David, ed. Science & Religion: Christian & Muslim Perspectives. 2012. 160p. pap. 24.95 ***(978-1-58901-914-0(8))*** Georgetown Univ. Pr.

Martin, Dale B. Sex & the Single Savior: Gender & Sexuality in Biblical Interpretation. annot. ed. 2006. (ENG., Illus.). 268p. per. 30.00 *(978-0-664-23046-3(6))* Westminster John Knox Pr.

Martoia, Ron. The Bible As Improv: Seeing & Living the Script in New Ways, 1 vol. 2010. (ENG.). 224p. pap. 14.99 *(978-0-310-28770-4(7))* Zondervan.

Martoia, Ron & McKnight, Scot. The Blue Parakeet: Rethinking How You Read the Bible, 1 vol. 2008. (ENG.). 192p. 18.99 *(978-0-310-28488-8(0))* Zondervan.

Martus, Steffen, et al, eds. Das Buch der Bucher - Gelesen: Lesarten der Bibel in den Wissenschaften und Kunsten. (GER., Illus.). 488p. 82.95 *(978-3-03910-839-8(5))* Lang, Peter CHE. Dist: Lang, Peter Publishing, Inc.

Marx, Alfred. Systemes Sacrificiels de l'Ancien Testament: Formes et Fonctions du Culte Sacrificiel a Yhwh. 260p. *(978-90-04-14286-2(X))* BRILL.

Masalha, Nur. The Bible & Zionism: Invented Traditions, Archaeology & Post-Colonialism in Palestine-Israel. 2007. (ENG.). 384p. 126.00 *(978-1-84277-760-2(2))*; per. 36.00 *(978-1-84277-761-9(0))* Zed Bks., Ltd. GBR. Dist: Macmillan.

Matassa, Lidia D. & Silverman, Jason M., eds. Text, Theology, & Trowel: New Investigations in the Biblical World. 2011. 232p. pap. 26.00 ***(978-1-60899-942-2(4)***, Pickwick Pubns.) Wipf & Stock Pubs.

Mathison, Keith A. From Age to Age: The Unfolding of Biblical Eschatology. 2009. *(978-0-87552-745-1(0))* P & R Publishing.

Maynard, M. C. Evil, Pain & Suffering. 2007. 60p. per. 10.00 *(978-1-4257-4423-6(0))* Xlibris Corp.

Mayo, Philip L. Those Who Call Themselves Jews: The Church & Judaism in the Apocalypse of John. 2006. (Princeton Theological Monographs). 218p. pap. 24.00 *(978-1-59752-558-9(8)*, Pickwick Pubns.) Wipf & Stock Pubs.

McCabe, Elizabeth A. An Examination of the Isis Cult with Preliminary Exploration into New Testament Studies. 2007. (ENG., Illus.). 128p. per. 30.50 *(978-0-7618-3402-1(8))* Univ. Pr. of America, Inc.

McCalla, Arthur & McCalla. The Creationist Debate: The Encounter Between the Bible & the Historical Mind. 2006. (ENG.). 248p. 39.95 *(978-0-8264-8002-6(0))* Continuum International Publishing Group, Ltd. GBR. Dist: National Bk. Network.

McClelland, Alexander. A Brief Treatise on the Canon & Interpretation of the Holy Scriptures. 2006. 240p. per. 20.99 *(978-1-4255-2120-2(7))* MPublishing.

McCosker, Philip. What Is It That the Scripture Says? Essays in Biblical Interpretation, Translation, & Reception in Honour of Henry Wansbrough OSB. 2007. (Library of New Testament Studies: Vol. 316). (ENG., Illus.). 362p. 190.00 *(978-0-567-04353-5(3)*, T&T Clark Int'l) Continuum International Publishing Group, Ltd. GBR. Dist: National Bk. Network.

McDonald, Lee Martin, et al. From Biblical Criticism to Biblical Faith: Essays in Honor of Lee Martin Mcdonald. 2007. 450p. 45.00 *(978-0-88146-052-0(4))* Mercer Univ. Pr.

McDonnell, Carole. Seeds of Bible Study. 2008. 292p. pap. 19.94 *(978-1-4357-0811-2(3))* Lulu Enterprises Inc.

McDonnell, Kilian. God Drops & Loses Things. 2009. 88p. pap. 11.95 *(978-0-9740992-4-8(4))* Liturgical Pr.

McDowell, Josh & McDowell, Sean. Experience Your Bible. 2012. 208p. pap. 13.99 ***(978-0-7369-2873-1(1))*** Harvest Hse. Pubs.

McKenzie, Janet P., compiled by. Devotion to St. Joseph: Read-Aloud Stories, Poems, & Prayers for Catholic Children. 2011. (Illus.). 130p. (J). pap. 14.95 ***(978-1-934185-41-4(8))*** Biblio Resource Pubns., Inc.

McKenzie, John L. How Relevant Is the Bible? And Other Commentaries on Scripture. 2009. (John L. Mckenzie Reprints Ser.). 220p. pap. 24.00 *(978-1-60608-047-4(4))* Wipf & Stock Pubs.

McKenzie, Steven L. How to Read the Bible: History, Prophecy, Literature — Why Modern Readers Need to Know the Difference & What It Means for Faith Today. 2009. (ENG.). 224p. pap. 16.95 *(978-0-19-538330-0(3))* Oxford Univ. Pr., Inc.

McLean, B. H. Biblical Interpretation & Philosophical Hermeneutics. 2012. (ENG., Illus.). 322p. (C). 99.00 ***(978-1-107-01949-2(4))***; pap. 29.99 ***(978-1-107-68340-2(8))*** Cambridge Univ. Pr.

McNicol, Allan J., et al, eds. Resourcing New Testament Studies: Literary, Historical, & Theological Essays in Honor of David L. Dungan. (ENG., Illus.). 2011. 238p. pap. 44.95 ***(978-0-567-56547-1(5))*** 2009. 240p. 120.00 *(978-0-567-02754-2(6))* Continuum International Publishing Group, Ltd. GBR. (T&T Clark Int'l). Dist: National Bk. Network.

M'Crie, Thomas. Lectures on the Book of Esther. 2006. pap. 25.00 *(978-1-59925-091-5(8))* Solid Ground Christian Bks.

Medeiros, John Manimas. The Primacy of Stewardship: The Handbook for Christians Who Believe in Democracy. 2008. 183p. ring bd. 30.00 *(978-0-9821860-0-8(2))* JManimas Publishing.

Meynet, Roland. Treatise on Biblical Rhetoric. 2012. (ENG.). XII, 464p. ***(978-90-04-22418-6(1))*** BRILL.

Miles, Henry A. (Henry Adolphus). The Gospel Narratives: Their origin, Peculiarities & Transmission. by Henry A. Miles ... 2006. 124p. per. 16.99 *(978-1-4255-0851-7(0))* MPublishing.

Miller, J. R. Mini-Guide to the Contents of the Books of the Bible. pap. 0.99 *(978-0-87377-163-4(X))* GAM Pubns.

Miller, Keith Graber & Berry, Malinda Elizabeth. Wrestling with the Text: Young Adult Perspectives on Scripture. 2007. (Journeys with Scripture Ser.: 2). 192p. pap. 19.95 *(978-1-931038-37-9(6))* Cascadia Publishing Hse., LLC.

Miller, Patrick D., et al, eds. Interpretations, CD-ROM Edition, 43 vols. 2006. (Interpretation Ser.). (AKK & ENG.). cd-rom 800.00 *(978-0-664-23143-9(8))* Westminster John Knox Pr.

Miller, Sally. The Bible Is a Girl's Best Friend: Experiencing a Fresh Encounter with God's Word. 2007. 224p. pap. 12.99 *(978-0-7369-2029-2(3))* Harvest Hse. Pubs.

Miller, Stephen M. Incredible Mysteries of the Bible, 1 vol. 2008. (Zondervan Visual Reference Ser.). (ENG., Illus.). 96p. 12.99 *(978-0-310-25594-9(5))* Zondervan.

Milligan, William. Discussions on the Apocalypse. 2008. 306p. pap. 26.00 *(978-1-55635-763-3(X))* Wipf & Stock Pubs.

Mills, Lucinda. Spiritual Devotional Study Guide. 2008. 92p. pap. 11.00 *(978-1-4357-1950-7(6))* Lulu Enterprises Inc.

Mimouni, S. C. La circoncision dane le monde judeen aux epoques grecque et Romaine. 2007. (Collection de la Revue des Etudes Juives Ser.). (FRE.). 388p. (C). pap. 87.00 *(978-90-429-1968-6(X))* Peeters Pubs. & Booksellers BEL. Dist: Brown, David Bk. Co., The.

Mitchell, Bill. Biblical Anomalies. 2007. 92p. per. 12.50 *(978-1-59858-396-0(4))* Dog Ear Publishing, LLC.

Mitchell, Eric Alan. A Literary Examination of the Function of Satire in the Mispat Hammelek of I Samuel 8. 2007. 508p. 139.95 *(978-0-7734-5311-1(3))* Mellen, Edwin Pr., The.

Moberly, R. W. L. Prophecy & Discernment. 2008. (Cambridge Studies in Christian Doctrine Ser.). (ENG.). 300p. pap. 44.00 *(978-0-521-05104-0(5))* Cambridge Univ. Pr.

Moe, John. They Testify of Me. 2007. (Insight Ser.). 48p. pap. 5.99 *(978-0-7586-1466-7(7))* Concordia Publishing Hse.

Montague, George T. Understanding the Bible: A Basic Introduction to Biblical Interpretation. rev. ed. 2007. (Illus.). 274p. per. 19.95 *(978-0-8091-4344-3(5)*, 4344-3) Paulist Pr.

Moon, Byung-Ho. Christ the Mediator of the Law: Calvin's Christological Understanding of the Law as the Rule of Living & Life-Giving. 2006. (Studies in Christian History & Thought: Ser.). 336p. pap. 32.00 *(978-1-59752-782-8(3)*, Wipf and Stock) Wipf & Stock Pubs.

Moore, James W. How God Takes Our Little & Makes it Much. 2010. 86p. pap. 11.00 *(978-1-4267-0878-7(5))* Abingdon Pr.

Moore, Stephen D. The Bible in Theory: Critical & Postcritical Essays. 2011. XIV, 466p. *(978-90-04-18701-6(4))* BRILL.

—The Bible in Theory: Critical & Postcritical Essays. 2010. xiv, 465p. *(978-1-58983-507-8(7))*; *(978-1-58983-506-1(9))* Society of Biblical Literature.

Morgan, Christopher & Peterson, Robert. Suffering & the Goodness of God. Morgan, Christopher W. & Peterson, Robert A., eds. 2008. (Theology in Community Ser.). 256p. 23.99 *(978-1-58134-859-0(2))* Crossway.

Morgan, Donn. Fighting with the Bible: Why Scripture Divides Us & How It Can Bring Us Together. 2007. 144p. per. 15.00 *(978-1-59627-058-9(6)*, Seabury Bks.) Church Publishing, Inc.

Morgan, G. Campbell. Living Messages of the Books of the Bible. 2010. (G. Campbell Morgan Reprint Ser.). 446p. pap. 49.00 *(978-1-60899-293-5(4)*, Wipf and Stock) Wipf & Stock Pubs.

—Living Messages of the Books of the Bible: Genesis to Malachi. 2010. (G. Campbell Morgan Reprint Ser.). 638p. pap. 66.00 *(978-1-60899-302-4(7)*, Wipf and Stock) Wipf & Stock Pubs.

Morrow, William. Protest Against God: The Eclipse of a Biblical Tradition. 2007. 264p. per. *(978-1-906055-34-9(3))* Sheffield Phoenix Pr.

Morton, Glenn R. Genesis 1 Vol. 1: The Pathway Papers. 2006. 6.00 *(978-0-9648227-4-0(1))* DMD Publishing Co.

Moss, Leonard. The Evolutionary Sequence in Tragedy & the Bible. 2009. (ENG.). 232p. pap. 24.00 *(978-1-934542-04-0(0))* Davies Group Pubs., The.

Mossman, Stephen. Marquard von Lindau & the Challenges of Religious Life in Late Medieval Germany: The Passion, the Eucharist, the Virgin Mary. 2010. (Oxford Modern Languages & Literature Monographs). (ENG.). 384p. 120.00 *(978-0-19-957554-1(1))* Oxford Univ. Pr., Inc.

Mother Angelica & Arroyo, Raymond. Mother Angelica's Private & Pithy Lessons from the Scriptures. Arroyo, Raymond, ed. 2008. (ENG.). 256p. 17.95 *(978-0-385-51986-1(9))* Knopf Doubleday Publishing Group.

Moulton, Richard G. The Modern Reader's Bible. 2009. 114p. pap. *(978-0-217-09328-6(0))* Books LLC.

Mueller, Warren M. Truth Seeker: Bible Topics. 2nd ed. 2012. 284p. ***(978-1-58982-827-8(5)***, Millennial Mind Publishing) American Bk. Publishing Group.

Mueller, Warren M. Truth Seeker: Straight Talk from the Bible. 2007. (ENG.). 236p. 19.95 *(978-1-58982-402-7(4)*, Millennial Mind Publishing) American Bk. Publishing Group.

Murphy, Rondo A. Bible Twists & Turns. 2009. 194p. pap. 19.99 *(978-1-4415-5909-8(4))* Xlibris Corp.

Mutschler, Bernhard. Glaube in den Pastoralbriefen: Pistis als Mitte christlicher Existenz. 2010. (GER., Illus.). 487p. 237.50 *(978-3-16-150544-7(1))* Mohr Siebeck GmbH & Co. KG DEU. Dist: Coronet Bks.

Neher, Martin. Wesen und Wirken der Weisheit in der Sapientia Salomonis. (Beihefte zur Zeitschrift far die alttestamentliche Wissenschaft Ser.). (GER.). X, 274p. 210.00 ***(978-3-11-180518-4(2))*** De Gruyter, Walter Inc.

Nelson, Tommy. The Story of God: Understanding the Bible from Beginning to End. 2007. 264p. per. 15.99 *(978-1-928828-21-1(3))* Hudson Productions.

Neufeld, Dietmar. The Social Sciences & Biblical Translation. 2008. (SBL: Writings from the Greco-Roman World). 462p. (C). *(978-90-04-15746-0(8))* BRILL.

—The Social Sciences & Biblical Translation. 2008. 24.95 *(978-1-58983-347-0(3))* Society of Biblical Literature.

Newbigin, Lesslie. Walk Through the Bible. pap. 8.95 *(978-0-281-05253-0(0))* International Publishers Marketing.

Newman, Hillel I. Proximity to Power & Jewish Sectarian Groups of the Ancient Period: A Review of Lifestyle, Values, & Halacha in the Pharisees, Sadducees, Essenes, & Qumran. Ludlam, Ruth, ed. 2006. (Brill Reference Library of Judaism: Vol. 25). (Illus.). 332p. *(978-90-04-14699-0(7))* BRILL.

Neyrey, Jerome H. The Resurrection Stories. 2007. 112p. pap. 14.00 *(978-1-55635-206-5(9))* Wipf & Stock Pubs.

Nicholas, William C. & Nicholas, William C., Jr. I Saw the World End: An Introduction to the Bible's Apocalyptic Literature. 2007. (Illus.). 158p. per. 18.95 *(978-0-8091-4450-1(6)*, 4450-1) Paulist Pr.

North, Bob. The Way of Life: Volume One. 2008. 188p. 26.95 *(978-0-595-69772-4(0))*; pap. 16.95 *(978-0-595-45680-2(4))* iUniverse, Inc.

Nuss, Donald R. The Anatomies of God, the Bible, & Religion: Decoding the Old & New Testaments. 2010. 600p. 43.95 *(978-1-4502-5013-9(0))*; pap. 33.95 *(978-1-4502-5012-2(2))* iUniverse, Inc.

Nutu, Ela. Incarnate Word, Inscribed Flesh: John's Prologue & the Postmodern. 2007. (Illus.). 216p. *(978-1-905048-25-0(4))* Sheffield Phoenix Pr.

Oakman, Douglas E. Jesus & the Peasants. 2007. (Matrix: the Bible in Mediterranean Context: Ser.). (Illus.). 348p. pap. 38.00 *(978-1-59752-275-5(9))* Wipf & Stock Pubs.

Oberg, Ingemar. Luther & World Mission: A Historical & Systematic Study with Special Reference to Luther's Bible Exposition. Apel, Dean, tr. from GER. 2007. 522p. 51.99 *(978-0-570-03322-6(5))* Concordia Publishing Hse.

O'Donnell, Kevin. Their Hearts Burned: Walking with Jesus along the Emmaus Road: an Excursion Through the Old Testament. 2006. 208p. pap. 11.99 (978-0-8254-6117-0(0), Monarch Bks.) Lion Hudson PLC GBR. Dist: Kregel Pubns.

Oegema, Gerben S. Apocalyptic Interpretation of the Bible: Apocalypticism & Biblical Interpretation in Early Judaism, the Apostle Paul, the Historical Jesus & Their Reception History, Vol. 13. 2012. (Jewish & Christian Text Ser.). (ENG.). 208p. 110.00 (978-0-567-62208-2(8), T&T Clark Int'l) Continuum International Publishing Group, Ltd. GBR. Dist: National Bk. Network.

Oegema, Gerbern S. & Oegema. Pseudepigrapha & Christian Origins: Essays from the Studiorum Novi Testamenti Societas. Charlesworth, James H., ed. 2008. (Jewish & Christian Text Ser.). (ENG.). 312p. 140.00 (978-0-567-02719-1(8), T&T Clark Int'l) Continuum International Publishing Group, Ltd. GBR. Dist: National Bk. Network.

Okoye, James Chukwuma. Scripture in the Church: The Synod on the Word of God & the Post-Synodal Exhortation Verbum Domini. 2011. 24.95 (978-0-8146-5761-4(3)); E-Book (978-0-8146-8026-1(7)) Liturgical Pr.

Olbricht, Thomas H., et al, eds. Renewing Tradition: Studies in Texts & Contexts in Honor of James W. Thompson. 2006. (Princeton Theological Monographs). 334p. pap. 32.00 (978-1-59752-828-3(5), Pickwick Pubns.) Wipf & Stock Pubs.

Olmstead, Wesley G. Matthew's Trilogy of Parables: The Nation, the Nations & the Reader in Matthew 21:28-22:14. 2007. (Society for New Testament Studies Monograph Ser.). (ENG.). 292p. pap. 62.00 (978-0-521-03630-6(5)) Cambridge Univ. Pr.

Olofsson, Staffan. As a Deer Longs for Flowing Streams: A Study of the Septuagint Version of Ps 42-43 in Its Relation to the Hebrew Text. 2011. (De Septuaginta Investigatione Ser.). (ENG.). 235p. (C). 95.00 (978-3-525-53383-3(7)) Vandenhoeck & Ruprecht GmbH & Co. KG DEU. Dist: ISD.

Orme, William. Bibliotheca Biblica: A Select List of Books on Sacred Literature: With Notices, Biographical, Critical, & Bibliographical. 2009. pap. (978-1-57898-750-4(4)) Martino Publishing.

—Bibliotheca Biblica: A Select List of Books on Sacred Literature: with Notices, Biographical, Critical, & Bibliographical. 2009. 65.00 (978-1-57898-749-8(0)) Martino Publishing.

Paffenroth, Kim. More Than Mere Players: Shakespeare & the Bible on Life's Drama. 2007. 192p. pap. (978-0-8264-2838-7(X)) Continuum International Publishing Group, Ltd.

Palmer, Kelly A. Cowboy Revelations: A Voice Crying in the Wilderness. 2009. 103p. pap. 12.95 (978-1-4327-1225-9(X)) Outskirts Pr., Inc.

Papadima, Liviu, et al, eds. The Canonical Debate Today: Crossing Disciplinary & Cultural Boundaries. 2011. (ENG., Illus.). 355p. pap. 99.00 (978-90-420-3281-1(2)) Rodopi.

Parker, Jeff I. Biblical Answers to Doctrinal Questions. 2008. 266p. pap. 27.95 (978-1-60441-074-7(4)) PublishAmerica, Inc.

Parsons, James C. The Living Word: Or, Bible Truths & Lessons, for the Family, the School, & the Church ... 2006. 160p. per. 18.99 (978-1-4255-1211-8(9)) MPublishing.

Paterson-Smyth, J. The Old Documents & the New Bible - an Easy Lesson for People in Biblical Criticism. 2007. 256p. per. (978-1-4067-8865-5(1), Pomona Pr.) Read Bks.

Patrick, Dale & Scult, Allen. Rhetoric & Biblical Interpretation. 2009. (Library of Hebrew Bible/Old Testament Studies, the Ser.). (ENG.). 171p. 29.95 (978-0-567-44036-5(2), T&T Clark) Continuum International Publishing Group, Ltd. GBR. Dist: National Bk. Network.

Pelikan, Jaroslav, ed. Luther's Works 18: Lectures on Minor Prophets I. 30.00 (978-0-570-06418-3(X)) Concordia Publishing Hse.

Penniman, Josiah H. A Book about the English Bible. 2007. (ENG.). 454p. 52.95 (978-0-548-02673-1(4)) Kessinger Publishing, LLC.

Peters, David A. The Many Faces of Biblical Humor: A Compendium of the Most Delightful, Romantic, Humorous, Ironic, Sarcastic, or Pathetically Funny Stories & Statements in Scripture. 2007. (ENG.). 444p. per. 56.99 (978-0-7618-3958-3(5)) Hamilton Bks.

Peters, Eileen. Standing in the Stillness. 2009. 96p. pap. 10.99 (978-1-61579-176-7(0)) Xulon Pr., Inc.

Peterson, Eugene. Cómete Este Libro (Eat This Book) 2011. (SPA.). pap. 12.95 (978-1-58802-621-7(3)) Editorial Patmos.

Peterson, Eugene H. The Invitation: A Simple Guide to the Bible. 2007. (Hollywood Nobody Ser.). (ENG., Illus.). 208p. 16.99 (978-1-60006-233-9(4)) NavPress Publishing Group.

—The Jesus Way: A Conversation on the Ways That Jesus Is the Way. 2011. 304p. pap. 17.00 (978-0-8028-6703-2(0)) 2007. 289p. 22.00 (978-0-8028-2949-8(X)) Eerdmans, William B. Publishing Co.

Peterson, Eugene H. & Santucci, Peter. Eat This Book: Study Guide. 2006. 48p. per. 6.00 (978-0-8028-3263-4(6)) Eerdmans, William B. Publishing Co.

—The Jesus Way Study Guide. 2007. 63p. per. 6.00 (978-0-8028-4566-5(5)) Eerdmans, William B. Publishing Co.

Pettinggill, William & Torrey, R. A. 1001 Bible Questions Answered. 2011. (ENG.). 496p. pap. 14.95 (978-0-88486-479-0(0)) Bristol Park Bks.

Philipps, James. Understanding the Bible. 2007. (Jump Starts for Catechists Ser.). 44p. pap. 4.95 (978-1-58595-629-6(5)) Twenty-Third Pubns./Bayard.

Pierce, Stephen E. Stones of the Bible: A Guide to their Identification & Significance. 2006. (Illus.). 167p. (YA). spiral bd. 19.95 (978-0-9767811-6-5(6), True Potential) True Potential Publishing, Inc.

Pink, Arthur W. Profiting from the Word. 2011. 106p. pap. 9.99 (978-1-61203-336-5(9)) Bottom of the Hill Publishing.

Pink, Arthur Waddington. A W Pink's Studies in the Scriptures - 1932-33. 2008. 588p. pap. 33.99 (978-1-58960-235-9(8)) Sovereign Grace Pubs., Inc.

Pizarro, Rudy A. The Holy Trinity & the Gambler. 2008. 300p. pap. 17.99 (978-1-60647-244-6(5)) Xulon Pr., Inc.

Plotz, David. Good Book: The Bizarre, Hilarious, Disturbing, Marvelous, & Inspiring Things I Learned When I Read Every Single Word of the Bible. (P. S. Ser.). 2010. (ENG.). 352p. pap. 14.99 (978-0-06-137425-8(3), HarperPerennial) 2009. (ENG.). 320p. 26.99 (978-0-06-137424-1(5)) 2009. 496p. pap. 26.99 (978-0-06-171995-0(1), HarperLuxe) HarperCollins Pubs.

Pokorný, Petr. A Commentary on the Gospel of Thomas: From Interpretations to the Interpreted. 2011. (ENG.). 190p. pap. 44.95 (978-0-567-50749-5(1), T&T Clark Int'l) Continuum International Publishing Group, Ltd. GBR. Dist: National Bk. Network.

Polkinghorne, John. Testing Scripture: A Scientist Explores the Bible. 2011. 128p. pap. 17.99 (978-1-58743-313-9(3)) Brazos Pr.

Ponessa, Joseph & Manhardt, Laurie Watson. David & the Psalms. 2006. (Come & See Catholic Bible Study Ser.). (Illus.). 202p. per. 19.95 (978-1-931018-37-1(5)) Emmaus Road Publishing.

Pontifical Biblical Commission. The Interpretation of the Bible in the Church. 144p. pap. 5.95 (978-0-8198-3670-0(2), 332-132) Pauline Bks. & Media.

Popplewell, Pat Galen. Bible Interpretation. 2009. 192p. pap. 14.99 (978-1-60791-410-5(7)) Xulon Pr., Inc.

Porter, Stanley E. Dictionary of Biblical Criticism & Interpretation. 2009. (ENG.). 424p. (C). pap. 44.95 (978-0-415-55274-5(5)) 2007. 496p. 250.00 (978-0-415-20100-1(4)) Routledge.

Porter, Stanley E., ed. The Messiah in the Old & New Testaments. 2007. (McMaster New Testament Studies). 268p. per. 29.00 (978-0-8028-0766-3(6)) Eerdmans, William B. Publishing Co.

—Paul's World. 2007. (Pauline Studies Ser.). 284p. (978-90-04-16272-3(0)) BRILL.

Potter, James. Mysteries of the Bible - Adam to Abram the Primeval Er. 2009. 328p. pap. 19.95 (978-1-61529-001-7(X)) Vision Publishing.

Poulin, Richard. How to Be Eternally Blessed. 2008. 112p. pap. 10.99 (978-1-4389-2921-7(8)) AuthorHouse.

Powys, David J. 'Hell': A Hard Look at a Hard Question: The Fate of the Unrighteous in New Testament Thought. 2007. (Paternoster Biblical Monographs: Ser.). 518p. pap. 54.00 (978-1-59752-756-9(4), Wipf and Stock) Wipf & Stock Pubs.

Premnath, Devadasan Nithya & Sugirtharajah, R. S. Border Crossings: Cross-Cultural Hermeneutics. 2007. 179p. per. 40.00 (978-1-57075-745-7(3)) Orbis Bks.

Presutta, David. The Biblical Cosmos Versus Modern Cosmology: Why the Bible Is Not the Word of God. 2007. 360p. per. 24.95 (978-1-59526-829-7(4), Llumina Pr.) Aeon Publishing Inc.

Prewitt, Jay Steven. Have You Received since You Believed? 2007. 140p. per. 24.95 (978-1-4241-7481-2(3)) PublishAmerica, Inc.

Price, Lynn F. One in Thine Hand: The Stick of Judah & the Stick of Joseph. 2007. 365p. per. 21.99 (978-0-88290-816-8(2)) Cedar Fort, Inc./CFI Distribution.

Priddy, Eugene. Keep from Stumbling! 2008. 324p. per. 17.99 (978-1-60477-443-6(6)) Xulon Pr., Inc.

Pritz, Ray. The Works of Their Hands: Man-Made Things in the Bible. 2009. (Illus.). xxvii, 485p. (978-0-8267-0039-1(X)) United Bible Societies.

Professor Stuart's Postscript to his Letter to the Editors of the Biblical Repertory. 2010. pap. 18.88 (978-1-61143-171-1(9)) Gorgias Pr., LLC.

Puhalo, Lazar. Ikon As Scripture. Date not set. (Illus.). 54p. pap. (978-1-879038-55-4(2), 9025) Synaxis Pr.

Purcell, Everett. True Story about the Sign of Jonah. 2007. 108p. (ENG.). 18.99 (978-1-60266-250-6(9)); per. 10.99 (978-1-60266-249-0(5)) Xulon Pr., Inc.

Pyper, Hugh S. The Unchained Bible: Cultural Appropriations of Biblical Texts. 2012. (ENG.). 176p. 100.00 (978-0-567-16690-6(2), T&T Clark Int'l) Continuum International Publishing Group, Ltd. GBR. Dist: National Bk. Network.

Pyper, Hugh S. & Vander Stichele, Caroline. Text, Image, & Otherness in Children's Bibles: What Is in the Picture? 2012. pap. (978-1-58983-661-7(8)) Society of Biblical Literature.

Rae, Murray & Rae. History & Hermeneutics. 2006. (ENG.). 176p. 60.00 (978-0-567-08092-9(7), T&T Clark Int'l) Continuum International Publishing Group, Ltd. GBR. Dist: National Bk. Network.

Raharimanantsoa, Mamy. Mort et Esperance Selon la Bible Hebraique. 2006. (Coniectanea Biblica Old Testament Ser.: Vol. 53). (FRE.). 532p. (C). pap. (978-91-22-02142-1(6)) Almqvist & Wiksell International.

Rainey, Les. The Collected Writings of les Rainey. 2008. 424p. per. (978-1-897117-31-6(0)) 2007. 620p. per. (978-1-897117-30-9(2)) Gospel Folio Pr.

—The Collected Writings of les Rainey Volume 1. 2007. 196p. per. (978-1-897117-29-3(9)) Gospel Folio Pr.

Randall, Lonnie O. And Ye Shall Know the Truth: Answers from the Bible. Date not set. (Illus.). iv, 145p. pap. 10.00 (978-0-9677302-0-2(1)) Joy Enterprises.

Ranieri, John & Ranieri, John J. Disturbing Revelation: Leo Strauss, Eric Voegelin, & the Bible. 2009. (ENG.). 288p. (C). 47.50 (978-0-8262-1836-0(9)) Univ. of Missouri Pr.

Ransdell, Lisa (Bee). To Babel or Not: Confused? So Am I. 2008. 101p. pap. 16.95 (978-1-60563-431-9(X)) PublishAmerica, Inc.

Rasbeary, James. What's Wrong with the Old Black Book? 2009. 263p. pap. 19.99 (978-0-557-05353-7(6)) Lulu Enterprises Inc.

Rasbeary, James / M. What's Wrong with the Old Black Book: An Understandable Guide to the Debate Surrounding the King James Bible. 2007. 261p. per. (978-0-9788703-9-3(5)) Calvary Publishing.

Reagan, Wesley C., ed. The Higley Lesson Commentary: 1933-2008. 2007. (Higley Lesson Commentary Ser.). (Illus.). 530p. per. 15.95 (978-1-886763-32-6(1)) Higley Publishing Corp.

—The Higley Lesson Commentary: Based on the International Sunday School Lessons. 2007. (Illus.). 530p. 19.95 (978-1-886763-33-3(X)) Higley Publishing Corp.

—The Higley Lesson Commentary: Based on the International Sunday School Lessons, King James Version, 77th Annual Volume. 2009. (Higley Lesson Commentary Ser.). (Illus.). 520p. pap. 15.95 (978-1-886763-36-4(4)) Higley Publishing Corp.

Reed, David. LEFT BEHIND Answered Verse by Verse. 2008. 144p. per. 11.96 (978-1-4357-0873-0(3)) Lulu Enterprises Inc.

Reeves, Robert. Blessed Assurance; the Lord Reigns! 2007. 296p. per. 15.99 (978-1-60266-155-4(3)) Xulon Pr., Inc.

Reiland, Robert. Jesus & the Third Temple: The Complete Guide to the Ancient History & Secret Rituals of the Red Heifer Ceremony. 3rd ed. 2008. (Illus.). 692p. pap. 34.95 (978-1-59772-036-6(4), Your Own World Bks.) Your Own World, Inc.

Remember the Heart of the Bible - Love God / Love Neighbor. 2008. 192p. pap. 16.95 (978-0-9747656-5-5(1)) Eagle's Nest Pr.

Rhodes, David. Faith in Dark Places - P. 112p. 10.00 (978-0-281-04986-8(6)) SPCK Publishing GBR. Dist: Pilgrim Pr., The/United Church Pr.

Rhodes, Ron. Commonly Misunderstood Bible Verses: Clear Explanations for the Difficult Passages. 2008. 300p. pap. 14.99 (978-0-7369-2175-6(3)) Harvest Hse. Pubs.

—What Does the Bible Say About — ? 2007. 400p. pap. 14.99 (978-0-7369-1903-6(1)) Harvest Hse. Pubs.

Rich, Ben E. Mr. Durant of Salt Lake City: that Mormon. 2008. 132p. 28.95 (978-1-4357-5632-8(0)); pap. 13.95 (978-1-4357-5630-4(4)) Lulu Enterprises Inc.

Richards, Larry. Como Entender el Antiguo Testamento: How to Understand the Old. (SPA.). (978-84-7228-591-0(X), 220158) Clie, Editorial.

Riddell, Elder Donnie L. Dare to Go Against the Grain of the Porcupines: (Church Traditions & State Interpretations) 2008. 108p. pap. 16.95 (978-1-60672-902-1(0)) PublishAmerica, Inc.

Riell, Howard M. Enoch & the Book of Coincidences III: Promise. 2006. 134p. per. 14.95 (978-1-58939-927-3(7)) Virtualbookworm.com Publishing, Inc.

Roberts, D. Let Me See Your Form: Seeking Poetic Structure in the Song of Songs. 2007. (Studies in the History of Judaism Ser.). (ENG.). per. 57.99 (978-0-7618-2913-3(X)) Univ. Pr. of America, Inc.

Robertson Smith, W. The Old Testament in the Jewish Church - Twelve Lectures on Biblical Criticism. 2007. 460p. per. (978-1-4067-8822-8(8), Pomona Pr.) Read Bks.

Robertson, Stan. Why Was That Tree in the Garden, Anyway? 2009. 400p. pap. 24.95 (978-1-58982-528-4(4), Millennial Mind Publishing) American Bk. Publishing Group.

Robinson, Henry W., ed. Record & Revelation. reprint ed. 35.50 (978-0-404-15354-0(2)) AMS Pr., Inc.

Rochester, Stuart. Good News at Gerasa: Transformative Discourse & Theological Anthropology in Mark's Gospel. 2011. (ENG.). 349p. pap. 77.95 (978-3-0343-0294-4(0)) Lang, Peter AG GBR. Dist: Lang, Peter.

Rogerson, J. W. According to the Scriptures? The Challenge of Using the Bible in Social, Moral & Political Questions. 2007. (Biblical Challenges in the Contemporary World Ser.). (ENG.). 192p. (C). 99.95 (978-1-84553-127-0(2)); per. 29.95 (978-1-84553-128-7(0)) Equinox Publishing Ltd. GBR. Dist: ISD.

Rollins, Wayne G. & Kille, D. Andrew, eds. Psychological Insight into the Bible: Texts & Readings. 2007. 291p. per. 28.00 (978-0-8028-4155-1(4)) Eerdmans, William B. Publishing Co.

Rooke, Deborah, ed. A Question of Sex? Gender & Difference in the Hebrew Bible & Beyond. 2007. 200p. (978-1-906055-20-2(3)) Sheffield Phoenix Pr.

Root, Michael & Buckley, James Joseph. Sharper Than a Two-Edged Sword: Preaching, Teaching, & Living the Bible. Root, Michael & Buckley, James J., eds. 2008. (Illus.). 112p. pap. 16.00 (978-0-8028-6271-6(3)) Eerdmans, William B. Publishing Co.

Rose Publishing Staff. The Bible at a Glance. 2008. (Rose Bible Basics Ser.). (ENG., Illus.). 112p. pap. 12.99 (978-1-59636-200-0(6)) Rose Publishing.

—Pop Spirituality & the Truth: The Real Secret of a New Earth. 2009. 14p. 3.99 (978-1-59636-315-1(0)) Rose Publishing.

Rosner, Brian S. Greed as Idolatry: The Origin & Meaning of a Pauline Metaphor. 2007. 214p. per. 22.00 (978-0-8028-3374-7(8)) Eerdmans, William B. Publishing Co.

Rowland. Interpretation in Context. 2008. vii, 119p. pap. (978-0-281-05802-0(4)) SPCK Publishing.

Ruiz, Jean-Pierre. Readings from the Edges: The Bible & People on the Move. 2011. 192p. pap. 28.00 (978-1-57075-944-4(8)) Orbis Bks.

Ruzer, Serge. Mapping the New Testament: Early Christian Writings as a Witness for Jewish Biblical Exegesis. 2007. (Jewish & Christian Perspectives Ser.). 254p. (978-90-04-15892-4(8)) BRILL.

Ryan, Paschal. The Paschal Lamb. 2006. (ENG.). 188p. per. 24.95 (978-1-4241-5810-2(9)) PublishAmerica, Inc.

Ryken, Leland. Understanding English Bible Translation: The Case for an Essentially Literal Approach. 2009. 208p. pap. 12.99 (978-1-4335-0279-8(8)) Crossway.

S., J. Torah the Five Books of Moses the Inte. 2006. (HEB & ENG.). 400p. per. (978-956-291-335-5(X)) Editorial Benei Noaj.

Saarnivaara, Uuras. Can the Bible Be Trusted? Old & New Testament Introduction & Interpretation. 2008. 812p. pap. 74.00 (978-1-55635-699-5(4), Wipf and Stock) Wipf & Stock Pubs.

—Hath God Said? Who Is Right Ntilde; God or the Liberals. 2008. 294p. pap. 32.00 (978-1-55635-885-2(7), Wipf and Stock) Wipf & Stock Pubs.

Sabbath, R. Sacred Tropes: Tanakh, New Testament, & Qur'an as Literature & Culture. 2009. (Biblical Interpretation Ser.). 544p. (978-90-04-17752-9(3)) BRILL.

Sadler, M. F. The Lost Gospel & Its Contents. 2007. 168p. per. (978-1-4065-4254-7(7)) Dodo Pr.

Saith, Ebbie. The Last One: A Bible for Dummies. Date not set. 100p. Vol. I. pap. (978-1-891597-51-0(5)) Vol. II. pap. 9.99 (978-1-891597-52-7(3)) Mleecole Pub. (SDC Pr.).

Sawyer, Greg. How to Read & Understand the Bible. stu. ed. 3.45 (978-0-570-00646-6(5), 22-2767); 4.45 (978-0-570-00647-3(3), 22-2768) Concordia Publishing Hse.

Sawyer, John F. A. Sacred Texts & Sacred Meanings: Studies in Biblical Language & Literature. 2011. 480p. (978-1-906055-94-3(7)) Sheffield Phoenix Pr.

Sawyer, John F. A., ed. The Bible & Culture. 2006. (ENG., Illus.). 564p. 199.95 (978-1-4051-0136-3(9), Wiley-Blackwell) Wiley, John & Sons, Inc.

Sawyer, John F. A., ed. The Blackwell Companion to the Bible & Culture. 2012. (ENG.). 568p. pap. 44.95 (978-0-470-67488-8(1), Wiley-Blackwell) Wiley, John & Sons, Inc.

Schei, Kenneth A. An Atheist for Jesus: A Personal Journey of Discovery. 2nd rev. ed. 2007. ring bd. 17.95 (978-0-926491-03-8(2)) Synthesis.

Schissler Fiorenza, Elisabeth. Democratizing Biblical Studies: Toward an Emancipatory Educational Space. 2009. (ENG., Illus.). 232p. pap. 25.00 (978-0-664-23509-3(3)) Westminster John Knox Pr.

Scopello, M., ed. The Gospel of Judas in Context: Proceedings of the First International Conference on the Gospel of Judas, Paris, Sorbonne, October 27th-28th, 2006. 2008. (Nag Hammadi & Manichaean Studies). (FRE & ENG.). 424p. (978-90-04-16721-6(8)) BRILL.

Scott, Ian W. Paul's Way of Knowing: Story, Experience, & the Spirit. 2008. 368p. (C). pap. 50.00 (978-0-8010-3609-5(7)) Baker Academic.

Scripture Union. SUbstance. 2011. 82p. pap. (978-1-84427-527-4(2)) Scripture Union.

Seatts, Linda. The Truth about the Superior Lie: A book to resurrect the lives of African-Americans crucified by the Lie, 1. 2007. 76p. (YA). (978-0-9793305-0-6(5)) Kittrell Publishing Hse.

Seiss, Joseph. The Apocalypse: Lectures on the Book of Revelation. 2007. 536p. per. 25.95 (978-1-60206-143-9(2)) Cosimo, Inc.

Sellew, Philip & Smith, James D., eds. The Fabric of Early Christianity: Reflections in Honor of Helmut Koester by Fifty Years of Harvard Students. 2006. (Illus.). 168p. pap. 20.00 (978-1-59752-974-7(5), Pickwick Pubns.) Wipf & Stock Pubs.

Senior, Donald & Collins, John J., eds. Catholic Study Bible. 2nd ed. 2011. (ENG.). 2560p. (C). 89.99 (978-0-19-529778-2(4)) Oxford Univ. Pr., Inc.

The Seven Churches of Asia: The Path of the Chosen Revealed. 2007. (Illus.). 343p. per. 19.99 (978-1-59886-940-8(X)) Tate Publishing & Enterprises, LLC.

Shea, John. The Spiritual Wisdom of the Gospels for Christian Preachers & Teachers: The Relentless Widow: Year C. 2006. 330p. per. 29.95 (978-0-8146-2915-4(6), Liturgical Pr. Bks.) Liturgical Pr.

Shelburne, Gene, et al. The Higley Lesson Commentary: KJV Based on the International Sunday School Lessons. Reagan, Wesley, ed. 77th ed. 2009. (Illus.). 520p. (J). 19.95 (978-1-886763-37-1(2)) Higley Publishing Corp.

Shen, Bing W. A Step Toward Cracking the Deutero-Isaiah Codes: His Name Is Israel! 2008. 244p. pap. 25.00 (978-0-9798435-0-1(2)) Zeroah Publishing LLC.

Shoulders, Kendall T. A Purpose-Filled God: Shadows of the Almighty. 2007. (ENG.). 108p. per. 11.95 (978-1-58736-818-9(8)) Wheatmark.

Siegel, Bob. I'd Like to Believe in Jesus, But... The Harder, Less Frequently Discussed Questions. 2007. 190p. per. 14.95 (978-1-59352-308-4(4)) Christian Services Publishing.

Silver, Abiel. Lectures on the Symbolic Character of the Sacred Scriptures, by Rev Abiel Silver. 2006. 292p. per. 23.99 (978-1-4255-2751-8(5)) MPublishing.

Silverman, Jason M. & Daughton, Amy, eds. A Land Like Your Own. 2010. 176p. pap. 20.00 (978-1-60899-454-0(6), Pickwick Pubns.) Wipf & Stock Pubs.

Skinner, Andrew. A Bible Fit for the Restoration: The Epic Struggle that Brought Us the King James Version. 2011. 128p. pap. 9.99 (978-1-59955-908-7(0)) Cedar Fort, Inc./CFI Distribution.

Sloat, John W. Moving Beyond the Christian Myth: The Next Step in Our Spiritual Evolution. 2011. (ENG., Illus.). 148p. pap. (978-1-926918-94-5(0), CCB Publishing) CCB Publishing.

Smith, Allen. Verse Abuse. 2007. 178p. per. 19.95 (978-1-887653-33-6(3)) Papito Publishing.

Smith, Barry. What Must I Do to Be Saved? Paul Parts Company with His Jewish Heritage. 2007. 304p. (978-1-905048-82-3(3)) Sheffield Phoenix Pr.

Smith, Christopher R. The Bible Without Chapters & Verses: Exploring Scripture's Inherent Designs. 2007. (ENG.). 152p. per. (978-1-894667-73-9(5)) Clements Publishing.

Smith, Eddie. Making Sense of Spiritual Warfare. 2008. 208p. pap. 14.99 (978-0-7642-0393-0(2)) Bethany Hse. Pubs.

Smith, Joseph Nathan. The Generations of Noah. 2008. 128p. pap. 16.99 (978-0-615-19309-0(9)) Smith, Joseph Nathan.

—Rest unto the Land. 2007. 188p. pap. 25.00 *(978-0-615-16189-1(8))* Smith, Joseph Nathan.

Smith, Melissa. The Ancient Word Series. 2008. 736p. pap. 25.95 *(978-1-60461-929-4(5))* Independent Pub.

Snodgrass, Klyne, ed. Ex Auditu - Volume 24: An International Journal of Theological Interpretation of Scripture. 2009. 218p. pap. 30.00 *(978-1-60608-740-4(1)*, Pickwick Pubns.) Wipf & Stock Pubs.

Sociedades Biblicas Unidas, creator. Santa Biblia-Rvr 1960-Letra Grande. l.t. ed. 2011. (SPA.). 1580p. pap. **(978-1-59877-199-2(X))** Deutsche Bibelgesellschaft.

Solutin, Pablo H. We Are Gods: Jesus Said So. 2007. 73p. pap. 16.95 *(978-1-60441-796-8(X))* PublishAmerica, Inc.

Soskice, Janet Martin. The Kindness of God: Metaphor, Gender, & Religious Language. 2008. (ENG.). 224p. pap. 21.95 *(978-0-19-826950-2(1))* Oxford Univ. Pr., Inc.

Soughers, Tara. Treasures of Darkness: Finding God When Hope Is Hidden. 2009. pap. 13.00 *(978-0-687-65543-4(9))* Abingdon Pr.

Soulen, Richard N. & Soulen, R. Kendall. Handbook of Biblical Criticism, Fourth Edition. 4th ed. 2011. (ENG.). 272p. pap. 30.00 **(978-0-664-23534-5(4))** Westminster John Knox Pr.

The Source of the Old & New Testaments. 2007.Tr. of source de l'ancien et du nouveau Testament. (Illus.). 241p. per. 27.50 *(978-0-9716674-4-0(6))* Kototama Bks.

Speck, Ralph. Is That Really What God Said? Volume One Bible Stories, Parables & Miracles Interpreted for Today's Living. 2007. 112p. per. 19.95 *(978-1-60441-070-9(1))* PublishAmerica, Inc.

Spell, David. Peter & Paul in Acts: A Comparison of Their Ministries - A Study in New Testament Apostolic Ministry. 2006. 218p. pap. 24.00 *(978-1-59752-784-2(X)*, Wipf and Stock) Wipf & Stock Pubs.

St. Augustine. On Christian Doctrine. Shaw, J. F., tr. from LAT. 2009. (ENG.). 192p. pap. 7.95 *(978-0-486-46918-8(2))* Dover Pubns., Inc.

Stalnaker, Leo. Mystic Symbolism in Bible Numerals. 2011. 150p. 40.95 **(978-1-258-00661-7(8))** Literary Licensing, LLC.

Stanard, Terry. Meet the man who can change your life Forever. 2007. (Illus.). 32p. 9.95 *(978-0-9794885-0-4(8))* Art of Faith Publishing.

Standard Publishing Staff. NIV Standard Lesson Commentary. l.t. ed. 2009. (ENG.). 520p. pap. 18.99 *(978-0-7847-2259-6(5))* Standard Publishing.

—NIV Standard Lesson Commentary with ECommentary. 2009. (Standard Lesson Commentary Ser.). (ENG.). 448p. 21.99 *(978-0-7847-2342-5(7))* Standard Publishing.

Starr, Chloe & Starr. Reading Christian Scriptures in China. 2008. (ENG.). 240p. 130.00 *(978-0-567-03292-8(2)*, T&T Clark Int'l) Continuum International Publishing Group, Ltd. GBR. Dist: National Bk. Network.

Stein, Robert H. A Basic Guide to Interpreting the Bible: Playing by the Rules. 2nd ed. 2011. (C). pap. 19.99 *(978-0-8010-3373-5(X))* Baker Academic.

Steiner, Rudolf. The Bible Begins with Reference to Foregoing Conditions of Old. 2006. pap. 12.95 *(978-1-4304-2535-9(0))* Kessinger Publishing, LLC.

—How Genesis Describes the Preparation for Lemuria until Moon. 2006. pap. 12.95 *(978-1-4304-2539-7(3))* Kessinger Publishing, LLC.

—Why Material Concepts Are Insufficient to Understand the Spiritual - 2006. pap. 9.95 *(978-1-4304-2525-0(3))* Kessinger Publishing, LLC.

Stendahl, Krister. Meanings: The Bible as Document & as Guide. 2nd ed. 2008. 272p. pap. 25.00 *(978-0-8006-6366-7(7))* Augsburg Fortress, Pubs.

Sterrett, T. Norton & Schultz, Richard L. How to Understand Your Bible. 3rd rev. ed. 2010. (ENG.). 205p. (Orig.). pap. 16.00 *(978-0-8308-1093-2(5)*, IVP Conn.) InterVarsity Pr.

Stevens, R. Paul. Work Matters: Lessons from Scripture. 2012. pap. **(978-0-8028-6596-7(4))** Eerdmans, William B. Publishing Co.

Stevenson, John. Gratitude: An Exposition of the Hundred & Third Psalm... . 2006. 336p. per. 23.99 *(978-1-4255-3383-0(3))* MPublishing.

Strand, Clark. How to Believe in God: Whether You Believe in Religion or Not. 2009. (ENG.). 256p. 24.95 *(978-0-7679-2069-8(4))* Knopf Doubleday Publishing Group.

Strba, Blazej. Take Off Your Sandals from Your Feet! An Exegetical Study of Josh 5, 13-15. 2008. 404p. pap. 82.95 *(978-3-631-57599-4(8))* Lang, Peter Publishing, Inc.

Strelan, Rick. Strange Acts: Studies in the Cultural World of the Acts of the Apostles. (Beihefte zur Zeitschrift fur die neutestamentliche Wissenschaft und die Kunde der älteren Kirche Ser.). (ENG.). XIV, 339p. 225.00 **(978-3-11-180088-2(1))** De Gruyter, Walter Inc.

Stripling, Scott. The Trowel & the Truth. 2007. 168p. per. 18.95 *(978-1-931178-28-0(3))* Vision Publishing.

Stubbs, Narelle C. & Clayton, Hilary M. Activate Your HOrse's Core: Unmounted Exercises for Dynamic Mobility, Strength & Balance. 2008. (Illus.). 32p. spiral bd. *(978-0-9747670-1-7(8))* Sport Horse Pubns.

Stuckenbruck, Loren T. Memory in the Bible & Antiquity. Stuckenbruck, Loren T. et al, eds. 2007. (Wissenschaftliche Untersuchungen Zum Neuen Testament Ser.). 394p. (C). 155.00 *(978-3-16-149251-8(X))* Mohr Siebeck GmbH & Co. KG DEU. Dist: Eisenbrauns, Inc.

Stuhlmacher, Peter. Schriftauslegung Auf Dem Wege Zur Biblischen Theologie. 2011. (Forschungen Zur Religion und Literatur des Alten & Neuen Testament Ser.). (GER & ENG.). 487p. (C). 140.00 **(978-3-525-53555-4(4))** Vandenhoeck & Ruprecht GmbH & Co. KG DEU. Dist: ISD.

Stylianopoulos, Theodore G. Encouraged by the Scriptures: Essays on Scripture, Interpretation, & Life. 2011. **(978-1-935317-22-7(9))** Holy Cross Orthodox Pr.

Sugirtharajah. Readings in Indian Christian Theology. (Illus.). 272p. 14.95 *(978-0-281-04622-5(0))* International Publishers Marketing.

Sugirtharajah, R. S. Exploring Postcolonial Biblical Criticism: History, Method, Practice. 2011. (ENG.). 224p. 87.95 *(978-1-4051-5856-5(5))*; pap. 34.95 *(978-1-4051-5857-2(3))* Wiley, John & Sons, Inc. (Wiley-Blackwell).

—Troublesome Texts: The Bible in Colonial & Contemporary Culture. 2008. 172p. *(978-1-906055-38-7(6))* Sheffield Phoenix Pr.

Supreme, Ali. My Interpretation. 2008. 172p. pap. 14.95 *(978-0-9744282-8-4(0))* Wide View Entertainment & Media, Inc.

Swain, Scott R. Trinity, Revelation, & Reading: A Theological Introduction to the Bible & its Interpretation. 2011. (ENG.). 168p. 90.00 *(978-0-567-25525-9(5))*; pap. 27.95 *(978-0-567-26540-1(4))* Continuum International Publishing Group, Ltd. GBR. (T&T Clark Int'l). Dist: National Bk. Network.

Sweeney, Marvin A. Reading the Hebrew Bible after the Shoah: Engaging Holocaust Theology. 2008. 302p. (C). pap. 29.00 *(978-0-8006-3849-8(2)*, Fortress Pr.) Augsburg Fortress, Pubs.

Swindell, Anthony C. Reworking the Bible: The Literary Reception-History of Fourteen Biblical Stories. 2010. 356p. *(978-1-907534-01-0(6))* Sheffield Phoenix Pr.

Syswerda, Jean E. The Women's Devotional Guide to the Bible: A One-Year Plan for Studying, Praying, & Responding to God's Word. 2012. 384p. pap. 15.99 **(978-0-8499-2977-9(6))** Nelson, Thomas Inc.

Tate, W. Randolph. Biblical Interpretation: An Integrated Approach. 3rd ed. 2008. 400p. (C). 32.99 *(978-0-8010-4782-4(X))* Baker Academic.

Tharekadavil, Antony. Servant of Yahweh in Second Isaiah: Isaianic Servant Passages in Their Literary & Historical Context. 2007. (European University Studies 23 Ser.: Vol. 848). 204p. pap. *(978-3-631-57079-1(1))* Lang, Peter AG.

Thatcher, Adrian. The Savage Text: The Use & Abuse of the Bible. 2008. (Blackwell Manifestos Ser.: 15). (ENG.). 232p. pap. 33.95 *(978-1-4051-7016-1(6))*; 93.95 *(978-1-4051-7017-8(4))* Wiley, John & Sons, Inc. (Wiley-Blackwell).

Thomas, Ice. Breaking the apocalypse Code. 2007. pap. 14.99 *(978-1-59751-035-6(1))* Word For Today, The.

Thomas Nelson Publishing Staff, creator. Christmas A to Z: Unwrapping the Wonder of Seasonal Words & Phrases, 0 vols. 2007. (Illus.). 208p. 19.99 *(978-1-4185-2796-9(3))* Nelson, Thomas Inc.

Thompson, Henry. Historia Sagrada - Tomo III: Bible Unfolded: Life of Jesus. (SPA.). 512p. *(978-84-7228-965-9(6)*, 223046) Clie, Editorial.

Thomson, George F. Book of Pure Logic: Pure Logic Studies & Analysis of the Bible & of Life. 2009. 384p. pap. 19.99 *(978-1-4343-9536-8(7))* AuthorHouse.

Thurow, Kenneth D. A Place at the Table: Scripture, Sexuality, & Life in the Church. 2009. 140p. pap. 13.95 *(978-1-4401-1330-7(0))* iUniverse, Inc.

Tiller, Darryl J. Growing into Jesus: Six Building Blocks for Life in Christ. 2008. 122p. pap. 19.95 *(978-1-60474-869-7(9))* PublishAmerica, Inc.

Tilma, Mary. Ancient Book Relevant Faith. 2008. 184p. pap. 14.99 *(978-1-60647-950-6(4))* Xulon Pr., Inc.

Tischendorf, Constantin von. When Were Our Gospels Written? an Argument by Constantine Tischendorf with a Narrative of the Discovery of the Sinaitic Manuscript Tr & Pub by T. 2006. 132p. per. 16.99 *(978-1-4255-0941-5(X))* MPublishing.

Tobin, Paul. The Rejection of Pascal's Wager. 2009. (Illus.). 668p. pap. *(978-0-7552-0461-8(1))* Authors OnLine, Ltd.

Tony, Cartledge. Telling Stories: Tall Tales & Deep Truth. 2008. pap. 17.00 *(978-1-57312-515-4(6))* Smyth & Helwys Publishing, Inc.

Tov, Emanuel & Evans, Craig A., eds. Exploring the Origins of the Bible: Canon Formation in Historical, Literary, & Theological Perspective. 2008. (Acadia Studies in Bible & Theology Ser.). 272p. (C). pap. 28.00 *(978-0-8010-3242-4(3))* Baker Academic.

Treier, Daniel J. Introducing Theological Interpretation of Scripture: Recovering a Christian Practice. 2008. 224p. (C). pap. 22.00 *(978-0-8010-3178-6(8))* Baker Academic.

—Virtue & the Voice of God: Toward Theology as Wisdom. 2006. 278p. per. 30.00 *(978-0-8028-3074-6(9))* Eerdmans, William B. Publishing Co.

Troward, Thomas. Bible Mystery & Bible Meaning. 2007. 336p. 29.95 *(978-1-60206-995-4(6))*; (ENG.). per. 19.95 *(978-1-60206-212-2(9))* Cosimo, Inc.

—Bible Mystery & Bible Meaning. 2007. 272p. 29.99 *(978-1-59986-730-4(3))*; (ENG.). pap. 19.99 *(978-1-59986-870-7(9)*, FQ Classics) Filiquarian Publishing, LLC.

Tyndale, William. Doctrinal Treatises & Introductions to Different Portions of the Holy Scriptures. Walter, Henry, ed. 2008. 604p. 59.95 *(978-0-548-94480-6(6))* 2007. (ENG.). 608p. per. 44.95 *(978-0-548-60772-5(9))* Kessinger Publishing, LLC.

Ukpong, Justin S. African Interpretation of the Bible: A Reader. 2006. *(978-90-04-15114-7(1))* BRILL.

—African Interpretation of the Bible: A Reader. 2006. *(978-1-58983-242-8(6))* Society of Biblical Literature.

Umoren, Anthony Iffen. Paul & Power Christology: Exegesis & Theology of Romans 1:3-4 in Relation to Popular Power Christology in an African Context. 2007. XV, 207p. pap. 46.95 *(978-3-631-57554-3(8))* Lang, Peter Publishing, Inc.

Upchurch, Cackie & Yeary, Clifford, eds. Year of Sundays: Gospel Reflections 2009. 2008. 88p. pap. 2.00 *(978-0-8146-3100-3(2))* Liturgical Pr.

Urantia Foundation Staff, ed. The Urantia Book: Revealing the Mysteries of God, the Universe, Jesus, & Ourselves. 2008. (ENG.). 2097p. 27.95 *(978-0-911560-07-7(6))* Urantia Foundation.

van Kooten, George H. The Revelation of the Name YHWH to Moses: Perspectives from Judaism, the Pagan Graeco-Roman World, & Early Christianity. 2006. (Themes in Biblical Narrative Ser.: Vol. 9). 264p. *(978-90-04-15398-1(5))* BRILL.

Van Peursen, W. Th. Language & Interpretation in the Syriac Text of Ben Sira: A Comparative Linguistic & Literary Study. 2007. (Monographs of the Peshitta Institute Leiden Ser.). (Illus.). 473p. *(978-90-04-16394-2(8))* BRILL.

Van Vliet, Jason, ed. Living Waters from Ancient Springs: Essays in Honor of Cornelis Van Dam. 2011. 278p. pap. 31.00 **(978-1-60899-949-1(1)**, Pickwick Pubns.) Wipf & Stock Pubs.

Vanhoozer, Kevin J., et al. Theological Interpretation of the Old Testament: A Book-by-Book Survey. 2008. 336p. (C). pap. 19.99 *(978-0-8010-3624-8(0))* Baker Academic.

Veijola, Timo. Zeit und Zeitlichkeit im Judentum. 2009. (Judische Religion, Geschichte und Kultur (JRGK) Ser.). (GER & ENG., Illus.). 630p. (C). 164.00 *(978-3-525-54000-8(0))* Vandenhoeck & Ruprecht GmbH & Co. KG DEU. Dist: ISD.

Via, Dan O. & Via, Dan O., Jr. Divine Justice, Divine Judgment: Rethinking the Judgement of Nations. 2007. (Facets Ser.). 208p. per. 9.99 *(978-0-8006-3896-2(4)*, Fortress Pr.) Augsburg Fortress, Pubs.

Virtue, Doreen. Daily Guidance from Your Angels: 365 Angelic Messages to Soothe, Heal, & Open Your Heart. (ENG.). 2006. 400p. 24.95 *(978-1-4019-0771-6(7))* 2008. (Illus.). 256p. pap. 25.95 *(978-1-4019-1716-6(X))* Hay Hse., Inc.

Vogan, Charles. Knots Untied. 2007. 230p. pap. 16.95 *(978-0-615-13937-1(X))* Shenandoah Bible Ministries.

—Where the Paths Meet. 2007. (ENG.). 276p. per. 21.00 *(978-0-615-13928-9(0))* Shenandoah Bible Ministries.

Volf, Miroslav. Captive to the Word of God: Engaging the Scriptures for Contemporary Theological Reflection. 2010. 176p. pap. 18.00 *(978-0-8028-6590-8(9))* Eerdmans, William B. Publishing Co.

Waite, Th. D. The Dean Burgon Societies Messages from the 30th Annual Meeting, #18 in a Series. 2008. 204p. pap. 15.00 *(978-0-9820608-5-8(8))* Old Paths Pubns., Inc., The.

—Fundamentalist Deception on Bible Preservation. 2008. 172p. pap. 15.00 *(978-1-56848-049-7(0))* Old Paths Pubns., Inc., The.

Waite, Th. D. Pastor D. A. Fundamentalist Mis-Information on Bible Versions. 2008. pap. 15.00 *(978-1-56848-027-5(X))* Old Paths Pubns., Inc., The.

Walchenbach, John R. John Calvin as Biblical Commentator. 2010. (Illus.). 218p. pap. 24.00 *(978-1-60899-328-4(0)*, Wipf and Stock) Wipf & Stock Pubs.

Walck, Leslie W. & Walck. The Son of Man in the Parables of Enoch & in Matthew. 2011. (Jewish & Christian Texts in Contexts & Related Studies). (ENG.). 288p. 130.00 *(978-0-567-02729-0(5)*, T&T Clark Int'l) Continuum International Publishing Group, Ltd. GBR. Dist: National Bk. Network.

Walker, Henry. Seasons: God's Timing for Special Blessings. 2006. (Illus.). 83p. per. 8.95 *(978-1-59886-395-6(9))* Tate Publishing & Enterprises, LLC.

Wansbrough, Henry. Use & Abuse of the Bible: A Brief History of Biblical Interpretation. 2010. (ENG.). 224p. 22.95 *(978-0-567-09057-7(4)*, T&T Clark Int'l) Continuum International Publishing Group, Ltd. GBR. Dist: National Bk. Network.

Ware, James. Reading the Bible As Christian Scripture: Understanding the Writers' Use of Language. 2009. 124p. pap. 14.25 *(978-1-4251-8291-5(7))* Trafford Publishing.

Water, Mark. Bible Prophecy Made Easy: An Easy-to-Understandy Pocket Reference Guide. (Made Easy Ser.). pap. 4.99 *(978-1-85608-384-3(5))* Hunt, John Publishing Ltd. GBR. Dist: O. M. Literature.

—Bible Teachings Made Easy: An Easy-to-Understand Pocket Reference Guide. (Made Easy Ser.). (Illus.). 64p. pap. 4.99 *(978-1-85608-387-4(X))* Hunt, John Publishing Ltd. GBR. Dist: O. M. Literature.

—Learning the Word: A Made Easy Handbook on Studying the Bible. (Made Easy Handbooks Ser.). 320p. 14.95 *(978-1-56563-862-4(X))* Hendrickson Pubs. Marketing, LLC.

Watkins, Durrell. Wrestling with God Without Getting Pinned: Old Stories, New Thoughts, & Progressive Spirituality. 2010. 252p. pap. 17.95 *(978-1-4327-4896-8(3))* Outskirts Pr., Inc.

Watts, James W. Ritual & Rhetoric in Leviticus: From Sacrifice to Scripture. 2007. (ENG.). 278p. 104.00 *(978-0-521-87193-8(X))* Cambridge Univ. Pr.

Webb, Robert L. John the Baptizer & Prophet: A Sociohistorical Study. 2006. 446p. pap. 42.00 *(978-1-59752-966-0(9)*, Wipf and Stock) Wipf & Stock Pubs.

Webster, Allen. Dealing with Sexual Temptation. 2007. 0.35 *(978-1-933808-60-4(8))* House to House Heart to Heart Publishing, Inc.

—Seven Things a Loving God Hates. 2006. per. 7.95 *(978-1-933808-25-3(X))* House to House Heart to Heart Publishing, Inc.

—Seven Things God Hates: A Proud Look. 2007. 0.75 *(978-1-933808-83-3(7))* House to House Heart to Heart Publishing, Inc.

Welch, Adam C. The Psalter in Life, Worship & History. 2007. 128p. per. *(978-1-4067-8786-3(8)*, Pomona Pr.) Read Bks.

Welker Michael, et al. Calvin Today: Reformed Theology & the Future of the Church. Weinrich, Michael et al, eds. 2011. (ENG.). 240p. 120.00 *(978-0-567-13693-0(0)*, T&T Clark Int'l) Continuum International Publishing Group, Ltd. GBR. Dist: National Bk. Network.

Wenham, John. Christ & the Bible, Third Edition. 2009. 222p. pap. 24.00 *(978-1-60608-888-3(2)*, Wipf and Stock) Wipf & Stock Pubs.

Werline, Rodney Alan. Experientia: Inquiry into Religious Experience in Early Judaism & Christianity. Flannery, Frances & Shantz, Colleen, eds. 2008. (SBL - Symposium Ser.). 272p. *(978-90-04-16911-1(3))* BRILL.

Werline, Rodney Alan, et al. Experientia: Sites for Inquiry for Religious Experience in Early Judaism & Christianity. 2008. 272p. pap. 32.95 *(978-1-58983-368-5(6))* Society of Biblical Literature.

West, G. & de Wit, H., eds. African & European Readers of the Bible in Dialogue: In Quest of a Shared Meaning. 2008. 430p. *(978-90-04-16656-1(4))* BRILL.

West, Gerald O. Reading Other-Wise: Socially Engaged Biblical Scholars Reading with Their Local Communities. 2007. (SBL - Semeia Studies). 172p. *(978-90-04-15733-0(6))* BRILL.

—Reading Other-Wise: Socially Engaged Biblical Scholars Reading with Their Local Communities. 2007. (ENG.). 180p. per. 24.95 *(978-1-58983-273-2(6))* Society of Biblical Literature.

Westminster John Knox Press Staff. Interpretation, Complete Series Set. Achtemeier, Paul J. et al, eds. 2012. (ENG.). pap. 860.00 **(978-0-664-23923-7(4))** Westminster John Knox Pr.

Wheeler, Tompaul. Bible Readings: Straight Answers from the Bible. 2007. *(978-0-8280-1728-2(X))* Review & Herald Publishing Assn.

Whelchel, Lisa. The Busy Mom's Guide to Bible Study. 2010. (ENG.). 256p. pap. 16.99 *(978-1-4516-2377-2(1)*, Howard Bks.) Howard Books.

Wheless, Joseph. Is It God's Word. 2007. 520p. per. 25.50 *(978-1-60206-248-1(X))* Cosimo, Inc.

Whidden, Theodore L. The Bible Plumb Line: Cain's Wife & Other Perspectives. 2006. per. *(978-0-9786694-2-6(1)*, Heritage Ink Christian Publishing Co., LLC.

White, Ellen G. The Spirit of Prophecy by Ellen G White + 2006. (ENG.). 416p. per. 26.99 *(978-1-4255-4477-5(0))*; (ENG.). 412p. per. 26.99 *(978-1-4255-4385-3(5))*; 404p. per. 26.99 *(978-1-4255-4284-9(0))* MPublishing.

Wilkinson, Robert J. The Kabbalistic Scholars of the Antwerp Polyglot Bible. 2007. (Studies in the History of Christian Traditions). 141p. *(978-90-04-16251-8(8))* BRILL.

Williams, Derek. Authentic Guide to the Bible. 2007. (ENG.). 154p. pap. 14.99 *(978-1-85078-760-0(3))* Authentic Media.

Williams, H. D. The Covenant of Salt. 2010. 120p. pap. 13.00 *(978-0-9822230-7-9(2))* Old Paths Pubns., Inc., The.

—The Lie That Changed the Modern World. 2008. pap. 25.00 *(978-1-56848-042-8(3))* Old Paths Pubns., Inc., The.

Williams, Jane. Storyteller's Companion to the Bible I: Audio. 13.00 *(978-0-687-76229-3(4))* Abingdon Pr.

Williams, Marilyn. She Did What She Could. 2009. 181p. pap. 14.75 *(978-0-557-04254-8(2))* Lulu Enterprises Inc.

Williams, Peter. 2 Timothy. 2007. (Opening Up Ser.). (Illus.). 112p. per. 9.00 *(978-1-84625-065-1(X))* DayOne Pubns. GBR. Dist: STL Distribution North America.

Williams, Tim. Psalmball. 2011. 190p. pap. 14.99 **(978-1-61379-037-3(6))** Xulon Pr., Inc.

Willis, D. C. Subtle Deceit: A Layman Perspective. 2011. 172p. 23.89 **(978-1-4567-5546-1(3))**; pap. 13.73 **(978-1-4567-5547-8(1))** AuthorHouse.

Wilson, Paul Scott. The New Interpreter's Handbook of Preaching. 2008. 506p. 60.00 *(978-0-687-05556-2(3))* Abingdon Pr.

Wirzba, Norman. The Gift of Creation. 2009. *(978-1-935001-22-5(1))* Acclaim Pr., Inc.

Witherington, Ben, III. Letters & Homilies for Jewish Christians: A Socio-Rhetorical Commentary on Hebrews, James & Jude. 2007. (Letters & Homilies for Hellenized Christians Ser.). (ENG., Illus.). 656p. 40.00 *(978-0-8308-2932-3(6)*, IVP Acad.) InterVarsity Pr.

Wolf, Linda. Did That Really Come from the Bible? Everyday SSayings with a Biblical Origin. 2007. per. 12.99 *(978-0-9794384-1-7(1))* Be a Light Christian Publishing Co.

Wood, Charles M. Love That Rejoices in the Truth: Theological Explorations. 2009. 166p. pap. 19.00 *(978-1-55635-953-8(5)*, Cascade Bks.) Wipf & Stock Pubs.

—Love that Rejoices in the Truth: Theological Explorations. 2010. (ENG.). 166p. (C). pap. 42.50 *(978-0-227-17328-2(7))* Clarke, James Co., Ltd. GBR. Dist: Brown, David Bk. Co., The.

Wood, Henry. Life More Abundant Scriptural Truth in M. 2006. pap. 30.95 *(978-1-4286-3955-3(1))* Kessinger Publishing, LLC.

Wootton, D. This Is God Speaking. 2007. 84p. per. *(978-1-84693-042-3(1))* Best Global Publishing Ltd.

Wray, T. J. What the Bible Really Tells Us: The Essential Guide to Biblical Literacy. 2011. (ENG.). 264p. 24.95 *(978-0-7425-6253-0(0))* Rowman & Littlefield Publishers, Inc.

Wright, Charles Henry. Biblical Essays or Exegetical Studies on. 2006. pap. 28.95 *(978-1-4286-3616-3(1))* Kessinger Publishing, LLC.

Wright, Christopher J. H. Salvation Belongs to Our God: Celebrating the Bible's Central Story. 2008. (ENG.). 202p. pap. 16.00 *(978-0-8308-3306-1(4)*, IVP Acad.) InterVarsity Pr.

Wright, Gerald. Sabbatarian Concordance & Commentary. 167p. pap. 3.50 *(978-0-933672-35-2(7)*, C-1572) Star Bible & Tract Corp.

Wright, Stephen I. The Voice of Jesus: Studies in the Interpretation of Six Gospel Parables. 2007. (Paternoster Biblical & Theological Monographs). 304p. pap. 35.00 *(978-1-55635-649-0(8))* Wipf & Stock Pubs.

Wyckoff, John W. Pneuma & Logos. 2010. 168p. pap. 19.00 *(978-1-60899-483-0(X)* Wipf and Stock) Wipf & Stock Pubs.

Wynn, Charles M., Sr. And God Said, Let There Be Evolution! Reconciling the Book of Genesis, the Qur'an, & the Theory of Evolution. 2011. 198p. pap. 16.99 **(978-0-9846392-5-0(X))** All Things That Matter Pr.

B

Xeravits, Géza G., ed. Dualism in Qumran. 2010. (Library of Second Temple Studies, the Ser.). (ENG.). 208p. 120.00 *(978-0-567-23435-3(5),* T&T Clark Int'l) Continuum International Publishing Group, Ltd. GBR. Dist: National Bk. Network.

Yamauchi, Edwin M. Africa & the Bible. 2006. (Illus.). 304p. (C). pap. 26.00 *(978-0-8010-3119-9(2))* Baker Academic.

Yisrael, Bethuel. A Discussion of Biblical Scripture Translation: That Pertains to African-American History. 2007. pap. 14.00 *(978-0-8059-8425-5(9))* Dorrance Publishing Co., Inc.

Yoder, John Howard. To Hear the Word - Second Edition. 2009. 266p. pap. 29.00 *(978-1-60608-928-6(5),* Cascade Bks.) Wipf & Stock Pubs.

Young, Ian & Rezetko, Robert. Linguistic Dating of Biblical Texts, 2 vols. 2008. (BibleWorld Ser.). (ENG.). 512p. (C). pap. 39.95 *(978-1-84553-082-2(9))* Equinox Publishing Ltd. GBR. Dist: ISD.

Young, Sarah. Biblical Womanhood: Nine Studies for Individuals or Groups. 2010. 64p. pap. *(978-1-904889-07-6(7))* Good Bk. Co.

Zenos, Andrew C. The Elements of the Higher Criticism. 2007. (ENG.). 270p. 42.95 *(978-0-548-06873-1(9))* Kessinger Publishing, LLC.

Zeolla, Gary F. Scripture Workbook: for Personal & Group Bible Study & Teaching the Bible; Second Edition; Volume I: the Essentials of the Faith. 2008. 226p. pap. 19.95 *(978-0-557-00677-9(5))* Lulu Enterprises Inc.

Zuck, Roy, ed. Vital Biblical Issues: Examining Problem Passages of the Bible. 2011. 276p. pap. 30.00 ***(978-1-61097-399-1(2),*** Wipf and Stock) Wipf & Stock Pubs.

Zvi, Ehud Ben. Utopia & Dystopia in Prophetic Literature: Essays on Biblical & Related Themes in Honour of Lars Aejmelaeus. 2006. (Publications of the Finish Exegetical Society Ser.: Vol. 92). 298p. pap. 56.00 *(978-951-9217-47-5(9))* Finnish Exegetical Society FIN. Dist: Eisenbrauns, Inc.

BIBLE—CRITICISM, INTERPRETATION, ETC.—DATA PROCESSING

Del Barco, Javier. Computer Assisted Research on the Bible in the 21st Century. 2010. 116.00 *(978-1-60724-930-6(8))* Gorgias Pr., LLC.

Deppe, Dean B. All Roads Lead to the Text: Eight Methods of Inquiry: A Template for Model Exegesis with Exegetical Examples Employing Logos Bible Software. 2011. pap. 25.00 ***(978-0-8028-6594-6(1))*** Eerdmans, William B. Publishing Co.

I am a Dreamer. 2007. *(978-0-9792993-0-8(6))* Thang, Levi Sap Nei.

Lang, David. Macs in the Ministry, 0 vols. Lawson, Michael, ed. 2010. (Nelson's Tech Guides). 280p. pap. 29.99 *(978-1-4185-4172-9(9))* Nelson, Thomas Inc.

Negus, Christopher & Boronczyk, Timothy. CentOS. 2009. (Bible Ser.: 599). (ENG., Illus.). 984p. pap. 54.99 *(978-0-470-48165-3(X),* Wiley) Wiley, John & Sons, Inc.

Rose Publishing, creator. The Gospels: Lost & Found: PowerPoint. 2007. cd-rom 39.99 *(978-1-59636-155-3(7))* Rose Publishing.

—Why Trust the Bible? PowerPoint: Answers to the New Critics. 2007. cd-rom 39.99 *(978-1-59636-156-0(5))* Rose Publishing.

—100 Proofs for the Bible: PowerPoint: Old & New Testaments. 2007. cd-rom 39.99 *(978-1-59636-157-7(3))* Rose Publishing.

Software Storytellers Companion to the Bible New Testament. 79.00 *(978-0-687-06070-2(2))* Abingdon Pr.

Worth, Roland H. & Worth, Roland H., Jr. Biblical Studies on the Internet: A Resource Guide. 2nd rev. ed. 2008. (ENG.). 392p. pap. 49.95 *(978-0-7864-3625-5(5))* McFarland & Co., Inc. Pubs.

Zondervan Publishing Staff. KJV Holy Bible, 1 vol. 2007. (ENG.). cd-rom 9.99 *(978-0-310-93719-7(1))* Inspirio.

BIBLE—CRITICISM, INTERPRETATION, ETC.—HISTORY

Aaron - Aniconism, 30 vols., Vol. 1. 2009. (ENG., Illus.). XXIX, 612p. 333.00 *(978-3-11-018355-9(2))* De Gruyter, Walter Inc.

Anim - Atheism, Vol. 2. 2009. (ENG., Illus.). XXVI, 604p. 333.00 *(978-3-11-018370-2(6))* De Gruyter, Walter Inc.

Barrett, Lee C. & Stewart, Jon, eds. Kierkegaard & the Bible, 2 vols. 2010. (Kierkegaard Research: Sources, Reception & Resources Ser.). 352p. 134.95 *(978-1-4094-0443-9(9))* Ashgate Publishing Co.

Bellamah, Timothy. The Biblical Interpretation of William of Alton, 1 vol. 2011. (Oxford Studies in Historical Theology Ser.). (ENG.). 368p. 74.00 *(978-0-19-975360-4(1))* Oxford Univ. Pr., Inc.

Boer, Roland. Symposia: Dialogues Concerning the History of Biblical Interpretation. 2007. (BibleWorld Ser.). (ENG.). 172p. (C). 95.00 *(978-1-84553-101-0(9));* per. 29.95 *(978-1-84553-102-7(7))* Equinox Publishing Ltd. GBR. Dist: ISD.

Brinkmann, Hennig. Mittelalterliche Hermeneutik. (GER.). XV, 439p. 210.00 ***(978-3-11-183524-2(3))*** De Gruyter, Walter Inc.

Busi, Davide. I Primi Passi Di un Erudito: Angelo Maria Querini, Firenze e L'Oratio de Mosaicae Historiae Praestantia. 2008. (ITA.). 140p. *(978-88-8486-338-6(4))* La Compagnia della Stampa.

Cheyne, Thomas Kelly. Founders of Old Testament Criticism: Biographical, Descriptive & Critical Studies. 2007. (ENG.). 382p. 48.95 *(978-0-548-03524-5(5))* Kessinger Publishing, LLC.

Choi, John H. Traditions at Odds: The Reception of the Pentateuch in Biblical & Second Temple Period Literature. 2010. (Library of Hebrew Bible/Old Testament Studies). (ENG.). 288p. 140.00 *(978-0-567-26524-1(2),* T&T Clark Int'l) Continuum International Publishing Group, Ltd. GBR. Dist: National Bk. Network.

Dahan, Gilbert. Lire la Bible au Moyen-Age: Essais dhermeneutique Medievale. 2009. (Titre Courant Ser.). (FRE.). 448p. (C). 40.00 *(978-2-600-00538-8(2))* Droz, Librairie CHE. Dist: Brown, David Bk. Co., The.

Deanesly, Margaret. The Lollard Bible: And Other Medieval Biblical Versions. 2008. (ENG.). 508p. pap. 63.00 *(978-0-521-09073-5(3))* Cambridge Univ. Pr.

Deitz, Reginald W. What the Bible Can Mean for You. 2009. 110p. 34.95 *(978-1-104-85492-8(9))* 2007. (ENG.). 108p. per. 19.95 *(978-0-548-43889-3(7))* Kessinger Publishing, LLC.

Du Toit, Jaqueline S. Textual Memory: Ancient Archives, Libraries & the Hebrew Bible. 2011. 202p. ***(978-1-907534-15-7(6))*** Sheffield Phoenix Pr.

Duff, Archibald. History of Old Testament Criticism. 2009. 220p. 23.99 *(978-1-103-58397-3(2));* pap. 17.99 *(978-1-103-58396-6(4))* BiblioBazaar.

Ecclesiastes & the Pioneers. 2006. 90p. pap. 10.95 *(978-1-57258-486-0(6),* 945-6347) TEACH Services, Inc.

Encyclopedia of the Bible & its Reception. 2007. (ENG., Illus.). 9366.00 *(978-3-11-019904-8(1))* De Gruyter, Walter Inc.

Enos, Richard Leo & Thompson, Roger, eds. The Rhetoric of St. Augustine of Hippo: De Doctrina Christiana & the Search for a Distinctly Christian Rhetoric. 2008. (ENG.). 420p. (C). pap. 49.95 *(978-1-60258-008-4(1))* Baylor Univ. Pr.

Fairbairn, Andrew M. Place of Christ in Modern Theology. 2006. pap. 43.95 *(978-1-4286-4280-5(3))* Kessinger Publishing, LLC.

Farkasfalvy, Denis. Inspiration & Interpretation: A Theological Introduction to Sacred Scripture. 2010. 309p. pap. 34.95 *(978-0-8132-1746-8(6))* Catholic Univ. of America Pr.

Fortosis, Stephen. The Multilingual God: Translating God to Every People. 2011. ***(978-0-87808-468-5(1))*** Carey, William Library Pubs.

Foster, Paul. The Apocryphal Gospels: A Very Short Introduction. 2009. (Very Short Introductions Ser.). (ENG., Illus.). 144p. pap. 11.95 *(978-0-19-923694-7(1))* Oxford Univ. Pr., Inc.

Frampton, Travis L. & Frampton. Spinoza & the Rise of Historical Criticism of the Bible. 2007. (ENG.). 272p. 150.00 *(978-0-567-02593-7(4),* T&T Clark Int'l) Continuum International Publishing Group, Ltd. GBR. Dist: National Bk. Network.

Froehlich, Karlfried. Biblical Interpretaion from the Church Fathers to the Reformation. 2010. (Variorum Collected Studies). (Illus.). 366p. 170.00 *(978-1-4094-0365-4(3))* Ashgate Publishing Co.

Gerdmar, Anders. Roots of Theological Anti-Semitism: German Biblical Interpretation & the Jews, from Herder & Semler to Kittel & Bultmann. 2008. (Studies in Jewish History & Culture (Formerly Studies in E Ser.). 668p. *(978-90-04-16851-0(6))* BRILL.

Gundry, Robert H. The Old Is Better: New Testament Essays in Support of Traditional Interpretations. 2010. 468p. pap. 54.00 *(978-1-60899-830-2(4),* Wipf and Stock) Wipf & Stock Pubs.

Hamlin, Hannibal. Psalm Culture & Early Modern English Literature. 2007. (ENG.). 304p. pap. 63.00 *(978-0-521-03706-8(9))* Cambridge Univ. Pr.

Hauser, Alan J. & Watson, Duane F., eds. A History of Biblical Interpretation: The Ancient Periods. 2008. 558p. pap. 48.00 *(978-0-8028-6395-9(7))* Eerdmans, William B. Publishing Co.

—A History of Biblical Interpretation Vol. 2: The Medieval Through the Reformation Periods, 2 vols. 2008. 456p. 50.00 *(978-0-8028-4274-9(7))* Eerdmans, William B. Publishing Co.

Holsinger-Friesen, Thomas. Irenaeus & Genesis: A Study of Competition in Early Christian Hermeneutics. 2009. pap. 34.95 *(978-1-57506-700-1(5))* Eisenbrauns, Inc.

Horbury, William. Herodian Judaism & New Testament Study. 2006. (Wissenschaftliche Untersuchungen Zum Neuen Testament Ser.: Vol. 193). 268p. (C). 159.50 *(978-3-16-148877-1(6))* Mohr Siebeck GmbH & Co. KG DEU. Dist: Coronet Bks.

Jefferson, Thomas. The Jefferson Bible: The Life & Morals of Jesus of Nazareth. 2006. (Little Books of Wisdom Ser.). (ENG.). 104p. 9.95 *(978-1-55709-184-0(6))* Applewood Bks.

Jeffrey, David Lyle. Houses of the Interpreter: Reading Scripture, Reading Culture. 2009. (ENG.). 300p. (C). pap. 49.95 *(978-1-60258-239-2(4))* Baylor Univ. Pr.

Jenkins, Allan K. & Preston, Patrick. Biblical Scholarship & the Church: A Sixteenth Century Crisis of Authority. 2007. (Ashgate New Critical Thinking in Religion, Theology, & Biblical Studies). 340p. 124.95 *(978-0-7546-3703-5(4))* Ashgate Publishing Co.

Kelly, Christopher J. Cassian's Conferences: Scriptual Interpretation & the Monastic Ideal. 2012. (New Critical Thinking in Religion, Theology & Biblical Studies). 196p. 79.95 ***(978-1-4094-0559-7(1))*** Ashgate Publishing Co.

Ker, John. The Psalms in History & Biography. 2007. (ENG.). 244p. 41.95 *(978-0-548-12671-4(2))* Kessinger Publishing, LLC.

—Psalms in History & Biography. 2006. pap. 26.95 *(978-1-4286-3663-7(3))* Kessinger Publishing, LLC.

Kloppenborg, John S. & Newman, Judith H. Editing the Bible: Assessing the Task Past & Present. 2012. ***(978-90-04-21983-0(8))*** Society of Biblical Literature.

Kraus, Donald. Sex, Sacrifice, Shame, & Smiting: Is the Bible Always Right? 2008. 176p. pap. 18.00 *(978-1-59627-068-8(3),* Seabury Bks.) Church Publishing, Inc.

LaPorte, Charles. Victorian Poets & the Changing Bible. 2011. (Illus.). ix, 284p. E-Book ***(978-0-8139-3165-4(7));*** (ENG., 304p. (gr. 17). 45.00 *(978-0-8139-3158-6(4))* Univ. Pr. of Virginia.

Lehmann, Henning. Students of the Bible in 4th & 5th Century Syria: Seats of Learning, Sidelights & Syriacisms. 2008. (ENG., Illus.). 256p. (C). 55.00 *(978-87-7934-390-0(2))* Aarhus Universitetsforlag DNK. Dist: ISD.

Levering, Matthew. Participatory Biblical Exegesis: A Theology of Biblical Interpretation. 2008. (Reading the Scriptures Ser.). (ENG.). 344p. 60.00 *(978-0-268-03406-1(0));* pap. 25.00 *(978-0-268-03408-5(7))* Univ. of Notre Dame Pr.

Levy, Ian Christopher. The Letter to the Galatians. 2011. 312p. pap. 34.00 *(978-0-8028-2223-9(1))* Eerdmans, William B. Publishing Co.

Logie, Thomas D. Fighting the Good Fight. 2011. 332p. pap. 19.52 *(978-1-4269-5092-6(6))* Trafford Publishing.

Long, Burke O. Planting & Reaping Albright. 2008. 176p. per. 24.95 *(978-0-271-02834-7(3))* Pennsylvania State Univ. Pr.

Lubac, Henri De. History & Spirit: The Understanding of Scripture According to Origen. Nash, Anne Englund, tr. from FRE. 2007. 507p. pap. 24.95 *(978-0-89870-880-6(X))* Ignatius Pr.

Luman, J. W. A Verse by Verse Exegesis of Hebrews. I.t. ed. 2007. 136p. 20.00 *(978-0-9796285-0-4(4))* International Fellowship of Covenant Ministries, The.

Lumpkin, Joseph, ed. END of DAYS - the Apocalyptic Writings: The Apocalypse of Abraham, the Apocalypse of Thomas, 4th Ezra, & 2nd Baruch. 2007. (ENG.). 200p. per. 17.00 *(978-1-933580-38-8(0))* Fifth Estate, Inc.

Mandelbrote, Scott H. & Meer, Jitse M. van der, eds. Nature & Scripture in the Abrahamic Religions: Volume I: To 1700. 2009. (Brill's Ser. in Church History Ser.). 744p. *(978-90-04-17191-6(6))* BRILL.

—Nature & Scripture in the Abrahamic Religions: Volume II: 1700-Present. 2009. (Brill's Ser. in Church History Ser.). 584p. *(978-90-04-17192-3(4))* BRILL.

Marshall, Larry. The Mythical Life of Jesus. 2011. 280p. 27.48 *(978-1-4269-5296-8(1));* pap. 17.48 *(978-1-4269-5295-1(3))* Trafford Publishing.

Mcauliffe. With Reverence for the Word: Medieval Scriptural Exegesis in Judaism, Christianity, & Islam, 1 vol. McAuliffe, Jane Dammen et al, eds. 2010. (ENG.). 512p. pap. 39.95 *(978-0-19-975575-2(2))* Oxford Univ. Pr., Inc.

McKim, Donald K., ed. Dictionary of Major Biblical Interpreters. 2nd ed. 2007. (ENG., Illus.). 1134p. 55.00 *(978-0-8308-2927-9(X),* IVP Acad.) InterVarsity Pr.

Moore, Stephen D. & Sherwood, Yvonne. The Invention of the Biblical Scholar: A Critical Manifesto. 2011. 120p. pap. 18.00 *(978-0-8006-9774-7(X),* Fortress Pr.) Augsburg Fortress, Pubs.

Niehoff, Maren R. Jewish Exegesis & Homeric Scholarship in Alexandria. 2011. (ENG.). 236p. 85.00 *(978-1-107-00072-8(6))* Cambridge Univ. Pr.

Ocker, Christopher. Biblical Poetics Before Humanism & Reformation. 2008. (ENG., Illus.). 284p. pap. 41.00 *(978-0-521-08921-0(2))* Cambridge Univ. Pr.

Parris, David Paul. Reception Theory & Biblical Hermeneutics. 2009. (Princeton Theological Monographs). 344p. pap. 38.00 *(978-1-55635-653-7(6),* Pickwick Pubns.) Wipf & Stock Pubs.

Pietersen, Lloyd. Reading the Bible after Christendom. 2012. pap. ***(978-0-8361-9617-7(1))*** Herald Pr.

Preus, J. Samuel. Spinoza & the Irrelevance of Biblical Authority. 2009. (ENG.). 248p. pap. 36.00 *(978-0-521-09353-8(8))* Cambridge Univ. Pr.

Reventlow, Henning. History of Biblical Interpretation. 2009. 32.95 *(978-1-58983-459-0(3));* 49.95 *(978-1-58983-460-6(7));* 256p. pap. 29.95 *(978-1-58983-202-2(7));* 324p. pap. 36.95 *(978-1-58983-455-2(0))* Society of Biblical Literature.

Reventlow, Henning Graf. Biblical Studies & the Shifting of Paradigms, 1850-1914. Farmer, William R., ed. 2009. (Library of Hebrew Bible/Old Testament Studies, the Ser.). (ENG.). 297p. 49.95 *(978-1-4411-2589-7(2),* T&T Clark) Continuum International Publishing Group, Ltd. GBR. Dist: National Bk. Network.

Rogerson, John W. Bible & Criticism in Victorian Britain: Profiles of F. D. Maurice & William Robertson Smith. 2009. (Library of Hebrew Bible/Old Testament Studies, the Ser.). (ENG.). 188p. 39.95 *(978-0-567-54180-2(0),* T&T Clark) Continuum International Publishing Group, Ltd. GBR. Dist: National Bk. Network.

—W. M. L. de Wette, Founder of Modern Biblical Criticism: An Intellectual Biography. 2009. (Library of Hebrew Bible/Old Testament Studies, the Ser.). (ENG.). 313p. 55.00 *(978-0-567-23388-2(X),* T&T Clark) Continuum International Publishing Group, Ltd. GBR. Dist: National Bk. Network.

Rooke, Deborah W. Handel's Israelite Oratorio Libretti: Sacred Drama & Biblical Exegesis. 2012. (ENG.). 328p. 150.00 ***(978-0-19-927928-9(4))*** Oxford Univ. Pr., Inc.

Rummel, Erika. Biblical Humanism & Scholasticism in the Age of Erasmus. 2008. (Brill's Companions to the Christian Tradition Ser.: Vol. 9). 352p. (C). *(978-90-04-14573-3(7))* BRILL.

Sachau, Eduard, ed. Theodore of Mopsuestia: Syriac Fragments. 2010. (LAT.). 103.76 *(978-1-60724-911-5(1))* Gorgias Pr., LLC.

Sheldon, Henry. Unbelief in the Nineteenth Century. 2007. (ENG.). 408p. 49.95 *(978-0-548-05249-5(2))* Kessinger Publishing, LLC.

Shuger, Debora Kuller. The Renaissance Bible: Scholarship, Sacrifice, & Subjectivity. 2010. (ENG., Illus.). 313p. (C). pap. 39.95 *(978-1-60258-309-2(9))* Baylor Univ. Pr.

Smend, Rudolf. Vier Epitaphe - Die Basler Hebraistenfamilie Buxtorf. 2010. (Litterae et Theologia Ser.). (GER., Illus.). XIX, 51p. pap. 21.00 ***(978-3-11-022895-3(5))*** De Gruyter, Walter Inc.

Smyth, Mary Winslow. Biblical Quotations in Middle English Literature Before 1350. 2009. 380p. 26.99 *(978-1-110-00333-4(1));* pap. 20.99 *(978-1-110-00326-6(9))* BiblioBazaar.

—Biblical Quotations in Middle English Literature Before 1350. 2009. 192p. pap. *(978-1-151-73793-9(3))* Books LLC.

—Biblical Quotations in Middle English Literature Before 1350. 2008. 384p. 48.95 *(978-1-4369-8810-0(1));* pap. 33.95 *(978-1-4367-8840-3(4))* Kessinger Publishing, LLC.

Soulen, Richard N. Sacred Scripture: A Short History of Interpretation. 2010. (ENG.). 208p. pap. 25.00 *(978-0-664-23246-7(9))* Westminster John Knox Pr.

Sparks, Kenton L. God's Word in Human Words: An Evangelical Appropriation of Critical Biblical Scholarship. 2008. (Illus.). 416p. (C). pap. 28.00 *(978-0-8010-2701-7(2))* Baker Academic.

Spijker, Ienje van 't. The Multiple Meaning of Scripture: The Role of Exegesis in Early Christian & Medieval Culture. 2008. (LAT, FRE, GER & ENG.). 352p. *(978-90-04-17184-8(3))* BRILL.

Stewart, Jon & Barrett, Lee C., eds. Kierkegaard & the Bible, 2 vols., Vol. 1. 2010. (Kierkegaard Research: Sources, Reception & Resources Ser.). 294p. 124.95 *(978-1-4094-0285-5(1))* Ashgate Publishing Co.

Stroumsa, Guy G. Kanon und Kultur: Zwei Studien zur Hermeneutik des antiken Christentums. (Hans-Lietzmann-Vorlesungen Ser.). (GER.). XXV, 66p. 45.00 ***(978-3-11-177273-8(X))*** De Gruyter, Walter Inc.

Thompson, John L. Reading the Bible with the Dead: What You Can Learn from the History of Exegesis That You Can't Learn from Exegesis Alone. 2007. 324p. per. 20.00 *(978-0-8028-0753-3(4))* Eerdmans, William B. Publishing Co.

Tinkle, Theresa. Gender & Power in Medieval Exegesis. 2010. (New Middle Ages Ser.). (ENG.). 212p. 84.00 *(978-0-230-10435-8(5))* Palgrave Macmillan.

Tyson, Joseph B. Luke, Judaism, & the Scholars: Critical Approaches to Luke-Acts. 2010. pap. 24.94 *(978-1-57003-964-5(X))* Univ. of South Carolina Pr.

Under Construction. 2008. (Judaism in Context Ser.: 5). 75.00 *(978-1-59333-698-1(5))* Gorgias Pr., LLC.

Vicchio, Stephen J. Job in the Ancient World. 2006. (Image of the Biblical Job: A History: Ser.). 266p. pap. 27.00 *(978-1-59752-532-9(4),* Wipf and Stock) Wipf & Stock Pubs.

—Job in the Medieval World. 2006. (Image of the Biblical Job: A History: Ser.). 264p. pap. 27.00 *(978-1-59752-533-6(2),* Wipf and Stock) Wipf & Stock Pubs.

—Job in the Modern World. 2006. (Image of the Biblical Job: A History: Ser.). 258p. pap. 26.00 *(978-1-59752-534-3(0),* Wipf and Stock) Wipf & Stock Pubs.

Walters, Stanley D., ed. Go Figure! Figuration in Biblical Interpretation. 2008. (Princeton Theolgoical Monograph Ser.). 174p. pap. 20.00 *(978-1-55635-579-0(3),* Pickwick Pubns.) Wipf & Stock Pubs.

Watt, John & Lossl, Josef. Interpreting the Bible & Aristotle in Late Antiquity: The Alexandrian Commentary Tradition from Rome to Baghdad. 2011. (Illus.). 360p. 134.95 ***(978-1-4094-1007-2(2))*** Ashgate Publishing Co.

Weeter, Mark L. John Wesley's View & Use of Scripture. 2007. 260p. pap. 27.00 *(978-1-59752-876-4(5),* Wipf and Stock) Wipf & Stock Pubs.

Westcott, Brooke Foss. The Bible in the Church. 2008. 344p. 28.99 *(978-0-559-65467-1(7));* pap. 31.75 *(978-0-559-65464-0(2))* BiblioBazaar.

Wink, Walter. The Bible in Human Transformation: Toward a New Paradigm in Bible Study. 2010. (Facets Ser.). 96p. pap. 9.99 *(978-0-8006-9633-7(6),* Fortress Pr.) Augsburg Fortress, Pubs.

Yeo, John Ji-Won. Plundering the Egyptians: The Old Testament & Historical Criticism at Westminster Theological Seminary (1929-1998) 2010. vi, 318p. *(978-0-7618-4960-5(2))* Univ. Pr. of America, Inc.

BIBLE—CRITICISM, INTERPRETATION, ETC.—N. T.

see also Demythologization

Adewuyi, Femi. Ordinances & Laws of the New Covenant: Bible Expository. 2009. 68p. pap. *(978-1-84748-333-1(X))* Athena Pr.

Akers, Regina Dawn. The Holy Spirit's Interpretation of the New Testament: A Course in Understanding & Acceptance. 2008. (ENG.). 608p. per. 36.00 *(978-1-84694-085-9(0))* Hunt, John Publishing Ltd. GBR. Dist: National Bk. Network.

Allen, Pauline & Sim, David C., eds. Ancient Jewish & Christian Texts as Crisis Management Literature: Thematic Studies from the Centre for Early Christian Studies. 2012. (ENG.). 224p. 110.00 ***(978-0-567-28102-9(7),*** T&T Clark Int'l) Continuum International Publishing Group, Ltd. GBR. Dist: National Bk. Network.

Amalraj, Loyola. How to Experience the Spiritual Meaning of Gospel Texts: The Psychology of Reading Mystically. 2010. 172p. 99.95 *(978-0-7734-3814-9(9))* Mellen, Edwin Pr., The.

Anderholm, K. D. Understanding New Testament Judgments. unabr. ed. Date not set. 100p. (Orig.). pap. 6.99 *(978-0-9655407-1-1(5))* True Light Pubns.

Anderson, Paul N. John, Jesus, & History: Aspects of Historicity in the Fourth Gospel. Anderson, Paul N. et al, eds. 2009. 468p. pap. 49.95 *(978-1-58983-392-0(9))* Society of Biblical Literature.

—The Riddles of the Fourth Gospel: An Introduction to John. 2011. 288p. pap. 22.00 *(978-0-8006-0427-1(X),* Fortress Pr.) Augsburg Fortress, Pubs.

Angus-Green. Los Libros de la Biblia, A. T. The Books of the Bible, A. T. (SPA.). *(978-84-7645-017-8(6),* 223094) Clie, Editorial.

—Los Libros de la Biblia, N. T. The Books of the Bible, N. T. (SPA.). *(978-84-7645-019-2(2),* 223095) Clie, Editorial.

Arzt-Grabner, Peter & Kreinecker, Christina M., eds. Light from the East. Papyrologische Kommentare zum Neuen Testament: Akten des internationalen Symposions vom 3. -4. Dezember 2009 am Fachbereich Bibelwissenschaft und Kirchengeschichte der Universitat Salzburg. 2010. (Philippika Ser.). (ENG & GER.). 237p. (C). pap. 72.00 *(978-3-447-06291-6(6))* Harrassowitz, Otto Verlag DEU. Dist: ISD.

Attridge, Harold W., et al. Method & Meaning: Essays on New Testament Interpretation in Honor of Harold W. Attridge. 2011. ***(978-1-58983-631-0(6));*** ***(978-1-58983-632-7(4))*** Society of Biblical Literature.

Audi, Norman. They Came Back Rejoicing. 2009. 208p. pap. 15.99 *(978-1-60791-981-0(8))* Xulon Pr., Inc.

Aune, David Edward & Fotopoulos, John. The New Testament & Early Christian Literature in Greco-Roman Context: Studies in Honor of David E. Aune. 2006. (Supplements to Novum Testamentum Ser.: Vol. 122). (Illus.). 468p. (978-90-04-14304-3(1)) BRILL.

Bachmann, Michael. Von Paulus zur Apokalypse und weiter: Exegetische und rezeptionsgeschichtliche Studien zum Neuen Testament. 2011. (Novum Testamentum et Orbis Antiquus/Studien zur Umwelt des Neuen Testaments (NTOA/StUNT) Ser.). (GER., Illus.). 644p. (C). 116.00 (978-3-525-53398-7(5)) Vandenhoeck & Ruprecht GmbH & Co. KG DEU. Dist: ISD.

Baker Publishing Group Staff. A Walk Thru the Life of Peter: Growing Bold Faith. 2009. (Walk Thru the Bible Discussion Guides). 60p. pap. 7.99 (978-0-8010-7172-0(0)) Baker Bks.

Banks, Robert & Banks, Robert, Jr., eds. Reconciliation & Hope: New Testament Essays on Atonement & Eschatology. 2006. 318p. pap. 32.00 (978-1-59752-989-1(3), Wipf and Stock) Wipf & Stock Pubs.

Barclay, William. Insights - Forgiveness: What the Bible Tells Us about Forgiveness. 2012. (Insights Ser.). 80p. pap. 12.50 **(978-0-7152-0934-9(5))** Saint Andrew Pr., Ltd. GBR. Dist: Westminster John Knox Pr.

Barrs, Jerram. Learning Evangelism from Jesus. 2009. 288p. pap. 17.99 (978-1-4335-0318-4(2)) Crossway.

Barth, Markus. Rediscovering the Lord's Supper: Communion with Israel, with Christ, & among the Guests. 2006. 118p. pap. 16.00 (978-1-59752-851-1(X), Wipf and Stock) Wipf & Stock Pubs.

Basden, Paul & Dockery, David S., eds. The People of God. 2009. 368p. pap. 40.00 (978-1-60608-694-4(7), Wipf and Stock) Wipf & Stock Pubs.

Bauscher, David. Divine Contact-Discovery of the Original New Testament. 2007. 123p. pap. 19.96 (978-0-615-15604-0(5)) Bauscher, David.

Beale, G. K. & Carson, D. A., eds. Commentary on the New Testament Use of the Old Testament. 2007. 1280p. (C). 59.99 (978-0-8010-2693-5(8)) Baker Academic.

Beange, Amy. The Church As God's Temple. 2009. 88p. pap. (978-3-639-14904-3(1)) VDM Verlag Dr. Mueller e.K.

Beavis, Mary Ann. Jesus & Utopia: Looking for the Kingdom of God in the Roman World. 2006. 184p. per. 23.00 (978-0-8006-3562-6(0), Fortress Pr.) Augsburg Fortress, Pubs.

Bernstine, David J. The New Testament: Does It Speak for Itself? 2007. 69p. per. 8.99 (978-1-59886-933-0(7)) Tate Publishing & Enterprises, LLC.

Berry, Donald L. Holy Words & Holy Orders: As Dying, Behold We Live. 2009. (ENG.). 100p. pap. 19.99 (978-0-7618-4418-1(X)) Univ. Pr. of America, Inc.

Bieringer, R. The New Testament & Rabbinic Literature. 2009. 554p. (978-90-04-17588-4(1)) BRILL.

Black, C. Clifton & Watson, Duane F., eds. Words Well Spoken: George Kennedy's Rhetoric of the New Testament. 2008. (ENG.). 255p. 49.95 (978-1-60258-064-0(2)) Baylor Univ. Pr.

Blackburn, John. Seek Ye. 2007. 136p. (978-0-901860-02-6(6)); (ENG.). per. (978-0-901860-61-3(1)) Scripture Truth Pubns.

Blair, Alexander. Christian Ambivalence Toward Its Old Testament: Interactive Creativity versus Static Obedience. 2011. 420p. pap. 46.00 (978-1-60899-106-8(7), Wipf and Stock) Wipf & Stock Pubs.

Blanchard, John. Jesus: Dead or Alive? 2009. 40p. pap. (978-0-85234-697-6(2)) Evangelical Pr.

Bleek, Friedrich. Introduction to the New Testament. 2009. 464p. 35.99 (978-1-115-88618-5(5)); 42.99 (978-1-115-88617-8(7)) BiblioBazaar.

Blomberg, Craig L. Jesus & the Gospels: An Introduction & Survey, Second Edition. 2nd ed. 2009. (ENG., Illus.). 512p. 39.99 (978-0-8054-4482-7(3), B&H Academic) B&H Publishing Group.

Bock, Darrell & Charlesworth, James H., eds. Parables of Enoch, Early Judaism, Jesus, & Christian Origins. 2013. (Jewish & Christian Text Ser.). (ENG.). 272p. 120.00 (978-0-567-62406-2(4), T&T Clark Int'l) Continuum International Publishing Group, Ltd. GBR. Dist: National Bk. Network.

Bock, Darrell L. & Fanning, Buist M., eds. Interpreting the New Testament Text: Introduction to the Art & Science of Exegesis. 2006. (Illus.). 480p. 32.00 (978-1-58134-408-0(2)) Crossway.

Bockmuehl, Markus. Seeing the Word: Refocusing New Testament Study. 2006. (Studies in Theological Interpretation Ser.). (Illus.). 298p. (C). pap. 27.00 (978-0-8010-2761-1(6)) Baker Academic.

Borchert, Gerald L. Worship In The New Testament: Divine Mystery & Human Response. 2008. 224p. pap. 25.00 (978-0-8272-2514-5(8)) Chalice Pr.

Borg, Marcus J. Evolution of the Word: Reading the New Testament in the Order It Was Written. 2012. (ENG.). 608p. 29.99 **(978-0-06-208210-7(8)**, HarperOne) HarperCollins Pubs.

Borg, Marcus J. & Wright, N. T. The Meaning of Jesus: Two Visions. 2007. (Plus Ser.). (ENG.). 320p. pap. 15.99 (978-0-06-128554-7(4), HarperOne) HarperCollins Pubs.

Boteler, Lori. Messages That Will Form Your Life: 1995 Edition. Sei, Sheila, ed. 2007. per. 24.95 net. (978-0-9789555-9-5(5)) LoJo Publishing.

Bottrich, Christfried. Josephus und das Neue Testament: Wechselseitige Wahrnehmungen.II. Internationales Symposium zum Corpus Judaeo-Hellenisticum. 25.-28. Mai 2006, Greifswald. Bottrich, Christfried & Herzer, Jens, eds. 2007. (Wissenschaftliche Untersuchungen Zum Neuen Testament Ser.). 615p. (C). 195.00 (978-3-16-149368-3(0)) Mohr Siebeck GmbH & Co. KG DEU. Dist: Eisenbrauns, Inc.

Boxall, Ian. Revelation: Vision & Insight: An Introduction to the Apocalypse. (Illus.). 176p. 19.00 (978-0-281-05362-9(6)) SPCK Publishing GBR. Dist: Pilgrim Pr., The/United Church Pr.

Boyarin, Daniel. The Jewish Gospels: The Story of the Jewish Christ. 2012. (ENG., Illus.). 224p. 21.95 (978-1-59558-468-7(4)) New Pr., The.

Brawley, Robert L. Character Ethics & the New Testament: Moral Dimensions of Scripture. 2007. (ENG.). 269p. per. 30.00 (978-0-664-23066-1(0)) Westminster John Knox Pr.

Breytenbach, Cilliers, et al, eds. The New Testament Interpreted: Essays in Honor of Bernard C. Lategan. 2006. (Supplements to Novum Testamentum Ser.: Vol. 124). (Illus.). 404p. (978-90-04-15304-2(7)) BRILL.

Breytenbach, Cilliers & Hoppe, Rudolf. Neutestamentliche Wissenschaft nach 1945. Hauptvertreter der deutschsprachigen Exegese in der Darstellung ihrer Schüler: Hauptvertreter der deutschsprachigen Exegese in der Darstellung ihrer Schüler. 2008. (Illus.). xi, 486p. pap. (978-3-7887-2274-6(6)) Neukirchener Verlag.

Buitenwerf, Rieuward & Hollander, Harm. W., eds. Jesus, Paul, & Early Christianity: Studies in Honour of Henk Jan de Jonge. 2008. (Novum Testamentum Supplements Ser.). 480p. (C). (978-90-04-17033-9(2)) BRILL.

Burdette, Dallas R. Biblical Preaching & Teaching: Jesus & Our Privileges. 2009. 476p. 36.99 (978-1-61579-085-2(3)); pap. 24.99 (978-1-61579-084-5(5)) Xulon Pr., Inc.

Burge, Gary M. Jesus & the Jewish Festivals. 1 vol. 2012. (Ancient Context, Ancient Faith Ser.). (ENG.). 144p. pap. 14.99 **(978-0-310-28047-7(8))** Zondervan.

Burkett, Delbert. The Son of Man Debate: A History & Evaluation. 2007. (Society for New Testament Studies Monograph Ser.). (ENG.). 192p. pap. 44.00 (978-0-521-03745-7(X)) Cambridge Univ. Pr.

Burridge. New Testament Ethics Today. 240p. (978-0-567-08905-2(3)); pap. (978-0-567-08705-8(0)) Continuum International Publishing Group, Ltd. GBR. (T&T Clark). Dist: Continuum International Publishing Group, Inc.

Burridge, Richard A. Imitating Jesus: An Inclusive Approach to New Testament Ethics. 2007. 490p. 35.00 (978-0-8028-4458-3(8)) Eerdmans, William B. Publishing Co.

Cadwallader, Alan H. & Trainor, Michael, eds. Colossae in Space & Time: Linking to an Ancient City. 2011. (Novum Testamentum et Orbis Antiquus/Studien zur Umwelt des Neuen Testaments (NTOA/StUNT) Ser.). (ENG., Illus.). 368p. (C). 168.00 (978-3-525-53397-0(7)) Vandenhoeck & Ruprecht GmbH & Co. KG DEU. Dist: ISD.

Caldecott, Stratford. All Things Made New: The Mysteries of the World in Christ. 2011. pap. **(978-1-59731-129-8(4))** Perennis, Sophia.

Camery-Hoggatt, Jerry. Reading the Good Book Well: A Guide to Biblical Interpretation. 2007. 240p. per. 30.00 (978-0-687-64275-5(2)) Abingdon Pr.

Campbell, Constantine. Verbal Aspect, the Indicative Mood, & Narrative: Soundings in the Greek of the New Testament. 2007. (Studies in Biblical Greek Ser.: Vol. 13). (Illus.). (C). 308p. 119.95 (978-1-4331-0023-9(1)); 312p. pap. 34.95 (978-1-4331-0003-1(7)) Lang, Peter Publishing, Inc.

Campbell, William S. Paul & the Creation of Christian Identity. 2008. (T&T Clark Biblical Studies). (ENG.). 218p. 44.95 (978-0-567-03367-3(8), T&T Clark Int'l) Continuum International Publishing Group, Ltd. GBR. Dist: National Bk. Network.

Cantalamessa, Raniero. Jesus Began to Preach: The Mystery of God's Word. 2010. (ENG.). 112p. pap. 7.95 (978-0-8146-3304-5(8)) Liturgical Pr.

Caputo, John D. & Alcoff, Linda Martín, eds. St. Paul among the Philosophers. 2009. (Indiana Ser. in the Philosophy of Religion Ser.). (ENG.). 208p. 60.00 (978-0-253-35317-7(3), 0253353173); pap. 22.95 (978-0-253-22083-7(1), 0253220831) Indiana Univ. Pr.

Carey, Greg. Sinners: Jesus & His Earliest Followers. 2009. (ENG.). 200p. (C). pap. 29.95 (978-1-60258-146-3(0)) Baylor Univ. Pr.

Carroll, Richard C. Is Christ Divided? Approaching Our Conflicts in Christ. 2008. 288p. pap. 14.95 (978-1-57921-924-6(1)) WinePress Publishing.

Cassels, Walter R. A Reply to Dr. Lightfoot's Essays. 2007. (ENG.). 164p. pap. 19.99 (978-1-4264-7044-8(4)); 186p. pap. 21.99 (978-1-4264-7120-9(3)) BiblioBazaar.

Charles, Daniel. Jesus' Public Relations Slogan: ... My Works Testify of Me. 2008. 416p. 29.95 (978-1-934925-66-9(7), Eloquent Bks.) AEG Literary Publishing Services, Inc.

Chen, Diane G. A Pocketful of Verses: When Out-Of-Context Becomes the Norm. 2010. pap. 15.99 (978-1-57312-564-2(4)) Smyth & Helwys Publishing, Inc.

Childs, Brevard S. The Church's Guide for Reading Paul: The Canonical Shaping of the Pauline Corpus. 2008. 288p. pap. 28.00 (978-0-8028-6278-5(0)) Eerdmans, William B. Publishing Co.

Chilton, Bruce D. Beginning New Testament Study. (Illus.). 208p. 16.00 (978-0-281-04210-4(1)) SPCK Publishing GBR. Dist: Pilgrim Pr., The/United Church Pr.

Clark-Soles, Jaime & Clark-Soles. Death & the Afterlife in the New Testament. 2006. (ENG.). 272p. 110.00 (978-0-567-02902-7(6)); pap. 49.95 (978-0-567-02912-6(3)) Continuum International Publishing Group, Ltd. GBR. (T&T Clark Int'l). Dist: National Bk. Network.

Clivaz, Claire & Zumstein, Jean. Reading New Testament Papyri in Context: Lire des Papyrus du Nouveau Testament Dans Leur Contexte. 2012. (Bibliotheca Ephemeridum Theologicarum Lovaniensium Ser.). (FRE, GER & ENG., Illus.). 454p. (C). pap. 118.00 **(978-90-429-2506-9(X))** Peeters Pubs. & Booksellers BEL. Dist: Brown, David Bk. Co., The.

Colijn, Brenda B. Images of Salvation in the New Testament. 2010. (ENG.). 335p. pap. 25.00 (978-0-8308-3872-1(4), IVP Acad.) InterVarsity Pr.

Collins, Raymond F. The Power of Images in Paul. 2008. xv, 307p. (C). 49.95 (978-0-8146-5963-2(2)) Liturgical Pr.

Connelly, Douglas. The Book of Revelation for Blockheads: A User-Friendly Look at the Bible's Weirdest Book. 1 vol. 2007. (ENG.). 384p. pap. 16.99 (978-0-310-24909-2(0)) Zondervan.

Conyers, A. J. Last Things: The Heart of New Testament Eschatology. 2009. Orig. Title: The End: What Jesus REally Said about the Last Things. 160p. (C). pap. 14.00 (978-1-58731-450-6(9)) St. Augustine's Pr., Inc.

Couch, Mal, ed. A Biblical Theology of the Church. 2006. 336p. pap. 22.99 (978-0-8254-2411-3(9)) Kregel Pubns.

Court, John M., ed. New Testament Writers & the Old Testament: An Introduction. 2011. 140p. pap. 17.00 **(978-1-61097-048-8(9)**, Wipf and Stock) Wipf & Stock Pubs.

Cowper, B. Harris. Apocryphal Gospels. 2006. 580p. per. (978-1-4067-1502-6(6), Hesperides Pr.) Read Bks.

Crossan, John Dominic. The Power of Parables: How Fiction by Jesus Became Fiction about Jesus. 2012. (ENG.). 256p. 25.99 **(978-0-06-187569-4(4)**, HarperOne) HarperCollins Pubs.

Crossley, James. Reading the New Testament: Contemporary Approaches. 2010. (Reading Religious Texts). (ENG., Illus.). 200p. (C). pap. 30.95 (978-0-415-48531-9(2), Routledge) Taylor & Francis Group GBR. Dist: Taylor & Francis Group.

Crossley, James G. Jesus in an Age of Terror: Scholarly Projects for a New American Century. 2008. (BibleWorld Ser.). (ENG.). 284p. (C). 99.95 (978-1-84553-429-5(8)); pap. 34.95 (978-1-84553-430-1(1)) Equinox Publishing Ltd. GBR. Dist: ISD.

—The New Testament & Jewish Law. 2010. (Guides for the Perplexed Ser.). (ENG.). 144p. 80.00 (978-0-567-03433-5(X)); pap. 24.95 (978-0-567-03434-2(8)) Continuum International Publishing Group, Ltd. GBR. (T&T Clark Int'l). Dist: National Bk. Network.

—Reading the New Testament: Contemporary Approaches. 2010. (Reading Religious Texts). (ENG., Illus.). 200p. (C). 100.00 (978-0-415-48530-2(4)) Routledge.

Custer, Stewart. Critical Questions for New Testament Study. 2010. (978-1-60682-106-0(7)) BJU Pr.

Danove, Paul L. & Danove, Paul. Grammatical & Exegetical Study of New Testament Verbs of Transference: A Case Frame Guide to Interpretation & Translation. 2009. (Library of New Testament Studies, the Ser.). (ENG.). 258p. 130.00 (978-0-567-03116-7(0), T&T Clark Int'l) Continuum International Publishing Group, Ltd. GBR. Dist: National Bk. Network.

Daube, David. The New Testament & Rabbinic Judaism. 2011. 478p. pap. 55.00 **(978-1-61097-510-0(3)**, Wipf and Stock) Wipf & Stock Pubs.

Davies, W. D. & Daube, D., eds. The Background of the New Testament & its Eschatology. 2009. (ENG.). 584p. pap. 69.00 (978-0-521-09329-3(5)) Cambridge Univ. Pr.

Davis, Mike. The Atheist's Introduction to the New Testament: How the Bible Undermines the Basic Teachings of Christianity. 2008. 184p. pap. 18.95 (978-1-4327-2691-1(9)) Outskirts Pr., Inc.

Davis, Stacy. This Strange Story: Jewish & Christian Interpretation of the Curse of Canaan from Antiquity To 1865. 2008. (ENG.). 250p. per. 40.99 (978-0-7618-3879-1(1)) Univ. Pr. of America, Inc.

de Villiers, Pieter & van Henten, Jan Willem, eds. Coping with Violence in the New Testament. 2012. (Studies in Theology & Religion Ser.). (ENG., Illus.). **(978-90-04-22104-8(2))** BRILL.

Dean, Rynold Duane. Evangelical Hermeneutics & the New Testament Use of the Old Testament: If the Bugle Produces an Indistinct Sound... 2009. 273p. lib. bdg. 24.99 (978-0-9824481-0-6(4)) Veritypath Pubns.

Deines, Roland. Neues Testament und hellenistisch-jüdische Alltagskultur: Wechselseitige Wahrnehmungen. III. Internationales Symposium zum Corpus Judaeo-Hellenisticum Novi Testamenti 21.-24. Mai 2009, Leipzig. Herzer, Jens & Niebuhr, Karl W., eds. 2011. (Wissenschaftliche Untersuchungen zum Neuen Teastament Ser.). (GER.). 493p. 257.50 **(978-3-16-150170-8(5))** Mohr Siebeck GmbH & Co. KG DEU. Dist: Coronet Bks.

Deissmann, Adolf. The New Testament in the Light of Modern Research: The Haskell Lectures 1929. 2007. 204p. pap. 20.00 (978-1-55635-454-0(1), Wipf and Stock) Wipf & Stock Pubs.

DeMaris, Richard. Understanding the Social World of the New Testament. Neufeld, Dietmar, ed. 2009. (ENG., Illus.). 304p. (C). 110.00 (978-0-415-77581-6(7)) Routledge.

deSilva, David A. The Hope of Glory. 2009. 246p. pap. 27.00 (978-1-60608-412-0(7), Wipf and Stock) Wipf & Stock Pubs.

Disbrey, Claire. Wrestling with Life's Tough Issues: What Should a Christian Do? 2008. 185p. pap. 16.95 (978-1-59856-314-6(9)) Hendrickson Pubs. Marketing, LLC.

Donaldson, Terence L. Jews & Anti-Judaism in the New Testament: Decision Points & Divergent Interpretations. 2010. (ENG.). 192p. (C). pap. 24.95 (978-1-60258-263-7(7)) Baylor Univ. Pr.

Dungan, David L. Constantine's Bible: Politics & the Making of the New Testament. 2006. 236p. per. 18.00 (978-0-8006-3790-3(9), Fortress Pr.) Augsburg Fortress, Pubs.

Dyer, Keith & Neville, David, eds. Resurrection & Responsibility: Essays on Theology, Scripture, & Ethics in Honor of Thorwald Lorenzen. 2009. 290p. pap. 32.00 (978-1-60608-461-8(5), Pickwick Pubns.) Wipf & Stock Pubs.

Eddy, Paul Rhodes & Boyd, Gregory A. The Jesus Legend: A Case for the Historical Reliability of the Synoptic Jesus Tradition. 2007. 480p. (C). pap. 32.00 (978-0-8010-3114-4(1)) Baker Academic.

Edersheim, Alfred. Sketches of Jewish Social Life in the Days of Christ. 2007. 272p. per. 17.50 (978-1-60206-501-7(2)) Cosimo, Inc.

—Sketches of Jewish Social Life in the Days of Christ. 2008. 346p. 46.95 (978-1-4372-5207-1(9)); pap. 31.95 (978-1-4371-2463-7(1)) Kessinger Publishing, LLC.

Ehrman, Bart D. Forged: Writing in the Name of God — Why the Bible's Authors Are Not Who We Think They Are. (ENG.). 2012. 256p. pap. 15.99 **(978-0-06-201262-3(2))** 2011. 304p. 26.99 (978-0-06-201261-6(4)) HarperCollins Pubs. (HarperOne).

Eichhorn, Albert. The Lord's Supper in the New Testament. 2008. (SBL - History of Biblical Studies Ser.). 116p. (978-90-04-15734-7(4)) BRILL.

—The Lord's Supper in the New Testament. Cayzer, Jeffrey, tr. from GER. 2007. 116p. per. 14.95 (978-1-58983-274-9(4)) Society of Biblical Literature.

Ellens, Deborah L., et al. God's Word for Our World, Vol. 1. 2009. (Library of Hebrew Bible/Old Testament Studies, the Ser.). (ENG.). 336p. 55.00 (978-1-4411-7724-7(8)) Continuum International Publishing Group, Ltd. GBR. Dist: National Bk. Network.

Elliott, Matthew A. Faithful Feelings: Rethinking Emotion in the New Testament. 2006. 304p. pap. 21.99 (978-0-8254-2542-4(5)) Kregel Pubns.

Evans, Roger Steven. Issues of New Testament Anti-Judaism: Son of Man, Deicide, & Divine Predetermination. 2008. (ENG.). 120p. pap. 26.50 (978-0-7618-4143-2(1)) Univ. Pr. of America, Inc.

Farelly, Nicolas. The Disciples in the Fourth Gospel: A Narrative Analysis of Their Faith & Understanding. 2010. (Illus.). 273p. pap. 127.50 (978-3-16-150583-6(2)) Mohr Siebeck GmbH & Co. KG DEU. Dist: Coronet Bks.

Finlan, Stephen. The Apostle Paul & the Pauline Tradition. 2008. xiv, 229p. (C). pap. 29.95 (978-0-8146-5271-8(9)) Liturgical Pr.

—The Family Metaphor in Jesus' Teaching: Gospel & Ethics. 2009. 154p. pap. 18.00 (978-1-55635-938-5(1), Cascade Bks.) Wipf & Stock Pubs.

Finsterbusch, Karin, et al, eds. Human Sacrifice in Jewish & Christian Tradition. 2006. (Numen Book Series-Studies in the History of Religions). (Illus.). 365p. (978-90-04-15085-0(4)) BRILL.

Fisichella, Anthony J. One Solitary Life: Book III - the Christ Epoch. 2008. 276p. pap. 15.95 (978-1-4343-5413-6(X)) AuthorHouse.

Flores, José. Texto del Nuevo Testamento: New Testament Text. (SPA.). 256p. (978-84-7228-287-2(2), 220880) Clie, Editorial.

Foskett, Mary F. Between Experience & Interpretation: Engaging the Writings of the New Testament. Allen, Wesley, ed. 2008. 262p. pap. 29.50 (978-0-687-64739-2(8)) Abingdon Pr.

Foster, Paul, ed. New Testament Studies, 4 vols. 2010. (SAGE Benchmarks in Religious Studies). (Illus.). 1608p. 995.00 (978-1-84860-168-0(9), B01689C) SAGE Pubns., Ltd. GBR. Dist: SAGE Pubns., Inc.

Francis, James M. M. Adults as Children Vol. 17: Images of Childhood in the Ancient World & the New Testament. 2006. (Religions & Discourse Ser.: Vol. 17). 346p. pap. 68.95 (978-0-8204-6299-9(6)) Lang, Peter Publishing, Inc.

Freyne, Sean, et al. A Wandering Galilean: Essays in Honour of Sean Freyne. 2008. (978-90-04-17355-2(2)) BRILL.

Fridrichsen, Anton. Exegetical Writings: A Selection. Caragounis, Chrys C. & Fornberg, Tord, trs. 2011. 328p. pap. 36.00 **(978-1-61097-367-0(4)**, Wipf and Stock) Wipf & Stock Pubs.

Furnish, Victor. Moral Teaching of Paul. 3rd ed. 2009. 176p. pap. 18.00 (978-0-687-33293-9(1)) Abingdon Pr.

Garcia, Vince. The Resurrection Life Study Bible. 2007. 500p. per. 23.99 (978-1-60266-882-9(5)) Xulon Pr., Inc.

Gelpi, Donald L. Encountering Jesus Christ: Rethinking Christological Faith & Commitment. 2009. pap. (978-0-87462-742-8(7)) Marquette Univ. Pr.

George, Raymond. Communion with God in the New Testament. 2009. 296p. pap. 34.00 (978-1-60608-733-6(9), Wipf and Stock) Wipf & Stock Pubs.

Gilbert, George Holley. Greek Thought in the New Testament. 2011. 216p. 44.95 **(978-1-258-01921-1(3))** Literary Licensing, LLC.

Gooder, Paula, Sr. Searching for Meaning: An Introduction to Interpreting the New Testament. 2008. (ENG.). 256p. pap. 25.00 (978-0-664-23194-1(2)) Westminster John Knox Pr.

Grech, Prosper. An Outline of New Testament Spirituality. 2011. 160p. pap. 18.00 (978-0-8028-6560-1(7)) Eerdmans, William B. Publishing Co.

Greeley, Andrew M. Jesus: A Meditation on His Stories & His Relationships with Women. 2009. (ENG.). 176p. mass mkt. 6.99 (978-0-7653-5701-4(1), Forge Bks.) Doherty, Tom Assocs., LLC.

Green, Joel. Reading Scripture As Wesleyans. 2010. 186p. pap. 15.00 (978-1-4267-0691-2(X)) Abingdon Pr.

Gregory, Andrew & Tuckett, Christopher, eds. The New Testament & the Apostolic Fathers, 2 vols., Set. 2007. (ENG.). 926p. pap. 99.00 (978-0-19-923006-8(4)) Oxford Univ. Pr., Inc.

Grimm, Veronika. From Feasting to Fasting: The Evolution of a Sin. 2010. (ENG.). 304p. pap. 39.95 (978-0-415-58904-8(5)) Routledge.

Gurtner, Daniel M. The Torn Veil: Matthew's Exposition of the Death of Jesus. 2006. (Society for New Testament Studies Monograph Ser.). (ENG., Illus.). 320p. 117.00 (978-0-521-87064-1(X)) Cambridge Univ. Pr.

Gzella, Holger. Languages from the World of the Bible. 2011. **(978-1-934078-61-7(1))** De Gruyter, Walter Inc.

Hahn, Scott. Faith Charts, the Bible at a Glance. 2008. (Faith Charts Ser.). 6p. 7.95 (978-1-59276-483-9(5)) Our Sunday Visitor, Publishing Div.

Halbur, Virginia, ed. College Study Bible: New American Bible. 2007. (Illus.). 2048p. per. 37.95 (978-0-88489-907-5(1)) St. Mary's Pr.

Hanson, Anthony Tyrrell. The New Testament Interpretation of Scripture. 2011. 250p. pap. 28.00 **(978-1-61097-351-9(8)**, Wipf and Stock) Wipf & Stock Pubs.

Harris, Murray J. Jesus as God: The New Testament Use of Theos in Reference to Jesus. 2008. 379p. pap. 42.00 *(978-1-60608-108-2(X)*, Wipf and Stock) Wipf & Stock Pubs.

Hatina, Thomas R. & Hatina. Biblical Interpretation in Early Christian Gospels Vol. 2: The Gospel of Matthew, 5 vols. 2008. (Library of New Testament Studies, the Ser.). (ENG.). 256p. 130.00 *(978-0-567-04194-4(8)*, T&T Clark Int'l) Continuum International Publishing Group, Ltd. GBR. Dist: National Bk. Network.

Hearon, Holly, ed. The Bible in Ancient & Modern Media: Story & Performance. 2008. (Biblical Performance Criticism Ser.). 200p. pap. 23.00 *(978-1-55635-990-3(X)*, Cascade Bks.) Wipf & Stock Pubs.

Heininger, Bernhard. Die Inkulturation des Christentums: Aufsätze und Studien zum Neuen Testament und seiner Umwelt. 2010. (GER., Illus.). 433p. 217.50 *(978-3-16-150546-1(8))* Mohr Siebeck GmbH & Co. KG DEU. Dist: Coronet Bks.

Hengel, Martin. The Son of God: The Origin of Christology & the History of Jewish-Hellenistic Religion. 2007. 112p. pap. 14.00 *(978-1-55635-230-0(1)*, Wipf and Stock) Wipf & Stock Pubs.

Hengel, Martin & Bowden, John. The Son of God: The Origin of Christology & the History of Jewish-Hellenistic Religion. 2012. xii, 100p. pap. ***(978-0-334-01468-3(9)***, SCM Pr.) Hymns Ancient & Modern Ltd.

Hentschel, Anni. Diakonia im neuen Testament: Studien zur Semantik unter besonderer Berücksichtigung der Rolle von Frauen. Wissenschaftliche Untersuchungen zum Neuen Testament. 2007. (Wissenschaftliche Untersuchungen Zum Neuen Testament 2 Ser.: 226). 512p. (Orig.). (C). pap. 142.50 *(978-3-16-149086-6(X))* Mohr Siebeck GmbH & Co. KG DEU. Dist: Coronet Bks.

Hester, James D. & Hester, J. David. Rhetorics in the New Millennium: Promise & Fulfillment. 2010. (Studies in Antiquity & Christianity Ser.). (ENG.). 320p. pap. 70.00 *(978-0-567-34991-0(8)*, T&T Clark Int'l) Continuum International Publishing Group, Ltd. GBR. Dist: National Bk. Network.

Hester, James D. & Hester, J. David, eds. Rhetorics in the New Millennium: Promise & Fulfillment. 2009. (Studies in Antiquity & Christianity Ser.). (ENG.). 320p. 120.00 *(978-0-567-02752-8(X)*, T&T Clark) Continuum International Publishing Group, Ltd. GBR. Dist: National Bk. Network.

Hoeffner, R., et al, eds. Studien zu Einleitungsfragen und zur Theologie und Exegese des Neuen Testaments: Gesammelte Aufsatze von Peter Dschulnigg. 2010. (Biblical Tools & Studies). (GER.). 601p. (C). 116.00 *(978-90-429-2279-2(6))* Peeters Pubs. & Booksellers BEL. Dist: Brown, David Bk. Co., The.

Holder, R. Ward. A Companion to Paul in the Reformation. 2009. 690p. *(978-90-04-17492-4(3))* BRILL.

Holzapfel, Richard. Making Sense of the NT. 2010. 544p. 34.99 *(978-1-60641-668-6(5))* Deseret Bk. Co.

Holzapfel, Richard Neitzel & Wayment, Thomas A. The Life & Teachings of the New Testament Apostles: From the Day of Pentecost to the Apocalypse. 2010. x, 358p. 34.99 *(978-1-60641-824-6(6))* Deseret Bk. Co.

Horan, Michael. Jesus & the Trojan War: Myth & Meaning for Today. 2007. (ENG.). 252p. per. 29.90 *(978-1-84540-081-1(X))* Imprint Academic GBR. Dist: Ingram Pub. Services.

Horn, Friedrich W. Jenseits Von Indikativ und Imperativ. Zimmermann, Ruben, ed. 2009. (Wissenschaftliche Untersuchungen zum Nuen Testament Ser.). (GER., Illus.). 386p. 169.00 *(978-3-16-149997-5(2))* Mohr Siebeck GmbH & Co. KG DEU. Dist: Eisenbrauns, Inc.

Horsley, Richard A. Jesus in Context: Power, People, & Perfomance. 2008. 280p. (C). pap. 26.00 *(978-0-8006-6312-4(8)*, Fortress Pr.) Augsburg Fortress, Pubs.

Houlden, J. L. The Strange Story of the Gospels: Finding Doctrine Through Narrative. 144p. 14.00 *(978-0-281-05436-7(3))* SPCK Publishing GBR. Dist: Pilgrim Pr., The/United Church Pr.

Howard, J. Keir. Medicine, Miracle, & Myth in the New Testament. 2010. 132p. pap. 16.00 *(978-1-60899-244-7(6)*, Resource Pubns.) Wipf & Stock Pubs.

Hubbard, Norman. Right of Malachi: Exploring the Great Ideas of the New Testament. 2007. (Exploring the Great Ideas Ser.). (ENG.). 160p. per. 9.99 *(978-1-60006-053-3(6))* NavPress Publishing Group.

Humphrey, Edith McEwan & Humphrey, Edith M. And I Turned to See the Voice: The Rhetoric of Vision in the New Testament. 2007. (Studies in Theological Interpretation Ser.). 240p. (C). pap. 24.00 *(978-0-8010-3157-1(5))* Baker Academic.

Imperato, Robert. Portraits of Jesus: A Reading Guide. 2008. (Studies in the History of Judaism Ser.). (ENG.). 198p. pap. 24.50 *(978-0-7618-4325-2(6))* Univ. Pr. of America, Inc.

Indermark, John. Christ: Jesus Christ: A Portrait of God. 2006. (Great Themes of the Bible Ser.). (Illus.). 77p. per. 8.50 *(978-0-687-49020-2(0))* Abingdon Pr.

—Gospeled Lives: Encounters with Jesus, A Lenten Study. 2008. 144p. pap. 15.00 *(978-0-8358-9971-0(3))* Upper Room Bks.

Isaak, Jon M. New Testament Theology: Extending the Table. 2010. (Illus.). 404p. pap. 44.00 *(978-1-55635-293-5(X)*, Cascade Bks.) Wipf & Stock Pubs.

Jack, Zachary Michael. The Plowman Sings: The Essential Fiction, Poetry, & Drama of America's Forgotten Regionalist Jay G. Sigmund. 2008. (ENG.). 131p. pap. 28.50 *(978-0-7618-4282-8(9))* Univ. Pr. of America, Inc.

Jackson, Bernard S. Essays on Halakhah in the New Testament. 2007. (Jewish & Christian Perspectives Ser.). 264p. *(978-90-04-16273-0(9))* BRILL.

Jasper, David. Rhetoric, Power, & Community. 2009. (David Jasper Reprint Ser.). 184p. pap. 21.00 *(978-1-60608-831-9(9)*, Wipf and Stock) Wipf & Stock Pubs.

Jeremias, Joachim. Unknown Sayings of Jesus. Fuller, Reginald H., tr. 2008. 118p. pap. 15.00 *(978-1-55635-978-1(0))* Wipf & Stock Pubs.

Johnson, Andy & Brower, K. E. Holiness & Ecclesiology in the New Testament. Brower, Kent E. & Johnson, Andy, eds. 2007. 385p. per. 35.00 *(978-0-8028-4560-3(6))* Eerdmans, William B. Publishing Co.

Johnson, Jeffrey D. The Passionate Sacrifice: Genesis 22: Binding Isaac. 2007. 24p. pap. 3.00 *(978-1-55635-084-9(8)*, Wipf and Stock) Wipf & Stock Pubs.

Johnson, Nita (LaFond). Where Was God? 2008. (Illus.). 127p. *(978-0-9656528-7-2(4))* Graham, Robert J. Desktop Publishing.

Jones, Judith Kaye. The Women in the Gospel of John: The Divine Feminine. 2008. 16.99 *(978-0-8272-4257-9(3))* Chalice Pr.

Jones Sr., Carl L. It Isn't the Jefferson Bible. 2009. 266p. pap. 23.99 *(978-0-9748266-6-0(9))* Grampa Jones's Publishing Co.

Joynes, Christine. Perspectives on the Passion: Encountering the Bible through the Arts. 2008. (Library of New Testament Studies, the Ser.). (ENG.). 224p. 140.00 *(978-0-567-03362-8(7)*, T&T Clark Int'l) Continuum International Publishing Group, Ltd. GBR. Dist: National Bk. Network.

Judd, Frank F. & Strathearn, Gaye. How the New Testament Came to Be: 35th Annual Sidney B. Sperry Symposium. 2006. 432p. 24.95 *(978-1-59038-627-9(2))* Deseret Bk. Co.

—Sperry Syposium Classics: The New Testament. 2006. 464p. 24.95 *(978-1-59038-628-6(0))* Deseret Bk. Co.

Käsemann, Ernst, et al. On Being a Disciple of the Crucified Nazarene: Unpublished Lectures & Sermons. 2010. 352p. pap. 30.00 *(978-0-8028-6026-2(5))* Eerdmans, William B. Publishing Co.

Keefer, Kyle, ed. The New Testament as Literature. 2008. (Very Short Introductions Ser.). (ENG., Illus.). 144p. pap. 11.95 *(978-0-19-530020-8(3))* Oxford Univ. Pr., Inc.

Kelhoffer, James A. Persecution, Persuasion & Power: Readiness to Withstand Hardship as a Corroboration of Legitimacy in the New Testament. 2010. (Wissenschaftliche Untersuchungen zum Neuen Testament, No. 270 Ser.). 465p. 197.50 *(978-3-16-150612-3(X))* Mohr Siebeck GmbH & Co. KG DEU. Dist: Coronet Bks.

Kent, Charles Foster. The Origin & Permanent Value of the Old Testament. 2007. (ENG.). 160p. pap. 19.99 *(978-1-4264-3062-6(0))*; 180p. pap. 21.99 *(978-1-4264-3127-2(9))* BiblioBazaar.

Kenyon, Frederic G. Recent Developments in the Textual Criticism of the Greek Bible: The Schweich Lectures of the British Academy 1932. 2007. 130p. pap. 16.00 *(978-1-55635-370-3(7)*, Wipf and Stock) Wipf & Stock Pubs.

Kim, Kyoung-Shik. God Will Judge Each One According to Works: Judgment According to Works & Psalm 62 in Early Judaism & the New Testament. (Beihefte zur Zeitschrift far die neutestamentliche Wissenschaft und die Kunde der älteren Kirche Ser.). (ENG., XIII, 294p. 2011. Illus.). 210.00 ***(978-3-11-218955-9(8))*** 2010. 140.00 *(978-3-11-024776-3(3))* De Gruyter, Walter Inc.

Klein, Hans, et al, eds. Das Gebet im Neuen Testament: Vierte, europäische orthodox-westliche Exegetenkonferenz in Sambata de Sus, 4. — 8. August 2007. 2009. (GER.). 493p. 215.00 *(978-3-16-150102-9(0))* Mohr Siebeck GmbH & Co. KG DEU. Dist: Coronet Bks.

Koch, Dietrich-Alex & Horn, Friedrich Wilhelm. Hellenistisches Christentum: Schriftverstandnis, Ekklesiologie, Geschichte. 2008. (Novum Testamentum et Orbis Antiquus/Studien zur Umwelt des Neuen Testaments (NTOA/StUNT) Ser.). (GER., Illus.). 378p. (C). 137.00 *(978-3-525-54001-5(9))* Vandenhoeck & Ruprecht GmbH & Co. KG DEU. Dist: ISD.

Koester, Helmut, et al. Trajectories Through Early Christianity. 2006. 310p. pap. 30.00 *(978-1-59752-736-1(X)*, Wipf and Stock) Wipf & Stock Pubs.

Kostenberger, Andreas J. & Kruger, Michael J. The Heresy of Orthodoxy: How Contemporary Culture's Fascination with Diversity Has Reshaped Our Understanding of Early Christianity. 2010. 256p. pap. 17.99 *(978-1-4335-0143-2(0))* Crossway.

Köstenberger, Andreas J. & Kruger, Michael J. The Heresy of Orthodoxy: How Contemporary Culture's Fascination with Diversity Has Reshaped Our Understanding of Early Christianity. 2010. *(978-1-4335-1813-3(9))* Crossway.

Kraft, Robert A. Exploring the Scripturesque: Jewish Texts & Their Christian Contexts. 2009. (Supplements to the Journal for the Study of Judaism Ser.). 288p. *(978-90-04-17010-0(3))* BRILL.

Krans, Jan. Beyond What Is Written: Erasmus & Beza as Conjectural Critics of the New Testament. 2006. (New Testament Tools & Studies: Vol. 35). (Illus.). 394p. *(978-90-04-15286-1(5))* BRILL.

Kupor, Robert. Jesus the Misunderstood Jew: What the New Testament Really Says about the Man from Nazareth. 2007. 216p. 27.95 *(978-0-595-69314-6(8))*; per. 17.95 *(978-0-595-42404-7(X))* iUniverse, Inc.

Laansma, Jon C., et al, eds. New Testament Theology in Light of the ChurchÕs Mission: Essays in Honor of I. Howard Marshall. 2011. 418p. pap. 46.00 ***(978-1-61097-530-8(8)***, Cascade Bks.) Wipf & Stock Pubs.

Labahn, M. & Lehtipuu, O., eds. Anthropology in the New Testament & its Ancient Context: Papers from the EABS-Meeting in Piliscaba, Budapest. 2010. (Contributions to Biblical Exegesis & Theology Ser.). (ENG.). 276p. (C). pap. 56.00 *(978-90-429-2342-3(3))* Peeters Pubs. & Booksellers BEL. Dist: Brown, David Bk. Co., The.

Lampe, Peter, ed. Neutestamentliche Grenzgange: Symposium zur kritischen Rezeption der Arbeiten Gerd Theissens. 2009. (Novum testamentum/studien zur umwelt des NT Ser.). (GER.). 248p. (C). 98.00 *(978-3-525-53393-2(4))* Vandenhoeck & Ruprecht GmbH & Co. KG DEU. Dist: ISD.

Langton, Daniel R. The Apostle Paul in the Jewish Imagination: A Study in Modern Jewish-Christian Relations. 2010. (ENG.). 320p. 100.00 *(978-0-521-51740-9(0))* Cambridge Univ. Pr.

Lavin, Ron. Witness: The Reign of God & Missional Churches Today. 2007. 169p. per. *(978-0-7880-2434-4(5))* CSS Publishing Co.

Lee, Margaret Ellen & Scott, Bernard Brandon. Sound Mapping the New Testament. 2009. 416p. pap. 34.95 *(978-1-59815-015-5(4))* Polebridge Pr.

Lee, Michelle V. Paul, the Stoics, & the Body of Christ. 2006. (Society for New Testament Studies Monograph Ser.). (ENG.). 238p. 108.99 *(978-0-521-86454-1(2))* Cambridge Univ. Pr.

Lee, Simon S. Jesus' Transfiguration & the Believers' Transformation: A Study of the Transfiguration & Its Development in Early Christian Writings. 2009. (Wissenschaftliche Untersuchungen zum Nuen Testament Ser.). (Illus.). 244p. pap. 102.00 *(978-3-16-150003-9(2))* Mohr Siebeck GmbH & Co. KG DEU. Dist: Eisenbrauns, Inc.

Levering, Matthew. Predestination: Biblical & Theological Paths. 2011. (ENG.). 288p. 110.00 *(978-0-19-960452-4(5))* Oxford Univ. Pr., Inc.

Levine, Amy Jill. Jewish Context of the New Test. 2009. 128p. pap. 16.00 *(978-0-687-64544-2(1))* Abingdon Pr.

Levine, Amy-Jill. The Misunderstood Jew: The Church & the Scandal of the Jewish Jesus. 2006. (ENG.). 240p. 24.95 *(978-0-06-078966-4(2)*, HarperOne) HarperCollins Pubs.

Lichtenberger, Hermann & Mittmann-Richert, Ulrike. Biblical Figures in Deuterocanonical & Cognate Literature. 2009. (GER & ENG.). *(978-3-11-020368-4(5))* de Gruyter, Walter GmbH & Co. KG.

Liew, Tat-Siong Benny, ed. Reading Ideologies: Essays on the Bible & Interpretation in Honor of Mary Ann Tolbert. 2011. 386p. ***(978-1-907534-27-0(X))*** Sheffield Phoenix Pr.

Litke, Richard L. What Jesus Really Meant: Challenging Passages in the New Testament. 2011. pap. 15.99 *(978-0-8163-2479-8(4))* Pacific Pr. Publishing Assn.

Loader, William. Sexuality in the New Testament: Understanding the Key Texts. 2010. (ENG.). 176p. pap. 20.00 *(978-0-664-23161-3(6))* Westminster John Knox Pr.

Lohmeyer, Ernst. Ernst Lohmeyers Zcugnis im Kirchenkampf: Breslauer Universitatspredigten. Kohn, Andreas, ed. 2006. (GER.). 154p. (Orig.). (C). pap. 36.00 *(978-3-525-55382-4(X))* Vandenhoeck & Ruprecht GmbH & Co. KG DEU. Dist: ISD.

Longenecker, Bruce W. & Liebengood, Kelly D., eds. Engaging Economics: New Testament Scenarios & Early Christian Reception. 2009. (ENG.). 344p. pap. 32.00 *(978-0-8028-6414-7(7))* Eerdmans, William B. Publishing Co.

Ludemann, Gerd. Intolerance & the Gospel: Selected Text from the New Testament. 2006. (ENG.). 1p. 29.98 *(978-1-59102-468-2(4))* Prometheus Bks., Pubs.

Lyda, Hap C. S. History of Biblical Christianity: An Introductory Study of Beginning Christianity & the New Testament. 2006. *(978-0-9630629-6-3(4))* 21st Century Pr.

MacDonald, Nathan & Luzia Sutter Rehmann, eds. Decisive Meals: Table Politics in Biblical Literature. 2012. (Library of New Testament Studies). (ENG.). 200p. 110.00 ***(978-0-567-52601-4(1)***, T&T Clark Int'l) Continuum International Publishing Group, Ltd. GBR. Dist: National Bk. Network.

MacNair Jr., A. Stanley. To the Churches with Love: Biblical Studies of the Letters to the Seven Churches. 2011. 108p. 39.95 ***(978-1-258-05626-1(7))*** Literary Licensing, LLC.

MacRae, George W. Studies in the New Testament & Gnosticism. 2007. (Illus.). 278p. pap. 31.00 *(978-1-55635-595-0(5))* Wipf & Stock Pubs.

Marshall, I. Howard, ed. New Testament Interpretation: Essays on Principles & Methods. 2006. 406p. pap. 42.00 *(978-1-59752-696-8(7)*, Wipf and Stock) Wipf & Stock Pubs.

Martens, Peter W. Origen & Scripture: The Contours of the Exegetical Life. 2012. (Oxford Early Christian Studies). (ENG.). 352p. 125.00 ***(978-0-19-963955-7(8))*** Oxford Univ. Pr., Inc.

Martin, Dale B. New Testament History & Literature. 2012. (Open Yale Courses Ser.). (ENG., Illus.). 464p. pap. 18.00 ***(978-0-300-18085-5(3))*** Yale Univ. Pr.

Marty, William H. Surveying the New Testament. 3rd rev. ed. 2009. (ENG.). 308p. spiral bd. 31.63 *(978-0-7575-1788-4(9)*, 0757517889) Kendall Hunt Publishing Co.

Mason, Eric F., ed. A Teacher for All Generations (2 vol. Set) Essays in Honor of James C. VanderKam, 2 vols. 2011. (Supplements to the Journal for the Study of Judaism Ser.). (Illus.). lxx, 1004p. ***(978-90-04-21520-7(4))*** BRILL.

Massey, Lesly F. Women & the New Testament: An Analysis of Scripture in Light of New Testament Era Culture. alt. ed. 2012. (ENG.). 160p. pap. 25.00 ***(978-0-7864-6772-3(X))*** McFarland & Co., Inc. Pubs.

Matera, Frank J. New Testament Theology: Exploring Diversity & Unity. 2007. (ENG.). 485p. per. 50.00 *(978-0-664-23044-9(X))* Westminster John Knox Pr.

Mathews McGinnis, Claire, ed. As Those Who Are Taught: The Interpretation of Isaiah from the LXX to the SBL. 2006. (SBL - Symposium Ser.). 342p. *(978-90-04-13041-8(1))* BRILL.

McCollough, Charles. The Art of Parables: Reinterpreting the Teaching Stories of Jesus in Word & Sculpture. 2008. (ENG., Illus.). 256p. pap. 34.95 *(978-1-55145-563-1(3)*, Copperhouse) Wood Lake Publishing, Inc. CAN. Dist: Westminster John Knox Pr.

McComiskey, Douglas S. Lukan Theology in the Light of the Gospel's Literary Structure. 2007. (Paternoster Biblical Monographs: Ser.). 422p. pap. 43.00 *(978-1-59752-786-6(6)*, Wipf and Stock) Wipf & Stock Pubs.

McConkey, James H. The Book of Revelation: A Series of Outline Studies in the Apocalypse. 2011. 98p. 38.95 ***(978-1-258-04243-1(6))*** Literary Licensing, LLC.

McKenzie, John L. The New Testament Without Illusion. 2009. (John L. Mckenzie Reprint Ser.). 256p. pap. 28.00 *(978-1-60608-272-0(8)*, Wipf and Stock) Wipf & Stock Pubs.

—The Power & the Wisdom: An Interpretation of the New Testament. 2009. (John L. Mckenzie Reprints Ser.). (Illus.). 322p. pap. 35.00 *(978-1-60608-048-1(2))* Wipf & Stock Pubs.

McNamara, Martin. Targum & New Testament: Collected Essays. 2011. (Wissenschaftliche Untersuchungen zum Neuen Testament Ser.). 629p. 292.50 ***(978-3-16-150836-3(X))*** Mohr Siebeck GmbH & Co. KG DEU. Dist: Coronet Bks.

Merrill, Nan C. & Merrill. Journey into Love: From Fear to Freedom. 2007. (ENG., Illus.). 208p. pap. 16.95 *(978-0-8264-1904-0(6))* Continuum International Publishing Group, Ltd. GBR. Dist: National Bk. Network.

Metzner, Rainer. Die Prominenten Im Neuen Testament: Ein Prosopographischer Kommentar. 2008. (Novum Testamentum et Orbis Antiquus/Studien zur Umwelt des Neuen Testaments (NTOA/StUNT) Ser.). (GER.). 695p. (C). 117.00 *(978-3-525-53967-5(3))* Vandenhoeck & Ruprecht GmbH & Co. KG DEU. Dist: ISD.

Middleton, Paul, et al, eds. Paul, Grace & Freedom: Essays in Honour of John K. Riches. 2012. (ENG.). 234p. pap. 44.95 ***(978-0-567-38254-2(0)***, T&T Clark Int'l) Continuum International Publishing Group, Ltd. GBR. Dist: National Bk. Network.

Middleton, Paul & Middleton. Paul, Grace & Freedom: Essays in Honour of John K. Riches. Paddison, Angus & Wenell, Karen J., eds. 2009. (ENG.). 234p. 130.00 *(978-0-567-03318-5(X)*, T&T Clark Int'l) Continuum International Publishing Group, Ltd. GBR. Dist: National Bk. Network.

Miles, Jack. Christ: A Crisis in the Life of God. abr. ed. 2009. (Playaway Adult Nonfiction Ser.). (ENG.). 39.99 *(978-1-60812-720-7(6))* Findaway World, LLC.

Miller, Edward. The Oxford Debate on the Textual Criticism of the New Testament. 2009. 96p. pap. 10.00 *(978-0-9822230-1-7(3))* Old Paths Pubns., Inc., The.

Minear, Paul S. Images of the Church in the New Testament. 2007. (ENG.). 308p. pap. 52.00 *(978-0-227-17243-8(4))* Clarke, James Co., Ltd. GBR. Dist: Brown, David Bk. Co., The.

Moloney, Francis J. Mary. 2009. 80p. pap. 11.00 *(978-1-60608-965-1(X)*, Wipf and Stock) Wipf & Stock Pubs.

Moore, Daniel F. Jesus, an Emerging Jewish Mosaic: Jewish Perspectives, Post-Holocaust. 2012. (ENG.). 344p. pap. 55.00 ***(978-0-567-11855-4(X)***, T&T Clark Int'l) Continuum International Publishing Group, Ltd. GBR. Dist: National Bk. Network.

Moore, Daniel F. & Moore. Jesus, an Emerging Jewish Mosaic: Jewish Perspectives, Post-Holocaust. 2008. (Jewish & Christian Texts in Contexts & Related Studies). (ENG.). 344p. 155.00 *(978-0-567-02738-2(4)*, T&T Clark Int'l) Continuum International Publishing Group, Ltd. GBR. Dist: National Bk. Network.

Moreno, Art, Jr. The Letters. 2009. 300p. 49.50 *(978-0-557-03055-2(2))* Lulu Enterprises Inc.

Moule, C. F. D. Essays in New Testament Interpretation. 2008. (ENG.). 344p. pap. 46.00 *(978-0-521-09025-4(3))* Cambridge Univ. Pr.

Moyise. Evoking Scripture: Seeing the Old Testament in the New. 2008. (ENG., Illus.). 176p. 34.95 *(978-0-567-03325-3(2)*, T&T Clark Int'l) Continuum International Publishing Group, Ltd. GBR. Dist: National Bk. Network.

Moyise, Steve. Deuteronomy in the New Testament: The New Testament & the Scriptures of Israel. Menken, Maarten J.J., ed. 2007. (Library of New Testament Studies, the Ser.). (ENG.). 208p. 155.00 *(978-0-567-04549-2(8)*, T&T Clark Int'l) Continuum International Publishing Group, Ltd. GBR. Dist: National Bk. Network.

—Evoking Scripture: Seeing the Old Testament in the New. 2008. (ENG., Illus.). 176p. 120.00 *(978-0-567-03324-6(4)*, T&T Clark Int'l) Continuum International Publishing Group, Ltd. GBR. Dist: National Bk. Network.

Myers, Ched & Enns, Elaine, eds. Ambassadors of Reconciliation Vol. I: New Testament Reflections on Restorative Justice & Peacemaking. 2009. 192p. pap. 16.00 *(978-1-57075-831-7(X))* Orbis Bks.

New Testament Profiles, 3 vols., Set. Incl. Luke: Historian & Theologian. 3rd ed. Marshall, I. Howard. 252p. pap. 22.00 *(978-0-8308-1513-5(9)*, 1513, IVP Acad.); Matthew: Evangelist & Teacher (New Testament Profiles) France, R. T. 345p. 23.00 *(978-0-8308-1511-1(2)*, 1511); 1998. reprint ed. 2p. Set pap. 20.00 o.p. *(978-0-8308-1541-8(4))* InterVarsity Pr.

Neyrey, et al. The Social World of the New Testament: Insights & Models. 2008. 270p. (C). pap. *(978-1-59856-128-9(6))* Hendrickson Pubs. Marketing, LLC.

O. Living in the Victory of Jesus: Bible Lessons to Deepen Faith. 2008. 144p. pap. 10.99 *(978-1-60352-090-4(2))* UMI (Urban Ministries, Inc.).

O'Brien, Kelli S. Use of Scripture in the Markan Passion Narrative. 2010. (Library of New Testament Studies, the Ser.). (ENG.). 352p. 150.00 *(978-0-567-03379-6(1)*, T&T Clark Int'l) Continuum International Publishing Group, Ltd. GBR. Dist: National Bk. Network.

Oegema, Gerbern S. Early Judaism & Modern Culture: Literature & Theology. 2011. xvi, 236p. pap. 30.00 *(978-0-8028-6444-4(9))* Eerdmans, William B. Publishing Co.

Ogden, D. Kelly & Skinner, Andrew C. Verse by Verse, Acts Through Revelation. 2006. (Illus.). ix, 422p. 24.99 *(978-1-59038-590-6(X))* Deseret Bk. Co.

Olsson, Frank. Come to Think about It: Associations to the Sixty-Six Books of the Bible from a Philosophical Perspective. 2009. 248p. pap. 25.95 *(978-1-4269-1457-7(1))* Trafford Publishing.

Ostrander, Peter E. New Testament Healing. 2011. 334p. 28.99 ***(978-1-61379-285-8(9))***; pap. 18.99 ***(978-1-61379-284-1(0))*** Xulon Pr., Inc.

Page, John E. Prophecy in Order. 2009. 260p. pap. 16.99 *(978-1-60791-526-3(X))* Xulon Pr., Inc.

Park, Jung Eun Sophia. A Hermeneutic on Dislocation As Experience: Creating a Borderland, Constructing a Hybrid Identity. 2012. viii, 137p. ***(978-1-4331-1594-3(8))***; E-Book ***(978-1-4539-0190-8(6))*** Lang, Peter GmbH, Europaischer Verlag der Wissenschaften.

Parker, D. C. An Introduction to the New Testament Manuscripts & their Texts. 2008. (ENG., Illus.). 398p. 95.00 *(978-0-521-89553-8(7))* Cambridge Univ. Pr.

—An Introduction to the New Testament Manuscripts & Their Texts. 2008. (ENG., Illus.). 398p. pap. 40.00 *(978-0-521-71989-6(5))* Cambridge Univ. Pr.

Parker, David C. Manuscripts, Texts, Theology: Collected Papers, 1977-2007. 2009. (Arbeiten zur neutestamentlichen Textforschung Ser.). (ENG.). XII, 380p. 140.00 *(978-3-11-021193-1(9))* De Gruyter, Walter Inc.

Parker, David C. Textual Scholarship & the Making of the New Testament. 2012. (ENG., Illus.). 208p. 40.00 ***(978-0-19-965781-0(5))*** Oxford Univ. Pr., Inc.

Patte, Daniel, et al, eds. Greek Patristic & Eastern Orthodox Interpretations of Romans, Vol. 9. 2013. (Romans Through History & Culture Ser.). (ENG.). 224p. pap. 39.95 *(978-0-567-48092-7(5)*, T&T Clark Int'l) Continuum International Publishing Group, Ltd. GBR. Dist: National Bk. Network.

Patterson, Donald. Bible Discovery Series: Finding Tools to Read & Interpret Scripture. 2010. 96p. pap. *(978-0-8100-2269-0(9))* Northwestern Publishing Hse.

Petersen, Norman R. Literary Criticism for New Testament Critics. 2008. 92p. (Orig.). pap. 13.00 *(978-1-60608-115-0(2)*, Wipf and Stock) Wipf & Stock Pubs.

Pinkston, Ron. Our Father. 2009. 76p. pap. 10.99 *(978-0-9796620-2-7(8))* Selah Publishing Group, LLC.

Poll-van de Lisdonk, M. L. van, ed. VI-9 Annotationes in novum testamentum (pars Quinta) Ordinis sexti - Tomus Nonus. 2009. (Opera Omnia Desiderii Erasmi ndash; Erasmus, Opera Omnia Ser.). (LAT & MUL., Illus.). 496p. *(978-90-04-17564-8(4))* BRILL.

Pollard, Neal. Rise up & Build. 2007. *(978-0-929540-62-7(X))* Publishing Designs, Inc.

Pregeant, Russell. Knowing Truth, Doing Good: Engaging New Testament Ethics. 2008. 400p. per. 35.00 *(978-0-8006-3846-7(8)*, Fortress Pr.) Augsburg Fortress, Pubs.

Price, Craig. Biblical Exegesis of New Testament Greek: James. 2008. 294p. pap. 32.00 *(978-1-55635-972-9(1))* Wipf & Stock Pubs.

Prichard, Gerald R. Is Jesus Reasonable? A Logical Analysis of the Statements Attributed to Jesus Christ. 2009. (ENG.). 350p. pap. 36.99 *(978-0-7618-4651-2(4))* Univ. Pr. of America, Inc.

Puhalo, Lazar. Scripture & the Divine Liturgy: Scripture in the Liturgy. Date not set. 60p. pap. 5.50 *(978-1-879038-94-3(3)*, 9060) Synaxis Pr.

Ramsay, William, et al. Cities of St. Paul: And Other Biblical Sites in Asia Minor. 2012. 416p. 26.99 *(978-0-8254-3635-2(4))* Kregel Pubns.

Randall, Albert B. Holy Scriptures As Justifications for War: Fundamentalist Interpretations of the Torah, the New Testament, & the Qur'an. 2007. 280p. 109.95 *(978-0-7734-5217-6(6))* Mellen, Edwin Pr., The.

Redford, Douglas. The New Testament Church Vol. 2: Acts - Revelation. 2007. (Standard Reference Library NT Ser.). 304p. 19.99 *(978-0-7847-1901-5(2))* Standard Publishing.

Reed, Randall W. A Clash of Ideologies: Marxism, Liberation Theology, & Apocalypticism in New Testament Studies. 2010. (Princeton Theological Monographs). 194p. pap. 22.00 *(978-1-55635-514-1(9)*, Pickwick Pubns.) Wipf & Stock Pubs.

Reeves, Rodney. Spirituality According to Paul: Imitating the Apostle of Christ. 2011. (ENG.). 253p. pap. 20.00 ***(978-0-8308-3946-9(1)***, IVP Acad.) InterVarsity Pr.

Richard Benton, Benton & Richard Benton. God What Great Signs: Signs in the Heavens. 2009. 128p. 23.95 *(978-1-4401-7973-0(5))*; pap. 13.95 *(978-1-4401-7975-4(1))* iUniverse, Inc.

Rickards Mozley, John. The Divine Aspect of History: Volume 2. 2011. (ENG.). 520p. pap. 48.00 ***(978-1-107-60518-3(0))*** Cambridge Univ. Pr.

Ridges, David J. Your Study of the New Testament Made Easier: Part 1: Matthew, Mark, Luke & John. 2nd ed. 2010. (Gospel Studies). 467p. per. 24.99 *(978-1-59955-000-8(8))* Cedar Fort, Inc./CFI Distribution.

—Your Study of the New Testament Made Easier Part 2: Acts Through Revelation, Vol. 2. 2nd ed. 2010. (Gospel Studies). 469p. per. 24.99 *(978-1-59955-001-5(6))* Cedar Fort, Inc./CFI Distribution.

Riell, Howard Michael. Enoch & the Book of Coincidences Vi. 2008. 376p. pap. 16.95 *(978-1-60264-139-6(0))* Virtualbookworm.com Publishing, Inc.

Robb, Carol S. Wind, Sun, Soil, Spirit: Biblical Ethics & Climate Change. 2010. 176p. (C). pap. 20.00 *(978-0-8006-9706-8(5)*, Fortress Pr.) Augsburg Fortress, Pubs.

Robertson, A. T. Estudios en el Nuevo Testamento: Studies on the New Testament. (SPA.). *(978-84-7645-229-5(2)*, 223298) Clie, Editorial.

Robinson, John A. T. Twelve New Testament Studies. 2009. (Studies in Biblical Theology, First Ser.). 180p. pap. 21.00 *(978-1-60899-033-7(8)*, Wipf and Stock) Wipf & Stock Pubs.

Rohrbaugh, Richard L. The New Testament in Cross-Cultural Perspective. 2006. (Matrix: the Bible in Mediterranean Context: Ser.). (Illus.). 228p. pap. 25.00 *(978-1-59752-827-6(7)*, Cascade Bks.) Wipf & Stock Pubs.

Rowland, C. C. & Morray-Jones, C. R. A. Compendia Rerum Iudaicarum ad Novum Testamentum, The Mystery of God: Early Jewish Mysticism & the New Testament, Vol. 12. 2009. 694p. *(978-90-04-17532-7(6))* BRILL.

Rowlandson, Maurice L. The Riddle of the Gifts. 2007. 80p. pap. 14.95 *(978-1-84753-368-5(X))* Lulu Enterprises Inc.

Runesson, Anna. Exegesis in the Making: Postcolonialism & New Testament Studies. 2010. (Biblical Interpretation Ser.). (Illus.). xv, 254p. *(978-90-04-18836-5(3))* BRILL.

Sanday, William. The Authorship & Historical Character of the Fourth Gospel. 2009. 330p. pap. 30.75 *(978-1-115-80443-1(X))* BiblioBazaar.

Schäfer, Peter. Jesus in the Talmud. (ENG., Illus.). 232p. (C). 2009. pap. 22.95 *(978-0-691-14318-7(8))* 2007. 45.00 *(978-0-691-12926-6(6))* Princeton Univ. Pr.

Schaller, Berndt, et al. Judaistik und Neutestamentliche Wissenschaft: Standorte, Grenzen, Beziehungen. 2008. (Forschungen Zur Religion und Literatur des Alten & Neuen Testament Ser.). (GER., Illus.). 416p. (C). 111.00 *(978-3-525-53090-0(0))* Vandenhoeck & Ruprecht GmbH & Co. KG DEU. Dist: ISD.

Schenck, Kenneth. Paul: Prisoner of Hope. 2012. ***(978-0-89827-525-4(3))*** Wesleyan Publishing Hse.

Schmeller, Thomas, ed. Historiographie und Biographie Im Neuen Testament und Seiner Umwelt. 2009. (Novum Testamentum et Orbis Antiquus/Studien zur Umwelt des Neuen Testaments (NTOA/StUNT) Ser.). (GER.). 208p. (C). 77.00 *(978-3-525-53968-2(1))* Vandenhoeck & Ruprecht GmbH & Co. KG DEU. Dist: ISD.

Schreiter, Robert J. In Water & in Blood: A Spirituality of Solidarity & Hope. rev. ed. 2007. 137p. per. 18.00 *(978-1-57075-707-5(0))* Orbis Bks.

Scott, Bernard Brandon. The Trouble with Resurrection: From Paul to the Fourth Gospel. 2010. 264p. pap. 25.00 *(978-1-59815-020-9(0))* Polebridge Pr.

Scrivener, Frederick Henry Ambrose. A Plain Introduction to the Criticism of the New Testament: For the Use of Biblical Students. 2010. (Cambridge Library Collection - Religion Ser.). (ENG.). 536p. pap. 39.99 *(978-1-108-00746-7(5))* Cambridge Univ. Pr.

—A Plain Introduction to the Criticism of the New Testament for the Use of Biblical Students by Frederick Henry Scrivener. 2006. 536p. per. 29.99 *(978-1-4255-6059-1(8))* MPublishing.

Seay, Chris, et al, retold by. The Voice from on High: God Announces His Son as Israel's Liberating King. 0 vols. 2007. (Voice Ser.). 144p. pap. 14.99 *(978-0-529-12414-2(9))* Nelson, Thomas Inc.

Segovia, Fernando F. A Postcolonial Commentary on the New Testament Writings. Sugirtharajah, R. S., ed. 2009. (Bible & Postcolonialism Ser.). (ENG.). 480p. 44.95 *(978-0-567-63707-9(7)*, T&T Clark Int'l) Continuum International Publishing Group, Ltd. GBR. Dist: National Bk. Network.

Segovia, Fernando F., et al. A Postcolonial Commentary on the New Testament Writings. 2007. (Bible & Postcolonialism Ser.). (ENG.). 480p. 160.00 *(978-0-567-04563-8(3)*, T&T Clark Int'l) Continuum International Publishing Group, Ltd. GBR. Dist: National Bk. Network.

Shelly, Rubel. New Testament: A Book-by-Book Study. pap. 13.99 *(978-0-89098-012-5(8))* Twentieth Century Christian Bks.

Shepp, Victoria. Coyote Meets Jesus: Treasures in Folktales & Scripture. 2006. (Illus.). 107p. 16.75 *(978-0-88489-889-4(X))* St. Mary's Pr.

Shillington, V. George. New Testament in Context: A Literary & Theological Textbook. 2009. (ENG., Illus.). 352p. 34.95 *(978-0-567-03405-2(4)*, T&T Clark Int'l) Continuum International Publishing Group, Ltd. GBR. Dist: National Bk. Network.

Shillington, V. George & Shillington, V. G. The New Testament in Context: A Literary & Theological Textbook. 2009. (ENG., Illus.). 352p. 120.00 *(978-0-567-03404-5(6)*, T&T Clark Int'l) Continuum International Publishing Group, Ltd. GBR. Dist: National Bk. Network.

Silva, Moises. The Essential Companion to Life in Bible Times: Key Insights for Reading God's Word, 1 vol. 2011. (Essential Bible Companion Ser.). (ENG.). 144p. pap. 16.99 *(978-0-310-28688-2(3))* Zondervan.

Simmons, Albert C. I, Paul... God's Ambassador to the Gentiles. 2007. 356p. pap. 18.95 *(978-0-7414-4186-7(1))* Infinity Publishing.

Smith, William Frank. How Will We Know the Way? A reading guide for the New Testament. 2011. 156p. pap. 16.95 ***(978-1-4575-0327-6(1))*** Dog Ear Publishing, LLC.

So, Damon W. K. The Forgotten Jesus & the Trinity You Never Knew. 2010. (Illus.). 254p. pap. 28.00 *(978-1-60899-631-5(X)*, Wipf and Stock) Wipf & Stock Pubs.

Sorge, Bob. It's Not Business, It's Personal. 2009. (Illus.). 87p. pap. 9.00 *(978-0-9749664-6-5(0))* Oasis Hse.

Sperry Syposium Staff. The New Testament & the Latter-Day Saints. 2010. 256p. pap. 15.99 *(978-1-59955-486-0(0))* Cedar Fort, Inc./CFI Distribution.

Spicq, Ceslaus. Agape in the New Testament Vol. 1: Agape in the Synoptic Gospels. 2006. 168p. pap. 20.00 *(978-1-59752-856-6(0)*, Wipf and Stock) Wipf & Stock Pubs.

—Agape in the New Testament Vol. 2: Agape in the Epistles of St. Paul, the Acts of the Apostles & the Epistles of St. James, St. Peter, & St. Jude. 2006. (Agape in the New Testament Ser.). 460p. pap. 44.00 *(978-1-59752-857-3(9)*, Wipf and Stock) Wipf & Stock Pubs.

—Agape in the New Testament Vol. 3: Agape in the Gospels, Epistles, & Apocalypse of St. John. 2006. (Agape in the New Testament Ser.). 272p. pap. 27.00 *(978-1-59752-858-0(7)*, Wipf and Stock) Wipf & Stock Pubs.

—Agape in the New Testament, 3 Volumes. 2007. 900p. pap. 90.00 *(978-1-55635-344-4(8)*, Wipf and Stock) Wipf & Stock Pubs.

Stewart, Robert B. & Habermas, Gary R., eds. Memories of Jesus: A Critical Appraisal of James D. G. Dunn's Jesus Remembered. 2010. (ENG.). 352p. pap. 29.99 *(978-0-8054-4840-5(3)*, B&H Academic) B&H Publishing Group.

Stichele, Caroline Vander, et al. Contextualizing Gender in Early Christian Discourse: Thinking Beyond Thecla. 2009. (ENG.). 264p. 29.95 *(978-0-567-03036-8(9))*; 120.00 *(978-0-567-03035-1(0))* Continuum International Publishing Group, Ltd. GBR. (T&T Clark Int'l). Dist: National Bk. Network.

Stout, Stephen O. The Man Christ Jesus: The Humanity of Jesus in the Teaching of the Apostle Paul. 2011. 344p. pap. 38.00 ***(978-1-61097-287-1(2)***, Wipf and Stock) Wipf & Stock Pubs.

Strickert, Frederick M. Philip's City: From Bethsaida to Julias. 2011. 39.95 *(978-0-8146-5752-2(4))*; E-Book *(978-0-8146-8008-7(9))* Liturgical Pr.

Supernatural Religion V2 an Inquiry into. 2006. pap. 40.95 *(978-1-4286-5221-7(3))* Kessinger Publishing, LLC.

Tait, Michael. Torah in the New Testament: Papers Delivered at the Manchester-Lausanne Seminar of June 2008. Tait, Michael & Oakes, Peter, eds. 2010. (Library of New Testament Studies, the Ser.). (ENG.). 304p. 130.00 *(978-0-567-00673-8(5)*, T&T Clark Int'l) Continuum International Publishing Group, Ltd. GBR. Dist: National Bk. Network.

Tamberino, Tony. Scripture Sessions on the New Testament. ldr.'s ed. 2006. 102p. per. 18.95 *(978-0-88489-867-2(9))* St. Mary's Pr.

Tamberino, Tony & Shrader, Mary. Scripture Sessions on the New Testament. 2006. (YA). pap., wbk. ed. 7.25 *(978-0-88489-866-5(0))* St. Mary's Pr.

Tannehill, Robert C. The Shape of the Gospel: New Testament Essays. 2007. 254p. pap. 28.00 *(978-1-59752-511-4(1)*, Cascade Bks.) Wipf & Stock Pubs.

Tasker, R. V. G. The Greek New Testament. 2008. (GEC & GRE.). 460p. pap. 58.00 *(978-0-521-09026-1(1))* Cambridge Univ. Pr.

Tatum, Gregory. New Chapters in the Life of Paul: The Relative Chronology of His Career. 2006. (Catholic Biblical Quarterly Ser.: Vol. 41). ix, 145p. *(978-0-915170-39-5(6))* Catholic Biblical Assn. of America.

Taylor, John. Classics & the Bible: Hospitality & Recognition. 2007. (Classical Literature & Society Ser.). 192p. per. 34.95 *(978-0-7156-3481-3(X))* Duckworth Publishers GBR. Dist: International Publishers Marketing.

Theissen, Gerd. The New Testament: A Literary History. Maloney, Linda M., tr. from GER. 2011. 304p. (C). 49.00 *(978-0-8006-9785-3(5)*, Fortress Pr.) Augsburg Fortress, Pubs.

—Von Jesus zur urchristlichen Zeichenwelt: Neutestamentliche Grenzgänge im Dialog. 2011. (Novum Testamentum et Orbis Antiquus/Studien zur Umwelt des Neuen Testaments (NTOA/StUNT) Ser.). (GER.). 237p. (C). 81.00 *(978-3-525-55023-6(5))* Vandenhoeck & Ruprecht GmbH & Co. KG DEU. Dist: ISD.

Thomas Nelson Publishing Staff. The Voice New Testament, Designer Series, 0 vols. 2009. 480p. pap. 34.99 *(978-1-4185-4249-8(0))* Nelson, Thomas Inc.

—The Voice Reader's New Testament, 0 vols. 2009. 600p. pap. 9.99 *(978-1-4185-4215-3(6))* Nelson, Thomas Inc.

Thompson, Thomas L. & Verenna, Thomas S., eds. 'Is This Not the Carpenter?' The Question of the Historicity of the Figure of Jesus. 2012. (Copenhagen International Seminar Ser.). (ENG.). 296p. (C). 110.00 ***(978-1-84553-986-3(9))*** Equinox Publishing Ltd. GBR. Dist: ISD.

Thompson, Vivian & Ah Yee, Virginia. Intimate Moments with My Beloved King. 2007. 275p. per. 15.00 *(978-0-9797037-0-6(0))* Ah Yee, Virginia.

Towns, Elmer. Praying the New Testament: Praying the Scriptures with Elmer Towns. 2008. pap. 24.99 *(978-0-7684-2704-2(5))* Destiny Image Pubs.

Travis, Stephen. Christ & the Judgement of God: The Limits of Divine Retribution in New Testament Thought. 2009. *(978-1-84227-613-6(1))* Hendrickson Pubs. Marketing, LLC.

—Christ & the Judgment of God: The Limits of Divine Retribution in New Testament Thought. 2009. 448p. pap. *(978-1-59856-338-2(6))* Hendrickson Pubs. Marketing, LLC.

Trebilco, Paul. Self-designations & Group Identity in the New Testament. 2011. (ENG., Illus.). 392p. 99.00 ***(978-1-107-01299-8(6))*** Cambridge Univ. Pr.

Treneer, Mike. Advancing the Gospel: How the Gospel Bears Fruit & Grows. 2011. *(978-1-61747-157-5(7)*, NavPress Publishing Group.

Turner, Max, et al. The Spirit & Christ in the New Testament & Christian Theology: Essays in Honor of Max Turner. 2012. pap. ***(978-0-8028-6753-7(7))*** Eerdmans, William B. Publishing Co.

Twelftree, Graham H. In the Name of Jesus: Exorcism among Early Christians. 2007. 352p. (C). pap. 35.00 *(978-0-8010-2745-1(4))* Baker Academic.

Twelftree, Graham H. Jesus the Exorcist: A Contribution to the Study of the Historical Jesus. 2011. 286p. pap. 31.00 ***(978-1-61097-060-0(8)***, Wipf and Stock) Wipf & Stock Pubs.

Tyndale House Publishers Staff & Next Staff, prods. Manga Messiah. 2007. (ENG., Illus.). 288p. (YA). (gr. 5). pap. 12.99 *(978-1-4143-1680-2(1))* Tyndale Hse. Pubs.

Vaka'uta, Nasili. Reading Ezra 9/10 Tu'a-Wise: Rethinking Biblical Interpretation in Oceania. 2011. ***(978-1-58983-621-1(9))***; ***(978-1-58983-620-4(0))*** Society of Biblical Literature.

van Cangh, J. -M., ed. Les sources judaïques du Nouveau Testament: Receuil D'essais. 2008. (Bibliotheca Ephemeridum Theologicarum Lovaniensium Ser.). (FRE.). 718p. (C). pap. 122.00 *(978-90-429-1903-7(5))* Peeters Pubs. & Booksellers BEL. Dist: Brown, David Bk. Co., The.

van der Watt, Jan, ed. & contrib. by. Identity, Ethics, & Ethos in the New Testament. 2006. (Beihefte Zur Zeitschrift Für Die Neutestamentliche Wissenschaft und Die Kunde der älteren Kirche Ser.: Vol. 141). (ENG.). XIII, 645p. 231.00 *(978-3-11-018973-5(9))* De Gruyter, Walter Inc.

Vance, Laurence M. Greek Verbs in the New Testament & Their Principal Parts. 2006. (ENM.). 236p. per. *(978-0-9763448-2-7(3))* Vance Pubns.

Vanhoozer, Kevin J., ed. Theological Interpretation of the New Testament: A Book-by-Book Survey. 2008. 272p. (C). pap. 19.99 *(978-0-8010-3623-1(2))* Baker Academic.

Viola, Frank. From Eternity to Here: Rediscovering the Ageless Purpose of God, 1 vol. 2009. (ENG.). 320p. pap. 14.99 *(978-1-4347-6870-4(8))* Cook, David C.

—Reimagining Church: Pursuing the Dream of Organic Christianity. 2008. (ENG.). 320p. pap. 14.99 *(978-1-4347-6875-9(9))* Cook, David C.

Viola, Frank & Barna, George. Pagan Christianity? Exploring the Roots of Our Church Practices. (ENG.). 336p. 2012. pap. 14.99 ***(978-1-4143-6455-1(5))*** 2008. 17.99 *(978-1-4143-1485-3(X))* Tyndale Hse. Pubs. (BarnaBks.).

Vogan, Charles. Jesus & the New Testament. 2007. 351p. pap. 21.94 *(978-0-615-13930-2(2))* Shenandoah Bible Ministries.

Vööbus, Arthur. Investigations into the Text of the New Testament used by Rabbula of Edessa. 2010. pap. 20.80 *(978-1-61143-616-7(8))* Gorgias Pr., LLC.

Waite, Pastor D. A. Westcott & Hort's Greek Text & Theory Refuted. 2008. 48p. pap. 10.00 *(978-1-56848-004-6(0))* Old Paths Pubns., Inc., The.

Waite, Th. D. Fuzzy Facts from Fundamentalists. 2008. 112p. pap. 12.00 *(978-1-56848-032-9(6))* Old Paths Pubns., Inc., The.

Wake, William. The Forbidden Books of the New Testament. 2009. 300p. pap. 11.95 *(978-1-59594-816-8(3)*, Wingspan Pr.) WingSpan Publishing.

Warrington, Keith. Discovering Jesus in the New Testament, 1 vol. 2010. (ENG.). 240p. *(978-1-59856-011-4(5))* Hendrickson Pubs. Marketing, LLC.

Waters, Guy Prentiss. End of Deuteronomy in the Epistles of Paul. 2006. (Wissenshaftliche Untersuchungen zum Neuen Testament Ser.: 221). 302p. (Orig.). pap. 99.50 *(978-3-16-148891-7(1))* Mohr Siebeck GmbH & Co. KG DEU. Dist: Coronet Bks.

Watson, Duane F. The Rhetoric of the New Testament: A Bibliographic Survey. 2006. 182p. pap. 34.95 *(978-90-5854-028-7(6))* Deo Publishing NLD. Dist: Presbyterian Publishing Corp.

What Does the New Testament Say? *(978-0-382-00936-5(3))* Silver, Burdett & Ginn, Inc.

Wieland, George M. The Significance of Salvation: A Study of Salvation Language in the Pastoral Epistles. 2006. (Paternoster Biblical Monographs: Ser.). 384p. pap. 39.00 *(978-1-59752-721-7(1)*, Wipf and Stock) Wipf & Stock Pubs.

Wiertzema, John. The Coming Judgment of Islam. 2007. 168p. (ENG.). 21.99 *(978-1-60266-501-9(X))*; per. 13.99 *(978-1-60266-500-2(1))* Xulon Pr., Inc.

Wilson, R. McLachlan, tr. The Gospel of Philip: Translated from the Coptic Text with an Introduction & Commentary. 2011. 206p. 44.95 ***(978-1-258-04675-0(X))*** Literary Licensing, LLC.

Wilson, Robert McLachlan, et al. Text & Interpretation: Studies in the New Testament Presented to Matthew Black. Best, Ernest, ed. 2009. (ENG.). 288p. pap. 42.00 *(978-0-521-11479-0(9))* Cambridge Univ. Pr.

Winstanley, Edward William. Spirit in the New Testament: An Enquiry into the Use of the Word #928;#925;#917;#933;#924;#913; in All Passages, & a Survey of the Evidence Concerning the Holy Spirit. 2011. 175p. pap. 19.99 *(978-1-107-60024-9(3))* Cambridge Univ. Pr.

Witherington, Ben, III. The Indelible Image Vol. 1: The Theological & Ethical Thought World of the New Testament - The Individual Witnesses. 2009. (Indelible Image Set Ser.). (ENG.). 856p. 50.00 *(978-0-8308-3861-5(9)*, IVP Acad.) InterVarsity Pr.

—The Indelible Image Vol. 2: The Theological & Ethical Thought World of the New Testament - The Collective Witness. 2010. (Indelible Image Set Ser.). (ENG.). 838p. 50.00 *(978-0-8308-3862-2(7)*, IVP Acad.) InterVarsity Pr.

—What's in the Word: Rethinking the Socio-Rhetorical Character of the New Testament. 2009. (ENG.). 203p. pap. 29.95 *(978-1-60258-196-8(7))* Baylor Univ. Pr.

Women in the New Testament. 18.00 *(978-0-687-34304-1(6))* Abingdon Pr.

Wordsworth, John & White, Henry. Novum Testamentum Latine. 2007. (LAT.). 644p. per. *(978-1-84356-024-1(0))* Wallenberg, Simon Pr.

Wright, N. T. The Kingdom New Testament: A Contemporary Translation. 2012. 640p. pap. 16.99 ***(978-0-06-206492-9(4)***, HarperOne) HarperCollins Pubs.

—New Testament for Everyone: Complete Eighteen-Volume Set. 2011. (New Testament for Everyone Ser.). (ENG.). pap. 215.00 *(978-0-664-23826-1(2))* Westminster John Knox Pr.

—Paul: In Fresh Perspective. 2008. 203p. (C). pap. 20.00 *(978-0-8006-6357-5(8))* Augsburg Fortress, Pubs.

The Writings of S S Peter, James, & John; Together with Notices of Their Lives, & the Ten Commandments the Text Accurately Copied from an Editi. 2006. 144p. per. 16.99 *(978-1-4255-1062-6(0))* MPublishing.

Yinger, Kent L. The New Perspective on Paul: An Introduction. 2011. 120p. pap. 16.00 *(978-1-60899-463-2(5))* Cascade Bks.

Yoder Neufeld, Thomas R. Recovering Jesus: The Witness of the New Testament. 2007. (Illus.). 336p. (C). pap. 30.00 *(978-1-58743-202-6(1))* Brazos Pr.

Zacka, Jimi P. Possessions Démoniaques et Exorcismes Dans les églises Pentecôtistes D'Afrique Centrale: Une Relecture du "Ministère de Délivrance" à Partir de L'Évangile de Marc. 2010. (FRE.). 347p. *(978-9956-0-9183-6(9))* Cle, Editions.

Zimmermann, Ruben, et al, eds. Moral Language in the New Testament: The Interrelatedness of Language & Ethics in Early Christian Writings. Kontexte und Normen Neutestamentlicher Ethik / Contexts & Norms of New Testament Ethics. Band II. 2010. (Illus.). 457p. pap. 177.50 *(978-3-16-150354-2(6))* Mohr Siebeck GmbH & Co. KG DEU. Dist: Coronet Bks.

BIBLE—CRITICISM, INTERPRETATION, ETC.—N. T. ACTS

Adamczewski, Bartosz. Heirs of the Reunited Church: The History of the Pauline Mission in Paul's Letters, in the So-Called Pastoral Letters, & in the Pseudo-Titus Narrative of Acts. 2010. 178p. 57.95 *(978-3-631-60504-2(8))*

B

Lang, Peter GmbH, Europaischer Verlag der Wissenschaften DEU. Dist: Lang, Peter.

Alexander, Loveday & Alexander. Acts in Its Ancient Literary Context: A Classicist Looks at the Acts of the Apostles. 2007. (Library of New Testament Studies: Vol. 289). (ENG., Illus.). 304p. 140.00 *(978-0-567-08209-1(1)*, T&T Clark Int'l) Continuum International Publishing Group, Ltd. GBR. Dist: National Bk. Network.

Alexander, Paul, et al, eds. Trajectories in the Book of Acts: Essays in Honor of John Wesley Wyckoff. 2010. 394p. pap. 43.00 *(978-1-60608-540-0(9)*, Wipf and Stock) Wipf & Stock Pubs.

Anderson, Leith. The Jesus Revolution: Learning from Christ's First Followers. 2009. 152p. pap. 16.00 *(978-0-687-65398-0(3))* Abingdon Pr.

Ascough, Richard S. Lydia: Paul's Cosmopolitan Hostess. Malina, Bruce J., ed. 2009. 144p. pap. 14.95 *(978-0-8146-5269-5(7))* Liturgical Pr.

Atkinson, William. Baptism in the Spirit: Luke-Acts & the Dunn Debate. 2012. (ENG.). 164p. (C). pap. 30.00 ***(978-0-7188-9268-5(2))*** Lutherworth Pr., The GBR. Dist: Brown, David Bk. Co., The.

Atkinson, William P. Baptism in the Spirit: Luke-Acts & the Dunn Debate. 2011. 164p. pap. 19.00 *(978-1-60899-971-2(8)*, Pickwick Pubns.) Wipf & Stock Pubs.

Baker, Coleman A. Identity, Memory, & Narrative in Early Christianity: Peter, Paul, & Recategorization in the Book of Acts. 2011. (Illus.). 282p. pap. 31.00 ***(978-1-60899-514-1(3)***, Pickwick Pubns.) Wipf & Stock Pubs.

Barber, Cyril J. Come Before Winter: Profiles of Some of Paul's Friends ... & Some Who Were Not. 2008. 152p. pap. 17.00 *(978-1-60608-179-2(9))* Wipf & Stock Pubs.

Barr, Beth Allison, et al, eds. The Acts of the Apostles: Four Centuries of Baptist Interpretation. 2009. (ENG.). 1000p. 99.95 *(978-1-60258-186-9(X))* Baylor Univ. Pr.

Barreto, Eric D. Ethnic Negotiations: The Function of Race & Ethnicity in Acts 16. 2010. (Illus.). 230p. pap. 107.50 *(978-3-16-150609-3(X))* Mohr Siebeck GmbH & Co. KG DEU. Dist: Coronet Bks.

Barrier, Jeremy W. The Acts of Paul & Thecla: A Critical Introduction & Commentary. 2009. (GEC & ENG., Illus.). XX, 232p. pap. 117.50 *(978-3-16-149998-2(0))* Mohr Siebeck GmbH & Co. KG DEU. Dist: Coronet Bks.

Börstinghaus, Jens. Sturmfahrt und Schiffbruch: Zur lukanischen Verwendung eines literarischen Topos in Apostelgeschichte 27,1-28,6. 2010. (GER., Illus.). 572p. pap. 187.50 *(978-3-16-149996-8(4))* Mohr Siebeck GmbH & Co. KG DEU. Dist: Coronet Bks.

Blackaby, Henry. The Book of Acts, 0 vols. 2007. (Encounters with God Ser.). 112p. per. 9.99 *(978-1-4185-2642-9(8))* Nelson, Thomas Inc.

Bock, Darrell L. & Köstenberger, Andreas J. A Theology of Luke & Acts: Biblical Theology of the New Testament, 1 vol. 2012. (Biblical Theology of the New Testament Ser.). (ENG.). 512p. 39.99 ***(978-0-310-27089-8(8))*** Zondervan.

Bovon, Francois. Luke the Theologian: Fifty-Five Years of Research (1950-2005) 2nd ed. 2006. 445p. per. 39.95 *(978-1-932792-18-8(X))* Baylor Univ. Pr.

Brother, Yun. Living Water, 1 vol. 2008. (ENG.). 240p. pap. 14.99 *(978-0-310-28554-0(2))* Zondervan.

Campbell, William. The We Passages in the Acts of the Apostles: The Narrator as Narrative Character. 2007. 164p. per. 19.95 *(978-1-58983-205-3(1))* Society of Biblical Literature.

Campbell, William Sanger. The We Passages in the Acts of the Apostles: The Narrator as Narrative Character. 2007. (SBL - Studies in Biblical Literature Ser.). 150p. *(978-90-04-14676-1(8))* BRILL.

Chamness, Stefani O. Turn from Games & Lies to the Truth & from the Power of Satan unto God Acts 26: 18. deluxe ed. *(978-0-9631276-1-7(6))* Church of The Living God, The.

Churchill, Timothy W. R. Divine Initiative & the Christology of the Damascus Road Encounter. 2010. (Illus.). 336p. pap. 37.00 *(978-1-60899-325-3(6)*, Pickwick Pubns.) Wipf & Stock Pubs.

Czachesz, István & Czachesz, I. Commission Narratives: A Comparative Study of the Canonical & Apocryphal Acts. 2007. (Studies in Early Christian Apocrypha Ser.). (ENG.). 322p. (C). pap. 58.00 *(978-90-429-1845-0(4))* Peeters Pubs. & Booksellers BEL. Dist: Brown, David Bk. Co., The.

De Long, Kindalee Pfremmer. Surprised by God: Praise Responses in the Narrative of Luke-Acts. 2009. (Beihefte zur Zeitschrift für die neutestamentliche Wissenschaft und die Kunde der älteren Kirche Ser.). (ENG.). XIV, 331p. 105.00 *(978-3-11-022165-7(9))* De Gruyter, Walter Inc.

Eisen, Ute E. Die Poetik der Apostelgeschichte: Eine Narratologische Studie. 2006. (Novum Testamentum et Orbis Antiquus (Ntoa) Ser.: 58). (GER.). 294p. (C). 68.00 *(978-3-525-53961-3(4))* Vandenhoeck & Ruprecht GmbH & Co. KG DEU. Dist: ISD.

Everts, Don. Getting Your Feet Dirty: A down-to-Earth Look at Following Jesus. 2007. (ENG.). 132p. per. 8.00 *(978-0-8308-3604-8(7)*, IVP Bks.) InterVarsity Pr.

Flessen, Bonnie J. An Exemplary Man: Cornelius & Characterization in Acts 10. 2011. 206p. pap. 23.00 ***(978-1-61097-294-9(5)***, Pickwick Pubns.) Wipf & Stock Pubs.

Foss, Michael W. From Members to Disciples: Leadership Lessons from the Book of Acts. 2007. 100p. per. 16.00 *(978-0-687-46730-3(6))* Abingdon Pr.

Frey, Jörg, et al, eds. Die Apostelgeschichte im Kontext antiker und frahchristlicher Historiographie. 2009. (Beihefte zur Zeitschrift far die neutestamentliche Wissenschaft und die Kunde der älteren Kirche Ser.).Tr. of Acts of the Apostles in the Context of Ancient & Early Christian Historiography. (GER.). X, 703p. 321.00 ***(978-3-11-173653-2(9))*** De Gruyter, Walter Inc.

Frey, Jörg, et al, eds. Die Apostelgeschichte im Kontext antiker und frühchristlicher Historiographie. 2009. (Beihefte zur Zeitschrift für die neutestamentliche Wissenschaft und die Kunde der Älteren Kirche Ser.).Tr. of Acts of the Apostles in the Context of Ancient & Early Christian Historiography. (GER.). X, 703p. 210.00 *(978-3-11-021631-8(0))* De Gruyter, Walter Inc.

Girard, Robert C. The Book of Acts, 0 vols. Richards, Larry, ed. 2007. (Smart Guide to the Bible Ser.). (Illus.). 384p. per. 14.99 *(978-1-4185-0997-2(3))* Nelson, Thomas Inc.

Goodwin, Bennie. Acts: Luke's Portrait of the Early Christian Church. 2010. 108p. pap. 7.95 *(978-1-932715-54-5(1))* UMI (Urban Ministries, Inc.).

Gowler, David B. & Gowler, David. Host, Guest, Enemy & Friend: Portraits of the Pharisees in Luke & Acts. 2008. 422p. pap. 46.00 *(978-1-55635-690-2(0))* Wipf & Stock Pubs.

Harnack, Adolf. Luke the Physician: The Author of the Third Gospel & the Acts of the Apostles. 2008. 244p. pap. *(978-1-4437-1686-4(3))* Read Bks.

—Luke the Physician: The Author of the Third Gospel & the Acts of the Apostles. 2009. 240p. pap. 25.00 *(978-1-60608-439-7(9)*, Wipf and Stock) Wipf & Stock Pubs.

—Luke the Physician the Author of the Thi. 2006. pap. 28.95 *(978-1-4286-3475-6(4))* Kessinger Publishing, LLC.

Hartsock, Chad. Sight & Blindness in Luke-Acts: The Use of Physical Features in Characterization. 2008. (Biblical Interpretation Ser.). 232p. *(978-90-04-16535-9(5))* BRILL.

Hennecke, Matt. Acts of the Apostles. 2007. pap. 6.99 *(978-1-58427-192-5(2))* Guardian of Truth Foundation.

Horton, Dennis J. Death & Resurrection. 2009. 152p. pap. 17.00 *(978-1-60608-290-4(6)*, Pickwick Pubns.) Wipf & Stock Pubs.

—Death & Resurrection: The Shape & Function of a Literary Motif in the Book of Acts. 2011. (ENG.). 136p. pap. 38.00 *(978-0-227-17365-7(1))* Clarke, James Co., Ltd. GBR. Dist: Brown, David Bk. Co., The.

Houghtby-Haddon, Natalie K. Changed Imagination, Changed Obedience: Social Change, Social Imagination, & the Bent-over Woman in the Gospel of Luke. 2011. 190p. pap. 22.00 *(978-1-60899-675-9(1)*, Pickwick Pubns.) Wipf & Stock Pubs.

Hume, Douglas A. The Early Christian Community: A Narrative Analysis of Acts 2:41-47 & 4:32-35. 2011. (Wissenschaftliche Untersuchungen zum Neuen Testament, 2 / No. 298 Ser.). 187p. pap. 97.50 *(978-3-16-150729-8(0))* Mohr Siebeck GmbH & Co. KG DEU. Dist: Coronet Bks.

Huntington, Ray L., et al, eds. Shedding Light on the New Testament: Acts through Revelation. 2009. 288p. *(978-0-8425-2725-5(7)*, Brigham Young Univ. Religious Studies Ctr.) Brigham Young Univ.

Jeffery, Peter. Moving Out: With the Christian Faith. 2007. 126p. per. *(978-0-85234-609-9(3))* Evangelical Pr.

Kent, Homer A., Jr. Jerusalem to Rome: Studies in Acts. (Illus.). pap. 10.99 *(978-0-88469-056-6(3))* BMH Bks.

Koet, B. J. Dreams & Scriptures in Luke-Acts: Collected Essays. 2006. (Contributions to Biblical Exegesis & Theology Ser.: Vol. 42). (ENG & GER., Illus.). 232p. (C). 57.00 *(978-90-429-1750-7(4))* Peeters Pubs. & Booksellers BEL. Dist: Brown, David Bk. Co., The.

Land, Darin H. The Diffusion of Ecclesiastical Authority: Sociological Dimensions of Leadership in the Book of Acts. 2008. (Princeton Theological Monographs). 256p. pap. 28.00 *(978-1-55635-575-2(0)*, Pickwick Pubns.) Wipf & Stock Pubs.

Larkin, William J. & Trites, Allison A. Luke, Acts. 2006. (Cornerstone Biblical Commentary Ser.: 12). (ENG.). 688p. 34.99 *(978-0-8423-3438-9(6))* Tyndale Hse. Pubs.

Leod, F. Wayne Mac. Acts: Principles of Victory & Perseverance. 2006. (Light to My Path Ser.). (ENG.). 264p. per. 13.99 *(978-1-932805-01-7(X))* Authentic Media.

Lindemann, Andreas. Die Evangelien und die Apostelgeschichte: [in German]. 2009. 421p. 225.00 *(978-3-16-150041-1(5))* Mohr Siebeck GmbH & Co. KG DEU. Dist: Coronet Bks.

Longstreth, Jason. BTB Acts. 2007. 6.99 *(978-1-58427-198-7(1))* Guardian of Truth Foundation.

Malina, Bruce J. & Pilch, John J. Social-Science Commentary on the Book of Acts. 2008. (Illus.). 254p. per. 29.00 *(978-0-8006-3845-0(X)*, Fortress Pr.) Augsburg Fortress, Pubs.

Marty, William H. Lecture Notes for the Book of Acts. 3rd rev. ed. 2009. (ENG.). 114p. spiral bd. 28.45 *(978-0-7575-2690-9(X))* Kendall Hunt Publishing Co.

Matthews, Shelly. Perfect Martyr: The Stoning of Stephen & the Construction of Christian Identity. (ENG.). 2012. 240p. pap. 24.95 ***(978-0-19-992465-3(1))*** 2010. 224p. 65.00 *(978-0-19-539332-3(5))* Oxford Univ. Pr., Inc.

Maxwell, Kathy. Hearing Between the Lines: The Audience as Fellow-Worker in Luke-Acts & its Literary Milieu, Vol.. 425. 2010. (Library of New Testament Studies, the Ser.). (ENG., Illus.). 224p. 120.00 *(978-0-567-59291-0(X)*, T&T Clark Int'l) Continuum International Publishing Group, Ltd. GBR. Dist: National Bk. Network.

McCabe, David R. How to Kill Things with Words: Ananias & Sapphira under the Prophetic Speech-Act of Divine Judgment (Acts 4. 32-5. 11) 2011. (ENG.). 296p. 120.00 ***(978-0-567-52543-7(0)***, T&T Clark Int'l) Continuum International Publishing Group, Ltd. GBR. Dist: National Bk. Network.

McGhee, Quentin. Hechos del Espiritu Santo- Guia del Maestro. Moeckl, Trudy, ed. Segura, Sara & Segura, Maritza, trs. from ENG. 2011. Orig. Title: Acts of the Holy Spirit. (SPA.). lib. bdg. 10.00 *(978-1-931984-43-0(X))*, 4413-16S1 Faith & Action Team.

Meek, James A. Gentile Mission in Old Testament Citations in Acts: Text, Hermeneutic, & Purpose. 2009. (Library of New Testament Studies, the Ser.). (ENG.). 192p. 130.00 *(978-0-567-03380-2(5)*, T&T Clark Int'l) Continuum International Publishing Group, Ltd. GBR. Dist: National Bk. Network.

Miller, J. R. Devotional Hours with the Bible Volume Viii, from the Acts, the Epistles & Revelation. 2011. 154p. pap. 14.99 ***(978-1-61203-206-1(0))*** Bottom of the Hill Publishing.

Miller, John B. F. Convinced that God had Called Us: Dreams, Visions & the Perception of God's Will in Luke-Acts. 2006. (Biblical Interpretation Ser.: Vol. 85). 288p. *(978-90-04-15474-2(4))* BRILL.

Mittelstadt, Martin. Reading Luke-Acts in the Pentecostal Tradition: Reflections on the History & Status of Research. 2010. (ENG.). 232p. (C). pap. 14.95 *(978-0-9819651-7-8(2))* CPT Pr.

Moessner, David P., et al, eds. Paul & the Heritage of Israel: Luke's Narrative Claim upon Paul & Israel's Legacy. 2012. (Library of New Testament Studies). (ENG.). 400p. 120.00 *(978-0-567-40148-9(0)*, T&T Clark Int'l) Continuum International Publishing Group, Ltd. GBR. Dist: National Bk. Network.

Muñoz-Larrondo, Rubén. A Postcolonial Reading of the Acts of the Apostles. 2012. xiv, 249p. E-Book ***(978-1-4539-0237-0(6))*** Lang, Peter GmbH, Europaischer Verlag der Wissenschaften.

—A Postcolonial Reading of the Acts of the Apostles. 2011. (C). 80.95 ***(978-1-4331-1608-7(1))*** Lang, Peter Publishing, Inc.

Myers, Susan E. Spirit Epicleses in the Acts of Thomas. 2010. (Illus.). 276p. pap. 117.50 *(978-3-16-149472-7(5))* Mohr Siebeck GmbH & Co. KG DEU. Dist: Coronet Bks.

Need, Stephen W. Paul Today: Challenging Readings of Acts & the Epistles. 2007. (Essential Inquiries Ser.). (ENG.). 160p. per. 15.95 *(978-1-56101-296-1(3))* Cowley Pubns.

Öhler, Markus, ed. Aposteldekret und antikes Vereinswesen: Gemeinschaft und ihre Ordnung. 2011. (Wissenschaftliche Untersuchungen zum Neuen Testament Ser.). (GER.). 419p. 225.00 ***(978-3-16-150363-4(5))*** Mohr Siebeck GmbH & Co. KG DEU. Dist: Coronet Bks.

Padilla, Osvaldo. The Speeches of Outsiders in Acts: Poetics, Theology & Historiography. (Society for New Testament Studies Monograph Ser.). (ENG.). 2011. 284p. pap. 45.00 *(978-0-521-17532-6(1))* 2008. 288p. 127.00 *(978-0-521-89981-9(8))* Cambridge Univ. Pr.

Park, Hyung Dae & Park. Finding Herem? A Study of Luke-Acts in the Light of Herem. 2007. (Library of New Testament Studies). (HEB & ENG.). 240p. 130.00 *(978-0-567-04550-8(1)*, T&T Clark Int'l) Continuum International Publishing Group, Ltd. GBR. Dist: National Bk. Network.

Park, Sejin. Pentecost & Sinai: The Festival of Weeks as a Celebration of the Sinai Event. 2008. (Library of Hebrew Bible/Old Testament Studies, the Ser.). (ENG.). 304p. 130.00 *(978-0-567-02727-6(9)*, T&T Clark Int'l) Continuum International Publishing Group, Ltd. GBR. Dist: National Bk. Network.

Parker, David C. Codex Bezae: An Early Christian Manuscript & its Text. 2008. (LAT, GEC & ENG., Illus.). 376p. pap. 48.00 *(978-0-521-07236-6(0))* Cambridge Univ. Pr.

Parsons, Mikeal C. Body & Character in Luke & Acts: The Subversion of Physiognomy in Early Christianity. 2011. (ENG.). 192p. pap. 29.95 *(978-1-60258-380-1(3))* Baylor Univ. Pr.

Paulist Press. Praying with Saint Paul Using Lectio Divina: Acts of the Apostles. 2009. 72p. pap. 4.95 *(978-0-8091-4645-1(2))* Paulist Pr.

Pervo, Richard I. Dating Acts: Between the Evangelists & the Apologists. 2006. xiv, 513p. *(978-0-944344-73-6(9))* Polebridge Pr.

—The Mystery of Acts: Unraveling Its Story. 2008. 192p. pap. 20.00 *(978-1-59815-012-4(X))* Polebridge Pr.

Phillips, Thomas E. Acts Within Diverse Frames of Reference. 2009. 192p. pap. 30.00 *(978-0-88146-165-7(2))* Mercer Univ. Pr.

—Contemporary Studies in Acts. 2009. 224p. pap. 35.00 *(978-0-88146-145-9(8))* Mercer Univ. Pr.

—Paul, His Letters, & Acts. 2008. (ENG.). 250p. (C). pap. *(978-1-934269-34-3(4))* Univ. Readers.

Phillips, Thomas E. & Porter, Stanley E. Paul, His Letters, & Acts. 2009. 256p. *(978-1-59856-001-5(8))* Hendrickson Pubs. Marketing, LLC.

Pilgrim, Walter. Good News to the Poor: Wealth & Poverty in Luke - Acts. 2011. 198p. pap. 23.00 ***(978-1-61097-663-3(0)***, Wipf and Stock) Wipf & Stock Pubs.

Puskas, Charles B. The Conclusion of Luke-Acts Vols. 16-31: The Significance of Acts 28. 2008. 206p. pap. 21.00 *(978-1-55635-235-5(2)*, Pickwick Pubns.) Wipf & Stock Pubs.

Read-Heimerdinger, Jenny & Rius-Camps, Josep. Message of Acts in Codex Bezae Vol. 4: A Comparison with the Alexandrian Tradition, Acts 18. 24-28. 31 - Rome. 2009. (Library of New Testament Studies, the Ser.). (ENG.). 434p. 140.00 *(978-0-567-04899-8(3)*, T&T Clark Int'l) Continuum International Publishing Group, Ltd. GBR. Dist: National Bk. Network.

Rhoads, David, et al, eds. Luke-Acts & Empire: Essays in Honor of Robert L. Brawley. 2010. (Princeton Theological Monographs). 186p. pap. 21.00 *(978-1-60899-098-6(2)*, Pickwick Pubns.) Wipf & Stock Pubs.

Rius-Camps, Josep, et al. The Message of Acts in Codex Bezae Vol. 3: A Comparison with the Alexandrian Tradition - Acts 13. 1-18. 23, 3 vols. 2007. (Library of New Testament Studies). (ENG.). 416p. 155.00 *(978-0-567-03248-5(5)*, T&T Clark Int'l) Continuum International Publishing Group, Ltd. GBR. Dist: National Bk. Network.

Robertson, C. K. Conversations with Scripture: Acts of the Apostles. 2010. (Anglican Association of Biblical Scholars Ser.). 160p. pap. 18.00 *(978-0-8192-2372-2(7)*, Morehouse Publishing) Church Publishing, Inc.

Rowe, C. Kavin. Rethinking the Unity & Reception of Luke & Acts. Gregory, Andrew F., ed. 2010. 232p. 49.95 *(978-1-57003-916-4(X))* Univ. of South Carolina Pr.

—World Upside Down: Reading Acts in the Graeco-Roman Age. 2010. (ENG.). 312p. pap. 24.95 *(978-0-19-976761-8(0))* Oxford Univ. Pr., Inc.

Salmeier, Michael A. Restoring the Kingdom: The Role of God as the ÒOrdainer of Times & SeasonsÓ in the Acts of the Apostles. 2011. (Princeton Theological Monographs). 224p. pap. 25.00 ***(978-1-61097-098-3(5)***, Pickwick Pubns.) Wipf & Stock Pubs.

Samkutty, V J & Samkutty. The Samaritan Mission in Acts, Vol. 328. 2006. (Library of New Testament Studies: Vol. 328). (ENG., Illus.). 272p. 180.00 *(978-0-567-04464-8(5)*, T&T Clark Int'l) Continuum International Publishing Group, Ltd. GBR. Dist: National Bk. Network.

Schmithals, Walther. Paul & James. 2009. (Studies in Biblical Theology, First Ser.). 126p. pap. 16.00 *(978-1-60899-028-3(1)*, Wipf and Stock) Wipf & Stock Pubs.

Sellner, Hans Jorg. Das Heil Gottes: Studien Zur Soteriologie des Lukanischen Doppelwerks. 2007. (Beihefte Zur Zeitschrift Für Die Neutestamentliche Wissenschaft Und Die Kunde der älteren Kirche Ser.). (GER.). XIII, 591p. 196.00 *(978-3-11-019699-3(9))* De Gruyter, Walter Inc.

Shillington, V. George & Shillington. An Introduction to the Study of Luke-Acts. 2007. (T & T Clark Approaches to Biblical Studies). (ENG.). 168p. 39.95 *(978-0-567-03053-5(9)*, T&T Clark Int'l) Continuum International Publishing Group, Ltd. GBR. Dist: National Bk. Network.

Simpson, A. B. Hechos-Comentario Hechos De: Acts-Comment. to the Acts. (SPA.). *(978-84-7645-260-8(8)*, 223322) Clie, Editorial.

Skinner, Matthew L. The Trial Narratives: Conflict, Power, & Identity in the New Testament. 2010. (ENG.). 224p. pap. 35.00 *(978-0-664-23032-6(6))* Westminster John Knox Pr.

Sleeman, Matthew. Geography & the Ascension Narrative in Acts. 2009. (Society for New Testament Studies Monograph Ser.). (ENG.). 312p. 102.00 *(978-0-521-50962-6(9))* Cambridge Univ. Pr.

Smith, Mitzi J. The Literary Construction of the Other in the Acts of the Apostles: Charismatics, the Jews, & Women. 2012. (ENG.). 186p. pap. 30.00 ***(978-0-227-68022-3(7))*** Clarke, James Co., Ltd. GBR. Dist: Brown, David Bk. Co., The.

—The Literary Construction of the Other in the Acts of the Apostles: Charismatics, the Jews, & Women. 2010. (Princeton Theological Monographs). 186p. pap. 21.00 *(978-1-60899-384-0(1)*, Pickwick Pubns.) Wipf & Stock Pubs.

Smith, Richard G. Studies in Acts. 3.98 *(978-0-687-82659-9(4))* Abingdon Pr.

Spencer, F. Scott. The Gospel of Luke & Acts of the Apostles. 2008. (Interpreting Biblical Texts Ser.). (Illus.). 260p. per. 25.00 *(978-0-687-00850-6(6))* Abingdon Pr.

Standard Publishing Staff. Church. 2006. cd-rom 24.99 *(978-0-7847-1883-4(0))* Standard Publishing.

Stott, John. Acts: Seeing the Spirit at Work. 2008. (John Stott Bible Studies). (ENG.). 111p. pap. 8.00 *(978-0-8308-2161-7(9)*, IVP Conn.) InterVarsity Pr.

Thompson, Alan. One Lord, One People: The Unity of the Church in Acts in Its Literary Setting. 2008. (Library of New Testament Studies). (ENG.). 240p. 130.00 *(978-0-567-04559-1(5)*, T&T Clark Int'l) Continuum International Publishing Group, Ltd. GBR. Dist: National Bk. Network.

Thompson, Alan J. The Acts of the Risen Lord Jesus: Luke's Account of God's Unfolding Plan. 2011. (New Studies in Biblical Theology Ser.: Volume 27). (ENG.). 232p. pap. 24.00 *(978-0-8308-2628-5(9)*, IVP Acad.) InterVarsity Pr.

Thompson, Richard P. Keeping the Church in Its Place: The Church as Narrative Character in Acts. 2006. (ENG.). 320p. pap. 34.95 *(978-0-567-02645-3(0)*, T&T Clark Int'l) Continuum International Publishing Group, Ltd. GBR. Dist: National Bk. Network.

—Keeping the Church in Its Place: The Church as Narrative Character in the Book of Acts. 2006. (ENG.). 320p. 110.00 *(978-0-567-02654-5(X)*, T&T Clark Int'l) Continuum International Publishing Group, Ltd. GBR. Dist: National Bk. Network.

Torrey, Charles Cutler. The Composition & Date of Acts. 2009. 76p. pap. 16.75 *(978-1-113-66465-5(7))* BiblioBazaar.

—The Composition & Date of Acts. 2009. 58p. pap. *(978-0-217-07353-0(0))* Books LLC.

Troftgruben, Troy M. A Conclusion Unhindered: A Study of the Ending of Acts Within Its Literary Environment. 2010. (Illus.). 239p. pap. 117.50 *(978-3-16-150453-2(4))* Mohr Siebeck GmbH & Co. KG DEU. Dist: Coronet Bks.

Twelftree. People of the Spirit. 2009. xvii, 269p. pap. *(978-0-281-05536-4(X))* Baker Academic.

Twelftree, Graham H. People of the Spirit: Exploring Luke's View of the Church, 1 vol. 2009. 304p. (C). pap. 25.00 *(978-0-8010-3880-8(4))* Baker Academic.

Tyson, Joseph B. The Death of Jesus in Luke-Acts. 2010. pap. 24.95 *(978-1-57003-962-1(3))* Univ. of South Carolina Pr.

—Images of Judaism in Luke-Acts. 2010. pap. 24.94 *(978-1-57003-963-8(1))* Univ. of South Carolina Pr.

—Luke, Judaism, & the Scholars: Critical Approaches to Luke-Acts. 2010. pap. 24.94 *(978-1-57003-964-5(X))* Univ. of South Carolina Pr.

—Marcion & Luke-Acts: A Defining Struggle. annot. ed. 2006. 192p. 39.95 *(978-1-57003-650-7(0))* Univ. of South Carolina Pr.

Wade, Kenneth R. Paul: A Spiritual Journey. 2011. pap. 14.99 *(978-0-8163-2493-4(X))* Pacific Pr. Publishing Assn.

Walters, Patricia. The Assumed Authorial Unity of Luke & Acts: A Reassessment of the Evidence. 2009. (Society for New Testament Studies Monograph Ser.). (ENG., Illus.). 254p. 102.00 *(978-0-521-50974-9(2))* Cambridge Univ. Pr.

Walton, Steve. Leadership & Lifestyle: The Portrait of Paul in the Miletus Speech & 1 Thessalonians. 2007. (Society for New Testament Studies Monograph Ser.). (ENG.). 272p. (C). pap. 57.00 *(978-0-521-03638-2(0))* Cambridge Univ. Pr.

Weaver, John B. Plots of Epiphany: Prison-Escape in Acts of the Apostles. (Beihefte zur Zeitschrift fur die neutestamentliche Wissenschaft und die Kunde der älteren Kirche Ser.). (ENG.). XII, 335p. 225.00 ***(978-3-11-181864-1(0))*** De Gruyter, Walter Inc.

Williams, Charles Bray. The Participle in the Book of Acts. 2008. 87p. pap. 8.00 *(978-1-60608-354-3(5)*, Wipf and Stock) Wipf & Stock Pubs.

Wilson, J. M., tr. The Acts of the Apostles: Translated from the Codex Bezae with an Introduction on its Lucan Origin & Importance. 2011. 104p. pap. 11.00 *(978-1-61097-123-2(X)*, Wipf and Stock) Wipf & Stock Pubs.

Witherington, Ben, III, ed. History, Literature, & Society in the Book of Acts. 2007. (ENG.). 396p. pap. 79.00 *(978-0-521-04628-2(9))* Cambridge Univ. Pr.

Zeller, Edward. The Contents & Origin of the Acts of the Apostles: Critically Investigated, 2 Volumes. 2007. 645p. pap. 55.00 *(978-1-55635-505-9(X)*, Wipf and Stock) Wipf & Stock Pubs.

Zugmann, Michael. 'Hellenisten' in der Apostelgeschichte: Historische und exegetische Untersuchungen zu Apg 6,1; 9,29; 11,20. 2009. (Wissenschaftliche Untersuchungen zum Neuen Testament Ser.). (Illus.). 497p. pap. 167.50 *(978-3-16-149896-1(8))* Mohr Siebeck GmbH & Co. KG DEU. Dist: Coronet Bks.

Zwiep, Arie W. Christ, the Spirit & the Community of God: Essays on the Acts of the Apostles. 2010. (Wissenschaftliche Untersuchungen zum Neuen Testament Ser.). (Illus.). XVIII, 237p. pap. 117.50 *(978-3-16-150675-8(8))* Mohr Siebeck GmbH & Co. KG DEU. Dist: Coronet Bks.

BIBLE—CRITICISM, INTERPRETATION, ETC.—N. T. APOCRYPHAL BOOKS

Achtemeier, Paul J. Jesus & the Miracle Tradition. 2007. 274p. pap. 30.00 *(978-1-59752-364-6(X))* Wipf & Stock Pubs.

Attridge, Harold W. The Acts of Thomas. Hills, Julian V., ed. 2010. 130p. pap. 18.00 *(978-1-59815-021-6(9))* Polebridge Pr.

Baun, Jane. Tales from Another Byzantium: Celestial Journey & Local Community in the Medieval Greek Apocrypha. 2010. (ENG.). 474p. pap. 55.00 *(978-0-521-17749-8(9))* Cambridge Univ. Pr.

Bovon, François. New Testament & Christian Apocrypha. 2009. (Wissenschaftliche Untersuchungen zum Neuen Testament Ser.). (Illus.). 381p. 229.00 *(978-3-16-149050-7(9))* Mohr Siebeck GmbH & Co. KG DEU. Dist: Eisenbrauns, Inc.

Cowper, B. Harris. Apocryphal Gospels & Other Documents R. 2006. pap. 19.95 *(978-1-4286-4467-0(9)*, Kessinger Publishing, LLC.

Czachesz, Istvan, et al, eds. The Visio Pauli & the Gnostic Apocalypse of Paul. 2007. (Studies in Early Christian Apocrypha Ser.). (ENG., Illus.). 249p. (C). pap. 60.00 *(978-90-429-1851-1(9))* Peeters Pubs. & Booksellers BEL. Dist: Brown, David Bk. Co., The.

De Conick, April D. The Codex Judas Papers: Proceedings of the International Congress on the Tchacos Codex Held at Rice University, Houston Texas, March 13-16 2008. 2009. (Nag Hammadi & Manichaean Studies). 614p. *(978-90-04-18141-0(5))* BRILL.

DeSilva, David Arthur. The Jewish Teachers of Jesus, James, & Jude: What the First Family of Christianity Learned from the Apocrypha & Pseudepigrapha. 2012. (ENG.). 384p. 35.00 ***(978-0-19-532900-1(7))*** Oxford Univ. Pr., Inc.

Elliott, J. K., ed. The Apocryphal Jesus: Legends of the Early Church. 2008. (ENG.). 240p. pap. 32.95 *(978-0-19-954402-8(2))* Oxford Univ. Pr., Inc.

Foster, Paul. Non-Canonical Gospels. Foster, Paul, ed. 2008. (ENG.). 232p. 39.95 *(978-0-567-03302-4(3)*, T&T Clark Int'l) Continuum International Publishing Group, Ltd. GBR. Dist: National Bk. Network.

Foster, Paul, ed. Non-Canonical Gospels. 2008. (ENG.). 232p. 130.00 *(978-0-567-03301-7(5)*, T&T Clark Int'l) Continuum International Publishing Group, Ltd. GBR. Dist: National Bk. Network.

Frey, Jorg, et al, eds. Das Thomasevangelium: Entstehung - Rezeption - Theologie. 2008. (Beihefte zur Zeitschrift für die neutestamentliche Wissenschaft und die Kunde der Älteren Kirche Ser.). (GER.). IX, 545p. 147.00 *(978-3-11-020246-5(8))* De Gruyter, Walter Inc.

Glicksman, Andrew T. Wisdom of Solomon 10: A Jewish Hellenistic Reinterpretation of Early Israelite History through Sapiential Lenses. 2011. (Deuterocanonical & Cognate Literature Studies). (ENG., Illus.). XIV, 244p. 210.00 ***(978-3-11-214313-1(2))*** De Gruyter, Walter Inc.

Goodspeed, Edgar Johnson. Strange New Gospels. 2011. 122p. 40.95 ***(978-1-258-03988-2(5))*** Literary Licensing, LLC.

Hall, John R. Apocalypse: From Antiquity to the Empire of Modernity. 2009. (ENG.). 296p. 69.95 *(978-0-7456-4508-7(9))*; pap. 24.95 *(978-0-7456-4509-4(7))* Polity Pr. GBR. Dist: Wiley, John & Sons, Inc.

Hanson, Kenneth. Secrets from the Lost Bible. 2006. (ENG., Illus.). 248p. per. 14.95 *(978-1-57178-203-8(6))* Council Oak Bks.

Hone, William & Jones, Jeremiah, compiled by. The Apocryphal New Testament. 2010. 114.80 *(978-1-61719-219-7(8))* Gorgias Pr., LLC.

Jacobs, Alan & Watkins, eds. The Gnostic Gospels: Including the Gospel of Thomas the Gospel of Mary Magdalene. 2006. (Sacred Wisdom Ser.). (ENG., Illus.). 280p. 8.95 *(978-1-84293-121-9(0)*, Watkins Publishing) Duncan Baird Pubs. GBR. Dist: Sterling Publishing Co., Inc.

King, Karen L. The Secret Revelation of John. 2009. (Illus.). 416p. pap. 19.50 *(978-0-674-03055-8(9))* Harvard Univ. Pr.

Klauck, Hans-Josef. The Apocryphal Acts of the Apostles: An Introduction. 2008. (ENG.). 310p. (C). pap. 39.95 *(978-1-60258-159-3(2))* Baylor Univ. Pr.

Levine, Amy Jill, ed. A Feminist Companion to the New Testament Apocrypha. 2006. (Feminist Companion to the New Testament & Early Christian Writings). 292p. per. 21.00 *(978-0-8298-1754-6(9))* Pilgrim Pr., The/United Church Pr.

Lumpkin, Joseph B. The Gospel of Judas: The Man, His History, His Story. 2007. (ENG.). 148p. per. 14.99 *(978-1-933580-40-1(2))* Fifth Estate, Inc.

—Lost Scriptures & Divergent Doctrine: Lost Books of the Bible & Lost Doctrines of the Faith. 2007. (ENG.). 792p. per. 34.99 *(978-1-933580-39-5(9))* Fifth Estate, Inc.

Merkt, Andreas, et al, eds. Violence in the Apocalypse. 2011. (Novum Testamentum et Orbis Antiquus/Studien zur Umwelt des Neuen Testaments (NTOA/StUNT) Ser.). (ENG & GER.). 313p. (C). 95.00 *(978-3-525-53976-7(2))* Vandenhoeck & Ruprecht GmbH & Co. KG DEU. Dist: ISD.

Metzger, Bruce M. Apostolic Letters of Faith, Hope, & Love: Galatians, 1 Peter, & 1 John. 2006. 110p. pap. 15.00 *(978-1-59752-501-5(4)*, Cascade Bks.) Wipf & Stock Pubs.

National Geographic Society Staff, et al, eds. The Gospel of Judas. 2nd ed. 2008. (ENG., Illus.). 224p. pap. 12.95 *(978-1-4262-0048-9(X)*, National Geographic) National Geographic Society.

Newton, Tim. The Forgotten Gospels: Early, Lost, & Historical Writings on the Life & Teachings of Jesus. 2009. (ENG.). 160p. 20.00 *(978-1-58243-508-4(1)*, Counterpoint Pr.) Basic Bks. GBR. Dist: Perseus-PGW.

Nicklas, Tobias. Gospel Fragments. Kraus, Thomas J. & Kruger, Michael J., eds. 2009. (GEC & ENG., Illus.). 288p. 165.00 *(978-0-19-920815-9(8))* Oxford Univ. Pr., Inc.

Oegema, Gerbern S. Early Judaism & Modern Culture: Literature & Theology. 2011. xvi, 236p. pap. 30.00 *(978-0-8028-6444-4(9))* Eerdmans, William B. Publishing Co.

Oegema, Gerbern S. & Charlesworth, James H., eds. The Pseudepigrapha & Christian Origins: Essays from the Studiorum Novi Testamenti Societas. 2011. (ENG.). 312p. pap. 49.95 ***(978-0-567-43054-0(5)***, T&T Clark Int'l) Continuum International Publishing Group, Ltd. GBR. Dist: National Bk. Network.

Pagels, Elaine & King, Karen L. Reading Judas: The Gospel of Judas & the Shaping of Christianity. 2008. (ENG.). 224p. (gr. 12-18). 15.00 *(978-0-14-311316-4(X)*, Penguin (Non-Classics)) Penguin Group (USA) Inc.

Painchaud, Louis & Poirier, Paul-Hubert. Colloque International "L'évangile Selon Thomas et les Textes de Nag Hammadi", Québec, 29-31 Mai 2003. 2007. (Bibliotheque copte de nag hammadi. section Etudes Ser.). (FRE, GEC & ENG.). 652p. (C). pap. 116.00 *(978-90-429-2055-2(6))* Peeters Pubs. & Booksellers BEL. Dist: Brown, David Bk. Co., The.

Pate, C. Marvin. Reading Revelation: A Comparison of Four Interpretive Translations of the Apocalypse, 1 vol. 2009. 208p. pap. 29.99 *(978-0-8254-3367-2(3))* Kregel Pubns.

Perrin, Nicholas. Thomas, the Other Gospel. 2007. (ENG.). 160p. per. 25.00 *(978-0-664-23211-5(6))* Westminster John Knox Pr.

Porter, Stanley E. & Heath, Gordon L. The Lost Gospel of Judas: Separating Fact from Fiction. 2007. 127p. per. 16.00 *(978-0-8028-2456-1(0))* Eerdmans, William B. Publishing Co.

Rhodes, James N. Epistle of Barnabas Hermeneia. 2019. (Hermeneia Ser.). *(978-0-8006-6055-0(2))* Augsburg Fortress, Pubs.

Signori, Gabriela. Dying for the Faith, Killing for the Faith: Old-Testament Faith-Warriors (1 & 2 Maccabees) in Historical Perspective. 2011. (Brill's Studies in Intellectual History). (Illus.). xiii, 311p. ***(978-90-04-21105-6(5))*** BRILL.

Tuckett, Christopher, ed. The Gospel of Mary. 2007. (Oxford Early Christian Texts). (MUL & ENG., Illus.). 256p. 150.00 *(978-0-19-921213-2(9))* Oxford Univ. Pr., Inc.

William Hone Published 1820 Staff. The Apocryphal New Testament. 2007. pap. *(978-1-84830-013-2(1)*, Wildhern Pr.) Echo Library.

William Wake. The Suppressed Gospels & Epistles of the original New Testament of Jesus the Christ Volume 9: Hermas. 2007. (ENG.). 130p. pap. 18.99 *(978-1-4346-3926-4(6))*; 146p. pap. 19.99 *(978-1-4346-3927-1(4))* BiblioBazaar.

BIBLE—CRITICISM, INTERPRETATION, ETC.—N. T. COLOSSIANS

see Bible—Criticism, Interpretation, etc.—N. T. Epistles

BIBLE—CRITICISM, INTERPRETATION, ETC.—N. T. CORINTHIANS

see Bible—Criticism, Interpretation, etc.—N. T. Epistles

BIBLE—CRITICISM, INTERPRETATION, ETC.—N. T. EPHESIANS

see Bible—Criticism, Interpretation, etc.—N. T. Epistles

BIBLE—CRITICISM, INTERPRETATION, ETC.—N. T. EPISTLES

Here are entered books on the Epistles as a whole, or on one or more of the following, Colossians, Corinthians, Ephesians, Galatians, Hebrews, James, Epistles of John, Jude, Peter, Philemon, Romans, Thessalonians, Timothy, Titus.

Abasciano & Abasciano, Brian J. Paul's Use of the Old Testament in Romans 9:10-18: An Intertextual & Theological Exegesis. 2011. (Library of New Testament Studies). (ENG.). 272p. 120.00 *(978-0-567-03103-7(9)*, T&T Clark Int'l) Continuum International Publishing Group, Ltd. GBR. Dist: National Bk. Network.

Abernathy, David. Exegetical Summary of 1 Peter. 2nd ed. 2008. 184p. pap. 26.00 *(978-1-55671-193-0(X))* SIL International.

—Exegetical Summary of 2 Corinthians. 2nd ed. 2008. (GEC & ENG.). 436p. pap. 44.00 *(978-1-55671-206-7(5))* SIL International.

—Exegetical Summary of Romans 1-8. 2nd ed. 2008. 577p. pap. 48.00 *(978-1-55671-207-4(3))* SIL International.

—An Exegetical Summary of Romans 9-16. 2009. 390p. pap. 42.00 *(978-1-55671-233-3(2))* SIL International.

Achtemeier, Paul J. Romans. 2010. (Interpretation: A Bible Commentary Ser.). (ENG., Illus.). 256p. pap. 25.00 *(978-0-664-23438-6(0))* Westminster John Knox Pr.

Adewuya, J. Ayodeji. Holiness & Community in 2 Cor 6:14Ntilde;7:1: Paul's View of Communal Holiness in the Corinthian Correspondence. 2011. 248p. pap. 27.00 *(978-1-61097-194-2(9)*, Wipf and Stock) Wipf & Stock Pubs.

Aernie, Matthew D. Forensic Language & the Day of the Lord Motif in Second Thessalonians 1 & the Effects on the Meaning of the Text. 2011. (WEST Theological Monograph Ser.). 250p. pap. 28.00 ***(978-1-61097-486-8(7)***, Wipf and Stock) Wipf & Stock Pubs.

Akenson, Donald Harman. Saint Saul: A Skeleton Key to the Historical Jesus. (ENG.). 352p. *(978-0-7735-2090-5(2))* McGill-Queen's Univ. Pr.

Anderson, Clive. Opening up 2 Peter. 2007. (Opening up the Bible Ser.). (Illus.). 128p. pap. 9.00 *(978-1-84625-077-4(3))* DayOne Pubns. GBR. Dist: STL Distribution North America.

Anderson, Richard Lloyd. Understanding Paul. 2007. 464p. pap. 17.95 *(978-1-59038-729-0(5))* Desert Bks.

Anderson, Robert. Types in Hebrews. 2007. 196p. per. 9.45 *(978-1-60206-233-7(1))* Cosimo, Inc.

Artz-Grabner, Peter. 1. Korinther: Papyrologische Kommentare zum Neuen Testament. 2006. (Papyrologische Kommentare zum Neuen Testament Ser.: Vol. 2). (GER.). 576p. (C). 144.00 *(978-3-525-51001-8(2))* Vandenhoeck & Ruprecht GmbH & Co. KG DEU. Dist: ISD.

Ashley, Evelyn. Paul's Defense of His Ministerial Style: A Study of His Second Letter to the Corinthians. 2011. 352p. 129.95 *(978-0-7734-1557-7(2))* Mellen, Edwin Pr., The.

Attridge, Harold W. Essays on John & Hebrews. 2010. (Illus.). 443p. 257.50 *(978-3-16-150319-1(8))* Mohr Siebeck GmbH & Co. KG DEU. Dist: Coronet Bks.

Aymer, Margaret & Aymer. First Pure, Then Peaceable: Frederick Douglass Reads James. 2008. (Library of New Testament Studies, the Ser.). (ENG.). 164p. 130.00 *(978-0-567-03307-9(4)*, T&T Clark Int'l) Continuum International Publishing Group, Ltd. GBR. Dist: National Bk. Network.

Bachmann, Michael. Anti-Judaism in Galatians? Exegetical Studies on a Polemical Letter & on Paul's Theology. Brawley, Robert L., tr. from GER. 2009. (Illus.). 224p. pap. 45.00 *(978-0-8028-6291-4(8))* Eerdmans, William B. Publishing Co.

Backhaus, Knut. Der sprechende Gott: Gesammelte Studien zum Hebräerbrief. 2009. (Illus.). 344p. 177.50 *(978-3-16-150027-5(X))* Mohr Siebeck GmbH & Co. KG DEU. Dist: Coronet Bks.

Baker Publishing Group Staff. A Walk Thru the Book of Ephesians: Real Power for Daily Life. 2009. (Walk Thru the Bible Discussion Guides). 77p. pap. 7.99 *(978-0-8010-7167-6(4))* Baker Bks.

—A Walk Thru the Book of James: Faith that Endures. 2009. (Walk Thru the Bible Discussion Guides). 62p. pap. 7.99 *(978-0-8010-7170-6(4))* Baker Bks.

Barclay. Divine & Human Agency in Paul & His Cultural Environment. Barclay, John M. G. & Gathercole, Simon J., eds. 2008. (Library of New Testament Studies, the Ser.). (ENG.). 224p. 44.95 *(978-0-567-08443-9(4)*, T&T Clark Int'l) Continuum International Publishing Group, Ltd. GBR. Dist: National Bk. Network.

Barclay, Gathercole. Divine & Human Agency in Paul & his Cultural Environment, Vol. 335. 2007. (Library of New Testament Studies: Vol. 335). (ENG., Illus.). 224p. 155.00 *(978-0-567-08453-8(1)*, T&T Clark Int'l) Continuum International Publishing Group, Ltd. GBR. Dist: National Bk. Network.

Bass, Christopher David. That You May Know: Assurance of Salvation in 1 John. 2008. (New American Commentary Studies in Bible & Theology Ser.). (ENG.). 256p. 24.99 *(978-0-8054-4761-3(X)*, B&H Academic) B&H Publishing Group.

Bateman, Herbert W. & Bateman IV, Herbert W., eds. Four Views on the Warning Passages in Hebrews, 1 vol. 2007. 480p. pap. 29.99 *(978-0-8254-2132-7(2))* Kregel Pubns.

Batten, Alicia. What Are They Saying about the Letter of James? 2009. (What Are They Saying about ... ? Ser.). 128p. pap. 14.95 *(978-0-8091-4620-8(7))* Paulist Pr.

Bauckham. A Cloud of Witnesses: The Theology of Hebrews in Its Ancient Contexts. Bauckham, Richard et al, eds. 2008. (Library of New Testament Studies). (ENG.). 254p. 130.00 *(978-0-567-03388-8(0)*, T&T Clark Int'l) Continuum International Publishing Group, Ltd. GBR. Dist: National Bk. Network.

Bauer, Thomas Johann. Paulus und die kaiserzeitliche Epistolographie: Kontextualisierung und Analyse der Briefe an Philemon und an die Galater. 2011. (Wissenschaftliche Untersuchungen zum Neuen Testament Ser.). (GER., Illus.). 505p. 232.50 ***(978-3-16-150977-3(3))*** Mohr Siebeck GmbH & Co. KG DEU. Dist: Coronet Bks.

Baumert, Norbert. NOMOS und andere Vorarbeiten zur Reihe 'Paulus neu gelesen' 2010. (GER.). 519p. *(978-3-429-03303-3(9))* Echter Verlag GmbH.

Beck, David T. The Holy Spirit & the Renewal of All Things: Pneumatology in Paul & Jurgen Moltmann. 2010. (ENG.). 277p. pap. 48.00 *(978-0-227-17332-9(5))* Clarke, James Co., Ltd. GBR. Dist: Brown, David Bk. Co., The.

Becker, Joseph Peter. Paul's Usage of xapis in Corinthians 8-9: An Ontology of Grace. 2011. 432p. 139.95 ***(978-0-7734-1590-4(4))*** Mellen, Edwin Pr., The.

Bekken, Per Jarle. The Word Is near You: A Study of Deuteronomy 30:12-14 in Paul's Letter to the Romans in a Jewish Context. (Beihefte zur Zeitschrift fur die neutestamentliche Wissenschaft und die Kunde der älteren Kirche Ser.). (ENG.). 294p. 225.00 ***(978-3-11-187274-2(2))***; 2007. 140.00 *(978-3-11-019341-1(8))* De Gruyter, Walter Inc.

Benedict XVI, pseud. Saint Paul the Apostle. 2009. 122p. pap. 8.95 *(978-1-59276-615-4(3))* Our Sunday Visitor, Publishing Div.

Benyamini, Itzhak. Narcissist Universalism: A Psychoanalytic Reading of Paul's Epistles. 2012. (ENG.). 144p. 90.00 ***(978-0-567-22614-3(X)***, T&T Clark Int'l) Continuum International Publishing Group, Ltd. GBR. Dist: National Bk. Network.

Berg, Jim. Essential Virtues: Marks of the Christ-Centered Life. 2008. *(978-1-59166-883-1(2))* BJU Pr.

Bernard, David K. Justification & the Holy Spirit. 2007. 132p. 16.99 *(978-1-56722-704-8(X))* Word Aflame Pr.

Bienert, David C., et al. Paulus und Die Antike Welt: Beiträge Zur Zeit- und Religionsgeschichtlichen Erforschung des Paulinischen Christentums: [Festgabe Für Dietrich-Alex Koch Zum 65. Geburtstag]. 2008. (Forschungen Zur Religion und Literatur des Alten & Neuen Testament Ser.). (GER & ENG., Illus.). 248p. (C). 107.00 *(978-3-525-53088-7(9))* Vandenhoeck & Ruprecht GmbH & Co. KG DEU. Dist: ISD.

Bird, Jennifer G. Abuse, Power & Fearful Obedience: Reconsidering 1 Peter?s Commands to Wives. 2011. (Library of New Testament Studies). (ENG.). 180p. 130.00 *(978-0-567-42750-2(1)*, T&T Clark Int'l) Continuum International Publishing Group, Ltd. GBR. Dist: National Bk. Network.

Blackaby, Henry, et al. Ephesians, 0 vols. 2008. (Blackaby Bible Study Ser.). 96p. pap. 9.99 *(978-1-4185-2647-4(9))* Nelson, Thomas Inc.

—Romans, 0 vols. 2007. (Encounters with God Ser.). 112p. pap. 9.99 *(978-1-4185-2643-6(6))* Nelson, Thomas Inc.

Blackmon, Norma. A Bible Study in the Books of Galatians & Ephesians. 2011. pap. 12.99 *(978-1-61739-089-0(5))* Tate Publishing & Enterprises, LLC.

Blight, Richard C. An Exegetical Summary of 1 Timothy. 2009. 396p. pap. 42.00 *(978-1-55671-230-2(8))* SIL International.

Bischke, Folker, ed. Die Begründung und die Durchsetzung der Ethik bei Paulus. 2007. (Arbeiten Zur Bibel und Ihrer Geschichte Ser.: Vol. 25). 520p. (C). 82.00 *(978-3-374-02474-2(2))* Evangelische Verlagsanstalt GmbH DEU. Dist: Eisenbrauns, Inc.

Blumenthal, Christian. Prophetie und Gericht: Der Judasbrief als Zeugnis urchristlicher Prophetie. Bonner Biblische Beiträge 156. 2008. (Bonner Biblische Beitrage Ser.). (GER., Illus.). 416p. (C). 74.00 ***(978-3-89971-490-6(3)***, V&R unipress) Vandenhoeck & Ruprecht GmbH & Co. KG DEU. Dist: ISD.

Boers, Hendrikus. Christ in the Letters of Paul: In Place of a Christology. (Beihefte zur Zeitschrift fur die neutestamentliche Wissenschaft und die Kunde der älteren Kirche Ser.). (ENG.). XII, 361p. 255.00 ***(978-3-11-182561-8(2))***; 2006. 154.00 *(978-3-11-018992-6(5))* De Gruyter, Walter Inc.

Boice, James Montgomery. Renewing Your Mind in a Mindless World: Learning to Think & Act Biblically, 1 vol. 2009. 144p. pap. 10.99 *(978-0-8254-2572-1(7))* Kregel Pubns.

Bolton, Martha. If the Tongue's a Fire, Who Needs Salsa? 212p. pap. 10.99 *(978-0-8307-3446-7(5)*, Gospel Light) Gospel Light Pubns.

Borg, Marcus J. & Crossan, John Dominic. The First Paul: Reclaiming the Radical Visionary Behind the Church's Conservative Icon. 2009. (Playaway Adult Nonfiction Ser.). (ENG.). 59.99 *(978-1-60847-997-9(8))* Findaway World, LLC.

—The First Paul: Reclaiming the Radical Visionary Behind the Church's Conservative Icon. 2010. (ENG.). 240p. pap. 14.99 *(978-0-06-143073-2(0)*, HarperOne) HarperCollins Pubs.

Bowen. Isg 11: A Guide to Romans 2nd Ne. 3rd ed. 2009. (Illus.). xx, 280p. pap. *(978-0-281-06020-7(7))* SPCK Publishing.

Bowen, Roger. Guide to Romans. 16.00 *(978-0-687-85459-2(8))* Abingdon Pr.

Branick, Vincent P. Understanding Paul & His Letters. 2009. 464p. pap. 27.95 *(978-0-8091-4581-2(2))* Paulist Pr.

Brearley, Chris. Philemon. 2007. 72p. *(978-1-85345-453-0(2))* Crusade for World Revival.

Brickle, Jeffrey E. Aural Design & Coherence in the Prologue of First John. 2012. (ENG., Illus.). 176p. 110.00 ***(978-0-567-00404-8(X)***, T&T Clark Int'l) Continuum International Publishing Group, Ltd. GBR. Dist: National Bk. Network.

Brodie, Thomas. Intertextuality of the Epistles Explorat. 2006. (Illus.). 328p. *(978-1-905048-62-5(9))* Sheffield Phoenix Pr.

Brooke, George J. & Najman, Hindy. The Significance of Sinai: Traditions about Sinai & Divine Revelation in Judaism & Christianity. 2008. (Themes in Biblical Narrative Ser.). 384p. (C). *(978-90-04-17018-6(9))* BRILL.

Burns, Lanier. The Nearness of God: His Presence with His People. 2009. pap. *(978-1-59638-056-1(X))* P & R Publishing.

Burroughs, Jeremiah & Kistler, Don. Moses' Choice: With His Eye Fixed upon Heaven: Discovering the Happy Condition of a Self-Denying Heart with His Eye Fixed upon Heaven: Delivered in a Treatise upon Hebrews 11:25-26. 2012. ***(978-0-9826155-9-1(0))*** Northampton Pr., The.

Butt, Herbert W. Tests of Eternal Life: Studies in First John. pap. 0.99 *(978-0-87377-034-7(X))* GAM Pubns.

Buttery, Nathan. How to Be Sure: Seven Studies for Individuals or Groups. 2010. 56p. pap. *(978-1-904889-95-3(6))* Good Bk. Co.

Cameron, Ron & Miller, Merrill P. Redescribing Paul & the Corinthians. 2010. 323p. ***(978-90-04-18710-8(3))*** BRILL.

—Redescribing Paul & the Corinthians. 2011. xiii, 325p. *(978-1-58983-529-0(8))*; 340p. pap. *(978-1-58983-528-3(X))* Society of Biblical Literature.

Campbell. Medieval Readings of Romans. Campbell, William S. et al, eds. 2007. (Romans Through History & Culture Ser.). (ENG.). 250p. pap. 49.95 *(978-0-567-02706-1(6),* T&T Clark Int'l) Continuum International Publishing Group, Ltd. GBR. Dist: National Bk. Network.

Campbell, Douglas A. The Deliverance of God: An Apocalyptic Rereading of Justification in Paul. 2009. 1248p. 60.00 *(978-0-8028-3126-2(5))* Eerdmans, William B. Publishing Co.

Canclini, Arnoldo. Estoy Contigo, Pedro: I'm with You, Peter. (SPA.). 104p. *(978-84-7228-245-2(7),* 220382) Clie, Editorial.

Cathcart, Kevin J. Targumic & Cognate Studies: Essays in Honour of Martin Mcnamara. Maher, Michael, ed. 2009. (Library of Hebrew Bible/Old Testament Studies, the Ser.). (ENG.). 250p. 44.95 *(978-0-567-60396-8(2),* T&T Clark) Continuum International Publishing Group, Ltd. GBR. Dist: National Bk. Network.

Celano, Peter. To Live Is Christ: A 40-Day Journey with Saint Paul. 2009. (ENG.). 168p. (gr. 9). 17.99 *(978-1-55725-638-6(1))* Paraclete Pr., Inc.

Chamblin, J. Knox. Paul & the Self: Apostolic Teaching for Personal Wholeness. 2011. 286p. pap. 31.00 ***(978-1-61097-445-5(X),*** Wipf and Stock) Wipf & Stock Pubs.

Chester, Tim. Living in the Real World: Five Studies for Individuals or Groups. 2010. 64p. pap. *(978-1-904889-49-6(2))* Good Bk. Co.

Cheung, Luke Leuk. The Genre, Composition & Hermeneutics of the Epistle of James. 2006. (Paternoster Biblical Monographs). (ENG.). 388p. per. 39.99 *(978-1-84227-062-2(1),* Paternoster) Authentic Media.

—The Genre, Composition & Hermeneutics of the Epistle of James. 2007. (Paternoster Biblical Monographs: Ser.). 406p. pap. 41.00 *(978-1-59752-748-4(3),* Wipf and Stock) Wipf & Stock Pubs.

Clark, Kim. Armor: Divine Protection in a Darkening World. 2007. 320p. 21.95 *(978-1-59038-756-6(2))* Deseret Bk. Co.

Clarke, Andrew D. Secular & Christian Leadership in Corinth: A Socio-Historical & Exegetical Study of 1 Corinthians 1-6. 2006. (Paternoster Biblical Monographs: Ser.). 224p. pap. 25.00 *(978-1-59752-960-0(5),* Wipf and Stock) Wipf & Stock Pubs.

Cohick, Lynn H. Ephesians. 2010. (New Covenant Commentary Ser.). 190p. pap. 22.00 *(978-1-60608-141-9(1),* Cascade Bks.) Wipf & Stock Pubs.

Constantineanu, Corneliu. The Social Significance of Reconciliation in Paul's Theology Vol. 421: Narrative Readings in Romans. 2010. (Library of New Testament Studies, the Ser.). (ENG.). 272p. 130.00 *(978-0-567-58198-3(5),* T&T Clark Int'l) Continuum International Publishing Group, Ltd. GBR. Dist: National Bk. Network.

Cook, Gwendolyn Ann. The Power to Believe: It's not what you need, It's what you Believe! 2009. 160p. 22.49 *(978-1-4490-3053-7(X));* pap. 16.99 *(978-1-4490-3052-0(1))* AuthorHouse.

Cook, Jerry. The Monday Morning Church: Out of the Sanctuary & into the Streets. 2011. (ENG.). 224p. pap. 15.99 *(978-1-4516-3618-5(0),* Howard Bks.) Howard Books.

Coppins, Wayne. Interpretation of Freedom in the Letters of Paul: With Special Reference to the German Tradition. 2009. (Wissenschaftliche Untersuchungen zum Neuen Testament, 2 Ser.). (Illus.). 218p. 103.00 *(978-3-16-149969-2(7))* Mohr Siebeck GmbH & Co. KG DEU. Dist: Eisenbrauns, Inc.

Cosaert, Carl P. The Gospel in Galatia: Paul's Letter to the Galatians. 2011. *(978-0-8280-2560-7(6))* Review & Herald Publishing Assn.

Cosby, Michael R. Apostle on the Edge: An Inductive Approach to Paul. 2009. (Illus.). (ENG.). 320p. 35.00 *(978-0-664-23308-2(2));* xiii, 322p. *(978-0-664-23442-3(9))* Westminster John Knox Pr.

Crü, et al. Die pseudepigraphen Briefe an die Gemeinde in Thessaloniki: Studien zu ihrer Abfassung und zur jüdisch-christlichen Sozialgeschichte. 2010. (GER.). 336p. pap. *(978-3-17-021149-0(8))* Kohlhammer, W., GmbH.

Cripe, D. Earl. Faith & Liberty: Studies in the Letter of St. Paul to the Churches of Galatia. 2009. 312p. pap. 15.49 *(978-1-4389-7802-4(2))* AuthorHouse.

Criswell, David. Controversies in the Prophets: Isaiah through Malachi. 2007. (ENG.). 558p. pap. 14.95 *(978-1-4196-7204-0(5))* CreateSpace.

Crowe, Bob. So Great Salvation: Studies in the Book of Hebrews. 2009. 216p. pap. 16.99 *(978-1-4251-5946-7(X))* Trafford Publishing.

Cummins, Stephen Anthony. Paul & the Crucified Christ in Antioch: Maccabean Martyrdom & Galatians 1 And 2. 2007. (Society for New Testament Studies Monograph Ser.). (ENG.). 308p. pap. 63.00 *(978-0-521-03717-4(4))* Cambridge Univ. Pr.

Darden, John S. A Walk Through Ephesians. 2008. 83p. pap. 7.98 *(978-0-557-00631-1(7))* Lulu Enterprises Inc.

Darko, Daniel K. No Longer Living As the Gentiles: Differentiation & Shared Ethical Values in Ephesians 4:17- 6:9. 2008. (Library of New Testament Studies, the Ser.). (ENG.). 176p. 130.00 *(978-0-567-03308-6(2),* T&T Clark Int'l) Continuum International Publishing Group, Ltd. GBR. Dist: National Bk. Network.

Davids, Peter H. 2 Peter & Jude: A Handbook on the Greek Text. 2011. (Baylor Handbook on the Greek New Testament Ser.). (ENG.). 152p. pap. 29.95 *(978-1-60258-313-9(7))* Baylor Univ. Pr.

Desilva, David Arthur. Despising Shame: Honor Discourse & Community Maintenance in the Epistle to the Hebrews. 2nd ed. 2008. 428p. pap. 44.95 *(978-1-58983-400-2(3))* Society of Biblical Literature.

Desmond Ford. The Coming Worldwide Calvary: Christ Versus Antichrist. 2009. 168p. pap. 15.95 *(978-1-4401-7284-7(6))* iUniverse, Inc.

Dever, Mark. 12 Challenges Churches Face. 2008. 192p. 17.99 *(978-1-58134-944-3(0))* Crossway.

Dewey, Arthur J., et al. The Authentic Letters of Paul. 2010. (Illus.). 268p. pap. 27.00 *(978-1-59815-019-3(7))* Polebridge Pr.

Discover James. (Discover Your Bible Ser.). (KOR.). pap., tchr. ed. 4.95 *(978-1-55883-235-0(1),* 600215); pap., stu. ed. 3.25 *(978-1-55883-234-3(3),* 600210) C R C World Literature Ministries/Libros Desafio.

Discover Jesus in John: The Lives He Touched. (Discover Your Bible Ser.). (KOR.). pap., tchr. ed. 4.95 *(978-1-55883-215-2(7),* 600145); pap., stu. ed. 3.25 *(978-1-55883-212-1(2),* 600140) C R C World Literature Ministries/Libros Desafio.

Discover the Abundant Life: A Thematic Study of 2 Corinthians. (Discover Your Bible Ser.). pap., tchr. ed. 4.95 *(978-1-56212-261-4(4),* 152395) Faith Alive Christian Resources.

Docherty, Susan E. The Use of the Old Testament in Hebrews: A Case Study in Early Jewish Bible Interpretation. 2009. xi, 233p. *(978-3-16-149904-3(2))* Mohr Siebeck GmbH & Co. KG.

Dodd, C. H. The Johannine Epistles. 2008. 244p. *(978-1-4437-3256-7(7))* 2007. 240p. per. *(978-1-4067-8830-3(9))* Read Bks. (Pomona Pr.).

Dohrmann, Natalie B. & Stern, David, eds. Jewish Biblical Interpretation & Cultural Exchange: Comparative Exegesis in Context. 2008. (Jewish Culture & Contexts Ser.). (Illus.). 352p. (C). 69.95 *(978-0-8122-4074-0(X))* Univ. of Pennsylvania Pr.

Donfried, K. P., ed. 1 Timothy Reconsidered. 2008. (Colloquium Oecumenicum Paulinum Ser.). (ENG.). 201p. (C). pap. 67.00 *(978-90-429-2091-0(2))* Peeters Pubs. & Booksellers BEL. Dist: Brown, David Bk. Co., The.

du Preez, Ronald. Judging the Sabbath: Discovering What Can't Be Found in Colossians 2:16. 2008. (ENG.). pap. *(978-1-883925-62-8(2))* Andrews Univ. Pr.

Du Toit, Marietjie. A Study of 1 Peter 3:18-4:6: An Investigation into the Historical Background of the Doctrine of Christ's Descent into Hades. 2008. 108p. pap. *(978-3-639-08832-8(8))* VDM Verlag Dr. Mueller e.K.

Dubis, Mark. 1 Peter: A Handbook on the Greek Text. 2010. (Baylor Handbook on the Greek New Testament Ser.). (ENG.). 220p. (C). pap. 24.95 *(978-1-932792-62-1(7))* Baylor Univ. Pr.

Dunn, James D. G. The New Perspective on Paul. 2007. (Wissenschaftliche Untersuchungen Zum Neuen Testament Ser.). 539p. per. 36.00 *(978-0-8028-4562-7(2))* Eerdmans, William B. Publishing Co.

Eastman, Susan. Recovering Paul's Mother Tongue: Language & Theology in Galatians. 2007. 206p. per. 25.00 *(978-0-8028-3165-1(6))* Eerdmans, William B. Publishing Co.

Ehrensperger, Kathy. Paul & the Dynamics of Power: Communication & Interaction in the Early Christ-Movement. (Library of New Testament Studies, the Ser.). (ENG.). 2009. 256p. 39.95 *(978-0-567-61494-0(8))* 2007. 250p. 140.00 *(978-0-567-04374-0(6))* Continuum International Publishing Group, Ltd. GBR. (T&T Clark Int'l). Dist: National Bk. Network.

Ehrensperger, Kathy & Tucker, J. Brian, eds. Reading Paul in Context: Explorations in Identity Formation: Essays in Honour of William S. Campbell. 2010. (Library of New Testament Studies). (ENG.). 288p. 120.00 *(978-0-567-02467-1(9),* T&T Clark Int'l) Continuum International Publishing Group, Ltd. GBR. Dist: National Bk. Network.

Ehrman, Bart D. The Lost Gospel of Judas Iscariot: A New Look at Betrayer & Betrayed. 2008. (ENG.). 208p. pap. 15.95 *(978-0-19-534351-9(4))* Oxford Univ. Pr., Inc.

Elbers, Gerard H. Le Combat des Vainqueurs: L'Armure Complète de Dieu. 2008. (FRE.). 113p. pap. 8.95 *(978-2-921905-09-1(4))* Editions le mieux-etre CAN. Dist: AtlasBooks Distribution.

Elengabeka, Elvis. L' exploitation des Ecritures: L'intertextualité scripturaire dans les Epîtres Pastorales. 2009. (Europäische Hochschulschriften. Reihe 23: Theologie Ser.). (FRE.). 277p. pap. *(978-3-03911-810-6(2))* Lang, Peter.

Elliott, Neil. The Arrogance of Nations: Reading Romans in the Shadow of Empire. 2008. (Paul in Critical Contexts Ser.). (Illus.). 238p. 22.00 *(978-0-8006-3844-3(1),* Fortress Pr.) Augsburg Fortress, Pubs.

—Documents & Images for the Study of Paul. Reasoner, Mark, ed. 2010. (Illus.). 300p. (C). pap. 35.00 *(978-0-8006-6375-9(6),* Fortress Pr.) Augsburg Fortress, Pubs.

Ellis, J. Edward. Paul & Ancient Views of Sexual Desire: Paul's Sexual Ethics in 1 Thessalonians 4, 1 Corinthians 7 & Romans 1. 2007. (Library of New Testament Studies, the Ser.). (ENG.). 206p. 130.00 *(978-0-567-04538-6(2),* T&T Clark Int'l) Continuum International Publishing Group, Ltd. GBR. Dist: National Bk. Network.

Engberg-Pedersen, Troels. Cosmology & Self in the Apostle Paul: The Material Spirit. 2010. (ENG.). 304p. 110.00 *(978-0-19-955856-8(6))* Oxford Univ. Pr., Inc.

Engelbrecht, Edward & Deterding, Paul E. Colossians & 1 & 2 Thessalonians. 2012. ***(978-0-7586-2771-1(8))*** Concordia Publishing Hse.

Erasmus. Paraphrases on the Epistles to the Corinthians, Ephesians, Philippians, Colossians, & Thessalonians. Sider, Robert D., ed. 2009. (Collected Works of Erasmus Ser.). (ENG.). 760p. *(978-0-8020-9296-0(9))* Univ. of Toronto Pr.

Fagbemi, Stephen Ayodeji A. Who Are the Elect in 1 Peter? A Study in Biblical Exegesis & Its Application to the Anglican Church of Nigeria. 2007. (Studies in Biblical Literature Ser.). 304p. (C). 76.95 *(978-0-8204-9503-3(4))* Lang, Peter Publishing, Inc.

Fee, Gordon D. God's Empowering Presence: The Holy Spirit in the Letters of Paul. 2009. 967p. pap. 34.95 *(978-1-59856-432-7(3))* Hendrickson Pubs. Marketing, LLC.

Feldmeier, Reinhard. The First Letter of Peter: A Commentary on the Greek Text. 2008. 265p. pap. 34.95 *(978-1-60258-024-4(3))* Baylor Univ. Pr.

Ferrer, Blehl Vincent, ed. Realizations Newman's Own Selection of His Sermons. 2009. 192p. pap. 19.95 *(978-0-8146-3290-1(4),* Liturgical Pr. Bks.) Liturgical Pr.

Fetterhoff, Dean. The Making of a Man of God: Studies in I & II Timothy. pap. 5.99 *(978-0-88469-030-6(X))* BMH Bks.

Finger, Reta Halteman. Roman House Churches for Today: A Practical Guide for Small Groups. 2nd ed. 2007. 207p. per. 15.00 *(978-0-8028-0764-9(X))* Eerdmans, William B. Publishing Co.

Finney, Mark T. Honour & Conflict in the Ancient World: 1 Corinthians in its Greco-Roman Social Setting. 2012. (ENG.). 312p. 120.00 ***(978-0-567-05772-3(0),*** T&T Clark Int'l) Continuum International Publishing Group, Ltd. GBR. Dist: National Bk. Network.

Fiore, Benjamin. Pastoral Epistles. Date not set. (Sacra Pagina Ser.: No. 12). 29.95 *(978-0-8146-5814-7(8))* 2009. 264p. pap. 8.95 *(978-0-8146-5980-9(2),* Liturgical Pr. Bks.) Liturgical Pr.

Fitzgerald, Troy. Live Like You Mean It: Wisdom for the Journey Home. 2010. 15.99 *(978-0-8163-2380-7(1))* Pacific Pr. Publishing Assn.

Flebbe, Jochen. Solus Deus: Untersuchungen zur Rede von Gott im Brief des Paulus an die Römer. 2008. (Beihefte Zur Zeitschrift Für Die Neutestamentliche Wissenschaft und Die Kunde der älteren Kirche Ser.). (GER.). XIII, 509p. 175.00 *(978-3-11-020217-5(4))* De Gruyter, Walter Inc.

Flores, José. Cristologia de Pedro: Christology of Peter. (SPA.). 224p. *(978-84-7228-398-5(4),* 220214) Clie, Editorial.

Forman, Mark. The Politics of Inheritance in Romans. 2011. (Society for New Testament Studies Monograph Ser.). (ENG.). 284p. 90.00 *(978-0-521-76909-9(4))* Cambridge Univ. Pr.

Foster, Paul. The Gospel of Peter: Critical Edition, Introduction & Commentary. 2010. (Texts & Editions for New Testament Study Ser.). (Illus.). xvi, 555p. *(978-90-04-18094-9(X))* BRILL.

Frisius, Mark A. Tertullian's Use of the Pastoral Epistles, Hebrews, James, 1 & 2 Peter, & Jude. 2011. (C). 79.95 *(978-1-4331-1392-5(9))* Lang, Peter Publishing, Inc.

Gadenz, Pablo T. Called from the Jews & from the Gentiles: Pauline Ecclesiology in Romans 9-11. 2009. (Wissenschaftliche Untersuchungen zum Neuen Testament Ser.). (Illus.). XI, 393p. pap. 157.50 *(978-3-16-150091-6(1))* Mohr Siebeck GmbH & Co. KG DEU. Dist: Coronet Bks.

Gallagher, Steve. Pressing on Toward the Heavenly Calling: A 12-Week Study Through the Prison Epistles. 2007. (Walk Ser.). (ENG., Illus.). 144p. per. 10.99 *(978-0-9758832-6-6(7))* Pure Life Ministries.

Garcilazo, Albert V. The Corinthian Dissenters & the Stoics. 2007. (Studies in Biblical Literature Ser.: Vol. 106). (Illus.). 268p. (C). 71.95 *(978-0-8204-9521-7(2))* Lang, Peter Publishing, Inc.

Gardner, Thomas. John in the Company of Poets: The Gospel in Literary Imagination. 2011. (Studies in Christianity & Literature Ser.). (ENG.). 236p. 69.95 *(978-1-60258-315-3(3))* Baylor Univ. Pr.

Garlington, Don. Faith, Obedience, & Perseverance. 2009. 214p. pap. 24.00 *(978-1-60608-825-8(4),* Wipf and Stock) Wipf & Stock Pubs.

—The Obedience of Faith. 2009. 352p. pap. 39.00 *(978-1-60608-826-5(2),* Wipf and Stock) Wipf & Stock Pubs.

Gatumu, Kabiro wa. The Pauline Concept of Supernatural Powers: A Reading from the African Worldview. 2009. (Paternoster Biblical Monographs). 326p. pap. 38.00 *(978-1-60608-472-4(0),* Wipf and Stock) Wipf & Stock Pubs.

Gelardini, Gabriella. Hebrews: Contemporary MethodsûNew Insights. 2008. 316p. pap. 37.95 *(978-1-58983-386-9(4))* Society of Biblical Literature.

Genade, Aldred A. Persuading the Cretans: A Text-Generated Persuasion Analysis of the Letter to Titus. 2011. 148p. pap. 18.00 *(978-1-60899-330-7(2),* Wipf and Stock) Wipf & Stock Pubs.

Giffard Smith, Sheila. Talking & Walking with God. 2008. 336p. per. *(978-1-84748-264-8(4))* Athena Pr.

Gignilliat, Mark. Paul & Isaiah's Servants: Paul's Theological Reading of Isaiah 40-66 in 2 Corinthians 5:14-6:10. 2007. (Library of New Testament Studies). (ENG., Illus.). 212p. 130.00 *(978-0-567-04483-9(1),* T&T Clark Int'l) Continuum International Publishing Group, Ltd. GBR. Dist: National Bk. Network.

Gill, Malcolm. Jesus as Mediator: Politics & Polemic in 1 Timothy 2:1-7. 2008. 196p. pap. 61.95 *(978-3-03911-829-8(3))* Lang, Peter AG GBR. Dist: Lang, Peter.

Gilley, James W. God for Us: According to John: John 13-21. 2010. 157p. pap. 14.99 *(978-0-8163-2426-2(3))* Pacific Pr. Publishing Assn.

Gitau, Samson. Breaking the Shackles: Contemporary Perspectives in Paul's Letter to the Galatians. 2008. 228p. pap. 14.95 *(978-1-4389-2838-8(6))* AuthorHouse.

Glad, Clarence E. Paul & Philodemus: Adaptability in Epicurean & Early Christian Psychagogy. 2010. *(978-1-58983-502-3(6))* Society of Biblical Literature.

Gladd, Benjamin. Revealing the Mysterion: The Use of Mystery in Daniel & Second Temple Judaism with Its Bearing on First Corinthians. 2008. (Beihefte zur Zeitschrift far die neutestamentliche Wissenschaft und die Kunde der älteren Kirche Ser.). (ENG.). XXIV, 352p. 224.00 ***(978-3-11-173930-4(9))*** De Gruyter, Walter Inc.

Gladd, Benjamin L. Revealing the Mysterion: The Use of Mystery in Daniel & Second Temple Judaism with Its Bearing on First Corinthians. 2008. (Beihefte zur Zeitschrift für die neutestamentliche Wissenschaft und die Kunde der Älteren Kirche Ser.). (ENG.). XXIV, 352p. 147.00 *(978-3-11-020913-6(6))* De Gruyter, Walter Inc.

Glaser, Timo. Paulus als Briefroman erzählt: Studien zum antiken Briefroman und seiner christlichen Rezeption. Novum Testamentum et Orbis Antiquus / Studien zur Umwelt des Neuen Testaments 76. 2009. (Novum Testamentum et Orbis Antiquus/Studien zur Umwelt des Neuen Testaments (NTOA/StUNT) Ser.). (GER., Illus.). 376p. (C). 91.00 *(978-3-525-53389-5(6))* Vandenhoeck & Ruprecht GmbH & Co. KG DEU. Dist: ISD.

Gombis, Timothy G. The Drama of Ephesians: Participating in the Triumph of God. 2010. (ENG.). 188p. pap. 20.00 *(978-0-8308-2720-6(X),* IVP Acad.) InterVarsity Pr.

—Paul. 2010. (Guides for the Perplexed Ser.). (ENG.). 176p. 24.95 *(978-0-567-03394-9(5));* 80.00 *(978-0-567-03393-2(7))* Continuum International Publishing Group, Ltd. GBR. (T&T Clark Int'l). Dist: National Bk. Network.

González, Justo L. & Gonzalez, Catherine Gunsalus. For the Love of God: The Epistles of John. 2010. (ENG.). 116p. 6.50 *(978-1-933663-40-1(5),* WD/GBGM Bks.) General Board of Global Ministries, The United Methodist Church.

Gooder. Only the Third Heaven?, Vol. 313. 2006. (T & T Clark Library of Biblical Studies: Vol. 313). (ENG., Illus.). 256p. 155.00 *(978-0-567-04244-6(8),* T&T Clark Int'l) Continuum International Publishing Group, Ltd. GBR. Dist: National Bk. Network.

Goodrich, John. Paul as an Administrator of God in 1 Corinthians: Volume 152: The Graeco-Roman Context of 1 Corinthians. 2012. (Society for New Testament Studies Monograph Ser.: 152). (ENG., Illus.). 264p. 99.00 ***(978-1-107-01862-4(5))*** Cambridge Univ. Pr.

Goodwin, Thomas. The Works of Thomas Goodwin, Vol. 1. 2009. 598p. pap. 50.00 *(978-1-60608-590-5(5),* Wipf and Stock) Wipf & Stock Pubs.

Graham, Glenn H. Exegetical Summary of Ephesians. 2nd ed. 2008. 596p. pap. 49.00 *(978-1-55671-208-1(1))* SIL International.

Grant, L. M. First & Second Thessalonians, First & Second Timothy & Titus. 184p. 8.50 *(978-0-88172-159-1(X))* Believers Bookshelf, Inc.

Grenholm, Cristina & Patte, Daniel. Modern Interpretations of Romans: Tracking Their Hermeneutical/Theological Trajectory, Vol. 10. Grenholm, Cristina & Patte, Daniel, eds. 2013. (ENG.). 272p. pap. 39.95 ***(978-0-567-21503-1(2),*** T&T Clark Int'l) Continuum International Publishing Group, Ltd. GBR. Dist: National Bk. Network.

Group Publishing, creator. Galatians: Experiencing Freedom in Jesus. 2006. (Illus.). 108p. pap. 9.99 *(978-0-7644-3244-6(3))* Group Publishing, Inc.

Gumerlock, Francis X. Fulgentius of Ruspe on the Saving Will of God: The Development of a Sixth-Century African Bishop's Interpretation of 1 Timothy 2:4 During the Semi-Pelagian Controversy. 2009. 256p. 109.95 *(978-0-7734-4935-0(3))* Mellen, Edwin Pr., The.

Gupta, Nijay K. Worship that Makes Sense to Paul: A New Approach to the Theology & Ethics of Paul's Cultic Metaphors. (Beihefte zur Zeitschrift far die neutestamentliche Wissenschaft und die Kunde der älteren Kirche Ser.). (ENG., X, 263p. 2011. Illus.). 154.00 ***(978-3-11-173045-5(X))*** 2010. 98.00 *(978-3-11-022889-2(0))* De Gruyter, Walter Inc.

Hafemann, Scott J. Paul, Moses, & the History of Israel: The Letter/Spirit Contrast & the Argument from Scripture in 2 Corinthians 3. 2008. (Paternoster Biblical Monographs). 526p. pap. 64.00 *(978-1-59752-775-0(0))* Wipf & Stock Pubs.

—Suffering & Ministry in the Spirit: Paul's Defence of His Ministry in II Corinthians. abr. ed. 2006. (Paternoster Theological Monographs). (ENG.). 284p. pap. 39.99 *(978-0-85364-967-0(7),* Paternoster) Authentic Media.

—Suffering & the Spirit: An Exegetical Study of 2 Corinthians 2:4Ntilde;3:3 within the Context of the Corinthian Correspondence. 2011. 266p. pap. 29.00 *(978-1-61097-086-0(1),* Wipf and Stock) Wipf & Stock Pubs.

Haffner, Karl. Caught Between Two Worlds: A Survival Guide to End-Time Living. 2011. 143p. pap. 14.99 *(978-0-8163-2404-0(2))* Pacific Pr. Publishing Assn.

Hagen, Kenneth. Hebrews Commenting from Erasmus to Beze. 2011. 134p. pap. 17.00 ***(978-1-61097-350-2(X),*** Wipf and Stock) Wipf & Stock Pubs.

Hanson, Anthony Tyrrell. Studies in Paul's Technique & Theology. 2011. 344p. pap. 40.00 ***(978-1-61097-353-3(4),*** Wipf and Stock) Wipf & Stock Pubs.

Harmon, Matthew S. She Must & Shall Go Free: Paul's Isaianic Gospel in Galatians. 2010. (Beihefte zur Zeitschrift für die neutestamentliche Wissenschaft und die Kunde der Älteren Kirche Ser.). (ENG.). XI, 330p. 140.00 *(978-3-11-022175-6(6))* De Gruyter, Walter Inc.

Harrington, Daniel J. Meeting St. Paul Today: Understanding the Man, His Mission, & His Message. 2008. (ENG.). 160p. pap. 12.95 *(978-0-8294-2734-9(1))* Loyola Pr.

Harrington, Daniel J. & Keenan, James F., eds. Paul & Virtue Ethics: Building Bridges Between New Testament Studies & Moral Theology. 2010. (ENG.). 220p. 40.00 *(978-0-7425-9959-8(0))* Rowman & Littlefield Publishers, Inc.

Harrington, Daniel P. Meeting St. John Today: Understanding the Man, His Mission, & His Message. 2011. (ENG.). 144p. pap. 12.95 *(978-0-8294-2917-6(4))* Loyola Pr.

Harrison, James R. Paul & the Imperial Authorities at Thessalonica & Rome: A Study in the Conflict of Ideology. 2011. (Wissenschaftliche Untersuchungen zum Neuen Teastament Ser.). (GER.). 428p. 227.50 ***(978-3-16-149880-0(1))*** Mohr Siebeck GmbH & Co. KG DEU. Dist: Coronet Bks.

Harvey, Bruce J. YHWH Elohim: A Survey of Occurrences in the Leningrad Codex & Their Corresponding Septuagintal Renderings. 2011. (Library of Hebrew Bible/Old Testament Studies). (ENG., Illus.). 272p. 130.00 *(978-0-567-20748-7(X),* T&T Clark Int'l) Continuum International Publishing Group, Ltd. GBR. Dist: National Bk. Network.

Hausser, Detlef. Christusbekenntnis und Jesusüberlieferung bei Paulus. 2006. (Wissenschaftliche Untersuchungen Zum Neuen Testament 2 Ser.: Vol. 210). 416p. (C). pap. 135.00 *(978-3-16-148962-4(4))* Mohr Siebeck GmbH & Co. KG DEU. Dist: Coronet Bks.

Hayford, Jack W. 2 Corinthians, 1 & 2 Timothy, Titus: Ministering in the Spirit & Strength of Jesus, 0 vols. 2009. (Spirit-Filled Life Study Guide Ser.). 128p. pap. 9.99 *(978-1-4185-4120-0(6))* Nelson, Thomas Inc.

Heil, John Paul. Colossians: Encouragement to Walk in All Wisdom As Holy Ones in Christ. 2010. (ENG.). 242p. pap. 28.95 *(978-1-58983-484-2(4))* Society of Biblical Literature.

—Ephesians: Empowerment to Walk in Love for the Unity of All. 2007. (SBL - Studies in Biblical Literature Ser.). 360p. *(978-90-04-15125-3(7))* BRILL.

—Ephesians: Empowerment to Walk in Love for the Unity of All in Christ. 2007. (ENG.). 372p. per. 39.95 *(978-1-58983-267-1(1))* Society of Biblical Literature.

—Hebrews: Chiastic Structures & Audience Response. 2010. *(978-0-915170-45-6(0))* Catholic Biblical Assn. of America.

Heil, John Paul. The Letters of Paul as Rituals of Worship. 2012. (ENG.). 216p. pap. 35.00 ***(978-0-227-68007-0(3))*** Clarke, James Co., Ltd. GBR. Dist: Brown, David Bk. Co., The.

—The Letters of Paul as Rituals of Worship. 2011. 216p. pap. 24.00 *(978-1-60899-870-8(3),* Cascade Bks.) Wipf & Stock Pubs.

Hemphill, Ken, et al. You Are Gifted: Your Spiritual Gifts & the Kingdom of God, 1 vol. 2009. (ENG.). 240p. 17.99 *(978-0-8054-4862-7(4),* B&H Bks.) B&H Publishing Group.

Henderson, Warren. Glories Seen & Unseen: A Study of the Head Covering. 2007. 160p. per. 11.95 *(978-0-9795387-2-8(6))* Henderson, Warren.

Hering, James P. The Colossian & Ephesian Haustafeln in Theological Context: An Analysis of Their Origins, Relationship, & Message. 2007. (American University Studies VII: Theology & Religion Ser.). 296p. (C). 74.95 *(978-0-8204-9505-7(0))* Lang, Peter Publishing, Inc.

Hietanen, Mika & Hietanen. Paul's Argumentation in Galatians: A Pragma-Dialectical Analysis. 2007. (Library of New Testament Studies). (ENG., Illus.). 232p. 155.00 *(978-0-567-03127-3(6),* T&T Clark Int'l) Continuum International Publishing Group, Ltd. GBR. Dist: National Bk. Network.

Hills, Julian. The Epistle of the Apostles. 2009. 144p. pap. 18.00 *(978-1-59815-017-9(0))* Polebridge Pr.

Hiu, Elim. Regulations Concerning Tongues & Prophecy in 1 Corinthians 14.26-40: Relevance Beyond the Corinthian Church, Vol. 406. 2010. (Library of New Testament Studies, the Ser.). (ENG.). 240p. 130.00 *(978-0-567-54606-7(3),* T&T Clark Int'l) Continuum International Publishing Group, Ltd. GBR. Dist: National Bk. Network.

Hodge, Caroline Johnson. If Sons, Then Heirs: A Study of Kinship & Ethnicity in the Letters of Paul. 2007. (ENG.). 240p. 65.00 *(978-0-19-518216-3(2))* Oxford Univ. Pr., Inc.

Hoehner, Harold W., et al. Ephesians, Philippians, 1-2 Thessalonians Colossians, Philemon. 2008. (Cornerstone Biblical Commentary Ser.: 16). (ENG.). 456p. 29.99 *(978-0-8423-8344-8(1))* Tyndale Hse. Pubs.

Hogan, Pauline. "No Longer Male & Female" Interpreting Galatians 3:28 in Early Christianity. 2008. (Library of New Testament Studies, the Ser.). (ENG.). 240p. 140.00 *(978-0-567-03335-2(X),* T&T Clark Int'l) Continuum International Publishing Group, Ltd. GBR. Dist: National Bk. Network.

Hogeterp, Albert L. A. & Hogeterp, A. L. A. Paul & God's Temple: A Historical Interpretation of Cultic Imagery in the Corinthian Correspondence. 2006. (Biblical Tools & Studies: Vol. 2). (ENG.). 483p. (C). 95.00 *(978-90-429-1722-4(9))* Peeters Pubs. & Booksellers BEL. Dist: Brown, David Bk. Co., The.

Holloway, Paul A. Coping with Prejudice: 1 Peter in Social-Psychological Perspective. 2009. (Illus.). XVI, 317p. 177.50 *(978-3-16-149961-6(1))* Mohr Siebeck GmbH & Co. KG DEU. Dist: Coronet Bks.

Hooker, Morna D. From Adam to Christ: Essays on Paul. 2008. 208p. pap. 23.00 *(978-1-60608-024-5(5))* Wipf & Stock Pubs.

—Pauline Pieces. 2006. 96p. pap. 13.00 *(978-1-59752-520-6(0),* Wipf and Stock) Wipf & Stock Pubs.

Hooker, Morna D. & Hooker, Morna Dorothy. Paul: A Beginner's Guide. 2008. (Beginners Guide (Oneworld) Ser.). (ENG., Illus.). 224p. per. 14.95 *(978-1-85168-564-6(2))* Oneworld Pubns. GBR. Dist: National Bk. Network.

Horrell, David G. An Introduction to the Study of Paul. 2nd rev. ed. 2006. (T & T Clark Approaches to Biblical Studies). (ENG., Illus.). 176p. 29.95 *(978-0-567-04083-1(6),* T&T Clark Int'l) Continuum International Publishing Group, Ltd. GBR. Dist: National Bk. Network.

Horrell, David G. & Horrell. 1 Peter (New Testament Guides) 2008. (New Testament Guides). (ENG.). 138p. 80.00 *(978-0-567-03168-6(3));* (Illus.). 136p. 22.95 *(978-0-567-03169-3(1))* Continuum International Publishing Group, Ltd. GBR. (T&T Clark Int'l). Dist: National Bk. Network.

Horrell, David G., et al. Greening Paul: Rereading the Apostle in a Time of Ecological Crisis. 2010. (ENG.). 322p. (C). pap. 34.95 *(978-1-60258-290-3(4))* Baylor Univ. Pr.

Horsley, Richard A. Wisdom & Spiritual Transcendence at Corinth: Studies in First Corinthians. 2007. 182p. pap. 21.00 *(978-1-59752-844-3(7))* Wipf & Stock Pubs.

Howe, Bonnie. Because You Bear This Name: Conceptual Metaphor & the Moral Meaning of 1 Peter. 2006. (Biblical Interpretation Ser.: Vol. 81). (Illus.). 408p. *(978-90-04-15095-9(1))* BRILL.

—Because You Bear This Name: Conceptual Metaphor & the Moral Meaning of 1 Peter. 2008. 428p. pap. 49.95 *(978-1-58983-383-8(X))* Society of Biblical Literature.

Howell, Sarah L. Galatians: Breakaway to Freedom, 1. 2006. (Heart Stealers Bible Studies). (ENG.). 144p. (gr. 11). per. 12.99 *(978-0-89957-104-1(2))* AMG Pubs.

Hoyt, Herman A. Christ, God's Final Word to Man: An Exposition of the Epistle to the Hebrews. pap. 8.99 *(978-0-88469-009-2(1))* BMH Bks.

—The First Christian Theology Studies in Romans. pap. 7.99 *(978-0-88469-038-2(5))* BMH Bks.

Hubbard, Moyer V. Christianity in the Greco-Roman World: A Narrative Introduction, 1 vol. 2010. (ENG., Illus.). 290p. *(978-1-56563-663-7(5))* Hendrickson Pubs. Marketing, LLC.

Hughes, Philip E. The Divine Plan for Jew & Gentile. 2010. 32p. pap. 4.00 *(978-1-60899-470-0(8))* Wipf & Stock Pubs.

Hummel, Rand. Gratefully Yours. 2012. ***(978-1-60682-389-7(2))*** BJU Pr.

Hunt, Susan. Spiritual Mothering: The Titus 2 Model for Women Mentoring Women. 2009. 208p. pap. 15.99 *(978-1-4335-0313-9(1))* Crossway.

Huntington, Ray L., et al, eds. Shedding Light on the New Testament: Acts through Revelation. 2009. 288p. *(978-0-8425-2725-5(7),* Brigham Young Univ. Religious Studies Ctr.) Brigham Young Univ.

Hwang, Jin Ki. Mimesis & Apostolic Parousia in 1 Corinthians 4 & 5: An Apologetic-Mimetic Interpretation. 2010. (Illus.). x, 352p. 119.95 *(978-0-7734-3719-7(3))* Mellen, Edwin Pr., The.

II Corinthians. (People's Bible Commentary Ser.). 264p. 14.99 *(978-0-7586-0446-0(7));* (LifeLight Bible Studies: Course 21). stu. ed. 5.50 *(978-0-570-09432-6(1),* 20-2556); (LifeLight Bible Studies: Course 21). 6.50 *(978-0-570-09431-9(3),* 20-2555) Concordia Publishing Hse.

Inziku, John. Overcoming Divisive Behaviour: An Attempt to Interpret 1Cor 11, 17-34 from Another Perspective, Vol. 816. (European University Studies: Vol. 23). (Illus.). 389p. pap. 62.95 *(978-3-631-54310-8(7))* Lang, Peter Publishing, Inc.

Ironside, H. A. The Epistles of John & Jude. 2007. (Ironside Expository Commentaries Ser.). (Illus.). 192p. 19.99 *(978-0-8254-2923-1(4))* Kregel Pubns.

Ironside, Henry A. Estudios en Timoteo, Tito y Filemon: Lectures on Timothy, Titus & Philemon. (SPA.). *(978-84-7645-287-5(X),* 223374) Clie, Editorial.

—Estudios sobre I y II Tesalonicenses: Lectures on First & Second Thessalonians. (SPA.). *(978-84-7645-292-9(6),* 223297) Clie, Editorial.

—Estudios sobre Santiago I y II Pedro: Lectures on James & Peter. (SPA.). *(978-84-7645-374-2(4),* 223492) Clie, Editorial.

Jackson, Donald. The Saint John's Bible: An Introduction. 2008. (Illus.). 32p. per. 9.95 *(978-0-8146-9100-7(5),* Liturgical Pr. Bks.) Liturgical Pr.

Jackson, T. Ryan. New Creation in Paul's Letters: A Study of the Historical & Social Setting of a Pauline Concept. 2010. (Illus.). 240p. pap. 117.50 *(978-3-16-149999-9(9))* Mohr Siebeck GmbH & Co. KG DEU. Dist: Coronet Bks.

Jakes, T. D. Life Overflowing: 6 Pillars for Abundant Living. 2010. 448p. reprint ed. pap. 19.99 *(978-0-7642-0798-3(9))* Bethany Hse. Pubs.

Jennings, J. Nelson. God the Real Superpower: Rethinking Our Role in Missions. 2007. pap. *(978-1-59638-023-3(3))* P & R Publishing

Jeremiah, David. What to Do When You Don't Know What to Do. 2009. (ENG.). 256p. pap. 13.99 *(978-1-4347-6451-5(6))* Cook, David C.

Jervis, L. Ann. At the Heart of the Gospel: Suffering in the Earliest Christian Message. 2007. 149p. per. 14.00 *(978-0-8028-3993-0(2))* Eerdmans, William B. Publishing Co.

Johnson, Edna. A Semantic & Structural Analysis of Ephesians. 2008. 251p. pap. 30.00 *(978-1-55671-224-1(3))* SIL International.

Johnson, Matthew V. Onesimus Our Brother: Reading, Religion, Race, & Slavery in Philemon. Noel, James A., ed. 2012. (Paul in Critical Contexts Ser.). 176p. (C). 39.00 *(978-0-8006-6341-4(1),* Fortress Pr.) Augsburg Fortress, Pubs.

Jones, Peter Rhea. 1, 2, & 3 John. 2008. *(978-1-57312-036-9(3))* Smyth & Helwys Publishing, Inc.

Joseph, Abson. A Narratological Reading of 1 Peter. 2012. (ENG.). 224p. 120.00 ***(978-0-567-16625-8(2),*** T&T Clark Int'l) Continuum International Publishing Group, Ltd. GBR. Dist: National Bk. Network.

Joslin, Barry C. Hebrews, Christ & the Law: The Theology of the Mosaic Law in Hebrews 71 1018. 2008. (Paternoster Biblical Monographs). (ENG.). 353p. 49.99 *(978-1-84227-530-6(5),* Paternoster) Authentic Media.

—Hebrews, Christ, & the Law: The Theology of the Mosaic Law in Hebrews 7:1Ð10:18. 2009. (Paternoster Biblical Monographs). 354p. pap. 42.00 *(978-1-60608-474-8(7),* Wipf and Stock) Wipf & Stock Pubs.

Julien, Tom. Inherited Wealth: Studies in Ephesians. 2006. 141p. per. 7.99 *(978-0-88469-034-4(2))* BMH Bks.

Kahl, Brigitte. Galatians Re-Imagined: Readings with the Eyes of the Vanquished. 2010. (Paul in Critical Contexts Ser.). 272p. (C). 29.00 *(978-0-8006-3864-1(6),* Fortress Pr.) Augsburg Fortress, Pubs.

Kamudzandu, Israel. Abraham as Spiritual Ancestor: A Postcolonial Zimbabwean Reading of Romans 4. 280p. *(978-90-04-18164-9(4))* BRILL.

Kartzow, Marianne Bjelland. Gossip & Gender: Othering of Speech in the Pastoral Epistles. 2009. (Beihefte zur Zeitschrift für die neutestamentliche Wissenschaft und die Kunde der älteren Kirche Ser.). (ENG.). XVI, 241p. 126.00 *(978-3-11-021563-2(2));* 196.00 ***(978-3-11-173600-6(8))*** De Gruyter, Walter Inc.

Kelly, W. The Epistle to the Hebrews. 272p. 9.95 *(978-0-88172-155-3(7))* Believers Bookshelf, Inc.

—Exposition of the Epistles of John. 7.25 *(978-0-88172-100-3(X))* Believers Bookshelf, Inc.

—Notes on Romans. 8.95 *(978-0-88172-107-2(7))* Believers Bookshelf, Inc.

—Titus & Philemon. 6.95 *(978-0-88172-110-2(7))* Believers Bookshelf, Inc.

Kelly, William. The Pauline Epistles. (Introductory Lecture Ser.: Vol. 2). 551p. 7.95 *(978-0-88172-098-3(4))* Believers Bookshelf, Inc.

Kent, Homer A., Jr. Ephesians, the Glory of the Church. pap. 8.99 *(978-0-88469-078-8(4))* BMH Bks.

Kern, Philip H. Rhetoric & Galatians: Assessing an Approach to Paul's Epistle. 2007. (Society for New Testament Studies Monograph Ser.). (ENG.). 324p. pap. 47.00 *(978-0-521-04813-2(3))* Cambridge Univ. Pr.

Killen, W. D. The Ignatian Epistles Entirely Spurious. 2007. 72p. per. *(978-1-4065-1920-4(0))* Dodo Pr.

Kim, Yung Suk. Christ's Body in Corinth: The Politics of a Metaphor. 2008. (Paul in Critical Contexts Ser.). (Illus.). 152p. (C). pap. 29.00 *(978-0-8006-6285-1(7),* Fortress Pr.) Augsburg Fortress, Pubs.

King, Martha. Exegetical Summary of Colossians. 2nd ed. 2008. 346p. pap. 39.00 *(978-1-55671-203-6(0))* SIL International.

Kirk, J. R. Daniel. Unlocking Romans: Resurrection & the Justification of God. 2008. 256p. pap. 32.00 *(978-0-8028-6290-7(X))* Eerdmans, William B. Publishing Co.

Kistemaker, Simon. The Psalm Citations in the Epistle to the Hebrews. 2010. 164p. pap. 19.00 *(978-1-60899-721-3(9),* Wipf and Stock) Wipf & Stock Pubs.

Kittredge, Cynthia & Kittredge, Cynthia Briggs. Conversations with Scripture: The Gospel of John. 2007. (Anglican Association of Biblical Scholars Study Ser.). 144p. per. 18.00 *(978-0-8192-2249-7(6),* Morehouse Publishing) Church Publishing, Inc.

Klauck, Hans-Josef. Ancient Letters & the New Testament: A Guide to Context & Exegesis. 2006. 539p. per. 39.95 *(978-1-932792-40-9(6))* Baylor Univ. Pr.

Knowles, Michael P. We Preach Not Ourselves: Paul on Proclamation. 2008. 288p. (C). pap. 28.00 *(978-1-58743-211-8(0))* Brazos Pr.

Kraus, Thomas J. & Nicklas, Tobias, eds. Das Evangelium nach Petrus: Text, Kontexte, Intertexte. 2007. (Texte und Untersuchungen Zur Geschichte der Altchristlichen Literatur Ser.). (GER & ENG.). VIII, 384p. 154.00 *(978-3-11-019313-8(2))* De Gruyter, Walter Inc.

Kreitzer. Hierapolis in the Heavens: Studies in the Letter to the Ephesians. 2008. (Library of New Testament Studies, the Ser.). (ENG., Illus.). 160p. 130.00 *(978-0-567-04572-0(2),* T&T Clark Int'l) Continuum International Publishing Group, Ltd. GBR. Dist: National Bk. Network.

Kroll, Woodrow. Ephesians: Life in God's Family. 2007. (Back to the Bible Study Guides). 96p. pap. 7.99 *(978-1-58134-881-1(9))* Crossway.

Kulus, Chester W. One Tittle Shall in No Wise Pass: Destroying the Scholarly Myth that God Did Not Inspire the Vowels of the Old Testament. 2009. 456p. pap. 30.00 *(978-0-9820608-7-2(4))* Old Paths Pubns., Inc., The.

Kuma, Hermann V. A. The Centrality of Aiua (Blood) in the Theology of the Epistle to the Hebrews: An Exegetical & Philological Study. 2011. 129.95 *(978-0-7734-1461-7(4))* Mellen, Edwin Pr., The.

Kuske, David P. A Commentary on Romans 1-8. 2007. (GEC & ENG., Illus.). 460p. *(978-0-8100-1979-9(5))* Northwestern Publishing Hse.

Kwon, Oh-Young. 1 Corinthians 1Ð4: Reconstructing Its Social & Rhetorical Situation & Re-Reading it Cross-Culturally for Korean-Confucian Christians Today. 2010. 316p. pap. 35.00 *(978-1-60899-432-8(5),* Wipf and Stock) Wipf & Stock Pubs.

Ladd, Karol. Unfailing Love: A Woman's Walk Through First John. 2012. (Positive Woman Connection Ser.). 240p. pap. 12.99 ***(978-0-7369-2977-6(0))*** Harvest Hse. Pubs.

Lakey, Michael. Image & Glory of God. 2010. (Library of New Testament Studies, the Ser.). (ENG., Illus.). 224p. stu. ed. 120.00 *(978-0-567-18260-9(6),* T&T Clark Int'l) Continuum International Publishing Group, Ltd. GBR. Dist: National Bk. Network.

Langton, Daniel R. The Apostle Paul in the Jewish Imagination: A Study in Modern Jewish-Christian Relations. 2010. (ENG.). 320p. 100.00 *(978-0-521-51740-9(0))* Cambridge Univ. Pr.

Larkin, William J. Ephesians: A Handbook on the Greek Text. 2009. (Baylor Handbook on the Greek New Testament Ser.). (ENG.). 210p. pap. 24.95 *(978-1-60258-066-4(9))* Baylor Univ. Pr.

Lau, Te-Li. The Politics of Peace: Ephesians, Dio Chrysostom, & the Confucian Four Books. 2009. (Novum Testamentum Supplements Ser.). 376p. *(978-90-04-18053-6(2))* BRILL.

Lee, Brian J. Johannes Cocceius & the Exegetical Roots of Federal Theology: Reformation Developments in the Interpretation of Hebrews 7-10. 2009. (Reformed Historical Theology Ser.). (ENG.). 215p. (C). 65.00 *(978-3-525-56913-9(0))* Vandenhoeck & Ruprecht GmbH & Co. KG DEU. Dist: ISD.

Lee, Michelle V. Paul, the Stoics, & the Body of Christ. 2008. (Society for New Testament Studies Monograph Ser.). (ENG.). 240p. pap. 36.00 *(978-0-521-09143-5(8))* Cambridge Univ. Pr.

Leithart, Peter J. The Promise of His Appearing: An Exposition of Second Peter. 2006. (ENG.). 111p. pap. 15.00 *(978-1-59128-026-2(5))* Canon Pr.

Letson, Rickey. Sessions with Thessalonians: Being Faithful in a Confusing World. 2007. (Sessions Ser.). 82p. per. *(978-1-57312-491-1(5))* Smyth & Helwys Publishing, Inc.

Levering, Matthew & Dauphinais, Michael, eds. Reading Romans with St. Thomas Aquinas. 2012. (ENG.). 336p. 54.95 ***(978-0-8132-1962-2(0));*** pap. 34.95 ***(978-0-8132-1963-9(9))*** Catholic Univ. of America Pr.

Levy, Ian Christopher. The Letter to the Galatians. 2011. 312p. pap. 34.00 *(978-0-8028-2223-9(1))* Eerdmans, William B. Publishing Co.

Lewis, Agnes Smith, ed. Acta Mythologica Apostolorum in Arabic: Transcribed from an Arabic MS in the Convent of Deyr-Es-Suriani, Egypt, & from MSS in the Convent of St Catherine, on Mount Sinai. 2010. (Cambridge Library Collection - Religion Ser.). (ARA., Illus.). 254p. pap. 23.99 *(978-1-108-01898-2(X))* Cambridge Univ. Pr.

Liddon, H P. Explanatory Analysis of St. Paul's First Epistle to Timothy. 2008. 97p. pap. 8.00 *(978-1-55635-765-7(6))* Wipf & Stock Pubs.

Lincoln, Andrew. Hebrews: A Guide. 2006. (ENG.). 136p. 120.00 *(978-0-567-04363-4(0),* T&T Clark Int'l) Continuum International Publishing Group, Ltd. GBR. Dist: National Bk. Network.

Lingenfelter, W. M. Stepping Forward: A 39-Day Walk Through Ephesians. 2011. 168p. 30.95 ***(978-1-4497-2358-3(6));*** pap. 13.95 ***(978-1-4497-2357-6(8))*** Author Solutions, Inc. (WestBow Pr.).

Lockett, Darian. An Introduction to the Catholic Epistles. 2012. (ENG.). 160p. pap. 24.95 ***(978-0-567-17177-1(9));*** 100.00 ***(978-0-567-23655-5(2))*** Continuum International Publishing Group, Ltd. GBR. (T&T Clark Int'l). Dist: National Bk. Network.

Lockett, Darian. Purity & Worldview in the Epistle of James. 2008. (Library of New Testament Studies, the Ser.). (ENG.). 240p. 130.00 *(978-0-567-03311-6(2),* T&T Clark Int'l) Continuum International Publishing Group, Ltd. GBR. Dist: National Bk. Network.

Lockwood, Gregory & Dunker, Gary. 1 Corinthians. 2007. (Life Light Foundations Topical Bible Study Ser.). (Illus.). 31p. pap. 8.99 *(978-0-7586-1028-7(9))* Concordia Publishing Hse.

Longenecker, Bruce. Remember the Poor: Paul, Poverty, & the Greco-Roman World. 2010. 284p. pap. 25.00 *(978-0-8028-6373-7(6))* Eerdmans, William B. Publishing Co.

Longenecker, Richard N. Introducing Romans: Critical Issues in Paul's Most Famous Letter. 2011. 536p. pap. 40.00 *(978-0-8028-6619-6(0))* Eerdmans, William B. Publishing Co.

Lozada, Francisco, Jr., ed. New Currents Through John: A Global Perspective. 2006. (Society of Biblical Literature Academia Biblica Ser.). (Illus.). 248p. *(978-90-04-14672-3(5))* BRILL.

Lucado, Max. Book of 2 Corinthians: Remembering What Matters, 0 vols. 2007. (Inspirational Bible Study; Life Lessons with Max Lucado Ser.). 128p. per. 9.99 *(978-1-4185-0972-9(8))* Nelson, Thomas Inc.

—Book of Ephesians: Where You Belong, 0 vols. 2007. (Inspirational Bible Study; Life Lessons with Max Lucado Ser.). (Illus.). 128p. per. 9.99 *(978-1-4185-0953-8(1))* Nelson, Thomas Inc.

—Book of Galatians: Free in Christ, 0 vols. 2007. (Inspirational Bible Study; Life Lessons with Max Lucado Ser.). 128p. per. 9.99 *(978-1-4185-0970-5(1))* Nelson, Thomas Inc.

—Books of Colossians & Philemon: The Difference Christ Makes, 0 vols. 2007. (Inspirational Bible Study; Life Lessons with Max Lucado Ser.). 128p. per. 9.99 *(978-1-4185-0973-6(6))* Nelson, Thomas Inc.

Luckensmeyer, David. The Eschatology of First Thessalonians. 2009. (Novum Testamentum et Orbis Antiquus/Studien zur Umwelt des Neuen Testaments (NTOA/StUNT) Ser.). (ENG.). 463p. (C). 111.00 *(978-3-525-53969-9(X))* Vandenhoeck & Ruprecht GmbH & Co. KG DEU. Dist: ISD.

Lull, David John. The Spirit in Galatia: Paul's Interpretation of Pneuma as Divine Power. 2006. (Dissertation Series (Society of Biblical Literature) Ser.). 254p. pap. 26.00 *(978-1-59752-725-5(4),* Wipf and Stock) Wipf & Stock Pubs.

Lund, Enrique. Epistola a los Filipenses.T: of Paul's Letter to the Philippians. (SPA.). *(978-84-7645-060-4(5),* 223119) Clie, Editorial.

MacArthur, John. Colossians & Philemon, 0 vols. 2007. (MacArthur Bible Study Guides). 128p. per. 9.99 *(978-1-4185-0963-7(9))* Nelson, Thomas Inc.

—Ephesians: Our Immeasurable Blessings in Christ, 0 vols. 2006. (MacArthur Bible Study Guides). 128p. per. 9.99 *(978-1-4185-0886-9(1))* Nelson, Thomas Inc.

—The Fulfilled Family: God's Design for Your Home, 0 vols. 2008. 144p. pap. 12.99 *(978-1-4002-8044-5(3))* Nelson, Thomas Inc.

—Hebrews: Christ - Perfect Sacrifice, Perfect Priest, 0 vols. 2006. (MacArthur Bible Study Guides). 144p. per. 9.99 *(978-1-4185-0888-3(8))* Nelson, Thomas Inc.

—James, 0 vols. 2006. (MacArthur Bible Study Guides). (Illus.). 128p. per. 9.99 *(978-1-4185-0889-0(6))* Nelson, Thomas Inc.

—1, 2, 3, John & Jude: Established in Truth, Marked by Love, 0 vols. 2007. (MacArthur Bible Studies). 128p. pap. 9.99 *(978-1-4185-0965-1(5))* Nelson, Thomas Inc.

—1 & 2 Peter, 0 vols. 2006. (MacArthur Bible Studies). (Illus.). 128p. pap. 9.99 *(978-1-4185-0890-6(X))* Nelson, Thomas Inc.

—1 & 2 Thessalonians & Titus: Living Faithfully in View of Christ's Coming, 0 vols. 2007. (MacArthur Bible Studies). 128p. pap. 9.99 *(978-1-4185-0964-4(7))* Nelson, Thomas Inc.

—1 & 2 Timothy, 0 vols. 2006. (MacArthur Bible Studies). (Illus.). 128p. pap. 9.99 *(978-1-4185-0887-6(X))* Nelson, Thomas Inc.

—2 Corinthians: Words from a Caring Shepherd, 0 vols. 2007. (MacArthur Bible Study Guides). 128p. per. 9.99 *(978-1-4185-0962-0(0))* Nelson, Thomas Inc.

MacArthur, John F. God's High Calling for Women, 1 vol. 2009. (ENG.). 96p. pap. 7.99 *(978-0-8024-5304-4(X))* Moody Pubs.

MacDonald, James M. Life & Writings of St. John. 2006. pap. 40.95 *(978-1-4286-3708-5(7))* Kessinger Publishing, LLC.

Mackie, Scott D. Eschatology & Exhortation in the Epistle to the Hebrews: Kleine Schriften IV. 2007. (Wissenschaftliche Untersuchungen Zum Neuen Testament Ser.: 223). 284p. (Orig.). (C). pap. 85.00 *(978-3-16-149215-0(3))* Mohr Siebeck GmbH & Co. KG DEU. Dist: Eisenbrauns, Inc.

B

Mackintosh, Charles Henry & MacKintosh, Charles Henry. The All Sufficient Christ: Miscellaneous Writings of C. H. Mackintosh V1. 2011. 380p. 53.95 (978-1-258-01734-7(2)) Literary Licensing, LLC.

Macleay, Angus. Teaching 1 Peter: Unlocking the Book of 1st Peter for the Bible Teacher. 2008. (Teaching Ser.). (ENG.). 288p. pap. 10.99 (978-1-84550-347-5(3), Christian Focus) Christian Focus Pubns. GBR. Dist: STL Distribution North America.

Magda, Ksenija. Paul's Territoriality & Mission Strategy: Searching for the Geographical Awareness Paradigm Behind Romans. 2009. (Wissenschaftliche Untersuchungen zum Neuen Testament Ser.). (Illus.). 215p. pap. 115.00 (978-3-16-149990-6(5)) Mohr Siebeck GmbH & Co. KG DEU. Dist: Coronet Bks.

Malherbe, Abraham J. Paul & the Thessalonians: The Philosophic Tradition of Pastoral Care. 2011. 132p. pap. 16.00 (978-1-61097-355-7(0), Wipf and Stock) Wipf & Stock Pubs.

Man, Ron. Proclamation & Praise: Hebrews 2:12 & the Christology of Worship. 2007. 118p. pap. 15.00 (978-1-55635-056-6(2), Wipf and Stock) Wipf & Stock Pubs.

Marchal, Joseph A. Hierarchy, Unity, & Imitation: A Feminist Rhetorical Analysis of Power Dynamics in Paul's Letter to the Philippians. 2006. (Society of Biblical Literature Academia Biblica Ser.). 261p. (978-90-04-15115-4(X)) BRILL.

Marchal, Joseph A., ed. Studying Paul's Letters: Contemporary Perspectives & Methods. 2012. 256p. pap. 32.00 (978-0-8006-9818-8(5), Fortress Pr.) Augsburg Fortress, Pubs.

Marohl, Matthew J. Faithfulness & the Purpose of Hebrews: A Social Identity Approach. 2010. (ENG.). 228p. (C). pap. 42.50 (978-0-227-17337-4(6)) Clarke, James Co., Ltd. GBR. Dist: Brown, David Bk. Co., The.

—Faithfulness & the Purpose of Hebrews: A Social Identity Approach. 2007. (Princeton Theological Monograph Ser.). 228p. pap. 25.00 (978-1-55635-512-7(2), Pickwick Pubns.) Wipf & Stock Pubs.

Mason, Eric F. You Are a Priest Forever: Second Temple Jewish Messianism & the Priestly Christology of the Epistle to the Hebrews. 2008. (Studies on the Texts of the Desert of Judah). 229p. (978-90-04-14987-8(2)) BRILL.

Mason, James. My Father's Words in Stability. 2009. 33p. pap. 16.82 (978-0-557-03900-5(2)) Lulu Enterprises Inc.

Mayhall, Carole. Come Walk with Me: A Woman's Personal Guide to Knowing God & Mentoring Others. 2010. (ENG.). 224p. pap. 13.99 (978-0-307-45887-2(3), WaterBrook Pr.) Doubleday Religious Publishing Group, The.

Mbuvi, Andrew Mutua. Temple, Exile & Identity in 1 Peter. 2007. (Library of New Testament Studies, the Ser.). (ENG.). 192p. 130.00 (978-0-567-03142-6(X), T&T Clark Int'l) Continuum International Publishing Group, Ltd. GBR. Dist: National Bk. Network.

McCollum, Adam, intro. Jacob of Sarug's Homily on Simon Peter, when our Lord said 'Get behind me, Satan' 2009. (SYR & ENG.). pap. 50.00 (978-1-60724-214-7(1)) Gorgias Pr., LLC.

McCruden, Kevin B. Solidarity Perfected: Beneficent Christology in the Epistle to the Hebrews. 2008. (Beihefte zur Zeitschrift für die neutestamentliche Wissenschaft und die Kunde der Älteren Kirche Ser.). (ENG.). VIII, 159p. 105.00 (978-3-11-020554-1(8)) De Gruyter, Walter Inc.

McKenzie, Duncan W. The Antichrist & the Second Coming Vol. 1: A Preterist Examination. 2009. 468p. 36.99 (978-1-61579-038-8(1)); pap. 24.99 (978-1-61579-037-1(3)) Xulon Pr., Inc.

McKenzie, John L. Light on the Epistles: A Reader's Guide. 2009. (John L. Mckenzie Reprints Ser.). 212p. pap. 23.00 (978-1-60608-045-0(8)) Wipf & Stock Pubs.

McKinley, David. The Life You Were Born to Give: Why It's Better to Live Than to Receive, 0 vols. 2007. 192p. per. 12.99 (978-0-8499-1202-3(4)) Nelson, Thomas Inc.

McNaughton, Ian. 2 Thessalonians. 2008. (Opening Up Ser.). (Illus.). 96p. pap. (978-1-84625-117-7(6)) DayOne Pubns.

Meadows, James L. I, II & III John & Jude. pap. 5.50 (978-0-89098-409-3(3)) Twentieth Century Christian Bks.

—I Thessalonians. pap. 5.50 (978-0-89098-412-3(3)) Twentieth Century Christian Bks.

—II Corinthians & Galatians. pap. 5.50 (978-0-89098-397-3(6)) Twentieth Century Christian Bks.

Meyer, F. b. & Meyer, F. B. The Way into the Holiest. 2011. 174p. pap. 16.99 (978-1-61203-261-0(3)) Bottom of the Hill Publishing.

Meyer, Rudolf. Gramatica del Hebreo Biblico.Tr. of Grammar of the Biblical Hebrew. (SPA.). 496p. (978-84-7645-324-7(8), 223501) Clie, Editorial.

Mihaila, Corin. Paul-Apollos Relationship & Paul's Stance Toward Greco-Roman Rhetoric: An Exegetical & Socio-Historical Study of 1 Corinthians 1-4. 2009. (Library of New Testament Studies, the Ser.). (ENG.). 272p. 140.00 (978-0-567-18382-8(3), T&T Clark Int'l) Continuum International Publishing Group, Ltd. GBR. Dist: National Bk. Network.

Milinovich, Timothy. Now Is the Day of Salvation: An Audience-Oriented Study of 2 Corinthians 5:16Ntilde;6:2. 2011. 190p. pap. 22.00 (978-1-60899-764-0(2), Pickwick Pubns.) Wipf & Stock Pubs.

Milinovich, Timothy. Now Is the Day of Salvation: An Audience-Oriented Study of 2 Corinthians 5:16ü6:2. 2012. (ENG.). 190p. pap. (978-0-7188-9264-7(X)) Lutherworth Pr., The.

Miller, J. R. Devotional Hours with the Bible Volume Viii, from the Acts, the Epistles & Revelation. 2011. 154p. pap. 14.99 (978-1-61203-206-1(0)) Bottom of the Hill Publishing.

Miranda, Jose Porfirio & Eagleson, John. Being & the Messiah: The Message of St. John. 2006. 256p. pap. 26.00 (978-1-59752-816-0(1), Wipf and Stock) Wipf & Stock Pubs.

Mitchell, Alan C. Hebrews. 2007. (Sacra Pagina Ser.: No. 13). 357p. 29.95 (978-0-8146-5815-4(6)) Liturgical Pr.

Mitchell, Margaret M. Paul, the Corinthians & the Birth of Christian Hermeneutics. 2010. (ENG., Illus.). 192p. 85.00 (978-0-521-19795-3(3)) Cambridge Univ. Pr.

Mitton, C. Leslie. The Formation of the Pauline Corpus of Letters. 2009. 80p. pap. 11.00 (978-1-60608-416-8(X), Wipf and Stock) Wipf & Stock Pubs.

Moffitt, David M. Atonement & the Logic of Resurrection in the Epistle to the Hebrews. 2011. (Novum Testamentum Supplements Ser.). XX, 340p. (978-90-04-20651-9(5)) BRILL.

Moody, Dale. Apostasy. 7.00 (978-0-687-82119-8(3)) Abingdon Pr.

Morales, Rodrigo J. The Spirit & the Restoration of Israel: New Exodus & New Creation Motifs in Galatians. 2010. (Illus.). 209p. pap. 97.50 (978-3-16-150435-8(6)) Mohr Siebeck GmbH & Co. KG DEU. Dist: Coronet Bks.

Morgan-Wynne, John Eifion. The Cross in the Johannine Writings. 2011. 318p. pap. 35.00 (978-1-61097-251-2(1), Pickwick Pubns.) Wipf & Stock Pubs.

Morrison, James. A Critical Exposition of the Third Chapter of Paul's Epistle to the Romans. A Monograph. 2009. 444p. pap. 36.00 (978-1-60608-376-5(7), Wipf and Stock) Wipf & Stock Pubs.

Morrison, Michael D. Who Needs a New Covenant? Rhetorical Function of the Covenant Motif in the Argument of Hebrews. 2008. (Princeton Theological Monographs). (Illus.). 226p. pap. 25.00 (978-1-55635-804-3(0), Pickwick Pubns.) Wipf & Stock Pubs.

moshe, ben david. At the Gate of Rome (Hebrew) 2008. 526p. pap. 39.99 (978-1-4092-2747-2(2)) Lulu Enterprises Inc.

Moule, Handley C. Estudios sobre Colosenses: Lectures in Colossians. (SPA.). 176p. (978-84-7228-900-0(1), 222323) Clie, Editorial.

—Estudios sobre Efesios: Studies in Ephesians. (SPA.). 192p. (978-84-7228-902-4(8), 222333) Clie, Editorial.

—Estudios sobre Hebreos: Studies on Hebrews. (SPA.). (978-84-7645-092-5(3), 223154) Clie, Editorial.

Munzinger, Andre. Discerning the Spirits: Theological & Ethical Hermeneutics in Paul. 2007. (Society for New Testament Studies Monograph Ser.). (ENG., Illus.). 256p. 112.00 (978-0-521-87594-3(3)) Cambridge Univ. Pr.

Murphy-O'Connor, Jerome. Becoming Human Together: The Pastoral Anthropology of St. Paul, Third Edition. 2009. 280p. pap. 29.95 (978-1-58983-361-6(9)) Society of Biblical Literature.

Muther, Urs-Ullrich. Paulinische Ökonomie: Der Effizienzbegriff in 1. Korinther 12 und seine Bedeutung für die Gemeindekonzeption. 2010. (Religion in der Öffentlichkeit Ser.). (GER.). 386p. 90.95 (978-3-631-60941-5(8)) Lang, Peter GmbH, Europaischer Verlag der Wissenschaften DEU. Dist: Lang, Peter.

Nee, Watchman. Sit Walk Stand with Study Guide: The Process of Christian Maturity. 2008. 96p. pap. 8.99 (978-0-87508-973-7(9)) CLC Pubns.

Need, Stephen W. Paul Today: Challenging Readings of Acts & the Epistles. 2007. (Essential Inquiries Ser.). (ENG.). 160p. per. 15.95 (978-1-56101-296-1(3)) Cowley Pubns.

Nelson, Emmitt J. The Fruit of the Spirit. 2nd l.t. ed. 87p. (Orig.). pap. 9.00 (978-0-9664896-2-0(4)) Nelson Consulting, Inc.

Niang, A. C. & Niang, Aliou Cisse. Faith & Freedom in Galatia & Senegal: The Apostle Paul, Colonists & Sending Gods. 2009. (Biblical Interpretation Ser.). (Illus.). 192p. (978-90-04-17522-8(9)) BRILL.

Nicholl, Colin R. From Hope to Despair in Thessalonica: Situating 1 & 2 Thessalonians. 2008. (Society for New Testament Studies Monograph Ser.). (ENG.). 336p. pap. 48.00 (978-0-521-07307-3(3)) Cambridge Univ. Pr.

Nicholson, Suzanne. Dynamic Oneness. 2011. (ENG.). 294p. pap. 48.00 (978-0-227-17366-4(X)) Clarke, James Co., Ltd. GBR. Dist: Brown, David Bk. Co., The.

—Dynamic Oneness. 2009. 312p. pap. 33.00 (978-1-60608-326-0(0), Pickwick Pubns.) Wipf & Stock Pubs.

Nickle, Keith F. The Collection: A Study in Paul's Strategy. 2009. 176p. pap. 20.00 (978-1-60608-690-2(1), Wipf and Stock) Wipf & Stock Pubs.

Niebuhr, Karl-Wilhelm & Wall, Robert W., eds. Catholic Epistles & Apostolic Tradition. 2009. (ENG.). 570p. 69.95 (978-1-60258-215-6(7)) Baylor Univ. Pr.

Nienhuis, David R. Not by Paul Alone: The Formation of the Catholic Epistle Collection & the Christian Canon. 2007. (Illus.). 285p. 44.95 (978-1-932792-71-3(6)) Baylor Univ. Pr.

Norman, Dwayne & Mallette, Richard. The Mystery. 2010. 286p. pap. 13.99 (978-0-88144-520-6(7)) Yorkshire Publishing Group.

O'Brien, Peter T. Introductory Thanksgivings in the Letters of Paul. 2009. 322p. pap. 35.00 (978-1-60608-811-1(4), Wipf and Stock) Wipf & Stock Pubs.

Ochsenmeier, Erwin. Mal, Souffrance et Justice de Dieu Selon Romains 1-3: étude Exégétique et Théologique. 2007. (Beihefte Zur Zeitschrift Für Die Neutestamentliche Wissenschaft und Die Kunde der älteren Kirche Ser.). (FRE.). XII, 392p. 182.00 (978-3-11-019696-2(4)) De Gruyter, Walter Inc.

Ochsenmeier, Erwin. Mal, Souffrance et Justice de Dieu Selon Romains 1-3: Étude Exégétique et Théologique. (Beihefte zur Zeitschrift far die neutestamentliche Wissenschaft und die Kunde der älteren Kirche Ser.). (FRE.). XII, 392p. 300.00 (978-3-11-183373-6(9)) De Gruyter, Walter Inc.

Odell-Scott, David & Odell-Scott. Paul's Critique of Theocracy: A Theocracy in Corinthians & Galatians. 2009. (Library of New Testament Studies, the Ser.). (ENG.). 200p. 39.95 (978-0-567-28335-1(6), T&T Clark Int'l) Continuum International Publishing Group, Ltd. GBR. Dist: National Bk. Network.

Odell-Scott, David W. Reading Romans with Contemporary Philosophers & Theologians, Vol. 7. 2007. (Romans Through History & Culture Ser.). (ENG.). 304p. pap. 49.95 (978-0-567-02705-4(8), T&T Clark Int'l) Continuum International Publishing Group, Ltd. GBR. Dist: National Bk. Network.

O'Mahony, Kieran J. Do We Still Need St. Paul: A Contemporary Reading of the Apostle. 2009. (ENG.). 150p. pap. 24.95 (978-1-84730-171-0(1)) Veritas Pubns. IRL. Dist: Dufour Editions, Inc.

Orme, William. Memoir of the Controversy Respecting the Three Heavenly Witnesses, I John V 7 Including Critical Notices of the Principal Writers on Both Sides of T. 2006. 232p. per. 20.99 (978-1-4255-1969-8(5)) MPublishing.

Oropeza, B. J. Paul & Apostasy: Eschatology, Perseverance, & Falling Away in the Corinthian Congregation. 2007. 324p. pap. 36.00 (978-1-55635-333-8(2), Wipf and Stock) Wipf & Stock Pubs.

Otto, Diane. Guess What I Discovered on the Way to Church? 2007. 428p. per. 24.99 (978-1-60266-349-7(1)) Xulon Pr., Inc.

Paddison, Angus. Theological Hermeneutics & 1 Thessalonians. 2008. (Society for New Testament Studies Monograph Ser.). (ENG.). 248p. pap. 36.00 (978-0-521-09005-6(9)) Cambridge Univ. Pr.

Pahl, Michael W. & Pahl. Discerning the 'Word of the Lord' The 'Word of the Lord' in 1 Thessalonians 4:15. 2009. (Library of New Testament Studies, the Ser.). (ENG.). 216p. 120.00 (978-0-567-45565-9(3), T&T Clark Int'l) Continuum International Publishing Group, Ltd. GBR. Dist: National Bk. Network.

Palmer, Delano Vincent. Romans in Context: A Theological Appreciation of Paul's Magnum Opus. 2011. 328p. pap. 36.00 (978-1-60899-754-1(5), Resource Pubns.) Wipf & Stock Pubs.

Pate, C. Marvin. The Writings of John: A Survey of the Gospel Epistles, & Apocalypse, 1 vol. 2011. (ENG.). 560p. 44.99 (978-0-310-26737-9(4)) Zondervan.

Pedrone, Dino. True I D. 2008. 216p. per. 14.99 (978-1-60477-492-4(4)) Xulon Pr., Inc.

Perriman, Andrew. The Future of the People of God: Reading Romans Before & after Western Christendom. 2010. 188p. pap. 22.00 (978-1-60608-787-9(8), Cascade Bks.) Wipf & Stock Pubs.

Pettingill, W. L. Estudios Sencillos sobre Romanos: Simple Studies in Romans. (SPA.). 192p. (978-84-7228-866-9(8), 222326) Clie, Editorial.

—Estudios sobre la Epistola a Galatas: Studies on Galatians. (SPA.). 96p. (978-84-7228-893-5(5), 222329) Clie, Editorial.

Philip, Mayjee. Leveticus in Hebrews: A Transtextual Analysis of the Tabernacle Theme in the Letter to the Hebrews. 2011. 190p. 94.95 (978-3-0343-0257-9(6)) Lang, Peter AG GBR. Dist: Lang, Peter.

Phillips, Thomas E. Paul, His Letters, & Acts. 2008. (ENG.). 250p. (C). pap. (978-1-934269-34-3(4)) Univ. Readers.

Phillips, Thomas E. & Porter, Stanley E. Paul, His Letters, & Acts. 2009. 256p. (978-1-59856-001-5(8)) Hendrickson Pubs. Marketing, LLC.

Pierce, Chad T. Spirits & the Proclamation of Christ: 1 Peter 3:18-22 in Light of Sin & Punishment Traditions in Early Jewish & Christian Literature. 2011. (Wissenschaftliche Untersuchungen zum Neuen Testament Ser.). 289p. pap. 137.50 (978-3-16-150858-5(0)) Mohr Siebeck GmbH & Co. KG DEU. Dist: Coronet Bks.

Pizzuto, Vincent A. & Pizzuto, V. A. A Cosmic Leap of Faith: An Authorial, Structural, & Theological Investigation of the Cosmic Christology in Col. 1:15-20. 2006. (Contributions to Biblical Exegesis & Theology Ser.). (ENG.). 306p. (C). pap. 58.00 (978-90-429-1651-7(6)) Peeters Pubs. & Booksellers BEL. Dist: Brown, David Bk. Co., The.

Pollefeyt, Didier & Bieringer, Reimund, eds. Paul & Judaism: Crosscurrents in Pauline Exegesis & the Study of Jewish-Christian Relations. 2012. (ENG.). 272p. 110.00 (978-0-567-07280-1(0), T&T Clark Int'l) Continuum International Publishing Group, Ltd. GBR. Dist: National Bk. Network.

Portalatin, Antonio. Temporal Oppositions as Hermeneutical Categories in the Epistle to the Hebrews, Vol. 833. 2006. (European University Studies: Vol. 23). xvii,293p. pap. (978-0-8204-9946-8(3)) Lang, Peter AG.

Porter, Stanley E. The Pauline Canon. 2009. 272p. pap. 32.95 (978-1-58983-428-6(3)) Society of Biblical Literature.

Porterfield, Eric. Sessions with Colossians & Philemon: On the Move with God. 2007. (Sessions Ser.). 112p. per. (978-1-57312-494-2(X)) Smyth & Helwys Publishing, Inc.

Powers, Kevin. Augustine on Natural Theology. 2008. 96p. pap. (978-3-639-07114-6(X)) VDM Verlag Dr. Mueller e.K.

Rader, William H. The Church & Racial Hostility: A History of Interpretation of Ephesians 2:11Ð22. 2011. 284p. pap. 31.00 (978-1-61097-215-4(5), Wipf and Stock) Wipf & Stock Pubs.

Rascher, Angela. Schriftauslegung und Christologie Im Hebraerbrief. 2007. (Beihefte Zur Zeitschrift Für Die Neutestamentliche Wissenschaft und Die Kunde der älteren Kirche Ser.). (GER.). XII, 261p. 133.00 (978-3-11-019697-9(2)) De Gruyter, Walter Inc.

Rascher, Angela. Schriftauslegung und Christologie im Hebräerbrief. (Beihefte zur Zeitschrift far die neutestamentliche Wissenschaft und die Kunde der älteren Kirche Ser.). (GER.). XII, 261p. 225.00 (978-3-11-184548-7(6)) De Gruyter, Walter Inc.

Reasoner, Mark. The Strong & the Weak: Romans 14. 1-15. 13 in Context. 2007. (Society for New Testament Studies Monograph Ser.). (ENG., Illus.). 296p. pap. 62.00 (978-0-521-03664-1(X)) Cambridge Univ. Pr.

The Red Ember in the White Ash: Letting God Reignite Your Spiritual Passion. 2006. 191p. 12.99 (978-0-7369-1592-2(3)) Harvest Hse. Pubs.

Reyneveld, Clarence. Unlocking Galatians Again. 2007. 408p. per. 21.99 (978-1-60266-594-1(X)) Xulon Pr., Inc.

Richardson, John, Jr. God, Sex & Marriage: Guidance from 1 Corinthians 7. 2010. 88p. pap. (978-1-873166-70-3(2)) Good Bk. Co.

Roberts, Roy R. Life in the Pressure Cooker: Studies in James. pap. 5.99 (978-0-88469-036-8(9)) BMH Bks.

Roberts, Vaughan. Authentic Church: True Spirituality in a Culture of Counterfeits. 2011. 214p. (978-1-84474-518-0(X)); (ENG.). 213p. pap. 16.00 (978-0-8308-3798-4(1)) InterVarsity Pr. (IVP Bks.).

Robinson, Alan. The Treasures of St. Paul: Selected Themes from Paul's Theology & Ethics. 218p. pap. 19.95 (978-0-8189-9500-2(9)) St Pauls/Alba Hse. Pubs.

Robinson B.D., J. Armitage. The Gospel According to Peter & the Revelation of Peter. 2007. 104p. per. 10.45 (978-1-59462-767-5(3), Book Jungle) Standard Pubns., Inc.

Roh, Taeseong. Der Zweite Thessalonicherbrief Als Erneuerung Apokalyptischer Zeitdeutung. 2007. (Novum Testamentum et Orbis Antiquus/Studien zur Umwelt des Neuen Testaments (NTOA/StUNT) Ser.). (GER., Illus.). 140p. (C). 68.00 (978-3-525-53963-7(0)) Vandenhoeck & Ruprecht GmbH & Co. KG DEU. Dist: ISD.

Roitto, Rikard. Behaving As a Christ-Believer: A Cognitive Perspective on Identity & Behavior Norms in Ephesians. 2011. pap. 39.95 (978-1-57506-814-5(1)) Eisenbrauns, Inc.

Romans. (People's Bible Commentary Ser.). pap. 10.99 (978-0-570-04814-5(1), 12-8039) Concordia Publishing Hse.

Rose Publishing Staff. Dare to Love. 2009. 14p. 3.99 (978-1-59636-317-5(7)) Rose Publishing.

Roseveare, Helen. Living Faith: Willing to Be Stirred as a Pot of Paint. 2007. (Living Ser.). (ENG.). 224p. 10.99 (978-1-84550-295-9(7)) Christian Focus Pubns. GBR. Dist: STL Distribution North America.

Rudd, A. B. La Epistola a los Hebreos.Tr. of Letter to the Hebrews. (SPA.). (978-84-7645-073-4(7), 223136) Clie, Editorial.

Rudnick, Milton, et al. Lifelight: 1 Corinthians (New Format) 2007. pap. 8.99 (978-0-7586-1027-0(0)) Concordia Publishing Hse.

Rudolph, David J. A Jew to the Jews: Jewish Contours of Pauline Flexibility in 1 Corinthians 9:19-23. 2011. (Wissenschaftliche Untersuchungen zum Neuen Testament Ser.). 290p. pap. 137.50 (978-3-16-149293-8(5)) Mohr Siebeck GmbH & Co. KG DEU. Dist: Coronet Bks.

Ruf, Martin G. Die heiligen Propheten, eure Apostel und ich: Metatextuelle Studien zum zweiten Petrusbrief. 2011. (Wissenschaftliche Untersuchungen zum Neuen Testament, 2 / No. 300 Ser.). (GER.). 702p. pap. 197.50 (978-3-16-150592-8(1)) Mohr Siebeck GmbH & Co. KG DEU. Dist: Coronet Bks.

The Sacred Writings of Paul: Annotated & Explained. 2007. (SkyLight Illuminations Ser.). 171p. per. 16.99 (978-1-59473-213-3(2)) SkyLight Paths Publishing.

Sandt, Hubertus Waltherus Maria van de. Matthew, James, & Didache: Three Related Documents in Their Jewish & Christian Setting. Zangenberg, Jurgen, ed. 2008. 488p. (978-90-04-15748-4(4)) BRILL.

Sanger, Dieter & Konradt, Matthias. Das Gesetz im fruhen Judentum und im Neuen Testament: Festschrift fur Christoph Burchard zum 75. Geburtstag. 2006. (Novum Testatnentum et Orbis Antiquus Ser.). (GER & ENG.). 344p. (C). 137.00 (978-3-525-53958-3(4)) Vandenhoeck & Ruprecht GmbH & Co. KG DEU. Dist: ISD.

Schenck, Kenneth L. Cosmology & Eschatology in Hebrews: The Settings of the Sacrifice. 2010. (Society for New Testament Studies Monograph Ser.). (ENG.). 236p. pap. 36.99 (978-0-521-13047-9(6)) Cambridge Univ. Pr.

Schinkel, Dirk. Die Himmlische Burgerschaft: Untersuchungen zu Einem Urchristlichen Sprachmotiv Im Spannungsfeld Von Religoser Integration und Abgrenzung Im 1.und. 2007. (Forschungen Zur Religion und Literatur des Alten & Neuen Testament Ser.). (GER.). 224p. (C). 98.00 (978-3-525-53084-9(6)) Vandenhoeck & Ruprecht GmbH & Co. KG DEU. Dist: ISD.

Schirrmacher, Thomas. Paul in Conflict with the Veil. 2007. pap. (978-3-933372-46-8(1)) VTR Verlag fur Theologie und Religionswissenschaft.

Schliesser, Benjamin. Abraham's Faith in Romans 4: Paul's Concept of Faith in Light of the History of Reception of Genesis 15:6. 2007. (Wissenschaftliche Untersuchungen zum Neuen Testament 2 Ser.). 548p. (C). pap. 145.00 (978-3-16-149197-9(1)) Mohr Siebeck GmbH & Co. KG DEU. Dist: Coronet Bks.

Schlosser, J., ed. Paul et l'unite des Chretiens. 2010. (Colloquium Oecumenicum Paulinum Ser.). (FRE.). 251p. (C). pap. 67.00 (978-90-429-2312-6(1)) Peeters Pubs. & Booksellers BEL. Dist: Brown, David Bk. Co., The.

Schmidt, Eckart David. Heilig ins Eschaton: Heiligung und Heiligkeit als eschatologische Konzeption im 1. Thessalonicherbrief. 2010. (Beihefte zur Zeitschrift für die neutestamentliche Wissenschaft und die Kunde der älteren Kirche Ser.).Tr. of Sanctity in Eschatology. Sanctification & Sanctity as Eschatological Conceptions in the First Epistle to the Thessalonians. (GER.). XII, 506p. 182.00 (978-3-11-022169-5(1)); 280.00 (978-3-11-174070-6(6)) De Gruyter, Walter Inc.

Schmithals, Walther. Paul & James. 2009. (Studies in Biblical Theology, First Ser.). 126p. pap. 16.00 (978-1-60899-028-3(1), Wipf and Stock) Wipf & Stock Pubs.

Schnabel, Eckhard J. Paul the Missionary: Realities, Strategies, & Methods. 2008. (ENG.). 518p. pap. 32.00 (978-0-8308-2887-6(7), IVP Acad.) InterVarsity Pr.

Schnelle, U., ed. The Letter to the Romans. 2009. (Bibliotheca Ephemeridum Theologicarum Lovaniensium Ser.). (ENG, FRE & GER.). 894p. (C). pap. 124.00 (978-90-429-2199-3(4)) Peeters Pubs. & Booksellers BEL. Dist: Brown, David Bk. Co., The.

Schreech, Tamara. Discover Galatians. (Discover Your Bible Ser.). pap., stu. ed. 3.95 *(978-1-56212-389-5(0),* 152210) Faith Alive Christian Resources.

Schrock, Lynn D. Libres Para Servir - Galatas: Galatians: Outline & Exposition. (SPA.). *(978-84-7645-358-2(2),* 223454) Clie, Editorial.

Schweinsberg, Laurie. Adam - a Type of Christ? 2009. 80p. pap. *(978-3-639-15447-4(9))* VDM Verlag Dr. Mueller e.K.

Scroggie, W. Estudios en Filemon: Studies in Philemon. (SPA.). 144p. *(978-84-7228-832-4(3),* 222327) Clie, Editorial.

Seesengood, Robert Paul. Paul: A Brief History. 2010. (Blackwell Brief Histories of Religion Ser.). (ENG.). 264p. pap. 33.95 *(978-1-4051-7890-7(6));* 94.95 *(978-1-4051-7891-4(4))* Wiley, John & Sons, Inc. (Wiley-Blackwell).

Segundo, Juan L. Humanist Christology of Paul. Drury, John, tr. 2007. 254p. pap. 28.00 *(978-1-55635-600-1(5),* Wipf and Stock) Wipf & Stock Pubs.

Seid, Timothy W. The Second Chance for GodÕs People: Messages from Hebrews. 2008. 332p. pap. 37.00 *(978-1-55635-826-5(1),* Wipf and Stock) Wipf & Stock Pubs.

Sellin, Gerhard & Sänger, Dieter. Studien zu Paulus und zum Epheserbrief: Forschungen zur Religion und Literatur des Alten und Neuen Testaments 229. 2009. (Forschungen Zur Religion und Literatur des Alten & Neuen Testament Ser.). (GER.). 279p. (C). 98.00 *(978-3-525-53093-1(5))* Vandenhoeck & Ruprecht GmbH & Co. KG DEU. Dist: ISD.

Selvaggio, Anthony. The 24/7 Christian: Practical Help from the Book of James. 2008. 175p. pap. *(978-0-85234-687-7(5))* Evangelical Pr.

Shafer, Sonya. Middle Ages, Renaissance, Reformation & Epistles: A Family Study Handbook, 6 bks., Bk.4. 2010. 146p. pap. 15.95 *(978-1-61634-084-1(3))* Simply Charlotte Mason, LLC.

Shelly, Rubel. In Step with the Spirit: Galatians 5:22-23. pap. 8.99 *(978-0-89098-095-8(0))* Twentieth Century Christian Bks.

Shepherd, J. Barrie. Aspects of Love: An Exploration of 1 Corinthians 13. 2010. 126p. pap. 16.00 *(978-1-60899-720-6(0),* Wipf and Stock) Wipf & Stock Pubs.

Shkul, Minna & Shkul. Reading Ephesians: Exploring Social Entrepreneurship in the Text. 2010. (Library of New Testament Studies, the Ser.). (ENG., Illus.). 304p. 120.00 *(978-0-567-28777-9(7),* T&T Clark Int'l) Continuum International Publishing Group, Ltd. GBR. Dist: National Bk. Network.

Simmons, Carl, ed. Ephesians: Seeing Ourselves in Jesus. 2006. (Illus.). 111p. pap. 9.99 *(978-0-7644-3241-5(9))* Group Publishing, Inc.

—James: Showing Our Faith in Jesus. 2006. (Illus.). 111p. pap. 9.99 *(978-0-7644-3242-2(7))* Group Publishing, Inc.

—1 John: Living in the Light of Jesus. 2006. (Illus.). 95p. pap. 9.99 *(978-0-7644-3243-9(5))* Group Publishing, Inc.

Simpson, A. B. La Epistola a los Romanos.Tr. of Epistle to the Romans. (SPA.). *(978-84-7645-076-5(1),* 223130) Clie, Editorial.

Smit, Laura. II Corinthians: Serving in Weakness. l.t. ed. 5.25 *(978-1-56212-661-2(X),* 150120) Faith Alive Christian Resources.

Smith, Craig. Timothy's Task, Paul's Prospect: A New R. 2006. (ENG.). 280p. *(978-1-905048-29-8(7))* Sheffield Phoenix Pr.

Smith, David Raymond & Smith. 'Hand This Man over to Satan' Curse, Exclusion & Salvation in 1 Corinthians 5. 2009. (Library of New Testament Studies, the Ser.). (ENG.). 224p. 140.00 *(978-0-567-03387-1(2),* T&T Clark Int'l) Continuum International Publishing Group, Ltd. GBR. Dist: National Bk. Network.

Smith, Debra White. What Jane Austen Taught Me about Love & Romance. 2007. 192p. per. 11.99 *(978-0-7369-1889-3(2))* Harvest Hse. Pubs.

Snyder, Jackson. The Epistle of Barnabas: Revised Greek with Hebraic-English Translation. 2010. 108p. pap. 15.95 *(978-0-557-16576-6(8))* Lulu Enterprises Inc.

Standard Publishing Staff. Wise Advice. 2006. cd-rom 24.99 *(978-0-7847-1876-6(5))* Standard Publishing.

Starling, David I. Not My People: Gentiles as Exiles in Pauline Hermeneutics. 2011. (Beihefte zur Zeitschrift far die neutestamentliche Wissenschaft und die Kunde der älteren Kirche Ser.). (ENG., Illus.). XII, 254p. 210.00 ***(978-3-11-916515-0(3))*** De Gruyter, Walter Inc.

Starling, David Ian. Not My People: Gentiles As Exiles in Pauline Hermeneutics. 2011. (Beihefte zur Zeitschrift für die neutestamentliche Wissenschaft und die Kunde der älteren Kirche Ser.). (ENG.). XII, 254p. 140.00 ***(978-3-11-025960-5(5))*** De Gruyter, Walter Inc.

Stenstrup, Ken. Titus: Honoring the Gospel of God. 2010. 15.95 *(978-0-8146-5287-9(5))* Liturgical Pr.

Stepp, Paul. Philemon & Onesimus. 2008. 106p. pap. 9.95 *(978-1-4357-1089-4(4))* Lulu Enterprises Inc.

Stetzer, Ed & Nation, Philip. Compelled by Love: The Most Excellent Way to Missional Living. 2008. (ENG.). 224p. pap. 14.99 *(978-1-59669-227-5(8))* New Hope Pubs.

—Impulsados Por el Amor: El Camino Mas Excelente Al Estilo de Vida Misionero. 2008. (SPA & ENG.). 240p. pap. 14.99 *(978-1-59669-228-2(6))* New Hope Pubs.

Strange, David. Exegetical Summary of 2 Peter. 2nd ed. 2008. (GEC & ENG.). 312p. pap. 38.00 *(978-1-55671-202-9(2))* SIL International.

Strauch, Alexander. Love or Die: Christ's Wake-up Call to the Church. 2008. 112p. pap. 9.99 *(978-0-936083-28-5(X))* Lewis & Roth Pubs.

Streett, Daniel R. They Went Out from Us: The Identity of the Opponents in First John. 2011. (Beihefte zur Zeitschrift far die neutestamentliche Wissenschaft und die Kunde der älteren Kirche Ser.). (ENG., XVIII, 462p. Illus.). 280.00 ***(978-3-11-219047-0(5));*** 182.00 ***(978-3-11-024770-1(4))*** De Gruyter, Walter Inc.

—They Went Out from Us: The identity of the opponents in First John. 2011. 562p. pap. 69.00 ***(978-1-243-58363-5(0),*** Proquest, UMI Dissertation Publishing) BiblioBazaar.

Stutzman, Robert. Exegetical Summary of Galatians. 2nd ed. 2008. 265p. pap. 32.00 *(978-1-55671-201-2(4))* SIL International.

SUbstance 5: Telling Others. 2009. 80p. pap. *(978-1-84427-385-0(7))* Scripture Union.

Svendsen, Stefan N. Allegory Transformed: The Appropriation of Philonic Hermeneutics in the Letters to the Hebrews. 2009. 273p. pap. 117.50 *(978-3-16-149968-5(9))* Mohr Siebeck GmbH & Co. KG DEU. Dist: Coronet Bks.

Swanberg, Dennis. Is Your Love Tank Full? Or Are You Driving on Empty. 2009. (ENG.). 128p. pap. 10.95 *(978-1-4391-6841-7(5),* Howard Bks.) Howard Books.

Swete, Henry Barclay. The Akhmim Fragment of the Apocryphal Gospel of St Peter. 2007. 108p. per. 11.95 *(978-1-60206-450-8(4))* Cosimo, Inc.

Swindoll, Charles R. & Gaither, Mark. Insights on Romans. 2009. (Swindoll's New Testament Insights Ser.). (ENG.). 400p. 25.99 *(978-0-310-28430-7(9))* Zondervan.

Taeger, Jens-W. Johanneische Perspektiven: Aufsatze zur Johannesapokalypse und zum johanneischen Kreis 1984-2003. 2006. (Forschungen Zur Religion und Literatur des Alten & Neuen Testament Ser.: Vol. 215). (GER & ENG., Illus.). 254p. (C). 98.00 *(978-3-525-53082-5(X))* Vandenhoeck & Ruprecht GmbH & Co. KG DEU. Dist: ISD.

Talbert, Charles H., ed. Perspectives on First Peter. 2010. 157p. (Orig.). pap. 17.00 *(978-1-60899-836-4(3),* Wipf and Stock) Wipf & Stock Pubs.

Tambasco, Anthony J. In the Days of Paul: The Social World & Teaching of the Apostle. 2006. (Illus.). 132p. pap. 17.00 *(978-1-59752-836-8(6),* Wipf and Stock) Wipf & Stock Pubs.

Tamez, Elsa. Struggles for Power in Early Christianity: A Study of the First Letter of Timothy. Kinsler, Gloria, tr. from SPA. annot. ed. 2007. 163p. per. 22.00 *(978-1-57075-708-2(9))* Orbis Bks.

Tannehill, Robert C. Dying & Rising with Christ: A Study in Pauline Theology. 2006. 140p. pap. 18.00 *(978-1-59752-991-4(5),* Wipf and Stock) Wipf & Stock Pubs.

Taylor, Mark E. Text-Linguistic Investigation into the Discourse Structure of James. 2006. (Library of New Testament Studies: Vol. 311). (ENG., Illus.). 160p. 130.00 *(978-0-567-04463-1(7),* T&T Clark Int'l) Continuum International Publishing Group, Ltd. GBR. Dist: National Bk. Network.

Tenney, Merrill Chapin. Galatas: La Carta de Libertad: Galations: The Letter of Liberty. (SPA.). 229p. *(978-84-7228-077-9(2),* 220423) Clie, Editorial.

Theobald, Michael. Studien zum Corpus Iohanneum. 2011. (Wissenschaftliche Untersuchungen zum Neuen Testament, No. 267 Ser.). (GER.). 741p. 287.50 *(978-3-16-150284-2(1))* Mohr Siebeck GmbH & Co. KG DEU. Dist: Coronet Bks.

Thigpen, Paul. A Bible Study Guide for Catholics: St. Paul: Jubilee Year of the Apostle Paul Edition. 2008. per. 53.95 *(978-1-59276-423-5(1));* per. 8.95 *(978-1-59276-420-4(7))* Our Sunday Visitor, Publishing Div.

Thiselton, Anthony C. The Living Paul: An Introduction to the Apostle's Life & Thought. 2010. (ENG.). 190p. pap. 20.00 *(978-0-8308-3881-3(3),* IVP Acad.) InterVarsity Pr.

Thomas, C. Adrian. A Case for Mixed-Audience with Reference to the Warning Passages in the Book of Hebrews. 2008. 346p. (C). 80.95 *(978-1-4331-0331-5(1))* Lang, Peter Publishing, Inc.

Thomas, Kenneth J. & Thomas, Margaret Orr. Structure & Orality in 1 Peter: A Guide for Translators. 2006. (Illus.). xiii, 219p. *(978-0-8267-0460-3(3))* United Bible Societies.

Thomas, Matthew A. These Are the Generations: Identity, Covenant & the Toledot Formula. 2011. (Library Hebrew Bible/Old Testament Studies). (ENG.). 176p. 120.00 *(978-0-567-15141-4(7),* T&T Clark Int'l) Continuum International Publishing Group, Ltd. GBR. Dist: National Bk. Network.

Thomas Nelson Publishing Staff & Bertolini, Dewey. 1 & 2 Corinthians, 0 vols. Richards, Larry, ed. 2009. (Smart Guide to the Bible Ser.). 352p. pap. 14.99 *(978-1-4185-1013-8(0))* Nelson, Thomas Inc.

Thomas, Oral A. W. Biblical Resistance Hermeneutics Within a Caribbean Context. 2010. (BibleWorld Ser.). (ENG., Illus.). 246p. (C). 110.00 *(978-1-84553-656-5(8));* pap. 39.95 *(978-1-84553-657-2(6))* Equinox Publishing Ltd. GBR. Dist: ISD.

Thompson, Frederick M. Devotions from the Epistle of Romans. 2007. 280p. per. 15.99 *(978-1-60266-375-6(0))* Xulon Pr., Inc.

Thompson, James W. The Church in Exile: God's Counterculture in a Non-Christian World. 2011. 160p. pap. 12.99 *(978-0-89112-273-9(7),* Leafwood Pubs.) Abilene Christian Univ. Pr.

Thompson, Michael B. Clothed with Christ: The Example & Teaching of Jesus in Romans 12. 1Ntilde;15. 13. 2011. 292p. pap. 32.00 ***(978-1-61097-142-3(6),*** Wipf and Stock) Wipf & Stock Pubs.

Tidball, Derek J. In Christ, in Colossae: Sociological Perspectives on Colossians. 2011. 222p. pap. 25.00 ***(978-1-84227-736-2(7),*** Paternoster) Authentic Media.

Tolbert, Malcolm. Walking with the Lord: The Relevance of First John to the Contemporary Christian Life. 2008. 124p. pap. 15.00 *(978-1-55635-945-3(4),* Wipf and Stock) Wipf & Stock Pubs.

Tolmie, D. Francois, ed. Philemon in Perspective: Interpreting a Pauline Letter. 2010. (Beihefte zur Zeitschrift für die neutestamentliche Wissenschaft und die Kunde der älteren Kirche Ser.). (ENG.). XII, 394p. 140.00 *(978-3-11-022173-2(X))* De Gruyter, Walter Inc.

Toney, Carl N. Paul's Inclusive Ethic: Resolving Community Conflicts & Promoting Mission in Romans 14-15. 2008. XIII, 235p. pap. *(978-3-16-149741-4(4))* Mohr Siebeck GmbH & Co. KG.

Tozer, A. W. Living as a Christian: Teachings from First Peter. 2010. (ENG.). 224p. pap. 14.99 *(978-0-8307-4692-7(7))* Gospel Light Pubns.

Trail, Ronald L. Exegetical Summary of 1 Corinthians 1-9. 2nd ed. 2008. 370p. pap. 42.00 *(978-1-55671-204-3(9))* SIL International.

—Exegetical Summary of 1 Corinthians 10-16. 2nd ed. 2008. 382p. pap. 42.00 *(978-1-55671-205-0(7))* SIL International.

Treier, Daniel J. & Laansma, Jon C. Christology & Hermeneutics: Hebrews as an Interdisciplinary Case Study. Treier, Daniel J. & Laansma, Jon C., eds. 2012. (Library of New Testament Studies). (ENG.). 288p. 120.00 *(978-0-567-23859-7(8),* T&T Clark Int'l) Continuum International Publishing Group, Ltd. GBR. Dist: National Bk. Network.

Tucker, J. Brian. You Belong to Christ: Paul & the Formation of Social Identity in 1 Corinthians 1-4. 2010. 346p. pap. 38.00 *(978-1-60899-676-6(X),* Pickwick Pubns.) Wipf & Stock Pubs.

Ulrichs, Karl Frederich. Christusglaube: Studien zum Syntagma pistis Christou und zum paulinischen Verständnis von Glaube und Rechtfertigung. 2007. (Wissenschaftliche Untersuchungen Zum Neuen Testament 2 Ser.: 227). 311p. (Orig.). pap. 115.00 *(978-3-16-149216-7(1))* Mohr Siebeck GmbH & Co. KG DEU. Dist: Coronet Bks.

Van Der Watt, Jan & Van der Watt. Introduction to the Johannine Gospel & Letters. 2008. (T& T Clark Approaches to Biblical Studies). (ENG.). 162p. 22.95 *(978-0-567-03037-5(7),* T&T Clark Int'l) Continuum International Publishing Group, Ltd. GBR. Dist: National Bk. Network.

van der Watt, Jan & van der Watt. Introduction to the Johannine Gospel & Letters. 2008. (T& T Clark Approaches to Biblical Studies). (ENG., Illus.). 168p. 110.00 *(978-0-567-04584-3(6),* T&T Clark Int'l) Continuum International Publishing Group, Ltd. GBR. Dist: National Bk. Network.

Vandaalen. Guide to Galatians. 10.95 *(978-0-281-04501-3(1))* International Publishers Marketing.

Vanlandingham, Chris. Judgment & Justification in Early Judaism & the Apostle Paul. 2006. 384p. 29.95 *(978-1-56563-398-8(9))* Hendrickson Pubs. Marketing, LLC.

Vlachos, Chris A. The Law & the Knowledge of Good & Evil: The Edenic Background of the Catalytic Operation of the Law in Paul. 2008. 312p. pap. 34.00 *(978-1-59752-864-1(1),* Pickwick Pubns.) Wipf & Stock Pubs.

Vos, Geerhardus. La Ensenanza Epistola a los Hebreos: Teachings of the Letter to the Hebrews. (SPA.). 128p. *(978-84-7228-105-9(1),* 220370) Clie, Editorial.

Wade, Kenneth R. Paul: A Spiritual Journey. 2011. pap. 14.99 *(978-0-8163-2493-4(X))* Pacific Pr. Publishing Assn.

Waite, Th. D. Second Timothy, Preaching Verse by Verse. 2008. 256p. pap. 20.00 *(978-1-56848-060-2(1))* Old Paths Pubns., Inc., The.

Waite, Th. D. Pastor D. A. Romans, Preaching Verse by Verse. 2008. pap. 38.00 *(978-1-56848-047-3(4))* Old Paths Pubns., Inc., The.

Wallace, James Buchanan. Snatched into Paradise (2 Cor 12:1-10) Paul's Heavenly Journey in the Context of Early Christian Experience. 2011. (Beihefte zur Zeitschrift far die neutestamentliche Wissenschaft und die Kunde der älteren Kirche Ser.). (ENG., XII, 391p. Illus.). 210.00 ***(978-3-11-218885-9(3));*** 140.00 *(978-3-11-024784-8(4))* De Gruyter, Walter Inc.

Wallace, Mark. Living to Please God: Seven Studies for Individuals or Groups. 2010. 64p. pap. *(978-1-904889-53-3(0))* Good Bk. Co.

Walton, Steve. Leadership & Lifestyle: The Portrait of Paul in the Miletus Speech & 1 Thessalonians. 2007. (Society for New Testament Studies Monograph Ser.). (ENG.). 272p. (C). pap. 57.00 *(978-0-521-03638-2(0))* Cambridge Univ. Pr.

Watson, Francis. Paul, Judaism, & the Gentiles: Beyond the New Perspective. 2007. 400p. per. 32.00 *(978-0-8028-4020-2(5))* Eerdmans, William B. Publishing Co.

Watson, W. Scott. An Arabic Version of the Epistle of Dionysius the Areopagite to Timothy. 2010. 82.04 *(978-1-61143-530-6(7))* Gorgias Pr., LLC.

Weaver, Joel A. Theodoret of Cyrus on Romans 11:26: Recovering an Early Christian Elijah Redivivus Tradition. 202p. (C). 65.95 *(978-0-8204-8608-6(6))* Lang, Peter Publishing, Inc.

Webb. Reading James with New Eyes: Methodological Reassessments of the Letter of James. Webb, Robert L. & Kloppenborg, John S., eds. 2007. (Library of New Testament Studies). (ENG.). 208p. 140.00 *(978-0-567-03125-9(X),* T&T Clark Int'l) Continuum International Publishing Group, Ltd. GBR. Dist: National Bk. Network.

Webb, Martin & Webb. Reading Second Peter with New Eyes: Methodological Reassessments of the Letter of Second Peter. Webb, Robert L. & Watson, Duane F., eds. 2010. (Library of New Testament Studies, the Ser.). (ENG.). 224p. 140.00 *(978-0-567-03363-5(5),* T&T Clark Int'l) Continuum International Publishing Group, Ltd. GBR. Dist: National Bk. Network.

Webb, Robert L. & Bauman-Martin, Betsy, eds. Reading First Peter with New Eyes: Methodological Reassessments of the Letter of First Peter. 2007. (Library of New Testament Studies, the Ser.). (ENG.). 224p. 140.00 *(978-0-567-04562-1(5),* T&T Clark Int'l) Continuum International Publishing Group, Ltd. GBR. Dist: National Bk. Network.

Webb, Robert L., et al. Reading Jude with New Eyes: Methodological Reassessments of the Letter of Jude. Webb, Robert L. & Davids, Peter Hugh, eds. 2009. (Library of New Testament Studies, the Ser.). (ENG.). 176p. 140.00 *(978-0-567-03361-1(9),* T&T Clark Int'l) Continuum International Publishing Group, Ltd. GBR. Dist: National Bk. Network.

Wedderburn, A. J. M. Baptism & Resurrection: Studies in Pauline Theology against its Graeco-Roman Background. 2011. 496p. pap. 55.00 *(978-1-61097-087-7(X),* Wipf and Stock) Wipf & Stock Pubs.

Welborn, L. L. An End to Enmity: Paul & the Wrongdoer of Second Corinthians. 2011. (Beihefte zur Zeitschrift für die neutestamentliche Wissenschaft und die Kunde der älteren Kirche Ser.). (ENG.). XXVIII, 570p. 182.00 ***(978-3-11-026327-5(0));*** (Illus.). 280.00 ***(978-3-11-916381-1(3))*** De Gruyter, Walter Inc.

Wellman, Pat & McCullough, Jeannie. Hebrews Pt. 1: Covenant of Faith. 2006. (Wisdom of the Word Bible Study Ser.). (ENG.). 96p. spiral bd. 14.99 *(978-0-8341-2265-9(0),* 083-412-2650) Beacon Hill Pr. of Kansas City.

—Hebrews Pt. 2: Covenant of Faith. 2006. (Wisdom of the Word Bible Study Ser.). (ENG.). 96p. spiral bd. 14.99 *(978-0-8341-2275-8(8),* 083-412-2758) Beacon Hill Pr. of Kansas City.

Wendland, Ernst R. Finding & Translating the Oral-Aural Elements in Written Language: The Case of the New Testament Epistles. 2009. (Illus.). 444p. 129.95 *(978-0-7734-4959-6(0))* Mellen, Edwin Pr., The.

Wenham, David. Did St Paul Get Jesus Right? The Gospel According to Paul. 2011. (ENG., Illus.). 160p. pap. 12.95 *(978-0-7459-6248-1(3))* Lion Hudson PLC GBR. Dist: Independent Pubs. Group.

Westerhoff, Matthias. Das Paulusverständnis im Liber Graduum. 2008. (Patristische Texte und Studien Ser.).Tr. of Did the Author of the 'Book of Steps' Understand Paul? (GER.). XIV, 260p. 119.00 *(978-3-11-020732-3(X))* De Gruyter, Walter Inc.

Whaley, Charles. Prophetic, Post-Apostolic & Postmodern: Three Bible Studies from a Missionary to Japan. 2009. pap. *(978-1-57312-548-2(2))* Smyth & Helwys Publishing, Inc.

White, James R. The God Who Justifies: The Doctrine of Justification. 2007. 396p. pap. 27.00 *(978-0-7642-0481-4(5))* Bethany Hse. Pubs.

Whitlark, Jason A. Enabling Fidelity to God: Perseverance in Hebrews in Light of the Reciprocity Systems of the Ancient Mediterranean World. 2009. (Paternoster Biblical Monographs). 242p. pap. 27.00 *(978-1-60608-477-9(1),* Wipf and Stock) Wipf & Stock Pubs.

Wiersbe, Warren W. Ephesians: Gaining the Things That Money Can't Buy 2009. (WBS Ser.). (ENG.). 128p. pap. 8.99 *(978-0-7814-4568-9(X))* Cook, David C.

Wiles, Maurice F. Divine Apostle. 2009. (ENG.). 172p. pap. 28.99 *(978-0-521-11206-2(0))* Cambridge Univ. Pr.

Wiley, Tatha. Encountering Paul: Understanding the Man & His Message. 2010. (Come & See Ser.). (ENG.). 214p. 65.00 *(978-0-7425-5808-3(8));* 180p. pap. 22.50 *(978-0-7425-5809-0(6))* Rowman & Littlefield Publishers, Inc.

Wilk, Florian, et al, eds. Between Gospel & Election: Explorations in the Interpretation of Romans 9-11. 2010. (Illus.). 565p. 267.50 *(978-3-16-150533-1(6))* Mohr Siebeck GmbH & Co. KG DEU. Dist: Coronet Bks.

Willard, Louis Charles. A Critical Study of the Euthalian Apparatus. 2009. (Arbeiten zur neutestamentlichen Textforschung Ser.). (ENG.). XIV, 182p. 112.00 *(978-3-11-021567-0(5));* 168.00 ***(978-3-11-173601-3(6))*** De Gruyter, Walter Inc.

Williams, Guy. The Spirit World in the Letters of Paul the Apostle: A Critical Examination of the Role of Spiritual Beings in the Authentic Pauline Epistles. 2009. (Forschungen Zur Religion und Literatur des Alten & Neuen Testament Ser.). (ENG.). 336p. (C). 110.00 *(978-3-525-53095-5(1))* Vandenhoeck & Ruprecht GmbH & Co. KG DEU. Dist: ISD.

Williams, Martin. The Doctrine of Salvation in the First Letter of Peter. 2011. (Society for New Testament Studies Monograph Ser.). (ENG.). 340p. 99.00 ***(978-1-107-00328-6(8))*** Cambridge Univ. Pr.

Wilson, David. Lessons of Salvation in Galatians. 2007. 95p. per. 5.25 *(978-0-9786002-0-4(7))* Wilson, David.

Wilson, Todd A. Curse of the Law & the Crisis in Galatia: Reassessing the Purpose of Galatians. 2007. (Wissenschaftliche Untersuchungen Zum Neuen Testament 2 Ser.: 225). 185p. (Orig.). (C). pap. 79.50 *(978-3-16-149254-9(4))* Mohr Siebeck GmbH & Co. KG DEU. Dist: Coronet Bks.

Wischmeyer, Oda. Paul: Life, Setting, Work, Letters. 2012. (ENG., Illus.). 384p. 130.00 *(978-0-567-55991-3(2));* pap. 39.95 *(978-0-567-63091-9(9))* Continuum International Publishing Group, Ltd. GBR. (T&T Clark Int'l). Dist: National Bk. Network.

Woodcock, Anne & Woodcock, Peter. God & You: Six Studies for Individuals or Groups. 2010. 64p. pap. *(978-1-904889-61-8(1))* Good Bk. Co.

Yarbrough, Mark. Paul's Utilization of Preformed Traditions in 1 Timothy: An Evaluation of Paul's Literary, Rhetorical, & Theological Tactics. 2010. (Library of New Testament Studies, the Ser.). (ENG., Illus.). 256p. 130.00 *(978-0-567-25490-0(9),* T&T Clark Int'l) Continuum International Publishing Group, Ltd. GBR. Dist: National Bk. Network.

Yee, Tet-Lim N. Jews, Gentiles & Ethnic Reconciliation: Paul's Jewish identity & Ephesians. 2008. (Society for New Testament Studies Monograph Ser.). (ENG.). 328p. pap. 44.00 *(978-0-521-09146-6(2))* Cambridge Univ. Pr.

Yeo, K. K. Musing with Confucius & Paul: Toward a Chinese Christian Theology. 2008. 508p. pap. 55.00 *(978-1-55635-488-5(6))* Wipf & Stock Pubs.

Yeo, Khiok-Khng. Musing with Confucius & Paul: Toward a Chinese Christian Theology. 2008. (ENG.). 508p. pap. 58.00 *(978-0-227-17283-4(3))* Clarke, James Co., Ltd. GBR. Dist: Brown David Bk. Co., The.

Yinger, Kent L. Paul, Judaism, & Judgment according to Deeds. 2007. (Society for New Testament Studies Monograph Ser.). (ENG., Illus.). 336p. pap. 69.00 *(978-0-521-03669-6(0))* Cambridge Univ. Pr.

Young, Frances M. & Ford, David F. Meaning & Truth in Second Corinthians. 2008. 298p. pap. 33.00 *(978-1-55635-813-5(X))* Wipf & Stock Pubs.

Zangenberg, Jurgen & Sandt, Hubertus Waltherus Maria van de. Matthew, James, & Didache: Three Related Documents in Their Jewish & Christian Setting. 2008. 54.95 *(978-1-58983-358-6(9))* Society of Biblical Literature.
Zuntz, G. The Text of the Epistles: A Disquisition upon the Corpus Paulinum: The Schweich Lectures of the British Academy 1946. 2007. 314p. pap. 35.00 *(978-1-55635-372-7(3)*, Wipf and Stock) Wipf & Stock Pubs.
1 Peter & 1 John. ldr.'s ed. (LifeLight Bible Studies: Course 9). 6.50 *(978-0-570-09276-6(0)*, 20-2283) Concordia Publishing Hse.

BIBLE—CRITICISM, INTERPRETATION, ETC.—N. T. EPISTLES OF JOHN

see Bible—Criticism, Interpretation, etc.—N. T. Epistles

BIBLE—CRITICISM, INTERPRETATION, ETC.—N. T. GALATIANS

see Bible—Criticism, Interpretation, etc.—N. T. Epistles

BIBLE—CRITICISM, INTERPRETATION, ETC.—N. T. GOSPELS

Here are entered works on the Gospels as a whole, or on one or more of the Gospels: John, Luke, Mark, Matthew.

see also Q Hypothesis (Synoptics Criticism)

Abbott, Edwin A. Johannine Grammar. 2007. (ENG.). 712p. 65.95 *(978-0-548-15702-2(2))*; pap. 50.95 *(978-1-4304-5180-8(7))* Kessinger Publishing, LLC.
—Johannine Vocabulary: A Comparison of the Words of the Fourth Gospel with Those of the Three. 2007. (ENG.). 388p. 48.95 *(978-0-548-10039-4(X))* Kessinger Publishing, LLC.
—Miscellanea Evangelica: Volume 1. 2011. 108p. pap. 19.99 *(978-1-107-60026-3(X))* Cambridge Univ. Pr.
—Miscellanea Evangelica: Volume 2, Christ's Miracles of Feeding. 2011. 210p. pap. 22.99 *(978-1-107-60019-5(7))* Cambridge Univ. Pr.
Acosta, Dempsey R. The Path to See Like Jesus. 2008. 201p. pap. 13.95 *(978-1-4357-0084-0(8))* Lulu Enterprises Inc.
Adamczewski, Bartosz. The Gospel of the Narrative 'We' The Hypertextual Relationship of the Fourth Gospel to the Acts of the Apostles. 2010. 168p. 54.95 *(978-3-631-60505-9(6))* Lang, Peter GmbH, Europaischer Verlag der Wissenschaften DEU. Dist: Lang, Peter.
Adams, Dwayne H. The Sinner in Luke. 2007. (Evangelical Theological Society Monograph Ser.). 230p. pap. 25.00 *(978-1-55635-461-8(4)*, Pickwick Pubns.) Wipf & Stock Pubs.
Adams, Roy. The Wonder of Jesus: He Still Touches Hearts. 2007. *(978-0-8280-2065-7(5))* Review & Herald Publishing Assn.
Adamsbaum, Beryl. The time has come - Lent. 2008. 80p. pap. *(978-1-85345-486-8(9))* Crusade for World Revival.
Agboga, Ehis. Fifteen PS for Every Minister: Unveiling Matthew 10. 2010. 130p. pap. 16.00 *(978-1-60608-990-3(0)*, Resource Pubns.) Wipf & Stock Pubs.
Aheame-Kroll, Stephen. The Psalms of Lament in Mark's Passion: Jesus' Davidic Suffering. 2010. (Society for New Testament Studies Monograph Ser.). (ENG.). 256p. pap. 29.00 *(978-0-521-13040-0(9))* Cambridge Univ. Pr.
Aheame-Kroll, Stephen P. The Psalms of Lament in Mark's Passion: Jesus' Davidic Suffering. 2007. (Society for New Testament Studies Monograph Ser.). (ENG.). 254p. 99.00 *(978-0-521-88191-3(9))* Cambridge Univ. Pr.
Ahoua, Raymond. The Transference of the Three Mediating Institutions of Salvation from Caiaphas to Jesus: A Study of Jn 11, 45-54 in the Light of the Akan Myth of the Crossing of a River. 2008. 224p. pap. *(978-3-03911-466-5(2))* Lang, Peter.
Aichele. Phantom Messiah: Postmodern Fantasy & the Gospel of Mark. 2006. (ENG.). 272p. 120.00 *(978-0-567-02581-4(0)*, T&T Clark Int'l) Continuum International Publishing Group, Ltd. GBR. Dist: National Bk. Network.
Aichele, George. Simulating Jesus: Reality Effects in the Gospels. 2011. (BibleWorld Ser.). (ENG., Illus.). 258p. (C). 99.95 *(978-1-84553-680-0(0))*; pap. 34.95 *(978-1-84553-681-7(9))* Equinox Publishing Ltd. GBR. Dist: ISD.
Alaharasan, V. Antony. From Patmos to Paradise: John's Vision of Heaven. 2009. (Illus.). 128p. pap. 14.95 *(978-0-8091-4589-8(8))* Paulist Pr.
Alexander, William. The Leading Ideas of the Gospels. 2007. (ENG.). 362p. 46.95 *(978-0-548-01738-8(7))* Kessinger Publishing, LLC.
Alfaro, Juan. Conozca a Jesus: ¿Que Nos Dicen de él Mateo, Marcos, Lucas y Juan? 2008. (SPA.). 144p. 14.95 *(978-0-7648-1722-9(1))* Liguori Pubns.
—Getting to Know Jesus: What Do Matthew, Mark, Luke, & John Tell Us? 2008. 14.99 *(978-0-7648-1727-4(2))* Liguori Pubns.
Alonso, P. The Woman Who Changed Jesus. Crossing Boundaries in Mk 7,24-30. 2011. (Biblical Tools & Studies). (ENG.). 398p. (C). 99.00 ***(978-90-429-2387-4(3))*** Peeters Pubs. & Booksellers BEL. Dist: Brown, David Bk. Co., The.
Alsup, John E. The Post-Resurrection Appearance Stories of the Gospel Tradition: A History-of-Tradition Analysis. 2007. 308p. pap. 38.00 *(978-1-59752-970-9(2)*, Wipf and Stock) Wipf & Stock Pubs.
Altopp, Whitney. The Adolescent Beloved Disciple. 2010. 52p. pap. *(978-3-639-26712-9(5))* VDM Verlag Dr. Mueller e.K.
Anderson, Alicia & Myers, Alicia Rebecca. Characterizing Jesus: A Rhetorical Analysis on the Fourth Gospel's Use of Scripture in its Presentation of Jesus. 2012. (ENG.). 256p. 120.00 ***(978-0-567-23897-9(0)***, T&T Clark Int'l) Continuum International Publishing Group, Ltd. GBR. Dist: National Bk. Network.
Anderson, H. T. Codex Sinaiticus: the H. T. Anderson New Testament. 2010. 600p. pap. 35.65 *(978-0-557-27476-5(1))* Lulu Enterprises Inc.
Anderson, Janice Capel & Moore, Stephen D. Mark & Method: New Approaches in Biblical Studies. Anderson, Janice Capel & Moore, Stephen D., eds. 2nd rev. ed. 2008. (Illus.). 300p. per. 23.00 *(978-0-8006-3851-1(4)*, Fortress Pr.) Augsburg Fortress, Pubs.
Anderson, John L. Exegetical Summary of 1, 2, & 3 John. 2nd ed. 2008. 240p. pap. 29.00 *(978-1-55671-197-8(2))* SIL International.
Anderson, Ken/Ponder. The Gospel According to John the Baptist: The Hidden Life of Jesus & John As Seen Through John's Eyes. Anderson, Auburn/Ponder, ed. 2007. pap. 19.95 *(978-0-9793906-7-8(2))* Beam Me Up Lord Publishing Hse.
Anderson, Paul N. Fourth Gospel & the Quest for Jesus: Modern Foundations Reconsidered. 2008. (Library of New Testament Studies, the Ser.). (ENG.). 256p. 44.95 *(978-0-567-03330-7(9)*, T&T Clark Int'l) Continuum International Publishing Group, Ltd. GBR. Dist: National Bk. Network.
Appold, Mark L. The Oneness Motif of the Fourth Gospel: Motif Analysis & Exegetical Probe into the Fourth Gospel. 2011. 324p. pap. 36.00 ***(978-1-61097-543-8(X)***, Wipf and Stock) Wipf & Stock Pubs.
Arnold, John H. The Day Christ Lied: John 7:8 & its Critics. 2011. pap. 11.95 ***(978-0-7414-6528-3(0))*** Infinity Publishing.
Ashton, John. Understanding the Fourth Gospel. 2nd ed. (ENG.). 2009. 608p. pap. 49.95 *(978-0-19-954422-6(0))* 2007. 606p. 165.00 *(978-0-19-929761-0(4))* Oxford Univ. Pr., Inc.
Atkinson, William. Baptism in the Spirit: Luke-Acts & the Dunn Debate. 2012. (ENG.). 164p. (C). pap. 30.00 ***(978-0-7188-9268-5(2))*** Lutherworth Pr., The GBR. Dist: Brown, David Bk. Co., The.
Atkinson, William P. Baptism in the Spirit: Luke-Acts & the Dunn Debate. 2011. 164p. pap. 19.00 *(978-1-60899-971-2(8)*, Pickwick Pubns.) Wipf & Stock Pubs.
Atteberry, Mark. Free Refill: Coming Back for More of Jesus. 2007. 144p. 12.99 *(978-0-7847-1912-1(8))* Standard Publishing.
Attridge, Harold W. Essays on John & Hebrews. 2010. (Illus.). 443p. 257.50 *(978-3-16-150319-1(8))* Mohr Siebeck GmbH & Co. KG DEU. Dist: Coronet Bks.
Augustine, Saint. Homilies on the First Epistle of John. Doyle, Daniel E. & Martin, Thomas, eds. Ramsey, Boniface, tr. 2008. (Works of Saint Augustine A Translation for the 21st Century Ser.). 173p. per. 19.95 *(978-1-56548-289-0(1))* New City Pr.
Aus, Roger David. Feeding the Five Thousand: Studies in the Judaic Background of Mark 630-44 Par. & John 61-15. 2010. (Studies in Judaism Ser.). (ENG.). 218p. pap. 33.50 *(978-0-7618-5152-3(6))* Univ. Pr. of America, Inc.
—Feeding the Five Thousand: Studies in the Judaic Background of Mark 6:30-44 Par. & John 6:1-15. 2010. xvii, 187p. *(978-0-7618-5153-0(4))* Univ. Pr. of America, Inc.
Awodeyi, Jonah. This Jesus - Torah, Gospel & Quran. 2010. 86p. pap. 8.50 *(978-1-4457-6544-0(6))* Lulu Enterprises Inc.
Bajema, Edith. Discover Jesus in John: The Lives He Touched. (Discover Your Bible Ser.). 45p. pap., stu. ed. 3.25 *(978-1-56212-233-1(9)*, 152330) Faith Alive Christian Resources.
Baker Publishing Group Staff. A Walk Thru the Book of John: A Surprising Savior. 2009. 78p. pap. 7.99 *(978-0-8010-7173-7(9))* Baker Bks.
Baker, Todd D. Matthew 27: 25. 2008. 76p. pap. 10.95 *(978-0-595-53073-1(7))* iUniverse, Inc.
Balaguer, Vicente, ed. Understanding the Gospels. 2010. 196p. pap. 9.95 *(978-1-59417-071-3(1))* Scepter Pubs., Inc.
Baltes, Guido. Hebräisches Evangelium und synoptische Überlieferung: Untersuchungen zum hebräischen Hintergrund der Evangelien. 2011. (Wissenschaftliche Untersuchungen zum Neuen Testament Ser.). (GER., Illus.). 718p. pap. 199.50 ***(978-3-16-150953-7(6))*** Mohr Siebeck GmbH & Co. KG DEU. Dist: Coronet Bks.
Barker, Margaret. Christmas: The Original Story. 2008. 192p. pap. ***(978-0-281-06050-4(9))*** SPCK Publishing.
Barnhart, Bruno. The Good Wine: Reading John from the Center. 2008. 544p. (Orig.). pap. 60.00 *(978-1-60608-340-6(6))* Wipf & Stock Pubs.
Barrett, C. K. The Holy Spirit & the Gospel Tradition. 2011. 184p. pap. 20.00 ***(978-1-60899-727-5(8)***, Wipf and Stock) Wipf & Stock Pubs.
Barton, Stephen C. The Spirituality of the Gospels. 2006. 172p. pap. 20.00 *(978-1-59752-909-9(5)*, Wipf and Stock) Wipf & Stock Pubs.
Barton, Stephen C., ed. The Cambridge Companion to the Gospels. 2006. (Cambridge Companions to Religion Ser.). (ENG.). 312p. (C). 94.00 *(978-0-521-80766-1(2))* Cambridge Univ. Pr.
Bauckham, Richard. The Testimony of the Beloved Disciple: Narrative, History, & Theology in the Gospel of John. 2007. (Illus.). 320p. (C). pap. 30.00 *(978-0-8010-3485-5(X))* Baker Academic.
Baxter, Wayne. Israel's Only Shepherd: Matthew's Shepherd Motif & His Social Setting. 2012. (ENG.). 232p. 110.00 ***(978-0-567-06661-9(4)***, T&T Clark Int'l) Continuum International Publishing Group, Ltd. GBR. Dist: National Bk. Network.
Beck, Robert R. Banished Messiah. 2010. 222p. pap. 24.00 *(978-1-60608-556-1(5)*, Wipf and Stock) Wipf & Stock Pubs.
—Nonviolent Story: Narrative Conflict Resolution in the Gospel of Mark. 2009. 224p. (Orig.). pap. 25.00 *(978-1-60608-401-4(1)*, Wipf and Stock) Wipf & Stock Pubs.
Beck, Sanderson. The Good Message of Jesus the Christ: A Harmony, Synthesis, & Interpretation of the Gospels. Beck, Sanderson, ed. 2008. pap. 25.00 *(978-0-9792532-8-7(4))* World Peace Communications.
Becker, Eve-Marie. Das Markus-Evangelium im Rahmen antiker Historiographie. 2006. (Wissenschaftliche Untersuchungen Zum Neuen Testament Ser.: Vol. 194). 516p. (C). 232.50 *(978-3-16-148913-6(6))* Mohr Siebeck GmbH & Co. KG DEU. Dist: Coronet Bks.
Becker, Eve-Marie & Runesson, Anders, eds. Mark & Matthew I: Comparative Readings - Understanding the Earliest Gospels in Their First Century Settings. 2011. (Wissenschaftliche Untersuchungen Zum Neuen Testament Ser.: No. 271). IX, 491p. 275.00 ***(978-3-16-150837-0(8))*** Mohr Siebeck GmbH & Co. KG DEU. Dist: Coronet Bks.
Belle, G. Van, ed. The Death of Jesus in the Fourth Gospel. 2007. (Bibliotheca Ephemeridum Theologicarum Lovaniensium Ser.). (ENG., Illus.). 1003p. (C). pap. 102.00 *(978-90-429-1940-2(5))* Peeters Pubs. & Booksellers BEL. Dist: Brown, David Bk. Co., The.
Benedict XVI, pseud. Jesus of Nazareth: Holy Week: from the Entrance into Jerusalem to the Resurrection. 2011. 384p. 24.95 *(978-1-58617-500-9(9))* Ignatius Pr.
Bennema, Cornelis. Excavating John's Gospel: A Commentary for Today. 2008. 252p. pap. 29.00 *(978-1-55635-799-2(0))* Wipf & Stock Pubs.
Berard, Wayne-Daniel. When Christians Were Jews (That Is, Now) Recovering the Lost Jewishness of Christianity with the Gospel of Mark. 2006. (ENG.). 230p. per. 16.95 *(978-1-56101-280-0(7))* Cowley Pubns.
Betsworth, Sharon. Reign of God Is Such as These: A Socio-Literary Analysis of Daughters in the Gospel of Mark. 2010. (Library of New Testament Studies). (ENG.). 176p. 120.00 *(978-0-567-17531-1(6)*, T&T Clark Int'l) Continuum International Publishing Group, Ltd. GBR. Dist: National Bk. Network.
Beutler, Johannes. Do not be Afraid: The First Farewell Discourse in John's Gospel (Jn 14) 2011. (New Testament Studies in Contextual Exegesis - Neutestamentliche Studien zur kontextuellen Exegese Ser.). 146p. 43.95 *(978-3-631-61370-2(9))* Lang, Peter GmbH, Europaischer Verlag der Wissenschaften DEU. Dist: Lang, Peter.
Bible Study Combo: Alba House Gospels & Who Do You Say That I Am? 472p. 10.00 *(978-0-8189-0681-7(2))* St Pauls/Alba Hse. Pubs.
The Bible Study Guide (Volume 4) The Gospels. 2007. 20.00 *(978-0-9796940-4-2(3))* Foundations Publishing.
Bilezikian, Gilbert. The Liberated Gospel: A Comparison of the Gospel of Mark & Greek Tragedy. 2010. 160p. pap. 18.00 *(978-1-60899-617-9(4)*, Wipf and Stock) Wipf & Stock Pubs.
Binz, Stephen J. Jesus, the Suffering Servant. 2012. ***(978-1-58595-864-1(6))*** 2011. ***(978-1-58595-863-4(8))*** Twenty-Third Pubns./Bayard.
Bittleston, Kalmia. The Four Gospels: A Translation in Verse. 2007. 588p. *(978-0-86315-570-3(7))* Floris Bks.
Blackaby, Henry. The Gospel of John, 0 vols. 2007. (Encounters with God Ser.). 112p. per. 9.99 *(978-1-4185-2641-2(X))* Nelson, Thomas Inc.
—The Gospel of Luke, 0 vols. 2007. (Encounters with God Ser.). 112p. per. 9.99 *(978-1-4185-2640-5(1))* Nelson, Thomas Inc.
—The Gospel of Mark, 0 vols. 2007. (Encounters with God Ser.). 96p. per. 9.99 *(978-1-4185-2639-9(8))* Nelson, Thomas Inc.
—The Gospel of Matthew, 0 vols. 2007. (Encounters with God Ser.). 96p. per. 9.99 *(978-1-4185-1420-4(9))* Nelson, Thomas Inc.
Blackwell, John. A Whole New World: The Gospel of Mark: Great Insights into Transformation & Togetherness. 2007. viii, 111p. audio *(978-1-60037-231-5(7))* Morgan James Publishing.
Blackwood, Alan. The Theology of Judgement in the Fourth Gospel. 2008. 188p. pap. *(978-3-639-07340-9(1))* VDM Verlag Dr. Mueller e.K.
Blaine, Brad. Peter in the Gospel of John. 2007. (ENG.). 240p. per. 29.95 *(978-1-58983-272-5(8))* Society of Biblical Literature.
Blaine, Bradford B., Jr. Peter in the Gospel of John: The Making of an Authentic Disciple. 2007. (SBL - Academia Biblica Ser.). (Illus.). 224p. *(978-90-04-15732-3(8))* BRILL.
Blass, Friedrich. Philology of the Gospels. 2009. 276p. 34.99 *(978-1-113-86668-4(3))*; 262p. 30.99 *(978-1-110-91672-6(8))*; 262p. 30.99 *(978-1-110-88956-3(9))*; 262p. pap. 25.75 *(978-1-110-88955-6(0))*; 262p. pap. 25.75 *(978-1-110-91670-2(1))* BiblioBazaar.
—Philology of the Gospels. 2009. 118p. pap. 19.99 *(978-1-150-47069-1(0))* General Bks. LLC.
—Philology of the Gospels. 2009. 262p. 42.95 *(978-1-104-95096-5(0))*; pap. 27.95 *(978-1-104-89025-4(9))* Kessinger Publishing, LLC.
Blight, Richard C. Exegetical Summary of Luke 1-11. 2nd ed. 2008. 549p. pap. 46.00 *(978-1-55671-211-1(1))* SIL International.
—Exegetical Summary of Luke 12-24. 2nd ed. 2008. (GEC & ENG.). 581p. pap. 48.00 *(978-1-55671-213-5(8))* SIL International.
Blomberg, Craig L. The Historical Reliability of John's Gospel: Issues & Commentary. 2011. (ENG.). 346p. pap. 24.00 ***(978-0-8308-3871-4(6)***, IVP Acad.) InterVarsity Pr.
Blumenberg, Hans. Matthduspassion. 2009. *(978-0-8047-4067-8(4))*; pap. *(978-0-8047-4068-5(2))* Stanford Univ. Pr.
Bock, Darrell L. Jesus according to Scripture: Restoring the Portrait from the Gospels. 2007. 704p. (C). pap. 40.00 *(978-0-8010-3308-7(X))* Baker Academic.
Bock, Darrell L. & Köstenberger, Andreas J. A Theology of Luke & Acts: Biblical Theology of the New Testament, 1 vol. 2012. (Biblical Theology of the New Testament Ser.). (ENG.). 512p. 39.99 ***(978-0-310-27089-8(8))*** Zondervan.
Boe, Sverre. Cross-Bearing in Luke. 2010. (Illus.). 272p. pap. 117.50 *(978-3-16-150419-8(4))* Mohr Siebeck GmbH & Co. KG DEU. Dist: Coronet Bks.
Boice, James Montgomery. The Gospel of Matthew. 2006. 688p. pap. 39.95 *(978-0-8010-6659-7(X))* Baker Bks.
Boice, James Montgomery. The King Has Come: The Real Message of Christmas. 2008. (ENG.). pap. 10.99 *(978-1-84550-366-6(X))* Christian Focus Pubns. GBR. Dist: STL Distribution North America.
Bolt, Peter G. Jesus' Defeat of Death: Persuading Mark's Early Readers. 2008. (Society for New Testament Studies Monograph Ser.). (ENG., Illus.). 384p. pap. 53.00 *(978-0-521-06899-4(1))* Cambridge Univ. Pr.
Borchert, Gerald. Jesus of Nazareth: Background, Witnesses, & Significance. 2011. 256p. pap. 25.00 *(978-0-88146-266-1(7))* Mercer Univ. Pr.
Borg, Marcus J. Conversations with Scripture: The Gospel of Mark. 2009. (Anglican Association of Biblical Scholars Ser.). (Illus.). 160p. pap. 18.00 *(978-0-8192-2339-5(5)*, Morehouse Publishing) Church Publishing, Inc.
Borg, Marcus J. & Crossan, John Dominic. The First Christmas: What the Gospels Really Teach about Jesus's Birth. 2009. (ENG.). 272p. pap. 13.99 *(978-0-06-143071-8(4)*, HarperOne) HarperCollins Pubs.
—The Last Week: What the Gospels Really Teach about Jesus's Final Days in Jerusalem. 2007. (ENG.). 240p. pap. 13.99 *(978-0-06-087260-1(8)*, HarperOne) HarperCollins Pubs.
Bosetti, Elena. Matthew: The Journey Toward Hope. 2006. xvi, 252p. pap. *(978-0-8198-4848-2(4))* Pauline Bks. & Media.
Bovon, François. Luke the Theologian: Fifty-Five Years of Research (1950-2005) 2nd ed. 2006. 445p. per. 39.95 *(978-1-932792-18-8(X))* Baylor Univ. Pr.
Branden, Robert C. Satanic Conflict & the Plot of Matthew. 2006. (Studies in Biblical Literature: Vol. 89). (Illus.). 184p. (C). 62.95 *(978-0-8204-7916-3(0))* Lang, Peter Publishing, Inc.
Brock, Rita Nakashima. Journeys by Heart: A Christology of Erotic Power. 2008. 148p. pap. 18.00 *(978-1-60608-171-6(3)*, Wipf and Stock) Wipf & Stock Pubs.
Brown, Brian Arthur. Forensic Scriptures: Critical Analysis of Scripture & What the Qur'an Reveals about the Bible. 2009. 236p. pap. 26.00 *(978-1-60608-289-8(2)*, Cascade Bks.) Wipf & Stock Pubs.
Brown, John. Christ, the Way, the Truth, & the Life. 2011. 220p. pap. 14.99 ***(978-1-61203-077-7(7))*** Bottom of the Hill Publishing.
Brown, Raymond E. New Testament Essays. 2010. (ENG.). 368p. pap. 15.00 *(978-0-307-59164-7(6)*, Image) Doubleday Religious Publishing Group, The.
—Reading the Gospels with the Church: From Christmas Through Easter. 2008. 96p. (Orig.). pap. 13.00 *(978-1-55635-963-7(2))* Wipf & Stock Pubs.
Brown, Raymond Edward & Donahue, John R. Christ in the Gospels of the Liturgical Year. Witherup, Ronald D., ed. 2008. 456p. pap. 29.95 *(978-0-8146-1860-8(X))* Liturgical Pr.
Brown, Sherri. Gift upon Gift. 2010. (Princeton Theological Monographs). 286p. pap. 31.00 *(978-1-60899-391-8(4)*, Pickwick Pubns.) Wipf & Stock Pubs.
Bruce, Frederick Fyvie. The Pauline Circle. 2006. 106p. pap. 15.00 *(978-1-59752-982-2(6)*, Wipf and Stock) Wipf & Stock Pubs.
Bruehler, Bart B. A Public & Political Christ: The Social-Spatial Characteristics of Luke 18:35Ð19:43 & the Gospel as a Whole in Its Ancient Context. 2011. (Princeton Theological Monographs). 422p. pap. 46.00 ***(978-1-60608-851-7(3)***, Pickwick Pubns.) Wipf & Stock Pubs.
Burge, Gary M. Jesus, the Middle Eastern Storyteller, 1 vol. 2009. (Ancient Context, Ancient Faith Ser.). (ENG.). 112p. pap. 14.99 *(978-0-310-28045-3(1))* Zondervan.
Burkitt, F. C. The Gospel History & its Transmission. 2006. (Gorgias Theological Library: 15). 384p. 98.00 *(978-1-59333-529-8(6))* Gorgias Pr., LLC.
Burkitt, F. Crawford. The Gospel History & Its Transmission. 2007. (ENG.). 372p. 48.95 *(978-0-548-10816-1(1))* Kessinger Publishing, LLC.
Butler, Sheila. St Mark's Gospel. Bartlett, Cynthia, ed. 2009. (ENG., Illus.). pap., stu. ed. 37.50 *(978-1-4085-0458-1(8))* Nelson Thornes Ltd. GBR. Dist: Trans-Atlantic Pubns., Inc.
Buxbaum, J. G. In the Beginning Was the Word: The New Matthew Henry Commentary on the Book of John, Book I, Chapters 1-6. 2008. 332p. pap. 14.95 *(978-1-4327-2579-2(3))* Outskirts Pr., Inc.
Cabrido, John Aranda. The Portrayal of Jesus in the Gospel of Matthew: A Narrative-Critical & Theological Study. 2011. 139.95 *(978-0-7734-1406-8(1))* Mellen, Edwin Pr., The.
Cadwallader, Alan. Beyond the Word of a Woman: Recovering the Bodies of the Syrophoenician Woman. 2011. (ATF Biblical Ser.). (ENG.). 400p. (C). pap. 26.00 *(978-1-920691-85-1(5))* ATF Pr. AUS. Dist: Brown, David Bk. Co., The.
Campbell, Joan Cecelia. Kinship Relations in the Gospel of John. 2007. (Catholic Biblical Quarterly Ser.: Vol. 42). xiv, 246p. *(978-0-915170-41-8(8))* Catholic Biblical Assn. of America.
Cardenal, Ernesto. The Gospel in Solentiname. 2010. (Illus.). 656p. pap. 30.00 *(978-1-57075-902-4(2))* Orbis Bks.
Carroll, John. The Existential Jesus. 2009. (ENG.). 288p. (Orig.). pap. 15.95 *(978-1-58243-465-0(4)*, Counterpoint Pr.) Basic Bks. GBR. Dist: Perseus-PGW.
—The Existential Jesus. 2008. 288p. (Orig.). pap. 29.95 *(978-1-921215-17-9(8))* Scribe Pubns. AUS. Dist: Independent Pubs. Group.
Carruth, S., et al. Q 6: 37-42: Not Judging - the Blind Leading the Blind - the Disciple & the Teacher - the Speck & the Beam. 2011. (Documenta Q Ser.). (ENG & GER.). 428p. (C). pap. 125.00 *(978-90-429-2293-8(1))* Peeters Pubs. & Booksellers BEL. Dist: Brown, David Bk. Co., The.
Carter, Gary W., et al. John & Empire: Initial Explorations. 2008. (ENG.). 440p. 120.00 *(978-0-567-02703-0(1))*; pap. 42.95 *(978-0-567-02840-2(2))* Continuum International Publishing Group, Ltd. GBR. (T&T Clark Int'l). Dist: National Bk. Network.
Carter, Warren. John: Storyteller, Interpreter, Evangelist. 2006. 264p. per. 19.95 *(978-1-56563-523-4(X))* Hendrickson Pubs. Marketing, LLC.

Carver, Stephen S. The Ungospel: The Life & Teachngs of the Historical Jesus, Second Edition. 2010. 298p. pap. 33.00 *(978-1-60899-425-0(2)*, Wipf and Stock) Wipf & Stock Pubs.

Casey, Maurice. Aramaic Sources of Mark's Gospel. 2007. (Society for New Testament Studies Monograph Ser.). (ENG.). 292p. pap. 60.00 *(978-0-521-03613-9(5))* Cambridge Univ. Pr.

—Judaism, Jewish Identities, & the Gospel Tradition: Essays in Honour of Maurice Casey. Crossley, James G., ed. 2010. (BibleWorld Ser.). (ENG.). 240p. (C). 39.95 *(978-1-84553-284-0(8))*; 99.95 *(978-1-84553-283-3(X))* Equinox Publishing Ltd. GBR. Dist: ISD.

Cassidy, Richard J. Four Times Peter: Portrayals of Peter in the Four Gospels & at Philippi. 2007. (Interfaces Ser.). (Illus.). 154p. per. 15.95 *(978-0-8146-5178-0(X))* Liturgical Pr.

Chandler, Paul-Gordon. Songs in Waiting: Spiritual Reflections on Christ's Birth. 2009. (Illus.). 128p. 20.00 *(978-0-8192-2360-9(3)*, Morehouse Publishing) Church Publishing, Inc.

Chargois, Paige Lanier. Certain Women Called by Christ: Biblical Realities for Today. 2008. (ENG.). 176p. per. 12.99 *(978-1-59669-200-8(6))* New Hope Pubs.

Charnwood, Lord. According to Saint John. 2007. (ENG.). 336p. 45.95 *(978-0-548-03192-6(4))* Kessinger Publishing, LLC.

Chester. New Testament Commentaries Vol. 2: The Gospel According to St Matthew. (Black's New Testament Commentaries Ser.). pap. *(978-0-7136-4017-5(0)*, Burns & Oates) Continuum International Publishing Group, Ltd.

Chilton, Bruce, et al. A Comparative Handbook to the Gospel of Mark: Comparisons with Pseudepigrapha, the Qumran Schrolls, & Rabbinic Literature. 2009. (New Testament Gospels in their Judaic Contexts Ser.). xii, 596p. *(978-90-04-17973-8(9))* BRILL.

Cho, Sukmin. Jesus As Prophet in the Fourth Gospel. 2006. (ENG.). 384p. *(978-1-905048-42-7(4))* Sheffield Phoenix Pr.

Choe, An Sung. A Narrative Approach to the Identity of the Beloved Disciple. 2009. 144p. pap. *(978-3-639-12826-0(5))* VDM Verlag Dr. Mueller e.K.

Choi, Sungho. The Messianic Kingship of Jesus: A Study of Christology & Redemptive History in MatthewÕs Gospel with Special Reference to the ÒRoyal EnthronmentÓ Psalms. 2011. (WEST Theological Monograph Ser.). 254p. pap. 28.00 ***(978-1-61097-489-9(1)***, Wipf and Stock) Wipf & Stock Pubs.

Churton, Tobias. Kiss of Death: The True History of the Gospel of Judas. 2008. (ENG.). 320p. per. 19.95 *(978-1-905857-51-7(9)*, Watkins Publishing) Duncan Baird Pubs. GBR. Dist: Sterling Publishing Co., Inc.

Clivaz, C. L' Ange et la Sueur de Sang (Lc 22,43-44) Ou Comment on Pourrait Bien Encore Ecrire l'Histoire. 2010. (Biblical Tools & Studies). (FRE.). 733p. (C). 124.00 *(978-90-429-2278-5(8))* Peeters Pubs. & Booksellers BEL. Dist: Brown, David Bk. Co., The.

Cohen, Tim. Messiah, History, & the Tribulation Period Vol. 3: Conflict of the Aeons: Understanding the Protoevangelium (Genesis 3:15) Cohen, Tim, ed. 2006. pap. *(978-0-9662793-4-4(4))* Prophecy House, Inc.

Coloe, Mary L. Dwelling in the Household of God: Johannine Ecclesiology & Spirituality. 2007. 226p. per. 26.95 *(978-0-8146-5988-5(8))* Liturgical Pr.

Coloe, Mary L. & Thatcher, Tom. John, Qumran, & the Dead Sea Scrolls: Sixty Years of Discovery & Debate. 2011. *(978-90-04-20252-8(8))* BRILL.

—John, Qumran, & the Dead Sea Scrolls: Sixty Years of Discovery & Debate. 2011. 246p. pap. *(978-1-58983-546-7(8))* Society of Biblical Literature.

Continuum. The Gospel According to St. Luke. (Black's New Testament Commentaries Ser.). pap. *(978-0-7136-4477-7(X)*, Burns & Oates) Continuum International Publishing Group, Ltd.

Cook, Harry T. Resonance: Biblical Texts Speaking to 21st-century Inquirers. 2011. 130p. pap. 18.00 *(978-1-59815-029-2(4))* Polebridge Pr.

Cosaert, Carl P. The Text of the Gospels in Clement of Alexandria. 2008. (SBL - the New Testament in the Greek Fathers Ser.). 384p. *(978-90-04-16913-5(X))* BRILL.

—The Text of the Gospels in Clement of Alexandria. 2008. 388p. pap. 47.95 *(978-1-58983-372-2(4))* Society of Biblical Literature.

Coy, Jimmie Dean. Matthew A to Z + 2: An Easy Way to Learn the Gospel According to Matthew. 2008. (Illus.). 64p. 10.99 *(978-1-58169-276-1(5)*, Evergreen Pr.) Genesis Communications, Inc.

Craffert, Pieter F. Life of a Galilean Shaman: Jesus of Nazareth in Anthropological-Historical Perspective. 2008. (ENG., Illus.). 470p. pap. 64.00 *(978-0-227-17320-6(1))* Clarke, James Co., Ltd. GBR. Dist: Brown, David Bk. Co., The.

Crosby, Michael H. The Dysfunctional Church: Addiction & Codependency in the Family of Catholicism. 2011. 256p. (Orig.). pap. 28.00 *(978-1-61097-147-8(7)*, Wipf and Stock) Wipf & Stock Pubs.

Crossan, John Dominic. Four Other Gospels: Shadows on the Contour of Canon. 2008. 208p. pap. 23.00 *(978-1-55635-820-3(2))* Wipf & Stock Pubs.

Crouch, Kevin & Crouch, Tenya. The Gospel According to Elvis. 2007. (ENG., Illus.). 264p. per. 17.95 *(978-1-86074-655-0(1)*, BOB11539R) Bobcat Bks. GBR. Dist: Ingram Pub. Services.

Culpepper, R. Alan. Critical Readings of John 6. 2006. (ENG.). 308p. per. 29.95 *(978-1-58983-255-8(8))* Society of Biblical Literature.

Cygon, Joseph R. Journey Towards Self-Realization: An Interpretation of the Christian Gospels. 2011. 264p. 47.95 ***(978-1-258-00701-0(0))*** Literary Licensing, LLC.

Daise, Michael A. Feasts in John: Jewish Festivals & Jesus' "Hour" in the Fourth Gospel. (Wissenschaftliche Untersuchungen zum Neuen Testament 2 Reihe Ser.: Vol. 229). 222p. (C). pap. 75.00 *(978-3-16-149018-7(5))* Mohr Siebeck GmbH & Co. KG DEU. Dist: Eisenbrauns, Inc.

Dale, R. W. Living Christ & the Four Gospels. 2006. pap. 27.95 *(978-1-4286-4175-4(0))* Kessinger Publishing, LLC.

David Joy Staff. Mark & Its Subalterns: A Hermeneutical Paradigm for a Postcolonial Context. 2008. (BibleWorld Ser.). (ENG.). 240p. (C). 99.95 *(978-1-84553-327-4(5))*; 34.95 *(978-1-84553-328-1(3))* Equinox Publishing Ltd. GBR. Dist: ISD.

David, Wilson. God's Call to Planet Earth. 2007. 416p. per. 13.50 *(978-0-9786002-5-9(8))* Wilson, David.

Dawsey, James M. Peter's Last Sermon: Identity & Discipleship in the Gospel of Mark. 2010. 176p. pap. 25.00 *(978-0-88146-224-1(1))* Mercer Univ. Pr.

De Long, Kindalee Pfremmer. Surprised by God: Praise Responses in the Narrative of Luke-Acts. 2009. (Beihefte zur Zeitschrift für die neutestamentliche Wissenschaft und die Kunde der älteren Kirche Ser.). (ENG.). XIV, 331p. 105.00 *(978-3-11-022165-7(9))* De Gruyter, Walter Inc.

De Valdes, Juan. El Evangelio Segun Mateo: Gospel of Matthew - Reformation. (SPA.). 544p. *(978-84-7645-071-0(0)*, 223129) Clie, Editorial.

DeConick, April D. The Original Gospel of Thomas in Translation: With a Commentary & New English Translation of the Complete Gospel. 2006. (Early Christianity in Context Ser.: Vol. 286). (ENG., Illus.). 376p. 180.00 *(978-0-567-04382-5(7)*, T&T Clark Int'l) Continuum International Publishing Group, Ltd. GBR. Dist: National Bk. Network.

—Recovering the Original Gospel of Thomas: A History of the Gospel & Its Growth. 2006. (Early Christianity in Context Ser.). (ENG., Illus.). 288p. 55.00 *(978-0-567-04332-0(0)*, T&T Clark Int'l) Continuum International Publishing Group, Ltd. GBR. Dist: National Bk. Network.

—The Thirteenth Apostle: What the Gospel of Judas Really Says. 2nd rev. ed. 2009. (ENG., Illus.). 296p. 19.95 *(978-1-84706-568-1(6))* Continuum International Publishing Group, Ltd. GBR. Dist: National Bk. Network.

—Voices of the Mystics: Early Christian Discourse in the Gospels of John & Thomas & Other Ancient Christian Literature. 2013. (Journal for the Study of the New Testament Supplement: Vol. 157). (ENG.). 192p. pap. 55.00 *(978-0-567-08071-4(4)*, T&T Clark Int'l) Continuum International Publishing Group, Ltd. GBR. Dist: National Bk. Network.

DeConick, April D. & DeConick. The Thirteenth Apostle: What the Gospel of Judas Really Says. 2008. (ENG., Illus.). 224p. 27.95 *(978-0-8264-9964-6(3))* Continuum International Publishing Group, Ltd. GBR. Dist: National Bk. Network.

den Hollander, A. A. Virtuelle Vergangenheit: Die Textrekonstruktion einer verlorenen mittelniederlandischen Evangelienharmonie. Die Handschrift Utrecht Universitatsbibliothek 1009. 2007. (Bibliotheca Ephemeridum Theologicarum Lovaniensium Ser.). (GER.). 168p. (C). pap. 85.00 *(978-90-429-1989-1(2))* Peeters Pubs. & Booksellers BEL. Dist: Brown, David Bk. Co., The.

Denniston, John J. Give Them What You Have: Interpreting the New Testament for Today. 2008. 193p. pap. 19.99 *(978-0-7648-1620-8(9))* Liguori Pubns.

Desmond Ford. The Coming Worldwide Calvary: Christ Versus Antichrist. 2009. 168p. pap. 15.95 *(978-1-4401-7284-7(6))* iUniverse, Inc.

Digiacomo, James. Sundays with Jesus: Reflections for the Year of Matthew. 2007. 111p. per. 7.95 *(978-0-8091-4482-2(4)*, 4482-2) Paulist Pr.

Dimont, Max I. A Search for the Historical Jesus. 2011. (ENG.). 288p. pap. 11.95 *(978-1-59687-410-7(4))* IBks., Inc.

Discover Jesus in John: Why He Came. (Discover Your Bible Ser.). (KOR.). pap., tchr. ed. 6.95 *(978-1-55883-217-6(3)*, 600165); pap., stu. ed. 4.25 *(978-1-55883-214-5(9)*, 600160) C R C World Literature Ministries/Libros Desafio.

Discover Jesus in John: Why He Came. (Discover Your Bible Ser.). pap., stu. ed. 425.00 *(978-1-56212-450-2(1)*, 152350) Faith Alive Christian Resources.

Discover Mark. (Discover Your Bible Ser.). (KOR.). Vol. 1. pap., tchr. ed. 6.95 *(978-1-55883-204-6(1)*, 600125) Vol. 2. pap., tchr. ed. 6.95 *(978-1-55883-205-3(X)*, 600135) C R C World Literature Ministries/Libros Desafio.

Do, Maria Yen Thi. The Lucan Journey: A Study of Luke 9:28-36 & Acts 1:6-11 As an Architectural Pair. 2010. (Illus.). 357p. pap. *(978-3-0343-0092-6(1))* Lang, Peter.

Dodd, C. H. About the Gospels. 2008. (ENG.). 56p. pap. 20.99 *(978-0-521-09745-1(2))* Cambridge Univ. Pr.

—History & the Gospel. 2008. 192p. *(978-1-4437-3250-5(8))* 2007. 188p. per. *(978-1-4067-8804-4(X))* Read Bks. (Pomona Pr.).

Dodson, Derek S. Reading Dreams: An Audience-Critical Approach to the Dreams in the Gospel of Matthew. 2009. (Library of New Testament Studies, the Ser.). (ENG.). 240p. 130.00 *(978-0-567-57770-2(8)*, T&T Clark Int'l) Continuum International Publishing Group, Ltd. GBR. Dist: National Bk. Network.

Donehoo, Fred. Serving the Servant: Devotional Thoughts on the Book of Mark. 2008. *(978-1-59166-917-3(0))* BJU Pr.

Dowling, Elizabeth V. & Dowling. Taking Away the Pound: Women, Theology & the Parable of the Pounds in the Gospel of Luke. 2007. (Library of New Testament Studies). (ENG.). 272p. 155.00 *(978-0-567-04364-1(9)*, T&T Clark Int'l) Continuum International Publishing Group, Ltd. GBR. Dist: National Bk. Network.

Driggers, Ira Brent. Following God Through Mark: Theological Tension in the Second Gospel. 2007. (ENG.). 148p. per. 30.00 *(978-0-664-23095-1(4))* Westminster John Knox Pr.

Duran, Nicole Wilkinson & Duran. Power of Disorder: Ritual Elements in Mark's Passion Narrative. 2009. (Library of New Testament Studies, the Ser.). (ENG.). 142p. 120.00 *(978-0-567-03306-2(6)*, T&T Clark Int'l) Continuum International Publishing Group, Ltd. GBR. Dist: National Bk. Network.

Ebel, Eva. Lydia und Berenike: Zwei selbständige Frauen bei Lukas. 2009. (Biblische Gestalten Ser.). (GER.). 208p. (C). pap. 27.00 *(978-3-374-02681-4(8))* Evangelische Verlagsanstalt GmbH DEU. Dist: Brown, David Bk. Co., The.

Edmunds, Albert J. Buddhist & Christian Gospels Being Gos. 2006. pap. 27.95 *(978-1-4286-3844-0(X))* Kessinger Publishing, LLC.

Edwards, James R. The Hebrew Gospel & the Development of the Synoptic Tradition. 2009. (Illus.). 402p. pap. 36.00 *(978-0-8028-6234-1(9))* Eerdmans, William B. Publishing Co.

Eisele, Wilfried. Welcher Thomas? Studien zur Text- und Überlieferungsgeschichte des Thomasevangeliums. 2010. (GER., Illus.). XII, 308p. 197.50 *(978-3-16-150543-0(3))* Mohr Siebeck GmbH & Co. KG DEU. Dist: Coronet Bks.

Ekwugha, Maurice. Gospel of Deliverance. 2008. pap. 19.99 *(978-1-60647-099-2(X))* Xulon Pr., Inc.

Ellens, J. Harold. The Son of Man in the Gospel of John. 2010. 220p. *(978-1-906055-99-8(8))* Sheffield Phoenix Pr.

Ellsworth, Roger. Foundations of the Faith: A Step-by-Step Guide in the Gospel of John. 2006. (Illus.). 346p. pap. *(978-0-85234-615-0(8))* Evangelical Pr.

Elowsky, Joel C. & Oden, Thomas C., eds. John 1-10. 2007. (Ancient Christian Commentary on Scripture Ser.: New Testament Volume 4a). (ENG.). 421p. 50.00 *(978-0-8308-1489-3(2)*, IVP Acad.) InterVarsity Pr.

Elvey, Anne F. The Matter of the Text: Material Engagements between Luke & the Five Senses. 2011. 240p. ***(978-1-907534-16-4(4))*** Sheffield Phoenix Pr.

Estes, Douglas. The Temporal Mechanics of the Fourth Gospel: A Theory of Hermeneutical Relativity in the Gospel of John. 2008. (Biblical Interpretation Ser.: Vol. 92). 324p. *(978-90-04-16598-4(3))* BRILL.

Evans, Craig A. Fabricating Jesus: How Modern Scholars Distort the Gospels. (ENG., Illus.). 290p. 2008. pap. 16.00 *(978-0-8308-3355-9(2))* 2006. 24.00 *(978-0-8308-3318-4(8))* InterVarsity Pr. (IVP Bks.).

Evans-Perry, Sonja. Restore unto Me... My Passion, My Drive, My Life! 2011. (Illus.). 100p. pap. 15.00 ***(978-0-9774890-7-7(8))*** L.T.A. Productions.

Eyles Pierce, S. El Evangelio del Espiritu: The Gospel of the Spirit. (SPA.). 128p. *(978-84-7228-870-6(6)*, 220391) Clie, Editorial.

Farley, Lawrence. The Gospel of Matthew: The Torah for the Church. 2009. (Orthodox Bible Study Companion Ser.). 400p. pap. 22.95 *(978-0-9822770-7-2(5))* Conciliar Pr.

Felsch, Dorit. Die Feste im Johannesevangelium: Jüdische Tradition und christologische Deutung. 2011. (Wissenschaftliche Untersuchungen Zum Neuen Testament Ser.: No. 308). (GER.). 344p. pap. 157.50 ***(978-3-16-150888-2(2))*** Mohr Siebeck GmbH & Co. KG DEU. Dist: Coronet Bks.

Finnern, Sonke. Narratologie und biblische Exegese: Eine integrative Methode der Erzählanalyse und ihr Ertrag am Beispiel von Matthäus 28. 2010. (Illus.). 637p. pap. 197.50 *(978-3-16-150381-8(3))* Mohr Siebeck GmbH & Co. KG DEU. Dist: Coronet Bks.

Fisher, George Park. The Nature & Method of Revelation. 2007. (ENG.). 306p. 43.95 *(978-0-548-01050-1(1))* Kessinger Publishing, LLC.

Fleer, David. Preaching John's Gospel: The World It Imagines. 2008. 192p. pap. 20.00 *(978-0-8272-3007-1(9))* Chalice Pr.

Flores, Ernest R. Tempted to Leave the Cross: Renewing the Call to Discipleship. 2007. 130p. per. 14.00 *(978-0-8170-1524-4(8))* Judson Pr.

—Tentado a Dejar la Cruz: Renovando el Llamado al Discipulado. 2008.Tr. of Tempted to Leave the Cross: Renewing the Call to Discipleship. (SPA.). 160p. pap. 14.00 *(978-0-8170-1535-0(3))* Judson Pr.

Flores, José. Cristologia de Juan: Christology of John. (SPA.). 288p. *(978-84-7228-216-2(3)*, 220212) Clie, Editorial.

Fluitt, Michael. The Authority of the Believer. 2009. 100p. pap. 10.49 *(978-1-4490-1287-8(6))* AuthorHouse.

Focant, C. Marc, Un évangile étonnant: Recueil D'essais. 2006. (Bibliotheca Ephemeridum Theologicarum Lovaniensium Ser.). (FRE & ENG.). 402p. (C). pap. 87.00 *(978-90-429-1699-9(0))* Peeters Pubs. & Booksellers BEL. Dist: Brown, David Bk. Co., The.

Ford, J. Massyngbaerde. My Enemy Is My Guest: Jesus & Violence in Luke. 2010. 192p. pap. 22.00 *(978-1-60899-471-7(6)*, Wipf and Stock) Wipf & Stock Pubs.

Forster, N. Das Gemeinschaftliche Gebet in der Sicht des Lukas. 2007. (Biblical Tools & Studies). (GER & ENG.). 586p. (C). 124.00 *(978-90-429-1900-6(0))* Peeters Pubs. & Booksellers BEL. Dist: Brown, David Bk. Co., The.

Fortna. Gospel of Signs. 290p. *(978-0-521-07624-1(2))* Cambridge Univ. Pr.

Foster, Charles. The Christmas Myster. 2008. (ENG.). 128p. 13.99 *(978-1-85078-769-3(7))* Authentic Media.

Foster, P., et al, eds. New Studies in the Synoptic Problem: Oxford Conference, April 2008. 2011. (Bibliotheca Ephemeridum Theologicarum Lovaniensium Ser.). (ENG.). 968p. (C). pap. 124.00 *(978-90-429-2401-7(2))* Peeters Pubs. & Booksellers BEL. Dist: Brown, David Bk. Co., The.

The Four Gospels: Printed in Paragraphs from the Text of the Authorised Version. 2012. (ENG.). 246p. pap. 27.00 ***(978-1-107-68456-0(0))*** Cambridge Univ. Pr.

Fox, Emmet. Sermon on the Mount, the Gift Edition: The Key to Success in Life. 2012. 256p. 23.99 ***(978-0-06-222156-8(6)***, HarperOne) HarperCollins Pubs.

France. Divine Government. 13.00 *(978-0-687-85282-6(X))* Abingdon Pr.

Fraser, Giles, selected by. The Gospels, Jesus Christ. 2007. (Revolutions Ser.). (ENG.). 174p. per. 14.95 *(978-1-84467-176-2(3)*, 844176) Verso Bks. GBR. Dist: Norton, W. W. & Co., Inc.

Freedman, Harry. The Gospels' Veiled Agenda: Revolution, Priesthood & the Holy Grail. 2009. (ENG.). 246p. pap. 24.95 *(978-1-84694-260-0(8))* O Bks.,John Hunt.

French, Lachlen. Breath of Light. 2010. 480p. pap. *(978-0-9814278-6-7(3))* Kima Global Pubs.

Frey, Jörg, et al, eds. Die Apostelgeschichte im Kontext antiker und frühchristlicher Historiographie. 2009. (Beihefte zur Zeitschrift fur die neutestamentliche Wissenschaft und die Kunde der älteren Kirche Ser.).Tr. of Acts of the Apostles in the Context of Ancient & Early Christian Historiography. (GER.). X, 703p. 321.00 ***(978-3-11-173653-2(9))*** De Gruyter, Walter Inc.

Frey, Jorg, ed. Imagery in the Gospel of John: Terms, Forms, Themes & Theology of Johannine Figurative Language. 2006. (Wissenschaftliche Untersuchnugen Zum Neuen Testament Ser.: No. 200). (GER & ENG., Illus.). 504p. 195.00 *(978-3-16-149116-0(5))* Mohr Siebeck GmbH & Co. KG DEU. Dist: Coronet Bks.

Frey, Jörg, et al, eds. Die Apostelgeschichte im Kontext antiker und frühchristlicher Historiographie. 2009. (Beihefte zur Zeitschrift für die neutestamentliche Wissenschaft und die Kunde der Alteren Kirche Ser.).Tr. of Acts of the Apostles in the Context of Ancient & Early Christian Historiography. (GER.). X, 703p. 210.00 *(978-3-11-021631-8(0))* De Gruyter, Walter Inc.

Frost, Michael. Jesus the Fool. 2010. 214p. pap. 14.95 *(978-1-59856-358-0(0))* Hendrickson Pubs. Marketing, LLC.

Fuller, Michael E. The Restoration of Israel: Israel's Re-Gathering & the Fate of the Nations in Early Jewish Literature & Luke-Acts. 2006. (Beihefte Zur Zeitschrift Für Die Neutestamentliche Wissenschaft und die Kunde der Alteren Kirche Ser.). (ENG.). XI, 332p. 154.00 *(978-3-11-018896-7(1))* De Gruyter, Walter Inc.

Fuller, Michael E. The Restoration of Israel: Israel's Re-gathering & the Fate of the Nations in Early Jewish Literature & Luke-Acts. (Beihefte zur Zeitschrift fur die neutestamentliche Wissenschaft und die Kunde der älteren Kirche Ser.). (ENG.). XI, 332p. 255.00 ***(978-3-11-182836-7(0))*** De Gruyter, Walter Inc.

Fullmer, Paul M. & Fullmer. Resurrection in Mark's Literary-Historical Perspective. 2007. (Library of New Testament Studies). (ENG., Illus.). 272p. 160.00 *(978-0-567-04553-9(6)*, T&T Clark Int'l) Continuum International Publishing Group, Ltd. GBR. Dist: National Bk. Network.

Gathercole, Simon. The Gospel of Judas: Rewriting Early Christianity. 2007. (ENG., Illus.). 208p. 39.95 *(978-0-19-922584-2(2))* Oxford Univ. Pr., Inc.

Gerhardsson, Birger. The Testing of God's Son. Toy, John, tr. 2009. 82p. pap. 12.00 *(978-1-60608-691-9(X)*, Wipf and Stock) Wipf & Stock Pubs.

Getty-Sullivan, Mary Ann. Parables of the Kingdom: Jesus & the Use of Parables in the Synoptic Tradition. 2007. 191p. per. 3.95 *(978-0-8146-2993-2(8)*, Liturgical Pr. Bks.) Liturgical Pr.

Gilbrant, Ragnhild. Purity & Impurity. 2010. 268p. pap. *(978-3-639-23861-7(3))* VDM Verlag Dr. Mueller e.K.

Gilley, James W. God with Us: According to John. 2008. 13.99 *(978-0-8163-2285-5(6))* Pacific Pr. Publishing Assn.

Gingrich, Raymond E. Fellowship with the Word of Life: Studies in I, II, III John. pap. 7.99 *(978-0-88469-042-9(3))* BMH Bks.

Glunz, H. H. History of the Vulgate in England from Alcuin to Roger Bacon: Being an Inquiry into the Text of Some English Manuscripts of the Vulgate Gospels. 2010. (ENG.). 404p. pap. 31.99 *(978-0-521-17075-8(3))* Cambridge Univ. Pr.

Gordon, Mary. Reading Jesus: A Writer's Encounter with the Gospels. 2010. (ENG.). 240p. pap. 15.00 *(978-0-307-27762-6(3)*, Anchor) Knopf Doubleday Publishing Group.

Gordon, Samuel. Quiet Talks on John's Gospel. 2007. 260p. per. 21.95 *(978-1-60206-055-5(X))* Cosimo, Inc.

Gorman, Mary Jane. Tending Body, Heart, Mind & Soul: Following Jesus in Caring for Ourselves. 2006. 136p. per. 10.00 *(978-0-687-49210-7(6))* Abingdon Pr.

Gowler, David B. & Gowler, David. Host, Guest, Enemy & Friend: Portraits of the Pharisees in Luke & Acts. 2008. 422p. pap. 46.00 *(978-1-55635-690-2(0)*, Wipf & Stock Pubs.

Grant, Robert M. The Earliest Lives of Jesus. 2008. 144p. pap. 18.00 *(978-1-55635-934-7(9)*, Wipf and Stock) Wipf & Stock Pubs.

Graves, Robert & Podro, Joshua. The Nazarene Gospel Restored. Presley, John, ed. 2011. 1060p. 80.00 *(978-1-85754-667-5(9))* Carcanet Pr., Ltd. GBR. Dist: Independent Pubs. Group.

Gray, Ronald. Jesus's Gospel of Love & the Holocaust. 2008. 72p. pap. *(978-1-84748-294-5(5))* Athena Pr.

Green, Joel B. The Way of the Cross. 2009. 110p. pap. 14.00 *(978-1-60608-573-8(5)*, Wipf and Stock) Wipf & Stock Pubs.

Green, Joel B., ed. Methods for Luke. 2010. (Methods in Biblical Interpretation Ser.). (ENG.). 168p. (C). 85.00 *(978-0-521-86912-4(X))*; pap. 24.99 *(978-0-521-71781-6(7))* Cambridge Univ. Pr.

Grey, Mary. Gospel Treasure. 112p. 13.00 *(978-0-281-05267-7(0))* SPCK Publishing GBR. Dist: Pilgrim Pr., The/United Church Pr.

—Open Door on Mark. (Illus.). 142p. 10.00 *(978-0-281-04998-1(X))* SPCK Publishing GBR. Dist: Pilgrim Pr., The/United Church Pr.

Grimshaw, James P. The Matthean Community & the World: An Analysis of Matthew's Food Exchange. 2008. (Studies in Biblical Literature Ser.). 292p. (C). 84.95 *(978-1-4331-0083-3(5))* Lang, Peter Publishing, Inc.

Grindheim, Sigurd. Christology in the Synoptic Gospels: God or God's Servant 2012. (ENG.). 232p. 110.00 ***(978-0-567-00063-7(X))***; pap. 32.95 ***(978-0-567-24657-8(4))*** Continuum International Publishing Group, Ltd. GBR. (T&T Clark Int'l). Dist: National Bk. Network.

Gruen, Roger. Crossword John with Answers. 2008. 110p. pap. 14.50 *(978-0-615-18141-7(4))* Crossword Institute, The.

B

—Crossword John without Answers. 2008. 89p. pap. 13.50 *(978-0-615-18142-4(2))* Crossword Institute, The.

Gurtner, Daniel M. The Torn Veil: Matthew's Exposition of the Death of Jesus. 2010. (Society for New Testament Studies Monograph Ser.). (ENG.). 320p. pap. 39.99 *(978-0-521-18738-1(9))* Cambridge Univ. Pr.

Gurtner, Daniel M. & Nolland, John. Built upon the Rock: Studies in the Gospel of Matthew. Gurtner, Daniel M. & Nolland, John, eds. 2008. (Illus.). 331p. per. 34.00 *(978-0-8028-4563-4(0))* Eerdmans, William B. Publishing Co.

Guttenberger, Gudrun. Die Gottesvorstellung im Markusevangelium. (Beihefte zur Zeitschrift far die neutestamentliche Wissenschaft und die Kunde der älteren Kirche Ser.). (GER.). IX, 477p. 300.00 ***(978-3-11-182784-1(4))*** De Gruyter, Walter Inc.

Haldimann, Konrad. Rekonstruktion und Entfaltung: Exegetische Untersuchungen zu Joh 15 Und 16. (Beihefte zur Zeitschrift far die neutestamentliche Wissenschaft und die Kunde der älteren Kirche Ser.). (GER.). IX, 444p. 344.00 ***(978-3-11-185020-7(X))*** De Gruyter, Walter Inc.

Hall, John. What's Wrong with the Name it & Claim it Gospel? 2011. (ENG.). 50p. pap. 6.99 ***(978-1-4664-1576-8(2))*** CreateSpace.

Harnack, Adolf. Luke the Physician: The Author of the Third Gospel & the Acts of the Apostles. 2008. 244p. pap. *(978-1-4437-1686-4(3))* Read Bks.

—Luke the Physician: The Author of the Third Gospel & the Acts of the Apostles. 2009. 240p. pap. 25.00 *(978-1-60608-439-7(9),* Wipf and Stock) Wipf & Stock Pubs.

—Luke the Physician the Author of the Thi. 2006. pap. 28.95 *(978-1-4286-3475-6(4))* Kessinger Publishing, LLC.

Harrington, Daniel J. The Synoptic Gospels Set Free: Preaching without Anti-Semitism. 2009. (Stimulus Bks.). (Illus.). 256p. pap. 19.95 *(978-0-8091-4583-6(9))* Paulist Pr.

Harrington, Daniel J. Sj & Harrington, Daniel J. Meeting St. Luke Today. 2009. (ENG.). 144p. pap. 12.95 *(978-0-8294-2916-9(6))* Loyola Pr.

Harrington, Daniel P. Meeting St. John Today: Understanding the Man, His Mission, & His Message. 2011. (ENG.). 144p. pap. 12.95 *(978-0-8294-2917-6(4))* Loyola Pr.

Harrington, Todd. Resonating the Gospel Within a Post Christian Culture. 2008. 132p. pap. *(978-3-639-01382-5(4))* VDM Verlag Dr. Mueller e.K.

Harris, J. Rendel. The Gospel of the Twelve Apostles: Together with the Apocalypses of Each One of Them, Edited from the Syriac MS. with a Translation & Introduction. 2008. 60p. pap. 5.00 *(978-1-60608-351-2(1),* Wipf and Stock) Wipf & Stock Pubs.

Harrison, Everett F. John: The Gospel of Faith. 2011. 128p. 40.95 ***(978-1-258-08156-0(3))*** Literary Licensing, LLC.

Hartenstein, Judith. Charakterisierung im Dialog: Maria Magdalena, Petrus, Thomas und die Mutter Jesu im Johannesevangelium. 2007. (Novum Testamentum et Orbis Antiquus/Studien zur Umwelt des Neuen Testaments (NTOA/StUNT) Ser.). (GER., Illus.). 347p. (C). 86.00 *(978-3-525-53987-3(8))* Vandenhoeck & Ruprecht GmbH & Co. KG DEU. Dist: ISD.

Hartin, P. J. Exploring the Spirituality of the Gospels. 2011. pap. 14.95 *(978-0-8146-3317-5(X));* E-Book *(978-0-8146-3941-2(0))* Liturgical Pr.

Hartley, Donald E. The Wisdom Background & Parabolic Implications of Isaiah 6: 9-10 in the Synoptics. 2006. (Studies in Biblical Literature: Vol. 100). (Illus.). 430p. (C). 86.95 *(978-0-8204-8665-9(5))* Lang, Peter Publishing, Inc.

Hartsock, Chad. Sight & Blindness in Luke-Acts: The Use of Physical Features in Characterization. 2008. (Biblical Interpretation Ser.). 232p. *(978-90-04-16535-9(5))* BRILL.

Hatina, Thomas R., ed. Biblical Interpretation in Early Christian Gospels Vol. 3: The Gospel of Luke, 5 vols. 2010. (Library of New Testament Studies, the Ser.). (ENG.). 240p. 130.00 *(978-0-567-03309-3(0),* T&T Clark Int'l) Continuum International Publishing Group, Ltd. GBR. Dist: National Bk. Network.

Hays, Christopher. Luke's Wealth Ethics: A Study in Their Coherence & Character. 2010. 347p. pap. 147.50 *(978-3-16-150269-9(8))* Mohr Siebeck GmbH & Co. KG DEU. Dist: Coronet Bks.

Headlam, A. The Fourth Gospel As History. 2007. 152p. per. *(978-1-4067-8882-2(1),* Pomona Pr.) Read Bks.

Hedrick, Charles W. Unlocking the Secrets of the Gospel according to Thomas. 2010. 246p. pap. 27.00 *(978-1-55635-239-3(5),* Cascade Bks.) Wipf & Stock Pubs.

Heil, Christoph. Lukas und Q: Studien zur lukanischen Redaktion des Spruchevangeliums Q. (Beihefte zur Zeitschrift far die neutestamentliche Wissenschaft und die Kunde der älteren Kirche Ser.). (GER.). X, 444p. 240.00 ***(978-3-11-185277-5(6))*** De Gruyter, Walter Inc.

Henderson, Suzanne Watts. Christology & Discipleship in the Gospel of Mark. 2008. (Society for New Testament Studies Monograph Ser.). (ENG.). 304p. pap. 44.00 *(978-0-521-09139-8(X))* Cambridge Univ. Pr.

Hengel, Martin. Studies in the Gospel of Mark. 2012. 224p. pap. ***(978-0-334-02343-2(2),*** SCM Pr.) Hymns Ancient & Modern Ltd.

Herrmann, Florian. Strategien der Todesdarstellung in der Markuspassion: Ein literaturgeschichtlicher Vergleich. 2010. (Novum Testamentum et Orbis Antiquus/Studien zur Umwelt des Neuen Testaments (NTOA/StUNT) Ser.). (GER.). 407p. (C). 98.00 *(978-3-525-55011-3(1))* Vandenhoeck & Ruprecht GmbH & Co. KG DEU. Dist: ISD.

Hill, C. E. Who Chose the Gospels? Probing the Great Gospel Conspiracy. (ENG., Illus.). 2012. 320p. pap. 16.95 ***(978-0-19-964029-4(7))*** 2010. 240p. 27.95 *(978-0-19-955123-1(5))* Oxford Univ. Pr., Inc.

Hixson, J. B. Getting the Gospel Wrong. 2008. 408p. pap. 21.99 *(978-1-60647-098-5(1))* Xulon Pr., Inc.

Holloway, Gary. Matthew: Jesus Is King. 2007. (Meditative Commentary Ser.). 224p. per. 13.99 *(978-0-9767790-1-8(3),* Leafwood Pubs.) Abilene Christian Univ. Pr.

Holmas, Geir O. Prayer & Vindication in Luke Acts: The Theme of Prayer within the Context of the Legitimating & Edifying Objective of the Lukan Narrative. 2011. (Library of New Testament Studies). (ENG.). 320p. 130.00 *(978-0-567-01756-7(7),* T&T Clark Int'l) Continuum International Publishing Group, Ltd. GBR. Dist: National Bk. Network.

Holton, Bil & Holton, Cher. The Gospel of Mark: New Metaphysical Version. 2008. xi, 83p. *(978-1-893095-51-9(7))* Liberty Publishing Group.

Hooker, Morna D. Beginnings: Keys That Open the Gospels. 2010. 112p. pap. 14.00 *(978-1-60899-260-7(8),* Wipf and Stock) Wipf & Stock Pubs.

Hooker, Morna D. & Vincent, John J. The Drama of Mark. 2010. (ENG.). 80p. pap. 10.00 *(978-0-7162-0664-4(1))* Epworth Pr., The GBR. Dist: Westminster John Knox Pr.

Horman, John. A Common Written Greek Source for Mark & Thomas. 2011. (Studies in Christianity & Judaism Ser.). (ENG, COP & GEC.). 258p. (C). 85.00 *(978-1-55458-224-2(5))* Wilfrid Laurier Univ. Pr. CAN. Dist: Univ. of Toronto Pr.

Horsley, Richard A. Oral Performance, Popular Tradition, & Hidden Transcript in Q. 2006. (SBL - Semeia Studies). 229p. *(978-90-04-15120-8(6))* BRILL.

—Oral Performance, Popular Tradition, & Hidden Transcript in Q. 2006. vii, 229p. 35.95 *(978-1-58983-248-0(5))* Society of Biblical Literature.

Hoskins, Paul M. Jesus as the Fulfillment of the Temple in the Gospel of John. 2007. (Paternoster Biblical Monographs: Ser.). 300p. pap. 35.00 *(978-1-55635-223-2(9),* Wipf and Stock) Wipf & Stock Pubs.

Houghtby-Haddon, Natalie K. Changed Imagination, Changed Obedience: Social Change, Social Imagination, & the Bent-over Woman in the Gospel of Luke. 2011. 190p. pap. 22.00 *(978-1-60899-675-9(1),* Pickwick Pubns.) Wipf & Stock Pubs.

Hovey, Craig. To Share in the Body: A Theology of Martyrdom for Today's Church. 2008. 160p. (C). pap. 22.00 *(978-1-58743-217-0(X))* Brazos Pr.

Howard, Wilbert Francis. Fourth Gospel in Recent Criticism & Interpretation, 4th Edition. Barrett, C. K., ed. 2009. 342p. pap. 40.00 *(978-1-60608-720-6(7),* Wipf and Stock) Wipf & Stock Pubs.

Howell, Don N., Jr. The Passion of the Servant: A Journey to the Cross. 2009. 390p. pap. 43.00 *(978-1-60608-207-2(8),* Wipf and Stock) Wipf & Stock Pubs.

Howell, Timothy D. The Matthean Beatitudes in Their Jewish Origins: A Literary & Speech Act Analysis. 2011. (C). 89.95 ***(978-1-4331-1545-5(X))*** Lang, Peter Publishing, Inc.

Hudson, Gary W. The Secret Things: The Hidden Wisdom of the Gospel of Thomas. 2006. 24.95 *(978-0-9778517-1-3(0))* Unitive Life Pubns.

Huizenga, L. A. The New Isaac: Tradition & Intertextuality in the Gospel of Matthew. 2009. (Novum Testamentum Supplements Ser.). xx, 337p. *(978-90-04-17569-3(5))* BRILL.

Hultgren, Stephen. Narrative Elements in the Double Tradition: A Study of Their Place within the Framework of the Gospel Narrative. (Beihefte zur Zeitschrift far die neutestamentliche Wissenschaft und die Kunde der älteren Kirche Ser.). (ENG.). XVIII, 420p. 255.00 ***(978-3-11-181192-5(1))*** De Gruyter, Walter Inc.

Humphrey, Hugh Minear. The Gospel of Mark: An Indexed Bibliography 1980-2005. 2006. 348p. 119.95 *(978-0-7734-5553-5(1))* Mellen, Edwin Pr., The.

Hunt, Steven A. Rewriting the Feeding of the Five Thousand: John 6.1-15 As a Test Case for Johannine Dependence on the Synoptic Gospels. 2011. (Studies in Biblical Literature Ser.). (C). 87.95 *(978-1-4331-0606-4(X))* Lang, Peter Publishing, Inc.

Hwang, Won Ha. The theological role of signs in the Gospel of John. 2008. 252p. pap. *(978-3-639-09946-1(X))* VDM Verlag Dr. Mueller e.K.

Hylen, Susan. Allusion & Meaning in John 6. (Beihefte zur Zeitschrift far die neutestamentliche Wissenschaft und die Kunde der älteren Kirche Ser.). (ENG.). IX, 237p. 195.00 ***(978-3-11-179413-6(X))*** De Gruyter, Walter Inc.

Hylen, Susan. Imperfect Believers: Ambiguous Characters in the Gospel of John. 2009. (ENG.). 212p. pap. 25.00 *(978-0-664-23372-3(4))* Westminster John Knox Pr.

Inch, Morris. Matthew in the Messianic Tradition. 2006. (ENG.). 120p. per. 26.50 *(978-0-7618-3525-7(3))* Univ. Pr. of America, Inc.

Ironside, H. A. The Epistles of John & Jude. 2007. (Ironside Expository Commentaries Ser.). (Illus.). 192p. 19.99 *(978-0-8254-2923-1(4))* Kregel Pubns.

Ironside, Henry A. Estudios sobre Mateo: Lectures on Matthew. (SPA.). *(978-84-7645-160-1(1,* 223187) Clie, Editorial.

—Grandes Palabras del Evangelio: Great Words of the Gospel. (SPA.). *(978-84-7645-184-7(9),* 223223) Clie, Editorial.

Iverson, Kelly R. & Iverson. Gentiles in the Gospel of Mark: Even the Dogs under the Table Eat the Children's Crumbs, 339 vols. 2007. (Library of New Testament Studies: Vol. 339). (ENG.). 224p. 140.00 *(978-0-567-03131-0(4),* T&T Clark Int'l) Continuum International Publishing Group, Ltd. GBR. Dist: National Bk. Network.

Iverson, Kelly R. & Skinner, Christopher W. Mark As Story: Retrospect & Prospect. 2011. 309p. *(978-90-04-20253-5(6))* BRILL.

—Mark As Story: Retrospect & Prospect. 2011. xii, 309p. *(978-1-58983-549-8(2));* 322p. pap. *(978-1-58983-548-1(4))* Society of Biblical Literature.

Jack, Alison M. Scottish Fiction As Gospel Exegesis: Four Case Studies. 2010. 190p. *(978-1-906055-90-5(4))* Sheffield Phoenix Pr.

Jefferson, Thomas. The Jefferson Bible. 2010. 176p. pap. 19.95 *(978-0-557-38564-5(4))* Lulu Enterprises Inc.

—The Jefferson Bible: The Life & Morals Of. 2007. 100p. per. 8.99 *(978-1-60459-128-6(5))* Wilder Pubns., Ltd.

—The Jefferson Bible: The Life & Morals of Jesus of Nazareth Extracted Textually from the Gospels, Together with a Comparison of His Doctrines with T. 2011. 104p. pap. 4.35 ***(978-1-61427-028-7(7))*** Martino Publishing.

—The Jefferson Bible, Smithsonian Edition: The Life & Morals of Jesus of Nazareth. 2011. (ENG, LAT, FRE & GEC., Illus.). 200p. 35.00 *(978-1-58834-312-3(X))* Smithsonian Institution Pr.

—Jefferson Bible the Life & Morals of J. 2006. 96p. per. 9.99 *(978-1-59547-955-6(4))* NuVision Pubns., LLC.

—The Jefferson Bible, the Life & Morals of Jesus. 2009. 108p. 29.99 *(978-1-59547-569-5(9))* NuVision Pubns., LLC.

John. (People's Bible Commentary Ser.). 275p. pap. 12.99 *(978-0-570-05323-1(4),* 12-8049); (People's Bible Commentary Ser.). 288p. 14.99 *(978-0-7586-0442-2(4))*;Pt. 1. (LifeLight Bible Studies: Course 7). stu. ed. 5.50 *(978-0-570-09273-5(6),* 20-2274);Pt. 1. (LifeLight Bible Studies: Course 7). 6.50 *(978-0-570-09272-8(8),* 20-2273);Pt. 2. (LifeLight Bible Studies: Course 8). stu. ed. 5.50 *(978-0-570-09275-9(2),* 20-2279);Pt. 2. (LifeLight Bible Studies: Course 8). 6.50 *(978-0-570-09274-2(4),* 20-2278) Concordia Publishing Hse.

John, Vol. 19. 6.99 Westminster John Knox Pr.

John the Unafraid. 2007. (ENG.). 130p. 35.95 *(978-0-548-02053-1(1))* Kessinger Publishing, LLC.

Johnson, John Frederick. The Synoptic Gospels. 2011. 211p. *(978-1-57025-248-8(3))* Whole Person Assocs., Inc.

Johnson, S. R. Q 12: 33-34: Storing up Treasures in Heaven. 2007. (Documenta Q Ser.). (ENG.). 213p. (C). pap. 99.00 *(978-90-429-1949-5(3))* Peeters Pubs. & Booksellers BEL. Dist: Brown, David Bk. Co., The.

Johnson, Steven R. Seeking the Imperishable Treasure: Wealth, Wisdom, & a Jesus Saying. 2008. 200p. pap. 23.00 *(978-1-55635-244-7(1),* Cascade Bks.) Wipf & Stock Pubs.

Joubert, Johann. The Paraclete-Spirit in the Johannine Gospel: A comparative study of the Paraclete statements & references to the Holy Spirit in the Johannine Gospel. 2008. 548p. pap. *(978-3-639-09952-2(4))* VDM Verlag Dr. Mueller e.K.

Kadlecek, Jo. Desperate Women of the Bible: Lessons on Passion from the Gospels. 2006. 192p. pap. 15.00 *(978-0-8010-6618-4(2))* Baker Bks.

Kalellis, Peter M. God's Power Within You: Attitudes for Living. 2010. 112p. pap. 12.95 *(978-0-8091-4655-0(X))* Paulist Pr.

Kandiah, Krish. Dysciples: Why I fall asleep when I pray & twelve other discipleship Dysfunctions. 2009. (ENG.). 172p. 13.99 *(978-1-85078-824-9(3))* Authentic Media.

Karris, OFM, Robert J. Luke: Artist & Theologian: Luke's Passion Account as Literature. 2009. 138p. pap. 17.00 *(978-1-60608-453-3(4),* Wipf and Stock) Wipf & Stock Pubs.

Kashouh, Hikmat. The Arabic Versions of the Gospels: The Manuscripts & Their Families. 2011. (Arbeiten zur neutestamentlichen Textforschung Ser.). (ENG.). XIV, 761p. (gr. 17). 377.00 ***(978-3-11-022858-8(0))*** De Gruyter, Walter Inc.

Kealy, Sean P. A History or the Interpretation of the Gospel of Mark: Through the Nineteenth Century, 2 vols., Vol. I. 2007. 580p. 139.95 *(978-0-7734-5190-2(0))* Mellen, Edwin Pr., The.

—A History or the Interpretation of the Gospel of Mark: Volume II: the Twentieth Century, 2 vols. 720p. 159.95 *(978-0-7734-5117-9(X))* Mellen, Edwin Pr., The.

Keith, Chris. The Pericope Adulterae, the Gospel of John, & the Literacy of Jesus. 2009. (New Testament Tools, Studies & Documents Ser.). (Illus.). 366p. *(978-90-04-17394-1(3))* BRILL.

Kelber, Werner H. & Byrskog, Samuel, eds. Jesus in Memory: Traditions in Oral & Scribal Perspectives. 2009. (ENG.). 350p. 49.95 *(978-1-60258-235-4(1))* Baylor Univ. Pr.

Keller, Zsolt. Der Blutruf: Eine schweizerische Wirkungsgeschichte 1900-1950. 2006. (GER.). 200p. (C). pap. 36.00 *(978-3-525-55328-2(5))* Vandenhoeck & Ruprecht GmbH & Co. KG DEU. Dist: ISD.

Kelly, W. Exposition of the Gospel of Luke. 7.25 *(978-0-88172-102-7(6))* Believers Bookshelf, Inc.

—Exposition of the Gospel of Mark. 6.95 *(978-0-88172-103-4(4))* Believers Bookshelf, Inc.

Kelly, William. The Gospels. (Introductory Lecture Ser.: Vol. 1). 567p. 7.95 *(978-0-88172-097-6(6))* Believers Bookshelf, Inc.

Kezbere, Ilze. Umstrittener Monotheismus: Wahre und Falsche Apotheose im Lukanischen Doppelwerk. 2006. (Novum Testamentum et Orbis Antiquus (Ntoa) Ser.: 60). (GER.). 231p. (C). 59.00 *(978-3-525-53960-6(6))* Vandenhoeck & Ruprecht GmbH & Co. KG DEU. Dist: ISD.

Kierspel, Lars. The Jews & the World in the Fourth Gospel: Parallelism, Function, & Context. (Wissenschaftliche Untersuchungen zum Neuen Testament Ser.: No. 220). 283p. pap. 85.00 *(978-3-16-149069-9(X))* Mohr Siebeck GmbH & Co. KG DEU. Dist: Eisenbrauns, Inc.

Kilgallen, John J. Twenty Parables of Jesus in the Gospel of Luke. 2008. (ENG.). 178p. pap. 45.00 ***(978-88-7653-637-3(X))*** Biblical Institute Pr. ITA. Dist: Loyola Pr.

Klink, Edward W., III. Audience of the Gospels: The Origin & Function of the Gospels in Early Christianity. Klink, Edward W., III, ed. 3rd ed. 2010. (Library of New Testament Studies, the Ser.). (ENG.). 208p. 130.00 *(978-0-567-04536-2(6),* T&T Clark Int'l) Continuum International Publishing Group, Ltd. GBR. Dist: National Bk. Network.

Kilpatrick, G. D. Origins of the Gospel According to St. Matthew. 2007. 152p. pap. 35.00 *(978-0-86516-677-6(3))* Bolchazy-Carducci Pubs.

Kilpatrick, George Dunbar. The Origins of the Gospel According to St. Matthew. 2007. pap. 39.00 *(978-0-86516-667-7(6))* Bolchazy-Carducci Pubs.

Kim, Seong Hee. Mark, Women & Empire: A Korean Postcolonial Perspective. 2010. 192p. *(978-1-906055-64-6(5))* Sheffield Phoenix Pr.

Kim, Stephen S. The Miracles of Jesus According to John: Their Christological & Eschatological Significance. 2010. 240p. pap. 26.00 *(978-1-60608-259-1(0),* Wipf and Stock) Wipf & Stock Pubs.

Kim, Yongjae. Interpretation der Gebote im Markusevangelium. 2010. (Europäische Hochschulschriften. Reihe 23: Theologie Ser.). (GER.). 188p. pap. 53.95 *(978-3-631-59537-4(9))* Lang, Peter GmbH, Europaischer Verlag der Wissenschaften DEU. Dist: Lang, Peter.

Klassen, Steve. Trained by Jesus: Studies in the Gospel of Mark. 110p. pap. 3.60 *(978-0-921788-69-0(X))* Kindred Productions.

Klink, Edward W. The Sheep of the Fold: The Audience & Origin of the Gospel of John. 2007. (Society for New Testament Studies Monograph Ser.). (ENG.). 336p. 115.00 *(978-0-521-87582-0(X))* Cambridge Univ. Pr.

Klink III, Edward W. The Sheep of the Fold: The Audience & Origin of the Gospel of John. 2010. (Society for New Testament Studies Monograph Ser.). (ENG.). 336p. pap. 42.00 *(978-0-521-13044-8(1))* Cambridge Univ. Pr.

Klumbies, Paul-Gerhard. Der Mythos bei Markus. (Beihefte zur Zeitschrift far die neutestamentliche Wissenschaft und die Kunde der älteren Kirche Ser.). (GER.). IX, 375p. 255.00 ***(978-3-11-180552-8(2))*** De Gruyter, Walter Inc.

Knox, Wilfred L. The Sources of the Synoptic Gospels: Volume 1, St Mark. Chadwick, H., ed. 2011. (ENG.). 178p. pap. 21.99 *(978-0-521-18060-3(0))* Cambridge Univ. Pr.

—The Sources of the Synoptic Gospels: Volume 2, St Luke & St Matthew. Chadwick, H., ed. 2011. (ENG.). 182p. pap. 21.99 *(978-0-521-18075-7(9))* Cambridge Univ. Pr.

Kobel, Esther. Dining with John: Communal Meals & Identity Formation in the Fourth Gospel & its Historical & Cultural Context. 2011. (Biblical Interpretation Ser.). (Illus.). 375p. ***(978-90-04-21778-2(9))*** BRILL.

Koester, Craig R. The Word of Life: A Theology of John's Gospel. 2008. 264p. pap. 21.00 *(978-0-8028-2938-2(4))* Eerdmans, William B. Publishing Co.

Koet, B. J. Dreams & Scriptures in Luke-Acts: Collected Essays. 2006. (Contributions to Biblical Exegesis & Theology Ser.: Vol. 42). (ENG & GER., Illus.). 232p. (C). 57.00 *(978-90-429-1750-7(4))* Peeters Pubs. & Booksellers BEL. Dist: Brown, David Bk. Co., The.

Köstenberger, Andreas J. Father, Son & Spirit. 2008. pap. *(978-1-84474-253-0(9))* InterVarsity Pr.

Kraeling, Carl H. Anthropos & Son of Man: A Study in the Religious Syncretism of the Hellenistic Orient. 2007. (Gorgias Theological Library: 21). 72.00 *(978-1-59333-631-8(4))* Gorgias Pr., LLC.

Kreitzer, Larry. Gospel According to John. 11.00 *(978-0-687-82292-8(0))* Abingdon Pr.

Kuecker, Aaron. Spirit & The 'Other' Social Identity, Ethnicity & Intergroup Reconciliation in Luke-Acts. 2011. (Library of New Testament Studies). (ENG.). 296p. 120.00 *(978-0-567-23570-1(X),* T&T Clark Int'l) Continuum International Publishing Group, Ltd. GBR. Dist: National Bk. Network.

Kumlehn, Martina. Geoeffnete Augen: Gedeutete Zeichen: Historisch-Systematische und Erzaehltheoretisch-Hermeneutische: Studien Zur Rezeption und Didaktik des Johannesevangeliums in der Modernen Religionspaedagogik. 2007. (Praktische Theologie Im Wissenschaftsdiskurs Ser.). (GER.). XII, 419p. 154.00 *(978-3-11-019516-3(X))* De Gruyter, Walter Inc.

Kurtz, Dennis. Youth Engaging Scripture: Diving into the Sunday Gospels. 2007. 376p. per. 18.95 *(978-0-88489-912-9(8))* St. Mary's Pr.

Kysar, Robert. John, the Maverick Gospel. 3rd ed. 2007. (ENG., Illus.). 190p. per. 25.00 *(978-0-664-23056-2(3))* Westminster John Knox Pr.

Labahn, M., et al, eds. Repetitions & Variations in the Fourth Gospel: Style, Text, Interpretation. 2009. (Bibliotheca Ephemeridum Theologicarum Lovaniensium Ser.). (ENG.). 712p. (C). pap. 124.00 *(978-90-429-2154-2(4))* Peeters Pubs. & Booksellers BEL. Dist: Brown, David Bk. Co., The.

Labahn, Michael. Jesus als Lebensspender: Untersuchungen zu einer Geschichte der johanneischen Tradition anhand ihrer Wundergeschichten. (Beihefte zur Zeitschrift far die neutestamentliche Wissenschaft und die Kunde der älteren Kirche Ser.). (GER.). X, 559p. 388.00 ***(978-3-11-186882-0(6))*** De Gruyter, Walter Inc.

Larkin, William J. & Trites, Allison A. Luke, Acts. 2006. (Cornerstone Biblical Commentary Ser.: 12). (ENG.). 688p. 34.99 *(978-0-8423-3438-9(6))* Tyndale Hse. Pubs.

Lathrop, Gordon W. The Four Gospels on Sunday: The New Testament & the Reform of Christian Worship. 2011. 240p. (C). 49.00 ***(978-0-8006-9852-2(5),*** Fortress Pr.) Augsburg Fortress, Pubs.

Law, Henry. El Evangelio en el Exodo: The Gospel in Exodus. (SPA.). *(978-84-7645-096-3(6),* 223151) Clie, Editorial.

Le Donne, Anthony & Thatcher, Tom. The Fourth Gospel in First-Century Media Culture. 2011. (Library of New Testament Studies). (ENG.). 296p. 120.00 *(978-0-567-46468-2(7),* T&T Clark Int'l) Continuum International Publishing Group, Ltd. GBR. Dist: National Bk. Network.

Lehtipuu, Outi. The Afterlife Imagery in Luke's Story of the Rich Man & Lazarus. 2006. (Supplements to Novum Testamentum Ser.: Vol. 123). 361p. *(978-90-04-15301-1(2))* BRILL.

Leung, Mavis M. The Kingship-Cross Interplay in the Gospel of John: JesusÕ Death as Corroboration of His Royal Messiahship. 2011. 234p. pap. 26.00 ***(978-1-61097-242-0(2),*** Wipf and Stock) Wipf & Stock Pubs.

Lewis, Agnes Smith. Light on the Four Gospels from the Sinai Palimpsest. 2006. (Gorgias Theological Library: 16). 235p. 84.00 (978-1-59333-530-4(X)) Gorgias Pr., LLC.

Lewis, Karoline M. Rereading the Shepherd Discourse: Restoring the Integrity of John 9:39-10:21. 2008. (Studies in Biblical Literature Ser.). 232p. (C). 69.95 (978-1-4331-0190-8(4)) Lang, Peter Publishing, Inc.

Lierman, John, ed. Challenging Perspectives on the Gospel of John. 2006. (Wissenschaftliche Untersuchungen Zum Neuen Testament 2 Ser.: No. 219). 381p. pap. 125.00 (978-3-16-149113-9(0)) Mohr Siebeck GmbH & Co. KG DEU. Dist: Coronet Bks.

Lindars, Barnabas. Behind the Fourth Gospel. 2010. 84p. pap. 12.00 (978-1-60899-730-5(8), Wipf and Stock) Wipf & Stock Pubs.

Lindemann, Andreas. Die Evangelien und die Apostelgeschichte: [in German]. 2009. 421p. 225.00 (978-3-16-150041-1(5)) Mohr Siebeck GmbH & Co. KG DEU. Dist: Coronet Bks.

Linden, William M. The Historical Jesus for Beginners: A Primer on Contemporary Biblical Scholarship. 2008. 168p. pap. 23.00 (978-1-55635-338-3(3), Wipf and Stock) Wipf & Stock Pubs.

Ling, Timothy J. M. The Judaean Poor & the Fourth Gospel. 2008. (Society for New Testament Studies Monograph Ser.). (ENG.). 264p. pap. 40.00 (978-0-521-09142-8(X)) Cambridge Univ. Pr.

Littleton, John & Burke, Christy. Journeying Through the Year of Matthew: Reflection on the Gospel. 2011. (ENG.). 176p. pap. 24.95 (978-1-85607-724-8(1)) Columba Pr. IRL. Dist: Dufour Editions, Inc.

Litzman, Warren Lee, Sr. My Notes on the Final Gospel. 2007. 527p. per. (978-0-9794765-5-6(0)) Christ-life Publishing House.

Loftus, Francis. St Luke's Gospel. Bartlett, Cynthia, ed. 2009. (ENG., Illus.). pap., stu. ed. 37.50 (978-1-4085-0459-8(6)) Nelson Thornes Ltd. GBR. Dist: Trans-Atlantic Pubns., Inc.

Lohuizen, Wali van. A Psycho-Spiritual View on the Message of Jesus in the Gospels: Presence & Transformation in Some Logia As a Sign of Mysticism. 2010. (978-1-4331-0658-3(2)) Lang, Peter GmbH, Europaischer Verlag der Wissenschaften.

Lotz, Anne Graham. Pursuing More of Jesus, 0 vols. 2009. 400p. pap. 16.99 (978-0-8499-2094-3(9)) Nelson, Thomas Inc.

Love, Stuart L. Jesus & Marginal Women: The Gospel of Matthew in Social-Scientific Perspective. 2010. (ENG., Illus.). 275p. (C). pap. 43.00 (978-0-227-17316-9(3)) Clarke, James Co., Ltd. GBR. Dist: Brown, David Bk. Co., The.

—Jesus & Marginal Women: The Gospel of Matthew in Social-Scientific Perspective. 2008. (Matrix: the Bible in Mediterranean Context: Ser.). (Illus.). 276p. pap. 31.00 (978-1-59752-803-0(X)) Wipf & Stock Pubs.

Lozada, Francisco & Thatcher, Tom. New Currents Through John: A Global Perspective. 2006. (Resources for Biblical Study Ser.: No. 54). (Illus.). viii, 248p. 29.95 (978-1-58983-201-5(9)) Society of Biblical Literature.

Lucado, Max. Book of Matthew: The Carpenter King, 0 vols. 2007. (Inspirational Bible Study; Life Lessons with Max Lucado Ser.). 128p. per. 9.99 (978-1-4185-0969-9(8)) Nelson, Thomas Inc.

—3:16: The Numbers of Hope. l.t. ed. 2009. (ENG.). 320p. (YA). pap. 17.95 (978-1-59415-248-1(9), Walker Large Print) Cengage Gale.

—3:16: The Numbers of Hope, 0 vols. 2009. 240p. pap. 15.99 (978-0-8499-2101-8(5)) 2008. 176p. (YA). pap. 12.99 (978-1-4003-1108-8(X)) Nelson, Thomas Inc.

—3:16: The Numbers of Hope. l.t. ed. 2008. 329p. (YA). 30.95 (978-1-4104-0744-3(6)) Thorndike Pr.

—The 3:16 Promise: He Loves. He Gave. We Believe. We Live, 0 vols. 2007. 64p. per. 2.99 (978-0-8499-1919-0(3)) Nelson, Thomas Inc.

Ludemann, Gerd. Eyes That See Not: The Pope Looks at Jesus. 2008. 131p. per. 20.00 net. (978-1-59815-006-3(5)) Polebridge Pr.

Ludemann, Gerd. Jesus after 2000 Years. 2012. 720p. pap. (978-0-334-02776-8(4), SCM Pr.) Hymns Ancient & Modern Ltd.

Lunsford, Jack. The Holy Spirit of God. 2008. 448p. pap. 22.99 (978-1-60791-130-2(2)) Xulon Pr., Inc.

Lutzer, Erwin W. & Lutzer, Rebecca. Jesus, Lover of a Woman's Soul: How He Validated Women As Honored Daughters of God. 2007. pap. 14.99 (978-0-8423-8427-8(5)) Tyndale Hse. Pubs.

MacArthur, John, Jr. Commentary on the Books of the New Testament, Vol. 3 Matthew: Matthew16-23. 2008.Tr. of Matthew 16-23. (RUS.). 480p. (978-1-56773-028-9(0)) Slavic Gospel Assn.

MacArthur, John. Luke, 0 vols. 2007. (MacArthur Bible Study Guides). 160p. per. 9.99 (978-1-4185-0961-3(2)) Nelson, Thomas Inc.

—Matthew, 0 vols. 2007. (MacArthur Bible Study Guides). 160p. per. 9.99 (978-1-4185-0959-0(0)) Nelson, Thomas Inc.

—A Tale of Two Sons, 0 vols. 2008. 128p. pap. 9.99 (978-1-4185-2820-1(X)) Nelson, Thomas Inc.

—A Tale of Two Sons: An Astonishing Study of the Parable Jesus Told to Unveil God's Grace for You, 0 vols. 2010. 240p. pap. 15.99 (978-1-4002-0268-3(X)) Nelson, Thomas Inc.

—A Tale of Two Sons: The Inside Story of a Father, His Sons, & a Shocking Murder. l.t. ed. 2010. (ENG.). 384p. pap. 17.99 (978-1-59415-308-2(6)) Cengage Gale.

—1, 2, 3, John & Jude: Established in Truth, Marked by Love, 0 vols. 2007. (MacArthur Bible Studies). 128p. pap. 9.99 (978-1-4185-0965-1(5)) Nelson, Thomas Inc.

MacDonald, Dennis R. The Homeric Epics & the Gospel of Mark. 2010. 274p. pap. 29.00 (978-0-300-17261-4(3)) Yale Univ. Pr.

MacDonald, James M. Life & Writings of St John. 2006. pap. 40.95 (978-1-4286-3708-5(7)) Kessinger Publishing, LLC.

Mack, Burton L. Patterns of Persuasion in the Gospels. 2008. 240p. pap. 26.00 (978-1-60608-220-1(5), Wipf and Stock) Wipf & Stock Pubs.

Madden, Patrick J. Jesus' Walking on the Sea: An Investigation of the Origin of the Narrative Account. (Beihefte zur Zeitschrift far die neutestamentliche Wissenschaft und die Kunde der älteren Kirche Ser.). (ENG.). X, 156p. 225.00 (978-3-11-174375-2(6)) De Gruyter, Walter Inc.

Magpie Books, creator. The Giant Book of Dreams. 2007. 538p. 7.99 (978-1-84529-544-8(7)) Constable & Robinson Ltd. GBR. Dist: Book Sales, Inc.

Malbon, Elizabeth Struthers. Between Author & Audience in Mark: Narration, Characterization, Interpretation. 2009. xii, 196p. (978-1-906055-60-8(2)) Sheffield Phoenix Pr.

—Mark's Jesus: Characterization as Narrative Christology. 2009. (ENG., Illus.). 360p. 39.95 (978-1-60258-247-7(5)) Baylor Univ. Pr.

Mallen, Peter & Mallen. The Reading & Transformation of Isaiah in Luke-Acts. 2008. (Library of New Testament Studies, the Ser.). (ENG.). 258p. 130.00 (978-0-567-04566-9(6), T&T Clark Int'l) Continuum International Publishing Group, Ltd. GBR. Dist: National Bk. Network.

Marohl, Matthew J. Joseph's Dilemma: Honor Killing in the Birth Narrative of Matthew. 2008. 104p. pap. 13.00 (978-1-55635-825-8(3)) Wipf & Stock Pubs.

Marshall, Jonathan. Jesus, Patrons & Benefactors: Roman Palestine & the Gospel of Luke. 2009. (Wissenschaftliche Untersuchungen zum Neuen Testament Ser.). 383p. pap. 147.50 (978-3-16-149901-2(8)) Mohr Siebeck GmbH & Co. KG DEU. Dist: Coronet Bks.

Martin, Michael W. Judas & the Rhetoric of Comparison in the Fourth Gospel. 2010. (Illus.). 186p. (978-1-906055-87-5(4)) Sheffield Phoenix Pr.

Martinez, Roberto. The Question of John the Baptist & JesusÕ Indictment of the Religious Leaders: A Critical Analysis of Luke 7:18Ð35. 2011. 246p. pap. 27.00 (978-1-60899-459-5(7), Pickwick Pubns.) Wipf & Stock Pubs.

Mason, James. My Father's Words in Servitude. 2008. 114p. pap. 49.95 (978-0-557-01169-8(8)) Lulu Enterprises Inc.

Mathews, Shailer. The Student's Gospels: A Harmony of the Synoptics, the Gospel of John. Mathews, Shailer & Goodspeed, Edgar J., eds. Soares, Theodore G., tr. 2011. 264p. 47.95 (978-1-258-06119-7(8)) Literary Licensing, LLC.

Mathson, Patricia L. Plant the Seed: Sharing the Gospels with Children. 2011. (978-0-7648-2009-0(5)) Liguori Pubns.

Maurice, Frederick Denison. The Gospel of the Kingdom of Heaven: A Course of Lectures on the Gospel of St. Luke. 2007. (ENG.). 416p. 49.95 (978-0-548-33893-3(0)); per. 34.95 (978-1-4326-9819-5(2)) Kessinger Publishing, LLC.

Mauser, Ulrich W. Christ in the Wilderness. 2009. (Studies in Biblical Theology, First Ser.). 160p. pap. 18.00 (978-1-60899-021-4(4), Wipf and Stock) Wipf & Stock Pubs.

Maxwell, Kathy. Hearing Between the Lines: The Audience as Fellow-Worker in Luke-Acts & its Literary Milieu, Vol.. 425. 2010. (Library of New Testament Studies, the Ser.). (ENG., Illus.). 224p. 120.00 (978-0-567-59291-0(X), T&T Clark Int'l) Continuum International Publishing Group, Ltd. GBR. Dist: National Bk. Network.

May, David M. & Graves, Mike. Preaching Matthew: Interpretation & Proclamation. 2007. 152p. per. (978-0-8272-3005-7(2)) Chalice Pr.

Mbonu, Caroline N. Handmaid. 2010. 156p. pap. 18.00 (978-1-60899-761-9(8), Wipf and Stock) Wipf & Stock Pubs.

Mburu, Elizabeth W. Qumran & the Origins of Johannine Language & Symbolism. 2010. (Jewish & Christian Text Ser.). (ENG.). 240p. 130.00 (978-0-567-52371-6(3), T&T Clark Int'l) Continuum International Publishing Group, Ltd. GBR. Dist: National Bk. Network.

McClain, Elder Henry. The Complete Works of the Apostle John. 2007. 624p. 33.99 (978-1-4257-8605-2(7)) Xlibris Corp.

Mcdonnell, Rea & McDonnell, Rea. Into Heart of Mary. 2009. 160p. pap. 12.95 (978-1-59471-207-4(7)) Ave Maria Pr.

McIver, Robert K. Memory, Jesus, & the Synoptic Gospels. 2011. (978-1-58983-561-0(1)); pap. (978-1-58983-560-3(3)) Society of Biblical Literature.

McKenzie, John L. Light on the Gospels: A Reader's Guide. 2009. (John L. Mckenzie Reprints Ser.). 220p. pap. 24.00 (978-1-60608-147-1(0)) Wipf & Stock Pubs.

McKnight, Scot. The Real Mary: Why Evangelical Christians Can Embrace the Mother of Jesus. 2006. 176p. 19.95 (978-1-55725-523-5(7)) Paraclete Pr., Inc.

Mcquade, Pamela. Knowing Jesus. 2006. pap. 4.97 (978-1-59789-526-2(1)) Barbour Publishing, Inc.

McWhirter, Jocelyn. The Bridegroom Messiah & the People of God: Marriage in the Fourth Gospel. 2008. (Society for New Testament Studies Monograph Ser.). (ENG.). 192p. pap. 33.00 (978-0-521-09022-3(9)) Cambridge Univ. Pr.

Mead, G. R. S. Pistis Sophi: The Gnostic text of Jesus, Mary, Mary Magdalene, Jesus, & His Disciples. 2009. 224p. pap. 9.99 (978-1-60459-717-2(8)) Wilder Pubns., Ltd.

Meek, James A. Gentile Mission in Old Testament Citations in Acts: Text, Hermeneutic, & Purpose. 2009. (Library of New Testament Studies, the Ser.). (ENG.). 192p. 130.00 (978-0-567-03380-2(5), T&T Clark Int'l) Continuum International Publishing Group, Ltd. GBR. Dist: National Bk. Network.

Members of the Faculty of Theology of the University. Navarre Bible: St. Luke. (Navarre Bible Ser.). (ENG & LAT., Illus.). 285p. pap. 14.95 (978-1-85182-040-5(X)) Four Courts Pr. IRL. Dist: International Specialized Bk. Services.

Metzger, James A. Consumption & Wealth in Luke's Travel Narrative. 2007. (Biblical Interpretation Ser.). 218p. (978-90-04-16261-7(5)) BRILL.

Meynet, Roland. A New Introduction to the Synoptic Gospels. 2010. (ENG.). 440p. (C). lib. bdg. 43.99 (978-1-934996-11-9(4)) Convivium Pr., Inc.

Mihalios, Stefanos. The Danielic Eschatological Hour in the Johannine Literature. 2011. (Library of New Testament Studies). (ENG.). 224p. 120.00 (978-0-567-36720-4(7), T&T Clark Int'l) Continuum International Publishing Group, Ltd. GBR. Dist: National Bk. Network.

Miller, J. R. Devotional Hours with the Bible Volume V, from the Gospels, on the Life of Christ. 2011. 138p. pap. 14.99 (978-1-61203-203-0(6)) Bottom of the Hill Publishing.

—Devotional Hours with the Bible Volume VI, from the Gospel of Matthew. 2011. 142p. pap. 14.99 (978-1-61203-204-7(4)) Bottom of the Hill Publishing.

Miller, John B. F. Convinced that God had Called Us: Dreams, Visions & the Perception of God's Will in Luke-Acts. 2006. (Biblical Interpretation Ser.: Vol. 85). 288p. (978-90-04-15474-2(4)) BRILL.

Milton, Michael A. Oh, the Deep, Deep Love of Jesus: Expository Messages from John 17. 2007. 106p. pap. 15.00 (978-1-59752-218-2(X), Wipf and Stock) Wipf & Stock Pubs.

Miranda, Jose Porfirio & Eagleson, John. Being & the Messiah: The Message of St. John. 2006. 256p. pap. 26.00 (978-1-59752-816-0(1), Wipf and Stock) Wipf & Stock Pubs.

Mittelstadt, Martin. Reading Luke-Acts in the Pentecostal Tradition: Reflections on the History & Status of Research. 2010. (ENG.). 232p. (C). pap. 14.95 (978-0-9819651-7-8(2)) CPT Pr.

Mligo, Elia Shabani. Jesus & the Stigmatized: Reading the Gospel of John in a Context of HIV/AIDSÐRelated Stigmatization in Tanzania. 2011. 474p. pap. 52.00 (978-1-60899-706-0(5), Pickwick Pubns.) Wipf & Stock Pubs.

Moessner, David P., et al, eds. Paul & the Heritage of Israel: Luke's Narrative Claim upon Paul & Israel's Legacy. 2012. (Library of New Testament Studies). (ENG.). 400p. 120.00 (978-0-567-40148-9(0), T&T Clark Int'l) Continuum International Publishing Group, Ltd. GBR. Dist: National Bk. Network.

Moloney, Francis J. Beginning the Good News: A Narrative Approach. 2006. 176p. (Orig.). pap. 21.00 (978-1-59752-985-3(0), Wipf and Stock) Wipf & Stock Pubs.

—The Johannine Son of Man. 2nd ed. 2007. 346p. pap. 38.00 (978-1-55635-583-7(1)) Wipf & Stock Pubs.

Montefiore, Hugh & Turner, H. E. W. Thomas & the Evangelists. 2009. (Studies in Biblical Theology, First Ser.). 128p. pap. 16.00 (978-1-60899-022-1(2), Wipf and Stock) Wipf & Stock Pubs.

Moore, Stephen. Empire & Apocalypse Postcolonialism an. 2006. 172p. (978-1-905048-85-4(8)); (ENG.). per. (978-1-905048-86-1(6)) Sheffield Phoenix Pr.

Morgan, Elisa. She Did What She Could (SDWSC) Five Words of Jesus That Will Change Your Life. 2009. (ENG.). 144p. 9.99 (978-1-4143-3378-6(1)) Tyndale Hse. Pubs.

Morgan, G. Campbell. The Gospel According to Mark. 2010. (G. Campbell Morgan Reprint Ser.). 350p. pap. 39.00 (978-1-60899-300-0(0), Wipf and Stock) Wipf & Stock Pubs.

Morgan-Wynne, John Eifion. The Cross in the Johannine Writings. 2011. 318p. pap. 35.00 (978-1-61097-251-2(1), Pickwick Pubns.) Wipf & Stock Pubs.

Morlan, David S. Conversion in Luke & Paul: an Exegetical & Theological Exploration. 2012. (Library of New Testament Studies). (ENG.). 224p. 120.00 (978-0-567-20913-9(X), T&T Clark Int'l) Continuum International Publishing Group, Ltd. GBR. Dist: National Bk. Network.

Morrill, Bruce & Parker, David C., eds. 2. the Full Collation of Chapter 18:2. 1 List of the Manuscripts & Comparative Description. 2. 2. Collation Results & Main List Vol. 5. 2013. (Arbeiten zur neutestamentlichen Textforschung Ser.). (ENG & GER., Illus.). 1400p. 487.00 (978-3-11-018675-8(6)) De Gruyter, Walter Inc.

Moss, Charlene McAfee. The Zechariah Tradition & the Gospel of Matthew. 2008. (Beihefte Zur Zeitschrift Für Die Neutestamentliche Wissenschaft und Die Kunde der älteren Kirche Ser.). (ENG.). X, 271p. 133.00 (978-3-11-019695-5(6)) De Gruyter, Walter Inc.

Mosse, Martin. The Three Gospels: New Testament History Introduced by the Synoptic Problem. 2007 (Paternoster Biblical Monographs). (Illus.). 414p. pap. 50.00 (978-1-55635-660-5(9)) Wipf & Stock Pubs.

Mulloorparambil, Sebastian. Messianic Rejection & Matthean Redaction: A Study of the Temple Cleansing in Mt. 21:12-17. 2007. xvi, 371p. pap. (978-81-89958-01-5(1), Library of Congress — New Delhi Overseas Office) Dharmaram Publications.

Myers, Ched. Binding the Strong Man: A Political Reading of Mark's Story of Jesus. 20th ed. 2008. (Illus.). 560p. pap. 28.00 (978-1-57075-797-6(6)) Orbis Bks.

Nadella, Raj. Dialogue Not Dogma: Many Voice in the Gospel of Luke. 2011. (Library of New Testament Studies). (ENG.). 160p. 110.00 (978-0-567-14543-7(3), T&T Clark Int'l) Continuum International Publishing Group, Ltd. GBR. Dist: National Bk. Network.

Naickanparampil, Michael. The Gospel of Mark: Themes Explored. 2009. xvi, 259p. pap. (978-81-7086-511-7(5), Library of Congress — New Delhi Overseas Office) Asian Trading Corp.

Nappa, Amy. Thirsty: Meeting Jesus at Your Deepest Need. 2008. (Redefining Life Ser.). (ENG.). 224p. pap. 14.99 (978-1-60006-093-9(5)) NavPress Publishing Group.

Need, Stephen W. The Gospels Today: Challenging Readings of John, Mark, Luke & Matthew. 2007. (ENG.). 160p. per. 15.95 (978-1-56101-297-8(1)) Cowley Pubns.

Newton, Isaac. Observations upon the Prophecies of Daniel, & the Apocalypse of St John. 2009. 148p. 29.99 (978-1-59547-550-3(8)) NuVision Pubns., LLC.

Neyrey, Jerome H. The Gospel of John in Cultural & Rhetorical Perspective. 2009. (ENG.). 512p. pap. 37.00 (978-0-8028-4866-6(4)) Eerdmans, William B. Publishing Co.

—An Ideology of Revolt: John's Christology in Social-Science Perspective. 2007. (Illus.). 272p. pap. 30.00 (978-1-55635-269-0(7)) Wipf & Stock Pubs.

—The Passion According to Luke: A Redaction Study of Luke's Soteriology. 2007. (Illus.). 240p. pap. 26.00 (978-1-55635-207-2(7)) Wipf & Stock Pubs.

Nicholls, Rachel. Walking on the Water: Reading Mt. 14:22-33 in the Light of its Wirkungsgeschichte. 2007. (Biblical Interpretation Ser.). (Illus.). 220p. (978-90-04-16374-4(3)) BRILL.

Nichols, Ichabod. Hours with the Evangelists by I Nichols. 2006. 420p. per. 26.99 (978-1-4255-4587-1(4)) MPublishing.

Nielsen, Jesper Tang. Die Kognitive Dimension of Kreuzes. 2009. (Wissenschaftliche Untersuchungen zum Nuen Testament Ser.). (Illus.). 335p. pap. 118.00 (978-3-16-150017-6(2)) Mohr Siebeck GmbH & Co. KG DEU. Dist: Eisenbrauns, Inc.

Nissen, Johannes. New Testament & Mission: Historical & Hermeneutical Perspectives. 4th ed. 196p. pap. 36.95 (978-3-631-56097-6(4)) Lang, Peter Publishing, Inc.

Obielosi, Dominic Chukwunonso. Servant of God in John. 2008. (Europäische Hochschulschriften. Reihe 23: Theologie Ser.). 330p. pap. 81.95 (978-3-631-58068-4(1)) Lang, Peter GmbH, Europäischer Verlag der Wissenschaften DEU. Dist: Lang, Peter.

O'Leary, Matthew's Judaization of Mark: Examined in the Context of the Use of Sources in Graeco-Roman Antiquity. 2006. (Library of New Testament Studies: Vol. 323). (ENG., Illus.). 240p. 130.00 (978-0-567-03104-4(7), T&T Clark Int'l) Continuum International Publishing Group, Ltd. GBR. Dist: National Bk. Network.

Ovenda, Job. The Word of God: What it Really Meant. 2009. 610p. pap. 19.95 (978-1-4327-1186-3(5)) Outskirts Pr., Inc.

Owens, W. R., ed. The Gospels: Authorized King James Version. 2011. (Oxford World's Classics Ser.). (ENG., Illus.). 352p. pap. 12.95 (978-0-19-954117-1(5)) Oxford Univ. Pr., Inc.

Oyen, Geert van, et al. The Trial & Death of Jesus: Essays on the Passion Narrative in Mark. 2006. (Contributions to Biblical Exegesis & Theology Ser.). (ENG.). 268p. (C). pap. 58.00 (978-90-429-1834-4(9)) Peeters Pubs. & Booksellers BEL. Dist: Brown, David Bk. Co., The.

Page, Christopher. Mark's Gospel: Awakening the Voice Within. 180p. 15.95 (978-1-55126-450-9(1)) Forward Movement Pubns.

Palu, Ma'afu. Jesus & Time: An Interpretation of Mark 1. 15. 2012. (Library of New Testament Studies). (ENG.). 320p. 120.00 (978-0-567-42410-5(3), T&T Clark Int'l) Continuum International Publishing Group, Ltd. GBR. Dist: National Bk. Network.

Pappas Thm, C. H. In Defense of the Authenticity of 1 John: 7. 2011. 148p. pap. 13.95 (978-1-61507-766-3(9)) Cross Bks. Publishing.

Parfitt, John. Gossiping the Gospel: Exploring the Gospel Readings. 2007. 192p. per. (978-1-84401-968-7(3)) Athena Pr.

Park. Mark's Memory Resources & the Controversy Stories (Mark 2:1-3:6) An Application of the Frame Theory of Cognitive Science to the Markan Oral-Aural Narrative. 2009. (Linguistic Biblical Studies). (978-90-04-17962-2(3)) BRILL.

Park, Hyung Dae & Park. Finding Herem? A Study of Luke-Acts in the Light of Herem. 2007. (Library of New Testament Studies). (HEB & ENG.). 240p. 130.00 (978-0-567-04550-8(1), T&T Clark Int'l) Continuum International Publishing Group, Ltd. GBR. Dist: National Bk. Network.

Park, Sejin. Pentecost & Sinai: The Festival of Weeks as a Celebration of the Sinai Event. 2008. (Library of Hebrew Bible/Old Testament Studies, the Ser.). (ENG.). 304p. 130.00 (978-0-567-02727-6(9), T&T Clark Int'l) Continuum International Publishing Group, Ltd. GBR. Dist: National Bk. Network.

Parker, David C. Codex Bezae: An Early Christian Manuscript & its Text. 2008. (LAT, GEC & ENG., Illus.). 376p. pap. 48.00 (978-0-521-07236-6(0)) Cambridge Univ. Pr.

Parker, Neil Ronald. The Marcan Portrayal of the Jewish Unbeliever: A Function of the Marcan References to Jewish Scripture: the Theological Basis of a Literary Construct. 2008. (Studies in Biblical Literature Ser.: Vol. 79). 364p. (C). 82.95 (978-0-8204-7483-0(5)) Lang, Peter Publishing, Inc.

Parsenios, George L. Rhetoric & Drama in the Johannine Lawsuit Motif. 2010. (Illus.). 175p. 157.50 (978-3-16-150262-0(0)) Mohr Siebeck GmbH & Co. KG DEU. Dist: Coronet Bks.

Parsons, Ernest William. A Historical Examination of Some Non-Markan Elements of Luke. 2009. 80p. pap. 7.00 (978-1-60608-754-1(1), Wipf and Stock) Wipf & Stock Pubs.

Parsons, Mikeal C. Body & Character in Luke & Acts: The Subversion of Physiognomy in Early Christianity. 2011. (ENG.). 192p. pap. 29.95 (978-1-60258-380-1(3)) Baylor Univ. Pr.

—Luke: Storyteller, Interpreter, Evangelist. 2007. (Illus.). 230p. per. 19.95 (978-1-56563-483-1(7)) Hendrickson Pubs. Marketing, LLC.

Pasala, Solomon. The "Drama" of the Messiah in Matthew 8 & 9: A Study from a Communicative Perspective. 2008. 365p. pap. (978-3-03911-650-8(9)) Lang, Peter.

Pastorelli, David. Le Paraclet Dans le Corpus Johannique. 2006. (Beihefte Zur Zeitschrift Für Die Neutestamentliche Wissenschaft und Die Kunde der

älteren Kirche Ser.). (FRE.). XII, 343p. 154.00 *(978-3-11-019045-8(1))* De Gruyter, Walter Inc.
Pate, C. Marvin. The Writings of John: A Survey of the Gospel Epistles, & Apocalypse, 1 vol. 2011. (ENG.). 560p. 44.99 *(978-0-310-26737-9(4))* Zondervan.
Patriquin, Norm. The Bible's Redemption Pattern & Numeric Map. 2009. 312p. pap. 18.99 *(978-1-60791-448-8(4))* Xulon Pr., Inc.
Patton, Carl S. Sources of the Synoptic Gospels. 2007. (ENG.). 288p. 43.95 *(978-0-548-11599-2(0))* Kessinger Publishing, LLC.
Pazdan, Mary Margaret. Becoming God's Beloved in the Company of Friends: A Spirituality of the Fourth Gospel. 2007. 134p. pap. 17.00 *(978-1-55635-462-5(2),* Cascade Bks.) Wipf & Stock Pubs.
Penley, Paul T. Common Tradition Behind Synoptic Sayings of Judgment & John's Apocalypse: An Oral Interpretive Tradition of OT Prophetic Material. 2010. (Library of New Testament Studies, the Ser.). (ENG.). 208p. 120.00 *(978-0-567-62765-0(9),* T&T Clark Int'l) Continuum International Publishing Group, Ltd. GBR. Dist: National Bk. Network.
Pennington, Jonathan T. Heaven & Earth in the Gospel of Matthew. 2007. (Novum Testamentum Supplements Ser.). (Illus.). 416p. *(978-90-04-16205-1(4))* BRILL.
—Heaven & Earth in the Gospel of Matthew. 2009. 416p. (C). pap. 43.00 *(978-0-8010-3728-3(X))* Baker Academic.
Perkins, Pheme. Introduction to the Synoptic Gospels. 2009. (ENG.). 336p. pap. 23.00 *(978-0-8028-6553-3(4))* 2007. 312p. 28.00 *(978-0-8028-1770-9(X))* Eerdmans, William B. Publishing Co.
Perrianne, Brownback. Engaging the Culture: A Book for Leaders & Reformers Who are Committed to the Gospel ... 2006. per. *(978-1-59872-683-1(8))* Instant Pub.
Peterson, Eugne H. Tell It Slant: A Conversation on the Language of Jesus in His Stories & Prayers. 2008. 264p. 24.00 *(978-0-8028-2954-2(6))* Eerdmans, William B. Publishing Co.
Pettingill, W. L. Estudios Sencillos sobre Mateo: Simple Studies on Matthew. (SPA.). *(978-84-7645-107-6(5),* 223161) Clie, Editorial.
Phelan, Geoffrey L. Crucifixion & the Death Cry of Jesus Christ. 2009. 188p. pap. 14.99 *(978-1-60791-768-7(8))* Xulon Pr., Inc.
Phillips, Richard D. Jesus the Evangelist: Learning to Share the Gospel from the Book of John. 2007. 195p. *(978-1-56769-088-0(2))* Reformation Pubs.
Pilgrim, Walter. Good News to the Poor: Wealth & Poverty in Luke - Acts. 2011. 198p. pap. 23.00 *(978-1-61097-663-3(0),* Wipf and Stock) Wipf & Stock Pubs.
Piper, John. What Jesus Demands from the World. 2006. 400p. 21.99 *(978-1-58134-845-3(2))* Crossway.
—What Jesus Demands from the World. 2011. 400p. pap. 17.99 *(978-1-4335-2057-0(5))* Crossway.
Pizzalato, Brian. An Unforgivable Sin? 2009. 56p. pap. *(978-3-639-17699-5(5))* VDM Verlag Dr. Mueller e.K.
Plese, Zlatko. Poetics of the Gnostic Universe: Narrative & Cosmology in the Apocryphon of John. 2006. (Nag Hammadi & Manichaean Studies: Vol. 52). 329p. *(978-90-04-11674-0(5))* BRILL.
Plisch, Uwe-Karsten. The Gospel of Thomas: Original Text with Commentary. Robinson, Gesine Schenke, tr. 2010. (Illus.). 281p. 69.99 *(978-3-438-05133-2(8))* American Bible Society.
Powell, Mark Allan, ed. Methods for Matthew. 2009. (Methods in Biblical Interpretation Ser.). (ENG.). 278p. (C). 90.00 *(978-0-521-88808-0(5));* (Illus.). pap. 27.99 *(978-0-521-71614-7(4))* Cambridge Univ. Pr.
Pramann, Susanne. Point of View im Markusevangelium: Eine Tiefenbohrung. 2008. (Europäische Hochschulschriften. Reihe 23: Theologie Ser.). 324p. pap. 81.95 *(978-3-631-58299-2(4))* Lang, Peter GmbH, Europaischer Verlag der Wissenschaften DEU. Dist: Lang, Peter.
Pratt, Maureen. Beyond Pain: Job, Jesus & Joy. 2010. pap. 14.95 *(978-1-58595-786-6(0))* Twenty-Third Pubns./Bayard.
Prince, Benny. Why Tithing Is NOT for the Church. 2008. 148p. per. 9.50 *(978-0-9801438-2-9(9))* Avid Readers Publishing Group.
Queen, Chuck. The Good News According to Jesus: A New Kind of Christianity for a New Kind of Christian. 2009. pap. *(978-1-57312-528-4(8))* Smyth & Helwys Publishing, Inc.
Quy, Roger. All about Jesus: The Single Story from Matthew, Mark, Luke, & John. 2007. (ENG.). 254p. pap. 14.99 *(978-1-932805-73-4(7))* Authentic Media.
Ramsay, W. M. Was Christ Born at Bethlehem? A Study on the Credibility of St. Luke. 2009. 288p. pap. 25.00 *(978-1-60608-382-6(1,* Wipf and Stock) Wipf & Stock Pubs.
Rasimus, Tuomas. The Legacy of John: Second-Century Reception of the Fourth Gospel. 2009. xi, 406p. *(978-90-04-17633-1(0))* BRILL.
Redelings, David A. The Epistemological Basis for Belief According to JohnÕs Gospel: Miracles & Message in Their Essentials As Non-Fictional Grounds for Knowledge of God. 2011. 238p. pap. 26.00 ***(978-1-61097-180-5(9),*** Pickwick Pubns.) Wipf & Stock Pubs.
Reid, Barbara E. Los Parabolas: Predicandolas y Vivendolas: El Evangelio Segun San Mateo. Rodriguez-Galarza, Gerardo, tr. from ENG. 2008. (SPA.). 288p. per. 6.24 *(978-0-8146-3054-9(5),* Liturgical Pr. Bks.) Liturgical Pr.
Reiprich, Torsten. Das Mariageheimnis: Maria Von Nazareth und Die Bedeutung Familiärer Beziehungen Im Markusevangelium. 2008. (Forschungen Zur Religion und Literatur des Alten & Neuen Testament Ser.). (GER., Illus.). 336p. (C). 98.00 *(978-3-525-53086-3(2))* Vandenhoeck & Ruprecht GmbH & Co. KG DEU. Dist: ISD.
Rejecting Religion - Embracing Grace. 2010. (ENG.). pap. 12.00 ***(978-1-889973-10-4(6))*** Plain Truth Ministries.
Rhoads, David, et al, eds. Luke-Acts & Empire: Essays in Honor of Robert L. Brawley. 2010. (Princeton Theological Monographs). 186p. pap. 21.00 *(978-1-60899-098-6(2),* Pickwick Pubns.) Wipf & Stock Pubs.
Richards, John. The Spirit of God with All People: Recognizing & Confirming the Non-Orthodox of Jesus. 2009. (ENG., Illus.). 192p. pap. 18.00 *(978-0-981911-0-6(2))* Loyalsock Publishing, LLC.
Richards, Larry & Gibson, Joyce L., eds. The Book of Luke, 0 vols. 2007. (Smart Guide to the Bible Ser.). (Illus.). 352p. per. 14.99 *(978-1-4185-0996-5(5))* Nelson, Thomas Inc.
Richardson, Barrie. Curtain Call. 2011. (Illus.). 263p. 50.00 ***(978-0-945296-68-3(1))*** Hermetic Pr., Inc.
Richey, Lance Byron. Roman Imperial Ideology & the Gospel of John. 2007. (Catholic Biblical Quarterly Ser.). *(978-0-915170-43-2(4))* Catholic Biblical Assn. of America.
Ringe, Matthew S. Jesus' Parable of the Rich Fool: Luke 12:13-34 among Ancient Conversations on Death & Possessions. 2011. 320p. pap. 36.95 ***(978-1-58983-614-3(6)); (978-1-58983-615-0(4))*** Society of Biblical Literature.
Roberts, Mark D. Can We Trust the Gospels? Investigating the Reliability of Matthew, Mark, Luke, & John. 2007. (Illus.). 216p. pap. 12.99 *(978-1-58134-866-8(5))* Crossway.
Robinson B.D., J. Armitage. The Gospel According to Peter & the Revelation of Peter. 2007. 104p. per. 10.45 *(978-1-59462-767-5(3),* Book Jungle) Standard Pubns., Inc.
Robinson, James. The Problem of History in Mark: And Other Marcan Studies. 2010. (ENG.). *(978-0-227-17277-3(9))* Clarke, James Co., Ltd.
Robinson, John A. T. The Priority of John. Coakley, J. F., ed. 2011. 460p. pap. 56.00 *(978-1-61097-102-7(7),* Wipf and Stock) Wipf & Stock Pubs.
Robinson, John A. T. & Coakley, J. F. The Priority of John. 2012. 443p. ***(978-0-334-02273-2(8),*** SCM Pr.) Hymns Ancient & Modern Ltd.
Rochester, Stuart. Transformative Discourse in Mark's Gospel: With Special Reference to Mark 5, 1-20. 2011. 344p. pap. *(978-3-0343-0293-7(2))* Hudson Hills Pr. LLC.
Rodriguez, Rafael. Structuring Early Christian Memory: Jesus in Tradition, Performance. 2010. (Library of New Testament Studies, the Ser.). (ENG.). 304p. 140.00 *(978-0-567-26420-6(3),* T&T Clark Int'l) Continuum International Publishing Group, Ltd. GBR. Dist: National Bk. Network.
Rogers, E. Kent. 12 Miracles of Spiritual Growth: A Path of Healing from the Gospels. 2012. (ENG.). 232p. pap. 15.95 ***(978-0-87785-343-5(6))*** Swedenborg Foundation, Inc.
Rolver, Olaf. Christliche Existenz zwischen den Gerichten Gottes: Untersuchungen zur Eschatologie des Matthausevangeliums. 2010. (Bonner Biblische Beitrage Ser.). (GER.). 642p. (C). 102.00 *(978-3-89971-767-9(8))* Vandenhoeck & Ruprecht GmbH & Co. KG DEU. Dist: ISD.
Ross, Hugh McGregor. Thirty Essays on the Gospel of Thomas. 2nd ed. 2008. 204p. per. *(978-1-904808-12-1(3))* Evertype.
Rowe, C. Kavin. Early Narrative Christology: The Lord in the Gospel of Luke 2009. (ENG.). 290p. (C). pap. 40.00 *(978-0-8010-3591-3(0))* Baker Academic.
—Early Narrative Christology: The Lord in the Gospel of Luke. 2006. (Beihefte Zur Zeitschrift Für Die Neutestamentliche Wissenschaft und Die Kunde der älteren Kirche Ser.). (ENG., Illus.). VIII, 276p. 133.00 *(978-3-11-018995-7(X))* De Gruyter, Walter Inc.
—Rethinking the Unity & Reception of Luke & Acts. Gregory, Andrew F., ed. 2010. 232p. 49.95 *(978-1-57003-916-4(X))* Univ. of South Carolina Pr.
Ruprecht, Louis A. This Tragic Gospel: How John Corrupted the Heart of Christianity. 2008. (ENG.). 256p. 24.95 *(978-0-7879-8778-7(6),* Jossey-Bass) Wiley, John & Sons, Inc.
Ryle, J. C. Los Evangelios Explicados - Juan: Gospels Explained - John. (SPA.). 432p. *(978-84-7228-348-0(8),* 220396) Clie, Editorial.
—Los Evangelios Explicados - Lucas: Gospels Explained - Luke. (SPA.). 592p. *(978-84-7228-346-6(1),* 220395) Clie, Editorial.
—Los Evangelios Explicados - Marcos: Gospels Explained - Mark. (SPA.). *(978-84-7228-347-3(X),* 220394) Clie, Editorial.
—Los Evangelios Explicados - Mateo: Gospels Explained - Matthew. (SPA.). 250p. *(978-84-7228-349-7(6),* 220393) Clie, Editorial.
Sabin, Marie Noonan. Reopening the Word: Reading Mark as Theology in the Context of Early Judaism. 2011. (ENG.). 316p. pap. 29.95 ***(978-0-19-989574-8(0))*** Oxford Univ. Pr., Inc.
Sadananda, Daniel Rathnakara. The Johannine Exegesis of God: An Exploration into the Johannine Understanding of God. (Beihefte zur Zeitschrift far die neutestamentliche Wissenschaft und die Kunde der älteren Kirche Ser.). (ENG.). XIV, 356p. 255.00 ***(978-3-11-185286-7(5))*** De Gruyter, Walter Inc.
Salomone, Rev. Gaetano. The Secret Gospel of Mark & the Burial Shroud of Jesus. 2011. 154p. pap. 19.99 ***(978-1-4363-6908-4(8))*** Xlibris Corp.
Samkutty, V J & Samkutty. The Samaritan Mission in Acts, Vol. 328. 2006. (Library of New Testament Studies: Vol. 328). (ENG., Illus.). 272p. 180.00 *(978-0-567-04464-8(5),* T&T Clark Int'l) Continuum International Publishing Group, Ltd. GBR. Dist: National Bk. Network.
Samuel. Postcolonial Reading of Mark's Story of Jesus. 2007. (Library of New Testament Studies). (ENG.). 206p. 155.00 *(978-0-567-03132-7(2),* T&T Clark Int'l) Continuum International Publishing Group, Ltd. GBR. Dist: National Bk. Network.
Sanday, W. Gospels in the Second Century. 2006. pap. *(978-1-4068-0013-5(9))* Echo Library.
Sanders, E. P. The Tendencies of the Synoptic Tradition. 2006. (ENG.). 344p. pap. 69.00 *(978-0-521-03131-8(1))* Cambridge Univ. Pr.
Sandt, Hubertus Waltherus Maria van de. Matthew, James, & Didache: Three Related Documents in Their Jewish & Christian Setting. Zangenberg, Jurgen, ed. 2008. 488p. *(978-90-04-15748-4(4))* BRILL.
Santamaria, Gloria. Evangelio Poetico: The Gospel on Poetry. (SPA.). 128p. *(978-84-7228-126-4(4),* 220387) Clie, Editorial.
Sayles, Guy. Matthew: Living as Disciples of Jesus. 2006. (Annual Bible Study Ser.). (Illus.). 160p. per. *(978-1-57312-474-4(5))* Smyth & Helwys Publishing, Inc.
Schaberg, Jane. Illegitimacy of Jesus A Feminist Theolog. 20th ed. 2006. 332p. *(978-1-905048-83-0(1));* per. *(978-1-905048-84-7(X))* Sheffield Phoenix Pr.
Schleritt, Frank. Der Vorjohanneische Passionsbericht: Eine Historisch-Kritische und Theologische Untersuchung Zu Joh 2,13-11: 11,47-14,31 und 18,1-20,29. 2007. (Beihefte Zur Zeitschrift Für Die Neutestamentliche Wissenschaft und Die Kunde der älteren Kirche Ser.). (GER.). XIX, 650p. 210.00 *(978-3-11-019698-6(0))* De Gruyter, Walter Inc.
Schmidt, Frederick W. Jr. & Schmidt, Frederick W. Conversations with Scripture: The Gospel of Luke. 2009. (Anglican Association of Biblical Scholars Ser.). 144p. pap. 18.00 *(978-0-8192-2361-6(1),* Morehouse Publishing) Church Publishing, Inc.
Schmidt, Karl Matthias. Wege des Heils: Erzahlstrukturen und Rezeptionskontexte des Markusevangeliums. 2010. (Novum Testamentum et Orbis Antiquus/Studien zur Umwelt des Neuen Testaments (NTOA/StUNT) Ser.). (GER., Illus.). 609p. (C). 123.00 *(978-3-525-53395-6(0))* Vandenhoeck & Ruprecht GmbH & Co. KG DEU. Dist: ISD.
Schmiedel, Paul W. The Johannine Writings. Canney, Maurice A., tr. 2007. (ENG.). 304p. 43.95 *(978-0-548-08339-0(8))* Kessinger Publishing, LLC.
Schonborn, Christoph Cardinal. Behold, God's Son! Encountering Christ in the Gospel of Mark. Taylor, Henry, tr. from GER. 2007. 238p. pap. 16.95 *(978-1-58617-177-3(1))* Ignatius Pr.
Schreiber, Stefan. Weihnachtspolitik: Lukas 1-2 und das Goldene Zeitalter. 2009. (Novum Testamentum et Orbis Antiquus/Studien zur Umwelt des Neuen Testaments (NTOA/StUNT) Ser.). (GER., Illus.). 174p. (C). 68.00 *(978-3-525-53392-5(6))* Vandenhoeck & Ruprecht GmbH & Co. KG DEU. Dist: ISD.
Schubert, Judith. The Gospel of John: Question by Question. 2008. (Question by Question Ser.). 256p. pap. 19.95 *(978-0-8091-4549-2(9))* Paulist Pr.
Schuler, Mark & Middendorf, Michael P. Called by the Gospel: An Introduction to the New Testament. 2007. (Called by the Gospel Ser.). (Illus.). 410p. pap. 45.00 *(978-1-55635-526-4(2))* Wipf & Stock Pubs.
Scranton, J. Philip. Journey to & Through the Second Death. 2008. 176p. per. 13.99 *(978-1-60477-324-8(3))* Xulon Pr., Inc.
Sears, Edmund Hamilton. The Fourth Gospel, the Heart of Christ by Edmund H Sears. 2006. 564p. per. 32.99 *(978-1-4255-6194-9(2))* MPublishing.
Seay, Chris. The Voice Revealed: The True Story of the Last Eyewitness, 0 vols. 2007. (Voice Ser.). 96p. pap. 2.99 *(978-0-529-12355-8(X))* Nelson, Thomas Inc.
Seay, Chris, et al. The Voice of Romans: The Gospel According to Paul, 0 vols. 2008. 144p. pap. 9.99 *(978-0-529-12361-9(4))* Nelson, Thomas Inc.
Sellner, Hans Jorg. Das Heil Gottes: Studien Zur Soteriologie des Lukanischen Doppelwerks. 2007. (Beihefte Zur Zeitschrift Für Die Neutestamentliche Wissenschaft und Die Kunde der älteren Kirche Ser.). (GER.). XIII, 591p. 196.00 *(978-3-11-019699-3(9))* De Gruyter, Walter Inc.
Selvaggio, Anthony T. The Seven Signs: Seeing the Glory of Christ in the Gospel of John. 2010. pap. *(978-1-60178-083-6(4))* Reformation Heritage Bks.
Sesboüé, Bernard. Gospel & Tradition. 2011. pap. 25.95 *(978-1-934996-17-1(3))* Convivium Pr., Inc.
Shaw, Frances. Discernment of Revelation in the Gospel of Matthew. 370p. pap. 68.95 *(978-3-03910-564-9(7))* Lang, Peter Publishing, Inc.
Shaw, M. Thomas. Conversations with Scripture & with Each Other: Spiritual Formation for Lay Leaders. 2008. (ENG.). 132p. pap. 16.95 *(978-0-7425-6279-0(4))* Rowman & Littlefield Publishers, Inc.
Shea, John. Following Jesus. 2010. 128p. pap. 15.00 *(978-1-57075-721-1(6))* Orbis Bks.
Shea, Ron. The Gospel (Chinese, Simplified) Housel, Peter et al, trs. from ENG. 2007. (CHI.). *(978-0-9777070-3-4(2))* Clear Gospel Campaign.
Shea, Ronald. The Gospel (Chinese, Traditional) Housel, Peter et al, trs. 2007. (CHI.). *(978-0-9777070-2-7(4))* Clear Gospel Campaign.
—The Gospel (English) 2007. *(978-0-9777070-0-3(8))* Clear Gospel Campaign.
—The Gospel (Japanese) Matsuno, Toshi, tr. 2007. *(978-0-9777070-4-1(0))* Clear Gospel Campaign.
Shelford, Melvia Thomas. The Christ As John Knew Him: Lectures on the Gospel According to John. 2011. 98p. 38.95 ***(978-1-258-04510-4(9))*** Literary Licensing, LLC.
Sherton, Tim. Jesus in Luke's Gospel, Book 1, Vol. 1. 2006. (Daily Readings From... Ser.). (Illus.). 65p. (J). pap. 7.00 *(978-1-84625-014-9(5))* DayOne Pubns. GBR. Dist: STL Distribution North America.
—Jesus in Luke's Gospel, Book 2, Vol. 2. 2006. (Daily Readings From... Ser.). (Illus.). 64p. (J). pap. 7.00 *(978-1-84625-048-4(X))* DayOne Pubns. GBR. Dist: STL Distribution North America.
Sheridan, Ruth. Retelling Scripture: "The Jews" & the Scriptural Citations in John 1:19-12:50. 2012. (ENG., Illus.). 312p. ***(978-90-04-21442-2(9))*** BRILL.
Shiell, William David. Sessions with Matthew. 2008. per. 12.00 *(978-1-57312-501-7(6))* Smyth & Helwys Publishing, Inc.
Shillington, V. George & Shillington. An Introduction to the Study of Luke-Acts. 2007. (T & T Clark Approaches to Biblical Studies). (ENG.). 168p. 39.95 *(978-0-567-03053-5(9),* T&T Clark Int'l) Continuum International Publishing Group, Ltd. GBR. Dist: National Bk. Network.
Shults, Fount. Father's Love Journey. 2007. 364p. per. 19.99 *(978-1-60266-263-6(0))* Xulon Pr., Inc.
Siegert, Folker. Das Johannesevangelium in seiner ursprünglichen Gestalt: Wiederherstellung und Kommentar. Schriften des Institutum Judaicum Delitzschianum, Band 7. 2008. (Schriften des Institutum Judaicum Delitzschianum Ser.). (GER.). 856p. (C). 204.00 *(978-3-525-50147-4(1))* Vandenhoeck & Ruprecht GmbH & Co. KG DEU. Dist: ISD.
Sigal, Phillip. The Halakah of Jesus of Nazareth According to the Gospel of Matthew. 2007. 29.95 *(978-1-58983-282-4(5))* Society of Biblical Literature.
—The Halakhah of Jesus of Nazareth According to the Gospel of Matthew. 2008. (SBL - Studies in Biblical Literature Ser.). 262p. *(978-90-04-15742-2(5))* BRILL.
Sim, David & Repschinski, Boris. Matthew & His Christian Contemporaries. 2008. (Library of New Testament Studies, the Ser.). (ENG.). 222p. 130.00 *(978-0-567-04453-2(X),* T&T Clark Int'l) Continuum International Publishing Group, Ltd. GBR. Dist: National Bk. Network.
Sivertsen, Barbara J. The Three Pillars: How Family Politics Shaped the Earliest Church & the Gospel of Mark. 2010. 156p. pap. 18.00 *(978-1-60899-603-2(4),* Wipf and Stock) Wipf & Stock Pubs.
Skinner, Christopher. John & Thomas-Gospels in Conflict? 2009. 250p. 59.95 *(978-0-7618-4518-6(X))* Univ. Pr. of America, Inc.
Skinner, Christopher W. John & ThomasNtilde;Gospels in Conflict? Johannine Characterization & the Thomas Question. 2009. (Princeton Theological Monographs). 270p. pap. 30.00 *(978-1-60608-614-8(6),* Pickwick Pubns.) Wipf & Stock Pubs.
Skinner, Matthew L. The Trial Narratives: Conflict, Power, & Identity in the New Testament. 2010. (ENG.). 224p. pap. 35.00 *(978-0-664-23032-6(6))* Westminster John Knox Pr.
Smith, Abner. The Combined Gospel of Jesus Christ. 2009. 332p. pap. 22.50 *(978-1-4251-5016-7(0))* Trafford Publishing.
Smith, D. Moody. The Fourth Gospel in Four Dimensions: Judaism & Jesus, the Gospels & Scripture. 2008. 288p. pap. 29.95 *(978-1-57003-763-4(9))* Univ. of South Carolina Pr.
Smith, Daniel A. & Smith. The Post-Mortem Vindication of Jesus in the Sayings Gospel Q, Vol. 328. 2007. (Library of New Testament Studies). (ENG.). 224p. 145.00 *(978-0-567-04474-7(2),* T&T Clark Int'l) Continuum International Publishing Group, Ltd. GBR. Dist: National Bk. Network.
Smith, David Oliver. Matthew, Mark, Luke, & Paul: The Influence of the Epistles on the Synoptic Gospels. 2011. 346p. pap. 38.00 ***(978-1-61097-319-9(4),*** Resource Pubns.) Wipf & Stock Pubs.
Smith, William Benjamin. The Birth of the Gospel: A Study of the Origin & Purport of the Primitive Allegory of the Jesus. Gulick, Addison, ed. 2011. 256p. 47.95 ***(978-1-258-07524-8(5))*** Literary Licensing, LLC.
Soc Hoo, Gilbert. The Pedagogy of the Johannine Jesus. 2009. 304p. pap. *(978-3-639-17456-4(9))* VDM Verlag Dr. Mueller e.K.
Soskice, Janet Martin. The Sisters of Sinai: How Two Lady Adventurers Discovered the Hidden Gospels. 2010. (Vintage Ser.). (ENG., Illus.). 336p. pap. 16.95 *(978-1-4000-3474-1(4),* Vintage) Knopf Doubleday Publishing Group.
Spaulding, Mary B. & Spaulding. Commemorative Identities: Jewish Social Memory & the Johannine Feast of Booths. 2009. (Library of New Testament Studies, the Ser.). (ENG.). 224p. 130.00 *(978-0-567-16061-4(0),* T&T Clark Int'l) Continuum International Publishing Group, Ltd. GBR. Dist: National Bk. Network.
Speer, Roberto E. El Evangelio de Juan - Sugestiones: Introduction to the Gospel of John. (SPA.). *(978-84-7645-151-9(2),* 223197) Clie, Editorial.
Spencer, F. Scott. The Gospel of Luke & Acts of the Apostles. 2008. (Interpreting Biblical Texts Ser.). (Illus.). 260p. per. 25.00 *(978-0-687-00850-6(6))* Abingdon Pr.
Spencer, Patrick E. & Spencer. Rhetorical Texture & Narrative Trajectories of the Lukan Galilean Ministry Speeches: Hermeneutical Appropriation by Authorial Readers of Luke-Acts. 2007. (Library of New Testament Studies). (ENG., Illus.). 264p. 155.00 *(978-0-567-03130-3(6),* T&T Clark Int'l) Continuum International Publishing Group, Ltd. GBR. Dist: National Bk. Network.
Spinella, Frank. The Cloak & the Parchments. 2009. 206p. pap. 23.00 *(978-1-60899-072-6(9))* Wipf & Stock Pubs.
Spong, John Shelby. Jesus for the Non-Religious. 2008. 336p. per. 14.99 *(978-0-06-077841-5(5),* HarperOne) HarperCollins Pubs.
St. Clair, Raquel A. Call & Consequences: A Womanist Reading of Mark. 2008. 224p. (C). pap. 23.00 *(978-0-8006-3902-0(2),* Fortress Pr.) Augsburg Fortress, Pubs.
Stanton, Vincent Henry. The Gospels as Historical Documents, Part I: The Early Use of the Gospels. 2008. 303p. pap. 26.00 *(978-1-60608-275-1(2),* Wipf and Stock) Wipf & Stock Pubs.
—The Gospels as Historical Documents, Part III: The Fourth Gospel. 2008. 303p. pap. 26.00 *(978-1-60608-277-5(9),* Wipf and Stock) Wipf & Stock Pubs.
Sterner, Rob. Kingdom of Power, Power of Kingdom: The Opposing World Views of Mark & Chariton. 2010. 232p. pap. 26.00 *(978-1-60899-008-5(7),* Pickwick Pubns.) Wipf & Stock Pubs.
Steiner, Rudolf. The Gospel of St. Luke. 203p. 22.00 *(978-0-88010-218-6(7))* SteinerBooks, Inc.
—The Gospel of St Mark: A Course of Twelve Lectures, Basel 1912. Collison, H., ed. 2011. 250p. 46.95 ***(978-1-258-00755-3(X))*** Literary Licensing, LLC.
Steiner, Rudolf. The Gospel of St. Matthew. 237p. pap. 12.95 *(978-0-85440-630-2(1))* Steiner, Rudolf Pr. GBR. Dist: Steiner, Rudolf Pr.

Stevens, William & Burton, Ernest. A Harmony of the Gospels. 2007. 296p. per. 14.95 (978-1-933993-49-2(9)) Apocryphile Pr.

Stewart, Eric C. Gathered around Jesus: An Alternative Spatial Practice in the Gospel of Mark. 2008. (Matrix: the Bible in Mediterranean Context Ser.). 252p. pap. 28.00 (978-1-60608-084-9(9), Cascade Bks.) Wipf & Stock Pubs.

—Gathered Around Jesus: An Alternative Spatial Practice in the Gospel of Mark. 2009. (ENG.). 251p. (C). pap. 43.00 (978-0-227-17317-6(1)) Clarke, James Co., Ltd. GBR. Dist: Brown, David Bk. Co., The.

Streeter, Burnett Hillman. The Four Gospels: A Study of Origins, Treating of the Manuscript Tradition, Sources, Authorship, & Dates. 2008. 654p. pap. 56.00 (978-1-55635-797-8(4)) Wipf & Stock Pubs.

Strelan, Rick. Luke the Priest: The authority of the author of the third Gospel. 2008. 204p. 99.95 (978-0-7546-6259-4(4)) Ashgate Publishing Co.

Subash, William J. The Dreams of Matthew 1: 18-2:23: Tradition, Form, & Theological Investigation. 2011. (C). 78.95 **(978-1-4331-1625-4(1))** Lang, Peter Publishing, Inc.

—The Dreams of Matthew 1:18-2:23: Tradition, Form, & Theological Investigation. 2012. xv, 222p. E-Book **(978-1-4539-0260-8(0))** Lang, Peter GmbH, Europaischer Verlag der Wissenschaften.

Subramanian, Dheena. Jesus, the Yogi. 2009. 84p. pap. (978-1-926582-07-8(1)) Insomniac Pr.

Swain, Scott R. & Köstenberger, Andreas J. Father, Son & Spirit: The Trinity & John's Gospel. 2008. (New Studies in Biblical Theology Ser.: Volume 24). (ENG., Illus.). 224p. pap. 22.00 (978-0-8308-2625-4(4), IVP Acad.) InterVarsity Pr.

Swanson, Richard W. Provoking the Gospel of Matthew: A Storyteller's Commentary: Year A. 2007. 447p. (978-0-8298-1691-4(7)) Pilgrim Pr., The/United Church Pr.

Swidler, Leonard J. Jesus Was a Feminist: What the Gospels Reveal about His Revolutionary Perspective. 2007. (ENG.). 352p. per. 19.95 (978-1-58051-218-3(6), Sheed & Ward) Rowman & Littlefield Publishers, Inc.

Talbot, Elizabeth Viera. John: God Became Flesh. 2010. pap. 1.99 (978-0-8163-2403-3(4)) Pacific Pr. Publishing Assn.

Tan, Yak-Whee. Re-Presenting the Johannine Community: A Postcolonial Perspective. 2007. (Studies in Biblical Literature Ser.). 240p. (C). 69.95 (978-0-8204-9733-4(9)) Lang, Peter Publishing, Inc.

Tekula, Charles F. The Gospel of Pure Human Kindness. 2007. 68p. per. 10.00 (978-1-4257-8474-4(7)) Xlibris Corp.

Temple, P. J. The Boyhood Consciousness of Christ. 2009. 256p. pap. 22.00 (978-1-60608-503-5(4), Wipf and Stock) Wipf & Stock Pubs.

Thatcher, Tom. Jesus the Riddler: The Power of Ambiguity in the Gospels. 2006. (ENG., Illus.). 188p. per. 30.00 (978-0-664-22640-4(X)) Westminster John Knox Pr.

Thatcher, Tom, ed. Jesus, the Voice, & the Text: Beyond the Oral & the Written Gospel. 2008. (ENG.). 310p. 39.95 (978-1-932792-60-7(0)) Baylor Univ. Pr.

—What We Have Heard from the Beginning: The Past, Present, & Future of Johannine Studies. 2007. 425p. per. 39.95 (978-1-60258-010-7(3)) Baylor Univ. Pr.

Thatcher, Tom & Moore, Stephen D. Anatomies of Narrative Criticism: The Past, Present, & Futures of the Fourth Gospel As Literature. 2008. pap. 35.95 (978-1-58983-370-8(8)) Society of Biblical Literature.

Thatcher, Tom & Moore, Stephen D., eds. Anatomies of Narrative Criticism: The Past, Present, & Futures of the Fourth Gospel as Literature. 2008. 314p. (978-90-04-16912-8(1)) BRILL.

Theophilos, Michael. The Abomination of Desolation in Matthew 24. 15. 2012. (ENG., Illus.). 296p. 120.00 **(978-0-567-55468-0(6)**, T&T Clark Int'l) Continuum International Publishing Group, Ltd. GBR. Dist: National Bk. Network.

Thomas, et al. The Gnostic Gospels of Thomas, Mary, & John. 2009. 84p. pap. 8.95 (978-1-60459-718-9(6)) Wilder Pubns., Ltd.

Thomas, Bill. The Road to Victory: A Pre-Easter Home Study. 2007. 58p. per. (978-0-7880-2440-5(X)) CSS Publishing Co.

Thompson, Alan. One Lord, One People: The Unity of the Church in Acts in Its Literary Setting. 2008. (Library of New Testament Studies). (ENG.). 240p. 130.00 (978-0-567-04559-1(5), T&T Clark Int'l) Continuum International Publishing Group, Ltd. GBR. Dist: National Bk. Network.

Thurneysen, Eduard. The Sermon on the Mount. Robinson, William Childs, tr. 2010. (ENG.). 84p. pap. 12.00 (978-1-60899-575-2(5)) Wipf & Stock Pubs.

Thurston, Bonnie B. Spiritual Landscape of Mark. 2008. 104p. pap. 12.95 (978-0-8146-1864-6(2)) Liturgical Pr.

Tippett, Alan R. & Redford, Shawn B. The Jesus Documents. 2011. **(978-0-87808-466-1(5))** Carey, William Library Pubs.

Titley, Robert. A Poetic Discontent: Austin Farrer & the Gospel of Mark. 2010. (Library of New Testament Studies, the Ser.). (ENG.). 240p. 130.00 (978-0-567-28321-4(6), T&T Clark Int'l) Continuum International Publishing Group, Ltd. GBR. Dist: National Bk. Network.

Tolbert, Malcolm. The Disturbing Galilean: Essays about Jesus. 2009. pap. (978-1-57312-530-7(X)) Smyth & Helwys Publishing, Inc.

Tovey, Derek. Jesus, Story of God: John's Story of Jesus. 2007. 191p. per. 8.00 (978-1-920691-73-8(1)) ATF Pr. AUS. Dist: International Publishers Marketing.

Tremmel, Robert. The Four Gospels. 2011. 152p. 29.99 **(978-1-4568-4262-8(5))**; pap. 19.99 **(978-1-4568-4261-1(7))** Xlibris Corp.

Trench, Richard Chenevix. Studies in the Gospels. 2008. 346p. 46.95 (978-1-4366-1213-5(6)); (ENG.). 348p. per. 31.95 (978-0-548-82526-6(2)) Kessinger Publishing, LLC.

—Studies in the Gospels by Richard Chenevix Trench. 2006. 616p. per. 34.99 (978-1-4255-6547-3(6)) MPublishing.

Trost, Travis Darren. Who Should Be King in Israel? A Study on Roman Imperial Politics, the Dead Sea Scrolls, & the Fourth Gospel. 2011. xii, 242p. (978-1-4331-1151-8(9)) Lang, Peter GmbH, Europaischer Verlag der Wissenschaften.

Troxler, J. Allen. Doing Justice to the Unjust Steward: An Exegetical Examination of Luke 16:1-13 & Its Context. 2007. (978-0-8204-8623-9(X)) Lang, Peter Publishing, Inc.

Tsutserov, Alexander. Glory, Grace, & Truth: Ratification of the Sinaitic Covenant according to the Gospel of John. 2009. 288p. pap. 32.00 (978-1-55635-976-7(4), Pickwick Pubns.) Wipf & Stock Pubs.

Tuckett, Christopher, ed. The Gospel of Mary. 2007. (Oxford Early Christian Texts). (MUL & ENG., Illus.). 256p. 150.00 (978-0-19-921213-2(9)) Oxford Univ. Pr., Inc.

Tukasi, Emmanuel O. Determinism & Petitionary Prayer in John & the Dead Sea Scrolls: An Ideological Reading of John & the Rule of the Community (1QS) Smedes, Taede, ed. 2008. (Library of Second Temple Studies, the Ser.). (ENG.). 192p. 130.00 (978-0-567-03346-8(5), T&T Clark Int'l) Continuum International Publishing Group, Ltd. GBR. Dist: National Bk. Network.

Twelftree. People of the Spirit. 2009. xvii, 269p. pap. (978-0-281-05536-4(X)) Baker Academic.

Twelftree, Graham H. People of the Spirit: Exploring Luke's View of the Church, 1 vol. 2009. 304p. (C). pap. 25.00 (978-0-8010-3880-8(4)) Baker Academic.

Tyndale House Publishers Staff. NTV: Evangelio De Juan [Gospel of John], Demoss Ed., Sc. 2009. 96p. pap. 0.99 (978-1-4143-3163-8(0), Tyndale Espanol) Tyndale Hse. Pubs.

Tyson, Janet. Jesus, Mary, & Child: Samaritan Blood & the Kingdom at Shiloh. 2006. (Illus.). 428p. per. 22.95 (978-0-9735341-9-1(2)) EcceNova Editions CAN. Dist: Ingram Pub. Services.

Tyson, Joseph B. The Death of Jesus in Luke-Acts. 2010. pap. 24.95 (978-1-57003-962-1(3)) Univ. of South Carolina Pr.

—Images of Judaism in Luke-Acts. 2010. pap. 24.94 (978-1-57003-963-8(1)) Univ. of South Carolina Pr.

—Luke, Judaism, & the Scholars: Critical Approaches to Luke-Acts. 2010. pap. 24.94 (978-1-57003-964-5(X)) Univ. of South Carolina Pr.

—Marcion & Luke-Acts: A Defining Struggle. annot. ed. 2006. 192p. 39.95 (978-1-57003-650-7(0)) Univ. of South Carolina Pr.

Udny, E. Francis. The Animal's Place in Evolution & Our Duty Towards Them - 2006. pap. 12.95 (978-1-4304-3046-9(X)) Kessinger Publishing, LLC.

Upchurch, Cackie. Year of Sundays 2010. 2009. 88p. pap. 3.00 (978-0-8146-3626-8(8), Liturgical Pr. Bks.) Liturgical Pr.

Upchurch, Cackie & Yeary, Clifford, eds. Year of Sundays. 2011. 80p. pap. 2.00 **(978-0-8146-3644-2(6))** Liturgical Pr.

Urion, M.D., David. Compassion as a Subversive Activity: Illness, Community, & the Gospel of Mark. 2006. (ENG.). 144p. per. 14.95 (978-1-56101-279-4(3)) Cowley Pubns.

Valantasis, Richard, et al. The Gospels & Christian Life in History & Practice. 2009. (ENG.). 288p. 99.00 (978-0-7425-5921-9(1)); pap. 37.50 (978-0-7425-5922-6(X)) Rowman & Littlefield Publishers, Inc.

Van Belle, G., et al, eds. Miracles & Imagery in Luke & John: Festschrift Ulrich Busse. 2008. (Bibliotheca Ephemeridum Theologicarum Lovaniensium Ser.). (ENG., Illus.). 287p. (C). pap. 114.00 (978-90-429-2115-3(3)) Peeters Pubs. & Booksellers BEL. Dist: Brown, David Bk. Co., The.

van de Sandt, H., et al, eds. Life Beyond Death in Matthew's Gospel: Religious Metaphor or Bodily Reality? 2011. (Biblical Tools & Studies). (ENG., Illus.). 302p. (C). 99.00 **(978-90-429-2518-2(3))** Peeters Pubs. & Booksellers BEL. Dist: Brown, David Bk. Co., The.

Van Der Watt, Jan & Van der Watt. Introduction to the Johannine Gospel & Letters. 2008. (T& T Clark Approaches to Biblical Studies). (ENG.). 162p. 22.95 (978-0-567-03037-5(7), T&T Clark Int'l) Continuum International Publishing Group, Ltd. GBR. Dist: National Bk. Network.

van der Watt, Jan & van der Watt. Introduction to the Johannine Gospel & Letters. 2008. (T& T Clark Approaches to Biblical Studies). (ENG., Illus.). 168p. 110.00 (978-0-567-04584-3(6), T&T Clark Int'l) Continuum International Publishing Group, Ltd. GBR. Dist: National Bk. Network.

Viviano, Benedict. Matthew & His World: The Gospel of the Open Jewish Christians: Studies in Biblical Theology. 2007. (Novum Testamentum et Orbis Antiquus/Studien zur Umwelt des Neuen Testaments (NTOA/StUNT) Ser.). (ENG.). 309p. (C). 75.00 (978-3-525-53964-4(9)) Vandenhoeck & Ruprecht GmbH & Co. KG DEU. Dist: ISD.

Voorwinde, Stephen. Jesus' Emotions in the Gospels. 2011. (Illus.). 272p. (ENG.). 120.00 (978-0-567-62040-8(9)); pap. 34.95 (978-0-557-43061-8(8)) Continuum International Publishing Group, Ltd. GBR. (T&T Clark Int'l). Dist: National Bk. Network.

Wallace, Peter M. Living Loved: Knowing Jesus as the Lover of Your Soul. 2007. 176p. per. 18.00 (978-1-59627-065-7(9), Seabury Bks.) Church Publishing, Inc.

Walters, Patricia. The Assumed Authorial Unity of Luke & Acts: A Reassessment of the Evidence. (Society for New Testament Studies Monograph Ser.). (ENG.). 2011. 256p. pap. 35.99 (978-0-521-18397-0(9)) 2009. (Illus.). 254p. 102.00 (978-0-521-50974-9(2)) Cambridge Univ. Pr.

Waterford, William Bede. The Difference Between Hearing & Reading about Jesus: Aural Versus Literal Meanings of Biblical Texts (Mark 6:30-8:27a) 340p. 119.95 (978-0-7734-5259-6(1)) Mellen, Edwin Pr., The.

Way, Jim. The Question: A Survey of the Questions Asked by the World's Most Influential Leader. 2009. 124p. pap. 15.00 (978-1-60608-229-4(9), Wipf and Stock) Wipf & Stock Pubs.

Weaver, Joanna. Lazarus Awakening: Finding Your Place in the Heart of God. l.t. ed. 2011. 439p. 30.99 **(978-1-4104-4033-4(8))** Thorndike Pr.

Webb, Geoff R. Mark at the Threshold: Applying Bakhtinian Categories to Markan Characterisation. 2008. 276p. (978-90-04-16774-2(9)) BRILL.

Wells, Chris Albert. Jesus: God, Man or Party Label? the Dead Sea Scrolls' Messiah Code. 2010. 314p. 28.50 (978-1-60860-946-8(4), Eloquent Bks.) AEG Literary Publishing Services, Inc.

Wendt, Hans Hinrich. The Gospel According to St. John: An Inquiry into Its Genesis & Historical Value. 2009. 272p. pap. 23.00 (978-1-60608-379-6(1), Wipf and Stock) Wipf & Stock Pubs.

Werner, Ernest. Rod of Jesse: On the Jesus of the Gospels & Doubt of his Existence. Werner, Ernest, ed. 2008. 352p. 19.95 (978-0-9799424-0-2(3)) Dward Lion Pr.

Wheeler, Michael. St John & the Victorians. 2011. (ENG., Illus.). 288p. 90.00 **(978-0-521-50972-5(6))** Cambridge Univ. Pr.

White, Gregory, ed. The Net Bible Synopsis of the Four Gospels. 2009. 312p. pap. 19.95 (978-0-7375-0153-7(7)) Biblical Studies Pr.

White, James Boyd. Connecting to the Gospel: Texts, Sermons, Commentaries. 2010. 226p. pap. 25.00 (978-1-60899-135-8(0), Wipf and Stock) Wipf & Stock Pubs.

White, L. Michael. Scripting Jesus: The Gospels in Rewrite. 2010. 528p. 28.99 (978-0-06-122879-7(6), HarperOne) HarperCollins Pubs.

Why Four Gospels? The Historical Origins of the Gospels. 2nd rev. ed. 2010. 124p. pap. 11.99 (978-1-893729-87-2(7)) Energion Pubns.

Wiarda, Timothy. Interpreting Gospel Narratives: Scenes, People, & Theology, 1 vol. 2010. (ENG.). 256p. pap. 24.99 (978-0-8054-4843-6(8), B&H Academic) B&H Publishing Group.

Wiersbe, Warren W. Be Transformed (John 13-21) Christ's Triumph Means Your Transformation 2009. (Be Series Commentary Ser.). (ENG.). 192p. pap. 12.99 (978-1-4347-6738-7(8)) Cook, David C.

Wilkens, Hermann. Kata Markon. (GER.). 116p. 28.95 (978-3-631-34879-6(7)) Lang, Peter Publishing, Inc.

Wilkens, Lorenz. Figuren der Vermittlung in den Evangelien: Eine religionsphilosophische Studie. 2008. 130p. pap. 39.95 (978-3-631-57097-5(X)) Lang, Peter GmbH, Europaischer Verlag der Wissenschaften DEU. Dist: Lang, Peter.

Willis, Mike. BTB John. 2007. pap. 6.99 (978-1-58427-193-2(0)) Guardian of Truth Foundation.

—BTB Luke. 2007. 6.99 (978-1-58427-208-3(2)) Guardian of Truth Foundation.

Willitts, Joel. Matthew's Messianic Shepherd-King: In Search of 'the Lost Sheep of the House of Israel' 2007. (Beihefte zur Zeitschrift für die neutestamentliche Wissenschaft und die Kunde der Älteren Kirche Ser.). (ENG.). IX, 270p. 140.00 (978-3-11-019343-5(4)); 210.00 **(978-3-11-915999-9(9))** De Gruyter, Walter Inc.

Willitts, Joel & Bird, Michael F., eds. Paul & the Gospels: Christologies, Conflicts, & Convergences. 2011. (Library of New Testament Studies). (ENG.). 288p. 120.00 (978-0-567-61742-2(4), T&T Clark Int'l) Continuum International Publishing Group, Ltd. GBR. Dist: National Bk. Network

Wills, Garry. What Jesus Meant. 2007. (ENG.). 176p. (gr. 12-18). 14.00 (978-0-14-303880-1(X), Penguin (Non-Classics)) Penguin Group (USA) Inc.

—What the Gospels Meant. 2009. (ENG.). 224p. (gr. 12-18). 15.00 (978-0-14-311512-0(X), Penguin (Non-Classics)) Penguin Group (USA) Inc.

Wilson, David. Lessons of Salvation in 1 John. 2007. 142p. per. 6.95 (978-0-9786002-3-5(1)) Wilson, David.

Wilson, J. M., tr. The Acts of the Apostles: Translated from the Codex Bezae with an Introduction on its Lucan Origin & Importance. 2011. 104p. pap. 11.00 (978-1-61097-123-2(X), Wipf and Stock) Wipf & Stock Pubs.

Winn, Adam. Mark & the Elijah-Elisha Narrative: Considering the Pracice of Greco-Roman Imitation in the Search for Markan Source Material. 2010. 148p. pap. 18.00 (978-1-60899-201-0(2), Pickwick Pubns.) Wipf & Stock Pubs.

Wire, Antoinette Clark. The Case for Mark Composed in Performance. 2010. (Biblical Performance Criticism Ser.). 238p. pap. 26.00 (978-1-60899-858-6(4), Cascade Bks.) Wipf & Stock Pubs.

Wise, Isaac Mayer. The Martyrdom of Jesus of Nazareth: A Historic-Critical Treatise on the Last Chapters of the Gospel. 2008. 136p. pap. 26.95 (978-1-4437-4890-2(0)) Research Pr.

Witherington, Ben, III. What Have They Done with Jesus? Beyond Strange Theories & Bad History — Why We Can Trust the Bible. 2006. (Illus.). 352p. 24.95 (978-0-06-112001-5(4), HarperOne) HarperCollins Pubs.

Wong, Solomon Hon-fai. The Temple Incident in Mark 11,15-19: The Disclosure of Jesus & the Marcan Faction. 2009. (New Testament Studies in Contextual Exegesis - Neutestamentliche Studien zur kontextuellen Exegese Ser.). 252p. 69.95 (978-3-631-58957-1(3)) Lang, Peter GmbH, Europaischer Verlag der Wissenschaften DEU. Dist: Lang, Peter.

Wood, Frederick. El Evangelio Segun Pablo: The Gospel According to Paul. (SPA.). (978-84-7645-095-6(8), 223147) Clie, Editorial.

Wright, William M. Rhetoric & Theology: Figural Reading of John 9. 2009. (Beihefte zur Zeitschrift für die neutestamentliche Wissenschaft und die Kunde der älteren Kirche Ser.). (ENG.). XII, 248p. 126.00 (978-3-11-022163-3(2)); 196.00 **(978-3-11-174150-5(8))** De Gruyter, Walter Inc.

Yamazaki-Ransom, Kazuhiko. The Roman Empire in Luke's Narrative. 2010. (Library of New Testament Studies, the Ser.). (ENG., Illus.). 256p. 130.00 (978-0-567-36439-5(9), T&T Clark Int'l) Continuum International Publishing Group, Ltd. GBR. Dist: National Bk. Network.

Yasin, Ibn. The Authenticity of the Gospel of Barnabas. 2011. 130p. 29.99 **(978-1-4568-5453-9(4))**; pap. 19.99 **(978-1-4568-5452-2(6))** Xlibris Corp.

Yee, Gale A. Jewish Feasts & the Gospel of John. 2007. 96p. (Orig.). pap. 13.00 (978-1-55635-645-2(5)) Wipf & Stock Pubs.

Yieh, John Yueh-Han. One Teacher: Jesus' Teaching Role in Matthew's Gospel Report. (Beihefte zur Zeitschrift far die neutestamentliche Wissenschaft und die Kunde der älteren Kirche Ser.). (ENG.). XVII, 395p. 255.00 **(978-3-11-181857-3(8))** De Gruyter, Walter Inc.

Zangenberg, Jurgen & Sandt Hubertus Waltherus Maria van de. Matthew, James, & Didache: Three Related Documents in Their Jewish & Christian Setting. 2008. 54.95 (978-1-58983-358-6(9)) Society of Biblical Literature.

Zegarelli, Gregg Robert. One (Divine Version) The Unified Gospel of Jesus for Christians. ltd. ed. 2006. per. 24.99 (978-0-9789906-0-2(9)) One Unified Gospel Pr.

—One (Universal Version) The Unified Gospel of Jesus for Non-Christians & Christian Empirical Study. 2006. 300p. per. 24.95 (978-0-9789906-1-9(7)) One Unified Gospel Pr.

BIBLE—CRITICISM, INTERPRETATION, ETC.—N. T. HEBREWS

see Bible—Criticism, Interpretation, etc.—N. T. Epistles

BIBLE—CRITICISM, INTERPRETATION, ETC.—N. T. JAMES

see Bible—Criticism, Interpretation, etc.—N. T. Epistles

BIBLE—CRITICISM, INTERPRETATION, ETC.—N. T. JOHN

see Bible—Criticism, Interpretation, etc.—N. T. Gospels

BIBLE—CRITICISM, INTERPRETATION, ETC.—N. T. JUDE

see Bible—Criticism, Interpretation, etc.—N. T. Epistles

BIBLE—CRITICISM, INTERPRETATION, ETC.—N. T. LUKE

see Bible—Criticism, Interpretation, etc.—N. T. Gospels

BIBLE—CRITICISM, INTERPRETATION, ETC.—N. T. MARK

see Bible—Criticism, Interpretation, etc.—N. T. Gospels

BIBLE—CRITICISM, INTERPRETATION, ETC.—N. T. MATTHEW

see Bible—Criticism, Interpretation, etc.—N. T. Gospels

BIBLE—CRITICISM, INTERPRETATION, ETC.—N. T. PETER

see Bible—Criticism, Interpretation, etc.—N. T. Epistles

BIBLE—CRITICISM, INTERPRETATION, ETC.—N. T. PHILEMON

see Bible—Criticism, Interpretation, etc.—N. T. Epistles

BIBLE—CRITICISM, INTERPRETATION, ETC.—N. T.—PHILIPPIANS

Cassidy, Richard J. Four Times Peter: Portrayals of Peter in the Four Gospels & at Philippi. 2007. (Interfaces Ser.). (Illus.). 154p. per. 15.95 (978-0-8146-5178-0(X)) Liturgical Pr.

Fabricatore, Daniel. Form of God, Form of a Servant - An Examination of the Greek Noun Imorphei in Philippians 26-7. 2009. (ENG.). 250p. pap. 35.99 (978-0-7618-4828-8(2)) Univ. Pr. of America, Inc.

Fabricatore, Daniel J. Form of God Form of a Servant: An Examination of the Greek Noun Imorphei in Philippians 26-7. 2010. (ENG.). 250p. 61.99 (978-0-7618-4827-1(4)) Univ. Pr. of America, Inc.

—Form of God, Form of a Servant: An Examination of the Greek Noun [morphe] in Philippians 2:6-7. 2010. (Illus.). xiii, 283p. E-Book (978-0-7618-4829-5(0)) Univ. Pr. of America, Inc.

Gan, Jonathan. The Metaphor of Shepherd in the Hebrew Bible: A Historical-Literary Reading. 2007. (ENG.). 146p. per. 30.50 (978-0-7618-3754-1(X)) Univ. Pr. of America, Inc.

Green, Timothy. Philippians: Lectio Divina for Youth. 2007. (ENG.). 80p. pap. 7.99 (978-0-8341-5021-8(2), 083-415-0212) Beacon Hill Pr. of Kansas City.

Hargreaves, John. Guide to Philippians. 16.00 (978-0-687-85458-5(X)) Abingdon Pr.

Hell, John Paul. Philippians: Let Us Rejoice in Being Conformed to Christ. 2010. (ENG.). 224p. pap. 25.95 (978-1-58983-482-8(8)) Society of Biblical Literature.

Hellerman, Joseph H. Reconstructing Honor in Roman Philippi: Carmen Christi as Cursus Pudorum. 2008. (Society for New Testament Studies Monograph Ser.). (ENG.). 252p. pap. 40.00 (978-0-521-09083-4(0)) Cambridge Univ. Pr.

Holloway, Paul A. Consolation in Philippians: Philosophical Sources & Rhetorical Strategy. 2007. (Society for New Testament Studies Monograph Ser.). (ENG.). 224p. pap. 50.00 (978-0-521-03624-5(0)) Cambridge Univ. Pr.

Houghton, John. Philippians - Cover to Cover Study Guide. 2007. 72p. (978-1-85345-421-9(4)) Crusade for World Revival.

Jervis, L. Ann. At the Heart of the Gospel: Suffering in the Earliest Christian Message. 2007. 149p. per. 14.00 (978-0-8028-3993-0(2)) Eerdmans, William B. Publishing Co.

Keown, Mark J. Congregational Evangelism in Philippians: The Centrality of an Appeal for Gospel Proclamation to the Fabric of Philippians. 2009. (Paternoster Biblical Monographs). 382p. pap. 46.00 (978-1-60608-475-5(5), Wipf and Stock) Wipf & Stock Pubs.

Kimmel, June. A Life Surrendered. 2007. 98p. per. 6.95 (978-1-59166-728-5(3)) BJU Pr.

Ladd, Karol. A Woman's Passionate Pursuit of God: Creating a Positive & Purposeful Life. 2011. 224p. pap. 12.99 (978-0-7369-2964-6(9)) Harvest Hse. Pubs.

Little, Edward S. Joy in Disguise: Meeting Jesus in the Dark Times. 2009. 160p. pap. 18.00 *(978-0-8192-2328-9(X)*, Morehouse Publishing) Church Publishing, Inc.

Lucado, Max. Book of Philippians: Guide to Joy, 0 vols. 2007. (Inspirational Bible Study; Life Lessons with Max Lucado Ser.). 128p. per. 9.99 *(978-1-4185-0971-2(X))* Nelson, Thomas Inc.

MacArthur, John. Philippians: Christ, the Source of Joy & Strength, 0 vols. 2007. (MacArthur Bible Study Guides). 128p. per. 9.99 *(978-1-4185-0960-6(4))* Nelson, Thomas Inc.

Marchal, Joseph. Hierarchy, Unity, & Imitation: A Femin. 2006. viii, 261p. pap. 39.95 *(978-1-58983-243-5(4))* Society of Biblical Literature.

Oakes, Peter. Philippians: From People to Letter. 2007. (Society for New Testament Studies Monograph Ser.). (ENG., Illus.). 248p. (C). pap. 55.00 *(978-0-521-03661-0(5))* Cambridge Univ. Pr.

Owens, Daniel. A Joy That Is Real. 2006. 191p. pap., per. 11.99 *(978-0-7814-4187-2(0)*, 0781441870) Cook, David C.

Park, M. Sydney & Park. Submission Within the Godhead & the Church in the Epistle to the Philippians: An Exegetical & Theological Examination of the Concept of Submission in Philippians 2 & 3. 2007. (Library of New Testament Studies, the Ser.). (ENG.). 224p. 155.00 *(978-0-567-04551-5(X)*, T&T Clark Int'l) Continuum International Publishing Group, Ltd. GBR. Dist: National Bk. Network.

Parker, David. Reading Philippians Now & Then. 2011. 212p. pap. ***(978-3-639-32665-9(2))*** VDM Verlag Dr. Mueller e.K.

Rosell Nebreda, Sergio. Christ Identity: A Social-Scientific Reading of Philippians 2. 5-11. 2011. (Forschungen Zur Religion und Literatur des Alten & Neuen Testament Ser.). (ENG.). 391p. (C). 129.00 *(978-3-525-53254-6(7))* Vandenhoeck & Ruprecht GmbH & Co. KG DEU. Dist: ISD.

Simmons, Carl, ed. Philippians: Sharing the Joy of Jesus. 2006. (Group's BibleSense Ser.). (Illus.). 92p. pap. 9.99 *(978-0-7644-3225-5(7))* Group Publishing, Inc.

BIBLE—CRITICISM, INTERPRETATION, ETC.—N. T. REVELATION

Adams, Angela. The Stars Will Fall from Heaven: Cosmic Catastrophe in the New Testament & Its World. 2007. (Library of New Testament Studies, the Ser.). (ENG.). 320p. 150.00 *(978-0-567-08912-0(6)*, T&T Clark Int'l) Continuum International Publishing Group, Ltd. GBR. Dist: National Bk. Network.

Adams, Patricia. A Charted Journey Through Revelation. 2008. 196p. pap. 19.99 *(978-1-4343-9652-5(5))* AuthorHouse.

Afzal, Cameron. The Mystery of the Book of Revelation: Reenvisioning the End of Time. 2008. 164p. (C). 99.95 *(978-0-7734-5183-4(8))* Mellen, Edwin Pr., The.

Akin, Jack T. The Story of Revelation: A Modern Interpretation of Facts & Mysticism in John's Book. 2011. 108p. 39.95 ***(978-1-258-05544-8(9))*** Literary Licensing, LLC.

Allen, Cady H. The Message of the Book of Revelation. 2007. (ENG.). 180p. 37.95 *(978-0-548-08644-5(3))* Kessinger Publishing, LLC.

Apocalipsis, No. 4. (SPA., Illus.). 0.39 *(978-0-945792-78-9(6)*, 496123) Editorial Unilit.

Aune, David E. Apocalypticism, Prophecy & Magic in Early Christianity: Collected Essays. 2006. (Wissenschaftliche Untersuchungen zum Neuen Testament Ser.: No. 199). 482p. 215.00 *(978-3-16-149020-0(7))* Mohr Siebeck GmbH & Co. KG DEU. Dist: Coronet Bks.

Babb, Eileen. Further Revelations of Silas: A Spirit Guide. 2009. 124p. pap. 14.95 *(978-1-4092-6184-1(0))* Lulu Enterprises Inc.

Baker Publishing Group Staff. Apocalyptic Thought in Early Christianity, 1 vol. Daly, Robert S. J., ed. 2009. (Holy Cross Studies in Patristic Theology & History Ser.). 304p. (C). pap. 33.00 *(978-0-8010-3627-9(5))* Baker Academic.

Bandy, Alan S. The Prophetic Lawsuit in the Book of Revelation. 2010. 356p. *(978-1-906055-97-4(1))* Sheffield Phoenix Pr.

Banger, Dene. The Spirit of Prophecy. 2009. 642p. pap. 23.99 *(978-1-4415-3012-7(6))* Xlibris Corp.

Barchuck, Ivan. Explicacion del Libro de Apocalipsis: The Book of Revelation Explained, 1 vol. 2008. (SPA.). 400p. pap. 10.99 *(978-84-7228-169-1(8)*, 220403) Clie, Editorial ESP. Dist: Zondervan.

Barr, David L. The Reality of Apocalypse: Rhetoric & Politics in the Book of Revelation. 2007. (SBL - Symposium Ser.). 306p. *(978-90-04-15107-9(9))* BRILL.

Barr, David L. Tales of the End: A Narrative Commentary on the Book of Revelation. 2011. xiii, 377p. ***(978-1-59815-033-9(2))*** Polebridge Pr.

Beale, G. K. The Use of Daniel in Jewish Apocalyptic Literature & in the Revelation of St. John. 2010. 364p. pap. 40.00 *(978-1-60899-530-1(5)*, Wipf and Stock) Wipf & Stock Pubs.

Belew, Dell. The Woman, the Red Dragon, & the End of the Age: 2006. pap. 13.99 *(978-1-60034-479-4(8))* Xulon Pr., Inc.

Bennett-Ryan, Monica. Tribulation. 2007. 216p. per. 14.99 *(978-1-60034-959-1(5))* Xulon Pr., Inc.

Bible Study Combo: Alba House Gospels & Who Do You Say That I Am? 472p. 10.00 *(978-0-8189-0681-7(2))* St Pauls/Alba Hse. Pubs.

Blanco, Jack J. Visions & Dreams: Hope for the Future, Courage for Today: A Fresh Look at Daniel & Revelation. 2010. pap. 6.99 *(978-0-8127-0478-5(9))* Autumn Hse. Publishing Co.

Bock, Emil. Apocalypse of Saint John. 3rd rev. ed. 208p. pap. 30.00 *(978-0-86315-539-0(1))* Floris Bks. GBR. Dist: SteinerBooks, Inc.

Bock, Stephen R. Symbols of Revelation. 2008. 273p. per. 15.99 *(978-1-60247-836-7(8))* Tate Publishing & Enterprises, LLC.

Bohr, Stephen. Prophecy's Dr. Jekyll & Mr. Hyde. 2008. 80p. 7.95 *(978-1-933291-28-4(1))* Remnant Pubns.

—Worship at Satan's Throne. 2008. (ENG.). 144p. pap. 11.95 *(978-1-933291-27-7(3))* Remnant Pubns.

Boone, Dan. Answers for Chicken Little: Lessons for Faith Communities. 2007. (In Sight Media Ser.). (ENG.). pap. 24.99 *(978-0-8341-2330-4(4)*, 0834123304) Beacon Hill Pr. of Kansas City.

Boothe, Milton. Views on the Revelation. 2006. 276p. per. 20.95 *(978-1-59886-379-6(7))* Tate Publishing & Enterprises, LLC.

Boteler, Lori. Genesis to Psalms Questions & Answers: Student Edition. 2006. per. 19.95 net. *(978-0-9789555-3-3(6))* LoJo Publishing.

Braaten, Mark. Come, Lord Jesus: A Study of Revelation. 2007. 157p. per. 14.95 *(978-0-8146-3172-0(X))* Liturgical Pr.

Bradam, Michael. The Rapture & the Sixth Seal: A New Interpretation of the Rapture & the Book of Revelation. 2008. 256p. pap. 20.95 *(978-1-4327-3180-9(7))* Outskirts Pr., Inc.

Braddock, Brian. The End Times: Is the rule of man on Earth coming to an End? 2009. 150p. pap. 11.95 *(978-1-4327-4056-6(3))* Outskirts Pr., Inc.

Bradley/Toussaint. God's Roadmap to Peace: A Study of the Book of Revelation. 2011. (ENG.). 298p. pap. 32.95 ***(978-0-7618-5520-0(3))*** Hamilton Bks.

Bridges, B. C. A Window to Secrets & Mysteries in the Bible. 2011. 64p. pap. 9.95 *(978-1-4497-1054-5(9)*, WestBow Pr.) Author Solutions, Inc.

Brittingham, Les. Revelation Unraveled: The Future Is Now. 2007. pap. 17.99 *(978-1-60266-195-0(2))* Xulon Pr., Inc.

Brother John of Taize. I Am the Beginning & the End: Creation Stories & Visions of Fulfillment in the Bible. 2007. 167p. per. *(978-0-8189-1248-1(0))* St Pauls/Alba Hse. Pubs.

Brownfield, D., David E., Th. How It All Ends. 2007. 73p. pap. 14.95 *(978-1-4241-9752-1(X))* PublishAmerica, Inc.

Broyles, Danny. Creation to Revelation: The Continuing Story of Truth. 2009. 384p. pap. 20.99 *(978-1-61579-377-8(1))* Xulon Pr., Inc.

Brubacher, Willis S. To Seal up Vision & Prophecy. 2009. 296p. pap. 15.49 *(978-1-4389-5988-7(5))* AuthorHouse.

Bunch, Taylor G. The Seven Epistles of Christ. 2007. *(978-0-9744082-3-1(9))* Orion Publishing Co.

Burney, Gerry. Revelation, Apostasy, End, Times, & This Generation. 2009. 172p. pap. 14.99 *(978-1-60791-623-9(1))* Xulon Pr., Inc.

Carman, Oneal. The Final Triumph: The Book of Revelation Revealed. Date not set. 235p. (Orig.). (C). pap. 12.95 *(978-0-9649675-0-2(2))* Gospel Gold Pubns.

Charles, R. H. The British Academy Lectures on the Apocalypse: The Schweich Lectures 1919. 2008. 88p. pap. 8.00 *(978-1-60608-242-3(6)*, Wipf and Stock) Wipf & Stock Pubs.

Chick, Jack T. Queen of All. 2007.Tr. of Reina de Todos. (SPA.). 160p. pap. 9.95 *(978-0-7589-0645-8(5))* Chick Pubns., Inc.

Christensen, Reg. Fear Not: Messages of Hope, Healing, & Peace in the Book of Revelation. 2010. xii, 264p. ***(978-1-59811-995-4(8))*** Covenant Communications.

Christensen, Ronald R. The Little Book. 2010. 32p. pap. 6.00 *(978-0-557-66295-1(8))* Lulu Enterprises Inc.

Clouser, G. B. M. The Patmos Vision: A Study of the Apocalypse. 2011. 254p. 47.95 ***(978-1-258-05143-3(5))*** Literary Licensing, LLC.

Cohen, Tim. Messiah, History, & the Tribulation Period Vol. 1: Biblical Interpretation (Hermeneutics) Cohen, Tim, ed. 2006. pap. *(978-0-9662793-2-0(8))* Prophecy House, Inc.

—Messiah, History, & the Tribulation Period Vol. 5: The Real Rapture & Other Prophetic Mysteries: Understanding the Revelation (Apocalypse) Cohen, Tim, ed. 2006. (Illus.). pap. *(978-0-9662793-6-8(0))* Prophecy House, Inc.

—Messiah, History, & the Tribulation Period Vol. 6: Messiah's Preeminence in History & Prophecy: the Heart of Israelology, Eschatology, & God's Holy Days. Cohen, Tim, ed. 2006. pap. *(978-0-9662793-7-5(9))* Prophecy House, Inc.

—Messiah, History, & the Tribulation Period Vol. 7: The Harmony of Weeks: God's Inspired Grand Unified Theology Unveiled. Cohen, Tim, ed. 2006. pap. *(978-0-9662793-8-2(7))* Prophecy House, Inc.

Cox, Clyde C. Prophetical Events & the Great Tribulation: A Study of Prophecy in Revelation. 2011. 126p. 40.95 ***(978-1-258-08749-4(9))*** Literary Licensing, LLC.

Critser, Sherman L. & Miller, David L. Equipping the Church for Difficult Times: A training manual based on the Book of Revelation. 2009. 148p. pap. 14.99 *(978-1-60791-659-8(2))* Xulon Pr., Inc.

Dalrymple, Rob. Revelation & the Two Witnesses: The Implications for Understanding JohnÕs Depiction of the People of God & His Hortatory Intent. 2011. 174p. pap. 20.00 ***(978-1-61097-138-6(8)***, Wipf and Stock) Wipf & Stock Pubs.

Daniel, Thesina Claudia. Revelation has Begun. 2007. 396p. per. 25.95 *(978-0-9678621-6-3(7))* Gardenia Publishing.

Daniels, T. Scott. Seven Deadly Spirits: The Message of Revelation's Letters for Today's Church, 1 vol. 2009. 160p. (C). pap. 20.00 *(978-0-8010-3171-7(0))* Baker Academic.

Darby, J. N. Estudios sobre el Libro de Apocalipsis: Study on the Book of Revelation. (SPA.). *(978-84-399-5725-6(4)*, 220385) Clie, Editorial.

Davis, James L. Unveiling Revelation: The Prophetic Visions of St. John of Patmos. 2009. 228p. pap. 15.99 *(978-1-60791-185-2(X))* Xulon Pr., Inc.

De Waal, Kayle B. A Socio-Rhetorical Interpretation of the Seven Trumpets of Revelation: The Apocalyptic Challenge to Earthly Empire. 2012. ***(978-0-7734-2567-5(5))*** Mellen, Edwin Pr., The.

Delorme, Jean & Donegani, Isabelle. L'Apocalypse de Jean: Révélation Pour le Temps de la Violence et du Désir, 2 vols. 2010. (FRE.). *(978-2-204-09170-1(7))*; *(978-2-204-08894-7(3))*; pap. *(978-2-204-09231-9(2))* Editions du Cerf.

DeSilva, David Arthur. Seeing Things John's Way: The Rhetoric of the Book of Revelation. 2009. (ENG.). 416p. pap. 40.00 *(978-0-664-22449-3(0))* Westminster John Knox Pr.

Diedricks, Louis. The Day of the Lord. 2010. 76p. pap. 13.95 *(978-1-936198-05-4(3))* Hillcrest Publishing Group, Inc.

Dochhorn, Jan. Schriftgelehrte Prophetie: Der eschatologische Teufelsfall in Apc Joh 12 und seine Bedeutung für das Verständnis der Johannesoffenbarung. 2010. (Wissenschaftliche Untersuchungen zum Neuen Testament, No. 268 Ser.). (GER.). 492p. 227.50 *(978-3-16-150608-6(1))* Mohr Siebeck GmbH & Co. KG DEU. Dist: Coronet Bks.

Dow, Lois K. Fuller. Images of Zion: Biblical Antecedents for the New Jerusalem. 2010. 298p. *(978-1-906055-95-0(5))* Sheffield Phoenix Pr.

Drummonds, Audrey T. The Book of Revelation Vol. 2: A Study of Christ in You, the Hope of Glory. 2007. 160p. per. 14.95 *(978-0-595-46825-6(X))* iUniverse, Inc.

Ebner, Martin & Esch-Wermling, Elisabeth, eds. Kaiserkult, Wirtschaft und spectacula: Zum politischen und gesellschaftlichen Umfeld der Offenbarung. 2011. (Novum Testamentum et Orbis Antiquus/Studien zur Umwelt des Neuen Testaments (NTOA/StUNT) Ser.). (GER., Illus.). 200p. (C). 81.00 *(978-3-525-53396-3(9))* Vandenhoeck & Ruprecht GmbH & Co. KG DEU. Dist: ISD.

Farrer, Austin. A Rebirth of Images: The Making of St. John's Apocalypse. 2007. (Illus.). 350p. pap. 35.00 *(978-1-59752-949-5(4)*, Wipf and Stock) Wipf & Stock Pubs.

Finamore, Stephen. God, Order, & Chaos: Rene Girard & the Apocalypse. 2009. (Paternoster Biblical Monographs Ser.). 315p. pap. 37.00 *(978-1-60608-604-9(9)*, Wipf and Stock) Wipf & Stock Pubs.

Flower, Marilyn O. The Woman Clothed by the Sun with the Moon under Her Feet. 2010. 208p. pap. *(978-3-8383-8270-8(6))* Lambert Academic Publishing.

Folkenberg, Robert. Getting Back to the Heart of Adventism. 2009. pap. 13.99 *(978-0-8163-2347-0(X))* Pacific Pr. Publishing Assn.

Fowler, Franklin S. When the Church Rides the Beast: Unfolding a Rome-Centered Mystery! (Revelation Chapters 17, 13 & 18:1-8) 2011. 200p. pap. 15.04 ***(978-1-4269-6925-6(2))*** Trafford Publishing.

—When "The" Church Rides the Beast: Unfolding a Rome-Centered Mystery!: (Revelation Chapters 17, 13 & 18:1-8) 2009. (Illus.). x, 185p. ***(978-0-9789263-1-1(5))*** Christian Heritage Foundation.

Gaebelein, Arno C. El Libro de Apocalipsis: The Revelation of Jesus. (SPA.). 176p. *(978-84-7228-944-4(3)*, 223020) Clie, Editorial.

Geoffrey of Auxerre. Geoffrey of Auxerre: On the Apocalypse, No. 42. Gibbons, Joseph, tr. from LAT. (Cistercian Fathers Ser.). 230p. *(978-0-87907-642-9(9))* Cistercian Pubns., Inc.

Gillispie, Mary Ann. Endtime Reapers. 2008. 456p. pap. 27.99 *(978-1-4251-4072-4(6))* Trafford Publishing.

God's Definition of Revelation: Revelation 10.4, Daniel 12.4. (Illus.). 13p. pap. *(978-0-9714351-0-0(3))* Shaw, John R.

Grace, Bob. Revelation Revealed. 2011. 158p. 29.99 ***(978-1-4568-0338-4(7))***; pap. 19.99 ***(978-1-4568-0337-7(9))*** Xlibris Corp.

Graf, Jutta. Von Schatten und Bildern zur Wahrheit: Die Erschließung der Offenbarung bei John Henry Newman. 2009. (Linzer Philosophisch-Theologische Beiträge Ser.). (GER.). 268p. 72.95 *(978-3-631-58968-7(9))* Lang, Peter GmbH, Europaischer Verlag der Wissenschaften DEU. Dist: Lang, Peter.

Graves, David. The Seven Messages of Revelation & Vassal Treaties. 2009. 137.00 *(978-1-60724-568-1(X))* Gorgias Pr., LLC.

Greszczyszyn, Andrew. The Book of Revelation Code. 2010. 198p. pap. *(978-1-926582-68-9(3))* Insomniac Pr.

Gumerlock, Francis X., intro. & notes. The Seven Seals of the Apocalypse: Medieval Texts in Translation. 2009. pap. 11.00 *(978-1-58044-108-7(4))* Medieval Institute Pubns.

Gunkel, Hermann. Creation & Chaos in the Primeval Era & the Eschaton: Religio-Historical Study of Genesis 1 & Revelation 12. Whitney, K. William, tr. from GER. 2006. (Biblical Resource Ser.). 442p. pen. 36.00 *(978-0-8028-2804-0(3))* Eerdmans, William B. Publishing Co.

Gunnink, Jerrien. Revelation 101: What in the World Is Jesus Doing Now. 2009. 96p. pap. 10.99 *(978-1-61579-611-3(8))* Xulon Pr., Inc.

Guttesen, Poul F. Leaning into the Future. 2009. (Princeton Theological Monographs). 278p. pap. 31.00 *(978-1-55635-513-4(0)*, Pickwick Pubns.) Wipf & Stock Pubs.

Hadjiantoniou, G.A. The Postman of Patmos: Striking Messages on the Seven Letters to the Seven Churches of Revelation. 2011. 148p. 40.95 ***(978-1-258-05295-9(4))*** Literary Licensing, LLC.

Hall, John R. Apocalypse: From Antiquity to the Empire of Modernity. 2009. (ENG.). 296p. 69.95 *(978-0-7456-4508-7(9))*; pap. 24.95 *(978-0-7456-4509-4(7))* Polity Pr. GBR. Dist: Wiley, John & Sons, Inc.

Hand, Brian R. The Worthy Champion: A Christology of the Book of Revelation Based on Elements of Its Literary Composition. 2008. (Illus.). 287p. pap. 22.95 *(978-1-59166-825-1(5))* BJU Pr.

Harrington, Daniel P. Meeting St. John Today: Understanding the Man, His Mission, & His Message. 2011. (ENG.). 144p. pap. 12.95 *(978-0-8294-2917-6(4))* Loyola Pr.

Harrington, Wilfrid J. Revelation. 2008. (Sacra Pagina Ser.). 278p. pap. 24.95 *(978-0-8146-5977-9(2)*, Liturgical Pr. Bks.) Liturgical Pr.

Hassell, Eddie. Someone Should Tell You: Startling Revelations & Truths to Help You Understand & Improve Your Life. 2009. (ENG.). 306p. 33.95 *(978-1-4327-5180-7(8))* Outskirts Pr., Inc.

Hawley, Charles Arthur. The Teaching of Apocrypha & Apocalypse 1925. 2007. (ENG.). 184p. 37.95 *(978-0-548-05638-7(2))* Kessinger Publishing, LLC.

Hayford, Jack W. Revelation, 0 vols. 2008. (Spirit-Filled Life Study Guide Ser.). 128p. pap. 9.99 *(978-1-4185-3330-4(0))* Nelson, Thomas Inc.

Hays, Richard B. & Alkier, Stefan, eds. Revelation & the Politics of Apocalyptic Interpretation. 2012. (ENG.). 230p. 49.95 ***(978-1-60258-561-4(X))*** Baylor Univ. Pr.

Herbers, M. James. This Generation of the Latter Days, Volume I Dispensationalism & God's Original Purpose of Creation. 2011. 264p. pap. 18.00 ***(978-0-557-89677-6(0))*** Lulu Enterprises Inc.

Herms, Ronald. An Apocalypse for the Church & for the World: The Narrative Function of Universal Language in the Book of Revelation. (Beihefte zur Zeitschrift far die neutestamentliche Wissenschaft und die Kunde der älteren Kirche Ser.). (ENG.). XV, 299p. 225.00 ***(978-3-11-181860-3(8))***; 2006. 140.00 *(978-3-11-019312-1(4))* De Gruyter, Walter Inc.

Hern, Robert. Bible Answers: The end of this age & the beginning of the thousand year Reign. 2009. 53p. pap. 10.95 *(978-1-4327-2431-3(2))* Outskirts Pr., Inc.

Herrick, Rick. The Case Against Evangelical Christianity. 2006. 206p. per. 14.95 *(978-0-9791304-2-7(5))* Charles River Pr.

Heukelum, Richard Van. Priority Mail: The Seven Churches of Revelation. 2007. (Illus.). 70p. pap. *(978-0-87227-523-2(X))* Regular Baptist Pr.

Hiles, Lynn. The Revelation of Jesus Christ: An Open Letter to the Church from a Modern Perspective of the Book of Revelation. 2007. 261p. per. 17.99 *(978-0-7684-2435-5(6))* Destiny Image Pubs.

Hilliard, Jack. Understanding Revelation. 2008. 432p. 33.99 *(978-1-60791-055-8(1))* 2007. 408p. per. 21.99 *(978-1-60266-650-4(4))* Xulon Pr., Inc.

Hodge, Kent. Rediscovering Revelation: I Will Build My Church. 2011. 156p. 28.99 ***(978-1-4634-1272-2(X))***; pap. 15.49 ***(978-1-4634-1273-9(8))*** AuthorHouse.

Hongisto, Leif. Experiencing the Apocalypse at the Limits of Alterity. 2010. (Biblical Interpretation Ser.). (Illus.). 292p. *(978-90-04-18563-0(1))* BRILL.

Hort, Fenton John Anthony. The Apocalypse of St John, I-III: The Greek Text with Introduction, Commentary, & Additional Notes. 2010. (Cambridge Library Collection - Religion Ser.). (ENG.). 104p. pap. 19.99 *(978-1-108-00757-3(0))* Cambridge Univ. Pr.

Hoskier, H. C. The Complete Commentary of Oecumenius on the Apocalypse: Now Printed for the First Time from Manuscripts at Messina, Rome, Salonika, & Athos. 2008. 273p. pap. 23.00 *(978-1-60608-329-1(5)*, Wipf and Stock) Wipf & Stock Pubs.

Houghton, John. Revelation - Chapters 1-3. 2008. 72p. *(978-1-85345-461-5(3))* Crusade for World Revival.

Hoyt, Edyth Armstrong. Studies in the Apocalypse of John of Patmos. 2011. 262p. 47.95 ***(978-1-258-04498-5(6))*** Literary Licensing, LLC.

Hoyt, Herman A. Studies in Revelation. pap. 7.99 *(978-0-88469-118-1(7))* BMH Bks.

Huber, Lynn R. & Huber. Like a Bride Adorned: Reading Metaphor in John's Apocalypse. 2007. (Emory Studies in Early Christianity Ser.). (ENG.). 232p. pap. 80.00 *(978-0-567-02674-3(4)*, T&T Clark Int'l) Continuum International Publishing Group, Ltd. GBR. Dist: National Bk. Network.

Hudson, Gary W. Revelation ~ Awakening the Christ Within: The Book of Revelation as the Christian Book of Death & Rebirth. 2006. (Illus.). 256p. 24.95 *(978-0-9778517-2-0(9))* Unitive Life Pubns.

Hudson, Henry T. Reviewing the Revelation. 2009. 288p. pap. 20.95 *(978-1-4401-4711-1(6))* iUniverse, Inc.

Huettner, Charles H. Jesus Reveals Revelation. 2007. 248p. pap. 15.95 *(978-1-60145-319-8(1))* Booklocker.com, Inc.

Hughes, Chris. Revelation Revealed. 2007. (ENG.). 21.99 *(978-1-60034-835-8(1))* Xulon Pr., Inc.

Huntington, Ray L., et al, eds. Shedding Light on the New Testament: Acts through Revelation. 2009. 288p. *(978-0-8425-2725-5(7))*, Brigham Young Univ. Religious Studies Ctr.) Brigham Young Univ.

Isaac Newton. Observations upon the Prophecies of Daniel & the Apocalypse of St John. 2011. 204p. pap. 5.89 ***(978-1-60386-402-2(4)***, Watchmaker Publishing) Wexford College Pr.

Jackson, Celia Sprinkle. Revelations. 2008. 296p. pap. 21.99 *(978-1-4343-7724-1(5))* AuthorHouse.

Jastrembowska, Elzbieta. Cities of the Apocalypse. 2012. (ENG.). 240p. pap. 24.95 *(978-1-84368-046-8(7))* Pallas Athene GBR. Dist: Independent Pubs. Group.

Kingdom Quotes Staff. Notes on the Seven Churches: (Of the Revelation) pap. *(978-0-930179-19-9(6))* Johns Enterprises.

—The Seven Churches: (Of the Revelation) pap. *(978-0-930179-18-2(8))* Johns Enterprises.

—Three Urgent Messages: (From the Book of Revelation) pap. *(978-0-930179-15-1(3))* Johns Enterprises.

Kirsch, Jonathan. History of the End of the World: How the Most Controversial Book in the Bible Changed the Course of Western Civilization. 2007. (ENG., Illus.). 352p. pap. 14.95 *(978-0-06-134987-4(9)*, HarperOne) HarperCollins Pubs.

Knight, Jonathan. Revelation. 2011. 212p. ***(978-1-906055-06-6(8))***; pap. ***(978-1-906055-07-3(6))*** Sheffield Phoenix Pr.

Knudsen, Dean. Unveiling Final Jesus: Portraits of Christ in the Book of Revelation. 2009. 124p. 21.95 *(978-1-4389-9508-3(3))*; pap. 11.95 *(978-1-4389-9509-0(1))* AuthorHouse.

Kramer, Robert L. A Guided Tour Through the Revelation. 2009. 248p. pap. 15.99 *(978-1-60791-598-0(7))* Xulon Pr., Inc.

Kraus, Wolfgang, ed. Beiträge zur urchristlichen Theologiegeschichte. 2009. (Beihefte zur Zeitschrift far die neutestamentliche Wissenschaft und die Kunde der älteren Kirche Ser.).Tr. of Studies on the History of Early Christian Theology. (GER.). XVI, 560p. 280.00 ***(978-3-11-173599-3(0))*** De Gruyter, Walter Inc.

Kraus, Wolfgang, ed. Beiträge zur urchristlichen Theologiegeschichte. 2009. (Beihefte zur Zeitschrift für die neutestamentliche Wissenschaft und die Kunde der älteren Kirche Ser.).Tr. of Studies on the History of Early Christian Theology. (GER.). XVI, 560p. 182.00 *(978-3-11-021565-6(9))* De Gruyter, Walter Inc.

Kraybill, J. Nelson & Baker Publishing Group Staff. Apocalypse & Allegiance: Worship, Politics, & Devotion in the Book of Revelation, 1 vol. 2010. (ENG., Illus.). 192p. pap. 21.99 *(978-1-58743-261-3(7))* Brazos Pr.

Kremer, Don. The Chronological Order of Revelation. 2007. 296p. per. 17.99 *(978-1-60266-351-0(3))* Xulon Pr., Inc.

Lear, Gilberto. Discursos Sobre el Libro De: Lectures on Revelation. (SPA.). 224p. *(978-84-7228-957-4(5)*, 223017) Clie, Editorial.

Ledesma, Henry Grenryk. The little book: the sound of the seventh Trumpet. 2007. 176p. 35.49 *(978-1-4357-0171-7(2))*; 35.34 *(978-1-4303-2856-8(8))* Lulu Enterprises Inc.

Lee, Richard. Understanding Leviathan: The Key to Apostle John's the Revelation. 2009. 280p. 30.95 *(978-0-595-70998-4(2))*; pap. 20.95 *(978-0-595-46137-0(9))* iUniverse, Inc.

Lichtenwalter, Larry L. Revelation's Great Love Story: More Than I Ever Imagined. 2008. (ENG.). 141p. pap. 12.99 *(978-0-8127-0460-0(6))* Review & Herald Publishing Assn.

Lockyer, Herbert. The Four Horsemen of the Apocalypse. 2011. 30p. 35.95 ***(978-1-258-04239-4(8))*** Literary Licensing, LLC.

—The Four Women of the Apocalypse. 2011. 34p. 35.95 ***(978-1-258-04358-2(0))*** Literary Licensing, LLC.

Lowery, Robert. Revelation's Rhapsody: Listening to the Lyrics of the Lamb: How to Read the Book of Revelation. 2006. (Illus.). 222p. *(978-0-89900-946-9(8))* College Pr. Publishing Co., Inc.

Lunceford, Joe E. Parody & Counterimaging in the Apocalypse. 2009. 312p. pap. 34.00 *(978-1-60608-177-8(2)*, Wipf and Stock) Wipf & Stock Pubs.

Lyons, William John & Økland, Jorunn. The Way the World Ends? The Apocalypse of John in Culture & Ideology. 2009. x, 317p. *(978-1-906055-43-1(2))* Sheffield Phoenix Pr.

MacArthur, John. Revelation: The Christian's Ultimate Victory, 0 vols. 2006. (MacArthur Bible Study Guides). 144p. per. 9.99 *(978-1-4185-0891-3(8))* Nelson, Thomas Inc.

MacDonald, James M. Life & Writings of St John. 2006. pap. 40.95 *(978-1-4286-3708-5(7))* Kessinger Publishing, LLC.

Malcolm, Maxine. The Harlot Demon Unveiled: The Death Angel. 2011. 168p. 22.23 ***(978-1-4634-0989-0(3))***; pap. 15.00 ***(978-1-4634-0991-3(5))*** AuthorHouse.

Martino, Michael. Understanding the Book of Revelation. 2010. 108p. pap. 19.96 *(978-0-557-24688-5(1))* Lulu Enterprises Inc.

Mbosowo, Donald E. Understanding the Book of Revelation: The Mystery of the Book of Revelation Is finally Revealed. 2010. 216p. pap. 15.99 *(978-1-60957-810-7(4))* Xulon Pr., Inc.

McCahan, Jon. Revelation: Deception, Judgment & the Coming Kingdom. 2007. 320p. per. 17.99 *(978-1-60266-486-9(2))* Xulon Pr., Inc.

McConkey, James H. The Book of Revelation a Series of Outline Studies in the Apocalypse. 2007. 104p. per. 9.45 *(978-1-59462-608-1(1)*, 646, Book Jungle) Standard Pubns., Inc.

McConkie, Clay. The Final Countdown: The Seven Final Events Before the Second Coming. 2007. 103p. per. 10.99 *(978-1-59955-017-6(2))* Cedar Fort, Inc./CFI Distribution.

McDonough, Sean M. YHWH at Patmos: Rev. 1:4 in Its Hellenistic & Early Jewish Setting. 2011. 286p. pap. 31.00 ***(978-1-61097-155-3(8)***, Wipf and Stock) Wipf & Stock Pubs.

McDowell, Danny. Apostasia: A Corrupt Church for a Corrupt Age. 2011. 276p. pap. 17.48 *(978-1-4269-5912-7(5))* Trafford Publishing.

McKnight, William John. The Apocalypse of Jesus Christ, a Reappearance V1: John to the Seven Churches. 2011. 358p. 51.95 ***(978-1-258-04156-4(1))*** Literary Licensing, LLC.

McNicol, Allan J. The Conversion of the Nations in Revelation. 2011. (Library of New Testament Studies). (ENG.). 176p. 110.00 *(978-0-567-02608-8(6)*, T&T Clark Int'l) Continuum International Publishing Group, Ltd. GBR. Dist: National Bk. Network.

Miller, J. R. Devotional Hours with the Bible Volume Viii, from the Acts, the Epistles & Revelation. 2011. 154p. pap. 14.99 ***(978-1-61203-206-1(0))*** Bottom of the Hill Publishing.

Miller, Leslie. La Ira del Cordero del Apocalipsis.Tr. of Angry lamb of Revelation. (SPA.). 200p. *(978-84-7228-497-5(2)*, 220502) Clie, Editorial.

Millet, Robert L. Making Sense of the Book of Revelation. 2011. 160p. pap. 18.99 *(978-1-60641-944-1(7))* Deseret Bk. Co.

Mills, Kevin. Approaching Apocalypse: Unveiling Revelation in Victorian Writing. 2007. 228p. (C). *(978-0-8387-5627-0(1))*; (ENG.). 49.50 *(978-1-61148-237-9(2))* Bucknell Univ. Pr.

Moore, Stephen. Empire & Apocalypse Postcolonialism an. 2006. 172p. *(978-1-905048-85-4(8))*; (ENG.). per. *(978-1-905048-86-1(6))* Sheffield Phoenix Pr.

Morgan, Ian Charles. Revelation Revealed. 2010. 164p. pap. 19.99 *(978-0-557-28013-1(3))* Lulu Enterprises Inc.

Morton, Russell S. The One upon the Throne & the Lamb: A Tradition Historical/Theological Analysis of Revelation 4-5. 2007. (Studies in Biblical Literature Ser.). 262p. (C). 70.95 *(978-1-4331-0071-0(1))* Lang, Peter Publishing, Inc.

Myers, Ivor. War in Heaven. 2009. *(978-1-933291-45-1(1))* Remnant Pubns.

Nelson, Floyd & Nelson, Wanda. Revelation: The Interpretation of Revelation & the Trinity Mark'666. 2011. 108p. 21.23 ***(978-1-4567-1268-6(3))***; pap. 12.68 ***(978-1-4567-1266-2(7))*** AuthorHouse.

Newman, Sharan. The Real History of the End of the World: Apocalyptic Predictions from Revelation & Nostradamus to Y2k & 2012. 2010. (ENG., Illus.). 336p. (gr. 12-18). 15.00 *(978-0-425-23253-8(0)*, Berkley Trade) Penguin Group (USA) Inc.

Newport, Kenneth G. C. Apocalypse & Millennium: Studies in Biblical Eisegesis. 2008. (ENG., Illus.). 264p. (C). pap. 40.00 *(978-0-521-06845-1(2))* Cambridge Univ. Pr.

Newton, Isaac. Observations upon the Prophecies of Daniel, & the Apocalypse of St John. 2007. (ENG.). 176p. per. *(978-1-4065-5033-7(7))* Dodo Pr.

—Observations upon the Prophecies of Daniel, & the Apocalypse of St John. 2007. 120p. per. *(978-1-4068-3454-3(8))* Echo Library.

—Observations upon the Prophecies of Daniel, & the Apocalypse of St John. 2007. (ENG.). 148p. per. 12.99 *(978-1-59547-841-2(8))* NuVision Pubns., LLC.

—Observations upon the Prophecies of Daniel & the Apocalypse of St. John: In Two Parts. 2007. (ENG.). 188p. pap. 19.99 *(978-1-4346-0577-1(9))*; 208p. pap. 22.99 *(978-1-4346-0652-5(X))* BiblioBazaar.

Newton, Jon. Revelation Reclaimed: The Use & Misuse of the Apocalypse. 2009. (ENG.). 124p. 19.99 *(978-1-84227-612-9(3)*, Paternoster) Authentic Media.

Oeland, W. B. God's Kingdom in Revelation: John's Synopsis of the Bible. 2007. 48p. pap. 9.00 *(978-0-8059-7621-2(3))* Dorrance Publishing Co., Inc.

Opoku-Gyimah, Fred. End Time Prophecy. 2009. 92p. pap. 10.99 *(978-1-60791-281-1(3))* Xulon Pr., Inc.

Ostten, Steven H. Practical Studies in the Book of Revelation. 2007. per. *(978-1-60208-055-3(0))* FBC Pubns. & Printing.

Pagels, Elaine. Revelations: Visions, Prophecy, & Politics in the Book of Revelation. 2012. (ENG.). 256p. (gr. 12). 27.95 ***(978-0-670-02334-9(5)***, Viking Adult) Penguin Group (USA) Inc.

Pahl, Michael W. The Beginning & the End: Rereading GenesisÕs Stories & Revelation's Visions. 2011. 118p. pap. 15.00 ***(978-1-60899-927-9(0)***, Cascade Bks.) Wipf & Stock Pubs.

Pate, C. Marvin. Reading Revelation: A Comparison of Four Interpretive Translations of the Apocalypse, 1 vol. 2009. 208p. pap. 29.99 *(978-0-8254-3367-2(3))* Kregel Pubns.

—The Writings of John: A Survey of the Gospel Epistles, & Apocalypse, 1 vol. 2011. (ENG.). 560p. 44.99 *(978-0-310-26737-9(4))* Zondervan.

Paulien, Jon. Seven Keys: Unlocking the Secrets of Revelation. 2009. pap. 13.99 *(978-0-8163-2373-9(9))* Pacific Pr. Publishing Assn.

Perry, Peter S. The Rhetoric of Digressions: Revelation 7:1-17 & 10:1-11:13 & Ancient Communication. 2009. X, 297p. pap. 127.50 *(978-3-16-150001-5(6))* Mohr Siebeck GmbH & Co. KG DEU. Dist: Coronet Bks.

Police, Floyd. Talks on Revelation. 2006. 27.00 *(978-0-8059-8276-3(0))* Dorrance Publishing Co., Inc.

Potter, Cheri Lynn. Revelations Sealed. 2011. 432p. 34.99 ***(978-1-4568-6629-7(X))***; pap. 23.99 ***(978-1-4568-6628-0(1))*** Xlibris Corp.

Prevost, Jean-Pierre. How to Read the Apocalypse. Bowden, John & Lydamore, Margaret, trs. from FRE. 2012. (Illus.). x, 118p. ***(978-0-334-02101-8(4)***, SCM Pr.) Hymns Ancient & Modern Ltd.

Pryse, James. The Apocalypse Unsealed. 2007. 236p. per. 13.95 *(978-1-60206-247-4(1))* Cosimo, Inc.

Quamina, Alvan. Let's Get Real: A Contemporary Study of the Book of the Revelation. 2006. (ENG.). 324p. per. 29.95 *(978-1-4241-5906-2(7))* PublishAmerica, Inc.

Resseguie, James L. The Revelation of John: A Narrative Commentary, 1 vol. 2009. 288p. (C). pap. 26.00 *(978-0-8010-3213-4(X))* Baker Academic.

Revelation. (People's Bible Commentary Ser.). 228p. pap. 10.99 *(978-0-570-04986-9(5)*, 12-8048); (People's Bible Commentary Ser.). 240p. 13.99 *(978-0-7586-0453-8(X))*; (LifeLight Bible Studies: Course 15). stu. ed. 5.50 *(978-0-570-09289-6(2)*, 20-2317); (LifeLight Bible Studies: Course 15). 6.50 *(978-0-570-09288-9(4)*, 20-2316) Concordia Publishing Hse.

Revelation ... Unveiling the End, Act 3: The Final Curtain. 2007. per. 16.99 *(978-1-57972-738-3(7))* Insight for Living.

Ridges, David J. The Book of Revelation Made Easier. 2010. 144p. pap. 11.99 *(978-1-59955-418-1(6))* Cedar Fort, Inc./CFI Distribution.

Risbeck, John S. Daniel & Revelation Bound Together. Berry, Marian G., ed. 2010. (Illus.). 327p. spiral bd. 29.95 *(978-1-57258-537-9(4))* TEACH Services, Inc.

Robinson B.D., J. Armitage. The Gospel According to Peter & the Revelation of Peter. 2007. 104p. per. 10.45 *(978-1-59462-767-5(3)*, Book Jungle) Standard Pubns., Inc.

Rodriguez, Jacob M. Hidden Kings: Revealing the Man God Made You to Be. 2007. per. 15.00 *(978-1-59872-816-3(4))* Instant Pub.

Rose Publishing, creator. Understanding the Book of Revelation. 2008. 39.90 *(978-1-59636-300-7(2))* Rose Publishing.

Ryan, James. The Revelation Handbook: Surviving the Great Tribulation. 2007. 124p. per. 11.95 *(978-1-59800-955-2(9))* Outskirts Pr., Inc.

Ryan, Sean Michael. Hearing at the Boundaries of Vision: Education Informing Cosmology in Revelation 9. 2012. (ENG., Illus.). 296p 120.00 ***(978-0-567-60489-7(6)***, T&T Clark Int'l) Continuum International Publishing Group, Ltd. GBR. Dist: National Bk. Network.

Sanchez, David A. From Patmos to the Barrio: Subverting Imperial Myths. 2008. 222p. (C). pap. 21.00 *(978-0-8006-6259-2(8)*, Fortress Pr.) Augsburg Fortress, Pubs.

Scavone, Frank. The New Heaven & the New Earth. 2011. 24p. pap. 8.99 *(978-1-61215-775-7(0))* Xulon Pr., Inc.

Scheg, Lawrence. King of Kings & Lord of Lords. 2007. (Illus.). 237p. pap. 20.00 *(978-0-9742756-2-8(X))* Sierra Publishing & Booksellers.

Schmiedel, Paul W. The Johannine Writings. Canney, Maurice A., tr. 2007. (ENG.). 304p. 43.95 *(978-0-548-08339-0(8))* Kessinger Publishing, LLC.

Seiss, J. A. The Apocalypse V1: A Series of Special Lectures on the Revelation of Jesus Christ. 2011. 458p. 57.95 ***(978-1-258-09260-3(3))*** Literary Licensing, LLC.

—The Apocalypse V2: A Series of Special Lectures on the Revelation of Jesus Christ. 2011. 460p. 57.95 ***(978-1-258-06734-2(X))*** Literary Licensing, LLC.

Shepardson, Dale. Unveiling the Mysteries of Our Times. 2009. 336p. pap. 22.95 *(978-1-4401-3176-9(7))* iUniverse, Inc.

Silva, Kittim. Apocalipsis Revelacion Jesucristo: The Revelation of Jesus Christ. (SPA.). 268p. *(978-84-7228-971-0(0)*, 223057) Clie, Editorial.

Smith, F. g. & Smith, F. G. The Revelation Explained. 2010. (Illus.). 204p. pap. 15.85 *(978-1-153-71906-3(1))* General Bks. LLC.

Smith, Frederick George. The Revelation Explained. 2008. 364p. 31.99 *(978-0-554-24563-8(9))* 2008. 364p. 29.99 *(978-0-554-33866-8(1))* 2006. (ENG.). 324p. pap. 23.99 *(978-1-4264-6874-2(1))* 2006. (ENG.). 362p. pap. 26.99 *(978-1-4264-6956-5(X))* BiblioBazaar.

Smith, J. E. The Revelation in Plain English. 2006. pap. 16.00 *(978-0-8059-6981-8(0))* Dorrance Publishing Co., Inc.

Snow, Roger. Fifty Ways to Leave Left Behind. 2007. 212p. per. 13.99 *(978-1-60247-560-1(1))* Tate Publishing & Enterprises, LLC.

Sodano, Vincent. Counting Sheep: The Number 666 of Revelation 13: 18 Explained. 2007. 160p. per. 12.95 *(978-1-4327-0359-2(5))* Outskirts Pr., Inc.

Stephens, Mark B. Annihilation or Renewal? The Meaning & Function of New Creation in the Book of Revelation. 2011. (Wissenschaftliche Untersuchungen Zum Neuen Testament Ser.). 354p. pap. 157.50 ***(978-3-16-150838-7(6))*** Mohr Siebeck GmbH & Co. KG DEU. Dist: Coronet Bks.

Stevens, Gerald L., ed. Essays on Revelation: Appropriating Yesterday's Apocalypse in Today's World. 2010. (Illus.). 240p. pap. 26.00 *(978-1-60608-879-1(3)*, Pickwick Pubns.) Wipf & Stock Pubs.

Stevens, Minister Howard. Seven Mysteries of the Book of Revelation Revealed: The End of the Church Age. 2009. 136p. pap. 14.99 *(978-1-61579-506-2(5))* Xulon Pr., Inc.

Stevenson, Gregory. Power & Place: Temple & Identity in the Book of Revelation. (Beihefte zur Zeitschrift far die neutestamentliche Wissenschaft und die Kunde der älteren Kirche Ser.). (ENG.). XVII, 368p. 255.00 ***(978-3-11-180818-5(1))*** De Gruyter, Walter Inc.

Stramara, Daniel F. God's Timetable: The Book of Revelation & the Feast of Seven Weeks. 2011. 202p. pap. 22.00 *(978-1-60899-638-4(7)*, Pickwick Pubns.) Wipf & Stock Pubs.

Strauch, Alexander. Love or Die: Christ's Wake-up Call to the Church. 2008. 112p. pap. 9.99 *(978-0-936083-28-5(X))* Lewis & Roth Pubs.

Strauss, Lehman. The Book of the Revelation: Outlined Studies. 2008. 381p. pap. 17.99 *(978-0-88469-090-0(3))* BMH Bks.

Streett, Matthew. Here Comes the Judge: Violent Pacifism in the Book of Revelation. 2012. (Library of New Testament Studies). (ENG., Illus.). 296p. 120.00 ***(978-0-567-03539-4(5)***, T&T Clark Int'l) Continuum International Publishing Group, Ltd. GBR. Dist: National Bk. Network.

Swain, Lincoln. The Why People: A Crowd Impossible to Number. 2008. 88p. per. 12.95 *(978-0-9760535-9-0(4))* Atomic Quill Pr.

Taeger, Jens-W. Johanneische Perspektiven: Aufsatze zur Johannesapokalypse und zum johanneischen Kreis 1984-2003. 2006. (Forschungen Zur Religion und Literatur des Alten & Neuen Testament Ser.: Vol. 215). (GER & ENG., Illus.). 254p. (C). 98.00 *(978-3-525-53082-5(X))* Vandenhoeck & Ruprecht GmbH & Co. KG DEU. Dist: ISD.

Tapley, William. Revelation Unraveled: Hidden Secrets of the Apocalypse. 2007. 140p. (YA). per. 12.95 *(978-0-9798722-0-4(0))* Canterbury Pr.

Teeter, David. The Days of the Prophets: What We Can Learn from Biblical Prophecy. 2009. 123p. pap. 12.95 *(978-1-4327-3559-3(4))* Outskirts Pr., Inc.

Theobald, Michael. Studien zum Corpus Iohanneum. 2011. (Wissenschaftliche Untersuchungen zum Neuen Testament, No. 267 Ser.). (GER.). 741p. 287.50 *(978-3-16-150284-2(1))* Mohr Siebeck GmbH & Co. KG DEU. Dist: Coronet Bks.

Thomas, David Andrew. Revelation 19 in Historical & Mythological Context. 2008. (Studies in Biblical Literature Ser.). 214p. (C). 68.95 *(978-1-4331-0252-3(8))* Lang, Peter Publishing, Inc.

Thomas, Rodney Lawrence. Magical Motifs in the Book of Revelation, Vol. 416. 2010. (Library of New Testament Studies, the Ser.). (ENG.). 240p. 130.00 *(978-0-567-22686-0(7)*, T&T Clark Int'l) Continuum International Publishing Group, Ltd. GBR. Dist: National Bk. Network.

Tonstad, Sigve K. & Tonstad. Saving God's Reputation: The Theological Function of Pistis Iesou in the Cosmic Narratives of Revelation. 2007. (Library of New Testament Studies: Vol. 337). (ENG., Illus.). 250p. 170.00 *(978-0-567-04494-5(7)*, T&T Clark Int'l) Continuum International Publishing Group, Ltd. GBR. Dist: National Bk. Network.

Tóth, Franz. Der himmlische Kult: Wirklichkeitskonstruktion und Sinnbildung in der Johannesoffenbarung. 2006. (Arbeiten Zur Bibel und Ihrer Geschichte Ser.: Vol. 22). 613p. 79.00 *(978-3-374-02427-8(0))* Evangelische Verlagsanstalt GmbH DEU. Dist: Eisenbrauns, Inc.

Trail, Ronald L. Exegetical Summary of Revelation 1-11. 2nd ed. 2008. 243p. pap. 29.00 *(978-1-55671-198-5(0))* SIL International.

—Exegetical Summary of Revelation 11-22. 2nd ed. 2008. 238p. pap. 29.00 *(978-1-55671-196-1(4))* SIL International.

Tregelles, Samuel Prideaux. The Book of Revelation in Greek Edited from Ancient Authorities. 2009. (Cambridge Library Collection - Religion Ser.). (ENG.). 208p. pap. 22.99 *(978-1-108-00745-0(7))* Cambridge Univ. Pr.

Van Groningen, Gerard. The Progress of Revelation in the Old Testament. 2006. 84p. pap. 13.00 *(978-1-59752-629-6(0)*, Resource Pubns.) Wipf & Stock Pubs.

van Wert, Leon G. The Jewish Popes: The Two Harbingers of the End Times. 2009. 27.99 *(978-1-60604-687-6(X))* Tate Publishing & Enterprises, LLC.

Victoria, T. Un livre de feu dans un siecle de Fer: Les lectures de l'Apocalypse dans la litterature francaise de la Renaissance. 2009. (Bibliotheca Ephemeridum Theologicarum Lovaniensium Ser.). (FRE.). 609p. (C). pap. 124.00 *(978-90-429-2132-0(3))* Peeters Pubs. & Booksellers BEL. Dist Brown, David Bk. Co., The.

Vilyus, Donald J. Revelation Update: Volume One. 2006. 85p. per. 8.95 *(978-1-59824-277-5(6))* E-BookTime LLC.

Wagner, Richard & Helyer, Larry R. The Book of Revelation for Dummies. 2008. (ENG., Illus.). 342p. pap. 21.99 *(978-0-470-04521-3(3)*, For Dummies) Wiley, John & Sons, Inc.

Weikert, Vicki. Behold He Cometh, a Study in Revelation. 2008. 82p. pap. 16.95 *(978-1-60441-487-5(1))* PublishAmerica, Inc.

Weinland, Ronald. God's Final Witness 2008. 2007. 244p. per. 14.00 *(978-0-9753240-7-3(1))* The-End.Com, Inc.

Wiersbe, Warren W. Colossians: Become the Whole Person God Intends You to Be. 2009. (WBS Ser.). (ENG.). 128p. pap. 8.99 *(978-0-7814-4567-2(1))* Cook, David C.

Wilkins, Harry A. Prepare to Meet Thy God Jehovah. 2006. 15.00 *(978-0-8059-7337-2(0))* Dorrance Publishing Co., Inc.

Wilson, Mark. Charts on the Book of Revelation: Literary, Historical, & Theological Perspectives. 2007. (Kregel Charts of the Bible & Theology Ser.). (Illus.). 136p. pap. 21.99 *(978-0-8254-3939-1(6))* Kregel Pubns.

—The Victor Sayings in the Book of Revelation. 2007. 294p. pap. 32.00 *(978-1-55635-146-4(1)*, Wipf and Stock) Wipf & Stock Pubs.

Witetschek, S. Ephesische Enthullungen 1: Fruhe Christen in einer antiken Grosstadt. Zugleich ein Beitrag zur Frage nach den Kontexten der Johannesapokalypse. 2008. (Biblica Tools & Studies). (GER.). 526p. (C). 111.00 *(978-90-429-2108-5(0))* Peeters Pubs. & Booksellers BEL. Dist: Brown, David Bk. Co., The.

Witherington, Ben Iii. Revelation & the End Times Participant's Guide: Unraveling God's Message of Hope. 2010. 112p. pap. 10.00 *(978-0-687-66006-3(8))* Abingdon Pr.

Witulski, Thomas. Die Johannesoffenbarung und Kaiser Hadrian: Studien Zur Datierung der Neutestamentlichen Apokalpyse. 2007. (Forschungen Zur Religion und Literatur des Alten & Neuen Testament Ser.). (GER.). 415p. (C). 117.00 *(978-3-525-53085-6(4))* Vandenhoeck & Ruprecht GmbH & Co. KG DEU. Dist: ISD.

BIBLE—CRITICISM, INTERPRETATION, ETC.—N. T. ROMANS

see Bible—Criticism, Interpretation, etc.—N. T. Epistles

BIBLE—CRITICISM, INTERPRETATION, ETC.—N. T. THESSALONIANS

see Bible—Criticism, Interpretation, etc.—N. T. Epistles

BIBLE—CRITICISM, INTERPRETATION, ETC.—N. T. TIMOTHY

see Bible—Criticism, Interpretation, etc.—N. T. Epistles

BIBLE—CRITICISM, INTERPRETATION, ETC.—N. T. TITUS

see Bible—Criticism, Interpretation, etc.—N. T. Epistles

BIBLE—CRITICISM, INTERPRETATION, ETC.—O. T.

Ackroyd, Peter R. & Lindars, Barnabas. Words & Meanings. 2009. (ENG.). 260p. pap. 38.99 *(978-0-521-11205-5(2))* Cambridge Univ. Pr.

Adams, Samuel L. Wisdom in Transition: Act & Consequence in Second Temple Instructions. 2008. (Supplements to the Journal for the Study of Judaism Ser.). 320p. *(978-90-04-16566-3(5))* BRILL.

Ahn, John J. Exile as Forced Migrations: A Sociological, Literary, & Theological Approach on the Displacement & Resettlement of the Southern Kingdom of Judah. (Beihefte zur Zeitschrift far die alttestamentliche Wissenschaft Ser.). (ENG., 2011. Illus.). XVIII, 306p. 196.00 ***(978-3-11-175389-8(1))*** 2010. 320p. 126.00 *(978-3-11-024095-5(5))* De Gruyter, Walter Inc.

Ahn, John J. & Middlemas, Jill. By the Irrigation Canals of Babylon: Approaches to the Study of the Exile. 2012. (Library of Hebrew Bible/Old Testament Studies). (ENG.). 208p. 120.00 *(978-0-567-52694-0(4)*, T&T Clark Int'l) Continuum International Publishing Group, Ltd. GBR. Dist: National Bk. Network.

Aitken, James K., et al, eds. On Stone & Scroll: Essays in Honour of Graham Ivor Davies. 2011. (Beihefte zur Zeitschrift far die alttestamentliche Wissenschaft

Ser.). (ENG., Illus.). XXVIII, 576p. 280.00 (978-3-11-175624-0(6)) De Gruyter, Walter Inc.

Ajayi, Joel A. A. A Biblical Theology of Gerassapience. 2010. (Studies in Biblical Literature Ser.). 280p. (C). 79.95 (978-1-4331-0785-6(6)) Lang, Peter Publishing, Inc.

Albrektson, Bertil. Text, Translation, Theology: Selected Essays on the Hebrew Bible. 2010. (Society for Old Testament Study Ser.). 154p. 89.95 (978-0-7546-6908-1(4)) Ashgate Publishing Co.

Alexander, Larry D. Sunday school lessons from the Apostle Paul's letter to the Romans. 2007. 77p. pap. 15.51 (978-0-615-15342-1(9)) Alexander, Larry D.

Allison, Dale C. Testament of Abraham. (Commentaries on Early Jewish Literature Ser.). (ENG.). XVI, 527p. 224.00 (978-3-11-179960-5(3)) De Gruyter, Walter Inc.

Alter, Robert. The Art of Biblical Narrative. 2nd ed. 2011. (ENG.). 272p. (gr. 9). pap. 16.99 (978-0-465-02255-7(3)) Basic Bks.

Amit, Yaira & Naaman, Nadav. Essays on Ancient Israel in Its near Eastern Context: A Tribute to Nadav Naaman. 2006. (Illus.). 466p. 59.50 (978-1-57506-128-3(7)) Eisenbrauns, Inc.

Andreopoulos, Andreas, et al, eds. Meditations of the Heart: The Psalms in Early Christian Thought & Practice. Essays in Honour of Andrew Louth. 2011. (Studia Traditionis Theologiae Ser.). (ENG., Illus.). 301p. (C). pap. 102.00 (978-2-503-53433-6(3)) Brepols Pubs. BEL. Dist: ISD.

Angel, Hayyim J. Revealed Texts, Hidden Meanings: Finding the Religious Significance in Tanakh. 2009. (978-1-60280-128-8(2)) Ktav Publishing Hse., Inc.

Arbel, Daphna V. & Orlov, Andrei A., eds. With Letters of Light: Studies in the Dead Sea Scrolls, Early Jewish Apocalypticism, Magic & Mysticism. 2010. (Ekstasis: Religious Experience from Antiquity to the Middle Ages Ser.). 640p. 182.00 (978-3-11-022201-2(9)) De Gruyter, Walter Inc.

Augustin, Matthias & Niemann, Hermann Michael, eds. Thinking Towards New Horizons: Collected Communications to the XIXth Congress of the International Organization for the Study of the Old Testament, Ljubljana 2007. 2009. (Beiträge zur Erforschung des Alten Testaments und des Antiken Judentums Ser.). (FRE, GER & ENG., Illus.). 212p. pap. 56.95 (978-3-631-58447-7(4)) Lang, Peter GmbH, Europaischer Verlag der Wissenschaften DEU. Dist: Lang, Peter.

Auld, A. G. & Eynikel, E., eds. For & against David: Story & History in the Books of Samuel. 2010. (Bibliotheca Ephemeridum Theologicarum Lovaniensium Ser.). (ENG, FRE & GER.). 397p. (C). pap. 111.00 (978-90-429-2284-6(2)) Peeters Pubs. & Booksellers BEL. Dist: Brown, David Bk. Co., The.

Auld, A. Graeme. Understanding Poets & Prophets: Essays in Honour of George Wishart Anderson. 2009. (Library of Hebrew Bible/Old Testament Studies, the Ser.). (ENG.). 445p. 75.00 (978-0-567-41156-3(7), T&T Clark) Continuum International Publishing Group, Ltd. GBR. Dist: National Bk. Network.

Avishur, Yitzhak. Comparative Studies in Biblical & Ugaritic Languages & Litratures. 2007. 238p. 60.00 (978-965-7162-14-9(9)) Archaeological Ctr. Pubns. ISR. Dist: Eisenbrauns, Inc.

Avrahami, Yael. Senses of Scripture: Sensory Experience in the Hebrew Bible. 2011. (Library Hebrew Bible/Old Testament Studies). (ENG.). 328p. 140.00 (978-0-567-53092-9(2), T&T Clark Int'l) Continuum International Publishing Group, Ltd. GBR. Dist: National Bk. Network.

Baab, Lynne M. Prayers of the Old Testament, 1 vol. 2010. (LifeGuide Bible Studies). (ENG.). 64p. pap. 8.00 (978-0-8308-3138-8(X), IVP Conn.) InterVarsity Pr.

Bacher, Wilhelm. Abraham Ibn Esra Als Grammatiker: Ein Beitrag Zur Geschichte der Hebräischen Sprachwissenschaft. 2010. 194p. pap. 23.75 (978-1-147-72132-4(7)) BiblioBazaar.

Bacher, Wilhelm. Abraham Ibn Esra als Grammatiker: Ein Beitrag zur Geschichte der hebräischen Sprachwissenschaft. (GER.). 192p. 135.00 (978-3-11-125803-4(3)) De Gruyter, Mouton DEU. Dist: de Gruyter, Walter GmbH & Co. KG.

Baker, David L. Tight Fists or Open Hands? Wealth & Poverty in Old Testament Law. 2009. (ENG.). 440p. pap. 36.00 (978-0-8028-6283-9(7)) Eerdmans, William B. Publishing Co.

Baker, David W., et al. Illustrated Bible Backgrounds Commentary: Old Testament, 1 vol. Walton, John H., ed. 2011. (Zondervan Illustrated Bible Backgrounds Commentary Ser.). (ENG.). 2928p. 249.95 (978-0-310-25572-7(4)) Zondervan.

Baker Publishing Group Staff. The Prayers of David: Becoming a Person after God's Own Heart. 2007. 160p. 12.99 (978-0-7642-0288-9(X)) Bethany Hse. Pubs.

Bal, Mieke. Anti-Covenant: Counter-Reading Women's Lives in the Hebrew Bible. 2009. (Library of Hebrew Bible/Old Testament Studies, the Ser.). (ENG.). 39.95 (978-0-567-46347-0(8), T&T Clark) Continuum International Publishing Group, Ltd. GBR. Dist: National Bk. Network.

Barton, George. Tiamat. 2010. pap. 19.24 (978-1-61719-040-7(3)) Gorgias Pr., LLC.

Barton, John. The Canon Literature & Theology: Collected Works of John Barton. 2007. (Society for Old Testament Study Ser.). 308p. 124.95 (978-0-7546-5451-3(6)) Ashgate Publishing Co.

—Religious Diversity in Ancient Israel & Judah. Stavrakopoulou, Francesca, ed. 2010. (ENG.). 224p. 34.95 (978-0-567-03216-4(7), T&T Clark Int'l) Continuum International Publishing Group, Ltd. GBR. Dist: National Bk. Network.

Basden, Paul & Dockery, David S., eds. The People of God. 2009. 368p. pap. 40.00 (978-1-60608-894-4(7), Wipf and Stock) Wipf & Stock Pubs.

Bechtel, Carol M. Touching the Altar: The Old Testament for Christian Worship. Conseil, ed. 2008. (Calvin Institute of Christian Worship Liturgical Studies). (Illus.). 211p. per. 18.00 (978-0-8028-2848-4(5)) Eerdmans, William B. Publishing Co.

Becking, Bob & Grabbe, Lester L. Between Evidence & Ideology: Essays on the History of Ancient Israel Read at the Joint Meeting of the Society for Old Testament Study & the Oud Testamentisch Werkgezelschap, Lincoln, July 2009. 2011. (Illus.). xiv, 234p. (978-90-04-18737-5(5)) BRILL.

Becking, Bob & Human, Dirk J., eds. Exile & Suffering: A Selection of Papers Read at the 50th Anniversary Meeting of the Old Testament Society of South Africa OTWSA/OTSSA Pretoria, August 2007. 2008. 304p. (978-90-04-17104-6(5)) BRILL.

Becking, Bob, et al. From Babylon to Eternity: The Exile Remembered & Constructed in Text & Tradition. 2010. (BibleWorld Ser.). (ENG., Illus.). 120p. (C). 99.95 (978-1-84553-305-2(4)) Equinox Publishing Ltd. GBR. Dist: ISD.

—From Babylon to Eternity: The Exile Remembered & Constructed in Text & Tradition. Cannegieter, Alex, ed. 2010. (BibleWorld Ser.). (ENG., Illus.). 120p. (C). 29.95 (978-1-84553-306-9(2)) Equinox Publishing Ltd. GBR. Dist: ISD.

Bembry, Jason. Yahweh's Coming of Age. 2011. (978-1-57506-172-6(4)) Eisenbrauns, Inc.

Ben-Dov, Jonathan. Head of All Years: Astronomy & Calendars at Qumran in Their Ancient Context. 2008. (Illus.). 352p. (978-90-04-17088-9(X)) BRILL.

Ben Zvi, Ehud, ed. Perspectives on Hebrew Scriptures: Comprising the Contents of Journal of Hebrew Scriptures, Vol. 6. 2008. (Gorgias Perspectives on Hebrew Scriptures Ser.: 3). 125.00 (978-1-59333-976-0(3)) Gorgias Pr., LLC.

—Perspectives on Hebrew Scriptures V. 2009. 164.00 (978-1-60724-326-7(1)) Gorgias Pr., LLC.

—Perspectives on Hebrew Scriptures VI. 2010. 26.32 (978-1-61143-004-2(6)) Gorgias Pr., LLC.

Ben Zvi, Ehud, et al, eds. A Palimpsest: Rhetoric, Ideology, Stylistics, & Language Relating to Persian Israel. 2009. 117.32 (978-1-60724-584-1(1)) Gorgias Pr., LLC.

Ben Zvi, Ehud & Levin, Christoph, eds. The Concept of Exile in Ancient Israel & its Historical Contexts. (Beihefte zur Zeitschrift für die alttestamentliche Wissenschaft Ser.). 2011. (ENG., Illus.). XII, 388p. 210.00 (978-3-11-173479-8(X)) 2010. 400p. 140.00 (978-3-11-022177-0(2)) De Gruyter, Walter Inc.

Benedict, Marion J. The God of the Old Testament in Relation to War. 2010. 192p. pap. 16.00 (978-1-60899-376-5(0), Wipf and Stock) Wipf & Stock Pubs.

Benjamin, Mara H. Rosenzweig's Bible: Reinventing Scripture for Jewish Modernity. 2009. (ENG., Illus.). 222p. 80.00 (978-0-521-89526-2(X)) Cambridge Univ. Pr.

Berger, David. The Jewish-Christian Debate in the High Middle Ages: A Critical Edition of the Nizzahon Vetus. 2008. 616p. pap. 60.00 (978-1-59740-545-4(0)) ACLS Humanities E-Book.

Bergmann, Claudia D. Childbirth As a Metaphor for Crisis: Evidence from the Ancient near East, the Hebrew Bible, & 1QH XI, 1-18. 2008. (Beihefte zur Zeitschrift für die alttestamentliche Wissenschaft Ser.). (ENG.). X, 267p. 119.00 (978-3-11-020042-3(2)) De Gruyter, Walter Inc.

Bergmann, Claudia D. Childbirth as a Metaphor for Crisis: Evidence from the Ancient near East, the Hebrew Bible, & 1QH XI, 1-18. 2008. (Beihefte zur Zeitschrift far die alttestamentliche Wissenschaft Ser.). (ENG.). X, 267p. 182.00 (978-3-11-173517-7(6)) De Gruyter, Walter Inc.

Bergmann, Michael, et al. Divine Evil? The Moral Character of the God of Abraham. 2011. (ENG.). 352p. 125.00 (978-0-19-957673-9(4)) Oxford Univ. Pr., Inc.

Bergsma, John S. The Jubilee from Leviticus to Qumran: A History of Interpretation. 2006. (Vetus Testamentum Supplements Ser.). 348p. (978-90-04-15299-1(7)) BRILL.

Bester, Dorte. Körperbilder in den Psalmen: Studien zu Psalm 22 und verwandten Texten. 2007. 304p. (C). pap. 75.00 (978-3-16-149361-4(3)) Mohr Siebeck GmbH & Co. KG DEU. Dist: Eisenbrauns, Inc.

Bickerman, E. J. Studies in Jewish & Christian History: A New Edition in English Including the God of the Maccabees. Tropper, Amram, ed. 2007. (Ancient Judaism & Early Christianity Ser.). 1218p. (978-90-04-15294-6(6)) BRILL.

Bickerman, Elias J. Studies in Jewish & Christian History. 2011. 1242p. pap. (978-90-04-20606-9(X)) BRILL.

Biggs, Charles & Grant-Henderson, Anna. A Way into the Old Testament. 2007. (ENG.). 196p. (C). pap. 8.00 (978-1-920691-81-3(2)) ATF Pr. AUS. Dist: Brown, David Bk. Co., The.

Black, et al. The Artifice of Love: Grotesque Bodies in the Song of Songs. 2009. (Library of Hebrew Bible/Old Testament Studies, the Ser.: Vol. 392). (ENG., Illus.). 304p. 125.00 (978-0-8264-6985-4(X), T&T Clark Int'l) Continuum International Publishing Group, Ltd. GBR. Dist: National Bk. Network.

Blair, Judit M. De-Demonising the Old Testament: An Investigation of Azazel, Lilith, Deber, Qeteb & Reshef in the Hebrew Bible. 2009. 266p. pap. 117.50 (978-3-16-150131-9(4)) Mohr Siebeck GmbH & Co. KG DEU. Dist: Coronet Bks.

Blake, Robert P. Ancient Georgian Versions of the Old Testament. 2010. pap. 19.36 (978-1-61143-411-8(4)) Gorgias Pr., LLC.

Block, Daniel I. Israel: Ancient Kingdom or Late Invention? 2008. (ENG., Illus.). 368p. pap. 27.99 (978-0-8054-4679-1(6), B&H Academic) B&H Publishing Group.

Boda, Mark J. A Severe Mercy: Sin & Its Remedy in the Old Testament. 2009. x, 622p. 59.50 (978-1-57506-164-1(3)) Eisenbrauns, Inc.

Boda, Mark J., et al. Seeking the Favor of God. 2006. 35.95 (978-1-58983-261-9(2)) Society of Biblical Literature.

Bovati, Pietro. Re-establishing Justice: Legal Terms, Concepts & Procedures in the Hebrew Bible. 2009. (Library of Hebrew Bible/Old Testament Studies, the Ser.). (ENG.). 478p. 75.00 (978-0-567-05265-0(6), T&T Clark) Continuum International Publishing Group, Ltd. GBR. Dist: National Bk. Network.

Bowker, John. The Targums & Rabbinic Literature: An Introduction to Jewish Interpretations of Scripture. 2009. (ENG.). 408p. pap. 51.00 (978-0-521-09771-0(1)) Cambridge Univ. Pr.

Branch, Robin Gallaher. Jeroboam's Wife. 2009. 220p. pap. 16.95 (978-1-56563-745-0(3)) Hendrickson Pubs. Marketing, LLC.

Brent, Allen. A Political History of Early Christianity. 2009. (ENG.). 344p. 44.95 (978-0-567-03175-4(6)); 140.00 (978-0-567-03174-7(8)) Continuum International Publishing Group, Ltd. GBR. (T&T Clark Int'l). Dist: National Bk. Network.

Brett, Mark G. Biblical Criticism in Crisis? The Impact of the Canonical Approach on Old Testament Studies. 2008. (ENG.). 252p. pap. 53.00 (978-0-521-04748-7(X)) Cambridge Univ. Pr.

Brettler, Marc Zvi. God Is King: Understanding an Israelite Metaphor. 2009. (Library of Hebrew Bible/Old Testament Studies, the Ser.). (ENG.). 219p. 39.95 (978-0-567-64081-9(7), T&T Clark) Continuum International Publishing Group, Ltd. GBR. Dist: National Bk. Network.

—How to Read the Jewish Bible. 2007. (ENG.). 400p. per. 19.95 (978-0-19-532522-5(2)) Oxford Univ. Pr., Inc.

—Minhah Le-Nahum: Biblical & Other Studies Presented to Nahum M. Sarna in Honour of his 70th Birthday. Fishbane, Michael, ed. 2009. (Library of Hebrew Bible/Old Testament Studies, the Ser.). (ENG.). 337p. 55.00 (978-0-567-33802-0(9), T&T Clark) Continuum International Publishing Group, Ltd. GBR. Dist: National Bk. Network.

Bridge, Steven L. Getting the Old Testament: What It Meant to Them, What It Means for Us. 2009. 248p. (C). pap. 16.99 (978-0-8010-4574-5(6)) Baker Academic.

—Getting the Old Testament: What It Meant to Them, What It Means for Us. 2009. (Illus.). 190p. 14.95 (978-1-59856-045-9(X)) Hendrickson Pubs. Marketing, LLC.

Bridgeman, Valerie & Page, Hugh. The Africana Bible: Reading Israel's Scriptures from Africa & the African Diaspora. 2009. 512p. 39.00 (978-0-8006-2125-4(5), Fortress Pr.) Augsburg Fortress, Pubs.

Britt, Brian. Rewriting Moses: The Narrative Eclipse of the Text. 2009. (Library of Hebrew Bible/Old Testament Studies, the Ser.). (ENG.). 256p. 44.95 (978-0-567-09205-2(4), T&T Clark Int'l) Continuum International Publishing Group, Ltd. GBR. Dist: National Bk. Network.

Brooke, George J. & Najman, Hindy. The Significance of Sinai: Traditions about Sinai & Divine Revelation in Judaism & Christianity. 2008. (Themes in Biblical Narrative Ser.). 384p. (C). (978-90-04-17018-6(9)) BRILL.

Brown, William P. The Seven Pillars of Creation: The Bible, Science, & the Ecology of Wonder, 1 vol. 2010. (ENG., Illus.). 352p. 29.95 (978-0-19-973079-7(2)) Oxford Univ. Pr., Inc.

Brueggemann, Walter. Great Prayers of the Old Testament. 2008. (ENG.). 176p. pap. 15.00 (978-0-664-23174-3(8)) Westminster John Knox Pr.

—Journey to the Common Good. 2010. (ENG.). 120p. pap. 17.00 (978-0-664-23516-1(6)) Westminster John Knox Pr.

—A Pathway of Interpretation: The Old Testament for Pastors & Students. 2008. 180p. pap. 21.00 (978-1-55635-589-9(0)) Wipf & Stock Pubs.

—An Unsettling God: The Heart of the Hebrew Bible. 2009. 192p. (C). pap. 22.00 (978-0-8006-6363-6(2), Fortress Pr.) Augsburg Fortress, Pubs.

Burchett, Author Walter, BA. Heavenly angel lay lay & guardian angel shadow guess the real age of the Earth. 2007. 48p. pap. 14.95 (978-0-615-17488-4(4)) Crossover Ministries.

Burnette-Bletsch, Rhonda. Studying the Old Testament: A Companion. 2007. 305p. 30.00 (978-0-687-64623-4(5)) Abingdon Pr.

Burns, Duncan Thorburn. Far from Minimal: Celebrating the Work & Influence of Philip R. Davies. Burns, Duncan Thorburn et al, eds. 2012. (Library of Hebrew Bible/Old Testament Studies, the Ser.). (ENG., Illus.). 576p. 180.00 (978-0-567-02717-7(1), T&T Clark Int'l) Continuum International Publishing Group, Ltd. GBR. Dist: National Bk. Network.

Buttery, Nathan. David: God's True King: Six Studies for Individuals or Groups. 2010. (Good Book Guides). 64p. pap. (978-1-904889-98-4(0)) Good Bk. Co.

Byassee, Jason. Praise Seeking Understanding: Reading the Psalms with Augustine. 2007. (Radical Traditions Ser.). 290p. per. 32.00 (978-0-8028-4012-7(4)) Eerdmans, William B. Publishing Co.

Campbell, Antony F. Making Sense of the Bible: Difficult Texts & Modern Faith. 2010. xiii, 306p. pap. 24.95 (978-0-8091-4634-5(7)) Paulist Pr.

Cantrell, Deborah O'Daniel. The Horsemen of Israel: Horses & Chariotry in Monarchic Israel (Ninth-Eighth Centuries B.C.E.) 2011. (978-1-57506-204-4(6)) Eisenbrauns, Inc.

Carmichael, Calum M. Law & Narrative in the Bible: The Evidence of the Deuteronomic Laws & the Decalogue. 2008. 356p. pap. 39.00 (978-1-60608-039-9(3)) Wipf & Stock Pubs.

Carpenter, Eugene E. Biblical Itinerary: In Search of Method, Form & Content. Essays in Honor of George W. Coats. 2009. (Library of Hebrew Bible/Old Testament Studies, the Ser.). (ENG.). 194p. 39.95 (978-0-567-48892-3(6), T&T Clark) Continuum International Publishing Group, Ltd. GBR. Dist: National Bk. Network.

Carr, Robert. The Catholic Revolutionary Movement. 2008. 145p. pap. 11.95 (978-1-4357-2079-4(2)) Lulu Enterprises Inc.

Carroll, M. Daniel & Lapsley, Jacqueline E., eds. Character Ethics & the Old Testament: Moral Dimensions of Scripture. 2007. (ENG., Illus.). 260p. per. 30.00 (978-0-664-22936-8(0)) Westminster John Knox Pr.

Carroll, Robert P. Text as Pretext: Essays in Honour of Robert Davidson. 2009. (Library of Hebrew Bible/Old Testament Studies, the Ser.). (ENG.). 307p. 49.95 (978-0-567-43776-1(0), T&T Clark) Continuum International Publishing Group, Ltd. GBR. Dist: National Bk. Network.

Carson, D. A. & Williamson, Hugh Godfrey Maturin, eds. It Is Written: Scripture Citing Scripture - Essays in Honour of Barnabas Lindars, SSF. 2009. (ENG.). 408p. pap. 53.00 (978-0-521-09762-8(2)) Cambridge Univ. Pr.

Carstens, Pernille & Lemche, Niels Peter, eds. The Reception & Remembrance of Abraham. 2011. 100.00 (978-1-4632-0054-1(4)) Gorgias Pr., LLC.

Carvalho, Corrine L. Encountering Ancient Voices (Second Edition) A Guide to Reading the Old Testament. 2nd ed. 2010. pap. 49.95 (978-1-59982-050-7(1), 9781599820507) St. Mary's Pr.

Castoro, Michael, Sr. Old Testament Scriptures. Date not set. 3.99 (978-0-9660781-5-2(2)) Castoro, Michael Angelo Jr.

Chalcraft, David & Chalcraft. Max Weber & the Sociology of Biblical Social Worlds. 2013. (Library of Hebrew Bible/Old Testament Studies, the Ser.). (ENG.). 224p. 120.00 (978-0-567-02758-0(9), T&T Clark Int'l) Continuum International Publishing Group, Ltd. GBR. Dist: National Bk. Network.

Cherry, Shai. Torah Through Time: Understanding Bible Commentary, from the Rabbinic Period to Modern Times. 2007. (ENG., Illus.). 208p. pap. 25.00 (978-0-8276-0848-1(9)) Jewish Pubn. Society.

Cheyne, T. K. Aids to the Devout Study of Criticism: Part I: the David Narrative, Part II: the Book of Psalms. 2009. 405p. pap. 34.00 (978-1-60608-500-4(X), Wipf and Stock) Wipf & Stock Pubs.

Childs, Brevard. Myth & Reality in the Old Testament. 2009. (Studies in Biblical Theology, First Ser.). 112p. pap. 15.00 (978-1-60899-035-1(4), Wipf and Stock) Wipf & Stock Pubs.

Christensen, Duane L. The Writings in the Tanakh. 2006. 140p. pap. (978-1-930566-32-3(8), BIBAL Pr.) Scott, D.& F. Publishing, Inc.

Chung, Youn Ho. The Sin of the Calf: The Rise of the Bible's Negative Attitude Toward the Golden Calf. 2010. (Library of Hebrew Bible/Old Testament Studies). (ENG.). 256p. 130.00 (978-0-567-42590-4(8), T&T Clark Int'l) Continuum International Publishing Group, Ltd. GBR. Dist: National Bk. Network.

Cohen, Chaim & Paul, Shalom M. Birkat Shalom: Studies in the Bible, Ancient near Eastern Literature, & Post-Biblical Judaism: Presented to Shalom M. Paul on the Occasion of His Seventieth Birthday, 2. 2008. (C). 99.50 (978-1-57506-145-0(7)); 99.50 (978-1-57506-155-9(4)); 99.50 (978-1-57506-154-2(6)) Eisenbrauns, Inc.

Cohen, Naomi G. Philo's Scriptures: Citations from the Prophets & Writings: Evidence for a Haftarah Cycle in Second Temple Judaism. 2007. (Supplements to the Journal for the Study of Judaism Ser.). 278p. (978-90-04-16312-6(3)) BRILL.

Cohen, Norman J. Masking & Unmasking Ourselves: Interpreting Biblical Texts on Clothing & Identity. 2012. (ENG.). 240p. 24.99 (978-1-58023-461-0(5)) Jewish Lights Publishing.

Coogan, Michael D. A Brief Introduction to the Old Testament: The Hebrew Bible in Its Context. 2nd ed. 2011. (ENG., Illus.). 480p. (C). pap. 54.95 (978-0-19-983011-4(8)) Oxford Univ. Pr., Inc.

Coogan, Michael D. The Old Testament. 2008. (Very Short Introductions Ser.). (ENG., Illus.). 144p. per. 11.95 (978-0-19-530505-0(1)) Oxford Univ. Pr., Inc.

Coogan, Michael David. Old Testament: A Historical & Literary Introduction to the Hebrew Scriptures, 1 vol. 2nd ed. 2010. (ENG.). 592p. (C). pap. 69.95 (978-0-19-537840-5(7)) Oxford Univ. Pr., Inc.

Cook, Johann & Cook, J. Septuagint & Reception: Essays Prepared for the Association for the Study of the Septuagint in South Africa. 2009. 422p. (978-90-04-17725-3(6)) BRILL.

Cotrozzi, Stefano. Expect the Unexpected: Aspects of Pragmatic Foregrounding in Old Testament Narratives, Vol. 510. 2010. (Library of Hebrew Bible/Old Testament Studies, the Ser.). (ENG., Illus.). 320p. 120.00 (978-0-567-56838-0(5), T&T Clark Int'l) Continuum International Publishing Group, Ltd. GBR. Dist: National Bk. Network.

Courson, Jon. Praying Thru the Tabernacle: A Biblical Model for Effective Prayer. 2007. (ENG., Illus.). 72p. per. 6.99 (978-0-9789472-0-0(7)) Searchlight.

Court, John M., ed. New Testament Writers & the Old Testament: An Introduction. 2011. 140p. pap. 17.00 (978-1-61097-048-8(9), Wipf and Stock) Wipf & Stock Pubs.

Crenshaw, James L. Old Testament Wisdom: An Introduction. 3rd ed. 2010. (ENG.). 320p. pap. 35.00 (978-0-664-23459-1(3)) Westminster John Knox Pr.

—Prophets, Sages, & Poets. 2006. 285p. per. 29.99 (978-0-8272-2988-4(7)) Chalice Pr.

Crouch, C. L. War & Ethics in the Ancient near East: Military Violence in Light of Cosmology & History. 2009. (Beihefte Zur Zeitschrift Fur Die Alttestamentliche Wissenschaft Ser.). (ENG.). XII, 248p. 105.00 (978-3-11-022351-4(1)); 168.00 (978-3-11-173975-5(9)) De Gruyter, Walter Inc.

Cryer, Frederick H. Divination in Ancient Israel & its near Eastern Environment: A Socio-Historical Investigation. 2009. (Library of Hebrew Bible/Old Testament Studies, the Ser.). (ENG.). 367p. 60.00 (978-0-567-37849-1(7), T&T Clark) Continuum International Publishing Group, Ltd. GBR. Dist: National Bk. Network.

Dahm, Ulrike. Opferkult und Priestertum in Alt-Israel: Ein kultur- und religionswissenschaftlicher Beitrag. (Beihefte zur Zeitschrift far die alttestamentliche Wissenschaft Ser.). (GER.). XII, 318p. 210.00 (978-3-11-180471-2(2)) De Gruyter, Walter Inc.

Davidson, Richard M. Flame of Yahweh: Sexuality in the Old Testament. 2007. 844p. per. (978-1-56563-847-1(6)) Hendrickson Pubs. Marketing, LLC.

Davies, Eryl W. Immoral Bible: Approaches to Biblical Ethics. 2010. (ENG.). 192p. 34.95 (978-0-567-30549-7(X)); 120.00 (978-0-567-26162-5(X)) Continuum International Publishing Group, Ltd. GBR. (T&T Clark Int'l). Dist: National Bk. Network.

Davies, Graham I., et al. On Stone & Scroll: Essays in Honour of Graham Ivor Davies. 2011. (Beihefte zur Zeitschrift für die alttestamentliche Wissenschaft Ser.). 182.00 (978-3-11-022805-2(X)) De Gruyter, Walter Inc.

Davies, Philip R. Memories of Ancient Israel: An Introduction to Biblical History — -Ancient & Modern. 2008. (ENG.). 208p. pap. 25.00 (978-0-664-23288-7(4)) Westminster John Knox Pr.

—The Origins of Biblical Israel. 2009. (Library of Hebrew Bible/Old Testament Studies, the Ser.). (ENG.). 208p. pap. 49.95 (978-0-567-13761-6(9), T&T Clark Int'l) Continuum International Publishing Group, Ltd. GBR. Dist: National Bk. Network.

—Whose Bible Is It Anyway? 2009. (Library of Hebrew Bible/Old Testament Studies, the Ser.). (ENG.). 150p. 27.95 (978-0-567-43885-0(6), T&T Clark) Continuum International Publishing Group, Ltd. GBR. Dist: National Bk. Network.

Davis, Ellen F. Scripture, Culture, & Agriculture: An Agrarian Reading of the Bible. 2008. (ENG.). 252p. (C). 90.00 (978-0-521-51834-5(2)); pap. 27.00 (978-0-521-73223-9(9)) Cambridge Univ. Pr.

Davison, W. T. WisdomLiterature of the Old Testament. 2006. pap. 30.95 (978-1-4286-4426-7(1)) Kessinger Publishing, LLC.

Dawson, David Allan. Text-Linguistics & Biblical Hebrew. 2009. (Library of Hebrew Bible/Old Testament Studies, the Ser.). (ENG.). 242p. 39.95 (978-0-567-22685-3(9), T&T Clark) Continuum International Publishing Group, Ltd. GBR. Dist: National Bk. Network.

de Lagarde, Paul. Semitica: Writings on Semitic Ephemera. 2008. (GER.). pap. 44.20 (978-1-59333-894-7(5)) Gorgias Pr., LLC.

de Lange, Nicholas, ed. Jewish Reception of Greek Bible Versions: Studies in Their Use in Late Antiquity & the Middle Ages. 2009. (Text & Studies in Medieval & Eary Modern Judaism Ser.). (Illus.). 338p. 195.00 (978-3-16-149779-7(1)) Mohr Siebeck GmbH & Co. KG DEU. Dist: Coronet Bks.

Dell, Katharine. Ethical & Unethical in the Old Testament: God & Humans in Dialogue, Vol. 528. 2010. (Library of Hebrew Bible/Old Testament Studies, the Ser.). (ENG., Illus.). 304p. 150.00 (978-0-567-21709-7(4), T&T Clark Int'l) Continuum International Publishing Group, Ltd. GBR. Dist: National Bk. Network.

—Opening the Old Testament. 2008. (ENG., Illus.). 240p. 99.95 (978-1-4051-2500-0(4), Wiley-Blackwell) Wiley, John & Sons, Inc.

Dell, Katharine J. Opening the Old Testament. 2008. (ENG., Illus.). 240p. per. 44.95 (978-1-4051-2501-7(2), Wiley-Blackwell) Wiley, John & Sons, Inc.

Dever, William G., et al. Confronting the Past: Archaeological & Historical Essays on Ancient Israel in Honor of William G. Dever. 2006. (Illus.). 376p. 69.50 (978-1-57506-117-7(1)) Eisenbrauns, Inc.

Dietrich, Walter, et al. Diasynchron: Beiträge zur Exegese, Theologie und Rezeption der Hebräischen Bibel. Walter Dietrich zum 65. Geburtstag. 2009. (GER., Illus.). 448p. (978-3-17-020822-3(5)) Kohlhammer, W., GmbH.

Distefano, Michel G. Inner-Midrashic Introductions & Their Influence on Introductions to Medieval Rabbinic Bible Commentaries. 2009. (Studia Judaica Ser.). (ENG.). XVI, 227p. 98.00 (978-3-11-021368-3(0)); 154.00 (978-3-11-173641-9(5)) De Gruyter, Walter Inc.

Doane, Alger Nicolaus & Stoneman, William P. Purloined Letters: The Twelfth-Century Reception of the Anglo-Saxon Illustrated Hexateuch (British Library, Cotton Claudius B. IV) 2011. (978-0-86698-443-0(7)) Arizona State Univ., Arizona Ctr. for Medieval & Renaissance Studies.

Dobos, Kroly Dniel, et al. With Wisdom As a Robe: Qumran & Other Jewish Studies in Honour of Ida Fröhlich. 2008. (GER & ENG., Illus.). xviii, 549p. (978-1-906055-57-8(2)) Sheffield Phoenix Pr.

Dolansky, Shawna. Now You See It, Now You Don't: Biblical Perspectives on the Relationship Between Magic & Religion. 2008. 119p. 24.50 (978-1-57506-805-3(2)) Eisenbrauns, Inc.

Doyle, Tsarina & Doyle, Brian. Words with Teeth: Metaphors & the Psalms of Imprecation. 2014. (Library of Hebrew Bible/Old Testament Studies, the Ser.). (ENG., Illus.). 144p. 105.00 (978-0-567-02772-6(4), T&T Clark Int'l) Continuum International Publishing Group, Ltd. GBR. Dist: National Bk. Network.

Driver, S. R. Sermons on Subjects Connected with the O. 2006. pap. 27.95 (978-1-4286-3681-1(1)) Kessinger Publishing, LLC.

—Sermons on Subjects Connected with the Old Testament. 2009. 254p. 34.99 (978-1-115-11457-8(3)); 30.99 (978-1-115-11455-4(7)) BiblioBazaar.

—Sermons on Subjects Connected with the Old Testament. 2007. (ENG.). 272p. 42.95 (978-0-548-12688-2(7)) Kessinger Publishing, LLC.

Duff, Archibald. History of Old Testament Criticism. 2009. 220p. 23.99 (978-1-103-58397-3(2)); pap. 17.99 (978-1-103-58396-6(4)) BiblioBazaar.

Dunteman, Paul L. The Christian Life & the History of Israel. 2009. 484p. pap. 24.99 (978-1-60791-274-3(0)) Xulon Pr., Inc.

Eberhardt, Gonke. JHWH und die Unterwelt: Spuren einer Kompetenzausweitung JHWHs im Alten Testament. 2007. (Forschungen zum Alten Testament, 2.Reihe: Vol. 23). 450p. (C). pap. 119.00 (978-3-16-149306-5(0)) Mohr Siebeck GmbH & Co. KG DEU. Dist: Eisenbrauns, Inc.

Eckhardt, John J. Behemoth & Leviathan. pap. 5.00 (978-1-883927-02-8(1)) Crusaders Ministries.

Edelman, Diana Vikander & Ben Zvi, Ehud, eds. The Production of Prophecy: Constructing Prophecy & Prophets in Yehud. 2009. (BibleWorld Ser.). (ENG.). 224p. (C). 99.95 (978-1-84553-499-8(9)); pap. 39.95 (978-1-84553-500-1(6)) Equinox Publishing Ltd. GBR. Dist: ISD.

Egger-Wenzel, Renate, ed. Ben Sira's God: Proceedings of the International Ben Sira Conference, Durham - Ushaw College 2001. (Beihefte zur Zeitschrift far die alttestamentliche Wissenschaft Ser.). (ENG.). VIII, 393p. 255.00 (978-3-11-179958-2(1)) De Gruyter, Walter Inc.

Eidevall, Goran, et al. Enigmas & Images: Studies in Honor of Tryggve N. D. Mettinger. 2011. pap. 42.95 (978-1-57506-813-8(3)) Eisenbrauns, Inc.

Eiselen, Frederick Carl. The Christian View of the Old Testament. 2011. 132p. pap. 12.99 (978-1-61203-060-9(2)) Bottom of the Hill Publishing.

Ellens, J. Harold & Greene, John T., eds. Probing the Frontiers of Biblical Studies. 2009. (Princeton Theological Monographs). 314p. pap. 35.00 (978-1-60608-460-1(7), Pickwick Pubns.) Wipf & Stock Pubs.

Eran, Mordechai & Shavit, Yaacov. The Hebrew Bible Reborn: From Holy Scripture to the Book of Books: A History of Biblical Culture & the Battles over the Bible in Modern Judaism. Naor, Chaya, tr. from HEB. 2007. (Studia Judaica: Forschungen Zur Wissenschaft des Judentums Ser.). (ENG.). X, 566p. 196.00 (978-3-11-019141-7(5)) De Gruyter, Walter Inc.

Eskenazi, Tamara C. Second Temple Studies: Vol. 2: Temple & Community in the Persian Period. Richards, Kent H., ed. 2009. (Library of Hebrew Bible/Old Testament Studies, the Ser.). (ENG.). 313p. 55.00 (978-0-567-11229-3(2), T&T Clark) Continuum International Publishing Group, Ltd. GBR. Dist: National Bk. Network.

Eslinger, Lyle. Ascribe to the Lord: Biblical & Other Essays in Memory of Peter C. Craigie. 2009. (Library of Hebrew Bible/Old Testament Studies, the Ser.). (ENG.). 75.00 (978-0-567-61023-2(3), T&T Clark) Continuum International Publishing Group, Ltd. GBR. Dist: National Bk. Network.

Falk, Dean. Parabiblical Texts: Strategies for Extending the Scriptures among the Dead Sea Scrolls. 2007. (Library of Second Temple Studies, the Ser.). (ENG., Illus.). 202p. 130.00 (978-1-84127-242-9(6), T&T Clark Int'l) Continuum International Publishing Group, Ltd. GBR. Dist: National Bk. Network.

Faur, Jose. The Horizontal Society, Vol. 1: Understanding the Covenant & Alphabetic Judaism. 2008. (Emunot: Jewish Philosophy & Kabbalah Ser.: Volume 1). (ENG.). 456p. 70.00 (978-1-934843-13-0(X)) Academic Studies Pr.

—The Horizontal Society, Vol. 2: Understanding the Covenant & Alphabetic Judaism. 2nd ed. 2008. (Emunot: Jewish Philosophy & Kabbalah Ser.: Volume 2). (ENG.). 220p. 60.00 (978-1-934843-18-5(0)) Academic Studies Pr.

Ferrell, James L. The Hidden Christ: Beneath the Surface of the Old Testament. 2012. pap. 24.99 (978-1-60908-915-3(4)) 2009. 29.95 (978-1-59038-477-0(6)) Deseret Bk. Co.

Finkelstein, Israel, et al. The Quest for the Historical Israel: Debating Archaeology & the History of Early Israel: Lectures Delivered at the Annual Colloquium of the Institute for Secular Humanistic Judaism, Detroit, October 2005. 2007. (978-90-401-5738-7(3)) BRILL.

—The Quest for the Historical Israel: Debating Archaeology & the History of Early Israel: Lectures Delivered at the Annual Colloquium of the Institute for Secular Humanistic Judaism, Detroit, October 2005. 2007. (Archaeology & Biblical Studies). 24.95 (978-1-58983-277-0(9)) Society of Biblical Literature.

Finsterbusch, Karin, et al, eds. Human Sacrifice in Jewish & Christian Tradition. 2006. (Numen Book Series-Studies in the History of Religions). (Illus.). 365p. (978-90-04-15085-0(4)) BRILL.

Firth, David G. & Wegner, Paul D. Presence, Power, & Promise: The Role of the Spirit of God in the Old Testament. 2011. (978-1-84474-534-0(1), IVP Acad.) InterVarsity Pr.

Firth, David G. & Wegner, Paul D., eds. Presence, Power & Promise: The Role of the Spirit of God in the Old Testament. 2011. (ENG.). 415p. pap. 30.00 (978-0-8308-3957-5(7), IVP Acad.) InterVarsity Pr.

Fleming, Daniel. The Legacy of Israel in Judah's Bible: History, Politics, & the Reinscribing of Tradition. 2012. (ENG.). 320p. (978-1-107-02431-1(5)); pap. (978-1-107-66999-4(5)) Cambridge Univ. Pr.

Flesher, Paul V. M. & Chilton, Bruce. The Targums: A Critical Introduction. 2011. 575p. pap. 69.95 (978-1-60258-385-6(4)); (ENG., Illus.). pap. 69.95 (978-1-60258-382-5(X)) Baylor Univ. Pr.

Flesher, Paul V. M. & Chilton, Bruce D. The Targums: A Critical Introduction. 2011. (Studies in the Aramaic Interpretation of Scripture). (Illus.). XVIII, 558p. (978-90-04-21769-0(X)) BRILL.

Frame, Grant & Eichler, Barry L. A Common Cultural Heritage: Studies on Mesopotamia & the Biblical World in Honor of Barry L. Eichler. 2011. (978-1-934309-37-7(0), CDL Pr.) Univ. Pr. of Maryland.

Frankel, David. The Land of Canaan & the Destiny of Israel: Theologies of Territory in the Hebrew Bible. 2011. 49.50 (978-1-57506-202-0(X)) Eisenbrauns, Inc.

Frazer, James George. Folk-lore in the Old Testament. 2010. pap. 76.72 (978-1-61719-818-2(8)); pap. 76.72 (978-1-61719-833-5(1)) Gorgias Pr., LLC.

Frendo, Anthony J. Pre-Exilic Israel, the Hebrew Bible, & Archaeology: Integrating Text & Artefact. 2011. (Library Hebrew Bible/Old Testament Studies). 144p. 120.00 (978-0-567-41563-9(5), T&T Clark Int'l) Continuum International Publishing Group, Ltd. GBR. Dist: National Bk. Network.

Friedman, Richard Elliott & Dolansky, Shawna. The Bible Now, 1 vol. 2011. (ENG.). 272p. 27.95 (978-0-19-531163-1(9)) Oxford Univ. Pr., Inc.

—Sacred History, Sacred Literature: Essays on Ancient Israel, the Bible, & Religion in Honor of R. E. Friedman on His Sixtieth Birthday. 2008. (Illus.). xiv, 348p. 49.50 (978-1-57506-151-1(1)) Eisenbrauns, Inc.

Gatti, Nicoletta & Ossom-Batsa, George. Journeying with the Old Testament. 2011. (Alte Testament im Dialog - an Outline of an Old Testament Dialogue Ser.). (ENG.). 189p. pap. (978-3-0343-1006-2(4)) Lang, Peter.

Gelander, Shamai. From Two Kingdoms to One Nation - Israel & Judah: Studies in Division & Unification. 2011. (978-90-04-20346-4(X)) BRILL.

George, Elizabeth. Una Mujer Conforme al Corazon de Dios. pap. 3.99 (978-0-7899-1409-5(3)) Editorial Unilit.

Gerstenberger, Erhard S. Wesen und Herkunft des Apodiktischen Rechts. 2009. 170p. pap. 20.00 (978-1-60608-491-5(7), Wipf and Stock) Wipf & Stock Pubs.

Gertz, Jan Christian, ed. Grundinformation Altes Testement: Eine Einfuhrung in Literatur, Religion und Geschichte des Alten Testaments. 2008. (GER., Illus.). 640p. (C). pap. 50.00 (978-3-8252-2745-6(6)) Vanderhoeck & Ruprecht GmbH & Co. KG DEU. Dist: ISD.

Gertz, Jan Christian, et al. T&T Clark Handbook of the Old Testament: An Introduction to the Literature, Religion & History of the Old Testament. 2012. (ENG.). 872p. 160.00 (978-0-567-42529-4(0)); pap. 49.95 (978-0-567-25368-2(6)) Continuum International Publishing Group, Ltd. GBR. (T&T Clark Int'l). Dist: National Bk. Network.

Gignilliat, Mark S. A Brief History of Old Testament Criticism: From Benedict Spinoza to Brevard Childs, 1 vol. 2012. (ENG.). 192p. pap. 16.99 (978-0-310-32532-1(3)) Zondervan.

Gladson, Jerry A. The Five Exotic Scrolls of the Hebrew Bible: The Prominence, Literary Structure, & Liturgical Significance of the Megilloth. 2009. 500p. 129.95 (978-0-7734-4749-3(0)) Mellen, Edwin Pr., The.

Gleicher, Jules. Political Themes in the Hebrew Scriptures. 2010. (ENG.). 268p. 84.00 (978-0-230-61822-0(7)) Palgrave Macmillan.

Gomes, Jules. The Sanctuary of Bethel & the Configuration of Israelite Identity. 2006. (Beihefte Zur Zeitschrift Für Die Alttestamentliche Wissenschaft Ser.). (ENG.). XX, 303p. 133.00 (978-3-11-018993-3(3)) De Gruyter, Walter Inc.

Gomes, Jules Francis. The Sanctuary of Bethel & the Configuration of Israelite Identity. (Beihefte zur Zeitschrift far die alttestamentliche Wissenschaft Ser.). (ENG.). XX, 303p. 225.00 (978-3-11-182965-4(0)) De Gruyter, Walter Inc.

Gordon, R. P. Hebrew Bible & Ancient Versions: Selected Essays of Robert P. Gordon. 2006. (Ashgate Contemporary Thinkers on Religion Ser.). 408p. 150.00 (978-0-7546-5617-3(9)) Ashgate Publishing Co.

Gordon, R. P. Studies on the Text & Versions of the Hebrew Bible in Honour of Robert Gordon. Khan, Geoffrey & Lipton, Diana, eds. 2011. (ENG.). XXII, 436p. (978-90-04-21730-0(4)) BRILL.

Gottheil, Richard J. H. Some Early Jewish Bible Criticism. 2010. 81.80 (978-1-61143-393-7(2)) Gorgias Pr., LLC.

Gottlieb, Michah, ed. Moses Mendelssohn: Writings on Judaism, Christianity, & the Bible. 2011. (Tauber Institute Series for the Study of European Jewry & the Brandeis Library of Modern Jewish Thought Ser.). 296p. (C). 85.00 (978-1-58465-684-5(0)); (ENG.). pap. 26.00 (978-1-58465-685-2(9)) Univ. Pr. of New England. (Brandeis University Press).

Gottwald, Norman K. The Politics of Ancient Israel. 2007. (Library of Ancient Israel Ser.). (ENG.). 388p. per. 45.00 (978-0-664-23234-4(5)) Westminster John Knox Pr.

Grabbe, Lester L., et al. The Historian & the Bible. 2010. (Library of Hebrew Bible/Old Testament Studies). (ENG., Illus.). 256p. 140.00 (978-0-567-20268-0(2), T&T Clark Int'l) Continuum International Publishing Group, Ltd. GBR. Dist: National Bk. Network.

Graham, M. Patrick. Chronicler as Author: Studies in Text & Texture. McKenzie, Steven L., ed. 2009. (Library of Hebrew Bible/Old Testament Studies, the Ser.). (ENG.). 424p. 70.00 (978-0-567-04662-8(1), T&T Clark) Continuum International Publishing Group, Ltd. GBR. Dist: National Bk. Network.

—History & Interpretation: Essays in Honour of John H. Hayes. Brown, William P. & Kuan, Jeffrey K., eds. 2009. (Library of Hebrew Bible/Old Testament Studies, the Ser.). (ENG.). 267p. 44.95 (978-0-567-11205-7(5), T&T Clark) Continuum International Publishing Group, Ltd. GBR. Dist: National Bk. Network.

—Worship & the Hebrew Bible: Essays in Honor of John T. Willis. McKenzie, Steven L. & Marrs, Richard R., eds. 2009. (Library of Hebrew Bible/Old Testament Studies, the Ser.). (ENG.). 284p. 49.95 (978-0-567-31680-6(7), T&T Clark) Continuum International Publishing Group, Ltd. GBR. Dist: National Bk. Network.

Green, Deborah A. The Aroma of Righteousness: Scent & Seduction in Rabbinic Life & Literature. 2011. (ENG.). 272p. 69.95 (978-0-271-03767-7(9)) Pennsylvania State Univ. Pr.

Green, Phil. SUbstance. 2010. 80p. pap. (978-1-84427-525-0(6)) Scripture Union.

Green, Steven D. The Tribe of Ephraim: Covenant & Bloodline. 2007. pap. 16.99 (978-0-88290-822-9(7)) Cedar Fort, Inc./CFI Distribution.

Greengus, Samuel. Laws in the Bible & in Early Rabbinic Collections: The Legal Legacy of the Ancient near East. 2011. 330p. pap. 36.00 (978-1-60899-946-0(7), Cascade Bks.) Wipf & Stock Pubs.

Greenspahn, Frederick E., ed. The Hebrew Bible: New Insights & Scholarship. 2007. (ENG.). 256p. pap. 22.00 (978-0-8147-3188-8(0)) New York Univ. Pr.

Grey, Jacqueline. Them, Us & Me: How the Old Testament Speaks to People Today. 2010. (Illus.). 248p. pap. 27.00 (978-1-60899-590-5(9)) Wipf & Stock Pubs.

Groves, J. Alan, et al. Eyes to See, Ears to Hear: Essays in Memory of J. Alan Groves. 2010. (Illus.). xxxiii, 225p. pap. (978-1-59638-122-3(1)) P & R Publishing.

Grunhaus, Naomi. The Challenge of Received Tradition: Dilemmas of Interpretation in Radak's Biblical Commentaries. 2012. 272p. 74.00 (978-0-19-985840-8(3)) Oxford Univ. Pr., Inc.

Guillaume, Philippe. Land, Credit & Crisis: Agrarian Finance in the Hebrew Bible. 2012. (BibleWorld Ser.). (ENG., Illus.). 308p. (C). 110.00 (978-1-84553-927-6(3)) Equinox Publishing Ltd. GBR. Dist: ISD.

Gzella, Holger. Languages from the World of the Bible. 2011. (978-1-934078-61-7(1)) De Gruyter, Walter Inc.

HaCohen, Ran. Reclaiming the Hebrew Bible: German-Jewish Reception of Biblical Criticism. Engel, Michelle, tr. (Studia Judaica Ser.). 2011. (ENG., Illus.). 250p. 196.00 (978-3-11-214252-3(7)) 2010. 280p. 126.00 (978-3-11-024756-5(9)) De Gruyter, Walter Inc.

Hahn, Scott. Faith Charts, the Bible at a Glance. 2008. (Faith Charts Ser.). 6p. 7.95 (978-1-59276-483-9(5)) Our Sunday Visitor, Publishing Div.

Halberstam, Chaya T. & Fonrobert, Charlotte. Law & Truth in Biblical & Rabbinic Literature. 2010. (ENG.). 240p. 34.95 (978-0-253-35411-2(0), 0253354110) Indiana Univ. Pr.

Hamilton, Mark W. The Body Royal: The Social Poetics of Kingship in Ancient Israel. 2008. 336p. pap. 37.95 (978-1-58983-382-1(1)) Society of Biblical Literature.

Hanson, Anthony Tyrrell. Studies in Paul's Technique & Theology. 2011. 344p. pap. 40.00 (978-1-61097-353-3(4), Wipf and Stock) Wipf & Stock Pubs.

Harper, William Rainey & Harper, William R. The Priestly Element in the Old Testament: An Aid to Historical Study. 2007. 300p. pap. 30.00 (978-1-55635-218-8(2), Wipf and Stock) Wipf & Stock Pubs.

Hartman, Geoffrey H. The Third Pillar: Essays in Judaic Studies. 2011. (Jewish Culture & Contexts Ser.). (Illus.). 248p. (C). 39.95 (978-0-8122-4316-1(1)) Univ. of Pennsylvania Pr.

Harvey, Charles D. Finding Morality in the Diaspora? Moral Ambiguity & Transformed Morality in the Books of Esther. (Beihefte zur Zeitschrift far die alttestamentliche Wissenschaft Ser.). (ENG.). XIV, 274p. 180.00 (978-3-11-186952-0(0)) De Gruyter, Walter Inc.

Haskell, Ellen Davina. Suckling at My Mother's Breasts: The Image of a Nursing God in Jewish Mysticism. 2012. (SUNY Series in Western Esoteric Traditions Ser.). (ENG.). 176p. 75.00 (978-1-4384-4381-2(1)) State Univ. of New York Pr.

Hauser, Alan. Art & Meaning: Rhetoric in Biblical Literature. Gunn, David M. & Clines, David J. A., eds. 2009. (Library of Hebrew Bible/Old Testament Studies, the Ser.). (ENG.). 266p. 44.95 (978-0-567-44863-7(0), T&T Clark) Continuum International Publishing Group, Ltd. GBR. Dist: National Bk. Network.

Hazony, Yoram. The Philosophy of Hebrew Scripture: An Introduction. 2012. (ENG.). 240p. (978-1-107-00317-0(2)); (Illus.). pap. (978-0-521-17667-5(0)) Cambridge Univ. Pr.

Heine, Ronald E. Reading the Old Testament with the Ancient Church: Exploring the Formation of Early Christian Thought. 2007. (Evangelical Ressourcement Ser.). 208p. (C). pap. 24.00 (978-0-8010-2777-2(2)) Baker Academic.

Heskett, Randall. Bible as a Human Witness to Divine Revelation: Hearing the Word of God Through Historically Dissimilar Traditions. Irwin, Brian, ed. 2010. (Library of Hebrew Bible/Old Testament Studies, the Ser.). (ENG., Illus.). 394p. 150.00 (978-0-567-02851-8(6), T&T Clark Int'l) Continuum International Publishing Group, Ltd. GBR. Dist: National Bk. Network.

Hess, Richard S., et al. Critical Issues in Early Israelite History. 2008. 324p. (C). 44.50 (978-1-57506-804-6(4)) Eisenbrauns, Inc.

Hill, Robert C. Of Prophets & Poets: Antioch Fathers on the Bible. 2007. pap. (978-1-885652-92-8(5)) Holy Cross Orthodox Pr.

—Reading the Old Testament in Antioch. 2010. (978-1-58983-497-2(6)) Society of Biblical Literature.

Hillel, Daniel. The Natural History of the Bible: An Environmental Exploration of the Hebrew Scriptures. 2007. (ENG., Illus.). 376p. (gr. 17). pap. 27.00 (978-0-231-13363-0(4)) Columbia Univ. Pr.

Holden, Lynn A. Forms of Deformity. 2009. (Library of Hebrew Bible/Old Testament Studies, the Ser.). (ENG.). 370p. 60.00 (978-1-4411-2079-3(3), T&T Clark) Continuum International Publishing Group, Ltd. GBR. Dist: National Bk. Network.

Holton, Bil. The Gospel of Matthew: New Metaphysical Version. Holton, Cher, ed. 2007. 100p. 21.95 (978-1-893095-49-6(5), Prosperity Publishing Hse.) Liberty Publishing Group.

Holzapfel, Richard Neitzel, et al. Jehovah & the World of the Old Testament. 2009. 45.95 (978-1-60641-136-0(5)) Deseret Bk. Co.

Honor, Leo L. Sennacherib's Invasion of Palestine. (Columbia University, Contributions to Oriental History & Philology Ser.: No. 12). reprint ed. 27.50 (978-0-404-50542-4(2)) AMS Pr., Inc.

—Sennacherib's Invasion of Palestine: A Critical Source Study. 2007. (Analecta Gorgiana Ser.: 32). per. 34.00 (978-1-59333-626-4(8)) Gorgias Pr., LLC.

Hopkins, Denise Dombkowski & Koppel, Michael Sherwood. Grounded in the Living Word: The Old Testament & Pastoral Care Practices. 2010. 248p. pap. 20.00 (978-0-8028-6368-3(X)) Eerdmans, William B. Publishing Co.

Horsley, Richard A. Scribes, Visionaries, & the Politics of Second Temple Judea. 2007. (ENG.). 261p. per. 30.00 (978-0-664-22991-7(3)) Westminster John Knox Pr.

Houston, Walter & Houston. Contending for Justice: Ideologies & Theologies of Social Justice in the Old Testament. 2009. (ENG.). 304p. 55.00 (978-0-567-03354-3(6), T&T Clark Int'l) Continuum International Publishing Group, Ltd. GBR. Dist: National Bk. Network.

Howard, Roger. The Arctic Gold Rush: The New Race for Tomorrow's Natural Resources. 2009. (ENG., Illus.). 272p. 29.95 (978-1-4411-8110-7(5))

Continuum International Publishing Group, Ltd. GBR. Dist: National Bk. Network.

Huizenga, L. A. The New Isaac: Tradition & Intertextuality in the Gospel of Matthew. 2009. (Novum Testamentum Supplements Ser.). xx, 337p. *(978-90-04-17569-3(5))* BRILL.

Hundley, Michael B. Keeping Heaven on Earth: Safeguarding the Divine Presence in the Priestly Tabernacle. 2011. (Forschungen zum Alten Testament, 2 / No. 50 Ser.). 266p. pap. 120.00 *(978-3-16-150697-0(9))* Mohr Siebeck GmbH & Co. KG DEU. Dist: Coronet Bks.

Hunt, Alice & Hunt. Missing Priests: The Zadokites in Tradition & History, Vol. 452. 2006. (Library of Hebrew Bible/Old Testament Studies). (ENG.). 242p. 145.00 *(978-0-567-02852-5(6)*, T&T Clark Int'l) Continuum International Publishing Group, Ltd. GBR. Dist: National Bk. Network.

Ibn Ezra, Abraham ben Meir & Goodman, Mordechai S. The Sabbath Epistle of Rabbi Abraham Ibn Ezra: 'Iggeret Hashabbat. 2008. *(978-1-60280-111-0(8))* Ktav Publishing Hse., Inc.

Isaacs, Roger D. Talking with God: The Radioactive Ark of the Testimony: Communication Through It. Protection from It. Williams Miller, Janice, ed. 2010. (Illus.). 514p. 29.95 *(978-1-4125-4997-4(3)*, Sacred Closet Bks.) Publishing Institute, Inc., The.

Isaak, Jon M. & Martens, E. A. The Old Testament in the Life of God's People: Essays in Honor of Elmer A. Martens. 2009. (Illus.). xxvii, 349p. 49.50 *(978-1-57506-158-0(9))* Eisenbrauns, Inc.

Jacobs, Irving. The Midrashic Process: Tradition & Interpretation in Rabbinic Judaism. 2008. (ENG.). 236p. pap. 36.00 *(978-0-521-07611-1(0))* Cambridge Univ. Pr.

Janzen, David. The Social Meanings of Sacrifice in the Hebrew Bible: A Study of Four Writings. (Beihefte zur Zeitschrift fur die alttestamentliche Wissenschaft Ser.). (ENG.). XII, 300p. 225.00 ***(978-3-11-181253-3(7))*** De Gruyter, Walter Inc.

John Holdsworth Staff. Lies, Sex & Politicians: Communicating the Old Testament in Contemporary Culture. 2011. 178p. pap. ***(978-0-334-04340-9(9)***, SCM Pr.) Hymns Ancient & Modern Ltd.

Johnstone, William. Chronicles & Exodus: An Analogy & its Application. 2009. (Library of Hebrew Bible/Old Testament Studies, the Ser.). (ENG.). 331p. 55.00 *(978-0-567-22326-5(4)*, T&T Clark) Continuum International Publishing Group, Ltd. GBR. Dist: National Bk. Network.

Jones, Bill. Putting Together the Puzzle of the Old Testament. 2007. (ENG., Illus.). 237p. (J). per. 16.99 *(978-1-932805-94-9(X)*, Paternoster) Authentic Media.

Jordan, W. G. Biblical Criticism & Modern Thought or the Place of the Old Testament Documents in the Life of Today. 2007. (ENG.). 332p. 45.95 *(978-0-548-03380-7(3))* Kessinger Publishing, LLC.

Kaiser, Walter C., Jr. The Majesty of God in the Old Testament: A Guide for Preaching & Teaching. 2007. 176p. (C). pap. 20.00 *(978-0-8010-3244-8(X))* Baker Academic.

Kaiser, Walter C., Jr., ed. Classical Evangelical Essays in Old Testament Interpretation. 2008. 265p. pap. 29.00 *(978-1-60608-025-2(3))* Wipf & Stock Pubs.

Kaiseratt, Harold. Our False Christianity: How it Started. 2010. pap. 12.95 *(978-0-533-16353-3(6))* Vantage Pr., Inc.

Kaltner, John, et al. The Uncensored Bible: The Bawdy & Naughty Bits of the Good Book. (ENG.). 224p. 2009. pap. 13.99 *(978-0-06-123885-7(6))* 2008. 19.95 *(978-0-06-123884-0(8))* HarperCollins Pubs. (HarperOne).

Kaminsky, Joel S. Yet I Loved Jacob: Reclaiming the Biblical Concept of Election. 2007. 242p. per. 31.00 *(978-0-687-02534-3(6))* Abingdon Pr.

Kamionkowski, S. Tamar & Kim, Wonil, eds. Bodies, Embodiment, & Theology of the Hebrew Bible, Vol. 465. 2010. (Library of Hebrew Bible/Old Testament Studies, the Ser.). (ENG., Illus.). 272p. 130.00 *(978-0-567-54799-6(X)*, T&T Clark Int'l) Continuum International Publishing Group, Ltd. GBR. Dist: National Bk. Network.

Kavanagh, Preston. The Exilic Code: Ciphers, Word Links, & Dating in Exilic & Post-Exilic Biblical Literature. 2008. 328p. pap. 35.00 *(978-1-55635-070-2(6)*, Pickwick Pubns.) Wipf & Stock Pubs.

—The Shaphan Group: The Fifteen Authors Who Shaped the Hebrew Bible. 2011. 154p. pap. 18.00 *(978-1-60608-611-7(1)*, Pickwick Pubns.) Wipf & Stock Pubs.

Keehus, Magnus N. Jesus: Is He the Messiah of Israel? ÒWho will Declare His Generation?Ó A Dialogue Based on the Tanakh, Talmud, & Targumim; the Dead Sea Scrolls; & the New Testament. 2011. 308p. pap. 34.00 *(978-1-60899-825-8(8)*, Wipf and Stock) Wipf & Stock Pubs.

Kelle, Brad E. & Ames, Frank Ritchel. Writing & Reading War: Rhetoric, Gender, & Ethics in Biblical & Modern Contexts. 2008. 280p. pap. 34.95 *(978-1-58983-354-8(6))* Society of Biblical Literature.

Kelle, Brad E., et al. Interpreting Exile: Interdisciplinary Studies of Displacement & Deportation in Biblical & Modern Contexts. 2011. ***(978-1-58983-604-4(9))***; ***(978-1-58983-605-1(7))*** Society of Biblical Literature.

Kennett, R. H. Old Testament Essays. 2012. (ENG.). 282p. pap. 45.00 ***(978-1-107-66398-5(9))*** Cambridge Univ. Pr.

Kennett, Robert Hatch. The Church of Israel: Studies & Essays. Cook, S. A., ed. 2012. (ENG.). 308p. pap. 42.99 ***(978-1-107-68048-7(4))*** Cambridge Univ. Pr.

Kent, Charles Foster. The Origin & Permanent Value of the Old Testament. 2008. 184p. 22.99 *(978-0-554-32101-1(7))*; 25.99 *(978-0-554-22798-6(3))* BiblioBazaar.

—The Origin & Permanent Value of the Old Testament. 2007. 144p. per. *(978-1-4065-1900-6(6))* Dodo Pr.

Kim, Sang-Kee. Das Menschenbild in der biblischen Urgeschichte und in ihren altorientalischen Parallelen. 2007. (GER.). 250p. pap. *(978-3-8325-1500-3(3))* Logos Verlag Berlin.

Kirkpatrick. Function of Ancient Historiography in Biblical & Cognate Studies. 2008. (Library of Hebrew Bible/Old Testament Studies, the Ser.). (ENG.). 192p. 120.00 *(978-0-567-02715-3(5)*, T&T Clark Int'l) Continuum International Publishing Group, Ltd. GBR. Dist: National Bk. Network.

Klein-Braslavy, Sara. Maimonides As a Biblical Interpreter. 2011. (Emunot: Jewish Philosophy & Kabbalah Ser.). (ENG.). 260p. 69.00 *(978-1-936235-28-5(5))* Academic Studies Pr.

Klein, Michael L. On the Jewish Targums: Collected Essays. 2011. (Illus.). xvi, 296p. *(978-90-04-20295-5(1))* BRILL.

Klement, Herbert H. & Steinberg, Julius. Themenbuch Zur Theologie des Alten Testaments. 2007. (GER., Illus.). 342p. *(978-3-7655-9545-5(4))*; *(978-3-417-29545-0(9))* Brockhaus, R. Verlag GmbH & Co.

Klepper, Deeana Copeland. The Insight of Unbelievers: Nicholas of Lyra & Christian Reading of Jewish Text in the Later Middle Ages. (Jewish Culture & Contexts Ser.). (Illus.). 240p. (C). 2008. pap. 24.95 *(978-0-8122-2021-6(8))* 2007. 59.95 *(978-0-8122-3991-1(1))* Univ. of Pennsylvania Pr.

Knight, Douglas A. Tradition & Theology in the Old Testament. 2007. (ENG.). 356p. per. 35.95 *(978-1-58983-280-0(9))* Society of Biblical Literature.

Knight, Douglas A. & Levine, Amy-Jill. The Meaning of the Bible: What the Jewish Scriptures & Christian Old Testament Can Teach Us. (ENG.). 448p. 2012. pap. 19.99 ***(978-0-06-206773-9(7))*** 2011. 29.99 *(978-0-06-112175-3(4))* HarperCollins Pubs. (HarperOne).

Knoppers, Gary N. & Grabbe, Lester L., eds. Exile & Restoration Revisited: Essays on the Babylonian & Persian Periods in Memory of Peter R. Ackroyd. 2011. (ENG.). 237p. pap. 44.95 ***(978-0-567-28083-1(7)***, T&T Clark Int'l) Continuum International Publishing Group, Ltd. GBR. Dist: National Bk. Network.

Knoppers, Gary N. & Ristau, Kenneth A. Community Identity in Judean Historiography: Biblical & Comparative Perspectives. 2009. 44.50 *(978-1-57506-165-8(1))* Eisenbrauns, Inc.

Knowles, Melody D. Centrality Practiced: Jerusalem in the Religious Practice of Yehud & the Diaspora in the Persian Period. 2006. (Archaeology & Biblical Studies: No. 16). 181p. *(978-90-04-13775-2(0))* BRILL.

Korngold, Jamie S. God in the Wilderness: Rediscovering the Spirituality of the Great Outdoors with the Adventure Rabbi. 2008. 160p. pap. 12.99 *(978-0-385-52049-2(2)*, Three Leaves) Doubleday Religious Publishing Group, The.

Korpel, Marjo C. A. & De Hoop, Raymond, eds. The Impact of Unit Delimitation on Exegesis. 2008. (Pericope Ser.). 293p. *(978-90-04-17162-6(2))* BRILL.

Kraft, Robert A. Exploring the Scripturesque: Jewish Texts & Their Christian Contexts. 2009. (Supplements to the Journal for the Study of Judaism Ser.). 288p. *(978-90-04-17010-0(3))* BRILL.

Kratz, Reinhard G. Composition of the Narrative Books of the Old Testament. 2010. (ENG.). 352p. 72.00 *(978-0-567-08921-2(5)*, T&T Clark Int'l) Continuum International Publishing Group, Ltd. GBR. Dist: National Bk. Network.

Kratz, Reinhard G. & Spieckermann, Hermann, eds. One God - One Cult - One Nation: Archaeological & Biblical Perspectives. (Beihefte zur Zeitschrift far die alttestamentliche Wissenschaft Ser.). (Illus.). 2011. XX, 463p. 210.00 ***(978-3-11-174103-1(6))*** 2010. (ENG., XIX, 463p. 140.00 *(978-3-11-022357-6(0))* De Gruyter, Walter Inc.

Kravitz, Kathryn F., et al. Bringing the Hidden to Light: The Process of Interpretation: Studies in Honor of Stephen A. Geller. 2007. 49.50 *(978-1-57506-124-5(4))* Eisenbrauns, Inc.

Kugel, James L. How to Read the Bible: A Guide to Scripture, Then & Now. 2008. (ENG., Illus.). 848p. pap. 21.00 *(978-0-7432-3587-7(8)*, Free Pr.) Free Pr.

—The Ladder of Jacob: Ancient Interpretations of the Biblical Story of Jacob & His Children. 2006. (ENG., Illus.). 296p. (C). 24.95 *(978-0-691-12122-2(2))* Princeton Univ. Pr.

Kugel, James L., et al. The Idea of Biblical Interpretation: Essays in Honor of James L. Kugel. 2008. 628p. pap. 65.95 *(978-1-58983-387-6(2))* Society of Biblical Literature.

Kuntz, J. Kenneth. The People of Ancient Israel. 2009. 576p. pap. 41.00 *(978-1-60608-880-7(7)*, Wipf and Stock) Wipf & Stock Pubs.

Lang, Bernhard. Hebrew Life & Literature: Selected Essays of Bernhard Lang. 2008. (Society for Old Testament Study Ser.). (Illus.). 292p. 114.95 *(978-0-7546-6618-9(2))* Ashgate Publishing Co.

Lange, Armin & Romheld, K. F. Diethard, eds. Wege zur Hebraischen Bibel: Denken - Sprache - Kultur. in memoriam Hans-Peter Muller. 2009. (Forschungen Zur Religion und Literatur des Alten & Neuen Testament Ser.). (GER., Illus.). 247p. (C). 96.00 *(978-3-525-53092-4(7))* Vandenhoeck & Ruprecht GmbH & Co. KG DEU. Dist: ISD.

Lange, Armin & Weigold, Matthias. Biblical Quotations & Allusions in Second Temple Jewish Literature. 2011. (Journal of Ancient Judaism. Supplements (JAJ. S) Ser.). (ENG.). 384p. (C). 122.00 *(978-3-525-55028-1(6))* Vandenhoeck & Ruprecht GmbH & Co. KG DEU. Dist: ISD.

Lawrence, Jonathan David. Washing in Water: Trajectories of Ritual Bathing in the Hebrew Bible & Second Temple Literature. 2006. (SBL - Academia Biblica Ser.). (Illus.). 294p. *(978-90-04-14670-9(9))* BRILL.

—Washing in Water: Trajectories of Ritual Bathing in the Hebrew Bible & Second Temple Literature. 2006. (Illus.). xix, 294p. 47.95 *(978-1-58983-199-5(3))* Society of Biblical Literature.

Lee, Eunny P. The Vitality of Enjoyment in Qohelet's Theological Rhetoric. (Beihefte zur Zeitschrift far die alttestamentliche Wissenschaft Ser.). (ENG.). XIV, 168p. 180.00 ***(978-3-11-182780-3(1))*** De Gruyter, Walter Inc.

Lefkovitz, Lori. In Scriptures: The First Stories of Jewish Sexual Identities. 2010. (ENG.). 204p. (C). (gr. 13-17). 55.00 *(978-0-7425-4704-9(3))* Rowman & Littlefield Publishers, Inc.

Lefkovitz, Lori Hope. In Scripture: The First Stories of Jewish Sexual Identities. 2011. 204p. pap. 19.95 ***(978-0-7425-4705-6(1))*** Rowman & Littlefield Publishers, Inc.

Legaspi, Michael C. & Michaelis, Johann David. The Death of Scripture & the Rise of Biblical Studies, 1 vol. 2010. (Oxford Studies in Historical Theology Ser.). (ENG.). 240p. 74.00 *(978-0-19-539435-1(6))* Oxford Univ. Pr., Inc.

Lehrer, Alice Becker. If We Could Hear Them Now: Encounters with Legendary Jewish Heroines. 2009. 176p. 19.95 *(978-965-524-031-3(2)*, Urim Fiction) Urim Pubns. ISR. Dist: Coronet Bks.

Lemche, Niels Peter. The Old Testament Between Theology & History: A Critical Survey. 2008. (ENG., Illus.). 504p. pap. 50.00 *(978-0-664-23245-0(0))* Westminster John Knox Pr.

Leuchter, Mark, et al, eds. From Babel to Babylon: Essays on Biblical History & Literature in Honor of Brian Peckham. 2006. (Library of Hebrew Bible/Old Testament Studies, the Ser.). (ENG., Illus.). 400p. 180.00 *(978-0-567-02892-1(5)*, T&T Clark Int'l) Continuum International Publishing Group, Ltd. GBR. Dist: National Bk. Network.

Leuchter, Mark & Hutton, Jeremy Michael. Levites & Priests in History & Tradition: Edited by Mark Leuchter & Jeremy M. Hutton. 2011. ***(978-1-58983-607-5(3))***; ***(978-1-58983-606-8(5))*** Society of Biblical Literature.

Leung Lai, Barbara M. Through The 'I'-Window: The Inner Life of Characters in the Hebrew Bible. 2011. 212p. ***(978-1-907534-20-1(2))*** Sheffield Phoenix Pr.

Levenson, Alan T. The Making of the Modern Jewish Bible: How Scholars in Germany, Israel, & America Transformed an Ancient Text. 2011. (ENG.). 262p. 54.95 *(978-1-4422-0516-1(4))* Rowman & Littlefield Publishers, Inc.

Levenson, Jon D. Resurrection & the Restoration of Israel: The Ultimate Victory of the God of Life. 2008. (ENG.). 304p. per. 18.00 *(978-0-300-13635-7(8))* Yale Univ. Pr.

Levi, Gerson B. Gnomic Literature in Bible & Apocrypha: With Special Reference to the Gnomic Fragments & Their Bearing on the Proverb Collections. 2007. 114p. pap. 10.00 *(978-1-55635-648-3(X)*, Wipf and Stock) Wipf & Stock Pubs.

Levin, Christoph. Fortschreibungen: Gesammelte Studien zum Alten Testament. (Beihefte zur Zeitschrift far die alttestamentliche Wissenschaft Ser.). (GER.). 360p. 255.00 ***(978-3-11-185230-0(X))*** De Gruyter, Walter Inc.

Levinas, Emmanuel & Levinas. Beyond the Verse: Talmudic Readings & Lectures. Mole, Gary D., tr. from FRE. 2007. (Continuum Impacts Ser.). (ENG.). 240p. 32.95 *(978-0-8264-9903-5(1))* Continuum International Publishing Group, Ltd. GBR. Dist: National Bk. Network.

Levine, Aaron, ed. The Oxford Handbook of Judaism & Economics, 1 vol. 2010. (Oxford Handbooks Ser.). (ENG., Illus.). 736p. 150.00 *(978-0-19-539862-5(9))* Oxford Univ. Pr., Inc.

Levine, Baruch A. & Gross, Andrew. In Pursuit of Meaning: Collected Studies of Baruch A. Levine. 2011. 109.50 *(978-1-57506-206-8(2))*; *(978-1-57506-208-2(9))*; *(978-1-57506-207-5(0))* Eisenbrauns, Inc.

Levinson, Bernard M. Gender & Law in the Hebrew Bible & the Ancient near East. Frymer-Kensky, Tikva & Matthews, Victor H., eds. 2009. (Library of Hebrew Bible/Old Testament Studies, the Ser.). (ENG.). 256p. 44.95 *(978-0-567-54500-8(8)*, T&T Clark) Continuum International Publishing Group, Ltd. GBR. Dist: National Bk. Network.

—Legal Revision & Religious Renewal in Ancient Israel. (ENG.). 232p. 2010. pap. 27.99 *(978-0-521-17191-5(1))* 2008. 84.00 *(978-0-521-51344-9(8))* Cambridge Univ. Pr.

Levinson, Bernard M. The Right Chorale: Studies in Biblical Law & Interpretation. 2011. pap. 49.50 ***(978-1-57506-210-5(0))*** Eisenbrauns, Inc.

Levtow, Nathaniel B. Images of Others: Iconic Politics in Ancient Israel. 2008. 211p. (C). 39.50 *(978-1-57506-146-7(5))* Eisenbrauns, Inc.

Liesen, Jan & Beentjes, Pancratius, eds. Visions of Peace & Tales of War. 2010. XII, 436p. 147.00 *(978-3-11-022277-7(9))* De Gruyter, Walter Inc.

—Visions of Peace & Tales of War: [Print + Online]. 2010. 440p. 180.00 *(978-3-11-022279-1(5))* De Gruyter, Walter Inc.

Linares, Joe. Proclaiming God's Stories: How to Preach Old Testament Historical Narrative. 2008. *(978-1-59166-926-5(X))* BJU Pr.

Lipschits, Oded, et al. Judah & the Judeans in the Achaemenid Period: Negotiating Identity in an International Context. 2011. (ENG., Illus.). 600p. 64.50 *(978-1-57506-197-9(X))* Eisenbrauns, Inc.

Lipschitz, Oded, et al. Judah & the Judeans in the Fourth Century B. C. E. 2007. 59.50 *(978-1-57506-130-6(9))* Eisenbrauns, Inc.

Little, Ann M. Abraham in Arms: War & Gender in Colonial New England. 2007. (Early American Studies). (Illus.). 272p. (C). per. 24.95 *(978-0-8122-1961-6(9))* Univ. of Pennsylvania Pr.

Loader, William R. G. Philo, Josephus, & the Testaments on Sexuality: Attitudes Towards Sexuality in Writings of Philo, Josephus, & the Testaments of the Twelve Patriarchs. 2011. pap. 65.00 ***(978-0-8028-6641-7(7))*** Eerdmans, William B. Publishing Co.

Lombaard, Christo. The Old Testament & Christian Spirituality: Collected Methodological Essays, South African & General Perspectives. 2012. pap. ***(978-1-58983-652-5(9))*** Society of Biblical Literature.

Longman, Tremper, III. Old Testament Commentary Survey. 4th ed. 2007. 160p. (C). pap. 16.00 *(978-0-8010-3123-6(0))* Baker Academic.

Lorberbaum, Yair. Disempowered King: Monarchy in Classical Jewish Literature. 2011. (Robert & Arlene Kogod Library of Judaic Studies). (ENG.). 232p. 140.00 *(978-1-4411-5429-3(9))*; pap. 44.95 *(978-1-4411-4088-3(3))* Continuum International Publishing Group, Ltd. GBR. Dist: National Bk. Network.

Lunceford, Joe E. Biblical WomenNtilde;Submissive? 2009. 208p. pap. 23.00 *(978-1-60608-178-5(0)*, Wipf and Stock) Wipf & Stock Pubs.

Lyes, D. C. Jewish Origins. 2007. 380p. per. 36.18 *(978-1-4251-2144-0(6))* Trafford Publishing.

Lyons, Williams/L. A History of Modern Scholarship on the Biblical Word Herem: The Contributions of Walter C. Kaiser, Jr. , Peter C. Craigie, & Tremper Longman, III. 2009. vi, 219p. *(978-0-7734-3834-7(3))* Mellen, Edwin Pr., The.

MacArthur, John. Before Abraham: Creation, Sin, & the Nature of God, 0 vols. 2008. (MacArthur Old Testament Study Guides). 128p. pap. 9.99 *(978-1-4185-3322-9(X))* Nelson, Thomas Inc.

—The Father of Israel: Trusting God's Promises, 0 vols. 2008. (MacArthur Old Testament Study Guides). (ENG.). 128p. pap. 9.99 *(978-1-4185-3323-6(8))* Nelson, Thomas Inc.

MacDonald, Nathan. What Did the Ancient Israelites Eat? Diet in Biblical Times. 2008. (Illus.). 160p. pap. 16.00 *(978-0-8028-6298-3(5))* Eerdmans, William B. Publishing Co.

Mafico, Temba L. J. Yahweh's Emergence as "Judge" among the Gods: A Study of the Hebrew Root ¿pt. 2006. 212p. 109.95 *(978-0-7734-5518-4(3))* Mellen, Edwin Pr., The.

Magdalino, P. The Old Testament in Byzantium. Nelson, Robert, ed. 2010. (Dumbarton Oaks Byzantine Symposia & Colloquia Ser.). (Illus.). 300p. 35.00 *(978-0-88402-348-7(6))* Dumbarton Oaks.

Mahusay, Nancy. The History of Redemption. 2007. 388p. per. 19.99 *(978-1-60266-737-2(3))* Xulon Pr., Inc.

Malena, Sarah & Miano, David. Milk & Honey: Essays on Ancient Israel & the Bible in Appreciation of the Judaic Studies Program at the University of California, San Diego. 2007. (Illus.). 44.50 *(978-1-57506-127-6(9))* Eisenbrauns, Inc.

Malseed, John. Following God Through the Bible: An Overview of the Old Testament. 2006. (Following God Through the Bible Ser.). (ENG.). 320p. (gr. 11). per. 14.99 *(978-0-89957-340-3(1))* AMG Pubs.

Marsden, Richard, ed. The Old English Heptateuch & Aelfric's Libellus de Veteri Testamento et Novo, Vol. 1. 2009. (Early English Text Society Original Ser.). (ANG & ENG., Illus.). 410p. 135.00 *(978-0-19-956143-8(5))* Oxford Univ. Pr., Inc.

Marti, Karl. Zeitschrift Für Die Alttestamentliche Wissenschaft, Volumes 23-24. 2010. 684p. pap. 47.75 *(978-1-146-55437-4(0))*; 770p. pap. 53.75 *(978-1-148-13511-3(1))*; 766p. pap. 53.75 *(978-1-145-91011-9(4))* BiblioBazaar.

Marti, Karl & Stade, Bernhard. Zeitschrift Für Die Alttestamentliche Wissenschaft, Volumes 23-24. 2010. 692p. pap. 48.75 *(978-1-148-69083-4(2))*; 350p. pap. 32.75 *(978-1-149-06812-0(4))*; 766p. pap. 53.75 *(978-1-143-96136-6(6))*; 698p. pap. 48.75 *(978-1-145-97427-2(9))*; 712p. pap. 49.75 *(978-1-145-86740-6(5))*; 682p. pap. 47.75 *(978-1-143-42406-9(9))*; 746p. pap. 52.75 *(978-1-145-95423-8(8))*; 654p. pap. 46.75 *(978-1-143-84291-7(X))*; 722p. pap. 49.75 *(978-1-145-33542-4(X))*; 650p. pap. 46.75 *(978-1-146-15528-1(X))* BiblioBazaar.

Marty, William H. A Survey of the Old Testament: Student Notes. rev. ed. 2010. (ENG.). 228p. spiral bd. 33.75 *(978-0-7575-3332-7(9))* Kendall Hunt Publishing Co.

Mason, Eric F., ed. A Teacher for All Generations (2 vol. Set) Essays in Honor of James C. VanderKam, 2 vols. 2011. (Supplements to the Journal for the Study of Judaism Ser.). (Illus.). lxx, 1004p. ***(978-90-04-21520-7(4))*** BRILL.

Mason, Roger. Propaganda & Subversion in Old Testament. 208p. 19.00 *(978-0-281-05015-4(5))* SPCK Publishing GBR. Dist: Pilgrim Pr., The/United Church Pr.

Matsier, Nicolaas. De Bijbel Volgens. 3rd ed. (DUT.). 239p. *(978-90-234-1005-8(X))* De Bezige Bij B.V., Uitgeverij.

Matthews, Victor H. More Than Meets the Ear: Discovering the Hidden Contexts of Old Testament Conversations. 2008. 288p. pap. 30.00 *(978-0-8028-0384-9(9))* Eerdmans, William B. Publishing Co.

McCabe, Elizabeth A. Women in the Biblical World: A Survey of Old & New Testament Perspectives. 2009. (ENG.). 200p. pap. 31.50 *(978-0-7618-4677-2(8))* Univ. Pr. of America, Inc.

McClenney-Sadler, Madeline Gay. Recovering the Daughter's Nakedness: A Formal Analysis of Israelite Kinship Terminology & the Internal Logic of Leviticus 18. 2007. (Library of Hebrew Bible/Old Testament Studies, the Ser.). (ENG.). 160p. 140.00 *(978-0-567-02676-7(0)*, T&T Clark Int'l) Continuum International Publishing Group, Ltd. GBR. Dist: National Bk. Network.

McConville, J. G. Reading the Law: Studies in Honour of Gordon J. Wenham. Möller, Karl, ed. 2007. (Library of Hebrew Bible/Old Testament Studies, the Ser.). (ENG.). 228p. 140.00 *(978-0-567-02642-2(6)*, T&T Clark Int'l) Continuum International Publishing Group, Ltd. GBR. Dist: National Bk. Network.

McConville, J. G., et al. A God of Faithfulness: Essays in Honour of J. Gordon McConville on His 60th Birthday. Grant, Jamie A. et al, eds. 2011. (Library Hebrew Bible/Old Testament Studies). (ENG., Illus.). 240p. 120.00 *(978-0-567-26436-7(X)*, T&T Clark Int'l) Continuum International Publishing Group, Ltd. GBR. Dist: National Bk. Network.

McCurdy, James Frederic. History Prophecy & the Monuments or Is. 2006. (ENG.). pap. 38.95 *(978-1-4286-5397-9(X))*; pap. 37.95 *(978-1-4286-5395-5(3))* Kessinger Publishing, LLC.

McKenzie, John L. The Old Testament Without Illusions. 2009. (John L. Mckenzie Reprints Ser.). 268p. pap. 29.00 *(978-1-60608-044-3(X))* Wipf & Stock Pubs.

—The Two-Edged Sword: An Interpretation of the Old Testament. 2009. (John L. Mckenzie Reprints Ser.). 340p. pap. 37.00 (978-1-60608-049-8(0)) Wipf & Stock Pubs.

McNaught, Doug. The Scarlet Thread. 2007. 137p. pap. 21.01 (978-1-84753-409-5(0)) Lulu Enterprises Inc.

Meade, Stanley. We Time-Traveled the Old Testament. 2008. 278p. pap. 27.95 (978-1-60610-185-8(4)) PublishAmerica, Inc.

Merrick, Britt. Big God: What Happens When We Trust Him. 2010. (ENG.). 240p. 19.99 (978-0-8307-5222-5(6)) Gospel Light Pubns.

Miano, David. Shadow on the Steps: Time Measurement in Ancient Israel. 2011. (Sbl - Resources for Biblical Study Ser.). (ENG.). XX, 268p. (978-90-04-17799-4(X)) BRILL.

—Shadow on the Steps: Time Measurement in Ancient Israel. 2010. (978-1-58983-478-1(X)); (978-1-58983-479-8(8)) Society of Biblical Literature.

Middlemas, Jill. The Templeless Age: An Introduction to the History, Literature, & Theology of the Exile. 2007. (ENG.). 174p. per. 25.00 (978-0-664-23130-9(6)) Westminster John Knox Pr.

Middlemas, Jill, et al, eds. The Centre & the Periphery: A European Tribute to Walter Brueggemann. 2010. 250p. (978-1-906055-86-8(6)) Sheffield Phoenix Pr.

Mies, Francoise. L' Esperance de Job. 2007. (Bibliotheca Ephemeridum Theologicarum Lovaniensium Ser.). (FRE & ENG.). 653p. (C). pap. 126.00 (978-90-429-1698-2(2)) Peeters Pubs. & Booksellers BEL. Dist: Brown, David Bk. Co., The.

Miles, Johnny. Constructing the Other in Ancient Israel & the Us. 2011. (Illus.). 404p. (978-1-907534-05-8(9)) Sheffield Phoenix Pr.

Miller, Robert D. Oral Tradition in Ancient Israel. 2011. (Biblical Performance Criticism: Ser.). 170p. pap. 20.00 (978-1-61097-271-0(6), Cascade Bks.) Wipf & Stock Pubs.

Miller, Toby & Miller, Patrick D. The Religion of Ancient Israel. 2007. (Library of Ancient Israel Ser.). (ENG.). 356p. per. 50.00 (978-0-664-23237-5(X)) Westminster John Knox Pr.

Mitchell, Eric & England, Archie. Old Testament Survey: A Student's Guide. 2nd ed. 2007. (ENG., Illus.). 240p. per. 27.99 (978-0-8054-4027-0(5), B&H Bks.) B&H Publishing Group.

Mitchell, Eric & House, Paul R. Old Testament Survey. 2nd rev. ed. 2007. (ENG., Illus.). 368p. 39.99 (978-0-8054-4036-2(4), B&H Academic) B&H Publishing Group.

Mittleman, Alan L. A Short History of Jewish Ethics: Conduct & Character in the Context of Covenant. 2011. (ENG.). 224p. 84.95 (978-1-4051-8942-2(8), Wiley-Blackwell) Wiley, John & Sons, Inc.

—A Short History of Jewish Ethics: Conduct & Character in the Context of Covenant. 2012. (ENG.). 224p. pap. 34.95 (978-1-4051-8941-5(X), Wiley-Blackwell) Wiley, John & Sons, Inc.

Mniler, Walter. Jesus the Keeper of the Truth. 2009. 316p. pap. 15.49 (978-1-4389-6416-4(1)) AuthorHouse.

Mobley, Gregory. The Stories Behind the Story: A Narrative Companion to the Hebrew Bible. 2011. pap. 25.00 (978-0-8028-3746-2(8)) Eerdmans, William B. Publishing Co.

Moore, Megan Bishop & Kelle, Brad E. Biblical History & Israel's Past. 2011. pap. 46.00 (978-0-8028-6260-0(8)) Eerdmans, William B. Publishing Co.

Morris, Dennis. RELIGION the Greatest Confidence Trick in History. 2007. 300p. pap. 22.96 (978-1-84753-600-6(X)) Lulu Enterprises Inc.

Morrow, William. Protest Against God: The Eclipse of a Bi. 2006. (ENG.). 264p. (978-1-905048-20-5(3)) Sheffield Phoenix Pr.

Muffs, Yochanan. The Personhood of God: Biblical Theology, Human Faith & the Divine Image. 2009. (ENG.). 240p. pap. 18.99 (978-1-58023-338-5(4)) Jewish Lights Publishing.

Nelson-Jones, Richard. Double Redaction of the Deuteronomistic History. 2009. (Library of Hebrew Bible/Old Testament Studies, the Ser.). (ENG.). 185p. 39.95 (978-0-567-26651-4(6), T&T Clark) Continuum International Publishing Group, Ltd. GBR. Dist: National Bk. Network.

Nichols, Aiden. Lovely, Like Jerusalem: The Fulfillment of the Old Testament in Christ & the Church. 2007. 279p. pap. 16.95 (978-1-58617-168-1(2)) Ignatius Pr.

Nigosian, Solomon & Nigosian, S. A. Magic & Divination in the Old Testament. 2008. (ENG.). 149p. (C). 69.50 (978-1-84519-296-9(6)) Sussex Academic Pr. GBR. Dist: International Specialized Bk. Services.

Nissinen, Martti, ed. Congress Volume Helsinki 2010. 2012. (Vetus Testamentum Supplements Ser.). (ENG, FRE & GER., Illus.). XVI, 568p. (978-90-04-20514-7(4)) BRILL.

Noll, K. L. & Schramm, Brooks, eds. Raising up a Faithful Exegete. 2010. 54.50 (978-1-57506-201-3(1)) Eisenbrauns, Inc.

North, Christopher R. The Old Testament Interpretation of History. 2009. 226p. pap. 26.00 (978-1-60608-714-5(2), Wipf and Stock) Wipf & Stock Pubs.

—The Thought of the Old Testament. 2009. 62p. pap. 9.00 (978-1-60608-712-1(6), Wipf and Stock) Wipf & Stock Pubs.

Obinwa, Ignatius M. C. Yahweh My Refuge: A Critical Analysis of Psalm 71, Vol. 839. 2006. (European Universities Studies 23 Ser.). (Illus.). 221p. pap. (978-3-631-55903-1(8)) Lang, Peter AG.

Ochs, Peter. The Return to Scripture in Judaism & Christianity: Essays in Postcritical Scriptural Interpretation. Ochs, Peter, ed. 2008. 388p. pap. 42.00 (978-1-55635-815-9(6), Wipf and Stock) Wipf & Stock Pubs.

Ochs, Peter & Johnson, William Stacy, eds. Crisis, Call, & Leadership in the Abrahamic Traditions. 2009. (ENG.). 288p. 95.00 (978-0-230-61825-1(1)) Palgrave Macmillan.

Oded, Bustenay & Millard, A. R. Homeland & Exile: Biblical & Ancient near Eastern Studies in Honour of Bustenay Oded. Galil, Gershon & Geller, Mark, eds. 2009. (Illus.). 672p. (978-90-04-17889-2(9)) BRILL.

O'Donnell, Douglas Sean. God's Lyrics: Rediscovering Worship Through Old Testament Songs. 2010. pap. (978-1-59638-172-8(8)) P & R Publishing.

Olsson, Frank. Come to Think about It: Associations to the Sixty-Six Books of the Bible from a Philosophical Perspective. 2009. 248p. pap. 25.95 (978-1-4269-1457-7(1)) Trafford Publishing.

Olyan, Saul M. Disability in the Hebrew Bible: Interpreting Mental & Physical Differences. 2008. (ENG.). 200p. 95.00 (978-0-521-88807-3(7)) Cambridge Univ. Pr.

—Priesthood & Cult in Ancient Israel. Anderson, Gary A., ed. 2009. (Library of Hebrew Bible/Old Testament Studies, the Ser.). (ENG.). 217p. 39.95 (978-0-567-47072-0(5), T&T Clark) Continuum International Publishing Group, Ltd. GBR. Dist: National Bk. Network.

—Social Inequality in the World of the Text: The Significance of Ritual & Social Distinctions in the Hebrew Bible: The Significance of Ritual & Social Distinctions in the Hebrew Bible. 2011. (Journal of Ancient Judaism. Supplements (JAJ. S) Ser.). (ENG.). 240p. (C). 89.00 (978-3-525-55024-3(3)) Vandenhoeck & Ruprecht GmbH & Co. KG DEU. Dist: ISD.

Orr, James. The Problem of the Old Testament Considered with Reference to Recent Criticism. 2009. 614p. 45.99 (978-1-115-36897-1(4)); pap. 45.75 (978-1-115-36893-3(1)) BiblioBazaar.

—The Problem of the Old Testament Considered with Reference to Recent Criticism. 2007. (ENG.). 610p. 59.95 (978-0-548-05238-9(7)) Kessinger Publishing, LLC.

Ostriker, Alicia. For the Love of God: The Bible as an Open Book. 2007. (ENG.). 184p. (C). pap. 19.95 (978-0-8135-4503-5(X)) Rutgers Univ. Pr.

Ottley, Robert Lawrence. Aspects of the Old Testament, 1897. 2007. (Bampton Lectures). 468p. pap. 35.00 (978-1-55635-163-1(1), Wipf and Stock) Wipf & Stock Pubs.

Otwell, John H. And Sarah Laughed: The Status of Woman in the Old Testament. 224p. 2009. 33.00 (978-1-59740-319-1(9)) 2008. pap. 22.00 (978-1-59740-692-5(9)) ACLS Humanities E-Book.

Page, John E. Prophecy in Order. 2009. 260p. pap. 16.99 (978-1-60791-526-3(X)) Xulon Pr., Inc.

Panorama of the Old Testament. pap. 3.99 (978-0-89096-480-2(8)) Twentieth Century Christian Bks.

Park, Sejin. Pentecost & Sinai: The Festival of Weeks as a Celebration of the Sinai Event. 2008. (Library of Hebrew Bible/Old Testament Studies, the Ser.). (ENG.). 304p. 130.00 (978-0-567-02727-6(9), T&T Clark Int'l) Continuum International Publishing Group, Ltd. GBR. Dist: National Bk. Network.

Parkey, W. C. Treasures & Truths. 2006. 292p. pap. 14.99 (978-1-56722-699-7(X)) Word Aflame Pr.

Patrick, Dale. Old Testament Law. 2011. 288p. (Orig.). pap. 32.00 (978-1-61097-241-3(4), Wipf and Stock) Wipf & Stock Pubs.

Patterson, Donald. Bible Discovery Series: Finding Tools to Read & Interpret Scripture. 2010. 96p. pap. (978-0-8100-2269-0(9)) Northwestern Publishing Hse.

Perdue, Leo G. & Niang, Aliou. Israel & Empire: A Postcolonial History of Israel & Early Judaism. 2013. (ENG.). 336p. 130.00 (978-0-567-05409-8(8)); pap. 39.95 (978-0-567-24328-7(1)) Continuum International Publishing Group, Ltd. GBR. (T&T Clark Int'l). Dist: National Bk. Network.

Perl, Gil. The Pillar of Volozhin: Rabbi Naftali Zvi Yehuda Berlin & the World of 19th Century Lithuanian Torah Scholarship. 2012. (Studies in Orthodox Judaism Ser.). (ENG.). 325p. 80.00 (978-1-936235-70-4(6)) Academic Studies Pr.

Perry, T. A. & Perry, T. Anthony. God's Twilight Zone: Wisdom in the Hebrew Bible. 2008. 206p. per. (978-1-59856-227-9(4)) Hendrickson Pubs. Marketing, LLC.

Petersen, David L., et al. Method Matters: Essays on the Interpretation of the Hebrew Bible in Honor of David L. Petersen. 2009. 49.95 (978-1-58983-444-6(5)) Society of Biblical Literature.

Pfoh, Emanuel & Chalcraft, David J., eds. Anthropology & the Bible. 2010. 102.80 (978-1-60724-956-6(1)) Gorgias Pr., LLC.

Phelps, William Lyon. Human Nature in the Bible. 2011. 174p. pap. 18.99 (978-1-61279-063-3(1)) Publishing in Motion.

Portman, Joel. No King in Israel. 2008. 228p. pap. (978-1-897117-62-0(0)) Gospel Folio Pr.

Prichard, Gerald R. Is Jesus Reasonable? A Logical Analysis of the Statements Attributed to Jesus Christ. 2009. (ENG.). 350p. 83.99 (978-0-7618-4650-5(6)) Univ. Pr. of America, Inc.

Prouser, Ora Horn & Horn Prouser, Ora. Esau's Blessing: How the Bible embraces those with special Needs. 2011. (ENG.). pap. 17.50 (978-1-934730-35-5(1)) Yehuda, Ben Pr.

Rand, Michael & Decter, Jonathan P., eds. Studies in Arabic & Hebrew Letters in Honor of Raymond P. Scheindlin. 2007. (Gorgias Précis Portfolios Ser.: 1). (HEB & ENG.). 86.00 (978-1-59333-701-8(9)) Gorgias Pr., LLC.

Raphael, Rebecca & Raphael. Biblical Corpora: Representations of Disability in Hebrew Biblical Literature. 2008. (Library of Hebrew Bible/Old Testament Studies, the Ser.). (ENG.). 176p. 110.00 (978-0-567-02822-0(X), T&T Clark Int'l) Continuum International Publishing Group, Ltd. GBR. Dist: National Bk. Network.

Rapoport, Sandra E. Biblical Seductions. 2011. 540p. 49.50 (978-1-60280-154-7(1)); pap. 29.50 (978-1-60280-170-7(3)) Ktav Publishing Hse., Inc.

Ratheiser, Gershom M. H. Mitzvoth Ethics & the Jewish Bible: The End of Old Testament Theology. 2007. (Library of Hebrew Bible/Old Testament Studies). (ENG.). 436p. 170.00 (978-0-567-02962-1(X), T&T Clark Int'l) Continuum International Publishing Group, Ltd. GBR. Dist: National Bk. Network.

Redditt, Paul L. & Schart, Aaron, eds. Thematic Threads in the Book of the Twelve. (Beihefte zur Zeitschrift fur die alttestamentliche Wissenschaft Ser.). (ENG.). XV, 376p. 240.00 (978-3-11-182759-9(3)) De Gruyter, Walter Inc.

Reeves, John C. Pursuing the Text: Studies in Honor of Ben Zion Wacholder on the Occasion of his Seventieth Birthday. Kampen, John, ed. 2009. (Library of Hebrew Bible/Old Testament Studies, the Ser.). (ENG.). 434p. 75.00 (978-0-567-65007-8(3), T&T Clark) Continuum International Publishing Group, Ltd. GBR. Dist: National Bk. Network.

Reventlow, Henning Graf. The Decalogue in Jewish & Christian Tradition. Hoffman, Yair, ed. 2010. (Library of Hebrew Bible/Old Testament Studies, the Ser.). (ENG., Illus.). 192p. 110.00 (978-0-567-21867-4(8), T&T Clark Int'l) Continuum International Publishing Group, Ltd. GBR. Dist: National Bk. Network.

—Justice & Righteousness: Biblical Themes & their Influence. Hoffman, Yair, ed. 2009. (Library of Hebrew Bible/Old Testament Studies, the Ser.). (ENG.). 258p. 44.95 (978-0-567-21207-8(6), T&T Clark) Continuum International Publishing Group, Ltd. GBR. Dist: National Bk. Network.

Rezetko, Robert, et al, eds. Reflection & Refraction: Studies in Biblical Historiography in Honour of A. Graeme Auld. 2006. (Supplements to Vetus Testamentum Ser.: Vol. 113). (Illus.). 572p. (978-90-04-14512-2(5)) BRILL.

Richard Benton, Benton & Richard Benton. God What Great Signs: Signs in the Heavens. 2009. 128p. 23.95 (978-1-4401-7973-0(5)); pap. 13.95 (978-1-4401-7975-4(1)) iUniverse, Inc.

Richter, Sandra L. The Epic of Eden: A Christian Entry into the Old Testament. 2008. (ENG., Illus.). 263p. pap. 24.00 (978-0-8308-2577-6(0), IVP Acad.) InterVarsity Pr.

Rickards Mozley, John. The Divine Aspect of History: Volume 1. 2011. (ENG.). 428p. pap. 48.00 (978-1-107-60517-6(2)) Cambridge Univ. Pr.

Roberg, Robert. God According to Jesus. 2008. 110p. pap. 19.95 (978-1-4357-3112-7(3)) Lulu Enterprises Inc.

Robinson, H. W. Record & Revelation - Essays on the Old Testament by Members of the Society for Old Testament Study. 2007. 552p. per. (978-1-4067-9581-3(X), Pomona Pr.) Read Bks.

Robinson, Henry W., ed. Record & Revelation. reprint ed. 35.50 (978-0-404-15354-0(2)) AMS Pr., Inc.

Roehrs, Walter R. Survey of Covenant History: A Historical Overview of the Old Testament. 208p. 20.99 (978-0-570-04260-0(7), 53-1020) Concordia Publishing Hse.

Rogers, Robert William. Cuneiform Parallels to the Old Testament. 2009. 596p. 30.99 (978-1-103-02092-8(7)); pap. 24.99 (978-1-103-02089-8(7)) BiblioBazaar.

Rogerson, John. Old Testament Criticism in the Nineteenth Century. 2010. 336p. pap. 39.00 (978-1-60899-733-6(2), Wipf and Stock) Wipf & Stock Pubs.

Rogerson, John, ed. Beginning Old Testament Study. 2nd ed. 176p. 17.95 (978-0-281-05103-8(8)) International Publishers Marketing.

Rogerson, John W. Bible & Criticism in Victorian Britain: Profiles of F. D. Maurice & William Robertson Smith. 2009. (Library of Hebrew Bible/Old Testament Studies, the Ser.). (ENG.). 188p. 39.95 (978-0-567-54180-2(X), T&T Clark) Continuum International Publishing Group, Ltd. GBR. Dist: National Bk. Network.

Rogerson, John W. & Carroll, Mark Daniel. Theory & Practice in Old Testament Ethics: The Contribution of John Rogerson. 2009. (Library of Hebrew Bible/Old Testament Studies, the Ser.). (ENG.). 168p. 29.95 (978-1-4411-0075-7(X), T&T Clark Int'l) Continuum International Publishing Group, Ltd. GBR. Dist: National Bk. Network.

Rollston, Chris A. Writing & Literacy in the World of Ancient Israel: Epigraphic Evidence from the Iron Age. 2010. (Illus.). xix, 171p. (978-1-58983-107-0(1)) Society of Biblical Literature.

Ronning, John L. The Jewish Targums & John's Logos Theology, 1 vol. 2010. (ENG., Illus.). 400p. (978-1-59856-306-1(8)) Hendrickson Pubs. Marketing, LLC.

Rooke, Deborah W. Embroidered Garments: Priests & Gender in Biblical Israel. Rooke, Deborah W., ed. 2009. (Illus.). 182p. (978-1-906055-77-6(7)) Sheffield Phoenix Pr.

Rooke, Deborah W. Zadok's Heirs: The Role & Development of the High Priesthood in Ancient Israel. 2012. (Oxford Theological Monographs). (ENG.). 404p. pap. 55.00 (978-0-19-966111-4(1)) Oxford Univ. Pr., Inc.

Rowe, Bede. The Old Testament. 2009. 265p. pap. 21.50 (978-1-4092-7402-5(0)) Lulu Enterprises Inc.

Rowland, C. C. & Morray-Jones, C. R. A. Compendia Rerum Iudaicarum ad Novum Testamentum, The Mystery of God: Early Jewish Mysticism & the New Testament, Vol. 12. 2009. 694p. (978-90-04-17532-7(6)) BRILL.

Rusca, Ruth. Feminine Mysteries in the Bible: The Soul Teachings of the Daughters of the Goddess. 2008. (ENG.). 1p. pap. 15.00 (978-1-59143-088-9(7)) Bear & Co.

Russell, D. S. The Old Testament Pseudepigrapha: Patriarchs & Prophets in Early Judaism. 2012. 160p. pap. (978-0-334-02229-9(0), SCM Pr.) Hymns Ancient & Modern Ltd.

Russell, Stephen C. Images of Egypt in Early Biblical Literature: Cisjordan-Israelite, Transjordan-Israelite, & Judahite Portrayals. 2009. (Beihefte Zur Zeitschrift Fur Die Alttestamentliche Wissenschaft Ser.). (ENG.). XX, 280p. 112.00 (978-3-11-022171-8(3)); 168.00 (978-3-11-173478-1(1)) De Gruyter, Walter Inc.

Sadler, Rodney S., Jr. Can a Cushite Change His Skin? An Examination of Race, Ethnicity, & Othering in the Hebrew Bible. 2009. (Library Hebrew Bible/Old Testament Studies). (ENG.). 192p. pap. 49.95 (978-0-567-02765-8(1), T&T Clark Int'l) Continuum International Publishing Group, Ltd. GBR. Dist: National Bk. Network.

Saebo, Magne, ed. Hebrew Bible / Old Testament: The History of its Interpretation, II: from the Renaissance to the Englightenment. 2008. (Hebrew Bible / Old Testament Ser.). (ENG.). 1248p. (C). 231.00 (978-3-525-53982-8(7)) Vandenhoeck & Ruprecht GmbH & Co. KG DEU. Dist: ISD.

Salem, Sema'an I. The Origins of Biblical Stories, 1 vol. 2009. 258p. pap. 27.95 (978-1-60672-903-8(9)) PublishAmerica, Inc.

Salkin, Jeffrey K. Righteous Gentiles in the Hebrew Bible: Ancient Role Models for Sacred Relationships. 2008. 192p. pap. 18.99 (978-1-58023-364-4(3)) Jewish Lights Publishing.

Sassoon, Isaac S. D. The Status of Women in Jewish Tradition. 2011. 232p. 85.00 (978-1-107-00174-9(9)) Cambridge Univ. Pr.

Sayce, A. H. The Early History of the Hebrews. 2007. (ENG.). 506p. 55.95 (978-0-548-00634-4(2)) Kessinger Publishing, LLC.

—The Higher Criticism & the Verdict of the Monuments. 2007. (ENG.). 586p. 58.95 (978-0-548-01690-9(9)) Kessinger Publishing, LLC.

Schifferdecker, K. & Schifferdecker, Kathryn. Out of the Whirlwind: Creation Theology in the Book of Job. 2008. (Harvard Theological Studies: 61). 217p. pap. 25.00 (978-0-674-02597-4(0)) Harvard Univ. Pr.

Schipper, Jeremy. Parables & Conflict in the Hebrew Bible. 2009. (ENG.). 182p. 88.00 (978-0-521-76462-9(9)) Cambridge Univ. Pr.

Schloen, J. David & Stager, Lawrence E. Exploring the Longue Durée: Essays in Honor of Lawrence E. Stager. 2009. 69.50 (978-1-57506-161-0(9)) Eisenbrauns, Inc.

Schmid, Konrad & Nogalski, James. Genesis & the Moses Story: Israel's Dual Origins in the Hebrew Bible. 2010. 64.50 (978-1-57506-152-8(X)) Eisenbrauns, Inc.

Scholz, Susanne & Scholz. Introducing the Women's Hebrew Bible. 2007. (Introductions in Feminist Theology Ser.). (ENG.). 160p. 29.95 (978-0-567-08257-2(1), T&T Clark Int'l) Continuum International Publishing Group, Ltd. GBR. Dist: National Bk. Network.

Schroeder, Joy A. Dinah's Lament: The Biblical Legacy of Sexual Violence in Christian Interpretation. 2007. (Illus.). 330p. (C). 35.00 (978-0-8006-3843-6(3), Fortress Pr.) Augsburg Fortress, Pubs.

Schwartz. Perspectives on Purity & Purification in the Bible. Wright, David, ed. 2008. (Library of Hebrew Bible/Old Testament Studies, the Ser.). (ENG.). 128p. (978-0-567-02832-7(1), T&T Clark Int'l) Continuum International Publishing Group, Ltd.

Schweid, Eliezer. The Philosophy of the Bible as Foundation of Jewish Culture: Philosophy of Biblical Law. Levin, Leonard, tr. from HEB. 2nd ed. 2009. (Reference Library of Jewish Intellectual History Ser.). (ENG.). 216p. 50.00 (978-1-934843-01-7(6)); pap. 35.00 (975-1-934843-52-9(0)) Academic Studies Pr.

—The Philosophy of the Bible as Foundation of Jewish Culture: Philosophy of Biblical Narrative. Levin, Leonard, tr. from HEB. 2009. (Reference Library of Jewish Intellectual History Ser.). (ENG.). 224p. 50.00 (978-1-934843-00-0(8)); pap. 35.00 (978-1-934843-51-2(2)) Academic Studies Pr.

Scott, William R. A Simplified Guide to BHS: Critical Apparatus, Masora, Accents, Unusual Letters & Other Markings. 4th ed. 2007. pap. (978-1-930566-68-2(9), BIBAL Pr.) Scott, D.& F. Publishing, Inc.

Scroggie, W. El Encanto del Antiguo Testamento: The Charm of the Old Testament. (SPA.). (978-84-7228-879-9(X), 220356) Clie, Editorial.

Segal, Alan F. Sinning in the Hebrew Bible: How the Worst Stories Speak for Its Truth. 2012. (ENG.). 296p. (gr. 17). pap. 29.50 (978-0-231-15927-2(7)) Columbia Univ. Pr.

—Sinning in the Hebrew Bible: How the Worst Stories Speak for Its Truth. 2012. (ENG.). 296p. (gr. 17). 89.50 (978-0-231-15926-5(9)) Columbia Univ. Pr.

Shalev, Meir & Schoffman, Stuart. Beginnings: Reflections on the Bible's Intriguing Firsts. 2011. 304p. 25.00 (978-0-307-71718-4(6)) Doubleday Canada, Ltd. CAN. Dist: Random Hse., Inc.

Shannon, Trevor H. God's People & God's Plan. 2006. (ENG.). 260p. pap. (978-1-84401-760-7(5)) Athena Pr.

Sharp, Carolyn J. Irony & Meaning in the Hebrew Bible. 2008. (Indiana Studies in Biblical Literature Ser.). (ENG.). 376p. 39.95 (978-0-253-35244-6(4), 0253352444) Indiana Univ. Pr.

Shatz, David. Jewish Thought in Dialogue: Essays on Thinkers, Theologies & Moral Theories. 2010. (Judaism & Jewish Life Ser.). (ENG.). 480p. 65.00 (978-1-934843-42-0(3)) Academic Studies Pr.

Sherman, Hazel. Reading Zechariah: The Allegorical Tradition of Biblical Interpretation Through the Commentary of Didymus the Blind & Theodore of Mopsuestia. 2007. (Studies in Christian History & Thought Ser.). (ENG.). 280p. pap. 39.99 (978-1-84227-213-8(6), Paternoster) Authentic Media.

Silva, Moises. The Essential Companion to Life in Bible Times: Key Insights for Reading God's Word, 1 vol. 2011. (Essential Bible Companion Ser.). (ENG.). 144p. pap. 16.99 (978-0-310-28688-2(3)) Zondervan.

Singer, Jacob. Taboo in the Hebrew Scriptures. 2007. (ENG.). 136p. 35.95 (978-0-548-14177-9(0)) 2006. pap. 20.95 (978-1-4286-5382-5(1)) Kessinger Publishing, LLC.

Slater, Elizabeth & Clanton, Dan W., Jr. Daring, Disreputable & Devout: Interpreting the Hebrew Bible's Women in the Arts & Music. 2009. (ENG.).

B

208p. pap. 22.95 *(978-0-567-02701-6(5)*, T&T Clark Int'l) Continuum International Publishing Group, Ltd. GBR. Dist: National Bk. Network.

Slifkin, Nosson. Sacred Monsters: Mysterious & Mythical Creatures of Scripture, Talmud & Midrash. 2007. (Illus.). 380p. 37.50 *(978-1-933143-18-7(5))* Urim Pubns. ISR. Dist: Coronet Bks.

Sloane, Andrew. At Home in a Strange Land: Using the Old Testament in Christian Ethics. 2009. (C). pap. 21.99 *(978-0-8010-4840-1(0))* Baker Academic.

—At Home in a Strange Land: Using the Old Testament in Christian Ethics. 2008. 280p. pap. *(978-1-59856-084-8(0))* Hendrickson Pubs. Marketing, LLC.

Smend, Rudolf. Vier Epitaphe - Die Basler Hebraistenfamilie Buxtorf. 2010. (Litterae et Theologia Ser.). (GER., Illus.). XIX, 51p. pap. 21.00 ***(978-3-11-022895-3(5))*** De Gruyter, Walter Inc.

Smith, Hamilton. Elijah. 2nd ed. 2007. 80p. per. *(978-0-901860-68-2(9))* Scripture Truth Pubns.

Smith, Mark S. God in Translation: Deities in Cross-Cultural Discourse in the Biblical World. 2008. (Forschungen zum Alten Testament Ser.). (Illus.). 408p. 225.00 *(978-3-16-149543-4(8))* Mohr Siebeck GmbH & Co. KG DEU. Dist: Coronet Bks.

Smith, W. Robertson. The Old Testament in the Jewish Church: Twelve Lectures on Biblical Criticism. 2007. (ENG.). 460p. 52.95 *(978-0-548-36364-5(1))*; per. 37.95 *(978-0-548-30655-0(9))* Kessinger Publishing, LLC.

Sprott, T. H. Modern Study of the Old Testament & Inspiration. 2011. (ENG.). 218p. pap. 22.99 *(978-1-107-60053-9(7))* Cambridge Univ. Pr.

Stackert, Jeffrey, et al. Gazing on the Deep: Ancient near Eastern & Other Studies in Honor of Tsvi Abusch. 2010. *(978-1-934309-26-1(5)*, CDL Pr.) Univ. Pr. of Maryland.

Stade, Bernhard, ed. Zeitschrift für die alttestamentliche Wissenschaft. 2010. (GER.). 4500.00 *(978-1-61719-797-0(1))*; 4500.00 *(978-1-61719-783-3(1))*; 4500.00 *(978-1-61719-800-7(5))*; 4500.00 *(978-1-61719-774-1(2))*; 4500.00 *(978-1-61719-771-0(8))*; 4500.00 *(978-1-61719-792-5(0))*; 4500.00 *(978-1-61719-785-7(8))*; 4500.00 *(978-1-61719-769-7(6))*; 4500.00 *(978-1-61719-782-6(3))*; 4500.00 *(978-1-61719-779-6(3))*; 4500.00 *(978-1-61719-801-4(3))*; 4500.00 *(978-1-61719-788-8(2))*; 4500.00 *(978-1-61719-773-4(4))*; 4500.00 *(978-1-61719-784-0(X))*; 4500.00 *(978-1-61719-781-9(5))*; 4500.00 *(978-1-61719-787-1(4))*; 4500.00 *(978-1-61719-790-1(4))*; 4500.00 *(978-1-61719-772-7(6))*; 4500.00 *(978-1-61719-807-6(2))*; 4500.00 *(978-1-61719-803-8(X))*; 4500.00 *(978-1-61719-770-3(X))*; 4500.00 *(978-1-61719-778-9(5))*; 4500.00 *(978-1-61719-780-2(7))*; 4500.00 *(978-1-61719-786-4(6))*; 4500.00 *(978-1-61719-798-7(X))*; 4500.00 *(978-1-61719-791-8(2))*; 4500.00 *(978-1-61719-793-2(9))*; 4500.00 *(978-1-61719-777-2(7))*; 4500.00 *(978-1-61719-794-9(7))*; 4500.00 *(978-1-61719-768-0(8))*; 4500.00 *(978-1-61719-796-3(3))*; 4500.00 *(978-1-61719-805-2(6))*; 4500.00 *(978-1-61719-802-1(1))*; 4500.00 *(978-1-61719-767-3(X))*; 4500.00 *(978-1-61719-776-5(9))*; 4500.00 *(978-1-61719-806-9(4))*; 4500.00 *(978-1-61719-799-4(8))*; 4500.00 *(978-1-61719-795-6(5))*; 4500.00 *(978-1-61719-804-5(8))*; 4500.00 *(978-1-61719-775-8(0))*; 4500.00 *(978-1-61719-789-5(0))* Gorgias Pr., LLC.

Stade, D. Bernhard. Zeitschrift Für Die Alttestamentliche Wissenschaft. 2010. 364p. 38.99 *(978-1-140-47680-1(7))*; pap. 32.75 *(978-1-140-47681-8(5))* BiblioBazaar.

Stahlberg, Lesleigh Cushing. Sustaining Fictions: Intertextuality, Midrash, Translation, & the Literary Afterlife of the Bible. 2008. (Library of Hebrew Bible/Old Testament Studies, the Ser.). (ENG., Illus.). 256p. 140.00 *(978-0-567-02709-2(0)*, T&T Clark Int'l) Continuum International Publishing Group, Ltd. GBR. Dist: National Bk. Network.

Stavans, Ilan & Drache, Mordecai. With All Thine Heart: Love & the Bible. 2010. (ENG., Illus.). 200p. 21.95 *(978-0-8135-4797-8(0))* Rutgers Univ. Pr.

Stavrakopoulou, Francesca. Land of Our Fathers: The Roles of Ancestor Veneration in Biblical Land Claims. (Library Hebrew Bible/Old Testament Studies). (ENG.). 208p. 2012. pap. 44.95 ***(978-0-567-41188-4(5))*** Vol. 473. 2010. 110.00 *(978-0-567-02881-5(X))* Continuum International Publishing Group, Ltd. GBR. (T&T Clark Int'l). Dist: National Bk. Network.

Stavrakopoulou, Francesca. Religious Diversity in Ancient Israel & Judah. Barton, John, ed. 2010. (ENG.). 224p. 130.00 *(978-0-567-03215-7(9)*, T&T Clark Int'l) Continuum International Publishing Group, Ltd. GBR. Dist: National Bk. Network.

Steiner, Richard C. A Biblical Tradition in the Making: The Evolution & Impact of Saadia Gaon's Tafsir. 2011. (Harvard Center for Jewish Studies). Orig. Title: The Evolution & Impact of Saadia Gaon's Tafs#299;r. 198p. 55.00 *(978-0-674-03335-1(3))* Harvard Univ. Ctr. for Jewish Studies.

Steussy, Marti J. David. 2009. 268p. pap. 29.95 *(978-1-57003-845-7(7))* Univ. of South Carolina Pr.

Stone, Perry. Breaking the Jewish Code: Twelve Secrets That Will Transform Your Life, Family, Health, & Finances. 2009. (ENG.). 256p. 21.99 *(978-1-59979-467-9(5)*, Charisma Hse.) Charisma Media.

Stott, Katherine M. & Stott. Why Did They Write This Way? Reflections on References to Written Documents in the Hebrew Bible & Ancient Literature, 1 vol. 2008. (Library of Hebrew Bible/Old Testament Studies, the Ser.). (ENG.). 178p. 115.00 *(978-0-567-02736-8(8)*, T&T Clark Int'l) Continuum International Publishing Group, Ltd. GBR. Dist: National Bk. Network.

Stump, Eleonore. Wandering in Darkness: Narrative & the Problem of Suffering. 2010. (ENG.). 640p. 99.00 *(978-0-19-927742-1(7))* Oxford Univ. Pr., Inc.

Sun, Henry T. C. & Eades, Keith L., eds. Problems in Biblical Theology: Essays in Honor of Rolf Knierim. 2011. 420p. pap. 48.00 ***(978-1-61097-157-7(4)***, Wipf and Stock) Wipf & Stock Pubs.

Swedenborg, Emanuel. The Word of the Old Testament Explained V3. Acton, Alfred, tr. 2011. 584p. 63.95 ***(978-1-258-01079-9(8))*** Literary Licensing, LLC.

Sweeney, Marvin A. Tanak: A Theological & Critical Introduction to the Jewish Bible. 2011. 464p. (C). 59.00 *(978-0-8006-3743-9(7)*, Fortress Pr.) Augsburg Fortress, Pubs.

Tape, John. Old Testament Portraits of Christ. 2008. 102p. pap. 17.95 *(978-0-615-20656-1(5))* Tape, John Walter.

Taylor, Leisa. The God of Human Blood. 2006. 358p. per. 15.95 *(978-1-59405-089-3(9))* New Age World Publishing.

Thackeray, H. St. J. The Septuagint & Jewish Worship: A Study in Origins. 2007. (Illus.). 143p. pap. 20.00 *(978-1-55635-159-4(3)*, Wipf and Stock) Wipf & Stock Pubs.

Thompson, Michael E. W. Where Is the God of Justice? The Old Testament & Suffering. 2011. 236p. pap. 26.00 ***(978-1-61097-262-8(7)***, Pickwick Pubns.) Wipf & Stock Pubs.

Tice, Paul. Jumpin' Jehovah: Exposing the Atrocities of the Old Testament God. 3rd rev. ed. 2007. (ENG., Illus.). 104p. per. 13.95 *(978-1-58509-112-6(X))* Book Tree, The.

Tov, Emanuel. The Greek & Hebrew Bible: Collected Essays on the Septuagint. 2006. (ENG.). 616p. per. 49.95 *(978-1-58983-254-1(X))* Society of Biblical Literature.

—Textual Criticism of the Hebrew Bible. 3rd rev. ed. 2011. (Illus.). 512p. 90.00 *(978-0-8006-9664-1(6))* Augsburg Fortress, Pubs.

Trost, Travis Darren. Who Should Be King in Israel? A Study on Roman Imperial Politics, the Dead Sea Scrolls, & the Fourth Gospel. 2011. xii, 242p. *(978-1-4331-1151-8(9))* Lang, Peter GmbH, Europaischer Verlag der Wissenschaften.

Tullock, David R. The Shepherd's Crook. 2008. 112p. pap. 19.99 *(978-1-4363-2538-7(2))* Xlibris Corp.

van Cangh, J. -M., ed. Les sources judaiques du Nouveau Testament: Receuil D'essais. 2008. (Bibliotheca Ephemeridum Theologicarum Lovaniensium Ser.). (FRE.). 718p. (C). pap. 122.00 *(978-90-429-1903-7(5))* Peeters Pubs. & Booksellers BEL. Dist: Brown, David Bk. Co., The.

Van Seters, John. Changing Perspectives I: Studies in the History, Literature, & Religion of Biblical Israel. 2011. (Copenhagen International Seminar Ser.). (ENG., Illus.). 438p. (C). 120.00 *(978-1-84553-901-6(X))* Equinox Publishing Ltd. GBR. Dist: ISD.

Veijola, Timo, et al. Leben Nach der Weisung: Exegetisch-Historische Studien Zum Alten Testament. 2008. (Forschungen Zur Religion und Literatur des Alten & Neuen Testament Ser.). (GER & ENG., Illus.). 192p. (C). 84.00 *(978-3-525-53087-0(0))* Vandenhoeck & Ruprecht GmbH & Co. KG DEU. Dist: ISD.

Veras, Richard. Jesus of Israel: Finding Christ in the Old Testament. 2007. 142p. per. 11.99 *(978-0-86716-772-6(6)*, Servant Bks.) Franciscan Media.

Vern, Robyn. Dating Archaic Biblical Hebrew Poetry. 2011. 113.00 *(978-1-61143-921-2(3))* Gorgias Pr., LLC.

Viola, Frank. From Eternity to Here: Rediscovering the Ageless Purpose of God, 1 vol. 2009. (ENG.). 320p. pap. 14.99 *(978-1-4347-6870-4(8))* Cook, David C.

Vogan, Charles. Removing the Veil. 2007. (ENG.). 152p. per. 13.95 *(978-0-615-15796-2(3))* Shenandoah Bible Ministries.

Wagner, Andreas, ed. Anthropologische Aufbrüche: Alttestamentliche und interdisziplinäre Zugänge zur historischen Anthropologie. 2009. (Forschungen Zur Religion und Literatur des Alten & Neuen Testament Ser.). (GER., Illus.). 430p. (C). 96.00 *(978-3-525-53189-1(3))* Vandenhoeck & Ruprecht GmbH & Co. KG DEU. Dist: ISD.

Walsh, Jerome T. Old Testament Narrative: A Guide to Interpretation. 2010. (ENG.). 272p. pap. 30.00 *(978-0-664-23464-5(X))* Westminster John Knox Pr.

Walton, John H. Ancient near Eastern Thought & the Old Testament: Introducing the Conceptual World of the Hebrew Bible. 2006. (Illus.). 368p. (C). pap. 26.99 *(978-0-8010-2750-5(0))* Baker Academic.

Walzer, Michael. In God's Shadow: Politics in the Hebrew Bible. 2012. (ENG.). 256p. 28.00 ***(978-0-300-18044-2(6))*** Yale Univ. Pr.

Waschke, Ernst-Joachim. Der Gesalbte: Studien zur alttestamentlichen Theologie. (Beihefte zur Zeitschrift far die alttestamentliche Wissenschaft Ser.). (GER.). X, 339p. 255.00 ***(978-3-11-178666-7(8))*** De Gruyter, Walter Inc.

Waskow, Rabbi Arthur & Berman, Rabbi Phyllis. Freedom Journeys: The Tale of Exodus & Wilderness across Millennia. 2011. 300p. 24.99 *(978-1-58023-445-0(3))* Jewish Lights Publishing.

Watt, Eric. Unleash His Spirit. 2008. 136p. per. 13.99 *(978-1-60477-589-1(0))* Xulon Pr., Inc.

Webb, Diana. Women of God. 2010. pap. 13.99 *(978-1-59955-384-9(8))* Cedar Fort, Inc./CFI Distribution.

Weeks, Noel. Sources & Authors: Assumptions in the Study of Hebrew Bible Narrative. 2011. 137.65 ***(978-1-4632-0034-3(X))*** Gorgias Pr., LLC.

Weinberg, Joel. Citizen-Temple Community. 2009. (Library of Hebrew Bible/Old Testament Studies, the Ser.). (ENG.). 159p. 29.95 *(978-0-567-61111-6(6)*, T&T Clark) Continuum International Publishing Group, Ltd. GBR. Dist: National Bk. Network.

Weisberg, Dvora E. Levirate Marriage & the Family in Ancient Judaism. 2009. (HBI Series on Jewish Women Ser.). (ENG., Illus.). 276p. lib. bdg. 50.00 *(978-1-58465-781-1(2)*, Brandeis University Press) Univ. Pr. of New England.

Weissenberg, Hanne von, et al, eds. Changes in Scripture: Rewriting & Interpreting Authoritative Traditions in the Second Temple Period. 2011. (Beihefte zur Zeitschrift far die alttestamentliche Wissenschaft Ser.). (ENG.). VI, 436p. 252.00 ***(978-3-11-174967-9(3))***; 436p. 168.00 ***(978-3-11-024048-1(3))*** De Gruyter, Walter Inc.

Wellhausen, Julius. Prolegomena. 2007. (ENG.). 676p. pap. 34.99 *(978-1-4264-1727-6(6))* 2006. 602p. pap. 31.99 *(978-1-4264-1639-2(3))* BiblioBazaar.

—Prolegomena to the History of Ancient Israel. 2009. 664p. 35.99 *(978-0-559-13069-4(4))*; 39.99 *(978-0-559-13054-0(6))*; pap. 45.75 *(978-0-559-13064-9(3))*; pap. 46.75 *(978-0-559-13058-8(9))* BiblioBazaar.

Wendland, Ernst R. Prophetic Rhetoric: Case Studies in Text Analysis & Translation. 2009. pap. 25.99 *(978-1-60791-766-3(1))* Xulon Pr., Inc.

Westbrook, Raymond & Wells, Bruce. Everyday Law in Biblical Israel: An Introduction. 2009. (ENG.). 160p. pap. 25.00 *(978-0-664-23497-3(6))* Westminster John Knox Pr.

Whedbee, J. William. The Bible & the Comic Vision. 2009. (ENG.). 332p. pap. 46.00 *(978-0-521-09761-1(4))* Cambridge Univ. Pr.

Wigram, George V. The Englishman's Hebrew & Chaldee Concordance of the Old Testament. 2010. 808p. pap. 55.75 *(978-1-143-39230-6(2))* BiblioBazaar.

Williams, Ken. Finding Jesus in the Old Testament (the Jewish Scriptures) Discovering the Jewish Roots of Your Faith. 2007. 208p. per. 9.95 *(978-1-4327-1529-8(1))* Outskirts Pr., Inc.

Wilson, James. The Holy Spirit & the Endtimes: A Season of Unusual Miracles. 2008. pap. 16.99 *(978-0-7684-2695-3(2))* Destiny Image Pubs.

Wimpfheimer, Barry S. & Samuels, Beth. Wisdom of Bat Sheva: In Memory of Beth Samuels. 2009. *(978-1-60280-127-1(4))* Ktav Publishing Hse., Inc.

Witte, Markus. Philologische Notizen zu Hiob 21-27. (Beihefte zur Zeitschrift far die alttestamentliche Wissenschaft Ser.). (GER.). XI, 202p. 180.00 ***(978-3-11-187784-6(1))*** De Gruyter, Walter Inc.

Wolde, E. J. van. Reframing Biblical Studies: When Language & Text Meet Culture, Cognition, & Context. 2009. 402p. 44.50 *(978-1-57506-182-5(1))* Eisenbrauns, Inc.

Wolf, Robert & Lefkowitz, Zvi. Forgotten Children of the Bible: Conflict & Consequences. 2009. 87p. 18.95 *(978-1-934440-71-1(X)*, Devora Publishing) Simcha Media Group.

Wood, Alice. Of Wings & Wheels: A Synthetic Study of the Biblical Cherubim. 2008. (Beihefte Zur Zeitschrift Für Die Alttestamentliche Wissenschaft Ser.). (ENG.). XI, 253p. 105.00 *(978-3-11-020528-2(9))*; 168.00 ***(978-3-11-173872-7(8))*** De Gruyter, Walter Inc.

Wright, Christopher J. H. Knowing God the Father Through the Old Testament. 2007. (ENG.). 234p. per. 18.00 *(978-0-8308-2592-9(4)*, IVP Acad.) InterVarsity Pr.

Wyatt, N. The Archaeology of Myth: Papers on Old Testament Tradition. 2010. (BibleWorld Ser.). (ENG.). 123p. (C). 100.00 *(978-1-84553-357-1(7))* Equinox Publishing Ltd. GBR. Dist: ISD.

—The Archaeology of Myth: Papers on Old Testament Tradition. 2010. (BibleWorld Ser.). (ENG., Illus.). 123p. (C). pap. 45.00 *(978-1-84553-358-8(5)*, Equinox Publishing Ltd. GBR. Dist: ISD.

Xeravits, Géza G. & Dusek, Jan, eds. The Stranger in Ancient & Mediaeval Jewish Tradition: Papers Read at the First Meeting of the JBSCE, Piliscsaba 2009. 2010. (Deuterocanonical & Cognate Literature Studies). (ENG.). VIII, 251p. 168.00 ***(978-3-11-173203-9(7))*** De Gruyter, Walter Inc.

Xeravits, Géza G., ed. The Stranger in Ancient & Mediaeval Jewish Tradition: Papers Read at the First Meeting of the JBSCE, Piliscsaba 2009. 2010. (Deuterocanonical & Cognate Literature Studies). (ENG.). VIII, 251p. 105.00 *(978-3-11-022203-6(5))* De Gruyter, Walter Inc.

Yeo, John. Plundering the Egyptians: The Old Testament & Historical Criticism at Westminster Theological Seminary (1929-1998) 2009. (ENG.). 328p. pap. 38.99 *(978-0-7618-4959-9(9))* Univ. Pr. of America, Inc.

Yeo, John Ji-Won. Plundering the Egyptians: The Old Testament & Historical Criticism at Westminster Theological Seminary (1929-1998) 2010. vi, 318p. *(978-0-7618-4960-5(2))* Univ. Pr. of America, Inc.

Zdelar, Christopher & Paul, Christopher. The Bible (Is God's Picture Book) 2006. (ENG.). 204p. per. 24.95 *(978-1-4241-4716-8(6))* PublishAmerica, Inc.

Ziegler, Y. Promises to Keep: The Oath in Biblical Narrative. 2008. 320p. *(978-90-04-16843-5(5))* BRILL.

Zimmerli, Walther. The Law & the Prophets: A Study of the Meaning of the Old Testament. Clements, R. E., tr. 2010. 112p. pap. 14.00 *(978-1-60899-726-8(X)*, Wipf and Stock) Wipf & Stock Pubs.

Zornberg, Avivah Gottlieb. The Murmuring Deep: Reflections on the Biblical Unconscious. (ENG.). 2011. 480p. pap. 19.95 *(978-0-8052-1206-8(X))* 2009. 464p. 28.95 *(978-0-8052-4247-8(3))* Knopf Doubleday Publishing Group. (Schocken).

Zsengellér, József. Samaria, Samarians, Samaritans: Studies on Bible, History & Linguistics. 2011. (Studia Samaritana Ser.). (ENG.). XII, 323p. 140.00 ***(978-3-11-026804-1(3))*** De Gruyter, Walter Inc.

BIBLE—CRITICISM, INTERPRETATION, ETC.—O. T. AMOS

see Bible—Criticism, Interpretation, Etc.—O. T. Minor Prophets

BIBLE—CRITICISM, INTERPRETATION, ETC.—O. T. APOCRYPHAL BOOKS

Ames, Frank Ritchel. Writing & Reading War: Rhetoric, Gender, & Ethics in Biblical & Modern Contexts. Kelle, Brad E., ed. 2008. (SBL - Symposium Ser.). 280p. *(978-90-04-13759-2(9))* BRILL.

Angel. Chaos & the Son of Man: The Hebrew Chaoskampf Tradition in the Period 515 BCE to 200 CE. 2006. (Library of Second Temple Studies, the Ser.). (ENG.). 256p. 170.00 *(978-0-567-03098-6(9)*, T&T Clark Int'l) Continuum International Publishing Group, Ltd. GBR. Dist: National Bk. Network.

The Apocalypse of Abraham. 99p. reprint ed. 68.00 *(978-0-7222-9910-4(9))* Library Reprints, Inc.

The Apocalypse of Baruch. 96p. reprint ed. 68.00 *(978-0-7222-9909-8(5))* Library Reprints, Inc.

The Apocalypse of Ezra. reprint ed. 68.00 *(978-0-7222-9908-1(7))* Library Reprints, Inc.

The Ascension of Isaiah. 155p. reprint ed. 68.00 *(978-0-7222-9907-4(9))* Library Reprints, Inc.

Bachmann, Veronika. Die Welt Im Ausnahmezustand: Eine Untersuchung Zu Aussagegehalt und Theologie des Wächterbuches (1 Hen 1-36) 2009. (Beihefte Zur Zeitschrift Fur Die Alttestamentliche Wissenschaft Ser.). Tr. of World in a State of Emergency. a Study on the Content, Message & Theology of the Book of the Watchers (1 Enoch 1-36). (GER.). X, 299p. 126.00 *(978-3-11-022429-0(1))*; 196.00 ***(978-3-11-174146-8(X))*** De Gruyter, Walter Inc.

Baker Publishing Group Staff. The Apocrypha: The Deuterocanonical Books of the Old Testament, 1 vol. 2009. 320p. 14.99 *(978-0-8010-7220-8(4))* Baker Bks.

Beentjes, Pancratius C. & Beentjes, P. C., eds. Happy the One Who Meditates on Wisdom (Sir. 14,20) Collected Essays on the Book of Ben Sira. 2006. (Contributions to Biblical Exegesis & Theology Ser.). (ENG & GER., Illus.). 402p. (C). pap. 66.00 *(978-90-429-1751-4(2))* Peeters Pubs. & Booksellers BEL. Dist: Brown, David Bk. Co., The.

Beentjes, Pancratius Cornelis, et al. Rewriting Biblical History: Essays on Chronicles & Ben Sira in Honour of Pancratius C. Beentjes de Gruyter. 2011. ***(978-3-11-024093-1(9))*** De Gruyter, Walter Inc.

Boccaccini, Gabriele & Collins, John J., eds. The Early Enoch Literature. 2007. (Supplements to the Journal for the Study of Judaism Ser.). 367p. *(978-90-04-16154-2(6))* BRILL.

Boda, Mark J., et al, eds. Seeking the Favor of God. 2008. (SBL - Early Judaism & Its Literature Ser.). *(978-90-04-16914-2(8))* BRILL.

—Seeking the Favor of God: The Impact of Penitential Prayer beyond Second Temple Judaism. 2008. 324p. pap. 39.95 *(978-1-58983-389-0(9))* Society of Biblical Literature.

Boda, Mark J., et al. Seeking the Favor of God. 2006. (Early Judaism & Its Literature Ser.: No. 21). 250p. *(978-90-04-15124-6(9))* BRILL.

Branick, Vincent P. Understanding the Historical Books of the Old Testament. 2011. (Illus.). 304p. pap. 24.95 *(978-0-8091-4728-1(9))* Paulist Pr.

Bridgeman, Valerie & Page, Hugh. The Africana Bible: Reading Israel's Scriptures from Africa & the African Diaspora. 2009. 512p. 39.00 *(978-0-8006-2125-4(5)*, Fortress Pr.) Augsburg Fortress, Pubs.

Charles, R. & Morfill, W. The Book of the Secrets of Enoch. 2007. 144p. 19.99 *(978-1-59986-742-7(7))* Filiquarian Publishing, LLC.

Charles, R. H. More Lost Books of the Bible the Secrets. 2006. pap. 18.95 *(978-1-933993-19-5(7))* Apocryphile Pr.

Charlesworth, James H. & McDonald, Lee Martin, eds. Jewish & Christian Scriptures: The Function of 'Canonical' & 'Non-Canonical' Religious Texts. 2010. (Jewish & Christian Text Ser.). (ENG.). 256p. 120.00 *(978-0-567-61870-2(6)*, T&T Clark Int'l) Continuum International Publishing Group, Ltd. GBR. Dist: National Bk. Network.

Collins, John Joseph & Harlow, Daniel C. The "Other" in Second Temple Judaism: Essays in Honor of John J. Collins. 2011. (Illus.). 528p. 65.00 *(978-0-8028-6625-7(5))* Eerdmans, William B. Publishing Co.

Esler, Philip F. Sex, Wives, & Warriors: Reading Biblical Narrative with Its Ancient Audience. 2011. 422p. pap. 46.00 ***(978-1-60899-829-6(0)***, Cascade Bks.) Wipf & Stock Pubs.

Fried, Lisbeth S. Was 1 Esdras First? An Investigation into the Priority & Nature of First Esdras. 2011. 287p. *(978-90-04-20251-1(X))* BRILL.

—Was 1 Esdras First? An Investigation into the Priority & Nature of First Esdras. 2011. *(978-1-58983-545-0(X))*; 300p. pap. *(978-1-58983-544-3(1))* Society of Biblical Literature.

Garlington, Don. The Obedience of Faith. 2009. 352p. pap. 39.00 *(978-1-60608-826-5(2)*, Wipf and Stock) Wipf & Stock Pubs.

Glicksman, Andrew T. Wisdom of Solomon 10: A Jewish Hellenistic Reinterpretation of Early Israelite History Through Sapiential Lenses. 2011. (Deuterocanonical & Cognate Literature Studies). 140.00 ***(978-3-11-024764-0(X))*** De Gruyter, Walter Inc.

Goering, G. S. Wisdom's Root Revealed: Ben Sira & the Election of Israel. 2009. (Supplements to the Journal for the Study of Judaism Ser.). 326p. *(978-90-04-16579-3(7))* BRILL.

Gregory, Bradley. Like an Everlasting Signet Ring: Generosity in the Book of Sirach. 2010. (Deuterocanonical & Cognate Literature Studies). (ENG.). XVII, 378p. 196.00 ***(978-3-11-174054-6(4))*** De Gruyter, Walter Inc.

Gregory, Bradley C. Like an Everlasting Signet Ring: Generosity in the Book of Sirach. 2010. (Deuterocanonical & Cognate Literature Studies). (ENG.). XVII, 378p. 126.00 *(978-3-11-022366-8(X))* De Gruyter, Walter Inc.

Grupner, Axel & Wolter, Michael, eds. Moses in Biblical & Extra-Biblical Traditions. 2007. (Beihefte Zur Zeitschrift Für Die Alttestamentliche Wissenschaft Ser.). (ENG., Illus.). VIII, 277p. 140.00 *(978-3-11-019460-9(0))* De Gruyter, Walter Inc.

Gurtner, Daniel M. Second Baruch: A Critical Edition of the Syriac Text with Greek & Latin Fragments, English Translation, Introduction, & Concordances. 2009. (Jewish & Christian Text Ser.). (ENG & SYR.). 240p. 130.00 *(978-0-567-60940-3(5)*, T&T Clark) Continuum International Publishing Group, Ltd. GBR. Dist: National Bk. Network.

Gurtner, Daniel M. Second Baruch: A Critical Edition of the Syriac Text: With Greek & Latin Fragments, English Translation, Introduction, & Concordances. 2011. (ENG.). 240p. pap. 44.95 ***(978-0-567-04616-1(8)***, T&T Clark Int'l) Continuum International Publishing Group, Ltd. GBR. Dist: National Bk. Network.

Hanson, Kenneth. Secrets from the Lost Bible. 2006. (ENG., Illus.). 248p. per. 14.95 *(978-1-57178-203-8(6))* Council Oak Bks.

Harrington, Daniel J. The Maccabean Revolt. 2009. 144p. pap. 18.00 *(978-1-60899-113-6(X)*, Wipf and Stock) Wipf & Stock Pubs.

Hauglid, Brian. A Textual History of the Book of Abraham. 2011. (Brigham Young University - Studies in the Book of Abraham Ser.). (Illus.). 307p. 79.95 *(978-0-8425-2774-3(5)*, Maxwell, Neal A. Institute for Religious Scholarship) Brigham Young Univ.

Hawley, Charles Arthur. The Teaching of Apocrypha & Apocalypse 1925. 2007. (ENG.). 184p. 37.95 *(978-0-548-05638-7(2))* Kessinger Publishing, LLC.

Henze, Matthias. Jewish Apocalypticism in Late First Century Israel: Reading 'Second Baruch' in Context. 2011. (Texts & Studies in Ancient Judaism Ser.). 448p. 247.50 ***(978-3-16-150859-2(9))*** Mohr Siebeck GmbH & Co. KG DEU. Dist: Coronet Bks.

Joslyn-Siemiatkoski, Daniel & Joslyn-Siemiatkoski, Dani. Christian Memories of the Maccabean Martyrs. 2009. (ENG.). 272p. 89.00 *(978-0-230-60279-3(7))* Palgrave Macmillan.

Kearns, Conleth, et al. The Expanded Text of Ecclesiasticus: Its Teaching on the Future Life As a Clue to Its Origin. 2011. (Deuterocanonical & Cognate Literature Studies). (ENG., Illus.). VI, 333p. 140.00 ***(978-3-11-025258-3(9))*** De Gruyter, Walter Inc.

Knibb, Michael A. Essays on the Book of Enoch & Other Early Jewish Texts & Traditions. 2008. (Studia in Veteris Testamenti Pseudepigrapha Ser.). 450p. *(978-90-04-16725-4(0))* BRILL.

Lattke, Michael. The Odes of Solomon. Attridge, Harold, ed. 2009. (Hermeneia Ser.). 864p. (C). 84.00 *(978-0-8006-6056-7(0)*, Fortress Pr.) Augsburg Fortress, Pubs.

Levine, Amy Jill. Women Like This: New Perspectives on Jewish Women in the Greco-Roman World. 2008. 280p. pap. 28.00 *(978-1-59740-691-8(0))* ACLS Humanities E-Book.

Littman, Robert J. Septuagint Commentary Series, Volume Tobit: The Book of Tobit in Codex Sinaiticus. 2008. (Septuagint Commentary Ser.). 264p. (C). *(978-90-04-17107-7(X))* BRILL.

Macatangay, Francis M. The Wisdom Instructions in the Book of Tobit. 2011. (Deuterocanonical & Cognate Literature Studies). (ENG., XVII, 367p. Illus.). 210.00 ***(978-3-11-218946-7(9))***; 140.00 ***(978-3-11-025534-8(0))*** De Gruyter, Walter Inc.

Manekin, Charles Harry & Eisen, Robert. Philosophers & the Jewish Bible. 2008. (C). *(978-1-934309-20-9(6))* Univ. Pr. of Maryland.

Marcus, Ralph. Law in the Apocrypha. (Columbia University, Oriental Studies: No. 26). reprint ed. 27.50 *(978-0-404-50516-5(3))* AMS Pr., Inc.

Marttila, Marko. Foreign Nations in the Wisdom of Ben Sira: A Jewish Sage between Opposition & Assimilation. 2012. (Deuterocanonical & Cognate Literature Studies). (ENG.). X, 287p. (gr. 17). 140.00 ***(978-3-11-027010-5(2))*** De Gruyter, Walter Inc.

Miller, Geoffrey David. Marriage in the Book of Tobit. 2011. (Deuterocanonical & Cognate Literature Studies). (ENG., VIII, 260p. Illus.). 210.00 ***(978-3-11-218873-6(X))***; 140.00 *(978-3-11-024786-2(0))* De Gruyter, Walter Inc.

Moo, Jonathan A. Creation, Nature & Hope in 4 Ezra. 2011. (Forschungen Zur Religion und Literatur des Alten & Neuen Testament Ser.). (ENG.). 206p. (C). 81.00 *(978-3-525-53103-7(6))* Vandenhoeck & Ruprecht GmbH & Co. KG DEU. Dist: ISD.

Morrow, William. Protest Against God: The Eclipse of a Biblical Tradition. 2007. 264p. per. *(978-1-906055-34-9(3))* Sheffield Phoenix Pr.

Neufeld, Dietmar, et al. And So They Went Out: The Lives of Adam & Eve as Cultural Transformative Story. 2010. (ENG.). 208p. 130.00 *(978-0-567-02679-8(5)*, T&T Clark Int'l) Continuum International Publishing Group, Ltd. GBR. Dist: National Bk. Network.

Nickelsburg, George W. E. Resurrection, Immortality, & Eternal Life in Intertestamental Judaism & Early Christianity. 2007. (Harvard Theological Studies: 56). (Illus.). 285p. per. 27.95 *(978-0-674-02378-9(1))* Harvard Univ. Pr.

Orlov, Andrei. Divine Manifestations in the Slavonic Pseudepigrapha. 2009. 110.00 *(978-1-60724-407-3(1))* Gorgias Pr., LLC.

Orlov, Andrei A. Selected Studies in the Slavonic Pseudepigrapha. 2009. *(978-90-04-17879-3(1))* BRILL.

Platt, Jr. The Forgotten Books of Eden. 2007. 464p. per. 24.99 *(978-1-59547-874-0(4))* NuVision Pubns., LLC.

Reading between the Lines: Discovering Christ in the Old Testament. 2008. pap. 19.99 *(978-1-56722-727-7(9))* Word Aflame Pr.

Rey, Jean-Sebastien & Joosten, Jan, eds. The Texts & Versions of the Book of Ben Sira: Transmission & Interpretation. 2011. (Supplements to the Journal for the Study of Judaism Ser.). (FRE.). X, 354p. ***(978-90-04-20692-2(2))*** BRILL.

Robert Henry Charles, ed. The Book of Enoch. 2011. 404p. pap. 8.74 ***(978-1-60386-425-1(3)***, Merchant Bks.) Rough Draft Printing.

Schwartz, S. Were the Jews a Mediterranean Society? Reciprocity & Solidarity in Ancient Judaism. 2009. (ENG.). 224p. (C). 30.95 *(978-0-691-14054-4(5))* Princeton Univ. Pr.

Turner, Marie. God's Wisdom or the Devil's Envy: Death & Creation Deconstructing in the Wisdom of Solomon. 2009. (ATF Biblical Ser.). (ENG.). 324p. (C). pap. 18.00 *(978-1-921511-57-8(5))* ATF Pr. AUS. Dist: Brown, David Bk. Co., The.

Ulrich, Eugene & Flint, Peter W. Discoveries in the Judaean Desert XXXII: Qumran Cave 1. II: the Isaiah Scrolls: Part 1: Plates & Transcriptions, 2 vols. 2011. (Discoveries in the Judaean Desert Ser.). (HEB & ENG., Illus.). 176p. 180.00 *(978-0-19-956666-2(6))* Oxford Univ. Pr., Inc.

Wicks, Henry J. The Doctrine of God in the Jewish Apocryphal & Apocalyptic Literature. 2010. 178p. pap. *(978-1-152-05350-2(7))* Books LLC.

—The Doctrine of God in the Jewish Apocryphal & Apocalyptic Literature. 2008. 385p. pap. 33.00 *(978-1-60608-255-3(8)*, Wipf and Stock) Wipf & Stock Pubs.

Wright, Benjamin G. III. Praise Israel for Wisdom & Instruction: Essays on Ben Sira & Wisdom, the Letter of Aristeas & the Septuagint. 2008. (Supplements to the Journal for the Study of Judaism Ser.). 358p. (C). *(978-90-04-16908-1(3))* BRILL.

Xeravits, Géza G., ed. A Pious Seductress: Studies in the Book of Judith. 2012. (Deuterocanonical & Cognate Literature Studies). (ENG & GER.). VII, 225p. (gr. 17). 112.00 ***(978-3-11-027994-8(0))*** De Gruyter, Walter Inc.

Xeravits, Geza G. & Zsengellér, József. Studies in the Book of Ben Sira: Papers of the Third International Conference on the Deuterocanonical Books, Shime'on Centre, Pápa, Hungary, 18-20 May 2006. 2008. (Supplements to the Journal for the Study of Judaism Ser.). 282p. *(978-90-04-16906-7(7))* BRILL.

Xeravits, Géza G. & Zsengellér, József, eds. The Books of the Maccabees: History, Theology, Ideology: Papers of the Second International Conference on the Deuterocanonical Books, Pápa, Hungary, 9-11 June 2005. 2007. (Supplements to the Journal for the Study of Judaism Ser.: Vol. 118). (GER & ENG.). 252p. *(978-90-04-15700-2(X))* BRILL.

Ziade, Raphaelle. Les Martyrs Maccabees: de L'Histoire Juive Au Culte Chretien: Les Homelies de Gregoire de Nazianze et de Jean Chrysostome. 2006. (Supplements to Vigiliae Christianae Ser.). (FRE.). 392p. *(978-90-04-15384-4(5))* BRILL.

BIBLE—CRITICISM, INTERPRETATION, ETC.—O. T. CHRONICLES

see Bible—Criticism, Interpretation, Etc.—O. T. Historical Books

BIBLE—CRITICISM, INTERPRETATION, ETC.—O. T. DANIEL

see Bible—Criticism, Interpretation, Etc.—O. T. Prophets

BIBLE—CRITICISM, INTERPRETATION, ETC.—O. T. DEUTERONOMY

see Bible—Criticism, Interpretation, Etc.—O. T. Pentateuch

BIBLE—CRITICISM, INTERPRETATION, ETC.—O. T. ECCLESIASTES

see Bible—Criticism, Interpretation, etc.—O. T. Poetical Books

BIBLE—CRITICISM, INTERPRETATION, ETC.—O. T. ESTHER

see Bible—Criticism, Interpretation, Etc.—O. T. Historical Books

BIBLE—CRITICISM, INTERPRETATION, ETC.—O. T. EXODUS

see Bible—Criticism, Interpretation, Etc.—O. T. Pentateuch

BIBLE—CRITICISM, INTERPRETATION, ETC.—O. T. EZEKIEL

see Bible—Criticism, Interpretation, Etc.—O. T. Prophets

BIBLE—CRITICISM, INTERPRETATION, ETC.—O. T. EZRA

see Bible—Criticism, Interpretation, Etc.—O. T. Historical Books

BIBLE—CRITICISM, INTERPRETATION, ETC.—O. T. GENESIS

see Bible—Criticism, Interpretation, Etc.—O. T. Pentateuch

BIBLE—CRITICISM, INTERPRETATION, ETC.—O. T. HABAKKUK

see Bible—Criticism, Interpretation, Etc.—O. T. Minor Prophets

BIBLE—CRITICISM, INTERPRETATION, ETC.—O. T. HAGGAI

see Bible—Criticism, Interpretation, Etc.—O. T. Minor Prophets

BIBLE—CRITICISM, INTERPRETATION, ETC.—O. T. HISTORICAL BOOKS

Here are entered works on the historical Books as a whole, as well as on one or more of the following: Chronicles, Esther, Ezra, Joshua, Judges, Kings, Nehemiah, Ruth, Samuel.

Ackroyd, Peter R. Chronicler in His Age. 2009. (Library of Hebrew Bible/Old Testament Studies, the Ser.). (ENG.). 65.00 *(978-0-567-00132-0(6)*, T&T Clark) Continuum International Publishing Group, Ltd. GBR. Dist: National Bk. Network.

Adam, Klaus-Peter. Soundings in Kings: Perspectives & Methods in Contemporary Scholarship. Leuchter, Mark, ed. 2010. 224p. (C). pap. 32.00 *(978-0-8006-9716-7(2)*, Fortress Pr.) Augsburg Fortress, Pubs.

Andersson, Greger. Untamable Texts: Literary Studies & Narrative Theory in the Books of Samuel, Vol. 514. 2009. (Library of Hebrew Bible/Old Testament Studies, the Ser.). (ENG.). 304p. 130.00 *(978-0-567-52051-7(X)*, T&T Clark Int'l) Continuum International Publishing Group, Ltd. GBR. Dist: National Bk. Network.

Arnold, Patrick M. Gibeah: The Search for a Biblical City. 2009. (Library of Hebrew Bible/Old Testament Studies, the Ser.). (ENG.). 200p. 39.95 *(978-0-567-40212-7(6)*, T&T Clark) Continuum International Publishing Group, Ltd. GBR. Dist: National Bk. Network.

Bader, Mary. Sexual Violation in the Hebrew Bible. 2006. (Studies in Biblical Literature: Vol. 87). x,206p. (C). 69.95 *(978-0-8204-7873-9(3))* Lang, Peter Publishing, Inc.

Bailey, Randall C. David in Love & War: The Pursuit of Pursuit of Power in 2 Samuel 10-12. 2009. (Library of Hebrew Bible/Old Testament Studies, the Ser.). (ENG.). 39.95 *(978-0-567-37645-9(1)*, T&T Clark) Continuum International Publishing Group, Ltd. GBR. Dist: National Bk. Network.

Baker Publishing Group Staff. A Walk Thru the Book of Ruth: Loyalty & Love. 2009. (Walk Thru the Bible Discussion Guides). 60p. pap. 7.99 *(978-0-8010-7169-0(0))* Baker Bks.

—A Walk Thru the Life of Solomon: Pursuing a Heart of Integrity. 2009. (Walk Thru the Bible Discussion Guides). 59p. pap. 7.99 *(978-0-8010-7174-4(7))* Baker Bks.

Batterson, Mark. In a Pit with a Lion on a Snowy Day: How to Survive & Thrive When Opportunity Roars. 2006. (ENG.). 192p. pap. 13.99 *(978-1-59052-715-3(1)*, Multnomah) Doubleday Religious Publishing Group, The.

Beentjes, Pancratius. Tradition & Transformation in the Book of Chronicles. 2008. (Studia Semitica Neerlandica Ser.). 332p. (C). *(978-90-04-17044-5(8))* BRILL.

Beentjes, Pancratius Cornelis, et al. Rewriting Biblical History: Essays on Chronicles & Ben Sira in Honour of Pancratius C. Beentjes de Gruyter. 2011. ***(978-3-11-024093-1(9))*** De Gruyter, Walter Inc.

Begerau, Gunnar. Elia vom Krit zum Jordan: Eine Untersuchung zur literarischen Makrostruktur und theologischen Intention der Elia-Ahab-Erzählung (1 Kön 16,29 bis 2 Kön 2,25) 2008. (Europäische Hochschulschriften. Reihe 23: Theologie Ser.). (GER., Illus.). 322p. pap. 74.95 *(978-3-631-58386-9(9))* Lang, Peter GmbH, Europaischer Verlag der Wissenschaften DEU. Dist: Lang, Peter.

Ben Zvi, Ehud & Edelman, Diana Vikander. What Was Authoritative for Chronicles? 2011. ***(978-1-57506-218-1(6))*** Eisenbrauns, Inc.

Blenkinsopp, Joseph. Judaism, the First Phase: The Place of Ezra & Nehemiah in the Origins of Jdaism. 2009. (ENG.). 288p. pap. 30.00 *(978-0-8028-6450-5(3))* Eerdmans, William B. Publishing Co.

Boda, Mark J. & Redditt, Paul L., eds. Unity & Disunity in Ezra-Nehemiah: Redaction, Rhetoric, & Reader. 2008. 396p. *(978-1-906055-40-0(8))* Sheffield Phoenix Pr.

Bodi, Daniel. The Demise of the Warlord: A New Look at the David Story. 2010. xii, 270p. ***(978-1-906055-82-0(3))*** Sheffield Phoenix Pr.

Bodner, Keith. Jeroboam's Royal Drama. 2012. (ENG.). 192p. 85.00 ***(978-0-19-960187-5(9))***; pap. 27.95 ***(978-0-19-960188-2(7))*** Oxford Univ. Pr., Inc.

Bodner, Keith. 1 Samuel: A Narrative Commentary. 2008. 352p. *(978-1-906055-10-3(6))* Sheffield Phoenix Pr.

Böhler, Dieter. Jiftach und die Tora: Eine intertextuelle Auslegung von Ri 10,6-12,7. 2008. (Österreichische Biblische Studien Ser.). 414p. pap. 99.95 *(978-3-631-57780-6(X))* Lang, Peter GmbH, Europaischer Verlag der Wissenschaften DEU. Dist: Lang, Peter.

Borgman, Paul. David, Saul, & God: Rediscovering an Ancient Story. 2008. (ENG.). 352p. 35.00 *(978-0-19-533160-8(5))* Oxford Univ. Pr., Inc.

Bosworth, David Alan. The Story Within a Story in Biblical Hebrew Narrative. 2009. *(978-0-915170-44-9(2))* Catholic Biblical Assn. of America.

Boteler, Lori. A Common Sense Approach to Esther. 2007. per. 20.00 *(978-0-9798207-0-0(7))* LoJo Publishing.

Branick, Vincent P. Understanding the Historical Books of the Old Testament. 2011. (Illus.). 304p. pap. 24.95 *(978-0-8091-4728-1(9))* Paulist Pr.

Brenner, Athalya. Rehab the Whore (Joshua 2 & 6) 2010. (Vos Ser.). pap. *(978-90-5629-068-9(1)*, Vossiupers UvA) Amsterdam Univ. Pr.

Brown, A. Philip, II. Hope Amidst Ruin: A Literary & Theological Analysis of Ezra. 2008. *(978-1-59166-942-5(1))* BJU Pr.

Brueggemann, Walter. Divine Presence amid Violence: Contextualizing the Book of Joshua. 2009. 93p. pap. 13.00 *(978-1-60608-089-4(X)*, Cascade Bks.) Wipf & Stock Pubs.

Carson, Alexander. God's Providence Unfolded in the Book of Esther: Confidence in God in Times of Danger. 2011. 132p. 40.95 ***(978-1-258-05931-6(2))*** Literary Licensing, LLC.

Chavda, Mahesh & Chavda, Bonnie. Make Room for Your Miracle, 1 vol. 2009. 192p. pap. 13.99 *(978-0-8007-9470-5(2))* Chosen Bks.

Chisholm, Robert B., Jr. Interpreting the Historical Books: An Exegetical Handbook, 1 vol. 2006. (Handbooks for Old Testament Exegesis Ser.). 232p. pap. 19.99 *(978-0-8254-2764-0(9))* Kregel Pubns.

Christenson, Larry. The Mantle of Esther: Discovering the Power of Intercession. 2008. 160p. pap. 12.99 *(978-0-8007-9428-6(1))* Chosen Bks.

Clines, David J. A. Telling Queen Michal's Story: An Experiment in Comparative Interpretation. Eskenazi, Tamara C., ed. 2009. (Library of Hebrew Bible/Old Testament Studies, the Ser.). (ENG.). 301p. 49.95 *(978-0-567-48797-1(0)*, T&T Clark) Continuum International Publishing Group, Ltd. GBR. Dist: National Bk. Network.

Cross, Kevin. Building Your Financial Fortress in 52 Days: The Lessons of Nehemiah. 2009. 184p. pap. 14.99 *(978-0-88270-643-6(8))* Bridge-Logos Foundation.

Culver, Carolyn. Protected by God's Providence: The Book of Esther. 2007. 127p. *(978-0-87227-340-5(7))* Regular Baptist Pr.

Dalley, Stephanie. Esther's Revenge at Susa: From Sennacherib to Ahasuerus. 2008. (ENG., Illus.). 280p. 110.00 *(978-0-19-921663-5(0))* Oxford Univ. Pr., Inc.

Daschke, Derek. City of Ruins: Mourning the Destruction of Jerusalem Through Jewish Apocalypse. (Illus.). 222p. *(978-90-04-18181-6(4))* BRILL.

Davis, John J. The Birth of a Kingdom: Studies in I & II Samuel & I Kings I-II. pap. 10.99 *(978-0-88469-053-5(9))* BMH Bks.

—Conquest & Crisis: Studies in Joshua, Judges & Ruth. (Illus.). pap. 9.99 *(978-0-88469-052-8(0))* BMH Bks.

Davis Sr, Roderick A. Called to Speak His Word Boldly. 2008. 52p. per. 7.95 *(978-1-4327-2078-0(3))* Outskirts Pr., Inc.

Day, Linda. Three Faces of a Queen: Characterization in the Books of Esther. 2009. (Library of Hebrew Bible/Old Testament Studies, the Ser.). (ENG.). 254p. 44.95 *(978-0-8264-4643-5(4)*, T&T Clark) Continuum International Publishing Group, Ltd. GBR. Dist: National Bk. Network.

Debelak, Robert P., Jr. & Debelak Jr., Robert P. Hidden in Plain Sight: Esther & a Marginalized Hermeneutic. 2008. (Illus.). 170p. pap. 20.00 *(978-1-55635-499-1(1))* Wipf & Stock Pubs.

Dietrich, Walter. The Early Monarchy in Israel: The Tenth Century B. C. E. Vette, Joachim, tr. from GER. 2007. (SBL - Biblical Encyclopedia Ser.). (Illus.). 378p. *(978-90-04-15735-4(2))* BRILL.

—The Early Monarchy in Israel: The Tenth Century B. C. E. Vette, Joachim, tr. from GER. 2007. 396p. per. 47.95 *(978-1-58983-263-3(9))* Society of Biblical Literature.

Dillard Cpa, John. A Voice Of Nehemiah's Prayer. 2009. 92p. pap. 16.95 *(978-1-60703-656-2(8))* PublishAmerica, Inc.

Duke, Rodney K. Persuasive Appeal of the Chronicler: A Rhetorical Analysis. 2009. (Library of Hebrew Bible/Old Testament Studies, the Ser.). (ENG.). 192p. 39.95 *(978-0-567-37461-5(0)*, T&T Clark) Continuum International Publishing Group, Ltd. GBR. Dist: National Bk. Network.

Dutcher-Walls, Patricia. Narrative Art, Political Rhetoric: The Case of Athaliah & Joash. 2009. (Library of Hebrew Bible/Old Testament Studies, the Ser.). (ENG.). 198p. 39.95 *(978-0-567-35506-5(3)*, T&T Clark) Continuum International Publishing Group, Ltd. GBR. Dist: National Bk. Network.

Earl, Douglas S. The Joshua Delusion? Rethinking Genocide in the Bible. 2010. (Illus.). 190p. pap. 22.00 *(978-1-60899-892-0(4)*, Cascade Bks.) Wipf & Stock Pubs.

—Joshua Delusion? The. 2011. (ENG.). 174p. pap. 38.00 *(978-0-227-17376-3(7))* Clarke, James Co., Ltd. GBR. Dist: Brown, David Bk. Co., The.

—Reading Joshua As Christian Scripture. 2010. pap. 37.95 *(978-1-57506-701-8(3))* Eisenbrauns, Inc.

Echols, Charles L. & Echols. "Tell Me, O Muse" The Song of Deborah (Judges 5) in the Light of Heroic Poetry. 2008. (Library of Hebrew Bible/Old Testament Studies, the Ser.). (ENG.). 256p. 130.00 *(978-0-567-02694-1(9)*, T&T Clark Int'l) Continuum International Publishing Group, Ltd. GBR. Dist: National Bk. Network.

Edelman, Diana Vikander. King Saul in the Historiography of Judah. 2009. (Library of Hebrew Bible/Old Testament Studies, the Ser.). (ENG.). 347p. 60.00 *(978-0-567-38596-3(5)*, T&T Clark) Continuum International Publishing Group, Ltd. GBR. Dist: National Bk. Network.

Esler, Philip F. Sex, Wives, & Warriors: Reading Biblical Narrative with Its Ancient Audience. 2011. 422p. pap. 46.00 ***(978-1-60899-829-6(0)***, Cascade Bks.) Wipf & Stock Pubs.

Eslinger, Lyle. House of God or House of David: The Rhetoric of 2 Samuel 7. 2009. (Library of Hebrew Bible/Old Testament Studies, the Ser.). (ENG.). 118p. 27.95 *(978-0-567-57153-3(X)*, T&T Clark) Continuum International Publishing Group, Ltd. GBR. Dist: National Bk. Network.

Evans, Paul S. The Invasion of Sennacherib in the Book of Kings: A Source-Critical & Rhetorical Study of 2 Kings 18-19. 2009. 240p. *(978-90-04-17596-9(2))* BRILL.

Fields, Weston W. Sodom & Gomorrah: History & Motif in Biblical Narrative. 2009. (Library of Hebrew Bible/Old Testament Studies, the Ser.). (ENG.). 223p. 39.95 *(978-0-567-60250-3(8)*, T&T Clark) Continuum International Publishing Group, Ltd. GBR. Dist: National Bk. Network.

Frolov, Serge. The Turn of the Cycle: 1 Samuel 1-8 in Synchronic & Diachronic Perspectives. (Beihefte zur Zeitschrift fur die alttestamentliche Wissenschaft Ser.). (ENG.). XIV, 275p. 225.00 ***(978-3-11-182919-7(7))*** De Gruyter, Walter Inc.

Furtick, Steven. Sun Stand Still: What Happens When You Dare to Ask God for the Impossible. 2010. (ENG.). 224p. pap. 14.99 *(978-1-60142-322-1(5)*, Multnomah) Doubleday Religious Publishing Group, The.

Gale, Stanley D. The Prayer of Jehoshaphat: Seeing Beyond Life's Storms. 2007. 143p. pap. *(978-1-59638-062-2(4))* P & R Publishing.

Garrett, Ginger. Queen Esther's Secrets of Womanhood: A Biblical Rite of Passage for Your Daughter. 2006. (Navigators Reference Library). (ENG.). 144p. pap. 11.99 *(978-1-57683-986-7(9))* NavPress Publishing Group.

Giuliano, Angelo G., et al. Old Testament Foundations: Genesis Through Kings: Year One: Teacher Guidebook. 2007. (Catholic Biblical School Program Ser.). (Illus.). 80p. per. 19.95 *(978-0-8091-9585-5(2))* Paulist Pr.

Good, Roger. The Septuagint's Translation of the Hebrew Verbal System in Chronicles. 2009. *(978-90-04-15158-1(3))* BRILL.

Goode, Carol N. Change Matters: Which voice will you Follow? 2009. 86p. pap. 14.95 *(978-1-4489-2084-6(1))* PublishAmerica, Inc.

Gossai, Hemchand. Power & Marginality in the Abraham Narrative - Second Edition. 2nd ed. 2009. (Princeton Theological Monographs). 168p. pap. 19.00 *(978-1-55635-874-6(1)*, Pickwick Pubns.) Wipf & Stock Pubs.

Grabbe, Lester L. & Grabbe. Ahab Agonistes: The Rise & Fall of the Omri Dynasty. 2007. (Library of Hebrew Bible/Old Testament Studies). (ENG., Illus.). 368p. 160.00 *(978-0-567-04540-9(4)*, T&T Clark Int'l) Continuum International Publishing Group, Ltd. GBR. Dist: National Bk. Network.

Green, Adam. King Saul: The True History of the First Messiah. 2007. (ENG., Illus.). 272p. pap. 40.00 *(978-0-7188-3074-8(1))* Lutherworth Pr., The GBR. Dist: Brown, David Bk. Co., The.

Greenspoon, Leonard & Crawford, Sidnie White. Book of Esther in Modern Research. 2009. (Library of Hebrew Bible/Old Testament Studies, the Ser.). (ENG.). 370p. 60.00 *(978-1-4411-0305-5(8))* Continuum International Publishing Group, Ltd. GBR. Dist: National Bk. Network.

Greer, Rowan A. & Mitchell, Margaret Mary, intros. The "Belly-Myther" of Endor: Interpretations of 1 Kingdoms 28 in the Early Church. 2007. (SBL: Writings from the Greco-Roman World). 190p. (978-90-04-13062-3(4)) BRILL.

—The Belly-Myther of Endor: Interpretations of 1 Kingdoms 28 in the Early Church. 2007. (ENG.). 348p. per. 39.95 (978-1-58983-120-9(9)) Society of Biblical Literature.

Gressmann, Hugo. Narrative & Novella in Samuel: Studies by Hugo Gressmann & Other Scholars 1906-1923. 2009. (Library of Hebrew Bible/Old Testament Studies, the Ser.). (ENG.). 182p. 29.95 (978-0-567-59407-5(6), T&T Clark) Continuum International Publishing Group, Ltd. GBR. Dist: National Bk. Network.

Grossman, Jonathan. Esther: The Outer Narrative & the Hidden Reading. 2011. **(978-1-57506-221-1(6))** Eisenbrauns, Inc.

Guillaume, Philippe. Land & Calendar: The Priestly Document from Genesis 1 to Joshua 18. 2009. (Library of Hebrew Bible/Old Testament Studies, the Ser.). (ENG., Illus.). 256p. 120.00 (978-0-567-32200-5(9), T&T Clark Int'l) Continuum International Publishing Group, Ltd. GBR. Dist: National Bk. Network.

Hall, Sarah Lebhar. Conquering Character: The Characterization of Joshua in Joshua 1-11, Vol. 512. 2010. (Library of Hebrew Bible/Old Testament Studies, the Ser.). (ENG.). 256p. 120.00 (978-0-567-25703-1(7), T&T Clark Int'l) Continuum International Publishing Group, Ltd. GBR. Dist: National Bk. Network.

Hamilton, Victor P. Handbook on the Historical Books: Joshua, Judges, Ruth, Samuel, Kings, Chronicles, Ezra-Nehemiah, Esther. 2008. (Illus.). 560p. (C). pap. 37.00 (978-0-8010-3614-9(3)) Baker Academic.

Hammond, Michelle McKinney. How to Be Found by the Man You've Been Looking For. 2008. 160p. pap. 10.99 (978-0-7369-2411-5(6)) Harvest Hse. Pubs.

Harding, James E. The Love of David & Jonathan. Crossley, James G. & Davies, Philip R., eds. 2012. (BibleWorld Ser.). (ENG.). (C). 224p. pap. 40.00 **(978-1-84553-676-3(2))**; 448p. 120.00 **(978-1-84553-675-6(4))** Equinox Publishing Ltd. GBR. Dist: Brown, David Bk. Co., The, ISD.

Hawk, L. Daniel. Every Promise Fulfilled: Contesting Plots in Joshua. 2009. 172p. (Orig.). pap. 20.00 (978-1-60608-595-0(6), Wipf and Stock) Wipf & Stock Pubs.

—Joshua In 3-D: A Commentary on Biblical Conquest & Manifest Destiny. 2010. 316p. pap. 35.00 (978-1-60608-819-7(X)) Wipf & Stock Pubs.

Heller, Roy. Conversations with Scripture: The Book of Judges. 2011. (Anglican Association of Biblical Scholars Ser.). 160p. pap. 18.00 (978-0-8192-2756-0(0), Morehouse Publishing) Church Publishing, Inc.

—Power, Politics, & Prophecy: The Character of Samuel & the Deuteronomistic Evaluation of Prophecy. 2006. (Library of Hebrew Bible/Old Testament Studies: Vol. 440). (ENG.). 184p. 160.00 (978-0-567-02762-7(7), T&T Clark Int'l) Continuum International Publishing Group, Ltd. GBR. Dist: National Bk. Network.

Heller, Roy L. Conversations with Scripture: The Book of Judges. 2011. E-Book **(978-0-8192-2757-7(9)**, Morehouse Publishing) Church Publishing, Inc.

Hess, Richard S. Joshua. 2008. (Tyndale Old Testament Commentaries Ser.: Volume 6). (ENG., Illus.). 352p. pap. 16.00 (978-0-8308-4206-3(3), IVP Acad.) InterVarsity Pr.

Hession, Roy. Our Nearest Kinsman: The Story of Ruth & Our Redemption in Christ. 2007. (ENG.). 105p. pap. 8.99 (978-0-87508-857-0(0)) CLC Pubns.

Hogan, Karina. Theologies in Conflict in 4 Ezra: Wisdom Debate & Apocalyptic Solution. 2008. (Supplements to the Journal for the Study of Judaism Ser.). 280p. (C). (978-90-04-12969-6(3)) BRILL.

Holmstedt, Robert D. Ruth: A Handbook on the Hebrew Text. 2010. (Baylor Handbook on the Hebrew Bible Ser.). (ENG.). 180p. pap. 24.95 (978-1-932792-91-1(0)) Baylor Univ. Pr.

Horowitz, Elliott. Reckless Rites: Purim & the Legacy of Jewish Violence. 2008. (Jews, Christians, & Muslims from the Ancient to the Modern World Ser.). (ENG., Illus.). 360p. (C). pap. 26.95 (978-0-691-13824-4(9)) Princeton Univ. Pr.

Hugo, Philippe & Schenker, Adrian. Archaeology of the Books of Samuel: The Entangling of the Textual & Literary History. 2009. (FRE, GER & ENG.). (978-90-04-17957-8(7)) BRILL.

Hurowitz, Victor. I Have Built You an Exalted House: Temple Building in the Bible in Light of Mesopotamian & North-West Semitic Writings. 2009. (Library of Hebrew Bible/Old Testament Studies, the Ser.). (ENG.). 398p. 65.00 (978-0-567-02988-1(3), T&T Clark) Continuum International Publishing Group, Ltd. GBR. Dist: National Bk. Network.

Ijezie, Luke Emehiele. The Interpretation of the Hebrew Word Am [Hebrew Script] (People) in Samuel-Kings. 2006. 342p. pap. 67.95 (978-0-8204-8376-4(1)) Lang, Peter Publishing, Inc.

Ironside, Henry A. Estudios sobre el Libro de Ester: Lectures on the Book of Esther. (SPA.). (978-84-7645-154-0(7), 223199) Clie, Editorial.

Jackson, Robert. What a Man. 2009. 72p. pap. 10.49 (978-1-4343-9778-2(5)) AuthorHouse.

Japhet, Sara. From the Rivers of Babylon to the Highlands of Judah: Collected Studies on the Restoration Period. 2006. 469p. 49.50 (978-1-57506-121-4(X)) Eisenbrauns, Inc.

—The Ideology of the Book of Chronicles & Its Place in Biblical Thought. 2009. 49.50 (978-1-57506-159-7(7)) Eisenbrauns, Inc.

Jones, Gwilym H. Nathan Narratives. 2009. (Library of Hebrew Bible/Old Testament Studies, the Ser.). (ENG.). 196p. 39.95 (978-0-567-10870-8(8), T&T Clark) Continuum International Publishing Group, Ltd. GBR. Dist: National Bk. Network.

Jones, Ken. Jewish Reactions to the Destruction of Jerusalem in A. D. 70: Apocalypses & Related Pseudepigrapha. 2011. (Supplements to the Journal for the Study of Judaism Ser.). x, 305p. **(978-90-04-21027-1(X))** BRILL.

Kalimi, Isaac. New Perspectives on Ezra-Nehemiah: History & Historiography, Text, Literature, & Interpretation. 2012. **(978-1-57506-233-4(X))** Eisenbrauns, Inc.

Kelly, Brian E. Retribution & Eschatology in Chronicles. 2009. (Library of Hebrew Bible/Old Testament Studies, the Ser.). (ENG.). 279p. 44.95 (978-0-567-11373-3(6), T&T Clark) Continuum International Publishing Group, Ltd. GBR. Dist: National Bk. Network.

Kent, Grenville J. R. Say It Again, Sam: A Literary & Filmic Study of Narrative Repetition in 1 Samuel 28. 2011. 268p. pap. 29.00 **(978-1-60899-990-3(4)**, Pickwick Pubns.) Wipf & Stock Pubs.

Kent, Grenville Jr. Say it Again, Sam: A Literary & Filmic Study of Narrative Repetition in 1 Samuel 28. 2012. (ENG.). 268p. pap. 39.00 **(978-0-7188-9271-5(2))** Lutherworth Pr., The GBR. Dist: Brown, David Bk. Co., The.

Kim, Koowon. Incubation as a Type-Scene in the Aqhatu, Kirta, & Hannah Stories: A Form-Critical & Narratological Study of KTU 1.14 I-1.15 III, 1.17 I-ii, & 1 Samuel 1:1-2:11. 2011. (Vetus Testamentum Supplements Ser.). XIV, 370p. (978-90-04-20239-9(0)) BRILL.

Kim, Uriah Y. Identity & Loyalty in the David Story: A Postcolonial Reading. 2008. 242p. (978-1-906055-58-5(0)) Sheffield Phoenix Pr.

Koopmans, William T. Joshua 24 as Poetic Narrative. 2009. (Library of Hebrew Bible/Old Testament Studies, the Ser.). (ENG.). 522p. 75.00 (978-0-567-29387-9(4), T&T Clark) Continuum International Publishing Group, Ltd. GBR. Dist: National Bk. Network.

Koosed, Jennifer L. Gleaning Ruth: A Biblical Heroine & Her Afterlives. 2011. 184p. 39.95 (978-1-57003-983-6(6)) Univ. of South Carolina Pr.

Kuenen, Abraham. HistoricoCritical Inquiry into the Origi. 2006. pap. 33.95 (978-1-4286-5869-1(6)) Kessinger Publishing, LLC.

Landy, Yehuda. Purim & the Persian Empire: A Historical, Archaeological, & Geographical Perspective. 2010. (HEB & ENG., Illus.). xii, 104p. **(978-1-59826-519-4(9))** Feldheim Pubs.

Lang, Marshall. Gedeon y los Jueces: Gideon & Judges. (SPA.). (978-84-7645-005-5(2), 223079) Clie, Editorial.

Lau, Peter H. W. Identity & Ethics in the Book of Ruth: A Social Identity Approach. 2010. (Beihefte zur Zeitschrift fa1/4r die alttestamentliche Wissenschaft Ser.). 250p. 126.00 (978-3-11-024760-2(7)) De Gruyter, Walter Inc.

Lau, Peter Hon Wan. Identity & Ethics in the Book of Ruth: A Social Identity Approach. 2011. (Beihefte zur Zeitschrift far die alttestamentliche Wissenschaft Ser.). (ENG., Illus.). XII, 234p. 196.00 **(978-3-11-214311-7(6))** De Gruyter, Walter Inc.

Levin, Meir. The Dawn of Redemption: What the Books of Ruth & Yona Teach about Alienation, Despair & Return. 2009. 235p. pap. 19.95 (978-965-524-022-1(3)) Urim Pubns. ISR. Dist: Coronet Bks.

Linafelt, Tod, et al, eds. The Fate of King David Vol. 500: The Past & Present of a Biblical Icon. 2010. (Library of Hebrew Bible/Old Testament Studies, the Ser.). (ENG.). 352p. (978-0-567-51546-9(X), T&T Clark Int'l) Continuum International Publishing Group, Ltd.

Lozovyy, Joseph. Saul, Doeg, Nabal, & the "Son of Jesse" Readings in 1 Samuel 16-25. 2009. (Library Hebrew Bible/Old Testament Studies). (ENG.). 256p. 140.00 (978-0-567-02753-5(8), T&T Clark Int'l) Continuum International Publishing Group, Ltd. GBR. Dist: National Bk. Network.

Luke Gartner-Brereton Staff. The Ontology of Space in Biblical Hebrew Narrative. 2008. (BibleWorld Ser.). (ENG., Illus.). 140p. (C). 99.95 (978-1-84553-313-7(5)); 29.95 (978-1-84553-314-4(3)) Equinox Publishing Ltd. GBR. Dist: ISD.

McClymonds, Scott A. Building a Kingdom Business: A View from the Trenches - How You Can Create a Business with Significance & Impact for God. 2009. 208p. 25.99 (978-1-61579-103-3(5)); pap. 15.99 (978-1-61579-096-8(9)) Xulon Pr., Inc.

McConville, J. G. God & Earthly Power: An Old Testament Political Theology. 2008. (ENG.). 224p. 44.95 (978-0-567-04570-6(6), T&T Clark Int'l) Continuum International Publishing Group, Ltd. GBR. Dist: National Bk. Network.

McKenzie, Steven L. Introduction to the Historical Books: Strategies for Reading. 2010. 184p. pap. 18.00 (978-0-8028-2877-4(9)) Eerdmans, William B. Publishing Co.

McNeil, Diane. Ruth 3,000 Years of Sleeping Prophecy Awakened -Workbook. 2007. 100p. per. 11.99 (978-1-60266-400-5(5)) Xulon Pr., Inc.

Michelson, Marty Alan. Reconciling Violence & Kingship: A Study of Judges & 1 Samuel. 2012. (ENG.). 240p. pap. 40.00 **(978-0-227-68013-1(8))** Clarke, James Co., Ltd. GBR. Dist: Brown, David Bk. Co., The.

—Reconciling Violence & Kingship: A Study of Judges & 1 Samuel. 2011. 240p. pap. 26.00 **(978-1-60899-338-3(8)**, Pickwick Pubns.) Wipf & Stock Pubs.

Miller, Patrick D. & Roberts, J. J. M. The Hand of the Lord: A Reassessment of the "Ark Narrative" of 1 Samuel. 2007. 15.95 (978-1-58983-294-7(9)) Society of Biblical Literature.

Millgram, Hillel I. Four Biblical Heroines & the Case for Female Authorship: An Analysis of the Women of Ruth, Esther & Genesis 38. 2007. (ENG., Illus.). 279p. per. 39.95 (978-0-7864-3081-9(8)) McFarland & Co., Inc. Pubs.

—The Invention of Monotheist Ethics: Exploring the First Book of Samuel. 2009. (ENG.). 260p. pap. 36.99 (978-0-7618-4922-3(X)); 360p. pap. 41.99 (978-0-7618-4924-7(6)) Univ. Pr. of America, Inc.

Mitchell, Gordon. Together in the Land: A Reading of the Book of Joshua. 2009. (Library of Hebrew Bible/Old Testament Studies, the Ser.). (ENG.). 224p. 39.95 (978-0-567-05742-6(9), T&T Clark) Continuum International Publishing Group, Ltd. GBR. Dist: National Bk. Network.

Mohney, Nell W. Slay Your Giants: Life Lessons from the Story of David & Goliath. 2007. 172p. pap. 13.00 (978-0-687-49106-3(1), Dimensions For Living) Abingdon Pr.

Monroe, Lauren A. S. Josiah's Reform & the Dynamics of Defilement: Israelite Rites of Violence & the Making of a Biblical Text. 2011. (ENG.). 216p. 74.00 (978-0-19-977416-6(1)) Oxford Univ. Pr., Inc.

Muniesa, David. Una De Contra un Imperio: Samuel Vila: Faith Against an Empire: Samuel Vila. (SPA., Illus.). 432p. (978-84-7228-444-9(1), 220795) Clie, Editorial.

Nehsahn, Peter. Esther: A Practical Study through the Book of Esther in the Context of our Time: Woman, Thy Time Is Now. 2007. (ENG.). 100p. per. 11.99 (978-1-4141-0861-2(3)) Pleasant Word.

Oeste, Gordon K. Legitimacy, Illegitimacy, & the Right to Rule: Windows on Abimelech?s Rise & Demise in Judges 9. 2011. (Library Hebrew Bible/Old Testament Studies). (ENG., Illus.). 288p. 140.00 (978-0-567-23783-5(4), T&T Clark Int'l) Continuum International Publishing Group, Ltd. GBR. Dist: National Bk. Network.

Page, Frank. The Nehemiah Factor: 16 Characteristics of a Missional Leader. 2008. (ENG.). 208p. pap. 14.99 (978-1-59669-223-7(5)) New Hope Pubs.

Parker, Frieda P. Eleven Words: Eleven inspirational, informational, & motivational messages based on eleven powerful words of Biblical Scripture. 2009. 128p. pap. 12.99 (978-1-4389-1803-7(6)) AuthorHouse.

Perkins, Bill. Seis Batallas Que Todo Hombre Debe Ganar: Y los Antiguos Secretos para Triunfar. 2008. Orig. Title: Six Battles Every Man Must Win. (SPA.). 144p. pap. 9.99 (978-1-4143-2397-8(2), Tyndale Espanol) Tyndale Hse. Pubs.

—Six Battles Every Man Must Win: ... & the Ancient Secrets You'll Need to Succeed. 2011. (ENG.). 160p. pap. 12.99 (978-1-4143-3898-9(8)) Tyndale Hse. Pubs.

Person, Raymond F., Jr. The Deuteronomic History & the Book of Chronicles: Scribal Works in an Oral World. 2010. 218p. pap. 26.95 (978-1-58983-517-7(4)) Society of Biblical Literature.

Person, Raymond F. The Deuteronomic History & the Book of Chronicles: Scribal Works in an Oral World. 2010. xii, 205p. (978-1-58983-518-4(2)) Society of Biblical Literature.

Person, Raymond F. The Kings - Isaiah & Kings - Jeremiah Recensions. (Beihefte zur Zeitschrift far die alttestamentliche Wissenschaft Ser.). (ENG.). VIII, 127p. 150.00 **(978-3-11-188092-1(3))** De Gruyter, Walter Inc.

Peterson, H. Donl. The Story of the Book of Abraham: Mummies, Manuscripts, & Mormonism. 2008. (Illus.). 273p. pap. 18.99 (978-1-59955-140-1(3)) Cedar Fort, Inc./CFI Distribution.

Prime, Jonathan. Opening up Ruth. 2007. (Opening up the Bible Ser.). (Illus.). 96p. pap. 9.00 (978-1-84625-067-5(6)) DayOne Pubns. GBR. Dist: STL Distribution North America.

Pruzansky, Steve. Judges for our Time Contempora. 2009. 232p. 18.00 (978-965-229-437-1(3)) Gefen Publishing Hse., Ltd ISR. Dist: Strauss Consultants.

Rake, Mareike. 'Juda wird aufsteigen!' Untersuchungen zum ersten Kapitel des Richterbuches. 2006. (Beihefte Zur Zeitschrift Für Die Alttestamentliche Wissenschaft Ser.). (GER.). X, 184p. 112.00 (978-3-11-019072-4(9)) De Gruyter, Walter Inc.

Rawlinson, Jorge. Esdras y Nehemias.Tr. of Ezra & Nehemiah. (SPA.). (978-84-7645-079-6(6), 223141) Clie, Editorial.

Recker, Matthew. Living on the Edge of Eternity. 2007. 112p. per. (978-1-59166-769-8(0)) BJU Pr.

Reid, Debra. Esther. 2nd rev. ed. 2008. (Tyndale Old Testament Commentaries Ser.: Volume 13). (ENG.). 168p. pap. 16.00 (978-0-8308-4213-1(6), IVP Acad.) InterVarsity Pr.

Reiser, T. J. Gleanings from the Book of Ruth. 2008. 59p. pap. 16.95 (978-1-60563-054-0(3)) PublishAmerica, Inc.

Rezetko, Robert. Source & Revision in the Narratives of David's Transfer of the Ark: Text, Language & Story in 2 Samuel 6 & 1 Chronicles 13, 15-16. 6th ed. 2007. (Library of Hebrew Bible/Old Testament Studies: Vol. 470). (ENG.). 432p. 180.00 (978-0-567-02612-5(4), T&T Clark Int'l) Continuum International Publishing Group, Ltd. GBR. Dist: National Bk. Network.

Rossier, H. Second Kings. 11.50 (978-0-88172-182-9(4)) Believers Bookshelf, Inc.

Rossier, H. L. Meditations on First Kings. 210p. 8.95 (978-0-88172-165-2(4)) Believers Bookshelf, Inc.

Rowe, Jonathan Y. Michal's Moral Dilemma: A Literary, Anthropological & Ethical Interpretation. 2010. (Library of Hebrew Bible/Old Testament Studies). (ENG., Illus.). 272p. 130.00 (978-0-567-27179-2(X), T&T Clark Int'l) Continuum International Publishing Group, Ltd. GBR. Dist: National Bk. Network.

Samuel, Kenneth L. Solomon's Success: Four Essential Keys to Leadership. 2006. 109p. per. (978-0-8298-1572-6(4)) Pilgrim Pr., The/United Church Pr.

Saxegaard, Kristin Moen. Character Complexity in the Book of Ruth. 2010. (Illus.). 252p. pap. 117.50 (978-3-16-150385-6(6)) Mohr Siebeck GmbH & Co. KG DEU. Dist: Coronet Bks.

Schniedewind, William M. Word of God in Transition: From Prophet to Exegete in the Second Temple Period. 2009. (Library of Hebrew Bible/Old Testament Studies, the Ser.). (ENG.). 275p. 44.95 (978-0-567-62520-5(6), T&T Clark) Continuum International Publishing Group, Ltd. GBR. Dist: National Bk. Network.

Schwab, George M. Right in Their Own Eyes: The Gospel According to Judges. 2011. pap. **(978-1-59638-210-7(4))** P & R Publishing.

Schweitzer, Steven. Reading Utopia in Chronicles. 2009. (Library Hebrew Bible/Old Testament Studies). (ENG.). 224p. pap. 49.95 (978-0-567-36317-6(1), T&T Clark Int'l) Continuum International Publishing Group, Ltd. GBR. Dist: National Bk. Network.

Scranton, J. Philip. Samson As Christ: The Marvelous Opener of the Gates. 2009. 192p. pap. 14.99 (978-1-61579-312-9(7)) Xulon Pr., Inc.

Short, J. Randall. The Surprising Election & Confirmation of King David. 2010. (Harvard Theological Studies: 63). (ENG.). 250p. pap. 25.00 (978-0-674-05341-0(9)) Harvard Univ. Pr.

Sicker, Martin. The First Book of Samuel: A Study in Prophetic History. 2011. 424p. pap. 23.95 **(978-1-4620-4442-9(5))** iUniverse, Inc.

Sjöberg, Mikael. Wrestling with Textual Violence the Jeph. 2006. 264p. (978-1-905048-14-4(9)) Sheffield Phoenix Pr.

Soggie, Neil. Myth, God, & War: The Mythopoetic Inspiration of Joshua. 2007. (ENG.). 200p. pap. 35.99 (978-0-7618-3656-8(X)) Univ. Pr. of America, Inc.

Southwood, Katherine E. Ethnicity & the Mixed Marriage Crisis in Ezra 9-10: An Anthropological Approach. 2012. (ENG.). 304p. 135.00 **(978-0-19-964434-6(9))** Oxford Univ. Pr., Inc.

Steussy, Marti J. Samuel & His God. 2010. (Personalities of the Old Testament Ser.). (ENG.). 44.95 (978-1-57003-924-9(0)) Univ. of South Carolina Pr.

Stone, Lawson. From Tribal Confederation to Monarchic State. 2009. 140.00 (978-1-60724-342-7(3)) Gorgias Pr., LLC.

Suriano, Matthew J. The Politics of Dead Kings: Dynastic Ancestors in the Book of Kings & Ancient Israel. 2010. (HEB & ENG., Illus.). 223p. pap. 107.50 (978-3-16-150473-0(9)) Mohr Siebeck GmbH & Co. KG DEU. Dist: Coronet Bks.

Swindoll, Charles R. Hand Me Another Brick Bible Companion: Timeless Lessons on Leadership, 0 vols. 2007. (Illus.). 224p. per. 9.99 (978-1-4185-2751-8(3)) Nelson, Thomas Inc.

—Hand Me Another Brick: Timeless Lessons on Leadership: How Effective Leaders Motivate Themselves & Others, 0 vols. 2007. (Illus.). 256p. per. 14.99 (978-0-8499-1460-7(4)) Nelson, Thomas Inc.

Thelle, Rannfrid Irene. Approaches to the 'Chosen Place' Accessing a Biblical Concept. 2011. (ENG.). 256p. (gr. 17). 140.00 **(978-0-567-46807-9(0)**, T&T Clark) Continuum International Publishing Group, Ltd. GBR. Dist: National Bk. Network.

Thompson, Henry. Historia Sagrada - Tomo I: Bible Unfolded: Beginning to King. (SPA.). (978-84-7228-963-5(X), 223044) Clie, Editorial.

—Historia Sagrada - Tomo II: Bible Unfolded: King Jehu to Herod. (SPA.). 320p. (978-84-7228-964-2(8), 223045) Clie, Editorial.

Tino, Jozef. King & Temple in Chronicles: A Contextual Approach to their Relations. 2010. (Forschungen Zur Religion und Literatur des Alten & Neuen Testament Ser.). (ENG.). 183p. (C). 110.00 (978-3-525-53096-2(X)) Vandenhoeck & Ruprecht GmbH & Co. KG DEU. Dist: ISD.

Travis, Charlotte. A Study of Ezra & Nehemiah: Restoration Through Comfort & Strength. 2011. 344p. pap. 31.95 **(978-1-4627-0604-4(5))** Cross Bks. Publishing.

Treloar, Richard. Esther & the End of 'Final Solutions' 2008. (ATF Dissertation Ser.). (ENG.). 380p. (C). pap. 20.00 (978-1-920691-86-8(3)) ATF Pr. AUS. Dist: Brown, David Bk. Co., The.

Tucker, Mike. 10 Keys to a Happy Marriage: Relationship Secrets from the Book of Ruth. 2007. 143p. 12.99 (978-0-8163-2163-6(9)) Pacific Pr. Publishing Assn.

Tushima, Cephas. Saul's Progeny in the Reign of David. 2012. (ENG.). 372p. (C). pap. 50.00 **(978-0-227-68036-0(7))** Clarke, James Co., Ltd. GBR. Dist: Brown, David Bk. Co., The.

Ulrich, Dean R. From Famine to Fullness: The Gospel According to Ruth. 2007. 180p. per. (978-1-59638-009-7(8)) P & R Publishing.

van der Deijl, A. R. Protest or Propaganda: War in the Old Testament Book of Kings & in Contemporaneous Ancient near Eastern Texts. 2008. (Studia Semitica Neerlandica Ser.). 720p. (978-90-04-16855-8(9)) BRILL.

Van Seters, John. The Biblical Saga of King David. 2009. 49.50 (978-1-57506-170-2(8)) Eisenbrauns, Inc.

Vannoy, J. Robert. Covenant Renewal at Gilgal: A Study of 1 Samuel 11:14-12:25. 2008. 290p. pap. 32.00 (978-1-55635-946-0(2), Wipf and Stock) Wipf & Stock Pubs.

Vesely, David. Righteousness Exalts a Nation: God's Love Will Change America. 2009. 72p. pap. 10.99 (978-1-61579-263-4(5)) Xulon Pr., Inc.

Vialle, C. Une analyse comparee d'Esther TM et LXX: Regard sur deux recits d'une meme Histoire. 2010. (Bibliotheca Ephemeridum Theologicarum Lovaniensium Ser.). (FRE., Illus.). 463p. (C). pap. 111.00 (978-90-429-2285-3(0)) Peeters Pubs. & Booksellers BEL. Dist: Brown, David Bk. Co., The.

Waggoner, J. H. From Eden to Eden. 2009. 224p. pap. (978-0-217-69723-1(2)) Books LLC.

Walsh, Jerome T. Ahab: The Construction of a King. 2006. (Interfaces Ser.). (Illus.). 125p. per. 14.95 (978-0-8146-5176-6(3)) Liturgical Pr.

Webb, Barry G. The Book of the Judges: An Integrated Reading. 2008. 278p. pap. 31.00 (978-1-55635-932-3(2), Wipf and Stock) Wipf & Stock Pubs.

Whitcomb. Tabla de los Patriarcas y Jueces de A. T. - Chart of the O. T. Patriarchs & Judges. (Tablas Cronologicas - Chronological Chart Ser.). (SPA.). (978-1-56063-931-2(8)) Editorial Unilit.

Williamson, H. G. M. Studies in Persian Period History & Historiography. 2010. 340p. pap. 38.00 (978-1-60899-417-5(1)) Wipf & Stock Pubs.

Williamson, Hugh Godfrey Maturin. Israel in the Books of Chronicles. 2007. (ENG.). 184p. (C). pap. 27.99 *(978-0-521-03709-9(3))* Cambridge Univ. Pr.

Willis, Mike. BTB Ezra, Nehemiah, Esther. 2007. pap. 6.99 *(978-1-58427-188-8(4))* Guardian of Truth Foundation.

—BTB First & Second Kings. 2007. 6.99 *(978-1-58427-205-2(8))* Guardian of Truth Foundation.

Winkler, Neil N. Bringing the Prophets to Life: A Timely Look at a Timeless Story. 2011. ***(978-965-229-478-4(0))*** Gefen Bks.

Winn, Adam. Mark & the Elijah-Elisha Narrative: Considering the Pracice of Greco-Roman Imitation in the Search for Markan Source Material. 2010. 148p. pap. 18.00 *(978-1-60899-201-0(2)*, Pickwick Pubns.) Wipf & Stock Pubs.

Witcomb. Tabla de los Reyes/Profetas del A. T. - Chart of the O. T. Kings & Prophets. (Tablas Cronologicas Ser.). (SPA.). *(978-1-56063-932-9(6))* Editorial Unilit.

A Woman & Her World. (Other Studies). tchr. ed. 6.95 *(978-1-56212-682-7(2)*, 152305) Faith Alive Christian Resources.

Wong, Gregory T. K. Compositional Strategy of the Book of Judges: An Inductive, Rhetorical Study. 2006. (Supplements to Vetus Testamentum Ser.: Vol. 111). (Illus.). 287p. *(978-90-04-15086-7(2))* BRILL.

Wray Beal, Lissa M. & Wray Beal. The Deuteronomist's Prophet: Narrative Control of Approval & Disapproval in the Story of Jehu (2 Kings 9 & 10) 2007. (Library of Hebrew Bible/Old Testament Studies). (ENG., Illus.). 240p. 150.00 *(978-0-567-02657-6(4)*, T&T Clark Int'l) Continuum International Publishing Group, Ltd. GBR. Dist: National Bk. Network.

Wright, Jacob L. Rebuilding Identity: The Nehemiah-Memoir & its Earliest Readers. (Beihefte zur Zeitschrift far die alttestamentliche Wissenschaft Ser.). (ENG.). XIII, 372p. 255.00 ***(978-3-11-182898-5(0))*** De Gruyter, Walter Inc.

Yamada, Frank M. Configurations of Rape in the Hebrew Bible: A Literary Analysis of Three Rape Narratives. 2007. (Studies in Biblical Literature Ser.). (C). 63.95 *(978-1-4331-0167-0(X))* Lang, Peter Publishing, Inc.

Yee, Gale A. Judges & Method: New Approaches in Biblical Studies. 2nd rev. ed. 2007. (Illus.). 294p. pap. 23.00 *(978-0-8006-3858-0(1)*, Fortress Pr.) Augsburg Fortress, Pubs.

Zahnd, Brian. What to Do on the Worst Day of Your Life. 2009. (ENG.). 144p. 14.99 *(978-1-59979-726-7(7))* Charisma Media.

BIBLE—CRITICISM, INTERPRETATION, ETC.—O. T. HOSEA

see Bible—Criticism, Interpretation, Etc.—O. T. Minor Prophets

BIBLE—CRITICISM, INTERPRETATION, ETC.—O. T. ISAIAH

see Bible—Criticism, Interpretation, Etc.—O. T. Prophets

BIBLE—CRITICISM, INTERPRETATION, ETC.—O. T. JEREMIAH

see Bible—Criticism, Interpretation, Etc.—O. T. Prophets

BIBLE—CRITICISM, INTERPRETATION, ETC.—O. T. JOB

see Bible—Criticism, Interpretation, etc.—O. T. Poetical Books

BIBLE—CRITICISM, INTERPRETATION, ETC.—O. T. JOEL

see Bible—Criticism, Interpretation, Etc.—O. T. Minor Prophets

BIBLE—CRITICISM, INTERPRETATION, ETC.—O. T. JONAH

see Bible—Criticism, Interpretation, Etc.—O. T. Minor Prophets

BIBLE—CRITICISM, INTERPRETATION, ETC.—O. T. JOSHUA

see Bible—Criticism, Interpretation, Etc.—O. T. Historical Books

BIBLE—CRITICISM, INTERPRETATION, ETC.—O. T. JUDGES

see Bible—Criticism, Interpretation, Etc.—O. T. Historical Books

BIBLE—CRITICISM, INTERPRETATION, ETC.—O. T. KINGS

see Bible—Criticism, Interpretation, Etc.—O. T. Historical Books

BIBLE—CRITICISM, INTERPRETATION, ETC.—O. T. LAMENTATIONS

see Bible—Criticism, Interpretation, Etc.—O. T. Prophets

BIBLE—CRITICISM, INTERPRETATION, ETC.—O. T. LEVITICUS

see Bible—Criticism, Interpretation, Etc.—O. T. Pentateuch

BIBLE—CRITICISM, INTERPRETATION, ETC.—O. T. MALACHI

see Bible—Criticism, Interpretation, Etc.—O. T. Minor Prophets

BIBLE—CRITICISM, INTERPRETATION, ETC.—O. T. MICAH

see Bible—Criticism, Interpretation, Etc.—O. T. Minor Prophets

BIBLE—CRITICISM, INTERPRETATION, ETC.—O. T. MINOR PROPHETS

Here are entered works on the 12 minor prophets as a whole, as well as books on one or more of the minor prophets.

see also Bible—Criticism, Interpretation, Etc.—O. T. Prophets

Albertz, Rainer, et al, eds. Perspectives on the Formation of the Book of the Twelve: Methodological Foundations - Redactional Processes - Historical Insights. 2012. (Beihefte zur Zeitschrift für die alttestamentliche Wissenschaft Ser.). (ENG.). 420p. (gr. 17). 168.00 ***(978-3-11-028334-1(4))*** De Gruyter, Walter Inc.

Atchley, Ernest C. The Messiah & His Kingdom: Understanding the End Times through the Book of Zechariah. 2011. pap. 21.99 ***(978-1-61777-133-0(3))*** Tate Publishing & Enterprises, LLC.

Baker, David W. Nahum, Habakkuk, Zephaniah. 2009. (Tyndale Old Testament Commentaries Ser.: Volume 27). (ENG.). 120p. pap. 16.00 *(978-0-8308-4227-8(6)*, IVP Acad.) InterVarsity Pr.

Baker Publishing Group Staff. A Walk Thru the Book of Jonah: Experiencing God's Relentless Grace. 2009. (Walk Thru the Bible Discussion Guides). 60p. pap. 7.99 *(978-0-8010-7171-3(2))* Baker Bks.

Balserak, Jon. Establishing the Remnant Church in France: Calvin's Lectures on the Minor Prophets, 1556-1559. 2011. XIV, 226p. *(978-90-04-19144-0(5))* BRILL.

Barrett, Michael P. V. Love Divine & Unfailing: The Gospel According to Hosea. 2008. 200p. pap. *(978-1-59638-075-2(6))* P & R Publishing.

Barton, John. The Theology of the Book of Amos. 2012. (Old Testament Theology Ser.). (ENG.). 215p. 99.00 ***(978-0-521-85577-8(2))***; pap. 25.99 ***(978-0-521-67175-0(2))*** Cambridge Univ. Pr.

Ben Zvi, Ehud. Signs of Jonah: Reading & Rereading in Ancient Yehud. 2009. (Library of Hebrew Bible/Old Testament Studies, the Ser.). (ENG.). 208p. 39.95 *(978-0-567-22293-0(4)*, T&T Clark) Continuum International Publishing Group, Ltd. GBR. Dist: National Bk. Network.

Ben Zvi, Ehud, et al. Two Sides of a Coin: Juxtaposing Views on Interpreting the Book of the Twelve / the Twelve Prophetic Books. 2009. pap. 29.00 *(978-1-60724-303-8(2))* Gorgias Pr., LLC.

Bentley, Michael. Zephaniah. 2008. (Opening Up Ser.). (Illus.). 112p. pap. *(978-1-84625-111-5(7))* DayOne Pubns.

BenZvi, Ehud, ed. A Historical-Critical Study of the Book of Zephaniah. (Beihefte zur Zeitschrift far die attestamentliche Wissenschaft Ser.). (ENG.). XII, 389p. 270.00 ***(978-3-11-219081-4(5))*** De Gruyter, Walter Inc.

Bosman, Jan Petrus. Social Identity in Nahum: A Theological-Ethical Enquiry. 2008. 117.00 *(978-1-60724-001-3(7))* Gorgias Pr., LLC.

Bridger, Gordon. The Message of Obadiah, Nahum & Zephaniah. 2010. (Bible Speaks Today Ser.). (ENG.). 307p. pap. 18.00 *(978-0-8308-2434-2(0)*, IVP Acad.) InterVarsity Pr.

Brothwell, DeWayne. Mystery Babylon Finally Revealed: Babylonian Elite Bankers Corporations. 2010. 105p. pap. 15.95 *(978-1-4327-6558-3(2))* Outskirts Pr., Inc.

Butterworth, Mike. Structure & the Book of Zechariah. 2009. (Library of Hebrew Bible/Old Testament Studies, the Ser.). (ENG.). 328p. 55.00 *(978-0-567-43447-0(8)*, T&T Clark) Continuum International Publishing Group, Ltd. GBR. Dist: National Bk. Network.

Carroll, Mark Daniel. Contexts for Amos: Prophetic Poetics in Latin-American Perspective. 2009. (Library of Hebrew Bible/Old Testament Studies, the Ser.). (ENG.). 362p. 60.00 *(978-0-567-40027-7(1)*, T&T Clark) Continuum International Publishing Group, Ltd. GBR. Dist: National Bk. Network.

Coggins, Richard & Han, Jin H. Six Minor Prophets Through the Centuries: Nahum, Habakkuk, Zephaniah, Haggai, Zechariah & Malachi. 2011. (Blackwell Bible Commentaries Ser.: 29). (ENG., Illus.). 296p. 119.95 *(978-1-4051-7675-0(X)*, Wiley-Blackwell) Wiley, John & Sons, Inc.

Cowles, Henry. The Minor Prophets; with Notes, Critical, Explanatory, & Practical, Designed for Both Pastors & People by Rev Henry Cowles. 2006. 444p. per. 26.99 *(978-1-4255-4946-6(2))* MPublishing.

Curtis, Byron G. Up the Steep & Stony Road: The Book of Zechariah in Social-Location Trajectory Analysis. 2006. (Illus.). 330p. *(978-90-04-15112-3(5))* BRILL.

—Up the Steep & Stony Road: The Book of Zechariah in Social-Location Trajectory Analysis. 2006. 44.95 *(978-1-58983-238-1(8))* Society of Biblical Literature.

De La Torre, Miguel A. Liberating Jonah: Forming an Ethics of Reconciliation. 2007. (Illus.). 178p. per. 20.00 *(978-1-57075-743-3(7))* Orbis Bks.

Decorzant, Alain. Vom Gericht zum Erbarmen: Text und Theologie von Micha 6-7. 2010. (GER.). 263p. *(978-3-429-03319-4(5))* Echter Verlag GmbH.

Eddinger, Terry. Malachi: A Handbook on the Hebrew Text. 2012. (Baylor Handbook on the Hebrew Bible Ser.). (ENG.). 174p. pap. 29.95 ***(978-1-60258-427-3(3))*** Baylor Univ. Pr.

Garrett, Duane A. Amos: A Handbook on the Hebrew Text. 2008. (ENG.). 300p. (C). pap. 24.95 *(978-1-932792-69-0(4))* Baylor Univ. Pr.

Giddens, Pastor/Missionary Donald Louis. Jesus in the Minor Prophets: Hosea-Malachi. 2007. 286p. pap. 28.50 *(978-1-4357-0198-4(4))* Lulu Enterprises Inc.

Ginsberg, H. L., et al, trs. from HEB. The Five Megilloth & Jonah. (Bible Titles Ser.). (ENG & HEB., Illus.). 122p. 14.95 *(978-0-8276-0045-4(3))* Jewish Pubn. Society.

Glenny, W. Edward. Finding Meaning in the Text: Translation Technique & Theology in the Septuagint of Amos. 2009. 322p. *(978-90-04-17638-6(1))* BRILL.

Gunn-Danforth, Christine. Transforming Culture: A Model for Faith & Film in Hollywood. 2008. 212p. pap. 23.00 *(978-1-55635-996-5(9))* Wipf & Stock Pubs.

Haddox, Susan E. Metaphor & Masculinity in Hosea. 2011. (Studies in Biblical Literature Ser.). 254p. (C). 79.95 ***(978-1-4331-1356-7(2))*** Lang, Peter Publishing, Inc.

Hadjiev, Tchavdar S. The Composition & Redaction of the Book of Amos. 2009. (Beihefte zur Zeitschrift für die alttestamentliche Wissenschaft Ser.). (ENG.). XVIII, 247p. 112.00 *(978-3-11-021271-6(4))*; 168.00 ***(978-3-11-173597-9(4))*** De Gruyter, Walter Inc.

Hagedorn, Anselm C. Die Anderen Im Spiegel: Israels Auseinandersetzung Mit Den Völkern in Den Büchern Nahum, Zefanja, Obadja und Joel. 2012. (Beihefte zur Zeitschrift far die alttestamentliche Wissenschaft Ser.).Tr. of Others in the Mirror. (GER., Illus.). X, 379p. (gr. 17). E-Book 210.00 ***(978-3-11-174965-5(7))*** De Gruyter, Walter Inc.

Hagedorn, Anselm C. Die Anderen im Spiegel: Israels Auseinandersetzung mit den Völkern in den Büchern Nahum, Zefanja, Obadja und Joel. 2010. (Beihefte Zur Zeitschrift Für Die Alttestamentliche Wissenschaft Ser.).Tr. of Others in the Mirror. (GER.). 400p. 140.00 *(978-3-11-022856-4(4))* De Gruyter, Walter Inc.

Hagedorn, Anselm C. & Mein, Andrew, eds. Aspects of Amos: Exegesis & Interpretation. 2010. (Library of Hebrew Bible/Old Testament Studies). (ENG.). 192p. 120.00 *(978-0-567-24537-3(3)*, T&T Clark Int'l) Continuum International Publishing Group, Ltd. GBR. Dist: National Bk. Network.

Hallaschka, Martin. Haggai und Sacharja 1-8: Eine redaktionsgeschichtliche Untersuchung. (Beihefte zur Zeitschrift far die alttestamentliche Wissenschaft Ser.).Tr. of Haggai & Zechariah 1-8. A Redaction-Historical Study. (GER.). XII, 371p. 2011. 210.00 ***(978-3-11-174000-3(5))*** 2010. 140.00 *(978-3-11-022486-3(0))* De Gruyter, Walter Inc.

Hamborg, Graham R. Still Selling the Righteous: A Redaction-critical Investigation of Reasons for Judgment in Amos 2. 6-16. 2012. (ENG.). 304p. 150.00 ***(978-0-567-62563-2(X)***, T&T Clark Int'l) Continuum International Publishing Group, Ltd. GBR. Dist: National Bk. Network.

Handy, Lowell K. Jonah's World: Social Science & the Reading of Prophetic Story. 2008. (BibleWorld Ser.). (ENG.). 192p. (C). 95.00 *(978-1-84553-123-2(X))*; pap. 29.95 *(978-1-84553-124-9(8))* Equinox Publishing Ltd. GBR. Dist: ISD.

Harper, William. The Structure of Hosea 1: 2 — 3:5. 2010. 81.80 *(978-1-61143-529-0(3))* Gorgias Pr., LLC.

Heimbucher, Martin. Prophetische Auslegung: Das reformatorische Profil des Wolfgang Fabricius Capito ausgehend von seinen Kommentaren zu Habakuk und Hosea. 2008. (Europäische Hochschulschriften. Reihe 23: Theologie Ser.). (GER.). 450p. pap. 107.95 *(978-3-631-57759-2(1))* Lang, Peter GmbH, Europaischer Verlag der Wissenschaften DEU. Dist: Lang, Peter.

Henderson, Richard. The Jealousy of Jonah: A Christian Devotional Commentary on the Book of Jonah as Translated in the Authorised (King James) Version of the Bible. 2006. (ENG., Illus.). 85p. per. 13.95 *(978-1-85607-522-0(2))* Columba Pr. IRL. Dist: Dufour Editions, Inc.

Ho, Ahuva. The Targum of Zephaniah: Manuscripts & Commentary. 2009. *(978-90-04-17180-0(0))* BRILL.

Hong, Seong-Hyuk. The Metaphor of Illness & Healing in Hosea & Its Significance in the Socio-Economic Context of Eighth-Century Israel & Judah. 2006. (Studies in Biblical Literature: Vol. 95). xv, 193p. (C). 67.95 *(978-0-8204-8155-5(6))* Lang, Peter Publishing, Inc.

House, Paul R. Unity of the Twelve. 2009. (Library of Hebrew Bible/Old Testament Studies, the Ser.). (ENG.). 262p. 44.95 *(978-0-567-60642-6(2)*, T&T Clark) Continuum International Publishing Group, Ltd. GBR. Dist: National Bk. Network.

Howell, James C. What Does the Lord Require? Doing Justice, Loving Kindness, & Walking Humbly. 2012. (ENG.). 64p. pap. 12.00 ***(978-0-664-23694-6(4))*** Westminster John Knox Pr.

Iacono, Fred Paul Dello. The Jonah Prophecies. 2011. 742p. 34.99 ***(978-1-4568-3152-3(6))***; pap. 23.99 ***(978-1-4568-3151-6(8))*** Xlibris Corp.

Kealy, Sean P. An Interpretation of the Twelve Minor Prophets of the Hebrew Bible: The Emergence of Eschatology as a Theological Theme. 2009. 264p. 109.95 *(978-0-7734-4715-8(6))* Mellen, Edwin Pr., The.

Levin, Meir. The Dawn of Redemption: What the Books of Ruth & Yona Teach about Alienation, Despair & Return. 2009. 235p. pap. 19.95 *(978-965-524-022-1(3))* Urim Pubns. ISR. Dist: Coronet Bks.

Linville, James R. Amos & the Cosmic Imagination. 2008. (Society for Old Testament Study Ser.). 212p. 99.95 *(978-0-7546-5481-0(8))* Ashgate Publishing Co.

Lohrmann, Martin J. Bugenhagen's Jonah: Biblical Interpretation As Public Theology in the Reformation. 2012. ***(978-1-932688-71-9(4))*** Kirk Hse. Pubns.

Lux, Rü, et al. Prophetie und Zweiter Tempel: Studien zu Haggai und Sacharja. 2009. (GER.). 371p. 175.00 *(978-3-16-149630-5(5))* Mohr Siebeck GmbH & Co. KG DEU. Dist: Eisenbrauns, Inc.

Mack, Russell. Neo-Assyrian Prophecy & the Hebrew Bible: Nahum, Habakkuk, & Zephaniah. 2011. 160.30 ***(978-1-4632-0077-0(3))*** Gorgias Pr., LLC.

McGarvey, J. w. Jesus & Jonah. 2010. *(978-0-9819703-2-5(X))* DeWard Publishing Co., Ltd.

Meadowcroft, Tim. Haggai. 2006. 276p. *(978-1-905048-59-5(9))*; per. *(978-1-905048-60-1(2))* Sheffield Phoenix Pr.

Möller, Karl. Prophet in Debate: The Rhetoric of Persuasion in the Book of Amos. 2009. (Library of Hebrew Bible/Old Testament Studies, the Ser.). (ENG.). 372p. 60.00 *(978-0-567-00363-8(9)*, T&T Clark) Continuum International Publishing Group, Ltd. GBR. Dist: National Bk. Network.

Morris, Gerald. Prophecy, Poetry & Hosea. 2009. (Library of Hebrew Bible/Old Testament Studies, the Ser.). (ENG.). 167p. 29.95 *(978-0-567-04456-3(4)*, T&T Clark) Continuum International Publishing Group, Ltd. GBR. Dist: National Bk. Network.

Moss, Charlene McAfee. The Zechariah Tradition & the Gospel of Matthew. 2008. (Beihefte Zur Zeitschrift Für Die Neutestamentliche Wissenschaft und Die Kunde der älteren Kirche Ser.). (ENG.). X, 271p. 133.00 *(978-3-11-019695-5(6))* De Gruyter, Walter Inc.

Muldoon, Catherine L. In Defense of Divine Justice: An Intertextual Approach to the Book of Jonah. 2011. *(978-0-915170-46-3(9))* Catholic Biblical Assn. of America.

Neusner, Jacob. Rabbis & the Prophets. 2010. (Studies in Judaism Ser.). (ENG.). 226p. pap. 32.50 *(978-0-7618-5437-1(1))* Univ. Pr. of America, Inc.

Ntamushobora, Faustin. From Trials to Triumphs. 2009. 96p. pap. 13.00 *(978-1-60608-631-5(6)*, Wipf and Stock) Wipf & Stock Pubs.

Perry, T. Anthony. The Honeymoon Is Over: Jonah's Argument with God. 2006. 250p. per. 19.95 *(978-1-56563-672-9(4))* Hendrickson Pubs. Marketing, LLC.

Person, Raymond F., Jr. In Conversation with Jonah: Conversation Analysis, Literary Criticism & the Book of Jonah. 2009. (Library of Hebrew Bible/Old Testament Studies, the Ser.). (ENG.). 204p. 39.95 *(978-0-567-42593-5(2)*, T&T Clark) Continuum International Publishing Group, Ltd. GBR. Dist: National Bk. Network.

Petterson, Anthony Robert. Behold Your King: The Hope for the House of David in the Book of Zechariah. 2009. (Library of Hebrew Bible/Old Testament Studies, the Ser.). (ENG.). 304p. 150.00 *(978-0-567-09215-1(1)*, T&T Clark Int'l) Continuum International Publishing Group, Ltd. GBR. Dist: National Bk. Network.

Radine, Jason. The Book of Amos in Emergent Judah. 2010. (Illus.). 279p. pap. 117.50 *(978-3-16-150114-2(4))* Mohr Siebeck GmbH & Co. KG DEU. Dist: Coronet Bks.

Rollins, John & Reigns, J. C. The Elijah Chronicle: He Risked It All to Serve His God. 2008. 137p. pap. 13.95 *(978-1-4327-1085-9(0))* Outskirts Pr., Inc.

Rudnig-Zelt, Susanne. Hoscastudien: Redaktionskritische Untersuchungen zur Genese des Hoseabuches. 2006. (Forschungen Zur Religion und Literatur des Alten & Neuen Testament Ser.: Vol. 213). (GER.). 311p. (C). 90.00 *(978-3-525-53077-1(3))* Vandenhoeck & Ruprecht GmbH & Co. KG DEU. Dist: ISD.

Schwesig, Paul-Gerhard. Die Rolle der Tag-JHWHs-Dichtungen Im Dodekapropheton. 2006. (Beihefte Zur Zeitschrift Für Die Alttestamentliche Wissenschaft Ser.). (GER., Illus.). X, 347p. 154.00 ***(978-3-11-019017-5(6))*** De Gruyter, Walter Inc.

Shepherd, Michael B. The Twelve Prophets in the New Testament. 2010. (Studies in Biblical Literature Ser.). 126p. (C). 63.95 *(978-1-4331-1346-8(5))* Lang, Peter Publishing, Inc.

Sherwood, Yvonne. Prostitute & the Prophet: Hosea's Marriage in Literary-Theoretical Perspective. 2009. (Library of Hebrew Bible/Old Testament Studies, the Ser.). (ENG.). 357p. 60.00 *(978-1-4411-1714-4(6)*, T&T Clark) Continuum International Publishing Group, Ltd. GBR. Dist: National Bk. Network.

Soughers, Tara. Fleeing God: Fear, Call, & the Book of Jonah. 2007. (ENG.). 135p. per. 13.95 *(978-1-56101-295-4(5))* Cowley Pubns.

Steiger, Johann Anselm & Kühlmann, Wilhelm. Der Problematische Prophet: Die Biblische Jona-Figur in Exegese, Theologie, Literatur und Bildender Kunst. 2011. (Arbeiten zur Kirchengeschichte Ser.). (GER.). XII, 541p. 196.00 ***(978-3-11-026651-1(2))*** De Gruyter, Walter Inc.

Thorogood, David. Guide to Book of Amos. 16.00 *(978-0-687-85449-3(0))* Abingdon Pr.

Van Tassell, Ray C. Pressing into the Land of the Living. 2009. pap. 22.99 *(978-1-60791-855-4(2))* Xulon Pr., Inc.

Vesely, David. Righteousness Exalts a Nation: God's Love Will Change America. 2009. 72p. pap. 10.99 *(978-1-61579-263-4(5))* Xulon Pr., Inc.

Walton, John H., et al. The Minor Prophets, Job, Psalms, Proverbs, Ecclesiastes, Song of Songs, 1 vol. 2009. (Zondervan Illustrated Bible Backgrounds Commentary Ser.). (ENG.). 624p. 49.99 *(978-0-310-25577-2(5))* Zondervan.

Wenzel, H. Reading Zechariah with Zechariah 1: 1-6 as the Introduction to the Entire Book. 2011. (Contributions to Biblical Exegesis & Theology Ser.). (ENG.). 340p. (C). pap. 66.00 *(978-90-429-2454-3(3))* Peeters Pubs. & Booksellers BEL. Dist: Brown, David Bk. Co., The.

Weyde, Karl William. Prophecy & Teaching: Prophetic Authority, Form Problems, & the Use of Traditions in the Book of Malachi. (Beihefte zur Zeitschrift far die alttestamentliche Wissenschaft Ser.). (ENG.). XVII, 455p. 344.00 ***(978-3-11-175370-6(0))*** De Gruyter, Walter Inc.

Willis, Mike, ed. Minor Prophets, Volume I. 2007. *(978-1-58427-206-9(6))* Guardian of Truth Foundation.

—Minor Prophets, Volume II. 2007. *(978-1-58427-207-6(4))* Guardian of Truth Foundation.

Wöhrle, Jakob. Der Abschluss des Zwölfprophetenbuches: Buchübergreifende Redaktionsprozesse in den späten Sammlungen. 2008. (Beihefte Zur Zeitschrift Für Die Alttestamentliche Wissenschaft Ser.).Tr. of Conclusion of the Book of the Twelve Prophets (Dodecapropheton). (GER.). XII, 478p. 175.00 *(978-3-11-020674-6(9))* De Gruyter, Walter Inc.

Zapff, Burkard M. Redaktionsgeschichtliche Studien zum Michabuch im Kontext des Dodekapropheton. (Beihefte zur Zeitschrift far die alttestamentliche Wissenschaft Ser.). (GER.). XII, 331p. 300.00 ***(978-3-11-174761-3(1))*** De Gruyter, Walter Inc.

BIBLE—CRITICISM, INTERPRETATION, ETC.—O. T. NAHUM

see Bible—Criticism, Interpretation, Etc.—O. T. Minor Prophets

BIBLE—CRITICISM, INTERPRETATION, ETC.—O. T. NEHEMIAH

see Bible—Criticism, Interpretation, Etc.—O. T. Historical Books

BIBLE—CRITICISM, INTERPRETATION, ETC.—O. T. NUMBERS

see Bible—Criticism, Interpretation, Etc.—O. T. Pentateuch

BIBLE—CRITICISM, INTERPRETATION, ETC.—O. T. OBADIAH

see Bible—Criticism, Interpretation, Etc.—O. T. Minor Prophets

BIBLE—CRITICISM, INTERPRETATION, ETC.—O. T. PENTATEUCH

Here are entered works on the Pentateuch as a whole, as well as books on one or more of the following: Deuteronomy, Exodus, Genesis, Leviticus, Numbers.

see also J Document (Biblical Criticism)

Acosta, Ana M. Reading Genesis in the Long Eighteenth Century: From Milton to Mary Shelley. 2006. (Illus.) 204p. 110.00 *(978-0-7546-5613-5(6))* Ashgate Publishing Co.

Altmann, Peter. Festive Meals in Ancient Israel: Deuteronomy's Identity Politics in Their Ancient near Eastern Context. 2011. (Beihefte zur Zeitschrift für die alttestamentliche Wissenschaft Ser.). (ENG.). XII, 300p. 140.00 ***(978-3-11-025536-2(7))***; (Illus.). 210.00 ***(978-3-11-218947-4(7))*** De Gruyter, Walter Inc.

B

Ameth, Martin. Durch Adams Fall Ist Ganz Verderbt: Studien Zur Entstehung der Alttestamentlichen Urgeschichte. 2007. (Forschungen Zur Religion und Literatur des Alten & Neuen Testament Ser.: Vol. 217). (GER.). 268p. (C). 93.00 *(978-3-525-53080-1(3))* Vandenhoeck & Ruprecht GmbH & Co. KG DEU. Dist: ISD.

Amoa-Kodie, Paulius. The Hidden Treasury. 2011. 62p. 24.99 ***(978-1-4535-7810-0(2))***; pap. 15.99 ***(978-1-4535-7809-4(9))*** Xlibris Corp.

Anderson, Bradford A. Brotherhood & Inheritance: A Canonical Reading of the Esau & Edom Traditions. 2011. (ENG.). 288p. 140.00 ***(978-0-567-03473-1(9)***, T&T Clark Int'l) Continuum International Publishing Group, Ltd. GBR. Dist: National Bk. Network.

Anderson, H. & Forbes, A. Dean. A Key-Word-in-Context to the Pentateuch, Vol. 35, Pt. B. (Illus.). pap. 269.95 *(978-0-7734-4096-8(8))* Mellen, Edwin Pr., The.

Anderson, John Edward. Jacob & the Divine Trickster: A Theology of Deception & YHWH's Fidelity to the Ancestral Promise in the Jacob Cycle. 2011. ***(978-1-57506-219-8(4))*** Eisenbrauns, Inc.

Anthony a.k.a Emotional Soldier, Kevin. GENESIS ... the Beginning of Misunderstanding. 2008. 252p. pap. 24.95 *(978-1-4357-1511-0(X))* Lulu Enterprises Inc.

Amdt, Emily K. Demanding Our Attention: The Hebrew Bible As a Source for Christian Ethics. 2011. 240p. pap. 30.00 *(978-0-8028-6569-4(0))* Eerdmans, William B. Publishing Co.

Amold, Thomas. Two Stage Biblical Creation: Uniting Biblical Insights Uncovered by Ten Notable Creation Theories. 2008. 580p. pap. 20.00 *(978-0-9798961-0-1(X))* Amold, Thomas Publishing.

Baden, Joel S. The Composition of the Pentateuch: Renewing the Documentary Hypothesis. 2012. (Anchor Yale Bible Reference Library). (ENG.). 392p. 65.00 ***(978-0-300-15263-0(9))*** Yale Univ. Pr.

Baden, Joel S. J,E, & the Redaction of the Pentateuch. 2009. (Forschungen zum Alten Testament Ser.). (Illus.). 339p. 187.50 *(978-3-16-149930-2(1))* Mohr Siebeck GmbH & Co. KG DEU. Dist: Coronet Bks.

Bader, Mary. Sexual Violation in the Hebrew Bible. 2006. (Studies in Biblical Literature: Vol. 87). x,206p. (C). 69.95 *(978-0-8204-7873-9(3))* Lang, Peter Publishing, Inc.

Bader, Mary Anna. Tracing the Evidence: Dinah in Post-Hebrew Bible Literature. 2008. (Studies in Biblical Literature Ser.: Vol. 102). (C). 70.95 *(978-0-8204-8853-0(4))* Lang, Peter Publishing, Inc.

Baker Publishing Group Staff. A Walk Thru the Life of Joseph: The Power of Forgiveness. 2009. (Walk Thru the Bible Discussion Guides). 78p. pap. 7.99 *(978-0-8010-7168-3(2))* Baker Bks.

Bakhos, Carol. Ishmael on the Border: Rabbinic Portrayals of the First Arab. 207p. 2007. per. 29.95 *(978-0-7914-6760-2(0))* 2006. 60.00 *(978-0-7914-6759-6(7))* State Univ. of New York Pr.

Barker, Paul A. The Triumph of Grace in Deuteronomy: Faithless Israel, Faithful Yahweh in Deuteronomy. 2007. (Paternoster Biblical Monographs: Ser.). 308p. pap. 31.00 *(978-1-59752-787-3(4)*, Wipf and Stock) Wipf & Stock Pubs.

Barrett, Rob. Disloyalty & Destruction: Religion & Politics in Deuteronomy & the Modem World. 2009. (Library of Hebrew Bible/Old Testament Studies, the Ser.). (ENG.). 304p. 130.00 *(978-0-567-61414-8(X)*, T&T Clark Int'l) Continuum International Publishing Group, Ltd. GBR. Dist: National Bk. Network.

Barton, Stephen C. & Wilkinson, David, eds. Reading Genesis after Darwin. 2009. (ENG.). 272p. 99.00 *(978-0-19-538335-5(4))*; pap. 24.95 *(978-0-19-538336-2(2))* Oxford Univ. Pr., Inc.

Bartor, Assnat. Reading Law As Narrative: A Study in the Casuistic Laws of the Pentateuch. 2010. (SBL - Ancient Israel & Its Literature Ser.). (ENG.). X, 220p. *(978-90-04-17800-7(7))* BRILL.

—Reading Law As Narrative: A Study in the Casuistic Laws of the Pentateuch. 2010. (ENG.). 230p. pap. 27.95 *(978-1-58983-480-4(1))* Society of Biblical Literature.

Barwell, Daniel. Monkeys & Mystics No More: Proper exegesis of Genesis 1-2-3. 2009. 208p. pap. 15.99 *(978-1-4389-4222-3(2))* AuthorHouse.

Bayerisches Landesamt F Ur Denkmalpflege, ed. A Farewell to the Yahwist? The Composition of the Pentateuch in Recent European Interpretation. 2006. (Symposium Series. (Society of Biblical Literature) Ser.). 197p. lib. bdg. *(978-90-04-13766-0(1))* BRILL.

Bediako, Daniel. Genesis: 1-2. 2010. 440p. pap. *(978-3-639-27670-1(1))* VDM Verlag Dr. Mueller e.K.

—Theological Character: of the Patriarchal History. 2010. 184p. pap. *(978-3-639-28015-9(6))* VDM Verlag Dr. Mueller e.K.

Bekken, Per Jarle. The Word Is near You: A Study of Deuteronomy 30:12-14 in Paul's Letter to the Romans in a Jewish Context. (Beihefte zur Zeitschrift far die neutestamentliche Wissenschaft und die Kunde der älteren Kirche Ser.). (ENG.). 294p. 225.00 ***(978-3-11-187274-2(2))***; 2007. 140.00 *(978-3-11-019341-1(8))* De Gruyter, Walter Inc.

Benoit, Gregory C. PharaohÕs Magicians: Evolution, the Bible, & Modern Gnosticism. 2011. 232p. pap. 26.00 ***(978-1-61097-416-5(6)***, Wipf and Stock) Wipf & Stock Pubs.

Bergen, David A. Dischronology & Dialogic in the Bible's Primary Narrative. 2009. *(978-1-60724-105-8(6))* Gorgias Pr., LLC.

Berkowitz, Beth A. Defining Jewish Difference: From Antiquity to the Present. 2012. (ENG.). 288p. 90.00 ***(978-1-107-01371-1(2))*** Cambridge Univ. Pr.

Berman, Joshua A. Created Equal: How the Bible Broke with Ancient Political Thought, 1 vol. 2011. (ENG.). 264p. pap. 24.95 ***(978-0-19-983240-8(4))*** Oxford Univ. Pr., Inc.

Berman, Joshua A. & Berman, Joshua. Created Equal: How the Bible Broke with Ancient Political Thought. 2008. (ENG., Illus.). 264p. 39.95 *(978-0-19-537470-4(3))* Oxford Univ. Pr., Inc.

Bernat, David A. Sign of the Covenant: Circumcision in the Priestly Tradition. 2009. pap. 24.95 *(978-1-58983-409-5(7))* Society of Biblical Literature.

Beyerle, Stefan. Der Mosesegen im Deuteronomium: Eine text-, kompositions- und formkritische Studie zu Deuteronomium 33. (Beihefte zur Zeitschrift far die alttestamentliche Wissenschaft Ser.). (GER.). X, 345p. 240.00 ***(978-3-11-177047-5(8))*** De Gruyter, Walter Inc.

Bibb, Bryan D. & Bibb. Ritual Words & Narrative Worlds in the Book of Leviticus. 2008. (Library of Hebrew Bible/Old Testament Studies, the Ser.). (ENG.). 192p. 120.00 *(978-0-567-02713-9(9)*, T&T Clark Int'l) Continuum International Publishing Group, Ltd. GBR. Dist: National Bk. Network.

Bigalke, Ron J., Jr. The Genesis Factor: Myths & Realities. 2008. (Illus.). 254p. per. 13.99 *(978-0-89051-480-1(1))* Master Bks.

Black, Crofton. Pico's Heptaplus & Biblical Hermeneutics. 2006. (Studies in Medieval & Reformation Traditions: History, Culture, Religion, Ideas: Vol. 116). 265p. *(978-90-04-15315-8(2))* BRILL.

Blacketer, Raymond A. The School of God: Pedagogy & Rhetoric in Calvin's Interpretation of Deuteronomy. 2010. (Studies in Early Modern Religious Reforms Ser.). xvii, 300p. pap. 189.00 *(978-90-481-6995-5(X)*, 904816995X) Springer.

Block, Daniel I. How I Love Your Torah, O LORD! Literary & Theological Explorations on the Book of Deuteronomy. 2011. 270p. pap. 30.00 ***(978-1-61097-342-7(9)***, Cascade Bks.) Wipf & Stock Pubs.

Blyth, Caroline. The Narrative of Rape in Genesis 34: Interpreting Dinah's Silence. 2010. (ENG.). 272p. 125.00 *(978-0-19-958945-6(3))* Oxford Univ. Pr., Inc.

Boehm, Omri. The Binding of Isaac: A Religious Model of Disobedience. 2007. (Library of Hebrew Bible/Old Testament Studies). (ENG.). 164p. 125.00 *(978-0-567-02613-2(2)*, T&T Clark Int'l) Continuum International Publishing Group, Ltd. GBR. Dist: National Bk. Network.

Boehme, Jacob. The Bestial Man His Sickness & Mortality. 2006. pap. 9.95 *(978-1-4286-7365-6(2))* Kessinger Publishing, LLC.

—The Cause & Rise of the Curse of the Earth & of the Body Of. 2006. pap. 12.95 *(978-1-4286-7430-1(6))* Kessinger Publishing, LLC.

—How God Stood by Abraham in Temptation & Defended Him. 2006. pap. 9.95 *(978-1-4286-7341-0(5))* Kessinger Publishing, LLC.

—Mysterium Magnum: Volume One. 2007. 436p. 29.95 *(978-1-59731-216-5(9))*; per. 22.95 *(978-1-59731-214-1(2))* Perennis, Sophia.

—Mysterium Magnum: Volume Two. 2007. 448p. 29.95 *(978-1-59731-217-2(7))*; per. 22.95 *(978-1-59731-215-8(0))* Perennis, Sophia.

—Of the Holy Trinity & Divine Essence. 2006. pap. 9.95 *(978-1-4286-7364-9(4))* Kessinger Publishing, LLC.

—Of the Word or Heart of God. 2006. pap. 9.95 *(978-1-4286-7339-7(3))* Kessinger Publishing, LLC.

—What the Manifested God Is & of the Trinity. 2006. pap. 9.95 *(978-1-4286-7319-9(9))* Kessinger Publishing, LLC.

Bohigas, Joaquin. Genesis y Transfiguraciones de las Estrellas. (Ciencia para Todos Ser.). (SPA.). pap. 6.99 *(978-968-16-3440-7(3))* Fondo de Cultura Economica USA.

Boone, Dan & Tallman, Amy Boone. Dancing with the Law: The Ten Commandments. 2010. (ENG.). 128p. pap. 11.99 *(978-0-8341-2491-2(2)*, 9780834124912) Beacon Hill Pr. of Kansas City.

Boorer, Suzanne. The Promise of the Land as Oath: A Key to the Formation of the Pentateuch. (Beihefte zur Zeitschrift far die alttestamentliche Wissenschaft Ser.). (ENG.). XVI, 470p. 328.00 ***(978-3-11-181108-6(5))*** De Gruyter, Walter Inc.

Bosworth, David Alan. The Story Within a Story in Biblical Hebrew Narrative. 2009. *(978-0-915170-44-9(2))* Catholic Biblical Assn. of America.

Boteler, Lori. A Common Sense Approach to Exodus. 2008. per. 20.00 *(978-0-9798207-4-8(X))* LoJo Publishing.

—A Common Sense Approach to Genesis. 2007. per. 20.00 *(978-0-9789555-8-8(7))* LoJo Publishing.

Brother John of Taize. I Am the Beginning & the End: Creation Stories & Visions of Fulfillment in the Bible. 2007. 167p. per. *(978-0-8189-1248-1(0))* St Pauls/Alba Hse. Pubs.

Brown, Brian Arthur. Forensic Scriptures: Critical Analysis of Scripture & What the Qur'an Reveals about the Bible. 2009. 236p. pap. 26.00 *(978-1-60608-289-8(2)*, Cascade Bks.) Wipf & Stock Pubs.

Brown, Walt. In the Beginning: Compelling Evidence for Creation & the Flood. 8th exp. rev. ed. 2008. 456p. 34.95 *(978-1-878026-48-4(8))*; (Illus.). 29.95 *(978-1-878026-09-5(7))* Ctr. for Scientific Creation.

Brueggemann, Walter. Truth-Telling as Subversive Obedience. Hanson, K. C., ed. 2011. 126p. pap. 16.00 ***(978-1-61097-234-5(1)***, Cascade Bks.) Wipf & Stock Pubs.

Byron, John. Cain & Abel in Text & Tradition: Jewish & Christian Interpretations of the First Sibling Rivalry. 2011. 226p. *(978-90-04-19252-2(2))* BRILL.

Carlson, Richard F. & Longman, Tremper, III. Science, Creation & the Bible: Reconciling Rival Theories of Origins. 2010. (ENG.). 144p. pap. 16.00 *(978-0-8308-3889-9(9)*, IVP Acad.) InterVarsity Pr.

Carmichael, Calum M. Illuminating Leviticus: A Study of Its Laws & Institutions in the Light of Biblical Narratives. annot. ed. 2006. (ENG.). 224p. (gr. 17). 60.00 *(978-0-8018-8500-6(0))* Johns Hopkins Univ. Pr.

—The Laws of Deuteronomy. 2008. 277p. pap. 30.00 *(978-1-60608-038-2(5))* Wipf & Stock Pubs.

Chelst, Kenneth. Exodus & Emancipation: Biblical & African-American Slavery. 2009. (Illus.). 446p. 34.95 *(978-965-524-020-7(7))* Urim Pubns. ISR. Dist: Lambda Pubs., Inc.

Chernick, Michael L. "A Great Voice That Did Not Cease" The Growth of the Rabbinic Canon & Its Interpretation. 2009. 303p. 50.00 *(978-0-87820-461-8(X))* Hebrew Union College Pr.

Choi, John H. Traditions at Odds: The Reception of the Pentateuch in Biblical & Second Temple Period Literature. 2010. (Library of Hebrew Bible/Old Testament Studies). (ENG.). 288p. 140.00 *(978-0-567-26524-1(2)*, T&T Clark Int'l) Continuum International Publishing Group, Ltd. GBR. Dist: National Bk. Network.

Chung, Il-Seung. A Revisionist Reading of the Esau-Jacob Stories in Genesis 25-36: Understanding Esau in a Positive Light. 2011. (ENG.). 312p. 129.95 *(978-0-7734-3670-1(7))* Mellen, Edwin Pr., The.

Clay, Albert T. Origin of Biblical Traditions Hebrew Leg. 2006. pap. 26.95 *(978-1-4286-4379-6(6))* Kessinger Publishing, LLC.

Coats, John R. Original Sinners: Why Genesis Still Matters. 2010. (ENG., Illus.). 256p. pap. 15.00 *(978-1-4391-0210-7(4)*, Free Pr.) Free Pr.

Cohen, Norman J. Moses & the Journey to Leadership: Timeless Lessons of Effective Management from the Bible & Today's Leaders. 2006. 212p. 21.99 *(978-1-58023-227-2(2))* Jewish Lights Publishing.

Cohen, Tim. Messiah, History, & the Tribulation Period Vol. 3: Conflict of the Aeons: Understanding the Protoevangelium (Genesis 3:15) Cohen, Tim, ed. 2006. pap. *(978-0-9662793-4-4(4))* Prophecy House, Inc.

Cowles, Henry. The Pentateuch, in Its Progressive Revelations of God to Men. 2008. 428p. 30.99 *(978-0-554-49048-9(X))*; 32.99 *(978-0-554-49040-3(4))*; pap. 35.75 *(978-0-554-49042-7(0))*; pap. 34.75 *(978-0-554-49045-8(5))* BiblioBazaar.

—The Pentateuch, in Its Progressive Revelations of God to Men. 2006. 436p. per. 26.99 *(978-1-4255-4702-8(8))* MPublishing.

—The Pentateuch in Its Progressive Revelations of God to Men. 2007. (ENG.). 424p. 51.95 *(978-0-548-19783-7(0))*; 428p. per. 36.95 *(978-1-4325-0584-4(X))* Kessinger Publishing, LLC.

Croone, Angela M. Lucifer's Reign & Satan's Fall. 2011. 140p. 28.99 *(978-1-4269-4929-6(4))*; pap. 18.99 *(978-1-4269-4928-9(6))* Trafford Publishing.

Daube, David. Law & Wisdom in the Bible Vol. 2: David Daube's Gifford Lectures. Carmichael, Calum, ed. 2010. (ENG., Illus.). 248p. (gr. 14). pap. 49.95 *(978-1-59947-345-1(3))* Templeton Pr.

Davies, G. I. The Way of the Wilderness: A Geographical Study of the Wilderness Itineraries in the Old Testament. 2009. (Society for Old Testament Study Monographs). (ENG.). 152p. pap. 20.99 *(978-0-521-10409-8(2))* Cambridge Univ. Pr.

Davies, Gordon F. Israel in Egypt: Reading Exodus 1-2. 2009. (Library of Hebrew Bible/Old Testament Studies, the Ser.). (ENG.). 204p. 39.95 *(978-1-4411-6508-4(8)*, T&T Clark) Continuum International Publishing Group, Ltd. GBR. Dist: National Bk. Network.

Davis, John D. Genesis & Semitic Tradition. 2009. 172p. 22.99 *(978-1-113-93574-8(X))*; pap. 21.99 *(978-1-113-93571-7(5))*; pap. 16.99 *(978-1-113-93570-0(7))* BiblioBazaar.

—Genesis & Semitic Tradition. 2009. 100p. pap. 14.14 *(978-0-217-57902-5(7))* General Bks. LLC.

—Genesis & Semitic Tradition. 2009. 172p. 37.95 *(978-1-104-10131-2(9))*; pap. 22.95 *(978-1-104-09098-2(8))* Kessinger Publishing, LLC.

Davis, John J. Paradise to Prison: Studies in Genesis. pap. 17.95 *(978-0-88469-050-4(4))* BMH Bks.

Davis, Stacy. This Strange Story: Jewish & Christian Interpretation of the Curse of Canaan from Antiquity To 1865. 2008. (ENG.). 250p. per. 40.99 *(978-0-7618-3879-1(1))* Univ. Pr. of America, Inc.

Dawn, Marva J. In the Beginning, God: Creation, Culture, & the Spiritual Life. 2009. (ENG.). 124p. pap. 15.00 *(978-0-8308-3707-6(8)*, IVP Bks.) InterVarsity Pr.

Diamond, James S. Stringing the Pearls: How to Read the Weekly Torah Portion. 2008. (ENG.). 288p. pap. 18.00 *(978-0-8276-0868-9(3))* Jewish Pubn. Society.

Dicou, Bert. Edom, Israel's Brother & Antagonist: The Role of Edom in Biblical Prophecy & Story. 2009. (Library of Hebrew Bible/Old Testament Studies, the Ser.). (ENG.). 227p. 39.95 *(978-0-567-48381-2(9)*, T&T Clark) Continuum International Publishing Group, Ltd. GBR. Dist: National Bk. Network.

Dillmann, August. Die Genesis Erklärt. 2007. (Gorgias Occasional Historical Commentaries Ser.: 1). (GER.). 96.00 *(978-1-59333-676-9(4))* Gorgias Pr., LLC.

Dishi, Gad. Jacob's Family Dynamics: Climbing the Rungs of the Ladder. 2010. 232p. pap. *(978-1-936068-08-1(7)*, Devorah Publishing) Urim Pubns.

Donahou, Michael. A Comparison of the Egyptian Execration Ritual to Exodus 32: 19 & Jeremiah 19. 2010. 110.12 *(978-1-61143-546-7(3))* Gorgias Pr., LLC.

Douglas, Mary. Thinking in Circles: An Essay on Ring Composition. 2007. (Terry Lectures). (ENG., Illus.). 192p. 35.00 *(978-0-300-11762-2(0))* Yale Univ. Pr.

—Thinking in Circles: An Essay on Ring Composition. 2010. (Terry Lectures Ser.). (ENG., Illus.). 192p. pap. 24.00 *(978-0-300-16785-6(7))* Yale Univ. Pr.

Dozeman, Thomas, et al, eds. Pentateuch, Hexateuch, or Enneateuch? Identifying Literary Works in Genesis Through Kings. 2011. (SBL - Ancient Israel & Its Literature Ser.). (ENG.). X, 314p. *(978-90-04-20250-4(1))* BRILL.

Dozeman, Thomas B., ed. Methods for Exodus. 2010. (Methods in Biblical Interpretation Ser.). (ENG.). (C). 268p. 85.00 *(978-0-521-88367-2(9))*; (Illus.). 266p. pap. 24.99 *(978-0-521-71001-5(4))* Cambridge Univ. Pr.

Dozeman, Thomas B., et al, eds. The Pentateuch. 2011. (Forschungen zum Alten Testament Ser.). (Illus.). 596p. 257.50 ***(978-3-16-150613-0(8))*** Mohr Siebeck GmbH & Co. KG DEU. Dist: Coronet Bks.

Dozeman, Thomas B., et al. Pentateuch, Hexateuch, or Enneateuch: Identifying Literary Works in Genesis Through Kings. 2011. *(978-1-58983-542-9(5))*; *(978-1-58983-543-6(3))* Society of Biblical Literature.

Drazin, Israel & Wagner, Stanley M., intros. Onkelos on the Torah: Understanding the Bible Text the Book of Genesis. 2006. (HEB, ARC & ENG.). 400p. 35.00 *(978-965-229-342-8(3))* Gefen Publishing Hse., Ltd ISR. Dist: Gefen Bks.

Ebifegha, Michael. The Death of Evolution. 2007. 248p. (ENG.). 24.99 *(978-1-60034-977-5(3))*; per. 14.99 *(978-1-60034-976-8(5))* Xulon Pr., Inc.

Edayadiyil, George. Israel in the Light of the Exodus Event: An Analysis of the Impact of the Exodus Event in the Life of Old Testament People. 2009. xxvi, 241p. pap. *(978-81-7086-496-7(8)*, Library of Congress — New Delhi Overseas Office) Asian Trading Corp.

Ellis, Ralph. Eden in Egypt: Adam & Eve were Pharaoh Akhenaton & Nefertiti. 2009. 370p. pap. 20.00 *(978-1-931882-95-8(9))* Adventures Unlimited Pr.

Emerton, John Adney, et al. Genesis, Isaiah, & Psalms: A Festschrift to Honour Professor John Emerton for His Eightieth Birthday. 2010. 210p. *(978-90-04-18231-8(4))* BRILL.

Esler, Philip F. Sex, Wives, & Warriors: Reading Biblical Narrative with Its Ancient Audience. 2011. 422p. pap. 46.00 ***(978-1-60899-829-6(0)***, Cascade Bks.) Wipf & Stock Pubs.

Fajfr, Ruth S. The Book of Numbers. pap. 2.49 *(978-1-56632-027-6(5))* Revival Literature.

Feder, Avraham. Torah Through A Zionist Vision. 2008. 664p. 48.00 *(978-965-229-444-9(6))* Gefen Publishing Hse., Ltd ISR. Dist: Gefen Bks.

Feldman, Daniel Z. & Halpern, Stuart W., eds. Mitokh Ha-Ohel: Essays on the Weekly Parashah from the Rabbis & Professors of Yeshiva University. 2010. (ENG & HEB.). 518p. 29.95 *(978-1-59264-324-0(8)*, Maggid) Toby Pr. LLC, The.

Feldt, Laura. Signs of Wonder - Traces of Doubt: The Fantastic in Religious Narrative from Exodus to Elisha. (BibleWorld Ser.). (ENG.). 292p. (C). 2012. 100.00 *(978-1-84553-942-9(7))* 2011. pap. 39.95 *(978-1-84553-943-6(5))* Equinox Publishing Ltd. GBR. Dist: Brown, David Bk. Co., The.

Fesko, J. V. Last Things First: Unlocking Genesis 1-3 with the Christ of Eschatology. 2007. (Last Things First Ser.). (ENG.). 208p. per. 19.99 *(978-1-84550-229-4(9)*, Mentor) Christian Focus Pubns. GBR. Dist: STL Distribution North America.

—The Rule of Love: Broken, Fulfilled, & Applied. 2009. *(978-1-60178-063-8(X))* Reformation Heritage Bks.

Fields, Weston W. Sodom & Gomorrah: History & Motif in Biblical Narrative. 2009. (Library of Hebrew Bible/Old Testament Studies, the Ser.). (ENG.). 228p. 39.95 *(978-0-567-60250-3(8)*, T&T Clark) Continuum International Publishing Group, Ltd. GBR. Dist: National Bk. Network.

Finch, Paul R. The Passover Papers: Controversy, Myth, Fairy Tales & Nonsense! 2nd ed. 2008. xiii, 340p. pap. *(978-0-9800739-3-5(6))* B-F Enterprises Inc.

Fink, Uta Barbara. Joseph und Aseneth: Revision des griechischen Textes und Edition der zweiten Lateinischen Übersetzung. 2008. (Fontes et Subsidia Ad Bibliam Pertinentes Ser.). (GER.). XI, 353p. 147.00 *(978-3-11-020140-6(2))* De Gruyter, Walter Inc.

Fischer, Chuck. In the Beginning: The Art of Genesis. 2008. (ENG., Illus.). 12p. (gr. k-5). 35.00 *(978-0-316-11842-2(7))* Little Brown & Co.

Fischer, Richard James. Historical Genesis: From Adam to Abraham. 2008. (ENG., Illus.). 210p. 41.99 *(978-0-7618-3806-7(6))*; per. 19.99 *(978-0-7618-3807-4(4))* Univ. Pr. of America, Inc.

Fisher, Loren R. Genesis, A Royal Epic: Introduction, Translation, & Notes, 2nd Edition. 2011. 268p. pap. 29.00 ***(978-1-61097-301-4(1)***, Cascade Bks.) Wipf & Stock Pubs.

Fistill, Ulrich. Israel und Das Ostjordanland: Untersuchungen Zur Komposition Von Num 21,21-36,13 im Hinblick auf Die Entstehung des Buches Numeri. (GER.). 274p. 57.95 *(978-3-631-55891-1(0))* Lang, Peter Publishing, Inc.

Fleer, David & Bland, Dave. Reclaiming the Imagination: The Exodus As Paradigmatic Narrative for Preaching. 2009. 25.99 *(978-0-8272-3259-4(4))*; xi, 191p. E-Book *(978-0-8272-3265-5(9))*; xi, 191p. E-Book *(978-0-8272-3266-2(7))* Chalice Pr.

Ford, Clayton Howard. Who Really Wrote the Bible? 2010. pap. 15.99 *(978-1-61566-224-1(3))* Tate Publishing & Enterprises, LLC.

Ford, William A. God, Pharaoh & Moses: Explaining the Lord's Actions in the Exodus Plagues Narrative. 2007. (Paternoster Biblical Monographs). (ENG., Illus.). 267p. per. 36.99 *(978-1-84227-420-0(1)*, Paternoster) Authentic Media.

Los Fosiles y el Diluvio: Fossils & the Genesis Flood. (SPA.). *(978-84-7645-192-2(X)*, 223236) Clie, Editorial.

Fyler, John M. Language & the Declining World in Chaucer, Dante, & Jean de Meun. (Cambridge Studies in Medieval Literature Ser.). (ENG.). 2010. 322p. pap. 39.99 *(978-0-521-14771-2(9))* 2007. 380p. 127.00 *(978-0-521-87215-7(4))* Cambridge Univ. Pr.

Giddens, Pastor/Missionary Donald Louis. Jesus in Genesis. 2007. 381p. pap. 33.50 *(978-1-4357-0125-0(9))* Lulu Enterprises Inc.

Giere, S. D. A New Glimpse of Day One: Intertextuality, History of Interpretation, & Genesis 1. 1-5. 2009. (Beihefte zur Zeitschrift für die neutestamentliche Wissenschaft und die Kunde der älteren Kirche Ser.). (ENG.). XVII, 359p. 140.00 *(978-3-11-022433-7(X))*; 210.00 ***(978-3-11-174148-2(6))*** De Gruyter, Walter Inc.

Gillman, Neil. Traces of God: Seeing God in Torah, History & Everyday Life. 2008. (ENG.). 240p. pap. 16.99 *(978-1-58023-369-9(4))* Jewish Lights Publishing.

Giuliano, Angelo G., et al. Old Testament Foundations: Genesis Through Kings: Year One: Teacher Guidebook. 2007. (Catholic Biblical School Program Ser.). (Illus.). 80p. per. 19.95 *(978-0-8091-9585-5(2))* Paulist Pr.

Goligher, Liam. Joseph: The Hidden Hand of God. 2008. (ENG.). 208p. pap. 12.99 *(978-1-84550-368-0(6))* Christian Focus Pubns. GBR. Dist: STL Distribution North America.

Gonzales, Robert R. Where Sin Abounds. 2009. 310p. pap. 34.00 *(978-1-60608-747-3(9)*, Wipf and Stock) Wipf & Stock Pubs.

Gooding, D. W. The Account of the Tabernacle: Translation & Textual Problems of the Greek Exodus. 2009. (ENG.). 132p. pap. 28.99 *(978-0-521-11163-8(3))* Cambridge Univ. Pr.

Gorospe, Athena E. Narrative & Identity: An Ethical Reading of Exodus 4. 2007. (Biblical Interpretation Ser.). 380p. *(978-90-04-15855-9(3))* BRILL.

Gossai, Hemchand. Barrenness & Blessing: Abraham, Sarah & the Journey of Faith. 2010. (ENG.). 136p. pap. 33.00 *(978-0-7188-9216-6(X))* Lutherworth Pr., The GBR. Dist: Brown, David Bk. Co., The.

—Power & Marginality in the Abraham Narrative - Second Edition. 2nd ed. 2009. (Princeton Theological Monographs). 168p. pap. 19.00 *(978-1-55635-874-6(1)*, Pickwick Pubns.) Wipf & Stock Pubs.

Gouin, Walter Robert. Chronicles Iii: Moses 1490 Exodus, to Cyrus of Persia 485 Bce Chronological Hebrew History of Israel & Judah's Patriarchs, Judges, Kings, Prophets & Governors. 2011. 276p. 34.99 ***(978-1-4567-3870-9(4))***; pap. 22.00 ***(978-1-4567-3868-6(2))*** AuthorHouse.

Granerod, Gard. Abraham & Melchizedek: Scribal Activity of Second Temple Times in Genesis 14 & Psalm 110. 2010. (Beihefte Zur Zeitschrift Für Die Alttestamentliche Wissenschaft Ser.). (ENG.). XIV, 317p. 112.00 *(978-3-11-022345-3(7))* De Gruyter, Walter Inc.

Green, William Henry. The Higher Criticism of the Pentateuch. 2009. 200p. 30.99 *(978-1-115-01577-6(X))* 2009. 200p. 26.99 *(978-1-115-01576-9(1))* 2009. 200p. 26.99 *(978-1-115-01578-3(8))* 2009. 200p. pap. 16.99 *(978-1-115-01574-5(5))* 2009. 200p. pap. 21.99 *(978-1-115-01573-8(7))* 2008. 137p. 25.99 *(978-0-554-63703-7(0))* 2008. 137p. 22.99 *(978-0-554-63714-3(6))* 2008. 137p. pap. 24.75 *(978-0-554-63705-1(7))* 2008. 137p. pap. 23.75 *(978-0-554-63711-2(1))* BiblioBazaar.

—The Higher Criticism of the Pentateuch. 2009. 142p. pap. *(978-0-217-08403-1(6))* Books LLC.

—The Higher Criticism of the Pentateuch. 2007. (ENG.). 198p. 39.95 *(978-0-548-16516-4(5))*; 200p. per. 24.95 *(978-1-4304-6169-2(1))* Kessinger Publishing, LLC.

—The Pentateuch Vindicated from the Aspersions of Bishop Colenso. 2009. 200p. 22.99 *(978-1-103-72342-3(1))*; pap. 16.99 *(978-1-103-72339-3(1))* BiblioBazaar.

—The Pentateuch Vindicated from the Aspersions of Bishop Colenso. 2007. (ENG.). 194p. 37.95 *(978-0-548-19782-0(2))*; 196p. per. 22.95 *(978-1-4325-0583-7(1))* Kessinger Publishing, LLC.

—The Pentateuch Vindicated from the Aspersions of Bishop Colenso. 2006. 204p. per. 20.99 *(978-1-4255-1704-5(8))* MPublishing.

Gregory & Drobner, Hubertus R. Opera exegetica in Genesim: Gregorii Nysseni in Hexaemeron, Vol. 1. 2009. (GER & GEC., Illus.). 224p. *(978-90-04-13315-0(1))* BRILL.

Grypeou, E. & Spurling, H. The Exegetical Encounter between Jews & Christians in Late Antiquity. 2009. (Jewish & Christian Perspectives Ser.). *(978-90-04-17727-7(2))* BRILL.

Guillaume, Philippe. Land & Calendar: The Priestly Document from Genesis 1 to Joshua 18. 2009. (Library of Hebrew Bible/Old Testament Studies, the Ser.). (ENG., Illus.). 256p. 120.00 *(978-0-567-32200-5(9)*, T&T Clark Int'l) Continuum International Publishing Group, Ltd. GBR. Dist: National Bk. Network.

Gunkel, Hermann. Creation & Chaos in the Primeval Era & the Eschaton: Religio-Historical Study of Genesis 1 & Revelation 12. Whitney, K. William, tr. from GER. 2006. (Biblical Resource Ser.). 442p. per. 36.00 *(978-0-8028-2804-0(3))* Eerdmans, William B. Publishing Co.

—The Legends of Genesis. 2008. (ENG.). 136p. per. 20.75 *(978-1-4375-3184-8(9))*; 120p. per. 19.75 *(978-1-4375-3073-5(7))* BiblioBazaar.

—The Legends of Genesis. 2007. 188p. per. 17.50 *(978-1-60206-552-9(7))* Cosimo, Inc.

—The Legends of Genesis. Carruth, W. H., tr. 2007. (ENG.). 188p. 37.95 *(978-0-548-12231-0(8))* Kessinger Publishing, LLC.

Gurney, Robert J. M. Six-Day Creation: Does It Matter What You Believe? 2007. (Wise Choices Ser.). (Illus.). 64p. pap. 6.00 *(978-1-84625-097-2(8))* DayOne Pubns. GBR. Dist: STL Distribution North America.

Ha, John. Genesis 15: A Theological Compendium of Pentateuchal History. (Beihefte zur Zeitschrift far die alttestamentliche Wissenschaft Ser.). (GER.). XII, 244p. 196.00 ***(978-3-11-177873-0(8))*** De Gruyter, Walter Inc.

Halivini, David Weiss. Breaking the Tablets: Jewish Theology after the Shoah. Ochs, Peter, ed. 2007. (ENG.). 144p. 65.00 *(978-0-7425-5220-3(9))*; per. 23.95 *(978-0-7425-5221-0(7))* Rowman & Littlefield Publishers, Inc.

Hamilton, Mark W. On the Mountain with God: Freedom & Community in Exodus. 2009. 144p. 12.99 *(978-0-89112-638-6(4)*, Leafwood Pubs.) Abilene Christian Univ. Pr.

Hammer, Rabbi Reuven. The Torah Revolution: Fourteen Truths That Changed the World. 2011. 250p. 24.99 ***(978-1-58023-457-3(7))*** Jewish Lights Publishing.

Hargreaves, John. Guide to Genesis. 3.00 *(978-0-687-85447-9(4))* Abingdon Pr.

Harmon, Jerry R. Exodus 34:6-7: A Hermeneutical Key in the Openness Debate. 2008. *(978-1-4331-0154-0(8))* Lang, Peter Publishing, Inc.

Harrell, Daniel M. How to Be Perfect: One Church's Audacious Experiment in Living the Old Testament Book of Leviticus. 2011. (ENG.). 240p. 19.99 *(978-0-446-55717-7(X))* FaithWords.

Haynes, Stephen R. Noah's Curse: The Biblical Justification of American Slavery. 2007. (Religion in America Ser.). (ENG.). 336p. pap. 25.00 *(978-0-19-531307-9(0))* Oxford Univ. Pr., Inc.

Heck, Joel D. In the Beginning, God: Creation from God's Perspective. 2011. 3.99 *(978-0-7586-2738-4(6))* Concordia Publishing Hse.

Heijne, Camilla Hélena von. The Messenger of the Lord in Early Jewish Interpretations of Genesis. (Beihefte zur Zeitschrift far die alttestamentliche Wissenschaft Ser.). (ENG., Illus.). XVII, 417p. 2011. 252.00 ***(978-3-11-174221-2(0))*** 2010. 168.00 *(978-3-11-022684-3(7))* De Gruyter, Walter Inc.

Hendel, Ronald, ed. Reading Genesis: Ten Methods. 2010. (ENG.). 300p. (C). 85.00 *(978-0-521-51861-1(X))*; pap. 27.99 *(978-0-521-73239-0(5))* Cambridge Univ. Pr.

Hendricks, J. L. All the Bible Is Based on Just Three Verses. 2008. 116p. pap. 11.99 *(978-1-60647-731-1(5))* Xulon Pr., Inc.

Hensel, Benedikt. Die Vertauschung des Erstgeburtssegens in der Genesis: Eine Analyse der Narrativ-Theologischen Grundstruktur des Ersten Buches der Tora. 2011. (Beihefte zur Zeitschrift für die alttestamentliche Wissenschaft Ser.). (GER.). XIV, 387p. 182.00 ***(978-3-11-024792-3(5))*** De Gruyter, Walter Inc.

Hepner, Gershon. Legal Friction: Law, Narrative, & Identity Politics in Biblical Israel. 2010. (Studies in Biblical Literature Ser.). 1130p. (C). 149.95 *(978-0-8204-7462-5(2))* Lang, Peter Publishing, Inc.

Hilbrands, Walter. Heilige Oder Hure? Die Rezeptionsgeschichte Von Juda und Tamar (Genesis 38) Von der Antike Bis Zur Reformationszeit. 2007. (Contributions to Biblical Exegesis & Theology Ser.). (GER & ENG.). 315p. (C). pap. 64.00 *(978-90-429-1914-3(0))* Peeters Pubs. & Booksellers BEL. Dist: Brown, David Bk. Co., The.

Hoffmeier, James. Ancient Israel in Sinai: The Evidence for the Authenticity of the Wilderness Tradition, 1 vol. 2011. (ENG., Illus.). 384p. pap. 24.95 *(978-0-19-973169-5(1))* Oxford Univ. Pr., Inc.

Holsinger-Friesen, Thomas. Irenaeus & Genesis: A Study of Competition in Early Christian Hermeneutics. 2009. pap. 34.95 *(978-1-57506-700-1(5))* Eisenbrauns, Inc.

Hutton, Jeremy M. The Transjordanian Palimpsest: The Overwritten Texts of Personal Exile & Transformation in the Deuteronomistic History. 2009. (Beihefte zur Zeitschrift far die alttestamentliche Wissenschaft Ser.). (ENG.). XVIII, 450p. 140.00 *(978-3-11-020410-0(X))* De Gruyter, Walter Inc.

Hyde, Daniel R. God in Our Midst: The Tabernacle & Our Relationship with God. 2012. ***(978-1-56769-281-5(8))*** Reformation Pubs.

Infeld, Tsevi. Ketav Ivri, Ketav Ashuri: Shitat Hazal Al Pi Torat Ha-Maharal U-Vet Midrasho. 2008. (HEB., Illus.). 249p. *(978-1-59826-202-5(5))* Feldheim Pubs.

Ingersoll, Robert G. Some Mistakes of Moses. 2007. (ENG.). 280p. per. 22.95 *(978-1-58509-060-0(3))* Book Tree, The.

—Some Mistakes of Moses. 2010. 266p. 34.36 *(978-1-169-75234-4(9))*; 42.95 *(978-1-161-60128-2(7))* Kessinger Publishing, LLC.

Ingersoll, Robert Green. Some Mistakes of Moses. 2009. 134p. 29.99 *(978-1-59547-499-5(4))* NuVision Pubns., LLC.

Jacobs, Mignon R. Gender, Power, & Persuasion: The Genesis Narratives & Contemporary Portraits. 2007. (Illus.). 272p. (C). pap. 28.00 *(978-0-8010-2706-2(3))* Baker Academic.

Johnson, Joey. God Is Greater Than Family Mess. 2009. (ENG.). 214p. 24.99 *(978-0-9825303-5-1(8))* St. Paul Pr.

Johnstone, William. Chronicles & Exodus: An Analogy & its Application. 2009. (Library of Hebrew Bible/Old Testament Studies, the Ser.). (ENG.). 331p. 55.00 *(978-0-567-22326-5(4)*, T&T Clark) Continuum International Publishing Group, Ltd. GBR. Dist: National Bk. Network.

Jones, Jerry J. Cheated: What to Do when Life's Not Fair. 2007. 16.99 *(978-1-56722-710-9(4))* Word Aflame Pr.

Joo, Samantha. Provocation & Punishment: The Anger of God in the Book of Jeremiah & Deuteronomistic Theology. (Beihefte zur Zeitschrift far die alttestamentliche Wissenschaft Ser.). (ENG.). XIV, 320p. 225.00 ***(978-3-11-184527-2(3))***; 2006. 140.00 *(978-3-11-018994-0(1))* De Gruyter, Walter Inc.

Joyce, Robert E. A Perfect Creation: the Light behind the Dark Side of GENESIS. 2009. 181p. pap. 19.95 *(978-0-615-25155-4(2))* LifeCom.

Kearney, Jonathan F. Rashi: Linguist Despite Himself: A Study of the Linguistic Dimension of Rabbi Solomon Yishaqi's Commentary on Deuteronomy. 2010. (Library of Hebrew Bible/Old Testament Studies). (ENG., Illus.). 224p. 120.00 *(978-0-567-43856-0(2)*, T&T Clark Int'l) Continuum International Publishing Group, Ltd. GBR. Dist: National Bk. Network.

Kelly, William. The Pentateuch. (Introductory Lecture Ser.). 524p. 7.95 *(978-0-88172-099-0(2))* Believers Bookshelf, Inc.

Kendall, Calvin B., tr. from LAT. Bede - On Genesis. 2008. (Liverpool University Press - Translated Texts for Historians Ser.). (ENG.). 256p. pap. 29.95 *(978-1-84631-088-1(1))* Liverpool Univ. Pr. GBR. Dist: Chicago Distribution Ctr.

Kim, Yoon-Kyung. Augustine's Changing Interpretations of Genesis 1-3: From de Genesi contra Manichaeos to de Genesi ad Litteram. 2006. 208p. 109.95 *(978-0-7734-5670-9(8))* Mellen, Edwin Pr., The.

Kimball, A. Samuel. The Infanticidal Logic of Evolution & Culture. 2007. 363p. pap. 60.00 *(978-0-87413-952-5(X))* Univ. of Delaware Pr.

Kimuhu, Johnson M. Leviticus: The Priestly Laws & Prohibitions from the Perspective of Ancient near East & Africa. 2008. (Studies in Biblical Literature Ser.). 456p. (C). 89.95 *(978-1-4331-0200-4(5))* Lang, Peter Publishing, Inc.

King, Thomas J. The Realignment of the Priestly Literature: The Priestly Narrative in Genesis & Its Relation to Priestly Legislation & the Holiness School. 2008. (Princeton Theological Monographs). 200p. pap. 23.00 *(978-1-55635-612-4(9)*, Pickwick Pubns.) Wipf & Stock Pubs.

Klaiber, Walter. On Creation: Religion & Science in Dialogue. 2011. 212p. pap. 35.00 *(978-0-687-46687-0(3))* Abingdon Pr.

Klitsner, Judy. Subversive Sequels in the Bible: How Biblical Stories Mine & Undermine Each Other. 2009. (ENG.). 224p. 35.00 *(978-0-8276-0888-7(8))* Jewish Pubn. Society.

—Subversive Sequels in the Bible: How Biblical Stories Mine & Undermine Each Other. 2011. (ENG.). 250p. pap. 16.95 *(978-1-59264-339-4(6)*, Maggid) Toby Pr. LLC, The.

Klitsner, Shmuel. Wrestling Jacob: Deception, Identity, & Freudian Slips in Genesis. 2007. 182p. 23.95 *(978-965-7108-93-2(4))* Urim Pubns. ISR. Dist: Coronet Bks.

—Wrestling Jacob: Deception, Identity, & Freudian Slips in Genesis. 2009. 186p. pap. *(978-1-934730-16-4(5))* Yehuda, Ben Pr.

Knierim, Rolf P. Text & Concept in Leviticus 1:1-9: A Case in Exegetical Method. 2010. 134p. pap. 17.00 *(978-1-60899-416-8(3))* Wipf & Stock Pubs.

Knohl, Israel. The Sanctuary of Silence: The Priestly Torah & the Holiness School. 2007. 256p. 29.50 *(978-1-57506-131-3(7))* Eisenbrauns, Inc.

Knoppers, Gary N. & Levinson, Bernard M. The Pentateuch As Torah: New Models for Understanding Its Promulgation & Acceptance. 2007. 49.50 *(978-1-57506-140-5(6))* Eisenbrauns, Inc.

Koch, Christoph. Vertrag, Treueid, und Bund: Studien Zur Rezeption des Altorientalischen Vertragsrechts Im Deuteronomium und Zur Ausbildung der Bundestheologie Im Alten Testament. 2008. (Beihefte zur Zeitschrift für die alttestamentliche Wissenschaft Ser.). (GER.). XI, 374p. 147.00 *(978-3-11-020245-8(X))* De Gruyter, Walter Inc.

Kolatch, Yonatan. Masters of the Word: Traditional Jewish Bible Commentary from the First Through Tenth Centuries. 2006. (Illus.). *(978-0-88125-936-0(5))* Ktav Publishing Hse., Inc.

Kraus, Helen. Gender Issues in Ancient & Reformation Translations of Genesis 1-4. 2011. (ENG.). 256p. 125.00 *(978-0-19-960078-6(3))* Oxford Univ. Pr., Inc.

Kreuz, Gottfried & Pseudo-Hilary. Pseudo-Hilarius, Metrum in Genesin, Carmen de Evangelio: Einleitung, Text und Kommentar. 2006. (VERoFFENTLICHUNGEN der KOMMISSION ZUR HERAUSGABE des CORPUS der LATEINISCHEN KIRCHENVaTER Ser.). (GER., Illus.). 456p. (C). pap. 83.00 *(978-3-7001-3790-0(7))* Austrian Academy of Sciences Press AUT. Dist: Brown, David Bk. Co., The.

Kuenen, Abraham. HistoricoCritical Inquiry into the Origi. 2006. pap. 33.95 *(978-1-4286-5869-1(6))* Kessinger Publishing, LLC.

Kugel, James L. & Kugel, James L. The Ladder of Jacob: Ancient Interpretations of the Biblical Story of Jacob & His Children. 2009. (ENG., Illus.). 296p. pap. 22.95 *(978-0-691-14123-7(1))* Princeton Univ. Pr.

Kupfer, Christian Daniel. Mit Israel auf dem Weg durch die Wüste: Eine leserorientierte Exegese der Rebellionstexte in Exodus 15:22-17:7 und Numeri 11:1-20:13. 2011. (Oudtestamentische Studiën, Old Testament Studies). (GER.). X, 290p. ***(978-90-04-20919-0(0))*** BRILL.

L&L Publishing, creator. Genesis: The Book of Ages & Dominion in the Earth. 2007. 256p. pap. *(978-0-9799833-1-3(2))* L & L Publishing Co.

LaCocque, Andre. The Captivity of Innocence: Babel & the Yahwist. 2010. 206p. pap. 23.00 *(978-1-60899-353-6(1))* Wipf & Stock Pubs.

—Onslaught Against Innocence: Cain, Abel, & the Yahwist. 2008. 188p. pap. 22.00 *(978-1-55635-789-3(3))* Wipf & Stock Pubs.

—Onslaught Against Innocence: Cain, Abel & the Yahwist. 2010. (ENG.). 187p. (C). pap. 39.00 *(978-0-227-17319-0(8))* Clarke, James Co., Ltd. GBR. Dist: Brown, David Bk. Co., The.

Lamb, David T. Righteous Jehu & His Evil Heirs: The Deuteronomist's Negative Perspective on Dynastic Succession. 2008. (Oxford Theological Monographs). (ENG., Illus.). 320p. 125.00 *(978-0-19-923147-8(8))* Oxford Univ. Pr., Inc.

Lane, Nathan C. The Compassionate, but Punishing God: A Canonical Analysis of Exodus 34:6-7. 2010. 176p. pap. 20.00 *(978-1-60608-792-3(4)*, Pickwick Pubns.) Wipf & Stock Pubs.

Lanfer, Peter Thacher. Remembering Eden: The Reception History of Genesis 3: 22-24, 1 vol. 2012. (ENG.). 272p. 74.00 ***(978-0-19-992674-9(3))*** Oxford Univ. Pr., Inc.

Lange, Armin, et al. From Qumran to Aleppo: A Discussion with Emanuel Tov about the Textual History of Jewish Scriptures in Honor of his 65th Birthday. 2009. (Forschungen Zur Religion und Literatur des Alten & Neuen Testament Ser.). (GER & ENG., Illus.). 202p. (C). 98.00 *(978-3-525-53094-8(3))* Vandenhoeck & Ruprecht GmbH & Co. KG DEU. Dist: ISD.

Langer, Gerhard. Esau - Bruder und Feind. Langer, Gerhard, ed. 2009. (GER.). 341p. (C). pap. 48.00 *(978-3-525-50113-9(7))* Vandenhoeck & Ruprecht GmbH & Co. KG DEU. Dist: ISD.

Law, Henry. El Evangelio en el Exodo: The Gospel in Exodus. (SPA.). *(978-84-7645-096-3(6)*, 223151) Clie, Editorial.

Lawrence, Paul. The Books of Moses Revisited. 2011. 188p. pap. 22.00 ***(978-1-61097-417-2(4)***, Wipf and Stock) Wipf & Stock Pubs.

Le Roux. South African Perspectives on the Pentateuch Between Synchrony & Diachrony. Otto, Eckart & Roux, Jurie Hendrik, eds. 2008. (Library of Hebrew Bible/Old Testament Studies, the Ser.). (ENG., Illus.). 224p. 140.00 *(978-0-567-02992-8(1)*, T&T Clark Int'l) Continuum International Publishing Group, Ltd. GBR. Dist: National Bk. Network.

Leder, Arie C. Waiting for the Land: The Story Line of the Pentateuch. 2010. xii, 238p. pap. *(978-0-87552-196-1(7))* P & R Publishing.

Lee, Bernon. Between Law & Narrative. 2009. 110.00 *(978-1-59333-912-8(7))* Gorgias Pr., LLC.

Lemmelijn, Benedicte. A Plague of Texts? A Text-Critical Study of the So-Called 'Plagues Narrative' in Exodus 7:14-11:10. 2009. (Oudtestamentische Studiën, Old Testament Studies). 396p. *(978-90-04-17235-7(1))* BRILL.

Leveen, Adriane. Memory & Tradition in the Book of Numbers. 2007. (ENG.). 256p. 88.00 *(978-0-521-87869-2(1))* Cambridge Univ. Pr.

Levine, Michelle J. Nahmanides on Genesis: The Art of Biblical Portraiture. 2009. *(978-1-930675-69-8(0))* Brown Univ.

Levinson, Bernard M. The Right Chorale: Studies in Biblical Law & Interpretation. 2011. pap. 49.50 ***(978-1-57506-210-5(0))*** Eisenbrauns, Inc.

—The Right Chorale: Studies in Biblical Law & Interpretation. 2008. (Illus.). xxiii, 432p. *(978-3-16-149382-9(6))* Mohr Siebeck GmbH & Co. KG.

Lewis, Sheldon. Torah of Reconciliation. 2012. ***(978-965-229-541-5(8))*** Gefen Bks.

Lewy, Immanuel. The Growth of the Pentateuch: A Literary, Sociological & Biographical Approach. 2011. 288p. 48.95 ***(978-1-258-09735-6(4))*** Literary Licensing, LLC.

Lier, Gudrun. A Redaction History of the Pentateuchal Targums. 2010. 119.00 *(978-1-61719-181-7(7))* Gorgias Pr., LLC.

Lietaert Peerbolte, L. J., et al, eds. The Interpretation of Exodus: Studies in Honour of Cornelius Houtman. 2006. (Contributions to Biblical Exegesis & Theology Ser.). (ENG & GER., Illus.). 327p. (C). pap. 57.00 *(978-90-429-1806-1(3))* Peeters Pubs. & Booksellers BEL. Dist: Brown, David Bk. Co., The.

Likhtenshtain, Mosheh. Moses: Envoy of God, Envoy of His People: Leadership & Crisis from the Exodus to the Plains of Moab. 2008. *(978-1-60280-012-0(X))* Ktav Publishing Hse., Inc.

Lincicum, David. Paul & the Early Jewish Encounter with Deuteronomy. 2010. (Illus.). 301p. pap. 127.50 *(978-3-16-150386-3(4))* Mohr Siebeck GmbH & Co. KG DEU. Dist: Coronet Bks.

Lipton, Diana. Revisions of the Night: Politics & Promises in the Patriarchal Dreams of Genesis. 2009. (Library of Hebrew Bible/Old Testament Studies, the Ser.). (ENG.). 288p. 49.95 *(978-1-4411-2055-7(6)*, T&T Clark) Continuum International Publishing Group, Ltd. GBR. Dist: National Bk. Network.

Lipton, Diana & Pirson, Ron. Universalism & Particularism at Sodom & Gomorrah: Essays in Memory of Ron Pirson. 2012. pap. ***(978-1-58983-650-1(2))*** Society of Biblical Literature.

Lisewski, Krzysztof Dariusz. Studien zu Motiven und Themen zur Josefsgeschichte der Genesis. 2008. (Europäische Hochschulschriften. Reihe 23: Theologie Ser.). 504p. pap. 107.95 *(978-3-631-57773-8(7))* Lang, Peter GmbH, Europaischer Verlag der Wissenschaften DEU. Dist: Lang, Peter.

Lloyd-Jones, D. Martyn & Lloyd-Jones, Martyn. The Gospel in Genesis: From Fig Leaves to Faith. 2009. 160p. pap. 16.99 *(978-1-4335-0120-3(1))* Crossway.

Lodahl, Michael. Claiming Abraham: Reading the Bible & the Qur'an Side by Side, 1 vol. 2010. (ENG.). 240p. pap. 23.00 *(978-1-58743-239-2(0))* Brazos Pr.

Lohr, Joel N. Chosen & Unchosen: Conceptions of Election in the Pentateuch & Jewish-Christian Interpretation. 2009. xviii, 254p. 39.50 *(978-1-57506-171-9(6))* Eisenbrauns, Inc.

Longman, Tremper. Genesis Thru Numbers Vol. 1: Where Do We Come From? 2009. (QuickNotes Commentaries Ser.). (ENG.). 240p. pap. 9.99 *(978-1-59789-767-9(1)*, Barbour Bks.) Barbour Publishing, Inc.

Longman, Tremper, III. How to Read Exodus. 2009. (How to Read Ser.). (ENG.). 187p. pap. 16.00 *(978-0-8308-3858-5(9)*, IVP Acad.) InterVarsity Pr.

Lowrie, John M. Adam & His Times. 2006. 292p. per. 23.99 *(978-1-4255-2745-7(0))* MPublishing.

Luke Gartner-Brereton Staff. The Ontology of Space in Biblical Hebrew Narrative. 2008. (BibleWorld Ser.). (ENG., Illus.). 140p. (C). 29.95 *(978-1-84553-314-4(3))*; 99.95 *(978-1-84553-313-7(5))* Equinox Publishing Ltd. GBR. Dist: ISD.

Lutzer, Erwin W. Fracaso: Una Puerta Abierta Al Exito: Failure: Back Door to Success. (SPA.). *(978-84-7228-493-7(X)*, 220416) Clie, Editorial.

Lyons, Michael A. & Lyons, Michael. From Law to Prophecy: Ezekiel's Use of the Holiness Code. 2009. (Library of Hebrew Bible/Old Testament Studies, the Ser.). (ENG.). 240p. 120.00 *(978-0-567-02725-2(2)*, T&T Clark Int'l) Continuum International Publishing Group, Ltd. GBR. Dist: National Bk. Network.

MacArthur, John. The Exodus from Egypt: Moses & God's Mercy, 0 vols. 2008. (MacArthur Old Testament Study Guides). (ENG.). 128p. pap. 9.99 *(978-1-4185-3325-0(4))* Nelson, Thomas Inc.

Mackintosh, Charles H. Notes on the Book of Exodus. 2006. 364p. per. 26.99 *(978-1-4255-3725-8(1))* MPublishing.

Magid, Shaul. From Metaphysics to Midrash: Myth, History, & the Interpretation of Scripture in Lurianic Kabbala. 2008. (Indiana Studies in Biblical Literature Ser.). (ENG., Illus.). 368p. 39.95 *(978-0-253-35088-6(3)*, 0253350883) Indiana Univ. Pr.

Mann, Thomas W. Divine Presence & Guidance in Israelite Traditions: The Typology of Exaltation. 2010. 320p. pap. 35.00 *(978-1-60899-718-3(9)*, Wipf and Stock) Wipf & Stock Pubs.

Mason, Steven D. Eternal Covenant in the Pentateuch: The Contours of an Elusive Phrase. 2008. (Library of Hebrew Bible/Old Testament Studies, the Ser.). (ENG.). 272p. 140.00 *(978-0-567-02718-4(X)*, T&T Clark Int'l)

Continuum International Publishing Group, Ltd. GBR. Dist: National Bk. Network.

Maxfield, John A. Luther's Lectures on Genesis & the Formation of Evangelical Identity. 2008. (Sixteenth Century Essays & Studies: 80). (Illus.). 264p. 54.00 *(978-1-931112-75-8(4))* Truman State Univ. Pr.

McConkie, Clay & McConkie, John, illus. A Man Named Peleg: An Exploration into the Days of Peleg. 2007. 139p. per. 13.99 *(978-1-59955-024-4(5))* Cedar Fort, Inc./CFI Distribution.

McConville, J. G. God & Earthly Power: An Old Testament Political Theology. 2008. (ENG.). 224p. 44.95 *(978-0-567-04570-6(6)*, T&T Clark Int'l) Continuum International Publishing Group, Ltd. GBR. Dist: National Bk. Network.

McEntire, Mark. Struggling with God: An Introduction to the Pentateuch. 2008. (Mercer Student Guide Ser.). (Illus.). 249p. pap. 25.00 *(978-0-88146-101-5(6))* Mercer Univ. Pr.

McFadden, Olivia. A Bird in the Hand... Some Thoughts Concerning Evolution, Creation, & the Teaching of the Catholic Church. 2009. 53p. 19.99 *(978-1-4415-6270-8(2))* Xlibris Corp.

McKay, Heather A. Of Prophets' Visions & the Wisdom of Sages: Essays in Honour of R. Norman Whybray on his Seventieth Birthday. Clines, David J. A., ed. 2009. (Library of Hebrew Bible/Old Testament Studies, the Ser.). (ENG.). 335p. 55.00 *(978-0-567-35484-6(9)*, T&T Clark) Continuum International Publishing Group, Ltd. GBR. Dist: National Bk. Network.

McKenzie, Tracy J. Idolatry in the Pentateuch: An Innertextual Strategy. 2010. 148p. pap. 18.00 *(978-1-60608-607-0(3)*, Pickwick Pubns.) Wipf & Stock Pubs.

McKenzie, Vashti Murphy. Swapping Housewives: Rachel & Jacob & Leah. 2007. 142p. per. *(978-0-8298-1773-7(5))* Pilgrim Pr., The/United Church Pr.

Mettinger, Tryggve N. D. The Eden Narrative: A Literary & Religio-Historical Study of Genesis 2-3. 2008. xvii, 165p. 29.50 *(978-1-57506-141-2(4))* Eisenbrauns, Inc.

Millard, A. r. Essays on the Patriarchal Narratives. Millard, A. R. & Wiseman, D. J., eds. 2008. 250p. pap. 25.00 *(978-1-55635-666-7(8)*, Wipf and Stock) Wipf & Stock Pubs.

Milgram, Hillel I. Four Biblical Heroines & the Case for Female Authorship: An Analysis of the Women of Ruth, Esther & Genesis 38. 2007. (ENG., Illus.). 279p. per. 39.95 *(978-0-7864-3081-9(8))* McFarland & Co., Inc. Pubs.

Mira Digital Publishing. Dispensationalism: Essential Beliefs & Common Myths. 2008. 73p. pap. 9.95 *(978-0-9798539-1-3(5))* Theological Studies Pr.

Miguet, Françoise. La représentation du divin dans les récits du Pentateuque: Médiations syntaxiques et Narratives. 2008. (Vetus Testamentum Supplements Ser.). 544p. *(978-90-04-17051-3(0))* BRILL.

Moberly, R. W. L. The Theology of the Book of Genesis. 2009. (Old Testament Theology Ser.). (ENG.). 296p. (C). 78.99 *(978-0-521-86631-6(6))*; pap. 26.00 *(978-0-521-68538-2(9))* Cambridge Univ. Pr.

Monroe, Lauren A. S. Josiah's Reform & the Dynamics of Defilement: Israelite Rites of Violence & the Making of a Biblical Text. 2011. (ENG.). 216p. 74.00 *(978-0-19-977416-6(1))* Oxford Univ. Pr., Inc.

Moore, Michael S. WealthWatch: A Study of Socioeconomic Conflict in the Bible. 2011. 320p. pap. 35.00 ***(978-1-61097-296-3(1)***, Pickwick Pubns.) Wipf & Stock Pubs.

Moriya, Akio & Hata, Gohei. Pentateuchal Traditions in the Late Second Temple Period: Proceedings of the International Workshop in Tokyo August 28-31, 2007. 2012. (ENG.). ***(978-90-04-18453-4(8))*** BRILL.

Moroz, Vadim. The Genesis Theory of Moses: A New Decoding & Interpretation of Ancient Text. 2007. (Illus.). 115p. per. 22.50 *(978-0-9714982-6-6(1))* Frost Publishing.

Moyise, Steve. Deuteronomy in the New Testament: The New Testament & the Scriptures of Israel. Menken, Maarten J.J., ed. 2007. (Library of New Testament Studies, the Ser.). (ENG.). 208p. 155.00 *(978-0-567-04549-2(6)*, T&T Clark Int'l) Continuum International Publishing Group, Ltd. GBR. Dist: National Bk. Network.

Najman, Hindy. Seconding Sinai: The Development of Mosaic Discourse in Second Temple Judaism. 2009. 196p. pap. 24.95 *(978-1-58983-424-8(0))* Society of Biblical Literature.

Nataf, Francis. Redeeming Relevance in the Book of Exodus: Explorations in Text & Meaning. 2010. 142p. 21.95 *(978-965-524-037-5(1))* Urim Pubns. ISR. Dist: Coronet Bks.

—Redeeming Relevance in the Book of Genesis: Explorations in Text & Meaning. 2007. 125p. 21.95 *(978-965-7108-94-9(2))* Urim Pubns. ISR. Dist: Coronet Bks.

Navon, Chaim. Genesis & Jewish Thought. Strauss, David, tr. from HEB. 2008. 350p. 35.00 *(978-1-60280-000-7(6))* Ktav Publishing Hse., Inc.

Newman, Louis. Genesis: The Student's Guide, Pt. 2. pap. 4.95 *(978-0-8381-0404-0(5))* United Synagogue of America Bk. Service.

—Teacher's Supplement to Genesis the Student's Guide, Pt. 1. pap. 2.95 *(978-0-8381-0403-3(7))* United Synagogue of America Bk. Service.

Nibley, Hugh, et al. One Eternal Round. 2010. *(978-1-60641-237-4(X))* Deseret Bk. Co.

Nicholas, Dean Andrew. The Trickster Revisited: Deception As a Motif in the Pentateuch. 2008. (Studies in Biblical Literature Ser.). 70.95 *(978-1-4331-0226-4(9))* Lang, Peter Publishing, Inc.

Nihan, Christophe. From Priestly to Pentateuch: A Study in the Composition of the Book of Leviticus. 2007. (Forschungen zum Alten Testament, 2.Reihe: Vol. 25). 697p. (C). pap. 155.00 *(978-3-16-149257-0(9))* Mohr Siebeck GmbH & Co. KG DEU. Dist: Eisenbrauns, Inc.

O'Dowd, Ryan. The Wisdom of Torah: Epistemology in Deuteronomy & the Wisdom in Literature: Forschungen zur Religion und Literatur des Alten und Neuen Testaments 225. 2009. (Forschungen Zur Religion und Literatur des Alten & Neuen Testament Ser.). (ENG.). 213p. (C). 98.00 *(978-3-525-53089-4(7))* Vandenhoeck & Ruprecht GmbH & Co. KG DEU. Dist: ISD.

Pahl, Michael W. The Beginning & the End: Rereading GenesisÕs Stories & Revelation's Visions. 2011. 118p. pap. 15.00 ***(978-1-60899-927-9(0)***, Cascade Bks.) Wipf & Stock Pubs.

Pamela B H Victor. For Surely He Has Forgiven Me: The power of god's Love. 2009. 128p. pap. 13.95 *(978-1-4401-7240-3(4))* iUniverse, Inc.

Pangle, Thomas L. Political Philosophy & the God of Abraham. 2007. (ENG., Illus.). 304p. (gr. 17). per. 26.00 *(978-0-8018-8761-1(5))* Johns Hopkins Univ. Pr.

Park, Abraham. The Genesis Genealogies: God's Administration in the History of Redemption. 2009. (ENG.). 256p. 24.95 *(978-0-7946-0628-2(8)*, PeriplusEdition) Tuttle Publishing.

Parker, Andrew. The Genesis Enigma: Why the First Book of the Bible Is Scientifically Accurate. 2010. (ENG.). 320p. (gr. 12). 16.00 *(978-0-452-29655-8(2)*, Plume) Penguin Group (USA) Inc.

Pearce, Sarah J. K. The Land of the Body: Studies in Philo's Representation of Egypt. 2007. (Wissenschaftliche Untersuchungen Zum Neuen Testament Ser.). 365p. (C). 165.00 *(978-3-16-149250-1(1))* Mohr Siebeck GmbH & Co. KG DEU. Dist: Eisenbrauns, Inc.

Pink, Arthur W. Gleanings in Genesis. 2006. pap. 19.99 *(978-1-59986-929-2(2))* Filiquarian Publishing, LLC.

Polaski, Sandra Hack. Inside the Red Tent. 2006. (Popular Insights Ser.). 100p. per. 12.99 *(978-0-8272-3028-6(1))* Chalice Pr.

Pomykala, Kenneth. Israel in the Wilderness: Interpretations of the Biblical Narratives in Jewish & Christian Traditions. Pomykala, Kenneth E., ed. 2008. (Themes in Biblical Narrative Ser.). (Illus.). 246p. *(978-90-04-16424-6(3))* BRILL.

Porter, Andrew P. In the Beginning, Exodus: The Bible Then & Now. 2008. 222p. pap. 24.00 *(978-1-55635-310-9(3))* Wipf & Stock Pubs.

Postell, Seth D. Adam As Israel: Genesis 1-3 as the Introduction to the Torah & Tanakh. 2012. (ENG.). 216p. pap. 39.00 ***(978-0-227-68019-3(7))*** Clarke, James Co., Ltd. GBR. Dist: Brown, David Bk. Co., The.

Postell, Seth D. Adam as Israel: Genesis 1Ð3 as the Introduction to the Torah & Tanakh. 2011. 216p. pap. 24.00 *(978-1-61097-176-8(0)*, Pickwick Pubns.) Wipf & Stock Pubs.

Prescott, Deborah Lee. Imagery from Genesis in Holocaust Memoirs: A Critical Study. 2010. (ENG., Illus.). 204p. pap. 45.00 *(978-0-7864-4817-3(2))* McFarland & Co., Inc. Pubs.

Radau, Hugo. The Creation-Story of Genesis I. 2009. pap. 37.70 *(978-1-60724-245-1(1))* Gorgias Pr., LLC.

Randall, Albert B. Holy Scriptures As Justifications for War: Fundamentalist Interpretations of the Torah, the New Testament, & the Qur'an. 2007. 280p. 109.95 *(978-0-7734-5217-6(6))* Mellen, Edwin Pr., The.

Rao, Chilkuri Vasantha. Ecological & Theological Apsects of Some Animal Laws in the Pentateuch. 2011. 380p. 129.95 ***(978-0-7734-3918-4(8))*** Mellen, Edwin Pr., The.

Ravndal Hauge, Martin. Descent from the Mountain: Narrative Patterns in Exodus 19-40. 2009. (Library of Hebrew Bible/Old Testament Studies, the Ser.). (ENG.). 368p. 60.00 *(978-1-4411-9848-8(2)*, T&T Clark) Continuum International Publishing Group, Ltd. GBR. Dist: National Bk. Network.

Remley, Paul G. Old English Biblical Verse: Studies in Genesis, Exodus & Daniel. 2007. (Cambridge Studies in Anglo-Saxon England Ser.). (ENG.). 496p. pap. 90.00 *(978-0-521-03280-3(6))* Cambridge Univ. Pr.

Rendtorff, Rolf. Problem of the Process of Transmission in the Pentateuch. 2009. (Library of Hebrew Bible/Old Testament Studies, the Ser.). (ENG.). 39.95 *(978-0-567-18792-5(6)*, T&T Clark) Continuum International Publishing Group, Ltd. GBR. Dist: National Bk. Network.

Rendtorff, Rolf. Das Überlieferungsgeschichtliche Problem des Pentateuch. (GER.). VIII, 177p. 210.00 ***(978-3-11-174783-5(2))*** De Gruyter, Walter Inc.

Rendtorff, Rolf & Kugler, Robert A. The Book of Leviticus: Composition & Reception. 2006. (ENG.). 496p. per. 49.95 *(978-1-58983-251-0(5))* Society of Biblical Literature.

Rijkers, Fabian. Arbeit - ein Weg zum Heil? Vorstellungen und Bewertungen körperlicher Arbeit in der spätantiken und frühmittelalterlichen lateinischen Exegese der Schöpfungsgeschichte. 2009. (Beihefte zur Mediaevistik. Monographien, Editionen, Sammelbände Ser.). (GRE & GER.). 300p. pap. 72.95 *(978-3-631-58173-5(4))* Lang, Peter GmbH, Europaischer Verlag der Wissenschaften DEU. Dist: Lang, Peter.

Roberts, Scott. The Rise & Fall of the Nephilim: The Untold Story of Fallen Angels, Giants on the Earth, & Their Extraterrestrial Origins. 2012. (ENG., Illus.). 1p. pap. 16.99 *(978-1-60163-197-8(9)*, New Page Bks.) Career Pr., Inc.

Roberts, Scott Alan. The Rise & Fall of the Nephilim: The Untold Story of Fallen Angels, Giants on Earth, & Their Extraterrestrial Origins. 2012. 256p. E-Book ***(978-1-60163-629-4(6)***, New Page Bks.) Career Pr., Inc.

Robinson, George. Essential Torah: A Complete Guide to the Five Books of Moses. 2006. (ENG.). 720p. 35.00 *(978-0-8052-4186-0(8)*, Schocken) Knopf Doubleday Publishing Group.

Roemer, T. The Books of Leviticus & Numbers. 2008. (Bibliotheca Ephemeridum Theologicarum Lovaniensium Ser.). (ENG.). 742p. (C). pap. 124.00 *(978-90-429-2094-1(7))* Peeters Pubs. & Booksellers BEL. Dist: Brown, David Bk. Co., The.

Romer, T. & Schmid, K., eds. Les dernieres redactions du Pentateuque, de l'Hexateuque et de L'Enneateuque. 2006. (Bibliotheca Ephemeridum Theologicarum Lovaniensium Ser.). (ENG.). 276p. (C). pap. 95.00 *(978-90-429-1902-0(7))* Peeters Pubs. & Booksellers BEL. Dist: Brown, David Bk. Co., The.

Romer, Thomas C. & Romer. The So-Called Deuteronomistic History: A Sociological, Historical, & Literary Introduction. 2007. (ENG.). 224p. 36.95 *(978-0-567-03212-6(4)*, T&T Clark Int'l) Continuum International Publishing Group, Ltd. GBR. Dist: National Bk. Network.

Rose, Seraphim. Genesis, Creation, & Early Man: The Orthodox Christian Vision. 2nd ed. 2011. ***(978-1-887904-25-4(5))*** St. Herman Pr.

Rosenthal, Robert S. From Plagues to Miracles: The Transformational Journey of Exodus, from the Slavery of Ego to the Promised Land of Spirit. 2012. (ENG.). 256p. pap. 15.95 ***(978-1-4019-3130-8(8))*** Hay Hse., Inc.

Rothenberg, Naftali. Wisdom by the Week: The Weekly Torah Portion As an Inspiration for Thought & Creativity. 2011. ***(978-1-60280-199-8(1))*** Yeshiva Univ. Pr.

Rudie, Carol Veldman. Discover Exodus Vol. 1: Out of Oppression. (Discover Your Bible Ser.). 43p. pap., stu. ed. 4.95 *(978-1-56212-238-6(X)*, 152400) Faith Alive Christian Resources.

—Discover Genesis Vol. 1: Creation to Abraham. (Discover Your Bible Ser.). 47p. pap., stu. ed. 4.25 *(978-1-56212-228-7(2)*, 152220) Faith Alive Christian Resources.

Ruprecht, Louis A., Jr. God Gardened East: A Gardener's Meditation on the Dynamics of Genesis. 2007. (Illus.). 184p. pap. 21.00 *(978-1-55635-434-2(7))* Wipf & Stock Pubs.

Russell, Brian D. The Song of the Sea: The Date & Significance of Exodus 15:1-21. 2007. xiii, 215p. (C). 68.95 *(978-0-8204-8809-7(7))* Lang, Peter Publishing, Inc.

Sacks, Jonathan. Covenant & Conversation: Volume I: Genesis, the Book of Beginnings, 5 Volumes, Volume 1. 2009. 353p. 24.95 *(978-1-59264-020-1(6)*, Maggid) Toby Pr. LLC, The.

—Covenant & Conversation, Exodus: The Book of Redemption. 2010. 24.95 *(978-1-59264-021-8(4))* Toby Pr. LLC, The.

Sailhamer, John H. The Meaning of the Pentateuch: Revelation, Composition & Interpretation. 2009. (ENG.). 632p. pap. 40.00 *(978-0-8308-3867-7(8)*, IVP Acad.) InterVarsity Pr.

Sasso, Sandy Eisenberg. God's Echo: Exploring Scripture with Midrash. 2007. (ENG., Illus.). 168p. (gr. 13). 19.95 *(978-1-55725-478-8(8))* Paraclete Pr., Inc.

Schley, Donald G. Shiloh: A Biblical City in Tradition & History. 2009. (Library of Hebrew Bible/Old Testament Studies, the Ser.). (ENG.). 256p. 44.95 *(978-0-567-50312-1(7)*, T&T Clark) Continuum International Publishing Group, Ltd. GBR. Dist: National Bk. Network.

Schlimm, Matthew Richard. From Fratricide to Forgiveness: The Language & Ethics of Anger in Genesis. 2011. ***(978-1-57506-224-2(0))*** Eisenbrauns, Inc.

Schmutzer, Andrew J. Be Fruitful & Multiply: A Crux of Thematic Repetition in Genesis 1-11. 2009. (Illus.). 276p. pap. 30.00 *(978-1-60608-440-3(2))* Wipf & Stock Pubs.

Schneider, Bernard N. Deuteronomy: A Favored Book of Jesus. pap. 6.99 *(978-0-88469-051-1(2))* BMH Bks.

Schneider, Tammi J. Mothers of Promise: Women in the Book of Genesis. 2008. 240p. (C). pap. 24.00 *(978-0-8010-2949-3(X))* Baker Academic.

Schoenfeld, Devorah. Isaac on Jewish & Christian Altars: Polemic & Exegesis in Rashi & the Glossa Ordinaria. 2012. (Fordham Series in Medieval Studies (FUP) Ser.). (ENG.). 364p. 55.00 ***(978-0-8232-4349-5(4))*** Fordham Univ. Pr.

Schulmeister, Irene. Israels Befreiung Aus Ägypten: Eine Formeluntersuchung zur Theologie des Deuteronomiums. 2010. (Österreichische Biblische Studien Ser.). (GER.). 346p. 83.95 *(978-3-631-60210-2(3))* Lang, Peter GmbH, Europaischer Verlag der Wissenschaften DEU. Dist: Lang, Peter.

Schweid, Eliezer. The Philosophy of the Bible as Foundation of Jewish Culture: Philosophy of Biblical Law. Levin, Leonard, tr. from HEB. 2nd ed. 2009. (Reference Library of Jewish Intellectual History Ser.). (ENG.). 216p. 50.00 *(978-1-934843-01-7(6))*; pap. 35.00 *(978-1-934843-52-9(0))* Academic Studies Pr.

—The Philosophy of the Bible as Foundation of Jewish Culture: Philosophy of Biblical Narrative. Levin, Leonard, tr. from HEB. 2009. (Reference Library of Jewish Intellectual History Ser.). (ENG.). 224p. 50.00 *(978-1-934843-00-0(8))*; pap. 35.00 *(978-1-934843-51-2(2))* Academic Studies Pr.

Shachter. Ibn Ezra on Leviticus: The Straightforward Meaning. 19.95 *(978-0-88125-109-8(7))* Ktav Publishing Hse., Inc.

Shechter, Jack. The Land of Israel: Its Theological Dimensions: A Study of Promise & of a Land's Holiness. 2010. xii, 325p. *(978-0-7618-5129-5(1))* Univ. Pr. of America, Inc.

Shectman, Sarah. Women in the Pentateuch: A Feminist & Source-Critical Analysis. 2009. 220p. *(978-1-906055-72-1(6))* Sheffield Phoenix Pr.

Shepherd, Gary. What Your Pastor Will Not Talk About. 2009. pap. *(978-1-61584-356-5(6))* Independent Pub.

Shooter, Jonathan. The Haftara Handbook: Lessons from the Prophets for the Contemporary Jew. 2010. 381p. pap. *(978-1-936068-05-0(2)*, Devorah Publishing) Urim Pubns.

Shoulson, Mark. The Torah: Jewish & Samaritan Versions Compared. 2nd ed. 2008. 616p. *(978-1-904808-18-3(2))* Evertype.

Shropshire, Richard J. The Genesis Factor: Biblical Principles of Relationship, 1 vol. 2009. 160p. pap. 24.95 *(978-1-60836-510-4(7))* PublishAmerica, Inc.

Sicker, Martin. The Theopolitical Discourses of Moses: The Book of Deuteronomy in Political Perspective (Part 2) 2009. 332p. pap. 22.95 *(978-1-4401-4515-5(6))* iUniverse, Inc.

Simpson, A. B. Genesis y Exodo: Christ in the Bible: Genesis. (SPA.). *(978-84-7645-001-7(X)*, 223080) Clie, Editorial.

Singh Boora, Kulwant. Oneness & Monotheism: Book 2. 2009. 132p. pap. 30.00 *(978-1-4490-1338-7(4))* AuthorHouse.

Ska, Jean Louis. Exegesis of the Pentateuch: Exegetical Studies & Basic Questions. 2009. (Forschungen zum Alten Testament Ser.). (Illus.). 280p. 175.00 *(978-3-16-149905-0(0))* Mohr Siebeck GmbH & Co. KG DEU. Dist: Eisenbrauns, Inc.

—Introduction to Reading the Pentateuch. 2006. 285p. pap. 29.50 *(978-1-57506-122-1(8))* Eisenbrauns, Inc.

Smith, George. The Chaldean Account of Genesis. 2010. (ENG.). 354p. pap. 32.75 *(978-1-176-54131-3(5))* 2010. 378p. pap. 33.75 *(978-1-148-27416-4(2))* 2009. 344p. 36.99 *(978-1-116-50432-3(4))* 2009. 344p. 32.99 *(978-1-116-50433-0(2))* 2009. (ENG.). 342p. pap. 24.99 *(978-1-116-50436-1(7)*, BiblioLife) 2009. (ENG.). 342p. pap. 23.99 *(978-1-116-50437-8(5)*, BiblioLife) 2009. 344p. pap. 31.75 *(978-1-116-50435-4(9))* 2009. 344p. pap. 32.75 *(978-1-116-50434-7(0))* BiblioBazaar.

—The Chaldean Account of Genesis. 2009. 206p. pap. 19.99 *(978-1-150-16381-4(X))* General Bks. LLC.

Smith, Mark S. The Priestly Vision of Genesis 1. 2009. 176p. pap. 25.00 *(978-0-8006-6373-5(X)*, Fortress Pr.) Augsburg Fortress, Pubs.

Soloveitchik, Joseph B., et al. Abraham's Journey: Reflections on the Life of the Founding Patriarch. 2008. 252p. 25.00 *(978-1-60280-004-5(9))* Ktav Publishing Hse., Inc.

Somers, Gayle. Genesis Part II: God & His Family: Genesis 12-50, Pt. 2. 2006. (Hearts Aflame Ser.). 171p. per. 13.99 *(978-1-931018-33-3(2))* Emmaus Road Publishing.

Sonek, Krzysztof. Truth, Beauty, & Goodness in Biblical Narratives: A Hermeneutical Study of Genesis 21.1-21. 2009. (Beihefte zur Zeitschrift far die alttestamentliche Wissenschaft Ser.). (ENG.). 304p. 126.00 *(978-3-11-020974-7(8))* De Gruyter, Walter Inc.

Stern, Stephen J. The Unbinding of Isaac. 2011. *(978-1-4331-1160-0(8))* Lang, Peter Publishing, Inc.

Stone, Michael E., et al, eds. Noah & His Book(S) 2010. (ENG.). 394p. pap. 45.95 *(978-1-58983-488-0(7))* Society of Biblical Literature.

Taylor, Paul. The Six Days of Genesis. 2007. (Illus.). 221p. per. 13.99 *(978-0-89051-499-3(2))* Master Bks.

Thelle, Rannfrid Irene. Approaches to the 'Chosen Place' Accessing a Biblical Concept. 2011. (ENG.). 256p. (gr. 17). 140.00 ***(978-0-567-46807-9(0)***, T&T Clark) Continuum International Publishing Group, Ltd. GBR. Dist: National Bk. Network.

Thom, David. Apocalyptic Beasts with an Explanation A. 2006. pap. 36.95 *(978-1-4286-4708-4(2))* Kessinger Publishing, LLC.

Thomas, Matthew A. These Are the Generations: Identity, Covenant & the Toledot Formula. 2011. (Library Hebrew Bible/Old Testament Studies). (ENG.). 176p. 120.00 *(978-0-567-15141-4(7)*, T&T Clark Int'l) Continuum International Publishing Group, Ltd. GBR. Dist: National Bk. Network.

Thompson, Jim. The Physics of Genesis. 2008. 216p. pap. 17.99 *(978-1-4141-1160-5(6))* Pleasant Word.

Thomson, Jeremy. Genesis: Foundations of Reality. 2006. 72p. *(978-1-85345-404-2(4))* Crusade for World Revival.

Tigay, Jeffrey H., et al. Mishneh Todah: Studies in Deuteronomy & Its Cultural Environment: in Honor of Jeffrey H. Tigay. 2009. 69.50 *(978-1-57506-156-6(2))* Eisenbrauns, Inc.

Timmer, Daniel C. Creation, Tabernacle, & Sabbath: The Sabbath Frame of Exodus 31:12-17; 35:1-3 in Exegetical & Theological Perspective. 2009. (Forschungen Zur Religion und Literatur des Alten & Neuen Testament Ser.). (ENG.). 236p. (C). 98.00 *(978-3-525-53091-7(9))* Vandenhoeck & Ruprecht GmbH & Co. KG DEU. Dist: ISD.

Tjen, Anwar. On Conditionals in the Greek Pentateuch: A Study of Translation Syntax, Vol. 515. 2010. 216p. E-Book *(978-0-567-07483-6(8)*, T&T Clark) Continuum International Publishing Group, Ltd.

—On Conditionals in the Greek Pentateuch: A Study of Translation Syntax. (ENG.). 288p. 2012. pap. 49.95 ***(978-0-567-64286-8(0))*** Vol. 515. 2010. 130.00 *(978-0-567-57546-3(2))* Continuum International Publishing Group, Ltd. GBR. (T&T Clark Int'l). Dist: National Bk. Network.

Trevaskis, Leigh M. Holiness, Ethics & Ritual in Leviticus. 2011. 300p. ***(978-1-906055-98-1(X))*** Sheffield Phoenix Pr.

Troyer, Dwight O. Genesis 1-2-3. 2007. 208p. 24.99 *(978-1-60477-138-1(0))*; per. 14.99 *(978-1-60477-137-4(2))* Xulon Pr., Inc.

Vassar, John S. Recalling a Story Once Told: An Intertextual Reading of the Psalter & the Pentateuch. 2007. 192p. 45.00 *(978-0-88146-051-3(6))* Mercer Univ. Pr.

Vogt, Peter & Vogt, Peter T. Interpreting the Pentateuch: An Exegetical Handbook, 1 vol. 2009. (Handbook on Old Testament Exegesis Ser.). (ENG.). 224p. pap. 21.99 *(978-0-8254-2762-6(2))* Kregel Pubns.

Vogt, Peter T. Deuteronomic Theology & the Significance of Torah: A Reappraisal. 2006. 242p. 37.50 *(978-1-57506-107-8(4))* Eisenbrauns, Inc.

Vrolijk, Paul. Jacob's Wealth: An Examination into the Nature & Role of Material Possessions in the Jacob- Cycle (Gen 25:19-35:29) 2011. (Vetus Testamentum Supplements Ser.). (Illus.). XIV, 366p. *(978-90-04-20329-7(X))* BRILL.

Walton, John H. Genesis 1 As Ancient Cosmology. 2011. ***(978-1-57506-216-7(X))*** Eisenbrauns, Inc.

Walton, John H. The Lost World of Genesis One: Ancient Cosmology & the Origins Debate, 1 vol. 2009. (ENG.). 192p. pap. 16.00 *(978-0-8308-3704-5(3),* IVP Acad.) InterVarsity Pr.

Walton, John H., et al. Genesis, Exodus, Leviticus, Numbers, Deuteronomy, 1 vol. Carpenter, Eugene, ed. 2009. (Zondervan Illustrated Bible Backgrounds Commentary Ser.). (ENG.). 624p. 49.99 *(978-0-310-25573-4(2))* Zondervan.

Wardlaw, Terrance Randall, Jr. Conceptualizing Words for God Within the Pentateuch: A Cognitive-Semantic Investigation in Literary Context. 2008. (Library of Hebrew Bible/Old Testament Studies, the Ser.). (ENG., Illus.). 364p. 145.00 *(978-0-567-02737-5(6),* T&T Clark Int'l) Continuum International Publishing Group, Ltd. GBR. Dist: National Bk. Network.

Waters, Guy Prentiss. End of Deuteronomy in the Epistles of Paul. 2006. (Wissenshaftliche Untersuchungen zum Neuen Testament Ser.: 221). 302p. (Orig.). pap. 99.50 *(978-3-16-148891-7(1))* Mohr Siebeck GmbH & Co. KG DEU. Dist: Coronet Bks.

Weir, Heather E., ed. Let Her Speak for Herself: Nineteenth-Century Women Writing on Women in Genesis. 2006. (Illus.). 513p. per. 44.95 *(978-1-932792-53-9(8))* Baylor Univ. Pr.

Weisblum, Moshe Pinchas & Visblum, Mosheh. The Hermeneutics of Medieval Jewish Thought: Understanding the Linguistic Codes of Rashi & Nahmanides. 2007. 272p. *(978-0-7734-5288-6(5))* Mellen, Edwin Pr., The.

Wenham, Gordon J., et al, eds. He Swore an Oath: Biblical Themes from Genesis 12-50. 2nd ed. 2007. 222p. pap. 24.00 *(978-1-55635-732-9(X))* Wipf & Stock Pubs.

Westermann, Claus & Westermann. Genesis. Green, David E., tr. (ENG.). 356p. 60.00 *(978-0-567-04390-0(8),* Burns & Oates) Continuum International Publishing Group, Ltd. GBR. Dist: National Bk. Network.

Whitcomb, John. El Diluvio Del Genesis: The Genesis Flood. (SPA.). 800p. *(978-84-7228-717-4(3),* 220285) Clie, Editorial.

Whitcomb, John C. The World That Perished. pap. 9.99 *(978-0-88469-059-7(8))* BMH Bks.

Whitcomb, John C. & Morris, Henry M. The Genesis Flood. pap. 14.99 *(978-0-88469-067-2(9))* BMH Bks.

Wiebe, Phillip H. Starting with God: Studies in the Book of Genesis. 94p. pap. 3.60 *(978-0-921788-70-6(3))* Kindred Productions.

Willis, John T. The Role of Exodus 4: 24-26 in the Book of Exodus. 2010. (ENG & HEB.). 230p. pap. *(978-3-0343-0462-7(5))* Lang, Peter.

Willis, Mike. BTB Exodus & Leviticus. 2007. pap. 7.49 *(978-1-58427-189-5(2))* Guardian of Truth Foundation.

—Numbers-Deuteronomy. 2007. pap. 7.99 *(978-1-58427-203-8(1))* Guardian of Truth Foundation.

Wilson, Edmund. Israel & the Dead Sea Scrolls. 2011. (ENG.). 440p. pap. 34.95 ***(978-1-4128-4248-8(4))*** Transaction Pubs.

Wilson, Lindsay. Joseph, Wise & Otherwise: The Intersection of Wisdom & Covenant in Genesis 37-50. 2007. (Paternoster Biblical Monographs: Ser.). 374p. pap. 37.00 *(978-1-59752-773-6(4),* Wipf and Stock) Wipf & Stock Pubs.

Winkler, Gary. Let There Be... & There Was. 2009. 120p. pap. 14.95 *(978-0-557-09025-9(3))* Lulu Enterprises Inc.

Wood-Langford, Eve. Eden: The Buried Treasure. 2009. 296p. pap. 15.49 *(978-1-4490-1952-5(8))* AuthorHouse.

Woolford, P. M. The Genesis Grid. 2010. (Illus.). 468p. pap. 20.49 *(978-1-4490-8117-1(7))* AuthorHouse.

Yager, Michael. The God Manifesto: How Jews, Christians, & Muslims Can Return to Their God. 2007. 84p. per. 10.95 *(978-0-595-44562-2(4))* iUniverse, Inc.

Yamada, Frank M. Configurations of Rape in the Hebrew Bible: A Literary Analysis of Three Rape Narratives. 2007. (Studies in Biblical Literature Ser.). (C). 63.95 *(978-1-4331-0167-0(X))* Lang, Peter Publishing, Inc.

Yeshiva University Rabbis & Professors. Mitokh Ha'Ohel: Volume II: Essays on the Weekly Haftara Reading, 2, Vol. 2. Feldman, Rabbi Daniel Z. & Halpern, Stuart W., eds. 2011. 745p. 29.95 ***(978-1-61329-031-6(4),*** Maggid) Toby Pr. LLC, The.

Yoreh, Tzemah L. The First Book of God. 2010. (Beihefte zur Zeitschrift für die alttestamentliche Wissenschaft Ser.). (ENG.). XII, 293p. 126.00 *(978-3-11-022167-1(5));* 196.00 ***(978-3-11-173204-6(5))*** De Gruyter, Walter Inc.

Zeelander, Susan. Closure in Biblical Narrative. 2012. (Biblical Interpretation Ser.). (ENG., Illus.). xiii, 232p. ***(978-90-04-21822-2(X))*** BRILL.

Zornberg, Avivah Gottlieb. The Particulars of Rapture: Reflections on Exodus. 2011. (ENG.). 592p. pap. 21.95 *(978-0-8052-1237-2(X),* Knopf) Knopf Doubleday Publishing Group.

BIBLE—CRITICISM, INTERPRETATION, ETC.—O. T. POETICAL BOOKS

Here are entered works on the poetical books as a whole, as well as books on one or more of the following: Job, Ecclesiastes, Psalms, Proverbs, Song of Solomon. For works on Lamentations see Bible—Criticism, Interpretation, etc.—O. T. Prophets.

Abbott, H. Mark. A Psalm-Shaped Life. 2011. 136p. pap. 17.00 ***(978-1-61097-421-9(2),*** Wipf and Stock) Wipf & Stock Pubs.

Ahearne-Kroll, Stephen. The Psalms of Lament in Mark's Passion: Jesus' Davidic Suffering. 2010. (Society for New Testament Studies Monograph Ser.). (ENG.). 256p. pap. 29.00 *(978-0-521-13040-0(9))* Cambridge Univ. Pr.

Ahearne-Kroll, Stephen P. The Psalms of Lament in Mark's Passion: Jesus' Davidic Suffering. 2007. (Society for New Testament Studies Monograph Ser.). (ENG.). 254p. 99.00 *(978-0-521-88191-3(9))* Cambridge Univ. Pr.

Alexander, Joseph A. The Psalms Translated & Explained. 2007. (ENG.). 320p. 45.95 *(978-0-548-34794-2(8));* per. 30.95 *(978-0-548-29018-7(0))* Kessinger Publishing, LLC.

Alford, C. Fred. After the Holocaust: The Book of Job, Primo Levi, & the Path to Affliction. 2009. (ENG.). 184p. (C). 85.00 *(978-0-521-76632-6(X));* pap. 24.99 *(978-0-521-74706-6(6))* Cambridge Univ. Pr.

Allender, Dan B. & Longman, Tremper, III. Breaking the Idols of Your Heart: How to Navigate the Temptations of Life. 2007. (ENG.). 191p. per. 15.00 *(978-0-8308-3441-9(9),* IVP Bks.) InterVarsity Pr.

Ansberry, Christopher B. Be Wise, My Son, & Make My Heart Glad: An Exploration of the Courtly Nature of the Book of Proverbs. (Beihefte zur Zeitschrift fur die alttestamentliche Wissenschaft Ser.). (ENG., XVIII, 240p. 2011. Illus.). 210.00 ***(978-3-11-218875-0(6))*** 2010. 140.00 ***(978-3-11-024790-9(9))*** De Gruyter, Walter Inc.

Aquilina, Mik & Bailey, Christopher. Praying the Psalms with the Early Christians: Ancient Songs for Modern Hearts. 2009. 200p. pap. 12.95 *(978-1-59325-155-0(6))* Word Among Us Pr.

Arthur, Kay & De Lacy, Pete. Walking with God in Every Season: Ecclesiastes/Song of Solomon/Lamentations. 2010. (New Inductive Study Ser.). 112p. pap. 8.99 *(978-0-7369-2236-4(9))* Harvest Hse. Pubs.

Ash, Christopher. Bible Delight: Heartbeat of the Word of God - Psalm 119 for the Bible Teacher & Hearer. 2008. (ENG.). 208p. pap. 12.99 *(978-1-84550-360-4(0))* Christian Focus Pubns. GBR. Dist: STL Distribution North America.

—Out of the Storm: Grappling with God in the Book of Job. 2006. (ENG.). 112p. per. *(978-1-57383-387-5(8),* Regent College Publishing) Regent College Publishing.

Assis, Elie. Flashes of Fire: A Literary Analysis of the Song of Songs. 2009. (Library of Hebrew Bible/Old Testament Studies, the Ser.). (ENG., Illus.). 304p. 130.00 *(978-0-567-02764-1(3),* T&T Clark Int'l) Continuum International Publishing Group, Ltd. GBR. Dist: National Bk. Network.

Baildam, John D. Paradisal Love: Johann Gottfried Herder & the Song of Songs. 2009. (Library of Hebrew Bible/Old Testament Studies, the Ser.). (ENG.). 368p. 60.00 *(978-1-4411-4533-8(8),* T&T Clark) Continuum International Publishing Group, Ltd. GBR. Dist: National Bk. Network.

Baker Publishing Group Staff. Psalms to Soothe a Woman's Heart, 1 vol. 2009. 384p. 14.99 *(978-0-7642-0551-4(X))* Bethany Hse. Pubs.

Barker, James. Song of Solomon. 2009. 130p. pap. 11.99 *(978-0-9824931-4-4(2))* Faithful Life Pubs.

Barnes, Albert. Notes, Critical, Illustrative & Practical on the Book of Job, with a New Translation & an Introductory Dissertation. 2006. (ENG.). 388p. per. 26.99 *(978-1-4255-4140-8(2));* (ENG.). 388p. per. 26.99 *(978-1-4255-4139-2(9));* (ENG.). 444p. per. 26.99 *(978-1-4255-4887-2(3));* 440p. per. 26.99 *(978-1-4255-4853-7(9))* MPublishing.

Baroody, Anees T. Our Man of Patience. 2009. 122p. 24.99 *(978-1-115-08131-3(4));* 28.99 *(978-1-115-08133-7(0))* BiblioBazaar.

—Our Man of Patience. 2007. (ENG.). 122p. 35.95 *(978-0-548-06497-9(0))* Kessinger Publishing, LLC.

Barrett, Valerie. The Word Search Puzzle Book of Ecclesiastes. Lockman Foundation, tr. 2007. 88p. (YA). *(978-0-9798573-0-0(9))* Alberlynn Co.

Baumgartner, Walter. Jeremiah's Poems of Lament. 115p. pap. *(978-1-85075-115-1(3),* Burns & Oates) Continuum International Publishing Group, Ltd.

Becking, Bob & Peels, Eric, eds. Psalms & Prayers: Papers Read at the Joint Meeting of the Society of Old Testament Study & the Oud Testamentische Werkgezelschap in Nederland en België, Apeldoorn August 2006. 2007. (Oudtestamentische Studien Ser.: Vol. 55). 306p. *(978-90-04-16032-3(9))* BRILL.

Beckstrand, Robert G. Companion to the Psalter: A Devotional Guide to the Psalms. 2007. 335p. spiral bd. *(978-0-7880-2464-1(7))* CSS Publishing Co.

Beentjes, Pancratius Cornelis, et al. Rewriting Biblical History: Essays on Chronicles & Ben Sira in Honour of Pancratius C. Beentjes de Gruyter. 2011. ***(978-3-11-024093-1(9))*** De Gruyter, Walter Inc.

Belcher, Richard P. Jr. The Messiah & the Psalms: Preaching Christ from All the Psalms. 2006. (ENG.). 288p. per. 19.99 *(978-1-84550-074-0(1),* Mentor) Christian Focus Pubns. GBR. Dist: STL Distribution North America.

Berlejung, A., et al, eds. The Language of Qohelet in its Context: Essays in Honour of Prof. A. Schoors on the Occasion of his Seventieth Birthday. 2007. (Orientalia Lovaniensia Analecta Ser.). (ENG.). 241p. (C). 126.00 *(978-90-429-1910-5(8))* Peeters Pubs. & Booksellers BEL. Dist: Brown, David Bk. Co., The.

Berry, Donald K. Psalms & their Readers: Interpretive Strategies for Psalm 18. 2009. (Library of Hebrew Bible/Old Testament Studies, the Ser.). (ENG.). 160p. 29.95 *(978-0-567-31707-0(2),* T&T Clark) Continuum International Publishing Group, Ltd. GBR. Dist: National Bk. Network.

Bester, Dorte. Körperbilder in den Psalmen: Studien zu Psalm 22 und verwandten Texten. 2007. 304p. (C). pap. 75.00 *(978-3-16-149361-4(3))* Mohr Siebeck GmbH & Co. KG DEU. Dist: Eisenbrauns, Inc.

Bolin, Thomas. Vive Memor Mortis: Qoheleth & the Wisdom of his Day. (BibleWorld Ser.). (ENG.). (C). 2012. 95.00 *(978-1-84553-072-3(1))* 2011. pap. 26.95 *(978-1-84553-073-0(X))* Equinox Publishing Ltd. GBR. Dist: ISD.

Boss, Jeffrey. Human Consciousness of God in the Book of Job: A Theological & Psychological Commentary. 2010. (ENG.). 304p. 70.00 *(978-0-567-25389-7(9),* T&T Clark Int'l) Continuum International Publishing Group, Ltd. GBR. Dist: National Bk. Network.

Boteler, Lori. A Common Sens Approach toJob. 2007. 105p. per. 20.00 *(978-0-9798207-1-7(5))* LoJo Publishing.

Bridges, Charles. An Exposition of the Book of Proverbs V1. 2007. (ENG.). 496p. 53.95 *(978-0-548-09683-3(X))* Kessinger Publishing, LLC.

Brueggemann, Walter. Truth-Telling as Subversive Obedience. Hanson, K. C., ed. 2011. 126p. pap. 16.00 ***(978-1-61097-234-5(1),*** Cascade Bks.) Wipf & Stock Pubs.

Bullock, C. Hassell. An Introduction to the Old Testament Poetic Books. rev. ed. 2007. (ENG., Illus.). 336p. 33.99 *(978-0-8024-4157-7(2))* Moody Pubs.

Burnett. Diachronic & Synchronic: Reading the Psalms in Real Time - Proceedings of the Baylor Symposium on the Book of Psalms. 2007. (Library of Hebrew Bible/Old Testament Studies, the Ser.). (ENG., Illus.). 224p. 130.00 *(978-0-567-02686-6(8),* T&T Clark Int'l) Continuum International Publishing Group, Ltd. GBR. Dist: National Bk. Network.

Burrell, David B. Deconstructing Theodicy: Why Job Has Nothing to Say to the Puzzle of Suffering. 2008. 144p. (C). pap. 20.00 *(978-1-58743-222-4(6))* Brazos Pr.

Camp, Claudia V. Wise, Strange & Holy: The Strange Woman & the Making of the Bible. 2009. (Library of Hebrew Bible/Old Testament Studies, the Ser.). (ENG.). 376p. 60.00 *(978-0-567-19510-4(4),* T&T Clark) Continuum International Publishing Group, Ltd. GBR. Dist: National Bk. Network.

Canadian Biotechnology Advisory Committee Staff & Brueggemann, Walter. Praying the Psalms: Engaging Scripture & the Life of the Spirit. 2nd ed. 2007. (Illus.). 116p. pap. 14.00 *(978-1-55635-283-6(2),* Cascade Bks.) Wipf & Stock Pubs.

Carbajosa, Ignacio. The Character of the Syriac Version of Psalms: A Study of Psalms 90-150 in the Peshitta. 2008. (Monographs of the Peshitta Institute Leiden Ser.). 456p. (C). *(978-90-04-17056-8(1))* BRILL.

Carter, George. Book of Psalms. 2008. 332p. pap. 21.99 *(978-1-60647-878-3(8))* Xulon Pr., Inc.

Cartledge, Tony & Cartledge, Jan. Job: Into the Fire, Out of the Ashes. 2007. (Annual Bible Study Ser.). (Illus.). 79p. pap. 4.00 *(978-1-57312-497-3(4))* Smyth & Helwys Publishing, Inc.

Cartledge, Tony W. & Cartledge, Jan. Job: Into the Fire, Out of the Ashes. 2007. *(978-1-57312-496-6(6))* Smyth & Helwys Publishing, Inc.

Chester, Tim. Soul Songs: Exploring Love, Temptation, Guilt & Fear from the Psalms. 2010. 56p. pap. *(978-1-904889-96-0(4))* Good Bk. Co.

Cheyne, T. K. Origin & Religious Contents of the Psa. 2006. pap. 42.95 *(978-1-4286-3984-3(5))* Kessinger Publishing, LLC.

Chiel, Samuel & Dreher, Henry. The Healing Power of Psalms: Renewal, Hope & Acceptance from the World's Most Beloved Ancient Verses. 2007. (ENG.). 256p. per. 14.00 *(978-1-60094-040-8(4))* Da Capo Pr., Inc.

Clairmont, Patsy. Kaleidoscope of Proverbs: Bits & Pieces Held to the Light, 0 vols. 2010. 208p. 16.99 *(978-1-4002-0270-6(1))* Nelson, Thomas Inc.

Clarke, David. Kiss Me Like You Mean It: Solomon's Crazy in Love How-to Manual. 2009. 240p. pap. 14.99 *(978-0-8007-3329-2(0))* Revell.

Cook, Gwendolyn Ann. The Power to Believe: It's not what you need, It's what you Believe! 2009. 160p. 22.49 *(978-1-4490-3053-7(X));* pap. 16.99 *(978-1-4490-3052-0(1))* AuthorHouse.

Cottrill, Amy C. Language, Power, & Identity in the Lament Psalms of the Individual. 2008. (Library of Hebrew Bible/Old Testament Studies, the Ser.). (ENG.). 192p. 130.00 *(978-0-567-02728-3(7),* T&T Clark Int'l) Continuum International Publishing Group, Ltd. GBR. Dist: National Bk. Network.

Cox, Claude E. & Cox, C. E. Armenian Job: Reconstructed Greek Text, Critical Edition of the Armenian with English Translation. 2006. (Hebrew University Armenian Studies: Vol. 8). (ARM, ENG & GEC.). 446p. (C). pap. 85.00 *(978-90-429-1726-2(1))* Peeters Pubs. & Booksellers BEL. Dist: Brown, David Bk. Co., The.

Creach, Jerome F. D. The Destiny of the Righteous in the Psalms: The Destiny of the Righteous in the Psalms. 2008. (C). 21.99 *(978-0-8272-0634-2(8))* Chalice Pr.

Cumming, Charles G. Assyrian & Hebrew Hymns of Praise. (Columbia University, Oriental Studies: No. 12). reprint ed. 32.50 *(978-0-404-50502-8(3))* AMS Pr., Inc.

Cumming, Charles Gordon. The Assyrian & Hebrew Hymns of Praise. 2007. (Gorgias Theological Library: 22). 124.00 *(978-1-59333-669-1(1))* Gorgias Pr., LLC.

Daly-Denton, Margaret. Psalm-shaped Prayerfulness. 2011. 224p. pap. 24.95 ***(978-0-8146-3402-8(8))*** Liturgical Pr.

Daly-Denton, Margaret. Psalm-Shaped Prayerfulness: A Guide to the Christian Reception of the Psalms. 2011. (ENG.). 226p. pap. 26.95 *(978-1-85607-715-6(2))* Columba Pr. IRL. Dist: Dufour Editions, Inc.

Dell, Katharine. Seeking a Life That Matters: Wisdom for Today from the Book of Proverbs. 128p. pap. 13.00 *(978-0-232-52402-4(5))* Abingdon Pr.

Dell, Katharine J. The Book of Proverbs in Social & Theological Context. 2009. (ENG.). 236p. pap. 38.00 *(978-0-521-12106-4(X))* Cambridge Univ. Pr.

Dell, Katherine J. The Book of Job as Sceptical Literature. (Beihefte zur Zeitschrift far die alttestamentliche Wissenschaft Ser.). (ENG.). X, 259p. 195.00 ***(978-3-11-187694-8(2))*** De Gruyter, Walter Inc.

Dillon, Emile Joseph. The Sceptics of the Old Testament: Job - Koheleth - Agur. 2007. (ENG.). 214p. pap. 20.99 *(978-1-4264-3007-7(8));* 248p. pap. 22.99 *(978-1-4264-2954-5(1))* BiblioBazaar.

—The Sceptics of the Old Testament: Job - Koheleth - Agur. 2007. (ENG.). 164p. per. *(978-1-4068-6125-9(1))* Echo Library.

Doukhan, Jacques. Ecclesiastes: All Is Vanity. 2006. 128p. 1.97 *(978-0-8163-2177-3(9))* Pacific Pr. Publishing Assn.

Dow, Thomas Edward. When Storms Come: A Christian Look at Job. 2010. (McMaster Ministry Studies Ser.). 154p. pap. 18.00 *(978-1-60899-276-8(4),* Pickwick Pubns.) Wipf & Stock Pubs.

Drace, Jerry. From the Heart of a Father: Godly Counsel from Proverbs, 1 vol. 2009. (ENG.). 96p. 12.95 *(978-1-58980-749-5(9))* Pelican Publishing Co., Inc.

Eaton, John H. Psalms of the Way & the Kingdom: A Conference with the Commentators. 2009. (Library of Hebrew Bible/Old Testament Studies, the Ser.). (ENG.). 120p. 27.95 *(978-0-567-27489-2(6),* T&T Clark) Continuum International Publishing Group, Ltd. GBR. Dist: National Bk. Network.

Edwards, Sue. Proverbs: Ancient Wisdom for a Postmodern World, 1 vol. 2007. (Sue Edwards Inductive Bible Study Ser.). 96p. pap. 12.99 *(978-0-8254-2548-6(4));* pap. 12.99 *(978-0-8254-2547-9(6))* Kregel Pubns.

Egwim, S. C. A Contextual & Cross-cultural Study of Psalm 109. 2011. (Biblical Tools & Studies). (ENG.). 399p. (C). 99.00 ***(978-90-429-2468-0(3))*** Peeters Pubs. & Booksellers BEL. Dist: Brown, David Bk. Co., The.

Elliott, Mark W. The Song of Songs & Christology in the Early Church, 381 - 451. 2011. 216p. pap. 24.00 ***(978-1-61097-154-6(X),*** Wipf and Stock) Wipf & Stock Pubs.

Emerton, John Adney, et al. Genesis, Isaiah, & Psalms: A Festschrift to Honour Professor John Emerton for His Eightieth Birthday. 2010. 210p. *(978-90-04-18231-8(4))* BRILL.

Estes, Daniel J. Handbook on the Wisdom Books & Psalms, 1 vol. 2010. (ENG.). 448p. (C). pap. 34.99 *(978-0-8010-3388-4(X))* Baker Academic.

Farrar, Steve. Gettin' There - A Passage Through the Psalms: How a Man Finds His Way on the Trail of Life. 2007. (ENG.). 252p. pap. 16.99 *(978-1-59052-987-4(1),* Multnomah) Doubleday Religious Publishing Group, The.

Firth, David G. Surrendering Retribution in the Psalms: Responses to Violence in Individual Complaints. 2007. (Paternoster Biblical Monographs: Ser.). 192p. pap. 22.00 *(978-1-59752-758-3(0),* Wipf and Stock) Wipf & Stock Pubs.

Fisher, Loren R. The Many Voices of Job. 2009. 132p. pap. 16.00 *(978-1-60608-656-8(1),* Cascade Bks.) Wipf & Stock Pubs.

Fitzpatrick, Elyse. A Steadfast Heart: Experiencing God's Comfort in Life's Storms. 2006. 158p. pap. 12.99 incl. audio compact disk *(978-0-87552-747-5(7))* P & R Publishing.

Fontaine, Carole. Smooth Words: Women, Proverbs, & Performance in Biblical Wisdom. 2009. (Library of Hebrew Bible/Old Testament Studies, the Ser.). (ENG.). 310p. 49.95 *(978-0-567-24315-7(X),* T&T Clark) Continuum International Publishing Group, Ltd. GBR. Dist: National Bk. Network.

Ford, Yannick. The Gospel in Job. 2007. 112p. *(978-0-901860-77-4(8));* per. *(978-0-901860-76-7(X))* Scripture Truth Pubns.

Forti, Tova L. Animal Imagery in the Book of Proverbs. 2008. (Vetus Testamentum Supplements Ser.). 193p. *(978-90-04-16287-7(9))* BRILL.

Foster, Robert L. & Howard, David M., Jr. My Words Are Lovely: Studies in the Rhetoric of the Psalms. Howard, David M., Jr., ed. 2008. (Library of Hebrew Bible/Old Testament Studies, the Ser.). (ENG.). 356p. 140.00 *(978-0-567-02653-8(1),* T&T Clark Int'l) Continuum International Publishing Group, Ltd. GBR. Dist: National Bk. Network.

Fox, Michael V. A Time to Tear down & a Time to Build Up: A Rereading of Ecclesiastes. 2010. 440p. pap. 48.00 *(978-1-60899-496-0(1),* Wipf and Stock) Wipf & Stock Pubs.

Fryar, Jane L. I Have Set My King on Zion: A Women's Bible Study Devotional. 2008. (New Song Ser.). (Illus.). 224p. pap. 12.99 *(978-0-7586-1560-2(4))* Concordia Publishing Hse.

—Planted by Streams of Water: A Women's Bible Study Devotional. 2008. (New Song Ser.). (Illus.). 224p. pap. 12.99 *(978-0-7586-1559-6(0))* Concordia Publishing Hse.

Futato, Mark David & Futato, Mark D. Interpreting the Psalms: An Exegetical Handbook, 1 vol. 2007. (Handbooks for Old Testament Exegesis Ser.). (Illus.). 240p. pap. 20.99 *(978-0-8254-2765-7(7))* Kregel Pubns.

Gallagher, Steve. A Lamp unto My Feet: A 12-Week Study Through Psalm 119. 2006. (Walk Ser.). (ENG.). 144p. 10.99 *(978-0-9758832-5-9(9))* Pure Life Ministries.

Geering, Lloyd. Such Is Life! 2010. 220p. pap. 20.00 *(978-1-59815-023-0(5))* Polebridge Pr.

George, Elizabeth. Quiet Confidence for a Woman's Heart: The Power of God's Restoration & Healing. 2009. 240p. pap. 13.99 *(978-0-7369-2389-7(6))* Harvest Hse. Pubs.

Giddens, Pastor/Missionary Donald Louis. Jesus in the Psalms. 2007. 286p. pap. 28.50 *(978-1-4357-0124-3(0))* Lulu Enterprises Inc.

Giffard Smith, Sheila. Talking & Walking with God. 2008. 336p. per. *(978-1-84748-264-8(3))* Athena Pr.

Girard, René. Job: The Victim of His People. Freccero, Yvonne, tr. from FRE. (ENG.). 173p. *(978-0-485-11304-4(X))* Continuum International Publishing Group, Ltd.

Glickman, Craig. Solomon's Song of Love: Let a Song of Songs Inspire Your Own Love Story. 2009. (ENG.). 256p. pap. 17.95 *(978-1-4391-6842-4(3),* Howard Bks.) Howard Books.

Granerod, Gard. Abraham & Melchizedek: Scribal Activity of Second Temple Times in Genesis 14 & Psalm 110. 2010. (Beihefte Zur Zeitschrift Für Die Alttestamentliche Wissenschaft Ser.). (ENG.). XIV, 317p. 112.00 *(978-3-11-022345-3(7))* De Gruyter, Walter Inc.

Gregory. Gregory the Great on the Song of Songs. 2012. ***(978-0-87907-244-5(X))*** Liturgical Pr.

Groseclose, Win. The Egyptian Hallel Psalms: Reflections on Psalms 113-118. 2008. 143p. pap. 11.49 *(978-0-557-00414-0(4))* Lulu Enterprises Inc.

B

Guthrie, Nancy. Holding on to Hope: A Pathway Through Suffering to the Heart of God. 2006. (ENG.). 192p. per. 9.99 *(978-1-4143-1296-5(2))* Tyndale Hse. Pubs.

Hahn, Kimberly. Chosen & Cherished: Biblical Wisdom for Your Marriage. annot. ed. 2007. 253p. per. 14.99 *(978-0-86716-848-8(X)*, Servant Bks.) Franciscan Media.

—Chosen & Cherished: Biblical Wisdom for Your Marrige, 3 discs. 2007. 253p. pap. 59.99 *(978-0-86716-859-4(5)*, Servant Bks.) Franciscan Media.

—Graced & Gifted: Biblical Wisdom for the Homemaker's Heart. 2008. 224p. pap. 14.99 *(978-0-86716-891-4(9)*, Fischer Productions); pap. 59.99 incl. DVD *(978-0-86716-901-0(X)*, Servant Bks.) Franciscan Media.

Hahn, Kimberly. Legacy of Love: Biblical Wisdom for Parenting Teens & Young Adults. 2011. ***(978-1-61636-000-9(3)***, Servant Bks.) Franciscan Media.

Hamilton, James. The Royal Preacher. 2006. 396p. per. 26.99 *(978-1-4255-4192-7(5))* MPublishing.

Hamlin, Hannibal. Psalm Culture & Early Modern English Literature. 2007. (ENG.). 304p. pap. 63.00 *(978-0-521-03706-8(9))* Cambridge Univ. Pr.

Handy, Lowell K. Psalm 29 through Time & Tradition. 2011. (ENG.). 148p. pap. 38.00 *(978-0-227-17363-3(5))* Clarke, James Co., Ltd. GBR. Dist: Brown, David Bk. Co., The.

Handy, Lowell K., ed. Psalm 29 through Time & Tradition. 2009. (Princeton Theological Monographs). 160p. pap. 18.00 *(978-1-55635-529-5(7)*, Pickwick Pubns.) Wipf & Stock Pubs.

Haralambakis, Maria. The Testament of Job: Text, Narrative & Reception History. 2012. (Library of Second Temple Studies). (ENG.). 224p. 120.00 ***(978-0-567-57558-6(6)***, T&T Clark Int'l) Continuum International Publishing Group, Ltd. GBR. Dist: National Bk. Network.

Hargreaves, John. Guide to Psalms. 3.00 *(978-0-687-85456-1(3))* Abingdon Pr.

Harper, Lisa. What Every Girl Wants: A Portrait of Perfect Love & Intimacy in the Song of Solomon. 2009. (ENG.). 128p. pap. 9.99 *(978-1-4143-3003-7(0))* Tyndale Hse. Pubs.

Harrington, Daniel J. Why Do We Hope? Images in the Psalms. 2008. 109p. per. 14.95 *(978-0-8146-3085-3(5))* Liturgical Pr.

Hartmann, Dave. Curse God & Die: Four Possible Reasons for the Words of Job's Wife. 2010. pap. 10.99 *(978-1-61566-482-5(3))* Tate Publishing & Enterprises, LLC.

Hatton, Peter T. H. Contradiction in the Book of Proverbs: The Deep Waters of Counsel. 2008. (Society for Old Testament Study Ser.). 214p. 99.95 *(978-0-7546-6304-1(3))* Ashgate Publishing Co.

Hayhoe, D. The Creation Psalms of David. 40p. pap. 2.95 *(978-0-88172-148-5(4))* Believers Bookshelf, Inc.

Hickey, Marilyn. Enjoy Life: Moving Past Everyday Struggles, 0 vols. 2006. 160p. per. 12.99 *(978-1-59951-005-7(7))* Nelson, Thomas Inc.

Hiebert, Robert J. V., et al, eds. Old Greek Psalter: Studies in Honour of Albert Pietersma. 2009. (Library of Hebrew Bible/Old Testament Studies, the Ser.). (ENG.). 352p. 60.00 *(978-0-567-33206-6(3)*, T&T Clark) Continuum International Publishing Group, Ltd. GBR. Dist: National Bk. Network.

Hilber, John W. Cultic Prophecy in the Psalms. (Beihefte zur Zeitschrift far die alttestamentliche Wissenschaft Ser.). (ENG.). XIV, 268p. 225.00 ***(978-3-11-182779-7(8))*** De Gruyter, Walter Inc.

Hoffman, Yair. Blemished Perfection: The Book of Job in Context. 2009. (Library of Hebrew Bible/Old Testament Studies, the Ser.). (ENG.). 360p. 60.00 *(978-1-4411-6877-1(X)*, T&T Clark) Continuum International Publishing Group, Ltd. GBR. Dist: National Bk. Network.

Horovitz, Chaim / T. A Two Thousand Year History of the Influence of the Song of Songs on Religion, Literature, Music, & Art. 2011. (Illus.). 516p. 149.95 *(978-0-7734-3810-1(6))* Mellen, Edwin Pr., The.

Human, Dirk J. Psalms & Mythology. 2007. (T & T Clark Library of Biblical Studies). (ENG., Illus.). 288p. 140.00 *(978-0-567-02982-9(4)*, T&T Clark Int'l) Continuum International Publishing Group, Ltd. GBR. Dist: National Bk. Network.

Human, Dirk J. & Steyn, Gert Jacobus, eds. Psalms & Hebrews: Studies in Reception. (Library Hebrew Bible/Old Testament Studies). (ENG.). 320p. 2012. pap. 49.95 ***(978-0-567-19884-6(7))*** 2010. 130.00 *(978-0-567-15052-3(6))* Continuum International Publishing Group, Ltd. GBR. (T&T Clark Int'l). Dist: National Bk. Network.

Hunt, Patrick. Poetry in the Song of Songs. 2007. (Studies in Biblical Literature Ser.). xi, 368p. (C). 109.95 *(978-0-8204-8192-0(0))* Lang, Peter Publishing, Inc.

Hunter, Alistair G. & Hunter. Introduction to the Psalms. 2008. (T& T Clark Approaches to Biblical Studies). (ENG., Illus.). 168p. 21.95 *(978-0-567-03028-3(8)*, T&T Clark Int'l) Continuum International Publishing Group, Ltd. GBR. Dist: National Bk. Network.

Hunter, John C. Introduction to the Psalms. 2008. (T& T Clark Approaches to Biblical Studies). (ENG.). 168p. 110.00 *(978-0-567-03297-3(3)*, T&T Clark Int'l) Continuum International Publishing Group, Ltd. GBR. Dist: National Bk. Network.

Husband Sr., Bishop Darryl. Discovering the Winner Within. 2009. 183p. pap. 19.97 *(978-0-557-05035-2(9))* Lulu Enterprises Inc.

Inch, Morris A. Pain as a Means of Grace. 2009. 82p. pap. 11.00 *(978-1-60608-527-1(1)*, Wipf and Stock) Wipf & Stock Pubs.

Ironside, Henry A. Los Estudios sobre el Cantar de: Lecutres on the Song of Songs. (SPA.). *(978-84-7645-337-7(X)*, 223435) Clie, Editorial.

Jackson, David R. Crying Out for Vindication: The Gospel According to Job. 2007. (Gospel According to the Old Testament Ser.). 238p. per. 12.99 *(978-1-59638-025-7(X))* P & R Publishing.

Janecko, Benedict. The Psalms: Heartbeat of Life & Worship. 3rd ed. 2007. (ENG.). 96p. pap. 11.00 *(978-0-9773909-3-9(4))* St. Vincent Archabbey Pubns.

Janse, S. You Are My Son: The Reception History of Psalm 2 in Early Judaism & the Early Church. 2009. (Contributions to Biblical Exegesis & Theology Ser.). (ENG., Illus.). 189p. (C). pap. 66.00 *(978-90-429-2127-6(7))* Peeters Pubs. & Booksellers BEL. Dist: Brown, David Bk. Co., The.

Janzen, J. Gerald. At the Scent of Water: The Ground of Hope in the Book of Job. 2009. (ENG., Illus.). 152p. pap. 16.00 *(978-0-8028-4829-1(X))* Eerdmans, William B. Publishing Co.

Jennings, F. C. Meditations on Ecclesiastes. 143p. 5.95 *(978-0-88172-090-7(9))* Believers Bookshelf, Inc.

Jeremiah, David. Searching for Heaven on Earth: How to Find What Really Matters in Life, 0 vols. 2007. 352p. per. 14.99 *(978-0-7852-8920-3(8))* Nelson, Thomas Inc.

Jinkins, Michael. Invitation to Psalms. 2008. (Short-Term Disciple Bible Studies). 136p. per., instr.'s gde. ed. 11.50 *(978-0-687-65071-2(2))* Abingdon Pr.

Johnson, Timothy Jay. Now My Eye Sees You: Unveiling an Apocalyptic Job. 2009. 212p. *(978-1-906055-73-8(4))* Sheffield Phoenix Pr.

Jones, Hywel R. Job. 2007. (Evangelical Press Study Commentary Ser.). 304p. *(978-0-85234-664-8(6))* Evangelical Pr.

Jones, Scott C. Rumors of Wisdom: Job 28 As a Poetry. 2009. (Beihefte Zur Zeitschrift Fur Die Alttestamentliche Wissenschaft Ser.). (ENG.). XX, 293p. 126.00 *(978-3-11-021477-2(6))* De Gruyter, Walter Inc.

Jung, C. G. Answer to Job. 50th ed. 2010. (Jung Extracts Ser.). (ENG.). 144p. pap. 9.95 *(978-0-691-15047-5(8)*, Bollingen) Princeton Univ. Pr.

Kay, Roy. The Ethiopian Prophecy in Black American Letters. 2011. (History of African-American Religions Ser.). (ENG., Illus.). 240p. 74.95 *(978-0-8130-3732-5(8))* Univ. Pr. of Florida.

Keel, Othmar. The Symbolism of the Biblical World: Ancient near Eastern Iconography & the Book of Psalms. Hallett, Timothy J., tr. from GER. 2008. (Illus.). 422p. (C). 39.50 *(978-1-57506-014-9(0))* Eisenbrauns, Inc.

Kellner, Menachem. Torah in the Observatory: Gersonides, Maimonides, Song of Songs. 2010. (Emunot: Jewish Philosophy & Kabbalah Ser.). (ENG.). 376p. 49.00 *(978-1-934843-80-2(6))* Academic Studies Pr.

Kermani, Navid. The Terror of God: Attar, Job & the Metaphysical Revolt. 2011. (ENG.). 240p. 69.95 *(978-0-7456-4526-1(7))*; pap. 26.95 *(978-0-7456-4527-8(5))* Polity Pr. GBR. Dist: Wiley, John & Sons, Inc.

Kerr, Gordon. Mohammedan Controversy. 2006. 228p. per. *(978-1-4067-3674-8(0)*, Hesperides Pr.) Read Bks.

Kidner, Derek. Psalms 73-150, 1 vol. 2009. (Tyndale Old Testament Commentaries Ser.: Volume 16). (ENG.). 242p. pap. 16.00 *(978-0-8308-4216-2(0)*, IVP Acad.) InterVarsity Pr.

Kim, Kyoung-Shik. God Will Judge Each One According to Works: Judgment According to Works & Psalm 62 in Early Judaism & the New Testament. (Beihefte zur Zeitschrift far die neutestamentliche Wissenschaft und die Kunde der älteren Kirche Ser.). (ENG., XIII, 294p. 2011. Illus.). 210.00 ***(978-3-11-218955-9(8))*** 2010. 140.00 *(978-3-11-024776-3(3))* De Gruyter, Walter Inc.

Kim, Seenam. The Coherence of the Collections in the Book of Proverbs. 2007. 308p. pap. 34.00 *(978-1-55635-518-9(1)*, Pickwick Pubns.) Wipf & Stock Pubs.

Kimilike, Lechion Peter. Poverty in the Book of Proverbs: An African Transformational Hermeneutic of Proverbs on Poverty. 2008. (Bible & Theology in Africa Ser.). 394p. (C). 84.95 *(978-1-4331-0327-8(3))* Lang, Peter Publishing, Inc.

Kniep, Seth. Loving God's Word: 7 Strategies for Slaying Bible Apathy. 2007. (ENG.). 286p. per. 15.99 *(978-0-9718306-8-4(1))* LifeSong Pubs.

Kniep Seth. Loving God's Word: 7 Strategies for Slaying Bible Apathy. 2007. 286p. *(978-0-9718306-9-1(X))* LifeSong Pubs.

Knight, George R. Exploring Ecclesiastes & Song of Solomon: A Devotional Commentary. 2006. 234p. per. 16.99 *(978-0-8280-2018-3(3))* Review & Herald Publishing Assn.

Koh, Y. V. Royal Autobiography in the Book of Qoheleth. (Beihefte zur Zeitschrift far die alttestamentliche Wissenschaft Ser.). (ENG.). XVI, 234p. 180.00 ***(978-3-11-185424-3(8))***; 2006. 112.00 *(978-3-11-019228-5(4))* De Gruyter, Walter Inc.

Labahn, A. & Van Hecke, P., eds. Metaphors in the Psalms. 2010. (Bibliotheca Ephemeridum Theologicarum Lovaniensium Ser.). (ENG.). 369p. (C). pap. 111.00 *(978-90-429-2256-3(7))* Peeters Pubs. & Booksellers BEL. Dist: Brown, David Bk. Co., The.

Lange, Karin. Und am Morgen Freude: Die Texte unserer Gedanken und Empfindungen. 2009. (Übergänge. Studien zur Evangelischen und Katholischen Theologie/Religionspädagogik Ser.). (GER.). 376p. 79.95 *(978-3-631-59680-7(4))* Lang, Peter GmbH, Europaischer Verlag der Wissenschaften DEU. Dist: Lang, Peter.

Lebaka, Morakeng Edward Kenneth. Old Testament Psalms & Pedi Psalm-Like Songs. 2010. 236p. pap. *(978-3-639-25445-7(7))* VDM Verlag Dr. Mueller e.K.

Lee, Curtiss F. My Shepherd. 2008. 212p. pap. 15.00 *(978-1-59755-136-6(8)*, Advantage Inspirational) Advantage Bks.

Leithart, Peter J. Solomon among the Postmoderns. 2008. 176p. (C). pap. 22.00 *(978-1-58743-204-0(8))* Brazos Pr.

Lichtenstein, Aaron. The Book of Psalms in Plain English: A Contemporary Reading of Tehillim. 2007. 201p. *(978-965-7108-86-4(1))* Urim Pubns.

Lioy, Dan. The Divine Sabotage: An Expositional Journey Through Ecclesiastes. 2008. 192p. pap. 22.00 *(978-1-55635-961-3(6))* Wipf & Stock Pubs.

Lucado, Max. Safe in the Shepherd's Arms: Hope & Encouragement from Psalm 23, 0 vols. 2010. 144p. 12.99 *(978-1-4041-8771-9(5))* Nelson, Thomas Inc.

Lyke, Larry. I Will Espouse You Forever: The Song of Songs & the Theology of Love in the Hebrew Bible. 2007. 142p. pap. 19.00 *(978-0-687-64574-9(3))* Abingdon Pr.

MacCallum, Jess. I Married Wonder Woman ... Now What? A Superhero's Guide for Leading & Loving the Proverbs 31 Wife. 2007. (Marriage Ser.). (Illus.). 128p. per. 9.99 *(978-0-7847-1945-9(4))* Standard Publishing.

Macias, Kathi. How Can I Run a Tight Ship When I'm Surrounded by Loose Cannons? Proverbs 31 Discoveries for Yielding to the Master of the Seas. 2009. (ENG.). 208p. pap. 13.99 *(978-1-59669-204-6(9))* New Hope Pubs.

Maclaren, Alexander. The Life of David: As Reflected in His Psalms. 2007. (ENG.). 144p. pap. 18.99 *(978-1-4346-4299-8(2))*; 156p. pap. 21.99 *(978-1-4346-4300-1(X))* BiblioBazaar.

Magdalene, F. Rachel. On the Scales of Righteousness: Neo-Babylonian Trial Law & the Book of Job. 2007. (Brown Judaic Studies). *(978-1-930675-44-5(5))* Brown Judaic Studies.

Manning, E. Nathan. Hesiod & the Hebrews. 2010. 96p. pap. *(978-3-639-14820-6(7))* VDM Verlag Dr. Mueller e.K.

McCann, J. Clinton. Great Psalms of the Bible. 2009. (ENG.). 128p. pap. 17.00 *(978-0-664-23176-7(4))* Westminster John Knox Pr.

McCann, J. Clinton, Jr., ed. Shape & Shaping of the Psalter. 2009. (Library of Hebrew Bible/Old Testament Studies, the Ser.). (ENG.). 130p. 27.95 *(978-0-567-04169-2(7)*, T&T Clark) Continuum International Publishing Group, Ltd. GBR. Dist: National Bk. Network.

McCreesh, Thomas P. Biblical Sound & Sense: Poetic Sound Patterns in Proverbs 10-29. 2009. (Library of Hebrew Bible/Old Testament Studies, the Ser.). (ENG.). 164p. 29.95 *(978-1-4411-1873-8(X)*, T&T Clark) Continuum International Publishing Group, Ltd. GBR. Dist: National Bk. Network.

McElroy, Mark. Proverbs for Living. 2009. pap. *(978-0-9823842-1-3(1))* NextSunday Resources.

McGinniss, Mark. Contributions of Selected Rhetorical Devices to a Biblical Theology of the Song of Songs. 2011. 256p. pap. 29.00 *(978-1-60899-634-6(4)*, Wipf and Stock) Wipf & Stock Pubs.

McKelvey, Michael G. Moses, David & the High Kingship of Yahweh. 2011. 112.40 *(978-1-61143-682-2(6))* Gorgias Pr., LLC.

Millet-Gerard, Dominique. Le Signe et le Sceau: Variations litteraires sur le Cantique des Cantiques. 2010. (HISTOIRE des IDeES et CRITIQUE LITTeRAIRE Ser.). (FRE.). 408p. (C). pap. 112.00 *(978-2-600-01399-4(7))* Droz, Librairie CHE. Dist: Brown, David Bk. Co., The.

Morrow, William. Protest Against God: The Eclipse of a Bi. 2006. (ENG.). 264p. *(978-1-905048-20-5(3))* Sheffield Phoenix Pr.

Mowinckel, Sigmund & Biddle, Mark E. Psalm Studies. 2010. *(978-90-04-18702-3(2))*; *(978-90-04-18703-0(0))* BRILL.

—Psalm Studies. 2010. *(978-1-58983-510-8(7))*; *(978-1-58983-508-5(5))*; *(978-1-58983-509-2(3))*; *(978-1-58983-512-2(3))*; *(978-1-58983-511-5(5))* Society of Biblical Literature.

Mueller, Steven. Psalms: An Introductory Course. (Journeys Through God's Word Ser.). pap., stu. ed. 8.99 *(978-0-570-06890-7(8)*, 20-2818); pap. 8.99 *(978-0-570-06891-4(6)*, 20-2819) Concordia Publishing Hse.

Nasuti, Harry P. Defining the Sacred Songs: Genre, Tradition, & the Post-Critical Interpretation of the Psalms. 2009. (Library of Hebrew Bible/Old Testament Studies, the Ser.). (ENG.). 231p. 39.95 *(978-0-567-01344-6(8)*, T&T Clark) Continuum International Publishing Group, Ltd. GBR. Dist: National Bk. Network.

Nelson, Alissa Jones. Edward Said, Contrapuntal Hermeneutics & the Book of Job: Power, Subjectivity & Responsibility, in Biblical Interpretation. 2012. (BibleWorld Ser.). (ENG.). 224p. (C). 99.95 *(978-1-84553-889-7(7))* Equinox Publishing Ltd. GBR. Dist: Brown, David Bk. Co., The.

—Edward Said, Contrapuntal Hermeneutics, & the Book of Job: Power, Subjectivity & Responsibility in Biblical Interpretation. 2011. (BibleWorld Ser.). (ENG.). 224p. (C). pap. 35.00 *(978-1-84553-890-3(0))* Equinox Publishing Ltd. GBR. Dist: Brown, David Bk. Co., The.

Nelson, Tommy. The Book of Romance: What Solomon Says about Love, Sex, & Intimacy, 0 vols. 2007. 224p. per. 13.99 *(978-0-7852-8898-5(8))* Nelson, Thomas Inc.

Newsom, Carol A. The Book of Job: A Contest of Moral Imaginations. 2009. (ENG.). 320p. pap. 24.95 *(978-0-19-539628-7(6))* Oxford Univ. Pr., Inc.

Noegel, Scott B. Janus Parallelism in the Book of Job. 2009. (Library of Hebrew Bible/Old Testament Studies, the Ser.). (ENG.). 223p. 39.95 *(978-0-567-51218-5(5)*, T&T Clark) Continuum International Publishing Group, Ltd. GBR. Dist: National Bk. Network.

Noegel, Scott B. & Rendsburg, Gary. Solomon's Vineyard: Literary & Linguistic Studies in the Song of Songs. 2009. *(978-90-04-16925-8(3))* BRILL.

—Solomon's Vineyard: Literary & Linguistic Studies in the Song of Songs. 2009. 282p. pap. 34.95 *(978-1-58983-422-4(4))* Society of Biblical Literature.

Núñez Rivera, Valentín. Poesía y Biblia en el Siglo de Oro: Estudios Sobre Los Salmos y el Cantar de Los Cantares. 2010. (Biblioteca Áurea Hispánica Ser.). (SPA.). 294p. pap. 44.00 *(978-84-8489-531-2(9))* Iberoamericana Vervuert Publishing Corp.

Obinwa, Ignatius M. C. Yahweh My Refuge: A Critical Analysis of Psalm 71, Vol. 839. 2006. (European Universities Studies 23 Ser.). 221p. pap. *(978-0-8204-8745-8(7))* Lang, Peter AG.

O'Donnell, Douglas Sean. The Song of Solomon: An Invitation to Intimacy. 2012. ***(978-1-4335-2338-0(8))*** Crossway.

O'Neill, George. The Psalms & the Canticles of the Divine Office. Husslein, Joseph, ed. 2011. 326p. 50.95 ***(978-1-258-05642-1(9))*** Literary Licensing, LLC.

Pak, G. Sujin. The Judaizing Calvin: Sixteenth-Century Debates over the Messianic Psalms. 2009. (History Theology Ser.). (ENG.). 240p. 65.00 *(978-0-19-537192-5(5))* Oxford Univ. Pr., Inc.

Partow, Donna. Becoming the Woman God Wants Me to Be: A 90-Day Guide to Living the Proverbs 31 Life. 2008. 352p. pap. 13.99 *(978-0-8007-3072-7(0))* Revell.

Passaro, Angelo & Bellia, Giuseppe. The Wisdom of Ben Sira: Studies on Tradition, Redaction, & Theology. 2008. (Deuterocanonical & Cognate Literature Studies). (ENG.). XIII, 411p. 133.00 *(978-3-11-019499-9(6))* De Gruyter, Walter Inc.

Passaro, Angelo & Bellia, Giuseppe, eds. The Wisdom of Ben Sira: Studies on Tradition, Redaction, & Theology. 2008. (Deuterocanonical & Cognate Literature Studies). (ENG.). XIII, 411p. 210.00 ***(978-3-11-173665-5(2))*** De Gruyter, Walter Inc.

Passmore, Tim. The Journal: The Psalms & Proverbs. 2010. 270p. pap. 15.99 *(978-0-9840682-8-9(7))* Outcome Publishing.

Pastor's Day-Proverbs 4:11. 7.50 *(978-0-8054-5907-4(3))* B&H Publishing Group.

Patterson, Ben. God's Prayer Book: The Power & Pleasure of Praying the Psalms. 2008. (ENG.). 320p. pap. 14.99 *(978-1-4143-1665-9(8)*, SaltRiver) Tyndale Hse. Pubs.

Pemberton, Glenn. Hurting with God: Learning to Lament with the Psalms. 2012. (ENG.). 288p. pap. 19.99 ***(978-0-89112-400-9(4)***, ACU Pr.) Abilene Christian Univ. Pr.

Perdue, Leo G. Wisdom in Revolt: Metaphorical Theology in the Book of Job. 2009. (Library of Hebrew Bible/Old Testament Studies, the Ser.). (ENG.). 296p. 49.95 *(978-0-567-46547-4(0)*, T&T Clark) Continuum International Publishing Group, Ltd. GBR. Dist: National Bk. Network.

Pinçon, Bertrand, ed. L'énigme du Bonheur: Étude sur le sujet du bien dans le livre de Qohélet. 2008. (Vetus Testamentum Supplements Ser.). 320p. (C). *(978-90-04-16717-9(X))* BRILL.

Podzeit, Utz. Die Freude an der Tora als Weisung des Weges zum Vater: Auslegungen der Rabbinen und des Aurelius Augustinus zu Psalm 1. 2009. (GER.). 98p. pap. 35.95 *(978-3-631-59067-6(9))* Lang, Peter GmbH, Europaischer Verlag der Wissenschaften DEU. Dist: Lang, Peter.

Power, A. D. Side Lights on the Book of Proverbs. 2007. 80p. per. *(978-1-4067-8842-6(2)*, Pomona Pr.) Read Bks.

Pratt, Maureen. Beyond Pain: Job, Jesus & Joy. 2010. pap. 14.95 *(978-1-58595-786-6(0))* Twenty-Third Pubns./Bayard.

Proverbs: Wisdom for Living. (Discover Life Ser.). 16p. stu. ed. 5.35 *(978-1-56212-146-4(4)*, 153110) Faith Alive Christian Resources.

Raabe, Paul R. Psalm Structures: A Study of Psalms with Refrains. 2009. (Library of Hebrew Bible/Old Testament Studies, the Ser.). (ENG.). 219p. 39.95 *(978-0-567-20712-8(9)*, T&T Clark) Continuum International Publishing Group, Ltd. GBR. Dist: National Bk. Network.

Rabenau, Merten. Studien zum Buch Tobit. (Beihefte zur Zeitschrift far die alttestamentliche Wissenschaft Ser.). (GER.). VIII, 249p. 210.00 ***(978-3-11-177703-0(0))*** De Gruyter, Walter Inc.

Ramirez, Frank. Proverbs, Ecclesiastes, Song of Solomon. 2012. 112p. 9.00 ***(978-1-4267-1631-7(1))*** Abingdon Pr.

Retzlaff, Georg. Church Psalter: The Book of Psalms for Liturgical & Private Use. 2009. 216p. pap. 14.49 *(978-1-4389-4515-6(9))* AuthorHouse.

Reynolds, Kent Aaron. Torah as Teacher: The Exemplary Torah Student in Psalm 119. 249p. *(978-90-04-18268-4(3))* BRILL.

Rogal, Samuel J. The Lord is My Shepherd (Psalm 23) How Poets, Mystics, & Hymnodists Have Delved Its Deeper Meanings. 2006. 172p. *(978-0-7734-5480-4(2))* Mellen, Edwin Pr., The.

Rohde, Michael, ed. Der Knecht Hiob im Gespräch mit Mose: Eine traditions- und redaktionsgeschichtliche Studie zum Hiobbuch. 2007. (Arbeiten Zur Bibel und Ihrer Geschichte Ser.: Vol. 26). 256p. (C). 55.00 *(978-3-374-02475-9(0))* Evangelische Verlagsanstalt GmbH DEU. Dist: Eisenbrauns, Inc.

Rosengren Petersen, Allan. Royal God: Enthronement Festivals in Ancient Israel & Ugarit? 2009. (Library of Hebrew Bible/Old Testament Studies, the Ser.). (ENG.). 121p. 27.95 *(978-0-567-59793-9(8)*, T&T Clark) Continuum International Publishing Group, Ltd. GBR. Dist: National Bk. Network.

Ruth, Peggy Joyce. Psalm 91. 2012. (ENG.). 128p. pap. 8.99 ***(978-1-61638-583-5(9)***, Charisma Hse.) 2007. xiv, 237p. *(978-1-59979-095-4(5)*, Creation Hse.) Charisma Media.

Ruth, Peggy Joyce & Schum, Angelia. Psalm 91 Workbook: God's Shield of Protection. 2007. (Illus.). 137p. pap. 8.00 *(978-0-9708257-6-6(5))* Impact Christian Bks., Inc.

Schaap, James C. Sixty at Sixty: A Boomer Reflects on the Psalms. 2008. *(978-1-59255-440-9(7))* Faith Alive Christian Resources.

Schipper, Bernd U. Hermeneutik der Tora: Studien Zur Traditionsgeschichte Von Prov. 2 und Zur Komposition Von Prov. 1-9. 2012. (Beihefte zur Zeitschrift für die alttestamentliche Wissenschaft Ser.).Tr. of Hermeneutic of Torah. Studies on the Tradition of Prov 2 & the Composition of Prov 1-9. (GER.). XII, 336p. (gr. 17). 140.00 ***(978-3-11-027948-1(7))*** De Gruyter, Walter Inc.

Schuller, Robert A. Getting Through What You're Going Through, 0 vols. 2008. 224p. pap. 14.99 *(978-0-7852-8942-5(9))* Nelson, Thomas Inc.

Schweitzer, Steven James. In Celebration of Wisdom: Life & Meaning in Job, Proverbs, & Ecclesiastes. 2009. *(978-0-936273-42-6(9))* Institute of Mennonite Studies.

Segraves, Daniel L. The Messiah in the Psalms: Discovering Christ in Unexpected Places. 2007. pap. 14.99 *(978-1-56722-706-2(6))* Word Aflame Pr.

Selderhuis, Herman J. Calvin's Theology of the Psalms. 2007. (Texts & Studies in Reformation & Post-Reformation Thought Ser.). 304p. (C). pap. 35.00 (978-0-8010-3166-3(4)) Baker Academic.

Shapiro, Rabbi Rami, tr. & anno. Proverbs: Annotated & Explained. 2011. 176p. pap. 16.99 **(978-1-59473-310-9(4))** SkyLight Paths Publishing.

Silva, Kittim. Eclesiastes: Un Mensaje para Hoy: Ecclesiastes: A Message for Today. (SPA.). (978-84-7645-406-0(6), 223462) Clie, Editorial.

Smith, Janet. Dust or Dew: Immortality in the Ancient near East & in Psalm 49. 2011. 286p. pap. 31.00 (978-1-60899-661-2(1), Pickwick Pubns.) Wipf & Stock Pubs.

Smith, Janet K. Dust or Dew No. 49: Immortality in the Ancient near East & in Psalm. 2012. (ENG.). 286p. pap. 39.00 **(978-0-227-68021-6(9))** Clarke, James Co., Ltd. GBR. Dist: Brown, David Bk. Co., The.

Sneed, Mark R. Ecclesiastes in Social-Science Perspective: The Politics of Pessimism. 2012. **(978-1-58983-610-5(3)); (978-1-58983-635-8(9))** Society of Biblical Literature.

Stedman, Ray C. Let God Be God: Life-Changing Truths from the Book of Job. 2007. (ENG.). 256p. per. 12.99 (978-1-57293-180-0(9)) Discovery Hse. Pubs.

Stedman, Ray C. & Crowder, Bill. Singing the Songs of the Brokenhearted: Psalms That Comfort & Mend the Soul. 2009. (ENG.). 176p. pap. 11.99 (978-1-57293-274-6(0)) Discovery Hse. Pubs.

Stephen B Dawes Staff. Psalms. 2010. (SCM Studyguides Ser.). (ENG.). 256p. (C). pap. 29.99 (978-0-334-04342-3(5), SCM Pr.) Hymns Ancient & Modern Ltd GBR. Dist: Westminster John Knox Pr.

Storstein Haug, Kari. Interpreting Proverbs 11:18-31, Psalm 73, & Ecclesiastes 9:1-12 in Light of, & as a Response to, Thai Buddhist Interpretations: A Contribution to Christian-Buddhist Dialogue. 2012. (Studies in Systematic Theology Ser.). (ENG.). **(978-90-04-21011-0(3))** BRILL.

Stuart, M. Interpretation of Psalm XVI. 2010. 84.56 (978-1-61143-454-5(8)) Gorgias Pr., LLC.

SUbstance. 2010. 80p. pap. (978-1-84427-386-7(5)) Scripture Union.

Swindoll, Charles R. Job: A Man of Heroic Endurance, 0 vols. 2009. 400p. pap. 14.99 (978-1-4002-0250-8(7)) Nelson, Thomas Inc.

Tabb, Mark. How Can a Good God Let Bad Things Happen? 2008. (Living the Letters Ser.). (ENG.). 224p. pap. 14.99 (978-1-60005-268-1(7)) NavPress Publishing Group.

Taylor, Preston. Ecclesiastes Life Beneath the Blazing Su. 2006. pap. 13.99 (978-1-60034-523-4(9)) Xulon Pr., Inc.

Terrien, Samuel L. The Psalms & Their Meaning for Today. 2011. 278p. 47.95 **(978-1-258-10253-1(6))** Literary Licensing, LLC.

Thomas, Nathan. What's Stopping You? 2010. (978-1-60682-076-6(1)) BJU Pr.

Tietjen, Suzanne Davenport. The Sheep of His Hand: Reflections on the Psalms from a 21st Century Shepherd, 1 vol. 2009. 176p. 15.99 (978-0-8254-6298-6(3), Monarch Bks.) Lion Hudson PLC GBR. Dist: Kregel Pubns.

Toler, Stan & Brecheisen, Jerry. Maximum Integrity: Leadership Insights from the Psalms. 2006. (ENG.). 96p. per. 9.99 (978-0-8341-2283-3(9), 083-412-2839) Beacon Hill Pr. of Kansas City.

Tucker, Mike. Every Good Thing: Satisfying Your Hunger for God. 2007. (ENG.). 160p. per. 12.99 (978-0-8127-0449-5(5)) Autumn Hse. Publishing Co.

Turner, Charles W. Wise Words in a Wicked World: Studies in Proverbs. pap. 7.99 (978-0-88469-028-3(8)) BMH Bks.

Van der Lugt, Pieter. Cantos & Strophes in Biblical Hebrew Poetry II, Psalms 42-89. 2010. 580p. (978-90-04-18200-4(4)) BRILL.

Van Dyke, Henry. The Story of the Psalms. 2007. (ENG.). 272p. 42.95 (978-0-548-08416-8(5)) Kessinger Publishing, LLC.

Van Harn, Roger E. & Strawn, Brent A., eds. Psalms for Preaching & Worship: A Lectionary Commentary. 2009. (Illus.). 522p. pap. 35.00 (978-0-8028-6321-8(3)) Eerdmans, William B. Publishing Co.

Van Hecke, Pierre. From Linguistics to Hermeneutics: A Functional & Cognitive Approach to Job 12-14. 2010. (Studia Semitica Neerlandica Ser.). (Illus.). 550p. (978-90-04-18835-8(5)) BRILL.

Vassar, John S. Recalling a Story Once Told: An Intertextual Reading of the Psalter & the Pentateuch. 2007. 192p. 45.00 (978-0-88146-051-3(6)) Mercer Univ. Pr.

Verbin, N. Divinely Abused: A Philosophical Perspective on Job & his Kin. 2011. (ENG.). 184p. pap. 32.95 **(978-1-4411-3856-9(0))** Continuum International Publishing Group, Ltd. GBR. Dist: National Bk. Network.

Viking, creator. Psalms. 2006. (ENG.). 132p. (gr. 12-18). 20.00 (978-0-670-02855-9(X), Penguin Global) Penguin Group (USA) Inc.

Villanueva, F. G. The 'Uncertainty of a Hearing' A Study of the Sudden Change of Mood in the Psalms of Lament. 2008. (Vetus Testamentum Supplements Ser.). 300p. (978-90-04-16847-3(8)) BRILL.

Walker-Jones, Arthur. The Green Psalter: Resources for an Ecological Spirituality. 2009. 200p. (C). pap. 20.00 (978-0-8006-6302-5(0), Fortress Pr.) Augsburg Fortress, Pubs.

Wallace, Robert E. The Narrative Effect of Book IV of the Hebrew Psalter. 2007. (Studies in Biblical Literature Ser.). 144p. (C). 58.95 (978-1-4331-0092-5(4)) Lang, Peter Publishing, Inc.

Waltke, Bruce K., et al. The Psalms As Christian Worship: A Historical Commentary. 2010. xii, 626p. pap. 28.00 (978-0-8028-6374-4(4)) Eerdmans, William B. Publishing Co.

Washburn, Mark E. To Find & Enjoy the Love of Your Life: A Study in the Song of Solomon. 2009. 244p. pap. 18.99 (978-1-60799-086-4(5)) Tate Publishing & Enterprises, LLC.

Waters, Larry J. The Contribution of the Speeches of Elihu to the Argument about Suffering in the Book of Job: A Study in Narrative Continuity. 2009. 312p. 119.95 (978-0-7734-4799-8(7)) Mellen, Edwin Pr., The.

Watters, William R. Formula Criticism & the Poetry of the Old Testament. 2012. (Beihefte zur Zeitschrift far die alttestamentliche Wissenschaft Ser.). (ENG.). XVI, 227p. (gr. 17). E-Book 196.00 **(978-3-11-188348-9(5))** De Gruyter, Walter Inc.

Webster, Brian L. & Beach, David R. The Psalms: Key Insights for Reading God's Word, 1 vol. 2010. (Essential Bible Companion Ser.). (ENG., Illus.). 192p. pap. 17.99 (978-0-310-28689-9(1)) Zondervan.

Weeks, Stuart. Ecclesiastes & Scepticism. 2011. (Library Hebrew Bible/Old Testament Studies). (ENG.). 240p. 130.00 (978-0-567-25288-3(4), T&T Clark Int'l) Continuum International Publishing Group, Ltd. GBR. Dist: National Bk. Network.

Wegner, Paul, et al. Wise Parenting: Guidelines from the Book of Proverbs. 2009. (ENG.). 144p. pap. 11.99 (978-1-57293-352-1(6)) Discovery Hse. Pubs.

Westerwelle, Rich. What So Ever You Do Will Prosper: A look at the 1st Psalm. 2010. 200p. 24.99 (978-1-4490-5335-2(1)); pap. 14.95 (978-1-4490-5334-5(3)) AuthorHouse.

Whaley, Charles. Prophetic, Post-Apostolic & Postmodern: Three Bible Studies from a Missionary to Japan. 2009. pap. (978-1-57312-548-2(2)) Smyth & Helwys Publishing, Inc.

White, Willie. The Lord Is My Shepherd. 2007. 112p. per. 19.95 (978-1-4241-9036-2(3)) PublishAmerica, Inc.

Whybray, R. N. Wisdom in Proverbs. 2009. (Studies in Biblical Theology, First Ser.). 120p. pap. 15.00 (978-1-60899-019-1(2), Wipf and Stock) Wipf & Stock Pubs.

Whybray, R. Norman. Composition of the Book of Proverbs. 2009. (Library of Hebrew Bible/Old Testament Studies, the Ser.). (ENG.). 173p. 29.95 (978-1-4411-5599-3(6), T&T Clark) Continuum International Publishing Group, Ltd. GBR. Dist: National Bk. Network.

—Wealth & Poverty in the Book of Proverbs. 2009. (Library of Hebrew Bible/Old Testament Studies, the Ser.). (ENG.). 132p. 27.95 (978-1-4411-5374-6(8), T&T Clark) Continuum International Publishing Group, Ltd. GBR. Dist: National Bk. Network.

Wilhite, Jud. That Crazy Little Thing Called Love: The Soundtrack of Marriage, Sex, & Faith. 2007. (Marriage Ser.). 160p. 14.99 (978-0-7847-1944-2(6)) Standard Publishing.

Wolde, Ellen Van, ed. Job's God. 2011. 141p. pap. **(978-0-334-03080-5(3)**, SCM Pr.) Hymns Ancient & Modern Ltd.

, Word Worldwide, Word Worldwide. Comfort & Encouragement from the Psalms 1-50: A Study in the Psalms. 2009. (ENG.). 56p. mass mkt. 4.99 (978-1-84550-408-3(9)) Christian Focus Pubns. GBR. Dist: STL Distribution North America.

Worley, Joe. I can't get no Satisfaction. 2007. (ENG.). 236p. per. 14.99 (978-1-60266-109-7(X)) Xulon Pr., Inc.

Wright, Robert & Wright. Psalms of Solomon: A Critical Edition of the Greek Text. 2007. (Jewish & Christian Texts in Contexts & Related Studies). (ENG., Illus.). 238p. 150.00 (978-0-567-02643-9(4), T&T Clark) Continuum International Publishing Group, Ltd. GBR. Dist: National Bk. Network.

Wursten, Dick. Clément Marot & Religion: A Re-Assessment in View of His Psalm Paraphrases. 2010. (Brill's Ser. in Church History Ser.). (ENG., Illus.). 442p. (978-90-04-18456-5(2)) BRILL.

Xeravits, Geza G. & Zsengellér, József. Studies in the Book of Ben Sira: Papers of the Third International Conference on the Deuterocanonical Books, Shime'on Centre, Pápa, Hungary, 18-20 May 2006. 2008. (Supplements to the Journal for the Study of Judaism Ser.). 282p. (978-90-04-16906-7(7)) BRILL.

Zenger, E. The Composition of the Book of Psalms. 2010. (Bibliotheca Ephemeridum Theologicarum Lovaniensium Ser.). (ENG, FRE & GER., Illus.). 826p. (C). pap. 131.00 (978-90-429-2329-4(6)) Peeters Pubs. & Booksellers BEL. Dist: Brown, David Bk. Co., The.

Zim, Rivkah. English Metrical Psalms: Poetry as Praise & Prayer, 1535-1601. 2011. (ENG., Illus.). 346p. pap. 33.99 (978-0-521-17221-9(7)) Cambridge Univ. Pr.

BIBLE—CRITICISM, INTERPRETATION, ETC.—O. T. PROPHETS

Here are entered works on the prophets as a whole as well as those on one or more of the following: Isaiah, Daniel, Lamentations, Ezekiel, Jeremiah.

Adams, Jim. The Performative Nature & Function of Isaiah 40-55: Exploring the Use & Value of the Philosophical Notions of Speech Act Theory for Biblical Interpretation & Specifically Isaiah 40-55. 2006. (Library of Hebrew Bible/Old Testament Studies). (ENG.). 288p. 160.00 (978-0-567-02582-1(9), T&T Clark Int'l) Continuum International Publishing Group, Ltd. GBR. Dist: National Bk. Network.

Adeyemi, Femi. The New Covenant Torah in Jeremiah & the Law of Christ in Paul. 2006. (Studies in Biblical Literature: Vol. 94). (C). 81.95 (978-0-8204-8137-1(8)) Lang, Peter Publishing, Inc.

Ahn, John J. & Ahn. Thus Says the LORD: Essays on the Former & Latter Prophets in Honor of Robert R. Wilson. Ahn, John J. & Cook, Stephen L., eds. 2009. (Library of Hebrew Bible/Old Testament Studies, the Ser.). (ENG., Illus.). 352p. 140.00 (978-0-567-17804-6(8), T&T Clark Int'l) Continuum International Publishing Group, Ltd. GBR. Dist: National Bk. Network.

Alexander, Philip S., notes. The Targum of Lamentations: 17b. 2008. (Aramaic Bible Ser.). (Illus.). 224p. 99.95 (978-0-8146-5864-2(4)) Liturgical Pr.

Anderson, Bernard W. & Harrelson, Walter, eds. Israel's Prophetic Heritage: Essays in Honor of James Muilenburg. 2010. 258p. pap. 28.00 (978-1-60899-687-2(5), Wipf and Stock) Wipf & Stock Pubs.

Arthur, Kay & De Lacy, Pete. Walking with God in Every Season: Ecclesiastes/Song of Solomon/Lamentations. 2010. (New Inductive Study Ser.). 112p. pap. 8.99 (978-0-7369-2236-4(9)) Harvest Hse. Pubs.

Avioz, Michael. I SAT Alone: Jeremiah among the Prophets. 2009. (978-1-59333-854-1(6)) Gorgias Pr., LLC.

Bak, Dong H. Klagender Gott - klagende Menschen: Studien zur Klage im Jeremiabuch. (Beihefte zur Zeitschrift far die alttestamentliche Wissenschaft Ser.). (GER.). XIII, 273p. 196.00 **(978-3-11-178328-4(6))** De Gruyter, Walter Inc.

Ball, Terry. Making Sense of Isaiah, Insights & Modern Applications. 2009. 192p. 24.95 (978-1-60641-000-4(8)) Deseret Bk. Co.

Barnes, Albert. Notes, Critical, Illustrative & Practical, on the Book of Daniel: With an Introductory Dissertation. 2007. 500p. 53.95 (978-0-548-55938-3(4)); per. 38.95 (978-0-548-50094-1(0)) Kessinger Publishing, LLC.

Barry, John D. The Resurrected Servant in Isaiah. 2010. (ENG.). 180p. pap. 24.99 (978-1-60657-100-2(1), Authentic Bibles) Authentic Media.

Barstad, Hans & Kratz, Reinhard G., eds. Prophecy in the Book of Jeremiah. 2009. (Beihefte zur Zeitschrift far die alttestamentliche Wissenschaft Ser.). (ENG.). X, 289p. 109.00 (978-3-11-020506-0(8)) De Gruyter, Walter Inc.

Batten, Loring W. The Hebrew Prophet. 2007. 364p. 46.95 (978-0-548-11159-8(6)) Kessinger Publishing, LLC.

Beale, G. K. The Use of Daniel in Jewish Apocalyptic Literature & in the Revelation of St. John. 2010. 364p. pap. 40.00 (978-1-50899-530-1(5), Wipf and Stock) Wipf & Stock Pubs.

Bellinger, William H. & Farmer, William R., eds. Jesus & the Suffering Servant: Isaiah 53 & Christian Origins. 2009. 334p. pap. 37.00 (978-1-60608-564-6(6), Wipf and Stock) Wipf & Stock Pubs.

Beyer, Bryan E. & Beyer, Bryan. Encountering the Book of Isaiah: A Historical & Theological Survey. 2007. (Encountering Biblical Studies). (Illus.). 304p. (C). pap. 29.99 (978-0-8010-2645-4(8)) Baker Academic.

Blanchard, John. Major Points from the Minor Prophets. 2012. (ENG.). 280p. pap. **(978-0-85234-782-9(0))** Evangelical Pr.

Blanco, Jack J. Visions & Dreams: Hope for the Future, Courage for Today: A Fresh Look at Daniel & Revelation. 2010. pap. 6.99 (978-0-8127-0478-5(9)) Autumn Hse. Publishing Co.

Blenkinsopp, Joseph. Opening the Sealed Book: Interpretations of the Book of Isaiah in Late Antiquity. 2006. 315p. per. 25.00 (978-0-8028-4021-9(3)) Eerdmans, William B. Publishing Co.

Bohr, Stephen. Prophecy's Dr. Jekyll & Mr. Hyde. 2008. 80p. 7.95 (978-1-933291-28-4(1)) Remnant Pubns.

Branick, Vincent P. Understanding the Prophets & Their Books. 2012. **(978-1-61643-138-9(5))**; 352p. pap. 29.95 **(978-0-8091-4763-2(7))** Paulist Pr.

Brittingham, Les. Decoding Daniel. 2007. pap. 15.99 (978-1-60034-926-3(9)) Xulon Pr., Inc.

Bromell, Dale. The Seventieth Week of Daniel. 2008. 271p. pap. 27.95 (978-1-4241-4755-7(7)) PublishAmerica, Inc.

Brueggemann, Walter. The Theology of the Book of Jeremiah. 2006. (Old Testament Theology Ser.). (ENG.). 229p. per. 24.00 (978-0-521-60629-5(2)) Cambridge Univ. Pr.

Brueggemann, Walter & Canadian Biotechnology Advisory Committee. The Theology of the Book of Jeremiah. 2006. (Old Testament Theology Ser.). (ENG.). 229p. 64.99 (978-0-521-84454-3(1)) Cambridge Univ. Pr.

Butler, John G. Daniel: The Man of Loyalty. 2007. 427p. (978-1-889773-21-6(2)) LBC Pubns.

Chisholm, Robert B., Jr. Handbook on the Prophets. 2009. (C). pap. 34.99 (978-0-8010-3860-0(X)) Baker Academic.

Clements, R. E. Jerusalem & the Nations: Studies in the Book of Isaiah. 2011. 262p. **(978-1-905048-81-6(5))** Sheffield Phoenix Pr.

Clements, R. E. Prophecy & Covenant. 2009. (Studies in Biblical Theology, First Ser.). 136p. pap. 17.00 (978-1-60899-020-7(6), Wipf and Stock) Wipf & Stock Pubs.

Cohen, Raymond & Westbrook, Raymond. Isaiah's Vision of Peace in Biblical & Modern International Relations: Swords into Plowshares. 2008. (Culture & Religion in International Relations Ser.). (ENG., Illus.). 304p. 100.00 (978-1-4039-7735-9(6)) Palgrave Macmillan.

Cook, Paul M. A Sign & a Wonder: The Redactional Formation of Isaiah 18-20. 2011. 220p. (978-90-04-20591-8(3)) BRILL.

Cook, Stephen L. Conversations with Scripture: 2 Isaiah. 2008. (Anglican Association of Biblical Scholars Ser.). 176p. pap. 18.00 (978-0-8192-2149-0(X), Morehouse Publishing) Church Publishing, Inc.

Coomber, Matthew. Re-Reading the Prophets Through Corporate Globalization. 2010. 122.00 (978-1-60724-978-8(2)) Gorgias Pr., LLC.

Crane, Ashley S. Israel's Restoration: A Textual-Comparative Exploration of Ezekiel 36-39. 2008. (Vetus Testamentum Ser.). 324p. (978-90-04-16962-3(8)) BRILL.

Cuéllar, Gregory Lee. Voices of Marginality: Exile & Return in Second Isaiah 40-55 & the Mexican Immigrant Experience. 2008. (American University Studies VII: Theology & Religion Ser.). 184p. (C). 72.95 (978-1-4331-0180-9(7)) Lang, Peter Publishing, Inc.

Czovek, Tamas. Three Seasons of Charismatic Leadership: A Literary-Critical & Theological Interpretation of the Narrative of Saul, David & Solomon. 2008. (Regnum Studies in Mission Ser.). 302p. pap. 35.00 (978-1-59752-921-1(4), Wipf and Stock) Wipf & Stock Pubs.

Daschke, Derek. City of Ruins: Mourning the Destruction of Jerusalem Through Jewish Apocalypse. (Illus.). 222p. (978-90-04-18181-6(4)) BRILL.

Davidson, Steed Vernyl. Empire & Exile: Postcolonial Readings of the Book of Jeremiah. 2011. (Library Hebrew Bible/Old Testament Studies). 272p. 140.00 (978-0-567-43704-4(3), T&T Clark Int'l) Continuum International Publishing Group, Ltd. GBR. Dist: National Bk. Network.

Davies, Eryl W. Prophecy & Ethics: Isaiah & the Ethical Traditions of Israel. 2009. (Library of Hebrew Bible/Old Testament Studies, the Ser.). (ENG.). 185p. 39.95 (978-0-567-06865-1(X), T&T Clark) Continuum International Publishing Group, Ltd. GBR. Dist: National Bk. Network.

Davies, Philip R. Among the Prophets: Language, Image & Structure in the Prophetic Writings. Clines, David J. A., ed. 2009. (Library of Hebrew Bible/Old Testament Studies, the Ser.). (ENG.). 218p. 39.95 (978-1-4411-9648-4(X), T&T Clark) Continuum International Publishing Group, Ltd. GBR. Dist: National Bk. Network.

Davis, Ellen F. Swallowing the Scroll: Textuality & the Dynamics of Discourse in Ezekiel's Prophecy. 2009. (Library of Hebrew Bible/Old Testament Studies, the Ser.). (ENG.). 184p. 29.95 (978-1-4411-4299-3(1), T&T Clark) Continuum International Publishing Group, Ltd. GBR. Dist: National Bk. Network.

Day, John. Prophecy & the Prophets in Ancient Israel: Proceedings of the Oxford Old Testament Seminar. 2010. (Library of Hebrew Bible/Old Testament Studies). (ENG.). 480p. 180.00 (978-0-567-47364-6(3), T&T Clark Int'l) Continuum International Publishing Group, Ltd. GBR. Dist: National Bk. Network.

de Hulster, Izaak J. Iconographic Exegesis & Third Isaiah. 2009. (Forschungen zum Alten Testament Ser.). 352p. pap. 137.50 (978-3-16-150029-9(6)) Mohr Siebeck GmbH & Co. KG DEU. Dist: Coronet Bks.

de Jong, Matthijs J. Isaiah among the Ancient near Eastern Prophets: A Comparative Study of the Earliest Stages of the Isaiah Tradition & the Neo-Assyrian Prophecies. 2007. (Vetus Testamentum Supplements Ser.). (Illus.). 522p. (978-90-04-16161-0(9)) BRILL.

De Jonge, Henk Jan & Tromp, Johannes, eds. The Book of Ezekiel & Its Influence. 2007. (Illus.). 232p. 99.95 (978-0-7546-5583-1(0)) Ashgate Publishing Co.

Deane, William J. Daniel: Su Vida y Sus Tiempos: The Life & Times of Daniel. (SPA.). (978-84-7645-166-3(0), 223205) Clie, Editorial.

Dekker, Jaap. Zion's Rock-Solid Foundations: An Exegetical Study of the Zion Text in Isaiah 28:16. 2007. 408p. (C). (978-90-04-15665-4(8)) BRILL.

Dempsey, Carol J. Jeremiah: Preacher of Grace, Poet of Truth. 2007. (Interfaces Ser.). 124p. per. 19.95 (978-0-8146-5985-4(3)) Liturgical Pr.

Desueza, Edmond F. & Jones, Judith. Conversations with Scripture: The Book of Daniel. 2011. E-Book **(978-0-8192-2750-8(1)**, Morehouse Publishing) Church Publishing, Inc.

Diamond, A. R. Pete. Jeremiah (Dis)Placed: New Directions in Writing/Reading Jeremiah. Stulman, Louis & Diamond, A. R. Pete, eds. 2011. (Library of Hebrew Bible/Old Testament Studies). (ENG., Illus.). 336p. 140.00 (978-0-567-64122-9(8), T&T Clark Int'l) Continuum International Publishing Group, Ltd. GBR. Dist: National Bk. Network.

Drazin, Israel. Maimonides & the Biblical Prophets. 2010. (Maimonides Ser.). 335p. (978-965-229-430-2(6)) Gefen Publishing Hse., Ltd.

Duck, Daymond, ed. The Book of Daniel, 0 vols. 2007. (Smart Guide to the Bible Ser.). (Illus.). 384p. per. 14.99 (978-1-4185-0998-9(1)) Nelson, Thomas Inc.

Eidevall, Goran. Prophecy & Propaganda: Images of Enemies in the Book of Isaiah. 2009. pap. 34.95 (978-1-57506-806-0(0)) Eisenbrauns, Inc.

Eisenberg, Charles. The Book of Daniel- A Well Kept Secret. 2007. 436p. per. 24.99 (978-1-60477-180-0(1)) Xulon Pr., Inc.

Emerton, John Adney, et al. Genesis, Isaiah, & Psalms: A Festschrift to Honour Professor John Emerton for His Eightieth Birthday. 2010. 210p. (978-90-04-18231-8(4)) BRILL.

Étougé A., Patrick. The Transgression & the Abomination of Desolation. 2010. 112p. pap. (978-3-639-28397-6(X)) VDM Verlag Dr. Mueller e.K.

Evans, Craig A. To See & Not Perceive: Isaiah 6. 9-10 in Early Jewish & Christian Interpretation. 2009. (Library of Hebrew Bible/Old Testament Studies, the Ser.). (ENG.). 261p. 44.95 (978-0-567-12836-2(9), T&T Clark) Continuum International Publishing Group, Ltd. GBR. Dist: National Bk. Network.

Everson, A. Joseph & Kim, Hyun Chul Paul. The Desert Will Bloom: Poetic Visions in Isaiah. 2009. (978-90-04-16926-5(1)) BRILL.

—The Desert Will Bloom: Poetic Visions in Isaiah. 2009. 37.95 (978-1-58983-425-5(9)) Society of Biblical Literature.

Fanwar, Wann. Creation in Isaiah. 2008. 236p. pap. (978-3-8364-8736-8(5)) VDM Verlag Dr. Mueller e.K.

Farrar, Steve. Get in the Ark, 0 vols. 2008. 256p. pap. 14.99 (978-0-7852-9680-5(8)) Nelson, Thomas Inc.

Foreman, Benjamin A. Animal Metaphors & the People of Israel in the Book of Jeremiah. 2011. (Forschungen Zur Religion und Literatur des Alten & Neuen Testament Ser.). (ENG., Illus.). 283p. (C). 122.00 (978-3-525-53258-4(X)) Vandenhoeck & Ruprecht GmbH & Co. KG DEU. Dist: ISD.

Fox, Emmet. The Garden of Allah: A Study in Treatment. 2011. 50p. 35.95 **(978-1-258-00447-7(X))** Literary Licensing, LLC.

García-Alfonso, Cristina. Resolviendo: Narratives of Survival in the Hebrew Bible & in Cuba Today. 2010. (Studies in Biblical Literature Ser.). 134p. (C). 63.95 (978-1-4331-0704-7(X)) Lang, Peter Publishing, Inc.

Gevirtz, Gila. The Prophets Speaking Out for Justice. 2010. (978-0-87441-600-8(0)) Behrman Hse., Inc.

Gignilliat, Mark S. Karl Barth & the Fifth Gospel: Barth's Theological Exegesis of Isaiah. 2009. (Barth Studies). 182p. 99.95 (978-0-7546-5856-6(2)) Ashgate Publishing Co.

Gillispie, Mary Ann. Endtime Reapers. 2008. 456p. pap. 27.99 (978-1-4251-4072-4(6)) Trafford Publishing.

Gladd, Benjamin. Revealing the Mysterion: The Use of Mystery in Daniel & Second Temple Judaism with Its Bearing on First Corinthians. 2008. (Beihefte zur Zeitschrift far die neutestamentliche Wissenschaft und die Kunde der älteren Kirche Ser.). (ENG.). XXIV, 352p. 224.00 **(978-3-11-173930-4(9))** De Gruyter, Walter Inc.

Gladd, Benjamin L. Revealing the Mysterion: The Use of Mystery in Daniel & Second Temple Judaism with Its Bearing on First Corinthians. 2008. (Beihefte zur Zeitschrift für die neutestamentliche Wissenschaft und die Kunde der Älteren Kirche Ser.). (ENG.). XXIV, 352p. 147.00 (978-3-11-020913-6(6)) De Gruyter, Walter Inc.

Glaub, Garry. Here Am I! Send Me. 2007. 444p. (ENG.). 33.99 (978-1-60477-410-8(X)); per. 21.99 (978-1-60477-389-7(8)) Xulon Pr., Inc.

God's Definition of Revelation: Revelation 10.4, Daniel 12.4. (Illus.). 13p. pap. (978-0-9714351-0-0(3)) Shaw, John R.

Goldingay, John. Uprooting & Planting: Essays on Jeremiah for Leslie Allen, Vol. 359. 2007. (T & T Clark Library of Biblical Studies). (ENG., Illus.). 404p. 210.00 (978-0-567-02952-2(2), T&T Clark Int'l) Continuum International Publishing Group, Ltd. GBR. Dist: National Bk. Network.

Goldingay, John E., et al. Isaiah 40-55: A Critical & Exegetical Commentary, 2 vols. 2007. (International Critical Commentary on the Holy Scriptures of the Old & New Testaments Ser.). (ENG.). 864p. 240.00 (978-0-567-04143-2(3), T&T Clark Int'l) Continuum International Publishing Group, Ltd. GBR. Dist: National Bk. Network.

Gottwald, Norman K. Studies in the Book of Lamentations. 2010. (SCM's Studies in Biblical Theology, First Ser.). 128p. pap. 16.00 (978-1-60608-981-1(1), Wipf and Stock) Wipf & Stock Pubs.

Grabbe, Lester L. & Nissinen, Martti. Constructs of Prophecy in the Former & Latter Prophets & Other Texts. 2011. **(978-1-58983-600-6(6))**; **(978-1-58983-599-3(9))** Society of Biblical Literature.

Graves, Michael. Jerome's Hebrew Philology: A Study Based on his Commentary on Jeremiah. 2007. (Vigiliae Christianae Supplements Ser.). 236p. (978-90-04-16204-4(6)) BRILL.

Gregory, Susan. The Daniel Fast: Feed Your Soul, Strengthen Your Spirit, & Renew Your Body. 2010. (ENG.). 288p. pap. 14.99 (978-1-4143-3413-4(3)) Tyndale Hse. Pubs.

Grey, Jacqueline. Three's a Crowd: Pentecostalism, Hermeneutics, & the Old Testament. 2011. 220p. pap. 24.00 **(978-1-60899-805-0(3)**, Pickwick Pubns.) Wipf & Stock Pubs.

Guthrie, Thomas. Gospel in Ezekiel Illustrated in A Serie. 2006. pap. 34.95 (978-1-4286-3559-3(9)) Kessinger Publishing, LLC.

—The Gospel in Ezekiel Illustrated in a Series of Discourses. 2006. (Illus.). 404p. per. 26.99 (978-1-4255-4383-9(9)) MPublishing.

Harman, Allan M. A Study Commentary on Daniel. 2007. (Ep Study Commentary Ser.). (Illus.). 333p. (978-0-85234-649-5(2)) Evangelical Pr.

Harrington, Daniel J. The Maccabean Revolt. 2009. 144p. pap. 18.00 (978-1-60899-113-6(X), Wipf and Stock) Wipf & Stock Pubs.

Hartley, Donald E. The Wisdom Background & Parabolic Implications of Isaiah 6: 9-10 in the Synoptics. 2006. (Studies in Biblical Literature: Vol. 100). (Illus.). 430p. (C). 86.95 (978-0-8204-8665-9(5)) Lang, Peter Publishing, Inc.

Hawley, Charles Arthur. The Teaching of Apocrypha & Apocalypse 1925. 2007. (ENG.). 184p. 37.95 (978-0-548-05638-7(2)) Kessinger Publishing, LLC.

Hayes, Elizabeth. The Pragmatics of Perception & Cognition in MT Jeremiah 1:1-6:30: A Cognitive Linguistics Approach. 2008. (Beihefte Zur Zeitschrift Für Die Alttestamentliche Wissenschaft Ser.). (ENG.). XII, 272p. 168.00 **(978-3-11-173873-4(6))** De Gruyter, Walter Inc.

Hayes, Elizabeth R. The Pragmatics of Perception & Cognition in MT Jeremiah 1:1-6:30: A Cognitive Linguistics Approach. 2008. (Beihefte Zur Zeitschrift Für Die Alttestamentliche Wissenschaft Ser.). (ENG., Illus.). XII, 272p. 105.00 (978-3-11-020229-8(8)) De Gruyter, Walter Inc.

Hayes, John Haralson. Israel's Prophets & Israel's Past: Essays on the Relationship of Prophetic Texts & Israelite History in Honor of John H. Hayes. Kelle, Brad E. & Moore, Megan Bishop, eds. 2006. (Library of Hebrew Bible/Old Testament Studies). (ENG., Illus.). 384p. 220.00 (978-0-567-02652-1(3), T&T Clark Int'l) Continuum International Publishing Group, Ltd. GBR. Dist: National Bk. Network.

Hebbard, Aaron B. Reading Daniel as a Text in Theological Hermeneutics. 2008. (Princeton Theological Monographs). 256p. pap. 28.00 (978-1-60608-991-0(9), Pickwick Pubns.) Wipf & Stock Pubs.

—Reading Daniel As a Text in Theological Hermeneutics Pb. 2011. (ENG.). 243p. pap. 42.50 (978-0-227-17364-0(3)) Clarke, James Co., Ltd. GBR. Dist: Brown, David Bk. Co., The.

Heffelfinger, Katie M. I Am Large, I Contain Multitudes: Lyric Cohesion & Conflict in Second Isaiah. 2011. (Illus.). xv, 328p. (978-90-04-19383-3(9)) BRILL.

Heiks, Heidi. The Daily Source Book. 2008. 220p. pap. 16.95 (978-1-57258-558-4(7)) TEACH Services, Inc.

Heller, Roy. Power, Politics, & Prophecy: The Character of Samuel & the Deuteronomistic Evaluation of Prophecy. 2006. (Library of Hebrew Bible/Old Testament Studies: Vol. 440). (ENG.). 184p. 160.00 (978-0-567-02762-7(7), T&T Clark Int'l) Continuum International Publishing Group, Ltd. GBR. Dist: National Bk. Network.

Heschel, Abraham Joshua. The Prophets. 2007. 522p. 29.95 (978-1-59856-181-4(2)) Hendrickson Pubs. Marketing, LLC.

Heskett, Randall. Reading the Book of Isaiah: Destruction & Lament in the Holy Cities. 2011. (ENG., Illus.). 240p. 90.00 (978-0-230-11685-6(X)) Palgrave Macmillan.

Heskett, Randall & Heskett. Messianism Within the Scriptural Scroll of Isaiah, Vol. 456. 2007. (T & T Clark Library of Biblical Studies). (ENG.). 368p. 160.00 (978-0-567-02922-5(0), T&T Clark Int'l) Continuum International Publishing Group, Ltd. GBR. Dist: National Bk. Network.

Hildreth, Lewis E. Isaiah Saw the Glory of Jesus: A Study of the Book of Isaiah. 2006. 188p. pap. 16.99 (978-1-4141-0742-4(0)) Pleasant Word.

Hom, Mary Katherine Y. H. The Characterisation of the Assyrians in Isaiah: Synchronic & Diachronic Perspectives. 2012. (Library Hebrew Bible/Old Testament Studies). (ENG., Illus.). 256p. 130.00 **(978-0-567-63171-8(0)**, T&T Clark Int'l) Continuum International Publishing Group, Ltd. GBR. Dist: National Bk. Network.

Howard, Anna Aven. Creative Bible Lessons in Ezekiel: Ancient Revelations for a Postmodern Generation, 1 vol. 2007. (Creative Bible Lessons Ser.). (ENG.). 144p. (gr. 13). pap. 14.99 (978-0-310-26960-1(1)) Zondervan.

Howe, Thomas A. Daniel in the Preterists' Den: A Critical Look at Preterist Interpretations of Daniel. 2008. 742p. pap. 77.00 (978-1-55635-273-7(5), Wipf and Stock) Wipf & Stock Pubs.

Hyland Lavik, Marta. A People Tall & Smooth-Skinned: The Rhetoric of Isaiah 18. 2006. (Supplements to Vetus Testamentum Ser.). 274p. (978-90-04-15434-6(5)) BRILL.

Ironside, Henry A. Estudios sobre el Libro de Isaías: Lectures on the Book of Isaiah. (SPA.). (978-84-7645-195-3(4), 223242) Clie, Editorial.

Isaac Newton. Observations upon the Prophecies of Daniel & the Apocalypse of St John. 2011. 204p. pap. 5.89 **(978-1-60386-402-2(4)**, Watchmaker Publishing) Wexford College Pr.

Jindo, Job Y. Biblical Metaphor Reconsidered: A Cognitive Approach to Poetic Prophecy in Jeremiah 1-24. 2010. 39.95 (978-1-57506-936-4(9)) Eisenbrauns, Inc.

Job, John B. Jeremiah's Kings: A Study of the Monarchy in Jeremiah. 2006. (Society for Old Testament Study Monographs). (Illus.). 248p. 99.95 (978-0-7546-5505-3(9)) Ashgate Publishing Co.

Johnson, Dan G. From Chaos to Restoration: An Integrative Reading of Isaiah 24-27. 2009. (Library of Hebrew Bible/Old Testament Studies, the Ser.). (ENG.). 150p. 27.95 (978-0-567-06982-5(6), T&T Clark) Continuum International Publishing Group, Ltd. GBR. Dist: National Bk. Network.

Joo, Samantha. Provocation & Punishment: The Anger of God in the Book of Jeremiah & Deuteronomistic Theology. (Beihefte zur Zeitschrift far die alttestamentliche Wissenschaft Ser.). (ENG.). XIV, 320p. 225.00 **(978-3-11-184527-2(3))**; 2006. 140.00 (978-3-11-018994-0(1)) De Gruyter, Walter Inc.

Joyce, Paul M. After Ezekiel: Essays on the Reception of a Difficult Prophet. Mein, Andrew & Joyce, Paul M., eds. 2010. (Library of Hebrew Bible/Old Testament Studies). (ENG., Illus.). 304p. 130.00 (978-0-567-53369-2(7), T&T Clark Int'l) Continuum International Publishing Group, Ltd. GBR. Dist: National Bk. Network.

Kalmanofsky, Amy. Terror All Around: The Rhetoric of Horror in the Book of Jeremiah. 2008. (T & T Clark Library of Biblical Studies). (ENG.). 176p. 105.00 (978-0-567-02656-9(6), T&T Clark Int'l) Continuum International Publishing Group, Ltd. GBR. Dist: National Bk. Network.

Kempin, Albert J. Daniel for Today. 2007. per. 13.00 (978-1-60416-011-6(X)) Reformation Pubs.

Kimchi, David B. Commentary of David Kimchi on Isaiah. Finkelstein, Louis, ed. (Columbia University, Oriental Studies: No. 19). reprint ed. 32.50 (978-0-404-50509-7(0)) AMS Pr., Inc.

Kirkpatrick, A. F. The Doctrine of the Prophets. 2007. (ENG.). 564p. 58.95 (978-0-548-01903-0(7)) Kessinger Publishing, LLC.

Klein, Peter. Jesaja 40,1-11 als Prolog: Ein Beitrag zur Komposition Deuterojesajas. 2009. (Wiener Alttestamentliche Studien Ser.). (GER.). 332p. pap. 81.95 (978-3-631-57227-6(1)) Lang, Peter GmbH, Europaischer Verlag der Wissenschaften DEU. Dist: Lang, Peter.

Kooij, Arie van der, et al. Isaiah in Context: Studies in Honour of Arie Van der Kooij on the Occasion of His Sixty-Fifth Birthday. 2010. (978-90-04-18657-6(3)) BRILL.

Koyzis, Nancy Calvert & Weir, Heather E. Strangely Familiar: Protofeminist Interpretations of Patriarchal Biblical Texts. 2009. 304p. pap. 35.95 (978-1-58983-453-8(4)) Society of Biblical Literature.

Larocca-Pitts, Mark. The Day of Yahweh. 2009. 364p. pap. (978-3-639-14940-1(8)) VDM Verlag Dr. Mueller e.K.

Launderville, Dale F. Spirit & Reason: The Embodied Character of Ezekiel's Symbolic Thinking. 2007. 475p. per. 39.95 (978-1-60258-005-3(7)) Baylor Univ. Pr.

Lee, Nancy C. & Mandolfo, Carleen. Lamentations in Ancient & Contemporary Cultural Contexts. Lee, Nancy, ed. 2008. 160p. (C). (978-90-04-15747-7(6)) BRILL.

—Lamentations in Ancient & Contemporary Cultural Contexts. 2008. 288p. pap. 34.95 (978-1-58983-357-9(0)) Society of Biblical Literature.

Leuchter, Mark. The Polemics of Exile in Jeremiah 26-45. (ENG.). 2011. 336p. pap. 39.99 (978-0-521-18276-8(X)) 2007. 334p. 111.00 (978-0-521-87991-0(4)) Cambridge Univ. Pr.

Levitt Kohn, Risa. New Heart & a New Soul: Ezekiel, the Exile & the Torah. 2009. (Library of Hebrew Bible/Old Testament Studies, the Ser.). (ENG.). 160p. 29.95 (978-0-567-02233-2(1), T&T Clark) Continuum International Publishing Group, Ltd. GBR. Dist: National Bk. Network.

Lim, Bo H. The Way of the Lord in the Book of Isaiah. 2010. (Library of Hebrew Bible/Old Testament Studies). (ENG.). 224p. (978-0-567-02763-4(5), T&T Clark Int'l) Continuum International Publishing Group, Ltd.

Lotz, Anne Graham. I Saw the Lord: A Wake-up Call for Your Heart, 1 vol. 2007. (ENG.). 112p. (gr. 13). pap., instr.'s gde. ed. 9.99 (978-0-310-27520-6(2)) Zondervan.

—I Saw the Lord: A Wake-Up Call for Your Heart, 1 vol. 2007. (ENG.). 240p. (gr. 13). pap. 14.99 (978-0-310-28470-3(8)) Zondervan.

Lundbom, Jack R. Jeremiah Closer Up: The Prophet & the Book. 2010. 138p. (978-1-907534-07-2(5)) Sheffield Phoenix Pr.

Lyons, Michael A. & Lyons, Michael. From Law to Prophecy: Ezekiel's Use of the Holiness Code. 2009. (Library of Hebrew Bible/Old Testament Studies, the Ser.). (ENG.). 240p. 120.00 (978-0-567-02725-2(2), T&T Clark Int'l) Continuum International Publishing Group, Ltd. GBR. Dist: National Bk. Network.

Ma, Wonsuk. Until the Spirit Comes: The Spirit of God in the Book of Isaiah. 2009. (Library of Hebrew Bible/Old Testament Studies, the Ser.). (ENG.). 256p. 44.95 (978-0-567-13625-1(6), T&T Clark) Continuum International Publishing Group, Ltd. GBR. Dist: National Bk. Network.

MacIntosh, A. A. Isaiah XXI: A Palimpsest. 2009. (ENG.). 172p. pap. 31.99 (978-0-521-09462-7(3)) Cambridge Univ. Pr.

Macwilliam, Stuart. Queer Theory & the Prophetic Marriage Metaphor in the Hebrew Bible. 2011. (BibleWorld Ser.). (ENG., Illus.). 264p. (C). 99.95 (978-1-84553-672-5(X)); pap. 34.95 (978-1-84553-673-2(8)) Equinox Publishing Ltd. GBR. Dist: ISD.

Mallen, Peter & Mallen. The Reading & Transformation of Isaiah in Luke-Acts. 2008. (Library of New Testament Studies, the Ser.). (ENG.). 258p. 130.00 (978-0-567-04566-9(8), T&T Clark Int'l) Continuum International Publishing Group, Ltd. GBR. Dist: National Bk. Network.

Mandolfo, Carleen. Daughter Zion Talks Back to the Prophets: A Dialogic Theology of the Book of Lamentations. 2007. ix, 149p. 24.95 (978-1-58983-247-3(7)) Society of Biblical Literature.

Mandolfo, Carleen R. Daughter Zion Talks Back to the Prophets: A Dialogic Theology of the Book of Lamentations. 2007. (SBL - Semeia Studies). 149p. (978-90-04-15119-2(2)) BRILL.

Mathews, Claire R. Defending Zion: Edom's Desolation & Jacob's Restoration (Isaiah 34-35) in Context. (Beihefte zur Zeitschrift far die alttestamentliche Wissenschaft Ser.). (ENG.). XII, 190p. 210.00 **(978-3-11-177301-8(9))** De Gruyter, Walter Inc.

Mathews McGinnis, Claire, ed. As Those Who Are Taught: The Interpretation of Isaiah from the LXX to the SBL. 2006. (SBL - Symposium Ser.). 342p. (978-90-04-13041-8(1)) BRILL.

Matthews, Victor H. 101 Questions & Answers on the Prophets of Israel. 2007. (Responses to 101 Questions... Ser.). (Illus.). 160p. pap. 14.95 (978-0-8091-4478-5(6), 4478-5) Paulist Pr.

Mayfield, Tyler D. Literary Structure & Setting in Ezekiel. 2010. (Illus.). 240p. pap. 107.50 (978-3-16-150272-9(8)) Mohr Siebeck GmbH & Co. KG DEU. Dist: Coronet Bks.

McClain, Alva J. Daniel's Prophecy of the 70 Weeks. 2006. (Illus.). 73p. per. 8.99 (978-0-88469-211-9(6)) BMH Bks.

—Daniel's Prophecy of the Seventy Weeks. pap. 7.99 (978-0-88469-076-4(8)) BMH Bks.

McKay, Heather A. Of Prophets' Visions & the Wisdom of Sages: Essays in Honour of R. Norman Whybray on his Seventieth Birthday. Clines, David J. A., ed. 2009. (Library of Hebrew Bible/Old Testament Studies, the Ser.). (ENG.). 335p. 55.00 (978-0-567-35484-6(9), T&T Clark) Continuum International Publishing Group, Ltd. GBR. Dist: National Bk. Network.

McKenzie, Duncan W. The Antichrist & the Second Coming Vol. 1: A Preterist Examination. 2009. 468p. 36.99 (978-1-61579-038-6(1)); pap. 24.99 (978-1-61579-037-1(3)) Xulon Pr., Inc.

McKinney, Edward. From Nebuchadnezzar to Gorbachev, the Story of Babylon, Book 1 Of 3. 2010. 268p. pap. 29.95 (978-0-557-26850-4(8)) Lulu Enterprises Inc.

McTernan, John P. Only Jesus of Nazareth Can Be the God of Israel's Righteous Servant. 2007. 200p. per. 14.99 (978-1-60477-483-2(5)) Xulon Pr., Inc.

Meadowcroft, T. J. Aramaic Daniel & Greek Daniel: A Literary Comparison. 2009. (Library of Hebrew Bible/Old Testament Studies, the Ser.). (ENG.). 336p. 55.00 (978-0-567-30693-7(3), T&T Clark) Continuum International Publishing Group, Ltd. GBR. Dist: National Bk. Network.

Melugin, Roy F. The Formation of Isaiah 40-55. (Beihefte zur Zeitschrift far die alttestamentliche Wissenschaft Ser.). (ENG.). XII, 186p. 210.00 **(978-3-11-175445-1(6))** De Gruyter, Walter Inc.

Melugin, Roy F. New Visions of Isaiah. Sweeney, Marvin A., ed. 2009. (Library of Hebrew Bible/Old Testament Studies, the Ser.). (ENG.). 344p. 55.00 (978-0-567-11349-8(3), T&T Clark) Continuum International Publishing Group, Ltd. GBR. Dist: National Bk. Network.

Meyer, F. b. & Meyer, F. B. Choice Notes on Joshua Through 2 Kings. 2011. 182p. pap. 16.99 **(978-1-61203-266-5(4))** Bottom of the Hill Publishing.

Migsch, Herbert. Studien zum Jeremiabuch und andere Beiträge zum Alten Testament. 2010. (Österreichische Biblische Studien Ser.). (GER.). 358p. 75.95 (978-3-631-60171-6(9)) Lang, Peter GmbH, Europaischer Verlag der Wissenschaften DEU. Dist: Lang, Peter.

Mihalios, Stefanos. The Danielic Eschatological Hour in the Johannine Literature. 2011. (Library of New Testament Studies). (ENG.). 224p. 120.00 (978-0-567-36720-4(7), T&T Clark Int'l) Continuum International Publishing Group, Ltd. GBR. Dist: National Bk. Network.

Mills, Mary E. Urban Imagination in Biblical Prophecy. 2012. (Library Hebrew Bible/Old Testament Studies). (ENG.). 272p. 130.00 **(978-0-567-11141-8(5)**, T&T Clark Int'l) Continuum International Publishing Group, Ltd. GBR. Dist: National Bk. Network.

Mills, Mary E. & Mills. Alterity, Pain & Suffering in Isaiah, Jeremiah & Ezekiel, Vol. 479. 2007. (T & T Clark Library of Biblical Studies). (ENG.). 192p. 130.00 (978-0-567-02693-4(0), T&T Clark Int'l) Continuum International Publishing Group, Ltd. GBR. Dist: National Bk. Network.

Modine, Mitchel. The Dialogues of Jeremiah. 2009. 110.00 (978-1-60724-028-0(9)) Gorgias Pr., LLC.

Mol. Collective & Individual Responsibility: A Description of Corporate Personality in Ezekiel 18 And 20. 2009. (Studia Semitica Neerlandica Ser.). 300p. (978-90-04-17043-8(X)) BRILL.

Moon, Joshua. Jeremiah's New Covenant: An Augustinian Reading. 2011. pap. (978-1-57506-702-5(1)) Eisenbrauns, Inc.

Morgan, G. Campbell. Studies in the Prophecy of Jeremiah. 2010. (G. Campbell Morgan Reprint Ser.). 288p. pap. 32.00 (978-1-60899-297-3(7), Wipf and Stock) Wipf & Stock Pubs.

Morrow, William. Protest Against God: The Eclipse of a Bi. 2006. (ENG.). 264p. (978-1-905048-20-5(3)) Sheffield Phoenix Pr.

Moughtin-Mumby, Sharon. Sexual & Marital Metaphors in Hosea, Jeremiah, Isaiah, & Ezekiel. 2008. (Oxford Theological Monographs). (ENG.). 350p. 150.00 (978-0-19-923908-5(8)) Oxford Univ. Pr., Inc.

Murray, Andrew. Standing in the Gap. 2009. 101p. pap. (978-1-77036-052-5(2)) Christian Art Pubs.

—Wings Like Eagles. 2009. (Illus.). 69p. pap. (978-1-77036-053-2(0)) Christian Art Pubs.

Newton, Isaac. Observations upon the Prophecies of Daniel, & the Apocalypse of St John. 2007. (ENG.). 176p. per. (978-1-4065-5033-7(7)) Dodo Pr.

—Observations upon the Prophecies of Daniel, & the Apocalypse of St John. 2007. 120p. per. (978-1-4068-3454-3(8)) Echo Library.

—Observations upon the Prophecies of Daniel, & the Apocalypse of St John. 148p. 2009. 29.99 (978-1-59547-550-3(8)) 2007. (ENG.). per. 12.99 (978-1-59547-841-2(8)) NuVision Pubns., LLC.

—Observations upon the Prophecies of Daniel & the Apocalypse of St. John: In Two Parts. 2007. (ENG.). 188p. pap. 19.99 (978-1-4346-0577-1(9)); 208p. pap. 22.99 (978-1-4346-0652-5(X)) BiblioBazaar.

Nibley, Hugh. The COLL Works of Hugh Nibley,8. 2009. 512p. 45.95 (978-1-60641-054-7(7)) Deseret Bk. Co.

Nielsen, Kirsten. There Is Hope for a Tree: The Tree as Metaphor in Isaiah. 2009. (Library of Hebrew Bible/Old Testament Studies, the Ser.). (ENG.). 301p. 49.95 (978-0-567-58238-6(8), T&T Clark) Continuum International Publishing Group, Ltd. GBR. Dist: National Bk. Network.

Nixon Ph. D., Thomas C. The Prophecy of Daniel: Unsealed. 2008. 260p. pap. 15.99 (978-1-4389-2061-0(X)) AuthorHouse.

O'Brien, Julia M. Challenging Prophetic Metaphor: Theology & Ideology in the Prophets. 2008. (ENG.). 224p. pap. 25.00 (978-0-664-22964-1(6)) Westminster John Knox Pr.

O'Brien, Julia M. & Franke, Chris, eds. The Aesthetics of Violence in the Prophets, Vol. 517. 2010. (Library of Hebrew Bible/Old Testament Studies, the Ser.). (ENG., Illus.). 208p. 120.00 (978-0-567-54811-5(2), T&T Clark Int'l) Continuum International Publishing Group, Ltd. GBR. Dist: National Bk. Network.

O'Connell, Robert H. Concentricity & Continuity: The Literary Structure of Isaiah. 2009. (Library of Hebrew Bible/Old Testament Studies, the Ser.). (ENG.). 272p. 44.95 (978-0-567-63952-3(5), T&T Clark) Continuum International Publishing Group, Ltd. GBR. Dist: National Bk. Network.

O'Connor, Kathleen M. Jeremiah: Pain & Promise. 2011. 192p. (C). 49.00 (978-0-8006-2040-0(2), Fortress Pr.) Augsburg Fortress, Pubs.

O'Hare, Daniel M. Have You Seen, Son of Man? Studies in the Translation & Vorlage of LXX Ezekiel 40-48. 2010. **(978-1-58983-527-6(1))**; (978-1-58983-526-9(3)) Society of Biblical Literature.

Olley, John W. Ezekiel: A Commentary Based on Iezekiel in Codex Vaticanus. 2009. (Septuagint Commentary Ser.). 599p. (978-90-04-17713-0(2)) BRILL.

Opoku-Gyimah, Fred. End Time Prophecy. 2009. 92p. pap. 10.99 (978-1-60791-281-1(3)) Xulon Pr., Inc.

Osuji, A. C. Where Is the Truth? Narrative Exegesis & the Question of True & False Prophecy in Jer 26-29 (MT) 2010. (Bibliotheca Ephemeridum Theologicarum Lovaniensium Ser.). (ENG.). 485p. (C). pap. 111.00 (978-90-429-2084-2(X)) Peeters Pubs. & Booksellers BEL. Dist: Brown, David Bk. Co., The.

Parry, Robin & Thomas, Heath, eds. Great Is Thy Faithfulness? Reading Lamentations as Sacred Scripture. 2011. (Illus.). 310p. pap. 34.00 **(978-1-61097-453-0(0)**, Pickwick Pubns.) Wipf & Stock Pubs.

Patmore, Hector M. Adam, Satan, & the King of Tyre: The Interpretation of Ezekiel 28:11-19 in Late Antiquity. 2011. (Jewish & Christian Perspectives Ser.). **(978-90-04-20722-6(8))** BRILL.

Payne, David, et al. Isaiah 40-55, 2 vols., Vol. 2. 2007. (International Critical Commentary on the Holy Scriptures of the Old & New Testaments Ser.). (ENG.). 392p. 140.00 (978-0-567-03072-6(5), T&T Clark Int'l) Continuum International Publishing Group, Ltd. GBR. Dist: National Bk. Network.

—Isaiah 40-55 Vol. 1: A Critical & Exegetical Commentary, 2 vols. 2007. (International Critical Commentary on the Holy Scriptures of the Old & New Testaments Ser.). (ENG.). 424p. 140.00 (978-0-567-04461-7(0), T&T Clark Int'l) Continuum International Publishing Group, Ltd. GBR. Dist: National Bk. Network.

Person, Raymond F., Jr. The Deuteronomic History & the Book of Chronicles: Scribal Works in an Oral World. 2010. 218p. pap. 26.95 (978-1-58983-517-7(4)) Society of Biblical Literature.

Person, Raymond F. The Deuteronomic History & the Book of Chronicles: Scribal Works in an Oral World. 2010. xii, 205p. *(978-1-58983-518-4(2))* Society of Biblical Literature.

Petersen, David. Roles of Israel's Prophets. 2009. (Library of Hebrew Bible/Old Testament Studies, the Ser.). (ENG.). 131p. 27.95 *(978-1-85539-628-9(9),* T&T Clark) Continuum International Publishing Group, Ltd. GBR. Dist: National Bk. Network.

Pettingill, W. L. Estudios Sobre el Libro de Daniel: Studies on the Book of Daniel. (SPA.). *(978-84-7228-994-9(X),* 223065) Clie, Editorial.

Plant. Good Figs, Bad Figs: Judicial Differentiation in the Book of Jeremiah. 2008. (Library of Hebrew Bible/Old Testament Studies, the Ser.). (ENG.). 242p. 140.00 *(978-0-567-02687-3(6),* T&T Clark Int'l) Continuum International Publishing Group, Ltd. GBR. Dist: National Bk. Network.

Podhoretz, Norman. The Prophets: Who They Were, What They Are. 2010. (ENG.). 400p. pap. 24.99 *(978-1-4516-1293-6(1),* Free Pr.) Free Pr.

Rata, Tiberius. The Covenant Motif in Jeremiah's Book of Comfort: Textual & Intertextual Studies of Jeremiah 30-33. 2007. (Studies in Biblical Literature Ser.: Vol. 105). 192p. (C). 64.95 *(978-0-8204-9508-8(5))* Lang, Peter Publishing, Inc.

Redditt, Paul L. Introduction to the Prophets. 2008. 360p. pap. 26.00 *(978-0-8028-2896-5(5))* Eerdmans, William B. Publishing Co.

Reid, Stephen Breck. Prophets & Paradigms: Essays in Honor of Gene M. Tucker. 2009. (Library of Hebrew Bible/Old Testament Studies, the Ser.). (ENG.). 248p. 39.95 *(978-0-567-02773-3(2),* T&T Clark) Continuum International Publishing Group, Ltd. GBR. Dist: National Bk. Network.

Remley, Paul G. Old English Biblical Verse: Studies in Genesis, Exodus & Daniel. 2007. (Cambridge Studies in Anglo-Saxon England Ser.). (ENG.). 496p. pap. 90.00 *(978-0-521-03280-3(6))* Cambridge Univ. Pr.

Risbeck, John S. Daniel & Revelation Bound Together. Barry, Marian G., ed. 2010. (Illus.). 327p. spiral bd. 29.95 *(978-1-57258-537-9(4))* TEACH Services, Inc.

Robertson, O. Palmer. The Christ of the Prophets. 2008. pap. *(978-1-59638-066-0(7))* P & R Publishing.

Robinson, Freddie. The Book of Daniel Unsealed. pap. 12.95 *(978-0-9640487-2-0(8))* Transfiguration Production Co.

Robson, James. Word & Spirit in Ezekiel, Vol. 447. 2006. (T & T Clark Library of Biblical Studies: Vol. 447). (ENG.). 340p. 170.00 *(978-0-567-02622-4(1),* T&T Clark Int'l) Continuum International Publishing Group, Ltd. GBR. Dist: National Bk. Network.

Roosenberg, Tim & Lale, Tim. Islam & Christianity: The Coming Holy War. 2011. ***(978-0-8280-2592-8(4))*** Review & Herald Publishing Assn.

Rowland, Christopher. "Wheels Within Wheels" William Blake & the Ezekiel's Merkabah in Text & Image. 2007. (C). *(978-0-87462-587-5(4))* Marquette Univ. Pr.

Rowley, H. H. Darius the Mede & the Four World Empires in the Book of Daniel: A Historical Study of Contemporary Theories. 2006. (Illus.). 232p. pap. 25.00 *(978-1-59752-896-2(X),* Wipf and Stock) Wipf & Stock Pubs.

Sandy, D. Brent, et al. Prophecy & Apocalyptic: An Annotated Bibliography. 2007. (IBR Bibliographies Ser.). 240p. (C). pap. 28.00 *(978-0-8010-2601-0(6))* Baker Academic.

Sayour, George. Plans to Prosper You: Find Your Purpose Through Jeremiah 29. 2006. (ENG.). 240p. 30.99 *(978-1-4141-0764-6(1));* per. 17.99 *(978-1-4141-0765-3(X))* Pleasant Word.

Schafer, P. Origins of Jewish Mysticism. 2011. (ENG.). 416p. (C). pap. 35.00 *(978-0-691-14215-9(7))* Princeton Univ. Pr.

Scheetz, Jordan M. The Concept of Canonical Intertextuality & the Book of Daniel. 2012. (ENG.). 184p. pap. 30.00 ***(978-0-227-68020-9(0))*** Clarke, James Co., Ltd. GBR. Dist: Brown, David Bk. Co., The.

—The Concept of Canonical Intertextuality & the Book of Daniel. 2011. 184p. pap. 21.00 *(978-1-60899-516-5(X),* Pickwick Pubns.) Wipf & Stock Pubs.

Schenker, Adrian. Das Neue am Neuen Bund und das Alte am Alten: Jer 31 in der Hebraischen und Griechischen Bibel, von der Textgeschichte Zu Theologie, Synagoge und Kirche. 2006. (Forschungen Zur Religion und Literatur des Alten & Neuen Testament Ser.). (GER.). 108p. (C). pap. 54.00 *(978-3-525-53076-4(5))* Vandenhoeck & Ruprecht GmbH & Co. KG DEU. Dist: ISD.

Scheuer, Blaenka. The Return of YHWH: The Tension Between Deliverance & Repentance in Isaiah 40-55. 2008. (Beihefte Zur Zeitschrift Für Die Alttestamentliche Wissenschaft Ser.). (ENG.). XV, 175p. 105.00 *(978-3-11-019034-2(6))* De Gruyter, Walter Inc.

Schramm, Brooks. Opponents of Third Isaiah: Reconstructing the Cultic History of the Restoration. 2009. (Library of Hebrew Bible/Old Testament Studies, the Ser.). (ENG.). 216p. 39.95 *(978-0-567-10214-0(9),* T&T Clark) Continuum International Publishing Group, Ltd. GBR. Dist: National Bk. Network.

Schreiber, Mordecai. The Man Who Knew God: Decoding Jeremiah. 2009. (ENG.). 196p. 68.50 *(978-0-7391-4345-2(X));* pap. 29.50 *(978-0-7391-4346-9(8))* Lexington Bks.

Schultz, Richard L. Search for Quotation: Verbal Parallels in the Prophets. 2009. (Library of Hebrew Bible/Old Testament Studies, the Ser.). (ENG.). 400p. 65.00 *(978-0-567-61967-9(2),* T&T Clark) Continuum International Publishing Group, Ltd. GBR. Dist: National Bk. Network.

Seitz, Christopher R. The Goodly Fellowship of the Prophets: The Achievement of Association in Canon Formation, 1 vol. 2009. (Acadia Studies in Bible & Theology Ser.). 144p. (C). pap. 20.00 *(978-0-8010-3883-9(9))* Baker Academic.

—Prophecy & Hermeneutics: Toward a New Introduction to the Prophets. 2007. (Studies in Theological Interpretation Ser.). 272p. (C). pap. 23.00 *(978-0-8010-3258-5(X))* Baker Academic.

Selvaggio, Anthony T. The Prophets Speak of Him: Encountering Jesus in the Minor Prophets. 2006. (Emmaus Ser.). 196p. per. *(978-0-85234-612-9(3))* Evangelical Pr.

Silva, Kittim. Daniel: Historia y Profecia: History & Prophecy, 1 vol. 2009. (SPA.). 264p. pap. 12.99 *(978-84-7228-975-8(3),* 223038) Clie, Editorial ESP. Dist: Zondervan.

Silverman, Jason M. Persepolis & Jerusalem: Iranian Influence on the Apocalyptic Hermeneutic. 2012. (ENG., Illus.). 320p. 140.00 ***(978-0-567-20551-3(7),*** T&T Clark) Continuum International Publishing Group, Ltd. GBR. Dist: National Bk. Network.

Sink, Susan. The Art of the Saint John's Bible: A Reader's Guide to Wisdom Books & Prophets, Vol. 2. 2008. 128p. pap. 14.95 *(978-0-8146-9063-5(7))* Liturgical Pr.

Smith, E. A. The End of Seven Days. 2007. 139p. pap. 24.95 *(978-1-60441-829-3(X))* PublishAmerica, Inc.

Smith, Gary V. Isaiah 1-39, Vol. 15A. 2007. (New American Commentary Ser.). 696p. 32.99 *(978-0-8054-0115-8(6))* B&H Publishing Group.

Smith, J. M. Powis. The Prophet & His Problems. 2007. (ENG.). 260p. 42.95 *(978-0-548-08426-7(2))* Kessinger Publishing, LLC.

Smith, James E. Daniel: A Christian Interpretation. 2008. 420p. pap. 22.94 *(978-1-4357-0597-5(1))* Lulu Enterprises Inc.

Smith, R. D. Visions of Daniel: Fulfilled. 2007. Orig. Title: "". 124p. per. 14.95 *(978-1-57472-402-8(9))* Archer Ellison Publishing Co.

Smith, Uriah. The Sanctuary & the Twenty-Three Hundred Days of Daniel Viii, 14 by Uriah Smith. 2006. 388p. per. 26.99 *(978-1-4255-4071-5(6))* MPublishing.

Staton, Cecil. Interpreting Isaiah for Preaching & Teaching. 7.00 *(978-0-687-82353-6(6))* Abingdon Pr.

Stefanovic, Zdravko. Aramaic of Daniel in the Light of Old Aramaic. 2009. (Library of Hebrew Bible/Old Testament Studies, the Ser.). (ENG.). 128p. 27.95 *(978-0-567-17443-7(3),* T&T Clark) Continuum International Publishing Group, Ltd. GBR. Dist: National Bk. Network.

Stein, Valerie A. Anti-Cultic Theology in Christian Biblical Interpretation: A Study of Isaiah 66:1-4 & Its Reception. 2007. (Studies in Biblical Literature: Vol. 97). 178p. (C). 62.95 *(978-0-8204-8618-5(3))* Lang, Peter Publishing, Inc.

Steinmann, Andrew E. Daniel. 2008. (Concordia Commentary Ser.). 42.99 *(978-0-7586-0695-2(8))* Concordia Publishing Hse.

Stromberg, Jacob. Isaiah after Exile: The Author of Third Isaiah as Reader & Redactor of the Book. 2011. (ENG.). 320p. 125.00 *(978-0-19-959391-0(4))* Oxford Univ. Pr., Inc.

Sweeney, Marvin A. Form & Intertextuality in Prophetic & Apocalyptic Literature. 2010. 308p. pap. 34.00 *(978-1-60899-418-2(X),* Wipf and Stock) Wipf & Stock Pubs.

Swint, Mark. Compare Isaiah: A Look at Biblical Scriptures in the Book of Mormon. 2009. pap. 12.99 *(978-0-88290-960-8(6))* Cedar Fort, Inc./CFI Distribution.

Taylor, Preston. Ezekiel Gods Prophet & His Puzzling Bo. 2006. pap. 15.99 *(978-1-60034-524-1(7))* Xulon Pr., Inc.

Thelle, Rannfrid Irene. Approaches to the 'Chosen Place' Accessing a Biblical Concept. 2011. (ENG.). 256p. (gr. 17). 140.00 ***(978-0-567-46807-9(0),*** T&T Clark) Continuum International Publishing Group, Ltd. GBR. Dist: National Bk. Network.

Thurman, William C. The Sealed Book of Daniel Opened. 2009. 194p. pap. 17.42 *(978-1-151-00849-7(4))* General Bks. LLC.

Tooman, William A. Gog of Magog: Reuse of Scripture & Compositional Technique in Ezekiel 38-39. 2011. (Forschungen zum Alten Testament Ser.). 354p. pap. 157.50 ***(978-3-16-150857-8(2))*** Mohr Siebeck GmbH & Co. KG DEU. Dist: Coronet Bks.

Tooman, William A. & Lyons, Michael A. Transforming Visions: Transformations of Text, Tradition, & Theology in Ezekiel. 2011. (ENG.). 350p. pap. 48.00 *(978-0-227-17368-8(6))* Clarke, James Co., Ltd. GBR. Dist: Brown, David Bk. Co., The.

Tooman, William A. & Lyons, Michael A., eds. Transforming Visions. 2009. (Princeton Theological Monographs). (Illus.). 378p. pap. 42.00 *(978-1-55635-285-0(9),* Pickwick Pubns.) Wipf & Stock Pubs.

Towns, Elmer L. The Daniel Fast for Spiritual Breakthrough. 2010. (ENG.). 192p. pap. 12.99 *(978-0-8307-5473-1(3))* Gospel Light Pubns.

Tregelles, S. P. Tregelles on Daniel: Remarks on the Prophetic Visions in the Book of Daniel. 2007. 254p. pap. 25.00 *(978-1-55635-615-5(3),* Wipf and Stock) Wipf & Stock Pubs.

Troxel, Ronald L. Prophetic Literature: From Oracles to Books. (ENG.). 288p. 2012. 89.95 ***(978-1-4051-8846-3(4))*** 2011. pap. 34.95 ***(978-1-4051-8845-6(6))*** Wiley, John & Sons, Inc. (Wiley-Blackwell).

Uhlig, Torsten. The Theme of Hardening in the Book of Isaiah: An Analysis of Communicative Action. 2009. 423p. pap. 167.50 *(978-3-16-150143-2(8))* Mohr Siebeck GmbH & Co. KG DEU. Dist: Coronet Bks.

Umoren, Gerald. The Salvation of the Remnant in Isaiah: 11-12. 2007. 316p. per. 29.95 *(978-1-58112-375-3(2),* Dissertation.com) Universal Pubs.

Valeta, David M. Lions & Ovens & Visions: A Satirical Reading of Daniel 1-6. 2008. xii, 230p. *(978-1-905048-53-3(X))* Sheffield Phoenix Pr.

Van der Kooij, A. & Van der Meer, M. N., eds. Old Greek of Isaiah: Issues & Perspectives. Papers read at the Conference on the Septuagint of Isaiah, held in Leiden 10-11 April 2008. 2010. (Contributions to Biblical Exegesis & Theology Ser.). (ENG.). 253p. (C). pap. 56.00 *(978-90-429-2351-5(2))* Peeters Pubs. & Booksellers BEL. Dist: Brown, David Bk. Co., The.

van der Meer, Willem. Structural Analysis of Biblical & Canaanite Poetry. 2009. (Library of Hebrew Bible/Old Testament Studies, the Ser.). (ENG.). 75.00 *(978-0-567-57423-7(7),* T&T Clark) Continuum International Publishing Group, Ltd. GBR. Dist: National Bk. Network.

Waggoner, J. H. From Eden to Eden. 2009. 224p. pap. *(978-0-217-69723-1(2))* Books LLC.

Werner, Wolfgang. Studien zur alttestamentlichen Vorstellung vom Plan Jahwes. (Beihefte zur Zeitschrift fur die alttestamentliche Wissenschaft Ser.). (GER.). XII, 334p. 238.00 ***(978-3-11-179199-9(8))*** De Gruyter, Walter Inc.

Whaley, Charles. Prophetic, Post-Apostolic & Postmodern: Three Bible Studies from a Missionary to Japan. 2009. pap. *(978-1-57312-548-2(2))* Smyth & Helwys Publishing, Inc.

Whybray, R. N. The Heavenly Counsellor in Isaiah XI 13-14: A Study of the Sources of the Theology of Deutero-Isaiah. 2009. (Society for Old Testament Study Monographs). (ENG.). 100p. pap. 31.99 *(978-0-521-09627-0(8))* Cambridge Univ. Pr.

Wiersbe, Warren W. Be Comforted (Isaiah) Feeling Secure in the Arms of God, 1 vol. 2009. (BE Ser. Commentary Ser.). (ENG.). 192p. pap. 12.99 *(978-1-4347-6615-1(2))* Cook, David C.

Williamson. Isaiah 13-27 (Icc) 2011. (International Critical Commentary Ser.). 640p. 120.00 *(978-0-567-03058-0(X),* T&T Clark Int'l) Continuum International Publishing Group, Ltd. GBR. Dist: National Bk. Network.

Williamson, H. G. M. Holy, Holy, Holy: The Story of a Liturgical Formula. 2008. (Julius-Wellhausen-Vorlesung Ser.). (ENG.). IV, 36p. pap. 28.00 *(978-3-11-020716-3(8))* De Gruyter, Walter Inc.

Williamson, H. G. M. & InterVarsity Press Staff. Interpreting Isaiah: Issues & Approaches, 1 vol. Firth, David G. & Williamson, H. G. M., eds. 2009. (ENG.). 287p. pap. 28.00 *(978-0-8308-3703-8(5),* IVP Acad.) InterVarsity Pr.

Willis, Amy Merrill. Dissonance & the Drama of Divine Sovereignty in the Book of Daniel. 2010. (Library of Hebrew Bible/Old Testament Studies, the Ser.). (ENG.). 240p. 130.00 *(978-0-567-37948-1(5),* T&T Clark Int'l) Continuum International Publishing Group, Ltd. GBR. Dist: National Bk. Network.

Wilson, Robert Dick. Studies in the Book of Daniel. 2009. 268p. pap. *(978-0-217-05878-0(7))* Books LLC.

Witcomb. Tabla de los Reyes/Profetas del A. T. - Chart of the O. T. Kings & Prophets. (Tablas Cronologicas Ser.). (SPA.). *(978-1-56063-932-9(6))* Editorial Unilit.

Woods, Julie. Jeremiah 48 as Christian Scripture. 2011. pap. 42.50 *(978-0-227-17378-7(3))* Clarke, James Co., Ltd. GBR. Dist: Brown, David Bk. Co., The.

Woods, Julie Irene. Jeremiah 48 as Christian Scripture. 2010. (Princeton Theological Monographs). 372p. pap. 41.00 *(978-1-60899-842-5(8),* Pickwick Pubns.) Wipf & Stock Pubs.

BIBLE—CRITICISM, INTERPRETATION, ETC.—O. T. PROVERBS

see Bible—Criticism, Interpretation, etc.—O. T. Poetical Books

BIBLE—CRITICISM, INTERPRETATION, ETC.—O. T. PSALMS

see Bible—Criticism, Interpretation, etc.—O. T. Poetical Books

BIBLE—CRITICISM, INTERPRETATION, ETC.—O. T. RUTH

see Bible—Criticism, Interpretation, Etc.—O. T. Historical Books

BIBLE—CRITICISM, INTERPRETATION, ETC.—O. T. SAMUEL

see Bible—Criticism, Interpretation, Etc.—O. T. Historical Books

BIBLE—CRITICISM, INTERPRETATION, ETC.—O. T. SONG OF SOLOMON

see Bible—Criticism, Interpretation, etc.—O. T. Poetical Books

BIBLE—CRITICISM, INTERPRETATION, ETC.—O. T. WISDOM LITERATURE

Perdue, Leo G. The Sword & the Stylus. 2008. 528p. pap. 38.00 *(978-0-8028-6245-7(4))* Eerdmans, William B. Publishing Co.

Sink, Susan. The Art of the Saint John's Bible: A Reader's Guide to Wisdom Books & Prophets, Vol. 2. 2008. 128p. pap. 14.95 *(978-0-8146-9063-5(7))* Liturgical Pr.

BIBLE—CRITICISM, INTERPRETATION, ETC.—O. T. ZECHARIAH

see Bible—Criticism, Interpretation, Etc.—O. T. Minor Prophets

BIBLE—CRITICISM, INTERPRETATION, ETC.—O. T. ZEPHANIAH

see Bible—Criticism, Interpretation, Etc.—O. T. Minor Prophets

BIBLE—CRITICISM, INTERPRETATION, ETC.—THEORY, METHODS, ETC.

see Bible—Hermeneutics

BIBLE—CRITICISM, TEXTUAL

see also Bible—Versions

Burgon, Dean John William. The Cause of Corruption of the Traditional Text, Vol. II. 2008. pap. 20.00 *(978-1-888328-03-5(7))* Old Paths Pubns., Inc., The.

Burgon, John William. The Causes of the Corruption of the Traditional Text of the Holy Gospels. 2009. 304p. 24.99 *(978-0-559-11331-4(5));* 28.99 *(978-0-559-11314-7(5));* pap. 28.75 *(978-0-559-11325-3(0));* pap. 23.99 *(978-0-559-11319-2(6))* BiblioBazaar.

—The Causes of the Corruption of the Traditional Text of the Holy Gospels. Edward Miller, ed. 2007. 308p. per. 24.95 *(978-1-60206-454-6(7))* Cosimo, Inc.

—The Traditional Text of the Holy Gospels. 2007. 344p. per. 24.95 *(978-1-60206-646-5(9))* Cosimo, Inc.

Campbell, Gordon. Bible: The Story of the King James Version 1611-2011. (ENG., Illus.). 2011. 368p. pap. 18.95 *(978-0-19-969301-6(3))* 2010. 256p. 24.95 *(978-0-19-955759-2(4))* Oxford Univ. Pr., Inc.

Edwards, Brian H. Why Twenty Seven? How Can We Be Sure That We Have the Right Books in the New Testament? 2007. 253p. per. *(978-0-85234-650-1(6))* Evangelical Pr.

Fuller, David O. True or False: The Westcott-Hort Textual Theory Examined. 317p. reprint ed. pap. 11.95 *(978-0-944355-12-1(9))* Institute for Biblical Textual Studies, The.

Gryson, R. Scientiam Salutis: Quarante annees de recherches sur l'Antiquite Chretienne. 2008. (Bibliotheca Ephemeridum Theologicarum Lovaniensium Ser.). (FRE.). 879p. (C). pap. 128.00 *(978-90-429-1904-4(3))* Peeters Pubs. & Booksellers BEL. Dist: Brown, David Bk. Co., The.

Hays, Richard B., et al, eds. Reading the Bible Intertextually. 2009. (MUL & ENG., Illus.). 310p. 49.95 *(978-1-60258-180-7(0))* Baylor Univ. Pr.

Hendrickson Publishers, creator. Nestle-Aland Novum Testamentum Graece-FL-Wide Margin. 27th ed. 2007. 812p. 59.95 *(978-1-59856-200-2(2))* Hendrickson Pubs. Marketing, LLC.

Hernandez, Juan, Jr. Scribal Habits & Theological Influences in the Apocalypse: The Singular Readings of Sinaiticus, Alexandrinus & Ephraemi. 2006. (Wissenschaftliche Untersuchungen Zum Neuen Testament 2 Ser.: No. 218). 259p. pap. 125.00 *(978-3-16-149112-2(2))* Mohr Siebeck GmbH & Co. KG DEU. Dist: Coronet Bks.

Johnson, S. R. Q 12: 33-34: Storing up Treasures in Heaven. 2007. (Documenta Q Ser.). (ENG.). 213p. (C). pap. 99.00 *(978-90-429-1949-5(3))* Peeters Pubs. & Booksellers BEL. Dist: Brown, David Bk. Co., The.

Jongkind, Dirk. Scribal Habits of Codex Sinaiticus. 2007. 78.00 *(978-1-59333-422-2(2))* Gorgias Pr., LLC.

Karrer, Martin, et al. Von der Septuaginta Zum Neuen Testament: Textgeschichtliche Erörterungen. 2010. (Arbeiten zur neutestamentlichen Textforschung Ser.). (GER.). IX, 461p. 182.00 ***(978-3-11-024001-6(7))*** De Gruyter, Walter Inc.

Klindworth, Duane O. Falconry: Testifying to the Indictment of Corrupt Bibles. 2008. (Illus.). 78p. per. *(978-0-9795247-0-7(9))* Klindworth Pubns.

Korpel, Marjo C. A., et al, eds. Method in Unit Delimitation. 2007. (Pericope Ser.). (Illus.). 231p. *(978-90-04-15567-0(3))* BRILL.

Krans, Jan. Beyond What Is Written: Erasmus & Beza as Conjectural Critics of the New Testament. 2006. (New Testament Tools & Studies: Vol. 35). (Illus.). 394p. *(978-90-04-15286-1(5))* BRILL.

McCosker, Philip. What Is It That the Scripture Says? Essays in Biblical Interpretation, Translation, & Reception in Honour of Henry Wansbrough OSB. 2007. (Library of New Testament Studies: Vol. 316). (ENG., Illus.). 362p. 190.00 *(978-0-567-04353-5(3),* T&T Clark Int'l) Continuum International Publishing Group, Ltd. GBR. Dist: National Bk. Network.

Muncey, R. W. The New Testament Text of Saint Ambrose. 2008. (ENG.). 200p. pap. 31.99 *(978-0-521-09149-7(7))* Cambridge Univ. Pr.

Royse, James R. Scribal Habits in Early Greek New Testament Papyri. 2007. (New Testament Tools & Studies). 1024p. *(978-90-04-16181-8(3))* BRILL.

Schmid, U. B. & Parker, D. C., eds. The New Testament in Greek IV: the Gospel According to St. John: Edited by the American & British Committees of the International Greek New Testament Project: Volume Two the Majuscules. 2007. (New Testament Tools, Studies & Documents Ser.). 558p. *(978-90-04-16313-3(1))* BRILL.

Scrivener, Frederick H. Adversaria Critica Sacra: With a Short Explanatory Introduction. 2006. 274p. pap. 27.00 *(978-1-55635-060-3(0),* Wipf and Stock) Wipf & Stock Pubs.

Seitz, Christopher R. The Goodly Fellowship of the Prophets: The Achievement of Association in Canon Formation, 1 vol. 2009. (Acadia Studies in Bible & Theology Ser.). 144p. (C). pap. 20.00 *(978-0-8010-3883-9(9))* Baker Academic.

Trajtmann, Uri. Torah: Biblia Hebreo / Español - el Libro de Genesis. 2007. 208p. *(978-956-291-256-3(6))* Editorial Benei Noaj.

Van Peursen, Wido & Thoutenhoof, Ernst D., eds. Text Comparison & Digital Creativity: The Production of Presence & Meaning in Digital Text Scholarship. 2010. (Scholarly Communication Ser.). (Illus.). 325p. *(978-90-04-18865-5(7))* BRILL.

Waite, Th. D. Pastor D. A. The Case for the King James Bible, A Summary of the Evidence & Argument. 2008. pap. 14.00 *(978-1-56848-011-4(3))* Old Paths Pubns., Inc., The.

—Fundamentalist Distortions on Bible Versions. 2008. pap. 12.00 *(978-1-56848-021-3(0))* Old Paths Pubns., Inc., The.

Werner, A. Frances. Truth in Translation: Accuracy & Surprising Bias in the Old Testament. 2008. 150p. pap. 44.00 *(978-0-9789763-1-6(2))* ARTB Publishing.

White, James R. The King James Only Controversy: Can You Trust Modern Translations? 2nd expurg. ed. 2009. 368p. reprint ed. pap. 15.99 *(978-0-7642-0605-4(2))* Bethany Hse. Pubs.

Williams, M. D. Origin of the Critical Text. 2008. 164p. pap. 16.00 *(978-0-9820608-4-1(X))* Old Paths Pubns., Inc., The.

Williamson, H. G. M. Holy, Holy, Holy: The Story of a Liturgical Formula. 2008. (Julius-Wellhausen-Vorlesung Ser.). (ENG.). IV, 36p. pap. 28.00 *(978-3-11-020716-3(8))* De Gruyter, Walter Inc.

Wilshire, Leland E. Insight into Two Biblical Passages: Anatomy of a Prohibition I Timothy 2:12, the TLG Computer, & the Christian Church. 2010. (ENG.). 154p. pap. 26.50 *(978-0-7618-5207-0(7))* Univ. Pr. of America, Inc.

BIBLE—CRITICISM, TEXTUAL—N. T.

Baldwin, Clinton S. The So-Called Mixed Text: An Examination of the Non-Alexandrian & Non-Byzantine Text-Type in the Catholic Epistles. 2011. (978-1-4331-0755-9(4)) Lang, Peter GmbH, Europaischer Verlag der Wissenschaften.

Belle, G. Van, ed. The Death of Jesus in the Fourth Gospel. 2007. (Bibliotheca Ephemeridum Theologicarum Lovaniensium Ser.). (ENG., Illus.). 1003p. (C). pap. 102.00 (978-90-429-1940-2(X)) Peeters Pubs. & Booksellers BEL. Dist: Brown, David Bk. Co., The.

Brogue, David. La Divina Autoridad Del Nuevo Test. The Divine Authority of the N. T. (SPA.). (978-84-7645-486-2(4), 223345) Clie, Editorial.

Burgon, Dean John William. The Traditional Text of the Holy Gospels, Volume I. 2008. pap. 20.00 (978-1-888328-02-8(9)) Old Paths Pubns., Inc., The.

Culy, Martin M., et al. Luke: A Handbook on the Greek Text. 2010. (Baylor Handbook on the Greek New Testament Ser.). (ENG.). 816p. (C). pap. 49.95 (978-1-60258-291-0(2)) Baylor Univ. Pr.

Davids, Peter H. 2 Peter & Jude: A Handbook on the Greek Text. 2011. (Baylor Handbook on the Greek New Testament Ser.). (ENG.). 152p. pap. 29.95 (978-1-60258-313-9(7)) Baylor Univ. Pr.

Ehrman, Bart D. Misquoting Jesus: The Story Behind Who Changed the Bible & Why. 2007. (Plus Ser.). (ENG., Illus.). 256p. pap. 14.99 (978-0-06-085951-0(2), HarperOne) HarperCollins Pubs.

—The Orthodox Corruption of Scripture: The Effect of Early Christological Controversies on the Text of the New Testament. 2011. (ENG.). 416p. pap. 29.95 (978-0-19-973978-3(1)) Oxford Univ. Pr., Inc.

—Whose Word Is It? The Story Behind Who Changed the New Testament & Why. 2008. 256p. (978-1-84706-314-4(4)) Continuum International Publishing Group, Ltd.

Ellis, E. Earle. The Making of the New Testament Documents. 2009. 544p. pap. 59.95 (978-1-58983-438-5(0)) Society of Biblical Literature.

Fantin, Joseph D. The Greek Imperative Mood in the New Testament: A Cognitive & Communicative Approach. 2010. (Studies in Biblical Greek Ser.). 424p. (C). 91.95 (978-0-8204-7487-8(8)) Lang, Peter Publishing, Inc.

Fortna. Gospel of Signs. 290p. (978-0-521-07624-1(2)) Cambridge Univ. Pr.

Gwynn, John. On a Syriac MS. Belonging to the Collection of Archbishop Ussher. 2010. pap. 21.76 (978-1-61719-579-2(0)) Gorgias Pr., LLC.

Haldimann, Konrad. Rekonstruktion und Entfaltung: Exegetische Untersuchungen zu Joh 15 Und 16. (Beihefte zur Zeitschrift far die neutestamentliche Wissenschaft und die Kunde der älteren Kirche Ser.). (GER.). IX, 444p. 344.00 (978-3-11-185020-7(X)) De Gruyter, Walter Inc.

Harris, J. Rendel. New Testament Autographs. 2009. pap. 72.28 (978-1-60724-543-8(4)) Gorgias Pr., LLC.

Holding, James Patrick. Trusting the New Testament. 2009. 304p. pap. 21.99 (978-1-60791-733-5(5)) Xulon Pr., Inc.

Hull, Robert F. The Story of the New Testament Text: Movers, Materials, Motives, Methods, & Models. 2010. xiv, 229p. (978-1-58983-520-7(4)); (978-1-58983-521-4(2)) Society of Biblical Literature.

—The Story of the New Testament Text: Movers, Motives, Materials, Methods, & Models. 2011. XIV, 230p. (978-90-04-18707-8(3)) BRILL.

Jones, Timothy Paul. Misquoting Truth: A Guide to the Fallacies of Bart Ehrman's Misquoting Jesus. 2007. (ENG., Illus.). 176p. per. 15.00 (978-0-8308-3447-1(8), IVP Bks.) InterVarsity Pr.

Kenyon, Frederic G. Recent Developments in the Textual Criticism of the Greek Bible. 2010. 95.12 (978-1-61143-501-6(3)) Gorgias Pr., LLC.

Miller, Edward. The Oxford Debate on the Textual Criticism of the New Testament. 2009. 96p. pap. 10.00 (978-0-9822230-1-7(3)) Old Paths Pubns., Inc., The.

Miller, M. A. Edward. A Guide to the Textual Criticism of the New Testament. 2008. pap. 15.00 (978-1-888328-09-7(6)) Old Paths Pubns., Inc., The.

Moir, I. A. Codex Climaci Rescriptus Graecus. 2009. (ENG.). 140p. pap. 23.99 (978-0-521-10527-9(7)) Cambridge Univ. Pr.

Moorman, J. A. Early Manuscripts, Church Fathers & the Authorized Version with Manuscript Digests & Summaries. 2008. pap. 25.00 (978-1-56848-048-0(2)) Old Paths Pubns., Inc., The.

Parker, D. C. & Houghton, H. A. G., eds. Textual Variation: Theological & Social Tendencies? 2008. 105.00 (978-1-59333-789-6(2)) Gorgias Pr., LLC.

Robinson, Maurice A., et al, eds. The Greek New Testament for Beginning Readers: The Byzantine Greek Text & Verb Parsing. 2010. 796p. (978-3-941750-24-1(0)) VTR Verlag fur Theologie und Religionswissenschaft.

Rodgers, Peter R. Text & Story: Narrative Studies in New Testament Textual Criticism. 2011. 136p. pap. 17.00 (978-1-61097-304-5(6), Pickwick Pubns.) Wipf & Stock Pubs.

Royse, James Ronald. Scribal Habits in Early Greek New Testament Papyri. 2010. (978-1-58983-522-1(0)) Society of Biblical Literature.

Sandnes, Karl Olav. The Gospel "According to Homer & Virgil" Cento & Canon. 2011. XII, 280p. (978-90-04-18718-4(9)) BRILL.

Scrivener, Frederick Henry Ambrose. Adversaria Critica Sacra: With a Short Explanatory Introduction. 2010. (Cambridge Library Collection - Religion Ser.). (ENG.). 284p. pap. 23.99 (978-1-108-00748-1(1)) Cambridge Univ. Pr.

Scrivener, Frederick Henry Ambrose, ed. An Exact Transcript of the Codex Augiensis: A Graco-Latin Manuscript of S. Paul's Epistles, Deposited in the Library of Trinity College, Cambridge - To Which Is Added a Full Collation of Fifty Manuscripts. 2010. (Cambridge Library Collection - Religion Ser.). (ENG., Illus.). 668p. pap. 45.00 (978-1-108-00749-8(X)) Cambridge Univ. Pr.

Shepherd, Michael B. The Twelve Prophets in the New Testament. 2010. (Studies in Biblical Literature Ser.). 126p. (C). 63.95 (978-1-4331-1346-8(5)) Lang, Peter Publishing, Inc.

Streeter, Burnett Hillman. The Four Gospels: A Study of Origins, Treating of the Manuscript Tradition, Sources, Authorship, & Dates. 2008. 654p. pap. 56.00 (978-1-55635-797-8(4)) Wipf & Stock Pubs.

Taylor, Mark E. Text-Linguistic Investigation into the Discourse Structure of James. 2006. (Library of New Testament Studies: Vol. 311). (ENG., Illus.). 160p. 130.00 (978-0-567-04463-1(7), T&T Clark Int'l) Continuum International Publishing Group, Ltd. GBR. Dist: National Bk. Network.

Tischendorf, Constantin, ed. Novum Testamentum Graece: Eighth Edition. 2007. 468p. pap. 40.00 (978-1-55635-563-9(7), Wipf and Stock) Wipf & Stock Pubs.

Trail, Ronald L. Exegetical Summary of Revelation 1-11. 2nd ed. 2008. 243p. pap. 29.00 (978-1-55671-198-5(0)) SIL International.

—Exegetical Summary of Revelation 11-22. 2nd ed. 2008. 238p. pap. 29.00 (978-1-55671-196-1(4)) SIL International.

Tregelles, Samuel Prideaux. The Book of Revelation in Greek Edited from Ancient Authorities. 2009. (Cambridge Library Collection - Religion Ser.). (ENG.). 208p. pap. 22.99 (978-1-108-00745-0(7)) Cambridge Univ. Pr.

Valset, Jon. Searching for the Truth in the New Testament. 2011. 640p. 45.95 (978-1-4502-8930-6(4)) iUniverse, Inc.

Wachtel, Klaus & Holmes, Michael W. The Textual History of the Greek New Testament. 2011. (978-1-58983-624-2(3)); (978-1-58983-625-9(1)) Society of Biblical Literature.

Waite, Th. D. Pastor D. A. Burgon's Warnings on Revision of the Textus Receptus & the King James Bible. 2008. pap. 12.00 (978-1-56848-013-8(X)) Old Paths Pubns., Inc., The.

—First Timothy, Preaching Verse by Verse. 2008. pap. 20.00 (978-1-56848-055-8(5)) Old Paths Pubns., Inc., The.

Zuck, Roy, ed. Vital New Testament Issues: Examining New Testament Passages & Problems. 2006. (Vital Issues Ser.). 288p. pap. 28.00 (978-1-59752-684-5(3), Wipf and Stock) Wipf & Stock Pubs.

BIBLE—CRITICISM, TEXTUAL—O. T.

Ausloos, H., et al, eds. Translating a Translation: The LXX & its Modern Translations in the Context of Early Judaism. 2008. (Bibliotheca Ephemeridum Theologicarum Lovaniensium Ser.). (ENG.). 317p. (C). pap. 116.00 (978-90-429-2038-5(6)) Peeters Pubs. & Booksellers BEL. Dist: Brown, David Bk. Co., The.

Ben Zvi, Ehud, ed. Perspectives on Hebrew Scriptures: Comprising the Contents of Journal of Hebrew Scriptures, Vol. 6. 2008. (Gorgias Perspectives on Hebrew Scriptures Ser.: 3). 125.00 (978-1-59333-976-0(3)) Gorgias Pr., LLC.

—Perspectives on Hebrew Scriptures V. 2009. 164.00 (978-1-60724-326-7(1)) Gorgias Pr., LLC.

—Perspectives on Hebrew Scriptures VI. 2010. 26.32 (978-1-61143-004-2(6)) Gorgias Pr., LLC.

Burchard, C. A Minor Edition of the Armenian Version of Joseph & Aseneth. 2010. (Hebrew University Armenian Studies). (ENG.). 211p. (C). pap. 63.00 (978-90-429-2041-5(6)) Peeters Pubs. & Booksellers BEL. Dist: Brown, David Bk. Co., The.

Clines, David J. A. Esther Scroll: The Story of the Story. 2009. (Library of Hebrew Bible/Old Testament Studies, the Ser.). (ENG.). 262p. 44.95 (978-0-567-57864-8(X), T&T Clark) Continuum International Publishing Group, Ltd. GBR. Dist: National Bk. Network.

Collver, Albert B. Hosea/Joel/Amos: Faithfulness amid Unfaithfulness. 2010. (God's Word for Today Ser.). 112p. pap. 8.99 (978-0-7586-1716-3(X)) Concordia Publishing Hse.

Eitan, Israel. Contribution to Biblical Lexicography. (Columbia University, Contributions to Oriental History & Philology Ser.: No. 10). reprint ed. 29.50 (978-0-404-50540-0(6)) AMS Pr., Inc.

Ginsburg, Christian D. Jacob Ben Chajim Ibn Adonijah's Introduction to the Rabbinic Bible: Hebrew & English with Explanatory Notes. 2009. 414p. pap. 35.00 (978-1-60608-443-4(7), Wipf and Stock) Wipf & Stock Pubs.

Gooding, D. W. The Account of the Tabernacle: Translation & Textual Problems of the Greek Exodus. 2009. (ENG.). 132p. pap. 28.99 (978-0-521-11163-8(3)) Cambridge Univ. Pr.

—Relics of Ancient Exegesis: A Study of the Miscellanies in 3 Reigns 2. 2009. (Society for Old Testament Study Monographs). (ENG.). 144p. pap. 20.99 (978-0-521-10413-5(0)) Cambridge Univ. Pr.

Gordon, R. P. Studies on the Text & Versions of the Hebrew Bible in Honour of Robert Gordon. Khan, Geoffrey & Lipton, Diana, eds. 2011. (ENG.). XXII, 436p. (978-90-04-21730-0(4)) BRILL.

Hadjiev, Tchavdar S. The Composition & Redaction of the Book of Amos. 2009. (Beihefte zur Zeitschrift für die alttestamentliche Wissenschaft Ser.). (ENG.). XVIII, 247p. 112.00 (978-3-11-021271-6(4)); 168.00 (978-3-11-173597-9(4)) De Gruyter, Walter Inc.

Hallermayer, Michaela. Text und Überlieferung des Buches Tobit. (Deuterocanonical & Cognate Literature Studies). (GER.). IX, 209p. 195.00 (978-3-11-181307-3(X)); 2007. 119.00 (978-3-11-019496-8(1)) De Gruyter, Walter Inc.

Hayes, Elizabeth. The Pragmatics of Perception & Cognition in MT Jeremiah 1:1-6:30: A Cognitive Linguistics Approach. 2008. (Beihefte Zur Zeitschrift Für Die Alttestamentliche Wissenschaft Ser.). (ENG.). XII, 272p. 168.00 (978-3-11-173873-4(6)) De Gruyter, Walter Inc.

Hayes, Elizabeth R. The Pragmatics of Perception & Cognition in MT Jeremiah 1:1-6:30: A Cognitive Linguistics Approach. 2008. (Beihefte Zur Zeitschrift Für Die Alttestamentliche Wissenschaft Ser.). (ENG., Illus.). XII, 272p. 105.00 (978-3-11-020229-8(8)) De Gruyter, Walter Inc.

Hiebert, Robert J. V., et al, eds. Old Greek Psalter: Studies in Honour of Albert Pietersma. 2009. (Library of Hebrew Bible/Old Testament Studies, the Ser.). (ENG.). 352p. 60.00 (978-0-567-33206-6(3), T&T Clark) Continuum International Publishing Group, Ltd. GBR. Dist: National Bk. Network.

Jacobs, Mignon R. Conceptual Coherence of the Book of Micah. 2009. (Library of Hebrew Bible/Old Testament Studies, the Ser.). (ENG.). 288p. 49.95 (978-0-567-30287-8(3), T&T Clark) Continuum International Publishing Group, Ltd. GBR. Dist: National Bk. Network.

Jones, Scott C. Rumors of Wisdom: Job 28 As a Poetry. 2009. (Beihefte Zur Zeitschrift Fur Die Alttestamentliche Wissenschaft Ser.). (ENG.). XX, 293p. 126.00 (978-3-11-021477-2(6)) De Gruyter, Walter Inc.

Kearns, Conleth. The Expanded Text of Ecclesiasticus: Its Teaching on the Future Life as a Clue to its Origin. Beentjes, Pancratius C., ed. 2011. (Deuterocanonical & Cognate Literature Studies). (ENG., Illus.). VI, 333p. 210.00 (978-3-11-219102-6(1)) De Gruyter, Walter Inc.

Kearns, Conleth, et al. The Expanded Text of Ecclesiasticus: Its Teaching on the Future Life As a Clue to Its Origin. 2011. (Deuterocanonical & Cognate Literature Studies). (ENG., Illus.). VI, 333p. 140.00 (978-3-11-025258-3(9)) De Gruyter, Walter Inc.

Ledo, Michael. The Bronze Age Bible. 2010. 52p. pap. 7.99 (978-0-557-38757-1(4)) Lulu Enterprises Inc.

Martin, Gary D. Multiple Originals: New Approaches to Hebrew Bible Textual Criticism. 2011. XIV, 342p. (978-90-04-18704-7(9)) BRILL.

—Multiple Originals: New Approaches to Hebrew Bible Textual Criticism. 2010. (978-1-58983-513-9(1)); (978-1-58983-514-6(X)) Society of Biblical Literature.

Mazor, Yair. Who Wrought the Bible? Unveiling the Bible's Aesthetic Secrets. 2008. (ENG.). 232p. pap. 26.95 (978-0-299-22844-6(4)); (Illus.). 60.00 (978-0-299-22840-8(1)) Univ. of Wisconsin Pr.

Mutius, Hans-Georg von. Nichtmasoretische Bibelzitate im Midrasch ha-Gadol (13. /14. Jahrhundert) 2010. (Judentum und Umwelt. Realms of Judaism Ser.). (GER.). 152p. 47.95 (978-3-631-60826-5(8)) Lang, Peter GmbH, Europaischer Verlag der Wissenschaften DEU. Dist: Lang, Peter.

Naville, Edouard. The Text of the Old Testament; the British Academy; the Schweich Lectures 1915. 2007. (ENG.). 108p. 33.95 (978-0-548-05235-8(2)) Kessinger Publishing, LLC.

Schramm, Brooks. Opponents of Third Isaiah: Reconstructing the Cultic History of the Restoration. 2009. (Library of Hebrew Bible/Old Testament Studies, the Ser.). (ENG.). 216p. 39.95 (978-0-567-10214-0(9), T&T Clark) Continuum International Publishing Group, Ltd. GBR. Dist: National Bk. Network.

Stephenson, Maude A. A Commentary on the Five Scrolls: Song of Songs, Ruth, Lamentations, Ecclesiastes, Esther. 2011. 130p. 40.95 (978-1-258-06019-0(1)) Literary Licensing, LLC.

Talmon, Shemaryahu. Text & Canon of the Hebrew Bible: Collected Studies. 2010. 54.50 (978-1-57506-192-4(9)) Eisenbrauns, Inc.

Tooman, William A. & Lyons, Michael A. Transforming Visions: Transformations of Text, Tradition, & Theology in Ezekiel. 2011. (ENG.). 350p. pap. 48.00 (978-0-227-17368-8(6)) Clarke, James Co., Ltd. GBR. Dist: Brown, David Bk. Co., The.

Tov, Emanuel. Textual Criticism of the Hebrew Bible. 3rd rev. ed. 2011. (Illus.). 512p. 90.00 (978-0-8006-9664-1(6)) Augsburg Fortress, Pubs.

Ulrich, Eugene Charles, et al. The Biblical Qumran Scrolls: Transcriptions & Textual Variants. 2009. (Vetus Testamentum Supplements Ser.). 812p. (978-90-04-18038-3(9)) BRILL.

Van Der Louw, Theo A. W. Transformations in the Septuagint: Towards an Interaction of Septaguint Studies & Translation Studies. 2007. (Contributions to Biblical Exegesis & Theology Ser.). (ENG., Illus.). 404p. (C). pap. 61.00 (978-90-429-1888-7(8)) Peeters Pubs. & Booksellers BEL. Dist: Brown, David Bk. Co., The.

van Keulen, P. S. F. & van Pcursen, W. T. Corpus Linguistics & Textual History: A Computer-Assisted Interdisciplinary Approach to the Peshitta. 2006. (Studia Semitica Neerlandica - SSN Ser.: Vol. 48). (GER.). 37p. 109.00 (978-90-232-4194-2(0)) Van Gorcum & Co. B.V. NLD. Dist: Eisenbrauns, Inc.

Varzonovtseva, Milena. The Secret Books of the Bogomils. 2008. 84p. pap. (978-3-639-06125-3(X)) VDM Verlag Dr. Mueller e.K.

Wajdenbaum, Philippe. Argonauts of the Desert: Structural Analysis of the Hebrew Bible. 2011. (Copenhagen International Seminar Ser.). (ENG.). 324p. (C). 99.95 (978-1-84553-924-5(9)) Equinox Publishing Ltd. GBR. Dist: ISD.

Walters, Peter. The Text of the Septuagint: Its Corruptions & their Emendation. 2009. (ENG.). 440p. pap. 46.00 (978-0-521-10293-3(6)) Cambridge Univ. Pr.

Willis, Mike, ed. Great Texts of the Old Testament - 2007 Lectures. 2007. 14.95 (978-1-58427-195-6(7)) Guardian of Truth Foundation.

Zandstra, Sidney. Witness of "The Vulgate," "Peshitta" & "Septuagint" to the Text of "Zephaniah" (Columbia University, Contributions to Oriental History & Philology Ser.: No. 4). reprint ed. 24.50 (978-0-404-50534-9(1)) AMS Pr., Inc.

BIBLE—CULTUS

see Worship in the Bible

BIBLE—CURIOSA

see Bible—Miscellanea

BIBLE—DATA PROCESSING

see Bible—Criticism, Interpretation, etc.—Data Processing

BIBLE—DEVOTIONAL LITERATURE

see Bible—Meditations

BIBLE—DICTIONARIES

Abercrombie, Melvin. Does God Have a Penis? 2006. 276p. per. 20.00 (978-1-4251-0115-2(1)) Trafford Publishing.

Allen, Richard J. New Testament Who's Who: A Comprehensive Guide to the People in the New Testament. 2010. (Illus.). xvii, 221p. (978-1-60861-072-3(1)) Covenant Communications, Inc.

American Bible Society, contrib. by. Greek New Testament-FL. 2011. (ENG.). 69.99 (978-3-438-05137-0(0)) American Bible Society.

Bacote, Vincent, ed. Precepts for Living 2009-2010 W/CD-ROM. 2009. (Precepts for Living Ser.). 504p. pap. 21.95 (978-1-60352-685-2(4)) UMI (Urban Ministries, Inc.).

Barclay, William. New Testament Words. 2012. 288p. pap. (978-0-334-01139-2(6), SCM Pr.) Hymns Ancient & Modern Ltd.

Beck, James R. & Beck, John A. Zondervan Dictionary of Biblical Imagery, 1 vol. 2010. (ENG.). 288p. 29.99 (978-0-310-29285-2(9)) Zondervan.

Beharrell, T. G. (Thomas G.). A Complete Alphabetically Arranged Biblical Biography. 2006. 516p. per. 29.99 (978-1-4255-5752-2(X)) MPublishing.

Botterweck, G. Johannes, et al, eds. Theological Dictionary of the Old Testament, Vol. 15. Green, David E., tr. from GER. 2006. (Theological Dictionary of the Old Testament Ser.). 793p. 65.00 (978-0-8028-2339-7(4)) Eerdmans, William B. Publishing Co.

Bridgeforth, Pastor Garrick Sr. Words of the Bible Explained: Bible Word Dictionary. 2011. 262p. 29.99 (978-1-4653-5242-2(2)); pap. 19.99 (978-1-4653-5241-5(4)) Xlibris Corp.

Brown, John. Brown's Dictionary of Bible Characters. Stonier, Geoffrey, ed. 2007. (ENG.). 596p. 29.99 (978-1-84550-266-9(3), Christian Heritage) Christian Focus Pubns. GBR. Dist: STL Distribution North America.

Browning, W. R. F. A Dictionary of the Bible. 2nd ed. (Oxford Paperback Reference Ser.). (ENG., Illus.). 2011. 432p. pap. 19.95 (978-0-19-954398-4(4)) 2010. 464p. 65.00 (978-0-19-954399-1(2)) Oxford Univ. Pr., Inc.

Bryan, Timothy. Bible People Prophets. pap. 5.95 (978-0-687-07405-1(3)) Abingdon Pr.

Burer, Michael H., et al. A New Reader's Lexicon of the Greek New Testament. 2008. 512p. 34.99 (978-0-8254-2009-2(1)) Kregel Pubns.

Comfort, Philip Wesley & Elwell, Walter A. Tyndale Bible Dictionary. 2008. (Tyndale Reference Library). (ENG.). 1352p. 34.99 (978-1-4143-1945-2(2)) Tyndale Hse. Pubs.

Common English Bible (Firm) Staff, contrib. by. CEB Bible Dictionary. 2011. 448p. pap. 24.95 (978-1-60926-024-8(4)) Christian Resources Development Corp.

Coogan, Michael D., ed. The Oxford Encyclopedia of the Books of the Bible, 2 vols. 2011. (Oxford Encyclopedias of the Bible Ser.). (ENG., Illus.). 1280p. 395.00 (978-0-19-537737-8(0)) Oxford Univ. Pr., Inc.

Coogan, Michael D., et al. The New Oxford Annotated Bible. 4th rev. ed. 2010. (ENG., Illus.). 2096p. 42.99 (978-0-19-528950-3(1)) Oxford Univ. Pr., Inc.

Croy, N. Clayton. A Primer of Biblical Greek. 2007. 264p. pap. 29.00 incl. cd-rom (978-0-8028-6000-2(1)) Eerdmans, William B. Publishing Co.

Danker, Frederick William & Krug, Kathryn. The Concise Greek-English Lexicon of the New Testament. 2009. (GEC & ENG., Illus.). 408p. 55.00 (978-0-226-13615-8(9)) Univ. of Chicago Pr.

Douglas, J. D. & Tenney, Merrill C. Bible Dictionary, 1 vol. 2008. (ENG.). 608p. lthr. 19.99 (978-0-310-29304-0(9)) Zondervan.

—NIV Compact Dictionary of the Bible, 1 vol. 2009. (NIV Compact Ser.). (ENG.). 704p. pap. 6.99 (978-0-310-28568-7(2)) Zondervan.

Douglas, J. T. & Tenney, Merrill Chapin. Zondervan Illustrated Bible Dictionary: The Most Accurate & Comprehensive Bible Dictionary Available, 1 vol. 2011. (Premier Reference Ser.). (ENG., Illus.). 1616p. 29.99 (978-0-310-22983-4(9)) Zondervan.

Easton, M. G. Illustrated Bible Dictionary. 2006. (ENG.). 39.95 (978-1-59605-947-4(8), Cosimo Classics) Cosimo, Inc.

Editorial Castilla La Vieja Staff. Dictionary of the Bible (English-Spanish/Spanish-English) 2008.Tr. of Diccionario de la Biblia (Español-Inglés/Inglés-Español). (SPA & ENG.). 600p. 75.00 (978-0-9765947-4-1(9)) Editorial Castilla La Vieja.

Eerdmans Dictionary of the Bible. 2010. (978-90-5356-503-2(5)) Amsterdam Univ. Pr.

Encyclopedia of the Bible & its Reception. 2007. (ENG., Illus.). 9366.00 (978-3-11-019904-8(1)) De Gruyter, Walter Inc.

The Essential IVP Reference Collection 3. 0. 2008. (ENG.). 1p. cd-rom 190.00 (978-0-8308-2447-2(2), IVP Acad.) InterVarsity Pr.

Evins, Karlen. I Didn't Know That Came from the Bible. 2008. 192p. 16.99 (978-0-8249-4740-8(1), GuidepostsBooks) Ideals Pubns.

Ezekiel. (People's Bible Commentary Ser.). 288p. 14.99 (978-0-7586-0433-0(5)) Concordia Publishing Hse.

Fischer, Jean. 199 Bible People, Places, & Things. 2009. (Value Bks.). (ENG.). 160p. pap. 1.99 (978-1-60260-381-3(2), Barbour Bks.) Barbour Publishing, Inc.

Fohrer, Georg, et al, eds. Hebrew & Aramaic Dictionary of the Old Testament. (ENG.). XVI, 332p. (C). 56.00 (978-3-11-176077-3(1)) De Gruyter, Walter Inc.

Gilmore. Concise Dictionary of Bible Origins. 2nd ed. 2007. (ENG.). 256p. 130.00 (978-0-567-03096-2(2), T&T Clark Int'l) Continuum International Publishing Group, Ltd. GBR. Dist: National Bk. Network.

Gilmore, Alec & Gilmore. Concise Dictionary of Bible Origins & Interpretation. 2nd ed. 2007. (ENG.). 256p. 39.95 (978-0-567-03097-9(0), T&T Clark Int'l) Continuum International Publishing Group, Ltd. GBR. Dist: National Bk. Network.

Godoy, Pope. Diccionario Geográfico Del Nuevo Testamento. 2010. (SPA., Illus.). 140p. (978-84-8005-152-1(3)) 1El Almendro de Cordoba, Ediciones, S.L.

Green, Kevin. Zondervan All in One Bible Reference Guide. 2008. 675p. (978-0-310-61164-6(4)) Zondervan.

Grimm, Carl Ludwig Willibald & Thayer, Joseph Henry. A Greek-English Lexicon of the New Testament. 2010. (GRE.). 169.52 *(978-1-61719-677-5(0))* Gorgias Pr., LLC.

Hahn, Scott, ed. Catholic Bible Dictionary. 2009. (ENG., Illus.). 1008p. 45.00 *(978-0-385-51229-9(5))* Knopf Doubleday Publishing Group.

Hastings, James & Selbie, John A., eds. A Dictionary of the Bible. 2010. 955.60 *(978-1-61719-216-6(3))*; 955.60 *(978-1-61719-219-0(X))*; 955.60 *(978-1-61719-215-9(5))*; 955.60 *(978-1-61719-217-3(1))* Gorgias Pr., LLC.

Hickie, W. Greek-English Lexicon to the New Testament. 2007. 224p. per. 24.95 *(978-1-60206-774-5(0))* Cosimo, Inc.

Hillyer, Norman & Holman Reference Editorial Staff. Holman Giant Print Illustrated Bible Dictionary. 2008. (ENG., Illus.). 400p. 19.99 *(978-0-8054-9497-6(9)*, Holman Reference) B&H Publishing Group.

Holman Reference Editorial Staff, creator. Holman Illustrated Pocket Bible Dictionary: Pocket Reference Edition. 2007. (Illus.). 395p. per. 9.99 *(978-1-58640-314-0(1)*, Holman Pubs.) B&H Publishing Group.

Intervarsity Press. The Ivp Bible Dictionary Series. 6p. 300.00 *(978-0-8308-2900-2(8))* InterVarsity Pr.

Jacobson, Rolf A. & Jacobson, Karl N. Crazy Book: A Not-So-Stuffy Dictionary of Biblical Terms. 2009. 288p. pap. 17.99 *(978-0-8066-5765-3(0))*, Augsburg Bks.) Augsburg Fortress, Pubs.

Kingdom Quotes Staff. New Testament Dictionary of Sins. pap. *(978-0-930179-37-3(4))* Johns Enterprises.

Knight, George W., ed. KJV Super Giant Print Dictionary & Concordance. 2007. (ENG., Illus.). 1248p. 24.99 *(978-0-8054-9492-1(8)*, Holman Reference) B&H Publishing Group.

Knight, George W. & Ray, Rayburn W. The Quicknotes Bible Dictionary. 2009. (QuickNotes Commentaries Ser.). (ENG.). 352p. pap. 4.99 *(978-1-60260-442-1(8)*, Barbour Bks.) Barbour Publishing, Inc.

Livingstone Corporation Staff & Fackler, Mark. Big Ideas of the Bible. 2010. (ENG., Illus.). 240p. pap. 9.99 *(978-1-60260-697-5(8)*, Barbour Bks.) Barbour Publishing, Inc.

Longman III, Tremper & Enns, Peter, eds. Dictionary of the Old Testament: Wisdom, Poetry & Writings - A Compendium of Contemporary Biblical Scholarship. 2008. (IVP Bible Dictionary Ser.). (ENG., Illus.). 991p. 60.00 *(978-0-8308-1783-2(2)*, IVP Acad.) InterVarsity Pr.

Losch, Richard R. All the People in the Bible: An A-Z Guide to the Saints, Scoundrels, & Other Characters in Scripture. 2008. 578p. pap. 26.00 *(978-0-8028-2454-7(4))* Eerdmans, William B. Publishing Co.

Mandel, David. Who's Who in the Jewish Bible. 2007. (ENG.). 550p. per. 30.00 *(978-0-8276-0863-4(2))* Jewish Pubn. Society.

Manser, Martin H. & Reid, Debra. The Compact Guide to the Bible. 2010. (Compact Encyclopedia Ser.). (ENG., Illus.). 192p. pap. 14.95 *(978-0-7459-5313-7(1))* Lion Hudson PLC GBR. Dist: Independent Pubs. Group.

McClintock, John & Strong, James. Cyclopaedia of Biblical, Theological, & Ecclesiastical Literature: Cyclopaedia of Biblical Literature, Vol. 1 10. 250.00 *(978-0-405-00020-1(0)*, 11917) Ayer Co. Pubs., Inc.

McQuade, Pamela L. The QuickNotes Dictionary of Bible Places. 2010. (QuickNotes Commentaries Ser.). (ENG.). 256p. pap. 9.99 *(978-1-60260-846-7(6)*, Barbour Bks.) Barbour Publishing, Inc.

Mounce, William D. Complete Expository Dictionary of Old & New Testament Words, 1 vol. Mounce, William D. et al, eds. 2006. (ENG, GEC & HEB.). 1344p. 29.99 *(978-0-310-24878-1(7))* Zondervan.

Muraoka, T. A Greek-Hebrew/Aramaic Two-way Index to the Septuagint. 2010. (ENG.). 394p. (C). 87.00 *(978-90-429-2356-0(3))* Peeters Pubs. & Booksellers BEL. Dist: Brown, David Bk. Co., The.

Newman, Barclay M., Jr. A Concise Greek-English Dictionary of the New Testament. 2006. 203p. pap. 1999.00 *(978-1-59856-165-4(0))* Hendrickson Pubs. Marketing, LLC.

Powell, Mark Allan. Bible Dictionary. 2009. 464p. pap. 19.99 *(978-0-06-146907-7(6)*, HarperOne) HarperCollins Pubs.

—Harpercollins Bible Dictionary. 3rd rev. ed. 2011. (ENG.). 1280p. 47.99 *(978-0-06-146906-0(8)*, HarperOne) HarperCollins Pubs.

Rand, W. W., ed. Diccionario de la Santa Biblia, 0 vols. 2006. (SPA., Illus.). 768p. per. 19.99 *(978-0-89922-726-9(0))* Grupo Nelson.

Reed, David. Dictionary of J. W. ese. 2010. 127p. pap. 10.98 *(978-0-557-22685-6(6))* Lulu Enterprises Inc.

Robinson, Edward. A Greek & English Lexicon of the New Testament. 2009. 820p. 38.99 *(978-1-116-42677-9(3))*; 49.99 *(978-1-116-42676-2(5))*; pap. 54.75 *(978-1-116-42679-3(X))* BiblioBazaar.

Sakenfeld, Katharine Doob. The New Interpreter's Dictionary of the Bible, 5 vols., Set. 2009. (Illus.). 400.00 *(978-0-687-33346-2(6))* Abingdon Pr.

—The New Interpreter's Dictionary of the Bible Vol. 5: S - Z, 5 vols. 2009. (New Interpreter's Dictionary of the Bible Ser.). (Illus.). 1075p. 79.99 *(978-0-687-33395-0(4))* Abingdon Pr.

Sakenfeld, Katharine Doob, ed. New Interpreter's Dictionary of the Bible Vol. 3, 5 vols., Vol. 3. 2008. (New Interpreter's Dictionary of the Bible Ser.). (Illus.). 936p. 79.99 *(978-0-687-33365-3(2))* Abingdon Pr.

—The New Interpreter's Dictionary of the Bible Vol. 4, 5 Vols. 2009. (New Interpreter's Dictionary of the Bible Ser.). (Illus.). 79.99 *(978-0-687-33375-2(X))* Abingdon Pr.

—The New Interpreter's Dictionary of the Bible - A-C Vol. 1, 5 vols. 2006. (New Interpreter's Dictionary of the Bible Ser.). (Illus.). 843p. pap. 79.99 *(978-0-687-05427-5(3))* Abingdon Pr.

Sakenfeld, Katharine Doob, et al, eds. The New Interpreter's Dictionary of the Bible Vol. 2: D-H, 5 vols. 2007. (New Interpreter's Dictionary of the Bible Ser.). (Illus.). 1012p. 79.99 *(978-0-687-33355-4(5))* Abingdon Pr.

Sandefur, Joy, ed. Bible Dictionary. 2008. (Dominican Ser.) (ENG.). 303p. (C). pap. 25.00 *(978-1-920691-93-6(6))* ATF Pr. AUS. Dist: Brown, David Bk. Co., The.

Sawyer, John F. A. A Concise Dictionary of the Bible & Its Reception. 2009. (ENG.). 256p. pap. 30.00 *(978-0-664-22338-0(9))* Westminster John Knox Pr.

Sidebotham, Jay. The New Testament from A-Z: A Spirited Journey Through the Christian Scriptures. 2007. (Illus.). 112p. per. 10.00 *(978-0-8192-2274-9(7)*, Morehouse Publishing) Church Publishing, Inc.

Silva. Zondervan Pictorial Encyclopedia of the Bible, Vol. 1. rev. ed. 2009. 56.00 *(978-0-310-20973-7(0))* Zondervan.

Silva, Moises. Key Insights for Reading God's Word, 1 vol. 2011. (Essential Bible Companion Ser.). (ENG.). 240p. pap. 16.99 *(978-0-310-27821-4(X))* Zondervan.

Silva, Moises & Tenney, Merrill Chapin. The Zondervan Encyclopedia of the Bible. 2009. 56.00 *(978-0-310-24134-8(0))*; 56.00 *(978-0-310-24132-4(4))*; 56.00 *(978-0-310-24133-1(2))*; 55.99 *(978-0-310-24135-5(9))* Zondervan.

Smith, William. Smith's Handi-Reference Bible Dictionary. Peloubet, Francis & Peloubet, Mary, eds. 2008. (AMG Handi-Reference Ser.). (ENG.). 800p. (gr. 11). pap. 9.99 *(978-0-89957-115-7(8))* AMG Pubs.

Standard Publishing Staff. Dictionary & Bible Skills Activities. 2006. (HeartShaper Resources-Elementary Ser.). (ENG.). (J). (gr. 1-5). cd-rom 14.99 *(978-0-7847-1874-2(1))* Standard Publishing.

Strong, James. Compact Reference Library Set. 2007. 2816p. pap. 34.99 *(978-0-7180-0729-4(8))* Nelson, Thomas Inc.

Tenney, Merrill C. The Zondervan Encyclopedia of the Bible, 1 vol. rev. ed. 2009. (ENG.). 5616p. 279.99 *(978-0-310-24136-2(7))* Zondervan.

Tyndale House Publishers Staff, prod. NLT Desktop Concordance. 2008. (Tyndale Desktop Reference Ser.). (ENG.). 320p. pap. 14.99 *(978-1-4143-2200-1(3))* Tyndale Hse. Pubs.

Vila-Escuain. Nuevo Diccionario Biblico Ilust.-Tela: New Illustrated Bible Dictionary, 1 vol. 2008. (SPA., Illus.). 1264p. 29.99 *(978-84-7645-049-9(4)*, 222442) Clie, Editorial ESP. Dist: Zondervan.

Vila, Samuel. Enciclopedia de Dificultades Biblicas: Encyclopedia of Bible Difficulties. (SPA.). 232p. *(978-84-7228-636-8(3)*, 220358) Clie, Editorial.

Watts, John D. W. Lists of Words Occurring Frequently in the Hebrew Bible. 2008. 32p. pap. 5.00 *(978-1-60608-010-8(5)*, Wipf and Stock) Wipf & Stock Pubs.

Wright, William Aldis. The Bible Word-Book: A Glossary of Archaic Words & Phrases in the Authorised Version of the Bible & Book of Common Prayer. 2010. (Cambridge Library Collection - Religion Ser.). 698p. pap. 43.00 *(978-1-108-02464-8(5))* Cambridge Univ. Pr.

Young, G. Douglas. Young's Bible Dictionary. 2007. (Tyndale Reference Ser.). (ENG., Illus.). 576p. per. 13.99 *(978-1-4143-1568-3(6))* Tyndale Hse. Pubs.

Zondervan. The Zondervan Encyclopedia of the Bible: Revised Full-Color Edition, 1 vol. rev. ed. 2011. (ENG.). 44.80 ***(978-0-310-49517-8(2))***; (ENG.). 44.80 ***(978-0-310-49518-5(0))***; (ENG.). 44.80 ***(978-0-310-49514-7(8))***; (ENG.). 44.80 ***(978-0-310-49515-4(6))***; (SPA.). 44.80 ***(978-0-310-49516-1(4))*** Zondervan.

Zondervan Publishing Staff. Concordance Dictionary Topical Bible, 1 vol. 2008. (ENG.). 688p. 19.99 *(978-0-310-28309-6(4))* Zondervan.

BIBLE—DRAMA

see Bible As Literature; Bible Plays; Mysteries and Miracle-Plays

BIBLE—ECONOMICS

see also Christianity and Economics

Haan, Roelf. The Economics of Honor: Biblical Reflections on Money & Property. Hielema, Bert, tr. from DUT. 2009. 152p. pap. 15.00 *(978-0-8028-6012-5(5))* Eerdmans, William B. Publishing Co.

Muir, James C. Business Men of the Bible: A Study of the Advance Agents of Trade & Commerce. 2007. (ENG.). 112p. 34.95 *(978-0-548-05886-2(5))* Kessinger Publishing, LLC.

BIBLE—ETHICS

see Ethics in the Bible

BIBLE—ETHNOLOGY

see Ethnology in the Bible

BIBLE—EVIDENCES, AUTHORITY, ETC.

Here are entered works which attempt to establish the truth of statements in the Bible and to present the Bible as a book whose principles should be followed. Works which discuss the Bible as a divinely inspired book are entered under Bible—Inspiration.

see also Bible—Quotations, Early

Alexander, Archibald. Evidence of the Authenticity, Inspiration & Canonical Authority of the Holy Scriptures. (Works of Reverend Archibald Alexander). 308p. reprint ed. lib. bdg. 49.00 *(978-0-932051-73-8(1))* Reprint Services Co.

—Evidences of the Authenticity, Inspiration, & Canonical Authority of the Holy Scriptures. 2009. 192p. pap. 19.99 *(978-1-150-14392-2(4))* General Bks. LLC.

Allert, Craig D. A High View of Scripture? The Authority of the Bible & the Formation of the New Testament Canon. 2007. (Evangelical Ressourcement Ser.). 204p. (C). pap. 22.00 *(978-0-8010-2778-9(0))* Baker Academic.

Anderson, Cheryl. Ancient Laws & Contemporary Controversies: The Need for Inclusive Biblical Interpretation, 1 vol. 2009. (ENG.). 208p. 25.00 *(978-0-19-530550-0(7))* Oxford Univ. Pr., Inc.

Bailey, Ruben. In the Course of a Dream EMANUEL for LOVE. 2007. 252p. pap. 23.50 *(978-0-615-15178-6(7))* Bailey, Ruben.

Baker-Fletcher, Garth Kasimu & Baker-Fletcher, Garth. Bible Witness in Black Churches. 2009. (Black Religion/Womanist Thought/Social Justice Ser.). (ENG.). 208p. 84.00 *(978-0-230-61771-1(9))* Palgrave Macmillan.

Baltz, Frederick. The Mystery of the Beloved Disciple: New Evidence, Complete Answer. 2011. pap. 12.95 *(978-0-7414-6205-3(2))* Infinity Publishing.

Barbalho, Valquirio. The Third & Last Testament. 2009. 680p. pap. 25.99 *(978-1-4389-5097-6(7))* AuthorHouse.

Barr, James & Barton, John. Bible & Interpretation: The Collected Essays of James Barr, 3 vols. 2012. (ENG.). 696p. 230.00 ***(978-0-19-969290-3(4))***; 792p. 230.00 ***(978-0-19-969289-7(0))*** Oxford Univ. Pr., Inc.

Barr, James, et al. Bible & Interpretation: The Collected Essays of James Barr, 3 vols. 2012. (ENG.). 736p. 230.00 ***(978-0-19-969288-0(2))*** Oxford Univ. Pr., Inc.

Bauckham, Richard. Jesus & the Eyewitnesses: The Gospels As Eyewitness Testimony. 2008. 552p. pap. 26.00 *(978-0-8028-6390-4(6))* Eerdmans, William B. Publishing Co.

Beale, G. K. The Erosion of Inerrancy in Evangelicalism: Responding to New Challenges to Biblical Authority. 2008. 304p. pap. 22.00 *(978-1-4335-0203-3(8))* Crossway.

Beeke, Joel R. & Kistler, Don. Sola Scriptura! The Protestant Position on the Bible. 2nd ed. 2009. *(978-1-56769-183-2(8))* Reformation Pubs.

Bieringer, R. & Elsbernd, M., eds. Normativity of the Future: Reading Biblical & Other Authoritative Texts in an Eschatological Perspective. 2010. (Annua Nuntia Lovaniensia Ser.). (ENG.). 402p. (C). pap. 87.00 *(978-90-429-2227-3(3))* Peeters Pubs. & Booksellers BEL. Dist: Brown, David Bk. Co., The.

Bock, Darrell L. Can I Trust the Bible? 2007. (RZIM Critical Questions Discussion Guides). (ENG.). 74p. per. 8.00 *(978-0-8308-3152-4(5)*, IVP Conn.) InterVarsity Pr.

Boice, James M. Our Sovereign God. 2008. 180p. per. 16.00 *(978-1-59925-134-9(5))* Solid Ground Christian Bks.

Bovell, Carlos R. By Good & Necessary Consequence: A Preliminary Genealogy of Biblicist Foundationalism. 2009. 188p. pap. 22.00 *(978-1-60608-457-1(7)*, Wipf and Stock) Wipf & Stock Pubs.

Bovell, Carlos R., ed. Interdisciplinary Perspectives on the Authority of Scripture: Historical, Biblical, & Theoretical Perspectives. 2011. 424p. pap. 47.00 ***(978-1-60899-347-5(7)***, Pickwick Pubns.) Wipf & Stock Pubs.

Brown, William P. Engaging Biblical Authority: Perspectives on the Bible as Scripture. 2007. (ENG.). 158p. per. 20.00 *(978-0-664-23057-9(1))* Westminster John Knox Pr.

Brug, John F. Bible Discovery Series: Using Archaeology to Study the Bible: Digging for Insights. 2010. pap. *(978-0-8100-2233-1(8))* Northwestern Publishing Hse.

Brusati, Celeste, et al, eds. The Authority of the Word: Reflecting on Image & Text in Northern Europe, 1400-1700. 2011. (ENG., Illus.). XL I, 710p. ***(978-90-04-21515-3(8))*** BRILL.

Cahill, Mark. One Heartbeat Away: Your Journey into Eternity. 2006. (ENG.). pap. 14.99 *(978-0-9643665-7-2(6))* Biblical Discipleship Pubs.

—A un Solo Latido de Distancia: Tu Viaje a la Eternidad. 2007. (SPA., Illus.). pap. 16.99 *(978-0-9643665-5-8(X))* Biblical Discipleship Pubs.

Candler, Warren A. Manual de Evidencias Cristianas: Christian Evidence Manual. (SPA.). *(978-84-7645-009-3(5)*, 223074) Clie, Editorial.

Crawford, Gayleen. Evidence & Science That Confirms the Bible. 2008. 176p. pap. *(978-1-55452-300-9(1))* Essence Publishing.

Down, David. Unveiling the Kings of Israel: Revealing the Bible's Archaeological History. 2011. (Illus.). 170p. ***(978-0-89051-609-6(X))*** Master Bks.

[Dunn, Henry]. Liber Librorum: Its Structure, Limitations, & Purpose. A Friendly Communication to A Reluctant Sceptic. 2006. 240p. per. 20.99 *(978-1-4255-2021-2(9)*,) MPublishing.

Edwards, Rex. An Adventure into Discovery. 2010. (Illus.). 195p. pap. 13.95 *(978-1-57258-613-0(3))* TEACH Services, Inc.

Evans, G. R. The Language & Logic of the Bible: The Road to Reformation. 2009. (ENG.). 220p. pap. 31.99 *(978-0-521-09293-7(0))* Cambridge Univ. Pr.

The Evidences of Christianity in their External Division. 2010. pap. 19.00 *(978-1-61143-177-3(8))* Gorgias Pr., LLC.

Fluhrer, Gabriel N. E. Solid Ground: The Inerrant Word of God in an Errant World. 2012. pap. ***(978-1-59638-403-3(4))*** P & R Publishing.

Fountain, Edwin B. & Ramsey, Willard A. The Signature of God Confronts the Forgeries of Men: How Human Subjectivism Has Eroded Confidence in the Authority of Scripture. 2007. *(978-0-9625220-7-9(4))* Millennium III Pubs., L.P.

Frendo, Anthony J. Pre-Exilic Israel, the Hebrew Bible, & Archaeology: Integrating Text & Artefact. 2011. (Library Hebrew Bible/Old Testament Studies). 144p. 120.00 *(978-0-567-41553-9(5)*, T&T Clark Int'l) Continuum International Publishing Group, Ltd. GBR. Dist: National Bk. Network.

Freund, Richard A. Digging Through the Bible: Modern Archaeology & the Ancient Bible. (ENG., 352p. 2009. Illus.). pap. 18.95 *(978-0-7425-4645-5(4))* 2008. 47.95 *(978-0-7425-4644-8(6))* Rowman & Littlefield Publishers, Inc.

Garner, David B. Did God Really Say? Affirming the Truthfulness & Trustworthiness of Scripture. 2012. pap. ***(978-1-59638-399-9(2))*** P & R Publishing.

Gaussen, Louis. The Divine Inspiration of Scripture. 2007. (ENG.). 400p. 24.99 *(978-1-85792-449-7(5))* Christian Focus Pubns. GBR. Dist: STL Distribution North America.

Geisler, Norman L. & Howe, Thomas. Making Sense of Bible Difficulties: Clear & Concise Answers from Genesis to Revelation, 1 vol. 2009. 272p. pap. 13.99 *(978-0-8010-7188-1(7))* Baker Bks.

Geldenhuys, J. Norval. Supreme Authority: The Authority of the Lord, His Apostles & the New Testament. 2008. 126p. pap. 11.00 *(978-1-55635-768-8(0))* Wipf & Stock Pubs.

George, Timothy & George, Denise, eds. Why I Preach That the Bible is Literally True. (Library of Baptist Classics). pap. 19.99 *(978-0-8054-2077-7(0))* B&H Publishing Group.

Ghosh, Kantik. The Wycliffite Heresy: Authority & the Interpretation of Texts. 2009. (Cambridge Studies in Medieval Literature Ser.). (ENG.). 316p. pap. 42.00 *(978-0-521-10987-1(6))* Cambridge Univ. Pr.

Gruen, George & Gruen, Jean. Let's Witness to Jews: A Practical Guide for Sharing Your Faith- an Individual or Small Group Study. 2009. pap. 14.99 *(978-1-60799-260-8(4))* Tate Publishing & Enterprises, LLC.

Hackett, Stuart C. The Reconstruction of the Christian Revelation Claim: A Philosophical & Critical Apologetic. 2009. 350p. pap. 39.00 *(978-1-60608-367-3(8)*, Wipf and Stock) Wipf & Stock Pubs.

Ham, Ken & Hodge, Bodie. How Do We Know the Bible Is True? 2011. pap. 14.99 *(978-0-89051-633-1(2))* Master Bks.

Ham, Steve. In God We Trust: Why biblical authority matters for every Believer. 2010. (ENG.). 224p. pap. 12.99 *(978-0-89051-583-9(2))* Master Bks.

Henderson, Warren, 8th. The Bible: Myth or Divine Truth? 2008. 64p. pap. 8.95 *(978-0-9795387-7-3(7))* Henderson, Warren.

Hill, Richard J. "Dick". A Glimpse of the Christ: Glimpses of God's Grace. 2007. (ASM & ENG.). 216p. per. 17.99 *(978-1-4141-0812-4(5))* Pleasant Word.

Hutchinson, Robert J. The Politically Incorrect Guide to the Bible. 2007. (Politically Incorrect Guides). (ENG.). 262p. per. 19.95 *(978-1-59698-520-9(8))* Regnery Publishing, Inc., An Eagle Publishing Co.

Istafanous, Abd-el-Masih. Calvin's Doctrine of Biblical Authority. 2010. 240p. pap. 27.00 *(978-1-60899-644-5(1)*, Wipf and Stock) Wipf & Stock Pubs.

Jeffrey, Grant R. The Signature of God, Revised Edition: Conclusive Proof that Every Teaching, Every Command, Every Promise in the Bible Is True. l.t. ed. 2010. (ENG.). 416p. pap. 17.99 *(978-1-59415-338-9(8))* Cengage Gale.

—The Signature of God, Revised Edition: Conclusive Proof That Every Teaching, Every Command, Every Promise in the Bible Is True. 3rd ed. 2010. (ENG.). 336p. pap. 14.99 *(978-0-307-44484-4(8)*, WaterBrook Pr.) Doubleday Religious Publishing Group, The.

King, L. W. Legends of Babylon & Egypt in Relation to Hebrew Tradition. 2007. 172p. per. *(978-1-4065-1948-8(0))* Dodo Pr.

Kissinger, Thomas / Mark. The Noble Berean: And they searched the scriptures daily, whether those things were So..., 5 volumes, Volume 1. 2007. 104p. pap. 12.95 *(978-0-9785134-1-2(X))* Straightway Publishing Co.

Kroll, Woodrow. Taking Back the Good Book: How America Forgot the Bible & Why It Matters to You. 2007. 224p. 19.99 *(978-1-58134-826-2(6))* Crossway.

Kwok, Dennis & College, Faculty of Febc. Verbal Plenary Preservation of the Bible, a Course on the Doctrine of Verbal Plenary Preservation. 2008. 176p. pap. 15.00 *(978-0-9817985-4-7(3))* Old Paths Pubns., Inc., The.

Law, David R. Historical Critical Method: A Guide for the Perplexed. 2012. (ENG.). 344p. 90.00 ***(978-0-567-11130-2(X))***; pap. 27.95 ***(978-0-567-40012-3(3))*** Continuum International Publishing Group, Ltd. GBR. (T&T Clark Int'l). Dist: National Bk. Network.

Lee, William. The Inspiration of Holy Scripture, Its Nature & Proof: Eight Discourses, Preached Before the University of Dublin, by William Lee ... 2006. 484p. pap. 29.99 *(978-1-4255-5389-0(3))*; 480p. per. 29.99 *(978-1-4255-5330-2(3))* MPublishing.

Levy, Ian Christopher. Holy Scripture & the Quest for Authority at the End of the Middle Ages. 2012. (ND Reading the Scriptures Ser.). (ENG.). 352p. pap. 38.00 ***(978-0-268-03414-6(1))*** Univ. of Notre Dame Pr.

Lewis, Tayler. The Divine Human in the Scriptures. 2009. 142p. pap. *(978-0-217-38306-6(8))* Books LLC.

—The Divine Human in the Scriptures. 2007. (ENG.). 410p. 49.95 *(978-0-548-17927-7(1))*; 412p. per. 34.95 *(978-1-4304-7976-5(0))* Kessinger Publishing, LLC.

—The Divine Human in the Scriptures. 2006. 412p. per. 26.99 *(978-1-4255-4445-4(2))* MPublishing.

Lutzer, Erwin W. Seven Reasons Why You Can Trust the Bible. 2008. (ENG.). 208p. pap. 13.99 *(978-0-8024-8433-8(6))* Moody Pubs.

MacArthur, John F. Why Believe the Bible? 2008. (ENG., Illus.). 192p. 14.99 *(978-0-8307-4564-7(5))* Gospel Light Pubns.

Mal, Mary. Where Are We in God's Timing? Examining the Evidence. Date not set. spiral bd. incl. audio *(978-0-9659430-3-1(8))* Mal, Mary.

Marcellino, Dennis. The Proof: That God Exists & the Bible Is True. 2009. *(978-0-945272-33-5(2))* Lighthouse Pubns., Inc.

—Why Are We Here Workbook. 2007. 152p. per. 19.95 *(978-0-945272-12-0(X))* Lighthouse Publishing.

McDowell, Josh & Williams, Thomas. The Relational Word: A Biblical Design to Reclaim & Transform the Next Generation. annot. ed. 2006. 249p. per. 13.99 *(978-1-932587-83-8(7))* Green Key Bks.

McGowan, A. T. B. The Divine Authenticity of Scripture: Retrieving an Evangelical Heritage. 2008. (ENG.). 229p. pap. 22.00 *(978-0-8308-2879-1(6)*, IVP Acad.) InterVarsity Pr.

McIlvaine, Charles Pettit. The Evidences of Christianity; in Their External, or Historical, Division: Exhibited in A Course of Lectures, by Charles Pettit McIlvaine ... Revised. 2006. 416p. per. 26.99 *(978-1-4255-4475-1(4))* MPublishing.

B

McNaught, Doug. Reclaiming the Bible from the Enlightened. 2007. 338p. 43.95 *(978-1-84753-654-9(9))* Lulu Enterprises Inc.
Meitlis, Itzhak. Excavating the Bible: New Archaeological Evidence for the Historical Reliability of Scripture. 2012. ***(978-0-935437-41-6(X))*** Bartleby Pr.
Moore, James. Heretics from Heaven: How a Few Church Rejects Changed the World. 2011. 208p. pap. 17.95 *(978-1-4497-1228-0(2),* WestBow Pr.) Author Solutions, Inc.
Moorman, Jack. Forever Settled, A Survey of the Documents & History of the Bible. 2008. pap. 20.00 *(978-1-888328-06-6(1))* Old Paths Pubns., Inc., The.
Mullins, E. Y. Manual de Evidencias Cristianas: Christian Evidence Manual. (SPA.). *(978-84-7645-181-6(4),* 223226) Clie, Editorial.
Mulloorparambil, Sebastian. Dynamism of the Word of God & Biblical Personalities. 2009. xiv, 285p. pap. *(978-81-89958-22-0(4),* Library of Congress — New Delhi Overseas Office) Dharmaram Publications.
Murray, John. Calvin on Scripture & Divine Sovereignty. 2009. 84p. pap. 12.00 *(978-1-59925-203-2(1))* Solid Ground Christian Bks.
Nettles, Kenneth James. The Supernatural Origin of the Bible. 2011. 178p. 42.95 ***(978-1-258-05582-0(1))*** Literary Licensing, LLC.
Nicholas, David R. Foundations of Biblical Inerrancy. pap. 2.99 *(978-0-88469-104-4(7))* BMH Bks.
Nichols, Stephen J. & Brandt, Eric T. Ancient Word, Changing Worlds: The Doctrine of Scripture in a Modern Age. 2009. 176p. pap. 16.99 *(978-1-4335-0260-6(7))* Crossway.
Paley, William. The Miscellaneous Works of William Paley. 2009. 370p. pap. *(978-0-217-09257-9(8))* Books LLC.
Palmer, B. M. (Benjamin Morgan). Death in the Home: A Christian Father Responds Loss. 2008. (ENG.). 102p. reprint ed. pap. 12.95 *(978-0-9800370-1-2(8))* Reformed Academic Pr.
Pinnock, Clark H. & Callen, Barry L. The Scripture Principle: Reclaiming the Full Authority of the Bible. 3rd ed. 2009. *(978-0-9819582-5-5(7))* Emeth Pr.
Piper, John. Why We Believe the Bible: A Study Guide to the DVD Featuring John Piper. 2009. (John Piper Small Group Ser.). 192p. pap. 11.99 *(978-1-4335-0771-7(4))* Crossway.
Price, Robert M. Inerrant the Wind: The Evangelical Crisis of Biblical Authority. 2008. (ENG.). 345p. bds. 25.98 *(978-1-59102-676-1(8))* Prometheus Bks., Pubs.
Quist, Allen. Many Convincing Proofs: A Biblical Approach to Christian Apologetics. 2008. (Illus.). 81p. pap. 12.95 *(978-0-931057-00-7(0))* Lutheran Synod Bk. Co.
Rawlinson, George. The Historical Evidences of the Truth of the Scripture Records States Anew. 2006. 460p. per. 29.99 *(978-1-4255-5095-0(9))* MPublishing.
Rogers, Henry. Reason & Faith; Their Claims & Conflicts. 2007. 80p. per. *(978-1-4068-3996-8(5))* Echo Library.
Rose Publishing Staff. Why Trust the Bible? 2008. (Rose Bible Basics Ser.). (ENG., Illus.). 112p. pap. 12.99 *(978-1-59636-201-7(4))* Rose Publishing.
—Why Trust the Bible? Answers to the New Critics. 2007. 12p. 3.99 *(978-1-59636-139-3(5))* Rose Publishing.
Satta, Ronald F. The Sacred Text: Biblical Authority in Nineteenth-Century America. 2007. (Princeton Theological Monographs). 132p. pap. 16.00 *(978-1-55635-298-0(0),* Pickwick Pubns.) Wipf & Stock Pubs.
—True & Reasonable: In Defense of the Christian Faith. 2009. 96p. pap. 13.00 *(978-1-60608-486-1(0),* Wipf and Stock) Wipf & Stock Pubs.
Sheetz, Paul. Three Faces of Eden. 2006. 27.99 *(978-1-59781-658-8(2));* pap. 17.99 *(978-1-59781-657-1(4))* Xulon Pr., Inc.
Sorenson, Thomas C. Liberating Christianity: Overcoming Obstacles to Faith in the New Millennium. 2008. 238p. pap. 26.00 *(978-1-60608-072-6(5),* Wipf and Stock) Wipf & Stock Pubs.
Sproul, R. C. Can I Trust the Bible? 2009. *(978-1-56769-182-5(X))* Ligonier Ministries.
Stevenson, Jeffery S. All People, All Times: Rethinking Biblical Authority in Churches of Christ. 2009. 292p. pap. 16.99 *(978-1-60791-539-3(1))* Xulon Pr., Inc.
Stewart, Robert, ed. The Reliability of the New Testament: Bart Ehrman & Daniel Wallace in Dialogue. 2011. 224p. (C). pap. 22.00 *(978-0-8006-9773-0(1),* Fortress Pr.) Augsburg Fortress, Pubs.
Stott, John, ed. The Anglican Communion & Scripture: Papers from the First International Consultation of the Evangelical Fellowship in the Anglican Communion, Canterbury, UK, June 1993. 2011. 198p. pap. 23.00 ***(978-1-61097-559-9(6),*** Wipf and Stock) Wipf & Stock Pubs.
Thomas, J. D. We Be Brethren: A Study in Biblical Interpretation. 2011. 276p. 47.95 ***(978-1-258-10042-1(8))*** Literary Licensing, LLC.
Thomson, William. Aids to Faith; a Series of Theological Essays by Several Writers Being a Reply to Essays & Reviews Ed by William Thomson. 2006. 544p. (ENG.). per. 29.99 *(978-1-4255-6026-3(1));* per. 29.99 *(978-1-4255-6025-6(3))* MPublishing.
Topping, Richard R. Revelation Scripture & Church: Theological Hermeneutic Thought of James Barr Paul Ricoeur & Hans Frei. 2007. (Ashgate New Critical Thinking in Religion, Theology & Biblical Studies Ser.). 252p. 114.95 *(978-0-7546-5802-3(3))* Ashgate Publishing Co.
Torrey, R. A. The Bible & Its Christ: Being Noonday. 2006. 20.95 *(978-1-4286-3764-1(8))* Kessinger Publishing, LLC.
—Is the Bible the Inerrant Word of God: And Was the Body of Jesus Raised from the Dead? 2007. (ENG.). 184p. 37.95 *(978-0-548-09724-3(0))* Kessinger Publishing, LLC.
Trench, Richard Chenevix. The Fitness of Holy Scripture for Unfolding the Spiritual Life of Men II Christ the Desire of All Nations, or, the Unconscious Prophecies of Heathen. 2006. 268p. per. 23.99 *(978-1-4255-2370-1(6))* MPublishing.
Turnage, C. L. The Bible. . . An Extraterrestrial Transmission: Is Planet X Planet Heaven? rev. ed. Date not set. (Illus.). 159p. reprint ed. 20.00 *(978-0-9645885-4-7(4))* Flying Disk Pubns.
Tyler, James Endell. Primitive Christian Worship. 2008. 376p. 29.99 *(978-0-554-34159-0(X));* 31.99 *(978-0-554-24856-1(5))* BiblioBazaar.
—Primitive Christian Worship. 2009. 230p. pap. 18.71 *(978-0-217-03173-8(0))* Books LLC.
—Primitive Christian Worship. 2006. pap. *(978-1-4068-3373-7(8))* Echo Library.
Tyner, M. J. Is the Bible the Infallible Word of God? 2007. per. 1.00 *(978-0-9789909-2-3(7))* True-Way Tracts.
Van Den Belt, Henk. The Authority of Scripture in Reformed Theology: Truth & Trust. 2008. (Studies in Reformed Theology Ser.). 384p. *(978-90-04-16307-2(7))* BRILL.
Veith, Gene Edward. Why God Gave Us a Book. 2011. pap. ***(978-1-59638-378-4(X))*** P & R Publishing.
Waite, D. A. Jr. & Waite, D. A. A Warning!! on Gail Riplinger's Kjb & Multiple Inspiration Heresy. 2010. 140p. pap. 13.00 *(978-1-56848-069-5(5))* Old Paths Pubns., Inc., The.
Watson, Richard. An Apology for the Bible: In a Series of Letters Addressed to Thomas Paine. 2011. 127p. pap. 19.99 *(978-1-107-60004-1(9))* Cambridge Univ. Pr.
Webster, Allen. You Gotta Be Dumb to Believe the Bible. Right? 2007. 0.35 *(978-1-933808-64-2(0))* House to House Heart to Heart Publishing, Inc.
Whitcomb, John C. The World That Perished: An Introduction to Biblical Catastrophism. 3rd ed. 2009. (Illus.). 178p. pap. 18.00 *(978-0-88469-266-9(3))* BMH Bks.
Williams, Philip Lee. The Archaeological Evidence of Noah's Flood. 2011. (ENG., Illus.). 411p. 34.95 *(978-0-9793102-2-5(9))* Christian Leaders & Scholars Pr.
Wright, N. T. The Last Word: Scripture & the Authority of God — Getting Beyond the Bible Wars. 2006. 160p. pap. 12.99 *(978-0-06-087261-8(6),* HarperOne) HarperCollins Pubs.

BIBLE—EVIDENCES, AUTHORITY, ETC.—N. T.

Bauckham, Richard. Jesus & the Eyewitnesses: The Gospels as Eyewitness Testimony. 2006. 538p. 32.00 *(978-0-8028-3162-0(1))* Eerdmans, William B. Publishing Co.
Bruce, F. F. The New Testament Documents: Are they Reliable? 2009. 84p. pap. 8.99 *(978-1-60459-866-7(2))* Wilder Pubns., Ltd.
Bruce, Frederick Fyvie & Bruce, F. F. Are the New Testament Documents Reliable? 2011. 124p. pap. 8.95 ***(978-1-61427-058-4(9))*** Martino Publishing.
Ehrman, Bart D. Forged: Writing in the Name of God — Why the Bible's Authors Are Not Who We Think They Are. (ENG.). 2012. 256p. pap. 15.99 ***(978-0-06-201262-3(2))*** 2011. 304p. 26.99 *(978-0-06-201261-6(4))* HarperCollins Pubs. (HarperOne).
Greenleaf, Simon. The Testimony of the Evangelists, Examined by the Rules of Evidence Administered in Courts of Justice with an Appendix Containing a History of the Most Ancient Manuscript Copies of the New Testament, & a Comparison of Their Text with That of the King James, [1874]. fac. ed. 2009. 636p. 35.95 *(978-1-58477-095-4(3))* Lawbook Exchange, Ltd., The.
Holding, James Patrick. Trusting the New Testament. 2009. 304p. pap. 21.99 *(978-1-60791-733-5(5))* Xulon Pr., Inc.
Lewis, Frank. The Irenaeus Testimony to the Fourth Gospel. 2009. pap. 37.70 *(978-1-60724-277-2(X))* Gorgias Pr., LLC.
Lewis, Frank Grant. The Irenaeus Testimony to the Fourth Gospel: Its Extent, Meaning & Value. 2008. 64p. pap. 6.00 *(978-1-60608-279-9(5),* Wipf and Stock) Wipf & Stock Pubs.
Nast, William. The Gospel Records: Their Genuineness, Authenticity, Historic Verity, & inspiration, with Some Preliminary Remarks on the Gospel History. by William. 2006. 380p. per. 26.99 *(978-1-4255-4009-8(0))* MPublishing.
Price, Robert M. Night of the Living Savior. 2011. vii, 239p. pap. 21.95 *(978-1-57884-010-6(4))* American Atheist Pr.
Taylor, C. The Witness of Hermas to the Four Gospels. 2008. 156p. pap. 13.00 *(978-1-60608-292-8(2),* Wipf and Stock) Wipf & Stock Pubs.
Wesley, John. John Wesley's Notes on Paul's Epistle to the Romans. 2011. 82p. 37.95 ***(978-1-258-08790-6(1))*** Literary Licensing, LLC.

BIBLE—EVIDENCES, AUTHORITY, ETC.—O. T.

Albright, William Foxwell. Archaeology & the Religion of Israel. 2006. (Old Testament Library). (ENG.). 247p. per. 40.00 *(978-0-664-22742-5(2))* Westminster John Knox Pr.
Ben Zvi, Ehud & Edelman, Diana Vikander. What Was Authoritative for Chronicles? 2011. ***(978-1-57506-218-1(6))*** Eisenbrauns, Inc.
Carr, David McLain. The Formation of the Hebrew Bible: A New Reconstruction, 1 vol. 2011. (ENG.). 544p. 74.00 *(978-0-19-974260-8(X))* Oxford Univ. Pr., Inc.
Eran, Mordechai & Shavit, Yaacov. The Hebrew Bible Reborn: From Holy Scripture to the Book of Books: A History of Biblical Culture & the Battles over the Bible in Modern Judaism. Naor, Chaya, tr. from HEB. 2007. (Studia Judaica: Forschungen Zur Wissenschaft des Judentums Ser.). (ENG.). X, 566p. 196.00 *(978-3-11-019141-7(5))* De Gruyter, Walter Inc.
Finkelstein, Israel, et al. The Quest for the Historical Israel: Debating Archaeology & the History of Early Israel: Lectures Delivered at the Annual Colloquium of the Institute for Secular Humanistic Judaism, Detroit, October 2005. 2007. *(978-90-401-5738-7(3))* BRILL.
—The Quest for the Historical Israel: Debating Archaeology & the History of Early Israel: Lectures Delivered at the Annual Colloquium of the Institute for Secular Humanistic Judaism, Detroit, October 2005. 2007. (Archaeology & Biblical Studies). 24.95 *(978-1-58983-277-0(9))* Society of Biblical Literature.
Grabbe, Lester L., et al. The Historian & the Bible. 2010. (Library of Hebrew Bible/Old Testament Studies). (ENG., Illus.). 256p. 140.00 *(978-0-567-20268-0(2),* T&T Clark Int'l) Continuum International Publishing Group, Ltd. GBR. Dist: National Bk. Network.
Keith, Alexander. Evidence of the Truth of the Christian Religion Derived from the Literal Fulfillment of Prophecy. 2009. 286p. 34.99 *(978-1-113-99889-7(X))* BiblioBazaar.
Lightner, Robert. A Biblical Case for Total Inerrancy: How Jesus Viewed the Old Testament. 2007. 204p. per. 24.00 *(978-1-57978-650-2(2))* Baptist Standard Bearer, Inc.
Oswalt, John & Oswalt, John N. The Bible among the Myths: Unique Revelation or Just Ancient Literature?, 1 vol. 2009. (ENG.). 208p. pap. 17.99 *(978-0-310-28509-0(7))* Zondervan.
Wilson, Robert. A Scientific Investigation of the Old Testament. 2007. 196p. per. 18.99 *(978-1-59925-105-9(1))* Solid Ground Christian Bks.

BIBLE—EXAMINATIONS, QUESTION-BOOKS, ETC.

see Bible—Catechisms

BIBLE—EXEGESIS

see Bible—Commentaries; Bible—Hermeneutics

BIBLE—FEMINIST CRITICISM

Here are entered works on the criticism of the Bible from the standpoint of feminist theology or feminist theory. Works on how feminism is or ought to be viewed from the standpoint of the Bible are entered under Bible and Feminism.
see also Bible and Feminism

Abraham, Joseph. Eve: Accused or Acquitted? An Analysis of Feminist Readings of the Creation Narrative Texts in Genesis 1-3. 2007. (Paternoster Biblical Monographs: Ser.). 312p. pap. 31.00 *(978-1-59752-767-5(X),* Wipf and Stock) Wipf & Stock Pubs.
Bellis, Alice Ogden. Helpmates, Harlots, & Heroes: Women's Stories in the Hebrew Bible. 2nd ed. 2007. (ENG.). 306p. per. 30.00 *(978-0-664-23028-9(8))* Westminster John Knox Pr.
Bird, Jennifer G. Abuse, Power & Fearful Obedience: Reconsidering 1 Peter?s Commands to Wives. 2011. (Library of New Testament Studies). (ENG.). 180p. 130.00 *(978-0-567-42750-2(1),* T&T Clark Int'l) Continuum International Publishing Group, Ltd. GBR. Dist: National Bk. Network.
Bundesen, Lynne. The Feminine Spirit: Recapturing the Heart of Scripture. 2007. (ENG.). 208p. per. 17.95 *(978-0-7879-8495-3(7),* Jossey-Bass) Wiley, John & Sons, Inc.
Calvert-Koyzis, Nancy. Breaking Boundaries: Female Biblical Interpreters Who Challenged the Status Quo. Weir, Heather E., ed. 2010. (Library of Hebrew Bible/Old Testament Studies). (ENG.). 224p. 130.00 *(978-0-567-59503-4(X),* T&T Clark Int'l) Continuum International Publishing Group, Ltd. GBR. Dist: National Bk. Network.
Calvert-Koyzis, Nancy & Weir, Heather, eds. Breaking Boundaries: Female Biblical Interpreters Who Challenged the Status Quo. 2012. (Library Hebrew Bible/Old Testament Studies). (ENG.). 224p. pap. 44.95 ***(978-0-567-37503-2(X),*** T&T Clark Int'l) Continuum International Publishing Group, Ltd. GBR. Dist: National Bk. Network.
Camp, Claudia V. Wise, Strange & Holy: The Strange Woman & the Making of the Bible. 2009. (Library of Hebrew Bible/Old Testament Studies, the Ser.). (ENG.). 376p. 60.00 *(978-0-567-19510-4(4),* T&T Clark) Continuum International Publishing Group, Ltd. GBR. Dist: National Bk. Network.
Day, Linda & Pressler, Carolyn, eds. Engaging the Bible in a Gendered World: An Introduction to Feminist Biblical Interpretation. 2006. (ENG., Illus.). 260p. per. 30.00 *(978-0-664-22910-8(7))* Westminster John Knox Pr.
deGroot, Christiana & Taylor, Marion Ann. Recovering Nineteenth-Century Women Interpreters of the Bible. 2007. (SBL - Symposium Ser.). 246p. *(978-90-04-15109-3(5))* BRILL.
—Recovering Nineteenth-Century Women Interpreters of the Bible. 2007. (ENG.). 256p. per. 34.95 *(978-1-58983-220-6(5))* Society of Biblical Literature.
Eskenazi, Tamara Cohn. The Torah: A Women's Commentary. 2007. 1350p. 75.00 *(978-0-8074-1081-3(0))* URJ Pr.
Forth, Sarah S. Eve's Bible: A Woman's Guide to the Old Testament. 2009. (ENG.). 336p. pap. 17.95 *(978-0-312-56518-3(6),* St. Martin's Griffin) St. Martin's Pr.
Goldstein, Elyse, ed. The Women's Torah Commentary: New Insights from Women Rabbis on the 45 Weekly Torah Portions. 2008. 496p. pap. 19.99 *(978-1-58023-370-5(8))* Jewish Lights Publishing.
Gossai, Hemchand. Power & Marginality in the Abraham Narrative - Second Edition. 2nd ed. 2009. (Princeton Theological Monographs). 168p. pap. 19.00 *(978-1-55635-874-6(1),* Pickwick Pubns.) Wipf & Stock Pubs.
Holloway, Steven, et al, eds. In the Wake of Tikva Frymer-Kensky. 2009. 105.00 *(978-1-59333-977-7(1))* Gorgias Pr., LLC.
Jackson, Melissa. Comedy & Feminist Interpretation of the Hebrew Bible: A Subversive Collaboration. 2012. (ENG.). 288p. 125.00 ***(978-0-19-965677-6(0))*** Oxford Univ. Pr., Inc.
Kelso, Julie. O Mother, Where Art Thou? An Irigarayan Reading of the Book of Chronicles. 2008. (BibleWorld Ser.). (ENG.). 224p. (C). 99.95 *(978-1-84553-323-6(2));* pap. 34.95 *(978-1-84553-324-3(0))* Equinox Publishing Ltd. GBR. Dist: ISD.
Kim, Seong Hee. Mark, Women & Empire: A Korean Postcolonial Perspective. 2010. 192p. *(978-1-906055-64-6(5))* Sheffield Phoenix Pr.
Kostenberger, Margaret, et al. Jesus & the Feminists: Who Do They Say That He Is? 2008. 256p. pap. 19.99 *(978-1-58134-959-7(9))* Crossway.
Köstenberger, Margaret Elizabeth. Jesus & the Feminists: Who Do They Say That He Is? 2008. pap. *(978-1-58134-595-7(X))* Crossway.
Koyzis, Nancy Calvert & Weir, Heather E. Strangely Familiar: Protofeminist Interpretations of Patriarchal Biblical Texts. 2009. 304p. pap. 35.95 *(978-1-58983-453-8(4))* Society of Biblical Literature.
Kwok, Pui-Lan, ed. Women's Sacred Scripture. 2011. pap. ***(978-0-334-03049-2(8),*** SCM Pr.) Hymns Ancient & Modern Ltd.
Lavigne, Langley. Sex, Sheepskin Rugs 'n' Bless My Soul. 2008. (Illus.). 448p. pap. *(978-1-84748-242-6(2))* Athena Pr.
Levine, Amy Jill. A Feminist Companion to Patristic Literature. 2008. (Feminist Companion to the New Testament & Early Christian Writings Ser.). (ENG., Illus.). 256p. 49.95 *(978-0-567-04555-3(2));* 160.00 *(978-0-567-04554-6(4))* Continuum International Publishing Group, Ltd. GBR. (T&T Clark Int'l). Dist: National Bk. Network.
Mandolfo, Carleen. Daughter Zion Talks Back to the Prophets: A Dialogic Theology of the Book of Lamentations. 2007. ix, 149p. 24.95 *(978-1-58983-247-3(7))* Society of Biblical Literature.
Marchal, Joseph. Hierarchy, Unity, & Imitation: A Femin. 2006. viii, 261p. pap. 39.95 *(978-1-58983-243-5(4))* Society of Biblical Literature.
O'Brien, Julia M. Challenging Prophetic Metaphor: Theology & Ideology in the Prophets. 2008. (ENG.). 224p. pap. 25.00 *(978-0-664-22964-1(6))* Westminster John Knox Pr.
Rusca, Ruth. Feminine Mysteries in the Bible: The Soul Teachings of the Daughters of the Goddess. 2008. (ENG.). 1p. pap. 15.00 *(978-1-59143-088-9(7))* Bear & Co.
Rushton, Kathleen P. The Parable of the Woman in Childbirth of John 16: A Metaphor for the Death & Glorification of Jesus. 2011. 404p. 139.95 *(978-0-7734-1500-3(9))* Mellen, Edwin Pr., The.
Scholz, Susanne & Scholz. Introducing the Women's Hebrew Bible. 2007. (Introductions in Feminist Theology Ser.). (ENG.). 160p. 29.95 *(978-0-567-08257-2(1),* T&T Clark Int'l) Continuum International Publishing Group, Ltd. GBR. Dist: National Bk. Network.
Sherwood, Yvonne. Prostitute & the Prophet: Hosea's Marriage in Literary-Theoretical Perspective. 2009. (Library of Hebrew Bible/Old Testament Studies, the Ser.). (ENG.). 357p. 60.00 *(978-1-4411-1714-4(8),* T&T Clark) Continuum International Publishing Group, Ltd. GBR. Dist: National Bk. Network.
Society of Biblical Literature Staff, contrib. by. The Bible & Women: An Encyclopaedia of Exegesis & Cultural History. 2011. ***(978-1-58983-634-1(0));*** ***(978-1-58983-565-8(4));*** 500p. pap. ***(978-1-58983-564-1(6))*** Society of Biblical Literature.
Stanton, Elizabeth Cady. The Woman's Bible. 2008. 476p. 31.99 *(978-0-554-32429-6(6))* 2008. 476p. 33.99 *(978-0-554-23126-6(3))* 2007. (ENG.). 428p. pap. 26.99 *(978-1-4264-3777-9(3))* 2007. (ENG.). 472p. pap. 30.99 *(978-1-4264-3847-9(8))* BiblioBazaar.
Turner, John Douglas & Corrigan, Kevin. Plato's Parmenides & Its Heritage: History & Interpretation from the Old Academy to Later Platonism & Gnosticism. 2009. *(978-90-04-17793-2(0))* BRILL.
Wallace, David R. The Gospel of God: Romans as Paul's Aeneid. 2008. 244p. pap. 27.00 *(978-1-55635-437-3(1),* Pickwick Pubns.) Wipf & Stock Pubs.
Weir, Heather E., ed. Let Her Speak for Herself: Nineteenth-Century Women Writing on Women in Genesis. 2006. (Illus.). 513p. per. 44.95 *(978-1-932792-53-9(8))* Baylor Univ. Pr.
Wooten, Barbara Boone. Destiny Denied: The Veiling of Women in the Traditional Church. 2008. (ENG.). 304p. pap. 14.99 *(978-1-59979-193-7(5),* Creation Hse.) Charisma Media.

BIBLE—FESTIVALS

see Fasts and Feasts

BIBLE—FOLKLORE

see Jews—Folklore

BIBLE—FORM CRITICISM

see Bible—Criticism, Form

BIBLE—GARDENS

see Nature in the Bible

BIBLE—GENEALOGY

see Genealogy in the Bible

BIBLE—GEOGRAPHY

see also Ecclesiastical Geography

Bartlett, W. H. Footsteps of Our Lord & His Apostles in Syria, Greece & Italy: A Succession of Visits to the Scenes of New Testament Narrative. 2007. (ENG.). 286p. 43.95 *(978-0-548-03617-4(9))* Kessinger Publishing, LLC.
Beck, John A. The Land of Milk & Honey: An Introduction to the Geography of Israel. 2006. (ENG., Illus.). 205p. per. 29.99 *(978-0-7586-0056-1(9))* Concordia Publishing Hse.
Beck, John A., et al. A Visual Guide to Bible Events: Fascinating Insights into Where They Happened & Why. 2009. 272p. 39.99 *(978-0-8010-1285-3(6))* Baker Bks.
Booram, Beth. The Wide Open Spaces of God: A Journey with God Through the Landscapes of Life. 2007. 189p. per. 14.00 *(978-0-687-49096-7(0),* Dimensions For Living) Abingdon Pr.
Burge, Gary M. The Bible & the Land, 1 vol. 2009. (Ancient Context, Ancient Faith Ser.). (ENG.). 112p. pap. 14.99 *(978-0-310-28044-6(3))* Zondervan.
Camp, Claudia V. & Berquist, Jon L. Constructions of Space II: The Biblical City & Other Imagined Spaces. Camp, Claudia V., ed. 2008. (Library of Hebrew

Bible/Old Testament Studies, the Ser.). (ENG., Illus.). 176p. 120.00 *(978-0-567-02708-5(2),* T&T Clark Int'l) Continuum International Publishing Group, Ltd. GBR. Dist: National Bk. Network.

Caughey, Ellen. 40 Fascinating Places of the Bible. 2008. (Value Books Ser.). (ENG.). 96p. pap. 0.99 *(978-1-60260-021-8(X),* Barbour Bks.) Barbour Publishing, Inc.

Curtis, Adrian. Oxford Bible Atlas. 4th ed. 2009. (ENG., Illus.). 240p. pap. 24.95 *(978-0-19-956046-2(3))* Oxford Univ. Pr., Inc.

Davies, G. I. The Way of the Wilderness: A Geographical Study of the Wilderness Itineraries in the Old Testament. 2009. (Society for Old Testament Study Monographs). (ENG.). 152p. pap. 20.99 *(978-0-521-10409-8(2))* Cambridge Univ. Pr.

DeVries, LaMoine F. Cities of the Biblical World: An Introduction to the Archaeology, Geography, & History of Biblical Sites. 2006. (Illus.). 420p. pap. 40.00 *(978-1-55635-120-4(8),* Wipf and Stock) Wipf & Stock Pubs.

Godoy, Pope. Diccionario Geográfico Del Nuevo Testamento. 2010. (SPA., Illus.). 140p. *(978-84-8005-152-1(3))* 1El Almendro de Cordoba, Ediciones, S.L.

Jacobs, Dennis. The Seventh World Empire. 2007. 124p. per. 15.95 *(978-0-9766046-1-7(2))* DRAYJAC Publishing Co.

Jensen, Fred M. Experience the Presence of God. 2009. 328p. 28.99 *(978-1-60791-309-2(7))* Xulon Pr., Inc.

Kallai, Zecharia. Studies in Biblical Historiography & Geography: Collection of Studies. 2010. (Beiträge zur Erforschung des Alten Testaments und des Antiken Judentums Ser.). 266p. 57.95 *(978-3-631-59362-2(7))* Lang, Peter GmbH, Europäischer Verlag der Wissenschaften DEU. Dist: Lang, Peter.

Laan, Ray Vander. Faith Lessons on the Prophets & Kings of Israel Discovery Guide, 1 vol. exp. rev. ed. 2008. (Faith Lessons Ser.). (ENG.). 208p. pap. 9.99 *(978-0-310-27961-7(5))* Zondervan.

—Promised Land, 1 vol., Vol. 1. rev. exp. ed. 2008. (Faith Lessons Ser.). (ENG.). 160p. pap. 9.99 *(978-0-310-27957-0(7))* Zondervan.

Laan, Ray Vander & Sorenson, Amanda. Early Church, 1 vol., Vol. 5. exp. rev. ed. 2008. (Faith Lessons Ser.). (ENG.). 192p. pap. 9.99 *(978-0-310-27971-6(2))* Zondervan.

Laan, Ray Vander, et al. Life & Ministry of the Messiah Discovery Guide Revised & Expanded, 1 vol. rev. ed. 2008. (Faith Lessons Ser.). (ENG.). 304p. pap. 9.99 *(978-0-310-27964-8(X))* Zondervan.

Leeman, Bernard. Queen of Sheba & Biblical Scholarship. 280p. 84.95 *(978-1-59221-117-3(8))* Africa World Pr.

Marchadour, Alain, et al. The Land, the Bible, & History: Toward the Land That I Will Show You. 3rd ed. 2010. (Abrahamic Dialogues Ser.). (ENG.). 232p. pap. 26.00 *(978-0-8232-2660-3(3))* Fordham Univ. Pr.

Martin, James C., et al. A Visual Guide to Gospel Events: Fascinating Insights Into Where They Happened & Why. 2010. 208p. 29.99 *(978-0-8010-1311-9(9))* Baker Bks.

Miller, Hugh. Testimony of the Rocks. 2010. pap. 76.24 *(978-1-61719-652-2(5))* Gorgias Pr., LLC.

Niesiolowski-Spanò, Lukasz. The Origin Myths of Holy Places in the Old Testament: A Study of Aetiological Narratives. 2011. (Copenhagen International Seminar Ser.). (ENG.). 314p. (C). 110.00 *(978-1-84553-334-2(6))* Equinox Publishing Ltd. GBR. Dist: ISD.

Old Testament Palestine: Tribal Divisions & Cities of Refuge. 2007. (Abingdon Class Maps Ser.). 13.75 *(978-0-687-23277-2(5))* Abingdon Pr.

Race, Marianne & Brink, Laurie. In This Place: Reflections on the Land of the Gospels for the Liturgical Cycles. 2008. 238p. pap. 26.00 *(978-1-55635-906-4(3),* Wipf and Stock) Wipf & Stock Pubs.

Rasmussen, Carl G. Atlas of the Bible, 1 vol. rev. ed. 2010. (ENG.). 256p. 39.99 *(978-0-310-27050-8(2))* Zondervan.

Ritter, Carl. Comparative Geography of Palestine & T. 2006. 412p. per. *(978-1-4067-2163-8(8),* Hesperides Pr.) Read Bks.

—The Comparative Geography of Palestine & the Sinaitic Peninsula. 2009. 320p. pap. *(978-0-217-62340-7(9))* Books LLC.

—The Comparative Geography of Palestine & the Sinaitic Peninsula. 2009. 292p. pap. 23.46 *(978-0-217-38090-4(5));* 312p. pap. 23.46 *(978-0-217-38092-8(1))* General Bks. LLC.

Robinson, Edward. Biblical Researches in Palestine, 1838-52 a Journal of Travels in the Year 1838 by E Robinson & E Smith Drawn up from the Original Diaries, Wit. 2006. 648p. pap. 36.99 *(978-1-4255-6693-7(6));* 700p. pap. 38.99 *(978-1-4255-7404-8(1));* 616p. per. 34.99 *(978-1-4255-6553-4(0))* MPublishing.

Schlier, Heinrich. Principalities & Powers in the New Testament. reprint ed. 32.50 *(978-0-404-18432-2(4))* AMS Pr., Inc.

Schwarz, Joseph. A Descriptive Geography & Brief Historical Sketch of Palestine by Rabbi Joseph Schwarz Translated by Isaac Leeser. 2006. 532p. per. 29.99 *(978-1-4255-5953-3(0))* MPublishing.

Sleeman, Matthew. Geography & the Ascension Narrative in Acts. 2009. (Society for New Testament Studies Monograph Ser.). (ENG.). 312p. 102.00 *(978-0-521-50962-6(9))* Cambridge Univ. Pr.

Stutzman, Linford. Sailing Acts Following an Ancient Voyage, 1 vol. 2006. (ENG., Illus.). 300p. pap. 14.95 *(978-1-56148-546-8(2))* Good Bks.

Thurston, Bonnie B. Spiritual Landscape of Mark. 2008. 104p. pap. 12.95 *(978-0-8146-1864-6(2))* Liturgical Pr.

Timm, Stefan. Eusebius und die Heilige Schrift: Die Schriftvorlagen des Onomastikons der biblischen Ortsnamen. 2010. (Texte und Untersuchungen zur Geschichte der altchristlichen Literatur Ser.). Tr. of Eusebius & the Holy Scripture. (GER.). XIV, 653p. 210.00 *(978-3-11-022600-3(6))* De Gruyter, Walter Inc.

Weir, James. In Search of Eden: The Course of an Obsession. 2007. (Armchair Traveller Ser.). (ENG., Illus.). 174p. 19.95 *(978-1-905791-07-1(0))* Haus Publishing GBR. Dist: Consortium Bk. Sales & Distribution.

BIBLE—GEOGRAPHY—MAPS

Bacote, Vincent, ed. Precepts for Living 2009-2010 W/CD-ROM. 2009. (Precepts for Living Ser.). 504p. pap. 21.95 *(978-1-60352-685-2(4))* UMI (Urban Ministries, Inc.).

Beitzel, Barry J. The New Moody Atlas of the Bible. 2009. (ENG.). 304p. 49.99 *(978-0-8024-0441-1(3))* Moody Pubs.

Capper, Brian, et al. The Penguin Historical Atlas of the Bible Lands. 2009. (ENG., Illus.). 144p. (gr. 12). 20.00 *(978-0-14-102687-9(1),* Penguin (Non-Classics)) Penguin Group (USA) Inc.

Currid, John D. & Barrett, David P. Crossway ESV Bible Atlas. 2010. 352p. 55.00 *(978-1-4335-0192-0(9))* Crossway.

Curtis, Adrian. Oxford Bible Atlas. 4th ed. 2009. (ENG., Illus.). 240p. pap. 24.95 *(978-0-19-956046-2(3))* Oxford Univ. Pr., Inc.

Dowley, Tim. Bible Atlas. 2008. (St. Joseph Bible Resource Ser.). (Illus.). 32p. pap. 4.95 *(978-0-89942-654-9(9))* Catholic Bk. Publishing Corp.

—St. Joseph Atlas of the Bible. 2007. (Illus.). 96p. pap. 9.95 *(978-0-89942-655-6(7))* Catholic Bk. Publishing Corp.

Hammond World Atlas Corporation Staff. Atlas of the Bible Lands. 4th rev. ed. 2008. (Illus.). 64p. per. 9.85 *(978-0-8437-0983-4(9))* Hammond World Atlas Corp.

Hammond World Atlas Corporation Staff, creator. Atlas of the Bible Lands. 4th rev. ed. 2008. (Illus.). 64p. 14.95 *(978-0-8437-0982-7(0))* Hammond World Atlas Corp.

Holman Bible Atlas: Shelftalker. *(978-0-8400-3602-5(7))* B&H Publishing Group.

Hudson, Christopher D. & Barrett, David. Bible Atlas & Companion. 2008. (Bible Reference Library). (ENG., Illus.). 176p. pap. 9.99 *(978-1-59789-779-2(5),* Barbour Bks.) Barbour Publishing, Inc.

Isbouts, Jean-Pierre. The Biblical World: An Illustrated Atlas. 2007. (ENG., Illus.). 368p. 40.00 *(978-1-4262-0138-7(9),* National Geographic) National Geographic Society.

Lawrence, Paul. The IVP Atlas of Bible History. 2006. (ENG., Illus.). 190p. 45.00 *(978-0-8308-2452-6(9),* IVP Acad.) InterVarsity Pr.

Pritchard, James B. Atlas of Bible History. Page, Nick, ed. 2008. (ENG., Illus.). 192p. pap. 25.95 *(978-0-06-145195-9(9),* HarperOne) HarperCollins Pubs.

Rainey, Anson F. & Notley, R. Steven. Carta's New Century Handbook & Atlas of the Bible. (Illus.). 280p. *(978-965-220-703-6(9),* Debolsillo) Carta, The Israel Map & Publishing Co., Ltd.

Rainey, Anson F. & Notley, Steven. The Sacred Bridge: Carta's Historical Atlas of the Bible. 4th ed. 2006. (Illus.). 448p. 110.00 *(978-965-220-529-2(X))* Carta, The Israel Map & Publishing Co., Ltd. ISR. Dist: Coronet Bks.

Rose Publishing. Life of Apostle Paul. 2006. cd-rom 39.99 *(978-1-59636-083-9(6))* Rose Publishing.

Rose Publishing Staff. Then & Now Bible Maps: Compare Bible Times with Modern Day. 2007. (ENG.). 12p. 3.99 *(978-1-59636-130-0(1))* Rose Publishing.

—Then & Now Bible Maps Insert. 2008. (ENG., Illus.). 44p. 16.99 *(978-1-59636-293-2(6))* Rose Publishing.

Rose Publishing Staff, ed. Deluxe Then & Now Bible Map Book with CD-ROM. 2007. 40p. 29.99 *(978-1-59636-163-8(8))* Rose Publishing.

—Rose Book of Bible Charts, Vol. 2. 2008. (ENG.). 192p. 29.99 *(978-1-59636-275-8(8))* Rose Publishing.

Schwartz, Dan. Eleh Mas'ei. 32.95 *(978-1-58330-266-8(2))* Feldheim Pubs.

Smith, William. An Atlas of Ancient Geography, Biblical & Classical: Maps of the Ancient World. 2012. (ENG., Illus.). 240p. 475.00 *(978-1-84885-352-2(1))* I. B. Tauris & Co., Ltd. GBR. Dist: Macmillan.

Thomas Nelson. Nelson's Complete Book of Bible Maps & Charts, 3rd Edition, 0 vols. 2010. 512p. pap. 19.99 *(978-1-4185-4171-2(0))* Nelson, Thomas Inc.

BIBLE—GLOSSARIES, VOCABULARIES, ETC.

see Bible—Dictionaries

BIBLE—HANDBOOKS, MANUALS, ETC.

Abingdon Press Staff. The Essential Bible Handbook. 2009. 800p. 24.99 *(978-1-4267-0059-0(8))* Abingdon Pr.

Beers, V. Gilbert. Manual de Descubrimientos Biblicos: Discovery Bible Handbook. (SPA.). *(978-84-7645-339-1(6),* 223377) Clie, Editorial.

Clinton, Tim & Hawkins, Ron. The Quick-Reference Guide to Biblical Counseling. 2009. 288p. pap. 24.99 *(978-0-8010-7225-3(5))* Baker Bks.

Dipardo, Armando. Compendio Biblico Doctrinal: Doctrinal Handbook of the Bible. (SPA.). *(978-84-499-0067-9(0),* 220184) Clie, Editorial.

George, Jim. The Bare Bones Bible Handbook: 10 Minutes to Understanding Each Book of the Bible. 2006. (Bare Bones Bible Ser.). (Illus.). 325p. per. 13.99 *(978-0-7369-1654-7(7))* Harvest Hse. Pubs.

—The Bare Bones Bible Handbook for Teens: Getting to Know Every Book in the Bible. 2008. (Bare Bones Bible Ser.). 336p. pap. 12.99 *(978-0-7369-2386-6(1))* Harvest Hse. Pubs.

Halley, Henry H. & Halley, Henry Hampton. Halley's Bible Handbook, 1 vol. deluxe ed. 2007. (ENG., Illus.). 960p. 24.99 *(978-0-310-25994-7(0))* Zondervan.

Ham, Ken, et al. Answers Academy: Biblical Apologetics for Real Life! 2006. 199.00 *(978-1-893345-48-5(3))* Answers in Genesis Ministries.

House, H. Wayne. Chronological & Background Charts of the New Testament, 1 vol. 2nd ed. 2009. (ZondervanCharts Ser.). (ENG.). 176p. pap. 19.99 *(978-0-310-28293-8(4))* Zondervan.

Hunt, June. Counseling Through Your Bible Handbook: Providing Biblical Hope & Practical Help for 50 Everyday Problems. 2008. 442p. per. 14.99 *(978-0-7369-2181-7(8))* Harvest Hse. Pubs.

Knight, George W. Quicknotes Bible Handbook. 2009. (QuickNotes Commentaries Ser.). (ENG.). 352p. pap. 4.99 *(978-1-60260-444-5(4),* Barbour Bks.) Barbour Publishing, Inc.

Manley, G. T. Nuevo Auxiliar Biblico: New Bible Handbook. (SPA.). *(978-84-7645-211-0(X),* 223257) Clie, Editorial.

Manser, Martin. CLC Bible Companion: Flexicover. 2011. 848p. pap. 24.99 ***(978-1-936143-23-8(2))*** CLC Pubns.

Miller, Stephen M. The Complete Guide to the Bible. 2007. (Bible Reference Library). (ENG., Illus.). 528p. per. 19.99 *(978-1-59789-374-9(9),* Barbour Bks.) Barbour Publishing, Inc.

Rose Publishing Staff. Then & Now Bible Maps Insert. 2008. (ENG., Illus.). 44p. 16.99 *(978-1-59636-293-2(6))* Rose Publishing.

Rose Publishing Staff, ed. Rose Book of Bible Charts, Vol. 2. 2008. (ENG.). 192p. 29.99 *(978-1-59636-275-8(8))* Rose Publishing.

Steinmann, Andrew. From Abraham to Paul: A Biblical Chronology. 2011. 79.99 ***(978-0-7586-2799-5(8))*** Concordia Publishing Hse.

Strong, James. Compact Reference Library Set. 2007. 2816p. pap. 34.99 *(978-0-7180-0729-4(8))* Nelson, Thomas Inc.

Thomas Nelson. Nelson's Complete Book of Bible Maps & Charts, 3rd Edition, 0 vols. 2010. 512p. pap. 19.99 *(978-1-4185-4171-2(0))* Nelson, Thomas Inc.

Wiebe, Dianna. Biblical Feasts & Holy Days: A Chronological Study of the Sabbath, the Seven Feasts of the Lord, & Purim, Vols. 2. 2007. (Stick Figure Ser.). 48p. pap. 14.95 *(978-1-59873-019-7(3))* Grapevine Studies.

Wiebe, Dianna & Wiebe, Dianna. Biblical Feasts & Holy Days: A Chronological Study of the Sabbath, the Seven Feasts of the Lord, & Purim, Vols. 2. 2007. (Stick Figure Ser.). (Illus.). 80p. pap., stu. ed. 19.95 *(978-1-59873-020-3(7))* Grapevine Studies.

Wright, Charles H. H. The Bible Readers' Aids. 2007. 360p. 46.95 *(978-0-548-06795-6(3))* Kessinger Publishing, LLC.

BIBLE—HARMONIES

Abbott, Edwin A. Indices to Diatessarica: With a Specimen of Research. 2006. 216p. pap. 24.00 *(978-1-59752-891-7(9),* Wipf and Stock) Wipf & Stock Pubs.

Acland, John Edward. Little Gidding & Its Inmates in the Time of King Charles I. 2008. 48p. pap. *(978-1-4099-0575-2(6))* Dodo Pr.

Alber, Erasmus. Evangelienharmonie. Homer, Petra, ed. 2009. (GER.). XV, 214p. 126.00 *(978-3-11-020910-5(1))* De Gruyter, Walter Inc.

Beck, Sanderson. The Good Message of Jesus the Christ: A Harmony, Synthesis, & Interpretation of the Gospels. Beck, Sanderson, ed. 2008. pap. 25.00 *(978-0-9792532-8-7(4))* World Peace Communications.

Blanco, Jack J. Savior: Four Gospels. One Story: A Fresh Look at Jesus Christ, His Ministry, & His Teachings. 2008. (ENG.). 154p. pap. 12.99 *(978-0-8127-0469-3(X))* Review & Herald Publishing Assn.

—Witness: A Fresh Look at the New Testament Church. 2009. pap. 17.99 *(978-0-8127-0491-4(6))* Autumn Hse. Publishing Co.

Calvin, John. Commentary on a Harmony of the Evangelists V2: Matthew, Mark, & Luke. Pringle, William, tr. 2011. 456p. 57.95 ***(978-1-258-02053-8(X))*** Literary Licensing, LLC.

Cohen, Tim. Messiah, History, & the Tribulation Period Vol. 6: Messiah's Preeminence in History & Prophecy: the Heart of Israelology, Eschatology, & God's Holy Days. Cohen, Tim, ed. 2006. pap. *(978-0-9662793-7-5(9))* Prophecy House, Inc.

—Messiah, History, & the Tribulation Period Vol. 7: The Harmony of Weeks: God's Inspired Grand Unified Theology Unveiled. Cohen, Tim, ed. 2006. pap. *(978-0-9662793-8-2(7))* Prophecy House, Inc.

Costa, Isaac da. The Four Witnesses. 2006. 504p. per. 29.99 *(978-1-4255-5603-7(5))* MPublishing.

David, Earl, Jr. The 8 Days of Holy Week. 2010. pap. 19.50 *(978-1-935529-73-6(0)),* Intermedia Publishing Group.

den Hollander, A. A. Virtuele Vergangenheit: Die Textrekonstruktion einer verlorenen mittelniederlandischen Evangelienharmonie. Die Handschrift Utrecht Universitatsbibliothek 1009. 2007. (Biblioteca Ephemeridum Theologicarum Lovaniensium Ser.). (GER.). 168p. (C). pap. 85.00 *(978-90-429-1989-1(2))* Peeters Pubs. & Booksellers BEL. Dist: Brown, David Bk. Co., The.

Dewey, Arthur J. & Miller, Robert J. The Complete Gospel Parallels. 2012. xi, 417p. ***(978-1-59815-035-3(9))*** Polebridge Pr.

Mathews, Shailer. The Student's Gospels: A Harmony of the Synoptics, the Gospel of John. Mathews, Shailer & Goodspeed, Edgar J., eds. Soares, Theodore G., tr. 2011. 264p. 47.95 ***(978-1-258-06119-7(8))*** Literary Licensing, LLC.

Moore, Mark E. The Chronological Life of Christ. 2007. (Illus.). 704p. *(978-0-89900-955-1(7))* College Pr. Publishing Co., Inc.

Newsome, James D. & Newsome, James, eds. A Synoptic Harmony of Samuel, Kings, & Chronicles: With Related Passages from Psalms, Isaiah, Jeremiah, & Ezra. 2006. 276p. pap. 28.00 *(978-1-59752-994-5(X),* Wipf and Stock) Wipf & Stock Pubs.

Sharman, Henry. Records of the Life of Jesus. 2007. 256p. per. 14.95 *(978-1-933993-54-6(5))* Apocryphile Pr.

Smith, Abner. The Gospel Harmony of Jesus Christ. 2009. 304p. 32.50 *(978-1-4251-9110-8(X))* Trafford Publishing.

Smith, Joseph & Bishop, Patrick A. The Gospels in Harmony: The Illustrated, Combined Accounts of the Life of Christ from Matthew, Mark, Luke, John, & Joseph Smith Translation. 2010. (Illus.). vii, 213p. *(978-1-60861-096-9(9))* Covenant Communications.

Where to Find It in the Bible. 2009. pap. *(978-1-59636-344-1(4))* Rose Publishing.

BIBLE—HERMENEUTICS

Here are entered works on the principles of Biblical Criticism. Critical works on the Bible are entered under Bible—Criticism, Interpretation, etc.

Attridge, Harold W., et al. Method & Meaning: Essays on New Testament Interpretation in Honor of Harold W. Attridge. 2011. ***(978-1-58983-632-7(4)); (978-1-58983-631-0(6))*** Society of Biblical Literature.

Baildam, John D. Paradisal Love: Johann Gottfried Herder & the Song of Songs. 2009. (Library of Hebrew Bible/Old Testament Studies, the Ser.). (ENG.). 368p. 60.00 *(978-1-4411-4533-8(8),* T&T Clark) Continuum International Publishing Group, Ltd. GBR. Dist: National Bk. Network.

Bates, Matthew W. The Hermeneutics of the Apostolic Proclamation: The Center of Paul's Method of Scriptural Interpretation. 2012. (ENG.). 415p. 69.95 ***(978-1-60258-328-3(5))*** Baylor Univ. Pr.

Bauckham, Richard. The Bible in Politics, Second Edition: How to Read the Bible Politically. 2nd ed. 2011. (ENG.). 192p. pap. 25.00 *(978-0-664-23708-0(8))* Westminster John Knox Pr.

Beal, S. T. L. Foundations of Christianity The Historical Jesus & His World. 2009. 352p. pap. 17.99 *(978-1-4389-2671-1(5))* AuthorHouse.

Bednar, Lawrence. Evidence of the Divine Hand on the Traditional Texts of Holy Scripture. 2006. (ENG.). 446p. (C). per. 18.95 *(978-0-9760563-7-9(2))* Mechling Bookbindery.

Bergen, Wesley. Voyages in Uncharted Waters Essays on Th. 2006. 248p. *(978-1-905048-57-1(2))* Sheffield Phoenix Pr.

Berkhof, Luis. Principios de Interpretacion Biblica: Principles of Biblical Interpretation. (SPA.). 201p. *(978-84-7228-078-6(0),* 220716) Clie, Editorial.

Billings, J. Todd. The Word of God for the People of God: An Entryway to the Theological Interpretation of Scripture. 2010. (Illus.). 256p. pap. 18.00 *(978-0-8028-6235-8(7))* Eerdmans, William B. Publishing Co.

Bock, Darrell L. & Fanning, Buist M., eds. Interpreting the New Testament Text: Introduction to the Art & Science of Exegesis. 2006. (Illus.). 480p. 32.00 *(978-1-58134-408-0(2))* Crossway.

Bohmeier, Ute. Exegetische Methodik in Pirke de-Rabbi Elieser, Kapitel 1-24 Nach der Edition Venedig 1544, unter Berücksichtigung der Edition Warschau 1852. 2008. (Judentum und Umwelt. Realms of Judaism Ser.). 582p. pap. 124.95 *(978-3-631-57847-6(4))* Lang, Peter GmbH, Europäischer Verlag der Wissenschaften DEU. Dist: Lang, Peter.

Borchert, Gerald. Jesus of Nazareth: Background, Witnesses, & Significance. 2011. 256p. pap. 25.00 *(978-0-88146-266-1(7))* Mercer Univ. Pr.

Bos, Rein. We Have Heard That God Is with You: Preaching the Old Testament. 2008. 336p. pap. 28.00 *(978-0-8028-0770-0(4))* Eerdmans, William B. Publishing Co.

Bowald, Mark Alan. Divine & Human Agency in Contemporary Biblical Hermeneutics: Rendering God's Word. 2007. 214p. 99.95 *(978-0-7546-5877-1(5))* Ashgate Publishing Co.

Brauch, Manfred & Brauch, Manfred T. Abusing Scripture: The Consequences of Misreading the Bible, 1 vol. 2009. (ENG.). 293p. pap. 18.00 *(978-0-8308-2579-0(7),* IVP Acad.) InterVarsity Pr.

Brettler, Marc Zvi, et al. The Bible & the Believer: How to Read the Bible Critically & Religiously. 2012. (ENG., Illus.). 224p. 27.95 ***(978-0-19-986300-6(8))*** Oxford Univ. Pr., Inc.

Briggs, Richard S. Reading the Bible Wisely: An Introduction to Taking Scripture Seriously. 2011. 166p. pap. 19.00 ***(978-1-61097-288-8(0),*** Cascade Bks.) Wipf & Stock Pubs.

Briggs, Richard S. The Virtuous Reader: Old Testament Narrative & Interpretive Virtue, 1 vol. 2010. (Studies in Theological Interpretation Ser.). (ENG.). 288p. (C). pap. 27.00 *(978-0-8010-3843-3(X))* Baker Academic.

Brown, Jeannine K. Scripture as Communication: Introducing Biblical Hermeneutics. 2007. (Illus.). 320p. (C) pap. 27.99 *(978-0-8010-2788-8(8))* Baker Academic.

Brown, Raymond E. The Sensus Plenior of Sacred Scripture. 2008. 192p. pap. 22.00 *(978-1-60608-070-2(9))* Wipf & Stock Pubs.

Butler, Trent. Six Ways to Study the Bible. 2010. 168p. pap. 16.99 *(978-0-8272-3470-3(8))* Chalice Pr.

Camery-Hoggatt, Jerry. Reading the Good Book Well: A Guide to Biblical Interpretation. 2007. 240p. per. 30.00 *(978-0-687-64275-5(2))* Abingdon Pr.

Carroll, Mark Daniel. Contexts for Amos: Prophetic Poetics in Latin-American Perspective. 2009. (Library of Hebrew Bible/Old Testament Studies, the Ser.). (ENG.). 362p. 60.00 *(978-0-567-40027-7(1),* T&T Clark) Continuum International Publishing Group, Ltd. GBR. Dist: National Bk. Network.

Carvalho, Corrine L. Primer on Biblical Methods. 2009. (ENG.). 93p. (C). pap. 15.95 *(978-1-59982-015-6(3),* St. Mary's Pr.

Chafer, Rollin Thomas. The Science of Biblical Hermeneutics: An Outline Study of Its Laws. 2011. 94p. 38.95 ***(978-1-258-05377-2(2))*** Literary Licensing, LLC.

Chapman, C. L. Rightly Dividing the Word of Truth. 2010. 272p. 24.95 *(978-1-4269-3919-8(1));* pap. 14.95 *(978-1-4269-3918-1(3))* Trafford Publishing.

Cherry, Shai. Torah Through Time: Understanding Bible Commentary, from the Rabbinic Period to Modern Times. 2007. (ENG., Illus.). 208p. pap. 25.00 *(978-0-8276-0848-1(9))* Jewish Pubn. Society.

Cheung, Luke Leuk. The Genre, Composition & Hermeneutics of the Epistle of James. 2006. (Paternoster Biblical Monographs). (ENG.). 388p. per. 39.99 *(978-1-84227-062-2(1),* Paternoster) Authentic Media.

—The Genre, Composition & Hermeneutics of the Epistle of James. 2007. (Paternoster Biblical Monographs: Ser.). 406p. pap. 41.00 (978-1-59752-748-4(3), Wipf and Stock) Wipf & Stock Pubs.

Clark-Soles, Jaime. Engaging the Word: The New Testament & the Christian Believer. 2010. (ENG., Illus.). 160p. pap. 20.00 (978-0-664-23114-9(4)) Westminster John Knox Pr.

Coffen, Richard W. Wake up Your Bible Study: Getting the Most from Your Time with God. 2007. (ENG.). 201p. per. 14.99 (978-0-8127-0440-2(1)) Autumn Hse. Publishing Co.

Cohen, Tim. Messiah, History, & the Tribulation Period: Multi-Volume Set, 7 vols., Cohen, Tim, ed. rev. ed. 2006. (Illus.). pap. (978-0-9662793-1-3(X), BK-02) Prophecy House, Inc.

—Messiah, History, & the Tribulation Period Vol. 1: Biblical Interpretation (Hermeneutics) Cohen, Tim, ed. 2006. pap. (978-0-9662793-2-0(8)) Prophecy House, Inc.

—Messiah, History, & the Tribulation Period Vol. 7: The Harmony of Weeks: God's Inspired Grand Unified Theology Unveiled. Cohen, Tim, ed. 2006. pap. (978-0-9662793-8-2(7)) Prophecy House, Inc.

Coleson, Joseph. Treasure the Word: A Layperson's Guide to Interpreting Scripture. 2009. 14.99 (978-0-89827-412-7(5)) Wesleyan Publishing Hse.

Conder, Tim & Rhodes, Daniel. Free for All: Rediscovering the Bible in Community. 2009. (Emersion). (Illus.). 256p. pap. 16.99 (978-0-8010-7147-8(X)) Baker Bks.

Dahan, Gilbert. Lire la Bible au Moyen-Age: Essais dhermeneutique Medievale. 2009. (Titre Courant Ser.). (FRE.). 448p. (C). 40.00 (978-2-600-00538-8(2)) Droz, Librairie CHE. Dist: Brown, David Bk. Co., The.

Dare, Helen & Woodman, Simon. The Plainly Revealed Word of God? Baptist Hermeneutics in Theory & Practice. 2011. 256p. pap. 40.00 (978-0-88146-237-1(3)) Mercer Univ. Pr.

Debelak, Robert P., Jr. & Debelak Jr., Robert P. Hidden in Plain Sight: Esther & a Marginalized Hermeneutic. 2008. (Illus.). 170p. pap. 20.00 (978-1-55635-499-1(1)) Wipf & Stock Pubs.

Debelak, Robert P. Jr. Hidden in Plain Sight: Esther & a Marginalised Hermeneutic. 2008. (ENG.). 156p. pap. 33.00 (978-0-7188-9181-7(3)) Lutherworth Pr., The GBR. Dist: Brown, David Bk. Co., The.

Dozeman, Thomas B., ed. Methods for Exodus. 2010. (Methods in Biblical Interpretation Ser.). (ENG.). (C). 268p. 85.00 (978-0-521-88367-2(9)); (Illus.). 266p. pap. 24.99 (978-0-521-71001-5(4)) Cambridge Univ. Pr.

Duffy, Maria. Paul Ricoeur's Pedagogy of Pardon: A Narrative Theory of Memory & Forgetting. 2009. (ENG., Illus.). 208p. 120.00 (978-1-84706-474-5(4)) Continuum International Publishing Group, Ltd. GBR. Dist: National Bk. Network.

Dulaney, Robert C. Hermeneutics. 40p. pap. 2.95 (978-1-56794-160-9(5), C-2494) Star Bible & Tract Corp.

Duvall, J. Scott. Grasping God's Word Laminated Sheet, 1 vol. 2007. (Zondervan Get an A! Study Guides). (ENG.). 4p. 6.99 (978-0-310-27514-5(8)) Zondervan.

Duvall, J. Scott & Hays, J. Daniel. Grasping God's Word: A Hands-On Approach to Reading, Interpreting, & Applying the Bible, 1 vol. 3rd ed. 2012. (ENG.). 464p. (C). 39.99 **(978-0-310-49257-3(2))** Zondervan.

Edwards, Richard M. Scriptural Perspicuity in the Early English Reformation in Historical Theology. 2008. (Studies in Biblical Literature Ser.). 48.95 (978-0-8204-7057-3(0)) Lang, Peter Publishing, Inc.

Evans, G. R. The Language & Logic of the Bible: The Road to Reformation. 2009. (ENG.). 220p. pap. 31.99 (978-0-521-09293-7(0)) Cambridge Univ. Pr.

Fairbairn, Patrick. Hermeneutical Manual; or, Introduction to the Exegetical Study of the Scriptures of the New Testament. 2006. 532p. per. 29.99 (978-1-4255-5915-1(8)) MPublishing.

Farkasfalvy, Denis. Inspiration & Interpretation: A Theological Introduction to Sacred Scripture. 2010. 309p. pap. 34.95 (978-0-8132-1746-8(6)) Catholic Univ. of America Pr.

Fowl, Stephen E. Theological Interpretation of Scripture. 2009. (Cascade Companions Ser.). 108p. pap. 13.00 (978-1-55635-241-6(7), Cascade Bks.) Wipf & Stock Pubs.

Fowl, Stephen E., et al. Reading Scripture with the Church: Toward a Hermeneutic for Theological Interpretation. 2006. 156p. (C). pap. 20.00 (978-0-8010-3173-1(7)) Baker Academic.

Francis, Leslie J. & Village, Andrew. Preaching: With All Our Souls - A Study in Hermeneutics & Psychological Type. 2008. (ENG.). 184p. 27.95 (978-0-8264-9326-2(2)) Continuum International Publishing Group, Ltd. GBR. Dist: National Bk. Network.

Froehlich, Karlfried. Biblical Interpretaion from the Church Fathers to the Reformation. 2010. (Variorum Collected Studies). (Illus.). 366p. 170.00 (978-1-4094-0365-4(3)) Ashgate Publishing Co.

Glabach, Wilfried E. Reclaiming the Book of Revelation: A Suggestion of New Readings in the Local Church. 2007. (American University Studies: Vol. 259). xii, 212p. 70.95 (978-0-8204-9504-0(2)); 226p. (C). 68.95 (978-1-4331-0054-3(1)) Lang, Peter Publishing, Inc.

Goldsworthy, Graeme. Gospel-Centered Hermeneutics: Foundations & Principles of Evangelical Biblical Interpretation. 2007. (ENG.). 341p. 29.00 (978-0-8308-2839-5(7), IVP Acad.) InterVarsity Pr.

Gooder. Searching for Meaning: A Practical Guide to Interpreting the New Testament. 2008. 256p. pap. (978-0-281-05835-8(0)) Westminster John Knox Pr.

Gooder, Paula, Sr. Searching for Meaning: An Introduction to Interpreting the New Testament. 2008. (ENG.). 256p. pap. 25.00 (978-0-664-23194-1(2)) Westminster John Knox Pr.

Gottwald. Bible & Liberation. 584p. 45.00 (978-0-281-04719-2(7)) International Publishers Marketing.

Granados, Jose, et al, eds. Opening up the Scriptures: Joseph Ratzinger & the Foundations of Biblical Interpretation. 2008. 176p. pap. 25.00 (978-0-8028-6011-8(7)) Eerdmans, William B. Publishing Co.

Green, Garrett. Theology, Hermeneutics, & Imagination: The Crisis of Interpretation at the End of Modernity. 2007. (ENG.). 244p. pap. 51.00 (978-0-521-04531-5(2)) Cambridge Univ. Pr.

Green, Joel B., ed. Hearing the New Testament: Strategies for Interpretation. 2nd ed. 2010. 432p. pap. 28.00 (978-0-8028-6420-8(1)) Eerdmans, William B. Publishing Co.

—Methods for Luke. 2010. (Methods in Biblical Interpretation Ser.). (ENG.). 168p. (C). 85.00 (978-0-521-88912-4(X)); pap. 24.99 (978-0-521-71781-6(7)) Cambridge Univ. Pr.

Habets, Myk, ed. The Spirit of Truth: Reading Scripture & Constructing Theology with the Holy Spirit. 2010. 238p. pap. 26.00 (978-1-60899-321-5(3), Pickwick Pubns.) Wipf & Stock Pubs.

Hahn, Scott, ed. Letter & Spirit for the Sake of Our Salvation: The Truth & Humility of God's Word, 6. 2011. 440p. pap. (978-1-931018-68-5(5)) Emmaus Road Publishing.

Hampton, David. Narrative Theology As A Hermeneutic Approach. 2009. 95p. pap. 20.00 (978-0-557-09996-2(X)) Lulu Enterprises Inc.

Hartill, J. Edwin & Hartill, J. E. Principles of Biblical Hermeneutics, 1 vol. 2007. (ENG., Illus.). 128p. pap. 24.99 (978-0-310-27255-7(6)) Zondervan.

Hawkins, Beth & Stahlberg, Lesleigh Cushing, eds. Scrolls of Love: Ruth & the Song of Songs. 3rd ed. 2006. (ENG., Illus.). 408p. 80.00 (978-0-8232-2571-2(2)) Fordham Univ. Pr.

Hawkins, Peter S., et al, eds. Scrolls of Love: Ruth & the Song of Songs. 3rd ed. 2006. (ENG., Illus.). 408p. per. 30.00 (978-0-8232-2572-9(0)) Fordham Univ. Pr.

Hayes, John H. & Holladay, Carl R. Biblical Exegesis: A Beginner's Handbook. 3rd ed. 2007. (ENG.). 236p. per. 25.00 (978-0-664-22775-3(9)) Westminster John Knox Pr.

Hays, Richard B. & Alkier, Stefan, eds. Revelation & the Politics of Apocalyptic Interpretation. 2012. (ENG.). 230p. 49.95 **(978-1-60258-561-4(X))** Baylor Univ. Pr.

Hebbard, Aaron B. Reading Daniel as a Text in Theological Hermeneutics. 2008. (Princeton Theological Monographs). 256p. pap. 28.00 (978-1-60608-991-0(9), Pickwick Pubns.) Wipf & Stock Pubs.

—Reading Daniel As a Text in Theological Hermeneutics Pb. 2011. (ENG.). 243p. pap. 42.50 (978-0-227-17364-0(3)) Clarke, James Co., Ltd. GBR. Dist: Brown, David Bk. Co., The.

Hendel, Ronald, ed. Reading Genesis: Ten Methods. 2010. (ENG.). 300p. (C). 85.00 (978-0-521-51861-1(X)); pap. 27.99 (978-0-521-73239-0(5)) Cambridge Univ. Pr.

Holland, Scott. How Do Stories Save Us? An Essay on the Question with the Theological Hermeneutics of David Tracy in View. 2007. (Louvain Theological & Pastoral Monographs). 277p. pap. 45.00 (978-0-8028-4564-1(9)) Eerdmans, William B. Publishing Co.

Holland, Scott & Holland, S. How Do Stories Save Us? an Essay on the Question with the Theological Hermeneutics of David Tracy in View: An Essay on the Question with the Theological Hermeneutics of David Tracy in View. 2006. (Louvain Theological & Pastoral Monographs: Vol. 35). (ENG.). 227p. (C). pap. 38.00 (978-90-429-1786-6(5)) Peeters Pubs. & Booksellers BEL. Dist: Brown, David Bk. Co., The.

Holter, Knut & Jonker, Louis C. Global Hermeneutics? Reflections & Consequences. 2010. (978-1-58983-477-4(1)) Society of Biblical Literature.

Human, Dirk J. & Steyn, Gert Jacobus, eds. Psalms & Hebrews: Studies in Reception. (Library Hebrew Bible/Old Testament Studies). (ENG.). 320p. 2012. pap. 49.95 **(978-0-567-19884-6(7))** 2010. 130.00 (978-0-567-15052-3(6)) Continuum International Publishing Group, Ltd. GBR. (T&T Clark Int'l). Dist: National Bk. Network.

Iverson, Kelly R. & Skinner, Christopher W. Mark As Story: Retrospect & Prospect. 2011. 309p. (978-90-04-20253-5(6)) BRILL.

—Mark As Story: Retrospect & Prospect. 2011. xii, 309p. (978-1-58983-549-8(2)); 322p. pap. (978-1-58983-548-1(4)) Society of Biblical Literature.

James, Rob. Faith, Belief, & Scripture: Anglicanism & Homosexuality. 2011. 192p. pap. **(978-1-86335-924-5(9))** Common Ground Publishing Pty, Ltd.

Jasper, David. Readings in the Canon of Scripture. 2009. (David Jasper Reprint Ser.). 180p. pap. 21.00 (978-1-60608-835-7(1), Wipf and Stock) Wipf & Stock Pubs.

Jensen, Alexander S. Theological Hermeneutics. 2007. (Scm Core Text Ser.). 237p. per. (978-0-334-02901-4(5)) Hymns Ancient & Modern Ltd.

Joy, David. Bible & Hermeneutics. 2010. 184p. (978-81-7821-247-0(1), Library of Congress — New Delhi Overseas Office) Christava Sahitya Samithy Bookshop, CSS.

Jungling, Laurie, ed. Lutheran Perspectives on Biblical Interpretation: The 2009 Hein-Fry Lectures. 2011. 130p. pap. 16.00 (978-1-932688-56-6(0), Lutheran Univ. Pr.) Kirk Hse. Pubs.

—Teaching the Bible in the Parish, & Beyond: The 2010 Hein-Fry Lectures. 2011. 130p. pap. 16.00 (978-1-932688-58-0(7)) Kirk Hse. Pubs.

Kaiser, Walter C., Jr., et al. Introduction to Biblical Hermeneutics: The Search for Meaning, 1 vol. rev. enl. ed. 2007. (ENG.). 352p. 34.99 (978-0-310-27951-8(8)) Zondervan.

Kanyoro, Musimbi R. A. Introduction to Feminist Cultural Hermeneutics: A Key to African Women's Liberation Theology. (Introductions in Feminist Theology Ser.). 99p. pap. (978-0-8264-6054-7(2)) Continuum International Publishing Group, Ltd.

Kasiri, Hamid. Mit den Augen des Anderen: Zur Entwicklung des Umgangs mit der Hl. Schrift im Katholizismus des 20. Jahrhunderts. 2009. (Europäische Hochschulschriften. Reihe 23: Theologie Ser.). (GER.). 202p. pap. 57.95 (978-3-631-59174-1(8)) Lang, Peter GmbH, Europaischer Verlag der Wissenschaften DEU. Dist: Lang, Peter.

Kay, James F. Preaching & Theology. 2008. (Preaching & Its Partners Ser.). 166p. per. 19.99 (978-0-8272-2991-4(7)) Chalice Pr.

Kinnamon, Michae & Linn, Jan. Disciples: Reclaiming Our Identity, Reforming Our Practice. 2009. 176p. pap. 19.99 (978-0-8272-0635-9(6)) Chalice Pr.

Kuruvilla, Abraham & Kuruvilla. Text to Praxis: Hermeneutics & Homiletics in Dialogue. 2009. (Library of New Testament Studies, the Ser.). (ENG.). 240p. 130.00 (978-0-567-53854-3(0), T&T Clark Int'l) Continuum International Publishing Group, Ltd. GBR. Dist: National Bk. Network.

Kyomya, Michael. Interpreting Scripture: Context, Harmony, & Application, 1 vol. 2010. (Hippo Ser.). (ENG.). 128p. pap., instr.'s gde. ed. 12.99 (978-9966-00-308-9(8)) Zondervan.

Kysar, Robert & Webb, Joseph M. Preaching to Postmoderns: New Perspectives for Proclaiming the Message. 2006. 239p. per. 19.95 (978-1-56563-400-8(4)) Hendrickson Pubs. Marketing, LLC.

Lancaster, Irene. Deconstructing the Bible. 2007. (Illus.). 256p. 39.95 (978-0-415-44444-6(6)) Routledge.

Lawrence, Louise J. Word in Place. 2009. (Illus.). xx, 171p. pap. (978-0-281-06112-9(2)) SPCK Publishing.

Leithart, Peter J. & Leithart, Peter. Deep Exegesis: The Mystery of Reading Scripture. 2009. (ENG.). 253p. pap. 29.95 (978-1-60258-069-5(3)) Baylor Univ. Pr.

Levering, Matthew. Participatory Biblical Exegesis: A Theology of Biblical Interpretation. 2008. (Reading the Scriptures Ser.). (ENG.). 344p. 60.00 (978-0-268-03406-1(0)); pap. 25.00 (978-0-268-03408-5(7)) Univ. of Notre Dame Pr.

Lincoln. Christology & Scripture: Interdisciplinary Perspectives. Lincoln, Andrew T. & Paddison, Angus, eds. 2008. (Library of New Testament Studies, the Ser.). (ENG.). 238p. 44.95 (978-0-567-04567-6(6), T&T Clark Int'l) Continuum International Publishing Group, Ltd. GBR. Dist: National Bk. Network.

Lincoln, Andrew T., et al, eds. Christology & Scripture: Interdisciplinary Perspectives. 2007. (Library of New Testament Studies). (ENG.). 240p. 130.00 (978-0-567-03091-7(1), T&T Clark Int'l) Continuum International Publishing Group, Ltd. GBR. Dist: National Bk. Network.

Lowder, Poncho. Pursue God: How Do You Develop a Thriving Relationship with God? 2011. (ENG.). 160p. pap. 11.99 **(978-0-8307-6180-7(2))** Gospel Light Pubns.

Luman, J. W. A Verse by Verse Exegesis of Hebrews. l.t. ed. 2007. 136p. 20.00 (978-0-9796285-0-4(4)) International Fellowship of Covenant Ministries, The.

Martoia, Ron & McKnight, Scot. The Blue Parakeet: Rethinking How You Read the Bible, 1 vol. 2008. (ENG.). 192p. 18.99 (978-0-310-28488-8(0)) Zondervan.

Martus, Steffen, et al, eds. Das Buch der Bucher - Gelesen: Lesarten der Bibel in den Wissenschaften und Kunsten. (GER., Illus.). 488p. 82.95 (978-3-03910-839-8(5)) Lang, Peter CHE. Dist: Lang, Peter Publishing, Inc.

McDonald, Olivia M. Acknowledging God in the Decisions of State: A Biblically Informed Treatise on Public Policy for the Integration of Knowledge, Action, & Faith in the Exercise of Biblical Statesmanship. 2008. (Illus.). 157p. 59.95 (978-0-9778294-0-8(5)) Grace Hse. Publishing.

McKenzie, Steven L. Introduction to the Historical Books: Strategies for Reading. 2010. 184p. pap. 18.00 (978-0-8028-2877-4(9)) Eerdmans, William B. Publishing Co.

McKnight, Edgar. Postmodern Use of the Bible. 288p. 16.00 (978-0-687-33178-9(1)) Abingdon Pr.

McLean, B. H. Biblical Interpretation & Philosophical Hermeneutics. 2012. (ENG., Illus.). 322p. (C). 99.00 **(978-1-107-01949-2(4))**; pap. 29.99 **(978-1-107-68340-2(8))** Cambridge Univ. Pr.

McVey, Steve. 52 Lies Heard in Church Every Sunday: And Why the Truth Is So Much Better. 2011. 256p. pap. 12.99 (978-0-7369-3864-8(8)) Harvest Hse. Pubs.

Mitchell, Margaret M. Paul, the Corinthians & the Birth of Christian Hermeneutics. 2010. (ENG., Illus.). 192p. 85.00 (978-0-521-19795-3(3)) Cambridge Univ. Pr.

Moore, Mark E. Seeing God in HD: God's Word in Today's World. 2008. (978-0-89900-930-8(1)) College Pr. Publishing Co., Inc.

Muenscher, Joseph. Manual of Biblical Interpretation. 2009. 182p. pap. 19.99 (978-0-217-86265-3(9)) General Bks. LLC.

—Manual of Biblical Interpretation. 2007. (ENG.). 324p. 45.95 (978-0-548-16958-2(6)); per. 30.95 (978-1-4304-6698-7(7)) Kessinger Publishing, LLC.

—Manual of Biblical Interpretation. 2006. 328p. per. 23.99 (978-1-4255-3272-7(1)) MPublishing.

Munzinger, Andrè. Discerning the Spirits: Theological & Ethical Hermeneutics in Paul. 2011. (Society for New Testament Studies Monograph Ser.). (ENG.). 256p. pap. 35.99 (978-0-521-16856-4(2)) Cambridge Univ. Pr.

Nelson, Alissa Jones. Edward Said, Contrapuntal Hermeneutics & the Book of Job: Power, Subjectivity & Responsibility, in Biblical Interpretation. 2012. (BibleWorld Ser.). (ENG.). 224p. (C). 99.95 (978-1-84553-889-7(7)) Equinox Publishing Ltd. GBR. Dist: Brown, David Bk. Co., The.

—Edward Said, Contrapuntal Hermeneutics, & the Book of Job: Power, Subjectivity & Responsibility in Biblical Interpretation. 2011. (BibleWorld Ser.). (ENG.). 224p. (C). pap. 35.00 (978-1-84553-890-3(0)) Equinox Publishing Ltd. GBR. Dist: Brown, David Bk. Co., The.

Nielson, Kathleen Buswell. Bible Study: Following the Ways of the Word. 2011. pap. (978-1-59638-205-3(8)) P & R Publishing.

Oranekwu, George. Indeed, he would never speak to them except in Parables (Mark 4:34) A Hermeneutical Correlation of Parables in Mark 4 to the Traditional Igbo Culture. 2008. 286p. (gr. 11). pap. 37.95 (978-3-88939-837-6(5)) IKO Verlag fur Interkulturelle Kommunikation DEU. Dist: Transaction Pubs.

Osborne, Grant R. The Hermeneutical Spiral: A Comprehensive Introduction to Biblical Interpretation. 2nd rev. ed. 2006. (ENG., Illus.). 624p. per. 30.00 (978-0-8308-2826-5(5), IVP Acad.) InterVarsity Pr.

Panna, George. A Theological Biblical Model for the Liberation of Marginals in Indi. 2010. 492p. pap. (978-3-639-25768-7(5)) VDM Verlag Dr. Mueller e.K.

Park. Mark's Memory Resources & the Controversy Stories (Mark 2:1-3:6) An Application of the Frame Theory of Cognitive Science to the Markan Oral-Aural Narrative. 2009. (Linguistic Biblical Studies). (978-90-04-17962-2(3)) BRILL.

Parris, David Paul. Reception Theory & Biblical Hermeneutics. 2009. (Princeton Theological Monographs). 344p. pap. 38.00 (978-1-55635-653-7(6), Pickwick Pubns.) Wipf & Stock Pubs.

Petersen, David L., et al. Method Matters: Essays on the Interpretation of the Hebrew Bible in Honor of David L. Petersen. 2009. 49.95 (978-1-58983-444-6(5)) Society of Biblical Literature.

Pink, Arthur W. Interpretation of the Scriptures. 2011. 128p. pap. 14.99 **(978-1-61203-339-6(3))** Bottom of the Hill Publishing.

Plummer, Robert L. 40 Questions about Interpreting the Bible, 1 vol. 2010. (40 Questions & Answers Ser.). (ENG.). 352p. pap. 17.99 (978-0-8254-3498-3(X)) Kregel Pubns.

Pokorný, Petr. Hermeneutics as a Theory of Understanding, Volume 1. Bryson-Gustová, Anna, tr. from CZE. 2010. pap. 30.00 (978-0-8028-2721-0(7)) Eerdmans, William B. Publishing Co.

Powell, Mark Allan, ed. Methods for Matthew. 2009. (Methods in Biblical Interpretation Ser.). (ENG.). 278p. (C). 90.00 (978-0-521-88808-0(5)); (Illus.). pap. 27.99 (978-0-521-71614-7(4)) Cambridge Univ. Pr.

Pregeant, Russell. Reading the Bible for All the Wrong Reasons. 2011. (Illus.). 160p. (C). pap. 14.99 (978-0-8006-9844-7(4), Fortress Pr.) Augsburg Fortress, Pubs.

Premnath, Devadasan Nithya & Sugirtharajah, R. S. Border Crossings: Cross-Cultural Hermeneutics. 2007. 179p. per. 40.00 (978-1-57075-745-7(3)) Orbis Bks.

Rae, Murray & Rae. History & Hermeneutics. 2006. (ENG.). 176p. 60.00 (978-0-567-08092-9(7), T&T Clark Int'l) Continuum International Publishing Group, Ltd. GBR. Dist: National Bk. Network.

Ratke, David C., ed. Hearing the Word: Lutheran Hermeneutics — A Vision of Life under the Gospel. 2006. (ENG.). 108p. pap. 12.00 (978-1-932688-19-1(6), Lutheran Univ. Pr.) Kirk Hse. Pubs.

Ratzinger, Joseph, et al. The Ratzinger Reader: Mapping a Theological Journey. Boeve, Lieven & Mannion, Gerard, eds. 2010. (ENG.). 304p. 130.00 (978-0-567-03213-3(2)); pap. 34.95 (978-0-567-03214-0(0)) Continuum International Publishing Group, Ltd. GBR. (T&T Clark Int'l). Dist: National Bk. Network.

Reventlow, Henning Graf. Creative Biblical Exegesis: Christian & Jewish Hermeneutics through the Centuries. Uffenheimer, Benjamin, ed. 2009. (Library of Hebrew Bible/Old Testament Studies, the Ser.). (ENG.). 225p. 39.95 (978-1-4411-7123-8(1), T&T Clark) Continuum International Publishing Group, Ltd. GBR. Dist: National Bk. Network.

Robinson, James M. Language, Hermeneutic, & History: Theology after Barth & Bultmann. 2007. 260p. pap. 29.00 (978-1-59752-881-8(1)) Wipf & Stock Pubs.

Rosenblatt, Samuel. The Interpretation of the Bible in the Mishnah. 2008. 106p. pap. 9.00 (978-1-60608-030-6(X)) Wipf & Stock Pubs.

Rowland. Interpretation in Context. 2008. vii, 119p. pap. (978-0-281-05802-0(4)) SPCK Publishing.

Sanday, William. The Authorship & Historical Character of the Fourth Gospel. 2009. 330p. pap. 30.75 (978-1-115-80443-1(X)) BiblioBazaar.

Schenck, Kenneth. Making Sense of God's Word. 2009. (978-0-89827-376-2(5)) Wesleyan Publishing Hse.

Schwarz, W. Principles & Problems of Biblical Translation: Some Reformation Controversies & their Background. 2009. (ENG.). 248p. pap. 34.99 (978-0-521-09753-6(3)) Cambridge Univ. Pr.

Segovia, Fernando F., et al. Postcolonial Biblical Criticism: Interdisciplinary Intersections. 2007. (Bible & Post-Colonialism Ser.). (ENG.). 216p. 39.95 (978-0-567-04530-0(7), T&T Clark Int'l) Continuum International Publishing Group, Ltd. GBR. Dist: National Bk. Network.

Seitz, Christopher R. Prophecy & Hermeneutics: Toward a New Introduction to the Prophets. 2007. (Studies in Theological Interpretation Ser.). 272p. (C). pap. 23.00 (978-0-8010-3258-5(X)) Baker Academic.

Selby, Rosalind. The Comical Doctrine: An Epistemology of New Testament Hermeneutics. 2006. (Paternoster Biblical Monographs: Ser.). 318p. pap. 32.00 (978-1-59752-997-6(4), Wipf and Stock) Wipf & Stock Pubs.

Snodgrass, Klyne, ed. Ex Auditu - Volume 24: An International Journal of Theological Interpretation of Scripture. 2009. 218p. pap. 30.00 (978-1-60608-740-4(1), Pickwick Pubns.) Wipf & Stock Pubs.

Sociedades Biblicas Unidas, creator. Santa Biblia-Rvr 1960-Letra Grande. l.t. ed. 2011. (SPA.). 1580p. pap. **(978-1-59877-199-2(X))** Deutsche Bibelgesellschaft.

Sparks, Kenton L. Sacred Word, Broken Word: Preparing for Theological Interpretation of Scripture. 2012. pap. **(978-0-8028-6718-6(9))** Eerdmans, William B. Publishing Co.

Spinks, D. Christopher & Spinks. Bible & the Crisis of Meaning: Debates on the Theological Interpretation of Scripture. 2007. (ENG., Illus.). 224p. 130.00 *(978-0-567-03210-2(8)*, T&T Clark Int'l) Continuum International Publishing Group, Ltd. GBR. Dist: National Bk. Network.

Sproul, R. C. Knowing Scripture, 1 vol. 2nd rev. ed. 2009. (ENG.). 152p. (Orig.). pap. 15.00 *(978-0-8308-3723-6(X)*, IVP Bks.) InterVarsity Pr.

St. Augustine. On Christian Doctrine. Shaw, J. F., tr. from LAT. 2009. (ENG.). 192p. pap. 7.95 *(978-0-486-46918-8(2))* Dover Pubns., Inc.

Stewart, Robert B. The Quest of the Hermeneutical Jesus: The Impact of Hermeneutics on the Jesus Research of John Dominic Crossan & N. T. Wright. 2008. (ENG.). 180p. 62.99 *(978-0-7618-4095-4(8))*; pap. 34.99 *(978-0-7618-4096-1(6))* Univ. Pr. of America, Inc.

Stuart, Douglas. Old Testament Exegesis, Fourth Edition: A Handbook for Students & Pastors. 4th ed. 2009. (ENG.). 224p. pap. 25.00 *(978-0-664-23344-0(9))* Westminster John Knox Pr.

Sugirtharajah, R. S. Interpretation Matters: Postcolonial Biblical Interpretation. 2010. (ENG.). pap. 25.00 *(978-0-334-04334-8(4)*, SCM Pr.) Hymns Ancient & Modern Ltd GBR. Dist: Westminster John Knox Pr.

Sugirtharajah, R. S., ed. Voices from the Margin: Interpreting the Bible in the Third World. 3rd rev. exp. ed. 2006. 506p. per. 35.00 *(978-1-57075-686-3(4))* Orbis Bks.

Sugirtharajah, R. S. & Sugirtharajah. Still at the Margins: Biblical Scholarship Fifteen Years after Voices from the Margin. Sugirtharajah, R. S., ed. 2008. (ENG.). 176p. 130.00 *(978-0-567-03221-8(3)*, T&T Clark Int'l) Continuum International Publishing Group, Ltd. GBR. Dist: National Bk. Network.

Sweeney, Marvin A. Reading the Hebrew Bible after the Shoah: Engaging Holocaust Theology. 2008. 302p. (C). pap. 29.00 *(978-0-8006-3849-8(2)*, Fortress Pr.) Augsburg Fortress, Pubs.

Swindell, Anthony Charles. How Contemporary Novelists Rewrite Stories from the Bible: The Interpretation of Scripture in Literature. 2009. 364p. 119.95 *(978-0-7734-4764-6(4))* Mellen, Edwin Pr., The.

Tate, W. Randolph. Biblical Interpretation an Integrated Approach. 3rd ed. 2008. 400p. *(978-1-59856-080-0(8))* Hendrickson Pubs. Marketing, LLC.

Terry, M. S. Hermeneutica: Biblical Hermeneutics. (SPA.). *(978-84-7645-013-0(3)*, 223089) Clie, Editorial.

Thiselton, Anthony C. Hermeneutics: An Introduction. 2009. 424p. pap. 30.00 *(978-0-8028-6410-9(4))* Eerdmans, William B. Publishing Co.

Thompson, Mark D. A Clear & Present Word: The Clarity of Scripture. 2006. (New Studies in Biblical Theology Ser.: Volume 21). (ENG.). 196p. per. 22.00 *(978-0-8308-2622-3(X)*, IVP Acad.) InterVarsity Pr.

Tillmann, Thomas. Hermeneutik und Bibelexegese Beim Jungen Goethe. 2006. (Historia Hermeneutica. Series Studia Ser.). (GER.). XII, 286p. 154.00 *(978-3-11-019068-7(0))* De Gruyter, Walter Inc.

Tischendorf, Constantin, ed. Vetus Testamentum Graece: Sixth Edition. 2007. 1386p. pap. 100.00 *(978-1-55635-331-4(6)*, Wipf and Stock) Wipf & Stock Pubs.

Topping, Richard R. Revelation Scripture & Church: Theological Hermeneutic Thought of James Barr Paul Ricoeur & Hans Frei. 2007. (Ashgate New Critical Thinking in Religion, Theology & Biblical Studies Ser.). 252p. 114.95 *(978-0-7546-5802-3(3))* Ashgate Publishing Co.

Treier, Daniel J. Introducing Theological Interpretation of Scripture: Recovering a Christian Practice. 2008. 224p. (C). pap. 22.00 *(978-0-8010-3178-6(8))* Baker Academic.

Treier, Daniel J. & Laansma, Jon C. Christology & Hermeneutics: Hebrews as an Interdisciplinary Case Study. Treier, Daniel J. & Laansma, Jon C., eds. 2012. (Library of New Testament Studies). (ENG.). 288p. 120.00 *(978-0-567-23859-7(8)*, T&T Clark Int'l) Continuum International Publishing Group, Ltd. GBR. Dist: National Bk. Network.

Twelftree, et al. Spirit & Scripture: Biblical Hermeneutics in the Renewal Tradition. Wright, Archie T. & Spawn, Kevin L., eds. 2012. (ENG.). 248p. 120.00 ***(978-0-567-03406-9(2)***, T&T Clark Int'l) Continuum International Publishing Group, Ltd. GBR. Dist: National Bk. Network.

Van Ess, Leandri. Vetus Testamentum Graecum, Editione Sixtina. 2007. 1064p. pap. 90.00 *(978-1-55635-569-1(6)*, Wipf and Stock) Wipf & Stock Pubs.

Van Hecke, Pierre. From Linguistics to Hermeneutics: A Functional & Cognitive Approach to Job 12-14. 2010. (Studia Semitica Neerlandica Ser.). (Illus.). 550p. *(978-90-04-18835-8(5))* BRILL.

Vanhoozer, Kevin J. Biblical Narrative in the Philosophy of Paul Ricoeur: A Study in Hermeneutics & Theology. 2007. (ENG.). 324p. pap. 61.00 *(978-0-521-04390-8(5))* Cambridge Univ. Pr.

Vessey, Etal. Calling of the Nations. 2010. (Green College Thematic Lecture Ser.). *(978-0-8020-9241-0(1))* Univ. of Toronto Pr.

Village, Andrew. The Bible & Lay People: An Empirical Approach to Ordinary Hermeneutics. 2007. (Explorations in Practical, Pastoral & Empirical Theology Ser.). 206p. 99.95 *(978-0-7546-5801-6(5))* Ashgate Publishing Co.

Virkler, Henry A. & Ayayo, Karelynne Gerber. Hermeneutics: Principles & Processes of Biblica Interpretation. 2nd ed. 2007. (Illus.). 256p. (C). pap. 21.99 *(978-0-8010-3138-0(9))* Baker Academic.

Warner, Sharon. Unlocking the Message of the Bible. 2008. 24.99 *(978-0-8272-3807-7(X))* Chalice Pr.

Webb, Robert L. & Bauman-Martin, Betsy, eds. Reading First Peter with New Eyes: Methodological Reassessments of the Letter of First Peter. 2007. (Library of New Testament Studies, the Ser.). (ENG.). 224p. 140.00 *(978-0-567-04562-1(5)*, T&T Clark Int'l) Continuum International Publishing Group, Ltd. GBR. Dist: National Bk. Network.

Weisblum, Moshe Pinchas & Visblum, Mosheh. The Hermeneutics of Medieval Jewish Thought: Understanding the Linguistic Codes of Rashi & Nahmanides. 2007. 272p. *(978-0-7734-5288-6(5))* Mellen, Edwin Pr., The.

Westphal, Merold. Whose Community? Which Interpretation? Philosophical Hermeneutics for the Church, 1 vol. 2009. (Church & Postmodern Culture Ser.). 160p. (C). pap. 20.00 *(978-0-8010-3147-2(8))* Baker Academic.

Wilshire, Leland E. Insight into Two Biblical Passages: Anatomy of a Prohibition I Timothy 2:12, the TLG Computer, & the Christian Church. 2010. (ENG.). 154p. pap. 26.50 *(978-0-7618-5207-0(7))* Univ. Pr. of America, Inc.

Wyckoff, John W. Pneuma & Logos. 2010. 168p. pap. 19.00 *(978-1-60899-483-0(X)*, Wipf and Stock) Wipf & Stock Pubs.

Xun, Chen. Theological Exegesis in the Canonical Context: Brevard Springs Childs' Methodology of Biblical Theology. 2010. (Studies in Biblical Literature Ser.). 322p. (C). 83.95 *(978-1-4331-0955-3(7))* Lang, Peter Publishing, Inc.

Yamasaki, Gary & Yamasaki. Watching a Biblical Narrative: Point of View in Biblical Exegesis. 2008. (ENG.). 240p. 160.00 *(978-0-567-02695-8(7)*, T&T Clark Int'l) Continuum International Publishing Group, Ltd. GBR. Dist: National Bk. Network.

Yee, Gale A. Judges & Method: New Approaches in Biblical Studies. 2nd rev. ed. 2007. (Illus.). 294p. pap. 23.00 *(978-0-8006-3858-0(1)*, Fortress Pr.) Augsburg Fortress, Pubs.

Yoder, John Howard. To Hear the Word - Second Edition. 2009. 266p. pap. 29.00 *(978-1-60608-928-6(5)*, Cascade Bks.) Wipf & Stock Pubs.

Young, Frances M. Biblical Exegesis & the Formation of Christian Culture. 2007. (ENG.). 340p. pap. 69.00 *(978-0-521-04513-1(4))* Cambridge Univ. Pr.

Zwiep, A W. Tussen Tekst en Lezer: Een Historische Inleiding in de Bijbelse Hermeneutiek. 2009. (DUT.). *(978-90-8659-342-2(9))* VU Univ. Pr.

BIBLE—HERMENEUTICS—HISTORY

see Bible—Criticism, Interpretation, Etc.—History

BIBLE—HIGHER CRITICISM

see Bible—Criticism, Interpretation, etc.; Bible—Introductions

BIBLE—HISTORIOGRAPHY

Amit, Yaira & Naaman, Nadav. Essays on Ancient Israel in Its near Eastern Context: A Tribute to Nadav Naaman. 2006. (Illus.). 466p. 59.50 *(978-1-57506-128-3(7))* Eisenbrauns, Inc.

Becker, Eve-Marie. Das Markus-Evangelium im Rahmen antiker Historiographie. 2006. (Wissenschaftliche Untersuchungen Zum Neuen Testament Ser.: Vol. 194). 516p. (C). 232.50 *(978-3-16-148913-6(6))* Mohr Siebeck GmbH & Co. KG DEU. Dist: Coronet Bks.

Becking, Bob & Grabbe, Lester L. Between Evidence & Ideology: Essays on the History of Ancient Israel Read at the Joint Meeting of the Society for Old Testament Study & the Oud Testamentisch Werkgezelschap, Lincoln, July 2009. 2011. (Illus.). xiv, 234p. *(978-90-04-18737-5(5))* BRILL.

Berquist, Jon, ed. Approaching Yehud: New Approaches to the Study of the Persian Period. 2007. (Semeia Studies). 260p. per. 29.95 *(978-1-58983-145-2(4))* Society of Biblical Literature.

Berquist, Jon L. Approaching Yehud: New Approaches to the Study of the Persian Period. 2007. *(978-90-04-13078-4(0))* BRILL.

Blomberg, Craig L. & Blomberg, Craig. The Historical Reliability of the Gospels. 2nd rev. ed. 2007. (ENG., Illus.). 416p. per. 24.00 *(978-0-8308-2807-4(9)*, IVP Acad.) InterVarsity Pr.

Frey, Jörg, et al, eds. Die Apostelgeschichte im Kontext antiker und frühchristlicher Historiographie. 2009. (Beihefte zur Zeitschrift far die neutestamentliche Wissenschaft und die Kunde der älteren Kirche Ser.).Tr. of Acts of the Apostles in the Context of Ancient & Early Christian Historiography. (GER.). X, 703p. 321.00 ***(978-3-11-173653-2(9))*** De Gruyter, Walter Inc.

Frey, Jörg, et al, eds. Die Apostelgeschichte im Kontext antiker und frühchristlicher Historiographie. 2009. (Beihefte zur Zeitschrift für die neutestamentliche Wissenschaft und die Kunde der Alteren Kirche Ser.).Tr. of Acts of the Apostles in the Context of Ancient & Early Christian Historiography. (GER.). X, 703p. 210.00 *(978-3-11-021631-8(0))* De Gruyter, Walter Inc.

Garbini, Giovanni. Myth & History in the Bible. 2009. (Library of Hebrew Bible/Old Testament Studies, the Ser.). (ENG.). 192p. 39.95 *(978-0-567-01839-7(3)*, T&T Clark) Continuum International Publishing Group, Ltd. GBR. Dist: National Bk. Network.

Geoghegan, Jeffrey C. The Time, Place, & Purpose of the Deuteronomistic History: The Evidence of "Until This Day" 2006. (Brown Judaic Studies: No. 347). (Illus.). xviii, 203p. *(978-1-930675-27-8(5))* Brown Judaic Studies.

Gilmour, Rachelle. Representing the Past: A Literary Analysis of Narrative Historiography in the Book of Samuel. 2011. (Illus.). XII, 336p. *(978-90-04-20340-2(0))* BRILL.

Glicksman, Andrew T. Wisdom of Solomon 10: A Jewish Hellenistic Reinterpretation of Early Israelite History Through Sapiential Lenses. 2011. (Deuterocanonical & Cognate Literature Studies). 140.00 ***(978-3-11-024764-0(X))*** De Gruyter, Walter Inc.

—Wisdom of Solomon 10: A Jewish Hellenistic Reinterpretation of Early Israelite History through Sapiential Lenses. 2011. (Deuterocanonical & Cognate Literature Studies). (ENG., Illus.). XIV, 244p. 210.00 ***(978-3-11-214313-1(2))*** De Gruyter, Walter Inc.

Grabbe, Lester L., et al. The Historian & the Bible. 2010. (Library of Hebrew Bible/Old Testament Studies). (ENG., Illus.). 256p. 140.00 *(978-0-567-20268-0(2)*, T&T Clark Int'l) Continuum International Publishing Group, Ltd. GBR. Dist: National Bk. Network.

Jonker, Louis, ed. Historiography & Identity (Re)Formulation in Second Temple Historiographical Literature. 2010. (Library of Hebrew Bible/Old Testament Studies, the Ser.). (ENG.). 192p. 110.00 *(978-0-567-41062-7(5)*, T&T Clark Int'l) Continuum International Publishing Group, Ltd. GBR. Dist: National Bk. Network.

Kalimi, Isaac. The Retelling of Chronicles in Jewish Tradition & Literature: A Journey Through History. 2009. 59.50 *(978-1-57506-149-8(X))* Eisenbrauns, Inc.

Kallai, Zecharia. Studies in Biblical Historiography & Geography: Collection of Studies. 2010. (Beiträge zur Erforschung des Alten Testaments und des Antiken Judentums Ser.). 266p. 57.95 *(978-3-631-59362-2(7))* Lang, Peter GmbH, Europaischer Verlag der Wissenschaften DEU. Dist: Lang, Peter.

Kavanagh, Preston. The Shaphan Group: The Fifteen Authors Who Shaped the Hebrew Bible. 2011. 154p. pap. 18.00 *(978-1-60608-611-7(1)*, Pickwick Pubns.) Wipf & Stock Pubs.

Kirkpatrick. Function of Ancient Historiography in Biblical & Cognate Studies. 2008. (Library of Hebrew Bible/Old Testament Studies, the Ser.). (ENG.). 192p. 120.00 *(978-0-567-02715-3(5)*, T&T Clark Int'l) Continuum International Publishing Group, Ltd. GBR. Dist: National Bk. Network.

Knoppers, Gary N. & Ristau, Kenneth A. Community Identity in Judean Historiography: Biblical & Comparative Perspectives. 2009. 44.50 *(978-1-57506-165-8(1))* Eisenbrauns, Inc.

Leeman, Bernard. Queen of Sheba & Biblical Scholarship. 280p. 84.95 *(978-1-59221-117-3(8))* Africa World Pr.

Levinson, Bernard M. Legal Revision & Religious Renewal in Ancient Israel. (ENG.). 232p. 2010. pap. 27.99 *(978-0-521-17191-5(1))* 2008. 84.00 *(978-0-521-51344-9(8))* Cambridge Univ. Pr.

Moore, Megan Bishop & Kelle, Brad E. Biblical History & Israel's Past. 2011. pap. 46.00 *(978-0-8028-6260-0(8))* Eerdmans, William B. Publishing Co.

Oswalt, John & Oswalt, John N. The Bible among the Myths: Unique Revelation or Just Ancient Literature?, 1 vol. 2009. (ENG.). 208p. pap. 17.99 *(978-0-310-28509-0(7))* Zondervan.

Spinella, Frank. The Cloak & the Parchments. 2009. 206p. pap. 23.00 *(978-1-60899-072-6(9))* Wipf & Stock Pubs.

Warkentin, A. A Harmony of the Kings. 2007. (Illus.). 245p. pap. 21.00 *(978-1-55635-754-1(0))* Wipf & Stock Pubs.

Wineland, John D., et al, eds. My Father's World: Celebrating the Life of Reuben G. Bullard. 2011. 234p. pap. 26.00 ***(978-1-60608-879-8(X)***, Wipf and Stock) Wipf & Stock Pubs.

BIBLE—HISTORY

Here are entered works on the history of Bible texts, versions, and printing. For works on historical events see Bible—History of Biblical Events or Bible—History of Contemporary Events.

Advanced Bible History: For Lutheran Schools in the Words of Holy Scripture. 447p. pap. 14.99 *(978-0-570-03974-7(6)*, 12-3009) Concordia Publishing Hse.

Armstrong, Karen. The Bible: A Biography. 2008. (Books That Changed the World Ser.). (ENG.). 176p. pap. 14.00 *(978-0-8021-4384-6(9)*, Grove Pr.) Grove/Atlantic, Inc.

—The Bible: A Biography. l.t. ed. 2008. (Books That Changed the World Ser.). 375p. 30.95 *(978-1-4104-0378-0(5))* Thorndike Pr.

Arnold, Clinton E. How We Got the Bible: A Visual Journey, 1 vol. Arnold, Clinton E., ed. 2008. (Zondervan Visual Reference Ser.). (ENG., Illus.). 96p. 12.99 *(978-0-310-25306-8(3))* Zondervan.

Aune, David E. Apocalypticism, Prophecy & Magic in Early Christianity: Collected Essays. 2006. (Wissenschaftliche Untersuchungen zum Neuen Testament Ser.: No. 199). 482p. 215.00 *(978-3-16-149020-0(7))* Mohr Siebeck GmbH & Co. KG DEU. Dist: Coronet Bks.

A Bible History a Concordia Classic Edition: Student Workbook. 160p. stu. ed., wbk. ed. 9.50 *(978-0-7586-0289-3(8))* Concordia Publishing Hse.

A Bible History a Concordia Classic Edition: Teacher Guide. 128p. tchr. ed. 14.00 *(978-0-7586-0290-9(1))* Concordia Publishing Hse.

Bigelow, John. The Bible That Was Lost & Is Found. 2010. (ENG.). 132p. pap. 20.75 *(978-1-177-57286-6(9))* 2010. 132p. pap. 20.75 *(978-1-141-57183-3(8))* 2009. 126p. 21.99 *(978-1-103-82644-5(1))* 2009. 128p. pap. 15.99 *(978-1-103-82635-3(2))* BiblioBazaar.

—The Bible That Was Lost & Is Found. 2009. 72p. pap. 14.14 *(978-0-217-91002-6(5))* General Bks. LLC.

—The Bible That Was Lost & Is Found. 2007. (ENG.). 124p. 35.95 *(978-0-548-19309-9(6))*; 128p. per. 20.95 *(978-1-4304-9906-0(0))* Kessinger Publishing, LLC.

Blech, Arthur. The Causes of Anti-Semitism: A Critique of the Bible. 2010. 512p. 29.95 *(978-1-59079-068-7(5))* Select Bks.

Boynton, Susan & Reilly, Diane J. The Practice of the Bible in the Middle Ages: Production, Reception, & Performance in Western Christianity. 2011. (Columbia Journalism Review Bks). (Illus.). 400p. E-Book 1.99 *(978-0-231-52739-2(X))* Columbia Univ. Pr.

Boynton, Susan & Reilly, Diane J., eds. The Practice of the Bible in the Middle Ages: Production, Reception, & Performance in Western Christianity. 2011. (ENG., Illus.). 376p. (gr. 17). 89.50 *(978-0-231-14826-9(7))*; pap. 29.50 *(978-0-231-14827-6(5))* Columbia Univ. Pr.

Bragg, Melvyn. The Book of Books: The Radical Impact of the King James Bible 1611-2011. 2012. (ENG.). 368p. pap. 16.95 ***(978-1-61902-010-8(6)***, Counterpoint) Counterpoint LLC.

Bragg, Melvyn. The Book of Books: The Radical Impact of the King James Bible 1611-2011. 2011. (ENG., Illus.). 368p. 28.00 *(978-1-58243-781-1(5)*, Counterpoint) Counterpoint LLC.

Brake, Donald L. A Visual History of the English Bible: The Tumultuous Tale of the World's Bestselling Book. 2008. (Illus.). 352p. 29.99 *(978-0-8010-1316-4(X))*; 256p. pap. 14.99 *(978-0-8010-6821-8(5))* Baker Bks.

Brown, Michelle P. In the Beginning: Bibles Before the Year 1000. 2006. (ENG., Illus.). 368p. 45.00 *(978-1-58834-240-9(9))* Smithsonian Institution Pr.

Burton, Keith Augustus. The Blessing of Africa: The Bible & African Christianity. 2007. (ENG.). 294p. per. 22.00 *(978-0-8308-2762-6(5)*, IVP Acad.) InterVarsity Pr.

Campbell, Gordon. Bible: The Story of the King James Version 1611-2011. 2010. (ENG., Illus.). 256p. 24.95 *(978-0-19-955759-2(4))* Oxford Univ. Pr., Inc.

Chami, Sami & Abaidia, Mourad. Alph. 2009. 172p. pap. 65.00 *(978-1-60860-485-2(3)*, Strategic Bk. Publishing) AEG Literary Publishing Services, Inc.

Chilton, Bruce & Saldarini, Anthony J., eds. The Cambridge Companion to the Bible. 2nd rev. ed. 2007. (ENG., Illus.). 734p. per. 38.99 *(978-0-521-69140-6(0))* Cambridge Univ. Pr.

Clay, Albert T. The Origin of Biblical Traditions: Hebrew Legends in Babylonia & Israel. 2007. (Ancient near East: Classic Studies: Ser.). (Illus.). 224p. pap. 24.00 *(978-1-59752-718-7(1)*, Wipf and Stock) Wipf & Stock Pubs.

Comfort, Philip W. Origen De la Biblia (Origin of The Bible), Sc. 2011. 384p. pap. 12.99 *(978-1-4143-1719-9(0)*, Tyndale Espanol) Tyndale Hse. Pubs.

Conant, H. C. The English Bible: History of the Translation of the Holy Scriptures into the English Tongue: With Specimens of the Old English Versions. 2006. *(978-1-57898-611-8(7))* Martino Publishing.

Condit, Blackford. The History of the English Bible: Extending from Earliest Saxon Translations to the Present Anglo-American Revision: with Special Reference to the Protestant Religion & the English Language. 2008. 85.00 *(978-1-57898-610-1(9))* Martino Publishing.

Conner, Kenneth E. They Captured the Spirit. 2007. 220p. per. 12.95 *(978-1-60364-001-5(0)*, Honey Locust Pr.) Wolfmont, LLC.

Darden, John S. A Walk Through the Holy Land. 2010. 83p. pap. 7.98 *(978-0-557-00630-4(9))* Lulu Enterprises Inc.

de Hamel, Christopher. Bibles: An Illustrated History from Papyrus to Print. 2011. (Illus.). 192p. pap. 19.00 *(978-1-85124-298-6(8))* Bodleian Library GBR. Dist: Chicago Distribution Ctr.

Deanesly, Margaret. The Lollard Bible: And Other Medieval Biblical Versions. 2008. (ENG.). 508p. pap. 63.00 *(978-0-521-09073-5(3))* Cambridge Univ. Pr.

deGroot, Christiana & Taylor, Marion Ann. Recovering Nineteenth-Century Women Interpreters of the Bible. 2007. (SBL - Symposium Ser.). 246p. *(978-90-04-15109-3(5))* BRILL.

Deloe, Jesse B. Sweeter Than Honey. pap. 5.99 *(978-0-88469-105-1(5))* BMH Bks.

Dickey, Darryl O. Revelations of the Bible: Lifting the Veil on the History & Creation of the Bible. 2010. 364p. pap. 24.75 *(978-1-4251-8863-4(X))* Trafford Publishing.

Dove, Mary. The First English Bible: The Text & Context of the Wycliffite Versions. 2011. (Cambridge Studies in Medieval Literature Ser.). (ENG.). 334p. pap. 39.99 *(978-0-521-17547-0(X))* Cambridge Univ. Pr.

Earle, Ralph, et al. How We Got Our Bible: Third Edition. 3rd ed. 2010. (ENG.). 128p. pap. 12.99 *(978-0-8341-2495-0(5)*, 9780834124950) Beacon Hill Pr. of Kansas City.

Ferrell, Lori Anne. The Bible & the People. 2008. (ENG., Illus.). 288p. 32.50 *(978-0-300-11424-9(9))* Yale Univ. Pr.

Flores, José. Historia de la Biblia en Espana: History of the Bible in Spain. (SPA., Illus.). 320p. *(978-84-7228-399-2(2)*, 220463) Clie, Editorial.

Foreman, Iris A. His Name Forever: The Story Behind the Name of God. 2011. 144p. pap. 16.95 ***(978-1-4490-4029-1(2))*** AuthorHouse.

Gameson, Richard, ed. The Early Medieval Bible: Its Production, Decoration & Use. 2009. (Cambridge Studies in Palaeography & Codicology Ser.). (ENG., Illus.). 264p. pap. 36.99 *(978-0-521-10001-4(1))* Cambridge Univ. Pr.

Garcia, Carmen. Mis Primeras Historias de la Biblia. (SPA.). 384p. *(978-1-4054-1485-2(5))* Parragon, Inc.

Goodspeed, Edgar Johnson. The Making of the English New Testament. 2011. 138p. 40.95 ***(978-1-258-05086-3(2))*** Literary Licensing, LLC.

Graves, Kersey. The Bible of Bibles. 2009. 346p. pap. *(978-1-4589-0996-1(4))* Books LLC.

—The Bible of Bibles. 2007. (ENG.). 388p. per. 18.45 *(978-1-60206-258-0(7))* Cosimo, Inc.

Greenberg, Rabbi Ben. Covenantal Promise & Destiny: Wisdom for Life. 2010. 108p. 25.00 *(978-0-557-57574-6(X))* Lulu Enterprises Inc.

Greer, Rowan A. & Mitchell, Margaret Mary, intros. The Belly-Myther of Endor: Interpretations of 1 Kingdoms 28 in the Early Church. 2007. (ENG.). 348p. per. 39.95 *(978-1-58983-120-9(9))* Society of Biblical Literature.

Gwynn, John. On a Syriac MS. Belonging to the Collection of Archbishop Ussher. 2010. pap. 21.76 *(978-1-61719-579-2(0))* Gorgias Pr., LLC.

Halder, Francis. The Greatest World War. 2011. 52p. pap. 12.15 *(978-1-4567-7315-1(1))* AuthorHouse.

Hansen, David. In their Sandals. 2007. pap. 9.99 *(978-1-60266-032-8(8))* Xulon Pr., Inc.

Harnack, Adolf. Bible Reading in the Early Church. 2009. 172p. 26.99 *(978-1-110-64637-1(2))*; pap. 20.75 *(978-1-110-64634-0(8))* BiblioBazaar.

B

Harris, Rendel. The Origin of the Prologue to St John's Gospel. 2011. (ENG.). 76p. pap. 36.99 ***(978-1-107-68843-8(4))*** Cambridge Univ. Pr.

Hill, Robert C. Of Prophets & Poets: Antioch Fathers on the Bible. 2007. pap. *(978-1-885652-92-8(5))* Holy Cross Orthodox Pr.

Historias de la Biblia Vol. I. Tr. of Lion Bible Stories. (SPA., Illus.). 10.99 *(978-1-56063-171-2(6),* 490352) Editorial Unilit.

Holloway, Steven. Orientalism Assyriology & the Bible. 2006. (Illus.). 592p. *(978-1-905048-37-3(8))* Sheffield Phoenix Pr.

Holloway, Steven, ed. Orientalism, Assyriology & the Bible. 2007. 592p. per. *(978-1-906055-33-2(5))* Sheffield Phoenix Pr.

Hull, Robert F. The Story of the New Testament Text: Movers, Materials, Motives, Methods, & Models. 2010. xiv, 229p. *(978-1-58983-521-4(2));* *(978-1-58983-520-7(4))* Society of Biblical Literature.

Judd, Frank F. & Strathearn, Gaye. How the New Testament Came to Be: 35th Annual Sidney B. Sperry Symposium. 2006. 432p. 24.95 *(978-1-59038-627-9(2))* Deseret Bk. Co.

Kahler, James C. A Charted History of the Bible. 2007. (Illus.). 35p. pap. 5.99 *(978-1-890120-51-1(0))* DayStar Publishing.

Kee, Howard Clark, et al. The Cambridge Companion to the Bible. Chilton, Bruce, ed. 2nd rev. ed. 2007. (ENG., Illus.). 734p. 120.00 *(978-0-521-86997-3(8))* Cambridge Univ. Pr.

Keeler, Bronson C. A Short History of the Bible. 2009. 84p. pap. *(978-1-151-64064-2(6))* Books LLC.

Kent, Charles Foster. The Origin & Permanent Value of the Old Testament. 2008. 184p. 25.99 *(978-0-554-22798-6(3))* 2008. 184p. 22.99 *(978-0-554-32101-1(7))* 2007. (ENG.). 160p. pap. 19.99 *(978-1-4264-3062-6(0))* 2007. (ENG.). 180p. pap. 21.99 *(978-1-4264-3127-2(9))* BiblioBazaar.

—The Origin & Permanent Value of the Old Testament. 2007. 144p. per. *(978-1-4065-1900-6(6))* Dodo Pr.

Kenyon, Frederic G. Our Bible & the Ancient Manuscripts. 2011. 298p. pap. 26.00 ***(978-1-61097-756-2(4),*** Wipf and Stock) Wipf & Stock Pubs.

Kenyon, Frederic G. Our Bible & the Ancient Manuscripts Be. 2006. pap. 31.95 *(978-1-4286-5003-9(2))* Kessinger Publishing, LLC.

Kroll, Woodrow. Taking Back the Good Book: How America Forgot the Bible & Why It Matters to You. 2007. 224p. 19.99 *(978-1-58134-826-2(6))* Crossway.

Laan, Ray Vander. Faith Lessons on the Prophets & Kings of Israel Discovery Guide, 1 vol. exp. rev. ed. 2008. (Faith Lessons Ser.). (ENG.). 208p. pap. 9.99 *(978-0-310-27961-7(5))* Zondervan.

—Promised Land, 1 vol., Vol. 1. rev. exp. ed. 2008. (Faith Lessons Ser.). (ENG.). 160p. pap. 9.99 *(978-0-310-27957-0(7))* Zondervan.

Lawrence, Paul. The IVP Atlas of Bible History. 2006. (ENG., Illus.). 190p. 45.00 *(978-0-8308-2452-6(9),* IVP Acad.) InterVarsity Pr.

Ledo, Michael. The Bronze Age Bible. 2010. 52p. pap. 7.99 *(978-0-557-38757-1(4))* Lulu Enterprises Inc.

Lieb, Michael, et al. The Oxford Handbook of the Reception History of the Bible. 2011. (ENG., Illus.). 752p. 150.00 *(978-0-19-920454-0(3))* Oxford Univ. Pr., Inc.

Lovett, Richard. Printed English Bible 1525 1885. 2007. 212p. per. *(978-1-4067-8997-3(6),* Pierides Pr.) Read Bks.

Lupas, Liana. On Eagles' Wings: The King James Turns 400. Lupas, Liana & Pongracz, Patricia C., eds. 2011. pap. 29.95 ***(978-0-9777839-8-4(7))*** Museum of Biblical Art.

Lyons, Vernon C. The Revivals in the Bible. 2009. 216p. pap. 17.99 *(978-1-4141-1338-8(2))* Pleasant Word.

Marsden, Richard & Matter, E. Ann. The New Cambridge History of the Bible: From 600 To 1450. 2012. (New Cambridge History of the Bible Ser.). (ENG., Illus.). 1068p. 190.00 ***(978-0-521-86006-2(7))*** Cambridge Univ. Pr.

Masonic Service Association. The Gutenberg Bible: Five Hundredth Anniversary of the Invention of Printing from Moveable Type & the First Printed Great Light. 2011. 28p. 35.95 ***(978-1-258-10565-5(9))*** Literary Licensing, LLC.

McAfee, Cleland Boyd & Mcafee, Cleland Boyd. The Greatest English Classic, a Study of the King James Version of the Bible & It's Influence on Live & Literature. 2011. 146p. pap. 12.99 ***(978-1-61203-235-1(4))*** Bottom of the Hill Publishing.

McComb, Samuel. The Making of the English Bible. 2009. 78p. pap. *(978-1-151-37606-0(X))* Books LLC.

Moore, Helen & Reid, Julian, eds. Manifold Greatness: The Making of the King James Bible. 2011. (Illus.). 208p. pap. 35.00 *(978-1-85124-349-5(6))* Bodleian Library GBR. Dist: Chicago Distribution Ctr.

Mosse, Martin. The Three Gospels: New Testament History Introduced by the Synoptic Problem. 2007. (Paternoster Biblical Monographs). (Illus.). 414p. pap. 50.00 *(978-1-55635-660-5(9))* Wipf & Stock Pubs.

Muller, Walter. Unchaste Deception. 2008. 193p. pap. 17.50 *(978-1-4092-0829-7(X))* Lulu Enterprises Inc.

Mutius, Hans-Georg von. Nichtmasoretische Bibelzitate im Midrasch ha-Gadol (13. /14. Jahrhundert) 2010. (Judentum und Umwelt. Realms of Judaism Ser.). (GER.). 152p. 47.95 *(978-3-631-60826-5(8))* Lang, Peter GmbH, Europaischer Verlag der Wissenschaften DEU. Dist: Lang, Peter.

Newman, Tom. A Brief History of the Bible. 2010. pap. 27.99 *(978-1-61566-273-9(1))* Tate Publishing & Enterprises, LLC.

Noort, Edward, et al. The Land of Israel in Bible, History, & Theology: Studies in Honour of Ed Noort. 2009. *(978-90-04-17515-0(6))* BRILL.

Norton, David. The King James Bible: A Short History from Tyndale to Today. 2011. (Illus.). 232p. (ENG.). 65.00 *(978-0-521-85149-7(1));* pap. 24.99 *(978-0-521-61688-1(3))* Cambridge Univ. Pr.

Ogden, Arthur M. The Development of the New Testament. rev. ed. 100p. reprint ed. pap., wbk. ed. 3.95 *(978-0-9646497-0-5(5))* Ogden Pubns.

Pope, Kyle. How We Got the Bible. 2010. 106p. pap. 12.95 *(978-1-58427-298-4(8))* Guardian of Truth Foundation.

Publishing, Rose. Rose Book of Bible & Christian History Time Lines: More Than 6000 Years at a Glance. 2006. (ENG., Illus.). 31p. 29.99 *(978-1-59636-084-6(4))* Rose Publishing.

Rasimus, Tuomas. The Legacy of John: Second-Century Reception of the Fourth Gospel. 2009. xi, 406p. *(978-90-04-17633-1(0))* BRILL.

Ray, T. C. The Intention of it All: Mysteries & Misunderstood Scriptures of the Bible Decoded. 2010. 392p. pap. 17.99 *(978-1-4520-9102-0(1))* AuthorHouse.

Reuss, Eduard. History of the Canon of the Holy Scriptures in the Christian Church. Hunter, David, tr. 2007. 416p. pap. 35.00 *(978-1-55635-747-3(8))* Wipf & Stock Pubs.

Roberts, Vaughan. Missing the Point? Finding Our Place in the Turning Points of History. 2008. (ENG.). 28p. 5.99 *(978-1-85078-763-1(8))* Authentic Media.

Rogerson, John. Old Testament Criticism in the Nineteenth Century. 2010. 336p. pap. 39.00 *(978-1-60899-733-6(2),* Wipf and Stock) Wipf & Stock Pubs.

Romer. Testament: Bible & History. (Illus.). 368p. 35.00 *(978-0-948397-12-7(8))* O'Mara, Michael Bks., Ltd. GBR. Dist: Trans-Atlantic Pubns., Inc.

Sawyer, John F. A. A Concise Dictionary of the Bible & Its Reception. 2009. (ENG.). 256p. pap. 30.00 *(978-0-664-22338-0(9))* Westminster John Knox Pr.

Schwarz, W. Principles & Problems of Biblical Translation: Some Reformation Controversies & their Background. 2009. (ENG.). 248p. pap. 34.99 *(978-0-521-09753-6(3))* Cambridge Univ. Pr.

Setzer, Claudia & Shefferman, David, eds. The Bible & American Culture: A Sourcebook. 2011. (ENG.). 296p. (C). pap. 36.95 *(978-0-415-57811-0(6))* Routledge.

Sheehan, Jonathan. The Enlightenment Bible: Translation, Scholarship, Culture. 2007. (ENG., Illus.). 296p. (C). per. 26.95 *(978-0-691-13069-9(8))* Princeton Univ. Pr.

Short, Charles. The New Revision of King James' Revision of the New Testament. 2009. pap. 72.28 *(978-1-60724-540-7(X))* Gorgias Pr., LLC.

Skinner, Andrew. A Bible Fit for the Restoration: The Epic Struggle that Brought Us the King James Version. 2011. 128p. pap. 9.99 ***(978-1-59955-908-7(0))*** Cedar Fort, Inc./CFI Distribution.

Smith, Robert Bruce. Cultural Perspectives on the Bible: A Beginner's Guide. 2007. 224p. per. 18.00 *(978-0-9785165-7-4(5))* Drinian Pr., LLC.

Smith, Sue Ellen. Visions & Messages. 2007. 44p. pap. 8.95 *(978-0-7414-4130-0(6))* Infinity Publishing.

Smyth, J. Paterson. The Bible in the Making in the Light of Modern Research. 2007. (ENG.). 224p. 39.95 *(978-0-548-06792-5(9))* Kessinger Publishing, LLC.

Spencer, Nick. Freedom & Order: History, Politics & the English Bible. (ENG.). 2012. 384p. pap. 13.95 ***(978-0-340-99624-9(2))*** 2011. (Illus.). 320p. 26.95 *(978-0-340-99623-2(4))* Hodder General Publishing Div. GBR. (Hodder & Stoughton). Dist: Independent Pubs. Group.

Spong, John Shelby. Re-Claiming the Bible for a Non-Religious World. 2011. (ENG.). 432p. 28.99 *(978-0-06-201128-2(6),* HarperOne) HarperCollins Pubs.

Stanfill, Brenda Richie. Fatal Errors. 2007. 125p. pap. 19.95 *(978-1-60441-846-0(X))* PublishAmerica, Inc.

Sumner, Tracy Macon. How Did We Get the Bible? 2009. (Value Bks.). (ENG.). 160p. pap. 2.99 *(978-1-60260-363-9(4),* Barbour Bks.) Barbour Publishing, Inc.

Swete, Henry Barclay & Ottley, Richard Rusden. An Introduction to the Old Testament in Greek. Thackeray, H. J., ed. 2011. (GRE & ENG.). 156.80 *(978-1-61143-842-0(X))* Gorgias Pr., LLC.

Theissen, Gerd. The New Testament: A Literary History. Maloney, Linda M., tr. from GER. 2011. 304p. (C). 49.00 *(978-0-8006-9785-3(5),* Fortress Pr.) Augsburg Fortress, Pubs.

Tobin, Paul. The Rejection of Pascal's Wager. 2009. (Illus.). 668p. pap. *(978-0-7552-0461-8(1))* Authors OnLine, Ltd.

Tov, Emanuel & Evans, Craig A., eds. Exploring the Origins of the Bible: Canon Formation in Historical, Literary, & Theological Perspective. 2008. (Acadia Studies in Bible & Theology Ser.). 272p. (C). pap. 28.00 *(978-0-8010-3242-4(3))* Baker Academic.

Townley, James. Illustrations of Biblical Literature, Exhibiting the History & Fate of the Sacred Writings, from the Earliest Period to the Present Century; Includi. 2006. 612p. per. 34.99 *(978-1-4255-6495-7(X));* 608p. per. 34.99 *(978-1-4255-6496-4(8))* MPublishing.

Trevelyon, Thomas. The Trevelyon Miscellany of 1608: A Facsimile of Folger Shakespeare Library MS V. B. 232. 2007. (ENG., Illus.). 648p. 750.00 ***(978-0-295-98659-3(X))*** Folger Shakespeare Library.

van der Toorn, Karel & van der Toorn, K. Scribal Culture & the Making of the Hebrew Bible. 2009. 416p. pap. 23.00 *(978-0-674-03254-5(3))* Harvard Univ. Pr.

Vermes, Geza. The Story of the Scrolls: The Miraculous Discovery & True Significance of the Dead Sea Scrolls. 2010. (ENG.). 272p. pap. 17.00 *(978-0-14-104615-0(5),* Penguin Global) Penguin Group (USA) Inc.

Waite, Th. D. Fundamentalist Deception on Bible Preservation. 2008. 172p. pap. 15.00 *(978-1-56848-049-7(0))* Old Paths Pubns., Inc., The.

Wansbrough, Henry. The Story of the Bible: How It Came to Us. 2006. *(978-1-59235-072-8(0));* 140p. per. 11.95 *(978-1-59325-072-0(X))* Word Among Us Pr.

Weisberg, David B. Leaders & Legacies in Assyriology & Bible: The Collected Essays of David B. Weisberg. 2012. ***(978-1-57506-230-3(5))*** Eisenbrauns, Inc.

Westbrook, Vivienne. Long Travail & Great Paynes: A Politics of Reformation Revision. 2010. (Studies in Early Modern Religious Reforms Ser.). 232p. pap. 129.00 *(978-90-481-5699-3(8),* 9048156998) Springer.

Wilkinson, Robert J. Orientalism, Aramaic & Kabbalah in the Catholic Reformation: The First Printing of the Syriac New Testament. 2007. (Studies in the History of Christian Traditions). 288p. *(978-90-04-16250-1(X))* BRILL.

Yutang, Lin. A Bible for the Liberal. Runes, Dagobert D., ed. 2011. 380p. 53.95 ***(978-1-258-01060-7(7))*** Literary Licensing, LLC.

BIBLE—HISTORY OF BIBLICAL EVENTS

Here are entered works on the history of events related in the Bible. Works on history contemporary with the history of Biblical events, including archaeological, social, and cultural materials that shed light on the Bible, are entered under Bible—History of Contemporary Events.

Anderson, Clive. Face2face Sennacherib: Encountering Assyrias great & terrifying Ruler. 2007. (Face2face With Ser.). 96p. 9.00 *(978-1-84625-076-7(5))* DayOne Pubns. GBR. Dist: STL Distribution North America.

Barnhart, David. Living in the Times of the Signs. 2007. 492p. (ENG.). 35.99 *(978-1-60477-052-0(X));* per. 23.99 *(978-1-60477-051-3(1))* Xulon Pr., Inc.

Beitzel, Barry J. The New Moody Atlas of the Bible. 2009. (ENG.), 304p. 49.99 *(978-0-8024-0441-1(3))* Moody Pubs.

Booker, Richard. Discovering the Miracle of the Scarlet Thread in Every Book of the Bible: A Simple Plan for Understanding the Bible. 2009. pap. 15.99 *(978-0-7684-3111-7(5))* Destiny Image Pubs.

Buechel, Eugene. Wowapi Wakan, Wicowoyake Yuptecelapi Kin: Bible History in the Language of the Teton Sioux Indians. 2011. 350p. 51.95 ***(978-1-258-01551-0(X))*** Literary Licensing, LLC.

Capper, Brian, et al. The Penguin Historical Atlas of the Bible Lands. 2009. (ENG., Illus.). 144p. (gr. 12). 20.00 *(978-0-14-102687-9(1),* Penguin (Non-Classics)) Penguin Group (USA) Inc.

Caughey, Ellen. 40 Fascinating Places of the Bible. 2008. (Value Books Ser.). (ENG.). 96p. pap. 0.99 *(978-1-60260-021-8(X),* Barbour Bks.) Barbour Publishing, Inc.

Chumbley, Charles Melvin. The Man Invincible or What Is It All About: This Book We Call the Bible. 2011. 310p. 48.95 ***(978-1-258-05107-5(9))*** Literary Licensing, LLC.

Cohen, Tim. Messiah, History, & the Tribulation Period: Multi-Volume Set, 7 vols., Cohen, Tim, ed. rev. ed. 2006. (Illus.). pap. *(978-0-9662793-1-3(X),* BK-02) Prophecy House, Inc.

—Messiah, History, & the Tribulation Period Vol. 2, Vol. 3: The Prophetic Stage: Signs of the Times. Cohen, Tim, ed. 2006. pap. *(978-0-9662793-3-7(6))* Prophecy House, Inc.

—Messiah, History, & the Tribulation Period Vol. 4: Biblical Chronology: the Young Creation. Cohen, Tim, ed. 2006. pap. *(978-0-9662793-5-1(2))* Prophecy House, Inc.

—Messiah, History, & the Tribulation Period Vol. 6: Messiah's Preeminence in History & Prophecy: the Heart of Israelology, Eschatology, & God's Holy Days. Cohen, Tim, ed. 2006. pap. *(978-0-9662793-7-5(9))* Prophecy House, Inc.

—Messiah, History, & the Tribulation Period Vol. 7: The Harmony of Weeks: God's Inspired Grand Unified Theology Unveiled. Cohen, Tim, ed. 2006. pap. *(978-0-9662793-8-2(7))* Prophecy House, Inc.

Currid, John D. & Barrett, David P. Crossway ESV Bible Atlas. 2010. 352p. 55.00 *(978-1-4335-0192-0(9))* Crossway.

De Graaf, S. G. El Pueblo de la Promesa: Desde la Creacion Hasta la Conquista de Canaan, Vol. I. (SPA.). 415p. pap. 16.00 *(978-1-55883-065-3(0),* 6700-2510C) Libros Desafio.

Drane, John. The World of the Bible. 2010. (ENG., Illus.). 256p. 34.95 *(978-0-7459-5250-5(X))* Lion Hudson PLC GBR. Dist: Independent Pubs. Group.

Ellwood, Thomas. Sacred History V1 or the Historical Part. 2006. pap. 42.95 *(978-1-4286-5228-6(0))* Kessinger Publishing, LLC.

—Sacred History V2 or the Historical Part. 2006. pap. 42.95 *(978-1-4286-5227-9(2))* Kessinger Publishing, LLC.

Eskenazi, Tamara C. Second Temple Studies: Vol. 2: Temple & Community in the Persian Period. Richards, Kent H., ed. 2009. (Library of Hebrew Bible/Old Testament Studies, the Ser.). (ENG.). 313p. 55.00 *(978-0-567-11229-3(2),* T&T Clark) Continuum International Publishing Group, Ltd. GBR. Dist: National Bk. Network.

Exum, J. Cheryl & Nutu, Ela. Between the Text & the Canvas: The Bible & Art in Dialogue. Exum, J. Cheryl & Nutu, Ela, eds. 2007. (Illus.). 264p. *(978-1-906055-19-6(X))* Sheffield Phoenix Pr.

Foakes-Jackson, F. J. The Biblical History of the Hebrews. 2007. 516p. per. *(978-1-4067-8795-5(7),* Pomona Pr.) Read Bks.

Freund, Richard A. Digging Through the Bible: Modern Archaeology & the Ancient Bible. (ENG., 352p. 2009. Illus.). pap. 18.95 *(978-0-7425-4645-5(4))* 2008. 47.95 *(978-0-7425-4644-8(6))* Rowman & Littlefield Publishers, Inc.

Goheen, Michael W. & Bartholomew, Craig G. The True Story of the Whole World: Finding Your Place in the Biblical Drama. 2009. *(978-1-59255-476-8(8))* Faith Alive Christian Resources.

Goldenberg, Robert. The Origins of Judaism: From Canaan to the Rise of Islam. 2007. (ENG., Illus.). 312p. 82.99 *(978-0-521-84453-6(3));* per. 25.99 *(978-0-521-60628-8(4))* Cambridge Univ. Pr.

Hancock, Jimmie L. Bad News from the Good Book. 2010. 180p. pap. 22.00 *(978-0-557-48474-4(X))* Lulu Enterprises Inc.

Headley, J. H. Sacred Plains. 2007. (ENG.). 242p. 41.95 *(978-0-548-00551-4(6))* Kessinger Publishing, LLC.

Headley, Joel Tyler. Sacred Scenes & Characters. 2007. (ENG.). 210p. 39.95 *(978-0-548-17806-5(2));* 212p. per. 24.95 *(978-1-4304-7829-4(2))* Kessinger Publishing, LLC.

—Sacred Scenes & Characters. 2006. 220p. per. 20.99 *(978-1-4255-1832-5(X))* MPublishing.

Hudson, Christopher D. & Barrett, David. Bible Atlas & Companion. 2008. (Bible Reference Library). (ENG., Illus.). 176p. pap. 9.99 *(978-1-59789-779-2(5),* Barbour Bks.) Barbour Publishing, Inc.

Hughes, Jeremy. Secrets of the Times: Myth & History in Biblical Chronology. 2009. (Library of Hebrew Bible/Old Testament Studies, the Ser.). (ENG.). 312p. 49.95 *(978-0-567-25414-6(3),* T&T Clark) Continuum International Publishing Group, Ltd. GBR. Dist: National Bk. Network.

Hurlbut, Jesse Lyman. Hurlbut's Story of the Bible, Unabridged & Fully Illustrated in Bw. 2011. (Illus.). 976p. ***(978-1-84902-455-6(3))*** Benediction Classics.

Isbouts, Jean-Pierre. The Biblical World: An Illustrated Atlas. 2007. (ENG., Illus.). 368p. 40.00 *(978-1-4262-0138-7(9),* National Geographic) National Geographic Society.

Israel Antiquities Authority. The Dead Sea Scrolls: Union Station Kansas City. 2007. per. *(978-1-933245-07-2(7))* Documentary Media LLC.

Johnson, Don. The Road to Heaven. 2007. 276p. per. 15.99 *(978-1-60266-181-3(2))* Xulon Pr., Inc.

Jones, Marjorie K. Mankind-Creatures Emerged Before the First Named Man. 2008. 120p. pap. 10.99 *(978-1-4343-7763-0(6))* AuthorHouse.

Keller, Werner. The Bible As History. 2008. 180p. pap. *(978-965-91241-5-2(5))* Editorial Benei Noaj.

Kent, Charles Foster. The Makers & Teachers of Judaism. 2008. 456p. 31.99 *(978-0-554-33320-5(1));* 33.99 *(978-0-554-24017-6(3))* BiblioBazaar.

—The Makers & Teachers of Judaism. 2007. 336p. per. *(978-1-4065-1899-3(9))* Dodo Pr.

—The Makers & Teachers of Judaism: From the Fall of Jerusalem to the Death of Herod the Great. 2007. 402p. pap. 26.99 *(978-1-4264-5583-4(6));* 452p. pap. 30.99 *(978-1-4264-5631-2(X))* BiblioBazaar.

Knoppers, Gary N. & Grabbe, Lester L., eds. Exile & Restoration Revisited: Essays on the Babylonian & Persian Periods in Memory of Peter R. Ackroyd. 2011. (ENG.). 237p. pap. 44.95 ***(978-0-567-28083-1(7),*** T&T Clark Int'l) Continuum International Publishing Group, Ltd. GBR. Dist: National Bk. Network.

Leana, Christina. The Last Testament: Of Christina. 2007. 316p. per. 29.95 *(978-1-4241-7853-7(3))* PublishAmerica, Inc.

Leeman, Bernard. Queen of Sheba & Biblical Scholarship. 280p. 84.95 *(978-1-59221-117-3(8))* Africa World Pr.

Magnuson, JoAnn G., notes. Israel Study Manual. 2007. per. 19.95 *(978-0-9795810-0-7(1))* Magnuson, JoAnn.

Marchadour, Alain, et al. The Land, the Bible, & History: Toward the Land That I Will Show You. 3rd ed. 2010. (Abrahamic Dialogues Ser.). (ENG.). 232p. pap. 26.00 *(978-0-8232-2660-3(3))* Fordham Univ. Pr.

Okoro, Onyeije Chukwudum. Repentance from Dead Works: Vol. I. of the Foundation of Biblical Faith. 2009. 248p. 29.95 *(978-0-595-50026-0(9));* pap. 19.95 *(978-0-595-50474-9(4))* iUniverse, Inc.

Pillar, Russell. The Crisis Driven Church: Discover the Cure for Crisis Living. 2007. 180p. per. 13.99 *(978-0-9795480-3-1(9))* Insight Publishing Group.

Pritchard, James B. Atlas of Bible History. Page, Nick, ed. 2008. (ENG., Illus.). 192p. pap. 25.95 *(978-0-06-145195-9(9),* HarperOne) HarperCollins Pubs.

Rainey, Anson F. & Notley, R. Steven. Carta's New Century Handbook & Atlas of the Bible. (Illus.). 280p. *(978-965-220-703-6(9),* Debolsillo) Carta, The Israel Map & Publishing Co., Ltd.

Rasmussen, Carl G. Atlas of the Bible, 1 vol. rev. ed. 2010. (ENG.). 256p. 39.99 *(978-0-310-27050-8(2))* Zondervan.

Reeve, Joseph. The History of the Holy Bible, Comprising the Most Remarkable Events in the Old & New Testaments, Interspersed with Moral & Instructive Reflection. 2006. 616p. per. 34.99 *(978-1-4255-6533-6(6))* MPublishing.

Rhone, Charles E. Yahweh Numbers the Nations. 2008. xxii, 444p. pap. *(978-0-9702569-1-1(4))* Bible Numbers Communications.

Sedulius, et al. Sedulii Opera Omnia: Una Cum Excerptis Ex Remigii Expositione in Sedulii Paschale Carmen. 2007. (Corpus Scriptorum Christianorum Orientalium Ser.). (LAT.). xlvii, 532p. (C). 78.00 *(978-3-7001-3681-1(1))* Austrian Academy of Sciences Press AUT. Dist: Brown, David Bk. Co., The.

Shanks, Hershel. Scholars on the Record: Insightful Interviews on Bible & Archaeology. 2009. (Illus.). 254p. *(978-1-935335-23-8(5))* Biblical Archaeology Society.

Sloan, William Wilson. A Survey of the New Testament. 2011. 308p. 48.95 ***(978-1-258-07280-3(7))*** Literary Licensing, LLC.

Smits, Jan. No Cunningly Devised Fables: The Bible As History. 2011. ***(978-1-77069-084-4(0))*** Word Alive Pr.

Spring, Gardiner. First Things: A Series of Lectures on the Great Facts & Moral Lessons First Revealed to Mankind. by Gardiner Spring ... 2006. 400p. per. 26.99 *(978-1-4255-4286-3(7))* MPublishing.

—First Things: A Series of Lectures on the Great Facts & Moral Lessons First Revealed to Mankind, by Gardiner Spring ... 2006. 400p. per. 26.99 *(978-1-4255-4287-0(5))* MPublishing.

Van Zleer, Raymond. The Antichrist Whom Christ Declared: A Biblical Study of Whom Jesus Christ Considered the Antichrist to Be, & Its Implications for Today's World. 2008. (ENG.). 140p. per. 12.95 *(978-1-4251-0346-0(4))* Trafford Publishing.

Warren, Ulysses Grant. The Bible in Story & Art: Containing over Two Hundred Masterpieces of Sacred Art. 2011. 488p. 58.95 **(978-1-258-04681-1(4))** Literary Licensing, LLC.

Watts, Isaac. Short View of the Whole Scripture Histor. 2006. pap. 28.95 *(978-1-4286-4711-4(2))* Kessinger Publishing, LLC.

Williams, Marcia D. Why the Ships Came. 2007. 164p. pap. 17.95 *(978-1-4303-1622-0(5))* Lulu Enterprises Inc.

Williams, Philip Lee. The Archaeological Evidence of Noah's Flood. 2011. (ENG., Illus.). 411p. 34.95 *(978-0-9793102-2-5(9))* Christian Leaders & Scholars Pr.

Willis, Mike. Intertestamental Period. 2007. pap. 7.99 *(978-1-58427-199-4(X))* Guardian of Truth Foundation.

Yemane, Elias. Mephibosheth: Transformation by a Covenant Love. 2007. 181p. per. 15.99 *(978-1-60247-443-7(5))* Tate Publishing & Enterprises, LLC.

Yonge, Charlotte M. The Chosen People: A Compendium of Sacred & Church History for School-Children. by the Author of the Heir of Redclyffe. 2006. 200p. (gr. 4-7). per. 18.99 *(978-1-4255-1633-8(5))* MPublishing.

Zed. Ancient Voices. 2010. pap. 26.95 *(978-0-692-01082-2(3))* Khonsu Publishing.

BIBLE—HISTORY OF BIBLICAL EVENTS—CHRONOLOGY

see Bible—Chronology

BIBLE—HISTORY OF BIBLICAL EVENTS—HISTORIOGRAPHY

see Bible—Historiography

BIBLE—HISTORY OF BIBLICAL EVENTS—JUVENILE LITERATURE

see Bible Stories

BIBLE—HISTORY OF BIBLICAL EVENTS—N. T.

Anderson, Paul N. John, Jesus, & History: Aspects of Historicity in the Fourth Gospel. Anderson, Paul N. et al, eds. 2009. 468p. pap. 49.95 *(978-1-58983-392-0(9))* Society of Biblical Literature.

Anderson, Paul N., et al, eds. John, Jesus, & History, Volume I: Critical Appraisals of Critical Views. 2007. (SBL - Symposium Ser.). (Illus.). 346p. *(978-90-04-15743-9(3))* BRILL.

Anderson, Paul N., et al. John, Jesus, & History. 2007. *(978-90-04-16916-6(4))* Society of Biblical Literature.

Anderson, Poul, et al, eds. John, Jesus, & History: Critical Appraisals of Critical Views. 2007. (Illus.). 356p. per. 37.95 *(978-1-58983-293-0(0))* Society of Biblical Literature.

Boyer. Tabla Cronologica del Nuevo Testamento - Chronological Chart of the New Testament. (Tablas Cronologicas - Chronological Chart Ser.). (SPA.). *(978-1-56063-935-0(0))* Editorial Unilit.

Daniel-Rops, Henri & O'Kelly, Donal. The Book of Life: The Story of the New Testament. 2009. *(978-1-933184-49-4(3))* Sophia Institute Pr.

Deissmann, Adolf. The New Testament in the Light of Modern Research: The Haskell Lectures 1929. 2007. 204p. pap. 20.00 *(978-1-55635-454-0(1),* Wipf and Stock) Wipf & Stock Pubs.

Edwards, Brian H. & Anderson, Clive. Kings, Pharaohs & Bandits: The World of Abraham to Esther. 2008. (Footsteps of the Past Ser.). (Illus.). 32p. pap. *(978-1-84625-035-4(6))* DayOne Pubns.

—Romans, Gladiators & Games: The Roman World of the First Christians. 2008. (Footsteps of the Past Ser.). (Illus.). 32p. pap. *(978-1-84625-036-1(6))* DayOne Pubns.

Graf, Friedrich Wilhelm & Wiegandt, Klaus. Die Anfänge des Christentums. 2009. (GER., Illus.). 505p. pap. *(978-3-596-18277-0(8))* Fischer Taschenbuch Verlag.

Herbst, Eva. Tales & Customs of the Ancient Hebrews. 2008. (Illus.). 76p. pap. 7.95 *(978-1-59915-292-9(4))* Yesterday's Classics.

Kremer, Don. The Chronological Order of Revelation. 2007. 296p. per. 17.99 *(978-1-60266-351-0(3))* Xulon Pr., Inc.

McBirnie, William Steuart. The Search for the Twelve Apostles. 2008. (ENG., Illus.). 288p. pap. 14.99 *(978-1-4143-2004-5(3))* Tyndale Hse. Pubs.

Metcalf, R. C. Colliding with Christ. 2008. 260p. (ENG.). 25.99 *(978-1-60477-626-3(9))*; per. 15.99 *(978-1-60477-625-6(0))* Xulon Pr., Inc.

Moore, Megan Bishop & Kelle, Brad E. Biblical History & Israel's Past. 2011. pap. 46.00 *(978-0-8028-6260-0(8))* Eerdmans, William B. Publishing Co.

Patten, Priscilla & Patten, Rebecca. The World of the Early Church: A Companion to the New Testament. 2008. 276p. pap. 30.00 *(978-1-55635-860-9(1))* Wipf & Stock Pubs.

Pool, Elizabeth. The Unexpected Messiah. 2007. (ENG.). 312p. 45.95 *(978-0-548-08428-1(9))* Kessinger Publishing, LLC.

Schmithals, Walther. Paul & James. 2009. (Studies in Biblical Theology, First Ser.). 126p. pap. 16.00 *(978-1-60899-028-3(1),* Wipf and Stock) Wipf & Stock Pubs.

Schroter, Jens. Von Jesus zum Neuen Testament. 2007. (Wissenschaftliche Untersuchungen Zum Neuen Testament Ser.: 204). 441p. (C). 157.50 *(978-3-16-149231-0(5))* Mohr Siebeck GmbH & Co. KG DEU. Dist: Coronet Bks.

Smith, Daniel A. Revisiting the Empty Tomb: The Early History of Easter. 2010. 192p. (C). 29.00 *(978-0-8006-9701-3(4),* Fortress Pr.) Augsburg Fortress, Pubs.

Theron, Daniel J. Evidence of Tradition: Selected Source Material for the Study of the History of the Early Church, the New Testament Books, & the New Testament Canon. 2009. 149p. pap. 13.00 *(978-1-60608-588-2(3),* Wipf and Stock) Wipf & Stock Pubs.

White, Ellen G. The Acts of the Apostles in the Proclamation of the Gospel of Jesus Christ. 2009. 456p. pap. *(978-0-217-56901-9(3))* Books LLC.

—The Acts of the Apostles in the Proclamation of the Gospel of Jesus Christ. 2007. (ENG.). 628p. 60.95 *(978-0-548-02728-8(5))* Kessinger Publishing, LLC.

BIBLE—HISTORY OF BIBLICAL EVENTS—O. T.

Acolatse, Joachim. Samson: God's Mighty Man of Faith. 2010. pap. 12.99 *(978-1-61663-198-7(8))* Tate Publishing & Enterprises, LLC.

Ahn, John J. Exile as Forced Migrations: A Sociological, Literary, & Theological Approach on the Displacement & Resettlement of the Southern Kingdom of Judah. (Beihefte zur Zeitschrift fur die alttestamentliche Wissenschaft Ser.). (ENG., 2011. Illus.). XVIII, 306p. 196.00 **(978-3-11-175389-8(1))** 2010. 320p. 126.00 *(978-3-11-024095-5(5))* De Gruyter, Walter Inc.

Ajiake, Matthew. Nephilim: The First Human Clones: Why Their Existence Led to Noah's Flood. 2006. 228p. 19.99 *(978-1-60012-000-8(8))* Sonika Publishing.

Becking, Bob & Human, Dirk J., eds. Exile & Suffering: A Selection of Papers Read at the 50th Anniversary Meeting of the Old Testament Society of South Africa OTWSA/OTSSA Pretoria, August 2007. 2008. 304p. *(978-90-04-17104-6(5))* BRILL.

Bergant, Dianne. Israel's Story: Part One. 2006. 99p. per. 9.95 *(978-0-8146-3046-4(4))* Liturgical Pr.

—Israel's Story: Part Two. 2007. 112p. per. 9.95 *(978-0-8146-3047-1(2),* Liturgical Pr. Bks.) Liturgical Pr.

Bergant, Dianne & CSA Staff. La historia de Israel: Primera Parte. 2008. (SPA.). 120p. pap. 9.95 *(978-0-8146-1712-0(3))* Liturgical Pr.

The Biblical Antiquities of Philo. 280p. reprint ed. 68.00 *(978-0-7222-9912-8(5))* Library Reprints, Inc.

Blenkinsopp, Joseph. Gibeon & Israel: The Role of Gibeon & the Gibeonites in the Political & Religious History of Early Israel. 2009. (Society for Old Testament Study Monographs). (ENG.). 168p. pap. 28.99 *(978-0-521-11541-4(8))* Cambridge Univ. Pr.

Books of the Way. Old Testament History in Chronological Order. 2007. (YA). per. 36.95 *(978-0-9793995-6-5(4))* Bks. of the Way.

Boyer. Tabla Cronologica del Periodo Intertestamentario - Chronological Chart of the Period Between the Testaments. (Tablas Cronologicas Ser.). (SPA.). *(978-1-56063-934-3(2))* Editorial Unilit.

Callahan, Gertrude E. Through the Old Testament & the Apocryph. 2011. 328p. 50.95 **(978-1-258-05840-1(5))** Literary Licensing, LLC.

Cameron, Ernestine. The Kingdom - Holiness unto the Lord. 2009. 256p. pap. 16.99 *(978-1-60791-806-6(4))* Xulon Pr., Inc.

Coogan, Michael D. A Brief Introduction to the Old Testament: The Hebrew Bible in Its Context. 2nd ed. 2011. (ENG., Illus.). 480p. (C). pap. 54.95 **(978-0-19-983011-4(8))** Oxford Univ. Pr., Inc.

Coogan, Michael David. Old Testament: A Historical & Literary Introduction to the Hebrew Scriptures, 1 vol. 2nd ed. 2010. (ENG.). 592p. (C). pap. 69.95 *(978-0-19-537840-5(7))* Oxford Univ. Pr., Inc.

Dalley, Stephanie. Esther's Revenge at Susa: From Sennacherib to Ahasuerus. 2008. (ENG., Illus.). 280p. 110.00 *(978-0-19-921663-5(0))* Oxford Univ. Pr., Inc.

Daniel-Rops, Henri & O'Kelly, Donal. The Book of Books: The Story of the Old Testament. 2009. pap. *(978-1-933184-48-7(5))* Sophia Institute Pr.

Davies, Philip R. Memories of Ancient Israel: An Introduction to Biblical History—Ancient & Modern. 2008. (ENG.). 208p. pap. 25.00 *(978-0-664-23288-7(4))* Westminster John Knox Pr.

—The Origins of Biblical Israel. 2009. (Library of Hebrew Bible/Old Testament Studies, the Ser.). (ENG.). 208p. pap. 49.95 *(978-0-567-13761-6(9),* T&T Clark Int'l) Continuum International Publishing Group, Ltd. GBR. Dist: National Bk. Network.

DesCamp, Mary Therese. Metaphor & Ideology: Liber Antiquitatum Biblicarum & Literary Methods through a Cognitive Lens. 2007. (Biblical Interpretation Ser.). (Illus.). 388p. *(978-90-04-16179-5(1))* BRILL.

Down, David. Unveiling the Kings of Israel: Revealing the Bible's Archaeological History. 2011. (Illus.). 170p. **(978-0-89051-609-6(X))** Master Bks.

Evenson, Wallace. Adam to Christ: An Accurate Account of Old Testament Chronology. 2009. 160p. pap. 12.99 *(978-1-4389-3742-7(3))* AuthorHouse.

Feiler, Bruce. Where God Was Born: A Daring Adventure Through the Bible's Greatest Stories. 2007. (P. S. Ser.). (ENG., Illus.). 416p. pap. 14.95 *(978-0-06-057489-5(5),* William Morrow Paperbacks) HarperCollins Pubs.

Fritz, Volkmar. The Emergence of Israel in the 12th & 11th Centuries BCE. 2011. **(978-1-58983-262-6(0))**; **(978-1-58983-633-4(2))** Society of Biblical Literature.

Fry, T. C. Old Testament History for Schools. 2007. 202p. 39.95 *(978-0-548-06476-4(8))* Kessinger Publishing, LLC.

Garbini, Giovanni. Myth & History in the Bible. 2009. (Library of Hebrew Bible/Old Testament Studies, the Ser.). (ENG.). 192p. 39.95 *(978-0-567-01839-7(3),* T&T Clark) Continuum International Publishing Group, Ltd. GBR. Dist: National Bk. Network.

Gelb, Norman. Kings of the Jews: The Origins of the Jewish Nation. 2010. (ENG., Illus.). 250p. pap. 22.00 *(978-0-8276-0913-6(2))* Jewish Pubn. Society.

Gertz, Jan Christian, et al. T&T Clark Handbook of the Old Testament: An Introduction to the Literature, Religion & History of the Old Testament. 2012. (ENG.). 872p. 160.00 *(978-0-567-42529-4(0))*; pap. 49.95 *(978-0-567-25368-2(6))* Continuum International Publishing Group, Ltd. GBR. (T&T Clark Int'l). Dist: National Bk. Network.

Gessner. The Death of Abel. 2007. (ENG.). 172p. 37.95 *(978-0-548-08298-0(7))* Kessinger Publishing, LLC.

Gottwald, Norman K. The Hebrew Bible: A Brief Socio-Literary Introduction. 2008. (Illus.). 412p. (C). pap. 45.00 *(978-0-8006-6308-7(X),* Fortress Pr.) Augsburg Fortress, Pubs.

Grabbe, Lester L. Judah Between East & West: The Transition from Persian to Greek Rule (ca. 400-200 BCE) Grabbe, Lester L. & Lipschits, Oded, eds. 2011. (Library of Second Temple Studies, the Ser.). (ENG.). 336p. 140.00 *(978-0-567-04684-0(2),* T&T Clark Int'l) Continuum International Publishing Group, Ltd. GBR. Dist: National Bk. Network.

Graham, William Creighton & May, Herbert Gordon. Culture & Conscience: An Archaeological Study of the New Religious Past in Ancient Palestine. 2011. 386p. 53.95 **(978-1-258-01724-8(5))** Literary Licensing, LLC.

Gray, Jonathan. Suprise Witness: Global events during the Flood, 3 vols., Vol. 2. 2008. (Illus.). 236p. pap. 19.95 *(978-1-57258-554-6(4))* TEACH Services, Inc.

Guerber, H. A. The Story of the Chosen People. 2009. (Illus.). 296p. pap. 12.95 *(978-1-59915-331-5(9))* Yesterday's Classics.

Hayes, John Haralson. Israel's Prophets & Israel's Past: Essays on the Relationship of Prophetic Texts & Israelite History in Honor of John H. Hayes. Kelle, Brad E. & Moore, Megan Bishop, eds. 2006. (Library of Hebrew Bible/Old Testament Studies). (ENG., Illus.). 384p. 220.00 *(978-0-567-02652-1(3),* T&T Clark Int'l) Continuum International Publishing Group, Ltd. GBR. Dist: National Bk. Network.

Holloway, Steven W. Pitcher Is Broken: Memorial Essays for Gösta W. Ahlström. Handy, Lowell K., ed. 2009. (Library of Hebrew Bible/Old Testament Studies, the Ser.). (ENG.). 474p. 75.00 *(978-0-567-46666-2(3),* T&T Clark) Continuum International Publishing Group, Ltd. GBR. Dist: National Bk. Network.

Hughes, Chris. Rahab: Encountering the Woman Snatched from Destruction. Robinson, Simon J., ed. 2008. (Face 2 Face Ser.). 80p. pap. *(978-1-84625-135-1(4))* DayOne Pubns.

Jones, Julia. Tamar, Bathsheba & Tamar: Encountering Three Women with Messed-up Lives. Robinson, Simon J., ed. 2008. (Face 2 Face Ser.). 72p. pap. *(978-1-84625-141-2(9))* DayOne Pubns.

Josephus, Flavius. The Antiquities of the Jews. 2008. 492p. 31.99 *(978-0-554-35383-8(0))* 2008. 552p. 32.99 *(978-0-554-32740-2(6))* 2008. 596p. 36.99 *(978-0-554-24522-5(1))* 2008. 552p. 35.99 *(978-0-554-23437-3(8))* 2008. 492p. 33.99 *(978-0-554-26080-8(8))* 2008. 596p. 33.99 *(978-0-554-33825-5(4))* 2007. (ENG.). 450p. pap. 26.99 *(978-1-4346-0359-3(8))* 2007. (ENG.). 532p. pap. 30.99 *(978-1-4264-6772-1(9))* 2007. (ENG.). 504p. pap. 30.99 *(978-1-4264-4391-6(9))* Vol. 1. 2007. (ENG.). 488p. pap. 30.99 *(978-1-4346-0432-3(2))* Vol. 2. 2007. (ENG.). 592p. pap. 32.99 *(978-1-4264-6835-3(0))* Vol. 3. 2007. (ENG.). 550p. pap. 31.99 *(978-1-4264-4429-6(X))* BiblioBazaar.

—The Antiquities of the Jews. Whiston, William, tr. 2007. (ENG.). 700p. per. *(978-1-4065-4663-7(1))*; 568p. per. *(978-1-4065-4664-4(X))* Dodo Pr.

Kent, Charles Foster. Israel's Historical & Biographical Narratives. 2007. (ENG.). 560p. 57.95 *(978-0-548-04502-2(X))* Kessinger Publishing, LLC.

Kurtz, J. H. (Johann Heinrich). History of the Old Covenant. 2006. 540p. per. 29.99 *(978-1-4255-5985-4(9))*; 440p. per. 26.99 *(978-1-4255-4807-0(5))*; 524p. per. 29.99 *(978-1-4255-5838-3(0))* MPublishing.

Lemaire, André. The Birth of Monotheism: The Rise & Disappearance of Yahwism. 2007. *(978-1-880317-99-0(0))* Biblical Archaeology Society.

Leuchter, Mark, et al, eds. From Babel to Babylon: Essays on Biblical History & Literature in Honor of Brian Peckham. 2006. (Library of Hebrew Bible/Old Testament Studies, the Ser.). (ENG., Illus.). 400p. 180.00 *(978-0-567-02892-1(5),* T&T Clark Int'l) Continuum International Publishing Group, Ltd. GBR. Dist: National Bk. Network.

Lyda, Hap C. S. History of Biblical Judaism: An Introductory Study of the Bible. 5th ed. 2008. (ENG.). 272p. (C). per. 26.00 *(978-0-9630629-8-7(0))* 21st Century Pr.

MacArthur, John. The Father of Israel: Trusting God's Promises, 0 vols. 2008. (MacArthur Old Testament Study Guides). (ENG.). 128p. pap. 9.99 *(978-1-4185-3323-6(8))* Nelson, Thomas Inc.

—A House Divided: Elijah & the Kings of Israel, 0 vols. 2009. (MacArthur Old Testament Study Guides). 128p. pap. 9.99 *(978-1-4185-3691-6(1))* Nelson, Thomas Inc.

MacKenzie, R. A. F. Faith & History in the Old Testament. 2009. (ENG.). 132p. pap. 40.00 *(978-0-8166-5822-0(6))* Univ. of Minnesota Pr.

Miller, J. Maxwell & Hayes, John H. A History of Ancient Israel & Judah. 2nd ed. 2006. (ENG., Illus.). 562p. per. 40.00 *(978-0-664-22358-8(3))* Westminster John Knox Pr.

Mills, Dorothy. The People of Ancient Israel. 2007. 212p. (ENG.). 25.95 *(978-1-59731-380-3(7))*; per. 18.50 *(978-1-59731-355-1(6))* Perennis, Sophia.

Muir, James C. The Spade & the Scriptures. 2007. (ENG.). 208p. 39.95 *(978-0-548-07489-3(5))* Kessinger Publishing, LLC.

Obeng, Kwadwo. We Are All Africans; Exposing the Negative Influence of the Judeo-Christian-Islamic Religions on Africans. 2009. 796p. pap. 85.95 *(978-1-935097-31-0(8))* Hillcrest Publishing Group, Inc.

Oded, Bustenay & Millard, A. R. Homeland & Exile: Biblical & Ancient near Eastern Studies in Honour of Bustenay Oded. Galil, Gershon & Geller, Mark, eds. 2009. (Illus.). 672p. *(978-90-04-17889-2(9))* BRILL.

Pearl, Michael, et al. La Biblia Kingstone, Vol. 1. 2011. 192p. pap. 17.99 **(978-1-61328-020-1(3))** Kingstone Media Group.

Philo. The Biblical Antiquities of Philo. 2007. 284p. per. 20.95 *(978-1-60206-567-3(5))* Cosimo, Inc.

Portier-Young, Anathea. Apocalypse Against Empire: Theologies of Resistance in Early Judaism. 2010. 480p. pap. 50.00 *(978-0-8028-6598-4(4))* Eerdmans, William B. Publishing Co.

Pseudo-Philo. The Biblical Antiquities of Philo. 2009. 174p. pap. *(978-1-4588-6257-0(7))* Books LLC.

—The Biblical Antiquities of Philo. James, M. R., tr. 2006. 280p. pap. 28.00 *(978-1-59752-962-4(1),* Wipf and Stock) Wipf & Stock Pubs.

Pytlik, George. Daniel: God's Messenger to Our Times. 2010. 37.95 *(978-0-578-05455-1(8))*; pap. 24.97 *(978-0-578-05376-9(4))* Illuminosity Pr.

Short, J. Randall. The Surprising Election & Confirmation of King David. 2010. (Harvard Theological Studies: 63). (ENG.). 250p. pap. 25.00 *(978-0-674-05341-0(9))* Harvard Univ. Pr.

Spencer, F. Ernest. Old Testament History. 2007. (ENG.). 126p. 35.95 *(978-0-548-06475-7(X))* Kessinger Publishing, LLC.

Stith, D. Matthew. The Coups of Hazael & Jehu: Building an Historical Narrative. 2008. (Gorgias Dissertations in Biblical Studies: 3). 95.00 *(978-1-59333-833-6(3))* Gorgias Pr. LLC.

Thompson, Darren. Why the Bible Is Historically Accurate. 2nd ed. 2007. 101p. pap. 15.31 *(978-1-4303-1062-4(6))* Lulu Enterprises Inc.

Translations of Early Documents: Hellenistic-Jewish Texts, 6 Vols. reprint ed. 362.40 *(978-0-7222-9913-5(3))* Library Reprints, Inc.

Translations of Early Documents: Palestinian-Jewish & Cognate Texts. reprint ed. 761.60 *(978-0-7222-9920-3(6))* Library Reprints, Inc.

Tullock, John & McEntire, Mark. The Old Testament Story. 9th rev. ed. 2011. (ENG.). 416p. (C). pap. 108.60 *(978-0-205-09783-8(9),* Prentice Hall) Prentice Hall PTR.

Turnbull, Ralph G. Later Hebrew History & Prophets. 2011. 102p. 39.95 **(978-1-258-08975-7(0))** Literary Licensing, LLC.

Watts, John D. W. How We Got Our Bible: Files from an Alttestamentler's Hard Drive. 2011. 246p. pap. 27.00 *(978-1-60899-394-9(9),* Wipf and Stock) Wipf & Stock Pubs.

Whitcomb. Tabla Cronologica/Cautividad Babilonica I-II - Chart of Babylonia Captivity I-II. (Tablas Cronologicas - Chronological Chart Ser.). (SPA.). *(978-1-56063-933-6(4))* Editorial Unilit.

—Tabla de los Patriarcas y Jueces de A. T. - Chart of the O. T. Patriarchs & Judges. (Tablas Cronologicas - Chronological Chart Ser.). (SPA.). *(978-1-56063-931-2(8))* Editorial Unilit.

Wiebe, Dianna. Old Testament Overview: A Chronological Study of the Major Characters & Events of the Old Testament: Beginner. 2007. (Stick Figure Ser.). 104p. per. 18.95 *(978-1-59873-002-9(9))*; (Illus.). 208p. per. 23.95 *(978-1-59873-000-5(2))* Grapevine Studies.

Wilson, R. Andrew. Write Like Hemingway: Writing Lessons You Can Learn from the Master. 2009. (ENG.). 256p. pap. 16.95 *(978-1-59869-896-1(6))* Adams Media Corp.

Witcomb. Tabla de los Reyes/Profetas del A. T. - Chart of the O. T. Kings & Prophets. (Tablas Cronologicas Ser.). (SPA.). *(978-1-56063-932-9(6))* Editorial Unilit.

BIBLE—HISTORY OF BIBLICAL EVENTS—POETRY

Alter, Robert. The Art of Biblical Poetry. 2nd ed. 2011. (ENG.). 320p. (gr. 9). pap. 18.00 *(978-0-465-02256-4(1))* Basic Bks.

Anlezark, Daniel. Old Testament Narratives. 2011. (Dumbarton Oaks Medieval Library). (ENG & ANG.). 368p. 29.95 *(978-0-674-05319-9(2))* Harvard Univ. Pr.

Azriel, Yakov. In the Shadow of a Burning Bush: Poems on Exodus. 2008. 120p. pap. 15.95 *(978-1-56809-122-8(2),* Time Being Pr.) Time Being Bks.

Azriel, Yakov. Swimming in Moses' Well: Poems on Numbers. 2011. 120p. pap. 15.95 **(978-1-56809-144-0(3),** Time Being Pr.) Time Being Bks.

Bloch, Ariel & Bloch, Chana, trs. The Song of Songs: The World's First Great Love Poem. 2006. (Modern Library Classics Ser.). (ENG & HEB.). 256p. pap. 16.00 *(978-0-8129-7620-5(7),* Modern Library) Random House Publishing Group.

Chansky, Norman M. Essence of the Psalms: Poems Inspired by the Sacred Text. 2008. 128p. pap. 16.00 *(978-1-55635-500-4(9),* Resource Pubns.) Wipf & Stock Pubs.

Coopland, Lisa. A Bond of Perfectness. 2006. 136p. per. 10.99 *(978-1-59886-206-5(5))* Tate Publishing & Enterprises, LLC.

Davis, Brad. Like Those Who Dream: Book Five of Opening King David. 2008. 74p. pap. 16.00 *(978-0-9798451-8-5(1))* Antrim Hse.

Dawes, Kwame. Gomer's Song. 2007. (Black Goat Ser.). (ENG.). 72p. per. 14.95 *(978-1-933354-44-6(5))* Akashic Bks.

Fares, Laila. Rising from the East: Coptic Praises. 2006. (ENG.). 108p. per. 16.95 *(978-1-4241-4845-5(6))* PublishAmerica, Inc.

Finch Jr, Arthur. A Book of Bible Poetry Volume 4. 2010. 69p. pap. 15.97 *(978-0-557-36398-8(5))* Lulu Enterprises Inc.

Greenwald, David. A Love Song for Eternity. 2006. (ENG.). 188p. per. 24.95 *(978-1-4241-3913-2(9))* PublishAmerica, Inc.

Kugel, James L. The Great Poems of the Bible: A Reader's Companion with New Translations. 2008. (ENG.). 352p. pap. 21.99 *(978-1-4165-8902-0(3),* Free Pr.) Free Pr.

Milton, John. Milton: Paradise Lost. 2008. 352p. 28.99 *(978-0-554-35678-5(3))*; 29.99 *(978-0-554-26375-5(0))* BiblioBazaar.

—Milton: Paradise Lost. 2008. 256p. pap. *(978-1-4099-1785-4(1))* Dodo Pr.

—Paradise Lost, a Poem in Twelve Books by John Milton; with Explanatory Notes & a Life of the Author, by Rev H Stebbing. 2006. 324p. per. 23.99 *(978-1-4255-3202-4(0))* MPublishing.

—Paradise Regained. (ENG.). 108p. 2007. per. 9.95 *(978-1-60312-027-2(0))* 2006. 22.95 *(978-1-59818-167-8(X))* Aegypan.

—Paradise Regained. 2007. (ENG.). 64p. pap. 16.99 *(978-1-4346-0490-3(X))*; 76p. pap. 18.99 *(978-1-4346-0523-8(X))* BiblioBazaar.

Milton, John & Danielson, Dennis Richard. Milton: Paradise Lost. 2008. 560p. pap. *(978-1-57383-426-1(2))* Regent College Publishing.

Moore Stenhouse, Sharon. Mormism: Bible Study Exercises. 2010. 48p. pap. 10.00 *(978-0-557-25964-9(9))* Lulu Enterprises Inc.

Poultney, Wilfred Howard. More Biblical Ballads. 2006. (ENG., Illus.). 76p. pap. *(978-1-84401-790-4(7))* Athena Pr.

Rothwell, Allen Edward. The Old Bible in Rhyme. 2011. 192p. 42.95 ***(978-1-258-09721-9(4))*** Literary Licensing, LLC.

Song of Solomon. 2008. pap. *(978-1-60208-160-4(3))* FBC Pubns. & Printing.

Ward, Jean Elizabeth, Poet Laureate. Serene Speculations. 2008. 152p. pap. 22.50 *(978-1-4357-1049-8(5))* Lulu Enterprises Inc.

Wood, Matt P. Say Goodbye, Darkness, 1 vol. 2009. 124p. pap. 19.95 *(978-1-60813-638-4(8))* PublishAmerica, Inc.

BIBLE—HISTORY OF CONTEMPORARY EVENTS

Here are entered works on history contemporary with the history of Biblical events, including archaeological, social, and cultural materials that shed light on the Bible. Works on the history of events related in the Bible are entered under Bible—History of Biblical Events.

Bienert, David C., et al. Paulus und Die Antike Welt: Beiträge Zur Zeit- und Religionsgeschichtlichen Erforschung des Paulinischen Christentums: [Festgabe Für Dietrich-Alex Koch Zum 65. Geburtstag]. 2008. (Forschungen Zur Religion und Literatur des Alten & Neuen Testament Ser.). (GER & ENG., Illus.). 248p. (C). 107.00 *(978-3-525-53088-7(9))* Vandenhoeck & Ruprecht GmbH & Co. KG DEU. Dist: ISD.

Carr, David M. & Conway, Colleen M. An Introduction to the Bible: Sacred Texts & Imperial Contexts. 2010. (ENG., Illus.). 408p. 110.95 *(978-1-4051-6738-3(6))*; pap. 61.95 *(978-1-4051-6737-6(8))* Wiley, John & Sons, Inc. (Wiley-Blackwell).

Cohen, Tim. Messiah, History, & the Tribulation Period: Multi-Volume Set, 7 vols., Cohen, Tim, ed. rev. ed. 2006. (Illus.). pap. *(978-0-9662793-1-3(X)*, BK-02) Prophecy House, Inc.

—Messiah, History, & the Tribulation Period Vol. 2, Vol. 3: The Prophetic Stage: Signs of the Times. Cohen, Tim, ed. 2006. pap. *(978-0-9662793-3-7(6))* Prophecy House, Inc.

Collomb, Jean. Les Derniers Temps? 2009. 324p. pap. 22.92 *(978-1-4269-1824-7(0))* Trafford Publishing.

Conder, Claude. The Bible & the East. 2007. (ENG.). 246p. 41.95 *(978-0-548-05186-3(0))* Kessinger Publishing, LLC.

Darlow, Richard. Moses in Ancient Egypt the Hidden Story. 2007. 219p. pap. 24.96 *(978-1-4303-0053-3(1))* Lulu Enterprises Inc.

Drane, John. The World of the Bible. 2010. (ENG., Illus.). 256p. 34.95 *(978-0-7459-5250-5(X))* Lion Hudson PLC GBR. Dist: Independent Pubs. Group.

Exploring God's Word: Grade 8 - Contemporary Issues. (Voyages Ser.). tchr. ed., spiral bd. 32.95 *(978-0-570-00305-2(9)*, 57-0822) Concordia Publishing Hse.

Fairweather, William. Background of the Gospels or Judaism in. 2006. pap. 38.95 *(978-1-4286-4434-2(2))* Kessinger Publishing, LLC.

Hopkins, David C. The Highlands of Canaan: Agricultural Life in the Early Iron Age. (Social World of Biblical Antiquity Ser.: Vol. 3). (Illus.). 315p. pap. *(978-0-907459-39-2(0)*, Burns & Oates) Continuum International Publishing Group, Ltd.

Keller, Werner. The Bible As History. 2008. 204p. pap. *(978-965-00-6016-9(2))* Editorial Benei Noaj.

Ling, Timothy J. M. The Judaean Poor & the Fourth Gospel. 2008. (Society for New Testament Studies Monograph Ser.). (ENG.). 264p. pap. 40.00 *(978-0-521-09142-8(X))* Cambridge Univ. Pr.

Marchadour, Alain, et al. The Land, the Bible, & History: Toward the Land That I Will Show You. 3rd ed. 2010. (Abrahamic Dialogues Ser.). (ENG.). 232p. pap. 26.00 *(978-0-8232-2660-3(3))* Fordham Univ. Pr.

Rainey, Anson F. & Notley, R. Steven. Carta's New Century Handbook & Atlas of the Bible. (Illus.). 280p. *(978-965-220-703-6(9)*, Debolsillo) Carta, The Israel Map & Publishing Co., Ltd.

Rasmussen, Carl G. Atlas of the Bible, 1 vol. rev. ed. 2010. (ENG.). 256p. 39.99 *(978-0-310-27050-8(2))* Zondervan.

Spurgeon, Charles H. The Bible & the Newspaper. 2010. 228p. pap. 25.75 *(978-1-141-56325-8(8))* BiblioBazaar.

—The Bible & the Newspaper. 2009. 94p. pap. 20.00 *(978-0-217-23254-8(X))* General Bks. LLC.

—The Bible & the Newspaper. 2008. 224p. 39.95 *(978-1-4372-1284-6(0))*; pap. 24.95 *(978-1-4370-8349-1(8))* Kessinger Publishing, LLC.

BIBLE—HISTORY OF CONTEMPORARY EVENTS—N. T.

Guignebert, Charles. Jewish World in the Time of Jesus. 2006. 328p. per. *(978-1-4067-3231-3(1)*, Hesperides Pr.) Read Bks.

Metzner, Rainer. Die Prominenten Im Neuen Testament: Ein Prosopographischer Kommentar. 2008. (Novum Testamentum et Orbis Antiquus/Studien zur Umwelt des Neuen Testaments (NTOA/StUNT) Ser.). (GER.). 695p. (C). 117.00 *(978-3-525-53967-5(3))* Vandenhoeck & Ruprecht GmbH & Co. KG DEU. Dist: ISD.

Patten, Priscilla & Patten, Rebecca. The World of the Early Church: A Companion to the New Testament. 2008. 276p. pap. 30.00 *(978-1-55635-860-9(1))* Wipf & Stock Pubs.

Thompson, Virgil F. The New Testament in Contemporary Life. 2012. (ENG.). 192p. pap. 30.00 ***(978-0-7575-9841-8(2))*** Kendall Hunt Publishing Co.

BIBLE—HISTORY OF CONTEMPORARY EVENTS—O. T.

Ahn, John J. Exile as Forced Migrations: A Sociological, Literary, & Theological Approach on the Displacement & Resettlement of the Southern Kingdom of Judah. (Beihefte zur Zeitschrift far die alttestamentliche Wissenschaft Ser.). (ENG., 2011. Illus.). XVIII, 306p. 196.00 ***(978-3-11-175389-8(1))*** 2010. 320p. 126.00 *(978-3-11-024095-5(5))* De Gruyter, Walter Inc.

Allen, Joel Stevens. The Despoliation of Egypt in Pre-Rabbinic, Rabbinic, & Patristic Traditions. 2008. (Vigiliae Christianae Ser.: Vol. 92). 328p. (C). *(978-90-04-16745-2(5))* BRILL.

Carr, David M. Introduction to the Old Testament: Sacred Texts & Imperial Contexts of the Hebrew Bible. 2010. (Wiley Desktop Editions Ser.). (ENG., Illus.). 296p. pap. 39.95 *(978-1-4051-8467-0(1)*, Wiley-Blackwell) Wiley, John & Sons, Inc.

Carr, G. Lloyd & Carr, David M. An Introduction to the Old Testament: Sacred Texts & Imperial Contexts of the Hebrew Bible. 2010. (ENG., Illus.). 296p. 99.95 *(978-1-4051-8468-7(X)*, Wiley-Blackwell) Wiley, John & Sons, Inc.

Graham, M. Patrick. History & Interpretation: Essays in Honour of John H. Hayes. Brown, William P. & Kuan, Jeffrey K., eds. 2009. (Library of Hebrew Bible/Old Testament Studies, the Ser.). (ENG.). 267p. 44.95 *(978-0-567-11205-7(5)*, T&T Clark) Continuum International Publishing Group, Ltd. GBR. Dist: National Bk. Network.

Holzapfel, Richard Neitzel, et al. Jehovah & the World of the Old Testament. 2009. 45.95 *(978-1-60641-136-0(5))* Deseret Bk. Co.

Matthews, Victor Harold. Old Testament Parallels (New Revised & Expanded Third Edition) Laws & Stories from the Ancient near East. 3rd rev. exp. ed. 2007. (Illus.). 448p. per. 22.95 *(978-0-8091-4435-8(2)*, 4435-2) Paulist Pr.

More Lost Books of the Bible: The Book O. 2006. pap. 18.95 *(978-1-933993-21-8(9))* Apocryphile Pr.

Pritchard, J. B. The Ancient near East - an Anthology of Texts & Pictures. 2010. (ENG., Illus.). 664p. (C). 85.00 *(978-0-691-14725-3(6))* Princeton Univ. Pr.

Pritchard, James Bennett. The Ancient Near East: An Anthology of Texts & Pictures. 2010. (ENG., Illus.). 664p. (C). pap. 39.50 *(978-0-691-14726-0(4))* Princeton Univ. Pr.

Schley, Donald G. Shiloh: A Biblical City in Tradition & History. 2009. (Library of Hebrew Bible/Old Testament Studies, the Ser.). (ENG.). 256p. 44.95 *(978-0-567-50312-1(7)*, T&T Clark) Continuum International Publishing Group, Ltd. GBR. Dist: National Bk. Network.

Stith, D. Matthew. The Coups of Hazael & Jehu: Building an Historical Narrative. 2008. (Gorgias Dissertations in Biblical Studies: 3). 95.00 *(978-1-59333-833-6(3))* Gorgias Pr., LLC.

Tullock, John & McEntire, Mark. The Old Testament Story. 9th rev. ed. 2011. (ENG.). 416p. (C). pap. 108.60 *(978-0-205-09783-8(9)*, Prentice Hall) Prentice Hall PTR.

Van Seters, John. Changing Perspectives I: Studies in the History, Literature, & Religion of Biblical Israel. 2011. (Copenhagen International Seminar Ser.). (ENG., Illus.). 438p. (C). 120.00 *(978-1-84553-901-6(X))* Equinox Publishing Ltd. GBR. Dist: ISD.

Weippert, Manfred. Historisches Textbuch zum Alten Testament: Grundrisse zum Alten Testament. 2010. (Grundrisse Zum Alten Testament Ser.). (GER.). 654p. (C). 108.00 *(978-3-525-51693-5(2))* Vandenhoeck & Ruprecht GmbH & Co. KG DEU. Dist: ISD.

BIBLE—HOMILETICAL USE

Aaron, Charles L., Jr., et al. Sermons on the Gospel Readings: Series II, Cycle A. 2007. 484p. per. 37.95 *(978-0-7880-2453-5(1))* CSS Publishing Co.

Alexander, Eric J. What Is Biblical Preaching? 2008. 32p. pap. *(978-1-59638-113-1(2))* P & R Publishing.

Allen, Ronald J. & Williamson, Clark M. Preaching the Old Testament: A Lectionary Commentary. annot. ed. 2007. (ENG.). 309p. 30.00 *(978-0-664-23068-5(7))* Westminster John Knox Pr.

Anderson, Russell F. Lectionary Preaching Workbook: Series V, Cycle A. 2007. 394p. per. 47.95 *(978-0-7880-2488-7(4))* CSS Publishing Co.

—Lectionary Preaching Workbook Series V Cycle A. 2007. 49.95 *(978-0-7880-2489-4(2))* CSS Publishing Co.

Ayers, James. Finding the Story: Hard Texts, Homiletical Narratives, & Hearing God's Voice. 2007. 226p. per. *(978-0-7880-2445-0(0))* CSS Publishing Co.

Bartlett, David L. & Taylor, Barbara Brown, eds. Advent Through Transfiguration, Year A, 12 vols., Vol. 1. 2010. (Feasting on the Word Ser.). (ENG.). 472p. 40.00 *(978-0-664-23104-0(7))* Westminster John Knox Pr.

—Lent Through Eastertide, 12 vols., Vol. 2. 2010. (Feasting on the Word Ser.). (ENG.). 560p. 40.00 *(978-0-664-23105-7(5))* Westminster John Knox Pr.

—Pentecost & Season after Pentecost - Year C Vol. 3, Vol. 3. 2010. (Feasting on the Word Ser.). (ENG.). 408p. 40.00 *(978-0-664-23102-6(0))* Westminster John Knox Pr.

—Season after Pentecost 2 (Propers 17 - Reign of Christ) Vol. 4, 12 vols., Year C, Vol. 4. 2010. (Feasting on the Word Ser.). (ENG.). 360p. 40.00 *(978-0-664-23103-3(9))* Westminster John Knox Pr.

Bos, Rein. We Have Heard That God Is with You: Preaching the Old Testament. 2008. 336p. pap. 28.00 *(978-0-8028-0770-0(4))* Eerdmans, William B. Publishing Co.

Brauninger, Dallas A. Preaching the Miracles. 2008. 142p. pap. *(978-0-7880-2576-1(7))* CSS Publishing Co.

Brittain, John N., et al. Sermons on the Second Readings: Series II, Cycle A. 2007. 500p. per. 37.95 *(978-0-7880-2452-8(3))* CSS Publishing Co.

Brooks, Gennifer Benjamin. Good News Preaching: Offering the Gospel in Every Sermon. 2011. (ENG.). 158p. pap. 20.00 ***(978-0-8298-1917-5(7))*** 2009. *(978-0-8298-1822-2(7))* Pilgrim Pr., The/United Church Pr.

Brueggemann, Walter. Truth-Telling as Subversive Obedience. Hanson, K. C., ed. 2011. 126p. pap. 16.00 ***(978-1-61097-234-5(1)***, Cascade Bks.) Wipf & Stock Pubs.

Css Publishing Company, compiled by. Sermons on the Second Readings, Series III , Cycle C. 2009. (Illus.). 450p. pap. 37.95 *(978-0-7880-2620-1(8))* CSS Publishing.

Deeg, Alexander. Predigt und Derascha: Homiletische Textlekture im Dialog im dem Judentum. 2006. (Arbeiten zür Pastoraltheologie. Liturgik und Hymnologie: Vol. 48). (GER.). 608p. (C). pap. 116.00 *(978-3-525-62390-9(9))* Vandenhoeck & Ruprecht GmbH & Co. KG DEU. Dist: ISD.

Dever, Mark, et al. Preaching the Cross. 2007. (Together for the Gospel Ser.). 176p. 19.99 *(978-1-58134-828-6(2))* Crossway.

Eswine, Zack. Preaching to a Post-Everything World: Crafting Biblical Sermons That Connect with Our Culture. 2008. 288p. pap. 20.00 *(978-0-8010-9194-0(2))* Baker Bks.

Fretheim, Terence E. Exodus: Interpretation: A Bible Commentary for Teaching & Preaching. 2010. (Interpretation Ser.). (ENG.). 336p. pap. 30.00 *(978-0-664-23619-9(7))* Westminster John Knox Pr.

Gibson, Scott M., ed. Preaching the Old Testament. 2006. 224p. pap. 17.00 *(978-0-8010-6623-8(9))* Baker Bks.

Glabach, Wilfried E. Reclaiming the Book of Revelation: A Suggestion of New Readings in the Local Church. 2007. (American University Studies: Vol. 259). xii, 212p. 70.95 *(978-0-8204-9504-0(2))* Lang, Peter Publishing, Inc.

Hare, Douglas R. A. & Hare, Douglas. Matthew. 2009. (Interpretation, a Bible Commentary for Teaching & Preaching Ser.). (ENG.). 352p. pap. 30.00 *(978-0-664-23433-1(X))* Westminster John Knox Pr.

Hell, John Paul. Worship in the Letter to the Hebrews. 2011. (ENG.). 326p. pap. 36.00 ***(978-1-60899-947-7(5)***, Cascade Bks.) Wipf & Stock Pubs.

Holbert, John C. Preaching Job. 2011. 204p. pap. 22.00 ***(978-1-61097-278-9(3)***, Wipf and Stock) Wipf & Stock Pubs.

Johnson, Dennis E. Him We Proclaim: Preaching Christ from All the Scriptures. 2007. 494p. per. 24.99 *(978-1-59638-054-7(3))* P & R Publishing.

Keeney, William E. Preaching the Parables. 2008. 101p. pap. *(978-0-7880-2547-1(3))* CSS Publishing Co.

Kent, Grenville J. R., et al, eds. Reclaiming the Old Testament for Christian Preaching. 2010. (ENG.). 256p. pap. 23.00 *(978-0-8308-3887-5(2)*, IVP Acad.) InterVarsity Pr.

Kitchen, John. The Pastoral Epistles for Pastors. 2009. (ENG.). 624p. 39.99 *(978-1-934952-02-3(8))* Kress Christian Pubns.

Kuruvilla, Abraham & Kuruvilla. Text to Praxis: Hermeneutics & Homiletics in Dialogue. 2009. (Library of New Testament Studies, the Ser.). (ENG.). 240p. 130.00 *(978-0-567-53854-3(0)*, T&T Clark Int'l) Continuum International Publishing Group, Ltd. GBR. Dist: National Bk. Network.

Kysar, Robert & Webb, Joseph M. Preaching to Postmoderns: New Perspectives for Proclaiming the Message. 2006. 239p. per. 19.95 *(978-1-56563-400-8(4))* Hendrickson Pubs. Marketing, LLC.

Leininger, David E. Lectionary Tales for the Pulpit. 2008. 286p. pap. *(978-0-7880-2545-7(7))* CSS Publishing Co.

—Lectionary Tales for the Pulpit: Series VI, Cycle A. 2007. (Lectionary Tales for the Pulpit Ser.). 185p. per. *(978-0-7880-2454-2(X))* CSS Publishing Co.

Linares, Joe. Proclaiming God's Stories: How to Preach Old Testament Historical Narrative. 2008. *(978-1-59166-926-5(X))* BJU Pr.

Lott, David B., ed. New Proclamation: Year B, 2010, Easter Through Christ the King. 2012. 256p. (C). pap. 25.00 *(978-0-8006-9772-3(3))* Augsburg Fortress, Pubs.

—New Proclamation: Year B, 2011-2012, Advent through Holy Week. 2011. 256p. (C). pap. 25.00 *(978-0-8006-9771-6(5))* Augsburg Fortress, Pubs.

Lott, David B., et al. Commentary on Feasts: Holy Days & Other Celebrations. Lott, David B., ed. 2007. (New Proclamation Ser.). (Illus.). 288p. per. 26.00 *(978-0-8006-6228-8(8)*, Fortress Pr.) Augsburg Fortress, Pubs.

Matera, Frank J. Preaching Romans: Proclaiming God's Saving Grace. 2010. 14.95 *(978-0-8146-3318-2(8))* Liturgical Pr.

Mead, Patrick. Expository Nuggets from 1 Peter. 2008. 48p. pap. 8.95 *(978-0-615-20068-2(0))* Machaira Touch Ministries, Inc.

Mohler, R. Albert, Jr. Proclame la Verdad, 1 vol. 2010. Orig. Title: He Is Not Silent. (SPA.). 176p. pap. 9.99 *(978-0-8254-1811-2(9)*, Editorial Portavoz) Kregel Pubns.

Moore, Beth. Praying God's Word Day by Day. 2006. (ENG.). 382p. 14.99 *(978-0-8054-4420-9(3))* B&H Publishing Group.

Nappa, Mike. Interactive Illustrations-the Gospels: For Every Preacher, Teacher, & Small Group Leader. 2010. (Interactive Illustrations Ser.). (ENG.). 160p. pap. 12.99 *(978-0-7847-2357-9(5))* Standard Publishing.

Nelson, Michael T. The Seven Signs - Volume 1: A Spirit-filled Look at the Gospel According to John. 2010. pap. 21.99 *(978-1-61663-387-5(5))* Tate Publishing & Enterprises, LLC.

—The Seven Signs - Volume 2: A Spirit-filled Look at the Gospel According to John. 2010. pap. 20.99 *(978-1-61663-386-8(7))* Tate Publishing & Enterprises, LLC.

O'Brien, Mark. Sunday Matters: Reflections on the Lectionary Readings Year B. 2011. (ENG.). 206p. (C). pap. 35.00 ***(978-1-921817-16-8(X))*** ATF Pr. AUS. Dist: Brown, David Bk. Co., The.

O'Grady, John F. Preaching the Gospel of John. 2009. 176p. pap. 16.95 *(978-0-8091-4619-2(3))* Paulist Pr.

Old, Hughes Oliphant. The Modern Age, 1789-1889, 7 vols., Vol. 6. 2007. (Reading & Preaching of the Scriptures in the Worship of the Christian Church Ser.). 997p. per. 50.00 *(978-0-8028-3139-2(7))* Eerdmans, William B. Publishing Co.

Powell, Mark Allan. What Do They Hear? Bridging the Gap Between Pulpit & Pew. 2007. (Illus.). 107p. per. 16.00 *(978-0-687-64205-2(1))* Abingdon Pr.

Reid, Barbara E. Los Parabolas: Predicandolas y Vivendolas: El Evangelio Segun San Mateo. Rodriguez-Galarza, Gerardo, tr. from ENG. 2008. (SPA.). 288p. per. 6.24 *(978-0-8146-3054-9(5)*, Liturgical Pr. Bks.) Liturgical Pr.

Reid, Robert Stephen, ed. Slow of Speech & Unclean Lips. 2009. 216p. pap. 24.00 *(978-1-60608-521-9(2)*, Cascade Bks.) Wipf & Stock Pubs.

Robinson, Haddon W. Biblical Preaching: The Development & Delivery of Expository Messages. 2nd rev. ed. 2007. (Illus.). 256p. (C). (gr. 13-18). 21.99 *(978-0-8010-2262-3(2))* Baker Academic.

Rodriguez, Rafael A. Homiletica Simplificada: Homiletics Simplified. (SPA.). *(978-84-7645-305-6(1)*, 223448) Clie, Editorial.

Root, Michael & Buckley, James Joseph. Sharper Than a Two-Edged Sword: Preaching, Teaching, & Living the Bible. Root, Michael & Buckley, James J., eds. 2008. (Illus.). 112p. pap. 16.00 *(978-0-8028-6271-6(3))* Eerdmans, William B. Publishing Co.

Saunders, Stanley P. Preaching the Gospel of Matthew: Proclaiming God's Presence. 2010. (ENG.). 312p. pap. 25.00 *(978-0-664-22920-7(4))* Westminster John Knox Pr.

Schifrin, Amy C. Lectionary Worship Workbook: Series III, Cycle A. 2007. (Illus.). 206p. per. 34.95 *(978-0-7880-2465-8(5))* CSS Publishing Co.

—Lectionary Worship Workbook Series III, Cycle A. 2007. 208p. 36.95 *(978-0-7880-2466-5(3))* CSS Publishing Co.

Scroggie, W. Manual Biblico Homiletico: Homiletics Bible Manual. (SPA.). 528p. *(978-84-7228-831-7(5)*, 223346) Clie, Editorial.

Shea, John. The Spiritual Wisdom of the Gospels for Christian Preachers & Teachers: The Relentless Widow: Year C. 2006. 330p. per. 29.95 *(978-0-8146-2915-4(6)*, Liturgical Pr. Bks.) Liturgical Pr.

Sheffield, Richard Louie. Preaching the Parables: Series IV, Cycle A: I Love to Tell the Story. 2007. 115p. per. 14.95 *(978-0-7880-2458-0(2))* CSS Publishing Co.

Sloyan, Gerard Stephen & Sloyan, Gerard. John. 2009. (Interpretation, a Bible Commentary for Teaching & Preaching Ser.). (ENG.). 360p. pap. 25.00 *(978-0-664-23436-2(4))* Westminster John Knox Pr.

Smith, James. Comentario Homiletico de la Biblia: Handfuls on Purpose. (SPA.). Vol. I. *(978-84-7645-332-2(9)*, 223449) Vol. II. *(978-84-7645-333-9(7)*, 223460) Vol. III. *(978-84-7645-359-9(0)*, 223489) Vol. IV. *(978-84-7645-360-5(4)*, 223490) Vol. V. *(978-84-7645-416-9(3)*, 223506) Vol. VI. *(978-84-7645-405-3(8)*, 223511) Vol. VII. *(978-84-7645-448-0(1)*, 223530) Vol. XIII. *(978-84-7645-449-7(X)*, 223524) Clie, Editorial.

Soards, Marion L. Preaching the Revised Common Lectionary: Electronic Edition. Date not set. 60.00 *(978-0-687-01435-4(2))* Abingdon Pr.

Spurgeon, Charles H. My Sermon Notes. 2009. 178p. pap. *(978-1-150-22600-7(5))* Books LLC.

Staton, Cecil. Interpreting Isaiah for Preaching & Teaching. 7.00 *(978-0-687-82353-6(6))* Abingdon Pr.

Steffen, Tom A. Reconnecting God's Story to Ministry: Crosscultural Storytelling at Home & Abroad. 2006. (ENG., Illus.). 250p. (Orig.). per. 14.99 *(978-1-932805-06-2(0))* Authentic Media.

Stevenson, Peter K. & Wright, Stephen I. Preaching the Atonement. 2009. (ENG.). 224p. pap. 25.00 *(978-0-664-23328-0(7))* Westminster John Knox Pr.

—Preaching the Incarnation. 2010. (ENG.). 328p. pap. 20.00 *(978-0-664-23280-1(9))* Westminster John Knox Pr.

Stuart, Douglas. Old Testament Exegesis, Fourth Edition: A Handbook for Students & Pastors. 4th ed. 2009. (ENG.). 224p. pap. 25.00 *(978-0-664-23344-0(9))* Westminster John Knox Pr.

Swanson, Richard W. Provoking the Gospel of John: A Storyteller's Commentary, Years a, B, & C. 2010. *(978-0-8298-1866-6(9))* Pilgrim Pr., The/United Church Pr.

Turnbull, Ralph G. Later Hebrew History & Prophets. 2011. 102p. 39.95 ***(978-1-258-08975-7(0))*** Literary Licensing, LLC.

Vila, Samuel. Manual de Homiletica: Manual of Homiletics, 1 vol. 2008. (SPA.). 232p. pap. 7.99 *(978-84-7228-125-7(6)*, 220565) Clie, Editorial ESP. Dist: Zondervan.

Wansbrough, Henry. The Sunday Word: A Commentary on the Sunday Readings. 2012. (ENG.). 328p. (gr. 17). 34.95 ***(978-1-4411-4419-5(6)***, Burns & Oates) Continuum International Publishing Group, Ltd. GBR. Dist: National Bk. Network.

Wegner, Paul D. Using Old Testament Hebrew in Preaching: A Guide for Students & Pastors, 1 vol. 2009. 176p. pap. 17.99 *(978-0-8254-3936-0(1))* Kregel Pubns.

Westberg, Daniel & Fuller, Reginald H., eds. Preaching the Lectionary: The Word of God for the Church Today. 3rd ed. 2006. 616p. per. 29.95 *(978-0-8146-2792-1(7)*, Liturgical Pr. Bks.) Liturgical Pr.

Wilhelm, Dawn Ottoni. Preaching the Gospel of Mark: Proclaiming the Power of God. 2008. (ENG.). 312p. pap. 25.00 *(978-0-664-22921-4(2))* Westminster John Knox Pr.

Williamson, Lamar, Jr. Mark. 2009. (Interpretation, a Bible Commentary for Teaching & Preaching Ser.). (ENG.). 312p. pap. 25.00 *(978-0-664-23434-8(8))* Westminster John Knox Pr.

BIBLE—ILLUSTRATIONS

Here are entered works containing the complete text with accompanying pictures, works containing illustrations which have been reissued separately without text, and works about Bible illustrations.

see also subdivision Art under names of Bible characters, e.g. Jesus Christ—Art

Adult Bible Studies Illustrated Winter 2008-2009. 2008. pap. 7.00 *(978-0-687-64738-5(X),* Cokesbury) Abingdon Pr.

Bachelard, Gaston, et al. Marc Chagall - Dessins pour la Bible: Bilder für die Bibel - Drawings for the Bible. 2011. (FRE, GER & ENG., Illus.). 208p. 120.00 ***(978-3-7913-4566-6(4))*** Prestel Publishing.

Bank House Books. The Hieroglyphical Bible. 2011. 156p. ***(978-1-904408-90-1(7))*** Bank House Bks.

Beckett, Wendy. Sister Wendy's Bible Treasury: Stories & Wisdom Through the Eyes of Great Painters. 2012. ***(978-1-57075-972-7(3))*** Orbis Bks.

Bernabò, Massimo & Arduini, Franca. Il Tetravangelo Di Rabbula: Firenze, Biblioteca Medicea Laurenziana, Plut. 1.56: L'illustrazione Del Nuovo Testamento Nella Siria Del VI Secolo. 2008. (ITA & ENG., Illus.). ix, 174p. *(978-88-8498-516-3(1))* Storia e Letteratura.

Biblia Pauperum. 195.00 *(978-0-9633632-0-6(4))* Ebory, Inc.

Biblical Illustrator. 4.00 *(978-0-7673-4747-1(1))* LifeWay Christian Resources.

Bisley, Simon, illus. Simon Bisley's Illustrations from the Bible: A Work in Progress. 2007. per. 21.95 *(978-1-932413-78-6(2))* Heavy Metal Magazine.

Blake, William, et al. Genesis: William Blake's Last Illuminated Work. 2012. (ENG., Illus.). 100p. 80.00 ***(978-0-87328-247-5(7))*** Huntington Library Pr.

Brewer, Christopher. Art That Tells the Story. Brewer, Christopher, ed. 2011. (ENG.). pap. 24.99 *(978-0-615-42601-3(8))* Gospel through Shared Experience.

Broca, Lilian, et al. The Hidden & the Revealed: The Queen Esther Mosaics of Lilian Broca. 2011. ***(978-965-229-560-6(4))*** Gefen Bks.

Brubaker, Leslie. Vision & Meaning in Ninth-Century Byzantium: Image as Exegesis in the Homilies of Gregory of Nazianzus. 2008. (Cambridge Studies in Palaeography & Codicology Ser.). (ENG., Illus.). 572p. pap. 55.00 *(978-0-521-10191-3(6))* Cambridge Univ. Pr.

Brusati, Celeste, et al, eds. The Authority of the Word: Reflecting on Image & Text in Northern Europe, 1400-1700. 2011. (ENG., Illus.). XLII, 710p. ***(978-90-04-21515-3(8))*** BRILL.

Burt, David. 25 Sketches about Proverbs. 2006. (ENG.). 173p. per. 12.99 *(978-0-85476-871-4(8))* Kingsway Pubns. GBR. Dist: STL Distribution North America.

Bussagli, Marco. Angels. Giammanco, Rosanna, tr. from ITA. 2007. (ENG., Illus.). 780p. 19.95 *(978-0-8109-9436-2(4))* Abrams.

Christian Art Gifts, creator. For You, Graduate. 2009. (For You... Ser.). (Illus.). 79p. *(978-1-77036-119-5(7))* Christian Art Pubs.

—For You, Mom: ... Because I Love You. 2009. (For You... Ser.). (Illus.). 78p. *(978-1-77036-117-1(0))* Christian Art Pubs.

—For You, with Love. 2009. (Illus.). 79p. *(978-1-77036-235-2(5))* Christian Art Pubs.

Clifton, James, et al, contrib. by. Scripture for the Eyes: Bible Illustration in Netherlandish Prints of the Sixteenth Century. 2009. (Illus.). 224p. pap. 49.95 *(978-0-9777839-3-9(6))* Museum of Biblical Art.

De Rynck, Patrick. How to Read Bible Stories & Myths in Art: Decoding the Old Masters from Giotto to Goya. 2009. (ENG., Illus.). 360p. pap. 37.50 *(978-0-8109-8400-4(8))* Abrams.

Degl'Innocenti, Martina & Marinone, Stella. Bible Stories. 2010. (ENG., Illus.). 612p. 19.95 *(978-0-8109-8996-2(4))* Abrams.

Derbes, Anne & Sandona, Mark. The Usurer's Heart: Giotto, Enrico Scrovegni, & the Arena Chapel in Padua. 2008. (ENG., Illus.). 312p. 75.00 *(978-0-271-03256-6(1))* Pennsylvania State Univ. Pr.

Doré, Gustave, illus. Scenes from the Bible. 2008. 384p. 24.99 *(978-0-7858-2311-7(5),* 0785823115, Chartwell) Book Sales, Inc.

Ennis, Solomon. In His Image: Illustrations & Meditations from an African-Centered Christian Perspective. 2011. (ENG., Illus.). 110p. 39.95 *(978-0-88378-299-6(5))* Third World Press.

Exell, Joseph S. The Biblical Illustrator. 2009. (ENG.). 706p. 47.99 *(978-1-117-71555-1(8));* pap. 32.99 *(978-1-117-71557-5(4),* BiblioLife); pap. 48.75 *(978-1-117-71556-8(6),* BiblioLife) BiblioBazaar.

Forlaget Illuminated Sweden Staff, ed. Bible Illuminated: The Book, Old Testament. 2009. 526p. pap. 45.00 *(978-91-976694-5-0(8))* Illuminated World SWE. Dist: Midpoint Trade Bks., Inc.

Gealt, Adelheid M. & Knox, George. Domenico Tiepolo: A New Testament. 2006. (ENG., Illus.). 888p. 75.00 *(978-0-253-34809-8(9),* 0253348099) Indiana Univ. Pr.

Ghiberti, Lorenzo, et al. The Gates of Paradise: Lorenzo Ghiberti's Renaissance Masterpiece. 2007. (Illus.). 182p. pap. *(978-1-932543-16-2(3))* High Museum of Art.

Giffen, Keith & Elliott, Dave. The Bible - Eden. 2nd ed. 2010. (Illus.). 112p. pap. 17.99 *(978-1-60010-718-4(4))* Idea & Design Works, LLC.

Graham-Dixon, Andrew. Michelangelo & the Sistine Chapel. 2009. 240p. 24.95 *(978-1-60239-368-4(0))* Skyhorse Publishing Co., Inc.

Grisanti, Michael A. The Kregel Pictorial Guide to the Old Testament, 1 vol. 2010. (Kregel Pictorial Guide Ser.). (ENG.). 32p. pap. 9.99 *(978-0-8254-2690-2(1))* Kregel Pubns.

Illuminated Tehilim in Hebrew. 2007. *(978-0-9753982-3-4(7))* Benbenisty, Samuel & Baruch.

Illuminated Tehilim in Hebrew/English. 2007. *(978-0-9753982-4-1(5))* Benbenisty, Samuel & Baruch.

Illuminated World Staff. Bible Illuminated: The Book, New Testament. 2008. 288p. pap. 35.00 *(978-91-976694-4-3(X))* Illuminated World SWE. Dist: Midpoint Trade Bks., Inc.

Israel, Ruth Ben. Bible Illuminations. 2010. 264p. 40.00 *(978-965-229-477-7(2))* Gefen Publishing Hse., Ltd ISR. Dist: Gefen Bks.

Jackson, Donald. The Saint John's Bible: An Introduction. 2008. (Illus.). 32p. per. 9.95 *(978-0-8146-9100-7(5),* Liturgical Pr. Bks.) Liturgical Pr.

Jackson, Donald, illus. Praying the Word: Illuminated Prayers & Wisdom from the Saint John's Bible. 2008. 72p. *(978-0-8146-9093-2(9),* Liturgical Pr. Bks.) Liturgical Pr.

—The Saint John's Bible Vol. 1: Pentateuch. 2006. 158p. 69.95 *(978-0-8146-9052-9(1))* Liturgical Pr.

—The Saint John's Bible Vol. 2: Historical Books. 2010. 276p. 79.95 *(978-0-8146-9053-6(X),* St. John's Bible Bks.) Liturgical Pr.

—The Saint John's Bible Vol. 3: Prophets. 2007. 232p. 69.95 *(978-0-8146-9054-3(8))* Liturgical Pr.

—The Saint John's Bible Vol. 4: Wisdom Books. 2007. 136p. 64.95 *(978-0-8146-9055-0(6))* Liturgical Pr.

Kind David Illuminated Psalms. 2007. *(978-0-9753982-1-0(0))* Benbenisty, Samuel & Baruch.

Kitto, John. A Pictorial Life of Our Savior. 2007. (ENG.). 310p. 45.95 *(978-0-548-01534-6(1))* Kessinger Publishing, LLC.

Kossonogi, Alon. Jesus Boat Study Companion. 2009. pap. 14.95 *(978-0-01-247567-6(X))* STL Distribution North America.

L & W Bible Discoverers Teaching Pictures. 6.25 *(978-0-7673-5390-8(0))* LifeWay Christian Resources.

L & W Bible Learners Teaching Pictures. 6.25 *(978-0-7673-5446-2(X))* LifeWay Christian Resources.

L & W Bible Searchers Teaching Pictures. 6.25 *(978-0-7673-5334-2(X))* LifeWay Christian Resources.

La Farge, John. The Gospel Story in Art. 2008. 438p. 51.95 *(978-1-4365-4105-3(0))* 2007. (ENG.). 440p. per. 36.95 *(978-0-548-74634-9(6))* Kessinger Publishing, LLC.

Ladis, Andrew. Giotto's O: Narrative, Figuration, & Pictorial Ingenuity in the Arena Chapel. 2008. (ENG., Illus.). 208p. 75.00 *(978-0-271-03407-2(6))* Pennsylvania State Univ. Pr.

Lopez, Omar R. G O D's Biblical Evolutions: An Interpretive Fantasy about Life's Beginnings. 2008. 212p. per. 14.95 *(978-1-4327-1956-2(4))* Outskirts Pr., Inc.

Lubbock, Jules. Storytelling in Christian Art from Giotto to Donatello. 2006. (Illus.). 353p. 50.00 *(978-0-300-11727-1(2))* Yale Univ. Pr.

Melion, Walter S. Scripture for the Eyes: Bible Illustration in Netherlandish Prints of the Sixteenth Century. Clifton, James, ed. 2009. (ENG., Illus.). 224p. 65.00 *(978-1-904832-66-9(0))* Giles, D. Ltd. GBR. Dist: Antique Collectors' Club.

Moore, Karen. For You, Dad: ... Because I Love You. 2009. (For You... Ser.). (Illus.). 87p. *(978-1-77036-115-7(4))* Christian Art Pubs.

Morgan, Nigel. Illuminating The End of Time: The Getty Apocalypse Manuscript. 2012. (ENG., Illus.). 180p. 75.00 *(978-1-60606-071-1(6),* J. Paul Getty Museum) Getty Pubns.

O'Hear, Natasha F. H. Contrasting Images of the Book of Revelation in Late Medieval & Early Modern Art: A Case Study in Visual Exegesis. 2011. (ENG., Illus.). 304p. 150.00 *(978-0-19-959010-0(9))* Oxford Univ. Pr., Inc.

O'Kane, Martin. Painting the Text: The Artist As Biblical Interpreter. 2007. (Illus.). 252p. *(978-1-905048-36-6(X))* Sheffield Phoenix Pr.

—Painting the Text: The Artist as Biblical Interpreter. 2009. (Illus.). 250p. pap. *(978-1-906055-92-9(0))* Sheffield Phoenix Pr.

Papadaki-Oekland, S. Byzantine Illuminated Manuscripts of the Book of Job: A Preliminary Study of the Miniature Illustrations, Its Origin & Development. 2009. (ENG & GEC., Illus.). 478p. (C). 218.00 *(978-2-503-53232-5(2))* Brepols Pubs. BEL. Dist: ISD.

Perlove, Shelley Karen & Silver, Larry. Rembrandt's Faith: Church & Temple in the Dutch Golden Age. 2009. (ENG., Illus.). 512p. 100.00 *(978-0-271-03406-5(8))* Pennsylvania State Univ. Pr.

Pongracz, Patricia. Biblical Art & the Asian Imagination. 2007. *(978-0-9777839-2-2(8))* Museum of Biblical Art.

Pongracz, Patricia C., et al. The Christian Story: Five Asian Artists Today. 2007. (ENG., Illus.). 168p. pap. 39.95 *(978-1-904832-20-1(2))* Giles, D. Ltd. GBR. Dist: Antique Collectors' Club.

Radke, Gary & contrib. by. The Gates of Paradise: Lorenzo Ghiberti's Renaissance Masterpiece. 2007. (Illus.). 182p. 45.00 *(978-1-932543-15-5(5))* High Museum of Art.

Radke, Gary M., ed. The Gates of Paradise: Lorenzo Ghiberti's Renaissance Masterpiece. 2007. (ENG., Illus.). 184p. 45.00 *(978-0-300-12615-0(8))* Yale Univ. Pr.

Rias-Baker, Georgette. Top of the Ninth & I'm Winning: Be a Victorious Winner. 2009. 128p. pap. 11.95 *(978-1-4327-4224-9(8))* Outskirts Pr., Inc.

Richardson, Jan. The Intimate Apocalypse: Notes on a Pilgrimage into Revelation. 2007. (Illus.). 28p. pap. 19.00 *(978-0-9778162-2-4(2),* Wanton Gospeller Pr.

Roberston, A. T. Imagenes Verbales en el N. T. Word Pictures in the N. T., 6 vols. (SPA.). II. *(978-84-7645-325-4(6),* 223350)III. *(978-84-7645-347-6(7),* 223446)IV. *(978-84-7645-382-7(5),* 223353)V. *(978-84-7645-400-8(7),* 223470)VI. *(978-84-7645-414-5(7),* 223505) Clie, Editorial.

Robinson, George W. The Overflowing Heart: Illustrations for the Gospel of Matthew. 2007. 59p. pap. 8.95 *(978-0-7414-4339-7(2))* Infinity Publishing.

Rowland, Christopher. Blake & the Bible. 2011. (ENG., Illus.). 320p. 50.00 *(978-0-300-11260-3(2))* Yale Univ. Pr.

Spier, Jeffrey. Late Antique & Early Christian Gems. 2007. (Spatantike, Fruhes Christentum, Byzanz Ser.). (ENG.). 374p. (C). 337.00 *(978-3-89500-434-6(0))* Reichert, Ludwig Dr. DEU. Dist: Brown, David Bk. Co., The.

—Picturing the Bible: The Earliest Christian Art. (Illus.). 2009. (ENG.). 328p. pap. 50.00 *(978-0-300-14934-0(4))* 2007. xv, 309p. pap. *(978-0-912804-47-7(5))* Yale Univ. Pr.

Strachan, James. Early Bible Illustrations: A Short Study Based on some Fifteenth & Early Sixteenth Century Printed Texts. 2009. (ENG.). 188p. pap. 31.99 *(978-0-521-10002-1(X))* Cambridge Univ. Pr.

Verkerk, Dorothy. Early Medieval Bible Illumination & the Ashburnham Pentateuch. 2011. (ENG., Illus.). 272p. pap. 34.99 *(978-1-107-40200-3(X))* Cambridge Univ. Pr.

Warren, Ulysses Grant. The Bible in Story & Art: Containing over Two Hundred Masterpieces of Sacred Art. 2011. 488p. 58.95 ***(978-1-258-04681-1(4))*** Literary Licensing, LLC.

Willoughby, Harold R. Codex 2400 abd its Miniatures. 2011. 111.25 *(978-1-61143-943-4(4))* Gorgias Pr., LLC.

Yarbrough, Robert W. The Kregel Pictorial Guide to the New Testament, 1 vol. 2010. (Kregel Pictorial Guide Ser.). 32p. pap. 9.99 *(978-0-8254-4170-7(6))* Kregel Pubns.

Yeo, K. K. The Spirit Hovers: Journeying through Chaos with Prayers. 2011. 124p. pap. 15.00 ***(978-1-61097-506-3(5),*** Cascade Bks.) Wipf & Stock Pubs.

Yeo, K. K. The Spirit Intercedes. 2009. 132p. pap. 16.00 *(978-1-60608-794-7(0),* Cascade Bks.) Wipf & Stock Pubs.

York, Karen S. Sons of Adam, Daughters of Eve: Biblical Images in Art from Tulsa Collections. 2007. (Illus.). 110p. pap. *(978-0-9799851-0-2(2))* Sherwin Miller Museum of Jewish Art, The.

BIBLE—IN LITERATURE

Ackerman, The Bible As in Literature: Anthology. 2nd ed. (Points of Departure Ser.). (Illus.). viii, 472p. 8.97 *(978-0-673-29424-1(2))* Addison-Wesley Longman, Inc.

Alter, Robert. Pen of Iron: American Prose & the King James Bible. 2010. (ENG.). 208p. 19.95 *(978-0-691-12881-8(2))* Princeton Univ. Pr.

Anonby, John A. The Kenyan Epic Novelist Ngugi: His Secular Reconfiguration of Biblical Themes. 2006. 224p. 109.95 *(978-0-7734-5496-5(9))* Mellen, Edwin Pr., The.

Arellano, Ignacio & Fine, Ruth. La Biblia en la Literatura Del Siglo de Oro. 2010. (SPA., Illus.). 477p. pap. 75.00 *(978-84-8489-446-9(0),* Iberoamericana Vervuert Publishing Corp.

Benfell, V. Stanley. The Biblical Dante. 2011. (Toronto Italian Studies). (ENG.). 288p. ***(978-1-4426-4274-4(2))*** Univ. of Toronto Pr.

Cook, Albert Stanburrough. Biblical Quotations in Old English Prose Writers. 2008. 420p. 30.99 *(978-0-559-43911-7(3));* pap. 33.75 *(978-0-559-43910-0(5))* BiblioBazaar.

Cook, Albert Stanburrough, et al. Biblical Quotations in Old English Prose Writers. 2010. 420p. pap. 34.75 *(978-1-144-20344-1(9))* BiblioBazaar.

Courtmanche, Jason Charles. How Nathaniel Hawthorne's Narratives Are Shaped by Sin: His Use of Biblical Typology in His Four Major Works. 2008. 268p. 109.95 *(978-0-7734-5017-2(3))* Mellen, Edwin Pr., The.

DeCook, Travis & Galey, Alan, eds. Shakespeare the Bible & the History of the Material Book: Contested Scriptures. 2011. (Routledge Studies in Shakespeare Ser.). (ENG., Illus.). 220p. (C). 125.00 *(978-0-415-88350-4(4))* Routledge.

Drosnin, Michael. Bible Code III: Saving the World. 2010. (ENG.). 232p. 26.00 *(978-0-615-39963-8(0))* Worldmedia, Inc.

Exum, J. Cheryl. Retellings: The Bible in Literature, Music, Art, & Film. 2007. pap. *(978-90-04-16572-4(X))* BRILL.

Fohrman, David. The Beast that Crouches at the Door: Adam & Eve, Cain & Abel, & Beyond... 2007. 216p. pap. 24.95 *(978-1-932687-79-8(3),* Devora Publishing) Simcha Media Group.

Forrest, William Mentzel. Biblical Allusions in Poe. 2011. 208p. 44.95 ***(978-1-258-01587-9(0))*** Literary Licensing, LLC.

Fox, Michael & Sharma, Manish, eds. Old Englterature & the Old Testament. 2011. (Toronto Anglo-Saxon Ser.). (Illus.). 400p. ***(978-0-8020-9854-2(1))*** Univ. of Toronto Pr.

Gardner, Thomas. John in the Company of Poets: The Gospel in Literary Imagination. 2011. (Studies in Christianity & Literature Ser.). (ENG.). 236p. 69.95 *(978-1-60258-315-3(3))* Baylor Univ. Pr.

Hamlin, Hannibal. Psalm Culture & Early Modern English Literature. 2007. (ENG.). 304p. pap. 63.00 *(978-0-521-03705-8(9))* Cambridge Univ. Pr.

Hass, Andrew, et al. The Oxford Handbook of English Literature & Theology. 2007. (Oxford Handbooks Ser.). (ENG.). 908p. 175.00 *(978-0-19-927197-9(6))* Oxford Univ. Pr., Inc.

Horan, Michael. Jesus & the Trojan War: Myth & Meaning for Today. 2007. (ENG.). 252p. per. 29.90 *(978-1-84540-081-1(X))* Imprint Academic GBR. Dist: Ingram Pub. Services.

Hsiao, Eric Yi-Huan. Celestial Light, Shine Inward. 2008. 156p. pap. *(978-3-8364-9208-9(3))* VDM Verlag Dr. Mueller e.K.

Hyde, Virginia. The Risen Adam. 2008. pap. 24.95 *(978-0-271-02845-3(9))* Pennsylvania State Univ. Pr.

Jacobson, Howard. The Exagoge of Ezekiel. 2009. (ENG & GEC.). 264p. pap. 38.99 *(978-0-521-12243-5(0))* Cambridge Univ. Pr.

Jasper, David. Readings in the Canon of Scripture. 2009. (David Jasper Reprint Ser.). 180p. pap. 21.00 *(978-1-60608-835-7(1),* Wipf and Stock) Wipf & Stock Pubs.

—The Sacred & Secular Canon in Romanticism. 2009. (David Jasper Reprint Ser.). 168p. pap. 19.00 *(978-1-60608-834-0(3),* Wipf and Stock) Wipf & Stock Pubs.

Jones, Beth Felker. Touched by a Vampire: Discovering the Hidden Messages in the Twilight Saga. 2009. (ENG.). 192p. pap. 13.99 *(978-1-60142-278-1(4),* Multnomah) Doubleday Religious Publishing Group, The.

Killinger, John. The Life, Death, & Resurrection of Harry Potter. 2009. 192p. pap. 17.00 *(978-0-88146-162-8(8))* Mercer Univ. Pr.

LaPorte, Charles. Victorian Poets & the Changing Bible. 2011. (Illus.). ix, 284p. E-Book ***(978-0-8139-3165-4(7))***; (ENG.), 304p. (gr. 17). 45.00 *(978-0-8139-3158-6(4))* Univ. Pr. of Virginia.

Lemon, Rebecca, et al, eds. The Blackwell Companion to the Bible in English Literature. (ENG.). 720p. 2012. pap. 44.95 ***(978-0-470-67499-4(7))*** 2009. (Wiley-Blackwell Companions to Religion Ser.: 29). 199.95 *(978-1-4051-3160-5(8))* Wiley, John & Sons, Inc. (Wiley-Blackwell).

Manser, Martin H. The Facts on File Dictionary of Allusions. 2008. (Writer's Reference Library). 544p. (gr. 6-12). 75.00 *(978-0-8160-7105-0(5))* Facts On File, Inc.

Mills, Kevin. Approaching Apocalypse: Unveiling Revelation in Victorian Writing. 2007. 228p. (C). *(978-0-8387-5627-0(1));* (ENG.). 49.50 *(978-1-61148-237-9(2))* Bucknell Univ. Pr.

Milton, John. John Milton, Paradise Lost: The Biblically Annotated Edition. Stallard, Matthew, ed. 2011. 600p. pap. 24.00 *(978-0-88146-268-5(3));* 60.00 *(978-0-88146-236-4(5))* Mercer Univ. Pr.

Neusner, Jacob. Habakkuk, Jonah, Nahum, & Obadiah in Talmud & Midrash: A Source Book. 2007. (Studies in Judaism Ser.). (ENG.). 186p. per. 33.99 *(978-0-7618-3697-1(7))* Univ. Pr. of America, Inc.

Núñez Rivera, Valentín. Poesía y Biblia en el Siglo de Oro: Estudios Sobre Los Salmos y el Cantar de Los Cantares. 2010. (Biblioteca Áurea Hispánica Ser.). (SPA.). 294p. pap. 44.00 *(978-84-8489-531-2(9))* Iberoamericana Vervuert Publishing Corp.

O'Reilly, Terence. The Bible in the Literary Imagination of the Spanish Golden Age: Images & Texts from Columbus to Velazquez. 2010. (ENG.). 65.00 *(978-0-916101-63-3(0))* St. Joseph's Univ. Pr.

Rowland, Christopher. "Wheels Within Wheels" William Blake & the Ezekiel's Merkabah in Text & Image. 2007. (C). *(978-0-87462-587-5(4))* Marquette Univ. Pr.

Russell, Heather & Bassard, Katherine Clay. Transforming Scriptures: African American Women Writers & the Bible. 2010. (ENG.). 180p. 44.95 *(978-0-8203-3090-7(6))* Univ. of Georgia Pr.

Schwartz, Regina M. Remembering & Repeating: Biblical Creation in Paradise Lost. 2011. (ENG.). 156p. pap. 24.99 *(978-0-521-17729-0(4))* Cambridge Univ. Pr.

Shaheen, Naseeb. Biblical References in Shakespeare's Plays. 2011. (ENG.). 880p. 125.00 ***(978-1-61149-358-0(7))*** Univ. of Delaware Pr.

Shuger, Debora Kuller. The Renaissance Bible: Scholarship, Sacrifice, & Subjectivity. 2010. (ENG., Illus.). 313p. (C). pap. 39.95 *(978-1-60258-309-2(9))* Baylor Univ. Pr.

Stein, Arnold. Answerable Style: Essays on Paradise Lost. 2009. (ENG.). 180p. pap. 40.00 *(978-0-8166-5372-5(2))* Univ. of Minnesota Pr.

Stevens, Jennifer. The Historical Jesus & the Literary Imagination 1860-1920. 2010. (Liverpool University Press - English Association Monographs). (ENG.). 312p. 95.00 *(978-1-84631-470-4(4))* Liverpool Univ. Pr. GBR. Dist: Chicago Distribution Ctr.

Streete, Adrian, ed. Early Modern Drama & the Bible: Contexts & Readings, 1570-1625. 2011. (Early Modern Literature in History Ser.). (ENG., Illus.). 280p. 85.00 ***(978-0-230-30109-2(6))*** Palgrave Macmillan.

Stubbings, Hilda U. Milton's "First Couple" Love & Alienation in Paradise Lost. Date not set. 350p. (C). lib. bdg. 55.00 *(978-1-880622-06-3(8))* Rubena Pr.

Swindell, Anthony Charles. How Contemporary Novelists Rewrite Stories from the Bible: The Interpretation of Scripture in Literature. 2009. 364p. 119.95 *(978-0-7734-4764-6(4))* Mellen, Edwin Pr., The.

Taylor, John. Classics & the Bible: Hospitality & Recognition. 2007. (Classical Literature & Society Ser.). 192p. per. 34.95 *(978-0-7156-3481-3(X))* Duckworth Publishers GBR. Dist: International Publishers Marketing.

The Bush Theatre. Sixty-Six Books: A Contemporary Response to the King James Bible. 2012. (ENG.). 352p. pap. 30.95 ***(978-1-84943-227-6(9))*** Oberon Bks., Ltd. GBR. Dist: Consortium Bk. Sales & Distribution.

Tichy, Henrietta. Biblical Influences in English Literature: A Survey of Studies. 2011. 72p. 36.95 ***(978-1-258-06490-7(1))*** Literary Licensing, LLC.

Woodman, Thomas & Knight, Mark, eds. Biblical Religion & the Novel 1700-2000. 2006. 170p. 110.00 *(978-0-7546-5117-8(7))* Ashgate Publishing Co.

Wordsworth, Charles. Shakespeare's Knowledge & Use of the Bible. 2010. 320p. 36.76 *(978-1-163-21389-6(6));* pap. 24.76 *(978-1-162-74189-5(9))* Kessinger Publishing, LLC.

Wright, T. R. D. H. Lawrence & the Bible 2009. (ENG.). 288p. pap. 41.00 *(978-0-521-09322-4(8))* Cambridge Univ. Pr.

Wright, Terry R. The Genesis of Fiction: The Modern Novel As Biblical Exegesis. 2007. 200p. 99.95 *(978-0-7546-1668-9(1))* Ashgate Publishing Co.

BIBLE—INDEXES

Here are entered works which list the ideas of the Bible and give the passages where the idea rather than the exact word occurs. Works which list the words of the Bible and give the passages where each word occurs are entered under Bible—Concordances.

Alward, Benjamin B. Handy Scripture Guide. 2011. 236p. 46.95 ***(978-1-258-10504-4(7))*** Literary Licensing, LLC.

Ed. Pub. Concepts Staff, prod. What Did Jesus Say? Bible Verses on Issues You Deal With. 2010. (ENG.). 192p. (J). pap. 9.99 *(978-1-4143-3180-5(0))* Tyndale Hse. Pubs.

Graham, Merry & Bye, Rachel. Scriptures at Your Fingertips: 200 Topics & 2000 Verses. 2006. (ENG.). 256p. pap. 12.99 *(978-1-58229-613-5(8)*, Howard Bks.) Howard Books.

Graham, Merry & Graham, Tiffany Michelle. Scriptures at Your Fingertips for Teens: Over 250 Topics & 2000 Verses. 2008. (ENG.). 288p. (J). pap. 13.99 *(978-1-4165-7910-6(9)*, Howard Bks.) Howard Books.

Green, Kevin. Zondervan All in One Bible Reference Guide. 2008. 675p. ***(978-0-310-61164-6(4))*** Zondervan.

Hunt, June. The Complete Biblical Counseling Concordance: Every Scripture Verse You'll Need to Apply the Bible to Life's Problems. 2013. 352p. mass mkt. 11.99 *(978-0-7369-2330-9(6))* Harvest Hse. Pubs.

Mason, Amy E. & Beers, Ronald A. Bible Promises to Live By. 2007. (ENG.). 176p. per. 3.99 *(978-1-4143-1355-9(1))* Tyndale Hse. Pubs.

McGlynn, Jackie. I Am ... in the Garden. 2011. 40p. pap. 13.95 ***(978-1-4497-1701-8(2)***, WestBow Pr.) Author Solutions, Inc.

Meredith, Joel L. Meredith's Complete Book of Bible Lists: A One-of-a-Kind Collection of Bible Facts. 2009. 480p. pap. 12.99 *(978-0-7642-0339-8(8))* Bethany Hse. Pubs.

Puen, Ray. Is That in the Bible? Fascinating Insights & Discoveries in the Book of Books. 2008. 96p. per. *(978-0-9795930-0-0(X))* Regency Pr.

Religious Tract and Book Society for Ireland, Dublin Staff. The Scripture Text Book. 2006. 288p. per. 23.99 *(978-1-4255-2624-5(1))* MPublishing.

Rhodes, Ron. Find It Fast in the Bible: A Quick Topical Reference. 2009. 208p. pap. 7.99 *(978-0-7369-2656-0(9))* Harvest Hse. Pubs.

Simmons, Charles. A Scripture Manual. 2009. 480p. pap. *(978-0-217-66648-0(5))*; 444p. pap. *(978-1-4432-7109-7(8))* Books LLC.

—A Scripture Manual. 2009. 422p. pap. 24.67 *(978-0-217-76910-5(1))* General Bks. LLC.

—A Scripture Manual. 2007. (ENG.). 524p. 55.95 *(978-0-548-04754-5(5))* Kessinger Publishing, LLC.

—A Scripture Manual. 2006. (ENG.). 532p. per. 29.99 *(978-1-4255-5913-7(1))* MPublishing.

Strong, James. The New Strong's Expanded Exhaustive Concordance of the Bible, 0 vols. 2010. 2000p. 39.99 *(978-1-4185-4168-2(0))* Nelson, Thomas Inc.

—The New Strong's Expanded Exhaustive Concordance of the Bible, Supersaver, 0 vols. 2010. 2000p. 39.99 *(978-1-4185-4237-5(7))* Nelson, Thomas Inc.

Where to Find It in the Bible. 2009. pap. *(978-1-59636-344-1(4))* Rose Publishing.

BIBLE—INERRANCY

see Bible—Evidences, Authority, etc.

BIBLE—INFLUENCE

Armstrong, Karen. The Bible: A Biography. 2008. (Books That Changed the World Ser.). (ENG.). 176p. pap. 14.00 *(978-0-8021-4384-6(9)*, Grove Pr.) Grove/Atlantic, Inc.

—The Bible: A Biography. l.t. ed. 2008. (Books That Changed the World Ser.). 375p. 30.95 *(978-1-4104-0378-0(5))* Thorndike Pr.

Besserman, Lawrence. Biblical Paradigms in Medieval English Literature. 2011. (ENG., Illus.). 236p. (C). 125.00 ***(978-0-415-89794-5(7))*** Routledge.

Bielo, James S., ed. The Social Life of Scriptures: Cross-Cultural Perspectives on Biblicism. 2009. (Signifying (on)Scriptures Ser.). (ENG., Illus.). 272p. (C). 72.00 *(978-0-8135-4605-6(2))*; pap. 28.95 *(978-0-8135-4606-3(0))* Rutgers Univ. Pr.

Bieringer, R. & Elsbernd, M., eds. Normativity of the Future: Reading Biblical & Other Authoritative Texts in an Eschatological Perspective. 2010. (Annua Nuntia Lovaniensia Ser.). (ENG.). 402p. (C). pap. 87.00 *(978-90-429-2227-3(3))* Peeters Pubs. & Booksellers BEL. Dist: Brown, David Bk. Co., The.

Bland, Jay. The Generation of Edward Hyde: The Animal Within, from Plato to Darwin to Robert Louis Stevenson. 2010. 374p. pap. 74.95 *(978-3-0343-0135-0(9))* Lang, Peter AG GBR. Dist: Lang, Peter.

Boer, Roland. Cave Droppings: Nick Cave & Religion. 2012. (Studies in popular Music Ser.). (ENG.). (C). 224p. 95.00 ***(978-1-908049-67-4(7))***; 192p. pap. 25.00 ***(978-1-908049-66-7(9))*** Equinox Publishing Ltd. GBR. Dist: ISD, Brown, David Bk. Co., The.

Boillet, Élise. L'Arétin et la Bible. 2007. (Travaux d'Humanisme et Renaissance Ser.). (FRE & ENG., Illus.). 592p. (C). 205.00 *(978-2-600-01058-0(0))* Droz, Libraire CHE. Dist: Brown, David Bk. Co., The.

Bragg, Melvyn. The Book of Books: The Radical Impact of the King James Bible 1611-2011. 2012. (ENG.). 368p. pap. 16.95 ***(978-1-61902-010-8(6)***, Counterpoint) Counterpoint LLC.

Bragg, Melvyn. The Book of Books: The Radical Impact of the King James Bible 1611-2011. 2011. (ENG., Illus.). 368p. 28.00 *(978-1-58243-781-1(5)*, Counterpoint) Counterpoint LLC.

Choi, John H. Traditions at Odds: The Reception of the Pentateuch in Biblical & Second Temple Period Literature. 2010. (Library of Hebrew Bible/Old Testament Studies). (ENG.). 288p. 140.00 *(978-0-567-26524-1(2)*, T&T Clark Int'l) Continuum International Publishing Group, Ltd. GBR. Dist: National Bk. Network.

Culbertson, Philip Leroy. The Bible in/and Popular Culture: A Creative Encounter. Culbertson, Philip & Wainwright, Elaine M., eds. 2011. (ENG.). VIII, 210p. ***(978-90-04-18699-6(9))*** BRILL.

Exum, J. Cheryl. Retellings: The Bible in Literature, Music, Art, & Film. 2007. pap. *(978-90-04-16572-4(X))* BRILL.

Glen, Marie & glen, marie. As It Was in the Beginning. 2009. 82p. pap. 14.95 *(978-0-615-23587-5(5))* Inner-monastery.com.

Hastings, Kirk. What Is Truth? A Handbook for Separating Fact from Fiction in a Propaganda-Filled World, 1 vol. 2009. 200p. pap. 24.95 *(978-1-60836-298-1(1))* PublishAmerica, Inc.

Horovitz, Chaim / T. A Two Thousand Year History of the Influence of the Song of Songs on Religion, Literature, Music, & Art. 2011. (Illus.). 516p. 149.95 *(978-0-7734-3810-1(6))* Mellen, Edwin Pr., The.

Jeffrey, David L. The Bible & the University, 1 vol. Jeffrey, David Lyle et al, eds. 2007. (Scripture & Hermeneutics Ser.). (ENG.). 352p. (gr. 13). pap. 34.99 *(978-0-310-23418-0(2))* Zondervan.

Ker, John. The Psalms in History & Biography. 2007. (ENG.). 244p. 41.95 *(978-0-548-12671-4(2))* Kessinger Publishing, LLC.

—Psalms in History & Biography. 2006. pap. 26.95 *(978-1-4286-3663-7(3))* Kessinger Publishing, LLC.

Kirsch, Jonathan. History of the End of the World: How the Most Controversial Book in the Bible Changed the Course of Western Civilization. 2007. (ENG., Illus.). 352p. pap. 14.95 *(978-0-06-134987-4(9)*, HarperOne) HarperCollins Pubs.

Kroll, Woodrow. Taking Back the Good Book: How America Forgot the Bible & Why It Matters to You. 2007. 224p. 19.99 *(978-1-58134-826-2(6))* Crossway.

LaPorte, Charles. Victorian Poets & the Changing Bible. 2011. (Illus.). ix, 284p. E-Book ***(978-0-8139-3165-4(7))***; (ENG.), 304p. (gr. 17). 45.00 *(978-0-8139-3158-6(4))* Univ. Pr. of Virginia.

Larsen, Timothy. A People of One Book: The Bible & the Victorians. 2011. (ENG.). 336p. 55.00 *(978-0-19-957009-6(4))* Oxford Univ. Pr., Inc.

Lemon, Rebecca, et al, eds. The Blackwell Companion to the Bible in English Literature. 2009. (Wiley-Blackwell Companions to Religion Ser.: 29). (ENG.). 720p. 199.95 *(978-1-4051-3160-5(8)*, Wiley-Blackwell) Wiley, John & Sons, Inc.

Martus, Steffen, et al, eds. Das Buch der Bucher - Gelesen: Lesarten der Bibel in den Wissenschaften und Kunsten. (GER., Illus.). 488p. 82.95 *(978-3-03910-839-8(5))* Lang, Peter CHE. Dist: Lang, Peter Publishing, Inc.

Matthews, John. The Influence of the Bible in Improving the Understanding & Moral Character. 2010. 226p. pap. 18.00 *(978-1-59925-144-8(2))* Solid Ground Christian Bks.

McAfee, Cleland Boyd & Mcafee, Cleland Boyd. The Greatest English Classic, a Study of the King James Version of the Bible & It's Influence on Live & Literature. 2011. 146p. pap. 12.99 ***(978-1-61203-235-1(4))*** Bottom of the Hill Publishing.

Merenfeld De Moscu. The Unconscious & the Bible. 2010. 392p. pap. *(978-3-8383-7216-7(6))* Lambert Academic Publishing.

Mills, Kevin. Approaching Apocalypse: Unveiling Revelation in Victorian Writing. 2007. 228p. (C). *(978-0-8387-5627-0(1))*; (ENG.). 49.50 *(978-1-61148-237-9(2))* Bucknell Univ. Pr.

Mobley, Kendal P. & Montgomery, Helen Barrett. Helen Barrett Montgomery: Boxed Set: the Global Mission of Domestic Feminism / the Bible & Missions. 2009. 640p. 69.95 *(978-1-60258-189-0(4))* Baylor Univ. Pr.

Montgomery, Helen Barrett. The Bible & Missions. 2009. (Illus.). 200p. (ENG.). pap. 29.95 *(978-1-60258-188-3(6))*; *(978-1-60258-156-2(8))* Baylor Univ. Pr.

—The Bible & Missions. 2009. 276p. 24.99 *(978-1-103-22367-1(4))*; pap. 18.99 *(978-1-103-22365-7(8))* BiblioBazaar.

—The Bible & Missions. 2009. 166p. pap. *(978-0-217-57210-1(3))* Books LLC.

—The Bible & Missions. 2008. 274p. 42.95 *(978-1-4365-8332-9(2))* 2007. (ENG.). 276p. per. 27.95 *(978-0-548-78088-6(9))* Kessinger Publishing, LLC.

Newcombe, Jerry. The Book That Made America: How the Bible Formed Our Nation. 2009. (ENG., Illus.). 304p. pap. 18.95 *(978-0-9824929-0-1(1))* Nordskog Publishing, Inc.

Nutu, Ela. Incarnate Word, Inscribed Flesh: John's Prologue & the Postmodern. 2007. (Illus.). 216p. *(978-1-905048-25-0(4))* Sheffield Phoenix Pr.

Osherow, Michele. Biblical Women's Voices in Early Modern England. 2009. (Women & Gender in the Early Modern World Ser.). (Illus.). 202p. 99.95 *(978-0-7546-6674-5(3))* Ashgate Publishing Co.

Parker, David. Reading Philippians Now & Then. 2011. 212p. pap. ***(978-3-639-32665-9(2))*** VDM Verlag Dr. Mueller e.K.

Sanders, Theresa. Approaching Eden: Adam & Eve in Popular Culture. 2009. (ENG.). 264p. 37.50 *(978-0-7425-6333-9(2))* Rowman & Littlefield Publishers, Inc.

Sawyer, John F. A., ed. The Bible & Culture. 2006. (ENG., Illus.). 564p. 199.95 *(978-1-4051-0136-3(9)*, Wiley-Blackwell) Wiley, John & Sons, Inc.

Sawyer, John F. A., ed. The Blackwell Companion to the Bible & Culture. 2012. (ENG.). 568p. pap. 44.95 ***(978-0-470-67488-8(1)***, Wiley-Blackwell) Wiley, John & Sons, Inc.

Schweid, Eliezer. The Philosophy of the Bible as Foundation of Jewish Culture: Philosophy of Biblical Narrative. Levin, Leonard, tr. from HEB. 2009. (Reference Library of Jewish Intellectual History Ser.). (ENG.). 224p. 50.00 *(978-1-934843-00-0(8))*; pap. 35.00 *(978-1-934843-51-2(2))* Academic Studies Pr.

Spencer, Nick. Freedom & Order: History, Politics & the English Bible. 2011. (ENG., Illus.). 320p. 26.95 *(978-0-340-99623-2(4)*, Hodder & Stoughton) Hodder General Publishing Div. GBR. Dist: Independent Pubs. Group.

Stern, Max. Bible & Music: Influences of the Old Testament on Western Music. 2011. ***(978-1-60280-166-0(5))*** Ktav Publishing Hse., Inc.

Tadmor, Naomi. The Social Universe of the English Bible: Scripture, Society, & Culture in Early Modern England. 2010. (Illus.). 224p. 95.00 *(978-0-521-76971-6(X))* Cambridge Univ. Pr.

The Bush Theatre. Sixty-Six Books: A Contemporary Response to the King James Bible. 2012. (ENG.). 352p. pap. 30.95 ***(978-1-84943-227-6(9))*** Oberon Bks., Ltd. GBR. Dist: Consortium Bk. Sales & Distribution.

Valkeakari, Tuire. Religious Idiom & the African American Novel, 1952-1998. 2007. (ENG.). 272p. 59.95 *(978-0-8130-3055-5(2))* Univ. Pr. of Florida.

Wainwright, Elaine Mary & Culbertson, Philip Leroy. The Bible In/And Popular Culture: Creative Encounter. 2010. vii, 210p. *(978-1-58983-494-1(1))*; *(978-1-58983-493-4(3))* Society of Biblical Literature.

Webster, Allen. You Gotta Be Dumb to Believe the Bible. Right? 2007. 0.35 *(978-1-933808-64-2(0))* House to House Heart to Heart Publishing, Inc.

Wheeler, Michael. St John & the Victorians. 2011. (ENG., Illus.). 288p. 90.00 ***(978-0-521-50972-5(6))*** Cambridge Univ. Pr.

White, James Boyd. Connecting to the Gospel: Texts, Sermons, Commentaries. 2010. 226p. pap. 25.00 *(978-1-60899-135-8(0)*, Wipf and Stock) Wipf & Stock Pubs.

BIBLE—INSPIRATION

Here are entered works which discuss the Bible as a divinely inspired book. Works which attempt to establish the truth of statements in the Bible and to present the Bible as a book whose principles should be followed are entered under Bible—Evidences, Authority, etc.

see also Bible—Evidences, Authority, etc.

Akpa, Michael Onyedikachi. The Identity & Role of Michael in the Narrative of the War in Heaven. 2010. 360p. pap. *(978-3-639-27947-4(6))* VDM Verlag Dr. Mueller e.K.

Alexander, Archibald. Evidence of the Authenticity, Inspiration & Canonical Authority of the Holy Scriptures. (Works of Reverend Archibald Alexander). 308p. reprint ed. lib. bdg. 49.00 *(978-0-932051-73-8(1))* Reprint Services Co.

—Evidences of the Authenticity, Inspiration, & Canonical Authority of the Holy Scriptures. 2009. 192p. pap. 19.99 *(978-1-150-14392-2(4))* General Bks. LLC.

Alexander, T. Desmond. From Eden to the New Jerusalem: An Introduction to Biblical Theology, 1 vol. 2009. 208p. pap. 19.99 *(978-0-8254-2015-3(6))* Kregel Pubns.

Alexander, Terry G. Beyond Revelation: The Last Eden. 2010. 196p. pap. *(978-1-933641-36-2(3))* Bible Belt Pubns.

Allert, Craig D. A High View of Scripture? The Authority of the Bible & the Formation of the New Testament Canon. 2007. (Evangelical Ressourcement Ser.). 204p. (C). pap. 22.00 *(978-0-8010-2778-9(0))* Baker Academic.

Arthur W. Pink. The Divine Inspiration of the Bible. 2011. 144p. pap. 4.29 ***(978-1-60386-419-0(9)***, Watchmaker Publishing) Wexford College Pr.

Atkins, Fred. How to Maintain a Positive Attitude During the Difficult Times, 1 vol. 2009. 90p. pap. 16.95 *(978-1-60563-160-8(4))* PublishAmerica, Inc.

Badhai, Melinda Lis Solomon. Image & Likeness: Unveiling the Twenty-Seven Dimensions of Man... Condensed Version. 2011. 84p. pap. 9.95 *(978-1-4497-1217-4(7)*, WestBow Pr.) Author Solutions, Inc.

Barbeau, Jeffrey W. Coleridge, the Bible, & Religion. 2007. (Nineteenth-Century Major Lives & Letters Ser.). (ENG.). 248p. 95.00 *(978-0-230-60134-5(0))* Palgrave Macmillan.

The Beginning of Mankind. 2007. per. 14.95 *(978-0-9788520-5-4(2))* TanosBooks Publishing.

Berrigan, Daniel. The Nightmare of God: The Book of Revelation. 2009. (Daniel Berrigan Reprint Ser.). 126p. pap. 15.00 *(978-1-60608-470-0(4)*, Wipf and Stock) Wipf & Stock Pubs.

Bezet, D. L. "Rocky". True Riches: How to Enrich Your Life. 2009. 140p. pap. 14.99 *(978-1-61579-459-1(X))* Xulon Pr., Inc.

The Bible in 90 Days: Whole-Church Challenge - Session 1 with no Teacher, 1 vol. 2009. 2.99 *(978-0-310-94807-0(X))*; (ENG.). 2.99 *(978-0-310-94809-4(6))*; (ENG.). 4.99 *(978-0-310-94808-7(8))* Zondervan.

Bickle, Mike, notes. Book of Revelation NKJV. 2009. (Illus.). 139p. pap. 10.00 *(978-0-9823262-0-6(3))* Forerunner Books.

Biela, Frank. The Book of Revelation. 2007. 312p. pap. 14.95 *(978-1-59919-022-8(2)*, Ivan Pr.) Elim Publishing.

Billings, Cliff. Last Stand at Megiddo: A Study of the Book of Revelation. 2010. pap. 21.99 *(978-1-61566-781-9(4))* Tate Publishing & Enterprises, LLC.

Bock, Darrell L. Can I Trust the Bible? 2007. (RZIM Critical Questions Discussion Guides). (ENG.). 74p. per. 8.00 *(978-0-8308-3152-4(5)*, IVP Conn.) InterVarsity Pr.

Bovell, Carlos R. Inerrancy & the Spiritual Formation of Younger Evangelicals. 2007. 186p. pap. 21.00 *(978-1-59752-861-0(7)*, Wipf and Stock) Wipf & Stock Pubs.

Bowman, Bob. A Chosen Life Study: Conversations, Scriptures & Poems. 2009. 200p. pap. 19.99 *(978-1-4490-0123-0(8))* AuthorHouse.

Brice, Niambi Ngeri. Teacher Journal: A Book of Revelations. 2010. 68p. pap. 11.99 *(978-1-4490-1754-5(1))* AuthorHouse.

Britt, Dmin. Revelation for Dummies! 2011. 106p. pap. 11.99 ***(978-1-61379-292-6(1))*** Xulon Pr., Inc.

Brownlee, Edward L. Simply Revelation. 2011. pap. 18.99 ***(978-1-61777-736-3(6))*** Tate Publishing & Enterprises, LLC.

btmi.org, www. & Larry E. Wolfe, Evangelist. The Priesthood of the Apocalypse (the 144 Thousand) 2009. 132p. pap. 12.96 *(978-0-578-02168-3(4))* Wolfe, Larry E.

Burgon, Dean John William. Inspiration & Interpretation. 2008. pap. 29.00 *(978-1-888328-04-2(5))* Old Paths Pubns., Inc., The.

Caldecott, Stratford. All Things Made New: The Mysteries of the World in Christ. 2011. pap. ***(978-1-59731-129-8(4))*** Perennis, Sophia.

Carpenter, Anne. Revel in Revelations. 2010. 244p. pap. 15.99 *(978-1-61579-722-6(X))* Xulon Pr., Inc.

Cartrett, Shannon. One Extraordinary Life to Come an in-Depth Study of the Book of Revelation. 2009. spiral bd. 17.99 *(978-1-61623-241-2(2))* Independent Pub.

Collins, Bishop K. D. Ninth Hour. 2009. 232p. pap. 15.99 *(978-1-60791-658-1(4))* Xulon Pr., Inc.

Collins, Debra J. The Book of Revelation in Blonde. 2009. 144p. pap. 24.95 *(978-1-61546-599-6(5))* PublishAmerica, Inc.

Conner, Bobby. The Shepherd's Rod Volume XIII: The Kingdom Company. 2007. 64p. per. 8.00 *(978-0-9801639-0-2(0))* EaglesView Ministries.

Countryman, Jack. Treasure of God's Word, 0 vols. 2010. 176p. 16.99 *(978-1-4041-8976-8(9))* Nelson, Thomas Inc.

Dana, H. E. The Epistles & Apocalypse of John: A Brief Commentary. 2011. 160p. 41.95 ***(978-1-258-05666-7(6))*** Literary Licensing, LLC.

Daniele, Elizabeth. Revelation & Bible Prophecy Syr. 2009. 248p. pap. 15.38 *(978-0-557-16354-0(4))* Lulu Enterprises Inc.

Darden, John S. A Walk Through Revelation. 2010. 150p. pap. 10.98 *(978-0-557-00632-8(5))* Lulu Enterprises Inc.

Darst, G. Albert. The Revelation of Jesus Christ in the Old Testament. 2010. 356p. 32.99 *(978-1-60957-587-8(3))*; pap. 20.99 *(978-1-60957-586-1(5))* Xulon Pr., Inc.

Dickey, Darryl O. Revelations of the Bible: Lifting the Veil on the History & Creation of the Bible. 2010. 364p. pap. 24.75 *(978-1-4251-8863-4(X))* Trafford Publishing.

Divietro, Kirk. Cleaning-up Hazardous Materials. 2010. 418p. pap. 25.00 *(978-1-56848-068-8(7))* Old Paths Pubns., Inc., The.

Dobbs, H. A. He That Overcomes: A Study in the Book of Revelation. 2011. 340p. 39.95 ***(978-1-4497-3063-5(9))***; pap. 24.95 ***(978-1-4497-3062-8(0))*** Author Solutions, Inc. (WestBow Pr.).

Dodge, Esther. The Apocalypse & the Twentieth Century. 2011. 152p. 41.95 ***(978-1-258-04188-5(X))*** Literary Licensing, LLC.

Duarte, Armando. The Return of the High Priest. 2011. 44p. pap. 21.99 ***(978-1-4568-9478-8(1))*** Xlibris Corp.

[Dunn, Henry]. Liber Librorum: Its Structure, Limitations, & Purpose. A Friendly Communication to A Reluctant Sceptic. 2006. 240p. per. 20.99 *(978-1-4255-2021-2(9))* MPublishing.

Earley, Dave. 21 Reasons Bad Things Happen to Good People. 2008. (21 Most Ser.). (ENG.). 176p. pap. 4.99 *(978-1-60260-219-9(0)*, Barbour Bks.) Barbour Publishing, Inc.

Ebenhoe, Joseph R. The Prophecy Puzzle: Fitting Prophecy from the Whole Bible into the Book of Revelation. 2008. 252p. pap. 15.99 *(978-1-60647-661-1(0))* Xulon Pr., Inc.

Eldridge, Gary. Apocalypse... the Unveiling of Jesus Christ Coming King in the Book of Revelation. 2010. pap. 16.99 *(978-1-61579-704-2(1))* Xulon Pr., Inc.

Ewald, Georg Heinrich August. Abhandlungen Zur Orientalischen und Biblischen Literatur. 2010. (GER & ENG.). 166p. pap. 19.00 *(978-1-60899-604-9(2))* Wipf & Stock Pubs.

Farabaugh, David. A Pew Sitters Devotions in Revelation: Guide to Devotions in Revelation. 2009. pap. 13.99 *(978-1-60696-952-6(8))* Tate Publishing & Enterprises, LLC.

Farkasfalvy, Denis. Inspiration & Interpretation: A Theological Introduction to Sacred Scripture. 2010. 309p. pap. 34.95 *(978-0-8132-1746-8(6))* Catholic Univ. of America Pr.

Ferrari, Andrea. John Diodatis Doctrine of Holy Scripture. 2006. pap. 16.00 *(978-1-892777-98-0(3))* Reformation Heritage Bks.

Freeman, Eugene D. M. The End of the World Is Not Yet: Israel Is the Key Puzzle to Watch Resist EU's World Government the Church Must Resist its Adversaries. 2010. 132p. pap. 12.60 *(978-1-4269-3075-1(5))* Trafford Publishing.

Frishcosy, Unofficial Pastor Douglas E. Back Way into Heaven: Living for Life. 2008. 60p. pap. 16.95 *(978-1-60474-978-6(4))* PublishAmerica, Inc.

Garcia-Rivera, Alejandro. The Garden of God: A Theological Cosmology. 2009. (Theology & the Sciences Ser.). 176p. (C). pap. 22.00 *(978-0-8006-6358-2(6)*, Fortress Pr.) Augsburg Fortress, Pubs.

Garza Th.D, Al. The Jewish Unveiling of Revelation & the End. 2009. 152p. 30.00 *(978-0-557-11944-8(8))* Lulu Enterprises Inc.

Gaussen, Louis. The Divine Inspiration of Scripture. 2007. (ENG.). 400p. 24.99 *(978-1-85792-449-7(5))* Christian Focus Pubns. GBR. Dist: STL Distribution North America.

George, Timothy & George, Denise, eds. Why I Preach That the Bible is Literally True. (Library of Baptist Classics). pap. 19.99 *(978-0-8054-2077-7(0))* B&H Publishing Group.

Gettys, Joseph M. How to Study the Revelation. 2011. 132p. 40.95 ***(978-1-258-02367-6(9))*** Literary Licensing, LLC.

Gonzalez, Jonas. The Counting: 666, 1 vol. 2009. 49p. pap. 16.95 *(978-1-60813-489-2(X))* PublishAmerica, Inc.

Goodrick, Edward W. Is My Bible the Inspired Word of God? Lubeck, Ray, ed. rev. ed. 2007. (Illus.). 140p. (Orig.). pap. 17.00 *(978-1-55635-376-5(6)*, Wipf and Stock) Wipf & Stock Pubs.

Grant, James Ralph. Letters to the Seven Churches & Other Sermons. James, E. S., ed. 2011. 112p. 39.95 ***(978-1-258-09276-4(X))*** Literary Licensing, LLC.

HaLevi, Moshe Ben Yoseph. Revelation of the Bible: The Book of Genesis. 2011. 284p. 30.95 *(978-1-4502-8558-2(9))*; pap. 20.95 *(978-1-4502-8559-9(7))* iUniverse, Inc.

Hancock, Janet. That We May Know Him. 2007. 248p. pap. *(978-1-57258-456-3(4)*, 945-6317) TEACH Services, Inc.

Harris, R. Laird. Inspiration & Canonicity of the Scriptures. 2008. 348p. pap. 38.00 *(978-1-55635-887-6(3))* Wipf & Stock Pubs.

Haugabook, Phyllis. God's Favor 4 Teen Girls. 2009. 88p. pap. 10.99 *(978-1-60791-555-3(3))* Xulon Pr., Inc.

Hayden, Valda. Through the Valley: A Stunning Revelation of the Good Shepherd's Care for His Flock. Comprehensively Outlined in Psalm 23. 2009. 116p. pap. 11.99 *(978-1-61579-106-4(X))* Xulon Pr., Inc.

Heidt, William G. The Book of the Apocalypse: New Testament Reading Guide, No. 14. 2011. 130p. 40.95 ***(978-1-258-04434-3(X))*** Literary Licensing, LLC.

Hilliard, Jack. Understanding Revelation. 2008. 432p. 33.99 *(978-1-60791-055-8(1))* Xulon Pr., Inc.

Hodge, Archibald A. & Warfield, Benjamin B. Inspiration. 2008. 118p. pap. 10.00 *(978-1-55635-761-9(3))* Wipf & Stock Pubs.

Holland, Carl. Revelation Simplified. 2007. 200p. per. 14.99 *(978-1-60477-353-8(7))* Xulon Pr., Inc.

James, Randy L. Unraveling the Revelation: Devotional Readings from the Apocalypse, written from an A-millennial Perspective. 2010. 208p. pap. 15.00 *(978-1-4520-0783-0(7))* AuthorHouse.

Jeffrey, Grant R. The Signature of God, Revised Edition: Conclusive Proof that Every Teaching, Every Command, Every Promise in the Bible Is True. l.t. ed. 2010. (ENG.). 416p. pap. 17.99 *(978-1-59415-338-9(8))* Cengage Gale.

—The Signature of God, Revised Edition: Conclusive Proof That Every Teaching, Every Command, Every Promise in the Bible Is True. 3rd ed. 2010. (ENG.). 336p. pap. 14.99 *(978-0-307-44484-4(8)*, WaterBrook Pr.) Doubleday Religious Publishing Group, The.

Johnson, Arnold. God's Truth about the End of Time. 2011. 128p. 28.95 *(978-1-4497-1296-9(7))*; pap. 11.95 *(978-1-4497-1294-5(0))* Author Solutions, Inc. (WestBow Pr.).

Johnson, James R. All Power to the Lamb. 2011. 580p. 40.99 ***(978-1-61379-124-0(0))***; pap. 27.99 ***(978-1-61379-123-3(2))*** Xulon Pr., Inc.

Journey, Michael. Beyond the Seen: Journey Within, A Story Recollecting the Path Through the Depths of Sorrow to the Heights of Joy in Discovering the Revelation of Our True Birthright & Spiritual Essence. 2010. 232p. 33.95 *(978-1-4497-0638-8(X))*; pap. 17.95 *(978-1-4497-0636-4(3))* Author Solutions, Inc. (WestBow Pr.).

Kelly, William. God's Inspiration of the Scriptures. 2007. 484p. (ENG.). *(978-0-901860-56-9(5))*; per. *(978-0-901860-51-4(4))* Scripture Truth Pubns.

Kwok, Dennis & College, Faculty of Febc. Verbal Plenary Preservation of the Bible, a Course on the Doctrine of Verbal Plenary Preservation. 2008. 176p. pap. 15.00 *(978-0-9817985-4-7(3))* Old Paths Pubns., Inc., The.

Lajeunesse, Brian. Defy the Darkness. 2008. 100p. pap. 16.95 *(978-1-60703-386-8(0))* PublishAmerica, Inc.

Lee, Sang-Hwan. Revelation & Trinity: The Formative Influence of the Revelation of the Triune God in Calvin's 1559 Institutes & Barth's Church Dogmatics. 2011. 416p. 36.95 *(978-1-4502-7872-0(8))*; pap. 26.95 *(978-1-4502-7871-3(X))* iUniverse, Inc.

Lee, William. The Inspiration of Holy Scripture, Its Nature & Proof: Eight Discourses, Preached Before the University of Dublin, by William Lee ... 2006. 484p. pap. 29.99 *(978-1-4255-5389-0(3))*; 480p. per. 29.99 *(978-1-4255-5330-2(3))* MPublishing.

Lightner, Robert. A Biblical Case for Total Inerrancy: How Jesus Viewed the Old Testament. 2007. 204p. per. 24.00 *(978-1-57978-650-2(2))* Baptist Standard Bearer, Inc.

Marder, John. You're God's Gift to Teachers: Passages of Biblical Encouragement for Teachers. 2008. 184p. pap. 13.95 *(978-1-4327-3699-6(X))* Outskirts Pr., Inc.

Martin, Roy. The Book of Revelation from Alpha to Omega. 2011. pap. 25.99 *(978-1-61739-845-2(4))* Tate Publishing & Enterprises, LLC.

Mathews, Susan Fournier. The Book of Revelation: Question by Question. 2009. (Question by Question Bible Study Commentary Ser.). 224p. pap. 19.95 *(978-0-8091-4585-0(5))* Paulist Pr.

Mayer, Ladde. Israel Yesterday, the Body of Christ Today, Israel Tomorrow: Understanding the Relationship Between Israel's Kingdom Program & the Body of Christ Plus A Commentary on the Book of Revelation. 2010. 460p. 38.95 *(978-1-4502-3839-7(4))*; pap. 28.95 *(978-1-4502-3837-3(8))* iUniverse, Inc.

McKisic, Kelvin. Illuminating Revelation: A Study in the Book of Revelation. 2008. 244p. 24.99 *(978-1-60647-649-9(1))*; pap. 14.99 *(978-1-60647-648-2(3))* Xulon Pr., Inc.

Meier, Fred. Understanding the Times. 2006. (ENG.). 84p. per. 11.99 *(978-1-4141-0733-2(1))* Pleasant Word.

Miesner, Donald M. Keys to Revelation. 2011. 154p. pap. 29.99 ***(978-0-7586-3413-9(7))*** Concordia Publishing Hse.

Moorman, Jack. Forever Settled, A Survey of the Documents & History of the Bible. 2008. pap. 20.00 *(978-1-888328-06-6(1))* Old Paths Pubns., Inc., The.

Morgan, Nigel. Illuminating The End of Time: The Getty Apocalypse Manuscript. 2012. (ENG., Illus.). 180p. 75.00 *(978-1-60606-071-1(6)*, J. Paul Getty Museum) Getty Pubns.

Morritt, Robert. Early Explorations in the American Southwest. 2011. 176p. pap. ***(978-3-8443-8723-0(4))*** Lambert Academic Publishing.

Mueller, Steven P. Revelation: An Introductory Course. (Journeys Through God's Word Ser.). pap., stu. ed. 8.99 *(978-0-570-07819-7(9)*, 20-2820); pap. 8.99 *(978-0-570-07820-3(2)*, 20-2821) Concordia Publishing Hse.

Nester, Curtis E. Faith Will Keep You Afloat. 2009. 160p. pap. 14.99 *(978-1-60791-690-1(8))* Xulon Pr., Inc.

O'Hear, Natasha F. H. Contrasting Images of the Book of Revelation in Late Medieval & Early Modern Art: A Case Study in Visual Exegesis. 2011. (ENG., Illus.). 304p. 150.00 *(978-0-19-959010-0(9))* Oxford Univ. Pr., Inc.

Page, Marian. Bitterness: How It Can Effect You Physically, Emotionally & Spiritually. 2006. (ENG.). 64p. per. 10.99 *(978-1-4141-0780-6(3))* Pleasant Word.

Palladino Sr., Michael L. Why I Believe in the Rapture. 2010. 328p. pap. 21.99 *(978-1-4490-8325-0(0))* AuthorHouse.

Palmer, B. M. (Benjamin Morgan). Death in the Home: A Christian Father Responds Loss. 2008. (ENG.). 102p. reprint ed. pap. 12.95 *(978-0-9800370-1-2(8))* Reformed Academic Pr.

Patton, Francis L. (Francis Landrey). The Inspiration of the Scriptures by the Rev Francis L Patton. 2006. 144p. per. 16.99 *(978-1-4255-1060-2(4))* MPublishing.

Peale, Norman Vincent. Spirit Lifters. 2011. 26p. 35.95 ***(978-1-258-00467-5(4))*** Literary Licensing, LLC.

Pennington, Ray. The Answer to All Your Questions about the Book of Revelation. 2010. 230p. 25.99 *(978-1-60957-564-9(4))*; pap. 15.99 *(978-1-60957-563-2(6))* Xulon Pr., Inc.

Pink, Arthur. Divine Inspiration of the Bible. 2007. 112p. per. 11.99 *(978-1-58960-392-9(3))* Sovereign Grace Pubs., Inc.

Pink, Arthur W. The Divine Inspiration of the Bible. 2011. 98p. (Orig.). pap. 9.99 ***(978-1-61203-329-7(6))*** Bottom of the Hill Publishing.

Presley, Dale M. Way Truth: Life. 2009. 172p. 22.49 *(978-1-4490-3425-2(X))*; pap. 11.99 *(978-1-4490-3424-5(1))* AuthorHouse.

Ray, Walter. Gods Plan for Our Age. 2009. 252p. pap. 14.49 *(978-1-4389-3666-6(4))* AuthorHouse.

Richardson, Robert F. Justice Pending: The Revelation of God's Inconvenient Truth. 2010. 424p. 42.95 *(978-1-4497-0362-2(3))*; pap. 27.95 *(978-1-4497-0361-5(5))* Author Solutions, Inc. (WestBow Pr.).

Rogers, Henry. Reason & Faith; Their Claims & Conflicts. 2007. 80p. per. *(978-1-4068-3996-8(5))* Echo Library.

Rogers, John G. The Gentile Valley of Bones. 2010. pap. 12.99 *(978-1-61663-164-2(3))* Tate Publishing & Enterprises, LLC.

Rothhaar, Gary Alan. The Revelation of Jesus Christ Clear & Understandable. 2011. 146p. pap. 19.99 ***(978-1-4653-5530-0(8))*** Xlibris Corp.

Sampson, Shellie. Revelation Now: Viewing the Tragedies & Triumph of Believers: Building Faith for Life Now. 2010. 164p. 24.95 *(978-1-4401-9749-9(0))*; (ENG.). pap. 14.95 *(978-1-4401-9747-5(4))* iUniverse, Inc.

Satta, Ronald F. The Sacred Text: Biblical Authority in Nineteenth-Century America. 2007. (Princeton Theological Monographs). 132p. pap. 16.00 *(978-1-55635-298-0(0)*, Pickwick Pubns.) Wipf & Stock Pubs.

Sedinger, Ione L. The Good News of the Apocalypse: Dancing Your Way Through the Bible. 2010. 380p. 34.95 *(978-1-4502-5474-8(8))*; pap. 24.95 *(978-1-4502-5473-1(X))* iUniverse, Inc.

Seiss, Joseph A. Letters to the Seven Churches. 2011. 344p. 51.95 ***(978-1-258-03231-9(7))*** Literary Licensing, LLC.

The Seven Churches of Asia: The Path of the Chosen Revealed. 2007. (Illus.). 343p. per. 19.99 *(978-1-59886-940-8(X))* Tate Publishing & Enterprises, LLC.

Simpson, William D. Living in the Hope of My Imagination: A Compelling Story that Proves the Bible to be A Living Revelation of God. 2010. 264p. pap. 16.99 *(978-0-88144-488-9(X)*, Thorncrown Publishing) Yorkshire Publishing Group.

Skelton, Kenneth. The Names of Man: A Divine Revelation of Who God Created You to Be. 2011. pap. 10.99 ***(978-1-61777-811-7(7))*** Tate Publishing & Enterprises, LLC.

Smolarz, Sebastian R. Covenant & the Metaphor of Divine Marriage in Biblical Thought: A Study with Special Reference to the Book of Revelation. 2010. 404p. pap. 44.00 *(978-1-60899-455-7(4)*, Wipf and Stock) Wipf & Stock Pubs.

Storms, C. Samuel. To the One Who Conquers: 50 Daily Meditations on the Seven Letters of Revelation 2-3. 2008. 239p. *(978-1-4335-0455-6(3))* Crossway.

Struyk, M. J. God's Plan for Victory in the Life of His Children, 1 vol. 2010. 51p. pap. 16.95 *(978-1-4489-7028-5(8))* PublishAmerica, Inc.

Swain, Scott R. Trinity, Revelation, & Reading: A Theological Introduction to the Bible & its Interpretation. 2011. (ENG.). 168p. 90.00 *(978-0-567-25525-9(5))*; pap. 27.95 *(978-0-567-26540-1(4))* Continuum International Publishing Group, Ltd. GBR. (T&T Clark Int'l). Dist: National Bk. Network.

Topping, Richard R. Revelation Scripture & Church: Theological Hermeneutic Thought of James Barr Paul Ricoeur & Hans Frei. 2007. (Ashgate New Critical Thinking in Religion, Theology & Biblical Studies Ser.). 252p. 114.95 *(978-0-7546-5802-3(3))* Ashgate Publishing Co.

Tucker, R. E. A Visitation from Jesus: Orders from Headquarters. 2011. 332p. pap. 21.49 ***(978-1-4634-1915-8(5))*** AuthorHouse.

Tuella. A New Book of Revelations. 160p. pap. 14.00 *(978-0-938294-85-6(7))* Inner Light - Global Communications.

Upton, Jerry N. Revelation of Christ. 2011. 332p. pap. 18.99 ***(978-1-61379-482-1(7))*** Xulon Pr., Inc.

Upton, Jerry N. & Ukiwe, David. Revelation of Christ. 2015 332p. 28.99 ***(978-1-61379-483-8(5))*** Xulon Pr., Inc.

Vanderslice, Debbie. Shameless: An 8-Week Study to Freedom Through God's Redemption. 2008. (ENG.). 224p. pap. 12.99 *(978-1-59669-216-9(2))* New Hope Pubs.

Vanover, S. T. Holocaust # 2. 2007. 144p. pap. 15.00 *(978-0-8059-7528-4(4))* Dorrance Publishing Co., Inc.

Vassal, Joy. Turn Around & See the Lord. 2009. 276p. 26.99 *(978-1-60647-893-6(1))*; pap. 16.99 *(978-1-60647-892-9(3))* Xulon Pr., Inc.

Vince, Benjamin Lee. The Bible, Re-Write It or Re-Read It: Do We Really Need Another Version of the Bible? 2008. 252p. pap. 16.99 *(978-1-4343-8304-4(0))* AuthorHouse.

Vtlez, Jost D. Un Nombre 13 Revelaciones. 2009. 108p. pap. 12.49 *(978-1-4389-2731-2(2))* AuthorHouse.

Wahlstedt, Carl. Brokenwing of an Angel. 2009. 178p. pap. 17.99 *(978-1-4490-0603-7(5))* AuthorHouse.

Walthall, Bill. The Love Revelation. 2008. 268p. pap. 17.00 *(978-1-59755-125-0(2)*, Advantage Inspirational) Advantage Bks.

Westcott, Brooke Foss. Thoughts on Revelation & Life: Being Selections from the Writings of Brooke Foss Westcott, D. D, D. C. L. Phillips, Stephen, ed. 2007. (Illus.). 398p. pap. 34.00 *(978-1-55635-752-7(4))* Wipf & Stock Pubs.

White, C. Randy. The Apocalypse: Expository Messages from Revelation: the Revelation of the Redeemer. 2007. 303p. per. 16.95 *(978-1-59824-425-0(6))* E-BookTime LLC.

Wilson, Philip Whitwell. The Vision We Forget. 2007. (ENG.). 286p. 43.95 *(978-0-548-01658-9(5))* Kessinger Publishing, LLC.

Wilton, Don & Wilton, Donald. A Hope & a Future: Overcoming Discouragement, 1 vol. 2009. (ENG.). 256p. pap. 16.99 *(978-0-8054-4555-8(2)*, B&H Bks.) B&H Publishing Group.

Winfrey, Melvin. The Beast That Was, & Is Not, & yet Is. 2009. 136p. *(978-1-4389-9879-4(1))* AuthorHouse.

Witulski, Thomas. Die Johannesoffenbarung und Kaiser Hadrian: Studien Zur Datierung der Neutestamentlichen Apokalpyse. 2007. (Forschungen Zur Religion und Literatur des Alten & Neuen Testament Ser.). (GER.). 415p. (C). 117.00 *(978-3-525-53085-6(4))* Vandenhoeck & Ruprecht GmbH & Co. KG DEU. Dist: ISD.

Woodson, K. L. Delivered into Destiny, 1 vol. 2009. 53p. pap. 12.95 *(978-1-4489-8183-0(2))* PublishAmerica, Inc.

Zia, Mark J. What Are They Saying about Biblical Inspiration? 2011. (What Are They Saying about ... ? Ser.). 128p. pap. *(978-0-8091-4699-4(1))* Paulist Pr.

BIBLE—INTERLINEAR TRANSLATIONS

Bauscher, David. The Aramaic-English Interlinear New Testament. 2008. 621p. 54.98 *(978-1-4357-3462-3(9))* Lulu Enterprises Inc.

Berry, George. Interlinear Hebrew-English Old Testament. 2007. 420p. per. 19.95 *(978-1-933993-52-2(9))* Apocryphile Pr.

Green, Sr. Larger Print Interlinear Hebrew Greek English Bible. 2007. 728p. per. 52.99 *(978-1-58960-481-0(4))*; (ENG.). 812p. per. 58.99 *(978-1-58960-484-1(9))* Sovereign Grace Pubs., Inc.

—Larger Print Interlinear Hebrew Greek English Bible, Volume 3 of 3 Volumes. 2007. 756p. per. 52.99 *(978-1-58960-483-4(0))* Sovereign Grace Pubs., Inc.

Green, Sr., tr. Larger Print Interlinear Hebrew Greek English Bible. 2007. 728p. per. 52.99 *(978-1-58960-482-7(2))* Sovereign Grace Pubs., Inc.

The Interlinear Bible Hebrew - English: The Book of Genesis. 2006. 252p. per. *(978-956-291-340-9(6))* Editorial Benei Noaj.

Magiera, Janet M. Aramaic Peshitta New Testament Translation, 3 vols. 2009. (SYR & ENG.). ***(978-0-9679613-9-2(4)***, LWM Pubns.) Light of the Word Ministry.

Magiera, Janet M. & Magiera, Janet. Aramaic Peshitta New Testament Translation, 3 vols. 2009. (SYR & ENG.). ***(978-0-9679613-8-5(6))***; ***(978-0-9820085-0-8(3))*** Light of the Word Ministry. (LWM Pubns.).

MKL Resources, LLC. Interlinear Bible: With Strong's Numbers, Greek, & Hebrew. 2011. 800p. pap. 36.49 *(978-1-4520-1823-2(5))* AuthorHouse.

Pentateuco, Biblia. Antiguo Testamento Interlineal: Interlinear Hebrew - Sp. O. T., 1 vol., Vol. 1. 2009. (SPA.). 876p. 34.99 *(978-84-7645-397-1(3)*, 223518) Clie, Editorial ESP. Dist: Zondervan.

BIBLE—INTERPRETATION

see Bible—Commentaries; Bible—Criticism, Interpretation, etc.; Bible—Hermeneutics

BIBLE—INTRODUCTIONS

Anderson, William Angor. Introduction to the Bible: Overview, Historical Context, & Cultural Perspectives. 2012. ***(978-0-7648-2119-6(9))*** Liguori Pubns.

Augsburg Fortress, creator. The Lutheran Handbook II. 2007. (Illus.). 304p. per. 14.99 *(978-0-8066-7037-9(1))* Augsburg Fortress, Pubs.

Babb, Reverend Joe R. A History of the Bible. 2010. (ENG.). 116p. pap. 15.00 *(978-0-9827611-2-0(0)*, Catch the Spirit of Appalachia) Ammons Communications, Ltd.

Barbour Publishing, Inc. Staff & Stedman, Ray C. Aventurándonos en el Conocimiento de la Biblia. 2010. (SPA.). 880p. pap. 16.99 *(978-1-60485-129-8(5))* Discovery Hse. Pubs.

Barton, John. The Bible: The Basics. 2010. (Illus.). x, 190p. (C). 19.95 ***(978-0-203-85998-8(7))*** Routledge.

Beers, V. Gilbert. Manual de Descubrimientos Biblicos: Discovery Bible Handbook. (SPA.). *(978-84-7645-339-1(6)*, 223377) Clie, Editorial.

Binz, Stephen J. Introduccion a la Biblia Una Guia Catolica para el Estudio de las Escrituras. 2007. (SPA.). 94p. per. 8.95 *(978-0-8146-1711-3(5)*, Liturgical Pr. Bks.) Liturgical Pr.

Blankenbaker, Frances & Mears, Henrietta. What the Bible Is All about for Young Explorers-Japanese. 2011. (JPN., Illus.). 364p. pap. 34.50 ***(978-4-264-01802-5(1))*** Word of Life Press Ministries JPN. Dist: STL Distribution North America.

Boyett, Jason & Boyett. Pocket Guide to the Bible No. 1: A Little Book about the Big Book. 2009. (ENG., Illus.). 208p. pap. 12.95 *(978-0-470-37309-5(1)*, Jossey-Bass) Wiley, John & Sons, Inc.

Carr, David M. & Conway, Colleen M. An Introduction to the Bible: Sacred Texts & Imperial Contexts. 2010. (ENG., Illus.). 408p. 110.95 *(978-1-4051-6738-3(6))*; pap. 61.95 *(978-1-4051-6737-6(8))* Wiley, John & Sons, Inc. (Wiley-Blackwell).

Connelly, Douglas. The Bible for Blockheads: A User-Friendly Look at the Good Book, 1 vol. rev. ed. 2007. (ENG., Illus.). 480p. pap. 19.99 *(978-0-310-27388-2(9))* Zondervan.

Coogan, Michael D., ed. The Oxford Encyclopedia of the Books of the Bible, 2 vols. 2011. (Oxford Encyclopedias of the Bible Ser.). (ENG., Illus.). 1280p. 395.00 *(978-0-19-537737-8(0))* Oxford Univ. Pr., Inc.

Cram101 Textbook Reviews. Outlines & Highlights for Understanding the Bible by Harris, Isbn: 0767429168. 2011. 478p. pap. 37.95 ***(978-1-61830-049-2(0))*** Cram101 Inc.

Croft, Andy & Pilavachi, Mike. Storylines Your Map to Understanding the Bible. 2nd ed. 2010. 207p. ***(978-1-4347-0037-7(2))*** Kingsway Pubns.

Daley, John. Getting to Know the Bible. 2006. 64p. pap. 5.95 *(978-0-7648-1509-6(1))* Liguori Pubns.

David, Patricia J. Through the Bible: A Comprehensive, Sequential Bible Survey Study & Reference Source. 2008. (Illus.). 385p. pap. 28.99 *(978-0-89827-396-0(X))* Wesleyan Publishing Hse.

Dawes, Gregory W. Introduction to the Bible. 2007. (New Collegeville Bible Commentary Ser.). (Illus.). 80p. per. 6.95 *(978-0-8146-2835-5(4))* Liturgical Pr.

Deming, Lynne Mobberley. A User's Guide to the Bible. 2010. (Insights: Bible Studies for Growing Faith Ser.). 62p pap. 9.00 *(978-1-60899-220-1(9))* Wipf & Stock Pubs.

Dever, Mark. What Does God Want of Us Anyway? A Quick Overview of the Whole Bible. 2010. pap. *(978-1-4335-1416-6(8))*; 128p. 12.99 *(978-1-4335-1415-9(X))* Crossway.

Drane, John. Introducing the Bible. 2nd rev. ed. 2011. 736p. pap. 65.00 *(978-0-8006-9840-9(1)*, Fortress Pr.) Augsburg Fortress, Pubs.

Ellie Claire Staff, creator. Everything but the Bible: Black Floral. 2008. (ENG.). lthr. 29.99 *(978-1-934770-89-4(2))* Ellie Claire & Summerside Pr.

—Everything but the Bible: Traditional, Black. 2008. (ENG.). lthr. 29.99 *(978-1-934770-88-7(4))* Ellie Claire & Summerside Pr.

Essex, Barbara J. Bible for Vital Congregations. 2008. *(978-0-8298-1732-4(8))* Pilgrim Pr., The/United Church Pr.

George, Jim. The Bare Bones Bible Handbook: 10 Minutes to Understanding Each Book of the Bible. 2006. (Bare Bones Bible Ser.). (Illus.). 325p. per. 13.99 *(978-0-7369-1654-7(7))* Harvest Hse. Pubs.

—The Bare Bones Bible Handbook for Teens: Getting to Know Every Book in the Bible. 2008. (Bare Bones Bible Ser.). 336p. pap. 12.99 *(978-0-7369-2386-6(1))* Harvest Hse. Pubs.

Gilbert, Christopher. A Complete Introduction to the Bible: A Literary & Historical Introduction to the Bible. 2009. (Illus.). 320p. pap. 24.95 *(978-0-8091-4552-2(9))* Paulist Pr.

Gospel Light. Depending on Jesus: Jesus Provides What We Truly Need in Every Life Challenge. 2011. (SonRise National Park Ser.). (ENG.). 144p. (gr. 13). pap. 12.99 ***(978-0-8307-5996-5(4))*** Gospel Light Pubns.

Gudgel, David. Owner's Guide to Using Your Bible. 2009. 124p. pap. 11.99 *(978-1-60791-913-1(3))* Xulon Pr., Inc.

Hammond, Jonathan. The Bible the Only Infallible Book for the Perishing World. 2009. 328p. pap. 18.99 *(978-1-60791-117-3(5))* Xulon Pr., Inc.

Hargrove, Verna. First Step for Christians. 2009. 73p. pap. 12.00 *(978-0-557-19931-0(X))* Lulu Enterprises Inc.

Harper, Lisa. What the Bible Is All about for Women: A Book of 66 Devotions. 2007. (ENG.). 224p. per. 14.99 *(978-0-8307-4406-0(1))* Gospel Light Pubns.

Harris, Stephen. Understanding the Bible. 8th ed. 2010. (ENG., Illus.). 592p. (C). pap. 98.33 *(978-0-07-340744-9(5)*, 0073407445) McGraw-Hill Cos., The.

Hauer, Christian E. & Young, William A. Introduction to the Bible. 8th rev. ed. 2011. (ENG.). 400p. (C). pap. 92.00 ***(978-0-205-05165-6(0)***, Prentice Hall) Prentice Hall PTR.

Hole, Frank. The Gospels & Acts. 2007. 392p. *(978-0-901860-46-0(8))* Scripture Truth Pubns.

Ishida, Hiroshi. Manga Introduction to the Bible-Japanese. 2011. (JPN.). 176p. pap. 28.00 ***(978-4-264-02722-5(5))*** Word of Life Press Ministries JPN. Dist: STL Distribution North America.

Jenkins, Simon. The Bible from Scratch. 2006. (Illus.). 259p. per. 16.75 *(978-0-88489-940-2(3))* St. Mary's Pr.

—The Bible from Scratch: A Lightning Tour from Genesis to Revelation. 2009. (ENG., Illus.). 256p. pap. 14.95 *(978-0-7459-4154-7(0))* Lion Hudson PLC GBR. Dist: Independent Pubs. Group.

Jenks, Gregory C. The Once & Future Bible: An Introduction to the Bible for Religious Progressives. 2011. 268p. pap. 29.00 *(978-1-60899-961-3(0)*, Wipf and Stock) Wipf & Stock Pubs.

Knight, George W. Quicknotes Bible Handbook. 2009. (QuickNotes Commentaries Ser.). (ENG.). 352p. pap. 4.99 *(978-1-60260-444-5(4)*, Barbour Bks.) Barbour Publishing, Inc.

Knight, Trevor F. God's Wonderful Word: Introducing Each Book of the Bible. 2007. 151p. pap. 13.00 *(978-1-84625-072-9(2))* DayOne Pubns. GBR. Dist: STL Distribution North America.

Kugler, Robert & Hartin, Patrick. An Introduction to the Bible. 2009. (ENG., Illus.). 600p. 50.00 *(978-0-8028-4636-5(X))* Eerdmans, William B. Publishing Co.

Lang, J. Stephen. Guideposts Know the Bible in 30 Days. 2008. (ENG.). 432p. 24.99 *(978-0-8249-4733-0(9)*, GuidepostsBooks) Ideals Pubns.

Latkovich, Sallie. Mining the Meaning of the Bible: Beyond the Literal Word. 2011. 64p. *(978-0-7648-1982-7(8))* Liguori Pubns.

Levy, Steve. Bible Overview. 2008. (ENG.). pap. 11.99 *(978-1-84550-378-9(3))* Christian Focus Pubns. GBR. Dist: STL Distribution North America.

Linafelt, Tod. The Hebrew Bible As Literature: A Very Short Introduction. 2010. (ENG.). 144p. pap. 11.95 *(978-0-19-530007-9(6))* Oxford Univ. Pr., Inc.

Mattam, Zacharias. Meeting Christ in the Scriptures: A Comprehensive Introduction to the Bible. 2009. (Illus.). xii, 327p. pap. *(978-81-87370-49-9(1),* Library of Congress — New Delhi Overseas Office) Kristu Jyoti Pubns., Kristu Jyoti College.

McDonald, Lee. Origin of the Bible Guide Perp. 2011. (Guides for the Perplexed Ser.). (ENG.). 272p. pap. 27.95 *(978-0-567-13932-0(8),* T&T Clark Int'l) Continuum International Publishing Group, Ltd. GBR. Dist: National Bk. Network.

McKenzie, Steven L. How to Read the Bible: History, Prophecy, Literature — Why Modern Readers Need to Know the Difference & What It Means for Faith Today. 2009. (ENG.). 224p. pap. 16.95 *(978-0-19-538330-0(3))* Oxford Univ. Pr., Inc.

Messenger Magazine, Various. A Dunker Guide to the Bible. 2010. (Illus.). 226p. pap. 15.95 *(978-0-87178-137-6(9))* Brethren Pr.

Miller, Stephen. User's Guide to the Bible. 2007. (Questions of Faith Ser.). (Illus.). 125p. pap. 14.95 *(978-1-59856-138-8(3))* Hendrickson Pubs. Marketing, LLC.

Miller, Stephen M. User's Guide to the Bible. 2007. (Questions of Faith Ser.). (Illus.). 125p. pap. 9.97 *(978-1-59856-232-3(0))* Hendrickson Pubs. Marketing, LLC.

Mitchell, Alison. The Book of Beginnings: Bible Discovery for Children. 2010. 80p. (J). pap. *(978-1-873166-93-2(1))* Good Bk. Co.

—The Book of Beginnings: Bible Discovery for Families. 2010. 48p. (J). pap. *(978-1-873166-92-5(3))* Good Bk. Co.

Paprocki, Joe. The Bible Blueprint: A Catholic's Guide to Understanding & Embracing God's World. rev. ed. 2009. (ENG.). 144p. pap. 9.95 *(978-0-8294-2898-8(4))* Loyola Pr.

—Los Planos de la Biblia: Una Guía Católica para Entender y Acoger la Palabra de Dios. Arias, Miguel, tr. from ENG. 2009. (SPA.). 144p. pap. 9.95 *(978-0-8294-2858-2(5))* Loyola Pr.

Parker, William J. Scripture 101: An Intro to Reading the Bible. 2009. 160p. pap. 14.95 *(978-0-7648-1700-7(C),* Liguori) Liguori Pubns.

Publications International Staff. Daily Dose of Knowledge Bible. 2009. 384p. 19.95 *(978-1-4127-1541-6(5))* Publications International, Ltd.

Riches, John. The Bible. 2010. (Brief Insight Ser.). (ENG.). 232p. 14.95 *(978-1-4027-7536-9(9))* Sterling Publishing Co., Inc.

Rogers, Cris. The Bible Book by Book: A Journey Through Its People, Places & Themes, 1 vol. 2011. (Illus.). 208p. pap. 19.99 *(978-0-85721-016-6(5),* Monarch Bks.) Lion Hudson PLC GBR. Dist: Kregel Pubns.

Rogerson, J. W. An Introduction to the Bible. 3rd ed. 2012. (BibleWorld Ser.). (ENG.). 240p. (C). pap. 29.95 *(978-1-84553-707-4(6))* Equinox Publishing Ltd. GBR. Dist: ISD.

Rose Publishing (Torrance, Calif.) Staff, contrib. by. Parables & Other Favorite Bible Studies. 2010. pap. *(978-1-59636-416-5(5))* Rose Publishing.

Royer, Darline Kantola & Burk, Dorsey. An Introduction to the Bible. 2011. *(978-0-7577-4215-6(7))* Word Aflame Pr.

Ruff, Jerry, Sr., ed. Understanding the Bible: A Guide to Reading the Scriptures. 2008. (Illus.). ix, 99p. pap. 12.95 *(978-0-88489-852-8(0))* St. Mary's Pr.

Russell, Gilbert & Russell, Judith. Introduction to the Bible. 2011. 96p. pap. 13.95 *(978-1-4670-6025-7(9))* AuthorHouse.

Saarnivaara, Uuras. Can the Bible Be Trusted? Old & New Testament Introduction & Interpretation. 2008. 812p. pap. 74.00 *(978-1-55635-699-5(4),* Wipf and Stock) Wipf & Stock Pubs.

Satta, Ronald F. A Survey of the Bible: An Overview of the Sixty-Six Canonical Books of Sacred Scripture. 2008. 246p. pap. 27.00 *(978-1-60608-068-9(7),* Wipf and Stock) Wipf & Stock Pubs.

Schehr, Timothy P. The Bible Made Easy: A Book-by-Book Introduction. 2006. 246p. per. 5.95 *(978-0-86716-598-2(7))* Franciscan Media.

Snodgrass, Diann. Understanding Who God Is. 2010. 108p. pap. 11.95 *(978-1-4520-3657-1(8))* AuthorHouse.

Strickland, William P. A Manual of Biblical Literature. 2006. 420p. per. 26.99 *(978-1-4255-4523-9(8))* MPublishing.

Sumney, Jerry L. The Bible: An Introduction. 2009. 320p. pap. 42.00 *(978-0-8006-6374-2(8),* Fortress Pr.) Augsburg Fortress, Pubs.

Swain, Scott R. Trinity, Revelation, & Reading: A Theological Introduction to the Bible & its Interpretation. 2011. (ENG.). 168p. 90.00 *(978-0-567-25525-9(5));* pap. 27.95 *(978-0-567-26540-1(4))* Continuum International Publishing Group, Ltd. GBR. (T&T Clark Int'l). Dist: National Bk. Network.

Swenson, Kristin. Bible Babel: Making Sense of the Most Talked about Book of All Time. 2011. (ENG.). 368p. pap. 14.99 *(978-0-06-172826-6(8),* HarperPerennial) HarperCollins Pubs.

Taylor, Justin. As It Was Written: An Introduction to the Bible. 2007. (Illus.). 168p. pap. 19.00 *(978-1-55635-521-9(1))* Wipf & Stock Pubs.

Tice, Rico & Shammas, Sam. How to Run the Course. 2010. (Christianity Explored Ser.). 153p. pap. *(978-1-906334-60-4(9))* Good Bk. Co.

Tidwell, Josiah Blake. The Bible Book by Book: A Manual for the Outline Study of the Bible by Book. 2007. 188p. pap. 19.99 *(978-1-4346-2739-1(X));* 210p. pap. 22.99 *(978-1-4346-2772-8(1))* BiblioBazaar.

Tidwell, Josiah Blake. The Bible Book by Books, a Manual for the Outline Study of the Bible by Books. 2011. 152p. pap. 14.99 ***(978-1-61203-238-2(9))*** Bottom of the Hill Publishing.

Tinsley, Sarah V. Bible in a Nutshell, Daily Devotional Version. I.t. ed. 2010. 436p. pap. 29.95 *(978-1-4357-3113-4(1))* Lulu Enterprises Inc.

Wafer, G. Arnold. Start Right, Finish Strong: What Every Christian Should Know. 2010. pap. 21.99 *(978-1-60799-713-9(4))* Tate Publishing & Enterprises, LLC.

Walker, Peter. The Lion Companion to the Bible. 2011. (ENG., Illus.). 320p. 29.95 *(978-0-7459-5292-5(5))* Lion Hudson PLC GBR. Dist: Independent Pubs. Group.

Weaver, Dean M. Singing & Sighing Through the Psalms: Scaling the Heights of Hope & Sounding the Depths of Depression. 2007. (Illus.). 364p. spiral bd. 25.00 *(978-0-943195-02-5(0))* Multiple Ministries.

Webster, Allen. A Brief Introduction to the Bible. 2007. 0.75 *(978-1-933808-82-6(9))* House to House Heart to Heart Publishing, Inc.

Williams, Marion H. Beyond Adam & Eve: 50 Things You Need to Know Before You Get to Heaven. 2007. (Illus.). 340p. pap. 12.95 *(978-0-9797845-0-7(6))* Recamier Publishing, LLC.

Winter, David. The Bible Made Clear. 2008. (ENG., Illus.). 160p. pap. 14.95 *(978-0-7459-5273-4(9))* Lion Hudson PLC GBR. Dist: Independent Pubs. Group.

Witherup, Ronald D. The Bible Companion: A Catholic Handbook for Beginners. 2nd ed. 2009. (ENG.). 264p. pap. 14.95 *(978-0-8245-2547-7(7))* Crossroad Publishing Co., The.

BIBLE—INTRODUCTIONS—APOCRYPHA AND APOCRYPHAL BOOKS

Bouwman, Hans. In Remembrance of These Things. 2007. 100p. per. *(978-1-897117-41-5(8))* Gospel Folio Pr.

Dentan, Robert C. The Apocrypha, Bridge of the Testaments: A Reader's Guide to the Apocryphal Books of the Old Testament. 2011. 130p. 40.95 ***(978-1-258-04913-3(9))*** Literary Licensing, LLC.

Ehrman, Bart D. & Plese, Zlatko. The Apocryphal Gospels: Texts & Translations, 1 vol. 2011. (ENG.). 624p. 35.00 *(978-0-19-973210-4(8))* Oxford Univ. Pr., Inc.

Fairweather, Stephen. The Missing Book of Genesis. 2010. 328p. pap. 17.99 *(978-1-4490-9238-2(1))* AuthorHouse.

Goodspeed, Edgar J., tr. The Apocryph: An American Translation. 2011. 506p. 60.95 ***(978-1-258-04282-0(7))*** Literary Licensing, LLC.

Harwood, William. Biblical Apocryph: Books Excluded from the King James Version. Strozier, M. Stefan & Torke, Kyle, eds. 2010. 562p. 49.95 *(978-1-935444-32-9(8))* World Audience Pubs.

James, M. R. The Lost Apocrypha of the Old Testament: Their Titles & Fragments. 2007. 124p. pap. 12.00 *(978-1-55635-289-8(1),* Wipf and Stock) Wipf & Stock Pubs.

Johnson, Norman B. & Johnson, Norman B. Prayer in Apocrypha & Pseudepigraph: A Study of the Jewish Concept of God. 2011. 82p. 37.95 ***(978-1-258-03761-1(0))*** Literary Licensing, LLC.

Platt, Jr. The Forgotten Books of Eden. 2007. 280p. per. 17.50 *(978-1-60206-551-2(9))* Cosimo, Inc.

William Wake, Archbishop. The Forbidden Books - the Suppressed Gospels & Epistles of the Original New Testament. 2008. 601p. pap. 36.95 *(978-1-84799-838-5(0))* Lulu Enterprises Inc.

BIBLE—INTRODUCTIONS—N. T.

Here are entered introductions to the New Testament as a whole, or to any part except the Gospels, which are listed separately below.

Adams, Edward. Parallel Lives of Jesus: A Guide to the Four Gospels. 2011. (ENG.). 200p. pap. 25.00 ***(978-0-664-23331-0(7))*** Westminster John Knox Pr.

Barbieri, Tony. Covenant Series- Book 1: An Introduction to the New Covenant. 2011. pap. 14.95 *(978-0-7414-6390-6(3))* Infinity Publishing.

Barclay, William. Barclay's Guide to the New Testament. 2008. (ENG.). 351p. pap. 30.00 *(978-0-664-23256-6(6))* Westminster John Knox Pr.

Barr, David L. New Testament Story: An Introduction. 4th rev. ed. 2008. (ENG., Illus.). 608p. (C). per. 73.95 *(978-0-534-62748-5(X))* Wadsworth.

Beal, Timothy. Biblical Literacy: The Essential Bible Stories Everyone Needs to Know. 2010. (ENG.). 368p. pap. 15.99 *(978-0-06-171867-0(X),* HarperOne) HarperCollins Pubs.

Berding, Kenneth & Williams, Matt, eds. What the New Testament Authors Really Cared About: A Survey of Their Writings, 1 vol. 2008. 240p. pap. 24.99 *(978-0-8254-2539-4(5))* Kregel Pubns.

Boring, M. Eugene. An Introduction to the New Testament: History, Literature, Theology. 2012. (ENG.). 584p. pap. 40.00 ***(978-0-664-25592-3(2))*** Westminster John Knox Pr.

Carson, D. A. & Moo, Douglas J. Introducing the New Testament: A Short Guide to Its History & Message, 1 vol. Naselli, Andrew David, ed. abr. ed. 2010. (ENG.). 160p. (C). pap. 12.99 *(978-0-310-29149-7(6))* Zondervan.

Cory, Catherine. A Voyage Through the New Testament. 2007. (ENG., Illus.). 560p. (C). per. 73.00 *(978-0-13-049495-5(X),* Prentice Hall) Prentice Hall PTR.

Cousar, Charles B. An Introduction to the New Testament: Witnesses to God's New Work. annot. ed. 2006. (ENG.). 215p. per. 30.00 *(978-0-664-22413-4(X))* Westminster John Knox Pr.

Cram101 Textbook Reviews. Outlines & Highlights for New Testament: A Students Introduction by Stephen L. Harris, ISBN. 2011. 462p. pap. 37.95 ***(978-1-61812-203-2(7))*** Cram101 Inc.

—Outlines & Highlights for New Testament Story: An Introduction by Barr, ISBN. 2011. 320p. pap. 33.95 ***(978-1-61830-047-8(4))*** Cram101 Inc.

Davies, Stevan L. The New Testament: An Analytical Approach. 2011. pap. 37.00 ***(978-1-59815-036-0(7))*** Polebridge Pr.

Deibler, Ellis/W., Jr. A Translator's Translation: Of the New Testament. 2008. 560p. 19.95 *(978-0-9640069-4-2(4))* Cummins Works.

Driscoll, Mark. On the New Testament. 2008. (Book You'll Actually Read Ser.). 88p. pap. 9.99 *(978-1-4335-0134-0(1))* Crossway.

Ehrman, Bart D. The New Testament: A Historical Introduction to the Early Christian Writings. 5th ed. 2011. (Illus.). xxxvii, 536p. ***(978-0-19-975755-8(0));*** (ENG., 608p. (C). pap. 64.95 *(978-0-19-975753-4(4))* Oxford Univ. Pr., Inc.

Geisler, Norman L. A Popular Survey of the New Testament. 2008. (Illus.). 352p. 34.99 *(978-0-8010-1299-0(6))* Baker Bks.

Goodspeed, Edgar J. The Story of the New Testament. 2010. (Illus.). 160p. pap. 14.00 *(978-1-60899-542-4(9),* Wipf and Stock) Wipf & Stock Pubs.

Goodspeed, Edgar Johnson. Matthew, Apostle & Evangelist: A Study on the Authorship of the First Gospel. 2011. 176p. 42.95 ***(978-1-258-03426-9(3))*** Literary Licensing, LLC.

Harris, Stephen. The New Testament: A Student's Introduction. 6th ed. 2008. (ENG., Illus.). 528p. (C). pap. 86.00 *(978-0-07-338653-9(7),* 0073386537) McGraw-Hill Cos., The.

Harris, Stephen L. The New Testament: A Student's Introduction. 7th ed. 2011. (ENG., Illus.). 544p. (C). pap. 86.00 *(978-0-07-353582-1(6),* 0073535826) McGraw-Hill Cos., The.

Hiebert, D. Edmond. An Introduction to the New Testament: Volume 1: the Gospels & Acts, Volume 2: the Pauline Epistles, Volume 3: the Non-Pauline Epistles, 3 vols. 2006. 973p. pap. 24.99 *(978-1-884543-74-6(X))* Authentic Media.

Holzapfel, Richard Neitzel, et al. Jesus Christ & the World of the New Testament: An Illustrated Reference for Latter-day Saints. 2006. 39.95 *(978-1-59038-442-8(3))* Deseret Bk. Co.

Hort, Fenton John Anthony. Prolegomena to St Paul's Epistles to the Romans & the Ephesians. 2009. (Cambridge Library Collection - Religion Ser.). (ENG.). 208p. pap. 22.99 *(978-1-108-00751-1(1))* Cambridge Univ. Pr.

Hunter, A. M. Introducing New Testament Theology. 2012. 160p. pap. ***(978-0-334-00699-2(6),*** SCM Pr.) Hymns Ancient & Modern Ltd.

Johnson, Luke Timothy. The New Testament: A Very Short Introduction. 2010. (Illus.). xii, 146p. pap. *(978-0-19-530838-9(7))* Oxford Univ. Pr., Inc.

—The New Testament: A Very Short Introduction, 1 vol. 2010. (Very Short Int Ser.). (ENG., Illus.). 160p. pap. 11.95 *(978-0-19-973570-9(0))* Oxford Univ. Pr., Inc.

—The Writings of the New Testament. 3rd rev. ed. 2010. 544p. (C). pap. 49.00 *(978-0-8006-6361-2(6),* Fortress Pr.) Augsburg Fortress, Pubs.

Köstenberger, Andreas J., et al. The Cradle, the Cross, & the Crown: An Introduction to the New Testament, 1 vol. 2009. (ENG.). 976p. 59.99 *(978-0-8054-4365-3(7),* B&H Academic) B&H Publishing Group.

Kruse, Colin G. John. 2008. (Tyndale New Testament Commentaries Ser.: Volume 4). (ENG.). 389p. pap. 17.00 *(978-0-8308-4234-6(9),* IVP Acad.) InterVarsity Pr.

Loader, William. The New Testament with Imagination: A Fresh Approach to Its Writings & Themes. 2007. (Illus.). 206p. per. 16.00 *(978-0-8028-2746-3(2))* Eerdmans, William B. Publishing Co.

Moffatt, James. An Introduction to the Literature of the New Testament. 2009. 702p. 46.99 *(978-1-115-16898-4(3));* 39.99 *(978-1-115-16897-7(5));* pap. 48.75 *(978-1-115-16896-0(7))* BiblioBazaar.

Motyer, Stephen. New Testament Introduction. 2008. (St. Joseph Bible Resource Ser.). (Illus.). 32p. pap. 4.95 *(978-0-89942-652-5(2))* Catholic Bk. Publishing Corp.

Pfleiderer, Otto. Primitive Christianity V4: Its Writings & Teachings in Their Historical. Montgomery, W., tr. 2007. pap. 42.95 *(978-1-4304-4975-1(6))* Kessinger Publishing, LLC.

Pilch, John J. Introducing the Cultural Context of the New Testament. 2007. (Hear the Word! (Wipf & Stock) Ser.). 270p. pap. 30.00 *(978-1-55635-186-0(0),* Wipf and Stock) Wipf & Stock Pubs.

Piso, Roman & Gallus, Jay. Piso Christ: A Book of the New Classical Scholarship. 2010. 192p. (ENG.). 24.95 *(978-1-4269-3044-7(5));* pap. 14.95 *(978-1-4269-2996-0(X))* Trafford Publishing.

Powell, Mark Allan. Introducing the New Testament: A Historical, Literary, & Theological Survey. 2009. 544p. (C). 44.99 *(978-0-8010-2868-7(X))* Baker Academic.

Prat, Ferdinand. The Theology of Saint Paul, 2 Volumes. Stoddard, John L., tr. 2010. 1060p. pap. 117.00 *(978-1-60899-685-8(9),* Wipf and Stock) Wipf & Stock Pubs.

Pregeant, Russell. Encounter with the New Testament: An Interdisciplinary Approach. 2009. 400p. (C). pap. 30.00 *(978-0-8006-6348-3(9),* Fortress Pr.) Augsburg Fortress, Pubs.

Puskas, Charles B. & Robbins, C. Michael. An Introduction to the New Testament, Second Edition. 2011. 394p. pap. 43.00 ***(978-1-60608-785-5(1),*** Cascade Bks.) Wipf & Stock Pubs.

Puskas, Charles B. & Robbins, Michael C. An Introduction to the New Testament, 2nd Edition. 2012. (ENG.). 394p. (C). pap. 50.00 ***(978-0-7188-9265-4(8))*** Lutterworth Pr., The GBR. Dist: Brown, David Bk. Co., The.

Ralph, Margaret Nutting. A Walk Through the New Testament: An Introduction for Catholics. 2009. 352p. pap. 19.95 *(978-0-8091-4582-9(0))* Paulist Pr.

Royer, Darline Kantola & Burk, Dorsey. Survey of the New Testament. 2011. ***(978-0-7577-4217-0(3))*** Word Aflame Pr.

Schenck, Kenneth. God's Plan Fulfilled: A Guide to Understanding the New Testament. 2009. *(978-0-89827-378-6(1))* Wesleyan Publishing Hse.

Smith, William Frank. How Will We Know the Way? A reading guide for the New Testament. 2011. 156p. pap. 16.95 ***(978-1-4575-0327-6(1))*** Dog Ear Publishing, LLC.

Swain, K. W. A Great Silence in the Land. 2010. 168p. 28.99 *(978-1-4520-6792-6(9));* pap. 15.49 *(978-1-4520-6791-9(0))* AuthorHouse.

Wilder, Terry L., et al. Faithful to the End: An Introduction to Hebrews Through Revelation. 2007. (ENG.). 496p. (C). 34.99 *(978-0-8054-2625-0(6),* B&H Academic) B&H Publishing Group.

Zahn, Theodor. Introduction to the New Testament. 2009. 448p. pap. *(978-0-217-49267-6(3));* 442p. pap. *(978-0-217-49264-5(9));* 474p. pap. *(978-0-217-49261-4(4))* Books LLC.

—Introduction to the New Testament. 2009. 448p. pap. 29.69 *(978-0-217-85379-8(X))* General Bks. LLC.

BIBLE—INTRODUCTIONS—N. T. GOSPELS

Alexander, Mae W., et al. Under the Palm of Deborah: Counsel from Wise Women of God. 2008. 188p. pap. 14.99 *(978-1-933972-14-5(9))* PriorityONE Pubns.

Alexander, T. D. Discovering Jesus: Why Four Gospels to Portray One Person? 2010. 144p. pap. 12.99 *(978-1-4335-2005-1(2))* Crossway.

Alfaro, Juan. Homilías Sobre Los Evangelios de Domingos. 2011. (SPA.). 160p. pap. 16.95 ***(978-0-8146-3359-5(5))*** Liturgical Pr.

Bailey, Jeffrey & Bailey. Interfaith Relation. 2013. (Guides for the Perplexed Ser.). (ENG.). 176p. 24.95 *(978-0-567-03419-9(4),* T&T Clark Int'l) Continuum International Publishing Group, Ltd. GBR. Dist: National Bk. Network.

Bauscher, David. The Original Aramaic Gospels in Plain English. 2007. 257p. pap. 26.50 *(978-0-615-15681-1(9))* Bauscher, David.

Boccardo, James. Unsilenced: How to Voice the Gospel. 2010. 188p. pap. 13.95 *(978-1-61507-174-6(1))* Cross Bks. Publishing.

Breakthrough Prayer. 2009. (ENG.). 32p. 2.95 *(978-0-9792335-1-7(8))* Faith Christian Fellowship.

Buttrick, David. Speaking Conflict: Stories of a Controversial Jesus. 2007. (ENG.). 222p. per. 30.00 *(978-0-664-23089-0(X))* Westminster John Knox Pr.

Chaffin, Eric. Everything I Know about God I Learned from Football. 2008. 220p. pap. 14.99 *(978-1-60604-621-0(7))* Tate Publishing & Enterprises, LLC.

Clutterbuck, Ivan. Another Look at St John's Gospel. 2006. 88p. per. *(978-0-85244-496-2(6))* Gracewing, Ltd.

Crook, Zeba A. Parallel Gospels: A Synopsis of Early Christian Writing. 2011. (ENG.). 362p. (C). 44.95 ***(978-0-19-973941-7(2))*** Oxford Univ. Pr., Inc.

Gregory, Daniel Seely. Why Four Gospels or the Gospel for All T. 2006. pap. 26.99 *(978-1-4255-3749-4(9))* MPublishing.

Harding, Mark & Nobbs, Alanna. The Content & the Setting of the Gospel Tradition. 2010. 600p. pap. 55.00 *(978-0-8028-3318-1(7))* Eerdmans, William B. Publishing Co.

Holiday, Ivan. The Bouncer's Bible: 2nd Edition. 2011. 155p. pap. 19.95 ***(978-1-4327-7089-1(6))*** Outskirts Pr., Inc.

Jones, Khandi. Who Is He? A study of Jesus & the Gospels. 2008. 42p. pap. 10.95 *(978-1-4357-3231-5(6))* Lulu Enterprises Inc.

Levingston, Harold. The Modern Words of God. 2008. 344p. pap. 29.95 *(978-1-60672-372-2(3))* PublishAmerica, Inc.

Linhart, Terry. Middle School Talksheets: 50 Ready-to-Use Discussions on the Life of Christ, 1 vol. 2008. (TalkSheets Ser.). (ENG.). 112p. pap. 16.99 *(978-0-310-28553-3(4))* Zondervan.

McKenzie, John L. Light on the Gospels: A Reader's Guide. 2009. (John L. Mckenzie Reprints Ser.). 220p. pap. 24.00 *(978-1-60608-147-1(0))* Wipf & Stock Pubs.

Phillips, Wallace. All Dressed up & No Place to Go: Closed Doors at the Lord's House. 2007. 104p. pap. 12.95 *(978-0-9772483-8-4(0))* Diakonia Publishing.

Puskas, Charles B. & Crump, David. An Introduction to the Gospels & Acts. 2008. (Illus.). 232p. pap. 19.00 *(978-0-8028-4557-3(6))* Eerdmans, William B. Publishing Co.

Rey, Stevie. The Hillbilly Bible: John. 2008. 105p. pap. 9.99 *(978-0-615-17925-4(8))* Reynolds, Stephen.

Scholz, Daniel J. Jesus in the Gospels & Acts: Introducing the New Testament. 2009. (Illus.). 272p. pap. 30.95 *(978-0-88489-955-6(1))* St. Mary's Pr.

Scroggie, W. Graham. A Guide to the Gospels: A Comprehensive Analysis of the Four Gospels, 1 vol. 2010. 688p. pap. 35.99 *(978-0-8254-3904-9(3),* Kregel Classics) Kregel Pubns.

Shaia, Alexander & Gaugy, Michelle. The Hidden Power of the Gospels: Four Questions, Four Paths, One Journey. 2010. (ENG.). 384p. 26.99 *(978-0-06-189801-3(5),* HarperOne) HarperCollins Pubs.

Stedman, Ray C. Adventuring Through the Life of Christ: A Bible Handbook on the Gospels & Acts. 2009. (ENG.). 128p. pap. 9.99 *(978-1-57293-311-8(9))* Discovery Hse. Pubs.

Streeter, B. H. The Washington Manuscript of the Gospels: The Harvard Theological Review V19, No. 2, April 1926. Moore, George F., ed. 2011. 12p. pap. 35.95 ***(978-1-258-05519-6(8))*** Literary Licensing, LLC.

Sullivan, Kathleen M. I Had Lunch with God: Gospel Inspirations for Tough Times. 2008. pap. 19.95 *(978-0-9776458-5-5(1))* Corby Books.

Taylor, C. The Witness of Hermas to the Four Gospels. 2008. 156p. pap. 13.00 *(978-1-60608-292-8(2),* Wipf and Stock) Wipf & Stock Pubs.

Taylor, Vincent. The Gospels: A Short Introduction. 2009. 112p. pap. 14.00 *(978-1-60608-709-1(6),* Wipf and Stock) Wipf & Stock Pubs.

BIBLE—INTRODUCTIONS—O. T.

Here are entered introductions to the Old Testament as a whole, or to any part except Apocryphal writings, which are listed separately under Bible—Introductions—Apocrypha and Apocryphal Books.

Archer, Gleason & Archer, Gleason, Jr. A Survey of Old Testament Introduction. rev. ed. 2007. (ENG., Illus.). 512p. 39.99 *(978-0-8024-8434-5(4))* Moody Pubs.

Bandstra, Barry L. Reading the Old Testament: Intr to Hebrew Bible. 4th ed. 2008. (ENG.). 576p. (C). pap. 148.95 *(978-0-495-39105-0(0))* Wadsworth.

Barstad, Hans M. A Brief Guide to the Hebrew Bible. 2010. (ENG.). 256p. pap. 30.00 *(978-0-664-23325-9(2))* Westminster John Knox Pr.

Bauer-Levesque, Angela. The Indispensable Guide to the Old Testament: An Introduction. 2009. *(978-0-8298-1780-5(8))* Pilgrim Pr., The/United Church Pr.

Beal, Timothy. Biblical Literacy: The Essential Bible Stories Everyone Needs to Know. 2010. (ENG.). 368p. pap. 15.99 *(978-0-06-171867-0(X)*, HarperOne) HarperCollins Pubs.

Bullock, C. Hassell. An Introduction to the Old Testament Prophetic Books. rev. ed. 2007. (ENG.). 480p. 34.99 *(978-0-8024-4154-6(8))* Moody Pubs.

Carr, David M. Introduction to the Old Testament: Sacred Texts & Imperial Contexts of the Hebrew Bible. 2010. (Wiley Desktop Editions Ser.). (ENG., Illus.). 296p. pap. 39.95 *(978-1-4051-8467-0(1)*, Wiley-Blackwell) Wiley, John & Sons, Inc.

Carr, G. Lloyd & Carr, David M. An Introduction to the Old Testament: Sacred Texts & Imperial Contexts of the Hebrew Bible. 2010. (ENG., Illus.). 296p. 99.95 *(978-1-4051-8468-7(X)*, Wiley-Blackwell) Wiley, John & Sons, Inc.

Childs, Brevard S. Introduction to Old Testament As Scripture. 2010. 692p. pap. 36.00 *(978-0-8006-9833-1(9)*, Fortress Pr.) Augsburg Fortress, Pubs.

Collins, John J. A Short Introduction to the Hebrew Bible. 2007. (Illus.). 336p. per. 39.00 *(978-0-8006-6207-3(5)*, Fortress Pr.) Augsburg Fortress, Pubs.

Davis, Dale Ralph. The Word Became Flesh: How to Preach from Old Testament Narrative Texts. 2006. (ENG.). 160p. per. 16.99 *(978-1-84550-192-1(6)*, Mentor) Christian Focus Pubns. GBR. Dist: STL Distribution North America.

De Wette, Wilhelm Martin Leberecht. A Critical & Historical Introduction to the Canonical Scriptures of the Old Testament, from the German of Wilhelm Martin Leberecht de Wette; Transla. 2006. 572p. per. 32.99 *(978-1-4255-6277-9(9))* MPublishing.

Dentan, Robert C. The Apocrypha, Bridge of the Testaments: A Reader's Guide to the Apocryphal Books of the Old Testament. 2011. 130p. 40.95 ***(978-1-258-04913-3(9))*** Literary Licensing, LLC.

Dick, Michael B. Reading the Old Testament: An Inductive Introduction. 2008. (Illus.). 367p. incl. cd-rom *(978-1-56563-953-9(7))* Hendrickson Pubs. Marketing, LLC.

Drane, John. Introducing the Old Testment. 3rd rev. ed. 2011. 386p. pap. 45.00 *(978-0-8006-9613-3(4)*, Fortress Pr.) Augsburg Fortress, Pubs.

Driscoll, Mark. On the Old Testament. 2008. (Book You'll Actually Read Ser.). 96p. pap. 9.99 *(978-1-4335-0135-7(X))* Crossway.

Driver, S. R. An Introduction to the Literature of the Old Testament. 2009. 578p. 37.99 *(978-1-110-38327-6(4))*; pap. 42.75 *(978-1-110-38321-4(5))* BiblioBazaar.

Evans, Mary J. Old Testament Introduction. 2008. (St. Joseph Bible Resource Ser.). (Illus.). 32p. pap. 4.95 *(978-0-89942-656-3(5))* Catholic Bk. Publishing Corp.

Gottwald, Norman K. The Hebrew Bible: A Brief Socio-Literary Introduction. 2008. (Illus.). 412p. (C). pap. 45.00 *(978-0-8006-6308-7(X)*, Fortress Pr.) Augsburg Fortress, Pubs.

—A Light to the Nations: An Introduction to the Old Testament. 2009. 640p. pap. 70.00 *(978-1-60608-980-4(3)*, Wipf and Stock) Wipf & Stock Pubs.

Gravett, Sandra L., et al, eds. An Introduction to the Hebrew Bible: A Thematic Approach. 2008. (ENG., Illus.). 552p. pap. 40.00 *(978-0-664-23030-2(X))* Westminster John Knox Pr.

Harris, Rick W. Survey of Old Testament: Student's Edition. 2011. 482p. 34.99 ***(978-1-4628-9323-2(6))***; pap. 23.99 ***(978-1-4628-9324-9(4))*** Xlibris Corp.

—Survey of Old Testament: Teacher's Edition. 2011. 488p. 34.99 ***(978-1-4628-9188-7(8))***; pap. 23.99 ***(978-1-4628-9187-0(X))*** Xlibris Corp.

Howard, David M., Jr. An Introduction to the Old Testament Historical Books. 2007. (ENG., Illus.). 456p. 34.99 *(978-0-8024-4155-3(6))* Moody Pubs.

Hummel, Horace D. The Word Becoming Flesh: An Introduction to the Origin, Purpose & Meaning of the Old Testament. 736p. 27.99 *(978-0-570-03989-1(4)*, 12-3017) Concordia Publishing Hse.

Jewish Publication Society Staff, compiled by. The Jewish Bible: A JPS Guide. 2008. (JPS Guides). (ENG., Illus.). 300p. pap. 22.00 *(978-0-8276-0851-1(9))* Jewish Pubn. Society.

Jones, Sonia. Old Testament Alive! 2010. *(978-0-9810470-8-9(4))* Erser & Pond Pubs., Ltd.

Kent, Charles Foster. The Origin & Permanent Value of the Old Testament. 2008. 184p. 22.99 *(978-0-554-32101-1(7))* 2008. 184p. 25.99 *(978-0-554-22798-6(3))* 2007. (ENG.). 160p. pap. 19.99 *(978-1-4264-3062-6(0))* 2007. (ENG.). 180p. pap. 21.99 *(978-1-4264-3127-2(9))* BiblioBazaar.

—The Origin & Permanent Value of the Old Testament. 2007. 144p. per. *(978-1-4065-1900-6(5))* Dodo Pr.

Kim, Heerak Christian. Psalms of Solomon: A New Translation & Introduction. 2008. 140p. 25.00 *(978-1-59689-079-4(7))*; (ENG.). pap. 50.00 *(978-1-59689-080-0(0))* Hermit Kingdom Pr., The. (Hermit Kingdom Pr., The).

Lennox, Stephen J. God's Story Revealed: A Guide for Understanding the Old Testament. 2009. *(978-0-89827-377-9(3))* Wesleyan Publishing Hse.

Loken, Israel P. The Old Testament Prophetic Books: An Introduction. 2010. 466p. pap. 24.99 *(978-1-61579-789-9(0))* Xulon Pr., Inc.

Longman, Tremper, III, et al. Daniel: Faith under Pressure, 1 vol. 2010. (Bringing the Bible to Life Ser.). (ENG.). 160p. pap. 7.99 *(978-0-310-32042-5(9))* Zondervan.

—An Introduction to the Old Testament. 2nd ed. 2006. (ENG., Illus.). 640p. 34.99 *(978-0-310-26341-8(7))* Zondervan.

McFadyen, John Edgar. Introduction to the Old Testament. 2009. 370p. 33.99 *(978-1-115-67263-4(0))* 2009. 370p. pap. 31.75 *(978-1-115-67265-8(7))* 2009. 370p. pap. 32.75 *(978-1-115-67264-1(9))* 2008. 252p. 24.99 *(978-0-554-31676-5(5))* 2008. 252p. 27.99 *(978-0-554-22373-5(2))* 2007. (ENG.). 256p. pap. 21.99 *(978-1-4264-2166-2(4))* 2006. 248p. pap. 22.99 *(978-1-4264-2234-8(2))* BiblioBazaar.

—Introduction to the Old Testament. 2009. 208p. pap. *(978-0-217-49274-4(6))* Books LLC.

Navarre Bible Editors. Introduction to the Bible: Old Testament. 2012. (Illus.). 256p. pap. 14.95 *(978-1-84682-204-9(1))* Four Courts Pr. IRL. Dist: International Specialized Bk. Services.

Pilch, John J. Introducing the Cultural Context of the Old Testament. 2007. (Hear the Word! (Wipf & Stock) Ser.). 234p. pap. 26.00 *(978-1-55635-185-3(2)*, Wipf and Stock) Wipf & Stock Pubs.

Platzner, Robert & Harris, Stephen. The Old Testament: An Introduction to the Hebrew Bible. 2nd rev. ed. 2007. (ENG., Illus.). 528p. (C). per. 86.00 *(978-0-07-299051-5(1)*, 007299051I) McGraw-Hill Cos., The.

Royer, Darline Kantola & Burk, Dorsey. Survey of the Old Testament. 2011. ***(978-0-7577-4216-3(5))*** Word Aflame Pr.

Seitz, Christopher R. Prophecy & Hermeneutics: Toward a New Introduction to the Prophets. 2007. (Studies in Theological Interpretation Ser.). 272p. (C). pap. 23.00 *(978-0-8010-3258-5(X))* Baker Academic.

Sharp, Carolyn J. Old Testament Prophets for Today. 2009. (For Today Ser.). (ENG.). 128p. pap. 13.00 *(978-0-664-23178-1(0))* Westminster John Knox Pr.

—Wrestling the Word: The Hebrew Scriptures & the Christian Believer. 2010. (ENG.). 176p. pap. 20.00 *(978-0-664-23067-8(9))* Westminster John Knox Pr.

Stulman, Louis & Kim, Paul. You Are My People: An Introduction to Prophetic Literature. 2010. 304p. pap. 25.00 *(978-0-687-46565-1(6))* Abingdon Pr.

Swete, Henry Barclay. An Introduction to the Old Testament in Greek: With an Appendix Containing the Letter of Aristeas. Thackeray, Henry St. John, ed. 2010. (Cambridge Library Collection - Religion Ser.). (ENG.). 612p. pap. 43.00 *(978-1-108-00758-0(9))* Cambridge Univ. Pr.

Thieman, John E. A Religious History of the Old Testament. 2008. (Illus.). iii, 211p. pap. *(978-0-615-26261-1(9))* DaCapo Foundation.

Thomas Nelson Publishing Staff & Peters, Angie. The Life of Solomon, 0 vols. Richards, Larry, ed. 2009. (Smart Guide to the Bible Ser.). (Illus.). 384p. pap. 14.99 *(978-1-4185-1012-1(2))* Nelson, Thomas Inc.

Tullock, John & McEntire, Mark. The Old Testament Story. 9th rev. ed. 2011. (ENG.). 416p. (C). pap. 108.60 *(978-0-205-09783-8(9)*, Prentice Hall) Prentice Hall PTR.

Walton, John H. Survey of the Old Testament, 1 vol. 2007. (Zondervan Get an A! Study Guides Ser.). (ENG., Illus.). 6p. 6.99 *(978-0-310-27318-9(8))* Zondervan.

Wolf, Herbert. An Introduction to the Old Testament Pentateuch. 2007. (ENG.). 336p. 33.99 *(978-0-8024-4156-0(4))* Moody Pubs.

BIBLE—ISLAMIC INTERPRETATIONS

A, Abdullahi. From Islam to Christianity: Muhammad in the Bible Facts or Fiction. 2008. 101p. pap. 16.95 *(978-1-4092-0833-4(8))* Lulu Enterprises Inc.

Islamic Perspective Davi. 2006. pap. 14.95 *(978-1-56744-738-5(4))* Kazi Pubns., Inc.

Islamic Perspective Jaco. 2006. pap. 16.50 *(978-1-56744-737-8(6))* Kazi Pubns., Inc.

Lodahl, Michael. Claiming Abraham: Reading the Bible & the Qur'an Side by Side, 1 vol. 2010. (ENG.). 240p. pap. 23.00 *(978-1-58743-239-2(0))* Brazos Pr.

Michael, S. & McAlister, L. Dare to Explore2. 2011. 184p. pap. 16.99 ***(978-1-61379-748-8(6))*** Xulon Pr., Inc.

Saddique. Life, the Universe & the Quran. 2011. (Illus.). 156p. pap. 18.87 ***(978-1-4520-8868-6(3))*** AuthorHouse.

Schmitz, Bertram. Paulus und der Koran. 2010. (GER.). 212p. (C). pap. 32.00 *(978-3-525-51007-0(1))* Vandenhoeck & Ruprecht GmbH & Co. KG DEU. Dist: ISD.

Thomas, David. Christian Doctrines in Islamic Theology. 2008. 384p. *(978-90-04-16935-7(0))* BRILL.

Vicchio, Stephen J. Biblical Figures in the Islamic Faith. 2008. 298p. pap. 33.00 *(978-1-55635-304-8(9))* Wipf & Stock Pubs.

BIBLE—JUVENILE LITERATURE

see also Bible Stories

Bible Stories. 2009. 60p. pap. *(978-0-217-31622-4(0))* Books LLC.

Bible Stories. (Israel Wall Maps Ser.). (HEB.). 18.95 *(978-0-7834-3343-1(3))* Map Link.

Helm, David R. The Big Picture Story Bible. 2010. 456p. (J). 29.99 *(978-1-4335-2391-5(4))* Crossway.

Lee, Young Shin. Death, Resurrection, & the Great Commission, 1 vol. Rogers, Bud et al, eds. 2009. (Z Graphic Novels / Manga Bible Ser.). (ENG.). 224p. (J). pap. 6.99 *(978-0-310-71293-0(9))* Zondervan.

Lloyd-Jones, Sally. The Jesus Storybook Bible: Every Story Whispers His Name, 1 vol. 1t. ed. 2011. (ENG.). 352p. (J). 22.99 *(978-0-310-72605-0(0))* Zonderkidz.

Loth, Paul J. My First Study Bible: Exploring God's Word on My Own! 2011. 440p. (J). 16.99 *(978-1-4003-1690-8(1))* Nelson, Thomas Inc.

Noah's Ark. (Stories from the Bible Ser.). 32p. *(978-1-4054-3787-5(1))* Parragon, Inc.

Under the Baobab Tree: Claiming Roots, Kindling Hope, Spreading God's Love. 4.00 *(978-0-687-08741-9(4))* Abingdon Pr.

BIBLE—LANGUAGE, STYLE

see also Aramaic Language; Bible—Parables; Bible As Literature; Greek Language, Biblical; Hebrew Language

Abbott, Edwin A. Johannine Vocabulary: A Comparison of the Words of the Fourth Gospel with Those of the Three. 2007. (ENG.). 388p. 48.95 *(978-0-548-10039-4(X))* Kessinger Publishing, LLC.

Adams, James Rowe. From Literal to Literary: The Essential Reference Book for Biblical Metaphors. 2nd ed. 2008. 387p. per. *(978-0-8298-1788-1(3))* Pilgrim Pr., The/United Church Pr.

Avishur, Yitzhak. Comparative Studies in Biblical & Ugaritic Languages & Litratures. 2007. 238p. 60.00 *(978-965-7162-14-9(9)*, Archaeological Ctr. Pubns. ISR. Dist: Eisenbrauns, Inc.

Bandstra, Barry. Genesis 1-11: A Handbook on the Hebrew Text. 2008. (Baylor Handbook on the Hebrew Bible Ser.). (ENG & HEB., Illus.). 600p. pap. 39.95 *(978-1-932792-70-6(8))* Baylor Univ. Pr.

Barnstone, Willis. The Poems of Jesus Christ. 2012. (ENG.). 320p. 26.95 ***(978-0-393-08357-6(8)***, 8357) Norton, W. W. & Co., Inc.

Barr, James. Biblical Words for Time. 2009. (Studies in Biblical Theology, First Ser.). 222p. pap. 24.00 *(978-1-60899-023-8(0)*, Wipf and Stock) Wipf & Stock Pubs.

Barrick, W. Boyd & Barrick. BMH As Body Language: A Lexical & Iconographical Study of the Word BMH When Not a Reference to Cultic Phenomena in Biblical & Post-Biblical Hebrew. 2008. (Library of Hebrew Bible/Old Testament Studies, the Ser.). (ENG.). 208p. 120.00 *(978-0-567-02658-3(2)*, T&T Clark Int'l) Continuum International Publishing Group, Ltd. GBR. Dist: National Bk. Network.

Bauscher, David. The Original Aramaic Gospels in Plain English. 2007. 257p. pap. 26.50 *(978-0-615-15681-1(9))* Bauscher, David.

Beck, James R. & Beck, John A. Zondervan Dictionary of Biblical Imagery, 1 vol. 2010. (ENG.). 288p. 29.99 *(978-0-310-29285-2(9))* Zondervan.

Beck, John A. God As Storyteller: Seeking Meaning in Biblical Narrative. 2008. 24.99 *(978-0-8272-1254-1(2))* Chalice Pr.

Becking, Bob & Peels, Eric, eds. Psalms & Prayers: Papers Read at the Joint Meeting of the Society of Old Testament Study & the Oud Testamentische Werkgezelschap in Nederland en België, Apeldoorn August 2006. 2007. (Oudtestamentische Studien Ser.: Vol. 55). 306p. *(978-90-04-16032-3(9))* BRILL.

Ben Zvi, Ehud, et al, eds. A Palimpsest: Rhetoric, Ideology, Stylistics, & Language Relating to Persian Israel. 2009. 117.32 *(978-1-60724-584-1(1))* Gorgias Pr., LLC.

Benner, Jeff A. A Mechanical Translation of the Book of Exodus. 2009. 444p. 29.95 *(978-1-60264-391-8(1))* Virtualbookworm.com Publishing, Inc.

Berlejung, A., et al, eds. The Language of Qohelet in Its Context: Essays in Honour of Prof. A. Schoors on the Occasion of his Seventieth Birthday. 2007. (Orientalia Lovaniensia Analecta Ser.). (ENG.). 241p. (C). 126.00 *(978-90-429-1910-5(8))* Peeters Pubs. & Booksellers BEL. Dist: Brown, David Bk. Co., The.

Berlin, Adele. The Dynamics of Biblical Parallelism. 2007. (Biblical Resource Ser.). (HEB & ENG.). 200p. per. 21.00 *(978-0-8028-0397-9(0))* Eerdmans, William B. Publishing Co.

Black, C. Clifton & Watson, Duane F., eds. Words Well Spoken: George Kennedy's Rhetoric of the New Testament. 2008. (ENG.). 255p. 49.95 *(978-1-60258-064-0(2))* Baylor Univ. Pr.

Black, David Alan & Broadman and Holman Publishers Staff. Learn to Read New Testament Greek, 1 vol. 3rd ed. 2009. (ENG.). 272p. 29.99 *(978-0-8054-4493-3(9)*, B&H Academic) B&H Publishing Group.

Blumfield, Fiona. Further Biblical Hebrew. 2010. pap. 38.00 *(978-1-61143-662-4(1))* 2009. 116.00 *(978-1-59333-948-7(8))* Gorgias Pr., LLC.

Bons, Eberhard & Kraus, Thomas J., eds. Et sapienter et Eloquenter: Studies on Rhetorical & Stylistic Features of the Septuagint. 2011. (Forschungen Zur Religion und Literatur des Alten & Neuen Testament Ser.). (ENG.). 165p. (C). 91.00 *(978-3-525-53261-4(X))* Vandenhoeck & Ruprecht GmbH & Co. KG DEU. Dist: ISD.

Burer, Michael H., et al. A New Reader's Lexicon of the Greek New Testament. 2008. 512p. 34.99 *(978-0-8254-2009-2(1))* Kregel Pubns.

Butterworth, Mike. Structure & the Book of Zechariah. 2009. (Library of Hebrew Bible/Old Testament Studies, the Ser.). (ENG.). 328p. 55.00 *(978-0-567-43447-0(8)*, T&T Clark) Continuum International Publishing Group, Ltd. GBR. Dist: National Bk. Network.

Caird, George B. The Language & Imagery of the Bible. 2009. 288p. pap. 29.95 *(978-0-7156-1579-9(3))* Duckworth Publishers GBR. Dist: International Publishers Marketing.

Callaham, Scott N. Modality & the Biblical Hebrew Infinitive Absolute. 2010. (Abhandlungen Für Die Kunde des Morgenlandes Ser.). (ENG.). 343p. (C). pap. 117.00 *(978-3-447-06158-2(6))* Harrassowitz, Otto Verlag DEU. Dist: ISD.

Campbell, Constantine. Verbal Aspect, the Indicative Mood, & Narrative: Soundings in the Greek of the New Testament. 2007. (Studies in Biblical Greek Ser.: Vol. 13). (Illus.). (C). 308p. 119.95 *(978-1-4331-0023-9(1))*; 312p. pap. 34.95 *(978-1-4331-0003-1(7)*, Lang, Peter Publishing, Inc.

Campbell, Constantine R. Verbal Aspect & Non-Indicative Verbs: Further Soundings in the Greek of the New Testament. 2008. (Studies in Biblical Greek Ser.). (C). 170p. 89.95 *(978-1-4331-0418-3(0))*; (GEC & ENG.). 176p. pap. 34.95 *(978-1-4331-0299-8(4)*, Lang, Peter Publishing, Inc.

Caragounis, Chrys C. The Development of Greek & the New Testament: Morphology, Syntax, Phonology, & Textual Transmission. 2007. 752p. (C). pap. 75.00 *(978-0-8010-3230-1(X))* Baker Academic.

Choi, Kyoungwon. An Analysis of Subject-Before-Finite-Verb Clauses: An Analysis of Subject-Before-Finite-Verb Clauses in the Book of Genesis Based on Traditional Grammarians. 2008. 136p. pap. *(978-3-639-10031-0(X))* VDM Verlag Dr. Mueller e.K.

Clabeaux, John & Clabeaux, J. NT Greek: A Systems Approach. 2009. (Illus.). 375p. pap. 50.00 *(978-1-58966-186-8(9))* Univ. of Scranton Pr.

Clasby, Nancy Tenfelde. God, the Bible, & Human Consciousness. 2008. (ENG.). 272p. 95.00 *(978-0-230-60543-5(6))* Palgrave Macmillan.

Conklin, Blane. Oath Formulas in Biblical Hebrew. 2011. 34.50 *(978-1-57506-203-7(8))* Eisenbrauns, Inc.

Contributions to Hebrew Syncnymy. 2007. (Analecta Gorgiana Ser.: 42). per. 29.00 *(978-1-59333-850-3(3))* Gorgias Pr., LLC.

Coogan, Michael D. A Brief Introduction to the Old Testament: The Hebrew Bible in Its Context. 2nd ed. 2011. (ENG., Illus.). 480p. (C). pap. 54.95 ***(978-0-19-983011-4(8))*** Oxford Univ. Pr., Inc.

Coogan, Michael David. Old Testament: A Historical & Literary Introduction to the Hebrew Scriptures, 1 vol. 2nd ed. 2010. (ENG.). 592p. (C). pap. 69.95 *(978-0-19-537840-5(7))* Oxford Univ. Pr., Inc.

Cotrozzi, Stefano. Expect the Unexpected: Aspects of Pragmatic Foregrounding in Old Testament Narratives, Vol. 510. 2010. (Library of Hebrew Bible/Old Testament Studies, the Ser.). (ENG., Illus.). 320p. 120.00 *(978-0-567-56838-0(5)*, T&T Clark Int'l) Continuum International Publishing Group, Ltd. GBR. Dist: National Bk. Network.

Crystal, David. Begat: The King James Bible & the English Language. 2011. (ENG.). 320p. pap. 16.95 *(978-0-19-969518-8(0))* Oxford Univ. Pr., Inc.

Davies, Gordon F. Israel in Egypt: Reading Exodus 1-2. 2009. (Library of Hebrew Bible/Old Testament Studies, the Ser.). (ENG.). 204p. 39.95 *(978-1-4411-6508-4(8)*, T&T Clark) Continuum International Publishing Group, Ltd. GBR. Dist: National Bk. Network.

Davies, Philip R. Among the Prophets: Language, Image & Structure in the Prophetic Writings. Clines, David J. A., ed. 2009. (Library of Hebrew Bible/Old Testament Studies, the Ser.). (ENG.). 218p. 39.95 *(978-1-4411-9648-4(X)*, T&T Clark) Continuum International Publishing Group, Ltd. GBR. Dist: National Bk. Network.

Dawson, David Allan. Text-Linguistics & Biblical Hebrew. 2009. (Library of Hebrew Bible/Old Testament Studies, the Ser.). (ENG.). 242p. 39.95 *(978-0-567-22685-3(9)*, T&T Clark) Continuum International Publishing Group, Ltd. GBR. Dist: National Bk. Network.

Decker, Rodney J. & Decker, Rodney. Koine Greek Reader: Selections from the New Testament, Septuagint, & Early Christian Writers, 1 vol. 2007. 312p. pap. 25.99 *(978-0-8254-2442-7(9))* Kregel Pubns.

DeRouchie, Jason. A Call to Covenant Love: Text Grammar & Literary Structure in Deuteronomy 5, 11. 2007. 32.00 ***(978-1-59333-674-5(8))*** Gorgias Pr., LLC.

Dodson, Joseph R. The "Powers" of Personification: Rhetorical Purpose in the Book of Wisdom & the Letter to the Romans. 2008. (Beihefte zur Zeitschrift fur die neutestamentliche Wissenschaft und die Kunde der älteren Kirche Ser.). (ENG.). XII, 264p. 147.00 *(978-3-11-020976-1(4))* De Gruyter, Walter Inc.

Duckwitz, Norbert H. O. Reading the Gospel of St. Mark in Greek: A Beginning with Introduction, Notes, Vocabulary, & Grammatical Appendix. 2011. pap. 19.00 ***(978-0-86516-776-5(1))*** Bolchazy-Carducci Pubs.

Dunlap, John. An Answer Key to a Primer of Ecclesiastical Latin: A Supplement to the Text. 2006. 168p. per. 19.95 *(978-0-8132-1469-6(6))* Catholic Univ. of America Pr.

Eddinger, Terry. Malachi: A Handbook on the Hebrew Text. 2012. (Baylor Handbook on the Hebrew Bible Ser.). (ENG.). 174p. pap. 29.95 ***(978-1-60258-427-3(3))*** Baylor Univ. Pr.

Eng, Milton. The Days of Our Years: A Lexical Semantic Study of the Life Cycle in Biblical Israel. 2011. (Library of Hebrew Bible/Old Testament Studies, the Ser.). (ENG., Illus.). 192p. 110.00 *(978-0-567-02503-6(9)*, T&T Clark Int'l) Continuum International Publishing Group, Ltd. GBR. Dist: National Bk. Network.

Eslinger, Lyle. House of God or House of David: The Rhetoric of 2 Samuel 7. 2009. (Library of Hebrew Bible/Old Testament Studies, the Ser.). (ENG.). 118p. 27.95 *(978-0-567-57153-3(X)*, T&T Clark) Continuum International Publishing Group, Ltd. GBR. Dist: National Bk. Network.

Everson, A. Joseph & Kim, Hyun Chul Paul. The Desert Will Bloom: Poetic Visions in Isaiah. 2009. *(978-90-04-16926-5(1))* BRILL.

—The Desert Will Bloom: Poetic Visions in Isaiah. 2009. 37.95 *(978-1-58983-425-5(9))* Society of Biblical Literature.

Fantin, Joseph D. The Greek Imperative Mood in the New Testament: A Cognitive & Communicative Approach. 2010. (Studies in Biblical Greek Ser.). 424p. (C). 91.95 *(978-0-8204-7487-8(8))* Lang, Peter Publishing, Inc.

Fox, Michael V. A Time to Tear down & a Time to Build Up: A Rereading of Ecclesiastes. 2010. 440p. pap. 48.00 *(978-1-60899-496-0(1)*, Wipf and Stock) Wipf & Stock Pubs.

Frey, Jorg, ed. Imagery in the Gospel of John: Terms, Forms, Themes & Theology of Johannine Figurative Language. 2006. (Wissenschaftliche Untersuchungen Zum Neuen Testament Ser.: No. 200). (GER & ENG., Illus.). 504p. 195.00 *(978-3-16-149116-0(5))* Mohr Siebeck GmbH & Co. KG DEU. Dist: Coronet Bks.

Futato, Mark D. Beginning Biblical Hebrew. 2009. (Illus.). 351p. reprint ed. 44.95 *(978-1-57506-022-4(1))* Eisenbrauns, Inc.

Garrett, Duane A. Amos: A Handbook on the Hebrew Text. 2008. (ENG.). 300p. (C). pap. 24.95 *(978-1-932792-69-0(4))* Baylor Univ. Pr.

Garrett, Duane A. & DeRouchie, Jason S. A Modern Grammar for Biblical Hebrew. 2009. (ENG.). 432p. 49.99 *(978-0-8054-4962-4(0)*, B&H Academic) B&H Publishing Group.

Garrett, Duane A., et al. A Modern Grammar for Biblical Hebrew Workbook, 1 vol. 2009. (ENG., Illus.). 320p. pap. 39.99 (978-0-8054-4963-1(9), B&H Academic) B&H Publishing Group.

Gevirtz, Gila & Rank, Ellen J. [Kol Yisrael] 3: The Prayers of Our People 3. 2011. (HEB., Illus.). 96p. (978-0-87441-821-7(6)) Behrman Hse., Inc.

Gladson, Jerry A. The Five Exotic Scrolls of the Hebrew Bible: The Prominence, Literary Structure, & Liturgical Significance of the Megilloth. 2009. 500p. 129.95 (978-0-7734-4749-3(0)) Mellen, Edwin Pr., The.

Glenny, W. Edward. Finding Meaning in the Text: Translation Technique & Theology in the Septuagint of Amos. 2009. 322p. (978-90-04-17638-6(1)) BRILL.

Graves, Michael. Jerome's Hebrew Philology: A Study Based on his Commentary on Jeremiah. 2007. (Vigiliae Christianae Supplements Ser.). 236p. (978-90-04-16204-4(6)) BRILL.

Grimm, Carl Ludwig Willibald & Thayer, Joseph Henry. A Greek-English Lexicon of the New Testament. 2010. (GRE.). 169.52 (978-1-61719-677-5(0)) Gorgias Pr., LLC.

Gutierrez, Ben, et al. Learn to Read New Testament Greek: Supplemental Exercises for Greek Grammar Students. Croteau, David A., ed. 2009. (ENG.). 256p. pap., wbk. ed. 28.99 (978-0-8054-4792-7(X)) B&H Publishing Group.

Hackett, Jo Ann. Basic intro to biblical hebrew W/cd, 1 vol. 2010. (ENG & HEB., Illus.). 330p. 39.95 (978-1-59856-028-2(X)) Hendrickson Pubs. Marketing, LLC.

Halper, B. The Participial Formations of the Geminate Verbs. 2011. (GER, HEB, SYR & ARA.). 110.80 (978-1-61143-981-6(7)) Gorgias Pr., LLC.

Hamlin, Hannibal & Jones, Norman W., eds. The King James Bible after Four Hundred Years: Literary, Linguistic, & Cultural Influences. 2010. (ENG., Illus.). 378p. 39.99 (978-0-521-76627-6(6)) Cambridge Univ. Pr.

Harris, Murray J. Prepositions & Theology in the Greek New Testament, 1 vol. 2012. (ENG.). 192p. (C). 42.99 (978-0-310-49392-1(7)) Zondervan.

Hayes, Elizabeth. The Pragmatics of Perception & Cognition in MT Jeremiah 1:1-6:30: A Cognitive Linguistics Approach. 2008. (Beihefte Zur Zeitschrift Für Die Alttestamentliche Wissenschaft Ser.). (ENG.). XII, 272p. 168.00 (978-3-11-173873-4(6)) De Gruyter, Walter Inc.

Hayes, Elizabeth R. The Pragmatics of Perception & Cognition in MT Jeremiah 1:1-6:30: A Cognitive Linguistics Approach. 2008. (Beihefte Zur Zeitschrift Für Die Alttestamentliche Wissenschaft Ser.). (ENG., Illus.). XII, 272p. 105.00 (978-3-11-020229-8(8)) De Gruyter, Walter Inc.

Hecke, P. van. Metaphor in the Hebrew Bible. 2006. (Bibliotheca Ephemeridum Theologicarum Lovaniensium Ser.: Vol. 187). (ENG & GER., Illus.). 271p. (C). pap. 95.00 (978-90-429-1640-1(0)) Peeters Pubs. & Booksellers BEL. Dist: Brown, David Bk. Co., The.

Heffelfinger, Katie M. I Am Large, I Contain Multitudes: Lyric Cohesion & Conflict in Second Isaiah. 2011. (Illus.). xv, 328p. (978-90-04-19383-3(9)) BRILL.

Heil, John Paul. Hebrews: Chiastic Structures & Audience Response. 2010. (978-0-915170-45-6(0)) Catholic Biblical Assn. of America.

Henderson, Warren. Hallowed Be Thy Name. 2007. 164p. per. (978-1-897117-45-3(0)) Gospel Folio Pr.

Herms, Ronald. An Apocalypse for the Church & for the World: The Narrative Function of Universal Language in the Book of Revelation. (Beihefte zur Zeitschrift far die neutestamentliche Wissenschaft und die Kunde der älteren Kirche Ser.). (ENG.). XV, 299p. 225.00 (978-3-11-181860-3(8)); 2006. 140.00 (978-3-11-019312-1(4)) De Gruyter, Walter Inc.

Hewett, James A. & Robbins, C. Michael. New Testament Greek: A Beginning & Intermediate Grammar with CD. 2009. 275p. (978-1-59856-141-8(3)) Hendrickson Pubs. Marketing, LLC.

Hill. Greek Words Hebrew Meanings. 2009. (ENG.). 352p. pap. 46.00 (978-0-521-10886-7(1)) Cambridge Univ. Pr.

Hogeterp, Albert L. A. & Hogeterp, A. L. A. Paul & God's Temple: A Historical Interpretation of Cultic Imagery in the Corinthian Correspondence. 2006. (Biblical Tools & Studies: Vo. 2). (ENG.). 483p. (C). 95.00 (978-90-429-1722-4(9)) Peeters Pubs. & Booksellers BEL. Dist: Brown, David Bk. Co., The.

Howard, Roger. The Arctic Gold Rush: The New Race for Tomorrow's Natural Resources. 2009. (ENG., Illus.). 272p. 29.95 (978-1-4411-8110-7(5)) Continuum International Publishing Group, Ltd. GBR. Dist: National Bk. Network.

Howson, John Saul. The Metaphors of St Paul & Companions of St Paul. 2008. 328p. 25.99 (978-0-559-19011-7(5)); pap. 29.75 (978-0-559-19009-4(3)) BiblioBazaar.

—The Metaphors of St Paul & Companions of St Paul. 2007. (ENG.). 318p. 45.95 (978-0-548-16767-0(2)); 320p. per. 30.95 (978-1-4304-6479-2(8)) Kessinger Publishing, LLC.

—The Metaphors of St Paul & Companions of St Paul. 2006. 312p. per. 23.99 (978-1-4255-3296-3(9)) MPublishing.

Infeld, Tsevi. Ketav Ivri, Ketav Ashuri: Shitat Hazal Al Pi Torat Ha-Maharal U-Vet Midrasho. 2008. (HEB., Illus.). 249p. (978-1-59826-202-5(5)) Feldheim Pubs.

Isaacs, Roger D. Talking with God: The Radioactive Ark of the Testimony: Communication Through It. Protection from It. Williams Miller, Janice, ed. 2010. (Illus.). 514p. 29.95 (978-1-4125-4997-4(3), Sacred Closet Bks.) Publishing Institute, Inc., The.

Jacobs, Victor / Stephen. Arthrous Occurrence & Function in the Pauline Corpus, with Particular Focus on the Text of Romans. 2010. (Illus.). iv, 317p. (978-0-7734-3769-2(X)) Mellen, Edwin Pr., The.

Jeanie Strand Chilton. Eastern Customs of the Bible: The Teachings of Bishop K. C. Pillai. 2010. 108p. pap. 13.50 (978-1-4251-2163-1(2)) Trafford Publishing.

Jones, Scott C. Rumors of Wisdom: Job 28 As a Poetry. 2009. (Beihefte Zur Zeitschrift Fur Die Alttestamentliche Wissenschaft Ser.). (ENG.). XX, 293p. 126.00 (978-3-11-021477-2(6)) De Gruyter, Walter Inc.

Joosten, Jan, et al, eds. Voces Biblicae: Septuagint Greek & its Significance for the New Testament. 2007. (Contributions to Biblical Exegesis & Theology Ser.). (ENG.). 170p. (C). pap. 57.00 (978-90-429-1915-0(9)) Peeters Pubs. & Booksellers BEL. Dist: Brown, David Bk. Co., The.

Joosten, Jan & Bons, Eberhard. Septuagint Vocabulary: Pre-History, Usage, Reception. 2011. (GER.). 224p. pap. (978-1-58983-585-6(9)) Society of Biblical Literature.

Jost, Garry. Heart, Soul, Mind, & Strength. 2008. 160p. pap. (978-3-639-02181-3(9)) VDM Verlag Dr. Mueller e.K.

Kearney, Jonathan F. Rashi: Linguist Despite Himself: A Study of the Linguistic Dimension of Rabbi Solomon Yishaqi's Commentary on Deuteronomy. 2010. (Library of Hebrew Bible/Old Testament Studies). (ENG., Illus.). 224p. 120.00 (978-0-567-43856-0(2), T&T Clark Int'l) Continuum International Publishing Group, Ltd. GBR. Dist: National Bk. Network.

Kent, Grenville Jr. Say it Again, Sam: A Literary & Filmic Study of Narrative Repetition in 1 Samuel 28. 2012. (ENG.). 268p. pap. 39.00 (978-0-7188-9271-5(2)) Lutherworth Pr., The GBR. Dist: Brown, David Bk. Co., The.

Kern, Philip H. Rhetoric & Galatians: Assessing an Approach to Paul's Epistle. 2007. (Society for New Testament Studies Monograph Ser.). (ENG.). 324p. pap. 47.00 (978-0-521-04813-2(3)) Cambridge Univ. Pr.

Kim, Seenam. The Coherence of the Collections in the Book of Proverbs. 2007. 308p. pap. 34.00 (978-1-55635-518-9(1), Pickwick Pubns.) Wipf & Stock Pubs.

Klauck, Hans-Josef. Ancient Letters & the New Testament: A Guide to Context & Exegesis. 2006. 539p. per. 39.95 (978-1-932792-40-9(6)) Baylor Univ. Pr.

Konsmo, Erik. The Pauline Metaphors of the Holy Spirit: The Intangible Spirit's Tangible Presence in the Life of the Christian. 2010. (Studies in Biblical Literature Ser.). 242p. (C). 75.95 (978-1-4331-0691-0(4)) Lang, Peter Publishing, Inc.

Kox, Norbert H. The Holy Cipher: Who Changed God's Name? 2008. 145p. pap. 16.95 (978-0-615-16142-6(1)) Apocalypse Hse.

Kreinecker, Christina M. Koptische Zeugen der Auferstehungsberichte. 2008. (Arbeiten zur neutestamentlichen Textforschung Ser.).Tr. of Coptic Traditions of the Accounts of the Resurrection. XII, 274p. (COP, GEC & GER.). 147.00 (978-3-11-020920-4(9)); (GER.). 224.00 (978-3-11-173869-7(8)) De Gruyter, Walter Inc.

Labahn, A. & Van Hecke, P., eds. Metaphors in the Psalms. 2010. (Bibliotheca Ephemeridum Theologicarum Lovaniensium Ser.). (ENG.). 369p. (C). pap. 111.00 (978-90-429-2256-3(7)) Peeters Pubs. & Booksellers BEL. Dist: Brown, David Bk. Co., The.

Lagarde, Paul, ed. Bibliothecae Syriacae. 2007. 256p. pap. 22.00 (978-1-55635-714-5(1)) Wipf & Stock Pubs.

Leavins, Daniel. Verbs of Leading in the Hebrew Bible. 2011. 145.00 (978-1-61143-925-0(6)) Gorgias Pr., LLC.

Lee. Paul's Gospel in Romans: A Discourse Analysis of Rom 1:16-8:39. 2009. (Linguistic Biblical Studies). (978-90-04-17963-9(1)) BRILL.

Litke, Richard L. What Jesus Really Meant: Challenging Passages in the New Testament. 2011. pap. 15.99 (978-0-8163-2479-8(4)) Pacific Pr. Publishing Assn.

Lockett, Darian. Purity & Worldview in the Epistle of James. 2008. (Library of New Testament Studies, the Ser.). (ENG.). 240p. 130.00 (978-0-567-03311-6(2), T&T Clark Int'l) Continuum International Publishing Group, Ltd. GBR. Dist: National Bk. Network.

Malena, Sarah & Miano, David. Milk & Honey: Essays on Ancient Israel & the Bible in Appreciation of the Judaic Studies Program at the University of California, San Diego. 2007. (Illus.). 44.50 (978-1-57506-127-6(9)) Eisenbrauns, Inc.

Marguerat, D., et al, eds. L' intrigue dans le recit Biblique: Quatrieme colloque international du RRENAB, Universite Laval, Quebec, 29 mai-1er Juin 2008. 2010. (Bibliotheca Ephemeridum Theologicarum Lovaniensium Ser.). (FRE.). 479p. (C). pap. 99.00 (978-90-429-2328-7(8)) Peeters Pubs. & Booksellers BEL. Dist: Brown, David Bk. Co., The.

Martin, Lee Roy. Introduction to Biblical Hebrew. 3rd rev. ed. 2009. (C). pap. 17.95 (978-0-9819651-5-4(6)) CPT Pr.

Mathewson, David. Verbal Aspect in the Book of Revelation: The Function of Greek Verb Tenses in John's Apocalypse. 2010. (Linguistic Biblical Studies). 206p. (978-90-04-18668-2(9)) BRILL.

McCreesh, Thomas P. Biblical Sound & Sense: Poetic Sound Patterns in Proverbs 10-29. 2009. (Library of Hebrew Bible/Old Testament Studies, the Ser.). (ENG.). 164p. 29.95 (978-1-4411-1873-8(X), T&T Clark) Continuum International Publishing Group, Ltd. GBR. Dist: National Bk. Network.

Meyer, Mark. A Comparative Dialectical Study of Genitive Constructions in Aramaic Translations of Exodus. 2010. 140.00 (978-1-61143-002-8(X)) Gorgias Pr., LLC.

Monferrer-Sala, Juan Pedro & Urbán, Ángel, eds. Sacred Text: Explorations in Lexicography. 2009. (Studien zur romanischen Sprachwissenschaft und interkulturellen Kommunikation Ser.). 328p. 83.95 (978-3-631-59741-5(X)) Lang, Peter GmbH, Europaischer Verlag der Wissenschaften DEU. Dist: Lang, Peter.

Moorman, Jack A. Missing in Modern Bibles, the Old Heresy Revived. 2009. 124p. pap. 14.00 (978-0-9822230-4-8(8)) Old Paths Pubns., Inc., The.

Morgenstern, Mira. Conceiving a Nation: The Development of Political Discourse in the Hebrew Bible. 2009. (ENG.). 232p. 65.00 (978-0-271-03473-7(4)) Pennsylvania State Univ. Pr.

Moshavi, A. Mosak. Word Order in the Biblical Hebrew Finite Clause: A Syntactic & Pragmatic Analysis of Preposing. 2010. 42.50 (978-1-57506-191-7(0)) Eisenbrauns, Inc.

Mounce, William. Biblical Greek Survival Kit, 1 vol. 2006. (ENG.). audio compact disk 29.99 (978-0-310-27582-4(2)) Zondervan.

Mounce, William D. Biblical Greek, 1 vol. 2011. (ENG & GEC.). 224p. pap. 19.99 (978-0-310-32606-9(0)) Zondervan.

—Greek for the Rest of Us: Using Greek Tools Without Mastering Biblical Languages, 1 vol. 2007. (ENG., Illus.). 320p. (gr. 13). pap. 24.99 (978-0-310-28289-1(6)) Zondervan.

Niccacci, Alviero. Syntax of the Verb in Classical Hebrew Prose. 2009. (Library of Hebrew Bible/Old Testament Studies, the Ser.). (ENG.). 27.95 (978-0-567-21372-3(2), T&T Clark) Continuum International Publishing Group, Ltd. GBR. Dist: National Bk. Network.

Nicholson, Suzanne. Dynamic Oneness. 2009. 312p. pap. 33.00 (978-1-60608-326-0(0), Pickwick Pubns.) Wipf & Stock Pubs.

Noegel, Scott B. Janus Parallelism in the Book of Job. 2009. (Library of Hebrew Bible/Old Testament Studies, the Ser.). (ENG.). 223p. 39.95 (978-0-567-51218-5(5), T&T Clark) Continuum International Publishing Group, Ltd. GBR. Dist: National Bk. Network.

Novenson, Matthew V. Christ among the Messiahs: Christ Language in Paul & Messiah Language in Ancient Judaism, 1 vol. 2012. (ENG.). 256p. 74.00 (978-0-19-984457-9(7)) Oxford Univ. Pr., Inc.

O'Brien, Julia M. Challenging Prophetic Metaphor: Theology & Ideology in the Prophets. 2008. (ENG.). 224p. pap. 25.00 (978-0-664-22964-1(6)) Westminster John Knox Pr.

O'Connell, Robert H. Concentricity & Continuity: The Literary Structure of Isaiah. 2009. (Library of Hebrew Bible/Old Testament Studies, the Ser.). (ENG.). 272p. 44.95 (978-0-567-63952-3(5), T&T Clark) Continuum International Publishing Group, Ltd. GBR. Dist: National Bk. Network.

Ortlund, Eric. Theophany & Chaoskampf: The Interpretation of Theophanic Imagery in the Baal Epic, Isaiah, & the Twelve. 2010. 104.00 (978-1-61719-160-2(4)) Gorgias Pr., LLC.

Park. Mark's Memory Resources & the Controversy Stories (Mark 2:1-3:6) An Application of the Frame Theory of Cognitive Science to the Markan Oral-Aural Narrative. 2009. (Linguistic Biblical Studies). (978-90-04-17962-2(3)) BRILL.

Peacock, George M. Unlocking the Idioms: An LDS Perspective on Understanding Scriptural Idioms. 2009. pap. 15.99 (978-1-59955-241-5(8)) Cedar Fort, Inc./CFI Distribution.

Petersen, Norman R. The Gospel of John & the Sociology of Light: Language & Characterization in the Fourth Gospel. 2008. 176p. pap. 20.00 (978-1-60608-114-3(4), Wipf and Stock) Wipf & Stock Pubs.

Peterson, Eugne H. Tell It Slant: A Conversation on the Language of Jesus in His Stories & Prayers. 2008. 264p. 24.00 (978-0-8028-2954-2(6)) Eerdmans, William B. Publishing Co.

Porter, Stanley E. & Adams, Sean A., eds. Paul & the Ancient Letter Form. 2009. (978-90-04-18163-2(6)) BRILL.

Porter, Stanley E., et al. Fundamentals of New Testament Greek. 2010. (GEC & ENG.). xxi, 466p. 40.00 (978-0-8028-2827-9(2)) Eerdmans, William B. Publishing Co.

Pratico, Gary D., et al. Basics of Biblical Hebrew Workbook. 2nd ed. 2007. (ENG., Illus.). 304p. (gr. 13). pap. 22.99 (978-0-310-27022-5(7)) Zondervan.

Pratt, Samuel Jackson. The Sublime & Beautiful of Scripture Being Essays on Select Passages of Sacred Composition. 2007. (ENG.). 258p. 42.95 (978-0-548-03659-4(4)) Kessinger Publishing, LLC.

Price, Craig. Biblical Exegesis of New Testament Greek: James. 2008. 294p. pap. 32.00 (978-1-55635-972-9(1)) Wipf & Stock Pubs.

Pyper, Hugh S. & Vander Stichele, Caroline. Text, Image, & Otherness in Children's Bibles: What Is in the Picture? 2012. pap. (978-1-58983-661-7(8)) Society of Biblical Literature.

Ravndal Hauge, Martin. Descent from the Mountain: Narrative Patterns in Exodus 19-40. 2009. (Library of Hebrew Bible/Old Testament Studies, the Ser.). (ENG.). 368p. 60.00 (978-1-4411-9848-8(2), T&T Clark) Continuum International Publishing Group, Ltd. GBR. Dist: National Bk. Network.

Rees, Margo. Lishan Didan, Targum Didan: Translation Language in a Neo-Aramaic Targum Tradition. 2007. 75.00 (978-1-59333-426-0(5)) Gorgias Pr., LLC.

Reisman, Yisroel. Pathways of the Prophets: A Treasury of Torah Thought & Law - Looking at Ourselves Through the Lens of the Prophets. 2009. (ArtScroll Ser.). 467p. (978-1-4226-0893-7(X)) Mesorah Pubns., Ltd.

Renner, Rick. Sparkling Gems from the Greek: 365 Greek Word Studies for Every Day of the Year to Sharpen Your Understanding of God's Word. 2007. (DRA.). 1046p. 34.95 (978-0-9725454-2-6(5)) Teach All Nations.

Roberts, D. Let Me See Your Form: Seeking Poetic Structure in the Song of Songs. 2007. (Studies in the History of Judaism Ser.). (ENG.). per. 57.99 (978-0-7618-2913-3(X)) Univ. Pr. of America, Inc.

Robinson, Thomas A. Mastering New Testament Greek: Essential Tools for Students. 2006. 230p. pap. incl. cd-rom (978-1-56563-576-0(0)) Hendrickson Pubs. Marketing, LLC.

Rooker, Mark F. Biblical Hebrew in Transition: The Language of the Book of Ezekiel. 2009. (Library of Hebrew Bible/Old Testament Studies, the Ser.). (ENG.). 222p. 39.95 (978-0-567-02883-9(6), T&T Clark) Continuum International Publishing Group, Ltd. GBR. Dist: National Bk. Network.

Rosenau, William. Hebraisms in the Authorized Version of the Bible. 2009. 288p. 24.99 (978-1-103-22156-1(6)); pap. 18.99 (978-1-103-22155-4(8)) BiblioBazaar.

Rothschild, Clare K. Hebrews As Pseudepigraphon: The History & Significance of the Pauline Attribution of Hebrews. 2009. (Illus.). xvii, 287p. (978-3-16-149826-8(7)) Mohr Siebeck GmbH & Co. KG.

Runge, Steven E. Discourse Grammar of the Greek New Testament: A Practical Introduction for Teaching & Exegesis. 2010. (GEC & ENG., Illus.). 384p. 49.95 (978-1-59856-583-6(4)) Hendrickson Pubs. Marketing, LLC.

Sacks, Robert D. Beginning Biblical Hebrew: Intentionality & Grammar. 2010. (ENG., Illus.). 205p. pap. 18.00 (978-1-888009-33-0(0)) Green Lion Pr.

Sanders, Seth L. The Invention of Hebrew. (Traditions Ser.). (ENG., Illus.). 280p. 2011. pap. 35.00 (978-0-252-07835-4(7)) 2009. 50.00 (978-0-252-03284-4(5)) Univ. of Illinois Pr.

Sawyer, John F. A. Sacred Texts & Sacred Meanings: Studies in Biblical Language & Literature. 2011. 480p. (978-1-906055-94-3(7)) Sheffield Phoenix Pr.

Schultz, Richard L. Search for Quotation: Verbal Parallels in the Prophets. 2009. (Library of Hebrew Bible/Old Testament Studies, the Ser.). (ENG.). 400p. 65.00 (978-0-567-61967-9(2), T&T Clark) Continuum International Publishing Group, Ltd. GBR. Dist: National Bk. Network.

Sellin, Gerhard. Allegorie - Metapher - Mythos - Schrift: Beiträge zur religiösen Sprache im Neuen Testament und in seiner Umwelt. Sanger, Dieter, ed. 2011. (Novum Testamentum et Orbis Antiquus/Studien zur Umwelt des Neuen Testaments (NTOA/StUNT) Ser.). (GER.). 306p. (C). 81.00 (978-3-525-55020-5(0)) Vandenhoeck & Ruprecht GmbH & Co. KG DEU. Dist: ISD.

Seybold, Klaus. Studien Zu Sprache und Stil der Psalmen. 2010. (Beihefte zur Zeitschrift für die alttestamentliche Wissenschaft Ser.). (GER.). VIII, 358p. 126.00 (978-3-11-024097-9(1)) De Gruyter, Walter Inc.

Shead, Stephen. Radical Frame Semantics & Biblical Hebrew: Exploring Lexical Semantics. 2011. (Biblical Interpretation Ser.). (Illus.). XXVIII, 378p. (978-90-04-18839-6(8)) BRILL.

Sidebottom, E. M. The Christ of the Fourth Gospel. 2010. 240p. pap. 27.00 (978-1-60899-746-6(4), Wipf and Stock) Wipf & Stock Pubs.

Sim, Margaret G. Marking Thought & Talk in New Testament Greek. 2011. (ENG.). 242p. pap. 42.50 (978-0-227-17377-0(5)) Clarke, James Co., Ltd. GBR. Dist: Brown, David Bk. Co., The.

Smith, Mark S. The Origins & Development of the Waw-Consecutive: Northwest Semitic Evidence from Ugarit to Qumran. 2009. pap. (978-1-57506-935-7(0)) Eisenbrauns, Inc.

Smolarz, Sebastian R. Covenant & the Metaphor of Divine Marriage in Biblical Thought: A Study with Special Reference to the Book of Revelation. 2010. 404p. pap. 44.00 (978-1-60899-455-7(4), Wipf and Stock) Wipf & Stock Pubs.

Spencer, Aida Besancon. Paul's Literary Style: A Stylistic & Historical Comparison of II Corinthians 11:16-12:13, Romans 8:9-39, & Philippians 3:2-4:13. 2007. (ENG., Illus.). 266p. per. 42.99 (978-0-7618-3954-5(2)) Univ. Pr. of America, Inc.

Steinmann, Andrew E. Intermediate Biblical Hebrew. 2010. 264p. pap. 49.99 (978-0-7586-2516-8(2)) Concordia Publishing Hse.

Stevens, Gerald. New Testament Greek Intermediate: From Morphology to Translation. 2009. (ENG., Illus.). 638p. pap. 64.00 (978-0-7188-9200-5(3)) Lutherworth Pr., The GBR. Dist: Brown, David Bk. Co., The.

—New Testament Greek Primer. 2nd ed. 2009. (ENG & GEC., Illus.). 620p. pap. 64.00 (978-0-7188-9206-7(2)) Lutherworth Pr., The GBR. Dist: Brown, David Bk. Co., The.

Stevens, Gerald L. New Testament Greek Intermediate: From Morphology to Translation. 2008. (Illus.). 638p. pap. 50.00 (978-1-55635-580-6(7)) Wipf & Stock Pubs.

—New Testament Greek Primer. 2nd ed. 2007. (Illus.). 620p. pap. 49.00 (978-1-55635-348-2(0), Cascade Bks.) Wipf & Stock Pubs.

—New Testament Greek Primer, Third Edition. 2010. 620p. pap. 49.00 (978-1-60899-467-0(8), Cascade Bks.) Wipf & Stock Pubs.

Taiwo, Moses. Paul's Rhetoric in 1 Corinthians: 29b-30. 2008. 244p. pap. (978-3-639-01048-0(5)) VDM Verlag Dr. Mueller e.K.

Tooman, William A. & Lyons, Michael A. Transforming Visions: Transformations of Text, Tradition, & Theology in Ezekiel. 2011. (ENG.). 350p. pap. 48.00 (978-0-227-17368-8(6)) Clarke, James Co., Ltd. GBR. Dist: Brown, David Bk. Co., The.

Tooman, William A. & Lyons, Michael A., eds. Transforming Visions. 2009. (Princeton Theological Monographs). (Illus.). 378p. pap. 42.00 (978-1-55635-285-0(9), Pickwick Pubns.) Wipf & Stock Pubs.

Tregelles, Samuel Prideaux, ed. The Greek New Testament: Edited from Ancient Authorities, with Their Various Readings in Full, & the Latin Version of Jerome. 2010. (Cambridge Library Collection - Religion Ser.). (ENG.). 284p. pap. 23.99 (978-1-108-00713-9(9)); 212p. pap. 22.99 (978-1-108-00715-3(5)); 196p. pap. 19.99 (978-1-108-00714-6(7)); 232p. pap. 22.99 (978-1-108-00712-2(0)) Cambridge Univ. Pr.

Tregelles, Samuel Prideaux, et al, eds. The Greek New Testament: Edited from Ancient Authorities, with Their Various Readings in Full, & the Latin Version of Jerome. 2010. (Cambridge Library Collection - Religion Ser.). (ENG.). 248p. pap. 23.99 (978-1-108-00711-5(2)) Cambridge Univ. Pr.

Valeta, David M. Lions & Ovens & Visions: A Satirical Reading of Daniel 1-6. 2008. xii, 230p. (978-1-905048-53-3(X)) Sheffield Phoenix Pr.

Van der Lugt, Pieter. Cantos & Strophes in Biblical Hebrew Poetry II, Psalms 42-89. 2010. 580p. (978-90-04-18200-4(4)) BRILL.

van der Meer, Willem. Structural Analysis of Biblical & Canaanite Poetry. 2009. (Library of Hebrew Bible/Old Testament Studies, the Ser.). (ENG.). 75.00 *(978-0-567-57423-7(7),* T&T Clark) Continuum International Publishing Group, Ltd. GBR. Dist: National Bk. Network.

Van Pelt, Miles V. Basics of Biblical Aramaic: Complete Grammar, Lexicon, & Annotated Text, 1 vol. 2011. (ENG.). 304p. pap. 44.99 *(978-0-310-49391-4(9))* Zondervan.

Van Pelt, Miles V. & Pratico, Gary D. Graded Reader of Biblical Hebrew: A Guide to Reading the Hebrew Bible, 1 vol. 2006. (ENG.). 256p. 18.99 *(978-0-310-25157-6(5))* Zondervan.

Vern, Robyn. Dating Archaic Biblical Hebrew Poetry. 2011. 113.00 *(978-1-61143-921-2(3))* Gorgias Pr., LLC.

Voitila, Anssi, et al. Scripture in Transition: Essays on Septuagint, Hebrew Bible, & Dead Sea Scrolls in Honour of Raija Sollamo. Voitila, Anssi & Jokiranta, Jutta, eds. 2008. (Supplements to the Journal for the Study of Judaism Ser.). 700p. *(978-90-04-16582-3(7))* BRILL.

Waite, Pastor D. A. A Critical Answer to James Price's King James Onlyism. 2009. 188p. pap. 15.00 *(978-1-56848-063-3(6))* Old Paths Pubns., Inc., The.

Waite, Th. D. Pastor D. A. A Critical Answer to Michael Sproul's God's Word Preserved. 2008. pap. 15.00 *(978-1-56848-058-9(X))* Old Paths Pubns., Inc., The.

Walker, Robert. Bible Treatise. 2011. 28p. pap. 5.99 ***(978-1-937129-05-7(5))*** Faithful Life Pubs.

Wallace, Daniel B. Gramatica Griega/Sintaxis Del Nt, 1 vol. 2011. (Biblioteca Teologica Vida Ser.). (SPA.). 624p. 29.99 ***(978-0-8297-5919-8(0))*** Vida Pubs.

Watson, Edward W. Paul, His Roman Audience, & the Adopted People of God: Understanding the Pauline Metaphor of Adopton in Romans as Authorial Audience. 2008. 252p. 109.95 *(978-0-7734-4927-5(2))* Mellen, Edwin Pr., The.

Watts, James W. Psalm & Story: Inset Hymns in Hebrew Narrative. 2009. (Library of Hebrew Bible/Old Testament Studies, the Ser.). (ENG.). 244p. 39.95 *(978-0-567-56410-8(X),* T&T Clark) Continuum International Publishing Group, Ltd. GBR. Dist: National Bk. Network.

—Ritual & Rhetoric in Leviticus: From Sacrifice to Scripture. 2007. (ENG.). 278p. 104.00 *(978-0-521-87193-8(X))* Cambridge Univ. Pr.

Webster, Brian L. Biblical Hebrew. 2009. (ENG., Illus.). 380p. (C). 125.00 incl. cd-rom *(978-0-521-88542-3(6))*; pap. 44.00 incl. cd-rom *(978-0-521-71284-2(X))* Cambridge Univ. Pr.

Weeks, Noel. Sources & Authors: Assumptions in the Study of Hebrew Bible Narrative. 2011. 137.65 ***(978-1-4632-0034-3(X))*** Gorgias Pr., LLC.

Whittaker, Molly. New Testament Greek Grammar: Key to Exercises. 48p. pap. 7.00 *(978-0-334-00830-9(1))* Hymns Ancient & Modern Ltd GBR. Dist: Morehouse Publishing.

Williams, Charles Bray. The Participle in the Book of Acts. 2008. 87p. pap. 8.00 *(978-1-60608-354-3(6),* Wipf and Stock) Wipf & Stock Pubs.

Winstanley, Edward William. Spirit in the New Testament: An Enquiry into the Use of the Word Pneuma in All Passagas, & a Survey of the Evidence Concerning the Holy Spirit. 2008. (Illus.). 174p. pap. 15.00 *(978-1-55635-772-5(9))* Wipf & Stock Pubs.

Wischmeyer, Oda & Scornaienchi, Lorenzo. Polemik in der frühchristlichen Literatur: Texte und Kontexte. 2010. (Beihefte zur Zeitschrift für die neutestamentliche Wissenschaft und die Kunde der älteren Kirche Ser.). (GER.). VII, 686p. 196.00 ***(978-3-11-022353-8(8))*** De Gruyter, Walter Inc.

Witherington, Ben, III. New Testament Rhetoric: An Introduction Guide to the Art of Persuasion in & of the New Testament. 2008. 284p. pap. 28.00 *(978-1-55635-929-3(2))* Wipf & Stock Pubs.

Wolde, E. J. van. Reframing Biblical Studies: When Language & Text Meet Culture, Cognition, & Context. 2009. 402p. 44.50 *(978-1-57506-182-5(1))* Eisenbrauns, Inc.

Wong, Gregory T. K. Compositional Strategy of the Book of Judges: An Inductive, Rhetorical Study. 2006. (Supplements to Vetus Testamentum Ser.: Vol. 111). (Illus.). 287p. *(978-90-04-15086-7(2))* BRILL.

Younger, K. Lawson, Jr. Ancient Conquest Accounts: A Study in Ancient near Eastern & Biblical History Writing. 2009. (Library of Hebrew Bible/Old Testament Studies, the Ser.). (ENG.). 383p. 65.00 *(978-0-567-55704-9(9),* T&T Clark) Continuum International Publishing Group, Ltd. GBR. Dist: National Bk. Network.

Zewi, Tamar. Parenthesis in Biblical Hebrew. 2007. (Studies in Semitic Languages & Linguistics Ser.). *(978-90-04-16243-3(7))* BRILL.

Zimmermann, Christiane. Die Namen des Vaters: Studien zu ausgewählten neutestamentlichen Gottesbezeichnungen. 2007. (Ancient Judaism & Early Christianity Ser.). (GER.). 728p. *(978-90-04-15812-2(X))* BRILL.

Zuck, Roy, ed. Vital New Testament Issues: Examining New Testament Passages & Problems. 2006. (Vital Issues Ser.). 288p. pap. 28.00 *(978-1-59752-684-5(3),* Wipf and Stock) Wipf & Stock Pubs.

BIBLE—LAW

see Jewish Law; Law (Theology)

BIBLE—LITERARY CRITICISM

see Bible—Criticism, interpretation, etc.; Bible—Introductions; Bible As Literature

BIBLE—LITURGICAL USE

see also Lectionaries

Aernie, Jeffrey W. Is Paul also among the Prophets? An Examination of the Relationship between Paul & the Old Testament Prophetic Tradition in 2 Corinthians. 2012. (Library of New Testament Studies). (ENG.). 320p. 120.00 ***(978-0-567-17572-4(3),*** T&T Clark Int'l) Continuum International Publishing Group, Ltd. GBR. Dist: National Bk. Network.

Braulik, Georg & Lohfink, Norbert. Osternacht und Altes Testament - Ergänzungsband: Vertonung des Vigilvorschlags durch Godehard Joppich. 2008. (Österreichische Biblische Studien Ser.). (GER., Illus.). 172p. 56.95 *(978-3-631-56994-8(7))* Lang, Peter GmbH, Europaischer Verlag der Wissenschaften DEU. Dist: Lang, Peter.

Brauninger, Dallas A. In the Beginning Was the Word: Scriptures for the Lectionary Speaking Choir. 2008. *(978-0-7880-2571-6(6))* CSS Publishing Co.

Camille, Alice. God's Word Is Alive. 2007. (Illus.). 398p. per. 19.95 *(978-0-87946-339-7(2))* ACTA Pubns.

Eckardt Jr, Burnell F. The New Testament in His Blood. 2010. 118p. pap. 18.00 *(978-0-557-55043-2(2))* Lulu Enterprises Inc.

Farrow, Michael G., compiled by. Psalm Verses of the Orthodox Liturgy: Psalms Used at the Antiphons, at the Entrance, at the Prokeimenon & Alleluia, & at Communion, along with Their Biblical Citations According to Both the Greek & Slav Usages. 2011. *(978-0-88141-873-6(0))* St. Vladimir's Seminary Pr.

Greisen, Thomas A., et al. Living Liturgy: Spirituality, Celebration, & Catechesis for Sundays & Solemnities - Year A 2008. 2007. (Illus.). 320p. per. 16.95 *(978-0-8146-2745-7(5),* Liturgical Pr. Bks.) Liturgical Pr.

Grisbrooke, W. Jardine, ed. The Liturgical Portions of the Apostolic Contitutions. 2009. 88.00 *(978-1-60724-368-7(7))* Gorgias Pr., LLC.

Hahn, Scott, compiled by. Spirit & Life: Essays on Interpreting the Bible in Ordinary Time. 2009. 162p. mass mkt. 15.95 *(978-1-931018-53-1(7))* Emmaus Road Publishing.

Hahn, Scott W. & Scott, David, eds. Letter & Spirit, Volume 4: Temple & Contemplation: God's Presence in the Cosmos, Church, & Human Heart. 2008. (Letter & Spirit Ser.). 336p. pap. 15.95 *(978-1-931018-52-4(9))* Emmaus Road Publishing.

Hawkes-Teeples, Steven. The Liturgical Commentaries: St symeon of Thessalonika. 2011. (Studies & Texts). (ENG, GEC & GRE.). 310p. 90.00 *(978-0-88844-168-3(1))* Pontifical Institute of Mediaeval Studies, Dept. of Pubns. CAN. Dist: Univ. of Toronto Pr.

Houlden, Leslie & Rogerson, John, eds. Common Worship Lectionary: A Scripture Commentary (Year B) 296p. 32.00 *(978-0-281-05326-1(X))* SPCK Publishing GBR. Dist: Pilgrim Pr., The/United Church Pr.

Kerr, Gordon. Mohammedan Controversy. 2006. 228p. per. *(978-1-4067-3674-8(0),* Hesperides Pr.) Read Bks.

Latkovich, Sallie. Mining the Meaning of the Bible: Beyond the Literal Word. 2011. 64p. *(978-0-7648-1982-7(8))* Liguori Pubns.

Living Liturgy Sunday Missal 2010. 2009. 384p. pap. 9.95 *(978-0-8146-3306-9(4),* Liturgical Pr. Bks.) Liturgical Pr.

Lott, David B., ed. New Proclamation: Year B, 2010, Easter Through Christ the King. 2012. 256p. (C). pap. 25.00 *(978-0-8006-9772-3(3))* Augsburg Fortress, Pubs.

—New Proclamation: Year B, 2011-2012, Advent through Holy Week. 2011. 256p. (C). pap. 25.00 *(978-0-8006-9771-6(5))* Augsburg Fortress, Pubs.

McKenna, Megan. Lent: Daily Readings. 2008. (ENG.). 176p. pap. 22.95 *(978-1-84730-104-8(5))* Veritas Pubns. IRL. Dist: Dufour Editions, Inc.

Nasr, Constantine. The Bible in the Liturgy. 75p. spiral bd. 9.95 *(978-1-880321-01-0(7))* Theosis Publishing Co.

O'Driscoll, Herbert. The Word Today: Reflections on the Readings of the Revised Common Lectionary. 14.95 *(978-1-55126-337-3(8),* 1446); 14.95 *(978-1-55126-334-2(3),* 1536); Vol. 2. 14.95 *(978-1-55126-335-9(1),* 1537); Vol. 2. 14.95 *(978-1-55126-338-0(6),* 1462); Vol. 3. 18.95 *(978-1-55126-336-6(X),* 1538); Vol. 3. 18.95 *(978-1-55126-339-7(4),* 1463) Forward Movement Pubns.

Old, Hughes Oliphant. The Modern Age, 1789-1889, 7 vols., Vol. 6. 2007. (Reading & Preaching of the Scriptures in the Worship of the Christian Church Ser.). 997p. per. 50.00 *(978-0-8028-3139-2(7))* Eerdmans, William B. Publishing Co.

O'Neill, George. The Psalms & the Canticles of the Divine Office. Husslein, Joseph, ed. 2011. 326p. 50.95 ***(978-1-258-05642-1(9))*** Literary Licensing, LLC.

Pontifical Biblical Commission. The Interpretation of the Bible in the Church. 144p. pap. 5.95 *(978-0-8198-3670-0(2),* 332-132) Pauline Bks. & Media.

Race, Marianne & Brink, Laurie. In This Place: Reflections on the Land of the Gospels for the Liturgical Cycles. 2008. 238p. pap. 26.00 *(978-1-55635-906-4(3),* Wipf and Stock) Wipf & Stock Pubs.

Simple Guide to the Daily Mass Readings 2007. 2006. 3.00 *(978-1-56854-583-7(5),* READ07) Liturgy Training Pubns.

The Word Among Us, ed. Abide in My Word 2010: Mass Readings at Your Fingertips. 2009. 584p. pap. 16.50 *(978-1-59325-157-4(2))* Word Among Us Pr.

The Word Among Us Press Staff, ed. Abide in My Word 2012: Mass Readings at Your Fingertips. 2011. 600p. pap. 16.50 *(978-1-59325-187-1(4))* Word Among Us Pr.

Westberg, Daniel & Fuller, Reginald H., eds. Preaching the Lectionary: The Word of God for the Church Today. 3rd ed. 2006. 616p. per. 29.95 *(978-0-8146-2792-1(7),* Liturgical Pr. Bks.) Liturgical Pr.

Witvliet, John D. The Biblical Psalms in Christian Worship: A Brief Introduction & Guide to Resources. 2007. (Calvin Institute of Christian Worship Liturgical Studies). 169p. per. 16.00 *(978-0-8028-0767-0(4))* Eerdmans, William B. Publishing Co.

World Among Us Press, creator. Abide in My Word: Mass Readings at Your Fingertips. 2006. 610p. per. 15.50 *(978-1-59325-078-2(9))* Word Among Us Pr.

Zimmerman, Joyce. Living Liturgy for Extraordinary Ministers of Holy Communion. Harmon, Kathleen, ed. 2011. 128p. pap. 9.95 ***(978-0-8146-3334-2(X))*** Liturgical Pr.

Zimmerman, Joyce, ed. Living Liturgy Year C 2010. 2009. 336p. pap. 16.95 *(978-0-8146-2747-1(1),* Liturgical Pr. Bks.) Liturgical Pr.

Zimmerman, Joyce Ann, et al, eds. Living Liturgy for Extraordinary Ministers of Holy Communion: Year A 2008. 2007. (Illus.). 135p. per. 6.95 *(978-0-8146-3084-6(7),* Liturgical Pr. Bks.) Liturgical Pr.

Zyromski, Page McKean. How to Pray with the Bible. 2010. (ENG.). 128p. pap. 14.99 *(978-1-55725-691-1(8))* Paraclete Pr., Inc.

BIBLE—MANUSCRIPTS

see also Dead Sea Scrolls

Anderson, H. T. Codex Sinaiticus: the H. T. Anderson New Testament. 2010. 600p. pap. 35.65 *(978-0-557-27476-5(1))* Lulu Enterprises Inc.

Arzt-Grabner, Peter & Kreinecker, Christina M., eds. Light from the East. Papyrologische Kommentare zum Neuen Testament: Akten des internationalen Symposions vom 3. -4. Dezember 2009 am Fachbereich Bibelwissenschaft und Kirchengeschichte der Universitat Salzburg. 2010. (Philippika Ser.). (ENG & GER.). 237p. (C). pap. 72.00 *(978-3-447-06291-6(6))* Harrassowitz, Otto Verlag DEU. Dist: ISD.

Baldwin, Clinton S. The So-Called Mixed Text: An Examination of the Non-Alexandrian & Non-Byzantine Text-Type in the Catholic Epistles. 2011. ***(978-1-4331-0755-9(4))*** Lang, Peter GmbH, Europaischer Verlag der Wissenschaften.

Brown, Michelle, comment. Holkham Bible (Facsimile Edition) 2007. (ENG.). 180p. (C). 99.50 *(978-0-7123-0990-5(X))* British Library, The GBR. Dist: Chicago Distribution Ctr.

Brown, Michelle P. In the Beginning: Bibles Before the Year 1000. 2006. (ENG., Illus.). 368p. 45.00 *(978-1-58834-240-9(9))* Smithsonian Institution Pr.

Cambridge University Library. Catalogue of the Hebrew Manuscripts Preserved in the University Library, Cambridge. 2006. 260p. per. 23.99 *(978-1-4255-2228-5(9))* MPublishing.

Cobb, Tyrone W. It Is Written. 2010. 396p. pap. 20.99 *(978-1-61579-965-7(6))* Xulon Pr., Inc.

Crouch, Earl. Do You Know? 2007. 192p. per. 24.95 *(978-1-4241-7391-4(4))* PublishAmerica, Inc.

De Troyer, K., et al, eds. Prophecy after the Prophets? the Contribution of the Dead Sea Scrolls to the Understanding of Biblical & Extra-Biblical Prophecy. 2009. (Contributions to Biblical Exegesis & Theology Ser.). (ENG.). 242p. (C). pap. 61.00 *(978-90-429-2135-1(8))* Peeters Pubs. & Booksellers BEL. Dist: Brown, David Bk. Co., The.

Doane, Alger Nicolaus & Stoneman, William P. Purloined Letters: The Twelfth-Century Reception of the Anglo-Saxon Illustrated Hexateuch (British Library, Cotton Claudius B. IV) 2011. ***(978-0-86698-443-0(7))*** Arizona State Univ., Arizona Ctr. for Medieval & Renaissance Studies.

Ehrman, Bart D. Misquoting Jesus: The Story Behind Who Changed the Bible & Why. 2007. (Plus Ser.). (ENG., Illus.). 256p. pap. 14.99 *(978-0-06-085951-0(2),* HarperOne) HarperCollins Pubs.

Emmenegger, Gregor. Der Text des koptischen Psalters aus al-Mudil: Ein Beitrag zur Textgeschichte der Septuaginta und zur Textkritik koptischer Bibelhandschriften, mit der kritischen Neuausgabe des Papyrus 37 der British Library London (U) und des Papyrus 39 der Leipziger Universitätsbibliothek (2013) 2007. (Texte und Untersuchungen zur Geschichte der altchristlichen Literatur Ser.: Vol. 159). (GEC & GER., Illus.). XXVIII, 391p. 182.00 *(978-3-11-019948-2(3))* De Gruyter, Walter Inc.

Evans, Craig A. & Zacharias, Daniel H., eds. Jewish & Christian Scripture as Artifact & Canon. 2011. (ENG.). 338p. pap. 55.00 ***(978-0-567-29329-9(7),*** T&T Clark Int'l) Continuum International Publishing Group, Ltd. GBR. Dist: National Bk. Network.

Gameson, Richard, ed. The Early Medieval Bible: Its Production, Decoration & Use. 2009. (Cambridge Studies in Palaeography & Codicology Ser.). (ENG., Illus.). 264p. pap. 36.99 *(978-0-521-10001-4(1))* Cambridge Univ. Pr.

Gastgeber, Christian & Fussel, Stephan. Bible Manuscripts. Fingernagel, Andreas, ed. 25th ed. 2008. (ENG., Illus.). 320p. 29.99 *(978-3-8365-0299-3(2))* TASCHEN DEU. Dist: Ingram Pub. Services.

Gesing, Cheryl & Schmigotzki, Tiffany. Undiscovered Treasure: The untold secret of ephraim & Manasseh. 2007. 348p. per. 17.99 *(978-1-60266-877-5(9))* Xulon Pr., Inc.

Gottheil, Richard J. H. Some Hebrew Manuscripts in Cairo. 2010. (HEB.). 86.00 *(978-1-61143-394-4(0))* Gorgias Pr., LLC.

Hatch, William. Specimens of Greek New Testament Handwriting from the Second to the Sixteenth Century, 2 Vols. 2009. Set; Vols. 1-2. 820.00 *(978-1-60724-420-2(9))*Set; Vols.1-2. 820.00 *(978-1-60724-419-6(5))* Gorgias Pr., LLC.

Hatch, William & Kiraz, George. The Greek Manuscripts of the New Testament at Mount Sinai. 2009. 390.00 *(978-1-60724-416-5(0))*; 390.00 *(978-1-60724-415-8(2))* Gorgias Pr., LLC.

Haugld, Brian. A Textual History of the Book of Abraham. 2011. (Brigham Young University - Studies in the Book of Abraham Ser.). (Illus.). 307p. 79.95 *(978-0-8425-2774-3(5),* Maxwell, Neal A. Institute for Religious Scholarship) Brigham Young Univ.

Hernandez, Juan, Jr. Scribal Habits & Theological Influences in the Apocolypse: The Singular Readings of Sinaiticus, Alexandrinus & Ephraemi. 2006. (Wissenschaftliche Untersuchungen Zum Neuen Testament 2 Ser.: No. 218). 259p. pap. 125.00 *(978-3-16-149112-2(2))* Mohr Siebeck GmbH & Co. KG DEU. Dist: Coronet Bks.

Hill, Charles E. & Kruger, Michael J. The Early Text of the New Testament. 2012. (ENG.). 448p. 175.00 ***(978-0-19-956636-5(4))*** Oxford Univ. Pr., Inc.

Hurtado, Larry W. The Freer Biblical Manuscripts: Fresh Studies of an American Treasure Trove. 2006. (SBL - Text-Critical Studies). (Illus.). 308p. *(978-90-04-14679-2(2))* BRILL.

Johnson, Shelia D. A Scripture A Day Will Keep Satan Away. 2010. 68p. pap. 11.49 *(978-1-4520-2953-5(9))* AuthorHouse.

Jones, Timothy Paul. Misquoting Truth: A Guide to the Fallacies of Bart Ehrman's Misquoting Jesus. 2007. (ENG., Illus.). 176p. per. 15.00 *(978-0-8308-3447-1(8),* IVP Bks.) InterVarsity Pr.

Kenyon, Frederic G. Our Bible & the Ancient Manuscripts. 2011. 298p. pap. 26.00 ***(978-1-61097-756-2(4),*** Wipf and Stock) Wipf & Stock Pubs.

Kenyon, Frederic G. Our Bible & the Ancient Manuscripts Be. 2006. pap. 31.95 *(978-1-4286-5003-9(2))* Kessinger Publishing, LLC.

Klein, Michael L. Targumic Manuscripts in the Cambridge Genizah Collections. 2006. (Genizah Ser.). 136p. 60.00 *(978-1-905739-03-5(6))* Archaeopress GBR. Dist: Brown, David Bk. Co., The.

Kooten, Geurt Hendrik van & Ruiten, J. Van. The Prestige of the Pagan Prophet Balaam in Judaism, Early Christianity & Islam. Kooten, George H. van & Ruiten, Jacques van, eds. 2008. (Themes in Biblical Narrative Ser.). 344p. *(978-90-04-16564-9(9))* BRILL.

Korpel, Marjo C. A., et al, eds. Method in Unit Delimitation. 2007. (Pericope Ser.). (Illus.). 231p. *(978-90-04-16567-0(3))* BRILL.

Kraus, Thomas J. Ad Fontes: Original Manuscripts & Their Significance for Studying Early Christianity - Selected Essays. 2007. (Texts & Editions for New Testament Study Ser.). (MUL., Illus.). 304p. *(978-90-04-16182-5(1))* BRILL.

Lake, Kirsopp & New, Silva, eds. Six Collations of New Testament Manuscripts. 2007. (Illus.). 254p. pap. 22.00 *(978-1-55635-700-8(1))* Wipf & Stock Pubs.

Lewis, Agnes Smith. Light on the Four Gospels from the Sinai Palimpsest. 2006. (Gorgias Theological Library: 16). 235p. 84.00 *(978-1-59333-530-4(X))* Gorgias Pr., LLC.

Living Scripture's Story: 52 Interactive Devotions. 64p. 9.99 *(978-0-570-06848-8(7),* 20-2724) Concordia Publishing Hse.

McBirnie, William Steuart. The Search for the Twelve Apostles. 2008. (ENG., Illus.). 288p. pap. 14.99 *(978-1-4143-2004-5(3))* Tyndale Hse. Pubs.

McKendrick, Scot. In a Monastery Library: Preserving Codex Sinaiticus & the Greek Written Heritage. 2007. (ENG., Illus.). 48p. pap. 13.00 *(978-0-7123-4940-6(5))* British Library, The GBR. Dist: Chicago Distribution Ctr.

McKendrick, Scot & Doyle, Kathleen. Bible Manuscripts: 1400 Years of Scribes & Scripture. 2007. (ENG., Illus.). 159p. 35.00 *(978-0-7123-4922-2(7))* British Library, The GBR. Dist: Chicago Distribution Ctr.

Miller, Gene E. Understanding Each Book of the Bible. 2007. 180p. per. 24.95 *(978-1-60441-199-7(6))* PublishAmerica, Inc.

Morrill, Bruce & Parker, David C., eds. 2. the Full Collation of Chapter 18:2. 1 List of the Manuscripts & Comparative Description. 2. 2. Collation Results & Main List Vol. 5. 2013. (Arbeiten zur neutestamentlichen Textforschung Ser.). (ENG & GER., Illus.). 1400p. 487.00 *(978-3-11-018675-8(6))* De Gruyter, Walter Inc.

Parker, D. C. Codex Sinaiticus: The Story of the World's Oldest Bible. 2010. (Illus.). 216p. *(978-0-7123-5803-3(X))* British Library, The.

—Codex Sinaiticus: The Story of the World's Oldest Bible. 2010. 222p. 39.95 *(978-1-59856-390-0(4))* Hendrickson Pubs. Marketing, LLC.

—An Introduction to the New Testament Manuscripts & their Texts. 2008. (ENG., Illus.). 398p. 95.00 *(978-0-521-89553-8(7))* Cambridge Univ. Pr.

—An Introduction to the New Testament Manuscripts & Their Texts. 2008. (ENG., Illus.). 398p. pap. 40.00 *(978-0-521-71989-6(5))* Cambridge Univ. Pr.

Pope, Kyle. How We Got the Bible. 2010. 106p. pap. 12.95 *(978-1-58427-298-4(8))* Guardian of Truth Foundation.

Ray, T. C. The Intention of it All: Mysteries & Misunderstood Scriptures of the Bible Decoded. 2010. 392p. pap. 17.99 *(978-1-4520-9102-0(1))* AuthorHouse.

Royse, James Ronald. Scribal Habits in Early Greek New Testament Papyri. 2010. *(978-1-58983-522-1(0))* Society of Biblical Literature.

Sanders, Henry A. The New Testament Manuscript in the Freer Collection Pt. 1: The Washington Manuscript of the Four Gospels. 2008. (Ancient Texts & Translations Ser.). 270p. pap. 23.00 *(978-1-60608-206-5(X),* Wipf and Stock) Wipf & Stock Pubs.

—Old Testament Manuscripts in the Freer Collection. 2010. pap. 61.60 *(978-1-61719-354-5(2))*; (GRE.). pap. 61.60 *(978-1-61719-337-8(2))* Gorgias Pr., LLC.

Schmid, U. B. & Parker, D. C., eds. The New Testament in Greek IV: the Gospel According to St. John: Edited by the American & British Committees of the International Greek New Testament Project: Volume Two the Majuscules. 2007. (New Testament Tools, Studies & Documents Ser.). 558p. *(978-90-04-16313-3(1))* BRILL.

Scrivener, Frederick Henry Ambrose. A Full & Exact Collation of about Twenty Greek Manuscripts of the Holy Gospels: Deposited in the British Museum, the Archiepiscopal Library at Lambeth. 2009. (Cambridge Library Collection - Religion Ser.). (ENG.). 260p. pap. 23.99 *(978-1-108-00747-4(3))* Cambridge Univ. Pr.

Smith, Dudley. Faith Is Our Victory. 2009. 131p. pap. 16.99 *(978-0-557-05000-0(6))* Lulu Enterprises Inc.

—The TIME of the END. 2009. 304p. pap. 19.99 *(978-0-557-06035-1(4))* Lulu Enterprises Inc.

B

Stegemann, Hartmut & Schuller, Eileen, eds. Discoveries in the Judaean Desert, vol. XL: Qumran Cave 1. III: 1QHodayot a: with Incorporation of 4QHodayot a-f & 1QHodayot B. Newsom, Carol, tr. from HEB. 2009. (Discoveries in the Judaean Desert Ser.). (FRE, ENG & HEB., Illus.). 410p. 199.00 *(978-0-19-955005-0(0))* Oxford Univ. Pr., Inc.

Stone, Robert C. The Language of the Latin Text of Codex Bezae. 2009. 200p. pap. 17.00 *(978-1-60608-750-3(9)*, Wipf and Stock) Wipf & Stock Pubs.

Ulrich, Eugene & Flint, Peter W. Discoveries in the Judaean Desert XXXII: Qumran Cave 1. II: the Isaiah Scrolls: Part 1: Plates & Transcriptions, 2 vols. 2011. (Discoveries in the Judaean Desert Ser.). (HEB & ENG., Illus.). 176p. 180.00 *(978-0-19-956666-2(6))* Oxford Univ. Pr., Inc.

—Discoveries in the Judaean Desert XXXII: Qumran Cave 1: II. the Isaiah Scrolls: Part 2: Introductions, Commentary, & Textual Variants, 2 vols. 2011. (Discoveries in the Judaean Desert Ser.). (HEB & ENG., Illus.). 240p. 145.00 *(978-0-19-956667-9(4))* Oxford Univ. Pr., Inc.

Wineland, John D. & Wineland, John, eds. The Light of Discovery: Studies in Honor of Edwin M. Yamauchi. 2007. (Evangelical Theological Society Monograph Ser.). (Illus.). 338p. pap. 32.00 *(978-1-55635-045-0(7)*, Pickwick Pubns.) Wipf & Stock Pubs.

Yeap, Chee Seng. Bible Verses on Prosperity. 2007. 97p. pap. 18.86 *(978-1-4357-0501-2(7))* Lulu Enterprises Inc.

BIBLE—MAPS

see Bible—Geography—Maps

BIBLE—MEDICINE, HYGIENE, ETC.

see Medicine in the Bible

BIBLE—MEDITATIONS

Adams, James R. Flickers from a Burning Candle. Adams, Patricia, ed. (Illus.). 200p. (Orig.). pap. 12.95 *(978-0-9618060-2-6(8))* Sheer Joy! Pr.

Arterburn, Stephen & Stoop, David. The Life Recovery: A Biblical Guide Through the Twelve Steps. 2007. (ENG.). 128p. per., wbk. ed. 9.99 *(978-1-4143-1328-3(4))* Tyndale Hse. Pubs.

—The Life Recovery Devotional: Thirty Meditations from Scripture for Each Step in Recovery. 2009. (ENG.). 400p. pap. 12.99 *(978-1-4143-3004-4(9))* Tyndale Hse. Pubs.

—The Life Recovery Journal: Becoming a New You - One Step at a Time. 2009. (ENG.). 128p. pap. 9.99 *(978-1-4143-2823-2(0))* Tyndale Hse. Pubs.

Bales, David O. Scenes of Glory: Subplots of God's Long Story. 2008. *(978-0-7880-2554-9(6))* CSS Publishing Co.

Balogh, Raymond L., Jr. Biblical Reflections: Devotionals from a Different Angle. 2008. (ENG.). 21.95 *(978-1-60037-313-8(5))*; 155p. per. 11.95 *(978-1-60037-234-6(1))* Morgan James Publishing.

Banks, William L. Daily Manna II. 2011. pap. 18.95 *(978-0-7414-6404-0(7))* Infinity Publishing.

Barclay, William. Daily Devotions with William Barclay: 365 Meditations on the Heart of the New Testament. 2008. (ENG.). 384p. 20.00 *(978-0-664-23270-2(1))* Westminster John Knox Pr.

Barnes, Bob. Five Minutes in the Bible for Men. 2010. 272p. pap. 12.99 *(978-0-7369-2697-3(6))* Harvest Hse. Pubs.

Beeke, Joel R., ed. Milk & Honey. 2010. 400p. *(978-1-60178-111-6(3))* Reformation Heritage Bks.

Beers, Ron & Mason, Amy E. The One Year Mini Daily Inspiration. 2009. (ENG.). 384p. 12.99 *(978-1-4143-2024-3(8))* Tyndale Hse. Pubs.

Beers, Ronald A. & Mason, Amy E. TouchPoints for Students. 2009. (ENG.). 288p. pap. 4.99 *(978-1-4143-2021-2(3))* Tyndale Hse. Pubs.

Begg, Alistair, ed. Evening by Evening: A New Edition of the Classic Devotional Based on the ESV Bible. rev. ed. 2008. 384p. 21.99 *(978-1-58134-982-5(3))* Crossway.

Benner, Juliet. Contemplative Vision: A Guide to Christian Art & Prayer. 2010. (ENG.). 191p. pap. 17.00 *(978-0-8308-3544-7(X)*, IVP Bks.) InterVarsity Pr.

Bergant, Dianne. The Word for Every Season: Reflections on the Lectionary Readings (Cycle A) 2010. 208p. pap. 19.95 *(978-0-8091-4673-4(8))* Paulist Pr.

—The Word for Every Season: Reflections on the Lectionary Readings (Cycle C) 2009. 208p. pap. 16.95 *(978-0-8091-4607-9(X))* Paulist Pr.

Berndt, Jodie. Praying the Scriptures for Your Teenagers: Discover How to Pray God's Will for Their Lives, 1 vol. 2007. (ENG.). 304p. pap. 12.99 *(978-0-310-27351-6(X))* Zondervan.

Biddle, Daniel. The Secret of the Seven Pillars. 2007. 248p. (ENG.). 24.99 *(978-1-60266-785-3(3))*; per. 14.99 *(978-1-60266-784-6(5))* Xulon Pr., Inc.

Biermann, Joel D. Psalms of Divine Wisdom: A Man's Journey Through the Psalms. 2009. (Blessed Is the Man Ser.). (Illus.). 192p. pap. 9.99 *(978-0-7586-1658-6(9))* Concordia Publishing Hse.

—Psalms of the Messiah: A Man's Journey Through the Psalms. 2009. (Blessed Is the Man Ser.). (Illus.). 192p. pap. 9.99 *(978-0-7586-1722-4(4))* Concordia Publishing Hse.

Biermann, Joel D. & Baker, Robert C. Psalms of Lament: A Man's Journey Through the Psalms. 2010. (Blessed Is the Man Ser.). (Illus.). 192p. pap. 9.99 *(978-0-7586-1723-1(2))* Concordia Publishing Hse.

Binz, Steve. Conversing with God in Lent: Praying the Sunday Mass Readings with Lectio Divina. 2010. 112p. pap. 9.95 *(978-1-59325-165-9(3))* Word Among Us Pr.

Birkel, Michael Lawrence. Encuentro con Las Escrituras. 2007. (SPA.). pap. *(978-0-944350-70-6(4))* Friends United Pr.

Blackaby, Henry. Experiencing God (Revised) Leader Kit. 2007. 179.95 incl. DVD *(978-1-4158-5895-0(0))* LifeWay Christian Resources.

Blackaby, Henry T., et al. Experiencing God Member Book: Knowing & Doing the Will of God. 2007. (Illus.). 272p. per. 14.95 *(978-1-4158-5838-7(1))* LifeWay Christian Resources.

Boa, Kenneth & Boa, Karen. A Guided Tour of the Bible: A One-Year Journey Through 365 Key Chapters of the Bible. 2007. (ENG., Illus.). 373p. per. 14.99 *(978-1-932805-92-5(3))* Authentic Media.

Bonikowsky, Andy. Just a Minute. 2010. *(978-1-60682-065-0(6))* BJU Pr.

Booram, Beth. The Wide Open Spaces of God: A Journey with God Through the Landscapes of Life. 2007. 189p. per. 14.00 *(978-0-687-49096-7(0)*, Dimensions For Living) Abingdon Pr.

Booth, Bradley. Time Warp: Been There, Done That? 2010. 368p. *(978-0-8280-2495-2(2))* Review & Herald Publishing Assn.

Bosetti, Elena. John: The Word of Light. 2009. 176p. pap. 14.95 *(978-0-8198-3990-9(6))* Pauline Bks. & Media.

Bostrom, Kathleen Long, et al, eds. Daily Feast: Meditations from Feasting on the Word, Year C. 2012. (Feasting on the Word Ser.). (ENG.). 584p. lthr. 25.00 ***(978-0-664-23798-1(3))*** Westminster John Knox Pr.

Bostrom, Kathleen Long & Caldwell, Elizabeth F., eds. Daily Feast: Meditations from Feasting on the Word, Year B. 2011. (Feasting on the Word Ser.). (ENG.). 480p. im. lthr. 25.00 *(978-0-664-23797-4(5))* Westminster John Knox Pr.

Briner, Bob & Pritchard, Ray. Leadership Lessons of Jesus: A Timeless Model for Today's Leaders. 2008. (ENG.). 240p. 14.99 *(978-0-8054-4520-6(X)*, B&H Bks.) B&H Publishing Group.

Briscoe, Jill. The Garden of Grace: Treasures from the Golden Book. 2007. (Illus.). 160p. 13.99 *(978-0-8254-6132-3(4)*, Monarch Bks.) Lion Hudson PLC GBR. Dist: Kregel Pubns.

Bryce, Brady. Echoing the Story. 2010. 138p. pap. 17.00 *(978-1-60899-818-0(5)*, Resource Pubns.) Wipf & Stock Pubs.

Burne, Martin J. Remember Lot's Wife: Scriptural Reflections on How to Lose Your Life & Save It. 2007. 170p. per. *(978-0-8189-1241-2(3))* St Pauls/Alba Hse. Pubs.

Butcher, Catherine. Special to God, 1 vol. 2009. (ENG.). 112p. pap. *(978-1-85345-508-7(3))* Crusade for World Revival.

Camille, Alice. 2010: A Book of Grace-Filled Days. 2009. (ENG.). 408p. pap. 11.95 *(978-0-8294-2525-3(X))* Loyola Pr.

Campbell, Alexander. Pilgrim Prayers for Mealtime. 2009. 128p. pap. 16.00 *(978-1-60608-575-2(1)*, Wipf and Stock) Wipf & Stock Pubs.

Campbell, Lorne. Mettle for New Christians. 2008. 96p. (YA). pap. *(978-1-85345-459-2(1))* Crusade for World Revival.

Carroll, Norm. Miracles, Messages, & Metaphors: Unlocking the Wisdom of the Bible. 2010. 400p. pap. 16.95 *(978-0-9823140-1-2(9))* Synergy Bks.

Carson, D. A. For the Love of God Vol. 1: A Daily Companion for Discovering the Riches of God's Word. 2nd ed. 2006. 400p. pap. 19.99 *(978-1-58134-815-6(0))* Crossway.

—For the Love of God Vol. 2: A Daily Companion for Discovering the Riches of God's Word. 2nd ed. 2006. 416p. pap. 19.99 *(978-1-58134-816-3(9))* Crossway.

Carter, George. Book of Psalms. 2008. 332p. pap. 21.99 *(978-1-60647-878-3(8))* Xulon Pr., Inc.

Chalmers, Thomas. Sabbath Scripture Readings II - Spiritual Meditations from the Old Testament. 2008. 520p. pap. 35.00 *(978-1-59925-192-9(2))* Solid Ground Christian Bks.

Church, Clarice Wyatt Bell. Win with the Word. 2006. (Illus.). 256p. pap. 12.99 *(978-0-9766578-2-8(1))* Dove Publishing, Inc.

Crosby, Cindy, ed. Ancient Christian Devotional: A Year of Weekly Readings. 2007. (Ancient Christian Devotional Set Ser.). (ENG.). 294p. per. 17.00 *(978-0-8308-3431-0(1)*, IVP Bks.) InterVarsity Pr.

—Ancient Christian Devotional: Lectionary Cycle C. 2009. (Ancient Christian Devotional Set Ser.). (ENG.). 304p. pap. 18.00 *(978-0-8308-3528-7(8)*, IVP Bks.) InterVarsity Pr.

Cuartas Londoño, Rómulo, et al. La Biblia: Libro de Contemplación. 2010. (SPA.). 598p. *(978-84-8353-268-3(9))* Monte Carmelo, Editorial.

Dateno, Maria Grace & Marsh, Emily. Teens Share the Word. 2011. pap. *(978-0-8198-7437-5(X))* Pauline Bks. & Media.

Dateno, Maria Grace & Trouvé, Marianne Lorraine. Easter Grace: Daily Gospel Reflections. 2011. pap. *(978-0-8198-2362-5(7))* Pauline Bks. & Media.

David, Patricia J. John: Lectio Divina for Youth. 2007. (ENG.). 80p. pap. 7.99 *(978-0-8341-5022-5(0)*, 083-415-0220) Beacon Hill Pr. of Kansas City.

Davis, Andrea & Radtke, Nancy. Hidden Treasures of the Spirit. 2008. 140p. pap. 14.99 *(978-1-60791-108-1(6))* Xulon Pr., Inc.

Davis, Gerald. Coaching with the Scriptures. 2008. 184p. pap. 14.99 *(978-1-60647-782-3(X))* Xulon Pr., Inc.

Des Cotes, Rob. Higher Than I: Meditations for Spiritual Direction. 2007. 104p. per. *(978-1-894667-67-8(0))*; *(978-1-894667-66-1(2))* Clements Publishing.

Des Cotes, Rob. Ultreia: Meditations for Spiritual Direction. 2010. 14.95 ***(978-1-894667-70-8(0))*** Clements Publishing.

DeVries, Catherine & Pulley, Kelly. My Time with God: Book of Devotions, 1 vol. 2007. (Beginners Bible Ser.). (ENG., Illus.). 192p. (J). (gr. -1-1). 12.99 *(978-0-310-71481-1(8))* Zondervan.

Dumm, Demetrius. So We Do Not Lose Heart: Biblical Wisdom for All Our Days. 2006. 272p. pap. *(978-0-9773909-1-5(8))* St. Vincent Archabbey Pubns.

Dunlap, Judith. Bringing Home the Gospel: A Weekly Journal for Catholic Parents: The Year of Mark. 2008. 128p. pap. 10.95 *(978-0-86716-781-8(5))* Franciscan Media.

—Bringing Home the Gospel: The Year of Matthew: A Weekly Journal for Catholic Parents. 2007. 126p. per. 10.95 *(978-0-86716-780-1(7))* Franciscan Media.

Edward A. Vinson. At Sea - Meditations on the Psalms. 2010. 452p. 34.99 *(978-1-4535-1661-4(1))*; pap. 23.99 *(978-1-4535-1660-7(3))* Xlibris Corp.

Edwards, Judson. Hidden Treasures: Walking the Back Roads of the Bible in Search of Truth. 2007. 184p. per. 16.00 *(978-1-57312-483-6(4))* Smyth & Helwys Publishing, Inc.

Eggert, Ron, compiled by. Tozer on the Almighty God: A 366-Day Devotional. 2007. (Tozer for Today Ser.). 386p. pap. 16.99 *(978-1-60066-133-4(5))* WingSpread Publishers.

Elkins, Stephen. LullaBible, 0 vols. 2010. (Illus.). 208p. (J). 16.99 *(978-1-4003-1561-1(1))* Nelson, Thomas Inc.

Elliott, Don. The Journey: A trip through the Bible. 2009. 432p. pap. 19.95 *(978-1-934453-03-2(X))* PLC Pubns.

Ellsworth, Roger. When Heaven Calls Your Name: People in the Bible Who Heard God Speak. 2008. (Reflections (DayOne) Ser.). (Illus.). 103p. pap. *(978-1-84625-102-3(8))* DayOne Pubns.

Esmond, Dwain. 24-7-365: A Year in the Word. 2008. 377p. (YA). 14.99 *(978-0-8280-2336-8(0))* Review & Herald Publishing Assn.

Evans, Tony. Time to Get Serious: Daily Devotions to Keep You Close to God. 2007. 352p. pap. 16.99 *(978-1-58134-951-1(3))* Crossway.

Faley, Roland J. Reflections on the Weekday Lectionary Readings. 2010. 576p. pap. 39.95 *(978-0-8091-4541-6(3))* Paulist Pr.

Fashbaugh, Earl. Snapshots: Sixty-Six Books of the Bible: A Devotional. 2011. 264p. pap. 13.99 ***(978-1-4269-6427-5(7))*** Trafford Publishing.

Ferguson, Nancy. S'More Time with God. 2011. 128p. 12.99 *(978-0-8170-1663-0(5))* Judson Pr.

First Place 4 Health. Healthy Summer Living. 2009. (First Place Ser.). (ENG.). 192p. pap. 14.99 *(978-0-8307-4722-1(2))* Gospel Light Pubns.

Fitzpatrick, Carol Lynn. 365 One-Minute Meditations from Daily Wisdom for Women. 2009. (One minute Meditations Ser.). (ENG.). 384p. pap. 9.99 *(978-1-60260-371-4(5)*, Barbour Bks.) Barbour Publishing, Inc.

Fotinos, Joel & Gold, August. Little Daily Wisdom: 365 Inspiring Bible Verses to Change Your Life. 2009. (ENG.). 371p. (gr. 13). pap. 14.99 *(978-1-55725-648-5(9))* Paraclete Pr., Inc.

Fowler, Lynn. My Little Chats with God. 2009. (ENG.). 119p. pap. 14.96 *(978-1-4092-6561-0(7))* Lulu Enterprises Inc.

France, Dick. Timothy, Titus, & Hebrews: A Guide for Reflection & Prayer. 2007. (Daily Bible Commentary Ser.). 217p. per. 12.95 *(978-1-59856-195-1(2))* Hendrickson Pubs. Marketing, LLC.

Freeman, J. D. Life on the Uplands, an Interpretation of the Twenty-Third Psalm. 2007. 144p. per. *(978-1-4067-8867-9(8)*, Pomona Pr.) Read Bks.

Froehle, Virginia Ann. Loving Yourself More: 101 Meditations on Self-Esteem for Women. rev. ed. 2007. 156p. per. 12.95 *(978-1-59471-131-2(3))* Ave Maria Pr.

Gibbs, Pam. Esther: The Role of a Life Time: A Bible Study for Teen Girls. 2008. (Illus.). 103p. pap. *(978-1-4158-6604-7(X))* B&H Publishing Group.

Goan, Sean. Let the Reader Understand: The Sunday Readings of Year A. 2007. (ENG.). 125p. pap. 18.95 *(978-1-85607-590-9(7))* Columba Pr. IRL. Dist: Dufour Editions, Inc.

Gross, Thomas Pelham. Israel's Holocaust & Resurrection. 2009. 236p. pap. 15.99 *(978-1-60791-727-4(0))* Xulon Pr., Inc.

Guilmette, Emile. Twenty Steps on the Way to Glory. 2006. pap. 10.00 *(978-0-8059-7005-0(3))* Dorrance Publishing Co., Inc.

Gunnell, Rhonda K. Smiling on the Inside. 2006. 77p. pap. 16.95 *(978-1-4241-4917-9(7))* PublishAmerica, Inc.

Guthrie, Thomas. The Angels' Song. 2008. 58p. pap. *(978-1-4099-5814-7(0))* Dodo Pr.

—The Angels' Song. 2009. 144p. 35.95 *(978-1-104-42202-8(6))*; pap. 20.95 *(978-1-104-38170-7(2))* Kessinger Publishing, LLC.

Hanson, Joe, et al. Psalms of Praise: A Man's Journey Through the Psalms. 2010. (Blessed Is the Man Ser.). (Illus.). 192p. pap. 9.99 *(978-0-7586-1724-8(0))* Concordia Publishing Hse.

Harrison House, Inc. Staff. Scripture Confessions for Teens. 2009. 32p. pap. 1.99 *(978-1-57794-923-7(4))* Harrison House Pubs.

Hawkins, Pamela C. Behold! Cultivating Attentiveness in the Season of Advent. 2011. 112p. 14.00 *(978-0-8358-1062-3(3))* Upper Room Bks.

Hayford, Jack W. Rebuilding the Real You: The Definitive Guide to the Holy Spirit's Work in Your Life. 2009. (ENG.). 240p. pap. 14.99 *(978-1-59979-471-6(3)*, Charisma Hse.) Charisma Media.

Heath, Elaine A. We Were the Least of These: Reading the Bible with Survivors of Sexual Abuse. 2011. 196p. (C). pap. 19.99 *(978-1-58743-271-2(4))* Brazos Pr.

Hemphill, Ken. God Is: Devotions Empowered by Biblical Statements of Faith. 2008. (Kingdom Promises Ser.). (ENG.). 128p. pap. 3.99 *(978-0-8054-4766-8(0)*, B&H Bks.) B&H Publishing Group.

—God Will: Devotions Empowered by Biblical Statements of Faith. 2008. (Kingdom Promises Ser.). (ENG.). 128p. pap. 3.99 *(978-0-8054-4768-2(7)*, B&H Bks.) B&H Publishing Group.

Henry, Gary. Enthusiastic Ideas: A Good Word for Every Day of the Year. 2012. (ENG.). 388p. pap. 18.95 *(978-0-9713710-2-6(4))* WordPoints.

—More Enthusiastic Ideas: Another Good Word for Every Day of the Year. 2013. (ENG.). 388p. pap. 18.95 *(978-0-9713710-3-3(2))* WordPoints.

Hermes, Kathryn J. Cherished by the Lord: 100 Meditations. 2012. 240p. 12.95 ***(978-0-8198-1605-4(1))*** Pauline Bks. & Media.

Heyer, Walt. Perfected with Love: A Powerful & Inspiring True Story. 2009. 116p. pap. 11.99 *(978-1-60791-838-7(2))* Xulon Pr., Inc.

Hollar, Larry, ed. Hunger for the Word: Lectionary Reflections on Food & Justice: Year C. 2006. (Illus.). 224p. per. 19.95 *(978-0-8146-3009-9(X))* Liturgical Pr.

Hommerding, Alan J. Everyday Psalms: 150 Meditations for Living the Lord's Songs. 2009. 159p. pap. 12.95 *(978-1-58459-433-8(0))* World Library Pubns.

Hope for Every Moment: 365 Inspirational Thoughts for Every Day of the Year. 2007. 369p. 13.99 *(978-0-7684-2397-6(X))* Destiny Image Pubs.

Howe, Thomas A. What the Bible Really Says? Breaking the Apocalypse Code. 2009. 212p. pap. 23.00 *(978-1-55635-858-6(X)*, Wipf and Stock) Wipf & Stock Pubs.

Howell, James C. 40 Treasured Bible Verses: A Devotional. 2011. (ENG.). 152p. pap. 15.00 *(978-0-664-23653-3(7))* Westminster John Knox Pr.

Indermark, John. Way Words: A Daily Itinerary for Lent. 2011. 112p. pap. 10.00 ***(978-1-4267-3065-8(9))*** Abingdon Pr.

Jacobson, Diane L. Book of Faith Lenten Journey: Water Marks. 2011. ***(978-1-4514-0262-9(7))*** Augsburg Fortress, Pubs.

James, Sharon. The Dawn of Heaven Breaks: Anticipating Eternity. 2007. 153p. per. *(978-0-85234-641-9(7))* Evangelical Pr.

Jenkins, Ava. Word 52: A Weekly Dose of Scripture & Poetry. 2008. 57p. pap. 12.50 *(978-0-615-19037-2(5))* Towdah Unlimited Publishing.

Jeske, Mark A. Time of Grace: A Devotional Companion. 2010. 394p. 19.99 *(978-0-7586-1913-6(8))* Concordia Publishing Hse.

Jones, Zane. Holy Words of God to Live By. 2009. 80p. pap. 10.99 *(978-1-60791-005-3(5))* Xulon Pr., Inc.

K.Camplin, Miriam. Constant Fellowship: A Handbook on Scripture Meditation. 2011. pap. 12.99 ***(978-1-61346-145-7(3))*** Tate Publishing & Enterprises, LLC.

Kalas, J. Ellsworth. Men Worth Knowing: Biblical Meditations for Daily Living. 2007. (ENG.). 118p. per. 15.00 *(978-0-664-23059-3(8))* Westminster John Knox Pr.

Kibbey, Sue Nilson & Slaughter, Carolyn, eds. Transformation Journal: A One Year Journey Through the Bible. 2007. 320p. pap. 22.00 *(978-0-687-64215-1(9))* Abingdon Pr.

King, Claude. Experiencing God: Knowing & Doing the Will of God. 2007. 64p. pap. 6.95 *(978-1-4158-5839-4(X))* LifeWay Christian Resources.

Kirk, Sandy Davis. The Masterpiece: Painted in Blood, Floodlit with Glory. 2007. 71p. per. 8.99 *(978-1-58158-107-2(6))* McDougal Publishing Co.

Knight, David. Immersed in Christ Invitation 3: Prophet. 2010. 4.95 *(978-0-87029-433-4(4))* Abbey Pr.

—Immersed in Christ Promise 5. 2010. 1.95 *(978-0-87029-438-9(5))* Abbey Pr.

—Immersed in Christ Reflections 5. 2010. 0.95 *(978-0-87029-437-2(7))* Abbey Pr.

—Immersed in Christ Through Immersion in the Mass: Lectionary Reflections for Each Day of Lent 2011. 2011. 5.95 *(978-0-87029-456-3(3))* Abbey Pr.

Knight, David M. Experiencing the Mass — Five Moments of Mystery: Daily Reflections for Lent 2011. 2010. 4.95 *(978-0-87029-452-5(0))* Abbey Pr.

Knight, David M. Immersed in Christ: Faith Formation Series. 2009. ***(978-0-87029-435-8(0))*** Abbey Pr.

Konold, Bruce. The Way of the Cross: A Good Friday Devotional Guide. 2007. *(978-0-9786075-4-8(6))* Burning Bush Communications.

Kurtz, Dennis. Youth Engaging Scripture: Diving into the Sunday Gospels. 2007. cd-rom 17.75 *(978-0-88489-913-6(6))* St. Mary's Pr.

Kurtz, Dennis, et al. Day by Day with People of the Bible: Reflections for Teens. 2007. 384p. per. 13.75 *(978-0-88489-922-8(5))* St. Mary's Pr.

Lauretta Justin, Pastor James Justin. Express Yourself. 2011. 82p. pap. 10.99 ***(978-1-61379-512-5(2))*** Xulon Pr., Inc.

Levy, Bryna Jocheved. Waiting for Rain: Reflections at the Turning of the Year. 2008. (ENG., Illus.). 300p. 24.00 *(978-0-8276-0841-2(1))* Jewish Pubn. Society.

Lewis, Audie G., compiled by. A los Pies del Maestro: Devocional Diario, 1 vol. 2006. (SPA.). 384p. (gr. 11). pap. 14.99 *(978-0-8297-4729-4(X))* Vida Pubs.

Lewis, C. S. The C. S. Lewis Bible. 2010. (ENG.). 1600p. 34.99 *(978-0-06-198208-8(3)*, HarperOne) HarperCollins Pubs.

Lewis, Patsy. Simply Listening: 12 Months with God. 2009. (ENG.). 256p. pap. 14.99 *(978-0-8341-2441-7(6)*, 9780834124417) Beacon Hill Pr. of Kansas City.

Livingstone. Fruit of the Spirit. 2008. (God's Promises Ser.). (ENG.). 160p. 3.99 *(978-1-934068-99-1(3))* Authentic Media.

—God's Promises on His Love. 2008. (God's Promises Ser.). (ENG.). 160p. 3.99 *(978-1-934068-97-7(7))* Authentic Media.

Lucas, Jeff. Life with Lucas: Daily Readings Throughout the Year, Book 2. 2009. 334p. pap. *(978-1-85345-500-1(8))* Crusade for World Revival.

Lyons, George. Revelation: Lectio Divina for Youth. 2007. (Ancient Faith Ser.). (ENG.). 80p. per. 7.99 *(978-0-8341-5014-0(X)*, 083-415-014X) Beacon Hill Pr. of Kansas City.

MacArthur, John. Moments of Truth: Unleashing God's Word One Day at a Time. 2012. 400p. pap. 16.99 ***(978-1-4002-0371-0(6))*** Nelson, Thomas Inc.

MacDonald, James. Ancient Wisdom: The Book of Proverbs with Devotions for Today. 2007. 160p. 14.99 *(978-0-8054-4428-5(9))* B&H Publishing Group.

Mahoney, Beth. Grant Us Peace: Rosary Meditations for Those Who Mourn. 2008. (Holy Cross Family Ministry Ser.). 49p. pap. 4.95 *(978-1-59471-164-0(X))* Ave Maria Pr.

Marr, Steve. Proverbs for Business. 2006. 256p. pap. 5.99 *(978-0-8007-8751-6(X))* Revell.

Mary And Carman Lando. Scripture Reflections. 2009. 56p. pap. 31.99 *(978-1-4415-1537-7(2))* Xlibris Corp.

Maxwell, Marcus. Ephesians to Colossians & Philemon: A Guide for Reflection & Prayer. 2007. (Daily Bible Commentary Ser.). 277p. per. 12.95 *(978-1-59856-194-4(4))* Hendrickson Pubs. Marketing, LLC.

McAlpine, Campbell. Wisdom from Above: God's Wisdom from the Book of Proverbs. 2007. 351p. pap. *(978-1-903725-94-8(1))* New Wine Pr.

McKenna, Megan. Advent, Christmas, & Epiphany: Stories & Reflections on the Daily Readings. 2008. 256p. pap. 19.95 *(978-1-56548-301-9(4))* New City Pr.

—Advent, Christmas & Epiphany: Stories & Reflections on the Sunday & Daily Readings. 2008. 512p. pap. 39.90 *(978-1-56548-302-6(2))* New City Pr.

McWhorter, Jane. Roses in December. 2007. *(978-0-929540-58-0(1))* Publishing Designs, Inc.

Monroe, Irene. Let Your Light Shine Like a Rainbow Always: Meditations on Bible Prayers for Not-So-Everyday Moments. 2008. 402p. pap. 14.95 *(978-1-59350-077-1(7))* Alyson Pubns.

Montague, George T. Holy Spirit, Make Your Home in Me: Biblical Meditations on Receiving the Gift of the Spirit. 2008. 205p. per. 12.95 *(978-1-59325-128-4(9))* Word Among Us Pr.

Moore, Beth & Broadman and Holman Publishers Staff. Scriptures & Quotations from Praying God's Word, 1 vol. 2009. (Quick Word with Beth Moore Ser.). (ENG.). 192p. 9.99 *(978-0-8054-3280-0(9))* B&H Publishing Group.

—Scriptures & Quotations from When Godly People Do Ungodly Things, 1 vol. 2009. (Quick Word with Beth Moore Ser.). (ENG.). 96p. 9.99 *(978-0-8054-3281-7(7))* B&H Publishing Group.

Moretz, Jim. Mark: Lectio Divina for Youth. 2007. (Ancient Faith Ser.). (ENG.). 80p. per. 7.99 *(978-0-8341-5015-7(8)*, 083-415-0158) Beacon Hill Pr. of Kansas City.

Moule, Handley C. G. The Second Epistle to Timothy: Short Devotional Studies on the Dying Letter of St. Paul. 2007. 180p. pap. 18.00 *(978-1-55635-252-2(2)*, Wipf and Stock) Wipf & Stock Pubs.

Murdy, Kay. A Closer Walk with Jesus: Reading & Praying the Daily Gospels for Lent. 2009. pap. *(978-0-89390-688-7(3))* Resource Pubns., Inc.

Nall, Marvin P. God's Encouraging Word. 2008. 248p. pap. 14.99 *(978-1-60647-524-9(X))* Xulon Pr., Inc.

Nee, Watchman. Changed into His Likeness. 2007. (ENG.). 161p. pap. 9.99 *(978-0-87508-859-4(7))* CLC Pubns.

—Changed into His Likeness. 2007. per. 8.00 *(978-1-4245-0786-3(3))* Treasures Media Inc.

Neff, LaVonne. 2008. A Book of Grace-Filled Days. 2007. 400p. per. 10.95 *(978-0-8294-1874-3(1))* Loyola Pr.

Nemecek, F. Dean. Reflections of a Soldier & Servant. 2008. 388p. pap. 21.99 *(978-1-4141-1165-8(1))* Pleasant Word.

Ness, Dave. Serving God. 2007. 378p. pap. 14.99 *(978-0-9778614-7-7(3))* Partnership Pubns.

Neufeld, Henry E. & Neufeld, Jody. Along Bible Paths: Summer Devotions. 2010. 164p. pap. 9.99 *(978-1-893729-83-4(4))* Energion Pubns.

Newton, Richard. Bible Blessings. 2008. 336p. 45.95 *(978-1-4369-7263-5(9))*; pap. 30.95 *(978-1-4367-8816-8(1))* Kessinger Publishing, LLC.

—Bible Blessings. 2006. 336p. per. 23.99 *(978-1-4255-3384-7(1))* MPublishing.

Nichols, John. A Wind Swept over the Waters: Reflections on 60 Favorite Bible Passages. 2007. (ENG.). 1p. per. 15.00 *(978-1-55896-527-0(0)*, Skinner Hse. Bks.) Unitarian Universalist Assn.

Nielson, Merritt J. Ashes to Fire Year B Devotional: Daily Reflections from Ash Wednesday to Pentecost. 2011. (ENG.). 192p. lthr. 19.99 ***(978-0-8341-2762-3(8)***, 9780834127623) Beacon Hill Pr. of Kansas City.

Nisbet, Jim. An Artist Walks the Way of Sorrows. 2006. 8.99 *(978-0-9789221-0-8(7)*, NSST-PM-SOTC-1) Nisbet Scripture Study Tapes.

Nix, Echol Lee, Sr., et al. The Inspiration of the Holy Spirit. 2011. 160p. pap. 20.00 ***(978-1-60306-121-6(5)***, NewSouth Bks.) NewSouth, Inc.

Oden, Thomas C. & Elowsky, Joel C., eds. On the Way to the Cross: 40 Days with the Church Fathers. 2011. (ENG.). 130p. pap. 10.00 ***(978-0-8308-3567-6(9)***, IVP Bks.) InterVarsity Pr.

Ogilvie, Lloyd J. The Essence of His Presence: How Christ Wants to Bless Your Life. 2007. 304p. 14.99 *(978-0-7369-1728-5(4))* Harvest Hse. Pubs.

O'Loughlin, Thomas. Liturgical Resources for Matthew's Year: Sundays in Ordinary Time in Year A. 2007. (ENG.). 332p. pap. 26.95 *(978-1-85607-593-0(1))* Columba Pr. IRL. Dist: Dufour Editions, Inc.

Omartian, Stormie. The Power of a Praying Woman: A Bible Study Workbook for Video Curriculum. 2006. (Power of a Praying Series! Ser.). (Illus.). 151p. per. 14.95 *(978-1-933376-46-2(5))* Sampson Resources.

—The Power of a Praying Woman: Leader Guide for Video Curriculum. 2006. (Illus.). 40p. pap. 8.95 *(978-1-933376-47-9(3))* Sampson Resources.

O'Steen-Grant, Mae. Lavender & Peach. 2009. 265p. pap. 18.95 *(978-1-4327-3910-2(7))* Outskirts Pr., Inc.

Paintner, Christine Valters. Lectio Divina — the Sacred Art: Transforming Words & Images into Heart-Centered Prayer. 2011. 192p. pap. 16.99 *(978-1-59473-300-0(7))* SkyLight Paths Publishing.

Parks, Marty. Quiet Moments for Worship Leaders: Scriptures, Meditations, & Prayers. 2008. (ENG.). 160p. pap. 12.99 *(978-0-8341-2372-4(X)*, 9780834123724) Beacon Hill Pr. of Kansas City.

The Path of Justice. 2010. (Walking Bible Studies). 96p. 10.00 *(978-1-4267-1173-2(5))* Abingdon Pr.

Patty, Sandi. A New Day: A Guided Journal. 2011. (ENG.). 224p. pap. 15.99 *(978-1-4516-4331-2(4)*, Howard Bks.) Howard Books.

Paulist Press Staff. The Catholic Prayer Bible (NRSV) Lectio Divina Edition. 2010. 1968p. 39.95 *(978-0-8091-0587-8(X))*; pap. 29.95 *(978-0-8091-4663-5(0))* Paulist Pr.

Pearson, Carol Lynn. The Lord Is My Shepherd: Inspiration for Couples, 1 vol. 2009. (ENG.). 64p. 9.99 *(978-1-4236-0586-7(1))* Gibbs Smith, Publisher.

Peckham, Colin N. Joshua: A Devotional Commentary. 2007. (Exploring the Bible Ser.). (Illus.). 235p. pap. 13.00 *(978-1-84625-093-4(5))* DayOne Pubns. GBR. Dist: STL Distribution North America.

Phillips, Abby. I Come to the Garden Alone: Meditations from a Psalmist's Heart. 2007. 67p. pap. 9.95 *(978-0-7414-3842-3(9))* Infinity Publishing.

Phillips, John. 100 Devotions for Pastors & Church Leaders Vol. 1: Ideas & Inspiration for Your Sermons, Lessons, Church Events, Newsletters, & Web Sites. 2007. 224p. pap. 14.99 *(978-0-8254-3375-7(4))* Kregel Pubns.

—100 Devotions for Pastors & Church Leaders Vol. 2: Ideas & Inspiration for Your Sermons, Lessons, Church Events, Newsletters, & Web Sites. 2008. 216p. pap. 14.99 *(978-0-8254-3388-7(6))* Kregel Pubns.

Pride, Kathy. What the Bible Is All about for Moms: God's Loving Promises for You & Your Family. 2010. (ENG.). 240p. pap. 14.99 *(978-0-8307-5160-0(2))* Gospel Light Pubns.

Pursley, Ovit G. Counseling with God's Word: From A to W. 2011. 224p. pap. 15.86 *(978-1-4269-5015-5(2))* Trafford Publishing.

Ralph, Margaret Nutting. Breaking Open the Lectionary: Lectionary Readings in their Biblical Context for RCIA, Faith Sharing Groups & Lectors - Cycle A. 2007. 240p. pap. 19.95 *(978-0-8091-4471-6(9)*, 4471-6) Paulist Pr.

Reid, Barbara E. Abiding Word: Sunday Reflections for Year B. 2011. 18.95 *(978-0-8146-3312-0(9))* Liturgical Pr.

Reinders, Philip F., compiled by. Seeking God's Face: Praying with the Bible Through the Church Year. 2010. *(978-1-59255-498-0(9))* Faith Alive Christian Resources.

Reverend, Monroe. Let Your Light Shine Like a Rainbow 365 Days a Year. 2008. 402p. pap. 14.95 *(978-1-59350-076-4(9))* Alyson Pubns.

Reynolds, Carolyn. Wisdom from God-Meditations from Carolyn. 2007. (ENG.). 92p. per. 9.99 *(978-1-60034-840-2(8))* Xulon Pr., Inc.

Rigsby, Sandy & Mason, Steve. Exploring the Sunday Lectionary: A Teenager's Guide to the Readings Cycle C. 2006. 191p. per. 19.95 *(978-0-8091-9582-4(8)*, 4410-7) Paulist Pr.

Rogers, Geanine Noel. God's Message. 2011. 52p. pap. 9.95 ***(978-1-4497-1880-0(9)***, WestBow Pr.) Author Solutions, Inc.

Rohr, Richard. Wondrous Encounters: Scripture for Lent. 2011. 143p. pap. 8.99 *(978-0-86716-987-4(7))* Franciscan Media.

Rosage, David E. Bread of Life: Opening Our Hearts to Jesus & the Eucharist. 2008. 142p. pap. 18.00 *(978-1-60608-202-7(7)*, Wipf and Stock) Wipf & Stock Pubs.

Ryan, Sharon Catherine. Live Your Life: How to Abandon Your Miserable Existence Without Killing Yourself & Others along the Way. 2008. 94p. *(978-0-9809436-0-3(4))* Arden Agencies, Inc.

Sanders, Anthony R. Start Your Day with God: Daily Meditation for Your Spiritual Growth. 2009. 420p. 34.99 *(978-1-61579-119-4(1))*; pap. 22.99 *(978-1-60791-932-2(X))* Xulon Pr., Inc.

Savage, Warren J. & McSweeny, Mary Ann. Mindful Meditations for Every Day of Lent & Easter: Years a, B, & C. 2011. *(978-0-7648-1969-8(0))* Liguori Pubns.

Schatz, Larry. Walking with the Word: Daily Ventures into 15 Books of the Bible. 2008. 384p. (YA). (gr. 9-18). pap. 13.75 *(978-0-88489-993-8(4))* St. Mary's Pr.

Schmitt, Robin, et al. Book of Devotions. 2008. (ENG.). 416p. (J). pap. 12.99 *(978-0-310-71447-7(8))* Zondervan.

Schneider, M. Valerie. 10 Wise & Wonderful Stories for Children: Celebrating Holidays & Holy Days. 2007. (Illus.). 60p. per. 14.95 *(978-1-58595-614-2(7))* Twenty-Third Pubns./Bayard.

Schroeder, Frederick, intro. Cada Dia Es un Don. 2006. (Illus.). 192p. vinyl bd. 6.99 *(978-0-89942-163-6(6))* Catholic Bk. Publishing Corp.

Schwartz, Avraham. Hearts on Fire: Inspirational Thoughts on Selected Verses from the Psalms. 2007. 176p. per. *(978-956-310-008-2(5))* Editorial Benei Noaj.

Sedlacek, Ronald S. Echoes from the Valley: A Daily Devotional Written by Man Behind the Razor Wire. Sedlacek, Ronald S., ed. 321p. pap. 14.95 *(978-0-9725055-0-5(4))* E & C Endeavers.

Slaughter, Carolyn. Transformation Journal: A Daily Walk in the Word. Kibbey, Sue Nilson, ed. 2008. 211p. pap. 24.50 *(978-0-687-65502-1(1))* Abingdon Pr.

Smart, Dominic. 40 days with Paul: A Journey that could change your World. 2010. (ENG., Illus.). 128p. 10.99 *(978-1-84550-567-7(0))* Christian Focus Pubns. GBR. Dist: STL Distribution North America.

Smith, Ann. Written on My Heart. 2009. pap. *(978-1-57312-549-9(0))* Smyth & Helwys Publishing, Inc.

Smith, Chuck. Wisdom for Today: Genesis - Revelation Daily Devotional. 2007. lthr. 24.99 *(978-1-59751-031-8(9))* Word For Today, The.

Sonnenberg, Alaine. Shine On. 2010. pap. 10.99 *(978-1-61663-826-9(5))* Tate Publishing & Enterprises, LLC.

Spanish devotional / Devocional. 2011. 384p. pap. 13.99 *(978-0-7586-1750-7(X))* Concordia Publishing Hse.

Spurgeon, C. H. Morning & Evening: Daily Readings. 2009. 468p. pap. 12.99 *(978-1-60459-676-2(7))* Wilder Pubns., Ltd.

Spurgeon, Charles H. Evening by Evening: A New Edition of the Classic Devotional Based on the Holy Bible, English Standard Version. Begg, Alistair, ed. 2009. 384p. im. lthr. 21.99 *(978-1-4335-1359-6(5))* Crossway.

—Morning & Evening - Matt Tan/Blue: Daily Readings. 2007. (ENG.). 768p. 22.99 *(978-1-84550-183-9(7)*, Christian Heritage) Christian Focus Pubns. GBR. Dist: STL Distribution North America.

—Morning by Morning: A New Edition of the Classic Devotional Based on the Holy Bible, English Standard Version. Begg, Alistair, ed. 2009. 384p. im. lthr. 21.99 *(978-1-4335-1358-9(7))* Crossway.

—Morning by Morning & Evening by Evening: A New Edition of the Classic Devotional Based on the ESV Bible. Begg, Alistair, ed. 2009. 768p. im. lthr. 39.99 *(978-1-4335-1360-2(9))* Crossway.

Standard Publishing Staff. Standard Companion Devotions. 2009. (ENG.). 384p. pap. 9.99 *(978-0-7847-2253-4(6))* Standard Publishing.

Stapleton, Jean. Read with Me: 365 Family Readins Giving an Overview of the Bible. 2006. (ENG., Illus.). 432p. per. 14.99 *(978-1-84550-148-8(9)*, Christian Focus) Christian Focus Pubns. GBR. Dist: STL Distribution North America.

Stevens, Becca. The Path of Peace. 2010. (Walking Bible Studies). 96p. 10.00 *(978-1-4267-0978-4(1))* Abingdon Pr.

Storms, Sam. The Hope of Glory: 100 Daily Meditations on Colossians. 2008. 368p. pap. 17.99 *(978-1-58134-931-3(9))* Crossway.

—A Sincere & Pure Devotion to Christ: 100 Daily Meditations on 2 Corinthians. 2010. 240p. pap. 25.99 *(978-1-4335-1311-4(0))* Crossway.

Strang, Joy, ed. By Love Transformed: A Collection of Inspirational Readings. 2006. (Illus.). 382p. 14.99 *(978-1-59185-981-9(6)*, Charisma Hse.) Charisma Media.

Strauss, Ed. The Ultimate Devo for Boys: 365 Daily Devotions. 2009. (2:52 Ser.). (ENG.). 416p. (J). pap. 12.99 *(978-0-310-71314-2(5))* Zonderkidz.

Sweezy, Loy B. Encouraging Scriptures. 2008. 140p. pap. 13.99 *(978-0-9717546-4-5(0))* Sweezy, Loy B.

Swindoll, Charles R. Great Days with the Great Lives, 0 vols. 2007. (Great Lives from God's Word Ser.). 384p. per. 14.99 *(978-0-8499-1888-9(X))* Nelson, Thomas Inc.

Thompson, Nancy Eden. The Spirit & the Bride Say Come: Meditations from the Song of Solomon. 2009. 110p. pap. 14.95 *(978-1-4327-3635-4(3))* Outskirts Pr., Inc.

Tomberg, Valentin. Christ & Sophia: Anthroposophic Meditations on the Old Testament, New Testament, & Apocalypse. Bruce, R. H., tr. from GER. 2011. Orig. Title: Anthroposophisch Betrachtungen über des Alte Testament; Anthroposophische Betrachtungen über das Neue Testament; Geisteswissenschaftliche Betrachtungen über die Apokalypse des Johannes. 472p. pap. 40.00 *(978-0-88010-735-8(9))* SteinerBooks, Inc.

Towns, Elmer L. Praying the Gospels: Mathew, Mark, Luke, & John. 2007. (Praying the Scriptures Ser.). 305p. per. 15.99 *(978-0-7684-2439-3(9))* Destiny Image Pubs.

Tracy, Pamela Kaye. Promesas para Cada Dia: Refrigerio Espiritual paraa Mujeres. 2010. (Spiritual Refreshment for Women Ser.).Tr. of Everyday Promises. (ENG & SPA.). 224p. pap. 4.99 *(978-1-60260-868-9(7)*, Casa Promesa) Barbour Publishing, Inc.

Union & Communion or, Thoughts on the Song of Solomon. 2007. 96p. per. 8.95 *(978-1-60206-422-5(9))* Cosimo, Inc.

Urquhart, Colin. My Dear Son. 224p. pap. *(978-0-340-55809-6(1)*, Hodder & Stoughton) Hodder General Publishing Div.

Van, Breemen Peter. God of Our Deepest Longings. 2009. 128p. pap. 12.95 *(978-1-59471-200-5(X))* Ave Maria Pr.

VanderVelde, Clarence J. My Rock & My Salvation: Meditations on Forgiveness, God's Providence, & the Christian Life. 2008. pap. *(978-0-921100-80-5(9))* Inheritance Pubns.

Wade, Loron. Simply Put: What God's Been Saying All Along. 2009. 223p. pap. 14.99 *(978-0-8280-2477-8(4))* Review & Herald Publishing Assn.

Waite, Yvonne S. My Daily Bible Blessings from My Daily Bible Reading. 2011. 664p. pap. 30.00 ***(978-1-56848-079-4(2))*** Old Paths Pubns., Inc., The.

Walking Bible Study: The Path of Love. 2010. (Walking Bible Studies). 96p. 10.00 *(978-1-4267-1174-9(3))* Abingdon Pr.

Walters, J. Donald. Rays of the One Light: Weekly Commentaries on the Bible & the Bhagavad Gita. 2nd ed. 2007. (ENG.). 143p. per. 17.95 *(978-1-56589-208-8(9))* Crystal Clarity Pubs.

Ware, James. Reading the Bible As Christian Scripture: Understanding the Writers' Use of Language. 2009. 124p. pap. 14.25 *(978-1-4251-8291-5(7))* Trafford Publishing.

Watkins, Duane. Lessons from the Road. 2006. (ENG.). 24.99 *(978-1-60034-445-9(3))*; pap. 14.99 *(978-1-60034-444-2(5))* Xulon Pr., Inc.

Webb, James. Morning Meditation. 2007. 192p. 21.99 *(978-1-60477-227-2(1))*; per. 13.99 *(978-1-60477-226-5(3))* Xulon Pr., Inc.

Wesley, Edna. The Prelude: A Woman Named Job. 2007. 44p. pap. 8.95 *(978-0-7414-4075-4(X))* Infinity Publishing.

Westminster John Knox Press. A Year with the Bible 2012, 10 pks. 2011. (Year with the Bible Ser.). (ENG.). 28p. pap. 15.00 *(978-0-664-23809-4(2))* Westminster John Knox Pr.

Whelchel, Lisa. Busy Mom's Guide to Wisdom. 2011. (Motherhood Club Ser.). (ENG.). 128p. pap. 10.99 *(978-1-4516-4323-7(3)*, Howard Bks.) Howard Books.

White, Fred & White, Fred D. The Daily Writer: 366 Meditations to Cultivate a Productive & Meaningful Writing Life. 2008. (ENG., Illus.). 336p. pap. 17.99 *(978-1-58297-529-0(9)*, Writer's Digest Bks.) F&W Media, Inc.

Wiederkehr, Macrina. Abide: Keeping Vigil with the Word of God. 2011. E-Book ***(978-0-8146-3958-0(5))*** Liturgical P.

Wild, Jean. Rainbows & Promises: Fifty-Two Readings from the Bible with Selections from Well-Loved Hymns 2007. (52 Readings Ser.). 112p. pap. 9.00 *(978-1-84625-098-9(5))* DayOne Pubns. GBR. Dist: STL Distribution North America.

Wilson, Neil S., ed. The One Year Daily Wisdom. 2006. (ENG.). 384p. per. 12.99 *(978-1-4143-1496-9(5))* Tyndale Hse. Pubs.

Wolf, Carlene. The Power of the Word: -Spiritual Guidance for the Journey of Your Life. 2008. (Illus.). 804p. *(978-1-60800-000-5(1))* LifeReloaded.

Wolgemuth, Robert. NIV Letters to God Bible, 1 vol. movie tie-in ed. 2010. (ENG.). 1056p. lthr. 34.99 *(978-0-310-94943-5(2))* Zondervan.

Wood, Barry G. Bible Secrets Revealed. 2008. 184p. pap. 13.99 *(978-1-60477-861-8(X))* Xulon Pr., Inc.

Wooding, Mamie, et al. Nirv Adventure Bible: Book of Devotions 365 Days of Adventure. 2008. (ENG.). 416p. (J). pap. 12.99 *(978-0-310-71448-4(6))* Zondervan.

Wright, Eric E. Down a Country Road: 52 Seasonal Readings from Out Where the Sky Springs Free. 2008. (52 Readings Ser.). (Illus.). 192p. pap. *(978-1-84625-106-1(0))* DayOne Pubns.

Yogananda, Paramhansa. Spiritual Relationships. 2007. (Wisdom of Yogananda Ser.: Vol. 3). (ENG., Illus.). 156p. per. 9.95 *(978-1-56589-224-8(0))* Crystal Clarity Pubs.

Young, Sarah. Dear Jesus: Seeking His Life in Your Life, 0 vols. 2007. 256p. 13.99 *(978-1-4041-0495-2(X))* Nelson, Thomas Inc.

Zondervan. Bible Promises for You, 1 vol. 2006. (ENG.). 176p. pap. 1.99 *(978-0-310-81268-5(2))* Inspirio.

Zondervan Publishing Staff. Bible Promises for You, 1 vol. 2006. (ENG.). 176p. pap., pap. 95.52 *(978-0-310-81291-3(7))* Zondervan.

—God's Words of Life for Graduates: From the New International Version, 1 vol. 2007. (ENG.). 208p. (gr. 13). pap. 9.99 *(978-0-310-81726-0(9))* Inspirio.

BIBLE—MEDITATIONS—N. T.

Alexander, Loveday. Acts: Daily Bible Commentary: A Guide for Reflection & Prayer. 2007. (Daily Bible Commentary Ser.). 195p. per. 12.95 *(978-1-59856-189-0(8))* Hendrickson Pubs. Marketing, LLC.

Anderson, Ken/Ponder. The Gospel According to Jesus. Anderson, Auburn/Ponder, ed. 2007. pap. 19.95 *(978-0-9793906-8-5(0))* Beam Me Up Lord Publishing Hse.

—The Gospel According to John the Baptist: The Hidden Life of Jesus & John As Seen Through John's Eyes. Anderson, Auburn/Ponder, ed. 2007. pap. 19.95 *(978-0-9793906-7-8(2))* Beam Me Up Lord Publishing Hse.

Bacon, Philip W. Believing Like Jesus: The Kingdom of God, 1 vol. 2009. 100p. pap. 16.95 *(978-1-61582-573-8(8))* PublishAmerica, Inc.

Boice, James Montgomery. To the Glory of God: A 40-Day Devotional on the Book of Romans. 2010. 192p. pap. 14.99 *(978-0-8010-7279-6(4))* Baker Bks.

Bowen, George. Love Revealed: Meditations on the Parting Words of Jesus with His Disciples in Chapters Xiii. , Xiv. , Xv. , Xvi. , Xvii. , of the Gospel by John. 2006. 396p. per. 26.99 *(978-1-4255-4232-0(8))* MPublishing.

Briley, Terry. Meditative Commentary: Revelation: Jesus the Lamb. 2009. (Meditative Commentary Ser.). 122p. pap. 10.99 *(978-0-89112-559-4(0)*, Leafwood Pubs.) Abilene Christian Univ. Pr.

Brumbaugh, Renae. Morning Coffee with James. 2009. pap. 12.99 *(978-0-8272-2336-3(6))* Chalice Pr.

Burridge, Richard A. John: A Guide for Reflection & Prayer. 2007. (Daily Bible Commentary Ser.). 248p. per. 12.95 *(978-1-59856-188-3(X))* Hendrickson Pubs. Marketing, LLC.

Carlson, Melody. Life: A Teen Devotional, 1 vol. 2009. (Words from the Rock Ser.). 192p. (YA). pap. 11.99 *(978-0-8007-3255-4(3))* Revell.

—True: A Teen Devotional. 2008. (Words from the Rock Ser.). 192p. (YA). pap. 11.99 *(978-0-8007-3254-7(5))* Revell.

Christ, Jennifer. Journeying with Matthew: Five Minute Preparation for each Sunday Liturgy. 2007. (Illus.). 80p. pap. 7.95 *(978-0-8091-4477-8(8)*, 4477-8) Paulist Pr.

Colborn, Frank. Luke's Notebook: Meditations on the Gospel. 2009. 90p. pap. 11.00 *(978-0-557-15306-0(9))* Lulu Enterprises Inc.

Cooper, Phyllis A. Questions God Asks in the Hebrew Scriptures. 2008. pap. 13.00 *(978-0-8059-7929-9(8))* Dorrance Publishing Co., Inc.

Courson, Jon. A Day's Journey: 365 Meditations from the New Testament. 2008. 448p. pap. 14.99 *(978-0-9789472-1-7(5))* Searchlight.

Craghan, John F. The Gospels of the Weekday Lectionary: Commentary & Reflections. 2010. 29.95 *(978-0-8146-3338-0(2))*; E-Book 19.95 *(978-0-8146-3933-7(X))* Liturgical Pr.

Daughters of St. Paul Staff. Lenten Grace Daily Gospel Reflections. 2008. v, 147p. pap. *(978-0-8198-4525-2(6))* Pauline Bks. & Media.

DeLashmutt, Gary. Loving God's Way: A Fresh Look at the One Another Passages. 2007. (ENG.). 144p. pap. 14.99 *(978-1-59067-007-1(8))* Xenos Christian Fellowship.

Digiacomo, James. Sundays with Jesus: Reflections for the Year of Matthew. 2007. 111p. per. 7.95 *(978-0-8091-4432-2(4)*, 4482-2) Paulist Pr.

Dunlap, Judith. Bringing Home the Gospel: A Weekly Journal for Catholic Parents. 2006. 128p. per. 10.95 *(978-0-86716-782-5(3))* Franciscan Media.

Dunn, James D. G. Romans: A Guide for Reflection & Prayer. 2007. (Daily Bible Commentary Ser.). 189p. per. 12.95 *(978-1-59856-190-6(1))* Hendrickson Pubs. Marketing, LLC.

Durepos, Joseph. A Still More Excellent Way: How St. Paul Points Us to Jesus. 2008. (ENG.). 136p. pap. 10.95 *(978-0-8294-2758-5(9))* Loyola Pr.

Duvall, J. Scott & Verbrugge, Verlyn D. Devotions on the Greek New Testament, 1 vol. 2012. (ENG.). 160p. pap. 16.99 ***(978-0-310-49254-2(8))*** Zondervan.

Fenton, John. Galatians, 1 & 2 Thessalonians: A Guide for Reflection & Prayer. 2007. (Daily Bible Commentary Ser.). 191p. per. 12.95 *(978-1-59856-193-7(6))* Hendrickson Pubs. Marketing, LLC.

Fitzpatrick, Elyse. Comforts from the Cross: Celebrating the Gospel One Day at a Time. 2009. 146p. *(978-1-4335-0556-0(8))* Crossway.

Fitzpatrick, Elyse M. Comforts from the Cross: Celebrating the Gospel One Day at a Time. 2011. 152p. pap. 14.99 *(978-1-4335-2821-7(5))* Crossway.

Flowers, Thomas. Walking Humbly: Scripture Meditations in Verse. 2009. (Illus.). 80p. pap. 9.95 *(978-0-8091-4571-3(5))* Paulist Pr.

Franklin, Barbara Jean. Through Another Lens: Reflections on the Gospels, Year A. 2010. vi, 137p. pap. *(978-0-7648-1908-7(9))* Liguori Pubns.

—Through Another Lens: Reflections on the Gospels, Year C. 2009. 144p. pap. 14.95 *(978-0-7648-1773-1(6)*, Liguori) Liguori Pubns.

Green, Timothy. Philippians: Lectio Divina for Youth. 2007. (ENG.). 80p. pap. 7.99 *(978-0-8341-5021-8(2)*, 083-415-0212) Beacon Hill Pr. of Kansas City.

Guthrie, Nancy. Hoping for Something Better: Refusing to Settle for Life as Usual. 2007. (ENG.). 240p. per. 14.99 *(978-1-4143-1307-8(1)*, SaltRiver) Tyndale Hse. Pubs.

Harris, Don. The Red Letter Questions: Meditations on the Questions Jesus Asked. 2007. 333p. per. 12.99 *(978-0-88270-332-9(3))* Bridge-Logos Foundation.

Holloway, Gary. John: Believing in Jesus. 2007. (Meditative Commentary Ser.). 143p. per. 10.99 *(978-0-89112-504-4(3)*, Leafwood Pubs.) Abilene Christian Univ. Pr.

—Letters of Peter, John & Jude: Living in Jesus. 2008. (Meditative Commentary Ser.). 96p. pap. 8.99 *(978-0-89112-557-0(4)*, Leafwood Pubs.) Abilene Christian Univ. Pr.

—Meditative Commentary Series: Hebrews & James: Brother Jesus. 2007. (Meditative Commentary Ser.). 111p. pap. 11.99 *(978-0-89112-505-1(1)*, Leafwood Pubs.) Abilene Christian Univ. Pr.

Jacobs, Donald R. Consider Jesus: Daily Reflections on the Book of Hebrews. 2006. 367p. 15.99 *(978-0-8361-9348-0(2))*; pap. 11.99 *(978-0-8361-9347-3(4))* Herald Pr.

Jimenez, C. Mas Que Vencedores.Tr. of More Than Winners. (SPA.). 10.99 *(978-0-7899-0206-1(0)*, 550048) Editorial Unilit.

Jones, Kevin. Understanding Easter: "The Seven Last Words": A Resource Book for Personal Study, Lent & Easter Groups. 2007. 140p. pap. *(978-0-9549462-1-0(9))* Heart of Oak.

Kirvan, John J. Abide in Love: The Gospel Spirituality of John the Evangelist. 2006. (30 Days with a Great Spiritual Teacher Ser.: 17). 205p. per. 8.95 *(978-1-59471-098-8(8))* Ave Maria Pr.

Kurtz, Dennis. Youth Engaging Scripture: Diving into the Sunday Gospels. 2007. 376p. per. 18.95 *(978-0-88489-912-9(8))* St. Mary's Pr.

Laurie, Greg. Walking with Jesus: Daily Inspiration from the Gospel of John. 2007. 320p. pap. 16.00 *(978-0-8010-6815-7(0))* Baker Bks.

Lavender, Earl. Meditative Commentary Series: 1 & 2 Corinthians: Jesus, Cross, Church. 2008. (Meditative Commentary Ser.). 143p. pap. 11.99 *(978-0-89112-560-0(4)*, Leafwood Pubs.) Abilene Christian Univ. Pr.

—Meditative Commentary Series: Mark: Jesus Is God's Son. 2007. (Meditative Commentary Ser.). 143p. pap. 11.99 *(978-0-89112-551-8(5)*, Leafwood Pubs.) Abilene Christian Univ. Pr.

Lucado, Max. And the Angels Were Silent. 2009. (Bestseller Collection). 224p. 9.99 *(978-0-8499-2130-8(9))* Nelson, Thomas Inc.

—A Gentle Thunder: Hearing God Through the Storm. 2012. 240p. pap. 15.99 ***(978-0-8499-4733-9(2))*** Nelson, Thomas Inc.

Lucado, Max. A Gentle Thunder: Hearing God through the Storm, 0 vols. 2009. (Bestseller Collection). 256p. 9.99 *(978-0-8499-2148-3(1))* Nelson, Thomas Inc.

MacIntosh, Mike. Thirty Days: A Devotional Through Colossians. 2007. 67p. pap. *(978-1-60412-009-7(6))* Horizon Pr.

Mangiaracina, George. A Lenten Journey with Jesus Christ & St. John of the Cross. 2009. 280p. pap. 14.95 *(978-0-9841707-2-2(3))* Christus Publishing, LLC.

Martin, George. Meeting Jesus in the Gospels. 2009. 149p. pap. 13.99 *(978-0-86716-900-3(1)*, Servant Bks.) Franciscan Media.

Martini, Carlo Maria. The Gospel According to St. Paul: Meditations on His Life & Letters. Daigle-Williamson, Marsha, tr. from SPA. 2008. 127p. pap. 10.95 *(978-1-59325-145-1(9))* Word Among Us Pr.

Miller, David LeRoy. Book of Faith Lenten Journey: Marks of the Christian. 2009. *(978-0-8066-9764-2(4))* Augsburg Fortress, Pubs.

Miller, J. R. Devotional Hours with the Bible Volume I, from the Creation to the Exodus. 2011. 180p. pap. 14.99 ***(978-1-61203-199-6(4))*** Bottom of the Hill Publishing.

—Devotional Hours with the Bible Volume II , from the Exodus Through the Life of David. 2011. 156p. pap. 14.99 ***(978-1-61203-200-9(1))*** Bottom of the Hill Publishing.

—Devotional Hours with the Bible Volume III , Gleanings from the Psalms. 2011. 144p. pap. 14.99 ***(978-1-61203-201-6(X))*** Bottom of the Hill Publishing.

—Devotional Hours with the Bible Volume Vii, from the Gospel of John. 2011. 160p. pap. 14.99 ***(978-1-61203-205-4(2))*** Bottom of the Hill Publishing.

Mills, William C. Let Us Attend: Reflections on the Gospel of Mark for the Lenten Season. 2008. 108p. pap. 13.95 *(978-1-933275-26-0(X)*, Orthodox Research Institute) Cocheco Falls Publishing.

—A 30 Day Retreat: A Personal Guide to Spiritual Renewal. 2010. 176p. pap. 16.95 *(978-0-8091-4642-0(8))* Paulist Pr.

Murray, Andrew. The True Vine: Meditations for A Month on John XV. 2011. 130p. pap. 6.95 ***(978-1-61427-154-3(2))*** Martino Publishing.

O'Connor, Jerome Murphy. 1 Corinthians: A Guide for Reflection & Prayer. 2007. (Daily Bible Commentary Ser.). 1999p. per. 12.95 *(978-1-59856-191-3(X))* Hendrickson Pubs. Marketing, LLC.

Paulien, Jon. The Gospel from Patmos: Everyday Insights for Living from the Last Book of the Bible. 2007. 379p. *(978-0-8280-2092-3(2))* Review & Herald Publishing Assn.

Personal Promise Bible, ed. Personal Promise Bible Complete Old & New Testaments Regular Print: Personalized Text. 2007. 970p. lthr. 95.00 *(978-0-9759578-3-7(X))* Personal Promise Bible.

Peterson, Eugene H. A Year with Jesus: Daily Readings & Meditations. 2006. (ENG.). 432p. 19.95 *(978-0-06-111843-2(5)*, HarperOne) HarperCollins Pubs.

Power, Edmund. Blessed Be God: Hymns of St Paul. 2009. (Illus.). 64p. 9.95 *(978-0-8189-1299-3(5))* St Pauls/Alba Hse. Pubs.

Schlafer, David J. The Shattering Sound of Amazing Grace: Disquieting Tales from Saint John's Gospel. 2006. (ENG.). 112p. per. 12.95 *(978-1-56101-247-3(5))* Cowley Pubns.

Shields, Ann. Deeper Conversion: Extraordinary Grace for Ordinary Times. 2008. 112p. per. 11.99 *(978-0-86716-811-2(0)*, Servant Bks.) Franciscan Media.

—To Be Like Jesus: Inspiration from the Gospel of Luke. 2010. 128p. pap. 11.99 *(978-0-86716-951-5(6)*, Servant Bks.) Franciscan Media.

Silf, Margaret. Wayfaring. 2009. 256p. pap. 16.95 *(978-1-933495-17-0(0)*, Sorin Bks.) Ave Maria Pr.

Spencer, Aida Besancon. 2 Corinthians: A Guide for Reflection & Prayer. 2007. (Daily Bible Commentary Ser.). 231p. per. 12.95 *(978-1-59856-192-0(8))* Hendrickson Pubs. Marketing, LLC.

Spurgeon, Charles H. Matthew & Mark. 2007. (Devotional Thoughts on the Bible Ser.). 337p. pap. *(978-0-85234-663-1(8))* Evangelical Pr.

Standfield, Anne. Seasons of Comfort & Joy: Meditations in Verse Based on Select Scripture Readings. 2008. (Reflections (DayOne) Ser.). (Illus.). 90p. pap. *(978-1-84625-103-0(6))* DayOne Pubns.

Steagald, Tom. Shadows, Darkness, & Dawn: A Lenten Journey with Jesus. 2010. 158p. *(978-0-8358-1032-6(1))* Upper Room Bks.

Stevan, Sergio. Jesus & the Women of Faith, Hope, & Love. 2011. *(978-0-7648-2027-4(3))* Liguori Pubns.

Storms, C. Samuel. A Sincere & Pure Devotion to Christ Vol. 1: 100 Daily Meditations on 2 Corinthians. 2010. 240p. pap. 15.99 *(978-1-4335-1150-9(9))* Crossway.

—A Sincere & Pure Devotion to Christ Vol. 2: 100 Daily Meditations on 2 Corinthians. 2010. 288p. pap. 15.99 *(978-1-4335-1308-4(0))* Crossway.

—To the One Who Conquers: 50 Daily Meditations on the Seven Letters of Revelation 2-3. 2008. 239p. *(978-1-4335-0455-6(3))* Crossway.

Various Contributors. A Year in the New Testament: Meditations for Each Day of the Church Year. 2011. 400p. pap. 29.99 *(978-0-7586-2590-8(1))* Concordia Publishing Hse.

Voie, Gerald. Seeing Jesus Again for the First Time. 2007. 156p. per. 24.95 *(978-1-4241-9383-7(4))* PublishAmerica, Inc.

Wager, Dave. Beyond the Deception: Learning to Defend the Truth. 2007. (ENG.). 87p. pap. 11.95 *(978-1-60265-003-9(9))* Grace Acres Pr.

Wansbrough, Henry. Luke: A Guide for Reflection & Prayer. 2007. (Daily Bible Commentary Ser.). 215p. per. 12.95 *(978-1-59856-187-6(1))* Hendrickson Pubs. Marketing, LLC.

Wright, Allan F. Jesus in the House: Gospel Reflections on Christ's Presence in the Home. 2007. 190p. per. 14.95 *(978-0-86716-791-7(2))* Franciscan Media.

Wright, N. T. Lent for Everyone - Mark, Year B: A Daily Devotional. 2012. (Lent for Everyone Ser.). (ENG.). 144p. pap. 15.00 ***(978-0-664-23894-0(7))*** Westminster John Knox Pr.

Xvi, Pope Benedict. The Joy of Knowing Christ: Meditations on the Gospels. 2009. 144p. pap. 11.95 *(978-1-59325-151-2(3))* Word Among Us Pr.

BIBLE—MEDITATIONS—O. T.

Bolton, Martha. Don't Jump to Conclusions Without a Bungee Cord. 210p. pap. 10.99 *(978-0-8307-3414-6(7)*, Gospel Light) Gospel Light Pubns.

Branon, Dave, et al. My Soul Thirsts for God: Reflections on the Psalms from Our Daily Bread. 2009. (ENG.). 208p. pap. 11.99 *(978-1-57293-324-8(0))* Discovery Hse. Pubs.

Chilson, Richard & Kirvan, John, eds. You Shall Not Want-Rev. 2009. 120p. pap. 9.95 *(978-1-59471-156-5(9))* Ave Maria Pr.

Cook, Robert. The Jerusalem Church: Learn Not the Way of the Heathen. 2010. pap. 10.99 *(978-1-61566-546-4(3))* Tate Publishing & Enterprises, LLC.

Crosby, David E. You Excel Them All: Proverbs 31 Daily Devotional Guide, 1 vol. 2010. (ENG., Illus.). 64p. 12.95 *(978-1-58980-807-2(X))* Pelican Publishing Co., Inc.

Deeley, Mary & Deeley, Mary Katharine. Mothers, Lovers, Priests, Prophets, & Kings. 2010. xiii, 120p. pap. *(978-0-7648-1938-4(0))* Liguori Pubns.

DeLeon, Roy. Praying with the Body: Bringing the Psalms to Life. 2009. (Active Prayer Ser.). (ENG.). 150p. (gr. 13). pap. 18.99 *(978-1-55725-589-1(X))* Paraclete Pr., Inc.

Edris, Cheryl D. The Inescapable Presence: A Study of Genesis. 2010. pap. 13.99 *(978-1-60799-973-7(0))* Tate Publishing & Enterprises, LLC.

Evans, William. The Shepherd Psalm. 2011. 58p. pap. 8.99 ***(978-1-61203-290-0(7))*** Bottom of the Hill Publishing.

Ferguson, Sinclair. Faithful God. 2007. 157p. pap. 10.99 *(978-1-85049-216-0(6))* Bryntirion Pr. GBR. Dist: Spring Arbor Distributors, Inc.

Flowers, Thomas. God's Invitation: Meditations on a Covenant Relationship. 2011. 128p. pap. 12.95 *(978-0-8091-4712-0(2))* Paulist Pr.

Hyun, Keumju Jewel & Lathrop, Cynthia Davis, eds. Some Men Are Our Heroes: Stories by Women about the Men Who Have Greatly Influenced Their Lives. 2010. (House of Prisca & Aquila Ser.). 132p. pap. 17.00 *(978-1-60608-628-5(6)*, Wipf and Stock) Wipf & Stock Pubs.

Ingram, Chip. Finding God When You Need Him Most. 2007. 224p. pap. 14.99 *(978-0-8010-6812-6(6))* Baker Bks.

James, Sharon. Gentle Rain on Tender Grass: Daily Readings from the Pentateuch. 2006. (Illus.). per. *(978-0-85234-630-3(1))* Evangelical Pr.

Kamenetsky, Mordechai. The Parsha Parables Anthology: Stories & Anecdotes That Shed New Light on the Weekly Torah Portion & Holidays. 2008. 880p. 72.99 *(978-1-58330-304-7(9))* Feldheim Pubs.

Keller, W. Phillip & Keller, W. P. A Shepherd Looks at Psalm 23, 1 vol. 2007. (ENG.). 128p. 15.99 *(978-0-310-27442-1(7))*; 144p. (gr. 13). mass mkt. 4.99 *(978-0-310-27441-4(9))*; 144p. (gr. 13). pap. 12.99 *(978-0-310-27443-8(5))* Zondervan.

Kephart, Lore. Continuing Paths to Prayer: A Little Book of Old Testament Devotions. 2007. (Paths to Prayer Ser.). (Illus.). 114p. 19.95 *(978-1-57736-399-6(X))* Providence Hse Pubs.

Leibowitz, Yeshayahu. Accepting the Yoke of Heaven: Commentary on the Weekly Torah Portion. Himelstein, Shmuel, tr. 2006. 203p. per. 15.95 *(978-965-7108-77-2(2))* Urim Pubns. ISR. Dist: Coronet Bks.

Machowski, Marty. Long Story Short: Ten-Minute Devotions to Draw Your Family to God. 2010. 416p. pap. 19.99 *(978-1-935273-81-3(7))* New Growth Pr.

Meninger, William. A Joyful Noise: A Monastic Approach to the Psalms. 2011. 160p. pap. *(978-0-8091-4687-1(8))* Paulist Pr.

Moore, Beth. Esther: It's Tough Being a Woman. 2008. pap. 277.75 *(978-1-4158-5289-7(8))* LifeWay Christian Resources.

Newton, Linda. Better Than Jewels: 31 Days of Biblical Insight for a Woman Seeking God. 2009. 136p. 12.95 *(978-1-59317-369-2(5))* Warner Pr. Pubs.

—Sapphires from Psalms: 31 Gems of Encouragement for a Woman Seeking God. 2010. 136p. 12.95 *(978-1-59317-511-5(6))* Warner Pr. Pubs.

Pastor, Janzen, frwd. ... & GOD Smiled. 2008. (Illus.). 98p. per. *(978-0-9735907-4-6(2))* Destination Publishing.

Pearson, Carol Lynn. The Lord Is My Shepherd: Inspiration for Mothers. 2010. 64p. *(978-1-4236-0585-0(3))* Gibbs Smith, Publisher.

Personal Promise Bible, ed. Personal Promise Bible Complete Old & New Testaments Regular Print: Personalized Text. 2007. 970p. lthr. 95.00 *(978-0-9759578-3-7(X))* Personal Promise Bible.

Peterson, Eugene H. Run with the Horses: The Quest for Life at Its Best. 2nd rev. ed. 2009. (ENG.). 213p. pap. 15.00 *(978-0-8308-3706-9(X)*, IVP Bks.) InterVarsity Pr.

Rankin, Jerry. In the Secret Place: A Pilgrimage through the Psalms, 1 vol. 2009. (ENG.). 352p. pap. 14.99 *(978-0-8054-4881-8(0)*, B&H Bks.) B&H Publishing Group.

Remmell, Harry N. Modern Psalms. 2009. 128p. pap. 14.99 *(978-1-60791-280-4(5))* Xulon Pr., Inc.

Rhodes, Schuyler. A Journey Through the Psalms: Reflections for Worried Hearts & Troubled Times: Preaching the Psalms, Cycles a, B, C. 2009. *(978-0-7880-2627-0(5))* CSS Publishing Co.

Ross, Michael F. The Light of the Psalms: Deepening Your Faith with Every Psalm. 2006. (ENG.). 288p. per. 15.99 *(978-1-84550-150-1(0))* Christian Focus Pubns. GBR. Dist: STL Distribution North America.

Schaap, James C. Honest to God: Psalms for Scribblers, Scrawlers, & Sketchers. 2010. *(978-1-59255-526-0(8))* Faith Alive Christian Resources.

—Sixty at Sixty: A Boomer Reflects on the Psalms. 2008. *(978-1-59255-440-9(7))* Faith Alive Christian Resources.

Septién, Pia. Las Mujeres Del Antiguo Testamento: Sus Vidas Son Nuestra Esperanza. 2011. (SPA.). ***(978-0-7648-2054-0(0))*** Liguori Pubns.

—The Women of the Old Testament: Their Lives Are Our Hope. 2012. ***(978-0-7648-2204-9(7))*** Liguori Pubns.

Smith, Teresa S. Through the Darkest Valley: The Lament Psalms & One Woman's Lifelong Battle Against Depression. 2009. 210p. pap. 23.00 *(978-1-60608-528-8(X)*, Resource Pubns.) Wipf & Stock Pubs.

Snyder, Walter. Our Suffering Savior Daily Devotions. 2006. (Illus.). 57p. 2.29 *(978-0-7586-1025-6(4))* Concordia Publishing Hse.

Spurgeon, Charles H. The Pentateuch. 2007. (Devotional Thoughts on the Bible Ser.). 222p. per. *(978-0-85234-654-9(9))* Evangelical Pr.

Stevens, Wesley. Learning to Sing in a Strange Land: When a Loved One Goes to Prison. 2009. 210p. pap. 23.00 *(978-1-59752-535-0(9)*, Resource Pubns.) Wipf & Stock Pubs.

Storms, Sam. More Precious Than Gold: 50 Daily Meditations on the Psalms. 2009. 288p. pap. 15.99 *(978-1-4335-0261-3(5))* Crossway.

Stricker, K. C. Coming Out of Egypt Vol. 1: Journey Out of Idolatry Begins. 2008. 602p. pap. 59.00 *(978-1-55635-087-0(2))* Wipf & Stock Pubs.

Talking Back to God: Speaking Your Heart to God through the Psalms. 2010. 224p. pap. 14.99 *(978-0-89112-646-1(5)*, Leafwood Pubs.) Abilene Christian Univ. Pr.

Timmer, John. The Kingdom Equation: A Fresh Look at the Parables of Jesus. 2nd ed. 2008. 90p. per. *(978-1-59255-411-9(3))* Faith Alive Christian Resources.

Tripp, Paul David. A Shelter in the Time of Storm: Meditations on God & Trouble. 2009. 160p. pap. 12.99 *(978-1-4335-0598-0(3))* Crossway.

—Whiter Than Snow: Meditations on Sin & Mercy. 2008. 160p. pap. 12.99 *(978-1-4335-0230-9(5))* Crossway.

Welch, Henry James. Beloved of Beloved, Bride of Brides, Song of Songs. 2010. 464p. pap. *(978-1-77069-017-2(4))* Word Alive Pr.

Wiersbe, Warren W. Be Committed: Doing God's Will Whatever the Cost. 2008. (Be Ser.). (ENG.). 192p. pap. 12.99 *(978-1-4347-6848-3(1))* Cook, David C.

—Prayer, Praise & Promises: A Daily Walk Through the Psalms. 2011. 384p. 17.99 *(978-0-8010-1395-9(X))* Baker Bks.

BIBLE—MEMORIZATION

Braier, Gail. Signs of Faith: Roadside Reminders of God's Word. 2007. spiral bd. 7.99 *(978-0-9793751-0-1(X))* Traveling Word, LLC.

Hempe, Isaiah. E-Z Memory Book of Psalms. 2010. 272p. pap. 15.99 *(978-0-9840725-1-4(9))* Tzyon Pr.

Holford, Karen. 100 Creative Ways to Learn Memory Verses. 2009. *(978-0-8127-0505-8(X))* Autumn Hse. Publishing Co.

Kang, Joshua Choonmin. Scripture by Heart: Devotional Practices for Memorizing God's Word. 2010. (ENG.). 166p. pap. 15.00 *(978-0-8308-3536-2(9)*, IVP Bks.) InterVarsity Pr.

Kingswood, Jeff. From the Lips of Little Ones. 2008. 164p. (J). pap. 10.00 *(978-1-884527-24-1(8))* Crown & Covenant Pubns.

Lewis, R. M. A System for Memorizing God's Word. 2008. 120p. pap. 13.95 *(978-1-4357-0671-2(4))* Lulu Enterprises Inc.

Lingo, Susan. Scripture Memory Makers. 2007. 108p. pap. 13.99 *(978-0-9760696-5-2(2))* Lingo, Susan Bks.

Lingo, Susan L. Making Scripture Memorable. 2007. 132p. (gr. -1 — 1). pap. 12.99 *(978-0-9760696-1-4(X))* Lingo, Susan Bks.

Marshall, Andrea. Remember Remember: Teaching Memory Verses to Children. 2010. (Click Ser.). 64p. pap. *(978-1-905564-75-0(9))* Good Bk. Co.

BIBLE—MIRACLES

see Jesus Christ—Miracles; Miracles

BIBLE—MISCELLANEA

Adeleye, Modupe O. Search the Scriptures: Topical questions & Answers. 2011. 86p. pap. 15.99 ***(978-1-4628-7227-5(1))*** Xlibris Corp.

Adrian, Werner. New Discoveries in the Divine Inspiration of the Bible: The Impossibility of Refuting Its Authorship & the Four Gospels. 2008. (ENG.). 272p. 21.99 *(978-1-59979-460-0(8)*, Creation Hse.) Charisma Media.

Akenson, Donald Harman. Surpassing Wonder: The Invention of the Bible & the Talmuds. 672p. pap. *(978-0-7735-2289-3(1))* McGill-Queen's Univ. Pr.

Amazing Bible Trivia. Date not set. pap. *(978-0-87162-530-4(X))* Warner Pr. Pubs.

American Bible Society Staff. Inside the Mysteries of the Bible: New Perspectives on Ancient Truths. rev. ed. 2006. (ENG., Illus.). 176p. pap. 19.95 *(978-1-933405-91-9(0))* Time Home Entertainment, Inc.

Barbour Publishing, Inc. 365-Day Fun Bible Fact Book. 2010. (ENG.). 384p. pap. 9.99 *(978-1-60260-848-1(2)*, Barbour Bks.) Barbour Publishing, Inc.

Beers, Ronald A. & Mason, Amy E. TouchPoints for Recovery. 2009. (ENG.). 288p. pap. 4.99 *(978-1-4143-2023-6(X))* Tyndale Hse. Pubs.

Bell, James S. Bible Answer Book: Over 260 of the Most Frequently Asked Questions. 2010. (ENG.). 240p. pap. 15.99 *(978-1-4022-3745-4(6))* Sourcebooks, Inc.

Bible Clothes. Date not set. 1.50 *(978-0-906731-76-5(3))* Christian Focus Pubns. GBR. Dist: Spring Arbor Distributors, Inc.

Bible Colours. Date not set. pap. 1.50 *(978-0-906731-77-2(1))* Christian Focus Pubns. GBR. Dist: Spring Arbor Distributors, Inc.

Bickel, Bruce & Jantz, Stan. Bible Answers 101: A User-Friendly Guide to Life's Biggest Questions. 2009. (Christianity 101 Ser.). 272p. pap. 13.99 *(978-0-7369-2525-9(2))* Harvest Hse. Pubs.

Bowen, Barbara M. Strange Scriptures That Perplex the Western Mind. 132p. 2010. pap. 16.76 *(978-1-163-18724-1(0))* 2008. 35.95 *(978-1-4367-0682-7(3))* 2007. (ENG.). per. 20.95 *(978-1-4325-8891-5(5))* Kessinger Publishing, LLC.

Buckingham. En Todas Estas Cosas: In All These Things. (SPA.). 304p. *(978-84-7228-020-5(9)*, 220354) Clie, Editorial.

Cardenal, Ernesto. The Gospel in Solentiname. 2010. (Illus.). 656p. pap. 30.00 *(978-1-57075-902-4(2))* Orbis Bks.

Casey, Wilson. Do You Know Your Bible? A Fun Quiz on the Good Book. 2007. (ENG.). 48p. per. 5.95 *(978-1-4022-0884-3(7))* Sourcebooks, Inc.

Chamness, Stefani O. The Answer to Every Question Is in the Bible. deluxe ed. *(978-0-9631276-0-0(8))* Church of The Living God, The.

Christian Vision Literature Staff. What the Bible Says about Satan. 2008. 196p. pap. 18.95 *(978-1-4357-0678-1(1))* Lulu Enterprises Inc.

Collins, Joshua. Did God Plant the Forbidden Tree? 2010. 175p. pap. ***(978-1-935434-42-9(X))*** Global Education Advance.

Cunningham, Eva. Bible Secret: Mysteries of the Bible. 2010. 70p. pap. 15.99 *(978-1-4500-5400-3(5))* Xlibris Corp.

Danyans, Eugenio. Platillos Volantes & la Biblia: Flying Saucers & the Bible. (SPA., Illus.). 196p. *(978-84-7228-172-1(8)*, 220694) Clie, Editorial.

Darden, John S. Bible Topics Volume One. 2010. 88p. pap. 7.98 *(978-0-557-00628-1(7))* Lulu Enterprises Inc.

Davidson, George. Why Are There No Cats in the Bible? And Other Fascinating Facts to Expand Your Knowledge of the Bible. 2009. (ENG., Illus.). 192p. 9.99 *(978-0-7858-2493-0(6)*, 0785824936, Castle Bks., Inc.) Book Sales, Inc.

Dirks, Jerald. What You Weren't Taught in Sunday School. 2011. ***(978-1-59008-069-6(6))*** amana pubns.

Dodge, Esther. The Apocalypse & the Twentieth Century. 2011. 152p. 41.95 ***(978-1-258-04188-5(X))*** Literary Licensing, LLC.

Dowley, Tim. Bible Facts & Figures. 2008. (St. Joseph Bible Resource Ser.). (Illus.). 32p. pap. 4.95 *(978-0-89942-653-2(0))* Catholic Bk. Publishing Corp.

Fernandez, Adolfo. Plantas en las Aagradas Escrituras: Plants in the Holy Scriptures. (SPA., Illus.). 96p. *(978-84-7228-273-5(2)*, 220691) Clie, Editorial.

Geisler, Norman L. & Howe, Thomas. Making Sense of Bible Difficulties: Clear & Concise Answers from Genesis to Revelation, 1 vol. 2009. 272p. pap. 13.99 *(978-0-8010-7188-1(7))* Baker Bks.

Giles, Terry. A Doubter's Guide to the Bible. 2009. 156p. pap. 14.00 *(978-0-687-65833-6(0))* Abingdon Pr.

Goldingay, John. Key Questions about Christian Faith: Old Testament Answers. 2010. *(978-1-59856-430-3(7))* Hendrickson Pubs. Marketing, LLC.

Good News of Great Joy: Large. 5.00 *(978-0-687-00733-2(X))* Abingdon Pr.

Good News of Great Joy: Offering Envelope. 4.50 *(978-0-687-00582-6(5))* Abingdon Pr.

Good News of Great Joy: Regular. 4.50 *(978-0-687-00642-7(2))* Abingdon Pr.

Hammari, Kimiko. The Old Testament Puzzle Book. 2009. 96p. pap. 8.99 *(978-1-59955-368-9(6))* Cedar Fort, Inc./CFI Distribution.

Hammer, Shalom. The Family Rashi Book. 2010. 223p. *(978-1-934440-88-9(4),* Devorah Publishing) Urim Pubns.

—The Family Rashi Book. 2010. (ENG.). 223p. pap. 19.95 *(978-1-936068-16-6(8),* Devorah Publishing) Urim Pubns. ISR. Dist: Lambda Pubs., Inc.

Hammond, F. Rompiendo las Maldiciones.Tr. of Breaking of Curses. (SPA.). 3.99 *(978-958-9354-09-4(2),* 550051) Editorial Unilit.

Hancock, Jimmie L. All the Questions in the Bible, Kjv. 2011. 232p. pap. 19.95 ***(978-1-257-93011-1(7))*** Lulu Enterprises Inc.

Hanegraaff, Hank. The Bible Answer Book: Volume 2, 0 vols., Vol. 2. 2007. 256p. 14.99 *(978-1-4041-0303-0(1))* Nelson, Thomas Inc.

Houdmann, S. Michael. Got Questions? Bible Questions Answered - Answers to the Questions People Are Really Asking. 2009. 720p. 47.99 *(978-1-4141-1202-2(5))*; pap. 31.99 *(978-1-4141-1208-4(4))* Pleasant Word.

Howard Books Staff. Puzzlements & Predicaments of the Bible: The Weird, the Wacky, & the Wondrous. 2008. (ENG., Illus.). 288p. pap. 18.99 *(978-1-4165-6676-2(7),* Howard Bks.) Howard Books.

Howard Books Staff, contrib. by. Mysteries & Intrigues of the Bible. 2007. (ENG.). 320p. pap. 19.99 *(978-1-4165-4356-5(2),* Howard Bks.) Howard Books.

Isaacs, Roger D. Talking with God: The Radioactive Ark of the Testimony: Communication Through It. Protection from It. Williams Miller, Janice, ed. 2010. (Illus.). 514p. 29.95 *(978-1-4125-4997-4(3),* Sacred Closet Bks.) Publishing Institute, Inc., The.

Kovacs, Joe. Shocked by the Bible. 2007. 25.95 *(978-0-9790451-3-4(4),* WND Bks.) WND Bks, Inc.

—Shocked by the Bible: The Most Astonishing Facts You've Never Been Told, 0 vols. 2008. 224p. 22.99 *(978-0-8499-2011-0(6))* Nelson, Thomas Inc.

Laney, J. Carl. Answers to Tough Questions: A Survey of Problem Passages & Issues from Every Book of the Bible. 2010. 352p. pap. 39.00 *(978-1-60899-840-1(1),* Wipf and Stock) Wipf & Stock Pubs.

Lang, J. Stephen. The Big Book of Bible Bloopers: A Lighthearted Look at the Misquotes, Misconceptions, & Misunderstandings of the World's Bestselling Book. 2007. 272p. pap. 11.99 *(978-0-7369-2136-7(2))* Harvest Hse. Pubs.

—Curiosidades de la Biblia: The Complete Book of Bible Trivia, Vol.2. 256p. 10.95 *(978-958-607-927-3(9))* Sociedad de San Pablo COL. Dist: St Pauls/Alba Hse. Pubs.

Lang, Stephen. Curiosidades de la Biblia, Vol. 1.Tr. of Complete Book of Bible Trivia. (SPA.). 192p. 7.95 *(978-958-607-738-5(1))* Sociedad de San Pablo COL. Dist: St Pauls/Alba Hse. Pubs.

LeBeau, Byron. The Curs-Ed Net. 2007. 284p. (ENG.). 25.99 *(978-1-60477-223-4(9))*; per. 15.99 *(978-1-60477-149-7(6))* Xulon Pr., Inc.

Littleton, Mark. The Bible Bathroom Book: Information for Those Who Have Only Minutes to Read. 2008. (ENG.). 320p. pap. 19.99 *(978-1-4165-4359-6(7),* Howard Bks.) Howard Books.

Manser, Martin H. The Ultimate Bible Fact & Quiz Book. Chartwell Books Staff, ed. 2009. (ENG., Illus.). 384p. spiral bd. 9.99 *(978-0-7858-2161-8(9),* 0785821619, Chartwell) Book Sales, Inc.

Matthews, Victor H. 101 Questions & Answers on the Historical Books of the Bible. 2009. (Responses to 101 Questions... Ser.). 160p. pap. 16.95 *(978-0-8091-4618-5(5))* Paulist Pr.

McDonnell, Kilian. God Drops & Loses Things. 2009. 88p. pap. 11.95 *(978-0-9740992-4-8(4))* Liturgical Pr.

McTavish, T. J. A Biblical Miscellany: 176 Pages of Offbeat, Zesty, Vitally Unnecessary Facts, Figures, & Tidbits about the Bible, 0 vols. 2007. 176p. per. 9.99 *(978-0-8499-1745-5(X))* Nelson, Thomas Inc.

Miller, Stephen M. Incredible Mysteries of the Bible, 1 vol. 2008. (Zondervan Visual Reference Ser.). (ENG., Illus.). 96p. 12.99 *(978-0-310-25594-9(5))* Zondervan.

Mulder, William. Compa-erismo con dios y el Pr+jimo. 2006. pap. 17.99 *(978-1-59781-978-7(6))* Xulon Pr., Inc.

Publications International Staff. Daily Dose of Knowledge Bible. 2009. 384p. 19.95 *(978-1-4127-1541-6(5))* Publications International, Ltd.

Reed, Wanda. Amazing Bible Facts: A Great Way to Test Your Knowledge. 2011. 312p. pap. 22.95 *(978-1-4497-1344-7(0),* WestBow Pr.) Author Solutions, Inc.

Rhodes, Ron. Commonly Misunderstood Bible Verses: Clear Explanations for the Difficult Passages. 2008. 300p. pap. 14.99 *(978-0-7369-2175-6(3))* Harvest Hse. Pubs.

—What Does the Bible Say About — ? 2007. 400p. pap. 14.99 *(978-0-7369-1903-6(1))* Harvest Hse. Pubs.

Rusca, Ruth. Feminine Mysteries in the Bible: The Soul Teachings of the Daughters of the Goddess. 2008. (ENG.). 1p. pap. 15.00 *(978-1-59143-088-9(7))* Bear & Co.

Tribby, Jeffery L. A Little Collection of Truths. 2009. 236p. pap. 14.99 *(978-1-60791-510-2(3))* Xulon Pr., Inc.

Troward, Thomas. Bible Mystery & Bible Meaning. 2007. 336p. 29.95 *(978-1-60206-995-4(6))* Cosimo, Inc.

—Bible Mystery & Bible Meaning. 2007. 272p. 29.99 *(978-1-59986-730-4(3))* Filiquarian Publishing, LLC.

Turnage, C. L. The Bible. . . An Extraterrestrial Transmission: Is Planet X Planet Heaven? rev. ed. Date not set. (Illus.). 159p. reprint ed. 20.00 *(978-0-9645885-4-7(4))* Flying Disk Pubns.

Waton, Harry. The Key to the Bible. 2007. (ENG.). 108p. 33.95 *(978-0-548-08341-3(X))* Kessinger Publishing, LLC.

BIBLE—MUSIC

see Music in the Bible

BIBLE—MUSICAL INSTRUMENTS

see Music in the Bible

BIBLE—NAMES

see Names in the Bible

BIBLE—NATURAL HISTORY

see Nature in the Bible

BIBLE—NUMBERS

see Numbers in the Bible

BIBLE—NUMISMATICS

Bressett, Kenneth. Money of the Bible. 2nd ed. 2007. (Illus.). 114p. 29.95 *(978-0-7948-2389-4(0))* Whitman Publishing LLC.

Dow, Joseph A. Ancient Coins Through the Bible. 2011. pap. 59.99 ***(978-1-61777-135-4(X))*** Tate Publishing & Enterprises, LLC.

BIBLE—OUTLINES, SYLLABI, ETC.

see Bible—Study and Teaching—Outlines, Syllabi, etc.

BIBLE—PARABLES

see also Jesus Christ—Parables

Adams, Jay Edward. Preaching with Parables. 2007. (Ministry Monographs for Modern Times Ser.). 64p. per. 11.55 *(978-1-889032-54-2(9))* Timeless Texts, Inc.

Anderson, Ken/Ponder. The Millennium Raptures Parable Episode I. 2007. pap. 15.95 *(978-0-9793906-0-9(5))* Beam Me Up Lord Publishing Hse.

—The Millennium Tribulation Parable Episode II. 2007. pap. 15.95 *(978-0-9793906-1-6(3))* Beam Me Up Lord Publishing Hse.

—The Millennium Trilogy in Three Parable Episodes. Anderson, Auburn/Ponder, ed. 2007. pap. 24.95 *(978-0-9793906-3-0(X))* Beam Me Up Lord Publishing Hse.

—The Next Millennium Parable Episode III: A Thousand Years Living in the New Earth & Heaven & Lucifer's Final Return. Anderson, Auburn/Ponder, ed. 2007. pap. *(978-0-9793906-2-3(1))* Beam Me Up Lord Publishing Hse.

—The Trinity of God's Living Truth Manuscripts 2012 (or Later?) Prophecy of Regeneration & Renewal World Without End. Anderson, Auburn/Ponder, ed. 2010. Orig. Title: 2010. 132p. pap. 19.95 *(978-0-9793906-9-2(9))* Beam Me Up Lord Publishing Hse.

Arnot, William. The Parables of Our Lord. 2008. 476p. 33.99 *(978-0-554-29739-2(6))* 2008. 476p. 31.99 *(978-0-554-39042-0(6))* 2007. (ENG.). 426p. pap. 26.99 *(978-1-4346-8316-8(8))* 2007. (ENG.). 474p. pap. 30.99 *(978-1-4346-8317-5(6))* BiblioBazaar.

—The Parables of Our Lord. 2009. 318p. pap. *(978-1-4589-3226-6(5))* Books LLC.

—The Parables of Our Lord. 2009. 448p. pap. *(978-1-4099-7503-8(7))* Dodo Pr.

Barclay, William. Insights - Parables: What the Bible Tells Us about Jesus' Miracles. 2011. (Insights Ser.). 80p. pap. 12.50 ***(978-0-7152-0932-5(9))*** Saint Andrew Pr., Ltd. GBR. Dist: Westminster John Knox Pr.

Boccaccini, Gabriele, ed. Enoch & the Messiah Son of Man: Revisiting the Book of Parables. 2007. 600p. pap. 50.00 *(978-0-8028-0377-1(6))* Eerdmans, William B. Publishing Co.

Boyd, Sherrill J. Tares among Us: Masquerading as True Believers. 2009. pap. 14.99 *(978-1-60696-950-2(1))* Tate Publishing & Enterprises, LLC.

Braxton, Virgie. Random Parables. 2008. 92p. pap. 10.99 *(978-1-60647-668-0(8))* Xulon Pr., Inc.

Bunyan, John. The Pharisee & the Publican. 2009. 128p. pap. 7.99 *(978-1-60450-617-4(2),* Serenity Pubs.) Arc Manor.

—The Pharisee & the Publican. 2008. 160p. 22.99 *(978-0-554-38783-3(2))* 2008. 160p. 25.99 *(978-0-554-29480-3(X))* 2007. (ENG.). 140p. pap. 18.99 *(978-1-4346-7726-6(5))* 2007. (ENG.). 156p. pap. 21.99 *(978-1-4346-7727-3(3))* BiblioBazaar.

—The Pharisee & the Publican. 2007. 116p. per. *(978-1-4068-2397-4(X))* Echo Library.

Caspi, Mishael M. & Greene, John T. Parables & Fables as Distinctive Jewish Literary Genres: The Origins & Structure of Indirect Speech about God. 2012. 372p. 129.95 ***(978-0-7734-2598-9(5))*** Mellen, Edwin Pr., The.

Cordova, Maria. The Kingdom of the Son of Man on Earth. 2009. 272p. pap. 16.99 *(978-1-61579-159-0(0))* Xulon Pr., Inc.

Drysdale. Holiness in the Parables. pap. 7.99 *(978-0-88019-044-2(2))* Schmul Publishing Co., Inc.

Evans, Roderick L. I Will Open My Mouth in Parables: Examining the Parables of the Hidden Treasure & of the Unmerciful Servant. 2009. 66p. pap. 11.95 *(978-1-60141-043-6(3),* 285715) Kingdom Builders Publishing.

Funk, Robert W. Funk on Parables: Collected Essays. 2006. 220p. per. *(978-0-944344-99-6(2))* Polebridge Pr.

Garcia, Zen. Lucifer - Father of Cain. 2010. 312p. pap. 19.96 *(978-0-557-36908-9(8))* Lulu Enterprises Inc.

Hargreaves, John. Guide to the Parables. 16.00 *(978-0-687-85445-5(8))* Abingdon Pr.

Hunter, A. M. Interpreting the Parables. 2012. 126p. pap. ***(978-0-334-00685-5(6),*** SCM Pr.) Hymns Ancient & Modern Ltd.

Jeanie Strand Chilton. Eastern Customs of the Bible: The Teachings of Bishop K. C. Pillai. 2010. 108p. pap. 13.50 *(978-1-4251-2163-1(2))* Trafford Publishing.

Moore, Michael S. WealthWatch: A Study of Socioeconomic Conflict in the Bible. 2011. 320p. pap. 35.00 ***(978-1-61097-296-3(1),*** Pickwick Pubns.) Wipf & Stock Pubs.

Negri, Antonio. The Labor of Job: The Biblical Text as a Parable of Human Labor. Mandarini, Matteo, tr. from ITA. 2009. (New Slant: Religion, Politics, Ontology Ser.). (ENG.). 168p. 74.95 *(978-0-8223-4622-7(2))*; pap. 21.95 *(978-0-8223-4634-0(6))* Duke Univ. Pr.

Oranekwu, George. Indeed, he would never speak to them except in Parables (Mark 4:34) A Hermeneutical Correlation of Parables in Mark 4 to the Traditional Igbo Culture. 2008. 286p. (gr. 11). pap. 37.95 *(978-3-88939-837-6(5))* IKO Verlag fur Interkulturelle Kommunikation DEU. Dist: Transaction Pubs.

Sadlack, Emil & Otto. The Desolations of the Sanctuary. 2010. 324p. pap. 22.70 *(978-0-557-27598-4(9))* Lulu Enterprises Inc.

Schipper, Jeremy. Parables & Conflict in the Hebrew Bible. 2009. (ENG.). 182p. 88.00 *(978-0-521-76462-9(9))* Cambridge Univ. Pr.

Shua, Rafael. The Sand Table: A Tactical Approach to Revelation. 2009. 364p. pap. 20.99 *(978-1-61579-134-7(5))* Xulon Pr., Inc.

Smith, Kenneth W. Sheldon Jackson Parables. 2007. 152p. per. 14.95 *(978-0-595-44748-0(1))* iUniverse, Inc.

Van Loon, Michelle. Uprooted: Growing a Parable Life from the Inside Out. 2006. 173p. per. *(978-1-932902-62-4(7))* FaithWalk Publishing.

Voris, Steven J. Preaching Parables: A Metaphorical Interfaith Approach. annot. ed. 2008. 224p. pap. 19.95 *(978-0-8091-4506-5(5))* Paulist Pr.

White, Ellen G. Living the Life of the Lifegiver: Making Simple the Parables & Teachings of Jesus. 2007. (Life-Giving Secrets: Vol. 3). 320p. (Orig.). pap. 11.99 *(978-1-883012-67-0(8))* Remnant Pubns.

Wright, Stephen I. The Voice of Jesus: Studies in the Interpretation of Six Gospel Parables. 2007. (Paternoster Biblical & Theological Monographs). 304p. pap. 35.00 *(978-1-55635-649-0(8))* Wipf & Stock Pubs.

Young, Brad H. The Parables: Jewish Tradition & Christian Interpretation. 2008. 332p. pap. 24.95 *(978-1-59856-303-0(3))* Hendrickson Pubs. Marketing, LLC.

BIBLE—PARAPHRASES

Adams, Henry Wright. The Book of Job in Poetry; or, a Song in the Night. 2006. 384p. per. 26.99 *(978-1-4255-4093-7(7))* MPublishing.

Alcuinus, Flaccus Albinus, tr. Book of Jasher Referred to in Joshua & Second Samuel. 2009. 536p. 49.99 *(978-1-61534-103-0(X))*; pap. 28.99 *(978-1-61534-101-6(3))* EZreads Pubns., LLC.

Ayvazian, Andrea & Augarten, Ellen. Psalms in Ordinary Voices: A Reinterpretation of the 150 Psalms by Women, Men & Children. 2010. pap. *(978-1-935052-31-9(4))* White River Pr.

Belknap, Jeremy. Sacred Poetry; Consisting of Psalms & Hymns. 2006. 520p. per. 29.99 *(978-1-4255-5751-5(1))* MPublishing.

Bell, Rob & Golden, Don. Jesus Wants to Save Christians: A Manifesto for the Church in Exile. 2012. (ENG.). 240p. pap. 14.99 ***(978-0-06-212582-8(6),*** HarperOne) HarperCollins Pubs.

Bell, Rob, et al. Jesus Wants to Save Christians: A Manifesto for the Church in Exile, 1 vol. 2008. (ENG., Illus.). 224p. 19.99 *(978-0-310-27502-2(4))* Zondervan.

Bible. N.T. Galatians. English. Paraphra. Law & Grace: A paraphrase of the Epistle to the churches of Galatia. by William Morris ... 2011. 28p. pap. 11.99 ***(978-1-4181-9345-4(3))*** MPublishing.

Brown, John. The Psalms of David in Metre; with Annotations, Explaining the Sense, & Animating the Devotion, by John Brown. 2006. 372p. per. 26.99 *(978-1-4255-3912-2(2))* MPublishing.

Church Psalmist; or, Psalms & Hymns, Designed for the Public, Social & Private Use of Evangelical Christians. 2006. 652p. per. 36.99 *(978-1-4255-6721-7(5))* MPublishing.

Church Psalmist; or, Psalms & Hymns for the Public, Social & Private Use of Evangelical Christians. 2006. 680p. per. 36.99 *(978-1-4255-6803-0(3))* MPublishing.

Daye, Stephen. The Bay Psalm Book: The Whole Booke of Psalmes Faithfully Translated into English Metre. 2007. 316p. per. 11.50 *(978-1-60206-096-8(7))* Cosimo, Inc.

Erasmus. Collected Works of Erasmus. Sider, Robert D., ed. Simpson, Dean, tr. from LAT. 2008. (Collected Works of Erasmus Ser.). (ENG.). 408p. *(978-0-8020-9299-1(3))* Univ. of Toronto Pr.

—Paraphrases on the Epistles to the Corinthians, Ephesians, Philippians, Colossians, & Thessalonians. Sider, Robert D., ed. 2009. (Collected Works of Erasmus Ser.). (ENG.). 760p. *(978-0-8020-9296-0(9))* Univ. of Toronto Pr.

Ingraham, Margaret B. This Holy Alphabet: Lyric Poems Adapted from Psalm 119. 2009. (ENG.). 80p. (gr. 13). pap. 14.99 *(978-1-55725-655-3(1))* Paraclete Pr., Inc.

Knight, Robert. A Critical Commentary on the Epistle of St. Paul the Apostle to the Romans. 2009. 660p. pap. 56.00 *(978-1-60608-686-5(3),* Wipf and Stock) Wipf & Stock Pubs.

More Lost Books of the Bible: The Book O. 2006. pap. 18.95 *(978-1-933993-21-8(9))* Apocryphile Pr.

Parry, J. H., prod. Sefer Ha-Yashar or the Book of Jasher. unabr. ed. 2007. (ENG.). 280p. per. *(978-1-897352-33-4(1))* Providence University.

Prayerful Psalms for Everyone. 2007. *(978-0-9793490-3-4(6))* Dynasty Publishing, Inc.

Sewall, Henry D. Collection of Psalms & Hymns for Socia. 2006. pap. 36.95 *(978-1-4286-5927-8(7))* Kessinger Publishing, LLC.

Tolstoy, Leo & Condren, Dustin. The Gospel in Brief: The Life of Jesus. 2011. (ENG.). 224p. pap. 12.99 *(978-0-06-199345-9(X),* HarperPerennial) HarperCollins Pubs.

Vasquez, James. Prophets of the Old Testament: A classic collection of biblical heroes in Verse. 2010. pap. 24.99 *(978-1-61566-116-9(6))* Tate Publishing & Enterprises, LLC.

Westcott, Frederick Brooke. Colossians: A Letter to Asia. 2007. 210p. pap. 22.00 *(978-1-55635-169-3(0),* Wipf and Stock) Wipf & Stock Pubs.

Williams, Jane. Storyteller's Companion to the Bible I: Audio. 13.00 *(978-0-687-76229-3(4))* Abingdon Pr.

Zim, Rivkah. English Metrical Psalms: Poetry as Praise & Prayer, 1535-1601. 2011. (ENG., Illus.). 346p. pap. 33.99 *(978-0-521-17221-9(7))* Cambridge Univ. Pr.

BIBLE—PATRISTIC QUOTATIONS

see Bible—Quotations, Early

BIBLE—PERIODICALS

Elbert, Paul. Journal of Biblical & Pneumatological Research: Volume Three 2011. 2011. 158p. pap. 25.00 ***(978-1-61097-651-0(7),*** Wipf and Stock) Wipf & Stock Pubs.

Elbert, Paul, ed. Journal of Biblical & Pneumatological Research. 2010. 148p. pap. 25.00 *(978-1-60899-903-3(3),* Wipf and Stock) Wipf & Stock Pubs.

—Journal of Biblical & Pneumatological Research: Volume One 2009. 2009. 144p. pap. 25.00 *(978-1-60608-932-3(3),* Wipf and Stock) Wipf & Stock Pubs.

Hupper, William G. An Index to English Periodical Literature on the Old Testament & Ancient near Eastern Studies, 2 vols., Vol. 9. 2011. (ATLA Bibliography Ser.). (ENG.). 1438p. (gr. 17). 200.00 *(978-0-8108-7805-1(4))* Scarecrow Pr., Inc.

Tischendorf, Constantin, ed. Vetus Testamentum Graece: Sixth Edition. 2007. 1386p. pap. 100.00 *(978-1-55635-331-4(6),* Wipf and Stock) Wipf & Stock Pubs.

Van Ess, Leandri. Vetus Testamentum Graecum, Editione Sixtina. 2007. 1064p. pap. 90.00 *(978-1-55635-569-1(6),* Wipf and Stock) Wipf & Stock Pubs.

Zimmerman, Joyce. Living Liturgy for Extraordinary Ministers of Holy Communion. Harmon, Kathleen, ed. 2011. 128p. pap. 9.95 ***(978-0-8146-3334-2(X))*** Liturgical Pr.

BIBLE—PHILOLOGY

see Greek Language, Biblical; Hebrew Language

BIBLE—PHILOSOPHY

Graham, James Robert. A Philosophy of Scripture, Cosmology, V1: A Connected Commentary on the Book of Genesis. 2011. 332p. 50.95 ***(978-1-258-01209-0(X))*** Literary Licensing, LLC.

Hazony, Yoram. The Philosophy of Hebrew Scripture: An Introduction. 2012. (ENG.). 240p. ***(978-1-107-00317-0(2))***; (Illus.). pap. ***(978-0-521-17667-5(0))*** Cambridge Univ. Pr.

Hirst, Jon & Hirst, Mindy. Through the River: Understanding Your Assumptions about Truth. 2009. (ENG.). 207p. pap. 14.99 *(978-1-934068-03-8(9))* Authentic Media.

Olsson, Frank. Come to Think about It: Associations to the Sixty-Six Books of the Bible from a Philosophical Perspective. 2009. 248p. pap. 25.95 *(978-1-4269-1457-7(1))* Trafford Publishing.

Rasimus, Tuomas, et al, eds. Stoicism in Early Christianity. 2010. (C). pap. 40.00 *(978-0-8010-3951-5(7))* Baker Academic.

Rasimus, Tuomas, et al. Stoicism in Early Christianity. 2010. *(978-1-59856-445-7(5))* Hendrickson Pubs. Marketing, LLC.

Schweid, Eliezer. The Philosophy of the Bible as Foundation of Jewish Culture: Philosophy of Biblical Law. Levin, Leonard, tr. from HEB. 2nd ed. 2009. (Reference Library of Jewish Intellectual History Ser.). (ENG.). 216p. 50.00 *(978-1-934843-01-7(6))*; pap. 35.00 *(978-1-934843-52-9(0))* Academic Studies Pr.

—The Philosophy of the Bible as Foundation of Jewish Culture: Philosophy of Biblical Narrative. Levin, Leonard, tr. from HEB. 2009. (Reference Library of Jewish Intellectual History Ser.). (ENG.). 224p. 50.00 *(978-1-934843-00-0(8))*; pap. 35.00 *(978-1-934843-51-2(2))* Academic Studies Pr.

Vanhoozer, Kevin J. Biblical Narrative in the Philosophy of Paul Ricoeur: A Study in Hermeneutics & Theology. 2007. (ENG.). 324p. pap. 61.00 *(978-0-521-04390-8(5))* Cambridge Univ. Pr.

Waite, Pastor D. A., compiled by. Gnosticism: The Doctrinal Foundation of the New Bible Versions. 2009. 246p. pap. 20.00 *(978-0-9822230-2-4(1))* Old Paths Pubns., Inc., The.

Zegarelli, Gregg Robert. One (Divine Version) The Unified Gospel of Jesus for Christians. ltd. ed. 2006. per. 24.99 *(978-0-9789906-0-2(9))* One Unified Gospel Pr.

—One (Universal Version) The Unified Gospel of Jesus for Non-Christians & Christian Empirical Study. 2006. 300p. per. 24.95 *(978-0-9789906-1-9(7))* One Unified Gospel Pr.

BIBLE—PICTURES, ILLUSTRATIONS, ETC.

see Bible—Illustrations

BIBLE—POETRY

see Bible—History of Biblical Events—Poetry

BIBLE—POLITCAL SCIENCE

see Politics in the Bible

BIBLE—POLITICS

see Politics in the Bible

BIBLE—PRAYERS

see also Jesus Christ—Prayers; Lord's Prayer; Prayer—Biblical Teaching

Abingdon, Press, ed. Whats in the Bible about Praye. 2009. (Why Is That in the Bible & Why Should I Care? Ser.). 67p. pap. 8.00 *(978-0-687-65284-6(7))* Abingdon Pr.

Bible Prayer. 4.50 *(978-0-687-05162-5(2))* Abingdon Pr.

Boda, Mark, et al, eds. Seeking the Favor of God: Volume 2. 2007. 300p. per. 39.95 *(978-1-58983-278-7(7))* Society of Biblical Literature.

Boda, Mark J., et al, eds. Seeking the Favor of God. 2008. (SBL - Early Judaism & Its Literature Ser.). *(978-90-04-16914-2(8))* BRILL.

—Seeking the Favor of God: The Impact of Penitential Prayer beyond Second Temple Judaism. 2008. 324p. pap. 39.95 *(978-1-58983-389-0(9))* Society of Biblical Literature.

Boda, Mark J. & Falk, Daniel K., eds. Seeking the Favor of God. Volume 2: The Development of Penitential Prayer in Second Temple Jerusalem. 2007. (SBL - Early Judaism & Its Literature Ser.). 284p. *(978-90-04-15739-2(5))* BRILL.

Boda, Mark J., et al. Seeking the Favor of God. 2006. (Early Judaism & Its Literature Ser.: No. 21). 250p. *(978-90-04-15124-6(9))* BRILL.

—Seeking the Favor of God. 2006. 35.95 *(978-1-58983-261-9(2))* Society of Biblical Literature.

Bounds, Edward M. Prayer & Praying Men. 2007. (Authentic Original Classic Ser.). 191p. per. 13.99 *(978-0-7684-2546-8(8))* Destiny Image Pubs.

—Prayer & Praying Men. 2009. 164p. 36.95 *(978-1-104-42469-5(X))*; pap. 21.95 *(978-1-104-36665-0(7))* Kessinger Publishing, LLC.

Brueggemann, Walter. Great Prayers of the Old Testament. 2008. (ENG.). 176p. pap. 15.00 *(978-0-664-23174-3(8))* Westminster John Knox Pr.

Canham, Elizabeth. Praying the Bible. 128p. pap. 1.95 *(978-0-88028-231-4(2),* 1615) Forward Movement Pubns.

Claiborne, Shane & Wilson-Hartgrove, Jonathan. Becoming the Answer to Our Prayers: Prayer for Ordinary Radicals. 2008. (ENG.). 125p. pap. 13.00 *(978-0-8308-3622-2(5),* IVP Bks.) InterVarsity Pr.

Cottrell, Stephen. How to Pray: Alone, with Others, at Any Time, in Any Place. 3rd ed. 2010. (ENG.). xiv, 159p. pap. 13.99 *(978-0-7151-4222-6(4))* Church Hse. Publishing GBR. Dist: Westminster John Knox Pr.

Denny, Randal Earl. Where the Action Is: A Study of Acts 5 To 8. 2007. 126p. pap. 16.00 *(978-1-55635-384-0(7),* Wipf and Stock) Wipf & Stock Pubs.

Duplantis, Mark. The Constitution for the House of God. 2006. (ENG.). 64p. pap. 7.99 *(978-1-59979-016-9(5),* Creation Hse.) Charisma Media.

Earley, Dave. The 21 Most Effective Prayers of the Bible. 2008. (21 Most Ser.). (ENG.). 176p. pap. 4.99 *(978-1-60260-216-8(6),* Barbour Bks.) Barbour Publishing, Inc.

Greenberg, Moshe. Biblical Prose Prayer: As a Window to the Popular Religion of Ancient Israel. 2008. 76p. pap. 11.00 *(978-1-55635-111-2(9),* Wipf and Stock) Wipf & Stock Pubs.

Gutman, Ariel & Van Peursen, Wido. The Two Syriac Versions of the Prayer of Manasseh. 2011. 111.00 ***(978-1-4632-0050-3(1))*** Gorgias Pr., LLC.

Hairston, K. C. The Forgotten Rules of Prayer. 2006. (ENG.). 192p. per. 9.99 *(978-1-932805-85-7(0))* Authentic Media.

Holloway, Gary. Praying Dangerously: Daring Prayers for Meaningful Faith. 2010. (Illus.). 240p. pap. 14.99 *(978-0-89112-675-1(9),* Leafwood Pubs.) Abilene Christian Univ. Pr.

Hunt, Susan. Prayers of the Bible: Equipping Women to Call on God in Truth. 2011. pap. ***(978-1-59638-387-6(9))*** P & R Publishing.

Johnston, Louie, Jr. Prayers of the Bible: Study of the 184 Prayers from Ordinary people that God Answered. 2006. lib. bdg. 24.00 *(978-0-9659022-7-4(7))* Blue Wing Publishing.

—Prayers of the Bible Study Guide: Workbook. 2006. per. 12.00 *(978-0-9659022-8-1(5))* Blue Wing Publishing.

Kleinig, John W. Lord's Song: The Basis, Function & Significance of Choral Music in Chronicles. 2009. (Library of Hebrew Bible/Old Testament Studies, the Ser.). (ENG.). 236p. 39.95 *(978-0-567-02417-6(2),* T&T Clark) Continuum International Publishing Group, Ltd. GBR. Dist: National Bk. Network.

Law, Philip, ed. Praying with the Bible. 2007. (ENG.). 160p. 20.00 *(978-0-664-23272-6(8))* Westminster John Knox Pr.

Mark D. Spencer. A Portrait of Intercession. 2010. 152p. 26.94 *(978-1-4269-2267-1(1))* Trafford Publishing.

Merrill, Nan C. Psalms for Praying: An Invitation to Wholeness. 10th anniv. ed. 2006. (ENG.). 320p. 32.95 *(978-0-8264-1905-7(4))* Continuum International Publishing Group, Ltd. GBR. Dist: National Bk. Network.

Merrill, Nan C. & Merrill. Psalms for Praying: An Invitation to Wholeness. 10th anniv. ed. 2006. (ENG.). 320p. pap. 22.95 *(978-0-8264-1906-4(2))* Continuum International Publishing Group, Ltd. GBR. Dist: National Bk. Network.

Monroe, Irene. Let Your Light Shine Like a Rainbow Always: Meditations on Bible Prayers for Not-So-Everyday Moments. 2008. 402p. pap. 14.95 *(978-1-59350-077-1(7))* Alyson Pubns.

Morrow, William. Protest Against God: The Eclipse of a Bi. 2006. (ENG.). 264p. *(978-1-905048-20-5(3))* Sheffield Phoenix Pr.

—Protest Against God: The Eclipse of a Biblical Tradition. 2007. 264p. per. *(978-1-906055-34-9(3))* Sheffield Phoenix Pr.

Neita-Bailey, Brigette. Prayer Flames: The Effectual Fervent Prayer. 2011. 58p. 24.99 ***(978-1-4628-7334-0(0))***; pap. 15.99 ***(978-1-4628-7333-3(2))*** Xlibris Corp.

Pink, Arthur W. Gleanings from Paul. 2011. 274p. pap. 16.99 ***(978-1-61203-090-6(4))*** Bottom of the Hill Publishing.

—A Guide to Fervent Prayer. 2011. 148p. pap. 14.99 ***(978-1-61203-093-7(9))*** Bottom of the Hill Publishing.

Prince, Benny. Praying & Confessing Blessings from God's Word. 2008. 112p. per. 8.50 *(978-0-9801438-1-2(0))* Avid Readers Publishing Group.

Rankin, Jerry. In the Secret Place: A Pilgrimage through the Psalms, 1 vol. 2009. (ENG.). 352p. pap. 14.99 *(978-0-8054-4881-8(0),* B&H Bks.) B&H Publishing Group.

Saul, Stuart. Clearings Uncommon Words for Common Life. 2006. (ENG.). 25.99 *(978-1-60034-451-0(8))*; pap. 15.99 *(978-1-60034-450-3(X))* Xulon Pr., Inc.

Towns, Elmer L. Praying the Book of Acts: And the General Epistles. 2007. 227p. per. 15.99 *(978-0-7684-2493-5(3))* Destiny Image Pubs.

Wiles, Gordon P. Paul's Intercessory Prayers: The Significance of the Intercessory Prayer Passages in the Letters of St Paul. 2007. (Society for New Testament Studies Monograph Ser.). (ENG.). 364p. pap. 45.00 *(978-0-521-04835-4(4))* Cambridge Univ. Pr.

BIBLE—PRINTING

see Bible—History; Bible—Publication and Distribution

BIBLE—PROPHECIES

see also Apocalyptic Literature; Messiah—Prophecies; Prophets

Abdul-Malak, Michael. The Birth Pangs: An Obstetrician Unveils Jesus' Timeline for Earth's Final Travail. 2010. pap. 26.99 *(978-1-60799-403-9(8))* Tate Publishing & Enterprises, LLC.

Aigrain, René & Englebert, Omer. Prophecy Fulfilled: The Old Testament Realized in the New. Sheppard, Lancelot C., tr. 2011. 288p. 48.95 ***(978-1-258-09575-8(0))*** Literary Licensing, LLC.

American Bible Society Staff. Bible Prophecies: Faith, History & Hope. 2009. (ENG.). 128p. (YA). (gr. 8-17). 24.95 *(978-1-60320-068-4(1))* Time Home Entertainment, Inc.

Amoa-Kodie, Paulius. The Hidden Treasury. 2011. 62p. 24.99 ***(978-1-4535-7810-0(2))***; pap. 15.99 ***(978-1-4535-7809-4(9))*** Xlibris Corp.

Anderson, Ken/Ponder. The Answers Are Revealed: "About Aliens, Global Events, & Mankind's Future" Anderson, Auburn/Ponder, ed. 2007. pap. 15.95 *(978-0-9793906-4-7(8))* Beam Me Up Lord Publishing Hse.

—The Millennium Raptures Parable Episode I. 2007. pap. 15.95 *(978-0-9793906-0-9(5))* Beam Me Up Lord Publishing Hse.

—The Millennium Tribulation Parable Episode II. 2007. pap. 15.95 *(978-0-9793906-1-6(3))* Beam Me Up Lord Publishing Hse.

—The Millennium Trilogy in Three Parable Episodes. Anderson, Auburn/Ponder, ed. 2007. pap. 24.95 *(978-0-9793906-3-0(X))* Beam Me Up Lord Publishing Hse.

—The Next Millennium Parable Episode III: A Thousand Years Living in the New Earth & Heaven & Lucifer's Final Return. Anderson, Auburn/Ponder, ed. 2007. pap. *(978-0-9793906-2-3(1))* Beam Me Up Lord Publishing Hse.

—The Trinity of God's Living Truth Manuscripts 2012 (or Later?) Prophecy of Regeneration & Renewal World Without End. Anderson, Auburn/Ponder, ed. 2010. Orig. Title: 2010. 132p. pap. 19.95 *(978-0-9793906-9-2(9))* Beam Me Up Lord Publishing Hse.

Andrews Sr., James R. Your Sons & Daughters Shall Prophesy, 1 vol. 2009. 48p. pap. 16.95 *(978-1-60749-277-1(6))* PublishAmerica, Inc.

Ankerberg, John, et al. Israel under Fire: The Prophetic Chain of Events That Threatens the Middle East. 2009. 224p. pap. 13.99 *(978-0-7369-2584-6(8))* Harvest Hse. Pubs.

Aquino, Leora. Heart to Heart Talk with Abba: Why my Lord Is this Happening? 2007. 575p. pap. *(978-0-9794966-0-8(8))* Aquino, Larissa.

Assaf, Bruce. Behind the Veil of Radical Islam. 2007. 112p. per. *(978-1-55452-252-1(8))* Essence Publishing.

Baker, Todd Damon. Messengers of Messiah. 2006. pap. 13.99 *(978-1-60034-398-8(8))* Xulon Pr., Inc.

Bakley, Kurt B. Prophecies that Have, Will, or Didn't Happen. 2011. 64p. pap. 15.49 *(978-1-4567-1262-4(4))* AuthorHouse.

Banger, Dene. The Spirit of Prophecy. 2009. 642p. pap. 23.99 *(978-1-4415-3012-7(6))* Xlibris Corp.

Barber, Allen M. The Day of the Lord, the Key to Understanding End-Time Prophecy: A Critical Examination of Pretribulationism. 2011. pap. 29.99 ***(978-1-61777-167-5(8))*** Tate Publishing & Enterprises, LLC.

Barnes, James. Unveiling of the Middleman: The Truth about Prophecy. 2011. 80p. pap. 20.11 *(978-1-4567-2383-5(9))* AuthorHouse.

Barnhart, David. Living in the Times of the Signs. 2007. 492p. (ENG.). 35.99 *(978-1-60477-052-0(X))*; per. 23.99 *(978-1-60477-051-3(1))* Xulon Pr., Inc.

Basic bible Prophecy. 2006. pap. 13.99 *(978-1-60034-413-8(5))* Xulon Pr., Inc.

Beck, Kevin A. This Book Will Change Your World: How All Things Become New. 2009. pap. 16.95 *(978-1-934049-04-4(2))* Bimillennial Pr.

Bene Yeshua. The Book of Masahel. 2007. 120p. pap. 9.95 *(978-0-9796799-0-2(7))* Bene Yeshua Temple.

Bennett, David Malcolm. The Origins of Left Behind Eschatology. 2010. 418p. pap. 22.99 *(978-1-61579-667-0(3))* Xulon Pr., Inc.

Berry, James R. What We See from Afar. 2008. 152p. pap. 13.99 *(978-1-60647-445-7(6))* Xulon Pr., Inc.

Beshore, F. Kenton & Keller, R. William. When? When Will the Rapture Take Place? 2011. 320p. 32.95 *(978-1-4502-8871-2(5))*; pap. 22.95 *(978-1-4502-8870-5(7))* iUniverse, Inc.

Black, Harry. The Four Horses of the Apocalypse & Other Expositions on Revelation, Chapters 1-8. 2011. 38p. 35.95 ***(978-1-258-04308-7(4))*** Literary Licensing, LLC.

Blanco, Jack J. Visions & Dreams: Hope for the Future, Courage for Today: A Fresh Look at Daniel & Revelation. 2010. pap. 6.99 *(978-0-8127-0478-5(9))* Autumn Hse. Publishing Co.

Bloise, Remo Capra. The Shape. 2007. 44p. per. 17.95 *(978-1-4327-0505-3(9))* Outskirts Pr., Inc.

Bock, Stephen R. Symbols of Revelation. 2008. 273p. per. 15.99 *(978-1-60247-836-7(8))* Tate Publishing & Enterprises, LLC.

Boersma, David. Prophets of the Bible. 2008. 388p. 29.99 *(978-1-4257-3849-5(4))*; pap. 19.99 *(978-1-4257-3848-8(6))* Xlibris Corp.

Bondar, Alan. Reading the Bible Through New Covenant Eyes, 1 vol. 2010. 336p. pap. 29.95 *(978-1-4489-8428-2(9))* PublishAmerica, Inc.

Booker, Richard. The End of All Things Is at Hand: Are You Ready? 2009. 242p. pap. 15.99 *(978-0-88270-615-3(2))* Bridge-Logos Foundation.

Breshears, Jason M. When the Sun Darkens. 2009. 128p. pap. 14.95 *(978-1-58509-117-1(0))* Book Tree, The.

Briggs, Charles August. Messianic Prophecy the Prediction of the. 2006. pap. 42.95 *(978-1-4286-4207-2(2))* Kessinger Publishing, LLC.

Brown, C. E. Two Witnesses. 2008. 237p. pap. 19.95 *(978-1-60563-201-8(5))* PublishAmerica, Inc.

Brown, Randy. Apostolic Insight into the Prophetic: Identify the Prophet in You. 2007. 424p. per. 26.95 *(978-0-595-46605-4(2))* iUniverse, Inc.

Brownfield, D., David E., Th. How It All Ends. 2007. 73p. pap. 14.95 *(978-1-4241-9752-1(X))* PublishAmerica, Inc.

Brubacher, Willis S. To Seal up Vision & Prophecy. 2009. 296p. pap. 15.49 *(978-1-4389-5988-7(5))* AuthorHouse.

btmi.org, www. & E. Wolfe, Evangelist Larry. The People of the Apocalypse. 2007. 317p. pap. 17.50 *(978-0-615-17103-6(6))* Wolfe, Larry E.

Bullinger, Ethelbert. Commentary on Revelation: Or, the Apocalypse. 2007. 752p. per. 21.95 *(978-1-60206-112-5(2))* Cosimo, Inc.

Bynoe, Keithlind . R. E. What Is the Time? 2007. 288p. per. 15.99 *(978-1-60477-297-5(2))* Xulon Pr., Inc.

Campbell, Stacey & Campbell, Wesley. Ecstatic Prophecy. 2008. 256p. pap. 19.00 *(978-0-8007-9449-1(4))* Chosen Bks.

Carfrey, Daniel R. The Mysterious Disappearance: Why the Pre-Tribulation Rapture Is A Fundamental Doctrine of Biblical Prophecy. 2008. 68p. pap. 9.99 *(978-1-60647-683-3(1))* Xulon Pr., Inc.

Carroll, Robert P. When Prophecy Failed: Reactions & Responses to Failure in the Old Testament Prophetic Traditions. 2011. 256p. ***(978-1-85931-045-8(1),*** SCM Pr.) Hymns Ancient & Modern Ltd.

Chapman, Jimmie L. Armageddon Is Approaching. 2010. 278p. pap. 23.96 *(978-0-557-33736-1(4))* Lulu Enterprises Inc.

—Entering the Great Tribulation. 2009. 122p. pap. 16.99 *(978-0-557-10807-7(1))* Lulu Enterprises Inc.

—The Visions of Daniel. 2009. pap. 16.99 *(978-1-60799-058-1(X))* Tate Publishing & Enterprises, LLC.

Cherol, Christina. Let the Reader Understand Matthew 24:15. 2006. 159p. pap. 24.95 *(978-1-4241-4045-9(5))* PublishAmerica, Inc.

Chris Sandoval. The Failure of Bible Prophecy: A Skeptic's Review of the Evidence. 2010. 196p. pap. 14.99 *(978-1-4269-2383-8(X))* Trafford Publishing.

Cobb, Tyrone W. The Beginning & the End. 2009. 214p. pap. 15.99 *(978-1-61579-077-7(2))* Xulon Pr., Inc.

Cohen, Tim. Messiah, History, & the Tribulation Period Vol. 2, Vol. 3: The Prophetic Stage: Signs of the Times. Cohen, Tim, ed. 2006. pap. *(978-0-9662793-3-7(6))* Prophecy House, Inc.

—Messiah, History, & the Tribulation Period Vol. 3: Conflict of the Aeons: Understanding the Protoevangelium (Genesis 3:15) Cohen, Tim, ed. 2006. pap. *(978-0-9662793-4-4(4))* Prophecy House, Inc.

—Messiah, History, & the Tribulation Period Vol. 4: Biblical Chronology: the Young Creation. Cohen, Tim, ed. 2006. pap. *(978-0-9662793-5-1(2))* Prophecy House, Inc.

—Messiah, History, & the Tribulation Period Vol. 5: The Real Rapture & Other Prophetic Mysteries: Understanding the Revelation (Apocalypse) Cohen, Tim, ed. 2006. (Illus.). pap. *(978-0-9662793-6-8(0))* Prophecy House, Inc.

Collins, Anthony. A Discourse of the Grounds & Reasons of the Christian Religion. 2009. 182p. pap. *(978-1-150-42289-8(0))* Books LLC.

Congdon, Robert. The European Union & the Supra-Religion. 2007. 296p. per. 15.99 *(978-1-60266-679-5(2))* Xulon Pr., Inc.

Connelly, Douglas. Bible Prophecy & End Times. 2009. (Indispensable Guide to Practically Everything Ser.). (ENG., Illus.). 256p. pap. 15.99 *(978-0-8249-4772-9(X),* Guideposts) Ideals Pubns.

Connor, John. Diamonds for the Bride. 2008. 536p. 63.50 *(978-1-84799-173-7(4))* Lulu Enterprises Inc.

Coombe, Doug. America's Bitter End in Prophecy. 2008. 240p. per. *(978-1-55452-239-2(0),* Guardian Bks.) Essence Publishing.

Cox, Clyde C. Prophetical Events & the Great Tribulation: A Study of Prophecy in Revelation. 2011. 126p. 40.95 ***(978-1-258-08749-4(9))*** Literary Licensing, LLC.

Criswell, David. Controversies in the Prophets: Isaiah through Malachi. 2007. (ENG.). 558p. pap. 14.95 *(978-1-4196-7204-0(5))* CreateSpace.

Crone, Billy. The Final Countdown. 2010. 288p. pap. 14.52 *(978-0-615-25027-4(0))* Get a Life! International.

Daniele, Elizabeth. Revelation & Bible Prophecy Syr. 2009. 248p. pap. 15.38 *(978-0-557-16354-0(4))* Lulu Enterprises Inc.

Daniels, Thomas A. The Last 4 Visions of Daniel: Some Startling Revelations. 2007. (Illus.). 320p. per. 22.99 *(978-1-59886-775-6(X))* Tate Publishing & Enterprises, LLC.

Darden, John S. A Walk Through Bible Prophecy. 2010. 139p. pap. 11.01 *(978-0-557-00627-4(9))* Lulu Enterprises Inc.

—A Walk Through Revelation. 2010. 150p. pap. 10.98 *(978-0-557-00632-8(5))* Lulu Enterprises Inc.

Darter, Francis M. Zion's Redemption: The Church of Jesus Christ of Latter Day Saints. 2007. (ENG.). 232p. 41.95 *(978-0-548-04870-2(3))* Kessinger Publishing, LLC.

Davis, Cecelia G. Death of a World: Time Is Running Out. 2008. 310p. per. 18.95 *(978-0-9793146-2-9(3))* Cecelia Enterprises.

Davis, David. The Elijah Legacy. 2007. (ENG., Illus.). 300p. pap. 14.95 *(978-981-04-9721-7(0))* Word Prodns.

Davis, Ellen F. Swallowing the Scroll: Textuality & the Dynamics of Discourse in Ezekiel's Prophecy. 2009. (Library of Hebrew Bible/Old Testament Studies, the Ser.). (ENG.). 184p. 29.95 *(978-1-4411-4299-3(1),* T&T Clark) Continuum International Publishing Group, Ltd. GBR. Dist: National Bk. Network.

Davis, James L. Unveiling Revelation: The Prophetic Visions of St. John of Patmos. 2009. 228p. pap. 15.99 *(978-1-60791-185-2(X))* Xulon Pr., Inc.

Deakins, Billy Lemmon & Deakins, John R. The Beasts of Prophecy. 2011. 446p. pap. 19.99 ***(978-1-61720-285-8(1))*** Wilder Pubns., Ltd.

Dieleman, Jaap. The Coming of the King of Kings. 2007. (ENG.). 240p. per. 14.99 *(978-1-60266-100-4(6))* Xulon Pr., Inc.

Douglass, Herbert E. Red Alert: Hurtling into Eternity: Interpreting Today's Headlines in Light of Bible Prophecy. 2011. pap. 15.99 ***(978-0-8163-2488-0(3))*** Pacific Pr. Publishing Assn.

Duck, Daymond. Prophecies of the Bible, 0 vols. 2007. (Smart Guide to the Bible Ser.). (Illus.). 352p. per. 14.99 *(978-1-4185-0995-8(7))* Nelson, Thomas Inc.

—Return from Exile, 0 vols. Richards, Larry, ed. 2008. (Smart Guide to the Bible Ser.). (Illus.). 384p. per. 14.99 *(978-1-4185-1004-6(1))* Nelson, Thomas Inc.

Dumond, Joseph F. The Prophecies of Abraham: Declaring the end from the beginning, & from ancient times things that are not yet Done. 2010. (Illus.). 244p. pap. 60.99 *(978-1-4490-4752-8(1))* AuthorHouse.

Edelman, Diana Vikander & Ben Zvi, Ehud, eds. The Production of Prophecy: Constructing Prophecy & Prophets in Yehud. 2009. (BibleWorld Ser.). (ENG.). 224p. (C). 99.95 *(978-1-84553-499-8(9))*; pap. 39.95 *(978-1-84553-500-1(6))* Equinox Publishing Ltd. GBR. Dist: ISD.

Edghill, Ernest Arthur. Inquiry into the Evidential Value of Pro. 2006. pap. 48.95 *(978-1-4286-4369-7(9))* Kessinger Publishing, LLC.

Edior, Rev. Martin. Prophetic Messages & Predictions. 2011. 70p. pap. 15.99 ***(978-1-4628-6399-0(X))*** Xlibris Corp.

EDWARDS, Larry D. The Mystery Revealed! A Commentary on the Book of Revelation in the Holy Bible. 2008. 480p. 35.99 *(978-1-60647-728-1(5))*; pap. 23.99 *(978-1-60647-727-4(7))* Xulon Pr., Inc.

Ennis, Perry. Prepare for the Coming of Mess. 2007. 451p. pap. 17.77 *(978-0-9796887-3-7(6))* Menorah Bks. LLC.

Evans, John S. The Prophecies of Daniel. 2008. 280p. 25.99 *(978-1-60477-904-2(7))* Xulon Pr., Inc.

—The Prophecies of Daniel 2. 2008. 280p. pap. 15.99 *(978-1-60477-903-5(9))* Xulon Pr., Inc.

Fairbarn, Patrick. Profecia: Naturaleza, Funcion E: Biblical Prophecy. (SPA.). 384p. *(978-84-7228-935-2(4),* 223059) Clie, Editorial.

Falkenberg, Lorence A. The Last Chapter. 2008. 176p. 21.99 *(978-1-60647-220-0(8))*; pap. 13.99 *(978-1-60647-219-4(4))* Xulon Pr., Inc.

Ferguson, Larry. Red River Rising. 2007. 320p. (ENG.). 27.99 *(978-1-60477-195-4(X))*; per. 17.99 *(978-1-60477-194-7(1))* Xulon Pr., Inc.

Finley, Robert. The Time Is at Hand. 2008. 308p. pap. 18.99 *(978-1-60791-026-8(8))* Xulon Pr., Inc.

Fletcher, Jim & Fletcher, Jim F. It's the End of the World as We Know It (And I Feel Fine) How to Stop Worrying & Learn to Love These End Times. 2009. (ENG., Illus.). 224p. pap. 14.99 *(978-1-59979-472-3(1))* Charisma Media.

Flowers, Doyle W., Jr. Jesus Really Is Coming Back... Soon! 2008. (Illus.). 112p. pap. 16.95 *(978-1-60743-764-2(3))* Operation GoTo Pr., LLC.

Ford, James Stuart. Israel: God's Time Clock! 2008. 88p. pap. 9.99 *(978-1-60477-867-0(9))* Xulon Pr., Inc.

Foster, Ronald. The Plight of the Jew. 2007. 13.00 *(978-0-8059-8852-9(1))* Dorrance Publishing Co., Inc.

Frederick, William. The Coming Epiphany. 2007. 244p. pap. 15.95 *(978-1-4303-1383-0(8))* Lulu Enterprises Inc.

Froese, Arno. How Democracy Will Elect the Antichrist. 2nd rev. ed. 2008. (Illus.). 349p. 17.95 *(978-0-937422-64-9(9),* Olive Pr., The) Midnight Call.

—Preparing for the Mark of the Beast. 2006. 240p. 16.95 *(978-0-937422-63-2(0),* Olive Pr., The) Midnight Call.

Furguson, Barbara. Call Me Ann. 2007. 152p. per. *(978-1-906210-45-8(4))* Grosvenor Hse. Publishing Ltd.

Gamboa, Efren M. America Because I Have Loved You, I Have Made You Rich! The Inevitable Truth of America Bible Prophecy 2012 666. 2011. 144p. 31.23 ***(978-1-4634-0147-4(7))***; pap. 20.68 ***(978-1-4634-0148-1(5))*** AuthorHouse.

Gansle, Daniel J. Your World, Your Future, & Bible Prophecy. 2007. 275p. pap. 16.95 *(978-0-7414-4328-1(7))* Infinity Publishing.

Gaunt, Bonnie. The Great Prophetic Design: Found in Africa. 2009. (Bible Code Ser.). (Illus.). 146p. pap. 12.95 *(978-1-931882-97-2(5))* Adventures Unlimited Pr.

Gentry, Kenneth L., Jr. The Charismatic Gift of Prophecy. 170p. (Orig.). pap. 9.95 *(978-1-877818-06-6(2))* Footstool Pubns.

Gerbasi, Jerome. Prophetic Harmony of the Lamp of God. 2006. pap. 17.99 *(978-1-60034-604-0(9))* Xulon Pr., Inc.

Gerner, Terri J. The One Deadly Mistake... We All Make: No Subtitle. 2008. 212p. pap. 14.99 *(978-1-60647-242-2(9))* Xulon Pr., Inc.

Gillispie, Mary Ann. Endtime Reapers. 2008. 456p. pap. 27.99 *(978-1-4251-4072-4(6))* Trafford Publishing.

Glas, Gerrit, et al, eds. Hearing Visions & Seeing Voices: Psychological Aspects of Biblical Concepts & Personalities. 2007. (ENG., Illus.). xviii, 326p. 149.00 *(978-1-4020-5938-4(6)*, 1402059388) Springer.
Glaub, Garry. Here Am I! Send Me. 2007. 444p. (ENG.). 33.99 *(978-1-60477-410-8(X))*; per. 21.99 *(978-1-60477-389-7(8))* Xulon Pr., Inc.
God's Definition of Revelation: Revelation 10.4, Daniel 12.4. (Illus.). 13p. pap. *(978-0-9714351-0-0(3))* Shaw, John R.
Golightly Marshall, Brian Leonard. The Strawman Burneth. 2008. 496p. pap. 26.95 *(978-1-4092-2056-5(7))* Lulu Enterprises Inc.
González, Ann Camelia. Aunt Laura's Prophecies: God Speaks to His People, 1 vol. 2010. 192p. pap. 24.95 *(978-1-4489-4216-9(0))* PublishAmerica, Inc.
Goodwin, Samuel. Just How Dumb Do You Think I Am? 2008. 192p. pap. 13.99 *(978-1-60477-673-7(0))* Xulon Pr., Inc.
Grabbe, Lester L. & Nissinen, Martti. Constructs of Prophecy in the Former & Latter Prophets & Other Texts. 2011. ***(978-1-58983-600-6(6))***; ***(978-1-58983-599-3(9))*** Society of Biblical Literature.
Gray, Larry S. & Hart, Michael J. The Armageddon Project: Tales from the Kingdom Hall. 2009. 451p. pap. 18.95 *(978-1-4327-5014-5(3))* Outskirts Pr., Inc.
Green, Michael, Sr. The Last Hour 6. 2006. (ENG.). 116p. per. 13.95 *(978-1-59800-742-8(4))* Outskirts Pr., Inc.
Gregersen, Paul & Cook, Edmund. Bible Prophecies Of 9-11. 2007. 324p. per. 20.99 *(978-1-60477-029-2(5))* Xulon Pr., Inc.
Gribben Crawford & Shenton, Tim. The Life of Rowland Hill: 'The Second Whitefield' 2006. (Emmaus Ser.). (Illus.). 144p. per. *(978-0-85234-610-5(7))* Evangelical Pr.
Guest, Glenn. Steps Toward the Mark of the Beast. 2007. 160p. per. *(978-1-55452-187-6(4)*, Guardian Bks.) Essence Publishing.
Guest, Glenn A. Steps Toward the Mark of the Beast. 2007. pap. *(978-1-55452-188-3(2))* Essence Publishing.
Guinness, H. Grattan. Romanism & the Reformation: From the Standpoint of Prophecy. 2009. 408p. pap. 33.00 *(978-1-55635-618-6(8)*, Wipf and Stock) Wipf & Stock Pubs.
Hagee, John. Can America Survive? 10 Prophetic Signs That We Are the Terminal Generation. l.t. ed. 2011. (ENG.). 547p. pap. 17.99 *(978-1-59415-373-0(6))* Cengage Gale.
—Can America Survive? 10 Prophetic Signs That We Are the Terminal Generation. 2010. (ENG.). 288p. 22.99 *(978-1-4391-8985-6(4)*, Howard Bks.) Howard Books.
—Can America Survive? Updated Edition: Startling Revelations & Promises of Hope. 2011. (ENG.). 320p. pap. 14.99 *(978-1-4391-9056-2(9)*, Howard Bks.) Howard Books.
—Earth's Final Moments. 2011. ***(978-1-61638-596-5(0))***; E-Book ***(978-1-61638-574-3(X))*** Charisma Media. (Charisma Hse.).
—Financial Armageddon: What You Must Do to Survive the Devastation of an Economic Collapse! 2008. (ENG.). 144p. pap. 10.99 *(978-1-59979-603-1(1)*, Frontline) Charisma Media.
—Jerusalem Countdown: A Prelude to War. rev. exp. ed. 2006. (ENG.). 272p. pap. 14.99 *(978-1-59979-089-3(0)*, Frontline) Charisma Media.
—Knowing the Secrets of God, 0 vols. 2008. 324p. pap. 17.99 *(978-0-8499-2886-4(9))* Nelson, Thomas Inc.
Hairfield, Steven. Metaphysical Interpretation of the Bible. 2006. 808p. 39.95 *(978-0-9720080-5-1(5))* InnerCircle Publishing.
Hamilton, Gavin. Maranatha. (SPA.). 162p. *(978-84-7228-003-8(9)*, 220572) Clie, Editorial.
Hammond, Edmund Berkeley. Understanding Bible Prophecy. 2011. 148p. pap. 14.95 ***(978-1-4620-2120-8(4))*** iUniverse, Inc.
Hartman, Roger. Unfolding the Mysteries of Revelation. 2010. 228p. pap. 15.99 *(978-1-60957-479-6(6))* Xulon Pr., Inc.
Hathaway, David. Babylon in Europe: What Bible Prophecy Reveals about the European Union. 2006. 74p. pap. *(978-1-903725-82-5(8))* New Wine Pr.
Hayden, Timothy John. The Vision by the Tigris. 2006. (ENG.). 248p. per. 18.95 *(978-1-57258-446-4(7)*, 945-6307) TEACH Services, Inc.
Hayes, Norvel. The Reality of Prophecy & Visions. pap. 1.00 *(978-0-89274-098-7(1))* Harrison House Pubs.
Hayford, Jack W. Revelation, 0 vols. 2008. (Spirit-Filled Life Study Guide Ser.). 128p. pap. 9.99 *(978-1-4185-3330-4(0))* Nelson, Thomas Inc.
Heiks, Heidi. The Daily Source Book. 2008. 220p. pap. 16.95 *(978-1-57258-558-4(7))* TEACH Services, Inc.
Hellen, John. The Bible Is No Fairy Tale! The Compelling Evidence Proving the Bible to be God's True & Inspired Word. 2009. 236p. pap. 12.99 *(978-1-60799-029-1(6))* Tate Publishing & Enterprises, LLC.
Hemenway, Harold. European History Foretold. 2007. 204p. per. 14.99 *(978-1-60266-796-9(9))* Xulon Pr., Inc.
Hengstenberg, E. W. Christology of the Old Testament, 2 Volumes. 2008. 1396p. pap. 118.00 *(978-1-55635-739-8(7)*, Wipf and Stock) Wipf & Stock Pubs.
Herbers, M. James. This Generation of the Latter Days, Volume I Dispensationalism & God's Original Purpose of Creation. 2011. 264p. pap. 18.00 ***(978-0-557-89677-6(0))*** Lulu Enterprises Inc.
Hershey, Lori O'Mel. Fast Approaching. 2009. 188p. pap. 19.99 *(978-1-4343-6363-3(5))* AuthorHouse.
Hickson, Rachel. Eat the Word, Speak the Word: Exercising a Bible-Based Prophetic Ministry, 1 vol. 2010. 192p. pap. 14.99 *(978-1-85424-971-5(1)*, Monarch Bks.) Lion Hudson PLC GBR. Dist: Kregel Pubns.
Hitchcock, Mark. The Amazing Claims of Bible Prophecy: What You Need to Know in These Uncertain Times. 2010. 240p. pap. 13.99 *(978-0-7369-2645-4(3))* Harvest Hse. Pubs.
—Cashless: Bible Prophecy, Economic Chaos, & the Future Financial Order. 2009. (Illus.). 224p. pap. 13.99 *(978-0-7369-2644-7(5))* Harvest Hse. Pubs.
—Iran: the Coming Crisis: Radical Islam, Oil, & the Nuclear Threat. 2006. (ENG.). 224p. pap. 13.99 *(978-1-59052-764-1(X)*, Multnomah) Doubleday Religious Publishing Group, The.
—The Late Great United States: What Bible Prophecy Reveals about America's Last Days. l.t. ed. 2010. (ENG.). pap. 17.99 *(978-1-59415-337-2(X))* Cengage Gale.
—The Late Great United States: What Bible Prophecy Reveals about America's Last Days. 2010. (ENG.). 208p. pap. 14.99 *(978-1-60142-141-8(9)*, Multnomah) Doubleday Religious Publishing Group, The.
—The Late Great United States: What Bible Prophecy Reveals about America's Last Days. l.t. ed. 2010. (ENG.). 30.99 *(978-1-4104-2720-5(X))* Thorndike Pr.
—Middle East Burning. 2012. 256p. pap. 13.99 ***(978-0-7369-3996-6(2))*** Harvest Hse. Pubs.
—What on Earth Is Going On? 2006. 128p. pap. 7.99 *(978-1-60142-042-8(0)*, Multnomah) Doubleday Religious Publishing Group, The.
—2012, the Bible, & the End of the World. 2009. 192p. pap. 12.99 *(978-0-7369-2651-5(8))* Harvest Hse. Pubs.
Hodge, Kent. Rediscovering Revelation: I Will Build My Church. 2011. 156p. 28.99 ***(978-1-4634-1272-2(X))***; pap. 15.49 ***(978-1-4634-1273-9(8))*** AuthorHouse.
Hoffman, Kimber. Ancient Prophecies, Current Headlines. 2007. 152p. per. 13.95 *(978-1-57258-463-1(7)*, 945-6324) TEACH Services, Inc.
Hospers, Gerrit Hendrik. The Principle of Spiritualization in Hermeneutics. 2011. 54p. 36.95 ***(978-1-258-04991-1(0))*** Literary Licensing, LLC.
Howe, Thomas A. Daniel in the Preterists' Den: A Critical Look at Preterist Interpretations of Daniel. 2008. 742p. pap. 77.00 *(978-1-55635-273-7(5)*, Wipf and Stock) Wipf & Stock Pubs.
Hrubik, Vladimir. When They Say Peace Seek Shelter: The Road to Evade the Antichrist. 2009. 384p. pap. 19.99 *(978-1-4389-3342-9(8))* AuthorHouse.
Hubbard, R. Dean. Letter to Israel: God's Countdown for Mankind. 2006. (ENG., Illus.). 352p. pap. 16.99 *(978-1-59185-991-8(3)*, Creation Hse.) Charisma Media.
Hull, Robert. Welcome to Planet Earth - 2050 - Population Zero. 2011. 464p. pap. 20.23 ***(978-1-4634-2604-0(6))*** AuthorHouse.
Hunt, David. Countdown to the Second Coming: A Chronology of Prophetic Earth Events Happening Now. 2007. (ENG.). 96p. per. 7.99 *(978-1-928660-19-4(3))* Berean Call, The.
Hurd, Richard. An Introduction to the Study of the Prophecies Concerning the Christian Church, And In Particular, Concerning the Church of Papal Rome. 2006. pap. 31.95 *(978-1-4286-4696-4(5))* Kessinger Publishing, LLC.
Iacono, Fred Paul Dello. The Jonah Prophecies. 2011. 742p. 34.99 ***(978-1-4568-3152-3(6))***; pap. 23.99 ***(978-1-4568-3151-6(8))*** Xlibris Corp.
Is Truth Relative or Objective? 2008. pap. *(978-0-9789909-5-4(1))* True-Way Tracts.
Isaac Newton. Observations upon the Prophecies of Daniel & the Apocalypse of St John. 2011. 204p. pap. 5.89 ***(978-1-60386-402-2(4)***, Watchmaker Publishing) Wexford College Pr.
James, John. Get Ready! It'll Be Painful! Prepare for Persecution! 2009. 58p. pap. 10.00 *(978-0-692-00451-7(3))* James, John.
—Hijackers of Biblical Prophecy: Doctrines & Trends Countering Jesus' Imminent Return. 2008. 67p. per. 10.00 net. *(978-0-615-17945-2(2))* James, John.
James, Zealous. Where Will You Spend Eternity. 2009. 388p. pap. 20.99 *(978-1-60791-111-1(6))* Xulon Pr., Inc.
JANZEN, Waldemar. Mark of the Beast, Trumpets & Armageddon. 2009. 123p. pap. 17.92 *(978-0-557-06172-3(5))* Lulu Enterprises Inc.
Jeffrey. Armageddon: Appointment with Destiny. pap. 12.95 *(978-0-921714-00-2(9))* Spring Arbor Distributors, Inc.
Jeffrey, Grant R. Countdown to the Apocalypse: Learn to Read the Signs That the Last Days Have Begun. 2008. (ENG., Illus.). 240p. pap. 13.99 *(978-1-4000-7441-9(X)*, WaterBrook Pr.) Doubleday Religious Publishing Group, The.
—The New Temple & the Second Coming: The Prophecy That Points to Christ's Return in Your Generation. 2007. (ENG., Illus.). 224p. pap. 13.99 *(978-1-4000-7107-4(0)*, WaterBrook Pr.) Doubleday Religious Publishing Group, The.
Jeremiah, David. The Coming Economic Armageddon: What Bible Prophecy Warns about the New Global Economy. (ENG.). 2011. 320p. pap., pap. 14.99 *(978-0-446-56593-6(8))* 2010. (Illus.). 320p. 23.99 *(978-0-446-56594-3(6))* 2010. 496p. 25.99 *(978-0-446-57415-0(5))* FaithWords.
—What in the World Is Going On? 10 Prophetic Clues You Cannot Afford to Ignore. l.t. ed. 2010. (ENG.). 384p. pap. 17.99 *(978-1-59415-334-1(5))* Cengage Gale.
—What in the World Is Going On? 10 Prophetic Clues You Cannot Afford to Ignore, 0 vols. 2010. 288p. pap. 15.99 *(978-0-7852-3117-2(X))* Nelson, Thomas Inc.
Jeremiah, David & Carlson, C. C. The Handwriting on the Wall, 0 vols. 2008. 144p. pap. 14.99 *(978-0-7852-9690-4(5))* Nelson, Thomas Inc.
Jindo, Job Y. Biblical Metaphor Reconsidered: A Cognitive Approach to Poetic Prophecy in Jeremiah 1-24. 2010. 39.95 *(978-1-57506-936-4(9))* Eisenbrauns, Inc.
Johnson, Barton Warren. A Vision of the Ages: Or the Lectures on the Apocalypse. 2011. 362p. 51.95 ***(978-1-258-01302-8(9))*** Literary Licensing, LLC.
Johnson, Dwight. Journey into Time. 2006. 244p. per. 14.95 *(978-1-57258-452-5(1)*, 945-6313) TEACH Services, Inc.
Joyner, Rick. Taking the Land Part 1. 2009. 170p. pap. 9.99 *(978-1-59933-826-2(2))* MorningStar Pubns., Inc.
kallen, stuart. Prophecies & Soothsayers. 2011. (Mysterious & Unknown Ser.). (Illus.). 80p. (YA). (gr. 7-12). lib. bdg. 27.95 *(978-1-60152-184-2(7))* ReferencePoint Pr., Inc.
Kaltner, John & Kaltner. Inspired Speech: Prophecy in the Ancient near East Essays in Honor of Herbert B. Huffmon. Stulman, Louis, ed. 2008. (Library of Hebrew Bible/Old Testament Studies, the Ser.). (ENG., Illus.). 450p. 55.00 *(978-0-567-04569-0(2)*, T&T Clark Int'l) Continuum International Publishing Group, Ltd. GBR. Dist: National Bk. Network.
Kaltner, John & Stulman, Louis, eds. Inspired Speech: Prophecy in the Ancient near East Essays in Honor of Herbert B. Huffmon: 378. 2008. (Library of Hebrew Bible/Old Testament Studies, the Ser.). 448p. *(978-0-567-03395-6(3)*, T&T Clark) Continuum International Publishing Group, Ltd.
Kaplan, Jacob H. Psychology of Prophecy: A Study of the Prophetic Mind as Manifested by the Ancient Hebrew Prophets. 2007. 68.00 *(978-1-59333-743-8(4))* Gorgias Pr., LLC.
Keehus, Magnus N. Jesus: Is He the Messiah of Israel? ÒWho will Declare His Generation?Ó A Dialogue Based on the Tanakh, Talmud, & Targumim; the Dead Sea Scrolls; & the New Testament. 2011. 308p. pap. 34.00 *(978-1-60899-825-8(8)*, Wipf and Stock) Wipf & Stock Pubs.
Keith, Alexander. Evidence of the Truth of the Christian Religion Derived from the Literal Fulfillment of Prophecy. 2009. 286p. pap. 34.99 *(978-1-113-99889-7(X))* BiblioBazaar.
Kennedy, W. H. The Last Great War. 2011. 112p. pap. 11.95 *(978-1-4497-1405-5(6)*, WestBow Pr.) Author Solutions, Inc.
King, Dr. Dorothy. The Seven Seals of Revelation. 2007. 336p. pap. 32.50 *(978-1-4116-4349-9(6))* Lulu Enterprises Inc.
King, Eljay. Israel, a Different Version: An Extensive Study of Prophecy. 2008. 124p. pap. 10.99 *(978-1-60647-046-6(9))* Xulon Pr., Inc.
Kinsella, Jack. The Last Generation: Ten Signs of the End of the Age. 2007. (ENG.). 240p. pap. 15.99 *(978-0-9767811-8-9(2)*, TPPress) True Potential Publishing, Inc.
Kleiner, Edward. The Indestructible Jew: The Real Truth about Anti-Semitism. 2006. *(978-0-9779189-5-9(5))* Waldenhouse Pubs., Inc.
Kling, Peter. Letters to Earth You Can Survive Armageddon! 2009. 360p. 29.95 *(978-1-60911-033-8(1)*, Eloquent Bks.) AEG Literary Publishing Services, Inc.
Knezacek, Daniel. The Spirit of Prophecy: A Groundbreaking New Analysis of the Bible's End-Times Prophecies. 2011. 376p. pap. 24.95 *(978-1-4502-7793-8(4))* iUniverse, Inc.
Knight, George R. The Apocalyptic Vision & the Neutering of Adventism. 2008. pap. 10.99 *(978-0-8280-2385-6(9))* Review & Herald Publishing Assn.
Kramer, W. P. Revelation Exposed Plain & Simple: The Rapture or the Tribulation: Is There Really A Choice. 2010. 400p. pap. 21.95 *(978-1-4327-5017-6(8))* Outskirts Pr., Inc.
LaHaye, Tim. Understanding Bible Prophecy for Yourself. 2009. (Tim LaHaye Prophecy Library). 256p. pap. 14.99 *(978-0-7369-2538-9(4))* Harvest Hse. Pubs.
Lang, Dean. Is This the End? 2011. 294p. 29.99 ***(978-1-4568-7447-6(0))***; pap. 19.99 ***(978-1-4568-7446-9(2))*** Xlibris Corp.
Lateer, Andrew James. Maranatha: Biblical Prophecy about the End of the Age in Plain English. 2011. 320p. pap. 22.95 ***(978-1-4497-2716-1(6)***, WestBow Pr.) Author Solutions, Inc.
Lawhorn, Zane. Finding America: Published Version. 2008. 316p. pap. 24.94 *(978-1-4357-4701-2(1))* Lulu Enterprises Inc.
Lee, Richard. Understanding Leviathan: The Key to Apostle John's the Revelation. 2009. 280p. 30.95 *(978-0-595-70998-4(2))*; pap. 20.95 *(978-0-595-46137-0(9))* iUniverse, Inc.
Leonard, Beth. The Seven Sorrows Bible Study for Catholics: What We Can Learn from Our Mother of Sorrows. 2010. 88p. pap. 15.99 *(978-1-4490-5137-2(5))* AuthorHouse.
Lever, A. B. And God Said. 2007. 332p. per. 17.99 *(978-1-60477-115-2(1))* Xulon Pr., Inc.
Litmer, Greg. Messianic Prophecies. 2010. 122p. pap. 14.95 *(978-1-58427-300-4(3))* Guardian of Truth Foundation.
Lord, Eleazar. The Messiah in Moses & the Prophets. 2006. 332p. per. 23.99 *(978-1-4255-3328-1(0))* MPublishing.
Lowry, Montecue J. Military Miracles & Biblical Prophecy: The Hand of God in History. 2010. 753p. 59.95 *(978-1-4327-4668-1(5))*; pap. 41.95 *(978-1-4327-4583-7(2))* Outskirts Pr., Inc.
Madden, Deborah. The Paddington Project: Richard Brothers's Journey to Jerusalem. 2010. (ENG., Illus.). 320p. 90.00 *(978-0-7190-8238-2(2))* Manchester Univ. Pr. GBR. Dist: Macmillan.
Maitland, Brownlow. The Argument from Prophecy. 2008. 109p. 24.99 *(978-0-554-73575-7(X))*; 126p. 27.99 *(978-0-554-73570-2(9))*; 109p. pap. 23.75 *(978-0-554-73574-0(1))*; 109p. pap. 24.75 *(978-0-554-73572-6(5))* BiblioBazaar.
—The Argument from Prophecy. 2009. 96p. pap. *(978-0-217-29520-8(7))* Books LLC.
Maitland, Charles. The Apostles' School of Prophetic Interpretation. 2009. 472p. pap. 40.00 *(978-1-60608-752-7(5)*, Wipf and Stock) Wipf & Stock Pubs.
Manty, Jeffrey A. Prophecy Code II: A Last Days Revelation of Allah in Scripture & What It Means to the World. 2006. 160p. pap. 14.95 *(978-1-58736-675-8(4))* Wheatmark.
Marrs, Texe W. Mysterious Monuments: Encyclopedia of Secret Illuminati Designs, Masonic Architecture, & Occult Places. 2008. (Illus.). 618p. *(978-1-930004-46-7(X))* Rivercrest Industries.
Martin, Russell. How Christians Got Left Behind. 2011. pap. 14.95 ***(978-0-7414-6576-4(0))*** Infinity Publishing.
Massegee, Charles. The Rise & Fall of the Antichrist: Islam, Allah, & the Antichrist in Prophecy. 2011. 450p. pap. 29.95 ***(978-1-4327-7335-9(6))*** Outskirts Pr., Inc.
Mccarty, Philip W. All the Way from Kingdom Come: Basic Futu. 2006. 132p. per. 13.95 *(978-0-595-40370-7(0))* iUniverse, Inc.
McClain, Alva J. Daniel's Prophecy of the 70 Weeks. 2006. (Illus.). 73p. per. 8.99 *(978-0-88469-211-9(6))* BMH Bks.
—Daniel's Prophecy of the Seventy Weeks. 2007. (ENG.). 64p. per. 16.95 *(978-1-4325-8204-3(6))* Kessinger Publishing, LLC.
McCracken, Lester. When Jesus Said He Would Return. 2007. (ENG.). 116p. per. 11.95 *(978-1-58736-858-5(7))* Wheatmark.
McGee, J. Vernon. On Prophecy: Man's Fascination with the Future, 0 vols. 2008. (Thru the Bible Ser.). 256p. pap. 14.99 *(978-0-8499-2911-3(3))* Nelson, Thomas Inc.
McGowan, Victor. The Revelation & the History of Christendom: Prophecy Fulfilled to the End of Our Time. 2011. 88p. pap. 9.95 *(978-1-4502-7809-6(4))* iUniverse, Inc.
McKane, William. Prophets & Wise Men. 2009. (Studies in Biblical Theology, First Ser.). 136p. pap. 17.00 *(978-1-60899-030-6(3)*, Wipf and Stock) Wipf & Stock Pubs.
McKenzie, Shane. All the Evidence Indicates His Return Is Near. 2009. 176p. pap. 12.95 *(978-1-60860-678-8(3)*, Eloquent Bks.) AEG Literary Publishing Services, Inc.
McMurray, Carl. Esteemed of God: Studying Daniel the man & his prophecies of the time between the Testaments. 2007. 84p. pap. 7.70 *(978-0-9774754-3-8(3))* Spiritbuilding.
McTernan, John P. As America Has Done to Israel. 2008. (Illus.). 320p. per. 13.99 *(978-1-60374-038-8(4))* Whitaker Hse.
Mealey, Andrew. Future Sight: Exposing Spiritual Monsters & Catastrophic Events. 2nd ed. 2010. *(978-0-9656384-0-1(5))* NorRem Publishing.
—Last Exodus: Every Race, People, & Tribe Inherit God's Promised Land. 2nd ed. 2010. pap. *(978-0-9656384-2-5(1))* NorRem Publishing.
Melekin, Embaye. The African Bible: The Records of the Abyssinian Prophets. 2011. 730p. pap. 23.99 ***(978-1-4628-6191-0(1))*** Xlibris Corp.
Mendola, John. The Last Days. 2006. 32p. *(978-1-931274-23-4(1))* Essence Publishing.
Miller, Stephen M. The Complete Guide to Bible Prophecy. 2010. (ENG.). 384p. pap. 16.99 *(978-1-60260-300-4(6)*, Barbour Bks.) Barbour Publishing, Inc.
Mira Digital Publishing. Dispensationalism: Essential Beliefs & Common Myths. 2008. 73p. pap. 9.95 *(978-0-9798539-1-3(5))* Theological Studies Pr.
Missler, Chuck. Prophecy 20/20: Profiling the Future Through the Lens of Scripture, 0 vols. 2006. (Illus.). 288p. per. 13.99 *(978-0-7852-1889-0(0))* Nelson, Thomas Inc.
Mitchel, Alvin. Prelude to the Apocalypse of Jesus Christ. 2007. spiral bd. 0.01 net. *(978-1-60402-558-3(1))* Independent Pub.
Moore, Marvin. Challenge to the Remnant. 2008. pap. 16.99 *(978-0-8163-2273-2(2))* Pacific Pr. Publishing Assn.
—Could It Really Happen? Revelation 13 in the Light of History & Current Events. 2007. 287p. 16.99 *(978-0-8163-2185-8(X))* Pacific Pr. Publishing Assn.
Morton, Richard G. The Papal Beast & the Irs. 2011. 162p. pap. 24.95 ***(978-1-4560-9588-8(9))*** PublishAmerica, Inc.
Moseley, E. H. Jew & His Destiny. 2007. 76p. per. *(978-1-4067-8877-8(5)*, Pomona Pr.) Read Bks.
Moy, Randy & Moy, Nancy. Horror to Glory: The Great Day of the Lord Is at Hand! Who Can Endure It? 2009. 362p. pap. 20.99 *(978-1-60791-889-9(7))* Xulon Pr., Inc.
Muganda, Leonidas & Standley, Edwin. Automated Cars Prophesied by William Branham. 2009. 120p. pap. 11.99 *(978-1-60791-434-1(4))* Xulon Pr., Inc.
Myers, Ralph. The Biblical Interpretation of the Number 666. 2010. 136p. pap. 14.95 *(978-1-4327-4890-6(4))* Outskirts Pr., Inc.
Nelson, N I. The Second War in Heaven, As Now Being Waged by Lucifer Through Hitler As a Dummy. 2011. 298p. 48.95 ***(978-1-258-05445-8(0))*** Literary Licensing, LLC.
Newton, Isaac. Observations upon the Prophecies of Daniel, & the Apocalypse of St John. 2007. (ENG.). 176p. per. *(978-1-4065-5033-7(7))* Dodo Pr.
—Observations upon the Prophecies of Daniel, & the Apocalypse of St John. 2007. 120p. per. *(978-1-4068-3454-3(8))* Echo Library.
—Observations upon the Prophecies of Daniel, & the Apocalypse of St John. 2007. (ENG.). 148p. per. 12.99 *(978-1-59547-841-2(8))* NuVision Pubns., LLC.
—Observations upon the Prophecies of Daniel & the Apocalypse of St John. 2008. 248p. per. 9.99 *(978-1-59986-580-5(7))* Filiquarian Publishing, LLC.
—Observations upon the Prophecies of Daniel & the Apocalypse of St. John: In Two Parts. 2007. (ENG.). 188p. pap. 19.99 *(978-1-4346-0577-1(9))*; 208p. pap. 22.99 *(978-1-4346-0552-5(X))* BiblioBazaar.
Ngaruiya, Joed. The New World Order Versus God's Plan for the Next 1,000 Years & Beyond. 2007. xvii, 248p. pap. *(978-1-57258-448-8(3))* TEACH Services, Inc.
Nixon Ph. D., Thomas C. The Prophecy of Daniel: Unsealed. 2008. 260p. pap. 15.99 *(978-1-4389-2061-0(X))* AuthorHouse.

B

Noel, Ted. A Primer on the Book of Revelation. 2009. 222p. pap. 24.00 *(978-1-55635-532-5(7),* Resource Pubns.) Wipf & Stock Pubs.

O'Donnell, Martin. Postresurrection. 2006. pap. 13.99 *(978-1-60034-522-7(0))* Xulon Pr., Inc.

Oliver, Edward. Prophets & Frauds. 2007. 360p. per. 15.95 *(978-1-60264-015-3(7))* Virtualbookworm.com Publishing, Inc.

Overton, Bradley E. Searching for the Gospel Truth: What Your Minister Doesn't Want You to Know. 2008. 264p. pap. 19.95 *(978-1-4327-1976-0(9))* Outskirts Pr., Inc.

Page, John E. Prophecy in Order. 2009. 260p. pap. 16.99 *(978-1-60791-526-3(X))* Xulon Pr., Inc.

Panko, Bill & Panko, Margaret. Prophetic Commands. Date not set. 150p. (Orig.). pap. 14.95 *(978-1-885342-25-6(X))* Creative Ways.

Paulien, Jon. Armageddon at the Door: An Insider's Guide to the Book of Revelation. 2008. (ENG., Illus.). 192p. pap. 15.99 *(978-0-8127-0477-8(0))* Autumn Hse. Publishing Co.

Payne, J. L. On Borrowed Time! Peace, Crime, Sex, War. 2006. pap. 21.00 *(978-0-9758957-9-5(6))* Church Hse. Pubs.

Pearl, Alfred Eugene. The Gates of Hell. 2008. 108p. pap. 11.99 *(978-1-60647-273-6(9))* Xulon Pr., Inc.

Pharr, W. Larry. The Rapture Examined, Explained & Exposed. 2007. 236p. (ENG.). 24.99 *(978-1-60477-020-9(1))*; per. 14.99 *(978-1-60477-000-1(7))* Xulon Pr., Inc.

Pinkston, John A. Woe! Woe! Woe! & then Armageddon: A Prophecy of the End Time. 2011. 124p. 23.95 *(978-1-4502-9732-5(3))*; pap. 13.95 *(978-1-4502-9730-1(7))* iUniverse, Inc.

Pitts, F. E. A Defence of Armageddon, or Our Great Country Foretold in the Holy Scriptures in Two Discourses Delivered in the Capitol of the United States, at Th. 2006. 120p. per. 16.99 *(978-1-4255-0773-2(5))* MPublishing.

—The USA in Bible Prophecy. 58p. reprint ed. pap. 4.00 *(978-0-934666-49-7(0))* Artisan Pubs.

Prasch, James Jacob. Israel, the Church & the Jews. 2008. (ENG.). 324p. pap. 14.99 *(978-0-9779535-6-1(4))* 21st Century Pr.

Presley, Dale M. Way Truth: Life. 2009. 172p. 22.49 *(978-1-4490-3425-2(X))*; pap. 11.99 *(978-1-4490-3424-5(1))* AuthorHouse.

Prince, Derek. Prophetic Guide to the End Times: Facing the Future Without Fear. 2008. 224p. per. 13.99 *(978-0-8007-9445-3(1))* Chosen Bks.

Prophet, Phantom. His Dream Interpreters. 2009. 416p. 34.99 *(978-1-60791-208-8(2))*; pap. 22.99 *(978-1-60791-207-1(4))* Xulon Pr., Inc.

Pyatt, Thomas J. There Is Only One Way, Amen! 2007. (Illus.). 152p. per. 14.95 *(978-0-9767079-4-3(2))* Pyatt, Thomas J.

Quiles, John J. America in Prophecy. 2008. 360p. per. 19.99 *(978-1-60477-707-9(9))* Xulon Pr., Inc.

Reiland, Robert. Jesus & the Third Temple: The Complete Guide to the Ancient History & Secret Rituals of the Red Heifer Ceremony. 3rd ed. 2008. (Illus.). 692p. pap. 34.95 *(978-1-59772-036-6(4),* Your Own World Bks.) Your Own World, Inc.

Rhodes, Ron. Bible Prophecy: Find It Quick... Every Bible Verse on the End Times. 2010. 176p. pap., instr.'s hndbk. ed. 9.99 *(978-0-7369-2847-2(2))* Harvest Hse. Pubs.

—The End Times in Chronological Order. 2012. 240p. pap. 13.99 ***(978-0-7369-3778-8(1))*** Harvest Hse. Pubs.

—The Middle East Conflict: What You Need to Know. 2009. (Quick Reference Guides). 3.99 *(978-0-7369-2649-2(6))* Harvest Hse. Pubs.

—Northern Storm Rising: Russia, Iran, & the Emerging End-Times Military Coalition Against Israel. 2008. 246p. per. 13.99 *(978-0-7369-2174-9(5))* Harvest Hse. Pubs.

—Oil Shock. 2010. 224p. pap. 13.99 *(978-0-7369-2846-5(4))* Harvest Hse. Pubs.

Rhody, Donald. Watching for the Day. 2011. pap. 24.99 ***(978-1-61346-436-6(3))*** Tate Publishing & Enterprises, LLC.

Ridges, David J. 65 Signs of the Times: Leading up to the Second Coming. 2009. pap. 14.99 *(978-1-59955-366-5(X))* Cedar Fort, Inc./CFI Distribution.

Riley, Leah Bassinger. As in the Days of Noah: The UFO Phenomenon Exposed. 2008. 73p. pap. 16.95 *(978-1-60563-694-8(0))* PublishAmerica, Inc.

Robbins, Bill. The Latter Days at the Time of the End. 2008. 230p. pap. 16.95 *(978-0-7414-4476-9(3))* Infinity Publishing.

Robinson, Tony. The Scroll of the Gospel According to King David: Discovering a Prophecy of the Death, Burial & Resurrection of Yeshua in II Samuel 15:10-20:2. 2009. 178p. pap. 16.99 *(978-1-60791-738-0(6))* Xulon Pr., Inc.

—The Scroll of the Gospel of David. 2008. 200p. pap. 16.99 *(978-1-60647-161-6(9))* Xulon Pr., Inc.

Rogers, Adrian. Apocalipsis: el Fin de Los Tiempos: El Triunfo del Cordero de Dios. 2007. 273p. per. 9.99 *(978-0-8054-3275-6(2),* B&H Bks.) B&H Publishing Group.

Rohrig, George. God's Glorious Church: Understanding the Purposes of God. 2011. 148p. 22.23 *(978-1-4567-1680-6(8))*; pap. 11.70 *(978-1-4567-1681-3(6))* AuthorHouse.

Roosenberg, Tim & Lale, Tim. Islam & Christianity: The Coming Holy War. 2011. ***(978-0-8280-2592-8(4))*** Review & Herald Publishing Assn.

Rosemarie. The Signs That God Speaks and, the Mysteries of the Universe. 2010. 64p. pap. 9.95 *(978-1-4502-5323-9(7))* iUniverse, Inc.

Rosenberg, Joel C. Epicenter: Why the Current Rumblings in the Middle East Will Change Your Future. (ENG., Illus.). 2008. 112p. pap., stu. ed., pupil's gde. ed. 7.99 *(978-1-4143-2154-7(6))* 2006. 336p. 19.99 *(978-1-4143-1135-7(4))* 2008. 432p. pap. 14.99 *(978-1-4143-1136-4(2))* Tyndale Hse. Pubs.

—Epicentro: Entérese Cómo los Acontecimientos en el Medio Oriente Cambiarán Su Futuro. 2007.Tr. of Epicenter: Why the Current Rumblings in the Middle East Will Change Your Future. (SPA., Illus.). 368p. per. 14.99 *(978-1-4143-1584-3(8),* Tyndale Espanol) Tyndale Hse. Pubs.

Ross, C. M. Until the Time of the End: The True Story of the Mark, the Number & the Beast. 2006. (ENG.). 128p. per. 13.95 *(978-0-7414-3160-8(2))* Infinity Publishing.

Rowe, David L. God's Strange Work: William Miller & the End of the World. 2008. (Library of Religious Biography). (Illus.). 280p. pap. 24.00 *(978-0-8028-0380-1(6))* Eerdmans, William B. Publishing Co.

Rudman, Burton S. The Bible Between the Lines, 1 vol. 2010. 138p. pap. 24.95 *(978-1-4489-4761-4(8))* PublishAmerica, Inc.

Rutherford, J. F. Government. 2006. pap. 31.95 *(978-1-4304-4193-9(3))* Kessinger Publishing, LLC.

Saini, Herman. Satan vs. God: From the Flood to Abraham's Call. 2009. 472p. 36.99 *(978-1-60791-031-2(4))*; pap. 24.99 *(978-1-60791-030-5(6))* Xulon Pr., Inc.

Sanders, Jennifer E. Daughters of God, Come to Me! 2010. 200p. 29.99 *(978-1-4500-9625-6(5))*; pap. 19.99 *(978-1-4500-9624-9(7))* Xlibris Corp.

Sandford, John & Sandford, Paula. The Elijah Task: A Call to Today's Prophets & Intercessors. annot. ed. 2006. (ENG.). 240p. pap. 14.99 *(978-1-59979-020-6(3),* Charisma Hse.) Charisma Media.

Santana, J. William. Last Keepers of the Covenant. 2009. 340p. 18.99 *(978-1-60696-384-5(8))* Tate Publishing & Enterprises, LLC.

Scofield, C. I. Que Dicen los Profetas? (What Do the Prophets Say?) (SPA.). 112p. *(978-84-7228-966-6(4),* 223051) Clie, Editorial.

Seed, Hal. Future History: Understanding the Book of Daniel & End Times Prophecy. 2007. 206p. pap. *(978-0-9797878-0-5(7))* HalSeedBooks.

Seitz, Christopher R. Prophecy & Hermeneutics: Toward a New Introduction to the Prophets. 2007. (Studies in Theological Interpretation Ser.). 272p. (C). pap. 23.00 *(978-0-8010-3258-5(X))* Baker Academic.

Shannon, Jill. The Seduction of Christianity: Overcoming the Lukewarm Spirit of the Church. 2010. 380p. *(978-0-7684-3462-0(9))*; *(978-0-7684-3463-7(7))*; E-Book *(978-0-7684-9108-1(8))* Destiny Image Pubs.

Sharbaugh, Norm. Red Sky's a Blazin' 2008. (Illus.). 200p. pap. 15.99 *(978-1-60647-801-1(X))* Xulon Pr., Inc.

Shaw, Kenneth M. Comes a Thief: When the Glass Breaks, Book II, 1 vol. 2010. 72p. pap. 19.95 *(978-1-61582-152-5(X))* PublishAmerica, Inc.

Shields, R. D. The Armageddon Scenario. 2009. 240p. pap. 15.99 *(978-1-60791-538-6(3))* Xulon Pr., Inc.

Shinkoskey, Robert Kimball. Do My Prophets No Harm: Revelation & Religious Liberty in the Bible. 2011. 224p. pap. 25.00 *(978-1-60899-845-6(2),* Resource Pubns.) Wipf & Stock Pubs.

Short, Bob R. The Scroll. 2008. 284p. pap. 17.99 *(978-1-60647-047-3(7))* Xulon Pr., Inc.

Shua, Rafael. The Sand Table: A Tactical Approach to Revelation. 2009. 364p. pap. 20.99 *(978-1-61579-134-7(5))* Xulon Pr., Inc.

Shulman, George M. American Prophecy: Race & Redemption in American Political Culture. 2008. 320p. (ENG.). 75.00 *(978-0-8166-3074-5(7))*; pap. 25.00 *(978-0-8166-3075-2(5))* Univ. of Minnesota Pr.

Siacunco, Sergio B. And the Word Was Made Flesh. 2009. 232p. pap. 15.99 *(978-1-60791-250-7(3))* Xulon Pr., Inc.

Simpson, A. B. Profecias de Isaias (Prophecy of Isaiah) (SPA.). 320p. *(978-84-7228-998-7(2),* 223061) Clie, Editorial.

Smith, Carol. Bible Prophecy Handbook. 2010. (Value Bks.). (ENG.). 160p. pap. 2.99 *(978-1-60260-874-0(1),* Barbour Bks.) Barbour Publishing, Inc.

Smith, Craig. Tough Questions - Real Answers: How Can I Know God's Will? 2008. 132p. per. 7.99 *(978-0-9755135-2-1(4))* Shepherd Project Pr.

Smith, Dudley. The TIME of the END. 2009. 304p. pap. 19.99 *(978-0-557-06035-1(4))* Lulu Enterprises Inc.

Smith, R. Payne. Prophecy: A Preparation for Christ. 2007. (ENG.). 112p. 34.95 *(978-0-548-09755-7(0))* Kessinger Publishing, LLC.

Smith, Robert W. & Smith, Elisabeth A., eds. Scriptural & Secular Prophecies Pertaining to the Last Days Including Prophecies by Members of the Church of Jesus Christ of Latter Day Saints. 2007. (ENG.). 288p. 43.95 *(978-0-548-04877-1(0))* Kessinger Publishing, LLC.

Smith, Uriah. The United States in the Light of Prophecy: An Exposition of Rev. 13:11-17. 2007. (ENG.). 116p. pap. 18.99 *(978-1-4346-2683-7(0))*; 124p. pap. 19.99 *(978-1-4346-2688-2(1))* BiblioBazaar.

—The United States in the Light of Prophecy; Or, an Exposition of Rev. 13. 2006. 180p. per. 18.99 *(978-1-4255-1387-0(5))* MPublishing.

Smith, Worth. The House of Glory: Prophecies & Allied Messages of the Holy Bible & the Great Pyramid of Gizeh 1948. 2007. (ENG.). 158p. 36.95 *(978-0-548-05400-0(2))* Kessinger Publishing, LLC.

Sodano, Vincent. Counting Sheep: In the Name of the Beast. 2008. 120p. pap. 11.95 *(978-1-4327-3376-6(1))* Outskirts Pr., Inc.

Spicer, William Ambrose. Our Day: In the Light of Prophecy. 2008. 396p. pap. 14.95 *(978-1-59594-814-4(7),* Wingspan Pr.) WingSpan Publishing.

Spirit, T. H. The Last Epistle: Armageddon. 2011. 288p. pap. 15.19 *(978-1-4567-4137-2(3))* AuthorHouse.

St John the Evangelist. Revelation & Other Prophetic Books of the Bible. 2007. (Thrift Edition Ser.). (ENG., Illus.). 256p. per. 3.95 *(978-0-486-45644-7(7))* Dover Pubns., Inc.

Standish, Colin D. & Standish, Russell R. The European Union, the North American Union, the Papacy, & Globalism. 2007. 192p. per. 13.95 *(978-0-923309-97-8(7))* Hartland Pubns.

Stone, Jack. Set up to Worship the Antichrist: God sends them a powerful delusion so that they will believe the lie. 2 Thess. 2:10 (NIV) 2009. 130p. pap. 14.95 *(978-1-4327-2894-6(6))* Outskirts Pr., Inc.

Stone, Perry F. Nightmare along Pennsylvania Avenue: Prophetic Insight into America's Role in the Coming End Times. 2009. (ENG.). 336p. 21.99 *(978-1-59979-860-8(3),* Frontline) Charisma Media.

Stuart, Moses. Hints on the Interpretation of Prophecy by M Stuart. 2006. 200p. per. 18.99 *(978-1-4255-1656-7(4))* MPublishing.

Study in Daniel. 2007. (Illus.). 153p. pap. 10.00 *(978-0-9798178-0-3(6))* Christian Word Bks.

Sullivan, Bob. Escape the Global Storm. 2008. 256p. 25.99 *(978-1-60477-774-1(5))* Xulon Pr., Inc.

—Escape the Global Storm: A Personal Guarantee from the God of Abraham, Isaac & Jacob. 2008. 256p. pap. 15.99 *(978-1-60477-773-4(7))* Xulon Pr., Inc.

Taylor, Hudson. The Countdown Has Started. 2007. pap. 16.00 *(978-0-8059-8510-8(7))* Dorrance Publishing Co., Inc.

Teed, Alison. Voices Crying in the Wilderness. 2008. 276p. (ENG.). 25.99 *(978-1-60477-416-0(9))*; per. 15.99 *(978-1-60477-415-3(0))* Xulon Pr., Inc.

Teeter, David. The Days of the Prophets: What We Can Learn from Biblical Prophecy. 2009. 123p. pap. 12.95 *(978-1-4327-3559-3(4))* Outskirts Pr., Inc.

The Omega church. Obama the Great: Given Great Dominion. 2008. (Illus.). 21p. 9.99 *(978-0-9744246-1-3(7))* WayneLizco.

Thomas, C. L. Memoirs: Reflections of the Fathers Heart. 2011. 142p. pap. 14.99 ***(978-1-61379-461-6(4))*** Xulon Pr., Inc.

Thomas, Ice. Breaking the apocalypse Code. 2007. pap. 14.99 *(978-1-59751-035-6(1))* Word For Today, The.

Thompson, Richard David. Almost Midnight. 2009. 255p. pap. *(978-1-905991-22-8(3))* New Wine Pr.

Tregelles, S. P. Tregelles on Daniel: Remarks on the Prophetic Visions in the Book of Daniel. 2007. 254p. pap. 25.00 *(978-1-55635-615-5(3),* Wipf and Stock) Wipf & Stock Pubs.

Trent D.D., Kenneth E. Types of Christ in the Old Testament: A Conservative Approach to Old Testament Typology. 2010. 160p. 30.95 *(978-1-61507-148-7(2))*; pap. 13.99 *(978-1-61507-147-0(4))* Cross Bks. Publishing.

Tsukahira, Peter. God's Tsunami. 2006. 208p. pap. 14.95 *(978-0-9655551-3-5(5))* Word Prodns.

Tucker, Birdella A. & Renteria, Mary. Do You See What I See. 2008. 336p. 32.99 *(978-1-4257-5351-1(5))*; pap. 22.99 *(978-1-4257-5341-2(8))* Xlibris Corp.

Tunstall, Jim. The Seed of the Woman: The Story of an Ancient Prophecy Fulfilled. 2011. 192p. 27.99 ***(978-1-4520-9061-0(0))*** AuthorHouse.

Ty Collins. Biblical Current Events: A Current Events Study Guide. 2009. 108p. pap. 10.99 *(978-1-4389-6151-4(0))* AuthorHouse.

Tyner, M. J. Why Is Bible Prophecy So Amazing? 2007. (Illus.). 2p. per. 1.00 *(978-0-9789909-4-7(3))* True-Way Tracts.

Ungar, Larry L. Right at the Door: Prophetic Overview of the Final Days. 2009. 348p. pap. 18.99 *(978-1-61579-421-8(2))* Xulon Pr., Inc.

van Wert, Leon G. The Jewish Popes: The Two Harbingers of the End Times. 2009. 27.99 *(978-1-60604-687-6(X))* Tate Publishing & Enterprises, LLC.

Vilardi, Michael. The Time of His Coming: The Fictionalized Account of the Coming of Christ That Could Come True. 2006. pap. 16.99 *(978-1-58158-101-0(7),* Serenity Bks.) McDougal Publishing Co.

Vincent, Robert L. & Vincent, Consuelo M. The Prophecy & Testament: The Book of True Revealing. 2006. (Illus.). 608p. per. 40.00 *(978-1-4251-0020-9(1))* Trafford Publishing.

Vine, W. E. Prophecy, 0 vols. 2010. (Vine's Topical Commentaries Ser.). 256p. 29.99 *(978-1-4185-4308-2(X))* Nelson, Thomas Inc.

Wagner, Clarence. Lessons from the Land of the Bible. 2007. (Illus.). 239p. pap. *(978-0-9773852-4-9(8))* Hebraic Heritage Pr.

Waldron, Samuel E. More of the End Times Made Simple. 2009. 225p. pap. 19.99 *(978-1-879737-69-3(8))* Calvary Pr.

Walker, Neville Earl. Making Wise the Simple: Behaviors, Attitudes & Principles of the Body of Christ. 2007. 456p. per. 29.95 *(978-1-4120-9616-4(2))* Trafford Publishing.

Walvoord, John F. & Hitchcock, Mark. Armageddon, Oil & Terror: What the Bible Says about the Future of America, the Middle East, & the End of Western Civilization. rev. ed. 2007. (ENG., Illus.). 240p. per. 14.99 *(978-1-4143-1582-9(1))* Tyndale Hse. Pubs.

Ward, Henderson. One Minute to Midnight on God's Clock. 2009. (J). pap. 23.99 *(978-1-60799-630-9(8))* Tate Publishing & Enterprises, LLC.

Warn, Charles Lathrup. Today, As in the Days of Noah. 2011. 66p. 36.95 ***(978-1-258-05429-8(9))*** Literary Licensing, LLC.

Watkins, Ray. The Day the Eagle Falls: The United States in Prophecy. 2008. 146p. pap. 11.95 *(978-0-7414-4520-9(4))* Infinity Publishing.

Welch, Leslie. Revelation. 2011. 96p. pap. 19.95 ***(978-1-4626-4227-4(6))*** PublishAmerica, Inc.

Wendland, Ernst R. Prophetic Rhetoric: Case Studies in Text Analysis & Translation. 2009. pap. 25.99 *(978-1-60791-766-3(1))* Xulon Pr., Inc.

Wilson, Loren Henry. The Lady & the Dragon. 2011. 170p. 29.99 ***(978-1-4568-5779-0(7))***; pap. 19.99 ***(978-1-4568-5778-3(9))*** Xlibris Corp.

Wilson, Philip Whitwell. The Vision We Forget. 2007. (ENG.). 286p. 43.95 *(978-0-548-01658-9(5))* Kessinger Publishing, LLC.

Winfrey, Melvin. The Beast That Was, & Is Not, & yet Is. 2009. 144p. 22.49 *(978-1-4389-8994-5(6))*; 144p. pap. 15.49 *(978-1-4389-8993-8(8))*; 136p. *(978-1-4389-9879-4(1))* AuthorHouse.

Winrod, Gerald B. The United States & Russia in Prophecy: And the Red Horse of the Apocalypse. 2011. 40p. 35.95 ***(978-1-258-00726-3(6))*** Literary Licensing, LLC.

Winthrop, Edward. The Premium Essay on the Characteristics & Laws of Prophetic Symbols by the Rev Edward Winthrop. 2006. 216p. per. 20.99 *(978-1-4255-1783-0(8))* MPublishing.

Wolf, Robert & Glazerson, Mati. Light Out of Darkness: Surviving the End of Days. 2009. 108p. 18.95 *(978-1-934440-72-8(8),* Devora Publishing) Simcha Media Group.

Woods, Julie. Jeremiah 48 as Christian Scripture. 2011. pap. 42.50 *(978-0-227-17378-7(3))* Clarke, James Co., Ltd. GBR. Dist: Brown, David Bk. Co., The.

Woods, Julie Irene. Jeremiah 48 as Christian Scripture. 2010. (Princeton Theological Monographs). 372p. pap. 41.00 *(978-1-60899-842-5(8),* Pickwick Pubns.) Wipf & Stock Pubs.

Woolsey, Edwin L. The Voice of Seven Thunders: Shadows of Things to Come. 2011. 248p. 26.59 ***(978-1-4634-0629-5(0))***; pap. 16.95 ***(978-1-4634-0630-1(4))*** AuthorHouse.

Wright, Lester. Read It & Run. 2006. pap. 13.99 *(978-1-60034-361-2(9))* Xulon Pr., Inc.

Wright, Robert. Proving It - Eschatology That Makes Sense in Four Research Reports. 2007. (ENG.). 368p. per. 23.95 *(978-1-59594-126-8(6),* Wingspan Pr.) WingSpan Publishing.

Zachary, John. Science & Religion Series, 4 vols. Incl. Mysterious Numbers of the Sealed Revelation. Webster, Donald, ed. (Illus.). 87p. pap. 4.99 *(978-0-9640404-4-1(1))*; Prophecies of Nostradamus & a Scientific Approach to Scripture. 3.99 *(978-0-9640404-6-5(8))*; Scientific Evidence for the Second Coming of Christ. Webster, Donald, ed. (Illus.). 77p. pap. 4.99 *(978-0-9640404-3-4(3))*; Threshold of Eternity. (Illus.). 213p. pap. 9.99 *(978-0-9640404-1-0(7))*; 1994. 17.97 *(978-0-9640404-0-3(9))* Harvard Hse.

BIBLE—PSYCHOLOGY

see also Christianity—Psychology; Psychology, Religious

Clinton, Tim & Hawkins, Ron. The Quick-Reference Guide to Biblical Counseling. 2009. 288p. pap. 24.99 *(978-0-8010-7225-3(5))* Baker Bks.

Delitzsch, Franz. A System of Biblical Psychology. Wallis, Robert Ernest, tr. 2007. (ENG.). 600p. 59.95 *(978-0-548-09991-9(X))* Kessinger Publishing, LLC.

Forster, Jonathan Langs. Biblical Psychology in Four Parts. 2006. pap. 30.95 *(978-1-4286-4856-2(9))* Kessinger Publishing, LLC.

Fox, Michael V. A Time to Tear down & a Time to Build Up: A Rereading of Ecclesiastes. 2010. 440p. pap. 48.00 *(978-1-60899-496-0(1),* Wipf and Stock) Wipf & Stock Pubs.

Garnett, Colin. The Biblical Link to Addictions: An Understandable Guide through the Spiritual, Emotional & Psychological Madness of Addiction. 2011. 108p. pap. 13.32 ***(978-1-4567-7324-3(0))*** AuthorHouse.

Glas, Gerrit, et al, eds. Hearing Visions & Seeing Voices: Psychological Aspects of Biblical Concepts & Personalities. (ENG., Illus.). xviii, 326p. 2010. pap. 149.00 *(978-90-481-7482-9(1),* 9048174821) 2007. 149.00 *(978-1-4020-5938-4(8),* 1402059388) Springer.

Hunt, June. Counseling Through Your Bible Handbook: Providing Biblical Hope & Practical Help for 50 Everyday Problems. 2008. 442p. per. 14.99 *(978-0-7369-2181-7(8))* Harvest Hse. Pubs.

Johnson, Aubrey R. The Vitality of the Individual in the Thought of Ancient Israel. 2nd ed. 2006. 166p. pap. 15.00 *(978-1-59752-900-6(1),* Wipf and Stock) Wipf & Stock Pubs.

Johnson, Dennis E. & Fitzpatrick, Elyse M. Counsel from the Cross: Connecting Broken People to the Love of Christ. 2009. 240p. pap. 15.99 *(978-1-4335-0317-7(4))* Crossway.

Johnson, Eric L. Foundations for Soul Care: A Christian Psychology Proposal. 2007. (ENG., Illus.). 716p. 45.00 *(978-0-8308-2567-7(3),* IVP Acad.) InterVarsity Pr.

Kaplan, Kalman J. & Schwartz, Matthew B. The Seven Habits of the Good Life: How the Biblical Virtues Free Us from the Seven Deadly Sins. 2008. (ENG.). 134p. pap. 16.95 *(978-0-7425-3275-5(5))* Rowman & Littlefield Publishers, Inc.

Kaplan, Kalman J. & Scwartz, Matthew B. The Seven Habits of the Good Life: How the Biblical Virtues Free Us from the Seven Deadly Sins. 2006. (ENG.). 136p. 19.95 *(978-0-7425-3274-8(7))* Rowman & Littlefield Publishers, Inc.

Leung Lai, Barbara M. Through The 'I'-Window: The Inner Life of Characters in the Hebrew Bible. 2011. 212p. ***(978-1-907534-20-1(2))*** Sheffield Phoenix Pr.

Meech, John L. Paul in Israel's Story: Self & Community at the Cross. 2006. (AAR Academy Ser.). (ENG.). 192p. 75.00 *(978-0-19-530694-1(5))* Oxford Univ. Pr., Inc.

Powlison, David/Arthur. The Biblical Counseling Movement: History & Context. 2009. 432p. pap. 39.99 *(978-1-935273-13-4(2))* New Growth Pr.

Richards, Larry. Psicologia & la Biblia: Psychology & the Bible. (SPA.). *(978-84-7228-364-0(X),* 220729) Clie, Editorial.

Rollins, Wayne G. & Kille, D. Andrew, eds. Psychological Insight into the Bible: Texts & Readings. 2007. 291p. per. 28.00 *(978-0-8028-4155-1(4))* Eerdmans, William B. Publishing Co.

Rosenthal, Robert S. From Plagues to Miracles: The Transformational Journey of Exodus, from the Slavery of Ego to the Promised Land of Spirit. 2012. (ENG.). 256p. pap. 15.95 ***(978-1-4019-3130-8(8))*** Hay Hse., Inc.

Strawn, Brent A. The Bible & the Pursuit of Happiness. 2012. (ENG.). 368p. 99.00 ***(978-0-19-979573-4(8))***; pap. 35.00 ***(978-0-19-979574-1(6))*** Oxford Univ. Pr., Inc.

Wilson, J. Barry. Psycho Bible: Where Modern Psychology Meets Timeless Wisdom. 2010. pap. 12.99 *(978-1-61566-137-4(9))* Tate Publishing & Enterprises, LLC.

Woodward, John B. Man As Spirit, Soul, & Body: A Study of Biblical Psychology. 2nd ed. 2007. pap. *(978-1-931527-63-7(6))* Grace Ministries.

Zornberg, Avivah Gottlieb. The Murmuring Deep: Reflections on the Biblical Unconscious. (ENG.). 2011. 480p. pap. 19.95 *(978-0-8052-1206-8(X))* 2009. 464p. 28.95 *(978-0-8052-4247-8(3))* Knopf Doubleday Publishing Group. (Schocken).

BIBLE—PUBLICATION AND DISTRIBUTION

American Bible Society. Address of the Managers to Its Auxiliaries, Members & Friends, in Regard to a General Supply of the United States with the Sacred Scriptures. 2011. 18p. pap. 11.99 ***(978-1-4181-9049-1(7))*** MPublishing.

Brother David & David, Brother. Project Pearl: The 1 Million Smuggled Bibles That Changed China, 1 vol. 2008. (Illus.). 320p. pap. 13.99 *(978-0-8254-6195-8(2)*, Monarch Bks.) Lion Hudson PLC GBR. Dist: Kregel Pubns.

Brown, Michelle P. In the Beginning: Bibles Before the Year 1000. 2006. (ENG., Illus.). 368p. 45.00 *(978-1-58834-240-9(9))* Smithsonian Institution Pr.

Den Hollander, A A & Francois, W., eds. Infant Milk or Hardy Nourishment? The Bible for Lay People & Theologians in the Early Modern Period. 2009. (Bibliotheca Ephemeridum Theologicarum Lovaniensium Ser.). (GER, FRE & ENG., Illus.). 488p. (C). pap. 116.00 *(978-90-429-2144-3(7))* Peeters Pubs. & Booksellers BEL. Dist: Brown, David Bk. Co., The.

Home Evangelization: A View of the Wants & Prospects of Our Country, Based on Facts & Relations of Colportage. by One of the Secretaries of the Am. 2006. 176p. per. 18.99 *(978-1-4255-1375-7(1))* MPublishing.

Kirkbride Bible Company, creator. Thompson Chain Reference Bible-KJV. 2011. im. lthr. 89.99 ***(978-0-88707-658-9(0))*** Kirkbride, B.B. Bible Co., Inc.

Mobley, Kenda P. & Montgomery, Helen Barrett. Helen Barrett Montgomery: Boxed Set the Global Mission of Domestic Feminism / the Bible & Missions. 2009. 640p. 69.95 *(978-1-60258-189-0(4))* Baylor Univ. Pr.

Montgomery, Helen Barrett. The Bible & Missions. 2009. (Illus.). 200p. (ENG.). pap. 29.95 *(978-1-60258-188-3(6))*; *(978-1-60258-156-2(8))* Baylor Univ. Pr.

—The Bible & Missions. 2009. 276p. 24.99 *(978-1-103-22367-1(4))*; pap. 18.99 *(978-1-103-22365-7(8))* BiblioBazaar.

—The Bible & Missions. 2009. 166p. pap. *(978-0-217-57210-1(3))* Books LLC.

—The Bible & Missions. 2008. 274p. 42.95 *(978-1-4365-8332-9(2))* 2007. (ENG.). 276p. per. 27.95 *(978-0-548-78088-6(9))* Kessinger Publishing, LLC.

Smith, Culling Eardley, intro. The encyclical letter of Our Lord Pope Gregory XVI. 2010. (LAT & ITA.). 85.76 *(978-1-61719-001-8(2))* Gorgias Pr., LLC.

Zondervan. NIV Life Application Study Bible. 2011. (ENG.). 2528p. lthr. 69.99 ***(978-0-310-43449-8(1))*** Zondervan.

Zondervan Publishing Staff. NIV Life Application Study Bible. 2011. (ENG.). 2528p. lthr. 69.99 ***(978-0-310-43459-7(9))*** Zondervan.

BIBLE—QUOTATIONS

Here are entered collections of quotations from or about the Bible.

Andry, Duane. Blogosphere Madness 2010: More Ravings of a Religious Fanatic 2009: Dogmasphere. 2010. 296p. spiral bd. *(978-0-9798444-0-9(1))* Andry, Duane & Assocs.

—The Great Consolidation: Reconciling the Family of God. 2007. 390p. spiral bd. *(978-0-9798444-2-3(8))* Andry, Duane & Assocs.

—Reconciliation: The Children of Abraham. 2007. 531p. 48.95 *(978-0-9798444-1-6(X))* Andry, Duane & Assocs.

Armstrong, Dave. Bible Proofs for Catholic Truths: A Source Book for Apologists & Inquirers. 2009. xiv, 445p. pap. 15.95 *(978-1-933184-57-9(4))* Sophia Institute Pr.

Barbour Publishing. NLV Gift & Award 2. 2009. (New life Bible Ser.). (ENG.). 960p. pap. 7.97 *(978-1-59789-806-5(6)*, Barbour Bks.) Barbour Publishing, Inc.

Barbour Publishing Staff. The Bible Promise Book: God's Promises for You. gif. ed. 2007. (Bible Promise Bks.). (ENG.). 176p. pap. 9.99 *(978-1-59789-679-5(9)*, Barbour Bks.) Barbour Publishing, Inc.

Beals, Timothy J. The Red Letters: The Sayings & Teachings of Jesus. Beals, Timothy J., ed. 2009. 160p. tchr. ed. 16.99 *(978-1-4335-0140-1(6))* Crossway.

Beers, Ronald A. & Mason, Amy E. TouchPoints for Men: God's Answers for Your Daily Needs. rev. ed. 2010. (ENG.). 288p. pap. 4.99 *(978-1-4143-2018-2(3))* Tyndale Hse. Pubs.

—TouchPoints for New Believers. 2009. (ENG.). 288p. pap. 4.99 *(978-1-4143-2022-9(1))* Tyndale Hse. Pubs.

Berke, Molly L. Shepard, ed. Quote, Unquote Vol. 5: Spiritual Quotes for Inspired Moments, 5 vols. 2007. 158p. spiral bd. 14.95 *(978-0-9791848-0-2(0)*, Quote, Unquote) Autumn Leaves, a Creativity Co.

The Bible's Promises for Life (from the Holy Bible, English Standard Version / Redesign) 2011. 160p. pap. 5.99 ***(978-1-4335-3171-2(2))*** Crossway.

The Bible's Promises for Women (from the Holy Bible, English Standard Version / Redesign) 2011. 160p. pap. 5.99 ***(978-1-4335-3170-5(4))*** Crossway.

Black, C. Clifton. The Eighth Day of Creation: An Anthology of Christian Scripture. 2008. 376p. 24.00 *(978-0-8028-6272-3(1))* Eerdmans, William B. Publishing Co.

Blair, Alexander. Christian Ambivalence Toward Its Old Testament: Interactive Creativity versus Static Obedience. 2011. 420p. pap. 46.00 *(978-1-60899-106-8(7)*, Wipf and Stock) Wipf & Stock Pubs.

Bosserman, Beth. Medicine from God: Scripture Verses to Encourage & Comfort the Sick. 2010. 128p. pap. 14.99 *(978-1-4141-1473-6(7))* Pleasant Word.

Brady, Gwendolyn Hall. Joy Cometh in the Morning: A Compilation of Inspirational Verses from the Holy Bible New Testament in the King James Version. 2009. 64p. pap. 12.00 *(978-1-4251-9053-8(7))* Trafford Publishing.

Capri, Roger William. The Way of Holiness. 2010. pap. 13.95 *(978-0-7414-5768-4(7))* Infinity Publishing.

Chamberlain, Diane K. The Rainbow in the Storm: Finding Hope Where There Isn't Any. 2009. (ENG.). 272p. pap. 22.00 *(978-1-58982-535-2(7)*, Millennial Mind Publishing) American Bk. Publishing Group.

Chen, Diane G. A Pocketful of Verses: When Out-Of-Context Becomes the Norm. 2010. pap. *(978-1-57312-564-2(4))* Smyth & Helwys Publishing, Inc.

Christian Art Gifts, creator. For You, Graduate. 2009. (For You... Ser.). (Illus.). 79p. *(978-1-77036-119-5(7))* Christian Art Pubs.

—For You, Mom: ... Because I Love You. 2009. (For You... Ser.). (Illus.). 78p. *(978-1-77036-117-1(0))* Christian Art Pubs.

—For You, with Love. 2009. (Illus.). 79p. *(978-1-77036-235-2(5))* Christian Art Pubs.

—199 Favorite Bible Verses for Leaders. 2009. (199 Favorite Bible Verses For... Ser.). 127p. pap. *(978-1-77036-123-2(5))* Christian Art Pubs.

—199 Favorite Bible Verses for Men. 2009. (199 Favorite Bible Verses For... Ser.). 125p. pap. *(978-1-77036-121-8(9))* Christian Art Pubs.

—199 Favorite Bible Verses for Teens. 2009. (199 Favorite Bible Verses For... Ser.). (Illus.). 127p. pap. *(978-1-77036-124-9(3))* Christian Art Pubs.

Cole, Judith Carol. How to Handle Your Relationship. 2009. (ENG.). 236p. pap. 18.95 *(978-1-4401-8167-2(5))* iUniverse, Inc.

Collins, Anthony. A Discourse of the Grounds & Reasons of the Christian Religion. 2009. 182p. pap. *(978-1-150-42289-8(0))* Books LLC.

Collins, K. D. Wounded Witnesses. 2006. pap. 9.99 *(978-1-60034-362-9(7))* Xulon Pr., Inc.

Cook, Albert S., ed. Biblical Quotations in Old English Prose Writers. 2007. (ENG.). 404p. 49.95 *(978-0-548-25577-3(6))*; 408p. per. 34.95 *(978-1-4325-5925-7(1))* Kessinger Publishing, LLC.

Countryman, Jack. God's Wisdom for Your Every Need, 0 vols. 2009. 272p. im. lthr. 14.99 *(978-1-4041-8755-9(3))* Nelson, Thomas Inc.

Davidson, George. Why Are There No Cats in the Bible? And Other Fascinating Facts to Expand Your Knowledge of the Bible. 2009. (ENG., Illus.). 192p. 9.99 *(978-0-7858-2493-0(6)*, 0785824936, Castle Bks., Inc.) Book Sales, Inc.

Dear Child, Love, Daddy. 2008. 372p. pap. 19.99 *(978-1-60647-100-5(7))* Xulon Pr., Inc.

Dell, Katharine. Seeking a Life That Matters: Wisdom for Today from the Book of Proverbs. 128p. pap. 13.00 *(978-0-232-52402-4(5))* Abingdon Pr.

Durden, Timothy J. 101 Biblical Words. 2009. 156p. pap. 14.99 *(978-1-61579-328-0(3))* Xulon Pr., Inc.

Eastep, Sandy. Cooking 2 Live: Recipe & Memories-A Holiday Collection. 2007. 208p. 29.95 *(978-0-9792705-2-9(9))* Cooking 2 Live.

—Cooking 2 Live: The Natural Way. 2007. 184p. per. 19.95 *(978-0-9792705-1-2(0))* Cooking 2 Live.

—Cooking 2 Live the Natural Way. 2007. 184p. 27.95 *(978-0-9792705-0-5(2))* Cooking 2 Live.

Ed. Pub. Concepts Staff, prod. What Did Jesus Say? Bible Verses on Issues You Deal With. 2010. (ENG.). 192p. (J). pap. 9.99 *(978-1-4143-3180-5(0))* Tyndale Hse. Pubs.

Eichler, Dolores M. Why? Oh Why Do I Do What I Do (Quotes from Scriptures or Bible) Coming to Christ. (Happy Heart Ser.: No. 1-882283-09-0). (Illus.). (Orig.). 48p. pap. 3.00 *(978-1-882283-02-6(3))*; 45p. reprint ed. pap. 3.00 *(978-1-882283-00-2(7))* Eichler, Dolores M.

Ellie Claire Staff. Joy of the Lord Is My Strength, 1 vol. 2010. (ENG.). 128p. 9.99 *(978-1-935416-55-5(3))* Ellie Claire & Summerside Pr.

Forster, Ed. 101 Everyday Sayings from the Bible. 2008. (Illus.). xi, 195p. pap. *(978-0-9792266-3-2(5))* Salvation Army National Pubns., The.

Frey, Harold. Prisoners of the Paradigm. 2008. 368p. pap. 19.99 *(978-1-60647-251-4(8))* Xulon Pr., Inc.

Furguson, Barbara. Call Me Ann. 2007. 152p. per. *(978-1-906210-45-8(4))* Grosvenor Hse. Publishing Ltd.

Graham, Merry & Bye, Rachel. Scriptures at Your Fingertips: 200 Topics & 2000 Verses. 2006. (ENG.). 256p. pap. 12.99 *(978-1-58229-613-5(8)*, Howard Bks.) Howard Books.

Graham, Merry & Graham, Tiffany Michelle. Scriptures at Your Fingertips for Teens: Over 250 Topics & 2000 Verses. 2008. (ENG.). 288p. (J). pap. 13.99 *(978-1-4165-7910-6(9)*, Howard Bks.) Howard Books.

Grier, Derek. 60 Minutes of Wisdom: Insight in an Instant. 2009. (ENG.). 96p. pap. 7.99 *(978-1-59979-724-3(0)*, Creation Hse.) Charisma Media.

Hancock, Jimmie L. All the Questions in the Bible, Kjv. 2011. 232p. pap. 19.95 ***(978-1-257-93011-1(7))*** Lulu Enterprises Inc.

Houtman, A. & Sysling, H. Alternative Targum Traditions: The Use of Variant Readings for the Study in Origin & History of Targum Jonathan. 2009. (Studies in the Aramaic Interpretation of Scripture). 314p. *(978-90-04-17842-7(2))* BRILL.

Hummel, Rand. Turn Away Wrath: Meditations to Control Anger & Bitterness. 2007. 165p. per. *(978-1-59166-734-6(8))* BJU Pr.

Jacobson, Nelly P. Bible Quotes: Searching for the Word. 2011. pap. 24.99 ***(978-1-61777-034-0(5))*** Tate Publishing & Enterprises, LLC.

Kale, Shelly, ed. Alpha & Omega: Visions of the Millennium. 2006. (Illus.). 76p. reprint ed. 17.00 *(978-1-4223-5423-0(7))* DIANE Publishing Co.

Kangosa, Guy-Angelo. Die Bedeutung der Jesaja-Zitate für die lukanische Christologie: Eine exegetische Untersuchung mit Ausblick auf den afrikanischen Kontext. 2008. (Europäische Hochschulschriften. Reihe 23: Theologie Ser.). 240p. pap. 61.95 *(978-3-631-57686-1(2))* Lang, Peter GmbH, Europaischer Verlag der Wissenschaften DEU. Dist: Lang, Peter.

Katz, Art. The Holocaust - Where was God? An Inquiry into the Biblical Roots of Tragedy. 6th rev. ed. 2008. (ENG.). 91p. pap. 10.00 *(978-0-9749631-0-5(0))* Burning Bush Pr.

Kerrigan, Michael P. Saint Paul the Apostle for Every Day: A Vision That Inspires, a Mission for Life. 2008. (Illus.). 128p. pap. 6.95 *(978-0-8091-4567-6(7))* Paulist Pr.

Kilgore, Kay Wheeler & Countryman, J. God's Promises for Your Every Need, 0 vols. 2006. 352p. im. lthr. 9.97 *(978-1-4041-0411-2(9))* Nelson, Thomas Inc.

Kistemaker, Simon. The Psalm Citations in the Epistle to the Hebrews. 2010. 164p. pap. 19.00 *(978-1-60899-721-3(9)*, Wipf and Stock) Wipf & Stock Pubs.

Koenig-Bricker, Woodeene. Listening to God with Mother Teresa. 2010. 128p. 12.95 *(978-1-59276-789-2(3))* Our Sunday Visitor, Publishing Div.

Kollmann, Bernd. Die Verheißung des Neuen Bundes: Wie alttestamentliche Texte im Neuen Testament fortwirken. Kollmann, Bernd, ed. 2010. (Biblisch-Theologische Schwerpunkte Ser.). (GER., Illus.). 284p. (C). pap. 41.00 *(978-3-525-61616-1(3))* Vandenhoeck & Ruprecht GmbH & Co. KG DEU. Dist: ISD.

Kugel, James L., ed. Prayers That Cite Scripture. 2006. (Harvard Center for Jewish Studies). (Illus.). 119p. 27.50 *(978-0-674-01971-3(7))* Harvard Univ. Ctr. for Jewish Studies.

Lafleur, Jacque. The Science of Salvation: Forty-nine Instant Sermons Especially for Lay Pastors. 2009. 396p. pap. 22.95 *(978-1-57258-586-7(2))* TEACH Services, Inc.

Lange, Armin & Weigold, Matthias. Biblical Quotations & Allusions in Second Temple Jewish Literature. 2011. (Journal of Ancient Judaism. Supplements (JAJ. S) Ser.). (ENG.). 384p. (C). 122.00 *(978-3-525-55028-1(6))* Vandenhoeck & Ruprecht GmbH & Co. KG DEU. Dist: ISD.

Lee, Jaerock. The Power of God. 2008. 164p. pap. *(978-1-55452-257-6(9))* Essence Publishing.

Livingstone Corporation Staff. God's Promises on Character. 2008. (God's Promises Ser.). (ENG.). 160p. 3.99 *(978-1-934068-90-8(X))* Authentic Media.

—God's Promises on Healing. 2008. (God's Promises Ser.). (ENG.). 160p. 3.99 *(978-1-934068-91-5(8))* Authentic Media.

—God's Promises on Knowing Him. 2008. (God's Promises Ser.). (ENG.). 160p. 3.99 *(978-1-934068-88-5(8))* Authentic Media.

Livingstone Staff. God's Promises on Praise & Worship. 2008. (God's Promises Ser.). (ENG.). 160p. 3.99 *(978-1-934068-89-2(6))* Authentic Media.

Lucado, Max. Fear Not: For I Am with You Always, 0 vols. 2009. 224p. 14.99 *(978-1-4041-8775-7(8))* Nelson, Thomas Inc.

Lyda, Hope. Prayers of Comfort for Those Who Hurt. 2009. 48p. 12.99 *(978-0-7369-2562-4(7))* Harvest Hse. Pubs.

Madrid, Patrick. 150 Bible Verses Every Catholic Should Know. 2008. pap. *(978-0-86716-902-7(8)*, Servant Bks.) Franciscan Media.

Mahusay, Nancy. The History of Redemption. 2007. 388p. per. 19.99 *(978-1-60266-737-2(3))* Xulon Pr., Inc.

Manser, Martin. Scapegoats, Shambles & Shibboleths: The Queen's English from the King James Bible. 2009. (ENG.). 272p. pap. 19.95 ***(978-0-340-97979-2(8)***, Hodder & Stoughton) Hodder General Publishing Div. GBR. Dist: Independent Pubs. Group.

Mason, Amy E. & Beers, Ronald A. Bible Promises to Live By. 2007. (ENG.). 176p. per. 3.99 *(978-1-4143-1355-9(1))* Tyndale Hse. Pubs.

Masonic Service Association. Bible Quotations for Masonic Speakers. 2011. 38p. 35.95 ***(978-1-258-10585-3(3))*** Literary Licensing, LLC.

Mayo, William D. That's in the Bible? Scripture's User-Friendly Impact on Everyday Conversation. 2011. 224p. 24.95 ***(978-1-4634-7436-2(9))***; pap. 14.95 ***(978-1-4634-7437-9(7))*** AuthorHouse.

Menken, Maarten J.J. & Moyise, Steve, eds. Genesis in the New Testament. 2012. (Library of New Testament Studies). (ENG.). 224p. 120.00 ***(978-0-567-56302-6(2)***, T&T Clark Int'l) Continuum International Publishing Group, Ltd. GBR. Dist: National Bk. Network.

Moore, Karen. For You, Dad: ... Because I Love You. 2009. (For You... Ser.). (Illus.). 87p. *(978-1-77036-115-7(4))* Christian Art Pubs.

Morey, Robert A. A Bible Handbook on Slander & Gossip. 2009. (Illus.). 240p. pap. 15.99 *(978-1-61579-356-3(9))* Xulon Pr., Inc.

Moyise. Evoking Scripture: Seeing the Old Testament in the New. 2008. (ENG., Illus.). 176p. 34.95 *(978-0-567-03325-3(2)*, T&T Clark Int'l) Continuum International Publishing Group, Ltd. GBR. Dist: National Bk. Network.

Moyise, Steve. Evoking Scripture: Seeing the Old Testament in the New. 2008. (ENG., Illus.). 176p. 120.00 *(978-0-567-03324-6(4)*, T&T Clark Int'l) Continuum International Publishing Group, Ltd. GBR. Dist: National Bk. Network.

Mutius, Hans-Georg von. Nichtmasoretische Bibelzitate im Midrasch ha-Gadol (13. /14. Jahrhundert) 2010. (Judentum und Umwelt. Realms of Judaism Ser.). (GER.). 152p. 47.95 *(978-3-631-60826-5(8))* Lang, Peter GmbH, Europaischer Verlag der Wissenschaften DEU. Dist: Lang, Peter.

Newell, Lloyd D. He Shall Fulfill All of His Promises: Daily Hope & Encouragement from the Scriptures. 2010. 18.99 *(978-1-60641-837-6(8))* Deseret Bk. Co.

O'Brien, Kelli S. Use of Scripture in the Markan Passion Narrative. 2010. (Library of New Testament Studies, the Ser.). (ENG.). 352p. 150.00 *(978-0-567-03379-6(1)*, T&T Clark Int'l) Continuum International Publishing Group, Ltd. GBR. Dist: National Bk. Network.

Overton, Jan. Through the Word Today. 2009. 383p. pap. 29.89 *(978-0-557-15347-3(6))* Lulu Enterprises Inc.

Patty, Sandi. A New Day: A Guided Journal. 2011. (ENG.). 224p. pap. 15.99 *(978-1-4516-4331-2(4)*, Howard Bks.) Howard Books.

Peavy, Karin. Hot Chocolate for the Spirit. 2007. 112p. (ENG.). 13.99 *(978-1-60266-722-8(5))*; per. 10.99 *(978-1-60266-721-1(7))* Xulon Pr., Inc.

Petersen, Randy. 99 Bible Promises for Tough Times. 2009. (99 Ways Ser.). (ENG.). 112p. pap. 5.99 *(978-0-307-45838-4(5)*, WaterBrook Pr.) Doubleday Religious Publishing Group, The.

Porter, Stanley E., ed. Hearing the Old Testament in the New Testament. 2006. (McMaster New Testament Studies). 316p. per. 29.00 *(978-0-8028-2846-0(9))* Eerdmans, William B. Publishing Co.

Powers, Kevin. Augustine on Natural Theology. 2008. 96p. pap. *(978-3-639-07114-6(X))* VDM Verlag Dr. Mueller e.K.

Reid, Garnett. Deuteronomy 6 In 3D: An Ancient Plan for Modern Parents. 2010. (Illus.). 47p. pap. 4.99 *(978-0-89265-626-4(3))* Randall Hse. Pubns.

Rhodes, Ron. 1001 Unforgettable Quotes about God, Faith, & the Bible. 2011. 256p. pap. 11.99 *(978-0-7369-2848-9(0))* Harvest Hse. Pubs.

Rothman, Joel. Super Quiz Who Said? Bible Quotes. 2008. pap. 7.95 *(978-1-934872-22-2(9))* JR Pubns.

Salem, Sema'an I. The Origins of Biblical Stories, 1 vol. 2009. 258p. pap. 27.95 *(978-1-60672-903-8(9))* PublishAmerica, Inc.

Saunders, Gartrell. A Poignant Place in Him. 2010. 118p. pap. 11.99 *(978-1-60957-604-2(7))* Xulon Pr., Inc.

Shepherd, Michael B. The Twelve Prophets in the New Testament. 2010. (Studies in Biblical Literature Ser.). 126p. (C). 63.95 *(978-1-4331-1345-8(5))* Lang, Peter Publishing, Inc.

Sheridan, Ruth. Retelling Scripture: "The Jews" & the Scriptural Citations in John 1:19-12:50. 2012. (ENG., Illus.). 312p. ***(978-90-04-21442-2(3))*** BRILL.

Skaggs, Gene. Biblical Quotes from A Course in Miracles Reinterpreted. 2007. 187p. pap. 15.00 *(978-0-9800049-0-8(X))* One Miracle.

Small, Shawn. The Via Crucis. 2008. (Illus.). 174p. 14.95 *(978-1-57736-401-6(5))* Providence Hse Pubs.

Smith, Michael W. Friends are Friends Forever, 0 vols. 2009. 256p. pap. 13.99 *(978-0-7852-9746-8(4))* Nelson, Thomas Inc.

Smyth, Mary Winslow. Biblical Quotations in Middle English Literature Before 1350. 2009. 380p. 26.99 *(978-1-110-00333-4(1))*; pap. 20.99 *(978-1-110-00326-6(9))* BiblioBazaar.

—Biblical Quotations in Middle English Literature Before 1350. 2009. 192p. pap. *(978-1-151-73793-9(3))* Books LLC.

—Biblical Quotations in Middle English Literature Before 1350. 2008. 384p. 48.95 *(978-1-4369-8810-0(1))*; pap. 33.95 *(978-1-4367-8840-3(4))* Kessinger Publishing, LLC.

Snuffer, Denver C., Jr. Nephi' Isaiah: A Prophetic Look at the Latter Days. 2006. 310p. per. 20.99 *(978-0-9740158-3-5(0))* Mill Creek Pr., LLC

Snyder, Henry Nelson. Selections from the Old Testament. 2009. 236p. 23.99 *(978-1-103-74572-2(7))*; pap. 17.99 *(978-1-103-74570-8(0))* BiblioBazaar.

Snyder, Henry Nelson, ed. Selections from the Old Testament. 2007. (ENG.). 232p. 41.95 *(978-0-548-06861-4(2))* Kessinger Publishing, LLC.

Sonnenberg, Alaine. Shine On. 2010. pap. 10.99 *(978-1-61663-826-9(5))* Tate Publishing & Enterprises, LLC.

Southern, Daniel. The Message of Leadership: 31 Essential Insights from Proverbs. 2007. (Acts 29 Ser.). (ENG.). 144p. per. 11.99 *(978-1-60006-085-4(4))* NavPress Publishing Group.

Starling, David I. Not My People: Gentiles as Exiles in Pauline Hermeneutics. 2011. (Beihefte zur Zeitschrift far die neutestamentliche Wissenschaft und die Kunde der älteren Kirche Ser.). (ENG., Illus.). XII, 254p. 210.00 ***(978-3-11-916515-0(8))*** De Gruyter, Walter Inc.

Starling, David Ian. Not My People: Gentiles As Exiles in Pauline Hermeneutics 2011. (Beihefte zur Zeitschrift für die neutestamentliche Wissenschaft und die Kunde der älteren Kirche Ser.). (ENG.). XII, 254p. 140.00 ***(978-3-11-025960-5(5))*** De Gruyter, Walter Inc.

Steyn, Gert J. A Quest for the Assumed LXX Vorlage of the Explicit Quotations in Hebrews. 2011. (Forschungen Zur Religion und Literatur des Alten & Neuen Testament Ser.). (ENG., Illus.). 458p. (C). 203.00 *(978-3-525-53099-3(4))* Vandenhoeck & Ruprecht GmbH & Co. KG DEU. Dist: ISD.

Strong, Terri. Inspiration for Life's Journey. 2011. 80p. pap. 9.99 ***(978-1-4634-4612-3(8))*** AuthorHouse.

Sturley, John. Help! I Don't Understand What Is Happening to My Church: A Layman's Field Guide to Calvinist Controversy. 2008. 404p. pap. 24.99 *(978-1-60647-073-2(6))* Xulon Pr., Inc.

Swint, Mark. Compare Isaiah: A Look at Biblical Scriptures in the Book of Mormon. 2009. pap. 12.99 *(978-0-88290-960-8(6))* Cedar Fort, Inc./CFI Distribution.

Thomas Paine. The Age of Reason. Moncure Daniel Conway, ed. 2010. 220p. pap. 5.49 *(978-1-60386-340-7(0)*, Watchmaker Publishing) Wexford College Pr.

Thompson, Nan. God's Events, Now & Forever: A Study of End-Time Events. 2009. 24.99 *(978-1-60791-685-7(1))*; pap. 14.99 *(978-1-60791-684-0(3))* Xulon Pr., Inc.

Tims, Riva. When It All Falls Apart: Find Healing, Joy & Victory Through the Pain. 2012. (ENG.). 224p. pap. 14.99 ***(978-1-61638-471-5(9)***, Charisma Hse.) Charisma Media.

Vocatio, creator. Pearls of Wisdom from God. 2007. (Illus.). 144p. 11.99 *(978-0-9792342-1-7(2))* Vocatio Pubs.

—Treasures of God's Promises. 2007. (Illus.). 144p. 11.99 *(978-0-9792342-0-0(4))* Vocatio Pubs.

Walters, Winsome. I Can Learn to Pray the Lord's Prayer the Prayer of the Kingdom. 2008. 260p. 25.99 *(978-1-60477-310-1(3))*; pap. 15.99 *(978-1-60477-309-5(X))* Xulon Pr., Inc.

Washington, William T. The New Manifest Destiny: The Pathway to Continuous Personal Enrichment; the Roadmap to Enduring National Greatness. 2007. 187p. per. 12.99 *(978-1-59886-671-1(0))* Tate Publishing & Enterprises, LLC.

Waters, Guy Prentiss. End of Deuteronomy in the Epistles of Paul. 2006. (Wissenshaftliche Untersuchungen zum Neuen Testament Ser.: 221). 302p. (Orig.). pap. 99.50 *(978-3-16-148891-7(1))* Mohr Siebeck GmbH & Co. KG DEU. Dist: Coronet Bks.

Williams, Rose. A Beginning Latin Christian Reader: De Bonis Cogitationibus. 2010. (LAT & ENG.). pap. 19.00 *(978-0-86516-750-6(8))* Bolchazy-Carducci Pubs.

Williams, T. K. The Just Shall Live by Faith. Huntley, Yolanda, ed. 2010. 152p. pap. 12.95 *(978-0-578-05053-9(6))* Vision Pubns.

Wright, Carolyn Shores, illus. Little Messengers of Comfort. 2009. 64p. 9.99 *(978-0-7369-2481-8(7))* Harvest Hse. Pubs.

—Little Messengers of Hope. 2009. 64p. 9.99 *(978-0-7369-2482-5(5))* Harvest Hse. Pubs.

Wright, William. New Testament Quotations from the Old. pap. 1.49 *(978-0-87377-120-7(6))* GAM Pubns.

Xenophontos, George. Duty of Don't: An Inspirational Collection of 101 Original Quotes. 2009. 81p. pap. 11.95 *(978-1-4327-3634-7(5))* Outskirts Pr., Inc.

Yahweh, Almighty & Fair, Collinson. Incest, Sodomy & Other Dirty Passages from the Filthiest Book Ever Written. 2011. 102p. pap. 14.95 ***(978-1-59654-744-5(8)***, olympiapress.com) Disruptive Publishing.

Zacharias, Ravi. There Is a Plan, 1 vol. 2009. (ENG.). 96p. pap. 9.99 *(978-0-310-31849-1(1))* Zondervan.

BIBLE—QUOTATIONS, EARLY

Here are entered works on quotations from the Bible found in early Christian literature, and allusions and references thereto.

Aland, Kurt. Synopsis Quattuor Evangeliorum: Locis Parallelis Evangeliorum Apocryphorum et Patrum Adhibitis Edidit. 15th ed. 2007. 606p. *(978-1-59856-014-5(X))* Deutsche Bibelgesellschaft.

Muncey, R. W. The New Testament Text of Saint Ambrose. 2008. (ENG.). 200p. pap. 31.99 *(978-0-521-09149-7(7))* Cambridge Univ. Pr.

Oxford Society of Historical Theology Staff. The New Testament in the Apostolic Fathers. 2008. 160p. 22.99 *(978-0-559-49252-5(9))*; pap. 20.75 *(978-0-559-49248-8(0))* BiblioBazaar.

BIBLE—READERS

see Readers—Bible

BIBLE—READING

Abingdon. Gospels & the Early Church Runner's Reader: Matthew - Acts. 2008. 128p. pap. 6.00 *(978-0-687-33468-1(3))* Abingdon Pr.

Arias, Benjamin Franklin. Agenda Biblica: Con una Guia de Lecturas Diarias. 2010. (SPA.). 144p. pap. 13.14 *(978-1-4269-3483-4(1))* Trafford Publishing.

Bahkou, Abjar. On the Road to Emmaus: Youth Devotional Journey Through Christian Faith. 2011. 140p. pap. 13.95 ***(978-1-4620-1670-9(7))*** iUniverse, Inc.

The Bible in 90 Days: Whole-Church Challenge - Session 1 with no Teacher, 1 vol. 2009. (ENG.). 2.99 *(978-0-310-94809-4(6))*; (ENG.). 4.99 *(978-0-310-94808-7(8))*; 2.99 *(978-0-310-94807-0(X))* Zondervan.

The Bible in 90 Days: Whole-Church Challenge - Session 10 with Jack Modesett, 1 vol. 2009. 4.99 *(978-0-310-94835-3(5))*; 2.99 *(978-0-310-94834-6(7))*; 2.99 *(978-0-310-94836-0(3))* Zondervan.

The Bible in 90 Days: Whole-Church Challenge - Session 10 with John Walton, 1 vol. 2009. 4.99 *(978-0-310-94344-0(2))*; 2.99 *(978-0-310-94345-7(0))*; 2.99 *(978-0-310-94314-3(0))* Zondervan.

The Bible in 90 Days: Whole-Church Challenge - Session 11 with Jack Modesett, 1 vol. 2009. 2.99 *(978-0-310-94839-1(8))*; 2.99 *(978-0-310-94837-7(1))*; 4.99 *(978-0-310-94838-4(X))* Zondervan.

The Bible in 90 Days: Whole-Church Challenge - Session 11 with Mark Strauss, 1 vol. 2009. 2.99 *(978-0-310-94347-1(7))*; 2.99 *(978-0-310-94315-0(9))*; 4.99 *(978-0-310-94346-4(9))* Zondervan.

The Bible in 90 Days: Whole-Church Challenge - Session 12 with Jack Modesett, 1 vol. 2009. 2.99 *(978-0-310-94842-1(8))*; 4.99 *(978-0-310-94841-4(X))*; 2.99 *(978-0-310-94840-7(1))* Zondervan.

The Bible in 90 Days: Whole-Church Challenge - Session 12 with Mark Strauss, 1 vol. 2009. 4.99 *(978-0-310-94348-8(5))*; 2.99 *(978-0-310-94349-5(3))*; 2.99 *(978-0-310-94316-7(7))* Zondervan.

The Bible in 90 Days: Whole-Church Challenge - Session 13 with Jack Modesett, 1 vol. 2009. 2.99 *(978-0-310-94845-2(2))*; 4.99 *(978-0-310-94844-5(4))*; 2.99 *(978-0-310-94843-8(6))* Zondervan.

The Bible in 90 Days: Whole-Church Challenge - Session 13 with Mark Strauss, 1 vol. 2009. (ENG.). 2.99 *(978-0-310-94351-8(5))*; 4.99 *(978-0-310-94350-1(7))*; 2.99 *(978-0-310-94317-4(5))* Zondervan.

The Bible in 90 Days: Whole-Church Challenge - Session 14 with Jack Modesett, 1 vol. 2009. (ENG.). 2.99 *(978-0-310-94855-1(X))*; 2.99 *(978-0-310-94854-4(1))*; (ENG.). 4.99 *(978-0-310-94326-6(4))* Zondervan.

The Bible in 90 Days: Whole-Church Challenge - Session 14 with Mark Strauss, 1 vol. 2009. 2.99 *(978-0-310-94305-1(1))*; (ENG.). 2.99 *(978-0-310-94327-3(2))*; (ENG.). 4.99 *(978-0-310-94853-7(3))* Zondervan.

The Bible in 90 Days: Whole-Church Challenge - Session 2 with Jack Modesett, 1 vol. 2009. (ENG.). 4.99 *(978-0-310-94811-7(8))*; 2.99 *(978-0-310-94810-0(X))*; (ENG.). 2.99 *(978-0-310-94812-4(6))* Zondervan.

The Bible in 90 Days: Whole-Church Challenge - Session 2 with John Walton, 1 vol. 2009. 2.99 *(978-0-310-94306-8(X))*; (ENG.). 2.99 *(978-0-310-94329-7(9))*; (ENG.). 4.99 *(978-0-310-94328-0(0))* Zondervan.

The Bible in 90 Days: Whole-Church Challenge - Session 3 with Jack Modesett, 1 vol. 2009. (ENG.). 4.99 *(978-0-310-94814-8(2))*; (ENG.). 2.99 *(978-0-310-94815-5(0))*; 2.99 *(978-0-310-94813-1(4))* Zondervan.

The Bible in 90 Days: Whole-Church Challenge - Session 3 with John Walton, 1 vol. 2009. (ENG.). 2.99 *(978-0-310-94331-0(0))*; (ENG.). 4.99 *(978-0-310-94330-3(2))*; 2.99 *(978-0-310-94307-5(8))* Zondervan.

The Bible in 90 Days: Whole-Church Challenge - Session 4 with Jack Modesett, 1 vol. 2009. (ENG.). 4.99 *(978-0-310-94817-9(7))*; 2.99 *(978-0-310-94816-2(9))*; (ENG.). 2.99 *(978-0-310-94818-6(5))* Zondervan.

The Bible in 90 Days: Whole-Church Challenge - Session 4 with John Walton, 1 vol. 2009. (ENG.). 2.99 *(978-0-310-94333-4(7))*; 2.99 *(978-0-310-94308-2(6))*; (ENG.). 4.99 *(978-0-310-94332-7(9))* Zondervan.

The Bible in 90 Days: Whole-Church Challenge - Session 5 with Jack Modesett, 1 vol. 2009. 2.99 *(978-0-310-94819-3(3))*; (ENG.). 4.99 *(978-0-310-94820-9(7))*; (ENG.). 2.99 *(978-0-310-94821-6(5))* Zondervan.

The Bible in 90 Days: Whole-Church Challenge - Session 5 with John Walton, 1 vol. 2009. (ENG.). 2.99 *(978-0-310-94335-8(3))*; 2.99 *(978-0-310-94309-9(4))*; (ENG.). 4.99 *(978-0-310-94334-1(5))* Zondervan.

The Bible in 90 Days: Whole-Church Challenge - Session 6 with Jack Modesett, 1 vol. 2009. 2.99 *(978-0-310-94822-3(3))*; (ENG.). 2.99 *(978-0-310-94824-7(X))*; (ENG.). 4.99 *(978-0-310-94823-0(1))* Zondervan.

The Bible in 90 Days: Whole-Church Challenge - Session 6 with John Walton, 1 vol. 2009. (ENG.). 2.99 *(978-0-310-94337-2(X))*; (ENG.). 4.99 *(978-0-310-94336-5(1))*; 2.99 *(978-0-310-94310-5(8))* Zondervan.

The Bible in 90 Days: Whole-Church Challenge - Session 7 with Jack Modesett, 1 vol. 2009. (ENG.). 4.99 *(978-0-310-94826-1(6))*; 2.99 *(978-0-310-94825-4(8))*; (ENG.). 2.99 *(978-0-310-94827-8(4))* Zondervan.

The Bible in 90 Days: Whole-Church Challenge - Session 7 with John Walton, 1 vol. 2009. (ENG.). 2.99 *(978-0-310-94339-6(6))*; (ENG.). 4.99 *(978-0-310-94338-9(8))*; 2.99 *(978-0-310-94311-2(6))* Zondervan.

The Bible in 90 Days: Whole-Church Challenge - Session 8 with Jack Modesett, 1 vol. 2009. 2.99 *(978-0-310-94828-5(2))*; (ENG.). 2.99 *(978-0-310-94830-8(4))*; (ENG.). 4.99 *(978-0-310-94829-2(0))* Zondervan.

The Bible in 90 Days: Whole-Church Challenge - Session 8 with John Walton, 1 vol. 2009. (ENG.). 4.99 *(978-0-310-94340-2(X))*; (ENG.). 2.99 *(978-0-310-94341-9(8))*; 2.99 *(978-0-310-94312-9(4))* Zondervan.

The Bible in 90 Days: Whole-Church Challenge - Session 9 with Jack Modesett, 1 vol. 2009. 2.99 *(978-0-310-94831-5(2))*; (ENG.). 4.99 *(978-0-310-94832-2(0))*; (ENG.). 2.99 *(978-0-310-94833-9(9))* Zondervan.

The Bible in 90 Days: Whole-Church Challenge - Session 9 with John Walton, 1 vol. 2009. 4.99 *(978-0-310-94342-6(6))* Zondervan.

Briggs, Richard S. Reading the Bible Wisely: An Introduction to Taking Scripture Seriously. 2011. 166p. pap. 19.00 ***(978-1-61097-288-8(0)***, Cascade Bks.) Wipf & Stock Pubs.

Bryce, Brady. Echoing the Story. 2010. 138p. pap. 17.00 *(978-1-60899-818-0(5)*, Resource Pubns.) Wipf & Stock Pubs.

Burchett, Author Walter, BA. Heavenly angel lay lay explains which bible to read, which bible not to read, & Why. 2007. 49p. pap. 14.95 *(978-0-615-17484-6(1))* Crossover Ministries.

Campbell, Lorne. Mettle for New Christians. 2008. 96p. (YA). pap. *(978-1-85345-459-2(1))* Crusade for World Revival.

Carson, D. A. For the Love of God Vol. 1: A Daily Companion for Discovering the Riches of God's Word. 2nd ed. 2006. 400p. pap. 19.99 *(978-1-58134-815-6(0))* Crossway.

—For the Love of God Vol. 2: A Daily Companion for Discovering the Riches of God's Word. 2nd ed. 2006. 416p. pap. 19.99 *(978-1-58134-816-3(9))* Crossway.

Carter, Archie. The Sunday Morning Experience 2. 2010. 330p. pap. 18.99 *(978-1-60957-187-0(8))* Xulon Pr., Inc.

Cole, Martin. Connecting You with God's Word. 2010. (Engage Ser.). (YA). 8p. *(978-1-906334-23-9(4))*; 128p. pap. *(978-1-906334-06-2(4))*; 128p. pap. *(978-1-906334-05-5(6))*; 128p. pap. *(978-1-906334-07-9(2))*; 128p. pap. *(978-1-906334-04-8(8))*; 128p. pap. *(978-1-906334-03-1(X))*; 128p. pap. *(978-1-906334-08-6(0))* Good Bk. Co.

Cooper, Ted. The Bible in 90 Days - Whole-Church Challenge: 14 Sessions, 1 vol. 2009. (ENG.). 160p. pap., instr.'s gde. ed. 9.99 *(978-0-310-94184-2(9))* Zondervan.

Cornes, Andrew. One2One: 24 Studies for Bible Reading Partnerships. 2010. (One2One Ser.). 64p. pap. *(978-1-873166-99-4(0))* Good Bk. Co.

Cover to Cover: A Journey through the Scriptures. 2007. spiral bd. 14.95 *(978-0-9792354-0-5(5))* Dream Word Bks.

Crain, Jeanie C. Reading the Bible as Literature. 2010. (ENG.). 256p. 69.95 *(978-0-7456-3507-1(5))*; pap. 24.95 *(978-0-7456-3508-8(3))* Polity Pr. GBR. Dist: Wiley, John & Sons, Inc.

Davies, Gordon F. Israel in Egypt: Reading Exodus 1-2. 2009. (Library of Hebrew Bible/Old Testament Studies, the Ser.). (ENG.). 204p. 39.95 *(978-1-4411-6508-4(8)*, T&T Clark) Continuum International Publishing Group, Ltd. GBR. Dist: National Bk. Network.

Deanesly, Margaret. The Lollard Bible: And Other Medieval Biblical Versions. 2008. (ENG.). 508p. pap. 63.00 *(978-0-521-09073-5(3))* Cambridge Univ. Pr.

Den Hollander, A A & Francois, W., eds. Infant Milk or Hardy Nourishment? The Bible for Lay People & Theologians in the Early Modern Period. 2009. (Bibliotheca Ephemeridum Theologicarum Lovaniensium Ser.). (GER, FRE & ENG., Illus.). 488p. (C). pap. 116.00 *(978-90-429-2144-3(7))* Peeters Pubs. & Booksellers BEL. Dist: Brown, David Bk. Co., The.

Dennis, A. J. Speaking of God. 112p. 9.00 *(978-0-281-04612-6(3))* SPCK Publishing GBR. Dist: Pilgrim Pr., The/United Church Pr.

Dickson, Lance. The Spiritual Journey of a Confused Man. 2010. 124p. pap. 11.99 *(978-1-60957-555-7(5))* Xulon Pr., Inc.

Earnhardt, John. Bible Marking Guide. 2008. 32p. 1.99 *(978-0-8280-2400-6(6))* Review & Herald Publishing Assn.

Esmond, Dwain. 24-7-365: A Year in the Word. 2008. 377p. (YA). 14.99 *(978-0-8280-2336-8(0))* Review & Herald Publishing Assn.

Fee, Gordon D. & Stuart, Douglas. How to Read the Bible Book by Book: A Guided Tour, 1 vol. 2009. (ENG.). 448p. pap. 6.99 *(978-0-310-28573-1(9))* Zondervan.

Foltz, Thea. Tombstone Treats for God's Kids. 2007. 72p. per. 11.99 *(978-1-60266-515-6(X))* Xulon Pr., Inc.

Funk, Mary Margaret. Lectio Matters: Before the Burning Bush: Through the Revelatory Texts of Scripture, Nature & Experience. 2010. (ENG.). 216p. 19.95 *(978-1-4411-5169-8(9))* Continuum International Publishing Group, Ltd. GBR. Dist: National Bk. Network.

Garcia, Clara E. Peace of Mind II. 2006. pap. 8.00 *(978-0-8059-6764-7(8))* Dorrance Publishing Co., Inc.

Gillaspie, Pam. Ablaze: Igniting Spiritual Passion for Life Through Reading God's Word. 2006. 171p. per. 10.99 *(978-1-932587-64-7(0))* Green Key Bks.

Goodrich O.P., Kevin. Plugging into God's Story. 2007. 220p. per. 14.99 *(978-1-60266-148-6(0))* Xulon Pr., Inc.

Gray, Tim. Praying Scripture for a Change: An Introductin to Lectio Divina. 2009. 127p. pap. 12.99 *(978-1-934217-48-1(4))* Ascension Pr.

Greenstein. Reader Responsibility: The Making of Meaning in Biblical Narrative. 2013. (Library Hebrew Bible/Old Testament Studies). (ENG.). 256p. 120.00 *(978-0-8264-6345-6(2))* Continuum International Publishing Group, Ltd. GBR. Dist: National Bk. Network.

Grey, Mary. How to Read the Bible. 2nd ed. (Illus.). 160p. 10.00 *(978-0-281-05014-7(7))* SPCK Publishing GBR. Dist: Pilgrim Pr., The/United Church Pr.

Grudem, Wayne, et al, eds. Understanding the Big Picture of the Bible: A Guide to Reading the Bible Well. 2012. 160p. pap. 14.99 ***(978-1-4335-3162-0(3))*** Crossway.

Guiden, Timothy Alan. Journey for the Soul. 2008. 372p. pap. 17.99 *(978-1-4389-2411-3(9))* AuthorHouse.

Guthrie, George. Reading God's Story: A Chronological Reading Bible. 2011. (ENG.). 1440p. 19.99 *(978-1-4336-0112-5(5))*; pap. 16.99 *(978-1-4336-0111-8(7)*, Holman Pubs.) B&H Publishing Group.

Hardin, Brian. Passages: How Reading the Bible in a Year Will Change Everything for You, 1 vol. 2011. (ENG.). 224p. pap. 14.99 *(978-0-310-32919-0(1))* Zondervan.

Harnack, Adolf. Bible Reading in the Early Church. 2009. 172p. 26.99 *(978-1-110-64637-1(2))*; pap. 20.75 *(978-1-110-64634-0(8))* BiblioBazaar.

Hickson, Jerry A. God's Word for Me: Six Tracks for Reading Through the Bible in a Year. 2011. pap. ***(978-1-59317-561-0(2))*** Warner Pr. Pubs.

Jaynes, Steve. How to Read the Bible for Understanding & Power. 2006. 344p. per. 24.95 *(978-1-59886-424-3(6))* Tate Publishing & Enterprises, LLC.

Kaylor, Robert. Come to the Manger Scriptures for the Church Seasons Advent 2008. 2008. (Sftcs Ser.). 48p. pap., stu. ed. 6.50 *(978-0-687-64711-8(8))*; 24p. pap. 6.50 *(978-0-687-64721-7(5))* Abingdon Pr.

Kimbrough, Robin Harris. God's Grace Revealed in Word. 2007. 39p. pap. 6.50 *(978-0-687-64182-6(9))*; pap. 9.00 *(978-0-687-64311-0(2))* Abingdon Pr.

Kuhn, Karl Allen. Having Words with God: The Bible As Conversation. 2008. 248p. (C). pap. 25.00 *(978-0-8006-6280-6(6)*, Fortress Pr.) Augsburg Fortress, Pubs.

Lasine, Stuart. Weighing Hearts: Character, Judgment, & the Ethics of Reading the Bible. 2012. (Library Hebrew Bible/Old Testament Studies). (ENG.). 320p. 160.00 ***(978-0-567-43081-6(2)***, T&T Clark Int'l) Continuum International Publishing Group, Ltd. GBR. Dist: National Bk. Network.

Le Grys, Alan. Shaped by God's Story: making sense of the Bible. 2010. 169p. pap. 25.50 *(978-1-4461-4178-6(0))* Lulu Enterprises Inc.

Marnie D. Givhan. An Invitation to Know Him: For Yourself. 2009. 268p. pap. 22.49 *(978-1-4343-1896-1(6))* AuthorHouse.

McKeever, James M. The Victory Bible Reading Plan. 16p. (C). pap. 1.25 *(978-0-86694-102-0(9))* Omega Pubns.

Miller, J. R. Silent Times, a Book to Help in Reading the Bible into Life. 2011. 126p. pap. 12.99 ***(978-1-61203-175-0(7))*** Bottom of the Hill Publishing.

Mulholland, M. Robert & Thompson, Marjorie J. The Way of Scripture. 2010. *(978-0-8358-1034-0(8))* Upper Room Bks.

Mutambanengwe, Florence. Read 31 Smaller Books of the Bible in 31 Days. 2010. (Illus.). 392p. pap. 82.99 *(978-1-4520-1045-8(5))* AuthorHouse.

Newell, Roger J. The Feeling Intellect: Reading the Bible with C. S. Lewis. 2010. 128p. pap. 16.00 *(978-1-60899-138-9(5))* Wipf & Stock Pubs.

Nichols, Stephen J. Welcome to the Story: Reading, Loving, Living God's Word. 2011. 176p. pap. 15.99 *(978-1-4335-2230-7(6))* Crossway.

Patrick, Dan. Second Most Important Book You'll Ever Read, 0 vols. 2009. 240p. pap. 14.99 *(978-0-8499-2935-9(0))* Nelson, Thomas Inc.

Patterson, Donald. Bible Discovery Series: Finding Tools to Read & Interpret Scripture. 2010. 96p. pap. *(978-0-8100-2269-0(9))* Northwestern Publishing Hse.

Peterson, Eugene H. The Invitation: A Simple Guide to the Bible. 2007. (Hollywood Nobody Ser.). (ENG., Illus.). 208p. 16.99 *(978-1-60006-233-9(4))* NavPress Publishing Group.

Phelps, William Lyon. Reading the Bible. 2007. (ENG.). 140p. 35.95 *(978-0-548-06583-9(7))* Kessinger Publishing, LLC.

Pink, Arthur W. Beneficios de la Lectura de la Biblia: Benefits of Bible Reading. (SPA.). 144p. *(978-84-7228-621-4(5)*, 220095) Clie, Editorial.

Poelman, Roger. How to Read the Bible. 2009. *(978-1-933184-66-1(3))* Sophia Institute Pr.

Robinson, Julia M. The Hand of Almighty God. 2010. 140p. 29.99 *(978-1-4500-6430-9(2))*; pap. 19.99 *(978-1-4500-6429-3(9))* Xlibris Corp.

Roozeboom, Bev. Unlocking the Treasure: A Bible Study for Moms Entrusted with Special-Needs Children. 2011. 132p. pap. 16.95 ***(978-1-4497-1599-1(0)***, WestBow Pr.) Author Solutions, Inc.

Sanders, Rachel L. And He Is My Source: My God with a capital G. 2009. 148p. pap. 15.00 *(978-1-4389-1707-8(4))* AuthorHouse.

Scott, James M. The Bible Reader's Companion: Over 2000 Questions & Answers on Every Book of the Bible. 2006. 400p. per. 20.99 *(978-1-59886-353-6(3))* Tate Publishing & Enterprises, LLC.

Smith, Dudley. What's the Bible About? 1. 2010. 171p. pap. 17.99 *(978-0-557-06469-4(4))* Lulu Enterprises Inc.

Smith, William Frank. How Will We Know the Way? A reading guide for the New Testament. 2011. 156p. pap. 16.95 ***(978-1-4575-0327-6(1))*** Dog Ear Publishing, LLC.

Studzinski, Raymond. Reading to Live: The Evolving Practice of Lectio Divina. 2009. pap. *(978-0-87907-231-5(8))* Cistercian Pubns., Inc.

Swain, Scott R. Trinity, Revelation, & Reading: A Theological Introduction to the Bible & its Interpretation. 2011. (ENG.). 168p. 90.00 *(978-0-567-25525-9(5))*; pap. 27.95 *(978-0-567-26540-1(4))* Continuum International Publishing Group, Ltd. GBR. (T&T Clark Int'l). Dist: National Bk. Network.

Tague, Matthew. Read the Word. 2008. 164p. pap. 14.99 *(978-1-60647-633-8(5))* Xulon Pr., Inc.

Thompson, Marjorie J. The Way of Scripture: Leader's Guide. 2010. *(978-0-8358-1033-3(X))* Upper Room Bks.

Tippett, Marilyn. Closing the GAP with Guaranteed Applied Phonics: For Reading in the Bible. 2007. (Illus.). 24p. 20.00 *(978-0-9797257-0-8(4))* Home Education.

Trachtman, Chaim. Women & Men in Communal Prayer: Halakhic Perspectives. 2010. (ENG & HEB.). *(978-1-60280-152-3(5))* Ktav Publishing Hse., Inc.

Tseng, Samuel C. Uncovering Hidden Treasures: Practical Bible Study Methods by Example. 2011. 204p. 33.95 *(978-1-4497-1277-8(0))*; pap. 17.95 *(978-1-4497-1276-1(2))* Author Solutions, Inc. (WestBow Pr.).

Tyndale House Publishers Staff, prod. The One Year Chronological Bible NIV. 2007. (ENG.). 1728p. 24.99 *(978-1-4143-1409-9(4))* Tyndale Hse. Pubs.

Where to Find It in the Bible. 2009. pap. *(978-1-59636-344-1(4))* Rose Publishing.

Wilson, Cheryl. Abigail: Woman of Wisdom, Courage, & Action! Bible Study for Small Groups. 2011. pap. 7.99 *(978-1-61739-836-0(5))* Tate Publishing & Enterprises, LLC.

World Bible Translation Center. Large Print Bible-OE-Easy-to-Read Version. l.t. ed. 2010. 1808p. pap. *(978-1-935189-06-0(9))* World Bible Translation Ctr., Inc.

Yoder, John Howard. To Hear the Word - Second Edition. 2009. 266p. pap. 29.00 *(978-1-60608-928-6(5)*, Cascade Bks.) Wipf & Stock Pubs.

Zondervan Publishing Staff. The Bible in 90 Days: Whole-Church Challenge Leader's Pack, 1 vol. 2009. (ENG.). pap. 54.99 *(978-0-310-94185-9(7))* Zondervan.

BIBLE—RELATION OF N. T. TO O. T.

Ahearne-Kroll, Stephen. The Psalms of Lament in Mark's Passion: Jesus' Davidic Suffering. 2010. (Society for New Testament Studies Monograph Ser.). (ENG.). 256p. pap. 29.00 *(978-0-521-13040-0(9))* Cambridge Univ. Pr.

Ahearne-Kroll, Stephen P. The Psalms of Lament in Mark's Passion: Jesus' Davidic Suffering. 2007. (Society for New Testament Studies Monograph Ser.). (ENG.). 254p. 99.00 *(978-0-521-88191-3(9))* Cambridge Univ. Pr.

Aigrain, René & Englebert, Omer. Prophecy Fulfilled: The Old Testament Realized in the New. Sheppard, Lancelot C., tr. 2011. 288p. 48.95 ***(978-1-258-09575-8(0))*** Literary Licensing, LLC.

Anderson, Bernard W., ed. The Old Testament & Christian Faith: A Theological Discussion. 2010. 286p. pap. 31.00 *(978-1-60899-686-5(7)*, Wipf and Stock) Wipf & Stock Pubs.

Bailey, Randall C. David in Love & War: The Pursuit of Pursuit of Power in 2 Samuel 10-12. 2009. (Library of Hebrew Bible/Old Testament Studies, the Ser.). (ENG.). 39.95 *(978-0-567-37645-9(1)*, T&T Clark) Continuum International Publishing Group, Ltd. GBR. Dist: National Bk. Network.

Beale, G. K. & Carson, D. A., eds. Commentary on the New Testament Use of the Old Testament. 2007. 1280p. (C). 59.99 *(978-0-8010-2693-5(8))* Baker Academic.

Beaton, Richard. Isaiah's Christ in Matthew's Gospel. 2007. (Society for New Testament Studies Monograph Ser.). (ENG.). 260p. pap. 55.00 *(978-0-521-03610-8(0))* Cambridge Univ. Pr.

Blair, Alexander. Christian Ambivalence Toward Its Old Testament: Interactive Creativity versus Static Obedience. 2011. 420p. pap. 46.00 *(978-1-60899-106-8(7)*, Wipf and Stock) Wipf & Stock Pubs.

Boda, Mark J. After God's Own Heart: The Gospel According to David. 2007. 186p. per. *(978-0-87552-653-9(5))* P & R Publishing.

Brickner, David & Robinson, Rich. Christ in the Feast of Pentecost. 2008. (ENG., Illus.). 240p. per. 12.99 *(978-0-8024-1402-1(8))* Moody Pubs.

Carson, D. A. & Williamson, Hugh Godfrey Maturin, eds. It Is Written: Scripture Citing Scripture - Essays in Honour of Barnabas Lindars, SSF. 2009. (ENG.). 408p. pap. 53.00 *(978-0-521-09762-8(2))* Cambridge Univ. Pr.

Casillas, Ken. The Law & the Christian: God's Light Within God's Limits. 2007. (Biblical Discernment for Difficult Issue Ser.). 70p. per. (978-1-59166-797-1(6)) BJU Pr.

Cryer, Frederick H. Qumran between the Old & New Testaments. Thompson, Thomas L., ed. 2009. (Library of Hebrew Bible/Old Testament Studies, the Ser.). (ENG.). 398p. 65.00 (978-1-4411-5692-1(5), T&T Clark) Continuum International Publishing Group, Ltd. GBR. Dist: National Bk. Network.

De Long, Kindalee Pfremmer. Surprised by God: Praise Responses in the Narrative of Luke-Acts. 2009. (Beihefte zur Zeitschrift für die neutestamentliche Wissenschaft und die Kunde der älteren Kirche Ser.). (ENG.). XIV, 331p. 105.00 (978-3-11-022165-7(9)) De Gruyter, Walter Inc.

Dean, Rynold Duane. Evangelical Hermeneutics & the New Testament Use of the Old Testament: If the Bugle Produces an Indistinct Sound... 2009. 273p. lib. bdg. 24.99 (978-0-9824481-0-6(4)) Veritypath Pubns.

Eguridu, Paul. Prayer Works. 2010. (ENG.). pap. 14.99 (978-0-7684-3270-1(7)) Destiny Image Pubs.

Flesher, Paul V. M. & Chilton, Bruce. The Targums: A Critical Introduction. 2011. 575p. pap. 69.95 (978-1-60258-385-6(4)) Baylor Univ. Pr.

Flesher, Paul V. M. & Chilton, Bruce D. The Targums: A Critical Introduction. 2011. (Studies in the Aramaic Interpretation of Scripture). (Illus.). XVIII, 558p. (978-90-04-21769-0(X)) BRILL.

Granerod, Gard. Abraham & Melchizedek: Scribal Activity of Second Temple Times in Genesis 14 & Psalm 110. 2010. (Beihefte Zur Zeitschrift Für Die Alttestamentliche Wissenschaft Ser.). (ENG.). XIV, 317p. 112.00 (978-3-11-022345-3(7)) De Gruyter, Walter Inc.

Gregory, Bryan R. Longing for God in an Age of Discouragement: The Gospel According to Zechariah. 2010. pap. (978-1-59638-142-1(6)) P & R Publishing.

Hartley, Donald E. The Wisdom Background & Parabolic Implications of Isaiah 6: 9-10 in the Synoptics. 2006. (Studies in Biblical Literature: Vol. 100). (Illus.). 430p. (C). 86.95 (978-0-8204-8665-9(5)) Lang, Peter Publishing, Inc.

Horbury, William. Herodian Judaism & New Testament Study. 2006. (Wissenschaftliche Untersuchungen Zum Neuen Testament Ser.: Vol. 193). 268p. (C). 159.50 (978-3-16-148877-1(6)) Mohr Siebeck GmbH & Co. KG DEU. Dist: Coronet Bks.

Huizenga, L. A. The New Isaac: Tradition & Intertextuality in the Gospel of Matthew. 2009. (Novum Testamentum Supplements Ser.). xx, 337p. (978-90-04-17569-3(5)) BRILL.

Isaak, Jon M. & Martens, E. A. The Old Testament in the Life of God's People: Essays in Honor of Elmer A. Martens. 2009. (Illus.). xxvii, 349p. 49.50 (978-1-57506-158-0(9)) Eisenbrauns, Inc.

Jackson, David R. Crying Out for Vindication: The Gospel According to Job. 2007. (Gospel According to the Old Testament Ser.). 238p. per. 12.99 (978-1-59638-025-7(X)) P & R Publishing.

Karrer, Martin, et al. Von der Septuaginta Zum Neuen Testament: Textgeschichtliche Erörterungen. 2010. (Arbeiten zur neutestamentlichen Textforschung Ser.). (GER.). IX, 461p. 182.00 (978-3-11-024001-6(7)) De Gruyter, Walter Inc.

Kim, Kyoung-Shik. God Will Judge Each One According to Works: Judgment According to Works & Psalm 62 in Early Judaism & the New Testament. 2011. (Beihefte zur Zeitschrift far die neutestamentliche Wissenschaft und die Kunde der älteren Kirche Ser.). (ENG., Illus.). XIII, 294p. 210.00 (978-3-11-218955-9(8)) De Gruyter, Walter Inc.

Kim, Stephen S. The Miracles of Jesus According to John: Their Christological & Eschatological Significance. 2010. 240p. pap. 26.00 (978-1-60608-259-1(0), Wipf and Stock) Wipf & Stock Pubs.

Koet, B. J. Dreams & Scriptures in Luke-Acts: Collected Essays. 2006. (Contributions to Biblical Exegesis & Theology Ser.: Vol. 42). (ENG & GER., Illus.). 232p. (C). 57.00 (978-90-429-1750-7(4)) Peeters Pubs. & Booksellers BEL. Dist: Brown, David Bk. Co., The.

Kollmann, Bernd. Die Verheißung des Neuen Bundes: Wie alttestamentliche Texte im Neuen Testament fortwirken. Kollmann, Bernd, ed. 2010. (Biblisch-Theologische Schwerpunkte Ser.). (GER., Illus.). 284p. (C). pap. 41.00 (978-3-525-61616-1(3)) Vandenhoeck & Ruprecht GmbH & Co. KG DEU. Dist: ISD.

Kraft, Robert A. Exploring the Scripturesque: Jewish Texts & Their Christian Contexts. 2009. (Supplements to the Journal for the Study of Judaism Ser.). 288p. (978-90-04-17010-0(3)) BRILL.

Kunhiyop, Samuel Waje & Berding, Kenneth. Counterpoints - Three Views on the New Testment Use of the Old Testment. 2008. (Counterpoints: Bible & Theology Ser.). (ENG.). 224p. pap. 16.99 (978-0-310-27333-2(1)) Zondervan.

Lee, Richard. Understanding Leviathan: The Key to Apostle John's the Revelation. 2009. 280p. 30.95 (978-0-595-70998-4(2)); pap. 20.95 (978-0-595-46137-0(9)) iUniverse, Inc.

Lee, Seung Yeal. Knowing God through Journey & Pilgrimage: A Scriptural Study of Journey, Jesus' Pilgrimages, & Their Significance to the Feasts of Passover, Pentecost, & Tabernacles. 2011. 276p. pap. 30.00 (978-1-60899-819-7(3), Wipf and Stock) Wipf & Stock Pubs.

Mallen, Peter & Mallen. The Reading & Transformation of Isaiah in Luke-Acts. 2008. (Library of New Testament Studies, the Ser.). (ENG.). 258p. 130.00 (978-0-567-04566-9(8), T&T Clark Int'l) Continuum International Publishing Group, Ltd. GBR. Dist: National Bk. Network.

Mathews, Kenneth A. Leviticus: Holy God, Holy People. 2009. (Preaching the Word Ser.). 288p. 32.99 (978-1-4335-0628-4(9)) Crossway.

McNamara, Martin. Targum & Testament Revisited: Aramaic Paraphrases of the Hebrew Bible: A light on the New Testament, Second Edition. 2010. viii, 359p. pap. 32.00 (978-0-8028-6275-4(6)) Eerdmans, William B. Publishing Co.

Meek, James A. Gentile Mission in Old Testament Citations in Acts: Text, Hermeneutic, & Purpose. 2009. (Library of New Testament Studies, the Ser.). (ENG.). 192p. 130.00 (978-0-567-03380-2(5), T&T Clark Int'l) Continuum International Publishing Group, Ltd. GBR. Dist: National Bk. Network.

Meyer, Jason C. The End of the Law: Mosaic Covenant in Pauline Theology. 1 vol. 2009. (ENG.). 352p. 19.99 (978-0-8054-4842-9(X), B&H Academic) B&H Publishing Group.

Moe, John. They Testify of Me. 2007. (Insight Ser.). 48p. pap. 5.99 (978-0-7586-1466-7(7)) Concordia Publishing Hse.

Moyise. Evoking Scripture: Seeing the Old Testament in the New. 2008. (ENG., Illus.). 176p. 34.95 (978-0-567-03325-3(2), T&T Clark Int'l) Continuum International Publishing Group, Ltd. GBR. Dist: National Bk. Network.

Moyise, Steve. Evoking Scripture: Seeing the Old Testament in the New. 2008. (ENG., Illus.). 176p. 120.00 (978-0-567-03324-6(4), T&T Clark Int'l) Continuum International Publishing Group, Ltd. GBR. Dist: National Bk. Network.

Ochsenmeier, Erwin. Mal, Souffrance et Justice de Dieu Selon Romains 1-3: étude Exégétique et Théologique. 2007. (Beihefte Zur Zeitschrift Für Die Neutestamentliche Wissenschaft und Die Kunde der älteren Kirche Ser.). (FRE.). XII, 392p. 182.00 (978-3-11-019696-2(4)) De Gruyter, Walter Inc.

Ochsenmeier, Erwin. Mal, Souffrance et Justice de Dieu Selon Romains 1-3: Étude Exégétique et Théologique. (Beihefte zur Zeitschrift far die neutestamentliche Wissenschaft und die Kunde der älteren Kirche Ser.). (FRE.). XII, 392p. 300.00 (978-3-11-183373-6(9)) De Gruyter, Walter Inc.

O'Donnell, Kevin. Their Hearts Burned: Walking with Jesus along the Emmaus Road: an Excursion Through the Old Testament. 2006. 208p. pap. 11.99 (978-0-8254-6117-0(0), Monarch Bks.) Lion Hudson PLC GBR. Dist: Kregel Pubns.

Ovenda, Job. The Word of God: What it Really Meant. 2009. 610p. pap. 19.95 (978-1-4327-1186-3(5)) Outskirts Pr., Inc.

Parker, Neil R. A Directory of Putative References to the Old Testament in the Gospel of Mark. 2011. (ENG.). 392p. 129.95 (978-0-7734-3937-5(4)) Mellen, Edwin Pr., The.

Penley, Paul T. Common Tradition Behind Synoptic Sayings of Judgment & John's Apocalypse: An Oral Interpretive Tradition of OT Prophetic Material. 2010. (Library of New Testament Studies, the Ser.). (ENG.). 208p. 120.00 (978-0-567-62765-0(9), T&T Clark Int'l) Continuum International Publishing Group, Ltd. GBR. Dist: National Bk. Network.

Porter, Stanley E., ed. Hearing the Old Testament in the New Testament. 2006. (McMaster New Testament Studies). 316p. per. 29.00 (978-0-8028-2846-0(9)) Eerdmans, William B. Publishing Co.

Porter, Stanley E. & Stanley, Christopher D. As It Is Written: Studying Paul's Use of Scripture. 2008. 392p. pap. 44.95 (978-1-58983-359-3(7)) Society of Biblical Literature.

Porter, Stanley E. & Stanley, Christopher D., eds. As It Is Written: Studying Paul's Use of Scripture. 2008. (SBL - Symposium Ser.). 388p. (978-90-04-15749-1(2)) BRILL.

Rascher, Angela. Schriftauslegung und Christologie Im Hebraerbrief. 2007. (Beihefte Zur Zeitschrift Für Die Neutestamentliche Wissenschaft und Die Kunde der älteren Kirche Ser.). (GER.). XII, 261p. 133.00 (978-3-11-019697-9(2)) De Gruyter, Walter Inc.

Rascher, Angela. Schriftauslegung und Christologie im Hebräerbrief. (Beihefte zur Zeitschrift far die neutestamentliche Wissenschaft und die Kunde der älteren Kirche Ser.). (GER.). XII, 261p. 225.00 (978-3-11-184548-7(6)) De Gruyter, Walter Inc.

Scheetz, Jordan M. The Concept of Canonical Intertextuality & the Book of Daniel. 2011. 184p. pap. 21.00 (978-1-60899-516-5(X), Pickwick Pubns.) Wipf & Stock Pubs.

Seitz, Christopher R. The Goodly Fellowship of the Prophets: The Achievement of Association in Canon Formation, 1 vol. 2009. (Acadia Studies in Bible & Theology Ser.). 144p. (C). pap. 20.00 (978-0-8010-3883-9(9)) Baker Academic.

She, King L. The Use of Exodus in Hebrews. 2011. (C). 77.95 (978-1-4331-1381-9(3)) Lang, Peter Publishing, Inc.

Silverman, Jason M. & Daughton, Amy, eds. A Land Like Your Own. 2010. 176p. pap. 20.00 (978-1-60899-454-0(6), Pickwick Pubns.) Wipf & Stock Pubs.

Sparks, Adam. One of a Kind. 2009. 352p. pap. 39.00 (978-1-60608-345-1(7), Pickwick Pubns.) Wipf & Stock Pubs.

Stanley, Christopher D. Paul & the Language of Scripture: Citation Technique in the Pauline Epistles & Contemporary Literature. 2008. (Society for New Testament Studies Monograph Ser.). (ENG.). 412p. pap. 53.00 (978-0-521-07796-5(6)) Cambridge Univ. Pr.

van Cangh, J. -M., ed. Les sources judaiques du Nouveau Testament: Receuil D'essais. 2008. (Bibliotheca Ephemeridum Theologicarum Lovaniensium Ser.). (FRE.). 718p. (C). pap. 122.00 (978-90-429-1903-7(5)) Peeters Pubs. & Booksellers BEL. Dist: Brown, David Bk. Co., The.

Veras, Richard. Jesus of Israel: Finding Christ in the Old Testament. 2007. 142p. per. 11.99 (978-0-86716-772-6(6), Servant Bks.) Franciscan Media.

Waters, Guy Prentiss. End of Deuteronomy in the Epistles of Paul. 2006. (Wissenshaftliche Untersuchungen zum Neuen Testament Ser.: 221). 302p. (Orig.). pap. 99.50 (978-3-16-148891-7(1)) Mohr Siebeck GmbH & Co. KG DEU. Dist: Coronet Bks.

Whittemore, William Stewart. But Who Do You Say That I Am? 2009. 160p. pap. 14.99 (978-1-60791-949-0(4)) Xulon Pr., Inc.

Willis, Mike. Intertestamental Period. 2007. pap. 7.99 (978-1-58427-199-4(X)) Guardian of Truth Foundation.

BIBLE—REVELATION

see Bible—Inspiration

BIBLE—SCIENCE

see Bible and Science

BIBLE—SERMONS

Here are entered works containing sermons which are successively based on at least one whole book of the Bible, virtually forming a commentary in sermon form.

Acatrinei, Nicoleta. Saint Jean Chrysostome et L'Homo Oeconomicus. 2008. 176p. pap. 14.95 (978-1-933275-20-8(0), Orthodox Research Institute) Cocheco Falls Publishing.

Bacote, Vincent, ed. Precepts for Living Commentary Pastor's Edition 2009-2010: Pastor's Edition. 3rd ed. 2009. (Precepts for Living Ser.). 29.95 (978-1-60352-688-3(9)) UMI (Urban Ministries, Inc.).

Baxter, Richard. What we must do to be Saved. 2010. 52p. pap. 12.00 (978-1-4466-3185-0(0)) Lulu Enterprises Inc.

Beck, Norman A. Lectionary Scripture Notes, Cycle B. 2011. 350p. pap. 30.95 (978-0-7880-2636-2(4)) CSS Publishing.

Bell, Richie. Sunday Morning Volume 2: Inspirational Sermon Guide for Busy Pastors. 2011. 144p. pap. 14.95 (978-1-4620-5168-7(5)) iUniverse, Inc.

Belsky, Yisroel. Einei Yisroel: Shemos. 2007. 24.95 (978-1-60091-000-5(9)) Israel Bookshop Pubns.

Black, Harry. Prophecy Sermons with Bible Chart. 2007. (ENG.). 168p. 36.95 (978-0-548-06563-1(2)) Kessinger Publishing, LLC.

Booher, Terry L. Booher Classics. 2006. per. 6.00 (978-1-60208-029-4(1)) FBC Pubns. & Printing.

Brown, Marc D., et al. Does Your Church Have a Prayer? In Mission Toward the Promised Land. 2009. 75p. pap. 9.00 (978-0-88177-567-9(3)) Discipleship Resources.

Burdette, Dallas R. Biblical Preaching & Teaching: Jesus & Our Privileges. 2009. 476p. 36.99 (978-1-61579-085-2(3)); pap. 24.99 (978-1-61579-084-5(5)) Xulon Pr., Inc.

Burgon, Dean John William. Inspiration & Interpretation. 2008. pap. 29.00 (978-1-888328-04-2(5)) Old Paths Pubns., Inc., The.

Churchville, John Elliot. Sermons for Subversives: The Gospel of Jesus for Liberation of the Oppressed & Social Justice for the Poor. 2006. 169p. pap. 12.95 (978-0-7414-3594-1(2)) Infinity Publishing.

Clements, R. Songs of Experience. 192p. 10.99 (978-1-85792-019-2(8)) Christian Focus Pubns. GBR. Dist: Spring Arbor Distributors, Inc.

Company, Css Publishing, compiled by. Lectionary Tales for the Pulpit, Series VII, Cycle B for the Revised Common Lectionary. 2011. (Illus.). 196p. pap. 19.95 (978-0-7880-2665-2(8)) CSS Publishing.

—Navigating the Sermon for Cycle B of the Revised Common Lectionary. 2011. 318p. pap. 39.95 (978-0-7880-2670-6(4)) CSS Publishing.

Coulter, Fred R. God's Plan for Mankind Revealed by His Sabbath & Holy Days: + 4 Audio CD's in MP3 Format. 2007. 608p. pap. 32.95 (978-0-9675479-8-5(9)) York Publishing Co.

Counsell, Michael. The 2012 Canterbury Preacher's Companion: 150 Complete Sermons for Sundays, Festivals & Special Occasions. 2011. 348p. pap. 26.99 (978-1-84825-059-8(2), Canterbury Pr. Norwich) Hymns Ancient & Modern Ltd GBR. Dist: Westminster John Knox Pr.

Cundiff, Margaret. Living by the Book. 2.00 (978-0-687-85689-3(2)) Abingdon Pr.

Currid, John D. Calvin & the Biblical Languages. 2007. (ENG.). 128p. per. 16.99 (978-1-84550-212-6(4)) Christian Focus Pubns. GBR. Dist: STL Distribution North America.

Davis, Carlos. Reclaiming the Faith Sermons by a Liberal Christian Wil Bailey. 2010. 148p. pap. 14.95 (978-0-595-47324-3(5)) iUniverse, Inc.

Deiss, Lucien. God's Word Is Our Joy: Advent, Christmas, Lent & Easter, Cycle A. Date not set. pap. 14.95 (978-0-937690-27-7(9)) World Library Pubns.

—God's Word Is Our Joy: Advent, Christmas, Lent, Easter, Cycle B. Date not set. pap. 14.95 (978-0-937690-29-1(5)) World Library Pubns.

—God's Word Is Our Joy: Advent, Christmas, Lent, Easter, Cycle C. Date not set. pap. 14.95 (978-0-937690-31-4(7)) World Library Pubns.

—God's Word Is Our Joy: Sundays 2-34 of the Year, Cycle A. Date not set. pap. 17.95 (978-0-937690-28-4(7)) World Library Pubns.

—God's Word Is Our Joy: Sundays 2-34 of the Year, Cycle C. Date not set. pap. 17.95 (978-0-937690-32-1(5)) World Library Pubns.

Discover the Sermon on the Mount. (Discover Your Bible Ser.) (KOR.). pap., tchr. ed. 4.95 (978-1-55883-229-9(7), 600235); pap., stu. ed. 3.25 (978-1-55883-228-2(9), 600230) C R C World Literature Ministries/Libros Desafio.

Durham, James. Christ Crucified: The Marrow of the Gospel in 72 Sermons on Isaiah 53. Coldwell, Christopher, ed. & pref. by. Carstairs, John, pref. 2nd ed. 2007. 703p. 45.00 (978-0-941075-46-6(X)) Naphtali Pr.

Dykes, Donna Stokes, ed. Dancing on the Buckle of the Bible Belt. 2007. 160p. per. 11.99 (978-0-9723884-3-6(5)) Pair'o'Docs Pr.

Escobar, Mark A. On Bits & Pieces: Along with Crooked Lines. 2009. 280p. pap. 15.49 (978-1-4389-1932-4(8)) AuthorHouse.

Farrar, F. W. Everyday Christian Life or Sermons by the Way. 2007. (ENG.). 306p. 43.95 (978-0-548-02107-1(4)) Kessinger Publishing, LLC.

Finney, Charles Grandison. Principles of Righteousness Vol. 1: Finney's Lessons on Romans. Parkhurst, Louis Gifford, ed. 2006. (Illus.). 208p. per. 16.95 (978-0-9778063-0-3(1)) Agion Pr.

Fleer, David & Bland, Dave. Reclaiming the Imagination: The Exodus As Paradigmatic Narrative for Preaching. 2009. 25.99 (978-0-8272-3259-4(4)); xi, 191p. E-Book (978-0-8272-3266-2(7)); xi, 191p. E-Book (978-0-8272-3265-5(9)) Chalice Pr.

Hall, David W. Preaching Like Calvin: Sermons from the 500th Anniversary Celebration. 2010. pap. (978-1-59638-097-4(7)) P & R Publishing.

Hobbs, Michael. I Call Him Lord, He Calls Me Son. 2010. 173p. pap. 13.67 (978-0-557-08351-0(6)) Lulu Enterprises Inc.

Hoch, Robert P. Breathing Patterns: A Teacher's Reflections on Calling, Equipping, & Sending. 2010. 174p. pap. 20.00 (978-1-60608-526-4(3), Wipf and Stock) Wipf & Stock Pubs.

Hoeksema, Homer C. Redeemed with Judgment, Volume 1: Sermons on Isaiah, 2 vols. Hoeksema, Mark H., ed. 2007. (ENG.). 464p. 32.00 (978-0-916206-97-0(1)) Reformed Free Publishing Assn.

—Redeemed with Judgment, Volume 2: Sermons on Isaiah, vols. 2, 2. Hoeksema, Mark H., ed. 2008. (ENG.). 640p. 32.00 (978-0-916206-98-7(X)) Reformed Free Publishing Assn.

James. Time to Speak. 224p. 19.00 (978-0-281-05042-0(2)) SPCK Publishing GBR. Dist: Pilgrim Pr., The/United Church Pr.

Keach, Benjamin. The Marrow of True Justification. 2007. 100p. per. 11.99 (978-1-59925-114-1(0)) Solid Ground Christian Bks.

Kinn, James W. Teach, Delight, Persuade: Scriptural Homilies for Years a, B, & C. 2009. vii, 368p. (978-1-59525-026-1(3)) Hillenbrand Bks.

Kollamparampil, Thomas. Jacob of Sarug's Homily on Epiphany: Complete Homilies of Jacob of Sarug: Fascicle 8. 2007. (Texts from Christian Late Antiquity: 4). per. 39.00 (978-1-59333-736-0(1)) Gorgias Pr., LLC.

—Jacob of Sarug's Homily on Palm Sunday: Complete Homilies of Jacob of Sarug: Fascicle 18. 2007. (Texts from Christian Late Antiquity: 5). per. 29.00 (978-1-59333-737-7(X)) Gorgias Pr., LLC.

Letellier, Robert. Sunday & Feastday Sermons: Cycles a, B, & C. 2011. (978-0-8189-1331-0(2), St. Pauls) St Pauls/Alba Hse. Pubs.

Lucas, Colleen. The Bible-Sermon Companion. pap. (978-0-9634547-0-6(6)) Lucas Assocs.

MacArthur, John. Truth Endures: Landmark Sermons from Forty Years of Unleashing God's Truth One Verse at a Time. 2011. 240p. pap. 16.99 (978-1-4335-2450-9(3)) Crossway.

Mahlangu-Ngcobo, Mankekolo. Restore Me: 40 Healing Sermons. 2010. 256p. (ENG.). 29.95 (978-1-4502-1633-3(1)); pap. 19.95 (978-1-4502-1631-9(5)) iUniverse, Inc.

Martin, John C. The Gospel According to Matthew. 2010. 432p. pap. 20.49 (978-1-4520-6225-9(0)); 492p. pap. 23.49 (978-1-4520-2466-0(9)) AuthorHouse.

Maurice, Frederick D. The Prayer - Book Considered Especially in Reference to the Romish System: Nineteen Sermons Preached in teh Chapel of Lincoln's Inn, & the Lord's Prayer: Nineteen Sermons Preached in the Chapel of Lincoln's Inn in the Months of February, March, & April 1848. 2010. 416p. pap. 36.00 (978-1-60899-713-8(8), Wipf and Stock) Wipf & Stock Pubs.

McIntyre, Ralph J. Feeding the Inner-Man: 85 Select Sermons. 2009. 452p. pap. 24.99 (978-1-61579-350-1(X)) Xulon Pr., Inc.

McMickle, Marvin A. Shaping the Claim: Moving from Text to Sermon. 2008. (Elements of Preaching Ser.). 96p. (C). pap. 12.00 (978-0-8006-0429-5(6) Fortress Pr.) Augsburg Fortress, Pubs.

Morgan, G. Campbell. Searchlights from the Word. 2010. (G. Campbell Morgan Reprint Ser.). 424p. pap. 46.00 (978-1-60899-291-1(8)) Wipf & Stock Pubs.

Murphy, Neal. The Psalms. 2008. 544p. 34.99 (978-1-4363-7623-5(8)); pap. 23.99 (978-1-4363-7622-8(X)) Xlibris Corp.

Nan. Twelve Months of Sundays: Life Lessons from Spirit-Filled Teaching. 2008. 27.99 (978-1-60647-616-1(5)); pap. 17.99 (978-1-60647-615-4(7)) Xulon Pr., Inc.

Payne, Brian. Exposing Christianity: My Way of Sharing an Alternative to the Church's Truth. 2007. 76p. per. 16.95 (978-1-4241-9413-1(X)) PublishAmerica, Inc.

Prickett, T. A. A Portrait of Jesus: Sermons from Matthew. 2010. 192p. 24.99 (978-1-4520-1322-0(5)); pap. 14.49 (978-1-4520-1323-7(3)) AuthorHouse.

Richard, Ramesh. Preparing Expository Sermons: A Seven-Step Method for Biblical Preaching. rev. ed. 2007. (Illus.). 224p. (gr. 13-18). pap. 16.99 (978-0-8010-9119-3(5), Scripture Sculp) Baker Bks.

Romauldo Turner. The Bible God's Surprising Dual Guide for Either Truth or Deception. 2009. 560p. pap. 69.50 (978-1-4269-2358-6(9)) Trafford Publishing.

Rothan, Michael W. 61 Minutes: Reflections & Homilies for the Year of Luke. 2009. 232p. pap. 19.95 (978-1-4490-2028-6(3)) AuthorHouse.

Rucker, Pastor Kenneth W. A Pastor's Biblical Formula for Preaching the Word of God: Book of Powerful Sermons. 2011. 380p. pap. 24.95 (978-1-4502-7140-0(5)) iUniverse, Inc.

Service, John. Salvation - Here & Hereafter - Sermons & Essays. 2010. 272p. pap. 29.95 (978-1-4455-9994-6(5)) Palmer Pr., The.

Sheals, William L. Walking in Authority: Biblical Examples for Modern Times. 2007. 104p. per. 11.95 (978-0-595-42441-2(4)) iUniverse, Inc.

Simora, Timothy W. Words to Live By... Food for the Soul, maybe Food for Thought. 2007. 109p. per. 10.95 (978-1-59824-505-9(8)) E-BookTime LLC.

Slater, John. Sermons of John Slater. 2007. 132p. per. (978-1-905022-29-8(8)) Covenanters Pr.

Smith, L. Ted. A Listening Season: Sermons for Advent & Christmas. 2010. 62p. pap. 9.95 (978-0-557-72193-1(8)) Lulu Enterprises Inc.

B

Smith, Sholom. Shabbos with Rav Pam: The Rosh HaYeshivah's Inspiring Thoughts on the Weekly Torah Readings. 2007. (ArtScroll Ser.). xxv, 290p. *(978-1-4226-0578-3(7))* Mesorah Pubns., Ltd.

Spurgeon, Charles H. Sermones Doctrinales.Tr. of Spurgeon's Sermons on Doctrine. (SPA.). 192p. *(978-84-7228-895-9(1)*, 220316) Clie, Editorial.

Stillie, Pastor Dave. One Clear Truth: A Series of Sermons from Each Book of the Bible, Preached to the Body of Christ Meeting at First Southern Baptist Church, Rawlins, Wyoming. 2007. pap. 23.99 *(978-1-60266-075-5(1))* Xulon Pr., Inc.

Tauber, Jack. Divrei Ya'akov: Lessons from Shemot. 2008. 395p. 24.95 *(978-1-934440-00-1(0)*, Devora Publishing) Simcha Media Group.

Taylor, J. Bernard. Looks to Lift the Spirit. 2011. 152p. 29.99 ***(978-1-4568-7318-9(0))***; pap. 19.99 ***(978-1-4568-7317-2(2))*** Xlibris Corp.

Tholuck's Interpretation of the Sermon on the Mount. 2010. pap. 17.92 *(978-1-61143-161-2(1))* Gorgias Pr., LLC.

Turner, William Clair, Jr. Preaching That Makes the Word Plain: Doing Theology in the Crucible of Life. 2008. 130p. pap. 17.00 *(978-1-55635-586-8(6))* Wipf & Stock Pubs.

Upchurch, Cackie & Yeary, Clifford, eds. A Year of Sundays: Gospel Reflections 2009. 2007. (Little Rock Scripture Study Ser.). 88p. per. 2.00 *(978-0-8146-3122-5(3)*, Liturgical Pr. Bks.) Liturgical Pr.

Wilton, Clyde C. The Good News: Book of Sermons. 2011. 212p. 25.45 *(978-1-4269-5991-2(5))*; pap. 15.45 *(978-1-4269-5990-5(7))* Trafford Publishing.

Winn, Robert E. Eusebius of Emesa: Church & Theology in the Mid-Fourth Century. 2011. 304p. 69.95 ***(978-0-8132-1876-2(4))*** Catholic Univ. of America Pr.

Wood, Charles R. Sermon Outlines on the Inner Life, 1 vol. 2006. (Wood Sermon Outline Ser.). 64p. pap. 5.99 *(978-0-8254-4153-0(6))* Kregel Pubns.

BIBLE—SERMONS—N. T.

Augustine. Love One Another, My Friends: St. Augustine's Homilies on the First Letter of John. Leinenweber, John, tr. 2009. 127p. pap. 16.00 *(978-1-60608-386-4(4)*, Wipf and Stock) Wipf & Stock Pubs.

Bales, David O. To the Cross & Beyond. 2010. (Illus.). 136p. pap. 14.95 ***(978-0-7880-2634-8(8))*** CSS Publishing.

Black, Harry. The Four Horses of the Apocalypse & Other Expositions on Revelation, Chapters 1-8. 2011. 38p. 35.95 ***(978-1-258-04308-7(4))*** Literary Licensing, LLC.

Calvin, John. The Mystery of Godliness & Other Sermons: Calvin's Sermons. 2011. 212p. 44.95 ***(978-1-258-04061-1(1))*** Literary Licensing, LLC.

Carter, William G. God in Present Tense: Cycle B Sermons for Pentecost 2, Based on the Gospel Text. 2011. ***(978-0-7880-2671-3(2))*** CSS Publishing Co.

Cartwright, David R. Eyes of Faith: Cycle B Sermons for Pentecost 1 Based on the Gospel Texts. 2011. ***(978-0-7880-2668-3(2))*** CSS Publishing Co.

Christian Art Gifts, creator. John 3:16. 2008. 400p. pap. *(978-1-77036-010-5(7))* Christian Art Pubs.

Chrysostom, John & Ashworth, J. Homilies on the Second Epistle to the Corinthians. 2010. pap. 61.48 *(978-1-61143-366-1(5))* Gorgias Pr., LLC.

Chrysostom, John & Copeland, William John. Commentary on Galatians & Homilies on Ephesians. 2010. pap. 65.80 *(978-1-61143-364-7(9))* Gorgias Pr., LLC.

Chrysostom, John & Cotton, W.C. Homilies on Philippians, Colossians, & 1-2 Thessalonians. Tweed, James, tr. 2010. pap. 85.48 *(978-1-61143-365-4(7))* Gorgias Pr., LLC.

Chrysostom, John & Marriot, Charles. Homilies on the Acts of the Apostles. 2010. pap. 58.60 *(978-1-61143-361-6(4))*; pap. 64.96 *(978-1-61143-360-9(6))* Gorgias Pr., LLC.

Chrysostom, John & Prevost, George. Homilies on the Gospel of St. Matthew. 2010. pap. 67.00 *(978-1-61143-363-0(0))*; pap., pap. 63.64 *(978-1-61143-362-3(2))* Gorgias Pr., LLC.

Chrysostom, John & Tweed, James. Homilies on 1-2 Timothy, Titus, & Philemon. 2010. pap. 63.88 *(978-1-61143-367-8(3))* Gorgias Pr., LLC.

Church, John R. Divine Healing. 2011. 48p. 35.95 ***(978-1-258-02061-3(0))*** Literary Licensing, LLC.

Clarke, John W. The View from the Cross: Cycle B Sermons for Lent & Easter Based on the Gospel Texts. 2011. ***(978-0-7880-2664-5(X))*** CSS Publishing Co.

Crotts, Stephen M. A Fine Gospel for Preaching: Cycle B Sermons for Pentecost 3 Based on the Gospel Texts. 2011. ***(978-0-7880-2667-6(4))*** CSS Publishing Co.

Cueni, R. Robert. When Walls Shift & the Ceiling Collapses: Cycle C Sermons for Pentecost 3, Proper 23 Through Thanksgiving Based on the Gospel Texts. 2012. ***(978-0-7880-2677-5(1))*** CSS Publishing Co.

Digiacomo, James. Sundays with Jesus: Reflections for the Year of Matthew. 2007. 111p. per. 7.95 *(978-0-8091-4482-2(4)*, 4482-2) Paulist Pr.

Doriani, Daniel M., et al. The Incarnation in the Gospels. 2008. v, 227p. *(978-1-59638-140-7(X))* P & R Publishing.

Elder, Robert J. Sermons on the Gospel Readings. 2008. 408p. pap. *(978-0-7880-2544-0(9))* CSS Publishing Co.

Everett, Tony. Show-and-Tell. 2010. (Illus.). 120p. pap. 14.95 ***(978-0-7880-2629-4(1))*** CSS Publishing.

Fleer, David. Preaching John's Gospel: The World It Imagines. 2008. 192p. pap. 20.00 *(978-0-8272-3007-1(9))* Chalice Pr.

Fortner, Donald S. Discovering Christ in Hebrews. 2007. *(978-0-9548624-4-2(9))* Go Pubns.

Gibson Mbs, Dean. A Sermon: If Not God, Then Satan! (John 8. 2011. 90p. 24.99 ***(978-1-4628-8042-3(8))***; pap. 15.99 ***(978-1-4628-8041-6(X))*** Xlibris Corp.

Hasler, Richard A. Facing the Future with Hope: Sermons for Advent, Christmas, & Epiphany: Cycle B Gospel Texts. 2011. ***(978-0-7880-2644-7(5))*** CSS Publishing Co.

Hong, John Sungchul. The Genealogy of Jesus Christ: Evangelistic Sermons on the Covenant from Matthew 1:1. 2010. 96p. 29.00 *(978-1-60947-006-7(0))* Emeth Pr.

Hough, J. W. The Mode of Baptism; a Discourse Delivered in the First Congregational Church, of Jackson, Mich , April 18, 1869, & Repeated April 25 1869. 2011. 30p. pap. 11.99 ***(978-1-4181-9380-5(1))*** MPublishing.

Hughes, Albert. The Whole Armour of God. 2011. 142p. 40.95 ***(978-1-258-05958-3(4))*** Literary Licensing, LLC.

Lenski, R. C. H. Saint Paul: A Brief Series of Evening Texts Made Ready for Pulpit Work. 2008. 247p. pap. 21.00 *(978-1-60608-281-2(7)*, Wipf and Stock) Wipf & Stock Pubs.

Lloyd-Jones, Martyn. Compelling Christianity. 2007. (Studies in the Book of Acts). 288p. 25.00 *(978-1-58134-832-3(0))* Crossway.

—Living Water: Studies in John 4. 2009. 736p. 40.00 *(978-1-4335-0127-2(9))* Crossway.

Lohmeyer, Ernst. Ernst Lohmeyers Zeugnis im Kirchenkampf: Breslauer Universitatspredigten. Kohn, Andreas, ed. 2006. (GER.). 154p. (Orig.). (C). pap. 36.00 *(978-3-525-55382-4(X))* Vandenhoeck & Ruprecht GmbH & Co. KG DEU. Dist: ISD.

MacKenzie, R. Sheldon. The Master Teacher: Sermons from Mark. 2007. 170p. *(978-0-7880-2189-3(3)*, Fairway Pr.) CSS Publishing Co.

Matera, Frank J. Preaching Romans: Proclaiming God's Saving Grace. 2010. 14.95 *(978-0-8146-3318-2(8))* Liturgical Pr.

May, David M. & Graves, Mike. Preaching Matthew: Interpretation & Proclamation. 2007. 152p. per. *(978-0-8272-3005-7(2))* Chalice Pr.

Morgan, George Campbel. Studies in the Gospels V1 the Gospel Acc. 2006. pap. 30.95 *(978-1-4286-4551-6(9))* Kessinger Publishing, LLC.

—Studies in the Gospels V2 the Gospel Acc. 2006. pap. 31.95 *(978-1-4286-4552-3(7))* Kessinger Publishing, LLC.

—Studies in the Gospels V3 the Gospel Acc. 2006. pap. 28.95 *(978-1-4286-4553-0(5))* Kessinger Publishing, LLC.

—Studies in the Gospels V4 the Gospel Acc. 2006. pap. 31.95 *(978-1-4286-4554-7(3))* Kessinger Publishing, LLC.

Papineau, Andre. Homilies to Transform Hearts & Minds. 2010. pap. *(978-0-89390-690-0(5))* Resource Pubns., Inc.

Peale, Norman Vincent. How to Turn Enemies into Friends. 2011. 16p. pap. 35.95 ***(978-1-258-00363-0(5))*** Literary Licensing, LLC.

Phillips, Buran F., tr. from GER. Friedrich Schleiermacher's Interpretation of the Epistle to the Colossians: A Series of Sermons (1830-1831) 2009. 320p. 119.95 *(978-0-7734-4689-2(3))* Mellen, Edwin Pr., The.

Puhalo, Lazar. Sermons on Matthew. Date not set. 67p. pap. 5.00 *(978-1-879038-71-4(4)*, 9041) Synaxis Pr.

Robinson, J. Armitage, ed. St. Paul's Epistle to the Ephesians. 2010. pap. 54.16 *(978-1-61719-325-5(9))* Gorgias Pr., LLC.

Russell, Daniel. Preaching the Apocalypse. 2007. (ENG.). 256p. 42.95 *(978-0-548-09202-6(8))* Kessinger Publishing, LLC.

Rutledge, Fleming. Not Ashamed of the Gospel: Sermons from Paul's Letter to the Romans. 2007. 411p. per. 19.00 *(978-0-8028-2737-1(3))* Eerdmans, William B. Publishing Co.

Sproul, R. C. Romans. 2009. pap. *(978-1-4335-0686-4(6))* Crossway.

—1-2 Peter. 2011. (St. Andrew's Expositional Commentary Ser.). 304p. 27.99 *(978-1-4335-2289-5(6))* Crossway.

Stedman, Ray. God's Unfinished Book: Journeying Through the Book of Acts. 2008. (ENG.). 336p. pap. 14.99 *(978-1-57293-231-9(7))* Discovery Hse. Pubs.

Stedman, Ray C. The Fight of Faith: Studies in the Pastoral Letters of Paul - I & II Timothy & Titus. 2009. (ENG.). 320p. pap. 12.99 *(978-1-57293-266-1(X))* Discovery Hse. Pubs.

Suskovic, Scott. Sermons on the Second Readings. 2008. 378p. pap. *(978-0-7880-2543-3(0))* CSS Publishing Co.

Thomas, Derek. How the Gospel Brings Us All the Way Home. 2011. *(978-1-56769-256-3(7))* Reformation Pubs.

Tozer, A. W. And He Dwelt among Us: Teachings from the Gospel of John. 2009. (ENG.). 224p. pap. 12.99 *(978-0-8307-4691-0(9))* Gospel Light Pubns.

Tyndale, William. The Parable of the Wicked Mammon. 2010. 102p. pap. 34.95 *(978-1-4092-2793-9(6))* Lulu Enterprises Inc.

Watson, Thomas & Kistler, Don. Heaven Taken by Storm, or, The Holy Violence a Christian Is to Put Forth in His Pursuit after Glory. 2007. iv, 143p. *(978-0-9798579-3-5(7))* Northampton Pr., The.

Wood, Charles R. Sermon Outlines on First Corinthians. 2006. (Wood Sermon Outline Ser.). 64p. pap. 5.99 *(978-0-8254-4142-4(0))* Kregel Pubns.

BIBLE—SERMONS—O. T.

Allen, Ronald J. & Williamson, Clark M. Preaching the Old Testament: A Lectionary Commentary. annot. ed. 2007. (ENG.). 309p. 30.00 *(978-0-664-23068-5(7))* Westminster John Knox Pr.

Anonimo. Biblia de Bosquejos y Sermones: Genesis 12-50, 1 vol. 2007. (Biblia/Bosque/Serm Ser.). (SPA.). 472p. pap. 27.99 *(978-0-8254-0726-0(5)*, Editorial Portavoz) Kregel Pubns.

Barkley, Gary W., tr. Origen. 2009. 294p. pap. 29.95 *(978-0-8132-1432-0(7))* Catholic Univ. of America Pr.

Bates, J. H. The Christian Faith the Safeguard of Freedom a Thanksgiving Sermon; Preached in the Presbyterian Church of Antrim, N H , November 29th 1855. 2011. 22p. pap. 11.99 ***(978-1-4181-9124-5(8))*** MPublishing.

Bevere, Allan R. The Character of Our Discontent. 2010. 128p. pap. 12.99 *(978-1-893729-78-0(8))* Energion Pubns.

Brandt, Brad & Kress, Eric. God in Everyday Life: The Book of Ruth for Expositors & Biblical Counselors. 2007. (ENG.). 187p. per. 14.99 *(978-0-9772262-5-2(5))* Kress Christian Pubns.

Bush, Charles Peck. The Fugitive Slave Law: A sermon preached in the Fourth Congregational church, Norwich, Conn. , June 25th, 1854. by Rev. Charles P. Bush, pastor. Publi. 2011. 20p. pap. 11.99 ***(978-1-4181-9070-5(5))*** MPublishing.

Calvin, John. Sermons from Job. Nixon, LeRoy, tr. 2011. 312p. pap. 25.00 ***(978-1-59925-258-2(9))*** Solid Ground Christian Bks.

Copp, Joseph A. The Atlantic Telegraph: As illustrating the providence & benevolent designs of God. A discourse, preached in the Broadway Church, Chelsea, August 8, 2011. 20p. pap. 11.99 ***(978-1-4181-9083-5(7))*** MPublishing.

Css Publishing Company, compiled by. Sermons on the First Readings, Series III , Cycle C. 2009. (Illus.). 426p. pap. 37.95 *(978-0-7880-2619-5(4))* CSS Publishing.

David, Avishai C. Discourses of Rav Yosef Dov Halevi Soloveitchik on the Weekly Parshah: Darosh Darash Yosef. 2011. (ENG.). 472p. 29.95 *(978-965-524-046-7(0))* Urim Pubns. ISR. Dist: Lambda Pubs., Inc.

Davidson, A. B. Waiting upon God. Paterson, J. A., ed. 2007. (ENG.). 388p. 48.95 *(978-0-548-12202-0(4))* Kessinger Publishing, LLC.

Davis, Dale Ralph. The Word Became Flesh: How to Preach from Old Testament Narrative Texts. 2006. (ENG.). 160p. per. 14.99 *(978-1-84550-192-1(6)*, Mentor) Christian Focus Pubns. GBR. Dist: STL Distribution North America.

Desmaretz, John. The Bible & Human Sexuality: What the Old Testament Says About. 2007. (ENG.). 236p. per. 24.95 *(978-1-4241-5859-1(1))* PublishAmerica, Inc.

Everett, Tony. Show-and-Tell. 2010. (Illus.). 120p. pap. 14.95 ***(978-0-7880-2629-4(1))*** CSS Publishing.

Everett, Tony S., et al. Sermons on the First Readings: Series II, Cycle A. 2007. 410p. per. *(978-0-7880-2451-1(5))* CSS Publishing Co.

Gannett, Ezra S. The Atlantic Telegraph: A discourse delivered in the First Church, August 8, 1858. Published by Request. 2011. 22p. pap. 11.99 ***(978-1-4181-9162-7(0))*** MPublishing.

Gibson, Scott M., ed. Preaching the Old Testament. 2006. 224p. pap. 17.00 *(978-0-8010-6623-8(9))* Baker Bks.

Greidanus, Sidney. Preaching Christ from the Genesis: Foundations for Expository Sermons. 2007. 518p. per. 30.00 *(978-0-8028-2586-5(9))* Eerdmans, William B. Publishing Co.

Hill, Robert C., tr. St John Chrysostom. 2009. 288p. pap. 29.95 *(978-0-8132-1496-2(3))* Catholic Univ. of America Pr.

Hodge, Charles. Sermons Preached Before the Congregation of the Presbyterian Church: Corner of Fifth Avenue & Nineteenth Street, at the Memorial services, October. 2011. 78p. pap. 14.99 ***(978-1-4255-0297-3(0))*** MPublishing.

Holbert, John C. Preaching Job. 2011. 204p. pap. 22.00 ***(978-1-61097-278-9(3)***, Wipf and Stock) Wipf & Stock Pubs.

Ironside, H. A. Joshua. 2008. (Ironside Expository Commentaries Ser.). (Illus.). 144p. 19.99 *(978-0-8254-2927-9(7))* Kregel Pubns.

Johnston, Jerry. Daniel: Principles of Leadership, Success, & Achievement. 2007. (Illus.). x, 372p. *(978-1-934438-00-8(6))* First Family Inspirations.

Jones, Martyn Lloyd. Faith on Trail: Why Do the Wicked Prosper? 2008. (ENG.). 176p. pap. 9.99 *(978-1-84550-375-8(9)*, Christian Heritage) Christian Focus Pubns. GBR. Dist: STL Distribution North America.

Kamenetsky, Mordechai. The Parsha Parables Anthology: Stories & Anecdotes That Shed New Light on the Weekly Torah Portion & Holidays. 2008. 880p. 72.99 *(978-1-58330-304-7(9))* Feldheim Pubs.

Kendall, R. T. A Man after God's own Heart. 2008. (ENG.). 400p. 19.99 *(978-1-84550-422-9(4))* Christian Focus Pubns. GBR. Dist: STL Distribution North America.

Long, S. P. Prophetic Pearls. 2007. (ENG.). 512p. 55.95 *(978-0-548-02811-7(7))* Kessinger Publishing, LLC.

Malphono, Narsai. Homilies of Mar Narsai Malphono on Joseph, Son of Jacob. 2010. (SYR.). pap. 25.36 *(978-1-61719-921-9(4))* Gorgias Pr., LLC.

Mandeville, Henry. Reflections on the Goodness of God to a Nation Three Score & Ten Years Old: A sermon preached in the Fourth Presbyterian church, Albany, on Thanksgi. 2011. 30p. pap. 11.99 ***(978-1-4181-9379-9(8))*** MPublishing.

Miller, Dana & Hansbury, Mary, trs. Jacob of Sarug's Homily on Zacchaeus the Tax Collector. 2010. (SYR.). pap. 46.00 *(978-1-61719-660-7(6))* Gorgias Pr., LLC.

Nebenzahl, Avigdor. Jerusalem Stone: Sefer Bereishis, 5 vols., Vol. 1. Klein, Nehemiah, tr. from HEB. & adapted by by. 2010. (ENG.). 388p. *(978-0-9779629-5-2(4))* Rossi Pubns.

Origen. Homilies on Judges. Dively Lauro, Elizabeth, tr. from FRE. 2009. 144p. 29.95 *(978-0-8132-0119-1(5))* Catholic Univ. of America Pr.

—Homilies on Numbers, 1 vol. Hall, Christopher A., ed. Scheck, Thomas P., tr. from LAT. 2009. (Ancient Christian Texts). (ENG.). 196p. 60.00 *(978-0-8308-2905-7(9)*, IVP Acad.) InterVarsity Pr.

Ostrovksy, Solomon. Sermons from the Mount. 2007. vi, 205p. pap. *(978-0-917842-06-1(5))* Frydland, Rachmiel Pubs.

Rutledge, Fleming. And God Spoke to Abraham: Preaching from the Old Testament. 2011. 440p. pap. 30.00 ***(978-0-8028-6606-6(9))*** Eerdmans, William B. Publishing Co.

Saul, Stuart. Clearings Uncommon Words for Common Life. 2006. (ENG.). 25.99 *(978-1-60034-451-0(8))*; pap. 15.99 *(978-1-60034-450-3(X))* Xulon Pr., Inc.

Scheck, Thomas P., tr. from LAT. Origen: Homilies 1-14 on Ezekiel. 2010. (Ancient Christian Writers Ser.). 224p. 31.95 *(978-0-8091-0567-0(5))* Paulist Pr.

Tauber, Jack. Yalkut Yaakov: Insights, Reflections, & Divrei Torah from the Book of Genesis. 2008. 240p. 24.95 *(978-1-934440-52-0(3)*, Devora Publishing) Simcha Media Group.

Welch, John W. The Sermon on the Mount in the Shadow of the Temple. 2009. (Society for Old Testament Study Ser.). 266p. 99.95 *(978-0-7546-5164-2(9))* Ashgate Publishing Co.

Zilbershtain, Yitshak ben David Yosef & Tsoran, Mosheh Mikhael. Aleinu L'shabei'ach: [Alenu Le-Shabeah]: Wisdom, Stories, & Inspiration. 2009. (ArtScroll Ser.). *(978-1-4226-0954-5(5))* Mesorah Pubns., Ltd.

BIBLE—SOCIOLOGY

see Sociology, Biblical

BIBLE—STORIES

see Bible Stories

BIBLE—STUDY AND TEACHING

see also Bible—Textbooks

Aaberg, Dennis G. Topic Bible Studies Addressing Everyday Problems & Questions. 2009. 184p. pap. 16.99 *(978-1-61579-209-2(0))* Xulon Pr., Inc.

Abingdon. Amazing Bible Race Director's Manual, Leg 1: Genesis-Deuteronomy. 2007. 16p. 30.00 *(978-0-687-46520-0(6))* Abingdon Pr.

—PowerXpress Christmas Around the World Disciple. 2.95 incl. cd-rom *(978-0-687-00089-0(0))* Abingdon Pr.

—Walk It Out Director's Manual. 2008. 14.00 *(978-0-687-65222-8(7))* Abingdon Pr.

Abingdon Press, creator. Law: Genesis-Deuteronomy: Leg 1. 2007. (Amazing Bible Race Ser.). (Illus.). 127p. per. 7.50 *(978-0-687-46510-1(9))* Abingdon Pr.

—Word Up! Speaking & Living for Jesus. 2007. (Fifth in Abingdon's Afro-Centric Intergenerational Program Ser.). 62.00 *(978-0-687-64300-4(7))* Abingdon Pr.

Abingdon Press Staff, ed. What's in the Bible about Life Together? What's in the Bible & Why Should I Care? 2009. (Why Is That in the Bible & Why Should I Care? Ser.). 80p. pap. 8.00 *(978-0-687-65304-1(5))* Abingdon Pr.

Abingdon Youth, creator. History Leg 2 Joshua - Esther. 2007. (Amazing Bible Race Ser.). cd-rom 30.00 *(978-0-687-33398-1(9))* Abingdon Pr.

Abington Press, creator. History, Leg 2: Joshua-Esther. 2007. (Amazing Bible Race Ser.). (Illus.). 127p. per. 6.00 *(978-0-687-33408-7(X))* Abingdon Pr.

Adult Bible Studies Illustrated Winter 2008-2009. 2008. pap. 7.00 *(978-0-687-64738-5(X)*, Cokesbury) Abingdon Pr.

Adult Bible Studies Teacher Winter 2009-10. 2009. 8.25 *(978-0-687-65933-3(7)*, Cokesbury) Abingdon Pr.

Adult Bible Teacher: Fall 2006. 2006. pap. *(978-1-59843-066-0(1))* Incorporated Trustees of the Gospel Worker Society, The.

Adult Bible Teacher: Winter, 2006/2007. 2006. pap. *(978-1-59843-067-7(X))* Incorporated Trustees of the Gospel Worker Society, The.

Aldridge, Mark. Calling All Catholics: A Message from the Word of God. 2009. pap. 14.99 *(978-1-60799-942-3(0))* Tate Publishing & Enterprises, LLC.

Allen, Byron. His Excellent Name: A Thirty Day Devotional Study Based on Bible Names of God. 2009. 256p. pap. 16.99 *(978-1-61579-463-8(8))* Xulon Pr., Inc.

Allen, Dale. Discover & Recover. 2008. 172p. pap. 16.99 *(978-1-60791-033-6(0))* Xulon Pr., Inc.

Amazing Bible Race: Letters & Prophecy. 2010. 128p. 10.00 *(978-1-4267-1011-7(9))* Abingdon Pr.

American Bible Society, creator. Large Print Bible-NRSV. l.t. ed. 2011. 2250p. 35.99 ***(978-0-564-09444-8(7))*** American Bible Society.

American Bible Society Staff. The Essential Study Bible: Everything You Need for a Deeper Understanding of the Bible. 2011. (ENG.). 1888p. (gr. 12-18). 19.95 *(978-1-58542-736-9(5)*, Tarcher) Penguin Group (USA) Inc.

Ames, Frank Richtel & Miller, Charles William. Foster Biblical Scholarship: Essays in Honor of Kent Harold Richards. 2011. XX, 358p. *(978-90-04-18711-5(1))* BRILL.

—Foster Biblical Scholarship: Essays in Honor of Kent Harold Richards. 2010. *(978-1-58983-534-4(4))*; *(978-1-58983-533-7(6))* Society of Biblical Literature.

Anders, Max. What You Need to Know about the Holy Spirit in 12 Lessons. 2011. 192p. pap. 12.99 *(978-1-4185-4629-8(1))* Nelson, Thomas Inc.

Anderson, Bernhard W. The Unfolding Drama of the Bible. 4th rev. ed. 2006. (Illus.). 112p. per. 15.00 *(978-0-8006-3560-2(4))* Augsburg Fortress, Pubs.

Anderson, Brian & Whitwer, Glynnis. Small Group in a Box Volume #2: Six Habits of Highly Effective Christians. 2007. 75.00 *(978-0-9798104-7-3(7))* Ampelon Publishing, LLC.

Anderson, Jason. Taking A Minute (Girl) 3. 0: Finding Solitude with God. 2009. pap. 11.00 *(978-1-58588-167-3(8))* Winword Publishing.

—Taking A Minute (Guy) 3. 0: Finding Solitude with God. 2009. pap. 11.00 *(978-1-58588-166-6(X))* Winword Publishing.

Anderson, Neil T. Freedom in Christ Bible: A Life-Changing Discipleship Program. 2008. (ENG.). 104p. pap., stu. ed. 9.99 *(978-0-8307-4653-8(6))* Gospel Light Pubns.

Anderson, Winston. Holy Water: You can Lead a Horse to Water but you can't make him Drink. 2008. 312p. per. 14.95 *(978-1-59800-911-8(7))* Outskirts Pr., Inc.

Andria R. Smith. Guidance from the Heart: A Christian Resource Guide for Young People. 2010. 200p. pap. 16.95 *(978-0-595-48267-2(8))* iUniverse, Inc.

Ankerberg, John & Burroughs, Dillon. Bible Basics in 60 Seconds. 2011. 144p. mass mkt. 6.99 *(978-0-7369-3932-4(6))* Harvest Hse. Pubs.

Applying Luther's Catechism. tchr. ed. 34.95 *(978-0-570-05509-9(1),* 54-0914); stu. ed. 10.95 *(978-0-570-05508-2(3),* 54-0910) Concordia Publishing Hse.

Ark, Dan Vander. Fit to Follow: A Study of Discipleship. (Crossroads Ser.). 103p. pap., tchr. ed. 15.95 *(978-0-930265-78-6(5),* 120055) Faith Alive Christian Resources.

—Honest to God: A Study of the Psalms. (Crossroads Ser.). 109p. pap., tchr. ed. 14.50 *(978-0-930265-41-0(6),* 120005) Faith Alive Christian Resources.

—Live It! A Study of James. (Crossroads Ser.). 99p. pap., tchr. ed. 15.95 *(978-0-930265-69-4(6),* 120025) Faith Alive Christian Resources.

Armistead, Kathy. How God Takes Our Little & Makes it Much Leaders Guide. 2010. 70p. pap. 11.00 *(978-1-4267-0879-4(3))* Abingdon Pr.

Armstrong, Jack. With Friends Like These, Who Needs Enemies. 2007. pap. 12.95 *(978-0-9796747-0-9(0))* ACCP, Inc.

Arnott, John. Manifestations & Prophetic Symbolism in a Move of the Spirit. 2008. 78p. pap. *(978-1-905991-27-3(4))* New Wine Pr.

Arthur, Kay. Having a Real Relationship with God. 2009. (40-Minute Bible Studies). (ENG., Illus.). 64p. pap. 7.99 *(978-0-307-45760-8(5),* WaterBrook Pr.) Doubleday Religious Publishing Group, The.

—How Do You Walk the Walk You Talk? 2009. (40-Minute Bible Studies). (ENG.). 64p. pap. 7.99 *(978-0-307-45763-9(X),* WaterBrook Pr.) Doubleday Religious Publishing Group, The.

—Lord, Teach Me to Study the Bible in 28 Days. 2008. 173p. pap. 11.99 *(978-0-7369-2383-5(7))* 2006. (Illus.). 156p. per. 9.99 *(978-0-7369-1603-5(2))* Harvest Hse. Pubs.

Arthur, Kay, et al, contrib. by. Faithful Abundant True Weekend Retreat & Study Guide: Three Lives Going Deeper Still. 2010. (Faithful, Abundant, True Ser.). (Illus.). 155p. pap. *(978-1-4158-6898-0(0))* LifeWay Christian Resources.

Arthur, Kay, et al. Living Like You Belong to God. 2009. (40-Minute Bible Studies). (ENG.). 96p. pap. 7.99 *(978-0-307-45866-7(0),* WaterBrook Pr.) Doubleday Religious Publishing Group, The.

—Loving God & Others: the Heart of True Faith. 2009. (40-Minute Bible Studies). (ENG.). 96p. pap. 7.99 *(978-0-307-45868-1(7),* WaterBrook Pr.) Doubleday Religious Publishing Group, The.

Artrip, Jerry L. Science in the Pulpit. 2009. 68p. pap. 9.95 *(978-1-4401-0835-8(8))* iUniverse, Inc.

Ash, Christopher. Teaching Romans Volume 2: Unlocking Romans 916 for the Bible Teacher. 2009. (Teaching Ser.). 288p. 12.99 *(978-1-84550-456-4(9))* Christian Focus Pubns. GBR. Dist: STL Distribution North America.

Asomugha, Lilian I. Are You Living in Someone Else s Mind. 2010. 86p. pap. 10.99 *(978-1-60957-534-2(2))* Xulon Pr., Inc.

Atkins, Carla. Bible Study Notebook 2009. 2008. 132p. pap. 12.49 *(978-1-4389-1244-8(7))* AuthorHouse.

Avital, Moshe. Quiz Me on Nach - Mazo, Chaim, ed. 2011. 224p. pap. 20.00 ***(978-1-936778-95-9(5))*** Mazo Pubs.

Avital, Moshe. Quiz Me on the Torah. 2007. 168p. per. 18.00 *(978-965-7344-17-0(4))* Mazo Pubs.

Bacote, Vincent. Precepts for Living Personal Study Guide 2009-2010. 2009th ed. 2009. (Precepts for Living Ser.). 140p. pap. 7.95 *(978-1-60352-684-5(6))* UMI (Urban Ministries, Inc.).

Bacote, Vincent, ed. Precepts for Living Annual Commentary 2009-2010. 12th ed. 2009. (Precepts for Living Ser.). 504p. pap. 16.95 *(978-1-60352-687-6(0))* UMI (Urban Ministries, Inc.).

Bacote,, Vincent, ed. Precepts for Living Annual Commentary 2009-2010. 12th l.t. ed. 2009. (Precepts for Living Ser.). 504p. pap. 19.95 *(978-1-60352-686-9(2))* UMI (Urban Ministries, Inc.).

Bacote, Vincent, ed. Precepts for Living Commentary Pastor's Edition 2009-2010: Pastor's Edition. 3rd ed. 2009. (Precepts for Living Ser.). 29.95 *(978-1-60352-688-3(9))* UMI (Urban Ministries, Inc.).

Baker, Jenny. Through the Bible: 12 Lessons to Help Students Navigate the Big Picture. 2009. 144p. pap. 29.99 *(978-0-7644-3891-2(3))* Group Publishing, Inc.

Bakr, Rita. From Milk to Meat. 2009. pap. *(978-1-61584-464-7(3))* Independent Pub.

Ball, Wanda L., 1st. Kids Ask the Darndest Things about God & the Beginning: Answers from the First Five Books of the Bible. 2007. 132p. per. 15.00 *(978-0-9800069-0-2(2))* Ball Pubns.

Ballester, Gonzalo Torrente. Fragmentos de Apocalipsis. (Classicos Contemporaneos Comentados Ser.). (SPA., Illus.). 536p. 19.95 *(978-84-233-2733-1(7),* DE7337) Ediciones Destino ESP. Dist: Continental Bk. Co., Inc.

Bankens, Pastor Rodney. A New Beginning. 2010. 140p. pap. 14.99 *(978-1-60957-605-9(5))* Xulon Pr., Inc.

Baptist Adults. 1.49 *(978-0-7673-5698-5(5))* LifeWay Christian Resources.

Barclay, William. The New Daily Study Bible, 17 vols., Set. 2011. (New Daily Study Bible Ser.). (ENG.). cd-rom 175.00 *(978-0-664-23806-3(8))* Westminster John Knox Pr.

Barr, Robert. In the World but Not of It-Serving Christ in the Modern World: God's Principles for Living. 2008. (Illus.). 192p. pap. 18.95 *(978-1-4327-3312-4(5))* Outskirts Pr., Inc.

Barrows, E. P. Companion to the Bible. 2006. pap. *(978-1-4065-1083-6(1))* Dodo Pr.

Beal, Timothy. Biblical Literacy: The Essential Bible Stories Everyone Needs to Know. 2010. (ENG.). 368p. pap. 15.99 *(978-0-06-171867-0(X),* HarperOne) HarperCollins Pubs.

BECOMING ONE Bible Study: A Guide for Uniting Jewish & Gentile Believers. 2007. per. 11.95 *(978-0-9790338-4-1(5))* Rodgers, Edwin Inc.

BECOMING ONE (the Book) 2007. per. 10.95 *(978-0-9790338-2-7(9))* Rodgers, Edwin Inc.

Beechick, Ruth. A Biblical Home Education: Building Your Homeschool on the Foundation of God's Word. 2007. (ENG.). 224p. pap. 14.99 *(978-0-8054-4454-4(8),* B&H Bks.) B&H Publishing Group.

Beers, Ronald A. & Beers, V. Gilbert. The Complete Book of Life's Questions: With Answers from the Bible. 2007. (ENG.). 784p. per. 14.97 *(978-1-4143-0730-5(6))* Tyndale Hse. Pubs.

Beginning Old Testament Study. 6.00 *(978-0-687-85086-0(X))* Abingdon Pr.

Bell, James Stuart & Sumner, Tracy. Bible Study Book: All You Need to Start Your Own Bible Study Group. 2007. (ENG., Illus.). 304p. pap. 19.95 *(978-1-59869-398-0(0))* Adams Media Corp.

Bell, James Stuart & Townsend, Susan B. A Cup of Comfort Book of Bible Promises: Stories That Celebrate God's Encouraging Words. 2010. (ENG.). 336p. 14.95 *(978-1-59869-855-8(9))* Adams Media Corp.

Bennett, Christopher Joseph. Here a Little, There a Little: Isaiah 28:9-10. 2008. 160p. pap. 12.95 *(978-1-4327-2495-5(9))* Outskirts Pr., Inc.

Bible Companion Series: Inductive Study Edition. cd-rom 119.00 *(978-1-57822-003-8(3))* Loizeaux/Bible Companion Software.

Bible Companion Series: Professional Edition. cd-rom 299.00 *(978-1-57822-045-8(9))* Loizeaux/Bible Companion Software.

Bible Companion Series: Standard Edition. cd-rom 89.00 *(978-1-57822-029-8(7))* Loizeaux/Bible Companion Software.

A Bible History a Concordia Classic Edition: Teacher Guide. 128p. tchr. ed. 14.00 *(978-0-7586-0290-9(1))* Concordia Publishing Hse.

The Bible in 90 Days: Whole-Church Challenge - Session 1 with no Teacher, 1 vol. 2009. (ENG.). 2.99 *(978-0-310-94809-4(6))*; 2.99 *(978-0-310-94807-0(X))*; (ENG.). 4.99 *(978-0-310-94808-7(8))* Zondervan.

The Bible in 90 Days: Whole-Church Challenge - Session 10 with Jack Modesett, 1 vol. 2009. 2.99 *(978-0-310-94834-6(7))*; 4.99 *(978-0-310-94835-3(5))*; 2.99 *(978-0-310-94836-0(3))* Zondervan.

The Bible in 90 Days: Whole-Church Challenge - Session 10 with John Walton, 1 vol. 2009. 2.99 *(978-0-310-94345-7(0))*; 2.99 *(978-0-310-94314-3(0),*; 4.99 *(978-0-310-94344-0(2))* Zondervan.

The Bible in 90 Days: Whole-Church Challenge - Session 11 with Jack Modesett, 1 vol. 2009. 2.99 *(978-0-310-94837-7(1))*; 4.99 *(978-0-310-94838-4(X))*; 2.99 *(978-0-310-94839-1(8))* Zondervan.

The Bible in 90 Days: Whole-Church Challenge - Session 11 with Mark Strauss, 1 vol. 2009. 2.99 *(978-0-310-94347-1(7))*; 2.99 *(978-0-310-94315-0(9))*; 4.99 *(978-0-310-94346-4(9))* Zondervan.

The Bible in 90 Days: Whole-Church Challenge - Session 12 with Jack Modesett, 1 vol. 2009. 2.99 *(978-0-310-94840-7(1))*; 2.99 *(978-0-310-94842-1(5))*; 4.99 *(978-0-310-94841-4(X))* Zondervan.

The Bible in 90 Days: Whole-Church Challenge - Session 12 with Mark Strauss, 1 vol. 2009. 4.99 *(978-0-310-94348-8(5))*; 2.99 *(978-0-310-94349-5(3))*; 2.99 *(978-0-310-94316-7(7))* Zondervan.

The Bible in 90 Days: Whole-Church Challenge - Session 13 with Jack Modesett, 1 vol. 2009. 2.99 *(978-0-310-94843-8(6))*; 4.99 *(978-0-310-94844-5(4))*; 2.99 *(978-0-310-94845-2(2))* Zondervan.

The Bible in 90 Days: Whole-Church Challenge - Session 13 with Mark Strauss, 1 vol. 2009. 4.99 *(978-0-310-94350-1(7))*; 2.99 *(978-0-310-94317-4(5))*; (ENG.). 2.99 *(978-0-310-94351-8(5))* Zondervan.

The Bible in 90 Days: Whole-Church Challenge - Session 14 with Jack Modesett, 1 vol. 2009. (ENG.). 4.99 *(978-0-310-94326-6(4))*; 2.99 *(978-0-310-94854-4(1))*; (ENG.). 2.99 *(978-0-310-94855-1(X))* Zondervan.

The Bible in 90 Days: Whole-Church Challenge - Session 14 with Mark Strauss, 1 vol. 2009. 2.99 *(978-0-310-94305-1(1))*; (ENG.). 4.99 *(978-0-310-94853-7(3))*; (ENG.). 2.99 *(978-0-310-94327-3(2))* Zondervan.

The Bible in 90 Days: Whole-Church Challenge - Session 2 with Jack Modesett, 1 vol. 2009. (ENG.). 4.99 *(978-0-310-94811-7(8))*; 2.99 *(978-0-310-94810-0(X))*; (ENG.). 2.99 *(978-0-310-94812-4(6))* Zondervan.

The Bible in 90 Days: Whole-Church Challenge - Session 2 with John Walton, 1 vol. 2009. 2.99 *(978-0-310-94306-8(X))*; (ENG.). 2.99 *(978-0-310-94329-7(9))*; (ENG.). 4.99 *(978-0-310-94328-0(0))* Zondervan.

The Bible in 90 Days: Whole-Church Challenge - Session 3 with Jack Modesett, 1 vol. 2009. (ENG.). 2.99 *(978-0-310-94815-5(0))*; 2.99 *(978-0-310-94813-1(4))*; (ENG.). 4.99 *(978-0-310-94814-8(2))* Zondervan.

The Bible in 90 Days: Whole-Church Challenge - Session 3 with John Walton, 1 vol. 2009. 2.99 *(978-0-310-94307-5(8))*; (ENG.). 2.99 *(978-0-310-94331-0(0))*; (ENG.). 4.99 *(978-0-310-94330-3(2))* Zondervan.

The Bible in 90 Days: Whole-Church Challenge - Session 4 with Jack Modesett, 1 vol. 2009. (ENG.). 4.99 *(978-0-310-94817-9(7))*; (ENG.). 2.99 *(978-0-310-94818-6(5))*; 2.99 *(978-0-310-94816-2(9))* Zondervan.

The Bible in 90 Days: Whole-Church Challenge - Session 4 with John Walton, 1 vol. 2009. (ENG.). 2.99 *(978-0-310-94333-4(7))*; 2.99 *(978-0-310-94308-2(6))*; (ENG.). 4.99 *(978-0-310-94332-7(9))* Zondervan.

The Bible in 90 Days: Whole-Church Challenge - Session 5 with Jack Modesett, 1 vol. 2009. (ENG.). 2.99 *(978-0-310-94821-6(5))*; (ENG.). 4.99 *(978-0-310-94820-9(7))*; 2.99 *(978-0-310-94819-3(3))* Zondervan.

The Bible in 90 Days: Whole-Church Challenge - Session 5 with John Walton, 1 vol. 2009. 2.99 *(978-0-310-94309-9(4))*; (ENG.). 4.99 *(978-0-310-94334-1(5))*; (ENG.). 2.99 *(978-0-310-94335-8(3))* Zondervan.

The Bible in 90 Days: Whole-Church Challenge - Session 6 with Jack Modesett, 1 vol. 2009. (ENG.). 2.99 *(978-0-310-94824-7(X))*; 2.99 *(978-0-310-94822-3(3))*; (ENG.). 4.99 *(978-0-310-94823-0(1))* Zondervan.

The Bible in 90 Days: Whole-Church Challenge - Session 6 with John Walton, 1 vol. 2009. (ENG.). 4.99 *(978-0-310-94336-5(1))*; 2.99 *(978-0-310-94310-5(8))*; (ENG.). 2.99 *(978-0-310-94337-2(X))* Zondervan.

The Bible in 90 Days: Whole-Church Challenge - Session 7 with Jack Modesett, 1 vol. 2009. (ENG.). 2.99 *(978-0-310-94827-8(4))*; 2.99 *(978-0-310-94825-4(8))*; (ENG.). 4.99 *(978-0-310-94826-1(6))* Zondervan.

The Bible in 90 Days: Whole-Church Challenge - Session 7 with John Walton, 1 vol. 2009. (ENG.). 4.99 *(978-0-310-94338-9(8))*; 2.99 *(978-0-310-94311-2(6))*; (ENG.). 2.99 *(978-0-310-94339-6(6))* Zondervan.

The Bible in 90 Days: Whole-Church Challenge - Session 8 with Jack Modesett, 1 vol. 2009. 2.99 *(978-0-310-94828-5(2))*; (ENG.). 4.99 *(978-0-310-94829-2(0))*; (ENG.). 2.99 *(978-0-310-94830-8(4))* Zondervan.

The Bible in 90 Days: Whole-Church Challenge - Session 8 with John Walton, 1 vol. 2009. (ENG.). 2.99 *(978-0-310-94341-9(8))*; 2.99 *(978-0-310-94312-9(4))*; (ENG.). 4.99 *(978-0-310-94340-2(X))* Zondervan.

The Bible in 90 Days: Whole-Church Challenge - Session 9 with Jack Modesett, 1 vol. 2009. 2.99 *(978-0-310-94831-5(2))*; (ENG.). 4.99 *(978-0-310-94832-2(0))*; (ENG.). 2.99 *(978-0-310-94833-9(9))* Zondervan.

The Bible in 90 Days: Whole-Church Challenge - Session 9 with John Walton, 1 vol. 2009. 4.99 *(978-0-310-94342-6(6))* Zondervan.

Bible Study Combo: Alba House Gospels & Who Do You Say That I Am? 472p. 10.00 *(978-0-8189-0681-7(2))* St Pauls/Alba Hse. Pubs.

The Bible Study Guide, Vol. 6. 2007. 100.00 *(978-0-9796940-0-4(0))* Foundations Publishing.

BibleZone Live! All Ages at Jesus' Feet. incl. audio compact disk *(978-0-687-04240-1(2))* Abingdon Pr.

BibleZone Live! All Ages by the Waters. incl. audio compact disk *(978-0-687-04231-9(3))* Abingdon Pr.

BibleZone Live! All Ages in a Foreign Land. incl. audio compact disk *(978-0-687-04243-2(7))* Abingdon Pr.

BibleZone Live! All Ages in God's House. incl. audio compact disk *(978-0-687-04236-4(4))* Abingdon Pr.

BibleZone Live! All Ages in Jerusalem. incl. audio compact disk *(978-0-687-04238-8(0))* Abingdon Pr.

BibleZone Live! All Ages in the City of David. incl. audio compact disk *(978-0-687-04237-1(2))* Abingdon Pr.

BibleZone Live! All Ages in the Garden. incl. audio compact disk *(978-0-687-04233-3(X))* Abingdon Pr.

BibleZone Live! All Ages in the Land of the Messiah. incl. audio compact disk *(978-0-687-04241-8(0))* Abingdon Pr.

BibleZone Live! All Ages in the Peaceful Kingdom. incl. audio compact disk *(978-0-687-04232-6(1))* Abingdon Pr.

BibleZone Live! All Ages in the Wilderness. incl. audio compact disk *(978-0-687-04234-0(8))* Abingdon Pr.

BibleZone Live! All Ages Inside Mud & Stone. incl. audio compact disk *(978-0-687-04239-5(9))* Abingdon Pr.

BibleZone Live! All Ages on the Road. incl. audio compact disk *(978-0-687-04242-5(9))* Abingdon Pr.

BibleZone Live! Older Elementary Teacher Book by the Waters. 29.99 *(978-0-687-08399-2(0))* Abingdon Pr.

BibleZone Live! Preschool Teacher Book by the Waters. 29.99 *(978-0-687-08388-6(5))* Abingdon Pr.

Bielo, James. Words upon the Word: An Ethnography of Evangelical Group Bible Study. 2009. (ENG.). 208p. 70.00 *(978-0-8147-9121-9(2))*; pap. 21.00 *(978-0-8147-9122-6(0))* New York Univ. Pr.

Bigelow, Kevin Jay. A Biblical Quest for Truth: A Personal or Small Group Study Guide. 2009. pap. 12.99 *(978-1-60799-447-3(X))* Tate Publishing & Enterprises, LLC.

Binz, Stephen J. Introduction to the Bible: A Catholic Guide to Studying Scripture. 2007. 90p. per. 8.95 *(978-0-8146-1700-7(X))* Liturgical Pr.

Bird, Richard. The Integrated Gospels. 2010. 242p. pap. 15.99 *(978-1-60957-329-4(3))* Xulon Pr., Inc.

Black, Suzy. Faith & Finance: Creating Godly Wealth in A Worldly System. 2009. 164p. pap. 14.99 *(978-1-60791-660-4(6))* Xulon Pr., Inc.

Blackaby, Henry, et al. Encounters with God: Life-Changing Encounters with God, 0 vols. 2007. 208p. pap. 17.99 *(978-1-4185-2804-1(8))* Nelson, Thomas Inc.

—Hebrews, 0 vols. 2008. (Encounters with God Ser.). 128p. pap. 9.99 *(978-1-4185-2652-8(5))* Nelson, Thomas Inc.

—James, 0 vols. 2008. (Encounters with God Ser.). 96p. pap. 9.99 *(978-1-4185-2653-5(3))* Nelson, Thomas Inc.

Blair, John Michael. Who Is Jesus? Deep Truths of the Bible Revealed in Small Group Bible Studies. 2011. 240p. 33.95 ***(978-1-4497-3056-7(6))***; pap. 17.95 ***(978-1-4497-3055-0(8))*** Author Solutions, Inc. (WestBow Pr.).

Blanchard, John. How to Enjoy Your Bible. 2007. 185p. per. *(978-0-85234-670-9(0))* Evangelical Pr.

Boer, Roland. Bakhtin & Genre Theory in Biblical Studies. 2007. (SBL - Semeia Studies). *(978-90-04-15737-8(9))* BRILL.

—Last Stop Before Antarctica: The Bible & Postcolonialism in Australia. 2nd ed. 2008. 217p. (C). *(978-90-04-13080-7(2))* BRILL.

—Last Stop Before Antarctica: The Bible & Postcolonialism in Australia. 2nd ed. 2008. 216p. pap. 24.95 *(978-1-58983-348-7(1))* Society of Biblical Literature.

Boer, Roland, ed. Bakhtin & Genre Theory in Biblical Studies. 2007. 248p. per. 25.95 *(978-1-58983-276-3(0))* Society of Biblical Literature.

Bohren, H. Benjamin, et al. And Still We Rise: A Six-Part Study on Personal & Congregational Transformation. 2007. (Illus.). 37p. pap. 19.99 *(978-0-8272-0054-8(4))* Chalice Pr.

Bolton, B. J. Trabajando Con los Ninos: ICL Bible Learning Activities. (SPA.). 208p. *(978-84-7228-684-9(3),* 220900) Clie, Editorial.

Bondar, Alan. Reading the Bible Through New Covenant Eyes, 1 vol. 2010. 336p. pap. 29.95 *(978-1-4489-8428-2(9))* PublishAmerica, Inc.

Booher, Terry L. Choice Bible Chapters. 2006. per. 3.00 *(978-1-60208-014-0(3))* FBC Pubns. & Printing.

Booth, Edwin P. Letters to Live By: A Course for Young People. 2011. 158p. 41.95 ***(978-1-258-09144-6(5))*** Literary Licensing, LLC.

Boyd, Eleanor. The Gospel in Genesis. 2008. 168p. pap. 9.95 *(978-0-9769695-7-0(2))* Polyventure Pubns.

Boyd-Taylor, C. Reading Between the Lines: The Interlinear Paradigm for Septuagint Studies. 2011. (Biblical Tools & Studies). (ENG.). 472p. (C). 108.00 *(978-90-429-2250-1(8))* Peeters Pubs. & Booksellers BEL. Dist: Brown, David Bk. Co., The.

Bradberry, Mary Ann. WEE Learn: Curriculum Guide for Pre-K. 2007. (Illus.). 688p. 219.95 *(978-1-4158-5202-6(2))* LifeWay Christian Resources.

Bradfield, B. Wayne. No One Has Hired Us: Bible Truths for the Unemployed. 2011. 116p. pap. 11.95 *(978-1-4497-0943-3(5),* WestBow Pr.) Author Solutions, Inc.

Braley, Ron. Finding the End of the World. 2011. 516p. 38.99 ***(978-1-61379-145-5(3))***; pap. 26.99 ***(978-1-61379-144-8(5))*** Xulon Pr., Inc.

Brathwaite, Chris. Jude: A Biblical Study of the Book of Jude. 2010. 76p. pap. 14.95 *(978-1-934449-38-7(5))* Legacy Publishing Services, Inc.

—Walking with James: A Biblical Study of the Book of James. 2007. 76p. per. 14.95 *(978-0-9776777-9-5(6))* Legacy Publishing Services, Inc.

Brehm, David. Celebrate the Sunday Readings: Cycle C. 258p. pap. 24.95 *(978-0-15-950608-0(5))* Harcourt Religion Pubs.

Breslauer, S. Daniel. Decoding Religion in the Bible: Learning to Recognize Diversity of Biblical Texts. 2006. (C). pap. 30.00 net. *(978-1-59738-001-0(6))* Sloan Publishing.

Brestin, Dee. The God of All Comfort Bible Study Guide: Finding Your Way into His Arms Through Scripture & Song, 1 vol. 2009. (ENG.). 208p. pap. 12.99 *(978-0-310-94882-7(7))* Zondervan.

Bridgeman, Les. A Teacher's Notebook. 2010. 344p. pap. 31.95 *(978-1-4497-0114-7(0,* WestBow Pr.) Author Solutions, Inc.

Britt, Don Juan. Serpent's Kiss: The Bible's Best-Kept Secrets Exposed. 2009. 64p. pap. 12.50 *(978-1-4269-1709-7(0))* Trafford Publishing.

Brown, Joyce. Discovering Together. 2007. 16p. 2.00 *(978-0-687-49186-5(X))* Abingdon Pr.

—Learning to Use My Bible: A Special Study for Children in Grades 3 & 4. 2007. (Illus.). 96p. pap., tchr. ed. 31.50 *(978-0-687-64567-1(0))* Abingdon Pr.

Brown, Marc D., et al. Does Your Church Have a Prayer? In Mission Toward the Promised Land. 2009. 75p. pap. 9.00 *(978-0-88177-567-9(3))* Discipleship Resources.

Brown, Michael Joseph. What They Don't Tell You, Second Edition: A Survivor's Guide to Biblical Studies. 2011. (ENG.). 176p. pap. 16.95 *(978-0-664-23594-9(8))* Westminster John Knox Pr.

Bruce, Barbara A. Triangular Teaching: A New Way of Teaching the Bible to Adults. 2007. (Illus.). 192p. per. 15.00 *(978-0-687-64352-3(X))* Abingdon Pr.

Bruce, Frederick Fyvie. The Pauline Circle. 2006. 106p. pap. 15.00 *(978-1-59752-982-2(6),* Wipf and Stock) Wipf & Stock Pubs.

Bull, Michael. Bible Matrix: An Introduction to the DNA of the Scriptures. 2010. 236p. (ENG.). 33.95 *(978-1-4497-0264-9(3))*; pap. 17.95 *(978-1-4497-0263-2(5))* Author Solutions, Inc. (WestBow Pr.).

Burdette, Dallas R. Biblical Preaching & Teaching. 2010. 758p. pap. 31.99 *(978-1-60957-918-0(6))* Xulon Pr., Inc.

Burrell, Jackie. The King: Drawing Closer to the Heart of God. 2010. pap. 12.99 *(978-1-61566-145-9(X))* Tate Publishing & Enterprises, LLC.

Burt, C. David, ed. The Miracle of Pentecost: Acts 2:1-11 in many different Languages. 2007. lib. bdg. 75.00 *(978-0-9793800-6-8(5))* Partridge Hill Pr.

Burton, Sharon. Let the Children Come to Me: Bible Stories for Children. 2011. pap. 8.99 *(978-1-61739-243-6(X))* Tate Publishing & Enterprises, LLC.

Butler, Basil Christopher. The Catholic Church & the Bible. 2011. *(978-1-933184-79-1(5))* Sophia Institute Pr.

Caesar, Fran. Love Is All: A Love Story. 2009. 136p. pap. 15.99 *(978-1-4389-2456-4(9))* AuthorHouse.

Call to Me: 2007 Elementary School Planner - NIV Scripture. 2007. 128p. spiral bd. 10.00 *(978-0-9794300-0-8(3),* 7-ES-N) God's Word in Time.

Call to Me: 2007 High School Planner - KJV Scripture. 2007. 128p. spiral bd. 10.00 *(978-0-9794300-4-6(6),* 7-HS-K) God's Word in Time.

Call to Me: 2007 High School Planner - NIV Scripture. 2007. 128p. spiral bd. 10.00 *(978-0-9794300-2-2(X),* 7-HS-N) God's Word in Time.

Call to Me: 2007 Middle School Planner - KJV Scripture. 2007. 128p. spiral bd. 10.00 *(978-0-9794300-3-9(8),* 7-MS-K) God's Word in Time.

Call to Me: 2007 Middle School Planner - NIV Scripture. 2007. 128p. spiral bd. 10.00 *(978-0-9794300-1-5(1),* 7-MS-N) God's Word in Time.

Campbell, Tracey L. The Spiritual Ties to Physical Health: A Biblical Study. 2010. (Illus.). 178p. pap. 14.95 *(978-1-4327-4811-1(4))* Outskirts Pr., Inc.

Capaccio, Salvatore. Crying Wisdom. 2010. 328p. pap. 18.99 *(978-1-60957-525-0(3))* Xulon Pr., Inc.

B

Carlisle, Randy. A Coach's Guide to Bible Quizzing. 2010. 155p. pap. 14.00 (978-0-557-54188-1(3)) Lulu Enterprises Inc.

Carver, Freda. El Emperador De los Muertos: Emperor of Death. (SPA.). (978-84-399-3992-4(2), 220351) Clie, Editorial.

Castleman, Robbie F. The Story of Scripture: The Unfolding Drama of the Bible. 2008. (LifeGuide Bible Studies). (ENG.). 96p. pap. 8.00 (978-0-8308-3129-6(0), IVP Conn.) InterVarsity Pr.

Cavins, Jeff, et al. The Bible Timeline 4-Part Study: Study Materials. 2007. (Great Adventure Ser.). 44.95 (978-1-932645-98-9(5)) Ascension Pr.

Cburnett, The Scribe. A Parallel Guide to the Scriptures: ~ it Is Written ~. 2011. 160p. 24.99 **(978-1-4634-0972-2(9))**; pap. 16.95 **(978-1-4634-0973-9(7))** AuthorHouse.

Cervone, John & Fleagle, Arnold R. Foundations 1: Basic Building Block for Building a Life of Faith. 2008. 79p. (978-1-60066-093-1(2)) WingSpread Publishers.

Chambers, Arron & Karpenske, Nancy. Go! Group Member Discussion Guide: From Studio Audience to Center Stage. 2009. (ENG.). 64p. pap. 6.99 (978-0-7847-2283-1(8)) Standard Publishing.

Chapman, C. R. Apocalyptic Tremors: Study the Revelation Like Never Before. 2011. 260p. pap. 27.95 **(978-1-4497-1961-6(9)**, WestBow Pr.) Author Solutions, Inc.

Chelson, Paul & Dyer, Craig. Training Conference Notebook. 2010. (Christianity Explored Ser.). 24p. pap. (978-1-906334-66-6(8)) Good Bk. Co.

Chester, Tim. Mark 1-8: the Coming King: Ten Studies for Individuals or Groups. 2010. (Good Book Guides). 96p. pap. (978-1-904889-28-1(X)) Good Bk. Co.

Chester, Tim & Moll, Ed. Gospel-Centred Family: Becoming the Family God Wants You to Be. 2010. (Gospel-centred Ser.). 96p. pap. (978-1-906334-70-3(6)) Good Bk. Co.

Chesterton, Chris & Ward, David T. 144 Talks for Totally Awesome Kids: Messages with a Meaning For 8-12s, 1 vol. 2007. (Illus.). 368p. per. 19.99 (978-0-8254-6147-7(2), Monarch Bks.) Lion Hudson PLC GBR. Dist: Kregel Pubns.

Christian Growth. 0.75 (978-0-89265-510-6(0)) Randall Hse. Pubns.

Christmyer, Sarah. A Quick Journey Through the Bible. 2007. (Great Adventure Ser.). 24.95 (978-1-934217-18-4(2)) Ascension Pr.

—A Quick Journey Through the Bible: 8-Part Leader's Guide. 2007. 16.95 (978-1-934217-12-2(3)) Ascension Pr.

—A Quick Journey Through the Bible 8-Part Student Workbook: 8-Part Student Workbook. 2007. 11.95 (978-1-934217-11-5(5)) Ascension Pr.

—A Quick Journey Through the Bible Student Pack: An 8-Part Introduction to the Bible Timeline. 2007. (Great Adventure Ser.). 19.95 (978-1-934217-17-7(4)) Ascension Pr.

Claim it! Feel it! Live it! Youth Ministry Sampler. 2007. 70.00 (978-0-687-64413-1(5)) Abingdon Pr.

Clergyman, A. Thoughts on the Virgin Birth - an Irenicon. 2009. pap. 29.00 (978-1-60724-275-8(3)) Gorgias Pr., LLC.

Cloud, David W. Dynamic Equivalency: Death Knell of Pure Scripture. Date not set. 47p. pap. 2.50 (978-1-58318-040-2(0), WOL059B) Way of Life Literature.

Cloud, Henry, et al. ReGroup: Training Groups to Be Groups, 1 vol. 2007. (ENG.). 160p. pap., instr.'s gde. ed. 9.99 (978-0-310-27785-9(X)) Zondervan.

Cloud, Thomas & Ragsdale, Trey. Circle of Fellowship: A Men's Small Group Discussion Guide Designed to Make Disciples of Jesus. 2009. 152p. pap. 14.99 (978-1-60791-199-9(X)) Xulon Pr., Inc.

Clubb, Ray. God's Guidance: How it Works; How to Get It. 2011. 184p. pap. 16.03 **(978-1-4490-7295-7(X))** AuthorHouse.

Cobb, Randall. Why Bible Study?, 1 vol. 2009. 81p. pap. 16.95 (978-1-60836-267-7(1)) PublishAmerica, Inc.

Coffen, Richard W. Wake up Your Bible Study: Getting the Most from Your Time with God. 2007. (ENG.). 201p. per. 14.99 (978-0-8127-0440-2(1)) Autumn Hse. Publishing Co.

Cohen, Gary G. El Ultimo Suspiro del Planeta Tierra: Civilization's Last Hurrah. (SPA.). 248p. (978-84-7228-275-9(9), 220918) Clie, Editorial.

Cohen, Ronna. Messianic Bible Study: First Steps to Studying God's Word. 2008. pap. (978-0-9774694-6-8(8)) Lindenville Publishing.

Colagiovanni, Vinny. The Kingdom. 2011. 82p. pap. 10.99 **(978-1-61215-455-8(7))** Xulon Pr., Inc.

Compilado. Viaje Maravilloso A los Tiempos Biblicos (Maes.) - Amazing Journey (Teacher) pap. (978-1-56063-957-2(1)) Editorial Unilit.

Conder, Tim & Rhodes, Daniel. Free for All: Rediscovering the Bible in Community. 2009. (Emersion). (Illus.). 256p. pap. 16.99 (978-0-8010-7147-8(X)) Baker Bks.

Cone, Christopher. Prolegomena: Introductory Notes on Bible Study & Theological Method. 2007. pap. 24.00 (978-0-9765930-1-0(7)) Exegetica Publishing & Biblical Resources.

Connelly, Douglas. The Book of Psalms, 0 vols. Richards, Larry, ed. 2008. (Smart Guide to the Bible Ser.). 416p. pap. 14.99 (978-1-4185-1010-7(6)) Nelson, Thomas Inc.

Conybeare, F. C. & Stock, George. Selections from the Septuagint: According to the Text of Swete. 2007. 314p. pap. 28.00 (978-1-55635-330-7(8)) Wipf & Stock Pubs.

Cook Communications, creator. International Lesson Commentary NIV: September 2007 - August 2008. 2007. (International Bible Lesson Commentary NIV Ser.). 430p. per. 14.99 (978-0-7814-4503-0(5)) Cook, David C.

Cook, David. Teaching Acts: Unlocking the Book of Acts for the Bible Teacher. 2007. (ENG.). 304p. per. 10.99 (978-1-84550-255-3(8)) Christian Focus Pubns. GBR. Dist: STL Distribution North America.

Cooper, Alicia R. Purse Prayer. 2009. 64p. pap. 14.95 (978-1-4389-6648-9(2)) AuthorHouse.

Cooper, Clayton Sedgwick. The Bible & Modern Life. 2009. 256p. 30.99 (978-1-110-41307-2(6)); pap. 25.75 (978-1-110-41304-1(1)) BiblioBazaar.

—The Bible & Modern Life. 2007. (ENG.). 254p. 42.95 (978-0-548-06790-1(2)) Kessinger Publishing, LLC.

Cooper, Ted. The Bible in 90 Days - Whole-Church Challenge: 14 Sessions, 1 vol. 2009. (ENG.). 160p. pap., instr.'s gde. ed. 9.99 (978-0-310-94184-2(9)) Zondervan.

Cooper, Velyn. Biblical Journeys: Passages Through Time & into Eternity. 2010. pap. 12.99 (978-1-61566-974-5(4)) Tate Publishing & Enterprises, LLC.

Cooper, Velyn. What Does the Bible Say About. 2011. pap. 14.99 **(978-1-61777-369-3(7))** Tate Publishing & Enterprises, LLC.

Cosgrove, Julie B. PRAYING- Bringing Power & Purpose to Your Prayers. 2010. 98p. pap. 14.42 (978-0-557-18134-6(8)) Lulu Enterprises Inc.

—Song Notes. 2010. 166p. pap. 14.99 (978-0-557-35806-9(X)) Lulu Enterprises Inc.

Coverdell, Donald. Precious & Very Great Promises. 2009. 172p. pap. 19.88 (978-0-557-05095-6(2)) Lulu Enterprises Inc.

Cox, R. Kenneth. Sound Doctrine. 2009. 76p. pap. 16.49 (978-0-557-07551-5(3)) Lulu Enterprises Inc.

Crossan, John Dominic. The Cross That Spoke: The Origins of the Passion Narrative. 2008. (Illus.). 454p. pap. 50.00 (978-1-55635-819-7(9)) Wipf & Stock Pubs.

Crump, Dennis G. Approaching the Holy: A Season in God's House. 2007. 168p. per. 10.95 (978-1-4327-0365-3(X)) Outskirts Pr., Inc.

Curtis, Bryan C. Combating Bible Illiteracy. 2010. 496p. 36.99 (978-1-60957-024-8(3)) Xulon Pr., Inc.

Czaplinski, Evangelist Edward J. Time Is Running Out. 2008. 500p. pap. 34.95 (978-1-4241-9231-1(5)) PublishAmerica, Inc.

Daley, John. Getting to Know the Bible. 2006. 64p. pap. 5.95 (978-0-7648-1509-6(1)) Liguori Pubns.

Dalgliesh, Ryan. Love Notes. 2008. 236p. per. 14.99 (978-1-60477-687-4(0)) Xulon Pr., Inc.

Dator, Joanne M. Reflections in Light. 2008. 196p. pap. 15.99 (978-1-4389-2016-0(4)) AuthorHouse.

David C. Cook Publishing Company Staff. Deeper Space Music & Bible Memory Guide. 2007. (Vacation Bible School Ser.). 48p. (J). (gr. 3-12). pap. 6.99 (978-1-4347-9959-3(X)) Cook, David C.

—Lesson Commentary, September 2008-August 2009: Deep Truth, Bold Faith, Changed Lives. Lioy, Daniel, ed. 2008. (Bible-in-Life Lesson Commentary Ser.). 424p. pap. 14.99 (978-1-4347-9936-4(0)) Cook, David C.

Davis, Andrea & Radtke, Nancy. Hidden Treasures of the Spirit. 2008. 140p. pap. 14.99 (978-1-60791-108-1(6)) Xulon Pr., Inc.

Davis, Reginald F. Bible Study for Busy Pastors & Ministers: Ready-made Lessons to Transform Members into Disciples & an Audience into an Army. 2011. 154p. pap. 18.00 (978-1-61097-218-5(X), Resource Pubns.) Wipf & Stock Pubs.

Day, Jackson. Bible Storytelling Tools. 2007. 208p. pap. 25.00 (978-0-9797324-2-3(5)) Day, H. Jackson.

Deane, Andy. Learn to Study the Bible. 2009. 248p. pap. 15.99 (978-1-60791-576-8(6)) Xulon Pr., Inc.

Deissmann, G. Adolf. Bible Studies. 2010. 402p. 38.99 (978-1-140-17879-8(2)); pap. 34.75 (978-1-140-17880-4(6)) BiblioBazaar.

DeLacy, Pete & Arthur, Kay. Key Principles of Biblical Fasting. 2009. (40-Minute Bible Studies). (ENG.). 96p. pap. 7.99 (978-0-307-45765-3(6), WaterBrook Pr.) Doubleday Religious Publishing Group, The.

Deloe, Jesse B. Sweeter Than Honey. pap. 5.99 (978-0-88469-105-1(5)) BMH Bks.

Dennis, Barry. The Saviour of All Men. 2011. pap. 14.99 (978-1-61739-902-2(7)) Tate Publishing & Enterprises, LLC.

Di Pardo, Armando. Tratado de Introduccion Biblica: Introduction to Bible Study, AM. (SPA.). (978-84-399-7101-6(X), 220903) Clie, Editorial.

DiMarco, Hayley. Hotness. (Pocket Bible Study & Journal Ser.). 128p. (YA). 2009. pap. 7.99 (978-0-8007-3414-5(9)) 2008. pap. 14.99 (978-0-8007-3223-3(5)) Revell.

—Mean. 2008. (Pocket Bible Study & Journal Ser.). 128p. (YA). pap. 14.99 (978-0-8007-3221-9(9)) Revell.

—Sex: A Pocket Bible Study & Journal. 2008. (Pocket Bible Study & Journal Ser.). (Illus.). 128p. (YA). pap. 14.99 (978-0-8007-3222-6(7)) Revell.

DiMari, Christina. You're Designed to Shine: Leader Guide: Six Sessions for Girls Ages 8 To 88. 2008. 64p. pap. 19.99 (978-0-7644-3693-2(7)) Group Publishing, Inc.

Dingwall, Cindy. More Bible Times with Kids: 200+ Bible-Based Activities to Use with Children. 2006. (Illus.). 154p. per. 24.00 (978-0-687-49230-5(0)) Abingdon Pr.

Disciple III Video Series. 150.00 incl. VHS (978-0-687-76256-9(1)) Abingdon Pr.

Disciple IV. 30.00 (978-0-687-09667-1(7)) Abingdon Pr.

Disciple IV under the Tree of Life Video 2. 60.00 (978-0-687-04596-9(7)) Abingdon Pr.

Disciple IV under the Tree of Life Video 3. 60.00 (978-0-687-04616-4(5)) Abingdon Pr.

Disciple IV under the Tree of Life Video 4. 60.00 (978-0-687-04636-2(X)) Abingdon Pr.

Disciple IV under the Tree of Life Video I. 60.00 (978-0-687-04586-0(X)) Abingdon Pr.

Disciple Youth Teacher Helps. 2nd ed. 5.00 (978-0-687-71687-6(X)) Abingdon Pr.

Discover Acts. (Discover Your Bible Ser.). (KOR.). Vol. 1. pap., tchr. ed. 6.95 (978-1-55883-220-6(3), 600175) Vol. 2. pap., tchr. ed. 6.95 (978-1-55883-221-3(1), 600185) Vol. 2. pap., stu. ed. 4.25 (978-1-55883-219-0(X), 600180) C R C World Literature Ministries/Libros Desafio.

Dole, Anita S. Bible Study Notes Vol. 1, 6 vols., Vol. 1. Woofenden, William Ross, ed. 2012. (ENG.). 456p. pap. 20.00 **(978-0-87785-358-9(4))** Swedenborg Foundation, Inc.

—Bible Study Notes Vol. 2, 6 vols., Vol. 2. Woofenden, William Ross, ed. 2012. (ENG.). 448p. pap. 20.00 **(978-0-87785-359-6(2))** Swedenborg Foundation, Inc.

—Bible Study Notes Vol. 3, 6 vols., Vol. 3. Woofenden, William Ross, ed. 2012. (ENG.). 432p. pap. 20.00 **(978-0-87785-360-2(6))** Swedenborg Foundation, Inc.

—Bible Study Notes Vol. 4, 6 vols., Vol. 4. Woofenden, William Ross, ed. 2012. (ENG.). 432p. pap. 20.00 **(978-0-87785-361-9(4))** Swedenborg Foundation, Inc.

—Bible Study Notes Vol. 5, 6 vols., Vol. 5. Woofenden, William Ross, ed. 2012. (ENG.). 384p. pap. 20.00 **(978-0-87785-362-6(2))** Swedenborg Foundation, Inc.

—Bible Study Notes Vol. 6, 6 vols., Vol. 6. Woofenden, William Ross, ed. 2012. (ENG.). 416p. pap. 20.00 **(978-0-87785-363-3(0))** Swedenborg Foundation, Inc.

Doulos, Kris. How Satan Deceives You. 2009. 236p. pap. 14.99 (978-1-4389-9742-1(6)) AuthorHouse.

Downing, Donald R. Heart Almanac Expository & Curriculum: A Complete Expository & Curriculum of the Heart. 2008. 156p. pap. 16.99 (978-1-60647-689-5(0)) Xulon Pr., Inc.

Duncan, Joshua J., ed. Healing Scriptures. 3rd ed. 2007. 76p. pap. 10.00 (978-0-9798321-0-9(1)) Duncan & Duncan Gifts & Bks.

Dungy, Tony. Dare to Be Uncommon Men's Bible Study: Discovering How to Impact Your World. 2009. 96p. pap. 9.99 (978-0-7644-3920-9(0)) Group Publishing, Inc.

—Quiet Strength: Men's Bible Study: Discovering God's Game Plan for a Winning Life. 2007. (Illus.). 80p. per. 9.99 (978-0-7644-3662-8(7)) Group Publishing, Inc.

Dutra, Sharon. Be Transformed. 2011. 274p. pap. 18.99 **(978-1-61379-058-8(9))** Xulon Pr., Inc.

Eade, Alfred Thompson. The New Panorama Bible Study Course: Panorama No. 1 the Plan of the Ages, No.1. 2007. (Illus.). 28p. 24.99 (978-0-9799734-0-6(6)) Oak Knoll Publishing.

—The New Panorama Bible Study Course: Panorama Study No. 2 the Study of Angelology, No.2. deluxe ed. 2008. (Illus.). 33p. 24.99 (978-0-9799734-1-3(4)) Oak Knoll Publishing.

—The New Panorama Bible Study Course: Panorama Study No. 3 the 2nd Coming of Christ, No.3. deluxe ed. 2008. (Illus.). 36p. 24.99 (978-0-9799734-2-0(2)) Oak Knoll Publishing.

Earley, Dave. Las 21 Oraciones Más Efectivas de la Biblia. 2010.Tr. of 21 Most Effective Prayers of the Bible. (ENG & SPA.). 176p. pap. 3.99 (978-1-60260-873-3(3), Casa Promesa) Barbour Publishing, Inc.

Easter, Howard G., Jr. Biblenotes: Get Wisdom, Knowledge, & Understanding. 2008. 148p. pap. 15.99 (978-1-60477-663-8(3)) Xulon Pr., Inc.

EBS Adult Bible Study Guide. 3.15 (978-0-7673-4123-3(6)) LifeWay Christian Resources.

EBS Adult Commentary. 4.60 (978-0-7673-4958-1(X)) LifeWay Christian Resources.

EBS Adult Leader Guide. 4.00 (978-0-7673-4944-4(X)) LifeWay Christian Resources.

EBS Adult Leader Pack. 16.50 (978-0-7673-5086-0(3)) LifeWay Christian Resources.

EBS Adult Learner Guide. 1.50 (978-0-7673-4930-7(X)); 1.50 (978-0-7673-4887-4(7)) LifeWay Christian Resources.

Edwards, Cynthia. Quiz Me! A Through-the-Bible-in-A-Year Quiz Book. 2010. pap. 13.99 (978-1-61566-464-1(5)) Tate Publishing & Enterprises, LLC.

Edwards, Gene. The Shocking Story of the History of Bible Study. 2007. per. 14.95 (978-0-9778033-3-0(3)) Seedsowers, The.

Ellens, J. Harold & Greene, John T., eds. Probing the Frontiers of Biblical Studies. 2009. (Princeton Theological Monographs). 314p. pap. 35.00 (978-1-60608-460-1(7), Pickwick Pubns.) Wipf & Stock Pubs.

Ellis, Gwen. Read & Share Curriculum - Unit 1, 0 vols. 2010. 129.99 (978-1-4003-1551-2(4)) Nelson, Thomas Inc.

Ellis, Larry W. Sermon Notes: Volume 1. 2009. (ENG.). 186p. pap. 12.99 (978-0-9819672-4-0(8)) St. Paul Pr.

Ellsworth, Roger. Malachi. 2007. (Opening Up Ser.). (Illus.). 96p. per. 9.00 (978-1-84625-033-0(1)) DayOne Pubns. GBR. Dist: STL Distribution North America.

Engelbrecht, Edward. Complete Bible Handbook for Students. 2011. 544p. pap. 23.99 **(978-0-7586-2968-5(0))** Concordia Publishing Hse.

Enns, Peter. Telling God's Story: A Parents' Guide to Teaching the Bible. 2011. (Telling God's Story Ser.). (ENG., Illus.). 140p. pap. 11.95 (978-1-933339-46-7(2), 333946) Peace Hill Pr.

Errett, Isaac. Evenings with the Bible. 2009. 384p. 26.99 (978-1-103-95812-2(7)); pap. 20.99 (978-1-103-95804-7(6)) BiblioBazaar.

—Evenings with the Bible. 2009. 240p. pap. (978-1-4590-7136-0(0)) Books LLC.

The Essential IVP Reference Collection 3. 0. 2008. (ENG.). 1p. cd-rom 190.00 (978-0-8308-2447-2(2), IVP Acad.) InterVarsity Pr.

Estudios Biblicos Lifeway Para Adultos Manual Para el Lider. 3.25 (978-0-7673-5002-0(2)) LifeWay Christian Resources.

ESV Study Bible (Cowhide, Deep Brown) 2010. 2752p. lthr. 179.99 (978-1-4335-2178-2(4), Crossway Bibles) Crossway.

Evans, John. How to Study the Bible: A Discussion & Workbook in 12 Lessons. 2007. 108p. per. 7.95 (978-1-4327-1791-9(X)) Outskirts Pr., Inc.

Evans, Mary J. & Kroeger, Catherine Clark, eds. The Women's Study Bible 3112. 2009. (ENG.). 2016p. 49.99 (978-0-19-529129-2(8)) Oxford Univ. Pr., Inc.

Evans, William. Esquema Didactico Para el Est. Biblia: Teaching Charts for Bible Study. (SPA.). (978-84-7645-432-9(5), 223465) Clie, Editorial.

Everett, Luke. Stepping Out in Faith: How God's Plan for One Family Changed Thousands of Lives. 2007. (Illus.). 132p. pap. 16.00 (978-1-55635-389-5(8), Wipf and Stock) Wipf & Stock Pubs.

Exploring God's Word: Grade 4 - Teacher Kit. (Voyages Ser.). 190.00 incl. audio, cd-rom (978-0-570-00273-4(7), 57-0410) Concordia Publishing Hse.

Exploring God's Word: Grade 5 - Teacher Kit. (Voyages Ser.). 54.95 incl. audio, cd-rom (978-0-570-00280-2(X), 57-0512) Concordia Publishing Hse.

Exploring God's Word: Grade 6 - Teacher Kit. (Voyages Ser.). 200.00 incl. audio, cd-rom (978-0-570-00285-7(0), 57-0610) Concordia Publishing Hse.

Exploring God's Word: Grade 8 - Teacher Kit. (Voyages Ser.). 210.00 incl. audio, cd-rom (978-0-570-00299-4(0), 57-0810) Concordia Publishing Hse.

Fanning, Tolbert. The True Method of Searching the Scriptures, by Talbot [I] Fanning. 2006. 144p. per. 16.99 (978-1-4255-1106-7(6)) MPublishing.

Farmer. The Pastor's Bible Study Volume Five, 5 vols. 2008. 336p. 35.00 (978-0-687-49584-9(9)) Abingdon Pr.

Fay, Benjamin G. Tratado de Biblia Sintetica: Topical Bible Study Book. (SPA.). (978-84-499-0068-6(9), 220898) Clie, Editorial.

FBS Bible Teaching for 1s & 2s Leader Guide. 4.00 (978-0-7673-5611-4(X)) LifeWay Christian Resources.

FBS Bible Teaching for 3s-Pre-K Leader Guide. 4.00 (978-0-7673-5597-1(0)) LifeWay Christian Resources.

FBS Bible Teaching for Kindergarten Leader Guide. 4.00 (978-0-7673-5569-8(5)) LifeWay Christian Resources.

FBS Bible Teaching for Preschoolers Leader Guide. 4.00 (978-0-7673-4086-1(8)) LifeWay Christian Resources.

FBS Early Bible Steps Learner Guide. 1.50 (978-0-7673-5226-0(2)) LifeWay Christian Resources.

FBS Youth Teacher. 3.35 (978-0-7673-4988-8(1)) LifeWay Christian Resources.

Fee, Gordon D. & Hubbard, Robert L., Jr., eds. The Eerdmans Companion to the Bible. 2009. (Illus.). 816p. 39.00 (978-0-8028-3823-0(5)) Eerdmans, William B. Publishing Co.

Fields, Lee M. Hebrew for the Rest of Us, 1 vol. 2008. (ENG.). 304p. pap. 29.99 (978-0-310-27709-5(4)) Zondervan.

Fifty-Two Weeks with the Bible. 6.00 (978-1-890569-30-3(5)) General Board of Global Ministries, The United Methodist Church.

Finlay, Randy. Seeing from Heaven. 2010. 344p. 33.95 (978-1-4502-7761-7(6)); pap. 23.95 (978-1-4502-7759-4(4)) iUniverse, Inc.

Finley, Jeanne Torrence. Blessings of the Manger Student: An Advent Study Based on the Revised Common Lectionary. 2010. (Sftcs Ser.). pap. 7.00 (978-0-687-46696-2(2)) Abingdon Pr.

Fireside Catholic Bibles, creator. Personal Study Bible-Nab-Giant Print. l.t. ed. 2006. 2239p. per. 34.95 (978-1-55665-444-2(8)) Fireside Catholic Bibles.

First Place 4 Health (Organization) Staff & First Place 4 Health. Daily Victory, Daily Joy. 2009. (First Place 4 Health Ser.). (ENG.). 224p. 19.99 (978-0-8307-4724-5(9)) Gospel Light Pubns.

Fleming, Bruce C. E. Women & Men in the Light of Eden. 2011. 94p. pap. 10.99 **(978-1-61579-690-8(8))** Xulon Pr., Inc.

Flessner, Stephen. Just Cross References: Bible Cross References in a New Light. 2011. pap. 26.99 (978-1-61739-891-9(8)) Tate Publishing & Enterprises, LLC.

Force, J. E. & Popkin, R. H., eds. The Books of Nature & Scripture: Recent Essays on Natural Philosophy, Theology & Biblical Criticism in the Netherlands of Spinoza's Time & the British Isles of Newton's Time: Recent Essays on Natural Philosophy, Theology & Biblical Criticism in the Netherlands of Spinoza's Time & the British Isles of Newton's Time. 2010. (International Archives of the History of Ideas / archives internationales d'histoire des Idées Ser.). 232p. pap. 219.00 (978-90-481-4321-4(7), 9048143217) Springer.

Ford, Michael. The bible of the Adversary. 2009. 335p. 43.95 (978-0-557-04429-0(4)) Lulu Enterprises Inc.

Forge, Anvil. Living Each Day Led by the Spirit. 2008. 128p. (ENG.). 21.99 (978-1-60477-776-5(1)); per. 13.99 (978-1-60477-775-8(3)) Xulon Pr., Inc.

Foster, Annette. Culture Fair Fridays. 2008. 104p. pap. 10.99 (978-1-60791-096-1(9)) Xulon Pr., Inc.

French Bible. 1115p. 27.99 (978-2-85300-118-2(0)) Société Biblique Française FRA. Dist: American Bible Society.

French, Bill. Glimpses of Canaan Land. 2009. 276p. pap. 15.49 (978-1-4389-3994-0(9)) AuthorHouse.

Frey, Harold. Prisoners of the Paradigm. 2008. 368p. pap. 19.99 (978-1-60647-251-4(8)) Xulon Pr., Inc.

Futato, Mark D. Pocket Paradigms: For Biblical Hebrew. 2008. 66p. pap. 9.00 (978-1-59752-449-0(2), Wipf and Stock) Wipf & Stock Pubs.

Gaffney, Dave. These Things Must Happen: A Lesson from the Fig Tree. 2011. pap. 24.99 (978-1-61739-966-4(3)) Tate Publishing & Enterprises, LLC.

Galfo, Guy S. The Interwoven Gospels: The Ministry of Christ. 2009. 264p. pap. 26.99 *(978-1-61579-320-4(8))* Xulon Pr., Inc.
Gallagher, Steve. He Leads Me Beside Still Waters: A 12week Study Through the Choicest Psalms. 2009. (Walk Ser.). (ENG.). 144p. pap. 10.99 *(978-0-9800286-0-7(4))* Pure Life Ministries.
Gardner, Durrelle. The Gospel Revealed: God's Plain Truth. 2009. 288p. pap. 16.99 *(978-1-60791-610-9(X))* Xulon Pr., Inc.
Garlow, James L. The Covenant: Lessons for Faith Communities. 2007. (ENG.). pap. 24.99 *(978-0-8341-2331-1(2)*, 0834123312) Beacon Hill Pr. of Kansas City.
Gatti, Nicoletta & Ossom-Batsa, George. Journeying with the Old Testament. 2011. (Alte Testament im Dialog - an Outline of an Old Testament Dialogue Ser.). (ENG.). 189p. pap. ***(978-3-0343-1006-2(4))*** Lang, Peter.
Gaughan, Nancy C. Building Trust: God as Our Role Model in Parenting. 2008. 192p. pap. 24.95 *(978-1-60703-915-0(X))* PublishAmerica, Inc.
Gd.P, A. Wake Wachmann. A View from the Horizontal Forest: Views from the Pews on Issues Some Preachers Don't Get Paid to Talk About. 2009. 140p. pap. 14.99 *(978-1-60791-930-8(3))* Xulon Pr., Inc.
Geisler, Norman L. L. . & Nix, William E. E. From God to Us: How We Got Our Bible. 2012. (ENG.). 432p. pap. 21.99 ***(978-0-8024-2882-0(7))*** Moody Pubs.
Gelabert, Pedro. La Biblia del Abuelo.Tr. of Grandfather's Bible. (SPA.). *(978-84-7228-543-9(X)*, 220097) Clie, Editorial.
Getting Along Early. (Conflict Resolution Curriculum Ser.). tchr. ed. 26.00 *(978-0-570-09972-7(2)*, 22-2712) Concordia Publishing Hse.
Gibson, Cay. Christmas Mosaic: An Illustrated Book Study for Christmas. 2007. 210p. (J). spiral bd. 19.99 *(978-0-9798469-1-5(9))* Hillside Education.
Giddens, Pastor/Missionary Donald Louis. Jesus in Isaiah. 2008. 236p. pap. 25.50 *(978-1-4357-1257-7(9))* Lulu Enterprises Inc.
Gilbert, Debbie. R U Mad Journal. 2007. 151p. per. 11.99 *(978-1-59886-791-6(1))* Tate Publishing & Enterprises, LLC.
Glahn, Sandra. Cappuccino with Colossians. 2007. (Coffee Cup Bible Studies). (ENG.). 176p. spiral bd. 12.99 *(978-0-89957-234-5(0))* AMG Pubs.
—Premium Roast with Ruth. 2007. (Coffee Cup Bible Studies). (ENG.). 176p. (gr. 11). spiral bd. 12.99 *(978-0-89957-236-9(7))* AMG Pubs.
God Is Forgiving. 2.99 *(978-0-7847-0853-8(3))* Standard Publishing.
God Is Holy. 2.99 *(978-0-7847-0873-6(8))* Standard Publishing.
God Is Inside Us. 2.99 *(978-0-7847-0874-3(6))* Standard Publishing.
God Is Our Caregiver. 2.99 *(978-0-7847-0858-3(4))* Standard Publishing.
God Is Powerful. 2.99 *(978-0-7847-0852-1(5))* Standard Publishing.
God Is Sovereign. 2.99 *(978-0-7847-0860-6(6))* Standard Publishing.
God, the Only God. 2.99 *(978-0-7847-0870-5(3))* Standard Publishing.
God's Action Plan. 112p. tchr. ed. 19.95 *(978-0-570-09801-0(7)*, 22-2486) Concordia Publishing Hse.
Goines, R. L. Angelic Encounter: El. 2010. 190p. pap. 14.99 *(978-1-60957-793-3(0))* Xulon Pr., Inc.
Gospel Light. Depending on Jesus: Jesus Provides What We Truly Need in Every Life Challenge. 2011. (SonRise National Park Ser.). (ENG.). 144p. (gr. 13). pap. 12.99 ***(978-0-8307-5996-5(4))*** Gospel Light Pubns.
Graham, John M. The Foundation & Focus for Living: A Doctrinal Study of Scripture. 2009. 62p. pap. 15.99 *(978-1-4500-0663-7(9))* Xlibris Corp.
Grandville, Conrado. Donde, Como y Porque Esta Escrito? Understanding & Interpreting. (SPA.). *(978-84-7645-139-7(3)*, 223139) Clie, Editorial.
Gray, William R. The Destruction of America Is Coming Soon: Where Is America in the Bible? 2011. 80p. pap. 8.95 ***(978-1-4620-1945-8(5))*** iUniverse, Inc.
Green, Ken. Bible Reading for Amateurs. (Illus.). 112p. pap. *(978-0-340-74540-3(1)*, Hodder & Stoughton) Hodder General Publishing Div.
Gregory, Peter. How to Study Your Bible: An Introduction. 2008. 80p. 7.95 *(978-1-933291-30-7(3))* Remnant Pubns.
Grice, Charles. A God Who Dreams: Why the Gospels Call Us to Become as Little Children. 2009. 428p. pap. 24.95 *(978-1-4389-8218-2(6))* AuthorHouse.
Griffin, Anthony L., et al. Christian Living Study Guide. 2009. 80p. pap. 21.99 *(978-1-4259-0017-5(8))* AuthorHouse.
Group Publishing, creator. Drama Team Leader Manual. 2009. (Rome: Paul & the Underground Church Ser.). (Illus.). 46p. pap. 9.99 *(978-0-7644-3776-2(3))* Group Publishing, Inc.
—Egypt Joseph's Journey from Prison to Palace: Building Blocks Family Devotional. 2010. pap. 16.99 *(978-0-7644-3948-3(0))* Group Publishing, Inc.
—Egypt Joseph's Journey from Prison to Palace Family Time Teaching Kit. 2010. 14.99 *(978-0-7644-3940-7(5))* Group Publishing, Inc.
—Egypt Joseph's Journey from Prison to Palace: Notes from the Nile Student Book. 2010. (Illus.). pap. 3.09 *(978-0-7644-3941-4(3))* Group Publishing, Inc.
—Extolo Leader Manual. 2009. (Rome: Paul & the Underground Church Ser.). (Illus.). 76p. pap. 9.99 *(978-0-7644-3777-9(1))* Group Publishing, Inc.
—Family Time Leader Manual. 2009. (Rome: Paul & the Underground Church Ser.). (Illus.). 56p. pap. 9.99 *(978-0-7644-3814-1(X))* Group Publishing, Inc.
—Family Time Teaching Kit Leader Manual. 2009. (Rome: Paul & the Underground Church Ser.). 14.99 *(978-0-7644-3815-8(8))* Group Publishing, Inc.
—Postcards from Rome: Student Book. 2009. (Rome: Paul & the Underground Church Ser.). pap. 3.09 *(978-0-7644-3781-6(X))* Group Publishing, Inc.
Group Publishing Staff, contrib. by. Group's The Humongous Book of Preschool Ideas 2. 2008. pap. *(978-0-7644-3813-4(1))* Group Publishing, Inc.
Group Publishing Staff & MOPS International, Inc Staff, contrib. by. Lively Bible Lessons for MOPPETS. 2007. pap. *(978-0-7644-3573-7(6))* Group Publishing, Inc.
Grupo Nelson, creator. Biblia Plenitud-NVI-FL. 2008. (Illus.). 2110p. 49.99 *(978-0-89922-015-4(0))* Nelson, Thomas Inc.
Guinness, Bryan. It's Simpler Than You Think: Uncovering God's Will for Your Life. 2011. 152p. 24.95 ***(978-1-4620-0581-9(0))***; pap. 14.95 ***(978-1-4620-0580-2(2))*** iUniverse, Inc.
Gustafson, Eleanor. Stones Study Guide. 2009. 52p. pap. 6.99 *(978-1-60374-103-3(8))* Whitaker Hse.
Hahn, Scott, ed. Ignatius Catholic Study Bible: New Testament. 2010. 700p. lthr. 39.95 *(978-1-58617-485-9(1))* Ignatius Pr.
Hahn, Scott & Mitch, Curtis. Ignatius Catholic Study Bible: The Letter to the Hebrews. 2007. 60p. pap. 9.95 *(978-1-58617-191-9(7))* Ignatius Pr.
Hahn, Scott & Mitch, Curtis, eds. Ignatius Catholic Study Bible: New Testament. 2010. 700p. 31.95 *(978-1-58617-484-2(3))* Ignatius Pr.
Halbur, Virginia, ed. The Catholic Youth Bible. 3rd rev. ed. 2010. 34.95 *(978-0-88489-788-0(5))* St. Mary's Pr.
—The Catholic Youth Bible: New American Bible - Pray It, Study It, Live It. 3rd ed. 2010. 34.95 *(978-0-88489-779-8(6))*; pap. 26.95 *(978-0-88489-777-4(X))* St. Mary's Pr.
—The Catholic Youth Bible: New American Bible Translation - Pray It, Study It, Live It. 3rd ed. 2010. lthr. 41.95 *(978-0-88489-780-4(X))* St. Mary's Pr.
—The Catholic Youth Bible: Pray It Study It Live It. 3rd rev. ed. 2010. pap. 26.95 *(978-0-88489-787-3(7))* St. Mary's Pr.
—Leader Guide for the Catholic Youth Bible, Third Edition. 2010. spiral bd. 29.95 *(978-1-59982-030-9(7))* St. Mary's Pr.
—Saint Mary's Press College Study Bible. 2007. (Illus.). 2048p. 42.95 *(978-0-88489-962-4(4))* St. Mary's Pr.
Haldane, Robert. The Authenticity & Inspiration of the Holy Scriptures. 2007. 205p. per. 18.00 *(978-1-55635-746-6(X))* Wipf & Stock Pubs.
Hale, Elnader. I Gotta Have It. 2009. 174p. pap. 19.96 *(978-0-557-06239-3(X))* Lulu Enterprises Inc.
Haley-Escuain. Dicc. Dificultades Y: Encyclopedia of Bible Difficulties, 1 vol. 2009. (SPA.). 600p. 29.99 *(978-84-7645-323-0(X)*, 223309) Clie, Editorial ESP. Dist: Zondervan.
Hammond, Jonathan. The Bible the Only Infallible Book for the Perishing World. 2009. 328p. pap. 18.99 *(978-1-60791-117-3(5))* Xulon Pr., Inc.
Hamrick, Frank & Thornton, champ. Dynamic Christian Living. 2nd ed. 2008. (ENG., Illus.). 252p. pap. 14.95 *(978-1-59557-050-5(0))* Positive Action For Christ.
Hanegraaff, Hank. The Complete Bible Answer Book, 0 vols. collector's ed. 2009. 560p. 21.99 *(978-1-4041-1381-7(9))* Nelson, Thomas Inc.
Hanson, Buddy. Bottom Line Theology. 2007. 292p. pap. 19.95 *(978-0-9719812-3-2(X))* Hanson Group.
—Making Your Daily Reads. 2008. 180p. pap. 20.00 *(978-0-9771773-8-7(6))* Hanson Group.
Hardmeier, Christof. Prophetie Im Streit Vor Dem Untergang Judas: Erzählkommunikative Studien Zur Entstehungssituation der Jesaja- Und Jeremiaerzählungen in II Reg 18-20 und Jer 37-40. (Beihefte zur Zeitschrift fur die alttestamentliche Wissenschaft Ser.). (GER.). XVII, 506p. 240.00 ***(978-3-11-178388-8(X))*** De Gruyter, Walter Inc.
Harris, Janice L., et al. Discovering A Christlike Character (Book 4) CHRISTIAN SCHOOL Edition: Student Workbook. Snyder, Barb, ed. 2007. (Illus.). 196p. spiral bd., wbk. ed. 19.95 *(978-1-930547-51-3(X))* Deeper Roots Pubns. & Media.
—Discovering A Christlike Character (Book 4) CHRISTIAN SCHOOL Edition: TEACHER's Guide. Snyder, Barb & Harris, JoAnna, eds. 2007. (Illus.). 282p. tchr. ed., spiral bd. 28.95 *(978-1-930547-50-6(1))* Deeper Roots Pubns. & Media.
—Discovering A Christlike Character (Book 4) HOME SCHOOL Edition: TEACHER's Guide - Snyder, Barb, ed. 2007. (Illus.). 334p. tchr. ed., spiral bd. 28.95 *(978-1-930547-62-9(5))* Deeper Roots Pubns. & Media.
—Discovering A Christlike Character (Book 4) HOME SCHOOL: Student Workbook- Snyder, Barb & Harris, JoAnna, eds. 2007. (Illus.). 296p. spiral bd., wbk. ed. 19.95 *(978-1-930547-63-6(3))* Deeper Roots Pubns. & Media.
Harrison, Earl. Kingdom Character. 2009. 72p. pap. 15.99 *(978-1-4415-4950-1(1))* Xlibris Corp.
Hart, Tom, et al. Being a Disciple. 2009. (40-Minute Bible Studies). (ENG.). 80p. pap. 7.99 *(978-0-307-45756-1(7)*, WaterBrook Pr.) Doubleday Religious Publishing Group, The.
Harthan, Jan. The B-I-B-L-E. 2008. 152p. pap. 13.99 *(978-1-60647-361-0(1))*; 280p. per. 15.99 *(978-1-60477-584-6(X))* Xulon Pr., Inc.
Hatmaker, Jennifer. A Modern Girl's Guide to Bible Study: A Refreshingly Unique Look at God's Word. 2006. (Modern Girl's Bible Study Ser.). (ENG., Illus.). 208p. per. 12.99 *(978-1-57683-891-4(9))* NavPress Publishing Group
Hawkins, James F. Lift up My Soul: Taking Flight on the Winds of Faith. 2007. 70p. pap. 9.00 *(978-0-687-49085-1(5))* Abingdon Pr.
Hawkins, Tim. The Cry of My Heart - Bible Study: 7 Bible Studies for Small Groups. 2010. 48p. (YA). pap. *(978-1-905564-79-8(1))* Good Bk. Co.
Hayden, Wesley. Weekly Nuggets of Wisdom. 2007. 208p. pap. 19.95 *(978-0-9764945-9-1(0))* Williams, Benjamin Publishing.
Hayes, Kate. For the Tough Times: Does God Care When I Am Hurting? 2006. (Re: Action: Small Group Resources Ser.). (Illus.). 48p. pap. 8.00 *(978-1-85999-622-5(1))* Scripture Union GBR. Dist: STL Distribution North America.
Hayford, Jack W. 2 Corinthians, 1 & 2 Timothy, Titus: Ministering in the Spirit & Strength of Jesus, 0 vols. 2009. (Spirit-Filled Life Study Guide Ser.). 128p. pap. 9.99 *(978-1-4185-4120-0(6))* Nelson, Thomas Inc.
Headlund, Peggy L. The Spirit Guides. 2008. 216p. 24.99 *(978-1-60477-738-3(9))*; pap. 14.99 *(978-1-60477-737-6(0))* Xulon Pr., Inc.
Heald, Cynthia. Becoming a Woman of Faith: Fixing our eyes on Jesus, the author & perfecter of faith. Hebrews 12:2. 2009. (Becoming a Woman Of ... Ser.). (ENG.). 112p. pap. 9.99 *(978-1-61521-021-3(0))* NavPress Publishing Group.
—Becoming a Woman of Simplicity: I Am Afraid That, As the Serpent Deceived Eve by His Craftiness, Your Minds Will Be Led Astray from the Simplicity & Purity of Devotion to Christ. 2 Corinthians 11:3. 2009. (Becoming a Woman Of ... Ser.). (ENG.). 144p. pap. 9.99 *(978-1-60006-663-4(1))* NavPress Publishing Group.
Heart & Soul: a Bible Study Series for Women in the Workplace: Faith Shared. (Bible Studies). 6.99 *(978-0-7586-0068-4(2))* Concordia Publishing Hse.
Heitzig, Lenya & Rose, Penny Pierce. Live Deeply: A Study in the Parables of Jesus. 2009. (Fresh Life Ser.). (ENG.). 288p. pap. 14.99 *(978-1-4347-9986-9(7))* Cook, David C.
—Live Relationally: Lessons from the Women of Genesis. 2009. (Fresh Life Ser.). (ENG.). 288p. pap. 17.99 *(978-1-4347-6748-6(5))* Cook, David C.
Hendricks, Howard G. & Hendricks, William D. Interpretación Bíblica - una Introducción (Living by the Book: the Art & Science of Reading the Bible) 2011. (SPA.). 378p. pap. 24.95 ***(978-1-58802-440-4(7))*** Editorial Patmos.
—Living by the Book: The Art & Science of Reading the Bible. 2007. (ENG., Illus.). 400p. per. 18.99 *(978-0-8024-0823-5(0))* Moody Pubs.
—Living by the Book Workbook: The Art & Science of Reading the Bible. 2007. (ENG., Illus.). 232p. per. 16.99 *(978-0-8024-9538-9(9))* Moody Pubs.
Henley, Karyn. Behavior Management. (Children's Ministry Folders). pap., tchr. ed. 2.99 *(978-0-7847-0687-9(5)*, 42237) Standard Publishing.
—Learning Centers. (Children's Ministry Folders). tchr. ed. 2.99 *(978-0-7847-0681-7(6)*, 42231) Standard Publishing.
—Learning Strengths. (Children's Ministry Folders). tchr. ed. 2.99 *(978-0-7847-0688-6(3)*, 42238) Standard Publishing.
—Parents: Teaching Partners. (Children's Ministry Folders). tchr. ed. 2.99 *(978-0-7847-0685-5(9)*, 42235) Standard Publishing.
—Storytelling. (Children's Ministry Folders). tchr. ed. 2.99 *(978-0-7847-0690-9(5)*, 42240) Standard Publishing.
Hickey, Marilyn. Bible Encounter: Classic Library Edition. 24.95 *(978-1-56441-031-3(5))* Hickey, Marilyn Ministries.
Higgs, Charles & Long, Greg. Get Your Bible Out of the Saddle Bag! Genesis Through Esther. 2011. 80p. pap. 9.95 ***(978-1-4497-3081-9(7)***, WestBow Pr.) Author Solutions, Inc.
Hill, Harriet S. & Hill, Margaret. Translating the Bible into Action: How the Bible Can Be Relevant in All Languages & Cultures. 2008. (Illus.). 320p. pap. *(978-1-903689-53-0(8))* Piquant Editions Ltd.
Hill, Louis. Seven Foolish Questions: An Exhortation to Today's Church as Taught from the Book of Malachi. 2010. pap. 13.99 *(978-1-61663-561-9(4))* Tate Publishing & Enterprises, LLC.
Hill, Richard J. ", et al. A Glimpse of the Chosen: Glimpses of God's Elective Grace. 2010. 140p. 28.95 *(978-1-61507-210-1(1))* Cross Bks. Publishing.
Hill, Trevis. The Bible Study Journal. 2010. pap. 9.99 *(978-1-61566-242-5(1))* Tate Publishing & Enterprises, LLC.
Holdsworth, John. Getting Started with the Bible: A Guide for Complete Beginners. 2008. 178p. pap. 14.99 *(978-1-85311-846-3(X))* Canterbury Pr.
Holford, Karen. 100 Creative Ways to Learn Memory Verses. 2009. *(978-0-8127-0505-8(X))* Autumn Hse. Publishing Co.
Holland, Carl E. The Truth. 2008. 224p. pap. 14.99 *(978-1-60477-919-6(5))* Xulon Pr., Inc.
Holland, Deborah. The Word Within the Word. 2007. 128p. per. 10.95 *(978-1-59858-313-7(1))* Dog Ear Publishing, LLC.
Holloway, Elnora & Lamb, Connie. Shaping Little Minds for the Future. 2009. 72p. pap. 15.49 *(978-1-4389-7277-0(6))* AuthorHouse.
Holmes, Eric. 8 Great Wonders. 2006. pap. 17.99 *(978-1-60034-626-2(X))* Xulon Pr., Inc.
Holton, Betty J. Come Boldly to the Throne: Child of the King. 2011. 9?p. pap. 14.95 *(978-1-4327-6862-1(X))* Outskirts Pr., Inc.
Hopkins, Willodine, et al. Significant Women in the Signs of God. 2010. 248p. pap. 14.49 *(978-1-4490-7095-3(7))* AuthorHouse.
Howard, Marcos L. Arqueolog a b Blica. 2010. 102p. pap. 12.99 *(978-1-60957-831-2(7))* Xulon Pr., Inc.
Hudson, Anneke O. Bevilacqua. 2007. 212p. per. 14.99 *(978-1-60477-332-3(4))* Xulon Pr., Inc.
Hudson, Leslie & Lovett Neal, M. Ed. The Mother-in-Law Trap: Avoid the Pitfalls & Enjoy Your In-Laws. 2009. 152p. pap. 13.99 *(978-1-4490-0709-6(0))* AuthorHouse.
Huffnagle, Sylvia. Bible Living Quiz Book: 964 Q/A - Rated According to Difficulty. 2006. 393p. per. 20.95 *(978-1-59824-302-4(0))* E-BookTime LLC.
Hunt, Alice. Second Temple Studies IV: Historiography & History. 2012. (Library Hebrew Bible/Old Testament Studies). (ENG.). 144p. 110.00 *(978-0-567-45699-1(4)*, T&T Clark Int'l) Continuum International Publishing Group, Ltd. GBR. Dist: National Bk. Network.
Hunt, Josh. Good Questions Have Groups Talking; How to teach using Questions. 2010. 213p. pap. 19.99 *(978-0-557-58465-9(5))* Lulu Enterprises Inc.
Hunt, Marvin. 100 Bible Topics: Made Plain & Simple. 2008. (Illus.). 256p. pap. 14.95 *(978-0-9703236-3-7(8))* Spruce Street Publishing.
Hybels, Bill, et al. The Passion Story: Uphill Faith, 1 vol. 2009. (New Community Bible Study Ser.). (ENG.). 96p. pap. 7.99 *(978-0-310-28061-3(3))* Zondervan.
Intervarsity Press. Christian Basics Bible Studies, 16 titles, Set. 13p. (Orig.). pap., wbk. ed. 91.00 *(978-0-8308-2025-2(6)*, 2025) InterVarsity Pr.
—LifeGuide Bible Studies, 73 bks., Set. 91p. pap., wbk. ed. 637.00 *(978-0-8308-1100-7(1)*, 1100) InterVarsity Pr.
Irvine, Rebecca. Adventures with the Word of God: Making Scripture Study Exciting for the Entire Family. 2008. pap. 12.99 *(978-0-88290-845-8(6))* Cedar Fort, Inc./CFI Distribution.
., Krazy. Alphabetical Bible: A Beginner's Bible. 2011. 800p. 34.99 ***(978-1-4628-6029-6(X))***; pap. 23.99 ***(978-1-4628-6028-9(1))*** Xlibris Corp.
Jackson, Delphine G. ABC's of Outreach Ministries. 2007. pap. 12.00 *(978-0-8059-8477-4(1))* Dorrance Publishing Co., Inc.
Jacobson, Diane L., et al. Opening the Book of Faith. 2009. 144p. pap. 12.99 *(978-0-8066-8061-3(X))* Augsburg Fortress, Pubs.
James, Ewin. Prosperity or Greed? Exposing the errors & dangers of the Prosperity Gospel. 2009. 88p. pap. 12.95 *(978-1-4327-4747-3(9))* Outskirts Pr., Inc.
Jefferson, Thomas. Jefferson Bible, or the Life & Morals of Jesus of Nazareth. 2010. 174p. pap. 5.95 *(978-1-57898-878-5(0))* Martino Publishing.
Jensen, Fred M. A Study of the Foundation of Justification. 2011. 214p. 29.99 ***(978-1-4535-1137-4(7))***; pap. 19.99 ***(978-1-4535-1136-7(9))*** Xlibris Corp.
Jeys, Margaret Sturgill. Revelation for the Common Man: Book 1. 2010. 220p. (ENG.). 24.99 *(978-1-4490-8445-5(1))*; pap. 14.49 *(978-1-4490-8444-8(3))* AuthorHouse.
Johnson, Jan. Spiritual Disciplines Companion: Bible Studies & Practices to Transform Your Soul, 1 vol. 2009. (ENG.). 315p. pap. 20.00 *(978-0-8308-3523-2(7)*, IVP Bks.) InterVarsity Pr.
Johnson, Joey. The Biblical World Through New Glasses: Seeing the Bible through its Cultural Context. 2011. (ENG.). 172p. pap. 13.99 ***(978-0-9838328-7-4(0))*** St. Paul Pr.
Johnson, Kurt W. How to Give a Bible Study: Suggestions for Finding Bible Study Interests & Effective Tips for Leading Them to Christ. 2007. 1.99 *(978-0-8163-2230-5(9))* Pacific Pr. Publishing Assn.
Johnson, Wallace F. Following the Good Shepherds. 2010. 299p. pap. *(978-1-61663-631-9(3))* Tate Publishing & Enterprises, LLC.
Johnston, Louie, Jr. Prayers of the Bible Study Guide: Workbook. 2006. per. 12.00 *(978-0-9659022-8-1(5))* Blue Wing Publishing.
Jones, Stewart. Through the Bible in 365 Days. 2009. 300p. pap. 35.50 *(978-1-4452-2936-2(6))* Lulu Enterprises Inc.
Kahler, Clay A. The Unashamed: Learning the Inductive Method of Bible Study. 2011. (Sharing the Word: Ser.). 204p. pap. 22.00 ***(978-1-61097-612-1(6)***, Wipf and Stock) Wipf & Stock Pubs.
Kaiser, Walter C., Jr. & Walter, Kaiser D., Jr. Archaeological Study Bible: An Illustrated Walk Through Biblical History & Culture, 1 vol. Garrett, Duane, ed. 2009. (ENG.). 2336p. lthr. 89.99 *(978-0-310-94860-5(6))* Zondervan.
Keck, Leander E. New Interpreter's Bible, 12 vols. 780.00 *(978-0-687-06347-5(7))* Abingdon Pr.
Keller-Scholz, Rick. Teaching Activities Manual for Breakthrough! the Bible for Young Catholics: Getting to Know Jesus. 2007. 108p. spiral bd. 16.75 *(978-0-88489-979-2(9))* St. Mary's Pr.
Kellmeyer, Steve. The Sensible Scripture Study. 2007. 104p. per. 9.95 *(978-1-60104-003-9(2))* Bridegroom Pr.
Kendrick, Stephen, et al. The Love Dare Bible Study. 2009. (Illus.). 93p. pap. 9.75 *(978-1-4158-6655-9(4))* LifeWay Christian Resources.
Kenney, Garrett C. Mark's Gospel: Lectures & Lessons. 2007. (ENG.). 136p. pap. 29.50 *(978-0-7618-3709-1(4))* Univ. Pr. of America, Inc.
Kent, Dayna. Gospel Handbook. 2007. 164p. 34.50 *(978-1-4303-1167-5(3))* Lulu Enterprises Inc.
King, Cinda. Walking with Moses, Talking with God: Lessons Learned from an Unlikely Leader. 2008. 168p. pap. 10.99 *(978-0-89265-667-7(0))* Randall Hse. Pubns.
Kingdom Quotes Staff. Can Dead People Speak to Us? pap. *(978-0-930179-42-7(0))* Johns Enterprises.
—Cases of Demonic Possession in the Holy Bible. pap. *(978-0-930179-21-2(8))* Johns Enterprises.
Kirk, Marilyn. The Word Says. 2007. 493p. pap. 24.95 *(978-0-9801420-0-6(8))* Ketch Publishing.
Kirkbride Bible Company, creator. Thompson Chain Reference Bible-KJV. 2010. 1923p. im. lthr. 73.99 *(978-0-88707-614-5(9))*; (ENG., Illus.). im. lthr. *(978-0-88707-615-2(7))* Kirkbride, B.B. Bible Co., Inc.
Kirkwood-Hatchett, Queen. A General Study of the Books of the Bible. 2006. 184p. per. 19.99 *(978-1-59858-258-1(5))* Dog Ear Publishing, LLC.
Kizer, Drew. The Cast of the Cross. 2008. 168p. (YA). pap. 9.00 *(978-0-9725894-4-4(9))* Riddle Creek Publishing.
Klein, William W. Handbook for Personal Bible Study: Enriching Your Experience with God's Word. 2008. (Navigators Reference Library). (ENG.). 448p. 19.99 *(978-1-60006-117-2(6))* NavPress Publishing Group.
Kloster, Julie. The Eternal Truths of Narnia: Bible Studies & Leader's Guide. 2008. 98p. pap. 13.99 *(978-0-88270-616-0(0)*, Bridge-Logos) Bridge-Logos Foundation.
Knack, Brian L. Made for W. A. R. 52 Weeks of Wisdom & Revelation, 1 vol. 2009. 133p. pap. 24.95 *(978-1-4489-1759-4(X))* PublishAmerica, Inc.
Knotts, J. L. The Master & His Church. 2010. 162p. pap. 14.99 *(978-1-60957-429-1(X))* Xulon Pr., Inc.
Knuckle, Rose. Daily Grace. 2008. 604p. 33.99 *(978-1-4389-3274-3(X))*; pap. 23.49 *(978-1-4389-3275-0(8))* AuthorHouse.
Kok, Elsa. A Woman with a Past, a God with a Future: Embracing God's Transforming Love. 2006. (ENG., Illus.). 160p. per. 12.99 *(978-1-59669-001-1(1))* New Hope Pubs.

B

Kroeger, Catherine Clark & Evans, Mary J., eds. The Women's Study Bible: New Insights For All God's People. 2nd ed. 2009. (ENG., Illus.). 1892p. 34.99 *(978-0-19-529125-4(5))* Oxford Univ. Pr., Inc.

Kuipers, Ken. A. D. A Study of Church History. (Crossroads Ser.). 133p. tchr. ed. 16.25 *(978-0-930265-45-8(9)*, 120015) Faith Alive Christian Resources.

L & W Bible Discoverers Teaching Pictures. 6.25 *(978-0-7673-5390-8(0))* LifeWay Christian Resources.

L & W Bible Learners Teaching Pictures. 6.25 *(978-0-7673-5446-2(X))* LifeWay Christian Resources.

L & W Bible Searchers Teaching Pictures. 6.25 *(978-0-7673-5334-2(X))* LifeWay Christian Resources.

Laan, Ray Vander. Walking with God in the Desert, 1 vol. 2010. (Faith Lessons Ser.). (ENG.). 336p. pap. 10.99 *(978-0-310-32993-0(0))* Zondervan.

Laan, Ray Vander, et al. The Death & Resurrection of the Messiah Discovery Guide Revised & Expanded, 1 vol. rev. ed. 2008. (Faith Lessons Ser.). (ENG.). 224p. pap. 9.99 *(978-0-310-27968-6(2))* Zondervan.

—Life & Ministry of the Messiah Discovery Guide Revised & Expanded, 1 vol. rev. ed. 2008. (Faith Lessons Ser.). (ENG.). 304p. pap. 9.99 *(978-0-310-27964-8(X))* Zondervan.

Ladd, John D. Commentary on the Book of Enoch. 2008. 440p. pap. 24.99 *(978-1-60647-451-8(0))* Xulon Pr., Inc.

LaHaye, Tim. How to Study the Bible for Yourself. l.t. ed. 2007. (Walker Large Print Ser.). (ENG., Illus.). 273p. per. 16.95 *(978-1-59415-173-6(3)*, Walker Large Print) Cengage Gale.

—How to Study the Bible for Yourself. 2006. (Illus.). 173p. per. 12.99 *(978-0-7369-1696-7(2))* Harvest Hse. Pubs.

Lake, S. D. The Pagans Are Revolting. 2010. 128p. 23.95 *(978-1-4502-4391-9(6))*; pap. 13.95 *(978-1-4502-4389-6(4))* iUniverse, Inc.

Langerock, Daniel. David: Man after God's Heart. 2009. 48p. pap. 9.99 *(978-0-9821153-5-0(0))* Living Waters Publishing Co.

Lawrence, Randall G. & Law, David R. Reading the Bible: An Introduction to Biblical Interpretation. 2012. (ENG.). 288p. pap. 29.95 *(978-0-567-03412-0(7)*, T&T Clark Int'l) Continuum International Publishing Group, Ltd. GBR. Dist: National Bk. Network.

—Reading the Bible (h) 2012. (ENG.). 288p. 130.00 *(978-0-567-03411-3(9)*, T&T Clark Int'l) Continuum International Publishing Group, Ltd. GBR. Dist: National Bk. Network.

Lawson, David, et al. The Essentials of Effective Prayer. 2009. (40-Minute Bible Studies). (ENG., Illus.). 104p. pap. 7.99 *(978-0-307-45770-7(2)*, WaterBrook Pr.) Doubleday Religious Publishing Group, The.

—Fatal Distractions: Conquering Destructive Temptations. 2011. (40-Minute Bible Studies). (ENG.). 112p. pap. 7.99 *(978-0-307-72981-1(6)*, WaterBrook Pr.) Doubleday Religious Publishing Group, The.

—Forgiveness: Breaking the Power of the Past. 2009. (40-Minute Bible Studies). (ENG., Illus.). 96p. pap. 7.99 *(978-0-307-45759-2(1)*, WaterBrook Pr.) Doubleday Religious Publishing Group, The.

—How Do You Know God's Your Father? 2009. (40-Minute Bible Studies). (ENG.). 64p. pap. 7.99 *(978-0-307-45762-2(1)*, WaterBrook Pr.) Doubleday Religious Publishing Group, The.

—How to Make Choices You Won't Regret. 2009. (40-Minute Bible Studies). (ENG.). 80p. pap. 7.99 *(978-0-307-45764-6(8)*, WaterBrook Pr.) Doubleday Religious Publishing Group, The.

—Rising to the Call of Leadership. 2009. (40-Minute Bible Studies). (ENG., Illus.). 112p. pap. 7.99 *(978-0-307-45769-1(9)*, WaterBrook Pr.) Doubleday Religious Publishing Group, The.

—Turning Your Heart Toward God. 2010. (40-Minute Bible Studies). (ENG.). 112p. pap. 7.99 *(978-0-307-45872-8(5)*, WaterBrook Pr.) Doubleday Religious Publishing Group, The.

—Understanding Spiritual Gifts. 2010. (40-Minute Bible Studies). (ENG.). 96p. pap. 7.99 *(978-0-307-45870-4(9)*, WaterBrook Pr.) Doubleday Religious Publishing Group, The.

Lawson, Glenn. The Word- How Simple Can it Be? 2011. pap. 9.95 ***(978-0-7414-6565-8(5))*** Infinity Publishing.

Leach, Ted. Faith Questions - How Does the Bible Shape My Faith? A Study of Biblical Interpretation & Faith Development. 2006. (Faithquestions Ser.). 102p. per. 10.00 *(978-0-687-49739-3(6))* Abingdon Pr.

LeaderTreks, creator. River Running Vol 1 Facilitator's Guide: Leadership in Motion. 2007. (ENG.). 24p. (YA). 19.95 *(978-1-934577-51-6(0))* LeaderTreks NFP.

—River Running Vol 1 Student Guide: Leadership in Motion. 2007. (ENG.). 32p. (YA). 9.95 *(978-1-934577-50-9(2))* LeaderTreks NFP.

—River Running Vol 2 Facilitator's Guide: Leadership in Motion. 2007. (ENG.). 32p. (YA). 19.95 *(978-1-934577-53-0(7))* LeaderTreks NFP.

—River Running Vol 2 Student Guide: Leadership in Motion. 2007. (ENG.). 40p. (YA). 9.95 *(978-1-934577-52-3(9))* LeaderTreks NFP.

Leak, Spencer. It's Time Truth Speaks. 2010. pap. 24.99 *(978-1-61579-812-4(9))* Xulon Pr., Inc.

The Learning Bible. cd-rom 24.95 *(978-1-58516-117-1(9))* American Bible Society.

Leddy, Jim. The Simple Truth. 2008. 380p. pap. 20.99 *(978-1-60647-828-8(1))* Xulon Pr., Inc.

Lee, James. The Kingdom of Heaven Is at Hand! 2010. 330p. pap. 18.99 *(978-1-60957-548-9(2))* Xulon Pr., Inc.

Lee, Rebecca. Pure in Heart Pt. 1: Who's in My Heart? 2009. 192p. pap. 12.99 *(978-1-60799-468-8(2))* Tate Publishing & Enterprises, LLC.

Lee, Richard Steward. Becoming an Effective Biblical Counselor: A Handbook Manual for Counselors. 2008. 156p. pap. 17.99 *(978-1-4389-1290-5(0))* AuthorHouse.

Legaspi, Michael C. The Death of Scripture & the Rise of Biblical Studies. 2011. (ENG.). 240p. pap. 24.95 ***(978-0-19-984588-0(3))*** Oxford Univ. Pr., Inc.

Lehmann, Henning. Students of the Bible in 4th & 5th Century Syria: Seats of Learning, Sidelights & Syriacisms. 2008. (ENG., Illus.). 256p. (C). 55.00 *(978-87-7934-390-0(2))* Aarhus Universitetsforlag DNK. Dist: ISD.

Leuzarder, John. The Gospel for Children. 2008. (Illus.). 40p. per. 8.95 *(978-0-9767582-8-0(8))* Shepherd Pr. Inc.

Life Application Study Bible Staff & Tyndale House Publishers Staff. Life Application Study Bible NKJV. 2006. (ENG., Illus.). 2560p. 79.99 *(978-0-8423-4041-0(6))* Tyndale Hse. Pubs.

Life Publishers, prod. La Biblie Esprit et Vie. 2007.Tr. of Full Life Study Bible. (FRE.). *(978-0-7361-0366-4(X))*; *(978-0-7361-0367-1(8))*; mass mkt. *(978-0-7361-0365-7(1))*; mass mkt. *(978-0-7361-0360-2(0))*; lthr. *(978-0-7361-0368-8(6))* Life Pubs. International.

—Fire Bible: Student Edition - Deluxe. 2007. (YA). lthr. *(978-0-7361-0364-0(3))* Life Pubs. International.

—Fire Bible: Student Edition - Standard. 2007. (YA). lthr. *(978-0-7361-0363-3(5))* Life Pubs. International.

LifeLight: Ephesians / 1 & 2 Thessalonians. 2011. 80p. pap. 8.99 *(978-0-7586-1195-6(1))* Concordia Publishing Hse.

Lifetogether. Sermon on the Mount. 2011. (Deepening Life Together Ser.). (Illus.). 125p. pap. 8.99 *(978-0-8010-6919-2(X))* Baker Bks.

Little III, Pastor Robert G. Four Faces of God. 2007. pap. *(978-0-9778728-8-6(2))* Bush Publishing Inc.

Little Lamb. True Humanity. 2011. 108p. 21.23 ***(978-1-4634-3235-5(6))***; pap. 10.68 ***(978-1-4634-3236-2(4))*** AuthorHouse.

Littleton, Jeanette Gardner & Littleton, Mark. What's in the Bible for Teens. Richards, Larry, ed. 2007. 352p. (YA). pap. 17.99 *(978-0-7642-0386-2(X))* Bethany Hse. Pubs.

Livingstone. God's Promises on Simplicity. 2008. (God's Promises Ser.). (ENG.). 160p. 3.99 *(978-1-934068-98-4(5))* Authentic Media.

Livingstone, des. God's Promises on Prayer. 2008. (God's Promises Ser.). (ENG.). 160p. 3.99 *(978-1-934068-96-0(9))* Authentic Media.

Lloyd, Lynnette. The Bible, Fact or Fiction? Exciting & Compelling Facts to Consider. 2009. (Illus.). 175p. pap. 11.95 *(978-1-4327-2342-2(1))* Outskirts Pr., Inc.

Loges, Shirley. Lessons of Love: A Studt Guide to the Chronological Bible. 2007. (ENG.). 480p. per. 28.99 *(978-1-59755-103-8(1)*, Advantage Inspirational) Advantage Bks.

Londeree, Danielle J. Total Heart Makeover. 2011. 112p. 28.95 ***(978-1-4497-1681-3(4))***; pap. 11.95 ***(978-1-4497-1679-0(2))*** Author Solutions, Inc. (WestBow Pr.).

Longman, Tremper. One Chronicles Thru Job Vol. 4: Timeless Stories & Life Lessons. 2009. (QuickNotes Commentaries Ser.: Vol. 4.1). (ENG.). 240p. pap. 9.99 *(978-1-59789-770-9(1)*, Barbour Bks.) Barbour Publishing, Inc.

Loop, Katherine A. Beyond Numbers: A Practical Guide to Teaching Math Biblically. 2nd ed. 2011. (Illus.). 116p. pap. 8.99 ***(978-0-9773611-3-7(6))*** Christian Perspective.

Lotz, Anne Graham. Into the Word: 52 Life-Changing Bible Studies for Individuals & Groups, 1 vol. 2009. (ENG.). 320p. pap. 14.99 *(978-0-310-32538-3(2))* Zondervan.

—The Vision of His Glory, 0 vols. 2009. 384p. pap. 16.99 *(978-0-8499-2095-0(7))* Nelson, Thomas Inc.

Lowe, Jeff. Greater Works: And How to Perform Miracles. 2009. 260p. pap. 16.99 *(978-1-61579-034-0(9))* Xulon Pr., Inc.

Loy, Keith. Celebrate Colossians. 2009. 80p. pap. 7.99 *(978-0-89827-391-5(9))* Wesleyan Publishing Hse.

Lucado, Max. Gente Comun, 0 vols. 2009. (SPA.). 256p. pap. 13.99 *(978-1-60255-267-8(3))* Grupo Nelson.

—Outlive Your Life: Joining God's Plan to Change the World. 2010. (Outlive Your Life Ser.). (Illus.). 174p. pap., wbk. ed., pupil's gde. ed. *(978-1-4158-6878-2(6))* LifeWay Christian Resources.

Luke 1. (LifeLight Bible Studies: Course 22). pap., stu. ed. 5.50 *(978-0-570-09586-6(7)*, 20-2741); pap. 6.50 *(978-0-570-09585-9(9)*, 20-2740) Concordia Publishing Hse.

Lumpkin, Ronald B. From God's Hands to My Hands. 2008. 132p. per. 13.99 *(978-1-60477-121-3(6))* Xulon Pr., Inc.

LW Bible Discoverers. 1.55 *(978-0-7673-5376-2(5))* LifeWay Christian Resources.

LW Bible Discoverers Teacher. 3.75 *(978-0-7673-5418-9(4))* LifeWay Christian Resources.

LW Bible Learners Teacher. 3.75 *(978-0-7673-5474-5(5))* LifeWay Christian Resources.

LW Bible Searchers Teacher. 3.75 *(978-0-7673-5362-5(5))* LifeWay Christian Resources.

LW Directions Bible Studies for Adults 18-24. 1.55 *(978-0-7673-4562-0(2))* LifeWay Christian Resources.

Lynn, Dennis G. 101 Reflections. 2008. (Illus.). 144p. pap. 14.99 *(978-1-60647-956-8(3))* Xulon Pr., Inc.

Lyons, Michael. The Preachers Bible Study: Advance Bible Study. 2007. (C). 13.95 *(978-0-9778314-2-5(6))* High Praise Publishing.

MacArthur, John. The First King: Prophets & the Power of God's Voice, 0 vols. 2009. (MacArthur Old Testament Study Guides). (Illus.). 128p. pap. 9.99 *(978-1-4185-3404-2(8))* Nelson, Thomas Inc.

—How to Study the Bible, 1 vol. 2009. (ENG.). 144p. pap. 7.99 *(978-0-8024-5303-7(1))* Moody Pubs.

—The MacArthur LifeWorks Library, 0 vols. 2008. cd-rom 89.99 *(978-1-4185-2793-8(9))* Nelson, Thomas Inc.

MacArthur, John, ed. The MacArthur Study Bible, 0 vols. 2006. 2240p. lthr. 99.99 *(978-0-7180-1902-0(4))* Nelson, Thomas Inc.

—MacArthur Study Bible-NASB, 0 vols. 2007. 2208p. im. lthr. 74.99 *(978-0-7180-2076-7(6))*; (Illus.). 2208p. im. lthr. 74.99 *(978-0-7180-2075-0(8))*; (Illus.). 2043p. 49.99 *(978-0-7180-2005-7(7))* Nelson, Thomas Inc.

—MacArthur Study Bible-NKJV. 2006. 2240p. 44.99 *(978-0-7180-1899-3(0))*; 74.99 *(978-0-7180-1900-6(8))*; 84.99 *(978-0-7180-1923-5(7))* Nelson, Thomas Inc.

Maiden, Peter. Discipleship - Bible Study. 2007. (Keswick Foundations Ser.). (ENG.). 144p. 14.99 *(978-1-85078-762-4(X))* Authentic Media.

Mal, Mary. Yes, Let's Have a Bible Study, Especially with a Jehovah's Witness, 2 vols., Set. Incl. Vol. I. iii, 152p. spiral bd. 18.00 *(978-0-9659430-0-0(3))*; Vol. II. spiral bd. *(978-0-9659430-1-7(1))*; 1997. Set pap. 35.00 *(978-0-9659430-2-4(X))* Mal, Mary.

Malcolm, Wesley J. Humble Obedience Leverages Your Basic Instructions Before Leaving Earth: A Compliment to Your Daily Bible Study. 2010. 288p. 25.99 *(978-1-4490-4048-2(9))* AuthorHouse.

Maner, Gary. Aistheterion. 2008. 148p. per. 13.99 *(978-1-60477-603-4(X))* Xulon Pr., Inc.

Marcus, Deborah. Create in Me a Clean Heart. 2011. 222p. pap. 15.99 ***(978-1-61379-248-3(4))*** Xulon Pr., Inc.

Margesson, Nick. A Wonderful Word: Five youth group sessions from Genesis to Revelation. 2009. (ENG., Illus.). 64p. pap. 9.99 *(978-1-84550-461-8(5))* Christian Focus Pubns. GBR. Dist: STL Distribution North America.

Marshall, Andrea. Remember Remember: Teaching Memory Verses to Children. 2010. (Click Ser.). 64p. pap. *(978-1-905564-75-0(9))* Good Bk. Co.

Martin, Dale B. Pedagogy of the Bible: An Analysis & Proposal. 2008. (ENG.). 144p. pap. 25.00 *(978-0-664-23306-8(6))* Westminster John Knox Pr.

Martinez, J. M. La Biblia Dice... According to the Bible. (SPA.). *(978-84-7645-054-3(0)*, 223116) Clie, Editorial.

Mathison, John Ed. Transformed Living in Tough Times Devotions. 2010. 128p. pap. 10.00 *(978-0-687-66032-2(7))* Abingdon Pr.

Matthew: Audio Dramatization Based Word for Word on the Visual Bible's Epic Motion Picture. (People's Bible Commentary Ser.). 454p. pap. 12.99 *(978-0-570-04963-0(6)*, 12-8047);Pt. 1. pap. 8.99 *(978-0-570-07815-9(6)*, 20-3300);Pt. 2. pap. 8.99 *(978-0-570-07847-0(4)*, 20-3310) Concordia Publishing Hse.

Matthews, Leah. Facing Change. 2010. (Insights: Bible Studies for Growing Faith Ser.). 48p. pap. 7.00 *(978-1-60899-222-5(5)*, Wipf and Stock) Wipf & Stock Pubs.

Maxwell, Chris & Standard Publishing Staff. Season One: Episodes 40-52. Cain, Kristi & Derico, Laura, eds. ldr.'s ed. 2008. (Faith Cafe Ser.). (ENG., Illus.). 64p. pap. 14.99 *(978-0-7847-2207-7(2))* Standard Publishing.

—Season One: Episodes 40-52 - Participant's Guide. Cain, Kristi & Derico, Laura, eds. 2008. (Faith Cafe Ser.). (ENG., Illus.). 32p. pap. 3.99 *(978-0-7847-2208-4(0))* Standard Publishing.

Maydell, Karl. Total Triumph: Bible-Study-Commentary. 2009. 248p. pap. 20.95 *(978-1-4327-4038-2(5))* Outskirts Pr., Inc.

Mayhue, Richard. How to Study the Bible. 2006. (ENG.). 208p. pap. 11.99 *(978-1-84550-203-4(5)*, Christian Focus) Christian Focus Pubns. GBR. Dist: STL Distribution North America.

Maynard, M. C. Evil, Pain & Suffering. 2007. 60p. per. 10.00 *(978-1-4257-4423-6(0))* Xlibris Corp.

Mazza, Biagio. How to Teach Scripture. 2010. 112p. pap. 10.95 *(978-0-8091-4630-7(4))* Paulist Pr.

McDonnell, Carole. Seeds of Bible Study. 2008. 292p. pap. 19.94 *(978-1-4357-0811-2(3))* Lulu Enterprises Inc.

McDowell, Josh. Josh Mcdowell's Guide to Understanding Your Bible. 2006. 125p. pap. 11.99 *(978-1-932587-65-4(9))* Green Key Bks.

McDowell, Josh & Pitts, Cindy Ann. Is the Bible Personally from God? Workbook, Grade 1-3. 2006. 48p. 5.99 *(978-1-932587-92-0(6))* Green Key Bks.

—Is the Bible Personally from God? Workbook, Grades 4-6. 2006. 48p. (J). 5.99 *(978-1-932587-93-7(4))* Green Key Bks.

McGarvey, J. w. A Guide to Bible Study. 2010. *(978-0-9819703-4-9(6))* DeWard Publishing Co., Ltd.

McGarvey, J. W. & Willett, Herbert L. A Guide to Bible Study. 2009. (ENG.). 160p. 30.99 *(978-1-117-09456-4(1))* BiblioBazaar.

McIntyre, Louis, Sr. GOD's LOVE & YOU. 2009. 86p. pap. 7.50 *(978-0-557-04382-8(4))* Lulu Enterprises Inc.

McKinney, Leslie Ann. Accepted in the Beloved: A Devotional Bible Study for Women on Finding Healing & Wholeness in God's Love. 2008. (House of Prisca & Aquila Ser.). 56p. pap. 10.00 *(978-1-55635-936-1(5))* Wipf & Stock Pubs.

McLean, Max & Bird, Warren. Unleashing the Word: Rediscovering the Public Reading of Scripture, 1 vol. 2009. (ENG.). 128p. pap. 24.99 *(978-0-310-29270-8(0))* Zondervan.

Meadors, Edward P. Creation, Sin, Covenant, & Salvation: A Primer for Biblical Theology. 2011. 140p. pap. 17.00 ***(978-1-61097-072-3(1)***, Cascade Bks.) Wipf & Stock Pubs.

Mears, Henrietta C. God's Plan: Discover What the Bible Says about Finding Yourself in His Grand Design. 2008. (ENG., Illus.). 336p. pap. 14.99 *(978-0-8307-4562-3(9))* Gospel Light Pubns.

Mears, Henrietta C. & Graham, Billy. What the Bible Is All About. 2007. (ENG., Illus.). 448p. 22.99 *(978-0-8307-4329-2(4))* Gospel Light Pubns.

Meding, Gwen. Come & Rest: A Bible Study for all Who Thirst For More. 2008. 244p. pap. 19.99 *(978-1-4141-1159-9(2))* Pleasant Word.

Meek, James A. A New Kind of Life. (Discover Life Ser.). tchr. ed. 7.35 *(978-1-56212-586-8(9)*, 153135) Faith Alive Christian Resources.

Melbourne, Bertram. The Busy People Bible Study Plan: Strategies for Personal Time with God Amidst Life's Hectic Pace. 2009. 78p. pap. 14.95 *(978-1-60352-067-6(8))* UMI (Urban Ministries, Inc.).

—The Busy People Bible Study Plan Journal: 52 Weeks to Developing a Deeper Relationship with God. 2009. 104p. pap. 9.95 *(978-1-60352-601-2(3))* UMI (Urban Ministries, Inc.).

Melick, Jr., Richard R., Richard R & Melick, Shera. Teaching that Transforms: Facilitating Life Change through Adult Bible Teaching, 1 vol. 2010. (ENG.). 352p. 29.99 *(978-0-8054-4856-6(X)*, B&H Academic) B&H Publishing Group.

Merrill, Timothy. Community: Our Community Now & in God's Future. 2007. (Great Themes of the Bible Ser.). (Illus.). 85p. per. 8.50 *(978-0-687-64342-4(2))* Abingdon Pr.

Mi Dios es Creador (My God Is Creator) Quarter 1, Level 1. (Caminando con Jesus (Walking with Jesus) Series A). (SPA.). tchr. ed. 3.50 *(978-0-570-05101-5(0)*, 16-1801) Concordia Publishing Hse.

Mi Dios es Grande (My God Is Big) Quarter 3, Level 1. (Caminando con Jesus (Walking with Jesus) Series A). (SPA.). tchr. ed. 3.50 *(978-0-570-05103-9(7)*, 16-1803) Concordia Publishing Hse.

Miller, Calvin. Gentleness: Cultivating Spirit-Given Character. 2008. (Fruit of the Spirit Study Guide Ser.). (ENG.). 128p. per. 9.99 *(978-1-4185-2843-0(9))* Nelson, Thomas Inc.

—Love: Cultivating Spirit-Given Character, 0 vols. 2008. (Fruit of the Spirit Study Guide Ser.). (ENG.). 128p. per. 9.99 *(978-1-4185-2841-6(2))* Nelson, Thomas Inc.

—Patience: Cultivating Spirit-Given Character. 2008. (Fruit of the Spirit Ser.). (ENG., Illus.). 128p. per. 9.99 *(978-1-4185-2836-2(6))* Nelson, Thomas Inc.

—Peace: Cultivating Spirit-Given Character. 2008. (Fruit of the Spirit Study Guide Ser.). (ENG.). 128p. per. 9.99 *(978-1-4185-2838-6(2))* Nelson, Thomas Inc.

Miller, George. The Shekinah Glory. 2007. 108p. (ENG.). 18.99 *(978-1-60266-848-5(5))*; per. 10.99 *(978-1-60266-847-8(7))* Xulon Pr., Inc.

Miller, George L. Bible Lights. 2009. 472p. 34.50 *(978-1-60860-170-7(6)*, Eloquent Bks.) AEG Literary Publishing Services, Inc.

Miller, Holly. The Face of an Arrow. 2011. 230p. pap. 15.95 ***(978-1-4327-6933-8(2))*** Outskirts Pr., Inc.

Miller, Linda Ray. Call of the Deep: Diving into God's Way of Life. 2008. 71p. pap. 9.00 *(978-0-687-64986-0(2))* Abingdon Pr.

Miller, Linda Ray, ed. Toddlers & Twos. 19.99 *(978-0-687-05727-6(2))* Abingdon Pr.

Mills, Robert. Whom Alone We Worship & Serve. 2007. 132p. pap. 18.95 *(978-1-934453-00-1(5))* PLC Pubns.

Mills, Sheri D. Doing it God's Way. 2010. 124p. pap. 11.99 *(978-1-60957-671-4(3))* Xulon Pr., Inc.

Millson, Sid. Forty Days Through the Bible. 2010. 110p. 25.00 *(978-1-935271-62-8(8))*; pap. 12.00 *(978-1-935271-61-1(X))* Published by Westview, Inc.

Milthaler, Matthew. E-Merge 2. 0 Small Group Leader's Guide for Younger Youth. 2007. pap. 18.00 *(978-0-687-64299-1(X))* Abingdon Pr.

—EMerge 1. 0: small-group leader's guide for younger Youth: Developing Youth as Fully Devoted Disciples. 2007. 48p. pap. 18.00 incl. cd-rom *(978-0-687-33599-2(X))* Abingdon Pr.

Missick, Stephen Andrew. The Hammer of God. 2010. 454p. pap. 24.99 *(978-1-60957-289-1(0))* Xulon Pr., Inc.

Mister, G. Marie. Who Man Could Have Been in the Body of Christ. 2009. 276p. pap. 20.00 *(978-1-4259-0949-9(3))* AuthorHouse.

Mitch, Stacy. Courageous Generosity: A Bible Study for Women on Heroic Sacrifice. 2009. (Courageous Studies for Women Ser.). 98p. pap. 9.95 *(978-1-931018-57-9(X))* Emmaus Road Publishing.

Mitchell, Alison. The Book of Beginnings: Bible Discovery for Children. 2010. 80p. (J). pap. *(978-1-873166-93-2(1))* Good Bk. Co.

—The Book of Beginnings: Bible Discovery for Families. 2010. 48p. (J). pap. *(978-1-873166-92-5(3))* Good Bk. Co.

—Check It Out: Bible Discovery for Families. 2010. (Table Talk Ser.). 48p. (J). pap. *(978-1-904889-13-7(1))* Good Bk. Co.

—Comings & Goings: Bible Discovery for Families. 2010. (Illus.). 48p. (J). pap. *(978-1-873166-97-0(4))* Good Bk. Co.

—End to End: Bible Discovery for Families. 2010. (Table Talk Ser.). 48p. (J). pap. *(978-1-904889-17-5(4))* Good Bk. Co.

—Footprints: Bible Discovery for Children. 2010. 80p. (J). pap. *(978-1-873166-51-2(6))* Good Bk. Co.

—Footprints: Bible Discovery for Families. 2010. (Table Talk Ser.). 48p. (J). pap. *(978-1-873166-53-6(2))* Good Bk. Co.

—Heroes & Zeros: Bible Discovery for Children. 2010. 80p. (J). pap. *(978-1-873166-69-7(9))* Good Bk. Co.

—The Promise Keeper: Bible Discovery for Children. 2010. 80p. (J). pap. *(978-1-873166-36-9(2))* Good Bk. Co.

—The Promise Keeper: Bible Discovery for Families. 2010. (Table Talk Ser.). 48p. (J). pap. *(978-1-873166-35-2(4))* Good Bk. Co.

—The Real King: Bible Discovery for Children. 2010. (XTB Ser.). 80p. (J). pap. *(978-1-904889-08-3(5))* Good Bk. Co.

—The Real King: Bible Discovery for Families. 2010. (Table Talk Ser.). 48p. (J). pap. *(978-1-904889-09-0(3))* Good Bk. Co.
—Travels Unravelled: Bible Discovery for Children. 2010. 80p. (J). pap. *(978-1-873166-10-9(9))* Good Bk. Co.
—Travels Unravelled: Bible Discovery for Families. 2010. 48p. (J). pap. *(978-1-873166-77-2(X))* Good Bk. Co.
—Trick or Treat?, 25 vols. 2010. 6p. (J). *(978-1-906334-29-1(3))* Good Bk. Co.
—Way to Go: Bible Discovery for Children. 2010. (XTB Ser.). 80p. (J). pap. *(978-1-904889-10-6(7))* Good Bk. Co.
—Way to Go: Bible Discovery for Families. 2010. (Table Talk Ser.). 48p. (J). pap. *(978-1-904889-11-3(5))* Good Bk. Co.
—Write & Wrong: Bible Discovery for Children. 2010. (XTB Ser.). 76p. (J). pap. *(978-1-904889-14-4(X))* Good Bk. Co.
Mitchell, Shirley. Jesus Lives: Ask Me How I Know. 2009. 292p. pap. 18.99 *(978-1-60791-597-3(9))* Xulon Pr., Inc.
Mligo, Elia Shabani. Jesus & the Stigmatized: Reading the Gospel of John in a Context of HIV/AIDS-Related Stigmatization in Tanzania. 2011. 474p. pap. 52.00 ***(978-1-60899-706-0(5)***, Pickwick Pubns.) Wipf & Stock Pubs.
Monroy, Juan A. La Biblia en el Quijote.Tr. of Bible in Quijote. (SPA.). 192p. *(978-84-7228-468-5(9)*, 220099) Clie, Editorial.
Monteith, Stanley. Brotherhood of Darkness. 2009. (ENG.). 160p. pap. 12.95 *(978-0-9817643-7-5(1))* Anomalos Publishing, LLC.
Moody, Dwight Lyman. Pleasure & Profit in Bible Study & Anecdotes, Incidents & Illustrations. 2007. 248p. per. *(978-1-4067-8874-7(0)*, Pomona Pr.) Read Bks.
Moore, Beth. A Woman's Heart: God's Dwelling Place. 2007. (Illus.). 222p. per. 14.95 *(978-1-4158-5581-2(1))* LifeWay Christian Resources.
—A Woman's Heart Leader's Guide: God's Dwelling Place. 2007. 31p. pap. 6.95 *(978-1-4158-5579-9(X))* LifeWay Christian Resources.
Moore, Leola O. In-Souls Power Steps Bible Study. 2007. 12.99 *(978-0-9760126-9-6(3))* In-Souls Pubns.
Moore, William. The Elder Shall Serve the Younger. 2007. 108p. per. 10.99 *(978-1-60266-164-6(2))* Xulon Pr., Inc.
Morgan, G. Campbell. Los Grandes Capitulos de la Biblia: Great Chapters of the Bible, 2 bks. (SPA.). Bk. I. 200p. *(978-84-7228-881-2(1)*, 222330)Bk. II. *(978-84-7228-882-9(X)*, 222331) Clie, Editorial.
—Ultimo Mensaje de Dios al Hombre: God's Last Word to Man. (SPA.). 144p. *(978-84-7228-852-2(8)*, 220919) Clie, Editorial.
Morris, Bruce T. A Funny Thing Happened on the Way Through My Bible Study. 2008. 184p. pap. 13.99 *(978-1-60647-028-2(0))* Xulon Pr., Inc.
Morris, Trena M. Momma Said, You Gotta Pray: Mini-Devotional Prayers. 2011. 48p. 24.99 ***(978-1-4628-8393-6(1))***; pap. 15.99 ***(978-1-4628-8392-9(3))*** Xlibris Corp.
Moskala, Jiri, ed. Christ, Salvation, & the Eschaton: Essays in Honor of Hans K. Larondelle. 2009. (Illus.). 500p. (C). pap. 20.00 *(978-0-9706380-2-1(7))* Andrew's Univ., Theological Seminary, Old Testament Dept.
Moss, James D. Into the Bible Every Day: Notes & Observations. 2007. 428p. per. 24.99 *(978-1-60266-978-9(3))* Xulon Pr., Inc.
Moulton, Richard G. The Literary Study of the Bible. 2009. 550p. 43.99 *(978-1-115-30725-3(8))*; pap. 40.75 *(978-1-115-30720-8(7))*; pap. 41.75 *(978-1-115-30721-5(5))* BiblioBazaar.
Mueller, A. C. & Rake, Tim. 1 & 2 Timothy/Titus. 2006. (God's Word for Today Ser.). 120p. pap. 8.99 *(978-0-7586-1355-4(5))* Concordia Publishing Hse.
Murphy, Dennis J., ed. The Church & the Bible: Official Documents of the Catholic Church. 2nd enl. ed. 2007. xcvi, 1048p. 24.95 *(978-0-8189-1250-4(2)*, St. Pauls) St Pauls/Alba Hse. Pubns.
Murray, Ted. Lessons from Ezra. 2007. 84p. per. *(978-0-901860-75-0(1))* Scripture Truth Pubns.
My Daily Catholic Bible: NAB Edition. rev. ed. 2011. 1552p. pap. 24.95 ***(978-1-59276-144-9(5))*** Our Sunday Visitor, Publishing Div.
Navajo Bible. 1125p. 31.99 *(978-1-58516-194-2(2))* American Bible Society.
Nee, Watchman. Escudrinad las Escrituras.Tr. of Search the Scriptures. (SPA.). *(978-84-7645-289-9(6)*, 223342) Clie, Editorial.
Neede, Lilian Pickering. God's Woman Unveiled: Proverbs 31 Footprints in the New Millennium. 2009. 308p. 28.99 *(978-1-60791-848-6(X))*; pap. 18.99 *(978-1-60791-847-9(1))* Xulon Pr., Inc.
Nelson, Ray. Because. God Said So! 2008. 332p. pap. 29.95 *(978-1-60441-425-7(1))* PublishAmerica, Inc.
Newman, Gale. The Truth about the Lie. 2009. 220p. pap. 15.99 *(978-1-60791-020-6(9))* Xulon Pr., Inc.
Newton, R. Heber. The Right & Wrong Uses of the Bible. 2008. 204p. 27.99 *(978-0-554-24197-5(3))* 2008. 204p. 24.99 *(978-0-554-33500-1(X))* 2007. (ENG.). 180p. pap. 19.99 *(978-1-4264-5925-2(4))* BiblioBazaar.
—The Right & Wrong Uses of the Bible. 2007. (ENG.). 172p. per. *(978-1-4065-5034-4(5))* Dodo Pr.
—The Right & Wrong Uses of the Bible. 2007. (ENG.). 268p. 42.95 *(978-0-548-10006-6(3))* Kessinger Publishing, LLC.
—Right & Wrong Uses of the Bible. 2006. pap. *(978-1-4068-3455-0(6))* Echo Library.
—The Right & Wrong Uses of the Bible. lt. ed. 2007. 202p. pap. 22.99 *(978-1-4264-5993-1(9))* BiblioBazaar.
Nicholes, Lou. Job. 2007. 140p. per. 13.99 *(978-1-60266-309-1(2))* Xulon Pr., Inc.
Nickelson, Ronald L., ed. Standard Lesson Commentary: KJV. 2007. (Standard Lesson Commentary: KJV Ser.). (Illus.). 448p. 19.99 *(978-0-7847-2079-0(7))*; 512p. per. 16.99 *(978-0-7847-2082-0(7))* Standard Publishing.
—Standard Lesson Commentary-KJV: International Sunday School Lessons. 56th ed. 2008. (Standard Lesson Commentary: KJV Ser.). (Illus.). 448p. 19.99 *(978-0-7847-2195-7(5))* Standard Publishing.
—Standard Lesson Commentary: NIV. 2007. (Standard Lesson Commentary: NIV Ser.). (Illus.). 512p. per. 16.99 *(978-0-7847-2083-7(5))*; 448p. per. 14.99 *(978-0-7847-2080-6(0))* Standard Publishing.
Nickelson, Ronald L. & Underwood, Jonathan, eds. KJV Standard Lesson Commentary: International Sunday School Lessons. 2008. (Standard Lesson Commentary: KJV Ser.). (Illus.). 448p. pap. 15.99 *(978-0-7847-2194-0(7))*; 512p. pap. 18.99 *(978-0-7847-2200-8(5))* Standard Publishing.
—NIV Standard Lesson Commentary: International Sunday School Lessons. 2008. (Standard Lesson Commentary: NIV Ser.). (Illus.). 447p. pap. 15.99 *(978-0-7847-2196-4(3))*; 512p. pap. 18.99 *(978-0-7847-2201-5(3))* Standard Publishing.
—Standard Lesson Commentary: International Sunday School Lessons. 2007. (Standard Lesson Commentary: KJV Ser.). (Illus.). 448p. per. 14.99 *(978-0-7847-2078-3(9))* Standard Publishing.
Ninos y Mujeres en la Biblia (Children & Women in the Bible) Quarter 2, Level 2. (Caminando con Jesus (Walking with Jesus) Series A). (SPA.). tchr. ed. 3.50 *(978-0-570-05127-5(4)*, 16-2802) Concordia Publishing Hse.
Norwood, James E. Christ As Conqueror & Reconciler: Theological Implications for the Church's Role in Deliverance. 2008. 124p. 24.95 *(978-0-9785352-4-7(3))* Word & Spirit Pr.
Novelli, Michael. Enter the Story: Seven Experiences to Unlock the Bible for Your Students, 1 vol. 2010. (ENG.). 176p. pap. 18.99 *(978-0-310-66927-2(8))* Zondervan.
Una Nueva Vida (A New Life) Quarter 3, Level 2. (Caminando con Jesus (Walking with Jesus) Series B). (SPA.). tchr. ed. 3.50 *(978-0-570-05131-2(2)*, 16-2903) Concordia Publishing Hse.
Nuss, Donald R. The Anatomies of God, the Bible, & Religion: Decoding the Old & New Testaments. 2010. 600p. 43.95 *(978-1-4502-5013-9(0))*; pap. 33.95 *(978-1-4502-5012-2(2))* iUniverse, Inc.
Nwaduba, Michael. A Simple Guide for Bible Study. 2008. 212p. 24.99 *(978-1-4343-8934-3(0))*; pap. 14.49 *(978-1-4343-8933-6(2))* AuthorHouse.
Oesch, Jackie. Making the Bible Yours: A Journey into the Heart of God. 2009. 88p. pap. 12.99 *(978-1-60791-778-6(5))* Xulon Pr., Inc.
Ogunkoya, Olukayode. Godly Parents, Godly Children. 2011. 68p. pap. 10.99 ***(978-1-61215-507-4(3))*** Xulon Pr., Inc.
Olive, Diaphero. Top Secret: The 12th Apostle of the Lamb. 2007. 252p. per. 19.95 *(978-1-4327-0685-2(3))* Outskirts Pr., Inc.
One Room Sunday School Teacher Guide: Spring. tchr. ed. 12.00 *(978-0-687-03598-4(8))* Abingdon Pr.
One Room Sunday School Teacher Guide: Winter. tchr. ed. 10.50 *(978-0-687-03597-7(X))* Abingdon Pr.
Orr, William W. The Anguish of Earth's Tribulation. (Prophecy Ser.). 48p. reprint ed. pap. 3.50 *(978-0-944412-01-5(7))* Glad Tidings.
—Believer's First Bible Course. (Basic Bible Ser.). 48p. reprint ed. pap. 3.50 *(978-0-944412-00-8(9))* Glad Tidings.
Ortberg, John, et al. New Community Series Library, ZCS, 1 vol. 2008. (New Community Bible Study Ser.). pap., pap., pap. 83.88 *(978-0-310-65025-6(9))* Zondervan.
O'Steen-Grant, Mae. Lavender & Peach. 2009. 265p. pap. 18.95 *(978-1-4327-3910-2(7))* Outskirts Pr., Inc.
Our Life in Christ Bk. 5: Adult Bible Study. rev. ed. 6.50 *(978-0-570-07920-0(9))* Concordia Publishing Hse.
Our Life in Christ Bk. 8: Adult Bible Study. rev. ed. 6.50 *(978-0-570-07923-1(3)*, 20-3242) Concordia Publishing Hse.
Oxford, ed. The Catholic Bible. 2nd ed. 2011. (ENG.). 2464p. (C). 89.99 *(978-0-19-981256-1(X))*; 49.99 *(978-0-19-529790-4(3))*; pap. 39.99 *(978-0-19-529791-1(1))* Oxford Univ. Pr., Inc.
Pacwa, Mitch. St. Paul & the Power of the Cross. 2008. (Illus.). 120p. pap. 8.95 *(978-1-59276-552-2(1))* Our Sunday Visitor, Publishing Div.
Page, Nick. The Bible Book: A User's Guide. 2008. (ENG., Illus.). 416p. pap. 22.95 *(978-0-00-711967-7(4))* HarperCollins Pubs. Ltd. GBR. Dist: Independent Pubs. Group.
Patrick, Dan. Second Most Important Book You'll Ever Read, 0 vols. 2009. 240p. pap. 14.99 *(978-0-8499-2935-9(0))* Nelson, Thomas Inc.
Patterson, Donald. Bible Discovery Series: Finding Tools to Read & Interpret Scripture. 2010. 96p. pap. *(978-0-8100-2269-0(9))* Northwestern Publishing Hse.
Patterson, Richard. Father Said to Tell You. 2006. pap. 12.99 *(978-0-9767889-2-8(6))* Morningstar Publishing.
Pavlantos, Stephanie. The Few, the Humble, the Church. 2008. 140p. pap. 13.99 *(978-1-60647-265-1(8))* Xulon Pr., Inc.
Pearch, Steve, frwd. Back to the Source: 10 Steps for Personal Bible Study. 2007. 138p. per. 14.95 *(978-0-9790966-0-0(X))* Pearch Publishing, LLC.
Peck, John A. Called to Serve. 2009. 68p. pap. 20.00 *(978-1-4357-4194-2(3))* Lulu Enterprises Inc.
—Called to Serve Leader's Edition. 2009. 68p. pap. 25.00 *(978-1-4357-4195-9(1))* Lulu Enterprises Inc.
Pedrone, Dino. He Must Be The. 2011. 90p. pap. 10.99 ***(978-1-61215-516-6(2))*** Xulon Pr., Inc.
Pedrone, Dino. What in the World Is God Doing? A Verse-by-Verse Study of Romans. 2009. 320p. pap. 18.99 *(978-1-60791-955-1(9))* Xulon Pr. Inc
Penn-Lewis, Jessie. Como Entender Ensen. y Misterios Cruz: How to Understand the Teachings. (SPA.). 104p. *(978-84-7228-888-1(9)*, 222312) Clie, Editorial.
Pennington, Mark. The Scripture Memory Workbook. 2007. spiral bd. 0.01 net. *(978-1-60402-175-2(6))* Independent Pub.
Pennington, Ray. The Answer to All Your Questions about the Book of Revelation. 2010. 230p. 25.99 *(978-1-60957-564-9(4))*; pap. 15.99 *(978-1-60957-563-2(6))* Xulon Pr., Inc.
Penson, Lynn. Esther: For such a time as This, 1 vol. 2009. (Cover to Cover Bible Study Ser.). 72p. pap. *(978-1-85345-511-7(3))* Crusade for World Revival.
Perkins, Robert. Bringing Home the Message: How Community Can Multiply the Power of the Preached Word. 2010. 238p. 31.99 *(978-0-557-46023-6(9))* Lulu Enterprises Inc.
Perrotta, Kevin. The Our Father: A Guided Discovery for Groups & Individuals. 2007. (Six Weeks with the Bible Ser.). 88p. per. 7.95 *(978-0-8294-2167-5(X))* Loyola Pr.
Peters, Linda. The Bible: Fitting Together the Pieces. 2010. 258p. pap. 16.99 *(978-1-61579-282-5(1))* Xulon Pr., Inc.
Peterson, David H. A Firm Foundation. 2008. 196p. per. 13.99 *(978-1-60477-437-5(1))* Xulon Pr., Inc.
Peterson, Eugene H. The Invitation: A Simple Guide to the Bible. 2007. (Hollywood Nobody Ser.). (ENG., Illus.). 208p. 16.99 *(978-1-60006-233-9(4))* NavPress Publishing Group.
Pettingell, Karen. Study Guide For: Teach Me, Lord, to Dance: an Interview with Jesus. 2007. 76p. per. 11.99 *(978-0-9786487-1-8(4))* Frankie Dove Publishing.
Philipps, James. Make Room for Scripture: An Invitation to Catechists & Teachers. 2010. 168p. pap. 14.95 *(978-1-58595-775-0(5))* Twenty-Third Pubns./Bayard.
Pierce, Chad J. Disciples. 2008. (Illus.). 149p. *(978-1-59255-433-1(4))* Faith Alive Christian Resources.
Pierce-Norton, Mary Jane. Gender & Learning: Gifted Equally, Taught Differently. 2008. 96p. pap. 10.00 *(978-0-687-65472-7(6))* Abingdon Pr.
Pierce, Wesley. Bible Study Made Simple! 2011. 134p. pap. 16.95 ***(978-1-57472-500-1(9))*** Archer Ellison Publishing Co.
Pilavachi, Mike & Croft, Andy. Storylines: Your Map to Understanding the Bible, 1 vol. 2010. (ENG.). 208p. pap. 12.99 *(978-1-4347-6475-1(3))* Cook, David C.
Pitre, Roy. Where Is the Fire of the Book of Acts? 2007. pap. 16.99 *(978-1-60266-034-2(4))* Xulon Pr., Inc.
Pitt, David. All Life Is Dependent on the Word Relationship. 2008. (Illus.). 50p. pap. 22.95 *(978-0-9798246-3-0(X)*, Seraphina Fr.) Hillcrest Publishing Group, Inc.
Pitt, Patricia D. Return to Eden: The Place Called There. 2007. (J). per. *(978-1-59872-812-5(1))* Instant Pub.
Platt, Rita J. An Undivided Heart: Experiencing the Intimacy of Jesus' Touch. 2009. (Sword of Lyric Ser.). (ENG.). 128p. pap. 9.99 *(978-1-60006-388-6(8))* NavPress Publishing Group.
Platt, Rutherford H. The Forgotten Books of Eden. 2009. 464p. 42.99 *(978-1-59547-512-1(5))* NuVision Pubns., LLC.
Platt, Rutherford H., ed. The Forgotten Books of Eden. 2006. 280p. pap. 22.95 *(978-1-58509-270-3(3))* Book Tree, The.
Ponessa, Joseph & Manhardt, Laurie Watson. David & the Psalms. 2006. (Come & See Catholic Bible Study Ser.). (Illus.). 202p. per. 19.95 *(978-1-931018-37-1(5))* Emmaus Road Publishing.
Possi, Peter. The Bible Study Challenge. 2008. 113p. pap. 17.95 *(978-1-4092-0573-9(8))* Lulu Enterprises Inc.
Powell, Kara, ed. Listening to God: Junior High Group Study. 2012. (Uncommon Ser.). (ENG.). 192p. pap. 14.99 ***(978-0-8307-6136-4(5))*** Gospel Light Pubns.
Powell, Kara Eckmann. The Armor of God. 2011. pap. ***(978-0-8307-5899-9(2))*** Gospel Light Pubns.
Power, Freddie. Behind Closed Doors: God Brings Life after Abuse. 2010. 84p. pap. 26.49 *(978-1-4389-8701-9(3))* AuthorHouse.
PowerXpress Dance for Joy. 9.95 incl. audio compact disk *(978-0-687-09517-9(4))* Abingdon Pr.
PowerXpress Esther. 9.95 incl. audio compact disk *(978-0-687-09514-8(X))* Abingdon Pr.
PowerXpress Feasts & Festivals. 9.95 incl. audio compact disk *(978-0-687-07922-3(5))* Abingdon Pr.
PowerXpress Jesus Calms the Storm. 9.95 incl. audio compact disk *(978-0-687-09457-8(7))* Abingdon Pr.
PowerXpress Journey to the Cross. 9.95 incl. audio compact disk *(978-0-687-09268-8(4))* Abingdon Pr.
PowerXpress Life in Bible Times. 9.95 incl. audio compact disk *(978-0-687-09437-0(2))* Abingdon Pr.
PowerXpress Ten Lepers. 9.95 incl. audio compact disk *(978-0-687-08101-1(7))* Abingdon Pr.
Prasch, James Jacob. Israel, the Church & the Jews. 2008. (ENG.). 324p. pap. 14.99 *(978-0-9779535-6-1(4))* 21st Century Pr.
Pratico, Gary D., et al. Basics of Biblical Hebrew Workbook. 2nd ed. 2007. (ENG., Illus.). 304p. (gr. 13). pap. 22.99 *(978-0-310-27022-5(7))* Zondervan.
Price, Cheryl. Living in the Excellence of Jesus - Adult Workbook. Carey, Evangeline, ed. 2007. 100p. pap. 2.99 *(978-1-934056-65-3(0))* UMI (Urban Ministries, Inc.).
Price, Cheryl L. Living in the Excellence of Jesus! Carey, Evangeline, ed. 2007. 148p. per. 9.89 *(978-1-934056-63-9(4))* UMI (Urban Ministries, Inc.).
Pries, Jeff & Ward, John. Crossing. 2007. (Liquid Ser.). (ENG., Illus.). 112p. instr.'s gde. ed. 24.99 *(978-1-4185-2759-4(9))* Nelson, Thomas Inc.
—Live at Five, 0 vols. 2007. (Liquid Ser.). (ENG., Illus.). 112p. 24.99 *(978-1-4185-2757-0(2))* Nelson, Thomas Inc.
—Mirror Image. 2007. (Liquid Ser.). (ENG., Illus.). 112p. 24.99 *(978-1-4185-2761-7(0))* Nelson, Thomas Inc.
Purifoy, Thomas & Rogers, Jonathan. Modern Parables, Volume 1: Living in the Kingdom of God. 2007. 196p. pap. 8.99 *(978-0-9798524-1-1(2))*; DVD, audio compact disk 129.00 *(978-0-9798524-0-4(4))* Compass Cinema.
R. E. A. L. 2009. 32p. pap. 5.99 *(978-0-7644-3955-1(3))* Group Publishing, Inc.
Radcliffe, Duane & Ross, Marcus. The Precepts & Doctrines of Men. 2010. 292p. pap. 20.95 *(978-1-4502-5116-7(1))* iUniverse, Inc.
Radke, Nancy L. & Miller, Alison D. I Know My Bible, Volume 2: The Books of History. 2011. (Illus.). 59p. (J). 3.99 ***(978-0-9802148-4-0(X)***, Show & Tell Bible) Bedrock Video Productions LLC.
Rainey, Barbara. Growing Together in Truth: Character Stories for Families. 2011. (Character Stories for Families Ser.). (ENG., Illus.). 38p. 12.99 ***(978-1-60200-500-6(1))*** FamilyLife.
Rainey, Dennis & Rainey, Barbara. FamilyLife Bible Study for Couples, 0 vols. 2010. 128p. pap. 9.99 *(978-1-4185-4303-7(9))* Nelson, Thomas Inc.
Rapaport. Ashmedai the King of DemonsA Guide to de. 2006. 60p. per. *(978-956-291-327-0(9))* Editorial Benei Noaj.
Read, Tim. Angels Do Not Have Wings. 2011. 92p. pap. 19.95 ***(978-1-4626-1752-4(2))*** PublishAmerica, Inc.
Reagan, Wesley C., ed. The Higley Lesson Commentary: 1933-2008. 2007. (Higley Lesson Commentary Ser.). (Illus.). 530p. pap. 15.95 *(978-1-886763-32-6(1))* Higley Publishing Corp.
—The Higley Lesson Commentary: Based on the International Sunday School Lessons. 2007. (Illus.). 530p. 19.95 *(978-1-886763-33-3(X))*, Higley Publishing Corp.
—The Higley Lesson Commentary: Based on the International Sunday School Lessons, King James Version, 77th Annual Volume. 2009. (Higley Lesson Commentary Ser.). (Illus.). 520p. pap. 15.95 *(978-1-886763-36-4(4))* Higley Publishing Corp.
Reasons, Allen. The Gospel of Luke: Good News of Great Joy. 2009. 212p. pap. *(978-1-934731-41-3(2))* Baptistway.
Reed, Mark. Route 66: Travel Through the Bible. 3rd ed. 2009. (ENG.). pap. 16.95 *(978-1-59557-109-0(4)*, Positive Action Bible Curriculum) Positive Action For Christ.
Reese, Pastor James R. 100 Most Asked Questions about the Bible. 2011. 220p. 24.59 ***(978-1-4634-3468-7(5))***; pap. 15.79 ***(978-1-4634-3469-4(3))*** AuthorHouse.
Rev. J. A. Jefferson. Bible Study Guide: Man's Relationship to His Eternal God. 2009. 184p. pap. 19.49 *(978-1-4389-0411-5(8))* AuthorHouse.
Reverend O. L. Johnson, O. L. Johnson & Reverend O.L. Johnson. Exploring the Holy Scriptures: The Back to Basics Series. 2009. 108p. 22.95 *(978-1-4401-6454-5(1))*; pap. 12.95 *(978-1-4401-6455-2(X))* iUniverse, Inc.
Richards, Larry. Indispensable Guide to Practically Everything. 2009. (Indispensable Guide to Practically Everything Ser.). (ENG., Illus.). 256p. pap. 15.99 *(978-0-8249-4769-9(X))* Ideals Pubns.
—The Life of Moses, 0 vols. Peters, Angie, ed. 2008. (Smart Guide to the Bible Ser.). 384p. pap. 14.99 *(978-1-4185-1009-1(2))* Nelson, Thomas Inc.
Richards, Larry, ed. Indispensable Guide to Practically Everything, 0 vols. 2006. (Smart Guide to the Bible Ser.). (Illus.). 352p. per. 14.99 *(978-1-4185-0988-0(4))* Nelson, Thomas Inc.
Richardson, John, Jr. Get into the Bible: From First Creation to New Creation - The Unfolding Plan of God in Scripture. 2010. 48p. pap. *(978-1-873166-08-6(7))* Good Bk. Co.
Riden, Darryl E. The Young Theologian's Handbook. 2011. 248p. pap. 15.99 ***(978-1-61379-177-6(1))*** Xulon Pr., Inc.
Ries, Xavier. New Believers Study Guide. 2006.Tr. of Nuevos Creyentes Guida de Estudio. 111p. per. *(978-0-9773829-6-5(6))* Calvary Chapel Pasadena.
Rimmer, Harry. La Llave del Problema: Answers to Key Bible Questions. (SPA.). 190p. *(978-84-7228-004-5(7)*, 220542) Clie, Editorial.
Robert Duprey. Scriptures of the Christianity - the Holy Bible. 2009. 176p. pap. 19.95 *(978-1-4269-2142-1(X))* Trafford Publishing.
Roberts, Oral. This Is Your Abundant Life in Jesus Christ: Bible Studies in Abundant Life. 2011. 130p. 40.95 ***(978-1-258-00789-8(4))*** Literary Licensing, LLC.
Robertson, Chuck. A Simple Man's Study of Esther. 2009. pap. 11.99 *(978-1-60696-672-3(3))* Tate Publishing & Enterprises, LLC.
Robertson, Norman. Ministering in the Power of the Holy Spirit. pap. 20.00 *(978-0-9636898-2-5(7))* Robertson, Norman Ministries.
—The Supernatural Church. pap. 20.00 *(978-0-9636898-0-1(0))* Robertson, Norman Ministries.
Robinson, Rodney. Let the Word of God Explain Itself. 2011. 45p. pap. 8.99 ***(978-1-61215-581-4(2))*** Xulon Pr., Inc.
Rodgers, Edwin. BECOMING ONE (Leader's Guide) 2007. per 4.95 *(978-0-9790338-3-4(7))* Rodgers, Edwin Inc.
Rohrig, George. God's Glorious Church: Understanding the Purposes of God. 2011. 148p. 22.23 *(978-1-4567-1680-6(8))*; pap. 11.70 *(978-1-4567-1681-3(6))* AuthorHouse.
Roncace, Mark & Gray, Patrick. Teaching the Bible Through Popular Culture & the Arts. 2008. 393p. *(978-90-04-15116-1(8))* BRILL.
—Teaching the Bible Through Popular Culture & the Arts. 2007. (Resources for Biblical Study Ser.). 37.95 *(978-1-58983-244-2(2))* Society of Biblical Literature.
Root, Michael & Buckley, James Joseph. Sharper Than a Two-Edged Sword: Preaching, Teaching, & Living the Bible. Root, Michael & Buckley, James J., eds. 2008. (Illus.). 112p. pap. 16.00 *(978-0-8028-6271-6(3))* Eerdmans, William B. Publishing Co.

B

Rosan, Dan. Soldiers of Christ Bible Study: Daily Bible Study. 2010. 72p. pap. 12.95 *(978-1-4327-5715-1(6))* Outskirts Pr., Inc.

Roshwald, Mordecai. Biblical Revisions & para-Biblical Visions. Strozier, M. Stefan & Torke, Kyle, eds. 2008. 184p. pap. 20.00 *(978-1-935444-00-8(X))* World Audience Pubs.

Ross, Hugh. El Creador y el Cosmos. Date not set. (SPA.). 224p. pap. 11.99 *(978-0-311-05047-5(6),* Editorial Mundo Hispano) Casa Bautista de Publicaciones.

Rossi, Antony. Who Am I? (Early Intervention Books Ser.). 23.10 *(978-0-7362-0036-3(3));* Vol. 6. 3.85 *(978-1-56334-984-3(1))* Hampton-Brown Bks.

Rossi, Antony & Rossi, Francesco. Who Am I? 2009. (Illus.). 40p. (J). 14.95 *(978-0-9816641-6-3(4))* Forks Pr.

Rottmann, Erik. One Truth, Many Lies. 2011. 96p. pap. 17.99 ***(978-0-7586-2824-4(2))*** Concordia Publishing Hse.

Royer, Katherine. Nursery Stories of Jesus. 2009. 52p. pap. 12.00 *(978-1-60899-140-2(7),* Resource Pubns.) Wipf & Stock Pubs.

Rudman, Burton S. Biography of the Sacred, 1 vol. 2009. 144p. pap. 24.95 *(978-1-60836-909-6(9))* PublishAmerica, Inc.

Ruggiero, Louis. The Tower of Deception. 2008. pap. 14.95 *(978-0-9801357-2-5(9))* Tree of Life Publishing Hse.

Russell, Gilbert & Russell, Judith. Introduction to the Bible. 2011. 96p. pap. 13.95 ***(978-1-4670-6025-7(9))*** AuthorHouse.

Ryrie, Charles C. The Ryrie KJV Study Bible. 2008. (ENG.). 2336p. 39.99 *(978-0-8024-8908-1(7))* Moody Pubs.

Saint Mary's Press Staff, contrib. by. The Catholic Youth Bible. 3rd ed. 2010. *(978-0-88489-791-0(5))* St. Mary's Pr.

Samuelson, Christine. Healer of the Broken Heart. 2008. 148p. pap. 15.99 *(978-1-60477-870-0(9))* Xulon Pr., Inc.

Sanusi, Idowu. Learn & Test Your Understanding of Bible. 2009. 164p. pap. 17.95 *(978-1-4327-1190-0(3))* Outskirts Pr., Inc.

Saphir, Adolph. The Divine Unity of Scripture. 2009. 372p. 31.99 *(978-1-116-36628-0(2));* 33.99 *(978-1-116-36629-7(0));* pap. 32.75 *(978-1-116-36631-0(2));* pap. 33.75 *(978-1-116-36630-3(4))* BiblioBazaar.

—The Divine Unity of Scripture. 2009. 192p. pap. *(978-0-217-07451-3(0))* Books LLC.

Sarah, Christmyer. The Bible Timeline Guided Journal. 2007. (Great Adventure Ser.). 227p. 14.95 *(978-1-934217-16-0(6))* Ascension Pr.

Sargent, Alan E. Changing Your Stars: Empowerment for a Different Destiny. 2011. pap. 12.99 *(978-1-61739-948-0(5))* Tate Publishing & Enterprises, LLC.

Scheppmann, Susanne. Birds in My Mustard Tree: How to Grow Your Faith. 2008. 151p. pap. 10.99 *(978-0-89265-668-4(9))* Randall Hse. Pubns.

Schlieker, Paul. What's Missing Inside You? 2006. pap. 16.99 *(978-1-60034-518-0(2))* Xulon Pr., Inc.

Schultz, Karl A. How to Pray with the Bible: The Ancient Prayer Form of Lectio Divina Made Simple. 2007. 157p. per. 9.95 *(978-1-59276-216-3(6))* Our Sunday Visitor, Publishing Div.

Scimasass, Rico T. & a.k.a. Barranger, Jack. Rico's Irreverent Bible Studies. 2009. 112p. pap. 13.95 *(978-1-58509-123-2(5))* Book Tree, The.

Scroggie, W. Es la Biblia la Palabra de Dios? Is the Bible the Word of God? (SPA.). 96p. *(978-84-7228-843-0(9),* 222321) Clie, Editorial.

Seelye, Edward Eli. Bible Emblems. 2006. 224p. per. 20.99 *(978-1-4255-1873-8(7))* MPublishing.

Segovia, Fernando F. & Tolbert, Mary Ann, eds. Teaching the Bible: The Discourses & Politics of Biblical Pedagogy. 2009. 386p. pap. 29.00 *(978-0-8006-9698-6(0))* Augsburg Fortress, Pubs.

Seiple, D. & Weidmann, Frederick W., eds. Enigmas & Powers: Engaging the Work of Walter Wink for Classroom, Church, & World. 2007. (Princeton Theological Monographs). 168p. pap. 19.00 *(978-1-55635-290-4(5),* Pickwick Pubns.) Wipf & Stock Pubs.

Sell, Alan P. F., ed. The Bible in Church, Academy, & Culture: Essays in Honour of the Reverend Dr. John Tudno Williams. 2011. 302p. pap. 33.00 *(978-1-60899-475-5(9),* Pickwick Pubns.) Wipf & Stock Pubs.

Senior, Donald & Collins, John J. Catholic Study Bible. 2nd ed. 2011. (ENG.). 2560p. (C). 49.99 *(978-0-19-529775-1(X));* pap. 39.99 *(978-0-19-529776-8(8))* Oxford Univ. Pr., Inc.

Shahin, Gloria. Liturgy & Sacraments: Teacher Guide. 2010. pap. 26.25 *(978-1-59982-047-7(1))* St. Mary's Pr.

Shalev, Zur. Sacred Words & Worlds: Geography, Religion, & Scholarship, 1550-1700. 2011. (History of Science & Medicine Library). (Illus.). 320p. ***(978-90-04-20935-0(2))*** BRILL.

Shammas, Sam. Invitations. 2010. (Christianity Explored Ser.). *(978-1-904889-40-3(9))* Good Bk. Co.

Sharbaugh, Norm. Red Sky's a Blazin' 2008. (Illus.). 200p. pap. 15.99 *(978-1-60647-801-1(X))* Xulon Pr., Inc.

Shelburne, Gene, et al. The Higley Lesson Commentary: KJV Based on the International Sunday School Lessons. Reagan, Wesley, ed. 77th ed. 2009. (Illus.). 520p. (J). 19.95 *(978-1-886763-37-1(2))* Higley Publishing Corp.

Shelton, Asher Elishama. Vessels of Honor & Dishonor: A Poetic Reference Book of Biblical Characters. 2009. 336p. pap. 18.99 *(978-1-61579-005-0(5))* Xulon Pr., Inc.

Sheveland, Jerry & Sheveland, Dee. Come & Follow: Encountering Jesus: an 8-week study through Mark's Gospel. 2011. 142p. pap. 12.99 ***(978-0-935797-03-9(3))*** Harvest Pubns.

Shirer, Priscilla. Jonah: Navigating a Life Interrupted. 2010. 157p. pap. *(978-1-4158-6849-2(2))* LifeWay Christian Resources.

Shirer, Priscilla, et al. Anointed, Transformed, Redeemed: A Study of David. 2008. (Illus.). 148p. pap. 18.00 *(978-1-4158-6585-9(X))* LifeWay Christian Resources.

Simpson, Amy. Into the Word: How to Get the Most from Your Bible. 2008. (Hollywood Nobody Ser.). (ENG.). 80p. (YA). pap. 8.99 *(978-1-60006-094-6(3),* Th1nk Bks.) NavPress Publishing Group.

Sims, Timothy. In Defense of the Word of Faith: An Apologetic Response to Encourage Charismatic Believers. 2008. 284p. 26.99 *(978-1-4389-1823-5(2));* pap. 16.99 *(978-1-4389-1824-2(0))* AuthorHouse.

Sing! A New Creation. ldr.'s ed. 49.95 *(978-1-56212-812-8(4),* 400205) Faith Alive Christian Resources.

Singer-Towns, Brian. Biblical Literacy Made Easy: A Practical Guide for Catechists, Teachers, & Youth Ministers. 2008. (Illus.). 69p. pap. 7.25 *(978-0-88489-956-3(X))* St. Mary's Pr.

Singer-Towns, Brian, ed. Catholic Youth Bible. 2007. (Illus.). 1600p. (YA). lthr. 39.95 *(978-0-88489-664-7(1));* lthr. 45.95 *(978-0-88489-663-0(3))* St. Mary's Pr.

Sisk, William B. The Mystery of Iniquity: God's Revelation of Good & Evil. 2008. 199p. pap. 24.95 *(978-1-60563-747-1(5))* PublishAmerica, Inc.

Skelton, Stephen. John Wayne Movie Bible Study (Study Guide) 2009. (ENG.). 48p. 7.99 *(978-0-9817549-8-7(8))* Primetime Parable Ministries.

—Mayberry Moments VOL 1 Leader / Participant Guide. 2008. (ENG.). 44p. 5.99 *(978-0-9791259-9-7(5))* Primetime Parable Ministries.

—Mayberry Moments VOL 2 Leader / Participant Guide. 2008. (ENG.). 44p. 5.99 *(978-0-9817549-1-8(0))* Primetime Parable Ministries.

—Primetime Moments VOL 1 Leader / Participant Guide. 2008. (ENG.). 44p. 5.99 *(978-0-9817549-3-2(7))* Primetime Parable Ministries.

Smith-Christopher, Daniel L. Jonah, Jesus, & Other Good Coyotes: Speaking Peace to Power in the Bible. annot. ed. 2007. 194p. pap. 22.00 *(978-0-687-34383-6(6))* Abingdon Pr.

Smith, Christopher R. Daniel / Revelation: Understanding the Books of the Bible Study. 2011. (Understanding the Books of the Bible Ser.). (ENG.). 143p. pap. 8.99 *(978-1-60657-057-9(9),* Authentic Bibles) Authentic Media.

—Proverbs / Ecclesiastes / James: Understanding the Books of the Bible Study. 2011. (Understanding the Books of the Bible Ser.). (ENG.). 138p. pap. 8.99 *(978-1-60657-056-2(0),* Authentic Bibles) Authentic Media.

Smith, Dudley. Faith Is Our Victory. 2009. 131p. pap. 16.99 *(978-0-557-05000-0(6))* Lulu Enterprises Inc.

—The TIME of the END. 2009. 304p. pap. 19.99 *(978-0-557-06035-1(4))* Lulu Enterprises Inc.

Smith, J. Translated Hallelujahs: A Linguistic & Exegetical Commentary on Select Septuagint Psalms. 2011. (Contributions to Biblical Exegesis & Theology Ser.). (ENG.). 300p. (C). pap. 56.00 *(978-90-429-2384-3(9))* Peeters Pubs. & Booksellers BEL. Dist: Brown, David Bk. Co., The.

Smith, Robert. Biblical Charity. 29p. pap. 2.99 *(978-0-9652883-2-3(3))* Audubon Pr. & Christian Bk. Service.

Smith, Robert Bruce. Cultural Perspectives on the Bible: A Beginner's Guide. 2007. 224p. per. 18.00 *(978-0-9785165-7-4(5))* Drinian Pr., LLC.

Smith, Sandra Bivens. Never Thirst Again: Journey to the Well. 2011. 96p. pap. 13.95 ***(978-1-4497-1431-4(5),*** WestBow Pr.) Author Solutions, Inc.

Smith, William, Jr. Entre los Dos Testamentos.Tr. of Between the Two Testaments. (SPA.). *(978-84-7645-018-5(4),* 223088) Clie, Editorial.

Smith, Willie Mae. The Witch Hidden in My House. 2008. 52p. pap. 9.99 *(978-1-60266-147-9(2))* Xulon Pr., Inc.

Soles, Richard V., Jr. The Bible Belt. 2008. 127p. pap. 14.95 *(978-0-557-03212-9(1))* Lulu Enterprises Inc.

Sonnenberg, Roger. God's Grace in the Fifties. (Yearbook Bible Studies). 6.99 *(978-0-570-06946-1(7),* 20-3051) Concordia Publishing Hse.

—God's Grace in the Forties. (Yearbook Bible Studies). 6.99 *(978-0-570-06945-4(9),* 20-3050) Concordia Publishing Hse.

—God's Grace in the Seventies. 6.99 *(978-0-570-06948-5(3),* 20-3053) Concordia Publishing Hse.

Speck, Samuel L. Bible Readings for Bible Students & for the Home & Fireside. 2007. 20.00 *(978-1-60416-056-7(X))* Reformation Pubs.

Speck, Samuel L. & Riggle, Herbert M. Bible Readings for Bible Students & for the Home & Fireside. 2007. per. 13.00 *(978-1-60416-055-0(1))* Reformation Pubs.

Spencer, Melle. Can Anything Good Come from Seinfeld? 2010. pap. 10.99 *(978-1-61663-252-6(6))* Tate Publishing & Enterprises, LLC.

Spradlin, Dwayne. From the Garden to the Gathering. 2008. 66p. pap. 10.00 *(978-0-9801420-4-4(0))* Ketch Publishing.

Spurgeon, Charles H. The Treasury of David. 2010. 488p. pap. 38.75 *(978-1-148-91074-1(3));* 504p. pap. 39.75 *(978-1-148-96910-7(1));* 508p. pap. 39.75 *(978-1-142-49405-6(5))* BiblioBazaar.

—The Treasury of David. 2009. 106p. pap. *(978-0-217-30920-2(8));* 200p. pap. *(978-1-4589-0822-3(4));* 546p. pap. *(978-1-4589-4156-5(6))* Books LLC.

—The Treasury of David. 2009. 364p. pap. 33.59 *(978-1-4589-0823-0(2))* General Bks. LLC.

Spurling, Marshall. Ladder. 2006. pap. 17.99 *(978-1-60034-182-3(9))* Xulon Pr., Inc.

Stampley, C. D., Enterprises Staff, Enterprises D. Stampley, contrib. by. Sagrada Biblia Guadalupana Pasta Negra. 2007. (SPA.). 600p. *(978-0-580-87055-2(3))* B S I Standards.

Stanbrough, David L. What about Santa Claus & Christians at Christmas? How to Teach Your Children the Real Meaning of Christmas - from the Bible. 2008. 60p. pap. 10.95 *(978-1-4327-2892-2(X))* Outskirts Pr., Inc.

Standard Publishing Staff. Media. 2006. cd-rom 24.99 *(978-0-7847-1888-9(1))* Standard Publishing.

—NIV Standard Lesson Commentary. l.t. ed. 2009. (ENG.). 520p. pap. 18.99 *(978-0-7847-2259-6(5))* Standard Publishing.

—NIV Standard Lesson Commentary with ECommentary. 2009. (Standard Lesson Commentary Ser.). (ENG.). 448p. 21.99 *(978-0-7847-2342-5(7))* Standard Publishing.

—Standard Companion Devotions. 2009. (ENG.). 384p. pap. 9.99 *(978-0-7847-2253-4(6))* Standard Publishing.

Standard Publishing Staff, creator. Conquering Crisis: Lessons from the Life of Job. 2007. (Encounter Bible Lessons Ser.). cd-rom 24.99 *(978-0-7847-1879-7(2))* Standard Publishing.

—Encounter: The Magazine. 2009. (Encounter Curriculum Ser.). (Illus.). pap. 17.99 *(978-0-7847-5430-6(6))* Standard Publishing.

Stanley, Charles F. Developing a Servant's Heart: Give of Yourself & Receive from God, 0 vols. 2008. (Life Principles Study Ser.). 128p. per. 9.99 *(978-1-4185-2811-9(0))* Nelson, Thomas Inc.

—Discovering Your Identity: Find Yourself Fully in Christ, 0 vols. 2008. (Life Principles Study Ser.). 128p. per. 9.99 *(978-1-4185-2817-1(X))* Nelson, Thomas Inc.

—Experiencing Success God's Way: Achieve the Goals God Helps You to Set, 0 vols. 2009. (Life Principles Study Ser.). 128p. pap. 9.99 *(978-1-4185-4125-5(7))* Nelson, Thomas Inc.

—Exploring the Depths of God's Love, 0 vols. 2009. (Life Principles Study Ser.). 128p. pap. 9.99 *(978-1-4185-4114-9(1))* Nelson, Thomas Inc.

—Preparing for Christ's Return, 0 vols. 2009. (Life Principles Study Ser.). 128p. pap. 9.99 *(978-1-4185-4118-7(4))* Nelson, Thomas Inc.

—Sharing the Gift of Encouragement: Being Blessed by Blessing Others, 0 vols. 2008. (Life Principles Study Ser.). 128p. per. 9.99 *(978-1-4185-2812-6(9))* Nelson, Thomas Inc.

—Winning on the Inside: Facing Trials & Defeating Temptation, 0 vols. 2008. (Life Principles Study Ser.). 128p. per. 9.99 *(978-1-4185-2816-4(1))* Nelson, Thomas Inc.

—10 Principles for Studying Your Bible, 0 vols. 2008. 160p. per. 7.99 *(978-1-4002-0097-9(0))* Nelson, Thomas Inc.

—30 Life Principles, 0 vols. 2008. 160p. pap. 9.99 *(978-1-4185-3108-9(1))* Nelson, Thomas Inc.

Stanley, Thomas. Study Guide for Reading the Bible the Law Vol 1. 2011. 188p. pap. 13.95 ***(978-1-4620-2684-5(2))*** iUniverse, Inc.

Stansfield, Michael. Covenant Promise of Joseph: The Key to Solving the Jewish/Palestinian Conflict. 2009. 416p. pap. 21.99 *(978-1-60799-277-6(9))* Tate Publishing & Enterprises, LLC.

Stapleton, Jean. Read with Me: 365 Family Readins Giving an Overview of the Bible. 2006. (ENG., Illus.). 432p. per. 14.99 *(978-1-84550-148-8(9),* Christian Focus) Christian Focus Pubns. GBR. Dist: STL Distribution North America.

Starks, Edward Andrew Th. D. The Christian Lifestyle Study Bible & Commentary. 2009. 724p. 34.99 *(978-1-4363-8143-7(6));* pap. 23.99 *(978-1-4363-8142-0(8))* Xlibris Corp.

Stavrakopoulou, Francesca. How to Read the Hebrew Bible. 2012. (ENG., Illus.). 256p. (C). 108.00 *(978-0-415-47142-8(7))* Routledge.

Steck, Odil H. Studien zu Tritojesaja. (Beihefte zur Zeitschrift far die alttestamentliche Wissenschaft Ser.). (GER.). XIV, 294p. 196.00 ***(978-3-11-188067-9(2))*** De Gruyter, Walter Inc.

Steinberg, Joseph. The Book of Y. 2008. (ENG.). 176p. 15.99 *(978-1-86024-568-8(4))* Authentic Media.

Steiner, Rudolf. Bible & Wisdom. 32p. pap. 3.95 *(978-0-919924-26-0(3),* 1083) Steiner Bk. Ctr. CAN. Dist: SteinerBooks, Inc.

Steinmann, Andrew E. Intermediate Biblical Hebrew. 2010. 264p. pap. 49.99 *(978-0-7586-2516-8(2))* Concordia Publishing Hse.

Stephen, Skelton. Gilligan's Island Bible Study Study Guide. 2007. (ENG.). 42p. pap. 7.99 *(978-0-9791259-5-9(2))* Entertainment Ministry, The.

Stewart, Ann Marie. Preparing My Heart for Motherhood. 2009. 174p. pap. 12.99 *(978-0-89957-027-3(5))* AMG Pubs.

Street, Linda. When We Move to Heaven: A Family Love Story. 2009. 296p. pap. 16.99 *(978-1-60791-037-4(3))* Xulon Pr., Inc.

Stuart, Moses. Exegetical Essays on Several Words Relating to Future Punishment. 2009. 86p. pap. 15.58 *(978-1-151-63453-5(0))* General Bks. LLC.

—Exegetical Essays on Several Words Relating to Future Punishment. 2008. 160p. 36.95 *(978-1-4369-0571-8(0));* pap. 21.95 *(978-1-4368-4150-4(X))* Kessinger Publishing, LLC.

Student Bible. deluxe ed. (Illus.). 24.99 *(978-0-529-10821-0(6));* 31.99 *(978-0-529-11139-5(X))* Nelson, Thomas Inc.

Sub FBS All Youth Leader Pack. 79.35 *(978-0-633-05077-1(6))* LifeWay Christian Resources.

Sub FBS Collegiate Learner Guide. 11.55 *(978-0-633-05048-1(2))* LifeWay Christian Resources.

Sub FBS Life Answers. ldr.'s ed. 18.95 *(978-0-633-05052-8(0))* LifeWay Christian Resources.

Sub FBS Life Answers Leader Pack. 81.15 *(978-0-633-05084-9(9))* LifeWay Christian Resources.

Sub FBS Life Truths. ldr.'s ed. 18.95 *(978-0-633-05054-2(7))* LifeWay Christian Resources.

Sub FBS Life Truths Leader Pack. 79.35 *(978-0-633-05085-6(7))* LifeWay Christian Resources.

Sub FBS Preteen Teaching Pictures. 45.15 *(978-0-633-05089-4(X))* LifeWay Christian Resources.

Sub FBS the Herschel Hobbs Commentary. 21.95 *(978-0-633-05127-3(6))* LifeWay Christian Resources.

Subscription FBS Adult Leader Guide HCSB. 18.95 *(978-0-633-05040-5(7))* LifeWay Christian Resources.

Summers, Oliver E. What Is God up to? - Why Earth?- Why Eternity? 2008. 380p. pap. 23.99 *(978-1-60647-635-2(1))* Xulon Pr., Inc.

Swaggart, Jimmy. The Expositor's Study Bible - Loose-Leaf Edition. 2007. 99.95 *(978-1-934655-37-5(6))* Swaggart, Jimmy Ministries.

Swanson, Reuben J. Reflections on Biblical Themes by an Octogenarian. 2007. 210p. pap. 24.00 *(978-1-59752-877-1(3),* Wipf and Stock) Wipf & Stock Pubs.

Swenson, Kristin. Bible Babel: Making Sense of the Most Talked about Book of All Time. 2010. (ENG.). 368p. 24.99 *(978-0-06-172829-7(2))* HarperCollins Pubs.

Swindoll, Charles R. Esther -Revised- Bible Study Guide, 0 vols. 2008. 120p. pap. 9.99 *(978-0-8499-9074-8(2))* Nelson, Thomas Inc.

Teacher Resource Pack - Preschool: Summer 2001. (Faith Weaver Ser.). 19.99 incl. audio compact disk *(978-0-7644-1128-1(4))* Group Publishing, Inc.

Ted, Cooper, reader. In 90 Days: Church Campaign Kit. 2009. (ENG.). pap., pap. 99.99 *(978-0-310-94154-5(7))* Zondervan.

Teeters, Jim. Going Intergenerational. 2010. 100p. pap. 14.00 *(978-1-59498-021-3(7))* Barclay Pr., Inc.

Thomas Nelson. The Chronological Guide to the Bible, 0 vols. 2010. 464p. pap. 24.99 *(978-1-4185-4175-0(3))* Nelson, Thomas Inc.

Thomas Nelson Publishing Staff. The Chronological Study Bible, 0 vols. 2009. 1728p. 74.99 *(978-1-4185-4251-1(2))* Nelson, Thomas Inc.

—Precious Moments Holy Bible - Blue NKJV, 0 vols. 2009. 1088p. 17.99 *(978-1-4003-1519-2(0))* Nelson, Thomas Inc.

—Precious Moments Holy Bible - Pink NKJV, 0 vols. 2009. 1088p. 17.99 *(978-1-4003-1518-5(2))* Nelson, Thomas Inc.

Thomas Nelson Publishing Staff, ed. KJV Family Bible. 2009. 508p. 29.99 *(978-1-4185-4110-1(9))* Nelson, Thomas Inc.

Thomas Nelson Publishing Staff & Thomas Nelson. Expanded: New Testament, 0 vols. 2009. 672p. 29.99 *(978-0-7180-1984-6(9))* Nelson, Thomas Inc.

—Expanded Bible NT, 0 vols. 2009. 672p. pap. 19.99 *(978-0-7180-1916-7(4))* Nelson, Thomas Inc.

Thomas, W. Griffith. Metodos de Estudio Biblico: Methods for Bible Study. (SPA.). 112p. *(978-84-7228-868-3(4),* 220591) Clie, Editorial.

Thomason, Krista. Determined Not to be Desperate. 2009. pap. 10.99 *(978-1-60799-494-7(1))* Tate Publishing & Enterprises, LLC.

The Thompson Chain-Reference Bible. lthr. 77.95 *(978-0-88707-392-2(1))* Kirkbride, B.B. Bible Co., Inc.

The Thompson Chain-Reference Bible. lthr. 77.95 *(978-0-88707-393-9(X))* Kirkbride, B.B. Bible Co., Inc.

The Thompson Chain-Reference Bible. lthr. 77.95 *(978-0-88707-395-3(6))* Kirkbride, B.B. Bible Co., Inc.

Thompson, David W. The Stranger's Compass. 2009. 116p. pap. 11.99 *(978-1-60791-389-4(5))* Xulon Pr., Inc.

—A Stranger's Journey. 2007. 124p. per. 10.99 *(978-1-60477-471-9(1))* Xulon Pr., Inc.

Thompson, Marjorie J. The Way of Scripture: Leader's Guide. 2010. *(978-0-8358-1033-3(X))* Upper Room Bks.

Thompson, Nan. God's Events, Now & Forever: A Study of End-Time Events. 2009. 24.99 *(978-1-60791-685-7(1));* pap. 14.99 *(978-1-60791-684-0(3))* Xulon Pr., Inc.

Tidwell, Josiah Blake. The Bible Book by Book: A Manual for the Outline Study of the Bible by Book. 2007. 188p. pap. 19.99 *(978-1-4346-2739-1(X));* 210p. pap. 22.99 *(978-1-4346-2772-8(1))* BiblioBazaar.

Tidwell, Josiah Blake. The Bible Book by Book, a Manual for the Outline Study of the Bible by Books. 2011. 152p. pap. 14.99 ***(978-1-61203-238-2(9))*** Bottom of the Hill Publishing.

Tiegreen, Chris. Story Thru the Bible: An Interactive Way to Connect with God's Word. 2011. (NavPress Devotional Readers Ser.). 336p. pap. 24.99 *(978-1-61521-820-2(3))* NavPress Publishing Group.

Time with God. (Friendship Ser.). 10.50 *(978-1-56212-751-0(9),* 300650) Faith Alive Christian Resources.

Tinsley, Sarah V. Bible in a Nutshell, Daily Devotional Version. 2008. 436p. pap. 34.95 *(978-1-4357-3025-0(9))* Lulu Enterprises Inc.

—Bible in a Nutshell, New Edition. 2008. 292p. pap. 28.95 *(978-1-4357-2794-6(0))* Lulu Enterprises Inc.

—Bible in a Nutshell Study Guide. 2008. 148p. pap. 21.50 *(978-1-4357-3087-8(9))* Lulu Enterprises Inc.

Tjjohnson. Chapter & Verse, Crosswords & Other Puzzles: Verse Variety. 2011. 188p. pap. 19.95 ***(978-1-4670-4208-6(0))*** AuthorHouse.

To Die For: Life Study of John the Baptist. 2007. (YA). *(978-1-934577-22-6(7))* LeaderTreks NFP.

Torrey, R. A. Evidencias Cristianas: The Bible & Its Christ. (SPA.). *(978-84-7645-085-7(0),* 223134) Clie, Editorial.

—How to Study the Bible for Greatest Profit. 2009. 124p. 24.99 *(978-1-110-47599-5(3));* pap. 19.75 *(978-1-110-47598-8(5))* BiblioBazaar.

—What the Bible Teaches: The Truths of the Bible Made Plain, Simple & Understandable. 2008. 502p. per. 24.95 *(978-1-59856-273-6(8))* Hendrickson Pubs. Marketing, LLC.

Torrey, Ruben A. Como Estudiar la Biblia: How to Study the Bible. (SPA.). 128p. *(978-84-7228-677-1(0),* 220166) Clie, Editorial.

Travis, Charlotte. A Study of 1 & 2 Timothy: Guarding Truth. 2011. 188p. pap. 19.95 (978-1-61507-799-1(5)) Cross Bks. Publishing.
Turrentine, Haywood. The Invisible Chain That Enslaves Us: The Clergy's Misuse of the King James Version of the Bible. 2009. 148p. 22.95 (978-1-60860-417-3(9), Eloquent Bks.) AEG Literary Publishing Services, Inc.
Tyndale House Publishers Staff, prod. Operation Worship Holy Bible. 2009. (ENG.). 1008p. pap. 5.99 (978-1-4143-3386-1(2)); pap. 5.99 (978-1-4143-3387-8(0)); pap. 5.99 (978-1-4143-3385-4(4)) Tyndale Hse. Pubs.
Tyndale House Publishers Staff & Bright Media Foundation Staff, prods. Discover God Study Bible. 2007. (ENG., Illus.). 2480p. 59.99 (978-0-8423-6919-0(8)) Tyndale Hse. Pubs.
—The Discover God Study Bible. 2007. (ENG., Illus.). 2480p. lthr. 59.99 (978-0-8423-6923-7(6)) Tyndale Hse. Pubs.
Under His Wings Bible Studies: Emptiness/Abundance. stu. ed. 5.50 (978-0-570-06933-1(5), 20-3207); 5.50 (978-0-570-06932-4(7), 20-3206) Concordia Publishing Hse.
Under His Wings Bible Studies: Fear/Confidence. stu. ed. 5.50 (978-0-570-06937-9(8), 20-3211); 5.50 (978-0-570-06936-2(X), 20-3210) Concordia Publishing Hse.
Under His Wings Bible Studies: Guilt/Forgiveness. stu. ed. 5.50 (978-0-570-06939-3(4), 20-3213); 5.50 (978-0-570-06938-6(6), 20-3212) Concordia Publishing Hse.
Under His Wings Bible Studies: Tempest/Refuge. stu. ed. 5.50 (978-0-570-06935-5(1), 20-3209); 5.50 (978-0-570-06934-8(3), 20-3208) Concordia Publishing Hse.
Underwood, Richard & Boley, Brian. Understanding Doctrine. 2010. (Learn2Lead Ser.). 64p. pap. (978-1-905564-71-2(6)) Good Bk. Co.
—Understanding the Bible. 2010. (Learn2Lead Ser.). 72p. pap. (978-1-905564-70-5(8)) Good Bk. Co.
Ungnad, Arthur. Selected Babylonian Business & Legal Terms of the Hammurabi Period. 2009. 106p. pap. 9.00 (978-1-60608-381-9(3), Wipf and Stock) Wipf & Stock Pubs.
United State Confraternity of Catholic Bishops, creator. Study Bible-NABRE. 2011. (ENG.). im. lthr. 35.97 (978-1-55665-426-8(X)) Fireside Catholic Bibles.
Upton, Christy. Come Away with Me: Living Life in His Presence. 2009. 172p. pap. 12.99 (978-1-4389-5547-6(2)) AuthorHouse.
Urick, Steve. Nowmillennial Dispensationalism: A Biblical Examination of the Millennium & the Kingdom of God. 2009. 128p. pap. 13.99 (978-1-4389-9993-7(3)) AuthorHouse.
Van Der Veer, Andrew. Bible Lessons for Juniors: (four volume Set) 2007. (J). (978-1-60178-016-4(8)) Reformation Heritage Bks.
Van Kampen, Beverly. The Bible Study Teacher's Guide. 2006. 192p. per. (978-1-932902-63-1(5)) FaithWalk Publishing.
Van Kempen, Case. 1, 2, 3 John: Living in the Light of Love. pap., stu. ed. 7.95 (978-1-59255-202-3(1), 150330); pap. 8.95 (978-1-59255-204-7(8), 150335) Faith Alive Christian Resources.
Van Schooneveld, Amber & Van Schooneveld, Mike. Passport to Prayer: A Journey of Compassion. 2009. (Illus.). 114p. pap. 12.99 (978-0-7644-3840-0(9)) Westminster John Knox Pr.
Vander Griend, Alvin J. Small Groups That Work. (Healthy Church Ser.). 2.95 (978-1-56212-713-8(6), 216771) Faith Alive Christian Resources.
Vander Kam, Henry. Bible Lessons: The Book of Amos. 2007. 100p. pap. 8.00 (978-0-9793677-1-7(9)) Reformed Fellowship, Inc.
—Bible Lessons: The Books of II Timothy & Titus. 2007. 100p. pap. 8.00 (978-0-9793677-0-0(0)) Reformed Fellowship, Inc.
Vereen, Bob. A Man's Strategy for Conquering Temptation. 2009. (40-Minute Bible Studies). (ENG.). 112p. pap. 7.99 (978-0-307-45761-5(3), WaterBrook Pr.) Doubleday Religious Publishing Group, The.
Vereen, Bob, et al. Living a Life of True Worship. 2009. (40-Minute Bible Studies). (ENG., Illus.). 96p. pap. 7.99 (978-0-307-45766-0(4), WaterBrook Pr.) Doubleday Religious Publishing Group, The.
—Living Victoriously in Difficult Times. 2009. (40-Minute Bible Studies). (ENG.). 96p. pap. 7.99 (978-0-307-45767-7(2), WaterBrook Pr.) Doubleday Religious Publishing Group, The.
Vinas, Jaime. La Biblia - Guia de Comprension. 2008. 364p. pap. 17.99 (978-1-4259-6612-6(8)) AuthorHouse.
Vincent, Ray. Let the Bible Be Itself. 2009. (ENG.). 160p. pap. 24.95 (978-1-84694-148-1(2)) Hunt, John Publishing Ltd. GBR. Dist: National Bk. Network.
Vine, W. E. W. E. Vine Essential Library, 1 vol. 2009. cd-rom 49.99 (978-1-4185-4368-6(3)) Nelson, Thomas Inc.
Visual Resources for Bible Teaching. pap. 11.00 (978-0-8307-2299-0(8)) Gospel Light Pubns.
Vogan, Charles. Ten Keys to the Bible. 2007. (ENG.). 592p. per. 32.00 (978-0-615-13933-3(7)) Shenandoah Bible Ministries.
Vukovich, R. A. Masked: Timeless, Thought-Provoking, & Spiritually Challenging. 2011. 180p. 30.95 (978-1-4497-1684-4(9)); pap. 13.95 (978-1-4497-1682-0(2)) Author Solutions, Inc. (WestBow Pr.).
Waite, Th. D. The Superior Foundation of the King James Bible. 2008. 108p. pap. 12.00 (978-1-56848-062-6(8)) Old Paths Pubns., Inc., The.
Walker, James Barr. The Bible in School. 2011. 26p. pap. 11.99 (978-1-4181-9236-5(8)) MPublishing.
Walker, Robert. Bible Treatise. 2011. 28p. pap. 5.99 (978-1-937129-05-7(5)) Faithful Life Pubs.
Walkin, Cardinal & Walkin, Cardinal N. Praying for Miracles. 2007. 400p. per. (978-1-905529-95-7(3)) Grosvenor Hse. Publishing Ltd.
Walkin, Newton. Praying for Miracles. 2011. 534p. 38.99 (978-1-60957-041-5(3)); pap. 26.99 (978-1-60957-040-8(5)) Xulon Pr., Inc.
Walsh, Sheila. WOF: Embracing God's Design for Your Life - TP Edition, 0 vols. 2009. (Women of Faith Study Guide Ser.). 144p. pap. 9.99 (978-1-4185-3225-3(8)) Nelson, Thomas Inc.
Wampach, Jane. Adventures of Zeke & Jimmy: The Tales of Two Dogs. 2008. 160p. pap. 13.99 (978-1-60477-965-3(9)) Xulon Pr., Inc.
Ward, John & Pries, Jeff. Fork in the Road, Kit. ldr.'s ed. 2007. (Liquid Ser.). (ENG., Illus.). 112p. 24.99 (978-1-4185-2763-1(7)) Nelson, Thomas Inc.
—Money Talks. 2008. (Liquid Ser.). (ENG.). 112p. 24.99 (978-1-4185-2765-5(3)); (Illus.). pap., instr.'s gde. ed. 9.99 (978-1-4185-3355-7(6)) Nelson, Thomas Inc.
Ware, George W. Jesus Christ, a Complete Harmony: Narrating the Four Gospels in Chronological Order (NRVS) pap., tchr. ed. 0.95 (978-1-56794-241-5(5), C-3027) Star Bible & Tract Corp.
Warfield, Benjamin B. Estudios Biblicos y Teologicos: Biblical & Theological Studies. (SPA.). (978-84-7645-497-8(X), 223567) Clie, Editorial.
Water, Mark. The Bible Made Easy: An Easy-to-Understand Pocket Reference Guide. (Made Easy Ser.). (Illus.). 64p. pap. 4.99 (978-1-85608-293-8(8)) Hunt, John Publishing Ltd. GBR. Dist: O. M. Literature.
—The Bible Made Plain & Simple. 128p. pap. 14.95 (978-1-56563-893-8(X)) Hendrickson Pubs. Marketing, LLC.
—Bible Study Made Easy: An Easy-to-Understand Pocket Reference Guide. (Made Easy Ser.). (Illus.). 64p. pap. 4.99 (978-1-85608-386-7(1)) Hunt, John Publishing Ltd. GBR. Dist: O. M. Literature.
Webster, Sheila. Truthfinder. 2007. 112p. per. 10.99 (978-1-60266-346-6(7)) Xulon Pr., Inc.
Wells, Laura Marie. A Marian Bible Study: Bringing Scripture to Life for Moms. 2006. (Illus.). 110p. per. 9.95 (978-1-59276-222-4(0)) Our Sunday Visitor, Publishing Div.
Wesleyan Publishing House, creator. Wesley Bible Lesson Commentary: For Teachers & Students. 2009. (Illus.). 398p. pap. 21.99 (978-0-89827-414-1(1)) Wesleyan Publishing Hse.
West, Robert M. How to Study the Bible. 2007. (Value Bks.). (ENG.). 96p. per. 1.49 (978-1-59789-706-8(X), Barbour Bks.) Barbour Publishing, Inc.
West, Theresa. Biblical Nutrients: VITAMINS A, B, C, D,E, F & G. 2011. 54p. pap. 15.99 (978-1-4628-7186-5(0)) Xlibris Corp.
Wezeman, Phyllis Vos. 50 Interactive Bible Stories for Children Ages 5-8. 2009. 80p. (J). pap. 16.95 (978-1-58595-701-9(1), Twenty-Third Pubns./Bayard.
White, Cookie. And I Heard God Whisper, Walk with Me. 2010. 122p. pap. 11.99 (978-1-60957-405-5(2)) Xulon Pr., Inc.
White, Hugh C. Narration & Discourse in the Book of Genesis. 2003. (ENG.). 328p. (C). pap. 39.99 (978-0-521-05026-5(X)) Cambridge Univ. Pr.
Whittle, Rodney E. Exploring the Word. 2009. 376p. pap. 23.99 (978-1-61579-256-6(2)); 392p. pap. 23.99 (978-1-61579-255-9(4)) Xulon Pr., Inc.
Wiersbe, Warren W. Be Holy (Leviticus) Becoming Set Apart for God. 2010. (BE Series Commentary Ser.). (ENG.). 208p. pap. 12.99 (978-1-4347-0053-7(4)) Cook, David C.
—Philippians: Even When Things Go Wrong, You Can Have Joy. 2007. (Wiersbe Bible Study Ser.). (ENG.). 128p. per. 8.99 (978-0-7814-4570-2(1)) Cook, David C.
Williams. The Miracle of Biblical Inspiration. 2009. 132p. pap. 15.00 (978-0-9820608-6-5(6)) Old Paths Pubns., Inc., The.
Williams, Matt, ed. The Last Days of Jesus Participant's Guide: Six In-Depth Studies Connecting the Bible to Life, 1 vol. 2009. (ENG.). 144p. pap. 9.99 (978-0-310-29302-6(2)) Zondervan.
—The Life of Jesus Participant's Guide: Six In-Depth Studies Connecting the Bible to Life, 1 vol. 2009. (ENG.). 144p. pap. 9.99 (978-0-310-29301-9(4)) Zondervan.
Williams, Paul & Cooper, Barry. If You Could Ask God One Question. 2010. (Christianity Explored Ser.). 128p. pap. (978-1-904889-45-8(X)) Good Bk. Co.
Willimon, William H. & Green, Joel B. New Revised Standard Version - NRSV - the Welsey Study Bible: Imitation Leather - Tan/Green. 2009. 1616p. pap. 49.95 (978-0-687-64503-9(4)) Abingdon Pr.
Willingham, Angela. Temple Time Bible Study Guide & Personal Journal II-Relationships. Willingham, Angela, ed. 2007. 70p. spiral bd. 15.00 (978-0-9772049-2-2(8)) New Beginnings Holistic Fitness Ministries, Inc.
Willis, Charles. Effectively Teaching Adult Bible Class. 2008. 80p. pap. 6.95 (978-1-58427-234-2(1)) Guardian of Truth Foundation.
Willis, Mike. How to Study the Bible - Truth in Life. 2007. 5.99 (978-1-58427-196-3(5)) Guardian of Truth Foundation.
Wilson, Glenda. Journey into Purroelving Yourself Throug. 2006. 148p. per. 14.95 (978-1-931178-26-6(7)) Vision Publishing.
Winford, Rick & Stephenson, Andy. Taking the Plunge: Leaders Guide. 2011. (Ultimate Adventure Ser.). (ENG., Illus.). 113p. pap. 16.00 (978-1-59317-527-6(2)) Warner Pr. Pubs.
Wink, Walter. The Bible in Human Transformation: Toward a New Paradigm in Bible Study. 2010. (Facets Ser.). 96p. pap. 9.99 (978-0-8006-9633-7(6), Fortress Pr.) Augsburg Fortress, Pubs.
—Transforming Bible Study. 2009. 176p. pap. 20.00 (978-1-60608-665-0(0), Wipf and Stock) Wipf & Stock Pubs.
Witnessing to Unchurched Family Members. 12.99 (978-0-570-06850-1(9), 20-3022) Concordia Publishing Hse.
Wolgemuth, Bobbie. God's Wisdom for a Mother's Heart: A Bible Study for Moms, 0 vols. 2010. 128p. pap. 9.99 (978-1-4185-4304-4(7)) Nelson, Thomas Inc.
Wolgemuth, Robert & Wolgemuth, Bobbie. Couples of the Bible: A One Year Devotional Study of Couples in Scripture, 1 vol. 2012. (ENG.). 432p. 22.99 (978-0-310-33268-8(0)) Zondervan.
Women of Faith. Being Yourself: How Do I Take off This Mask?, 0 vols. 2008. (Women of Faith Study Guides). 128p. 9.99 (978-1-4185-2936-9(2)) Nelson, Thomas Inc.
—Imagine, 0 vols. 2010. (Women of Faith Study Guide Ser.). 128p. spiral bd. 9.99 (978-1-4185-4186-6(9)) Nelson, Thomas Inc.
Won, Dal Joon, ed. The New Interpreter's Study Bible. 2008. (KOR.). 2342p. 28.00 (978-0-687-49733-1(7)) Abingdon Pr.
Wood, Barry G. Bible Secrets Revealed. 2008. 184p. pap. 13.99 (978-1-60477-861-8(X)) Xulon Pr., Inc.
World Bible Translation Center, creator. Holy Bible: Easy-to-Read. 2007. 1039p. pap. 3.95 (978-1-932438-45-1(9)) World Bible Translation Ctr., Inc.
—Malayalam Holy Bible-FL: Easy to Read. 2007. 1238p. 11.95 (978-1-932438-78-9(5)) World Bible Translation Ctr., Inc.
World Bible Translation Ctr, tr. La Biblia. 2008. (SPA.). 969p. 8.95 (978-1-932438-28-4(9)) World Bible Translation Ctr., Inc.
Worship & Liturgy: God Speaks We Respond. (Touchpoint Ser.). 40p. pap., stu. ed. 2.99 (978-0-570-09557-6(3), 20-2501) 30p. pap. 2.99 (978-0-570-09558-3(1), 20-2502) Concordia Publishing Hse.
Wright, Charles H. H. The Bible Readers' Aids. 2007. 360p. 46.95 (978-0-548-06795-6(3)) Kessinger Publishing, LLC.
Wright, Lacie. Covenant for Kids! Teacher's Edition. 2008. 60p. pap. 11.95 (978-0-615-20657-8(3)) Wright, Lacie.
Young. The Fish Tale of Ichthys. 2011. 300p. pap. 18.99 (978-1-61379-349-7(9)) Xulon Pr., Inc.
Young & York, Jeff. The Fish Tale of Ichthys. 2015. 300p. 28.99 (978-1-61379-350-3(2)) Xulon Pr., Inc.
Young People's Bible Teacher: Winter, 2006/2007. 2006. pap. (978-1-59843-055-4(6)) Incorporated Trustees of the Gospel Worker Society, The.
Young People's Bible Teacher Vol. 4: Fall 2006. 2006. pap. (978-1-59843-054-7(8)) Incorporated Trustees of the Gospel Worker Society, The.
Youngblood, Michael. Bible Study Manual: An Easy Step by Step Guide to Bible Study - Book One. 2010. 68p. pap. 26.00 (978-1-4520-3837-7(6)) AuthorHouse.
Zeolla, Gary F. Scripture Workbook: for Personal & Group Bible Study & Teaching the Bible; Second Edition; Volume I: the Essentials of the Faith. 2008. 226p. pap. 19.95 (978-0-557-00677-9(5)) Lulu Enterprises Inc.
Zodhiates, Spiros & Baker, Warren, eds. Key Word Study Bible KJV. 2008. (Key Word Study Bibles Ser.). (ENG., Illus.). 2304p. (gr. 11). 49.99 (978-0-89957-745-6(8)) AMG Pubs.
—Key Word Study Bible KJV: Bonded Black. 3rd exp. ed. 2008. (Key Word Study Bibles Ser.). (ENG., Illus.). 2304p. (gr. 11). lthr. 69.99 (978-0-89957-745-3(6)) AMG Pubs.
—Key Word Study Bible KJV: Bonded Burgundy. 2008. (Key Word Study Bibles Ser.). (ENG., Illus.). 2304p. (gr. 11). lthr. 69.99 (978-0-89957-747-0(4)) AMG Pubs.
—Key Word Study Bible KJV: Genuine Black. 3rd exp. ed. 2008. (Key Word Study Bibles Ser.). (ENG., Illus.). 2304p. (gr. 11). lthr. 79.99 (978-0-89957-748-7(2)) AMG Pubs.
—Key Word Study Bible KJV: Genuine Burgundy. 3rd exp. ed. 2008. (Key Word Study Bibles Ser.). (ENG., Illus.). 2304p. (gr. 11). lthr. 79.99 (978-0-89957-749-4(0)) AMG Pubs.
—Key Word Study Bible NASB. 3rd exp. ed. 2008. (Key Word Study Bibles Ser.). (ENG., Illus.). 2156p. (gr. 11). 49.99 (978-0-89957-750-0(4)) AMG Pubs.
—Key Word Study Bible NASB: Bonded Black. 3rd exp. ed. 2008. (Key Word Study Bibles Ser.). (ENG., Illus.). 2156p. (gr. 11). lthr. 69.99 (978-0-89957-751-7(2)) AMG Pubs.
—Key Word Study Bible NASB: Bonded Burgundy. 3rd exp. ed. 2008. (Key Word Study Bibles Ser.). (ENG., Illus.). 2156p. (gr. 11). lthr. 69.99 (978-0-89957-752-4(0)) AMG Pubs.
—Key Word Study Bible NASB: Genuine Black. 3rd exp. ed. 2008. (Key Word Study Bibles Ser.). (ENG., Illus.). 2156p. (gr. 11). lthr. 79.99 (978-0-89957-753-1(9)) AMG Pubs.
—Key Word Study Bible NASB: Genuine Burgundy. 3rd exp. ed. 2008. (Key Word Study Bibles Ser.). (ENG., Illus.). 2156p. (gr. 11). lthr. 79.99 (978-0-89957-754-8(7)) AMG Pubs.
ZOE Ministries International. Captivated by Their Character. 2011. 248p. pap. 15.99 (978-1-61215-823-5(4)) Xulon Pr., Inc.
Zeller, John. Maravilla de la Biblia: Wonder of the Bible. (SPA.). (978-84-7228-025-0(X), 220575) Clie, Editorial.
Zondervan. NIV Life Application Study Bible. 2011. (ENG.). 2528p. lthr. 69.99 (978-0-310-43449-8(1)) Zondervan.
—NIV Quest Study Bible, Personal Size: The Question & Answer Bible, 1 vol. 2012. (ENG.). 2080p. lthr. 59.99 (978-0-310-41025-6(8)) Zondervan.
—Niv Youth Quest Study Bible, 1 vol. 2012. (ENG.). 1920p. (YA). lthr. 44.99 (978-0-310-73383-6(9)) Zondervan.
Zondervan Bibles Staff. Is Heaven Real? Meditations on Scriptures about the Afterlife. 2011. (ENG.). 96p. pap. 5.99 (978-0-310-44346-9(6)) Zondervan.
Zondervan Publishing Staff. The Bible in 90 Days: Whole-Church Challenge Leader's Pack, 1 vol. 2009. (ENG.). pap. 54.99 (978-0-310-94185-9(7)) Zondervan.
—Celebrate Recovery Bible, 1 vol. 2007. (ENG.). 1696p. pap. 24.99 (978-0-310-93810-1(4)) Zondervan.
—Concordance Dictionary Topical Bible, 1 vol. 2008. (ENG.). 688p. 19.99 (978-0-310-28309-6(4)) Zondervan.
—An Illustrated Walk Through Biblical History & Culture, 1 vol. rev. ed. 2008. (ENG.). 2336p. lthr. 109.99 (978-0-310-93958-0(5)) Zondervan.
—NASB Thinline Bible, 1 vol. rev. ed. 2008. (ENG.). 2528p. lthr. 69.99 (978-0-310-94119-4(9)) Zondervan.
Zondervan Publishing Staff. NIV Life Application Study Bible. 2011. (ENG.). 2528p. lthr. 69.99 (978-0-310-43459-7(9)) Zondervan.
Zondervan Publishing Staff, creator. Celebrate Recovery Bible, 1 vol. 2007. (ENG.). 1696p. 34.99 (978-0-310-92849-2(4)) Zondervan.

BIBLE—STUDY AND TEACHING—BIBLIOGRAPHY

Lang, Bernhard, ed. International Review of Biblical Studies: Internationale Zeitschriftenschau Fur Bibelwissenschaft und Grenzgebiete Revue Internationale des Etudes Bibliques. (International Review of Biblical Studies). 2008. 538p. pap. (978-90-04-16551-9(7)) 2007. 554p. pap. (978-90-04-15583-1(X)) BRILL.

BIBLE—STUDY AND TEACHING—DATA PROCESSING

Finger, Reta Halteman. Roman House Churches for Today: A Practical Guide for Small Groups. 2nd ed. 2007. 207p. per. 15.00 (978-0-8028-0764-9(X)) Eerdmans, William B. Publishing Co.
Jeremiah, David. David Jeremiah Essential Library, 1 vol. 2009. cd-rom 49.99 (978-1-4185-4367-9(5)) Nelson, Thomas Inc.
MacArthur, John. John MacArthur Essential Library, 1 vol. 2009. cd-rom 49.99 (978-1-4185-4371-6(3)) Nelson, Thomas Inc.
Naef, Thomas. Holy Bits. 2010. 104.00 (978-1-60724-327-4(X), Gorgias Pr., LLC.
Navigators Staff, et al. Topical Memory System Life Issues: Hide God's Word in Your Heart. 2009. (Becoming a Woman Of ... Ser.). (ENG.). 2p. 14.99 (978-1-60006-671-9(2)) NavPress Publishing Group.
Navigators, The. Topical Memory System Accessory Card Set. 2008. 80p. pap. 6.99 (978-1-60006-434-0(5)) NavPress Publishing Group.
—Topical Memory System Life Issues Memory Verse Cards. 2009. 48p. pap. (978-1-61521-127-2(6)) NavPress Publishing Group.
Rose Publishing. Life of Apostle Paul. 2006. cd-rom 39.99 (978-1-59636-083-9(6)) Rose Publishing.
—Names of God. 2006. cd-rom 39.99 (978-1-59636-081-5(X)) Rose Publishing.
—Names of Jesus. 2006. cd-rom 39.99 (978-1-59636-082-2(8)) Rose Publishing.
Thomas Nelson. Counseling Essential Library, 1 vol. 2009. cd-rom 49.99 (978-1-4185-4369-3(1)) Nelson, Thomas Inc.
—Essential Bible Study Library, 0 vols. 2009. cd-rom 19.97 (978-1-4185-4319-8(5)) Nelson, Thomas Inc.
—Preacher's Essential Library, 1 vol. 2009. cd-rom 49.99 (978-1-4185-4370-9(5)) Nelson, Thomas Inc.
Trebilco, Paul. The Early Christians in Ephesus from Paul to Ignatius. 2007. 826p. per. 85.00 (978-0-8028-0769-4(0)) Eerdmans, William B. Publishing Co.
Verion 2.0 Upgrade. cd-rom 29.00 (978-1-57822-035-9(1)) Loizeaux/Bible Companion Software.

BIBLE—STUDY AND TEACHING—OUTLINES, SYLLABI, ETC.

Anyabwile, Thabiti & Woodcock, Anne. Ephesians: God's Big Plan for Christ's New People: 10 Studies for Individuals or Groups. 2010. (Good Book Guides). 96p. pap. (978-1-907377-09-9(3)) Good Bk. Co.
Bedogne, Vincent Frank. New Testament TransLine: A Literal Translation in Outline Format. 2008. 1056p. pap. 100.00 (978-1-55635-935-4(7), Wipf and Stock) Wipf & Stock Pubs.
Burns, Jim. Outlines & Messages. 2008. (Uncommon Ser.). (ENG.). 208p. 34.99 (978-0-8307-4633-0(1)) Gospel Light Pubns.
Collins, Katy. Tell Me More about Your Life! Children's Ministry Curriculum. 2010. 72p. pap. 10.95 (978-1-4401-7399-8(0)) iUniverse, Inc.
Crowter, Phil. Preaching God's Big Story: Talk Outlines for a Bible Overview. 2010. (Pray, Prepare, Preach Ser.). 96p. pap. (978-1-906334-57-4(9)) Good Bk. Co.
—Preaching Mark: Talk Outlines for the Gospel of Mark. 2010. (Pray, Prepare, Preach Ser.). 160p. pap. (978-1-906334-63-5(3)) Good Bk. Co.
—Preaching Philippians: Talk Outlines for the Book of Philippians. 2010. (Pray, Prepare, Preach Ser.). 64p. pap. (978-1-906334-92-5(7)) Good Bk. Co.
Davies, Rupert E. Studies in 1 Corinthians. 2009. 94p. pap. 14.00 (978-1-60608-719-0(3), Wipf and Stock) Wipf & Stock Pubs.
Dole, Anita S. Bible Study Notes, 6 vols. Set. Woofenden, William R., ed. 2nd ed. 2012. pap. 120.00 (978-0-87785-357-2(6)) Swedenborg Foundation, Inc.
Heck, Joel. History & Literature of the Old Testament. rev. ed. 2010. (ENG.). 238p. spiral bd. 88.00 (978-0-7575-7771-0(7)) Kendall Hunt Publishing Co.
Leadership Ministries Worldwide, creator. The Preachers Outline & Sermon Bible-KJV: Ezra, Nehemiah, Esther. 2007. (Preacher's Outline & Sermon Bible-KJV Ser.). 404p. per. 35.99 (978-1-57407-201-3(3)) Leadership Ministries Worldwide.
McGhee, Quentin. The Life & Teachings of Christ- Teacher's Guide: Synoptic Gospels. Moeckl, Trudy, ed. 4th rev. ed. 2011. pap. 10.00 (978-1-931984-46-1(8), 4414-13e1) Faith & Action Team.
Morgan, G. Campbell. Searchlights from the Word. 2010. (G. Campbell Morgan Reprint Ser.). 424p. pap. 46.00 (978-1-60899-291-1(8)) Wipf & Stock Pubs.
Poelman, Roger. How to Read the Bible. 2009. (978-1-933184-66-1(3)) Sophia Institute Pr.
Preacher's Outline & Sermon Bible, Daniel-Hosea (KJV) 2008. pap. 39.99 (978-1-57407-226-6(9)) Leadership Ministries Worldwide.

B

Preacher's Outline & Sermon Bible, Ezekiel (NIV) 2007. pap. 39.99 *(978-1-57407-230-3(7))* Leadership Ministries Worldwide.
Preacher's Outline & Sermon Bible, Habakkuk-Malachi (KJV) 2009. pap. 39.99 *(978-1-57407-241-9(2))* Leadership Ministries Worldwide.
The Preacher's Outline & Sermon Bible, Jeremiah 2, Lamentations, KJV: Jeremiah 2, Lamentations. 2006. pap. 39.99 *(978-1-57407-222-8(6))* Leadership Ministries Worldwide.
The Preacher's Outline & Sermon Bible, Jeremiah 2-Lamentations, KJV: Jeremiah 2, Lamentations. 2006. ring bd. 44.99 *(978-1-57407-223-5(4))* Leadership Ministries Worldwide.
Preacher's Outline & Sermon Bible, Joel-Nahum (NIV) 2009. pap. 39.99 *(978-1-57407-239-6(0))* Leadership Ministries Worldwide.
Taylor, B. C. Analisis General Libros de la Biblia: Bible Book Outlines. (SPA.). *(978-84-7645-059-8(1)*, 223125) Clie, Editorial.
Tidwell, Josiah Blake. Bible Book by Book. 2006. pap. *(978-1-4068-0978-7(0))* Echo Library.
—Bible Period by Period. 2006. pap. *(978-1-4068-0979-4(9))* Echo Library.
Wood, Charles R. The Heroes of the Faith, 1 vol. 2008. (Wood Sermon Outline Ser.). 64p. pap. 5.99 *(978-0-8254-4179-0(X))* Kregel Pubns.

BIBLE—STUDY AND TEACHING—N. T.

Aland, Kurt. Supplementa Zu Den Neutestamentlichen und Den Kirchengeschichtlichen Entwürfen. Köster, Beate et al, eds. (GER., Illus.). VII, 516p. 270.00 ***(978-3-11-188538-4(0))*** De Gruyter, Walter Inc.
Anderholm, K. D. Understanding New Testament Judgments. unabr. ed. Date not set. 100p. (Orig.). pap. 6.99 *(978-0-9655407-1-1(5))* True Light Pubns.
Anderson, William Angor. The Gospel of Matthew: A Scripture Study & Reflection. 2012. ***(978-0-7648-2120-2(2))*** Liguori Pubns.
Arthur, Kay & Arndt, Janna. A Sneak Peek into the Future: Revelation 8-22. 2007. (Discover 4 Yourself Inductive Bible Studies for Kids Ser.). (Illus.). 203p. (J). (gr. 4-7). per. 11.99 *(978-0-7369-2036-0(6))* Harvest Hse. Pubs.
Arthur, Kay & De Lacy, Pete. Experiencing the Real Power of Faith. 2011. (New Inductive Study Ser.). 120p. pap. 8.99 *(978-0-7369-1273-0(8))* Harvest Hse. Pubs.
Awmi, creator. Grace: The Power of the Gospel Study Guide: the Power of the Gospel. 2007. spiral bd. 35.00 *(978-1-59548-066-8(8))* Wommack, Andrew Ministries, Inc.
Bailey, Brian J. Colossians & Philemon. 122p. pap. 10.00 *(978-0-9630837-8-4(3))* Zion Christian Pubs.
Baker Publishing Group Staff. A Walk Thru the Book of Ephesians: Real Power for Daily Life. 2009. (Walk Thru the Bible Discussion Guides). 77p. pap. 7.99 *(978-0-8010-7167-6(4))* Baker Bks.
—A Walk Thru the Book of James: Faith that Endures. 2009. (Walk Thru the Bible Discussion Guides). 62p. pap. 7.99 *(978-0-8010-7170-6(4))* Baker Bks.
—A Walk Thru the Book of John: A Surprising Savior. 2009. 78p. pap. 7.99 *(978-0-8010-7173-7(9))* Baker Bks.
—A Walk Thru the Life of Peter: Growing Bold Faith. 2009. (Walk Thru the Bible Discussion Guides). 60p. pap. 7.99 *(978-0-8010-7172-0(0))* Baker Bks.
Baker Publishing Group Staff & Life Together Staff. Acts, 1 vol. 2009. (Deepening Life Together Ser.). 128p. pap. 8.99 *(978-0-8010-6842-3(8))* Baker Bks.
—Ephesians, 1 vol. 2009. (Deepening Life Together Ser.). 96p. pap. 8.99 *(978-0-8010-6845-4(2))* Baker Bks.
—John, 1 vol. 2009. (Deepening Life Together Ser.). 128p. pap. 8.99 *(978-0-8010-6844-7(4))* Baker Bks.
—Revelation, 1 vol. 2009. (Deepening Life Together Ser.). 128p. pap. 8.99 *(978-0-8010-6846-1(0))* Baker Bks.
—Romans, 1 vol. 2009. (Deepening Life Together Ser.). 128p. pap. 8.99 *(978-0-8010-6843-0(6))* Baker Bks.
Barnett, Albert Edward. The Letters of Paul. 2011. 160p. 41.95 ***(978-1-258-05057-3(9))*** Literary Licensing, LLC.
Bartholomew, J. J. The Identity of Jesus. 2010. 124p. pap. 11.99 *(978-1-60957-629-5(2))* Xulon Pr., Inc.
Bartunek, John. The Better Part: A Christ-Centered Resource for Personal Prayer. 2008. (Illus.). 1019p. pap. 35.95 *(978-1-933271-10-1(8))* Circle Pr.
Belchen, Richard P. Ministry Helps in John. 60p. pap. 6.95 *(978-0-925703-18-7(4))* Crown Pubns., Inc.
—Teaching Helps in Hebrews. 56p. pap. 6.95 *(978-0-925703-16-3(8))* Crown Pubns., Inc.
—Teaching Helps in II Corinthians. 38p. pap. 6.95 *(978-0-925703-15-6(X))* Crown Pubns., Inc.
—Teaching Helps in James. 64p. pap. 6.95 *(978-0-925703-17-0(6))* Crown Pubns., Inc.
Berger, Steve. 40 Days with the Word of Promise, 0 vols. 2008. 128p. pap. 9.99 *(978-1-4185-3419-6(6))* Nelson, Thomas Inc.
The Bible Study Guide (Volume 4) The Gospels. 2007. 20.00 *(978-0-9796940-4-2(3))* Foundations Publishing.
The Bible Study Guide (Volume 5) Acts through II Corinthians. 2007. 20.00 *(978-0-9796940-5-9(1))* Foundations Publishing.
Blackaby, Henry, et al. Ephesians, 0 vols. 2008. (Blackaby Bible Study Ser.). 96p. pap. 9.99 *(978-1-4185-2647-4(9))* Nelson, Thomas Inc.
—1, 2, 3 John & Jude, 0 vols. 2008. (Encounters with God Ser.). 96p. pap. 9.99 *(978-1-4185-2655-9(X))* Nelson, Thomas Inc.
—1 & 2 Peter: A Blackaby Bible Study Series, 0 vols. 2008. (Encounters with God Ser.). 96p. pap. 9.99 *(978-1-4185-2654-2(1))* Nelson, Thomas Inc.
—1 & 2 Thessalonians: A Blackaby Bible Study Series, 0 vols. 2008. (Encounters with God Ser.). 128p. pap. 9.99 *(978-1-4185-2650-4(9))* Nelson, Thomas Inc.
—1 & 2 Timothy & Titus, 0 vols. 2008. (Encounters with God Ser.). 128p. pap. 9.99 *(978-1-4185-2651-1(7))* Nelson, Thomas Inc.
Bock, Darrell. Acts - Ephesians. 2006. (Bible Knowledge Ser.). 512p. 44.99 *(978-0-7814-3445-4(9)*, 0781434459) Cook, David C.
Bock, Darrell L. Luke. 2010. (IVP New Testament Commentary Ser.: Volume 3). (ENG.). 412p. pap. 20.00 *(978-0-8308-4003-8(6)*, IVP Acad.) InterVarsity Pr.
Boice, James Montgomery. Renewing Your Mind in a Mindless World: Learning to Think & Act Biblically, 1 vol. 2009. 144p. pap. 10.99 *(978-0-8254-2572-1(7))* Kregel Pubns.
Boomsma, Sylvia. Discover 1 Corinthians: Wisdom for Living. (Discover Your Bible Ser.). pap., stu. ed. 3.25 *(978-1-56212-243-0(6)*, 152380) Faith Alive Christian Resources.
Bowen. Guide to Romans. (Illus.). 256p. 13.00 *(978-0-281-04953-0(X))* SPCK Publishing GBR. Dist: Pilgrim Pr., The/United Church Pr.
Bowen, Roger. Guide to Romans. 16.00 *(978-0-687-85459-2(8))* Abingdon Pr.
Brady, Steve. All You Need Is Christ. 2007. (ENG.). 200p. 12.99 *(978-1-85078-748-8(4))* Authentic Media.
Breytenbach, Cilliers & Hoppe, Rudolf. Neutestamentliche Wissenschaft nach 1945. Hauptvertreter der deutschsprachigen Exegese in der Darstellung ihrer Schüler: Hauptvertreter der deutschsprachigen Exegese in der Darstellung ihrer Schüler. 2008. (Illus.). xi, 486p. pap. *(978-3-7887-2274-6(6))* Neukirchener Verlag.
Brown, Aleck A. New Testament Handbook: A Guided Approach to Understanding the New Testament. 2008. 292p. 32.99 *(978-1-4269-0099-0(6))*; pap. 24.99 *(978-1-4251-8516-9(9))* Trafford Publishing.
Brunger, Robert. He Is Not Here. 2009. (Illus.). 308p. pap. 15.49 *(978-1-4389-1581-4(0))* AuthorHouse.
Burge, Gary M. & Strauss, Mark L. John: Meet God Face to Face. 2009. (NLT Study Ser.). (ENG.). 176p. pap. 7.99 *(978-1-4143-2196-7(1))* Tyndale Hse. Pubs.
Burningham, Janet. Monday Nights by the Sea of Galilee: 30 Stories & Scripture Lessons for Family Home Evening Based on the Four Gospels of the New Testament. 2010. pap. 10.99 *(978-1-59955-472-3(0))* Cedar Fort, Inc./CFI Distribution.
Butt, Christian. Kindertheologische Untersuchungen zu Auferstehungsvorstellungen von Grundschulerinnen und Grundschulern. 2009. (Arbeiten zur Religionspadagogik Ser.). (GER., Illus.). 307p. (C). 54.00 *(978-3-89971-720-4(1))* Vandenhoeck & Ruprecht GmbH & Co. KG DEU. Dist: ISD.
Carter, James E. The Gospel of Mark: Jesus' Works & Words. 2007. 154p. pap. *(978-1-931060-98-1(3))* Baptistway.
Christianity Today International Staff. Crash Course on Revelation. 2009. (Crash Course Bible Studies). (ENG.). 96p. pap. 7.99 *(978-0-7847-2250-3(1))* Standard Publishing.
Clinton, John. Are You Thinking Like A Pharesee? 2008. pap. 12.95 *(978-0-9801357-4-9(5))* Tree of Life Publishing Hse.
Conrey, Linda. Theology of Dance: (A Study in the Old & New Testaments) 2008. 114p. lib. bdg. 12.00 *(978-0-9791327-1-1(1))* Redemption Ministries International.
Cook, David. The Unheeded Christ: Jesus Demands Serious Obedience. 2008. (ENG.). 176p. pap. 10.99 *(978-1-84550-369-7(4))* Christian Focus Pubns. GBR. Dist: STL Distribution North America.
Cooper, Barry & Shammas, Sam. English Made Easy. 2010. (Christianity Explored Ser.). 64p. pap., pupil's gde. ed. *(978-1-904889-36-6(0))*; 96p. pap. *(978-1-904889-35-9(2))* Good Bk. Co.
Coy, Jimmie Dean. Matthew A to Z + 2: An Easy Way to Learn the Gospel According to Matthew. 2008. (Illus.). 64p. 10.99 *(978-1-58169-276-1(5)*, Evergreen Pr.) Genesis Communications, Inc.
Cummings, Glenn Earle. A Verse by Verse Study of the Book of Revelation: In Depth, yet easy to understand, study of this prophetic Book. 2007. 228p. pap. 20.00 *(978-0-9800465-1-9(3))* Cummings, Glenn.
Day, Jackson. New Testament Bible Stories. 2007. 224p. pap. 25.00 *(978-0-9797324-1-6(7))* Day, H. Jackson.
Deelen, Marion. A Message for Today: A Study in Mark's Gospel. 2008. (Geared for Growth Ser.). (ENG.). 56p. 4.99 *(978-1-84550-413-7(5))* Christian Focus Pubns. GBR. Dist: STL Distribution North America.
Dilling, David R. The Gospel of John. 2008. 273p. pap. 24.50 *(978-1-4357-2296-5(5))* Lulu Enterprises Inc.
Dymally, Billye. Absolute Truth. 2007. 154p. pap. 12.95 *(978-0-7414-3854-6(2))* Infinity Publishing.
Echevarria, Michelle. Only Believe: Increasing Faith by the Word of God. 2008. 112p. 22.95 *(978-0-595-50167-0(2))*; pap. 12.95 *(978-0-595-50371-1(3))* iUniverse, Inc.
Edwards, Sue. Ephesians: Finding Your Identity & Purpose in Christ, 1 vol. 2007. (Sue Edwards Inductive Bible Study Ser.). 96p. pap. 12.99 *(978-0-8254-2549-3(2))* Kregel Pubns.
Ericson, Norman R. & Moo, Douglas J. James: Live What You Believe. 2009. (NLT Study Ser.). (ENG.). 128p. pap. 7.99 *(978-1-4143-2197-4(X))* Tyndale Hse. Pubs.
Evans, Craig A. Early Christian Literature & Intertextuality: Thematic Studies, 2 vols. Zacharias, Danny, ed. 2009. (Library of New Testament Studies, the Ser.). (ENG.). 312p. 140.00 *(978-0-567-58475-5(5)*, T&T Clark Int'l) Continuum International Publishing Group, Ltd. GBR. Dist: National Bk. Network.
—Early Christian Literature & Intertextuality: Volume 2: Exegetical Studies, 2 vols. Zacharias, Danny, ed. 2009. (Library of New Testament Studies, the Ser.). (ENG.). 264p. 120.00 *(978-0-567-34100-6(3)*, T&T Clark Int'l) Continuum International Publishing Group, Ltd. GBR. Dist: National Bk. Network.
Fee, Gordon D. Philippians. 2010. (IVP New Testament Commentary Ser.: Volume 11). (ENG.). 204p. pap. 17.00 *(978-0-8308-4011-3(7)*, IVP Acad.) InterVarsity Pr.
Fields, Doug & McGill, Matt. Rooted: New Testament: 6 New Testament Studies to Equip Your Students to Study God's Word. 2006. pap. 49.00 incl. cd-rom *(978-0-7644-6000-5(5))* Group Publishing, Inc.
Follin, Marc. Colossians. 2010. 58p. pap. 12.99 *(978-1-60957-461-1(3))* Xulon Pr., Inc.
Galfo, Guy S. The Interwoven Gospels: The Ministry of Christ. 2009. 264p. pap. 16.99 *(978-1-60477-892-2(X))* Xulon Pr., Inc.
Garland, David E. & Lee-Thorp, Karen. Mark: Gospel of the Servant King, 1 vol. 2010. (Bringing the Bible to Life Ser.). (ENG.). 160p. pap. 7.99 *(978-0-310-32043-2(7))* Zondervan.
Glahn, Sandra. Frappe with Philippians. 2009. (Coffee Cup Bible Studies). (ENG., Illus.). 160p. (gr. 11). spiral bd. 12.99 *(978-0-89957-396-0(7))* AMG Pubs.
Goodspeed, Edgar J. New Chapters in New Testament Study. 2011. 236p. 46.95 ***(978-1-258-03291-3(0))*** Literary Licensing, LLC.
Griggs, Donald L. & Johnson, Earl S., Jr., Earl S. Matthew's Gospel from Scratch: The New Testament for Beginners. 2011. (Bible from Scratch Ser.). (ENG.). 112p. pap. 13.00 *(978-0-664-23485-0(2))* Westminster John Knox Pr.
Gromacki, Robert G. New Testament Survey. 2008. 448p. (C). pap. 40.00 *(978-0-8010-3626-2(7))* Baker Academic.
Guptill, Tim. 1 & 2 Peter: Lectio Divina for Youth. 2008. (Ancient Faith Ser.: Vol. 1). (ENG.). 80p. pap. 7.99 *(978-0-8341-5025-6(5)*, 9780834150256) Beacon Hill Pr. of Kansas City.
Hahn, Scott & Mitch, Curtis. Ignatius Catholic Study Bible: The Letters of St. James, St. Peter & St. Jude. 2008. (Ignatius Catholic Study Bible Ser.). 65p. pap. 9.95 *(978-1-58617-248-0(4))* Ignatius Pr.
Haines, Mark. Hebrews: Lectio Divina for Youth. 2008. (Ancient Faith Ser.). (ENG.). 80p. pap. 7.99 *(978-0-8341-5024-9(7)*, 9780834150249) Beacon Hill Pr. of Kansas City.
Hargreaves, John. Guide to Philippians. 16.00 *(978-0-687-85458-5(X))* Abingdon Pr.
Hayford, Jack W. John: Living Beyond the Ordinary, 0 vols. 2010. (Spirit-Filled Life Study Guide Ser.). 128p. pap. 9.99 *(978-1-4185-4122-4(2))* Nelson, Thomas Inc.
Heil, John Paul. Worship in the Letter to the Hebrews. 2011. (ENG.). 326p. pap. 36.00 ***(978-1-60899-947-7(5)***, Cascade Bks.) Wipf & Stock Pubs.
Hemphill, Ken. Eternal Impact: The Passion of Kingdom-Centered Communities. 2008. (ENG.). 93p. pap. 6.95 *(978-1-4276-2735-3(5))* Auxano Pr.
—Eternal Impact: The Passion of Kingdom-Centered Communities. 2008. (ENG.). 240p. per. 14.99 *(978-0-8054-4660-9(5)*, B&H Bks.) B&H Publishing Group.
Higgins, William H. The Healing Works of Jesus: An Inspiring & Concise Reference of the Healings Jesus Performed in the Four Gospels. 2007. 154p. *(978-0-9789002-0-5(0))* Faith Library Pubns., Inc.
Hill, Gary. The Discovery Bible: New Testament. Archer, Gleason L., Jr., ed. 610p. 17.95 *(978-0-88469-202-7(7))* BMH Bks.
Holloway, Gary. Matthew: Jesus Is King. 2007. (Meditative Commentary Ser.). 224p. per. 13.99 *(978-0-9767790-1-8(3)*, Leafwood Pubs.) Abilene Christian Univ. Pr.
Hybels, Bill, et al. Romans 8: Inseparable, 1 vol. 2009. (New Community Bible Study Ser.). (ENG.). 96p. pap. 7.99 *(978-0-310-28059-0(1))* Zondervan.
—Titus: Spiritual Influence, 1 vol. 2009. (New Community Bible Study Ser.). (ENG.). 96p. pap. 7.99 *(978-0-310-28058-3(3))* Zondervan.
II Corinthians. (People's Bible Commentary Ser.). 264p. 14.99 *(978-0-7586-0446-0(7))*; (LifeLight Bible Studies: Course 21). stu. ed. 5.50 *(978-0-570-09432-6(1)*, 20-2556); (LifeLight Bible Studies: Course 21). 6.50 *(978-0-570-09431-9(3)*, 20-2555) Concordia Publishing Hse.
Jackman, David & Philip, William. Teaching Matthew: Unlocking the Gospel of Matthew for the Bible Teacher. 2009. (ENG.). 240p. 12.99 *(978-1-84550-480-9(1))* Christian Focus Pubns. GBR. Dist: STL Distribution North America.
Jasper, David. The New Testament & the Literary Imagination. 2009. (David Jasper Reprint Ser.). 126p. pap. 16.00 *(978-1-60608-833-3(5)*, Wipf and Stock) Wipf & Stock Pubs.
Jastrembowska, Elzbieta. Cities of the Apocalypse. 2012. (ENG.). 240p. pap. 24.95 *(978-1-84368-046-8(7))* Pallas Athene GBR. Dist: Independent Pubs. Group.
Jeremiah, David. What to Do When You Don't Know What to Do. 2009. (ENG.). 256p. pap. 13.99 *(978-1-4347-6451-5(6))* Cook, David C.
Jesus, Name above All Names, Preschool: Thematic Unit: Our Names. (Scripture Bites Ser.). pap., tchr. ed. 5.99 *(978-0-7847-9070-0(1))* Standard Publishing.
Jones, Duane. Jesus Was a Middle Schooler Too. 2007. 84p. per. 9.99 *(978-1-60477-011-7(2))* Xulon Pr., Inc.
Kelley, Dee. Acts: The Church Ignited: Part 1. McCullough, Jeannie, ed. 2006. (Wisdom of the Word Ser.). (ENG.). 96p. spiral bd. 14.99 *(978-0-8341-2281-9(2)*, 083-412-2812) Beacon Hill Pr. of Kansas City.
—Acts: The Church Ignited: Part 2. McCullough, Jeannie, ed. 2006. (Wisdom of the Word Ser.). (ENG.). 96p. spiral bd. 14.99 *(978-0-8341-2282-6(0)*, 083-412-2820) Beacon Hill Pr. of Kansas City.
Kok, Joel. Romans: Getting It All Together. l.t. ed. 5.25 *(978-1-56212-649-0(0)*, 150001) Faith Alive Christian Resources.
Köstenberger, Andreas J. & Wilder, Terry L., eds. Entrusted with the Gospel: Paul's Theology in the Pastoral Epistles, 1 vol. 2010. (ENG.). 352p. pap. 19.99 *(978-0-8054-4841-2(1)*, B&H Academic) B&H Publishing Group.
Kreitzer, Larry. Gospel According to John. 11.00 *(978-0-687-82292-8(0))* Abingdon Pr.
Larsen, David R. How to Remember Everything in the New Testament & General Conference. 2006. 205p. per. 14.99 *(978-1-55517-997-7(5))* Cedar Fort, Inc./CFI Distribution.
Lee, Richard. Understanding Leviathan: The Key to Apostle John's the Revelation. 2009. 280p. 30.95 *(978-0-595-70998-4(2))*; pap. 20.95 *(978-0-595-46137-0(9))* iUniverse, Inc.
Letters & Prophecy: Romans - Revelation. 2008. 128p. pap. 6.00 *(978-0-687-33488-9(8))*; cd-rom 30.00 *(978-0-687-33478-0(0))* Abingdon Pr.
Lifetogether. James. 2011. (Deepening Life Together Ser.). (Illus.). 121p. pap. 8.99 *(978-0-8010-6869-0(X))* Baker Bks.
—Matthew. 2010. (Deepening Life Together Ser.). 24.99 *(978-0-8010-3052-9(8))*; pap. 8.99 *(978-0-8010-6922-2(X))* Baker Bks.
—Paul. 2011. (Deepening Life Together Ser.). (Illus.). 89p. pap. 8.99 *(978-0-8010-6905-5(X))* Baker Bks.
LifeWay Press Staff, contrib. by. Colossians: Navigating Successfully Through Cultural Chaos: Connect with God, Connect with Others, Connect with Life. 2008. 175p. pap. 13.95 *(978-1-4158-6712-9(7))* LifeWay Christian Resources.
Linhart, Terry. High School Talksheets, 1 vol. 2008. (TalkSheets Ser.). (ENG.). 112p. pap. 16.99 *(978-0-310-28552-6(6))* Zondervan.
Livingstone Corporation Staff. The Complete New Testament Resource for Youth Workers, Volume 1, 1 vol. 2009. (ENG.). 416p. pap. 29.99 *(978-0-310-27335-6(8))* Zondervan.
Long, Alfred T., Sr. Grasping at the Wind: How to Go from Ashes to Beauty Using God's Word-Practical Biblical Solutions for Complex Life Problems. 2008. 152p. pap. 13.99 *(978-1-60477-983-7(7))* Xulon Pr., Inc.
Lopez, Diane D. Por el amor de Dios: Guia de Estudio. 2010. (SPA.). pap. 3.00 ***(978-1-933663-44-9(8)***, WD/GBGM Bks.) General Board of Global Ministries, The United Methodist Church.
Lotz, Anne Graham. Pursuing More of Jesus. 2009. 108p. pap. *(978-1-4158-6648-1(1))* LifeWay Christian Resources.
Luck, G. Coleman. James: Christian Faith in Action. 2011. 124p. 40.95 ***(978-1-258-09031-9(7))*** Literary Licensing, LLC.
Luther, Martin. Commentary on Galatians. 2007. 26.98 *(978-1-4245-0792-4(8))* Treasures Media Inc.
Lynn, David. High School: 50 Ready-to-Use New Testament Discussions, 1 vol. 2009. (TalkSheets Ser.). (ENG.). 128p. pap. 14.99 *(978-0-310-66871-8(9))* Zondervan.
—Middle School Talksheets, 1 vol. 2009. (TalkSheets Ser.). (ENG.). 128p. pap. 14.99 *(978-0-310-66872-5(7))* Zondervan.
Madsen, Jon. The New Testament: A Rendering. (Illus.). 608p. 29.50 *(978-0-86315-184-2(1)*, 1869) Floris Bks. GBR. Dist: SteinerBooks, Inc.
Margesson, Nick. Keep on Going: Seven Youth Group Sessions on 1 Thessalonians. 2009. (Junction TnT Ministries Ser.). (ENG.). 80p. pap. 9.99 *(978-1-84550-462-5(3))* Christian Focus Pubns. GBR. Dist: STL Distribution North America.
Marie, Carol. The Law Fulfilled: Why God's Appointed Feasts Were Foreordained for the New Testament Church. 2009. (J). pap. 13.99 *(978-1-60799-419-0(4))* Tate Publishing & Enterprises, LLC.
McAllister, Stephen A. What God Has Promised You: Ancient Wisdom for Modern Times: Reflections for Individual & Group Study from Paul's Epistle to the Romans. 2009. *(978-1-926645-08-7(1))* BPS Bks.
McCallum, Brian K. The Day of the Lord. 2009. 46p. pap. 7.95 *(978-0-89276-950-6(5))* Faith Library Pubns., Inc.
McDowell, Josh. Christ up Close & Personal: Adult Group 8 Sesion Leader Guide. 2006. 128p. 17.99 *(978-1-932587-87-6(X))* Green Key Bks.
—Christ up Close & Personal: Youth Group 8 Session Leader Guide. 2006. 128p. (YA). 17.99 *(978-1-932587-89-0(6))* Green Key Bks.
—Christ up Close & Personal / Adult Group Course Kit. 2006. pap. 159.99 incl. DVD *(978-1-932587-86-9(1))* Green Key Bks.
—Christ up Close & Personal / Youth Group Course Kit. 2006. 128p. (YA). DVD 129.99 *(978-1-932587-88-3(8))* Green Key Bks.
McGhee, Quentin. Hechos del Espíritu Santo- Guía del Maestro. Moeckl, Trudy, ed. Segura, Sara & Segura, Maritza, trs. from ENG. 2011. Orig. Title: Acts of the Holy Spirit. (SPA.). lib. bdg. 10.00 *(978-1-931984-43-0(3)*, 4413-16S1) Faith & Action Team.
McKisic, Kelvin. Illuminating Revelation: A Study in the Book of Revelation. 2008. 244p. 24.99 *(978-1-60647-649-9(1))*; pap. 14.99 *(978-1-60647-648-2(3))* Xulon Pr., Inc.
Miller, Kathy Collard. Paul & the Prison Epistles, 0 vols. Richards, Larry, ed. 2008. (Smart Guide to the Bible Ser.). 352p. pap. 14.99 *(978-1-4185-1007-7(6))* Nelson, Thomas Inc.
Mills, William C. Let Us Attend: Reflections on the Gospel of Mark for the Lenten Season. 2008. 108p. pap. 13.95 *(978-1-933275-26-0(X)*, Orthodox Research Institute) Cocheco Falls Publishing.
—A Light to the Gentiles: Reflections on the Gospel of Luke. 2008. 128p. pap. 13.95 *(978-1-933275-25-3(1)*, Orthodox Research Institute) Cocheco Falls Publishing.
Moo, Douglas J. & Harrison, Sean A. Romans: Know the Truth. 2009. (NLT Study Ser.). (ENG.). 160p. pap. 7.99 *(978-1-4143-2198-1(8))* Tyndale Hse. Pubs.
Moticheck, Shawn S. Removing the Veil. 2008. 180p. pap. 24.95 *(978-1-60703-786-6(6))* PublishAmerica, Inc.

Nestle, Eberhard. Introduction to the Textual Criticism of the Greek New Testament. 2009. 254p. pap. *(978-0-217-49296-6(7))* Books LLC.
—Introduction to the Textual Criticism of the Greek New Testament. Edie, William, tr. 2007. (ENG.). 388p. 48.95 *(978-0-548-13140-4(6))* Kessinger Publishing, LLC.
—Introduction to the Textual Criticism of the Greek New Testament. Menzies, Allan, ed. Edie, William, tr. 2006. (ENG.). 388p. per. 33.95 *(978-1-4286-4192-1(0))* Kessinger Publishing, LLC.
The New Testament. 16.00 *(978-0-687-05287-5(4))* Abingdon Pr.
The New Testament. 2009. 426p. pap. *(978-1-4588-9144-0(5))* Books LLC.
The New Testament. 2008. 29.90 *(978-1-60591-037-6(6))* Title Player, Inc.
Nielson, Kathleen Buswell. Colossians & Philemon: Contiue to Live in Him. 2007. (Living Word Bible Studies). 124p. spiral bd. *(978-1-59638-073-8(X))* P & R Publishing.
O'Higgins, Paul & O'Higgins, Nuala. New Testament Believers & the Law. pap. 3.95 *(978-0-944795-04-0(8))* Reconciliation Outreach, Inc.
Olshine, David. The Philippians, Colossians, First & Second Thessalonians, 1 vol. 2009. (Studies on the Go Ser.). (ENG.). 176p. pap. 8.99 *(978-0-310-28549-6(6))* Zondervan.
Paulien, Jon. The Gospel from Patmos: Everyday Insights for Living from the Last Book of the Bible. 2007. 379p. *(978-0-8280-2092-3(2))* Review & Herald Publishing Assn.
Peckham, David T. 101 Thoughts from the Word: New Testament. 2008. 224p. pap. 14.49 *(978-1-4389-0852-6(0))* AuthorHouse.
Pink, Arthur W. Exposition of the Gospel of John. 2011. 630p. pap. 29.99 ***(978-1-61203-320-4(2))*** Bottom of the Hill Publishing.
Polich, Laurie. John, 1 vol. 2006. (Studies on the Go Ser.). (ENG., Illus.). 128p. (gr. 13). pap. 9.99 *(978-0-310-27200-7(9))* Zondervan.
—Romans, 1 vol. 2009. (Studies on the Go Ser.). (ENG.). 128p. pap. 8.99 *(978-0-310-66874-9(3))* Zondervan.
Porter, J. R. & Porter, J.R. Jesucristo: Vida, Escenario, Doctrina, Interpretaciones, Jesus en el Arte. Gutierrez, Margarita, tr. 2009. (SPA.). 240p. pap. 15.95 *(978-84-8076-723-1(5))* Blume ESP. Dist: Independent Pubs. Group.
PowerXpress Jesus in the Temple. 9.95 incl. audio compact disk *(978-0-687-09348-9(1))* Abingdon Pr.
PowerXpress Kingdom Parables. 9.95 incl. audio compact disk *(978-0-687-04153-4(8))* Abingdon Pr.
PowerXpress Man Beside the Pool. 2006. 10.50 *(978-0-687-04072-8(8))* Abingdon Pr.
Rake, Timothy A. & Dunker, Gary. 2 Corinthians. 2007. (Life Light Foundations Topical Bible Study Ser.). (Illus.). 32p. pap. 8.99 *(978-0-7586-1096-6(3))* Concordia Publishing Hse.
Rogers, Adrian. Apocalipsis: el Fin de Los Tiempos: El Triunfo del Cordero de Dios. 2007. 273p. per. 9.99 *(978-0-8054-3275-6(2),* B&H Bks.) B&H Publishing Group.
Sayles, Guy. Matthew: Living as Disciples of Jesus. 2006. (Annual Bible Study Ser.). (Illus.). 160p. per. *(978-1-57312-474-4(5))* Smyth & Helwys Publishing, Inc.
Schubert, Judith. The Gospel of John: Question by Question. 2008. (Question by Question Ser.). 256p. pap. 19.95 *(978-0-8091-4549-2(9))* Paulist Pr.
Simmons, Carl, ed. Ephesians: Seeing Ourselves in Jesus. 2006. (Illus.). 111p. pap. 9.99 *(978-0-7644-3241-5(9))* Group Publishing, Inc.
—James: Showing Our Faith in Jesus. 2006. (Illus.). 111p. pap. 9.99 *(978-0-7644-3242-2(7))* Group Publishing, Inc.
—Phillipians: Sharing the Joy of Jesus. 2006. (Group's BibleSense Ser.). (Illus.). 92p. pap. 9.99 *(978-0-7644-3225-5(7))* Group Publishing, Inc.
—1 John: Living in the Light of Jesus. 2006. (Illus.). 95p. pap. 9.99 *(978-0-7644-3243-9(5))* Group Publishing, Inc.
Sloan, William Wilson. A Survey of the New Testament. 2011. 308p. 48.95 ***(978-1-258-07280-3(7))*** Literary Licensing, LLC.
Smith, Ebbie C. The Gospel of Matthew: Hope in the Resurrected Christ: Adult Bible Teaching Guide. 2008. 154p. pap. *(978-1-934731-22-2(6))* Baptistway.
Steele M.Div, M.A., A. T. The Exegetical Study Guide Series: An Expositor's Field Manual Matthew 24 And 2Peter. 2009. 328p. pap. 22.95 *(978-1-4401-5187-3(3))* iUniverse, Inc.
Stott, John. Acts: Seeing the Spirit at Work. 2008. (John Stott Bible Studies). (ENG.). 111p. pap. 8.00 *(978-0-8308-2161-7(9),* IVP Conn.) InterVarsity Pr.
Study Guide for the Apostles by Pope Bendict XVI. 2007. 62p. pap. 4.95 *(978-1-59276-409-9(6))* Our Sunday Visitor, Publishing Div.
Sutherland, J. D. Richard. The Hanging Death of Jesus Christ-and Other New Testament Occurrences. 2009. 64p. pap. 9.95 *(978-1-4401-3205-6(4))* iUniverse, Inc.
Talbot, Dee Dee. The Word Made Flesh: Study Guide 4. 2007. 240p. pap. 21.50 *(978-1-4303-1554-4(7))* Lulu Enterprises Inc.
Terrell, Patricia Elyse & Terrell. Paul's Parallels: An Echoes Synopsis, 592 vols. 2009. (ENG., Illus.). 1008p. 225.00 *(978-0-567-02745-0(7),* T&T Clark Int'l) Continuum International Publishing Group, Ltd. GBR. Dist: National Bk. Network.
Thoene, Bodie & Thoene, Brock. Why a Shepherd? More than just a name... it is the reason he was Sent. 2007. 96p. mass mkt. 2.99 *(978-0-9770565-3-8(8))* Parable Group, The.
Thomas, Bill. The Critical Questions - - & More: Three Pre-Easter Bible Studies. 2007. *(978-0-7880-2509-9(0))* CSS Publishing Co.
—The Critical Questions ... & More: Three Pre-Easter Bible Studies. 2008. 133p. per. 15.95 *(978-0-7880-2524-2(4))* CSS Publishing Co.
Thomas, Jesse. Church & the Kingdom A New Testament S. 2006. 328p. per. 33.00 *(978-1-57978-521-5(2))* Baptist Standard Bearer, Inc.
Thomas Nelson. The Word of Promise Next Generation New Testament Devotional: How Should a Christian Live?, 0 vols. 2010. 176p. pap. 15.99 *(978-1-4003-1560-4(3))* Nelson, Thomas Inc.
Twomey, Jay. Radical Paulitics: Readings of Paul in Contemporary Culture. 2012. (Library of New Testament Studies). (ENG.). 184p. 100.00 *(978-0-567-10413-7(3),* T&T Clark Int'l) Continuum International Publishing Group, Ltd. GBR. Dist: National Bk. Network.
Tyndale House Publishers Staff, prod. Galatians & Ephesians. 2009. (Life Application Bible Studies: NLT Ser.). (ENG.). 120p. pap. 7.99 *(978-1-4143-2644-3(0))* Tyndale Hse. Pubs.
—James. 2008. (Life Application Bible Studies: NLT Ser.). (ENG.). 96p. pap. 7.99 *(978-1-4143-2560-6(6))* Tyndale Hse. Pubs.
—John. 2008. (Life Application Bible Studies: NLT Ser.). (ENG.). 144p. pap. 7.99 *(978-1-4143-2561-3(4))* Tyndale Hse. Pubs.
—Luke. 2009. (Life Application Bible Studies: NLT Ser.). (ENG.). 160p. pap. 7.99 *(978-1-4143-2649-8(1))* Tyndale Hse. Pubs.
—1 & 2 Peter & Jude. 2009. (Life Application Bible Studies: NLT Ser.). (ENG.). 104p. pap. 7.99 *(978-1-4143-2651-1(3))* Tyndale Hse. Pubs.
—1 Corinthians. 2009. (Life Application Bible Studies: NLT Ser.). (ENG.). 112p. pap. 7.99 *(978-1-4143-2648-1(3))* Tyndale Hse. Pubs.
Underwood, Ed. Reborn to Be Wild: Reviving Our Radical Pursuit of Jesus, 1 vol. 2010. (ENG.). 320p. pap. 16.99 *(978-1-4347-0017-9(8))* Cook, David C.
Upchurch, Catherine, et al. The Four Gospels: Catholic Personal Study Edition. 2009. 288p. pap. 19.95 *(978-0-8146-3631-2(4))* Liturgical Pr.
Violi, Unicio J. Monarch Notes on the New Testament. (C). 4.95 *(978-0-671-00625-9(8),* Arco) Peterson's.
Wallace, Daniel B. New Testament Greek Syntax Laminated Sheet, 1 vol. 2009. (Zondervan Get an A! Study Guides). (ENG.). 6p. pap. 6.99 *(978-0-310-29208-1(5))* Zondervan.
Walters, Dennis, contrib. by. The Letters of Saint Paul to the Thessalonians, Timothy, & Titus. 2nd ed. 2007. (Ignatius Catholic Study Bible Ser.). 63p. pap. 9.95 *(978-1-58617-162-9(3))* Ignatius Pr.
Waterloo, Bob. Revelation: Verse by Verse. 2009. 168p. pap. 14.99 *(978-1-60791-923-0(0))* Xulon Pr., Inc.
Wauck, Mark A., tr. Letters of Saint Paul. 2008. 300p. pap. *(978-0-8189-1272-6(3))* Pauline Bks. & Media.
Wezeman, Phyllis. BIBLE BASICS Lessons for Life: New Testament Epistles of Paul: Romans - Philemon. 2007. 19.95 *(978-0-9774304-2-0(1))* Active Learning Associates, Inc.
—BIBLE BASICS Lessons for Life: New Testament Genereal Epistles/Prophecy: Hebrews - Revelation. 2007. 15.95 *(978-0-9774304-3-7(X))* Active Learning Associates, Inc.
Whelan, Mary Jane. Jesus Is Calling: Saint John Version. l.t. ed. 2006. (Illus.). 89p. spiral bd., wbk. ed. 16.99 *(978-0-9786924-3-8(8))* Royal Reign Pubns.
—Jesus Is Calling: Saint Luke Version. l.t. ed. 2006. (Illus.). 108p. spiral bd., wbk. ed. 16.99 *(978-0-9786924-2-1(X))* Royal Reign Pubns.
—Jesus Is Calling: St. Mark Version. l.t. ed. 2006. (Illus.). 80p. spiral bd., wbk. ed. 14.99 *(978-0-9786924-1-4(1))* Royal Reign Pubns.
Widdowson, Frederick. Ephesians, A Bible Study. 2010. 69p. pap. 9.99 *(978-0-557-55662-5(7))* Lulu Enterprises Inc.
Wiersbe, Warren W. Romans: How to Be Right with God, Yourself, & Others. 2008. (WBS Ser.). (ENG.). 144p. pap. 8.99 *(978-0-7814-4572-6(8))* Cook, David C.
—The Wiersbe Bible Study Series: Proverbs: God's Guidebook to Wise Living, 1 vol. 2010. (Wiersbe Bible Study Ser.). (ENG.). 160p. pap. 8.99 *(978-1-4347-6511-6(3))* Cook, David C.
Wigram, George. The Analytical Greek Lexicon of the New Testament. 2007. 504p. per. 19.95 *(978-1-933993-51-5(0))* Apocryphile Pr.
Wilkinson, Bruce. Secrets of the Vine Leader's Guide: Breaking Through to Abundance. 2006. (ENG., Illus.). 80p. per. 10.99 *(978-1-59052-858-7(1),* Multnomah) Doubleday Religious Publishing Group, The.
WILLHAUCK. Living in Gods Light. pap. 8.50 *(978-0-687-02197-0(9))* Abingdon Pr.
Williams, Michael E. Ephesians, Philippians, Colossians: Living with Faithfulness & Joy. 2008. 158p. pap. *(978-1-934731-16-1(1))* Baptistway.
Witherington, Ben Iii. Revelation & the End Times Participant's Guide: Unraveling God's Message of Hope. 2010. 112p. pap. 10.00 *(978-0-687-66006-3(8))* Abingdon Pr.
Woods, Guy N. How to Study the New Testament Effectively: Shared Insights Gained from a Lifetime of Study. 136p. pap. 6.99 *(978-0-89225-416-3(5))* Gospel Advocate Co., Inc.
World Bible Translation Center, creator. Arabic New Testament-FL-Easy to Read. 2007. 446p. pap. 7.50 *(978-977-6124-98-1(4))* World Bible Translation Ctr., Inc.
Younger, Carol Davis & Younger, Brett. Mark: Finding Ourselves in the Story. 2010. pap. *(978-1-57312-566-6(0))* Smyth & Helwys Publishing, Inc.
Zuber, Rand. Men of Whom the World Was Not Worthy. 2011. 54p. pap. 9.95 ***(978-1-58427-331-8(3))*** Guardian of Truth Foundation.

BIBLE—STUDY AND TEACHING—O. T.

Abingdon. Amazing Bible Race, Director's Manual, Leg 3 CD-ROM. 2007. cd-rom 30.00 *(978-0-687-33418-6(7))* Abingdon Pr.
—The Amazing Bible Race, Runner's Reader, Leg 3. 2007. pap. 6.00 *(978-0-687-33428-5(4))* Abingdon Pr.
—Isaiah - Malachi. 2008. 128p. 30.00 *(978-0-687-33438-4(1))* Abingdon Pr.
Answers in Genesis. stu. ed. *(978-0-89051-233-3(7))* Master Bks.
Arthur, Kay & de Lacy, Pete. Finding Hope When Life Seems Dark: Hosea/Micah/Nahum/Habakkuk/Zephaniah. 2006. (New Inductive Study Ser.). (Illus.). 108p. per. 8.99 *(978-0-7369-1825-1(6))* Harvest Hse. Pubs.
Arthur, Kay & De Lacy, Pete. Isaiah. 2008. (New Inductive Study Ser.). (Illus.). 160p. pap. 8.99 *(978-0-7369-2305-7(5))* Harvest Hse. Pubs.
Ascham, John Bayne. The Religion of Israel. 2007. (ENG.). 238p. 41.95 *(978-0-548-07100-7(4))* Kessinger Publishing, LLC.
Avery, Joseph L., Jr. Study the Word in a Year: Old Testament Questions & Answers. 2007. 50p. pap. 9.00 *(978-0-8059-7642-7(6))* Dorrance Publishing Co., Inc.
Baker Publishing Group Staff. A Walk Thru the Book of Jonah: Experiencing God's Relentless Grace. 2009. (Walk Thru the Bible Discussion Guides). 60p. pap. 7.99 *(978-0-8010-7171-3(2))* Baker Bks.
—A Walk Thru the Book of Ruth: Loyalty & Love. 2009. (Walk Thru the Bible Discussion Guides). 60p. pap. 7.99 *(978-0-8010-7169-0(0))* Baker Bks.
—A Walk Thru the Life of Joseph: The Power of Forgiveness. 2009. (Walk Thru the Bible Discussion Guides). 78p. pap. 7.99 *(978-0-8010-7168-3(2))* Baker Bks.
—A Walk Thru the Life of Solomon: Pursuing a Heart of Integrity. 2009. (Walk Thru the Bible Discussion Guides). 59p. pap. 7.99 *(978-0-8010-7174-4(7))* Baker Bks.
Beck, William. Discovering jesus in the old Testament. 2007. pap. 15.99 *(978-1-60034-920-1(X))* Xulon Pr., Inc.
Belchen, Richard P. Teaching Helps in Malachi. 38p. pap. 6.95 *(978-0-925703-63-7(X))* Crown Pubns., Inc.
Bellinzoni, Arthur J. Old Testament: An Introduction to Biblical Scholarship. 2008. (ENG., Illus.). 375p. bds. 29.98 *(978-1-59102-673-0(3))* Prometheus Bks., Pubs.
Berquist, Jon L. & Hunt, Alice. Focusing Biblical Studies: The Crucial Nature of the Persian & Hellenistic Periods: Essays in Honor of Douglas A. Knight. 2012. (Library Hebrew Bible/Old Testament Studies). (ENG.). 224p. 130.00 *(978-0-567-62894-7(9),* T&T Clark Int'l) Continuum International Publishing Group, Ltd. GBR. Dist: National Bk. Network.
The Bible Study Guide (Volume 1) Genesis through Esther. 2007. 20.00 *(978-0-9796940-1-1(9))* Foundations Publishing.
The Bible Study Guide (Volume 3) Isaiah through Malachi. 2007. 20.00 *(978-0-9796940-3-5(5))* Foundations Publishing.
The Bible Study Guide(Volume 2) Job through song of Salomon. 2007. 20.00 *(978-0-9796940-2-8(7))* Foundations Publishing.
Boonstra, Harry. Isaiah: Encounters with the Living God. l.t. ed. 5.95 *(978-1-56212-830-2(2),* 150221) Faith Alive Christian Resources.
Brueggemann, Walter. A Pathway of Interpretation: The Old Testament for Pastors & Students. 2008. 180p. pap. 21.00 *(978-1-55635-589-9(0))* Wipf & Stock Pubs.
Buck, Thomas, et al. God's Old Testament People. tchr. ed. 11.50 *(978-0-570-01531-4(6),* 22-2260) Concordia Publishing Hse.
Bullock, Robert H. Hammer on the Rock: The Message of the Prophet Jeremiah. 2011. 66p. 36.95 ***(978-1-258-02805-3(0))*** Literary Licensing, LLC.
Burkholder, Connie. Exodus: Freed for the Journey with God. 2007. 6?p. pap. 6.95 *(978-0-87178-069-0(0))* Brethren Pr.
Burningham, Janet. Monday Nights in Jerusalem. 2009. 144p. pap. 14.99 *(978-1-59955-377-1(5))* Cedar Fort, Inc./CFI Distribution.
Christianity Today International Staff. Crash Course on Psalms. 2009. (Crash Course Bible Studies). (ENG.). 96p. pap. 7.99 *(978-0-7847-2249-7(8))* Standard Publishing.
Cloud, David W. Proverbs: Wisdom of the Wise & Foolish. Date not set. pap. 19.95 *(978-1-58318-007-5(9),* WOL Proverbs) Way of Life Literature.
Crumpler, Anne B. Entering the Psalms: Leader's Guide. 2009. pap. 15.00 *(978-0-8358-9975-8(6))* Upper Room Bks.
Davies, Philip R. & Vikander Edelman, Diana, eds. The Historian & the Bible: Essays in Honour of Lester L. Grabbe. 2012. (Library Hebrew Bible/Old Testament Studies). (ENG.). 256p. pap. 44.95 ***(978-0-567-54620-3(9),*** T&T Clark Int'l) Continuum International Publishing Group, Ltd. GBR. Dist: National Bk. Network.
Day, Jackson. Old Testament Bible Stories. 2007. 252p. pap. 25.00 *(978-0-9797324-0-9(9))* Day, H. Jackson.
Debelak, Robert P. Jr. Hidden in Plain Sight: Esther & a Marginalised Hermeneutic. 2008. (ENG.). 156p. pap. 33.00 *(978-0-7188-9181-7(3))* Lutherworth Pr., The GBR. Dist: Brown, David Bk. Co., The.
Dickson, Edward L. Genesis. 2008. 408p. pap. 22.99 *(978-1-60647-354-2(9))* Xulon Pr., Inc.
Draper Jr., James T. Difficult Times, Encouraging Words. 2009. 188p. pap. 14.99 *(978-1-61507-016-9(8))* Cross Bks. Publishing.
Drazin, Israel. A Rational Approach to Judaism & Torah Commentary. 2007. 237p. 23.95 *(978-965-7108-91-8(8))* Urim Pubns. ISR. Dist: Coronet Bks.
Driscoll, Helen W. A Guide to Old Testament Bible Study. 2008. 304p. 28.99 *(978-1-60477-767-3(2));* pap. 18.99 *(978-1-60477-766-6(4),* Xulon Pr., Inc.
Dunker, Gary. Deuteronomy: God's Word for a New Generation. 2008. (God's Word for Today Ser.). 120p. pap. 8.99 *(978-0-7586-1553-4(1))* Concordia Publishing Hse.
—1 & 2 Samuel: God's Grace Through Kings. 2008. (God's Word for Today Ser.). 120p. pap. 8.99 *(978-0-7586-1554-1(X))* Concordia Publishing Hse.
Dymally, Billye. Absolute Truth. 2007. 154p. pap. 12.95 *(978-0-7414-3854-6(2))* Infinity Publishing.
Edwards, Sue. Proverbs: Ancient Wisdom for a Postmodern World, 1 vol. 2007. (Sue Edwards Inductive Bible Study Ser.). 96p. pap. 12.99 *(978-0-8254-2548-6(4));* pap. 12.99 *(978-0-8254-2547-9(6))* Kregel Pubns.
—Psalms: Authentic Worship for Today's Women, 1 vol. 2009. (Sue Edwards Inductive Bible Study Ser.). 96p. pap. 12.99 *(978-0-8254-2544-8(1))* Kregel Pubns.
Exploring God's Word: Grade 7 - Old Testament Teacher Kit. (Voyages Ser.). 200.00 incl. audio, cd-rom *(978-0-570-00291-8(5),* 57-0710) Concordia Publishing Hse.
Fyall, Bob. Teaching Amos: Unlocking the Prophecy of Amos for the Bible Teacher. 2006. (ENG.). 160p. per. 10.99 *(978-1-84550-142-6(X))* Christian Focus Pubns. GBR. Dist: STL Distribution North America.
Giddens, Pastor/Missionary Donald Louis. Jesus in Genesis. 2007. 331p. pap. 33.50 *(978-1-4357-0125-0(9))* Lulu Enterprises Inc.
Giuliano, Angelo G., et al. Old Testament Foundations: Genesis Through Kings: Year One: Teacher Guidebook. 2007. (Catholic Biblical School Program Ser.). (Illus.). 80p. per. 19.95 *(978-0-8091-9585-5(2))* Paulist Pr.
—Old Testament Foundations: Genesis Through Kings Year One Student Workbook. 2007. (Illus.). 115p. pap. 16.95 *(978-0-8091-9584-8(4))* Paulist Pr.
Glahn, Sandra. Kona with Jonah. 2009. (Coffee Cup Bible Studies). (ENG., Illus.). 160p. (gr. 11). spiral bd. 12.99 *(978-0-89957-395-3(9))* AMG Pubs.
Glover, Sterling E. Obsession. 2011. (Illus.). 160p. pap. 12.95 ***(978-1-4327-6585-9(X))*** Outskirts Pr., Inc.
Golden, Kevin S. Minor Prophets. 2009. (LifeLight Ser.). 80p. pap., pupil's gde. ed. 8.99 *(978-0-7586-1180-2(3))* Concordia Publishing Hse.
Hargreaves, John. Guide to Genesis. 3.00 *(978-0-687-85447-9(4))* Abingdon Pr.
—Guide to Psalms. 3.00 *(978-0-687-85455-1(3))* Abingdon Pr.
Hayford, Jack W. Genesis: Promises & Beginnings, 0 vols. 2009. (Spirit-Filled Life Study Guide Ser.). 128p. pap. 9.99 *(978-1-4185-4119-4(2))* Nelson, Thomas Inc.
—Hebrews: Beyond the Veil, 0 vols. 2009. (Spirit-Filled Life Study Guide Ser.). 128p. pap. 9.99 *(978-1-4185-4121-7(4))* Nelson, Thomas Inc.
Heck, Joel. History & Literature of the Old Testament. rev. ed. 2010. (ENG.). 238p. spiral bd. 88.00 *(978-0-7575-7771-0(7))* Kendall Hunt Publishing Co.
Henderson, Betty. Grace for Every Trial. 2008. 128p. pap. 7.95 *(978-1-59166-918-0(9))* BJU Pr.
Houghton, John. Isaiah 1-39: Prophet to the Nations, 1 vol. 2009. (Cover to Cover Bible Study Ser.). 72p. pap. *(978-1-85345-510-0(5))* Crusade for World Revival.
Hunting, Harold B. Hebrew Life & Times. 2008. 192p. 22.99 *(978-0-554-33199-7(3))* 2008. 192p. 25.99 *(978-0-554-23896-8(9))* 2006. (ENG.). 170p. pap. 19.99 *(978-1-4264-5131-7(8))* 2006. (ENG.). 190p. pap. 21.99 *(978-1-4264-5432-5(5))* BiblioBazaar.
—Hebrew Life & Times. 2010. (Illus.). 92p. pap. 20.00 *(978-1-77045-589-4(2))* General Bks. LLC.
Hunting, Harold B. 1879-1958. Hebrew Life & Times. 2010. (ENG.). 212p. pap. 24.75 *(978-1-176-65696-3(1))* BiblioBazaar.
Hunting, Harold B. Hebrew Life & Times. 2009. 208p. 28.99 *(978-1-110-67398-8(1));* pap. 23.75 *(978-1-110-67397-1(3))* BiblioBazaar.
—Hebrew life & Times. 2009. (ENG.). 207p. pap. 20.99 *(978-1-110-67393-3(0),* BiblioLife) BiblioBazaar.
Isaacson, Marlys J. Picture Me Reading Favorite Bible Stories! Classroom Teacher's Manual: Old Testament Stories, Sight Word Activities, & Phonics Instruction. 2007. 154p. (C). spiral bd. 15.00 *(978-0-9743916-5-5(4))* Picture Me Reading!
—Picture Me Reading Favorite Bible Stories! Manual for Teaching One-on-One: Old Testament Stories, Sight Word Activities, & Phonics Instruction. 2007. 42p. 5.00 *(978-0-9743916-4-9(6))* Picture Me Reading!
Johnson, Bob O. Effective Teaching Resources, Old Testament Bible Survey Course. 2010. 162p. pap. 16.99 *(978-1-61579-817-9(X))* Xulon Pr., Inc.
—Student Study Guide, Old Testament Bible Survey Course. 2010. 202p. pap. 17.99 *(978-1-61579-818-6(8))* Xulon Pr., Inc.
Kearney, Jonathan. Rashi ndash; Linguist despite Himself: A Study of the Linguistic Dimension of Rabbi Solomon Yishaqirsquo;s Commentary on Deuteronomy. 2012. (Library Hebrew Bible/Old Testament Studies). (ENG.). 224p. pap. 44.95 ***(978-0-567-09558-9(4),*** T&T Clark Int'l) Continuum International Publishing Group, Ltd. GBR. Dist: National Bk. Network.
Kettner, Edward & Richter, Elaine. LifeLight: Minor Prophets. 2009. 80p. pap. 8.99 *(978-0-7586-1179-6(X))* Concordia Publishing Hse.
Kim, Hoon. Creative Bible Lessons in Genesis, 1 vol. 2006. (Creative Bible Lessons Ser.). (ENG., Illus.). 144p. (gr. 13). pap. 16.99 *(978-0-310-27093-5(6))* Zondervan.
Kirkpatrick. Function of Ancient Historiography in Biblical & Cognate Studies. 2008. (Library of Hebrew Bible/Old Testament Studies, the Ser.). (ENG.). 192p. 120.00 *(978-0-567-02715-3(5),* T&T Clark Int'l) Continuum International Publishing Group, Ltd. GBR. Dist: National Bk. Network.
Knoppers, Gary N. Exile & Restoration Revisited: Essays on the Babylonian & Persian Periods in Memory of Peter R. Ackroyd. Grabbe, Lester L., ed. 2009. (Library of Second Temple Studies, the Ser.). (ENG.). 237p. 130.00 *(978-0-567-12256-8(5),* T&T Clark Int'l) Continuum International Publishing Group, Ltd. GBR. Dist: National Bk. Network.
Koedoot, Gerrit. Deuteronomy: Keeping the Promises. l.t. ed. 5.25 *(978-1-56212-650-6(4),* 15011) Faith Alive Christian Resources.
Kok, Joel. Judges: Doing as We See Fit. l.t. ed. 5.25 *(978-1-56212-553-7(9),* 150041) Faith Alive Christian Resources.

B

Lasiter, Cindy. Diamonds in the Rough: Learning How to Apply God's Principles for Living Through the Study of Old Testament Characters. 2009. 200p. pap. 17.99 *(978-1-60791-218-7(X))* Xulon Pr., Inc.

Leavitt, Dennis H. & Christensen, Richard O. Scripture Study for Latter-Day Saint Families: The Old Testament. 2009. 21.99 *(978-1-60641-141-4(1))* Deseret Bk. Co.

Lifetogether. Proverbs. 2010. (Deepening Life Together Ser.). 24.99 *(978-0-8010-3054-3(4))*; pap. 8.99 *(978-0-8010-6967-3(X))* Baker Bks.

—Psalms. 2011. (Deepening Life Together Ser.). (Illus.). 85p. pap. 8.99 *(978-0-8010-6855-3(X))* Baker Bks.

—Ruth. 2011. (Deepening Life Together Ser.). (Illus.). 87p. pap. 8.99 *(978-0-8010-6872-0(X))* Baker Bks.

Loken, Israel P. The Old Testament Historical Books: An Introduction. 2008. 452p. pap. 23.99 *(978-1-60647-238-5(0))* Xulon Pr., Inc.

—The Old Testament Prophetic Books: An Introduction. 2010. 466p. pap. 24.99 *(978-1-61579-789-9(0))* Xulon Pr., Inc.

Lowry, Rich. Reforming Kings: Cult & Society in First Temple Judah. 2009. (Library of Hebrew Bible/Old Testament Studies, the Ser.). (ENG.). 236p. 39.95 *(978-1-4411-0052-8(0)*, T&T Clark) Continuum International Publishing Group, Ltd. GBR. Dist: National Bk. Network.

MacArthur, John. End of an Era: The Rise & Fall of Solomon, 0 vols. 2009. (MacArthur Old Testament Study Guides). 128p. pap. 9.99 *(978-1-4185-3406-4(4))* Nelson, Thomas Inc.

—Finally in the Land: Canaan & the Kinsman Redeemer, 0 vols. 2009. (MacArthur Old Testament Study Guides). (Illus.). 128p. pap. 9.99 *(978-1-4185-3403-5(X))* Nelson, Thomas Inc.

—Jacob & Egypt: The Sovereignty of God, 0 vols. 2008. (MacArthur Old Testament Study Guides). (ENG.). 128p. pap. 9.99 *(978-1-4185-3324-3(6))* Nelson, Thomas Inc.

—The Restoration of a Sinner: David's Heart Revealed, 0 vols. 2009. (MacArthur Old Testament Study Guides). 128p. pap. 9.99 *(978-1-4185-3405-9(6))* Nelson, Thomas Inc.

Mahusay, Nancy. The History of Redemption. 2007. 388p. 31.99 *(978-1-60266-738-9(1))*; per. 19.99 *(978-1-60266-737-2(3))* Xulon Pr., Inc.

March, W. Eugene & Griggs, Donald L. Genesis from Scratch: The Old Testament for Beginners. 2010. (Bible from Scratch Ser.). (ENG., Illus.). 112p. pap. 13.00 *(978-0-664-23507-9(7))* Westminster John Knox Pr.

Mason, James. My Father's Words in Faithfulness & Courage. 2008. 37p. pap. 16.98 *(978-0-557-02690-6(3))* Lulu Enterprises Inc.

Mathews, Danny. Royal Motifs in the Pentateuchal Portrayal of Moses. 2012. (Library Hebrew Bible/Old Testament Studies). (ENG.). 176p. 120.00 ***(978-0-567-11614-7(X)**, T&T Clark Int'l)* Continuum International Publishing Group, Ltd. GBR. Dist: National Bk. Network.

Maurice Price, Ira. Compendio de la Historia Del A. T. An Outline of Old Testament. (SPA.). *(978-84-7645-425-1(2)*, 223331) Clie, Editorial.

McConville, James Gordon & Millar, J. G. Time & Place in Deuteronomy. 2009. (Library of Hebrew Bible/Old Testament Studies, the Ser.). (ENG.). 155p. 29.95 *(978-1-4411-8905-9(X)*, T&T Clark) Continuum International Publishing Group, Ltd. GBR. Dist: National Bk. Network.

McFarland, Alex. Stand: Diving into God's Words - A Discovery of Psalm 119. 2009. (Stand Ser.: 1). (ENG.). 144p. (YA). pap. 12.99 *(978-1-58997-482-1(4))* Tyndale Hse. Pubs.

—Stand: Seeking the Way of God - A Discovery of Genesis 37-47. 2009. (Stand Ser.: 3). (ENG.). 160p. (YA). pap. 12.99 *(978-1-58997-484-5(0))* Tyndale Hse. Pubs.

—Stand: Unleashing the Wisdom of God - A Discovery of Proverbs. 2009. (Stand Ser.: 2). (ENG.). 144p. (YA). pap. 12.99 *(978-1-58997-483-8(2))* Tyndale Hse. Pubs.

McGinnis, Marilyn. Discover Judges. 2009. (Illus.). 94p. pap. *(978-1-59255-482-9(2))* Faith Alive Christian Resources.

McKenzie, Steven L. & Kaltner, John. The Old Testament: Its Background, Growth, & Content. 2007. (Illus.). 382p. pap. 34.00 *(978-0-687-03901-2(0))* Abingdon Pr.

Mills, William C. Feasts of Faith: Reflections on the Major Feast Days. 2008. 172p. pap. 13.95 *(978-1-933275-23-9(5)*, Orthodox Research Institute) Cocheco Falls Publishing.

Minter, Kelly. Hannah's One Wish: A Bible Study for Teen Girls. 2007. 120p. 10.95 *(978-1-4158-5254-5(5))* LifeWay Christian Resources.

Mitchell, Marilyn. Women's Stories for God's Glory. 2009. 80p. pap. 14.99 *(978-1-4490-1773-6(8))* AuthorHouse.

Motyer, Alec. The Story of the Old Testament: Men with a Message. Stott, John, ed. 2010. (ENG.). 400p. 19.99 *(978-1-84550-506-6(9))* Christian Focus Pubns. GBR. Dist: STL Distribution North America.

Nordberg, Bette. Jeremiah: A Bright Light in a Dark Season. 2008. (Following God Through the Bible Ser.). (ENG.). 160p. pap. 14.99 *(978-0-89957-030-3(5))* AMG Pubs.

Ogden, Graham. Qoheleth. 2007. (ENG.). 256p. *(978-1-906055-08-0(4))*; 2nd ed. per. *(978-1-906055-09-7(2))* Sheffield Phoenix Pr.

Olshine, David. Proverbs, 1 vol. 2009. (Studies on the Go Ser.). (ENG.). 176p. pap. 8.99 *(978-0-310-28548-9(8))* Zondervan.

Overduin, Nick. Job: Challenging a Silent God. l.t. ed. 5.25 *(978-1-56212-659-9(8)*, 150101) Faith Alive Christian Resources.

Piersma, John H. Bible Lessons: The Book of Daniel. 2007. per. 8.00 *(978-0-9793677-4-7(7))* Reformed Fellowship, Inc.

Porterfield, Alicia Davis & Porterfield, Eric. Proverbs — Living Wisely, Loving Well: Annual Bible Study: Teaching Guide. 2009. pap. *(978-1-57312-545-1(8))* Smyth & Helwys Publishing, Inc.

Rae, Frederick J. How to Teach the Old Testament. 2007. (ENG.). 252p. 41.95 *(978-0-548-06208-1(0))* Kessinger Publishing, LLC.

Ranck, Doug. Creative Bible Lessons in Job, 1 vol. 2007. (Creative Bible Lessons Ser.). (ENG.). 160p. pap. 16.99 *(978-0-310-27219-9(X))* Zondervan.

Redding, Mary Lou. Meeting God in Scripture: Entering the Old Testament. 2008. 111p. per. 15.00 *(978-0-8358-9946-8(2))* Upper Room Bks.

Reitman, James. Unlocking Wisdom: Forming Agents of God in the House of Mourning - A Canonical-Linguistic Exposition of the Books of Job & Ecclesiastes. 2008. (ENG., Illus.). 384p. per. 19.99 *(978-0-9779535-5-4(6))* 21st Century Pr.

Rockwell, Willard F. Character Caveat: A Miniseries of Mighty Messages. 2010. pap. 16.99 *(978-1-61566-962-2(0))* Tate Publishing & Enterprises, LLC.

Rogerson, John, ed. Beginning Old Testament Study. 2nd ed. 176p. 17.95 *(978-0-281-05103-8(8))* International Publishers Marketing.

Rydelnik, Michael & Broadman and Holman Publishers Staff. The Messianic Hope: Is the Hebrew Bible Really Messianic? 2010. (ENG.). 224p. 19.99 *(978-0-8054-4654-8(0)*, B&H Academic) B&H Publishing Group.

Schmutzer, Andrew, et al. Genesis: See Our Story Begin. 2009. (NLT Study Ser.). (ENG.). 224p. pap. 8.99 *(978-1-4143-2199-8(6))* Tyndale Hse. Pubs.

Schroeder, John D. Old Testament Stories from the Backside: A Video Study. ldr.'s ed. 2007. (Behind the Pages Ser.). 40p. pap. 11.00 *(978-0-687-64204-5(3))* Abingdon Pr.

Scott, Johnny & Christ In Youth Staff. Connect: A 9-Week Small Group Collision-Living the Faith. 2010. (Rock Your Face off Jr. High Resource Ser.). (ENG.). 128p. 14.99 *(978-0-7847-2405-7(9))* Standard Publishing.

Seyda, Robert R. To God's Heart: The Psalms for Today. 2007. 526p. per. 59.95 *(978-0-9785609-9-7(X))* New Global Publishing.

Shomaker, Cynthia. From Moab to Bethlehem... Journey to the King - A Devotional Study on the Book of Ruth. 2009. 416p. 34.99 *(978-1-60791-164-7(7))*; pap. 22.99 *(978-1-60791-163-0(9))* Xulon Pr., Inc.

Stahl, Nanette. Law & Liminality in the Bible. 2009. (Library Hebrew Bible/Old Testament Studies). (ENG.). 104p. pap. 27.95 *(978-0-567-54205-2(X)*, T&T Clark) Continuum International Publishing Group, Ltd. GBR. Dist: National Bk. Network.

Tarazi, Paul N. Old Testament Introduction, 3 vols., Set. Incl. Historical Traditions. (Illus.). 173p. 1990. pap. 16.00 *(978-0-88141-105-8(1))*; Prophetic Traditions. 207p. 1994. pap. 18.00 *(978-0-88141-106-5(X))*; Psalms & Wisdom. (Illus.). 207p. 1996. pap. 16.00 *(978-0-88141-107-2(8))*; 587p. Set pap. 36.00 *(978-0-88141-108-9(6))* St. Vladimir's Seminary Pr.

Thorogood, David. Guide to Book of Amos. 16.00 *(978-0-687-85449-3(0))* Abingdon Pr.

Towns, Elmer. Praying Your Way Out of Bondage: Prayers From Exodus & Leviticus. 2009. pap. 17.99 *(978-0-7684-2759-2(2))* Destiny Image Pubs.

Vander Hart, Mark. Bible Studies on Jacob. 2007. per. 8.00 *(978-0-9793677-7-9(8))* Reformed Fellowship, Inc.

Vos, Clarence. The Prophets: Hearing the Word of the Lord. l.t. ed. 5.25 *(978-1-56212-660-5(1)*, 150111) Faith Alive Christian Resources.

Wager, Dave. Beyond the Resistance: Learning to Face Adversity. 2007. (Intimate Warrior Ser.). 104p. per. 11.95 *(978-1-60265-001-5(2)*, BTR) Grace Acres Pr.

Walk Thru the Bible. OT39 Old Testament Flashcards: The Keyword Learning SystemTM. 2012. (Bible Survey Ser.). 11.95 ***(978-1-59834-198-0(7))*** Walk Thru the Bible Ministry.

Wiersbe, Warren W. Be Amazed (Minor Prophets) Restoring an Attitude of Wonder & Worship, 1 vol. 2010. (BE Series Commentary Ser.). (ENG.). 224p. pap. 12.99 *(978-1-4347-6505-5(9))* Cook, David C.

—Ruth/Esther: Doing God's Will Whatever the Cost. 2008. (Wiersbe Bible Study Ser.). (ENG.). 128p. pap. 8.99 *(978-0-7814-4573-3(6))* Cook, David C.

BIBLE—SYMBOLISM

see Symbolism in the Bible

BIBLE—TEACHINGS

see Bible—Theology

BIBLE—TEXTBOOKS

Here are entered textbooks for the study of the Bible for all age levels.

Arnold, Bill T. & Beyer, Bryan E. Encountering the Old Testament: A Christian Survey. 2nd ed. 2008. (Encountering Biblical Studies). (Illus.). 528p. (C). 49.99 *(978-0-8010-3170-0(2))* Baker Academic.

Arthur, Kay & De Lacy, Pete. The Coming of God's Kingdom: Matthew. 2009. (New Inductive Study Ser.). (Illus.). 128p. pap. 7.99 *(978-0-7369-2512-9(0))* Harvest Hse. Pubs.

—Experiencing the Miracles of Jesus: Mark. 2010. (New Inductive Study Ser.). 112p. pap. 8.99 *(978-0-7369-2513-6(9))* Harvest Hse. Pubs.

—The God Who Cares & Knows You. 2008. (New Inductive Study Ser.). (Illus.). 159p. per. 8.99 *(978-0-7369-2193-0(1))* Harvest Hse. Pubs.

—The Key to Living by Faith: Hebrews. 2009. (New Inductive Study Ser.). 112p. pap. 8.99 *(978-0-7369-2306-4(3))* Harvest Hse. Pubs.

Baker Publishing Group Staff & Life Together Staff. Revelation, 1 vol. 2009. (Deepening Life Together Ser.). 128p. pap. 8.99 *(978-0-8010-6846-1(0))* Baker Bks.

—Romans, 1 vol. 2009. (Deepening Life Together Ser.). 128p. pap. 8.99 *(978-0-8010-6843-0(6))* Baker Bks.

Barclay, William & Law, Philip. Mark: A Guide to the New Daily Study Bible. 2010. (ENG.). 64p. pap. 7.00 *(978-0-664-23418-8(6))* Westminster John Knox Pr.

—Matthew: A Guide to the New Daily Study Bible. 2010. (ENG.). 64p. pap. 7.00 *(978-0-664-23417-1(8))* Westminster John Knox Pr.

Beynon, Nigel & Sach, Andrew. Dig Deeper: Tools for Understanding God's Word. 2010. 160p. pap. 14.99 *(978-1-58134-971-9(8))* Crossway.

Binz, Stephen J. Abraham: Father of All Believers. 2011. (Ancient-Future Bible Study: Experience Scripture Through Lectio Divina Ser.). 192p. pap. 11.99 *(978-1-58743-277-4(3))* Brazos Pr.

—David: Shepherd & King of Israel. 2011. (Ancient-Future Bible Study: Experience Scripture Through Lectio Divina Ser.). pap. 11.99 *(978-1-58743-280-4(3))* Brazos Pr.

—Jesus, the Messianic King, Part 2: Matthew 17-28. 2010. 136p. pap. 12.95 *(978-1-58595-816-0(6))* Twenty-Third Pubns./Bayard.

—Jesus, the Suffering Servant. 2012. ***(978-1-58595-864-1(6))*** 2011. ***(978-1-58595-863-4(8))*** Twenty-Third Pubns./Bayard.

Binz, Stephen J. Paul: Apostle to All the Nations. 2011. (Ancient-Future Bible Study: Experience Scripture Through Lectio Divina Ser.). pap. 11.99 *(978-1-58743-278-1(1))* Brazos Pr.

Blackwell, John. A Whole New World: The Gospel of Mark: Great Insights into Transformation & Togetherness. 2007. viii, 111p. audio *(978-1-60037-231-5(7))* Morgan James Publishing.

Bunch, Cindy, ed. Advent of the Savior. 2009. (LifeGuide Bible Studies). (ENG., Illus.). 64p. pap. 8.00 *(978-0-8308-3136-4(3)*, IVP Conn.) InterVarsity Pr.

Burge, Gary M., et al. New Testament in Antiquities, 1 vol. 2009. (ENG., Illus.). 496p. 49.99 *(978-0-310-24495-0(1))* Zondervan.

Burnette-Bletsch, Rhonda. Studying the Old Testament: A Companion. 2007. 305p. 30.00 *(978-0-687-64623-4(5))* Abingdon Pr.

Caldwell, Chris. James: Gaining True Wisdom. 2011. ***(978-0-9823842-4-4(6))*** Smyth & Helwys Publishing, Inc.

Carmody, Timothy R. The Gospel of Mark: Question by Question. 2010. (Question by Question Bible Study Commentary Ser.). 128p. pap. 16.95 *(978-0-8091-4636-9(3))* Paulist Pr.

Caron, Gerald. Mark in the Lectionary: An Ecumenical Guide to the Sunday Gospels. 2008. 208p. pap. 19.95 *(978-0-8091-4591-1(X))* Paulist Pr.

Cartledge, Tony W. Old Testament Promises to God. 2009. pap. *(978-0-9821806-8-6(3))* NextSunday Resources.

Carvalho, Corrine L. The Book of Ezekiel: Question by Question. 2010. (Question by Question Bible Study Commentary Ser.). 224p. pap. *(978-0-8091-4678-9(9))* Paulist Pr.

—Encountering Ancient Voices (Second Edition) A Guide to Reading the Old Testament. 2nd ed. 2010. pap. 49.95 *(978-1-59982-050-7(1)*, 9781599820507) St. Mary's Pr.

Cassady, David. Colossians: Living the Faith Faithfully. 2009. pap. *(978-0-9823842-8-2(9))* NextSunday Resources.

Chargois, Paige Lanier. Certain Women Called by Christ: Biblical Realities for Today. 2008. (ENG.). 176p. per. 12.99 *(978-1-59669-200-8(6))* New Hope Pubs.

Collver, Albert B. Ezra & Nehemiah: The Lord Is Faithful. 2009. (God's Word for Today Ser.). 120p. pap. 8.99 *(978-0-7586-1649-4(X))* Concordia Publishing Hse.

Cordeiro, Wayne. The Divine Mentor: Growing Your Faith as You Sit at the Feet of the Savior. 2008. 240p. pap. 13.99 *(978-0-7642-0579-8(X))* Bethany Hse. Pubs.

Cram101 Textbook Reviews. Outlines & Highlights for New Testament: A Students Introduction by Stephen L. Harris, ISBN. 2011. 462p. pap. 37.95 ***(978-1-61812-203-2(7))*** Cram101 Inc.

Curry, Bruce. The Bible & the Quest of Life. 2007. (ENG.). 328p. 45.95 *(978-0-548-06791-8(0))* Kessinger Publishing, LLC.

Dant, James & Dant, James C. How Does the Church Decide? 2009. pap. *(978-0-9821806-6-2(7))* NextSunday Resources.

Davenport, Gene L. Powers & Principalities. 2010. (Insights: Bible Studies for Growing Faith Ser.). 56p. pap. 8.00 *(978-1-60899-217-1(9)*, Wipf and Stock) Wipf & Stock Pubs.

David, Patricia J. John: Lectio Divina for Youth. 2007. (ENG.). 80p. pap. 7.99 *(978-0-8341-5022-5(0)*, 083-415-0220) Beacon Hill Pr. of Kansas City.

Davies, Stevan L. The New Testament: An Analytical Approach. 2011. pap. 37.00 ***(978-1-59815-036-0(7))*** Polebridge Pr.

Duvall, J. Scott & Hays, J. Daniel. Living God's Word: Discovering Our Place in the Great Story of Scripture, 1 vol. 2012. (ENG.). 352p. (C). 34.99 ***(978-0-310-29210-4(7))*** Zondervan.

Dyet, James T. Unsolved Mysteries? Answers from the Book of Genesis. 2007. 55p. pap. *(978-1-59402-509-9(6))* Regular Baptist Pr.

Edwards, Sue. Ephesians: Finding Your Identity & Purpose in Christ, 1 vol. 2007. (Sue Edwards Inductive Bible Study Ser.). 96p. pap. 12.99 *(978-0-8254-2549-3(2))* Kregel Pubns.

Engle, Joel. The Exchange: Tired of Living the Christian Life on Your Own? 2007. (Illus.). 128p. pap. 7.95 *(978-1-4158-5270-5(7))* LifeWay Christian Resources.

Essex, Barbara J. Bold & Brazen: Exploring Biblical Prophets. 2010. 128p. 16.00 *(978-0-8298-1873-4(1))* Pilgrim Pr., The/United Church Pr.

First Place 4 Health. Balanced Living. 2010. (First Place Ser.). (ENG.). 256p. 19.99 *(978-0-8307-5396-3(6))* Gospel Light Pubns.

First Place 4 Health & First Place 4 Health. Celebrate Success. 2009. (First Place Ser.). (ENG.). 256p. 19.99 *(978-0-8307-4755-9(9))* Gospel Light Pubns.

Franklin, Ryan. The Bible Made Simple. 2010. *(978-1-56722-741-3(4))* Word Aflame Pr.

Frigge, Marielle. Beginning Biblical Studies. 2009. (ENG.). 197p. (C). pap. 29.95 *(978-1-59982-002-6(1))* St. Mary's Pr.

Gettys, Joseph M. How to Study Luke. 2011. 146p. 40.95 ***(978-1-258-02591-5(4))*** Literary Licensing, LLC.

Green, Timothy. Philippians: Lectio Divina for Youth. 2007. (ENG.). 80p. pap. 7.99 *(978-0-8341-5021-8(2)*, 083-415-0212) Beacon Hill Pr. of Kansas City.

Griggs, Donald L. & Johnson, Earl S., Jr., Earl S. Matthew's Gospel from Scratch: The New Testament for Beginners. 2011. (Bible from Scratch Ser.). (ENG.). 112p. pap. 13.00 *(978-0-664-23485-0(2))* Westminster John Knox Pr.

Griggs, Donald L. & Walaskay, Paul W. Luke's Gospel from Scratch: The New Testament for Beginners. 2011. (Bible from Scratch Ser.). (ENG.). 136p. pap. 13.00 *(978-0-664-23499-7(2))* Westminster John Knox Pr.

Grimsrud, Ted. God's Healing Strategy, Revised Edition: An Introduction to the Bible's Main Themes. 2011. 190p. pap. 17.95 ***(978-1-931038-88-1(0))*** Cascadia Publishing Hse., LLC.

Gundry, Robert H. A Survey of the New Testament, 1 vol. 2007. (Zondervan Get an A! Ser.). (ENG.). 6p. 6.99 *(978-0-310-27314-1(5))* Zondervan.

Hahn, Kimberly & Barber, Michael. Genesis to Jesus: Studying Scripture from the Heart of the Church. 2007. (Journey Through Scripture Ser.). (Illus.). 133p. per. 9.99 *(978-0-86716-837-2(4)*, Servant Bks.) Franciscan Media.

Hahn, Scott & Socias, James. Comprender Las Escrituras: Curso Completo para el Estudio de la Biblia. 2010. (SPA.). *(978-1-936045-33-4(8))* Midwest Theological Forum.

—Faith & Revelation: Knowing God Through Sacred Scripture. 2009. *(978-1-936045-01-3(X))* Midwest Theological Forum.

—Understanding the Scriptures. 2010. *(978-1-936045-12-9(5))* Midwest Theological Forum.

Harbour, Brian L. Ephesians, Philippians, Colossians: Living with Faithfulness & Joy. 2008. 142p. pap. *(978-1-934731-14-7(5))* Baptistway.

Harris, Stephen. Exploring the Bible. 2009. (ENG., Illus.). 480p. (C). pap. 67.00 *(978-0-07-340736-4(4)*, 0073407364) McGraw-Hill Cos., The.

—The New Testament: A Student's Introduction. 6th ed. 2008. (ENG., Illus.). 528p. (C). pap. 86.00 *(978-0-07-338653-9(7)*, 0073386537) McGraw-Hill Cos., The.

Harris, Stephen L. The New Testament: A Student's Introduction. 7th ed. 2011. (ENG., Illus.). 544p. (C). pap. 86.00 *(978-0-07-353582-1(6)*, 0073535826) McGraw-Hill Cos., The.

Heer, Ken. Ephesians: Lectio Divina for Youth. 2009. (Ancient Faith Ser.). (ENG.). 80p. pap. 7.99 *(978-0-8341-5028-7(X)*, 9780834150287) Beacon Hill Pr. of Kansas City.

Henry, Barbara. Making Disciples in Your Community: Coming Together to Grow in Christ. 2009. (Following God Discipleship Ser.). (ENG.). 176p. (gr. 11). pap. 14.99 *(978-0-89957-346-5(0))* AMG Pubs.

Hill, Bill. Moses: From the Burning Bush to the Promised Land. 2009. pap. *(978-0-9823842-7-5(0))* NextSunday Resources.

Hoeck, Andreas & Manhardt, Laurie. Come & See: Ezekiel, Hebrews, Revelation. 2010. 224p. pap. 19.95 *(978-1-931018-65-4(0))* Emmaus Road Publishing.

Hybels, Bill, et al. Nehemiah, 1 vol. 2008. (New Community Bible Study Ser.). (ENG.). 96p. pap. 7.99 *(978-0-310-28055-2(9))* Zondervan.

Indermark, John. Immersion Bible Studies: Luke. 2011. 103p. 9.00 *(978-1-4267-0983-8(8))* Abingdon Pr.

Johnson, Kevin. Follow: Walk in the Rhythm of Jesus, 1 vol. 2009. (Higher Ser.). (ENG.). 112p. pap. 8.99 *(978-0-310-28264-8(0))* Zondervan.

—Soar, 1 vol. 2009. (Higher Ser.). (ENG.). 112p. pap. 8.99 *(978-0-310-28267-9(5))* Zondervan.

—Thrive, 1 vol. 2009. (Higher Ser.). (ENG.). 112p. pap. 8.99 *(978-0-310-28265-5(9))* Zondervan.

Jordan, Rick. A Holy & Surprising Birth. 2009. pap. *(978-0-9823842-9-9(7))* NextSunday Resources.

Kelley, Dee. Acts: The Church Ignited: Part 1. McCullough, Jeannie, ed. 2006. (Wisdom of the Word Ser.). (ENG.). 96p. spiral bd. 14.99 *(978-0-8341-2281-9(2)*, 083-412-2812) Beacon Hill Pr. of Kansas City.

—Acts: The Church Ignited: Part 2. McCullough, Jeannie, ed. 2006. (Wisdom of the Word Ser.). (ENG.). 96p. spiral bd. 14.99 *(978-0-8341-2282-6(0)*, 083-412-2820) Beacon Hill Pr. of Kansas City.

Kelley, Rhonda H. Personal Holiness: A Biblical Study for Developing a Holy Lifestyle. rev. ed. 2010. (Woman's Guide Ser.). (ENG.). 176p. pap. 14.99 *(978-1-59669-257-2(X))* New Hope Pubs.

—Spiritual Wellness: A Personal Study of Colossians. rev. ed. 2010. (Woman's Guide Ser.). (ENG.). 176p. pap. 14.99 *(978-1-59669-259-6(6))* New Hope Pubs.

Lassiter, Perry. The Gospel of Luke: Good News of Great Joy. 2009. 188p. pap. *(978-1-934731-39-0(0))* Baptistway.

Latkovich, Sallie. Excavando en el Significado de la Biblia: Más Allá de Las Palabras. 2011.Tr. of Mining the Meaning of the Bible: Beyond the Literal Word. (SPA.). 64p. *(978-0-7648-2050-2(8))* Liguori Pubns.

Laurie, Greg. Beyond: A Devotional. 2007. (ENG.). 320p. per. 14.99 *(978-1-59052-831-0(X)*, Multnomah) Doubleday Religious Publishing Group, The.

Lavin, Ronald J. The Eagle: "Don't Despair" Passages in the Gospel of John. 2008. *(978-0-7880-2555-6(4))* CSS Publishing Co.

—The Servant Lord: Challenging & Encouraging Passages in the Gospel of Mark. 2009. *(978-0-7880-2609-6(7))* CSS Publishing Co.

Leiter, David A. Peace in Isaiah. 2011. ***(978-0-87178-166-6(2))*** Brethren Pr.

Lucas & Lucas, Ernest C. Exploring the Old Testament, Vol. 3. 2008. (Exploring the Bible Ser.). (ENG.). 311p. 30.00 *(978-0-8308-2543-1(6)*, IVP Acad.) InterVarsity Pr.

March, W. Eugene & Griggs, Donald L. Genesis from Scratch: The Old Testament for Beginners. 2010. (Bible from Scratch Ser.). (ENG., Illus.). 112p. pap. 13.00 *(978-0-664-23507-9(7))* Westminster John Knox Pr.

Mason, Eric Farrel & McCruden, Kevin B. Reading the Epistle to the Hebrews: A Resource for Students. 2011. **(978-1-58983-608-2(1))**; (978-1-58983-509-9(X)) Society of Biblical Literature.
Maxwell, David R. 1, 2, & 3 John: Love & Hate, Light & Darkness. 2009. (God's Word for Today Ser.). 120p. pap. 8.99 (978-0-7586-1653-1(8)) Concordia Publishing Hse.
May, David M. Easter Confessions. 2009. pap. (978-0-9821806-5-5(9)) NextSunday Resources.
McCullar, Michael D. Annual Bible Study: James. 2011. **(978-1-57312-604-5(7))** Smyth & Helwys Publishing, Inc.
McCullar, Michael D. & Letson, Rickey. Sessions with Mark: Following Jesus at Full Speed. 2008. pap. (978-1-57312-517-8(2)) Smyth & Helwys Publishing, Inc.
Miller, William T. The Book of Exodus: Question by Question. 2009. (Question by Question Bible Study Commentary Ser.). 352p. pap. 21.95 (978-0-8091-4612-3(6)) Paulist Pr.
Moore, Dwayne. Pure Praise for Youth: A Heart-Focused Study on Worship. 2011. pap. **(978-0-7644-6657-1(7)**, Group) Group Publishing, Inc.
Moore, Mark. Acts: Lectio Divina for Youth. 2009. (Ancient Faith Ser.). (ENG.). 80p. pap. 7.99 (978-0-8341-5027-0(1), 9780834150270) Beacon Hill Pr. of Kansas City.
Mulholland, M. Robert & Thompson, Marjorie J. The Way of Scripture. 2010. (978-0-8358-1034-0(8)) Upper Room Bks.
Myers, Charles D., Jr. & Griggs, Donald L. Mark's Gospel from Scratch: The New Testament for Beginners. 2010. (Bible from Scratch Ser.). (ENG.). 112p. pap. 13.00 (978-0-664-23486-7(0)) Westminster John Knox Pr.
Myers, Kristen. Coffee with the Savior: A Bible Study for Women. 2010. (Lutheran Difference Ser.). 128p. pap. 8.99 (978-0-7586-1755-2(0)) Concordia Publishing Hse.
Nash, Robert N. Embracing the Word of God. 2009. 63p. pap. (978-0-9823842-6-8(2)) NextSunday Resources.
Neff, Robert W. & Ramirez, Frank. The Chronicler. 2010. (978-0-87178-132-1(8), FaithQuest) Brethren Pr.
Nielson, Kathleen Buswell. Joshua: All God's Good Promises. 2008. 143p. spiral bd. 12.99 (978-1-59638-105-6(1)) P & R Publishing.
—Proverbs: The Ways of Wisdom. 2007. (Living Word Bible Studies). 182p. spiral bd. 12.99 (978-1-59638-081-3(0)) P & R Publishing.
—1 & 2 Thessalonians: Living the Gospel to the End. 2008. 145p. spiral bd. 12.99 (978-1-59638-104-9(3)) P & R Publishing.
Packer, J. I. & Nystrom, Carolyn. Abiding in Christ. 2009. (LifeGuide Bible Studies). (ENG.). 64p. pap. 8.00 (978-0-8308-3125-8(8), IVP Conn.) InterVarsity Pr.
Parkey, W. C. Treasures & Truths. 2006. 292p. pap. 14.99 (978-1-56722-699-7(X)) Word Aflame Pr.
Pennock, Michael. Encountering Jesus in the New Testament. 2009. (Illus.). 332p. (YA). pap., stu. ed. 24.95 (978-1-59471-165-7(8)) Ave Maria Pr.
Plummer, Robert L. 40 Questions about Interpreting the Bible, 1 vol. 2010. (40 Questions & Answers Ser.). (ENG.). 352p. pap. 17.99 (978-0-8254-3498-3(X)) Kregel Pubns.
Porterfield, Alicia Davis & Porterfield, Eric. Proverbs — Living Wisely, Loving Well: Annual Bible Study: Study Guide. 2009. pap. (978-1-57312-546-8(6)) Smyth & Helwys Publishing, Inc.
Pregeant, Russel. Encounter with the New Testament: An Interdisciplinary Approach. 2009. 400p. (C). pap. 30.00 (978-0-8006-6348-3(9), Fortress Pr.) Augsburg Fortress, Pubs.
Ramirez, Frank. The Household of God. 2009. pap. 7.95 (978-0-87178-126-0(3), FaithQuest) Brethren Pr.
Richardson, John, Jr. Get into the Bible: From First Creation to New Creation - The Unfolding Plan of God in Scripture. 2010. 48p. pap. (978-1-873166-08-6(7)) Good Bk. Co.
Rigsby, Sandy & Mason, Steve. Exploring the Sunday Lectionary: A Teenager's Guide to the Readings - Cycle A. 2007. 208p. pap. 19.95 (978-0-8091-9583-1(6), 9583-1) Paulist Pr.
Royer, Darline Kantola & Burk, Dorsey. An Introduction to the Bible. 2011. **(978-0-7577-4215-6(7))** Word Aflame Pr.
Setzer, Robert B. Sessions with John: The Vocabulary of Grace. 2010. pap. (978-1-57312-560-4(1)) Smyth & Helwys Publishing, Inc.
Stanley, Christopher. The Hebrew Bible: A Comparative Approach. 2009. 560p. (C). pap. 42.00 (978-0-8006-6347-6(0), Fortress Pr.) Augsburg Fortress, Pubs.
Stott, John. Acts: Seeing the Spirit at Work. 2008. (John Stott Bible Studies). (ENG.). 111p. pap. 8.00 (978-0-8308-2161-7(9), IVP Conn.) InterVarsity Pr.
—Christian Leadership, 1 vol. 2009. (LifeGuide Bible Studies). (ENG.). 64p. pap. 8.00 (978-0-8308-3126-5(6), IVP Conn.) InterVarsity Pr.
—Galatians: Experiencing the Grace of Christ. 2008. (John Stott Bible Studies). (ENG.). 64p. pap. 8.00 (978-0-8308-2164-8(3), IVP Conn.) InterVarsity Pr.
—Revelation: The Triumph of Christ. 2008. (John Stott Bible Studies). (ENG.). 64p. pap. 8.00 (978-0-8308-2023-8(X), IVP Conn.) InterVarsity Pr.
—Romans: Encountering the Gospel's Power. 2008. (John Stott Bible Studies). (ENG.). 112p. pap. 8.00 (978-0-8308-2165-5(1), IVP Conn.) InterVarsity Pr.
—1 & 2 Thessalonians: Living in the End Times. 2008. (John Stott Bible Studies). (ENG.). 63p. pap. 8.00 (978-0-8308-2166-2(X), IVP Conn.) InterVarsity Pr.
Taege, Marlys. The Heart of Jesus: Women in the Gospel of Luke. 2009. 224p. pap. 12.99 (978-0-7586-1659-3(7)) Concordia Publishing Hse.
University Bible Fellowship, compiled by. Back to the Gospel: Spiritual Help for a Troubled Church. 2009. pap. 15.99 (978-0-9819826-5-6(4)) UBF Pr.
Upper Room (Publisher: Nashville, contrib. by. Entering the Psalms: Participant's Workbook. 2009. 10.00 (978-0-8358-9973-4(X)) Upper Room Bks.
Wellman, Pat & McCullough, Jeannie. Hebrews Pt. 1: Covenant of Faith. 2006. (Wisdom of the Word Bible Study Ser.). (ENG.). 96p. spiral bd. 14.99 (978-0-8341-2265-9(0), 083-412-2650) Beacon Hill Pr. of Kansas City.
—Hebrews Pt. 2: Covenant of Faith. 2006. (Wisdom of the Word Bible Study Ser.). (ENG.). 96p. spiral bd. 14.99 (978-0-8341-2275-8(8), 083-412-2758) Beacon Hill Pr. of Kansas City.
Whitfield, Raymond. Job. 2010. (Insights: Bible Studies for Growing Faith Ser.). 56p. pap. 8.00 (978-1-60899-219-5(5), Wipf and Stock) Wipf & Stock Pubs.
Wiersbe, Warren W. Acts - Put Your Faith Where the Action Is. 2010. (Wiersbe Bible Study Ser.). (ENG.). 144p. pap. 8.99 (978-0-7814-0422-8(3)) Cook, David C.
—Be Comforted (Isaiah) Feeling Secure in the Arms of God, 1 vol. 2009. (BE Ser. Commentary Ser.). (ENG.). 192p. pap. 12.99 (978-1-4347-6615-1(2)) Cook, David C.
—John: Get to Know the Living Savior. 2010. 186p. (978-0-7814-0490-7(8)) Kingsway Pubns.
—Psalms: Glorifying God for Who He Is. 2010. 176p. (978-0-7814-0491-4(6)) Kingsway Pubns.
Younger, Carol Davis. The Gospel of Matthew: Hope in the Resurrected Christ: Adult Bible Study Guide. 2008. 137p. pap. (978-1-934731-20-8(X)) Baptistway.

BIBLE—TEXTUAL CRITICISM

see Bible—Criticism, Textual

BIBLE—THEOLOGY

Here are entered works on the theology of the Bible, considered apart from the later theology of the church.

see also Worship in the Bible

also subdivision Biblical Teaching under subjects, e.g. Atonement—Biblical Teaching; Family—Biblical Teaching

Abingdon Press, ed. Whats in the Bible & Where D. 2009. (Why Is That in the Bible & Why Should I Care? Ser.). 112p. pap. 10.00 (978-0-687-65324-9(X)) Abingdon Pr.
Ackley, Esther Lee. Believest thou Me?, 1 vol. 2010. 582p. pap. 34.95 (978-1-4512-9116-2(7)) PublishAmerica, Inc.
Ackroyd, Peter R. Chronicler in His Age. 2009. (Library of Hebrew Bible/Old Testament Studies, the Ser.). (ENG.). 65.00 (978-0-567-00132-0(6), T&T Clark) Continuum International Publishing Group, Ltd. GBR. Dist: National Bk. Network.
Acts 1. ldr.'s ed. (LifeLight Bible Studies: Course 13). 6.50 (978-0-570-09284-1(1), 20-2306) Concordia Publishing Hse.
Acts 2. ldr.'s ed. (LifeLight Bible Studies: Course 14). 6.50 (978-0-570-09286-5(8), 20-2311) Concordia Publishing Hse.
Adams, Shari Dawson. The Bible & Sinbearing: New Questions about Old Answers. 2009. pap. 20.00 (978-1-61623-816-2(X)) Independent Pub.
Adrian, Werner. New Discoveries in the Divine Inspiration of the Bible: The Impossibility of Refuting Its Authorship & the Four Gospels. 2008. (ENG.). 272p. 21.99 (978-1-59979-460-0(8), Creation Hse.) Charisma Media.
Adult Bible Study. (KOR.). 2.31 (978-0-7673-4193-6(7)) LifeWay Christian Resources.
Aertsen, Jan A. & Pickavé, Martin, eds. Ende und Vollendung: Eschatologische Perspektiven im Mittelalter. (Miscellanea Mediaevalia Ser.). (GER., Illus.). XIII, 763p. 538.00 **(978-3-11-180901-4(3))** De Gruyter, Walter Inc.
Afanasiev, Nicholas. The Church of the Holy Spirit. Plekon, Michael, ed. Permiakov, Vitaly, tr. from RUS. 2007. (ENG., Illus.). 416p. 45.00 (978-0-268-02030-9(2)) Univ. of Notre Dame Pr.
Aiken, Brett. Dreaming Your Reality: Seeing God's Vision Come to Life. 2010. 88p. pap. 12.99 (978-1-4520-2350-2(6)) AuthorHouse.
Alexander-Reindorf, Deaconess Floria. I Exist in All Planes at the Same Time: Anthology Three. 2011. 408p. pap. 36.95 **(978-1-4502-1342-4(1))** iUniverse, Inc.
Alexander, T. Desmond & Gathercole, Simon, eds. Heaven on Earth. 2006. (ENG.). 224p. per. 19.99 (978-1-84227-272-5(1), Paternoster) Authentic Media.
Alexander, T. Desmond & Rosner, Brian S., eds. New Dictionary of Biblical Theology. (978-0-85111-976-2(X)) Bow Historical Bks.
Allen, Diogenes & Springsted, Eric O. Philosophy for Understanding Theology. 2nd ed. 2007. (ENG.). 267p. per. 30.00 (978-0-664-23180-4(2)) Westminster John Knox Pr.
Allen, Lee W. God's Plan for His Creation & Eternity: Biblical Theology. 2010. 177p. (ENG.). 29.95 (978-1-4327-5076-3(3)); pap. 15.95 (978-1-4327-4623-0(5)) Outskirts Pr., Inc.
Amoabeng, Benedict Kofi. Christianity & Alcohol (Wine) Is It A Sin to Drink Alcohol (Wine) As A Christian? 2010. 28p. pap. 13.99 (978-1-4490-8621-3(7)) AuthorHouse.
Andry, Duane. From the Beginning: The Methodology of God. 2011. 452p. 39.59 **(978-1-4634-0172-6(8))**; pap. 30.35 **(978-1-4634-0171-9(X))** AuthorHouse.
Ann, Spangler. Mujeres de la Biblia/Women of the Bible, 1 vol. 2008. (SPA.). 432p. 14.99 (978-0-8297-5126-0(2)) Vida Pubs.
Aquinas, Thomas. Umma Theologica of St. Thomas Aquinas, Vol. 5. pap. (978-0-87061-068-4(6), Christian Classic) Ave Maria Pr.
Arendell, Randy. Modern Church: Where Tradition Trumps Truth. 2008. 220p. (ENG.). 24.99 (978-1-60477-669-0(2)); per. 14.99 (978-1-60477-668-3(4)) Xulon Pr., Inc.
Asomugha, Lilian I. Are You Living in Someone Else's Mind? 2010. 92p. pap. 10.49 (978-1-4490-8865-1(1)) AuthorHouse.
Attridge, Harold W. & Society of Biblical Literature Staff. The HarperCollins Study Bible. Meeks, Wayne A. & Bassler, Jouette M., eds. rev. ed. 2006. (ENG.). 2272p. per. 39.99 (978-0-06-122840-7(0), HarperOne) HarperCollins Pubs.
Aubrey, Roger. The Circle of Life. 2007. 128p. per. 13.99 (978-1-60266-185-1(5)) Xulon Pr., Inc.
Bachota, Joseph T. Word of Faith Preachers: How Misinterpretation of Scripture Might Lead You Astray. 2010. 260p. pap. 19.95 (978-1-4502-3145-9(4)) iUniverse, Inc.
Bacote, Vincent. Precepts for Living Personal Study Guide 2009-2010. 2009th ed. 2009. (Precepts for Living Ser.). 140p. pap. 7.95 (978-1-60352-684-5(6)) UMI (Urban Ministries, Inc.).
Baker, James R. Prophecy Unsealed. 2011. 254p. pap. 16.99 **(978-1-61215-834-1(X))** Xulon Pr., Inc.
Baker, Jonathan & Davage, William, eds. Who Is This Man? Christ in the Renewal of the Church. 2006. (ENG.). 224p. 34.95 (978-0-8264-8157-3(4)) Continuum International Publishing Group, Ltd. GBR. Dist: National Bk. Network.
Barr, James & Barton, John. Bible & Interpretation: The Collected Essays of James Barr, 3 vols. 2012. (ENG.). 696p. 230.00 **(978-0-19-969290-3(4))**; 792p. 230.00 **(978-0-19-969289-7(0))** Oxford Univ. Pr., Inc.
Barr, James, et al. Bible & Interpretation: The Collected Essays of James Barr, 3 vols. 2012. (ENG.). 736p. 230.00 **(978-0-19-969288-0(2))** Oxford Univ. Pr., Inc.
Barrett, Mary. Back to the Beginning: Remembering Your First Love. 2009. 132p. pap. 13.95 (978-1-4401-3369-5(7)) iUniverse, Inc.
Barrett, Michael. The Beauty of Holiness: A Guide to Biblical Worship. 2006. 285p. per. 14.99 (978-1-932307-62-7(1)) Emerald Hse. Group, Inc.
Barth, Markus. Justification. Woodruff, A M, III, tr. 2006. 90p. pap. 13.00 (978-1-59752-850-4(1), Wipf and Stock) Wipf & Stock Pubs.
Barthelemy, Jean-Dominique. God & His Image: An Outline of Biblical Theology. Dean, Dom Aldhelm, tr. from FRE. 2007. 296p. per. 16.95 (978-1-58617-082-0(1)) Ignatius Pr.
Basics for Believers: An Introduction to Reformed Teachings. 4.25 (978-1-56212-669-8(5), 150910) Faith Alive Christian Resources.
Bauckham, Richard & Mosser, Carl. The Gospel of John & Christian Theology. Bauckham, Richard & Mosser, Carl, eds. 2008. 404p. per. 32.00 (978-0-8028-2717-3(9)) Eerdmans, William B. Publishing Co.
Benson, Clarence H. & Morgan, Robert J. Exploring Theology: A Guide for Systematic Theology & Apologetics. 2007. 336p. pap. 19.99 (978-1-58134-962-7(9)) Crossway.
Berner, Michael. The Anti-Theology of Jesus. 2007. 164p. per. 13.99 (978-1-60266-457-9(9)) Xulon Pr., Inc.
Billings, J. Todd. The Word of God for the People of God: An Entryway to the Theological Interpretation of Scripture. 2010. (Illus.). 256p. pap. 18.00 (978-0-8028-6235-8(7)) Eerdmans, William B. Publishing Co.
Bird, Michael F. Saving Righteousness of God: Studies on Paul, Justification & the New Perspective. 2008. (Paternoster Biblical Monographs Ser.). (ENG.). 250p. pap. 39.99 (978-1-84227-465-1(1), Paternoster) Authentic Media.
—The Saving Righteousness of God: Studies on Paul, Justification & the New Perspective. 2007. (Paternoster Biblical Monographs). 266p. pap. 30.00 (978-1-55635-274-4(3), Wipf and Stock) Wipf & Stock Pubs.
Bisagno, John. And Then Shall the End Come. 2007. 188p. per. 13.99 (978-1-60266-856-0(6)) Xulon Pr., Inc.
Black, Vicki K. & Wenner, Peter W. Welcome to the Bible. 2007. 128p. per. 14.00 (978-0-8192-2236-7(4)) Church Publishing, Inc.
The Blessing Place Child Care Kit. (Midweek Curriculum Ser.). 36.75 (978-0-570-00317-5(2)) Concordia Publishing Hse.
Bock, Emil. Kings & Prophets: Saul, David, Solomon, Elijah, Jonah, Isaiah, & Jeremiah. 2nd rev. ed. 2007. 368p. pap. (978-0-86315-573-4(1)) Floris Bks.
books to uplift youth. Questions about the Bible People Are Afraid to Ask - Revised: An Afrikan Spiritual Interpretation. 2007. pap. 11.95 (978-0-9740031-3-9(1)) Bks. To Uplift Youth.
Bordwine, James E. The Pauline Doctrine of Male Headship: The Apostle Versus Biblical Feminists. 2009. 334p. pap. 37.00 (978-1-60608-568-4(9), Wipf and Stock) Wipf & Stock Pubs.
Bowman, Wayne B. Hidden in Plain Sight: Catechism versus the Bible. 2009. (J). pap. 15.99 (978-1-60799-779-5(7)) Tate Publishing & Enterprises, LLC.
Brannan, William J. Spiritual DNA. 2008. 272p. pap. 16.99 (978-1-60791-191-3(4)) Xulon Pr., Inc.
Breytenbach, Cilliers & Frey, Jorg, eds. Aufgabe und Durchführung einer Theologie des Neuen Testaments. 2007. (Wissenschaftliche Untersuchungen Zum Neuen Testament Ser.: 205). 376p. (C). 179.50 (978-3-16-149252-5(8)) Mohr Siebeck GmbH & Co. KG DEU. Dist: Coronet Bks.
Bright, William Marshall. Matthew for the Sunday School Teacher. 2011. 166p. pap. 24.95 **(978-1-4626-2264-1(X))** PublishAmerica, Inc.
Brink, Robert. A Few Thoughts about the Course. 2009. 232p. pap. 17.95 (978-1-59858-885-9(0)) Dog Ear Publishing, LLC.
Brisendine, Mark. Gleanings from Scripture for the Edification of the Church. 2007. 256p. per. 15.99 (978-1-60266-239-1(8)) Xulon Pr., Inc.
Broadwater, Donald A. God's Fire Starters. 2008. 244p. 25.99 (978-1-60647-870-7(2)); pap. 15.99 (978-1-60647-869-1(9)) Xulon Pr., Inc.
Brother, B. Ephesian Benchmarks: Sit-Walk-Stand: Christian Growth to Maturity. 2010. 96p. pap. 13.49 (978-1-4520-3541-3(5)) AuthorHouse.
Brown, Marc D., et al. Does Your Church Have a Prayer? In Mission Toward the Promised Land. 2009. 75p. pap. 9.00 (978-0-88177-567-9(3)) Discipleship Resources.
Brueggemann, Walter. Old Testament Theology: An Introduction. 2008. 433p. (C). pap. 34.00 (978-0-687-34090-3(X)) Abingdon Pr.
Brunt, John. Redemption in Romans. 2010. pap. 7.97 (978-0-8163-2387-5(9)) Pacific Pr. Publishing Assn.
Buckley, John W. Satan. 2007. 284p. 20.95 (978-1-4327-0992-1(5)); (ENG.). per. 10.95 (978-1-4327-1515-1(1)) Outskirts Pr., Inc.
Burke, Trevor J. Adopted into God's Family: Exploring a Pauline Metaphor. 2006. (New Studies in Biblical Theology Ser.: Volume 22). (ENG.). 237p. per. 23.00 (978-0-8308-2623-0(8), IVP Acad.) InterVarsity Pr.
Butler, R. Will. God Speaks: What the Bible Teaches about Itself. Bogue, Carl, ed. 2nd rev. ed. Date not set. pap. 6.95 (978-0-9658804-4-2(3)) Deo Volente Publishing.
Calhoun, Shayla L. I Read It, Like I Eat It!, 1 vol. 2010. 62p. pap. 19.95 (978-1-4489-3322-8(6)) PublishAmerica, Inc.
Capes, David B., et al. Rediscovering Paul: An Introduction to His World, Letters & Theology. 2011. (ENG.). 350p. pap. 25.00 **(978-0-8308-3941-4(0)**, IVP Acad.) InterVarsity Pr.
Carelock, Joyce L. Youth Halted Between: Bad Choices & God's Purpose. 2011. 190p. pap. 14.99 **(978-1-61379-377-0(4))** Xulon Pr., Inc.
Carner, James Alan. Isaiah Cry. 2010. 208p. 27.99 (978-1-4520-9041-2(6)); pap. 18.49 (978-1-4520-7669-0(3)) AuthorHouse.
Carter, Harold A., Jr. The Power of God's Negatives: A Contemporary Look at What God Does Not Want Us to Do. 2009. (ENG.). 161p. pap. 14.99 (978-0-9819672-8-8(0)) St. Paul Pr.
Carter, Paul. The Narrow Way. 2012. 216p. pap. **(978-1-77069-530-6(3))** Word Alive Pr.
Case, Justin. Satan Comes First - King of Babylon, Vol. 1. 2011. 222p. pap. 15.99 **(978-1-61215-826-6(9))** Xulon Pr., Inc.
Charles, Daniel. The Kingdom Years of the Chosen People. 2009. 324p. 26.50 (978-1-60693-291-9(8), Eloquent Bks.) AEG Literary Publishing Services, Inc.
Cho, Youngmo. Spirit & Kingdom in the Writings of Luke & Paul: An Attempt to Reconcile These Concepts. 2007. (Paternoster Biblical Monographs Ser.). 254p. pap. 27.00 (978-1-59752-798-9(X), Wipf and Stock) Wipf & Stock Pubs.
Chrishon, Brent Oliver. And There Is the Hiding of His Power. 2007. 154p. per. 12.95 (978-1-57258-459-4(9), 945-6320) TEACH Services, Inc.
Christian Art Gifts, des. 199 Favorite Bible Verses for Busy Moms. 2010. (Illus.). 126p. pap. (978-1-77036-439-4(0)) Christian Art Pubs.
—199 Favorite Bible Verses for Graduates. 2010. (Illus.). 123p. pap. (978-1-77036-438-7(2)) Christian Art Pubs.
Christian Vision Literature Staff. What the Bible Says about Satan. 2008. 196p. pap. 18.95 (978-1-4357-0678-1(1)) Lulu Enterprises Inc.
Chubb, Paul. Chronicles in Parallel. 2009. 304p. pap. 35.95 (978-1-4092-0423-7(5)) Lulu Enterprises Inc.
Clark, Madison. Establishing A Healthy Church: Things We Need to Know & Do in the Body of Christ. 2010. 132p. 21.49 (978-1-4520-1016-8(1)); pap. 11.99 (978-1-4520-1015-1(3)) AuthorHouse.
Clark, Terry Mathis. The Strength of a King: A Metaphorical Look at the Attributes & Amenities of a King & His Kingdom. 2008. 88p. pap. 11.95 (978-1-59858-616-9(5)) Dog Ear Publishing, LLC.
The Comparative Coincidence of Reason & Scripture. 2009. 184p. pap. (978-0-217-38089-8(1)) Books LLC.
Cook, Arthurine. In the Beginning. 2011. 50p. pap. 15.99 **(978-1-4568-5476-8(3))** Xlibris Corp.
Coote, Robert & Gottwald, Norman, eds. To Break Every Yoke: Essays in Honor of Marvin L. Chaney. 2007. (Illus.). 396p. (978-1-906055-27-1(0)) Sheffield Phoenix Pr.
Copeland, Gloria. Blessed Beyond Measure: Experience the Extraordinary Goodness of God. 2008. (ENG.). 208p. pap. 11.99 (978-0-446-51127-8(7)) FaithWords.
Corpas de Posada, Isabel. Teologia De Los Sacramentos. 192p. 6.95 (978-958-607-706-4(3)) Sociedad de San Pablo COL. Dist: St Pauls/Alba Hse. Pubs.
Coulange, Pierre. Dieu, Ami des Pauvres: Erude Sur la Connivence Entre le Tres-Haut et les Petits. 2007. (Orbis Biblicus et Orientalis Ser.: 223). 304p. 75.00 (978-3-7278-1574-4(4)) Editions Univ. Fribourg Suisse CHE. Dist: Eisenbrauns, Inc.
Craghan, John F. Precious Gifts: Biblical Reflections on the Eucharist. 2011. **(978-0-7648-2026-7(5))** Liguori Pubns.
Cramer, Paul. A Mormon on the Road to Emmaus. 2008. 260p. per. 15.99 (978-1-60477-686-7(2)) Xulon Pr., Inc.
Crawford-Frost, William A. The Philosophy of Integration: An Explanation of the Universe & of the Christian Religion. Bright, James Wilson, ed. 2007. 192p. 37.95 (978-0-548-01854-5(5)) Kessinger Publishing, LLC.
Culto Cristiano Himnario. (SPA.). 832p. 12.50 (978-0-570-09953-6(6), 15-3012) Concordia Publishing Hse.
Daniel Lee Staneart. Drawing a Line in the Sand. 2009. 256p. 24.99 (978-1-4389-6046-3(8)); pap. 14.49 (978-1-4389-6045-6(X)) AuthorHouse.
Daniels, J. B. The Wonder of God's Love. 2011. 106p. 24.99 **(978-1-4568-7710-1(0))** Xlibris Corp.
Darr, D. C. The Religion of Man vs. the Word of God: How Man Makes God Conform to Man's Image. 2010. pap. 10.99 (978-1-61663-222-9(4)) Tate Publishing & Enterprises, LLC.
Davenport, Gene L. Though the Mountains Tremble: Biblical Reflections on Contemporary Society. 2009. 218p. pap. 24.00 (978-1-55635-562-2(9), Wipf and Stock) Wipf & Stock Pubs.

B

Davidson, Jo Ann. Toward a Theology of Beauty: A Biblical Perspective. 2008. (ENG.). 224p. 68.50 *(978-0-7618-3946-0(1))*; pap. 38.99 *(978-0-7618-3947-7(X))* Univ. Pr. of America, Inc.

Davis, Justin A. Christchaphrenia: The Misconceptions of the Bible Destroying Christians Lives. 2010. 92p. pap. 13.99 *(978-1-4520-7692-8(8))* AuthorHouse.

Davis, Roberta. My Friend, the Story of Jesus, 1 vol. 2010. 64p. pap. 19.95 *(978-1-4489-5010-2(4))* PublishAmerica, Inc.

De Waal Dryden, J. Theology & Ethics in 1 Peter: Paraenetic Strategies for Christian Character Formation. 2006. (Wissenschaftliche Untersuchungen Zum Neuen Testament 2 Ser.: Vol. 209). 237p. (C). pap. 89.50 *(978-3-16-148910-5(1))* Mohr Siebeck GmbH & Co. KG DEU. Dist: Coronet Bks.

Deane-Drummond, Celia & Scott, Peter, eds. Future Perfect? God, Medicine & Human Identity. 2006. (ENG., Illus.). 232p. 120.00 *(978-0-567-03079-5(2)*, T&T Clark Int'l) Continuum International Publishing Group, Ltd. GBR. Dist: National Bk. Network.

Dearborn, Kerry. Baptised Imagination: The Theology of George MacDonald. 2006. (Ashgate Studies in Theology, Imagination & the Arts Ser.). (Illus.). 210p. 99.95 *(978-0-7546-5516-9(4))* Ashgate Publishing Co.

Dennison, John A. Jesus' Death & the Gathering of True Israel: The Johannine Appropriation of Restoration Theology in the Light of John 11.47-52. 2006. (Wissenschaftliche Untersuchungen Zum Neuen Testament 2 Ser.: No. 217). 429p. pap. 125.00 *(978-3-16-148821-4(0))* Mohr Siebeck GmbH & Co. KG DEU. Dist: Coronet Bks.

Desafios en la Escuela. (Bible Studies for Teens Vivencias de la Vida Real (Real Deal) Ser.).Tr. of School Challenges. (SPA.). 88p. 14.99 *(978-0-7586-0608-2(7))* Concordia Publishing Hse.

Dever, Mark. What Does God Want of Us Anyway? A Quick Overview of the Whole Bible. 2010. pap. *(978-1-4335-1416-6(8))*; 128p. 12.99 *(978-1-4335-1415-9(X))* Crossway.

Diaz, Gwendolyn Mitchell. Sticking up for What Is Right: Answers to the Moral Dilemmas Teenagers Face. 2008. 140p. pap. 14.99 *(978-1-60791-103-6(5))* Xulon Pr., Inc.

Dill, D. V. M. In the Beginnings. 2010. 394p. 32.99 *(978-1-60957-323-2(4))* Xulon Pr., Inc.

Dill, Steven E. In the Beginnings. 2010. 394p. pap. 20.99 *(978-1-60957-163-4(0))* Xulon Pr., Inc.

Dinsmore, Jim. It Seems to Me: An Attempt to Talk Sense about the Bible. 2011. 124p. pap. 11.95 ***(978-1-4497-1720-9(9)***, WestBow Pr.) Author Solutions, Inc.

Dohrmann, Natalie B. & Stern, David, eds. Jewish Biblical Interpretation & Cultural Exchange: Comparative Exegesis in Context. 2008. (Jewish Culture & Contexts Ser.). (Illus.). 352p. (C). 69.95 *(978-0-8122-4074-0(X))* Univ. of Pennsylvania Pr.

Dolen, Walter R. New Mind Papers. 2009. (ENG.). 382p. pap. 29.95 *(978-1-877981-38-8(9))* Becoming-One Pubns.

—Prophecy Papers. 2009. (ENG.). 186p. pap. 22.95 *(978-1-877981-36-4(2))* Becoming-One Pubns.

Donaldson, James. The Apostolical Fathers a Critical Account of Their Genuine Writings & of Their Doctrines. 2007. (ENG.). 418p. 49.95 *(978-0-548-03579-5(2))* Kessinger Publishing, LLC.

Doyle, Adelaide. Thoughts on a Sunday Afternoon. 2008. *(978-1-55452-214-9(5))* Essence Publishing.

Driscoll, Mark & Breshears, Gerry. Doctrine: What Christians Should Believe. 2010. pap. *(978-1-4335-0626-0(2))* Crossway.

—Doctrine: What Christians Should Believe. 2011. (Re:Lit:Vintage Jesus Ser.). 464p. pap. 17.99 *(978-1-4335-2757-9(X))* Crossway.

Duncan, Fred J. Super Jesus: Unraveling the Tough Questions about Jesus. 2010. pap. 10.99 *(978-1-61566-813-7(6))* Tate Publishing & Enterprises, LLC.

EBS Chinese Bible Studies Master. 2.31 *(978-0-7673-4165-3(1))* LifeWay Christian Resources.

Edwards, Lynette. Just a Little Talk with Jesus: You Can't be Spirit Led until you are Spirit Fed. 2011. 380p. pap. 21.14 ***(978-1-4269-7544-8(9))*** Trafford Publishing.

Ehiemua, Valentine. The Takeover. 2007. 160p. per. 13.99 *(978-1-60266-864-5(7))* Xulon Pr., Inc.

Ellers, Flo. Activating the Angelic: Keys to Releasing the Holy Spirit. 2008. pap. 15.99 *(978-0-7684-2706-6(1))* Destiny Image Pubs.

Elliott, Mark W. The Reality of Biblical Theology. 2007. 386p. pap. 87.95 *(978-3-03911-356-9(9))* Lang, Peter Publishing, Inc.

Ellis, Larry W. Sermon Notes: Volume 1. 2009. (ENG.). 186p. pap. 12.99 *(978-0-9819672-4-0(8))* St. Paul Pr.

Elstub, Colin. Contradiction & Controversy in the Bible. 2008. 163p. pap. 13.95 *(978-1-4092-3661-0(7))* Lulu Enterprises Inc.

Estrada, Hugo. El Espiritu Santo en la Biblia y en Nuestra Vida.Tr. of Holy Spirit in the Bible & in Our Lives. (SPA.). 128p. pap. 3.95 *(978-958-607-432-2(3))* Sociedad de San Pablo COL. Dist: St Pauls/Alba Hse. Pubs.

Estudios Biblicos Lifeway Para Adultos Manual Para el Particpante. 1.40 *(978-0-7673-4859-1(1))* LifeWay Christian Resources.

Étougé A., Patrick. The Transgression & the Abomination of Desolation. 2010. 112p. pap. *(978-3-639-28397-6(X))* VDM Verlag Dr. Mueller e.K.

Evans, Rev., William. Great Doctrines of the Bible. 2008. 256p. 28.99 *(978-0-554-21939-4(5))* 2008. 256p. 25.99 *(978-0-554-31242-2(5))* 2006. 262p. pap. 21.99 *(978-1-4264-1291-2(6))* BiblioBazaar.

—The Great Doctrines of the Bible. 2007. 244p. per. *(978-1-4065-3378-1(5))* Dodo Pr.

Evans, Charles G. B. Is Jesus God? An Examination & Refutation of Popular Cultic Views. 2010. 203p. pap. 13.95 *(978-1-4327-6290-2(7))* Outskirts Pr., Inc.

Evans, Roderick L. The Word was Made Flesh: The Principles of Christ versus the Personality of Christ. 2011. 64p. pap. 10.95 *(978-1-60141-093-1(X)*, 146053) Kingdom Builders Publishing.

Evans, Roderick L., comment. The Epistle of Titus: The Evans Practical Bible Commentary. 2009. (ENG.). 40p. pap. 11.95 *(978-1-60141-094-8(8)*, 319445) Kingdom Builders Publishing.

FaithWeaver: Bible Study Book FA02 Youth. *(978-0-7644-1435-0(6))* Group Publishing, Inc.

Farmer. The Pastor's Bible Study, 5 vols., Vol. 4. 2007. (New Interpreter's Bible Study Ser.). 35.00 *(978-0-687-49340-1(4))* Abingdon Pr.

Fee, Gordon D. Pablo, el Espiritu y el Pueblo de Dios, 1 vol. 2007. (Biblioteca Teologica Vida Ser.). (SPA.). 224p. (gr. 13). 14.99 *(978-0-8297-5387-5(7))* Vida Pubs.

Feldhahn, Shaunti & Feldhahn, Jeff. For Men Only: A Straightforward Guide to the Inner Lives of Women. 2007. (Walker Large Print Ser.). (ENG., Illus.). 246p. per. 17.95 *(978-1-59415-200-9(4)*, Walker Large Print) Cengage Gale.

Feldmeier, Reinhard & Spieckermann, Hermann. God of the Living: A Biblical Theology. 2011. (ENG.). 500p. 59.95 *(978-1-60258-394-8(3))* Baylor Univ. Pr.

Fergusson. Cosmos & the Creator. 128p. 15.00 *(978-0-281-05068-0(6))* SPCK Publishing GBR. Dist: Pilgrim Pr., The/United Church Pr.

Finley, Robert. The Time Is at Hand. 2008. 308p. pap. 18.99 *(978-1-60791-026-8(8))* Xulon Pr., Inc.

Finney, Jerald. Seperation of Church & State: God's Churches - Spiritual or Legal Entities? 2009. 108p. pap. 11.99 *(978-1-60791-341-2(0))* Xulon Pr., Inc.

Fisher, Douglas R. Surveying Truths in the Word of God: A New Inspirational Way to Study Your Bible. 2010. pap. 14.99 *(978-1-61566-583-9(8))* Tate Publishing & Enterprises, LLC.

Fitzmyer, Joseph A. The Interpretation of Scripture: In Defense of the Historical-Critical Method. 2008. 176p. pap. 18.95 *(978-0-8091-4504-1(9)*, 4504-1) Paulist Pr.

Flores, Said R. The Son of Man: Yeshua ha Messiah. 2008. 124p. pap. 11.99 *(978-1-60647-596-6(7))* Xulon Pr., Inc.

Ford, John & Ford, Katherine. When Evil Reigns: The Timeline of the Antichrist's Imminent Rise to Power. 2011. pap. 19.99 *(978-1-61663-661-6(0))* Tate Publishing & Enterprises, LLC.

Fowl, Stephen E. Engaging Scripture: A Model for Theological Interpretation. 2008. 228p. pap. 25.00 *(978-1-60608-112-9(8))* Wipf & Stock Pubs.

—Theological Interpretation of Scripture. 2009. (Cascade Companions Ser.). 108p. pap. 13.00 *(978-1-55635-241-6(7)*, Cascade Bks.) Wipf & Stock Pubs.

—Theological Interpretation of Scripture: Classic & Contemporary Readings. 2010. (ENG.). *(978-0-227-17268-1(X))* Clarke, James Co., Ltd.

Fowler, Stanley K. More Than a Symbol: The British Baptist Recovery of Baptismal Sacramentalism. 2007. (Studies in Baptist History & Thought Ser.). 309p. pap. 31.00 *(978-1-59752-733-0(5)*, Wipf and Stock) Wipf & Stock Pubs.

French, Donald W. The Holy Spirit of God. 2009. 380p. pap. 22.00 *(978-1-4389-7918-2(5))* AuthorHouse.

Fridrichsen, Anton. The Root of the Vine: Essays in Biblical Theology. 2011. 168p. 41.95 ***(978-1-258-07706-8(X))*** Literary Licensing, LLC.

Friesen, John & Friesen, Virginia. What's Your Church Like? 2007. 264p. per. 15.99 *(978-1-60266-607-8(5))* Xulon Pr., Inc.

Friesen, Patty. For the Beauty of the Earth: Women, Faith & Creation Care. 2009. (Illus.). 71p. pap. 8.99 *(978-0-8361-9496-8(9))* Herald Pr.

Fusion: Food. (Fusion Bible Study Ser.). 80p. 15.99 *(978-0-7586-0600-6(1))* Concordia Publishing Hse.

Fusion: Trees. (Fusion Bible Study Ser.). 80p. 15.99 *(978-0-7586-0601-3(X))* Concordia Publishing Hse.

Gaist, Byron J. Creative Suffering & the Wounded Healer: Analytical Psychology & Orthodox Christian Theology. 2010. 456p. pap. 29.95 *(978-1-933275-40-6(5)*, Orthodox Research Institute) Cocheco Falls Publishing.

Gamble, Richard C. The Whole Counsel of God. 2009. *(978-1-59638-182-7(5))*; *(978-1-59638-181-0(7))* P & R Publishing.

Garcia, Oscar. Aclarando Conceptos Teológicos y Doctrinales. 2010. 310p. pap. 18.95 *(978-1-4327-5161-6(1))* Outskirts Pr., Inc.

Gelfer, Joseph, ed. The Best of Journal of Men, Masculinities & Spirituality. 2010. 116.00 *(978-1-61143-003-5(8))* Gorgias Pr., LLC.

God's Power for Fathers. Date not set. pap. 3.95 *(978-0-937347-76-8(0))* C&D International.

Gore, Bruce W. Historical & Chronological Context of the Bible. 2010. 640p. pap. 34.95 *(978-1-4269-4359-1(8))* Trafford Publishing.

Gorman, Michael J. Reading Paul. 2008. (Cascade Companions: Ser.). 206p. pap. 22.00 *(978-1-55635-195-2(X))* Wipf & Stock Pubs.

Graf, Daniel. Unterwegs zu einer Biblischen Theologie: Perspektiven der Konzeption von Peter Stuhlmacher. 2011. (GER.). 374p. (C). 74.00 *(978-3-89971-815-7(1))* Vandenhoeck & Ruprecht GmbH & Co. KG DEU. Dist: ISD.

Green, Joel B. Seized by Truth: Readng the Bible as Scripture. 2007. 185p. per. 25.00 *(978-0-687-02355-4(6))* Abingdon Pr.

Grudem, Wayne A. Doctrina Cristiana: Veinte Puntos Bsicos Que Todo Cristiano Debe Conocer, 1 vol. Grudem, Elliot, ed. 2006. (SPA.). 144p. (gr. 11). per. 7.99 *(978-0-8297-4558-0(0))* Vida Pubs.

—Teologia Sistematica: Una Introduccion a la Doctrina Biblica, 1 vol. 2007. (SPA.). 1296p. 29.99 *(978-0-8297-4627-3(7))* Zondervan.

Grudem, Wayne A. & Thoennes, Erik. Systematic Theology, 1 vol. 2008. (Zondervan Get an A! Study Guides). (ENG.). 6p. pap. 6.99 *(978-0-310-27319-6(6))* Zondervan.

Guarino, Thomas G. & Guarino. Vattimo & Theology. 2009. (Philosophy & Theology Ser.). (ENG.). 200p. 32.95 *(978-0-567-03233-1(7))*; 110.00 *(978-0-567-03232-4(9))* Continuum International Publishing Group, Ltd. GBR. (T&T Clark Int'l). Dist: National Bk. Network.

Hagee, John. Knowing the Secrets of God, 0 vols. 2008. 324p. pap. 17.99 *(978-0-8499-2886-4(9))* Nelson, Thomas Inc.

Hahn, Scott W. Kinship by Covenant: A Canonical Approach to the Fulfillment of God's Saving Promises. 2009. (Anchor Yale Bible Reference Library). (ENG.). 608p. 50.00 *(978-0-300-14097-2(5))* Yale Univ. Pr.

Hamilton, James M., Jr. God's Indwelling Presence: The Holy Spirit in the Old & New Testaments. 2006. (NAC Studies in Bible & Theology). (ENG., Illus.). 320p. 19.99 *(978-0-8054-4383-7(5)*, B&H Academic) B&H Publishing Group.

Hanegraaff, Hank. HAS GOD SPOKEN? (International Edition) Proof of the Bible¿s Divine Inspiration. 2011. 400p. pap. 15.99 ***(978-0-8499-4891-6(6))*** Nelson, Thomas Inc.

Hanson, Robert. What Am I to Do? 2007. 96p. per. 9.99 *(978-1-60266-873-7(6))* Xulon Pr., Inc.

Harrington, Wilfrid. John: Spiritual Theologian: The Jesus of John. 2nd rev. ed. 2007. (ENG.). 103p. pap. 21.95 *(978-1-85607-594-7(X))* Columba Pr. IRL. Dist: Dufour Editions, Inc.

Helmer, Christine & Higbe, Charlene T. The Multivalence of Biblical Texts & Theological Meanings. 2006. (SBL - Symposium Ser.). (Illus.). 199p. *(978-90-04-15110-9(9))* BRILL.

Henrich, Sarah S. Great Themes of the Bible, Volume 2. 2007. (ENG.). 143p. per. 13.00 *(978-0-664-23064-7(4))* Westminster John Knox Pr.

Henry, Jerome A. The and Well Eternal. 2011. 452p. pap. 24.99 ***(978-1-61379-619-1(6))*** Xulon Pr., Inc.

Heschel, Susannah. The Aryan Jesus: Christian Theologians & the Bible in Nazi Germany. 2008. (ENG., Illus.). 360p. (C). 46.95 *(978-0-691-12531-2(7))* Princeton Univ. Pr.

Hilborn, David. Prosperity Gospel. pap. 7.99 *(978-0-9532992-1-8(X))* Acute GBR. Dist: O. M. Literature.

Hille, Kirk. Deceived by Light: The Truth about the End Times. 96p. 14.99 *(978-0-7586-0040-0(2))* Concordia Publishing Hse.

Hills, Julian V. Tradition & Composition in the Epistula Apostolorum. 2008. (Harvard Theological Studies: 57). (Illus.). 185p. pap. 22.95 *(978-0-674-02131-0(2))* Harvard Univ. Pr.

Hinneh, Joshua. Answers to Questions People Never Ask - But Should! 2011. 448p. 28.99 ***(978-1-4269-7080-1(3))***; pap. 18.99 ***(978-1-4269-7079-5(X))*** Trafford Publishing.

Hinson. Theology of Old Testament. (Illus.). 222p. 15.00 *(978-0-281-02927-3(X))* SPCK Publishing GBR. Dist: Pilgrim Pr., The/United Church Pr.

Hodge, Charles. Systematic Theology. 2010. 760p. pap. 52.75 *(978-1-178-19004-5(8))* 2010. 898p. pap. 59.75 *(978-1-178-14120-7(9))* 2010. (ENG.). 980p. pap. 63.75 *(978-1-178-02906-2(9))* 2010. (ENG.). 92p. pap. 18.75 *(978-1-178-02792-1(9))* 2010. 982p. pap. 63.75 *(978-1-178-15929-5(9))* 2010. 674p. pap. 47.75 *(978-1-178-10350-2(1))* 2010. 672p. pap. 47.75 *(978-1-177-07905-0(8))* 2010. 900p. pap. 59.75 *(978-1-177-24808-2(5))* 2010. (ENG.). 892p. pap. 59.75 *(978-1-177-02479-2(9))* 2010. 672p. pap. 47.75 *(978-1-177-24850-1(6))* 2010. 674p. pap. 47.75 *(978-1-178-14113-9(6))* 2010. 982p. pap. 63.75 *(978-1-149-85882-0(6))* 2010. 746p. 47.99 *(978-1-140-46937-7(1))* 2010. 746p. pap. 52.75 *(978-1-140-46938-4(X))* 2010. 666p. pap. 47.75 *(978-1-147-01840-0(5))* 2008. 88p. pap. 18.75 *(978-0-559-57081-0(3))* BiblioBazaar.

—Systematic Theology. 2010. 78p. pap. *(978-1-152-77826-9(9))* Books LLC.

—Systematic Theology. 2010. 510p. pap. 29.40 *(978-1-150-92952-6(9))*; 704p. pap. 75.28 *(978-1-154-86478-6(2))* General Bks. LLC.

—Systematic Theology. 2006. 668p. pap. 36.99 *(978-1-4255-6779-8(7))* MPublishing.

Hodge, Kent. Christ in You: An Introduction to the New Covenant & the Christian Life. 2009. 672p. 36.49 *(978-1-4389-5290-1(2))*; pap. 25.99 *(978-1-4389-5224-6(4))* AuthorHouse.

Hole, Frank. Hebrews to Revelation. 2007. 304p. *(978-0-901860-49-1(2))*; (Illus.). per. *(978-0-901860-45-3(X))* Scripture Truth Pubns.

Horner, Grant. Meaning at the Movies: Becoming a Discerning Viewer. 2010. 224p. pap. 16.99 *(978-1-4335-1228-5(9))* Crossway.

Hostetter, S. R. Battle & Victory Beneath the Surface. 2008. pap. 14.99 *(978-1-60477-148-0(8))* Xulon Pr., Inc.

Hunt, Joel D. For God So Loved the World. 2010. 170p. 22.99 *(978-1-60957-689-9(6))*; pap. 14.99 *(978-1-60957-688-2(8))* Xulon Pr., Inc.

Hutchings, Noah W. 40 Irrefutable Signs of the Last Generation. 2010. (Illus.). 212p. pap. *(978-1-933641-38-6(X))* Bible Belt Pubns.

Hymns of the Faithful Series: Advent/Christmas LG. (Bible Studies). 4.50 *(978-0-570-07939-2(X))* Concordia Publishing Hse.

Hynd. Theology in a third Voice. 2007. 196p. pap. 15.00 *(978-1-920691-36-3(7))* ATF Pr. AUS. Dist: International Publishers Marketing.

Inch, Morris A. In Christ & on Track: The Essential Paul. 2007. (ENG.). 102p. pap. 26.50 *(978-0-7618-3965-1(8))* Univ. Pr. of America, Inc.

Isaac, Allan S. Kingdom Dynamics of the Apostolic Community. 2009. 220p. 24.99 *(978-1-4389-7997-7(5))*; pap. 15.99 *(978-1-4389-7996-0(7))* AuthorHouse.

Jackson, Earl. The Sons of God & the Nephilim. 2008. 150p. pap. 13.95 *(978-0-557-03312-6(8))* Lulu Enterprises Inc.

Jacobs, Carolyn Y. Salt of the Earth: How Do We Compare? 2008. 84p. pap. 29.95 *(978-1-4343-8613-7(9))* AuthorHouse.

Jeremiah, David. Angels: Who They Are & How They Help — What the Bible Reveals. 2009. (ENG.). 240p. pap. 14.99 *(978-1-60142-269-9(5)*, Multnomah) Doubleday Religious Publishing Group, The.

Jeter, Hugh. 52 Estudios Biblicos: Ayudas Minsteriales para el Pastor. 2011.Tr. of 52 Bible Studies... (SPA.). 106p. spiral bd. 6.00 *(978-1-931984-89-8(1)*, 5027-00S1) Faith & Action Team.

Johnson, Alisa Miller. Divine Moments: Letters of Encouragement. 2009. 128p. pap. *(978-1-55452-385-6(0)*, Guardian Bks.) Essence Publishing.

Johnson, Jeffrey D. The Silent God: Why God Does Not Speak. 2007. 12p. pap. 2.00 *(978-1-55635-077-1(5)*, Wipf and Stock) Wipf & Stock Pubs.

Jones, Richard. Words of Comfort from God & Others. 2007. 80p. per. 9.99 *(978-0-9793079-3-5(7))* Double-Edged Publishing, Inc.

Joseph, Yvette. False Christianity: The Drug of Choice. 2006. (ENG.). 60p. per. 16.95 *(978-1-4241-5429-6(4))* PublishAmerica, Inc.

Joyce, Robert. God Says, We Say: the Interpersonal Act of Redemption. 2010. 301p. pap. 24.95 *(978-0-578-06653-0(X))* LifeCom.

Joyce, Robert E. God Said, We Said: the Interpersonal Act of Creation. 2010. 177p. pap. 17.95 *(978-0-9615722-9-7(9))* LifeCom.

Kaiser, Walter C. The Promise Plan of God: A Biblical Theology of the Old & New Testaments, 1 vol. 2008. (ENG., Illus.). 432p. (gr. 13). 34.99 *(978-0-310-27586-2(5))* Zondervan.

Kaiser, Walter C., Jr. Recovering the Unity of the Bible: One Continuous Story, Plan, & Purpose, 1 vol. 2009. (ENG.). 256p. 29.99 *(978-0-310-32024-1(0))* Zondervan.

—Toward an Exegetical Theology: Biblical Exegesis for Preaching & Teaching. 2007. 272p. (C). (gr. 13-18). pap. 28.00 *(978-0-8010-2197-8(9))* Baker Academic.

Kalas, J. Ellsworth. God's Promises That Keep Us. 2010. 144p. pap. 14.95 *(978-1-4267-1003-2(8))* Abingdon Pr.

Kalivoda, George. Back to Basics-Biblical Principles for Leading & Managing in the 21st Century. 2007. 236p. (ENG.). 24.99 *(978-1-60266-778-5(0))*; per. 14.99 *(978-1-60266-777-8(2))* Xulon Pr., Inc.

Kanaly, Pam. Will the Real Me Please Stand up - Let's Go Deeper: Companion Workbook. 2010. pap. 13.99 *(978-1-61566-667-6(2))* Tate Publishing & Enterprises, LLC.

Kanzlemar, Joseph. Graphic Illustrations of Biblical Truth. 2007. (Illus.). 261p. *(978-0-9797786-6-7(2))* Bible Based Studies.

Kennedy, Rick. Jesus, History, & Mt. Darwin: An Academic Excursion. 2008. (Illus.). 112p. pap. 14.00 *(978-1-55635-655-1(2))* Wipf & Stock Pubs.

Kenneson, Philip D., et al. The Shape of Our Lives: Study One in the Ekklisia Project. 2008. (Getting Your Feet Wet Ser.). 86p. pap. 12.00 *(978-1-60608-054-2(7))* Wipf & Stock Pubs.

Kern, Steve. No Other Gods - the Biblical Creation Worldview. 2007. pap. 24.99 *(978-0-9778085-7-1(2))* Amerisearch, Inc.

Kiesling, Tracey. Meet Me at the Well. 2006. 21.99 *(978-1-60034-939-3(0))*; (ENG.). pap. 13.99 *(978-1-60034-938-6(2))* Xulon Pr., Inc.

Kinsler, Kim. Impact Me & See. 2010. 168p. pap. 39.95 *(978-1-4520-0476-1(5))* AuthorHouse.

Knight, Richard. Thoughts, Images, & Expressions. 2007. 108p. per. 10.99 *(978-1-60266-456-2(0))* Xulon Pr., Inc.

Kremer, Pastor Don. The Chronological Order of the Endtimes. 2010. 344p. pap. 22.01 *(978-1-4520-5451-3(7))* AuthorHouse.

Kulikovsky, Andrew. Creation, Fall, Restoration: A Biblical Theology of Creation. 2009. (ENG.). 320p. 19.99 *(978-1-84550-446-5(1)*, Mentor) Christian Focus Pubns. GBR. Dist: STL Distribution North America.

Kusema, Wellingtone Garati. The Believers' Companion: A Concise Topical Handbook on Doctrine in the African Apostolic Church. 2011. 410p. pap. 14.99 ***(978-0-9557546-1-6(5))*** Heritage Pr.

Lack of Knowledge. 2006. per. 9.99 *(978-0-9788110-0-6(3))* Etacwa.

Lafleur, Stephen. Champion's Choice: Decision Making That Transforms Lives. 2008. 76p. pap. 9.99 *(978-1-60477-728-4(1))* Xulon Pr., Inc.

Lauder, Darrin. The Heart of Spiritual Warfare: A Biblical Theological Consideration of Some Crucial Issues. 2011. 228p. 24.59 *(978-1-4520-2723-4(4))*; pap. 14.03 *(978-1-4520-2724-1(2))* AuthorHouse.

Lawrence, Michael. Biblical Theology in the Life of the Church: A Guide for Ministry. 2010. (IXMarks Ser.). 240p. pap. 16.99 *(978-1-4335-1508-8(3))* Crossway.

Learning to Use My Bible: Student. rev. ed. stu. ed. 3.95 *(978-0-687-07206-4(9))* Abingdon Pr.

LeBlanc, Judy Azar. Theology 101 in Bite-Size Pieces: A Bird's Eye View of the Riches of Divine Grace. 2010. 124p. 28.95 *(978-1-4497-0707-1(6))*; pap. 11.95 *(978-1-4497-0706-4(8))* Author Solutions, Inc. (WestBow Pr.).

Leddy, Jim. The Simple Truth. 2008. 380p. pap. 20.99 *(978-1-60647-828-8(1))* Xulon Pr., Inc.

Levy, Steve. Bible Overview. 2008. (ENG.). pap. 11.99 *(978-1-84550-378-9(3))* Christian Focus Pubns. GBR. Dist: STL Distribution North America.

Lewis, Frederick E. Understanding the Bible & End Times. 2006. (Biblical Advanced Basics Ser.). (Illus.). 118p. per. 10.95 *(978-1-59886-386-4(X))* Tate Publishing & Enterprises, LLC.

Lin, Kent C. The Rationality of Christian Doctrines. 2009. 268p. pap. 16.99 *(978-1-60791-212-5(0))* Xulon Pr., Inc.

Lin, Zichun. Duo Yuan Xing Han Yu Shen Xue Quan Shi: A Polyphonic View on Sino-Christian Theology. 2008. (978-7-80254-081-1(X)) China Religion and Culture Publishing Hse.

Lindblad, Frank. The SpiritNtilde;Which Is from God. 2009. 270p. pap. 23.00 (978-1-50608-184-6(5), Wipf and Stock) Wipf & Stock Pubs.

Lindsay, Anna Robertson Brown. The Warriors. 2008. 156p. 25.99 (978-0-554-26902-3(3)) 2008. 156p. 22.99 (978-0-554-36205-2(8)) 2007. (ENG.). 136p. pap. 18.99 (978-1-4346-2109-2(X)) 2007. (ENG.). 154p. pap. 21.99 (978-1-4346-2137-5(5)) BiblioBazaar.

—The Warriors. 2009. 64p. pap. (978-0-217-28562-9(7)) Books LLC.

Lioy, Dan. Axis of Glory: A Biblical & Theological Analysis of the Temple Motif in Scripture. 2010. (Studies in Biblical Literature Ser.). 194p. (C). 59.95 (978-1-4331-1012-2(1)) Lang, Peter Publishing, Inc.

Livingstone Corporation Staff. God's Promises on Character. 2008. (God's Promises Ser.). (ENG.). 160p. 3.99 (978-1-934068-90-8(X)) Authentic Media.

Lorenzo, Michael J. God's Gradual Self-Revelation to Mankind. 2009. 236p. pap. 15.99 (978-1-59858-712-8(9)) Dog Ear Publishing, LLC.

Lowry, Mark. The Temple of Divine Truth: Second Edition. Lowry, Montecue J., ed. 2008. 164p. 17.95 (978-1-4327-2745-1(1)); pap. 9.95 (978-1-4327-2591-4(2)) Outskirts Pr., Inc.

Loze, Dennis. Modern Christianity: God's Law or Man's Law? 2010. 232p. pap. 15.99 (978-1-4520-8026-0(7)) AuthorHouse.

Luther, Martin. The Bondage of the Will. Cole, Henry, tr. 2007. (Illus.). 417p. per. 14.99 (978-1-932307-43-6(5)) Emerald Hse. Group, Inc.

Lw: Bible Searchers. 1.55 (978-0-7673-5320-5(X)) LifeWay Christian Resources.

LW Advanced Bible Study. 2.65 (978-0-7673-4873-7(7)) LifeWay Christian Resources.

MacGregor, Kirk R. A Molinist-Anabaptist Systematic Theology. 2007. (ENG.). 366p. per. 53.50 (978-0-7618-3851-7(1)) Univ. Pr. of America, Inc.

Malicoat, Cheryl. Cookie & Verse! A Spiritual Compilation. 2010. 108p. pap. 12.49 (978-1-4490-6505-8(8)) AuthorHouse.

Mann, Theodore H. Completely Unrelated Theological Articles. 2007. 135p. pap. 15.95 (978-1-4357-0126-7(7)) Lulu Enterprises Inc.

Manson, William. Jesus the Messiah - the Synoptic Tradition of the Revelation of God in Christ. 2007. 216p. per. (978-1-4067-8824-2(4), Pomona Pr.) Read Bks.

Manzanga, Peter. A Background Study of Life & Light in John's Gospel. 2010. 144p. pap. (978-3-639-26629-0(3)) VDM Verlag Dr. Mueller e.K.

March, W. Eugene. Great Themes of the Bible, Volume 1, Vol. 1. 2006. (ENG., Illus.). 143p. per. 13.00 (978-0-664-22918-4(2)) Westminster John Knox Pr.

Margesson, Nick. God Rules: Junction Book 3 Seven youth group sessions God's loving rule in the life of Joseph. 2010. (ENG.). 64p. 9.99 (978-1-84550-548-6(4)) Christian Focus Pubns. GBR. Dist: STL Distribution North America.

Martin, Paula. The Pretrib Rapture. 2008. 176p. pap. 13.99 (978-1-60477-777-2(X)) Xulon Pr., Inc.

Martucci, Jean. Preguntas Sobre La Biblia. 80p. 4.95 (978-958-607-198-7(7)) Sociedad de San Pablo COL. Dist: St Pauls/Alba Hse. Pubs.

Maspero, Giulio & Wozniak, Robert J., eds. Rethinking Trinitarian Theology: Disputed Questions & Contemporary Issues in Trinitarian Theology. 2012. (ENG.). 512p. 160.00 (978-0-567-60381-4(4)); pap. 44.95 (978-0-567-22546-7(1)) Continuum International Publishing Group, Ltd. GBR. (T&T Clark Int'l). Dist: National Bk. Network.

May, Stephen. Stardust & Ashes - P. 176p. 19.00 (978-0-281-05104-5(6)) SPCK Publishing GBR. Dist: Pilgrim Pr., The/United Church Pr.

Mayer, Frederick E. The Religious Bodies of America. 4th ed. 616p. 26.99 (978-0-7586-0231-2(6)) Concordia Publishing Hse.

Mayshack, John L. Cotton Patch Sermon Outlines. 2008. pap. 13.99 (978-1-60647-140-1(6)) Xulon Pr., Inc.

McCarter, Carlton. No More Drama. 2007. 104p. per. 9.99 (978-1-59886-773-2(3)) Tate Publishing & Enterprises, LLC.

McConnel, Francis J. Understanding the Scriptures. 2009. 66p. pap. (978-1-4099-5852-9(3)) Dodo Pr.

McCosker, Philip. What Is It That the Scripture Says? Essays in Biblical Interpretation, Translation, & Reception in Honour of Henry Wansbrough OSB. 2007. (Library of New Testament Studies: Vol. 316). (ENG., Illus.). 362p. 190.00 (978-0-567-04353-5(3), T&T Clark Int'l) Continuum International Publishing Group, Ltd. GBR. Dist: National Bk. Network.

McKenzie, John L. Myths & Realities: Studies in Biblical Theology. 2009. (John L. Mckenzie Reprints Ser.). 306p. pap. 33.00 (978-1-60608-050-4(4)) Wipf & Stock Pubs.

McRobbie, James. What the Bible Teaches. pap. 8.99 (978-0-88019-122-7(8)) Schmul Publishing Co., Inc.

Mead, James K. Biblical Theology: Issues, Methods, & Themes. 2007. (ENG., Illus.). 328p. per. 30.00 (978-0-664-22972-6(7)) Westminster John Knox Pr.

Meadors, Edward P. Creation, Sin, Covenant, & Salvation: A Primer for Biblical Theology. 2011. 140p. pap. 17.00 (978-1-61097-072-3(1), Cascade Bks.) Wipf & Stock Pubs.

Meadors, Edward P. & Meadors. Idolatry & the Hardening of the Heart: A Study in Biblical Theology. 2006. (ENG.). 224p. pap. 39.95 (978-0-567-02573-9(X), T&T Clark Int'l) Continuum International Publishing Group, Ltd. GBR. Dist: National Bk. Network.

Miller, George. The Shekinah Glory. 2007. 108p. (ENG.). 18.99 (978-1-60266-848-5(5)); per. 10.99 (978-1-60266-847-8(7)) Xulon Pr., Inc.

Miller, John James. Being Right with God: It's a Great Life. 2011. 228p. 33.95 (978-1-4497-0674-6(6)); pap. 17.95 (978-1-4497-0675-3(4)) Author Solutions, Inc. (WestBow Pr.).

Miller, Michael St. A. Reshaping the Contextual Vision in Caribbean Theology: Theoretical Foundations for Theology Which Is Contextual, Pluralistic, & Dialectical. 2007. (ENG.). 414p. 89.50 (978-0-7618-3784-8(1)); per. 57.99 (978-0-7618-3785-5(X)) Univ. Pr. of America, Inc.

Minear, Paul Sevier. Eyes of Faith: A Study in the Biblical Point of View. 320p. 2008. 45.95 (978-1-4367-0874-6(5)) 2007. (ENG.). per. 30.95 (978-1-4325-5578-8(2)) Kessinger Publishing, LLC.

Mitchell, Cordell W. Snapshots of Christ in Genesis: A Scriptural Study of Christology in Genesis. 2011. 528p. 44.95 (978-1-4497-1589-2(3)); pap. 34.95 (978-1-4497-1588-5(5)) Author Solutions, Inc. (WestBow Pr.).

Mitchell, Kenneth R. Justice & Generosity: The Teaching of the Bible Concerning the Poor. 2008. 422p. pap. 29.95 (978-1-60563-950-5(8)) PublishAmerica, Inc.

Moen, Skip. Spiritual Restoration: Reclaiming the Foundations of God's World Volume 1. 2008. 260p. pap. 15.99 (978-1-60647-555-3(X)) Xulon Pr., Inc.

Morgan, Nigel. The Douce Apocalypse: Picturing the End of the World in the Middle Ages. 2007. (BL - Treasures from the Bodleian Library). (ENG., Illus.). 120p. 45.00 (978-1-85124-360-0(7)) Bodleian Library GBR. Dist: Chicago Distribution Ctr.

Morris, Wayne. Theology Without Words: Theology in the Deaf Community. 2008. (Explorations in Practical, Pastoral & Empirical Theology Ser.). 192p. 99.95 (978-0-7546-6222-8(5)); pap. 39.95 (978-0-7546-6227-3(6)) Ashgate Publishing Co.

Mullooparambil, Sebastian. Dynamism of the Word of God & Biblical Personalities. 2009. xiv, 285p. pap. (978-81-89958-22-0(4), Library of Congress — New Delhi Overseas Office) Dharmaram Publications.

Murray, Richard K. Lift up Your Jawbone: Developing Samson-Like Strength Through Daily Word Confession. 2008. 136p. pap. 7.95 (978-1-4327-1742-1(1)) Outskirts Pr., Inc.

Murray, Robert. The Cosmic Covenant: Biblical Themes of Justice, Peace & the Integrity of Creation. 2007. per. 49.00 (978-1-59333-747-6(7)) Gorgias Pr., LLC.

Nelson, P. c. & Nelson, Peter Christopher. Bible Doctrines: Discover Profound Truths for Everyday Living. 75th ed. 2009. 144p. pap. (978-0-88243-858-0(1)) Gospel Publishing Hse.

New Life No Limits. Isaiah Homiletics Workbook. 2010. 264p. pap. 27.95 (978-1-4497-0649-4(5), WestBow Pr.) Author Solutions, Inc.

Niehaus, Jeffrey J. Ancient near Eastern Themes in Biblical Theology. 2008. 208p. pap. 18.99 (978-0-8254-3360-3(6)) Kregel Pubns.

Noll, K. L. & Schramm, Brooks, eds. Raising up a Faithful Exegete. 2010. 54.50 (978-1-57506-201-3(1)) Eisenbrauns, Inc.

Nwaduba, Michael. A Simple Guide for Bible Study. 2008. 212p. 24.99 (978-1-4343-8934-3(0)); pap. 14.49 (978-1-4343-8933-6(2)) AuthorHouse.

O'Day, Gail R. & Petersen, David L. Theological Bible Commentary. 2009. (ENG.). 504p. 50.00 (978-0-664-22711-1(2)) Westminster John Knox Pr.

Ofosuah, Beatrice N. The Secret Weapon. 2009. 84p. pap. 10.99 (978-1-60647-786-1(2)) Xulon Pr., Inc.

Olaribigbe, Evangelist K. Emmanuella. The Battle of the Mind & Power of the Tongue: No Subtitle. 2008. pap. 9.99 (978-1-60647-170-8(8)) Xulon Pr., Inc.

Oliphant, Winston. Why the Man Must Die. 2010. (ENG.). 86p. pap. 11.95 (978-1-60702-074-5(2), iTouch Pubs.) Higher Standard Enterprises, Inc.

One Perfect Hero: Jesus & the Five-Dimensional Narrative. 2006. 167p. per. 12.95 (978-1-59886-416-8(5)) Tate Publishing & Enterprises, LLC.

O'Neill, Andrew & O'Neill. Tillich. 2008. (Guides for the Perplexed Ser.). (ENG.). 176p. 24.95 (978-0-567-03291-1(4)); 110.00 (978-0-567-03290-4(6)) Continuum International Publishing Group, Ltd. GBR. (T&T Clark Int'l). Dist: National Bk. Network.

Onwubiko, Moses. Disaster: God's Warning Bell. 2009. 224p. pap. (978-1-55452-359-7(1), Guardian Bks.) Essence Publishing.

Our Life in Christ High School Bible Studies, Vol. 3. 19.99 (978-0-570-06944-7(0)) Concordia Publishing Hse.

Oægarro, Easton. God's Marvelous Threes: Part 1. 2008. 164p. pap. 11.99 (978-1-4343-8925-1(1)) AuthorHouse.

Packer, J. I. & Packer, Jim. 18 Words: The Most Important Words You Will Ever Know. 2008. (ENG.). 218p. pap. 12.99 (978-1-84550-327-7(9)) Christian Focus Pubns. GBR. Dist: STL Distribution North America.

Paddison, Angus. Scripture: A Very Theological Proposal. 2009. (ENG.). 184p. 39.95 (978-0-567-03424-3(0)); 130.00 (978-0-567-03423-6(2)) Continuum International Publishing Group, Ltd. GBR. (T&T Clark Int'l). Dist: National Bk. Network.

Palmer, Hedley. The Patterns of the Scripture: Unlocking the Chronological & Genealogical Coding of the Scriptures. 2011. 144p. pap. 80.00 (978-1-4269-5201-2(5)) Trafford Publishing.

Palmer, Kelly A. Cowboy Revelations: A Voice Crying in the Wilderness. 2009. 103p. pap. 12.95 (978-1-4327-1225-9(X)) Outskirts Pr., Inc.

Panteghini, Giacomo. El Gemido de la Creacion. (SPA.). 176p. 6.95 (978-958-607-945-7(7)) Sociedad de San Pablo ESP. Dist: St Pauls/Alba Hse. Pubs.

Pantuosco Jr., Louis. Got Questions? 2007. 216p. per. 14.99 (978-1-60477-192-3(5)) Xulon Pr., Inc.

Park, Mirae. Signs & Wonders: Super Natural Power in Daily Life. 2009. 248p. pap. 15.99 (978-1-61579-171-2(X)) Xulon Pr., Inc.

Partee, Milt. Christianity in Crisis: A wake-up call for the Church. 2010. 38p. pap. 10.95 (978-1-4490-8535-3(0)) AuthorHouse.

Paul, Bruce. The Living Waters of Eden: Exploring the Biblical, Scientific, & Historical Evidence Supporting Eden's Israel Location. 2007. (ENG.). 128p. per. 20.00 (978-0-9796251-0-7(6)) Robertson Publishing.

Paulson, Kay. The Wrap-up: 21 Days to learn what the Bible teaches about the End Of. 2007. (ENG.). 172p. per. 15.99 (978-1-60266-076-2(X)) Xulon Pr., Inc.

Peace, Truth, Love, & Joy: What the Bible Is All About. 2007. per. (978-0-9624064-7-8(3)) New Era Training.

Perdue, Leo. Biblical Theology. 2009. (Library of Biblical Theology Ser.). 337p. pap. 22.00 (978-0-687-34100-9(0)) Abingdon Pr.

Pittman, Sr. The Sign of Christ's Return. 2008. 324p. pap. 22.95 (978-1-4401-0398-8(4)) iUniverse, Inc.

Pizarro, Rudy A. The Holy Trinity & the Gambler. 2008. 300p. pap. 17.99 (978-1-60647-244-6(5)) Xulon Pr., Inc.

Pollmann, Karla & Vessey, Mark, eds. Augustine & the Disciplines: From Cassiciacum to Confessions. 2007. (ENG.). 272p. pap. 45.00 (978-0-19-923004-4(8)) Oxford Univ. Pr., Inc.

Price, Robert M. Inerrant the Wind: The Evangelical Crisis of Biblical Authority. 2008. (ENG.). 345p. bds. 25.98 (978-1-59102-676-1(8)) Prometheus Bks., Pubs.

Pugh, Jeffrey C. & Pugh. Religionless Christianity: Dietrich Bonhoeffer in Troubled Times. 2009. (ENG.). 192p. 120.00 (978-0-567-03258-4(2), T&T Clark Int'l) Continuum International Publishing Group, Ltd. GBR. Dist: National Bk. Network.

Raisanen, Heikki. Paul & the Law (2nd Edition) 2010. 352p. pap. 39.00 (978-1-60899-750-3(2), Wipf and Stock) Wipf & Stock Pubs.

Ray, Walter. Gods Plan for Our Age. 2009. 252p. pap. 14.49 (978-1-4389-3666-6(4)) AuthorHouse.

Reynolds, Yvonne. Elijah Uncloaked: A Man for All Ages - Yesterday, Today & Always. 2009. 209p. pap. 24.95 (978-1-60749-455-3(8)) PublishAmerica, Inc.

Richey, Jr. Survival. 2008. 156p. pap. 14.99 (978-1-60647-598-0(3)) Xulon Pr., Inc.

Robison, Willie. The 3 Biggest Problems in the Body of Christ & How to Solve Them. 2007. 216p. per. 14.99 (978-1-60477-108-4(9)) Xulon Pr., Inc.

Rogers, Glenn. Making Sense of the Bible: Understanding & Applying God's Message in Your Life. 2007. 184p. per. 18.95 (978-0-9792072-0-4(7)) Mission & Ministry Resources.

Rohr, Richard. Things Hidden: Scripture as Spirituality. 2008. 238p. per. 19.95 (978-0-86716-659-0(2)) Franciscan Media.

Rollins, John S. The P Attitudes. 2009. 192p. pap. 14.99 (978-1-60791-248-4(1)) Xulon Pr., Inc.

Root, Tiffany. For God so Loved the World: ... & Everyone in It. 2011. 140p. pap. 11.95 (978-1-4497-1640-0(7), WestBow Pr.) Author Solutions, Inc.

Root, Tiffany & VandeGuchte, Kirk. For God so Loved the World: ... & Everyone in It. 2011. (ENG.). 140p. 28.95 (978-1-4497-1642-4(3), WestBow Pr.) Author Solutions, Inc.

Roselli, Robert. The Theory of Livevolution: Great Society of the Un-dead. 2008. 440p. pap. 25.99 (978-1-60647-281-1(X)) Xulon Pr., Inc.

Roshwald, Mordecai. Biblical Revisions & para-Biblical Visions. Strozier, M. Stefan & Torke, Kyle, eds. 2008. 184p. pap. 20.00 (978-1-935444-00-8(X)) World Audience Pubs.

RUDEN, Sarah. Paul among the People: The Apostle Reinterpreted & Reimagined in His Own Time. 2011. (ENG.). 240p. pap. 14.00 (978-0-385-52257-1(6), Image) Doubleday Religious Publishing Group, The.

—Paul among the People: The Apostle Reinterpreted & Reimagined in His Own Time. 2010. (ENG.). 240p. 25.00 (978-0-375-42501-1(2), Pantheon) Knopf Doubleday Publishing Group.

Russell, Charles Taze. Studies in the Scriptures. 2009. 84p. pap. (978-0-217-05867-4(1)) Books LLC.

—Studies in the Scriptures. 2009. 112p. pap. 31.17 (978-0-217-56317-8(1)) General Bks. LLC.

Saer, Orlando. Iron Sharpens Iron: Leading Small Groups That Thrive. 2010. (ENG.). 144p. 10.99 (978-1-84550-575-2(1)) Christian Focus Pubns. GBR. Dist: STL Distribution North America.

Salesman, P. Eliecer. 70 Preguntas Sobre la Biblia.Tr. of 70 Questions on the Bible. (SPA.). 224p. pap. 5.95 (978-980-350-000-9(7)) Sociedad de San Pablo VEN. Dist: St Pauls/Alba Hse. Pubs.

Schnarrs, John. Jesus Christ Is Greek-Hebrew Name Is Yahshua. 2011. 160p. pap. 15.00 (978-1-4520-5985-3(3)) AuthorHouse.

Schreiner, Thomas R. Run to Win the Prize: Perseverance in the New Testament. 2010. 128p. pap. 15.99 (978-1-4335-1436-4(2)) Crossway.

Schulmeister, Irene. Israels Befreiung Aus Ägypten: Eine Formeluntersuchung zur Theologie des Deuteronomiums. 2010. (Österreichische Biblische Studien Ser.). (GER.). 346p. 83.95 (978-3-631-60210-2(3)) Lang, Peter GmbH, Europaischer Verlag der Wissenschaften DEU. Dist: Lang, Peter.

Schurb, Ken & Shuta, Richard. Advent 2. ldr.'s ed. (Advent Bible Study Series C). 5.00 (978-0-570-07824-1(5), 20-2859) Concordia Publishing Hse.

—Advent 3. ldr.'s ed. (Advent Bible Study Series A). pap. 4.99 (978-0-570-07828-9(8), 20-2863) Concordia Publishing Hse.

Schutz, John Howard. Paul & the Anatomy of Apostolic Authority. 2007. (New Testament Library). (ENG.). 307p. per. 40.00 (978-0-664-22812-5(7)) Westminster John Knox Pr.

Schweizer. Theological Introduction to New Testament. 192p. 19.95 (978-0-281-04602-7(6)) International Publishers Marketing.

Scornaienchi, Lorenzo. Sarx und Soma bei Paulus: Der Mensch zwischen Destruktivität und Konstruktivität. 2008. (Novum Testamentum et Orbis Antiquus/Studien zur Umwelt des Neuen Testaments (NTOA/StUNT) Ser.). (GER.). 388p. (C). 98.00 (978-3-525-53966-8(5)) Vandenhoeck & Ruprecht GmbH & Co. KG DEU. Dist: ISD.

Scott, Ian W. Paul's Way of Knowing: Story, Experience, & the Spirit. 2008. 368p. (C). pap. 50.00 (978-0-8010-3609-5(7)) Baker Academic.

Scouteris, Constantine B. Ecclesial Being: Contributions to Theological Dialogue. Veniamin, Christopher, ed. 2006. 188p. pap. 9.95 (978-0-9774983-1-4(X)) Mount Thabor Publishing.

Selby. Rescue. 128p. 13.00 (978-0-281-04897-7(5)) SPCK Publishing GBR. Dist: Pilgrim Pr., The/United Church Pr.

Sell, Alan P. F., ed. The Bible in Church, Academy, & Culture: Essays in Honour of the Reverend Dr. John Tudno Williams. 2011. 302p. pap. 33.00 (978-1-60899-475-5(9), Pickwick Pubns.) Wipf & Stock Pubs.

Sellers, Otis Q. Seed & Bread Vol. I. 2009. 472p. 30.99 (978-1-4389-2145-7(4)); pap. 20.49 (978-1-4389-2144-0(6)) AuthorHouse.

—Seed & Bread Vol. Ii. 2009. 468p. 30.99 (978-1-4389-2147-1(0)); pap. 20.49 (978-1-4389-2146-4(2)) AuthorHouse.

Sellman, Paul. The Tree of Life: A Biblical Study of Immortality & New Creation. 2010. 238p. pap. 15.95 (978-1-4327-5232-2(X)) Outskirts Pr., Inc.

Shittu, T. J. Flames of the End! The Revival Is Coming! 2010. pap. 9.99 (978-1-61566-477-1(7)) Tate Publishing & Enterprises, LLC.

Shoemaker, Mel. The Theology of the Four Gospels. 2011. 476p. 43.95 (978-1-4497-2926-4(6)); pap. 30.95 (978-1-4497-2925-7(8)) Author Solutions, Inc. (WestBow Pr.).

Shuster, Eric & Sale, Charles. The Biblical Roots of Mormonism. 2010. 288p. pap. 17.99 (978-1-59955-406-8(2)) Cedar Fort, Inc./CFI Distribution.

Sineath, Mark. The Truth Shall Set You Free: This Ain't Your Grandma's Church. 2008. 100p. per. 9.99 (978-1-60462-141-9(9)) Tate Publishing & Enterprises, LLC.

Sloan, Cyndi. Celebrate the Journey. 2006. per. 15.00 (978-1-59094-126-3(8)) Jawbone Publishing Corp.

Smith, Barry. What Must I Do to Be Saved? Paul Parts Company with His Jewish Heritage. 2007. 304p. (978-1-905048-82-3(3)) Sheffield Phoenix Pr.

Smith-Christopher, Daniel L. & Spignesi, Stephen. Lost Books of the Bible for Dummies. 2008. (ENG., Illus.). 366p. pap. 21.99 (978-0-470-24380-0(5), For Dummies) Wiley, John & Sons, Inc.

Smith, Joseph. Pearl of Great Price. 2007. (ENG.). 120p. 19.99 (978-1-59986-694-9(3)) 2006. pap. 9.99 (978-1-59986-966-7(7)) Filiquarian Publishing, LLC.

Soskice, Janet Martin. The Kindness of God: Metaphor, Gender, & Religious Language. 2008. (ENG.). 224p. 49.95 (978-0-19-826951-9(X)) Oxford Univ. Pr., Inc.

Sparks, Kenton L. Sacred Word, Broken Word: Preparing for Theological Interpretation of Scripture. 2012. pap. (978-0-8028-6718-6(9)) Eerdmans, William B. Publishing Co.

Spell, David. Peter & Paul in Acts: A Comparison of Their Ministries - A Study in New Testament Apostolic Ministry. 2006. 218p. pap. 24.00 (978-1-59752-784-2(X), Wipf and Stock) Wipf & Stock Pubs.

Spinks, Bryan D. Reformation & Modern Rituals & Theologies of Baptism: From Luther to Contemporary Practices. 2006. (Liturgy, Worship, & Society Ser.). (Illus.). 266p. pap. 29.95 (978-0-7546-5697-5(7)) Ashgate Publishing Co.

Stanley, Alan P. Did Jesus Teach Salvation by Works? The Role of Works in Salvation in the Synoptic Gospels. Baker, David W., ed. 2006. (Evangelical Theological Society Monograph Ser.). (Illus.). 436p. pap. 42.00 (978-1-59752-680-7(0), Pickwick Pubns.) Wipf & Stock Pubs.

Starks, Edward Andrew Th. D. The Christian Lifestyle Study Bible & Commentary. 2009. 724p. 34.99 (978-1-4363-8143-7(6)); pap. 23.99 (978-1-4363-8142-0(8)) Xlibris Corp.

Starr, James & Engberg-Pedersen, Troels, eds. Early Christian Paraenesis in Context. (Beihefte zur Zeitschrift far die neutestamentliche Wissenschaft und die Kunde der älteren Kirche Ser.). (ENG.). VII, 616p. 314.00 (978-3-11-182786-5(0)) De Gruyter, Walter Inc.

Stearns, Gail J. Open Your Eyes Toward Living More Deeply in the Present. 2010. 150p. pap. 19.00 (978-1-60899-635-3(2), Wipf and Stock) Wipf & Stock Pubs.

Steffen, Sylvester L. What Self-Donation Is: Kenosis, Eucharist & Green Religion - Book Two of the Justified Living Trilogy. 2010. 116p. 21.49 (978-1-4520-3496-6(6)); pap. 10.99 (978-1-4520-3495-9(8)) AuthorHouse.

Stetson, Eric. Christian Universalism: God's Good News for All People. 2008. 144p. pap. 14.95 (978-0-9670631-8-8(3)) Sparkling Bay Bks.

Stevenson, John R. In the Clift of the Rock: There Is A Place Where Man Can See God. 2009. 104p. pap. 10.99 (978-1-61579-178-1(7)) Xulon Pr., Inc.

Stott, John, ed. The Anglican Communion & Scripture: Papers from the First International Consultation of the Evangelical Fellowship in the Anglican Communion, Canterbury, UK, June 1993. 2011. 198p. pap. 23.00 (978-1-61097-559-9(6), Wipf and Stock) Wipf & Stock Pubs.

Studebaker, Steven M., ed. Defining Issues in Pentecostalism: Classical & Emergent. 2008. (McMaster Theological Studies). 222p. pap. 24.00 (978-1-55635-843-2(1), Pickwick Pubns.) Wipf & Stock Pubs.

Sturgeon, Ava. A Daughter's Worth: A Bible Study for Teenaged Girls. 2006. 186p. per. 15.95 (978-1-59886-398-7(3)) Tate Publishing & Enterprises, LLC.

Sub FBS Adult. ldr.'s ed. 18.95 (978-0-633-05039-9(3)) LifeWay Christian Resources.

Sub FBS Adult Learner Guide. 8.75 (978-0-633-05041-2(5)); 8.75 (978-0-633-05042-9(3)) LifeWay Christian Resources.

Sub FBS Adult Learner Guide HCSB. 8.75 (978-0-633-05043-6(1)) LifeWay Christian Resources.

B

Sub FBS All Youth Learner Guide. 9.15 *(978-0-633-05046-7(6))*; 8.75 *(978-0-633-05047-4(4))* LifeWay Christian Resources.

Sub FBS Grades 1-3 Learner Guide. 9.15 *(978-0-633-05049-8(0))* LifeWay Christian Resources.

Sub FBS Grades 4-6 Learner Guide. 9.15 *(978-0-633-05050-4(4))* LifeWay Christian Resources.

Sub FBS Leader Guide for Grades 1-3 And 4-6. 18.95 *(978-0-633-05051-1(2))* LifeWay Christian Resources.

Sub FBS Leader Pack for Grades 1-3 And 4-6. 79.35 *(978-0-633-05083-2(0))* LifeWay Christian Resources.

Sub FBS Life Truths Learner Guide. 9.95 *(978-0-633-05055-9(5))* LifeWay Christian Resources.

Sub FBS Preteen Learner Guide. 9.15 *(978-0-633-05060-3(1))* LifeWay Christian Resources.

Sub FBS Younger Youth. ldr.'s ed. 18.95 *(978-0-633-05068-9(7))* LifeWay Christian Resources.

Sub FBS Younger Youth Learner Guide. 9.15 *(978-0-633-05069-6(5))* LifeWay Christian Resources.

Sutton, Juan. Another More Excellent Way. 2009. 232p. pap. 15.99 *(978-1-60791-549-2(9))* Xulon Pr., Inc.

Taber, Tyler M. The Things Above: Thinking Through Tough Questions of the Christian Faith. 2011. 196p. pap. 17.95 ***(978-1-4497-2817-5(0)***, WestBow Pr.) Author Solutions, Inc.

Taggart, Ed. Angels Surround Us: The Truth about Angels & Fallen Angels. 256p. pap. 12.99 *(978-1-85792-681-1(1)*, Christian Focus) Christian Focus Pubns. GBR. Dist: Riverside.

Taylor, Sister Angela. Experiencing Ishmael Before Receiving Isaac. 2007. (ENG.). 48p. per. 16.95 *(978-1-4137-9024-5(0))* PublishAmerica, Inc.

Tentaciones. (Bible Studies for Teens Vivencias de la Vida Real (Real Deal) Ser.).Tr. of Temptations. (SPA.). 14.99 *(978-0-7586-0657-0(5))* Concordia Publishing Hse.

Terrell, Ronald & Terrell, Michael. It's All about You. 2008. 144p. (ENG.). 21.99 *(978-1-60477-346-0(4))*; per. 13.99 *(978-1-60477-345-3(6))* Xulon Pr., Inc.

Thomas, Michael. Jesus 100 B. C. 2011. 272p. pap. 16.00 *(978-1-4567-1844-2(4))* AuthorHouse.

Thomas, Taniesha. The Purposeful Process. 2009. 48p. pap. 12.42 *(978-0-557-14694-9(1))* Lulu Enterprises Inc.

Thompson, Mark D. A Clear & Present Word: The Clarity of Scripture. 2006. (New Studies in Biblical Theology Ser.: Volume 21). (ENG.). 196p. per. 22.00 *(978-0-8308-2622-3(X)*, IVP Acad.) InterVarsity Pr.

Tiller, Darryl J. Growing into Jesus: Six Building Blocks for Life in Christ. 2008. 122p. pap. 19.95 *(978-1-60474-869-7(9))* PublishAmerica, Inc.

Tilton, Hereward. The Quest for the Phoenix: Spiritual Alchemy & Rosicrucianism in the Work of Count Michael Maier (1569-1622) (Arbeiten zur Kirchengeschichte Ser.). (ENG.). VIII, 322p. 225.00 ***(978-3-11-180347-0(3))*** De Gruyter, Walter Inc.

Tinker, Melvin & Buttery, Nathan. Tales of the Unexpected: The Power of Jesus' Parables. 2006. (ENG.). 144p. per. 7.99 *(978-1-84550-116-7(0))* Christian Focus Pubns. GBR. Dist: STL Distribution North America.

Today's Light Bible Reading Program Set, 3 bks., Set 39.99 *(978-0-570-00537-7(X)*, 01-1943) Concordia Publishing Hse.

Torrey, R. A. What the Bible Teaches: The Truths of the Bible Made Plain, Simple & Understandable. 2008. 502p. per. 24.95 *(978-1-59856-273-6(8))* Hendrickson Pubs. Marketing, LLC.

Traill, Ian. Who Am I? 2008. 212p. pap. 21.00 *(978-1-931178-51-8(8))* Vision Publishing.

Treier, Daniel J. Introducing Theological Interpretation of Scripture: Recovering a Christian Practice. 2008. 224p. (C). pap. 22.00 *(978-0-8010-3178-6(8))* Baker Academic.

Turner, Debbie. Whispered Thunder. 2006. pap. 15.99 *(978-1-60034-871-6(8))* Xulon Pr., Inc.

Ty Collins. Biblical Current Events: A Current Events Study Guide. 2009. 108p. pap. 10.99 *(978-1-4389-6151-4(0))* AuthorHouse.

Umoren, Anthony Iffen. Paul & Power Christology: Exegesis & Theology of Romans 1:3-4 in Relation to Popular Power Christology in an African Context. 2007. XV, 207p. pap. 46.95 *(978-3-631-57554-3(8))* Lang, Peter Publishing, Inc.

Urquhart, John. The Inspiration & Accuracy of the Holy Scriptures. 2008. 582p. 58.95 *(978-1-4365-4874-8(8))* 2007. (ENG.). 584p. per. 43.95 *(978-0-548-71230-6(1))* Kessinger Publishing, LLC.

Varughese, T. V. Bible & Theology Mysteries Solved! Volume One: Subtitle: Amazing Solutions to 14 of the Most Puzzling Questions. 2009. pap. 14.99 *(978-1-60791-450-1(6))* Xulon Pr., Inc.

Veith, Gene Edward. Why God Gave Us a Book. 2011. pap. ***(978-1-59638-378-4(X))*** P & R Publishing.

Vinas, Jaime. La Biblia - Guia de Comprension. 2008. 364p. pap. 17.99 *(978-1-4259-6612-6(8))* AuthorHouse.

Voerding, Philip. The Trouble with Christianity: A Concise Outline of Christian History. 2009. 176p. 24.99 *(978-1-4389-8944-0(X))*; pap. 14.99 *(978-1-4389-8924-2(5))* AuthorHouse.

Vogel, Jane & Sytsma, Mary. Route 66: A Road Trip Through the Bible. (Bible Study Ser.). pap. 24.95 *(978-1-59255-201-6(3)*, 130715); pap. 7.95 *(978-1-59255-200-9(5)*, 130710) Faith Alive Christian Resources.

Waite, Th. D. Pastor D. A. Heresies of Westcott & Hort. 2008. pap. 12.00 *(978-1-56848-014-5(8))* Old Paths Pubns., Inc., The.

Wakefield, Wesley H. Bible Basis for Christian Security. pap. 2.99 *(978-0-88019-054-1(X))* Schmul Publishing Co., Inc.

Waldron, Samuel E. The End Times Made Simple: How Could Everybody Be So Wrong about Biblical Prophecy? 2007. (ENG.). 251p. pap. 19.99 *(978-1-879737-50-1(7))* Calvary Pr.

Walton, Heather & Ward, Frances, eds. Theological Reflection: Sources, Vol. 2. 2008. 455p. per. *(978-0-334-02977-5(3))* Hymns Ancient & Modern Ltd.

Ward, Tom. The Cry of A Warrior. 2009. 214p. pap. 19.95 *(978-0-557-07915-5(2))* Lulu Enterprises Inc.

Weaver, Kirk. Running the Race: Spiritual Family Time Activities for All Ages. 2007. (Family Time Activities Bks.). (Illus.). 95p. pap. 14.99 *(978-1-888685-30-5(1))* Effective Parenting, Inc.

Webster, John. The Domain of the Word: Scripture & Theological Reason. 2012. (ENG.). 240p. 120.00 ***(978-0-567-21294-8(7)***, T&T Clark Int'l) Continuum International Publishing Group, Ltd. GBR. Dist: National Bk. Network.

Westminster John Knox Press. Library of Christian Classics, 26 vols., Set. 2006. (Library of Christian Classics). (ENG.). pap. 600.00 *(978-0-664-23108-8(X))* Westminster John Knox Pr.

Westminster John Knox Press Staff. Library of Christian Classics, 26 vols., Set. Baillie, John et al, eds. 2006. (Library of Christian Classics Ser.). (ENG.). cd-rom 500.00 *(978-0-664-23086-9(5))* Westminster John Knox Pr.

White, C. Randy. The Apocalypse: Expository Messages from Revelation: the Revelation of the Redeemer. 2007. 303p. per. 16.95 *(978-1-59824-425-0(6))* E-BookTime LLC.

Whitmore, Shakeena. Doing Battle: Under Fire. 2009. 57p. pap. 14.95 *(978-1-4327-3885-3(2))* Outskirts Pr., Inc.

Wiebe, Martha M. When Religion Makes No(N) Sense. 2011. ***(978-1-77069-272-5(X))*** Word Alive Pr.

Wiggins, Bernetta. But First You Must Be Whole. 2008. 112p. pap. 11.95 *(978-1-4327-2271-5(9))* Outskirts Pr., Inc.

Wilcken, John. God in Our World. pap. 4.95 *(978-0-8189-7007-8(3))* St Pauls/Alba Hse. Pubs.

Williams, David T. Kenosis of God: The self-limitation of God - Father, Son, & Holy Spirit. 2009. 380p. pap. 24.95 *(978-1-4401-3223-0(2))* iUniverse, Inc.

Williams, Jr. Life in a Cage. 2007. (ENG.). 140p. 21.99 *(978-1-60034-967-6(6))* Xulon Pr., Inc.

Wilson, Christopher. Radically Changed: 37 Real Life Inspirational Stories. 2010. 352p. 28.49 *(978-1-4490-8145-4(2))* AuthorHouse.

Witherington, Ben, III. The Living Word of God: Rethinking the Theology of the Bible. 2007. 291p. 29.95 *(978-1-60258-017-6(0))* Baylor Univ. Pr.

Witherington, Ben. Living Word of God: Rethinking the Theology of the Bible. 2007. (ENG.). 291p. pap. 24.95 ***(978-1-60258-192-0(4))*** Baylor Univ. Pr.

Witherup, Ronald D. Scripture: Dei Verbum. 2006. (Rediscovering Vatican II Ser.). 160p. per. 15.95 *(978-0-8091-4428-0(X)*, 4428-X) Paulist Pr.

Wright, G. Ernest. The Rule of God: Essays in Biblical Theology. 2011. 140p. 40.95 ***(978-1-258-09476-8(2))*** Literary Licensing, LLC.

Wright, John Wesley. Telling God's Story: Narrative Preaching for Christian Formation. 2007. (ENG.). 166p. per. 19.00 *(978-0-8308-2740-4(4)*, IVP Acad.) InterVarsity Pr.

Wright, N. T. Justification: God's Plan & Paul's Vision, 1 vol. 2009. (ENG.). 279p. 25.00 *(978-0-8308-3863-9(5)*, IVP Acad.) InterVarsity Pr.

Wright, Thomas. The Scientific Proof of God & Vindication of the Bible Code. 2010. (Illus.). 238p. pap. *(978-0-7552-1266-8(5))* Authors OnLine, Ltd.

Xeravits, Géza G., ed. Dualism in Qumran. 2010. (Library of Second Temple Studies, the Ser.). (ENG.). 208p. 120.00 *(978-0-567-23435-3(5)*, T&T Clark Int'l) Continuum International Publishing Group, Ltd. GBR. Dist: National Bk. Network.

Xun, Chen. Theological Exegesis in the Canonical Context: Brevard Springs Childs' Methodology of Biblical Theology. 2010. (Studies in Biblical Literature Ser.). 322p. (C). 83.95 *(978-1-4331-0955-3(7))* Lang, Peter Publishing, Inc.

Yip, Francis Ching-Wah. Capitalism as Religion - A Study of Paul Tillich's Interpretation of Modernity. 2010. (Harvard Theological Studies: 59). (Illus.). 240p. pap. 22.95 *(978-0-674-02147-1(9))* Harvard Univ. Pr.

Zarley, Kermit. The Third Day Bible Code. 2006. 268p. per. 17.95 *(978-1-933538-43-3(0))* Synergy Bks.

Zylstra, Henry. Testament of Vision. 2009. 238p. 41.95 *(978-1-104-84606-0(3))* 2007. (ENG.). 236p. per. 26.95 *(978-0-548-44443-6(9))* Kessinger Publishing, LLC.

BIBLE—THEOLOGY—N. T.

Aageson, James W. Paul, the Pastoral Epistles, & the Early Church. Porter, Stanley E., ed. 2008. (Library of Pauline Studies). 235p. per. *(978-1-59856-041-1(7))* Hendrickson Pubs. Marketing, LLC.

Aejmelaeus, Lars. The Nordic Paul: Finnish Approaches to Pauline Theology. Mustakallio, Antti, ed. 2008. (Library of New Testament Studies, the Ser.). (ENG.). 264p. 140.00 *(978-0-567-03310-9(4)*, T&T Clark Int'l) Continuum International Publishing Group, Ltd. GBR. Dist: National Bk. Network.

Amazing Bible Race: Gospels & the Early Church. 2010. 128p. 10.00 *(978-1-4267-0898-5(X))* Abingdon Pr.

Arrington, French L. The Spirit-Anointed Jesus: A Study of the Gospel of Luke. 2008. 427p. *(978-1-59684-317-2(9))* Pathway Pr.

Barclay. Divine & Human Agency in Paul & His Cultural Environment. Barclay, John M. G. & Gathercole, Simon J., eds. 2008. (Library of New Testament Studies, the Ser.). (ENG.). 224p. 44.95 *(978-0-567-08443-9(4)*, T&T Clark Int'l) Continuum International Publishing Group, Ltd. GBR. Dist: National Bk. Network.

Barclay, Gathercole. Divine & Human Agency in Paul & His Cultural Environment, Vol. 335. 2007. (Library of New Testament Studies: Vol. 335). (ENG., Illus.). 224p. 155.00 *(978-0-567-08453-8(1)*, T&T Clark Int'l) Continuum International Publishing Group, Ltd. GBR. Dist: National Bk. Network.

Barclay, John M. G. & Sweet, John Philip McMurdo, eds. Early Christian Thought in its Jewish Context. 2007. (ENG., Illus.). 316p. pap. 61.00 *(978-0-521-04412-7(X))* Cambridge Univ. Pr.

Bassler, Jouette M. Navigating Paul: An Introduction to Key Theological Concepts. 2006. (ENG.). 139p. per. 20.00 *(978-0-664-22741-8(4))* Westminster John Knox Pr.

Bates, Matthew W. The Hermeneutics of the Apostolic Proclamation: The Center of Paul's Method of Scriptural Interpretation. 2012. (ENG.). 415p. 69.95 ***(978-1-60258-328-3(5))*** Baylor Univ. Pr.

Bauckham, Richard. The Epistle to the Hebrews & Christian Theology. Bauckham, Richard et al, eds. 2009. 480p. pap. 36.00 *(978-0-8028-2588-9(5))* Eerdmans, William B. Publishing Co.

Bauscher, Rev. David. The Original Aramaic New Testament in Plain English (with Notes) 2010. 560p. 44.98 *(978-1-4357-3692-4(3))* Lulu Enterprises Inc.

Bayer, Hans F. A Theology of Mark: The Dynamic Between Christology & Authentic Discipleship. 2012. pap. ***(978-1-59638-119-3(1))*** P & R Publishing.

Beardslee, William A. Human Achievement & Divine Vocation in the Message of Paul. 2009. (Studies in Biblical Theology, First Ser.). 142p. pap. 18.00 *(978-1-60899-024-5(9)*, Wipf and Stock) Wipf & Stock Pubs.

Beattie & Sarah Jane Boss, Tina. Marian Reader. 2007. (Illus.). 580p. 90.00 *(978-0-86012-341-5(3)*, Burns & Oates) Continuum International Publishing Group, Ltd. GBR. Dist: National Bk. Network.

Benedict XVI, pseud. Meeting Saint Paul with the Pope: Wednesday Audiences During the Pauline Jubilee Year. 2009. 144p. pap. 10.95 *(978-0-8091-4664-2(9))* Paulist Pr.

—Saint Paul the Apostle. 2009. 122p. pap. 8.95 *(978-1-59276-615-4(3))* Our Sunday Visitor, Publishing Div.

Bernard, David K. Justification & the Holy Spirit. 2007. 132p. 16.99 *(978-1-56722-704-8(X))* Word Aflame Pr.

Bernard, Thomas Dehany. The Progress of Doctrine in the New Testament. 2009. 260p. 24.99 *(978-1-103-47729-6(3))* 2009. 260p. pap. 18.99 *(978-1-103-47725-8(0))* 2009. 288p. 24.99 *(978-0-559-97092-4(7))* 2009. 288p. pap. 18.99 *(978-0-559-97091-7(9))* 2008. 288p. 25.99 *(978-0-559-84812-4(9))* 2008. 288p. pap. 27.75 *(978-0-559-84811-7(0))* BiblioBazaar.

—The Progress of Doctrine in the New Testament. 2006. 264p. per. 23.99 *(978-1-4255-2402-9(8))* MPublishing.

Bird, Michael F. & Sprinkle, Preston M. The Faith of Jesus Christ: Exegetical, Biblical, & Theological Studies, 1 vol. 2010. (ENG.). 356p. *(978-1-59856-429-7(3))* Hendrickson Pubs. Marketing, LLC.

Bock, Darrell L. & Köstenberger, Andreas J. A Theology of Luke & Acts: Biblical Theology of the New Testament, 1 vol. 2012. (Biblical Theology of the New Testament Ser.). (ENG.). 512p. 39.99 ***(978-0-310-27089-8(8))*** Zondervan.

Bockmuehl, Markus & Torrance, Alan J., eds. Scripture's Doctrine & Theology's Bible: How the New Testament Shapes Christian Dogmatics. 2008. 240p. (C). pap. 25.00 *(978-0-8010-3601-9(1))* Baker Academic.

Borg, Marcus J. & Crossan, John Dominic. The First Paul: Reclaiming the Radical Visionary Behind the Church's Conservative Icon. 2009. (Playaway Adult Nonfiction Ser.). (ENG.). 59.99 *(978-1-60847-997-9(8))* Findaway World, LLC.

—The First Paul: Reclaiming the Radical Visionary Behind the Church's Conservative Icon. 2010. (ENG.). 240p. pap. 14.99 *(978-0-06-143073-2(0)*, HarperOne) HarperCollins Pubs.

Bouttier, Michel. Christianity According to Paul. 2009. (Studies in Biblical Theology, First Ser.). 128p. pap. 16.00 *(978-1-60899-027-6(3)*, Wipf and Stock) Wipf & Stock Pubs.

Bovon, François. Luke the Theologian: Fifty-Five Years of Research (1950-2005) 2nd ed. 2006. 445p. per. 39.95 *(978-1-932792-18-8(X))* Baylor Univ. Pr.

Breton, Stanislas. A Radical Philosophy of Saint Paul. Ballan, Joseph N., tr. from FRE. 2011. (Insurrections: Critical Studies in Religion, Politics, & Culture Ser.). (ENG.). 184p. (gr. 17). 84.50 ***(978-0-231-15104-7(7))***; pap. 26.50 ***(978-0-231-15105-4(5))*** Columbia Univ. Pr.

Breytenbach, Cilliers & Du Toit, David S., eds. Focusing on Paul: Persuasion & Theological Design in Romans & Galatians. 2007. (Beihefte Zur Zeitschrift Für Die Neutestamentliche Wissenschaft und Die Kunde der älteren Kirche Ser.). (ENG., Illus.). XIV, 443p. 154.00 *(978-3-11-019512-5(7))* De Gruyter, Walter Inc.

Breytenbach, Cilliers & du Toit, David S., eds. Focusing on Paul: Persuasion & Theological Design in Romans & Galatians. (Beihefte zur Zeitschrift fur die neutestamentliche Wissenschaft und die Kunde der älteren Kirche Ser.). (ENG.). XIV, 443p. 255.00 ***(978-3-11-185305-5(5))*** De Gruyter, Walter Inc.

Bridges, Jerry & Bevington, Bob. The Great Exchange: My Sin for His Righteousness. 2007. 304p. pap. 15.99 *(978-1-58134-927-6(0))* Crossway.

Brower, K. E. Living As God's Holy People: Holiness & Community in Paul. 2011. 156p. pap. 18.00 *(978-1-84227-667-9(0)*, Paternoster) Authentic Media.

Buch-Hansen, Gitte. It Is the Spirit that Gives Life: A Stoic Understanding of Pneuma in John's Gospel. 2010. (Beihefte zur Zeitschrift für die neutestamentliche Wissenschaft und die Kunde der älteren Kirche Ser.). (ENG.). XVII, 502p. 182.00 *(978-3-11-022597-6(2))*; 280.00 ***(978-3-11-174111-6(7))*** De Gruyter, Walter Inc.

Bultmann, Rudolf. Theology of the New Testament. Grobel, Kendrick, tr. from GER. 2007. 648p. per. 39.95 *(978-1-932792-93-5(7))* Baylor Univ. Pr.

Burer, Michael H. Divine Sabbath Work. 2011. ***(978-1-57506-815-2(X))*** Eisenbrauns, Inc.

Butticaz, Simon David. L'identité de L'église Dans les Actes des Apôtres: De la Restauration D'Israël à la Conquête Universelle. 2010. (Beihefte zur Zeitschrift für die neutestamentliche Wissenschaft und die Kunde der älteren Kirche Ser.). (FRE.). XXII, 556p. 182.00 ***(978-3-11-022953-0(6))*** De Gruyter, Walter Inc.

Carter, Christopher L. The Great Sermon Tradition as a Fiscal Framework in 1 Corinthians: Towards a Pauline Theology of Material Possessions. 2010. (Library of New Testament Studies, the Ser.). (ENG.). 288p. 130.00 *(978-0-567-47304-2(X)*, T&T Clark Int'l) Continuum International Publishing Group, Ltd. GBR. Dist: National Bk. Network.

Cavins, Jeff & Sarah, Christmyer. Adventures in Acts Study Set: The Spread of the Kingdom. 2007. (Great Adventure Ser.). 29.95 *(978-1-932927-74-0(3))* Ascension Pr.

Chamblin, J. Knox. Paul & the Self: Apostolic Teaching for Personal Wholeness. 2011. 286p. pap. 31.00 ***(978-1-61097-445-5(X)***, Wipf and Stock) Wipf & Stock Pubs.

Chatham, James O. Creation to Revelation: A Brief Account of the Biblical Story. 2006. (Illus.). 186p. per. 14.00 *(978-0-8028-6322-5(1))* Eerdmans, William B. Publishing Co.

Clarke, Andrew D. Called to Serve: A Pauline Theology of Leadership. 2008. (Library of New Testament Studies, the Ser.). (ENG.). 220p. 130.00 *(978-0-567-04560-7(9)*, T&T Clark Int'l) Continuum International Publishing Group, Ltd. GBR. Dist: National Bk. Network.

Cocoris, G. Michael. Repentance: The Most Misunderstood Word in the Bible. 2010. 99p. pap. *(978-0-9799637-7-3(X))* Grace Gospel Pr.

Costerzee, Johannes Jacobus van. The Theology of the New Testament a Handbook for Bible Students by the Rev J J Van Oosterzee Tr from the Dutch by Maurice J Evans. 2006. 472p. per. 29.99 *(978-1-4255-5252-7(8))* MPublishing.

Crossley, James. Reading the New Testament: Contemporary Approaches. 2010. (Reading Religious Texts). (ENG., Illus.). 200p. (C). pap. 30.95 *(978-0-415-48531-9(2)*, Routledge) Taylor & Francis Group GBR. Dist: Taylor & Francis Group.

Crossley, James G. Reading the New Testament: Contemporary Approaches. 2010. (Reading Religious Texts). (ENG., Illus.). 200p. (C). 100.00 *(978-0-415-48530-2(4))* Routledge.

Crump, David. Knocking on Heaven's Door: A New Testament Theology of Petitionary Prayer. 2006. 352p. (C). pap. 28.00 *(978-0-8010-2689-8(X))* Baker Academic.

D'Elia, John A. Place at the Table: George Eldon Ladd & the Rehabilitation of Evangelical Scholarship in America. 2008. (ENG., Illus.). 288p. 45.00 *(978-0-19-534167-6(8))* Oxford Univ. Pr., Inc.

Denney, James. The Death of Christ, Abridged. Tasker, R. V. G., ed. 2008. 208p. pap. 23.00 *(978-1-55635-777-0(X)*, Wipf and Stock) Wipf & Stock Pubs.

DeWitt, Norman Wentworth. Epicurus & His Philosophy. 2009. (ENG.). 400p. pap. 60.00 *(978-0-8166-5745-2(9))* Univ. of Minnesota Pr.

—St. Paul & Epicurus. 2009. (ENG.). 212p. pap. 50.00 *(978-0-8166-5746-9(7))* Univ. of Minnesota Pr.

DiPaolo, Lawrence, Jr. Hymn Fragments Embedded in the New Testament: Hellenistic Jewish & Greco-Roman Parallels. 2008. 196p. 99.95 *(978-0-7734-4923-7(X))* Mellen, Edwin Pr., The.

Dunn, James. New Testament Theology: An Introduction. 2009. (Library of Biblical Theology Ser.). 232p. pap. 22.00 *(978-0-687-34120-7(5))* Abingdon Pr.

Dunn, James D. G. Did the First Christians Worship Jesus? The New Testament Evidence. 2010. (ENG.). 176p. pap. 20.00 *(978-0-664-23196-5(9))* Westminster John Knox Pr.

Dunning, Benjamin H. Specters of Paul: Sexual Difference in Early Christian Thought. 2011. (Divinations: Rereading Late Ancient Religion Ser.). 264p. (C). 55.00 *(978-0-8122-4307-9(2))* Univ. of Pennsylvania Pr.

Ebert, Daniel J. Wisdom Christology: How Jesus Becomes God's Wisdom for Us. 2011. pap. *(978-1-59638-102-5(7))* P & R Publishing.

Ellens, Deborah L., et al. God's Word for Our World, Vol. 1. 2009. (Library of Hebrew Bible/Old Testament Studies, the Ser.). (ENG.). 336p. 55.00 *(978-1-4411-7724-7(8))* Continuum International Publishing Group, Ltd. GBR. Dist: National Bk. Network.

Fee, Gordon D. Pauline Christology: An Exegetical-Theological Study. 2007. 707p. *(978-1-59856-035-0(2))* Hendrickson Pubs. Marketing, LLC.

Flew, R. Newton. Jesus & His Church. 2009. 192p. pap. 22.00 *(978-1-60608-722-0(3)*, Wipf and Stock) Wipf & Stock Pubs.

Friesen, Philip E. The Old Testament Roots of Nonviolence: Abraham's Personal Faith, Moses' Social Vision, Jesus' Fulfillment, & God's Work Today. 2010. 174p. pap. 20.00 *(978-1-60608-936-1(6)*, Wipf and Stock) Wipf & Stock Pubs.

Furnish, Victor Paul. Theology & Ethics in Paul. 2009. (New Testament Library). (ENG.). 352p. pap. 40.00 *(978-0-664-23336-5(8))* Westminster John Knox Pr.

Gaventa, Beverly Roberts. Our Mother Saint Paul. 2007. (ENG.). 218p. per. 25.00 *(978-0-664-23149-1(7))* Westminster John Knox Pr.

Glasson, T. F. Moses in the Fourth Gospel. 2009. (Studies in Biblical Theology, First Ser.). 116p. pap. 15.00 *(978-1-60899-029-0(X)*, Wipf and Stock) Wipf & Stock Pubs.

Gorman, Michael J. Inhabiting the Cruciform God: Kenosis, Justification, & Theosis in Paul's Narrative Soteriology. 2009. 208p. pap. 24.00 *(978-0-8028-6265-5(9))* Eerdmans, William B. Publishing Co.

Guttenberger, Gudrun. Die Gottesvorstellung im Markusevangelium. (Beihefte zur Zeitschrift far die neutestamentliche Wissenschaft und die Kunde der älteren Kirche Ser.). (GER.). IX, 477p. 300.00 ***(978-3-11-182784-1(4))*** De Gruyter, Walter Inc.

Haffner, Paul. New Testament Theology. 2008. 276p. pap. *(978-88-902268-0-9(3))* Gracewing, Ltd.

Hahn, Scott. Scott Hahn's Study Guide for the Lamb's Supper. 2010. (ENG.). 112p. pap. 9.99 *(978-0-307-58905-7(6),* Doubleday Religion) Doubleday Religious Publishing Group, The.

Hannan, Peter. Nine Portraits. 2nd rev. ed. 2009. (ENG.). 185p. pap. 22.95 *(978-1-85607-649-4(0))* Columba Pr. IRL. Dist: Dufour Editions, Inc.

Harink, Douglas, ed. Paul, Philosophy, & the Theopolitical Vision: Critical Engagements with Agamben, Badiou, Zizek, & Others. 2010. (Theopolitical Visions Ser.). 350p. pap. 39.00 *(978-1-60608-662-9(6),* Cascade Bks.) Wipf & Stock Pubs.

Hausser, Detlef. Christusbekenntnis und Jesusüberlieferung bei Paulus. 2006 (Wissenschaftliche Untersuchungen Zum Neuen Testament 2 Ser.: Vol. 210). 416p. (C). pap. 135.00 *(978-3-16-148962-4(4))* Mohr Siebeck GmbH & Co. KG DEU. Dist: Coronet Bks.

Heil, John Paul. The Letters of Paul as Rituals of Worship. 2012. (ENG.). 216p. pap. 35.00 ***(978-0-227-68007-0(3))*** Clarke, James Co., Ltd. GBR. Dist: Brown, David Bk. Co., The.

—The Letters of Paul as Rituals of Worship. 2011. 216p. pap. 24.00 *(978-1-60899-870-8(3),* Cascade Bks.) Wipf & Stock Pubs.

Helyer, Larry R. The Witness of Jesus, Paul & John: An Exploration in Biblical Theology. 2008. (ENG., Illus.). 432p. 32.00 *(978-0-8308-2888-3(5),* IVP Acad.) InterVarsity Pr.

Henderson, Ian. Myth in the New Testament. 2009. (Studies in Biblical Theology, First Ser.). 58p. pap. 8.00 *(978-1-60899-026-9(5),* Wipf and Stock) Wipf & Stock Pubs.

Hinlicky, Paul R. Divine Complexity: The Rise of Creedal Christianity. 2010. 304p. pap. 32.00 *(978-0-8006-9669-6(7),* Fortress Pr.) Augsburg Fortress, Pubs

Holland, Tom. Romans: the Divine Marriage: A Biblical Theological Commentary. 2011. 558p. pap. 56.00 ***(978-1-60899-809-8(6),*** Pickwick Pubns.) Wipf & Stock Pubs.

Holtz, Gudrun. Damit Gott sei Alles in Allem: Studien Zum Paulinischen und Fruehjuedischen Universalismus. 2007. (Beihefte Zur Zeitschrift Für Die Neutestamentliche Wissenschaft und Die Kunde der älteren Kirche Ser.). (GER.). XI, 650p. 210.00 *(978-3-11-019553-8(4))* De Gruyter, Walter Inc.

Hook, Norman. The Eucharist in the New Testament. 2009. 158p. pap. 18.00 *(978-1-60608-713-8(4),* Wipf and Stock) Wipf & Stock Pubs.

Hooker, Morna D. From Adam to Christ: Essays on Paul. 2008. 208p. pap. 23.00 *(978-1-60608-024-5(5))* Wipf & Stock Pubs.

Hunter, A. M. Introducing New Testament Theology. 2012. 160p. pap. ***(978-0-334-00699-2(6),*** SCM Pr.) Hymns Ancient & Modern Ltd.

Hurtado, Larry W. God in New Testament Theology. 2010. (Library of Biblical Theology Ser.). 176p. pap. 21.00 *(978-0-687-46545-3(1))* Abingdon Pr.

Isaak, Jon M. New Testament Theology: Extending the Table. 2010. (Illus.). 404p. pap. 44.00 *(978-1-55635-293-5(X),* Cascade Bks.) Wipf & Stock Pubs.

Jackson-McCabe, Matt A. Logos & Law in the Letter of James: The Law of Nature, the Law of Moses, & the Law of Freedom. 2010. *(978-1-58983-501-6(8))* Society of Biblical Literature.

Jeffery, Peter. Moving Out: With the Christian Faith. 2007. 126p. per. *(978-0-85234-609-9(3))* Evangelical Pr.

Jeremias, Joachim & Bowden, John. New Testament Theology. 2012. xvii, 330p. pap. ***(978-0-334-01144-6(2),*** SCM Pr.) Hymns Ancient & Modern Ltd.

Johnson, Luke Timothy. Prophetic Jesus, Prophetic Church: The Challenge of Luke-Acts to Contemporary Christians. 2011. 206p. pap. 23.00 ***(978-0-8028-0390-0(3))*** Eerdmans, William B. Publishing Co.

Judge, E. A. & Scholer, David M. Social Distinctives of the Christians in the First Century: Pivotal Essays. 2008. 232p. pap. *(978-1-56563-880-8(8))* Hendrickson Pubs. Marketing, LLC.

Kangosa, Guy-Angelo. Die Bedeutung der Jesaja-Zitate für die lukanische Christologie: Eine exegetische Untersuchung mit Ausblick auf den afrikanischen Kontext. 2008. (Europäische Hochschulschriften. Reihe 23: Theologie Ser.). 240p. pap. 61.95 *(978-3-631-57686-1(2))* Lang, Peter GmbH, Europaischer Verlag der Wissenschaften DEU. Dist: Lang, Peter.

Käsemann, Ernst, et al. On Being a Disciple of the Crucified Nazarene: Unpublished Lectures & Sermons. 2010. 352p. pap. 30.00 *(978-0-8028-6026-2(5))* Eerdmans, William B. Publishing Co.

Kim, Yung Suk. A Theological Introduction to PaulÕs Letters: Exploring a Threefold Theology of Paul. 2011. 162p. pap. 19.00 ***(978-1-60899-793-0(6),*** Cascade Bks.) Wipf & Stock Pubs.

Koester, Craig R. The Word of Life: A Theology of John's Gospel. 2008. 264p. pap. 21.00 *(978-0-8028-2938-2(4))* Eerdmans, William B. Publishing Co.

Konsmo, Erik. The Pauline Metaphors of the Holy Spirit: The Intangible Spirit's Tangible Presence in the Life of the Christian. 2010. (Studies in Biblical Literature Ser.). 242p. (C). 75.95 *(978-1-4331-0691-0(4))* Lang, Peter Publishing, Inc.

Kostenberger, Andreas J. A Theology of John's Gospel & Letters: The Word, the Christ, the Son of God, 1 vol. 2009. (Biblical Theology of the New Testament Ser.). (ENG.). 656p. 39.99 *(978-0-310-26986-1(5))* Zondervan.

Kuma, Hermann V. A. The Centrality of Aiua (Blood) in the Theology of the Epistle to the Hebrews: An Exegetical & Philological Study. 2011. 129.95 *(978-0-7734-1461-7(4))* Mellen, Edwin Pr., The.

Laansma, Jon C., et al, eds. New Testament Theology in Light of the ChurchÕs Mission: Essays in Honor of I. Howard Marshall. 2011. 418p. pap. 46.00 ***(978-1-61097-530-8(8),*** Cascade Bks.) Wipf & Stock Pubs.

Lathrop, John P. Answer the Prayer of Jesus: A Call for Biblical Unity. 2011. (House of Prisca & Aquila Ser.). 128p. pap. 16.00 *(978-1-60899-392-5(2),* Wipf and Stock) Wipf & Stock Pubs.

Lee. Paul's Gospel in Romans: A Discourse Analysis of Rom 1:16-8:39. 2009. (Linguistic Biblical Studies). *(978-90-04-17963-9(1))* BRILL.

Lightner, Robert P. Portraits of Jesus in the Gospel of John. 2007. 202p. pap. 23.00 *(978-1-59752-878-8(1),* Resource Pubns.) Wipf & Stock Pubs.

Loader, William. The New Testament with Imagination: A Fresh Approach to Its Writings & Themes. 2007. (Illus.). 206p. per. 16.00 *(978-0-8028-2746-3(2))* Eerdmans, William B. Publishing Co.

Long, D. Stephen. Hebrews: Belief: A Theological Commentary on the Bible. 2011. (Belief Ser.). (ENG.). 208p. 30.00 *(978-0-664-23251-1(5))* Westminster John Knox Pr.

Luz, Ulrich, et al. Ökumene im Neuen Testament und heute. 2009. (GER.). 339p. (C). pap. 48.00 *(978-3-525-56355-7(8))* Vandenhoeck & Ruprecht GmbH & Co. KG DEU. Dist: ISD.

Machen, J. Gresham. Origin of Pauls Religion. 2006. pap. 31.95 *(978-1-4286-4490-8(3))* Kessinger Publishing, LLC.

—Origin of Paul's Religion. 329p. reprint ed. 98.00 *(978-0-7222-2143-3(6))* Library Reprints, Inc.

Malbon, Elizabeth Struthers. Mark's Jesus: Characterization as Narrative Christology. 2009. (ENG., Illus.). 360p. 39.95 *(978-1-60258-247-7(5))* Baylor Univ. Pr.

Manson, T. W. On Paul & John. 2009. (Studies in Biblical Theology, First Ser.). 168p. pap. 19.00 *(978-1-60899-031-3(1),* Wipf and Stock) Wipf & Stock Pubs.

Marshall, I. Howard. A Concise New Testament Theology. 2008. (ENG.). 304p. pap. 23.00 *(978-0-8308-2878-4(8),* IVP Acad.) InterVarsity Pr.

Martin, Isaac D. The Mystery of Christ & the Church. 2007. 79p. (YA). (gr. 11). pap. 3.95 *(978-0-7399-2389-4(7))* Rod & Staff Pubs., Inc.

Matera, Frank J. New Testament Theology: Exploring Diversity & Unity. 2007. (ENG.). 485p. per. 50.00 *(978-0-664-23044-9(X))* Westminster John Knox Pr.

McComiskey, Douglas S. Lukan Theology in the Light of the Gospel's Literary Structure. 2007. (Paternoster Biblical Monographs: Ser.). 422p. pap. 43.00 *(978-1-59752-786-6(6),* Wipf and Stock) Wipf & Stock Pubs.

McDonough, Sean M. Christ as Creator: Origins of a New Testament Doctrine. 2010. (ENG.). 288p. 120.00 *(978-0-19-957647-0(5))* Oxford Univ. Pr., Inc.

McKnight, Scot. The King Jesus Gospel: The Original Good News Revisited, 1 vol. 2011. (ENG.). 192p. 19.99 *(978-0-310-49298-6(X))* Zondervan.

Miller, Ted. Into His Rest: Refuting Liberation Theology's Use of the Exodus with Hebrews 3-4. 2009. *(978-1-60682-000-1(1))* BJU Pr.

Mittelstadt, Martin. Reading Luke-Acts in the Pentecostal Tradition: Reflections on the History & Status of Research. 2010. (ENG.). 232p. (C). pap. 14.95 *(978-0-9819651-7-8(2))* CPT Pr.

Morales, Rodrigo J. The Spirit & the Restoration of Israel: New Exodus & New Creation Motifs in Galatians. 2010. (Illus.). 209p. pap. 97.50 *(978-3-16-150435-8(6))* Mohr Siebeck GmbH & Co. KG DEU. Dist: Coronet Bks.

Morgan, Christopher W. A Theology of James: Wisdom for God's People. 2010. pap. *(978-1-59638-084-4(5))* P & R Publishing.

Morgan, Robert. The Nature of New Testament Theology. 2009. (Studies in Biblical Theology, Second Ser.). 206p. pap. 23.00 *(978-1-60608-707-7(X),* Wipf and Stock) Wipf & Stock Pubs.

Morrison, Clinton D. The Powers That Be. 2009. (Studies in Biblical Theology, First Ser.). 144p. pap. 18.00 *(978-1-60899-025-2(7),* Wipf and Stock) Wipf & Stock Pubs.

Morrison, James. A Critical Exposition of the Third Chapter of Paul's Epistle to the Romans. A Monograph. 2009. 444p. pap. 36.00 *(978-1-60608-376-5(7),* Wipf and Stock) Wipf & Stock Pubs.

North, Christopher R. The Old Testament Interpretation of History. 2009. 226p. pap. 26.00 *(978-1-60608-714-5(2),* Wipf and Stock) Wipf & Stock Pubs.

O'Neill, Lynn I. The Manchild Vision. 2008. pap. 16.00 *(978-0-8059-7933-6(6))* Dorrance Publishing Co., Inc.

Oropeza, B. J. Paul & Apostasy: Eschatology, Perseverance, & Falling Away in the Corinthian Congregation. 2007. 324p. pap. 36.00 *(978-1-55635-333-8(2),* Wipf and Stock) Wipf & Stock Pubs.

Padilla, Osvaldo. The Speeches of Outsiders in Acts: Poetics, Theology & Historiography. 2008. (Society for New Testament Studies Monograph Ser.). (ENG.). 288p. 127.00 *(978-0-521-89981-9(8))* Cambridge Univ. Pr.

Pahl, Michael W. The Beginning & the End: Rereading GenesisÕs Stories & Revelation's Visions. 2011. 118p. pap. 15.00 ***(978-1-60899-927-9(0),*** Cascade Bks.) Wipf & Stock Pubs.

Pennington, Mcdonough, et al. Cosmology & New Testament Theology. 2008. (Library of New Testament Studies). (ENG.). 224p. 130.00 *(978-0-567-03143-3(8),* T&T Clark Int'l) Continuum International Publishing Group, Ltd. GBR. Dist: National Bk. Network.

Pentecost, J. Dwight. New Wine: A Study of Transition in the Book of Acts, 1 vol. 2010. (ENG.). 144p. pap. 10.99 *(978-0-8254-3597-3(8))* Kregel Pubns.

Phillips, Richard D. Saved by Grace: The Glory of Salvation in Ephesians 2. 2009. pap. *(978-1-59638-127-8(2))* P & R Publishing.

Piper, John. The Future of Justification: A Response to N. T. Wright. 2007. 240p. pap. 17.99 *(978-1-58134-964-1(5))* Crossway.

Plevnik, Joseph. What Are They Saying about Paul & the End Time? 2009. (What Are They Saying about ... ? Ser.). 144p. pap. 14.95 *(978-0-8091-4578-2(2))* Paulist Pr.

Porter, Stanley E., ed. Paul & His Theology. 2006. (Pauline Studies: Vol. 3). 454p. *(978-90-04-15408-7(6))* BRILL.

Prat, Ferdinand. The Theology of Saint Paul, 2 Volumes. Stoddard, John L., tr. 2010. 1060p. pap. 117.00 *(978-1-60899-685-8(9),* Wipf and Stock) Wipf & Stock Pubs.

Rambo, Shelly. Spirit & Trauma: A Theology of Remaining. 2010. (ENG.). 176p. pap. 25.00 *(978-0-664-23503-1(4))* Westminster John Knox Pr.

Ratke, David C. The New Perspective on Paul: Perennial Questions & Contemporary Challenges. 2012. ***(978-1-932688-67-2(6))*** Kirk Hse. Pubs.

Ratzinger, Joseph. Jesus of Nazareth. 2007. 200p. pap. 14.95 *(978-1-58617-198-8(4))* Ignatius Pr.

—Jesus of Nazareth. 62p. pap., stu. ed. 9.99 Vision Video.

Ratzinger, Joseph & Pope Benedict XVI. Jesus of Nazareth. Walker, Adrian J., tr. from GER. 2007. (ENG.). 400p. 26.00 *(978-0-385-52341-7(6),* Doubleday) Doubleday Religious Publishing Group, The.

Reeves, Rodney. Spirituality According to Paul: Imitating the Apostle of Christ. 2011. (ENG.). 253p. pap. 20.00 ***(978-0-8308-3946-9(1),*** IVP Acad.) InterVarsity Pr.

Richardson, Alan. An Introduction to the Theology of the New Testament. 2012. 423p. pap. ***(978-0-334-00709-8(7),*** SCM Pr.) Hymns Ancient & Modern Ltd.

Riley, William. King & Cultus in Chronicles: Worship & the Reinterpretation of History. 2009. (Library of Hebrew Bible/Old Testament Studies, the Ser.). (ENG.). 229p. 39.95 *(978-0-567-31259-4(3),* T&T Clark) Continuum International Publishing Group, Ltd. GBR. Dist: National Bk. Network.

Robertson, O. Palmer. God's People in the Wilderness: The Church in Hebrews. 2009. (ENG.). 160p. 17.99 *(978-1-84550-477-9(1),* Mentor) Christian Focus Pubns. GBR. Dist: STL Distribution North America.

Rolston, Holmes. Consider Paul, Apostle of Jesus Christ: Revelation & Inspiration in the Letters of Paul. 2011. 216p. 44.95 ***(978-1-258-02108-5(0))*** Literary Licensing, LLC.

Ronning, John L. The Jewish Targums & John's Logos Theology, 1 vol. 2010. (ENG., Illus.). 400p. *(978-1-59856-306-1(8))* Hendrickson Pubs. Marketing, LLC.

Samra, James G. & Samra. Being Conformed to Christ in Community: A Study of Maturity, Maturation & the Local Church in the Undisputed Pauline Epistles. 2006. (Library of New Testament Studies: Vol. 320). (ENG.). 280p. 140.00 *(978-0-567-04354-2(1),* T&T Clark Int'l) Continuum International Publishing Group, Ltd. GBR. Dist: National Bk. Network.

Schaefer, Charles W. The Great Evangelical Dilution. 2006. 232p. pap. 17.99 *(978-1-4141-0719-6(6))* Pleasant Word.

Schenck, Kenneth. Paul: Prisoner of Hope. 2012. ***(978-0-89827-525-4(3))*** Wesleyan Publishing Hse.

Schnelle, Udo. Theology of the New Testament, 1 vol. 2009. (ENG.). 896p. (C). 59.99 *(978-0-8010-3604-0(6))* Baker Academic.

Schreiner, Thomas R. Magnifying God in Christ: A Summary of New Testament Theology, 1 vol. 2010. (ENG.). 272p. (C). pap. 24.99 *(978-0-8010-3826-6(X))* Baker Academic.

—New Testament Theology: Magnifying God in Christ. 2008. 976p. (C). 45.00 *(978-0-8010-2680-5(6))* Baker Academic.

Schroter, Jens. Von Jesus zum Neuen Testament. 2007. (Wissenschaftliche Untersuchungen Zum Neuen Testament Ser.: 204). 441p. (C). 157.50 *(978-3-16-149231-0(5))* Mohr Siebeck GmbH & Co. KG DEU. Dist: Coronet Bks.

Scott, Jr., James Julius. New Testament Theology: A New Study of the Thematic Structure of the New Testament. 2008. (ENG.). 368p. 29.99 *(978-1-84550-256-0(6),* Mentor) Christian Focus Pubns. GBR. Dist: STL Distribution North America.

Scroggs, Robin. The People's Jesus: Trajectories in Early Christianity. Johnson, Marshall, ed. 2011. 240p. (C). 29.00 *(978-0-8006-9791-4(X),* Fortress Pr.) Augsburg Fortress, Pubs.

Sellin, Gerhard & Sänger, Dieter. Studien zu Paulus und zum Epheserbrief: Forschungen zur Religion und Literatur des Alten und Neuen Testaments 229. 2009. (Forschungen Zur Religion und Literatur des Alten & Neuen Testament Ser.). (GER.). 279p. (C). 98.00 *(978-3-525-53093-1(5))* Vandenhoeck & Ruprecht GmbH & Co. KG DEU. Dist: ISD.

Shauf, Scott. Theology as History, History as Theology: Paul in Ephesus in Acts 19. (Beihefte zur Zeitschrift für die neutestamentliche Wissenschaft und die Kunde der älteren Kirche Ser.). (ENG.). X, 377p. 255.00 ***(978-3-11-182501-4(9))*** De Gruyter, Walter Inc.

Sidebottom, E. M. The Christ of the Fourth Gospel. 2010. 240p. pap. 27.00 *(978-1-60899-746-6(4),* Wipf and Stock) Wipf & Stock Pubs.

Sleeman, Matthew. Geography & the Ascension Narrative in Acts. 2009. (Society for New Testament Studies Monograph Ser.). (ENG.). 312p. 102.00 *(978-0-521-50962-6(9))* Cambridge Univ. Pr.

Stanbury, Wendy. High Five. 2007. 64p. pap. *(978-1-84427-251-8(6))* Scripture Union.

Starling, David I. Not My People: Gentiles as Exiles in Pauline Hermeneutics. 2011. (Beihefte zur Zeitschrift fur die neutestamentliche Wissenschaft und die Kunde der älteren Kirche Ser.). (ENG., Illus.). XII, 254p. 210.00 ***(978-3-11-916515-0(8))*** De Gruyter, Walter Inc.

Steyn, Gert J. A Quest for the Assumed LXX Vorlage of the Explicit Quotations in Hebrews. 2011. (Forschungen Zur Religion und Literatur des Alten & Neuen Testament Ser.). (ENG., Illus.). 458p. (C). 203.00 *(978-3-525-53099-3(4))* Vandenhoeck & Ruprecht GmbH & Co. KG DEU. Dist: ISD.

Still, Todd D. & Horrell, David G. After the First Urban Christians: The Social-Scientific Study of Pauline Christianity Twenty-Five Years Later. Still, Todd D. & Horrell, David G., eds. 2009. (ENG., Illus.). 192p. 120.00 *(978-0-567-42774-8(9));* pap. 34.95 *(978-0-567-21967-1(4))* Continuum International Publishing Group, Ltd. GBR. (T&T Clark Int'l). Dist: National Bk. Network.

Stubbs, David L. Numbers, 1 vol. 2009. (Brazos Theological Commentary on the Bible Ser.). 272p. (C). 29.99 *(978-1-58743-140-1(8))* Brazos Pr.

Stuhlmacher, Peter. Schriftauslegung Auf Dem Wege Zur Biblischen Theologie. 2011. (Forschungen Zur Religion und Literatur des Alten & Neuen Testament Ser.). (GER & ENG.). 487p. (C). 140.00 ***(978-3-525-53555-4(4))*** Vandenhoeck & Ruprecht GmbH & Co. KG DEU. Dist: ISD.

Talbert, Charles H. & Whitlark, Jason A. Getting Saved: A Theology of Salvation in the New Testament. 2011. 320p. pap. 30.00 *(978-0-8028-6648-5(4))* Eerdmans, William B. Publishing Co.

Talbot, Elizabeth Viera. Luke: Salvation for All. 2011. pap. 1.99 *(978-0-8163-2482-8(4))* Pacific Pr. Publishing Assn.

Thigpen, Paul. A Bible Study Guide for Catholics: St. Paul: Jubilee Year of the Apostle Paul Edition. 2008. per. 8.95 *(978-1-59276-420-4(7));* per. 53.95 *(978-1-59276-423-5(1))* Our Sunday Visitor, Publishing Div.

Turner, Max, et al. The Spirit & Christ in the New Testament & Christian Theology: Essays in Honor of Max Turner. 2012. pap. ***(978-0-8028-6753-7(7))*** Eerdmans, William B. Publishing Co.

Vanhoozer, Kevin J., ed. Theological Interpretation of the New Testament: A Book-by-Book Survey. 2008. 272p. (C). pap. 19.99 *(978-0-8010-3623-1(2))* Baker Academic.

Vickers, Brian. Jesus' Blood & Righteousness: Paul's Theology of Imputation. 2006. 256p. pap. 14.99 *(978-1-58134-754-8(5))* Crossway.

Wilkens, Hermann. Kata Markon. (GER.). 116p. 28.95 *(978-3-631-34879-6(7))* Lang, Peter Publishing, Inc.

Wills, Garry. What Paul Meant. 2007. (ENG.). 208p. (gr. 12-18). 14.00 *(978-0-14-311263-1(5),* Penguin (Non-Classics)) Penguin Group (USA) Inc.

—What Paul Meant. lt. ed. 2007. (Thorndike Inspirational Ser.). 245p. 30.95 *(978-0-7862-9009-3(9))* Thorndike Pr.

Wilson, J. M., tr. The Acts of the Apostles: Translated from the Codex Bezae with an Introduction on its Lucan Origin & Importance. 2011. 104p. pap. 11.00 *(978-1-61097-123-2(X),* Wipf and Stock) Wipf & Stock Pubs.

Winstanley, Edward William. Spirit in the New Testament: An Enquiry into the Use of the Word Pneuma in All Passages, & a Survey of the Evidence Concerning the Holy Spirit. 2008. (Illus.). 174p. pap. 15.00 *(978-1-55635-772-5(9),* Wipf & Stock Pubs.

Wright, N. T. & Hurst, L. D., eds. The Glory of Christ in the New Testament Studies in Christology - in Memory of George Bradford Caird. 2006. 344p. pap. 35.00 *(978-1-59752-956-3(7),* Wipf and Stock) Wipf & Stock Pubs.

Zimmermann, Christiane. Die Namen des Vaters: Studien zu ausgewählten neutestamentlichen Gottesbezeichnungen. 2007. (Ancient Judaism & Early Christianity Ser.). (GER.). 728p. *(978-90-04-15812-2(X))* BRILL.

BIBLE—THEOLOGY—O. T.

Ajayi, Joel A. A. A Biblical Theology of Gerassapience. 2010. (Studies in Biblical Literature Ser.). 280p. (C). 79.95 *(978-1-4331-0785-6(6),)* Lang, Peter Publishing, Inc.

Anderson, Bernhard W. Contours of Old Testament Theology. 2011. 372p. (C). pap. 29.00 *(978-0-8006-9834-8(7),* Fortress Pr.) Augsburg Fortress, Pubs.

Baldwin, Joyce G. Haggai, Zechariah & Malachi. 2009. (Tyndale Old Testament Commentaries Ser.: Volume 28). (ENG.). 277p. pap. 16.00 *(978-0-8308-4228-5(4),* IVP Acad.) InterVarsity Pr.

Barton, John. Amos's Oracles Against the Nations. 2009. (Society for Old Testament Study Monographs). (ENG.). 96p. pap. 20.99 *(978-0-521-10408-1(4))* Cambridge Univ. Pr.

Barton, John. The Theology of the Book of Amos. 2012. (Old Testament Theology Ser.). (ENG.). 215p. 99.00 ***(978-0-521-85577-8(2));*** pap. 25.99 ***(978-0-521-67175-0(2))*** Cambridge Univ. Pr.

Begerau, Gunnar. Elia vom Krit zum Jordan: Eine Untersuchung zur literarischen Makrostruktur und theologischen Intention der Elia-Ahab-Erzählung (1 Kön 16,29 bis 2 Kön 2,25) 2008. (Europäische Hochschulschriften. Reihe 23: Theologie Ser.). (GER., Illus.). 322p. pap. 74.95 *(978-3-631-58366-9(9))* Lang, Peter GmbH, Europaischer Verlag der Wissenschaften DEU. Dist: Lang, Peter.

Bell, Robert D. The Theological Messages of the Old Testament Books. 2010. *(978-1-60682-159-6(8)); (978-1-59166-992-0(8))* BJU Pr.

Benedict XVI, pseud & Ratzinger, Joseph. Jesus of Nazareth. 2009. (Illus.) 432p. 24.95 *(978-0-8478-3271-2(6))* Rizzoli International Pubns., Inc.

Block, Daniel I. How I Love Your Torah, O LORD! Literary & Theological Explorations on the Book of Deuteronomy. 2011. 270p. pap. 30.00 ***(978-1-61097-342-7(9),*** Cascade Bks.) Wipf & Stock Pubs.

Boda, Mark J. A Severe Mercy: Sin & Its Remedy in the Old Testament. 2009. x, 622p. 59.50 *(978-1-57506-164-1(3))* Eisenbrauns, Inc.

Botterweck, G. Johannes, et al, eds. Theological Dictionary of the Old Testament, Vol. 15. Green, David E., tr. from GER. 2006. (Theological Dictionary of the Old Testament Ser.). 793p. 65.00 *(978-0-8028-2339-7(4))* Eerdmans, William B. Publishing Co.

Brueggemann, Walter. Teologia del Antiguo Testamento: Un Juicio A Yahve; Testimonio. Disputa. Defensa. 2007. (Biblioteca de Estudios Biblicos Minor Ser.). 816p. 65.00 *(978-84-301-1634-8(6))* Sigueme, Ediciones, S.A. ESP. Dist: Augsburg Fortress, Pubs.

Eucher, Christina, et al. The Witness of the Hebrew Bible for a New Testament Church. 2010. pap. *(978-0-87178-145-1(X))* Brethren Pr.

Carroll, Robert P. Text as Pretext: Essays in Honour of Robert Davidson. 2009. (Library of Hebrew Bible/Old Testament Studies, the Ser.). (ENG.). 307p. 49.95 *(978-0-567-43776-1(0),* T&T Clark) Continuum International Publishing Group, Ltd. GBR. Dist: National Bk. Network.

Cheyne, T. K. Origin & Religious Contents of the Psa. 2006. pap. 42.95 (978-1-4286-3984-3(5)) Kessinger Publishing, LLC.

Cox, Harvey & Paulsell, Stephanie. Lamentations & the Song of Songs: A Theological Commentary on the Bible. 2012. (Belief: A Theological Commentary on the Bible Ser.). (ENG.). 304p. 30.00 **(978-0-664-23302-0(3))** Westminster John Knox Pr.

Crenshaw, James L. A Whirlpool of Torment: Israelite Traditions of God As an Oppressive Presence. 2008. 148p. pap. 16.95 (978-1-58983-349-4(X)) Society of Biblical Literature.

Dietrich, Walter, et al. Diasynchron: Beiträge zur Exegese, Theologie und Rezeption der Hebräischen Bibel. Walter Dietrich zum 65. Geburtstag. 2009. (GER., Illus.). 448p. (978-3-17-020822-3(5)) Kohlhammer, W., GmbH.

Dumbrell, W. J. Covenant & Creation: A Theology of Old Testament Covenants. 2009. 218p. pap. 24.00 (978-1-60899-238-6(1), Wipf and Stock) Wipf & Stock Pubs.

Estelle, Bryan D., et al. The Law Is Not of Faith: Essays on Works & Grace in the Mosaic Covenant. 2009. pap. (978-1-59638-100-1(0)) P & R Publishing.

Fesko, J. V. Last Things First: Unlocking Genesis 1-3 with the Christ of Eschatology. 2007. (Last Things First Ser.). (ENG.). 208p. per. 19.99 (978-1-84550-229-4(9), Mentor) Christian Focus Pubns. GBR. Dist: STL Distribution North America.

Fosbroke, Hughell E. W. Divine Transcendence in the Old Testament. 2011. 28p. 35.95 **(978-1-258-01727-9(X))** Literary Licensing, LLC.

Friesen, Philip E. The Old Testament Roots of Nonviolence: Abraham's Personal Faith, Moses' Social Vision, Jesus' Fulfillment, & God's Work Today. 2010. 174p. pap. 20.00 (978-1-60608-936-1(6), Wipf and Stock) Wipf & Stock Pubs.

Gertz, Jan Christian, et al. T&T Clark Handbook of the Old Testament: An Introduction to the Literature, Religion & History of the Old Testament. 2012. (ENG.). 872p. 160.00 (978-0-567-42529-4(0)); pap. 49.95 (978-0-567-25368-2(6)) Continuum International Publishing Group, Ltd. GBR. (T&T Clark Int'l). Dist: National Bk. Network.

Glenny, W. Edward. Finding Meaning in the Text: Translation Technique & Theology in the Septuagint of Amos. 2009. 322p. (978-90-04-17638-6(1)) BRILL.

Glueck, Nelson. Hesed in the Bible. Epstein, Elias L., ed. Gottschalk, Alfred, tr. 2011. 118p. pap. 15.00 **(978-1-61097-124-9(8)**, Wipf and Stock) Wipf & Stock Pubs.

Goldingay, John. Key Questions about Christian Faith: Old Testament Answers. 2010. (978-1-59856-430-3(7)) Hendrickson Pubs. Marketing, LLC.

—Old Testament Theology Vol. 2: Israel's Faith. 2006. (Old Testament Theology Ser.). (ENG.). 891p. 50.00 (978-0-8308-2562-2(2), IVP Acad.) InterVarsity Pr.

Gordon, Robert P., ed. The God of Israel. 2007. (University of Cambridge Oriental Publications). (ENG.). 326p. 122.99 (978-0-521-87365-9(7)) Cambridge Univ. Pr.

Gregory, Bryan R. Longing for God in an Age of Discouragement: The Gospel According to Zechariah. 2010. pap. (978-1-59638-142-1(6)) P & R Publishing.

Groves, J. Alan, et al. Eyes to See, Ears to Hear: Essays in Memory of J. Alan Groves. 2010. (Illus.). xxxiii, 225p. pap. (978-1-59638-122-3(1)) P & R Publishing.

Hebbard, Aaron B. Reading Daniel as a Text in Theological Hermeneutics. 2008. (Princeton Theological Monographs). 256p. pap. 28.00 (978-1-60608-991-0(9), Pickwick Pubns.) Wipf & Stock Pubs.

—Reading Daniel As a Text in Theological Hermeneutics Pb. 2011. (ENG.). 243p. pap. 42.50 (978-0-227-17364-0(3)) Clarke, James Co., Ltd. GBR. Dist: Brown, David Bk. Co., The.

Hensel, Benedikt. Die Vertauschung des Erstgeburtssegens in der Genesis: Eine Analyse der Narrativ-Theologischen Grundstruktur des Ersten Buches der Tora. 2011. (Beihefte zur Zeitschrift für die alttestamentliche Wissenschaft Ser.). (GER.). XIV, 387p. 182.00 **(978-3-11-024792-3(5))** De Gruyter, Walter Inc.

Hrobon, Bohdan. Ethical Dimension of Cult in the Book of Isaiah. (Beihefte zur Zeitschrift far die alttestamentliche Wissenschaft Ser.). (ENG., 2011. Illus.). XIII, 256p. 196.00 **(978-3-11-215064-1(3))** 2010. 310p. 126.00 (978-3-11-024748-0(8)) De Gruyter, Walter Inc.

Iannucci, Anthony. Gleanings from Genesis. 2011. 348p. pap. 18.99 (978-1-61215-818-1(8)) Xulon Pr., Inc.

Jenson, Robert W. Ezekiel. 2009. 384p. (C). 32.99 (978-1-58743-166-1(1)) Brazos Pr.

Johnson, Norman B. & Johnson, Norman B. Prayer in Apocrypha & Pseudepigraph: A Study of the Jewish Concept of God. 2011. 82p. 37.95 **(978-1-258-03761-1(0))** Literary Licensing, LLC.

Kearns, Conleth. The Expanded Text of Ecclesiasticus: Its Teaching on the Future Life as a Clue to its Origin. Beentjes, Pancratius C., ed. 2011. (Deuterocanonical & Cognate Literature Studies). (ENG., Illus.). VI, 333p. 210.00 **(978-3-11-219102-6(1))** De Gruyter, Walter Inc.

Kearns, Conleth, et al. The Expanded Text of Ecclesiastius: Its Teaching on the Future Life As a Clue to Its Origin. 2011. (Deuterocanonical & Cognate Literature Studies). (ENG., Illus.). VI, 333p. 140.00 **(978-3-11-025258-3(9))** De Gruyter, Walter Inc.

Kinlaw, Dennis & Oswalt, John. Lectures in Old Testament Theology: Yahweh Is God Alone. 2010. 492p. pap. (978-0-915143-15-3(1)) Francis Asbury Society.

Kinlaw, Dennis F & Oswalt, John N. Lectures in Old Testament Theology. 2011. (ENG.). 496p. (C). pap. 29.95 **(978-1-59317-542-9(6))** Warner Pr. Pubs.

Klement, Herbert H. & Steinberg, Julius. Themenbuch Zur Theologie des Alten Testaments. 2007. (GER., Illus.). 342p. (978-3-417-29545-0(9)); (978-3-7655-9545-5(4)) Brockhaus, R. Verlag GmbH & Co.

Knight, George W. The Names of God: an Illustrated Guide. 2009. (ENG.). 256p. pap. 9.99 (978-1-60260-343-1(X), Barbour Bks.) Barbour Publishing, Inc.

Lange, Lyle W. Bible Discovery Series: Discovering the Heart of the Old Testament. 2010. pap. (978-0-8100-2245-4(1)) Northwestern Publishing Hse.

Lemaire, André. The Birth of Monotheism: The Rise & Disappearance of Yahwism. 2007. (978-1-880317-99-0(0)) Biblical Archaeology Society.

Lohr, Joel N. Chosen & Unchosen: Conceptions of Election in the Pentateuch & Jewish-Christian Interpretation. 2009. xviii, 254p. 39.50 (978-1-57506-171-9(6)) Eisenbrauns, Inc.

MacKenzie, R. A. F. Faith & History in the Old Testament. 2009. (ENG.). 132p. pap. 40.00 (978-0-8166-5822-0(6)) Univ. of Minnesota Pr.

Mason, Rex. Old Testament Pictures of God. 15.00 (978-0-687-82533-2(4)) Abingdon Pr.

McConville, J. G. & Williams, Stephen N. Joshua. 2010. 272p. pap. 20.00 (978-0-8028-2702-9(0)) Eerdmans, William B. Publishing Co.

McGinniss, Mark. Contributions of Selected Rhetorical Devices to a Biblical Theology of the Song of Songs. 2011. 256p. pap. 29.00 (978-1-60899-634-6(4), Wipf and Stock) Wipf & Stock Pubs.

McKenzie, John L. A Theology of the Old Testament. 2009. (John L. Mckenzie Reprint Ser.). 356p. pap. 39.00 (978-1-60608-273-7(6), Wipf and Stock) Wipf & Stock Pubs.

McKeown, James. Genesis. 2008. (Two Horizons Old Testament Commentary Ser.). 398p. per. 25.00 (978-0-8028-2705-0(5)) Eerdmans, William B. Publishing Co.

Merrill, Eugene H. Everlasting Dominion: A Theology of the Old Testament. 2006. (ENG.). 672p. 39.99 (978-0-8054-4026-3(7), B&H Academic) B&H Publishing Group.

Middlemas, Jill, et al, eds. The Centre & the Periphery: A European Tribute to Walter Brueggemann. 2010. 250p. **(978-1-906055-86-8(6))** Sheffield Phoenix Pr.

Miller, Patrick D. The Way of the Lord: Essays in Old Testament Theology. 2007. 341p. per. 30.00 (978-0-8028-3272-6(5)) Eerdmans, William B. Publishing Co.

Miller, Patrick D. & Roberts, J. J. M. The Hand of the Lord: A Reassessment of the "Ark Narrative" of 1 Samuel. 2007. 15.95 (978-1-58983-294-7(9)) Society of Biblical Literature.

Mirguet, Françoise. La représentation du divin dans les récits du Pentateuque: Médiations syntaxiques et Narratives. 2008. (Vetus Testamentum Supplements Ser.). 544p. (978-90-04-17051-3(0)) BRILL.

Moberly, R. W. L. The Theology of the Book of Genesis. 2009. (Old Testament Theology Ser.). (ENG.). 296p. (C). 78.99 (978-0-521-86631-6(6)); pap. 26.00 (978-0-521-68538-2(9)) Cambridge Univ. Pr.

Morris, Quinn. Echoes from the Old Testament: Wisdom for Teens. 2010. 132p. pap. 15.00 (978-1-4269-2973-1(0)) Trafford Publishing.

Muffs, Yochanan. The Personhood of God: Biblical Theology, Human Faith & the Divine Image. 2009. (ENG.). 240p. pap. 18.99 (978-1-58023-338-5(4)) Jewish Lights Publishing.

Neusner & Chilton, Bruce D. Torah Revealed, Torah Fulfilled: Scriptural Laws in Formative Judaism & Earliest Christianity. 2008. (ENG.). 256p. 130.00 (978-0-567-02739-9(2), T&T Clark Int'l) Continuum International Publishing Group, Ltd. GBR. Dist: National Bk. Network.

Nickelsburg, George W. E. Resurrection, Immortality, & Eternal Life in Intertestamental Judaism & Early Christianity. 2007. (Harvard Theological Studies: 56). (Illus.). 285p. per. 27.95 (978-0-674-02378-9(1)) Harvard Univ. Pr.

Nixon, John S. Redemption in Genesis: The Crossroads of Faith & Reason. 2011. pap. **(978-0-8163-2505-4(7))** Pacific Pr. Publishing Assn.

Pahl, Michael W. The Beginning & the End: Rereading GenesisÕs Stories & Revelation's Visions. 2011. 118p. pap. 15.00 **(978-1-60899-927-9(0)**, Cascade Bks.) Wipf & Stock Pubs.

Pentiuc, Eugen J. Jesus the Messiah in the Hebrew Bible. 2006. 188p. per. 24.95 (978-0-8091-4346-7(1), 4346-1) Paulist Pr.

Perry, T. Anthony. The Honeymoon Is Over: Jonah's Argument with God. 2006. 250p. per. 19.95 (978-1-56563-672-9(4)) Hendrickson Pubs. Marketing, LLC.

Pierce, Timothy M. Enthroned on Our Praise: An Old Testament Theology of Worship. Clendenen, E. Ray, ed. 2008. (New American Commentary Studies in Bible & Theology Ser.). (ENG.). 256p. (C). 19.99 (978-0-8054-4364-4(3), B&H Academic) B&H Publishing Group.

Pratt, Richard L. Mentor: 1 & 2 Chronicles. 2006. (Mentor Commentary Ser.). (ENG.). 736p. 39.99 (978-1-84550-144-0(6), Mentor) Christian Focus Pubns. GBR. Dist: STL Distribution North America.

Publishing, Rose. Christ in the Old Testament Pamphlet: Types & Illustrations of Jesus. 2007. 12p. 3.99 (978-1-59636-169-0(7)) Rose Publishing.

Rad, Gerhard Von. Old Testament Theology, Vol. 1. Stalker, D.M.G., tr. from GER. 2012. 496p. pap. **(978-0-334-01182-8(5)**, SCM Pr.) Hymns Ancient & Modern Ltd.

Reeves, John C. Pursuing the Text: Studies in Honor of Ben Zion Wacholder on the Occasion of his Seventieth Birthday. Kampen, John, ed. 2009. (Library of Hebrew Bible/Old Testament Studies, the Ser.). (ENG.). 434p. 75.00 (978-0-567-65007-8(3), T&T Clark) Continuum International Publishing Group, Ltd. GBR. Dist: National Bk. Network.

Rogerson, John W. A Theology of the Old Testament: Cultural Memory, Communication, & Being Human. 2010. 224p. (C). pap. 29.00 (978-0-8006-9715-0(4), Fortress Pr.) Augsburg Fortress, Pubs.

Rom-Shiloni, Dalit. God in Times of Destruction & Exiles. 2010. 684p. 43.00 (978-965-493-421-3(3)) Magnes Pr., Hebrew Univ., ISR. Dist: Gefen Bks.

Routledge, Robin. Old Testament Theology: A Thematic Approach, 1 vol. 2009. (ENG.). 384p. 32.00 (978-0-8308-2896-8(6), IVP Acad.) InterVarsity Pr.

Scharfstein, Sol. Torah & Commentary: The Five Books of Moses: Translation, Rabbinic & Contemporary Commentary. 2008. (Illus.). 532p. 49.50 (978-0-88125-973-5(X)); pap. 35.00 (978-1-60280-020-5(0)) Ktav Publishing Hse., Inc.

Selderhuis, Herman J. Calvin's Theology of the Psalms. 2007. (Texts & Studies in Reformation & Post-Reformation Thought Ser.). 304p. (C). pap. 35.00 (978-0-8010-3166-3(4)) Baker Academic.

Silva, Kittim. Predicando Sobre el Cantar de los Cantares: Preaching on the Song of Songs. (SPA.). (978-84-7645-288-2(8), 223364) Clie, Editorial.

—Predicando Sobre el Libro de Jonas: Preaching on the Book of Jonah. (SPA.). (978-84-7645-411-4(2), 223478) Clie, Editorial.

Snaith, Norman H. Distinctive Ideas of the Old Testament. 2009. 194p. pap. 23.00 (978-1-60608-724-4(X), Wipf and Stock) Wipf & Stock Pubs.

Stevens, Marty E. Theological Themes of the Old Testament. 2010. 184p. pap. 21.00 (978-1-60608-816-6(5), Cascade Bks.) Wipf & Stock Pubs.

Stone, Nathan. Names of God, 1 vol. 2010. (Moody Classics Ser.). (ENG.). 192p. pap. 7.99 (978-0-8024-5856-8(4)) Moody Pubs.

Sun, Henry T. C. & Eades, Keith L., eds. Problems in Biblical Theology: Essays in Honor of Rolf Knierim. 2011. 420p. pap. 48.00 **(978-1-61097-157-7(4)**, Wipf and Stock) Wipf & Stock Pubs.

Sweeney, Marvin A. Tanak: A Theological & Critical Introduction to the Jewish Bible. 2011. 464p. (C). 59.00 (978-0-8006-3743-9(7), Fortress Pr.) Augsburg Fortress, Pubs.

Theology of the Old Testament. 3.00 (978-0-687-85474-5(1)) Abingdon Pr.

Tino, Jozef. King & Temple in Chronicles: A Contextual Approach to their Relations. 2010. (Forschungen Zur Religion und Literatur des Alten & Neuen Testament Ser.). (ENG.). 183p. (C). 110.00 (978-3-525-53096-2(X)) Vandenhoeck & Ruprecht GmbH & Co. KG DEU. Dist: ISD.

Treitler, Wolfgang. Kein Diener zweier Herren! Der einzige Gott und viele Gegengötter. 2010. (Religion, Kultur, Recht Ser.). (GER.). 238p. 43.95 (978-3-631-59963-1(3)) Lang, Peter GmbH, Europaischer Verlag der Wissenschaften DEU. Dist: Lang, Peter.

Van Seters, John. Changing Perspectives I: Studies in the History, Literature, & Religion of Biblical Israel. 2011. (Copenhagen International Seminar Ser.). (ENG., Illus.). 438p. (C). 120.00 (978-1-84553-901-6(X)) Equinox Publishing Ltd. GBR. Dist: ISD.

Vogt, Peter T. Deuteronomic Theology & the Significance of Torah: A Reappraisal. 2006. 242p. 37.50 (978-1-57506-107-8(4)) Eisenbrauns, Inc.

Waddell James A., et al. The Messiah: A Comparative Study of the Enochic Son of Man & the Pauline Kyrios. 2011. (Jewish & Christian Text Ser.). (ENG.). 256p. 120.00 (978-0-567-58032-0(6), T&T Clark Int'l) Continuum International Publishing Group, Ltd. GBR. Dist: National Bk. Network.

Wanke, Roger Marcel. Praesentia Dei: Die Vorstellungen von der Gegenwart Gottes im Hiobbuch. 2011. (Beihefte Zur Zeitschrift Für Die Alttestamentliche Wissenschaft Ser.). Tr. of Praesentia Dei. the Conceptions of the Presence of God in the Book of Job. (GER.). 690p. 224.00 **(978-3-11-024762-6(3))** De Gruyter, Walter Inc.

Waterman, Leroy. Forerunners of Jesus. 2011. 168p. 41.95 **(978-1-258-02913-5(8))** Literary Licensing, LLC.

Willis, Amy Merrill. Dissonance & the Drama of Divine Sovereignty in the Book of Daniel. 2010. (Library of Hebrew Bible/Old Testament Studies, the Ser.). (ENG.). 240p. 130.00 (978-0-567-37948-1(5), T&T Clark Int'l) Continuum International Publishing Group, Ltd. GBR. Dist: National Bk. Network.

Wright, Christopher J. H. Knowing the Holy Spirit Through the Old Testament. 2006. (ENG.). 160p. per. 16.00 (978-0-8308-2591-2(6), IVP Acad.) InterVarsity Pr.

Wright, Ernest G. The Challenge of Israel's Faith. 2007. 132p. per. (978-1-4067-8866-2(X), Pomona Pr.) Read Bks.

Yinger, Kent L. Paul, Judaism, & Judgment according to Deeds. 2007. (Society for New Testament Studies Monograph Ser.). (ENG., Illus.). 336p. pap. 69.00 (978-0-521-03669-6(0)) Cambridge Univ. Pr.

BIBLE—TRANSLATING

Abernathy, David. Exegetical Summary of Romans 1-8. 2nd ed. 2008. 577p. pap. 48.00 (978-1-55671-207-4(3)) SIL International.

—An Exegetical Summary of Romans 9-16. 2009. 390p. pap. 42.00 (978-1-55671-233-3(2)) SIL International.

Allen, Larry & Neeley, Linda. Translator's Notes on Luke 9-16. 2010. 570p. spiral bd. 60.00 (978-1-55671-248-7(0)) SIL International.

Amélineau, Émile. The Sahidic Translation of the Book of Job. 2009. (COP & FRE.). pap. 37.70 (978-1-60724-271-0(0)) Gorgias Pr., LLC.

Ausloss, H., et al, eds. Translating a Translation: The LXX & its Modern Translations in the Context of Early Judaism. 2008. (Bibliotheca Ephemeridum Theologicarum Lovaniensium Ser.). (ENG.). 317p. (C). pap. 116.00 (978-90-429-2038-5(6)) Peeters Pubs. & Booksellers BEL. Dist: Brown, David Bk. Co., The.

Bacon, Francis. The Translation of Certain Psalms into English Verse. reprint ed. lib. bdg. 98.00 (978-0-7426-2037-7(9)) Classic Bks.

Barnwell, Katharine. Translator's Notes on Malachi. 2007. (Translator's Notes Ser.). 128p. spiral bd. 16.00 (978-1-55671-172-5(7)) SIL International.

Barnwell, Katharine & Kuhn, Hanni. Translator's Notes on Genesis 1-11. 2007. 248p. spiral bd. 22.00 (978-1-55671-173-2(5)) SIL International.

Bean, Mark Ellis. Translator's Notes on 1 Timothy. 2008. 196p. spiral bd. 24.00 (978-1-55671-212-8(X)) SIL International.

Benjamin, Mara H. Rosenzweig's Bible: Reinventing Scripture for Jewish Modernity. 2009. (ENG., Illus.). 222p. 80.00 (978-0-521-89526-2(X)) Cambridge Univ. Pr.

Blight, Richard C. Exegetical Summary of 1 & 2 Thessalonians. 2nd ed. 2008. 259p. pap. 32.00 (978-1-55671-200-5(6)) SIL International.

—An Exegetical Summary of 1 Timothy. 2009. 396p. pap. 42.00 (978-1-55671-230-2(8)) SIL International.

—Exegetical Summary of Luke 1-11. 2nd ed. 2008. 549p. pap. 46.00 (978-1-55671-211-1(1)) SIL International.

—Exegetical Summary of Luke 12-24. 2nd ed. 2008. (GEC & ENG.). 581p. pap. 48.00 (978-1-55671-213-5(8)) SIL International.

Brenner, Athalya. Bible Translation on the Threshold of the Twenty-First Century: Authority, Reception, Culture & Religion. van Henten, Jan Willem, ed. 2009. (Library of Hebrew Bible/Old Testament Studies, the Ser.). (ENG.). 208p. 39.95 (978-0-567-51279-6(7), T&T Clark) Continuum International Publishing Group, Ltd. GBR. Dist: National Bk. Network.

Bullard, Roger Aubrey & Hatton, Howard. A Handbook on Sirach. 2008. (978-0-8267-0203-6(1)) United Bible Societies.

—A Handbook on the Shorter Books of the Deuterocanon. 2006. (978-0-8267-0201-2(5)) United Bible Societies.

Campbell, Gordon. Bible: The Story of the King James Version 1611-2011. (ENG., Illus.). 2011. 368p. pap. 18.95 (978-0-19-969301-6(3)) 2010. 256p. 24.95 (978-0-19-955759-2(4)) Oxford Univ. Pr., Inc.

Carlton, Matthew E. Translator's Reference Translation of the Gospel of Luke. 2008. 495p. pap. 39.00 (978-1-55671-217-3(0)) SIL International.

Chemorion, Diphus. Community Participation in Scripture Version Design. 2010. 100.00 (978-1-60724-408-0(X)) Gorgias Pr., LLC.

Cook, E. M. A Glossary of Targum Onkelos: According to Alexander Sperber's Edition. 2008. (Studies in the Aramaic Interpretation of Scripture). (ARC & ENG.). 336p. (C). (978-90-04-14978-6(3)) BRILL.

Davies, Gordon F. Israel in Egypt: Reading Exodus 1-2. 2009. (Library of Hebrew Bible/Old Testament Studies, the Ser.). (ENG.). 204p. 39.95 (978-1-4411-6508-4(8), T&T Clark) Continuum International Publishing Group, Ltd. GBR. Dist: National Bk. Network.

Deibler, Ellis W., Jr. A Translation for Translators: Of the New Testament. 2008. 566p. 19.95 (978-0-9640069-3-5(6)) Cummins Works.

—A Translator's Translation: Of the New Testament. 2008. 560p. 19.95 (978-0-9640069-4-2(4)) Cummins Works.

Dekens, Carine Skupien. Traduire pour le peuple de Dieu: La syntaxe francaise dans la traduction de la Bible par Sebastien Castellion, Bale 1555. 2009. (Travaux d'Humanisme et Renaissance Ser.). (FRE., Illus.). 392p. (C). 137.00 (978-2-600-01300-0(8)) Droz, Librairie CHE. Dist: Brown, David Bk. Co., The.

Den Hollander, A A & Francois, W., eds. Infant Milk or Hardy Nourishment? The Bible for Lay People & Theologians in the Early Modern Period. 2009. (Bibliotheca Ephemeridum Theologicarum Lovaniensium Ser.). (GER, FRE & ENG., Illus.). 488p. (C). pap. 116.00 (978-90-429-2144-3(7)) Peeters Pubs. & Booksellers BEL. Dist: Brown, David Bk. Co., The.

Doubles, Malcolm C. The Seduction of the Church: How the Concern to Create Gender-Neutral Language in Bible & Song Is Being Misused to Betray Members' Faith. 2010. 176p. pap. 20.00 (978-1-60899-462-5(7), Wipf and Stock) Wipf & Stock Pubs.

Fee, Gordon D., et al. How to Choose a Translation for All Its Worth, 1 vol. 2007. (ENG., Illus.). 176p. (gr. 13). pap. 12.99 (978-0-310-27876-4(7)) Zondervan.

Findeisen, Raoul David, et al, eds. At Home in Many Worlds: Reading, Writing & Translating from Chinese & Jewish Cultures. 2010. (Veröffentlichungen des Ostasien-Instituts der Ruhr-Universität Bochum Ser.). (ENG.). 332p. (C). pap. 102.00 (978-3-447-06135-3(9)) Harrassowitz, Otto Verlag DEU. Dist: ISD.

Fisher, Loren R. The Many Voices of Job. 2009. 132p. pap. 16.00 (978-1-60608-656-8(1), Cascade Bks.) Wipf & Stock Pubs.

Foley, T. S. Biblical Translation in Chinese & Greek: Verbal Aspect in Theory & Practice. 2009. (Linguistic Biblical Studies). 472p. (978-90-04-17865-6(1)) BRILL.

Fortosis, Stephen. The Multilingual God: Translating God to Every People. 2011. **(978-0-87808-468-5(1))** Carey, William Library Pubs.

Gerber, Christine, et al. Gott Heisst Nicht Nur Vater: Zur Rede über Gott in Den Übersetzungen der "Bibel in Gerechter Sprache" 2008. (Biblisch-Theologische Schwerpunkte Ser.). (GER., Illus.). 256p. (C). pap. 27.00 (978-3-525-61609-3(0)) Vandenhoeck & Ruprecht GmbH & Co. KG DEU. Dist: ISD.

Glenny, W. Edward. Finding Meaning in the Text: Translation Technique & Theology in the Septuagint of Amos. 2009. 322p. (978-90-04-17638-6(1)) BRILL.

Glunz, H. H. History of the Vulgate in England from Alcuin to Roger Bacon: Being an Inquiry into the Text of Some English Manuscripts of the Vulgate Gospels. 2010. (ENG.). 404p. pap. 31.99 (978-0-521-17075-8(3)) Cambridge Univ. Pr.

Greenlee, J. Harold. An Exegetical Summary of Hebrews. 2nd ed. 2008. (Exegetical Summary Ser.). 592p. pap. 49.00 (978-1-55671-209-8(X)) SIL International.

—Exegetical Summary of James. 2nd ed. 2008. 214p. pap. 28.00 (978-1-55671-195-4(6)) SIL International.

—Exegetical Summary of Jude. 2nd ed. 2008. 82p. pap. 15.00 (978-1-55671-190-9(5)) SIL International.

—Exegetical Summary of Philippians. 2nd ed. 2008. 252p. pap. 32.00 (978-1-55671-199-2(9)) SIL International.

—Exegetical Summary of Titus & Philemon. 2nd ed. 2008. 147p. pap. 24.00 *(978-1-55671-192-3(1))* SIL International.

Groff, Randy & Neeley, Linda. Translator's Notes on Luke 1 - 8. 2009. 648p. spiral bd. 60.00 *(978-1-55671-228-9(6))* SIL International.

—Translator's Notes on Mark 1 - 8. 2008. 546p. spiral bd. 60.00 *(978-1-55671-214-2(6))* SIL International.

—Translator's Notes on Mark 9 - 16. 2008. 588p. spiral bd. 60.00 *(978-1-55671-215-9(4))* SIL International.

Hernández Guerrero, María José & Peña Martín, Salvador, eds. La traducción - Factor de Cambio. 2008. 286p. pap. *(978-3-03911-595-2(2))* Lang, Peter.

Hiebert, Robert J. V. Translation Is Required: The Septuagint in Retrospect & Prospect. 2011. XVIII, 248p. *(978-90-04-18708-5(1))* BRILL.

Hill, Harriet, et al. Bible Translation Basics: Communicating Scripture in a Relevant Way. 2011. 304p. pap. 29.00 ***(978-1-55671-269-2(3))*** SIL International.

Horner, George William. The Coptic Version of the New Testament in the Southern Dialect, Volume I. 2010. 664p. pap. 34.95 *(978-0-557-30236-9(6))* Lulu Enterprises Inc.

—The Coptic Version of the New Testament in the Southern Dialect, Volume II. 2010. 488p. pap. 34.95 *(978-0-557-30238-3(2))* Lulu Enterprises Inc.

—The Coptic Version of the New Testament in the Southern Dialect, Volume III. 2010. 428p. pap. 34.95 *(978-0-557-30240-6(4))* Lulu Enterprises Inc.

—The Coptic Version of the New Testament in the Southern Dialect, Volume IV. 2010. 468p. pap. 34.95 *(978-0-557-30242-0(0))* Lulu Enterprises Inc.

—The Coptic Version of the New Testament in the Southern Dialect, Volume V. 2010. 596p. pap. 34.95 *(978-0-557-30244-4(7))* Lulu Enterprises Inc.

—The Coptic Version of the New Testament in the Southern Dialect, Volume VI. 2010. 680p. pap. 34.95 *(978-0-557-30246-8(3))* Lulu Enterprises Inc.

—The Coptic Version of the New Testament in the Southern Dialect, Volume VII. 2010. 572p. pap. 34.95 *(978-0-557-30249-9(8))* Lulu Enterprises Inc.

Hughes, Aaron W. The Invention of Jewish Identity: Bible, Philosophy, & the Art of Translation. 2010. (ENG.). 202p. 70.00 *(978-0-253-35537-9(0),* 0253355370); pap. 24.95 *(978-0-253-22249-7(4),* 0253222494) Indiana Univ. Pr.

Israel, Hephzibah. Religious Transactions in Colonial South India: Language, Translation, & the Making of Protestant Identity. 2011. (Palgrave Studies in Cultural & Intellectual History Ser.). (ENG.). 286p. 85.00 *(978-0-230-10562-1(9))* Palgrave Macmillan.

Jenkins, Allan K. & Preston, Patrick. Biblical Scholarship & the Church: A Sixteenth Century Crisis of Authority. 2007. (Ashgate New Critical Thinking in Religion, Theology & Biblical Studies). 340p. 124.95 *(978-0-7546-3703-5(4))* Ashgate Publishing Co.

Joaquin, Arsenia R. Bible Words. 2009. 588p. pap. 26.95 *(978-0-9819570-8-1(0))* ASA Publishing Co.

—The Will Bible "New Testament" 2009. 632p. pap. 29.95 *(978-0-9819570-3-6(X))* ASA Publishing Co.

Johnson, Edna. A Semantic & Structural Analysis of Ephesians. 2008. 251p. pap. 30.00 *(978-1-55671-224-1(3))* SIL International.

Joosten, Jan & Bons, Eberhard. Septuagint Vocabulary: Pre-History, Usage, Reception. 2011. (GER.). 224p. pap. ***(978-1-58983-585-6(9))*** Society of Biblical Literature.

Joosten, Jan & Bons, Eberhard, eds. Septuagint Vocabulary: Pre-History, Usage, Reception. 2011. (SBL - Septuagint & Cognate Studies). (FRE, GER & ENG.). X, 212p. ***(978-90-04-21162-9(4))*** BRILL.

Kashouh, Hikmat. The Arabic Versions of the Gospels: The Manuscripts & Their Families. 2011. (Arbeiten zur neutestamentlichen Textforschung Ser.). (ENG.). XIV, 761p. (gr. 17). 377.00 ***(978-3-11-022858-8(0))*** De Gruyter, Walter Inc.

Krasovec, Joze. The Transformation of Biblical Proper Names. 2010. (Library of Hebrew Bible/Old Testament Studies, the Ser.). (ENG.). 176p. 110.00 *(978-0-567-45224-5(7),* T&T Clark Int'l) Continuum International Publishing Group, Ltd. GBR. Dist: National Bk. Network.

Kraus, Helen. Gender Issues in Ancient & Reformation Translations of Genesis 1-4. 2011. (ENG.). 256p. 125.00 *(978-0-19-960078-6(3))* Oxford Univ. Pr., Inc.

Kuske, David P. A Commentary on Romans 1-8. 2007. (GEC & ENG., Illus.). 460p. *(978-0-8100-1979-9(5))* Northwestern Publishing Hse.

Maxey, James A. From Orality to Orality: A New Paradigm for Contextual Translation of the Bible. 2009. (Biblical Performance Criticism Ser.). (Illus.). 221p. pap. 26.30 *(978-1-60608-324-6(4))* Cascade Bks.

Migsch, Herbert. Studien zum Jeremiabuch und andere Beiträge zum Alten Testament. 2010. (Österreichische Biblische Studien Ser.). (GER.). 358p. 75.95 *(978-3-631-60171-6(9))* Lang, Peter GmbH, Europaischer Verlag der Wissenschaften DEU. Dist: Lang, Peter.

Minor, Eugene E. Exegetical Summary of 2 Timothy. 2nd ed. 2008. 136p. pap. 22.00 *(978-1-55671-191-6(3))* SIL International.

Neufeld, Dietmar. The Social Sciences & Biblical Translation. 2008. (SBL: Writings from the Greco-Roman World). 462p. (C). *(978-90-04-15746-0(8))* BRILL.

—The Social Sciences & Biblical Translation. 2008. 24.95 *(978-1-58983-347-0(3))* Society of Biblical Literature.

O'Hare, Daniel M. Have You Seen, Son of Man? Studies in the Translation & Vorlage of LXX Ezekiel 40-48. 2010. *(978-1-58983-526-9(3)); (978-1-58983-527-6(1))* Society of Biblical Literature.

Olofsson, Staffan. Translation Technique & Theological Exegesis: Collected Essays on the Septuagint Version. 2009. pap. 39.95 *(978-1-57506-807-7(9))* Eisenbrauns, Inc.

Popjes, Jack. A Kick in the Pants. 2008. pap. 10.95 *(978-0-938978-46-6(2))* Wycliffe Bible Translators.

Porter, Stanley E. & Boda, Mark J., eds. Translating the New Testament: Text, Translation, Theology. 2009. (McMaster New Testament Studies). 384p. pap. 36.00 *(978-0-8028-6377-5(9))* Eerdmans, William B. Publishing Co.

Price, James D. A Theory for Biblical Translation: An Optimal Equivalence Model. 2008. (Illus.). 382p. 119.95 *(978-0-7734-5205-3(2))* Mellen, Edwin Pr., The.

Pritz, Ray. The Works of Their Hands: Man-Made Things in the Bible. 2009. (Illus.). xxvii, 485p. *(978-0-8267-0039-1(X))* United Bible Societies.

Rees, Margo. Lishan Didan, Targum Didan: Translation Language in a Neo-Aramaic Targum Tradition. 2007. 75.00 *(978-1-59333-426-0(5))* Gorgias Pr., LLC.

Reid, John Howard. Bible Wisdom: PSALMS of Praise & Power newly translated from the Greek Old Testament. 2010. 287p. pap. 15.50 *(978-0-557-16306-9(4))* Lulu Enterprises Inc.

Rosenberg, David. A Literary Bible: An Original Translation. 2009. (ENG.). 576p. 35.00 *(978-1-58243-514-5(6),* Counterpoint Pr.) Basic Bks. GBR. Dist: Perseus-PGW.

Ryken, Leland. Understanding English Bible Translation: The Case for an Essentially Literal Approach. 2009. 208p. pap. 12.99 *(978-1-4335-0279-8(8))* Crossway.

Stahlberg, Lesleigh Cushing. Sustaining Fictions: Intertextuality, Midrash, Translation, & the Literary Afterlife of the Bible. 2008. (Library of Hebrew Bible/Old Testament Studies, the Ser.). (ENG., Illus.). 256p. 140.00 *(978-0-567-02709-2(0),* T&T Clark Int'l) Continuum International Publishing Group, Ltd. GBR. Dist: National Bk. Network.

Strange, David. Exegetical Summary of 2 Peter. 2nd ed. 2008. (GEC & ENG.). 312p. pap. 38.00 *(978-1-55671-202-9(2))* SIL International.

Stutzman, Robert. Exegetical Summary of Galatians. 2nd ed. 2008. 265p. pap. 32.00 *(978-1-55671-201-2(4))* SIL International.

Thomas, Kenneth J. & Thomas, Margaret Orr. Structure & Orality in 1 Peter: A Guide for Translators. 2006. (Illus.). xiii, 219p. *(978-0-8267-0460-3(3))* United Bible Societies.

Trail, Ronald L. Exegetical Summary of 1 Corinthians 1-9. 2nd ed. 2008. 370p. pap. 42.00 *(978-1-55671-204-3(9))* SIL International.

—Exegetical Summary of 1 Corinthians 10-16. 2nd ed. 2008. 382p. pap. 42.00 *(978-1-55671-205-0(7))* SIL International.

—Exegetical Summary of Revelation 1-11. 2nd ed. 2008. 243p. pap. 29.00 *(978-1-55671-198-5(0))* SIL International.

—Exegetical Summary of Revelation 11-22. 2nd ed. 2008. 238p. pap. 29.00 *(978-1-55671-196-1(4))* SIL International.

Van Der Louw, Theo A. W. Transformations in the Septuagint: Towards an Interaction of Septuagint Studies & Translation Studies. 2007. (Contributions to Biblical Exegesis & Theology Ser.). (ENG., Illus.). 404p. (C). pap. 51.00 *(978-90-429-1888-7(8))* Peeters Pubs. & Booksellers BEL. Dist: Brown, David Bk. Co., The.

Voitila, Anssi, et al. Scripture in Transition: Essays on Septuagint, Hebrew Bible, & Dead Sea Scrolls in Honour of Raija Sollamo. Voitila, Anssi & Jokiranta, Jutta, eds. 2008. (Supplements to the Journal for the Study of Judaism Ser.). 700p. *(978-90-04-16582-3(7))* BRILL.

Wendland, Ernst. Galu Wamkota. 2007. 512p. (C). pap. *(978-99908-87-05-1(5))* Kachere Series, Bks. on Religion, Theology & Society in Malawi MWI. Dist: Michigan State Univ. Pr.

Wendland, Ernst R. Finding & Translating the Oral-Aural Elements in Written Language: The Case of the New Testament Epistles. 2009. (Illus.). 444p. 129.95 *(978-0-7734-4959-6(0))* Mellen, Edwin Pr., The.

—LiFE-Style Translating: A Workbook for Bible Translators. 2006. (Publications in Translation & Textlinguistics: 2). 347p. pap. 39.95 *(978-1-55671-167-1(0))* SIL International.

Werner, A. Frances. Truth in Translation: Accuracy & Surprising Bias in the Old Testament. 2008. 150p. pap. 44.00 *(978-0-9789763-1-6(2))* ARTB Publishing.

Williams, H. D. Wycliffe Controversies. 2008. 312p. pap. 20.00 *(978-0-9817339-8-2(0))* Old Paths Pubns., Inc., The.

Wilson, Derek A. The People's Bible: The Remarkable History of the King James Version. 2010. (ENG., Illus.). 224p. 24.95 *(978-0-7459-5351-9(4))* Lion Hudson PLC GBR. Dist: Independent Pubs. Group.

BIBLE—TRANSLATIONS

see Bible—Versions

BIBLE—TYPOLOGY

see Typology (Theology)

BIBLE—USE

see also Bible—Homiletical Use; Bible—Liturgical Use

Acker, Katina S. The Turning Point: When the Pleaser of Man Becomes a Servant of the Lord. 2009. 160p. 22.95 *(978-1-4389-9678-3(0))*; pap. 17.95 *(978-1-4389-9677-6(2))* AuthorHouse.

Adam, Gottfried, ed. Die Inhalte von Kinderbibeln. Kriterien ihrer Auswahl. 2008. (Arbeiten zur Religionspadagogik Ser.). (GER., Illus.). 365p. (C). 68.00 *(978-3-89971-489-0(X))* Vandenhoeck & Ruprecht GmbH & Co. KG DEU. Dist: ISD.

Barrett, Lee C. & Stewart, Jon, eds. Kierkegaard & the Bible, 2 vols. 2010. (Kierkegaard Research: Sources, Reception & Resources Ser.). 352p. 134.95 *(978-1-4094-0443-9(9))* Ashgate Publishing Co.

Berlinerblau, Jacques. Thumpin' It: The Use & Abuse of the Bible in Today's Presidential Politics. 2007. (ENG.). 190p. pap. 17.00 *(978-0-664-23173-6(X))* Westminster John Knox Pr.

Bielo, James S., ed. The Social Life of Scriptures: Cross-Cultural Perspectives on Biblicism. 2009. (Signifying (on)Scriptures Ser.). (ENG., Illus.). 272p. (C). 72.00 *(978-0-8135-4605-6(2))*; pap. 28.95 *(978-0-8135-4606-3(0))* Rutgers Univ. Pr.

Binz, Stephen J. Conversing with God in Scripture: A Contemporary Approach to Lectio Divina. 2008. 150p. per. 12.95 *(978-1-59325-126-0(2))* Word Among Us Pr.

Boa, Kenneth. Passionate Living: Praises & Promises - A Devotional. 2007. (ENG.). 157p. per. 12.99 *(978-1-932805-93-2(1))* Authentic Media.

—Passionate Living: Wisdom & Truth - A Devotional. 2007. (ENG.). 184p. per. 12.99 *(978-1-934068-26-7(8))* Authentic Media.

Brauch, Manfred & Brauch, Manfred T. Abusing Scripture: The Consequences of Misreading the Bible, 1 vol. 2009. (ENG.). 293p. pap. 18.00 *(978-0-8308-2579-0(7),* IVP Acad.) InterVarsity Pr.

Clinton, Tim & Hawkins, Ron. The Quick-Reference Guide to Biblical Counseling. 2009. 288p. pap. 24.99 *(978-0-8010-7225-3(5))* Baker Bks.

Cox, R. Kenneth. Sound Doctrine. 2009. 76p. pap. 16.49 *(978-0-557-07551-5(3))* Lulu Enterprises Inc.

Dawson, Jack E. The Passion Tree Devotional: The Story That Never Ends. 2006. (Illus.). 63p. *(978-1-892435-81-1(0))* Covenant Publishing, Inc.

de Lange, Nicholas, ed. Jewish Reception of Greek Bible Versions: Studies in Their Use in Late Antiquity & the Middle Ages. 2009. (Text & Studies in Medieval & Early Modern Judaism Ser.). (Illus.). 338p. 195.00 *(978-3-16-149779-7(1))* Mohr Siebeck GmbH & Co. KG DEU. Dist: Coronet Bks.

Emlet, Michael/Ray. CrossTalk: Where Life & Scripture Meet. 2009. 212p. pap. 15.99 *(978-1-935273-12-7(4))* New Growth Pr.

Ernest, James D. The Bible in Athanasius of Alexandria. 2010. *(978-1-58983-496-5(8))* Society of Biblical Literature.

Funk, Mary Margaret. Lectio Matters: Before the Burning Bush: Through the Revelatory Texts of Scripture, Nature & Experience. 2010. (ENG.). 216p. 19.95 *(978-1-4411-5169-8(9))* Continuum International Publishing Group, Ltd. GBR. Dist: National Bk. Network.

Gill, A. L., compiled by. God's Promises for Your Every Need, NKJV, 0 vols. 2008. 352p. im. lthr. 4.99 *(978-1-4041-8665-1(4))* Nelson, Thomas Inc.

Gray, Tim. Praying Scripture for a Change: An Introductin to Lectio Divina. 2009. 127p. pap. 12.99 *(978-1-934217-48-1(4))* Ascension Pr.

Isaak, Jon M. & Martens, E. A. The Old Testament in the Life of God's People: Essays in Honor of Elmer A. Martens. 2009. (Illus.). xxvii, 349p. 49.50 *(978-1-57506-158-0(9))* Eisenbrauns, Inc.

Jackson, Donald, illus. Praying the Word: Illuminated Prayers & Wisdom from the Saint John's Bible. 2008. 72p. *(978-0-8146-9093-2(9),* Liturgical Pr. Bks.) Liturgical Pr.

Kandiah, Krish. Route 66: Biblical Direction for the Road We Travel, 1 vol. 2011. (Illus.). 192p. pap. 13.99 *(978-0-85721-018-0(1),* Monarch Bks.) Lion Hudson PLC GBR. Dist: Kregel Pubns.

Kleuser, Louise C. The Bible Instructor: In Personal & Public Evangelism. 2007. (Illus.). 500p. pap. 22.95 *(978-1-57258-517-1(X))* TEACH Services, Inc.

Lane, Laura L. The Lutheran Study Bible Journal: Life by His Word. 2009. 640p. *(978-0-7586-1911-2(1))* Concordia Publishing Hse.

Leuzarder, John. The Gospel for Children. 2008. (Illus.). 40p. per. 8.95 *(978-0-9767582-8-0(8))* Shepherd Pr. Inc.

Mayo, William D. That's in the Bible? Scripture's User-Friendly Impact on Everyday Conversation. 2011. 224p. 24.95 ***(978-1-4634-7436-2(9))***; pap. 14.95 ***(978-1-4634-7437-9(7))*** AuthorHouse.

Miller, J. R. Silent Times, a Book to Help in Reading the Bible into Life. 2011. 126p. pap. 12.99 ***(978-1-61203-175-0(7))*** Bottom of the Hill Publishing.

O'Donnell, Douglas Sean. God's Lyrics: Rediscovering Worship Through Old Testament Songs. 2010. pap. *(978-1-59638-172-8(8))* P & R Publishing.

Okoye, James Chukwuma. Scripture in the Church: The Synod on the Word of God & the Post-Synodal Exhortation Verbum Domini. 2011. 24.95 *(978-0-8146-5761-4(3))*; E-Book *(978-0-8146-8026-1(7))* Liturgical Pr.

Omartian, Stormie. The Power of Praying Through the Bible Prayer Companion. 2010. 208p. pap. 9.99 *(978-0-7369-2784-0(0))* Harvest Hse. Pubs.

Orvis, David L., et al, eds. Psalms in the Early Modern World. 2011. (Illus.). 410p. 119.95 ***(978-1-4094-2282-2(8))*** Ashgate Publishing Co.

Paddison, Angus. Scripture: A Very Theological Proposal. 2009. (ENG.). 184p. 39.95 *(978-0-567-03424-3(0))*; 130.00 *(978-0-567-03423-6(2))* Continuum International Publishing Group, Ltd. GBR. (T&T Clark Int'l). Dist: National Bk. Network.

Paintner, Christine Valters & Wynkoop, Lucy. Lectio Divina: Contemplative Awakening & Awareness. 2008. (Illus.). 208p. pap. 18.95 *(978-0-8091-4531-7(6))* Paulist Pr.

Powlison, David/Arthur. The Biblical Counseling Movement: History & Context. 2009. 432p. pap. 39.99 *(978-1-935273-13-4(2))* New Growth Pr.

Prothero, Rowland. The Psalms in Human Life. 2008. 352p. pap. 25.00 *(978-1-59925-193-6(0))* Solid Ground Christian Bks.

Pyper, Hugh S. The Unchained Bible: Cultural Appropriations of Biblical Texts. 2012. (ENG.). 176p. 100.00 ***(978-0-567-16690-6(2),*** T&T Clark Int'l) Continuum International Publishing Group, Ltd. GBR. Dist: National Bk. Network.

Redding, Mary Lou. Meeting God in Scripture: Entering the Old Testament. 2008. 111p. per. 15.00 *(978-0-8358-9946-8(2))* Upper Room Bks.

Ronnegard, Per. Threads & Images: The Use of Scripture in Apophthegmata Patrum. 2010. 217p. pap. 35.95 *(978-1-57506-808-4(7))* Eisenbrauns, Inc.

Scheppmann, Susanne. Perplexing Proverbs-A Bible Study for Women: Following God Christian Living Series. 2007. (Following God Ser.). (ENG.). 192p. (gr. 11). pap. 14.99 *(978-0-89957-247-5(2))* AMG Pubs.

Stewart, Jon & Barrett, Lee C., eds. Kierkegaard & the Bible, 2 vols., Vol. 1. 2010. (Kierkegaard Research: Sources, Reception & Resources Ser.). 294p. 124.95 *(978-1-4094-0285-5(1))* Ashgate Publishing Co.

Stott, John, ed. The Anglican Communion & Scripture: Papers from the First International Consultation of the Evangelical Fellowship in the Anglican Communion, Canterbury, UK, June 1993. 2011. 198p. pap. 23.00 ***(978-1-61097-559-9(6),*** Wipf and Stock) Wipf & Stock Pubs.

Swenson, Kristin. Bible Babel: Making Sense of the Most Talked about Book of All Time. 2011. (ENG.). 368p. pap. 14.99 *(978-0-06-172826-6(8),* HarperPerennial) HarperCollins Pubs.

Thatcher, Adrian. The Savage Text: The Use & Abuse of the Bible. 2008. (Blackwell Manifestos Ser.: 15). (ENG.). 232p. pap. 33.95 *(978-1-4051-7016-1(6))*; 93.95 *(978-1-4051-7017-8(4),* Wiley, John & Sons, Inc. (Wiley-Blackwell).

Thomas Nelson Gift Books. God's Promises for Your Every Need, 0 vols. deluxe ed. 2008. 352p. lthr. 14.99 *(978-1-4041-8708-5(1))* Nelson, Thomas Inc.

Towns, Elmer. Praying for Your Second Hearing: Prayers From Deuteronomy & Numbers. 2009. pap. 17.99 *(978-0-7684-2760-8(6))* Destiny Image Pubs.

—Praying Your Way Out of Bondage: Prayers From Exodus & Leviticus. 2009. pap. 17.99 *(978-0-7684-2759-2(2))* Destiny Image Pubs.

Tyndale House Publishers Staff, creator. The One Year Chronological Bible. 2nd ed. 2007. (ENG.). 1728p. per. 19.99 *(978-1-4143-1408-2(6))* Tyndale Hse. Pubs.

Tyndale House Publishers Staff, prod. The One Year Chronological Bible NLT. 2007. (ENG.). 1728p. 24.99 *(978-1-4143-1407-5(8))* Tyndale Hse. Pubs.

Upper Room Books, creator. Entering the Old Testament: Participant's Workbook. 2008. (Meeting God in Scripture Ser.). 92p. per. 10.00 *(978-0-8358-9945-1(4))* Upper Room Bks.

Vang, Preben & Carter, Terry. Telling God's Story: The Biblical Narrative from Beginning to End. 2006. (ENG., Illus.). 352p. 29.99 *(978-0-8054-3282-4(5),* B&H Academic) B&H Publishing Group.

Wansbrough, Henry. Use & Abuse of the Bible: A Brief History of Biblical Interpretation. 2010. (ENG.). 224p. 22.95 *(978-0-567-09057-7(4),* T&T Clark Int'l) Continuum International Publishing Group, Ltd. GBR. Dist: National Bk. Network.

BIBLE—VERSIONS

Here are entered works on Versions of the Bible in any language except English. For English Version see subdivision Versions, English.

see also Language Question in the Church

Abingdon Press, creator. Mother's Bible-NRSV. 2008. (Illus.). 1103p. im. lthr. 21.95 *(978-0-687-64680-7(4))* Abingdon Pr.

Adult Bible Study Vietnamese Edition. 2.31 *(978-0-7673-4179-0(1))* LifeWay Christian Resources.

Aejmelaeus, A. On the Trail of the Septuagint Translators: Collected Essays. Revised & Expanded Edition. 2007. (Contributions to Biblical Exegesis & Theology Ser.). (ENG.). 316p. (C). pap. 64.00 *(978-90-429-1939-6(6))* Peeters Pubs. & Booksellers BEL. Dist: Brown, David Bk. Co., The.

Aland, Barbara, et al, eds. Greek-English New Testament-FL. 27th ed. 2006. 812p. 46.99 *(978-1-59856-176-0(6))* Hendrickson Pubs. Marketing, LLC.

—Greek New Testament-FL. 4th ed. 2006. 918p. 31.99 *(978-1-59856-171-5(5))* Hendrickson Pubs. Marketing, LLC.

—Novum Testamentum Graece-FL. 27th ed. 2006. 812p. 32.99 *(978-1-59856-172-2(3))*; 1015p. 59.99 *(978-1-59856-174-6(X))* Hendrickson Pubs. Marketing, LLC.

American Bible Society Staff, creator. Groot Nieuws Bijbel-FL. 2007. 64.99 *(978-90-6126-859-8(1))* American Bible Society.

—Large Print Bible-RV 1960-Zipper. l.t. ed. 2008. 22.99 *(978-1-59877-108-4(6))* American Bible Society.

Anonymous. The Bible. 2006. (ENG., Illus.). 2000p. (gr. 12-18). 17.00 *(978-0-14-144151-1(8),* Penguin Classics) Penguin Group (USA) Inc.

Attridge, Harold W. & Society of Biblical Literature, Meeting Staff. HarperCollins Study Bible. Meeks, Wayne A. & Bassler, Jouette M., eds. rev. ed. 2006. (ENG.). 2208p. stu. ed. 37.99 *(978-0-06-078683-0(3),* HarperOne) HarperCollins Pubs.

Attridge, Harold W. & Society of Biblical Literature Staff. Harper Collins Study Bible. Meeks, Wayne A. & Bassler, Jouette M., eds. rev. ed. 2006. (ENG., Illus.). 2208p. pap., stu. ed. 32.99 *(978-0-06-078684-7(1),* HarperOne) HarperCollins Pubs.

—The HarperCollins Study Bible. Meeks, Wayne A. & Bassler, Jouette M., eds. rev. ed. 2006. (ENG.). 2208p. 44.99 *(978-0-06-078685-4(X),* HarperOne) HarperCollins Pubs.

Ausloos, H., et al, eds. Translating a Translation: The LXX & its Modern Translations in the Context of Early Judaism. 2008. (Bibliotheca Ephemeridum Theologicarum Lovaniensium Ser.). (ENG.). 317p. (C). pap. 116.00 *(978-90-429-2038-5(6))* Peeters Pubs. & Booksellers BEL. Dist: Brown, David Bk. Co., The.

Ayers, Jerry. Yahweh's Breath Bible, Volume 1: Literal Strong's Version with Sacred Name Added. 2010. 760p. pap. 38.50 *(978-1-4520-1485-2(X))* AuthorHouse.

—Yahweh's Breath Bible, Volume 2: Literal Strong's Version with Sacred Name Added. 2010. 812p. pap. 38.50 *(978-1-4520-1488-3(4))* AuthorHouse.

Bach, Inka & Galle, Helmut. Deutsche Psalmendichtung vom 16. bis zum 20. Jahrhundert: Untersuchungen zur Geschichte einer lyrischen Gattung. (Quellen und Forschungen zur Sprach- und Kulturgeschichte der germanischen Völker. NF Ser.). (GER.). X, 461p. 321.00 ***(978-3-11-178702-2(8))*** De Gruyter, Walter Inc.

Baibala Hemolele.Tr. of The Hawaiian Bible. (HAW.). 34.95 *(978-0-681-30735-3(8))* Booklines Hawaii, Ltd.

Barbour Publishing, Inc. ¿Qué Dice la Biblia Sobre el Matrimonio? Respuestas Bíblicas para Preguntas de la Vida. 2010. (What the Bible Says About... Ser.).Tr. of What the Bible Says about Marriage. (ENG & SPA.). 192p. pap. 3.99 *(978-1-60260-871-9(7),* Casa Promesa) Barbour Publishing, Inc.

Bauscher, David. The Aramaic-English Interlinear New Testament. 2008. 621p. 54.98 *(978-1-4357-3462-3(9))* Lulu Enterprises Inc.

Bell, David. A Comparative Analysis of Formal Shifts in English Bible Translations. 2010. 552p. pap. *(978-3-8383-1683-3(5))* Lambert Academic Publishing.

Benjamin, Mara H. Rosenzweig's Bible: Reinventing Scripture for Jewish Modernity. 2009. (ENG., Illus.). 222p. 80.00 *(978-0-521-89526-2(X))* Cambridge Univ. Pr.

Berg, J. Frederic. The Influence of the Septuagint upon the Peshitta Psalter. 2010. 101.12 *(978-1-61719-178-7(7))* Gorgias Pr., LLC.

Besch, Werner. Deutscher Bibelwortschatz in der frühen Neuzeit: Auswahl - Abwahl - Veralten. 2008. (GER., Illus.). 278p. 65.95 *(978-3-631-57891-9(1))* Lang, Peter GmbH, Europaischer Verlag der Wissenschaften DEU. Dist: Lang, Peter.

Bible. N.T. English. 1867. The New Testament of Our Lord & Savior Jesus Christ the Common English Version, Cor by the Final Committee of the American Bible Union. 2011. 488p. pap. 29.99 ***(978-1-4181-8858-0(1))*** MPublishing.

Biblia del Discipulo.Tr. of Disciple's Bible. (SPA.). 20.99 *(978-1-56063-736-3(6),* 490087) Editorial Unilit.

Bickerman, E. J. Studies in Jewish & Christian History: A New Edition in English Including the God of the Maccabees. Tropper, Amram, ed. 2007. (Ancient Judaism & Early Christianity Ser.). 1218p. *(978-90-04-15294-6(6))* BRILL.

Black Compact Wide Margin Bible King James Version. 2008. 32.99 *(978-0-8340-0419-1(4));* lthr. 16.99 *(978-0-8340-0421-4(6))* Oxford Univ. Pr., Inc.

Blackaby, Henry, et al. 1 & 2 Peter: A Blackaby Bible Study Series, 0 vols. 2008. (Encounters with God Ser.). 96p. pap. 9.99 *(978-1-4185-2654-2(1))* Nelson, Thomas Inc.

Blake, Robert P. Ancient Georgian Versions of the Old Testament. 2010. pap. 19.36 *(978-1-61143-411-8(4))* Gorgias Pr., LLC.

Brayford, Susan. Genesis. 2007. (Septuagint Commentary Ser.). 468p. lib. bdg. *(978-90-04-15552-7(X))* BRILL.

Brewer, Julius A. The History of the New Testament Canon in the Syrian Church. 2010. pap. 24.40 *(978-1-61143-356-2(8))* Gorgias Pr., LLC.

Burgon, John William. The Traditional Text of the Holy Gospels. 2007. 344p. per. 24.95 *(978-1-60206-646-5(9))* Cosimo, Inc.

Burgundy Compact Wide Margin Bible King James Version. 2008. 17.99 *(978-0-8340-0420-7(8));* lthr. 16.99 *(978-0-8340-0422-1(4))* Oxford Univ. Pr., Inc.

Burkitt, F. Crawford. Fragments of the Books of Kings According to the Translation of Aquila. 2012. (ENG & GEC.). 58p. pap. 26.99 ***(978-1-107-60492-6(3))*** Cambridge Univ. Pr.

Carabetta, Natalie, illus. My First Catholic Bible-NRSV. 2007. 415p. (J). (gr. -1-3). 15.99 *(978-0-8146-3211-6(4))* Nelson, Thomas Inc.

Caribe Betania, creator. Biblia Letra Grande-RV 1960, 0 vols. l.t. ed. 2006. (SPA.). 1536p. lthr. 34.99 *(978-0-89922-708-5(2))* Grupo Nelson.

Carroll, Robert, ed. The Bible: Authorized King James Version with Apocrypha. 2008. (Oxford World's Classics Ser.). (ENG., Illus.). 1824p. pap. 18.95 *(978-0-19-953594-1(9))* Oxford Univ. Pr., Inc.

Chernorion, Diphus. Community Participation in Scripture Version Design. 2010. 100.00 *(978-1-60724-408-0(X))* Gorgias Pr., LLC.

Chinese Red Letter Edition Bible - Shen Edition. 1540p. 15.99 *(978-962-293-601-0(6))* Hong Kong Bible Society (HK) HKG. Dist: American Bible Society.

Chisley, J. r. Going Deeper: Notes for the Serious Bible Student. 2011. 141p. pap. 24.95 *(978-0-9841991-8-1(7))* Beckham Pubns. Group, Inc.

Christodoulou, Sophocles. Hidden Treasures in the Greek Text: Uncover the Riches of God's Word. 2009. (ENG.). 160p. 12.95 *(978-0-9824145-3-8(6))* Lifebridge Bks.

Chumash Bereishis (Book of Genesis) (HEB.). 243p. 8.50 *(978-0-87559-224-4(4))* Shalom, P. Pubns., Inc.

Clever, Charles Huntley. The Wise Shall Understand. 2009. 204p. 25.99 *(978-1-60791-307-8(0));* pap. 15.99 *(978-1-60791-575-1(8))* Xulon Pr., Inc.

Conner, Kenneth E. They Captured the Spirit. 2007. 220p. per. 12.95 *(978-1-60364-001-5(0),* Honey Locust Pr.) Wolfmont, LLC.

Conybeare, F. C. & Stock, St. George. Selections from the Septuagint. 2009. 324p. 32.99 *(978-1-115-88122-7(1));* 324p. 36.99 *(978-1-115-88121-0(3));* 324p. pap. 30.75 *(978-1-115-88123-4(X));* 324p. pap. 29.75 *(978-1-115-88124-1(8));* (GRE.). 322p. pap. 23.99 *(978-1-115-88126-5(4),* BiblioLife) BiblioBazaar.

Cook, E. M. A Glossary of Targum Onkelos: According to Alexander Sperber's Edition. 2008. (Studies in the Aramaic Interpretation of Scripture). (ARC & ENG.). 336p. (C). *(978-90-04-14978-6(3))* BRILL.

Cook, Johann & Cook, J. Septuagint & Reception: Essays Prepared for the Association for the Study of the Septuagint in South Africa. 2009. 422p. *(978-90-04-17725-3(6))* BRILL.

Copinger, Walter Arthur. Incunabula Biblica, or, the First Half Century of the Latin Bible: Being a Bibliographical Account of the Various Editions of the Latin Bible Between 1450 & 1500: with an Appendix Containing a Chronological List of the Editions of the Sixteenth Century. 2007. (Illus.). 301p. 125.00 *(978-1-57898-659-0(1))* Martino Publishing.

Cosaert, Carl P. The Text of the Gospels in Clement of Alexandria. 2008. (SBL - the New Testament in the Greek Fathers Ser.). 384p. *(978-90-04-16913-5(X))* BRILL.

—The Text of the Gospels in Clement of Alexandria. 2008. 388p. pap. 47.95 *(978-1-58983-372-2(4))* Society of Biblical Literature.

Cotos, Jorge L. Gramática Castellana: Adaptada para el Estudio Bíblico, 1 vol. 2008. (SPA.). 240p. pap. 9.99 *(978-84-7645-536-4(4))* Clie, Editorial ESP. Dist: Zondervan.

Coverdale, Miles & Coverdale, Miles, Jr. Remains of Myles Coverdale, Bishop of Exeter: Containing Prologues to the Translation of the Bible, Treatise on Death, Hope of the Faithful, Exhortation to the Carrying of Christ's Cross, Exposition upon the Twenty-Third Psalm, Confutation of the Treatise of John Standish, Defense of a Certain Poor Christian Man, Letters, Ghostly Psalms & Spiritual Songs. Pearson, George, ed. 2007. (Parker Society: Ser.). 641p. pap. 62.00 *(978-1-55635-066-5(X,* Wipf and Stock) Wipf & Stock Pubs.

Cox, Steven L. & Easley, Kendell H. HCSB Harmony of the Gospels. 2007. (ENG.). 400p. 24.99 *(978-0-8054-9444-0(8),* Holman Pubs.) B&H Publishing Group.

Curtice L. Rogers. And God Said. 2009. 52p. pap. 11.49 *(978-1-4389-5355-7(0))* AuthorHouse.

Czech Bible: Kralice 1613 Version. 1205p. 14.99 *(978-0-900185-94-6(5))* American Bible Society.

de Lange, Nicholas, ed. Jewish Reception of Greek Bible Versions: Studies in Their Use in Late Antiquity & the Middle Ages. 2009. (Text & Studies in Medieval & Early Modern Judaism Ser.). (Illus.). 338p. 195.00 *(978-3-16-149779-7(1))* Mohr Siebeck GmbH & Co. KG DEU. Dist: Coronet Bks.

De Young, Curtiss Paul, et al, eds. The Peoples' Bible. 2008. 1600p. (C). 35.00 *(978-0-8066-5625-0(5),* Fortress Pr.) Augsburg Fortress, Pubs.

Deutsche Bibelgesellschaft, creator. Novum Testamentum Latine-FL. 2006. 680p. 31.99 *(978-1-59856-175-3(8))* Hendrickson Pubs. Marketing, LLC.

Dove, Adrian. The Earliest Advocates of the English Bible: The Texts of the Medieval Debate. 2011. (University of Exeter Press - Exeter Medieval Texts & Studies). 236p. 100.00 *(978-0-85989-852-2(0))* Univ. of Exeter Pr. GBR. Dist: Chicago Distribution Ctr.

Dubis, Mark. 1 Peter: A Handbook on the Greek Text. 2010. (Baylor Handbook on the Greek New Testament Ser.). (ENG.). 220p. (C). pap. 24.95 *(978-1-932792-62-1(7))* Baylor Univ. Pr.

Duvall, J. Scott & Verbrugge, Verlyn D. Devotions on the Greek New Testament, 1 vol. 2012. (ENG.). 160p. pap. 16.99 ***(978-0-310-49254-2(8))*** Zondervan.

Edgar, Swift. The Vulgate Bible, Volume III: the Poetical Books: Douay-Rheims Translation, Volume III. 2011. (Dumbarton Oaks Medieval Library). (LAT & ENG.). 1232p. 29.95 *(978-0-674-99668-7(2))* Harvard Univ. Pr.

Edgar, Swift, et al. The Pentateuch: Douay-Rheims Translation, Volume I. 2010. (Dumbarton Oaks Medieval Library). (LAT & ENG.). 1200p. 29.95 *(978-0-674-05534-6(9))* Harvard Univ. Pr.

Edmunds, James. Discussion on Revision of the Holy Oracles & upon the Objects, Aims, Motives the Constitution, Organization, Facilities & Capacities of the Americ. 2006. 224p. per. 20.99 *(978-1-4255-1880-6(X))* MPublishing.

Edwards, Timothy. Exegesis in the Targum of Psalms: The Old, the New & the Rewritten. 2007. (Gorgias Dissertations in Biblical Studies: 1). 78.00 *(978-1-59333-432-1(X))* Gorgias Pr., LLC.

Ehrman, Bart D. Whose Word Is It? The Story Behind Who Changed the New Testament & Why. 2008. 256p. *(978-1-84706-314-4(4))* Continuum International Publishing Group, Ltd.

Eisele, Wilfried. Welcher Thomas? Studien zur Text- und Überlieferungsgeschichte des Thomasevangeliums. 2010. (GER., Illus.). XII, 308p. 197.50 *(978-3-16-150543-0(3))* Mohr Siebeck GmbH & Co. KG DEU. Dist: Coronet Bks.

Elliger, Karl, et al. Torah, Nevi'im U-Khetuvim: Biblia Hebraica Stuttgartensia. 5th ed. 2007. (HEB.). 1574p. 69.95 *(978-1-59856-199-9(5))* Hendrickson Pubs. Marketing, LLC.

Emmenegger, Gregor. Der Text des koptischen Psalters aus al-Mudil: Ein Beitrag zur Textgeschichte der Septuaginta und zur Textkritik koptischer Bibelhandschriften, mit der kritischen Neuausgabe des Papyrus 37 der British Library London (U) und des Papyrus 39 der Leipziger Universitätsbibliothek (2013) 2007. (Texte und Untersuchungen zur Geschichte der altchristlichen Literatur Ser.: Vol. 159). (GEC & GER., Illus.). XXVIII, 391p. 182.00 *(978-3-11-019948-2(3))* De Gruyter, Walter Inc.

Ewald, Georg Heinrich August. Abhandlungen Zur Orientalischen und Biblischen Literatur. 2010. (GER & ENG.). 166p. pap. 19.00 *(978-1-60899-604-9(2))* Wipf & Stock Pubs.

Farley, Lawrence. Universal Truth: The Catholic Epistles of James, Peter, Jude, & John. 2009. (Orthodox Bible Study Companion Ser.). 232p. pap. 15.95 *(978-1-888212-60-0(8))* Conciliar Pr.

Fee, Gordon D., et al. How to Choose a Translation for All Its Worth, 1 vol. 2007. (ENG., Illus.). 176p. (gr. 13). pap. 12.99 *(978-0-310-27876-4(7))* Zondervan.

Fireside Catholic Bibles, creator. Catholic Companion Bible-Nab-Giant Print. l.t. ed. 2006. (Illus.). 2239p. im. lthr. 54.95 *(978-1-55665-437-4(5))* Fireside Catholic Bibles.

Fireside Catholic Publishing, creator. Catholic Youth Bible-NAB. 2007. (Illus.). 1394p. im. lthr. 44.95 *(978-1-55665-462-6(6))* Fireside Catholic Bibles.

—New Catholic Answer Bible-NAB. 2007. (Illus.). 1394p. im. lthr. 49.95 *(978-1-55665-406-0(5))* Fireside Catholic Bibles.

Flesher, Paul V. M. & Chilton, Bruce. The Targums: A Critical Introduction. 2011. 575p. pap. 69.95 ***(978-1-60258-385-6(4))***; (ENG., Illus.). pap. 69.95 *(978-1-60258-382-5(X))* Baylor Univ. Pr.

Flesher, Paul V. M. & Chilton, Bruce D. The Targums: A Critical Introduction. 2011. (Studies in the Aramaic Interpretation of Scripture). (Illus.). XVIII, 558p. ***(978-90-04-21769-0(X))*** BRILL.

Foley, T. S. Biblical Translation in Chinese & Greek: Verbal Aspect in Theory & Practice. 2009. (Linguistic Biblical Studies). 472p. *(978-90-04-17865-6(1))* BRILL.

French Bible. 1115p. 27.99 *(978-2-85300-118-2(0))* Société Biblique Française FRA. Dist: American Bible Society.

French Bible: Segond Version. 984p. 12.99 *(978-1-58516-716-6(9))* American Bible Society.

Gerber, Christine, et al. Gott Heisst Nicht Nur Vater: Zur Rede über Gott in Den Übersetzungen der "Bibel in Gerechter Sprache" 2008. (Biblisch-Theologische Schwerpunkte Ser.). (GER., Illus.). 256p. (C). pap. 27.00 *(978-3-525-61609-3(0))* Vandenhoeck & Ruprecht GmbH & Co. KG DEU. Dist: ISD.

German Luther Bible with Apocrypha. 1125p. 49.99 *(978-3-438-01522-8(6))* Deutsche Bibelgesellschaft DEU. Dist: American Bible Society.

Giant print new american Bible. 2006. per. 54.95 *(978-1-59276-278-1(6))* Our Sunday Visitor, Publishing Div.

Gindin, Thamar Eiram. The Early Judaeo-Persian Tafsirs of Ezekiel: Text, Translation, Commentary. Vol. III: Commentary. 2011. (Veroffentlichungen zur Iranistik Ser.). (ENG.). 214p. (C). pap. 44.00 *(978-3-7001-3997-3(7))* Austrian Academy of Sciences Press AUT. Dist: Brown, David Bk. Co., The.

Ginsburg, Christian D. Introduction to the Massoretico-Critical Edition of the Hebrew Bible Pt. 2. 2007. (Dove Studies in Bible, Language, & History: Ser.). 1050p. pap. 78.00 *(978-1-59752-894-8(3),* Wipf and Stock) Wipf & Stock Pubs.

Glenny, W. Edward. Finding Meaning in the Text: Translation Technique & Theology in the Septuagint of Amos. 2009. 322p. *(978-90-04-17638-6(1))* BRILL.

Goodspeed, Edgar J., ed. The Translators to the Reader: Preface to the King James Version 1611. 2011. 54p. 36.95 ***(978-1-258-06120-3(1))*** Literary Licensing, LLC.

Gordon, R. P. Hebrew Bible & Ancient Versions: Selected Essays of Robert P. Gordon. 2006. (Ashgate Contemporary Thinkers on Religion Ser.). 408p. 150.00 *(978-0-7546-5617-3(9))* Ashgate Publishing Co.

Green, Jay P., Sr. KJ3 Literal Translation New Testament. 2006. 304p. per. 19.99 *(978-1-58960-472-8(5))* Sovereign Grace Pubs., Inc.

Greenfield, William. The Syriac New Testament: A Vocalized Text. 2006. 568p. 54.00 *(978-1-59333-503-8(2))* Gorgias Pr., LLC.

Greif, Michael. The VISIBLE KEYS: Newly Discovered Images that Spiritually Illustrate the Bible, Volume Two. 2008. 188p. pap. 60.98 *(978-0-615-18869-0(9))* Visible Glory.

Grife, Michael. The VISIBLE KEYS: Newly Discovered Images That Spiritually Illustrate the Bible, Volume One. 2008. 146p. pap. 47.80 *(978-0-615-19035-8(9))* Visible Glory.

Groseclose, Win. Saved from What? 2010. 80p. pap. 9.88 *(978-0-557-50536-4(4))* Lulu Enterprises Inc.

Gwynn, John. On a Syriac MS. Belonging to the Collection of Archbishop Ussher. 2010. pap. 21.76 *(978-1-61719-579-2(0))* Gorgias Pr., LLC.

Haar Romeny, R. B. ter. The Peshitta: Its Uses in Literature & Liturgy: Papers Read at the Third Peshitta Symposium. 2007. (Monographs of the Peshitta Institute Leiden Ser.). (Illus.). 412p. *(978-90-04-15658-6(5))* BRILL.

Hadas, Moses, ed. & tr. Aristeas to Philocrates. 2007. 244p. pap. 27.00 *(978-1-55635-506-6(8))* Wipf & Stock Pubs.

Hanon. Mi Primera Bible. 5.95 *(978-0-88271-096-9(6))* Regina Pr., Malhame & Co.

Harden, Jm. Dictionary of the Vulgate New Testament: A Dictionary of Ecclesiastical Latin. 2007. 140p. per. *(978-1-84356-017-3(8))* Wallenberg, Simon Pr.

Harper Bibles Staff. The Green Bible: Jesus Against Rome, Then & Now. 2008. (ENG.). 1408p. 29.95 *(978-0-06-162799-6(2),* HarperOne) HarperCollins Pubs.

—NRSV Go-Anywhere Bible: The Bible for Everyone Trusted, Accurate, Readable with Concordance. 2007. (ENG.). 46p. 29.95 *(978-0-06-124486-5(4),* HarperOne) HarperCollins Pubs.

Harper Bibles Staff, creator. NRSV XL. l.t. ed. 2007. (ENG.). 1608p. 34.99 *(978-0-06-124489-6(9),* HarperOne) HarperCollins Pubs.

Harper Collins Publishers Staff, creator. NRSV Go Anywhere Bible. 2007. (ENG.). 46p. 29.95 *(978-0-06-129048-0(3),* HarperOne) HarperCollins Pubs.

Harperone Staff. The Bible for Everyone Trusted, Accurate, Readable. l.t. ed. 2007. (ENG.). 1920p. 37.95 *(978-0-06-124487-2(2),* Harper San Francisco) HarperCollins Pubs.

Harrelson, Walter J., ed. New Revised Standard Version - the New Interpreter's Study Bible with the Apocrypha. 2008. 2360p. pap. 29.95 *(978-0-687-64733-0(9))* Abingdon Pr.

Harthan, Jan. The B-I-B-L-E. 2008. 280p. per. 15.99 *(978-1-60477-584-6(X))* Xulon Pr., Inc.

Harwood, William, et al. William Harwood Catalogue. 2009. 402p. pap. 29.00 *(978-1-935444-83-1(2))* World Audience Pubs.

Hatch, Edwin. Essays in Biblical Greek. 2009. 188p. pap. *(978-1-151-41239-3(2))* Books LLC.

—Essays in Biblical Greek. 2007. (ENG.). 302p. 43.95 *(978-0-548-25557-5(1));* 304p. per. 28.95 *(978-1-4326-5905-9(7))* Kessinger Publishing, LLC.

Hawley, Charles A. Critical Examination of the Peshitta Version of the Book of Ezra. (Columbia University, Contributions to Oriental History & Philology Ser.: No. 8). reprint ed. 27.50 *(978-0-404-50538-7(4))* AMS Pr., Inc.

Hendrickson Publishers, creator. Biblia Sacra Utriusque Testamenti Editio Hebraica et Graeca-FL. 2006. 109.99 *(978-1-59856-179-1(0))* Hendrickson Pubs. Marketing, LLC.

—Hendrickson Parallel Bible-PR-KJV/NKJV/NIV/NLT. 2008. 2871p. 49.95 *(978-1-59856-230-9(4));* 89.95 *(978-1-59856-231-6(2))* Hendrickson Pubs. Marketing, LLC.

—Nestle-Aland Novum Testamentum Graece-FL-Wide Margin. 27th ed. 2007. 812p. 59.95 *(978-1-59856-200-2(2))* Hendrickson Pubs. Marketing, LLC.

Hiebert, Robert J. V. Translation Is Required: The Septuagint in Retrospect & Prospect. 2010. *(978-1-58983-524-5(7)); (978-1-58983-523-8(9))* Society of Biblical Literature.

Hill, Charles E. & Kruger, Michael J. The Early Text of the New Testament. 2012. (ENG.). 448p. 175.00 ***(978-0-19-956636-5(4))*** Oxford Univ. Pr., Inc.

Ho, Ahuva. The Targum of Zephaniah: Manuscripts & Commentary. 2009. *(978-90-04-17180-0(0))* BRILL.

The Holy Bible. 2008. (ENG & SPA.). 1792p. 34.99 *(978-1-58134-956-6(4),* Crossway Bibles) Crossway.

The Holy Bible: Containing the Old & New Testaments, Newly Translated Out of the Original Tongues, & with the Former Translations Diligently Compared & Revised. 2006. *(978-1-57898-647-7(8))* Martino Publishing.

Honigman, Sylvie. The Septuagint & Homeric Scholarship in Alexandria: A Study in the Narrative of the 'Letter of Aristeas' 2012. (ENG.). 224p. (C). pap. 42.95 ***(978-0-415-51854-3(7))*** Routledge.

Horne, Thomas Hartwell. Manual of Biblical Bibliography: Comprising a Catalogue ... of the Principal Editions & Versions of the Holy Scriptures: Together with Notices of the Principal Philosophers, Critics, & Interpreters of the Bible. 2006. (ENG.). 450p. 75.00 *(978-1-57898-562-3(5))* Martino Publishing.

Horner, George William, ed. Coptic Version of the New Testament in the Southern Dialect. 2010. 1003.52 *(978-1-61719-475-7(1));* 1003.52 *(978-1-61719-474-0(3));* 1003.52 *(978-1-61719-476-4(X));* 1003.52 *(978-1-61719-472-6(7));* 1003.52 *(978-1-61719-478-8(6));* 1003.52 *(978-1-61719-473-3(5));* 1003.52 *(978-1-61719-477-1(8))* Gorgias Pr., LLC.

Houtman, A. & Sysling, H. Alternative Targum Traditions: The Use of Variant Readings for the Study in Origin & History of Targum Jonathan. 2009. (Studies in the Aramaic Interpretation of Scripture). 314p. *(978-90-04-17842-7(2))* BRILL.

Hughes, Aaron W. The Invention of Jewish Identity: Bible, Philosophy, & the Art of Translation. 2010. (ENG.). 202p. 70.00 *(978-0-253-35537-9(0),* 0253355370); pap. 24.95 *(978-0-253-22249-7(4),* 0253222494) Indiana Univ. Pr.

The Interlinear Bible Hebrew - English: The Book of Genesis. 2006. 252p. per. *(978-956-291-340-9(6))* Editorial Benei Noaj.

Israel, Hephzibah. Religious Transactions in Colonial South India: Language, Translation, & the Making of Protestant Identity. 2011. (Palgrave Studies in Cultural & Intellectual History Ser.). (ENG.). 286p. 85.00 *(978-0-230-10562-1(9))* Palgrave Macmillan.

Jemas, Bill. Genesis Rejuvenated. 2009. 114p. pap. 20.00 *(978-1-935444-87-9(5));* pap. 25.00 *(978-1-935444-95-4(6))* World Audience Pubs.

Jewish Family Bible, ed. Parallel Bible Hebrew / English: Tanakh, Biblia Hebraica - Volume I. 2007. 404p. per. *(978-956-291-482-6(8))* Editorial Benei Noaj.

—Parallel Bible Hebrew / English: Tanakh, Biblia Hebraica - Volume II. 2007. 548p. per. *(978-956-291-483-3(6))* Editorial Benei Noaj.

Jewish Publication Society of America, creator. The JPS Bible, Pocket Edition (Denim) 2008. (ENG.). 1104p. pap. 15.00 *(978-0-8276-0878-8(0))* Jewish Pubn. Society.

—The JPS Bible, Pocket Edition (Moss) 2008. (ENG.). 1104p. pap. 15.00 *(978-0-8276-0877-1(2))* Jewish Pubn. Society.

—The JPS Bible, Pocket Edition (Rose) 2008. (ENG.). 1104p. per. 15.00 *(978-0-8276-0876-4(4))* Jewish Pubn. Society.

—The JPS Bible, Pocket Edition (White) 2008. (ENG.). 1104p. pap. 30.00 *(978-0-8276-0879-5(9))* Jewish Pubn. Society.

Johnson, T. J. Chapter & Verse Crosswords & Other Puzzles. 2008. 100p. pap. 11.99 *(978-1-60477-320-0(0))* Xulon Pr., Inc.

Joosten, Jan, et al, eds. Voces Biblicae: Septuagint Greek & its Significance for the New Testament. 2007. (Contributions to Biblical Exegesis & Theology Ser.). (ENG.). 170p. (C). pap. 57.00 *(978-90-429-1915-0(9))* Peeters Pubs. & Booksellers BEL. Dist: Brown, David Bk. Co., The.

Joosten, Jan & Bons, Eberhard. Septuagint Vocabulary: Pre-History, Usage, Reception. 2011. (GER.). 224p. pap. ***(978-1-58983-585-6(9))*** Society of Biblical Literature.

Joosten, Jan & Bons, Eberhard, eds. Septuagint Vocabulary: Pre-History, Usage, Reception. 2011. (SBL - Septuagint & Cognate Studies). (FRE, GER & ENG.). X, 212p. ***(978-90-04-21162-9(4))*** BRILL.

Karrer, Martin & Kraus, Wolfgang. Die Septuaginta - Texte, Theologien, Einflüsse: 2. Internationale Fachtagung veranstaltet von Septuaginta Deutsch (LXX.D), Wuppertal 23.-27. Juli 2008. 2010. (GER., Illus.). 759p. 287.50 *(978-3-16-150225-5(6))* Mohr Siebeck GmbH & Co. KG DEU. Dist: Coronet Bks.

Kashouh, Hikmat. The Arabic Versions of the Gospels: The Manuscripts & Their Families. 2011. (Arbeiten zur neutestamentlichen Textforschung Ser.). (ENG.). XIV, 761p. (gr. 17). 377.00 ***(978-3-11-022858-8(0))*** De Gruyter, Walter Inc.

Kenyon, Frederic G. Our Bible & the Ancient Manuscripts. 2011. 298p. pap. 26.00 ***(978-1-61097-756-2(4),*** Wipf and Stock) Wipf & Stock Pubs.

—Our Bible & the Ancient Manuscripts Be. 2006. pap. 31.95 *(978-1-4286-5003-9(2))* Kessinger Publishing, LLC.

—Recent Develooments in the Textual Criticism of the Greek Bible: The Schweich Lectures of the British Academy 1932. 2007. 130p. pap. 16.00 *(978-1-55635-370-3(7),* Wipf and Stock) Wipf & Stock Pubs.

Kindig, Rhonda K. Found in Translation. 2011. 164p. pap. 13.95 ***(978-1-4497-1745-2(4),*** WestBow Pr.) Author Solutions, Inc.

Kinney, Angela M., ed. The Vulgate Bible, Volume IV: the Major Prophetical Books: Douay-Rheims Translation, Volume IV. 2012. (Dumbarton Oaks Medieval Library). (ENG & LAT.). 1168p. 29.95 ***(978-0-674-99669-4(0))*** Harvard Univ. Pr.

KJV Holy Bible Camo edition. 2007. pap. 12.99 *(978-0-9795850-0-5(7))* One Source Distribution, Inc.

Kohlenberger, John R., III, ed. The Comparative Psalter: Hebrew - Greek - English. 2007. (ENG.). 288p. 39.99 *(978-0-19-529760-7(1))* Oxford Univ. Pr., Inc.

Kushner, Aviya. And There Was Evening, & There Was Morning: Reading the Bible in Translation. 2013. (ENG.). 208p. 25.00 *(978-0-385-52082-9(4))* Spiegel & Grau.

Lacueva, Francisco. Nuevo Testamento Interlineal Griego: Interlinear Greek-Spanish N. T., 1 vol. 2008. (SPA.). 1040p. 34.99 *(978-84-7228-877-5(3),* 220494) Clie, Editorial ESP. Dist: Zondervan.

Lamberigts, M., et al. Lay Bibles in Europe 1450-1800. 2006. (Bibliotheca Ephemeridum Theologicarum Lovaniensium Ser.: Vol. 198). (ENG., Illus.). 360p. (C). pap. 115.00 *(978-90-429-1785-9(7))* Peeters Pubs. & Booksellers BEL. Dist: Brown, David Bk. Co., The.

Larkin, William J. Ephesians: A Handbook on the Greek Text. 2009. (Baylor Handbook on the Greek New Testament Ser.). (ENG.). 210p. pap. 24.95 *(978-1-60258-066-4(9))* Baylor Univ. Pr.

Lewis, Agnes Smith. A Translation of the Four Gospels from the Syriac of the Sinaitic Palimpsest. 2006. (Gorgias Theological Library: 17). 276p. 88.00 *(978-1-59333-531-1(8))* Gorgias Pr., LLC.

Life Pub, tr. from ENG. Bibla e Studimit Jeta e Plote: Full Life Study Bible - Albanian New Testament Language Edition. 2006. (ALB.). *(978-0-7361-0349-7(X))* Life Pubs. International.

—The Full Life Study Bible - Hindi Language: Full Life Study Bible - Hindi Language Edition. 2006. (HIN.). lib. bdg. *(978-0-7361-0359-6(7))* Life Pubs. International.

—The Victory Bible (the Full Life Study Bible) - Bengali Language: The Full Life Study Bible - Bengali Language Translation. 2006. (BEN.). *(978-0-7361-0358-9(9))* Life Pubs. International.

Livingstone Corporation Staff & Fackler, Mark. Holy Bible. 2006. (King James Bible Ser.). (ENG.). 576p. pap. 4.99 *(978-1-59789-515-6(6),* Barbour Bks.) Barbour Publishing, Inc.

Lucado, Max. He Still Moves Stones: Everyone Needs a Miracle, 0 vols. 2009. (Bestseller Collection). 240p. 9.99 *(978-0-8499-2133-9(3))* Nelson, Thomas Inc.

Margolis, Max L. The Story of Bible Translations. 2007. (ENG.). 160p. 36.95 *(978-0-548-26392-1(2));* per. 21.95 *(978-1-4326-6809-9(9))* Kessinger Publishing, LLC.

Mathews McGinnis, Claire, ed. As Those Who Are Taught: The Interpretation of Isaiah from the LXX to the SBL. 2006. (SBL - Symposium Ser.). 342p. *(978-90-04-13041-8(1))* BRILL.

McAfee, Cleland Boyd & Mcafee, Cleland Boyd. The Greatest English Classic, a Study of the King James Version of the Bible & It's Influence on Live & Literature. 2011. 146p. pap. 12.99 ***(978-1-61203-235-1(4))*** Bottom of the Hill Publishing.

McKendrick, Scot & Doyle, Kathleen. Bible Manuscripts: 1400 Years of Scribes & Scripture. 2007. (ENG., Illus.). 159p. 35.00 *(978-0-7123-4922-2(7))* British Library, The GBR. Dist: Chicago Distribution Ctr.

McNamara, Martin. Targum & Testament Revisited: Aramaic Paraphrases of the Hebrew Bible: A light on the New Testament, Second Edition. 2010. viii, 359p. pap. 32.00 *(978-0-8028-6275-4(6))* Eerdmans, William B. Publishing Co.

Muraoka, T. A Greek-English Lexicon of the Septuagint. 2010. (ENG.). 757p. (C). 138.00 *(978-90-429-2248-8(6))* Peeters Pubs. & Booksellers BEL. Dist: Brown, David Bk. Co., The.

—A Greek-Hebrew/Aramaic Two-way Index to the Septuagint. 2010. (ENG.). 394p. (C). 87.00 *(978-90-429-2356-0(3))* Peeters Pubs. & Booksellers BEL. Dist: Brown, David Bk. Co., The.

Murdock, James. The New Testament. 2009. 526p. pap. 45.00 *(978-1-60608-758-9(4),* Wipf and Stock) Wipf & Stock Pubs.

Navajo Bible. 1125p. 31.99 *(978-1-58516-194-2(2))* American Bible Society.

NIV. Date not set. mass mkt. *(978-0-312-99739-7(6),* St. Martin's Paperbacks) St. Martin's Pr.

Noyes, George R. The New Testament: Translated from the Greek Text of Tischendorf, by George R. Noyes ... 2006. 584p. per. 32.99 *(978-1-4255-6357-9(0))* MPublishing.

NRSV Premium Bible. 2010. 1152p. 36.00 *(978-1-4267-1141-1(7))* Abingdon Pr.

NRSV Premium Bible Bonded Leather Burgundy: Burgundy Bonded Leather. 2010. 1152p. 36.00 *(978-1-4267-1145-9(X))* Abingdon Pr.

O'Hare, Daniel M. Have You Seen, Son of Man? Studies in the Translation & Vorlage of LXX Ezekiel 40-48. 2010. *(978-1-58983-527-6(1));* *(978-1-58983-526-9(3))* Society of Biblical Literature.

Owles, R. The New Peace Treaty: (Between God & Humanity) 2007. 512p. per. 34.95 *(978-1-4241-4752-6(2))* PublishAmerica, Inc.

Oxford, ed. Essential Evangelical Parellel Bible. 2007. (ENG.). 3072p. 49.95 *(978-0-19-528180-4(2))* Oxford Univ. Pr., Inc.

Palmer, Nigel F. Bibelübersetzung und Heilsgeschichte: Studien zur Freiburger Perikopenhandschrift von 1462 und zu den deutschsprachigen Lektionaren des 15. Jahrhunderts. 2007. (Wolfgang Stammler Gastprofessur Für Germanische Philologie Ser.). (GER., Illus.). 252p. 133.00 *(978-3-11-019151-6(2))* De Gruyter, Walter Inc.

Peters, Melvin K. H. XII Congress of the International Organization for Septuagint & Cognate Studies, Leiden, 2004. 2006. (ENG.). 244p. per. 34.95 *(978-1-58983-258-9(2))* Society of Biblical Literature.

—XII Congress of the International Organization for Septuagint & Cognate Studies Leiden 2004 2006. (SBL - Septuagint & Cognate Studies). 232p. *(978-90-04-15122-2(2))* BRILL.

Peters, Melvin K. H., ed. Xiii Congress of the International Organization for Septuagint & Cognate Studies: Ljubljana 2007. 2008. 384p. pap. 45.95 *(978-1-58983-395-1(3))* Society of Biblical Literature.

Pietersma, Albert & Wright, Benjamin G. A New English Translation of the Septuagint. 2007. (ENG.). 1027p. 39.99 *(978-0-19-528975-6(7))* Oxford Univ. Pr., Inc.

Publishing, Barbour. KJV Gift & Award Bible - Burgundy. 2006. (King James Bible Ser.). (ENG.). 576p. pap. 4.99 *(978-1-59789-533-0(4),* Barbour Bks.) Barbour Publishing, Inc.

Rajak, Tessa. Translation & Survival: The Greek Bible & the Ancient Jewish Diaspora. 2009. (ENG.). 420p. 155.00 *(978-0-19-955867-4(1))* Oxford Univ. Pr., Inc.

Read-heimerdinger, Jenny & Rius-Camps, Josep. Luke's Demonstration to Theophilus: The Gospel & the Acts of the Apostles According to Codex Bezae. 2012. (ENG.). 752p. 200.00 ***(978-0-567-43888-1(0),*** T&T Clark Int'l) Continuum International Publishing Group, Ltd. GBR. Dist: National Bk. Network.

Reuss, Eduard. Bibliotheca Novi Testamenti Graeci: Cuius editiones ab initio typographiae ad nostram aetatem Impressas. 2007. (LAT.). 320p. 75.00 *(978-1-57898-661-3(3))* Martino Publishing.

Rias-Baker, Georgette. Top of the Ninth & I'm Winning: Be a Victorious Winner. 2009. 128p. pap. 11.95 *(978-1-4327-4224-9(8))* Outskirts Pr., Inc.

Rose Publishing Staff. Bible Translations Comparison Pamphlet. 2007. (ENG.). 12p. 3.99 *(978-1-59636-133-1(6))* Rose Publishing.

Rosenberg, David. A Literary Bible: An Original Translation. 2010. (ENG.). 704p. pap. 26.95 *(978-1-58243-619-7(3),* Counterpoint) Counterpoint LLC.

RV 1960 Staff. Biblia Tu Andar Diario. 2009. (Tu Andar Ser.).Tr. of Your Daily Walk Bible. (SPA.). 17.99 *(978-0-7899-0425-6(X),* 497545) Editorial Unilit.

Samoan Bible. 980p. 22.99 *(978-982-217-326-0(1))* Bible Society in the South Pacific FJI. Dist: American Bible Society.

Scarlata, M. W. Outside of Eden: Cain in the Ancient Versions of Genesis 4. 1-16. 2012. (Library Hebrew Bible/Old Testament Studies). (ENG.). 256p. 130.00 ***(978-0-567-44798-2(7),*** T&T Clark Int'l) Continuum International Publishing Group, Ltd. GBR. Dist: National Bk. Network.

Schwarz, W. Principles & Problems of Biblical Translation: Some Reformation Controversies & their Background. 2009. (ENG.). 248p. pap. 34.99 *(978-0-521-09753-6(3))* Cambridge Univ. Pr.

Scott, William R. A Simplified Guide to BHS: Critical Apparatus, Masora, Accents, Unusual Letters & Other Markings. 4th ed. 2007. pap. *(978-1-930566-68-2(9),* BIBAL Pr.) Scott, D.& F. Publishing, Inc.

Scrivener, F. H. A., ed. The New Testament in Greek: According to the Text Followed in the Authorised Version Together with the Variations Adopted in the Revised Version. 2010. (Cambridge Library Collection - Religion Ser.). 672p. pap. 45.00 *(978-1-108-02472-3(6))* Cambridge Univ. Pr.

Septuagint Version of the Old Testament. 2006. pap. 49.95 *(978-1-4286-4508-0(X));* pap. 50.95 *(978-1-4286-4507-3(1))* Kessinger Publishing, LLC.

Shahar, Ravi, tr. Horev, Keter-Crown Bible. 1178p. 34.99 *(978-1-58330-275-0(1))* Feldheim Pubs.

Shepard, S. E. The Reviser; a Monthly Periodical by S E Shepard [V 1, 1855]. 2006. 328p. per. 23.99 *(978-1-4255-3282-6(9))* MPublishing.

Spanish Bible RVR 1960 with Concordance. (SPA.). 1620p. lthr. 24.95 *(978-1-58516-224-6(8))* American Bible Society.

Spanish Kingsley's Meadow: 1-2-3 Cuenta Conmigo. 2.95 *(978-1-58516-540-7(9))* American Bible Society.

Stampley, C. D., Enterprises Staff, Enterprises D. Stampley, contrib. by. Sagrada Biblia Edicion Latinoamericana. 2007. 1305p. *(978-1-58087-110-5(0),* Stampley) Stampley, C. D. Enterprises, Inc.

Standard Publishing Staff. Reina-Valera Revision 1960. 2007. (Standard Full Color Bible Ser.). (SPA., Illus.). 1520p. 49.99 *(978-0-7847-2170-4(X))* Standard Publishing.

Standard Publishing Staff, creator. Standard Biblia a Todo Color-RVR. 2007. (Standard Full Color Bible Ser.). (SPA., Illus.). 1520p. 59.99 *(978-0-7847-2171-1(8))* Standard Publishing.

Sub FBS Adult. ldr.'s ed. 18.95 *(978-0-633-05039-9(3))* LifeWay Christian Resources.

Sub FBS Adult Learner Guide. 8.75 *(978-0-633-05041-2(5));* 8.75 *(978-0-633-05042-9(3))* LifeWay Christian Resources.

Sub FBS Adult Learner Guide HCSB. 8.75 *(978-0-633-05043-6(1))* LifeWay Christian Resources.

Sub FBS Advanced Bible Study Commentary. 21.95 *(978-0-633-05044-3(X))* LifeWay Christian Resources.

Sub FBS All Youth Learner Guide. 9.15 *(978-0-633-05046-7(6));* 8.75 *(978-0-633-05047-4(4))* LifeWay Christian Resources.

Sumney, Jerry L. Philippians: A Greek Student's Intermediate Reader. 2006. 161p. per. 14.95 *(978-1-56563-991-1(X))* Hendrickson Pubs. Marketing, LLC.

Taylor, Preston A. Ephesians. 2007. 436p. per. 21.99 *(978-1-60477-371-2(5))* Xulon Pr., Inc.

Thackeray, H. St. J. Some Aspects of the Greek Old Testament. 2007. 64p. pap. 10.00 *(978-1-55635-257-7(3),* Wipf and Stock) Wipf & Stock Pubs.

Thomas Nelson Publishing Staff. The King James Study Bible, 0 vols. 2008. 2206p. im. lthr. 79.99 *(978-0-7180-2476-5(1));* im. lthr. 69.99 *(978-0-7180-2456-7(7));* im. lthr. 69.99 *(978-0-7180-2451-2(6));* im. lthr. 79.99 *(978-0-7180-2478-9(8))* Nelson, Thomas Inc.

Thomas Nelson Publishing Staff, creator. Study Bible-KJV, 0 vols. 2008. (Illus.). 2206p. im. lthr. 69.99 *(978-0-7180-2475-8(3));* im. lthr. 69.99 *(978-0-7180-2477-2(X))* Nelson, Thomas Inc.

Timm, Stefan. Eusebius und die Heilige Schrift: Die Schriftvorlagen des Onomastikons der biblischen Ortsnamen. 2010. (Texte und Untersuchungen zur Geschichte der altchristlichen Literatur Ser.).Tr. of Eusebius & the Holy Scripture. (GER.). XIV, 653p. 210.00 *(978-3-11-022600-3(6))* De Gruyter, Walter Inc.

Topical Study Bible: NLT Second Edition. 2006. *(978-1-882536-87-0(8))* Bible League.

Tov, Emanuel. The Greek & Hebrew Bible: Collected Essays on the Septuagint. 2006. (ENG.). 616p. per. 49.95 *(978-1-58983-254-1(X))* Society of Biblical Literature.

Townsend, George. Indexes to All the Books of the New Testament Chiefly Abridged from Townsend. 2006. 164p. per. 18.99 *(978-1-4255-1303-0(4))* MPublishing.

Troxel, Ronald L. LXX-Isaiah as Translation & Interpretation: The Strategies of the Translator of the Septuagint of Isaiah. 2008. (Supplements to the Journal for the Study of Judaism Ser.). 309p. *(978-90-04-15394-3(2))* BRILL.

Tyndale House Publishers Staff, creator. Life Application Study Bible. 2006. (ENG., Illus.). 2560p. im. lthr. 69.99 *(978-1-4143-1293-4(8));* 2176p. im. lthr. 69.99 *(978-1-4143-1133-3(8))* Tyndale Hse. Pubs.

—The One Year Bible for New Believers: The Entire New Living Translation Arranged in 365 Daily Readings with Devotional Notes. 2nd ed. 2006. (ENG.). 1584p. per. 19.99 *(978-1-4143-0074-0(3))* Tyndale Hse. Pubs.

—The One Year Bible Premium Slimline. anniv. l.t. ed. 2006. (ENG.). 1440p. 24.99 *(978-1-4143-1245-3(8))* Tyndale Hse. Pubs.

Tyndale House Publishers Staff, prod. Holy Bible. 2nd l.t. ed. 2006. (ENG.). 1600p. 34.97 *(978-1-4143-1249-1(0));* 34.97 *(978-1-4143-1248-4(2))* Tyndale Hse. Pubs.

—Living Water New Testament NLT. 2006. (ENG.). 288p. pap. 3.99 *(978-1-4143-1241-5(5))* Tyndale Hse. Pubs.

—The One Year Bible Premium Slimline LP NLT. 10th anniv. l.t. ed. 2006. (ENG.) 1440p. pap. 19.99 *(978-1-4143-1244-6(X))* Tyndale Hse. Pubs.

Van der Kooij, A. & Van der Meer, M. N., eds. Old Greek of Isaiah: Issues & Perspectives. Papers read at the Conference on the Septuagint of Isaiah, held in Leiden 10-11 April 2008. 2010. (Contributions to Biblical Exegesis & Theology Ser.). (ENG.). 253p. (C). pap. 56.00 *(978-90-429-2351-5(2))* Peeters Pubs. & Booksellers BEL. Dist: Brown, David Bk. Co., The.

Van Der Louw, Theo A. W. Transformations in the Septuagint: Towards an Interaction of Septaguint Studies & Translation Studies. 2007. (Contributions to Biblical Exegesis & Theology Ser.). (ENG., Illus.). 404p. (C). pap. 61.00 *(978-90-429-1888-7(8))* Peeters Pubs. & Booksellers BEL. Dist: Brown, David Bk. Co., The.

Van der Pool, Charles Lynn, Sr., tr. The Apostolic Bible Polyglot. 2006.Tr. of Old & New Testament. (GEC.). im. lthr. 59.95 net. *(978-0-9632301-2-6(3))* Apostolic Pr.

van Keulen, P. S. F. & van Peursen, W. T. Corpus Linguistics & Textual History: A Computer-Assisted Interdisciplinary Approach to the Peshitta. 2006. (Studia Semitica Neerlandica - SSN Ser.: Vol. 48). (GER.). 37p. 109.00 *(978-90-232-4194-2(0))* Van Gorcum & Co. B.V. NLD. Dist: Eisenbrauns, Inc.

Vietnamese Bible. 997p. lthr. 19.99 *(978-1-58516-552-0(2))* American Bible Society.

Voitila, Anssi, et al. Scripture in Transition: Essays on Septuagint, Hebrew Bible, & Dead Sea Scrolls in Honour of Raija Sollamo. Voitila, Anssi & Jokiranta, Jutta, eds. 2008. (Supplements to the Journal for the Study of Judaism Ser.). 700p. *(978-90-04-16582-3(7))* BRILL.

Waite, D. A. Jr. & Waite, D. A. A Warning!! on Gail Riplinger's Kjb & Multiple Inspiration Heresy. 2010. 140p. pap. 13.00 *(978-1-56848-069-5(5))* Old Paths Pubns., Inc., The.

Waite, Jr. The Comparative Readability of the Authorized Version. 2008. 92p. pap. 12.00 *(978-1-56848-003-9(2))* Old Paths Pubns., Inc., The.

Waite, Pastor D. A. Westcott & Hort's Greek Text & Theory Refuted. 2008. 48p. pap. 10.00 *(978-1-56848-004-6(0))* Old Paths Pubns., Inc., The.

Waite, Th. D. Fundamentalist Deception on Bible Preservation. 2008. 172p. pap. 15.00 *(978-1-56848-049-7(0))* Old Paths Pubns., Inc., The.

—Fuzzy Facts from Fundamentalists. 2008. 112p. pap. 12.00 *(978-1-56848-032-9(6))* Old Paths Pubns., Inc., The.

Waite, Th. D. Pastor D. A. The Case for the King James Bible, A Summary of the Evidence & Argument. 2008. pap. 14.00 *(978-1-56848-011-4(3))* Old Paths Pubns., Inc., The.

—Fundamentalist Distortions on Bible Versions. 2008. pap. 12.00 *(978-1-56848-021-3(0))* Old Paths Pubns., Inc., The.

—Fundamentalist Mis-Information on Bible Versions. 2008. pap. 15.00 *(978-1-56848-027-5(X))* Old Paths Pubns., Inc., The.

—Romans, Preaching Verse by Verse. 2008. pap. 38.00 *(978-1-56848-047-3(4))* Old Paths Pubns., Inc., The.

Walther, Wilhelm. Die Deutsche Bibelubersetzung des Mittelalters. 766p. reprint ed. 148.00 *(978-0-7222-2136-5(3))* Library Reprints, Inc.

Wansbrough, Henry. The Story of the Bible: How It Came to Us. 2006. *(978-1-59235-072-8(0));* 140p. per. 11.95 *(978-1-59325-072-0(X))* Word Among Us Pr.

Wasserstein, Abraham & Wasserstein, David J. The Legend of the Septuagint: From Classical Antiquity to Today. 2009. (ENG.). 356p. pap. 41.00 *(978-0-521-10461-6(0))* Cambridge Univ. Pr.

Wayment, Thomas. The Complete Joseph Smith Translation of the Old Testament: A Side-By-Side Comparison with the King James Version. 2009. *(978-1-60641-131-5(4))* Deseret Bk. Co.

Wendland, Ernst R. Contextual Frames of Reference in Translation: A Coursebook for Bible Translators & Teachers. 2008. (Illus.). 340p. pap. *(978-1-905763-02-3(6))* St. Jerome Publishing.

Werner, A. Frances. Truth in Translation: Accuracy & Surprising Bias in the Old Testament. 2008. 150p. pap. 44.00 *(978-0-9789763-1-6(2))* ARTB Publishing.

Westcott, B. F. The Greek New Testament: With Comparative Apparatus Showing Variations from the Nestle-Aland & Robinson-Pierpont Editions. 2006. (GEC & ENG., Illus.). xxviii, 893p. spiral bd. 34.95 *(978-1-56563-674-3(0))* Hendrickson Pubs. Marketing, LLC.

Westcott, Brooke Foss & Hort, F. The New Testament in the Original Greek. 2007. 548p. per. 34.95 *(978-1-60206-775-2(9))* Cosimo, Inc.

Wire rack Display. (Shepherd's Notes). 112p. *(978-0-8400-3607-0(8))* B&H Publishing Group.

Wolf, Tony, illus. Catholic Bible for Little Children. 2006. 140p. (J). (gr. -1-3). 9.95 *(978-0-89942-997-7(1))* Catholic Bk. Publishing Corp.

The Women's Topical Bible. 19.99 *(978-1-56229-180-8(7),* Christian Living Bks., Inc.) Pneuma Life Publishing, Inc.

Wordsworth, John & White, Henry. Novum Testamentum Latine. 2007. (LAT.). 644p. per. *(978-1-84356-024-1(0))* Wallenberg, Simon Pr.

World Bible Translation Center, creator. Arabic New Testament-FL-Easy to Read. 2007. 446p. pap. 7.50 *(978-977-6124-98-1(4))* World Bible Translation Ctr., Inc.

—Malayalam Holy Bible-FL: Easy to Read. 2007. 1238p. 11.95 *(978-1-932438-78-9(5))* World Bible Translation Ctr., Inc.

—Nepali New Testament-FL. 2011. (HIN.). pap. 4.95 ***(978-1-935189-73-2(5))*** World Bible Translation Ctr., Inc.

World Bible Translation Center, creator. Urdu New Testament-FL: Easy to Read. 2007. 312p. pap. 4.50 *(978-1-932438-70-3(X))* World Bible Translation Ctr., Inc.

World Bible Translation Center, tr. Arabic New Testament AR102: Easy-to-Read Version. 2007. 446p. pap. 7.50 *(978-1-932438-30-7(0))* World Bible Translation Ctr., Inc.

—Arabic New Testament AR103: Easy-to-Read Version. 2007. 446p. pap. 7.50 *(978-1-935189-00-8(X))* World Bible Translation Ctr., Inc.

—Myanmarese (Burmese) New Testament. 2008. (BUR., Illus.). 461p. pap. 7.50 *(978-1-935189-01-5(8))* World Bible Translation Ctr., Inc.

World Bible Translation Ctr, creator. Gujarati Bible: Easy-to-Read Version. 2009. (Illus.). 1066p. vinyl bd. 11.95 *(978-1-932438-31-4(9))* World Bible Translation Ctr., Inc.

—Hindi Bible: Easy-to-Read Version. 2009. (Illus.). 1206p. vinyl bd. 11.95 *(978-1-932438-42-0(4))* World Bible Translation Ctr., Inc.

—Novo Testamento: Versao Facil de Ler. 2008. (Illus.). 392p. pap. 7.50 *(978-1-932438-34-5(3))* World Bible Translation Ctr., Inc.

World Publishing, creator. KJV Visual Reference Bible. 2007. (Illus.) im. lthr. 14.99 *(978-0-529-12074-8(7))* Nelson, Thomas Inc.

Wright, N. T. The Kingdom New Testament: A Contemporary Translation. 2011. 544p. 25.99 *(978-0-06-206491-2(6),* HarperOne) HarperCollins Pubs.

Wright, William Aldis. The Bible Word-Book: A Glossary of Archaic Words & Phrases in the Authorised Version of the Bible & Book of Common Prayer. 2010. (Cambridge Library Collection - Religion Ser.). 698p. pap. 48.00 *(978-1-108-02464-8(5))* Cambridge Univ. Pr.

Zandstra, Sidney. Witness of "The Vulgate," "Peshitta" & "Septuagint" to the Text of "Zephaniah" (Columbia University, Contributions to Oriental History & Philology Ser.: No. 4). reprint ed. 24.50 *(978-0-404-50534-9(1))* AMS Pr., Inc.

Zeolla, Gary F. Analytical-Literal Translation of the New Testament: Third Edition. 2007. 214p. pap. 21.95 *(978-0-615-16751-0(9))* Zeolla, Gary F.

—Companion Volume to the Analytical-Literal Translation: Third Edition. 2007. 142p. pap. 18.50 *(978-0-615-16633-9(4))* Zeolla, Gary F.

—Complete Concordance to the Analytical-Literal Translation: Second Edition. 2007. 408p. pap. 31.95 *(978-0-615-16752-7(7))* Zeolla, Gary F.

Zondervan. RVR 1960 Biblia de estudio, tapa dura, Con índice, 1 vol. 2007. (SPA.). 2144p. 49.99 *(978-0-8297-4485-9(1))* Zondervan.

Zondervan Publishing Staff. Manual: The Bible for Men. 2009. (ENG.). 1632p. lthr. 36.99 *(978-0-310-94099-9(0));* lthr. 59.99 *(978-0-310-94102-6(4));* lthr. 26.99 *(978-0-310-94101-9(6))* Zondervan.

—NIV Bible. 2010. (ENG.). 1152p. 24.99 *(978-0-310-94986-2(6))* Zondervan.

—True Identity: The Bible for Women - Becoming Who You Are in Christ, 1 vol. 2009. (ENG.). 1824p. lthr. 36.99 *(978-0-310-93891-0(0));* lthr. 24.99 *(978-0-310-93897-2(X));* lthr. 59.99 *(978-0-310-93944-3(5))* Zondervan.

Zondervan Publishing Staff, creator. The Story: Read the Bible as One Seamless Story from Beginning to End, 1 vol. 2007. (ENG., Illus.). 416p. 14.99 *(978-0-310-93698-5(5))* Zondervan.

BIBLE—VERSIONS—ILLUSTRATED EDITIONS
see Bible—Illustrations

BIBLE—VERSIONS—THEORY, METHODS, ETC.
see Bible—Translating

BIBLE—VERSIONS, ENGLISH

Abingdon. Gospels & the Early Church Runner's Reader: Matthew - Acts. 2008. 128p. pap. 6.00 (978-0-687-33468-1(3)) Abingdon Pr.

Abingdon Press, creator. Birthday Bible-NRSV. 2008. (Illus.). 1103p. im. lthr. 21.95 (978-0-687-65239-6(1)) Abingdon Pr.

—Graduation Bible-NRSV. abr. ed. 2008. (Illus.). 1103p. im. lthr. 21.95 (978-0-687-64710-1(X)) Abingdon Pr.

—Marriage Bible-NRSV. 2008. 1103p. im. lthr. 21.95 (978-0-687-64690-6(1)) Abingdon Pr.

Abingdon Press Staff. Caregiver's Bible-NRSV. 2008. (Illus.). 1136p. pap. 23.95 (978-0-687-64700-2(2), Abingdon Press) Abingdon Pr.

Adult Bible Studies for the Deaf. 2.31 (978-0-7673-4776-1(5)) LifeWay Christian Resources.

Alter, Robert. Pen of Iron: American Prose & the King James Bible. 2010. (ENG.). 208p. 19.95 (978-0-691-12881-8(2)) Princeton Univ. Pr.

American Bible Society. Committee On Ver. Report on the History & Recent Collation of the English Version of the Bible: Presented by the committee on versions to the Board of managers of The. 2011. 34p. pap. 11.99 **(978-1-4181-9450-5(6))** MPublishing.

Authentic Staff. Compact Bible-KJV. 2007. (ENG.). 826p. per. 6.99 (978-1-934068-23-6(3)) Authentic Media.

Baker Publishing Group Staff. Gift Bible. 2006. (ENG., Illus.). 1200p. 26.99 (978-0-521-61832-8(0)) Cambridge Univ. Pr.

—Holy Bible. 2006. (ENG.). 1274p. 22.99 (978-0-521-87383-3(5)) Cambridge Univ. Pr.

—KJV Concord Reference Bible. 1532p. 2008. (ENG., Illus.). lthr. 144.99 (978-0-521-70974-3(1)) 2007. lthr. 219.99 (978-0-521-70796-1(X)) Cambridge Univ. Pr.

—KJV Gift Bible. 2006. (ENG., Illus.). 1200p. 26.99 (978-0-521-60092-7(8)) Cambridge Univ. Pr.

—KJV Gift Bible Burgundy Hardcover KJ11. 2006. (ENG., Illus.). 1200p. 26.99 (978-0-521-61831-1(2)) Cambridge Univ. Pr.

—KJV Personal Concord Reference Bible. 2007. (ENG., Illus.). 1534p. im. lthr. 49.99 (978-0-521-70251-5(8)) Cambridge Univ. Pr.

—KJV Personal Concord Reference Bible. 2007. (ENG., Illus.). 1534p. im. lthr. 49.99 (978-0-521-70798-5(6)) Cambridge Univ. Pr.

—KJV Personal Concord Reference Black French Morocco KJ463XR. 2008. (ENG., Illus.). 1534p. lthr. 74.99 (978-0-521-70252-2(6)) Cambridge Univ. Pr.

—KJV Standard Text Bible. 2006. (ENG.). 1274p. lthr. 62.99 (978-0-521-69609-8(7)) Cambridge Univ. Pr.

—NASB Pitt Minion Reference Bible. rev. ed. 2006. (ENG., Illus.). 1120p. lthr. 144.99 (978-0-521-60412-3(5)) Cambridge Univ. Pr.

—NASB Wide-Margin Reference Bible. 2007. (ENG., Illus.). 1188p. lthr. 259.99 (978-0-521-70265-2(8)) Cambridge Univ. Pr.

—NASB Wide-Margin Reference Black French Morocco NS743XRM. 2007. (ENG., Illus.). 1188p. lthr. 169.99 (978-0-521-70264-5(X)) Cambridge Univ. Pr.

—NASB Wide-Margin Reference Green Hardcover NS743XRM. 2007. (ENG., Illus.). 1188p. 65.99 (978-0-521-70263-8(1)) Cambridge Univ. Pr.

—New American Standard Bible (NASB) 2006. (ENG., Illus.). 1120p. lthr. 99.99 (978-0-521-60410-9(9)) Cambridge Univ. Pr.

—NIV Single Column Text Bible. 2006. (ENG., Illus.). 1560p. lthr. 189.99 (978-0-521-69118-5(4)) Cambridge Univ. Pr.

—NIV Study Bible Black Goatskin NI686XRS. 2008. (ENG.). 2232p. lthr. 229.99 (978-0-521-70806-7(0)) Cambridge Univ. Pr.

Baker Publishing Group Staff, creator. King James Version Reference Bible (KJV) 2007. (Illus.). 1532p. lthr. 144.99 (978-0-521-70797-8(8)) Cambridge Univ. Pr.

Baker, Warren Patrick, ed. Giant Print Bible. l.t. ed. 2010. (AMG Giant Print Handy-Size Bibles Ser.). (ENG., Illus.). 2016p. (gr. 11). 29.99 (978-0-89957-998-6(1)); 29.99 (978-0-89957-997-9(3)) AMG Pubs.

Bardin & Marsee Publishing, creator. The Outdoor Bible-NAS: The New Testament, the Psalms & the Proverbs. 2008. 355p. pap. 36.95 (978-0-9792394-4-1(3)) Bardin & Marsee Publishing.

Bardin, Robert, creator. Outdoor Bible-NAS-Gospel of John Military. 2006. pap. 9.95 (978-0-9770169-7-6(8)) Bardin & Marsee Publishing.

Barker, Henry. English Bible Versions: A Tercentenary Memorial of the King James Version, from the New York Bible & Common Prayer Book Society. 2010. (Cambridge Library Collection - Religion Ser.). 387p. pap. 31.99 (978-1-108-02454-9(8)) Cambridge Univ. Pr.

Barton, John. The Bible: The Basics. 2008. (Basics Ser.). (Illus.). x, 190p. pap. 19.95 (978-0-415-41136-3(X)) Routledge.

Bloom, Harold. The Shadow of a Great Rock: A Literary Appreciation of the King James Bible. 2011. (ENG.). 320p. 28.00 (978-0-300-16683-5(4)) Yale Univ. Pr.

Bobrick, Benson. Wide As the Waters: The Story of the English Bible & the Revolution. 2010. (ENG.). 384p. pap. 23.99 (978-1-4516-1360-5(1)) Simon & Schuster.

Brake, Donald L. & Beach, Shelly. A Visual History of the King James Bible: The Dramatic Story of the World's Best-Known Translation. 2011. 272p. 24.99 (978-0-8010-1347-8(X)) Baker Bks.

Brown, John. The History of the English Bible. 2011. 164p. pap. 19.99 (978-1-107-40188-4(7)) Cambridge Univ. Pr.

—The History of the English Bible. 2008. 170p. 37.95 (978-1-4365-5378-0(4)) 2007. (ENG.). 172p. per. 22.95 (978-0-548-75592-1(2)) Kessinger Publishing, LLC.

Campbell, Gordon. Bible: The Story of the King James Version 1611-2011. 2011. (ENG., Illus.). 368p. pap. 18.95 (978-0-19-969301-6(3)) Oxford Univ. Pr., Inc.

Caribe Betania, creator. Large Print Bible-RV 1909, 0 vols. l.t. ed. 2006. (SPA.). 1104p. lthr. 29.99 (978-0-89922-727-6(9)) Grupo Nelson.

Chambers, Talbot W. (Talbot Wilson). A Companion to the Revised Old Testament. 2006. 292p. per. 23.99 (978-1-4255-2719-8(1)) MPublishing.

Collins Staff. The Holy Bible. 2008. (ENG., Illus.). 1152p. lthr. 39.95 (978-0-00-725976-2(X)) HarperCollins Pubs. Ltd. GBR. Dist: Independent Pubs. Group.

Common English Bible (Firm) Staff, contrib. by. CEB Bible Dictionary. 2011. 448p. pap. 24.95 **(978-1-60926-024-8(4))** Christian Resources Development Corp.

Conant, H. C. The English Bible: History of the Translation of the Holy Scriptures into the English Tongue: With Specimens of the Old English Versions. 2006. (978-1-57898-611-8(7)) Martino Publishing.

Concordia NIV Text Bible: And Lutheran Worship Hymnal, 2 bks., Set. 25.99 (978-0-570-00504-9(3), 01-1758) Concordia Publishing Hse.

Condit, Blackford. The History of the English Bible: Extending from Earliest Saxon Translations to the Present Anglo-American Revision: with Special Reference to the Protestant Religion & the English Language. 2008. 85.00 (978-1-57898-610-1(9)) Martino Publishing.

Crystal, David. Begat: The King James Bible & the English Language. (ENG.). 320p. 2011. pap. 16.95 (978-0-19-969518-8(0)) 2010. 24.95 (978-0-19-958585-4(7)) Oxford Univ. Pr., Inc.

Cullen, Joseph A. My God, My Companion. 2010. **(978-1-77069-080-6(8))** Word Alive Pr.

Dake, Finis J., Sr., comment. The Dake Reference Bible. lthr. 98.99 (978-1-55829-102-7(4)) Dake Publishing.

David C. Cook Publishing Company Staff. International Bible Lesson Commentary, KJV: The New Standard in Biblical Exposition Based on the ISSL. 2008. 424p. pap. 14.99 (978-1-4347-9975-3(1)) Cook, David C.

—International Bible Lesson Commentary, NIV: The New Standard in Biblical Exposition Based on the ISSL. 2008. 424p. pap. 14.99 (978-1-4347-9974-6(3)) Cook, David C.

Deanesly, Margaret. The Lollard Bible: And Other Medieval Biblical Versions. 2008. (ENG.). 508p. pap. 63.00 (978-0-521-09073-5(3)) Cambridge Univ. Pr.

Dove, Mary. The First English Bible: The Text & Context of the Wycliffite Versions. 2008. (Cambridge Studies in Medieval Literature Ser.). (ENG., Illus.). 332p. 119.00 (978-0-521-88028-2(9)) Cambridge Univ. Pr.

Edwards, Jonathan. The Blank Bible, 2 vols., Vol. 24. Stein, Stephen, ed. 2006. (Works of Jonathan Edwards). (ENG., Illus.). 1472p. 220.00 (978-0-300-10931-3(8)) Yale Univ. Pr.

Elmore, A. E. Lincoln's Gettysburg Address: Echoes of the Bible & Book of Common Prayer. 2nd ed. 2009. (ENG., Illus.). 280p. 32.95 (978-0-8093-2951-9(4)) Southern Illinois Univ. Pr.

Fields, Lee M. Hebrew for the Rest of Us, 1 vol. 2008. (ENG.). 304p. pap. 29.99 (978-0-310-27709-5(4)) Zondervan.

Fireside Bibles. Holy Bible: Catholic Companion Edition for Adults. l.t. ed. 1546p. 49.95 (978-1-55665-401-5(4)) Fireside Catholic Bibles.

Fireside Catholic Publishing, creator. New Catholic Companion Bible-NAB. 2007. (Illus.). 1394p. im. lthr. 42.95 (978-1-55665-320-9(4)); im. lthr. 42.95 (978-1-55665-351-3(4)); im. lthr. 42.95 (978-1-55665-336-0(0)) Fireside Catholic Bibles.

Fisch, Harold, tr. The Koren Chumash: Hebrew/English Five Books of Moses - Personal Size. 2010. (HEB & ENG.). 1300p. 29.95 (978-965-301-166-3(9), Koren Pubs.) Toby Pr. LLC, The.

—The Koren Chumash: Hebrew/English Five Books of Moses, Personal Size, Leather. 2010. (HEB & ENG.). 1300p. lthr. 39.95 (978-965-301-167-0(7), Koren Pubs.) Toby Pr. LLC, The.

—The Koren Chumash: Hebrew/English Five Books of Moses, Standard Size. 2010. (HEB & ENG.). 1300p. 34.95 (978-965-301-162-5(6), Koren Pubs.) Toby Pr. LLC, The.

Floor Dump with Volume Eight New International Version. 550.00 (978-0-687-01511-5(1)) Abingdon Pr.

Forster, Ed. 101 Everyday Sayings from the Bible. 2008. (Illus.). xi, 195p. pap. (978-0-9792266-3-2(5)) Salvation Army National Pubns., The.

Foster, Richard J., et al. The Life with God Bible NRSV. 2006. (Protestant Edition Ser.). (ENG.). 2048p. lthr. 39.99 (978-0-06-067107-5(6), HarperOne) HarperCollins Pubs.

Giant Print Bible. 22.97 (978-0-89957-990-0(6)) AMG Pubs.

Givens, Edmond Willie. Original King James Bible: The History before it is! 2008. 188p. pap. 15.99 (978-1-60477-946-2(2)) Xulon Pr., Inc.

GNT Mark's Gospel - The Learning Bible Edition. 128p. pap. 6.99 (978-1-58516-535-3(2)) American Bible Society.

Godspeed Bible KJV 525 Software Edition. 29.95 (978-0-687-01067-7(5)) Abingdon Pr.

Godspeed Bible New International Version 525 Software Edition. 34.95 (978-0-687-01069-1(1)) Abingdon Pr.

Goospeed Bible Greek/Hebrew 35 Software Edition. 29.95 (978-0-687-01070-7(5)) Abingdon Pr.

Greider, John C. The English Bible Translations & History. 2007. 316p. (ENG.). 29.99 (978-1-4257-8123-1(3)); per. 19.99 (978-1-4257-8103-3(9)) Xlibris Corp.

Haggart, G. P. The Infernal Truth, Series 1: Biblical Demonology. 2008. 20p. 15.50 (978-1-4357-0815-0(6)) Lulu Enterprises Inc.

Harper Bibles Staff. Holy Bible. 2008. (ENG.). 1568p. (gr. 13). 29.99 (978-0-06-145185-0(1), HarperOne) HarperCollins Pubs.

—NRSV Standard Bible. 2008. (ENG.). 1504p. 19.99 (978-0-06-144171-4(6)); 1568p. (gr. 13). 29.99 (978-0-06-124488-9(0)) HarperCollins Pubs. (HarperOne).

Harper Bibles Staff, creator. NRSV Standard Bible. 2008. (ENG., Illus.). 1504p. pap. 16.95 (978-0-06-144172-1(4), HarperOne) HarperCollins Pubs.

—NRSV XI. l.t. ed. 2007. (ENG.). 1824p. 39.99 (978-0-06-125577-9(7), HarperOne) HarperCollins Pubs.

Hendrickson Publishers, creator. Compact Reference Bible-KJV. 2006. 1590p. 19.95 (978-1-59856-108-1(1)); 19.95 (978-1-59856-107-4(3)); 14.97 (978-1-59856-115-9(4)); 14.97 (978-1-59856-119-7(7)); 14.97 (978-1-59856-118-0(9)) Hendrickson Pubs. Marketing, LLC.

—Compact Reference Bible-KJV-Magnetic Closure. 2006. 1590p. 24.95 (978-1-59856-109-8(X)); 24.95 (978-1-59856-110-4(3)); 24.95 (978-1-59856-111-1(1)); 17.97 (978-1-59856-127-2(8)); 17.97 (978-1-59856-125-8(1)); 17.97 (978-1-59856-129-6(4)) Hendrickson Pubs. Marketing, LLC.

—Giant Print Reference Bible-KJV. l.t. ed. 2006. 1644p. 24.97 (978-1-59856-087-9(5)); 1644p. im. lthr. 17.97 (978-1-59856-000-8(X)); 1644p. im. lthr. 17.97 (978-1-59856-021-3(2)); 1650p. im. lthr. 17.97 (978-1-59856-076-3(X)); 1644p. im. lthr. 27.95 (978-1-59856-086-2(7)); 1644p. im. lthr. 27.95 (978-1-59856-088-6(3)); 1644p. im. lthr. 27.95 (978-1-59856-090-9(5)); 1644p. 24.97 (978-1-59856-089-3(1)); 1644p. 34.95 (978-1-59856-091-6(3)); 1644p. 34.95 (978-1-59856-092-3(1)); 1644p. 39.95 (978-1-59856-093-0(X)); 1644p. 24.97 (978-1-59856-082-4(4)) Hendrickson Pubs. Marketing, LLC.

—Hendrickson Parallel Bible-PR-KJV/NKJV/NIV/NLT. 2008. 2871p. 89.95 (978-1-59856-234-7(7)) Hendrickson Pubs. Marketing, LLC.

—Minister's Bible-NASB-Deluxe. deluxe ed. 2006. (Hendrickson Minister's Bibles Ser.). 1138p. lthr. 175.00 (978-1-59856-008-4(5)) Hendrickson Pubs. Marketing, LLC.

—Parallel Bible-PR-NASB/Am. 2006. 1584p. 34.95 (978-1-59856-048-0(4)); 59.95 (978-1-59856-049-7(2)); 59.95 (978-1-59856-050-3(6)) Hendrickson Pubs. Marketing, LLC.

—Personal Size Giant Print Reference Bible-KJV. l.t. ed. 2006. 1644p. 29.95 (978-1-59856-103-6(0)); 29.95 (978-1-59856-105-0(7)); 29.95 (978-1-59856-099-2(9)); 19.97 (978-1-59856-104-3(9)); im. lthr. 19.95 (978-1-59856-095-4(6)); im. lthr. 19.95 (978-1-59856-097-8(2)); im. lthr. 14.97 (978-1-59856-100-5(6)); im. lthr. 14.97 (978-1-59856-096-1(4)) Hendrickson Pubs. Marketing, LLC.

—Pew Bible-KJV. 2007. 756p. 9.95 (978-1-59856-219-4(3)); 9.95 (978-1-59856-218-7(5)) Hendrickson Pubs. Marketing, LLC.

Heroes Merch Kit. 1152p. (978-0-8400-4238-5(8)) B&H Publishing Group.

Hochhalter, Kate. Analytical Rhyme Bible for Adults. 2006. pap. 20.50 (978-1-59330-417-1(X)) Aventine Pr.

Holman Bible Editorial Staff, ed. KJV Compact Cross Design Bible. l.t. ed. 2008. (ENG., Illus.). 1568p. im. lthr. 19.99 (978-1-58640-464-2(4), Holman Pubs.) B&H Publishing Group.

—KJV Compact Cross Design Bible, Burgundy. l.t. ed. 2008. (ENG., Illus.). 1568p. im. lthr. 19.99 (978-1-58640-465-9(2), Holman Pubs.) B&H Publishing Group.

Holman Reference Editorial Staff, ed. Holman Illustrated Pocket Bible Handbook. 3rd ed. 2007. (ENG., Illus.). 400p. per. 9.99 (978-1-58640-313-3(3), Holman Reference) B&H Publishing Group.

The Holy Bible: Containing the Old & New Testaments. 2007. pap. 17.00 (978-0-687-64318-9(X)); pap. 17.00 (978-0-687-64338-7(4)); pap. 17.00 (978-0-687-64328-8(7)) Abingdon Pr. (Cokesbury).

The Holy Bible: Containing the Old & New Testaments. 2007. (978-0-687-64239-7(6)); (978-0-687-64179-6(9)); (978-0-687-64348-6(1)); (978-0-687-64169-7(1)); (978-0-687-64159-8(4)); (978-0-687-64149-9(7)); (978-0-687-64129-1(2)); (978-0-687-64398-1(8)); (978-0-687-64388-2(0)); (978-0-687-64269-4(8)); (978-0-687-64259-5(0)); (978-0-687-64378-3(3)); (978-0-687-64358-5(9)); (978-0-687-64368-4(6)); ix, 1089p. (978-0-687-64249-6(3)); ix, 1089p. (978-0-687-64219-9(1)); ix, 1089p. (978-0-687-64229-8(9)); ix, 1089p. (978-0-687-64209-0(4)); ix, 1089p. (978-0-687-64189-5(6)); ix, 1089p. (978-0-687-64199-4(3)) Cokesbury.

Holy Bible: Sacramental Editions. 29.95 (978-1-55665-451-0(0), 4510); 29.95 (978-1-55665-464-0(2)) Fireside Catholic Bibles.

Holy Bible: Student Edition. 1458p. 19.99 (978-1-884543-52-4(9)) Authentic Media.

Horner, George William. The Coptic Version of the New Testament in the Northern Dialect, Volume I. 2010. 636p. pap. 34.95 (978-0-557-28357-6(4)) Lulu Enterprises Inc.

—The Coptic Version of the New Testament in the Northern Dialect, Volume II. 2010. 596p. pap. 34.95 (978-0-557-28385-9(X)) Lulu Enterprises Inc.

—The Coptic Version of the New Testament in the Northern Dialect, Volume III. 2010. 708p. pap. 34.95 (978-0-557-28405-4(8)) Lulu Enterprises Inc.

—The Coptic Version of the New Testament in the Northern Dialect, Volume IV. 2010. 604p. pap. 34.95 (978-0-557-28419-1(8)) Lulu Enterprises Inc.

—The Coptic Version of the New Testament in the Southern Dialect, Volume II. 2010. 488p. pap. 34.95 (978-0-557-30238-3(2)) Lulu Enterprises Inc.

Jackson, Donald. The Saint John's Bible: An Introduction. 2008. (Illus.). 32p. per. 9.95 (978-0-8146-9100-7(5), Liturgical Pr. Bks.) Liturgical Pr.

Jackson, Donald, illus. The Saint John's Bible Vol. 2: Historical Books. 2010. 276p. 79.95 (978-0-8146-9053-6(X), St. John's Bible Bks.) Liturgical Pr.

—The Saint John's Bible Vol. 3: Prophets. 2007. 232p. 69.95 (978-0-8146-9054-3(8)) Liturgical Pr.

—The Saint John's Bible Vol. 4: Wisdom Books. 2007. 136p. 64.95 (978-0-8146-9055-0(6)) Liturgical Pr.

Jeffrey, David Lyle, ed. The King James Bible & the World It Made. 2011. (ENG., Illus.). 209p. pap. 24.95 (978-1-60258-416-7(8)) Baylor Univ. Pr.

Johnston, Stephen, narrated by. Voice Only Bible-KJV. 2006. audio compact disk, audio compact disk 74.97 (978-1-59856-070-1(0)) Hendrickson Pubs. Marketing, LLC.

Johnston, Stephen, reader. Voice Only Bible-NASB. 2008. 29.97 (978-1-59856-136-4(7)) Hendrickson Pubs. Marketing, LLC.

JPS / Varda Books. JPS Hebrew-English Tanakh: CD / Web 2. 0 Edition. 2008. cd-rom 69.95 (978-1-59045-077-2(9)) Varda Bks.

Kaiser, Walter C., Jr. Archaeological Study Bible, 1 vol. Zondervan Publishing Staff & Garrett, Duane, eds. l.t. ed. 2008. (ENG.). 2336p. lthr. 89.99 (978-0-310-94084-5(2)) Zondervan.

Kaiser, Walter C., Jr. & Garrett, Duane, eds. An Illustrated Walk Through Biblical History & Culture, 1 vol. 2007. (ENG., Illus.). 2336p. 44.99 (978-0-310-93852-1(X)) Zondervan.

Kaiser, Walter C. & Kaiser. Archaeological Study Bible, 1 vol. Kaiser, Jr., Walter C., Walter C & Garrett, Duane, eds. rev. ed. 2007. (ENG., Illus.). 2336p. lthr. 84.99 (978-0-310-93844-6(9)) Zondervan.

Kirkbride Bible Company, creator. Text Bible-NIV. 2006. (Illus.). 1933p. im. lthr. 79.99 (978-0-88707-554-4(1)) Kirkbride, B.B. Bible Co., Inc.

—Thompson Abridged Reference Bible-KJV. 2007. (Illus.). 1827p. 74.99 (978-0-88707-561-2(4)); 64.99 (978-0-88707-560-5(6)); im. lthr. 69.99 (978-0-88707-565-0(7)); im. lthr. 59.99 (978-0-88707-564-3(9)); im. lthr. 69.99 (978-0-88707-563-6(0)); im. lthr. 59.99 (978-0-88707-562-9(2)) Kirkbride, B.B. Bible Co., Inc.

—Thompson Chain Reference Bible-KJV. 2007. 1923p. im. lthr. 64.99 (978-0-88707-578-0(9)); 1923p. 74.99 (978-0-88707-569-8(X)); (Illus.). 1910p. 74.99 (978-0-88707-567-4(3)); 5th ed. (Illus.). 1923p. im. lthr. 64.99 (978-0-88707-576-6(2)) Kirkbride, B.B. Bible Co., Inc.

—Thompson Chain Reference Bible-NIV. 2007. 1933p. im. lthr. 64.99 (978-0-88707-570-4(3)); 1933p. im. lthr. 64.99 (978-0-88707-574-2(6)); 5th ed. (Illus.). 1923p. im. lthr. 64.99 (978-0-88707-572-8(X)) Kirkbride, B.B. Bible Co., Inc.

KJV Cornerstone Master Study Bible: Cornerstone Tent. (Illus.). 2048p. (978-0-8400-3889-0(5)) B&H Publishing Group.

KJV Cornerstone Master Study Bible: Shelftalker. (Illus.). 2048p. (978-0-8400-3856-2(9)) B&H Publishing Group.

KJV Varsity Colors Collection: Shelftalkers packaged Alone. (978-0-8400-4117-3(9)) B&H Publishing Group.

Knight, George W., ed. KJV Super Giant Print Dictionary & Concordance. 2007. (ENG., Illus.). 1248p. 24.99 (978-0-8054-9492-1(8), Holman Reference) B&H Publishing Group.

Kraus, Donald. Choosing a Bible: For Worship, Teaching, Study, Preaching, & Prayer. 2007. (Illus.). 112p. per. 12.00 (978-1-59627-043-5(8)) Church Publishing, Inc.

Lamsa, George M. The Modern New Testament from Aramaic. 529p. pap. 24.95 (978-0-9675989-3-2(1)) Aramaic Bible Society,The.

Laurie, Greg, ed. New Believer's Bible NLT. 2007. (ENG., Illus.). 1280p. 29.99 (978-1-4143-0255-3(X)); per. 19.99 (978-1-4143-0254-6(1)) Tyndale Hse. Pubs.

Libronix Software Staff, et al, creators. Libronix Bible Software. 2008. (ENG.). 1p. cd-rom 49.99 (978-1-4143-2621-4(1)) Tyndale Hse. Pubs.

Logos Bible Software: Catholic Scholar's Pack. cd-rom 499.95 (978-1-57799-190-8(7)) Logos Research Systems, Inc.

Lucado, Max. The Lucado LifeWorks Library, 0 vols. 2011. cd-rom 14.99 (978-1-4185-2792-1(0)) Nelson, Thomas Inc.

MacArthur, John. The MacArthur Study Bible-NKJV, 0 vols. 2007. 2240p. im. lthr. 74.99 (978-0-7180-2074-3(X)) Nelson, Thomas Inc.

MacArthur, John, ed. The MacArthur Study Bible, 0 vols. 2006. 2240p. lthr. 99.99 (978-0-7180-1902-0(4)) Nelson, Thomas Inc.

—MacArthur Study Bible. 2007. (Illus.). 2043p. 84.99 (978-0-7180-2006-4(5)) Nelson, Thomas Inc.

—MacArthur Study Bible-NASB, 0 vols. 2007. 2208p. im. lthr. 74.99 (978-0-7180-2076-7(6)); (Illus.). im. lthr. 74.99 (978-0-7180-2075-0(8)) Nelson, Thomas Inc.

—MacArthur Study Bible-NKJV. 2006. 2240p. 44.99 (978-0-7180-1899-3(0)); 74.99 (978-0-7180-1900-6(8)); 84.99 (978-0-7180-1923-5(7)) Nelson, Thomas Inc.

Marks, Herbert. The English Bible: The Old Testament. 2012. (Norton Critical Editions Ser.). (ENG., Illus.). 2304p. (C). pap. 18.00 net. (978-0-393-92745-0(8), 92745) Norton, W. W. & Co., Inc.

Marquardt, H. Michael. The Four Gospels According to Joseph Smith. 2007. 436p. (ENG.). 33.99 (978-1-60477-026-1(0)); per. 21.99 (978-1-60477-025-4(2)) Xulon Pr., Inc.

Marsden, Richard. The Text of the Old Testament in Anglo-Saxon England. 2006. (Cambridge Studies in Anglo-Saxon England Ser.). (ENG.). 536p. pap. 95.00 (978-0-521-03125-7(7)) Cambridge Univ. Pr.

Maxwell, John C., ed. Maxwell Leadership Bible, Revised & Updated: Briefcase Edition, 0 vols. 2008. 1632p. 54.99 (978-0-7180-2528-1(8)) Nelson, Thomas Inc.

Mays, Milton. The People's Proverbs Bible: The Psalms Edition. 2007. 544p. *(978-1-57921-850-8(4))* WinePress Publishing.

McComb, Samuel. The Making of the English Bible. 2009. 78p. pap. *(978-1-151-37606-0(X))* Books LLC.

McKinney, Geneima. Concordance: A Journey of the Holy Bible, 1. 2007. 48p. spiral bd. 1.95 *(978-0-9789743-1-2(X))* Yeshua Productions.

McKinney, Geneima, told to. The Holy Bible Re-written: King James Version, 1. 2007. (Illus.). 1473p. per. 39.95 *(978-0-9789743-0-5(1))* Yeshua Productions.

Mitchell, Vernon. The New Testament. 2007. (ENG.). 312p. 27.99 *(978-1-60034-677-4(4))*; per. 17.99 *(978-1-60034-676-7(6))* Xulon Pr., Inc.

Moore, Helen & Reid, Julian, eds. Manifold Greatness: The Making of the King James Bible. 2011. (Illus.). 208p. pap. 35.00 *(978-1-85124-349-5(6))* Bodleian Library GBR. Dist: Chicago Distribution Ctr.

Mounce, William D. & Mounce. Greek & English Interlinear New Testament, 1 vol. 2008. (ENG.). 1216p. pap. 49.99 *(978-0-310-24164-5(2))* Zondervan.

Moynahan, Brian. If God Spare My Life. Date not set. mass mkt. *(978-0-312-98988-0(1)*, St. Martin's Paperbacks) St. Martin's Pr.

NASB Classic Companion. 2006. 1472p. 32.99 *(978-0-529-12315-2(0))*; im. lthr. 32.99 *(978-0-529-12314-5(2))* Nelson, Thomas Inc.

Nelson Bibles, creator. Maxwell Leadership Bible-NKJV, 0 vols. 2nd ed. 2007. 1649p. 39.99 *(978-0-7180-2015-6(4))*; 74.99 *(978-0-7180-2016-3(2))* Nelson, Thomas Inc.

—Stocking Stuffer Bible-KJV, 0 vols. 2007. 240p. im. lthr. 9.99 *(978-0-7180-2072-9(3))* Nelson, Thomas Inc.

The New Testament of Our Lord & Savior Jesus Christ the Common English Version, Cor by the Final Committee of the American Bible Union. 2006. 332p. per. 23.99 *(978-1-4255-3338-0(8))* MPublishing.

The New Testament of Our Lord & Saviour Jesus Christ, As Revised & Corrected by the Spirits. 2006. 336p. per. 23.99 *(978-1-4255-3429-5(5))* MPublishing.

Newborn, David. The King James Version of the Holy Bible Search Word Puzzle Book Of. 2007. pap. 16.99 *(978-1-60034-364-3(3))* Xulon Pr., Inc.

Nickelson, Ronald L., ed. Standard Lesson Commentary: KJV. 2007. (Standard Lesson Commentary: KJV Ser.). (Illus.). 448p. 19.99 *(978-0-7847-2079-0(7))*; 512p. per. 16.99 *(978-0-7847-2082-0(7))* Standard Publishing.

—Standard Lesson Commentary: NIV. 2007. (Standard Lesson Commentary: NIV Ser.). (Illus.). 448p. per. 14.99 *(978-0-7847-2080-6(0))*; 512p. per. 16.99 *(978-0-7847-2083-7(5))* Standard Publishing.

Nickelson, Ronald L. & Underwood, Jonathan, eds. Standard Lesson Commentary: International Sunday School Lessons. 2007. (Standard Lesson Commentary: KJV Ser.). (Illus.). 448p. per. 14.99 *(978-0-7847-2078-3(9))* Standard Publishing.

Night Lessons from Scripture Compiled by the Author of Amy Herbert. 2006. 392p. per. 26.99 *(978-1-4255-4188-0(7))* MPublishing.

NIV New Testament. 2007. per. 1.10 *(978-1-882536-90-0(8))* Bible League.

NLT TruthQuest Inductive Student Bible: 4-6 T. Q. Sheftakers packaged Together. 1506p. *(978-0-8400-4108-1(X))* B&H Publishing Group.

NRSV Bible Translation Committee. The New Revised Standard Version Bible with Apocrypha. Metzger, Bruce M., tr. 2006. (ENG.). 1616p. 44.99 *(978-0-19-528831-5(9))* Oxford Univ. Pr., Inc.

—The New Revised Standard Version Bible with Apocrypha: Pocket Edition. Metzger, Bruce M., tr. 2006. (ENG.). 1616p. 39.99 *(978-0-19-528829-2(7))* Oxford Univ. Pr., Inc.

Oxford, ed. English Standard Version Bible with Apocrypha. 2009. (ENG., Illus.). xiii, 1446p. 29.99 *(978-0-19-528910-7(2))* Oxford Univ. Pr., Inc.

—The New Oxford Annotated Bible, Augmented Third Edition, New Revised Standard Version. 2007. (ENG.). 2048p. 99.00 *(978-0-19-528878-0(5))* Oxford Univ. Pr., Inc.

—The NRSV Notetaker's Bible 9855A Deluxe Cloth. 2009. (ENG.). 1633p. 54.99 *(978-0-19-528921-3(8))* Oxford Univ. Pr., Inc.

—The Old Scofieldrg Study Bible. 2007. (ENG., Illus.). 1632p. 34.95 *(978-0-19-527474-5(1))* Oxford Univ. Pr., Inc.

Oxford University Press, creator. NRSV Pocket Bible. 2006. (ENG.). 1616p. 32.99 *(978-0-19-528826-1(2))* Oxford Univ. Pr., Inc.

—Pocket Bible-NRSV. 2006. (ENG.). 1616p. 32.99 *(978-0-19-528825-4(4))* Oxford Univ. Pr., Inc.

—Scofield Study Bible III. l.t. ed. 2008. (ENG., Illus.). 1968p. 79.99 *(978-0-19-528024-1(5))* Oxford Univ. Pr., Inc.

Paul, William E. English Language Bible Translators. alt. ed. 2009. (ENG.). 288p. pap. 49.95 *(978-0-7864-4243-0(3))* McFarland & Co., Inc. Pubs.

Petri, William. Universal King James Version: The Answer Bible. 2007. 776p. *(978-0-9787883-7-7(0)*, Beacon of Grace Ministries.

Pieters, Albertus, ed. The Scofield Bible. pap. 0.99 *(978-0-87377-070-5(6))* GAM Pubns.

The Preacher's Outline & Sermon Bible, Jeremiah 2, Lamentations, KJV: Jeremiah 2, Lamentations. 2006. pap. 39.99 *(978-1-57407-222-8(6))* Leadership Ministries Worldwide.

The Preacher's Outline & Sermon Bible, Jeremiah 2-Lamentations, KJV: Jeremiah 2, Lamentations. 2006. ring bd. 44.99 *(978-1-57407-223-5(4))* Leadership Ministries Worldwide.

Rasbeary, James / M. What's Wrong with the Old Black Book: An Understandable Guide to the Debate Surrounding the King James Bible. 2007. 261p. per. *(978-0-9788703-9-3(5))* Calvary Publishing.

The Resurrection Bible: An Expanded Version of the Modern New Testament from Aramaic that Documents the Law of Rebirth & Retribution. 62.95 *(978-0-9675989-4-9(X))* Aramaic Bible Society,The.

Rogal, Samuel J. The Lord is My Shepherd (Psalm 23) How Poets, Mystics, & Hymnodists Have Delved Its Deeper Meanings. 2006. 172p. *(978-0-7734-5480-4(2))* Mellen, Edwin Pr., The.

Ryken, Leland. Understanding English Bible Translation: The Case for an Essentially Literal Approach. 2009. 208p. pap. 12.99 *(978-1-4335-0279-8(8))* Crossway.

Ryrie, Charles C. The Ryrie KJV Study Bible. 2008. (ENG.). 2336p. 39.99 *(978-0-8024-8908-1(7))*; 2336p. 49.99 *(978-0-8024-8909-8(5))*; 2236p. 69.99 *(978-0-8024-8907-4(9))*; 2236p. 69.99 *(978-0-8024-8903-6(6))*; 2336p. 59.99 *(978-0-8024-8902-9(8))*; 2336p. lthr. 94.99 *(978-0-8024-8901-2(X))* Moody Pubs.

—The Ryrie Kjv Study Bible. 2008. (ENG.). 2336p. lthr. 84.99 *(978-0-8024-8900-5(1))* Moody Pubs.

—The Ryrie Kjv Study Bible. 2008. (ENG.). 2236p. 59.99 *(978-0-8024-8906-7(0))* Moody Pubs.

—The Ryrie NASB Study Bible. 2008. (ENG.). 2322p. 49.99 *(978-0-8024-8921-0(4))* Moody Pubs.

—The Ryrie NIV Study Bible. 2008. (ENG.). 2336p. 39.99 *(978-0-8024-8932-6(X))*; 2324p. 49.99 *(978-0-8024-8933-3(8))*; 2324p. 59.99 *(978-0-8024-8924-1(9))* Moody Pubs.

Scrivener, Frederick Henry Ambrose. The Authorized Version of the English Bible (1611) Its Subsequent Reprints & Modern Representatives. 2010. (Cambridge Library Collection - Religion Ser.). 324p. pap. 24.99 *(978-1-108-02463-1(7))* Cambridge Univ. Pr.

Singer-Towns, Brian, ed. Catholic Youth Bible. 2007. (Illus.). 1600p. (YA). lthr. 39.95 *(978-0-88489-664-7(1))*; lthr. 45.95 *(978-0-88489-663-0(3))* St. Mary's Pr.

Slim-Line New Testament: With Psalms & Proverbs. 544p. vinyl bd. 11.99 *(978-0-529-07452-2(4))* Nelson, Thomas Inc.

Smith, Joseph & Bishop, Patrick A. The Gospels in Harmony: The Illustrated, Combined Accounts of the Life of Christ from Matthew, Mark, Luke, John, & Joseph Smith Translation. 2010. (Illus.). vii, 213p. *(978-1-60861-096-9(9))* Covenant Communications.

Spencer, Nick. Freedom & Order: History, Politics & the English Bible. 2011. (ENG., Illus.). 320p. 26.95 *(978-0-340-99623-2(4)*, Hodder & Stoughton) Hodder General Publishing Div. GBR. Dist: Independent Pubs. Group.

Stabnow, David K. HCSB Super Giant Print Dictionary & Concordance. 2006. (ENG.). 1320p. 24.97 *(978-0-8054-9483-1(8)*, Holman Reference) B&H Publishing Group.

Standard Publishing Staff. Standard Full Color Bible-KJV. 2007 (Standard Full Color Bible Ser.). (ENG., Illus.). 1632p. 49.99 *(978-0-7847-2164-3(5))* Standard Publishing.

—Standard Full Color Bible-NIV. 2007. (Standard Full Color Bible Ser.). (ENG., Illus.). 1600p. 49.99 *(978-0-7847-2167-4(X))*; 59.99 *(978-0-7847-2168-1(8))* Standard Publishing.

Stanley, Charles F. The Charles F. Stanley Life Principles Bible. 2011 1760p. 39.99 ***(978-1-4185-5032-5(9))*** Nelson, Thomas Inc.

—The Charles F. Stanley Life Principles Bible, 0 vols. 2009. 1760p. 44.99 *(978-0-7180-2498-7(2))* Nelson, Thomas Inc.

Sumner, Tracy Macon. How Did We Get the Bible? 2009. (Value Bks.). (ENG.). 160p. pap. 2.99 *(978-1-60260-363-9(4)*, Barbour Bks.) Barbour Publishing, Inc.

Swanson, James A. & LaCosse, Patrick, compiled by. Comprehensive Concordance: A Comprehensive Concordance of Every Major Word in the Text of the New Living Translation. 2008. (Tyndale Reference Library). (ENG.). 1248p. 39.99 *(978-1-4143-1699-4(2))* Tyndale Hse. Pubs.

The Bush Theatre. Sixty-Six Books: A Contemporary Response to the King James Bible. 2012. (ENG.). 352p. pap. 30.95 ***(978-1-84943-227-6(9))*** Oberon Bks., Ltd. GBR. Dist: Consortium Bk. Sales & Distribution.

Thomas, Cecil K. Alexander Campbell & His New Version. 2011. 224p. pap. 19.00 ***(978-1-61097-563-6(4)**, Wipf and Stock)* Wipf & Stock Pubs.

Thomas Nelson Publishing Staff. The Chronological Study Bible, 0 vols. 2008. 1728p. 74.99 *(978-0-7180-2069-9(3))* Nelson, Thomas Inc.

—The Chronological Study Bible: Explore God's Word in Historical Order, 0 vols. 2008. (Illus.). 1728p. 44.99 *(978-0-7180-2068-2(5))* Nelson, Thomas Inc.

—KJV Personal Size Giant Print Reference Bible, 0 vols. 2008. 1952p. im. lthr. 44.99 *(978-0-7180-2471-0(0))*; (Illus.). im. lthr. 54.99 *(978-0-7180-2474-1(5))* Nelson, Thomas Inc.

—KJV Reference Bible, 0 vols. 2008. (Illus.). 1120p. im. lthr. 29.99 *(978-0-7180-2447-5(8))* Nelson, Thomas Inc.

—The Message-NKJV Parallel Bible, 0 vols. 2007. 1888p. 34.99 *(978-0-7180-1932-7(6))* Nelson, Thomas Inc.

—The NKJV Study Bible: Second Edition, 0 vols. 2nd ed. 2008. 2368p. 84.99 *(978-0-7180-2082-8(0))*; 74.99 *(978-0-7180-2080-4(4))* Nelson, Thomas Inc.

—Princess Bible: Lavender, 0 vols. 2008. 1218p. (J). im. lthr. 24.99 *(978-1-4003-1285-6(X))* Nelson, Thomas Inc.

Thomas Nelson Publishing Staff, contrib. by. KJV Pocket Bible. 2007. 1052p. 10.00 *(978-1-4185-2930-7(3))* Nelson, Thomas Inc.

Thomas Nelson Publishing Staff, creator. KJV Reference Bible, 0 vols. 2008 1120p. im. lthr. 39.99 *(978-0-7180-2467-3(2))*; (Illus.). im. lthr. 29.99 *(978-0-7180-2446-8(X))* Nelson, Thomas Inc.

—Orthodox Study Bible-OE-with Some NKJV: Acient Christianity Speaks to Today's World, 0 vols. 2008. (Illus.). 1984p. 69.99 *(978-0-7180-1908-2(3))* Nelson, Thomas Inc.

—Reference Bible-KJV, 0 vols. 2008. (Illus.). 1120p. im. lthr. 29.99 *(978-0-7180-2466-6(4))*; im. lthr. 39.99 *(978-0-7180-2468-0(0))*, im. lthr. 29.99 *(978-0-7180-2465-9(6))* Nelson, Thomas Inc.

Thomas Nelson Publishing Staff, et al. KJV Personal Size Giant Print Reference Bible, 0 vols. 2008. 1952p. im. lthr. 54.99 *(978-0-7180-2473-4(7))* Nelson, Thomas Inc.

Thompson, Frank Charles, ed. Thompson Chain-Reference Bible-KJV. 5th ed. 2006. 1923p. im. lthr. 69.99 *(978-0-88707-551-3(7))* Kirkbride, E.B. Bible Co., Inc.

—Thompson Chain Reference Bible-KJV. 5th ed. 2007. (Illus.). 1910p. im. lthr. 64.99 *(978-0-88707-566-7(5))*; im. lthr. 64.99 *(978-0-88707-568-1(1))* Kirkbride, B.B. Bible Co., Inc.

—Thompson-Chain Reference Study Bible-KJV. 5th ed. 2006. (Illus.). 1923p. im. lthr. 79.99 *(978-0-88707-552-0(5))* Kirkbride, B.B. Bible Co., Inc.

—Thompson Chain-Reference Study Bible-NIV. 2006. 1933p. im. lthr. 69.99 *(978-0-88707-553-7(3))* Kirkbride, B.B. Bible Co., Inc.

—Thompson Chain-Reference Study Bible-NIV-Handy Size. 2006. 1933p. per. 74.99 *(978-0-88707-558-2(4))*; im. lthr. 64.99 *(978-0-88707-556-3(8))*; im. lthr. 64.99 *(978-0-88707-557-5(6))*; (Illus.). im. lthr. 64.99 *(978-0-88707-555-1(X))* Kirkbride, B.B. Bible Co., Inc.

Trench, Richard Chenevix. On the Authorized Version of the New Testament in Connection with Some Recent Proposals for Its Revision. 2006. 196p. per. 18.99 *(978-1-4255-1597-3(5))* MPublishing.

Tyndale House Publishers Staff. The Life Recovery Bible NLT, Tutone. 2008. (ENG.). 1760p. im. lthr. 59.97 *(978-1-4143-2482-1(0))* Tyndale Hse. Pubs.

—Nuevo Testamento - Santa Biblia. 2009. (SPA.). 537p. im. lthr. 12.99 *(978-1-4143-3401-1(X)*, Tyndale Espanol) Tyndale Hse. Pubs.

—Santa Biblia. 2009. (SPA.). 537p. im. lthr. 12.99 *(978-1-4143-3402-8(8)*, Tyndale Espanol) Tyndale Hse. Pubs.

Tyndale House Publishers Staff, creator. Genesis 1-12. 2nd ed. 2008. (NLT Study Bible Ser.). (Illus.). 63p. pap. 1.99 *(978-1-4143-1757-1(3))* Tyndale Hse. Pubs.

—He Cares New Testament with Psalms & Proverbs. 2nd ed. 2007. (ENG.). 512p. per. 9.99 *(978-1-4143-1051-0(X))* Tyndale Hse. Pubs.

—Holy Bible. (ENG., l.t. ed. 2008. Illus.). 1952p. 59.99 *(978-1-4143-1935-8(1))* l.t. ed. 2007. 2160p. 24.99 *(978-1-4143-1405-1(1)*, l.t. ed. 2007. 2160p. 39.99 *(978-1-4143-1402-0(7))* l.t. ed. 2007. 2160p. 39.99 *(978-1-4143-1401-3(9))* l.t. ed. 2007. 2160p. im. lthr. 29.99 *(978-1-4143-1403-7(5))* l.t. ed. 2007. 2160p. im. lthr. 29.99 *(978-1-4143-1404-4(3))* 2nd l.t. ed. 2007. (Illus.). 1600p. im. lthr. 39.99 *(978-1-4143-1257-6(1))* 2nd l.t. ed. 2007. (Illus.). 1600p. im. lthr. 39.99 *(978-1-4143-1258-3(X))* Tyndale Hse. Pubs.

—Holy Bible, Giant Print NLT. l.t. ed. 2008. (ENG.). 1952p. 34.99 *(978-1-4143-1430-3(2))*; 69.99 *(978-1-4143-1966-5(X))*; im. lthr. 39.99 *(978-1-4143-1428-0(0))* Tyndale Hse. Pubs.

—Life Application Study Bible. 2007. (ENG., Illus.). 2176p. im. lthr. 59.99 *(978-1-4143-1421-1(3))*; 2816p. im. lthr. 79.99 *(978-1-4143-1627-7(5))* Tyndale Hse. Pubs.

—The Life Recovery Bible NLT. 2006. (ENG.). 1760p. 39.99 *(978-1-4143-0962-0(7))*; pap. 22.99 *(978-1-4143-0961-3(9))* Tyndale Hse. Pubs.

—NLT Study Bible. 2008. (ENG.). 2528p. 49.99 *(978-1-4143-2447-0(2))* lthr. 79.99 *(978-1-4143-2451-7(0))* Tyndale Hse. Pubs.

—NLT Study Bible. 2008. (ENG.). 2528p. lthr. 79.99 *(978-1-4143-2449-4(9))* Tyndale Hse. Pubs.

—NLT Study Bible, Tutone. 2008. (ENG.). 2528p. lthr. 79.99 *(978-1-4143-2453-1(7))*; lthr. 79.99 *(978-1-4143-2455-5(3))* Tyndale Hse. Pubs.

—24/7: A One Year Chronological Bible. 2008. (ENG.). 2224p. (YA). 24.99 *(978-1-4143-1410-5(8))*; pap. 17.99 *(978-1-4143-1411-2(6))* Tyndale Hse. Pubs.

Tyndale House Publishers Staff, prod. Life Application Study Bible. 2007. (ENG.). 2176p. im. lthr. 59.99 *(978-1-4143-1420-4(5))* Tyndale Hse. Pubs.

—Life Application Study Bible KJV, Personal Size. 2007. (ENG.). 2176p. pap. 24.99 *(978-1-4143-1419-8(1))* Tyndale Hse. Pubs.

—New Believer's Bible New Testament NLT. 2007. (ENG.). 448p. pap. 7.99 *(978-1-4143-0257-7(6))* Tyndale Hse. Pubs.

—Premium Gift Bible. gif. ed. 2009. (ENG.). 832p. lthr. 14.99 *(978-1-4143-3377-9(3))* Tyndale Hse. Pubs.

The Ultra Trim Bible. 1056p. lthr. 29.99 *(978-0-529-11137-1(3))* Nelson, Thomas Inc.

Vance, Laurence M. King James, His Bible, & Its Translators. 2006. 172p. per. 12.95 *(978-0-9763448-1-0(5))* Vance Pubns.

Voice Only Bible-KJV. 2006. audio compact disk, audio compact disk 99.95 *(978-1-56563-972-0(3))* Hendrickson Pubs. Marketing, LLC.

Waite, Th. D. The Contemporary English Version. 2008. 48p. pap. 10.00 *(978-1-56848-006-0(7))* Old Paths Pubns., Inc., The.

Weigle, Luther. The English New Testament - from Tyndale to the Revised Standard Version. 2007. 160p. per. *(978-1-4067-8855-6(4)*, Pomona Pr.) Read Bks.

Westbrook, Vivienne. Long Travail & Great Paynes: A Politics of Reformation Revision. 2010. (Studies in Early Modern Religious Reforms Ser.). 232p. pap. 129.00 *(978-90-481-5699-3(8)*, 9048156998) Springer.

White, James R. The King James Only Controversy: Can You Trust Modern Translations? 2nd expurg. ed. 2009. 368p. reprint ed. pap. 15.99 *(978-0-7642-0605-4(2))* Bethany Hse. Pubs.

Wilson, Derek A. The People's Bible: The Remarkable History of the King James Version. 2010. (ENG., Illus.). 224p. 24.95 *(978-0-7459-5351-9(4))* Lion Hudson PLC GBR. Dist: Independent Pubs. Group.

Wilton, Clyde C. The Wilton Translation of the New Testament: Translated from the Greek Text United Bible Societies Third Edition. 2010. 380p. 31.14 *(978-1-4269-4855-8(7))*; pap. 21.14 *(978-1-4269-4856-5(5))* Trafford Publishing.

Winter, David. The Reduced Bible. 2008. 128p. pap. 7.95 *(978-0-7459-5288-8(7))* Lion Hudson PLC GBR. Dist: Independent Pubs. Group.

Word of Life Press Staff, ed. Japanese-English Bilingual Bible New Testament-Niv. 2008. (JPN.). 576p. pap. 56.00 *(978-4-264-02605-1(9))* Word of Life Press Ministries JPN. Dist: STL Distribution North America.

Yancey, Philip & Stafford, Tim, eds. NIV Student Bible, 1 vol. 2009. (ENG.). 1472p. lthr. 49.99 *(978-0-310-94927-5(0))* Zondervan.

Zondervan Publishing Staff. Celebrate Recovery Bible, 1 vol. 2007. (ENG.). 1696p. pap. 24.99 *(978-0-310-93810-1(4))* Zondervan.

—The Faithgirlz! Bible. 2007. (Faithgirlz! Ser.). (ENG., Illus.). 1504p. (J). (gr. 5). lthr. 34.99 *(978-0-310-71583-2(0))* Zondervan.

—KJV/Archaeological Study Bible. Kaiser, Walter C. & Duane, Garrett, eds. rev. ed. 2008. (ENG.). 1728p. lthr. 64.99 *(978-0-310-94083-8(4))* Zondervan.

—Legacy Bible, 1 vol. Beshore, Kenton, ed. 2007. (ENG., Illus.). 1280p. lthr. 54.99 *(978-0-310-93802-6(3))* Zondervan.

—The Message Parallel Bible. 2006. (ENG.). 2624p. 39.99 *(978-0-310-93713-5(2))* Zondervan.

—New Men's Devotional Bible: New International Version, 1 vol. rev. ed. 2006. (ENG.). 1600p. lthr. 44.99 *(978-0-310-92858-4(3))* Zondervan.

—New Women's Devotional Bible. rev. ed. 2006. (ENG.). 1600p. lthr. 44.99 *(978-0-310-93615-2(2))* Zondervan.

—NIV Student Bible, 1 vol. Yancey, Philip & Stafford, Tim, eds. 2008. (ENG., Illus.). 1472p. lthr. 44.99 *(978-0-310-93851-4(1))* Zondervan.

—NIV Student Bible, 1 vol. Stafford, Tim & Yancey, Philip, eds. 2009. (ENG.). 1472p. lthr. 49.99 *(978-0-310-94926-8(2))* Zondervan.

—NIV Study Bible, 1 vol. rev. ed. 2008. (ENG.). 2368p. lthr. 79.99 *(978-0-310-93909-2(7))*; lthr. 89.99 *(978-0-310-93915-3(1))*; lthr. 79.99 *(978-0-310-93911-5(9))*; 39.99 *(978-0-310-93896-5(1))*; lthr. 74.99 *(978-0-310-93913-9(5))*; lthr. 69.99 *(978-0-310-93910-8(0))*; lthr. 59.99 *(978-0-310-93920-7(8))*; lthr. 74.99 *(978-0-310-93959-7(3))* Zondervan.

—Quest Study Bible, 1 vol. rev. ed. 2008. (ENG.). 1984p. lthr. 59.99 *(978-0-310-93876-7(7))* Zondervan.

—True Images: The Bible for Teen Girls. rev. ed. 2008. (ENG.). 1696p. (YA). lthr. 44.99 *(978-0-310-93979-5(8))* Zondervan.

—Zondervan King James Version Commentary-Old Testament, 1 vol. 2010. (ENG.). 1216p. 39.99 *(978-0-310-25139-2(7))* Zondervan.

—Zondervan Niv Study Bible Compact, 1 vol. rev. ed. 2008. (ENG.). 2368p. lthr. 39.99 *(978-0-310-93916-0(X))* Zondervan.

Zondervan Publishing Staff, creator. Archaeological Study Bible-NIV: An Illustrated Walk Through Biblical History & Culture, 1 vol. rev. l.t. ed. 2007. (ENG., Illus.). 2336p. 59.99 *(978-0-310-93850-7(3))* Zondervan.

—Aspire: The New Women of Color Study Bible: For Strength & Inspiration, 1 vol. 2007. (ENG.). 1760p. 39.99 *(978-0-310-93478-3(8))*; im. lthr. 49.99 *(978-0-310-93479-0(6))* Zondervan.

—Celebrate Recovery Bible, 1 vol. 2007. (ENG.). 1696p. 34.99 *(978-0-310-92849-2(4))* Zondervan.

—College Devotional Bible, 1 vol. 2007. (ENG.). 1664p. 27.99 *(978-0-310-93442-4(7))* Zondervan.

—The Faithgirlz! Bible. 2007. (Faithgirlz! Ser.). (ENG.). 1504p. (J). (gr. 5). pap. 22.99 *(978-0-310-71582-5(2))* Zondervan.

—Grandmother's Bible, 1 vol. 2008. (ENG., Illus.). 1712p. 34.99 *(978-0-310-93801-9(5))* Zondervan.

—The Message, 1 vol. 2007. (ENG.). 2624p. lthr. 64.99 *(978-0-310-93714-2(0))* Zondervan.

—New Men's Devotional Bible. rev. ed. 2006. (ENG.). 1600p. pap. 24.99 *(978-0-310-92856-0(7))* Zondervan.

—New Women's Devotional Bible. rev. ed. 2006. (ENG.). 1600p. 29.99 *(978-0-310-93613-8(6))*; pap. 24.99 *(978-0-310-93614-5(4))*; lthr. 44.99 *(978-0-310-93617-6(9))*; (Illus.). lthr. 44.99 *(978-0-310-93616-9(0))* Zondervan.

—NIV Student Bible, 1 vol. 2007. (ENG.). 1472p. lthr. 44.99 *(978-0-310-93856-9(2))* Zondervan.

—True Images: The Bible for Teen Girls. rev. ed. 2007. (ENG., Illus.). 1696p. (YA). 29.99 *(978-0-310-93661-9(6))*; (gr. 8-11). lthr. 44.99 *(978-0-310-93662-6(4))* Zondervan.

Zondervan Publishing Staff, ed. King James Version Compact Reference Bible, 1 vol. 2007. (ENG., Illus.). 1472p. lthr. 22.99 *(978-0-310-93786-9(8))* Zondervan.

—NASB Thinline Bible, 1 vol. 2008. (ENG.). 2528p. lthr. 69.99 *(978-0-310-94124-8(5))* Zondervan.

—NIV Holy Bible, 1 vol. 2007. (ENG.). cd-rom 9.99 *(978-0-310-93721-0(3))* Zondervan.

BIBLE—VESTMENTS

see Vestments in the Bible

BIBLE—WOMEN

see Women in the Bible

BIBLE—WORSHIP

see Worship in the Bible

BIBLE—ZOOLOGY

see Nature in the Bible

BIBLE AND ASTROLOGY

Darlison, Bill. The Gospel & the Zodiac. 2009. (ENG.). 304p. (gr. 12). pap. 14.95 (978-1-59020-160-2(4)) Overlook Pr., The.

—The Gospel & the Zodiac: The Secret Truth about Jesus. 2008. (ENG., Illus.). 304p. (gr. 12). 26.95 (978-1-59020-037-7(3)) Overlook Pr., The.

Jabbar, Malik H. The Biggest Lie Ever Told, 4th Edition. 4th exp. rev. ed. 2006. per. 9.95 (978-1-57154-007-2(5)) Rare Bks. Distributors.

Ledo, Michael. The Secret Astrology of the Bible. 2010. 274p. pap. 24.99 (978-0-557-38057-2(X)) Lulu Enterprises Inc.

Petersen, William. Astrología y Biblia: Astrology & the Bible. (SPA.). 64p. (978-84-7228-232-2(5), 220050) Clie, Editorial.

Stowe, Lyman E. Stowe's Bible Astrology. 2007. 268p. per. 18.45 (978-1-59462-756-9(8), Book Jungle) Standard Pubns., Inc.

—Stowe's Bible Astrology: The Bible Founded on Astrology. 2010. 266p. 42.95 (978-1-161-35544-4(8)) Kessinger Publishing, LLC.

Womack-El, Bishop. The Bible Is Astrology. 2008. 39.95 (978-0-9801316-0-4(X)) Radiant Light.

BIBLE AND EVOLUTION

see also Creationism; Evolution—Religious Aspects

Barton, Stephen C. & Wilkinson, David, eds. Reading Genesis after Darwin. 2009. (ENG.). 272p. 99.00 (978-0-19-538335-5(4)); pap. 24.95 (978-0-19-538336-2(2)) Oxford Univ. Pr., Inc.

Benoit, Gregory C. PharaohÕs Magicians: Evolution, the Bible, & Modern Gnosticism. 2011. 232p. pap. 26.00 (978-1-61097-416-5(6), Wipf and Stock) Wipf & Stock Pubs.

Birge, Mary Katherine, et al. Genesis, Evolution, & the Search for a Reasoned Faith. 2011. (ENG.). 148p. (C). pap. 26.95 (978-0-88489-755-2(9)) St. Mary's Pr.

Bosch, Kees van den. The Greatest Scientist Alive. 2011. 84p. pap. 41.99 (978-1-4568-3791-4(5)) Xlibris Corp.

Carr, H. Michael. Before Adam: The Biblical Origins of Mankind. 2007. (ENG.). 60p. per. 16.95 (978-1-4241-7820-9(7)) PublishAmerica, Inc.

Clark, E. J. & Agnew, B. Alexander. The Ark of Millions of Years Vol. 4: Book of Updates. 2011. 256p. pap. 16.95 (978-1-4567-2528-0(9)) AuthorHouse.

Cunningham, Mary. God in an Evolutionary World. 2007. (ENG., Illus.). 408p. (C). 37.95 (978-0-415-38014-0(6)) Routledge.

Cunningham, Mary Kathleen. God & Evolution. 2009. (Illus.). 224p. 99.00 (978-0-415-44349-4(0)) Routledge.

—God in an Evolutionary World. 2007. (Illus.). 408p. 125.00 (978-0-415-38013-3(8)) Routledge.

Cunningham, Mary Kathleen, ed. God & Evolution. 2009. (Illus.). 224p. 29.95 (978-0-415-44350-0(4)) Routledge.

Dean, Phillip. Creation ¿ God¿s Way: The First Chapter on Earth. 2006. 60p. per. 9.95 (978-1-60002-128-2(X), 3938) Mountain Valley Publishing, LLC.

DeWitt, David. Unraveling the Origins Controversy. 2007. (Illus.). 235p. pap. 14.99 (978-0-9796323-0-3(7)) Creation Curriculum, LLC.

Eristhee, Bishop Thomas. What Should We Believe? 2009. 96p. pap. 11.95 (978-1-4401-4237-6(8)) iUniverse, Inc.

Garratt, Samuel. World Without End. 2007. 312p. per. (978-1-4067-8991-1(7), Pierides Pr.) Read Bks.

Gatewood, Otis. There Is a God in Heaven. (RUS & ENG.). 380p. pap. 12.95 (978-1-56794-161-6(3), C-2571) Star Bible & Tract Corp.

Gitt, Werner. Did God Use Evolution? Observations from a Scientist of Faith. 2006. 142p. per. 9.99 (978-0-89051-483-2(6)) Master Bks.

Ham, Ken. The New Answers Book II. 2008. 300p. pap. (978-0-89051-537-2(9)) Master Bks.

Harwood, William. God, Jesus, & the Bible: The Origin & Evolution of Religion. 2009. 458p. 40.00 (978-1-935444-28-2(X)) World Audience Pubs.

Harwood, William, et al. God, Jesus, & the Bible. 2009. 458p. pap. 28.00 (978-1-935444-84-8(0)) World Audience Pubs.

Hassan, Imad. Shajara Code Decoded. 2009. (Illus.). 546p. pap. 23.49 (978-1-4490-0819-2(4)) AuthorHouse.

Howie, R. D. God's Master Plan: Creation or Evolution? 2012. (978-1-55452-707-6(4)) Essence Publishing.

Johnson, Robert Bowie, Jr. Sowing Atheism: The National Academy of Sciences' Sinister Scheme to Teach Our Children They're Descended from Reptiles. 2008. (ENG., Illus.). 128p. pap. 12.95 (978-0-9705438-5-1(9)) Solving Light Bks.

Kelly, Terry. Stars, Life & Intelligence: Being a Darwinian & a Believer. 2009. (ENG.). 130p. (C). pap. 36.00 (978-1-921511-69-1(9)) ATF Pr. AUS. Dist: Brown, David Bk. Co., The.

Lamoureux, Denis O. Evolutionary Creation: A Christian Approach to Evolution. 2008. (ENG., Illus.). 514p. pap. 64.00 (978-0-7188-9191-6(0)) Lutterworth Pr., The GBR. Dist: Brown, David Bk. Co., The.

—Evolutionary Creation: A Christian Approach to Evolution. 2008. 514p. pap. 55.00 (978-1-55635-581-3(5), Wipf and Stock) Wipf & Stock Pubs.

—I Love Jesus & I Accept Evolution. 2009. 202p. pap. 22.00 (978-1-55635-886-9(5), Wipf and Stock) Wipf & Stock Pubs.

Mandelbrote, Scott H. & Meer, Jitse M. van der, eds. Nature & Scripture in the Abrahamic Religions: Volume I: To 1700. 2009. (Brill's Ser. in Church History Ser.). 744p. (978-90-04-17191-6(6)) BRILL.

—Nature & Scripture in the Abrahamic Religions: Volume II: 1700-Present. 2009. (Brill's Ser. in Church History Ser.). 584p. (978-90-04-17192-3(4)) BRILL.

McCalla. Creationist Debate: The Encounter between the Bible & the Historical Mind. 2006. (ENG.). 248p. 140.00 (978-0-8264-6447-7(5)) Continuum International Publishing Group, Ltd. GBR. Dist: National Bk. Network.

McIntosh, Andy. Genesis for Today: The Relevance of the Creation/Evolution Debate to Today's Society. 4th ed. 2011. (Creation Points Ser.). (Illus.). 232p. pap. (978-1-84625-240-2(7)) DayOne Pubns.

—Genesis for Today: The Relevance of the Creation/Evolution Debate to Today's Society. 3rd ed. 2006. (Illus.). 230p. per. 13.00 (978-1-84625-051-4(X)) DayOne Pubns. GBR. Dist: STL Distribution North America.

Morris, Henry M., 3rd. 5 Reasons to Believe in Recent Creation. 2008. 48p. pap. 2.95 (978-0-932766-91-5(9)) Institute for Creation Research.

Nevin, Norman Cummings. Should Christians Embrace Evolution? Biblical & Scientific Responses. 2011. pap. (978-1-59638-230-5(9)) P & R Publishing.

Peters, Ted & Hewlett, Martinez. Can You Believe in God & Evolution? A Guide for the Perplexed. 2006. (Illus.). 98p. per. 12.00 (978-0-687-33551-0(5)) Abingdon Pr.

Savage, M. J. The Religion of Evolution. 2007. (ENG.). 254p. 42.95 (978-0-548-14957-7(7)); 256p. per. 27.95 (978-1-4304-4273-8(5)) Kessinger Publishing, LLC.

Scott, Mark. The Rest of the Greatest Story. 2010. 154p. pap. 14.99 (978-1-60957-106-1(1)) Xulon Pr., Inc.

Watson, David. El Gran Fraude Intelectual: The Great Brain Robbery. (SPA.). 160p. (978-84-7228-589-7(8), 220433) Clie, Editorial.

Webb, Stephen H. The Dome of Eden. 2009. 374p. pap. 41.00 (978-1-60608-741-1(X), Cascade Bks.) Wipf & Stock Pubs.

Whidden, Theodore L. The Bible Plumb Line: Cain's Wife & Other Perspectives. 2006. per. (978-0-9786684-2-6(1)) Heritage Ink Christian Publishing Co., LLC.

Whitcomb, John C. The Early Earth. pap. 9.99 (978-0-88469-060-3(1)) BMH Bks.

Whitelaw, Robert. Evolution & Bible. pap. 1.49 (978-0-87377-102-3(8)) GAM Pubns.

BIBLE AND FEMINISM

Here are entered works on how feminism is or ought to be viewed from the standpoint of the Bible. Works on the criticism of the Bible from the standpoint of feminist theology or feminist theory are entered under Bible—Feminist Criticism.

see also Bible—Feminist Criticism

Boer, Roland & +Iand, Jorunn, eds. Marxist Feminist Criticism of the Bible. 2008. 260p. (978-1-906055-35-6(1)) Sheffield Phoenix Pr.

Calvert-Koyzis, Nancy. Breaking Boundaries: Female Biblical Interpreters Who Challenged the Status Quo. Weir, Heather E., ed. 2010. (Library of Hebrew Bible/Old Testament Studies). (ENG.). 224p. 130.00 (978-0-567-59503-4(X), T&T Clark Int'l) Continuum International Publishing Group, Ltd. GBR. Dist: National Bk. Network.

Calvert-Koyzis, Nancy & Weir, Heather, eds. Breaking Boundaries: Female Biblical Interpreters Who Challenged the Status Quo. 2012. (Library Hebrew Bible/Old Testament Studies). (ENG.). 224p. pap. 44.95 (978-0-567-37503-2(X), T&T Clark Int'l) Continuum International Publishing Group, Ltd. GBR. Dist: National Bk. Network.

Grudem, Wayne A. & Grudem, Wayne. Evangelical Feminism: A New Path to Liberalism? 2006. 272p. pap. 15.99 (978-1-58134-734-0(0)) Crossway.

Kanyoro, Musimbi R. A. Introduction to Feminist Cultural Hermeneutics: A Key to African Women's Liberation Theology. (Introductions in Feminist Theology Ser.). 99p. pap. (978-0-8264-6054-7(2)) Continuum International Publishing Group, Ltd.

Osburn, Carroll D., ed. Essays on Women in Earliest Christianity, Volume 1. 2007. 566p. pap. 48.00 (978-1-55635-540-0(8)) Wipf & Stock Pubs.

—Essays on Women in Earliest Christianity, Volume 2. 2007. (Essays on Women in Earliest Christianity Ser.). 644p. pap. 55.00 (978-1-55635-541-7(6)) Wipf & Stock Pubs.

Ostriker, Alicia. For the Love of God: The Bible as an Open Book. 2007. (ENG.). 184p. (C). pap. 19.95 (978-0-8135-4503-5(X)) Rutgers Univ. Pr.

Phillips, Bob. Find It in the Bible for Women: Lists, Lists, & More Lists. 2007. (ENG.). 240p. pap. 15.99 (978-1-58229-640-1(5), Howard Bks.) Howard Books.

Poling, Nancy Werking. Had Eve Come First & Jonah Been a Woman. 2010. 128p. pap. 16.00 (978-1-60899-739-8(1), Resource Pubns.) Wipf & Stock Pubs.

Society of Biblical Literature Staff, contrib. by. The Bible & Women: An Encyclopaedia of Exegesis & Cultural History. 2011. (978-1-58983-634-1(0)); (978-1-58983-565-8(4)); 500p. pap. (978-1-58983-564-1(6)) Society of Biblical Literature.

BIBLE AND LAW

Adewuyi, Femi. Ordinances & Laws of the New Covenant: Bible Expository. 2009. 68p. pap. (978-1-84748-333-1(X)) Athena Pr.

Behrends, Okko. Der biblische Gesetzesbegriff: Auf den Spuren seiner Säkularisierung. 13. Symposion der Kommission 'Die Funktion des Gesetzes in Geschichte und Gegenwart' 2006. (Abhandl. D. akad. der wissensch. Phil. -hist. klasse 3. folge Ser.). (GER.). 389p. (C). 185.00 (978-3-525-82550-1(1)) Vandenhoeck & Ruprecht GmbH & Co. KG DEU. Dist: ISD.

Biliarsky, Ivan & Paun, Radu G. The Biblical Models of Power & Law: Papers of the International Conference, Bucharest, New Europe College 2005 = les Modèles Bibliques du Pouvoir et du Droit: Actes du Colloque International, Bucarest, New Europe College 2005. 2008. (FRE, MUL, GER & ENG., Illus.). 309p. pap. 72.95 (978-3-631-57240-5(9)) Lang, Peter GmbH, Europaischer Verlag der Wissenschaften DEU. Dist: Lang, Peter.

Blankenship, Lawrence L. Rev., 1st. The Divine Law: The Law of God & the Law of the States Vol. 1. 2007. (Illus.). 31p. 9.00 (978-0-9705440-0-1(6)) Divine Law, The.

Burnside, Jonathan. God, Justice, & Society: Aspects of Law & Legality in the Bible, 1 vol. 2010. (ENG., Illus.). 576p. 95.00 (978-0-19-975921-7(9)) Oxford Univ. Pr., Inc.

Daube, David. Studies in Biblical Law. 2008. (ENG.). 340p. (C). pap. 46.00 (978-0-521-08972-2(7)) Cambridge Univ. Pr.

O'Higgins, Paul & O'Higgins, Nuala. New Testament Believers & the Law. pap. 3.95 (978-0-944795-04-0(8)) Reconciliation Outreach, Inc.

BIBLE AND LITERATURE

see also Bible As Literature

Alter, Robert. Pen of Iron: American Prose & the King James Bible. 2010. (ENG.). 208p. 19.95 (978-0-691-12881-8(2)) Princeton Univ. Pr.

Bassard, Katherine Clay. Transforming Scriptures: African American Women Writers & the Bible. 2011. (ENG., Illus.). 180p. pap. 22.95 (978-0-8203-3880-4(X)) Univ. of Georgia Pr.

Deena, Seodial Frank H. & Szatek, Karoline, eds. From Around the Globe: Secular Authors & Biblical Perspectives. 2007. (ENG.). 342p. per. 51.50 (978-0-7618-3627-8(6)) Univ. Pr. of America, Inc.

Frye, Northrop. Words with Power: Being a Second Study of 'the Bible & Literature' Dolzani, Michael, ed. 2008. (Collected Works of Northrop Frye Ser.). (ENG.). 448p. (978-0-8020-9293-9(4)) Univ. of Toronto Pr.

Hass, Andrew, et al. The Oxford Handbook of English Literature & Theology. 2007. (Oxford Handbooks Ser.). (ENG.). 908p. 175.00 (978-0-19-927197-9(6)) Oxford Univ. Pr., Inc.

Jack, Alison. The Bible & Literature. 2012. 352p. pap. 45.00 (978-0-334-04166-5(X), SCM Pr.) Hymns Ancient & Modern Ltd GBR. Dist: Westminster John Knox Pr.

Lee, Alvin, ed. The Great Code: The Bible & Literature. 2006. (Collected Works of Northrop Frye Ser.). (ENG., Illus.). 464p. (978-0-8020-9120-8(2)) Univ. of Toronto Pr.

Lemon, Rebecca, et al, eds. The Blackwell Companion to the Bible in English Literature. (ENG.). 720p. 2012. pap. 44.95 (978-0-470-67499-4(7)) 2009. (Wiley-Blackwell Companions to Religion Ser.: 29). 199.95 (978-1-4051-3160-5(8)) Wiley, John & Sons, Inc. (Wiley-Blackwell).

McAfee, Cleland. The Greatest English Classic. 2006. 27.95 (978-1-59605-955-9(9), Cosimo Classics) Cosimo, Inc.

McAfee, Cleland Boyd & Mcafee, Cleland Boyd. The Greatest English Classic, a Study of the King James Version of the Bible & It's Influence on Live & Literature. 2011. 146p. pap. 12.99 (978-1-61203-235-1(4)) Bottom of the Hill Publishing.

Ostriker, Alicia. For the Love of God: The Bible as an Open Book. 2007. (ENG.). 184p. (C). pap. 19.95 (978-0-8135-4503-5(X)) Rutgers Univ. Pr.

Pardes, Ilana. Melville's Bibles. 2008. (Illus.). 202p. 65.00 (978-0-520-25454-1(6)); 192p. per. 26.95 (978-0-520-25455-8(4)) Univ. of California Pr.

Spencer, Jamie. Fictional Religion: Keeping the New Testament New. 2011. 164p. pap. 18.00 (978-1-59815-032-2(4)) Polebridge Pr.

Streete, Adrian, ed. Early Modern Drama & the Bible: Contexts & Readings, 1570-1625. 2011. (Early Modern Literature in History Ser.). (ENG., Illus.). 280p. 85.00 (978-0-230-30109-2(6)) Palgrave Macmillan.

Swindell, Anthony C. Reworking the Bible: The Literary Reception-History of Fourteen Biblical Stories. 2010. 356p. (978-1-907534-01-0(6)) Sheffield Phoenix Pr.

Swindell, Anthony Charles. How Contemporary Novelists Rewrite Stories from the Bible: The Interpretation of Scripture in Literature. 2009. 364p. 119.95 (978-0-7734-4764-6(4)) Mellen, Edwin Pr., The.

Tischler, Nancy M. Thematic Guide to Biblical Literature, 1 vol. 2007. 288p. 65.00 (978-0-313-33709-3(8), GR3709, Greenwood Pr.) Greenwood Publishing Group, Inc.

Woodman, Thomas & Knight, Mark, eds. Biblical Religion & the Novel 1700-2000. 2006. 170p. 110.00 (978-0-7546-5117-8(7)) Ashgate Publishing Co.

BIBLE AND SCIENCE

see also Creation; Modernist-Fundamentalist Controversy

Ackland, T. S. The Story of Creation As Told by Theology & by Science. 2008. 120p. pap. (978-1-4099-3425-7(X)) Dodo Pr.

Addinall, Peter. Philosophy & Biblical Interpretation: A Study in Nineteenth-Century Conflict. 2009. (ENG.). 344p. (C). pap. 46.00 (978-0-521-10840-9(3)) Cambridge Univ. Pr.

Bacon, Thomas Scott. The Reign of God Not the Reign of Law. 2007. (ENG.). 410p. 49.95 (978-0-548-15695-7(6)); pap. 34.95 (978-1-4304-5173-0(4)) Kessinger Publishing, LLC.

Baden-Powell, Baden Henry. Creation & Its Records. 2009. 126p. pap. (978-0-217-81434-8(4)) Books LLC.

Barefoot, Daniel. Ten Scriptual Reasons That the Earth Is Young. 2008. 80p. pap. 9.99 (978-1-60477-865-6(2)) Xulon Pr., Inc.

Barton, Stephen C. & Wilkinson, David, eds. Reading Genesis after Darwin. 2009. (ENG.). 272p. 99.00 (978-0-19-538335-5(4)); pap. 24.95 (978-0-19-538336-2(2)) Oxford Univ. Pr., Inc.

Becker, James. Evolution & the Bible. 2011. 226p. 46.95 (978-1-258-02397-3(0)) Literary Licensing, LLC.

Birks, Thomas Rawson. The Scripture Doctrine of Creation: With Reference to Religious Nihilism & Modern Theories of Development. 2009. (Cambridge Library Collection - Religion Ser.). 268p. pap. 23.99 (978-1-108-00022-2(3)) Cambridge Univ. Pr.

Bosch, Kees van den. The Greatest Scientist Alive. 2011. 84p. pap. 41.99 (978-1-4568-3791-4(5)) Xlibris Corp.

Breshears, Jason M. When the Sun Darkens. 2009. 128p. pap. 14.95 (978-1-58509-117-1(0)) Book Tree, The.

Brown, William P. The Seven Pillars of Creation: The Bible, Science, & the Ecology of Wonder, 1 vol. 2010. (ENG., Illus.). 352p. 29.95 (978-0-19-973079-7(2)) Oxford Univ. Pr., Inc.

Bullinger, E. W. The Witness of the Stars. 2007. 296p. per. 29.95 (978-1-60206-783-7(X)) Cosimo, Inc.

—The Witness of the Stars. 2011. 298p. pap. 9.45 (978-1-61427-078-2(3)) Martino Publishing.

Bullinger, Ethelbert. The Witness of the Stars. 2007. 296p. per. 10.95 (978-1-60206-046-3(0)) Cosimo, Inc.

Burney, Gerry. Science, Origins, & Ancient Civilizations: Scientific Evidence Withheld from School Textbooks. 2009. 158p. pap. 14.99 (978-1-60791-625-3(8)) Xulon Pr., Inc.

Cohen, Gary G. Biblical Decision Making, Intelligent Design, & Creation: A Book to Help Those Searching for Truth Especially with Regard to God & Creation. 2006. 292p. pap. 29.00 (978-1-59752-687-6(8), Resource Pubns.) Wipf & Stock Pubs.

Crawford, Gayleen. Evidence & Science That Confirms the Bible. 2008. 176p. pap. (978-1-55452-300-9(1)) Essence Publishing.

Curtiss, Harriett Augusta. Why There Is No Conflict Between Science & Religion or Between. 2006. pap. 9.95 (978-1-4286-8164-4(7)) Kessinger Publishing, LLC.

Davies, Thomas Alfred. Answer to Hugh Miller & Theoretic Geologists. 2006. 296p. per. 23.99 (978-1-4255-2775-4(2)) MPublishing.

Dawson, John William. Nature & the Bible a Course of Lectures Delivered in New York, in December, 1874, on the Morse Foundation of the Union Theological Seminary by J. 2006. 288p. per. 23.99 (978-1-4255-2576-7(8)) MPublishing.

—The Origin of the World According to Revelation & Science by J W Dawson. 2006. 448p. per. 26.99 (978-1-4255-4879-7(2)) MPublishing.

Derr, Louise Barrett. Experiencing Bible Science: A Lab Book for the Young at Heart. 2011. 316p. pap. 31.95 (978-1-4497-1088-0(3), WestBow Pr.) Author Solutions, Inc.

DeWitt, Calvin B. Earth-Wise: A Biblical Response to Environmental Issues. 2nd ed. 2008. 92p. per. (978-1-59255-414-0(8)) Faith Alive Christian Resources.

DeWitt, David. Unraveling the Origins Controversy. 2007. (Illus.). 235p. pap. 14.99 (978-0-9796323-0-3(7)) Creation Curriculum, LLC.

DeYoung, Donald B. Pioneer Explorers of Intelligent Design: Scientists Who Made a Difference. 2006. (Illus.). 101p. per. 12.99 (978-0-88469-073-3(3)) BMH Bks.

Dill, D. V. M. In the Beginnings. 2010. 394p. 32.99 (978-1-60957-323-2(4)) Xulon Pr., Inc.

Dill, Steven E. In the Beginnings. 2010. 394p. pap. 20.99 (978-1-60957-163-4(0)) Xulon Pr., Inc.

Erickson, Gary D. & Reynolds, David. Our Just Right World. 2009. (978-0-7577-3911-8(3)) Word Aflame Pr.

Fuller, Allan R. Thought: The Only Reality. 2010. 156p. pap. 13.95 (978-1-60844-590-5(9)) Dog Ear Publishing, LLC.

Green, Joel B. Body, Soul, & Human Life: The Nature of Humanity in the Bible. 2008. (Studies in Theological Interpretation Ser.). 240p. (C). pap. 24.00 (978-0-8010-3595-1(3)) Baker Academic.

Harris, Mark. The Bible & Science: Creation. 2011. (Biblical Challenges in the Contemporary World Ser.). (ENG.). 224p. (C). pap. 24.95 (978-1-84553-265-9(1)); 90.00 (978-1-84553-264-2(3)) Equinox Publishing Ltd. GBR. Dist: ISD.

Hassan, Imad. Shajara Code Decoded. 2009. (Illus.). 546p. pap. 23.49 (978-1-4490-0819-2(4)) AuthorHouse.

Hayes, Charles F. Bring University Students to Christ. 292p. 2015. 26.99 (978-1-61379-510-1(6)) 2011. pap. 16.99 (978-1-61379-509-5(2)) Xulon Pr., Inc.

Heck, Joel D. In the Beginning, God: Creation from God's Perspective. 2011. 3.99 (978-0-7586-2738-4(6)) Concordia Publishing Hse.

Hillis, Newell Dwight. The Influence of Christ in Modern Life Being a Study of the New Problems of the Church in American Society. 2007. (ENG.). 428p. 51.95 (978-0-548-01029-7(3)) Kessinger Publishing, LLC.

Hobrink, Ben. Modern Science in the Bible: Amazing Scientific Truths Found in Ancient Texts. 2011. (ENG., Illus.). 288p. 23.99 (978-1-4391-0892-5(7), Howard Bks.) Howard Books.

Hunt, Samuel. Episteme Scientia: The Law of All That Is. 2007. 248p. mass mkt. (978-0-9795445-0-7(5), Sunpiper Pr.) Sunpiper Media Publishing.

Isaacs, Roger D. Talking with God: The Radioactive Ark of the Testimony: Communication Through It. Protection from It. Williams Miller, Janice, ed. 2010. (Illus.). 514p. 29.95 (978-1-4125-4997-4(3), Sacred Closet Bks.) Publishing Institute, Inc., The.

Johnson, Robert Bowie, Jr. Sowing Atheism: The National Academy of Sciences' Sinister Scheme to Teach Our Children They're Descended from Reptiles. 2008. (ENG., Illus.). 128p. pap. 12.95 (978-0-9705438-5-1(9)) Solving Light Bks.

Kurtz, J. H. (Johann Heinrich). The Bible & Astronomy, an Exposition of the Biblical Cosmology, & Its Relations to Natural Science by John Henry Kurtz Translated from the Th. 2006. 536p. per. 29.99 (978-1-4255-5955-7(7)) MPublishing.

—History of the Old Covenant. 2006. 440p. per. 26.99 *(978-1-4255-4807-0(5))*; 524p. per. 29.99 *(978-1-4255-5838-3(0))*; 540p. per. 29.99 *(978-1-4255-5985-4(9))* MPublishing.
Lewis, Tayler. The Bible & Science; or, the World-Problem. 2006. 352p. per. 23.99 *(978-1-4255-3549-0(6))* MPublishing.
Linville, James R. Amos & the Cosmic Imagination. 2008. (Society for Old Testament Study Ser.). 212p. 99.95 *(978-0-7546-5481-0(8))* Ashgate Publishing Co.
Lord, Eleazar. The Epoch of Creation the Scripture Doctrine Contrasted with the Geological Theory by Eleazar Lord with an Introduction, by Richard W Dickinson. 2006. 312p. per. 23.99 *(978-1-4255-3002-0(8))* MPublishing.
Malczewski, Dan. God's Plan: What Every Christian Should Know. 2010. 232p. 33.95 *(978-1-4497-0341-7(0))*; pap. 17.95 *(978-1-4497-0340-0(2))* Author Solutions, Inc. (WestBow Pr.).
Mandelbrote, Scott H. & Meer, Jitse M. van der, eds. Nature & Scripture in the Abrahamic Religions: Volume I: To 1700. 2009. (Brill's Ser. in Church History Ser.) 744p. *(978-90-04-17191-6(6))* BRILL.
—Nature & Scripture in the Abrahamic Religions: Volume II: 1700-Present. 2009. (Brill's Ser. in Church History Ser.). 584p. *(978-90-04-17192-3(4))* BRILL.
Manimas, John. The Primacy of Stewardship: The Handbook for Christians Who Believe in Democracy. 2nd ed. 2009. 168p. pap. 25.00 *(978-0-9821860-2-2(9))* JManimas Publishing.
Maunder, E. Walter. The Astronomy of the Bible. 2007. 416p. per. 24.95 *(978-1-4344-0123-6(5))* Wildside Pr., LLC.
Medeiros, John Manimas. The Primacy of Stewardship: The Handbook for Christians Who Believe in Democracy. 2008. 183p. ring bd. 30.00 *(978-0-9821860-0-8(2))* JManimas Publishing.
Medved, David. Hidden Light: Science Secrets of the Bible. 2008. (Illus.). 170p. 24.95 *(978-1-59264-185-7(7))* Toby Pr. LLC, The.
Miller, Hugh. An the Testimony of the Rocks; or, Geology in Its Bearings on the Two Theologies, Natural & Revealed by Hugh Miller with Memorials of the Death. 2006. 532p. per. 29.99 *(978-1-4255-5923-6(9))*; 528p. per. 29.99 *(978-1-4255-5872-7(0))* MPublishing.
Mitchel, O. M. (Ormsby MacKnight). The Astronomy of the Bible by O M Mitchel with a Biographical Sketch. 2006. 336p. per. 23.99 *(978-1-4255-3385-4(X))* MPublishing.
Molloy, Gerald. Geology & Revelation: Or the Ancient History of the Earth Considered in the Light of Geological Facts & Revealed Religion / by Gerald Molloy. 2006. 384p. per. 26.99 *(978-1-4255-4054-8(6))* MPublishing.
Morris, Henry, III & Morris, Henry M. The Big Three: Major Events That Changed History Forever. 2009. 222p. pap. *(978-0-89051-562-4(X))* Master Bks.
Morris, Henry M., 3rd. 5 Reasons to Believe in Recent Creation. 2008. 48p. pap. 2.95 *(978-0-932766-91-5(9))* Institute for Creation Research.
Parker, Andrew. The Genesis Enigma: Why the First Book of the Bible Is Scientifically Accurate. 2010. (ENG.). 320p. (gr. 12). 16.00 *(978-0-452-29655-8(2)*, Plume) Penguin Group (USA) Inc.
Peabody, Andrew P. (Andrew Preston). Christianity & Science a Series of Lectures Delivered in New York, in 1874, on the Ely Foundation of the Union Theological Seminary by Andrew P P. 2006. 316p. per. 23.99 *(978-1-4255-3011-2(7))* MPublishing.
Poythress, Vern Sheridan. Redeeming Science: A God-Centered Approach. 2006. (Illus.). 384p. pap. 20.00 *(978-1-58134-731-9(6))* Crossway.
Read, John. Humour & Humanism in Chemistry. reprint ed. 42.50 *(978-0-404-18487-2(1))* AMS Pr., Inc.
Richards, Larry. Ciencia y Biblia, ? Se Contradicen? Science & Bible, Can We Believe. (SPA.). *(978-84-7228-378-7(X)*, 220160) Clie, Editorial.
Rock Solid Answers. 2009. 19.99 *(978-0-89051-567-9(0))* Master Bks.
Schroeder, Gerald L. & Schroeder, Gerald. God According to God: A Physicist Proves We've Been Wrong about God All Along. 2009. 256p. 25.99 *(978-0-06-171015-5(6)*, HarperOne) HarperCollins Pubs.
Sharp, G. Thomas. Science According to Moses, 3 vols., Set. Incl. Church in the Twenty-First Century. pap. *(978-0-9634981-5-1(0))*; Darwin's Twentieth Century Disciples. pap. *(978-0-9634981-3-7(4))*; Foundation of a Biblical World View. pap. *(978-0-9634981-6-8(9))*; 1996. pap. *(978-0-9634981-2-0(6))* Creation Truth Pubns.
Sivertsen, Barbara J. The Parting of the Sea: How Volcanoes, Earthquakes, & Plagues Shaped the Story of Exodus. 2009. (ENG., Illus.). 264p. (C). 39.95 *(978-0-691-13770-4(6))* Princeton Univ. Pr.
Smiles, Vincent M. The Bible & Science: Longing for God in a Science-Dominated World. 2011. E-Book *(978-0-8146-8006-3(2))* Liturgical Pr.
Smith, John Pye. The Relation Between the Holy Scriptures & Some Parts of Geological Science by John Pye Smith from the 4th London Ed , Greatly Enl. 2006. 428p. per. 26.99 *(978-1-4255-4660-1(9))* MPublishing.
Snoke, David. A Biblical Case for an Old Earth. 2006. (Illus.). 224p. pap. 18.00 *(978-0-8010-6619-1(0))* Baker Bks.
Stedman, Geoffrey Ernest. An Orthodox Understanding of the Bible with Physical Science. 2010. 310p. pap. 16.95 *(978-1-60911-725-2(5)*, Eloquent Bks.) AEG Literary Publishing Services, Inc.
Sturch, Richard L. From World to God? Or, New Dialogues Concerning Natural Religion. 2007. 152p. pap. 19.00 *(978-1-55635-053-5(8)*, Resource Pubns.) Wipf & Stock Pubs.
Taylor, Paul. The Six Days of Genesis. 2007. (Illus.). 221p. per. 13.99 *(978-0-89051-499-3(2))* Master Bks.
Thompson, Jim. The Physics of Genesis. 2008. 216p. pap. 17.99 *(978-1-4141-1160-5(6))* Pleasant Word.
Tokeley, Christopher J. Adam Ate with Dinosaurs. 2010. (ENG.). 158p. pap. ***(978-1-84748-708-7(4))*** Athena Pr.
Towers, Denis. Two Birdsone Stone. 2007. pap. 14.99 *(978-1-60034-899-0(8))* Xulon Pr., Inc.
Von Vett, Julie & Malone, Bruce. Inspired Evidence: Only One Reality. 2011. (ENG.). 432p. pap. 11.95 ***(978-0-9715911-3-4(X))*** Search for the Truth.
White, Richard. Bibles, Science & Sanity. 2007. 168p. per. 14.95 *(978-1-933912-80-6(4))* Westview Publishing Co., Inc.
Woolford, P. M. The Genesis Grid. 2010. (Illus.). 468p. pap. 20.49 *(978-1-4490-8117-1(7))* AuthorHouse.

BIBLE AND SPIRITUALISM

Claim it! Feel it! Live it! Youth Ministry Sampler. 2007. 70.00 *(978-0-687-64413-1(5))* Abingdon Pr.
Daniels, J. W. Spiritualism Versus Christianity; or, Spiritualism Thoroughly Exposed. 2006. 312p. per. 23.99 *(978-1-4255-2983-3(6))* MPublishing.
Davis, Andrew Jackson. The Approaching Crisis: Being A Review of Dr. Bushnell's Course of Lectures, on the Bible, Nature, Religion, Skepticism, & the Supernatural. 2006. 304p. per. 23.99 *(978-1-4255-2859-1(7))* MPublishing.
Doane, T. W. & Doane, T. W. Bible Myths & Their Parallels in Other Religions. 2010. 614p. 59.95 *(978-1-161-35605-2(3))* Kessinger Publishing, LLC.
Hare, Robert. Experimental Investigation of the Spirit Manifestations, Demonstrating the Existence of Spirits & Their Communion with Mortals Doctrine of the Spir. 2006. 484p. per. 29.99 *(978-1-4255-5374-6(5))* MPublishing.
Holman, Lorraine. Trials: Thanks a Lot! 2010. pap. 18.99 *(978-1-61663-308-0(5))* Tate Publishing & Enterprises, LLC.
Mamie D. Givhan. An Invitation to Know Him: For Yourself. 2009. 268p. pap. 22.49 *(978-1-4343-1896-1(6))* AuthorHouse.
McDonald, W. (William). Spiritualism Identical with Ancient Sorcery, New Testament Demonology, & Modern Witchcraft; with the Testimony of God & Man Against It by W Mdo. 2006. 228p. per. 20.99 *(978-1-4255-1908-7(3))* MPublishing.
Soles, Richard V., Jr. The Bible Belt. 2008. 127p. pap. 14.95 *(978-0-557-03212-9(1))* Lulu Enterprises Inc.
Sprague, E. W. All the Spiritualism of the Christian Bible & the Scripture Directly Opposing It. 2007. 396p. 49.95 *(978-0-548-28145-1(9))* Kessinger Publishing, LLC.
Watson, Samuel. The Clock Struck One, & Christian Spiritualist: Being A Synopsis of the investigations of Spirit intercourse by an Episcopal Bishop, Three Ministers. 2006. 212p. per. 20.99 *(978-1-4255-1759-5(5))* MPublishing.

BIBLE AND THEOSOPHY

Coon, Arthur M. Theosophy in Christianity. 2011. 24p. 35.95 ***(978-1-258-05395-6(0))*** Literary Licensing, LLC.
Pink, Arthur W. Writings of Arthur W Pink from Booklets & Pamphlets. 2011. 170p. pap. 16.99 ***(978-1-61203-346-4(6))*** Bottom of the Hill Publishing.

BIBLE AS LITERATURE

see also Bible—Criticism, Interpretation, etc.; Bible—Parables; Religious Literature
Ackerman. The Bible As in Literature: Anthology. 2nd ed. (Points of Departure Ser.). (Illus.). viii, 472p. 8.97 *(978-0-673-29424-1(2))* Addison-Wesley Longman, Inc.
Alexander, Joseph Addison. Notes on New Testament Literature & Ecclesiastical History. 2007. 340p. 46.95 *(978-0-548-54684-0(3))*; (ENG.). per. 31.95 *(978-0-548-47314-6(5))* Kessinger Publishing, LLC.
—Notes on New Testament Literature & Ecclesiastical History. 2006. 340p. per. 23.99 *(978-1-4255-3446-2(5))* MPublishing.
Alter, Robert. The World of Biblical Literature. 240p. 19.00 *(978-0-281-04654-6(9))* SPCK Publishing GBR. Dist: Pilgrim Pr., The/United Church Pr.
Andersson, Greger. Untamable Texts: Literary Studies & Narrative Theory in the Books of Samuel, Vol. 514. 2009. (Library of Hebrew Bible/Old Testament Studies, the Ser.). (ENG.). 304p. 130.00 *(978-0-567-52051-7(X)*, T&T Clark Int'l) Continuum International Publishing Group, Ltd. GBR. Dist: National Bk. Network.
Barr, David L. New Testament Story: An Introduction. 4th rev. ed. 2008. (ENG., Illus.). 608p. (C). per. 73.95 *(978-0-534-62748-5(X))* Wadsworth.
Beck, Bernard. Bible: The Greatest Marketing. 2010. (ENG.). 146p. pap. 23.99 *(978-0-7618-5256-8(5))* Hamilton Bks.
Briggs, Richard S. Reading the Bible Wisely: An Introduction to Taking Scripture Seriously. 2011. 166p. pap. 19.00 ***(978-1-61097-288-8(0)***, Cascade Bks.) Wipf & Stock Pubs.
Campbell, Lily B. Divine Poetry & Drama in Sixteenth-Century England. 2011. (ENG.). 278p. pap. 29.99 *(978-0-521-13701-0(2))* Cambridge Univ. Pr.
Carver, Stephen. An Introduction to the Literature of the Bible. 2010. (C). pap. 25.00 *(978-0-615-33004-4(5))* Carver, Stephen S.
Cook, Albert Stanburrough. The Bible & English Prose Style. 2009. 98p. pap. *(978-1-4588-6212-9(7))* Books LLC.
Cram101 Textbook Reviews. Outlines & Highlights for New Testament Story: An Introduction by Barr, ISBN. 2011. 320p. pap. 33.95 ***(978-1-61830-047-8(4))*** Cram101 Inc.
Dahan, Gilbert. Lire la Bible au Moyen-Age: Essais dhermeneutique Medievale. 2009. (Titre Courant Ser.). (FRE.). 448p. (C). 40.00 *(978-2-600-00538-8(2))* Droz, Librairie CHE. Dist: Brown, David Bk. Co., The.
Davidson, Jo Ann. Toward a Theology of Beauty: A Biblical Perspective. 2008. (ENG.). 224p. 68.50 *(978-0-7618-3946-0(1))*; pap. 38.99 *(978-0-7618-3947-7(X))* Univ. Pr. of America, Inc.
Firth, David G. & Grant, Jamie A., eds. Words & the Word: Explorations in Biblical Interpretation & Literary Theory, 1 vol. 2009. (ENG.). 352p. pap. 32.00 *(978-0-8308-2898-2(2)*, IVP Acad.) InterVarsity Pr.
Goodrich O.P., Kevin. Plugging into God's Story. 2007. 220p. per. 14.99 *(978-1-60266-148-6(0))* Xulon Pr., Inc.
Henn, Tom R. & Lutterworth Press Staff, creators. The Bible as Literature. 2008. (ENG.). 270p. pap. 42.50 *(978-0-7188-3091-5(1))* Lutterworth Pr., The GBR. Dist: Brown, David Bk. Co., The.
Hunt, Patrick. Poetry in the Song of Songs. 2007. (Studies in Biblical Literature Ser.). xi, 368p. (C). 109.95 *(978-0-8204-8192-0(0))* Lang, Peter Publishing, Inc.
Kim, Heerak Christian. Intricately Connected: Biblical Studies, Intertextuality, & Literary Genre. 2008. (ENG.). 112p. pap. 26.50 *(978-0-7618-4149-4(0))* Univ. Pr. of America, Inc.
Levi, Gerson B. Gnomic Literature in Bible & Apocrypha: With Special Reference to the Gnomic Fragments & Their Bearing on the Proverb Collections. 2007. 114p. pap. 10.00 *(978-1-55635-648-3(X)*, Wipf and Stock) Wipf & Stock Pubs.
Levine, Michelle J. Nahmanides on Genesis: The Art of Biblical Portraiture. 2009. *(978-1-930675-69-8(0))* Brown Univ.
Liss, Hanna & Oeming, Manfred. Literary Construction of Identity in the Ancient World: Proceedings of a Conference, Literary Fiction & the Construction of Identity in Ancient Literatures: Options & Limits of Modern Literary Approaches in the Exegesis of Ancient Texts, Heidelberg, July 10-13 2006. 2010. 49.50 *(978-1-57506-190-0(2))* Eisenbrauns, Inc.
Malkin, Yaakov. Judaism Without God? 2010. 120.00 *(978-1-60724-341-0(5))* Gorgias Pr., LLC.
Manser, Martin H., et al. Critical Companion to the Bible. 2009. (Critical Companion Ser.). (Illus.). 496p. (C). (gr. 9-18). 75.00 *(978-0-8160-7065-7(2))* Facts On File, Inc.
Maxwell, Kathy. Hearing Between the Lines: The Audience as Fellow-Worker in Luke-Acts & its Literary Milieu, Vol. 425. 2010. (Library of New Testament Studies, the Ser.). (ENG., Illus.). 224p. 120.00 *(978-0-567-59291-0(X)*, T&T Clark Int'l) Continuum International Publishing Group, Ltd. GBR. Dist: National Bk. Network.
Miles, Jack. Christ: A Crisis in the Life of God. abr. ed. 2009. (Playaway Adult Nonfiction Ser.). (ENG.). 39.99 *(978-1-60812-720-7(6))* Findaway World, LLC.
Moore, George Foot. The Literature of the Old Testament. 2009. 260p. 30.99 *(978-1-110-50192-2(7))* 2009. 258p. 30.99 *(978-1-110-50190-8(0))* 2009. 260p. pap. 25.75 *(978-1-110-50189-2(7))* 2009. 258p. pap. 25.75 *(978-1-110-50187-8(0))* 2008. 260p. 24.99 *(978-0-559-88508-2(3))* 2008. 260p. pap. 18.99 *(978-0-559-88507-5(5))* BiblioBazaar.
—The Literature of the Old Testament. 2009. 134p. pap. 19.56 *(978-1-150-90150-8(0))* General Bks. LLC.
—The Literature of the Old Testament. 2008. 256p. 42.95 *(978-1-4365-1811-6(3))* 2007. (ENG.). 260p. per. 27.95 *(978-0-548-71063-0(5))* Kessinger Publishing, LLC.
Niehaus, Jeffrey J. Ancient near Eastern Themes in Biblical Theology. 2008. 208p. pap. 18.99 *(978-0-8254-3360-3(6))* Kregel Pubns.
Pratt, Samuel Jackson. The Sublime & Beautiful of Scripture Being Essays on Select Passages of Sacred Composition. 2007. (ENG.). 258p. 42.95 *(978-0-548-03659-4(4))* Kessinger Publishing, LLC.
Stahlberg, Lesleigh Cushing. Sustaining Fictions: Intertextuality, Midrash, Translation, & the Literary Afterlife of the Bible. 2008. (Library of Hebrew Bible/Old Testament Studies, the Ser.). (ENG., Illus.). 256p. 140.00 *(978-0-567-02709-2(0)*, T&T Clark Int'l) Continuum International Publishing Group, Ltd. GBR. Dist: National Bk. Network.
Strickland, William P. A Manual of Biblical Literature. 2006. 420p. per. 26.99 *(978-1-4255-4523-9(8))* MPublishing.
Thatcher, Tom & Moore, Stephen D. Anatomies of Narrative Criticism: The Past, Present, & Futures of the Fourth Gospel As Literature. 2008. pap. 35.95 *(978-1-58983-370-8(8))* Society of Biblical Literature.
Thatcher, Tom & Moore, Stephen D., eds. Anatomies of Narrative Criticism: The Past, Present, & Futures of the Fourth Gospel as Literature. 2008. 314p. *(978-90-04-16912-8(1))* BRILL.
Tushima, Cephas T. A. The Fate of SaulÕs Progeny in the Reign of David. 2011. 372p. pap. 41.00 ***(978-1-60899-994-1(7)***, Pickwick Pubns.) Wipf & Stock Pubs.
Vila, Samuel. La Biblia y la Literatura Evangelica: The Bible Literature. (SPA.). 168p. *(978-84-7228-338-1(0)*, 220109) Clie, Editorial.
Watts, James W. Psalm & Story: Inset Hymns in Hebrew Narrative. 2009. (Library of Hebrew Bible/Old Testament Studies, the Ser.). (ENG.). 244p. 39.95 *(978-0-567-56410-8(X)*, T&T Clark) Continuum International Publishing Group, Ltd. GBR. Dist: National Bk. Network.

BIBLE GAMES AND PUZZLES

Adediji, Adeoti. Bible Word Search. 2011. 88p. 24.99 ***(978-1-4628-5193-5(2))***; pap. 15.99 ***(978-1-4628-5192-8(4))*** Xlibris Corp.
Amazing Bible Race: Letters & Prophecy. 2010. 128p. 10.00 *(978-1-4267-1011-7(9))* Abingdon Pr.
Banks, Cleaudia. The Ultimate Book of Various Biblical Puzzles. 2010. 184p. pap. 15.95 *(978-1-4327-4549-3(2))* Outskirts Pr., Inc.
Bannard, Diane M. Word Puzzles of the Bible from A to Z Word Scrambles. 2010. (ENG.). 96p. pap. 11.95 *(978-1-4259-3495-8(1))* AuthorHouse.
Barbour Publishing, Inc. Bible Crosswords 101, Vol. 1. 2010. (ENG.). 224p. pap. 4.99 *(978-1-60260-877-1(6)*, Barbour Bks.) Barbour Publishing, Inc.
—Bible Crosswords 101, Vol. 2. 2010. (ENG.). 224p. pap. 4.99 *(978-1-60260-878-8(4)*, Barbour Bks.) Barbour Publishing, Inc.
—Bible Word Search 101, Vol. 1. 2010. (ENG.). 224p. pap. 4.99 *(978-1-60260-879-5(2)*, Barbour Bks.) Barbour Publishing, Inc.
—Bible Word Search 101, Vol. 2. 2010. (ENG.). 224p. pap. 4.99 *(978-1-60260-880-1(6)*, Barbour Bks.) Barbour Publishing, Inc.
—Flip for Puzzles Volume 2. 2010. (ENG.). 224p. pap. 4.99 *(978-1-60260-790-3(7)*, Barbour Bks.) Barbour Publishing, Inc.
Barbour Publishing Staff. The 365 Day Bible Word Search Challenge: A Bible Word Search Puzzle for Every Day of the Year! 2007. (Bible puzzle Bks.). (ENG.). 384p. per. 9.99 *(978-1-59789-862-1(7)*, Barbour Bks.) Barbour Publishing, Inc.
Barrett, Valerie. The Word Search Puzzle Book of Ecclesiastes. Lockman Foundation, tr. 2007. 88p. (YA). *(978-0-9798573-0-0(9))* Alberlynn Co.
Bible Picture Word Game. (Illus.). 40p. pap. 8.00 *(978-1-58302-137-8(X))* One Way St., Inc.
David C. Cook Publishing Company Staff, creator. Bible Games That Teach. 2008. (Bible Fun Stuff for Preschool Ser.). (Illus.). 112p. (J). (gr. -1-k). pap. 19.99 *(978-1-4347-6863-6(5))* Cook, David C.
Dingwall, Cindy. More Bible Times with Kids: 200+ Bible-Based Activities to Use with Children. 2006. (Illus.). 154p. per. 24.00 *(978-0-687-49230-5(0))* Abingdon Pr.
Estiverne, Mario. Shame & the Exaltation of Jesus. 2011. 256p. 29.99 ***(978-1-4628-8801-6(1))***; pap. 19.99 ***(978-1-4628-8800-9(3))*** Xlibris Corp.
Fulwiler-Saltzman, Janet M. The Armor of God: Hide It in Your Heart Bible Verse Memorization Activity Book Series. 2008. 16p. (J). *(978-0-9755173-7-6(6))* Autumn Light Pubns.
—The Roman Road: Hide It in Your Heart Bible Verse Memorization Activity Book Series. 2008. 16p. (J). *(978-0-9755173-9-0(2))* Autumn Light Pubns.
—23rd Psalm: Hide It in Your Heart Bible Verse Memorization Activity Book Series. 2008. 16p. (J). *(978-0-9755173-8-3(4))* Autumn Light Pubns.
Gospel, Crosswords, Word Finds & Puzzles Vol. 1: (How Much Do You Know about the Word of God?) 2006. (YA). ring bd. 9.95 *(978-0-9787255-0-1(6))* Lively Hope Enterprises, Inc.
Group Publishing, creator. Apprenticeship Games Leader Manual. 2009. (Rome: Paul & the Underground Church Ser.). (Illus.). 38p. pap. 9.99 *(978-0-7644-3780-9(1))* Group Publishing, Inc.
—Games: 110 Out-of-This-World Games Kids Love. 2006. (Illus.). 126p. per. 17.99 *(978-0-7644-3438-9(1))* Group Publishing, Inc.
Gruen, Roger. Crossword John with Answers. 2008. 110p. pap. 14.50 *(978-0-615-18141-7(4))* Crossword Institute, The.
—Crossword John without Answers. 2008. 89p. pap. 13.50 *(978-0-615-18142-4(2))* Crossword Institute, The.
Hudson, Christopher. Bible Jumble. 2009. (ENG.). 224p. pap. 9.99 *(978-1-4143-2694-8(7))* Tyndale Hse. Pubs.
—Bible Promises Jumble Crosswords. 2009. (ENG.). 224p. pap. 9.99 *(978-1-4143-2695-5(5))* Tyndale Hse. Pubs.
Johnson, T. J. Chapter & Verse Crosswords & Other Puzzles. 2008. 100p. pap. 11.99 *(978-1-60477-320-0(0))* Xulon Pr., Inc.
Jones, Bill. Putting Together the Puzzle of the New Testament. 2009. (ENG.). 272p. pap. 16.99 *(978-1-60657-015-9(3))* Authentic Media.
King, A. Roy. The Bible Student's Quiz Book. 2010. 60p. pap. 9.95 *(978-0-557-29526-5(2))* Lulu Enterprises Inc.
Lion Staff. Libro Despegable (Concertina Puzzle Book) Regalos en la Primera Navidad (The First Christmas Present) (SPA.). 4.99 *(978-1-56063-202-3(X)*, 494002) Editorial Unilit.
Metcalfe, Nick. The Pool Bible. 2010. (ENG.). 192p. spiral bd. 14.99 *(978-0-7858-2602-6(5)*, 0785826025, Chartwell) Book Sales, Inc.
Mitchell, Alison. Comings & Goings: Bible Discovery for Children. 2010. (XTB Ser.). 96p. (J). pap. *(978-1-873166-25-3(7))* Good Bk. Co.
—Summer Signposts: Bible Discovery for Children & Families. 2010. 41p. (J). pap. *(978-1-873166-90-1(7))* Good Bk. Co.
—Way to Go: Bible Discovery for Children. 2010. (XTB Ser.). 80p. (J). pap. *(978-1-904889-10-6(7))* Good Bk. Co.
—Write & Wrong: Bible Discovery for Children. 2010. (XTB Ser.). 76p. (J). pap. *(978-1-904889-14-4(X))* Good Bk. Co.
Monfort, Peter L. T. The Best Ever Biblical Word Puzzles Easily Solved. 2007. 128p. per. 15.99 *(978-1-60266-795-2(0))* Xulon Pr., Inc.
Noble, Shiren T. Journey Through the Scriptures: Bible Games & Quizzes for Youth & Adults. Date not set. 30p. (Orig.). pap. 5.95 *(978-1-877971-07-5(3))* Middle Atlantic Regional Pr. of the Middle Atlantic Regional Gospel Ministries.
Parker, Timothy E. Challenging Puzzles from the Bible: Including Crosswords, Word Search, Cryptograms, & More. 2011. (ENG., Illus.). 160p. pap. 9.99 *(978-1-4391-9229-0(4)*, Howard Bks.) Howard Books.
—Extreme Puzzles from the Bible: Including Crosswords, Word Search, Cryptograms, & More. 2011. (ENG., Illus.). 160p. pap. 9.99 *(978-1-4391-9230-6(8)*, Howard Bks.) Howard Books.
—King James Games: Study Puzzles Crafted for the Learning & Memorization of God's Word. 2007. (ENG., Illus.). 360p. pap. 19.95 *(978-0-7407-6501-8(9))* Andrews McMeel Publishing.
Parolini, Steve, ed. On the Spot: No Prep Games for Youth Ministry. 2007. 24p. pap. 5.99 *(978-0-7644-3676-5(7))* Group Publishing, Inc.
Parrish, Marvin. Word Challenge. 2009. 132p. pap. 12.49 *(978-1-4490-2659-2(1))* AuthorHouse.
Paulun, Carl. Bible Firsts. 2006. pap. 10.99 *(978-1-60034-431-2(3))* Xulon Pr., Inc.

B

Pickett, Ted. Puzzling Encounters with Jesus. 2007. (ENG.). 60p. per. 16.95 (978-1-4241-6187-4(8)) PublishAmerica, Inc.

Publishing, Barbour. Men of the Bible. 2008. (Bible Puzzle Books Ser.). (ENG.). 192p. pap. 4.99 (978-1-60260-026-3(0), Barbour Bks.) Barbour Publishing, Inc.

—The World's Greatest Collection of Fun Bible Trivia. 2008. (Value Books Ser.). (ENG.). 96p. pap. 0.99 (978-1-60260-020-1(1), Barbour Bks.) Barbour Publishing, Inc.

Puzzle Society Staff. Pocket Posh King James Puzzles: People of the Bible. 2011. (ENG.). 128p. pap. 7.99 (978-1-4494-0318-8(2)) Andrews McMeel Publishing.

—Pocket Posh King James Puzzles: The Life of Jesus. 2011. (ENG.). 128p. pap. 7.99 (978-1-4494-0321-8(2)) Andrews McMeel Publishing.

—Pocket Posh King James Puzzles: The New Testament. 2011. (ENG.). 128p. pap. 7.99 (978-1-4494-0319-5(0)) Andrews McMeel Publishing.

—Pocket Posh King James Puzzles: The Old Testament. 2011. (ENG.). 128p. pap. 7.99 (978-1-4494-0320-1(4)) Andrews McMeel Publishing.

Ross, Mary H. Short & Sweet with a Treat: 52 Already Done, Ready-For Fun Family Home Evenings. 2008. (Illus.). 104p. pap. (978-1-59811-505-5(7)) Covenant Communications.

Sawyers, Jamie L. Work Quietly & Eat Your Own Bread: 42 Bible Verse & Inspirational Word Puzzles to Keep You from Being Idle. 2011. 64p. pap. 13.95 (978-1-4620-4026-1(8)) iUniverse, Inc.

Standke, Linda, et al. Bible Story Puzzle 'n' Learn! 2008. (ENG.). 176p. pap. 12.99 (978-1-60418-111-1(7)); (gr. 1-2). pap. 12.99 (978-1-60418-273-6(3)); (gr. 3-4). pap. 12.99 (978-1-60418-274-3(1)) Carson-Dellosa Publishing, LLC.

Timmerman, Charles. Everything Bible Crosswords Book: 150 Inspiring Puzzles to Test Your Knowledge of the Good Book. 2007. (ENG.). 192p. per. 9.95 (978-1-59869-338-6(7)) Adams Media Corp.

—The Everything Bible Word Search Book: 150 fun & inspirational Puzzles. 2009. (ENG.). 192p. pap. 9.95 (978-1-59869-798-8(6)) Adams Media Corp.

Timmerman, Charles. The Everything Large-Print Bible Word Search Book: 150 inspirational puzzles - now in large Print! 2011. (ENG.). 352p. pap. 15.95 (978-1-4405-3071-5(8)) Adams Media Corp.

Tjjohnson. Chapter & Verse, Crosswords & Other Puzzles: Verse Variety. 2011. 188p. pap. 19.95 (978-1-4670-4208-6(0)) AuthorHouse.

BIBLE IN LITERATURE

see Bible—In Literature

BIBLE IN THE SCHOOLS

see Religion in the Public Schools

BIBLE PLAYS

Here are entered works on the dramatization of Biblical events, collections of such dramatizations, and such individual plays as are not entered under the name of a principal character or other specific heading.

see also Liturgical Drama

also subdivision Drama under names of Biblical characters

Beadle, Richard, ed. The York Plays: Volume 1 the Text, 2 vols. 2009. (Early English Text Society Supplementary Ser.). (ENG., Illus.). 516p. 110.00 (978-0-19-957847-4(8)) Oxford Univ. Pr., Inc.

Beadle, Richard & Fletcher, Alan J., eds. The Cambridge Companion to Medieval English Theatre. 2nd rev. ed. 2008. (Cambridge Companions to Literature Ser.). (ENG., Illus.). 422p. 90.00 (978-0-521-86400-8(3)); 424p. pap. 30.00 (978-0-521-68254-1(1)) Cambridge Univ. Pr.

Everyman & Other Interludes - Mystery Plays & Miracle Plays. 2007. 220p. per. (978-1-4067-8905-8(4), Pierides Pr.) Read Bks.

Granger, Penny. The N-Town Play: Drama & Liturgy in Medieval East Anglia. 2009. (Westfield Medieval Studies: Volume 2). (Illus.). 264p. 90.00 (978-1-84384-189-0(4), D. S. Brewer) Boydell & Brewer, Ltd. GBR. Dist: Boydell & Brewer, Inc.

Leneman, Helen. The Performed Bible: The Story of Ruth in Opera & Oratorio. 2007. (Illus.). 276p. (978-1-905048-56-4(4)) Sheffield Phoenix Pr.

Lyle, Marie Caroline. The Original Identity of the York & Towneley Cycles. 2008. 122p. 24.99 (978-0-554-97349-4(9)); pap. 19.75 (978-0-554-97350-0(2)) BiblioBazaar.

Sugano, Douglas & Scherb, Victor I. The N-Town Plays. 2006. (ENM & ENG., Illus.). pap. 25.00 (978-1-58044-116-2(5)) Medieval Institute Pubns.

Young, Philip. Life & Times of 'Brother JuniperApos. 2009. (Illus.). 228p. pap. 15.99 (978-1-4343-5915-5(8)) AuthorHouse.

BIBLE PROTESTANT-CHURCH

Charles, R. H. The Book of Jubilees, or Little Genesis. 2010. 226p. pap. 8.95 (978-1-57898-895-2(0)) Martino Publishing.

BIBLE PUZZLES

see Bible Games and Puzzles

BIBLE STORIES

Abingdon. PowerXpress High Voltage Bible Experience Stations: Occupations in Bible Times. 99.00 (978-0-687-09503-2(4)) Abingdon Pr.

Achong, Pastor David A. Tell Us a Wonderful Story. 2008. 172p. pap. 15.00 (978-1-4343-7372-4(X)) AuthorHouse.

Aldredge-Clanton, Jann. God, A Word for Girls & Boys. 2007. 160p. pap. 18.00 (978-1-55635-280-5(8), Wipf and Stock) Wipf & Stock Pubs.

Almudevar, Antonio. Oro, Incienso & Mirra (Gold, Frankincense & Myrrh) (SPA.). 381p. (978-84-7228-790-7(4), 223013) Clie, Editorial.

Anthony, Michelle. The Big God Story. 2010. (Illus.). (J). E-Book (978-1-4347-0240-1(5)) Kingsway Pubns.

Armistead, Kathy. How God Takes Our Little & Makes It Much Leaders Guide. 2010. 70p. pap. 11.00 (978-1-4267-0879-4(3)) Abingdon Pr.

At the Feet of the Nazarene. Date not set. (978-0-9650204-2-8(8)) Neurotechtonics, Inc.

Baek, Andy. Water in the Gospel of John: Finding christ through Water. 2011. 96p. 24.99 (978-1-4500-8634-9(9)); pap. 15.99 (978-1-4500-8633-2(0)) Xlibris Corp.

Bauer, Judith, ed. The Illustrated 365 Day Catholic Childrens Bible. 2011. (ENG., Illus.). 445p. (J). (gr. -1-3). 24.96 (978-0-88271-274-1(8)) Regina Pr., Malhame & Co.

Beal, Timothy. Biblical Literacy: The Essential Bible Stories Everyone Needs to Know. 2010. (ENG.). 368p. pap. 15.99 (978-0-06-171867-0(X), HarperOne) HarperCollins Pubs.

Beck, John A., et al. A Visual Guide to Bible Events: Fascinating Insights into Where They Happened & Why. 2009. 272p. 39.99 (978-0-8010-1285-3(6)) Baker Bks.

Beers, V. Gilbert. Un Viaje a Través de la Biblia. 2010. Orig. Title: Journey Through the Bible. (SPA.). 416p. 24.99 (978-1-4143-2400-5(6), Tyndale Espanol) Tyndale Hse. Pubs.

Benson, Dan. El Hombre Total: The Total Man. (SPA.). 336p. (978-84-7228-435-7(2), 220468) Clie, Editorial.

Bible Stories. 2009. 60p. pap. (978-0-217-31622-4(0)) Books LLC.

Bible Stories. (Israel Wall Maps Ser.). (HEB.). 18.95 (978-0-7834-3343-1(3)) Map Link.

Bible Story Time Younger Pupil. 1.19 (978-0-7673-4074-8(4)) LifeWay Christian Resources.

Biers-Ariel, Matt. The Triumph of Eve & Other Subversive Bible Tales. 2007. 173p. per. 14.99 (978-1-59473-176-1(4)) SkyLight Paths Publishing.

Bing, Elder George. Alms Sunday School Lessons. 2008. 220p. pap. 17.00 (978-1-4389-3817-2(9)) AuthorHouse.

Blackwelder, Elizabeth. Camore: Jesus' Little Donkey. 2011. 92p. pap. 31.50 (978-1-4520-4892-5(4)) AuthorHouse.

Boa, Kenneth & Turner, John Alan. The 52 Greatest Stories of the Bible. 2008. (978-0-8307-4730-6(3)) Gospel Light Pubns.

—The 52 Greatest Stories of the Bible: A Devotional Study. 2008. (ENG.). 400p. 24.99 (978-0-8307-4582-1(3)) Gospel Light Pubns.

Boyle, Renita & Florian, Melanie. The Storytime Bible. 2011. (J). (978-0-8198-4884-0(0)) Pauline Bks. & Media.

Bremmer, Jan N. Greek Religion & Culture, the Bible & the Ancient near East. 2008. (Jerusalem Studies in Religion & Culture Ser.). 360p. (978-90-04-16473-4(1)) BRILL.

Brown, A. Leroy. Compass Points for Daily Living. 2011. 432p. 42.95 (978-1-4497-1437-6(4)); pap. 27.95 (978-1-4497-1436-9(6)) Author Solutions, Inc. (WestBow Pr.).

Bruce, Susan. God Opens Doors. pap. 9.00 (978-0-687-74021-5(5)) Abingdon Pr.

Burton, Sharon. Let the Children Come to Me: Bible Stories for Children. 2011. pap. 8.99 (978-1-61739-243-6(X)) Tate Publishing & Enterprises, LLC.

Byers, James. The Skunk's Gift. 2010. 28p. pap. 10.95 (978-1-61633-035-4(X)) Guardian Angel Publishing, Inc.

Caldwell, Randall. From Doubt to Destiny: A journey through the Process. 2009. 118p. pap. 11.95 (978-1-4327-3532-6(2)) Outskirts Pr., Inc.

Canclini, Arnoldo. Hijo Prodigo, Su Padre y Su Hermano: Prodigal Son, His Father & Brother. (SPA.). 128p. (978-84-7228-441-8(7), 220456) Clie, Editorial.

Carabetta, Natalie, illus. My First Catholic Bible-NRSV. 2007. 415p. (J). (gr. -1-3). 15.99 (978-0-8146-3211-6(4)) Nelson, Thomas Inc.

The Child's Scripture History. 2007. (ENG.). 144p. 35.95 (978-0-548-05159-7(3)) Kessinger Publishing, LLC.

Coldicutt, Sonia. Well of Living Water: The Story of a Man who was God. 2010. 220p. pap. 14.49 (978-1-4490-8692-3(6)) AuthorHouse.

Correa, Gil M. El Hijo Del Hombre: Son of Man. (SPA.). (978-84-7645-353-7(1), 223467) Clie, Editorial.

Craig, Kenneth W. The Big Picture of the Bible. 2008. (Illus.). 48p. pap. 4.99 (978-0-9798893-2-5(4)) DeWard Publishing Co., Ltd.

Curtis, Gladys Henry. The Miracle of the Mustard Seed. 2011. 28p. pap. 12.03 (978-1-4567-9661-7(5)) AuthorHouse.

Dalton, Nannette. The Road, the Road. 2006. 128p. pap. 14.99 (978-1-4141-0729-5(3)) Pleasant Word.

Daniels, J. B. The Wonder of God's Love. 2011. 106p. 24.99 (978-1-4568-7710-1(0)) Xlibris Corp.

Davenport, Richard A. Four Parables of Jesus. 2007. (Insight Ser.). 48p. pap. 5.99 (978-0-7586-1462-9(4)) Concordia Publishing Hse.

Dawes, Hillary. Surviving a Global Economic Crisis. 2008. 84p. pap. 10.99 (978-1-60647-730-4(7)) Xulon Pr., Inc.

Dempsey, Carol J. Reading the Bible, Transforming Conflict: Theology in Dialogue Series. 2011. 224p. pap. 26.00 (978-1-57075-914-7(6)) Orbis Bks.

Dennis, Trevor. The Book of Books. 2012. (ENG., Illus.). 480p. (J). (gr. 4-7). pap. 14.99 (978-0-7459-6912-1(7)) Lion Hudson PLC GBR. Dist: Independent Pubs. Group.

Digital Praise Inc. AMazing Bible: The Maze Game of Biblical Proportions, 0 vols. 2009. cd-rom 9.99 (978-1-4003-1571-0(9)) Nelson, Thomas Inc.

Elkins, Stephen. LullaBible, 0 vols. 2010. (Illus.). 208p. (J). 16.99 (978-1-4003-1561-1(1)) Nelson, Thomas Inc.

Engelbrecht, Edward & Pawlitz, Gail, eds. The Story Bible. 2011. 464p. (J). 29.99 (978-0-7586-1902-0(2)) Concordia Publishing Hse.

Ennis, Solomon. In His Image: Illustrations & Meditations from an African-Centered Christian Perspective. 2011. (ENG., Illus.). 110p. 39.95 (978-0-88378-299-6(5)) Third World Press.

Esler, Philip F. Sex, Wives, & Warriors: Reading Biblical Narrative with its Ancient Audience. 2012. (ENG.). 420p. (C). pap. 60.00 (978-0-227-67991-3(1)) Clarke, James Co., Ltd. GBR. Dist: Brown, David Bk. Co., The.

Fabrizius, Karl F. Bible Stories for Daily Prayer: Catechism Stories, 10 vols., Vol. 7. Bender, Peter C., ed. 2006. 230p. (J). ring bd. 20.00 (978-0-9725687-7-7(8)) Concordia Catechetical Academy.

Flegal, Daphna & Stickler, LeeDell. Delicious Bible Stories: No Cook Recipes That Teach. 2009. 64p. spiral bd. 11.00 (978-1-4267-0032-3(6)) Abingdon Pr.

Flores, José. El Hijo Eterno: The Eternal Son. (SPA.). 256p. (978-84-7228-745-7(9), 222338) Clie, Editorial.

Foltz, Thea. Tombstone Treats for God's Kids. 2007. 72p. per. 11.99 (978-1-60266-515-6(X)) Xulon Pr., Inc.

Freus, Zbigniew. Illustrated Family Bible. 2007. (Illus.). 424p. 24.99 (978-0-9792342-2-4(0)) Vocatio Pubs.

Ganeri, Anita. Noah & the Ark & Other Stories: Christianity. 2007. (Qeb Stories from Faiths Ser.). (Illus.). 36p. (J). (gr. -1-3). 19.95 (978-1-59566-380-1(0)) QEB Publishing Inc.

Glenys Irene Jones. The Story of Jesus & Stories from the Old Testament Told in Verse. 2009. (Illus.). 76p. pap. 27.49 (978-1-4389-9598-4(9)) AuthorHouse.

Goodings, Christina & Smith, Jamie. Esta Es Mi Biblia. 2010. (SPA., Illus.). 19p. (J). bds. 13.90 (978-1-55883-001-1(4)) C R C World Literature Ministries/Libros Desafio.

Gospel Light Publications Staff. Rock-Solid Followers: Helping Kids Discover Jesus' Love for Them & the World. 2008. (ENG.). 256p. (J). (gr. -1-7). 49.99 (978-0-8307-5114-3(9)) Gospel Light Pubns.

Gossai, Hemchand. Barrenness & Blessing: Abraham, Sarah, & the Journey of Faith. 2007. 136p. pap. 17.00 (978-1-55635-292-8(1)) Wipf & Stock Pubs.

Gray, James M. Synthetic Bible Studies. 2010. 246p. pap. (978-1-153-17141-0(4)) Books LLC.

—Synthetic Bible Studies. 2007. (ENG.). 344p. per. (978-1-4067-7299-9(2)) Read Bks.

Griswold, Barbara S. Suffering: God's Forge of Faith: Bible Stories for Adults of the Twenty-First Century. 2009. pap. 16.99 (978-1-60696-684-6(7)) Tate Publishing & Enterprises, LLC.

Grosshauser, Peter & Temple, Ed. Spark Story Bible. 2009. (J). (978-0-8066-7049-2(5)) Augsburg Fortress, Pubs.

Grossman, David. Lion's Honey: The Myth of Samson. Schoffman, Stuart, tr. from HEB. 2007. pap. (978-1-84195-923-8(5)) Canongate Bks.

Group Publishing, compiled by. Large-As-Life Bible Adventures: 13 Amazing You-Are-There Bible Experiences. 2007. (Illus.). 79p. pap. 24.99 incl. audio compact disk (978-0-7644-3549-2(3)) Group Publishing, Inc.

Hansen, David. In their Sandals. 2007. pap. 9.99 (978-1-60266-032-8(8)) Xulon Pr., Inc.

Hanson, Christopher Mark. The Forgotten Story of Mankind. 2009. 308p. pap. 21.50 (978-1-4092-8898-5(6)) Lulu Enterprises Inc.

Harper, Lisa. A Perfect Mess: Why You Don't Have to Worry about Being Good Enough for God. 2009. (ENG.). 224p. pap. 13.99 (978-1-4000-7479-2(7), WaterBrook Pr.) Doubleday Religious Publishing Group, The.

Harr, Victoria. A Grandmother's Life, As Told to Her Grandchild. 2008. 108p. pap. 12.00 (978-1-931178-52-5(6)) Vision Publishing.

Hartman, Bob. Anyone Can Tell a Bible Story: Bob Hartman's Guide to Storytelling - With over 50 Stories, 1 vol. 2011. (Illus.). 192p. pap. 16.99 (978-0-85721-007-4(6), Monarch Bks.) Lion Hudson PLC GBR. Dist: Kregel Pubns.

Hartman, Bob & Hartman, Bob. Telling the Bible: Over 100 Stories to Read Out Loud. 2007. 336p. pap. 19.99 (978-0-8254-6137-8(5), Monarch Bks.) Lion Hudson PLC GBR. Dist: Kregel Pubns.

Heitzig, Skip. The Daily God Book: Through the Bible - A Bird's-Eye View of the Bible in a Year. 2010. (ENG.). 384p. 14.99 (978-1-4143-1300-9(4)) Tyndale Hse. Pubs.

Henderson, Elsa. Wise Men Seek Him. 2011. 66p. pap. 10.99 (978-1-61379-293-3(X)) Xulon Pr., Inc.

Hernan, Miguel. Resplandor Azul: Tales for Children. (SPA.). 144p. (978-84-7228-972-7(9), 223029) Clie, Editorial.

Los Hijos de la Pequena Margarita: Children of Little Margaret. (SPA.). 80p. (978-84-7228-325-1(9), 220457) Clie, Editorial.

La Historia de un Lobo - A Wolf's Story. (SPA.). 214p. (978-1-56063-790-5(0)) Editorial Unilit.

Holder, Jennifer. Show & Tell Bible Stories. 2010. (ENG.). 208p. (J). 12.99 (978-0-7847-2129-2(7)) Standard Publishing.

Holmes, Andy. My Pajama Bible. 2008. (ENG., Illus.). 64p. (J). (gr. 3-7). bds. 12.99 (978-1-4143-1263-7(6)) Tyndale Hse. Pubs.

El Hombre Vestido de Negro: Man in Black. (SPA.). 344p. (978-84-7228-292-6(9), 220469) Clie, Editorial.

Honeycutt, Frank G. Marry a Pregnant Virgin: Unusual Bible Stories for New & Curious Christians. 2008. 256p. pap. 16.99 (978-0-8066-8036-1(9), Augsburg Bks.) Augsburg Fortress, Pubs.

Hopwood, Dave. The Road Trip: The Bloke's Bible. 2007. (ENG.). 224p. 14.99 (978-1-85078-753-2(0)) Authentic Media.

Hovde, Howard & Moore, Louis. Families of the Bible: How they Coped with Today's Problems. 2009. 126p. pap. 12.95 (978-1-934749-53-1(2)) Hannibal Bks.

Hronas, Georgia. Tell Us about the Angels, Grandma. 2006. (ENG., Illus.). 82p. pap. 13.95 (978-1-933654-04-1(X)) Light & Life Publishing Co.

Huegel, F. J. Hueso de Sus Huesos: Bone of His Bone. (SPA.). 120p. (978-84-7228-440-1(9), 220472) Clie, Editorial.

Hughes, Don. The Kingdom of Heaven Is Like... Finding Hope in the Stories of Jesus. 2008. pap. 14.99 (978-0-7684-2699-1(5)) Destiny Image Pubs.

Hughes, Ron. Refresh: 19 Ways to Boost Your Spiritual Life. 2011. 160p. pap. (978-1-926765-49-5(4)) Gospel Folio Pr.

Hurlbut, Jesse Lyman. Beautiful Bible Stories for Children. (ENG.). 240p. 2007. 41.95 (978-0-548-13353-8(0)) 2006. per. 26.95 (978-1-4286-4449-6(0)) Kessinger Publishing, LLC.

Hyatt, Lucinda & Hansen, Krissi. Little Lessons Learned: Stories for Children from the Bible. 2011. 44p. pap. 20.95 (978-1-61507-581-2(X)) Cross Bks. Publishing.

Inspirio, creator. The Gift of Prayer: Inspiring Stories of God's Work, 1 vol. 2007. (ENG., Illus.). 160p. 12.99 (978-0-310-81202-9(X)) Inspirio.

Jacobson, Ami & Mims, Robert. A Second Wind. 2008. 120p. pap. 11.99 (978-1-60647-841-7(9)) Xulon Pr., Inc.

Johnson, Wallace F. Following the Good Shepherds. 2010. 299p. pap. (978-1-61663-631-9(9)) Tate Publishing & Enterprises, LLC.

Jones, Arthur. The Bible's Cover-Stories Revealed: The Golden Keys That Unlock History. 2007. (ENG., Illus.). 36p. 24.95 (978-0-615-16074-0(3)) In God We Trust.

Jones, Colin D. Samson: Man of Strength, Man of Weakness. 2007. (People in the Bible Ser.). 94p. pap. 13.00 (978-1-84625-089-7(7)) DayOne Pubns. GBR. Dist: STL Distribution North America.

Keck, Lorena M. His Story: The Old Testament Told as a Chronological Story. 2010. 340p. pap. 24.95 (978-1-4497-0321-9(6), WestBow Pr.) Author Solutions, Inc.

Kidd, Virginia Bates. Stones of Grace. 2010. 72p. pap. 11.99 (978-1-61507-113-5(X)) Cross Bks. Publishing.

Koehler, Paul F. Telling God's Stories with Power: Biblical Storytelling in Oral Cultures. 2010. (978-0-87808-465-4(7)) Carey, William Library Pubs.

Korfker, Dena. Favorite Picture Stories from the Bible. 2011. 152p. 41.95 (978-1-258-02347-8(4)) Literary Licensing, LLC.

Kustra, Monika. Bible Stories for Preschoolers. 2011. (ENG.). 432p. (J). 16.99 (978-1-4143-3964-1(X), Tyndale Kids) Tyndale Hse. Pubs.

Kyle, Margaret. Bible Stories for All Ages - Year A: With Activities for the Very Young. 2007. (ENG., Illus.). 256p. per. 34.00 (978-1-55145-546-4(3)) Wood Lake Publishing, Inc. CAN. Dist: Westminster John Knox Pr.

Lacueva, Francisco. El Hombre: Su Grandeza y Su Miseria: Man: His Greatness & Misery, 1 vol. 2008. (SPA.). 224p. pap. 10.99 (978-84-7228-257-5(0), 220239) Clie, Editorial ESP. Dist: Zondervan.

Larsen, Carolyn. Classic Edition Bible Storybook. 2010. (J). (978-0-7847-2919-9(0)) Standard Publishing.

Latourette, Jane & Vischer, Phil. El Arca de Noe, 0 vols. Villalobos, Fernando, tr. 2007. (SPA., Illus.). 48p. 12.99 (978-0-89922-036-9(3)) Grupo Nelson.

Lawrence, Joy-Elizabeth, et al. Scary, Gross & Weird Stories from the Bible: Bloody Tent Pegs, Disembodied Fingers, & Suicidal Pigs... the Truths Buried in the Bizarre. Holbum, Kate S., ed. 2007. (Illus.). 133p. (J). (gr. 3-7). per. 19.99 (978-0-7644-3698-7(8)) Group Publishing, Inc.

Lee, Constance. Rahab of Jericho. 2010. 132p. pap. 12.49 (978-1-4490-4857-0(9)) AuthorHouse.

Lefeuvre, Amy. Hijos Prodigos: Prodigal Children. (SPA.). 104p. (978-84-7228-295-7(3), 220460) Clie, Editorial.

Lindeck, John. Mysterious Ways. 2009. 412p. pap. 17.99 (978-1-4389-5108-9(6)) AuthorHouse.

Lingo, Susan L. Kids-Tell-'Em Bible Stories. 2008. 116p. pap. 14.99 (978-1-935147-05-3(6)) Lingo, Susan Bks.

Linner, Kris. Women & the Word: Ten Narratives on God's Word. 2007. 85p. per. (978-0-7880-2446-7(9)) CSS Publishing Co.

Lopez, Omar R. G O D's Biblical Evolutions: An Interpretive Fantasy about Life's Beginnings. 2008. 212p. per. 14.95 (978-1-4327-1956-2(4)) Outskirts Pr., Inc.

Loth, Paul J. Bible Stories for Curious Kids: 800+ Questions to Explore! 2010. (ENG.). 320p. (J). 14.99 (978-0-7847-2127-8(0)) Standard Publishing.

Lucado, Max. Cast of Characters: Common People in the Hands of an Uncommon God. l.t. ed. 2009. (ENG.). 393p. pap. 17.99 (978-1-59415-294-8(2)) Cengage Gale.

—Cast of Characters: Common People in the Hands of an Uncommon God, 0 vols. 2010. 240p. pap. 15.99 (978-0-8499-2155-1(4)) Nelson, Thomas Inc.

Marty, William H. The Whole Bible Story: Everything That Happens in the Bible in Plain English. 2011. pap. (978-0-7642-9529-4(2)); pap. 12.99 (978-0-7642-0829-4(2)) Bethany Hse. Pubs.

Mason, Merrel. The Story of God's Love. 2006. (ENG.). 24.99 (978-1-59781-490-4(3)); pap. 14.99 (978-1-59781-489-8(X)) Xulon Pr., Inc.

McBride, O., Alfred. Fr. Mcbride's Guide to the Bible. 2008. 303p. pap. 14.95 (978-1-59276-480-8(0)) Our Sunday Visitor, Publishing Div.

McKarns, James E. Seldom-Told Bible Tales: Fifteen Eye-Opening Stories from the Bible. 2008. (978-0-7880-2612-6(7)) CSS Publishing Co.

McLeish, Kenneth. Stories & Legends Bible. Date not set. (Illus.). 324p. pap. 34.60 (978-0-582-03406-8(X)) Addison-Wesley Longman, Ltd. GBR. Dist: Trans-Atlantic Pubns., Inc.

Meeting the Master: Encounters with Christ Through a Series of Monologues. 2007. spiral bd. (978-0-9779521-1-3(8)) City on a Hill, Inc.

Milton, Ralph & Kyle, Margaret. Lectionary Story Bible - Year A. 2007. (ENG., Illus.). 240p. (J). 30.00 (978-1-55145-547-1(1)) Wood Lake Publishing, Inc. CAN. Dist: Westminster John Knox Pr.

Monroy, Juan A. Hombres de Fuego: Men of Fire. (SPA.). 160p. *(978-84-7228-473-9(5)*, 220467) Clie, Editorial.
Morgan, Robert. 100 Bible Verses Everyone Should Know by Heart. 2011. pap. 0.00 ***(978-1-59328-326-1(1))*** Graham, Billy Evangelistic Assn.
Morgan, Robert J. 100 Bible Verses Everyone Should Know by Heart. 2010. (ENG.). 288p. pap. 14.99 *(978-0-8054-4682-1(6)*, B&H Bks.) B&H Publishing Group.
—100 Bible Verses Everyone Should Know by Heart. Lt. ed. 2010. (ENG.). 352p. pap. 17.99 *(978-1-59415-341-9(8))* Cengage Gale.
Myers, Gary. A Brush with Angels: Compelling Tales of Biblical Proportion. 2011. pap. 14.99 *(978-0-89112-290-6(7)*, Leafwood Pubs.) Abilene Christian Univ. Pr.
Newton, Richard. Bible Models: The Shining Lights of Scripture. 2008. 484p. pap. 32.00 *(978-1-59925-154-7(X))* Solid Ground Christian Bks.
Osborne, Mary Pope & Boyce, Natalie Pope. Bible Stories. 2009. (Random House Book Of... Ser.). (ENG., Illus.). 176p. (J). (gr. 3-5). 24.99 *(978-0-375-82281-0(X))* Random Hse., Inc.
Owens, Virginia Stem. Daughters of Eve: Seeing Ourselves in Women of the Bible. 2007. (Navigators Reference Library). (ENG.). 256p. per. 13.99 *(978-1-60006-200-1(8))* NavPress Publishing Group.
Palmer, Bernard. Hijo Mio, Hijo Mio: My Son, My Son. (SPA.). 256p. *(978-84-7228-272-8(4)*, 220454) Clie, Editorial.
Peters, Angie. The Life of David, 0 vols. Richards, Larry, ed. 2008. (Smart Guide to the Bible Ser.). 384p. pap. 14.99 *(978-1-4185-1011-4(4))* Nelson, Thomas Inc.
Peterson, Gregory. How Do You Know When You Have Heard from God. 2010. 182p. pap. 14.99 *(978-1-60957-585-4(7))* Xulon Pr., Inc.
Phelps, William Lyon. Reading the Bible. 2007. (ENG.). 140p. 35.95 *(978-0-548-06583-9(7))* Kessinger Publishing, LLC.
Philipps, James. Make Room for Scripture: An Invitation to Catechists & Teachers. 2010. 168p. pap. 14.95 *(978-1-58595-775-0(5))* Twenty-Third Pubns./Bayard.
Ray, Thomas. And He Had No Sons. 2010. 112p. 21.99 *(978-1-4269-2673-0(1))*; pap. 11.99 *(978-1-4269-2672-3(3))* Trafford Publishing.
Rev. Marcia C. Fleischman. Wild Woman Theology: In the Arms of Loving Mother God. 2009. 136p. pap. 39.99 *(978-1-4389-2822-7(X))* AuthorHouse.
Rhodes, Paul. In Their Own Words. 2011. 86p. 24.99 ***(978-1-4568-6147-6(6))***; pap. 15.99 ***(978-1-4568-6146-9(8))*** Xlibris Corp.
Rikkers, Doris & Wynbeek Rikkers, Doris. Read with Me Bible for Toddlers, 1 vol. 2009. (ENG.). 288p. (J). 12.99 *(978-0-310-71877-2(5))* Zonderkidz.
Robb, Andy. 50 craziest bible Stories. 2008. 112p. (J). pap. *(978-1-85345-490-5(7))* Crusade for World Revival.
—50 weirdest bible Stories. 2008. 112p. (J). pap. *(978-1-85345-489-9(3))* Crusade for World Revival.
Roche, Paul. The Bible's Greatest Stories. 2012. (ENG.). 560p. (gr. 12). 7.95 *(978-0-451-53192-6(2)*, Signet Classics) Penguin Group (USA) Inc.
Rose Publishing, creator. 52 Key Bible Stories: Summary, Main Points, & Related Scriptures. 2009. (Illus.). pap. 39.90 *(978-1-59636-336-5(3))* Rose Publishing.
Rubenis, Juris & Subacs, Maris. Finding God in a Tangled World: Thoughts & Parables. 2007. (Illus.). 184p. 19.00 *(978-1-55725-495-5(8))* Paraclete Pr., Inc.
Rudman, Burton. God As Man Created Him. 2008. 80p. pap. 16.95 *(978-1-60474-846-8(X))* PublishAmerica, Inc.
Sala, Harold J. Y Seran una Sola Carne.Tr. of They Shall Be One Flesh. (SPA.). 176p. *(978-84-7228-729-7(7)*, 220974) Clie, Editorial.
Sangster, Margaret E. Stories from the Early Bible. 2007. (ENG.). 236p. 41.95 *(978-0-548-06733-8(3))* Kessinger Publishing, LLC.
Schillman, Gabe. War of God: Part One. 2008. 114p. pap. 19.95 *(978-1-60563-306-0(2))* PublishAmerica, Inc.
Schlink, M. Basilea. Huyendo Del Engano de Nuestro Tiempo: Escaping the Web of Deception. (SPA.). 72p. *(978-84-7228-241-4(4)*, 220475) Clie, Editorial.
Schnittjer, Gary E. Torah Story: An Apprenticeship on the Pentateuch. 2006. (ENG., Illus.). 560p. 44.99 *(978-0-310-24861-3(2))* Zondervan.
Schultz, Joani, et al, contrib. by. The Humongous Book of Preschool Ideas. 2007. 224p. (J). (gr. 3-7). per. 29.99 *(978-0-7644-3601-7(5))* Group Publishing, Inc.
Scorer, Donna & Kyle, Margaret. Seasons Growing Faith Board Books, Set. 2007. (ENG.). 8p. 35.00 *(978-1-55145-548-8(X))* Wood Lake Publishing, Inc. CAN. Dist: Westminster John Knox Pr.
Scott, Mark. The Rest of the Greatest Story. 2010. 154p. pap. 14.99 *(978-1-60957-106-1(1))* Xulon Pr., Inc.
Shaw, Edgar. The Untold Story: Revised Edition. 2010. 120p. 29.95 *(978-1-4520-0300-9(9))*; pap. 19.99 *(978-1-4520-0301-6(7))* AuthorHouse.
Siku. The Manga Bible: From Genesis to Revelation. 2008. (ENG., Illus.). 224p. pap. 13.99 *(978-0-385-52431-5(5)*, Galilee Trade) Doubleday Religious Publishing Group, The.
Silvani, Anita. The Strange Story of Ahrinziman. 2010. 296p. pap. 28.75 *(978-1-177-19004-6(4))* BiblioBazaar.
Simon, Mary Manz. Who Will Help? (Hear Me Read Classroom Sets Ser.). 32.00 *(978-0-570-05097-1(9))* Concordia Publishing Hse.
Sirkus, Louis C. Grandpa's Tales from the Bible. 2011. 188p. 42.95 ***(978-1-258-07939-0(9))*** Literary Licensing, LLC.
Sleeth, Matthew. The Gospel According to the Earth: Why the Good Book Is a Green Book. 2010. (ENG.). 208p. 22.99 *(978-0-06-173053-5(X)*, HarperOne) HarperCollins Pubs.
Smith, Gary A. Long, Long Ago. 0.50 *(978-0-687-50171-7(7))* Abingdon Pr.
Song, C. S. In the Beginning Were Stories, Not Texts. 2012. (ENG.). 180p. (C). pap. 30.00 ***(978-0-227-68023-0(5))*** Clarke, James Co., Ltd. GBR. Dist: Brown, David Bk. Co., The.
Standard Publishing Staff. 40 Instant Studies: Bible Truths. Eichenberger, Jim, ed. 2009. (True to Life Ser.). (ENG.). 96p. (YA). pap. 9.99 *(978-0-7847-2300-5(1))* Standard Publishing.
Stead, W. t., et al. The Blue Island. 2010. 156p. 30.99 *(978-1-140-52688-9(X))*; pap. 21.75 *(978-1-140-52689-6(8))* BiblioBazaar.
Stevens, R. Paul. Work Matters: Lessons from Scripture. 2012. pap. ***(978-0-8028-6696-7(4))*** Eerdmans, William B. Publishing Co.
Suchy, Gwen. Skits & Plays: In Poem & Praise. 2011. 160p. 30.95 ***(978-1-4497-1947-0(3))***; pap. 13.95 ***(978-1-4497-1945-6(7))*** Author Solutions, Inc. (WestBow Pr.).
Sutherland, Jo Ann. A Kingdom Story. 2011. 56p. pap. 20.00 *(978-1-4269-6163-2(4))* Trafford Publishing.
Swindell, Anthony C. Reworking the Bible: The Literary Reception-History of Fourteen Biblical Stories. 2010. 356p. *(978-1-907534-01-0(6))* Sheffield Phoenix Pr.
Swindoll, Charles R. A Bethlehem Christmas: Celebrating the Joyful Season, 0 vols. 2007. (Illus.). 192p. 14.99 *(978-1-4041-0468-6(2))* Nelson, Thomas Inc.
Taylor, Vern. Treasures in the Logos. 2010. 111p. 29.99 *(978-1-4500-7190-1(2))*; pap. 19.99 *(978-1-4500-7189-5(9))* Xlibris Corp.
Terry, J. O. Basic Bible Storying: Preparing & Presenting Bible Stories for Evangelism, Discipleship, Training, & Ministry. 2006. ring bd. *(978-0-9772433-0-3(3))* Church Starting Network.
The Master's Pen. Aaron & Erica's Garden. 2006. (ENG.). 18.99 *(978-1-60034-773-3(8))*; pap. 10.99 *(978-1-60034-318-6(X))* Xulon Pr., Inc.
Thomas Nelson Publishing Staff, creator. Christmas A to Z: Unwrapping the Wonder of Seasonal Words & Phrases, 0 vols. 2007. (Illus.). 208p. 19.99 *(978-1-4185-2796-9(3))* Nelson, Thomas Inc.
Tiegreen, Chris. Story Thru the Bible: An Interactive Way to Connect with God's Word. 2011. (NavPress Devotional Readers Ser.). 336p. pap. 24.99 *(978-1-61521-820-2(3))* NavPress Publishing Group.
Tony, Cartledge. Telling Stories: Tall Tales & Deep Truth. 2008. pap. 17.00 *(978-1-57312-515-4(6))* Smyth & Helwys Publishing, Inc.
Toulmin, Sarah. Baby's Little Bible. 2011. (ENG., Illus.). 160p. (J). (gr. k — 1). 9.99 *(978-0-7459-6272-6(6))* Lion Hudson PLC GBR. Dist: Independent Pubs. Group.
—Baby's Little Bible, Blue. 2011. (ENG., Illus.). 160p. (J). (gr. k — 1). 9.99 *(978-0-7459-6271-9(8))* Lion Hudson PLC GBR. Dist: Independent Pubs. Group.
Treanor, Oliver. The God Who Loved Stories. 143p. pap. 12.50 *(978-0-85439-571-2(7))* St. Paul Pubns. GBR. Dist: St Pauls/Alba Hse. Pubs.
Viola, Frank. God's Ultimate Passion: Unveiling the Purpose Behind Everything. 2007. 296p. per. 13.99 *(978-0-9789019-0-5(8))* Present Testimony Ministry.
Waddell, Helen. Stories from Holy Writ. 2009. 258p. 42.95 *(978-1-104-85393-8(0))* 2007. (ENG.). 256p. per. 27.95 *(978-0-548-39084-9(3))* Kessinger Publishing, LLC.
Waffle, Scott D. El Invernadero: His Tender Grapes. (SPA.). 208p. *(978-84-7228-430-2(1)*, 220497) Clie, Editorial.
Walton, John H. & Walton, Kim E. The Bible Story Handbook: A Resource for Teaching 175 Stories from the Bible. 2010. 448p. pap. 24.99 *(978-1-4335-0648-2(3))* Crossway.
Watt, Lloyd. The Blessing & the Birthright. 2007. (Illus.). 84p. per. *(978-1-84426-462-9(9))* Upfront Publishing Ltd.
Webb, G. & Walker, A., trs. from LAT. On the Nature & Dignity of Love. 63p. pap. *(978-1-901157-54-3(7))* St. Austin Pr.
Weinstock, Dawn Mirly. 120 Bible Stories. 2011. (J). ***(978-0-7586-1904-4(9))*** Concordia Publishing Hse.
Wells, Phillip P. Bible Stories & Religious Classics. Lt. ed. 2007. (ENG.). 438p. pap. 26.99 *(978-1-4264-4072-4(3))* 2006. 484p. pap. 24.99 *(978-1-4264-4131-8(2))* BiblioBazaar.
Wiley, Judi. The Manifold Cross. 2007. 244p. per. 14.99 *(978-1-60266-973-4(2))* Xulon Pr., Inc.
Wolf, Carol S. Biblical Storytelling in Youth Ministry: Twelve-Year-Olds, Chosen & Blessed: Hoglah, Deborah, Samuel, Jesus, & Jairus' Daughter. 2009. (Illus.). 62p. pap. *(978-0-7880-2217-3(2)*, Fairway Pr.) CSS Publishing Co.
Wyse, Marion. Oseas & la Espose Infiel: The Prophet & the Prostitute. (SPA.). 320p. *(978-84-7228-780-8(7)*, 220648) Clie, Editorial.
Yonge, Charlotte Mary. The Chosen People: A Compendium of Sacred & Church History for School-Children. 2009. 202p. (gr. 4-7). 32.99 *(978-1-116-77829-8(7))*; 28.99 *(978-1-116-77830-4(0))*; pap. 23.75 *(978-1-116-77832-8(7))*; pap. 24.75 *(978-1-116-77831-1(9))* BiblioBazaar.
Yonker, Nancy. Stories from the Shepherd's Heart: Stories about Sheep to Delight Both the Young & the Old Readers. 2010. 70p. pap. 10.99 *(978-1-61579-658-8(4))* Xulon Pr., Inc.
Zondervan. Niv Story: The Bible as One Continuing Story of God & His People, 1 vol. 2011. (ENG.). 512p. 19.99 *(978-0-310-95097-4(X))* Zondervan.
365 Bible Stories for Young Hearts. 2006. (Illus.). 448p. (J). (gr. -1-3). 17.99 *(978-1-58134-807-1(X))* Crossway.

BIBLE STORIES—N.T.

Ballestrero, Anastasio. Martha & Mary: Meeting Christ as Friend. pap. 11.50 *(978-0-8189-9483-8(5))* St Pauls/Alba Hse. Pubs.
Bauscher, David. The Aramaic-English Interlinear New Testament. 2008. 621p. 54.98 *(978-1-4357-3462-3(9))* Lulu Enterprises Inc.
Bishop, Mary Ann. Servants of the Most High God. 2008. (Illus.). 480p. pap. 26.99 *(978-1-60477-838-0(5))* Xulon Pr., Inc.
Corcoran, Peter. The Reminiscences of Mary: Unheard Voices from the Gospels. 2007. 100p. per. *(978-1-84401-907-6(1))* Athena Pr.
Crosse, Matthew. Panorama of Jesus & the New Testament. 2007. (Illus.). 36p. pap. 20.00 *(978-1-86118-930-1(3))* Third Millennium Pr., Ltd. GBR. Dist: STL Distribution North America.
Cushing, Richard. The Holy Gospel for Children. 2011. 188p. 42.95 ***(978-1-258-04923-2(6))*** Literary Licensing, LLC.
Day, Jackson. New Testament Bible Stories. 2007. 224p. pap. 25.00 *(978-0-9797324-1-6(7))* Day, H. Jackson.
DeMaris, Richard & Neufeld, Dietmar, eds. Understanding the Social World of the New Testament. 2009. (ENG., Illus.). 304p. (C). pap. 39.95 *(978-0-415-77582-3(5))* Routledge.
Fabrizius, Karl F. Bible Stories for Daily Prayer: New Testament Stories Year III, the Gospel of Luke, 10 vols., Vol. 6. Bender, Peter C., ed. 2007. 209p. (J). ring bd. 20.00 *(978-0-9725687-8-4(6))* Concordia Catechetical Academy.
Ferder, Fran. Enter the Story: Biblical Metaphors for Our Lives. 2010. 208p. pap. 18.00 *(978-1-57075-885-0(9))* Orbis Bks.
Fuentes, Miguel Angel. I. N. R. I. Jesus Nazareno: Rey de los Judios. 2007.Tr. of Jesus of Nazareth: King of the Jews. (SPA.). 338p. pap. 19.95 *(978-1-933871-05-9(9))* IVE Pr.
Hartman, Bob. Telling the Gospel: 70 Stories about Jesus to Read Out Loud, 1 vol. 2010. (Illus.). 240p. pap. 16.99 *(978-1-85424-961-6(4)*, Monarch Bks.) Lion Hudson PLC GBR. Dist: Kregel Pubns.
Hill, Amber. Ruth: the Reality of Redemption. 2010. 85p. pap. 12.00 *(978-0-557-48332-7(6))* Lulu Enterprises Inc.
Hungry Planet Media Staff, ed. Hungry Planet Bible Project: A Life-Changing New Testament Recording & DVD Documentary. 2011. (ENG.). 29.99 *(978-1-4143-3463-9(X))* Tyndale Hse. Pubs.
Hungry Planet Media Staff & Tyndale House Publishers Staff, prods. No Room at the Inn: Real Stories of How Faith Can Change Homelessness Includes the Christmas Story as Read by Families Touched by Homelessness. 2009. (Hungry Planet Bible Project Ser.). (ENG.). 2p. 14.99 *(978-1-4143-3572-8(5))* Tyndale Hse. Pubs.
Igbo New Testament. 2007. Orig. Title: Agba Ohuru. pap. *(978-1-882536-93-1(2))* Bible League.
Jones, Bill. Putting Together the Puzzle of the New Testament. 2009. (ENG.). 272p. pap. 16.99 *(978-1-60657-015-9(3))* Authentic Media.
Jones, Sonia. New Testament Alive! 2010. *(978-0-9810470-9-6(2))* Erser & Pond Pubs., Ltd.
Lucado, Max. He Still Moves Stones. 2011. (ENG.). 240p. pap. 15.99 ***(978-0-8499-4629-5(8))*** Nelson, Thomas Inc.
Lucas, Ross Thomas. The Greatest Stories Ever... Retold. 2010. 192p. 29.95 *(978-1-4520-6691-2(4))*; pap. 21.95 *(978-1-4520-6690-5(6))* AuthorHouse.
Lyster, William, ed. The Cave Church of Paul the Hermit: At the Monastery of St. Paul in Egypt. 2008. (ENG., Illus.). 416p. 75.00 *(978-0-300-11847-6(3))* Yale Univ. Pr.
Modi, Amarjit Singh & Temple, Elizabeth. Christ: Mother Mary's Gift of Light. 2008. 132p. pap. 13.95 *(978-1-4401-0263-9(5))* iUniverse, Inc.
Neeley, Deta Petersen & Neeley, Nathan Glen. A Child's Story of the New Testament, V1: Jesus of Nazareth. 2011. 176p. 42.95 ***(978-1-258-06370-2(0))*** Literary Licensing, LLC.
Neff, Merlin L. Warriors of the Cross. 2008. (J). *(978-0-8163-2268-8(6))* Pacific Pr. Pubns.
Picture Bible New Testament (Exclusive) 2009. (ENG.). 240p. (J). 14.99 *(978-1-4347-6486-7(9))* Cook, David C.
Pritchard, John. Living the Gospel Stories Today. 130p. 10.00 *(978-0-281-05365-0(0))* SPCK Publishing GBR. Dist: Pilgrim Pr., The/United Church Pr.
Rizzi, Giovanni. Paul of Tarsus: A Historical-Critical Reexamination & the Post-Biblical Tradition. 2009. pap. 17.95 *(978-1-61623-752-3(X))* Independent Pub.
Sivertsen, Barbara. The Parting of the Sea - How Volcanoes, Earthquakes, & Plagues Shaped the Story of Exodus. 2011. (ENG., Illus.). 264p. (C). pap. 22.95 *(978-0-691-15021-5(4))* Princeton Univ. Pr.
Standard Publishing Staff. 40 Instant Studies: New Testament. Eichenberger, Jim, ed. 2009. (True to Life Ser.). (ENG.). 96p. (YA). pap. 9.99 *(978-0-7847-2299-2(4))* Standard Publishing.
Thomas Nelson. Personal Size Giant Print Reference Bible, NKJV. 2010. im. lthr. 54.99 *(978-1-4185-4762-2(X))* Nelson, Thomas Inc.
Tidball, Charles S. Holy Visions, Sacred Stories: Authenticated Episodes in the Life of Jesus. 2012. (Illus.). 234p. pap. 20.00 *(978-0-88010-645-0(X))* SteinerBooks, Inc.
Townsend, Mark. Jesus Outside the Box: Twelve Spiritual Tales of the Unexpected. 2010. (ENG., Illus.). 80p. pap. 12.95 *(978-1-84694-326-3(4))* O Bks.,John Hunt.
Valenti, Connie Ann. Stories of Jesus: A Gospel of Faith & Imagination. 2012. (ENG.). 240p. pap. 20.00 ***(978-1-57075-960-4(X))*** Orbis Bks.
Williams, Michael E., ed. The Storyteller's Companion to the Bible Vol. 8: Daniel & Revelation. 2009. (Storyteller's Companion to the Bible Ser.). 208p. pap. 21.00 *(978-0-687-02652-4(0))* Abingdon Pr.
Wilson, Andrew. GodStories: Explorations in the Gospel of God, 1 vol. 2009. (ENG.). 304p. pap. 14.99 *(978-1-4347-6539-0(3))* Cook, David C.

BIBLE STORIES—O.T.

Abse. Old Testament Stories With Freudian Twist. 2010. (Illus.). 230p. pap. 34.95 *(978-1-85575-832-2(6))* Karnac Bks. GBR. Dist: Stylus Publishing, LLC.
Alloway, Rob. The Left Hand of God: And other uncommon tales from Esther, Nehemiah & Ezra. 2008. 276p. pap. *(978-1-57383-437-7(8))* Regent College Publishing.
Amery, Heather. The Usborne Little Book of Stories from the Old Testament. Tyler, Jenny, ed. 2008. (Usborne Miniature Editions Ser.). (Illus.). 70p. (J). (gr. -1-3). 6.99 *(978-0-7945-1941-4(5)*, Usborne) EDC Publishing.
Buck, Deanna Draper. My First Old Testament Stories. 2010. 36p. pap. 8.99 *(978-1-60641-689-1(8))* Deseret Bk. Co.
Caduto, Michael J. Abraham's Bind & Other Bible Tales of Trickery, Folly, Mercy & Love. 2006. 208p. 19.99 *(978-1-59473-186-0(1))* SkyLight Paths Publishing.
Campbell, Jim. The Stories of the Old Testament: A Catholic's Guide. 2007. (ENG.). 352p. per. 14.95 *(978-0-8294-2470-6(9))* Loyola Pr.
Cartledge, Tony W. Sessions with Samuel: Stories from the Edge. 2010. 98p. pap. *(978-1-57312-555-0(5))* Smyth & Helwys Publishing, Inc.
Daniels, Rosemary. The Jemima Chronicles: It's Jemima Time. 2009. 88p. pap. 10.95 *(978-0-595-53133-2(4))* iUniverse, Inc.
Day, Jackson. Old Testament Bible Stories. 2007. 252p. pap. 25.00 *(978-0-9797324-0-9(9))* Day, H. Jackson.
Downs, Victor. In the Beginning: Adventuring Through the Old Testament. 2011. 220p. 28.95 *(978-1-4567-2833-5(4))*; pap. 18.75 *(978-1-4567-2834-2(2))* AuthorHouse.
Drip Drop. (Hear Me Read Classroom Sets Ser.). 32.00 *(978-0-570-05099-5(5))* Concordia Publishing Hse.
Fabrizius, Karl F. Bible Stories for Daily Prayer: Old Testament Year III, the Monarchy to the Return of the Exiles, 10 vols., Vol. 3. Bender, Peter C., ed. 2006. 302p. (J). ring bd. 20.00 *(978-0-9725687-6-0(X))* Concordia Catechetical Academy.
Fant, Louie J., Jr., ed. Noah - In Sign Language. pap. 9.95 *(978-0-917002-10-6(5))* Joyce Media, Inc.
Faulkner, Sandy. Wholly God: The Story of a Perfect God & his Peculiar People. 2008. 160p. pap. 13.99 *(978-0-89112-572-3(8)*, Leafwood Pubs.) Abilene Christian Univ. Pr.
Fillmore Ness, Shirley. Mom's Old Testament Bible Stories: Heroes & Scoundrels. 2009. 248p. pap. 14.99 *(978-1-4490-5040-5(9))* AuthorHouse.
Ganeri, Anita. The Temple Lamp & Other Stories: Judaism. 2007. (Qeb Stories from Faiths Ser.). (Illus.). 36p. (J). (gr. -1-3). 19.95 *(978-1-59566-376-4(2))* QEB Publishing Inc.
Gladson, Jerry. The Strangest Books in the Bible. 2010. 164p. 29.99 *(978-1-4535-3494-6(6))*; pap. 19.99 *(978-1-4535-3493-9(8))* Xlibris Corp.
Glazer, Mel. And God Created Hope: Finding Your Way Through Grief from the Lessons of Early Biblical Stories. 2007. (ENG.). 256p. pap. 14.95 *(978-1-56924-267-4(4))* Da Capo Pr., Inc.
Greenwood, Val D., as told by. How Often Would I Have Gathered You: Stories from the Old Testament & Related Sources for Latter-Day Saints. 2007. 408p. (YA). 29.95 *(978-1-58982-380-8(X)*, Millennial Mind Publishing) American Bk. Publishing Group.
Isaacson, Marlys J. Picture Me Reading Favorite Bible Stories! Classroom Teacher's Manual: Old Testament Stories, Sight Word Activities, & Phonics Instruction. 2007. 154p. (C). spiral bd. 15.00 *(978-0-9743916-5-6(4))* Picture Me Reading!
—Picture Me Reading Favorite Bible Stories! Manual for Teaching One-on-One: Old Testament Stories, Sight Word Activities, & Phonics Instruction. 2007. 42p. 5.00 *(978-0-9743916-4-9(6))* Picture Me Reading!
Jensen, John W. It's All about Jesus. 2008. 108p. pap. 19.95 *(978-1-60703-524-4(3))* PublishAmerica, Inc.
Jones, Sonia. Old Testament Alive! 2010. *(978-0-9810470-8-9(4))* Erser & Pond Pubs., Ltd.
Jules, Jacqueline. Benjamin & the Silver Goblet. 2009. (Bible Ser.). (Illus.). 32p. (J). (gr. k-4). bds. 8.95 *(978-0-8225-8758-3(0)*, Kar-Ben Publishing) Lerner Publishing Group.
King, Adam (Ed). Panorama of the Old Testament. 2007. (Illus.). 36p. pap. 20.00 *(978-1-86118-925-7(7))* Third Millennium Pr., Ltd. GBR. Dist: STL Distribution North America.
King, Gwendolyn. God's Spoken Word: A Habakkuk 2:3 Story. 2010. 112p. 22.95 *(978-1-4502-7289-6(4))*; pap. 12.95 *(978-1-4502-7288-9(6))* iUniverse, Inc.
Lieb, Bob. The Golden Septre. 2008. 315p. per. *(978-0-9800096-9-9(3))* Calvary Publishing.
Lynn, David. More High School TalkSheets, Epic Old Testament Stories: 52 Ready-to-Use Discussions, 1 vol. 2012. (TalkSheets Ser.). (ENG.). 128p. pap. 14.99 ***(978-0-310-88938-0(3))*** Zondervan.
Marty Baker Th M., Baker Th M. & Marty Baker Th. M. Touring the Old Testament. 2009. 312p. pap. 30.95 *(978-1-4401-7347-9(8))* iUniverse, Inc.
Mesorah Publications, creator. Artscroll English Tanach-OE-Stone. 2011. 1416p. 34.99 *(978-1-4226-1039-8(X))* Mesorah Pubns., Ltd.
Mitchell, Kenneth R. Justice & Generosity: The Teaching of the Bible Concerning the Poor. 2008. 422p. pap. 29.95 *(978-1-60563-950-5(8))* PublishAmerica, Inc.
Morris, Quinn. Echoes from the Old Testament: Wisdom for Teens. 2010. 132p. pap. 15.00 *(978-1-4269-2973-1(0))* Trafford Publishing.
Mortimer, Favell Lee. Line upon Line: Or, A Second Series of the Earliest Religious instruction the Infant Mind Is Capable of Receiving. with Verses Illustrative of the Sub. 2006. 264p. per. 23.99 *(978-1-4255-2295-7(5))* MPublishing.
Nash, Audrey. Old Testament Story: Seeing the Old Testament as a Whole. 2008. 164p. pap. 11.99 *(978-1-4389-2873-9(4))* AuthorHouse.

Ness, Shirley Fillmore. Mom's Old Testament Bible Stories: Heroes & Scoundrels. 2009. 248p. 24.99 (978-1-4490-5039-9(5)) AuthorHouse.
Ochs, Vanessa. Sarah Laughed. 2011. (ENG.). 250p. pap. 16.00 (978-0-8276-0928-0(0)) Jewish Pubn. Society.
Once upon a Time. 13.00 incl. audio (978-0-687-76220-0(0)) Abingdon Pr.
Pearl, Michael, et al. La Biblia Kingstone, Vol. 1. 2011. 192p. pap. 17.99 **(978-1-61328-020-1(3))** Kingstone Media Group.
—The Kingstone Bible: Vol 1. 2011. 192p. pap. 17.99 **(978-1-61328-019-5(X))** Kingstone Media Group.
Perlstein, David. God's Others: Non-Israelites' Encounters with God in the Hebrew Bible. 2010. 380p. 34.95 (978-1-4502-2279-2(X)); pap. 24.95 (978-1-4502-2278-5(1)) iUniverse, Inc.
Rasell, Marc. Nehemiah the Sabbath Reformer. 2010. 100p. pap. 10.49 (978-1-4490-6677-2(1)) AuthorHouse.
Schroeder, John D. Old Testament Stories from the Backside: A Video Study. ldr.'s ed. 2007. (Behind the Pages Ser.). 40p. pap. 11.00 (978-0-687-64204-5(3)) Abingdon Pr.
Sivertsen, Barbara J. The Parting of the Sea: How Volcanoes, Earthquakes, & Plagues Shaped the Story of Exodus. 2009. (ENG., Illus.). 264p. (C). 39.95 (978-0-691-13770-4(6)) Princeton Univ. Pr.
Tankersley, Jean. Old Testament Saints & the Messiah. 2007. 240p. per. 14.99 (978-1-60477-251-7(4)) Xulon Pr., Inc.
Tappan, Eva March, ed. An Old, Old Storybook: Compiled from the Old Testament. 2007. (ENG.). 324p. 45.95 (978-0-548-05783-4(4)) Kessinger Publishing, LLC.
Thomas Nelson. Personal Size Giant Print Reference Bible, NKJV. 2010. im. lthr. 54.99 (978-1-4185-4762-2(X)) Nelson, Thomas Inc.
Trevor, Hart & Bauckham, Richard. Finding God in the Midst of Life: Old Stories for Contemporary Readers. 2007. (ENG.). pap. 16.99 (978-1-84227-472-9(4), Paternoster) Authentic Media.
Wallace, Peter. Connected: You & God in the Psalms. 2009. 208p. pap. 18.00 (978-0-8192-2308-1(5), Morehouse Publishing) Church Publishing, Inc.
Wheat, Charlotte. That Audacious, Impetuous Mother-of-All, Eve! 2008. 28p. per. 10.95 (978-1-4327-1887-9(8)) Outskirts Pr., Inc.
Withers, Benjamin C. The Illustrated Old English Hexateuch, Cotton Claudius B.IV: The Frontier of Seeing & Reading in Anglo-Saxon England. 2007. (Studies in Book & Print Culture Ser.). (ENG., Illus.). 464p. (978-0-8020-9104-8(0)) Univ. of Toronto Pr.
Woodman, Ros. David & Goliath. Date not set. pap. 1.75 (978-0-906731-25-3(9)) Christian Focus Pubns. GBR. Dist: Spring Arbor Distributors, Inc.

BIBLE TRANSLATING
see Bible—Translating; Bible—Versions

BIBLICAL ARAMAIC LANGUAGE
see Aramaic Language

BIBLICAL ARCHAEOLOGY
see Bible—Antiquities

BIBLICAL COSMOGONY
see Creation

BIBLICAL COSMOLOGY
see also Creation
Adrian B. Smith Staff. God, Energy & the Field. 2009. (ENG.). 160p. pap. 19.95 (978-1-84694-135-1(0)) Hunt, John Publishing Ltd. GBR. Dist: National Bk. Network.
Arnold, Thomas. Two Stage Biblical Creation: Uniting Biblical Insights Uncovered by Ten Notable Creation Theories. 2008. 580p. pap. 20.00 (978-0-9798961-0-1(X)) Arnold, Thomas Publishing.
Bruno, Joseph. And Now There Is Light... 2007. 252p. pap. 18.95 (978-0-615-13496-3(3)) Bruno, Joseph.
Engberg-Pedersen, Troels. Cosmology & Self in the Apostle Paul: The Material Spirit. 2010. (ENG.). 304p. 110.00 (978-0-19-955856-8(6)) Oxford Univ. Pr., Inc.
Fran Addeo. The God Zone: A Peaceful & Powerful State of Being. 2009. 172p. 25.95 (978-1-4401-6788-1(5)); pap. 15.95 (978-1-4401-6786-7(9)) iUniverse, Inc.
Haarsma, Deborah B. & Haarsma, Loren D. Origins: A Reformed Look at Creation, Design, & Evolution. 2007. (978-1-59255-227-6(7)) Faith Alive Christian Resources.
—Origins: Christian Perspectives on Creation, Evolution, & Intelligent Design. 2nd ed. 2011. (978-1-59255-573-4(X)) Faith Alive Christian Resources.
Lathrop, Gordon W. Holy Ground: A Liturgical Cosmology. 2009. 250p. (C). pap. 20.00 (978-0-8006-9655-9(7), Fortress Pr.) Augsburg Fortress, Pubs.
Lioy, Dan. Evolutionary Creation in Biblical & Theological Perspective. 2011. (Studies in Biblical Literature Ser.). 336p. (C). 87.95 **(978-1-4331-1624-7(3))** Lang, Peter Publishing, Inc.
Nicklas, Tobias & Zamfir, Korinna, eds. Theologies of Creation in Early Judaism & Ancient Christianity. 2010. (Deuterocanonical & Cognate Literature Studies). (ENG & GER.). XI, 447p. 140.00 (978-3-11-024630-8(9)) De Gruyter, Walter Inc.
Pennington, Mcdonough, et al. Cosmology & New Testament Theology. 2008. (Library of New Testament Studies). (ENG.). 224p. 130.00 (978-0-567-03143-3(8), T&T Clark Int'l) Continuum International Publishing Group, Ltd. GBR. Dist: National Bk. Network.
Ross, Hugh. Why the Universe Is the Way It Is. 2008. 240p. pap. 15.99 (978-0-8010-7196-6(8)) Baker Bks.
Ryan, Sean Michael. Hearing at the Boundaries of Vision: Education Informing Cosmology in Revelation 9. 2012. (ENG., Illus.). 296p. 120.00 **(978-0-567-60489-7(6)**, T&T Clark Int'l) Continuum International Publishing Group, Ltd. GBR. Dist: National Bk. Network.
Schenck, Kenneth L. Cosmology & Eschatology in Hebrews: The Settings of the Sacrifice. 2010. (Society for New Testament Studies Monograph Ser.). (ENG.). 236p. pap. 36.99 (978-0-521-13047-9(6)) Cambridge Univ. Pr.
Steenberg, Matthew C. & Steenberg, M. C. Irenaeus on Creation: The Cosmic Christ & the Saga of Redemption. 2008. (Vigiliae Christianae Supplements Ser.). 264p. (978-90-04-16682-0(3)) BRILL.
Swarbrick, D. Before Genesis to Revelation & Beyond. 2010. 276p. pap. 17.49 (978-1-4520-8908-9(6)) AuthorHouse.
Viser, Myron. Adding for Jesus. 2007. per. (978-0-9798066-0-5(7)) Viser, Myron.
Walton, John H. Genesis 1 As Ancient Cosmology. 2011. **(978-1-57506-216-7(X))** Eisenbrauns, Inc.
Walton, John H. The Lost World of Genesis One: Ancient Cosmology & the Origins Debate, 1 vol. 2009. (ENG.). 192p. pap. 16.00 (978-0-8308-3704-5(3), IVP Acad.) InterVarsity Pr.
Wilson, Douglas & Morin, Terry. The Forgotten Heavens: Six Essays on Cosmology. 2010. pap. (978-1-59128-071-2(0)) Canon Pr.
York, Dick. God's Eternal Purpose: The Making of Man in God's Image. York, Dick, ed. 2007. (Illus.). 128p. pap. 7.95 (978-1-889575-01-8(1)) SOF Pubs.

BIBLICAL GREEK
see Greek Language, Biblical

BIBLICAL LAW
see Jewish Law

BIBLICAL NAMES
see Names in the Bible

BIBLICAL NUMEROLOGY
see Numbers in the Bible

BIBLICAL RESEARCH
see Bible—Criticism, Interpretation, etc.

BIBLICAL SOCIOLOGY
see Sociology, Biblical

BIBLIOGRAPHERS
see also Librarians
Leu, Urs B. & Weidmann, Sandra. Conrad Gessner's Private Library. 2008. (History of Science & Medicine Library). (Illus.). 208p. (978-90-04-16723-0(4)) BRILL.
McKitterick, David. A Changing View from Amsterdam: Where Next with Book History? 2011. (Frederik Mullerlezing Ser.). 32p. pap. (978-90-5629-645-2(0)) Amsterdam Univ. Pr.

BIBLIOGRAPHERS—BIOGRAPHY
Proctor, Robert & Bowman, J. H. A Critical Edition of the Private Diaries of Robert Proctor: The Life of a Librarian at the British Museum. 2010. (Illus.). xxvii, 373p. 129.95 (978-0-7734-3634-3(0)) Mellen, Edwin Pr., The.

BIBLIOGRAPHIC CONTROL
see Bibliography—Methodology

BIBLIOGRAPHIC SEARCHING, ONLINE
see Online Bibliographic Searching

BIBLIOGRAPHICAL CITATIONS
Agrawal, Abha. EndNote 1 - 2 - 3 Easy! Reference MGMT for the Professional. 2nd ed. 2009. (ENG., Illus.). xxiii, 296p. 69.95 (978-0-387-95900-9(9)) Springer.
Barnett, Anthony. Citations followed On. 2010. (Illus.). 36p. 19.00 (978-0-907954-38-5(3), Allardyce Bk.) Allardyce, Barnett, Pubs. GBR. Dist: SPD-Small Pr. Distribution.
Bugeja, Michael & Dimitrova, Daniela V. Vanishing Act: The Erosion of Online Footnotes & Implications for Scholarship in the Digital Age. 2010. pap. 18.00 (978-1-936117-14-7(2)) Litwin Bks., LLC.
Gaines, Ann Graham. Don't Steal Copyrighted Stuff! Avoiding Plagiarism & Illegal Internet Downloading. 2008. (Prime Ser.). (Illus.). 192p. (J). (gr. 4-7). lib. bdg. 38.60 (978-0-7660-2861-6(5)) Enslow Pubs., Inc.
Greer, Michael. What Every Student Should Know about Citing Sources with MLA Documentation, Update Edition. 2009. (What Every Student Should Know about... (WESSKA Series) Ser.). (ENG.). (C). pap. 9.80 (978-0-205-71511-4(7)) Longman Publishing Group.
Hauptman, Robert. Documentation: A History & Critique of Attribution, Commentary, Glosses, Marginalia, Notes, Bibliographies, Works-Cited Lists, & Citation Indexing & Analysis. 2008. (ENG., Illus.). 240p. pap. 35.00 (978-0-7864-3333-9(7)) McFarland & Co., Inc. Pubs.
Heath, Marilyn. MLA Made Easy: Citation Basics for Beginners, 1 vol. 2009. 212p. pap. 35.00 (978-1-58683-343-5(X), A2653P) Libraries Unlimited, Inc.
Hunt, Fiona & Birks, Jane. More Hands-On Information Literacy Activities. 2008. 150p. 75.00 (978-1-55570-648-7(7)) Neal-Schuman Pubs., Inc.
Lipson, Charles. Cite Right: A Quick Guide to Citation Styles — MLA, APA, Chicago, the Sciences, Professions, & More. 2nd ed. 2011. (Chicago Guides to Writing, Editing, & Publishing Ser.). (ENG.). 224p. pap. 14.00 (978-0-226-48464-8(5)) Univ. of Chicago Pr.
—Cite Right, Second Edition: A Quick Guide to Citation Styles — MLA, APA, Chicago, the Sciences, Professions, & More. 2nd ed. 2011. (Chicago Guides to Writing, Editing, & Publishing Ser.). (ENG.). 224p. 42.00 (978-0-226-48463-1(7)) Univ. of Chicago Pr.
—Doing Honest Work in College: How to Prepare Citations, Avoid Plagiarism, & Achieve Real Academic Success. 2nd ed. 2008. (Chicago Guides to Academic Life Ser.). 260p. 37.50 (978-0-226-48476-1(9)); 202p. pap. 14.00 (978-0-226-48477-8(7)) Univ. of Chicago Pr.
Lunsford, Andrea A. & Muth, Marcia F. The St. Martin's Pocket Guide to Research & Documentation. 5th ed. 2011. (ENG.). 288p. (C). spiral bd. 9.95 (978-0-312-66192-2(4)) Bedford/Saint Martin's.
—The St. Martin's Pocket Guide to Research & Documentation with 2009 MLA & 2010 APA Updates. 4th ed. 2010. (ENG., Illus.). 288p. (C). spiral bd. 9.95 (978-0-312-66494-7(X)) Bedford/Saint Martin's.
—The St. Martin's Pocket Guide to Research & Documentation with 2009 MLA Update. 4th ed. 2009. (ENG.). 288p. (C). spiral bd. 9.95 (978-0-312-59460-2(7)) Bedford/Saint Martin's.
Mills, Elizabeth Shown. QuickSheet: Citing Online Historical Sources. 2007. pap. 5.95 (978-0-8063-1776-2(0)) Genealogical Publishing Co., Inc.
Moed, Henk F. Citation Analysis in Research Evaluation. 2010. (Information Science & Knowledge Management Ser.). xiv, 346p. pap. 119.00 (978-90-481-6938-2(0), 9048169380) Springer.
Neville, Colin. The Complete Guide to Referencing & Avoiding Plagiarism. 2nd ed. 2010. (ENG., Illus.). 288p. (C). pap. 40.00 (978-0-335-24103-3(4), 0335241034) McGraw-Hill Education GBR. Dist: McGraw-Hill Cos., The.
Pears, Richard & Shields, Graham. Cite Them Right: The essential referencing Guide, 2 vols. 8th ed. 2010. (Palgrave Study Guides). (ENG., Illus.). 112p. pap., instr.'s gde. ed. 22.00 (978-0-230-27231-6(2)) Palgrave Macmillan.
Pecorari, Diane. Academic Writing & Plagiarism: A Linguistic Analysis. 2010. (ENG.). 224p. pap. 44.95 (978-1-4411-3953-5(2)) Continuum International Publishing Group, Ltd. GBR. Dist: National Bk. Network.
—Academic Writing & Plagiarism: A Linguistic Anaylsis. 2008. (ENG.). 224p. 150.00 (978-0-8264-9166-4(9)) Continuum International Publishing Group, Ltd. GBR. Dist: National Bk. Network.
Pringle, Mike & Gonzales, John. The MLA Style of Documentation. 2009. (English MLA Updated Books Ser.). (ENG.). 72p. (C). pap. 15.20 (978-0-13-604973-9(7), Prentice Hall) Prentice Hall PTR.
Puckett, Jason. Zotero: A Guide for Librarians, Researchers, & Educators. 2011. pap. **(978-0-8389-8589-2(0))** Assn. of College & Research Libraries.
Schwartz, Linda Smoak. The Wadsworth Guide to MLA Documentation. 2nd ed. 2010. (ENG.). 336p. (C). spiral bd. 26.95 (978-1-111-34737-6(9)) Wadsworth.
—The Wadsworth Guide to MLA Documentation. 3rd ed. 2012. (ENG.). (C). spiral bd. 25.95 (978-1-4282-6344-4(6)) CENGAGE Learning.
Trimmer, Joseph. A Guide to MLA Documentation. 9th ed. 2012. (ENG., Illus.). 48p. (C). pap. 25.95 **(978-1-111-83707-5(4))** Wadsworth.
Williams, Kate & Carroll, Jude. Reference & Understand Plagiarism. 2011. (Palgrave Pocket Guides). (ENG., Illus.). 128p. pap. 10.00 **(978-0-230-57479-3(3))** Palgrave Macmillan.

BIBLIOGRAPHICAL CONTROL
see Bibliography—Methodology

BIBLIOGRAPHICAL EXHIBITIONS
see Books—History—Exhibitions

BIBLIOGRAPHICAL SEARCHING
see Searching, Bibliographical

BIBLIOGRAPHY
Here are entered works which discuss the theories, methods, history, etc. of the discipline of bibliography. Works on the topic of compiling national bibliographies are entered under Bibliography, National. Lists of titles published in an individual country are entered under the name of the country with subdivision Imprints, e.g. United States—Imprints. Lists of titles published in the language of one country without regard to place of publication are entered under the phrase headings of the type German Imprints. Lists of titles about an individual country are entered under the name of the country with subdivision Bibliography, e.g. United States—Bibliography.
see also Abstracting and Indexing Services; Anonyms and Pseudonyms; Archives; Best Books; Bio-Bibliography; Book Collecting; Bookbinding; Books; Cataloging; Catalogs; Editions; Errors and Blunders, Literary; First Editions; Incunabula; Indexes; Indexing; Information Storage and Retrieval Systems; Library Science; Manuscripts; Periodicals—Indexes; Printing; Reference Books; Searching, Bibliographical; Series (Publications); Titles of Books; Transmission of Texts; Unfinished Books
also names of literature, e.g. American Literature; and subdivision Bibliography under names of persons, places and subjects; and subdivision Imprints under names of countries, states, cities, etc.
Agrawal, Abha. EndNote 1 - 2 - 3 Easy! Reference MGMT for the Professional. 2nd ed. 2009. (ENG., Illus.). xxiii, 296p. 69.95 (978-0-387-95900-9(9)) Springer.
Ash, Russell & Lake, Brian. Bizarre Books: A Compendium of Classic Oddities. 2007. (Illus.). 224p. per. 14.95 (978-0-06-134665-1(9), HarperPerennial) HarperCollins Pubs.
Author Title & Subject Guide: [Print + EBookPLUS]. 2010. (978-3-11-023067-3(4)) Saur, K. G. Verlag GmbH & Co.
Bade, David. Responsible Librarianship: Library Policies for Unreliable Systems. 2008. (Illus.). 192p. pap. 22.00 (978-0-9778617-6-7(7), Library Juice Pr.) Litwin Bks., LLC.
Beaudiquez, Marcelle. Guide de Bibliographie Générale: Méthodologie et Pratique. (Bibliothèques et organismes Documentaires Ser.). (GER.). 280p. **(978-3-11-125386-2(4))** Saur, K. G. Verlag GmbH & Co.
Bibliographic Volume: International Organization Bibliography & Resources. 2010. (Yearbook of International Organizations 2010/2011 Ser.). XIV, 680p. (978-3-11-023034-5(8)) Saur, K. G. Verlag GmbH & Co.
Bradshaw, Henry. Collected Papers of Henry Bradshaw. 2011. 536p. pap. 39.99 (978-1-107-60005-8(7)) Cambridge Univ. Pr.
Brydges, Samuel E. Censura Literaria, 10 vols. in 5. reprint ed. 675.00 (978-0-404-01210-6(8)) AMS Pr., Inc.
Dibdin, Thomas Frognall. Reminiscences of a Literary Life. 2010. (Cambridge Library Collection - Printing & Publishing History Ser.). (Illus.). 444p. pap. 32.99 (978-1-108-00934-8(4)); (ENG., 608p. pap. 43.00 (978-1-108-00933-1(6)) Cambridge Univ. Pr.
Dwiggins, W. A., et al. Mss by Wad: Being A Collection of the Writings of Dwiggins on Various Subjects Some Critical, Some Philosophical, Some Whimsical. 2011. 168p. 41.95 **(978-1-258-05705-3(0))** Literary Licensing, LLC.
Eom, Sean B. Author Cocitation Analysis: Quantitative Methods for Mapping the Intellectual Structure of an Academic Discipline. 2008. (Illus.). 368p. 165.00 (978-1-59904-738-6(1)) IGI Global.
Ewen, Beth, ed. The Top Twenty-Five Book of Lists. 100p. pap. 16.95 (978-0-9634146-0-1(7)) Minneapolis-Saint Paul CityBusiness.
Ferguson, John. Some Aspects of Bibliography. 2010. 128p. pap. 19.75 (978-1-147-53780-2(1)); 122p. pap. 19.75 (978-1-141-12107-6(7)); 122p. pap. 19.75 (978-1-141-06195-2(3)) BiblioBazaar.
—Some Aspects of Bibliography. 2009. 68p. pap. (978-0-217-99471-2(7)) Books LLC.
Fink, Arlene. Conducting Research Literature Reviews: From the Internet to Paper. 3rd ed. 2009. (Illus.). 272p. (C). pap. 59.00 (978-1-4129-7189-8(6), B71898P) SAGE Pubns., Inc.
Fulton, Len, compiled by. Small Press Record of Books in Print. 2008. (ENG.). cd-rom 55.00 (978-0-916685-92-8(6)) Dustbooks.
Fulton, Len, ed. Small Press Record of Books in Print, 1, 33. 33rd ed. 2007. (ENG.). cd-rom 55.00 (978-0-916685-49-2(7)) Dustbooks.
Furrie, Betty. Understanding MARC Bibliographic: Machine-Readable Cataloging. 8th ed. 2009. (978-0-8444-9506-4(9)) Library of Congress.
Garnett, Richard. Essays in Librarianship & Bibliography. 2010. 368p. pap. 32.75 (978-1-145-03005-3(X)) 2009. 360p. 33.99 (978-1-113-70874-8(3)) 2009. 360p. pap. 31.75 (978-1-113-70870-0(0)) 2009. 360p. pap. 32.75 (978-1-113-70872-4(7)) BiblioBazaar.
—Essays in Librarianship & Bibliography. 2009. 194p. pap. (978-1-4590-4715-0(X)) Books LLC.
—Essays in Librarianship & Bibliography. 2007. (ENG.). 364p. per. (978-1-4067-0341-2(9)) Read Bks.
Gorman, Gary E. & Mahoney, Maureen M. Guide to current national Bibliographies in the Third World. Anderson, Dorothy [Vorr.], ed. (GER.). 328p. **(978-3-11-218534-6(X))** Saur, K. G. Verlag GmbH & Co.
Greenspan, Ezra & Rose, Jonathan, eds. Book History Volume 10. 2007. (Book History Ser.). (Illus.). 319p. 57.00 (978-0-271-02766-1(5)) Pennsylvania State Univ. Pr.
Haddad, Farid S. Annotated & Illustrated Bibliography: A Fragrant Rainbow in Two Hands-Full, 1 vol. 2007. (Illus.). 170p. pap. 40.00 (978-1-886465-23-7(1)) Shad D Board.
International Bibliography of Bibliographies 1959-88. rev. ed. 2007. Vol. 12, Pt. 2. (978-3-598-33750-5(7)) Vol. 12, Pt. 3. (978-3-598-33751-2(5)) Saur, K. G. Verlag GmbH & Co.
Kasinec, E. & Davis, Robert H. Slavic & Russian Books & Libraries: Occasional Essays & Notes. 2007. (978-0-88354-044-2(4)) Ross Publishing Incorporated.
Matthews, Brander. Ballads of Books. 2010. (ENG.). 184p. pap. 22.75 (978-1-145-64591-2(7)) 2010. (ENG.). 182p. pap. 22.75 (978-1-176-21170-4(6)) 2010. (ENG.). 186p. pap. 22.75 (978-1-176-21157-5(9)) 2009. 178p. 26.99 (978-1-110-82773-2(3)) 2009. 178p. pap. 21.75 (978-1-110-82772-5(5)) 2009. (ENG.). 177p. pap. 19.99 (978-1-110-82768-8(7), BiblioLife) 2009. (ENG.). 177p. pap. 21.99 (978-1-110-82769-5(5), BiblioLife) 2009. 180p. 22.99 (978-1-103-78208-6(8)) 2009. 180p. 22.99 (978-1-103-92043-3(X)) 2009. 180p. pap. 16.99 (978-1-103-78206-2(1)) 2009. 180p. pap. 16.99 (978-1-103-92036-5(7)) 2008. 180p. 22.99 (978-0-559-61745-4(3)) 2008. 180p. pap. 21.75 (978-0-559-61742-3(9)) 2008. 227p. 22.99 (978-0-554-72945-9(8)) 2008. 119p. 25.99 (978-0-554-72934-3(2)) 2008. 119p. pap. 22.75 (978-0-554-72936-7(9)) 2008. 227p. pap. 21.75 (978-0-554-72942-8(3)) BiblioBazaar.
—Ballads of Books. 2009. 96p. pap. (978-0-217-44341-8(9)); 102p. pap. (978-0-217-44343-2(5)); 90p. pap. (978-0-217-17915-7(0)) Books LLC.
—Ballads of Books. 2007. (ENG.). 180p. per. (978-1-4067-1800-3(9)) Read Bks.
Meulen, David L. Vander, ed. Studies in Bibliography Vol. 58: Papers of the Bibliographical Society of the University of Virginia. 2010. (ENG.). 300p. (gr. 17). 70.00 (978-0-8139-2878-4(8)) Univ. Pr. of Virginia.
National Information Standards Organization (U.S.) Staff & American National Standards Institute Staff, contrib. by. Holdings Statements for Bibliographic Items: An American National Standard. 2006. (National Information Standards Ser.). (978-1-880124-69-7(6)) NISO Pr.

Pollard, Alfred W. Old Picture Books with Other Essays on Bookish Subjects. 2009. 294p. 34.99 *(978-1-113-85442-1(1))*; pap. 23.99 *(978-1-113-85438-4(3))* BiblioBazaar.

Shields, Dario A. Ghetto Born, God Raised: It's Not Your Setbacks, It's How You Comeback. 2011. 284p. 29.99 ***(978-1-4634-1948-6(1))*** AuthorHouse.

Simon, Andre I. Biblioteca Vinaria. Date not set. reprint ed. 60.00 *(978-1-57898-123-6(9))* Martino Publishing.

Sterne, Laurence. The Complete Works & Life of Laurence Sterne, 12 Vols. reprint ed. lib. bdg. 1176.00 *(978-0-7426-2069-8(7))* Classic Bks.

Subject. 2009. (ENG.). XVIII, 988p. *(978-3-598-23909-0(2))* Saur, K. G. Verlag GmbH & Co.

Subject Guide. 2008. (ENG.). XVIII, 948p. *(978-3-598-23907-6(6))* Saur, K. G. Verlag GmbH & Co.

Superlccs 98: Schedule KF. Date not set. 215.00 *(978-0-7876-2351-7(2))* Cengage Gale.

Superlccs 98: Schedule KJ-KKZ. Date not set. 70.00 *(978-0-7876-2357-9(1))* Cengage Gale.

Superlccs 98: Schedule KZ. Date not set. 70.00 *(978-0-7876-2818-5(2))* Cengage Gale.

Superlccs 98: Schedule P-PM. Date not set. 60.00 *(978-0-7876-2375-3(X))* Cengage Gale.

Superlccs 98: Schedule PJ-PK. Date not set. 65.00 *(978-0-7876-2371-5(7))* Cengage Gale.

Superlccs 98: Schedule PL-PM. Date not set. 60.00 *(978-0-7876-2373-9(3))* Cengage Gale.

Taylor, Arlene G. Understanding FRBR: What It Is & How It Will Affect Our Retrieval Tools, 1 vol. 2007. (Illus.). 192p. per. 45.00 *(978-1-59158-509-1(0),* LU5090) Libraries Unlimited, Inc.

Villars, Pierre, et al. Bibliography, 3 vols. (ENG.). 2012. 4516p. 524.00 ***(978-3-11-027650-3(X))*** 2012. 4516p. (gr. 17). E-Book 727.00 ***(978-3-11-027666-4(6))*** 2011. (Illus.). XIV, 4152p. E-Book 587.00 ***(978-3-11-026896-6(5))*** 2011. XIV, 4152p. 391.00 ***(978-3-11-026844-7(2))*** De Gruyter, Walter Inc.

Wittgenstein - Zykan. 2010. XII, 503p. pap. *(978-3-11-023142-7(5))* Saur, K. G. Verlag GmbH & Co.

BIBLIOGRAPHY—BEST BOOKS
see Best Books

BIBLIOGRAPHY—BIBLIOGRAPHY
see Bibliography of Bibliographies

BIBLIOGRAPHY—BOOKS ISSUED IN SERIES
see Series (Publications)

BIBLIOGRAPHY—DICTIONARIES
see also Library Science—Dictionaries

Author Title & Subject Guide. 2012. (ENG., Illus.). XX, 1980p. ***(978-3-11-916301-9(5))*** Saur, K. G. Verlag GmbH & Co.

Diamond, Marie Josephine. Encyclopedia of World Writers, 1800 to the Present. 2nd rev. ed. 2011. 640p. (C). (gr. 9). 85.00 *(978-0-8160-8204-9(9))* Facts On File, Inc.

Stokes, Roy. Bibliographical Companion. 2011. (ENG.). 308p. pap. 40.00 *(978-0-8108-6047-6(3))* Scarecrow Pr., Inc.

Walter, Frank Keller. Abbreviations & Technical Terms Used in Book Catalogs & in Bibliographies. 2009. 182p. 22.99 *(978-1-116-46275-3(3))*; pap. 21.75 *(978-1-116-46277-7(X))* BiblioBazaar.

BIBLIOGRAPHY—EARLY PRINTED BOOKS
see Early Printed Books

BIBLIOGRAPHY—EDITIONS
see Editions

BIBLIOGRAPHY—EXHIBITIONS
see Books—History—Exhibitions

BIBLIOGRAPHY—FIRST EDITIONS
see First Editions

BIBLIOGRAPHY—HISTORY

Hauptman, Robert. Documentation: A History & Critique of Attribution, Commentary, Glosses, Marginalia, Notes, Bibliographies, Works-Cited Lists, & Citation Indexing & Analysis. 2008. (ENG., Illus.). 240p. pap. 35.00 *(978-0-7864-3333-9(7))* McFarland & Co., Inc. Pubs.

Mastrogregori, Massimo, ed. 2006. 2011. XVII, 372p. 405.00 ***(978-3-11-174179-6(6))*** 2010. 415p. 266.00 *(978-3-11-023140-3(9))* De Gruyter, Walter Inc.

Walbridge, Earle F., ed. The Papers of the Bibliographical Society of America, V45, First Quarter 1951. 2011. 110p. 39.95 ***(978-1-258-10035-3(5))*** Literary Licensing, LLC.

BIBLIOGRAPHY—METHODOLOGY
see also Bibliographical Citations; Bibliography, Critical

Academic Librarianship in the 21st Century. 2009. 69.00 *(978-1-60456-865-3(8))* Nova Science Pubs., Inc.

Andres, Ana. Measuring Academic Research: How to Undertake a Bibliometric Study. 2009. (Illus.). 200p. pap. 75.00 ***(978-1-84334-528-2(5))*** Neal-Schuman Pubs., Inc.

Badke, William. Research Strategies: Finding Your Way through the Information Fog. 2011. 284p. 30.95 *(978-1-4620-1019-6(9))*; 4th ed. (Illus.). pap. 20.95 *(978-1-4620-1017-2(2))* iUniverse, Inc.

Dane, Joseph A. Out of Sorts: On Typography & Print Culture. 2010. (Material Texts). (Illus.). 256p. (C). 59.95 *(978-0-8122-4294-2(7))* Univ. of Pennsylvania Pr.

Dane, Joseph A. What Is a Book? The Study of Early Printed Books. 2012. (ENG., Illus.). 288p. pap. 30.00 ***(978-0-268-02609-7(2))*** Univ. of Notre Dame Pr.

Raju, A. A. N. Legal Deposit & Bibliographical Control in India. 2009. 140p. 24.00 *(978-81-7000-555-1(8))* Ess Ess Pubns. IND. Dist: International Specialized Bk. Services.

BIBLIOGRAPHY—MICROSCOPIC AND MINIATURE EDITIONS
see Miniature Books

BIBLIOGRAPHY—MICROSCOPIC AND MINIATURE EDITIONS—SPECIMENS
see Miniature Books—Specimens

BIBLIOGRAPHY—OUT-OF-PRINT BOOKS
see Out-of-Print Books

BIBLIOGRAPHY—PAPERBACK EDITIONS
see Paperbacks

BIBLIOGRAPHY—PERIODICALS

Department of Information & Collections, ed. Annual Bibliography of the History of the Printed Book & Libraries: Volume 31. 2010. (Annual Bibliography of the History of the Printed Book & Libraries Ser.). lvi, 696p. pap. 459.00 *(978-90-481-6972-6(0),* 9048169720) Springer.

Dept. of Special Collections of the Koninklijke Bibliotheek, ed. Annual Bibliography of the History of the Printed Book & Libraries: Volume 29. 2010. (Annual Bibliography of the History of the Printed Book & Libraries Ser.). 698p. pap. 419.00 *(978-90-481-5929-1(6),* 9048159296) Springer.

—Annual Bibliography of the History of the Printed Book & Libraries: Volume 30. 2010. (Annual Bibliography of the History of the Printed Book & Libraries Ser.). 656p. pap. 429.00 *(978-90-481-6454-7(0),* 9048164540) Springer.

Meulen, David L. Vander, ed. Studies in Bibliography Vol. 56: Papers of the Bibliographical Society of the University of Virginia. 2007. (ENG.). 300p. (gr. 17). 70.00 *(978-0-8139-2530-1(4))* Univ. Pr. of Virginia.

—Studies in Bibliography Vol. 57: Papers of the Bibliographical Society of the University of Virginia. 2008. (ENG.). 300p. (gr. 17). 70.00 *(978-0-8139-2653-7(X))* Univ. Pr. of Virginia.

Wainwright, Alexander. The Princeton University Library Chronicle, V23, No 3, Spring 1962. Wainwright, Alexander, ed. 2011. 58p. 36.95 ***(978-1-258-01944-0(2))*** Literary Licensing, LLC.

BIBLIOGRAPHY—PIRATED EDITIONS
see Copyright—Unauthorized Reprints

BIBLIOGRAPHY—PROHIBITED BOOKS
see Prohibited Books

BIBLIOGRAPHY—RARE BOOKS
see Rare Books

BIBLIOGRAPHY—REFERENCE BOOKS
see Reference Books

BIBLIOGRAPHY—REPRINT EDITIONS
see Reprints (Publications)

BIBLIOGRAPHY—STUDY AND TEACHING

Bowers, Fredson. Studies in Bibliography. 2007. (ENG.). 340p. per. *(978-1-4067-7227-2(5))* Read Bks.

Repanovici, Angela. Marketing Strategies for Digital Repositories. 2010. 224p. pap. *(978-3-8383-8912-7(3))* Lambert Academic Publishing.

BIBLIOGRAPHY—THEORY, METHODS, ETC.
see Bibliography—Methodology

BIBLIOGRAPHY—UNION LISTS
see Union Catalogs

BIBLIOGRAPHY, CRITICAL
see also Books—History; Criticism, Textual

Dane, Joseph A. Abstractions of Evidence in the Study of Manuscripts & Early Printed Books. 2009. (Illus.). 184p. 99.95 *(978-0-7546-6501-4(1))* Ashgate Publishing Co.

Dane, Joseph A. What Is a Book? The Study of Early Printed Books. 2012. (ENG., Illus.). 288p. pap. 30.00 ***(978-0-268-02609-7(2))*** Univ. of Notre Dame Pr.

Rautenberg, Ursula. Buchwissenschaft in Deutschland: Ein Handbuch: Theorie und Forschung / Fachkommunikation, Lehre, Institutionen und Gesellschaften. Rautenberg, Ursula, ed. 2010.Tr. of Book Studies in Germany: A Handbook. (GER., Illus.). XXX, 1109p. 210.00 *(978-3-11-020036-2(8))* De Gruyter, Walter Inc.

Rautenberg, Ursula, ed. Buchwissenschaft in Deutschland: Ein Handbuch: Theorie und Forschung / Fachkommunikation, Lehre, Institutionen und Gesellschaften. 2010.Tr. of Book Studies in Germany: A Handbook. (GER.). XXX, 1109p. 321.00 ***(978-3-11-173658-7(X))*** De Gruyter, Walter Inc.

Tanselle, G. Thomas. Bibliographical Analysis: A Historical Introduction. 2009. (ENG.). 176p. (C). 77.00 *(978-0-521-76034-8(8))*; pap. 27.99 *(978-0-521-75762-1(2))* Cambridge Univ. Pr.

Williams, William Proctor & Abbott, Craig S. An Introduction to Bibliographical & Textual Studies. 4th ed. 2009. (ENG.). 200p. 37.50 *(978-1-60329-039-5(7))*; pap. 19.75 *(978-1-60329-040-1(0))* Modern Language Assn. of America.

BIBLIOGRAPHY, INTERNATIONAL

Mastrogregori, Massimo, ed. 2006. 2011. XVII, 372p. 405.00 ***(978-3-11-174179-6(6))*** 2010. 415p. 266.00 *(978-3-11-023140-3(9))* De Gruyter, Walter Inc.

BIBLIOGRAPHY, NATIONAL

Here are entered works on the topic of compiling national bibliographies. Lists of titles published in a specific country are entered under the names of the country, with subdivision imprints, e.g. United States—Imprints. Lists of titles published in the language of one country without regard to place of publication are entered under phrase headings of the type German Imprints. Lists of titles about a specific country are entered under the name of country, with subdivision bibliography, e.g. United States—Bibliography. Works which discuss the theories, methods, history, etc. of the discipline of bibliography are entered under Bibliography.

Bibliotheek, Koninklijke & National Library of the Netherlands Staff, eds. Brinkman's Cumulative Catalogue: Nationale Bibliografie van Nederland/Dutch National Bibliography. 2009. cd-rom *(978-3-598-40985-1(0))*; cd-rom *(978-3-598-40953-0(2))* Saur, K. G. Verlag GmbH & Co.

Brinkman's Cumulatieve Catalogus op CD-ROM, Ausgabe 2009/3. 2009. cd-rom *(978-3-598-40987-5(7))* Saur, K. G. Verlag GmbH & Co.

Raju, A. A. N. Legal Deposit & Bibliographical Control in India. 2009. 140p. 24.00 *(978-81-7000-555-1(8))* Ess Ess Pubns. IND. Dist: International Specialized Bk. Services.

Stahl, Harvey. Picturing Kingship: History & Painting in the Psalter of Saint Louis. 2008. (ENG., Illus.). 472p. 85.00 *(978-0-271-02863-7(7))* Pennsylvania State Univ. Pr.

Yumer, Maja, ed. National Bibliographies in the Digital Age: Guidance & New Directions: IFLA Working Group on Guidelines for National Bibliographies. 2009. (IFLA Series on Bibliographic Control Ser.). (ENG.). 140p. *(978-3-598-24287-8(5))* Saur, K. G. Verlag GmbH & Co.

BIBLIOGRAPHY OF BIBLIOGRAPHIES

K. G. Saur Editorial Staff, ed. International Bibliography of Bibliographies 1959-88. 2006. *(978-3-598-33733-8(7))* Saur, K. G. Verlag GmbH & Co.

Thomson Gale Staff. International Bibliography of Bibliographies 1959-88, Vol. 11, Pt. 2. rev. ed. 2007. (GER.). X, 445p. *(978-3-598-33748-2(5))* Saur, K. G. Verlag GmbH & Co.

Troike, Rudolph C. A Bibliography of Bibliographies of the Languages of the World, Vol. II. (Library & Information Sources in Linguistics Ser.: No. 19). *(978-90-272-3744-6(1))* Benjamins, John Publishing Co.

Walravens, Hartmut, ed. International Bibliography of Bibliographies, 1959-88, 2 vols. rev. ed. 2006. Vol. 11. 700p. *(978-3-598-33745-1(0))* Vol. 12, Pt. 1. 400p. *(978-3-598-33749-9(3))* Saur, K. G. Verlag GmbH & Co.

—International Bibliography of Bibliographies, 1959-88, 4 Vols., Vol. 12. rev. ed. 2006. 1200p. 950.00 *(978-3-598-33746-8(9))* Saur, K. G. Verlag GmbH & Co. DEU. Dist: Saur, K. G. Verlag GmbH & Co.

BIBLIOMANIA

Bartlett, Allison Hoover. The Man Who Loved Books Too Much: The True Story of a Thief, a Detective, & a World of Literary Obsession. 2010. (ENG.). 288p. (gr. 12). 15.00 *(978-1-59448-481-0(3),* Riverhead Trade (Paperbacks)) Penguin Group (USA) Inc.

Farren, Donald & Imholtz, August A., eds. The Baltimore Bibliophiles at Fifty, 1954-2004. 2009. 55.00 *(978-1-58456-251-1(X))* Oak Knoll Pr.

Hazlitt, W. Carew. The Book Collector. 2009. 364p. 33.99 *(978-1-113-62896-1(0))*; pap. 31.75 *(978-1-113-62894-7(4))* BiblioBazaar.

Lang, Andrew. Books & Bookmen. 2009. 166p. 22.99 *(978-1-110-00813-1(9))*; pap. 16.99 *(978-1-110-00811-7(2))* BiblioBazaar.

—Books & Bookmen. 2009. 66p. pap. *(978-0-217-44913-7(1))* Books LLC.

—Books & Bookmen. 2007. 92p. per. *(978-1-4065-2607-3(X))* Dodo Pr.

—Books & Bookmen. 2008. 160p. 36.95 *(978-1-4369-0470-4(6))*; pap. 21.95 *(978-1-4367-9121-2(9))* Kessinger Publishing, LLC.

Merryweather, F. Somner. Bibliomania in the Middle Ages. 2009. 250p. pap. *(978-1-4099-8324-8(2))* Dodo Pr.

Merryweather, Frederick Somner. Bibliomania in the Middle Ages. 2008. 264p. 28.99 *(978-0-554-29820-7(1))*; 25.99 *(978-0-554-39123-6(6))* BiblioBazaar.

BIBLIOTHERAPY
see also Hospital Libraries; Reading, Psychology Of; Therapeutics

Aubry, Timothy Richard. Reading as Therapy: What Contemporary Fiction Does for Middle-Class Americans. 2011. 268p. pap. 39.95 *(978-1-58729-955-1(0))* Univ. of Iowa Pr.

Clum, George A. & Watkins, Patti Lou, eds. Handbook of Self-Help Therapies. 2007. (ENG.). 472p. 85.95 *(978-0-8058-5171-7(2))* Routledge.

Grace, Cathy & Shores, Elizabeth F. After the Crisis: Using Storybooks to Help Children Cope. 2010. (ENG.). 64p. pap. 9.95 *(978-0-87659-129-1(2))* Gryphon Hse., Inc.

Halsted, Judith Wynn. Some of My Best Friends Are Books: Guiding Gifted Readers. 3rd ed. 2009. pap. 29.95 *(978-0-910707-96-1(0))* Great Potential Pr., Inc.

Hynes, Arlene & Hynes-Berry, Mary. Biblio/Poetry Therapy: A Handbook. 2011. 320p. pap. 14.95 *(978-0-87839-410-4(9))* North Star Pr. of St. Cloud.

Lee, Terry. A New Path at Midlife: Transformative Relationship & Story for Men. 2007. xi, 88p. pap. *(978-1-931342-08-7(3))* Men's Studies Pr.

Leibsohn, Dana. Script & Glyph: Pre-Hispanic History, Colonial Bookmaking, & the Historia Tolteca-Chichimeca. 2009. (Dumbarton Oaks Pre-Columbian Art & Archaeology Studies Ser.: 36). (Illus.). 250p. 49.95 *(978-0-88402-361-6(3))* Dumbarton Oaks.

Lund, Mary Ann. Melancholy, Medicine & Religion in Early Modern England: Reading 'the Anatomy of Melancholy' 2010. (ENG.). 236p. 95.00 *(978-0-521-19050-3(9))* Cambridge Univ. Pr.

Recob, Amy. Bibliotherapy: When Kids Need Books. 2008. 224p. pap. 18.95 *(978-0-595-52530-0(X))* iUniverse, Inc.

Tongguk Taehakkyo, Pusol Han'guk Munhak Yon'guso Staff, contrib. by. Pulga Ui Kul Ssugi Wa Pulgyo Munhak Ui Kanungsong. 2010. 341p. *(978-89-7801-259-1(0))* Dong-guk Univ. Pr.

BICAMERALISM
see Legislative Bodies

BICENTENNIAL CELEBRATION (UNITED STATES), 1976
see American Revolution Bicentennial, 1776-1976

BICETYLENE
see Acetylene

BICHELAMAR JARGON
see Bislama Language

BICHON FRISE

Beauchamp, Richard G. Bichon Frise. (Barron's Dog Bibles Ser.). 2009. *(978-0-7641-6229-9(2))* 2nd ed. 2006. (ENG., Illus.). 96p. pap. 8.99 *(978-0-7641-3405-0(1))* Barron's Educational Series, Inc.

Hood, Karen Jean Matsko. Bichon Frise: A Basic Guide to this Canine Breed. 2009. pap. 29.95 *(978-1-59434-201-1(6))*; 128p. 29.95 *(978-1-59808-921-9(8))* Whispering Pine Pr. International, Inc.

Waldorf Gewirtz, Elaine. Bichons Frises, 1 vol. 2008. (Animal Planet Pet Care Library). (ENG., Illus.). 120p. 11.95 *(978-0-7938-3788-5(X))* TFH Pubns., Inc.

Wyatt. Bichon Frise: Owners Campanion. (Illus.). 224p. 45.00 *(978-1-86126-196-0(9))* Crowood Pr., Ltd. GBR. Dist: Trafalgar Square Publishing.

BICHON HAVANAIS
see Bichon Frise

BICHON MALTAIS
see Bichon Frise

BICKERSTAFFE, ISAAC, CA. 1735-CA. 1812

Steele, Richard. Isaac Bickerstaff. 2006. (ENG.). pap. *(978-1-4068-3015-6(1))* Echo Library.

BICULTURALISM

Assanand, Sunaina. Clashing Cultures, Clashing Selves? 2008. 84p. pap. *(978-3-639-04400-3(2))* VDM Verlag Dr. Mueller e.K.

Darder, Antonia. A Dissident Voice: Essays on Culture, Pedagogy, & Power. 2011. (Illus.). xvi, 482p. E-Book ***(978-1-4539-0152-6(3))***; (C). 149.95 ***(978-1-4331-1400-7(3))***; (C). pap. 36.95 ***(978-1-4331-1399-4(6))*** Lang, Peter Publishing, Inc.

Hasegawa, Sumika. The Roles of Heritage Language Schools. 2009. 104p. pap. *(978-3-639-14694-3(8))* VDM Verlag Dr. Mueller e.K.

Kalra, V. S., et al, eds. A Postcolonial People: South Asians in Britain. 2008. (Columbia/Hurst Ser.). (ENG., Illus.). 448p. (gr. 17). pap. 32.50 *(978-0-231-70012-2(1))* Columbia Univ. Pr.

Kalra, V. S. & Sayyid, S., eds. A Postcolonial People: South Asians in Britain. 2008. (Columbia/Hurst Ser.). (ENG.). 448p. (gr. 17). 84.50 *(978-0-231-70011-5(3))* Columbia Univ. Pr.

Kuh, George D., et al. Piecing Together the Student Success Puzzle: Research, Propositions, & Recommendations: ASHE Higher Education Report. 2007. (J-B ASHE Higher Education Report Series (AEHE) Ser.: 116). (ENG.). 200p. pap. 29.00 *(978-0-7879-9776-2(5),* Jossey-Bass) Wiley, John & Sons, Inc.

McCarthy, Conal. Museums & Maori: Heritage Professionals, Indigenous Collections, Current Practice. 2011. (ENG.). 334p. pap. 36.95 ***(978-1-61132-077-0(1))***; (Illus.). 99.95 ***(978-1-61132-076-3(3))*** Left Coast Pr., Inc.

Millard, Gregory. Secession & Self: Quebec in Canadian Thought. 2008. (ENG.). 368p. (C). *(978-0-7735-3384-4(2))* McGill-Queen's Univ. Pr.

Olivos, Edward M., et al, eds. Bicultural Parent Engagement: Advocacy & Empowerment. 2011. (ENG.). 256p. 66.00 ***(978-0-8077-5265-4(7))***; pap. 31.95 ***(978-0-8077-5264-7(9))*** Teachers College Pr., Teachers College, Columbia Univ.

Phim, Navy. Reflections of a Khmer Soul. 2007. 164p. per. 14.95 *(978-1-58736-861-5(7))* Wheatmark.

Portilla, Elizabeth de la. They All Want Magic: Curanderas & Folk Healing. 2009. (Rio Grande/Rio Bravo Ser.: No. 16). pap. 19.95 *(978-1-60344-114-8(X))*; (ENG.). 160p. 45.00 *(978-1-60344-099-8(2))* Texas A&M Univ. Pr.

Smokowski, Paul & Bacallao, Martica. Becoming Bicultural: Risk, Resilience, & Latino Youth. 2011. (ENG., Illus.). 256p. 75.00 *(978-0-8147-4089-7(8))*; pap. 24.00 *(978-0-8147-4090-3(1))* New York Univ. Pr.

Stock, Bracha. Bracha Means Blessing: Scenes from a Bi-Cultural Adoption. 2007. 104p. per. 11.95 *(978-0-595-46338-1(X))* iUniverse, Inc.

Taniwha, Rosina. From Theory to Practice - the Bicultural Reality. 2010. 120p. pap. *(978-3-8383-6990-7(4))* Lambert Academic Publishing.

BICUSPID VALVE
see Mitral Valve

BICYCLE RACING

Abt, Samuel & Startt, James. In Pursuit of the Yellow Jersey: Bicycle Racing in the Year of the Troubled Tour. 16.95 *(978-1-892495-15-0(5))* Cycle Publishing/Van Der Plas Pubns.

Armstrong, Lance. Lance Armstrong: Images of a Champion. rev. ed. 2006. (ENG., Illus.). 248p. pap. 24.95 *(978-1-59486-506-0(X))* Rodale Pr., Inc.

Augendre, Jacques. Tour de France Annual 2004. 24.95 *(978-0-7603-2060-0(8))* MBI Publishing Co. LLC.

Balf, Todd. Major: A Black Athlete, a White Era, & the Fight to Be the World's Fastest Human Being. 2009. (ENG., Illus.). 320p. pap. 14.00 *(978-0-307-23659-3(5)*, Three Rivers Pr.) Crown Publishing Group.

Baroni, Francesco. The Bicycle: The Myth & the Passion. 2008. (ENG., Illus.). 304p. 35.00 *(978-88-544-0336-9(9))* White Star ITA. Dist: Random Hse., Inc.

Bauer, Kristian. Ride a Stage of the Tour de France: The Legendary Climbs & How to Ride Them. 2011. (ENG., Illus.). 224p. pap. 25.95 *(978-1-4081-3333-0(4))* A & C Black GBR. Dist: Macmillan.

Boulting, Ned. How I Won the Yellow Jumper: Dispatches from the Tour de France. 2011. (ENG., Illus.). 316p. pap. 24.95 ***(978-0-224-08335-5(X))*** Random Hse. GBR. Dist: Independent Pubs. Group.

Bouvet, Philippe, et al. Paris-Roubaix: A Journey Through Hell. Herlihy, David, tr. from FRE. 2007. (FRE., Illus.). 223p. 39.95 *(978-1-934030-09-7(0))* VeloPress.

—The Spring Classics: Cycling's Greatest One-Day Races. 2010. (ENG., Illus.). 224p. 39.95 *(978-1-934030-60-8(0))* VeloPress.

Brownlee, Nick. Vive le Tour! Amazing Tales of the Tour de France. 2010. (ENG., Illus.). 288p. pap. 14.95 *(978-1-906032-92-0(0))* Anova Bks. GBR. Dist: Independent Pubs. Group.

Bruyneel, Johan & Strickland, Bill. We Might as Well Win: On the Road to Success with the Mastermind Behind a Record-Setting Eight Tour de France Victories. 2008. (ENG., Illus.). 240p. 25.00 *(978-0-618-87937-3(4))* Houghton Mifflin Harcourt Trade & Reference Pubs.

—We Might as Well Win: On the Road to Success with the Mastermind Behind Eight Tour de France Victories. 2009. (ENG.). 240p. pap. 14.95 *(978-0-547-23773-2(1)*, Mariner Bks.) Houghton Mifflin Harcourt Trade & Reference Pubs.

Burney, Simon. Cyclocross: Training + Technique. 3rd ed. 2007. (ENG., Illus.). 230p. per. 18.95 *(978-1-934030-05-9(8))* VeloPress.

Cavendish, Mark. Boy Racer: My Journey to Tour de France Record-Breaker. 2010. (ENG., Illus.). 320p. pap. 21.95 *(978-1-934030-64-6(3))* VeloPress.

Clark, Jerry & Joss, Bill. Cyclosportives: A Competitor's Guide. 2011. (ENG., Illus.). 144p. pap. 27.95 *(978-1-84797-244-6(6))* Crowood Pr., Ltd. GBR. Dist: Independent Pubs. Group.

Clements, Frank. A Bike Ride Through My Life. 2011. 440p. 33.95 ***(978-1-4269-6317-9(3))***; pap. 23.95 ***(978-1-4269-6266-0(5))*** Trafford Publishing.

Connor, Jeff. Wide-Eyed & Legless: Inside the Tour de France. 2011. (ENG., Illus.). 192p. 19.95 ***(978-1-84596-171-8(4))*** Mainstream Publishing Co., Ltd. GBR. Dist: Independent Pubs. Group.

Daly, Tom. The Rás: The Story of Ireland's Unique Bike Race. 2012. (ENG., Illus.). 352p. pap. 26.95 ***(978-1-84889-148-7(2))*** Collins Pr., The IRL. Dist: Dufour Editions, Inc.

De Ruig, Ann. I've Grown Accustomed to His Butt: The Record of Three Long Distance Cycle Rides in Tandem Through South Africa by Two Geriatrics in Order to Share with You the Homeland I Love Close up & Personal. 2010. (Illus.). 204p. pap. 25.85 *(978-1-4520-8616-3(8))* AuthorHouse.

Doughty, Simon. The Long Distance Cyclists' Handbook. 2nd ed. 2006. (ENG., Illus.). 264p. per. 16.95 *(978-1-59228-948-6(7)*, Lyons Pr.) Globe Pequot Pr., The.

Drake, Geoff & Ochowicz, Jim. Team 7-Eleven: The Complete History of How an Unsung Band of American Cyclists Took on the World - & Won. 2011. (ENG., Illus.). 352p. 27.95 *(978-1-934030-53-0(8))* VeloPress.

Dzierzak, Lou. The Evolution of American Bicycle Racing. 2007. (ENG., Illus.). 256p. per. 17.95 *(978-0-7627-3901-1(0)*, Falcon Guides) Globe Pequot Pr., The.

Fife, Graeme. Tour de France: The History, the Legend, the Riders. (ENG., Illus.). 2011. 508p. pap. 19.95 ***(978-1-84596-762-8(3))*** 2010. 400p. pap. 21.95 *(978-1-84596-563-1(9))* 2009. 448p. pap. 21.95 *(978-1-84596-322-4(9))* 2008. 412p. per. 21.95 *(978-1-84596-256-2(7))* Mainstream Publishing Co., Ltd. GBR. Dist: Independent Pubs. Group.

Foot, John. Pedalare! Pedalare! 2011. (ENG., Illus.). 1p. pap. 31.00 *(978-0-7475-9521-2(6))* Bloomsbury Publishing.

Forrester, Auriel & Barfield, Mark. Starting Cycle Road Racing & Time. 2008. (ENG., Illus.). 128p. pap. 33.95 *(978-1-84797-014-5(1))* Crowood Pr., Ltd. GBR. Dist: Independent Pubs. Group.

Fotheringham, William. Fallen Angel: The Passion of Fausto Coppi. 2010. (ENG., Illus.). 292p. pap. 16.95 *(978-0-224-07450-6(4))* Random Hse. GBR. Dist: Independent Pubs. Group.

—Put Me Back on My Bike: In Search of Tom Simpson. 2007. (ENG., Illus.). 272p. pap. 16.95 *(978-0-224-08018-7(0))* Random Hse. GBR. Dist: Independent Pubs. Group.

Friel, Joe, intro. The Cyclist's Training Diary. 2007. (ENG., Illus.). 260p. spiral bd. 15.95 *(978-1-934030-08-0(2))* VeloPress.

Furia, Emily, compiled by. The Big Book of Bicycling: Everything You Need to Know, from Buying Your First Bike to Riding Your Best. 2010. *(978-1-60529-486-5(1))* Rodale Pr., Inc.

Gabriele, Michael. The Nutley Velodrome: The Final Chapter of the Golden Age of Cycling. 2011. 128p. pap. 19.99 *(978-1-59629-427-1(2))* History Pr., The.

Garcia, Leah & Lovejoy, Jilayne. Knack Cycling for Everyone: A Guide to Road, Mountain, & Commuter Biking. 2010. (Knack: Make It Easy Ser.). (ENG., Illus.). 256p. pap. 19.95 *(978-1-59921-871-7(2)*, Knack) Globe Pequot Pr., The.

Heine, Jan. The Competition Bicycle: A Photographic History. 2008. (Illus.). 176p. *(978-0-9765460-1-6(9))* Vintage Bicycle Pr.

Heine, Jan. The Competition Bicycle: The Craftsmanship of Speed - A Photographic History. 2012. (ENG., Illus.). 168p. 50.00 ***(978-0-8478-3841-7(2))*** Rizzoli International Pubns., Inc.

Homan, Andrew M. Life in the Slipstream: The Legend of Bobby Walthour Sr. 2011. (Illus.). 280p. 26.95 *(978-1-59797-685-5(7))* Potomac Bks., Inc.

Homer, Jill. Ghost Trails. 2009. 188p. pap. 15.96 *(978-0-557-02407-0(2))* Lulu Enterprises Inc.

Hon, Shek. BMX Riding Skills: The Guide to Flatland Tricks. 2010. (ENG., Illus.). 128p. pap. 16.95 *(978-1-55407-400-6(2))* Firefly Bks., Ltd.

Howard, Paul. Eat, Sleep, Ride: How I Braved Bears, Badlands, & Big Breakfasts in My Quest to Cycle the Tour Divide, 1 vol. 2011. (ENG., Illus.). 272p. pap. 16.95 *(978-1-55365-817-7(5)*, Greystone Bks.) D&M Pubs. Inc. CAN. Dist: Perseus-PGW.

Hoy, Chris. Chris Hoy: The Autobiography. (ENG., Illus.). 352p. 2010. pap. 14.95 *(978-0-00-731132-3(X))* 2009. 29.95 *(978-0-00-731131-6(1))* HarperCollins Pubs. Ltd. GBR. Dist: Independent Pubs. Group.

Johanson, Paula. Lance Armstrong: A Biography. 2011. E-Book *(978-0-313-38691-6(9)*, Greenwood Pr.) Greenwood Publishing Group, Inc.

Johanson, Paula Marie. Lance Armstrong: A Biography, 1 vol. 2011. (Greenwood Biographies Ser.). (Illus.). 153p. 35.00 *(978-0-313-38690-9(0)*, A3127C) Greenwood Publishing Group, Inc.

Johnson, Mark. Argyle Armada: Behind the Scenes of the Pro Cycling Life. 2012. (ENG., Illus.). 200p. 39.95 ***(978-1-934030-81-3(3))*** VeloPress.

Laborde, Christian. Le Tour de France Dans les Pyrénées: De 1910 à Lance Armstrong. 2010. (FRE., Illus.). 201p. *(978-2-7491-1387-6(3))* Le Cherche Midi Editeur.

Laget, Serge. Treas of the tour de France. 2007. (Illus.). 64p. *(978-1-84732-018-6(X))* Carlton Bks., Ltd.

Laget, Serge & Edwardes-Evans, Luke. The Official Treasures: le Tour de France. 2008. (Illus.). 64p. *(978-1-84732-086-5(4))* Carlton Bks., Ltd.

—The Official Treasures: le Tour de France: Fifth Edition. 2012. (ENG., Illus.). 64p. 45.00 ***(978-1-78097-087-5(0))*** Carlton Bks., Ltd. GBR. Dist: Sterling Publishing Co., Inc.

Laget, Serge & Edwardes-Evans, Luke. The Treasures of the Tour de France. 4th ed. 2010. (ENG., Illus.). 64p. 45.00 *(978-1-84732-550-1(5))* Carlton Bks., Ltd. GBR. Dist: Sterling Publishing Co., Inc.

Lee, Daniel. Belgian Hammer: Forging Young Americans into Professional Cyclists. 2011. (ENG., Illus.). 208p. pap. 15.00 ***(978-1-891369-91-9(1))*** Breakaway Bks.

McGann, Bill & McGann, Carol. The Story of the Tour de France. 2006. (Illus.). 316p. per. 15.95 *(978-1-59858-180-5(5))* Dog Ear Publishing, LLC.

—The Story of the Tour de France: 1965-2007. 2008. (ENG., Illus.). 392p. pap. 19.95 *(978-1-59858-608-4(4))* Dog Ear Publishing, LLC.

Millar, David. Racing Through the Dark: Crash. Burn. Coming Clean. Coming Back. 2012. (ENG., Illus.). 368p. 26.00 ***(978-1-4516-8268-7(9)***, Touchstone) Touchstone.

Molsberry, Robert. Tour de Faith: A Cyclist's Lessons for Living. 2007. (ENG.). 144p. per. 14.95 *(978-1-56101-316-6(1))* Cowley Pubns.

Moore, Gerry & Ritchie, Andrew. The Little Black Bottle: Choppy Warburton, His Mysterious Potion, & the Deaths of His Bicycle Racers. 2011. (Illus.). 160p. pap. 18.95 *(978-1-892495-67-9(8))* Cycle Publishing/Van Der Plas Pubns.

Moore, Richard. Sky's the Limit: British Cycling's Quest to Conquer the Tour de France. 2011. (ENG., Illus.). 352p. 26.95 ***(978-0-00-734183-2(0))*** HarperCollins Pubs. Ltd. GBR. Dist: Independent Pubs. Group.

—Sky's the Limit: Cavendish & Wiggins - The Quest to Conquer the Tour de France. (ENG., Illus.). 368p. *(978-0-00-734182-5(2))* Merril Pr.

Moore, Richard. Slaying the Badger: Greg Lemond, Bernard Hinault, & the Greatest Tour de France. 2012. (ENG., Illus.). 304p. pap. 18.95 ***(978-1-934030-87-5(2))*** VeloPress.

Muenzer, Lori-Ann. One Gear, No Breaks: Lori-Ann Muenzer's Ride to Belief, Belonging, & a Gold Medal. rev. ed. 2007. (ENG., Illus.). 256p. pap. 15.95 *(978-1-55263-883-5(9))* Key Porter Bks. CAN. Dist: Perseus-PGW.

Nye, Peter. Six Day Bicycle Races. 2010. (Illus.). 224p. 39.95 *(978-1-892495-49-5(X))* Cycle Publishing/Van Der Plas Pubns.

Oliver, Matt. Taupo 101. 2010. (Illus.). 170p. pap. *(978-1-877561-81-8(9))* First Edition Ltd.

Ortolani, Theresa, photos by. Endurance: Down & Dirty Off-Road Racing. 2009. (ENG., Illus.). 176p. 39.95 *(978-1-57687-517-9(2)*, powerHouse Bks.) powerHouse Cultural Entertainment, Inc.

Parkin, Joe. Come & Gone: A True Story of Blue-Collar Bike Racing in America. 2010. (ENG., Illus.). 208p. pap. 21.95 *(978-1-934030-54-7(6))* VeloPress.

Pellizzari, Paolo. Tours of the World. 2008. (ENG., Illus.). 168p. 45.00 *(978-88-7439-169-1(2))* 5 Continents ITA. Dist: Hachette Bk. Group.

Peveler, Willard. The Complete Book of Road Cycling & Racing. 2008. (ENG., Illus.). 240p. pap. 18.95 *(978-0-07-148937-9(1)*, 0071489371, International Marine/Ragged Mountain Pr.) McGraw-Hill Professional Publishing.

Pickering, Edward. Cycling for Competition: All you need to know about every type of racing, from track racing & time-trialling to cyclo-cross & triathlon, all shown in 200 Photographs. 2011. (ENG., Illus.). 96p. pap. 16.99 *(978-1-84476-827-1(9))* Anness Publishing GBR. Dist: National Bk. Network.

Pickering, Edward. Cycling for Sport: Mountain Bikes, Free Riding & Sportive Races: the Ultimate Guide to Moving up a Gear: the Challenges of off-Road & on-Road Cycling in over 230 Step-by-Step Photographs. 2012. (ENG., Illus.). 96p. pap. 17.99 ***(978-1-78019-016-7(6))*** Anness Publishing GBR. Dist: National Bk. Network.

Rendell, Matt. Blazing Saddles MMP: The Cruel & Unusual History of the Tour de France. 2nd ed. 2008. (Illus.). 304p. pap. *(978-1-84724-382-9(7)*, Quercus) Quercus.

—Kings of the Mountains: How Colombia's Cycling Heroes Changed Their Nation's History. (Illus.). 256p. 14.99 *(978-1-85410-911-8(1))* Aurum Pr., Ltd. GBR. Dist: Trafalgar Square Publishing.

—Olympic Gangster: The Legend of José Beyaert - Cycling Champion, Fortune Hunter & Outlaw. 2011. (ENG., Illus.). 352p. pap. 15.95 *(978-1-84596-593-8(0))* Mainstream Publishing Co., Ltd. GBR. Dist: Independent Pubs. Group.

Rendell, Matthew. Olympic Gangster: The Legend of José Beyaert - Cycling Champion, Fortune Hunter & Outlaw. 2009. (ENG., Illus.). 352p. pap. 22.95 *(978-1-84596-398-9(9))* Mainstream Publishing Co., Ltd. GBR. Dist: Independent Pubs. Group.

Riedy, Mark. The Cycling Trivia Book: 1001 Questions from the Velocipede to Lance. 2008. (ENG.). 288p. pap. 14.00 *(978-1-891369-79-7(2))* Breakaway Bks.

Ritchie, Andrew. Major Taylor: The Fastest Bicycle Rider in the World. 2nd ed. 2009. (Illus.). 240p. 39.95 *(978-1-892495-65-5(1))* Cycle Publishing/Van Der Plas Pubns.

Strickland, Bill. Tour de Lance: The Extraordinary Story of Cycling's Most Controversial Champion. 2011. (ENG., Illus.). 336p. pap. 16.00 *(978-0-307-58995-8(1)*, Three Rivers Pr.) Crown Publishing Group.

Stuart, James. Tour de France: A Visual History of the World's Greatest Bicycle Race. rev. ed. 2007. (Illus.). 158p. reprint ed. pap. 23.00 *(978-1-4223-9002-3(0))* DIANE Publishing Co.

Taylor, Amy. Lake Taupo Cycle Challenge Guide: Conquer New Zealand's Great Ride. 2009. (ENG., Illus.). 272p. pap. 19.95 *(978-0-9582916-1-3(6))* Awa Pr. NZL. Dist: Independent Pubs. Group.

Thomas, Steve, et al. The Racing Bike Book. 3rd ed. 2008. (ENG., Illus.). 176p. 29.95 *(978-1-84425-341-8(4)*, 1844253414) Haynes Publishing PLC GBR. Dist: MBI Distribution Services/Quayside Distribution.

Thompson, Christopher S. The Tour de France: A Cultural History. 2nd ed. 2008. (Illus.). 385p. pap. 24.95 *(978-0-520-25630-9(1))* Univ. of California Pr.

Walsh, David. From Lance to Landis: Inside the American Doping Controversy at the Tour de France. 2007. (ENG., Illus.). 352p. 24.95 *(978-0-345-49962-2(X)*, Ballantine Bks.) Random House Publishing Group.

Wheatcroft, Geoffrey. Le Tour: A History of the Tour de France. 2007. (ENG., Illus.). 396p. pap. 17.95 *(978-1-84739-086-8(2))* Simon & Schuster, Ltd. GBR. Dist: Independent Pubs. Group.

Wiggins, Bradley. In Pursuit of Glory. 2009. (ENG., Illus.). 288p. *(978-0-7528-9863-6(9))* Orion Bks. Ltd. GBR. Dist: Sterling Publishing Co., Inc.

Wiggins, Bradley. On Tour. 2010. (ENG., Illus.). 192p. pap. 26.95 ***(978-1-4091-3136-6(X))*** Orion Publishing Group, Ltd. GBR. Dist: Independent Pubs. Group.

Wilcockson, John. Lance: The Making of the World's Greatest Champion. (ENG.). 2010. 432p. pap. 15.95 *(978-0-306-81874-5(4))* 2009. (Illus.). 416p. 26.00 *(978-0-306-81587-4(7))* Da Capo Pr., Inc.

Wilcockson, John & VeloNews Editors. The 2007 Tour de France: A New Generation Takes the Stage. 2007. (Tour de France Ser.). (ENG., Illus.). 214p. per. 21.95 *(978-1-934030-10-3(4))* VeloPress.

Wills, Mike. Cycle Tour. 2008. 144p. pap. 28.95 *(978-1-77013-065-4(9))* Double Storey Bks. ZAF. Dist: International Publishers Marketing.

Woodland, Les. The Unknown Tour de France: The Many Faces of the World's Biggest Bicycle Race. 2nd rev. ed. 2009. (Illus.). 152p. 39.95 *(978-1-892495-63-1(5))* Cycle Publishing/Van Der Plas Pubns.

BICYCLE TOURING

Anderson, Shawn. Extra Mile America: Stories of Inspiration, Possibility & Purpose. 2010. 232p. pap. 19.95 *(978-0-9820974-2-7(5))* Goldmind Pr.

Bartulski, Barrie C. The Red Schwinn Bicycle: A Sentimental Journey. 2007. 128p. per. 13.95 *(978-0-595-41094-1(4))* iUniverse, Inc.

Beaumont, Mark. The Man Who Cycled the World. 2011. (ENG.). 400p. pap. 16.00 *(978-0-307-71665-1(1))* Broadway Bks.

Beryl Doiron With Bernie Doiron. Rusticoriders Cycle Afric: From Cairo to Cape Town. 2009. 208p. 29.95 *(978-1-4490-4970-6(2))* AuthorHouse.

Biers-Ariel, Matt. The Bar Mitzvah & the Beast: One Family's Cross-Country Ride of Passage by Bike. 2012. (ENG.). 256p. pap. ***(978-1-59485-672-3(9))***; E-Book ***(978-1-59485-673-0(7))*** Mountaineers Bks., The.

Brook, Nancy. Cycling, Wine, & Men: A Midlife Tour de France. 2011. (ENG.). 270p. pap. 16.95 *(978-1-60037-827-0(7))* Morgan James Publishing.

Byrne, David. Bicycle Diaries. 2010. (ENG.). 320p. (gr. 12). 16.00 *(978-0-14-311796-4(3)*, Penguin (Non-Classics)) Penguin Group (USA) Inc.

Chase, Sarah Leah. Pedaling Through Burgundy Cookbook. 2008. (ENG.). 192p. pap. 15.00 *(978-1-4223-9437-3(9))* DIANE Publishing Co.

Cox, Fred. Lancaster & Chester Counties. 2010. (25 Bicycle Tours Ser.). (ENG., Illus.). 176p. pap. 17.95 *(978-0-88150-884-0(5)*, 150884) Countryman Pr.

Dew, Josie. Long Cloud Ride: A Cycling Adventure Across New Zealand. 2008. (ENG., Illus.). 352p. pap. 17.95 *(978-0-7515-3584-6(2))* Little, Brown Bk. Group Ltd. GBR. Dist: Independent Pubs. Group.

Doiron, Beryl & Doiron, Bernie. Rusticoriders Cycle Afric: From Cairo to Cape Town. 2009. 208p. pap. 21.95 *(978-1-4490-4971-3(0))* AuthorHouse.

Doug Freedline. Summer Of 1977: A North American Bicycling Odyssey. 2009. 592p. 43.95 *(978-1-4401-5093-7(1))*; pap. 33.95 *(978-1-4401-0020-8(9))* iUniverse, Inc.

Dunlop, Ian, ed. Ontario Bicycle Touring Atlas. 2008. 124p. pap. *(978-1-894955-21-8(8))* Dun-Map, Inc.

Enfield, Edward. Downhill All the Way: Bicycling Across France. l.t. ed. 240p. 23.95 *(978-1-85695-202-6(9))* ISIS Large Print Bks. GBR. Dist: Transaction Pubs.

Enfield, Edward. Greece on My Wheels. 2012. (ENG., Illus.). 320p. pap. 14.95 ***(978-1-84953-168-9(4))*** Summerdale Pubs. GBR. Dist: Independent Pubs. Group.

Farmer, Daryl. Bicycling beyond the Divide: Two Journeys into the West. 2008. (Outdoor Lives Ser.). (ENG., Illus.). 331p. 26.95 *(978-0-8032-2034-8(0))* Univ. of Nebraska Pr.

Forsyth, Judith & Forsyth, Neil. Cycle Touring in Switzerland: Nine Tours on Switzerland's National Cycle Routes. 2010. (Illus.). 272p. pap. 22.95 *(978-1-85284-526-1(0))* Cicerone Pr. GBR. Dist: Midpoint Trade Bks., Inc.

Gill, Dominic. Take a Seat: One Man, One Tandem & Twenty Thousand Miles of Possibilities. 2010. (ENG., Illus.). 288p. pap. 16.95 *(978-0-7627-7069-4(4)*, Falcon Guides) Globe Pequot Pr., The.

Guise, Richard. From the Mull to the Cape: A Gentle Bike Ride on the Edge of theWilderness. 2008. (ENG., Illus.). 256p. pap. 14.95 ***(978-1-84024-674-2(X))*** Summerdale Pubs. GBR. Dist: Independent Pubs. Group.

—Two Wheels over Catalonia. 2011. (ENG., Illus.). 320p. pap. 13.95 ***(978-1-84953-144-3(7))*** Summerdale Pubs. GBR. Dist: Independent Pubs. Group.

Herlihy, David V. The Lost Cyclist: The Epic Tale of an American Adventurer & His Mysterious Disappearance. 2010. (ENG., Illus.). 336p. 26.00 *(978-0-547-19557-5(5))* Houghton Mifflin Harcourt Trade & Reference Pubs.

Homer, Jill. Be Brave, Be Strong: A Journey Across the Great Divide. 2011. 342p. pap. 19.95 ***(978-1-257-65858-9(1))*** Lulu Enterprises Inc.

Honeywell, Alice & Montgomery, Bobbi. Across America by Bicycle: Alice & Bobbi's Summer on Wheels. 2010. (ENG., Illus.). 300p. pap. 21.95 *(978-0-299-24884-0(4))* Univ. of Wisconsin Pr.

Howell, Joel D. Washtenaw County Bike Rides: A Guide to Road Rides in & around Ann Arbor. 2009. (ENG., Illus.). 96p. pap. 12.95 *(978-0-472-03330-0(1))* Univ. of Michigan Pr.

Humphreys, Alastair. Moods of Future Joys. 2nd rev. ed. 2007. (ENG.). 250p. pap. 12.95 *(978-1-903070-56-7(2))* Eye Bks. GBR. Dist: Independent Pubs. Group.

Jenkins, Mark. Off the Map: Bicycling Across Siberia. 2008. (ENG., Illus.). 256p. pap. 15.95 *(978-1-59486-764-4(X)*, Modern Times) Rodale Pr., Inc.

Knowlden, Martin. AA 50 Cycles to Country Pubs. 2006. (Walking Bks.). (ENG., Illus.). 208p. pap. 19.95 *(978-0-7495-4812-4(6))* Automobile Assn. GBR. Dist: Independent Pubs. Group.

Kurmaskie, Joe. Momentum Is Your Friend: The Metal Cowboy & His Pint-Sized Posse Take on America. 2006. (ENG., Illus.). 272p. 23.95 *(978-1-891369-65-0(2))* Breakaway Bks.

Lacy, Paul. Brooklyn Storefronts. 2008. (ENG., Illus.). 160p. pap. 17.95 *(978-0-393-33002-1(8)*, 33002) Norton, W. W. & Co., Inc.

Last, Antony. One Man & LEJOG: End-To-End on Two Wheels in Two Weeks. 2011. 80p. pap. 10.50 ***(978-1-4461-7196-7(5))*** Lulu Enterprises Inc.

Lilwall, Rob. Cycling Home from Siberia: 30,000 Miles, 3 Years, 1 Bicycle. 2011. (ENG., Illus.). 432p. pap. 14.99 *(978-1-4516-0786-4(5)*, Howard Bks.) Howard Books.

Lobigs, Martin. A Life on Wheels: Biking Alone from Newfoundland to Latin America: 1999-2004. 2007. (Illus.). 222p. per. *(978-1-897174-19-7(5))* Creative Bk. Publishing.

Lord, Stephen. Adventure Cycle-Touring. 2nd rev. ed. 2010. (ENG., Illus.). 312p. pap., instr.'s hndbk. ed. 21.95 *(978-1-905864-25-6(6))* Trailblazer Pubns. GBR. Dist: Globe Pequot Pr., The.

Lowthian, M. Russ. Minnesota: A Guide to the Greatest Bike Rides in Minnesota. 2007. (Road Biking Ser.). (ENG., Illus.). 232p. per. 15.95 *(978-0-7627-3801-4(4)*, Falcon Guides) Globe Pequot Pr., The.

Lynes, John. Ontario's Bike Paths & Rail Trails. 3rd ed. 2007. (Ulysses Green Escapes: Ontario's Bike Paths & Rail Trails Ser.). (Illus.). 172p. spiral bd. 17.95 *(978-2-89464-648-9(8))* Hunter Publishing, Inc.

Maka, Gwen. Riding with Ghosts. 2010. (Eye Classics Ser.). (ENG.). 288p. pap. 12.95 *(978-1-903070-77-2(5))* Eye Bks. GBR. Dist: Independent Pubs. Group.

Malusa, Jim. Into Thick Air: Biking to the Bellybutton of Six Continents. 2008. (ENG., Illus.). 336p. pap. 16.95 *(978-1-57805-141-0(X))* Sierra Club Bks.

Mark Jenkins. Off the Map: Bicycling Across Siberia. 2008. pap. 12.95 *(978-1-60529-913-6(8)*, Modern Times) Rodale Pr., Inc.

Mendoza, Louis G. A Journey Around Our America: A Memoir on Cycling, Immigration, & the Latinoization of the U. S. 2012. (ENG.). 222p. pap. 25.00 ***(978-0-292-74387-8(4))***; (Illus.). 55.00 ***(978-0-292-74208-6(8))*** Univ. of Texas Pr.

Meredith, Fred. Mountain Biking Texas: A Guide to the Greatest Bike Rides in Texas. 2009. (Road Biking Ser.). (Illus.). pap. 15.95 *(978-0-7627-3910-3(X)*, Falcon Guides) Globe Pequot Pr., The.

Mitchell, Michael D. Road to Glory. 2006. (ENG.). 31.99 *(978-1-4257-4021-4(9))*; pap. 21.99 *(978-1-4257-4020-7(0))* Xlibris Corp.

Murphy, Tim, ed. Journey to the Tar Sands. 2008. (ENG., Illus.). 96p. pap. 19.95 *(978-1-55277-039-9(7))* Lorimer, James & Co., Ltd., Pubs. CAN. Dist: Casemate Pubs. & Bk. Distributors, LLC.

Newlin, Larry. Coast to Coast on the Big O. 2009. 238p. pap. 15.95 *(978-1-60594-323-7(1),* Llumina Pr.) Aeon Publishing Inc.
Olverson, Eric. Eric on His Bike - a Home to Head For. 2011. (Illus.). 258p. pap. ***(978-0-7552-1343-6(2))*** Authors OnLine, Ltd.
Pintkowski, Mari. Shifting Gears: A Journey of Reinvention. 2011. 232p. 28.95 ***(978-1-4620-1740-9(1));*** pap. 18.95 ***(978-1-4620-1735-5(5))*** iUniverse, Inc.
Purdum, Stan & Fishel, Murray. Pedaling along the North Coast: Biking the Streets of Cleveland. 2011. 211p. pap. 19.95 *(978-1-931968-96-6(9))* Univ. of Akron Pr., The.
Rankin, Alan. Solo Round Scotland: The first single-handed circumnavigation by boat & Bike. 2010. (Illus.). 224p. pap. *(978-1-84995-003-9(2))* Whittles Publishing.
Shackleton, Andy. Arctic Cycle Two Wheels Ice & Fire. 2006. pap. *(978-1-904999-33-1(6))* Kennedy & Boyd.
Shaw, Mary. Linking Up. 3rd ed. 2007. pap. 4.00 *(978-0-9792108-1-5(X))* Great Allegheny Pr.
Stevens, Thomas. Around the World on a Bicycle. 2010. (ENG.). 606p. pap. 45.75 *(978-1-171-75083-3(8))* 2010. (ENG.). 568p. pap. 43.75 *(978-1-147-33993-7(X))* 2010. (ENG.). 498p. pap. 38.75 *(978-1-145-59394-7(1))* 2008. 508p. 32.99 *(978-0-554-36350-9(X))* 2008. 508p. 35.99 *(978-0-554-27047-0(1))* BiblioBazaar.
—Around the World on a Bicycle. 2010. 324p. pap. *(978-1-151-89934-7(8))* 2009. 350p. pap. *(978-0-217-44033-2(9))* Books LLC.
—Around the World on a Bicycle. 2010. 296p. pap. 37.30 *(978-1-151-89937-8(2));* 354p. pap. 16.91 *(978-1-152-18928-7(X))* General Bks. LLC.
—Around the World on A Bicycle Volume I. 2006. pap. *(978-1-4068-2204-5(3))* Echo Library.
—Around the World on A Bicycle Volume Ii. 2006. pap. *(978-1-4068-3038-5(0))* Echo Library.
—Around the World on a Bicycle Volume II: From Teheran to Yokohama. 2007. (ENG.). 452p. pap. 28.99 *(978-1-4346-2399-7(8)),* 504p. pap. 31.99 *(978-1-4346-2445-1(5))* BiblioBazaar.
Stuhaug, Dennis. Basic Essentials Bicycle Touring. 2nd ed. 2006. (Basic Essentials Ser.). (ENG., Illus.). 64p. per. 8.95 *(978-0-7627-4009-3(4),* Falcon Guides) Globe Pequot Pr., The.
Stutzman, Paul. Biking Through. 2011. 228p. 23.95 ***(978-0-9846449-0-2(3))*** Wandering Home Bks.
Thorness, Bill. Biking Puget Sound: 50 Rides from Olympia to the San Juans. 2007. (ENG., Illus.). 253p. per. 18.95 *(978-0-89886-943-9(9))* Mountaineers Bks., The.
Tim, Travis & Cindie, Travis. Down the Road in South America: A bicycle tour through poverty, paradise, & the places in Between. 2008. (ENG., Illus.). 284p. pap. 21.95 *(978-0-9754427-3-9(2))* Down The Road Publishing.
Travis, Tim & Travis, Cindie. Down the Road in Thailand, Cambodia & Vietnam: A Bicycle Tour Through War, Genocide & Forgiveness. 2010. (Illus.). 228p. pap. ***(978-0-9754427-6-0(7))*** Down The Road Publishing.
Trussell, John T. Road Biking Georgia: A Guide to the Greatest Bicycle Rides in Georgia. 2008. (Road Biking Ser.). (ENG., Illus.). 224p. per. 18.95 *(978-0-7627-3626-7(X),* Falcon Guides) Globe Pequot Pr., The.
Vande Kappelle, Robert P. The Invisible Mountain. 2010. 174p. pap. 20.00 *(978-1-60899-860-9(6),* Resource Pubns.) Wipf & Stock Pubs.
Vernon, Tom. Fat Man on a Bicycle: A Discovery of France. l.t. ed. 392p. 22.95 *(978-1-85695-201-9(0))* ISIS Large Print Bks. GBR. Dist: Transaction Pubs.
Winyard Sr., David C. Shore to Shore, A Father-and-Son Journey Across America. 2008. 284p. pap. 18.00 *(978-1-4303-1758-6(2))* Lulu Enterprises Inc.
Wolfe, D. H. No Excess Baggage: A world tour on two wheels - no motor but lots of Steam. 2009. 124p. pap. 35.99 *(978-1-4251-8600-5(9))* Trafford Publishing.
Zheutlin, Peter. Around the World on Two Wheels: Annie Londonderry's Extraordinary Ride. 2008. (ENG., Illus.). 40p. 14.95 *(978-0-8065-3066-6(9),* Citadel Pr.) Kensington Publishing Corp.

BICYCLE TOURING—GUIDEBOOKS

AA Publishing Staff, creator. London & the South Coast. 2007. (25 Cycle Rides Ser.). (ENG., Illus.). 112p. pap. 18.00 *(978-0-7495-5191-9(7))* Automobile Assn. GBR. Dist: Independent Pubs. Group.
Ainsley, Rob & Humphreys, Alastair. Thunder & Sunshine. 2008. (ENG.). 350p. pap. 12.95 *(978-1-903070-54-3(6))* Eye Bks. GBR. Dist: Independent Pubs. Group.
Barrett, Richard. Cycling in the Hebrides: Island Touring & Day Rides. 2012. (ENG., Illus.). 304p. pap. 24.95 ***(978-1-85284-643-5(7))*** Cicerone Pr. GBR. Dist: Midpoint Trade Bks., Inc.
Basch, Marty. The White Mountain Ride Guide. 2nd ed. 2007. pap. 14.95 *(978-0-9646510-4-3(1))* Top of the World Communications.
Baumgartner, Celeste. Ohio: A Guide to the State's Best Bike Rides. 2010. (Road Biking Ser.). (ENG., Illus.). 208p. pap. 16.95 *(978-0-7627-3963-9(0),* Falcon Guides) Globe Pequot Pr., The.
Benjaminse, Paul. Around Ireland on a Bike: The complete guide: maps, accommodation, practical Advice. 2012. (ENG., Illus.). 128p. spiral bd. 22.95 ***(978-1-84717-309-6(8))*** O'Brien Pr., Ltd., The IRL. Dist: Dufour Editions, Inc.
Botzman, Harvey. Finger Lakes Bicyclist's Tour Guide. 2nd rev. ed. 2011. (Illus.). 288p. per. 26.95 *(978-1-889602-33-2(7))* Cyclotour Guide Bks.
—'Round Lake Ontario: A Bicyclist's Tour Guide. 3rd ed. 2008. (Great Lakes Bicycle Touring Ser.: 1). (ENG., Illus.). 240p. per. 25.95 *(978-1-889602-34-9(5))* Cyclotour Guide Bks.
Brady, Patrick. Bicycling Los Angeles County: A Guide to Great Road Bike Rides. 2007. (Bicycling Ser.). (ENG., Illus.). 240p. per. 15.95 *(978-0-89732-950-7(3))* Menasha Ridge Pr., Inc.
Brundige, Don & Brundige, Sharron. Cycling Los Angeles. 3rd ed. 2007. (Illus.). 267p. per. 15.95 *(978-0-932653-81-9(2))* Sunbelt Pubns., Inc.
—Cycling Orange County: 58 Rides with Detailed Maps & Elevation Contours. 3rd ed. 2006. (Illus.). 205p. per. 14.95 *(978-0-932653-80-2(4))* Sunbelt Pubns., Inc.
Cantele, Andi Marie. Backroad Bicycling in Connecticut: 32 Scenic Rides on Country Lanes & Dirt Roads. 2nd ed. 2007. (Backroad Bicycling Ser.). (ENG., Illus.). 216p. per. 16.95 *(978-0-88150-730-0(X),* 150730) Countryman Pr.
Castle, Alan. The Grand Traverse of the Massif Central: By Mountain Bike, Road Bike or on Foot. 2010. (Illus.). 192p. pap. 22.95 *(978-1-85284-571-1(6))* Cicerone Pr. GBR. Dist: Midpoint Trade Bks., Inc.
Chestney, Linda. Bicycling New Hampshire's Seacoast. rev. ed. 2010. (Illus.). 160p. pap. 17.95 *(978-1-58465-871-9(1))* Univ. Pr. of New England.
Cooper, Tom. Cycle Touring in Ireland: 12 Routes Throughout Ireland. 2010. (Illus.). 256p. pap. 22.95 *(978-1-85284-562-9(7))* Cicerone Pr. GBR. Dist: Midpoint Trade Bks., Inc.
Copp, Nelson. Cycling Palm Springs Region. 2008. 160p. pap. 17.95 *(978-0-932653-93-2(6))* Sunbelt Pubns., Inc.
Cotton, Nick. Cycling Traffic-Free: Home Counties: Berkshire, Oxfordshire, Buckinghamshire, Bedfordshire, Hertfordshire, Essex & Sussex. 2010. (Cycling Traffic-Free Ser.). (ENG., Illus.). 112p. pap. 16.95 *(978-0-7110-3435-8(4),* Allan, Ian Publishing GBR. Dist: BookMasters Distribution Services (BDS).
Cottrell, Wayne. Road Biking Utah: A Guide to the State's Best Bike Rides. 2010. (Road Biking Ser.). (ENG., Illus.). 272p. pap. 16.95 *(978-0-7627-3962-2(2),* 1310310, Falcon Guides) Globe Pequot Pr., The.
Doherty, Tim. This Breathtaking World: Around the World by Bicycle 1997 - 1999. 2009. 273p. pap. 21.50 *(978-1-4452-2150-2(0))* Lulu Enterprises Inc.
Doughty, Simon. The Long Distance Cyclists' Handbook. 2nd ed. 2006. (ENG., Illus.). 264p. per. 16.95 *(978-1-59228-948-6(7),* Lyons Pr.) Globe Pequot Pr., The.
Duling, Sandra. Northern New England: A Guide to the Greatest Bike Rides in Vermont, New Hampshire, & Maine. 2008. (Road Biking Ser.). (ENG., Illus.). 200p. pap. 17.95 *(978-0-7627-3897-7(9),* Falcon Guides) Globe Pequot Pr., The.
Eastoe, Jane. Britain by Bike: A Two-Wheeled Odyssey Around Britain. 2010. (ENG., Illus.). 200p. 22.95 *(978-1-906388-71-3(7),* Batsford, B. T. Ltd.) Anova Bks. GBR. Dist: Sterling Publishing Co., Inc.
Enfield, Edward. Dawdling by the Danube. 2008. (ENG., Illus.). 240p. pap. 12.95 ***(978-1-84024-637-7(5))*** Summersdale Pubs. GBR. Dist: Independent Pubs. Group.
—Downhill All the Way. 2007. (ENG.). 224p. pap. 12.95 ***(978-1-84024-560-8(3))*** Summersdale Pubs. GBR. Dist: Independent Pubs. Group.
Evans, Jeremy. The C2C Cycle Route: Coast to Coast Across Northern England. 2011. (Illus.). 160p. pap. 21.95 *(978-1-85284-649-7(6))* Cicerone Pr. GBR. Dist: Midpoint Trade Bks., Inc.
Fox, Stephen. Cycle Touring in France: Eight Selected Cycle Tours. 2010. (Illus.). 256p. pap. 19.95 *(978-1-85284-432-5(9))* Cicerone Pr. GBR. Dist: Midpoint Trade Bks., Inc.
Fremantle, Tom. Johnny Ginger's Last Ride. 2007. 400p. per. 28.00 *(978-1-59048-249-0(2))* Long Riders' Guild Pr., The.
Gibney, James. A bit about Japan, India, New Zealand & Queensland Too. 2010. 130p. pap. 19.00 *(978-0-557-53506-4(9))* Lulu Enterprises Inc.
Hastings, Selina, et al. Cycling in the UK: The Official Guide to the National Cycle Network. 2009. (ENG., Illus.). 272p. 39.95 *(978-0-7495-6279-3(X))* Automobile Assn. GBR. Dist: Independent Pubs. Group.
Hosler, Raymond. Bay Area Bike Rides Deck. 2008. (ENG.). 50p. 14.95 *(978-0-8118-6526-5(6))* Chronicle Bks. LLC.
Hoven, Ray. Wisconsin Mountain Bike Trails. Date not set. (Illus.). 128p. pap. 14.95 *(978-1-57430-025-3(3))* American Bike Trails.
Hurst, Robert. The Bicycle Commuter's: Gear You Need * Clothing to Wear * Tips for Traffic * Roadside Repair. 2009. (Falcon Pocket Guides Ser.). (ENG., Illus.). 32p. instr.'s gde. ed. 9.95 *(978-0-7627-5127-3(4),* Falcon Guides) Globe Pequot Pr., The.
Iowa's Bike Trails. 2008. 160p. pap. 15.95 *(978-1-57430-140-3(3))* American Bike Trails.
James, David A., photos by. Cycling Arizona: The Statewide Road Biking Guide. 2007. (Illus.). 280p. pap. 19.95 *(978-1-56579-537-2(7))* Westcliffe Pubs.
Johnstone, Stuart A. Bike Paths of Massachusetts: A Guide to Rail-Trails & Other Car-Free Places. 3rd ed. 2006. (Illus.). 235p. pap. 17.95 *(978-0-9627990-6-8(8))* Active Pubns.
Kick, Peter W. Backroad Bicycling in the Hudson Valley & Catskills. 2006. (Countryman Guide Ser.). (ENG., Illus.). 224p. per. 16.95 *(978-0-88150-578-8(1),* 150578) Countryman Pr.
Knowlden, Martin. AA Britain's Favourite Pub Walks & Cycle Rides. 2006. (Walking Bks.). (ENG., Illus.). 256p. pap. 19.95 *(978-0-7495-4946-9(0))* Automobile Assn. GBR. Dist: Independent Pubs. Group.
Kraft, Skye. San Francisco & the Bay Area. 2008. (Mountain Bike! Ser.). (ENG., Illus.). 224p. pap., instr.'s gde. ed. 15.95 *(978-0-89732-659-9(8))* Menasha Ridge Pr., Inc.
Kunerth, Jeff & Kunerth, Gretchen. Florida's Paved Bike Trails: An Eco-Tour Guide. 2nd ed. 2008. (ENG., Illus.). 240p. pap. 16.95 *(978-0-8130-3255-9(5))* Univ. Pr. of Florida.
Lonely Planet Staff & Kennedy, Scott. Cycling New Zealand. 2nd ed. 2009. (Cycling Ser.). (ENG., Illus.). 372p. pap. 24.99 *(978-1-74059-121-8(6))* Lonely Planet Pubns.
Lonely Planet Staff & O'Carroll, Etain. Cycling Britain. 2nd ed. 2009. (Cycling Ser.). (ENG., Illus.). 380p. pap. 24.99 *(978-1-74104-042-5(6))* Lonely Planet Pubns.
Lonely Planet Staff, et al. Cycling Australia. 2nd ed. 2009. (Cycling Ser.). (ENG., Illus.). 372p. pap. 24.99 *(978-1-74104-040-1(X))* Lonely Planet Pubns.
—Cycling in Italy. 2nd rev. ed. 2009. (Cycling Ser.). (ENG., Illus.). 380p. pap. 24.99 *(978-1-74179-614-8(8))* Lonely Planet Pubns.
Lowthian, M. Russ. Road Biking Wisconsin: A Guide to Wisconsin's Greatest Bicycle Rides. 2008. (Road Biking Ser.). (ENG., Illus.). 248p. pap. 17.95 *(978-0-7627-3800-7(6),* Falcon Guides) Globe Pequot Pr., The.
Lyons, Steve. The Bicyclist's Guide to Northwest Connecticut. 271p. (Orig.). pap. 14.95 *(978-0-9632585-6-4(7))* Freewheel Pubns.
Massachusetts Bicycle Trails. 2008. 192p. pap. 16.95 *(978-1-57430-141-0(1))* American Bike Trails.
Mitchell, Nick. The End to End Cycle Route: Land's End to John o' Groats. 2012. (ENG., Illus.). 256p. pap. 21.95 ***(978-1-85284-670-1(4))*** Cicerone Pr. GBR. Dist: Midpoint Trade Bks., Inc.
Neumann, Phyllis L. Sonoma County Bike Trails: 29 Easy to Challenging Bicycle Rides for Touring & Mountain Bikes. 4th ed. 2008. (Bay Area Bike Trails Ser.). (ENG., Illus.). 128p. pap. 18.95 *(978-0-9769376-1-6(1))* Penngrove Pubns.
Purdum, Stan. Pedaling to Lunch. 2009. (ENG., Illus.). 314p. pap. 18.95 *(978-1-931968-59-1(4))* Univ. of Akron Pr., The.
Rosen, Jerry. Desert Journeys: A Guide for the Tucson Road Cyclist. Patchett, Kaye, ed. 2007. (Illus.). 80p. spiral bd. 25.00 *(978-0-9799800-0-8(3))* JR PHOTO.
Saint-Laurent, Carole. Cycling in France. 2nd rev. ed. (Illus.). 304p. spiral bd. 17.95 *(978-2-89464-348-8(9))* Hunter Publishing, Inc.
Sapp, Rick. Florida: A Guide to the Greatest Bike Rides in Florida. 2008. (Road Biking Ser.). (ENG., Illus.). 240p. pap. 16.95 *(978-0-7627-4448-0(0),* Falcon Guides) Globe Pequot Pr., The.
Selmes, Jules. Cycling Traffic Free: London. 2011. (ENG., Illus.). 129p. pap. 16.95 *(978-0-7110-3525-6(3))* Allan, Ian Publishing GBR. Dist: BookMasters Distribution Services (BDS).
Shidell, Doug. Bicycle Vacation Guide: Minnesota & Wisconsin. 4th rev. ed. 2008. (ENG., Illus.). 180p. pap. *(978-0-9746625-6-5(9))* Little Transport Pr.
Stinton, Sarah. Lands End to John O' Groats: Only Mad Dogs & Englishwomen. 2010. (Illus.). 218p. pap. *(978-0-7552-0499-1(9));* pap. *(978-0-7552-0498-4(0))* Authors OnLine, Ltd.
Stone, Laura. Himalaya by Bike: A Route & Planning Guide for Cyclists & Motor Cyclists. 2008. (ENG., Illus.). 336p. pap. 29.95 *(978-1-905864-04-1(3))* Trailblazer Pubns. GBR. Dist: Globe Pequot Pr., The.
ten Hoeve, Jaap. Who do you think you are? on the western climb of the Monte Zoncolan. 2010. 52p. pap. 27.95 *(978-1-4457-7563-0(8))* Lulu Enterprises Inc.
Terry, Keith. Nebraska's Cowboy Trail: A User's Guide. 2008. (ENG., Illus.). 116p. pap. 12.95 *(978-0-8032-9460-8(3),* Bison Bks.) Univ. of Nebraska Pr.
Time Out Guides Staff, ed. Time Out Cycle London. 2012. (ENG., Illus.). 224p. pap. 19.95 *(978-1-84670-236-5(4))* Time Out Guides Ltd. GBR. Dist: Perseus-PGW.
Touring Club of Italy. Italy by Bike: 105 Tours from the Alps to Sicily. 2nd rev. ed. 2008. (Dolce Vita Ser.). (ENG., Illus.). 240p. pap. *(978-88-365-4496-7(7))* Touring Club Italiano.
Trubshaw, Bob. Little-known Leicestershire & Rutland. 2nd ed. 2010. (Illus.). 147p. pap. *(978-1-905646-17-3(8))* Heart of Albion Pr.
Widing, Katherine. Bicycle Touring Holland: With Excursions into Belgium & Germany. 2010. (Cycling Resources Ser.). (Illus.). 296p. per. 18.95 *(978-1-892495-46-4(5))* Cycle Publishing/Van Der Plas Pubns.
Widing, Katherine. Bicycle Touring Holland: With Excursions into Neighboring Belgium & Germany. 2nd ed. 2012. (Cycling Resources Ser.). (Illus.). 296p. pap. 18.95 ***(978-1-892495-70-9(8))*** Cycle Publishing/Van Der Plas Pubns.

BICYCLES

see also Cycling; Mountain Bikes

Ames, Michael & Fuego, Jonny. Cruisers, 1 vol. 2009. (ENG., Illus.). 160p. pap. 21.99 *(978-1-4236-0267-5(6))* Gibbs Smith, Publisher.
Amrit, Sharma. Stability Analysis of Bicycles & Motorcycles: A Control Theoretic Perspective. 2011. 228p. pap. ***(978-3-639-32837-0(X))*** VDM Verlag Dr. Mueller e.K.
Andrews, Guy. The Custom Road Bike. 2012. (ENG., Illus.). 224p. pap. 29.95 ***(978-1-85669-813-9(0))*** King, Laurence Publishing GBR. Dist: Hachette Bk. Group.
Andrews, Guy & Laurence King Publishing Limited Staff. The Custom Road Bike. 2010. (ENG., Illus.). 224p. 50.00 *(978-1-85669-664-7(2))* King, Laurence Publishing GBR. Dist: Hachette Bk. Group.
Atkinson, Kevin. The Singer Story: Cars, Commercial Vehicles, Bicycles, Motorcycles. 2008. (ENG., Illus.). 256p. 120.00 *(978-1-874105-52-7(9),* 1874105529) Veloce Publishing Ltd. GBR. Dist: MBI Distribution Services/Quayside Distribution.
Baroni, Francesco. The Bicycle: The Myth & the Passion. 2008. (ENG., Illus.). 304p. 35.00 *(978-88-544-0336-9(9))* White Star ITA. Dist: Random Hse., Inc.
Blair, Timothy. Measuring Bicycle Compatibility in the Urban Environment. 2008. 216p. pap. *(978-3-639-06267-0(1))* VDM Verlag Dr. Mueller e.K.
Brady, Patrick. The No-Drop Zone: Everything You Need to Know about the Peloton, Your Gear, & Riding Strong. 2011. (ENG., Illus.). 288p. pap. 19.95 *(978-0-89732-660-5(1))* Menasha Ridge Pr., Inc.
Bridge, Raymond. Bike Touring: The Sierra Club Guide to Travel on Two Wheels. 2nd ed. 2009. (Sierra Club Outdoor Adventure Guide Ser.). (ENG., Illus.). 448p. pap. 18.95 *(978-1-57805-142-7(8))* Sierra Club Bks.
Burrows, Mike. Bicycle Design: The Search for the Perfect Machine. 2008. (Illus.). 160p. *(978-1-905005-68-0(7))* Snowbooks Ltd.
Card, Peter W. Early Cycle Lighting 1868-1948: Identification & Value Guide. 2007. (ENG., Illus.). 160p. 59.95 *(978-1-86126-964-5(1))* Crowood Pr., Ltd. GBR. Dist: Independent Pubs. Group.
—Early Vehicle Lighting. 2nd ed. 2008. (Shire Library). (ENG., Illus.). 56p. pap. 12.95 *(978-0-7478-0585-4(7))* Shire Pubns., Ltd. GBR. Dist: Random Hse., Inc.
Clayton, N., ed. Cycle History, Vol. 13. *(978-1-892495-08-2(2))* Cycle Publishing/Van Der Plas Pubns.
D'Arcy, Sean. Freestyle BMX Tricks: Flatland & Air. 2010. (ENG., Illus.). 128p. pap. 14.95 *(978-1-55407-818-9(0))* Firefly Bks., Ltd.
Dunn, Al. America from a Bicycle Seat. 2011. 74p. pap. 19.95 ***(978-1-4560-5502-8(X))*** PublishAmerica, Inc.
Edwards, Andrew & Leonard, Max. Fixed: Global Fixed-Gear Bike Culture. 2009. (ENG., Illus.). 144p. pap. 24.95 *(978-1-85669-645-6(6))* King, Laurence Publishing GBR. Dist: Hachette Bk. Group.
Embacher, Michael. Cyclepedia: A Century of Iconic Bicycle Design. 2011. (ENG.). 224p. 35.00 *(978-1-4521-0167-5(1))* Chronicle Bks. LLC.
Epperson, Bruce D. Peddling Bicycles to America: The Rise of an Industry. 2010. (ENG., Illus.). 302p. pap. 45.00 *(978-0-7864-4780-0(X))* McFarland & Co., Inc. Pubs.
Facchinetti, Paolo & Rubino, Guido. Campagnolo: 75 Years of Cycling Passion. 2008. (ENG., Illus.). 159p. 39.95 *(978-1-934030-37-0(6))* VeloPress.
Flaherty, Liz. Action Numeracy: Bikes. 2008. 32p. pap. 10.95 *(978-0-86431-800-8(6))* ACER Pr. AUS. Dist: International Specialized Bk. Services.
Furia, Emily, compiled by. The Big Book of Bicycling: Everything You Need to Know, from Buying Your First Bike to Riding Your Best. 2010. *(978-1-60529-486-5(1))* Rodale Pr., Inc.
Furia, Emily & Bicycling Magazine Editors. The Big Book of Bicycling: Everything You Need to Know, from Buying Your First Bike to Riding Your Best. 2010. (ENG., Illus.). 304p. pap. 21.99 *(978-1-60529-282-3(6))* Rodale Pr., Inc.
Garcia, Leah & Lovejoy, Jilayne. Knack Cycling for Everyone: A Guide to Road, Mountain, & Commuter Biking. 2010. (Knack: Make It Easy Ser.). (ENG., Illus.). 256p. pap. 19.95 *(978-1-59921-871-7(2),* Knack) Globe Pequot Pr., The.
Goddard, Stephen B. Colonel Albert Pope & His American Dream Machines: The Life & Times of a Bicycle Tycoon Turned Automotive Pioneer. alt. ed. 2008. (ENG.). 263p. pap. 39.95 *(978-0-7864-4089-4(9))* McFarland & Co., Inc. Pubs.
Grafton, Carol Belanger. 60 Great Bicycle Posters Platinum DVD & Book. 2012. (Dover Electronic Clip Art Ser.). (ENG., Illus.). 48p. pap. 19.95 *(978-0-486-99172-6(5))* Dover Pubns., Inc.
Graham, Brad & McGowan, Kathy. Bike, Scooter, & Chopper Projects for the Evil Genius. 2008. (Evil Genius Ser.). (ENG., Illus.). 300p. pap. 24.95 *(978-0-07-154526-6(3),* 0071545263, TAB/Electronics) McGraw-Hill Professional Publishing.
Greathouse, Lisa. Bikes & Boards: Forces & Motion. 2009. (Science Readers Ser.). 32p. (gr. 2-3). pap. 8.99 *(978-1-4333-0303-6(5))* Teacher Created Materials, Inc.
Hadland, Tony. Raleigh: Ups & Downs of the Iconic Bicycle Brand. 2011. (Cycling Resources Ser.). (Illus.). 360p. 49.95 *(978-1-892495-68-6(6))* Cycle Publishing/Van Der Plas Pubns.
Heine, Jan. The Competition Bicycle: A Photographic History. 2008. (Illus.). 176p. *(978-0-9765460-1-6(9))* Vintage Bicycle Pr.
—The Competition Bicycle: The Craftsmanship of Speed - A Photographic History. 2012. (ENG., Illus.). 168p. 50.00 ***(978-0-8478-3841-7(2))*** Rizzoli International Pubns., Inc.
Heine, Jan. The Golden Age of Handbuilt Bicycles: Craftsmanship, Elegance, & Function. 2009. (ENG., Illus.). 168p. 50.00 *(978-0-8478-3094-7(2))* Rizzoli International Pubns., Inc.
Herlihy, David V. Bicycle: The History. 2006. (ENG., Illus.). 480p. per. 30.00 *(978-0-300-12047-9(8))* Yale Univ. Pr.
Hon, Shek. BMX Riding Skills: The Guide to Flatland Tricks. 2010. (ENG., Illus.). 128p. pap. 16.95 *(978-1-55407-400-6(2))* Firefly Bks., Ltd.
International Police Mountain Bike Association. The Complete Guide to Public Safety Cycling. 2nd rev. ed. 2007. 254p. (C). pap. 32.95 *(978-0-7637-4433-5(6))* Jones & Bartlett Learning, LLC.
Jones, Ian. The Safety Bicycle. 2010. (Shire Library). (ENG., Illus.). 32p. pap. 11.95 *(978-0-85263-804-0(3))* Shire Pubns., Ltd. GBR. Dist: Random Hse., Inc.
Joyce, Jim, ed. & contrib. by. The Bicycle Book: Wit, Wisdom & Wanderings. 2007. (ENG., Illus.). 152p. per. 14.95 *(978-0-9729191-5-9(5))* Satya Hse. Pubns.
Kenney, Jay P. K. Great Road Rides Denver. 2010. (ENG.). 128p. pap. 12.95 *(978-1-55591-737-1(2))* Fulcrum Publishing.
Klanten, R. & S., Ehmann, eds. Velo: Bicycle Culture & Design. 2010. (Illus.). 240p. pap. 50.00 *(978-3-89955-284-3(9))* Die Gestalten Verlag DEU. Dist: Prestel Publishing.

Lamp, Frederick John. Connecticut by Bicycle: Fifty Great Scenic Routes. 2011. (Illus.). 160p. (978-0-7643-3794-9(7), Schiffer Publishing Ltd) Schiffer Publishing, Ltd.

Lapinskiene, Laura. From Ôhygienic Saddlesö to the Ôvehicle of Beautyö. 2008. 80p. pap. (978-3-639-07999-9(X)) VDM Verlag Dr. Mueller e.K.

Lasky, Julie. Bespoke: The Handbuilt Bicycle. 2010. (Illus.). 128p. pap. 35.00 (978-3-03778-204-0(8)) Lars Muller Pubs. CHE. Dist: Prestel Publishing.

McMullan, Rory. Biking to Work: A Beginner's Guide. 2008. (Chelsea Green Guides). (ENG., Illus.). 96p. pap. 7.95 (978-1-933392-98-1(3)) Chelsea Green Publishing.

Mionske, Bob. Bicycling & the Law: Your Rights as a Cyclist. 2007. (ENG., Illus.). 368p. per. 18.95 (978-1-931382-99-1(9)) VeloPress.

Noon, Bingo. How Much Does It Weigh? Design & Build Your Next Bike. Caliente, Bonita, ed. 2008. (Illus.). lib. bdg. 19.99 (978-0-9792754-0-1(7)) Robobike Pr.

Penn, Robert. It's All about the Bike: The Pursuit of Happiness on Two Wheels. 2011. (ENG., Illus.). 208p. 20.00 (978-1-60819-538-1(4)) Bloomsbury Publishing.

Phillips, Tom. Bicycles: Vintage People on Photo Postcards. 2011. (Bodleian Library - Photo Postcards from the Tom Phillips Archive Ser.). (Illus.). 112p. 25.00 (978-1-85124-368-6(2)) Bodleian Library GBR. Dist: Chicago Distribution Ctr.

Raborn, Craig. Guidance for Implementation of the AASHTO Strategic Highway Safety Plan. 2008. (Illus.). (978-0-309-09922-6(6)) Transportation Research Board.

Rosen, Paul. Framing Production: Technology, Culture, & Change in the British Bicycle Industry. 2008. (Inside Technology Ser.). (ENG., Illus.). 240p. (gr. 17). per. 19.00 (978-0-262-68170-4(6)) MIT Pr.

Slinn, Matthew. Build Your Own Electric Bicycle. 2010. (ENG., Illus.). 272p. pap. 24.95 (978-0-07-160621-9(1), 0071606211, TAB/Electronics) McGraw-Hill Professional Publishing.

Timm, Uwe. Der Mann auf dem Hochrad. (GER.). 97p. pap. (978-3-462-01757-1(8)) Kiepenheuer & Witsch GmbH & Company KG DEU. Dist: International Bk. Import Service, Inc.

Van Den Ouden, Eric-Jan, et al. Inventory of Bicycle Motion for the Design of a Bicycle Simulator. 2011. 124p. pap. (978-3-8443-8769-8(2)) Lambert Academic Publishing.

Velox. Velocipedes, Bicycles, & Tricycles: How to Make & How to Use Them, with A Sketch of Their History, Invention, & Progress (1869) 2008. 132p. 35.95 (978-1-4374-2399-0(X)); pap. 20.95 (978-1-4373-6062-2(9)) Kessinger Publishing, LLC.

Willard, FranceS. A Wheel Within a Wheel. 2007. 96p. per. 12.45 (978-1-59462-808-5(4), Book Jungle) Standard Pubns., Inc.

Williams, Eddie, photos by. Eddie Williams: Bike Messengers Life. New York City. 2010. (ENG., Illus.). 160p. pap. 35.00 (978-84-95471-99-4(X)) La Fabrica ESP. Dist: D.A.P./Distributed Art Pubs.

Yeager, Selene. Every Woman's Guide to Cycling: Everything You Need to Know, from Buying Your First Bike to Winning Your First Race. 2008. (ENG., Illus.). 320p. (gr. 12-18). 15.00 (978-0-451-22304-3(7), N A L Trade) Penguin Group (USA) Inc.

BICYCLES—JUVENILE LITERATURE

Mason, Paul. BMX & Mountain Biking: The World's Best Parks, Trails, Streets, & Techniques, 1 vol. 2010. (Passport to World Sports Ser.). (ENG.). 32p. (gr. 3-4). lib. bdg. 27.32 (978-1-4296-5499-9(6), Edge Bks.) Capstone Pr., Inc.

BICYCLES—MAINTENANCE AND REPAIR

Allwood, Melanie. The Total Bike Maintenance Book: DIY Repairs Made Easy. 2012. (ENG., Illus.). 304p. pap. 29.95 (978-1-84732-980-6(2)) Carlton Bks., Ltd. GBR. Dist: Sterling Publishing Co., Inc.

Andrews, Guy. Road Bike Maintenance. 2008. (Falcon Guides How to Ride Ser.). (Illus.). 199p. spiral bd. 19.95 (978-0-7627-4746-7(3), Falcon Guides) Globe Pequot Pr., The.

Barnett, John. Barnett's Manual DX 5. 06. 02. 2008. cd-rom 120.00 (978-0-9744952-8-6(X)) Barnett Group.

—Barnett's Manual DX 6. 08. 01. 2008. cd-rom 120.00 (978-0-9744952-9-3(8)) Barnett Group.

Bicycling Magazine's Complete Guide to Bicycle Maintenance & Repair: Including Road Bikes & Mountain Bikes. (Illus.). 352p. pap. 101.70 (978-0-87596-380-8(3)) Rodale Pr., Inc.

Big Blue Book of Bicycle Repair - 2nd Edition. 2nd ed. 2008. pap. (978-0-9765530-2-1(3)) Park Tool Co.

Big Blue Book of Bicycle Repair - German Edition. 2007. (GER.). per. (978-0-9765530-1-4(5)) Park Tool Co.

Downs, Todd. The Bicycling Guide to Complete Bicycle Maintenance & Repair: For Road & Mountain Bikes. 6th ed. 2010. (ENG., Illus.). 416p. pap. 23.99 (978-1-60529-487-2(X)) Rodale Pr., Inc.

Drinkell, Peter. The Bike Owner's Handbook. 2012. (ENG., Illus.). 112p. pap. 14.95 (978-0-9562053-8-4(0)) Cicada Bks. GBR. Dist: D.A.P./Distributed Art Pubs.

Forester, John. Effective Cycling. 7th ed. 2012. (ENG., Illus.). 624p. (gr. 17). pap. 37.95 (978-0-262-51694-5(2)) MIT Pr.

Haine, Charles. The Urban Biking Handbook: The DIY Guide to Building, Rebuilding, Tinkering with, & Repairing Your Bicycle for City Living. 2011. (ENG., Illus.). 208p. pap. 24.99 (978-1-59253-695-5(6), 1592536956) Quayside.

Jackson, Shelley Lynn & Clark, Ethan. The Chainbreaker Bike Book: A Rough Guide to Bicycle Maintenance. 2nd ed. 2008. (Illus.). 224p. per. 15.00 (978-0-9770557-3-9(6)) Microcosm Publishing.

Milson, Fred. Complete Bike Maintenance: For Road, Mountain, & Commuter Bicycles. exp. ed. 2011. (ENG., Illus.). 192p. pap. 21.99 (978-0-7603-4025-7(0), 0760340250, MVP Bks.) MBI Publishing Co. LLC.

Nodder, Chris. The Little Book of Bike Boo Boos - How to Fix Your Mountain Bike When You Are Miles from Civilization. 2008. 128p. pap. 17.50 (978-1-4357-1651-3(5)) Lulu Enterprises Inc.

Ruth, Karen. Bicycling: A Reintroduction - A Visual Guide to Choosing, Repairing, Maintaining & Operating a Bicycle. 2011. (ENG., Illus.). 128p. pap. 16.99 (978-1-58923-604-2(1), 1589236041, Fair Winds Press) Quayside.

Shanks, Daimeon. Essential Bicycle Maintenance & Repair. 2012. pap. 19.95 (978-1-4504-0707-6(2)) Human Kinetics Pubs.

Sidwells, Chris. Bicycle Repair Manual. rev. ed. 2008. (ENG., Illus.). 160p. (gr. 12). pap. 15.95 (978-0-7566-3394-3(X)) Dorling Kindersley Publishing, Inc.

Tracy, Sam. Roadside Bicycle Repair: A Pocket Manifesto. 2008. (ENG., Illus.). 120p. pap. 12.00 (978-1-933108-18-6(5)) Fulcrum Publishing.

Van Der Plas, Rob. Bicycle Repair: Maintenance & Repair of the Modern Bicycle. 2007. (Cycling Resources Ser.). (Illus.). 176p. (Orig.). pap. 24.95 (978-1-892495-55-6(4)) Cycle Publishing/Van Der Plas Pubns.

van der Plas, Rob & Baird, Stuart. Bicycle Technology: Understanding the Modern Bicycle & its Components. 2nd ed. 2010. (Cycling Resources Ser.). (Illus.). 320p. 39.95 (978-1-892495-66-2(X)) Cycle Publishing/Van Der Plas Pubns.

Zinn, Lennard. Zinn & the Art of Road Bike Maintenance. 3rd ed. 2009. (ENG., Illus.). 384p. pap. 24.95 (978-1-934030-42-4(2)) VeloPress.

BICYCLES AND TRICYCLES

see Bicycles; Tricycles

BIEDERMEIER STYLE

see Decoration and Ornament—Biedermeier Style

BIENVILLE, JEAN BAPTISTE LE MOYNE, SIEUR DE BIENVILLE, 1680-1768

see Le Moyne De Bienville, Jean Baptiste, 1680-1768

BIERCE, AMBROSE, 1842-1914

Bierce, Ambrose. Ambrose Bierce: the Devil's Dictionary, Tales, & Memoirs: The Devil's Dictionary, Tales, & Memoirs. Joshi, S. T., ed. 2011. (ENG.). 864p. (gr. 12). 35.00 (978-1-59853-102-2(6)) Library of America, The.

—The Collected Works of Ambrose Bierce: In the Midst of Life. 2011. 200p. (978-1-84902-314-6(X)) Benediction Classics.

Bierce, Ambrose. Essential Bierce: A Selection of the Writings of Ambrose Bierce. 2007. (California Legacy Ser.). 168p. per. (978-1-59714-054-6(6)) Santa Clara Univ., de Saisset Museum.

Griffin, Martin. Ashes of the Mind: War & Memory in Northern Literature, 1865-1900. 2009. 280p. 80.00 (978-1-55849-689-7(0)); (ENG.). pap. 29.95 net. (978-1-55849-690-3(4)) Univ. of Massachusetts Pr.

Mcwilliams, Carey. Ambrose Bierce: A Biography. 2011. 374p. 53.95 (978-1-258-06821-9(4)) Literary Licensing, LLC.

Neale, Walter C. Life of Ambrose Bierce. reprint ed. 20.00 (978-0-404-04668-2(1)) AMS Pr., Inc.

Owens, David M. The Devil's Topographer: Ambrose Bierce & the American War Story. 2006. (Illus.). 192p. 33.00 (978-1-57233-464-9(9)) Univ. of Tennessee Pr.

Starrett, Vincent. Ambrose Bierce. 2010. (ENG.). 56p. pap. 17.75 (978-1-171-78627-6(1)) 2009. (ENG.). 54p. pap. 16.99 (978-1-116-75836-8(9), BiblioLife) 2009. (ENG.). 54p. pap. 18.99 (978-1-116-75835-1(0), BiblioLife) 2009. 52p. pap. 17.75 (978-1-116-75833-7(4)) 2009. 52p. pap. 16.75 (978-1-116-75834-4(2)) BiblioBazaar.

—Ambrose Bierce. 2010. (Illus.). 28p. pap. 14.14 (978-1-154-45090-3(2)) General Bks. LLC.

—Ambrose Bierce. 2010. 52p. 25.56 (978-1-163-72452-1(1)) 2010. 52p. 31.95 (978-1-161-66705-9(9)) 2007. (ENG.). 108p. 31.95 (978-0-548-42505-3(1)) 2007. (ENG.). 52p. per. 16.95 (978-0-548-40195-8(0)) Kessinger Publishing, LLC.

—Ambrose Bierce. 2008. 52p. pap. (978-1-4097-7788-5(X)) Read Bks.

Talley, Sharon. Ambrose Bierce & the Dance of Death. 2010. (ENG.). xviii, 160p. 42.00 (978-1-57233-680-3(3)) Univ. of Tennessee Pr.

BIERCE, AMBROSE, 1842-1914—BIBLIOGRAPHY

Gaer, Joseph, ed. Ambrose Gwinett Bierce: Bibliography & Biographical Data. 2007. (ENG.). 108p. per. 19.95 (978-1-4325-7111-5(7)) Kessinger Publishing, LLC.

BIFURCATION THEORY

Ajbar, Abdelhamid & Alhumaizi, Khalid. Dynamics of the Chemostat. 2011. (ENG., Illus.). 368p. 99.95 (978-1-4398-6714-3(3), Chapman & Hall/CRC) CRC Pr. LLC.

Bardos, C., et al, eds. Bifurcation & Nonlinear Eigenvalue Problems: Proceedings, Universite de Paris XIII, Villetaneuse, France, October 2-4, 1978. 2008. (Lecture Notes in Mathematics Ser.). 308p. pap. 59.95 (978-3-540-09758-7(9)) Springer.

Barjaktarevic, John Paul. Bifurcations, Phase Transitions & Teleportation in Quantum Systems. 2009. 188p. pap. (978-3-639-18862-2(4)) VDM Verlag Dr. Mueller e.K.

Benoit, E., ed. Dynamic Bifurcations. 2008. (Lecture Notes in Mathematics Ser.). 226p. pap. 46.00 (978-3-540-54900-0(5)) Springer.

Berardi, Franco. Precarious Rhapsody: Semocapitalism & the Pathologies of the Post-Alpha Generation. 2009. (Illus.). 153p. pap. (978-1-57027-207-3(7)) AK Pr.

Bernardo, Mario, et al. Piecewise-smooth Dynamical Systems: Theory & Applications. 2010. (Applied Mathematical Sciences Ser.). (Illus.). xxii, 483p. pap. 119.00 (978-1-84996-548-4(X), 184996548X) Springer.

Braaksma, B., ed. Dynamical Systems & Bifurcations: Proceedings of a Workshop Held in Groningen, The Netherlands, April 16-20, 1984. 2008. (Lecture Notes in Mathematics Ser.). pap. 26.00 (978-3-540-15233-0(4)) Springer.

Bridges, T.J. & Furter, J.E. Singularity Theory & Equivariant Symplectic Maps. 2008. (Lecture Notes in Mathematics Ser.). 232p. pap. 59.95 (978-3-540-57296-1(1)) Springer.

Chow, Shui-Nee, et al. Normal Forms & Bifurcation of Planar Vector Fields. 2009. (ENG.). 484p. pap. 84.00 (978-0-521-10223-0(5)) Cambridge Univ. Pr.

Dercole, Fabio, et al. Analysis of Evolutionary Processes: The Adaptive Dynamics Approach & Its Applications. 2008. (Princeton Series in Theoretical & Computational Biology). (ENG., Illus.). 352p. (C). 85.00 (978-0-691-12006-5(4)) Princeton Univ. Pr.

Doi, Shinji, et al. Computational Electrophysiology: A first course in in silico medicine Vol. 2. 2010. (First Course in "in Silico Medicine" Ser.). (Illus.). 140p. pap. 89.95 (978-4-431-53861-5(5), 4431538615) Springer.

Dumortier, F., et al. Bifurcations of Planar Vector Fields: Nilpotent Singularities & Abelian Integrals. 2008. (Lecture Notes in Mathematics Ser.). 234p. pap. 59.95 (978-3-540-54521-7(2)) Springer.

Exadaktylos, George & Vardoulakis, Ioannis G., eds. Bifurcations, Instabilities, Degradation in Geomechanics. 2010. (ENG., Illus.). xvi, 470p. pap. 189.00 (978-3-642-08044-9(8), 3642080448) Springer.

Exadaktylos, George E. & Vardoulakis, Ioannis G., eds. Bifurcations, Instabilities, Degradation in Geomechanics. 2007. (ENG., Illus.). xvi, 470p. 189.00 (978-3-540-49341-9(7), 3540493417) Springer.

Feckan, Michal. Topological Degree Approach to Bifurcation Problems. (Topological Fixed Point Theory & Its Applications Ser.). (Illus.). ix, 261p. 2010. pap. 129.00 (978-90-481-7969-5(6), 9048179696) 2008. 129.00 (978-1-4020-8723-3(3)) Springer.

Field. Dynamics & Symmetry (V3) 2007. (ICP ADVANCED TEXTS in MATHEMATICS Ser.). (C). 150.00 (978-1-86094-828-2(6)) Imperial College Pr. GBR. Dist: World Scientific Publishing Co., Inc.

Francoise, J. P. Bifurcations of Planar Vector Fields: Proceedings of a Meeting held in Luminy, France, Sept. 18-22, 1989. 2008. (Lecture Notes in Mathematics Ser.). pap. 46.00 (978-3-540-53509-6(8)) Springer.

Ghergu, Marius & Radulescu, Vicentiu. Singular Elliptic Problems: Bifurcation & Asymptotic Analysis. 2008. (Math Applications Ser.). (ENG., Illus.). 320p. 80.00 (978-0-19-533472-2(8)) Oxford Univ. Pr., Inc.

Global Bifurcation of Periodic Solutions with Symmetry. 2008. (Lecture Notes in Mathematics Ser.). pap. 39.95 (978-3-540-19234-3(4)) Springer.

Haragus, Mariana & Iooss, Gérard. Local Bifurcations, Center Manifolds, & Normal Forms in Infinite-Dimensional Dynamical Systems. 2010. (Universitext Ser.). (Illus.). xiv, 325p. pap. 74.95 (978-0-85729-111-0(4), 0857291114) Springer.

Ikeda, Kiyohiro & Murota, Kazuo. Imperfect Bifurcation in Structures & Materials: Engineering Use of Group-Theoretic Bifurcation Theory. 2nd ed. 2010. (Applied Mathematical Sciences Ser.). (Illus.). xx, 517p. 84.95 (978-1-4419-7075-6(4), 1441970754); E-Book (978-1-4419-7296-5(X)) Springer.

Iooss, Gerard & Plotnikov, Pavel I. Small Divisor Problem in the Theory of Three-Dimensional Water Gravity Waves. 2009. (Memoirs of the American Mathematical Society Ser.). (Illus.). 128p. pap. 67.00 (978-0-8218-4382-6(6)) American Mathematical Society.

Ize, Antonio F., ed. Functional Differential Equations & Bifurcation. 2008. (Lecture Notes in Mathematics Ser.). 432p. pap. 69.95 (978-3-540-09986-4(7)) Springer.

Jager, Tobias H. The Creation of Strange Non-Chaotic Attractors in Non-Smooth Saddle-Node Bifurcations. 2009. (Memoirs of the American Mathematical Society Ser.). 106p. pap. 66.00 (978-0-8218-4427-4(X)) American Mathematical Society.

Kielhöfer, Hansjörg. Bifurcation Theory: An Introduction with Applications to Partial Differential Equations. 2nd ed. 2011. (Applied Mathematical Sciences Ser.). (ENG., Illus.). ix, 398p. 74.95 (978-1-4614-0501-6(7), 1461405017) Springer.

Kogan, J. Bifurcation of Extremals in Optimal Control. 2008. (Lecture Notes in Mathematics Ser.). pap. 26.00 (978-3-540-16818-8(4)) Springer.

Korman, Philip. Global Solution Curves for Semilinear Elliptic Equations. 2012. 245p. 90.00 (978-981-4374-34-7(2)) World Scientific Publishing Co., Inc.

Krauskopf, Bernd, et al, eds. Numerical Continuation Methods for Dynamical Systems: Path following & boundary value Problems. 2007. (Understanding Complex Systems Ser.). (Illus.). iv, 412p. 239.00 (978-1-4020-6355-8(5)) Springer.

Kuznetsov, Yuri. Elements of Applied Bifurcation Theory. 3rd ed. 2010. (Applied Mathematical Sciences Ser.). (Illus.). xxii, 631p. pap. 119.00 (978-1-4419-1951-9(1), 1441919511) Springer.

Leine, Remco I. & Nijmeijer, Henk. Dynamics & Bifurcations of Non-Smooth Mechanical Systems. (Lecture Notes in Applied & Computational Mechanics Ser.). (Illus.). xii, 236p. 2010. (ENG.). pap. 219.00 (978-3-642-06029-8(3), 3642060293) 2006. 219.00 (978-3-540-21987-3(0), 3540219870) Springer.

Magal, Pierre & Ruan, Shigui. Center Manifolds for Semilinear Equations with Non-Dense Domain & Applications to Hopf Bifurcation in Age Structured Models. 2009. (Memoirs of the American Mathematical Society Ser.). (Illus.). 71p. pap. 62.00 (978-0-8218-4653-7(1)) American Mathematical Society.

Mei, Zhen. Numerical Bifurcation Analysis for Reaction-Diffusion Equations. 2010. (Springer Series in Computational Mathematics Ser.). xiv, 414p. pap. 179.00 (978-3-642-08669-4(1), 3642086691) Springer.

Nagata, Wayne & Namachchivaya, N. Sri, eds. Bifurcation Theory & Spatio-Temporal Pattern Formation. 2006. (Fields Institute Communications Ser.: Vol. 49). (Illus.). 177p. 61.00 (978-0-8218-3725-2(7)) American Mathematical Society.

Rasmussen, Martin. Attractivity & Bifurcation for Nonautonomous Dynamical Systems. 2007. (Lecture Notes in Mathematics Ser.). (Illus.). xii, 216p. pap. 69.95 (978-3-540-71224-4(0)) Springer.

Rocsoreanu, C., et al. The FitzHugh-Nagumo Model: Bifurcation & Dynamics. 2010. (Mathematical Modelling: Theory & Applications Ser.). 248p. pap. 139.00 (978-90-481-5512-5(6), 9048155126) Springer.

Salvadori, L., ed. Bifurcation Theory & Applications: Lectures Given at the 2nd 1983 Session of the Centro Internationale Mathematico Estivo (C.I.M.E.) Held at Montecatini, Italy, June 24-July 2, 1983. 2008. (Lecture Notes in Mathematics Ser.). pap. 46.00 (978-3-540-12931-8(6)) Springer.

Sattinger, David H. Topics in Stability & Bifurcation Theory. 2008. (Lecture Notes in Mathematics Ser.). 204p. pap. 39.95 (978-3-540-06133-5(9), 3540061339) Springer.

Schaaf, R. Global Solution Branches of Two Point Boundary Value Problems. 2008. (Lecture Notes in Mathematics Ser.). pap. 39.95 (978-3-540-53514-0(4)) Springer.

Schlomiuk, Dana, ed. Bifurcations & Periodic Orbits of Vector Fields. 2010. (NATO Science Series C: (closed) Ser.). 496p. pap. 449.00 (978-90-481-4303-0(9), 9048143039) Springer.

Seydel, Radiger. Practical Bifurcation & Stability Analysis. 3rd ed. 2009. (Interdisciplinary Applied Mathematics Ser.). (Illus.). xv, 477p. 89.95 (978-1-4419-1739-3(X), 144191739X) Springer.

Sharifi, Hamid. Collocation Methods for the Numerical Bifurcation Analysis. 2010. 252p. pap. (978-3-8383-5194-0(0)) Lambert Academic Publishing.

Shi. Solution Set of Semilinear Elliptic... 2011. 400p. 65.00 (978-981-277-594-8(3)) World Scientific Publishing Co., Inc.

Sidorov, Nikolay, et al. Lyapunov-Schmidt Methods in Nonlinear Analysis & Applications. 2010. (Mathematics & Its Applications Ser.). 566p. pap. 209.00 (978-90-481-6150-8(9), 9048161509) Springer.

Simpson, David John Warwick. Bifurcations in Piecewise-Smooth Continuous Systems. 2010. (Illus.). xv, 238p. 102.00 (978-981-4293-84-6(9)) World Scientific Publishing Co., Inc.

Vandermeer, J. The Hamiltonian Hopf Bifurcation. 2008. (Lecture Notes in Mathematics Ser.). pap. 39.95 (978-3-540-16037-3(X)) Springer.

Wan, Richard, et al, eds. Bifurcations, Instabilities & Degradations in Geomaterials. 2011. (Springer Series in Geomechanics & Geoengineering Ser.). (Illus.). viii, 372p. 179.00 (978-3-642-18283-9(6), 3642182836) Springer.

Wilson, Alan. Catastrophe Theory & Bifurcation (Routledge Revivals) 2011. (Routledge Revivals Ser.). (ENG.). 354p. 140.00 (978-0-415-68782-9(9)) Routledge.

Zeraoulia, Elhadj. 2-D Quadratic Maps & 3-D Ode Systems: A Rigorous Approach. 2010. (Illus.). 356p. 108.00 (978-981-4307-74-1(2)) World Scientific Publishing Co., Inc.

BIG BAND MUSIC

Here are entered compositions not in a specific form or of a specific type for big band, and collections of compositions in several forms or types for big band.

see also Swing (Music)

Alfred Publishing Staff. At Last: Piano/Vocal/Guitar, Sheet. 2012. (Original Sheet Music Edition Ser.). (ENG.). 6p. pap. 3.99 (978-0-7390-8809-8(2)) Alfred Publishing Co., Inc.

American Dance Bands on Record & Film 1915-1942 Vol. 3 K-N. 2010. 968p. 125.00 (978-0-9825853-2-0(2)) Rustbooks Publishing.

Behrens, Jack. Big Bands & Great Ballrooms America I. 2006. (Illus.). 198p. pap. 19.49 (978-1-4259-6977-6(1)) AuthorHouse.

Berish, Andrew S. Lonesome Roads & Streets of Dreams: Place, Mobility, & Race in Jazz of the 1930s & '40s. 2012. (ENG., Illus.). 312p. 90.00 (978-0-226-04494-1(7)); pap. 30.00 (978-0-226-04495-8(5)) Univ. of Chicago Pr.

Big Band Albums: The Blanton-webster Band, Kate Michaels, a Hot Night in Paris, the Far East Suite, Chameleon, M. F. Horn Two, E=mc2, Black. 2010. 38p. pap. 14.14 (978-1-156-98983-8(3)) General Bks. LLC.

Big Band Hits. (Easy Keyboard Library). 9.95 (978-1-85909-142-5(3), Warner Bros. Pubns.) Alfred Publishing Co., Inc.

Hal Leonard Corporation Staff, creator. Big Band Vol. 9: Drum Play-Along. 2010. (ENG.). 40p. pap. 12.99 incl. audio compact disk (978-1-4234-1597-8(3), 1423415973) Leonard, Hal Corp.

—Big Band Ballads for Tenor or Bass Trombone. 2007. (ENG.). 24p. pap. 14.98 incl. audio compact disk (978-1-59615-465-0(9), 1596154659) Music Minus One.

—The Big Band Singer: Pro Vocal Men's Edition Volume 47. 2008. (ENG.). 32p. pap. 14.95 incl. audio compact disk (978-1-4234-6052-7(9), 1423460529) Leonard, Hal Corp.

—Big Band Standards: Pro Vocal Men's Edition Volume 50. 2008. (ENG.). 40p. pap. 14.99 incl. audio compact disk (978-1-4234-6055-8(3), 1423460553) Leonard, Hal Corp.

—Latin - Alto Sax: Big Band Play-along Volume 6. 2009. (ENG.). 24p. pap. 14.99 incl. audio compact disk *(978-1-4234-5874-6(5),* 1423458745) Leonard, Hal Corp.

Howland, John. Ellington Uptown: Duke Ellington, James P. Johnson, & the Birth of Concert Jazz. 2009. (Jazz Perspectives Ser.). (ENG., Illus.). 360p. pap. 29.95 *(978-0-472-03316-4(6))* Univ. of Michigan Pr.

Johnson, Richard J. & Shirley, Bernard H., compiled by. American Dance Bands on Record & Film 1915-1942, Vol. 1 A-E. 2010. 992p. 125.00 *(978-0-9825853-0-6(6))* Rustbooks Publishing.

—American Dance Bands on Record & Film 1915-1942 Vol. 2 E-J. 2010. 991p. 125.00 *(978-0-9825853-1-3(4))* Rustbooks Publishing.

—American Dance Bands on Record & Film 1915-1942 Vol. 4 O-S. 2010. 886p. 125.00 *(978-0-9825853-3-7(0))* Rustbooks Publishing.

—American Dance Bands on Record & Film 1915-1942 Vol. 5 T-Z Artist/Title Indexes. 2010. 125.00 *(978-0-9825853-4-4(9))* Rustbooks Publishing.

Leanza, Frank. The Golden Encyclopedia of Music Theory & Arranging. 2011. (Illus.). 263p. ***(978-0-934687-67-6(6))*** Crystal Pubs.

Scodwell, Tony. Big Band Classics Featuring Tony Scodwell: Trumpet Play-along Pack. 2008. (ENG.). 16p. pap. 14.99 incl. audio compact disk *(978-1-4234-4131-1(1),* 1423441311) Leonard, Hal Corp.

Stewart, Alex. Making the Scene: Contemporary New York City Big Band Jazz. 2007. (Illus.). 398p. 60.00 *(978-0-520-24953-0(4));* per. 27.95 *(978-0-520-24954-7(2))* Univ. of California Pr.

BIG BANDS

Here are entered works on bands generally of 10-15 solo instruments, predominantly winds, and sometimes including a vocalist, that perform jazz and popular music for social dancing.

American Dance Bands on Record & Film 1915-1942 Vol. 3 K-N. 2010. 968p. 125.00 *(978-0-9825853-2-0(2))* Rustbooks Publishing.

Behrens, Jack. Big Bands & Great Ballrooms America I. 2006. (Illus.). 198p. pap. 19.49 *(978-1-4259-6977-6(1))* AuthorHouse.

Big Band Musicians by Instrument: Big Band Clarinetists, Big Band Pianists, Big Band Saxophonists, Big Band Trumpet Players. 2010. 68p. pap. 14.14 *(978-1-157-78137-0(3))* General Bks. LLC.

Big Band Saxophonists: Jimmy Dorsey, Frank Foster, Bud Shank, Clifford Jordan, Buddy Tate, Guy Lafitte, Sam Most, Herbie Steward. 2010. 36p. pap. 14.14 *(978-1-156-98984-5(1))* General Bks. LLC.

Johnson, Richard J. & Shirley, Bernard H., compiled by. American Dance Bands on Record & Film 1915-1942, Vol. 1 A-E. 2010. 992p. 125.00 *(978-0-9825853-0-6(6))* Rustbooks Publishing.

—American Dance Bands on Record & Film 1915-1942 Vol. 2 E-J. 2010. 991p. 125.00 *(978-0-9825853-1-3(4))* Rustbooks Publishing.

—American Dance Bands on Record & Film 1915-1942 Vol. 4 O-S. 2010. 886p. 125.00 *(978-0-9825853-3-7(0))* Rustbooks Publishing.

—American Dance Bands on Record & Film 1915-1942 Vol. 5 T-Z Artist/Title Indexes. 2010. 125.00 *(978-0-9825853-4-4(9))* Rustbooks Publishing.

Llc, Books. Big Band Drummers: Buddy Rich, Jack Sperling, Louie Bellson, John Bernard Riley, Gene Krupa. 2010. 52p. pap. 19.99 *(978-1-155-88762-3(X))* General Bks. LLC.

Llc, Books, ed. Big Band Bandleaders: Benny Goodman, Lionel Hampton, Duke Ellington, Glenn Miller, Count Basie, Louis Prima, Cab Calloway, les Brown. 2010. 364p. pap. 43.71 *(978-1-156-82369-9(2))* General Bks. LLC.

—Big Band Clarinetists: Jimmy Dorsey, Irving Fazola, Heinie Beau. 2010. 20p. pap. 14.14 *(978-1-158-34337-9(X))* General Bks. LLC.

—Big Band Pianists: Henry Mancini, Luis Russell, Anselmo Sacasas, George Handy, Nat Pierce. 2010. 28p. pap. 14.14 *(978-1-158-34339-3(6))* General Bks. LLC.

Mayerhofer, Felix. Diary of a Young Musician: Final Days of the Big Band Era. 2006. (Illus.). 354p. per. 20.95 *(978-1-60002-198-5(0),* 4086) Mountain Valley Publishing, LLC.

Stewart, Alex. Making the Scene: Contemporary New York City Big Band Jazz. 2007. (Illus.). 398p. 60.00 *(978-0-520-24953-0(4));* per. 27.95 *(978-0-520-24954-7(2))* Univ. of California Pr.

BIG BANG THEORY

Al & Montani, Giovanni. Primordial Cosmology. 2011. 616p. 199.00 *(978-981-4271-00-4(4))* World Scientific Publishing Co., Inc.

Balbi, Amedeo. The Music of the Big Bang: The Cosmic Microwave Background & the New Cosmology. 2010. (Astronomers' Universe Ser.). Orig. Title: La musica del Big Bang. (Illus.). xvi, 160p. pap. 29.95 *(978-3-642-09749-2(9),* 3642097499) Springer.

Beahm, George. Unraveling the Mysteries of the Big Bang Theory: An Unabashedly Unauthorized TV Show Companion. 2011. (ENG.). 336p. pap. 14.95 *(978-1-936661-14-5(4))* BenBella Bks.

Bhagwat, A. V. Real Water in Mirage. 2009. 184p. 24.99 *(978-1-4389-2319-2(8));* pap. 14.49 *(978-1-4389-2318-5(X))* AuthorHouse.

Bignami, Giovanni F. We Are the Martians! Connecting Cosmology with Biology. 2012. (ENG., Illus.). xx, 200p. pap. 34.95 ***(978-88-470-2465-6(X),*** 884702465X) Springer.

Bradley, Tice. An Architecture for an Ur-Universe: Sequential Universal Events. 2011. 248p. pap. ***(978-3-639-30306-3(7))*** VDM Verlag Dr. Mueller e.K.

Bullard, Lucius. God's Big Bang. 2009. 208p. 25.50 *(978-1-60693-992-5(0),* Eloquent Bks.) AEG Literary Publishing Services, Inc.

Clegg, Brian. Before the Big Bang: The Prehistory of Our Universe. 2009. (ENG.). 320p. 25.99 *(978-0-312-38547-7(1))* St. Martin's Pr.

—Before the Big Bang: The Prehistory of the Universe. 2011. (ENG.). 320p. pap. 14.99 *(978-0-312-68028-2(7),* St. Martin's Griffin) St. Martin's Pr.

Combes, Francoise. Mysteries of Galaxy Formation. 2009. (Springer Praxis Books / Popular Astronomy Ser.). (ENG., Illus.). x, 208p. pap. 29.95 *(978-1-4419-0867-4(6),* 1441908676, Springer-Praxis) Springer.

Drexler, Jerome. Discovering Postmodern Cosmology. 2008. 292p. pap. 15.95 *(978-1-59942-987-8(X))* Universal Pubs.

Elsersawi, Amin. The Universe & Its Creation: The probability of God & Improbability of Science. 2011. 184p. pap. 17.00 *(978-1-4269-6278-3(9))* Trafford Publishing.

Farrell, John. The Day Without Yesterday: Lemaitre, Einstein, & the Birth of Modern Cosmology. 2006. (ENG., Illus.). 256p. per. 15.95 *(978-1-56025-902-2(7))* Basic Bks.

Frampton, Paul H. Did Time Begin? Will Time End? 2009. 116p. 32.00 *(978-981-4280-58-7(5))* World Scientific Publishing Co., Inc.

Frank, Adam. About Time: Cosmology & Culture at the Twilight of the Big Bang. 2011. (ENG.). 320p. 26.00 *(978-1-4391-6959-9(4),* Free Pr.) Free Pr.

Gasperini, Maurizio. The Universe Before the Big Bang: Cosmology & String Theory. 2010. (Astronomers' Universe Ser.). Orig. Title: This Is a significantly reworked & updated text in comparison to the original:L'universo prima del Big Bang - Cosmologia e teoria delle stringhe (publ. in 2002). (Illus.). xi, 208p. pap. 29.95 *(978-3-642-09384-5(1),* 3642093841) Springer.

Hall, Richard. The Big Bang: The Start of the Universe & Its Evolutional Challenges. 2007. 14.00 *(978-0-8059-7213-9(7))* Dorrance Publishing Co., Inc.

Hurt, John, narrated by. The Big Bang. (Expanding Universe Ser.). pap., tchr. ed. 29.95 incl. VHS *(978-1-930545-24-3(X),* 30005A) Choices, Inc.

Khan, Imran. Transverse Momentum Physics in Ha & Aa Interactions at High Energy. 2011. 80p. pap. ***(978-3-8443-8560-1(6))*** Lambert Academic Publishing.

Lago, Don. Starchild: The Human Meanings of the Big Bang Cosmos. 2009. 148p. pap. 14.95 *(978-1-935514-31-2(8))* Plain View Pr.

Levin, Frank. Calibrating the Cosmos: How Cosmology Explains Our Big Bang Universe. 2010. (Astronomers' Universe Ser.). (Illus.). x, 302p. pap. 39.95 *(978-1-4419-2152-9(4),* 1441921524) Springer.

López, Ricardo O. The Origin of the Universe & Life: A Puzzle for Science & Theology. 2007. *(978-1-59835-043-2(9))* Cambridge BrickHouse, Inc.

Magueijo, Joao. Faster Than the Speed of Light: The Story of a Scientific Speculation. 2006. (Illus.). 275p. reprint ed. pap. 20.00 *(978-1-4223-5883-2(6))* DIANE Publishing Co.

Marvin G. Back. Theory of the Total Universe. 2009. 52p. pap. 12.00 *(978-1-4389-6271-9(1))* AuthorHouse.

May, Brian, et al. Bang! The Complete History of the Universe. 2nd ed. 2008. (ENG., Illus.). 170p. 32.95 *(978-0-8018-8985-1(5))* Johns Hopkins Univ. Pr.

McPherson, Stephanie Sammartino. Stephen Hawking. 2006. (Biography Ser.). (Illus.). 112p. lib. bdg. 29.27 *(978-0-8225-5950-4(1),* Twenty-First Century Bks.) Lerner Publishing Group.

Metzger, Lenard. Common Sense Cosmology. 2010. 104p. pap. 10.98 *(978-0-557-51848-7(2))* Lulu Enterprises Inc.

Novak, Richey. Me & the Big Bang: Confessions of a Modern-Day Mystic. 2010. 216p. (ENG.). 27.95 *(978-1-4502-3412-2(7));* pap. 17.95 *(978-1-4502-3411-5(9))* iUniverse, Inc.

O'Connell, Jason R. & Hale, Alice L., eds. The Big Bang: Theory, Assumptions & Problems. 2012. (Physics Research & Technology Ser.). 331p. 140.00 *(978-1-61324-577-4(7))* Nova Science Pubs., Inc.

Pasion, Ronald Emil F. Absolute Beginning: A Presentation of the Primordial Spin with a Ripple Effect Expansion from a Single Point Origin Mode. 2011. pap. 14.99 ***(978-1-61346-560-8(2))*** Tate Publishing & Enterprises, LLC.

Peebles, P. James E., et al, eds. Finding the Big Bang. 2009. (ENG., Illus.). 596p. 76.00 *(978-0-521-51982-3(9))* Cambridge Univ. Pr.

Penrose, Roger. Cycles of Time: An Extraordinary New View of the Universe. 2012. (Vintage Ser.). (ENG., Illus.). 304p. pap. 15.95 ***(978-0-307-27846-3(8),*** Vintage) Knopf Doubleday Publishing Group.

Ratcliffe, Martin. Cosmology & the Evolution of the Universe, 1 vol. Jones, Lauren V. & Slater, Timothy F., eds. 2009. (Greenwood Guides to the Universe Ser.). 207p. 65.00 *(978-0-313-34079-6(X),* GR4079) Greenwood Publishing Group, Inc.

Rubakov, Valery A. & Gorbunov, Dmitry S. Introduction to the Theory of the Early Universe: Hot Big Bang Theory. 2011. 488p. pap. 78.00 *(978-981-4343-97-8(8))* 2010. 500p. 158.00 *(978-981-4322-24-9(5))* World Scientific Publishing Co., Inc.

Sarkar, Subir. The Big Bang. 2008. (Illus.). 300p. 110.00 *(978-0-521-58194-3(X))* Cambridge Univ. Pr.

—The Big Bang Laboratory for Particle Physics. 2008. (Illus.). 300p. pap. 39.95 *(978-0-521-58830-0(8))* Cambridge Univ. Pr.

Vaas, Rüdiger, ed. Beyond the Big Bang: Prospects for an Eternal Universe. 2009. (Frontiers Collection). (Illus.). 600p. 89.95 *(978-3-540-71422-4(7),* 3540714227) Springer.

Weymiens, Wolf. Introduction to Modern Cosmology. 2011. 92p. pap. ***(978-3-8383-3589-6(9))*** Lambert Academic Publishing.

Woolfson. Time, Space, Stars & Man. 2009. (Illus.). 300p. 124.00 *(978-1-84816-272-3(3))* World Scientific Publishing Co., Inc.

Woolfson, M. M. Time, Space, Stars, & Man: The Story of the Big Bang. 2009. (Illus.). xi, 422p. pap. 71.00 *(978-1-84816-273-0(1))* World Scientific Publishing Co., Inc.

BIG BEND REGION (TEX.)

Browne, Byron. Driving Southwest Texas: On the Road in Big Bend Country. 2010. *(978-1-60949-072-0(X))* History Pr., The.

Cox, Mike. Big Bend Tales. 2011. (Illus.). 128p. pap. 19.99 ***(978-1-60949-330-1(3))*** History Pr., The.

Dayton, Gage H., et al. Frogs & Toads of Big Bend National Park. 2007. (W. L. Moody, Jr., Natural History Ser.: 36). (ENG., Illus.). 64p. pap. 12.95 *(978-1-58544-576-9(2))* Texas A&M Univ. Pr.

Evans, James H., photos by. Crazy from the Heat: A Chronicle of Twenty Years in the Big Bend. 2011. (ENG., Illus.). 192p. 55.00 *(978-0-292-72659-8(7))* Univ. of Texas Pr.

Glendinning, Jim. Adventures in the Big Bend: A Travel Guide. 3rd ed. 2006. (Illus.). 305p. per. 18.95 *(978-0-9745048-4-1(X))* Iron Mountain Pr.

Koch, Peter & Price, June Cooper. Exploring the Big Bend Country. 2007. (ENG., Illus.). 192p. pap. 19.95 *(978-0-292-71655-1(9))* Univ. of Texas Pr.

Pearson, John R., ed. Road Guide to Paved & Improved Dirt Roads of Big Bend National Park. 2010. (Illus.). 48p. pap. 1.95 *(978-0-912001-02-9(X))* Big Bend Natural History Assn., Inc.

BIG BUSINESS

see also Cartels; Economies of Scale; Industrial Concentration; Industries—Size; Trusts, Industrial

Adachi, Yuko. Building Big Business in Russia: The Impact of Informal Corporate Governance Practices. 2012. (ENG., Illus.). 208p. (C). pap. 44.95 ***(978-0-415-62541-8(6))*** Routledge.

American Bar Association, Section of Antitrust Law Staff, contrib. by. Interlocking Directorates: Handbook on Section 8 of the Clayton ACT. 2011. ix, 102p. pap. ***(978-1-60442-876-6(7))*** American Bar Assn.

Ashton, Robert. The City & the Court 1603-1643. 2008. (ENG.). 264p. pap. 37.99 *(978-0-521-07137-6(2))* Cambridge Univ. Pr.

Atkinson, Edward. The Industrial Progress of the Nation. 2009. (ENG.). 408p. 41.99 *(978-1-117-33674-9(3));* pap. 33.75 *(978-1-117-33675-6(1))* BiblioBazaar.

Best/Kahn, ed. The Global Industrial Complex: Systems of Domination. 2011. (ENG., Illus.). 344p. 85.00 ***(978-0-7391-3697-3(6))*** Lexington Bks.

Binda, Veronica. The Dynamics of Big Business: Structure, Strategy, & Impact in Italy & Spain. 2012. (Routledge International Studies in Business History Ser.). (ENG.). 264p. (C). 125.00 *(978-0-415-89614-6(2))* Routledge.

Bunker, Robert J., ed. Narcos over the Border: Gangs, Cartels & Mercenaries. 2010. (ENG., Illus.). 256p. (C). 133.00 *(978-0-415-56072-6(1))* Routledge.

Coll, Steve. Private Empire: ExxonMobil & American Power. 2012. (ENG.). 688p. (gr. 12). 36.00 ***(978-1-59420-335-0(0),*** Penguin Pr. HC, The) Penguin Group (USA) Inc.

Conason, Joe. It Can Happen Here: Authoritarian Peril in the Age of Bush. 2008. (ENG.). 256p. pap. 16.99 *(978-0-312-37930-8(7),* St. Martin's Griffin) St. Martin's Pr.

Gant, Tina. International Directory of Company Histories, 100. 2009. (International Directory of Company Histories Ser.). (ENG.). 704p. 312.00 *(978-1-55862-634-8(4))* Cengage Gale.

Glover, John D. The Attack on Big Business. 2011. 390p. 53.95 ***(978-1-258-08249-9(7))*** Literary Licensing, LLC.

Halebsky, Stephen. Small Towns & Big Business: Challenging Wal-Mart Superstores. (ENG.). 248p. 2010. pap. 34.99 *(978-0-7391-2241-9(X))* 2009. 83.99 *(978-0-7391-2240-2(1))* Lexington Bks.

Hassard, John, et al. Managing in the Modern Corporation: The Intensification of Managerial Work in the USA, UK & Japan. (ENG.). 288p. 2011. pap. 55.00 *(978-0-521-18987-3(X))* 2009. (Illus.). 98.00 *(978-0-521-84582-3(3))* Cambridge Univ. Pr.

Hendrick, Burton J. The Age of Big Business. 2007. 76p. per. *(978-1-4068-1730-0(9))* Echo Library.

Hendrick, Burton Jesse. The Age of Big Business: A Chronicle of the Captains of Industry. 2009. 204p. 23.99 *(978-0-559-96350-6(5))* 2009. 204p. pap. 17.99 *(978-0-559-96345-2(9))* 2008. 132p. 24.99 *(978-0-554-69262-3(7))* 2008. 141p. pap. 23.75 *(978-0-554-69259-3(7))* 2008. 141p. 27.99 *(978-0-554-69252-4(X))* 2008. 141p. pap. 24.75 *(978-0-554-69254-8(6))* BiblioBazaar.

—The Age of Big Business: A Chronicle of the Captains of Industry. 2007. 96p. per. *(978-1-4065-5363-5(8))* Dodo Pr.

—The Age of Big Business: A Chronicle of the Captains of Industry. (Chronicles of America Ser.). 196p. reprint ed. 88.00 *(978-0-7222-7109-4(3))* Library Reprints, Inc.

International Directory of Company Histories. 2011. (ENG.). 312.00 *(978-1-55862-791-8(X),* St. James Pr.) 2011. (ENG.). 312.00 *(978-1-55862-790-1(1),* St. James Pr.) 2011. (ENG.). 312.00 *(978-1-55862-789-5(8),* St. James Pr.) 2011. (ENG.). 312.00 *(978-1-55862-788-8(X),* St. James Pr.) 2011. 312.00 *(978-1-55862-787-1(1),* St. James Pr.)101. 2009. (ENG.). 736p. 312.00 *(978-1-55862-635-5(2))*102. 2009. (ENG.). 704p. 312.00 *(978-1-55862-636-2(0))* Vol. 108. 2009. (ENG.). 312.00 *(978-1-4144-4104-7(5))* Vol. 109. 2010. (ENG.). 312.00 *(978-1-4144-4105-4(3))* Vol. 110. 2010. (ENG.). 312.00 *(978-1-4144-4106-1(1))* Vol. 111. 2010. (ENG.). 312.00 *(978-1-4144-4107-8(X))* Vol. 112. 2010. (ENG.). 312.00 *(978-1-4144-4108-5(8))* Vol. 113. 2010. (ENG.). 312.00 *(978-1-4144-4109-2(6))* Cengage Gale.

Intl Dir Co Hist. 2009. (International Directory of Company Histories Ser.). (ENG.). 752p. 312.00 *(978-1-55862-640-9(9));* 752p. 312.00 *(978-1-55862-639-3(5));* 720p. 312.00 *(978-1-55862-638-6(7));* 768p. 312.00 *(978-1-55862-637-9(9))* Cengage Gale.

Joyner, Mark & Joyner. Integration Marketing: How Small Businesses Become Big Businesses & Big Businesses Become Empires. 2009. (ENG., Illus.). 160p. 22.95 *(978-0-470-45459-6(8),* Wiley) Wiley, John & Sons, Inc.

Langlois, Richard N. The Dynamics of Industrial Capitalism: Schumpeter, Chandler, & the New Economy. 2007. (Graz Schumpeter Lectures). (Illus.). 122p. 140.00 *(978-0-415-77167-2(6))* Routledge.

Lee, Moosung & Shim, Jae-Seung. The Korean Economic System: Governments, Big Business & Financial Institutions. 2008. (Asian Finance & Development Ser.). (Illus.). 220p. 114.95 *(978-0-7546-7078-0(3))* Ashgate Publishing Co.

Lowe, Jim. Retail Giants - Friend or Foe? 2009. (Illus.). 64p. pap. *(978-1-84748-547-2(2))* Athena Pr.

Mayhew, Anne. Narrating the Rise of Big Business in the USA: How Economists Explain Standard Oil & Wal-Mart. 2008. (Routledge International Studies in Business History Ser.). 208p. 143.00 *(978-0-415-77534-2(5))* Routledge.

Mclaren/Best/Kahn/No. The Global Industrial Complex: Systems of Domination. 2011. (ENG., Illus.). 344p. pap. 36.95 ***(978-0-7391-3698-0(4))*** Lexington Bks.

Moltz, Barry J. & McCray, Becky. Small Town Rules: How Big Brands & Small Businesses Can Prosper in a Connected Economy. 2012. (Que Biz-Tech Ser.). (ENG.). 224p. 24.99 ***(978-0-7897-4920-8(3))*** Que.

Pederson, Jay P. International Directory of Company Histories, 99. 2009. (International Directory of Company Histories Ser.). (ENG.). 736p. 312.00 *(978-1-55862-633-1(6))* Cengage Gale.

Quinn, Theodore K. Unconscious Public Enemies. 2011. 252p. 46.95 ***(978-1-258-09024-1(4))*** Literary Licensing, LLC.

Quinn, Theodore Kinget. Giant Business: Threat to Democracy. 2011. 318p. 50.95 ***(978-1-258-00519-1(0))*** Literary Licensing, LLC.

Rothkopf, David. Power Inc: The Epic Rivalry Between Big Business & Government-and the Reckoning That Lies Ahead. 2012. (ENG., Illus.). 448p. 30.00 ***(978-0-374-15128-7(8))*** Farrar, Straus & Giroux.

Rowley, Chris. Globalization & Competitiveness. 2009. 280p. pap. 39.95 *(978-0-415-56830-2(7))* Routledge.

Sato, Kazuo, ed. Industry & Business in Japan. 2010. (ENG.). 496p. 150.00 *(978-0-415-59185-0(6))* Routledge.

Syman, Stefanie. The Subtle Body: The Story of Yoga in America, 1 vol. 2011. (ENG., Illus.). 400p. pap. 17.00 *(978-0-374-53284-0(2))* Farrar, Straus & Giroux.

Wood, John C. & Wood, Michael C., eds. Alfred D. Chandler: Critical Evaluation. 2008. (Critical Evaluations in Business & Management Ser.). (Illus.). 800p. 720.00 *(978-0-415-45476-6(X))* Routledge.

BIG GAME HUNTING

see also Tiger Hunting

Adams, Chuck. Super Slam! Adventures with North American Big Game. 2008. (ENG., Illus.). 352p. pap. 19.95 *(978-0-9795131-8-3(9))* Woods N' Water Pr., Inc.

An Annotated Bibliography of African Big Game Hunting Books 1785-1999. 2011. (ENG., Illus.). 313p. 85.00 ***(978-1-882458-42-4(7))*** Trophy Room Bks.

Boone and Crockett Club Staff. An American Elk Retrospective: Vintage Photos & Memorabilia from the Boone & Crockett Club Archives. 2011. (ENG., Illus.). 320p. 34.95 *(978-0-940864-70-2(3),* 940870) Boone & Crockett Club.

—Legendary Hunts: Short Stories from the Boone & Crockett Awards. Steffen, Mark B., ed. 2006. (ENG., Illus.). 352p. per. 19.95 *(978-0-940864-54-2(1),* 940854) Boone & Crockett Club.

Buckner, Eldon L. & Reneau, Jack. A Boone & Crockett Club Field Guide to Measuring & Judging Big Game. 2nd ed. 2010. (ENG., Illus.). 304p. pap. 24.95 *(978-0-940864-66-5(5),* 940866) Boone & Crockett Club.

Coolidge Jr., Harold J. & Roosevelt, Theodore. Three Kingdoms of Indo-Chin. 2011. 368p. 53.95 ***(978-1-258-05838-8(3))*** Literary Licensing, LLC.

Doctari. Africa's Most Dangerous: The Southern Buffalo (Syncerus Caffer Caffer) 2nd ed. 2007. (Illus.). xii, 237p. ***(978-1-57157-277-6(5))*** Safari Pr., Inc.

Donarski, Daniel J. & Donarski, Daniel J., Jr. 21 Days in Africa: A Hunter's Safari Journal. 2008. (ENG., Illus.). 232p. 29.95 *(978-0-8117-0288-1(X))* Stackpole Bks.

Grinnell, George Bird. American Big Game in Its Haunts. 2008. 320p. 28.99 *(978-0-554-32127-1(0));* 29.99 *(978-0-554-22824-2(6))* BiblioBazaar.

—American Big Game in Its Haunts. 2009. 68p. pap. *(978-0-217-67969-5(2))* Books LLC.

—American Big Game in Its Haunts. 2007. 204p. per. *(978-1-4068-1569-6(1))* Echo Library.

—American Big Game in Its Haunts: The Book of the Boone & Crockett Club. 2007. (ENG.). 280p. pap. 21.99 *(978-1-4264-3176-0(7));* 318p. pap. 24.99 *(978-1-4264-3211-8(9))* BiblioBazaar.

Hibben, Frank C. Hunting American Lions. 2007. (ENG.). 244p. per. *(978-1-4067-1081-6(4))* Read Bks.

Houston, Jay. Ultimate Elk Hunting: Strategies, Techniques & Methods. 2008. (Complete Hunter Ser.). (ENG., Illus.). 128p. 24.95 *(978-1-58923-353-9(0),* 1589233530, Creative Publishing International) Quayside.

Kelley, Sean. Hog Hunting with Dogs: The Hogdoggers Bible. 2009. 84p. pap. 39.99 *(978-1-4490-3295-1(8))* AuthorHouse.

King, Robert & Terry, Robert. The Hunting Guide to Big Game. (Illus.). 497p. 24.95 *(978-0-9633501-0-7(2))* King's Outdoor World, LLC.

Lee, Kenneth Fuller. Big Game Hunting & Marksmanship: A Manual on the Rifles, Marksmanship & Methods. 2011. 260p. 47.95 ***(978-1-258-03715-4(7))*** Literary Licensing, LLC.

Maartens, Basie. The Last Safari: An Autobiography. 2007. (Illus.). xix, 211p. ***(978-1-58160-572-3(2))*** Paladin Pr.

B

Mace, Dorsey. Hunting Memories, Treasures of A Lifetime. 2011. 220p. pap. 50.48 **(978-1-4634-0371-3(2))** AuthorHouse.

McIntyre, Thomas, ed. Wild & Fair: Tales of Hunting Big Game in North America. 2008. (ENG., Illus.). 229p. 34.95 *(978-1-57157-248-6(1))* Safari Pr., Inc.

Reneau, Jack & Buckner, Eldon L. Measuring & Scoring North American Big Game Trophies. 3rd ed. 2009. (ENG., Illus.). 176p. pap. 29.95 *(978-0-940864-63-4(0),* 940863) Boone & Crockett Club.

—Records of North American Big Game: A Book of the Boone & Crockett Club Containing Tabulations of Outstanding North American Big-Game Tropies, Compiled from Data in the Club's Big-Game Records Archives. 12th ed. 2008. (ENG., Illus.). 928p. pap. 34.95 *(978-0-940864-61-0(4),* 940861) Boone & Crockett Club.

Rocky Mountain Elk Foundation Staff. Elk Hunting Q & A: Expert Advice from Bugle Magazine. Burgess, Don, ed. rev. ed. 2007. (Rocky Mountain Elk Foundation Ser.). (ENG.). 176p. per. 12.95 *(978-1-59228-986-8(X),* Lyons Pr.) Globe Pequot Pr., The.

Roosevelt, Theodore. African Game Trails: An Account of the African Wanderings of an American Hunter-Naturalist. 2009. (ENG.). 529p. 49.95 *(978-1-57157-331-5(3))* Safari Pr., Inc.

—American Big-Game Hunting. 2009. 398p. pap. 31.45 *(978-1-4446-4649-8(4))* Audubon Pr. & Christian Bk. Service.

Roosevelt, Theodore & Brown, Arthur Erwin. American Big Game in Its Haunts. Grinnell, George Bird, ed. 2007. (ENG.). 276p. per. *(978-1-4065-4741-2(7))* Dodo Pr.

Sandlos, John. Hunters at the Margin: Native People & Wildlife Conservation in the Northwest Territories. 2008. (Nature History Society Ser.). (ENG., Illus.). 360p. pap. 36.95 *(978-0-7748-1363-1(6))* Univ. of Washington Pr.

Sherwood, Morgan. Big Game in Alaska: A History of Wildlife & People. 2008. (Illus.). 224p. pap. 24.95 *(978-1-60223-034-7(X))* Univ. of Alaska Pr.

Smith, James A. & Andrews, Harris. The Pocket Field Dressing Guide: The Complete Guide to Dressing Game. 2007. (Illus.). 160p. per. 7.95 *(978-0-88317-364-0(6))* Stoeger Publishing Co.

Speth, John D. The Paleoanthropology & Archaeology of Big-Game Hunting: Protein, Fat, or Politics? 2010. (Interdisciplinary Contributions to Archaeology Ser.). (Illus.). xxxiii, 325p. 199.00 *(978-1-4419-6732-9(X),* 144196732X) Springer.

Spiro, Jonathan. Defending the Master Race: Conservation, Eugenics, & the Legacy of Madison Grant. 2008. (ENG., Illus.). 508p. 39.95 *(978-1-58465-715-6(4))* Univ. Pr. of New England.

Spomer, Ron. Big Game Hunters Guide to Wyoming. 2008. 518p. pap. 28.95 *(978-1-932098-41-9(0))* Wilderness Adventures Pr., Inc.

Steffen, Mark B., et al, eds. Boone & Crockett Club's 26th Big Game Awards, 2004-2006. 2007. (ENG., Illus.). 736p. 44.95 *(978-0-940864-57-3(6))* Boone & Crockett Club.

Sutherland, James. The Adventures of an Elephant Hunter. 2008. 346p. 46.95 *(978-1-4366-5242-1(1));* 348p. pap. 31.95 *(978-0-548-86173-8(0))* Kessinger Publishing, LLC.

Swan, G. P., et al. Hunting Africa: A Practical Guide. 2nd ed. 2009. (Illus.). 372p. pap. 30.95 *(978-1-919938-70-7(2))* International Publishers Marketing.

Theroux, Paul. The End of the Game: The Last Word from Paradise. Beard, Peter & Wiener, Nina, eds. 2008. (ENG., Illus.). 280p. 39.99 *(978-3-8365-0530-7(4))* TASCHEN DEU. Dist: Ingram Pub. Services.

Thomas, E. Donnall, Jr. Longbows in the Far North. 2007. (ENG., Illus.). 144p. per. 16.95 *(978-0-8117-3434-9(X))* Stackpole Bks.

Wainwright, Geoff. Hunting for Trouble. 2007. (Illus.). 275p. *(978-1-57157-232-5(5))* Safari Pr., Inc.

Young, Gayne C. Texas Safari: The Game Hunter's Guide to Texas. 2007. (Illus.). 248p. per. 19.95 *(978-0-9717667-9-2(7))* Hardy, John M. Publishing Co.

BIG HORN COUNTY (WYO.)

Nottingham, Marvin A., ed. Victor & Connections to Pacific Spiny Lobster: Tales of Land & Sea. 2011. 108p. 22.95 *(978-1-4502-9273-3(9));* pap. 12.95 *(978-1-4502-9274-0(7))* iUniverse, Inc.

Slack, Judy, et al. Big Horn City. 2011. (Images of America Ser.). (Illus.). 128p. pap. 21.99 *(978-0-7385-8156-9(9))* Arcadia Publishing.

BIG SANDY VALLEY

Crowe-Carraco, Carol. The Big Sandy. 2009. (Kentucky Bicentennial Bookshelf Ser.). (ENG.). pap. 25.00 *(978-0-8131-9272-7(2))* Univ. Pr. of Kentucky.

Thomas, Jean. Big Sandy. 2007. 324p. per. *(978-1-4067-5500-8(1))* Read Bks.

BIG SUR (CALIF.)

Hopkins, Nancy & Hopkins, Heidi. These Are My Flowers: Raising a Family on the Big Sur Coast. 2007. (Illus.). 160p. *(978-0-9702294-3-4(7))* Glyph Publishing Arts.

Steakley, Douglas. Photographing Big Sur: Where to Find Perfect Shots & How to Take Them. 2011. (Photographer's Guide Ser.). (ENG., Illus.). 96p. pap. 15.95 *(978-0-88150-928-1(0),* 150928) Countryman Pr.

BIG THICKET (TEX.)

Bonney, Lorraine G. The Big Thicket Guidebook: Exploring the Backroads & History of Southeast Texas. Gunter, Pete A. Y. & Johnston, Maxine, eds. 2011. (Temple Big Thicket Ser.). (Illus.). 848p. 29.95 **(978-1-57441-318-2(X))** Univ. of North Texas Pr.

Watson, Geraldine Ellis. Big Thicket Plant Ecology: An Introduction. 3rd ed. 2006. (Temple Big Thicket Ser.: 5). (ENG., Illus.). 152p. per. 14.95 *(978-1-57441-214-7(0))* Univ. of North Texas Pr.

BIGAMY

see also Polygamy

McDougall, Sara. Bigamy & Christian Identity in Late Medieval Champagne. 2012. (Middle Ages Ser.). 240p. (C). 55.00 **(978-0-8122-4398-7(6))** Univ. of Pennsylvania Pr.

Schama, Chloë. Wild Romance: A Victorian Story of a Marriage, a Trial, & a Self-Made Woman. 2010. (ENG., Illus.). 272p. 24.00 *(978-0-8027-1736-8(5))* Walker & Co.

Thomson, Mary Turner. The Other Mrs Jordan: A True Story of Bigamy & Betrayal. 2007. (ENG., Illus.). 240p. pap. 22.95 *(978-1-84596-287-6(7))* Mainstream Publishing Co., Ltd. GBR. Dist: Independent Pubs. Group.

Welsh, Stanley L. What Price a Tear? Costs of the Practice 1884-1896. 2007. *(978-0-8425-2666-1(8),* Brigham Young Univ. Pr.) Brigham Young Univ.

BIGELOW, JOHN, 1817-1911

Bigelow, John. Jamaica In 1850. 2006. 228p. per. 20.99 *(978-1-4255-1961-2(X))* MPublishing.

BIGFOOT

see Sasquatch

BIGHORN SHEEP

Meloy, Ellen. Eating Stone: Imagination & the Loss of the Wild. 2006. (Vintage Ser.). (ENG.). 352p. pap. 15.00 *(978-1-4000-3177-1(X),* Vintage) Knopf Doubleday Publishing Group.

Towell, Dale E. Rocky Mountain Bighorn Sheep. 2007. *(978-1-57864-410-0(0))* Donning Co. Pubs.

BIGOTRY

see Toleration

BIHAR (INDIA)

Caube, Kamala Nayana. Jatiyom Ka Rajanitikarana: [Bihara Mem Pichari Jatiyom Ke Ubhara Ki Dastana]. 2008. (HIN.). 279p. *(978-81-8143-735-8(7),* Library of Congress — New Delhi Overseas Office) Vani Prakashan.

Jannuzi, F. Tomasson. Agrarian Crisis in India: The Case of Bihar. 2011. (ENG.). 246p. pap. 25.00 *(978-0-292-72923-0(5))* Univ. of Texas Pr.

Kumar, Ashwani. Community Warriors: State, Peasants & Caste Armies in Bihar. 2009. (Anthem Press India Ser.). (ENG.). 240p. pap. 40.00 *(978-1-84331-709-8(5))* Anthem Pr. GBR. Dist: Books International, Inc.

Mishra, Rajeshwar. Dynamics of Social Inclusion in a Plural Society. 2011. 176p. pap. **(978-3-8433-9089-7(4))** Lambert Academic Publishing.

Nitisa Kumara & Pathaka, Narendra. Vikasita Bihara Ki Khoja. 2010. (HIN., Illus.). 279p. *(978-81-7315-887-2(8),* Library of Congress — New Delhi Overseas Office) Prabhat Prakashan.

Singh, Rakesh. Impact of Iron Ore Mining on Wildlife Habitat. 2010. 192p. pap. *(978-3-8383-5416-3(8))* Lambert Academic Publishing.

Sinha, Nitin. Communication & Colonialism in Eastern India: Bihar, 1760sndash;1880s. 2012. (Anthem Modern South Asian History Ser.). (Illus.). 330p. 99.00 **(978-0-85728-448-8(7))** Anthem Pr. GBR. Dist: Books International, Inc.

Tiwary, Nishant. Celebrating Bihar: The Charm of Champaran. 2012. (ENG., Illus.). 104p. 99.00 **(978-0-19-808375-7(0))** Oxford Univ. Pr., Inc.

BIKES

see Bicycles

BIKO, STEVE, 1946-1977

Alexander, Amanda & Mngxitama, Andile. Biko Lives! Contesting the Legacies of Steve Biko. Gibson, Nigel, ed. 2008. (Contemporary Black History Ser.). (ENG.). 304p. pap. 31.00 *(978-0-230-60649-4(0))* Palgrave Macmillan.

Mngxitama, Andile, et al. Biko Lives! Contesting the Legacies of Steve Biko. Alexander, Amanda et al, eds. 2008. (Contemporary Black History Ser.). (ENG.). 304p. 95.00 *(978-0-230-60519-0(2))* Palgrave Macmillan.

Van Wyk, Chris, ed. Celebrating Steve Biko: We Write What We Like. 2011. (Columbia/Hurst Ser.). (ENG.). 224p. (gr. 17). 50.00 *(978-0-231-15430-7(5));* pap. 19.50 *(978-0-231-15431-4(3))* Columbia Univ. Pr.

Wilson, Lindy. Steve Biko. 2011. (Pocket History Guides). (Illus.). 150p. pap. 15.99 **(978-1-77009-963-0(8))** Jacana Media ZAF. Dist: Independent Pubs. Group.

BILDUNGSROMANS

Bolton, Jonathan. Blighted Beginnings: Coming of Age in Independent Ireland. 2010. (ENG.). 266p. 61.50 *(978-1-61148-353-6(0))* Bucknell Univ. Pr.

Bruford, W.H. The German Tradition of Self-Cultivation: 'Bildung' from Humboldt to Thomas Mann. 2010. (ENG.). 304p. pap. 42.00 *(978-0-521-12900-8(1))* Cambridge Univ. Pr.

Collins, Walter. Tracing Personal Expansion: Reading Selected Novels as Modern African Bildungsroman. 2006. (ENG.). 150p. per. 31.50 *(978-0-7618-3483-0(4))* Univ. Pr. of America, Inc.

Doub, Yolanda A. Journeys of Formation: The Spanish American Bildungsroman. 2010. (Currents in Comparative Romance Languages & Literatures Ser.). 118p. (C). 62.95 *(978-1-4331-0882-2(8))* Lang, Peter Publishing, Inc.

Esty, Joshua & Esty, Jed. Unseasonable Youth: Modernism, Colonialism, & the Fiction of Development. 1 vol. 2011. (Modernist Literature & Culture Ser.). (ENG.). 304p. 49.95 **(978-0-19-985796-8(2))** Oxford Univ. Pr., Inc.

Kociatiewicz, Justyna. Towards the Antibildungsroman: Saul Bellow & the Problem of the Genre. 2008. XIV, 156p. pap. 46.95 *(978-3-631-57574-1(2))* Lang, Peter Publishing, Inc.

Levine, George. How to Read the Victorian Novel. 2007. (How to Study Literature Ser.). (ENG.). 200p. 110.95 *(978-1-4051-3055-4(5));* per. 32.95 *(978-1-4051-3056-1(3))* Wiley, John & Sons, Inc. (Wiley-Blackwell).

Ligon, Alison D. Traversing Caribbean Thresholds: Coming of Age Stories in Selected Works of Anglophone Fiction. 2009. *(978-1-4331-0629-3(9))* Lang, Peter Publishing, Inc.

Minden, Michael. The German Bildungsroman: Incest & Inheritance. 2011. (Cambridge Studies in German Ser.). (ENG.). 304p. pap. 39.99 *(978-0-521-14280-9(6))* Cambridge Univ. Pr.

Summerfield, Giovanna & Downward, Lisa. New Perspectives on the European Bildungsroman. (ENG.). 2012. 208p. pap. 32.95 **(978-1-4411-0853-1(X))** 2010. 192p. 120.00 *(978-0-8264-3430-2(4))* Continuum International Publishing Group, Ltd. GBR. Dist: National Bk. Network.

Voßkamp, Wilhelm & Vosskamp, Wilhelm. Der Roman eines Lebens: Die Aktualität der Bildung und ihre Geschichte im Bildungsroman. 2009. (GER., Illus.). 210p. *(978-3-940432-42-1(3))* Berlin Univ. Pr.

BILE ACIDS

Häussinger, D., et al, eds. Bile Acids As Metabolic Integrators & Therapeutics: 21st International Bile Acid Meeting Falk Symposium 175, Freiburg, October 2010. Special Topic Issue:'Digestive Diseases 2011, Vol. 29, No. 1' 2011. (Illus.). 124p. pap. **(978-3-8055-9727-2(4))** Karger, S. AG.

—Bile Acids as Metabolic Integrators & Therapeutics: 21st International Bile Acid MeetingFalk Symposium 175, Freiburg, October 2010 Reprint of 'Digestive Diseases 2011, Vol. 29, No. 1' 2011. (Illus.). 124p. pap. **(978-3-8055-9804-0(1))** Karger, S. AG.

Jenkins, Gareth J. & Hardie, Laura, eds. Bile Acids: Toxicology & Bioactivity. 2008. (Issues in Toxicology Ser.). (ENG., Illus.). 176p. 118.00 *(978-0-85404-846-5(4))* Royal Society of Chemistry, The GBR. Dist: Ingram Pub. Services.

Keppler, D., et al, eds. Bile Acid Biology & Therapeutic Actions. 2009. (Falk Symposium Ser.). (ENG., Illus.). 320p. 259.00 *(978-1-4020-9643-3(7))* Springer.

—Bile Acids: Biological Actions & Clinical Relevance. 2007. (Falk Symposium Ser.). (Illus.). 288p. 359.00 *(978-1-4020-6251-3(6),* 1402062516) Springer.

BILE DUCTS

Bristow, Allen & Kircher, Kim. The Next 15 Minutes: Strength from the Top of the Mountain. 2011. (ENG.). 260p. pap. 15.95 **(978-1-933016-11-5(6))** Behler Pubns., LLC.

Clavien, Pierre Alain. Diseases of the Gallbladder & Bile Ducts: Diagnosis & Treatment. Baillie, John & Clavien, Pierre-Alain, eds. 2nd rev. ed. 2006. (ENG., Illus.). 448p. 295.00 *(978-1-4051-2740-0(6),* Wiley-Blackwell) Wiley, John & Sons, Inc.

Guglielmi, Alfredo, et al, eds. Surgical Treatment of Hilar & Intrahepatic Cholangiocarcinoma. 2007. (Updates in Surgery Ser.). (Illus.). 241p. per. 159.00 *(978-88-470-0728-4(3))* Springer.

Hoe, L. van, et al. MR Cholangiopancreatography: Atlas with Cross-Sectional Imaging Correlation. 2nd ed. 2010. (Illus.). xx, 414p. pap. 249.00 *(978-3-642-06083-0(8),* 3642060838) Springer.

Lamps, Laura. Diagnostic Pathology: Hepatobiliary & Pancreas. 2011. (ENG., Illus.). 436p. 299.00 *(978-1-931884-56-3(0))* Lippincott Williams & Wilkins.

Ryu, Munemasa, et al. New Liver Anatomy from the view point of portal segmentation & drainage Vein. 2009. (ENG., Illus.). x, 196p. 239.00 *(978-4-431-95992-2(0),* 4431959920) Springer.

BILE DUCTS—CALCULI

see Gallstones

BILHARZIOSIS

see Schistosomiasis

BILIARY CALCULI

see Gallstones

BILIARY TRACT

see also Bile Ducts; Gallbladder; Liver

Bland, Kirby I., et al, eds. Liver & Biliary Surgery: Handbooks in General Surgery. 2010. (ENG., Illus.). xx, 350p. pap. 39.95 *(978-1-84996-428-9(9),* 1849964289) Springer.

Contemporary Surgical Management of Liver, Biliary Tract, & Pancreatic Disease. 2011. 169.00 *(978-981-4293-05-1(9))* World Scientific Publishing Co., Inc.

Jarnagin, William R. & Blumgart, Leslie H. Blumgart's Surgery of the Liver, Pancreas & Biliary Tract, 2 vols, Set. 5th ed. 2012. (ENG., Illus.). 1976p. 495.00 **(978-1-4377-1454-8(4),** Saunders) Elsevier - Health Sciences Div.

Karaliotas, Constantine Ch, et al, eds. Liver & Biliary Tract Surgery: Embryological Anatomy to 3D-Imaging & Transplant Innovations. 2007. (Illus.). 638p. 299.00 *(978-3-211-49275-8(5))* Springer Wien AUT. Dist: Springer.

Mahmoud, Sameh, et al. Parasites & Biliary Stones. 2010. 212p. pap. *(978-3-8383-7283-9(2))* Lambert Academic Publishing.

Odze, Robert D. & Goldblum, John R. Surgical Pathology of the GI Tract, Liver, Biliary Tract & Pancreas. Odze, Robert D. & Goldblum, John R., eds. Crawford, James M., ed. 2nd ed. 2008. (ENG., Illus.). 1392p. 369.00 *(978-1-4160-4059-0(5),* Saunders) Elsevier - Health Sciences Div.

BILIARY TRACT—DISEASES

see also Jaundice

Bennett, Joseph J. Biliary Tract Cancer: Surgical Oncology Clinics. 2009. (Clinics: Surgery Ser.: 18-2). (ENG., Illus.). xvi, 208p. 99.00 *(978-1-4377-0912-4(5),* Saunders) Elsevier - Health Sciences Div.

Berry. Mini Atlas of Diagnostic Radiology: Hepatobiliary & GI Imaging. 2009. (Anshan Gold Standard Mini Atlas Ser.). (ENG., Illus.). 350p. pap. 34.95 incl. cd-rom *(978-1-905740-16-1(6))* Anshan GBR. Dist: Publishers Storage & Shipping.

Borzellino, Giuseppe & Cordiano, C. Biliary Lithiasis: Basic Science, Current Diagnosis & Management. 2008. (Illus.). 480p. 269.00 *(978-88-470-0762-8(3))* Springer.

Dooley, James S., et al, eds. Sherlock's Diseases of the Liver & Biliary System. 12th ed. 2011. (ENG., Illus.). 792p. 209.95 *(978-1-4051-3489-7(5),* Wiley-Blackwell) Wiley, John & Sons, Inc.

Gerbes, A. L., ed. Ascites, Hyponatremia & Hepatorenal Syndrome: Progress in Treatment. 2010. (Frontiers of Gastrointestinal Research Ser.). (ENG., Illus.). 212p. *(978-3-8055-9591-9(3))* Karger, S. AG.

Krishnamurthy, Gerbail T. & Krishnamurthy, Shakuntala. Nuclear Hepatology: A Textbook of Hepatobiliary Diseases. 2nd ed. 2009. (ENG., Illus.). xii, 368p. 199.00 *(978-3-642-00647-0(7),* 3642006477) Springer.

Lillemoe. Mast Techn Hepatobiliary Panc Surg Cb. 2012. (Master Techniques in General Surgery Ser.). (ENG.). 400p. 229.00 **(978-1-60831-172-9(4))** Lippincott Williams & Wilkins.

Poston, Graeme J., et al, eds. Surgical Management of Hepatobiliary & Pancreatic Disorders, Second Edition. 2010. (ENG.). 512p. *(978-1-84184-693-4(7))* Informa Healthcare.

Reichen, Jürg, et al. Textbook of Hepatology: From Basic Science to Clinical Practice, 2 vols. Rizzetto, Mario et al, eds. 3rd rev. ed. 2007. (ENG., Illus.). 2360p. 800.00 *(978-1-4051-2741-7(4),* Wiley-Blackwell) Wiley, John & Sons, Inc.

Stevens, Peter. Gastrointestinal Endoscopy Clinics of North America: Intraductal Biliary & Pancreatic Endoscopy. 2009. (Clinics: Internal Medicine Ser.: 19-4). (ENG., Illus.). xiv, 528p. 99.00 *(978-1-4377-1222-3(3),* Saunders) Elsevier - Health Sciences Div.

Sutcliffe, Robert, et al. Liver & Pancreatobiliary Surgery: With Liver Transplantation. 2010. (ENG., Illus.). 336p. pap. 85.00 *(978-0-19-920538-7(8))* Oxford Univ. Pr., Inc.

Talley, Nicholas J. Practical Gastroenterology & Hepatology Vol. 3: Liver & Biliary Disease. 2010. (ENG., Illus.). 424p. 151.95 *(978-1-4051-8275-1(X),* Wiley-Blackwell) Wiley, John & Sons, Inc.

Thomas, Charles & Fuller, Clifton, eds. Biliary Tract & Gallbladder Cancer: Diagnosis & Therapy. 2008. 336p. 149.00 *(978-1-933864-42-6(7))* Demos Medical Publishing, LLC.

Thomas, Melanie. Patient Guide to Cancers of the Liver & Biliary Tract. 2007. spiral bd. 0.01 net. *(978-1-60402-256-8(6))* Independent Pub.

Yantiss, Rhonda K., ed. Frozen Section Library: Liver, Extrahepatic Biliary Tree & Gallbladder: Liver, Extrahepatic Biliary Tree & Gallbladder. 2011. (Frozen Section Library). (ENG., Illus.). xi, 179p. pap. 139.00 *(978-1-4614-0042-4(2),* 1461400422) Springer.

BILINGUAL COURT SERVICES

see Court Interpreting and Translating

BILINGUAL EDUCATION

see Education, Bilingual

BILINGUAL METHOD (LANGUAGE TEACHING)

see Language and Languages—Study and Teaching—Bilingual Method

BILINGUALISM

see also Code Switching (Linguistics); Education, Bilingual

Adams, J. N. Bilingualism & the Latin Language. 2008. (ENG.). 864p. pap. 77.00 *(978-0-521-73151-5(8))* Cambridge Univ. Pr.

Altarriba, Jeanette & Heredia, Roberto R. An Introduction to Bilingualism: Principles & Practies. 2007. *(978-1-4106-1885-6(4))* Routledge.

—An Introduction to Bilingualism: Principles & Processes. 2008. (ENG., Illus.). 392p. 135.00 *(978-0-8058-5134-2(8),* Psychology Press) Taylor & Francis Group GBR. Dist: Taylor & Francis Group.

Altarriba, Jeanette & Heredia, Roberto R., eds. An Introduction to Bilingualism: Principles & Processes. 2008. (ENG., Illus.). 392p. per. 60.38 *(978-0-8058-5135-9(6),* Psychology Press) Taylor & Francis Group GBR. Dist: Taylor & Francis Group.

Annabelle, David. The Developing Bilingual Lexicon. 2011. 268p. pap. **(978-3-639-33016-8(1))** VDM Verlag Dr. Mueller e.K.

Appel, Rene & Muysken, Pieter. Language Contact & Bilingualism. 2006. (Amsterdam Academic Archive Ser.). 228p. pap. *(978-90-5356-857-6(3),* Leiden Univ. Pr.) Amsterdam Univ. Pr.

Ardila, Alfredo, ed. Speech & Language Disorders in Bilinguals. 2007. 244p. 79.00 *(978-1-60021-560-5(2))* Nova Science Pubs., Inc.

Arnold, Christopher, et al. Bilingual Books - Biliterate Children: Learning to read through dual language Books. 2009. (Illus.). 188p. pap. 32.95 *(978-1-85856-460-9(3))* Trentham Bks. Ltd. GBR. Dist: Stylus Publishing, LLC.

Auer, Peter & Wei, Li, eds. Handbook of Multilingualism & Multilingual Communication. 2009. (Handbooks of Applied Linguistics). (ENG.). XX, 586p. pap. 56.00 *(978-3-11-021251-8(X))* De Gruyter, Mouton DEU. Dist: de Gruyter, Walter GmbH & Co. KG.

Baker, Colin. Foundations of Bilingual Education & Bilingualism. 5th ed. 2011. (Bilingual Education & Bilingualism Ser.). (ENG., Illus.). 512p. 139.95 *(978-1-84769-356-3(3));* pap. 39.95 *(978-1-84769-355-6(5))* Multilingual Matters GBR. Dist: Univ. of Toronto Pr.

Basterra, Maria del Rosario, et al, eds. Cultural Validity in Assessment: Addressing Linguistic & Cultural Diversity. 2010. (Language, Culture, & Teaching Ser.). (ENG., Illus.). 320p. 44.95 *(978-0-415-99980-9(4))* Routledge.

Bauer, Eurydice B. & Gort, Mileidis, eds. Early Biliteracy Development: How Young Bilinguals Make Use of Their Linguistic Resources - Research & Applications. 2011. (ENG & SPA., Illus.). 224p. 135.00 *(978-0-415-88017-6(3))* Routledge.

Bauer, Eurydice B. & GORT, Mileidis, eds. Early Biliteracy Development: How Young Bilinguals Make Use of Their Linguistic Resources - Research & Applications. 2011. (ENG & SPA., Illus.). 224p. pap. 42.95 (978-0-415-88019-3(1)) Routledge.

Belcher, Diane D. & Hirvela, Alan R., eds. The Oral-Literate Connection: Perspectives on L2 Speaking, Writing, & Other Media Interactions. 2008. (ENG., Illus.). 344p. pap. 32.50 (978-0-472-03232-7(1)) Univ. of Michigan Pr.

Berk-Seligson, Susan. Coerced Confessions: The Discourse of Bilingual Police Interrogations. 2009. (Language, Power & Social Process [LPSP] Ser.). (ENG.). XII, 261p. 125.00 (978-3-11-021348-5(6)) De Gruyter, Mouton DEU. Dist: de Gruyter, Walter GmbH & Co. KG.

Besters-Dilger, Juliane, ed. Language Policy & Language Situation in Ukraine: Analysis & Recommendations. 2008. (Illus.). 396p. pap. 81.95 (978-3-631-58389-0(3)) Lang, Peter GmbH, Europaischer Verlag der Wissenschaften DEU. Dist: Lang, Peter.

Bongartz, Christiane M. & Rymarczyk, Jutta, eds. Languages Across the Curriculum: Ein multiperspektivischer Zugang. 2010. (Fremdsprachendidaktik inhalts- und lernerorientiert Ser.). (ENG & GER.). 180p. pap. 57.95 (978-3-631-58388-3(5)) Lang, Peter GmbH, Europaischer Verlag der Wissenschaften DEU. Dist: Lang, Peter.

Brentari, Diane, ed. Sign Languages. 2010. (Cambridge Language Surveys Ser.). (ENG., Illus.). 714p. 160.00 (978-0-521-88370-2(9)) Cambridge Univ. Pr.

Bullock, Barbara E. & Toribio, Almeida Jacqueline, eds. The Cambridge Handbook of Linguistic Code-switching. (ENG.). 2012. 440p. pap. 50.00 **(978-1-107-60541-1(5))** 2009. (Illus.). 438p. 150.00 (978-0-521-87591-2(9)) Cambridge Univ. Pr.

Byrd Clark, Julie. Multilingualism, Citizenship, & Identity: Voices of Youth & Symbolic Investments in an Urban, Globalized World. 2011. (ENG.). 242p. pap. 44.95 **(978-1-4411-8251-7(9))** Continuum International Publishing Group, Ltd. GBR. Dist: National Bk. Network.

Caldwell, Earl F., ed. Bilinguals: Cognition, Education & Language Processing. 2010. (Languages & Linguistics Ser.). 313p. 98.00 (978-1-60741-710-1(3), Nova Biomedical Bks.) Nova Science Pubs., Inc.

Cameron, David R. & Simeon, Richard, eds. Language Matters: How Canadian Voluntary Associations Manage French & English. 2010. (ENG.). 232p. pap. 32.95 (978-0-7748-1504-8(3)) Univ. of Washington Pr.

Chain Yu, Chin. Understanding Malay Academic Underachievement in Singapore. 2011. 60p. pap. **(978-3-8443-0877-8(6))** Lambert Academic Publishing.

Chen, Linda & Mora-Flores, Eugenia. Balanced Literacy for English Language Learners, K-2. 2006. (Illus.). 240p. pap. 33.75 (978-0-325-00880-6(9), E00880) Heinemann.

Chin, Ng Bee & Wigglesworth, Gillian. Bilingualism: An Advanced Resource Book. 2007. (Routledge Applied Linguistics Ser.). (ENG., Illus.). 384p. 135.00 (978-0-415-34386-2(0)) Routledge.

Ciscel, Matthew H. The Language of the Moldovans: Romania, Russia, & Identity in an Ex-Soviet Republic. 2007. (ENG., Illus.). 186p. 62.99 (978-0-7391-1443-8(3)) Lexington Bks.

Cook, Vivian & Bassetti, Benedetta, eds. Language & Bilingual Cognition. 2010. (ENG., Illus.). 608p. 79.95 (978-1-84872-924-7(3), Psychology Press) Taylor & Francis Group GBR. Dist: Taylor & Francis Group.

Cram101 Textbook Reviews & Cram101 Textbook Reviews. Outlines & Highlights for an Introduction to Bilingualism by Jeanette Altarriba, Isbn: 9780805851359 0805851356. 2011. 144p. pap. 28.95 **(978-1-61490-038-2(8))** Cram101 Inc.

De Bot, Kees, et al. Modeling Bilingualism from Structure to Chaos: In Honor of Kees de Bot. 2011. (Illus.). vi, 308p. (978-90-272-8700-7(7)); (978-90-272-4182-5(1)) Benjamins, John Publishing Co.

De Courtivron, Isabelle. Lives in Translation. 2009. (ENG.). 192p. pap. 30.00 (978-0-230-61070-5(6)) Palgrave Macmillan.

de Groot, Annette M. B. Bilingual Cognition. 2010. (ENG., Illus.). 528p. 62.95 (978-1-84872-901-8(4), Psychology Press) Taylor & Francis Group GBR. Dist: Taylor & Francis Group.

De Houwer, Annick. Bilingual First Language Acquisition. 2009. (MM Texts). (ENG., Illus.). 405p. 39.95 (978-1-84769-148-4(X)); 129.95 (978-1-84769-149-1(8)) Multilingual Matters GBR. Dist: Univ. of Toronto Pr.

Dehkharghani, Rahim & Shamsfard, Mehrnoush. Bilingual Ontology Mapping. 2011. 88p. pap. **(978-3-8433-9010-1(X))** Lambert Academic Publishing.

Fasoli-Wormann, Daniela. Sprachkontakt und Sprachkonflikt in Paraguay: Mythos und Realitat der Bilinguismussituation. (Studien zur Allgemeinen und Romanischen Sprachwissenschaft: Bd. 8). (GER., Illus.). 374p. 43.95 (978-3-631-38340-7(1)) Lang, Peter Publishing, Inc.

Feng, Anwei, ed. English Language Education Across Greater China. 2011. (Bilingual Education & Bilingualism Ser.). 264p. E-Book (978-1-84769-351-8(2)) Multilingual Matters.

Field, Frederic. Key Concepts in Bilingualism. 2011. (Palgrave Key Concepts Ser.). (ENG., Illus.). 256p. pap. 23.00 (978-0-230-23233-4(7)) Palgrave Macmillan.

Finkin, Jordan D. A Rhetorical Conversation: Jewish Discourse in Modern Yiddish Literature. 2010. (ENG., Illus.). 184p. 65.00 (978-0-271-03630-4(3)) Pennsylvania State Univ. Pr.

Fishman, Joshua A., et al, eds. Bilingualism in the Barrio. (Indiana University Publications). (ENG.). 696p. 388.00 **(978-3-11-202705-9(1))**; 261.00 **(978-3-11-128030-1(6))** De Gruyter, Mouton DEU. Dist: de Gruyter, Walter GmbH & Co. KG.

Gafaranga, Joseph. Talk in Two Languages. 2008. (ENG., Illus.). 256p. 89.00 (978-1-4039-4861-8(5)) Palgrave Macmillan.

Gallagher, William B. & Gallagher, Christopher J. Cool Things Happen When You Speak a Foreign Language. 2008. 196p. pap. 14.50 (978-1-930008-08-3(2)) Willowgate Pr.

Gohard-Radenkovic, Aline, ed. Plurilinguisme, Interculturalite et Didactique des Langues Etrangeres dans un Contexte Bilingue Mehrsprachigkeit, Interkulturalitat und Fremdsprachendidaktik in Einem Zweisprachigen Kontext. (Transversales Ser.: Vol. 11). (FRE, GER & ENG., Illus.). xii, 284p. 45.95 (978-3-03910-770-4(4)) Lang, Peter Publishing, Inc.

Grosjean, Francois. Bilingual: Life & Reality. 2010. (Illus.). 304p. 26.95 (978-0-674-04887-4(3)) Harvard Univ. Pr.

Grosjean, François & Grosjean, Francois. Studying Bilinguals. 2008. (ENG., Illus.). 352p. 145.00 (978-0-19-928128-2(9)); pap. 50.00 (978-0-19-928129-9(7)) Oxford Univ. Pr., Inc.

Gyasi, Kwaku Addae. The Francophone African Text: Translation & the Postcolonial Experience. 2006. (Francophone Cultures & Literatures Ser.: Vol. 48). 142p. (C). 59.95 (978-0-8204-7830-2(X)) Lang, Peter Publishing, Inc.

Hadaway, Nancy L. & Young, Terrell A. Matching Books & Readers: Helping English Learners in Grades K-6. 2010. (Solving Problems in the Teaching of Literacy Ser.). (ENG.). 256p. (gr. k-6). 50.00 (978-1-60623-882-0(5)); pap. 27.00 (978-1-60623-881-3(7)) Guilford Pubns., Inc.

Handamo, Samuel. Language Use in Shone Town: A sociolinguistic Study. 2010. 128p. pap. (978-3-639-23126-7(0)) VDM Verlag Dr. Mueller e.K.

Haque, Eve. Multiculturalism Within a Bilingual Framework: Language & the Racial Ordering of Difference & Belonging in Canada. 2009. (ENG.). (978-1-4426-4078-8(2)); pap. (978-1-4426-1016-3(6)) Univ. of Toronto Pr.

Haugen, Einar. Blessings of Babel: Bilingualism & Language Planning. Problems & Pleasures. (Contributions to the Sociology of Language [CSL] Ser.). (ENG.). XII, 176p. 90.00 **(978-3-11-178130-3(5))** De Gruyter, Mouton DEU. Dist: de Gruyter, Walter GmbH & Co. KG.

Heller, Monica. Bilingualism: A Social Approach. Heller, Monica, ed. 2007. (Palgrave Advances Ser.). (ENG.). 384p. pap. 42.00 (978-1-4039-9678-7(4)) Palgrave Macmillan.

Heller, Monica, ed. Bilingualism: A Social Approach. 2007. (Palgrave Advances Ser.). (ENG.). 384p. 137.00 (978-1-4039-9677-0(6)) Palgrave Macmillan.

Herrera, Socorro G. & Murry, Kevin G. Mastering ESL & Bilingual Methods: Differentiated Instruction for Culturally & Linguistically Diverse. 2nd ed. 2010. (ENG.). (C). pap. 79.20 (978-0-13-707390-0(9)) Allyn & Bacon, Inc.

—Mastering ESL & Bilingual Methods: Differentiated Instruction for Culturally & Linguistically Diverse (CLD) Students. 2nd ed. 2010. (MyEducationKit Ser.). (ENG.). 456p. (C). pap. 75.20 (978-0-13-705669-9(9)) Allyn & Bacon, Inc.

Hokenson, Jan & Munson, Marcella. The Bilingual Text: History & Theory of Literary Self-Translation. 2006. 236p. pap. (978-1-900650-93-9(2)) St. Jerome Publishing.

Holling, Michelle. Latina/o Discourse in Vernacular Spaces: Somos de una Voz? 2011. (Race, Rites, & Rhetoric: Colors, Cultures, & Communication Ser.). (ENG., Illus.). 332p. 80.00 (978-0-7391-4648-4(3)) Lexington Bks.

Holling, Michelle A. & Calafell, Bernadette Marie. Latina/O Discourse in Vernacular Spaces: Somos de una Voz? 2010. (Illus.). xxv, 276p. (978-0-7391-4650-7(5)) Lexington Bks.

Huerta-Macias, Ana, ed. Adult Biliteracy: Sociocultural & Programmatic Responses. 2007. (Illus.). 225p. per. 33.95 (978-0-8058-5362-9(6)) Erlbaum, Lawrence Assocs., Inc.

Isurin, Ludmila, et al. Multidisciplinary Approaches to Code Switching. 2009. (Illus.). xviii, 364p. (978-90-272-4178-8(3)) Benjamins, John Publishing Co.

Jaensch, Carol. L3 Acquisition of the German Determiner Phrase. 2009. 288p. pap. (978-3-639-14066-8(4)) VDM Verlag Dr. Mueller e.K.

Jaffe, Alexandra. Teaching in Two Languages: Plural Identities & Classroom Practice. (Routledge Critical Studies in Multilingualism Ser.). (ENG.). 192p. (C). 2013. pap. 44.95 (978-0-415-68151-3(0)) 2012. 170.00 (978-0-415-68152-0(9)) Routledge.

Jarvis, Scott & Pavlenko, Aneta. Crosslinguistic Influence in Language & Cognition. (ENG.). 304p. 2010. 39.95 (978-0-415-87981-1(7)) 2007. (Illus.). 99.95 (978-0-8058-3885-5(6)) Routledge.

Javier, Rafael Art. The Bilingual Mind: Thinking, Feeling & Speaking in Two Languages. 2010. (Cognition & Language: A Series in Psycholinguistics Ser.). (Illus.). xiv, 154p. pap. 119.00 (978-1-4419-4041-4(3), 1441940413) Springer.

—Thinking, Feeling & Speaking in Two Languages: Implications for Education, Research, & Practice. 2007. (Cognition & Language: A Series in Psycholinguistics Ser.). (Illus.). xiv, 154p. 119.00 (978-0-387-30913-2(6), 0387309136) Springer.

Jenifer, Hermes. Attitudes to Bilingualism among Japanese Learners of English: How Successful Learners of a Second Language View Bilingualism & Their Own Bilingual Development. 2011. 164p. pap. **(978-3-639-33634-4(8))** VDM Verlag Dr. Mueller e.K.

Kanno, Yasuko. Language & Education in Japan: Unequal Access to Bilingualism. 2008. (ENG., Illus.). 240p. 89.00 (978-0-230-50694-7(1)) Palgrave Macmillan.

Kappler, Matthias. Turkish Language Contacts in Southeastern Europe. 2010. 114.56 (978-1-61719-106-0(X)) Gorgias Pr., LLC.

Kecskés, István. Cognitive Aspects of Bilingualism. Albertazzi, Liliana, ed. 2007. (ENG., Illus.). xiv, 362p. 169.00 (978-1-4020-5934-6(5), 1402059345) Springer.

Kecskes, Istvan. Situation-Bound Utterances in L1 & L2. (Studies on Language Acquisition [SOLA] Ser.). (ENG.). VIII, 228p. 225.00 **(978-3-11-180362-3(7))** De Gruyter, Mouton DEU. Dist: de Gruyter, Walter GmbH & Co. KG.

Kecskes, Istvan & Albertazzi, Liliana, eds. Cognitive Aspects of Bilingualism. 2010. (ENG.). xiv, 362p. pap. 169.00 (978-90-481-7480-5(5), 9048174805) Springer.

Knapp, Karlfried & Antos, Gerd, eds. Handbook of Multilingualism & Multilingual Communication. 2007. (Handbooks of Applied Linguistics). (ENG., Illus.). XX, 586p. 277.00 (978-3-11-018216-3(5)) De Gruyter, Mouton DEU. Dist: de Gruyter, Walter GmbH & Co. KG.

Konidaris, Ephie. The Code-Switching of Trilingual Montrealers - a Case Study. 2008. 132p. pap. (978-3-639-06369-1(4)) VDM Verlag Dr. Mueller e.K.

Koven, Michele. Selves in Two Languages: Bilinguals' Verbal Enactments of Identity in French & Portuguese. 2007. (Studies in Bilingualism Ser.: Vol. 34). 329p. (C). 132.00 (978-90-272-4145-0(7)) Benjamins, John Publishing Co. NLD. Dist: Benjamins, John Publishing Co.

Kradinova, Larisa. What's Preached vs. What's Practiced. 2010. 240p. pap. (978-3-639-22579-2(1)) VDM Verlag Dr. Mueller e.K.

Kroll, Judith F. & DeGroot, Annette M. B., eds. Handbook of Bilingualism: Psycholinguistic Approaches. 2009. (ENG.). 608p. pap. 42.95 (978-0-19-537365-3(0)) Oxford Univ. Pr., Inc.

Langdon, Davis & Langdon, Henriette W. Assessment & Intervention for Communication Disorders in Culturally & Linguistically Diverse Populations. 2007. (ENG.). 320p. (C). pap. 82.95 (978-1-4180-0139-1(2)) Delmar Cengage Learning.

Lasagabaster, David & Huguet Canalís, Ángel, eds. Multilingualism in European Bilingual Contexts: Language Use & Attitudes. 2006. (Multilingual Matters Ser.). (ENG., Illus.). 264p. (C). 139.95 (978-1-85359-930-9(1)); pap. 56.95 (978-1-85359-929-3(8)) Multilingual Matters GBR. Dist: Univ. of Toronto Pr.

Lee, Yu-Hsiu & Araya, Palachot. The Study of Language & Communication in Urban Refugees: A Sociolinguistic & Bilingual/Biliteracy Introduction to the Case of Thailand & Beyond. 2011. 84p. pap. **(978-3-639-32193-7(6))** VDM Verlag Dr. Mueller e.K.

Lefebvre, Claire, et al. L2 Acquisition & Creole Genesis: Dialogues. (Language Acquisition & Language Disorders Ser.: Vol. 42). (Illus.). vi, 433p. 150.00 (978-90-272-5302-6(1)) Benjamins, John Publishing Co.

Leikin, Mark, et al, eds. Current Issues in Bilingualism: Cognitive & Socio-linguistic Perspectives. 2011. (Literacy Studies). (ENG., Illus.). x, 265p. 139.00 **(978-94-007-2326-9(1)**, 9400723261) Springer.

Ludi, Georges & Py, Bernard. Etre Bilingue: Revue. 2nd ed. (Exploration Ser.). (FRE.). 29.95 (978-3-906766-63-8(2)) Lang, Peter CHE. Dist: Lang, Peter Publishing, Inc.

Mansoor, Sabiha, et al, eds. Emerging Issues in TEFL: Challenges for South Asia. 2009. (ENG.). 350p. 32.95 (978-0-19-547651-4(4)) Oxford Univ. Pr., Inc.

Mayor Marsán, Maricel, ed. & prologue by. Español o Espanglish ¿Cuál es el futuro de nuestra lengua en los Estados Unidos? ¿Cuál es el futuro de nuestra lengua en los Estados Unidos? Colección Senderos de la Narrativa (Segunda Edición) 2nd ed. 2006. (SPA., Illus.). 100p. per. 14.00 (978-0-9752716-7-4(9)) Ediciones Baquiana.

McNamara, Katalin. Bilingualism. 2008. 64p. pap. (978-3-8364-9396-3(9)) VDM Verlag Dr. Mueller e.K.

Mehler, Alexander & Romary, Laurent, eds. Handbook of Technical Communication. 2012. (Handbooks of Applied Linguistics [HAL] Ser.). (ENG.). 600p. 257.00 (978-3-11-018834-9(1)) De Gruyter, Mouton DEU. Dist: de Gruyter, Walter GmbH & Co. KG.

Montrul, Silvina. El Bilingüismo en el Mundo Hispanohablante. 2012. (SPA & ENG.). 352p. 99.95 **(978-0-470-65720-1(0))**; pap. 49.95 **(978-0-470-65721-8(9))** Wiley, John & Sons, Inc. (Wiley-Blackwell).

Moyer, Melissa G. & Wei, Li, eds. Research Methods in Bilingualism & Multilingualism. 2008. (GMLZ - Guides to Research Methods in Language & Linguistics Ser.). (ENG., Illus.). 424p. pap. 56.95 (978-1-4051-7900-3(7), Wiley-Blackwell) Wiley, John & Sons, Inc.

Munro, Gillian. Gaelic Communities Today: Coimhearsnachd na Gàidhlig An-diugh. 2010. (ENG., Illus.). 189p. pap. 39.50 (978-1-903765-85-2(4)) Dunedin Academic Pr. GBR. Dist: International Specialized Bk. Services.

Mutonga, Lovemore & Shumba, Milton. Consonant Cluster Input Structure Retention in English Loanwords. 2011. 96p. pap. **(978-3-8443-1182-2(3))** Lambert Academic Publishing.

Nerenberg, Shiraz. Language in the Bilingual Family. 2008. 144p. pap. (978-3-639-08656-0(2)) VDM Verlag Dr. Mueller e.K.

Niño-Murcia, Mercedes & Rothman, Jason. Bilingualism & Identity: Spanish at the Crossroads with Other Languages. 2008. (Illus.). (C). (978-90-272-4148-1(1)) Benjamins, John Publishing Co.

Otheguy, Ricardo & Zentella, Ana Celia. Spanish in New York: Language Contact, Dialectal Leveling, & Structural Continuity, 1 vol. 2012. (Oxford Studies in Sociolinguistics Ser.). 320p. 99.00 (978-0-19-973740-6(1)); pap. 35.00 (978-0-19-973739-0(8)) Oxford Univ. Pr., Inc.

Paradis, Michel. Declarative & Procedural Determinants of Second Languages. 2009. (Illus.). xii, 219p. (978-90-272-4176-4(7)); pap. (978-90-272-4177-1(5)) Benjamins, John Publishing Co.

Pavlenko, Aneta, ed. The Bilingual Mental Lexicon: Interdisciplinary Approaches. 2009. (Bilingual Education & Bilingualism Ser.). (ENG., Illus.). 240p. 39.95 (978-1-84769-124-8(2)); 99.95 (978-1-84769-125-5(0)) Multilingual Matters GBR. Dist: Univ. of Toronto Pr.

—Thinking & Speaking in Two Languages. 2011. (Bilingual Education & Bilingualism Ser.). (ENG., Illus.). 272p. 159.95 (978-1-84769-337-2(7)); pap. 49.95 (978-1-84769-336-5(9)) Multilingual Matters GBR. Dist: Univ. of Toronto Pr.

Pires, Acrisio & Rothman, Jason, eds. Minimalist Inquiries into Child & Adult Language Acquisition: Case Studies across Portuguese. 2009. (Studies on Language Acquisition [SOLA] Ser.). (ENG., Illus.). VIII, 354p. 168.00 (978-3-11-021534-2(9)) De Gruyter, Mouton DEU. Dist: de Gruyter, Walter GmbH & Co. KG.

Pires, Acrisio & Rothman, Jason, eds. Minimalist Inquiries into Child & Adult Language Acquisition: Case Studies across Portuguese. 2009. (Studies on Language Acquisition [SOLA] Ser.). (ENG.). VIII, 354p. 252.00 **(978-3-11-174077-5(3))** De Gruyter, Mouton DEU. Dist: de Gruyter, Walter GmbH & Co. KG.

Plaza Pust, Carolina & Morales López, Esperanza. Sign Bilingualism: Language Development, Interaction, & Maintenance in Sign Language Contact Situations. Pust, Carolina Plaza & Morales-Lopez, Esperanza, eds. 2008. (Studies in Bilingualism Ser.: Vol. 38). (Illus.). 379p. (C). (978-90-272-4149-8(X)) Benjamins, John Publishing Co.

Potowski, Kim & Cameron, Richard. Spanish in Contact: Policy, Social & Linguistic Inquiries. 2007. (SPA & ENG.). (C). 132.00 (978-90-272-1861-2(7)) Benjamins, John Publishing Co.

Pronk, Tijmen. The Slovene Dialect of Egg & Potschach in the Gailtal, Austria. 2009. (ENG., Illus.). 354p. 105.00 (978-90-420-2774-9(6)) Rodopi.

Pujolar, Joan. Gender, Heteroglossia & Power: A Sociolinguistic Study of Youth Culture. (Language, Power & Social Process [LPSP] Ser.). (ENG.). XIV, 352p. 196.00 **(978-3-11-174923-5(1))** De Gruyter, Mouton DEU. Dist: de Gruyter, Walter GmbH & Co. KG.

Rayfield, J. R. The Languages of a Bilingual Community. (Janua Linguarum. Series Practica Ser.). (ENG.). 118p. 210.00 **(978-3-11-174532-9(5))** De Gruyter, Mouton DEU. Dist: de Gruyter, Walter GmbH & Co. KG.

Reyes, Maria de la Luz, ed. Words Were All We Had: Becoming Biliterate Against the Odds. 2011. (Language & Literacy Ser.). (ENG., Illus.). 192p. 72.00 (978-0-8077-5181-7(2)) Teachers College Pr., Teachers College, Columbia Univ.

—Words Were All We Had: Becoming Biliterate Against the Odds. 2011. (Language & Literacy Ser.). (ENG., Illus.). 192p. pap. 32.95 (978-0-8077-5180-0(4)) Teachers College Pr., Teachers College, Columbia Univ.

Rivera, Klaudia M. & Huerta-Macias, Ana, eds. Adult Biliteracy: Sociocultural & Programmatic Responses. 2007. (Illus.). 225p. 130.00 (978-0-8058-5361-2(8)) Erlbaum, Lawrence Assocs., Inc.

Rubin, Joan. National bilingualism in Paraguay. (Janua Linguarum. Series Practica Ser.). (ENG.). 135p. 210.00 **(978-3-11-196509-3(0))**; 135.00 **(978-3-11-100098-5(2))** De Gruyter, Mouton DEU. Dist: de Gruyter, Walter GmbH & Co. KG.

Santana, J. Gabriel. Spoken Bilinguism. 2008. 380p. 29.99 (978-1-4363-8403-2(6)); pap. 19.99 (978-1-4363-8402-5(8)) Xlibris Corp.

Sanz, Cristina & Leow, Ronald P., eds. Implicit & Explicit Language Learning: Conditions, Processes, & Knowledge in SLA & Bilingualism. 2011. (Georgetown University Round Table on Languages & Linguistics Ser.). (ENG., Illus.). 242p. pap. 49.95 (978-1-58901-729-0(3)) Georgetown Univ. Pr.

Schmid, Monika S. Language Attrition. 2011. (Key Topics in Sociolinguistics Ser.). (ENG., Illus.). 296p. 110.00 (978-0-521-76040-9(2)); 306p. pap. 39.99 (978-0-521-75993-9(5)) Cambridge Univ. Pr.

Serrander, Ulrika. Bilingual Lexical Processing in Single Word Production: Swedish Learners of Spanish & the Effects of L2 Immersion. 2011. (Studia Linguistica Upsaliensia Ser.). (Illus.). 145p. pap. 57.50 **(978-91-554-7990-9(1))** Uppsala Universitet/Acta Universitatis Upsaliensis SWE. Dist: Coronet Bks.

Shanmugam, Kalirenawati. Malay-English Bilingualism in Malaysi. 2009. 76p. pap. (978-3-639-11011-1(0)) VDM Verlag Dr. Mueller e.K.

Taumoepeau, Mele. The Battle Rages On: Winner Undecided. 2011. 176p. pap. **(978-3-8443-1274-4(9))** Lambert Academic Publishing.

Tokuhama-Espinosa, Tracey. Living Languages: Multilingualism Across the Lifespan. 2007. (Illus.). 296p. 49.95 (978-0-275-99912-4(2), C9912, Praeger Pubs.) Greenwood Publishing Group, Inc.

Tufan, Sirin. Language Convergence in Gostivar Turkish - Macedoni. 2010. 328p. pap. (978-3-8383-4541-3(X)) Lambert Academic Publishing.

Valdés, Guadalupe, et al. Developing Minority Language Resources: The Case of Spanish in California. 2006. (Bilingual Education & Bilingualism Ser.: Vol. 58). (ENG., Illus.). 344p. 119.95 (978-1-85359-898-2(4)); pap. 49.95 (978-1-85359-897-5(6)) Multilingual Matters GBR. Dist: Univ. of Toronto Pr.

Vann, Robert E. Materials for the Sociolinguistic Description & Corpus-Based Study of Spanish in Barcelona: Toward a Documentation of Colloquial Spanish in Naturally Occurring Groups. 2009. (Illus.). 300p. 109.95 (978-0-7734-4871-1(3)) Mellen, Edwin Pr., The.

Verschik, Anna. Emerging Bilingual Speech: From Monolingualism to Code-Copying. (ENG.). 270p. 2011. pap. 44.95 **(978-1-4411-2744-0(5))** 2008. 150.00 (978-0-8264-9720-8(9)) Continuum International Publishing Group, Ltd. GBR. Dist: National Bk. Network.

Webber, Philip E. Pella Dutch: Portrait of a Language in an Iowa Community, an Expanded Edition. 2011. (Bur Oak Book Ser.). (ENG., Illus.). 196p. pap. 19.95 (978-1-60938-065-6(7)) Univ. of Iowa Pr.

Wei. Bilingualism, 4 vols. 2009. (Illus.). (978-0-415-46271-6(1)); (978-0-415-46273-0(8)); (978-0-415-46270-9(3)) Routledge.

Wei & Wei, Li. Bilingualism & Multilingualism, 4 vols. 2009. (Critical Concepts in Linguistics Ser.). (ENG., Illus.). 1833p. 1520.00 (978-0-415-46267-9(3)) Routledge.

Wei, Li. The Bilingualism Reader. 2nd rev. ed. 2007. (ENG., Illus.). 592p. (C). 168.00 (978-0-415-35554-4(0)) Routledge.

Wei, Li, ed. The Bilingualism Reader. 2nd rev. ed. 2007. (ENG., Illus.). 592p. (C). per. 49.95 (978-0-415-35555-1(9)) Routledge.

Wei, Li & Moyer, Melissa G., eds. Blackwell Guide to Research Methods in Bilingualism & Multilingualism. 2008. (GMLZ - Guides to Research Methods in Language & Linguistics Ser.). (ENG., Illus.). 424p. 116.95 (978-1-4051-2607-6(8), Wiley-Blackwell) Wiley, John & Sons, Inc.

Wigglesworth, Gillian & Chin, Ng Bee. Bilingualism: An Advanced Resource Book. 2007. (Routledge Applied Linguistics Ser.). (ENG., Illus.). 384p. per. 39.95 (978-0-415-34387-9(9)) Routledge.

Xavier, Martin-Rubio. Identity Construction in 2 Bilingual Communities: Clashing Nationalist Discourses. 2011. 392p. pap. **(978-3-639-32802-8(7))** VDM Verlag Dr. Mueller e.K.

Xu, Shelley Hong. Teaching English Language Learners: Literacy Strategies & Resources for K-6. 2010. (Tools for Teaching Literacy Ser.). (ENG., Illus.). 304p. (gr. k-6). 50.00 (978-1-60623-530-0(3)); pap. 27.00 (978-1-60623-529-4(X)) Guilford Pubns., Inc.

Zajícová, Lenka. El Bilingüismo Paraguayo: Usos y Actitudes Hacia el Guaraní y el Castellano. 2009. (SPA., Illus.). 324p. pap. 56.00 (978-84-8489-439-1(8)) Iberoamericana Vervuert Publishing Corp.

BILINGUALISM IN CHILDREN

Alhuqbani, Mohammed. Bilingual Children's Metalinguistic Awareness. 2008. 200p. pap. (978-3-639-07604-2(4)) VDM Verlag Dr. Mueller e.K.

Baker, Colin. Bilingualism. 3rd ed. 2007. (ENG., Illus.). 240p. pap. 19.95 (978-1-84769-000-5(9)) Multilingual Matters GBR. Dist: Univ. of Toronto Pr.

—A Parents' & Teachers' Guide to Bilingualism. 3rd ed. 2007. (Parents' & Teachers' Guides). (ENG., Illus.). 256p. 49.95 (978-1-84769-001-2(7)) Multilingual Matters GBR. Dist: Univ. of Toronto Pr.

Barron-Hauwaert, Suzanne. Bilingual Siblings: Language Use in Families. 2010. (Parents' & Teachers' Guides). (ENG., Illus.). 216p. 99.95 (978-1-84769-327-3(X)); pap. 29.95 (978-1-84769-326-6(1)) Multilingual Matters GBR. Dist: Univ. of Toronto Pr.

Blom, Wilhelmina Bernardina Theodora & Unsworth, Sharon. Experimental Methods in Language Acquisition Research. 2010. (Illus.). vii, 292p. (978-90-272-8795-3(3)); (978-90-272-1996-1(6)); pap. (978-90-272-1997-8(4)) Benjamins, John Publishing Co.

Cantone, Katja F. Code-switching in Bilingual Children. 2010. (Studies in Theoretical Psycholinguistics Ser.). xx, 276p. pap. 179.00 (978-90-481-7444-7(9), 9048174449) Springer.

Cantone, Katja F. & Cantone, Katja Francesca. Code-Switching in Bilingual Children. 2007. (Studies in Theoretical Psycholinguistics Ser.). (ENG., Illus.). xx, 276p. 179.00 (978-1-4020-5783-0(0), 1402057830) Springer.

Centeno, Jose A. Communication Disorders in Spanish Speakers: Theoretical Research & Clinical Aspects. Anderson, Raquel T. & Obler, Loraine K., eds. 2007. (ENG.). 272p. 119.95 (978-1-85359-972-9(7)) Multilingual Matters GBR. Dist: Univ. of Toronto Pr.

Centeno, Jose G. & Anderson, Raquel T. Communication Disorders in Spanish Speakers: Theoretical, Research & Clinical Aspects. Obler, Loraine K., ed. 2007. (ENG.). 272p. pap. 49.95 (978-1-85359-971-2(9)) Multilingual Matters GBR. Dist: Univ. of Toronto Pr.

Cunningham, Una. Growing up with Two Languages. 3rd rev. ed. 2011. (ENG.). 208p. 120.00 (978-0-415-59851-4(6)) Routledge.

—Growing up with Two Languages: A Practical Guide for the Bilingual Family. 3rd rev. ed. 2011. (ENG.). 208p. pap. 32.95 (978-0-415-59852-1(4)) Routledge.

Datta. Bilinguality & Literacy: Principles & Practice. Datta, Manjula, ed. 2nd rev. ed. 2007. (ENG., Illus.). 252p. 39.95 (978-0-8264-9330-9(0)) Continuum International Publishing Group, Ltd. GBR. Dist: National Bk. Network.

Datta, Manjula & Datta. Bilinguality & Literacy. 2nd rev. ed. 2007. (ENG., Illus.). 252p. 130.00 (978-0-8264-9329-3(7)) Continuum International Publishing Group, Ltd. GBR. Dist: National Bk. Network.

De Houwer, Annick. An Introduction to Bilingual Development. 2009. (MM Textbooks Ser.). (ENG., Illus.). 208p. 24.95 (978-1-84769-168-2(4)); 74.95 (978-1-84769-169-9(2)) Multilingual Matters GBR. Dist: Univ. of Toronto Pr.

Diehr, Bärbel & Rymarczyk, Jutta, eds. Researching Literacy in a Foreign Language among Primary School Learners / Forschung zum Schrifterwerb in der Fremdsprache bei Grundschülern. 2010. (Inquiries in Language Learning. Forschungen zu Psycholinguistik und Fremdsprachendidaktik Ser.). (ENG & GER.). 200p. 50.95 (978-3-631-59500-8(X)) Lang, Peter GmbH, Europaeischer Verlag der Wissenschaften DEU. Dist: Lang, Peter.

Durgunoglu, Aydin Yucesan & Goldenberg, Claude, eds. Language & Literacy Development in Bilingual Settings. 2010. (Challenges in Language & Literacy Ser.). (ENG.). 363p. (gr. k-12). 60.00 (978-1-60623-954-4(6)) Guilford Pubns., Inc.

Francis, Norbert. Bilingual Competence & Bilingual Proficiency in Child Development. 2011. (ENG., Illus.). 424p. (gr. 17). 55.00 (978-0-262-01639-1(7)) MIT Pr.

Fuller, Janet M. Bilingual Pre-Teens: Competing Ideologies & Multiple Identities in the U. S. & Germany. 2012. (Routledge Studies in Sociolinguistics Ser.). (ENG., Illus.). 188p. (C). 125.00 **(978-0-415-80728-9(X))** Routledge.

Garcia, Eugene E. & Náñez, José E. Bilingualism & Cognition: Informing Research, Pedagogy, & Policy. 2011. 264p. 69.95 *(978-1-4338-0879-1(X))* American Psychological Assn.

Geiger-Jaillet, Anemone, ed. Lehren und Lernen in deutschsprachigen Grenzregionen. 2010. (Mehrsprachigkeit in Europa/Multilingualism in Europe Ser.). (GER.). 227p. pap. (978-3-0343-0399-6(8)) Lang, Peter.

Gerngross, Günter & Puchta, Herbert. Playway to English Level 1 Pupil's Book. 2nd ed. 2009. (ENG.). 84p. pap. 19.66 (978-0-521-12996-1(6)) Cambridge Univ. Pr.

—Playway to English Level 1 Teacher's Book. 2nd ed. 2009. (ENG.). 176p. pap. 38.22 (978-0-521-12990-9(7)) Cambridge Univ. Pr.

Gerngross, Günter, et al. Playway to English Level 1 Activity Book with CD-ROM. 2nd ed. 2009. (ENG.). 64p. pap. 24.15 incl. cd-rom (978-0-521-12993-0(1)) Cambridge Univ. Pr.

—Playway to English Level 1 Teacher's Resource Pack with Audio CD. 2nd ed. 2009. (ENG.). 80p. pap. 39.31 incl. audio compact disk (978-0-521-12987-9(7)) Cambridge Univ. Pr.

Goldstein, Brian A., ed. Bilingual Language Development & Disorders in Spanish-English Speakers, Second Edition. 2nd ed. 2011. 416p. pap. 44.95 **(978-1-59857-171-4(0))** Brookes, Paul H. Publishing Co.

Gopaul-McNicol, Sharon-Ann, et al. A Test Review Guide for Bilingual Children Vol. 1: Cognitive Assessment. 163p. pap. 25.95 (978-0-9649476-3-4(3)) Lincoln Univ.

Gregory, Eve. Learning to Read in a New Language: Making Sense of Words & Worlds. 2nd ed. 2008. (Illus.). 256p. (C). 121.00 (978-1-4129-2856-4(7), B28564C); pap. 54.00 (978-1-4129-2857-1(5), B28564P) SAGE Pubns., Ltd. GBR. Dist: SAGE Pubns., Inc.

Grinstead, John. Hispanic Child Languages: Typical & Impaired Development. 2009. (978-90-272-5311-8(0)) Benjamins, John Publishing Co.

Gut, Ulrike. Bilingual Acquisition of Intonation: A Study of Children Speaking German & English. (Linguistische Arbeiten Ser.). (ENG.). X, 181p. 135.00 **(978-3-11-188504-9(6))** De Gruyter, Walter Inc.

Hagège, Claude. L'enfant Aux Deux Langues. (FRE., Illus.). 298p. (978-2-7381-0340-6(5)) Jacob, Odile.

Howes, Carollee & Pianta, Robert C. Dual Language Learners in the Early Childhood Classroom, NCRECE Series, Volume 3, Vol. 3. Downer, Jason, ed. 2011. (Illus.). 296p. pap. 36.95 (978-1-59857-182-0(6)) Brookes, Paul H. Publishing Co.

Kabuto, Bobbie. Becoming Biliterate. 2010. (Illus.). 160p. (C). pap. 41.95 (978-0-415-87180-8(8), Routledge) Taylor & Francis Group GBR. Dist: Taylor & Francis Group.

—Early Biliteracy. 2010. (ENG., Illus.). 160p. (C). 140.00 (978-0-415-87179-2(4), Routledge) Taylor & Francis Group GBR. Dist: Taylor & Francis Group.

Lucas, Tamara, ed. Teacher Preparation for Linguistically Diverse Classrooms: A Resource for Teacher Educators. 2010. (Illus.). 256p. (ENG.). 44.95 (978-0-415-99792-8(5)); 135.00 (978-0-415-99791-1(7)) Routledge.

McLeod, Sharynne & Goldstein, Brian, eds. Multilingual Aspects of Speech Sound Disorders in Children. 2011. (Communication Disorders Across Languages Ser.). (ENG., Illus.). 304p. 169.95 **(978-1-84769-513-0(2))**; pap. 49.95 **(978-1-84769-512-3(4))** Multilingual Matters GBR. Dist: Univ. of Toronto Pr.

Montanari, Elke. Crecer en una Familia Bilingue: La Educacion Plurilingue en Casa y en la Escuela. 2007. (SPA.). 198p. per. 18.95 (978-84-329-1864-3(4)) Grupo Editorial CEAC, S. A. ESP. Dist: Planeta Publishing Corp.

Nikolov, Marianne, ed. The Age Factor & Early Language Learning. 2009. (Studies on Language Acquisition [SOLA] Ser.). (ENG., X, 424p. Illus.). 140.00 (978-3-11-021827-5(5)); 210.00 **(978-3-11-173635-8(0))** De Gruyter, Mouton DEU. Dist: de Gruyter, Walter GmbH & Co. KG.

—Early Learning of Modern Foreign Languages: Processes & Outcomes. 2009. (Second Language Acquisition Ser.). (ENG., Illus.). 240p. 44.95 (978-1-84769-145-3(5)); 124.95 (978-1-84769-146-0(3)) Multilingual Matters GBR. Dist: Univ. of Toronto Pr.

Paradis, Johanne, et al. Dual Language Development & Disorders: A Handbook on Bilingualism & Second Language Learning, Second Edition, CLI Series, Vol. 17. 2nd ed. 2010. (Illus.). 296p. pap. 39.95 (978-1-59857-058-8(7)) Brookes, Paul H. Publishing Co.

Pearson, Barbara Zurer & Living Language Staff. Raising a Bilingual Child. l.t. ed. 2008. (ENG.). 368p. pap. 14.95 (978-1-4000-2334-9(3), Living Language) Random Hse. Information Group.

Prévost, Philippe. The Acquisition of French: The Development of Inflectional Morphology & Syntax in L1 Acquisition, Bilingualism, & L2 Acquisition. 2009. (978-90-272-5312-5(9)) Benjamins, John Publishing Co.

Qi, Ruying. The Bilingual Acquisition of English & Mandarin: Chinese Children in Australia. 2011. **(978-1-60497-774-5(4))** Cambria Pr.

Reyes, Sharon Adelman & Kleyn, Tatyana. Teaching in 2 Languages: A Guide for K-12 Bilingual Educators. 2010. (Illus.). 200p. pap. 34.95 (978-1-4129-7802-6(5), B78019P) Corwin Pr.

Smidt, Sandra. Supporting Multilingual Learners in the Early Years: Many languages - many Children. 2008. (Nursery World/Routledge Essential Guides for Early Years Practitioners Ser.). (Illus.). VIII, 152p. 32.50 (978-0-415-43801-8(2)) Routledge.

—Supporting Multilingual Learners in the Early Years: Many Languages, Many Children. 2007. (Nursery World/Routledge Essential Guides for Early Years Practitioners Ser.). (Illus.). VIII, 152p. 130.00 (978-0-415-43800-1(4)) Routledge.

Steinhardt, Ute. Der bilinguale Erstspracherwerb von Wortstellungsmustern Deutsch-Spanisch. 2009. (Europäische Hochschulschriften. Reihe 21: Linguistik Ser.). (GER.). 292p. pap. 72.95 (978-3-631-59481-0(X)) Lang, Peter GmbH, Europaeischer Verlag der Wissenschaften DEU. Dist: Lang, Peter.

Stow, Carol & Pert, Sean. Bilingual Speech Sound Screen with Punjabi Heritage Children. (Illus.). 30p. pap. (978-0-86388-563-1(2), 003-5289) Speechmark Publishing Ltd.

Ujj, Marietta. Bringing up Children to Be Bilingual. 2008. 72p. pap. (978-3-639-01128-9(7)) VDM Verlag Dr. Mueller e.K.

Vasquez, Olga A., et al. Pushing Boundaries: Language & Culture in a Mexicano Community. 2007. (ENG., Illus.). 240p. pap. 51.00 (978-0-521-04857-6(5)) Cambridge Univ. Pr.

Wang, Xiao-Lei. Learning to Read & Write in the Multilingual Family. 2011. 208p. E-Book (978-1-84769-371-6(7)) Multilingual Matters.

—Learning to Read & Write in the Multilingual Family. 2011. (Parents' & Teachers' Guides). (ENG., Illus.). 208p. 99.95 (978-1-84769-370-9(9)); pap. 29.95 (978-1-84769-369-3(5)) Multilingual Matters GBR. Dist: Univ. of Toronto Pr.

Yambi, Josephine. Bilingual & Biliteracy Development. 2010. 280p. pap. (978-3-639-25669-7(7)) VDM Verlag Dr. Mueller e.K.

Yip, Virginia & Matthews, Stephen. The Bilingual Child: Early Development & Language Contact. 2007. (Cambridge Approaches to Language Contact Ser.). (ENG., Illus.). 320p. 100.00 (978-0-521-83617-3(4)); per. 33.99 (978-0-521-54476-4(9)) Cambridge Univ. Pr.

BILINI

see Byliny

BILIOUS DISEASES AND BILIOUSNESS

see Biliary Tract—Diseases

BILIRUBIN

Novotny, Jakub F. & Sedlacek, Florian. Bilirubin: Chemistry, Regulation & Disorder. 2012. **(978-1-62100-911-5(4))** Nova Science Pubs., Inc.

BILL, MAX

Benedetti, Lorenzo, et al. Max Bill: No Beginning, No End. Museum MARTa Herford Staff, ed. 2008. (Illus.). 200p. pap. 50.00 (978-3-85881-214-8(5)) Scheidegger und Spiess AG, Verlag CHE. Dist: Chicago Distribution Ctr.

Brockhaus, Christoph. Georges Vantongerloo und seine Kreise von Mondrian bis Bill: 'Für eine neue Welt' 1886 -1965. 2009. 130.00 (978-3-85881-294-0(3)) Scheidegger und Spiess AG, Verlag CHE. Dist: Chicago Distribution Ctr.

BILL DRAFTING

see also Law—Language

Borda, Aldo Zammit, ed. Legislative Drafting. 2010. (ENG.). 160p. (C). 125.00 (978-0-415-59781-4(1)) Routledge.

Broberg, Morten & Fenger, Niels. Preliminary References to the European Court of Justice. 2010. (ENG.). 470p. 337.50 (978-0-19-956507-8(4)) Oxford Univ. Pr., Inc.

Brockwell, Camille E., ed. Committee Markups in the House of Representatives: Procedure & Strategy. 2010. (Laws & Legislation Ser.). 130.00 (978-1-61728-463-2(7)) Nova Science Pubs., Inc.

Butt, Peter & Castle, Richard. Modern Legal Drafting: A Guide to Using Clearer Language. 2nd rev. ed. 2006. (Illus.). 240p. per. 45.00 (978-0-521-67452-2(2)) Cambridge Univ. Pr.

Ekins, Richard. The Nature of Legislative Intent. 2012. (ENG.). 288p. 70.00 **(978-0-19-964699-9(6))** Oxford Univ. Pr., Inc.

Filson, Lawrence E. & Starkoff, Sandra L. The Legislative Drafter's Desk Reference, 00 vols. 2nd rev. ed. 2007. 608p. 125.00 (978-0-87289-411-2(8)) CQ Pr.

Guide for Preparation of Committee Reports: For the Use of the Staff of the Committee on Commerce, Science, & Transportation. 2009. ii, 89p. (978-0-16-084661-8(7), 552-070-40154-7) United States Government Printing Office.

Ilbert, Courtenay. Legislative Methods & Forms. 2008. 403p. 95.00 (978-1-58477-889-9(X)) Lawbook Exchange, Ltd., The.

Mader, Luzius & Tavares De Almeida, Marta, eds. Quality of Legislation - Principles & Instruments: Proceedings of the Ninth Congress of the International Association of Legislation (Ial) in Lisbon, June 24th-25th 2010. 2011. 355p. pap., pap. 111.00 **(978-3-8329-5245-7(4))** Nomos Verlagsgesellschaft DEU. Dist: International Specialized Bk. Services.

McLeod, Ian. Principles of Legislative & Regulatory Drafting. 2009. (ENG.). 209p. pap. 52.00 (978-1-84113-772-8(3)) Hart Publishing Ltd. GBR. Dist: International Specialized Bk. Services.

Sulakshin, S. Paket Zakonodatelnoi Initsiativy Po Organizatsii Natsionalnoi Sistemy Pravovykh Aktov V Rossiiskoi Federatsii. 2010. (RUS.). 75p. (978-5-91290-112-6(2)) Institut Zakonodatel'stva I Normativno-Pravovyh Razrabotok, ANO.

Xanthaki, Helen & Stefanou, Constantin. Drafting Legislation: A Modern Approach. 2008. (Modern Approach Ser.). (Illus.). 320p. 134.95 (978-0-7546-4903-8(2)) Ashgate Publishing Co.

BILL OF PARTICULARS

see Bills of Particulars

BILL OF RIGHTS (UNITED STATES)

see United States—Constitution

BILLBOARDS

Alfred Publishing Staff. Billboard Magazine Hot 100 50th Anniversary Songbook: Piano/Vocal/Chords. 2009. (Billboard Magazine Ser.). (ENG.). 272p. pap. 24.95 (978-0-7390-6077-3(5)) Alfred Publishing Co., Inc.

Clip Art. Vintage Pinback Button Art CD-ROM & Book. McCleery, Paul, ed. 2012. (Dover Electronic Clip Art Ser.). (ENG.). 48p. pap. 19.95 **(978-0-486-99211-2(X))** Dover Pubns., Inc.

Dhakshna, M. P. The 9 Emotions of Indian Cinema Hoardings. 2009. (ENG., Illus.). 96p. 35.00 (978-81-86211-27-4(6)) Tara Publishing IND. Dist: Perseus-PGW.

Krols, Birgit. Sensational Billboards in Advertising. 2008. (FRE, DUT & ENG., Illus.). 176p. pap. (978-90-76886-46-6(6)) Tectum B.V.B.A.

Marin, Dan. Signs of Opportunity: How Lamar Advertising Company Became the Biggest Business of Its Kind in the U.S.A. 2007. *(978-0-925417-57-2(2))* Acadian Hse. Publishing.

—Signs of Opportunity: How Lamar Advertising Grew into the Biggest Billboard Business in America. 2008. (Illus.). 196p. per. 15.95 (978-0-925417-61-9(0)) Acadian Hse. Publishing.

Noever, Peter, ed. How Many Billboards? 2010. (ENG., Illus.). 160p. pap. 40.00 (978-3-86984-039-0(0)) Verlag der Buchhandlung Walther Konig DEU. Dist: D.A.P./Distributed Art Pubs.

Office of the Federal Register (U.S.), compiled by. Code of Federal Regulations, Title 23, Highways, Revised as of April 1 2011. rev. ed. 2011. (ENG.). 639p. pap. 50.00 **(978-0-16-088405-4(5)**, Office of the Federal Register) United States Government Printing Office.

Tell, Darcy. Times Square Spectacular: Lighting up Broadway. 2007. (Illus.). 208p. 34.95 (978-0-06-088433-8(9)) Smithsonian Institution Pr.

Wolverton, Marvin L. & Stoops, Dwain. The Valuation of Billboards. 2006. (Illus.). xviii, 187p. (978-0-922154-90-6(2)) Appraisal Institute, The.

York, Joe. With Signs Following: Photographs from the Southern Religious Roadside. 2007. (ENG., Illus.). 67p. 25.00 (978-1-57806-975-0(0)) Univ. Pr. of Mississippi.

BILLIARDS

see also Pool (Game)

Adams, Carter, compiled by & frwd. A Practical Treatise on the Game of Billiards: Accurately Exibiting the Rules & Practice Admitted & Established by the First Players of the Present Day; & Illustrated with a Numerous Collectioin of Cases, Explanatory of Each of the Different Forms of the Game, Calculations for Betting, Tables of Odds, &C. &c. 2007. (Illus.). 304p. 50.00 (978-0-9793663-0-7(5)) Adams, Carter.

Barthelette, Bruce. Knack Pool & Billiards: Everything You Need to Know to Improve Your Game. 2011. (Knack: Make It Easy Ser.). (ENG., Illus.). 256p. pap. 19.95 (978-1-59921-959-2(X), Knack) Globe Pequot Pr., The.

Byrne, Robert. Byrne's Treasury of Trick Shots in Pool & Billiards. 2012. (ENG., Illus.). 320p. 24.95 **(978-1-61608-538-4(X)**, 608538) Skyhorse Publishing Co., Inc.

Christopher, Bruce. "Superstroke" 2008. 168p. per. (978-1-55452-269-9(2)) Essence Publishing.

—Superstroke Bruce Christopher My Winning Secrets. 2008. per. (978-1-55452-268-2(4), Epic Pr.) Essence Publishing.

Clarke, G. A Billiards & Snooker Compendium. 2008. (Illus.). 280p. pap. (978-1-899820-46-7(9)) Paragon Publishing, Rothersthorpe.

Consumer Dummies Staff & Leider, Nicholas. Pool & Billiards for Dummies. 2010. (ENG., Illus.). 384p. pap. 19.99 (978-0-470-56553-7(5), For Dummies) Wiley, John & Sons, Inc.

Dyer, R. A. The Hustler & the Champ: Willie Mosconi, Minnesota Fats, & the Rivalry That Defined Pool. 2007. (ENG., Illus.). 320p. 24.95 (978-1-59228-883-0(9), Lyons Pr.) Globe Pequot Pr., The.

Levi, Riso. Billiards in the Twentieth Century. 2008. 296p. (978-1-4437-3742-5(9), Obscure Pr.) Read Bks.

Morin, Pierre. Pool Techniques & Tricks. 2011. (ENG., Illus.). 260p. pap. 24.95 (978-1-55407-938-4(1)) Firefly Bks., Ltd.

Peall, Arthur F. All about Billiards & How to Pot. 2008. 276p. (978-1-4437-3457-8(8), Pomona Pr.) Read Bks.

Rutter, Paul A. The Barefoot Cue Ball: An Easy Entry into the Magic World of Cue Ball Manipulation & Some Entertaining Pool Stories. 2011. 124p. pap. 19.95 **(978-1-4670-3901-7(2))** AuthorHouse.

Sand, Allan. Safety Toolbox: Advanced Defensive Strategies & Tactical Tools. 2007. (ENG., Illus.). 182p. pap. 26.99 (978-0-9793454-1-8(3)) Billiard Gods Productions.

—Table Map Library. 2007. (ENG.). E-Book 35.00 incl. cd-rom (978-0-9793454-0-1(5)) Billiard Gods Productions.

Stein, Victor & Rubino, Paul. The Billiard Encyclopedia: An Illustrated History of the Sport, 3 vols. 3rd ed. 2008. (Illus.). 640p. 159.95 (978-0-615-17092-3(7)) Balkline Pr., Inc.

Vago, Mike. The Pocket Book of Pocket Billiards: The Rack, the Rules - And a Working Pool Table. 2011. (ENG., Illus.). 48p. bds. 15.95 (978-0-7611-6250-6(X), 076116250X) Workman Publishing Co., Inc.

Wertheim, L. Jon. Running the Table: The Legend of Kid Delicious, the Last Great American Pool Hustler. 2007. (ENG., Illus.). 272p. 24.00 (978-0-618-66474-0(2)) Houghton Mifflin Harcourt Publishing Co.

—Running the Table: The Legend of Kid Delicious, the Last Great American Pool Hustler. 2008. (ENG., Illus.). 288p. pap. 14.95 (978-0-547-08612-5(1), Mariner Bks.) Houghton Mifflin Harcourt Trade & Reference Pubs.

BILLIARDS, POCKET

see Pool (Game)

BILLIART, JULIE, 1751-1816

Clare, James. Life of the Venerable Servant of God Julie Billiart: Foundress And. 2007. pap. 36.95 (978-1-4304-5170-9(X)) Kessinger Publishing, LLC.

BILLINGS, JOHN SHAW, 1838-1913

Lydenberg, Harry Miller. John Shaw Billings Creator of the Nation. 2006. pap. 19.95 (978-1-4286-5612-3(X)) Kessinger Publishing, LLC.

BILLS, LEGISLATIVE

Den Hartog, Chris & Monroe, Nathan W. Agenda Setting in the U. S. Senate: Costly Consideration & Majority Party Advantage. 2011. (ENG., Illus.). 240p. 85.00 (978-1-107-00646-1(5)) Cambridge Univ. Pr.

Harris, Martha H., ed. North Carolina Legislation 2006: A Summary of Legislation in the 2006 General Assembly of Interest to North Carolina Public Officials. 2007. 243p. pap. 50.00 net. (978-1-56011-495-6(9)) Schl. of Government

—North Carolina Legislation 2007: A Summer of Legislation in the 2007 General Assembly of Interest to North Carolina Public Officials. 2007. pap. 50.00 net. *(978-1-56011-565-6(3))* Schl. of Government.
Markup of H.R. 5493, H.R. 5711, H.R. 5681, H.R. 5682, H.R. 5717, & Two Committee Resolutions: Meeting Before the Committee on House Administration, House of Representatives, One Hundred Eleventh Congress, Second Session, Held in Washington, DC, July 14, 2010. 2010. ii, 48p. *(978-0-16-086656-2(1),* 552-070-41634-0) United States Government Printing Office.
Markup of Several Bills: Meeting Before the Committee on House Administration, House of Representatives, One Hundred Eleventh Congress, First Session, Held in Washington, DC, June 10, 2009. 2009. ii, 132p. *(978-0-16-084372-3(3),* 552-070-39915-1) United States Government Printing Office.
Simamba, Bilika H. The Legislative Process: A Handbook for Public Officials. 2009. 268p. 24.99 *(978-1-4490-0219-0(6));* pap. 15.99 *(978-1-4490-0220-6(X))* AuthorHouse.
Stationery Office (U K), The, creator. Fifth Report of Session 2009-10. 2010. (HI Paper Ser.). 5p. pap. *(978-0-10-845933-7(0))* Stationery Office, The.
—House of Lords Delegated Power & Regulatory Reform Committee: Personal Care at Home Bill: 4th Report of Session 2009-10. 2010. (HI Paper Ser.). 15p. pap. *(978-0-10-844868-1(6))* Stationery Office, The.
Verschuuren, Jonathan. The Impact of Legislation: A Critical Analysis of Ex Ante Evaluation. 2009. *(978-90-04-17020-9(0))* BRILL.

BILLS AND NOTES
see Negotiable Instruments

BILLS OF CREDIT
see Letters of Credit; Negotiable Instruments

BILLS OF EXCHANGE
see also Acceptances; Checks; Discount; Foreign Exchange
Balogh, T. Studies in Financial Organization. 2011. (National Institute of Economic & Social Research Economic & Social Studies). (ENG.). 344p. pap. 28.99 *(978-1-107-64901-9(3))* Cambridge Univ. Pr.
Chaudhuri, Sushil & Denzel, Markus A., eds. Cashless Payments & Transactions from the Antiquity To 1914. 2008. (Beiträge zur Wirtschafts- und Sozialgeschichte (BWSG) Ser.). (ENG., Illus.). 195p. (C). pap. 52.00 *(978-3-515-09259-3(5))* Steiner, Franz Verlag Wiesbaden GmbH DEU. Dist: Brown, David Bk. Co., The.
Freund, Judith. Die Wechselverpflichtung im 19. Jahrhundert. 2008. (Rechtshistorische Reihe Ser.). (GER.). 468p. pap. 107.95 *(978-3-631-57831-5(8))* Lang, Peter GmbH, Europaischer Verlag der Wissenschaften DEU. Dist: Lang, Peter.
Malynes, Gerard, et al. Consuetudo, Vel, Lex Mercatoria: In Three Parts, According to the Essentials of Traffick.... Whereunto are Annexed the Following Tracts, viz. I. the Collection of Sea Laws. II. Advice Concerning Bills of Exchange. by John Marius. III. the Merchants Mirrour: or, Directions for the Perfect Ordering of Keeping of His Accompts. by Way of Debtor & Creditor, after the Italian Manner. by R. Dassome. IV. an Introduction to Merchants, 2 vols. 3rd ed. 2008. 395.00 *(978-1-58477-871-4(7))* Lawbook Exchange, Ltd., The.
Nishimura, Shizuya. The Decline of Inland Bills of Exchange in the London Money Market, 1855-1913. 2010. (ENG.). 144p. pap. 27.99 *(978-0-521-13147-6(2))* Cambridge Univ. Pr.

BILLS OF FARE
see Menus

BILLS OF LADING
Anton, Grete. Carriage of Goods by Se. 2010. 76p. pap. *(978-3-8383-7165-8(8))* Lambert Academic Publishing.
Debattista, Charles. Bills of Lading in Export Trade: Maritime & Shipping. 2nd ed. 2008. (Illus.). 335p. 525.00 *(978-1-84592-315-0(4),* Bloomsbury Professional) Bloomsbury Publishing Plc GBR. Dist: International Specialized Bk. Services.
Fontestad Portalés, Leticia & Portales, Leticia Fontestad. Conocimiento de Embarque Como Título Ejecutivo. 2007. (SPA.). 390p. *(978-84-8456-974-9(8))* Tirant lo Blanch.
Gaskell, Bills, et al. Bills of Lading: Law & Contracts. 2nd ed. 2012. 630.00 *(978-1-84311-398-0(8))* Informa Professional GBR. Dist: International Specialized Bk. Services.
Kang, Son-Jun. Chonja Sonna Chungkwonpop Chejong e Kwanhan Yon'gu. 2007. (KOR., Illus.). 168p. *(978-89-8323-596-1(9))* Korea Legislation Research Institute.
Kassem, Ahmad Hussam. Carriage of Goods by Se. 2010. 268p. pap. *(978-3-8383-4210-8(0))* Lambert Academic Publishing.
LexisNexis (Firm) Staff, contrib. by. Goods in Transit: Selected Statutes & Treaties. 2009. pap. *(978-1-4224-7569-0(7))* LexisNexis Matthew Bender.
Li, Qinchang. Hai Shang Huo Yun He Tong de Fa Lü Wen Ti Yan Jiu. 2010. (CHI.). iv, 205p. *(978-7-03-025879-3(7))* Science Pr.
Reynolds, Ruth. Shipowners Global Limitation Liab Conflict of Laws: Intl Regimes. 2010. *(978-90-411-2465-4(9))* Kluwer Law International.
Thomas, D. Rhidian, ed. The Carriage of Goods by Sea under the Rotterdam Rules. 2010. (Illus.). 459p. 477.00 *(978-1-84311-893-0(9))* Informa Professional GBR. Dist: International Specialized Bk. Services.
Todd, Paul. Bills of Lading & Bankers' Documentary Credits. 4th rev. ed. 2007. 335p. 531.00 *(978-1-84311-631-8(6))* Informa Professional GBR. Dist: International Specialized Bk. Services.

BILLS OF PARTICULARS
Jones, Hope. Learn to Be the Boss! A How-to Guide to Owning & Operating a Medical Billing Agency at Home. 2009. 72p. pap. 18.49 *(978-1-4490-4868-6(4))* AuthorHouse.

BILLY, THE KID
Clifford, Frank. Deep Trails in the Old West: A Frontier Memoir. Nolan, Frederick, ed. 2011. (ENG., Illus.). 336p. 29.95 *(978-0-8061-4186-2(7))* Univ. of Oklahoma Pr.
Dellinger, Harold. Billy the Kid: The Best Writings on the Infamous Outlaw. 2008. (ENG., Illus.). 224p. pap. 16.95 *(978-0-7627-4893-8(1),* TwoDot) Globe Pequot Pr., The.
Gardner, Mark L. To Hell on a Fast Horse: Billy the Kid, Pat Garrett, & the Epic Chase to Justice in the Old West. l.t. ed. 2010. (ENG.). 518p. pap. 26.99 *(978-0-06-194569-4(2),* HarperLuxe) HarperCollins Pubs.
Gardner, Mark Lee. To Hell on a Fast Horse: The Untold Story of Billy the Kid & Pat Garrett. 2011. (ENG.). 352p. pap. 14.99 *(978-0-06-136829-5(6),* Harper Paperbacks) HarperCollins Pubs.
Garrett, Pat. The Authentic Life of Billy the Kid: A Biography of William Bonney by the Sheriff Who Knew Him, & Killed Him. 2011. 158p. pap. 11.99 ***(978-1-61001-008-5(6))*** Red & Black Pubs.
Garrett, Pat F. The Authentic Life of Billy the Kid: Facsimile of Original 1927 Edition. 2007. (Illus.). 312p. per. 26.95 *(978-0-86534-572-0(4))* Sunstone Pr.
—Pat F. Garrett's the Authentic Life of Billy, the Kid. 2007. (ENG.). 224p. (C). pap. 24.95 *(978-0-8061-3869-5(6))* Univ. of Oklahoma Pr.
Hunt, Frazier. The Tragic Days of Billy the Kid: Facsimilie of 1956 Edition. 2009. 348p. pap. 29.95 *(978-0-86534-717-5(4))* Sunstone Pr.
Jameson, W. C. Billy the Kid: Beyond the Grave. 2008. (ENG.). 184p. pap. 16.95 *(978-1-58979-381-1(1))* Taylor Trade Publishing.
Moriedge, Phillip J. The 'Real' Wild West. 2009. 438p. pap. 37.95 *(978-0-9559765-0-6(2))* PJM Publishing GBR. Dist: Lulu Enterprises Inc.
Nolan, Frederick. The Billy the Kid Reader. 2007. (ENG., Illus.). 400p. 29.95 *(978-0-8061-3849-7(1))* Univ. of Oklahoma Pr.
Otero, Miguel Antonio. The Real Billy the Kid: With New Light on the Lincoln County War. 2006. (ENG., Illus.). 252p. per. 24.95 *(978-0-86534-547-8(3))* Sunstone Pr.
Poe, John William. The Death of Billy the Kid: Facsimile of the Original 1933 Edition with New Foreword by Marc Simmons. 2006. (Southwest Heritage Ser.). (Illus.). 124p. pap. 18.95 *(978-0-86534-532-4(5))* Sunstone Pr.
Simmons, Marc. Stalking Billy the Kid: Brief Sketches of a Short Life. 2006. (Illus.). 196p. pap. 22.95 *(978-0-86534-525-6(2))* Sunstone Pr.
—Stalking Billy the Kid Hardcover. 2006. 196p. 28.95 *(978-0-86534-577-5(5))* Sunstone Pr.
Siringo, Charles A. A Lone Star Cowboy. 2006. (Illus.). 291p. pap. 24.95 *(978-0-86534-533-1(3))* Sunstone Pr.
Tunstill, William. Billy the Kid & Me Were the Same. 105p. *(978-1-886709-07-2(6))* Outlaw Pubns.
Turk, David S. Blackwater Draw: Three Lives, Billy the Kid, & the Murders That Started the Lincoln County War. 2011. (Illus.). 155p. pap. *(978-0-86534-780-9(8))* Sunstone Pr.
Wallis, Michael. Billy the Kid: The Endless Ride. (ENG., Illus.). 352p. 2008. per. 17.95 *(978-0-393-33063-2(X),* 33063) 2007. 25.95 *(978-0-393-06068-3(3),* 6068) Norton, W. W. & Co., Inc.

BILOXI (MISS.)
Cummings, Samantha. Biloxi: With Gulfport & the Mississippi Gulf Coast. 2012. (Tourist Town Guides). 192p. pap. 14.95 *(978-1-935455-09-7(5))* Channel Lake, Inc.
Flowers, Richard R. The Chronicles of Beauvoir, the Last Home of Jefferson Davis: A History. 2009. (Illus.). xii, 368p. *(978-0-9840856-0-6(2))* Beauvoir Pr.
Manint, Matthew. Lazarus Speaks. 2010. 121p. pap. 10.34 *(978-0-557-31838-4(6))* Lulu Enterprises Inc.
Mason, Gilbert R. & Smith, James Patterson. Beaches, Blood, & Ballots: A Black Doctor's Civil Rights Struggle. 2007. (ENG., Illus.). 227p. per. 22.00 *(978-1-934110-28-7(0))* Univ. Pr. of Mississippi.

BILTMORE FOREST (N.C.)
Alexander, Bill. The Biltmore Nursery: A Botanical Legacy. 2007. (Illus.). 189p. pap., per. 26.99 *(978-1-59629-238-3(5))* History Pr., The.

BILUCHI LANGUAGE
see Baluchi Language

BIMETAL
see Laminated Metals

BIMETALLISM
see also Currency Question; Gold Standard; Precious Metals; Quantity Theory of Money; Silver; Silver Question
Algeo, Matthew. The President Is a Sick Man: Wherein the Supposedly Virtuous Grover Cleveland Survives a Secret Surgery at Sea & Vilifies the Courageous Newspaperman Who Dared Expose the Truth. (ENG.). 272p. 2012. pap. 16.95 ***(978-1-61374-456-7(0))*** 2011. (Illus.). 24.95 *(978-1-56976-350-6(X))* Chicago Review Pr., Inc.
Fisher, Irving. Mathematical Investigations in the Theory of Value & Prices, And. 2006. pap. 19.95 *(978-1-59605-938-2(9),* Cosimo Classics) Cosimo, Inc.
—Mathematical Investigations in the Theory of Value & Prices, & Appreciation & Interest. 2007. 244p. 34.95 *(978-1-60206-959-6(X))* Cosimo, Inc.
Laughlin, James Laurence. The History of Bimetallism in the United States. 2009. 280p. 42.95 *(978-1-104-34525-9(0));* pap. 27.95 *(978-1-104-30976-3(9))* Kessinger Publishing, LLC.
Redish, Angela. Bimetallism: An Economic & Historical Analysis. 2006. (Studies in Macroeconomic History Ser.). (ENG., Illus.). 292p. pap. 61.00 *(978-0-521-02893-6(0))* Cambridge Univ. Pr.

BIN LADEN, OSAMA, 1957-2011
Assessing U.S. Policy & Its Limits in Pakistan: Hearing Before the Committee on Foreign Relations, United States Senate, One Hundred Twelfth Congress, First Session, May 5, 2011. 2011. iii, 52p. ***(978-0-16-089388-9(7),*** 552-070-43372-4) United States Government Printing Office.
Atwan, Abdel Bari. The Secret History of Al Qaeda. 2nd rev. ed. 2008. 328p. pap. 19.95 *(978-0-520-25561-6(5))* Univ. of California Pr.
Bergen, Peter L. Manhunt: The Ten-Year Search for Bin Laden — From 9/11 to Abbottabad. 2012. (ENG., Illus.). 384p. 26.00 ***(978-0-307-95557-9(5),*** Crown) Crown Publishing Group.
Bergen, Peter L. The Osama Bin Laden I Know: An Oral History of Al Qaeda's Leader. 2006. (ENG., Illus.). 528p. pap. 16.00 *(978-0-7432-7892-8(5),* Free Pr.) Free Pr.
Coll, Steve. The Bin Ladens: An Arabian Family in the American Century. (ENG.). 688p. (gr. 12-18). 2009. 18.00 *(978-0-14-311481-9(6),* Penguin (Non-Classics)) 2008. 35.00 *(978-1-59420-164-6(1),* Penguin Pr. HC, The) Penguin Group (USA) Inc.
Donahue, Raymond V. The Death of Osama bin Laden & Related Operations. 2011. (Terrorism, Hot Spots & Conflict-Related Issues Ser.). 162p. 95.00 ***(978-1-61470-479-9(1))*** Nova Science Pubs., Inc.
Fury, Dalton. Kill Bin Laden: A Delta Force Commander's Account of the Hunt for the World's Most Wanted Man. (ENG.). 2011. 400p. mass mkt. 7.99 *(978-0-312-54741-7(2),* St. Martin's Paperbacks) 2009. (Illus.). 352p. pap. 14.99 *(978-0-312-56740-8(5),* St. Martin's Griffin) St. Martin's Pr.
Gard, Carolyn. The Attacks on the World Trade Center: February 26, 1993, & September 11 2001. 2009. (Terrorist Attacks Ser.). 64p. (gr. 5-5). 58.50 *(978-1-60853-314-5(X))* Rosen Publishing Group, Inc., The.
Graham, Bob B, ed. Joint Inquiry into Intelligence Community Activities Before & after the Terrorist Attacks of September 11 2001: Congressional Hearings. 2006. (Illus.). 867p. (C). reprint ed. pap. 95.00 *(978-1-4223-0632-1(1))* DIANE Publishing Co.
—Joint Inquiry into Intelligence Community Activities before & after the Terrorist Attacks of September 11 2001: Congressional Hearings, Vol. 2. 2006. 659p. (C). reprint ed. pap. 75.00 *(978-1-4223-0631-4(3))* DIANE Publishing Co.
Griffin, David Ray. Osama Bin Laden: Dead or Alive? 2009. (ENG.). 128p. pap. 15.00 *(978-1-56656-783-1(1),* Olive Branch Pr.) Interlink Publishing Group, Inc.
Gutman, Roy. How We Missed the Story: Osama Bin Laden, the Taliban, & the Hijacking of Afghanistan. 2008. (Illus.). 304p. 26.00 *(978-1-60127-024-5(0))* U. S. Institute of Peace Pr. (USIP Pr.).
Hurst, Brandon Franklin. Osama Bin Laden: The Final Days. 2011. 300p. pap. 16.95 ***(978-1-926893-77-8(8))*** Cogito Media Grp. CAN. Dist: Midpoint Trade Bks., Inc.
Issaki, Shimshon. Terror & Iraq: How We Can Better Combat Islamic Terrorism. 2008. 504p. 39.90 *(978-965-91351-0-3(6))* Issaki, Shimshon ISR. Dist: AtlasBooks Distribution.
Laddage, Reialdo. Tres vidas secretas/ Three Secret Lives. 2008. (SPA.). 155p. pap. *(978-987-1156-81-8(2))* Hidalgo, Adriana Editora S.A.
Life Magazine Staff. Brought to Justice: Osama Bin Laden's War on America & the Mission That Stopped Him. 2011. (ENG., Illus.). 96p. 19.99 ***(978-0-316-20173-5(1))*** Little Brown & Co.
Lo, Mbaye. Understanding Muslim Discourse: Discourse: Language, Tradition, & the Message of Bin Laden. 2009. (ENG.). 130p. pap. 24.50 *(978-0-7618-4748-9(0))* Univ. Pr. of America, Inc.
Naylor, R. T. Satanic Purses: Money, Myth, & Misinformation in the War on Terror. (ENG.). (C). 2008. 432p. pap. *(978-0-7735-3454-4(7))* 2006. 430p. *(978-0-7735-3150-5(5))* McGill-Queen's Univ. Pr.
Olsson, Peter Alan. The Cult of Osama: Psychoanalyzing Bin Laden & His Magnetism for Muslim Youths, 1 vol. 2007. (Praeger Security International Ser.). 184p. 44.95 *(978-0-275-99989-6(0),* C9989, Praeger Security International) Greenwood Publishing Group, Inc.
Pfarrer, Chuck. Seal Target Geronimo: The Inside Story of the Mission to Kill Osama Bin Laden. (ENG., 240p. 2012. Illus.). pap. 15.99 ***(978-1-250-01471-9(9),*** St. Martin's Griffin) 2011. 25.99 ***(978-1-250-00635-6(X))*** St. Martin's Pr.
Riedel, Bruce. The Search for al Qaeda: Its Leadership, Ideology, & Future. 2008. (ENG.). 224p. 26.95 *(978-0-8157-7414-3(1))* Brookings Institution Pr.
Robinson, Adam. Bin Laden: Behind the Mask of a Terrorist. 2011. (ENG., Illus.). 320p. pap. 14.95 *(978-1-61145-122-1(1),* 611122, Arcade Publishing) Skyhorse Publishing Co., Inc.
—Bin Laden: Behind the Mask of the Terrorist. 2006. (Illus.). 302p. reprint ed. 24.00 *(978-1-4223-5427-8(X))* DIANE Publishing Co.
Roshandel, Jalil & Chadha, Sharon. Jihad & International Security. annot. ed. 2006. (ENG.). 256p. pap. 30.00 *(978-1-4039-7192-0(7))* Palgrave Macmillan.
Rowell, James. Gandhi & Bin Laden: Religion at the Extremes. 2009. (ENG.). 158p. pap. 26.50 *(978-0-7618-4766-3(9))* Univ. Pr. of America, Inc.
Rowell, James L. Gandhi & Bin Laden: Religion at the Extremes. 2009. 147p. *(978-0-7618-4767-0(7))* Univ. Pr. of America, Inc.
Sandia National Laboratories & Sandia National Laboratories. Osama Bin Laden: A Case Study. 2011. 396p. pap. 49.00 ***(978-1-60888-128-4(8))*** Nimble Bks. LLC.
Sasson, Jean, et al. Growing up Bin Laden: Osama's Wife & Son Take Us Inside Their Secret World. (ENG., Illus.). 352p. 2010. pap. 15.99 *(978-0-312-56087-4(7),* St. Martin's Griffin) 2009. 25.99 *(978-0-312-56016-4(8))* St. Martin's Pr.
Scheuer, Michael. Imperial Hubris: Why the West Is Losing the War on Terror. 2007. per. 10.95 *(978-1-59797-159-1(6))* Potomac Bks., Inc.
—Osama Bin Laden, 1 vol. 2011. (ENG.). 288p. 19.95 *(978-0-19-973866-3(1))* Oxford Univ. Pr., Inc.
—Osama bin Laden. 2012. (ENG.). 320p. pap. 13.95 ***(978-0-19-989839-8(1))*** Oxford Univ. Pr., Inc.
Scheuer, Michael. Through Our Enemies' Eyes: Osama Bin Laden, Radical Islam, & the Future of America. rev. ed. 2007. (Illus.). per. 10.95 *(978-1-59797-162-1(6))* Potomac Bks., Inc.
Schultheis, Rob. Hunting Bin Laden: How Al-Qaeda Is Winning the War on Terror. 2008. 229p. 24.95 *(978-1-60239-244-1(7))* Skyhorse Publishing Co., Inc.
Schweitzer, Yoram & Shay, Shaul. The Globalization of Terror: The Challenge of Al-Qaida & the Response of the International Community. 2008. (ENG., Illus.). 242p. pap. 29.95 *(978-1-4128-0770-8(0))* Transaction Pubs.
Smucker, Philip. Al Qaeda's Great Escape: The Military & the Media on Terror's Trail. 2006. (Illus.). 229p. reprint ed. 27.00 *(978-1-4223-5759-0(7))* DIANE Publishing Co.
United States, Congress House Permanent Select Committee on Intelligence, contrib. by. Al-Qaeda: The Many Faces of an Islamist Extremist Threat. 2006. (ENG., Illus.). 47p. pap. 21.00 *(978-0-16-076897-2(7),* 052-070-07483-3) United States Government Printing Office.
United States Senate. Tora Bora Revisited: How We Failed to Get Bin Laden & Why It Matters Today (Decisive Battles of the 21st Century) 2009. 50p. pap. 20.63 *(978-1-60888-012-6(5))* Nimble Bks. LLC.

BINARY FORMS
see Forms, Binary

BINARY-QUATERNARY SYSTEM
see Binary System (Mathematics)

BINARY STARS
see Double Stars

BINARY SYSTEM (MATHEMATICS)
see also Error-Correcting Codes (Information Theory)
Ali Rahoma, Walid, et al. Binary System with Varying Mass. 2011. 120p. pap. ***(978-3-8443-1582-0(9))*** Lambert Academic Publishing.
Cosinschi, Eugen & Cosinschi, Micheline. Essai de logique ternaire sémiotique et Philosophique. 2009. (FRE.). 213p. pap. *(978-3-0343-0048-3(4))* Lang, Peter.
Drechsler, Rolf, et al. Test Pattern Generation using Boolean Proof Engines. 2009. (ENG., Illus.). xii, 192p. 139.00 *(978-90-481-2359-9(3),* 9048123593) Springer.
Justesen, Jim & Forchhammer, Siren. Two-Dimensional Information Theory & Coding: With Applications to Graphics Data & High-Density Storage Media. 2009. (ENG., Illus.). 184p. 69.00 *(978-0-521-88860-8(3))* Cambridge Univ. Pr.
Loos, O. G. Jordan Pairs. 2008. (Lecture Notes in Mathematics Ser.). 240p. pap. 46.00 *(978-3-540-07166-2(0))* Springer.
Michael, Munywoki, et al. Cycle Indices of Semidirect Product Groups: The Dihedral, Frobenious & the Internal Direct Product Groups. 2011. 52p. pap. ***(978-3-639-25998-8(X))*** VDM Verlag Dr. Mueller e.K.
Ochin, Evgeny. Systemy Liczbowe. 2010. 106p. pap. 14.50 *(978-1-4457-7534-0(4))* Lulu Enterprises Inc.
Robertson, Paul Francis. Basic Computer Science Mathematics Binary Computations Guide. 2006. 44p. per. 11.99 *(978-1-59879-145-7(1))* Lifevest Publishing, Inc.
Scientific Group Thermodata Europe Staff. Binary Systems Supplement 1. 2007. (Landolt-Börnstein: Numerical Data & Functional Relationships in Science & Technology - New Series / Physical Chemistry Ser.). (Illus.). xxviii, 365p. 7439.00 *(978-3-540-45279-9(6),* 3540452796) Springer.

BINDING OF BOOKS
see Bookbinding

BINDING THEORY (LINGUISTICS)
see Government-Binding Theory (Linguistics)

BINGE-PURGE COMPULSION
see Bulimia

BINGEN, HILDEGARD VON, SAINT, 1098-1179
see Hildegard, Saint, 1098-1179

BINGHAM, GEORGE CALEB, 1811-1899
Bingham, George Caleb. "But I Forget That I Am a Painter & Not a Politician" The Letters of George Caleb Bingham. 2011. (Illus.). xiv, 564p. ***(978-0-9816939-3-4(8))*** State Historical Society of Missouri.
Christ-Janer, Albert. George Caleb Bingham of Missouri: The Story of an Artist. 171p. reprint ed. lib. bdg. 88.00 *(978-0-7222-0390-3(X))* Library Reprints, Inc.
Gentzler, Lynn Wolf, ed. But I Forget That I am a Painter & Not a Politician: The Letters of George Caleb Bingham. 2011. (Illus.). 578p. pap. 25.00 ***(978-0-9816939-2-7(X))*** State Historical Society of Missouri.
Larkin, Lew. Bingham, Fighting Artist: The Story of Missouri's Immortal Painter, Patriot, Soldier & Statesman. 2011. 374p. 53.95 ***(978-1-258-07202-5(5))*** Literary Licensing, LLC.

B

BINGHAM, HIRAM, 1875-1956

Bingham, Robert Kim. Courageous Dissent: How Harry Bingham Defied His Government to Save Lives. 2007. (Illus.). 159p. pap. 20.00 *(978-0-9613602-3-8(2)*, 42007) Triune Bks.

Heaney, Christopher. Cradle of Gold: The Story of Hiram Bingham, a Real-Life Indiana Jones, & the Search for Machu Picchu. 2010. (ENG., Illus.). 304p. 27.00 *(978-0-230-61169-6(9))* Palgrave Macmillan.

BINGO

Auto Bingo Staff. Auto Bingo 1. Date not set. 2.95 *(978-1-879424-82-1(7))* Nickel Pr.

Duggleby, Sue & Duggleby, Ross. Musical Bingo. 2nd rev. ed. (Illus.). 20p. *(978-0-86388-507-5(1)*, 003-5226) Speechmark Publishing Ltd.

Findley, Violet. Sight Word Bingo Ladders: Fun-and-Easy Reproducible Games That Target & Teach 300 Key Sight Words. 2010. (ENG.). 80p. (gr. k-2). pap. 12.99 *(978-0-545-22063-7(7)*, Teaching Resources) Scholastic, Inc.

Lawton, Jeffrey. The Bingo Pinball War: United vs Bally, 1951-1957. 2010. (Illus.). 160p. 39.99 *(978-0-7643-3557-0(X))* Schiffer Publishing, Ltd.

Longo, Frank. SCRABBLE Bingo Crosswords. 2009. (ENG.). 64p. spiral bd. 5.95 *(978-1-4027-5976-5(2)*, Puzzlewright) Sterling Publishing Co., Inc.

White, Gisele. Professor Melonhead's Bingo Book: Educational Games for Students of All Ages. 2009. 280p. pap. 39.99 *(978-0-578-02403-5(9))* White, Gisele L.

BINOCULAR VISION

Evans, Bruce J. W. & Pickwell, David. Pickwell's Binocular Vision Anomalies. 5th rev. ed. 2007. (ENG., Illus.). 464p. 120.00 *(978-0-7506-8897-0(1)*, Butterworth-Heinemann) Elsevier - Health Sciences Div.

Fletcher, Robert & Stidwill, David. Normal Binocular Vision: Theory, Investigation & Practical Aspects. 2010. (ENG., Illus.). 280p. pap. 66.99 *(978-1-4051-9250-7(X)*, Wiley-Blackwell) Wiley, John & Sons, Inc.

Griffin, John R. & Grisham, I David. Binrevlar Anomalies: Diagnosis & Vision Therapy, 2 vols. 4th ed. 2006. (ENG., Illus.). pap. 80.00 incl. cd-rom *(978-0-929780-16-0(7))* Optometric Extension Program Fndtn.

McCoun, Jacques & Reeves, Lucien, eds. Binocular Vision: Development, Depth Perception & Disorders. 2010. (Eye & Vision Research Developments Ser.). (Illus.). xiv, 260p. 145.00 *(978-1-60876-547-8(4))* Nova Science Pubs., Inc.

Pugeault, Nicolas. Early Cognitive Vision: Feedback Mechanisms for the Disambiguation of Early Visual Representation. 2008. 180p. pap. *(978-3-639-09357-5(7))* VDM Verlag Dr. Mueller e.K.

Scheiman, Mitchell & Wick, Bruce. Clinical Management of Binocular Vision: Heterophoric, Accommodative, & Eye Movement Disorders. 3rd rev. ed. 2008. (ENG., Illus.). 608p. pap. 92.99 *(978-0-7817-7784-1(4))* Lippincott Williams & Wilkins.

BINOCULARS

Laguerre, Enrique A. Los Gemelos. 145p. pap. 10.95 *(978-1-56758-003-7(3))* Editorial Cultural, Inc.

Mullaney, James. A Buyer's & User's Guide to Astronomical Telescopes & Binoculars. 2007. (Patrick Moore's Practical Astronomy Ser.). (Illus.). 203p. pap. 29.95 *(978-1-84628-439-7(2)*, 1846284392) Springer.

Scagell, Robin & Frydman, David. Stargazing with Binoculars. 2nd rev. ed. 2011. (ENG., Illus.). 208p. pap. 19.95 *(978-1-55407-821-9(0))* Firefly Bks., Ltd.

Tonkin, Stephen F. Binocular Astronomy. 2006. (Patrick Moore's Practical Astronomy Ser.). (Illus.). 284p. per. 32.95 *(978-1-84628-308-6(6)*, 1846283086) Springer.

Yoder, Paul R. & Vukobratovich, Daniel. Field Guide to Binoculars & Scopes. 2011. (Field Guide Ser.). 152p. spiral bd. 39.00 ***(978-0-8194-8649-3(3))*** SPIE.

BINOMIAL THEOREM

Hilbe, Joseph M. Negative Binomial Regression. 2nd rev. ed. 2011. (ENG., Illus.). 572p. 85.00 *(978-0-521-19815-8(1))* Cambridge Univ. Pr.

Sequence & Series, Mathematical Induction & Binomial Theorem, Descriptive Statistics, Vol. 10. 160p. 6.95 *(978-0-87891-209-4(6))* Research & Education Assn.

BIO-BIBLIOGRAPHY

see also Authors

also subdivision Bio-Bibliography under names of countries, cities, etc. and under topical headings

Clauss, J. E. John D. MacDonald: A Checklist. reprint ed. pap. 17.95 *(978-0-88411-799-5(5))* Amereon LTD.

—Louis L'Amour Checklist. pap. 17.95 *(978-0-88411-244-0(6))* Amereon LTD.

Europa, contrib. by. International Who's Who of Authors & Writers 2008. 23rd rev. ed. 2007. 832p. 390.00 *(978-1-85743-428-6(5))* Routledge.

Farley, G. M. The Zane Grey Annotated Book Checklist. reprint ed. pap. 17.95 *(978-0-89190-768-8(8))* Amereon LTD.

Gale Editor, ed. The Writers Directory, 2 vols. 29th ed. 2011. 2820p. lib. bdg. 349.00 *(978-1-55862-835-9(5)*, St. James Pr.) Cengage Gale.

Heuer, Renate & Boelke-Fabian, Andrea. Lexikon Deutsch-Jüdischer Autoren. 2007. (GER.). XXV, 424p. ***(978-3-598-22695-3(0))***; XXVIII, 355p. ***(978-3-598-22692-2(6))*** Saur, K. G. Verlag GmbH & Co.

Hill, Grace Livingston & Paulsen, Joanna. Grace Livingston Hill: A Checklist. Date not set. reprint ed. pap. 12.95 *(978-0-89190-993-4(1)*, American Reprint Co.) Amereon LTD.

Lexington Who's Who, Inc. Staff. The Lexington Who's Who Registry, 1998-1999. Date not set. *(978-0-9672740-0-3(1))* Empire Executive & Professional Registry.

The Writers Directory, 2.0. 28th ed. 2011. 332.00 *(978-1-55862-798-7(7)*, St. James Pr.) Cengage Gale.

BIOACOUSTICS

see also Animal Sounds; Hearing; Sound Production by Animals

Au, Whitlow W. L. & Hastings, Mardi C. Principles of Marine Bioacoustics. 2010. (Modern Acoustics & Signal Processing Ser.). (Illus.). xvi, 680p. pap. 99.00 *(978-1-4419-2686-9(0)*, 1441926860) Springer.

Dhar, Sumitrajit & Hall, James W. Otoacoustic Emissions: Principles, Procedures, & Protocols. 2011. (Illus.). 150p. pap. 55.00 *(978-1-59756-342-0(0))* Plural Publishing, Inc.

Hastings, Mardi C. & Au, Whitlow W. L. Principles of Marine Bioacoustics. 2008. (Modern Acoustics & Signal Processing Ser.). (Illus.). 360p. 99.00 *(978-0-387-78364-2(4))* Springer.

Hill, Peggy S. M. Vibrational Communication in Animals. 2008. (Illus.). 272p. 44.00 *(978-0-674-02798-5(1))* Harvard Univ. Pr.

Institute of Acoustics (IOA) Staff, compiled by. Spring Conference of the Institute of Acoustics 2005: The Heart of Building Acoustics: What Makes it Tick? 2007. (Proceedings of the Institute of Acoustics Ser.). 122p. pap. 115.00 *(978-1-60423-991-1(3))* Curran Assocs., Inc.

—4th International Conference on Bio-Acoustics 2007. 2007. (Proceedings of the Institute of Acoustics Ser.). 283p. pap. 143.00 *(978-1-60423-808-2(9))* Curran Assocs., Inc.

Manley, Geoffrey A. & Fay, Richard R., eds. Active Processes & Otoacoustic Emissions in Hearing. 2010. (Springer Handbook of Auditory Research Ser.). (Illus.). xviii, 484p. pap. 159.00 *(978-1-4419-2443-8(4)*, 1441924434) Springer.

Manley, Geoffrey A., et al. Active Processes & Otoacoustic Emissions. 2007. (Springer Handbook of Auditory Research Ser.: Vol. 30). (Illus.). 512p. 159.00 *(978-0-387-71467-7(7))* Springer.

Mattson, Jill Ingeborg. Secret Sounds: Ultimate Healing: Your Personal Guide to a Better Life using Sharry Edward's Revolutionary. 2011. (ENG.). 277p. pap. 19.99 ***(978-0-9822814-2-0(0))*** Wings of Light.

Olson, E. S. & Böhnke, F., eds. Mechanics of the Ear & Otoacoustic Emissions: Dedicated to Prof. Wolfgang Arnold on the Occasion of his 65th Birthday: Special Issue: ORL 2006, Vol. 68, No. 6. (Illus.). 90p. pap. *(978-3-8055-8204-9(8))* Karger, S. AG.

Webb, Jacqueline F., et al, eds. Fish Bioacoustics. 2008. (Springer Handbook of Auditory Research Ser.). (Illus.). 318p. 149.00 *(978-0-387-73028-8(1))* Springer.

Webb, Jacqueline F. & Fay, Richard R., eds. Fish Bioacoustics. 2010. (Springer Handbook of Auditory Research Ser.). (Illus.). xiv, 322p. pap. 149.00 *(978-1-4419-2505-3(8)*, 1441925058) Springer.

BIOASSAY

see Biological Assay

BIOASTRONAUTICS

see Space Biology; Space Medicine

BIOBIBLIOGRAPHY

see Bio-Bibliography

BIOCERAMICS

see Ceramics in Medicine

BIOCHEMICAL ENGINEERING

see also Bioreactors; Fermentation

American Society of Mechanical Engineers Staff, contrib. by. Proceedings of the 6th International Conference on Nanochannels, Microchannels & Minichannels, 2008: Presented at 6th International Conference on Nanochannels, Microchannels & Minichannels, June 23-25, 2008, Darmstadt, Germany: Sponsored by ASME, 2 vols. 2008. (Illus.). xxxiii, 1948p. pap. *(978-0-7918-4834-0(5))* American Society of Mechanical Engineers, The.

Belkin, Shimshon S. & Gu, Man Bock, eds. Whole Cell Sensing Systems: Part I: Reporter Cells & Devices, 2 vols. 2010. (Advances in Biochemical Engineering Biotechnology Ser.). (ENG., Illus.). xii, 220p. 299.00 *(978-3-642-12361-0(9)*, 3642123619) Springer.

Blanch, Harvey W. & Clark, Douglas S. Biochem Eng 2e. 2nd ed. 2013. 169.95 ***(978-1-57444-644-9(4)***, CRC Press) Taylor & Francis Group GBR. Dist: Taylor & Francis Group.

Boudreau, Michael A. & McMillan, Gregory K. New Directions in Bioprocess Modeling & Control: Maximizing Process Analytical Technology Benefits. 2006. (ENG., Illus.). 338p. pap. 99.00 *(978-1-55617-905-1(7))* ISA.

Calam, C. T. Process Development in Antibiotic Fermentations. 2008. (Cambridge Studies in Biotechnology Ser.). (ENG.). 228p. pap. 53.00 *(978-0-521-06552-8(6))* Cambridge Univ. Pr.

Calvert, Paul & Narayan, Roger, eds. Computer Aided Biomanufacturing. 2011. (Wiley Reference Collection in Solid State & Material Science Ser.). (ENG., Illus.). 204p. 160.00 *(978-3-527-40906-8(8)*, Wiley-VCH) Wiley, John & Sons, Inc.

Carnazza, Santina. Phage Display as a Tool for Synthetic Biology. Guglielmino, Salvatore, ed. 2010. (Nanotechnology Science & Technology Ser.). 93p. pap. 43.00 *(978-1-60876-987-2(9))* Nova Science Pubs., Inc.

Chen, Hongzhang. Process Engineering in Plant-Based Products. 2009. (Environmental Science, Engineering & Technology Ser.). 89.00 *(978-1-60741-962-4(9))* Nova Science Pubs., Inc.

Chen, Jim & Tsai, Shau-Wei. Carica Papaya Lipase: A versatile enantioselectivity Biocatalyst. 2011. 160p. pap. ***(978-3-8443-1730-5(9))*** Lambert Academic Publishing.

Cortassa, S. An Introduction to Metabolic & Cellular Engineering. 2nd rev. ed. 2011. 448p. 120.00 ***(978-981-4365-71-0(8))***; pap. 60.00 ***(978-981-4365-72-7(6))*** World Scientific Publishing Co., Inc.

Cram101 Textbook Reviews Staff. Outlines & Highlights for Chemical, Biochemical, & Engineering Thermodynamics by Stanley I Sandler, Isbn: 9780471661740. 2009. 202p. pap. 30.95 *(978-1-4288-7452-7(6))* Cram101 Inc.

Daculsi, Guy & Layrolle, Pierre, eds. Bioceramics; Proceedings: International Symposium on Ceramics in Medicine (20th: 2007: Nantes, Frances), Vol. 2. 2008. 1428p. pap. *(978-0-87849-457-6(X))* Trans Tech Pubns., Ltd.

Datta, Ashim & Rakesh, Vineet. An Introduction to Modeling of Transport Processes: Applications to Biomedical Systems. 2009. (Cambridge Texts in Biomedical Engineering Ser.). (ENG., Illus.). 532p. 87.00 *(978-0-521-11924-5(3))* Cambridge Univ. Pr.

Dietrich, Heidi. Nanoassays for Biomolecular Research. 2010. 152p. pap. *(978-3-8383-5731-7(0))* Lambert Academic Publishing.

Dochain, Denis. Automatic Control of Bioprocesses. 2007. 256p. 150.00 *(978-1-905209-36-1(3))* ISTE/Hermes Science Publishing GBR. Dist: Independent Pubs. Group.

Dookeran, Mark. Ginger Beer. 2010. 124p. pap. *(978-3-639-24813-5(9))* VDM Verlag Dr. Mueller e.K.

Doran, Pauline M. Bioprocess Engineering Principles. 2nd ed. 2012. (ENG.). 928p. pap. 119.95 ***(978-0-12-220851-5(X)***, Academic Pr.) Elsevier Science & Technology Bks.

Dumont, Fabian E. & Sacco, Jack A. Biochemical Engineering. 2009. (Biotechnology in Agriculture, Industry & Medicine Ser.). (Illus.). xiv, 360p. 129.00 *(978-1-60741-257-1(8))* Nova Science Pubs., Inc.

Dutta, Rajiv. Fundamentals of Biochemical Engineering. 2010. (ENG., Illus.). xv, 292p. pap. 99.00 *(978-3-642-09674-7(3)*, 3642096743) Springer.

Ende, David J. am. Chemical Engineering in the Pharmaceutical Industry: R&D to Manufacturing. 2010. (ENG., Illus.). 887p. 199.95 *(978-0-470-42669-2(1)*, Wiley) Wiley, John & Sons, Inc.

Enfors, Sven-Olof. Physiological Stress Responses in Bioprocesses. 2010. (Advances in Biochemical Engineering Biotechnology Ser.). (Illus.). xi, 244p. pap. 309.00 *(978-3-642-05787-8(X)*, 364205787X) Springer.

Fersht, Alan R. The Selected Papers of Sir Alan Fersht: Development of Protein Engineering. 2010. (Illus.). 408p. 140.00 *(978-1-84816-554-0(4))* Imperial College Pr. GBR. Dist: World Scientific Publishing Co., Inc.

Fett-Neto, Arthur Germano, ed. Plant Secondary Metabolism Engineering: Methods & Applications. 2010. (Methods in Molecular Biology Ser.). (ENG., Illus.). x, 326p. 159.00 *(978-1-60761-722-8(6)*, 1607617226) Humana Pr.

Forciniti, Daniel. Industrial Bioseparations: Principles & Practice. 2008. (ENG., Illus.). 376p. 134.00 *(978-0-8138-2085-9(5)*, Wiley-Blackwell) Wiley, John & Sons, Inc.

Freitag, Ruth, ed. Modern Advances in Chromatography. 2011. (Advances in Biochemical Engineering Biotechnology Ser.). (ENG., Illus.). xii, 271p. pap. 329.00 *(978-3-642-07706-7(4)*, 3642077064) Springer.

Galindo, Enrique & Ramírez, Octavio R., eds. Advances in Bioprocess Engineering. 2010. (Illus.). 541p. pap. 489.00 *(978-90-481-4459-4(0)*, 9048144590) Springer.

—Advances in Bioprocess Engineering Volume II. 2010. 288p. pap. 179.00 *(978-90-481-4987-2(8)*, 9048149878) Springer.

Ghosh, Raja. Principles of Bioseparations Engineering. 2006. (Illus.). 265p. 69.00 *(978-981-256-892-2(1))* World Scientific Publishing Co., Inc.

Gottschalk, Uwe, ed. Process Scale Purification of Antibodies. 2009. (ENG., Illus.). 456p. 122.00 *(978-0-470-20962-2(3)*, Wiley-Interscience) Wiley, John & Sons, Inc.

Gutiérrez, Agustín & Marco, Santiago. Biologically Inspired Signal Processing for Chemical Sensing. 2009. (Illus.). xiii, 167p. E-Book *(978-3-642-00176-5(9))* Springer.

Haimi, Suvi. Bone Tissue Engineering. 2010. 84p. pap. *(978-3-8383-0203-4(6))* Lambert Academic Publishing.

Harding, S. E., ed. Biotechnology & Genetic Engineering Reviews, Vol. 26. 2010. (Biotechnology & Genetic Engineering Reviews Ser.). (ENG.). 464p. 147.00 *(978-1-904761-91-4(7))* Nottingham Univ. Pr. GBR. Dist: Independent Pubs. Group.

Heinzle, Elmar, et al. Development of Sustainable Bioprocesses: Modeling & Assessment. 2007. (ENG., Illus.). 316p. 215.00 *(978-0-470-01559-9(4)*, Wiley) Wiley, John & Sons, Inc.

Honary, Lou, et al. Biobased Lubricants & Greases: Technology & Products. 2011. (Tribology in Practice Ser.). (ENG., Illus.). 238p. 125.00 *(978-0-470-74158-0(9)*, Wiley) Wiley, John & Sons, Inc.

Huopalahti, Rainer, et al, eds. Bioactive Egg Compounds. 2010. (ENG., Illus.). xx, 298p. pap. 189.00 *(978-3-642-07238-3(0)*, 3642072380) Springer.

Jane's Chemical - Biological Handbook: Military. 15.00 *(978-0-7106-1873-3(5))* Jane's Information Group, Inc.

Jensen, Knud, ed. Peptide & Protein Design for Biopharmaceutical Applications. 2009. (ENG., Illus.). 306p. 160.00 *(978-0-470-31961-1(5)*, Wiley) Wiley, John & Sons, Inc.

Karasev, Alexander V. Plant-Produced Microbial Vaccines. 2009. (Current Topics in Microbiology & Immunology Ser.). (Illus.). x, 120p. 159.00 *(978-3-540-70857-5(X))* Springer.

Katoh, Shigeo & Yoshida, Fumitake. Biochemical Engineering: A Textbook for Engineers, Chemists & Biologists. 2009. (ENG., Illus.). 282p. pap. 77.00 *(978-3-527-32536-8(0)*, Wiley-VCH) Wiley, John & Sons, Inc.

Kobayashi, Takeshi. Recent Progress of Biochemical & Biomedical Engineering in Japan II. 2010. (Advances in Biochemical Engineering Biotechnology Ser.). (Illus.). xii, 239p. pap. 289.00 *(978-3-642-05801-1(9)*, 3642058019) Springer.

Kompala, Dhinakar S. Bioprocess Engineering: Fundamentals & Applications. 2013. (ENG.). 750p. (C). 119.95 *(978-0-8493-8083-9(9)*, CRC Press) Taylor & Francis Group GBR. Dist: Taylor & Francis Group.

Lutz, Stefan & Bornscheuer, Uwe Theo, eds. Protein Engineering Handbook, 2 vols. 2009. (ENG., Illus.). 1015p. 490.00 *(978-3-527-31850-6(X)*, Wiley-VCH) Wiley, John & Sons, Inc.

Marco, Santiago & Gutiérrez, Agustí, eds. Biologically Inspired Signal Processing for Chemical Sensing. 2009. (Studies in Computational Intelligence Ser.). (ENG., Illus.). xiv, 170p. 159.00 *(978-3-642-00175-8(0))* Springer.

Meyyappan, Narayanan & Parthiban, Rangasamy. A Novel Separation Technique Using Hydrotropes. 2011. 152p. pap. ***(978-3-8443-1354-3(0))*** Lambert Academic Publishing.

Najafpour, Ghasem. Biochemical Engineering & Biotechnology. 2006. (ENG., Illus.). 438p. 215.00 *(978-0-444-52845-2(8)*, Elsevier Science) Elsevier Science & Technology Bks.

New Trends & Developments in Biochemical Engineering. 2010. (Advances in Biochemical Engineering Biotechnology Ser.). (Illus.). ix, 303p. pap. 349.00 *(978-3-642-07323-6(9)*, 3642073239) Springer.

Nielsen, Jens. Biotechnology for the Future. 2010. (Advances in Biochemical Engineering Biotechnology Ser.). (Illus.). xiv, 229p. pap. 279.00 *(978-3-642-06527-9(9)*, 3642065279) Springer.

—Metabolic Engineering. 2010. (Advances in Biochemical Engineering Biotechnology Ser.). (Illus.). xi, 183p. pap. 279.00 *(978-3-642-07534-6(7)*, 3642075347) Springer.

Nyanhongo, Gibson Stephen, et al, eds. Biofunctionalization of Polymers & their Applications. 2011. (Advances in Biochemical Engineering Biotechnology Ser.). (ENG., Illus.). xvi, 288p. 309.00 ***(978-3-642-21948-1(9)***, 3642219489) Springer.

Ortendhal, Valter & Salchow, Hjalmar, eds. Ribosomal Proteins & Protein Engineering: Design, Selection & Applications. 2010. (Protein Science & Engineering Ser.). 89.00 *(978-1-60741-005-8(2))* Nova Science Pubs., Inc.

Paul, Etienne & Liu, Yu-tung, eds. Biological Sludge Minimization & Biomaterials/Bioenergy Recovery Technologies. 2012. (ENG.). 536p. 110.00 ***(978-0-470-76882-2(7)***, Wiley) Wiley, John & Sons, Inc.

Prado, Marcelo & Zavaglia, Cecília. Bioceramics 21: Selected Papers from the 21st International Symposium on Ceramics in Medicine, the Annual Meeting of the International Society for Ceramics in Medicine (ISCM), Búzios, Brazil, 21-24 October 2008. Prado, Marcelo & Zavaglia, Cecília, eds. 2009. (Key Engineering Materials Ser.). (Illus.). 758p. *(978-0-87849-353-1(0))* Trans Tech Pubns., Ltd.

Rhodes, Catherine. International Governance of Biotechnology. 2012. (ENG.). 256p. 90.00 *(978-1-84966-065-5(4)*, Hodder Arnold) Bloomsbury Publishing.

Royal Society of Chemistry Staff. Computational & Structural Approaches to Drug Discovery: Ligand-Protein Interactions. Stroud, Robert M., ed. 2007. (RSC Biomolecular Sciences Ser.). (ENG., Illus.). 400p. 232.00 *(978-0-85404-365-1(9))* Royal Society of Chemistry, The GBR. Dist: Ingram Pub. Services.

Sheehan, Mallorie N., ed. Protein Engineering: Design, Selection & Applications. 2010. (Protein Biochemistry, Synthesis, Structure & Cellular Functions Ser.). 59.00 *(978-1-61668-286-6(8))* Nova Science Pubs., Inc.

Smolke, Christina D. The Metabolic Pathway Engineering, 2 vols., Set. 2009. (Metabolic Pathway Engineering Handbook Ser.). (ENG., Illus.). 1259p. instr.'s hndbk. ed. 257.95 *(978-0-8493-3923-3(5)*, CRC Press) Taylor & Francis Group GBR. Dist: Taylor & Francis Group.

Smolke, Christina D., ed. The Metabolic Pathway Engineering Handbook, 2 vols., Vol. 2. 2009. (ENG., Illus.). 581p. 164.95 *(978-1-4200-7765-0(1)*, CRC Press) Taylor & Francis Group GBR. Dist: Taylor & Francis Group.

Stahl, Ulf, et al. Food Biotechnology. 2010. (Advances in Biochemical Engineering Biotechnology Ser.). (Illus.). xii, 269p. pap. 329.00 *(978-3-642-08946-6(1)*, 3642089461) Springer.

Stockar, Urs von & Wielen, Luuk van der, eds. Process Integration in Biochemical Engineering. 2010. (Advances in Biochemical Engineering Biotechnology Ser.). (Illus.). xviii, 191p. pap. 289.00 *(978-3-642-07818-7(4)*, 3642078184) Springer.

Tommasi, Tonia. Anaerobic Biohydrogen Production. 2011. 216p. pap. ***(978-3-8443-2700-7(2))*** Lambert Academic Publishing.

Torres, Nèstor V. & Voit, Eberhard O. Pathway Analysis & Optimization in Metabolic Engineering. 2011. (ENG., Illus.). 324p. pap. 60.00 *(978-0-521-17748-1(0))* Cambridge Univ. Pr.

Tsao, G. T., et al, eds. Biotechnology in China II: Chemicals, Energy & Environment. 2010. (Advances in Biochemical Engineering Biotechnology Ser.). (Illus.). xiv, 264p. 359.00 *(978-3-642-14994-8(4)*, 3642149944) Springer.

Uyar, Basar. Biohydrogen Production by Photosynthetic Bacteria in Solar Reactors. 2010. 160p. pap. *(978-3-8383-1521-8(9))* Lambert Academic Publishing.

Venkatasamy, Venkatram. Formation of Hgcdte by Electrochemical Atomic Layer Deposition. 2011. 116p. pap. ***(978-3-8443-2397-9(X))*** Lambert Academic Publishing.

Verpoorte, R., et al, eds. Applications of Plant Metabolic Engineering. (ENG.). xxii, 332p. 2010. pap. 179.00 *(978-90-481-7510-9(0)*, 9048175100) 2007. (Illus.). 179.00 *(978-1-4020-6030-4(0)*, 1402060300) Springer.

Vigild, Martin E., et al. Design & Development of Biological, Chemical, Food & Pharmaceutical Products. 2007. (ENG., Illus.). 310p. pap. 188.95 (978-0-470-06154-1(5), Wiley) Wiley, John & Sons, Inc.

Wang, Ting. Blending Petrodiesel with Biodiesel to Produce Ultra-Low Sulfur Diesel. 2010. 144p. pap. (978-3-8383-7988-3(8)) Lambert Academic Publishing.

Wendisch, Volker F. Amino Acid Biosynthesis - Pathways, Regulation & Metabolic Engineering. (Microbiology Monographs). (Illus.). x, 413p. 2010. pap. 319.00 (978-3-642-08018-0(9), 3642080189) 2007. 319.00 (978-3-540-48595-7(3)) Springer.

Wesselingh, Johannes A., et al. Design & Development of Biological, Chemical, Food & Pharmaceutical Products. 2007. (ENG., Illus.). 310p. pap. 79.95 (978-0-470-06155-8(3), Wiley) Wiley, John & Sons, Inc.

Wiley-VCH Staff, ed. Ullmann's Biotechnology & Biochemical Engineering, 2 vols. 2007. (ENG., Illus.). 874p. 570.00 (978-3-527-31603-8(5), Wiley-VCH) Wiley, John & Sons, Inc.

Wittrup, K. Dane & Verdine, Gregory L. Protein Engineering for Therapeutics, Part A. 2012. (ENG.). 392p. 187.00 (978-0-12-416039-2(5), Academic Pr.) Elsevier Science & Technology Bks.

—Protein Engineering for Therapeutics, Part B. 2012. (ENG.). 392p. 187.00 (978-0-12-396962-0(X), Academic Pr.) Elsevier Science & Technology Bks.

Young, D. C., et al. Computational Drug Design: A Guide for Computational & Medicinal Chemists. 2009. (ENG., Illus.). 307p. 117.00 (978-0-470-12685-1(X), Wiley-Interscience) Wiley, John & Sons, Inc.

Zhong, J. J., et al. Biotechnology in China I. 2009. (Advances in Biochemical Engineering / Biotechnology Ser.). (ENG., Illus.). xiii, 322p. 389.00 (978-3-540-88414-9(9), 3540884149) Springer.

BIOCHEMICAL EVOLUTION

see Molecular Evolution

BIOCHEMICAL GENETICS

Abd El Maksoud Zaied, Khalifa. Introduction to Biochemical Genetics. 2011. 224p. pap. (978-3-8443-9476-4(1)) Lambert Academic Publishing.

Ahmad, Shamim & Hanaoka, Fumio, eds. Molecular Mechanisms of Xeroderma Pigmentosum. 2008. (Advances in Experimental Medicine & Biology Ser.: Vol. 637). (Illus.). XXVII, 166p. (C). 199.00 (978-0-387-09598-1(5), 0387095985) Springer.

Ahmad, Shamim I. Diseases of DNA Repair. 2010. (Advances in Experimental Medicine & Biology Ser.). (ENG., Illus.). xxviii, 256p. 219.00 (978-1-4419-6447-2(9), 1441964479) Springer.

Å poner, Jirí & Lanka, Filip, eds. Computational studies of RNA & DNA. 2010. (Challenges & Advances in Computational Chemistry & Physics Ser.). xi, 638p. pap. 299.00 (978-90-481-7195-8(4), 9048171954) Springer.

Blau, N., et al. Laboratory Guide to the Methods in Biochemical Genetics. 2008. (Illus.). xii, 852p. 159.00 (978-3-540-76697-1(9)) Springer.

Committee on Qualifications of Biomarkers and Surrogate Endpoints in Chronic Disease & Institute of Medicine. Evaluation of Biomarkers & Surrogate Endpoints in Chronic Disease. 2010. (ENG.). 336p. pap. 47.00 (978-0-309-15129-0(5)) National Academies Pr.

Didenko, Didenko & Schaffer, David, eds. In Situ Detection of DNA Damage: Methods & Protocols. 2009. (Methods in Molecular Biology Ser.). (Illus.). 300p. 119.00 (978-1-60327-408-1(1)) Humana Pr.

Dkhil, Mohamed. Non-Steroidal Anti-Inflammatory Drug: Piroxicam. 2011. 72p. pap. (978-3-8443-1976-7(X)) Lambert Academic Publishing.

Doetsch, Paul. Mechanisms of DNA Repair, Pt. A. 2012. (ENG.). 408p. 161.00 (978-0-12-387665-2(6), Academic Pr.) Elsevier Science & Technology Bks.

Evans, Mark D. & Cooke, Marcus S., eds. Oxidative Damage to Nucleic Acids. 2010. (Molecular Biology Intelligence Unit Ser.). (Illus.). xvii, 228p. pap. 175.00 (978-1-4419-2503-9(1), 1441925031) Springer.

Fu, Haian, ed. Chemical Genomics. 2012. (ENG., Illus.). 344p. 150.00 (978-0-521-88948-3(0)) Cambridge Univ. Pr.

Geacintov, Nicholas E. & Broyde, Suse, eds. The Chemical Biology of DNA Damage. 2010. (ENG., Illus.). 471p. 185.00 (978-3-527-32295-4(7), Wiley-VCH) Wiley, John & Sons, Inc.

Jacoby, Edgar, ed. Chemogenomics: Methods & Applications. 2009. (Methods in Molecular Biology Ser.). (ENG., Illus.). viii, 315p. 129.00 (978-1-60761-273-5(9), 1607612739) Humana Pr.

Kimura, Honoka & Suzuki, Aoi. New Research on DNA Damage. 2008. (Illus.). xvi, 410p. 150.00 (978-1-60456-581-2(0)) Nova Science Pubs., Inc.

Kimura, Sakura & Shimizu, Sora. DNA Repair: New Research. 2012. (978-1-62100-756-2(1)) Nova Science Pubs., Inc.

Kocsis, Andor & Molnar, Hajna. Genotoxicity: Evaluation, Testing & Prediction. 2009. (Genetics - Research & Issues Ser.). (Illus.). xiv, 361p. 129.00 (978-1-60741-714-9(6), Nova Biomedical Bks.) Nova Science Pubs., Inc.

MARECHAL, Eric, et al, eds. Chemogenomics & Chemical Genetics: A User's Introduction for Biologists, Chemists & Informaticians. 2011. (Illus.). 270p. 129.00 (978-3-642-19614-0(4), 3642196144) Springer.

National Research Council Staff, et al, contrib. by. Validation of Toxicogenomic Technologies: A Workshop Summary. 2007. (ENG., Illus.). 98p. pap. 21.00 (978-0-309-10413-5(0)) National Academies Pr.

Parry, James M. & Parry, Elizabeth M., eds. Genetic Toxicology: Principles & Methods. 2011. (Methods in Molecular Biology Ser.). (ENG., Illus.). xvi, 433p. 139.00 (978-1-61779-420-9(1), 1617794201) Humana Pr.

Paull, Tanya. Mechanisms of DNA Damage Recognition. Paull, Tanya, ed. 2009. (Cancer Genetics Ser.). (Illus.). 250p. 139.00 (978-0-387-69136-7(7)) Springer.

Penning, Trevor M., ed. Chemical Carcinogenesis. 2011. (Current Cancer Research Ser.). (Illus.). xv, 440p. 189.00 (978-1-61737-994-9(8), 1617379948) Humana Pr.

Siddique, Yasir. Natural Plants Extract & Drug Genotoxicity. 2011. 92p. pap. (978-3-8443-9433-7(8)) Lambert Academic Publishing.

Sunkar, Ramanjulu, ed. MicroRNAs in Plant Development & Stress Responses. 2012. (Signaling & Communication in Plants Ser.). (ENG., Illus.). viii, 296p. 189.00 (978-3-642-27383-4(1), 3642273831) Springer.

Vanyushin, Boris F. & Ashapkin, Vasili V. DNA Methylation in Plants. 2008. pap. 39.00 (978-1-60692-051-0(0)) Nova Science Pubs., Inc.

Zanders, Edward D., ed. Chemical Genomics: Reviews & Protocols. 2010. (Methods in Molecular Biology Ser.). (Illus.). 296p. pap. 119.00 (978-1-61737-541-5(1), 1617375411) Humana Pr.

Zanders, Edward D., ed. Chemical Genomics & Proteomics: Reviews & Protocols. 2011. (Methods in Molecular Biology Ser.). (ENG., Illus.). xi, 243p. 119.00 (978-1-61779-348-6(5), 1617793485) Humana Pr.

BIOCHEMICAL MARKERS

Aldini, Giancarlo, et al. Biomarkers for Antioxidant Defense & Oxidative Damage: Principles & Practical Applications. 2010. (ENG., Illus.). 380p. 220.95 (978-0-8138-1535-0(5), Wiley-Blackwell) Wiley, John & Sons, Inc.

Azuaje, Francisco. Bioinformatics & Biomarker Discovery: Omic Data Analysis for Personalized Medicine. 2010. (ENG., Illus.). 248p. 149.95 (978-0-470-74460-4(X), Wiley) Wiley, John & Sons, Inc.

Bahn, Sabine & Guest, Paul. Biomarkers of Neurological & Psychiatric Disease. 2011. (ENG., Illus.). 470p. 198.00 (978-0-12-387718-5(0), Academic Pr.) Elsevier Science & Technology Bks.

Bianchi, Thomas S. & Canuel, Elizabeth A. Chemical Biomarkers in Aquatic Ecosystems. 2011. (ENG., Illus.). 392p. (C). 95.00 (978-0-691-13414-7(6)) Princeton Univ. Pr.

Birrer, M. J. Biomarkers in Ovarian Disease. 2008. pap. 175.00 (978-1-58603-807-6(9)) IOS Pr., Inc.

Bleavins, Michael R., et al, eds. Biomarkers in Drug Development: A Handbook of Practice, Application, & Strategy. 2010. (ENG., Illus.). 800p. 178.00 (978-0-470-16927-8(3), Wiley) Wiley, John & Sons, Inc.

Bondy, Stephen & Maiese, Kenneth, eds. Studies on Aging. 2010. (Oxidative Stress in Applied Basic Research & Clinical Practice Ser.). (ENG., Illus.). xvi, 472p. 239.00 (978-1-60761-601-6(7), 1607616017) Humana Pr.

Braunwald, Eugene. Biomarkers in Heart Failure, an Issue of Heart Failure Clinics. 2009. (Clinics: Internal Medicine Ser.: 5-4). (ENG.). 99.00 (978-1-4377-1446-3(3), Saunders) Elsevier - Health Sciences Div.

Carrillo, M. C. & Hampel, H., eds. Alzheimer's Disease - Modernizing Concept, Biological Diagnosis & Therapy. 2012. (Advances in Biological Psychiatry Ser.). (ENG., Illus.). 194p. (978-3-8055-9802-6(5)) Karger, S. AG.

Cazzola, Mario, et al, eds. Chronic Obstructive Pulmonary Disease: Outcomes & Biomarkers. 2009. ring bd. 229.95 (978-1-4200-8460-3(7), Informa Healthcare) Taylor & Francis Group GBR. Dist: Taylor & Francis Group.

Clarke, Charlotte H. & McCarthy, Diane L. Bankert, eds. SELDI-TOF Mass Spectrometry: Methods & Protocols. 2011. (Methods in Molecular Biology Ser.). (ENG., Illus.). x, 239p. 119.00 (978-1-61779-417-9(1), 1617794171) Humana Pr.

Committee on Developing Biomarker-Based Tools for Cancer Screening, Diagnosis, and Treatment. Cancer Biomarkers: The Promises & Challenges of Improving Detection & Treatment. Nass, Sharyl J. & Moses, Harold L., eds. 2007. (ENG., Illus.). 252p. per. 42.00 (978-0-309-10386-2(X)) National Academies Pr.

Committee on Qualification of Biomarkers and Surrogate Endpoints in Chronic Disease & Institute of Medicine. Perspectives on Biomarker & Surrogate Endpoint Evaluation: Discussion Forum Summary. 2011. (ENG.). 140p. pap. 33.75 (978-0-309-16324-8(2)) National Academies Pr.

Cong, Nguyen Van. Acetylcholinesterase As Biomarker of Pesticide Exposure & Effects. 2009. 96p. pap. (978-3-639-16827-3(5)) VDM Verlag Dr. Mueller e.K.

Dambinova, Svetlana, et al, eds. Biomarkers for Traumatic Brain Injury. 2012. (RSC Drug Discovery Ser.). (ENG., Illus.). 246p. 175.00 (978-1-84973-389-2(9)) Royal Society of Chemistry, The GBR. Dist: Ingram Pub. Services.

Edelstein, Charles L., ed. Biomarkers of Kidney Disease. 2010. (ENG., Illus.). 454p. 99.95 (978-0-12-375672-5(3), Academic Pr.) Elsevier Science & Technology Bks.

El-Metwally, Tarek H. Cancer Biology: an Updated Global Overview. 2009. (Cancer Etiology, Diagnosis & Treatments Ser.). pap. 43.00 (978-1-60876-193-7(2), Nova Biomedical Bks.) Nova Science Pubs., Inc.

Fietz, Susanne. Phytoplankton Pigments in Lake Baikal. 2008. 204p. pap. (978-3-8364-8933-1(3)) VDM Verlag Dr. Mueller e.K.

Forum on Neuroscience and Nervous System Disorders & Institute of Medicine. Glutamate-Related Biomarkers in Drug Development for Disorders of the Nervous System: Workshop Summary. 2011. (ENG.). 74p. pap. 21.00 (978-0-309-21221-2(9)) National Academies Pr.

Forum on Neuroscience and Nervous System Disorders & Institute of Medicine. Neuroscience Biomarkers & Biosignatures: Converging Technologies, Emerging Partnerships - Workshop Summary. 2008. (ENG.). 128p. pap. 32.50 (978-0-309-10889-8(6)) National Academies Pr.

Galimberti, Daniela & Scarpani, Elio. Biomarkers for Early Diagnosis of Alzheimer's Disease. 2008. 98.00 (978-1-60456-991-9(3)) Nova Science Pubs., Inc.

Gaze, David Christopher. Getting to the Heart of the Matter: Cardiac Troponin as a Cardiovascular Biomarker. 2012. (Cardiology Research & Clinical Developments Ser.). 125p. pap. 47.00 (978-1-61470-796-7(0)) Nova Science Pubs., Inc.

Gomase, Virendra & Gomase, Shruti. Biomarkers. 2010. 224p. pap. (978-3-639-17030-6(X)) VDM Verlag Dr. Mueller e.K.

Govorukhina, Natalia. Biomarker Discovery for Cervical Cancer: Methods & Approaches. 2008. 160p. pap. (978-3-8364-8401-5(3)) VDM Verlag Dr. Mueller e.K.

Hamdan, Mahmoud H. Cancer Biomarkers: Analytical Techniques for Discovery. 2007. (Wiley - Interscience Series on Mass Spectrometry Ser.: 25). (ENG., Illus.). 377p. 134.00 (978-0-471-74516-7(2), Wiley-Interscience) Wiley, John & Sons, Inc.

Imai, K. & Itoh, F., eds. Development of New Molecular Tumor Markers for Diagnosis & Therapy: 36th Meeting of the International Society of Oncology & BioMarkers, ISOBM 2008, Tokyo, October 2008: Abstracts. 2008. 100p. pap. (978-3-8055-8997-0(2)) Karger, S. AG.

Ingelsson, E., ed. Circulating Biomarkers in Cardiovascular Disease - Book Edition of Disease Markers. 2009. 94p. pap. 131.00 (978-1-60750-057-5(4)) IOS Pr., Inc.

Januzzi, James L. Cardiac Biomarkers in Clinical Practice. rev. ed. 2009. (Illus.). 900p. pap. 86.95 (978-0-7637-6161-5(3)) Jones & Bartlett Learning, LLC.

Keating, Peter & Cambrosio, Alberto. Biomedical Platforms: Realigning the Normal & the Pathological in Late-Twentieth-Century Medicine. 2006. (Inside Technology Ser.). (ENG., Illus.). 560p. (gr. 17). per. 29.00 (978-0-262-61215-9(1)) MIT Pr.

Keren, David, et al. Flow Cytometry in Clinical Diagnosis. 4th ed. 2007. (Illus.). 384p. 179.25 incl. cd-rom (978-0-89189-548-0(5)) American Society for Clinical Pathology.

Kim, S. R. & Hino, O., eds. Awaji Liver Symposium / Japan-Korea Liver Symposium [Bibliography & Price not Definite.]: 2nd Awaji Liver Symposium, & 3rd Japan-Korea Liver Symposium, November 2006: Special Issue: Digestive Diseases 2007, Vol. 25, No. 4. 2007. (Illus.). 54p. pap. (978-3-8055-8365-7(6)) Karger, S. AG.

Komar, Anton A., ed. Single Nucleotide Polymorphisms: Methods & Protocols. 2nd ed. 2009. (Methods in Molecular Biology Ser.). (ENG., Illus.). xiv, 466p. 129.00 (978-1-60327-410-4(3), 1603274103) Humana Pr.

Kristoff, Helen C. Cancer Biomarkers. 2010. (Cancer Etiology, Diagnosis & Treatments Ser.). 129.00 (978-1-61761-302-9(9), Nova Biomedical Bks.) Nova Science Pubs., Inc.

Levy, Mitchell M. Biomarkers in the Critically Ill Patient, an Issue of Critical Care Clinics. 2011. (Clinics: Internal Medicine Ser.: 27-2). (ENG., Illus.). 259p. 110.00 (978-1-4557-0432-3(6), Saunders) Elsevier - Health Sciences Div.

Lindau, Stacy, ed. 2006 Biomarker Proceedings. 2007. spiral bd. 0.00 (978-0-9769978-3-2(5)) Ctr. on Aging, Univ. of Chicago.

—2007 Biomarker Proceedings. 2008. spiral bd. 0.00 (978-0-9769978-4-9(3)) Ctr. on Aging, Univ. of Chicago.

Lorz, H. & Wenzel, G., eds. Molecular Marker Systems in Plant Breeding & Crop Improvement. 2007. (Biotechnology in Agriculture & Forestry Ser.). (Illus.). 476p. pap. 139.00 (978-3-540-74006-3(6)) Springer.

Lovestone, Simon, ed. Biomarkers in Brain Disease. 2009. (Annals of the New York Academy of Sciences Ser.: 38). (ENG., Illus.). 276p. pap. 134.95 (978-1-57331-772-6(1), Wiley-Blackwell) Wiley, John & Sons, Inc.

Lundblad, Roger L. Development & Application of Biomarkers. 2010. (ENG., Illus.). 297p. 149.95 (978-1-4398-1979-1(3), CRC Press) Taylor & Francis Group GBR. Dist: Taylor & Francis Group.

Michael S., Ritsner, ed. The Handbook of Neuropsychiatric Biomarkers, Endophenotypes & Genes: Volume IV: Molecular Genetic & Genomic Markers, 4 vols. 2009. (ENG., Illus.). xii, 232p. 159.00 (978-90-481-2297-4(X), 904812297X) Springer.

Morrow, David A., ed. Cardiovascular Biomarkers: Pathophysiology & Disease Management. 2010. (Contemporary Cardiology Ser.). (Illus.). 640p. pap. 229.00 (978-1-61737-620-7(5), 1617376205) Humana Pr.

National Research Council Staff, creator. Biosocial Surveys. 2007. (ENG., Illus.). 428p. per. 50.00 (978-0-309-10867-6(5)) National Academies Pr.

Papadopoulos, V. Stem Cells & Disease: Book Edition of Disease Markers. 2008. 88p. pap. 138.00 (978-1-58603-875-5(3)) IOS Pr., Inc.

Pardalos, Panos M., et al, eds. Data Mining for Biomarker Discovery. 2012. (Springer Optimization & Its Applications Ser.: 65). (ENG., Illus.). xiv, 246p. 124.00 (978-1-4614-2106-1(3), 1461421063) Springer.

Peters, K. E., et al. The Biomarker Guide Volume 2: Biomarkers & Isotopes in Petroleum Systems & Earth History, 2 vols. 2nd rev. ed. 2007. (ENG., Illus.). 704p. pap. 84.00 (978-0-521-03998-7(3)) Cambridge Univ. Pr.

Peters, Kenneth E., et al. The Biomarker Guide Vol. 1: Biomarkers & Isotopes in the Environment & Human History, 2 vols., Vol. 1. 2nd rev. ed. 2007. (ENG., Illus.). 492p. pap. 100.00 (978-0-521-78697-3(5)) Cambridge Univ. Pr.

Pivac, Nela, et al. Peripheral Biological Markers in Alcoholism. 2008. (Illus.). viii, 93p. pap. 39.00 (978-1-60456-617-8(5)); pap. 39.00 (978-1-60456-444-0(X), Nova Biomedical Bks.) Nova Science Pubs., Inc.

Rabbee, Nusrat, et al. Understanding Statistics in Exploratory Biomarker Analysis. 2011. (Illus.). 350p. 89.95 (978-1-4398-1171-9(7)) CRC Pr. LLC.

Rancourt, Giselle C., ed. Proteomics: Methods, Applications & Limitations. 2010. (Protein Biochemistry, Synthesis, Structure & Cellular Functions Ser.). (Illus.). xi, 194p. 69.00 (978-1-61668-691-8(X)) Nova Science Pubs., Inc.

Richter, Emily. Research Progress in Tumor Markers. Schäfer, Lilly, ed. 2008. (Illus.). xi, 123p. 185.00 (978-1-60456-692-5(2)) Nova Science Pubs., Inc.

Ritsner, Michael S. The Handbook of Neuropsychiatric Biomarkers, Endophenotypes & Genes Vol. I: Neuropsychological Endophenotypes & Biomarkers, 4 vols. 2009. (ENG., Illus.). xiv, 274p. 159.95 (978-1-4020-9463-7(9), 1402094639) Springer.

Ritsner, Michael S., ed. The Handbook of Neuropsychiatric Biomarkers, Endophenotypes & Genes: Volume II: Neuroanatomical & Neuroimaging Endophenotypes & Biomarkers, 4 vols. 2009. (ENG., Illus.). xii, 244p. 159.00 (978-1-4020-9830-7(8), 1402098308) Springer.

—The Handbook of Neuropsychiatric Biomarkers, Endophenotypes & Genes: Volume III: Metabolic & Peripheral Biomarkers, 4 vols. 2009. (ENG., Illus.). x, 214p. 159.00 (978-1-4020-9837-6(5), 1402098375) Springer.

Roboz John Staff. Mass Spectrometry in Cancer Research Second Edition. 2nd ed. 2009. (Illus.). 640p. 199.95 (978-0-8493-7390-9(5)) CRC Pr. LLC.

Rosner, Mitchell H. & Okusa, Mark. Biomarkers in Renal Disease. 2008. 89.00 (978-1-60456-113-5(0), Nova Biomedical Bks.) Nova Science Pubs., Inc.

Royal Society of Chemistry Staff. Biomarkers & Human Biomonitoring: Set, 2 vols. Knudsen, Lisbeth & Merlo, Domenico Franco, eds. 2011. (Issues in Toxicology Ser.). (ENG., Illus.). 776p. 352.00 (978-1-84973-124-9(1)) Royal Society of Chemistry, The GBR. Dist: Ingram Pub. Services.

—Biomarkers & Human Biomonitoring: Volume 1, 2 vols. Knudsen, Lisbeth & Merlo, Domenico Franco, eds. 2011. (Issues in Toxicology Ser.). (ENG., Illus.). 498p. 200.00 (978-1-84973-241-3(8)) Royal Society of Chemistry, The GBR. Dist: Ingram Pub. Services.

—Biomarkers & Human Biomonitoring: Volume 2, 2 vols. Knudsen, Lisbeth & Merlo, Domenico Franco, eds. 2011. (Issues in Toxicology Ser.). (ENG., Illus.). 278p. 200.00 (978-1-84973-242-0(6)) Royal Society of Chemistry, The GBR. Dist: Ingram Pub. Services.

Said, Harun M., et al. Brain-Cancer Associated Tumor Marker Genes Expression Pattern in Humans. 2010. (Cancer Etiology, Diagnosis & Treatments Ser.). (Illus.). xiii, 52p. pap. 43.00 (978-1-61728-011-5(9), Nova Biomedical Bks.) Nova Science Pubs., Inc.

Sargent, Daniel. Trial Design for Biomarkers, an Issue of Clinics in Laboratory Medicine. 2009. (Clinics: Internal Medicine Ser.). (ENG.). 240p. 99.00 (978-1-4377-0494-5(8), Saunders) Elsevier - Health Sciences Div.

Semizarov, Dimitri & Blomme, Eric. Genomics in Drug Discovery & Development. 2008. (ENG., Illus.). 496p. 139.00 (978-0-470-09604-8(7), Wiley) Wiley, John & Sons, Inc.

Siawaya, J. Fleury Djoba, ed. Molecular Markers of Infectious Diseases - Book Edition of Disease Markers. 2009. 88p. pap. 130.00 (978-1-60750-076-6(0)) IOS Pr., Inc.

Sioud, Mouldy. Target Discovery & Validation: Reviews & Protocols: Volume 1: Emerging Strategies for Targets & Biomarker Discovery, 2 vols. 2006. (Methods in Molecular Biology Ser.: Vol. 360). (Illus.). 354p. 179.00 (978-1-58829-656-6(3), 1588296563) Humana Pr.

—Target Discovery & Validation: Reviews & Protocols: Volume 2: Emerging Molecular Targets & Treatment Options, 2 vols., Vol. 2. 2006. (Methods in Molecular Biology Ser.: Vol. 361). (Illus.). 345p. 149.00 (978-1-58829-890-4(6), 1588298906) Humana Pr.

Sioud, Mouldy, ed. Target Discovery & Validation Reviews & Protocols: Emerging Molecular Targets & Treatment Options,Volume 2. 2010. (Methods in Molecular Biology Ser.). (Illus.). 356p. pap. 149.00 (978-1-61737-827-0(5), 1617378275) Humana Pr.

—Target Discovery & Validation Reviews & Protocols: Emerging Strategies for Targets & Biomarker Discovery, Volume 1. 2010. (Methods in Molecular Biology Ser.). (Illus.). 376p. pap. 179.00 (978-1-61737-699-3(X), 161737699X) Humana Pr.

Sjöberg, Klas. Serologic Markers in Screening for Coeliac Disease. 2011. 64p. pap. (978-3-8433-7931-1(9)) Lambert Academic Publishing.

Smoller, Bruce R. Practical Immunopathology of the Skin. 2010. (Current Clinical Pathology Ser.). (Illus.). 208p. pap. 179.00 (978-1-61737-389-3(3), 1617373893) Humana Pr.

Swapna, M. & Srivastava, Sangeeta. Molecular Marker Applications for Improving Sugar Content in Sugarcane. 2012. (SpringerBriefs in Plant Science Ser.). (ENG., Illus.). vii, 49p. pap. 49.95 (978-1-4614-2256-3(6), 1461422566) Springer.

Swenson, Lee I. Progress in Tumor Marker Research. 2007. 129.00 (978-1-60021-619-0(6)) Nova Science Pubs., Inc.

Tainsky, Michael A. Tumor Biomarker Discovery: Methods & Protocols. 2009. (Methods in Molecular Biology Ser.). (Illus.). xi, 332p. (ENG.). 129.00 (978-1-60327-810-2(9)); E-Book (978-1-60327-811-9(7)) Humana Pr.

Thongboonkerd, Visith. Proteomics in Nephrology: Towards Clinical Applications. 2008. (Contributions to Nephrology Ser.). (Illus.). 136p. (978-3-8055-8544-6(6)) Karger, S. AG.

Tollefsbol, Trygve O., ed. Biological Aging: Methods & Protocols. 2007. (Methods in Molecular Biology Ser.: Vol. 371). (Illus.). XVI, 414p. 199.00 (978-1-58829-658-0(X), 158829658X) Humana Pr.

Trull, Andrew K., et al, eds. Biomarkers of Disease: An Evidence-Based Approach. 2008. (ENG., Illus.). 520p. pap. 67.00 (978-0-521-08860-2(7)) Cambridge Univ. Pr.

Tuffaha, Muin S. A. Phenotypic & Genotypic Diagnosis of Malignancies: An Immunohistochemical & Molecular Approach. 2008. (ENG.). 298p. 159.95 (978-3-527-31881-0(X), Wiley-VCH) Wiley, John & Sons, Inc.

Turck, Chris, ed. Biomarkers for Psychiatric Disorders. 2008. (ENG., Illus.). x, 538p. 149.00 (978-0-387-79250-7(3), 0387792503) Springer.

—Biomarkers for Psychiatric Disorders. 2010. (ENG., Illus.). x, 538p. pap. 149.00 (978-1-4419-4631-7(4), 1441946314) Springer.

Vaidya, Vishal S. & Bonventre, Joseph V., eds. Biomarkers: In Medicine, Drug Discovery, & Environmental Health. 2010. (ENG., Illus.). 618p. 158.00 (978-0-470-45224-0(2), Wiley) Wiley, John & Sons, Inc.

B

Vallant, Rainer. Fullerene Derivatives - & Their Application in Bioanalytics. 2008. 84p. pap. *(978-3-639-00540-0(6))* VDM Verlag Dr. Mueller e.K.

Vivanco, Fernando. Cardiovascular Proteomics: Methods & Protocols. Vivanco, Fernando, ed. 2007. (Methods in Molecular Biology Ser.: Vol. 357). (Illus.). 432p. 159.00 *(978-1-58829-535-4(4)*, 1588295354) Humana Pr.

Vivanco, Fernando, ed. Cardiovascular Proteomics: Methods & Protocols. 2010. (Methods in Molecular Biology Ser.). (Illus.). 432p. pap. 159.00 *(978-1-61737-627-6(2)*, 1617376272) Humana Pr.

Vlahou, Antonia, ed. Clinical Proteomics. 2008. (Methods in Molecular Biology Ser.). (ENG., Illus.). xvi, 408p. 129.00 *(978-1-58829-837-9(X)*, 158829837X) Humana Pr.

—Clinical Proteomics: Methods & Protocols. 2010. (Methods in Molecular Biology Ser.). (Illus.). xvi, 408p. pap. 129.00 *(978-1-61737-799-0(6)*, 1617377996) Humana Pr.

Wang, Feng, ed. Biomarker Methods in Drug Discovery & Development. 2010. (Methods in Pharmacology & Toxicology Ser.). (Illus.). xviii, 396p. pap. 179.00 *(978-1-61737-925-3(5)*, 1617379255) Humana Pr.

—Biomarker Methods in Drug Discovery & Development. 2008. (Methods in Pharmacology & Toxicology Ser.). (Illus.). XX, 500p. 179.00 *(978-1-934115-23-7(1)*, 1934115231) Springer.

Williams, J. Andrew, et al, eds. Practical Utility of Biomarkers in Drug Discovery & Development: Biomarkers & in Vitro - In Vivo Correlations. 2012. (Wiley Series on Technologies for the Pharmaceutical Industry Ser.: 11). (ENG.). 408p. 135.00 ***(978-0-470-17083-0(2)***, Wiley) Wiley, John & Sons, Inc.

Wu, Alan H. B., ed. Cardiac Markers. 2nd ed. 2010. (Pathology & Laboratory Medicine Ser.). (Illus.). 488p. pap. 189.00 *(978-1-61737-319-0(2)*, 1617373192) Humana Pr.

BIOCHEMICAL REACTORS

see Bioreactors

BIOCHEMISTRY

see also Absorption (Physiology); Acid-Base Equilibrium; Biochemical Engineering; Biochemical Genetics; Biochemical Markers; Biodegradation; Bioelectrochemistry; Bioenergetics; Bioinorganic Chemistry; Biological Interfaces; Bioorganic Chemistry; Biosynthesis; Body Composition; Botanical Chemistry; Chemical Embryology; Clinical Biochemistry; Clinical Chemistry; Cytochemistry; Histochemistry; Immunochemistry; Metabolism; Microbiological Chemistry; Molecular Biology; Neurochemistry; Quantum Biochemistry; Xenobiotics

Abdullah, Nurhayati. Processing Oil Palm Empty Fruit Bunches. 2009. 180p. pap. *(978-3-639-10551-3(6))* VDM Verlag Dr. Mueller e.K.

Adam, Gerold, et al. Physikalische Chemie und Biophysik. 4th ed. (Springer-Lehrbuch Ser.). (Illus.). XIII, 617p. pap. 54.95 *(978-3-540-00066-2(6)*, 3540000666) Springer.

—Physikalische Chemie und Biophysik. 5th ed. 2011. 644p. pap. ***(978-3-642-00423-0(7))*** Springer Singapore Pte. Ltd.

Afanas'ev, Igor B. & Afanasev, Igor B. Signaling Mechanisms of Oxygen & Nitrogen Free Radicals. 2009. (ENG., Illus.). 220p. 164.95 *(978-1-4200-7374-4(5)*, CRC Press) Taylor & Francis Group GBR. Dist: Taylor & Francis Group.

Ahmed, Nessar & Smith, Chris. Clinical Biochemistry. 2011. (Fundamentals of Biomedical Science Ser.). (ENG., Illus.). 576p. pap. 59.95 *(978-0-19-953393-0(8))* Oxford Univ. Pr., Inc.

Akram, Muhammad, et al. Research in Applied Biochemistry & Medicine. 2011. 68p. pap. ***(978-3-8443-8042-2(6))*** Lambert Academic Publishing.

Alade, Olalekan. Media Evaluation for Bioethanol Production from Cassava Hydrolysate. 2010. 172p. pap. *(978-3-8383-7748-3(6))* Lambert Academic Publishing.

Alberts, Bruce, et al. Essential Cell Biology. (ENG.). 2010. 20.00 *(978-0-8153-4459-9(7))* 3rd rev. ed. 2009. (Illus.). 860p. 149.00 *(978-0-8153-4129-1(6))* Taylor & Francis Group. (Garland Science).

Allen, James & Allen, James P. Biophysical Chemistry. 2008. (ENG., Illus.). 512p. 129.95 *(978-1-4051-2436-2(9)*, Wiley-Blackwell) Wiley, John & Sons, Inc.

Amara, S. G., et al, eds. Reviews of Physiology, Biochemistry & Pharmacology 158. 2010. (Reviews of Physiology, Biochemistry & Pharmacology Ser.). (Illus.). iv, 161p. pap. 189.00 *(978-3-642-09089-9(3)*, 3642090893) Springer.

Amara, Susan G. Reviews of Physiology, Biochemistry & Pharmacology. 2008. (Reviews of Physiology, Biochemistry & Pharmacology Ser.). (Illus.). 155p. 219.00 *(978-3-540-77603-1(6)*, 3540776036) Springer.

American Chemical Society Staff. Chemistry in Context. 6th ed. 2008. 608p. pap. *(978-0-07-304876-5(3))* McGraw-Hill Cos., The.

Ameta, K. L., et al. The Biochemistry of Chalcones. 2011. 236p. pap. ***(978-3-8443-2258-3(2))*** Lambert Academic Publishing.

Annual Review of Biochemistry. 2006. 85.00 *(978-0-8243-0875-9(1))* Annual Reviews, Inc.

Armstrong, James. Issues in General, Organic & Biochemistry. 2011. (ENG.). 448p. (C). pap. 51.95 *(978-0-534-49352-3(1))* Brooks/Cole.

Arnold, Melvin T. Essentials of General Organic & Biochemistry. tchr. ed. *(978-0-03-005649-9(7))* Saunders College Publishing.

—Essentials of General Organic Biochemistry. 100p. pap. *(978-0-03-005687-1(X))* Saunders College Publishing.

Atkins, Peter & dePaula, Julio. Physical Chemistry for the Life Sciences Solutions Manual. 2nd ed. 2011. (ENG.). 225p. (C). pap. 49.95 *(978-1-4292-3125-1(4))* Freeman, W. H. & Co.

Bajorath, Jargen, ed. Chemoinformatics & Computational Chemical Biology. 2010. (Methods in Molecular Biology Ser.). (Illus.). x, 588p. 189.00 *(978-1-60761-838-6(9)*, 1607618389) Humana Pr.

Balch, William E., ed. Small GTPases in Disease, Part B, 2 vols. 2008. (Methods in Enzymology Ser.). (ENG., Illus.). 616p. 187.00 *(978-0-12-374311-4(7)*, Academic Pr.) Elsevier Science & Technology Bks.

Bamberg, E., et al, eds. Review of Physiology, Biochemistry & Pharmacology, Volume 158. 2007. (Reviews of Physiology, Biochemistry & Pharmacology Ser.). (Illus.). 160p. 189.00 *(978-3-540-71790-4(0))* Springer.

Banerjee, Ruma, ed. Redox Biochemistry. 2007. (ENG., Illus.). 317p. 134.00 *(978-0-471-78624-5(1)*, Wiley) Wiley, John & Sons, Inc.

BarCharts Inc., Staff. Biochemistry. 2009. (ENG.). 6p. 5.95 *(978-1-4232-0853-2(6))* Barcharts, Inc.

Baron, Suzanne. Lange Biochemistry & Genetics Flash Cards 2/E. 2nd ed. 2012. (LANGE FlashCards Ser.). (ENG.). 400p. pap. 35.00 ***(978-0-07-176580-0(8)***, 0071765808) McGraw-Hill Medical Publishing Div.

Barri, Thaer. Downsized, Membrane-Based & Environmentally Green Extraction Systems. 2010. 100p. pap. *(978-3-639-22107-7(9))* VDM Verlag Dr. Mueller e.K.

Barrow, John D., et al, eds. Fitness of the Cosmos for Life: Biochemistry & Fine-Tuning. 2007. (Cambridge Astrobiology Ser.). (ENG., Illus.). 526p. 117.00 *(978-0-521-87102-0(6))* Cambridge Univ. Pr.

Bartlett, Douglas H., ed. High-Pressure Bioscience & Biotechnology. 2010. (Annals of the New York Academy of Sciences Ser.: 45). (ENG.). 352p. pap. 130.00 *(978-1-57331-771-9(3)*, Wiley-Blackwell) Wiley, John & Sons, Inc.

Bateman, Graham, ed. Organic Chemistry & Biochemistry. 2011. (Facts at Your Fingertips: Introducing Chemistry Ser.). 64p. (YA). (gr. 7-12). lib. bdg. 35.65 *(978-1-936333-14-1(7))* Brown Bear Bks.

Bates, Margaret K. & Kerr, Regina M., eds. Nuclear Receptors. 2011. (Microbiology Research Advances Ser.). (Illus.). 199p. 89.00 *(978-1-61209-980-4(7))* Nova Science Pubs., Inc.

Bäuerlein, Edmund, ed. Handbook of Biomineralization Vol. 1: Biological Aspects & Structure Formation. 2009. (ENG.). 471p. 310.00 *(978-3-527-31804-9(6)*, Wiley-VCH) Wiley, John & Sons, Inc.

Beard, Daniel A. & Qian, Hong. Chemical Biophysics: Quantitative Analysis of Cellular Systems. (Cambridge Texts in Biomedical Engineering Ser.). (ENG., Illus.). (C). 2010. 330p. pap. 45.00 *(978-0-521-15824-4(9))* 2008. 336p. 94.00 *(978-0-521-87070-2(4))* Cambridge Univ. Pr.

Beek, B. Bioaccumulation New Aspects & Developments. 2010. (Handbook of Environmental Chemistry / Reactions & Processes Ser.). (Illus.). xiv, 284p. pap. 269.00 *(978-3-642-08293-1(9)*, 3642082939) Springer.

Begley, Tadhg P. Chemical Biology Vol. 3, 4 vols., Vol. 3. 2009. (ENG., Illus.). 818p. 348.00 *(978-0-470-47019-0(4)*, Wiley) Wiley, John & Sons, Inc.

Behrens, Peter & Bäuerlein, Edmund, eds. Biomineralization Vol. 2: Biomimetic & Bioinspired Chemistry. 2009. (ENG.). 443p. instr.'s hndbk. ed. 305.00 *(978-3-527-31805-6(4)*, Wiley-VCH) Wiley, John & Sons, Inc.

Ben-Naim, Arieh Y. Cooperativity & Regulation in Biochemical Processes. 2010. (ENG.). 358p. pap. 159.00 *(978-1-4419-3336-2(0)*, 1441933360) Springer.

Benoit-Cowper, et al. Experimental Biochemistry. 2nd ed. 2010. (ENG.). (C). pap. 33.33 *(978-0-536-50836-2(4))* Pearson Learning Solutions.

Berg, Jeremy M., et al. Biochemistry (Loose-Leaf) 6th ed. 2008. (ENG.). (C). 141.95 *(978-1-4292-3502-0(0))* Freeman, W. H. & Co.

—Lecture Notebook for Biochemistry. 6th ed. 2006. (ENG.). 600p. (C). pap. 30.95 *(978-0-7167-7157-9(8))* Freeman, W. H. & Co.

Bergethon, Peter R. The Physical Basis of Biochemistry: The Foundations of Molecular Biophysics. 2nd ed. 2010. (ENG., Illus.). xxx, 950p. 89.95 *(978-1-4419-6323-9(5)*, 1441963235) Springer.

Bergethon, Peter R. & Hallock, Kevin. The Physical Basis of Biochemistry: Solutions Manual to the Second Edition. 2010. (ENG., Illus.). x, 146p. pap. 39.95 *(978-1-4419-7363-4(X)*, 144197363X) Springer.

Bester, Kai. Personal Care Compounds in the Environment: Pathways, Fate & Methods for Determination. 2007. (ENG., Illus.). 263p. 230.00 *(978-3-527-31567-3(5)*, Wiley-VCH) Wiley, John & Sons, Inc.

Bettelheim, Frederick. Introduction to General, Organic & Biochemistry, Hybrid. 10th ed. 2012. (Cengage Learningrsquo;s New Hybrid Editions! Ser.). (ENG.). 768p. (C). pap. 165.95 ***(978-1-133-10982-2(9))*** Brooks/Cole.

Bettiol, Esther, et al, contrib. by. Reviews of Physiology, Biochemistry & Pharmacology, Vol. 157. 2006. (Reviews of Physiology, Biochemistry & Pharmacology Ser.). (Illus.). iv, 140p. 229.00 *(978-3-540-39688-8(8)*, 3540396888) Springer.

Bewley, C. A. Protein-Carbohydrate Interactions in Infectious Diseases. 2006. (RSC Biomolecular Sciences Ser.). (ENG., Illus.). 364p. 232.00 *(978-0-85404-802-1(2)*, 0854048022) Royal Society of Chemistry, The GBR. Dist: Ingram Pub. Services.

Bhagavan, N. V. & Ha, Chung-Eun. Essentials of Medical Biochemistry: With Clinical Cases. 2011. (ENG.). 600p. (C). pap. 89.95 *(978-0-12-095461-2(3)*, Academic Pr.) Elsevier Science & Technology Bks.

Biochemistry. (Illus.). stu. ed. *(978-81-85427-32-4(1))* T. R. Pubns. Private Ltd.

Biochemistry, Cell & Molecular Biology. (Graduate Record Examination Ser.: GRE-22). 49.95 *(978-0-8373-5272-5(X)*, GRE-22) National Learning Corp.

Biochemistry the Molecular Basis of Life International. 4th ed. 2008. 52p. (C). pap. 12.00 *(978-0-19-538470-3(9))* Oxford Univ. Pr., Inc.

Blomquist, Gary J. & Bagnéres, Anne-Geneviéve, eds. Insect Hydrocarbons: Biology, Biochemistry, & Chemical Ecology. 2010. (ENG., Illus.). 504p. 120.00 *(978-0-521-89814-0(5))* Cambridge Univ. Pr.

Bolognesi, Martino. Dioxygen Binding & Sensing Proteins: A Tribute to Beatrice & Jonathan Wittenberg. Bolognesi, Martino et al, eds. 2008. (Protein Reviews Ser.). xii, 264p. 219.00 *(978-88-470-0806-9(9))* Springer.

Brambl, Robert & Marzluf, George A. Biochemistry & Molecular Biology. 2nd ed. 2010. (Mycota Ser.). (Illus.). xxii, 447p. pap. 419.00 *(978-3-642-07652-7(1)*, 3642076521) Springer.

Bray, Dennis, et al. Essential Cell Biology. 3rd rev. ed. 2009. (ENG., Illus.). 860p. *(978-0-8153-4130-7(X))* Garland Publishing, Inc.

Breidenbach, Mark. A STRUCTURAL BASIS FOR CLOSTRIDIAL NEUROTOXIN TARGETSPECIFICITY. 2008. 80p. pap. *(978-3-639-10464-6(1))* VDM Verlag Dr. Mueller e.K.

Brown, Kate. General, Organic & Biochemistry. 2nd ed. Date not set. (Chemistry Ser.). tchr. ed. 1.00 *(978-0-87150-774-7(9))*; stu. ed. 14.25 net. *(978-0-87150-772-3(2))*; (Illus.). 809p. 44.25 net. *(978-0-87150-762-4(5))* Brooks/Cole. (Brooks/Cole).

—Introduction to Organic & Biochemistry. 3rd ed. Date not set. (Chemistry Ser.). stu. ed. 12.50 net. *(978-0-87150-739-6(0)*, Brooks/Cole) Brooks/Cole.

Brown, Kate & Clapp. General, Organic & Biochemistry. 2nd ed. Date not set. (Chemistry Ser.). lab manual ed. 21.25 net. *(978-0-87150-773-0(0)*, Brooks/Cole) Brooks/Cole.

Bunnage, Mark E., ed. New Frontiers in Chemical Biology: Enabling Drug Discovery. 2010. (RSC Drug Discovery Ser.). (ENG., Illus.). 328p. 213.00 ***(978-1-84973-125-6(X))*** Royal Society of Chemistry, The GBR. Dist: Ingram Pub. Services.

Buxbaum, Engelbert. Biophysical Chemistry of Proteins: An Introduction to Laboratory Methods. 2010. (ENG., Illus.). xvi, 510p. 209.00 *(978-1-4419-7250-7(1)*, 1441972501) Springer.

Cabilly, Shmuel, ed. Combinatorial Peptide Library Protocols. 2010. (Methods in Molecular Biology Ser.). 328p. pap. 119.00 *(978-1-61737-022-9(3)*, 1617370223) Humana Pr.

Campbell, Mary K. Biochemistry. 3rd ed. 184p. (C). tchr. ed. 26.75 *(978-0-03-025072-9(2))* Saunders College Publishing.

Campbell, Mary K. & Farrell, Shawn O. Biochemistry. 7th ed. 2011. (ENG.). (C). 272p. pap. 35.95 *(978-1-111-42566-1(3))*; 864p. 220.95 *(978-0-8400-6858-3(1))* Brooks/Cole.

Cancro, Michael P., ed. BLyS Ligands & Receptors. 2009. (Contemporary Immunology Ser.). (ENG., Illus.). 300p. 189.00 *(978-1-60327-012-0(4))* Humana Pr.

Carey, George W. The Chemistry of Human Life. 2010. 82p. 32.95 *(978-1-161-36266-4(5))* Kessinger Publishing, LLC.

Chapman, Joseph B. Biochemistry. 307p. reprint ed. 98.00 *(978-0-7222-9992-0(3))* Library Reprints, Inc.

Chow, Shein-Chung. Design & Analysis of Bioavailability & Bioequivalence Studies, Third Edition BABE-Solution bundle Version. 3rd rev. ed. 2009. (Chapman & Hall/CRC Biostatistics Ser.). (ENG.). 760p. 299.95 *(978-1-4398-1358-4(2)*, CRC Press) Taylor & Francis Group GBR. Dist: Taylor & Francis Group.

Civjan, Natanya. Natural Products in Chemical Biology. 2012. (ENG.). 418p. 125.00 ***(978-1-118-10117-9(0)***, Wiley) Wiley, John & Sons, Inc.

Clardy, Jon C., et al. Chemical Biology. 2009. (ENG.). 704p. 110.00 *(978-0-8153-4118-5(0)*, Garland Science) Taylor & Francis Group.

Cooper, Alan. Biophysical Chemistry. 2nd ed. 2011. (Tutorial Chemistry Texts). (ENG., Illus.). 244p. (C). pap. 35.00 ***(978-1-84973-081-5(4))*** Royal Society of Chemistry, The GBR. Dist: Ingram Pub. Services.

Cox, Michael M., et al. Absolute Ultimate Guide for Lehninger Principles of Biochemistry. 5th rev. ed. 2008. (ENG., Illus.). 600p. (C). pap., pupil's gde. ed. 69.95 *(978-1-4292-1241-0(1))* Freeman, W. H. & Co.

Cram101 Textbook Reviews. Outlines & Highlights for Fundamentals of Biochemistry: Life at the Molecular Level by Charlotte W. Pratt, Judith G. Voet, Donald J. Voet, ISBN. 2010. 472p. pap. 36.95 *(978-1-61698-611-7(5))* Cram101 Inc.

—Outlines & Highlights for Fundamentals of Biochemistry: Life at the Molecular Level by Donald J. Voet, Judith G. Voet, Charlotte W. Pratt, ISBN. 2010. 398p. pap. 35.95 *(978-1-61698-606-3(9))* Cram101 Inc.

—Outlines & Highlights for Introduction to General, Organic & Biochemistry by Frederick a Bettelheim, Mary K Campbell, William H Brown, Shawn O F. 2010. 288p. pap. 32.95 *(978-1-61698-614-8(X))* Cram101 Inc.

—Outlines & Highlights for Introduction to General, Organic & Biochemistry by Leo R Best, Morris Hein, Scott Pattison, Susan Arena, Isbn: 9780470129. 2010. 334p. pap. 33.95 *(978-1-61698-608-7(5))* Cram101 Inc.

—Outlines & Highlights for Principles of Biochemistry by David L Nelson, Michael M Cox, Isbn: 9780716771081. 2010. 632p. pap. 40.95 *(978-1-61698-615-5(8))* Cram101 Inc.

—Outlines & Highlights for Textbook of Biochemistry with Clinical Correlations by Thomas M Devlin, Isbn: 9780471678083. 2010. 680p. pap. 41.95 *(978-1-61698-609-4(3))* Cram101 Inc.

Cram101 Textbook Reviews Staff. Outlines & Highlights for Physical Chemistry by Tinoco, Isbn: 013095943x. 2007. 264p. pap. 14.95 *(978-1-4288-3022-6(7))* Cram101 Inc.

Crane, Mark. Derivation & Use of Environmental Quality & Human Health Standards for Chemical Substances in Water & Soil. 2009. (Illus.). 168p. 124.95 *(978-1-4398-0344-8(7)*, CRC Press) Taylor & Francis Group GBR. Dist: Taylor & Francis Group.

Crowther, John R. The ELISA Guidebook. 2nd ed. 2009. (Methods in Molecular Biology Ser.). (ENG., Illus.). xvi, 568p. 149.00 *(978-1-60327-253-7(4))* Humana Pr.

Dadgostar, Nafiseh. Colloidal Synthesis of Copper Nanoparticles. 2009. 128p. pap. *(978-3-639-19370-1(9))* VDM Verlag Dr. Mueller e.K.

De Lemos, James A., ed. Biomarkers in Heart Disease. 2008. (American Heart Association Clinical Ser.: 3). (ENG., Illus.). 256p. 136.95 *(978-1-4051-7571-5(0)*, Wiley-Blackwell) Wiley, John & Sons, Inc.

Demarest, Mark & University of North Texas Staff. Biochemistry Laboratory 3622/4560. rev. ed. 2011. (ENG.). 256p. spiral bd. 33.75 *(978-0-7575-7929-5(9))* Kendall Hunt Publishing Co.

Denissov, Sergey. Transcription Regulation of Human Genes. 2010. 184p. pap. *(978-3-8383-6748-4(0))* Lambert Academic Publishing.

Denniston, K. J. & Topping, Joseph J. Foundations of General, Organic, & Biochemistry. 2007. 167.19 *(978-0-07-351106-1(4))* McGraw-Hill Higher Education.

—General, Organic, & Biochemistry. 7th ed. 2010. *(978-0-07-340262-8(1))* McGraw-Hill Cos., The.

Denniston, K. J., et al. General, Organic, & Biochemistry. 6th ed. 2007. *(978-0-07-351110-8(2))* McGraw-Hill Cos., The.

Denniston, Katherine. General, Organic, & Biochemistry. 7th ed. 2010. (ENG.). (C). 219.33 *(978-0-07-740574-8(9)*, 0077405749, McGraw-Hill Science, Engineering & Mathematics) McGraw-Hill Higher Education.

Denniston, Katherine, et al. Chemistry (from General, Organic, & Biochemistry) 7th ed. 2010. (ENG.). 416p. (C). pap. 96.67 *(978-0-07-739764-7(9)*, 0077397649, McGraw-Hill Science, Engineering & Mathematics) McGraw-Hill Higher Education.

—A Laboratory Manual for General, Organic & Biochemistry. 7th ed. 2010. (ENG., Illus.). 448p. (C). spiral bd., lab manual ed. 98.00 *(978-0-07-729672-8(9)*, 0077296729, McGraw-Hill Science, Engineering & Mathematics) McGraw-Hill Higher Education.

—Loose Leaf General, Organic & Biochemistry. 7th ed. 2010. (ENG.). (C). ring bd. 147.33 *(978-0-07-740174-0(3)*, 0077401743, McGraw-Hill Science, Engineering & Mathematics) McGraw-Hill Higher Education.

—Organic & Biochemistry (from General, Organic, & Biochemistry) 7th ed. 2010. (ENG.). (C). pap. 122.33 *(978-0-07-739763-0(0)*, 0077397630, McGraw-Hill Science, Engineering & Mathematics) McGraw-Hill Higher Education.

—Student Study Guide/Solutions Manual General, Organic & Biochemistry. 7th ed. 2010. (ENG.). 576p. (C). pap. 68.67 *(978-0-07-729673-5(7)*, 0077296737, McGraw-Hill Science, Engineering & Mathematics) McGraw-Hill Higher Education.

Denniston, Katherine J. & Topping, Joseph J. Foundations of General, Organic, & Biochemistry. 2007. (ENG., Illus.). 688p. (C). 184.00 *(978-0-07-331183-8(9)*, 0073311839, McGraw-Hill Science, Engineering & Mathematics) McGraw-Hill Higher Education.

Denniston, Katherine J., et al. General, Organic & Biochemistry. (ENG., 928p. (C). 6th ed. 2007. Illus.). 175.94 *(978-0-07-722141-6(9)*, 0077221419) 7th ed. 2010. 210.33 *(978-0-07-735480-0(X)*, 007735480X) McGraw-Hill Higher Education. (McGraw-Hill Science, Engineering & Mathematics).

Devahastin, Sakamon, ed. Physicochemical Aspects of Food Engineering & Processing. 2010. (Contemporary Food Engineering Ser.). (ENG., Illus.). 382p. 159.95 *(978-1-4200-8241-8(8)*, CRC Press) Taylor & Francis Group GBR. Dist: Taylor & Francis Group.

Devasena, T. Enzymology. 2012. (ENG., Illus.). 568p. 44.95 ***(978-0-19-806443-5(8))*** Oxford Univ. Pr., Inc.

Devlin, Thomas M. Biochemistry with Clinical Correlations. 7th ed. 2010. (ENG., Illus.). 1240p. 210.95 *(978-0-470-28173-4(1)*, Wiley-Liss) Wiley, John & Sons, Inc.

—Textbook of Biochemistry with Clinical Correlations 6th Edition with Human Molecular Genetics 2nd Edition Set. 6th rev. ed. 2006. (ENG.). 1p. pap. 230.00 *(978-0-470-10989-2(0))* Wiley, John & Sons, Inc.

—Textbook of Biochemistry with Clinical Correlations, Seventh Edition Binder Ready Version. 7th ed. 2010. (ENG., Illus.). 1240p. (C). ring bd. 132.95 *(978-0-470-60152-5(3)*, Wiley-Liss) Wiley, John & Sons, Inc.

Donev, Rossen. Advances in Protein Chemistry & Structural Biology. 2011. (ENG.). 216p. 161.00 ***(978-0-12-386483-3(6)***, Academic Pr.) Elsevier Science & Technology Bks.

Dugave, Christophe, ed. Cis-trans Isomerization in Biochemistry. 2006. (ENG., Illus.). 368p. 250.00 *(978-3-527-31304-4(4)*, Wiley-VCH) Wiley, John & Sons, Inc.

Eguchi, Shoji. Bioactive Heterocyles I. 2010. (Topics in Heterocyclic Chemistry Ser.). xiv, 220p. pap. 239.00 *(978-3-642-06998-7(3)*, 3642069983) Springer.

Elliott, William H. & Elliott, Daphne C. Biochemistry & Molecular Biology. 4th ed. 2009. (ENG., Illus.). 636p. (Orig.). (C). pap. 124.95 *(978-0-19-922671-9(7))* Oxford Univ. Pr., Inc.

Elsersawi. Biochemistry of Aging: Wellness & Longevity. 2010. 340p. pap. 27.95 *(978-1-4490-7380-0(8))* AuthorHouse.

Endo, Masahiko, et al, eds. Endoglycosidases: Biochemistry, Biotechnology, Application. 2006. (ENG., Illus.). xv, 272p. 209.00 *(978-3-540-34494-0(2)*, 3540344942) Springer.

Engel, Paul. Pain-Free Biochemistry: An Essential Guide for the Health Sciences. 2010. (ENG., Illus.). 344p. pap. 59.95 *(978-0-470-06046-9(8))*; 159.95 *(978-0-470-06045-2(X))* Wiley, John & Sons, Inc. (Wiley).

Epple, Matthias & Bäuerlein, Edmund, eds. Biomineralization Vol. 3: Medical & Clinical Aspects. 2009. (ENG.). 424p. instr.'s hndbk. ed. 299.00 *(978-3-527-31806-3(2)*, Wiley-VCH) Wiley, John & Sons, Inc.

Evans, Onyancha, et al. Phytochemical & Antimicrobial Analysis of Kenyan Teclea Nobilis: Phytochemical & Antimicrobial Analysis of Teclea Nobilis Del. Used in Ethnomedicine in Kenya. 2011. 72p. pap. ***(978-3-639-32761-8(6))*** VDM Verlag Dr. Mueller e.K.

Ezhilarasi, Anbalagan. Molecular Taxonomic Studies on the Genus Anabaena Bory. 2010. 128p. pap. *(978-3-8383-8818-2(6))* Lambert Academic Publishing.

Falvey, D. Nitrene & Nitrenium Ions. 2012. (Wiley Series of Reactive Intermediates in Chemistry & Biology Ser.: 3). (ENG.). 408p. 125.00 (978-0-470-39059-7(X), Wiley-Interscience) Wiley, John & Sons, Inc.

Fedorov, Dmitri & Kitaura, Kazuo. The Fragment Molecular Orbital Method: Practical Applications to Large Molecular Systems. 2009. (ENG., Illus.). 288p. 133.95 (978-1-4200-7848-0(8), CRC Press) Taylor & Francis Group GBR. Dist: Taylor & Francis Group.

Fenton, Aron W., ed. Allostery: Methods & Protocols. 2011. (Methods in Molecular Biology Ser.). (ENG., Illus.). xviii, 439p. 139.00 (978-1-61779-333-2(7), 1617793337) Humana Pr.

Fermini, Bernard. Ion Channels. 2008. (Topics in Medicinal Chemistry Ser.). 239.00 (978-3-540-79728-9(9), 3540797289) Springer.

Fermini, Bernard & Priest, Birgit. Ion Channels. 2010. (Topics in Medicinal Chemistry Ser.). (Illus.). xiv, 171p. pap. 239.00 (978-3-642-09855-0(X), 364209855X) Springer.

Fishbein, James C., contrib. by. Advances in Molecular Toxicology, Vol. 2. 2008. (ENG., Illus.). 275p. 251.00 (978-0-444-53098-1(3), Elsevier Science) Elsevier Science & Technology Bks.

Florence, Alexander T. & Walters, Kenneth A. Surfactants in Biological Systems. Date not set. (Surfactant Science Ser.). (978-0-8247-0022-5(8)) Dekker, Marcel Inc.

Frank, Joachim, ed. Molecular Machines in Biology: Workshop of the Cell. 2011. (ENG., Illus.). 272p. 125.00 (978-0-521-19428-0(8)) Cambridge Univ. Pr.

Frohlich, Edward D. & Re, Richard N., eds. The Local Cardiac Renin-Angiotensin Aldosterone System. 2nd ed. 2009. (ENG., Illus.). xii, 184p. 189.00 (978-1-4419-0527-7(8), 1441905278) Springer.

Fromm, Herbert J. & Hargrove, Mark. Essentials of Biochemistry. 2012. (ENG., Illus.). xviii, 364p. 59.95 (978-3-642-19623-2(3), 3642196233) Springer.

Frost, Laura D. & Deal, S. Todd. General, Organic, & Biological Chemistry. 2011. (ENG.). (C). ring bd. 110.20 (978-0-321-79590-8(3), Prentice Hall) Prentice Hall PTR.

Fukuyama, Hidenao & Le Bihan, Denis, eds. Water: The Forgotten Biological Molecule. 2010. (ENG., Illus.). 399p. 99.95 (978-981-4267-52-6(X)) Pan Stanford Publishing SGP. Dist: Taylor & Francis Group.

Gao, Lu. Investigating the Mechanisms of Transcriptional Silencing in Yeast. 2010. 180p. pap. (978-3-639-22630-0(5)) VDM Verlag Dr. Mueller e.K.

Garg, Neha & Prakash, Anil. Primer Designing of Dreb1a & Dreb2a Genes. 2010. 124p. pap. (978-3-8383-9535-7(2)) Lambert Academic Publishing.

Garoutte, Michael P. General, Organic, & Biological Chemistry: A Guided Inquiry. 11th ed. 2006. (ENG., Illus.). 216p. (C). pap. 66.95 (978-0-471-76359-8(4), Wiley) Wiley, John & Sons, Inc.

Garrett, Reginald H. & Grisham, Charles M. Biochemistry. 3rd rev. ed. 2006. (ENG.). 1p. (C). 291.95 (978-0-495-39290-3(1)) Brooks/Cole.

Gault, Victor, et al. Understanding Bioanalytical Chemistry: Principles & Applications. 2009. (ENG., Illus.). 300p. 179.95 (978-0-470-02906-0(4)); 304p. pap. 75.00 (978-0-470-02907-7(2)) Wiley, John & Sons, Inc. (Wiley).

Gerber, Mariette & Hoffman, Richard. The Mediterranean Diet: Health & Science. 2011. (ENG., Illus.). 414p. pap. 77.99 (978-1-4443-3002-1(0), Wiley-Blackwell) Wiley, John & Sons, Inc.

Giansante, Carlo. Supramolecular Photoactive Systems. 2011. 312p. pap. (978-3-8443-3410-4(6)) Lambert Academic Publishing.

Gilbert, Lawrence I., ed. Insect Molecular Biology & Biochemistry. 2011. (ENG.). 574p. 99.95 (978-0-12-384747-8(8), Academic Pr.) Elsevier Science & Technology Bks.

Gilbert, Lawrence I. & Gill, Sarjeet S., eds. Insect Pharmacology: Channels, Receptors, Toxins & Enzymes. 2010. (ENG., Illus.). 392p. 93.95 (978-0-12-381447-0(2), Academic Pr.) Elsevier Science & Technology Bks.

Glass, Richard S. Sulfur's Role in the Modern World. 2011. 350p. 179.00 (978-90-481-3837-1(X), 904813837X) Springer.

Goel, Gautam. Reconstructing Biochemical Systems - Systems Modeling & Analysis Tools for Decoding Biological Designs. 2008. 144p. per. (978-3-8364-5878-8(0)) VDM Verlag Dr. Mueller e.K.

Gohlke, Holger, ed. Protein-Ligand Interactions. 2012. (Methods & Principles in Medicinal Chemistry Ser.). (ENG.). 359p. 185.00 (978-3-527-32966-3(8), Wiley-VCH) Wiley, John & Sons, Inc.

Goldstein, Richard A., et al. Modeling Protein Evolution & Its Bioinformatics Applications. 2009. (Chapman Hall/CRC Mathematical Biology & Medicine Ser.). 79.95 (978-1-58488-498-9(3), Chapman & Hall/CRC) CRC Pr. LLC.

Goswami, Alakananda. Physiological Studies in Eucalyptus Tereticornis: Lignin & Peroxidase Activity - Effect of Biochemical & Environmental Parameters on Lignification. 2008. 112p. pap. (978-3-639-06474-2(7)) VDM Verlag Dr. Mueller e.K.

Greim, Helmut & Albertini, Richard, eds. The Cellular Response to the Genotoxic Insult: The Question of Threshold for Genotoxic Carcinogens. 2012. (Issues in Toxicology Ser.). (ENG., Illus.). 334p. 270.00 (978-1-84973-177-5(2)) Royal Society of Chemistry, The GBR. Dist: Ingram Pub. Services.

Grimm, Bernhard, et al, eds. Chlorophylls & Bacteriochlorophylls: Biochemistry, Biophysics, Functions & Applications. (Advances in Photosynthesis & Respiration Ser.). (Illus.). 2010. xxix, 603p. pap. 449.00 (978-90-481-7140-8(7), 9048171407) 2006. 603p. 449.00 (978-1-4020-4515-8(8), 1402045158) Springer.

Grunwald, Peter. Biocatalysis. 2008. (Illus.). 700p. 163.00 (978-1-86094-744-5(1)); pap. 86.00 (978-1-86094-771-1(9)) Imperial College Pr. GBR. Dist: World Scientific Publishing Co., Inc.

Guijarro, Albert & Yusty, Miguel. The Origin of Chirality in the Molecules of Life: A Revision from Awareness to the Current Theories & Perspectives of this Unsolved Problem. 2008. (ENG., Illus.). 164p. (C). 160.00 (978-0-85404-156-5(7)) Royal Society of Chemistry, The GBR. Dist: Ingram Pub. Services.

Guinn, Denise & Brewer, Rebecca. Essentials of General, Organic & Biochemistry. 2009. (ENG.). 640p. (C). 124.95 (978-0-7167-6121-1(1)) Freeman, W. H. & Co.

Gunsteren, W. F. van, et al, eds. Computer Simulation of Biomolecular Systems: Theoretical & Experimental Applications Volume 3. 2010. (Computer Simulations of Biomolecular Systems Ser.). (ENG.). 644p. pap. 619.00 (978-90-481-8528-3(9), 9048185289) Springer.

Gupta, Vijai Kumar, et al. Fungal Biochemistry & Biotechnology. 2011. 280p. pap. (978-3-8433-5800-2(1)) Lambert Academic Publishing.

Haidar, Ziyad S. A Hybrid Core-Shell Rhop-1 Nanoparticulate Delivery System. 2010. 304p. pap. (978-3-8383-7700-1(1)) Lambert Academic Publishing.

Haider, Konrad & Schäffer, Andreas. Soil Biochemistry. 2009. (ENG.). 132p. 59.95 (978-1-57808-579-8(9)) BIOS Scientific Publishers Ltd. GBR. Dist: Taylor & Francis Group.

Hall, Simon Robert. Biotemplating: Complex Structures from Natural Materials. 2009. (Illus.). 300p. 85.00 (978-1-84816-403-1(3)) Imperial College Pr. GBR. Dist: World Scientific Publishing Co., Inc.

Hames, David & Hooper, Nigel. Instant Notes in Biochemistry. 4th rev. ed. 2011. (Instant Notes Ser.). (ENG., Illus.). 467p. (C). pap. 40.00 (978-0-415-60845-9(7), Taylor & Francis) Taylor & Francis Group GBR. Dist: Taylor & Francis Group.

Hammes, Gordon G. Physical Chemistry for the Biological Sciences. 2007. (Methods of Biochemical Analysis Ser.: 138). (ENG., Illus.). 388p. 122.00 (978-0-470-12202-0(1), Wiley-Interscience) Wiley, John & Sons, Inc.

Hänninen, Pekka & Härmä, Harri, eds. Lanthanide Luminescence: Photophysical, Analytical & Biological Aspects. 2011. (Springer Series on Fluorescence Ser.). (Illus.). xii, 385p. 409.00 (978-3-642-21022-8(8), 3642210228) Springer.

Hansen, Peter W. Chemical Physics Research Developments. 2011. (978-1-61122-068-1(8)) Nova Science Pubs., Inc.

Hauryliuk, Vasili. Translational Gtpases. 2009. 84p. pap. (978-3-639-12700-3(5)) VDM Verlag Dr. Mueller e.K.

Hein, Morris, et al. Introduction to General, Organic, & Biochemistry. 10th ed. 2011. (ENG., Illus.). 1120p. (C). 212.95 (978-0-470-59880-1(8), Wiley) Wiley, John & Sons, Inc.

Herdewijn, Piet & Kisakürek, M. Volkan, eds. Origin of Life: Chemical Approach. 2008. (ENG., Illus.). 429p. 220.00 (978-3-906390-50-5(0), Wiley-VCH) Wiley, John & Sons, Inc.

Hobsbaum, Angela, et al. Book Bands for Guided Reading: Organising Key Stage One Texts for the Literacy Hour, Vol. 3. 3rd rev. ed. 2011. (Illus.). 340p. 180.00 (978-0-85473-687-4(5)) CABI GBR. Dist: Stylus Publishing, LLC.

Horton, Derek. Advances in Carbohydrate Chemistry & Biochemistry. (ENG.). 2011. 314p. 241.00 (978-0-12-385520-6(9)) 2010. 562p. 241.00 (978-0-12-380854-7(5)) 2010. 456p. 241.00 (978-0-12-380856-1(1)) 2007. 460p. 241.00 (978-0-12-373920-9(9)) Elsevier Science & Technology Bks. (Academic Pr.).

Houston, Michael E. Biochemistry Primer for Exercise Science. 3rd rev. ed. 2006. (ENG., Illus.). 280p. (C). per. 43.00 (978-0-7360-5612-0(2)) Human Kinetics Pubs.

Huang, Qiaoyun, et al, eds. Soil Mineral — Microbe-Organic Interactions: Theories & Applications. 2010. (ENG., Illus.). xvi, 354p. pap. 189.00 (978-3-642-09647-1(6), 3642096476) Springer.

Huopalahti, Rainer, et al, eds. Bioactive Egg Compounds. 2010. (ENG., Illus.). xx, 298p. pap. 189.00 (978-3-642-07238-3(0), 3642072380) Springer.

Huynh-Ba, Kim, ed. Current Trends in Stability Testing to Support Global Markets. 2009. (Biotechnology: Pharmaceutical Aspects Ser.). (ENG., Illus.). xx, 268p. 189.00 (978-1-4419-0888-9(9), 1441908889) Springer.

Imbihl, Ronald, et al. Nonlinear Dynamics in Chemistry & Biochemistry. 2006. (ENG.). 400p. 175.00 (978-3-527-30824-8(5)) Wiley, John & Sons, Inc.

Inderjit & Mukerji, K. G., eds. Allelochemicals: Biological Control of Plant Pathogens & Diseases: Biological Control of Plant Pathogens & Diseases. 2010. (Disease Management of Fruits & Vegetables Ser.). vii, 214p. pap. 179.00 (978-90-481-7131-6(8), 9048171318) Springer.

Janson, Lee W. Biochemistry: the Big Picture. 2012. (LANGE the Big Picture Ser.). (ENG., Illus.). 418p. pap. 60.00 (978-0-07-163791-6(5), 0071637915) McGraw-Hill Medical Publishing Div.

Jenkins, Alicia J. & Lyons, Timothy J., eds. Lipoproteins in Diabetes Mellitus. 2009. (Contemporary Diabetes Ser.). 500p. 199.00 (978-1-60761-023-6(X)) Humana Pr.

Jia. Metabonomics in Modern Health Sciences & Traditional Medicine. 2011. 99.00 (978-981-283-694-6(2)) World Scientific Publishing Co., Inc.

Jin, Tian & Hereld, Dale, eds. Chemotaxis: Methods & Protocols. 2009. (Methods in Molecular Biology Ser.). (ENG., Illus.). xvi, 540p. 129.00 (978-1-60761-197-4(X), 160761197X) Humana Pr.

Jing, Hao. Chemical & Biological Effects of Maillard Reaction Products. 2009. 220p. pap. (978-3-639-17689-6(8)) VDM Verlag Dr. Mueller e.K.

Johnson, Michael L., et al. Biothermodynamics, Part D. 2011. (ENG.). 369p. 187.00 (978-0-12-386003-3(2), Academic Pr.) Elsevier Science & Technology Bks.

Jue, Thomas, et al, eds. Biomembrane Frontiers: Nanostructures, Models, & the Design of Life. 2009. (Handbook of Modern Biophysics Ser.). (ENG., Illus.). xvi, 324p. 259.00 (978-1-60761-313-8(1), 1607613131) Humana Pr.

K v s v, Prasad & K V S V, Prasad. Purification & Characterization of Detergent Stable Alkaline Protease. 2011. 84p. pap. (978-3-8443-1724-4(4)) Lambert Academic Publishing.

Kaldis, Philipp, ed. Cell Cycle Regulation. 2010. (Results & Problems in Cell Differentiation Ser.). (Illus.). xii, 374p. pap. 269.00 (978-3-642-07093-8(0), 3642070930) Springer.

Kalsi, P. S. & Kalsi, J. P. Bioorganic, Bioinorganic & Supramolecular Chemistry. 2nd ed. 2011. (Illus.). 414p. pap. (978-1-906574-79-6(0)) New Age Science, Ltd.

Kamkin, Andre & Kiseleva, Irina, eds. Mechanosensitivity of the Heart. 2009. (Mechanosensitivity in Cells & Tissues Ser.). (ENG., Illus.). xxxvii, 471p. 269.00 (978-90-481-2849-5(8), 9048128498) Springer.

Kangueane, Pandjassarame. Protein-Protein Interactions. 2011. (Biochemistry Research Trends Ser.). 145.00 (978-1-61761-548-1(X), Nova Biomedical Bks.) Nova Science Pubs., Inc.

Katoch, Rajan. Analytical Techniques in Biochemistry & Molecular Biology. 2011. (ENG., Illus.). xviii, 441p. 209.00 (978-1-4419-9784-5(9), 1441997849) Springer.

Keankeo, Watcharaporn. Weathering of Almandine Garnet. 2010. 72p. pap. (978-3-8383-6919-8(X)) Lambert Academic Publishing.

Kinfe, Esayas, et al. Nutritional Composition of Some Capsicum Varieties Grown in Ethiopi. 2011. 76p. pap. (978-3-8443-0594-4(7)) Lambert Academic Publishing.

Kirsh, Marvin. Uniqueness, Self Belonging & Intercourse in Nature. 2010. 128p. pap. (978-3-8383-6737-8(5)) Lambert Academic Publishing.

Kisselev, Alexei M. Insights into Stimuli-Responsive Polymers. 2009. 136p. pap. (978-3-639-16533-3(0)) VDM Verlag Dr. Mueller e.K.

Kiyota, Hiromasa. Marine Natural Products. 2010. (Topics in Heterocyclic Chemistry Ser.). xiv, 287p. pap. 269.00 (978-3-642-07028-0(0), 3642070280) Springer.

Klebe, Gerhard, ed. Virtual Screening: An Alternative or Complement to High Throughput Screening. 2010. 308p. pap. 182.00 (978-90-481-5584-2(3), 9048155843) Springer.

Klok, Harm-Anton & Schlaad, Helmut. Peptide Hybrid Polymers. 2010. (Advances in Polymer Science Ser.). xii, 160p. pap. 279.00 (978-3-642-06897-3(9), 3642068979) Springer.

Ko, Kyung Yuk. Egg Yolk Immunoglobulins & Ovotransferrin Of. 2008. 208p. pap. (978-3-639-08320-0(2)) VDM Verlag Dr. Mueller e.K.

Kohler, Robert E. From Medical Chemistry to Biochemistry: The Making of a Biomedical Discipline. 2008. (Cambridge Studies in the History of Medicine Ser.). (ENG., Illus.). 412p. pap. 53.00 (978-0-521-09047-6(4)) Cambridge Univ. Pr.

Kolpashchikov, Dmitry & Gerasimova, Yulia. Biochemistry I. rev. ed. 2011. (ENG.). 120.00 (978-0-7575-7664-5(8)) Kendall Hunt Publishing Co.

Konigsberger, LanChi & Konigsberger, Erich, eds. Biomineralization: Medical Aspects of Solubility. 2006. (ENG., Illus.). 302p. 270.00 (978-0-470-09209-5(2), Wiley) Wiley, John & Sons, Inc.

Konopka, Andrzej K. Chemical, Computational, & Systems Biology Series Typical Book. 2007. 350p. 79.95 (978-0-470-12239-6(0), Wiley-Interscience) Wiley, John & Sons, Inc.

Kornberg, Roger D., ed. Annual Review of Biochemistry, Vol. 76. 2007. 864p. 342.79 (978-0-8243-0876-6(X)) Annual Reviews, Inc.

Kornberg, Roger D., ed. Annual Review of Biochemistry 2011. 2011. 1133p. 240.00 (978-0-8243-0880-3(8)) Annual Reviews, Inc.

Krauss, Gerhard. Biochemistry of Signal Transduction & Regulation. 4th ed. 2008. (ENG.). 646p. pap. 160.00 (978-3-527-31397-6(4), Wiley-VCH) Wiley, John & Sons, Inc.

Krishnaswamy, N.R. Chemistry of Natural Proucts: A Unified Approach, Second Edition. 2nd rev. ed. 2010. (ENG., Illus.). 432p. 89.95 (978-1-4398-4965-1(X), CRC Press) Taylor & Francis Group GBR. Dist: Taylor & Francis Group.

Kropf, Michel. Imaging Ampa-Type Receptors in Hippocampal Neurons. 2009. 140p. pap. (978-3-639-13319-6(6)) VDM Verlag Dr. Mueller e.K.

Krüse, J., et al, eds. The Practical Applicability of Toxicokinetic Models in the Risk Assessment of Chemicals. 2010. 206p. pap. 135.00 (978-90-481-6147-8(9), 9048161479) Springer.

Kumar, Lalita S. & Kumar, Sanjiv. Chemistry of Natural Products: Amino Acids, Peptides, Proteins & Enzymes. 2007. (ENG., Illus.). 224p. 79.95 (978-1-4200-5917-5(3), CRC Press) Taylor & Francis Group GBR. Dist: Taylor & Francis Group.

Kürti, Lfszló & Corey, E. J. Molecules & Medicine. 2007. (ENG.). 272p. pap. 54.95 (978-0-470-22749-7(4), Wiley) Wiley, John & Sons, Inc.

Kurzynski, Michal. The Thermodynamic Machinery of Life. 2010. (Frontiers Collection). (Illus.). xiv, 431p. pap. 99.00 (978-3-642-06284-1(9), 3642062849) Springer.

Kvesitadze, George, et al. Biochemical Mechanisms of Detoxification in Higher Plants: Basis of Phytoremediation. 2010. (ENG., Illus.). x, 256p. pap. 239.00 (978-3-642-06702-0(6), 3642067026) Springer.

Lahiri Majumder, A. & Biswas, B. B., eds. Biology of Inositols & Phosphoinositides. 2006. (Subcellular Biochemistry Ser.). (Illus.). xii, 340p. 229.00 (978-0-387-27599-4(1), 0387275991) Springer.

Landesberg, Joseph M. eneral, Organic, & Biochemistry - Laboratory Experiments. 2011. (ENG.). 256p. (C). pap. 69.95 (978-1-111-42661-3(9)) Brooks/Cole.

Lang, Florian, ed. Serum & Glucocorticoid Inducible Kinase, Vol. 13. (Cellular Physiology & Biochemistry Ser.: Vol. 13, No. 1). (Illus.). (978-3-8055-7512-6(2)) Karger, S. AG.

Larijani, Banafshe, et al, eds. Chemical Biology: Techniques & Applications. 2006. (ENG., Illus.). 272p. 209.95 (978-0-470-09064-0(2)); per. 84.95 (978-0-470-09065-7(0)) Wiley, John & Sons, Inc. (Wiley).

Lehninger, Albert, et al. Lehninger Principles of Biochemistry. 5th ed. 2008. (ENG., Illus.). 1100p. (C). 218.95 (978-0-7167-7108-1(X)) Freeman, W. H. & Co.

Levine, Martin. Topics in Dental Biochemistry. 2011. (ENG., Illus.). xiii, 307p. 189.00 (978-3-540-88115-5(6), 3540881158) Springer.

Li, Xiaoling. Oral Bioavailability: Basic Principles, Advanced Concepts, & Applications. Hu, Ming, ed. 2011. (Wiley Series in Drug Discovery & Development Ser.: 16). (ENG., Illus.). 568p. 149.95 (978-0-470-26099-9(8), Wiley) Wiley, John & Sons, Inc.

Liao, Chiung-Feng. Thy Study of Electroluminescenct Polymers & Application in WPLED: The Next Generation Potential Luminescence Technology. 2008. 100p. pap. (978-3-639-11019-7(6)) VDM Verlag Dr. Mueller e.K.

Liebig, Justus. Animal Chemistry. 2009. 238p. pap. (978-0-217-17072-7(2)) Books LLC.

—Animal Chemistry, or, Chemistry in Its Applications to Physiology & Pathology by Baron Liebig Edited from the Author's Manuscript by William. 2006. 188p. per. 18.99 (978-1-4255-1560-7(6)) MPublishing.

Limbird, Lee E. Cell Surface Receptors: A Short Course on Theory & Methods. 3rd ed. 2010. (ENG., Illus.). xii, 219p. pap. 129.00 (978-1-4419-3571-7(1), 1441935711) Springer.

Lindhorst, Thisbe K. Essentials of Carbohydrate Chemistry & Biochemistry. 3rd ed. 2007. (ENG., Illus.). 332p. pap. 90.00 (978-3-527-31528-4(4), Wiley-VCH) Wiley, John & Sons, Inc.

Lisdat, Fred. Biosensing for the 21st Century. 2010. (Advances in Biochemical Engineering Biotechnology Ser.). (Illus.). xvi, 504p. pap. 599.00 (978-3-642-09444-6(9), 3642094449) Springer.

Litwack, Gerald. Human Biochemistry & Disease. 2008. (ENG., Illus.). 1272p. (C). 225.00 (978-0-12-452815-4(5), Academic Pr.) Elsevier Science & Technology Bks.

Lohff, Brigitte & Conrads, Hinderk. From Berlin to New York: Life & Work of the Almost Forgotten German-Jewish Biochemist Carl Neuberg (1877-1956) 2007. (Geschichte und Philosophie der Medizin. History & Philosophy of Medicine Ser.). (ENG., Illus.). 294p. (C). 68.00 (978-3-515-09062-9(2)) Steiner, Franz Verlag Wiesbaden GmbH DEU. Dist: Brown, David Bk. Co., The.

Lomova, T. N. & Zaikov, Gennadii Efremovich, eds. Chemical Processes with Participation of Biological & Related Compounds: Biophysical & Chemical Aspects of Porphyrins, Pigments, Drugs, Biodegradable Polymers & Nanofibers. 2008. (ENG., Illus.). 422p. 216.00 (978-90-04-16210-5(0), CRC Press) Taylor & Francis Group GBR. Dist: Taylor & Francis Group.

Lundblad, Roger L. Biochemistry & Molecular Biology. 4th rev. ed. 2010. (ENG., Illus.). 1264p. cd-rom 209.95 (978-0-8493-8744-9(2), CRC Press) Taylor & Francis Group GBR. Dist: Taylor & Francis Group.

—Biochemistry & Molecular Biology Compendium. 2007. (ENG., Illus.). 424p. 113.95 (978-1-4200-4347-1(1), CRC Press) Taylor & Francis Group GBR. Dist: Taylor & Francis Group.

—Handbook of Biochemistry & Molecular Biology. 4th rev. ed. 2010. (ENG., Illus.). 1098p. instr.'s hndbk. ed. 209.95 (978-0-8493-9168-2(7), CRC Press) Taylor & Francis Group GBR. Dist: Taylor & Francis Group.

Lynden-Bell, Ruth M. Water & Life: The Unique Properties of H20. 2010. (ENG., Illus.). 396p. 89.95 (978-1-4398-0356-1(0), CRC Press) Taylor & Francis Group GBR. Dist: Taylor & Francis Group.

Määttä, Juha. Structural & Functional Characterization of Engineered Avidin Proteins. 2010. (Acta Universitatis Tamperensis Ser.). (Illus.). 160p. pap. 82.50 (978-951-44-8103-1(8)) Tampere Univ. Pr. FIN. Dist: Coronet Bks.

MacDonald, Ian M. Protein Structural Domain Boundary Prediction - a ture of Experts Approach. 2008. 216p. per. (978-3-8364-3720-2(1)) VDM Verlag Dr. Mueller e.K.

MacDonald, Richard G. & Chaney, William G. Biochemistry. 2007. (LANGE USMLE Road Maps Ser.). (ENG., Illus.). 224p. (C). per. 36.00 (978-0-07-144205-3(7), 0071442057) McGraw-Hill Medical Publishing Div.

MacHina, Krishnamoorthy & Ronald Fernandes. Gastroprotective & Antisecretory Activity of Selenomethionine. 2011. 128p. pap. (978-3-8443-9183-1(6)) Lambert Academic Publishing.

MacLaren, Donald & Morton, James. Biochemistry for Sport & Exercise Metabolism. 2012. (ENG.). 264p. 140.00 (978-0-470-09184-5(3)); pap. 50.00 (978-0-470-09185-2(1)) Wiley, John & Sons, Inc. (Wiley).

Mahdi, Safiur Rahman, et al. Protein Secondary Structure Prediction. 2010. 80p. pap. (978-3-639-27366-3(4)) VDM Verlag Dr. Mueller e.K.

Mahmoud, Atef, et al. Physiological Studies on Reducing the Deleterious Effects: In Some Fresh-Cut Vegetables. 2011. 96p. pap. (978-3-639-32335-1(1)) VDM Verlag Dr. Mueller e.K.

Mathews, Christopher K., et al. Biochemistry. 4th ed. 2012. (ENG., Illus.). 1368p. (C). 226.67 (978-0-13-800464-4(1), Prentice Hall) Prentice Hall PTR.

Maughan, Ronald J. & Gleeson, Michael. The Biochemical Basis of Sports Performance. 2nd ed. 2010. (ENG., Illus.). 320p. 55.00 (978-0-19-920828-9(X)) Oxford Univ. Pr., Inc.

McDermott, Anne E. & Polenova, Tatyana, eds. Solid State NMR Studies of Biopolymers. 2010. (ENG., Illus.). 592p. 165.00 (978-0-470-72122-3(7), Wiley) Wiley, John & Sons, Inc.

Mcdougal, Owen & Steiner, Rick. General, Organic & Biological Chemistry. 2006. pap., stu. ed. 43.95 (978-0-471-69942-2(X)) Wiley, John & Sons, Inc.

B

McEwan, I. J. The Nuclear Receptor Superfamily: Methods & Protocols. 2009. (Illus.). x, 281p. (978-1-60327-575-0(4)); 240p. 119.00 (978-1-60327-574-3(6)) Humana Pr.

McKee, Gertrude & McKee, James. Biochemistry: The Molecular Basis of Life, 1 vol. 5th ed. 2011. (ENG.). 864p. (C). 154.95 (978-0-19-973084-1(9)) Oxford Univ. Pr., Inc.

McKee, Trudy & McKee, James R. Biochemistry: The Molecular Basis of Life. 5th ed. 2012. **(978-0-19-992046-4(X))** Oxford Univ. Pr., Inc.

McKee, Trudy & McKee, James R. Biochemistry the Molecular Basis of LIfe International. 4th ed. 2008. (Illus.). 848p. (C). pap. 145.00 (978-0-19-538469-7(5)) Oxford Univ. Pr., Inc.

McMahon, Robert J., ed. Avidin-Biotin Interactions: Methods & Applications. 2010. (Methods in Molecular Biology Ser.). (Illus.). xiv, 232p. pap. 119.00 (978-1-61737-657-3(4), 1617376574) Humana Pr.

McMurry, John, et al. Study Guide & Selected Solutions Manual for Fundamentals of General, Organic, & Biological Chemistry. 6th ed. 2009. (ENG.). 432p. (C). pap. 69.87 (978-0-321-61239-7(6), Prentice Hall) Prentice Hall PTR.

Meisenberg, Gerhard & Simmons, William H. Principles of Medical Biochemistry: With STUDENT CONSULT Online Access. 3rd ed. 2011. (ENG., Illus.). 608p. (C). pap. 69.95 (978-0-323-07155-0(4), Saunders) Elsevier - Health Sciences Div.

Michibata, Hitoshi, ed. Vanadium: Biochemical & Molecular Biological Approaches. 2011. (ENG., Illus.). xv, 228p. 129.00 **(978-94-007-0912-6(9)**, 9400709129) Springer.

Microbiology, Microbial Production of Industrial Chemicals [Bibliography & Price Not Definite.]. Gosset Lagarda, G., ed. 2008. (Illus.). 66p. pap. (978-3-8055-8444-9(X)) Karger, S. AG.

Middlecamp, Catherine & American Chemical Society Staff. Chemistry in Context: Applying Chemistry to Society. 7th ed. 2011. (ENG., Illus.). 592p. (C). pap. 158.67 (978-0-07-337566-3(7), 0073375667, McGraw-Hill Science, Engineering & Mathematics) McGraw-Hill Higher Education.

Miller, Andrew D. & Tanner, Julian. Essentials of Chemical Biology: Structure & Dynamics of Biological Macromolecules. 2008. (ENG., Illus.). 590p. 199.95 (978-0-470-84530-1(9), Wiley) Wiley, John & Sons, Inc.

—Essentials of Chemical Biology: Structure & Dynamics of Biological Macromolecules. 2008. (ENG., Illus.). 590p. pap. 94.95 (978-0-470-84531-8(7), Wiley) Wiley, John & Sons, Inc.

Miranda, Katrina. Chemical Biology of Nitric Oxide. 2008. 350p. 50.00 (978-0-8153-4147-5(4), Garland Science) Taylor & Francis Group.

Moore, John T. & Langley, Richard H. Biochemistry for Dummies. 2nd ed. 2011. (ENG., Illus.). 360p. pap. 19.99 (978-1-118-02174-3(6), For Dummies) Wiley, John & Sons, Inc.

Moran, Laurence A., et al. Principles of Biochemistry. 5th ed. 2011. (ENG.). 832p. (C). 189.67 **(978-0-321-70733-8(8)**, Prentice Hall) Prentice Hall PTR.

Moreira, Susana. Carbohydrate Binding Modules: Functions & Applications. Gama, Miguel, ed. 2010. (Biotechnology in Agriculture, Industry & Medicine Ser.). 76p. pap. 43.00 (978-1-60876-979-7(8)) Nova Science Pubs., Inc.

Moss, Tom & Leblanc, Benoît. DNA-Protein Interactions. 3rd ed. 2009. (Methods in Molecular Biology Ser.). (ENG., Illus.). xxiv, 610p. 149.00 (978-1-60327-014-4(0), 1603270140) Humana Pr.

Mousdale, David M. Biofuels: Biotechnology, Chemistry, & Sustainable Development. 2008. (ENG., Illus.). 424p. 129.95 (978-1-4200-5124-7(5), CRC Press) Taylor & Francis Group GBR. Dist: Taylor & Francis Group.

Murray, Robert, et al. Harpers Illustrated Biochemistry 29th Edition. 29th ed. 2012. (LANGE Basic Science Ser.). (ENG., Illus.). 818p. (C). pap. 60.00 **(978-0-07-176576-3(X)**, 007176576X) McGraw-Hill Medical Publishing Div.

Naidu, Ravendra. Chemical Bioavailability in Terrestrial Environments. 2008. (Developments in Soil Science Ser.: 32). (ENG., Illus.). 828p. 101.00 (978-0-444-52169-9(0), Elsevier Science) Elsevier Science & Technology Bks.

Naik, Pankaja. Biochemistry. 3rd ed. 2009. (ENG., Illus.). 640p. pap. 71.00 (978-0-07-163435-9(5), 0071634355) McGraw-Hill Professional Publishing.

Needham, Joseph, ed. The Chemistry of Life: Eight Lectures on the History of Biochemistry. 2008. (ENG.). 268p. pap. 36.99 (978-0-521-08885-5(2)) Cambridge Univ. Pr.

Nelson, David L., et al. Cellular Metabolic Map Study Guide for Principles of Biochemistry. 5th ed. 2008. (ENG.). 1p. (C). pap., pupil's gde. ed. 17.95 (978-1-4292-2339-3(1)) Freeman, W. H. & Co.

Neustadt, John & Pieczenik, Steve. A Revolution in Health through Nutritional Biochemistry. 2007. 136p. per. 18.95 (978-0-595-45340-5(6)) iUniverse, Inc.

Neve, Kim A. Functional Selectivity of G Protein-Coupled Receptor Ligands: New Opportunities for Drug Discovery. 2009. (Receptors Ser.). (ENG., Illus.). x, 226p. 219.00 (978-1-60327-334-3(4)) Humana Pr.

New Trends & Developments in Biochemical Engineering. 2010. (Advances in Biochemical Engineering Biotechnology Ser.). (Illus.). ix, 303p. pap. 349.00 (978-3-642-07323-6(9), 3642073239) Springer.

Newsholme, Eric A., et al. Functional Biochemistry in Health & Disease. 2nd ed. 2010. (ENG., Illus.). 560p. pap. 79.95 (978-0-471-93165-2(9), Wiley) Wiley, John & Sons, Inc.

Nicolau, Dan V. Nanodevices Based on Protein Molecular Motors: An Engineering Approach. 2008. (Fundamental Biomedical Technologies Ser.). 135.00 (978-0-387-30755-8(9), 0387307559) Springer.

Nielsen, Jens. Metabolic Engineering. 2010. (Advances in Biochemical Engineering Biotechnology Ser.). (Illus.). xi, 183p. pap. 279.00 (978-3-642-07534-6(7), 3642075347) Springer.

Norde, Willem. Colloids & Interfaces in Life Sciences & Bionanotechnology. 2nd rev. ed. 2011. (ENG., Illus.). 495p. 129.95 (978-1-4398-1718-6(9), CRC Press) Taylor & Francis Group GBR. Dist: Taylor & Francis Group.

Novartis Foundation Symposium Staff. Innate Immunity to Pulmonary Infection. 2007. (Novartis Foundation Symposia Ser.: 155). (ENG., Illus.). 238p. 195.00 (978-0-470-02656-4(1), Wiley) Wiley, John & Sons, Inc.

Nuclear Receptors in Development. 2006. (Advances in Developmental Biology Ser.). (ENG., Illus.). 448p. 133.00 (978-0-444-52873-5(3), Elsevier Science) Elsevier Science & Technology Bks.

Nussinovitch, Amos. Plant Gum Exudates of the World: Sources, Distribution, Properties, & Applications. 2009. (ENG., Illus.). 427p. 185.95 (978-1-4200-5223-7(3), CRC Press) Taylor & Francis Group GBR. Dist: Taylor & Francis Group.

Ochs. Biochemistry. rev. ed. 2011. 174.95 (978-0-7637-5736-6(5)) Jones & Bartlett Learning, LLC.

Ohshima, Hiroyuki. Biophysical Chemistry of Biointerfaces. 2010. (ENG., Illus.). 547p. 142.00 (978-0-470-16935-3(4), Wiley) Wiley, John & Sons, Inc.

Okeyo, David & Fry (), Jack. Environmental Plant Stress. 2011. 132p. pap. **(978-3-8443-1110-5(6))** Lambert Academic Publishing.

Ozsoz, Mehmet Sengun, ed. Electrochemical DNA Biosensors. 2012. (ENG., Illus.). 400p. 149.95 **(978-981-4241-77-9(6))** Pan Stanford Publishing SGP. Dist: Taylor & Francis Group.

Palanivelu, Peramachi. Bioinformatics Analyses of Eukaryotic Mrnas & Industrial Enzymes. 2010. 96p. pap. (978-3-8383-4184-2(8)) Lambert Academic Publishing.

Palmer, Michael. Biochemical Pharmacology. 2012. (ENG.). 428p. 99.95 (978-0-470-17445-6(5), Wiley) Wiley, John & Sons, Inc.

Pan, Dongli & Cooperman, Barry S. Transfer Rna Dynamics in Bacterial Protein Synthesis. 2008. 160p. pap. (978-3-639-08503-7(5)) VDM Verlag Dr. Mueller e.K.

Parson, William W. Modern Optical Spectroscopy: With Exercises & Examples from Biophysics & Biochemistry. 2009. (ENG., Illus.). xii, 530p. pap. 89.95 (978-3-540-95895-6(9), 3540958959) Springer.

Paul, Eldor A., ed. Soil Microbiology, Ecology & Biochemistry. 3rd ed. 2006. (ENG., Illus.). 552p. (C). 83.95 (978-0-12-546807-7(5), Academic Pr.) Elsevier Science & Technology Bks.

Pearce, Eli M., et al, eds. New Steps in Chemical & Biochemical Physics. Pure & Applied Science. 2010. (Physics Research & Technology Ser.). 235.00 (978-1-61668-923-0(4)) Nova Science Pubs., Inc.

Peet, Alisa. Basic Medical Biochemistry. Lieberman, Michael A. & Marks, Allan, eds. 4th rev. ed. 2012. (ENG., Illus.). 1024p. pap. 79.95 **(978-1-60831-572-7(X))** Lippincott Williams & Wilkins.

Pellissier, Hélène. Chiral Sulfur-Containing Ligands: Asymmetric Catalysis. 2009. (RSC Catalysis Ser.). (ENG., Illus.). 402p. (C). 224.00 (978-1-84755-924-1(7)) Royal Society of Chemistry, The GBR. Dist: Ingram Pub. Services.

Permyakov, Eugene & Permyakov. Metalloproteomics. 2009. (Wiley Series in Protein & Peptide Science Ser.: 2). (ENG., Illus.). 802p. 158.00 (978-0-470-39248-5(7), Wiley-Interscience) Wiley, John & Sons, Inc.

Pervitsky, Dmitry. Hno Adducts of Horse Myoglobin & Human Hemoglobin. 2010. 108p. pap. (978-3-8383-0158-7(7)) Lambert Academic Publishing.

Peters, Thomas. Bioactive Conformation I. 2010. (Topics in Current Chemistry Ser.). (Illus.). xii, 309p. pap. 319.00 (978-3-642-08035-7(9), 3642080359) Springer.

—Bioactive Conformation II, 2 vols. 2008. (Topics in Current Chemistry Ser.). (Illus.). 210p. 279.00 (978-3-540-49079-1(5), 3540490795) Springer.

Pfaff, Donald W. & Kieffer, Brigitte L., eds. Molecular & Biophysical Mechanisms of Arousal, Alertness & Attention. 2008. (Annals of the New York Academy of Sciences Ser.). (ENG., Illus.). 400p. pap. 139.95 (978-1-57331-703-0(9), Wiley-Blackwell) Wiley, John & Sons, Inc.

Polavarapu, Prasad L. Chiroptical Spectroscopy: Fundamentals & Applications. 2010. (Illus.). 312p. 139.95 (978-1-4200-9246-2(4)) CRC Pr. LLC.

Poortmans, J. R., ed. Principles of Exercise Biochemistry, Vol. 46. 3rd rev. ed. (Medicine & Sport Science Ser.: Vol. 46). (Illus.). (978-3-8055-7607-9(2)) Karger, S. AG.

Pratt & Pratt, Charlotte W. Essential Biochemistry, 2 Edition Binder Ready Version with Binder Set. 2011. pap. (978-0-470-55768-6(0)) Wiley, John & Sons, Inc.

—Essential Biochemistry, 2 Edition Binder Ready Version with WileyPLUS Set. 2011. pap. (978-0-470-55815-7(6)) Wiley, John & Sons, Inc.

Pratt, Charlotte W. & Cornely, Kathleen. Essential Biochemistry. 2nd ed. 2010. (ENG., Illus.). 744p. (C). 205.95 (978-0-470-50477-2(3), Wiley) Wiley, John & Sons, Inc.

—Essential Biochemistry: University of Texas at Austin, CH 369 Fundamentals of Biochemistry. 2008. (Illus.). 761p. pap. 70.95 incl. cd-rom (978-0-470-28637-5(X), Wiley) Wiley, John & Sons, Inc.

Priyadarshy, Satyam & Shanker, Latha. DNA Nanotechnology. 2010. (Illus.). 464p. 149.95 (978-1-4200-8633-1(2)) CRC Pr. LLC.

Puglisi, Joseph D., ed. Biophysics & the Challenges of Emerging Threats. 2009. (NATO Science for Peace & Security Series B: Physics & Biophysics Ser.). (ENG., Illus.). viii, 180p. 249.00 (978-90-481-2366-7(6), 9048123666); pap. 89.95 (978-90-481-2367-4(4), 9048123674) Springer.

Rabaey, Korneel. Bio-electrochemical Systems: From Extracellular Electron Transfer to Biotechnological Application. 2009. (Integrated Environmental Technology Ser.). (Illus.). 524p. (C). (978-1-84339-233-0(X)) IWA Publishing.

Raut, Indrayani, et al. Formulation & Evaluation of Gastroretentive Drug Delivery System. 2011. 136p. pap. **(978-3-8433-8832-0(6))** Lambert Academic Publishing.

Raymond, Kenneth W. General Organic & Biological Chemistry. 3rd ed. (ENG., Illus.). (C). 2010. 624p. 188.95 (978-0-470-50476-5(5)) 2009. 349p. pap., pupil's gde. ed. 61.95 (978-0-470-55495-1(9)) Wiley, John & Sons, Inc. (Wiley).

—General, Organic, & Biological Chemistry: An Integrated Approach, Binder Ready Book. 2nd ed. 2007. (ENG.). 656p. (C). ring bd. 113.95 (978-0-470-27985-4(0), Wiley) Wiley, John & Sons, Inc.

—General Organic & Biological Chemistry: An Integrated Approach with Wiley Plus Set. rev. ed. 2006. 82.00 net. (978-0-470-10394-4(9)) Wiley, John & Sons, Inc.

—General, Organic, & Biological Chemistry: Anintegrated Approach. 2nd ed. 2008. (ENG., Illus.). 640p. (C). stu. ed., per. 61.95 (978-0-470-22844-9(X), Wiley) Wiley, John & Sons, Inc.

Reed, Stephen Charles. Essential Physiological Biochemistry: An Organ-Based Approach. 2010. (ENG., Illus.). 342p. 159.95 (978-0-470-02635-9(9)); pap. 79.95 (978-0-470-02636-6(7)) Wiley, John & Sons, Inc. (Wiley).

Rejsek, Klement, et al. The Soil Amino Acids: Quality, Distribution & Site Ecology. 2010. (Advances in Environmental Research Ser.). 89.00 (978-1-61668-335-1(X)) Nova Science Pubs., Inc.

Rejsek, Klement, et al. Soil Amino Acids: Quality, Distribution & Site Ecology. 2011. (Environmental Science, Engineering & Technology Ser.). 236p. pap. 59.00 **(978-1-62100-511-7(9))** Nova Science Pubs., Inc.

Reviews of Physiology, Biochemistry & Pharmacology 139. 2010. (Reviews of Physiology, Biochemistry & Pharmacology Ser.). (Illus.). vi, 174p. pap. 159.00 (978-3-642-08497-3(4), 3642084974) Springer.

Reviews of Physiology, Biochemistry & Pharmacology 149. 2010. (Reviews of Physiology, Biochemistry & Pharmacology Ser.). (Illus.). iv, 106p. pap. 182.00 (978-3-642-05777-9(2), 3642057772) Springer.

Reviews of Physiology, Biochemistry & Pharmacology 151. 2010. (Reviews of Physiology, Biochemistry & Pharmacology Ser.). (Illus.). iv, 110p. pap. 219.00 (978-3-642-06043-4(9), 3642060439) Springer.

Rhoads, Robert E., ed. MiRNA Regulation of the Translational Machinery. 2009. (Progress in Molecular & Subcellular Biology Ser.). (ENG., Illus.). x, 115p. 159.00 (978-3-642-03102-1(1), 3642031021) Springer.

Richtering, Walter. Smart Colloidal Materials. 2010. (Progress in Colloid & Polymer Science Ser.). viii, 184p. pap. 259.00 (978-3-642-06923-9(1), 3642069231) Springer.

Roat-Malone, Rosette M. Bioinorganic Chemistry: A Short Course. 2nd ed. 2007. (ENG., Illus.). 544p. pap. 132.00 (978-0-471-76113-6(3), Wiley-Interscience) Wiley, John & Sons, Inc.

Rogers, Kara. The Components of Life: From Nucleic Acids to Carbohydrates. 2011. (Biochemistry, Cells, & Life Ser.). (Illus.). 264p. (YA). lib. bdg. 40.00 (978-1-61530-324-3(3)) Rosen Publishing Group, Inc., The.

Rogers, Kara, ed. The Chemical Reactions of Life: From Metabolism to Photosynthesis. 2011. (Biochemistry, Cells, & Life Ser.). (Illus.). 280p. (YA). 80.00 (978-1-61530-432-5(0)); 40.00 (978-1-61530-328-1(6)) Rosen Publishing Group, Inc., The.

—The Components of Life: From Nucleic Acids to Carbohydrates. 2011. (Biochemistry, Cells, & Life Ser.). (Illus.). 264p. (YA). 80.00 (978-1-61530-434-9(7)) Rosen Publishing Group, Inc., The.

—Fungi, Algae, & Protists. 2011. (Biochemistry, Cells, & Life Ser.). (Illus.). 232p. (YA). 80.00 (978-1-61530-464-6(9)) Rosen Publishing Group, Inc., The.

Rokita, Steven. Carbon-Centered Free Radicals & Radical Cations: Structure, Reactivity, & Dynamics. Forbes, Malcolm D., ed. 2010. (Wiley Series of Reactive Intermediates in Chemistry & Biology Ser.: 2). (ENG., Illus.). 370p. 139.00 (978-0-470-39009-2(3), Wiley) Wiley, John & Sons, Inc.

Romano, Francesco H. & Russo, Andrea, eds. Biocatalysis Research Progress. 2008. (Illus.). xv, 365p. 185.00 (978-1-60456-619-2(1)) Nova Science Pubs., Inc.

Royal Society of Chemistry Staff. Biophysical Approaches Determining Ligand Binding to Biomolecular Targets: Detection, Measurement & Modelling. Podjarny, Alberto et al. eds. 2011. (RSC Biomolecular Sciences Ser.). (ENG., Illus.). 362p. 213.00 **(978-1-84973-009-9(1))** Royal Society of Chemistry, The GBR. Dist: Ingram Pub. Services.

—Computational & Structural Approaches to Drug Discovery: Ligand-Protein Interactions. Stroud, Robert M., ed. 2007. (RSC Biomolecular Sciences Ser.). (ENG., Illus.). 400p. 232.00 (978-0-85404-365-1(9)) Royal Society of Chemistry, The GBR. Dist: Ingram Pub. Services.

—Metal Ions in Life Sciences Set: Volumes 5, 6, 7, 8, 9. Sigel, Astrid et al, eds. 2011. (Metal Ions in Life Sciences Ser.). (ENG.). 2530p. 800.00 (978-1-84973-119-5(5)) Royal Society of Chemistry, The GBR. Dist: Ingram Pub. Services.

—Metal Ions in Life Sciences Set: Volumes 7, 8, 9. Sigel, Astrid et al, eds. 2011. (Metal Ions in Life Sciences Ser.). (ENG.). 1442p. 496.00 **(978-1-84973-117-1(9))** Royal Society of Chemistry, The GBR. Dist: Ingram Pub. Services.

—Preclinical Drug Discovery Vol. 1: High Throughput Screening & Compound Progression Strategies. Gul, Sheraz, ed. 2011. (RSC Drug Discovery Ser.). (ENG.). 288p. 195.00 **(978-1-84973-134-8(9))** Royal Society of Chemistry, The GBR. Dist: Ingram Pub. Services.

Rudroff, Florian. Enzymatic Baeyer-Villiger Oxidation for Natural Product Synthesis. 2008. 200p. pap. (978-3-639-02093-9(6)) VDM Verlag Dr. Mueller e.K.

Ruiz, Antonio. Flow Through Optosensors. 2012. pap. **(978-1-61942-467-8(3))** Nova Science Pubs., Inc.

Sameer, Aga Syed. Aspects of Biochemistry. 2011. 228p. pap. **(978-3-8433-9269-3(2))** Lambert Academic Publishing.

Sampietro, Diego A., et al. Isolation, Identification & Characterization of Allelochemicals/Natural Products. 2009. (ENG., Illus.). 555p. 139.95 (978-1-57808-577-4(2)) BIOS Scientific Publishers Ltd. GBR. Dist: Taylor & Francis Group.

Sandberg, Kathryn & Mulroney, Susan E., eds. RNA Binding Proteins: New Concepts in Gene Regulation. 2010. (Endocrine Updates Ser.). 328p. pap. 228.00 (978-1-4419-4935-6(6), 1441949356) Springer.

Savitsky, Alexander P., et al. Small Animal Whole-Body Optical Imaging Based on Genetically Engineered Probes: 21-22 January 2008, San Jose, California, USA. 2008. (Proceedings of SPIE Ser.). (Illus.). 164p. pap. 70.00 (978-0-8194-7043-0(0)) SPIE.

Sawyer, Tomi K., ed. Chemical Biology: Concepts, Methods & Tools for Drug Discovery. 2010. (Methods & Principles in Medicinal Chemistry Ser.). 400p. 200.00 (978-3-527-32298-5(1), Wiley-VCH) Wiley, John & Sons, Inc.

Schmid, Rolf D., et al, eds. Modern Biooxidation: Enzymes, Reactions & Applications. 2007. (ENG., Illus.). 318p. 225.00 (978-3-527-31507-9(1), Wiley-VCH) Wiley, John & Sons, Inc.

Schomburg, Dietmar & Michal, Gerhard. Biochemical Pathways: An Atlas of Biochemistry & Molecular Biology. 2nd ed. 2012. (ENG., Illus.). 400p. 125.00 (978-0-470-14684-2(2), Wiley) Wiley, John & Sons, Inc.

Schügerl, Karl & Zeng, A. P., eds. Tools & Applications of Biochemical Engineering Science. 2010. (Advances in Biochemical Engineering Biotechnology Ser.). (Illus.). xviii, 274p. pap. 349.00 (978-3-642-07598-8(3), 3642075983) Springer.

Schulz, Stefan. The Chemistry of Pheromones & Other Semiochemicals I. 2010. (Topics in Current Chemistry Ser.). xii, 239p. pap. 299.00 (978-3-642-05872-1(8), 3642058728) Springer.

Schulz, Stefan, ed. The Chemistry of Pheromones & Other Semiochemicals II. 2010. (Topics in Current Chemistry Ser.). ix, 333p. pap. 369.00 (978-3-642-05964-3(3), 3642059643) Springer.

Schweda, F., et al, contrib. by. Reviews of Physiology, Biochemistry & Pharmacology. 2009. (Reviews of Physiology, Biochemistry & Pharmacology Ser.). (ENG.). 200p. 189.00 (978-3-540-87628-1(6), 3540876286) Springer.

Scott, Thomas & Eagleson, Mary. Concise Encyclopedia Biochemistry. 2nd ed. (ENG.). VIII, 649p. 196.00 **(978-3-11-179978-0(6))** De Gruyter, Walter Inc.

Semenza, Giorgio. Stories of Success: Personal Recollections. X. 2007. (Comprehensive Biochemistry Ser.: 45). (ENG., Illus.). 374p. 215.00 (978-0-444-52246-7(8), Elsevier Science) Elsevier Science & Technology Bks.

—Stories of Success: Personal Recollections XI. 2008. (Comprehensive Biochemistry Ser.: 46). (ENG., Illus.). 596p. 185.00 (978-0-444-53225-1(0), Elsevier Science) Elsevier Science & Technology Bks.

Sener, Bilge, ed. Innovations in Chemical Biology. 2008. (ENG., Illus.). xliv, 428p. 239.00 (978-1-4020-6954-3(5), 1402069545) Springer.

Senesi, Nicola & Wilkinson, Kevin J., eds. Biophysical Chemistry of Fractal Structures & Processes in Environmental Systems. 2008. (Series on Analytical & Physical Chemistry of Environmental Systems Ser.). (ENG., Illus.). 340p. 320.00 (978-0-470-01474-5(1), Wiley) Wiley, John & Sons, Inc.

Serganov, Alexander. Riboswitches: Methods & Protocols. 2009. (Illus.). xi, 365p. E-Book (978-1-59745-558-9(X)) Humana Pr.

Shah, Muhammad Ghani, et al. A Central Asaian Medicanal Plant Primula MacRophylla D Don. 2010. 164p. pap. (978-3-639-26393-0(6)) VDM Verlag Dr. Mueller e.K.

Sharpe, Philip C., et al, contrib. by. Reviews of Physiology, Biochemistry & Pharmacology, Vol. 159. 2007. (Reviews of Physiology, Biochemistry & Pharmacology Ser.). (Illus.). 189p. 189.00 (978-3-540-73799-5(5), 3540737995) Springer.

Shartava, Tsisana. Biological Aspects of Human Health & Well-Being. 2011. (Medicine & Biology Research Developments (Series Editor - Tsisana Shartava, M. D. - Tbilisi, Georgia) Ser.). 129.00 (978-1-61209-134-1(2)) Nova Science Pubs., Inc.

—Ligands, Polymers & Amino Acids. 2011. (Biochemistry Research Trends Ser.). 89.00 (978-1-61122-793-2(3), Nova Biomedical Bks.) Nova Science Pubs., Inc.

Sheehan, David. Physical Biochemistry: Principles & Applications. 2nd rev. ed. 2009. (ENG., Illus.). 422p. 199.95 (978-0-470-85602-4(5)); pap. 99.95 (978-0-470-85603-1(3)) Wiley, John & Sons, Inc. (Wiley).

Shishkina, Ludmila N., et al. Handbook of Chemistry, Biochemistry & Biology: New Frontiers. 2009. 195.00 (978-1-60741-861-0(4)) Nova Science Pubs., Inc.

Shukla, Girish. Soil Enzymology. Shukla, Girish & Varma, Ajit, eds. 2010. (Soil Biology Ser.). (ENG., Illus.). xvi, 385p. 209.00 (978-3-642-14224-6(9), 3642142249) Springer.

Siebert, F., et al. Vibrational Spectroscopy in Life Science. 2007. (Tutorials in Biophysics Ser.). (ENG.). 320p. 150.00 (978-3-527-40506-0(2), Wiley-VCH) Wiley, John & Sons, Inc.

Sigel, Astrid, et al, eds. Metal Ions in Life Sciences Set: Volumes 8, 9. 2011. (Metal Ions in Life Sciences Ser.). (ENG.). 834p. 320.00 **(978-1-84973-118-8(7))** Royal Society of Chemistry, The GBR. Dist: Ingram Pub. Services.

Sigel, Helmut, et al. Metal Ions in Life Sciences, 3 vols., Set. 2007. (ENG.). 1912p. 1200.00 (978-0-470-51324-8(1), Wiley) Wiley, John & Sons, Inc.

Simanjuntak, Tiurma Pt. The Indonesia's Preliminary Anti Salmonella Typhi Research: Anti Salmonella Typhi Activities of Non Aqueous Camellia Sinensis Crude Extract. 2011. 52p. pap. **(978-3-639-32439-6(0))** VDM Verlag Dr. Mueller e.K.

Simeonov, Lubomir I., et al, eds. Environmental Heavy Metal Pollution & Effects on Child Mental Development: Risk Assessment & Prevention Strategies. 2010. (NATO Science for Peace & Security Series C: Environmental Security

Ser.). xx, 361p. 229.00 *(978-94-007-0252-3(3)*, 9400702523); (ENG.). pap. 119.00 *(978-94-007-0255-4(8)*, 9400702558) Springer.

Simon, Melvin I. Biothermodynamics, Part C. 2011. (ENG., Illus.). 401p. 187.00 *(978-0-12-381268-1(2)*, Academic Pr.) Elsevier Science & Technology Bks.

Simon, Melvin I., et al. Two-Component Signaling Systems, Part C. 2010. (ENG., Illus.). 496p. 187.00 *(978-0-12-381347-3(6)*, Academic Pr.) Elsevier Science & Technology Bks.

Simonneaux, Gerard, ed. Bioorganometallic Chemistry. 2010. (Topics in Organometallic Chemistry Ser.). x, 222p. pap. 319.00 *(978-3-642-06958-1(4)*, 3642069584) Springer.

Smith, Janice. General Organic & Biological Chemistry. 2009. (ENG.). (C). ring bd., ring bd. 147.33 *(978-0-07-736666-7(2)*, 0077366662, McGraw-Hill Science, Engineering & Mathematics) McGraw-Hill Higher Education.

Smith, Janice Gorzynski. Loose Leaf Version for Principles of General, Organic, & Biochemistry. 2011. (ENG.). (C). ring bd. 130.00 *(978-0-07-743138-9(3)*, 0077431383, McGraw-Hill Science, Engineering & Mathematics) McGraw-Hill Higher Education.

—Package: Principles of General, Organic & Biochemistry. 2011. (ENG.). (C). 194.66 *(978-0-07-746845-3(7)*, 0077468457, McGraw-Hill Science, Engineering & Mathematics) McGraw-Hill Higher Education.

—Principles of General, Organic, & Biological Chemistry. 2011. (ENG., Illus.). 736p. (C). 185.67 *(978-0-07-351115-3(3)*, 0073511153, McGraw-Hill Science, Engineering & Mathematics) McGraw-Hill Higher Education.

—Student Study Guide/Solutions Manual for Principles of General, Organic & Biochemistry. 2011. (ENG.). 384p. (C). pap. 61.67 *(978-0-07-738562-0(4)*, 0077385624, McGraw-Hill Science, Engineering & Mathematics) McGraw-Hill Higher Education.

Stanforth, Stephen P. Natural Product Chemistry at a Glance. 2006. (Chemistry at a Glance Ser.). (ENG., Illus.). 152p. pap. 39.99 *(978-1-4051-4562-6(5)*, Wiley-Blackwell) Wiley, John & Sons, Inc.

Stoker, H. Stephen. General, Organic & Biological Chemistry. 4th ed. 2006. (ENG.). 432p. (C). pap., lab manual ed. 110.95 *(978-0-618-60608-5(4)*, 354232) Brooks/Cole.

Strehl, Robert. Finite Elemente Methoden mit Anwendung auf Probleme der Chemotaxis: Betrachtungen von Blow-Up, Aggregation und Musterbildung. 2010. 84p. pap. *(978-3-639-26017-5(1))* VDM Verlag Dr. Mueller e.K.

Suckling, Colin J., ed. Principles & Applications of Chemical Biology. 2009. (Illus.). 320p. *(978-1-4051-3333-3(3)*, Wiley-Blackwell) Wiley, John & Sons, Ltd.

Sun, RunCang. Cereal Straw As a Resource for Sustainable Biomaterials & Biofuels: Chemistry, Extractives, Lignins, Hemicelluloses & Cellulose. 2010. (ENG., Illus.). 300p. 275.00 *(978-0-444-53234-3(X))* Elsevier Science & Technology Bks.

Suryo Rahmanto, Adwin & Davies, Michael. Molecular Mechanisms of Photo-Oxidative Damage in Cells. 2011. 284p. pap. ***(978-3-8443-2712-0(6))*** Lambert Academic Publishing.

Teich, Mikulas & Needham, Dorothy. A Documentary History of Biochemistry, 1770-1940. (Illus.). 756p. *(978-0-7185-1341-2(X)*, Burns & Oates) Continuum International Publishing Group, Ltd.

Timberlake, Karen C. Chemistry: An Introduction to General, Organic, & Biological Chemistry with MasteringChemistry(r). 11th rev. ed. 2011. (ENG.). 744p. (C). 194.07 *(978-0-321-74104-2(8)*, Prentice Hall) Prentice Hall PTR.

Timbrell, John A. Biochemical Toxicology. 4th rev. ed. 2008. (ENG., Illus.). 464p. 100.00 *(978-0-8493-7302-2(6))* CRC Pr. LLC.

Toone, Eric J., ed. Advances in Enzymology & Related Areas of Molecular Biology, Volume 78. 2011. (Advances in Enzymology - & Related Areas of Molecular Biology Ser.: 240). (ENG.). 568p. 125.00 *(978-1-118-01428-8(6)*, Wiley) Wiley, John & Sons, Inc.

Toy, Eugene C., et al. Biochemistry. 2nd ed. 2008. (Lange Case Files Ser). (ENG., Illus.). 456p. (C). pap. 34.95 *(978-0-07-148665-1(8)*, 0071486658) McGraw-Hill Medical Publishing Div.

Trimm, Harold H. & Hunter, William, 3rd, eds. Recent Advances in Biochemistry. 2011. (ENG.). 308p. 99.95 *(978-1-926692-72-2(1))* Apple Academic Pr., Inc. CAN. Dist: Taylor & Francis Group.

Tro, Nivaldo J. Chemistry: A Molecular Approach. 2nd ed. 2010. (ENG.). 1224p. (C). 222.00 *(978-0-321-65178-5(2)*, Prentice Hall) Prentice Hall PTR.

Tymoczko, John L., et al. Biochemistry: A Short Course. (ENG.). (C). 2009. 720p. pap. 162.95 *(978-0-7167-5840-2(7))* 2nd ed. 2011. 800p. 162.95 ***(978-1-4292-8360-1(2))*** Freeman, W. H. & Co.

Tymoczko, John L., et al. Biochemistry: A Short Course (Loose Leaf) 2nd ed. 2011. (ENG.). 800p. (C). 105.95 ***(978-1-4641-0486-2(7))*** Freeman, W. H. & Co.

Urich, Klaus. Comparative Animal Biochemistry. King, P. J., tr. from GER. 2010. (ENG., Illus.). xvii, 782p. pap. 206.00 *(978-3-642-08181-1(9)*, 3642081819) Springer.

Valentine, Joan Selverstone. Biological Inorganic Chemistry: Structure & Reactivity. 2006. (Illus.). 739p. 98.25 *(978-1-891389-43-6(2))* Univ. Science Bks.

van Dooren, Tom. Biochemical & Immuno-Histochemical Analysis of APP-Processing & Amyloid Pathology in Single & Multiple Transgenic Mice as Models for Alzheimer's Disease. 2006. (Acta Biomedica Lovaniensia Ser.: Vol. 365). (Illus.). pap. 97.50 *(978-90-5867-544-6(0))* Leuven Univ. Pr. BEL. Dist: Cornell Univ. Pr.

Varfolomeev, Sergei Dmitrevich. Biochemical Physics Frontal Research. 2006. 133p. 225.00 *(978-1-60021-425-7(8))* Nova Science Pubs., Inc.

—New Trends in Biochemical Physics Research. 2006. (Illus.). 128p. (C). 225.00 *(978-1-60021-463-9(0))* Nova Science Pubs., Inc.

—Trends in Biochemical Physics Research. 2007. 89.00 *(978-1-60021-426-4(6))* Nova Science Pubs., Inc.

Vastiau, Ilse. In Vitro & In Vivo Analysis of the Role of PEX 19P Farnesylation & PEX 14P Phosphorylation in Peroxisome Biogenesis. 2006. (Illus.). 88p. (Orig.). pap. 57.50 *(978-90-5867-579-8(3))* Leuven Univ. Pr. BEL. Dist: Cornell Univ. Pr.

Vasudevan, D. M. Mini Atlas of Biochemistry. 2007. (Anshan Gold Standard Mini Atlas Ser.). (ENG., Illus.). 350p. pap. 34.95 *(978-1-905740-04-8(2))* Anshan GBR. Dist: Publishers Storage & Shipping.

Vazquez-Duhalt, R., ed. Environmental Biotransformations: A Written Symposium. 2008. (Illus.). 154p. pap. *(978-3-8055-8513-2(6))* Karger, S. AG.

Vermerris, Wilfred & Nicholson, Ralph. Phenolic Compound Biochemistry. 2006. (ENG., Illus.). xii, 276p. 179.00 *(978-1-4020-5163-0(8)*, 1402051638) Springer.

Visockiene, Zydrune. Energy Metabolism in Obesity & Diabetes. 2010. 176p. pap. *(978-3-8383-0300-0(8))* Lambert Academic Publishing.

Visscher, Maurice B. Chemistry & Medicine: Papers Presented at the Fiftieth Anniversary of the Founding of the Medical School of the University of Minnesota. 2009. (ENG.). 308p. pap. 60.00 *(978-0-8166-5941-8(9))* Univ. of Minnesota Pr.

Vivanco, Jorge M. & Weir, Tiffany, eds. Chemical Biology of the Tropics: An Interdisciplinary Approach. 2011. (Signaling & Communication in Plants Ser.). ix, 115p. 139.00 *(978-3-642-19079-7(0)*, 3642190790) Springer.

Vladimirov, Nikita, et al. Multiscale Modeling of Bacterial Chemotaxis. 2010. 132p. pap. *(978-3-8383-4246-7(1))* Lambert Academic Publishing.

Voet. Fundamentals of Biochemistry: With Student Companion Take Notes & MCAT Sample Test Set. stu. ed. 115.00 *(978-0-471-38128-0(4))* Wiley, John & Sons, Inc.

Voet & Pratt, Charlotte W. Fundamentals of Biochemistry 3E Take Note! 3rd ed. 2008. (Illus.). 14.95 *(978-0-470-22843-2(1))* Wiley, John & Sons, Inc.

Voet, et al. Fundamentals of Biochemistry: Life at the Molecular Level. (ENG.). (C). 3rd ed. 2008. Illus.). 360p. pap., stu. ed. 78.95 *(978-0-470-22842-5(3))* 3rd ed. 2008. ring bd. 143.95 *(978-0-470-27989-2(3))* 3rd ed. 2008. (Illus.). 1240p. 221.95 *(978-0-470-12930-2(1))* 4th ed. 2012. (Illus.). 1200p. 221.95 *(978-0-470-54784-7(7))* Wiley, John & Sons, Inc. (Wiley).

Voet, Donald & Voet, Judith G. Biochemistry. 4th ed. 2010. (ENG., Illus.). 1520p. (C). 244.95 *(978-0-470-57095-1(4)*, Wiley) Wiley, John & Sons, Inc.

—Biochemistry. 4th ed. 2011. (ENG.). 240p. (C). pap. 79.95 *(978-1-118-00814-0(6)*, Wiley) Wiley, John & Sons, Inc.

—Biochemistry, Fourth Edition Binder Ready Version. 4th ed. 2010. (ENG., Illus.). 1248p. (C). ring bd. 147.95 *(978-0-470-91745-9(8)*, Wiley) Wiley, John & Sons, Inc.

Voet, Donald, et al. The Bar & Beverage Book. 5th ed. 2012. (ENG., Illus.). 736p. 89.95 *(978-0-470-24845-4(9)*, Wiley) Wiley, John & Sons, Inc.

Voet, Donald, et al. Student Companion to Accompany Fundamentals of Biochemistry. 4th ed. 2012. (ENG.). 424p. (C). pap. 83.95 ***(978-1-118-21827-3(2)***, Wiley) Wiley, John & Sons, Inc.

Volff, Jean-Nicolas & Lankenau, Dirk-Henner. Transposons & the Dynamic Genome. 2009. (Genome Dynamics & Stability Ser.). (ENG., Illus.). xvi, 184p. 239.00 *(978-3-642-02004-9(6)*, 3642020046) Springer.

Volk, Talila, ed. Post-Transcriptional Regulation by Star Proteins: Control of RNA Metabolism in Development & Disease. 2010. (Advances in Experimental Medicine & Biology Ser.). (ENG., Illus.). xviii, 162p. 219.00 *(978-1-4419-7004-6(5)*, 1441970045) Springer.

Walker, Sharon & McMahon, David. Biochemistry Demystified. 2008. (Demystified Ser.). (ENG., Illus.). 370p. pap. 21.95 *(978-0-07-149599-8(1)*, 0071495991) McGraw-Hill Professional Publishing.

Walla, Peter Jomo. Modern Biophysical Chemistry: Detection & Analysis of Biomolecules. 2009. (ENG., Illus.). 310p. pap. 67.00 *(978-3-527-32360-9(0)*, Wiley-VCH) Wiley, John & Sons, Inc.

Wang, Li-Wen. Directed Evolution of the Aspergillus Niger Epoxide Hydrolase. 2008. 100p. pap. *(978-3-639-06015-7(6))* VDM Verlag Dr. Mueller e.K.

Waring, R. H., et al, eds. Molecules of Death. 2nd ed. 2007. (Illus.). 400p. (C). 124.00 *(978-1-86094-814-5(6))* Imperial College Pr. GBR. Dist: World Scientific Publishing Co., Inc.

Waring, R. H., et al. Molecules of Death. 2nd ed. 2007. (Illus.). 430p. pap. 86.00 *(978-1-86094-815-2(4))* Imperial College Pr. GBR. Dist: World Scientific Publishing Co., Inc.

Water & Metal Cations. 93.50 *(978-0-89955-335-1(4))* Business Ctr. for Academic Societies JPN. Dist: International Specialized Bk. Services.

Werther, Meike & Seitz, Harald. Protein - Protein Interaction. 2010. (Advances in Biochemical Engineering Biotechnology Ser.). (Illus.). xiv, 272p. pap. 279.00 *(978-3-642-08838-4(4)*, 3642088384) Springer.

Williams, Timothy C., ed. Chemotaxis: Types, Clinical Significance, & Mathematical Models. 2010. (Cell Biology Research Progress Ser.). 99.00 *(978-1-61728-495-3(5))* Nova Science Pubs., Inc.

Williamson, Michael. How Proteins Work. 2011. (ENG., Illus.). 464p. pap. 105.00 *(978-0-8153-4446-9(5)*, Garland Science) Taylor & Francis Group.

Wilson, Keith & Walker, John, eds. Principles & Techniques of Biochemistry & Molecular Biology. 7th rev. ed. 2010. (ENG., Illus.). 760p. (C). pap. 73.00 *(978-0-521-73167-6(4))* Cambridge Univ. Pr.

Woodbury. Basic Biochemistry for Pharmacy. rev. ed. 2011. 500p. pap. 68.95 *(978-0-7637-6384-8(5))* Jones & Bartlett Learning, LLC.

Wu, Ge. Assay Development: Fundamentals & Practice. 2010. (ENG., Illus.). 429p. 147.00 *(978-0-470-19115-6(5)*, Wiley) Wiley, John & Sons, Inc.

Yalovsky, Shaul, et al, eds. Integrated G Proteins Signaling in Plants. 2009. (Signaling & Communication in Plants Ser.). (ENG., Illus.). x, 336p. 239.00 *(978-3-642-03523-4(X)*, 364203523X) Springer.

Yamanaka, Tateo. Chemolithoautotrophic Bacteria: Biochemistry & Environmental Biology. 2008. (ENG., Illus.). xiv, 157p. 189.00 *(978-4-431-78540-8(X)*, 443178540X) Springer.

Yildiz, Fatih, et al. Applied Food Biochemistry. 2009. (ENG., Illus.). 521p. 174.95 *(978-0-8493-7499-9(5)*, CRC Press) Taylor & Francis Group GBR. Dist: Taylor & Francis Group.

Zaikov, Gennadii Efremovich, ed. Progress in Chemical & Biochemical Physics, Kinetics & Thermodynamics. 2008. (C). 185.00 *(978-1-60456-079-4(7))* Nova Science Pubs., Inc.

—Success in Chemistry & Biochemistry Vol. 4: Mind's Flight in Time & Space. 2009. 139.00 *(978-1-60692-343-6(9))* Nova Science Pubs., Inc.

Zaikov, Gennady E., et al. Modern Problems in Biochemical Physics: New Horizons. 2012. (Biochemistry Research Trends Ser.). 349p. 129.00 ***(978-1-61324-003-8(1))*** Nova Science Pubs., Inc.

Zaikowski, Lori, et al, eds. Chemical Evolution II: From the Origins of Life to Modern Society, 1 vol. 2010. (ACS Symposium Ser.). (ENG., Illus.). 376p. 150.00 *(978-0-8412-6980-4(7))* American Chemical Society.

Zapanta, Laura S. A Roadmap to Success in Biochemistry: Extra Help for Confusing Topics. rev. ed. 2011. (ENG.). 92p. spiral bd. 42.00 ***(978-0-7575-9345-1(3))*** Kendall Hunt Publishing Co.

Zatta & Zatta, Paolo. Metallothioneins in Biochemistry & Pathology. 2008. 146.00 *(978-981-277-893-2(4))* World Scientific Publishing Co., Inc.

Zeidler, Ute. Expression und Reinigung des GimC-Komplexes: Im Modellorganismus Saccharomyces cerevisiae. 2009. 112p. pap. *(978-3-639-20092-8(6))* VDM Verlag Dr. Mueller e.K.

Zewail. Physical Biology. 2008. (Illus.). 450p. (C). 177.00 *(978-1-84816-199-3(9))*; pap. 88.00 *(978-1-84816-200-6(6))* Imperial College Pr. GBR. Dist: World Scientific Publishing Co., Inc.

BIOCHEMISTRY—CONGRESSES

Cuyper, M. de & Bulte, Jeff W. M., eds. Physics & Chemistry Basis of Biotechnology. 2010. (Focus on Biotechnology Ser.). (Illus.). 340p. pap. 239.00 *(978-90-481-5741-9(2)*, 9048157412) Springer.

Proceedings from the 11th Annual International Conference on the Biochemistry of Exercise: Special issue of the International Journal of Sport Nutrition & Exercise Metabolism, Volume 11, Supplement 2001. 232p. 14.00 *(978-0-7360-4186-7(9))* Human Kinetics Pubs.

BIOCHEMISTRY—DICTIONARIES

Atwood, Teresa, et al. Oxford Dictionary of Biochemistry & Molecular Biology. Cammack, Richard, ed. 2nd rev. ed. 2006. (ENG., Illus.). 736p. 125.00 *(978-0-19-852917-0(1))* Oxford Univ. Pr., Inc.

Begley, Tadhg P. Chemical Biology, 4 vols. (ENG., Illus.). Set. 2009. 3204p. 1620.00 *(978-0-471-75477-0(3)*, Wiley-Interscience) Vol. 1. 2008. 742p. 348.00 *(978-0-471-75399-5(8)*, Wiley) Wiley, John & Sons, Inc.

—Wiley Encyclopedia of Chemical Biology, 4 vols., Vol. 4. 2009. (ENG., Illus.). 810p. 348.00 *(978-0-470-47020-6(8)*, Wiley) Wiley, John & Sons, Inc.

English-Japanese/Japanese-English Dictionary on Biochemistry. (ENG & JPN.). 95.00 *(978-0-7859-9691-0(5))* French & European Pubns., Inc.

Singleton, Paul. Dictionary of DNA & Genome Technology. 2nd ed. 2010. (ENG., Illus.). 426p. 149.95 *(978-0-470-74732-2(3))*; pap. 57.95 *(978-0-470-74731-5(5))* Wiley, John & Sons, Inc. (Wiley).

BIOCHEMISTRY—EXAMINATIONS, QUESTIONS, ETC.

Berg, Jeremy M., et al. Biochemistry Student Companion. 7th ed. 2011. (ENG.). 608p. (C). pap. 60.95 *(978-1-4292-3115-2(7))* Freeman, W. H. & Co.

Coomes, Marguerite Wilton, et al. GRE Biochemistry, Cell & Molecular Biology. 2nd ed. 2010. (GRE Test Preparation Ser.). (ENG.). 368p. (C). pap. 42.95 *(978-0-7386-0834-1(3))* Research & Education Assn.

Cox, Lynne, et al. Thrive in Biochemistry & Molecular Biology. 2012. (ENG., Illus.). 336p. pap. 69.95 ***(978-0-19-964548-0(5))*** Oxford Univ. Pr., Inc.

Cram101 Textbook Reviews Staff. Outlines & Highlights for Lippincotts Illustrated Reviews: Biochemistry by Pamela C Champe, Richard A Harvey, Denise R Ferrier, ISBN. 2009. 418p. pap. 35.95 *(978-1-4288-8296-6(0))* Cram101 Inc.

Harvey, Richard A. & Ferrier, Denise R. Biochemistry. 5th ed. 2010. (Lippincott's Illustrated Reviews Ser.). (ENG.). 544p. pap. 68.99 *(978-1-60831-412-6(X))* Lippincott Williams & Wilkins.

Lieberman, Michael A. & Ricer, Rick. Biochemistry. 2009. (Lippincott's Illustrated Q&a Review Ser.). (ENG., Illus.). 224p. pap. 44.99 *(978-1-60547-302-4(2))* Lippincott Williams & Wilkins.

Manzoul, Saad M. & Mohammed, Hussan. Biochemistry. 2nd ed. 2010. (Deja Review Ser.). (ENG., Illus.). 206p. (C). pap. 21.00 *(978-0-07-162717-7(0)*, 0071627170) McGraw-Hill Medical Publishing Div.

Pelley, John W. & Goljan, Edward F. Biochemistry. 3rd ed. 2010. (Rapid Review Ser.). (ENG., Illus.). 208p. (C). pap. 39.95 *(978-0-323-06887-1(1)*, Mosby) Elsevier - Health Sciences Div.

Smith, Mike. Chemistry: Equilibria, Energetics & Elements. 2009. 112p. pap., stu. ed. 22.50 *(978-0-340-95759-2(X))* Hodder Education GBR. Dist: Trans-Atlantic Pubns., Inc.

Swanson, Todd A., et al. Biochemistry, Molecular Biology, & Genetics. 5th rev. ed. 2009. (Board Review Ser.). (ENG., Illus.). 432p. pap. 45.99 *(978-0-7817-9875-4(2))* Lippincott Williams & Wilkins.

Wilson, Golder N. Biochemistry & Genetics. 4th ed. 2010. (PreTest Basic Science Ser.). (ENG., Illus.). 545p. (C). pap. 33.00 *(978-0-07-162348-3(5)*, 0071623485) McGraw-Hill Medical Publishing Div.

BIOCHEMISTRY—LABORATORY MANUALS

Bettelheim, Frederick A., et al. Lab Experiments for Organic & Biochemistry. 6th ed. 2007. (Illus.). xxiii, 554p. *(978-0-495-10656-2(9))*; *(978-0-495-18998-5(7))* Brooks/Cole.

Boyer, Rodney F. Biochemistry Laboratory: Modern Theory & Techniques. 2nd ed. 2010. (ENG.). 384p. (C). pap. 79.60 *(978-0-13-604302-7(X)*, Prentice Hall) Prentice Hall PTR.

Davenport, Anthony P., ed. Receptor Binding Techniques. (Methods in Molecular Biology Ser.). (Illus.). 2nd ed. 2010. 256p. pap. 139.00 *(978-1-61737-556-9(X)*, 161737556X) 3rd ed. 2012. (ENG., xxiv, 324p. 119.00 ***(978-1-61779-908-2(4)***, 1617799084) Humana Pr.

Giezen, Mark van der, ed. Protein Targeting Protocols. 2nd ed. 2010. (Methods in Molecular Biology Ser.). (Illus.). xv, 501p. pap. 179.00 *(978-1-61737-727-3(9)*, 1617377279) Humana Pr.

Hein, Morris, et al. Introduction to General Organic & Biochemistry. 10th ed. 2011. (ENG.). 512p. (C). pap., lab manual ed. 142.95 *(978-0-470-59881-6(6)*, Wiley) Wiley, John & Sons, Inc.

Landesberg, Joseph M. eneral, Organic, & Biochemistry - Laboratory Experiments. 2011. (ENG.). 256p. (C). pap. 69.95 *(978-1-111-42661-3(9))* Brooks/Cole.

Macaulay, David B., et al. General, Organic & Biological Chemistry: An Integrated Approach. 2nd ed. 2009. (ENG.). 344p. (C). pap., lab manual ed. 88.95 *(978-0-470-56171-3(8)*, Wiley) Wiley, John & Sons, Inc.

Mellick, Albert S. & Rodgers, Linda, eds. Lab Ref, Volume 2: A Handbook of Recipes, Reagents, & Other Reference Tools for Use at the Bench. 2006. (ENG., Illus.). 248p. spiral bd. 40.00 *(978-0-87969-815-7(2))* Cold Spring Harbor Laboratory Pr.

Narayan, Mahesh. Biochemistry Laboratory Manual. rev. ed. 2011. (ENG.). 32p. spiral bd. 30.75 *(978-1-60250-182-9(3))* Kendall Hunt Publishing Co.

Ninfa, Alexander J., et al. Fundamental Laboratory Approaches for Biochemistry & Biotechnology. 2nd ed. 2009. (ENG., Illus.). 480p. (C). pap. 93.95 *(978-0-470-08766-4(8)*, Wiley) Wiley, John & Sons, Inc.

Poole, Robert K., ed. Globins & Other Nitric Oxide-Reactive Proteins, Part A, 2 vols. 2008. (Methods in Enzymology Ser.). (ENG., Illus.). 672p. 187.00 *(978-0-12-374277-3(3)*, Academic Pr.) Elsevier Science & Technology Bks.

—Globins & Other Nitric Oxide-Reactive Proteins, Part B, 2 vols. 2008. (Methods in Enzymology Ser.). (ENG., Illus.). 712p. 187.00 *(978-0-12-374278-0(1)*, Academic Pr.) Elsevier Science & Technology Bks.

Rorer, Jeffrey R. Laboratory Manual for Basic Biological Chemistry. rev. ed. 2006. (ENG.). 86p. spiral bd. 44.45 *(978-0-7575-3059-3(1))* Kendall Hunt Publishing Co.

Selfe, Sara, et al. General, Organic, & Biochemistry. 2009. (ENG.). 285p. (C). pap., lab manual ed. 54.95 *(978-1-4292-2433-8(9))* Freeman, W. H. & Co.

Tainsky, Michael A. Tumor Biomarker Discovery: Methods & Protocols. 2009. (Illus.). xi, 332p. E-Book *(978-1-60327-811-9(7))* Humana Pr.

Timberlake, Karen C. Lab Manual for General, Organic, & Biological Chemistry. 2nd ed. 2010. (ENG.). 624p. (C). pap. 97.40 *(978-0-321-69529-1(1)*, Prentice Hall) Prentice Hall PTR.

Van der Giezen, Mark. Protein Targeting Protocols. 2nd ed. 2007. (Methods in Molecular Biology Ser.). (Illus.). XV, 501p. 179.00 *(978-1-58829-702-0(0)*, 1588297020) Humana Pr.

Wenk, Markus R. & Fernandis, Aaron Z. A Manual for Biochemistry Protocols. 2007. (Manuals in Biomedical Research Ser.). (Illus.). 127p. spiral bd. 47.00 *(978-981-270-066-7(8))* World Scientific Publishing Co., Inc.

BIOCHEMISTRY—MATHEMATICAL MODELS

Fatumo, Segun. Computational Analysis of Biochemical Networks. 2010. 148p. pap. *(978-3-639-24714-5(0))* VDM Verlag Dr. Mueller e.K.

Krishna, Ritesh. Derivation of Process Algebraic Models of Biochemical Systems. 2009. 144p. pap. *(978-3-639-20018-8(7))* VDM Verlag Dr. Mueller e.K.

Lecca, Paola & Laurenzi, Ian. Deterministic Versus Stochastic Modelling in Biochemistry & Systems Biology. 2012. 250p. 165.00 ***(978-1-907568-62-8(X))*** Woodhead Publishing Ltd. GBR. Dist: Ingram Pub. Services.

Schuster, Stefan. Theoretical Systems Biology of Metabolism: Mathematical Modelling of Biochemical Networks. 2013. (ENG., Illus.). 400p. 199.00 *(978-3-211-78268-2(0)*, 3211782680) Springer.

BIOCHEMISTRY—OUTLINES, SYLLABI, ETC.

Blel & Odian & Cram101 Textbook Reviews Staff. General, Organic, & Biochemistry. 2007. 284p. per. 15.95 *(978-1-4288-2932-9(6))* Cram101 Inc.

Cram101 Textbook Reviews. Outlines & Highlights for Biochemical Calculations: How to Solve Mathematical Problems in General Biochemistry by Irwin H. Segel. 2011. 90p. pap. 27.95 ***(978-1-61905-985-6(1))*** Cram101 Inc.

—Outlines & Highlights for Biochemistry: Molecular Basics of Life by Trudy Mckee, ISBN. 2011. 382p. pap. 34.95 ***(978-1-61490-423-6(5))*** Cram101 Inc.

—Outlines & Highlights for Biochemistry & Molecular Biology by William H Elliott, Isbn: 9780199226719 0199226717. 2011. 226p. pap. 30.95 ***(978-1-61490-431-1(6))*** Cram101 Inc.

—Outlines & Highlights for Biochemistry by Jeremy M Berg, Lubert Stryer, John L Tymoczko, Isbn: 9780716787242. 2010. 478p. pap. 37.95 *(978-1-61698-617-9(4))* Cram101 Inc.

—Outlines & Highlights for Concepts in Biochemistry, with the Interactive Concepts in Biochemistry by Rodney F Boyer, Isbn: 9780471661795. 2010. 238p. pap. 31.95 *(978-1-61698-616-2(6))* Cram101 Inc.

—Outlines & Highlights for Essentials of Biochemistry by Charlotte W Pratt, Kathleen Cornely, Isbn: 9780471393870. 2010. 344p. pap. 33.95 *(978-1-61698-603-2(4))* Cram101 Inc.

B

—Outlines & Highlights for Essentials of Chemical Biology by Andrew D Miller, Isbn: 9780470845318 0470845317. 2011. 246p. pap. 31.95 ***(978-1-61490-245-4(3))*** Cram101 Inc.

—Outlines & Highlights for Essentials of General, Organic, & Biological Chemistry by H Stephen Stoker, Sharon K Stoffels, Isbn: 9780618192823. 2010. 154p. pap. 29.95 *(978-1-61698-613-1(1))* Cram101 Inc.

—Outlines & Highlights for General Organic & Biochemistry: Connecting Chemistry to Your Life by Ira Blei, George Odian, ISBN. 2010. 240p. pap. 31.95 *(978-1-61698-607-0(7))* Cram101 Inc.

—Outlines & Highlights for General, Organic, & Biological Chemistry: Structures of Life by Timberlake, Karen. 2010. 680p. pap. 41.95 *(978-1-4288-5324-9(3))* Cram101 Inc.

—Outlines & Highlights for General, Organic, & Biological Chemistry by H Stephen Stoker, Isbn: 9780547152813 0547152817. 2011. 560p. pap. 38.95 ***(978-1-61490-182-2(1))*** Cram101 Inc.

—Outlines & Highlights for General, Organic, & Biological Chemistry by Janice Gorzynski Smith, Isbn: 9780077274290. 2010. 302p. pap. 32.95 *(978-1-61698-554-7(2))* Cram101 Inc.

—Outlines & Highlights for General Organic & Biological Chemistry by Kenneth W Raymond, Isbn: 9780470504765 0470504765. 2011. 366p. pap. 34.95 ***(978-1-61490-185-3(6))*** Cram101 Inc.

—Outlines & Highlights for General, Organic, & Biological Chemistry by Laura D Frost, Isbn: 9780805381788 0805381783. 2011. 272p. pap. 32.95 ***(978-1-61490-181-5(3))*** Cram101 Inc.

—Outlines & Highlights for Introduction to General, Organic & Biochemistry in the Laboratory by Leo R Best, Morris Hein, Scott Pattison, Susan Aren. 2010. 202p. pap. 30.95 *(978-1-61698-610-0(7))* Cram101 Inc.

—Outlines & Highlights for Lippincotts Illustrated Reviews: Biochemistry by Pamela C Champe, Richard A Harvey, Denise R Ferrier, ISBN. 2010. (Illus.). 478p. pap. 37.95 *(978-1-61698-604-9(2))* Cram101 Inc.

—Outlines & Highlights for Organic & Biochemistry for Today by Spencer L Seager, Michael R Slabaugh, Isbn. 2010. 82p. pap. 27.95 *(978-1-61698-612-4(3))* Cram101 Inc.

Cram101 Textbook Reviews. Outlines & Highlights for Organic & Biological Chemistry by H Stephen Stoker. 2011. 442p. pap. 36.95 ***(978-1-61905-782-1(4))*** Cram101 Inc.

Cram101 Textbook Reviews & Cram101 Textbook Reviews. Outlines & Highlights for Introduction to Organic & Biochemistry by Frederick a Bettelheim, Isbn: 9780495391166 0495391166. 2011. 278p. pap. 32.95 ***(978-1-61490-783-1(8))*** Cram101 Inc.

—Outlines Joseph J Topping; Robert L Caret, Isbn: 9780077354800 9780073. 2011. 268p. pap. 31.95 ***(978-1-61461-760-0(0))*** Cram101 Inc.

Cram101 Textbook Reviews Staff. Outlines & Highlights for Biochemistry by Berg, Isbn: 0716730510. 2007. 596p. pap. 22.95 *(978-1-4288-3034-9(0))* Cram101 Inc.

—Outlines & Highlights for Biochemistry by Campbell, Isbn. 2008. 256p. pap. 14.95 *(978-1-4288-5884-8(9))*; 244p. pap. 14.95 *(978-1-4288-5882-4(2))* Cram101 Inc.

—Outlines & Highlights for Biochemistry by Garrett, Isbn: 0495121121. 2008. 332p. pap. 16.95 *(978-1-4288-6113-8(0))* Cram101 Inc.

—Outlines & Highlights for Biochemistry by Jeremy M Berg, Lubert Stryer, John L Tymoczko, Isbn: 9780716787242. 2009. 418p. pap. 35.95 *(978-1-4288-8153-2(0))* Cram101 Inc.

—Outlines & Highlights for Biochemistry by Reginald H Garrett, Isbn: 9780495109358. 2009. 318p. pap. 33.95 *(978-1-4288-8881-4(0))* Cram101 Inc.

—Outlines & Highlights for Biochemistry by Voet, Isbn: 047119350x. 2007. 732p. pap. 26.95 *(978-1-4288-3030-1(8))* Cram101 Inc.

—Outlines & Highlights for Concepts in Biochemistry, with the Interactive Concepts in Biochemistry by Rodney F Boyer, Isbn: 9780471661795. 2009. 208p. pap. 30.95 *(978-1-4288-8154-9(9))* Cram101 Inc.

—Outlines & Highlights for Foundations of General, Organic, & Biochemistry by Denniston, Isbn: 0073511064. 2007. 128p. per. 11.95 *(978-1-4288-5732-2(X))* Cram101 Inc.

—Outlines & Highlights for Fundamentals of Biochemistry: Life at the Molecular Level by Charlotte W. Pratt, Judith G. Voet, Donald J. Voet, ISBN. 2009. 416p. pap. 35.95 *(978-1-4288-8156-3(5))* Cram101 Inc.

—Outlines & Highlights for General, Organic, & Biochemistry by Katherine J Denniston, Isbn: 9780077221416. 2009. 412p. pap. 35.95 *(978-1-4288-8682-7(6))* Cram101 Inc.

—Outlines & Highlights for General, Organic, & Biological Chemistry: An Integrated Approach by Kenneth W. Raymond, ISBN. 2009. 136p. pap. 28.95 *(978-1-4288-8297-3(9))* Cram101 Inc.

—Outlines & Highlights for General, Organic, & Biological Chemistry by H Stephen Stoker, Isbn: 9780618606061. 2009. 386p. pap. 34.95 *(978-1-4288-9657-4(0))* Cram101 Inc.

—Outlines & Highlights for Lippincotts Illustrated Reviews: Biochemistry by Pamela C Champe, Richard A Harvey, Denise R Ferrier, ISBN. 2009. 418p. pap. 35.95 *(978-1-4288-8296-6(0))* Cram101 Inc.

—Outlines & Highlights for Organic & Biochemistry, Chapters 10-23 from General, Organic, & Biochemistry by Katherine J Denniston, Isbn: 9780077240. 2009. 176p. pap. 29.95 *(978-1-4288-9054-1(8))* Cram101 Inc.

—Outlines & Highlights for Physical Chemistry: For the Biosciences by Raymond Chang, ISBN. 2009. 102p. pap. 27.95 *(978-1-4288-8178-5(6))* Cram101 Inc.

—Outlines & Highlights for Physical Chemistry: For the Chemical & Biological Sciences by Raymond Chang, ISBN. 2009. 80p. pap. 27.95 *(978-1-4288-8185-3(9))* Cram101 Inc.

—Outlines & Highlights for Principles of Biochemistry by David L Nelson, Michael M Cox, Isbn: 9780716771081. 2009. 544p. pap. 38.95 *(978-1-4288-8155-6(7))* Cram101 Inc.

—Outlines & Highlights for Principles of Biochemistry by Horton, Isbn: 0131453068. 2008. 348p. pap. 16.95 *(978-1-4288-6308-8(7))* Cram101 Inc.

—Outlines & Highlights for Principles of Physical Biochemistry by Holde, Isbn: 0130464279. 2008. 124p. pap. 11.95 *(978-1-4288-6312-5(5))* Cram101 Inc.

Harvey, Richard A. & Ferrier, Denise R. Biochemistry. 5th ed. 2010. (Lippincott's Illustrated Reviews Ser.). (ENG.). 544p. pap. 68.99 *(978-1-60831-412-6(X))* Lippincott Williams & Wilkins.

Kuchel, Philip & Ralston, Gregory B. Schaum's Easy Outline of Biochemistry, Revised Edition. 2011. (Schaum's Easy Outlines Ser.). (ENG.). 144p. (C). pap. 11.00 ***(978-0-07-177968-5(X)***, 007177968X) McGraw-Hill Cos., The.

Kuchel, Philip W., et al. Schaum's Outline of Biochemistry, Third Edition. 3rd rev. ed. 2011. (Schaum's Outline Ser.). (ENG., Illus.). 506p. pap. 21.95 *(978-0-07-147227-2(4)*, 0071472274) McGraw-Hill Cos., The.

Pelley, John W. & Goljan, Edward F. Biochemistry. 3rd ed. 2010. (Rapid Review Ser.). (ENG., Illus.). 208p. (C). pap. 39.95 *(978-0-323-06887-1(1)*, Mosby) Elsevier - Health Sciences Div.

Salway, J. G. Medical Biochemistry at a Glance. 3rd ed. 2012. (At a Glance Ser.). (ENG., Illus.). 176p. pap. 42.95 ***(978-0-470-65451-4(1)***, Wiley-Blackwell) Wiley, John & Sons, Inc.

Wilcox, R. Bruce. Biochemistry. 3rd rev. ed. 2009. (High-Yield Ser.). (ENG., Illus.). 128p. pap. 34.99 *(978-0-7817-9924-9(4))* Lippincott Williams & Wilkins.

BIOCHEMISTRY—PROBLEMS, EXERCISES, ETC.

Berg, Jeremy M., et al. Biochemistry Student Companion. 7th ed. 2011. (ENG.). 608p. (C). pap. 60.95 *(978-1-4292-3115-2(7))* Freeman, W. H. & Co.

Cox, et al. Lehninger Principles of Biochemistry. 5th ed. 2008. (Illus.). *(978-1-4292-1242-7(X))* Freeman, W. H. & Co.

Houghton, Toby & Woodward, Christine. AQA GCSE Science Biology. 2007. (Illus.). 240p. pap., stu. ed. 47.50 *(978-0-340-92797-7(6)*, Hodder Murray) Hodder Education GBR. Dist: Trans-Atlantic Pubns., Inc.

Knopp, James. Knopp's Knotes: A Biochemistry Workbook with Definitions Concepts Hints & Problems. 2010. 134p. spiral bd. 35.00 *(978-0-7575-8316-2(4))* Kendall Hunt Publishing Co.

Moorthy, Krish. Fundamentals of Biochemical Calculations. 2nd rev. ed. 2007. (ENG., Illus.). 192p. (C). per. 44.95 *(978-1-4200-5357-9(4)*, CRC Press) Taylor & Francis Group GBR. Dist: Taylor & Francis Group.

Swanson, Todd A., et al. Biochemistry. 5th rev. ed. 2007. (Underground Clinical Vignettes Ser.). (ENG., Illus.). 256p. per. 30.99 *(978-0-7817-6472-8(6))* Lippincott Williams & Wilkins.

BIOCHEMISTRY—RESEARCH

Baginski, Simon J., ed. Biochemistry Research Updates. 2011. (Biochemistry Research Trends Ser.). 129.00 *(978-1-61209-700-8(6))* Nova Science Pubs., Inc.

Davenport, Anthony P., ed. Receptor Binding Techniques. 2nd ed. 2010. (Methods in Molecular Biology Ser.). (Illus.). 256p. pap. 139.00 *(978-1-61737-556-9(X)*, 161737556X) Humana Pr.

MacDonald, Paul N., ed. Two-Hybrid Systems: Methods & Protocols. 2010. (Methods in Molecular Biology Ser.). (Illus.). 352p. pap. 149.00 *(978-1-61737-210-0(2)*, 1617372102) Humana Pr.

Sies, Helmut & Haeussinger, Dieter. Osmosensing & Osmosignaling. 2007. (ENG., Illus.). 632p. 187.00 *(978-0-12-373921-6(7)*, Academic Pr.) Elsevier Science & Technology Bks.

Vallant, Rainer. Fullerene Derivatives - & Their Application in Bioanalytics. 2008. 84p. pap. *(978-3-639-00540-0(6))* VDM Verlag Dr. Mueller e.K.

Xu, Rensheng, et al, eds. Introduction to Natural Products Chemistry. 2011. (ENG., Illus.). 381p. 89.95 *(978-1-4398-6076-2(9)*, CRC Press) Taylor & Francis Group GBR. Dist: Taylor & Francis Group.

BIOCHEMISTRY—STUDY AND TEACHING

Abrahamson, Julie K. Guided Inquiry Explorations into Organic & Biochemistry. 2009. 144p. pap. 37.95 *(978-1-935551-58-4(2))* Univ. Readers.

Horton, Robert & Scism, Allen. Study Guide for Principles of Biochemistry. 5th ed. 2011. (ENG.). 240p. (C). pap. 61.60 ***(978-0-321-75276-5(7)***, Prentice Hall) Prentice Hall PTR.

Smith, Janice Gorzynski & Berk, Erin Smith. Student Study Guide/Solutions Manual to accompany General, Organic & Biological Chemistry. 2009. (ENG.). 528p. (C). pap. 68.67 *(978-0-07-302658-9(1)*, 0073026581, McGraw-Hill Science, Engineering & Mathematics) McGraw-Hill Higher Education.

BIOCHEMISTRY—TECHNIQUE

Chen, Jian & Zhu, Yang, eds. Solid State Fermentation for Foods & Beverages. 2011. (Fermented Foods & Beverages Ser.). (Illus.). 472p. 179.95 *(978-1-4398-4496-0(8)*, CRC Press) Taylor & Francis Group GBR. Dist: Taylor & Francis Group.

Cooper, Terrance G. The Tools of Biochemistry. 2nd ed. 2007. (ENG.). 500p. 69.95 *(978-0-471-69054-2(6)*, Wiley-Interscience) Wiley, John & Sons, Inc.

Hof, Martin, et al. Fluorescence Spectroscopy in Biology: Advanced Methods & their Applications to Membranes, Proteins, DNA, & Cells. 2010. (Springer Series on Fluorescence Ser.). (Illus.). xix, 305p. pap. 199.00 *(978-3-642-06106-6(0)*, 3642061060) Springer.

Khan, Masood N. & Findlay, John W., eds. Ligand-Binding Assays: Development, Validation, & Implementation in the Drug Development Arena. 2009. (ENG., Illus.). 424p. 122.00 *(978-0-470-04138-3(2)*, Wiley) Wiley, John & Sons, Inc.

McLean, J. A. & Tobin, G. Animal & Human Calorimetry. 2007. (Illus.). 356p. pap. 74.00 *(978-0-521-04885-9(0))* Cambridge Univ. Pr.

BIOCHEMISTRY, QUANTUM

see Quantum Biochemistry

BIOCHEMISTS

Brady, Catherine. Elizabeth Blackburn & the Story of Telomeres: Deciphering the Ends of DNA. (ENG., Illus.). 408p. (gr. 17). 2009. pap. 16.95 *(978-0-262-51245-9(9))* 2007. 31.95 *(978-0-262-02622-2(8))* MIT Pr.

Clark, Ronald. The Life of Ernst Chain: Penicillin & Beyond. 2012. 227p. pap. ***(978-1-4482-0119-8(5)***, 144542, Bloomsbury Reader) Bloomsbury Publishing Plc.

Conrads, Hinderk, et al. Carl Neuberg — Biochemie, Politik und Geschichte: Lebenswege und Werk Eines Fast Verdrängten Forschers. 2006. (Geschichte und Philosophie der Medizin. History & Philosophy of Medicine Ser.). (GER., Illus.). 221p. (C). 68.00 *(978-3-515-08894-7(6))* Steiner, Franz Verlag Wiesbaden GmbH DEU. Dist: Brown, David Bk. Co., The.

Cormier, Milton J. My Journey: Into, Through & Beyond the Ivory Tower. 2007. (Illus.). 104p. per. 12.00 *(978-0-911041-01-9(X))* OPA Author Services.

Donnerer, Josef & Lembeck, Fred. The Chemical Languages of the Nervous System: History of Scientists & Substances. (Illus.). 228p. (C). *(978-3-8055-8004-5(5))* Karger, S. AG.

Lohff, Brigitte & Conrads, Hinderk. From Berlin to New York: Life & Work of the Almost Forgotten German-Jewish Biochemist Carl Neuberg (1877-1956) 2007. (Geschichte und Philosophie der Medizin. History & Philosophy of Medicine Ser.). (ENG., Illus.). 294p. (C). 68.00 *(978-3-515-09062-9(2))* Steiner, Franz Verlag Wiesbaden GmbH DEU. Dist: Brown, David Bk. Co., The.

Shepherd, Linda J. Lifting the Veil: The Feminine Face of Science. 2007. (ENG.). 352p. (Orig.). per. 22.95 *(978-0-595-45771-7(1)*, Backinprint.com) iUniverse, Inc.

Tu, Anthony T. Nomadic Academic Life of a Professor. 2009. *(978-0-615-27672-4(5))* Alaken, Inc.

BIOCLIMATOLOGY

see also Crops and Climate; Medical Climatology

Butler, David R., et al, eds. The Changing Alpine Treeline: The Example of Glacier National Park, MT, USA. 2009. (Developments in Earth Surface Processes Ser.: 12). (ENG., Illus.). 224p. 190.00 *(978-0-444-53364-7(8)*, Elsevier Science) Elsevier Science & Technology Bks.

Ebi, Kristie L., et al, eds. Biometeorology for Adaptation to Climate Variability & Change. 2008. (Biometeorology Ser.). (ENG., Illus.). viii, 284p. 189.00 *(978-1-4020-8920-6(1)*, 1402089201) Springer.

Groisman, Pavel Ya. & Ivanov, Sergiy, eds. Regional Aspects of Climate-Terrestrial-Hydrologic Interactions in Non-boreal Eastern Europe. 2009. (NATO Science for Peace & Security Series C: Environmental Security Ser.). (ENG., Illus.). x, 278p. 249.00 *(978-90-481-2240-0(6))*; pap. 109.00 *(978-90-481-2241-7(4))* Springer.

Hadlow, Leonard. Climate, Vegetation & Man. 7.95 *(978-0-8022-0654-1(9))* Philosophical Library, Inc.

Hodkinson, Trevor R., et al, eds. Climate Change, Ecology & Systematics. 2011. (Systematics Association Special Volume Ser.). (ENG., Illus.). 544p. 125.00 *(978-0-521-76609-8(5))* Cambridge Univ. Pr.

Houérou, Henry N. Bioclimatology & Biogeography of Africa. 2008. (ENG., Illus.). xiv, 242p. 189.00 *(978-3-540-85191-2(7)*, 3540851917) Springer.

Lowry, William P. & Lowry, Porter P. Fundamentals of Biometeorology: Interactions of Organisms & the Atmosphere, 2 vols., Vols. 1 & 2. (Illus.). 650p. pap. 66.00 *(978-1-882002-05-4(9))* Peavine Pubns.

Pearson, Richard & American Museum of Natural History, New York Staff. Driven to Extinction: The Impact of Climate Change on Biodiversity. 2011. (ENG., Illus.). 264p. 22.95 *(978-1-4027-7223-8(8))* Sterling Publishing Co., Inc.

Strelcova, Katarina. Bioclimatology & Natural Hazards. 2009. (ENG., Illus.). xvi, 298p. 199.00 *(978-1-4020-8875-9(2)*, 1402088752) Springer.

Vergara, Walter, et al. Assessment of the Impacts of Climate Change on Mountain Hydrology: Development of a Methodology Through a Case Study in Peru. 2011. (World Bank Studies). (ENG.). 180p. pap. 25.00 *(978-0-8213-8662-0(X)*, 9780821386620) World Bank Pubns.

BIOCOMPATIBILITY

see also Biomedical Materials

Amiard-Triquet, Claude, et al, eds. Tolerance to Environmental Contaminants. 2011. (Environmental & Ecological Risk Assessment Ser.). (ENG., Illus.). 464p. 129.95 *(978-1-4398-1770-4(7)*, CRC Press) Taylor & Francis Group GBR. Dist: Taylor & Francis Group.

Baèáková, L. Cell Colonization Control by Physical & Chemical Modification of Materials. 2008. pap. 29.00 *(978-1-60456-887-5(9))* Nova Science Pubs., Inc.

Barzegar, Ellaheh. Coating of Biomedical Mems. 2010. 88p. pap. *(978-3-8383-5656-3(X))* Lambert Academic Publishing.

Burger, Albert, et al, eds. Anatomy Ontologies for Bioinformatics: Principles & Practice. 2007. (Computational Biology Ser.). (Illus.). 344p. 149.00 *(978-1-84628-884-5(3))* Springer.

Dee, Kay C., et al. The Introduction to Tissue-Biomaterial Interactions. 2nd ed. 2008. 248p. 99.95 *(978-0-470-09630-7(6)*, Wiley-Liss) Wiley, John & Sons, Inc.

Di Silvio, L., ed. Cellular Response to Biomaterials. 2008. (Illus.). 648p. *(978-1-84569-358-9(2))* Woodhead Publishing Ltd.

Jabbari, Esmaiel. Biologically-responsive Hybrid Biomaterials: A Reference for Material Scientists & Bioengineers. 2010. (Illus.). 432p. 135.00 *(978-981-4295-67-3(1))* World Scientific Publishing Co., Inc.

Knoll, Wolfgang, ed. Handbook of Biofunctional Surfaces. 2012. (ENG.). 800p. 425.00 ***(978-981-4316-63-7(6))*** Pan Stanford Publishing SGP. Dist: Taylor & Francis Group.

Kumar, S. Ashok, et al, eds. Biocompatible Nanomaterials: Synthesis, Characterization & Applications. 2010. (Nanotechnology Science & Technology Ser.). 235.00 *(978-1-61668-677-2(4))* Nova Science Pubs., Inc.

Petoukhov, Sergey & He, Matthew. Symmetrical Analysis Techniques for Genetic Systems & Bioinformatics: Advanced Patterns & Applications. 2009. 404p. 245.00 *(978-1-60566-124-7(4))* IGI Global.

Sharma, C. P., et al. Bointegration of Medical Implant Materials. 2010. (ENG., Illus.). 384p. 229.95 *(978-1-4398-3064-2(9)*, CRC Press) Taylor & Francis Group GBR. Dist: Taylor & Francis Group.

Wang, Meng-Jiy & Tsai, Wei-Bor, eds. Biomaterials in Blood-Contacting Devices: Complications & Solutions. 2010. (Biomaterials - Properties, Production & Devices Ser.). 87p. pap. 43.00 *(978-1-60876-784-7(1))* Nova Science Pubs., Inc.

Yang, Ang & Shan, Yin. Intelligent Complex Adaptive Systems. 2008. (Illus.). 380p. 99.95 *(978-1-59904-717-1(9))* IGI Global.

BIOCOMPATIBLE MATERIALS

see Biomedical Materials

BIOCOMPUTERS

see Conscious Automata

BIODEGRADATION

see also Bioremediation

Abdel-Megeed, Ahmed & Mueller, Rudolf. Psychrophilic Degradation of Long Chain Alkanes. 2010. 172p. pap. *(978-3-639-23838-9(9))* VDM Verlag Dr. Mueller e.K.

Abdelrahman, Hany, et al. Biodegradation of Some Pesticides by Soil Microorganisms. 2010. 132p. pap. *(978-3-639-27506-3(3))* VDM Verlag Dr. Mueller e.K.

Aelion, Marjorie C. Env Isot Biorerned Biodegrad. 2009. (ENG., Illus.). 464p. 133.95 *(978-1-56670-661-2(0)*, CRC Press) Taylor & Francis Group GBR. Dist: Taylor & Francis Group.

Albertsson, A. C., ed. & contrib. by. Degradable Aliphatic Polyesters. 2010. (Advances in Polymer Science Ser.). (Illus.). xi, 179p. pap. 239.00 *(978-3-642-07597-1(5)*, 3642075975) Springer.

Bostrom, Helene, ed. Pernilla Zetterman: Behave. 2010. (ENG., Illus.). 112p. 55.00 *(978-3-7757-2467-8(2))* Hatje Cantz Verlag GmbH & Co KG DEU. Dist: D.A.P./Distributed Art Pubs.

Caneva, Giulia, et al. Plant Biology for Cultural Heritage: Biodeterioration & Conservation. 2009. (Illus.). 400p. pap. 70.00 *(978-0-89236-939-3(6))* Oxford Univ. Pr., Inc.

Chiellini, E., ed. Environmentally Compatible Food Packaging. 2008. (Illus.). 552p. *(978-1-84569-194-3(6))* Woodhead Publishing Ltd.

Danielski, Leandro. Supercritical Processing of Plant Materials. 2008. 200p. pap. *(978-3-639-02458-6(3))* VDM Verlag Dr. Mueller e.K.

Dillmann, P. Corrosion of Metallic Heritage Artefacts: Investigation, Conservation & Prediction of Long Term Behaviour. (Illus.). xxx, 378p. *(978-1-84569-239-1(X))* Woodhead Publishing Ltd.

Domb, Abraham J. & Kumar, Neeraj, eds. Biodegradable Polymers in Clinical Use & Clinical Development. 2011. (ENG., Illus.). 752p. 149.95 *(978-0-470-42475-9(3)*, Wiley) Wiley, John & Sons, Inc.

Epstein, Eliot. Industrial Composting: Environmental Engineering & Facilities Management. 2011. (ENG., Illus.). 334p. 139.95 *(978-1-4398-4531-8(X)*, CRC Press) Taylor & Francis Group GBR. Dist: Taylor & Francis Group.

Hesham, Abd El-Latif & Yang, Min. Biodegradation of Petroleum Compounds & Environmental Meta-Genomics. 2010. 180p. pap. *(978-3-8383-9341-4(4))* Lambert Academic Publishing.

Jamil, Shahid. Biodegradation. 2010. 96p. pap. *(978-3-639-23787-0(0))* VDM Verlag Dr. Mueller e.K.

Javaherdashti, Reza. Microbiologically Influenced Corrosion: An Engineering Insight. 2010. (Engineering Materials & Processes Ser.). (Illus.). xiv, 164p. pap. 129.00 *(978-1-84996-721-1(0)*, 1849967210) Springer.

Javaherdashti, Reza & Nikraz, Hamid. A Global Warning on Corrosion & Environment. 2010. 156p. pap. *(978-3-639-25429-7(5))* VDM Verlag Dr. Mueller e.K.

Jilani, Seema. Biodegradation of Hazardous Waste During Biological Treatment Process. 2009. (Illus.). 200p. pap. *(978-3-639-15303-3(0))* VDM Verlag Dr. Mueller e.K.

Jimenez, Alfonso & Zaikov, Gennadii Efremovich, eds. Recent Advances in Research on Biodegradable Polymers & Sustainable Composites, 2 vols., Vol. 1. 2009. (Illus.). 152p. 145.00 *(978-1-60692-095-4(2))* Nova Science Pubs., Inc.

Johnson, Brandon M. & Berkel, Zachary E. Biodegradable Materials: Production, Properties & Applications. 2011. (Materials Science & Technologies Ser.). 89.00 *(978-1-61122-804-5(2))* Nova Science Pubs., Inc.

Josephraj, Jegan & Rangasamy, Parthiban. Growth Kinetics & Degradation of Polycyclic Aromatic Hydrocarbons: Biodegradation of of Naphthalene, Phenanthrene & Anthracene, Surfactants Triton X-100 & Tween-80, Modeling. 2011. 196p. pap. ***(978-3-639-33565-1(1))*** VDM Verlag Dr. Mueller e.K.

Kabnoorkar, Panchshila & Deokule, Subhash. Biodeterioration of Chemical Constituents. 2011. 312p. pap. ***(978-3-8433-9160-3(2))*** Lambert Academic Publishing.

Kato, Sakura Y. Archaea: Structure, Habitats & Ecological Significance. 2011. (Microbiology Research Advances Ser.). 98.00 *(978-1-61761-932-8(9))*, Nova Biomedical Bks.) Nova Science Pubs., Inc.

Lendlein, Andreas & Sisson, Adam, eds. Handbook of Biodegradable Polymers: Synthesis, Characterization & Applications. 2011. (ENG., Illus.). 426p. 195.00 *(978-3-527-32441-5(0)*, Wiley-VCH) Wiley, John & Sons, Inc.

Liong, Min-Tze. Bioprocess Sciences & Technology. 2011. (Biochemistry Research Trends Ser.). (Illus.). 526p. 195.00 *(978-1-61122-950-9(2))* Nova Science Pubs., Inc.

Lucejko, Jeannette Jacqueline. Waterlogged Archaeological Wood. 2010. 176p. pap. *(978-3-639-25707-6(3))* VDM Verlag Dr. Mueller e.K.

Macek, Tomas, et al, eds. Phytoremediation & Rhizoremediation: Theoretical Background. 2006. (Focus on Biotechnology Ser.: Vol. 9). (ENG., Illus.). vi, 300p. 289.00 *(978-1-4020-4952-1(8)*, 1402049528) Springer.

May, Eric, et al. Heritage Microbiology & Science: Microbes, Monuments & Maritime Materials. 2008. (Special Publication). (ENG., Illus.). 320p. 176.00 ***(978-0-85404-141-1(9))*** Royal Society of Chemistry, The GBR. Dist: Ingram Pub. Services.

Miraftab, M. Fatigue failure of textile Fibres. Miraftab, M., ed. 2009. (Illus.). 320p. 209.95 *(978-1-4398-0210-6(6))* CRC Pr. LLC.

Pawley, Lyman E., ed. Leading-Edge Environmental Biodegradation Research. 2008. (Illus.). 351p. 129.00 *(978-1-60021-903-0(9))* Nova Science Pubs., Inc.

Pichiah, Saravanan. Biodegradation of Phenolic Compounds. 2010. 224p. pap. *(978-3-639-25498-3(8))* VDM Verlag Dr. Mueller e.K.

Sherif, El-Kadi. Bioplastic Production in Plastic Age: Alcaligenes Eutrophus the Bioplastic Maker. 2011. 152p. pap. ***(978-3-639-33516-3(3))*** VDM Verlag Dr. Mueller e.K.

Singh, Ajay & Ward, Owen P. Biodegradation & Bioremediation. 2010. (Soil Biology Ser.). (Illus.). xvii, 309p. pap. 249.00 *(978-3-642-05929-2(5)*, 3642059295) Springer.

Singh, S. N. & Tripathi, R. D., eds. Environmental Bioremediation Technologies. 2006. (ENG., Illus.). xx, 518p. 249.00 *(978-3-540-34790-3(9)*, 3540347909) Springer.

Uysal, Ayla. Effect of Biosurfactant on Chlorophenols Biodegradation. 2011. 104p. pap. ***(978-3-8383-2680-1(6))*** Lambert Academic Publishing.

Wang, B. Y. Environmental Biodegradation Research Focus. 2008. (C). 129.00 *(978-1-60021-904-7(7)*, Nova Biomedical Bks.) Nova Science Pubs., Inc.

Xu, Yunji & Webb, Colin. Biodegradable Plastic from Wheat. 2010. 244p. pap. *(978-3-8383-0755-8(0))* Lambert Academic Publishing.

Yu, Long. Biodegradable Polymer Blends & Composites from Renewable Resources. 2008. (ENG., Illus.). 488p. 150.00 *(978-0-470-14683-5(4)*, Wiley) Wiley, John & Sons, Inc.

Zaikov, Gennadii Efremovich & Krylova, Larisa Petrivna, eds. Biotechnology, Biodegradation, Water & Foodstuffs. 2008. 145.00 *(978-1-60692-097-8(9))* Nova Science Pubs., Inc.

Zhang, Changhong. Biodegradable Polyurethanes in Biomedical Engineering Field. 2010. 116p. pap. *(978-3-8383-7491-8(6))* Lambert Academic Publishing.

BIODETERIORATION

see Biodegradation

BIODIVERSITY

Here are entered works on the totality of the variety of living organisms, the genetic differences among them, and the communities and ecosystems in which they occur.

see also Species Diversity

Abaidoo, Samuel. The Role of Environmental Ethics in Human-Nature Interaction. 2010. 192p. pap. *(978-3-8383-1787-8(4))* Lambert Academic Publishing.

Abele, Doris, et al, eds. Oxidative Stress in Aquatic Ecosystems. 2011. (ENG., Illus.). 548p. 159.95 ***(978-1-4443-3548-4(0)***, Wiley-Blackwell) Wiley, John & Sons, Inc.

Abernathy, Greg, et al, eds. Kentucky's Natural Heritage: An Illustrated Guide to Biodiversity. 2010. (ENG., Illus.). 256p. 39.95 *(978-0-8131-2575-6(8))* Univ. Pr. of Kentucky.

Acktun, Gerhard. Viktualienmarkt G'schichten 2: Nachtschicht. 2011. (ENG.). 208p. pap. 60.00 *(978-3-9812410-2-0(9))* United Nations Pubns.

Adams, Jonathan. Species Richness: Patterns in the Diversity of Life. 2009. (Springer Praxis Books / Environmental Sciences Ser.). (Illus.). 320p. 189.00 *(978-3-540-74277-7(8))* Springer.

Agosti, Donat, ed. Ants: Standard Methods for Measuring & Monitoring Biodiversity. 2008. (ENG.). 80p. pap. 27.00 *(978-1-4379-5147-9(3))* DIANE Publishing Co.

Ahern, Jack, et al. Biodiversity Planning & Design: Sustainable Practices. 2007. (ENG., Illus.). 128p. 50.00 *(978-1-59726-108-1(4))*; pap. 40.00 *(978-1-59726-109-8(2))* Island Pr.

Alexiades, Miguel N., ed. Mobility & Migration in Indigenous Amazonia Contemporary Ethnoecological Perspectives. 2009. (Illus.). 304p. 90.00 *(978-1-84545-563-7(0))* Berghahn Bks., Inc.

Allsopp, Michelle, et al. State of the World's Oceans. 2008. (ENG., Illus.). xiv, 258p. 79.95 *(978-1-4020-9115-5(X)*, 140209115X) Springer.

Amend, Thora, et al, eds. Protected Landscapes & Agrobiodiversity Values. 2008. (ENG.). 139p. pap. 32.00 *(978-3-925064-48-7(6))* UICN Union Mondiale pour la Nature, Cecile Thiery CHE. Dist: Chicago Distribution Ctr.

Armah, Ayaa Kojo & Allotey, Lloyd Cyril. Spatial Assemblages of Tropical Intertidal Rocky Shore Communities in Ghana, West Africa. Lamptey, Emmanuel, ed. 2010. (Environmental Science, Engineering & Technology Ser.). 68p. pap. 43.00 *(978-1-61668-767-0(3)*, Nova Novinka) Nova Science Pubs., Inc.

Ash, Neville, et al. Ecosystems & Human Well-Being: A Manual for Assessment Practitioners. 2010. (ENG., Illus.). 288p. 70.00 *(978-1-59726-710-6(4))*; pap. 35.00 *(978-1-59726-711-3(2))* Island Pr.

Bachmann, Peter, et al, eds. Assessment of Biodiversity for Improved Forest Planning. 2010. (Forestry Sciences Ser.). 424p. pap. 289.00 *(978-90-481-4962-9(2)*, 9048149622) Springer.

Backlund, Peter, et al. The Effects of Climate Change on Agriculture, Land Resources, Water Resources, & Biodiversity in the United States. 2008. pap. 39.00 *(978-1-60456-989-6(1))* Nova Science Pubs., Inc.

Balian, E. V., et al, eds. Freshwater Animal Diversity Assessment. 2010. (Developments in Hydrobiology Ser.). 640p. pap. 239.00 *(978-90-481-7822-3(3)*, 9048178223) Springer.

Barceló, Damià & Petrovic, Mira, eds. The Ebro River Basin. 2011. (Handbook of Environmental Chemistry Ser.). (Illus.). xiv, 431p. 409.00 *(978-3-642-18031-6(0)*, 3642180310) Springer.

Battaglia, Bruno, et al, eds. Antarctic Communities: Species, Structure & Survival. 2009. (ENG., Illus.). 484p. pap. 61.00 *(978-0-521-11179-9(X))* Cambridge Univ. Pr.

Beaugrand, Gregory. Marine Biodiversity, Climatic Variability & Global Change. 2012. (Earthscan Oceans Ser.). (ENG.). 320p. (C). pap. 59.95 ***(978-0-415-51703-4(6))*** Routledge.

Beck, Erwin, et al. Gradients in a Tropical Mountain Ecosystem of Ecuador. 2010. (Ecological Studies). (Illus.). xxiv, 526p. pap. 289.00 *(978-3-642-09266-4(7)*, 3642092667) Springer.

Beck, Harald. Linking Amazon Forest Dynamics with Mammalian Diversity. 2008. (Illus.). 128p. pap. *(978-3-639-07513-7(7))* VDM Verlag Dr. Mueller e.K.

Bergstrom, D. M., et al, eds. Trends in Antarctic Terrestrial & Limnetic Ecosystems: Antarctica as a Global Indicator. 2010. (ENG.). xiv, 369p. pap. 159.00 *(978-90-481-7327-3(2)*, 9048173272) Springer.

Bevington, Douglas. The Rebirth of Environmentalism: Grassroots Activism from the Spotted Owl to the Polar Bear. 2009. (ENG., Illus.). 304p. pap. 35.00 *(978-1-59726-656-7(6))*; 70.00 *(978-1-59726-655-0(8))* Island Pr.

Bharucha, Erach. The Biodiversity of India. 2006. (ENG., Illus.). 39.95 *(978-1-890206-40-6(7))* Mapin Publishing Pvt. Ltd IND. Dist: National Bk. Network.

Bharucha, Erach, contrib. by. Wonders of the Indian Wilderness. 2008. (ENG., Illus.). 855p. (J). 100.00 *(978-0-7892-0999-3(3))* Abbeville Pr., Inc.

Bharucha, Erach & Rai, Jayalaxmi. The Biodiversity of India. (Illus.). 48p. 39.95 incl. cd-rom *(978-81-88204-06-9(4))* Mapin Publishing Pvt. Ltd IND. Dist: Antique Collectors' Club.

Bhati, Sulehka. Focus on Biodiversity Research. 2006. (Illus.). 320p. (C). 225.00 *(978-1-60021-372-4(3))* Nova Science Pubs., Inc.

Bhattacharya, Samik. Tropical Bamboo: Molecular Profiling & Genetic Diversity Study. 2010. 220p. pap. *(978-3-8383-7422-2(3))* Lambert Academic Publishing.

Bickel, Daniel John & Pape, Thomas, eds. Diptera Diversity: Status, Challenges & Tools. 2009. 304p. *(978-90-04-14897-0(3))* BRILL.

Bilotta, Eleonora & Pantano, Pietro. Cellular Automata & Complex Systems: Methods for Modeling Biological Phenomena. 2010. (Illus.). 361p. 245.00 *(978-1-61520-787-9(2))* IGI Global.

Birhane, Emiru, et al. Woody Species Diversity in Enclosures. 2010. 76p. pap. *(978-3-639-28273-3(6))* VDM Verlag Dr. Mueller e.K.

Botkin & Keller & Cram101 Textbook Reviews Staff. Environmental Science: Earth as a Living Planet. 2007. 276p. per. 15.95 *(978-1-4288-3102-5(9))* Cram101 Inc.

Botkin, Daniel B. Environmental Science: Earth as a Living Planet Wileyplus Set. 6th ed. 2007. 98.00 net. *(978-0-470-13202-9(7))* Wiley, John & Sons, Inc.

Botkin, Daniel B. & Keller, Edward A. Environmental Science: Earth as a Living Planet. 5th ed. 2006. pap. 62.95 *(978-0-470-07849-5(9))* Wiley, John & Sons, Inc.

Bradstock, Ross A., et al, eds. Flammable Australia: The Fire Regimes & Biodiversity of a Continent. 2009. (ENG., Illus.). 472p. pap. 47.00 *(978-0-521-12531-4(6))* Cambridge Univ. Pr.

Brand, Ulrich. Conflicts in Environmental Regulation & the Internationalisation of the State. 2010. 292p. pap. 39.95 *(978-0-415-58679-5(8))* Routledge.

Brand, Ulrich, et al. Conflicts in Environmental Regulation & the Internationalisation of the State: Contested Terrains. 2008. (Routledge/RIPE Studies in Global Political Economy Ser.). XIV, 282p. 140.00 *(978-0-415-45513-8(8))* Routledge.

Brockerhoff, Eckehard G., et al, eds. Plantation Forests & Biodiversity: Oxymoron or Opportunity? Oxymoron or Opportunity? 2009. (Topics in Biodiversity & Conservation Ser.). (ENG., Illus.). viii, 288p. 269.00 *(978-90-481-2806-8(4)*, 9048128064) Springer.

Broennimann, Olivier. Niche, Distribution & Global Change. 2010. 232p. pap. *(978-3-8383-7965-4(9))* Lambert Academic Publishing.

Brooks, E. G. E., et al. The Status & Distribution of Freshwater Biodiversity in Central Africa. 2011. (Illus.). x, 126p. pap. 18.00 ***(978-2-8317-1326-7(9))*** International League of Conservation Photographers.

Browne, Sheila A., ed. Aquatic Ecosystems. 2011. (Series: Marine Biology Ser.). (Illus.). xi, 229p. 95.00 *(978-1-61324-399-2(5))* Nova Science Pubs., Inc.

Brusca, Richard C. The Gulf of California: Biodiversity & Conservation. 2010. (ENG., Illus.). 400p. 75.00 *(978-0-8165-2739-7(3))* Univ. of Arizona Pr.

Bryce, Clayton W. Marine Biodiversity Survey of Mermaid Reef (Rowley Shoals), Scott & Seringapatam Reef, Western Australia, 2006. 2009. (Illus.). xv, 255p. *(978-1-920843-50-2(7))* Art Gallery of Western Australia, The.

Butlin, Roger, et al, eds. Speciation & Patterns of Diversity. 2009. (Ecological Reviews Ser.). (ENG., Illus.). 346p. pap. 66.00 *(978-0-521-70963-7(6))* Cambridge Univ. Pr.

Calcott, Brett & Sterelny, Kim, eds. The Major Transitions in Evolution Revisited. 2011. (Vienna Series in Theoretical Biology Ser.). (ENG., Illus.). 336p. (gr. 17). 50.00 *(978-0-262-01524-0(2))* MIT Pr.

Campton, John. Biology: Organisms & Biodiversity. 2010. (Illus.). 110p. (gr. 10-12). pap., stu. ed. 27.50 *(978-0-340-99194-7(1))* Hodder Education GBR. Dist: Trans-Atlantic Pubns., Inc.

Caplow, Susan. Conflict, Conservation, & Chaos. 2008. 84p. pap. *(978-3-8364-7689-8(4))* VDM Verlag Dr. Mueller e.K.

Carolinian Canada Coalition Staff. The Natural Treasures of Carolinian Canada: Discovering the Rich Natural Diversity of Ontario's Southwestern Heartland. Johnson, Lorraine, ed. 2007. (ENG., Illus.). 160p. pap. *(978-1-55028-990-9(X))* Lorimer, James & Co., Ltd., Pubs. CAN. Dist: Casemate Pubs. & Bk. Distributors, LLC.

Carpenter, David. Agriculture, Biodiversity & Markets: Livelihoods & Agroecology in Comparative Perspective. Lockie, Stewart, ed. 2009. (ENG., Illus.). 336p. 95.00 *(978-1-84407-776-2(4))* Routledge.

Ceccaldi, Hubert-Jean, et al, eds. Global Change: Mankind-Marine Environment Interactions - Proceedings of the 13th French-Japanese Oceanography Symposium. 2011. (ENG., Illus.). xii, 450p. 179.00 *(978-90-481-8629-7(3)*, 9048186293) Springer.

Chaikovskii, IU V., et al. Diatropika, Evoliutsiia I Sistematika: K Iubileiu Melena Sbornik Statei S Prilozheniem Polnogo Spiska Trudov S.V. Melena, Sostavlennogo I.A. Ignatevym. 2010. (RUS.). 407p. *(978-5-87317-695-3(7))* KMK Scientific Pr. Ltd., Russia.

Chattopadhyay Gupta, Anita. Bioeconomic Modelling for Fish Biodiversity & Profitability. 2010. 256p. pap. *(978-3-8383-5300-5(5))* Lambert Academic Publishing.

Chivian, Eric & Bernstein, Aaron, eds. Sustaining Life: How Human Health Depends on Biodiversity. 2008. (ENG., Illus.). 528p. 34.95 *(978-0-19-517509-7(3))* Oxford Univ. Pr., Inc.

Chopra, Kanchan, et al. Biodiversity Land Use Change & Human Well-Being: A Study of Aquaculture in the Indian Sunderbans. 2009. (ENG., Illus.). 360p. 49.95 *(978-0-19-806021-5(1))* Oxford Univ. Pr., Inc.

Cincotta, Richard P. & Gorenflo, Larry J., eds. Human Population: The Demography & Geography of Homo sapiens & Their Implications for Biological Diversity. 2011. (Ecological Studies). (Illus.). xix, 242p. 129.00 *(978-3-642-16706-5(3)*, 3642167063) Springer.

Claudia, Cerda. Valuing Biological Diversity in Chile: A Choice Experiment Approach. 2011. 208p. pap. ***(978-3-639-34026-6(4))*** VDM Verlag Dr. Mueller e.K.

, Collective, Collective. Singapore Biodiversity: An Encyclopedia of the Natural Environment. 2011. (ENG., Illus.). 496p. 50.00 *(978-981-4260-08-4(8)*, Didier Millet,Csi) Continental Sales, Inc.

Committee for the Workshop on Frontiers in Understanding Climate Change and Polar Ecosystems & National Research Council. Frontiers in Understanding Climate Change & Polar Ecosystems: Summary of a Workshop. 2011. (ENG.). 86p. pap. 21.00 *(978-0-309-21087-4(9))* National Academies Pr.

Cowan, Stuart, et al. Ecological Design. 10th anniv. ed. 2007. (ENG., Illus.). 256p. pap. 32.50 *(978-1-59726-141-8(6))* Island Pr.

Craig, Johnson, ed. Seaweed Invasions. 2nd ed. 2011. (Marine & Freshwater Botany Ser.). (ENG., Illus.). 190p. 140.00 *(978-3-11-024065-8(3))* De Gruyter, Walter Inc.

Cram101 Textbook Reviews & Cram101 Textbook Reviews. Outlines & Highlights for Life in the Worlds Oceans: Diversity, Distribution, & Abundance by Alasdair Mcintyre, ISBN. 2011. 200p. pap. 30.95 ***(978-1-61461-362-6(1))*** Cram101 Inc.

—Outlines & Highlights for Remote Sensing for Biodiversity & Wildlife Management: Synthesis & Applications by Steven E. Franklin, ISBN. 2011. 114p. pap. 28.95 ***(978-1-61461-331-2(1))*** Cram101 Inc.

Curci, Jonathan. The Protection of Biodiversity & Traditional Knowledge in International Law of Intellectual Property. 2009. (Cambridge Intellectual Property & Information Law Ser.). (ENG., Illus.). 360p. 118.00 *(978-0-521-19944-5(1))* Cambridge Univ. Pr.

Curry, Gordon B. & Humphries, Chris J., eds. Biodiversity Databases: Techniques, Politics, & Applications. 2007. (Systematics Association Special Volumes Ser.). (ENG., Illus.). 208p. 89.95 *(978-0-415-33290-3(7)*, CRC Press) Taylor & Francis Group GBR. Dist: Taylor & Francis Group.

Dallmeier, Francisco, et al. Climate Change, Biodiversity, & Sustainability in the Americas: Impacts & Adaptations. 2010. (ENG.). 216p. 59.95 *(978-0-9788460-7-7(9))* Smithsonian Institution Scholarly Pr.

Damania, Ardeshir B. Biodiversity in Agriculture: Domestication, Evolution, & Sustainability. Gepts, Paul et al, eds. 2012. (ENG., Illus.). 630p. (C). 140.00 ***(978-0-521-76459-9(9))***; pap. 70.00 ***(978-0-521-17087-1(7))*** Cambridge Univ. Pr.

Dirzo, Rodolfo, et al. Seasonally Dry Tropical Forests: Ecology & Conservation. 2011. (ENG.). 408p. 95.00 *(978-1-59726-703-8(1))*; pap. 50.00 *(978-1-59726-704-5(X))* Island Pr.

Dittmar, Katharina & Liberles, David A. Evolution after Gene Duplication. 2010. (ENG., Illus.). 358p. 105.95 *(978-0-470-59382-0(2)*, Wiley-Blackwell) Wiley, John & Sons, Inc.

Dodds, Felix & Djoghlaf, Ahmed, eds. Biodiversity & Ecosystem Insecurity: A Planet in Peril. 2011. (ENG., Illus.). 264p. 135.00 *(978-1-84971-219-4(0))*; pap. 39.95 *(978-1-84971-220-0(4))* Routledge.

Doebeli, Michael. Adaptive Diversification. 2011. (Monographs in Population Biology Ser.). (ENG., Illus.). 392p. (C). 110.00 *(978-0-691-12893-1(6))*; pap. 49.50 *(978-0-691-12894-8(4))* Princeton Univ. Pr.

Dove, Michael R., et al, eds. Beyond the Sacred Forest: Complicating Conservation in Southeast Asia. 2011. (New Ecologies for the Twenty-First Century Ser.). (ENG., Illus.). 392p. 94.95 *(978-0-8223-4781-1(4))* Duke Univ. Pr.

—Beyond the Sacred Forest: Complicating Conservation in Southeast Asia. 2011. (New Ecologies for the Twenty-First Century Ser.). (ENG., Illus.). 392p. pap. 26.95 *(978-0-8223-4796-5(2))* Duke Univ. Pr.

Dover, John, et al, eds. Lepidoptera Conservation in a Changing World. 2011. (Illus.). viii, 384p. 239.00 *(978-94-007-1441-0(6)*, 9400714416) Springer.

Elshibli, Sakina. Biodiversity of Date Palm. 2010. 68p. pap. *(978-3-639-24578-3(4))* VDM Verlag Dr. Mueller e.K.

Engell, James, et al, eds. Environment: An Interdisciplinary Anthology. 2008. (ENG., Illus.). 984p. per. 45.00 *(978-0-300-11077-7(4))* Yale Univ. Pr.

Environmental Literacy Council & National Science Teachers Association, contrib. by. Biodiversity: Resources for Environmental Literacy. 2007. (ENG.). 22p. pap. 10.95 *(978-1-933531-16-8(9))* National Science Teachers Assn.

Environmental Science: Earth as a Living Planet, Sixth Edition Desktop Edition. 2007. (Wiley Desktop Editions Ser.). 125.95 *(978-0-470-24076-2(8))* Wiley, John & Sons, Inc.

Everard, Mark. The Business of Biodiversity. 2009. (Illus.). 208p. 119.00 *(978-1-84564-208-2(2))* WIT Pr GBR. Dist: WIT Pr.

Farnham, Timothy J. Saving Nature's Legacy: Origins of the Idea of Biological Diversity. 2007. (ENG., Illus.). 288p. 47.00 *(978-0-300-12005-9(2))* Yale Univ. Pr.

Fedonkin, Mikhail A., et al. The Rise of Animals: Evolution & Diversification of the Kingdom Animalia. 2008. (ENG., Illus.). 344p. (gr. 17). 79.00 *(978-0-8018-8679-9(1))* Johns Hopkins Univ. Pr.

Ferry, Natalie. Effects of Insect Resistant Gm Crops on Target & Non-Target Insects. 2010. 404p. pap. *(978-3-8383-3913-9(4))* Lambert Academic Publishing.

Finney, Stanley C. & Berry, William B. N. The Ordovician Earth System. 2010. (Illus.). viii, 193p. pap. 60.00 *(978-0-8137-2466-9(X))* Geological Society of America, Inc.

Food and Agriculture Organization. Workshop on status & trends in aquatic genetic Resources: A basis for international policy; 8-10 May 2006, Victoria, British Columbia, Canada. Bartley, Devin M. et al, eds. 2007. (FAO Fisheries Proceedings Ser.: Vol. 5). (Illus.). 184p. pap. *(978-92-5-105818-3(0))* Food & Agriculture Organization of the United Nations.

Foottit, Robert G. & Adler, Peter H., eds. Insect Biodiversity: Science & Society. 2009. (ENG., Illus.). 656p. 169.95 *(978-1-4051-5142-9(0)*, Wiley-Blackwell) Wiley, John & Sons, Inc.

Freshwater animal diversity Assessment. 2008. (Developments in Hydrobiology Ser.). 239.00 *(978-1-4020-8258-0(4))* Springer.

Fukushi, K., ed. Southeast Asian Water Environment 2. 2007. (Southeast Asian Water Environment Ser.). (Illus.). 346p. (C). pap. *(978-1-84339-124-1(4))* IWA Publishing.

Fukushi, Kensuke. Southeast Asian Water Environment 4. 2010. (Southeast Asian Water Environment Ser.). (Illus.). 280p. (C). pap. *(978-1-84339-362-7(X))* IWA Publishing.

Getzin, Stephan. Structural Fire Effects in the World's Savannas. 2007. 108p. per. *(978-3-8364-3664-9(7))* VDM Verlag Dr. Mueller e.K.

Gillespie, Alexander. Conservation, Biodiversity & International Law. 2012. (New Horizons in Environmental & Energy Law Ser.). 616p. 225.00 ***(978-0-85793-515-1(1))*** Elgar, Edward Publishing, Inc.

Giuliani, Alessandro. Developing Markets for Agrobiodiversity: Securing Livelihoods in Dryland Areas. 2007. (Earthscan Research Editions Ser.). (ENG., Illus.). 144p. 117.00 *(978-1-84407-468-6(4))* Routledge.

Glaubrecht, Matthias, ed. Evolution in Action: Case studies in Adaptive Radiation, Speciation & the Origin of Biodiversity. 2010. (ENG., Illus.). xxv, 586p. 239.00 *(978-3-642-12424-2(0)*, 3642124240) Springer.

Goodman, Alan H., et al. Race: Are We So Different? 2012. (ENG., Illus.). 400p. 79.95 ***(978-0-470-65713-3(8))***; 396p. pap. 24.95 ***(978-0-470-65714-0(6))*** Wiley, John & Sons, Inc. (Wiley-Blackwell).

Griffiths, Huw I., et al, eds. Balkan Biodiversity: Pattern & Process in the European Hotspot. 2010. x, 367p. pap. 279.00 *(978-90-481-6732-6(9)*, 9048167329) Springer.

Gunter, Michael M. Building the Next Ark: How NGOs Work to Protect Biodiversity. 2006. (Illus.). 276p. pap. 22.95 *(978-1-58465-590-9(9))* Univ. Pr. of New England.

Gurr, Geoff M., et al, eds. Biodiversity & Insect Pests: Key Issues for Sustainable Management. 2012. (ENG.). 360p. 129.95 ***(978-0-470-65686-0(7)***, Wiley-Blackwell) Wiley, John & Sons, Inc.

Hafashimana, David. Diversity & Distribution of Forest Biodiversity in Western Ugand. 2010. 232p. pap. *(978-3-8383-9189-2(6))* Lambert Academic Publishing.

Harrison, Guy P. Race & Reality: What Everyone Should Know about Our Biological Diversity. 2009. (ENG.). 320p. pap. 20.00 *(978-1-59102-767-6(5))* Prometheus Bks., Pubs.

Hatcher, Paul & Battey, Nick. Biological Diversity: Exploiters & Exploited. 2011. (ENG., Illus.). 436p. 169.95 *(978-0-470-77806-7(7))*; pap. 83.95 *(978-0-470-77807-4(5))* Wiley, John & Sons, Inc. (Wiley).

B

Hawksworth, David L. & Bull, Alan T., eds. Forest Diversity & Management. 2010. (Topics in Biodiversity & Conservation Ser.). vi, 550p. pap. 249.00 *(978-90-481-7310-5(8)*, 9048173108) Springer.
—Human Exploitation & Biodiversity Conservation. 2007. (Topics in Biodiversity & Conservation Ser.). vi, 514p. 239.00 *(978-1-4020-5282-8(0)*, 1402052820) Springer.
—Plant Conservation & Biodiversity. 2007. (Topics in Biodiversity & Conservation Ser.). viii, 424p. 209.00 *(978-1-4020-6443-2(8)*, 1402064438) Springer.
Hickman, Cleveland P., Jr., et al. Animal Diversity. 5th ed. 2008. (ENG., Illus.). 480p. (C). pap. 133.67 *(978-0-07-296945-0(8)*, 0072969458, McGraw-Hill Science, Engineering & Mathematics) McGraw-Hill Higher Education.
Hodkinson, Trevor R., et al, eds. Climate Change, Ecology & Systematics. 2011. (Systematics Association Special Volume Ser.). (ENG., Illus.). 544p. 125.00 *(978-0-521-76609-8(5))* Cambridge Univ. Pr.
Hoke, Peter, et al. A Rapid Biological Assessment of North Lorma, Gola & Grebo National Forests, Liberia. Hoke, Peter et al, eds. 2007. (Conservation International Rapid Assessment Program Ser.). (Illus.). 112p. per. 19.95 *(978-1-934151-01-3(7))* Conservation International.
Houston Wilderness. Houston Atlas of Biodiversity. 2007. (ENG., Illus.). 128p. per. 23.95 *(978-1-58544-618-6(1))* Texas A&M Univ. Pr.
Huber, Bernhard A., et al. African Biodiversity: Molecules, Organisms, Ecosystems. 2010. xx, 443p. pap. 279.00 *(978-1-4419-3719-3(6)*, 1441937196) Springer.
Hunter, Malcolm L. & Schmiegelow, Fiona. Wildlife, Forests & Forestry: Principles of Managing Forests for Biological Diversity. 2nd ed. 2010. (ENG., Illus.). 288p. (C). pap. 95.60 *(978-0-13-501432-5(8)*, Prentice Hall) Prentice Hall PTR.
Jahanzeb, Bukhari, et al. Thrips Biodiversity,Climatic & Physico-Morphic Characters: Influence of Physico-Morphic Plant Characteristics in Bt Cotton Cultivars & Meteorological Factors on Incidence of Thrips (Thrips Tabaci) 2011. 108p. pap. ***(978-3-639-33039-7(0))*** VDM Verlag Dr. Mueller e.K.
Jarvis, Devra I., et al, eds. Managing Biodiversity in Agricultural Ecosystems. 2010. (ENG., Illus.). 512p. (gr. 17). pap. 34.50 *(978-0-231-13649-5(8))* Columbia Univ. Pr.
Johnson, Kurt E. & Howell, W. Mike. Backyard Biodiversity. 2011. (ENG.). 276p. (C). pap. 30.67 ***(978-1-256-37911-9(5))*** Pearson Learning Solutions.
Kadereit, Joachim W. & Jeffrey, Charles. Flowering Plants. Eudicots: Asterales. 2010. (Families & Genera of Vascular Plants Ser.). (Illus.). xii, 635p. pap. 449.00 *(978-3-642-06822-5(7)*, 3642068227) Springer.
Kaiser, Roman. Scent of the Vanishing Flora. 2011. (ENG.). 400p. 175.00 *(978-3-906390-64-2(0)*, Wiley) Wiley, John & Sons, Inc.
Kendall, Ronald J., et al, eds. Wildlife Toxicology: Emerging Contaminant & Biodiversity Issues. 2010. (ENG., Illus.). 340p. 119.95 *(978-1-4398-1794-0(4)*, CRC Press) Taylor & Francis Group GBR. Dist: Taylor & Francis Group.
Kervalishvili, P. J., ed. Complexity & Security. 2008. 430p. 161.00 *(978-1-58603-849-6(4))* IOS Pr., Inc.
Kindlmann, Pavel, ed. Himalayan Biodiversity in the Changing World. 2011. (ENG., Illus.). x, 226p. 189.00 ***(978-94-007-1801-2(2)***, 9400718012) Springer.
Kindlmann, Pavel, et al, eds. Aphid Biodiversity under Environmental Change: Patterns & Processes. 2010. (ENG., Illus.). x, 191p. 189.00 *(978-90-481-8600-6(5)*, 9048186005) Springer.
Kinoshita. Structural Colors in the Realm of Nature. 2008. (Illus.). xiii, 352p. 121.00 *(978-981-270-783-3(2))* World Scientific Publishing Co., Inc.
Knapp, Denise A., ed. Flora & Ecology of the Santa Monica Mountains. 2007. (Illus.). 198p. pap. 40.00 *(978-0-9796277-0-5(2))* Southern California Botanists.
Kole, Chittaranjan, ed. Wild Crop Relatives - Genomic & Breeding Resources: Temperate Fruits. 2011. (ENG.). xxii, 247p. 189.00 *(978-3-642-16056-1(5)*, 3642160565) Springer.
Korner, Christian & Spehn, Eva M., eds. Data Mining for Global Trends in Mountain Biodiversity. 2009. (ENG., Illus.). 200p. 113.95 *(978-1-4200-8369-9(4)*, CRC Press) Taylor & Francis Group GBR. Dist: Taylor & Francis Group.
Krebs, C. The Ecological World View. 2008. (Illus.). 558p. 70.00 *(978-1-84593-376-0(1))* Oxford Univ. Pr., Inc.
Krever, Vladimir. Biodiversity of the Caucasus Ecoregion. (Illus.). 132p. 50.50 *(978-5-94398-005-3(9))* Signar 5 RUS. Dist: Coronet Bks.
Kupiec. The Origin of Individuals. 2009. (Illus.). 200p. 91.00 *(978-981-270-499-3(X))* World Scientific Publishing Co., Inc.
Ladle, Richard. Biodiversity & Conservation, 4 vols. 2009. (Critical Concepts in the Environment Ser.). (Illus.). LXXXIV, 2980p. 1675.00 *(978-0-415-45654-8(1))* Routledge.
Ladle, Richard J. Biodiversity & Conservation, 5 vols. 2008. (Illus.). *(978-0-415-49112-9(6))* Routledge.
Lasso, Carlos A., et al, eds. Evaluacion Rapida de la Biodiversidad de los Ecosistemas Acuaticos en la Confluencia de los rios Orinoco y Ventuari, Estado Amazonas (Venezuela) RAP Bulletin of Biological Assessment, 30. 2006. (Conservation International Rapid Assessment Program Ser.). (SPA & ENG., Illus.). 240p. pap. 19.95 *(978-1-881173-46-5(1))* Conservation International.
Laverty, Melina F., et al. Biodiversity 101, 1 vol. 2008. (Science 101 Ser.). (Illus.). 220p. 49.95 *(978-0-313-34120-5(6)*, GR4120, Greenwood Pr.) Greenwood Publishing Group, Inc.
Leadley, Paul. Biodiversity Scenarios: Projections of 21st Century Change in Biodiversity, & Associated Ecosystem Services: A Technical Report for the Global Biodiversity Outlook 3. 2010. (Illus.). 132p. pap. 40.00 *(978-92-9225-218-2(6))* United Nations Environment Programme KEN. Dist: National Bk. Network.
Lee, Cathleen. The Future of Drylands. 2008. (Illus.). xvi, 855p. 309.00 *(978-1-4020-6969-7(3))* Springer.
Lee, E. Stanley, ed. Emerging Developments in Autonomous Systems Technologies: Artificial Life Innovations. 2012. 455p. 245.00 ***(978-1-4666-0273-1(2)***, Medical Information Science Reference) IGI Global.
Lee, E. Stanley & Chang, Ping-Teng. Emerging Developments in Autonomous Systems Technologies: Artificial Life Innovations. 2012. ***(978-1-4666-0275-5(9))*** IGI Global.
Lenné, Jillian M. & Wood, David. Agrobiodiversity Management for Food Security: A Critical Review. 2011. (Illus.). 256p. 145.00 *(978-1-84593-761-4(9))* CABI GBR. Dist: Stylus Publishing, LLC.
Licata, Ignazio & Sakaji, Ammar, eds. Crossing in Complexity: Interdisciplinary Application of Physics in Biological & Social Systems. 2010. (Illus.). viii, 264p. 195.00 *(978-1-61668-037-4(7))* Nova Science Pubs., Inc.
Liittschwager, David. One Cubic Foot: Surveys in Biodiversity. 2012. (Illus.). 224p. 45.00 ***(978-0-226-48123-4(9))*** Univ. of Chicago Pr.
Lindenmayer, David B. Large Scale Landscape Experiments: Lessons from Tumut. 2009. (Ecology, Biodiversity & Conservation Ser.). (ENG., Illus.). 304p. 150.00 *(978-0-521-88156-2(0))*; pap. 64.00 *(978-0-521-70778-7(1))* Cambridge Univ. Pr.
Liu, Jianguo, et al, eds. Sources, Sinks & Sustainability. 2011. (Cambridge Studies in Landscape Ecology Ser.). (ENG., Illus.). 544p. 130.00 *(978-0-521-19947-6(6))*; pap. 65.00 ***(978-0-521-14596-1(1))*** Cambridge Univ. Pr.
Loon, Rael. Hidden Wonders: The Small 5005 of Southern Africa Insects, Spiders, Frogs & Reptiles. 2008. (ENG.). 272p. pap. 38.95 *(978-1-77009-309-6(5))* Jacana Media ZAF. Dist: Independent Pubs. Group.
Lovejoy, Thomas E. & Hannah, Lee, eds. Climate Change & Biodiversity. 2006. (ENG., Illus.). 440p. per. 38.00 *(978-0-300-11980-0(1))* Yale Univ. Pr.
Maclaurin, James & Sterelny, Kim. What Is Biodiversity? 2008. (Illus.). 224p. 60.00 *(978-0-226-50080-5(2))*; (ENG., pap. 24.00 *(978-0-226-50081-2(0))* Univ. of Chicago Pr.
Magurran, Anne E. & McGill, Brian J. Biological Diversity: Frontiers in Measurement & Assessment. 2011. (ENG., Illus.). 400p. 135.00 *(978-0-19-958066-8(9))*; 376p. pap. 72.50 *(978-0-19-958067-5(7))* Oxford Univ. Pr., Inc.
Mahoney, Conner L. & Springer, Douglas A. Genetic Diversity. 2009. (Genetics - Research & Issues Ser.). (Illus.). xiii, 304p. 129.00 *(978-1-60741-176-5(8))* Nova Science Pubs., Inc.
Maier, Donald S. What's So Good about Biodiversity? A Call for Better Reasoning about Nature's Value. 2012. (International Library of Environmental, Agricultural & Food Ethics Ser.). (ENG., Illus.). ix, 546p. 229.00 ***(978-94-007-3990-1(7)***, 9400739907) Springer.
Makumbe, Milton. Woody Plant Species Diversity & Structure on Termitaria in Zimbabwe. 2010. 104p. pap. *(978-3-8383-7845-9(8))* Lambert Academic Publishing.
Mal, Suraj & Singh, R. B. Environmental Change & Biodiversity. 2009. (Illus.). 256p. 45.00 *(978-81-316-0301-7(6))* Rawat Pubns. IND. Dist: International Specialized Bk. Services.
Managi, Shunsuke, ed. The Economics of Biodiversity & Ecosystem Services. 2012. (Routledge Explorations in Environmental Economics Ser.). (ENG., Illus.). 256p. (C). 152.00 ***(978-0-415-62563-0(7))*** Routledge.
Markussen, Michael, et al, eds. Valuation & Conservation of Biodiversity: Interdisciplinary Perspectives on the Convention on Biological Diversity. 2010. (ENG., Illus.). xxx, 430p. pap. 249.00 *(978-3-642-06313-8(6)*, 3642063136) Springer.
Matthesius, Arne. West African Montane Forest Diversity. 2008. 124p. pap. *(978-3-639-02351-0(X))* VDM Verlag Dr. Mueller e.K.
Mazhar, Farhad, et al. Food Sovereignty & Uncultivated Biodiversity in South Asia: Essays on the Poverty of Food Policy & the Wealth of the Social Landscape. 2007. (Illus.). 75p. pap. 39.95 incl. cd-rom *(978-81-7188-614-2(0))* Academic Foundation IND. Dist: Independent Pubs. Group.
McCord, Edward LeRoy. The Value of Species. 2012. (ENG.). 184p. 25.00 ***(978-0-300-17657-5(0))*** Yale Univ. Pr.
McCullough, Jennifer, et al, eds. Rapid Biological Assessment of the Ajenjua Bepo & Mamang River Forest Reserves, Ghana: RAP Bulletin of Biological Assessment 50. 2009. 200p. pap. 19.95 *(978-1-934151-26-6(2))* Conservation International.
McGowan, A. & Smithers, A.B., eds. Special Publication 358 - Comparing the Geological & Fossil Records: Implications for Biodiversity Studies. 2011. (Illus.). 247p. ***(978-1-86239-336-3(2))*** Geological Society Publishing Hse.
McGowan, Alistair, et al, eds. Palaeogeography & Palaeobiogeography: Biodiversity in Space & Time. 2011. (Systematics Association Special Volumes Ser.). (ENG., Illus.). 239p. 119.95 *(978-1-4200-4551-2(2)*, CRC Press) Taylor & Francis Group GBR. Dist: Taylor & Francis Group.
McIntyre, Alasdair, ed. Life in the World's Oceans: Diversity, Distribution, & Abundance. 2010. (ENG., Illus.). 384p. 209.95 *(978-1-4051-9297-2(6)*, Wiley-Blackwell) Wiley, John & Sons, Inc.
McManis, Charles R., ed. Biodiversity & the Law: Intellectual Property, Biotechnology & Traditional Knowledge. 2007. (ENG., Illus.). 520p. 152.00 *(978-1-84407-349-8(1))* Routledge.
McManis, Charles R. & Busch, Lawrence, eds. Biodiversity & the Law: Intellectual Property, Biotechnology & Traditional Knowledge. 2009. (ENG., Illus.). 520p. pap. 72.00 *(978-1-84407-816-5(7))* Routledge.
McNeely, Jeffrey A., et al. The Wealth of Nautre: Ecosystem Services, Biodiversity, & Human Well-Being. 2011. (ENG., Illus.). 367p. 49.00 *(978-0-9841686-0-6(5))* International League of Conservation Photographers.
McShea, Daniel W. & Brandon, Robert N. Biology's First Law: The Tendency for Diversity & Complexity to Increase in Evolutionary Systems. 2010. (ENG., Illus.). 184p. 55.00 *(978-0-226-56225-4(5))*; pap. 20.00 *(978-0-226-56226-1(3))* Univ. of Chicago Pr.
Mekonnen, Amare, et al. Ecological Implications of River Flow Modification. 2010. 124p. pap. *(978-3-639-26147-9(X))* VDM Verlag Dr. Mueller e.K.
Mousset, Sophie. La Boudeuse en Amazonie Française. 2010. (FRE., Illus.). 121p. *(978-2-7424-2830-4(5))* Gallimard, Editions.
Mueller-Dombois, Dieter, et al. Biodiversity Assessment of Tropical Island Ecosystems: PABITRA Manual for Interactive Ecology & Management. 2007. pap. *(978-1-58178-074-1(5))* Bishop Museum Pr.
Muller, Norbert, et al, eds. Urban Biodiversity & Design. 2010. (Conservation Science & Practice Ser.). (ENG., Illus.). 648p. 189.95 *(978-1-4443-3266-7(X))*; pap. 94.95 *(978-1-4443-3267-4(8))* Wiley, John & Sons, Inc. (Wiley-Blackwell).
Müller, Werner E. G. & Grachev, Mikhael A. Biosilica in Evolution, Morphogenesis, & Nanobiotechnology: Case Study Lake Baikal. 2009. (Progress in Molecular & Subcellular Biology / Marine Molecular Biotechnology Ser.). (ENG., Illus.). xxii, 421p. 299.00 *(978-3-540-88551-1(X))* Springer.
Mushita, A. & Thompson, Carol B. Biopiracy of Biodiversity: Global Exchange As Enclosure. 2006. *(978-1-59221-502-7(5))*; pap. *(978-1-59221-503-4(3))* Africa World Pr.
Musila, Simon. Loss of Biodiversity in World Heritage Cultural Sites in Keny. 2011. 84p. pap. ***(978-3-8443-1697-1(3))*** Lambert Academic Publishing.
Naeem, Shahid, et al, eds. Biodiversity, Ecosystem Functioning, & Human Wellbeing: An Ecological & Economic Perspective. 2009. (ENG., Illus.). 384p. pap. 85.00 *(978-0-19-954796-8(3))* Oxford Univ. Pr., Inc.
Naselli-Flores, Luigi & Rossetti, Giampaolo, eds. Fifty Years after the Homage to Santa Rosalia: Old & New Paradigms on Biodiversity in Aquatic Ecosystems: Santa Rosalia 50 Years On. 2010. (Developments in Hydrobiology Ser.). 244p. 219.00 *(978-90-481-9907-5(7)*, 9048199077) Springer.
National Geographic Society Staff. Operation: Protecting Our Ecological Future. 2008. pap. 24.99 *(978-1-4276-3224-1(3))* Aardvark Global Publishing.
New, Tim R. 'In Considerable Variety' Introducing the Diversity of Australia's Insects. 2011. (ENG., Illus.). xi, 254p. 189.00 *(978-94-007-1779-4(2)*, 9400717792) Springer.
Newton, Adrian C. Biodiversity Loss & Conservation in Fragmented Forest Landscapes: The Forests of Montane Mexico & Temperate South America. 2007. (Illus.). 416p. 180.00 *(978-1-84593-261-9(7))* CABI GBR. Dist: Stylus Publishing, LLC.
Niamir, Aidin, et al. Distribution Modelling of the Short-Toed Eagle. 2010. 80p. pap. *(978-3-8383-7565-6(3))* Lambert Academic Publishing.
Northrop, Robert B. Introduction to Complexity & Complex Systems. 2010. (ENG., Illus.). 551p. 83.95 *(978-1-4398-3901-0(8)*, CRC Press) Taylor & Francis Group GBR. Dist: Taylor & Francis Group.
O'Brien, Kevin J. An Ethics of Biodiversity: Christianity, Ecology, & the Variety of Life. 2010. (ENG.). 240p. pap. 26.95 *(978-1-58901-645-3(9))* Georgetown Univ. Pr.
Okane, Steve, et al. Life in the Naturalife in the Natural World: Investigating Life's Diversity. 2nd rev. ed. 2011. (ENG.). 152p. spiral bd. 28.66 *(978-0-7575-6864-0(5))* Kendall Hunt Publishing Co.
Oksanen, Markku & Pietarinen, Juhani, eds. Philosophy & Biodiversity. 2007. (Cambridge Studies in Philosophy & Biology Ser.). (ENG.). 280p. pap. 62.00 *(978-0-521-03914-7(2))* Cambridge Univ. Pr.
Organisation for Economic Co-operation and Development Staff. Aspects Redistributifs des Politiques Pour la Biodiversité. 2008. 292p. pap. 63.00 *(978-92-64-03432-7(3))* Organization for Economic Cooperation & Development.
Organisation for Economic Co-Operation and Development Staff. Paying for Biodiversity: Enhancing the Cost-Effectiveness of Payments for Ecosystem Services. 2011. (ENG.). 196p. pap. 40.00 *(978-92-64-09026-2(6))* Organization for Economic Cooperation & Development.
Ouchley, Kelby. Bayou-Diversity: Nature & People in the Louisiana Bayou Country. 2011. (Illus.). 264p. 19.95 *(978-0-8071-3859-5(2))* Louisiana State Univ. Pr.
Padoch, C., et al, eds. Managing Biodiversity in Agricultural Ecosystems. 2007. (ENG., Illus.). 512p. (gr. 17). 80.00 *(978-0-231-13648-8(X))* Columbia Univ. Pr.
Pal, B. P. Search for New Genes. Bhat, S. R. et al, eds. 2007. (ENG., Illus.). 500p. 79.95 *(978-81-7188-632-6(9))* Academic Foundation IND. Dist: Independent Pubs. Group.
Paudel, Indra. Economics of Agricultural Biodiversity. 2011. 128p. pap. ***(978-3-8443-2884-4(X))*** Lambert Academic Publishing.
Pavé, Alain. On the Origins & Dynamics of Biodiversity: the role of Chance: The role of Chance. 2010. (ENG., Illus.). xviii, 178p. 129.00 *(978-1-4419-6243-0(3)*, 1441962433) Springer.
Pearson, Richard & American Museum of Natural History, New York Staff. Driven to Extinction: The Impact of Climate Change on Biodiversity. 2011. (ENG., Illus.). 264p. 22.95 *(978-1-4027-7223-8(8))* Sterling Publishing Co., Inc.
Pilgrim, Sarah & Pretty, Jules, eds. Nature & Culture: Rebuilding Lost Connections. 2010. (ENG., Illus.). 296p. 84.95 *(978-1-84407-821-9(3))* Routledge.
Pla, Laura, et al. Quantifying Functional Biodiversity. 2011. (SpringerBriefs in Environmental Science Ser.). (ENG., Illus.). ix, 98p. 49.95 ***(978-94-007-2647-5(3)***, 9400726473) Springer.
Primavesi, Anne. Cultivating Unity: Within the Biodiversity of God. 2011. 240p. pap. 20.00 ***(978-1-59815-031-5(6))*** Polebridge Pr.
Prins, H. H. T. & Langevelde, Frank van. Resource Ecology: Spatial & Temporal Dynamics of Foraging. 2008. (Wageningen UR Frontis Ser.). (Illus.). x, 304p. pap. 109.00 *(978-1-4020-6849-2(2)*, 1402068492) Springer.
Prins, Herbert H. T. & Langevelde, Frank van, eds. Resource Ecology: Spatial & Temporal Dynamics of Foraging. 2008. (Wageningen UR Frontis Ser.). (ENG., Illus.). x, 306p. pap. 219.00 *(978-1-4020-6848-5(4)*, 1402068484) Springer.
Pyers, Greg. Biodiversity, 6 vols., Set. Incl. Biodiversity of Coasts. 28.50 *(978-1-60870-069-1(0))*; Biodiversity of Coral Reefs. 28.50 *(978-1-60870-070-7(4))*; Biodiversity of Deserts. 28.50 *(978-1-60870-071-4(2))*; Biodiversity of Polar Regions. 28.50 *(978-1-60870-072-1(0))*; Biodiversity of Rain Forests. 28.50 *(978-1-60870-073-8(9))*; Biodiversity of Woodlands. 28.50 *(978-1-60870-074-5(7))*; 32p. (gr. 4-18). (Biodiversity Ser.). 2010. Set lib. bdg. 171.00 ***(978-1-60870-068-4(2))*** Marshall Cavendish Corp.
Queiroga, H., et al. Marine Biodiversity: Patterns & Processes, Assessment, Threats, Management & Conservation. 2010. (Developments in Hydrobiology Ser.). xvi, 356p. pap. 239.00 *(978-90-481-7109-5(1)*, 9048171091) Springer.
Rai, M. K., et al, eds. Medicinal Plants. 2012. (ENG., Illus.). 650p. 149.95 ***(978-1-57808-793-8(7))*** BIOS Scientific Publishers Ltd. GBR. Dist: Taylor & Francis Group.
Raven, Peter H. Biology. 8th ed. 2006. *(978-0-07-296581-0(9))* 9th ed. 2010. (Illus.). xxvi, 1279p. *(978-0-07-353222-6(3))* McGraw-Hill Cos., The.
Raven, Peter H., et al. Biology. 9th ed. 2010. (ENG., Illus.). 1344p. (C). 214.66 *(978-0-07-735002-4(2)*, 0077350022, McGraw-Hill Science, Engineering & Mathematics) McGraw-Hill Higher Education.
Raymund I. Veritas, ed. Biodiversity Research Developments. 2008. (Illus.). (C). 89.00 *(978-1-60456-253-8(6))* Nova Science Pubs., Inc.
Reichholf, Josef. The Demise of Diversity: Loss & Extinction. 2009. (Sustainability Project Ser.). 236p. (ENG.). pap. 14.95 *(978-1-906598-38-9(X))*; (Illus.). 14.95 *(978-1-906598-15-0(0))* Haus Publishing GBR. Dist: Consortium Bk. Sales & Distribution.
Relini, G. & Ryland, J. Biodiversity in Enclosed Seas & Artificial Marine Habitats: Proceedings of the 39th European Marine Biology Symposium, held in Genoa, Italy, 21-24 July 2004. (Developments in Hydrobiology Ser.). viii, 272p. 2010. pap. 199.00 *(978-90-481-7551-2(8)*, 9048175518) 2008. 199.00 *(978-1-4020-6155-4(2))* Springer.
Renema, Willem, ed. Biogeography, Time & Place: Distributions, Barriers & Islands. 2007. (Topics in Geobiology Ser.). (Illus.). 414p. 239.00 *(978-1-4020-6373-2(3))* Springer.
—Biogeography, Time & Place: Distributions, Barriers & Islands: Distributions, Barriers & Islands. 2010. (Topics in Geobiology Ser.). (Illus.). xii, 416p. pap. 239.00 *(978-90-481-7618-2(2)*, 9048176182) Springer.
Rex, Michael A. & Etter, Ron J. Deep-Sea Biodiversity: Pattern & Scale. 2010. (Illus.). 368p. 58.00 *(978-0-674-03607-9(7))* Harvard Univ. Pr.
Rial, Anabel, et al, eds. Rapid Assessment of the Biodiversity & Socio-Ecosystem Aspects of the Ramal de Calderas, Venezuelan Andes. 2011. (Conservation International - RAP Bulletin of Biological Assessment Ser.). 183p. pap. 19.95 *(978-1-934151-37-2(8))* Conservation International.
Richards, Stephen J., ed. A Rapid Biodiversity Assessment of the Kaijende Highlands, Enga Province, Papua New Guinea. 2007. (Conservation International Rapid Assessment Program Ser.). (Illus.). 94p. per. 19.95 *(978-1-934151-08-2(4))* Conservation International.
Richards, Stephen J. & Gamui, Banak G. Rapid Biological Assessments of the Nakanai Mountains & the Upper Strickland Basin: Surveying the Biodiversity of Papua New Guinea's Sublime Karst Environments. 2011. (Conservation International Rapid Assessment Program Ser.). (ENG.). 258p. pap. 19.95 *(978-1-934151-45-7(9))* Conservation International.
Rogstad, Steven H. & Pelikan, Stephan, eds. Genetic Diversity in Establishing Plant Populations. 2011. (ENG., Illus.). 330p. 139.95 *(978-1-57808-721-1(X))* BIOS Scientific Publishers Ltd. GBR. Dist: Taylor & Francis Group.
Romeo, Tony. Bacterial Biofilms. 2008. (Current Topics in Microbiology & Immunology Ser.). (ENG., Illus.). xii, 296p. 219.00 *(978-3-540-75417-6(2)*, 3540754172) Springer.
Rosa, Carlos Augusto & Peterdi, Gabor, eds. Biodiversity & Ecophysiology of Yeasts. 2010. (Yeast Handbook Ser.). (ENG., Illus.). x, 580p. pap. 449.00 *(978-3-642-06552-1(X)*, 364206552X) Springer.
Rosendal, G. K. The Convention on Biological Diversity & Developing Countries. 2010. (Environment & Policy Ser.). 336p. pap. 219.00 *(978-90-481-5488-3(X)*, 904815488X) Springer.
Roughgarden, Joan & Roughgarden, J. Evolution's Rainbow: Diversity, Gender, & Sexuality in Nature & People. 2nd ed. 2009. (ENG.). 484p. pap. 24.95 *(978-0-520-26012-2(0))* Univ. of California Pr.
Royal Society of Chemistry Staff. Biodiversity under Threat. Hester, R. E. & Harrison, R. M., eds. 2007. (Issues in Environmental Science & Technology Ser.). (ENG., Illus.). 290p. 96.00 *(978-0-85404-251-7(2))* Royal Society of Chemistry, The GBR. Dist: Ingram Pub. Services.
Saikia, Prasanta Kumar & Kakati Saikia, Malabika. Biodiversity in Deepor Beel Ramsar Site of Assam Indi. 2011. 132p. pap. ***(978-3-8433-8907-5(1))*** Lambert Academic Publishing.
Sala, Osvaldo E., et al, eds. Biodiversity Change & Human Health: From Ecosystem Services to Spread of Disease. 2009. (Scientific Committee on

Problems of the Environment (SCOPE) Ser.). (ENG.). 320p. pap. 45.00 *(978-1-59726-497-6(0))*; 2nd ed. 80.00 *(978-1-59726-496-9(2))* Island Pr.
Samways, Michael J., et al. Tropical Island Recovery: Cousine Island, Seychelles. 2010. (ENG., Illus.). 260p. 139.95 *(978-1-4443-3309-1(7)*, Wiley-Blackwell) Wiley, John & Sons, Inc.
Sanchez Bengoa, Dolores & Powell, Dave. TOP Biodiversity Cyprus 2010 Conference Proceedings. 2010. 410p. pap. 25.50 *(978-1-4457-8550-9(1))* Lulu Enterprises Inc.
Sandström, Ulf G. Biodiversity & Green Infrastructure in Urban Landscapes. 2008. 52p. pap. *(978-3-8364-6860-2(3))* VDM Verlag Dr. Mueller e.K.
Sarkar. An Introduction to Biodiversity Informatics. 2011. 79.00 *(978-981-283-680-9(2))*; pap. 39.00 *(978-981-283-452-2(4))* World Scientific Publishing Co., Inc.
Sarkar, Sahotra. Biodiversity & Environmental Philosophy: An Introduction. 2010. (Cambridge Studies in Philosophy & Biology Ser.). (ENG., Illus.). 280p. pap. 29.99 *(978-0-521-14342-4(X))* Cambridge Univ. Pr.
Sarkar, Sahotra & Margules, Christopher R. Systematic Conservation Planning. 2007. (Ecology, Biodiversity & Conservation Ser.). (ENG., Illus.). 278p. per. 79.99 *(978-0-521-70344-4(1))* Cambridge Univ. Pr.
—Systematic Conservation Planning. 2007. (Ecology, Biodiversity & Conservation Ser.). (ENG., Illus.). 278p. 160.00 *(978-0-521-87875-3(6))* Cambridge Univ. Pr.
Scherer-Lorenzen, Michael, et al. Forest Diversity & Function: Temperate & Boreal Systems. 2010. (Ecological Studies). (Illus.). xix, 400p. pap. 239.00 *(978-3-642-06065-X)*, 364206065X) Springer.
Schniler, Myriam. Polychaeta of the Deep Southern Ocean. 2008. 220p. pap. *(978-3-639-01823-3(0))* VDM Verlag Dr. Mueller e.K.
Schulz, Florian. Yellowstone to Yukon: Freedom to Roam. 2008. (ENG., Illus.). 192p. pap. 29.95 *(978-1-59485-104-9(2)*, Braided River) Mountaineers Bks., The.
Sd Bay: Call to Conservation. 2009. 344p. pap. 24.95 *(978-1-888691-20-7(4))* Univ. of California, California Sea Grant College System.
Segers, H. & Martens, K. Aquatic Biodiversity II: The Diversity of Aquatic Ecosystems. 2011. (Developments in Hydrobiology Ser.). (ENG.). x, 390p. pap. 249.00 *(978-90-481-6951-1(8)*, 9048169518) Springer.
Senaris, Josefa Celsa, et al, eds. Evaluacion Rapida de la Biodiversidad de los Ecosistemas Acuaticos de la Cuenca Alta del Rio Paragua, Estado Bolivar, Venezuela: RAP Bulletin of Biological Assessment # 49. 2009. (Conservation International Rapid Assessment Program Ser.). (Illus.). 308p. pap. 19.95 *(978-1-934151-13-6(0))* Conservation International.
Settele, Josef, ed. Atlas of Biodiversity Risk. 2010. (Illus.). 264p. 250.00 *(978-954-642-446-4(3))* Pensoft Pubs. BGR. Dist: Coronet Bks.
Shrestha, Pratima. Linking Socio-Economic, Landuse & Vegetation for Rhino Conservation. 2011. 116p. pap. ***(978-3-8443-1622-3(1))*** Lambert Academic Publishing.
Silvertown, Jonathan. Demons in Eden: The Paradox of Plant Diversity. 2008. (ENG., Illus.). 202p. pap. 16.00 *(978-0-226-75772-8(2))* Univ. of Chicago Pr.
Silvertown, Jonathan, ed. Fragile Web: What Next for Nature? 2010. (Illus.). 192p. pap. 25.00 *(978-0-226-75781-0(1))* Univ. of Chicago Pr.
Sime-Ngando, Télesphore & Niquil, Nathalie, eds. Disregarded Microbial Diversity & Ecological Potentials in Aquatic Systems. 2011. (Developments in Hydrobiology Ser.). (Illus.). vi, 118p. 139.00 *(978-94-007-1197-6(2)*, 9400711972) Springer.
Singh, Jagbir, ed. Biodiversity, Environment & Sustainability. 2008. (Illus.). 340p. pap. 47.50 *(978-81-7533-148-8(8))* M. D. Pubns. Pvt, Ltd. IND. Dist: Coronet Bks.
Sinha, Bhaskar. Ecological Analysis of a Sacred Landscape in Garhwal Himalya, Indi. 2011. 116p. pap. ***(978-3-8454-1402-7(2))*** Lambert Academic Publishing.
Sodhi, Navjot S. & Brook, Barry W. Southeast Asian Biodiversity in Crisis. 2011. (Cambridge Tropical Biology Ser.). (ENG.). 204p. pap. 60.00 ***(978-1-107-40313-0(8))*** Cambridge Univ. Pr.
Sodhi, Navjot S. & Ehrlich, Paul R. Conservation Biology for All. 2010. (ENG., Illus.). 400p. pap. 65.00 *(978-0-19-955424-9(2))* Oxford Univ. Pr., Inc.
Solan, Martin, et al, eds. Marine Biodiversity & Ecosystem Functioning: Frameworks, methodologies, & Integration. 2012. (ENG., Illus.). 280p. 125.00 ***(978-0-19-964225-0(7))***; pap. 62.99 ***(978-0-19-964226-7(5))*** Oxford Univ. Pr., Inc.
Spicer, John. Biodiversity: A Beginner's Guide. 2006. (Beginners Guide (Oneworld) Ser.). (ENG., Illus.). 192p. pap. 14.95 *(978-1-85168-471-7(9))* Oneworld Pubns. GBR. Dist: National Bk. Network.
Spicer, John I. Biodiversity. 2009. lib. bdg. 33.25 *(978-1-4358-5167-2(6))* Rosen Publishing Group, Inc., The.
Starr, Lisa, et al. Volume 3 - Diversity of Life. 13th ed. 2012. (ENG., Illus.). 208p. (C). pap. 44.95 ***(978-1-111-58067-4(7))*** Brooks/Cole.
Stokland, Jogeir N., et al. Biodiversity in Dead Wood. 2012. (Ecology, Biodiversity & Conservation Ser.). (ENG., Illus.). 524p. 120.00 ***(978-0-521-88873-8(5))***; 528p. pap. 60.00 ***(978-0-521-71703-8(5))*** Cambridge Univ. Pr.
Storch, David, et al, eds. Scaling Biodiversity. 2007. (Ecological Reviews Ser.). (ENG., Illus.). 500p. per. 84.00 *(978-0-521-69937-2(1))*; 498p. 157.99 *(978-0-521-87602-5(8))* Cambridge Univ. Pr.
Sumi, Akimasa, et al, eds. Adaptation & Mitigation Strategies for Climate Change. 2010. (ENG., Illus.). 356p. 229.00 *(978-4-431-99797-9(0)*, 4431997970) Springer.
Tandon, Pramod, et al. Biodiversity & Its Significance. 2007. (Illus.). xii, 370p. (C). *(978-81-88237-81-4(7))* I.K. International Publishing House Pvt. Ltd.
Tobin, Mitch. Endangered: Biodiversity on the Brink. 2010. (ENG., Illus.). 480p. 27.95 *(978-1-55591-721-0(6))* Fulcrum Publishing.
Tresca, Stefano. Biodiversity & Protected Areas: A Common Concern of Humankind. 2010. 176p. pap. 29.95 *(978-88-492-0938-2(3))* Gangemi ITA. Dist: International Publishers Marketing.
Trisurat, Yongyut, et al, eds. Land Use, Climate Change & Biodiversity Modeling: Perspectives & Applications. 2011. 350p. 180.00 *(978-1-60960-619-0(1))* IGI Global.
United Nations. Status & Potential of Commercial Bioprospecting Activities in Latin America & the Caribbean. 2007. (Medio Ambiente y Desarrollo Ser.). (ENG.). 68p. pap. 10.00 *(978-92-1-121648-6(6))* United Nations Pubns.
Urrego, Dunia H. Climate Change & History of Western Amazonian Forests. 2009. 152p. pap. *(978-3-639-13505-3(9))* VDM Verlag Dr. Mueller e.K.
Urza, Alexandra. Sustainable Development & Biological Diversity: A Case Study of Deforestation in Panama. 2008. 116p. pap. *(978-3-639-09453-4(0))* VDM Verlag Dr. Mueller e.K.
Usher, Michael. Conserving European biodiversity in the context of climate Change. 2007. (Nature & Environment Ser.: 149). 54p. pap. 15.00 *(978-92-871-6263-2(8))* Council of Europe FRA. Dist: Manhattan Publishing Co.
Valentine, James. Southern Appalachian Celebration: In Praise of Ancient Mountains, Old-Growth Forests, & Wilderness. 2011. (ENG., Illus.). 152p. 35.00 *(978-0-8078-3514-2(5))* Univ. of North Carolina Pr.
VanLeeuwe, Hilde. Managing the Mount Kenya Environment for People & Elephants. 2010. 320p. pap. *(978-3-8383-0040-5(8))* Lambert Academic Publishing.
Verde, Cinzia & di Prisco, Guido, eds. Adaptation & Evolution in Marine Environments Vol. 1: The Impacts of Global Change on Biodiversity. 2012. (From Pole to Pole Ser.). (ENG., Illus.). xxiv, 222p. 129.00 ***(978-3-642-27351-3(3)***, 3642273513) Springer.
—Adaptation & Evolution in Marine Environments, Vol 2: The Impacts of Global Change on Biodiversity. 2012. (From Pole to Pole Ser.). (ENG.). 200p. 139.00 ***(978-3-642-27348-3(3)***, 3642273483) Springer.
Victor M Toledo & Toledo, Victor M. La Biodiversidad de México: Inventarios, Manejos, Usos, Informática, Conservación E Importancia Cultural. 2011. (SPA.). 356p. pap. 30.00 ***(978-607-455-531-8(1))*** Fondo de Cultura Economica USA.
Vikström, Mariana. The Status of Traditional Knowledge. 2011. 60p. pap. ***(978-3-8443-0322-3(7))*** Lambert Academic Publishing.
Vivanco, Jorge M. & Weir, Tiffany, eds. Chemical Biology of the Tropics: An Interdisciplinary Approach. 2011. (Signaling & Communication in Plants Ser.). ix, 115p. 139.00 *(978-3-642-19079-7(0)*, 3642190790) Springer.
Waller, Donald M. The Vanishing Present: Wisconsin's Changing Lands, Waters, & Wildlife. Rooney, Thomas P., ed. 2008. (ENG., Illus.). 522p. 40.00 *(978-0-226-87171-4(1))* Univ. of Chicago Pr.
Waller, Donald M. & Rooney, Thomas P., eds. The Vanishing Present: Wisconsin's Changing Lands, Waters, & Wildlife. 2010. (ENG., Illus.). 536p. pap. 27.50 *(978-0-226-87173-8(8))* Univ. of Chicago Pr.
Waterton, Claire, et al. Barcoding Nature. 2011. (Genetics & Society Ser.). (ENG.). 224p. (C). 130.00 *(978-0-415-55479-4(9))* Routledge.
Wehrtmann, Ingo S. & Cortés, Jorge. Marine Biodiversity of Costa Rica, Central America. 2008. (Monographiae Biologicae Ser.). (Illus.). 550p. 169.00 *(978-1-4020-8277-1(0))* Springer.
Wiggins, Glenn. Biological Notes on an Old Farm: Common Things As Seen by a Museum Curator. 2008. (ENG., Illus.). 352p. 45.00 *(978-0-88854-463-6(4))* Royal Ontario Museum CAN. Dist: Univ. of Toronto Pr.
Wilke, Thomas, et al, eds. Patterns & Processes of Speciation in Ancient Lakes: Proceedings of the Fourth Symposium on Speciation in Ancient Lakes, Berlin, Germany, September 4-8 2006. (Developments in Hydrobiology Ser.). vi, 236p. 2010. (ENG.). pap. 189.00 *(978-90-481-8162-9(3)*, 9048181623) 2008. 189.00 *(978-1-4020-9581-8(3))* Springer.
Williams, Gina S. Mediterranean Ecosystems: Dynamics, Management & Conservation. 2011. (Earth Sciences in the 21st Century Ser.). 129.00 *(978-1-61209-146-4(6))* Nova Science Pubs., Inc.
Wright, Heather E., ed. A Rapid Biological Assessment of the Atewa Range Forest Reserve, Eastern Ghana. 2008. (Conservation International Rapid Assessment Program Ser.). (Illus.). 184p. per. 19.95 *(978-1-934151-09-9(2))* Conservation International.
Wynberg, Rachel, et al, eds. Indigenous Peoples, Consent & Benefit Sharing: Lessons from the San-Hoodia Case. 2009. (ENG., Illus.). xxxiii, 363p. 39.95 *(978-90-481-3122-8(7)*, 9048131227) Springer.
Zeigler, David. Understanding Biodiversity, 1 vol. 2007. (Illus.). 192p. 44.95 *(978-0-275-99459-4(7)*, C9459, Praeger Pubs.) Greenwood Publishing Group, Inc.
Zhelezov, Georgi, ed. Sustainable Development in Mountain Regions: Southeastern Europe. 2011. (ENG., Illus.). xiv, 291p. 129.00 *(978-94-007-0130-4(6)*, 9400701306) Springer.

BIODIVERSITY CONSERVATION

see also Ecosystem Management

Abdu-Raheem, Kamal. Biodiversity Conservation on Dwesa-Cwebe Communal Land. 2011. 80p. pap. ***(978-3-8454-2002-8(2))*** Lambert Academic Publishing.
Adams, Jonathan. Species Richness: Patterns in the Diversity of Life. 2009. (Springer Praxis Books / Environmental Sciences Ser.). (Illus.). 320p. 189.00 *(978-3-540-74277-7(8))* Springer.
Alonso, Leeanne E., et al, eds. Still Counting... Biodiversity Exploration for Conservation — The First 20 Years of the Rapid Assessment Program. 2011. (Illus.). 316p. pap. 20.00 *(978-1-934151-44-0(0))* Conservation International.
Alverson, William S., et al, eds. Rapid Biological & Social Inventories Report 20: Ecuador, Peru: Cuyabeno-Gueppi. 2008. (Illus.). 376p. pap. 30.00 *(978-0-914868-72-9(1))* Field Museum of Natural History, Div. of Pubns.
Asante-Yeboah, Evelyn. Assessing the Impacts of Silvicultural Systems on Ecosystem Services. 2011. 168p. pap. ***(978-3-8443-1833-3(X))*** Lambert Academic Publishing.
Askins, Robert A., et al, eds. Saving Biological Diversity: Balancing Protection of Endangered Species & Ecosystems. (ENG., Illus.). xviii, 230p. 2010. pap. 129.00 *(978-1-4419-3495-6(2)*, 1441934952) 2008. 129.00 *(978-0-387-09566-0(7)*, 0387095667) Springer.
Ausden, Malcolm. Habitat Management for Conservation: A Handbook of Techniques. 2008. (Techniques in Ecology & Conservation Ser.). (ENG., Illus.). 424p. 150.00 *(978-0-19-856872-8(X))*; 384p. per. 75.00 *(978-0-19-856873-5(8))* Oxford Univ. Pr., Inc.
Bajracharya, Leena. Biodiversity Conservation in Buffer Zone - Problems & Opportunities. 2011. 104p. pap. ***(978-3-8433-8447-6(9))*** Lambert Academic Publishing.
Balmford, Andrew. Wild Hope: On the Front Lines of Conservation Success. 2012. E-Book ***(978-0-226-03600-7(6))***; (ENG., Illus.). 264p. 26.00 ***(978-0-226-03597-0(2))*** Univ. of Chicago Pr.
Banker, Gary. The Year in Ecology & Conservation Biology 2011. Ostfeld, Richard S. & Schlesinger, William H., eds. 2011. (Annals of the New York Academy of Sciences Ser.: 78). (ENG., Illus.). 252p. pap. 130.00 *(978-1-57331-833-4(7)*, Wiley-Blackwell) Wiley, John & Sons, Inc.
Barthlott, Wilhelm & Winiger, Matthias, eds. Biodiversity: A Challenge for Development Research & Policy. 2010. (ENG., Illus.). xxi, 429p. pap. 169.00 *(978-3-642-08370-9(6)*, 3642083706) Springer.
Basnet, Khadga & Kindlmann, Pavel, eds. Himalayan Biodiversity: Linking research & Conservation. 2011. (ENG.). 250p. 129.00 *(978-90-481-2461-9(1)*, 9048124611) Springer.
Bayon, Ricardo. Conservation & Biodiversity Banking: A Guide to Setting up & Running Biodiversity Credit Trading Systems. Fox, Jessica & Carroll, Nathaniel, eds. 2007. (Environmental Market Insights Ser.). (ENG., Illus.). 320p. 125.00 *(978-1-84407-471-6(4))* Routledge.
Beck, Erwin, et al. Gradients in a Tropical Mountain Ecosystem of Ecuador. (Ecological Studies). (Illus.). 2010. xxiv, 526p. pap. 289.00 *(978-3-642-09266-4(7)*, 3642092667) 2008. 540p. 289.00 *(978-3-540-73525-0(9))* Springer.
Bharucha, Erach, contrib. by. Wonders of the Indian Wilderness. 2008. (ENG., Illus.). 855p. (J). 100.00 *(978-0-7892-0999-3(3))* Abbeville Pr., Inc.
Bhattarai, Ananda Mohan. Protection of Himalayan Biodiversity: International Environmental Law & a Regional Legal Framework. 2010. (Sage Law Ser.). (Illus.). 456p. (C). 39.95 *(978-81-321-0463-6(3)*, B04636C) SAGE Pubns., Inc.
Biber-Klemm, Susette & Cottier, Thomas, eds. Rights to Plant Genetic Resources & Traditional Knowledge: Basic Issues & Perspectives. 2006. 448p. 180.00 *(978-0-85199-033-0(9))* CABI GBR. Dist: Stylus Publishing, LLC.
Biosphere Reserves in the Mountains of the World: Excellence in the Clouds? Celebrating 40 years of UNESCO's MAB Programme: an Austrian Contribution. 2011. 120p. (C). pap. 44.00 ***(978-3-7001-6968-0(X)***, Austrian Academy of Sciences of Pr.) Austrian Academy of Sciences Press AUT. Dist: Brown, David Bk. Co., The.
Bishop, Josh, ed. The Economics of Ecosystems & Biodiversity in Business & Enterprise. 2012. (ENG., Illus.). 296p. pap. 62.00 *(978-1-84971-251-4(4))* United Nations Pubns.
Bishop, Joshua, et al. Building Biodiversity Business. 2009. 159p. pap. 30.00 *(978-2-8317-1019-8(7))* UICN Union Mondiale pour la Nature, Cecile Thiery CHE. Dist: Chicago Distribution Ctr.
Bobbink, R., et al, eds. Wetlands: Functioning, Biodiversity Conservation, & Restoration. 2006. (Ecological Studies Ser.). (Illus.). 315p. 169.00 *(978-3-540-33188-9(3)*, 3540331883) Springer.
Bobbink, R, (Utrecht University). Wetlands. 2008. (Ecological Studies). (Illus.). xxv, 315p. spiral bd. 109.00 *(978-3-540-77420-4(3))* Springer.
Boon, Philip, et al, eds. Assessing the Conservation Value of Freshwaters: An International Perspective. 2009. (Ecology, Biodiversity & Conservation Ser.). (ENG., Illus.). 304p. 150.00 *(978-0-521-84885-5(7))*; pap. 69.00 *(978-0-521-61322-4(1))* Cambridge Univ. Pr.
Buchs, Ann Kathrin. Schutz der Biodiversität durch Benefit-sharing? Das Beispiel pharmazeutischer Bioprospektierung. 2009. (Schriften zur Politischen Ökonomik / Political Economics, Competition & Regulation. Evolutorische und ökologische Aspekte Ser.). (GER.). 194p. pap. 56.95 *(978-3-631-58831-4(3))* Lang, Peter GmbH, Europaischer Verlag der Wissenschaften DEU. Dist: Lang, Peter.
Buck, Louise E., et al. Understanding Ecoagriculture: Ecoagriculture Discussion Paper Number 2. 2006. 63p. spiral bd. 0.00 *(978-0-9793871-1-1(6))* Ecoagriculture Partners.
Bull, Alan T., ed. Biodiversity & Conservation in Europe. 2008. (Topics in Biodiversity & Conservation Ser.). (Illus.). 439p. 219.00 *(978-1-4020-6864-5(6))* Springer.
Caldecott, Julian & Caldecott, Julian Oliver. Designing Conservation Projects. 2009. (ENG.). 336p. pap. 36.99 *(978-0-521-11796-8(8))* Cambridge Univ. Pr.
Carpenter, David. Agriculture, Biodiversity & Markets: Livelihoods & Agroecology in Comparative Perspective. Lockie, Stewart, ed. 2009. (ENG., Illus.). 336p. 96.00 *(978-1-84407-776-2(4))* Routledge.
Carroll, Nathaniel, et al. Conservation & Biodiversity Banking: A Guide to Setting up & Running Biodiversity Credit Trading Systems. Carroll, Nathaniel et al, eds. 2009. (Environmental Market Insights Ser.). (ENG., Illus.). 320p. pap. 47.95 *(978-1-84407-814-1(0))* Routledge.
Commission for Environmental Cooperation. Marine Ecoregions of North America. 2010. (ENG., Illus.). 186p. 30.00 *(978-2-923358-41-3(4))* Commission de cooperation environnementale/Commission for Environmental Cooperation CAN. Dist: Chicago Distribution Ctr.
Council of Europe Staff, compiled by. The Pan-European Ecological Network: Nature & Environment No. 146: taking Stock. 2007. (Nature & Environment Ser.: 146). (Illus.). 114p. pap. 35.00 *(978-92-871-6119-2(4))* Council of Europe FRA. Dist: Manhattan Publishing Co.
Cram101 Textbook Reviews & Cram101 Textbook Reviews. Outlines & Highlights for Molecular Approaches in Natural Resource Conservation & Management by J Andrew Dewoody, Isbn: 9780521515641. 2011. 112p. pap. 28.95 ***(978-1-61461-397-8(4))*** Cram101 Inc.
—Outlines & Highlights for Wildlife, Forests & Forestry: Principles of Managing Forests for Biological Diversity by Malcolm L. Hunter, ISBN. 2011. 80p. pap. 27.95 ***(978-1-61461-388-6(5))*** Cram101 Inc.
Damodar, Gaire. Community Based Biodiversity Conservation: Linkages Between Biodiversity Conservation & Rural Livelihoods Improvement. 2011. 92p. pap. ***(978-3-639-26806-5(7))*** VDM Verlag Dr. Mueller e.K.
De Boef, Walter Simon, et al, eds. Community Biodiversity Management: Promoting Resilience & the Conservation of Plant Genetic Resources. 2012. (ENG.). 320p. (C). 155.00 ***(978-0-415-50219-1(5))***; pap. 66.95 ***(978-0-415-50220-7(9))*** Earthscan LLC.
Deke, Oliver. Environmental Policy Instruments for Conserving Global Biodiversity. 2010. (Kieler Studien - Kiel Studies). (Illus.). xx, 392p. pap. 189.00 *(978-3-642-09294-7(2)*, 3642092942) Springer.
DeWoody, J. Andrew, et al, eds. Molecular Approaches in Natural Resource Conservation & Management. 2010. (ENG., Illus.). 392p. 130.00 *(978-0-521-51564-1(5))*; pap. 55.00 *(978-0-521-73134-8(8))* Cambridge Univ. Pr.
Dinerstein, Eric. Tigerland & Other Unintended Destinations. 2007. (ENG., Illus.). 296p. pap. 25.00 *(978-1-59726-152-4(1))* Island Pr.
Dlamini, Cliff. Financing of Protected Areas. 2011. 80p. pap. ***(978-3-8443-8719-3(6))*** Lambert Academic Publishing.
Dodds, Felix & Djoghlaf, Ahmed, eds. Biodiversity & Ecosystem Insecurity: A Planet in Peril. 2011. (ENG., Illus.). 264p. 135.00 *(978-1-84971-219-4(0))*; pap. 39.95 *(978-1-84971-220-0(4))* Routledge.
Dronamraju. Biotechnology & Biodiversity. 2008. 73.00 *(978-981-277-500-9(5))* World Scientific Publishing Co., Inc.
Duralappah, Anantha Kumar, et al, eds. Satoyama¿Satoumi Ecosystems & Human Well-Being: Socio-Ecological Production Landscapes of Japan. 2012. (ENG.). 520p. pap. 36.00 ***(978-92-808-1210-7(6))*** United Nations Pubns.
Eden Books Staff. Eden Project: The Guide 2010/11. 10th anniv. ed. 2011. (ENG., Illus.). 64p. pap. 9.95 ***(978-1-905811-66-3(7))*** Transworld Publishers Ltd. GBR. Dist: Independent Pubs. Group.
Eden Books Staff. Eden Project 2010-11. 2010. (ENG., Illus.). 65p. pap., instr.'s gde. ed. 9.95 *(978-1-905811-65-6(9))* Transworld Publishers Ltd. GBR. Dist: Independent Pubs. Group.
Eyzaguirre, Pablo B. & Linares, Olga F., eds. Home Gardens & Agrobiodiversity. 2010. (ENG., Illus.). 304p. pap. 29.95 *(978-1-58834-288-1(3))* Smithsonian Institution Pr.
Foissner, W. & Hawksworth, David Leslie, eds. Protist Diversity & Geographical Distribution. 2009. (Topics in Biodiversity & Conservation Ser.). (ENG., Illus.). viii, 212p. 239.00 *(978-90-481-2800-6(5)*, 9048128005) Springer.
Franklin, Steven. Remote Sensing for Biodiversity & Wildlife Management - Synthesis & Applications. 2009. (ENG., Illus.). 368p. 130.00 *(978-0-07-162247-9(0)*, 0071622470) McGraw-Hill Professional Publishing.
Fraser, Caroline. Rewilding the World: Dispatches from the Conservation Revolution. 2009. (ENG., Illus.). 416p. 28.50 *(978-0-8050-7826-8(6)*, Metropolitan Bks.) Holt, Henry & Co.
—Rewilding the World: Dispatches from the Conservation Revolution. 2010. (ENG., Illus.). 416p. pap. 18.00 *(978-0-312-65541-9(X))* Picador.
Gardner, Toby. Monitoring Forest Biodiversity: Improving Conservation Through Ecologically-Responsible Management. 2010. (Earthscan Forest Library). (ENG., Illus.). 388p. 99.95 *(978-1-84407-654-3(7))* Routledge.
Ghazoul, Jaboury & Sheil, Douglas. Tropical Rain Forest Ecology, Diversity, & Conservation. 2010. (ENG., Illus.). 496p. 125.00 *(978-0-19-928587-7(X))*; pap. 65.00 *(978-0-19-928588-4(8))* Oxford Univ. Pr., Inc.
Gibbs, James P. & Hunter, Malcolm L. Fundamentals of Conservation Biology. 3rd rev. ed. 2006. (ENG., Illus.). 516p. 82.95 *(978-1-4051-3545-0(X)*, Wiley-Blackwell) Wiley, John & Sons, Inc.
Gold, E. Richard & Bubela, Tania, eds. Genetic Resources & Traditional Knowledge: Case Studies & Conflicting Interests. 2012. (Elgar Intellectual Property & Global Development Ser.). 400p. 160.00 ***(978-1-84844-223-8(8))*** Elgar, Edward Publishing, Inc.
Gordon, Iain, ed. The Vicuña: The Theory & Practice of Community Based Wildlife Management. 2010. (ENG., Illus.). viii, 256p. pap. 89.95 *(978-1-4419-3483-3(9)*, 1441934839) Springer.
Gradel, Alexander. Monitoring & Forecasting of Forest Diversity. 2010. 92p. pap. *(978-3-8383-6582-4(8))* Lambert Academic Publishing.
Hakkenberg, Christopher. Greener Forests. 2008. 64p. pap. *(978-3-639-04016-6(3))* VDM Verlag Dr. Mueller e.K.

Hawksworth, David L. & Bull, Alan T., eds. Arthropod Diversity & Conservation. 2010. (Topics in Biodiversity & Conservation Ser.). viii, 528p. pap. 219.00 (978-90-481-7309-9(4), 9048173094) Springer.

—Biodiversity & Conservation in Europe. 2010. (Topics in Biodiversity & Conservation Ser.). xiii, 440p. pap. 219.00 (978-90-481-7743-1(X), 904817743X) Springer.

—Forest Diversity & Management. 2010. (Topics in Biodiversity & Conservation Ser.). vi, 550p. pap. 249.00 (978-90-481-7310-5(8), 9048173108) Springer.

—Human Exploitation & Biodiversity Conservation. 2010. (Topics in Biodiversity & Conservation Ser.). vi, 514p. pap. 239.00 (978-90-481-7329-7(9), 9048173299) Springer.

—Marine, Freshwater, & Wetlands Biodiversity Conservation. 2010. (Topics in Biodiversity & Conservation Ser.). vi, 402p. pap. 239.00 (978-90-481-7436-2(8), 9048174368) Springer.

—Vertebrate Conservation & Biodiversity. 2007. (Topics in Biodiversity & Conservation Ser.). (ENG., Illus.). x, 498p. 239.00 (978-1-4020-6319-0(9), 1402063199) Springer.

Hawksworth, David Leslie, ed. Management & the Conservation of Biodiversity. 2009. (Topics in Biodiversity & Conservation Ser.). (ENG., Illus.). viii, 352p. 239.00 (978-90-481-3844-9(2), 9048138442) Springer.

—Methods & Practice in Biodiversity Conservation. 2009. (Topics in Biodiversity & Conservation Ser.). (Illus.). viii, 320p. 239.00 (978-90-481-3848-7(5), 9048138485) Springer.

Hayward, Matthew & Somers, Michael J. G., eds. Fencing for Conservation: Restriction of Evolutionary Potential or a Riposte to Threatening Processes? 2011. (ENG., Illus.). xv, 320p. 209.00 (**978-1-4614-0901-4(2)**, 1461409012) Springer.

Helfman, Gene S. Fish Conservation: A Guide to Understanding & Restoring Global Aquatic Biodiversity & Fishery Resources. 2007. (ENG., Illus.). 608p. 170.00 (978-1-55963-595-0(9)); pap. 85.00 (978-1-55963-596-7(7)) Island Pr.

Henry, Robert. Plant Resources for Food, Fuel & Conservation. 2009. (ENG., Illus.). 200p. 79.95 (978-1-84407-721-2(7)) Routledge.

Hostetler, Mark E. The Green Leap: A Primer for Conserving Biodiversity in Subdivision Development. 2012. (ENG., Illus.). 205p. 65.00 (**978-0-520-27110-4(6)**); pap. 26.95 (**978-0-520-27111-1(4)**) Univ. of California Pr.

Hundera, Kitessa. Floristics & Phytogeographic Study of the Dodola Forest. 2011. 64p. pap. (**978-3-8443-2628-4(6)**) Lambert Academic Publishing.

HURD, Andrew & GRIFFIN, Julie. Adrift: Tales of Ocean Fragility. Campagna, Claudio et al, eds. 2009. (ENG., Illus.). 136p. pap. 34.00 (978-2-8317-1070-9(7)) UICN Union Mondiale pour la Nature, Cecile Thiery CHE. Dist: Chicago Distribution Ctr.

Hurford, Clive, et al, eds. Conservation Monitoring in Freshwater Habitats: Practical Guide & Case Studies. 2009. (ENG., Illus.). xv, 415p. 199.00 (978-1-4020-9277-0(6), 1402092776) Springer.

International Union for Conservation of, et al. Mediterranean Mountains in a Changing World: Guidelines for Developing Actions Plans. 2008. (Illus.). xi, 88p. pap. 18.00 (**978-2-8317-1058-7(8)**) International League of Conservation Photographers.

IUCN. Biodiversity: My Hotel in Action: A Guide to Sustainable Use of Biological Resources. 2009. (ENG.). 126p. pap. 20.00 (978-2-8317-1071-6(5)) UICN Union Mondiale pour la Nature, Cecile Thiery CHE. Dist: Chicago Distribution Ctr.

Izaguirre, Juan. Mexico's Implementation of the Cbd & the Cartagena Protocol in the Gmo Er. 2008. 252p. pap. (978-3-639-00224-9(5)) VDM Verlag Dr. Mueller e.K.

Jeffery, Michael I., et al, eds. Biodiversity Conservation, Law, & Livelihoods: Bridging the North-South Divide. 2008. (IUCN Academy of Environmental Law Research Studies). (ENG., Illus.). 612p. 178.00 (978-0-521-88503-4(5)) Cambridge Univ. Pr.

Jonathan Davies, ed. Conservation & Sustainable Development. 2012. (Earthscan Conservation & Development Ser.). (ENG., Illus.). 224p. (C). 84.95 (**978-1-84971-404-4(5)**) Routledge.

Juhasz, Thomas. Strategies for the Long Term Conservation of Biodiversity on Mauritius. 2008. 68p. pap. (978-3-8364-7634-8(7)) VDM Verlag Dr. Mueller e.K.

Junk, Wolfgang J., ed. Pantanal: Ecology, Biodiversity & Sustainable Management of A Large Neotropical Seasonal Wetland. 2011. (Illus.). 870p. 299.50 (**978-954-642-492-1(7)**) Pensoft Pubs. BGR. Dist: Coronet Bks.

Kafle, Gandhiv, et al. Status & Conservation of Ramsar Sites & Biodiversity in Nepal. 2010. 104p. pap. (978-3-8383-6947-1(5)) Lambert Academic Publishing.

Kakoma, Ibulaimu. Turning Science into Action: Biodiversity Conservation & Natural Resources Management in Africa. 2009. (978-1-59221-728-1(1)); pap. (978-1-59221-729-8(X)) Africa World Pr.

Kant, Promode. Forest Carbon Management in Indi. 2011. 208p. pap. (**978-3-8433-7472-9(4)**) Lambert Academic Publishing.

Kareiva, Peter & Marvier, Michelle. Conservation Science: Balancing the Needs of People & Nature. 2010. (ENG., Illus.). 576p. (C). 90.00 (978-1-936221-06-6(3)) Roberts & Co.

Kareiva, Peter, et al. Natural Capital: Theory & Practice of Mapping Ecosystem Services. 2011. (ENG., Illus.). 432p. 134.95 (978-0-19-958899-2(6)); pap. 69.95 (978-0-19-958900-5(3)) Oxford Univ. Pr., Inc.

Kassam, Karim-Aly S. Biocultural Diversity & Indigenous Ways of Knowing: Human Ecology in the Arctic. 2009. (Northern Lights Ser.). (ENG., Illus.). 288p. pap. 35.95 (978-1-55238-253-0(2)) Univ. of Calgary Pr. CAN. Dist: Chicago Distribution Ctr.

Kawakami, Kazuto & Okochi, Isamu, eds. Restoring the Oceanic Island Ecosystem: Impact & Management of Invasive Alien Species in the Bonin Islands. 2010. (Illus.). 228p. 179.00 (978-4-431-53858-5(5), 4431538585) Springer.

Khadka, Sarba Raj. Biodiversity Conservation in Nepal. 2011. 344p. pap. (**978-3-8433-8576-3(9)**) Lambert Academic Publishing.

Kieß, Carolin. Die Sanierung von Biodiversitätsschäden nach der europäischen Umwelthaftungsrichtlinie. 2008. 252p. pap. (978-3-540-75919-5(0)) Springer Singapore Pte. Ltd.

Kim, Ke Chung & Weaver, Robert D., eds. Biodiversity & Landscapes: A Paradox of Humanity. 2009. (ENG., Illus.). 448p. pap. 46.00 (978-0-521-11933-7(2)) Cambridge Univ. Pr.

Koike, Fumito, et al. Assessment & Control of Biological Invasion Risks. 2006. (ENG.). 216p. pap. 25.00 (978-4-87974-604-7(5)) UICN Union Mondiale pour la Nature, Cecile Thiery CHE. Dist: Chicago Distribution Ctr.

Kontoleon, Andreas. Agrobiodiversity, Conservation & Economic Development. Smale, Melinda & Pascual, Unai, eds. 2008. (Routledge Explorations in Environmental Economics Ser.). (ENG., Illus.). 456p. (C). 185.00 (978-0-415-46505-2(2)) Routledge.

Kontoleon, Andreas, et al, eds. Agrobiodiversity Conservation & Economic Development. 2011. (Illus.). 456p. pap. 42.95 (**978-0-415-61976-9(9)**) Routledge.

Kontoleon, Andreas, et al, eds. Biodiversity Economics: Principles, Methods & Applications. (ENG., Illus.). 692p. 2010. pap. 68.00 (978-0-521-15465-9(0)) 2007. 145.00 (978-0-521-86683-5(9)) Cambridge Univ. Pr.

Kraft, Steven, et al. The Law & Policy of Ecosystem Services. 2007. (ENG., Illus.). 360p. 75.00 (978-1-55963-094-8(9)) Island Pr.

—The Law & Policy of Ecosystem Services. 2007. (ENG., Illus.). 360p. pap. 40.00 (978-1-55963-095-5(7)) Island Pr.

Kumar, Pushpam, ed. The Economics of Ecosystems & Biodiversity: Ecological & Economic Foundations. (ENG.). 456p. (C). 2012. pap. 59.95 (**978-0-415-50108-8(3)**) 2010. (Illus.). 79.95 (978-1-84971-212-5(3)) Routledge.

LaBruna, Danielle/T. & Klemens, Michael W. Eastern Westchester Biotic Corridor. Bedford Addendum. 2007. pap. 10.00 (978-0-9792418-2-6(0)) Wildlife Conservation Society.

—Northern Wallkill Biodiversity Plan: Balancing Development & Environmental Stewardship in the Hudson River Estuary Watershed. 2007. pap. 10.00 (978-0-9792418-3-3(9)) Wildlife Conservation Society.

Ladle, Richard. Biodiversity & Conservation, 4 vols. 2009. (Critical Concepts in the Environment Ser.). (Illus.). LXXXIV, 2980p. 1675.00 (978-0-415-45654-8(1)) Routledge.

Ladle, Richard J. Biodiversity & Conservation, 5 vols. 2008. (Illus.). (978-0-415-49112-9(6)) Routledge.

Ladle, Richard J. & Whittaker, Robert J., eds. Conservation Biogeography. 2011. (ENG., Illus.). 320p. 159.95 (978-1-4443-3503-3(0)); pap. 79.95 (978-1-4443-3504-0(9)) Wiley, John & Sons, Inc. (Wiley-Blackwell).

Lane, David J. W., ed. Tropical Islands Biodiversity Crisis: The Indo-West Pacific. 2010. (Topics in Biodiversity & Conservation Ser.). (Illus.). 285p. 189.00 (978-94-007-0167-0(5), 9400701675) Springer.

Langhammer, Penny F., et al. Identification & Gap Analysis of Key Biodiversity Areas: Targets for Comprehensive Protected Area Systems. 2007. (Best Practice Protected Area Guidelines Ser.). (ENG.). 116p. (C). pap. 30.00 (978-2-8317-0992-5(X)) UICN Union Mondiale pour la Nature, Cecile Thiery CHE. Dist: Chicago Distribution Ctr.

Lawrence, Anna, ed. Taking Stock of Nature: Participatory Biodiversity Assessment for Policy, Planning & Practice. 2010. (ENG., Illus.). 302p. 105.00 (978-0-521-87681-0(8)) Cambridge Univ. Pr.

Leadley, Paul. Biodiversity Scenarios: Projections of 21st Century Change in Biodiversity, & Associated Ecosystem Services: A Technical Report for the Global Biodiversity Outlook 3. 2010. (Illus.). 132p. pap. 40.00 (978-92-9225-218-2(6)) United Nations Environment Programme KEN. Dist: National Bk. Network.

Lefroy, Ted, et al, eds. Biodiversity: Integrating Conservation & Production. 2009. (Illus.). 270p. pap. 70.00 (978-0-643-09458-1(X)) CSIRO Publishing AUS. Dist: Stylus Publishing, LLC.

Lévêque, Christian. Biodiversity Dynamics & Conservation: The Freshwater Fish of Tropical Africa. 2006. (ENG., Illus.). 456p. pap. 88.00 (978-0-521-03197-4(4)) Cambridge Univ. Pr.

Lichtfouse, Eric. Biodiversity, Biofuels, Agroforestry & Conservation Agriculture. Lichtfouse, Eric, ed. 2010. (Sustainable Agriculture Reviews Ser.). (Illus.). x, 390p. 209.00 (978-90-481-9512-1(8), 9048195128) Springer.

Lowe, Celia. Wild Profusion: Biodiversity Conservation in an Indonesian Archipelago. 2006. (In-Formation Ser.). (Illus.). (ENG.). 216p. (C). per. 25.95 (978-0-691-12462-9(0)); 196p. 58.00 (978-0-691-12461-2(2)) Princeton Univ. Pr.

Maass, Petra. The Cultural Context of Biodiversity: Seen & Unseen Dimensions of Indigenous Knowledge among Q'Eqchi' Communities in Guatemala. 2010. 283p. 72.95 (978-1-931968-80-5(2)) Univ. of Akron Pr., The.

Maffi, Luisa & Woodley, Ellen. Biocultural Diversity Conservation: A Global Sourcebook. 2010. (ENG., Illus.). 304p. pap. 57.95 (978-1-84407-921-6(X)) Routledge.

Maffi, Luisa & Woodley, Ellen, eds. Biocultural Diversity Conservation: A Global Sourcebook. 2010. (ENG., Illus.). 304p. 155.00 (978-1-84407-920-9(1)) Routledge.

Mahonge, Christopher. Co-managing complex social-ecological systems in Tanzania: The case of Lake Jipe Wetland. 2010. (ENG., Illus.). 206p. pap. 66.00 (978-90-8686-151-4(2)) Wageningen Academic Publishers NLD. Dist: Enfield Publishing & Distribution Co., Inc.

Makeeva, V. M., et al. Ekologo-Geneticheskii Podkhod K Okhrane Zhivotnykh Antropogennykh Ekosistem: (Na Primere Modelnykh Vidov V Moskve I Podmoskove) 2011. (RUS., Illus.). 154p. pap. (978-5-211-05795-1(3)) Moskovskovo Gosudarstvennogo Univ.

Markussen, Michael, et al, eds. Valuation & Conservation of Biodiversity: Interdisciplinary Perspectives on the Convention on Biological Diversity. 2010. (ENG., Illus.). xxx, 430p. pap. 249.00 (978-3-642-06313-8(6), 3642063136) Springer.

Maxted, Nigel. Agrobiodiversity Conservation: Securing the Diversity of Crop Wild Relatives & Landraces. 2012. (Illus.). 400p. 180.00 (**978-1-84593-851-2(8)**) CABI GBR. Dist: Stylus Publishing, LLC.

McElfish, James & Kihslinger, Rebecca. Nature-Friendly Land Use Practices at Multiple Scales. 2009. (Environmental Law Institute Ser.). (ENG.). 210p. pap. 39.95 (978-1-58576-140-1(0)) Environmental Law Institute.

McIntosh, Wayne V. & Cates, Cynthia L. Forestry & Biodiversity: Learning How to Sustain Biodiversity in Managed Forests. Bunnell, Fred L. & Dunsworth, Glen B., eds. 2010. (ENG., Illus.). 374p. pap. 39.95 (978-0-7748-1530-7(2)) Univ. of Washington Pr.

McNeely, Jeffrey A. & Mainka, Susan A. Conservation for a New Era. 2010. (ENG., Illus.). 220p. pap. 25.00 (978-2-8317-1178-2(9)) UICN Union Mondiale pour la Nature, Cecile Thiery CHE. Dist: Chicago Distribution Ctr.

Meadows, Brian. Preserving Biodiversity: The role of economics in international environmental Policy-making. 2011. (ENG.). 44p. pap. 8.95 (978-1-907962-09-7(3), Revive Pubns.) Cranmore Pubns. GBR. Dist: Lightning Source, Inc.

Meyer, Stephen M. The End of the Wild. 2006. (Boston Review Bks.). (ENG., Illus.). 96p. (gr. 17). 14.95 (978-0-262-13473-6(X)) MIT Pr.

Midiwo, Jacob & Clough, John, eds. Aspects of African Biodiversity: Proceedings of the Pan Africa Chemistry Network Biodiversity Conference, Nairobi, 10-12 September 2008. 2009. (Special Publication). (ENG., Illus.). 204p. 160.00 (978-1-84755-948-7(4)) Royal Society of Chemistry, The GBR. Dist: Ingram Pub. Services.

Mohanty, Pratap K., ed. Monitoring & Modelling Lakes & Coastal Environments. (ENG., Illus.). xii, 248p. 2010. pap. 149.00 (978-90-481-7688-5(3), 9048176883) 2008. 149.00 (978-1-4020-6645-0(7), 1402066457) Springer.

Muhumuza, Moses. The People of Mountains of the Moon. 2009. 88p. pap. (978-3-639-21127-6(8)) VDM Verlag Dr. Mueller e.K.

Mushita, A. & Thompson, Carol B. Biopiracy of Biodiversity: Global Exchange As Enclosure. 2006. (978-1-59221-502-7(5)); pap. (978-1-59221-503-4(3)) Africa World Pr.

Nakano, Shin-ichi, et al, eds. The Biodiversity Observation Network in the Asia-Pacific Region: Toward Further Development of Monitoring. 2012. (Ecological Research Monographs). (ENG., Illus.). xvi, 584p. 209.00 (**978-4-431-54031-1(8)**, 4431540318) Springer.

Nakashizuka, Tohru, ed. Sustainability & Diversity of Forest Ecosystems: An Interdisciplinary Approach. 2007. (Illus.). 90p. 109.00 (978-4-431-73237-2(3), 4431732373) Springer.

Nanjundaiah, Chikkavanu. Biodiversity,Indigenous Environmental Knowledge & Iprs. 2011. 148p. pap. (**978-3-8443-0978-2(0)**) Lambert Academic Publishing.

Ndenecho, Emmanuel Neba. Local Livelihoods & Protected Area Management Biodiversity Conservation Problems in Cameroon. 2011. 230p. pap. (**978-9956-717-54-5(1)**) Langaa Research & Publishing Common Initiative Group.

Newmark, W. D. Conserving Biodiversity in East African Forests: A Study of the Eastern Arc Mountains. 2010. (Ecological Studies). (Illus.). xii, 197p. pap. 129.00 (978-3-642-07629-9(7), 3642076297) Springer.

Nicholls, Henry. Lonesome George: The Life & Loves of a Conservation Icon. 2007. (MacSci Ser.). (ENG., Illus.). 256p. pap. 14.95 (978-0-330-45011-9(5)) Palgrave Macmillan.

Ninan, K. N., ed. Conserving & Valuing Ecosystem Services & Biodiversity: Economic, Institutional & Social Challenges. (ENG., Illus.). 432p. 2010. pap. 49.95 (978-1-84971-173-9(9)) 2008. 136.50 (978-1-84407-651-2(2)) Routledge.

Noe, Christine. Wilderness Expansion. 2010. 180p. pap. 56.00 (978-3-8383-4486-7(3)) Lambert Academic Publishing.

Ojoyi, Mercy. The Importance of GIS & Remote Sensing in Conservation: Application of Spatial Tools in Conservation. 2008. 104p. pap. (978-3-639-10248-2(7)) VDM Verlag Dr. Mueller e.K.

O'Reilly, Angus & Murphy, Doran. National Parks: Biodiversity, Conservation & Tourism. 2009. (Wildlife Protection, Destruction & Extinction Ser.). 129.00 (978-1-60741-465-0(1)) Nova Science Pubs., Inc.

Organisation for Economic Co-operation and Development Staff. People & Biodiversity Policies: Impacts, Issues, & Strategies for Policy Action. 2008. (ENG.). 200p. pap. 63.00 (978-92-64-03431-0(5)) Organization for Economic Cooperation & Development.

Pace, Thomas W., ed. New Developments in Biodiversity Conservation. 2011. (Series: Environmental Health - Physical, Chemical & Biological Factors Ser.). (Illus.). xii, 153p. 95.00 (978-1-61324-374-9(X)) Nova Science Pubs., Inc.

Paulsen, J., ed. Human Impacts on Tropical Forest Biodiversity & Genetic Resources. 2007. 500p. (C). 140.00 (978-0-85199-692-9(2)) Oxford Univ. Pr., Inc.

Pearson, Richard & American Museum of Natural History, New York Staff. Driven to Extinction: The Impact of Climate Change on Biodiversity. 2011. (ENG., Illus.). 264p. 22.95 (978-1-4027-7223-8(8)) Sterling Publishing Co., Inc.

Perfecto, Ivette, et al. Nature's Matrix: Linking Agriculture, Conservation & Food Sovereignty. 2009. (ENG., Illus.). 272p. 136.00 (978-1-84407-781-6(0)); pap. 34.95 (978-1-84407-782-3(9)) Routledge.

Pilgrim, Sarah & Pretty, Jules, eds. Nature & Culture: Rebuilding Lost Connections. 2010. (ENG., Illus.). 296p. 84.95 (978-1-84407-821-9(3)) Routledge.

Polisciano, Grazia & Farina, Olmo, eds. National Parks: Vegetation, Wildlife & Threats. 2010. (Wildlife Protection, Destruction & Extinction Ser.). 129.00 (978-1-60876-742-7(6)) Nova Science Pubs., Inc.

Primack, Richard B. A Primer of Conservation Biology. 4th rev. ed. 2008. (Illus.). 300p. (**978-0-87893-692-2(0)**) Sinauer Assocs., Inc.

Propper, Michael. Culture & Biodiversity in Central Kavango, Namibia. 2010. (ENG.). 456p. pap. 69.00 (978-3-496-02827-7(0), Art Stock Bks. Ltd/Csi) Continental Sales, Inc.

Puettmann, Klaus J., et al. A Critique of Silviculture: Managing for Complexity. 2008. (ENG., Illus.). 208p. 60.00 (978-1-59726-145-6(9)); 206p. pap. 30.00 (978-1-59726-146-3(7)) Island Pr.

Pungetti, Gloria, et al, eds. Sacred Species & Sites: Advances in Biocultural Conservation. 2012. (ENG., Illus.). 488p. 120.00 (**978-0-521-11085-3(8)**); pap. 60.00 (**978-0-521-12575-8(8)**) Cambridge Univ. Pr.

Rafferty, John P., ed. Conservation & Ecology. 2011. (Living Earth Ser.). (Illus.). 288p. (YA). 103.40 (978-1-61530-435-6(5)) Rosen Publishing Group, Inc., The.

Rai, Suresh C. Ecotourism & Biodiversity Conservation. 2011. (Economic Issues, Problems & Perspectives Tourism & Hospitality Development & Management Ser.). 158p. pap. 47.00 (**978-1-61324-242-1(5)**) Nova Science Pubs., Inc.

Raphael, Martin, et al, eds. Conservation of Rare or Little-Known Species: Biological, Social, & Economic Considerations. 2nd ed. 2007. (ENG., Illus.). 392p. 90.00 (978-1-59726-165-4(3)) Island Pr.

—Conservation of Rare or Little-Known Species: Biological, Social, & Economic Considerations. 2nd ed. 2007. (ENG., Illus.). 392p. pap. 45.00 (978-1-59726-166-1(1)) Island Pr.

Raymund I. Veritas, ed. Biodiversity Research Developments. 2008. (Illus.). (C). 89.00 (978-1-60456-253-8(6)) Nova Science Pubs., Inc.

Redlin, Janice L., ed. Saving the Natural World. 2006. (Understanding Global Issues Ser.). (Illus.). 56p. lib. bdg. 28.50 (978-1-59036-236-5(5)) Weigl Pubs., Inc.

Rescigno, Vittore & Maletta, Savario, eds. Biodiversity Hotspots. 2010. (Environmental Science, Engineering & Technology Ser.). (Illus.). xiv, 200p. 129.00 (978-1-60876-458-7(3)) Nova Science Pubs., Inc.

Restrepo Orrego, Carlos Ernesto. Apropiación Indebida de Recursos Genéticos, Biodiversidad y Conocimientos Tradicionales: "Biopiratería" 2006. (SPA.). 302p. pap. 25.00 (978-958-710-140-9(5)) Universidad Externado de Colombia COL. Dist: Siglo del Hombre.

Reynolds, Julian & Souty-Grosset, Catherine. Management of Freshwater Biodiversity: Crayfish as Bioindicators. 2011. (ENG., Illus.). 384p. 110.00 (**978-0-521-51400-2(2)**) Cambridge Univ. Pr.

Richerzhagen, Carmen. Protecting Biological Diversity: The Effectiveness of Access & Benefit-Sharing Regimes. 2010. (Routledge Studies in Development & Society Ser.). (ENG., Illus.). 266p. 125.00 (978-0-415-87224-9(3)) Routledge.

Roberts, Julian. Marine Environment Protection & Biodiversity Conservation: The Application & Future Development of the IMO's Particularly Sensitive Sea Area Concept. 2006. (ENG., Illus.). xxi, 289p. 219.00 (978-3-540-37697-2(6), 3540376976) Springer.

Rodriguez-Labajos, Beatriz, ed. Assessing Biodiversity Risks with Socio-Economic Methods: The ALARM Experience (Illustrated) 2009. 366p. pap. 147.50 (978-954-642-490-7(0)) Pensoft Pubs. BGR. Dist: Coronet Bks.

Roe, Dilys & Elliott, Joanna, eds. The Earthscan Reader in Poverty & Biodiversity Conservation. 2010. (Earthscan Reader Ser.). (ENG., Illus.). 416p. 136.00 (978-1-84407-842-4(6)) Routledge.

—Poverty & Biodiversity Conservation. 2010. (Earthscan Reader Ser.). (ENG., Illus.). 416p. pap. 39.95 (978-1-84407-843-1(4)) Routledge.

Rubioá, Irene M. Ecological Management: New Research. Alonso, Marta S., ed. 2008. (Illus.). 262p. (C). 129.00 (978-1-60456-786-1(4)) Nova Science Pubs., Inc.

Runas, Johan & Dahlgren, Theodor, eds. Grassland Biodiversity: Habitat Types, Ecological Processes & Environmental Impacts. 2010. (Environmental Science, Engineering & Technology Ser.). 145.00 (978-1-60876-542-3(3)) Nova Science Pubs., Inc.

Santilli, Juliana. Agrobiodiversity & the Law: Regulating Genetic Resources, Food Security & Cultural Diversity. 2011. xx, 348p. E-Book (**978-0-203-15525-7(4)**) Earthscan LLC.

—Agrobiodiversity & the Law: Regulating Genetic Resources, Food Security & Cultural Diversity. 2011. (ENG., Illus.). 368p. 99.95 (978-1-84971-372-6(3)) Routledge.

Savill, Peter, et al. Wytham Woods: Oxford's Ecological Laboratory. 2010. (ENG., Illus.). 288p. 99.00 (978-0-19-954320-5(8)) Oxford Univ. Pr., Inc.

Sax, Joseph. Ownership, Property, & Sustainability. 2011. 20p. (gr. 12). pap. 4.95 (978-1-60781-139-8(1)) Univ. of Utah Pr.

Scherr, Sara J. & McNeely, Jeffrey A. Farming with Nature: The Science & Practice of Ecoagriculture. Scherr, Sara J. & McNeely, Jeffrey A., eds. 2007. (ENG., Illus.). 472p. 75.00 (978-1-59726-127-2(0)); pap. 47.50 (978-1-59726-128-9(9)) Island Pr.

Schmid, Jutta & Alonso, Leeanne E., eds. Une Evaluation Biologique Rapide du Corridor Mantadia-Zahamena, Madagascar/A Rapid Biological Assessment of the Mantadia-Zahamena Corridor, Madagascar: Rap Bulletin of Biological Assessment #32. 2007. (Conservation International Rapid Assessment Program Ser.). (FRE & ENG., Illus.). 202p. per. 19.95 *(978-1-881173-86-1(0))* Conservation International.

Schmidt, John G. Alpine Environment: Geology, Ecology & Conservation. 2011. (Environmental Science, Engineering & Technology Ser.). (Illus.). x, 214p. 129.00 *(978-1-61209-392-5(2))* Nova Science Pubs., Inc.

Schmitz, Oswald J. Ecology & Ecosystem Conservation. 2007. (Foundations Contemporary Environmental Ser.). (ENG., Illus.). 184p. (C). pap. 22.50 *(978-1-59726-049-7(5))* Island Pr.

—Resolving Ecosystem Complexity. 2010. (Monographs in Population Biology Ser.). (ENG., Illus.). 176p. (C). pap. 35.00 *(978-0-691-12849-8(9))* Princeton Univ. Pr.

Seddon, Sue & Fry, Carolyn. The Last Great Plant Hunt: The Story of the Millennium Seed Bank Project. 2011. (Illus.). 192p. 46.00 *(978-1-84246-432-8(9))* Kew Publishing GBR. Dist: Chicago Distribution Ctr.

Settele, Josef, ed. Atlas of Biodiversity Risk. 2010. (Illus.). 264p. 250.00 *(978-954-642-446-4(3))* Pensoft Pubs. BGR. Dist: Coronet Bks.

Silvertown, Jonathan. Demons in Eden: The Paradox of Plant Diversity. 2008. (ENG., Illus.). 202p. pap. 16.00 *(978-0-226-75772-8(2))* Univ. of Chicago Pr.

Singh, R. B., ed. Biogeography & Biodiversity. 2009. (Illus.). 340p. 60.00 *(978-81-316-0248-5(6))* Rawat Pubns. IND. Dist: International Specialized Bk. Services.

Sivaperuman, C. Faunal Ecology & Conservation of the Great Indian Desert. 2008. (ENG., Illus.). xviii, 222p. 199.00 *(978-3-540-87408-9(9)*, 3540874089) Springer.

Sivasithamparam, K., et al, eds. Microorganisms in Plant Conservation & Biodiversity. 2010. (Illus.). 392p. pap. 259.00 *(978-90-481-6087-7(1)*, 9048160871) Springer.

Siy, Sherilyn. The Case of the Vanishing Tawilis. 2010. 112p. pap. *(978-3-639-26397-8(9))* VDM Verlag Dr. Mueller e.K.

Smagadi, Aphrodite. Medicinal Bioprospecting: Policy Options for Access & Benefit-Sharing. 2009. (Illus.). 231p. pap. 140.00 *(978-1-905221-36-3(3))* British Institute of International & Comparative Law GBR. Dist: International Specialized Bk. Services.

Smale, Melinda, ed. Farmers, Gene Banks & Crop Breeding: Economic Analyses of Diversity in Wheat, Maize, & Rice. 2010. (Natural Resource Management & Policy Ser.). 288p. pap. 159.00 *(978-1-4419-5068-0(0)*, 1441950680) Springer.

Soemodinoto, Arisetiarso. Relationship Between Tourism, National Park & Local People. 2010. 292p. pap. *(978-3-8383-9078-9(4))* Lambert Academic Publishing.

Spalding, Mark, et al. World Atlas of Mangroves. 2010. (Illus.). 336p. 99.95 *(978-1-84407-657-4(1))* Routledge.

Spenceley, Anna. Responsible Tourism: Critical Issues for Conservation & Development. Spenceley, Anna, ed. 2008. (ENG., Illus.). 416p. (C). 135.00 *(978-1-84407-639-0(3))* Routledge.

Spenceley, Anna, ed. Responsible Tourism: Critical Issues for Conservation & Development. 2010. (ENG., Illus.). 416p. pap. 49.95 *(978-1-84971-070-1(8))* Routledge.

Summers, Carolyn. Designing Gardens with Flora of the American East. 2010. (ENG., Illus.). 240p. pap. 23.95 *(978-0-8135-4707-7(5))* Rutgers Univ. Pr.

Sunderland, Terry C. H., et al, eds. Evidence-Based Conservation. 2012. (Earthscan Forest Library). (ENG., Illus.). 416p. (C). 125.00 ***(978-1-84971-394-8(4))*** Routledge.

Swaminathan, M. s. & Swaminathan, M. S. In Search of Biohappiness: Biodiversity & Food, Health & Livelihood Security. 2011. 184p. 88.00 ***(978-981-4329-32-3(0))*** World Scientific Publishing Co., Inc.

Thompson, Ken. Do We Need Pandas? The Uncomfortable Truth about Biodiversity. 2011. (ENG., Illus.). 160p. pap. 19.95 *(978-1-900322-86-7(2))* Green Bks. GBR. Dist: Chelsea Green Publishing.

Tibbett, Mark. Mining in Ecologically Sensitive Landscapes. 2012. (ENG.). 250p. (C). 129.95 ***(978-0-415-62091-8(0)***, CRC Press) Taylor & Francis Group GBR. Dist: Taylor & Francis Group.

Tomalin, Emma. Bio-Divinity & Biodiversity: The Limits to Religious Environmentalism for India. 2009. 230p. 99.95 *(978-0-7546-5588-6(1))* Ashgate Publishing Co.

Trisurat, Yongyut, et al, eds. Land Use, Climate Change & Biodiversity Modeling: Perspectives & Applications. 2011. 350p. 180.00 *(978-1-60960-619-0(1))* IGI Global.

United Nations. Dead Planet, Living Planet: Biodiversity & Ecosystem Restoration for Sustainable Development. 2010. 110p. pap. 30.00 *(978-82-7701-083-0(4))* United Nations Environment Programme KEN. Dist: National Bk. Network.

—Status & Potential of Commercial Bioprospecting Activities in Latin America & the Caribbean. 2007. (Medio Ambiente y Desarrollo Ser.). (ENG.). 68p. pap. 10.00 *(978-92-1-121648-6(6))* United Nations Pubns.

Usher, Michael. Conserving European biodiversity in the context of climate Change. 2007. (Nature & Environment Ser.: 149). 54p. pap. 15.00 *(978-92-871-6263-2(8))* Council of Europe FRA. Dist: Manhattan Publishing Co.

Vandermeer, John H. The Ecology of Agroecosystems. rev. ed. 2009. 392p. pap. 97.95 *(978-0-7637-7153-9(8))* Jones & Bartlett Learning, LLC.

Viaroli, P., et al. Lagoons & Coastal Wetlands in the Global Change Context: Impact & Management Issues: Selected papers of the International Conference CoastWetChange , Venice 26-28 April 2004. 2010. (Developments in Hydrobiology Ser.). vi, 170p. pap. 189.00 *(978-90-481-7501-7(1)*, 9048175011) Springer.

Viaroli, Pierluigi. Lagoons & Coastal Wetlands in the Global Change Context: Impact & Management Issues. 2008. (Developments in Hydrobiology Ser.). vi, 170p. 189.00 *(978-1-4020-6007-6(6))* Springer.

Victor M Toledo & Toledo, Victor M. La Biodiversidad de México: Inventarios, Manejos, Usos, Informática, Conservación E Importancia Cultural. 2011. (SPA.). 356p. pap. 30.00 ***(978-607-455-531-8(1))*** Fondo de Cultura Economica USA.

Villard, Marc-Andrè & Jonsson, Bengt Gunnar, eds. Setting Conservation Targets for Managed Forest Landscapes. 2009. (Conservation Biology Ser.). (ENG., Illus.). 426p. 132.00 *(978-0-521-87709-1(1))*; pap. 66.00 *(978-0-521-70072-6(8))* Cambridge Univ. Pr.

Vriesendorp, Corine, et al, eds. Ecuador: Cabeceras Cofanes-Chingual. 2010. (Field Museum - Rapid Biological Inventories Ser.). (ENG & SPA., Illus.). 318p. pap. 30.00 *(978-0-914868-73-6(X))* Field Museum of Natural History, Div. of Pubns.

—Peru: Sierra del Divisor. 2007. (Field Museum - Rapid Biological Inventories Ser.). (SPA & ENG., Illus.). 298p. per. 30.00 *(978-0-914868-69-9(1))* Field Museum of Natural History, Div. of Pubns.

Wale, Edilegnaw, et al, eds. The Economics of Managing Crop Diversity On-farm: Case studies from the Genetic Resources Policy Initiative. 2010. (Issues in Agricultural Biodiversity Ser.). (ENG., Illus.). 160p. 140.00 *(978-1-84971-221-7(2))* Routledge.

—The Economics of Managing Crop Diversity On-Farm: Case Studies from the Genetic Resources Policy Initiative. 2010. (Issues in Agricultural Biodiversity Ser.). (ENG., Illus.). 160p. pap. 49.95 *(978-1-84971-222-4(0))* Routledge.

Wambuguh, Oscar. Conservation of Biological Diversity in Developing Countries. 2010. 168p. pap. *(978-3-8383-4927-5(X))* Lambert Academic Publishing.

Wilson, Edward O. The Diversity of Life. 2010. (Questions of Science Ser.). (ENG., Illus.). 440p. pap. 21.95 *(978-0-674-05817-0(8)*, Belknap Pr.) Harvard Univ. Pr.

Wilson, Edward O. & New York State Biodiversity Research Institute Staff, contrib. by. Biological Diversity: The Oldest Human Heritage. (Illus.). ix, 58p. pap. *(978-1-55557-210-5(3))* New York State Museum.

Wittmer, Heidi, et al. The Economics of Ecosystems & Biodiversity in Local & Regional Policy & Management. 2012. (ENG., Illus.). 384p. 84.95 ***(978-1-84971-252-1(2))*** Routledge.

W'O Okot Uma, Rogers & Endeley, RoseMarie-Rita. Biodiversity & Gender for Sustainable Development: Perspectives. 2007. 256p. pap. 48.75 *(978-1-901127-30-0(3))* Studies Forum International GBR. Dist: Stylus Publishing, LLC.

Wolff, Matthias & Gardener, Mark, eds. The Role of Science for Conservation. 2012. (Routledge Explorations in Environmental Economics Ser.). (ENG., Illus.). 320p. (C). 125.00 *(978-0-415-68071-4(9))* Routledge.

Worboys, Graeme L., et al, eds. Connectivity Conservation Management: A Global Guide. 2010. (ENG., Illus.). 416p. 192.00 *(978-1-84407-603-1(2))*; pap. 79.95 *(978-1-84407-604-8(0))* Routledge.

Yahya, H. S. A. Biodiversity Conservation Ethics in Major Religions. 2010. 272p. 33.49 *(978-1-4520-6124-5(6))*; pap. 19.99 *(978-1-4520-6123-8(8))* AuthorHouse.

Yelfaanibe, Augustine. Biocultural Diversity & Natural Resources Management in Ghan. 2011. 132p. pap. ***(978-3-8443-3201-8(4))*** Lambert Academic Publishing.

Zachos, Frank E. & Habel, Jan Christian, eds. Biodiversity Hotspots: Distribution & Protection of Conservation Priority Areas. 2011. (ENG., Illus.). xvii, 546p. 139.00 *(978-3-642-20991-8(2)*, 3642209912) Springer.

Zhang, Wen-Jun. Grasslands: Types, Biodiversity & Impacts. 2011. (Environmental Health - Physical, Chemical & Biological Factors Ser.). 95.00 ***(978-1-61470-555-0(0))*** Nova Science Pubs., Inc.

BIODYNAMIC FARMING

see Organic Farming

BIODYNAMIC GARDENING

see Organic Gardening

BIOELECTRICITY

see Electrophysiology

BIOELECTROCHEMISTRY

Alkire, Richard C., et al, contrib. by. Bioelectrochemistry: Fundamentals, Applications & Recent Developments. 2012. (Advances in Electrochemical Sciences & Engineering Ser.: 31). (ENG., Illus.). 411p. 205.00 ***(978-3-527-32885-7(8)***, Wiley-VCH) Wiley, John & Sons, Inc.

Bartlett, P. N. Bioelectrochemistry: Fundamentals, Experimental Techniques & Applications. 2008. (ENG., Illus.). 494p. 275.00 *(978-0-470-84364-2(0)*, Wiley) Wiley, John & Sons, Inc.

Bernstein, Eias M. Bioelectrochemistry Research Developments. 2008. (Illus.). 239p. (C). 129.00 *(978-1-60456-360-3(5))* Nova Science Pubs., Inc.

Eliaz, Noam, ed. Applications of Electrochemistry & Nanotechnology in Biology & Medicine I, 2 vols. 2011. (Modern Aspects of Electrochemistry Ser.). (ENG., Illus.). xxiii, 425p. 189.00 *(978-1-4614-0346-3(4)*, 1461403464) Springer.

Eliaz, Noam, ed. Applications of Electrochemistry & Nanotechnology in Biology & Medicine II, 2 vols. 2011. (Modern Aspects of Electrochemistry Ser.). (ENG., Illus.). xx, 338p. 129.00 ***(978-1-4614-2136-8(5)***, 1461421365) Springer.

Fry, A., ed. Organic & Biological Electrochemistry (General) 2008. (ECS Transactions Ser.). 87p. pap. 62.00 *(978-1-60423-882-2(8))* Curran Assocs., Inc.

Geyer, Cyril. Electrodenitrification of Water Using the Enzyme Nitrate Reductase. 2010. 92p. pap. *(978-3-8383-1951-3(6))* Lambert Academic Publishing.

Hammerich, Ole & Ulstrup, Jens, eds. Bioinorganic Electrochemistry. 2007. (ENG., Illus.). xiv, 314p. 289.00 *(978-1-4020-6499-9(3)*, 1402064993) Springer.

Jaroszeski, Mark J., ed. Electrochemotherapy, Electrogenetherapy, & Transdermal Drug Delivery: Electrically Mediated Delivery of Molecules to Cells. 2010. (Methods in Molecular Medicine Ser.). (Illus.). 512p. pap. 140.00 *(978-1-61737-094-6(0)*, 1617370940) Humana Pr.

Koeppl, Heinz. Design & Analysis of Biomolecular Circuits: Engineering Approaches to Systems & Synthetic Biology. Koeppl, Heinz et al, eds. 2011. (ENG., Illus.). xiii, 402p. 179.00 *(978-1-4419-6765-7(6)*, 1441967656) Springer.

Ksenzhek, Octavian. Money: Virtual Energy. 2007. 212p. per. 25.95 *(978-1-58112-953-3(X))* Universal Pubs.

Rabaey, Korneel. Bio-electrochemical Systems: From Extracellular Electron Transfer to Biotechnological Application. 2009. (Integrated Environmental Technology Ser.). (Illus.). 524p. (C). *(978-1-84339-233-0(X))* IWA Publishing.

BIOENERGETICS

see also Cellular Signal Transduction; Energy Metabolism

Bakalova, Elena. Bio-Energy Diagnostics: Methods, procedures, Techniques. 2008. 208p. pap. 17.95 *(978-1-4401-0115-1(9))* iUniverse, Inc.

Berkin, Jeffrey W. Bioenergetics. 2011. (Biochemistry Research Trends Ser.). (Illus.). v, 265p. 129.00 *(978-1-61761-788-1(1))* Nova Science Pubs., Inc.

Cheetham, Norman W. H. Introducing Biological Energetics: How Energy & Information Control the Living World. 2010. (ENG., Illus.). 352p. 110.00 *(978-0-19-959371-2(X))*; pap. 55.95 *(978-0-19-957593-0(2))* Oxford Univ. Pr., Inc.

Cram101 Textbook Reviews. Outlines & Highlights for Exercise Physiology: Human Bioenergetics & Its Applications with PowerWeb Bind-in Card by George A. Brooks, ISBN. 2010. 398p. pap. 35.95 *(978-1-4288-5018-7(X))* Cram101 Inc.

Cuevas-Sosa, Alejandro. The Biotagonists of the Bioenergemal Unit. 2008. 488p. pap. *(978-1-906210-86-1(1))* Grosvenor Hse. Publishing Ltd.

Cuevas Sosa, Alejandro. Human Biotagonists: Bioenergemal Communication BELC. 2008. 644p. pap. 20.95 *(978-1-4327-2671-3(4))* Outskirts Pr., Inc.

Demirel, Yaar. Energy: Production, Conversion, Storage, Conservation, & Coupling. 2012. (Green Energy & Technology Ser.). (ENG., Illus.). xix, 507p. 89.95 ***(978-1-4471-2371-2(9)***, 1447123719) Springer.

Eden, Donna & Feinstein, David. Energy Medicine for Women: Aligning Your Body's Energies to Boost Your Health & Vitality. 2008. (ENG.). 352p. (gr. 12-18). 17.99 *(978-1-58542-647-8(4)*, Tarcher) Penguin Group (USA) Inc.

Essentials of Amino Acids in Sports. 2009. 99.50 *(978-1-58829-689-4(X))* Humana Pr.

Fairweather, I., ed. Cell Signalling in Prokaryotes & Lower Metazoa. 2012. (ENG.). viii, 412p. pap. 225.00 *(978-90-481-6483-7(4)*, 9048164834) Springer.

Feinstein, David & Eden, Donna. Energy Medicine: Balancing Your Body's Energies for Optimal Health, Joy, & VitalityUpdated & Expanded. rev. exp. ed. 2008. (ENG.). 432p. (gr. 12-18). 17.99 *(978-1-58542-650-8(4)*, Tarcher) Penguin Group (USA) Inc.

Gad, Gabriele. Keep Your Sacrum More Sacred. 2010. 112p. pap. 23.50 *(978-1-4457-2637-3(8))* Lulu Enterprises Inc.

Garby, Lars & Larsen, Poul S. Bioenergetics. 2008. (ENG., Illus.). 288p. pap. 38.99 *(978-0-521-06635-8(2))* Cambridge Univ. Pr.

Haynie, Donald. Biological Thermodynamics. 2nd rev. ed. 2008. (ENG., Illus.). 438p. pap. 64.00 *(978-0-521-71134-0(7))* Cambridge Univ. Pr.

Holst, Ulrich. The Healing Power of Energized Water: The New Science of Potentizing the World's Most Vital Resource. 2010. (ENG.). 1p. pap. 16.95 *(978-1-59477-338-9(6)*, Healing Arts Pr.) Inner Traditions International, Ltd.

Jorgensen, Sven Erik. Introduction to Systems Ecology. 2012. (Applied Ecology & Environmental Management Ser.). (ENG., Illus.). 360p. 99.95 *(978-1-4398-5501-0(3)*, CRC Press) Taylor & Francis Group GBR. Dist: Taylor & Francis Group.

Kang, Jie. Bioenergetics Primer for Exercise Science. 2007. (ENG., Illus.). 224p. (C). per. 44.00 *(978-0-7360-6241-1(6))* Human Kinetics Pubs.

Kerksick, Chad M., ed. Nutrient Timing. 2011. (ENG., Illus.). 373p. 79.95 ***(978-1-4398-3889-1(5)***, CRC Press) Taylor & Francis Group GBR. Dist: Taylor & Francis Group.

Kothari, Shanu. Bariatric & Metabolic Surgery, an Issue of Surgical Clinics. 2011. (Clinics: Surgery Ser.: 91-6). (ENG., Illus.). xv, 1140p. 110.00 ***(978-1-4557-1044-7(X)***, Saunders) Elsevier - Health Sciences Div.

Kurzynski, Michal. The Thermodynamic Machinery of Life. 2010. (Frontiers Collection). (Illus.). xiv, 431p. pap. 99.00 *(978-3-642-06284-1(9)*, 3642062349) Springer.

Levin, Robert, et al. Work Meets Life: Exploring the Integrative Study of Work in Living Systems. 2011. (ENG., Illus.). 272p. (gr. 17). 30.00 *(978-0-262-01412-0(2))* MIT Pr.

McNab, Brian K. Extreme Measures: The Ecological Energetics of Birds & Mammals. 2012. (ENG., Illus.). 336p. 100.00 ***(978-0-226-56122-6(4))***; pap. 35.00 ***(978-0-226-56123-3(2))*** Univ. of Chicago Pr.

Meyerhof, Wolfgang, et al, eds. Sensory & Metabolic Control of Energy Balance. 2010. (Results & Problems in Cell Differentiation Ser.). (Illus.). viii, 205p. 219.00 *(978-3-642-14425-7(X)*, 364214425X) Springer.

Nieri, Marco. Bioenergetic Landscape: La Progettazione Del Giardino Terapeutico Bioenergetico. 2009. (ITA., Illus.) 256p. *(978-88-513-0576-5(5))* Sistemi Editoriali.

Novogratz, Jacqueline. The Blue Sweater: Bridging the Gap Between Rich & Poor in an Interconnected World. 2009. (ENG., Illus.). 304p. 24.95 *(978-1-59486-915-0(4))* Rodale Pr., Inc.

Paehler, Moritz. Energyhomeostatic neurons of the mouse hypothalamus: Cellular properties of identified hypothalamic neurons that control energy balance in the mouse. 2011. 140p. pap. ***(978-3-8381-1942-7(8))*** Südwestdeutscher Verlag für Hochschulschriften AG & Co. KG.

Palmeira, Carlos & Moreno, António J., eds. Mitochondrial Bioenergetics: Methods & Protocols. 2011. (Methods in Molecular Biology Ser.). (ENG., Illus.). xi, 333p. 119.00 ***(978-1-61779-381-3(7)***, 1617793817) Humana Pr.

Pena, Antonio. La Energia y la Vida Bioenergia. (Ciencia para Todos Ser.). (SPA.). pap. 6.99 *(978-968-16-3479-7(9))* Fondo de Cultura Economica USA.

Peschek, Günter A., et al, eds. Bioenergetic Processes of Cyanobacteria: From Evolutionary Singularity to Ecological Diversity. 2011. (ENG., Illus.). xxxiv, 720p. 209.00 *(978-94-007-0352-0(X)*, 940070352X) Springer.

Saks, Valdur, ed. Molecular System Bioenergetics: Energy for Life. 2007. (ENG.). 633p. 270.00 *(978-3-527-31787-5(2)*, Wiley-VCH) Wiley, John & Sons, Inc.

Schäfer, G & Penefsky, Harvey. Bioenergetics: Energy Conservation & Conversion. 2010. (Results & Problems in Cell Differentiation Ser.). (Illus.). xviii, 312p. pap. 269.00 *(978-3-642-09736-2(7)*, 3642097367) Springer.

Schäfer, Günter, ed. Third European Bioenergetics Conference. 2009. (ENG., Illus.). 796p. pap. 95.00 *(978-0-521-10682-5(6))* Cambridge Univ. Pr.

Schafer, Gunter, et al. Bioenergetics: Energy Conservation & Conversion: Günter Schäfer, Harvey S. Penefsky, Editors. 2008. (Results & Problems in Cell Differentiation Ser.). (Illus.). 312p. 269.00 *(978-3-540-78621-4(X)*, 354078621X) Springer.

Schneider, Eric D. & Sagan, Dorion. Into the Cool: Energy Flow, Thermodynamics, & Life. 2006. (ENG., Illus.). 378p. per. 18.00 *(978-0-226-73937-3(6))* Univ. of Chicago Pr.

Scott, Christopher B. A Primer for the Exercise & Nutrition Sciences: Thermodynamics, Bioenergetics, Metabolism. 2010. (ENG., Illus.). xiv, 166p. pap. 99.00 *(978-1-61737-893-5(3)*, 1617378933) Humana Pr.

—A Primer for the Exercise & Nutrition Sciences: Thermodynamics, Bioenergetics, Metabolism. 2008. (ENG., Illus.). xiv, 166p. 99.00 *(978-1-60327-382-4(4)*, 1603273824) Springer.

Simpson, Stephen J. & Raubenheimer, David. The Nature of Nutrition: A Unifying Framework from Animal Adaptation to Human Obesity. 2012. (ENG., Illus.). 260p. (C). 49.50 ***(978-0-691-14565-5(2))*** Princeton Univ. Pr.

Smil, Vaclav. Energy in Nature & Society: General Energetics of Complex Systems. 2007. (ENG., Illus.). 496p. (gr. 17). per. 34.00 *(978-0-262-69356-1(9))* MIT Pr.

Smith, Kenneth. Awakening the Energy Body: From Shamanism to Bioenergetics. 2008. (ENG., Illus.). 1p. pap. 15.00 *(978-1-59143-084-1(4))* Bear & Co.

—Shamanism for the Age of Science. 2011. (ENG.). 1p. pap. 18.00 *(978-1-59143-119-0(0))* Bear & Co.

Smith, Kenneth. Shamanism for the Age of Science: Awakening the Energy Body. 2011. E-Book ***(978-1-59143-977-5(9))*** Bear & Co.

Urry, Dan W. What Sustains Life? Consilient Mechanisms for Proteing-Based Machines & Materials. 2006. (Illus.). xviii, 632p. 165.00 *(978-0-8176-4346-1(X)*, 081764346X) Springer.

Whipple, Thomas J. & Eckhardt, Robert. The Endurance Paradox: Bone Health for the Endurance Athlete. 2011. (ENG.). 220p. 94.00 *(978-1-59874-617-4(0))* Left Coast Pr., Inc.

BIOENERGY

see Biomass Energy

BIOENGINEERING

see also Agricultural Engineering; Biological Warfare; Bionics; Biosynthesis; Biotelemetry; Human Engineering; Life Support Systems (Space Environment)

American Society of Agricultural and Biological Engineers (ASABE) Staff, compiled by. Annual International Meeting of the American Society of Agricultural & Biological Engineers 2007. 2007. 7327p. pap. 1995.00 *(978-1-60423-961-4(1))* Curran Assocs., Inc.

American Society of Mechanical Engineers Staff, contrib. by. Advances in Aerospace Technology: IMECE 2008, 17 vols., Vol. 1. 2009. (ASME 2008 International Mechanical Engineering Congress & Exposition Ser.: Vol. 1). (Illus.). *(978-0-7918-4862-3(0))* American Society of Mechanical Engineers, The.

—Biomedical & Biotechnology Engineering: IMECE 2008, 17 vols. 2009. (ASME 2008 International Mechanical Engineering Congress & Exposition Ser.: Vol. 2). (Illus.). *(978-0-7918-4863-0(9))* American Society of Mechanical Engineers, The.

—Combustion Science & Engineering: IMECE 2008, 17 vols. 2009. (ASME 2008 International Mechanical Engineering Congress & Exposition Ser.: Vol. 3). (Illus.). *(978-0-7918-4864-7(7))* American Society of Mechanical Engineers, The.

—Design, Analysis, Control & Diagnosis of Fluid Power Systems: IMECE 2008, 17 vols. 2009. (ASME 2008 International Mechanical Engineering Congress & Exposition Ser.: Vol. 5). (Illus.). *(978-0-7918-4866-1(3))* American Society of Mechanical Engineers, The.

—Design & Manufacturing: IMECE 2008, 17 vols. 2009. (ASME 2008 International Mechanical Engineering Congress & Exposition Ser.: Vol. 4).

(Illus.). (978-0-7918-4865-4(5)) American Society of Mechanical Engineers, The.

—Electronics & Photonics: IMECE 2008, 17 vols. 2009. (ASME 2008 International Mechanical Engineering Congress & Exposition Ser.: Vol. 6). (Illus.). (978-0-7918-4867-8(1)) American Society of Mechanical Engineers, The.

—Emerging Technologies: Recent Advances in Engineering, IMECE 2008, 17 vols. 2009. (ASME 2008 International Mechanical Engineering Congress & Exposition Ser.: Vol. 7). (Illus.). (978-0-7918-4868-5(X)) American Society of Mechanical Engineers, The.

—Energy Systems; Analysis, Thermodynamics & Sustainability: Sustainable Products & Processes, IMECE 2008, 17 vols. 2009. (ASME 2008 International Mechanical Engineering Congress & Exposition Ser.: Vol. 8). (Illus.). (978-0-7918-4869-2(8)) American Society of Mechanical Engineers, The.

—Engineering Education & Professional Development: IMECE 2008, 17 vols. 2009. (ASME 2008 International Mechanical Engineering Congress & Exposition Ser.: Vol. 9). (Illus.). (978-0-7918-4870-8(1)) American Society of Mechanical Engineers, The.

—Heat Transfer, Fluid Flows, & Thermal Systems: Parts A, B, & C; IMECE 2008, 17 vols. 2009. (ASME 2008 International Mechanical Engineering Congress & Exposition Ser.: Vol. 10). (Illus.). (978-0-7918-4871-5(X)) American Society of Mechanical Engineers, The.

—Mechanical Systems & Control: IMECE 2008, 17 vols. 2009. (ASME 2008 International Mechanical Engineering Congress & Exposition Ser.: Vol. 11). (Illus.). (978-0-7918-4872-2(8)) American Society of Mechanical Engineers, The.

—Mechanics of Solids, Structures & Fluids: IMECE 2008, 17 vols. 2009. (ASME 2008 International Mechanical Engineering Congress & Exposition Ser.: Vol. 12). (Illus.). (978-0-7918-4873-9(6)) American Society of Mechanical Engineers, The.

—Nano-Manufacturing Technology: Micro & Nano Systems; Parts A & B, IMECE 2008, 17 vols. 2009. (ASME 2008 International Mechanical Engineering Congress & Exposition Ser.: Vol. 13). (Illus.). (978-0-7918-4874-6(4)) American Society of Mechanical Engineers, The.

—New Developments in Simulation Methods & Software for Engineering Applications: IMECE 2008, 17 vols. 2009. (ASME 2008 International Mechanical Engineering Congress & Exposition Ser.: Vol. 14). (Illus.). (978-0-7918-4875-3(2)) American Society of Mechanical Engineers, The.

—Proceedings of the ASME International Mechanical Engineering Congress & Exposition — 2009: Presented at 2009 ASME International Mechanical Engineering Congress & Exposition, November 13-19, 2009, Lake Buena Vista, Florida, USA, 15 vols. 2010. (Illus.). (978-0-7918-4380-2(7)); (978-0-7918-4379-6(3)); (978-0-7918-4378-9(5)); (978-0-7918-4377-2(7)); (978-0-7918-4376-5(9)); (978-0-7918-4386-4(6)); (978-0-7918-4387-1(4)); (978-0-7918-4388-8(2)); (978-0-7918-4375-8(0)); (978-0-7918-4374-1(2)); (978-0-7918-4382-6(3)); (978-0-7918-4383-3(1)); (978-0-7918-4381-9(5)); (978-0-7918-4385-7(8)); (978-0-7918-4384-0(X)) American Society of Mechanical Engineers, The.

—Proceedings of the ASME International Mechanical Engineering Congress & Exposition 2007: Presented at 2007 ASME International Mechanical Engineering Congress & Exposition, November 11-15, 2007, Seattle, Washington, USA. 2008. (Illus.). (978-0-7918-4306-2(8)); (978-0-7918-4310-9(6)); (978-0-7918-4309-3(2)); (978-0-7918-4308-6(4)); (978-0-7918-4304-8(1)); (978-0-7918-4305-5(X)); (978-0-7918-4302-4(5)); (978-0-7918-4295-9(9)); (978-0-7918-4296-6(7)); (978-0-7918-4297-3(5)); (978-0-7918-4298-0(3)); (978-0-7918-4299-7(1)); (978-0-7918-4300-0(9)); (978-0-7918-4307-9(6)) American Society of Mechanical Engineers, The.

—Processing & Engineering Applications of Novel Materials: IMECE 2008, 17 vols. 2009. (ASME 2008 International Mechanical Engineering Congress & Exposition Ser.: Vol. 15). (Illus.). (978-0-7918-4876-0(0)) American Society of Mechanical Engineers, The.

—Safety Engineering, Risk Analysis & Reliability Methods: IMECE 2008, 17 vols. 2009. (ASME 2008 International Mechanical Engineering Congress & Exposition Ser.: Vol. 16). (Illus.). (978-0-7918-4877-7(9)) American Society of Mechanical Engineers, The.

—Transportation Systems: IMECE 2008, 17 vols. 2009. (ASME 2008 International Mechanical Engineering Congress & Exposition Ser.: Vol. 17). (Illus.). (978-0-7918-4878-4(7)) American Society of Mechanical Engineers, The.

American Society of Mechanical Engineers Staff, ed. Advances in Bioengineering. 332p. 150.00 (978-0-7918-1934-0(5)) ASME Pr.

Anuntalabhochai, S., et al. Ion Beam Bioengineering Research. 2011. (Biotechnology in Agriculture, Industry & Medicine Ser.). pap. 43.00 (978-1-61209-529-5(1), Nova Novinka) Nova Science Pubs., Inc.

Arena, Paolo, et al. Bioengineered & Bioinspired Systems III: 2-4 May 2007 Maspalomas, Gran Canaria, Spain. 2007. (Proceedings of SPIE Ser.). (Illus.). 376p. pap. 90.00 (978-0-8194-6720-1(0)) SPIE.

Artmann, Gerhard M. & Chien, Shu. Bioengineering in Cell & Tissue Research. Artmann, Gerhard M. & Chien, Shu, eds. 2008. (Illus.). 500p. 159.00 (978-3-540-75408-4(3), 3540754083) Springer.

Barnes, Frank S. & Greenebaum, Ben. Bioengineering & Biophysical Aspects of Electromagnetic Fields. 3rd ed. 2006. (Handbook of Biological Effects of Electromagnetic Fields, 3Ed Ser.). (ENG., Illus.). 440p. 124.95 (978-0-8493-9539-0(9), 9539, CRC Press) Taylor & Francis Group GBR. Dist: Taylor & Francis Group.

Begg, Rezaul, et al. Computational Intelligence in Biomedical Engineering. 2007. (ENG., Illus.). 392p. 144.95 (978-0-8493-4080-2(2), CRC Press) Taylor & Francis Group GBR. Dist: Taylor & Francis Group.

Bioengineering Fluid Mechanics. 2011. 68.00 (978-981-4295-15-4(9)) World Scientific Publishing Co., Inc.

Borenstein, Jeffrey, ed. Micro & Nanoengineering of the Cell Microenvironment: Technologies & Applications. 2008. (Engineering in Medicine & Biology Ser.). (Illus.). 627p. 179.00 (978-1-59693-148-0(5)) Artech Hse., Inc.

Brebbia, C. A., ed. Modelling in Medicine & Biology. 2011. (Illus.). 220p. lib. bdg. 190.00 (978-1-84564-572-4(3)) WIT Pr GBR. Dist: WIT Pr.

—Modelling in Medicine & Biology VIII. 2009. (Transactions in Biomedicine & Health: 13). (Illus.). 352p. 239.00 (978-1-84564-183-2(3)) WIT Pr GBR. Dist: WIT Pr.

Brebbia, Carlos A., ed. Modelling in Medicine & Biology VII. 2007. (Transactions in Biomedicine & Health: 12). (Illus.). 352p. 232.00 (978-1-84564-089-7(6)) WIT Pr GBR. Dist: WIT Pr.

Chien. Introduction to Bioengineering (V4) 2008. pap. 61.00 (978-981-270-794-9(8)); (Illus.). xix, 542p. 110.00 (978-981-270-793-2(X)) World Scientific Publishing Co., Inc.

Chien, Shu. Tributes to Yuan-cheng Fung on His 90th Birthday: Biomechanics: from Molecules to Man. 2009. (Illus.). 364p. 88.00 (978-981-4289-87-0(6)) World Scientific Publishing Co., Inc.

Christensen, Douglas. Introduction to Biomedical Engineering: Biomechanics & Bioelectricity. 2009. (Synthesis Lectures on Biomedical Engineering Ser.). 262p. pap. 50.00 (978-1-59829-844-4(5)) Morgan & Claypool Pubs.

Committee on Improving Metrics for the Department of Defense, et al. Improving Metrics for the Department of Defense Cooperative Threat Reduction Program. 2012. (ENG.). 118p. pap. 38.00 **(978-0-309-22255-6(9))** National Academies Pr.

Conference, Arnold and Mabel Beckman Center, Irvine California, November 20-22, 2009 & The National Academies. NAKFI Synthetic Biology: Building a Nation's Inspiration: Interdisciplinary Research Team Summaries. 2010. (ENG.). 120p. pap. 31.00 (978-0-309-14942-6(8)) National Academies Pr.

Cram101 Textbook Reviews. Outlines & Highlights for Bioengineering Fundamentals by Ann Saterbak. 2010. 244p. pap. 31.95 (978-1-4288-5301-0(4)) Cram101 Inc.

Das, Sandhitsu. Seeing People Move Perception of Biological Motion by Intermediate-Level Motion Features & Its Use in Computer Vision. 2009. 120p. pap. (978-3-639-09891-4(9)) VDM Verlag Dr. Mueller e.K.

Davis, John & Stacey, Glyn N., eds. Medicines from Animal Cell Culture. 2007. (ENG.). 696p. 335.00 (978-0-470-85094-7(9), Wiley) Wiley, John & Sons, Inc.

Delvin, Edgard & Pham, Gisele. Vocabulary of Cell Engineering Vol. I: Cell Structure. 315p. pap. (978-0-660-57091-4(2)) Bow Historical Bks.

Di Carlo, Dino. Microfluidic Technologies for Single-Cell Analysis. 2009. 116p. pap. (978-3-639-13951-8(8)) VDM Verlag Dr. Mueller e.K.

do Carmo Nicoletti, Maria & Jain, Lakhmi C., eds. Computational Intelligence Techniques for Bioprocess Modelling, Supervision & Control. 2009. (Studies in Computational Intelligence Ser.). (Illus.). x, 346p. 179.00 (978-3-642-01887-9(4), 3642018874) Springer.

Dorgan, John R. & Ahmann, Dianne. Bioengineering for Sustainability: Materials & Fuels for the 21st Century. 2008. 400p. 115.00 (978-0-470-08574-5(6), Wiley-Interscience) Wiley, John & Sons, Inc.

Dunn, Stanley, et al. Bioengineering Bundle. 2008. (ENG.). pap. 111.00 (978-0-12-374859-1(3), Academic Pr.) Elsevier Science & Technology Bks.

Eibl, Regine, et al. Cell & Tissue Reaction Engineering. 2009. (Principles & Practice Ser.). (ENG., Illus.). xi, 363p. pap. 109.00 (978-3-642-01874-9(2), 3642018742) Springer.

Elsersawi, Amin. World of Nanobioengineering: Potential Big Ideas for the Future. 2010. 196p. pap. 19.99 (978-1-4520-3750-9(7)) AuthorHouse.

Emery, Christine. Selecting the President's Inner Cabinet. 2008. 144p. pap. (978-3-639-08100-8(5)) VDM Verlag Dr. Mueller e.K.

Farkas, Dora. Development of a Collagen Gel Sandwich Hepatocyte Bioreactor. 2010. 156p. pap. (978-3-8383-5016-5(2)) Lambert Academic Publishing.

Flynne, William G., ed. Biotechnology & Bioengineering. 2008. (Illus.). xii, 272p. 129.00 (978-1-60456-067-1(3), Nova Biomedical Bks.) Nova Science Pubs., Inc.

Frenay, Robert. Pulse: The Coming Age of Systems & Machines Inspired by Living Things. 2008. (ENG., Illus.). 576p. pap. 24.95 (978-0-8032-1777-5(3), Bison Bks.) Univ. of Nebraska Pr.

Ghallab, Yehya H. & Badawy, Wael. Lab-on-a-Chip: Techniques, Circuits, & Biomedical Applications. 2010. (Illus.). 330p. 129.00 (978-1-59693-418-4(2)) Artech Hse., Inc.

Howard, Daniel. Frontiers in the Covergence of Bioscience & Information Technologies; Proceedings. Conference on Frontiers in the Covergence of Bioscience & InformationTechnologies (2007: Jeju Island, Korea) 2007. 907p. pap. 288.00 (978-0-7695-2999-8(2)) IEEE Computer Society Pr.

IEEE Staff. 2007 IEEE 7th International Symposium on BioInformatics & BioEngineering. 2007. pap. 268.00 (978-1-4244-1509-0(8)) IEEE.

Jaramillo, Alfonso, ed. Model-Based Design in Synthetic Biology. 2010. (Illus.). 306p. 69.95 (978-1-4200-8355-2(4), Chapman & Hall/CRC) CRC Pr. LLC.

Jenkins, Christopher H. M. Bio-Inspired Engineering. 2011. 156p. 109.95 **(978-1-60650-223-5(9))** Momentum Pr.

Kai, Li. Chemical, Biological & Environmental Engineering: Proceedings of the International Conference on Cbee 2009. 2009. (Illus.). 548p. 212.00 (978-981-4293-46-4(6)) World Scientific Publishing Co., Inc.

King, Michael R. & Mody, Nipa A. Numerical & Statistical Methods for Bioengineering: Applications in MATLAB. 2010. (Cambridge Texts in Biomedical Engineering Ser.). (ENG., Illus.). 594p. (C). 115.00 (978-0-521-87158-7(1)) Cambridge Univ. Pr.

Kojic, Milos, et al. Computer Modeling in Bioengineering: Theoretical Background, Examples & Software. 2008. (ENG., Illus.). 466p. 165.00 (978-0-470-06035-3(2), Wiley) Wiley, John & Sons, Inc.

Madabhushi, Anant & Udupa, Jayaram. Generalized Scale: Theory, Algorithms & Applications in Medical Image Analysis. 2008. 176p. pap. (978-3-8364-7378-1(X)) VDM Verlag Dr. Mueller e.K.

Madhavan, Guruprasad, et al, eds. Career Development in Bioengineering & Biotechnology. 2008. (Series in Biomedical Engineering Ser.). (Illus.). XLVIII, 536p. pap. 59.95 (978-0-387-76494-8(1), 0387764941) Springer.

Maguire, Tim & Novik, Eric. Methods in Bioengineering: Alternatives to Animal Testing. 2010. (Illus.). 295p. 139.00 (978-1-60807-011-4(5)) Artech Hse., Inc.

Mahfouf, Mahdi. Intelligent Systems Modeling & Decision Support in Bioengineering. 2006. (Artech House Engineering in Medicine & Biology Ser.). (Illus.). 342p. 149.00 (978-1-58053-998-2(X)) Artech Hse., Inc.

Maina, John N. Bioengineering Aspects in the Design of Gas Exchangers: Comparative Evolutionary, Morphological, Functional, & Molecular Perspectives. 2011. (ENG., Illus.). xiv, 329p. 189.00 (978-3-642-20394-7(9), 3642203949) Springer.

Marbis, Juan. Co2 Enrichment & Hot Water Heat in a Greenhouse. 2010. 148p. pap. (978-3-8383-3145-4(1)) Lambert Academic Publishing.

Mehta, Manav. Mechanically Assisted Corrosion of Stainless Steel Alloys. 2009. 128p. pap. (978-3-639-14961-6(0)) VDM Verlag Dr. Mueller e.K.

Morgan. Slope Stabilization & Erosion Control: A Bioengineering Approac. 2nd rev. ed. 2009. (Illus.). CCLXXXVIIIp. 110.00 (978-0-415-42757-9(6)) Taylor & Francis Group.

National Academies Keck Futures Initiative Healthspan Steering Committee. The National Academies Keck Futures Initiative: The Future of Human Healthspan - Demography, Evolution, Medicine, & Bioengineering, Task Group Summaries. 2008. (ENG.). 140p. pap. 34.50 (978-0-309-11559-9(0)) National Academies Pr.

Oshida, Yoshiki. Bioscience & Bioengineering of Titanium Materials. 2006. (ENG., Illus.). 448p. 255.00 (978-0-08-045142-8(X), Elsevier Science) Elsevier Science & Technology Bks.

Ostafin, Agnes, et al. Nanoreactor Engineering for Life Sciences & Medicine. 2008. (Illus.). 330p. 129.00 (978-1-59693-158-9(2)) Artech Hse., Inc.

Pilla, Srikanth, ed. Handbook of Bioplastics & Biocomposites Engineering Applications. 2011. (Wiley-Scrivener Ser.: 24). (ENG., Illus.). 620p. 195.00 (978-0-470-62607-8(0), Wiley-Scrivener) Wiley, John & Sons, Inc.

Planning Committee on Information-Sharing Models and Guidelines for Collaboration: Applications to an Integrated One Health Biosurveillance Strategy-A Workshop & Institute of Medicine. Information Sharing & Collaboration: Applications to Integrated Biosurveillance: Workshop Summary. 2012. (ENG.). 112p. pap. 37.00 **(978-0-309-22403-1(9))** National Academies Pr.

Poon, Chi-Sang. Analysis of Complex Biosystems: Linear, Nonlinear & Adaptive Systems. 2010. (Illus.). (978-0-387-98843-6(2)) Springer.

Ramachandran Kb Staff. Process Engineering in Biotechnology. 2009. 600p. 169.95 (978-1-57444-515-2(4)) CRC Pr. LLC.

RodriGuez-VáZquez, Ángel, et al. Bioelectronics, Biomedical, & Bioinspired Systems V; & Nanotechnology V. 2011. (Proceedings of SPIE Ser.). 380p. pap. 105.00 **(978-0-8194-8657-8(4))** SPIE.

Rodriguez-Vázquez, Ángel, et al. Bioengineered & Bioinspired Systems IV: 4-6 May 2009, Dresden, Germany. 2009. (Proceedings of SPIE Ser.). (Illus.). 236p. pap. 70.00 (978-0-8194-7639-5(0)) SPIE.

Roelof van der Meer, Jan. Concepts & Engineering in Synthetic Biosensing. 2010. (Synthesis Lectures on Synthetic Biology Ser.). 100p. pap. 40.00 (978-1-59829-911-3(5)) Morgan & Claypool Pubs.

Sabounchi, Poorya. Lab-on-Chip for Pathogen Detection & Cell Analysis. 2008. 140p. pap. (978-3-8364-7261-6(9)) VDM Verlag Dr. Mueller e.K.

Sahan, Yasemin. Determination of Some Heavy Metal Content of Black Olives Cv Gemlik. 2011. 172p. pap. **(978-3-8443-3176-9(X))** Lambert Academic Publishing.

Saterbak, Ann, et al. Bioengineering Fundamentals. 2007. (ENG., Illus.). 552p. (C). 191.00 (978-0-13-093838-1(6), Prentice Hall) Prentice Hall PTR.

Soto-Gutierrez, Alejando, et al, eds. Methods in Bioengineering: Cell Transplantation. 2011. (Illus.). 320p. 139.00 (978-1-60807-015-2(8)) Artech Hse., Inc.

Srivastava, Sarvesh Kumar & Joshi, Namrata. Biosurfactant Production & Characterization. 2010. 96p. pap. (978-3-8383-6022-5(2)) Lambert Academic Publishing.

Starita, A., et al. Computational Intelligence & Bioengineering: Essays in Memory of Antonina Starita. 2009. (Illus.). 213p. 145.00 (978-1-60750-010-0(8)) IOS Pr., Inc.

Stavroulakis, Peter, ed. Biological Effects of Electromagnetic Fields: Mechanisms, Modeling, Biological Effects, Therapeutic Effects, International Standards, Exposure Criteria. 2010. (Illus.). xv, 793p. pap. 319.00 (978-3-642-07697-8(1), 3642076971) Springer.

Stokes, A. Eco- & Ground Bio-Engineering: The Use of Vegetation to Improve Slope Stability: Proceedings of the First International Conference on Eco-Engineering, 13-17 September 2004. 2007. (Developments in Plant & Soil Sciences Ser.). (Illus.). ix, 438p. 265.00 **(978-1-4020-5592-8(7),** 1402055927) Springer.

Stokes, A., et al, eds. Eco- & Ground Bio-Engineering: the Use of Vegetation to Improve Slope Stability: Proceedings of the First International Conference on Eco-Engineering 13-17 September 2004. 2010. (Developments in Plant & Soil Sciences Ser.). ix, 438p. pap. 265.00 (978-90-481-7403-4(1), 9048174031) Springer.

Tarbell, John M., ed. Advances in Bioengineering 1993. (BED Ser.: Vol. 26). 658p. pap. 90.00 (978-0-7918-1031-6(3)) American Society of Mechanical Engineers, The.

Taylor, John G. Bioengineering for Pollution Prevention. 2009. (Illus.). 189p. 79.00 (978-1-60692-900-1(3)) Nova Science Pubs., Inc.

Technology Research Editors, ed. Prosthetic Devices Bioengineering, 2007 Ed. 2007. pap. 128.50 (978-1-60030-501-6(6), Search-In-Print) CSA Journal Division.

Tripathi, G., ed. Cellular & Biochemical Science. 2010. 1392p. (C). pap. (978-81-88237-85-2(X)) I.K. International Publishing House Pvt. Ltd.

Uygun, Korkut & Lee, Charles Y., eds. Methods in Bioengineering: Organ Preservation & Reengineering. 2011. (Illus.). 282p. 139.00 (978-1-60807-013-8(1)) Artech Hse., Inc.

Vidakovic, Brani. Statistics for Bioengineering Sciences: With MATLAB & WinBUGS Support. 2011. (Springer Texts in Statistics Ser.). (ENG., Illus.). xvi, 753p. 129.00 **(978-1-4614-0393-7(6),** 1461403936) Springer.

Voigt, Chris, ed. Synthetic Biology: Methods for Part/Device Characterization & Chassis Engineering, 2 vols. 2011. (ENG., Illus.). 714p. 187.00 (978-0-12-385075-1(4), Academic Pr.) Elsevier Science & Technology Bks.

—Synthetic Biology Pt. B: Computer Aided Design & DNA Assembly, 2 vols. 2011. (ENG., Illus.). 550p. 187.00 (978-0-12-385120-8(3), Academic Pr.) Elsevier Science & Technology Bks.

Wang, Lawrence K. Environmental Bioengineering. 2010. (Illus.). xxviii, 867p. E-Book **(978-1-60327-031-1(0))** Humana Pr.

Wang, Lawrence K., et al, eds. Environmental Bioengineering, Vol. 11. 2007. (Handbook of Environmental Engineering Ser.). (Illus.). 465p. 209.00 (978-1-58829-493-7(5), 1588294935) Humana Pr.

Weber, Wilfried & Fussenegger, Martin, eds. Synthetic Gene Networks: Methods & Protocols. 2011. (Methods in Molecular Biology Ser.). (ENG., Illus.). xi, 393p. 139.00 **(978-1-61779-411-7(2),** 1617794112) Humana Pr.

Wilhelm, Klaus P., ed. Bioengineering of the Skin: Skin Imaging & Analysis. 2nd rev. ed. 2006. (Dermatology: Clinical & Basic Science Ser.). (Illus.). 497p. 250.00 (978-0-8493-3817-5(4)) Taylor & Francis Group.

Wittmann, Christoph. Biosystems Engineering II: Linking Cellular Networks & Bioprocesses, 2 vols. Wittmann, Christoph & Krull, Rainer, eds. 2010. (Advances in Biochemical Engineering Biotechnology Ser.). (Illus.). xii, 166p. 299.00 (978-3-642-13865-2(9), 3642138659) Springer.

Wittmann, Christoph & Krull, Rainer, eds. Biosystems Engineering I: Creating Superior Biocatalysts, 2 vols. 2010. (Advances in Biochemical Engineering Biotechnology Ser.). (Illus.). xiii, 247p. 299.00 (978-3-642-14230-7(3), 3642142303) Springer.

Wu, Wan-Yu. Metal-Containing Hydrogenated Amorphous Carbon Thin Films. 2009. 192p. pap. (978-3-639-14095-8(8)) VDM Verlag Dr. Mueller e.K.

Zagal, J. H., et al, eds. N4-Macrocyclic Metal Complexes. 2006. (Illus.). xviii, 814p. 224.00 (978-0-387-28429-3(X), 038728429X) Springer.

Zahn, Jeffrey D. Methods in Bioengineering: Biomicrofabrication & Biomicrofluidics. 2009. (Illus.). 384p. 129.00 (978-1-59693-400-9(X)) Artech Hse., Inc.

Zhang, Mingjun, et al. Life Science Automation Fundamentals & Applications. 2007. (Illus.). 507p. 179.00 (978-1-59693-105-3(1)) Artech Hse., Inc.

2007 IEEE 33rd Annual Northeast Bioengineering Conference. 2007. pap. 340.00 (978-1-4244-1032-3(0), 07CH37883) IEEE.

BIOETHICS

see also Biology—Social Aspects; Medical Ethics

Allen, James. Health Law & Medical Ethics. rev. ed. 2011. (ENG.). 272p. (C). pap. 73.27 incl. cd-rom **(978-0-13-502799-8(3),** Prentice Hall) Prentice Hall PTR.

Amendola, Adalgiso. Biopolitica, Bioeconomia e Processi Di Soggettivazione. 2008. (ITA.). 431p. (978-88-7462-231-3(7)) Quodlibet.

Anderson, Stanley. Reform in a Prison Hospital: A dramatic case study of bioethics, criminal justice & public Administration. 2009. 220p. pap. 17.95 (978-0-595-53208-7(X)) iUniverse, Inc.

Annas, George. American Bioethics: Crossing Human Rights & Health Law Boundaries. 2009. (ENG.). 264p. pap. 26.99 (978-0-19-539029-2(6)) Oxford Univ. Pr., Inc.

Annas, George J. Worst Case Bioethics: Death, Disaster, & Public Health, 1 vol. 2010. (ENG.). 360p. 39.95 (978-0-19-539173-2(X)) Oxford Univ. Pr., Inc.

Arnold, Denis G., ed. Ethics & the Business of Biomedicine. 2009. (ENG., Illus.). 302p. 93.00 (978-0-521-76431-5(9)); pap. 30.99 (978-0-521-74822-3(4)) Cambridge Univ. Pr.

Ashcroft, Richard Edmund, et al, eds. Principles of Health Care Ethics. 2nd rev. ed. 2007. (ENG., Illus.). 864p. 407.00 (978-0-470-02713-4(4), Wiley) Wiley, John & Sons, Inc.

Ashley, Benedict M., et al. Health Care Ethics: A Catholic Theological Analysis. 5th rev. ed. 2006. (ENG., Illus.). 352p. (C). pap. 39.95 (978-1-58901-116-8(3)) Georgetown Univ. Pr.

Atighetchi, Dariusch. Islamic Bioethics: Problems & Perspectives. 2008. (International Library of Ethics, Law, & the New Medicine Ser.). (ENG.). xiv, 378p. pap. 69.95 (978-1-4020-9615-0(1), 1402096151) Springer.

—Islamic Bioethics: Problems & Perspectives: Problems & Perspectives. 2006. (International Library of Ethics, Law, & the New Medicine Ser.: Vol. 31). (ENG.). xiv, 378p. 239.00 (978-1-4020-4961-3(7), 1402049617) Springer.

Austriaco, Nicanor Pier Giorgio. Biomedicine & Beatitude: An Introduction to Catholic Bioethics. 2011. (Corpus de Mosaiques Ser.). 336p. 44.95

(978-0-8132-1881-6(0)); (ENG.). pap. 24.95 ***(978-0-8132-1882-3(9))*** Catholic Univ. of America Pr.

Baldwin-Ragaven, Laurel E. Feminist Bioethics: At the Center, on the Margins. Scully, Jackie Leach & Fitzpatrick, Petya, eds. 2010. (ENG.). 328p. (C). (gr. 13-17). 75.00 *(978-0-8018-9424-4(7))* Johns Hopkins Univ. Pr.

Barry, Vincent. Bioethics in a Cultural Context: Philosophy, Religion, History, Politics. 2011. (ENG.). 464p. (C). pap. 57.95 *(978-0-495-81408-5(3))* Wadsworth.

Beauchamp, Tom L. Standing on Principles: Collected Essays, 1 vol. 2010. (ENG., Illus.). 320p. 55.00 *(978-0-19-973718-5(5))* Oxford Univ. Pr., Inc.

Beauchamp, Tom L., et al. Contemporary Issues in Bioethics. 7th ed. 2007. (ENG., Illus.). 816p. (C). per. 183.95 *(978-0-495-00673-2(4))* Wadsworth.

Bedau, Mark A. & Parke, Emily C., eds. The Ethics of Protocells: Moral & Social Implications of Creating Life in the Laboratory. 2009. (Basic Bioethics Ser.). (ENG., Illus.). 384p. (gr. 17). 55.00 *(978-0-262-01262-1(6))*; pap. 29.00 *(978-0-262-51269-5(6))* MIT Pr.

Bennett, Belinda & Tomossy, George F., eds. Globalization & Health: Challenges for health law & Bioethics. 2010. (International Library of Ethics, Law, & the New Medicine Ser.). xv, 218p. pap. 219.00 *(978-90-481-7067-8(2)*, 9048170672) Springer.

Berkshire Encyclopedia of Religion, Science, Medicine, & Bioethics. 2007. lib. bdg. 395.00 *(978-0-9770159-8-6(X))* Berkshire Publishing Group.

Bhattacharyya, Swasti. Magical Progeny, Modern Technology: A Hindu Bioethick of Assisted Reproductive Technology. 2006. 161p. per. 29.95 *(978-0-7914-6792-3(9))* State Univ. of New York Pr.

—Magical Progeny, Modern Technology: A Hindu Bioethics of Assisted Reproductive Technology. 2006. x, 161p. (C). 68.50 *(978-0-7914-6791-6(0))* State Univ. of New York Pr.

Borovecki, Ana. Ethics Committees in Croati. 2009. 104p. pap. *(978-3-639-17299-7(X))* VDM Verlag Dr. Mueller e.K.

Bosk, Charles L. What Would You Do? Juggling Bioethics & Ethnography. 2008. 288p. 50.00 *(978-0-226-06676-9(2))*; (ENG.). pap. 20.00 *(978-0-226-06677-6(0))* Univ. of Chicago Pr.

Brassington, Iain. Bioscience & the Good Life. 2013. (ENG.). 208p. 85.00 ***(978-1-84966-338-0(6)***, 21271) Bloomsbury Publishing.

Brennan, William. John Paul II: Confronting the Language Empowering the Culture of Death. 2008. xix, 151p. pap. *(978-1-932589-44-3(9)*, Sapientia Pr.) Ave Maria Univ.

Briggle, Adam, ed. A Rich Bioethics: Public Policy, Biotechnology, & the Kass Council. 2010. (ND Studies in Medical Ethics Ser.). (ENG.). 240p. pap. 30.00 *(978-0-268-02221-1(6))* Univ. of Notre Dame Pr.

Brimah, Josephus. The Ethics of Human Cloning. 2010. 192p. pap. *(978-3-8383-4783-7(8))* Lambert Academic Publishing.

Brockopp, Jonathan E. & Eich, Thomas. Muslim Medical Ethics: From Theory to Practice. Brockopp, Jonathan E. & Eich, Thomas, eds. 2008. (Illus.). 280p. pap. 24.95 *(978-1-57003-753-5(1))* Univ. of South Carolina Pr.

Brody, Howard. The Future of Bioethics. 2009. (ENG.). 288p. 49.95 *(978-0-19-537794-1(X))* Oxford Univ. Pr., Inc.

Buchanan, Allen E. Better Than Human: The Promise & Perils of Enhancing Ourselves, 1 vol. 2011. (Philosophy in Action Ser.). (ENG.). 208p. 21.95 *(978-0-19-979787-5(0))* Oxford Univ. Pr., Inc.

Camenisch, P. F., ed. Religious Methods & Resources in Bioethics. 2010. (Theology & Medicine Ser.). 356p. pap. 369.00 *(978-90-481-4235-4(0)*, 9048142350) Springer.

Caplan, Arthur L. Smart Mice, Not So Smart People: An Interesting & Amusing Guide to Bioethics. 2006. (ENG.). 224p. 23.95 *(978-0-7425-4171-9(1))* Rowman & Littlefield Publishers, Inc.

—Smart Mice, Not-So-Smart People: An Interesting & Amusing Guide to Bioethics. 2008. (ENG.). 224p. per. 19.95 *(978-0-7425-4172-6(X))* Rowman & Littlefield Publishers, Inc.

Caplan, Arthur L., et al. The Penn Center Guide to Bioethics. 2009. (Illus.). 700p. 65.00 *(978-0-8261-1522-5(5))* Springer.

Carlson, Elof Axel. Times of Triumph, Times of Doubt: Science & the Battle for Public Trust. 2006. (ENG.). 227p. 39.00 *(978-0-87969-805-8(5))* Cold Spring Harbor Laboratory Pr.

Carlson, Robert H., et al. Biology Is Technology: The Promise, Peril, & New Business of Engineering Life. 2011. (ENG., Illus.). 288p. pap. 21.95 *(978-0-674-06015-9(6))* Harvard Univ. Pr.

Carson, Ronald A. & Burns, C. R., eds. Philosophy of Medicine & Bioethics: A Twenty-Year Retrospective & Critical Appraisal. 2010. (Philosophy & Medicine Ser.). 360p. pap. 259.00 *(978-90-481-4569-0(4)*, 9048145694) Springer.

Catholic Medical Association Staff & National Catholic Bioethics Center Staff, contrib. by. A Catholic Guide to Ethical Clinical Research. 2009. (ENG.). 68p. pap. 9.95 *(978-0-935372-53-3(9))* National Catholic Bioethics Ctr., The.

Chadwick, Ruth, et al, eds. The Bioethics Reader: Editors' Choice. 2007. (ENG.). 600p. pap. 39.95 *(978-1-4051-7522-7(2)*, Wiley-Blackwell) Wiley, John & Sons, Inc.

Charrow, Robert. Law in the Laboratory: A Guide to the Ethics of Federally Funded Science Research. 2010. (ENG., Illus.). 336p. 80.00 *(978-0-226-10164-4(9))*; pap. 29.00 *(978-0-226-10165-1(7))* Univ. of Chicago Pr.

Cherry, Mark. Religious Perspectives on Bioethics. 2009. 244p. pap. 34.00 *(978-0-415-54413-9(0)*, Taylor & Francis) Taylor & Francis Group GBR. Dist: Taylor & Francis Group.

Cherry, Mark & Iltis, Ana Smith, eds. Pluralistic Casuistry: Moral Arguments, Economic Realities, & Political Theory. 2007. (Philosophy & Medicine Ser.). 272p. (C). 159.00 *(978-1-4020-6259-9(1))* Springer.

Cherry, Mark J. & Smith Iltis, Ana, eds. Pluralistic Casuistry: Moral Arguments, Economic Realities, & Political Theory. 2010. (Philosophy & Medicine Ser.). xii, 260p. pap. 159.00 *(978-90-481-7586-4(0)*, 9048175860) Springer.

Chochinov, Harvey Max & Breitbart, William, eds. Handbook of Psychiatry in Palliative Medicine, 1 vol. 2nd ed. 2012. (ENG.). 592p. pap. 59.99 ***(978-0-19-986286-3(9))*** Oxford Univ. Pr., Inc.

Ciancio, Jack. Where Christ Presides: A Quaker Perspective on Moral Discernment. 2009. 176p. pap. 15.99 ***(978-1-4141-1376-0(5))*** Pleasant Word.

Cohn, Felicia G. & Eckenwiler, Lisa A., eds. The Ethics of Bioethics: Mapping the Moral Landscape. 2007. (ENG.). 352p. (gr. 17). 50.00 *(978-0-8018-8609-6(0))* Johns Hopkins Univ. Pr.

Cole-Tuner, Ronald, ed. Design & Destiny: Jewish & Christian Perspectives on Human Germline Modification. 2008. (Basic Bioethics Ser.). (ENG.). 248p. (gr. 17). per. 23.00 *(978-0-262-53301-0(4))* MIT Pr.

Cole-Turner, Ronald, ed. Design & Destiny: Jewish & Christian Perspectives on Human Germline Modification. 2008. (Basic Bioethics Ser.). (ENG.). 248p. (gr. 17). 58.00 *(978-0-262-03373-2(9))* MIT Pr.

Comstock, Gary L., ed. Life Science Ethics. 2nd ed. 2010. (ENG., Illus.). xxix, 482p. 69.95 *(978-90-481-8791-1(5)*, 9048187915) Springer.

Conner, Lindsey. Learning about Social-Ethical Issues Using Evaluative Constructivism. 2010. 264p. pap. *(978-3-639-22937-0(1))* VDM Verlag Dr. Mueller e.K.

Cook, William A. Issues in Bioethics & the Concept of Scale. 2008. (American University Studies V: Philosophy Ser.: Vol. 202). 146p. (C). 58.95 *(978-1-4331-0199-1(8))* Lang, Peter Publishing, Inc.

Corkery, Padraig. Bioethics & the Catholic Moral Tradition. 2011. (ENG.). 144p. pap. 18.95 *(978-1-84730-245-8(9))* Veritas Pubns. IRL. Dist: Dufour Editions, Inc.

Cram101 Textbook Reviews. Outlines & Highlights for Bioethics: Introduction for the biosciences by Ben Mepham, ISBN. 2011. 610p. pap. 30.95 ***(978-1-61490-447-2(2))*** Cram101 Inc.

Cram101 Textbook Reviews & Cram101 Textbook Reviews. Outlines & Highlights for Bioethics: Principles, Issues, & Cases by Lewis Vaughn, ISBN. 2011. 86p. pap. 27.95 ***(978-1-61461-703-7(1))*** Cram101 Inc.

—Outlines & Highlights for Health Care Ethics by Thomas M Garrett, Isbn: 9780132187909 0132187906. 2011. 90p. pap. 27.95 ***(978-1-61490-165-5(1))*** Cram101 Inc.

Dabrock, Peter, et al. Trust in Biobanking: Dealing with Ethical, Legal & Social Issues in an Emerging Field of Biotechnology. Dabrock, Peter et al, eds. 2010. (Veröffentlichungen des Instituts für Deutsches, Europäisches und Internationales Medizinrecht, Gesundheitsrecht und Bioethik der Universitäten Heidelberg und Mannheim Ser.). (ENG.). 350p. pap. 139.00 *(978-3-540-78844-7(1)*, 3540788441) Springer.

Daniels, Norman & Sabin, James E. Setting Limits Fairly: Learning to Share Resources for Health. 2nd ed. 2008. (ENG., Illus.). 256p. pap. 29.99 *(978-0-19-532595-9(8))* Oxford Univ. Pr., Inc.

DeGrazia, David, et al. Biomedical Ethics. 7th ed. 2010. (ENG.). 752p. (C). pap. 121.33 *(978-0-07-340745-6(3)*, 0073407453) McGraw-Hill Cos., The.

Devettere, Raymond J. Practical Decision Making in Health Care Ethics: Cases & Concepts. 3rd rev. ed. 2009. (ENG.). 528p. (C). pap. 37.50 *(978-1-58901-251-6(8))* Georgetown Univ. Pr.

Dickson, Kanakulya & DE CUZZANI, Paola. Making Bioethics Global. 2010. 108p. pap. *(978-3-639-25716-8(2))* VDM Verlag Dr. Mueller e.K.

Dolgin & Dolgin, Janet. Bioethics & the Law. 2nd rev. ed. 2009. 144.00 *(978-0-7355-7620-9(3))* Wolters Kluwer Law & Business.

Dolgin, Janet L. & Shepherd, Lois L. Bioethics & the Law. 2nd ed. 2009. xxxviii, 899p. pap. *(978-0-7355-7621-6(1)*, Aspen Pubs.) Wolters Kluwer Law & Business.

Düwell, Marcus. Bioethics: Methods, Theories, Scopes. 2012. (Biomedical Law & Ethics Library). (ENG.). 352p. (C). 155.00 *(978-0-415-60991-3(7))* Routledge.

—The Contingent Nature of Life. 2008. (International Library of Ethics, Law, & the New Medicine Ser.). (C). 249.00 *(978-1-4020-6762-4(3))* Springer.

Düwell, Marcus, et al, eds. The Contingent Nature of Life: Bioethics & the Limits of Human Existence. 2010. (International Library of Ethics, Law, & the New Medicine Ser.). xv, 376p. pap. 249.00 *(978-90-481-7717-2(0)*, 9048177170) Springer.

Eastham, Scott. Biotech Time-Bomb: The Side-Effects Are the Main Effects. 2009. *(978-1-57273-904-8(5))* Hampton Pr., Inc.

Eberl, Jason T. Thomistic Principles & Bioethics. 2006. (Routledge Annals of Bioethics Ser.). (ENG.). 176p. (C). 161.00 *(978-0-415-77063-7(7))* Routledge.

Eckenwiler, Lisa A. & Cohn, Felicia G., eds. The Ethics of Bioethics: Mapping the Moral Landscape. 2007. (ENG.). 352p. (gr. 17). pap. 27.00 *(978-0-8018-8612-6(0))* Johns Hopkins Univ. Pr.

Education Development Center. Exploring Bioethics. 2009. 350p. ring bd. 0.00 *(978-0-89292-550-6(7))* Education Development Ctr., Inc.

Ekeke, Emeka C. Issues in Biomedical Ethics: A christian Perspective. 2011. 184p. pap. ***(978-3-8433-6203-0(3))*** Lambert Academic Publishing.

Ekland-Olson, Sheldon & Beicken, Julie. How Ethical Systems Change: Eugenics the Final Solution Bioethics. 2011. (Framing 21st Century Social Issues Ser.). (ENG.). 88p. pap. 9.95 ***(978-0-415-50162-0(8))*** Routledge.

Elliott, John M. Bioethics in Singapore: The Ethical Microcosm. 2010. 344p. 78.00 *(978-981-4327-10-7(7))*; pap. 39.00 *(978-981-4327-11-4(5))* World Scientific Publishing Co., Inc.

Engelhardt, H. Tristram, ed. Bioethics Critically Reconsidered: Having Second Thoughts. 2011. (Philosophy & Medicine Ser.). (ENG.). ix, 200p. 139.00 ***(978-94-007-2243-9(5)***, 9400722435) Springer.

Engelhardt Jr., H. Tristram & Rasmussen, L. M., eds. Bioethics & Moral Content: National Traditions of Health Care Morality: Papers Dedicated in Tribute to Kazumasa Hoshino. 2010. (Philosophy & Medicine / Asian Studies in Bioethics & the Philosophy of Medicine Ser.). 316p. pap. 189.00 *(978-90-481-5658-0(0)*, 9048156580) Springer.

Evans, John Hyde. The History & Future of Bioethics: A Sociological View. 2011. (ENG.). 272p. 45.00 ***(978-0-19-986085-2(8))*** Oxford Univ. Pr., Inc.

Ferber, Sarah. Bioethics in Historical Perspective: Medicine & Culture. 2013. (ENG.). 224p. (C). 85.00 *(978-1-4039-8723-5(8))*; pap. 29.95 *(978-1-4039-8724-2(6))* Palgrave Macmillan.

Fielder. Biomedical Engineering Ethics. 2007. (Synthesis Lectures on Biomedical Engineering Ser.). 40.00 *(978-1-59829-286-2(2))* Morgan & Claypool Pubs.

Fischer, Michael & Schrems, Ingeborg, eds. Ethik im Sog Der Ökonomie: Was entscheidet wirklich unser Leben? 2008. (Ethik transdisziplinär Ser.). 322p. pap. 81.95 *(978-3-631-57324-2(3))* Lang, Peter GmbH, Europaischer Verlag der Wissenschaften DEU. Dist: Lang, Peter.

Fisher, Anthony. Catholic Bioethics for a New Millennium. 2011. (ENG.). 346p. 90.00 ***(978-1-107-00958-5(8))***; pap. 29.99 ***(978-0-521-25324-6(1))*** Cambridge Univ. Pr.

Fisher, Johnna. Biomedical Ethics: A Canadian Focus. 2009. (ENG.). 544p. 65.00 *(978-0-19-542790-5(4))* Oxford Univ. Pr., Inc.

Foreman, Mark W. Christianity & Bioethics: Confronting Clinical Issues. 2011. 300p. pap. 33.00 ***(978-1-61097-370-0(4)***, Wipf and Stock) Wipf & Stock Pubs.

Foster, Charles. Human Dignity in Bioethics & Law. 2011. (ENG., Illus.). 218p. pap. 60.00 *(978-1-84946-177-1(5))* Hart Publishing Ltd. GBR. Dist: International Specialized Bk. Services.

Fox, Renee C. & Swazey, Judith P. Observing Bioethics. 2008. (ENG.). 432p. 45.00 *(978-0-19-536555-9(0))* Oxford Univ. Pr., Inc.

Frankel, Lorry R., et al, eds. Ethical Dilemmas in Pediatrics: Cases & Commentaries. 2009. (ENG.). 316p. pap. 46.00 *(978-0-521-11861-3(1))* Cambridge Univ. Pr.

Freeman, Michael A., ed. Law & Bioethics: Current Legal Issues Volume 11. 2008. (Current Legal Issues Ser.). (ENG.). 530p. 195.00 *(978-0-19-954552-0(9))* Oxford Univ. Pr., Inc.

Fry, Sara T., et al. Case Studies in Nursing Ethics. 4th rev. ed. 2010. 506p. pap. 86.95 *(978-0-7637-8031-9(6))* Jones & Bartlett Learning, LLC.

Furton, Edward James. Live the Truth: The Moral Legacy of John Paul II in Catholic Health Care. 2009. (ENG & SPA., Illus.). 344p. pap. 24.95 *(978-0-935372-49-6(0))* National Catholic Bioethics Ctr., The.

—Urged on by Christ: Catholic Health Care in Tension with Contemporary Culture. 2009. (SPA & ENG.). pap. 19.95 *(978-0-935372-52-6(0))* National Catholic Bioethics Ctr., The.

Galt, Kimberly A. & Paschal, Karen. Foundations in Patient Safety for Health Professionals. rev. ed. 2009. 250p. pap. 65.95 *(978-0-7637-6338-1(1))* Jones & Bartlett Learning, LLC.

García San José, Daniel I. Biolaw & Bioethics in Spain: Facing New Challenges of Science. 2010. 187p. *(978-84-92602-26-1(0))* Laborum, S.L., Ediciones.

—International Bio Law: An International Overview of Developments in Human Embryo Research & Experimentation. 2010. 209p. *(978-84-92602-28-5(7))* Laborum, S.L., Ediciones.

Gaskell, George & Bauer, Martin W., eds. Genomics & Society: Legal, Ethical & Social Dimensions. 2007. (Science in Society Ser.). (ENG., Illus.). 280p. per. 54.95 *(978-1-84407-114-2(6))* Routledge.

Gastmans, Chris, et al, eds. New Pathways for European Bioethics, 1 Vol. 2007. 224p. pap. 66.50 *(978-90-5095-670-3(X))* Intersentia Uitgevers N.V. BEL. Dist: International Specialized Bk. Services.

Glannon, Walter. Bioethics & the Brain. (ENG., Illus.). 2008. 256p. pap. 26.95 *(978-0-19-537194-9(1))* 2006. 348p. 49.99 *(978-0-19-530778-8(X))* Oxford Univ. Pr., Inc.

—Brain, Body, & Mind: Neuroethics with a Human Face, 1 vol. 2011. (ENG.). 288p. 45.00 *(978-0-19-973409-2(7))* Oxford Univ. Pr., Inc.

González Valenzuela, Juliana. Filosofía y Ciencias de la Vida. 2009. (Filosofia Ser.). 273p. pap. *(978-607-16-0057-8(X))* Fondo de Cultura Economica.

Gordijn, Bert & Gordijn, B. Medical Utopias: Ethical Reflections about Emerging Medical Technologies. 2006. (Ethical Perspectives Monograph Ser.). (ENG.). 287p. (C). 55.00 *(978-90-429-1700-2(8))* Peeters Pubs. & Booksellers BEL. Dist: Brown, David Bk. Co., The.

Gottweis, Herbert & Petersen, Alan, eds. Biobanks. 2007. (Illus.). 224p. 45.95 *(978-0-415-42738-8(X))* Routledge.

Green, Ronald M., et al, eds. Global Bioethics: Issues of Conscience for the Twenty-First Century. 2009. (Issues in Biomedical Ethics Ser.). (ENG., Illus.). 368p. 99.00 *(978-0-19-954659-6(2))* Oxford Univ. Pr., Inc.

Groenhout, Ruth E. Bioethics: A Reformed Look at Life & Death Choices. 2009. *(978-1-59255-263-4(3))* Faith Alive Christian Resources.

Gugelmann, Johann Friedrich. After Justification: Moral Epistemology in H. T. Engelhardt, Jr.'s Foundations of Bioethics. 2008. 148p. pap. *(978-3-639-09438-1(7))* VDM Verlag Dr. Mueller e.K.

Guha, Debashis. Educational Ethics: Practical & Professional Ethics, Vol. 4. 2007. 256p. pap. 14.00 *(978-81-8069-476-9(3))* Concept Publishing Co. IND. Dist: South Asia Bks.

Guinn, David E., ed. Handbook of Bioethics & Religion. 2006. (ENG., Illus.). 456p. 140.00 *(978-0-19-517873-9(4))* Oxford Univ. Pr., Inc.

Gunning, Jennifer & Holm, Soren. Ethics Law & Society: Volume Iii. 2007. (Ethics, Law & Society Ser.). (Illus.). 334p. 134.95 *(978-0-7546-7180-0(1))* Ashgate Publishing Co.

Gunning, Jennifer, et al. Ethics, Law & Society, Vol. 4. 2009. (Ethics, Law & Society Ser.). (Illus.). 438p. 144.95 *(978-0-7546-7646-1(3))* Ashgate Publishing Co.

Hall & Orentlicher, David. Bioethics & Public Health Law. 2nd ed. 2008. (Illus.). xxv, 687p. pap. 94.00 *(978-0-7355-7004-7(3)*, Aspen Pubs.) Wolters Kluwer Law & Business.

Häyry, Matti, et al, eds. Arguments & Analysis in Bioethics. 2010. (Illus.). 326p. pap. 96.00 *(978-90-420-2802-9(5))* Rodopi.

—Ethics in Biomedical Research: International Perspectives. 2007. (Value Inquiry Book Ser.: 186). 280p. per. 70.20 *(978-90-420-2179-2(9))* Rodopi.

Healey, Peter & Rayner, Steve, eds. Unnatural Selection: The Challenges of Engineering Tomorrow's People. 2008. (ENG., Illus.). 224p. 74.95 *(978-1-84407-622-2(9))* Routledge.

Hobbs, Suzanne Havala. Living Dairy-Free for Dummies. 2010. (ENG., Illus.). 360p. pap. 19.99 *(978-0-470-63316-8(6)*, For Dummies) Wiley, John & Sons, Inc.

Hoffmann, Thomas Sören & Schweidler, Walter, eds. Normkultur vs. Nutzenkultur: Über kulturelle Kontexte von Bioethik und Biorecht. 2006. (GER., Illus.). XI, 549p. 154.00 *(978-3-11-018978-0(X))* De Gruyter, Walter Inc.

Holland, Stephen, ed. Arguing about Bioethics. 2012. (Arguing about Philosophy Ser.). (ENG.). 624p. (C). 175.00 *(978-0-415-47632-4(1))*; pap. 50.00 *(978-0-415-47633-1(X))* Routledge.

Holm, Soren & Holm, Soren. Ethics, Law, & Society, Vol. 2. Holm, Soren & Holm, Soren, eds. 2006. (Ethics, Law & Society Ser.). (Illus.). 352p. 130.00 *(978-0-7546-4881-9(8))* Ashgate Publishing Co.

Holmes, Jeffrey & Humphrey, Jay D. Communication & Ethics in Biomedical. 2008. (Synthesis Lectures on Biomedical Engineering Ser.). 140p. pap. 30.00 *(978-1-59829-298-5(6))* Morgan & Claypool Pubs.

Holstein, Martha B., et al. Ethics, Aging, & Society: The Critical Turn. 2010. xxii, 298p. E-Book *(978-0-8261-1635-2(3))* Springer Publishing Co., Inc.

Hoshino, K., ed. Japanese & Western Bioethics: Studies in Moral Diversity. 2010. (Philosophy & Medicine Ser.). 264p. pap. 239.00 *(978-90-481-4719-9(0)*, 9048147190) Springer.

Houdy, Philippe, et al, eds. Nanoethics & Nanotoxicology. 2011. Orig. Title: Les nanosciences - nanotoxicologie et Nanoéthique. (ENG., Illus.). xliii, 620p. 199.00 *(978-3-642-20176-9(8)*, 3642201768) Springer.

Humber, James M. & Almeder, Robert F., eds. Is There a Duty to Die? 2010. (Biomedical Ethics Reviews (closed) Ser.). (ENG.). 232p. pap. 79.95 ***(978-1-61737-187-5(4)***, 1617371874) Humana Pr.

Iltis, Ana S., et al. At the Roots of Christian Bioethics: Critical Essays on the Thought of H. Tristram Engelhardt, Jr. 2009. *(978-0-9764041-8-7(4))* M & M Scrivener Pr.

Iltis, Ana Smith & Johnson, Sandra. Legal Perspectives on Bioethics. 2007. (Routledge Annals of Bioethics Ser.). (ENG.). 312p. 133.00 *(978-0-415-70148-8(1))* Routledge.

Ip, King-Tak, ed. The Bioethics of Regenerative Medicine. 2008. (Philosophy & Medicine Ser.). 196p. 139.00 *(978-1-4020-8966-4(X))* Springer.

Jacoby, Liva & Siminoff, Laura, eds. Empirical Methods for Bioethics: A Primer. 2008. (Advances in Bioethics Ser.). 200p. 111.95 *(978-0-7623-1266-5(1))* Emerald Group Publishing Ltd. GBR. Dist: Turpin Distribution Services Ltd.

Jasanoff, Sheila, ed. Reframing Rights: Bioconstitutionalism in the Genetic Age. 2011. (Basic Bioethics Ser.). (ENG., Illus.). 320p. (gr. 17). 50.00 *(978-0-262-01595-0(1))* MIT Pr.

Jasanoff, Sheila & Jasanoff, Richard D. Reframing Rights: Bioconstitutionalism in the Genetic Age. 2011. (Basic Bioethics Ser.). (ENG., Illus.). 320p. (gr. 17). pap. 25.00 *(978-0-262-51627-3(6))* MIT Pr.

Johnson, Lawrence. A Life-Centered Approach to Bioethics: Biocentric Ethics. 2010. (ENG., Illus.). 388p. 90.00 *(978-0-521-76626-5(5))*; 386p. pap. 29.99 *(978-0-521-15420-8(0))* Cambridge Univ. Pr.

Johnson, Sandra H. Health Law & Bioethics: Cases in Context. 2009. (Illus.). xix, 268p. pap., stu. ed. 42.00 *(978-0-7355-7767-1(6))* Wolters Kluwer Law & Business.

Johnstone, Megan-Jane. Bioethics: A Nursing Perspective. 5th rev. ed. 2008. (ENG., Illus.). xv, 472p. (C). pap. 73.95 *(978-0-7295-3873-2(7)*, Churchill Livingstone) Elsevier - Health Sciences Div.

Jones, A., et al, eds. Ethics in the Science & Technology Classroom: A New Approach to Teaching & Learning. 2010. 144p. *(978-94-6091-070-8(X))*; pap. *(978-94-6091-069-2(6))* Sense Pubs.

Jones, Gareth. Bioethics: When the Challenges of Life Become Too Much. 2011. (ATF Science & Theology Ser.). (ENG.). 296p. (C). per. 10.00 *(978-1-920691-79-0(0))* ATF Pr. AUS. Dist: Brown, David Bk. Co., The.

Jost, Timothy S. Readings in Comparative Health Law & Bioethics. 2nd ed. 2007. 432p. 48.00 *(978-1-59460-296-2(4))* Carolina Academic Pr.

Kaczor, Christopher. The Edge of Life: Human Dignity & Contemporary Bioethics. 2010. (Philosophy & Medicine / Catholic Studies in Bioethics Ser.). vii, 155p. pap. 149.00 *(978-90-481-6810-1(4)*, 9048168104) Springer.

Kaebnick, Gregory E., ed. The Ideal of Nature: Debates about Biotechnology & the Environment. 2011. (ENG.). 232p. (gr. 17). 55.00 *(978-0-8018-9888-4(9))* Johns Hopkins Univ. Pr.

Kamein, Anja J. A Theory of Unborn Life: From Abortion to Genetic Manipulation, 1 vol. 2012. (ENG.). 208p. 49.95 ***(978-0-19-978247-5(4))*** Oxford Univ. Pr., Inc.

Kaye, Jane & Stranger, Mark. Principles & Practice in Biobank Governance. 2009. (Illus.). 316p. 124.95 *(978-0-7546-7825-0(3))* Ashgate Publishing Co.

Kenny, Nuala & Shelton, Wayne, eds. Lost Virtue: Professional Character Development in Medical Education. 2006. (Advances in Bioethics Ser.).

B

(Illus.). 254p. 111.95 *(978-0-7623-1196-5(7))* Emerald Group Publishing Ltd. GBR. Dist: Turpin Distribution Services Ltd.

Keyes, W. Noel. Bioethical & Evolutionary Approaches to Medicine & the Law. 2007. (ENG.). 1230p. per. 179.95 *(978-1-59031-725-9(4))* American Bar Assn.

Kincaid, Harold & McKitrick, Jennifer, eds. Establishing Medical Reality: Essays in the Metaphysics & Epistemology of Biomedical Science. 2010. (Philosophy & Medicine Ser.). viii, 240p. pap. 159.00 *(978-90-481-7312-9(4)*, 9048173124) Springer.

King, Nancy M. P. & Hyde, Michael J., eds. Bioethics Public Moral Argument & Social Responsibility. 2011. (Routledge Annals of Bioethics Ser.). (ENG.). 196p. (C). 125.00 *(978-0-415-89855-3(2))* Routledge.

Knoepffler, Nikolaus, et al, eds. Humanbiotechnology as Social Challenge: An Interdisciplinary Introduction to Bioethics. 2007. (Ashgate Studies in Applied Ethics Ser.). (Illus.). 192p. 99.95 *(978-0-7546-5755-2(8))* Ashgate Publishing Co.

Kohlen, Helen & Remmers, Hartmut, eds. Bioethics, Care & Gender: Herausforderungen für Medizin, Pflege und Politik. 2010. (Pflegewissenschaft und Pflegebildung Ser.). (GER & ENG.). 265p. (C). 54.00 *(978-3-89971-546-0(2))* Vandenhoeck & Ruprecht GmbH & Co. KG DEU. Dist: ISD.

Konrad, Monica. Collaborators Collaborating: Counterparts in Anthropological Knowledge & International Research Relations. 2012. E-Book ***(978-0-85745-481-2(1))*** Berghahn Bks., Inc.

Konrad, Monica, ed. Collaborators Collaborating: Counterparts in Anthropological Knowledge & International Research Relations. 2012. (ENG.). 308p. 90.00 ***(978-0-85745-480-5(3))*** Berghahn Bks., Inc.

Kopelman, L. M., ed. Building Bioethics: Conversations with Clouser & Friends on Medical Ethics. 2010. (Philosophy & Medicine Ser.). 268p. pap. 159.00 *(978-90-481-5276-6(3)*, 9048152763) Springer.

Kortner, Ulrich Hj. Leib und Leben: Bioethische Erkundungen zur Leiblichkeit des Menschen. 2010. (Arbeiten zur Pastoraltheologie, Liturgik und Hymnologie Ser.). (GER.). 230p. (C). pap. 83.00 *(978-3-525-62412-8(3))* Vandenhoeck & Ruprecht GmbH & Co. KG DEU. Dist: ISD.

Kovács, László. Medizin - Macht - Metaphern: Sprachbilder in der Humangenetik und ethische Konsequenzen ihrer Verwendung. 2008. (Klinische Ethik. Biomedizin in Forschung und Praxis. Clinical Ethics. Biomedicine in Research & Practice Ser.). 234p. 56.95 *(978-3-631-58283-1(8))* Lang, Peter GmbH, Europaischer Verlag der Wissenschaften DEU. Dist: Lang, Peter.

Kuhse, Helga & Singer, Peter, eds. A Companion to Bioethics. 2nd ed. 2012. (Blackwell Companions to Philosophy Ser.: 106). (ENG.). 636p. pap. 44.95 ***(978-1-4443-5084-5(6)***, Wiley-Blackwell) Wiley, John & Sons, Inc.

Kuppuswamy, Chamundeeswari. The International Legal Governance of the Human Genome. 2009. (Genetics & Society Ser.). (ENG.). 224p. (C). 150.00 *(978-0-415-45857-3(9))* Routledge.

LaFleur, William R., et al, eds. Dark Medicine: Rationalizing Unethical Medical Research. 2008. (Bioethics & the Humanities Ser.). (ENG.). 280p. pap. 19.95 *(978-0-253-22041-7(6)*, 0253220416) Indiana Univ. Pr.

Lanigan, Barbara T., ed. Human Dignity & Bioethics. 2009. 145.00 *(978-1-60692-470-9(2))* Nova Science Pubs., Inc.

Lantos, John D., ed. Controversial Bodies: Thoughts on the Public Display of Plastinated Corpses. 2011. (ENG.). 160p. (gr. 17). 35.00 ***(978-1-4214-0271-0(8))*** Johns Hopkins Univ. Pr.

Lawler, Peter Augustine. Modern & american Dignity: Who We Are as Persons, & What That Means for Our Future. 2010. (ENG.). 288p. 26.95 *(978-1-935191-89-6(6))* ISI Bks.

Leies, John A., et al. Handbook on Critical Life Issues. 3rd ed. 2010. 279p. pap. 24.95 *(978-0-935372-58-8(X))* National Catholic Bioethics Ctr., The.

Leinhos, Mary R. The Logic & Legitimacy of American Bioethics. 2008. 276p. 109.95 *(978-1-60497-507-9(5))* Cambria Pr.

Lenk, Christian, et al, eds. Biobanks & Tissue Research: The Public, the Patient & the Regulation. 2011. (International Library of Ethics, Law & Technology Ser.). (Illus.). viii, 238p. 139.00 *(978-94-007-1672-8(9)*, 9400716729) Springer.

Levine, Carol. Clashing Views on Bioethical Issues. (Taking Sides Ser.). (ENG.). (C). 13th ed. 2009. 368p. pap. 48.00 *(978-0-07-354566-0(X)*, 007354566X) 14th ed. 2011. 416p. pap. 48.00 *(978-0-07-805011-4(1)*, 0078050111) McGraw-Hill Higher Education. (McGraw-Hill/Dushkin).

Levine, Carol. Taking Sides: Clashing Views on Bioethical Issues, Expanded. 14th ed. 2012. (Taking Sides Ser.). (ENG.). 416p. (C). pap. 48.00 ***(978-0-07-805012-1(X)***, 007805012X, McGraw-Hill/Dushkin) McGraw-Hill Higher Education.

Levy, Neil. Neuroethics: Challenges for the 21st Century. 2007. (ENG.). 360p. 130.00 *(978-0-521-86782-5(7))*; 364p. per. 61.00 *(978-0-521-68726-3(8))* Cambridge Univ. Pr.

Lindemann, Hilde, et al. Naturalized Bioethics: Toward Responsible Knowing & Practice. Lindemann, Hilde & Verkerk, Marian, eds. 2008. (ENG.). 292p. pap. 28.99 *(978-0-521-71940-7(2))* Cambridge Univ. Pr.

Lindsay, Ronald A. Future Bioethics: Overcoming Taboos, Myths, & Dogmas. 2008. (ENG.). 340p. 28.98 *(978-1-59102-624-2(5))* Prometheus Bks., Pubs.

Lizza, John P., ed. Defining the Beginning & End of Life: Readings on Personal Identity & Bioethics. 2009. (ENG., Illus.). 600p. (C). (gr. 13-17). 65.00 *(978-0-8018-9336-0(4))*; pap. 32.00 *(978-0-8018-9337-7(2))* Johns Hopkins Univ. Pr.

Loewy, Erich E. H. & Springer Loewy, Roberta. Textbook of Healthcare Ethics. 2nd ed. 2010. (ENG., Illus.). xiii, 382p. pap. 119.00 *(978-90-481-6358-8(7)*, 9048163587) Springer.

Lombardo, Paul A., ed. A Century of Eugenics in America: From the Indiana Experiment to the Human Genome Era. 2011. (Bioethics & the Humanities Ser.). (ENG.). 268p. pap. 24.95 *(978-0-253-22269-5(9)*, 0253222699) Indiana Univ. Pr.

Luna, Florencia. Bioethics & Vulnerability: A Latin American View. Herissone-Kelly, Peter, ed. Pakter, Laura, tr. 2006. (Value Inquiry Book Ser.: 180). 208p. per. 52.00 *(978-90-420-2073-3(3))* Rodopi.

Lustig, B. A., et al, eds. Altering Nature: Volume II: Religion, Biotechnology, & Public Policy. 2010. (Philosophy & Medicine Ser.). x, 346p. pap. 239.00 *(978-90-481-7764-6(2)*, 9048177642) Springer.

Macnair, Rachel M. & Zunes, Stephen, eds. Consistently Opposing Killing: From Abortion to Assisted Suicide, the Death Penalty, & War, 1 vol. 2008. (Illus.). 208p. 49.95 *(978-0-313-35278-2(X)*, C35278, Praeger Pubs.) Greenwood Publishing Group, Inc.

Malmqvist, Erik. Good Parents, Better Babies. 2009. 200p. pap. *(978-3-639-19197-4(8))* VDM Verlag Dr. Mueller e.K.

Mann, Scott. Bioethics in Perspective: Public Health, Corporate Power & the Political Economy, 1 vol. 2010. (ENG.). 296p. (C). pap. 55.00 *(978-0-521-75656-3(1))* Cambridge Univ. Pr.

Manson, Neil C. & O'Neill, Onora. Rethinking Informed Consent in Bioethics. 2007. (ENG.). 226p. 99.00 *(978-0-521-87458-8(0))*; pap. 41.00 *(978-0-521-69747-7(6))* Cambridge Univ. Pr.

May, Thomas. Bioethics in a Liberal Society: The Political Framework of Bioethics Decision Making. 2009. (ENG.). 152p. (gr. 17). pap. 27.00 *(978-0-8018-9282-0(1))* Johns Hopkins Univ. Pr.

May, William E. Catholic Bioethics & the Gift of Human Life. 2nd ed. 2007. 368p. per. 19.95 *(978-1-59276-330-6(8))* Our Sunday Visitor, Publishing Div.

Mazur, Grzegorz. Informed Consent, Proxy Consent, & Catholic Bioethics: For the Good of the Subject. 2011. (Philosophy & Medicine Ser.). (ENG.). xv, 241p. 139.00 ***(978-94-007-2195-1(1)***, 9400721951) Springer.

McDonald, Richard & Smith, Sheldon, eds. Bio-Ethics: Proceedings of the 9th Annual Utah Valley University Conference by the Faculty. 2008. (Illus.). 100p. pap. 9.95 *(978-0-9744261-4-3(8))* Press of the Ctr. for the Study of Ethics.

McGee, Glenn. Bioethics for Beginners: 60 Cases & Cautions from the Moral Frontier of Healthcare. 2012. (ENG.). 192p. 24.95 ***(978-0-470-65911-3(4)***, Wiley-Blackwell) Wiley, John & Sons, Inc.

McQueen, Moira. Bioethics Matters: A Catholic Perspective. 2009. (ENG.). 112p. 14.95 *(978-0-8264-3510-1(6)*, Burns & Oates) Continuum International Publishing Group, Ltd. GBR. Dist: National Bk. Network.

Mehlman, Maxwell J. The Price of Perfection: Individualism & Society in the Era of Biomedical Enhancement. 2009. (ENG.). 320p. 27.00 *(978-0-8018-9263-9(5))* Johns Hopkins Univ. Pr.

Mepham, Ben. Bioethics: An Introduction for the Biosciences. 2nd ed. 2008. (ENG., Illus.). 450p. (C). pap. 59.95 *(978-0-19-921430-3(1))* Oxford Univ. Pr., Inc.

Messer, Neil. Respecting Life: Theology & Bioethics. 2011. 224p. pap. 55.00 *(978-0-334-04333-1(6)*, SCM Pr.) Hymns Ancient & Modern Ltd GBR. Dist: Westminster John Knox Pr.

Miller, Franklin G., et al, eds. The Nature & Prospect of Bioethics: Interdisciplinary Perspectives. 2010. 216p. pap. 44.50 *(978-1-61737-144-8(0)*, 1617371440) Humana Pr.

Miller, Geoffrey. Extreme Prematurity: Practices, Bioethics & the Law. 2006. (ENG.). 240p. 86.00 *(978-0-521-86221-9(3))*; 299.00 *(978-0-521-68053-0(0))* Cambridge Univ. Pr.

Miller, Geoffrey, ed. Pediatric Bioethics. 2009. (ENG.). 304p. (C). 85.00 *(978-0-521-51798-0(2))*; (Illus.). pap. 29.99 *(978-0-521-13594-8(X))* Cambridge Univ. Pr.

Miller, Seumas & Selgelid, Michael. Ethical & Philosophical Consideration of the Dual-Use Dilemma in the Biological Sciences. 2008. VIII, 76p. (C). pap. 49.95 *(978-1-4020-8311-2(4)*, 1402083114) Springer.

Millum, Joseph & Emanuel, Ezekiel, eds. Global Justice & Bioethics, 1 vol. 2012. (ENG., Illus.). 336p. 45.00 ***(978-0-19-537990-7(X))*** Oxford Univ. Pr., Inc.

Mitchell, Daria, ed. Dying, As A Franciscan: Approaching Our Transitus to Eternal Life, Accompanying Others on the Way to Thriers. 2011. 118p. 19.95 ***(978-1-57659-221-2(9))*** Franciscan Institute Pubns.

Monsour, Daniel. Ethics & the New Genetics: An Integrated Approach. 2007. (Lonergan Studies). 240p. *(978-0-8020-9273-1(X))* Univ. of Toronto Pr.

Morrison, Eileen E. & Monagle, John F. Health Care Ethics: Critical Issues for the 21st Century. 2nd rev. ed. 2008. 441p. (C). pap. 109.95 *(978-0-7637-4526-4(X))* Jones & Bartlett Learning, LLC.

Munson, Ronald. Intervention & Reflection: Basic Issues in Bioethics. 9th ed. 2011. (ENG.). (C). 171.95 ***(978-1-133-58714-9(3))*** Wadsworth.

Munson, Ronald. The Woman Who Decided to Die: Challenges & Choices at the Edges of Medicine. 2009. (ENG.). 224p. 27.95 *(978-0-19-533101-1(X))* Oxford Univ. Pr., Inc.

Murray, Stuart J. & Holmes, Dave. Critical Interventions in the Ethics of Healthcare: Challenging the Principle of Autonomy in Biotehics. 2009. (Medical Law & Ethics Ser.). 258p. 124.95 *(978-0-7546-7396-5(0))* Ashgate Publishing Co.

Murray, Thomas H. & Johnston, Josephine, eds. Trust & Integrity in Biomedical Research: The Case of Financial Conflicts of Interest. 2010. (ENG., Illus.). 288p. (gr. 17). 50.00 *(978-0-8018-9626-2(6))* Johns Hopkins Univ. Pr.

Myser, Catherine, ed. Bioethics Around the Globe, 1 vol. 2011. (ENG.). 304p. 49.95 *(978-0-19-538609-7(4))* Oxford Univ. Pr., Inc.

Napier, Stephen, ed. Persons, Moral Worth, & Embryos: A Critical Analysis of Pro-Choice Arguments. 2011. (Philosophy & Medicine / Catholic Studies in Bioethics Ser.). (Illus.). xiv, 283p. 139.00 *(978-94-007-1601-8(X)*, 940071601X) Springer.

National Research Council Staff, creator. Biosocial Surveys. 2007. (ENG., Illus.). 428p. per. 50.00 *(978-0-309-10867-6(5))* National Academies Pr.

Nelson, Leonard J., III. Diagnosis Critical: The Urgent Threats Confronting Catholic Health Care. 2009. 350p. 29.95 *(978-1-59276-070-1(8))* Our Sunday Visitor, Publishing Div.

Nys, Thomas, et al. Autonomy & Paternalism: Reflections on the Theory & Practice of Health Care. Denier, Y. et al, eds. 2007. (Ethical Perspectives Ser.). (ENG.). 184p. (C). pap. 66.00 *(978-90-429-1880-1(2))* Peeters Pubs. & Booksellers BEL. Dist: Brown, David Bk. Co., The.

Oakley, Justin. Bioethics. 2009. (International Library of Essays in Public & Professional Ethics Ser.). 586p. 325.00 *(978-0-7546-2597-1(4))* Ashgate Publishing Co.

Oehlschlaeger, Fritz. Procreative Ethics. 2009. 380p. pap. 42.00 *(978-1-60608-230-0(2)*, Cascade Bks.) Wipf & Stock Pubs.

Orentlicher, David, et al. Bioethics & Public Health Law. 2nd ed. 2008. (Illus.). xxv, 687p. *(978-0-7355-7104-4(X)*, Aspen Pubs.) Wolters Kluwer Law & Business.

O'Mathuna, Donal P., et al, eds. Disaster Bioethics: Normative Issues When Nothing Is Normal. 2012. (Public Health Ethics Analysis Ser.). (ENG.). x, 190p. 139.00 ***(978-94-007-3863-8(3)***, 9400738633) Springer.

Pace, Tyler N., ed. Bioethics: Issues & Dilemmas. 2010. (Ethical Issues in the 21st Century Ser.). (Illus.). x, 143p. 99.00 *(978-1-61728-290-4(1))* Nova Science Pubs., Inc.

Parker, Michael. Ethical Problems & Genetics Practice. 2012. (Cambridge Bioethics & Law Ser.). (ENG., Illus.). 182p. 90.00 ***(978-1-107-02080-1(8))*** Cambridge Univ. Pr.

Parks, Jennifer A. & Wike, Victoria S. Bioethics in a Changing World. 2009. (ENG.). 816p. (C). pap. 107.60 *(978-0-13-615164-7(7)*, Prentice Hall) Prentice Hall PTR.

Pellegrino, Edmund D. Human Dignity & Bioethics. Pellegrino, Edmund D. et al, eds. 2009. (ND Studies in Medical Ethics Ser.). (ENG.). 576p. pap. 40.00 *(978-0-268-03892-2(9))* Univ. of Notre Dame Pr.

Pence, Gregory. Re-Creating Medicine: Ethical Issues at the Frontiers of Medicine. annot. ed. 2007. (ENG.). 208p. per. 17.95 *(978-0-8476-9691-8(X))* Rowman & Littlefield Publishers, Inc.

Persson, Ingmar & Savulescu, Julian. Unfit for the Future? The Need for Moral Enhancement. 2012. (ENG.). 160p. 35.00 ***(978-0-19-965364-5(X))*** Oxford Univ. Pr., Inc.

Pessini, Léo & Barchifontaine, Christian de Paul de. Ibero-American Bioethics: History & Perspectives. Lolas Stepke, Fernando, ed. Bulcock, Jennifer et al, trs. 2010. (Philosophy & Medicine Ser.). (Illus.). xx, 397p. 159.00 *(978-1-4020-9349-4(7)*, 1402093497) Springer.

Petersen, Alan. The Politics of Bioethics. 2010. (Routledge Studies in Science, Technology & Society Ser.). (ENG.). 176p. (C). 125.00 *(978-0-415-99006-6(8))* Routledge.

Pierce, Jessica & Randels, George. Contemporary Bioethics: A Reader with Cases. 2009. *(978-0-19-973637-9(5))*; (ENG.). 736p. (C). pap. 89.95 *(978-0-19-531382-6(8))* Oxford Univ. Pr., Inc.

Pollard, Irina. Bioscience Ethics. 2009. (ENG., Illus.). 332p. (C). 132.00 *(978-0-521-76828-3(4))*; pap. 45.99 *(978-0-521-74527-7(6))* Cambridge Univ. Pr.

Post, Linda Farber, et al. Handbook for Health Care Ethics Committees. 2006. (ENG., Illus.). 352p. (gr. 17). per. 35.00 *(978-0-8018-8448-1(9))* Johns Hopkins Univ. Pr.

President's Council on Bioethics (U.S.), compiled by. Human Dignity & Bioethics: Essays Commissioned by the President's Council on Bioethics: Essays Commissioned by the President's Council on Bioethics. 2008. (ENG., Illus.). 571p. pap. 49.00 *(978-0-16-080071-9(4))* United States Government Printing Office.

President's Council on Bioethics (U.S.), ed. Monitoring Stem Cell Research: A Report of the President's Council on Bioethics: A Report of the President's Council on Bioethics. 2011. (ENG.). 414p. pap. 37.00 ***(978-0-16-087900-5(0)***, President's Council on Bioethics) United States Government Printing Office.

Rabinow, Paul & Bennett, Gaymon. Designing Human Practices: An Experiment with Synthetic Biology. 2012. (ENG.). 200p. pap. 25.00 ***(978-0-226-70314-5(2))***; (Illus.). 75.00 ***(978-0-226-70313-8(4))*** Univ. of Chicago Pr.

Radau, Wiltrud Christine. Die Biomedizinkonvention des Europarates: Humanforschung - Transplantationsmedizin - Genetik, Rechtsanalyse und Rechtsvergleich. 2006. (MedR Schriftenreihe Medizinrecht Ser.). XIV, 423p. pap. 135.00 *(978-3-540-34475-9(6)*, 3540344756) Springer.

Radest, Howard. Bioethics: Catastrophic Events in a Time of Terror. 2009. (ENG.). 188p. 68.50 *(978-0-7391-3527-3(9))* Lexington Bks.

Radest, Howard B., ed. Biomedical Ethics. 2006. (Humanism Today Ser.). (ENG.). 250p. 30.98 *(978-1-59102-423-1(4))* Prometheus Bks., Pubs.

Rasmussen, Lisa, ed. Ethics Expertise: History, Contemporary Perspectives, & Applications. 2010. (Philosophy & Medicine Ser.). vii, 279p. pap. 169.00 *(978-90-481-6973-3(9)*, 9048169739) Springer.

Ratke, David C., ed. Theological Foundations in an Age of Biological Intervention. 2008. (ENG., Illus.). 160p. pap. 18.00 *(978-1-932688-32-0(3)*, Lutheran Univ. Pr.) Kirk Hse. Pubs.

Rawlinson, Mary C. & Lundeen, Shannon, eds. The Voice of Breast Cancer in Medicine & Bioethics. 2010. (Philosophy & Medicine Ser.). (Illus.). xix, 207p. pap. 199.00 *(978-90-481-7139-2(3)*, 9048171393) Springer.

Rehmann-Sutter, Christoph. Disclosure Dilemmas: Ethics of Genetic Prognosis after the 'Right to Know/Not to Know' Debate. Müller, Hansjakob, ed. 2009. (Medical Law & Ethics Ser.). (Illus.). 296p. 124.95 *(978-0-7546-7451-1(7))* Ashgate Publishing Co.

Rehmann-Sutter, Christoph, et al, eds. Bioethics in Cultural Contexts: Reflections on Methods & Finitude. 2010. (International Library of Ethics, Law, & the New Medicine Ser.). vii, 384p. pap. 279.00 *(978-90-481-7082-1(6)*, 9048170826) Springer.

Ren-Zong Qiu, ed. Bioethics: Asian Perspectives: A Quest for Moral Diversity. 2010. (Philosophy & Medicine / Asian Studies in Bioethics & the Philosophy of Medicine Ser.). 246p. pap. 169.00 *(978-90-481-6509-4(1)*, 9048165091) Springer.

Rettig, Salomon & Hayes, Timothy. Hermeneutics & Discourse Analysis in Social Psychology. 2012. (Psychology Research Progress Ser.). 168p. 129.00 *(978-1-61209-943-9(2))* Nova Science Pubs., Inc.

Rothman, Barbara Katz, et al, eds. Bioethical Issues, Sociological Perspectives. 2007. (Advances in Medical Sociology Ser.). (Illus.). 364p. 111.95 *(978-0-7623-1438-6(9))* Emerald Group Publishing Ltd. GBR. Dist: Turpin Distribution Services Ltd.

Rothstein, Mark A., ed. Genetics & Life Insurance: Medical Underwriting & Social Policy. 2009. (Basic Bioethics Ser.). (ENG., Illus.). 312p. (gr. 17). pap. 18.00 *(978-0-262-51259-6(9))* MIT Pr.

Rudman, Jack. Bioethics. 2011. (Regents College Examination Passbooks Ser.). spiral bd. 29.95 ***(978-0-8373-5917-5(1))*** National Learning Corp.

Sachedina, Abdulaziz. Islamic Biomedical Ethics: Principles & Application. 2011. (ENG.). 296p. pap. 24.95 ***(978-0-19-986023-4(8))*** Oxford Univ. Pr., Inc.

Sarkar, Sahotra. Biodiversity & Environmental Philosophy: An Introduction. 2010. (Cambridge Studies in Philosophy & Biology Ser.). (ENG., Illus.). 280p. pap. 29.99 *(978-0-521-14342-4(X))* Cambridge Univ. Pr.

Sassower, Raphael & Cutter, Mary Ann. Ethical Choices for Contemporary Medicine: Integrative Bioethics. 2007. (ENG.). 160p. (C). per. *(978-0-7735-3351-6(6))* McGill-Queen's Univ. Pr.

Sassower, Raphael & Cutter, Mary Ann Gardell. Ethical Choices for Contemporary Medicine: Integrative Bioethics. 2007. (ENG.). 160p. (C). *(978-0-7735-3350-9(8))* McGill-Queen's Univ. Pr.

Scarnecchia, D. Brian. Bioethics, Law, & Human Life Issues: A Catholic Perspective on Marriage, Family, Contraception, Abortion, Reproductive Technology, & Death & Dying. 2nd ed. 2010. (Catholic Social Thought Ser.). (ENG., Illus.). 460p. 63.00 *(978-0-8108-7422-0(9))* Scarecrow Pr., Inc.

Schaller, Barry R. Understanding Bioethics & the Law: The Promises & Perils of the Brave New World of Biotechnology, 1 vol. 2007. 264p. 49.95 *(978-0-275-99918-6(1)*, C9918, Praeger Pubs.) Greenwood Publishing Group, Inc.

Schenker, Joseph G., ed. Ethical Dilemmas in Assisted Reproductive Technologies. 2011. (ENG., Illus.). XXIII, 387p. 321.00 ***(978-3-11-916282-1(5))*** De Gruyter, Walter Inc.

Scully, Jackie Leach. Disability Bioethics: Moral Bodies, Moral Difference. 2008. (Feminist Constructions Ser.). (ENG.). 212p. 65.00 *(978-0-7425-5122-0(9))* Rowman & Littlefield Publishers, Inc.

Scully, Jackie Leach, et al, eds. Feminist Bioethics: At the Center, on the Margins. 2010. (ENG.). 328p. (C). (gr. 13-17). pap. 30.00 *(978-0-8018-9425-1(5))* Johns Hopkins Univ. Pr.

Shamoo, Adil E. & Resnik, David B. Responsible Conduct of Research. 2nd ed. 2009. (ENG., Illus.). 464p. pap. 39.95 *(978-0-19-536824-6(X))* Oxford Univ. Pr., Inc.

Shannon, Thomas A. & Kockler, Nicholas J. An Introduction to Bioethics: Fourth Edition - Revised & Updated. 4th ed. 2009. 320p. pap. 22.95 *(978-0-8091-4623-9(1))* Paulist Pr.

Shelp, E. E., ed. Theology & Bioethics: Exploring the Foundations & Frontiers. 2010. (Philosophy & Medicine Ser.). 344p. pap. 289.00 *(978-90-481-8408-8(8)*, 9048184088) Springer.

Shibles, W. A. & Maier, Barbara. The Philosophy & Practice of Medicine & Bioethics: A Naturalistic-Humanistic Approach. 2010. (International Library of Ethics, Law, & the New Medicine Ser.). (Illus.). 620p. 239.00 *(978-90-481-8866-6(0)*, 9048188660) Springer.

Simonstein, Frida, ed. Reprogen-ethics & the future of Gender. 2009. (International Library of Ethics, Law, & the New Medicine Ser.). (ENG.). xiv, 226p. 179.00 *(978-90-481-2474-9(3)*, 9048124743) Springer.

Singer, Peter. A Companion to Bioethics. Kuhse, Helga & Singer, Peter, eds. 2nd ed. 2009. (Blackwell Companions to Philosophy Ser.: 28). (ENG.). 640p. 209.95 *(978-1-4051-6331-6(3)*, Wiley-Blackwell) Wiley, John & Sons, Inc.

Smith, George Patrick. Law & Bioethics: Intersections along the Mortal Coil. 2012. E-Book ***(978-0-203-12251-8(8))*** Routledge.

Smith II, George P. Law & Bioethics: Intersections along the Mortal Coil. 2012. (ENG.). 224p. (C). 135.00 *(978-0-415-78335-4(6))* Routledge.

Solo, Pam & Pressburg, Gail. The Promise & Politics of Stem Cell Research, 1 vol. 2006. 192p. 39.95 *(978-0-275-99038-1(9)*, C9038, Praeger Pubs.) Greenwood Publishing Group, Inc.

Spielman, Bethany J. Bioethics in Law. 2006. 181p. per. 74.95 *(978-1-58829-434-0(X)*, 158829434X) Humana Pr.

Spiess, Constanze. Diskurshandlungen: Theorie und Methode linguistischer Diskursanalyse am Beispiel der Bioethikdebatte. 2011. (Sprache und Wissen Ser.). (GER., Illus.). XVIII, 594p. 182.00 ***(978-3-11-025880-6(3))*** De Gruyter, Walter Inc.

Steinberg, David, ed. Biomedical Ethics: A Multidisciplinary Approach to Moral Issues in Medicine & Biology. 2007. (Illus.). 346p. per. 40.00 (978-1-58465-643-2(3), Dartmouth College Press) Univ. Pr. of New England.
Steinbock, Bonnie, ed. The Oxford Handbook of Bioethics. (Oxford Handbooks Ser.). (ENG.). 768p. 2009. pap. 55.00 (978-0-19-956241-1(5)) 2007. 165.00 (978-0-19-927335-5(9)) Oxford Univ. Pr., Inc.
Sutton, Agneta. Christian Bioethics. 2008. (Guides for the Perplexed Ser.). (ENG.). 192p. 24.95 (978-0-567-03197-6(7), T&T Clark Int'l) Continuum International Publishing Group, Ltd. GBR. Dist: National Bk. Network.
Sutton, Agneta & Sutton. Christian Bioethics. 2008. (Guides for the Perplexed Ser.). (ENG.). 192p. 110.00 (978-0-567-03196-9(9), T&T Clark Int'l) Continuum International Publishing Group, Ltd. GBR. Dist: National Bk. Network.
Swiffen, Amy. Law, Ethics & the Biopolitical. 2012. (ENG.). pap. 42.79 **(978-0-415-62870-9(9))** 2011. 128p. 120.00 (978-0-415-57844-8(2)) Routledge.
Talbot, Marianne. Bioethics: An Introduction. 2012. (ENG., Illus.). 464p. (C). 95.00 **(978-0-521-88833-2(6))**; pap. 45.00 **(978-0-521-71459-4(1))** Cambridge Univ. Pr.
Tamayo, Ruy Pérez, et al. La Construcción de la Bioética: Textos de Bioética, Vol. 1. 2008. (Ciencia, Tecnología, Sociedad Ser.). (SPA.). 223p. pap. 17.95 (978-968-16-8391-7(9)) Fondo de Cultura Economica USA.
Tao Lai Po-wah, J., ed. China: Bioethics, Trust, & the Challenge of the Market: Bioethics, Trust, & the Challenge of the Market. 2010. (Philosophy & Medicine / Asian Studies in Bioethics & the Philosophy of Medicine Ser.). xii, 212p. pap. 159.00 (978-90-481-7714-1(6), 9048177146) Springer.
—Cross-Cultural Perspectives on the (Im)Possibility of Global Bioethics. 2010. (Philosophy & Medicine / Asian Studies in Bioethics & the Philosophy of Medicine Ser.). 420p. pap. 239.00 (978-90-481-5969-7(5), 9048159695) Springer.
Taylor, James St & Taylor, James Stacey. Practical Autonomy & Bioethics. 2009. (Routledge Annals of Bioethics Ser.). (ENG.). XVI, 212p. 126.00 (978-0-415-99740-9(2)) Routledge.
Taylor, James Stacey. Death Posthumous Harm & Bioethics. 2012. (Routledge Annals of Bioethics Ser.). (ENG.). 272p. (C). 125.00 **(978-0-415-51884-0(9))** Routledge.
Ten Have, H. A. & Gordijn, Bert, eds. Bioethics in a European Perspective. 2010. (International Library of Ethics, Law, & the New Medicine Ser.). (Illus.). 554p. pap. 359.00 (978-90-481-5872-0(9), 9048158729) Springer.
Tereskerz, Patrica M. Riding the Green Wave: Financial Conflicts of Interest in Industry-Sponsored Clinical Research. 2007. 240p. pap. 24.99 (978-1-55572-084-1(6)) Univ. Publishing Group, Inc.
Théry, Irène. Des Humains Comme les Autres: Bioéthique, Anonymat et Genre du Don. 2010. (FRE.). 309p. (978-2-7132-2265-8(6)) Ecole des Hautes Etudes en Sciences Sociales.
Thiele, Felix & Ashcroft, R. E., eds. Bioethics in a Small World. 2010. (Ethics of Science & Technology Assessment Ser.). xv, 138p. pap. 89.95 (978-3-642-06256-8(3), 3642062563) Springer.
Tollefsen, Christopher, ed. Bioethics with Liberty & Justice: Themes in the Work of Joseph M. Boyle. 2010. (Philosophy & Medicine Ser.). x, 190p. 139.00 (978-90-481-9790-3(2), 9048197902) Springer.
—John Paul II's Contribution to Catholic Bioethics. 2010. (Philosophy & Medicine / Catholic Studies in Bioethics Ser.). v, 191p. pap. 149.00 (978-90-481-6801-9(5), 9048168015) Springer.
Torre Díaz, Javier de la & Uríbarri Bilbao, Gabino. Mujer, Mujeres y Bioética. 2010. (SPA., Illus.). 247p. (978-84-8468-277-6(3)) Universidad Pontificia Comillas de Madrid.
Tubbs, James B., Jr. A Handbook of Bioethics Terms. 2009. (ENG.). 208p. (C). pap. 14.95 (978-1-58901-259-2(3)) Georgetown Univ. Pr.
Tubbs Jr., James B. Christian Theology & Medical Ethics Four Contemporary Approaches. 2010. (Theology & Medicine Ser.). 224p. pap. 219.00 (978-90-481-4601-7(1), 9048146011) Springer.
Turner, Leigh, et al, eds. The View from Here: Bioethics & the Social Sciences. 2007. (Sociology of Health & Illness Monographs: 6) (ENG.). 232p. per. 39.95 (978-1-4051-5269-3(9), Wiley-Blackwell) Wiley, John & Sons, Inc.
Valenzuela, Juliana González. Perspectivas de la Bioética. 2008. (Filosofía Ser.). (SPA.). 384p. pap. (978-968-16-8546-1(6)) Fondo de Cultura Economica.
Vallero, Daniel A. Biomedical Ethics for Engineers: Ethics & Decision Making in Biomedical & Biosystem Engineering. 2007. (Biomedical Engineering Ser.). (ENG., Illus.). 408p. 57.95 (978-0-7506-8227-5(2), Academic Pr.) Elsevier Science & Technology Bks.
VanDrunen, David. Bioethics & the Christian Life: A Guide to Making Difficult Decisions. 2009. 256p. pap. 19.99 (978-1-4335-0144-9(9)) Crossway.
Vaughn, Lewis. Bioethics: Principles, Issues, & Cases. 2009. (ENG., Illus.). 696p. (C). pap. 89.95 (978-0-19-518282-8(0)) Oxford Univ. Pr., Inc.
Vaux, Kenneth L. Ministry on the Edge: Reflections of an Interfaith Pioneer, Civil Rights Advocate, & the First Bioethicist. 2010. 284p. pap. 31.00 (978-1-60899-506-6(2)) Wipf & Stock Pubs.
Veatch, Robert M. Bioethics. 3rd rev. ed. 2011. (ENG., Illus.). 224p. (C). pap. 56.20 **(978-0-205-76562-1(9)**, Prentice Hall) Prentice Hall PTR.
Veatch, Robert M., et al. Case Studies in Biomedical Ethics: Decision-Making, Principles, & Cases. 2009. (ENG., Illus.). 480p. (C). pap. 59.95 (978-0-19-530972-0(3)) Oxford Univ. Pr., Inc.
Viafora, C., ed. Clinical Bioethics: A Search for the Foundations. 2010. (International Library of Ethics, Law, & the New Medicine Ser.). xix, 206p. pap. 169.00 (978-90-481-6905-4(4), 9048169054) Springer.
Voigt, Friedemann, ed. Religion in bioethischen Diskursen: Interdisziplinäre, internationale und interreligiöse Perspektiven.Tr. of Religion in the Bioethical Discourse. (GER.). VI, 337p. 2011. 126.00 **(978-3-11-174116-1(8))** 2010. 84.00 (978-3-11-022437-5(2)) De Gruyter, Walter Inc.
Wagner, Viqi. Biomedical Ethics. 2007. (Opposing Viewpoints Ser.). (ENG.). 256p. (J). (gr. 3-7). per. 27.50 (978-0-7377-3738-7(7)); (Illus.). pap. 39.70 (978-0-7377-3737-0(9)) Cengage Gale. (Greenhaven Pr., Inc.).
Walker, Margaret Urban. Naturalized Bioethics: Toward Responsible Knowing & Practice. Lindemann, Hilde & Verkerk, Marian, eds. 2008. (ENG.). 292p. 85.00 (978-0-521-89524-8(3)) Cambridge Univ. Pr.
Walters, LeRoy, et al, eds. Bibliography of Bioethics. (ENG.). Vol. 33. 2007. 848p. (978-1-883913-14-4(4)) Vol. 34. 2008. (978-1-883913-15-1(2)) Vol. 35. 2009. 80.00 (978-1-883913-16-8(0)) Georgetown Univ., Kennedy Institute of Ethics.
Waters, Brent. This Mortal Flesh: Incarnation & Bioethics, 1 vol. 2009. 208p. (C). pap. 22.00 (978-1-58743-251-4(X)) Brazos Pr.
Watson, Fuller. The Social Impact of Modern Biology. 2012. (ENG.). 272p. (C). pap. 42.95 **(978-0-415-61179-4(2))** Routledge.
Watts, Fraser, ed. Christians & Bioethics. 96p. 12.00 (978-0-281-05194-6(1)) SPCK Publishing GBR. Dist: Pilgrim Pr., The/United Church Pr.
Weingartner, Paul, ed. Rohstoff Mensch, das flüssige Gold der Zukunft? Ist Ethik Privatisierbar? 2008. (Wissenschaft und Religion. Veröffentlichungen des Internationalen Forschungszentrums für Grundfragen der Wissenschaften Salzburg Ser.). 294p. pap. 74.95 (978-3-631-57611-3(0)) Lang, Peter GmbH, Europaischer Verlag der Wissenschaften DEU. Dist: Lang, Peter.
Weisstub, David N. & Díaz Pintos, Guillermo, eds. Autonomy & Human Rights in Health Care: An International Perspective. 2010. (International Library of Ethics, Law, & the New Medicine Ser.). xiv, 401p. pap. 219.00 (978-90-481-7453-9(8), 9048174538) Springer.
Weisstub, David N. & Díaz Pintos, Guillermo, eds. Autonomy & Human Rights in Health Care: An International Perspective. 2007. (International Library of Ethics, Law, & the New Medicine Ser.). (ENG.). xiv, 401p. 219.00 (978-1-4020-5840-0(3), 1402058403) Springer.
Wiener, Gary. Bioethics in Mary Shelley's Frankenstein. 2010. (Social Issues in Literature Ser.). (ENG.). 224p. 38.45 (978-0-7377-5012-6(X)); pap. 26.50 (978-0-7377-5013-3(8)) Cengage Gale. (Greenhaven Pr., Inc.).
World Health Organization: Regional Office for South-East Asia. Casebook on Ethical Issues in International Health Research. 2010. (Nonserial Publication Ser.). (ENG.). 209p. pap. 48.00 (978-92-4-154772-7(3)) World Health Organization.
Wüstenberg, Ralf K. & Heuser, Stefan, eds. Bonhoeffer & the Biosciences: An Initial Exploration. 2010. (International Bonhoeffer Interpretations Ser.). 184p. 57.95 (978-3-631-59345-0(9)) Lang, Peter GmbH, Europaischer Verlag der Wissenschaften DEU. Dist: Lang, Peter.
Zhang, Joy Yueyue. The Cosmpolitanization of Science: Stem Cell Governance in China. 2012. (ENG., Illus.). 232p. 85.00 **(978-0-230-30259-4(9))** Palgrave Macmillan.
Zimmerman, Deena R. Mi Dor le Dor Genetics & Genetic Diseases: Jewish Legal & Ethical Perspectives. 2012. **(978-1-60280-163-9(0))** Ktav Publishing Hse., Inc.
Zylinska, Joanna. Bioethics in the Age of New Media. 2009. (ENG.). 248p. (gr. 17). 32.00 (978-0-262-24056-7(4)) MIT Pr.

BIOFEEDBACK TRAINING

Budzynski, Thomas H., et al, eds. Introduction to Quantitative EEG & Neurofeedback: Advanced Theory & Applications. 2nd ed. 2008. (ENG., Illus.). 528p. 103.00 (978-0-12-374534-7(9), Academic Pr.) Elsevier Science & Technology Bks.
Condron, James, et al. Cross Time Frequency Analysis of Autonomic Nervous System Activity. 2010. 272p. pap. (978-3-8383-4158-3(9)) Lambert Academic Publishing.
Evans, James R. Handbook of Neurofeedback: Dynamics & Clinical Applications. 2007. (Haworth Series in Neurotherapy). (ENG., Illus.). 278p. pap. 100.00 (978-0-7890-3360-4(7), Informa Healthcare) Taylor & Francis Group.
Hammond, D. Corydon. Lens: The Low Energy Neurofeedback System. 2007. (ENG., Illus.). 120p. per. 60.95 (978-0-7890-3568-4(5)) Routledge.
Larsen, Stephen. The Neurofeedback Solution. 2012. 392p. pap. 19.95 **(978-1-59477-366-2(1))** Inner Traditions International, Ltd.
Miller, Eric B. Bio-Guided Music Therapy: A Practitioner's Guide to the Clinical Integration of Music & Biofeedback. 2011. (ENG., Illus.). 256p. pap. (978-1-84905-844-5(X)) Kingsley, Jessica Ltd.
Nosko, Herwig. Alpha Neurofeedback Training in the Rehabilitation Process of Stroke Patients. 2008. (Illus.). 132p. pap. (978-3-8364-8046-8(8)) VDM Verlag Dr. Mueller e.K.
Pecherstorfer, Thomas. Neurofeedback & Hrv Biofeedback after Stroke. 2009. 84p. pap. (978-3-639-20962-4(1)) VDM Verlag Dr. Mueller e.K.
Peper, Erik, et al. Biofeedback Mastery: An Experiential Teaching & Self-Training Manual. 2009. (ENG.). 438p. pap. 80.00 (978-0-9842979-0-0(1)) Assn. for Applied Psychophysiology & Biofeedback.
Puckhaber, Heather L. New Research on Biofeedback. 2006. 225.00 (978-1-60021-362-5(6)) Nova Science Pubs., Inc.
Robbins, Jim. A Symphony in the Brain: The Evolution of the New Brain Wave Biofeedback. rev. ed. 2008. (ENG.). 272p. pap. 14.00 (978-0-8021-4381-5(4), Grove Pr.) Grove/Atlantic, Inc.
Schluep- Gerber, Mirjam. Neurofeedback: Neurofeedback als mögliche Therapieform bei ADS? Vorteile und Schwierigkeiten. 2010. 76p. pap. (978-3-639-22866-3(9)) VDM Verlag Dr. Mueller e.K.
Striefel, Sebastian. Practice Guidelines & Standards for Providers of Biofeedback & Applied Psychophysiological Services, 1999. rev. ed. Date not set. 56p. ring bd. 28.00 (978-1-887114-05-9(X)) Assn. for Applied Psychophysiology & Biofeedback.
Swingle, Paul G. Biofeedback for the Brain: How Neurotherapy Effectively Treats Depression, ADHD, Autism, & More. 2010. (ENG., Illus.). 232p. pap. 21.95 (978-0-8135-4779-4(2)) Rutgers Univ. Pr.
Tenenbaum, Gershon & Edmonds, W. Alex, eds. Case Studies in Applied Psychophysiology: Neurofeedback & Biofeedback Treatments for Advances in Human Performance. 2012. (ENG.). 342p. 79.95 **(978-0-470-97173-4(8)**, Wiley-Blackwell) Wiley, John & Sons, Inc.

BIOFILMS

Abedon, Stephen T. Bacteriophages & Biofilms: Ecology, Phage Therapy, Plaques. 2011. (Bacteriology Research Developments Ser.). (Illus.). ii, 138p. pap. 69.00 (978-1-61761-588-7(9), Nova Biomedical Bks.) Nova Science Pubs., Inc.
Allen, Christopher. Game Theoretic Analysis. 2011. 68p. pap. **(978-3-8443-0033-8(3))** Lambert Academic Publishing.
An, Yuehuei H. & Friedman, Richard J., eds. Handbook of Bacterial Adhesion: Principles, Methods, & Applications. 2010. (ENG.). 672p. pap. 199.00 (978-1-61737-192-9(0), 1617371920) Humana Pr.
Ariga, Katsuhiko. Organized Organic Ultrathin Films: Fundamentals & Applications. 2009. (ENG.). 288p. 150.00 (978-0-470-82362-0(3), Wiley) Wiley, John & Sons, Inc.
Babu, Mohammed. Effects of Algal Biofilms & Operational Conditions on Nitrogen Transformations & Removal in Waste Stabilization Ponds. 2011. (ENG.). 140p. pap. 59.95 (978-0-415-66946-7(4), CRC Press) Taylor & Francis Group GBR. Dist: Taylor & Francis Group.
Bailey, William C. Biofilms: Formation, Development & Properties. 2010. (Biotechnology in Agriculture, Industry & Medicine Ser.). 295.00 (978-1-61728-293-5(6), Nova Biomedical Bks.) Nova Science Pubs., Inc.
Balaban, Naomi, ed. Control of Biofilm Infections by Signal Manipulation. (Springer Series on Biofilms Ser.). (Illus.). 2010. xvi, 175p. pap. 159.00 (978-3-642-09309-8(4), 3642093094) 2008. 175p. 159.00 (978-3-540-73852-7(5)) Springer.
Beyenal, Haluk & Lewandowski, Zbigniew. Fundamentals of Biofilm Research. 2007. (ENG., Illus.). 480p. 149.95 (978-0-8493-3541-9(8), CRC Press) Taylor & Francis Group GBR. Dist: Taylor & Francis Group.
Bjarnsholt, Thomas, ed. Biofilm Infections. 2010. (ENG., Illus.). 350p. 209.00 (978-1-4419-6083-2(X), 144196083X) Springer.
Blaschek, Hans P., et al, eds. Biofilms in the Food Environment. 2007. (Institute of Food Technologists Ser.: 33). (ENG., Illus.). 208p. 199.95 (978-0-8138-2058-3(8), Wiley-Blackwell) Wiley, John & Sons, Inc.
Bott, T. Reg. Industrial Biofouling: Occurrence & Control. 2011. (ENG.). 220p. 260.00 (978-0-444-53224-4(2)) Elsevier Science & Technology Bks.
Camesano, Terri A. & Mello, Charlene M. Microbial Surfaces: Structure, Interactions, & Reactivity. 2008. (ACS Symposium Ser.). (ENG., Illus.). 130.00 (978-0-8412-7430-3(4)) American Chemical Society.
Cerca, Nuno. Staphylococcal Biofilms in Medical Devices. 2011. 208p. pap. **(978-3-8443-9041-4(3))** Lambert Academic Publishing.
Costerton, J. William. The Biofilm Primer. 2007. (Springer Series on Biofilms Ser.). (Illus.). 199p. 79.95 (978-3-540-68021-5(7), 3540680217) Springer.
—The Biofilm Primer. 2010. (Springer Series on Biofilms Ser.). (Illus.). viii, 199p. pap. 79.95 (978-3-642-08765-3(5), 3642087655) Springer.
Flemming, Hans-Curt, et al, eds. Biofilm Highlights. 2011. (Springer Series on Biofilms Ser.). (ENG., Illus.). xii, 243p. 189.00 (978-3-642-19939-4(3), 3642199399) Springer.
—Colloidal Transport in Porous Media. 2007. (ENG., Illus.). xii, 292p. 169.00 (978-3-540-71338-8(7), 3540713387) Springer.
Fratamico, P., et al, eds. Biofilms in the Food & Beverage Industries. 2009. (ENG., Illus.). 600p. 249.95 (978-1-4200-9484-8(X), CRC Press) Taylor & Francis Group GBR. Dist: Taylor & Francis Group.
—Biofilms in the Food & Beverage Industries. 2009. (Illus.). 576p. (978-1-84569-477-7(5)) Woodhead Publishing Ltd.
Frimmel, Fritz H., et al, eds. Colloidal Transport in Porous Media. 2010. (ENG., Illus.). xii, 292p. pap. 169.00 (978-3-642-09047-9(8), 3642090478) Springer.
Gomes, Fernanda. Staphylococcus Epidermidis Biofilms. 2011. 120p. pap. **(978-3-8443-8040-8(X))** Lambert Academic Publishing.
Kjelleberg, Staffan & Gibskov, Michael, eds. The Biofilm Mode of Life: Mechanisms & Adaptions. 2007. (ENG., Illus.). 300p. (C). 226.00 (978-1-904933-33-5(5), Taylor & Francis) Taylor & Francis Group GBR. Dist: Taylor & Francis Group.
Krumbein, W. E., et al, eds. Fossil & Recent Biofilms: A Natural History of Life on Earth. 2010. 504p. pap. 299.00 (978-90-481-6412-7(5), 9048164125) Springer.
Lear, Gavin & Lewis, Gillian D., eds. Microbial Biofilms: Current Research & Applications. 2012. (Illus.). 238p. 319.00 **(978-1-904455-96-7(4))** Caister Academic Pr. GBR. Dist: International Specialized Bk. Services.
Materials Research Society ( ) Staff, compiled by. Biofilm-Material Interactions: New Tools, Technologies, & Opportunities. 2007. (Materials Research Society Symposium Proceedings Ser.). 31p. pap. 40.00 (978-1-60423-410-7(5)) Curran Assocs., Inc.
Moriarty, T. Fintan, et al, eds. Biomaterials Associated Infection: Immunological Aspects & Antimicrobial Strategies. 2012. (ENG., Illus.). 320p. 159.00 **(978-1-4614-1030-0(4)**, 1461410304) Springer.
Nieberle, Sigrid. Literarhistorische Filmbiographien: Autorschaft und Literaturgeschichte im Kino. Mit Einer Filmographie 1909-2007. 2008. (Media & Cultural Memory / Medien und kulturelle Erinnerung Ser.). (GER., Illus.). VIII, 400p. 147.00 (978-3-11-020074-4(0)) De Gruyter, Walter Inc.
Nobile, Clarissa. Genetics & Genomics of Candida Albicans Biofilm Formation. 2008. 224p. pap. (978-3-639-07055-2(0)) VDM Verlag Dr. Mueller e.K.
Oleskin, Alexander V., et al. Symbiotic Biofilms & Brain Neurochemistry. 2010. (Illus.). viii, 57p. pap. 49.00 (978-1-61761-005-9(4)) Nova Science Pubs., Inc.
Paulson, Daryl S., ed. Handbook of Applied Biomedical Microbiology a Biofilms Approach: A Biofilms Approach. 2009. (ENG., Illus.). 176p. 133.95 (978-0-8493-7569-9(X), CRC Press) Taylor & Francis Group GBR. Dist: Taylor & Francis Group.
Percival, Steven, et al, eds. Biofilms & Veterinary Medicine. 2011. (Springer Series on Biofilms Ser.). (ENG., Illus.). xiv, 257p. 189.00 (978-3-642-21288-8(3), 3642212883) Springer.
Rodrigues, Diana, et al. Listeria Monocytogenes & Salmonella Enterica Entertidis. 2011. 176p. pap. **(978-3-8433-9272-3(2))** Lambert Academic Publishing.
Romeo, Tony. Bacterial Biofilms. (Current Topics in Microbiology & Immunology Ser.). (Illus.). xii, 296p. 2010. pap. 219.00 (978-3-642-09469-9(4), 3642094694) 2008. (ENG., 219.00 (978-3-540-75417-6(2), 3540754172) Springer.
Shirtliff, Mark & Leid, Jeff. The Role of Biofilms in Device-Related Infections. 2009. (Springer Series on Biofilms Ser.). (ENG., Illus.). xii, 272p. 189.00 (978-3-540-68113-7(2)) Springer.
Shunmugaperumal, Tamilvanan. Biofilm Eradication & Prevention: A Pharmaceutical Approach to Medical Device Infections. 2010. (ENG., Illus.). 431p. 158.00 (978-0-470-47996-4(5), Wiley) Wiley, John & Sons, Inc.
Shunmugaperumal, Tamilvanan. Preventive Strategies for Medical Device-Related Nosocomial Infections. 2011. 192p. pap. **(978-3-8443-0184-7(4))** Lambert Academic Publishing.
Sillankorva, Sanna, et al. Use of Bacteriophages to Control Biofilms. 2011. 192p. pap. **(978-3-8454-0611-4(9))** Lambert Academic Publishing.
Sousa, Cláudia. Staphylococcus Epidermidis. 2011. 252p. pap. **(978-3-8443-9134-3(7))** Lambert Academic Publishing.
St.Clair, Larry & Seaward, Mark. Biodeterioration of Stone Surfaces: Lichens & Biofilms as Weathering Agents of Rocks & Cultural Heritage. 2010. xvii, 292p. pap. 189.00 (978-90-481-6724-1(8), 9048167248) Springer.
Valdez, J. C. Biological & Chemical Studies to Support the Use of Lactobacill As a Strategy for Control of Biofilm-Producing Bacteria. 2011. pap. (978-1-61728-859-3(4)) Nova Science Pubs., Inc.
Wilson, Michael & Devine, Deirdre, eds. Medical Implications of Biofilms. 2011. (ENG.). 338p. pap. 65.00 **(978-1-107-40345-1(6))** Cambridge Univ. Pr.

BIOFUELS

see Biomass Energy

BIOGAS

see also Methane

Abbasi, Tasneem, et al. Biogas Energy. 2011. (SpringerBriefs in Environmental Science Ser.). (ENG., Illus.). xiii, 169p. pap. 49.95 **(978-1-4614-1039-3(8)**, 1461410398) Springer.
Biogas: Volumes 1 And 2. 2007. per. 19.95 (978-1-60322-031-6(3)) Knowledge Pubns. Corp.
Biogas Volume 3: A Chinese Biogas Manual. 2007. per. 24.95 (978-1-60322-039-2(9)) Knowledge Pubns. Corp.
Deublein, Dieter & Steinhauser, Angelika. Biogas from Waste & Renewable Resources: An Introduction. 2nd ed. 2010. (ENG., Illus.). 578p. 155.00 (978-3-527-32798-0(3), Wiley-VCH) Wiley, John & Sons, Inc.
Hoogendoorn, Alwin & Kasteren, Han J. M N. V. Transportation Biofuels: Novel Pathways for the Production of Ethanol, Biogas & Biodiesel. 2010. (RSC Green Chemistry Ser.). (ENG., Illus.). 208p. (C). 195.00 (978-1-84973-043-3(1)) Royal Society of Chemistry, The GBR. Dist: Ingram Pub. Services.
Horn, Svein Jarle. Seaweed Biofuels. 2009. 104p. pap. (978-3-639-15307-1(3)) VDM Verlag Dr. Mueller e.K.
Litonjua, Raphaël & Cvetkovski, Irene. Biogas: Production, Consumption & Applications. 2012. (Energy Science, Engineering & Technology Ser.). 252p. 95.00 **(978-1-61470-973-2(4))** Nova Science Pubs., Inc.
Mwirigi, Jecinta. Biogas Technology. 2011. 124p. pap. **(978-3-8443-2543-0(3))** Lambert Academic Publishing.
Nanda, Rajashree, et al. Anaerobic Digestion in Kitchen Waste Management to Produce Biogas. 2011. 68p. pap. **(978-3-8454-1484-3(7))**; pap. **(978-3-8454-0751-7(4))** Lambert Academic Publishing.
Plata, Adam. Optimale Standorte von Biogasanlagen: Eine Multikriterienanalyse mit GIS. 2009. 120p. pap. (978-3-639-18310-8(X)) VDM Verlag Dr. Mueller e.K.
Poliafico, Marco. Anaerobic Digestion: Decision Support Software. 2009. 216p. pap. (978-3-639-13567-1(9)) VDM Verlag Dr. Mueller e.K.
Roy, Smarajit. Understanding Waste = Bioenergy. 2011. 60p. pap. 12.10 **(978-1-4567-8354-9(8))** AuthorHouse.
Thangamani, Arumugam & Parthiban, Rangasamy. Management of Industrial Tannery Solid Waste for Biogas Production. 2011. (Illus.). 236p. pap. **(978-3-8433-8927-3(6))** Lambert Academic Publishing.
Zaman, Sheikh. Electricity from Poultry Waste in Bangladesh. 2011. 124p. pap. **(978-3-8443-0100-7(3))** Lambert Academic Publishing.

BIOGENESIS

see Life—Origin

B

BIOGEOCHEMICAL CYCLES

see also Nitrogen Cycle

Andersen, Tom. Pelagic Nutrient Cycles: Herbivores as Sources & Sinks. 2011. (Ecological Studies). (ENG., Illus.). xii, 300p. pap. 169.00 *(978-3-642-08279-5(3),* 3642082793) Springer.

Archer, David. The Global Carbon Cycle. 2010. (Princeton Primers in Climate Ser.). (ENG., Illus.). 224p. (C). pap. 24.95 *(978-0-691-14414-6(1))* Princeton Univ. Pr.

—The Global Carbon Cycle. 2010. (Princeton Primers in Climate Ser.). (ENG., Illus.). 224p. (C). 70.00 *(978-0-691-14413-9(3))* Princeton Univ. Pr.

Bashkin, Vladimir N. Modern Biogeochemistry: Environmental Risk Assessment. 2nd ed. 2010. (ENG.). xvi, 444p. pap. 239.00 *(978-90-481-7063-0(X),* 904817063X) Springer.

Bemmerer, Daniel. Experimental Study of the Carbon-Nitrogen-Oxygen Cycle at Low Energy. 2008. 100p. pap. *(978-3-8364-7343-9(7))* VDM Verlag Dr. Mueller e.K.

Bünemann, Else K., et al, eds. Phosphorus in Action: Biological Processes in Soil Phosphorus Cycling. 2010. (Soil Biology Ser.). (Illus.). xv, 483p. 209.00 *(978-3-642-15270-2(8),* 3642152708) Springer.

Cao, Long. Global Warming, Ocean Circulation, & the Carbon Cycle - an Integrated Modeling Study. 2008. 88p. pap. *(978-3-639-03147-8(4))* VDM Verlag Dr. Mueller e.K.

Chapin, III, F. Stuart, FStuart, et al. Principles of Terrestrial Ecosystem Ecology. 2nd ed. 2011. (ENG., Illus.). xv, 529p. pap. 69.95 ***(978-1-4419-9502-5(1),*** 1441995021) Springer.

Chen, Junying & Guô, Chuguang, eds. Ecosystem Ecology Research Trends. 2008. 364p. (C). 129.00 *(978-1-60456-183-8(1))* Nova Science Pubs., Inc.

Cram101 Textbook Reviews. Outlines & Highlights for Marine Biogeochemical Cycles by Open University. 2011. 102p. pap. 27.95 ***(978-1-61905-574-2(0))*** Cram101 Inc.

Cram101 Textbook Reviews & Cram101 Textbook Reviews. Outlines & Highlights for Chemical Oceanography & the Marine Carbon Cycle by Steven R Emerson, Isbn: 9780521833134 0521833132. 2011. 128p. pap. 28.95 ***(978-1-61490-404-5(9))*** Cram101 Inc.

Fantozzi, Laura, et al. Behaviour of Autotrophic Protists Facing Heavy Metal Challenges. 2010. 92p. pap. *(978-3-8383-7355-3(3))* Lambert Academic Publishing.

Gadd, Geoffrey Michael, ed. Fungi in Biogeochemical Cycles. 2011. (British Mycological Society Symposia Ser.). (ENG.). 490p. pap. 85.00 ***(978-1-107-40321-5(9))*** Cambridge Univ. Pr.

Gianguzza, Antonio, et al, eds. Chemistry of Marine Water & Sediments. 2012. (Environmental Science & Engineering / Environmental Science Ser.). (ENG., Illus.). xviii, 508p. pap. 349.00 *(978-3-642-07559-9(2),* 3642075592) Springer.

Handa, N., et al, eds. Dynamics & Characterization of Marine Organic Matter. 2010. (Ocean Sciences Research Ser.). 572p. pap. 309.00 *(978-90-481-5451-7(0),* 9048154510) Springer.

Krapivin, Vladimir F. Biogeochemical Cycles in Globalization & Sustainable Development. 2010. (Springer Praxis Books / Environmental Sciences Ser.). xxxviii, 562p. pap. 319.00 *(978-3-642-09471-2(6),* 3642094716) Springer.

Krapivin, Vladimir F. (Russian Academy of Sciences. Biogeochemical Cycles in Globalization & Sustainable Development. 2008. (Springer Praxis Books / Environmental Sciences Ser.). 319.00 *(978-3-540-75439-8(3),* 3540754393) Springer.

Kronvang, Brian, et al, eds. The Interactions Between Sediments & Water. 2010. (ENG.). x, 319p. pap. 219.00 *(978-90-481-7377-8(9),* 9048173779) Springer.

Leeuwe, M. A. van, et al. Phaeocystis, major link in the biogeochemical cycling of climate-relevant Elements. 2011. (ENG.). vi, 330p. pap. 109.00 *(978-90-481-7569-7(0),* 9048175690) Springer.

Macias, D. The Strait of Gibraltar: A Field Laboratory to Analyze Biological Response to Physical Forcing. 2010. pap. 49.00 *(978-1-61728-973-6(6))* Nova Science Pubs., Inc.

McPherson, Brian J. & Sundquist, E. T. Carbon Sequestration & Its Role in the Global Carbon Cycle. 2009. *(978-0-87590-448-1(3))* American Geophysical Union.

Mortensen, E., et al, eds. Nutrient Dynamics & Biological Structure in Shallow Freshwater & Brackish Lakes. 2010. (Developments in Hydrobiology Ser.). 528p. pap. 549.00 *(978-90-481-4360-3(8),* 9048143608) Springer.

Navratil, Tomas. Biogeochemistry of the II a Group Elements in a Forested Catchment. 2009. 120p. pap. *(978-3-639-17929-3(3))* VDM Verlag Dr. Mueller e.K.

Newman, Michael C. & Zuber, Sharon L., eds. Mercury Pollution: An Interdisciplinary Overview. 2011. (ENG., Illus.). 288p. 89.95 *(978-1-4398-3384-1(2),* CRC Press) Taylor & Francis Group GBR. Dist: Taylor & Francis Group.

Restelli, G. & Angeletti, G., eds. Dimethylsulphide: Oceans, Atmosphere & Climate (1992) Oceans, Atmosphere & Climate (1992) 2010. 416p. pap. 223.00 *(978-90-481-4325-2(X),* 904814325X) Springer.

Schafer, Karina. Water & Carbon Relations under Ambient & Elevated Atmospheric Co2. 2009. 144p. pap. *(978-3-639-12075-2(2))* VDM Verlag Dr. Mueller e.K.

Stefels, J., et al, eds. Phaeocystis, major link in the biogeochemical cycling of climate-relevant Elements. 2007. (ENG.). vi, 330p. 109.00 *(978-1-4020-6213-1(3),* 1402062133) Springer.

Tamminen, T. & Kuosa, H., eds. Eutrophication in Planktonic Ecosystems: Food Web Dynamics & Elemental Cycling: Food Web Dynamics & Elemental Cycling. 2011. (Developments in Hydrobiology Ser.). 356p. pap. 229.00 *(978-90-481-5041-0(8),* 9048150418) Springer.

Valentini, Riccardo, ed. Fluxes of Carbon, Water & Energy of European Forests. 2010. (Ecological Studies). (Illus.). xx, 274p. pap. 169.00 *(978-3-642-07848-4(6),* 3642078486) Springer.

Volk, Tyler. CO2 Rising: The World's Greatest Environmental Challenge. 2010. (ENG., Illus.). 240p. (gr. 17). pap. 12.95 *(978-0-262-51521-4(0))* MIT Pr.

Vymazal, Jan, ed. Water & Nutrient Management in Natural & Constructed Wetlands. 2010. (ENG., Illus.). x, 375p. 179.00 *(978-90-481-9584-8(5),* 9048195845) Springer.

Wangersky, Peter J. Estuaries. 2010. (Handbook of Environmental Chemistry / Water Pollution Ser.). (Illus.). xvi, 305p. pap. 249.00 *(978-3-642-05544-7(3),* 3642055443) Springer.

White, Philip J. & Hammond, John P., eds. The Ecophysiology of Plant-Phosphorus Interactions. 2010. (Plant Ecophysiology Ser.). xii, 292p. pap. 239.00 *(978-90-481-7881-0(9),* 9048178819) Springer.

BIOGEOCHEMISTRY

see also Biogeochemical Cycles

Baird, Andrew J. Carbon Cycling in Northern Peatlands. 2009. *(978-0-87590-449-8(1))* American Geophysical Union.

Bashkin, Vladimir N. Modern Biogeochemistry: Environmental Risk Assessment. 2nd ed. (ENG.). xvi, 444p. 2010. pap. 239.00 *(978-90-481-7063-0(X),* 904817063X) 2006. (Illus.). 239.00 *(978-1-4020-4182-2(9),* 1402041829) Springer.

Bhattacharya, Prosun, et al, eds. Arsenic in Soil & Groundwater Environment: Biogeochemical Interactions, Health Effects & Remediation. 2007. (Trace Metals & Other Contaminants in the Environment Ser.: 9). (ENG., Illus.). 684p. 129.00 *(978-0-444-51820-0(7),* Elsevier Science) Elsevier Science & Technology Bks.

Braids, Olin C. & Swarzenski, Peter, eds. Handbook of Soil & Groundwater Biogeochemistry, 2 vols. 2009. (Illus.). 1000p. 459.00 *(978-1-4020-9772-0(7))* Springer.

Bundschuh, Jochen & Zilberbrand, Michael, eds. Geochemical Modeling of Groundwater, Vadose & Geothermal Systems. 2011. (Multiphysics Modeling Ser.). (ENG.). 332p. 149.95 *(978-0-415-66810-1(7),* CRC Press) Taylor & Francis Group GBR. Dist: Taylor & Francis Group.

Cram101 Textbook Reviews. Outlines & Highlights for Biogeochemistry: An Analysis of Global Change by W. H. Schlesinger, ISBN. 2010. 102p. pap. 28.95 *(978-1-61698-618-6(2))* Cram101 Inc.

Cram101 Textbook Reviews. Outlines & Highlights for Introduction to Marine Biogeochemistry by Susan Libes. 2011. 88p. pap. 27.95 ***(978-1-61905-851-4(0))*** Cram101 Inc.

Descy, Jean-Pierre, et al, eds. Lake Kivu: Limnology & biogeochemistry of a tropical great Lake. 2012. (Aquatic Ecology Ser.: 5). (ENG., Illus.). x, 200p. 129.00 ***(978-94-007-4242-0(8),*** 9400742428) Springer.

Fry, Brian. Stable Isotope Ecology. 2008. (ENG., Illus.). xii, 308p. 79.95 *(978-0-387-30513-4(0),* 0387305130) Springer.

Han, Fengxiang X. Biogeochemistry of Trace Elements in Arid Environments. (Environmental Pollution Ser.). 2010. xxvi, 355p. pap. 249.00 *(978-90-481-7508-6(9),* 9048175089) 2009. (Illus.). xxvi, 366p. 249.00 *(978-1-4020-6023-6(8))* Springer.

Ittekkot, Venugopalan, et al, eds. The Silicon Cycle: Human Perturbations & Impacts on Aquatic Systems. 2006. (Scientific Committee on Problems of the Environment (SCOPE) Ser.). (ENG., Illus.). 296p. 100.00 *(978-1-59726-114-2(9))* Island Pr.

—The Silicon Cycle: Human Perturbations & Impacts on Aquatic Systems. 2006. (Scientific Committee on Problems of the Environment (SCOPE) Ser.). (ENG., Illus.). 296p. pap. 50.00 *(978-1-59726-115-9(7))* Island Pr.

Jiao, Nianzhi & Zhang, Chuanlun. Microbial Processes & Carbon Cycling in the Ocean. 2008. (Illus.). 87p. (C). pap. 29.00 *(978-1-60456-779-3(1))* Nova Science Pubs., Inc.

Kabata-Pendias, Alina & Mukherjee, Arun B. Trace Elements from Soil to Human. 2010. (ENG., Illus.). xxvi, 550p. pap. 219.00 *(978-3-642-06925-3(8),* 3642069258) Springer.

Kondratyev, Kirill Y. & Krapivin, Vladimir F. Global Carbon Cycle & Climate Change. 2010. (Springer Praxis Books / Environmental Sciences Ser.). (Illus.). xxii, 368p. pap. 289.00 *(978-3-642-05642-0(3),* 3642056423) Springer.

Lal, Rattan & Follett, Ronald F., eds. Soil Carbon Sequestration & the Greenhouse Effect: SSSA Special Publication 57. 2nd ed. 2009. (SSSA Special Publications: 57). (Illus.). xxviii, 410p. pap. 70.00 *(978-0-89118-850-6(9))* ASA-CSSA-SSSA.

Leeuwe, M. A. van, et al. Phaeocystis, major link in the biogeochemical cycling of climate-relevant Elements. 2011. (ENG.). vi, 330p. pap. 109.00 *(978-90-481-7569-7(0),* 9048175690) Springer.

Levia, Delphis F., et al, eds. Forest Hydrology & Biogeochemistry: Synthesis of Past Research & Future Directions. 2011. (Ecological Studies). (ENG., Illus.). xxii, 740p. 229.00 *(978-94-007-1362-8(2),* 9400713622) Springer.

Libes, Susan. Introduction to Marine Biogeochemistry. 2nd ed. 2009. (ENG., Illus.). 928p. (C). 82.95 *(978-0-12-088530-5(1),* Academic Pr.) Elsevier Science & Technology Bks.

Likens, Gene E., ed. Biogeochemistry of Inland Waters. 2010. (ENG.). 744p. 155.00 *(978-0-12-381996-3(2),* Academic Pr.) Elsevier Science & Technology Bks.

MacKenzie, Fred T., ed. Carbon in the Geobiosphere: Earth's Outer Shell. 2006. (Topics in Geobiology Ser.). (Illus.). 402p. 269.00 *(978-1-4020-4044-3(X),* 140204044X) Springer.

Mackenzie, Fred T. & Lerman, Abraham. Carbon in the Geobiosphere: - Earth's Outer Shell - 2010. (Topics in Geobiology Ser.). (Illus.). xxi, 402p. pap. 269.00 *(978-90-481-7022-7(2),* 9048170222) Springer.

Matzner, Egbert, ed. Biogeochemistry of Forested Catchments in a Changing Environment: A German Case Study. 2011. (Ecological Studies). (ENG., Illus.). xxii, 501p. pap. 319.00 *(978-3-642-05900-1(7),* 3642059007) Springer.

Mitchell, Ralph. Microbial Ecology of the Oceans. Kirchman, David L., ed. 2nd ed. 2008. (Wiley Series in Ecological & Applied Microbiology Ser.: 34). (ENG., Illus.). 620p. 120.95 *(978-0-470-04344-8(X),* Wiley-Liss) Wiley, John & Sons, Inc.

Navratil, Tomas. Biogeochemistry of the II a Group Elements in a Forested Catchment. 2009. 120p. pap. *(978-3-639-17929-3(3))* VDM Verlag Dr. Mueller e.K.

Nieder, R. & Benbi, D. K. Carbon & Nitrogen in the Terrestrial Environment. 2010. (ENG., Illus.). xii, 432p. pap. 159.00 *(978-90-481-7880-3(0),* 9048178800) Springer.

Nieder, Rolf & Benbi, Dinesh K. Carbon & Nitrogen in the Terrestrial Environment. 2008. (ENG., Illus.). xii, 432p. 159.00 *(978-1-4020-8432-4(3),* 1402084323) Springer.

Peters, Kenneth E., et al. The Biomarker Guide Vol. 1: Biomarkers & Isotopes in the Environment & Human History, 2 vols., Vol. 1. 2nd rev. ed. 2007. (ENG., Illus.). 492p. pap. 100.00 *(978-0-521-78697-3(5))* Cambridge Univ. Pr.

Rebalancing the Carbon Cycle: Hearing Before the Subcommittee on Energy & Resources of the Committee on Government Reform, House of Representatives, One Hundred Ninth Congress, Second Session, September 27, 2006. 2008. (Illus.). iii, 140p. *(978-0-16-082518-7(0),* 552-070-38553-3) United States Government Printing Office.

Roston, Eric. The Carbon Age: How Life's Core Element Has Become Civilization's Greatest Threat. 2009. (ENG., Illus.). 320p. pap. 16.00 *(978-0-8027-1751-1(9))* Walker & Co.

Rye, Robert O. Evolution of Ore Deposits & Technology Transfer Project: Isotope & Chemical Methods in Support of the U.S. Geological Survey Science Strategy, 2003-2008. 2010. (Illus.). ix, 43p. *(978-1-4113-2603-3(2))* United States Geological Survey.

Santini, Joanna M. & Ward, Seamus A., eds. The Metabolism of Arsenite. 2012. (Arsenic in the Environment Ser.). (ENG., Illus.). 218p. 119.95 ***(978-0-415-69719-4(0),*** CRC Press) Taylor & Francis Group GBR. Dist: Taylor & Francis Group.

Song, Jinming. Biogeochemical Processes of Biogenic Elements in China Marginal Seas. 2009. (Advanced Topics in Science & Technology in China Ser.). (ENG., Illus.). 676p. 219.00 *(978-3-642-04059-7(4),* 3642040594) Springer.

Stefels, J., et al, eds. Phaeocystis, major link in the biogeochemical cycling of climate-relevant Elements. 2007. (ENG.). vi, 330p. 109.00 *(978-1-4020-6213-1(3),* 1402062133) Springer.

Talling, Jack F. & Lemoalle, Jacques. Ecological Dynamics of Tropical Inland Waters. 2010. (ENG.). 452p. pap. 55.00 *(978-0-521-16940-0(2))* Cambridge Univ. Pr.

Vetrov, Alexander & Romankevich, Evgeny. Carbon Cycle in the Russian Arctic Seas. 2010. (ENG., Illus.). x, 332p. pap. 169.00 *(978-3-642-05991-9(0),* 3642059910) Springer.

Volk, Tyler. CO2 Rising: The World's Greatest Environmental Challenge. 2008. (ENG., Illus.). 240p. (gr. 17). 23.95 *(978-0-262-22083-5(0))* MIT Pr.

Wieder, R. Kelman, et al, eds. Biogeochemical Investigations at the Watershed, Landscape, & Regional Scales. 2010. 512p. pap. 199.00 *(978-90-481-5064-9(7),* 9048150647) Springer.

Wiggert, Jerry D. Indian Ocean Biogeochemical Processes & Ecological Variability. 2009. (Illus.). vii, 429p. *(978-0-87590-475-7(0))* American Geophysical Union.

Williams, Richard G. & Follows, Michael J. Ocean Dynamics & the Carbon Cycle: Principles & Mechanisms. 2011. (ENG., Illus.). 416p. (C). 73.00 *(978-0-521-84369-0(3))* Cambridge Univ. Pr.

BIOGEOGRAPHY

see also Phytogeography; Zoogeography

also subdivisions Geographical Distribution or Migration under names of organisms, e.g. Fishes—Geographical Distribution; Birds—Migration

Atkinson, K & Raw, M. Biogeography. 2007. (Illus.). 144p. pap. 34.50 *(978-1-84489-620-2(X))* Hodder Education GBR. Dist: Trans-Atlantic Pubns., Inc.

Bright, Michael. The Distribution of Species. 2008. (Timeline: Life on Earth Ser.). (ENG., Illus.). 56p. 33.50 *(978-1-4329-1654-1(8));* pap. 9.99 *(978-1-4329-1660-2(2))* Heinemann-Raintree. (NA-h).

Cox, C. Barry & Moore, Peter D. Biogeography: An Ecological & Evolutionary Approach. 8th ed. 2010. (ENG., Illus.). 520p. (C). pap. 111.95 *(978-0-470-63794-4(3),* Wiley); 456p. pap. 100.95 *(978-1-4051-7806-8(X),* Wiley-Blackwell) Wiley, John & Sons, Inc.

Ebach, Malte C. & Tangney, Raymond S., eds. Biogeography in a Changing World. 2006. (Systematics Association Special Volume Ser.: No. 70). (ENG., Illus.). 232p. 89.95 *(978-0-8493-8038-9(3),* CRC Press) Taylor & Francis Group GBR. Dist: Taylor & Francis Group.

Elewa, Ashraf M. T., ed. Migration of Organisms: Climate. Geography. Ecology. 2010. (ENG., Illus.). xiv, 332p. pap. 139.00 *(978-3-642-06591-0(0),* 3642065910) Springer.

Fet, Victor & Popov, Alexi, eds. Biogeography & Ecology of Bulgaria. 2007. (Monographiae Biologicae Ser.). (Illus.). xxi, 687p. (C). 289.00 *(978-1-4020-4417-5(8),* 1402044178) Springer.

Finney, Stanley C. & Berry, William B. N. The Ordovician Earth System. 2010. (Illus.). viii, 193p. pap. 60.00 *(978-0-8137-2466-9(X))* Geological Society of America, Inc.

Fontaneto, Diego, ed. Biogeography of Microscopic Organisms: Is Everything Small Everywhere? 2011. (Systematics Association Special Volume Ser.). (ENG., Illus.). 384p. 99.00 *(978-0-521-76670-8(2))* Cambridge Univ. Pr.

Franklin, Janet. Mapping Species Distributions: Spatial Inference & Prediction. 2010. (Ecology, Biodiversity & Conservation Ser.). (ENG., Illus.). 338p. pap. 59.99 *(978-0-521-70002-3(7))* Cambridge Univ. Pr.

Gailis, Mihails & Kalni?š, Stefans, eds. Biogeography. 2010. (Environmental Research Advances Ser.). 106.00 *(978-1-60741-494-0(5))* Nova Science Pubs., Inc.

Gollasch, Stephan, et al, eds. Bridging Divides: Maritime Canals as Invasion Corridors. 2010. (Monographiae Biologicae Ser.). (Illus.). xiii, 315p. pap. 219.00 *(978-90-481-7265-8(9),* 9048172659) Springer.

Groves, R. H. & Di Castri, F., eds. Biogeography of Mediterranean Invasions. 2008. (ENG.). 504p. pap. 95.00 *(978-0-521-06390-6(6))* Cambridge Univ. Pr.

Houérou, Henry N. Bioclimatology & Biogeography of Africa. 2008. (ENG., Illus.). xiv, 242p. 189.00 *(978-3-540-85191-2(7),* 3540851917) Springer.

Knapp, Sandra & Williams, David M. Beyond Cladistics: The Branching of a Paradigm. 2010. (Species & Systematics Ser.). (ENG., Illus.). 352p. 65.00 *(978-0-520-26772-5(9))* Univ. of California Pr.

Koenemann, Stefan, et al, eds. Phylogeography & Population Genetics in Crustacea. 2011. (Crustacean Issues Ser.). (ENG., Illus.). 400p. 139.95 ***(978-1-4398-4073-3(3),*** CRC Press) Taylor & Francis Group GBR. Dist: Taylor & Francis Group.

Krebs, Charles J. Ecology: The Experimental Analysis of Distribution & Abundance. 6th ed. 2008. (ENG., Illus.). 688p. (C). 155.67 *(978-0-321-50743-3(6))* Benjamin-Cummings Publishing Co.

Ladle, Richard J. & Whittaker, Robert J., eds. Conservation Biogeography. 2011. (ENG., Illus.). 320p. 159.95 *(978-1-4443-3503-3(0));* pap. 79.95 *(978-1-4443-3504-0(9))* Wiley, John & Sons, Inc. (Wiley-Blackwell).

Lupton, Darach. Irish Orchid Conservation. 2010. 264p. pap. *(978-3-8383-4776-9(5))* Lambert Academic Publishing.

MacArthur, Robert H. The Theory of Island Biogeography Revisited. Losos, Jonathan B. & Ricklefs, Robert E., eds. 2009. (ENG., Illus.). 494p. (C). 105.00 *(978-0-691-13652-3(1));* pap. 52.50 *(978-0-691-13653-0(X))* Princeton Univ. Pr.

McCarthy, Dennis. Here Be Dragons: How the Study of Animal & Plant Distributions Revolutionized Our Views of Life & Earth. (ENG., Illus.). 2011. 240p. pap. 18.95 *(978-0-19-959566-2(6))* 2009. 256p. 29.95 *(978-0-19-954246-8(5))* Oxford Univ. Pr., Inc.

Millington, Andrew C., et al, eds. The SAGE Handbook of Biogeography. 2011. (Illus.). 624p. 140.00 *(978-1-4129-1951-7(7),* B19517C) SAGE Pubns., Ltd. GBR. Dist: SAGE Pubns., Inc.

Morand, Serge & Krasnov, Boris R., eds. The Biogeography of Host-Parasite Interactions. 2010. (ENG., Illus.). 288p. 135.00 *(978-0-19-956134-6(6));* pap. 65.00 *(978-0-19-956135-3(4))* Oxford Univ. Pr., Inc.

Murray, Craig A., ed. Whales & Dolphins: Behavior, Biology & Distribution. 2010. (Animal Science, Issues & Professions Ser.). 59.00 *(978-1-61668-693-2(6))* Nova Science Pubs., Inc.

Okubo, Akira & Levin, Smon A. Diffusion & Ecological Problems: Modern Perspectives: Modern Perspectives. 2nd ed. 2010. (Interdisciplinary Applied Mathematics Ser.). (Illus.). xx, 467p. pap. 99.00 *(978-1-4419-3151-1(1),* 1441931511) Springer.

Parenti, Lynne R. & Ebach, Malte C. Comparative Biogeography: Discovering & Classifying Biogeographical Patterns of a Dynamic Earth. 2009. (Species & Systematics Ser.). (ENG., Illus.). 272p. 50.00 *(978-0-520-25945-4(9))* Univ. of California Pr.

Patterson, Bruce D. & Costa, Leonora Pires, eds. Bones, Clones, & Biomes: The History & Geography of Recent Neotropical Mammals. 2012. (ENG., Illus.). 432p. 65.00 ***(978-0-226-64919-1(9))*** Univ. of Chicago Pr.

Peterson, Townsend, et al. Ecological Niches & Geographic Distributions. 2011. (Monographs in Population Biology Ser.). (ENG., Illus.). 328p. (C). 80.00 ***(978-0-691-13686-8(6));*** pap. 49.50 ***(978-0-691-13688-2(2))*** Princeton Univ. Pr.

Renema, Willem, ed. Biogeography, Time & Place: Distributions, Barriers & Islands. 2007. (Topics in Geobiology Ser.). (Illus.). 414p. 239.00 *(978-1-4020-6373-2(3))* Springer.

—Biogeography, Time & Place: Distributions, Barriers & Islands: Distributions, Barriers & Islands. 2010. (Topics in Geobiology Ser.). (Illus.). xii, 416p. pap. 239.00 *(978-90-481-7618-2(2),* 9048176182) Springer.

Rescigno, Vittore & Maletta, Savario, eds. Biodiversity Hotspots. 2010. (Environmental Science, Engineering & Technology Ser.). (Illus.). xiv, 200p. 129.00 *(978-1-60876-458-7(3))* Nova Science Pubs., Inc.

Rutgers, Damien S., ed. Phylogeography: Concepts, Intraspecific Patterns & Speciation Processes. 2010. (Genetics - Research & Issues Ser.). (Illus.). xii, 209p. 59.00 *(978-1-60692-954-4(2))* Nova Science Pubs., Inc.

Singh, R. B., ed. Biogeography & Biodiversity. 2009. (Illus.). 340p. 60.00 *(978-81-316-0248-5(6))* Rawat Pubns. IND. Dist: International Specialized Bk. Services.

Smith, Charles H. & Beccaloni, George, eds. Natural Selection & Beyond: The Intellectual Legacy of Alfred Russel Wallace. (ENG., Illus.). 2010. 512p. pap.

Epstein, Barbara & Silvers, Robert B., eds. The Company They Kept: Writers on Unforgettable Friendships. 2006. (ENG.). 316p. 24.95 *(978-1-59017-203-2(5))* New York Review of Bks., Inc., The.
Europa Publications Staff. International Who's Who of Women 2008. 6th rev. ed. 2007. 963p. 560.00 *(978-1-85743-429-3(3))* Routledge.
Fetz, Bernhard & Hemecker, Wilhelm, eds. Theorie der Biographie: Grundlagentexte und Kommentar. 2011. (De Gruyter Studienbuch Ser.). (GER.). 300p. (C). pap. 35.00 *(978-3-11-023762-7(8))* De Gruyter, Walter Inc.
Gardner, Gerald & Bellows, Jim. 80: From Ben Bradlee to Lena Horne to Carl Reiner, Our Most Famous Eighty Year Olds, Reveal Why They Never Felt So Young. 2007. (ENG., Illus.). 320p. 29.99 *(978-1-4022-0840-9(5))* Sourcebooks, Inc.
Gorman, Robert F. Great Lives from History. 2008. 80.00 *(978-1-58765-352-0(4))*; 80.00 *(978-1-58765-355-1(9))*; 80.00 *(978-1-58765-351-3(6))*; 80.00 *(978-1-58765-353-7(2))*; 80.00 *(978-1-58765-354-4(0))*; 80.00 *(978-1-58765-346-9(X))*; 80.00 *(978-1-58765-347-6(8))*; 80.00 *(978-1-58765-348-3(6))*; 80.00 *(978-1-58765-350-6(8))*; 80.00 *(978-1-58765-349-0(4))* Salem Pr., Inc.
—Great Lives from History: The 20th Century, 10 vols., Set. 2008. 5200p. 795.00 *(978-1-58765-345-2(1))* Salem Pr., Inc.
Greenwald, Norman D. Portraits of Power: Berkshire Social Studies Series. Myers, Richard E., ed. 2011. 122p. 39.95 ***(978-1-258-09185-9(2))*** Literary Licensing, LLC.
Henderson, Archibald. Contemporary Immortals. 2007. (ENG.). 248p. per. *(978-1-4067-6029-3(3))* Read Bks.
Holden, Una P. Famous Faces. (Illus.). 40p. *(978-0-86388-029-2(0)*, 003-0141) Speechmark Publishing Ltd.
International Biographical Centre Staff, contrib. by. Dictionary of International Biography. 33rd rev. ed. 2007. v, 1185p. 490.00 *(978-1-903986-26-4(5))* Routledge.
Jeanne Wilkins Wilde, Wilkins Wilde & Jeanne Wilkins Wilde. Tell Me About: A Collection of Memoirs. 2009. 332p. 32.95 *(978-1-4401-7136-9(X))*; pap. 22.95 *(978-1-4401-7134-5(3))* iUniverse, Inc.
Justin, Wintle, ed. New Makers of Modern Culture, 2 vols. 2006. (ENG.). 1816p. 560.00 *(978-0-415-42547-6(6))*; 1800p. 265.00 *(978-0-415-42553-7(0))* Routledge.
Knowlden, Martin. Chat: Greatest Ever True Life Stories. 2006. (ENG.). 254p. per. 13.95 *(978-1-84454-326-7(9))* Blake, John Publishing, Ltd. GBR. Dist: Independent Pubs. Group.
Kogan, David S. The Diary of David S Kogan. Levin, Meyer, ed. 2011. 256p. 47.95 ***(978-1-258-09099-9(6))*** Literary Licensing, LLC.
Kumar, Satish & Whitefield, Freddie, eds. Visionaries of the 20th Century: The 20th Century's 100 Most Important Inspirational Leaders. 2007. (ENG., Illus.). 208p. pap. 25.00 *(978-1-933392-53-0(3))* Chelsea Green Publishing.
Lutz, Stuart. The Last Leaf: Voices of History's Last-Known Survivors. 2010. (ENG.). 275p. 26.00 *(978-1-61614-162-2(X))* Prometheus Bks., Pubs.
Lyons, Jeffrey. Stories My Father Told Me: Notes from the Lyons Den. 2011. (ENG., Illus.). 400p. 35.00 *(978-0-7892-1102-6(5))* Abbeville Pr., Inc.
Marsé, Juan. Senoras y Senores. (SPA.). 180p. *(978-84-7223-636-3(6)*, 6070) Tusquets Editores.
Muggeridge, Malcolm. Something Beautiful for God. 2009. (ENG., Illus.). 160p. 16.95 *(978-0-7459-5339-0(7))* Lion Hudson PLC GBR. Dist: Independent Pubs. Group.
Newsmakers. 2011. 272.00 *(978-1-4144-4755-1(8))* Cengage Gale.
Newsmakers 2009 Ed, 4 vols. 2009th rev. ed. 2008. (Newsmakers Ser.). (ENG.). 272.00 *(978-1-4144-0682-4(7))* Cengage Gale.
Newsmakers 2011, 4 vols. 2011th ed. 2010. (ENG.). 272.00 *(978-1-4144-4164-1(9))* Cengage Gale.
Parkin, Lance. Alan Moore. 2009. (Pocket Essential Ser.). (ENG.). 160p. pap. 12.95 *(978-1-84243-284-6(2))* Pocket Essentials GBR. Dist: Independent Pubs. Group.
People Magazine Editors. The Best & Worst of the Year 2008. Durkee, Cutler, ed. 2008. (ENG., Illus.). 144p. 29.95 *(978-1-933821-16-0(7)*, People Bks.) Time Home Entertainment, Inc.
Phelps, Robert H., ed. Men in the News: Biographical Sketches from the New York Times, Men & Women Who Made Headlines In 1959. 2011. 320p. 50.95 ***(978-1-258-09332-7(4))*** Literary Licensing, LLC.
Pratt, A. T. Camden, ed. People of the Period: A Collection of the Biographies of Upwards. 2007. 1100p. 825.00 *(978-4-901481-85-4(1))* Synapse, Edition JPN. Dist: Taylor & Francis Group.
Randall, Stephen. Movers & Shakers. Playboy Magazine Editors, ed. 2007. (Sport Ser.). 480p. 22.95 *(978-1-59582-044-0(2))* M Pr.
Reader's Digest Staff. True Lives. 2007. 160p. pap. 15.95 *(978-0-7621-0859-6(2))* Reader's Digest Assn., Inc., The.
Roberts, Frank C. Obituaries from 'the Times' 1971-1975. 647p. pap. *(978-0-903713-97-9(7))* Bow Historical Bks.
Scrib Ency Am Lives. 2009. (Scribner Encyclopedia of American Lives, Chronological Ser.). (ENG.). 650p. 218.00 *(978-0-684-31575-1(0))* Cengage Gale.
Sheeler, Jim. Obit: Inspiring Stories of Ordinary People That Led Extraordinary Lives. 2007. 242p. 24.95 *(978-0-87108-943-4(2))* Pruett Publishing Co.
Silvers, Robert B. & Epstein, Barbara, eds. The Company They Kept: Writers on Unforgettable Friendships. 2009. (ENG.). 316p. pap. 19.95 *(978-1-59017-334-3(1))* New York Review of Bks., Inc., The.
Thomson Gale Staff. Newsmakers, 4 vols. 2007th ed. 2006. (Newsmakers Ser.). (ENG.). 272.00 *(978-0-7876-8087-9(7))* Cengage Gale.
Vella, Charles G. Ethics in the Service of the Sick: Reflections & Experiences of Life at the San Raffaele Hospital. 2009. (ENG.). 200p. pap. 35.95 *(978-1-84730-166-6(5))* Veritas Pubns. IRL. Dist: Dufour Editions, Inc.
Wendt, Jana. A Matter of Principle: New Meetings with the Good, the Great & the Formidable. 2008. (ENG.). 304p. pap. 24.95 *(978-0-522-85525-8(3))* Melbourne Univ. Publishing AUS. Dist: Independent Pubs. Group.
Wintle, Justin. The Concise New Makers of Modern Culture. 2009. XX, 876p. pap. 79.95 *(978-0-415-47783-3(2))*; 180.00 *(978-0-415-47782-6(4))* Routledge.
Woollacott, Angela, et al, eds. Transnational Lives: Biographies of Global Modernity, 1700-Present. 2010. (Palgrave Macmillan Transnational History Ser.). (ENG., Illus.). 336p. 89.00 *(978-0-230-23870-1(X))* Palgrave Macmillan.

BIOGRAPHY—21ST CENTURY

A&C Black Staff, ed. Who's Who 2010. 2009. (Who's Who Ser.). (ENG., Illus.). 2608p. 395.00 *(978-1-4081-1414-8(3))* A & C Black GBR. Dist: Macmillan.
The International Who's Who 2008. 71st rev. ed. 2007. 2480p. 650.00 *(978-1-85743-415-6(3))* Routledge.
Justin, Wintle, ed. New Makers of Modern Culture, 2 vols. 2006. (ENG.). 1816p. 560.00 *(978-0-415-42547-6(6))*; 1800p. 265.00 *(978-0-415-42553-7(0))* Routledge.
Marquis Who's Who Staff. Who's Who in the World 2008. 25th anniv. ed. 2007. 2800p. 590.00 *(978-0-8379-1139-7(7))* Marquis Who's Who, LLC.
Newsmakers 2008, 8 vols. 2008th rev. ed. 2007. (Newsmakers Ser.). (ENG.). 272.00 *(978-0-7876-9620-7(X))* Cengage Gale.
Olbermann. The Worst Person in the World: And 202 Strong Contenders. 2007. (ENG.). 272p. pap. 14.95 *(978-0-470-58137-7(9)*, Wiley) Wiley, John & Sons, Inc.
Olbermann, Keith. The Worst Person in the World: And 202 Strong Contenders. (ENG.). 272p. 2007. per. 14.95 *(978-0-470-17369-5(6))* 2006. 22.95 *(978-0-470-04495-7(0))* Wiley, John & Sons, Inc. (Wiley).
People Magazine Editors. PEOPLE Yearbook 2011. 2011. (ENG., Illus.). 144p. 33.95 *(978-1-60320-145-2(9)*, People Bks.) Time Home Entertainment, Inc.
People Magazine Editors, ed. People Yearbook 2009. 2009. (ENG.). 144p. 29.95 *(978-1-60320-048-6(7))* Time Home Entertainment, Inc.
Pratt, A. T. Camden, ed. People of the Period: A Collection of the Biographies of Upwards. 2007. 1100p. 825.00 *(978-4-901481-85-4(1))* Synapse, Edition JPN. Dist: Taylor & Francis Group.
Smith, Vickie. My Life Book. 2009. 520p. pap. 39.98 *(978-0-615-20221-1(7))* Smith, Vickie.
Szwed, John. Alan Lomax: The Man Who Recorded the World. 2011. (ENG.). 448p. (gr. 12). 20.00 ***(978-0-14-312073-5(5)***, Penguin (Non-Classics)) Penguin Group (USA) Inc.
Thompson, Clifford, et al, eds. Current Biography Yearbook. 2011. (Current Biography Yearbook Ser.). (Illus.). 738p. 185.00 ***(978-0-8242-1113-4(3))*** Wilson, H.W.
Unknown. Who's Who 2012. 164th ed. 2012. (Who's Who Ser.). (ENG., Illus.). 2608p. 425.00 *(978-1-4081-4229-5(5))* A & C Black GBR. Dist: Macmillan.
Who's Who Publishing Staff. Who's Who 2011. Reference Book Staff, ed. 2011. (ENG., Illus.). 2650p. 395.00 *(978-1-4081-2856-5(X))* A & C Black GBR. Dist: Macmillan.
Woollacott, Angela, et al, eds. Transnational Lives: Biographies of Global Modernity, 1700-Present. 2010. (Palgrave Macmillan Transnational History Ser.). (ENG., Illus.). 336p. 89.00 *(978-0-230-23870-1(X))* Palgrave Macmillan.

BIOGRAPHY AS A LITERARY FORM

see also Autobiography

Abercrombie, Barbara. (WCS)Courage & Craft: Writing Your Life into Story. 2006. 162p. pap. 28.95 *(978-0-470-05424-6(7))* Wiley, John & Sons, Inc.
Angier, Carole & Cline, Sally. Life Writing: Writing Biography, Autobiography & Memoir. 2010. (ENG.). 288p. pap. 24.95 *(978-1-4081-2418-5(1)*, Methuen Drama) A & C Black GBR. Dist: Macmillan.
Arthur, Paul Longley, ed. International Life Writing. 2012. (ENG.). 176p. (C). 125.00 ***(978-0-415-52254-0(4))*** Routledge.
Backus, Irena. Life Writing in Reformation Europe: Lives of Reformers by Friends, Disciples & Foes. 2008. (St Andrews Studies in Reformation History Ser.) 302p. 134.95 *(978-0-7546-6055-2(9))* Ashgate Publishing Co.
Baggerman, Arianne, et al. Controlling Time & Shaping Self: Developments in Autobiographical Writing since the Sixteenth Century. 2011. (Illus.). 552p. ***(978-90-04-19500-4(9))*** BRILL.
Bates, Blanchard W. Literary Portraiture in the Historical Narrative of the French Renaissance. 2011. 176p. 42.95 ***(978-1-258-08991-7(2))*** Literary Licensing, LLC.
Bay, J. Christian. Biography & Biographies: Hints & Indications. 2011. 34p. 35.95 ***(978-1-258-06721-2(8))*** Literary Licensing, LLC.
Beizer, Janet L. Thinking Through the Mothers: Reimagining Women's Biographies. 2008. (Illus.). 296p. 47.50 *(978-0-8014-3851-6(9))* Cornell Univ. Pr.
Benton, Michael J. Literary Biography: An Introduction. 2009. (ENG., Illus.). 280p. 110.95 *(978-1-4051-9446-4(4)*, Wiley-Blackwell) Wiley, John & Sons, Inc.
Boldrini, Lucia. Autobiographies of Others. 2012. (Routledge Studies in Twentieth-Century Literature Ser.). (ENG., Illus.). 244p. (C). 125.00 ***(978-0-415-50737-0(5))*** Routledge.
Brintlinger, Angela & Morson, Gary Saul. Writing a Usable Past: Russian Literary Culture, 1917-1937. 2008. (Srlt Ser.). (ENG.). 253p. pap. 34.95 *(978-0-8101-2523-0(4))* Northwestern Univ. Pr.
Brown, Andrew. A Brief History of Biographies: From Plutarch to Celebs. 2011. (Brief Histories Ser.). (ENG.). 144p. pap. 15.95 *(978-1-84391-972-8(9))* Hesperus Pr. GBR. Dist: Independent Pubs. Group.
Brownley, Martine Wa. Reconsidering Biography: Contexts, Controversies, & Sir John Hawkin's Life of Johnson. 2011. (ENG.). 196p. 60.00 ***(978-1-61148-383-3(2))*** Bucknell Univ. Pr.
Burton, David Henry. Animating History: The Biographical Pulse. 2007. (ENG.). 45.00 *(978-0-916101-75-6(4))* St. Joseph's Univ. Pr.
Carver, George. Alms for Oblivion: Books, Men & Biography. Husslein, Joseph, ed. 2011. 334p. 50.95 ***(978-1-258-06597-3(5))*** Literary Licensing, LLC.
Clifford, James L. From Puzzles to Portraits: Problems of a Literary Biographer. 2011. (ENG.). 168p. pap. 30.00 ***(978-0-8078-3638-9(1))*** Univ. of North Carolina Pr.
Collett, Anne & D'Arcens, Louise, eds. The Unsociable Sociability of Women's Life Writing. 2010. (ENG., Illus.). 256p. 84.00 *(978-0-230-24647-8(8))* Palgrave Macmillan.
Cox, Patricia. Biography in Late Antiquity: A Quest for the Holy Man. 2011. 186p. 28.00 ***(978-1-59740-803-5(4))*** ACLS Humanities E-Book.
D'Amore, Jonathan. American Authorship & Autobiographical Narrative: Mailer, Wideman, Eggers. 2012. (American Literature Readings in the Twenty-First Century Ser.). (ENG., Illus.). 224p. 80.00 ***(978-0-230-39067-6(6))*** Palgrave Macmillan.
Davis, Bertram H. & Johnson, Samuel. Johnson Before Boswell: A Study of John Hawkins' Life of Samuel Johnson. 2011. 234p. 46.95 ***(978-1-258-08966-5(1))*** Literary Licensing, LLC.
Demoen, Kristoffel & Praet, Danny, eds. Theios Sophistès: Essays on Flavius Philostratus' Vita Apollonii. 2008. (Mnemosyne, Supplements Ser.). (Illus.). 400p. *(978-90-04-17109-1(6))* BRILL.
Dunn, Waldo H. English Biography. 344p. 2008. 46.95 *(978-1-4365-3053-3(9))*; 2007. (ENG.). per. 31.95 *(978-0-548-70004-4(4))* Kessinger Publishing, LLC.
—English Biography. 2007. (ENG.). 344p. per. *(978-1-4067-0189-0(0))* Read Bks.
Ellis, David. The Truth about William Shakespeare: Fact, Fiction & Modern Biographies. 2012. (ENG.). 192p. (gr. 17). 95.00 ***(978-0-7486-4656-1(3))*** Edinburgh Univ. Pr. GBR. Dist: Columbia Univ. Pr.
Erika Karres & Susan Bowman. Memoir Star: Start Telling Your Life Story. 2010. 172p. 25.95 *(978-1-4401-9932-5(9))*; pap. 15.95 *(978-1-4401-9930-1(2))* iUniverse, Inc.
Ferret, Olivier, et al, eds. Dictionnaire des Vies Privées (1722-1842) 2011. (FRE., Illus.). 572p. pap. *(978-0-7294-1009-0(9))* Voltaire Foundation GBR. Dist: Marston Bk. Services, Ltd.
Folger, Robert A. Writing as Poaching: Interpellation & Self-Fashioning in colonial relaciones de méritos y Servicios. 2011. (Medieval & Early Modern Iberian World Ser.). (Illus.). 208p. ***(978-90-04-21109-4(8))*** BRILL.
Gillies, Midge. Writing Lives: Literary Biography. 2009. (Cambridge Contexts in Literature Ser.). (ENG.). 128p. pap. 16.00 *(978-0-521-73231-4(X))* Cambridge Univ. Pr.
Goffin, N. Six Short Biographies. 2006. 160p. per. *(978-1-4067-3303-7(2)*, Hesperides Pr.) Read Bks.
Goldberg, Natalie. Old Friend from Far Away: The Practice of Writing Memoir. 2009. (ENG., Illus.). 336p. pap. 15.00 *(978-1-4165-3503-4(9)*, Free Pr.) Free Pr.
Grace, Claudia. Write for Life. 2008. 69p. pap. 19.95 *(978-0-615-18427-2(8))* Access Art Corp., International.
Guo, Jiulin. Zhongguo Er Shi Shi Ji Zhuan Ji Wen Xue Shi. 2009. (CHI., Illus.). *(978-7-203-06439-8(5))* Shaanxi People's Publishing Hse.
Habich, Robert D. Building Their Own Waldos: Emerson's First Biographers & the Politics of Life-Writing in the Gilded Age. 2011. (ENG.). 248p. pap. 29.95 *(978-1-58729-962-9(3))* Univ. of Iowa Pr.
Hamilton, J. Plutarch. 2nd ed. 2009. (Illus.). 286p. pap. 32.95 *(978-1-85399-574-3(6))* Bristol Classical Pr. GBR. Dist: International Publishers Marketing.
Hamilton, Nigel. Biography: A Brief History. 2010. (Illus.). 360p. pap. 17.00 *(978-0-674-03471-6(6))* Harvard Univ. Pr.
—How to Do Biography: A Primer. 2008. 400p. 22.95 *(978-0-674-02796-1(5))* Harvard Univ. Pr.
Hampl, Patricia & Tyler May, Elaine, eds. Tell Me True: Memoir, History & Writing a Life. 2011. (ENG.). 240p. pap. 18.95 *(978-0-87351-815-4(2)*, Borealis Bk.) Minnesota Historical Society Pr.
Harrison, Barbara, ed. Life Story Research, 4 vols. 2009. (SAGE Benchmarks in Social Research Methods Ser.). (Illus.). 1712p. 995.00 *(978-1-4129-3588-3(1)*, B35881C) SAGE Pubns., Ltd. GBR. Dist: SAGE Pubns., Inc.
Harte, Liam, ed. Modern Irish Autobiography: Self, Nation & Society. 2007. (ENG.). 288p. 100.00 *(978-1-4039-1268-8(8))* Palgrave Macmillan.
Haslam, Sara & Neale, Derek. Life-Writing. 2009. 200p. pap. 23.95 *(978-0-415-46153-5(7))* Routledge.
Hemecker, Wilhelm W. Die Biographie - Zur Grundlegung ihrer Theorie. Fetz, Bernhard, ed. 2009.Tr. of History & Theory of Biography. (GER.). VII, 563p. 140.00 *(978-3-11-020226-7(3))* De Gruyter, Walter Inc.
Hemecker, Wilhelm. Die Biographie - Beiträge zu ihrer Geschichte. Hemecker, Wilhelm, ed. 2009.Tr. of Biography - Contributions to its History. (GER.). VII, 508p. 140.00 *(978-3-11-021936-4(0))* De Gruyter, Walter Inc.
Higgitt, Rebekah. Recreating Newton: Newtonian Biography & the Making of Nineteenth-Century History of Science, 1 vol. 2007. (Science & Culture in the Nineteenth Century Ser.). (ENG., Illus.). 304p. 99.00 *(978-1-85196-906-7(3))* Pickering & Chatto Pubs., Ltd. GBR. Dist: Ashgate Publishing Co.
Hindmarsh, D. Bruce. The Evangelical Conversion Narrative: Spiritual Autobiography in Early Modern England. 2008. (ENG.). 400p. per. 55.00 *(978-0-19-923671-8(2))* Oxford Univ. Pr., Inc.
Holmgren, Beth, ed. The Russian Memoir: History & Literature. 2007. (Srlt Ser.). (ENG.). 264p. per. 27.95 *(978-0-8101-2426-4(9))* Northwestern Univ. Pr.
Jefferson, Ann. Biography & the Question of Literature in France. 2007. (ENG.). 438p. 165.00 *(978-0-19-927084-2(8))* Oxford Univ. Pr., Inc.
Johnson, Edgar. One Mighty Torrent: The Drama of Biography. 2011. 592p. 64.95 ***(978-1-258-09343-3(X))*** Literary Licensing, LLC.
Junod, Karen. Writing the Lives of Painters: Biography & Artistic Identity in Britain 1760-1810. 2011. (Oxford English Monographs). (ENG., Illus.). 264p. 110.00 *(978-0-19-959700-0(6))* Oxford Univ. Pr., Inc.
Kirby, Dawn Latta & Kirby, Dan. New Directions in Teaching Memoir: A Studio Workshop Approach. 2007. (Illus.). 208p. pap. 32.50 *(978-0-325-00668-0(7)*, E00668) Heinemann.
Kupferberg, Feiwel & Negroni, Catherine. Biography & Turning Points in Europe & America. Hackstaff, Karla B., ed. 2012. 276p. 110.00 ***(978-1-84742-860-6(6))*** Policy Pr. GBR. Dist: Chicago Distribution Ctr.
LaChapelle, Carol. Finding Your Voice, Telling Your Stories: 167 Ways to Tell Your Life Stories. 2008. (ENG.). 224p. pap. 14.95 *(978-1-933338-32-3(6)*, Marion Street Pr.) Acorn Guild Pr., LLC.
Lara, Adair. Naked, Drunk, & Writing: Shed Your Inhibitions & Craft a Compelling Memoir or Personal Essay. 2010. (ENG., Illus.). 256p. pap. 14.99 *(978-1-58008-480-2(X))* Ten Speed Pr.
Lazar, David, ed. Truth in Nonfiction: Essays. 2008. (ENG., Illus.). 212p. pap. 19.95 *(978-1-58729-654-3(3))* Univ. of Iowa Pr.
Ledoux, Denis. The Photo Scribe: A Writing Guide: How to Write the Stories Behind Your Photographs. 3rd ed. 2008. (Illus.). 127p. pap. 19.95 *(978-0-9742773-1-8(2))* Soleil Pr.
Lee, Hermione. Virginia Woolf's Nose: Essays on Biography. annot. ed. 2007. (ENG.). 160p. (C). per. 15.95 *(978-0-691-13044-6(2))* Princeton Univ. Pr.
Lehmann, Jürgen. Bekennen - Erzählen - Berichten: Studien Zu Theorie und Geschichte der Autobiographie. (Studien zur deutschen Literatur Ser.). (GER., Illus.). VIII, 289p. 135.00 ***(978-3-11-183971-4(0))*** De Gruyter, Walter Inc.
Lippincott, Sharon M. The Heart & Craft of Lifestory Writing: How to Transform Memories into Meaningful Stories. 2007. (Illus.). 275p. per. 16.95 *(978-0-9792998-0-3(2))* Lighthouse Point Pr.
Longaker, Mark. Contemporary Biography. 2011. 270p. 47.95 ***(978-1-258-07205-6(X))*** Literary Licensing, LLC.
—English Biography in the Eighteenth Century. 2011. 530p. 60.95 ***(978-1-258-07271-1(8))*** Literary Licensing, LLC.
Lustig, Irma S., ed. Boswell: Citizen of the World, Man of Letters. 2009. (ENG.). 296p. pap. 30.00 *(978-0-8131-9276-5(5))* Univ. Pr. of Kentucky.
MacDonald, Katherine. Biography in Early Modern France, 1540-1630: Forms & Functions. 2007. (Legenda Research Monographs in French Studies). (Illus.). 115p. 65.00 *(978-1-905981-11-3(2))* Maney Publishing GBR. Dist: Brown, David Bk. Co., The.
Machtans, Karolin. Zwischen Wissenschaft und autobiographischem Projekt: Saul Friedländer und Ruth Klüger. 2009. (Conditio Judaica Ser.). (GER.). XII, 291p. pap. *(978-3-484-65173-9(3))* Verlag Max Niemeyer.
Marasco, Gabriele. Political Autobiographies & Memoirs in Antiquity. (Brill's Companions in Classical Studies). *(978-90-04-18299-8(3))* BRILL.
Moore-Gilbert, Bart, et al. Postcolonial Life-Writing: Culture, Politics, & Self-Representation. 2009. (Routledge Research in Postcolonial Literatures Ser.). (ENG.). 200p. 110.00 *(978-0-415-44299-2(0))* Routledge.
Noonan, James, ed. Biography & Autobiography: Essays on Irish & Canadian History & Literature. (Illus.). 300p. pap. *(978-0-88629-209-6(3))* McGill-Queen's Univ. Pr.
North, Julian. The Domestication of Genius: Biography & the Romantic Poet. 2010. (ENG., Illus.). 288p. 99.00 *(978-0-19-957198-7(8))* Oxford Univ. Pr., Inc.
Norton, Lisa D. & Norton, Lisa Dale. Shimmering Images: A Handy Little Guide to Writing Memoir. 2008. (ENG., Illus.). 144p. pap. 14.99 *(978-0-312-38292-6(8)*, St. Martin's Griffin) St. Martin's Pr.
O'Neill, Edward Hayes. A History of American Biography, 1800-1935. 2011. 440p. 56.95 ***(978-1-258-06237-8(2))*** Literary Licensing, LLC.
Oxford University Press Staff, ed. Bronte Story. 3rd ed. 2008. (ENG.). 80p. 9.38 *(978-0-19-479109-0(2))* Oxford Univ. Pr., Inc.
Pritchard, Allan. English Biography in the Seventeenth Century: A Critical Survey. 2009. (ENG.). 320p. pap. *(978-1-4426-1033-0(6))* Univ. of Toronto Pr.
Quires Fernández, María Teresa. Stereophonie der Autobiographie: Autobiographisches Schreiben von Paaren am Beispiel von María Teresa León und Rafael Alberti. 2009. (Mimesis Ser.).Tr. of Stereophonic Autobiography. Concept & Model of Autobiographies Written by Couples using the example of María Teresa león & Rafael Alberti. (GER.). VI, 213p. pap. *(978-3-484-55048-3(1))* Verlag Max Niemeyer.
Rollyson, Carl. Biography: A User's Guide. 2008. (ENG.). 336p. 27.50 *(978-1-56663-780-0(5))* Dee, Ivan R. Pub.
Sappington, Joe. Joe Sap's Tales. 2008. 264p. 25.99 *(978-0-559-21468-4(5))*; pap. 26.75 *(978-0-559-21466-0(9))* BiblioBazaar.
—Joe Sap's Tales. 2009. 152p. pap. 19.99 *(978-1-150-74734-2(X))* General Bks. LLC.
—Joe Sap's Tales. 2007. (ENG.). 260p. 42.95 *(978-0-548-26738-7(3))*; per. 27.95 *(978-1-4326-7176-1(6))* Kessinger Publishing, LLC.

B

Saunders, Max. Self Impression: Life-Writing, Autobiografiction, & the Forms of Modern Literature. 2010. (ENG., Illus.). 500p. 95.00 *(978-0-19-957976-1(8))* Oxford Univ. Pr., Inc.

Schneider, Myra & Killick, John. Writing Your Self: Transforming Personal Material. 2010. (ENG., Illus.). 270p. 24.95 *(978-1-84706-252-9(0))*; 90.00 *(978-1-84706-251-2(2))* Continuum International Publishing Group, Ltd. GBR. Dist: National Bk. Network.

Sela, Ron. The Legendary Biographies of Tamerlane: Islam & Heroic Apocrypha in Central Asia. 2011. (Cambridge Studies in Islamic Civilization Ser.). (ENG., Illus.). 184p. 85.00 *(978-0-521-51706-5(0))* Cambridge Univ. Pr.

Smith, Thomas R., ed. Lifewriting Annual: Biographical & Autobiographical Studies, Vol. 2. 2008. 316p. 115.00 *(978-0-404-63422-3(2))* AMS Pr., Inc.

Stauffer, Donald A. English Biography Before 1700. 2011. 410p. 54.95 ***(978-1-258-07316-9(1))*** Literary Licensing, LLC.

Stuart, Duane Reed. Epochs of Greek & Roman Biography: Sather Classical Lectures, V4. 2011. 280p. 47.95 ***(978-1-258-07490-6(7))*** Literary Licensing, LLC.

Symons, A.J.A. The Quest for Corvo: An Experiment in Biography. 2011. 306p. 48.95 ***(978-1-258-08238-3(1))*** Literary Licensing, LLC.

Szwed, John. Alan Lomax: The Man Who Recorded the World. 2011. (ENG.). 448p. (gr. 12). 20.00 ***(978-0-14-312073-5(5)***, Penguin (Non-Classics)) Penguin Group (USA) Inc.

Taylor, Isaac. Beginnings of European Biography: From the Decline of the Roman Empire to the Reign of Charlemagne. 2007. (ENG.). 192p. 37.95 *(978-0-548-05056-9(2))* Kessinger Publishing, LLC.

Thayer, William Roscoe. The Art of Biography. 2007. (ENG.). 160p. 36.95 *(978-0-548-14863-1(5))* 2006. pap. 21.95 *(978-1-4286-6379-4(7))* Kessinger Publishing, LLC.

—The Art of Biography. 2008. 164p. pap. *(978-1-4097-8318-3(9))* Read Bks.

Traig, Jennifer. The Autobiographer's Handbook: The 826 National Guide to Writing Your Memoir. 2008. 256p. 15.00 *(978-1-4299-3092-5(6))*; (ENG.). pap. 15.00 *(978-0-8050-8713-0(3))* Holt, Henry & Co. (Holt Paperback).

Vance, John A., ed. Boswell's Life of Johnson: New Questions, New Answers. 2009. (ENG.). 288p. pap. 24.95 *(978-0-8203-3376-2(X))* Univ. of Georgia Pr.

Weintraub, E. Roy & Forget, Evelyn L. Economists' Lives: Biography & Autobiography in the History of Economics. abr. ed. 2007. (Annual Supplement to History of Political Economy Ser.). (ENG.). 402p. 59.95 *(978-0-8223-6683-6(5))* Duke Univ. Pr.

Wells, Matthew V. To Die & Not Decay: Autobiography & the Pursuit of Immortality in Early China. 2009. *(978-0-924304-58-3(8))* Assn. for Asian Studies, Inc.

Woollacott, Angela, et al, eds. Transnational Lives: Biographies of Global Modernity, 1700-Present. 2010. (Palgrave Macmillan Transnational History Ser.). (ENG., Illus.). 336p. 89.00 *(978-0-230-23870-1(X))* Palgrave Macmillan.

Yost, Paula Stallings & McNees, Pat, eds. My Words Are Gonna Linger: The Art of Personal History. 2009. (Illus.). 320p. pap. 19.95 *(978-0-9820134-0-3(X))* Personal History Pr.

Zoellner, Tom. Homemade Biography: How to Collect, Record, & Tell the Life Story of Someone You Love. 2007. (ENG.). 224p. pap. 16.95 *(978-0-312-34831-1(2)*, St. Martin's Griffin) St. Martin's Pr.

BIOGRAPHY IN PSYCHOLOGY

see Psychology—Biographical Methods

BIOINFORMATICS

Accardi, L., et al. Quantum Bio-Informatics II: From Quantum Information to Bio-Informatics. 2009. (Illus.). 356p. 152.00 *(978-981-4273-74-9(0))* World Scientific Publishing Co., Inc.

Accardi, Luigi, et al. Quantum Bio-Informatics III: From Quantum Information to Bio-Informatics, Tokyo University of Science, Japan, 11-14 March 2009. 2010. (Illus.). 512p. 178.00 *(978-981-4304-05-4(0))* World Scientific Publishing Co., Inc.

—Quantum Bioinformatics IV: From Quantum Information to Bio-Informatics - Tokyo University of Science, Japan, 10-13 March 2010. 2011. (Illus.). 504p. 190.00 *(978-981-4343-75-6(7))* World Scientific Publishing Co., Inc.

Aftab, Muhammad Nauman. Effect of Rna Interference & Microarray. 2010. 140p. pap. *(978-3-639-24218-8(1))* VDM Verlag Dr. Mueller e.K.

Aguda, Baltazar & Friedman, Avner. Models of Cellular Regulation. 2008. (Oxford Graduate Texts). (ENG., Illus.). 200p. 99.00 *(978-0-19-857091-2(0))* Oxford Univ. Pr., Inc.

Akram, Muhammad, et al. Text Book of Bioinformatics. 2011. 120p. pap. ***(978-3-8443-8711-7(0))*** Lambert Academic Publishing.

Akutsu, Tatsuya. Genome Informatics 2010: Genome Informatics Series - Proceedings of the 10th Annual International Workshop on Bioinformatics & Systems Biology (IBSB 2010) 2010. (Illus.). 244p. 99.00 *(978-1-84816-657-8(5))* Imperial College Pr. GBR. Dist: World Scientific Publishing Co., Inc.

Al. Biocomputing 2007. 251.00 *(978-981-270-417-7(5))* World Scientific Publishing Co., Inc.

—Genome Informatics 2007. 2007. 124.00 *(978-1-86094-984-5(3))* Imperial College Pr. GBR. Dist: World Scientific Publishing Co., Inc.

Al-Rubeai, Mohamed & Fussenegger, Martin, eds. Systems Biology. 2007. (Cell Engineering Ser.: Vol. 5). (Illus.). viii, 425p. 279.00 *(978-1-4020-5251-4(0)*, 1402052510) Springer.

Alterovitz, Gil & Ramoni, Marco, eds. Knowledge-Based Bioinformatics: From Analysis to Interpretation. 2010. (ENG., Illus.). 396p. 80.00 *(978-0-470-74831-2(1)*, Wiley) Wiley, John & Sons, Inc.

Altman, Russ B. Biocomputing 2008. 2007. 274.00 *(978-981-277-608-2(7))* World Scientific Publishing Co., Inc.

Altman, Russ B., et al, eds. Biocomputing 2009. 2008. 600p. 210.00 *(978-981-283-692-2(6))* World Scientific Publishing Co., Inc.

Anai, Hirokazu, et al. Algebraic Biology: Second International Conference, AB 2007. 2007. (Lecture Notes in Computer Science Ser.). (Illus.). 377p. per. 79.95 *(978-3-540-73432-1(5))* Springer.

Andersen, Stig Kjær. EHealth Beyond the Horizon - Get It There: Proceedings of MIE2008. 2008. (Illus.). xx, 887p. 308.00 *(978-1-58603-864-9(8))* IOS Pr., Inc.

Arabnia, Hamid, ed. Advances in Computational Biology: Proceedings of the 2009 International Conference on Bioinformatics & Computational Biology (BIOCOMP'09) 2010. (Advances in Experimental Medicine & Biology Ser.). (ENG., Illus.). xvii, 533p. 239.00 *(978-1-4419-5912-6(2)*, 1441959122) Springer.

Arabnia, Hamid R. & Tran, Quoc-Nam, eds. Software Tools & Algorithms for Biological Systems. 2011. (Advances in Experimental Medicine & Biology Ser.). (ENG., Illus.). xii, 778p. 239.00 *(978-1-4419-7045-9(2)*, 1441970452) Springer.

Arora, Dilip K., et al, eds. Bioinformatics: Applied Mycology & Biotechnology. 2006. (Applied Mycology & Biotechnology Ser.: 6). (ENG.). 350p. 235.00 *(978-0-444-51807-1(X)*, Elsevier Science) Elsevier Science & Technology Bks.

Arredondo, Tomas. Information Theoretics Based Sequence Pattern Discriminant Algorithms. 2010. 264p. pap. *(978-3-8383-3710-4(7))* Lambert Academic Publishing.

Arthur, Jonathan & Ng, See-Kiong, eds. Genome Informatics 2008. 2008. (Illus.). 260p. 124.00 *(978-1-84816-331-7(2))* World Scientific Publishing Co., Inc.

Ashlock, Daniel. Evolutionary Computation for Modeling & Optimization. 2010. (ENG., Illus.). xx, 572p. pap. 97.00 *(978-1-4419-1969-4(4)*, 1441919694) Springer.

Astakhov, Vadim, ed. Biomedical Informatics. 2009. (Methods in Molecular Biology Ser.). (ENG., Illus.). x, 270p. 149.00 *(978-1-934115-63-3(0)*, 1934115630) Humana Pr.

Ay, Ferhat. A Comparative Study on Biological Networks. 2011. 216p. pap. ***(978-3-8443-9466-5(4))*** Lambert Academic Publishing.

Azuaje, Francisco. Bioinformatics & Biomarker Discovery: Omic Data Analysis for Personalized Medicine. 2010. (ENG., Illus.). 248p. 149.95 *(978-0-470-74460-4(X)*, Wiley) Wiley, John & Sons, Inc.

Back, Ralph-Johan, et al, eds. Transactions on Computational Systems Biology XIII. 2011. (Lecture Notes in Computer Science / Transactions on Computational Systems Biology Ser.). (Illus.). vii, 193p. pap. 98.00 *(978-3-642-19747-5(7)*, 3642197477) Springer.

Bal, Harshawardhan & Hujol, Johnny. Java for Bioinformatics & Biomedical Applications. (ENG., Illus.). xviii, 342p. 2010. pap. 115.00 *(978-1-4419-4245-6(9)*, 1441942459) 2006. 115.00 *(978-0-387-37235-8(0)*, 0387372350) Springer.

Bandyopadhyay, Sanghamitra, et al, eds. Analysis of Biological Data: A Soft Computing Approach. 2007. (SCIENCE, ENGINEERING, & BIOLOGY INFORMATICS Ser.). 500p. (C). 104.00 *(978-981-270-780-2(8))* World Scientific Publishing Co., Inc.

Banka, Haider. Soft Computing for MacHine Learning & Bioinformatics. 2010. 200p. pap. *(978-3-639-26484-5(3))* VDM Verlag Dr. Mueller e.K.

Barh, Debmalya, ed. Omics. 2011. (ENG., Illus.). 613p. 139.95 ***(978-1-4398-5008-4(9)***, CRC Press) Taylor & Francis Group GBR. Dist: Taylor & Francis Group.

Barillot, Emmanuel, et al. Computational Systems Biology of Cancer. 2012. (Chapman & Hall/CRC Mathematical & Computational Biology Ser.). (ENG., Illus.). 452p. 79.95 ***(978-1-4398-3144-1(0)***, CRC Press) Taylor & Francis Group GBR. Dist: Taylor & Francis Group.

Barnes, Michael R., ed. Bioinformatics for Geneticists: A Bioinformatics Primer for the Analysis of Genetic Data. 2nd rev. ed. 2007. (ENG., Illus.). 576p. 229.95 *(978-0-470-02619-9(7))*; pap. 104.95 *(978-0-470-02620-5(0))* Wiley, John & Sons, Inc. (Wiley).

Bassi, Sebastian. Python for Bioinformatics. 2009. (Chapman & Hall/CRC Mathematical & Computational Biology Ser.). (ENG., Illus.). 587p. pap. 71.95 *(978-1-58488-929-8(2)*, Chapman & Hall/CRC) CRC Pr. LLC.

Bateman, A., ed. 15th Annual International Conference on Intelligent Systems for Molecular Biology & 6th European Conference on Computational Biology (ISMB/ECCB 2007) 2007. (Bioinformatics Ser.). 142p. pap. 95.00 *(978-1-60423-968-3(9))* Curran Assocs., Inc.

Bawa, Tejdeep Singh. Understanding Tertiary Interactions in Protein Structures. 2011. 64p. pap. ***(978-3-8433-9403-1(2))*** Lambert Academic Publishing.

Bazzan, Ana L. C. Advances in Bioinformatics & Computational Biology: Third Brazilian Symposium on Bioinformatics, BSB 2008, Sao Paulo, Brazil, August 28-30, 2008, Proceedings. 2008. (Lecture Notes in Computer Science / Lecture Notes in Bioinformatics Ser.). (Illus.). x, 183p. pap. 59.95 *(978-3-540-85556-9(4))* Springer.

Böckenhauer, Hans-Joachim & Bongartz, Dirk. Algorithmic Aspects of Bioinformatics. 2010. (Natural Computing Ser.). (Illus.). x, 396p. pap. 95.00 *(978-3-642-09100-1(8)*, 3642091008) Springer.

Böhm, Christian, et al, eds. Information Technology in Bio- And Medical Informatics: Second International Conference, Itbam 2011, Toulouse, France, August - September, Proceedings. 2011. (Lecture Notes in Computer Science / Information Systems & Applications, incl. Internet/Web, & HCI Ser.). (ENG., Illus.). xii, 188p. pap. 72.00 ***(978-3-642-23207-7(8)***, 3642232078) Springer.

Bel-Enguix, G. & Dahl, V., eds. Biology, Computation & Linguistics: New Interdisciplinary Paradigms - Frontiers in Artificial Intelligence & Applications. 2011. 256p. 160.00 ***(978-1-60750-761-1(7))*** IOS Pr., Inc.

Beliczynski, Bartlomiej, et al. Adaptive & Natural Computing Algorithms: 8th International Conference, ICANNGA 2007, Warsaw, Poland, April 11-14, 2007, Proceedings, Part I. 2007. (Lecture Notes in Computer Science / Theoretical Computer Science & General Issues Ser.). xxv, 851p. pap. 139.00 *(978-3-540-71589-4(4))* Springer.

—Adaptive & Natural Computing Algorithms: 8th International Conference, ICANNGA 2007, Warsaw, Poland, April 11-14, 2007, Proceedings, Part II. 2008. (Lecture Notes in Computer Science Ser.). xxvi, 761p. pap. 139.00 *(978-3-540-71590-0(8))* Springer.

Belostotsky, Dmitry A., ed. Plant Systems Biology. 2009. (Methods in Molecular Biology Ser.). (Illus.). 376p. 159.00 *(978-1-60327-562-0(2))* Humana Pr.

Berman, Jules J. Biomedical Informatics. 2006. (Illus.). 459p. per. 90.95 *(978-0-7637-4135-8(3))* Jones & Bartlett Learning, LLC.

—Perl Programming for Medicine & Biology. 2007. 407p. per. 69.95 *(978-0-7637-4333-8(X))* Jones & Bartlett Learning, LLC.

Berthold, Michael R., et al, eds. Complife 2007: The Third International Symposium on Computational Life Sciences. 2007. (AIP Conference Proceedings Ser.). (Illus.). 180p. 85.00 *(978-0-7354-0452-6(6))* American Institute of Physics.

Bertini, Ivano, et al, eds. NMR of Biomolecules: Towards Mechanistic Systems Biology. 2012. (ENG.). 650p. pap. 129.95 ***(978-3-527-32850-5(5)***, Wiley-VCH) Wiley, John & Sons, Inc.

Bessant, Conrad, et al. Building Bioinformatics Solutions: With Perl, R & MySQL. 2009. (ENG., Illus.). 224p. 135.00 *(978-0-19-923019-8(6))* Oxford Univ. Pr., Inc.

—Building Bioinformatics Solutions: With Perl, R & MySQL. Oxford Publishing Staff, ed. 2009. (ENG., Illus.). 224p. pap. 55.00 *(978-0-19-923023-5(4))* Oxford Univ. Pr., Inc.

Bingen, Jean, et al. Rough-Fuzzy Pattern Recognition: Applications in Bioinformatics & Medical Imaging. 2012. (Wiley Series in Bioinformatics Ser.: 3). (ENG., Illus.). 312p. 99.95 *(978-1-118-00440-1(X))* IEEE Computer Society Pr.

Bioinformatics Research & Development. 2008. (Communications in Computer & Information Science Ser.). spiral bd. 119.00 *(978-3-540-70598-7(8))* Springer.

Blaschke, Christian, ed. Linking, Literature, Information, & Knowledge for Biologie: Workshop of the BioLINK Special Interest Group, ISBM/ECCB 2009, Stockholm, June 28-29, 2009, Revised Selected Papers. 2010. (Lecture Notes in Computer Science / Lecture Notes in Bioinformatics Ser.). xii, 81p. pap. 72.00 *(978-3-642-13130-1(1)*, 3642131301) Springer.

Blobel, B. EHealth: Combining Health Telematics, Telemedicine, Biomedical Engineering & Bioinformatics to the Edge. 2008. pap. 111.00 *(978-1-58603-834-2(6))* IOS Pr., Inc.

Bongartz, Dirk & Bockenhauer, Hans-Joachim. Algorithmic Aspects of Bioinformatics. 2007. (Natural Computing Ser.). (Illus.). 396p. 95.00 *(978-3-540-71912-0(1)*, 3540719121) Springer.

Borodovsky, Mark, et al, eds. Bioinformatics Research & Applications: 6th International Symposium, ISBRA 2010, Storrs, CT, USA, May 23-26, 2010. Proceedings. 2010. (Lecture Notes in Computer Science / Lecture Notes in Bioinformatics Ser.). xii, 253p. pap. 72.00 *(978-3-642-13077-9(1)*, 3642130771) Springer.

Borodovsky, Mark & Ekisheva, Svetlana. Problems & Solutions in Biological Sequence Analysis. 2006. (Illus.). (ENG.). 366p. (C). 101.99 *(978-0-521-84754-4(0))*; 346p. per. 50.99 *(978-0-521-61230-2(6))* Cambridge Univ. Pr.

Bos, Lodewijk, et al, eds. Future Visions on Biomedicine & Bioinformatics 1: A Liber Amicorum in Memory of Swamy Laxminarayan. 2011. (Communications in Medical & Care Compunetics Ser.). (ENG., Illus.). vi, 168p. 179.00 *(978-3-642-15050-0(0)*, 3642150500) Springer.

—Future Visions on Biomedicine & Bioinformatics 2: A Liber Amicorum in Memory of Swamy Laxminarayan. 2011. (Communications in Medical & Care Compunetics Ser.). (Illus.). v, 105p. 129.00 *(978-3-642-19553-2(9)*, 3642195539) Springer.

Bosu, Orpita & Thukral, Simminder Kaur. Bioinformatics: Experiments, Tools, Databases, & Algorithms. 2007. (ENG., Illus.). 528p. 29.95 *(978-0-19-567683-9(1))* Oxford Univ. Pr., Inc.

Br, Guruprasad & Kumar. C., Sunil. Computational Biology of Alzheimer's Disease. 2010. 128p. pap. *(978-3-639-27177-5(7))* VDM Verlag Dr. Mueller e.K.

Brazma, Alvis. Proceedings of the 6th Asia-Pacific. . V6. 2007. 160.00 *(978-1-84816-108-5(5))* Imperial College Pr. GBR. Dist: World Scientific Publishing Co., Inc.

Bruggeman, Frank J., et al, eds. Systems Biology: Philosophical Foundations. 2007. (ENG., Illus.). 360p. 132.00 *(978-0-444-52085-2(6)*, Elsevier Science) Elsevier Science & Technology Bks.

Bruni, Renato, ed. Mathematical Approaches to Polymer Sequence Analysis & Related Problems. 2010. (ENG., Illus.). x, 248p. 189.00 *(978-1-4419-6799-2(0)*, 1441967990) Springer.

Bucher, Philipp, ed. Algorithms in Bioinformatics: 6th International Workshop, WABI 2006, Zurich, Switzerland, September 11-13, 2006, Proceedings. 2007. (Lecture Notes in Computer Science Ser.). (Illus.). 402p. per. 99.00 *(978-3-540-39583-6(0)*, 3540395830) Springer.

Bujnicki, Janusz M., ed. Practical Bioinformatics. 2007. (Nucleic Acids & Molecular Biology Ser.). (Illus.). 265p. pap. 109.00 *(978-3-540-74267-8(0))* Springer.

Burger, Albert, et al, eds. Anatomy Ontologies for Bioinformatics: Principles & Practice. (Computational Biology Ser.). (Illus.). 2010. xvi, 356p. pap. 149.00 *(978-1-84996-666-5(4)*, 1849966664) 2007. 344p. 149.00 *(978-1-84628-884-5(3))* Springer.

Burkowski, Forbes J. Structural Bioinformatics: An Algorithmic Approach. 2008. (Chapman & Hall/CRC Mathematical & Computational Biology Ser.). (ENG., Illus.). 429p. (C). 87.95 *(978-1-58488-683-9(8)*, Chapman & Hall/CRC) CRC Pr. LLC.

Cabestany, Joan, et al. Bio-Inspired Systems: Computational & Ambient Intelligence: 10th International Work-Conference on Artificial Neural Networks, IWANN 2009, Salamanca, Spain, June 10-12, 2009. Proceedings, Part I. 2009. (Lecture Notes in Computer Science / Theoretical Computer Science & General Issues Ser.). (ENG.). li, 1356p. pap. 189.00 *(978-3-642-02477-1(7)*, 3642024777) Springer.

Cagney, Gerard & Emili, Andrew, eds. Network Biology: Methods & Applications. 2011. (Methods in Molecular Biology Ser.). (ENG., Illus.). xv, 437p. 139.00 *(978-1-61779-275-5(6)*, 1617792756) Humana Pr.

Cannataro, Mario. Handbook of Research on Computational Grid Technologies for Life Sciences, Biomedicine, & Healthcare, 2 vols. Cannataro, Mario, ed. 2009. 1050p. 495.00 *(978-1-60566-374-6(3)*, Medical Information Science Reference) IGI Global.

Cassman, Marvin, et al. Systems Biology: International Research & Development. (ENG.). xvii, 262p. 2010. pap. 159.00 *(978-90-481-7375-4(2)*, 9048173752) 2007. (Illus.). 159.00 *(978-1-4020-5467-9(X)*, 140205467X) Springer.

Cerami, Ethan. XML for Bioinformatics. 2010. (Illus.). xv, 304p. pap. 99.00 *(978-1-4419-1998-4(8)*, 1441919988) Springer.

Chan, Jonathan H., et al, eds. Computational Systems-Biology & Bioinformatics: First International Conference, CSBio 2010, Bangkok, Thailand, November 3-5, 2010, Proceedings. 2010. (Communications in Computer & Information Science Ser.). xiii, 227p. pap. 84.00 *(978-3-642-16749-2(7)*, 3642167497) Springer.

Chao, Kun-Mao & Zhang, Louxin. Sequence Comparison: Theory & Methods. (Computational Biology Ser.). (Illus.). xx, 210p. 2010. pap. 119.00 *(978-1-84996-782-2(2)*, 1849967822) 2008. 119.00 *(978-1-84800-319-4(6))* Springer.

Chen, Jake & Sidhu, Amandeep S. Biological Database Modeling. 2007. (Illus.). 224p. 123.00 *(978-1-59693-258-6(9))* Artech Hse., Inc.

Chen, Jianer, et al, eds. Bioinformatics Research & Application: 7th International Symposium, ISBRA 2011, Changsha, China, May 27-29, 2011, Proceedings. 2011. (Lecture Notes in Computer Science / Lecture Notes in Bioinformatics Ser.). (Illus.). xiv, 454p. pap. 95.00 *(978-3-642-21259-8(X)*, 364221259X) Springer.

Chen, Shihyen. Topics in Computing Similarity & Distance. 2010. 104p. pap. *(978-3-639-23657-6(2))* VDM Verlag Dr. Mueller e.K.

Chen, Xue-wen, et al. Computational & Statistical Methods in Bioinformatics. 2010. (Illus.). 329p. 79.95 *(978-1-4200-7054-5(1)*, Chapman & Hall/CRC) CRC Pr. LLC.

Cheng, Gang. High-Performance Computational Modeling of Tissue Growth Processes: Insights on the Interplay of Cell Population & Mass Transfer Dynamics. 2008. 308p. pap. *(978-3-8364-6539-7(6))* VDM Verlag Dr. Mueller e.K.

Cheng, Maggie. Nano-Net: Third International Conference, NanoNet 2008, Boston, MS, USA, September 14-16, 2008. Revised Selected Papers. 2009. (Lecture Notes of the Institute for Computer Sciences, Social-Informatics & Telecommunications Engineering Ser.). (ENG., Illus.). xii, 131p. pap. 69.95 *(978-3-642-02426-9(2)*, 3642024262) Springer.

Chetty, Madhu, et al. Microarrays & Gene Expression in Bioinformatics. 2010. (Wiley Series in Bioinformatics Ser.). (ENG.). 304p. 99.95 *(978-0-470-18529-2(5)*, Wiley-Interscience) Wiley, John & Sons, Inc.

Ciccarelli, Francesca D. & Miklós, István. Comparative Genomics: International Workshop, RECOMB-CG 2009, Budapest, Hungary, September 27-29, 2009, Proceedings. 2009. (Lecture Notes in Computer Science / Lecture Notes in Bioinformatics Ser.). viii, 241p. pap. 72.00 *(978-3-642-04743-5(2)*, 3642047432) Springer.

Claverie, Jean-Michel & Notredame, Cedric. Bioinformatics for Dummies. 2nd rev. ed. 2006. (ENG., Illus.). 456p. per. 29.99 *(978-0-470-08985-9(7)*, For Dummies) Wiley, John & Sons, Inc.

Cohen-Boulakia, Sarah & Tannen, Val. Data Integration in the Life Sciences: 4th International Workshop, DILS 2007, Philadelphia, PA, USA, June 27-29, 2007, Proceedings. 2007. (Lecture Notes in Computer Science / Lecture Notes in Bioinformatics Ser.). xi, 282p. pap. 69.95 *(978-3-540-73254-9(3))* Springer.

Collins, M. W., et al, eds. Design & Information in Biology Vol. 2: From Molecules to Systems. 2006. (Design in Nature Ser.: 2). (Illus.). 512p. 285.00 *(978-1-85312-853-0(8))* WIT Pr GBR. Dist: WIT Pr.

Comparative Genomics. 2008. (Lecture Notes in Computer Science / Lecture Notes in Bioinformatics Ser.). spiral bd. 69.95 *(978-3-540-87988-6(9))* Springer.

Computational Life Sciences II: Second International Symposium, Complife 2006 Cambridge, UK, September 27-29, 2006 Proceedings. 2007. (Lecture Notes in Computer Science Ser.). (Illus.). 267p. per. 69.95 *(978-3-540-45767-1(4)*, 3540457674) Springer.

Computational Methods in Systems Biology. 2008. (Lecture Notes in Computer Science / Lecture Notes in Bioinformatics Ser.). spiral bd. 89.95 *(978-3-540-88561-0(7)*, 3540885617) Springer.

Cram101 Textbook Reviews. Outlines & Highlights for Bioinformatics by Shuba Gopal, Isbn: 9780073133645. 2010. 268p. pap. 31.95 *(978-1-61698-008-5(7))* Cram101 Inc.

Cram101 Textbook Reviews. Outlines & Highlights for Understanding Bioinformatics by Marketa J Zvelebil. 2011. 94p. pap. 27.95 ***(978-1-61490-952-1(0))*** Cram101 Inc.

Cram101 Textbook Reviews & Cram101 Textbook Reviews. Outlines & Highlights for Algorithms in Bioinformatics by Wing-Kin Sung, Isbn: 9781420070330. 2011. 76p. pap. 27.95 ***(978-1-61461-495-1(4))*** Cram101 Inc.

—Outlines & Highlights for Bioinformatics & Functional Genomics by Jonathan Pevsner, Isbn: 9780470085851. 2011. 418p. pap. 35.95 ***(978-1-61461-480-7(6))*** Cram101 Inc.

—Outlines & Highlights for Computational Intelligence & Pattern Analysis in Biology Informatics by Ujjwal Maulik, Isbn: 9780470581599. 2011. 60p. pap. 26.95 ***(978-1-61461-178-3(5))*** Cram101 Inc.

—Outlines & Highlights for Introduction to Bioinformatics by Arthur Lesk, Isbn: 9780199208043 0199208042. 2011. 176p. pap. 29.95 ***(978-1-61490-063-4(9))*** Cram101 Inc.

—Outlines & Highlights for Knowledge Discovery in Bioinformatics by Xiaohua Hu, Isbn: 9780471777960. 2011. 122p. pap. 28.95 ***(978-1-61461-157-8(2))*** Cram101 Inc.

—Outlines & Highlights for Machine Learning in Bioinformatics by Yanqing Zhang, Isbn: 9780470116623. 2011. 134p. pap. 28.95 ***(978-1-61461-171-4(8))*** Cram101 Inc.

Crary, J., et al. Handbook of Statistical Systems Biology. 2011. (ENG., Illus.). 530p. 190.00 *(978-0-470-71086-9(1),* Wiley) Wiley, John & Sons, Inc.

Dalkilic, Mehmet M., et al, eds. Data Mining & Bioinformatics: First International Workshop, VDMB 2006, Seoul, Korea, September 11, 2006: Revised Selected Papers. 2007. (Lecture Notes in Computer Science Ser.). (Illus.). VIII, 197p. pap. 69.95 *(978-3-540-68970-6(2),* 3540689702) Springer.

Dardel, Frederic & Kepes, Francois. Bioinformatics: Genomics & Post-Genomics. Hardy, Noah, tr. from FRE. 2006. (ENG., Illus.). 252p. 84.95 *(978-0-470-02001-2(6),* Wiley) Wiley, John & Sons, Inc.

Das, Dipon. Dna Repair Studies in Plasmodium Falciparum. 2011. 136p. pap. ***(978-3-8454-0383-0(7))*** Lambert Academic Publishing.

Daskalaki, Andriani, ed. Handbook of Research on Systems Biology Applications in Medicine, 2 vols. 2008. (Illus.). 982p. (C). 595.00 *(978-1-60566-076-9(0))* IGI Global.

Dear, Paul H. Bioinformatics. 2007. (ENG., Illus.). 294p. 125.00 ***(978-1-904842-23-1(2))*** Scion Publishing Ltd. GBR. Dist: Chicago Distribution Ctr.

Degano, Pierpaolo & Gorrieri, Roberto. Computational Methods in Systems Biology: 7th International Conference, CMSB 2008. 2009. (Lecture Notes in Computer Science / Lecture Notes in Bioinformatics Ser.). x, 329p. pap. 79.95 *(978-3-642-03844-0(1),* 3642038441) Springer.

Dehmer, Matthias, et al, eds. Applied Statistics for Network Biology: Methods in Systems Biology. 2011. (Quantitative & Network Biology (VCH) Ser.: 3). (ENG., Illus.). 478p. 159.95 *(978-3-527-32750-8(9),* Wiley-VCH) Wiley, John & Sons, Inc.

Dehmer, Matthias & Emmert-Streib, Frank, eds. Analysis of Complex Networks: From Biology to Linguistics. 2009. (ENG., Illus.). 480p. 232.00 *(978-3-527-32345-6(7),* Wiley-VCH) Wiley, John & Sons, Inc.

Delisi, Charles. Genome Informatics 2009: Genome Informatics Series Vol. 22 - Proceedings of the 9th Annual International Workshop on Bioinformatics & Systems Biology (ibsb 2009) 2010. (Illus.). 228p. 111.00 *(978-1-84816-569-4(2))* Imperial College Pr. GBR. Dist: World Scientific Publishing Co., Inc.

Demin, Oleg & Goryanin, Igor. Kinetic Modelling in Systems Biology. 2008. (Chapman & Hall/CRC Mathematical & Computational Biology Ser.). (ENG., Illus.). 360p. 85.95 *(978-1-58488-667-9(6),* C6676, Chapman & Hall/CRC) CRC Pr. LLC.

Dey, Dipak K., et al. Bayesian Modeling in Bioinformatics. 2010. (Chapman & Hall/CRC Biostatistics Ser.). (ENG., Illus.). 466p. 89.95 *(978-1-4200-7017-0(7),* Chapman & Hall/CRC) CRC Pr. LLC.

Dijkstra, Tjeerd M. H., et al, eds. Pattern Recognition in Bioinformatics: 5th IAPR International Conference, PRIB 2010, Nijmegen, the Netherlands, September 22-24, 2010, Proceedings. 2010. (Lecture Notes in Computer Science / Lecture Notes in Bioinformatics Ser.). xii, 442p. pap. 95.00 *(978-3-642-16000-4(X),* 364216000X) Springer.

Dogaru, Radu, et al. Advances in Computational Intelligence & Bioinformatics. 2006. (Studies in Computational Intelligence Ser.). 200p. *(978-3-540-29392-7(2),* 3540293922) Springer.

Draghici, Sorin. An Introduction to Statistics & Data Analysis for Bioinformatics Using R. 2012. (Chapman & Hall/CRC Mathematical & Computational Biology Ser.). (ENG., Illus.). 506p. 79.95 ***(978-1-4398-9236-7(9),*** Chapman & Hall/CRC) CRC Pr. LLC.

Draghici, Sorin, et al. Pathway Analysis of High Throughput Experiments. 2010. (Illus.). 306p. 79.95 *(978-1-58488-685-3(4),* Chapman & Hall/CRC) CRC Pr. LLC.

Dua, Sumeet. Data Mining for Bioinformatics. 2012. (ENG., Illus.). 328p. 89.95 *(978-0-8493-2801-5(2),* CRC Press) Taylor & Francis Group GBR. Dist: Taylor & Francis Group.

Dubitzky, Werner. Distributed, High-Performance & Grid Computing in Computational Biology: International Workshop, GCCB 2006, Eilat, Israel, January 21, 2007: Proceedings. 2007. (Lecture Notes in Computer Science Ser.). (Illus.). X, 192p. pap. 69.95 *(978-3-540-69841-8(8),* 3540698418) Springer.

Edwards, David, ed. Plant Bioinformatics: Methods & Protocols. (Methods in Molecular Biology Ser.). (Illus.). 2010. xv, 552p. pap. 189.00 *(978-1-61737-697-9(3),* 1617376973) 2008. 552p. 189.00 *(978-1-58829-653-5(9))* Humana Pr.

Edwards, David, et al. Bioinformatics: Tools & Applications. 2009. (ENG., Illus.). xii, 451p. 89.95 *(978-0-387-92737-4(9),* 0387927379) Springer.

Ehrenfeucht, Andrzej, et al. Computation in Living Cells: Gene Assembly in Ciliates. 2010. (Natural Computing Ser.). xiv, 202p. pap. 89.95 *(978-3-642-07401-1(4),* 3642074014) Springer.

Eisenhaber, Frank, ed. Discovering Biomolecular Mechanisms with Computational Biology. 2010. (Molecular Biology Intelligence Unit Ser.). (Illus.). xi, 147p. pap. 179.00 *(978-1-4419-4177-0(0),* 1441941770) Springer.

Elber, Ron. Protein Modeling with Bioinformatics & Biophysics. 2007. (Illus.). 350p. 89.95 *(978-0-387-32988-8(9),* 0387329889) Springer.

Elloumi, Mourad & Zomaya, Albert Y. Algorithms in Computational Molecular Biology: Techniques, Approaches & Applications. 2011. (Wiley Series in Bioinformatics Ser.: 16). (ENG., Illus.). 1080p. 158.00 *(978-0-470-50519-9(2),* Wiley) Wiley, John & Sons, Inc.

Elnitski, Laura. Advances in Genomic Sequence Analysis & Pattern Discovery. 2011. 236p. 90.00 *(978-981-4327-72-5(7))* World Scientific Publishing Co., Inc.

Eskin, Eleazar, et al. Systems Biology & Regulatory Genomics: Joint Annual RECOMB 2005 Satellite Workshops on Systems Biology, & on Regulatory Genomics, San Diego, CA, USA, December 2-4, 2005, Revised Selected Papers. 2007. (Lecture Notes in Computer Science Ser.). (Illus.). X, 259p. pap. 69.95 *(978-3-540-48293-2(8),* 3540482938) Springer.

Et. Clustering Challenges in Biological Ne. . 2009. (Illus.). 350p. 150.00 *(978-981-277-165-0(4))* Imperial College Pr. GBR. Dist: World Scientific Publishing Co., Inc.

Ewens, Warren J. & Grant, Gregory R. Statistical Methods in Bioinformatics: An Introduction. 2nd ed. 2010. (Statistics for Biology & Health Ser.). (Illus.). xx, 588p. pap. 115.00 *(978-1-4419-2302-8(0),* 1441923020) Springer.

Falus, Andras. Clinical Applications of Immunomics. 2009. (Immunomics Reviews: Ser.). 228p. 179.00 *(978-0-387-79207-1(4))* Springer.

Fan, Jianqing. New Developments in Biostatistics & Bioinformatics. Vol. 21. 2009. 292p. 94.00 *(978-981-283-743-1(4))* World Scientific Publishing Co., Inc.

Fei, Minrui, et al, eds. Life System Modeling & Intelligent Computing: International Conference on Life System Modeling & Simulation, LSMS 2010, & International Conference on Intelligent Computing for Sustainable Energy & Environment, ICSEE 2010, Wuxi, China, September 17-20, 2010, Proceedings, Part I. 2010. (Lecture Notes in Computer Science / Theoretical Computer Science & General Issues Ser.). xxii, 518p. pap. 107.00 *(978-3-642-15620-5(7),* 3642156207) Springer.

Feng, Jianfeng, et al, eds. Networks: From Biology to Theory. 2007. (ENG., Illus.). xxvi, 318p. 109.00 *(978-1-84628-485-4(6),* 1846284856) Springer.

—Networks: from Biology to Theory: From Biology to Theory. 2010. (ENG., Illus.). xxvi, 318p. pap. 109.00 *(978-1-84996-609-2(5),* 1849966095) Springer.

Fenyö, David, ed. Computational Biology. 2010. (Methods in Molecular Biology Ser.). (Illus.). xi, 327p. 159.00 *(978-1-60761-841-6(9),* 1607618419) Humana Pr.

Feytmans, Ernest & Appel, Ron D. Bioinformatics: A Swiss Perspective. 2009. 320p. 147.00 *(978-981-283-877-3(5))* World Scientific Publishing Co., Inc.

Fielding, Alan H. Cluster & Classification Techniques for the Biosciences. (ENG., Illus.). 258p. 2007. per. 60.00 *(978-0-521-61800-7(2))* 2006. 122.00 *(978-0-521-85281-4(1))* Cambridge Univ. Pr.

Flaig, Ruediger-Marcus. Bioinformatics Programming in Python: A Practical Course for Beginners. 2008. (ENG., Illus.). 428p. pap. 94.95 *(978-3-527-32094-3(6),* Wiley-VCH) Wiley, John & Sons, Inc.

Flower, Darren R. Bioinformatics for Vaccinology. 2008. (ENG., Illus.). 312p. pap. 104.95 *(978-0-470-02711-0(8),* Wiley) Wiley, John & Sons, Inc.

Flower, Darren R., ed. Immunoinformatics: Predicting Immunogenicity in Silico. 2010. (Methods in Molecular Biology Ser.). (Illus.). xv, 438p. pap. 149.00 *(978-1-61737-725-9(2),* 1617377252) Humana Pr.

Flower, Darren R., et al. Bioinformatics for Immunomics. 2010. (Illus.). xvi, 192p. E-Book ***(978-1-4419-0540-6(5))*** Springer.

Fogel, Gary B., et al, eds. Computational Intelligence in Bioinformatics. 2007. (IEEE Press Series on Computational Intelligence Ser.: 7). (ENG., Illus.). 355p. 99.95 *(978-0-470-10526-9(7),* Wiley-IEEE Pr.) Wiley, John & Sons, Inc.

Forsdyke, Donald R. Evolutionary Bioinformatics. 2nd ed. 2011. (ENG., Illus.). xxii, 509p. 209.00 *(978-1-4419-7770-0(8),* 1441977708) Springer.

Frishman, D., ed. Structural Bioinformatics of Membrane Proteins. 2010. (ENG., Illus.). 400p. 139.00 *(978-3-7091-0044-8(5),* 3709100445) Springer.

Frishman, D. & Valencia, Alfonso, eds. Modern Genome Annotation: The Biosapiens Network. 2010. (ENG., Illus.). xviii, 490p. pap. 259.00 *(978-3-211-99911-0(6),* 3211999116) Springer.

Frishman, Dmitrij & Carrasco Valencia, Alfonso. Modern Genome Annotation: The BioSapiens Network. 2008. (Illus.). 550p. 259.00 *(978-3-211-75122-0(X))* Springer.

Fulekar, M. H. Bioinformatics. 2008. (Illus.). xii, 246p. 159.00 *(978-1-4020-8879-7(5))* Springer.

Gaber, Mohamed Medhat, ed. Scientific Data Mining & Knowledge Discovery: Principles & Foundations. 2009. (ENG.). x, 400p. 99.00 *(978-3-642-02787-1(3),* 3642027873) Springer.

Galloway, Alexander R. & Thacker, Eugene. The Exploit: A Theory of Networks. 2007. (Electronic Mediations Ser.). 256p. 57.00 *(978-0-8166-5043-9(6));* (ENG.). pap. 18.95 *(978-0-8166-5044-6(6))* Univ. of Minnesota Pr.

Gassert. Bioinformatics. 2007. (Synthesis Lectures on Biomedical Engineering Ser.). 40.00 *(978-1-59829-322-7(2))* Morgan & Claypool Pubs.

Gentleman, Robert. R Programming for Bioinformatics. 2008. (Chapman & Hall/CRC Computer Science & Data Analysis Ser.). (ENG., Illus.). 328p. 75.95 *(978-1-4200-6367-7(7),* Chapman & Hall/CRC) CRC Pr. LLC.

Giancarlo, Raffaele & Hannenhalli, Sridhar. Algorithms in Bioinformatics. 2007. (Lecture Notes in Computer Science Ser.). (Illus.). 432p. pap. 89.95 *(978-3-540-74125-1(9))* Springer.

Gleich, Arnim von, et al. Potentials & Trends in Biomimetics. 2009. (Illus.). viii, 200p. 129.00 *(978-3-642-05245-3(2),* 3642052452) Springer.

Goel, Gautam. Reconstructing Biochemical Systems - Systems Modeling & Analysis Tools for Decoding Biological Designs. 2008. 144p. per. *(978-3-8364-5878-8(0))* VDM Verlag Dr. Mueller e.K.

Golan, Yona. Computational Proteomics: Protein Classification & Meta-Organization. 2010. (Chapman & Hall/CRC Mathematical & Computational Biology Ser.). (ENG., Illus.). 767p. (C). 89.95 *(978-1-58488-555-9(6),* Chapman & Hall/CRC) CRC Pr. LLC.

Goldstein, Richard A., et al. Modeling Protein Evolution & Its Bioinformatics Applications. 2009. (Chapman Hall/CRC Mathematical Biology & Medicine Ser.). 79.95 *(978-1-58488-498-9(3),* Chapman & Hall/CRC) CRC Pr. LLC.

Gollery, Martin. Handbook of Hidden Markov Models in Bioinformatics. 2008. (Chapman & Hall/CRC Mathematical & Computational Biology Ser.). (ENG., Illus.). 176p. 64.95 *(978-1-58488-684-6(6),* Chapman & Hall/CRC) CRC Pr. LLC.

Gomase, Virendra. Transcriptomics. 2009. (Illus.). 436p. pap. *(978-3-639-21486-4(2))* VDM Verlag Dr. Mueller e.K.

Gomase, Virendra S. & Tagore, Somnath. Transcriptomics. 2009. 500p. 150.00 *(978-1-84829-021-1(7))* Anshan GBR. Dist: Publishers Storage & Shipping.

Gonnet, Gaston & Scholl, Ralf. Scientific Computation. 2009. (ENG., Illus.). 250p. 68.00 *(978-0-521-84989-0(6))* Cambridge Univ. Pr.

González-Díaz, Humberto. Alignment-Free Models in Plant Genomics: Theoretical, Experimental, & Legal Issues. Agüero-Chapin, Guillermin et al, eds. 2010. (Agriculture Issues & Policies Ser.). 92p. pap. 43.00 *(978-1-61668-333-7(3))* Nova Science Pubs., Inc.

Gonzalez, Juan, et al, eds. Nature Inspired Cooperative Strategies for Optimization (NICSO 2010) 2010. (Studies in Computational Intelligence Ser.). (ENG.). 420p. 199.00 *(978-3-642-12537-9(9),* 3642125379) Springer.

Gopal, Shuba, et al. Bioinformatics: A Computing Perspective. 2008. (ENG., Illus.). 480p. (C). 160.67 *(978-0-07-313364-5(7),* 0073133647, McGraw-Hill Science, Engineering & Mathematics) McGraw-Hill Higher Education.

Gordon, Gavin J. Bioinformatics in Cancer & Cancer Therapy. 2008. (Cancer Drug Discovery & Development Ser.). (Illus.). 192p. 179.00 *(978-1-58829-753-2(5))* Humana Pr.

Gordon, Gavin J., ed. Bioinformatics in Cancer & Cancer Therapy. 2012. (Cancer Drug Discovery & Development Ser.). (ENG., Illus.). x, 192p. pap. 179.00 *(978-1-61737-758-7(9),* 1617377589) Humana Pr.

Gordon, Paul M. K., et al. Genome Annotation. 2012. (Chapman & Hall/CRC Mathematical & Computational Biology Ser.). (ENG., Illus.). 248p. 89.95 *(978-1-4398-4117-4(9),* Chapman & Hall/CRC) CRC Pr. LLC.

Gottweis, Herbert & Petersen, Alan, eds. Biobanks. 2007. (Illus.). 224p. 150.00 *(978-0-415-42737-1(1))* Routledge.

Gromiha, M. Michael & Penrose, Denise. Protein Bioinformatics: From Sequence to Function. 2010. (ENG., Illus.). 339p. pap. 74.95 *(978-81-312-2297-3(7),* Academic Pr.) Elsevier Science & Technology Bks.

Gu, Jenny & Gu. Structural Bioinformatics. Gu, Jenny & Bourne, Philip E., eds. 2nd ed. 2009. (ENG., Illus.). 1067p. 109.95 *(978-0-470-18105-8(2),* Wiley-Blackwell) Wiley, John & Sons, Inc.

Guha, Rajarshi & Bender, Andreas, eds. Computational Approaches in Cheminformatics & Bioinformatics. 2012. (ENG., Illus.). 292p. 115.00 *(978-0-470-38441-1(7),* Wiley) Wiley, John & Sons, Inc.

GuimarÃ£es, Katia S., et al. Advances in Bioinformatics & Computational Biology: 4th Brazilian Symposium on Bioinformatics, BSB 2009, Porto Alegre, Brazil, July 29-31, 2009, Proceedings. 2009. (Lecture Notes in Computer Science / Lecture Notes in Bioinformatics Ser.). (ENG.). xiii, 169p. pap. 69.95 *(978-3-642-03222-6(2),* 3642032222) Springer.

Gupta, Randhir Kumar, et al. Bioinformatics. 2011. 308p. pap. ***(978-3-8443-8855-8(9))*** Lambert Academic Publishing.

Hahne, Florian, et al. Bioconductor Case Studies. 2008. (Use R! Ser.). (Illus.). 283p. pap. 99.00 *(978-0-387-77239-4(1))* Springer.

Halbesleben, Jonathon R. B., ed. Medical Biochemoinformatics. 2008. 249p. (C). 98.00 *(978-1-60456-501-0(2))* Nova Science Pubs., Inc.

Hamelryck, Thomas, et al, eds. Bayesian Methods in Structural Bioinformatics. 2012. (Statistics for Biology & Health Ser.). (ENG., Illus.). xxii, 385p. 89.95 ***(978-3-642-27224-0(X),*** 364227224X) Springer.

Hammer, Barbara & Hitzler, Pascal, eds. Perspectives of Neural-Symbolic Integration. (Studies in Computational Intelligence Ser.). (Illus.). 2010. xii, 319p. pap. 199.00 *(978-3-642-09322-7(1),* 3642093221) 2007. 319p. 199.00 *(978-3-540-73953-1(X))* Springer.

Haney, Steven A. High Content Screening: Science, Techniques & Applications. Haney, Steven A., ed. 2008. (ENG., Illus.). 448p. 153.00 *(978-0-470-03999-1(X),* Wiley-Interscience) Wiley, John & Sons, Inc.

Harrington, David, ed. Designs for Clinical Trials: Perspectives on Current Issues. 2011. (Applied Bioinformatics & Biostatistics in Cancer Research Ser.). (ENG., Illus.). xiv, 204p. 189.00 *(978-1-4614-0139-1(9),* 1461401399) Springer.

Hasan, Laiq. Acceleration of Bioinformatics Sequence Alignment. 2011. 132p. pap. ***(978-3-8443-8768-1(4))*** Lambert Academic Publishing.

Havukkala, Ilkka. Biodata Mining & Visualization, Vol. 4. 2009. 300p. 88.00 *(978-981-279-036-1(5))* World Scientific Publishing Co., Inc.

He, Matthew & Petoukhov, Sergey. Mathematics of Bioinformatics: Theory, Methods & Applications. 2011. (Wiley Series in Bioinformatics Ser.: 11). (ENG., Illus.). 298p. 105.00 *(978-0-470-40443-0(4),* Wiley-Interscience) Wiley, John & Sons, Inc.

Heath, Lenwood S. & Ramakrishnan, Naren, eds. Problem Solving Handbook for Computational Biology & Bioinformatics. 2010. (ENG., Illus.). xvii, 347p. 129.00 *(978-0-387-09759-6(7),* 0387097597) Springer.

Hetherington, Alistair & Grierson, Claire, eds. Practical Systems Biology, Vol. 61. 2008. (Society for Experimental Biology Ser.). (Illus.). CCCp. 234.00 *(978-0-415-40780-9(X))* Taylor & Francis Group.

Hicks, Martin G. & Kettner, Carsten, eds. Proceedings of the International Beilstein Symposium on Glyco-Bioinformatics: Bits 'n' Bytes of Sugars. 2011. 177p. *(978-3-8325-2719-8(2))* Logos Verlag Berlin.

Hochreiter, Sepp & Wagner, Roland. Bioinformatics Research & Development. 2007. (Lecture Notes in Computer Science Ser.). (Illus.). XVI, 482p. pap. 109.00 *(978-3-540-71232-9(1),* 3540712321) Springer.

Holmes, Raquell M. A Cell Biologist's Guide to Modeling & Bioinformatics. 2007. (ENG., Illus.). 224p. 119.95 *(978-0-471-16420-3(8),* Wiley-Liss) Wiley, John & Sons, Inc.

Horvath, Steve. Weighted Network Analysis: Applications in Genomics & Systems Biology. 2011. (ENG., Illus.). xxiii, 421p. 209.00 *(978-1-4419-8818-8(1),* 1441988181) Springer.

Hu, Hai & Liebman, Michael. Biomedical Informatics in Translational Research. 2008. (Illus.). 364p. 95.00 *(978-1-59693-038-4(1))* Artech Hse., Inc.

Hu, Xiaohua, ed. Bioinformatics & Biomedicine; Proceedings. 2007. 444p. pap. 237.00 *(978-0-7695-3031-4(1))* IEEE Computer Society Pr.

Hu, Xiaohua & Pan, Yi, eds. Knowledge Discovery in Bioinformatics: Techniques, Methods, & Applications. 2007. (Wiley Series in Bioinformatics Ser.: 5). (ENG., Illus.). 379p. 124.00 *(978-0-471-77796-0(X),* Wiley-Interscience) Wiley, John & Sons, Inc.

Hu, Yingjie. Gene Selection Based on Consistency Modelling, Algorithms & Applications - Genetic Algorithm Application in Bioinformatics Data Analysis. 2008. 112p. pap. *(978-3-639-00883-8(9))* VDM Verlag Dr. Mueller e.K.

Huang, De-Shuang, et al, eds. Advanced Intelligent Computing: 7th International Conference, ICIC 2011, Zhengzhou, China, August 11-14, 2011. Revised Selected Papers. 2011. (Lecture Notes in Computer Science / Theoretical Computer Science & General Issues Ser.). (ENG., Illus.). xxi, 707p. pap. 131.00 ***(978-3-642-24727-9(X),*** 364224727X) Springer.

—Advanced Intelligent Computing. Theories & Applications: 6th International Conference on Intelligent Computing, Changsha, China, August 18-21, 2010. Proceedings. 2010. (Communications in Computer & Information Science Ser.). xvi, 580p. pap. 129.00 *(978-3-642-14830-9(1),* 3642148301) Springer.

—Advanced Intelligent Computing Theories & Applications: 6th International Conference on Intelligent Computing, ICIC 2010, Changsha, China, August 18-21, 2010, Proceedings. 2010. (Lecture Notes in Computer Science / Theoretical Computer Science & General Issues Ser.). xix, 689p. pap. 139.00 *(978-3-642-14921-4(9),* 3642149219) Springer.

—Advanced Intelligent Computing Theories & Applications: with Aspects of Artificial Intelligence: 6th International Conference on Intelligent Computing, ICIC 2010, Changsha, China, August 18-21, 2010, Proceedings. 2010. (Lecture Notes in Computer Science / Lecture Notes in Artificial Intelligence Ser.). xviii, 685p. pap. 139.00 *(978-3-642-14931-3(6),* 3642149316) Springer.

—Advanced Intelligent Computing Theories & Applications with Aspects of Contemporary Intelligent Computing Techniques: 4th International Conference on Intelligent Computing, ICIC 2008 Shanghai, China, September 15-18, 2008, Proceedings. 2008. (Communications in Computer & Information Science Ser.). (Illus.). 559p. pap. 129.00 *(978-3-540-85929-1(2))* Springer.

Huang, De-Shuang, et al. Advanced Intelligent Computing Theories & Applications with Aspects of Artificial Intelligence: Third International Conference on Intelligent Computing, ICIC 2007 Qingdao, China, August 21-24, 2007 Proceedings. 2007. (Lecture Notes in Computer Science Ser.). (Illus.). 1373p. pap. 219.00 *(978-3-540-74201-2(8))* Springer.

—Advanced Intelligent Computing Theories & Applications: with Aspects of Theoretical & Methodological Issues: Third International Conference on Intelligent Computing, ICIC 2007 Qingdao, China, August 21-24, 2007 Proceedings. 2007. (Lecture Notes in Computer Science Ser.). (Illus.). 1379p. pap. 189.00 *(978-3-540-74170-1(4))* Springer.

—Computational Intelligence & Bioinformatics: International Conference on Intelligent Computing, ICIC 2006, Kunming, China, August 16-19, 2006, Proceedings, Part III. 2006. (Lecture Notes in Computer Science Ser.). (Illus.). 803p. pap. 129.00 *(978-3-540-37277-6(6),* 3540372776) Springer.

Hubbard, Simon & Jones, Andy, eds. Proteome Bioinformatics. 2010. (Methods in Molecular Biology Ser.). (ENG., Illus.). xi, 403p. 129.00 *(978-1-60761-443-2(X),* 160761443X) Humana Pr.

Husmeier, Dirk, et al, eds. Probabilistic Modeling in Bioinformatics & Medical Informatics. 2010. (Advanced Information & Knowledge Processing Ser.). (Illus.). xx, 508p. pap. 139.00 *(978-1-84996-912-3(4),* 1849969124) Springer.

Ideker, Trey & Bafna, Vineet. Systems Biology & Computational Proteomics. 2007. (Lecture Notes in Bioinformatics Ser.). (Illus.). 129p. per. 79.95 *(978-3-540-73059-0(1))* Springer.

IEEE Computer Society Staff, contrib. by. OCCBIO 2009: 2009 Ohio Collaborative Conference on Bioinformatics: Proceedings. 15-17 June 2009, Case Western

University, Cleveland, Ohio. 2009. (Illus.). xi, 145p. pap. *(978-0-7695-3685-9(9))* IEEE Computer Society Pr.

IEEE Staff. 2007 IEEE 7th International Symposium on BioInformatics & BioEngineering. 2007. pap. 268.00 *(978-1-4244-1509-0(8))* IEEE.

—2008 8th IEEE International Symposium on BioInformatics & BioEngineering. 2008. pap. 376.00 *(978-1-4244-2844-1(0))* IEEE.

—2008 IEEE International Conference on Bioinformatics & Biomedicine Workshops. 2008. pap. 222.00 *(978-1-4244-2890-8(4))* IEEE.

IEEE Staff, ed. 2007 IEEE Symposium on Computational Intelligence in Bioinformatics & Computational Biology. 2007. pap. 274.00 *(978-1-4244-0710-1(9)*, 07EX1576) IEEE.

Iglesias, Pablo A. & Ingalls, Brian P., eds. Control Theory & Systems Biology. 2009. (ENG., Illus.). 358p. (gr. 17). 45.00 *(978-0-262-01334-5(7))* MIT Pr.

Institute of Electrical and Electronics Engineers, Inc. Staff. 2007 IEEE International Confernece on Bioinformatics & Biomedicine Workshops. 2007. pap. 214.00 *(978-1-4244-1604-2(3))* IEEE.

Introduction to Machine Learning & Bioinformatics. 2011. (C). 83.95 *(978-1-4200-1178-4(2)*, Chapman & Hall/CRC) CRC Pr. LLC.

Irwin, George, ed. Bio-Inspired Computational Intelligence & Applications. 2007. (Lecture Notes in Computer Science Ser.). (Illus.). 805p. pap. 139.00 *(978-3-540-74768-0(0))* Springer.

Irwin, George William & He, Guosen, eds. Life System Modeling & Simulation: International Conference, LSMS 2007 Shanghai, China, September 14-17, 2007 Proceedings. 2007. (Lecture Notes in Computer Science Ser.). (Illus.). 561p. pap. 109.00 *(978-3-540-74770-3(2))* Springer.

Isaev, Alexander. Introduction to Mathematical Methods in Bioinformatics. 2006. (Universitext Ser.). (Illus.). xiv, 298p. pap. 74.95 *(978-3-540-21973-6(0)*, 3540219730) Springer.

Ishida, Yoshiteru. Immunity-Based Systems: A Design Perspective. 2010. (Advanced Information Processing Ser.). (Illus.). xii, 177p. pap. 159.00 *(978-3-642-05661-1(X)*, 364205661X) Springer.

Iyengar, M. Sriram. Symbolic Systems Biology. rev. ed. 2010. 218p. 140.95 *(978-0-7637-5370-2(X))* Jones & Bartlett Learning, LLC.

Jin, Yaochu & Wang, Lipo, eds. Fuzzy Systems in Bioinformatics & Computational Biology. 2009. (Studies in Fuzziness & Soft Computing Ser.). (Illus.). xvi, 332p. 199.00 *(978-3-540-89967-9(7))* Springer.

Kadirkamanathan, Visakan, et al. Pattern Recognition in Bioinformatics: 4th IAPR International Conference, PRIB 2009, Sheffield, UK, September 7-9, 2009, Proceedings. 2009. (Lecture Notes in Computer Science / Lecture Notes in Bioinformatics Ser.). xiv, 452p. pap. 99.00 *(978-3-642-04030-6(6)*, 3642040306) Springer.

Kalet, Ira J. Principles of Biomedical Informatics. 2008. (ENG., Illus.). 504p. 82.95 *(978-0-12-369438-6(8)*, Academic Pr.) Elsevier Science & Technology Bks.

Kaneko, Kunihiko. Life as a Complex System: A Constructive & Dynamical System Approach to the Biological Sciences. 2006. (Understanding Complex Systems Ser.). (Illus.). xiv, 371p. 119.00 *(978-3-540-32666-3(9)*, 3540326669) Springer.

Kangueane, Pandjassarame. Bioinformation Discovery: Data to Knowledge in Biology. 2009. (ENG., Illus.). xxv, 166p. 183.00 *(978-1-4419-0518-5(9)*, 1441905189) Springer.

Karasavvas, Konstantinos. Adjusting Autonomy in Multi-Agent Bioinformatics Integration Systems. 2009. 148p. pap. *(978-3-639-16965-2(4))* VDM Verlag Dr. Mueller e.K.

Karch, Steven B. & Osterman, Andrei L., eds. Gene Essentiality: Protocols & Bioinformatics. 2007. (Methods in Molecular Biology Ser.). (Illus.). 400p. 99.50 *(978-1-59745-321-9(8))* Humana Pr.

Keith, Jonathan M. Bioinformatics, 2 vols. 2008. (Methods in Molecular Biology Ser.). (Illus.). 469p. 159.00 *(978-1-60327-428-9(6))* Humana Pr.

Keith, Jonathan M., ed. Bioinformatics: Volume I: Data, Sequence Analysis & Evolution. 2010. (Methods in Molecular Biology Ser.). (Illus.). xii, 562p. pap. 159.00 *(978-1-61737-730-3(9)*, 1617377309) Humana Pr.

—Bioinformatics: Volume II: Structure, Function & Applications, 2 vols. 2010. (Methods in Molecular Biology Ser.). (Illus.). xvi, 502p. pap. 159.00 *(978-1-61737-895-9(X)*, 161737895X) Humana Pr.

—Bioinformatics, Volume I: Data, Sequence Analysis & Evolution, 2 vols. 2008. (Methods in Molecular Biology Ser.). (Illus.). 562p. 159.00 *(978-1-58829-707-5(1))* Springer.

Kelemen, Árpád, et al, eds. Computational Intelligence in Bioinformatics. 2010. (Studies in Computational Intelligence Ser.). (Illus.). xvi, 326p. pap. 239.00 *(978-3-642-09550-4(X)*, 364209550X) Springer.

Kelemen, Árpád, et al. Computational Intelligence in Bioinformatics. 2007. (Studies in Computational Intelligence Ser.). (Illus.). 331p. 239.00 *(978-3-540-76802-9(5))* Springer.

Khatri, Indu & A. K. Sharma. Protein Secondary Structure Prediction. 2011. 64p. pap. ***(978-3-8443-1323-9(0))*** Lambert Academic Publishing.

Khuri, Sami, et al. Information, Technology in Bio- & Medical Informatics, ITBAM 2010: First International Conference, Bilbao, Spain, September 1-2, 2010, Proceedings. 2010. (Monographs in Contemporary Mathematics Ser.). xii, 236p. pap. 72.00 *(978-3-642-15019-7(5)*, 3642150195) Springer.

Kihara, Daisuke, ed. Protein Function Prediction for Omics Era. 2011. (ENG., Illus.). xiii, 310p. 209.00 *(978-94-007-0880-8(7)*, 9400770807) Springer.

Kinser, Jason. Python for Bioinformatics. 2008. (Illus.). 417p. pap. 86.95 *(978-0-7637-5186-9(3))* Jones & Bartlett Learning, LLC.

Kiritchenko, Svetlana. Hierarchical Text Categorization. 2009. 180p. pap. *(978-3-639-18340-5(1))* VDM Verlag Dr. Mueller e.K.

Knapp, Ernst-Walter, et al, eds. Genome Informatics 2008. 2008. 300p. 150.00 *(978-1-84816-299-0(5))* World Scientific Publishing Co., Inc.

Koch, Ina, et al, eds. Modeling in Systems Biology: The Petri Net Approach. 2010. (Computational Biology Ser.). (ENG., Illus.). xxiii, 364p. 129.00 *(978-1-84996-473-9(4)*, 1849964734) Springer.

Kolehmainen, Ville, et al. Adaptive & Natural Computing Algorithms: 9th International Conference, ICANNGA 2009, Kuopio, Finland, April 23-25, 2009, Revised Selected Papers. 2009. (Lecture Notes in Computer Science / Theoretical Computer Science & General Issues Ser.). xvi, 630p. pap. 129.00 *(978-3-642-04920-0(6)*, 3642049206) Springer.

Konopka, Andrzej K. Chemical, Computational, & Systems Biology Series Typical Book. 2007. 350p. 79.95 *(978-0-470-12239-6(0)*, Wiley-Interscience) Wiley, John & Sons, Inc.

Koyutürk, Mehmet, et al, eds. Functional Coherence of Molecular Networks in Bioinformatics. 2011. (ENG., Illus.). x, 228p. 189.00 *(978-1-4614-0319-7(7)*, 1461403197) Springer.

Krasnogor, Natalio, et al, eds. Nature Inspired Cooperative Strategies for Optimization (Nicso 2007) 2008. (Studies in Computational Intelligence Ser.). (ENG., Illus.). xiv, 520p. 199.00 *(978-3-540-78986-4(3)*, 3540789863) Springer.

—Nature Inspired Cooperative Strategies for Optimization (NICSO 2008) 2009. (Studies in Computational Intelligence Ser.). (ENG., Illus.). xxviii, 300p. 199.00 *(978-3-642-03210-3(9)*, 3642032109) Springer.

Kumar, Abhishek. Bioinformatic Analysis of Beta Barrel Porins. 2010. 76p. pap. *(978-3-639-24450-2(8))* VDM Verlag Dr. Mueller e.K.

Kumar, Sudhir & Filipski, Alan. Molecular Sequence Analysis: A Primer on Computational & Bioinformatic Approaches. 2009. 416p. pap. 69.95 *(978-0-471-65099-7(4)*, Wiley-Liss) Wiley, John & Sons, Inc.

Lambrix, Patrick & Kemp, Graham, eds. Data Integration in the Life Sciences: 7th International Conference, DILS 2010, Gothenburg, Sweden, August 25-27, 2010. Proceedings. 2010. (Lecture Notes in Computer Science / Lecture Notes in Bioinformatics Ser.). x, 215p. pap. 72.00 *(978-3-642-15119-4(1)*, 3642151191) Springer.

Larson, Richard S., ed. Bioinformatics & Drug Discovery. 2010. (Methods in Molecular Biology Ser.). (Illus.). 456p. pap. 169.00 *(978-1-61737-509-5(8)*, 1617375098) Humana Pr.

Lässig, M. & Valleriani, A., eds. Biological Evolution & Statistical Physics. 2010. (Lecture Notes in Physics Ser.). xi, 356p. pap. 129.00 *(978-3-642-07743-2(9)*, 3642077439) Springer.

Lazakidou, Athina A., ed. Biocomputation & Biomedical Informatics: Case Studies & Applications. 2009. 399p. 245.00 *(978-1-60566-768-3(4))* IGI Global.

Lecca, Paola, et al. Systemic Approaches in Bioinformatics & Computational Systems Biology: Recent Advances. 2011. ***(978-1-61350-435-2(7))***; ***(978-1-61350-437-6(3))***; E-Book ***(978-1-61350-436-9(5))*** IGI Global.

Lee, Jae K. Statistical Bioinformatics: For Biomedical & Life Science Researchers. 2010. (ENG., Illus.). 370p. pap. 110.95 *(978-0-471-69272-0(7)*, Wiley-Blackwell) Wiley, John & Sons, Inc.

Lee, Sang Yup, ed. Systems Biology & Biotechnology of Escherichia Coli. 2009. (ENG., Illus.). xxii, 466p. 249.00 *(978-1-4020-9393-7(4)*, 1402093934) Springer.

Lengauer, Thomas, ed. Bioinformatics: From Genomes to Therapies - Molecular Sequences & Structures, 3 vols., Vol. I. 2007. (ENG., Illus.). 1814p. 795.00 *(978-3-527-31278-8(1)*, Wiley-VCH) Wiley, John & Sons, Inc.

Leondes. Biomechanical Systems Technology (V3) 2009. 155.00 *(978-981-270-983-7(5))* World Scientific Publishing Co., Inc.

Leser, Ulf, et al. Data Integration in the Life Sciences: Third International Workshop, DILS 2006, Hinxton, UK, July 20-22, 2006: Proceedings. 2006. (Lecture Notes in Computer Science Ser.). (Illus.). XI, 298p. pap. 74.95 *(978-3-540-36593-8(1)*, 3540365931) Springer.

Lesk, Arthur. Introduction to Bioinformatics. 3rd ed. 2008. (ENG., Illus.). 432p. (C). pap. 59.95 *(978-0-19-920804-3(2))* Oxford Univ. Pr., Inc.

Lewis, P. D. & Swansea University. R for Medicine & Biology. 2009. 399p. pap. 86.95 *(978-0-7637-5808-0(6))* Jones & Bartlett Learning, LLC.

Li, Haifeng. Applications of MacHine Learning Techniques to Bioinformatics. 2008. 236p. pap. *(978-3-639-05440-8(7))* VDM Verlag Dr. Mueller e.K.

Li, Kang, et al, eds. Life System Modeling & Intelligent Computing: International Conference on Life System Modeling & Simulation, LSMS 2010, & International Conference on Intelligent Computing for Sustainable Energy & Environment, ICSEE 2010, Wuxi, China, September 17-20, 2010. Proceedings. 2010. (Lecture Notes in Computer Science / Lecture Notes in Bioinformatics Ser.). xviii, 719p. pap. 131.00 *(978-3-642-15614-4(2)*, 3642156142) Springer.

—Life System Modeling & Intelligent Computing: International Conference on Life System Modeling & Simulation, LSMS 2010, & International Conference on Intelligent Computing for Sustainable Energy & Environment, ICSEE 2010, Wuxi, China, September 17-20, 2010, Proceedings, Part I. 2010. (Communications in Computer & Information Science Ser.). xviii, 261p. pap. 84.00 *(978-3-642-15852-0(8)*, 3642158528) Springer.

—Life System Modeling & Intelligent Computing: International Conference on Life System Modeling & Simulation, LSMS 2010, & International Conference on Intelligent Computing for Sustainable Energy & Environment, ICSEE 2010, Wuxi, China, September 17-20, 2010, Proceedings, Part II. 2010. (Communications in Computer & Information Science Ser.). xviii, 255p. pap. 84.00 *(978-3-642-15858-2(7)*, 3642158587) Springer.

Liang, Kung-Hao. Bioinformatics for Biomedical Science & Clinical Applications. 2012. 250p. 165.00 ***(978-1-907568-44-2(1))*** Woodhead Publishing Ltd. GBR. Dist: Ingram Pub. Services.

Liebman. Clinical Bioinformatics. 2008. 320p. 74.95 *(978-0-471-45773-2(6)*, Wiley-Liss) Wiley, John & Sons, Inc.

Lieth, Claus-Wilhelm von der, et al, eds. Bioinformatics for Glycobiology & Glycomics: An Introduction. 2010. (ENG., Illus.). 494p. 174.95 *(978-0-470-01667-1(1)*, Wiley) Wiley, John & Sons, Inc.

Lin, Simon C. & Yen, Eric, eds. Data Driven E-Science: Use Cases & Successful Applications of Distributed Computing Infrastructures (ISGC 2010) 2011. (ENG.). xxii, 517p. 199.00 *(978-1-4419-8013-7(X)*, 144198013X) Springer.

Liu, Jia-Jie. Solving Some Sequence Problems on Run-Length Encoded Strings. 2008. 76p. pap. *(978-3-639-02265-0(3))* VDM Verlag Dr. Mueller e.K.

Liu, Limin Angela & Wei, Dongqing, eds. Interdisciplinary Research & Applications in Bioinformatics, Computational Biology, & Environmental Sciences. 2010. (Illus.). 350p. 245.00 *(978-1-60960-064-8(9)*, Medical Information Science Reference) IGI Global.

Lodhi, Huma M., et al. Elements of Computational Systems Biology. 2010. (Wiley Series in Bioinformatics Ser.: 8). (ENG., Illus.). 412p. 128.00 *(978-0-470-18093-8(5)*, Wiley) Wiley, John & Sons, Inc.

Loog, Marco, et al, eds. Pattern Recognition in Bioinformatics: 6th IAPR International Conference, PRIB 2011, Delft, the Netherlands, November 2-4, 2011, Proceedings. 2011. (Lecture Notes in Computer Science / Lecture Notes in Bioinformatics Ser.). (ENG., Illus.). x, 342p. pap. 83.00 ***(978-3-642-24854-2(3)***, 3642248543) Springer.

Lu, Henry Horng-Shing, et al, eds. Handbook of Statistical Bioinformatics. 2011. (Springer Handbooks of Computational Statistics Ser.). (ENG., Illus.). ix, 627p. 339.00 *(978-3-642-16344-9(0)*, 3642163440) Springer.

Lu, Jiantao. Assessment of the Use of Topological Quantities in Structural Bioinformatics. 2008. 108p. pap. *(978-3-639-04570-3(X))* VDM Verlag Dr. Mueller e.K.

Lyons-Weiler, James. Research in Biomedical Informatics. 2010. (ENG.). 384p. 89.95 *(978-0-470-04415-5(2)*, Wiley-Interscience) Wiley, John & Sons, Inc.

Maccuish, John David & Maccuish, Norah E. Clustering in Bioinformatics & Drug Discovery. 2010. (Chapman & Hall/CRC Mathematical & Computational Biology Ser.). (ENG., Illus.). 244p. 79.95 *(978-1-4398-1678-3(6)*, CRC Press) Taylor & Francis Group GBR. Dist: Taylor & Francis Group.

Mahdi, Safiur Rahman, et al. Protein Secondary Structure Prediction. 2010. 80p. pap. *(978-3-639-27366-3(4))* VDM Verlag Dr. Mueller e.K.

Maheshwari, Uma & Rebello, Santhosh. Soft Computing Methodologies for Cluster Analysis & Gene Prediction. 2011. 56p. pap. ***(978-3-8443-1761-9(9))*** Lambert Academic Publishing.

Majoros, William H. Methods for Computational Gene Prediction. 2007. (ENG., Illus.). 448p. 138.00 *(978-0-521-87751-0(2))*; per. 65.00 *(978-0-521-70694-0(7))* Cambridge Univ. Pr.

Man, Mustafa, et al. Bio-Informatics. 2011. 112p. pap. ***(978-3-8433-9069-9(X))*** Lambert Academic Publishing.

Mandoiu, Ion. Bioinformatics Research & Applications. 2008. (Lecture Notes in Computer Science / Lecture Notes in Bioinformatics Ser.). spiral bd. 99.00 *(978-3-540-79449-3(2)*, 3540794492) Springer.

Mandoiu, Ion, et al. Bioinformatics Research & Applications: 5th International Symposium, ISBRA 2009 Fort Lauderdale, FL, USA, May 13-16, 2009, Proceedings. 2009. (Lecture Notes in Computer Science / Lecture Notes in Bioinformatics Ser.). (ENG.). xvii, 336p. pap. 79.95 *(978-3-642-01550-2(6))* Springer.

Mandoiu, Ion & Zelikovsky, Alexander. Bioinformatics Algorithms: Techniques & Applications. 2008. (Wiley Series in Bioinformatics Ser.: 3). (ENG., Illus.). 500p. 153.00 *(978-0-470-09773-1(6)*, Wiley-Interscience) Wiley, John & Sons, Inc.

—Bioinformatics Research & Applications: Third International Symposium, ISBRA 2007, Atlanta, GA, USA, May 7-10, 2007, Proceedings. 2007. (Lecture Notes in Computer Science / Lecture Notes in Bioinformatics Ser.). xv, 653p. pap. 119.00 *(978-3-540-72030-0(8))* Springer.

Mansour Alzohairy, Ahmed. Bioinformatics. 2011. 108p. pap. ***(978-3-8443-2938-4(2))*** Lambert Academic Publishing.

Marchiori, Elena. Evolutionary Computation, Machine Learning & Data Mining in Bioinformatics. 2008. (Lecture Notes in Computer Science / Theoretical Computer Science & General Issues Ser.). pap. 69.95 *(978-3-540-78756-3(9)*, 3540787569) Springer.

Marchiori, Elena & Rajapakse, Jagath C., eds. Evolutionary Computation, Machine Learning & Data Mining in Bioinformatics: 5th European Conference, EvoBIO 2007, Valencia, Spain, April 11-13, 2007: Proceedings. 2007. (Lecture Notes in Computer Science Ser.: Vol. 4447). (Illus.). 302p. 79.95 *(978-3-540-71782-9(X)*, 354071782X) Springer.

Marcum, James A. The Conceptual Foundations of Systems Biology: An Introduction. 2009. (Systems Biology - Theory, Techniques & Applications Ser.). (Illus.). x, 155p. 89.00 *(978-1-60741-867-2(3))* Nova Science Pubs., Inc.

Marcus, Frederick. Bioinformatics & Systems Biology: Collaborative Research & Resources. (ENG., Illus.). xxvi, 288p. 2010. pap. 129.00 *(978-3-642-09706-5(5)*, 3642097065) 2008. 129.00 *(978-3-540-78352-7(0)*, 3540783520) Springer.

Markstein, Peter & Xu, Ying, eds. Computational Systems Bioinformatics: CSB2007 Conference Proceedings, Volume 6: University of California, San Diego, USA, 13-17 August 2007. 2007. (Series on Advances in Bioinformatics & Computational Biology). (Illus.). 454p. 164.00 *(978-1-86094-872-5(3))* Imperial College Pr. GBR. Dist: World Scientific Publishing Co., Inc.

Masulli, Francesco, et al. Computational Intelligence Methods for Bioinformatics & Biostatistics: 5th International Meeting, CIBB 2008 Vietri sul Mare, Italy, October 3-4, 2008 Revised Selected Papers. 2009. (Lecture Notes in Computer Science / Lecture Notes in Bioinformatics Ser.). (ENG.). xi, 294p. pap. 79.95 *(978-3-642-02503-7(X)*, 364202503X) Springer.

Masulli, Francesco. Computational Intelligence Methods for Bioinformatics & Biostatistics: 6th International Meeting, CIBB 2009, Genoa, Italy, October 15-17, 2009, Revised Selected Papers. Masulli, Francesco et al, eds. 2010. (Lecture Notes in Computer Science / Lecture Notes in Bioinformatics Ser.). xiii, 320p. pap. 83.00 *(978-3-642-14570-4(1)*, 3642145701) Springer.

Mathur, Sunil K. Statistical Bioinformatics: With R. 2010. (ENG., Illus.). 336p. (C). 69.95 *(978-0-12-375104-1(7)*, Academic Pr.) Elsevier Science & Technology Bks.

Mathura, Venkatarajan & Kangueane, Pandjassarame. Bioinformatics: A Concept-Based Introduction. 2010. (ENG., Illus.). xiv, 190p. pap. 69.95 *(978-1-4419-4658-4(6)*, 1441946586) Springer.

Mathura, Venkatarajan Kumara, et al. Bioinformatics: A Concept-Based Introduction. 2008. (ENG., Illus.). xiv, 190p. 69.95 *(978-0-387-84869-3(X)*, 038784869X) Springer.

Matthiesen, Rune, ed. Clinical Proteomics: Methods, Applications, & Tools. 2009. (Methods in Molecular Biology Ser.). (Illus.). 332p. 129.00 *(978-1-60327-193-6(7))* Humana Pr.

Matti, Mukhlis. Exploring a Bioinformatics Clustering Algorithm - Methodology, Experiments, Analysis. 2008. 172p. pap. *(978-3-639-03335-9(3))* VDM Verlag Dr. Mueller e.K.

Maulik, Ujjwal, et al. Computational Intelligence & Pattern Analysis in Biology Informatics. 2010. (Wiley Series in Bioinformatics Ser.: 13). (ENG., Illus.). 372p. 116.00 *(978-0-470-58159-9(X)*, Wiley) Wiley, John & Sons, Inc.

—Multiobjective Genetic Algorithms for Clustering: Applications in Data Mining & Bioinformatics. 2011. (ENG., Illus.). xvi, 281p. 69.95 *(978-3-642-16614-3(8)*, 3642166148) Springer.

May, Hope. Error Control Codinng Bioinformatics. 2007. (Synthesis Lectures on Biomedical Engineering Ser.). 40.00 *(978-1-59829-280-0(3))* Morgan & Claypool Pubs.

Mayer, Bernd, ed. Bioinformatics for Omics Data: Methods & Protocols. 2011. (Methods in Molecular Biology Ser.). (ENG., Illus.). xii, 584p. 159.00 *(978-1-61779-026-3(5)*, 1617790265) Humana Pr.

Meller, Jaroslaw & Nowak, Wieslaw, eds. Applications of Statistical & Machine Learning Methods in Bioinformatics. 2007. (Advances in Computational & Systems Biology Ser.: Vol. 1). 128p. pap. 32.95 *(978-0-8204-8793-9(7))* Lang, Peter Publishing, Inc.

Mendelow, Barry, et al, eds. Molecular Medicine for Clinicians. 2009. (ENG.). 518p. pap. 79.95 *(978-1-86814-465-5(8))* Witwatersrand Univ. Pr. Pubns. ZAF. Dist: Transaction Pubs.

Messaoudi, Abdelmonaem. Bioinformatics. 2011. 132p. pap. ***(978-3-8443-1361-1(3))*** Lambert Academic Publishing.

Meyers, Robert A., ed. Systems Biology. 2012. (ENG.). 726p. 216.95 ***(978-3-527-32607-5(3)***, Wiley-VCH) Wiley, John & Sons, Inc.

Mikhael, Joseph. Philosophy of Bioinformatics - Extended Cognition, Analogies & Mechanisms. 2007. 224p. per. *(978-3-8364-5374-5(6))* VDM Verlag Dr. Mueller e.K.

Milazzo, Paolo. Formal Modelling in Systems Biology. 2008. 168p. pap. *(978-3-8364-9483-0(3))* VDM Verlag Dr. Mueller e.K.

Mira, José, et al. Bioinspired Applications in Artificial & Natural Computation: Third International Work-Conference on the Interplay Between Natural & Artificial Computation, IWINAC 2009, Santiago de Compostela, Spain, June 22-26, 2009, Proceedings, Part II. 2009. (Lecture Notes in Computer Science / Theoretical Computer Science & General Issues Ser.). (ENG.). xxi, 532p. pap. 109.00 *(978-3-642-02266-1(9)*, 3642022669) Springer.

Misener, Stephen & Krawetz, Stephen A., eds. Bioinformatics Methods & Protocols. 2010. (Methods in Molecular Biology Ser.). 512p. pap. 109.00 *(978-1-61737-156-1(4)*, 1617371564) Humana Pr.

Mitra, Sushmita, et al. Introduction to Machine Learning & Bioinformatics. 2008. (Chapman & Hall/CRC Computer Science & Data Analysis Ser.). (ENG., Illus.). 384p. (C). 87.95 *(978-1-58488-682-2(X)*, Chapman & Hall/CRC) CRC Pr. LLC.

Miyano, Satoru. Genome Informatics 2007. 2007. (C). 181.00 *(978-1-86094-991-3(6))* Imperial College Pr. GBR. Dist: World Scientific Publishing Co., Inc.

Model, Mitchell & Tisdall, James. Bioinformatics Programming Using Python: Practical Programming for Biological Data. 2009. (Animal Guide Ser.). (ENG., Illus.). 528p. pap. 59.99 *(978-0-596-15450-9(X))* O'Reilly Media, Inc.

Mondaini, Rubem P., ed. Biomat 2006: International Symposium on Mathematical & Computational Biology. (Illus.). 400p. 188.00 *(978-981-270-768-0(9))* World Scientific Publishing Co., Inc.

Munn, Katherine & Smith, Barry, eds. Applied Ontology: An Introduction. 2009. (ENG., Illus.). 342p. 134.00 *(978-3-938793-98-5(8))* Ontos Verlag DEU. Dist: Transaction Pubs.

Nadkarni, Prakash M. Metadata-driven Software Systems in Biomedicine: Designing Systems that can adapt to Changing Knowledge. 2011. (Health Informatics Ser.). (ENG., Illus.). x, 336p. 89.95 ***(978-0-85729-509-5(8)***, 0857295098) Springer.

Najarian, Kayvan. Systems Biology & Bioinformatics: A Computational Approach. 2009. (ENG., Illus.). 190p. (C). 75.95 *(978-1-4200-4650-2(0)*, CRC Press) Taylor & Francis Group GBR. Dist: Taylor & Francis Group.

—Systems Biology & Bioinformatics: A Computational Approach - Solutions Manual. 2008. *(978-1-4398-0508-4(3))* CRC Pr. LLC.

Nakanishi, Shigetada, et al, eds. Systems Biology: The Challenge of Complexity. 2009. (ENG., Illus.). xv, 246p. 189.00 (978-4-431-87703-5(7), 4431877037) Springer.

Nan, Fei. Gamma-Secretase & Its Substrates: A Bioinformatics Approach. 2008. 76p. pap. (978-3-639-10212-3(6)) VDM Verlag Dr. Mueller e.K.

Nielsen, Jens & Jewett, Michael C. Metabolomics: A Powerful Tool in Systems Biology. 2010. (Topics in Current Genetics Ser.). (Illus.). xvi, 284p. pap. 249.00 (978-3-642-09418-7(X), 364209418X) Springer.

Niiranen, Samuli & Ribeiro, André, eds. Information Processing & Biological Systems. 2011. (Intelligent Systems Reference Library). (Illus.). x, 230p. 129.00 (978-3-642-19620-1(9), 3642196209) Springer.

Niknejad, Amir. Applications of Linear Algebra to Dna Microarrays. 2009. 76p. pap. (978-3-639-17994-1(3)) VDM Verlag Dr. Mueller e.K.

Norberto de Souza, Osmar, et al, eds. Advances in Bioinformatics & Computational Biology: 6th Brazilian Symposium on Bioinformatics, BSB 2011, Brasília, Brazil, August 10-12, 2011, Proceedings. 2011. (Lecture Notes in Computer Science / Lecture Notes in Bioinformatics Ser.). (Illus.). ix, 83p. pap. 72.00 (**978-3-642-22824-7(0)**, 3642228240) Springer.

Ochs, Michael F., et al, eds. Biomedical Informatics in Cancer Research. 2010. (ENG., Illus.). xviii, 354p. 179.00 (978-1-4419-5712-2(X), 144195712X) Springer.

Ohya, Masanori & Volovich, I. Mathematical Foundations of Quantum Information & Computation & Its Applications to Nano- & Bio-Systems. 2011. (Theoretical & Mathematical Physics Ser.). (ENG., Illus.). xix, 759p. 169.95 (978-94-007-0170-0(5), 9400701705) Springer.

Okun, Oleg & Skarlas, Lambros. Feature Selection & Ensemble Methods for Bioinformatics: Algorithmic Classification & Implementations. 2011. 350p. 245.00 (978-1-60960-557-5(8), Medical Information Science Reference) IGI Global.

Omatu, Sigeru, et al. Distributed Computing, Artificial Intelligence, Bioinformatics, Soft Computing & Ambient Assisted Living: 10th International Work-Conference on Artificial Neural Networks, IWANN 2009 Workshops, Salamanca, Spain, June 10-12, 2009. Proceedings, Part II. 2009. (Lecture Notes in Computer Science / Theoretical Computer Science & General Issues Ser.). (ENG.). iii, 1304p. pap. 189.00 (978-3-642-02480-1(7), 3642024807) Springer.

Palanivelu, Peramachi. Bioinformatics Analyses of Eukaryotic Mrnas & Industrial Enzymes. 2010. 96p. pap. (978-3-8383-4184-2(8)) Lambert Academic Publishing.

Palsson, Bernhard. Systems Biology: Simulation of Dynamic Network States. 2011. (ENG., Illus.). 332p. 75.00 (978-1-107-00159-6(5)) Cambridge Univ. Pr.

Pan, Yi, et al, eds. Transactions on Computational Systems Biology V. 2006. (Lecture Notes in Computer Science Ser.). (Illus.). 128p. pap. 79.95 (978-3-540-36048-3(4), 3540360484) Springer.

Paradis, Emmanuel. Analysis of Phylogenetics & Evolution with R. 2nd ed. 2011. (Use R! Ser.). (ENG., Illus.). xiv, 386p. pap. 64.95 (**978-1-4614-1742-2(2)**, 1461417422) Springer.

Parida, Laxmi. Pattern Discovery in Bioinformatics: Theory & Algorithms. 2007. (Chapman & Hall/CRC Mathematical & Computational Biology Ser.). (ENG., Illus.). 512p. 89.95 (978-1-58488-549-8(1), C5491, Chapman & Hall/CRC) CRC Pr. LLC.

Parsia, Bijan & Dumontier, Michel. Bio-Ontologies. 2010. (Wiley Series in Bioinformatics Ser.). (ENG.). 400p. 125.00 (978-0-470-50496-3(X), Wiley) Wiley, John & Sons, Inc.

Pattern Recognition in Bioinformatics. 2008. (Lecture Notes in Computer Science / Lecture Notes in Bioinformatics Ser.). spiral bd. 99.00 (978-3-540-88434-7(3), 3540884343) Springer.

Paun, Gheorghe, et al. Membrane Computing: 10th International Workshop, WMC 2009, Curtea de Arges, Romania, August 24-27, 2009, Revised, Selected & Invited Papers. 2010. (Lecture Notes in Computer Science / Theoretical Computer Science & General Issues Ser.). ix, 487p. pap. 99.00 (978-3-642-11466-3(0), 3642114660) Springer.

Peltz, Gary, ed. Computational Genetics & Genomics: Tools for Understanding Disease. 2010. (Illus.). 320p. pap. 135.00 (978-1-61737-409-8(1), 1617374091) Humana Pr.

Petoukhov, Sergey & He, Matthew. Symmetrical Analysis Techniques for Genetic Systems & Bioinformatics: Advanced Patterns & Applications. 2009. 404p. 245.00 (978-1-60566-124-7(4)) IGI Global.

Pettifer, Stephen & Attwood, Teresa K. Bioinformatics & Computer Science. 2014. (ENG.). 304p. 170.00 (978-0-470-03550-4(1), Wiley) Wiley, John & Sons, Inc.

Pevsner, Jonathan. Bioinformatics & Functional Genomics. 2nd ed. 2009. (ENG., Illus.). 992p. pap. 104.95 (978-0-470-08585-1(1), Wiley-Blackwell) Wiley, John & Sons, Inc.

Pevzner, Pavel & Shamir, Ron, eds. Bioinformatics for Biologists. 2011. (ENG., Illus.). 392p. (C). 150.00 (**978-1-107-01146-5(9)**); pap. 60.00 (**978-1-107-64887-6(4)**) Cambridge Univ. Pr.

Pham, Tuân, ed. Computational Biology: Issues & Applications in Oncology. 2009. (Applied Bioinformatics & Biostatistics in Cancer Research Ser.). (Illus.). viii, 309p. 209.00 (978-1-4419-0810-0(2), 1441908102) Springer.

Pham, Tuân & Zhou, Xiaobo, eds. 2009 International Conference on Computational Models for Life Sciences (CMLS-09) 2010. (AIP Conference Proceedings / Mathematical & Statistical Phsyics Ser.). 160p. pap. 114.00 (978-0-7354-0747-3(9), 073540747X, AIP Pr.) Springer.

Pham, Tuan D. Computational Models for Life Sciences - Cmls '07. 2007. (AIP Conference Proceedings / Mathematical & Statistical Phsyics Ser.). (Illus.). xiv, 362p. 149.00 (978-0-7354-0466-3(6)) American Institute of Physics.

Pham, Tuan D., et al, eds. Advanced Computational Methods for Biocomputing & Bioimaging. 2006. 215p. (C). 129.00 (978-1-60021-278-9(6)) Nova Science Pubs., Inc.

Pham, Tuan D., et al, eds. 2011 International Symposium on Computational Models for Life Sciences (CMLS-11) 2011. (AIP Conference Proceedings / Mathematical & Statistical Phsyics Ser.). 356p. pap. 163.00 (**978-0-7354-0931-5(5)**, 0735409315, AIP Pr.) Springer.

Piramanayagam, Shanmughavel. Bioinformatics Applications in Forestry. 2010. 224p. pap. (978-3-639-24747-3(7)) VDM Verlag Dr. Mueller e.K.

Pizzuti, Clara, et al. Evolutionary Computation, Machine Learning & Data Mining in Bioinformatics: 7th European Conference, EvoBIO 2009 Tübingen, Germany, April 15-17, 2009 Proceedings. 2009. (Lecture Notes in Computer Science / Theoretical Computer Science & General Issues Ser.). xii, 203p. pap. 69.95 (978-3-642-01183-2(7)) Springer.

Pizzuti, Clara, et al, eds. Evolutionary Computation, Machine Learning & Data Mining in Bioinformatics: 8th European Conference, EvoBIO 2010, Istanbul, Turkey, April 7-9, 2010, Proceedings. 2010. (Lecture Notes in Computer Science / Theoretical Computer Science & General Issues Ser.). (Illus.). xii, 249p. pap. 72.00 (978-3-642-12210-1(8), 3642122108) Springer.

—Evolutionary Computation, Machine Learning & Data Mining in Bioinformatics: 9th European Conference, EvoBIO 2011, Torino, Italy, April 27-29, 2011, Proceedings. 2011. (Lecture Notes in Computer Science / Theoretical Computer Science & General Issues Ser.). (Illus.). xii, 188p. pap. 72.00 (978-3-642-20388-6(4), 3642203884) Springer.

Plotkin, Gordon, ed. Transactions on Computational Systems Biology VI. 2007. (Lecture Notes in Computer Science Ser.). (Illus.). VII, 247p. pap. 79.95 (978-3-540-45779-4(8), 3540457798) Springer.

Pociot, Flemming. BetaSys: Systems Biology of Regulated Exocytosis in Pancreatic ß-Cells. Pociot, Flemming et al, eds. 2011. (Systems Biology Ser.). (ENG., Illus.). xviii, 558p. 209.00 (978-1-4419-6955-2(1), 1441969551) Springer.

Polanski, Andrzej & Kimmel, Marek. Bioinformatics. 2007. (ENG., Illus.). xviii, 376p. 2010. pap. 89.95 (978-3-642-06332-9(2), 3642063322) 2007. 89.95 (978-3-540-24166-9(3), 3540241663) Springer.

Posada, David, ed. Bioinformatics for DNA Sequence Analysis. 2009. (Methods in Molecular Biology Ser.). (ENG., Illus.). xiv, 354p. 129.00 (978-1-58829-910-9(4), 1588299104) Humana Pr.

Priami, Corrado. Computational Methods in Systems Biology: International Conference, CMSB 2006, Trento, Italy, October 18-19, 2006, Proceedings. 2006. (Lecture Notes in Computer Science Ser.). (Illus.). 322p. pap. 79.95 (978-3-540-46166-1(3), 3540461663) Springer.

—Transactions on Computational Systems Biology: Computational Models for Cell Processes. 2009. (Lecture Notes in Computer Science / Transactions on Computational Systems Biology Ser.). viii, 335p. pap. 113.00 (978-3-642-04185-3(X), 364204185X) Springer.

—Transactions on Computational Systems Biology VII. 2006. (Lecture Notes in Computer Science / Transactions on Computational Systems Biology Ser.). (Illus.). vii, 185p. pap. 79.95 (978-3-540-48837-8(5)) Springer.

Priami, Corrado, et al. Transactions on Computational Systems Biology X. 2008. (Lecture Notes in Computer Science / Transactions on Computational Systems Biology Ser.). vii, 197p. pap. 89.95 (978-3-540-92272-8(5)) Springer.

Priami, Corrado. Transactions on Computational Systems Biology XII: Special Issue on Modeling Methodologies. 2010. (Lecture Notes in Computer Science / Transactions on Computational Systems Biology Ser.). ix, 263p. pap. 99.00 (978-3-642-11711-4(2), 3642117112) Springer.

Priami, Corrado, ed. Transactions on Computational Systems Biology IX. 2008. (Lecture Notes in Bioinformatics Ser.). (Illus.). 152p. pap. 79.95 (978-3-540-88764-5(4)) Springer.

Prokop, Ales & Michelson, Seth. Systems Biology in Biotech & Pharma: A Changing Paradigm. 2012. (SpringerBriefs in Pharmaceutical Science & Drug Development Ser.). (ENG., Illus.). xviii, 127p. pap. 49.95 (**978-94-007-2848-6(4)**, 9400728484) Springer.

Przytycka, Teresa & Sagot, Marie-France, eds. Algorithms in Bioinformatics: 11th International Workshop, WABI 2011, Saarbrücken, Germany, September 5-7, 2011, Proceedings. 2011. (Lecture Notes in Computer Science / Lecture Notes in Bioinformatics Ser.). (ENG., Illus.). 378p. pap. 83.00 (**978-3-642-23037-0(7)**, 3642230377) Springer.

Qazi, Wajahat & Ahmed, Khalil. MacHine Learning in Bioinformatics. 2010. 132p. pap. (978-3-639-25372-6(8)) VDM Verlag Dr. Mueller e.K.

Raducanu, Razvan & Xu, Chunxiao. Proceedings of the 2011 3rd International Conference on Future Computer & Communication (ICFCC 2011) Iasi, Romania, June 3-5, 2011. 2011. (Illus.). 503p. (**978-0-7918-5971-1(1)**) American Society of Mechanical Engineers, The.

Rajapakse, Jagath C., et al. Pattern Recognition in Bioinformatics: International Workshop, PRIB 2007, Singapore, October 1-2, 2007, Proceedings. 2007. (Lecture Notes in Computer Science / Lecture Notes in Bioinformatics Ser.). xviii, 410p. pap. 89.95 (978-3-540-75285-1(4), 3540752854) Springer.

Rajapakse, Jagath Chandana, et al. Pattern Recognition in Bioinformatics: International Workshop, PRIB 2006, Hong Kong, China, August 20, 2006, Proceedings. 2006. (Lecture Notes in Computer Science Ser.). (Illus.). 166p. pap. 69.95 (978-3-540-37446-6(9), 3540374469) Springer.

Rajasekaran, S. Bioinformatics & Computational Biology: First International Conference, BICoB 2009, New Orleans, la, USA, April 8-10, 2009, Proceedings. 2009. (Lecture Notes in Computer Science / Lecture Notes in Bioinformatics Ser.). xiv, 450p. pap. 99.00 (978-3-642-00726-2(0)) Springer.

Ramdayal, Kavisha. Analytical Methods in Bioinformatics. 2010. 84p. pap. (978-3-8383-8910-3(7)) Lambert Academic Publishing.

Ramsden, Jeremy. Bioinformatics: An Introduction. 2nd ed. 2009. (Computational Biology Ser.). (ENG., Illus.). xvi, 272p. 69.95 (978-1-84800-256-2(4)) Springer.

Ranganathan, Shoba, et al, eds. Immunoinformatics. 2007. (Immunomics Reviews: Ser.). (Illus.). 200p. 159.00 (978-0-387-72967-1(4)) Springer.

Rangwala, Huzefa & Karypis, George, eds. Introduction to Protein Structure Prediction: Methods & Algorithms. 2010. (Wiley Series in Bioinformatics Ser.: 14). (ENG., Illus.). 516p. 132.00 (978-0-470-47059-6(3), Wiley) Wiley, John & Sons, Inc.

Ranka, Sanjay, et al. Contemporary Computing: Second International Conference, IC3 2009, Noida, India, August 17-19, 2009. Proceedings. 2009 (Communications in Computer & Information Science Ser.). (ENG.). xviii, 662p. pap. 139.00 (978-3-642-03546-3(9), 3642035469) Springer.

Rao, C. R., et al. Bioinformatics: High Performance Parallel Computer Architectures. 2012. (Handbook of Statistics Ser.: 28). (ENG.). 712p. 250.00 (**978-0-444-51875-0(4)**, North Holland) Elsevier Science & Technology Bks.

Rao, C. R., ed. Bioinformatics: High Performance Parallel Computer Architectures. 2010. (Embedded Multi-Core Systems Ser.). (ENG., Illus.). 370p. 129.95 (978-1-4398-1488-8(0), CRC Press) Taylor & Francis Group GBR. Dist: Taylor & Francis Group.

Rattray, Magnus, et al, eds. Learning & Inference in Computational Systems Biology. 2009. (Computational Molecular Biology Ser.). (ENG., Illus.). 376p. (gr. 17). 42.00 (978-0-262-01386-4(X)) MIT Pr.

Revett, Kenneth. Bioinformatics for Computer Science: Foundations in Molecular Biology. 2012. 270p. pap. (**978-1-907568-22-0(0)**, Biohealthcare Publishing (Oxford) Limited) Woodhead Publishing Ltd.

Rigden, Daniel John. From Protein Structure to Function with Bioinformatics. 2008. (Illus.). xvi, 328p. 109.00 (978-1-4020-9057-8(9)) Springer.

Rigoutsos, Isidore & Stephanopoulos, Gregory, eds. Networks, Models, & Applications, 2 vols. 2006. (Series in Systems Biology Ser.). (ENG., Illus.). 366p. 75.00 (978-0-19-530080-2(7)) Oxford Univ. Pr., Inc.

—Systems Biology: Volume I: Genomics, 2 vols., Vol. 1. 2006. (Series in Systems Biology Ser.). (ENG., Illus.). 336p. 75.00 (978-0-19-530081-9(5)) Oxford Univ. Pr., Inc.

Riley, Michael C. Knowledge Discovery in Bioinformatics. 2009. 368p. pap. (978-3-639-19508-8(6)) VDM Verlag Dr. Mueller e.K.

Rissanen, Jorma, et al, eds. Information Theoretic Methods for Bioinformatics. 2008. 132p. per. 21.00 (978-977-454-014-1(X)) Hindawi Publishing Corp.

Rizzo, Riccardo & Lisboa, Paulo J. G., eds. Computational Intelligence Methods for Bioinformatics & Biostatistics: 7th International Meeting, CIBIB 2010, Palermo, Italy, September 16-18, 2010, Revised Selected Papers. 2011. (Lecture Notes in Computer Science / Lecture Notes in Bioinformatics Ser.). (ENG., Illus.). xiii, 288p. pap. 83.00 (**978-3-642-21945-0(4)**, 3642219454) Springer.

Robinson, Peter N. & Bauer, Sebastian. Introduction to Bio-Ontologies. 2011. (Chapman & Hall/CRC Mathematical & Computational Biology Ser.). (ENG., Illus.). 517p. 79.95 (978-1-4398-3665-1(5), Chapman & Hall/CRC) CRC Pr. LLC.

Rocha, Armando Freitas da, et al. The Brain: Fuzzy Arithmetic to Quantum Computing: Fuzzy Arithmetic to Quantum Computing. 2010. (Studies in Fuzziness & Soft Computing Ser.). vii, 227p. pap. 199.00 (978-3-642-06005-2(6), 3642060056) Springer.

Rocha, Miguel P., et al, eds. Advances in Bioinformatics: 4th International Workshop on Practical Applications of Computational Biology & Bioinformatics 2010 (IWPACBB 2010) 2010. (Advances in Intelligent & Soft Computing Ser.). 240p. pap. 219.00 (978-3-642-13213-1(8), 3642132138) Springer.

—5th International Conference on Practical Applications of Computational Biology & Bioinformatics. 2011. (Advances in Intelligent & Soft Computing Ser.). (Illus.). xvi, 400p. pap. 259.00 (978-3-642-19913-4(5), 3642199135) Springer.

Rodriguez-Ezpeleta, Naiara, et al, eds. Bioinformatics for High Throughput Sequencing. 2011. (ENG., Illus.). xi, 255p. 189.00 (**978-1-4614-0781-2(8)**, 1461407818) Springer.

Rosenberg, Michael. Sequence Alignment: Methods, Models, Concepts, & Strategies. 2011. (ENG.). 360p. pap. 39.95 (978-0-520-27131-9(9)) Univ. of California Pr.

Rosenberg, Michael S. Sequence Alignment: Methods, Models, Concepts, & Strategies. Rosenberg, Michael S., ed. 2009. (ENG., Illus.). 288p. 60.00 (978-0-520-25697-2(2)) Univ. of California Pr.

Royston, Patrick & Lambert, Paul C. Flexible Parametric Survival Analysis Using Stata: Beyond the Cox Model. 2011. (ENG.). 339p. pap. 79.95 (978-1-59718-079-5(3), Stata Pr.) StataCorp LP.

Sagot, Marie-France & Walter, Maria Emília M. T. Advances in Bioinformatics & Computational Biology: Second Brazilian Symposium on Bioinformatics, BSB 2007, Angra dos Reis, Brazil, August 29-31, 2007, Proceedings. 2007. (Lecture Notes in Computer Science / Lecture Notes in Bioinformatics Ser.). xii, 177p. pap. 79.95 (978-3-540-73730-8(8)) Springer.

Sakakibara, Yasubumi. Genome Informatics 2009: Proceedings of the 20th International Conference. 2009. (Illus.). 240p. 122.00 (978-1-84816-562-5(5)) Imperial College Pr. GBR. Dist: World Scientific Publishing Co., Inc.

Salehi, Sara. Automated Biomedical Text Fragmentation. 2009. 120p. pap. (978-3-639-21627-1(X)) VDM Verlag Dr. Mueller e.K.

Salzberg, Steven L. & Warnow, Tandy. Algorithms in Bioinformatics: 9th International Workshop, WABI 2009, Philadelphia, USA, September 12-13, 2009. Proceedings. 2009. (Lecture Notes in Computer Science / Lecture Notes in Bioinformatics Ser.). (Illus.). xi, 430p. pap. 99.00 (978-3-642-04240-9(6), 3642042406) Springer.

Samuelsson, Tore. Genomics & Bioinformatics: An Introduction to Programming Tools. 2012. (ENG., Illus.). 300p. (C). 120.00 (**978-1-107-00856-4(5)**); pap. 50.00 (**978-1-107-40124-2(0)**) Cambridge Univ. Pr.

Sankoff, David, et al, eds. Proceedings of the 5th Asia-Pacific Bioinformatics Conference. 2007. (Series on Advances in Bioinformatics & Computational Biology). (Illus.). 374p. 150.00 (978-1-86094-783-4(2)) Imperial College Pr. GBR. Dist: World Scientific Publishing Co., Inc.

Sarkar. An Introduction to Biodiversity Informatics. 2011. 79.00 (978-981-283-680-9(2)); pap. 39.00 (978-981-283-452-2(4)) World Scientific Publishing Co., Inc.

Sawai, Hidefumi, ed. Biological Functions for Information & Communication Technologies: Theory & Inspiration. 2011. (Studies in Computational Intelligence Ser.). Orig. Title: Life & ICT - Inspiring Life-like functions into ICT. (Illus.). xi, 280p. 129.00 (978-3-642-15101-9(9), 3642151019) Springer.

Schapire, Robert & Freund, Yoav. Boosting: Models, Applications & Extensions. 2010. (ENG., Illus.). 288p. 69.95 (978-1-4398-1415-4(5), Chapman & Hall/CRC) CRC Pr. LLC.

Seckbach, Joseph & Rubin, Eitan, eds. The New Avenues in Bioinformatics. 2010. (Cellular Origin, Life in Extreme Habitats & Astrobiology Ser.). xxvi, 281p. pap. 269.00 (978-90-481-6694-7(2), 9048166942) Springer.

Seiffert, Udo, et al, eds. Bioinformatics Using Computational Intelligence Paradigms. 2010. (Studies in Fuzziness & Soft Computing Ser.). viii, 216p. pap. 169.00 (978-3-642-06173-8(7), 3642061737) Springer.

Selzer, Paul M., et al. Applied Bioinformatics: An Introduction. 2008. (Illus.). 287p. pap. 49.95 (978-3-540-72799-6(X), 354072799X) Springer.

Sengupta, Anirvan M. Modeling Biomolecular Networks: An Introduction to Systems Biology. 2012. (ENG., Illus.). 208p. 69.50 (978-0-19-856804-9(5)) Oxford Univ. Pr., Inc.

Sensen, Christoph W. Advanced Imaging in Biology & Medicine: Technology, Software Environments, Applications. 2008. (ENG., Illus.). xii, 445p. 219.00 (978-3-540-68992-8(3), 3540689923) Springer.

Sharma, Kal Renganathan. Bioinformatics: Sequence Alignment & Markov Models. 2008. (ENG., Illus.). 320p. (C). 115.00 (978-0-07-159306-9(3), 0071593063) McGraw-Hill Professional Publishing.

Sharma, Naveen & Rathore, Madhu. Emerging Trends: Applied Biotechnology. 2011. 184p. pap. (**978-3-8443-9630-0(8)**) Lambert Academic Publishing.

Shatkay, Hagit & Craven, Mark. Mining the Biomedical Literature. 2012. (**978-0-262-01769-5(5)**) MIT Pr.

Shen, Shiyi. Theory & Mathematical Methods in Bioinformatics. 2010. (Biological & Medical Physics, Biomedical Engineering Ser.). (Illus.). xvi, 445p. pap. 219.00 (978-3-642-09429-3(5), 3642094295) Springer.

Shen, Shiyi & Tuszynski, J. A. Theory & Mathematical Methods in Bioinformatics. 2008. (Biological & Medical Physics, Biomedical Engineering Ser.). (Illus.). XVI, 445p. (C). 219.00 (978-3-540-74890-8(3), 3540748903) Springer.

Shin. Large-Scale Genome Sequence Processing. 2006. (Illus.). xii, 236p. 97.00 (978-1-86094-635-6(6)) World Scientific Publishing Co., Inc.

Shoshani, Arie & Rotem, Doron. Scientific Data Management: Challenges, Existing Technology, & Deployment. 2009. (Chapman & Hall/CRC Computational Science Ser.). (ENG., Illus.). 590p. 89.95 (978-1-4200-6980-8(2), Chapman & Hall/CRC) CRC Pr. LLC.

Sidhu, Amandeep S., et al, eds. Biomedical Data & Applications. 2009. (Studies in Computational Intelligence Ser.). (Illus.). x, 346p. 199.00 (978-3-642-02192-3(1), 3642021921) Springer.

Simon, Matthew. Emergent Computation: Emphasizing Bioinformatics. 2010. (Biological & Medical Physics, Biomedical Engineering Ser.). (Illus.). xiv, 423p. pap. 139.00 (978-1-4419-1963-2(5), 1441919635) Springer.

Skiadas, Christos H., ed. Advances in Data Analysis: Theory & Applications to Reliability & Inference, Data Mining, Bioinformatics, Lifetime Data, & Neural Networks. 2009. (Statistics for Industry & Technology Ser.). (ENG., Illus.). xxi, 346p. 159.00 (978-0-8176-4798-8(8), 0817647988) Birkhauser Verlag AG CHE. Dist: Springer.

Slezak, Dominik, et al. Bio-Science & Bio-Technology: International Conference, BSBT 2009 Held as Part of the Future Generation Information Technology Conference, FGIT 2009 Jeju Island, Korea, December 10-12, 2009 Proceedings. 2009. (Communications in Computer & Information Science Ser.). xii, 151p. pap. 89.95 (978-3-642-10615-6(3), 3642106153) Springer.

Smolinski, Tomasz G. Applications of Computational Intelligence in Biology. 2008. (Studies in Computational Intelligence Ser.). 239.00 (978-3-540-78533-0(7)) Springer.

Smolinski, Tomasz G., et al, eds. Applications of Computational Intelligence in Biology: Current Trends & Open Problems. 2010. (Studies in Computational Intelligence Ser.). (Illus.). xxvi, 428p. pap. 239.00 (978-3-642-09730-0(8), 3642097308) Springer.

—Computational Intelligence in Biomedicine & Bioinformatics: Current Trends & Applications. 2010. (Studies in Computational Intelligence Ser.). (Illus.). xxiv, 432p. pap. 199.00 (978-3-642-08969-5(0), 3642089690) Springer.

Solan, Zach. Unsupervised Learning of Natural Languages. 2009. 128p. pap. (978-3-639-14508-3(9)) VDM Verlag Dr. Mueller e.K.

Sorin, Draghici. Bioinf Dat Desgn Impl & Usge. 2009. (Illus.). 79.95 (978-1-58488-497-2(5)) CRC Pr. LLC.

Sperschneider, Volker. Bioinformatics: Problem Solving Paradigms. (ENG., Illus.). xviii, 290p. 2010. pap. 69.95 (978-3-642-09726-3(X), 364209726X) 2008. 69.95 (978-3-540-78505-7(1), 3540785051) Springer.

Splendiani, Andrea & Romano, Paolo. Semantic Web for the Life Sciences. 2012. (Chapman & Hall/CRC Mathematical & Computational Biology Ser.). (Illus.). 356p. 79.95 (978-1-4398-7360-1(7), Chapman & Hall/CRC) CRC Pr. LLC.

St. Clair, Caroline, et al. Exploring Bioinformatics: A Project-Based Approach. 2009. 360p. pap. 125.95 (978-0-7637-5829-5(9)) Jones & Bartlett Learning, LLC.

Stewart, C. Neal, ed. Plant Biotechnology & Genetics: Principles, Techniques & Applications. 2008. (ENG., Illus.). 416p. 117.00 (978-0-470-04381-3(4), Wiley-Interscience) Wiley, John & Sons, Inc.

Stojanovic, Nikola, ed. Computational Genomics: Current Methods. 2007. (ENG., Illus.). 200p. (C). 244.00 (978-1-904933-30-4(0), Taylor & Francis) Taylor & Francis Group GBR. Dist: Taylor & Francis Group.

Stolovitzky, Gustavo. The Challenges of Systems Biology: Community Efforts to Harness Biological Complexity. Califano, Andrea & Kahlem, Pascal, eds. 2009. (Annals of the New York Academy of Sciences Ser.: 9). (ENG., Illus.). 300p. pap. 134.95 (978-1-57331-751-1(9), Wiley-Blackwell) Wiley, John & Sons, Inc.

Structural Bioinformatics. 2011. (C). 83.95 (978-1-4200-1179-1(0), Chapman & Hall/CRC) CRC Pr. LLC.

Suh, Sang C., et al. Biomedical Engineering: Health Care Systems, Technology & Techniques. 2011. (Illus.). xiii, 285p. E-Book (978-1-4614-0116-2(X)) Springer.

Sundes, Joakim, et al. Computing the Electrical Activity in the Heart. 2006. (Monographs in Computational Science & Engineering: Vol. 1). (Illus.). xii, 318p. 129.00 (978-3-540-33432-3(7), 3540334327) Springer.

Sung, Wing-Kin. Algorithms in Bioinformatics: A Practical Introduction. 2009. (Chapman & Hall/CRC Mathematical & Computational Biology Ser.). (ENG., Illus.). 407p. (C). 87.95 (978-1-4200-7033-0(9), Chapman & Hall/CRC) CRC Pr. LLC.

Systems Bioinformatics: An Engineering Case-Based Approach. 2007. (Bioinformatics & Biomedical Imaging Ser.: Vol. 29). (Illus.). 386p. 99.00 incl. cd-rom (978-1-59693-124-4(8)) Artech Hse., Inc.

Systems Biology & Bioinformatics. 2011. (C). 71.95 (978-1-4200-4651-9(9), CRC Press) Taylor & Francis Group GBR. Dist: Taylor & Francis Group.

Tannier, Eric. Comparative Genomics: International Workshop, RECOMB-CG 2010, Ottawa, Canada, October 9-11, 2010, Proceedings. 2010. (Lecture Notes in Computer Science / Lecture Notes in Bioinformatics Ser.). xii, 303p. pap. 83.00 (978-3-642-16180-3(4), 3642161804) Springer.

Tesler, Glenn & Durand, Dannie. Comparative Genomics: RECOMB 2007, International Workshop, RECOMB-CG 2007, San Diego, CA, USA, September 16-18, 2007, Proceedings. 2007. (Lecture Notes in Computer Science / Lecture Notes in Bioinformatics Ser.). xii, 193p. pap. 69.95 (978-3-540-74959-2(4)) Springer.

Thacker, Eugene. The Global Genome: Biotechnology, Politics, & Culture. 2006. (Leonardo Bks.). (ENG., Illus.). 464p. (gr. 17). per. 27.95 (978-0-262-70116-7(2)) MIT Pr.

Thapar, Vishal. Applied Algorithms for Bioinformatics Problems. 2009. 136p. pap. (978-3-639-19788-4(7)) VDM Verlag Dr. Mueller e.K.

Torshin, Ivan Y. Physiology & Medicine: Bioinformatics in the Post-Genomic ERA. 2007. (Bioinformatics in the Post-Genomic ERA Ser.). 302p. 89.00 (978-1-60021-752-4(4)) Nova Science Pubs., Inc.

Tramontano, Anna. Introduction to Bioinformatics. 2006. (Mathematical & Computational Biology Ser.). (ENG., Illus.). 192p. (C). per. 67.95 (978-1-58488-569-6(6), Chapman & Hall/CRC) CRC Pr. LLC.

Transactions on Computational Systems Biology VIII. 2007. (Lecture Notes in Bioinformatics Ser.). (Illus.). 101p. pap. 79.95 (978-3-540-76638-4(3)) Springer.

Trent, R. J. Clinical Bioinformatics. (Methods in Molecular Medicine Ser.: Vol. 141). (Illus.). 2008. xi, 382p. (978-1-60327-148-6(1)) 2007. 382p. 129.00 (978-1-58829-791-4(8)) Humana Pr.

Trent, Ronald J. A., ed. Clinical Bioinformatics. 2010. (Methods in Molecular Medicine Ser.). (Illus.). xi, 382p. pap. 129.00 (978-1-61737-781-5(3), 1617377813) Humana Pr.

Tretter, Felix, et al, eds. Systems Biology in Psychiatric Research: From High-Throughput Data to Mathematical Modeling. 2010. (ENG., Illus.). 378p. 179.95 (978-3-527-32503-0(4), Wiley-VCH) Wiley, John & Sons, Inc.

Triggle, David J. & Taylor, John B. Comprehensive Medicinal Chemistry II, 8 vols., Set. 2006. (ENG., Illus.). 7200p. 7030.00 (978-0-08-044513-7(6), Elsevier Science) Elsevier Science & Technology Bks.

Tuteja, Renu. Bioinformatics: Genome Bioinformatics & Computational Biology. 2012. (978-1-62100-913-9(0)) Nova Science Pubs., Inc.

Tuyls, Karl, et al, eds. Knowledge Discovery & Emergent Complexity in Bioinformatics: First International Workshop, KDECB 2006, Ghent, Belgium, May 10, 2006, Revised Selected Papers. 2007. (Lecture Notes in Computer Science Ser.). (Illus.). 182p. per. 69.95 (978-3-540-71036-3(1), 3540710361) Springer.

Tveito, Aslak, et al, eds. Simula Research Laboratory: By Thinking Constantly about It. 2009. (ENG., Illus.). x, 656p. 119.00 (978-3-642-01155-9(1), 3642011551) Springer.

Uchida, Shizuka. Annotating New Genes: From in Silico Screening to Validations by Experiments. 2012. 200p. 165.00 (978-1-907568-68-8(9)) Woodhead Publishing Ltd. GBR. Dist: Ingram Pub. Services.

Ussery, David W., et al. Computing for Comparative Microbial Genomics: Bioinformatics for Microbiologists. 2009. (Computational Biology Ser.). (Illus.). 282p. 89.95 (978-1-84800-254-8(8)) Springer.

Valiente, Gabriel. Combinatorial Pattern Matching Algorithms in Computational Biology using Perl & R. 2009. (Chapman & Hall/CRC Mathematical & Computational Biology Ser.). (ENG., Illus.). 368p. 92.95 (978-1-4200-6973-0(X), Chapman & Hall/CRC) CRC Pr. LLC.

Van Helden, Jacques. Statistics Applied to Bioinformatics. 2011. 400p. 130.00 (978-0-19-922675-7(X)); pap. 60.00 (978-0-19-922676-4(8)) Oxford Univ. Pr., Inc.

Vanneschi, Leonardo, et al. Genetic Programming: 12th European Conference, EuroGP 2009 Tübingen, Germany, April, 15-17, 2009 Proceedings. 2009. (Lecture Notes in Computer Science / Theoretical Computer Science & General Issues Ser.). xiii, 363p. pap. 79.95 (978-3-642-01180-1(2)) Springer.

Villmann, Thomas, et al. Similarity-Based Clustering: Recent Developments & Biomedical Applications. 2009. (Lecture Notes in Computer Science / Lecture Notes in Artificial Intelligence Ser.). (ENG., Illus.). xi, 203p. pap. 69.95 (978-3-642-01804-6(1), 3642018041) Springer.

Voit, Eberhard. A First Course in Systems Biology. 2012. (ENG., Illus.). 496p. (C). pap. 125.00 (978-0-8153-4467-4(8), Garland Science) Taylor & Francis Group.

Wang, Edwin, ed. Cancer Systems Biology. 2010. (Chapman & Hall/CRC Mathematical & Computational Biology Ser.). (ENG., Illus.). 455p. 89.95 (978-1-4398-1185-6(7), CRC Press) Taylor & Francis Group GBR. Dist: Taylor & Francis Group.

Wang, Jason T. L., et al, eds. Data Mining in Bioinformatics. 2010. (Advanced Information & Knowledge Processing Ser.). (Illus.). xi, 340p. pap. 139.00 (978-1-84996-894-2(2), 1849968942) Springer.

Wang, Jason T. L. & Herbert, Katherine G. Bioinformatics Database Systems. 2011. (Illus.). 300p. 79.95 (978-1-4398-1247-1(0), CRC Press) Taylor & Francis Group GBR. Dist: Taylor & Francis Group.

Wang, Junbai, et al, eds. Next Generation Microarray Bioinformatics: Methods & Protocols. 2011. (Methods in Molecular Biology Ser.). (ENG., Illus.). xvi, 401p. 139.00 (978-1-61779-399-8(X), 161779399X) Humana Pr.

Wang, Lin, et al. New Antibody Microarray Tube for Cellular Localization & Signaling Pathways. 2008. (Illus.). 160p. 219.00 (978-3-540-74340-8(5)) Springer.

Wehrens, Ron. Chemometrics with R: Multivariate data analysis in the natural sciences & life Sciences. 2011. (Use R Ser.). (Illus.). xiv, 285p. pap. 59.95 (978-3-642-17840-5(5), 3642178405) Springer.

Westerhoff, Hans & Hayes, Neil, eds. Methods in Systems Biology. 2011. (ENG.). 668p. 187.00 (978-0-12-385118-5(1), Academic Pr.) Elsevier Science & Technology Bks.

Westhead, David & Hodgman, Charlie. Bioinformatics. 2nd rev. ed. 2008. (Instant Notes Ser.). (Illus.). 300p. 40.00 (978-0-415-39494-9(5), Taylor & Francis) Taylor & Francis Group GBR. Dist: Taylor & Francis Group.

Wilusz, Jeffrey. Post-Transcriptional Gene Regulation. 2008. (Methods in Molecular Biology Ser.). 129.00 (978-1-58829-783-9(7)) Humana Pr.

Wilusz, Jeffrey, ed. Post-Transcriptional Gene Regulation. 2010. (Methods in Molecular Biology Ser.). (Illus.). xviii, 318p. pap. 129.00 (978-1-61737-776-1(7), 1617377767) Humana Pr.

Winters-Hilt, Stephen. MacHine-Learning Based Sequence Analysis, Bioinformatics & Nanopore Transduction Detection. 2011. 434p. 37.00 (978-1-257-64525-1(0)) Lulu Enterprises Inc.

Wittmann, Christoph. Biosystems Engineering II: Linking Cellular Networks & Bioprocesses, 2 vols. Wittmann, Christoph & Krull, Rainer, eds. 2010. (Advances in Biochemical Engineering Biotechnology Ser.). (Illus.). xiii, 166p. 299.00 (978-3-642-13865-2(9), 3642138659) Springer.

Wong, Stephen & Li, Chung-Sheng, eds. Life Science Data Mining. 2006. (SCIENCE, ENGINEERING, & BIOLOGY INFORMATICS Ser.). (Illus.). 370p. 121.00 (978-981-270-064-3(1)); pap. 69.00 (978-981-270-065-0(X)) World Scientific Publishing Co., Inc.

Wong, Stephen T. C. & Zhou, Xiaobo. Computational Systems Bioinformatics: Methods & Biomedical Applications. 2008. (Illus.). 387p. 96.00 (978-981-270-704-8(2)) World Scientific Publishing Co., Inc.

Wu. Lecture Notes on Computational Struc... 2008. (Illus.). xii, 230p. 121.00 (978-981-270-589-1(9)) World Scientific Publishing Co., Inc.

Wu, Cathy H. & Chen, Chuming. Bioinformatics for Comparative Proteomics. 2011. (Illus.). xiii, 387p. E-Book (978-1-60761-977-2(6)) Humana Pr.

Wu, Cathy H. & Chen, Chuming, eds. Bioinformatics for Comparative Proteomics. 2010. (Methods in Molecular Biology Ser.). (ENG., Illus.). xiii, 387p. 139.00 (978-1-60761-976-5(8), 1607619768) Humana Pr.

Wu, J. L., et al, eds. Complex Medical Engineering. 2010. (ENG., Illus.). xii, 619p. pap. 209.00 (978-4-431-99816-7(0), 4431998160) Springer.

Wu, Weili & Daescu, Ovidiu, eds. Combinatorial Optimization & Applications: 4th International Conference, COCOA 2010, Kailua-Kona, HI, USA, December 18-20, 2010, Proceedings, Part II. 2010. (Lecture Notes in Computer Science / Theoretical Computer Science & General Issues Ser.). xvi, 416p. pap. 95.00 (978-3-642-17460-5(4), 3642174604) Springer.

Xia, Xuhua. Bioinformatics & the Cell: Modern Computational Approaches in Genomics, Proteomics & Transcriptomics. (ENG., Illus.). xvi, 352p. 2010. pap. 159.00 (978-1-4419-4391-0(9), 1441943919) 2007. 159.00 (978-0-387-71336-6(0), 0387713360) Springer.

Xu. Applications of Fuzzy Logic in Bioinformatics. 2008. (Illus.). xix, 225p. 112.00 (978-1-84816-258-7(8)) Imperial College Pr. GBR. Dist: World Scientific Publishing Co., Inc.

—Computational Systems Bioinformatics: CSB 2008 Conference Proceedings, Volume 7: Stanford University, USA, 26-29 August 2008. 2008. (Illus.). xiii, 340p. 142.00 (978-1-84816-263-1(4)) Imperial College Pr. GBR. Dist: World Scientific Publishing Co., Inc.

—Computational Systems Bioinformatics(V4) 2006. (Illus.). xvi, 400p. 164.00 (978-1-86094-700-1(X)) World Scientific Publishing Co., Inc.

Xu, Hua. Data Analysis for Mass Spectrometry-Based Proteomics: Novel Data Analysis Methods & Algorithms forIdentification of Peptides & Proteins by Use ofTandem Mass Spectrometry. 2008. (Illus.). 236p. pap. (978-3-639-10525-4(7)) VDM Verlag Dr. Mueller e.K.

Xu, Ying, et al, eds. Computational Methods for Protein Structure Prediction & Modeling: Volume 2: Structure Prediction. 2010. (Biological & Medical Physics, Biomedical Engineering Ser.). (Illus.). xx, 322p. pap. 209.00 (978-1-4419-2206-9(7), 1441922067) Springer.

Yang, Haiqin, et al. Sparse Learning under Regularization Framework. 2011. 152p. pap. (978-3-8443-3030-4(5)) Lambert Academic Publishing.

Yang, Zheng Rong. Machine Learning Approaches to Bioinformatics, Vol. 5. 2010. (Illus.). 336p. 107.00 (978-981-4287-30-2(X)) World Scientific Publishing Co., Inc.

Ye, Shui Qing. Bioinformatics: A Practical Approach. 2007. (Chapman & Hall/CRC Mathematical & Computational Biology Ser.). (ENG., Illus.). 648p. 89.95 (978-1-58488-810-9(5), Chapman & Hall/CRC) CRC Pr. LLC.

Young, Paul G., et al. Exploring Genomes: Web-Based Bioinformatics Tutorials. 9th rev. ed. 2007. (ENG.). 51p. (C). pap. 20.95 (978-0-7167-0178-0(9)) Freeman, W. H. & Co.

Yu, Shi, et al. Kernel-based Data Fusion for Machine Learning: Methods & Applications in Bioinformatics & Text Mining. 2011. (Studies in Computational Intelligence Ser.). (Illus.). xiv, 214p. 129.00 (978-3-642-19405-4(2), 3642194052) Springer.

Zelkowitz, Marvin, ed. Advances in Computers: Computational Biology & Bioinformatics. 2006. (ENG.). 334p. 171.00 (978-0-12-012168-7(9), Academic Pr.) Elsevier Science & Technology Bks.

Zeng, Erliang. Bioinformatic Analysis for Exploring Biological Relationships. 2009. 202p. pap. (978-3-639-18192-0(1)) VDM Verlag Dr. Mueller e.K.

Zhang, Aidong. Advanced Analysis of Gene Expression Microarray Data. 2006. (Illus.). 339p. 98.00 (978-981-256-645-4(7)) World Scientific Publishing Co., Inc.

Zhang, Shuxing. Structure/Ligand-Based Drug Design & Structure Bioinformatics. 2009. 116p. pap. (978-3-639-16415-2(6)) VDM Verlag Dr. Mueller e.K.

Zhang, Yanqing & Rajapakse, Jagath C. Machine Learning in Bioinformatics. 2008. (Wiley Series in Bioinformatics Ser.: 4). (ENG., Illus.). 456p. 124.00 (978-0-470-11662-3(5), Wiley) Wiley, John & Sons, Inc.

Zhou, Jie. Complex Sciences: First International Conference, Complex 2009, Shanghai, China, February 23-25, 2009. Revised Papers. 2009. (Lecture Notes of the Institute for Computer Sciences, Social-Informatics & Telecommunications Engineering Ser.). (ENG.). xxxi, 1189p. pap. 169.00 (978-3-642-02465-8(3), 3642024653) Springer.

—Complex Sciences: First International Conference, Complex 2009, Shanghai, China, February 23-25, 2009. Revised Papers, Part II. 2009. (Lecture Notes of the Institute for Computer Sciences, Social-Informatics & Telecommunications Engineering Ser.). (ENG.). xxxii, 1236p. pap. 171.00 (978-3-642-02468-9(8), 3642024688) Springer.

Zhu, Yangyong & Xiong, Yun. Sheng Wu Shu Ju Zheng He Yu Wa Jue. 2009. (CHI., Illus.). (978-7-309-06614-2(6)) Fudan Univ. Pr.

Zomaya, Albert Y. & Talbi, El-Ghazali, eds. Grid Computing for Bioinformatics & Computational Biology. 2007. (Wiley Series in Bioinformatics Ser.: 1). (ENG., Illus.). 392p. 153.00 (978-0-471-78409-8(5), Wiley-Interscience) Wiley, John & Sons, Inc.

Zvelebil, Marketa J. & Baum, Jeremy O. Understanding Bioinformatics. 2007. (ENG., Illus.). 798p. 124.00 (978-0-8153-4024-9(9), Garland Science) Taylor & Francis Group.

2007 1st International Conference on Bioinformatics & Biomedical Engineering. 2007. pap. 340.00 (978-1-4244-1119-1(X), 07EX1744) IEEE.

BIOINORGANIC CHEMISTRY

Cowan, J. A. Bioinorganic Chemistry: An Introduction. 3rd ed. 2008. 535p. 99.95 (978-0-471-78408-1(7), Wiley-VCH) Wiley, John & Sons, Inc.

Crabb, Eleanor. Metals & Life. 2009. (ENG., Illus.). 232p. (C). pap. 40.00 (978-1-84973-059-4(8)) Royal Society of Chemistry, The GBR. Dist: Ingram Pub. Services.

Crichton, Robert. Biological Inorganic Chemistry: A New Introduction to Molecular Structure & Function. 2nd ed. 2012. (ENG., Illus.). 472p. pap. 94.95 (978-0-444-53782-9(1)) Elsevier Science & Technology Bks.

Gomes, Claudio M. & Wittung-Stafshede, Pernilla, eds. Protein Folding & Metal Ions. 2010. (ENG., Illus.). 308p. 149.95 (978-1-4398-0964-8(X), CRC Press) Taylor & Francis Group GBR. Dist: Taylor & Francis Group.

Hughes, Jason G. & Robinson, Alton J., eds. Inorganic Biochemistry: Research Progress. 2008. (Illus.). 345p. (C). 185.00 (978-1-60456-708-3(2)) Nova Science Pubs., Inc.

Karlin, Kenneth D., et al, eds. Copper-Oxygen Chemistry. 2011. (Wiley Series of Reactive Intermediates in Chemistry & Biology Ser.: 8). (ENG., Illus.). 488p. 135.00 (978-0-470-52835-8(4), Wiley) Wiley, John & Sons, Inc.

Makai, Mihály. Group Theory Applied to Boundary Value Problems with Applications to Reactor Physics. Mercê, Ana Lucia Ramalho et al, eds. 2010. (Chemistry Research & Applications Ser.). 195.00 (978-1-61728-785-5(7)) Nova Science Pubs., Inc.

Merce, Ana Lucia Ramalho, et al, eds. Molecular & Supramolecular Bioinorganic Chemistry: Applications in Medical Sciences. 2008. (Illus.). 246p. 98.00 (978-1-60456-679-6(5)) Nova Science Pubs., Inc.

Metzler-Nolte, Nils & Kraatz, Heinz-Bernhard, eds. Concepts & Models in Bioinorganic Chemistry. 2006. (ENG., Illus.). 469p. pap. 80.00 (978-3-527-31305-1(2), Wiley-VCH) Wiley, John & Sons, Inc.

Metzler-Nolte, Nils & Schatzschneider, Ulrich. Bioinorganic Chemistry: A Practical Course. 2009. (ENG., Illus.). IX, 138p. (C). pap. 63.00 (978-3-11-020954-9(3)) De Gruyter, Walter Inc.

Ochiai, Ei-Ichiro. Bioinorganic Chemistry: A Survey. 2nd ed. 2008. (ENG., Illus.). 360p. (C). pap. 93.95 (978-0-12-088756-9(8), Academic Pr.) Elsevier Science & Technology Bks.

Rehder, Dieter. Bioinorganic Vanadium Chemistry. 2008. (Inorganic Chemistry: a Textbook Ser.: 31). (ENG., Illus.). 224p. pap. 80.00 (978-0-470-06516-7(8), Wiley) Wiley, John & Sons, Inc.

Roat-Malone, Rosette M. Bioinorganic Chemistry: A Short Course. 2nd ed. 2007. (ENG., Illus.). 544p. pap. 132.00 (978-0-471-76113-6(3), Wiley-Interscience) Wiley, John & Sons, Inc.

Ruiz-Hitzky, Eduardo, et al, eds. Bio-inorganic Hybrid Nanomaterials: Strategies, Syntheses, Characterization & Applications. 2008. (ENG., Illus.). 521p. 249.00 (978-3-527-31718-9(X), Wiley-VCH) Wiley, John & Sons, Inc.

Schneider, Manfred P. Chemical Probes in Biology: Science at the Interface of Chemistry, Biology & Medicine: Proceedings of the NATO Advanced Study Institute, Island of Spetses, Greece, 18-30 August 2002. 2008. (NATO Science Series II: Mathematics, Physics & Chemistry Ser.). 420p. pap. 129.00 (978-1-4020-1770-4(7)) Springer.

Schulzke, Carola & Samuel, Prinson P., eds. Molybdenum & Tungsten Cofactor Model Chemistry. 2010. (Chemistry Research & Applications Ser.). pap. 43.00 (978-1-61668-750-2(9)) Nova Science Pubs., Inc.

Scott, Robert A., ed. Applications of Physical Methods to Inorganic & Bioinorganic Chemistry. 2007. (EIC Bks.: 2). (ENG., Illus.). 594p. 255.00 (978-0-470-03217-6(0), Wiley-Interscience) Wiley, John & Sons, Inc.

Scott, Robert A. & Lukehart, Charles M., eds. Nanomaterials: Inorganic & Bioinorganic Perspectives. 2009. (EIC Bks.). (ENG., Illus.). 856p. 390.00 (978-0-470-51644-7(5), Wiley) Wiley, John & Sons, Inc.

Solomon, Edward I., et al, eds. Computational Inorganic & Bioinorganic Chemistry. 2009. (EIC Bks.). (ENG., Illus.). 614p. 230.00 (978-0-470-69997-3(3), Wiley) Wiley, John & Sons, Inc.

Stochel, Grazyna, et al. Bioinorganic Photochemistry. 2009. (ENG., Illus.). 398p. 210.00 (978-1-4051-6172-5(8), Wiley-Blackwell) Wiley, John & Sons, Inc.

Sun, Hongzhe, ed. Biological Chemistry of Arsenic, Antimony & Bismuth. 2011. (ENG., Illus.). 400p. 175.00 (978-0-470-71390-7(9), Wiley) Wiley, John & Sons, Inc.

Williams, R. J. P. Bioinorganic Chemistry: Trace Element Evolution from Anaerobes to Aerobes. 2010. (Structure & Bonding Ser.). (Illus.). x, 207p. pap. 244.00 (978-3-642-08340-2(4), 3642083404) Springer.

Zaikov, Gennadii Efremovich, ed. Modern Tendencies in Organic & Bioorganic Chemistry: Today & Tomorrow. 2008. (Illus.). viii, 423p. 185.00 (978-1-60456-295-8(1)) Nova Science Pubs., Inc.

BIOINTERFACES

see Biological Interfaces

BIOLINGUISTICS

see also Neurolinguistics; Psycholinguistics

Bickerton, Derek & Szathmáry, Eörs, eds. Biological Foundations & Origin of Syntax. 2009. (Strungmann Forum Reports). (ENG., Illus.). 492p. (gr. 17). 45.00 (978-0-262-01356-7(8)) MIT Pr.

Boeckx, Cedric & Di Sciullo, Anna Maria, eds. The Biolinguistic Enterprise: New Perspectives on the Evolution & Nature of the Human Language Faculty. 2011. (ENG., Illus.). 576p. 150.00 (978-0-19-955327-3(0)) Oxford Univ. Pr., Inc.

Cattell, Ray. An Introduction to Mind, Consciousness & Language. 2006. (ENG., Illus.). 256p. 49.95 (978-0-8264-5516-1(6)) Continuum International Publishing Group, Ltd. GBR. Dist: National Bk. Network.

—Mind, Consciousness & Language: An Introduction. 2006. (ENG., Illus.). 256p. 190.00 (978-0-8264-5515-4(8)) Continuum International Publishing Group, Ltd. GBR. Dist: National Bk. Network.

Cuevas-Sosa, Alejandro. Life Does Not Die - Bioenergemity,Biointuitionability & Biocommunication. 2011. 862p. pap. (978-1-908105-72-1(0)) Grosvenor Hse. Publishing Ltd.

Dedrick, D. Naming the Rainbow: Colour Language, Colour Science, & Culture. 2010. (Synthese Library). 226p. pap. 179.00 (978-90-481-5094-6(9), 9048150949) Springer.

Di Sciullo, Anna Maria & Boeckx, Cedric, eds. The Biolinguistic Enterprise: New Perspectives on the Evolution & Nature of the Human Language Faculty. 2011. (ENG., Illus.). 576p. pap. 55.00 (978-0-19-955328-0(9)) Oxford Univ. Pr., Inc.

Grein, Marion & Weigand, Edda. Dialogue & Culture. 2007. (Illus.). (C). (978-90-272-1018-0(7)) Benjamins, John Publishing Co.

Moro, Andrea. The Boundaries of Babel: The Brain & the Enigma of Impossible Languages. 2010. (Current Studies in Linguistics Ser.). (ITA & ENG., Illus.). 280p. (gr. 17). pap. 19.00 (978-0-262-51506-1(7)) MIT Pr.

—The Boundaries of Babel: The Brain & the Enigma of Impossible Languages. Caponigro, Ivano & Kane, Daniel B., trs. from ITA. 2008. (Current Studies in Linguistics Ser.). (ITA & ENG., Illus.). 280p. (gr. 17). 38.00 (978-0-262-13498-9(5)) MIT Pr.

Mukherji, Nirmalangshu. The Primacy of Grammar. (ENG., Illus.). 298p. (gr. 17). 2012. pap. 21.00 (978-0-262-51743-0(4)) 2010. 45.00 (978-0-262-01405-2(X)) MIT Pr.

Piattelli-Palmarini, Massimo, et al, eds. Of Minds & Language: A Dialogue with Noam Chomsky in the Basque Country. (ENG., Illus.). 2011. 472p. pap. 35.00 (978-0-19-954467-7(0)) 2009. 480p. 60.00 (978-0-19-954466-0(2)) Oxford Univ. Pr., Inc.

Pinker, Steven. The Language Instinct: How the Mind Creates Language. 2007. (P. S. Ser.). (ENG., Illus.). 576p. pap. 15.99 (978-0-06-133646-1(7), HarperPerennial) HarperCollins Pubs.

Romporti, Simeon & Vykypel, Bohumil. On the Biological Nature of Natural Language & Other Essays. 2008. (Travaux Linguistiques de Brno Ser.: Vol. 04). 60p. pap. (978-3-89586-315-8(7)) Lincom GmbH.

Samuels, Bridget D. Phonological Architecture: A Biolinguistic Approach. 2011. (ENG., Illus.). 272p. 125.00 (978-0-19-969435-8(4)); pap. 55.00 (978-0-19-969436-5(2)) Oxford Univ. Pr., Inc.

BIOLOGICAL ANTHROPOLOGY

see Physical Anthropology

BIOLOGICAL APPARATUS AND SUPPLIES

Dössel, Olaf & Becks, Thomas, eds. World Congress on Medical Physics & Biomedical Engineering, September 7-12, 2009 Munich, Germany: Diagnostic & Therapeutic Instrumentation, Clinical Engineering, Vol. 25/VII 2009. (IFMBE Proceedings Ser.). (Illus.). xxiv, 946p. pap. 469.00 (978-3-642-03834-6(0), 3642038840) Springer.

Enderle, John. Bioinstrumentation. 2006. (Synthesis Lectures on Biomedical Engineering Ser.). 220p. pap. 40.00 (978-1-59829-132-2(7)) Morgan & Claypool Pubs.

BIOLOGICAL ASSAY

Annual Book of ASTM Standards 2007; Section 2: Nonferrous Metal Products; V.02.04: Nonferrous Metals-Nickel, Cobalt, Lead, Tin, Zinc, Cadmium, Precious, Reactive, Refractory Metals & Alloys. 2007. 1243p. pap. 248.00 (978-0-8031-4304-3(4)) American Society for Testing & Materials.

Buss, Antony D. & Butler, Mark S., eds. Natural Product Chemistry for Drug Discovery. 2009. (RSC Biomolecular Sciences Ser.). (ENG., Illus.). 458p. 232.00 (978-0-85404-193-0(1)) Royal Society of Chemistry, The GBR. Dist: Ingram Pub. Services.

Clemons, Paul A., et al. Cell-Based Assays for High-Throughput Screening: Methods & Protocols. 2009. (Methods in Molecular Biology Ser.). (Illus.). 248p. 129.00 (978-1-60327-544-6(4)) Humana Pr.

Corey, Michael J. Coupled Bioluminescent Assays: Methods, Evaluations, & Applications. 2008. (ENG., Illus.). 308p. 139.00 (978-0-470-10883-3(5), Wiley) Wiley, John & Sons, Inc.

Giardi, Maria Teresa & Piletska, Elena. Biotechnological Applications of Photosynthetic Proteins: Biochips, Biosensors & Biodevices. 2010. (Biotechnology Intelligence Unit Ser.). xiv, 218p. pap. 209.00 (978-1-4419-4110-7(X), 144194110X) Springer.

Govindaraju, Z. Statistical Techniques in Bioassay. 2nd rev. enl. ed. (Illus.). (978-3-8055-7119-7(4)) Karger, S. AG.

Guan, Jun-Lin, ed. Cell Migration: Developmental Methods & Protocols. 2010. (Methods in Molecular Biology Ser.). (Illus.). 364p. pap. 149.00 (978-1-61737-532-3(2), 1617375322) Humana Pr.

Kelley, Marian & Prabhakar, Uma, eds. Validation of Cell-Based Assays in the GLP Setting: A Practical Guide. 2008. (ENG., Illus.). 312p. 169.95 (978-0-470-02876-6(9), Wiley) Wiley, John & Sons, Inc.

Lugnier, Claire, ed. Phosphodiesterase Methods & Protocols. 2010. (Methods in Molecular Biology Ser.). (Illus.). 336p. pap. 119.00 (978-1-61737-487-6(3), 1617374873) Humana Pr.

Makkar, Harinder P. S. Quantification of Tannins in Tree & Shrub Foliage: A Laboratory Manual. 2010. 116p. pap. 139.00 (978-90-481-6428-8(1), 9048164281) Springer.

Martin, Stewart & Murray, J. Clifford. Angiogenesis Protocols. 2nd ed. 2009. (Illus.). xi, 358p. (978-1-59745-241-0(6)) Humana Pr.

Peng, Shiqi, et al. Pharmaceutical Bioassays: Methods & Applications. 2009. (ENG., Illus.). 497p. 139.00 (978-0-470-22760-2(5), Wiley) Wiley, John & Sons, Inc.

Quevauviller, Philippe, et al, eds. Chemical Marine Monitoring: Policy Framework & Analytical Trends. 2011. (Water Quality Measurements Ser.: 24). (ENG., Illus.). 466p. 180.00 (978-0-470-74765-0(X), Wiley) Wiley, John & Sons, Inc.

Shen, Xun, et al, eds. Bioluminescence & Chemiluminescence: Light Emission - Biology & Scientific Applications. 2008. (Illus.). 480p. 178.00 (978-981-283-957-2(7)) World Scientific Publishing Co., Inc.

Sigurdsson, Einar M., ed. Amyloid Proteins. 2010. (Methods in Molecular Biology Ser.). (Illus.). 408p. pap. 134.00 (978-1-61737-502-6(0), 1617375020) Humana Pr.

Vemuri, Mohan C. Stem Cell Assays. 2007. (Methods in Molecular Biology Ser.). (Illus.). 443p. 199.00 (978-1-58829-744-0(6)) Humana Pr.

2007 Annual Book of ASTM Standards: Section 2: Nonferrous Metal Products; V.02.02: Aluminum & Magnesium Alloys. 2007. 845p. pap. 199.00 (978-0-8031-4300-5(1)) American Society for Testing & Materials.

BIOLOGICAL CHEMISTRY

see Biochemistry

BIOLOGICAL CLOCKS

see Biological Rhythms

BIOLOGICAL CLOCKS, DAILY

see Circadian Rhythms

BIOLOGICAL COMPATIBILITY

see Biocompatibility

BIOLOGICAL CONSTITUTION OF HUMAN BEINGS

see Human Beings—Constitution

BIOLOGICAL CONTROL OF INSECTS

see Insect Pests—Biological Control

BIOLOGICAL CONTROL SYSTEMS

see also Biofeedback Training; Body Temperature—Regulation; Cellular Control Mechanisms; Cellular Signal Transduction; Homeostasis; Metabolism—Regulation

Abbass, Hussein A. & Wiles, Janet, eds. Progress in Artificial Life: Third Australian Conference, ACAL 2007 Gold Coast, Australia, December 4-6, 2007 Proceedings. 2007. (Lecture Notes in Artificial Intelligence Ser.). (Illus.). 402p. pap. 89.95 (978-3-540-76930-9(7)) Springer.

Ågren, Göran & Andersson, Folke. Terrestrial Ecosystem Ecology: Principles & Applications. 2011. (ENG., Illus.). 348p. (C). pap. 59.00 (978-1-107-64825-8(4)) Cambridge Univ. Pr.

Al-Rubeai, Mohamed & Fussenegger, Martin, eds. Systems Biology. 2010. (Cell Engineering Ser.). viii, 425p. pap. 279.00 (978-90-481-7322-8(1), 9048173221) Springer.

Almeida e Costa, Francesco. Advances in Artificial Life: 9th European Conference, ECAL 2007, Lisbon, Portugal, September 10-14, 2007, Proceedings. 2007. (Lecture Notes in Computer Science / Lecture Notes in Artificial Intelligence Ser.). (Illus.). xviii, 1215p. pap. 179.00 (978-3-540-74912-7(8)) Springer.

Arabnia, Hamid R. & Tran, Quoc-Nam, eds. Software Tools & Algorithms for Biological Systems. 2011. (Advances in Experimental Medicine & Biology Ser.). (ENG., Illus.). xii, 778p. 239.00 (978-1-4419-7045-9(2), 1441970452) Springer.

Beard, Daniel A. Biosimulation: Simulation of Living Systems. 2012. (Cambridge Texts in Biomedical Engineering Ser.). (ENG., Illus.). 320p. 90.00 (978-0-521-76823-8(3)) Cambridge Univ. Pr.

Beard, Daniel A. & Qian, Hong. Chemical Biophysics: Quantitative Analysis of Cellular Systems. (Cambridge Texts in Biomedical Engineering Ser.). (ENG., Illus.). (C). 2010. 330p. pap. 45.00 (978-0-521-15824-4(9)) 2008. 336p. 94.00 (978-0-521-87070-2(4)) Cambridge Univ. Pr.

Bello, Isaac, et al. An Antioxidant from Nature. 2010. 76p. pap. (978-3-8383-7794-0(X)) Lambert Academic Publishing.

Ben Amar, Martine, et al. New Trends in the Physics & Mechanics of Biological Systems: Lecture Notes of the les Houches Summer School: Volume 92, July 2009. 2011. (ENG., Illus.). 368p. 72.00 (978-0-19-960583-5(1)) Oxford Univ. Pr., Inc.

Bertini, Ivano, et al, eds. NMR of Biomolecules: Towards Mechanistic Systems Biology. 2012. (ENG.). 650p. pap. 129.95 (978-3-527-32850-5(5), Wiley-VCH) Wiley, John & Sons, Inc.

Bose, Chinmoy K. Role of Nonlinear Dynamics in Endocrine Feedback. 2009. (Mathematics Research Developments Ser.). 89.00 (978-1-60741-948-8(3), Nova Biomedical Bks.) Nova Science Pubs., Inc.

Brodeur, Jacques & Boivin, Guy, eds. Trophic & Guild Interactions in Biological Control. 2006. (Progress in Biological Control Ser.: Vol. 3). (Illus.). x, 249p. 189.00 (978-1-4020-4766-4(5), 1402047665) Springer.

Buchanan, Mark, et al, eds. Networks in Cell Biology. 2010. (ENG., Illus.). 280p. 75.00 (978-0-521-88273-6(7)) Cambridge Univ. Pr.

Cassman, Marvin, et al. Systems Biology: International Research & Development. 2010. (ENG.). xvii, 262p. pap. 159.00 (978-90-481-7375-4(2), 9048173752) Springer.

Chambers, James J. & Kramer, Richard H., eds. Photosensitive Molecules for Controlling Biological Function. 2011. (Neuromethods Ser.). (ENG., Illus.). xiv, 298p. 119.00 (978-1-61779-030-0(3), 1617790303) Humana Pr.

Chen, Luonan, et al. Biomolecular Networks: Methods & Applications in Systems Biology. 2009. (Wiley Series in Bioinformatics Ser.: 10). (ENG., Illus.). 391p. 117.00 (978-0-470-24373-2(2), Wiley) Wiley, John & Sons, Inc.

Choi, Sangdun. Introduction to Systems Biology. 2007. (Illus.). 542p. 134.00 (978-1-58829-706-8(3)) Humana Pr.

Citro, Massimo. The Basic Code of the Universe. 2011. (ENG., Illus.). 1p. 24.95 (978-1-59477-391-4(2)) Inner Traditions International, Ltd.

Citro, Massimo. The Basic Code of the Universe: The Science of the Invisible in Physics, Medicine, & Spirituality. 2011. (Illus.). 320p. E-Book (978-1-59477-950-3(3), Park Street Pr.) Inner Traditions International, Ltd.

Collins, M. W., et al, eds. Design & Information in Biology Vol. 2: From Molecules to Systems. 2006. (Design in Nature Ser.: 2). (Illus.). 512p. 285.00 (978-1-85312-853-0(8)) WIT Pr GBR. Dist: WIT Pr.

Corne, David, et al. Membrane Computing: 9th International Workshop, WMC 2008, Edinburgh, UK, July 28-31, 2008, Revised Selected & Invited Papers. 2009. (Lecture Notes in Computer Science / Theoretical Computer Science & General Issues Ser.). ix, 403p. pap. 89.95 (978-3-540-95884-0(3)) Springer.

Cosentino, Carlo & Bates, Declan, eds. Feedback Control in Systems Biology. 2011. (ENG., Illus.). 296p. 89.95 (978-1-4398-1690-5(5), CRC Press) Taylor & Francis Group GBR. Dist: Taylor & Francis Group.

Daskalaki, Andriani, ed. Handbook of Research on Systems Biology Applications in Medicine, 2 vols. 2008. (Illus.). 982p. (C). 595.00 (978-1-60566-076-9(0)) IGI Global.

De Jong, Daan A., ed. Progress in Biological Cybernetics Research. 2008. (Illus.). (C). 120.00 (978-1-60021-968-9(3)) Nova Science Pubs., Inc.

DeGangi, Georgia A. The Dysregulated Adult: Integrated Treatment Approaches. 2012. (Practical Resources for the Mental Health Professional Ser.). (ENG.). 518p. pap. 59.95 (978-0-12-385011-9(8), Academic Pr.) Elsevier Science & Technology Bks.

Delucchi, V. L., ed. Studies in Biological Control. 2011. (International Biological Programme Synthesis Ser.). (ENG, RUS, FRE & SPA., Illus.). 322p. pap. 39.99 (978-0-521-28164-5(4)) Cambridge Univ. Pr.

Dembski, William A. No Free Lunch: Why Specified Complexity Cannot Be Purchased Without Intelligence. Dembski, William A., ed. 2nd ed. 2007. (ENG., Illus.). 432p. pap. 28.95 (978-0-7425-5810-6(X)) Rowman & Littlefield Publishers, Inc.

Drobne, Damjana, et al. Nanostructures in Biological Systems: Theory & Applications. 2011. 300p. 149.00 (978-981-4267-20-5(1)) Pan Stanford Publishing SGP. Dist: Independent Pubs. Group.

Dubitzky, Werner, et al, eds. Understanding the Dynamics of Biological Systems: Lessons Learned from Integrative Systems Biology. 2011. (ENG.). xiv, 238p. 189.00 (978-1-4419-7963-6(8), 1441979638) Springer.

Eichmann, Klaus. The Network Collective: Rise & Fall of a Scientific Paradigm. 2009. (Illus.). 310p. 159.00 (978-3-7643-8372-5(0)) Birkhauser Verlag AG CHE. Dist: Springer.

Feltz, Bernard, et al, eds. Self-organization & Emergence in Life Sciences. 2010. (Synthese Library). xii, 360p. pap. 289.00 (978-90-481-6997-9(6), 9048169976) Springer.

Feng, David Dagan & Zaytoon, Janan, eds. Modelling & Control in Biomedical Systems 2006. 2006. (IPV - IFAC Proceedings Volume Ser.). (ENG., Illus.). 920p. pap. 140.00 (978-0-08-044530-4(6), Elsevier Science) Elsevier Science & Technology Bks.

Ferro, Marcello. High Efficiency Real-Time Sensor/Actuator Control & Data Processing. 2010. 92p. pap. (978-3-639-25356-6(6)) VDM Verlag Dr. Mueller e.K.

Filloux, Alain A.M., ed. Bacterial Regulatory Networks. 2012. 400p. 360.00 (978-1-908230-03-4(7)) Caister Academic Pr. GBR. Dist: International Specialized Bk. Services.

Fuchs, Armin & Jirsa, V. K. Coordination: Neural, Behavioral & Social Dynamics. Fuchs, Armin & Jirsa, Viktor K., eds. 2008. (Understanding Complex Systems Ser.). (Illus.). 354p. 159.00 (978-3-540-74476-4(2)) Springer.

Fuchs, Armin & Jirsa, Viktor K., eds. Coordination: Neural, Behavioral & Social Dynamics: Neural, Behavioral & Social Dynamics. 2010. (Understanding Complex Systems Ser.). (Illus.). xiv, 356p. pap. 159.00 (978-3-642-09389-0(2), 3642093892) Springer.

Gould, Juli, et al, eds. Classical Biological Control of Bemisia tabaci in the United States - A Review of Interagency Research & Implementation. 2010. (Progress in Biological Control Ser.). xviii, 343p. pap. 189.00 (978-90-481-7708-0(1), 9048177081) Springer.

Govil, Girjesh & Chary, K. V. R. NMR in Biological Systems: From Molecules to Human. 2008. (Focus on Structural Biology Ser.). (Illus.). 521p. 149.00 (978-1-4020-6679-5(1)) Springer.

Grodzinsky, Alan J. Fields, Forces, & Flows in Biological Systems. 2011. (ENG., Illus.). 308p. 120.00 (978-0-8153-4212-0(8), Garland Science) Taylor & Francis Group.

Guerriero, Maria Luisa. Intuitive Formal Modelling of Biological Systems. 2011. 152p. pap. (978-3-8383-6269-4(1)) Lambert Academic Publishing.

Iglesias, Pablo A. & Ingalls, Brian P., eds. Control Theory & Systems Biology. 2009. (ENG., Illus.). 358p. (gr. 17). 45.00 (978-0-262-01334-5(7)) MIT Pr.

Jirsa, Viktor K. & Kelso, J.A.Scott. Coordination Dynamics: Issues & Trends: Issues & Trends. 2010. (Understanding Complex Systems Ser.). xiv, 272p. pap. 189.00 (978-3-642-05790-8(X), 364205790X) Springer.

Khoo, M. C. K., ed. Bioengineering Approaches to Pulmonary Physiology & Medicine. 2010. (ENG.). 253p. pap. 199.00 (978-1-4419-3260-0(7), 1441932607) Springer.

Klipp, Edda, et al. Systems Biology: A Textbook. 2009. (ENG., Illus.). 592p. pap., stu. ed. 100.00 (978-3-527-31874-2(7), Wiley-VCH) Wiley, John & Sons, Inc.

Kuldell, Natalie & Lerner, Neal. Genome Refactoring. 2009. (Synthesis Lectures on Synthetic Biology Ser.). (Illus.). 66p. pap. 25.00 (978-1-59829-947-2(6)) Morgan & Claypool Pubs.

Lessard, Charles. Basic Feedback Controls in Biomedicine. 2009. (Synthesis Lectures on Biomedical Engineering Ser.). 210p. pap. 45.00 (978-1-59829-950-2(6)) Morgan & Claypool Pubs.

Levin, Robert, et al. Work Meets Life: Exploring the Integrative Study of Work in Living Systems. 2011. (ENG., Illus.). 272p. (gr. 17). 30.00 (978-0-262-01412-0(2)) MIT Pr.

Linke, H. & Mansson, Alf. Controlled Nanoscale Motion. 2007. (Lecture Notes in Physics Ser.: Vol. 711). (Illus.). XX, 412p. 159.00 (978-3-540-49521-5(5), 3540495215) Springer.

MacDonald, N. Biological Delay Systems: Linear Stability Theory. Cannings, C. et al, eds. 2008. (Cambridge Studies in Mathematical Biology Ser.). (ENG.). 248p. pap. 53.00 (978-0-521-04816-3(8)) Cambridge Univ. Pr.

Macedonio, Michele A. & Dunford, Marie. The Athlete's Guide to Making Weight. 2009. (ENG., Illus.). 272p. pap. 17.95 (978-0-7360-7586-2(0)) Human Kinetics Pubs.

Macey. Introduction to Modeling Biological Systems. 2011. (ENG.). 256p. 99.95 (978-0-471-46259-0(4), Wiley-Liss) Wiley, John & Sons, Inc.

Markstein, Peter & Xu, Ying, eds. Computational Systems Bioinformatics: CSB2007 Conference Proceedings, Volume 6: University of California, San Diego, USA, 13-17 August 2007. 2007. (Series on Advances in Bioinformatics & Computational Biology). (Illus.). 454p. 164.00 (978-1-86094-872-5(3)) Imperial College Pr. GBR. Dist: World Scientific Publishing Co., Inc.

Méndez-Acosta, Hugo Oscar, et al, eds. Selected Topics in Dynamics & Control of Chemical & Biological Processes. 2007. (Lecture Notes in Control & Information Sciences Ser.). x, 319p. 179.00 (978-3-540-73187-0(3), 3540731873) Springer.

Minati, Gianfranco, et al, eds. Systemics of Emergence: Research & Development. 2010. (ENG., Illus.). xix, 745p. pap. 165.00 (978-1-4419-3961-6(X), 144193961X) Springer.

Moroz, Adam. The Common Extremalities in Biology & Physics: Maximum Energy Dissipation Principle in Chemistry, Biology, Physics & Evolution. 2nd ed. 2011. (ENG.). 394p. 150.00 (978-0-12-385187-1(4)) Elsevier Science & Technology Bks.

Nielsen, Jens & Jewett, Michael. Metabolomics: A Powerful Tool in Systems Biology. 2007. (Topics in Current Genetics Ser.). (Illus.). 299p. 249.00 (978-3-540-74718-5(4), 3540747184) Springer.

Peper, Erik, et al. Biofeedback Mastery: An Experiential Teaching & Self-Training Manual. 2009. (ENG.). 438p. pap. 80.00 (978-0-9842979-0-0(1)) Assn. for Applied Psychophysiology & Biofeedback.

Polani, D., et al, eds. Fifth German Workshop on Artificial Life: Abstracting & Synthesizing the Principle of Living Systems. (INFIX). 274p. pap. 55.00 (978-1-58603-242-5(9)) IOS Pr., Inc.

Potter, Steve. Biology: Control in Cells & in Organisms. 2010. (Illus.). 112p. pap., stu. ed. 22.50 (978-0-340-94953-5(8)) Hodder Education GBR. Dist: Trans-Atlantic Pubns., Inc.

Queinnec, Isabelle, et al, eds. Biology & Control Theory: Current Challenges. 2007. (Lecture Notes in Control & Information Sciences Ser.). (Illus.). 340p. pap. 169.00 (978-3-540-71987-8(3)) Springer.

Rao, Vadrevu Sree Hari & Rao, Ponnada Raja Sekhara. Dynamic Models & Control of Biological Systems. 2009. (ENG., Illus.). xiii, 275p. 189.00 (978-1-4419-0358-7(5), 1441903585) Springer.

Roelof van der Meer, Jan. Concepts & Engineering in Synthetic Biosensing. 2010. (Synthesis Lectures on Synthetic Biology Ser.). 100p. pap. 40.00 (978-1-59829-911-3(5)) Morgan & Claypool Pubs.

Skjeltorp, Arne T. & Belushkin, Alexander V., eds. Dynamics of Complex Interconnected Systems: Networks & Bioprocesses: Networks & Bioprocesses. 2006. (NATO Science Ser.: Vol. 232). (Illus.). xv, 211p. 169.00 (978-1-4020-5028-2(3), 1402050283); XV, 211p. pap. 89.95 (978-1-4020-5029-9(1), 1402050291) Springer.

Swishchuk, Anatoly & Jianhong Wu. Evolution of Biological Systems in Random Media: Limit Theorems & Stability: Limit Theorems & Stability. 2010. (Mathematical Modelling: Theory & Applications Ser.). 216p. pap. 129.00 (978-90-481-6398-4(6), 9048163986) Springer.

Systems Bioinformatics: An Engineering Case-Based Approach. 2007. (Bioinformatics & Biomedical Imaging Ser.: Vol. 29). (Illus.). 386p. 99.00 incl. cd-rom (978-1-59693-124-4(8)) Artech Hse., Inc.

Szallasi, Zoltan. System Modeling in Cellular Biology: From Concepts to Nuts & Bolts. Stelling, Jorg & Periwal, Vipul, eds. 2010. (ENG.). 464p. (gr. 17). pap. 28.00 (978-0-262-51422-4(2)) MIT Pr.

Tresilian, James. Sensorimotor Control & Learning: An Introduction to the Behavioral Neuroscience of Action. 2012. (ENG., Illus.). 912p. (C). 100.00 (978-0-230-37105-7(1)) Palgrave Macmillan.

Virnik, Elena. Analysis of Positive Descriptor Systems. 2008. 152p. pap. (978-3-639-06058-4(X)) VDM Verlag Dr. Mueller e.K.

Wagner, Andreas. Robustness & Evolvability in Living Systems. 2007. (Princeton Studies in Complexity). (ENG., Illus.). 384p. (C). per. 49.95 (978-0-691-13404-8(9)) Princeton Univ. Pr.

Wilkinson, Darren J. Stochastic Modelling for Systems Biology. 2nd rev. ed. 2011. (Chapman & Hall/CRC Mathematical & Computational Biology Ser.). (ENG., Illus.). 363p. 89.95 (978-1-4398-3772-6(4), CRC Press) Taylor & Francis Group GBR. Dist: Taylor & Francis Group.

Williams, Thomas O., ed. Biological Cybernetics Research Trends. 2007. 129.00 (978-1-60021-568-1(8)) Nova Science Pubs., Inc.

Xu. Computational Systems Bioinformatics: CSB 2008 Conference Proceedings, Volume 7: Stanford University, USA, 26-29 August 2008. 2008. (Illus.). xii, 340p. 142.00 (978-1-84816-263-1(4)) Imperial College Pr. GBR. Dist: World Scientific Publishing Co., Inc.

Zhang, Qingling, et al. Complexity, Analysis & Control of Singular Biological Systems. 2012. (Lecture Notes in Control & Information Sciences Ser.). (ENG., Illus.). xvi, 236p. pap. 109.00 (978-1-4471-2302-6(6), 1447123026) Springer.

BIOLOGICAL DEGRADATION

see Biodegradation

BIOLOGICAL DIVERSITY

see Biodiversity

BIOLOGICAL DIVERSITY CONSERVATION

see Biodiversity Conservation

BIOLOGICAL ELECTROCHEMISTRY

see Bioelectrochemistry

BIOLOGICAL ELECTRONICS

see Electronics in Biology

BIOLOGICAL ENGINEERING

see Bioengineering

BIOLOGICAL FORM

see Morphology

BIOLOGICAL FUELS

see Biomass Energy

BIOLOGICAL ILLUSTRATION

Brafman, David & Schrader, Stephanie. Insects & Flowers: The Art of Maria Sibylla Merian. 2008. (Illus.). 52p. pap. 9.95 (978-0-89236-929-4(9)) Oxford Univ. Pr., Inc.

Elphick, Jonathan. Birds: The Art of Ornithology. 2008. (ENG., Illus.). 336p. 19.95 *(978-0-8478-3134-0(5))* Rizzoli International Pubns., Inc.

Rossi-Wilcox, Susan M., et al. Drawing upon Nature: Studies for the Blaschkas' Glass Models. 2007. (Illus.). 167p. pap. 24.95 *(978-0-87290-166-7(1))* Corning Museum of Glass.

Ursyn, Anna. Biologically-Inspired Computing for the Arts: Scientific Data Through Graphics. 2012. ***(978-1-4666-0944-0(3))*** IGI Global.

Ursyn, Anna, ed. Biologically-Inspired Computing for the Arts: Scientific Data through Graphics. 2012. 320p. 190.00 ***(978-1-4666-0942-6(7))***, Information Science Reference) IGI Global.

BIOLOGICAL INDICATORS
see Indicators (Biology)

BIOLOGICAL INORGANIC CHEMISTRY
see Bioinorganic Chemistry

BIOLOGICAL INTERFACES
see also Membranes (Biology)

Cram101 Textbook Reviews & Cram101 Textbook Reviews. Outlines & Highlights for Physics of Surfaces & Interfaces by Harald Ibach. 2011. 202p. pap. 30.95 ***(978-1-61812-464-7(1))*** Cram101 Inc.

Eguchi, Koichi, et al, eds. Science & Technology in Catalysis: 5th Tokyo Conference on Advanced Catalytic Science & Technology. 2007. (Studies in Surface Science & Catalysis Ser.: 172). (ENG., Illus.). 652p. 260.00 *(978-0-444-53202-2(1),* Elsevier Science) Elsevier Science & Technology Bks.

Förch, Renate, et al, eds. Surface Design: Applications in Bioscience & Nanotechnology. 2009. (ENG., Illus.). 532p. 171.00 *(978-3-527-40789-7(8),* Wiley-VCH) Wiley, John & Sons, Inc.

Gorb, S., ed. Functional Surfaces in Biology: Little Structures with Big Effects, 2 vols., Vol. 1. 2009. (ENG., Illus.). xviii, 390p. 199.00 *(978-1-4020-6696-2(1),* 1402066961) Springer.

—Functional Surfaces in Biology: adhesion related Phenomena, 2 vols. 2009. (ENG., Illus.). xviii, 270p. 179.00 *(978-1-4020-6694-8(5),* 1402066945) Springer.

Gorb, Stanislav S. N., ed. Functional Surfaces in Biology, 2 vols. 2009. xviii, 660p. 329.00 *(978-1-4020-9994-6(0),* 1402099940) Springer.

Helburn, Robin & Vitha, Mark F., eds. Interfaces & Interphases in Analytical Chemistry, 1 vol. 2011. (ACS Symposium Ser.). (ENG., Illus.). 298p. 150.00 *(978-0-8412-2604-3(0))* American Chemical Society.

Knoll, Wolfgang, ed. Handbook of Biofunctional Surfaces. 2012. (ENG.). 800p. 425.00 ***(978-981-4316-63-7(6))*** Pan Stanford Publishing SGP. Dist: Taylor & Francis Group.

Landheer, D., ed. Bioelectronics, Biointerfaces, & Biomedical Applications 2. 2007. (ECS Transactions Ser.). 41p. pap. 36.00 *(978-1-60423-378-0(8))* Curran Assocs., Inc.

Materials Research Society ( ) Staff, compiled by. Biosurfaces & Biointerfaces. 2007. (Materials Research Society Symposium Proceedings Ser.). 240p. pap. 115.00 *(978-1-60423-406-0(7))* Curran Assocs., Inc.

Nestor & Favret, Eduardo A. Functional Properties of Bio-Inspired Surfaces: Characterization & Technological Applications. 2009. 416p. 141.00 *(978-981-283-701-1(9))* World Scientific Publishing Co., Inc.

Norde, Willem. Colloids & Interfaces in Life Sciences & Bionanotechnology. 2nd rev. ed. 2011. (ENG., Illus.). 495p. 129.95 *(978-1-4398-1718-6(9),* CRC Press) Taylor & Francis Group GBR. Dist: Taylor & Francis Group.

Ohshima, Hiroyuki. Electrical Phenomena at Interfaces & Biointerfaces: Fundamentals & Applications in Nano-, Bio-, & Environmental Sciences. 2012. (ENG., Illus.). 872p. 175.00 ***(978-0-470-58255-8(3),*** Wiley) Wiley, John & Sons, Inc.

Parise, James. MOLECULAR INTERACTIONS AT THE CHEMISTRY-BIOLOGY INTERFACE: The Design of Interfacial Biomaterials & the Modulation of Galectin-3 Aggregation With Multivalent Saccharide Ligands. 2008. 160p. pap. *(978-3-639-09799-3(8))* VDM Verlag Dr. Mueller e.K.

Pradier, C. -M. & Chabal, Y. J., eds. Biointerface Characterization by Advanced IR Spectroscopy. 2011. (ENG.). 344p. 147.00 *(978-0-444-53558-0(6))* Elsevier Science & Technology Bks.

Schramm, Laurier L. Dictionary of Nanotechnology, Colloid & Interface Science. 2008. (ENG.). 298p. 175.00 *(978-3-527-32203-9(5),* Wiley-VCH) Wiley, John & Sons, Inc.

Surfaces in Biomaterials Foundation Staff, compiled by. BioInterface 2003. 2007. 69p. pap. 137.00 *(978-1-60423-688-0(4))* Curran Assocs., Inc.

—BioInterface 2005. 2007. 57p. pap. 137.00 *(978-1-60423-690-3(6))* Curran Assocs., Inc.

—Biointerface Conference 2006. 2007. 50p. pap. 85.00 *(978-1-60423-979-9(4))* Curran Assocs., Inc.

—Role of the Government in the Biomaterials Industry Workshop & BioInterface 2004. 2007. 99p. pap. 137.00 *(978-1-60423-689-7(2))* Curran Assocs., Inc.

Wang, Zhiguo. MicroRNA Interference Technologies. (ENG., Illus.). xii, 193p. 2010. pap. 179.00 ***(978-3-642-10151-9(8),*** 3642101518) 2009. 179.00 *(978-3-642-00488-9(1),* 3642004881) Springer.

Zhang, Sam, ed. Biological & Biomedical Coatings Handbook, 2 vols. 2011. (Advances in Materials Science & Engineering Ser.). (ENG., Illus.). 976p. 249.95 *(978-1-4398-2125-1(9),* CRC Press) Taylor & Francis Group GBR. Dist: Taylor & Francis Group.

BIOLOGICAL INVASIONS
Here are entered works on processes in which organisms become established in a region where they previously did not exist and then rapidly expand their range.
see also Natural Selection

Alexander, Jeff. Pandora's Locks: The Opening of the Great Lakes-St. Lawrence Seaway. (ENG., Illus.). 431p. 2011. pap. 19.95 *(978-0-87013-872-0(3))* 2009. 29.95 *(978-0-87013-857-7(X))* Michigan State Univ. Pr.

Allen, Robert B. & Lee, William G., eds. Biological Invasions in New Zealand. 2012. (Ecological Studies). (ENG., Illus.). xxiv, 457p. pap. 269.00 *(978-3-642-06759-4(X),* 364206759X) Springer.

Boersma, P. Dee. Invasive Species in the Pacific Northwest. Reichard, Sarah & Van Buren, Amy, eds. 2006. (ENG., Illus.). 276p. pap. 29.95 *(978-0-295-98596-1(8))* Univ. of Washington Pr.

Capdevila-Arguelles, Laura & Zilletti, Bernardo, eds. Issues in Bioinvasion Science: EEI 2003: a Contribution to the Knowledge on Invasive Alien Species. 2011. (ENG.). vi, 150p. pap. 79.95 *(978-90-481-6745-6(0),* 9048167450) Springer.

Carlton, James T. & Eldredge, Lucius G. Marine Bioinvasions of Hawaii: The Introduced & Cryptogenic Marine & Estuarine Animals & Plants of the Hawaiian Archipelago. 2009. (Illus.). 202p. *(978-1-58178-096-3(6))* Bishop Museum Pr.

Galil, S., Bella, S & Cohen, N., Andrew, N. Bridging Divides: Maritime Canals as Invasion Corridors. Gollasch, Stephan, ed. 2006. (Monographiae Biologicae Ser.). (ENG., Illus.). xiii, 315p. 219.00 *(978-1-4020-5046-6(1),* 1402050461) Springer.

Gherardi, Francesca, ed. Biological invaders in inland waters: Profiles, distribution, & Threats: Profiles, distribution, & Threats. 2010. (Invading Nature - Springer Series in Invasion Ecology Ser.). xxx, 734p. pap. 239.00 *(978-90-481-7509-3(7),* 9048175097) Springer.

Golani, Daniel & Applebaum-Golani, Brenda, eds. Fish Invasions of the Mediterranean Sea: Change & Renewal. 2010. (Faunistica Ser.). 332p. pap. 132.50 *(978-954-642-526-3(5))* Pensoft Pubs. BGR. Dist: Coronet Bks.

Gollasch, Stephan, et al, eds. Bridging Divides: Maritime Canals as Invasion Corridors. 2010. (Monographiae Biologicae Ser.). (Illus.). xiii, 315p. pap. 219.00 *(978-90-481-7265-8(9),* 9048172659) Springer.

Groves, R. H. & Di Castri, F., eds. Biogeography of Mediterranean Invasions. 2008. (ENG.). 504p. pap. 95.00 *(978-0-521-06390-6(6))* Cambridge Univ. Pr.

Hamilton, Garry. Super Species: The Creatures That Will Dominate the Planet. 2010. (Illus.). 272p. 35.00 *(978-1-55407-630-7(7))* Firefly Bks., Ltd.

Hendrix, Paul F., ed. Biological Invasions Belowground: Earthworms as Invasive Species: Earthworms as Invasive Species. (ENG.). iv, 132p. 2010. pap. 89.95 *(978-90-481-7366-2(3),* 9048173663) 2006. 89.95 *(978-1-4020-5428-0(9),* 1402054289) Springer.

Joubert, Leonie. Invaded: The Biological Invasion of South Africa. 2009. (ENG.). 368p. pap. 39.95 *(978-1-86814-478-5(X))* Witwatersrand Univ. Pr. Pubns. ZAF. Dist: Transaction Pubs.

Keller, Reuben P., et al, eds. Bioeconomics of Invasive Species: Integrating Ecology, Economics, Policy, & Management. 2009. (ENG., Illus.). 320p. 99.00 *(978-0-19-536798-0(7));* pap. 49.95 *(978-0-19-536797-3(9))* Oxford Univ. Pr., Inc.

Koike, Fumito, et al. Assessment & Control of Biological Invasion Risks. 2006. (ENG.). 216p. pap. 25.00 *(978-4-87974-604-7(5))* UICN Union Mondiale pour la Nature, Cecile Thiery CHE. Dist: Chicago Distribution Ctr.

Leland, John. Aliens in the Backyard: Plant & Animal Imports into America. 2010. (Illus.). 248p. pap. 21.95 *(978-1-57003-958-4(5))* Univ. of South Carolina Pr.

Lockwood, Julie L., et al. Invasion Ecology. 2006. (ENG., Illus.). 312p. per. 84.95 *(978-1-4051-1418-9(5),* Wiley-Blackwell) Wiley, John & Sons, Inc.

Minnich, Richard A. California's Fading Wildflowers: Lost Legacy & Biological Invasions. 2008. (Illus.). 360p. 55.00 *(978-0-520-25353-7(1))* Univ. of California Pr.

Nentwig, Wolfgang. Biological Invasions. 2008. (Ecological Studies). (Illus.). 441p. pap. 99.00 *(978-3-540-77375-7(4))* Springer.

—Biological Invasions. 2006. (Ecological Studies). (Illus.). XXV, 441p. 289.00 *(978-3-540-36919-6(8),* 3540369198) Springer.

Perrings, Charles, et al, eds. Bioinvasions & Globalization: Ecology, Economics, Management, & Policy. 2010. (ENG., Illus.). 288p. 140.00 *(978-0-19-956015-8(3))* Oxford Univ. Pr., Inc.

Perrings, Charles, et al. Bioinvasions & Globalization: Ecology, Economics, Management, & Policy. 2010. (ENG., Illus.). 288p. 70.00 *(978-0-19-956016-5(1))* Oxford Univ. Pr., Inc.

Pimentel,, David, David, ed. Biological Invasions. 2nd rev. ed. 2011. (ENG., Illus.). 463p. 119.95 *(978-1-4398-2990-5(X),* CRC Press) Taylor & Francis Group GBR. Dist: Taylor & Francis Group.

Richardson, David M., ed. Fifty Years of Invasion Ecology: The Legacy of Charles Elton. 2011. (ENG., Illus.). 456p. 180.00 *(978-1-4443-3585-9(5));* pap. 84.95 *(978-1-4443-3586-6(3))* Wiley, John & Sons, Inc. (Wiley-Blackwell).

Rilov, Gil. Biological Invasions in Marine Ecosystems. 2008. (Ecological Studies). (Illus.). xxvi, 641p. 289.00 *(978-3-540-79235-2(X))* Springer.

Roy, Helen E. & Wajnberg, E. From Biological Control to Invasion: The Ladybird Harmonia Axyridis As a Model Species. 2008. (Illus.). 287p. 119.00 *(978-1-4020-6938-3(3),* 1402069383) Springer.

Roy, Helen E. & Wajnberg, Eric, eds. From Biological Control to Invasion: the Ladybird Harmonia axyridis as a Model Species: The Ladybird Harmonia axyridis as a Model Species. 2010. (Illus.). vi, 290p. pap. 119.00 *(978-90-481-7771-4(5),* 9048177715) Springer.

United States, Government Accountability Office Staff, contrib. by. Invasive Forest Pests. 2006. (Illus.). 92p. 125.00 *(978-1-60021-461-5(4))* Nova Science Pubs., Inc.

Wilcox, Charles P. & Turpin, Randall B., eds. Invasive Species: Detection, Impact & Control. 2008. 89.00 *(978-1-60692-252-1(1))* Nova Science Pubs., Inc.

Williams, Gill. 100 Alien Invaders: Animals & Plants That Are Changing Our World. 2011. (ENG., Illus.). 160p. 24.99 *(978-1-84162-359-7(8))* Bradt Travel Guides GBR. Dist: Globe Pequot Pr., The.

Williams, Peter A. & Clout, Michael N., eds. Invasive Species Management: A Handbook of Principles & Techniques. 2009. (Techniques in Ecology & Conservation Ser.). (ENG., Illus.). 320p. pap. 59.95 *(978-0-19-921633-8(9))* Oxford Univ. Pr., Inc.

BIOLOGICAL LABORATORIES

Adams, David. Effective Learning in the Life Sciences: How Students Can Achieve Their Full Potential. 2011. (ENG., Illus.). 288p. 149.95 ***(978-0-470-66156-7(9));*** pap. 79.95 ***(978-0-470-66157-4(7))*** Wiley, John & Sons, Inc. (Wiley).

Aziz, Hassan. Assessment of Laboratory Safety Knowledge among University Students. 2008. 96p. pap. *(978-3-639-08180-0(3))* VDM Verlag Dr. Mueller e.K.

Biobanking: How the Lack of a Coherent Policy Allowed the Veterans Administration to Destroy an Irreplaceable Collection of Legionella Samples: Hearing Before the Subcommittee on Investigations & Oversight, Committee on Science & Technology, One Hundred Tenth Congress, Second Session, September 9, 2008. 2008. (Illus.). iv, 514p. *(978-0-16-082631-3(4),* 552-070-38649-1) United States Government Printing Office.

Committee on Anticipating Biosecurity Challenges of the Global Expansion of High-Containment Biological Laboratories, et al. Biosecurity Challenges of the Global Expansion of High Containment Biological Laboratories. 2012. (ENG.). 216p. pap. 46.00 ***(978-0-309-22575-5(2))*** National Academies Pr.

Committee on Laboratory Security and Personnel Reliability Assurance Systems for Laboratories Conducting Research on Biological Select Agents and Toxins & National Research Council. Responsible Research with Biological Select Agents & Toxins. 2010. (ENG.). 188p. pap. 32.00 *(978-0-309-14535-0(X))* National Academies Pr.

Germs, Viruses, & Secrets: Government Plans to Move Exotic Disease Research to the Mainland United States: Hearing Before the Subcommittee on Oversight & Investigations of the Committee on Energy & Commerce, House of Representatives, One Hundred Tenth Congress, Second Session, May 22, 2008. 2008. (Illus.). iii, 538p. *(978-0-16-086822-1(X),* 552-070-41738-9) United States Government Printing Office.

Germs, Viruses, & Secrets: The Silent Proliferation of Bio-Laboratories in the United States: Hearing Before the Subcommittee on Oversight & Investigations of the Committee on Energy & Commerce, House of Representatives, One Hundred Tenth Congress, First Session, October 4, 2007. 2008. (Illus.). v, 267p. *(978-0-16-082525-5(3),* 552-070-38560-6) United States Government Printing Office.

Institute for Laboratory Animal Research. Animal Research in a Global Environment: Meeting the Challenges: Proceedings of the November 2008 International Workshop. 2011. (ENG.). 284p. pap. 45.00 ***(978-0-309-21502-2(1))*** National Academies Pr.

King, Kenneth. Germs Gone Wild: How the Unchecked Development of Domestic Bio-Defense Threatens America. 2011. (ENG.). 384p. pap. 16.95 *(978-1-60598-268-7(7),* 605268) Pegasus Bks.

Pal, S. B., ed. Handbook of Laboratory Health & Safety Measures. 2nd ed. 2012. (ENG.). 592p. pap. 404.00 *(978-90-481-4032-9(3),* 9048140323) Springer.

Salerno Reynolds M Staff. Laboratory Biosecurity Handbook. 2007. (ENG., Illus.). 208p. 113.95 *(978-0-8493-6475-4(2),* CRC Press) Taylor & Francis Group GBR. Dist: Taylor & Francis Group.

Samuels, Damon S., ed. Biosafety & Biosecurity Issues in High-Containment Laboratories. 2010. (Defense, Security & Strategies Ser.). (Illus.). ix, 288p. 195.00 *(978-1-61668-706-9(1))* Nova Science Pubs., Inc.

Schmitt. Laboratory Exercises in Biology. 2nd rev. ed. 2011. (ENG.). 268p. spiral bd. 57.95 ***(978-0-7575-9370-3(4))*** Kendall Hunt Publishing Co.

Separation Systems for Commercial Biotechnology. 2007. per. 4250.00 *(978-1-59623-263-1(3))* BCC Research.

Strengthening Security & Oversight at Biological Research Laboratories: Hearing Before the Subcommittee on Terrorism & Homeland Security of the Committee on the Judiciary, United States Senate, One Hundred Eleventh Congress, First Session, September 22, 2009. 2010. iii, 98p. *(978-0-16-085755-3(4),* 552-070-40973-4) United States Government Printing Office.

Zhou, Michael. Regulated Bioanalytical Laboratories: Technical & Regulatory Aspects from Global Perspectives. 2011. (ENG., Illus.). 526p. 132.00 *(978-0-470-47659-8(1),* Wiley) Wiley, John & Sons, Inc.

BIOLOGICAL LITERATURE

Seidensticker, Peter. Aisthesis: Wahrnehmung der Farben in den Pflanzenbeschreibungen der frühen deutschen Kräuterbücher. 2010. (Zeitschrift fur Dialektologie und Linguistik - Beihefte Ser.). (GER., Illus.). 98p. (C). pap. 44.00 *(978-3-515-09623-2(X))* Steiner, Franz Verlag Wiesbaden GmbH DEU. Dist: Brown, David Bk. Co., The.

Shatkay, Hagit & Craven, Mark. Mining the Biomedical Literature. 2012. ***(978-0-262-01769-5(5))*** MIT Pr.

BIOLOGICAL MAGNETISM
see Biomagnetism

BIOLOGICAL MARKERS
see Biochemical Markers

BIOLOGICAL MECHANICS
see Biomechanics

BIOLOGICAL MODELS
see also Biology—Mathematical Models; Stereology

Aguda, Baltazar & Friedman, Avner. Models of Cellular Regulation. 2008. (Oxford Graduate Texts). (ENG., Illus.). 200p. 99.00 *(978-0-19-857091-2(0))* Oxford Univ. Pr., Inc.

Al-Jumaily, Ahmed & Alizad, Azra, eds. Biomedical Applications of Vibration & Acoustics in Therapy, Bioeffect & Modeling. 2008. (Illus.). 350p. 139.00 *(978-0-7918-0275-5(2))* ASME Pr.

Anderson, Alexander R. A. & Rejniak, Katarzyna A., eds. Single-Cell-Based Models in Biology & Medicine. 2007. (Mathematics & Biosciences in Interaction Ser.). (Illus.). 349p. 249.00 *(978-3-7643-8101-1(9))* Birkhauser Verlag AG CHE. Dist: Springer.

Buxbaum, Engelbert. Biophysical Chemistry of Proteins: An Introduction to Laboratory Methods. 2010. (ENG., Illus.). xvi, 510p. 209.00 *(978-1-4419-7250-7(1),* 1441972501) Springer.

Computational Methods in Systems Biology. 2008. (Lecture Notes in Computer Science / Lecture Notes in Bioinformatics Ser.). spiral bd. 89.95 *(978-3-540-88561-0(7),* 3540885617) Springer.

Cram101 Textbook Reviews & Cram101 Textbook Reviews. Outlines & Highlights for Physics in Molecular Biology by Kim Sneppen. 2011. 72p. pap. 27.95 ***(978-1-61830-495-7(X))*** Cram101 Inc.

Creager, Angela N. H., et al, eds. Science Without Laws: Model Systems, Cases, Exemplary Narratives. 2007. (Science & Cultural Theory Ser.). (ENG., Illus.). 296p. (C). 89.95 *(978-0-8223-4046-1(1));* per. 24.95 *(978-0-8223-4068-3(2))* Duke Univ. Pr.

Cristini, Vittorio & Lowengrub, John. Multiscale Modeling of Cancer: An Integrated Experimental & Mathematical Modeling Approach. 2010. (ENG., Illus.). 298p. 125.00 *(978-0-521-88442-6(X))* Cambridge Univ. Pr.

Darowski, Marek & Ferrari, Gianfranco. Comprehensive Models of Cardiovascular & Respiratory Systems: Their Mechanical Support & Interactions. 2009. (Cardiology Research & Clinical Developments Ser.). 98.00 *(978-1-60876-212-5(2))* Nova Science Pubs., Inc.

Dochain, Denis, ed. Automatic Control of Bioprocesses. 2008. (Iste Ser.: 305). (ENG., Illus.). 288p. 174.00 *(978-1-84821-025-7(6),* Wiley-ISTE) Wiley, John & Sons, Inc.

Eichinger, Ludwig & Rivero-Crespo, Francisco. Dictyostelium Discoideum Protocols. Eichinger, Ludwig & Rivero-Crespo, Francisco, eds. 2006. (Methods in Molecular Biology Ser.). (Illus.). 580p. 209.00 *(978-1-58829-623-8(7),* 1588296237) Humana Pr.

Elsheikh, Ahmed, ed. Understanding Corneal Biomechanics through Experimental Assessment & Numerical Simulation. 2010. (Eye & Vision Research Developments Ser.). 73p. pap. 43.00 *(978-1-60876-694-9(2))* Nova Science Pubs., Inc.

Emerging Model Organisms: A Laboratory Manual, Vol. 1. 2008. (ENG., Illus.). 592p. 158.00 *(978-0-87969-826-3(8));* pap. 89.00 *(978-0-87969-872-0(1))* Cold Spring Harbor Laboratory Pr.

Emerging Model Organisms: A Laboratory Manual, Vol. 2. 2010. (ENG., Illus.). 624p. 162.00 *(978-0-87969-945-1(0));* pap. 91.00 *(978-0-87969-865-2(9))* Cold Spring Harbor Laboratory Pr.

Et. Clustering Challenges in Biological Ne. . 2009. (Illus.). 350p. 150.00 *(978-981-277-165-0(4))* Imperial College Pr. GBR. Dist: World Scientific Publishing Co., Inc.

Feng, David Dagan & Zaytoon, Janan, eds. Modelling & Control in Biomedical Systems 2006. 2006. (IPV - IFAC Proceedings Volume Ser.). (ENG., Illus.). 920p. pap. 140.00 *(978-0-08-044530-4(6),* Elsevier Science) Elsevier Science & Technology Bks.

Ghaemi, S. Nassir. The Rise & Fall of the Biopsychosocial Model: Reconciling Art & Science in Psychiatry. 2009. (ENG., Illus.). 272p. (gr. 17). 52.00 *(978-0-8018-9390-2(9))* Johns Hopkins Univ. Pr.

Greenwald, Mark. Human Experimental Therapeutic Models in Opioid Dependence. 2008. (Illus.). 82p. pap. 29.00 *(978-1-60456-807-3(0))* Nova Science Pubs., Inc.

Heinke, Dietmar. Computational Modelling in Behavioural Neuroscience: Closing the Gap Between Neurophysiology & Behaviour. Mavritsaki, Eirini, ed. 2009. (Advances in Behavioural Brain Science Ser.). (ENG., Illus.). 376p. (C). 110.00 *(978-1-84169-738-3(9),* Psychology Press) Taylor & Francis Group GBR. Dist: Taylor & Francis Group.

Iglesias, Pablo A. & Ingalls, Brian P., eds. Control Theory & Systems Biology. 2009. (ENG., Illus.). 358p. (gr. 17). 45.00 *(978-0-262-01334-5(7))* MIT Pr.

Ionescu, Armand Mihai. Membrane Computing: Traces, Neural Inspired Models, Controls. 2009. 184p. pap. *(978-3-639-16858-7(5))* VDM Verlag Dr. Mueller e.K.

Irwin, George William & He, Guosen, eds. Life System Modeling & Simulation: International Conference, LSMS 2007 Shanghai, China, September 14-17, 2007 Proceedings. 2007. (Lecture Notes in Computer Science Ser.). (Illus.). 561p. pap. 109.00 *(978-3-540-74770-3(2))* Springer.

Jaramillo, Alfonso, ed. Model-Based Design in Synthetic Biology. 2010. (Illus.). 306p. 69.95 *(978-1-4200-8355-2(4),* Chapman & Hall/CRC) CRC Pr. LLC.

Khoo, M. C. K., ed. Bioengineering Approaches to Pulmonary Physiology & Medicine. 2010. (ENG.). 253p. pap. 199.00 *(978-1-4419-3260-0(7),* 1441932607) Springer.

Koch, Wijnand F. R. M. & Marani, Enrico. Early Development of the Human Pelvic Diaphragm. 2007. (Advances in Anatomy, Embryology & Cell Biology Ser.). (Illus.). x, 114p. pap. 159.00 *(978-3-540-68006-2(3),* 3540680063) Springer.

Koonin, Eugene V., et al. Power Laws, Scale-Free Networks & Genome Biology. 2010. (Molecular Biology Intelligence Unit Ser.). xix, 257p. pap. 219.00 *(978-1-4419-3846-6(X),* 144193846X) Springer.

Krabs, Werner & Pickl, Stefan. Modelling, Analysis & Optimization of Biosystems. 2010. (ENG., Illus.). xii, 203p. pap. 139.00 *(978-3-642-09066-0(4),* 3642090664) Springer.

Krabs, Werner & Pickl, Stefan Wolfgang. Modelling, Analysis & Optimization of Biosystems. 2007. (ENG., Illus.). xii, 203p. 139.00 *(978-3-540-71452-1(9),* 3540714529) Springer.

Krishnan, Kannan & Andersen, Melvin, eds. Quantitative Modeling in Toxicology. 2010. (ENG., Illus.). 504p. 170.00 *(978-0-470-99809-0(1),* Wiley) Wiley, John & Sons, Inc.

Lenhart, Suzanne & Workman, John T. Optimal Control Applied to Biological Models. 2007. (Chapman & Hall/CRC Mathematical & Computational Biology Ser.). (ENG., Illus.). 280p. (C). 99.95 *(978-1-58488-640-2(4),* Chapman & Hall/CRC) CRC Pr. LLC.

Leondes. Biomechanical Systems Technology (V3) 2009. 155.00 *(978-981-270-983-7(5))* World Scientific Publishing Co., Inc.

Li, Kang, et al, eds. Life System Modeling & Intelligent Computing: International Conference on Life System Modeling & Simulation, LSMS 2010, & International Conference on Intelligent Computing for Sustainable Energy & Environment, ICSEE 2010, Wuxi, China, September 17-20, 2010, Proceedings. 2010. (Lecture Notes in Computer Science / Lecture Notes in Bioinformatics Ser.). xviii, 719p. pap. 131.00 *(978-3-642-15614-4(2),* 3642156142) Springer.

—Life System Modeling & Intelligent Computing: International Conference on Life System Modeling & Simulation, LSMS 2010, & International Conference on Intelligent Computing for Sustainable Energy & Environment, ICSEE 2010, Wuxi, China, September 17-20, 2010, Proceedings, Part I. 2010. (Communications in Computer & Information Science Ser.). xviii, 261p. pap. 84.00 *(978-3-642-15852-0(8),* 3642158528) Springer.

Macagnano, Antonella, et al. Advanced Topics in Cell Model Systems. 2009. 89.00 *(978-1-60692-906-3(2))* Nova Science Pubs., Inc.

McArthur, Robert A. & Borsini, Franco, eds. Animal & Translational Models for CNS Drug Discovery, 3 vols. 2008. (ENG., Illus.). 1376p. 210.00 *(978-0-12-373861-5(X),* Academic Pr.) Elsevier Science & Technology Bks.

Miftahof, Roustem, et al. Mathematical Modeling & Simulation in Enteric Neurobiology. 2009. 280p. 124.00 *(978-981-283-480-5(X))* World Scientific Publishing Co., Inc.

Moallem, Azin & Simone A. Ludwig, /. Using Swarm Intelligence for Distributed Job Scheduling on the Grid. 2010. 104p. pap. *(978-3-8383-0241-8(9))* Lambert Academic Publishing.

Mondaini, Rubem P. Mathematical Modelling of Biosystems. 2008. (Applied Optimization Ser.). 159.00 *(978-3-540-76783-1(5))* Springer.

Myslobodsky, Michael S. & Weiner, Ina, eds. Contemporary Issues in Modeling of Psychopathology. 2010. (Neurobiological Foundation of Aberrant Behaviors Ser.). 336p. pap. 199.00 *(978-1-4419-4996-7(8),* 1441949968) Springer.

National Council on Radiation Protection and Measurements Staff & National Council on Radiation Protection and Measurements, Scientific Committee 57-17 on Radionuclide Dosimetry Model for Wounds Staff, contrib. by. Development of a Biokinetic Model for Radionuclide-Contaminated Wounds & Procedures for Their Assessment, Dosimetry, & Treatment: Recommendations of the National Council on Radiation Protection & Measurements, December 14, 2006. 2007. (NCRP Reports: No. 156). *(978-0-929600-93-2(2))* National Council on Radiation Protection & Measurements.

Northrop, Robert B. Signals & Systems Analysis in Biomedical Engineering, Second Edition. 2nd rev. ed. 2010. (Biomedical Engineering Ser.). (ENG., Illus.). 654p. (C). 104.95 *(978-1-4398-1251-8(9),* CRC Press) Taylor & Francis Group GBR. Dist: Taylor & Francis Group.

Peters, Sheila Annie. Physiologically Based Pharmacokinetic (PBPK) Modeling & Simulations: Principles, Methods, & Applications in the Pharma Industry. 2012. (ENG.). 448p. 115.00 ***(978-0-470-48406-7(3),*** Wiley) Wiley, John & Sons, Inc.

Phillips, Rob, et al. Physical Biology of the Cell. 2008. (ENG., Illus.). 800p. pap. 136.00 *(978-0-8153-4163-5(6),* Garland Science) Taylor & Francis Group.

Phillips, Rob, et al. Physical Biology of the Cell. 2nd rev. ed. 2012. (ENG., Illus.). 950p. pap. 145.00 ***(978-0-8153-4450-6(3),*** Garland Science) Taylor & Francis Group.

Quarteroni, A., et al, eds. Complex Systems in Biomedicine. 2010. (ENG., Illus.). xiv, 292p. pap. 109.00 *(978-88-470-1555-5(3),* 8847015553) Springer.

Rasmussen, Steen, et al, eds. Protocells: Bridging Nonliving & Living Matter. 2008. (ENG., Illus.). 712p. (gr. 17). 75.00 *(978-0-262-18268-3(8))* MIT Pr.

Renugopalakrishnan, V. & Lewis, Randy V., eds. Bionanotechnology: Proteins to Nanodevices. 2010. (ENG.). xiv, 296p. pap. 229.00 *(978-90-481-7078-4(8),* 9048170788) Springer.

Rosato, Ezio, ed. Circadian Rhythms: Methods & Protocols. (Methods in Molecular Biology Ser.). (Illus.). 2010. xiv, 578p. pap. 189.00 *(978-1-61737-553-8(5),* 1617375535) 2007. 578p. 189.00 *(978-1-58829-417-3(X),* 158829417X) Humana Pr.

Siddiqui, Khawar Sohail & Thomas, Torsten. Protein Adaptation in Extremophiles. 2008. (Illus.). (C). 120.00 *(978-1-60456-019-0(3))* Nova Science Pubs., Inc.

Sjöbring, U. & Taylor, J. D., eds. Models of Exacerbations in Asthma & COPD [Bibliography & Price not Definite.]. 2007. (Contributions to Microbiology Ser.). (Illus.). 146p. *(978-3-8055-8332-9(X))* Karger, S. AG.

Smith, Thomas J. & Kriebel, David. A Biologic Approach to Environmental Assessment & Epidemiology, 1 vol. 2010. (ENG., Illus.). 448p. 67.50 *(978-0-19-514156-6(3))* Oxford Univ. Pr., Inc.

Smolinski, Tomasz G. Computational Intelligence in Biomedicine & Bioinformatics. 2008. (Studies in Computational Intelligence Ser.). (Illus.). xxiv, 432p. 199.00 *(978-3-540-70776-9(X))* Springer.

Smolinski, Tomasz G., et al, eds. Computational Intelligence in Biomedicine & Bioinformatics: Current Trends & Applications. 2010. (Studies in Computational Intelligence Ser.). (Illus.). xxiv, 432p. pap. 199.00 *(978-3-642-08969-5(0),* 3642089690) Springer.

Smolke, Christina D. The Metabolic Pathway Engineering Handbook: Fundamentals, 2 vols. Smolke, Christina D., ed. 2009. (ENG., Illus.). 678p. 164.95 *(978-1-4398-0296-0(3),* CRC Press) Taylor & Francis Group GBR. Dist: Taylor & Francis Group.

Tsonis, Panagiotis Antonios. Animal Models in Eye Research. 2008. (ENG., Illus.). 232p. 142.00 *(978-0-12-374169-1(6),* Academic Pr.) Elsevier Science & Technology Bks.

Twine, Richard. Animals as Biotechnology: Ethics, Sustainability & Critical Animal Studies. 2010. (Science in Society Ser.). (ENG., Illus.). 232p. 84.95 *(978-1-84407-830-1(2))* Routledge.

van Meurs, Willem L. Modeling & Simulation in Biomedical Engineering: Applications in Cardiorespiratory Physiology. 2011. (ENG., Illus.). 224p. 100.00 *(978-0-07-171445-7(6),* 0071714456) McGraw-Hill Professional Publishing.

Wilson, Daniel R., et al. The Evolutionary Epidemiology of Mania & Depression: A Theoretical & Empirical Interpretation of Mood Disorders. (Illus.). 412p. 129.95 *(978-0-7734-5209-1(5))* Mellen, Edwin Pr., The.

Wingender, Edgar, ed. Biological Petri Nets - Volume 162 Studies in Health Technology & Informatics. 2011. 316p. 174.00 ***(978-1-60750-703-1(X))*** IOS Pr., Inc.

Wrzesinski, Krzysztof. Molecular Markers Associated with Hepatotoxicity Development of in Vitro Test System Based on Human Cells. 2009. 208p. pap. *(978-3-639-16755-9(4))* VDM Verlag Dr. Mueller e.K.

Xie, Ping. Tetrahymena & Human Telomerase Enzymes: Model & Dynamics of Processive Nucleotide & Repeat Addition Translocations. 2012. pap. ***(978-1-62100-982-5(3))*** Nova Science Pubs., Inc.

Zaman, Muhammad H., ed. Statistical Mechanics of Cellular Systems & Processes. 2009. (ENG., Illus.). 228p. 80.00 *(978-0-521-88608-6(2))* Cambridge Univ. Pr.

BIOLOGICAL MOLECULES

see Biomolecules

BIOLOGICAL MONITORING

Here are entered works on the assessment of human exposure to noxious agents by measuring the toxic agent and/or metabolite in biological specimens, e.g. blood, hair, etc.

see also Indicators (Biology)

Angerer, Jürgen & Greim, Helmut, eds. Biomonitoring Methods: From the MAK-Collection for Occupational Health & Safety, Vol. 11. 2008. (MAK-Collection for Occupational Health & Safety. Part IV: Biomonitoring Methods (DFG) Ser.). (ENG.). 321p. 299.00 *(978-3-527-31596-3(9),* Wiley-VCH) Wiley, John & Sons, Inc.

Drexler, Hans & Greim, Helmut, eds. The MAK-Collection for Occupational Health & Safety Pt. II: BAT Value Documentations. 2010. (MAK-Collection for Occupational Health & Safety. Part II: BAT Value Documentations (DFG) Ser.). (ENG.). 240p. 160.00 *(978-3-527-32614-3(6),* Wiley-VCH) Wiley, John & Sons, Inc.

Greim, Helmut, ed. MAK Value Documentations, Vol. 24. 2007. (MAK-Collection for Occupational Health & Safety. Part I: MAK Value Documentations (DFG) Ser.). (ENG., Illus.). 196p. 189.00 *(978-3-527-31594-9(2),* Wiley-VCH) Wiley, John & Sons, Inc.

—MAK Value Documentations Vol. 25, Pt. 1, Vol. 25, Pt. 1. 2009. (MAK-Collection for Occupational Health & Safety. Part I: MAK Value Documentations (DFG) Ser.). (ENG.). 328p. 285.00 *(978-3-527-31958-9(1),* Wiley-VCH) Wiley, John & Sons, Inc.

Guide to Occupational Exposure Values 2007. 2007. spiral bd. 59.95 *(978-1-882417-70-4(4))* American Conference of Governmental Industrial Hygienists.

Hawley, Chris. Hazardous Materials Air Monitoring & Detection Devices. 2nd rev. ed. 2006. (ENG., Illus.). 192p. (C). per. 106.95 *(978-1-4180-3831-1(8))* Delmar Cengage Learning.

Kim, Young J. & Platt, Ulrich, eds. Advanced Environmental Monitoring. 2007. (ENG., Illus.). xxii, 420p. 239.00 *(978-1-4020-6363-3(6),* 1402063636) Springer.

Krolski, Michael E. & Lunchick, Curt, eds. Non-Dietary Human Exposure & Risk Assessment, 1 vol. 2011. (ACS Symposium Ser.). (ENG., Illus.). 128p. 150.00 *(978-0-8412-2588-6(5))* American Chemical Society.

Lawson, Glenn E. & Reynolds, John G., eds. Antiterrorism & Homeland Defense: Polymers & Materials. 3rd ed. 2008. (ACS Symposium Ser.). (ENG., Illus.). 284p. (C). 145.00 *(978-0-8412-3964-7(9))* American Chemical Society.

Merrill, Ray M. Environmental Epidemiology: Principles & Methods. 2007. 483p. (C). pap. 89.95 *(978-0-7637-4152-5(3))* Jones & Bartlett Learning, LLC.

National Research Council (U.S.), Committee on Human Biomonitoring for Environmental Toxicants Staff, contrib. by. Human Biomonitoring for Environmental Chemicals. 2006. (ENG., Illus.). 316p. pap. 55.00 *(978-0-309-10272-8(3))* National Academies Pr.

Ness, Shirley A. Air Monitoring for Toxic Exposures: An Integrated Approach. 2nd ed. 2007. 352p. pap., stu. ed. 20.00 *(978-0-471-29222-7(2),* Wiley); 640p. 98.95 *(978-0-471-29199-2(4))* Wiley, John & Sons, Inc.

Royal Society of Chemistry Staff. Biomarkers & Human Biomonitoring: Set, 2 vols. Knudsen, Lisbeth & Merlo, Domenico Franco, eds. 2011. (Issues in Toxicology Ser.). (ENG., Illus.). 776p. 352.00 ***(978-1-84973-124-9(1))*** Royal Society of Chemistry, The GBR. Dist: Ingram Pub. Services.

—Biomarkers & Human Biomonitoring: Volume 1, 2 vols. Knudsen, Lisbeth & Merlo, Domenico Franco, eds. 2011. (Issues in Toxicology Ser.). (ENG., Illus.). 498p. 200.00 ***(978-1-84973-241-3(8))*** Royal Society of Chemistry, The GBR. Dist: Ingram Pub. Services.

—Biomarkers & Human Biomonitoring: Volume 2, 2 vols. Knudsen, Lisbeth & Merlo, Domenico Franco, eds. 2011. (Issues in Toxicology Ser.). (ENG., Illus.). 278p. 200.00 ***(978-1-84973-242-0(6))*** Royal Society of Chemistry, The GBR. Dist: Ingram Pub. Services.

Valério Marques, A. P., ed. Positional Responses in Lichen Transplant Biomonitoring of Trace Element Air Pollution. 2008. 160p. pap. 87.00 *(978-1-58603-928-8(8))* IOS Pr., Inc.

2007 TLVs(r) & BEIs(r) Book. 2007. spiral bd. 39.95 *(978-1-882417-69-8(0))* American Conference of Governmental Industrial Hygienists.

BIOLOGICAL NAMES

see Biology—Nomenclature

BIOLOGICAL NEURAL NETWORKS

see Neural Networks (Neurobiology)

BIOLOGICAL NOMENCLATURE

see Biology—Nomenclature

BIOLOGICAL ORGANIC CHEMISTRY

see Bioorganic Chemistry

BIOLOGICAL OXIDATION

see Oxidation, Physiological

BIOLOGICAL PARENTS

see Birthparents

BIOLOGICAL PEST CONTROL

see Pests—Biological Control

BIOLOGICAL PHYSICS

see Biophysics

BIOLOGICAL PRODUCTIVITY

see also Food Chains (Ecology); Primary Productivity (Biology)

Riegler, Johannes. Comparative Optimisation of Perfusion Based Bioprocesses. 2010. 64p. pap. *(978-3-639-22947-9(9))* VDM Verlag Dr. Mueller e.K.

Westlake, D. F., et al. The Production Ecology of Wetlands: The IBP Synthesis. Westlake, D. F. et al, eds. 2009. (ENG., Illus.). 592p. pap. 74.00 *(978-0-521-11330-4(X))* Cambridge Univ. Pr.

BIOLOGICAL PRODUCTS

see also Biologicals

Barnes, Richard, et al. Animal Logic. 2009. (ENG., Illus.). 160p. 65.00 *(978-1-56898-861-0(3))* Princeton Architectural Pr.

Bhattacharyya, Lokesh & Rohrer, Jeffrey S. Applications of Ion Chromatography in the Analysis of Pharmaceutical & Biological Products. 2012. (ENG.). 476p. 125.00 ***(978-0-470-46709-1(6),*** Wiley) Wiley, John & Sons, Inc.

Bitterlich, Ahmed & Fischl, Sahar, eds. Bioactive Compounds: Types, Biological Activities & Health Effects. 2012. (Biotechnology in Agriculture, Industry & Medicine Ser.). 450p. 325.00 ***(978-1-61324-865-2(2))*** Nova Science Pubs., Inc.

Boehncke, Wolf-Henning & Radeke, Heinfried, eds. Biologics in General Medicine. 2007. (Illus.). 190p. 199.00 *(978-3-540-29017-9(6))* Springer.

Cavagnaro, Joy A., ed. Preclinical Safety Evaluation of Biopharmaceuticals: A Science-Based Approach to Facilitating Clinical Trials. 2008. (ENG., Illus.). 1072p. 178.00 *(978-0-470-10884-0(3),* Wiley-Interscience) Wiley, John & Sons, Inc.

Chen, Guo-Qiang, ed. Plastics from Bacteria: Natural Functions & Applications. 2010. (Microbiology Monographs). (ENG., Illus.). x, 450p. 239.00 *(978-3-642-03286-8(9),* 3642032869) Springer.

Civjan, Natanya. Natural Products in Chemical Biology. 2012. (ENG.). 418p. 125.00 ***(978-1-118-10117-9(0),*** Wiley) Wiley, John & Sons, Inc.

Colfer, Carol J. Pierce. Human Health & Forests: A Global Overview of Issues, Practice, & Policy. Colfer, Carol J. Pierce, ed. 2008. (People & Plants International Conservation Ser.). (ENG., Illus.). 400p. (C). 127.00 *(978-1-84407-532-4(X))* Routledge.

Daniel J. Gutiérrez. Follow-on Biologics: Background & Issues. 2011. (Series: Biotechnology in Agriculture, Industry & Medicine Ser.). 115.00 *(978-1-61122-076-6(9),* Nova Biomedical Bks.) Nova Science Pubs., Inc.

Diederich, Marc, ed. Natural Compounds & Their Role in Apoptotic Cell Signaling Pathways. 2009. (Annals of the New York Academy of Sciences Ser.: 29). (ENG., Illus.). 400p. pap. 154.95 *(978-1-57331-737-5(3),* Wiley-Blackwell) Wiley, John & Sons, Inc.

Dunford, Nurhan T., ed. Food & Industrial Bioproducts & Bioprocessing. 2012. (ENG., Illus.). 392p. 199.95 ***(978-0-8138-2105-4(3),*** Wiley-Blackwell) Wiley, John & Sons, Inc.

Dutton, Roshni & Scharer, Jeno. Advanced Technologies in Biopharmaceutical Processing. 2006. (ENG., Illus.). 284p. 233.00 *(978-0-8138-0517-7(1),* Wiley-Blackwell) Wiley, John & Sons, Inc.

Ehrlich, Hermann. Biological Materials of Marine Origin. 2010. (Biologically-Inspired System Ser.). 450p. 239.00 *(978-90-481-9129-1(7),* 9048191297) Springer.

Ekins, Sean & Xu, Jinghai J., eds. Drug Efficacy, Safety, & Biologics Discovery: Emerging Technologies & Tools. 2009. (Wiley Series on Technologies for the Pharmaceutical Industry Ser.: 4). (ENG., Illus.). 424p. 128.00 *(978-0-470-22555-4(6),* Wiley) Wiley, John & Sons, Inc.

Essa, M. Mohamed, et al. Natural Products & Their Active Compounds on Disease Prevention. 2012. ***(978-1-62100-153-9(9))*** Nova Science Pubs., Inc.

Forum on Drug Discovery, Development and Translation Staff & Institute of Medicine Staff. Accelerating the Development of Biomarkers for Drug Safety: Workshop Summary. 2009. (ENG.). 100p. pap. 21.00 *(978-0-309-13124-7(3))* National Academies Pr.

Gopalaswamy, Smita & Gopalaswamy, Venky. Combination Products: Regulatory Challenges & Successful Product Development. 2008. (ENG., Illus.). 264p. 149.95 *(978-1-4200-6446-9(0),* CRC Press) Taylor & Francis Group GBR. Dist: Taylor & Francis Group.

Hajek, Ann E., et al, eds. Use of Microbes for Control & Eradication of Invasive Arthropods. 2010. (Progress in Biological Control Ser.). xvi, 366p. pap. 189.00 *(978-90-481-7910-7(6),* 9048179106) Springer.

Hefferon, Kathleen Laura. Biopharmaceuticals in Plants: Toward the Next Century of Medicine. 2009. (ENG., Illus.). 224p. 99.95 *(978-1-4398-0474-2(5),* CRC Press) Taylor & Francis Group GBR. Dist: Taylor & Francis Group.

Honary, Lou, et al. Biobased Lubricants & Greases: Technology & Products. 2011. (Tribology in Practice Ser.). (ENG., Illus.). 238p. 125.00 *(978-0-470-74158-0(9),* Wiley) Wiley, John & Sons, Inc.

Hui, Y. H., et al, eds. Handbook of Plant-Based Fermented Foods & Beverages. 2nd rev. ed. 2012. (ENG., Illus.). 821p. 199.95 ***(978-1-4398-4904-0(8),*** CRC Press) Taylor & Francis Group GBR. Dist: Taylor & Francis Group.

Iason, Glenn R., et al, eds. The Ecology of Plant Secondary Metabolites: From Genes to Global Processes. 2012. (Ecological Reviews Ser.). (ENG., Illus.). 352p. 120.00 ***(978-0-521-19326-9(5))***; pap. 60.00 ***(978-0-521-15712-4(9))*** Cambridge Univ. Pr.

ISPE Good Practice Guide: Development of Investigational Therapeutic Biological Products. 2007. 86p. *(978-1-931879-58-3(3))* International Society for Pharmaceutical Engineering.

Ivanov, Volodymyr, et al. Biogranulation Technologies for Wastewater Treatment: Microbial Granules. 2006. (Waste Management Ser.: 6). (ENG., Illus.). 308p. 205.00 *(978-0-08-045022-3(9),* Pergamon) Elsevier Science & Technology Bks.

Jornitz, Maik W. & Meltzer, Theodore H., eds. Filtration & Purification in the Biopharmaceutical Industry. 2nd rev. ed. 2008. (Drugs & the Pharmaceutical Sciences Ser.). (ENG., Illus.). 816p. 350.00 *(978-0-8493-7953-6(9),* Informa Healthcare) Taylor & Francis Group GBR. Dist: Taylor & Francis Group.

Kirkham, Bruce, et al. The Handbook of Biological Therapy. 2009. (ENG., Illus.). 176p. pap. 55.00 *(978-0-19-920816-6(6))* Oxford Univ. Pr., Inc.

Liong, Min-Tze. Bioprocess Sciences & Technology. 2011. (Biochemistry Research Trends Ser.). (Illus.). 526p. 195.00 *(978-1-61122-950-9(2))* Nova Science Pubs., Inc.

Mire-Sluis, Anthony R. State of the Art Analytical Methods for the Characterization of Biological Products & Assessment of Comparability: Natcher Building, National Institutes of Health (NIH), Bethesda, MD, USA, June 10-13, 2003: Proceedings of a Symposium, Vol. 122. (Developments in Biologicals Ser.: Vol. 122). (Illus.). *(978-3-8055-7998-8(5))* Karger, S. AG.

Mohdaly, A. Extraction of Metabolites from Plant Tissues. Smetanska, I., ed. 2010. (Food Science & Technology Ser.). 72p. pap. 43.00 *(978-1-61668-252-1(3))* Nova Science Pubs., Inc.

Mollah, Hamid, et al. Application of Risk Management for Pharmaceutical & Biological Products Manufacturing. 2012. (Wiley Series in Biotechnology & Bioengineering Ser.). (ENG.). 350p. 89.95 *(978-0-470-55234-6(4),* Wiley) Wiley, John & Sons, Inc.

Nassar, Ala F., ed. Biotransformation & Metabolite Elucidation of Xenobiotics: Characterization & Identification. 2010. (ENG., Illus.). 328p. 116.00 *(978-0-470-50478-9(1),* Wiley) Wiley, John & Sons, Inc.

Nielson, Hanne Morck & Jorgensen, Lene, eds. Delivery Technologies for Biopharmaceuticals: Peptides, Proteins, Nucleic Acids & Vaccines. 2010. (ENG., Illus.). 442p. 185.00 *(978-0-470-72338-8(6),* Wiley) Wiley, John & Sons, Inc.

Oldham, Oldham, ed. Principles of Cancer Biotherapy. 5th ed. 2009. (ENG., Illus.). xii, 744p. 289.00 *(978-90-481-2277-6(5),* 9048122775) Springer.

PDR Staff. PDR Supplements 2007: PDR Combined Supp A/B. 61st rev. ed. 2007. (Illus.). 300p. 46.95 *(978-1-56363-600-4(X))* PDR Network, LLC.

Ramawat. Biotechnology: Secondary Metabolites. 2nd rev. ed. 2007. (ENG., Illus.). 586p. 79.95 *(978-1-57808-428-9(8))* BIOS Scientific Publishers Ltd. GBR. Dist: Taylor & Francis Group.

Rauter, Amélia Pilar, et al, eds. Natural Products in the New Millennium: Prospects & Industrial Application: Prospects & Industrial Application. 2010. (Proceedings of the Phytochemical Society of Europe Ser.). 540p. pap. 329.00 *(978-90-481-6186-7(X),* 904816186X) Springer.

Ravensberg, Willem. A Roadmap to the Successful Development & Commercialization of Microbial Pest Control Products for Control of Arthropods. 2011. (Progress in Biological Control Ser.). (ENG., Illus.). xxv, 383p. 179.00 *(978-94-007-0436-7(4),* 9400704364) Springer.

Reuters, Thomson. PDR Supplement B, 2009, Vol. 63. 2009. 300p. pap. 46.95 *(978-1-56363-715-5(4))* PDR Network, LLC.

—2009 PDR Supplement A, Vol. 63. 2009. 300p. pap. 46.95 *(978-1-56363-714-8(6))* PDR Network, LLC.

Reuters, Thomson, ed. 2009 Physicians' Desk Reference: (PDR) (Library/ Hospital edition) 63rd ed. 2008. (Illus.). 3500p. 94.95 *(978-1-56363-703-2(0))* PDR Network, LLC.

—2009 Physicians' Desk Reference (PDR) PDR (Bookstor edition) 63rd ed. 2008. 3500p. 94.95 *(978-1-56363-704-9(9))* PDR Network, LLC.

Rey, Louis & May, Joan C., eds. Freeze-Drying/Lyophilization of Pharmaceutical & Biological Products, Third Edition. 3rd rev. ed. 2010. (Drugs & the Pharmaceutical Sciences Ser.). (ENG., Illus.). 578p. *(978-1-4398-2575-4(0))* Informa Healthcare.

Rieger, Paula. Pocket Guide to Biotherapy. Date not set. (Nursing Ser.). 200p. pap. 31.25 *(978-0-7637-0543-5(8))* Jones & Bartlett Learning, LLC.

Sheets, Rebecca & Petricciani, John C. Vaccine Cell Substrates 2004: National Institutes of Health (NIH), Doubletree Hotel, Rockville, Md., USA, June 29-July 1, 2004, Vol. 123. (Developments in Biologicals Ser.: Vol. 123). (Illus.). 366p. pap. *(978-3-8055-7999-5(3))* Karger, S. AG.

Smolke, Christina D. The Metabolic Pathway Engineering Handbook: Fundamentals, 2 vols. Smolke, Christina D., ed. 2009. (ENG., Illus.). 678p. 164.95 *(978-1-4398-0296-0(3),* CRC Press) Taylor & Francis Group GBR. Dist: Taylor & Francis Group.

Stuart, M. C., et al, eds. WHO Model Formulary 2008. 2009. (Nonserial Publication Ser.). (ENG.). 650p. pap. 48.00 *(978-92-4-154765-9(0))* World Health Organization.

Suk, Kyoungho. Research Focus on Natural Products & the Body's Immune & Inflammatory Systems. 2007. 89.00 *(978-1-60021-751-7(6))* Nova Science Pubs., Inc.

Thomson, creator. Physicians Desk Reference: Supplement B, Vol. 61. 61st rev. ed. 2007. (Physicians' Desk Reference Supplements A & B Ser.). per. 46.95 *(978-1-56363-599-1(2))* PDR Network, LLC.

Thomson Healthcare, creator. Physicians' Desk Reference Supplement A, Vol. 61. 61st rev. ed. 2007. (Physicians' Desk Reference Supplements A & B Ser.). (Illus.). 288p. pap. 46.95 *(978-1-56363-598-4(4))* PDR Network, LLC.

Tokusoglu, Ozlem. Fruit & Cereal Bioactives: Sources, Chemistry, & Applications. 2011. (ENG., Illus.). 473p. 169.95 *(978-1-4398-0665-4(9),* CRC Press) Taylor & Francis Group GBR. Dist: Taylor & Francis Group.

Tovey, Michael G., ed. Detection & Quantification of Antibodies to Biopharmaceuticals: Practical & Applied Considerations. 2011. (ENG., Illus.). 448p. 135.00 *(978-0-470-56666-4(3),* Wiley) Wiley, John & Sons, Inc.

Vogel, Joseph Henry, ed. The Museum of Bioprospecting, Intellectual Property, & the Public Domain: A Place, A Process, A Philosophy. 2011. (Environmental Conventions: Transdisciplinary Approaches Ser.). 174p. pap. 40.00 *(978-0-85728-416-7(9))* Anthem Pr. GBR. Dist: Books International, Inc.

Walsh, G. & Murphy, B., eds. Biopharmaceuticals, an Industrial Perspective. 2010. 524p. pap. 399.00 *(978-90-481-5237-7(2),* 9048152372) Springer.

Wetzel, Suzanne, et al. Bioproducts from Canada's Forests: New Partnerships in the Bioeconomy. (ENG.). xv, 257p. 2010. pap. 209.00 *(978-90-481-7248-1(9),* 9048172489) 2006. (Illus.). 209.00 *(978-1-4020-4991-0(9),* 1402049919) Springer.

Whitmore, Elaine. Development of FDA-Regulated Medical Products: A Translational Approach. 2nd ed. 2012. ***(978-0-87389-833-1(8))*** ASQ Quality Pr.

Wink, Michael. Functions & Biotechnology of Plant Secondary Metabolites, Volume 39, 2nd Edition. 2nd ed. 2010. (Annual Plant Reviews Ser.: 46). (ENG., Illus.). 424p. 219.95 *(978-1-4051-8528-8(7),* Wiley-Blackwell) Wiley, John & Sons, Inc.

World Health Organization. WHO Expert Committee on Biological Standardization: Fifty-sixth Report. 2007. (Technical Report Series, No 941 Ser.). (ENG.). 350p. pap. 60.00 *(978-92-4-120941-0(0))* World Health Organization.

—WHO Expert Committee on Drug Dependence: Thirty-fourth Report. 2006. (Technical Report Series, No 942 Ser.). (ENG.). 30p. pap. 16.80 *(978-92-4-120942-7(9))* World Health Organization.

BIOLOGICAL PSYCHIATRY

Here are entered works dealing with that branch of psychiatry which emphasizes a multidisciplinary (physiological, neurological, pharmacological and genetic) approach to psychiatric disorders.

see also Neuropsychiatry; Psychobiology; Psychodynamic Psychotherapy

Banaschewski, Tobias & Rohde, L. A. Biological Child Psychiatry: Recent Trends & Developments. 2008. (Advances in Biological Psychiatry Ser.). (Illus.). 256p. *(978-3-8055-8482-1(2))* Karger, S. AG.

Barber, Charles. Comfortably Numb: How Psychiatry Is Medicating a Nation. 2009. (Vintage Ser.). (ENG.). 304p. pap. 15.95 *(978-0-307-27495-3(0),* Vintage) Knopf Doubleday Publishing Group.

Blows, William T. The Biological Basis of Mental Health Nursing. 2nd rev. ed. 2011. (ENG., Illus.). 336p. (C). 140.00 *(978-0-415-57097-8(2));* pap. 45.95 *(978-0-415-57098-5(0))* Routledge.

Cram101 Textbook Reviews & Cram101 Textbook Reviews. Outlines & Highlights for Biological Psychiatry by Michael Trimble, Isbn: 9780470688946. 2011. 140p. pap. 28.95 ***(978-1-61461-262-9(5))*** Cram101 Inc.

—Outlines & Highlights for Brain & Behavior: An Introduction to Biological Psychology by Bob Garrett, ISBN. 2011. 134p. pap. 28.95 ***(978-1-4288-5924-1(1))*** Cram101 Inc.

Fatemi, S. Hossein & Clayton, Paula J. The Medical Basis of Psychiatry. 3rd ed. 2008. (ENG., Illus.). xxii, 802p. 229.00 *(978-1-58829-917-8(1),* 1588299171) Springer.

Gabbard, Glen O. Principles of Psychodynamic Psychotherapy. 2009. cd-rom 69.00 *(978-0-89042-348-6(2))* American Psychiatric Publishing, Inc.

Ghaemi, S. Nassir. The Rise & Fall of the Biopsychosocial Model: Reconciling Art & Science in Psychiatry. 2009. (ENG., Illus.). 272p. (gr. 17). 52.00 *(978-0-8018-9390-2(9))* Johns Hopkins Univ. Pr.

Glenyn, Bernice C., et al, eds. Celiac Disease: Etiology, Diagnosis, & Treatment. 2008. (Illus.). xi, 261p. 129.00 *(978-1-60692-634-5(9))* Nova Science Pubs., Inc.

Kaschka, W. P., ed. Perspectives in Affective Disorders: International Symposium '25 Years Weissenau Depression Unit', Weissenau, Germany, September 14-15, 2001, Vol. 21. (Advances in Biological Psychiatry Ser.: Vol. 21). (Illus.). *(978-3-8055-7439-6(8))* Karger, S. AG.

Luecken, Linda J. & Gallo, Linda C. Handbook of Physiological Research Methods in Health Psychology. 2007. (Illus.). 472p. 150.00 *(978-1-4129-2605-8(X),* B2605XC) SAGE Pubns., Inc.

Maccabe, James, ed. Beyond Nature & Nurture in Psychiatry: Genes, Environment & Their Interplay. 2006. (ENG., Illus.). 256p. 130.00 *(978-0-415-37300-5(X),* Informa Healthcare) Taylor & Francis Group GBR. Dist: Taylor & Francis Group.

McLaren, Niall. Humanizing Psychiatrists: Toward a Humane Psychiatry: An Application of the Philosophy of Science to Psychiatry. 2010. *(978-1-61599-061-0(5));* pap. *(978-1-61599-060-3(7))* Loving Healing Pr., Inc.

—Humanizing Psychiatry: The Biocognitive Model. 2010. *(978-1-61599-012-2(7));* pap. *(978-1-61599-011-5(9))* Loving Healing Pr., Inc.

Muller, René J. Doing Psychiatry Wrong: A Critical & Prescriptive Look at a Faltering Profession. 2007. (ENG.). 136p. per. 36.50 *(978-0-88163-469-3(7))* Routledge.

Myslobodsky, Michael S. & Weiner, Ina, eds. Contemporary Issues in Modeling of Psychopathology. 2010. (Neurobiological Foundation of Aberrant Behaviors Ser.). 336p. pap. 199.00 *(978-1-4419-4996-7(8),* 1441949968) Springer.

Noll, Richard. American Madness: The Rise & Fall of Dementia Praecox. 2011. 408p. 45.00 *(978-0-674-04739-6(7))* Harvard Univ. Pr.

Smoller, Jordan. The Other Side of Normal: How Biology Is Providing the Clues to Unlock the Secrets of Normal & Abnormal Behavior. 2012. (ENG.). 400p. 27.99 *(978-0-06-149219-8(1),* Morrow, William & Co.); 640p. pap. 27.99 *(978-0-06-206497-4(5),* HarperLuxe) HarperCollins Pubs.

Smoller, Jordan W. The Other Side of Normal: How Biology Is Providing the Clues to Unlock the Secrets of Normal & Abnormal Behavior. 2012. ***(978-0-06-149220-4(5),*** Morrow, William & Co.) HarperCollins Pubs.

Trimble, Michael R. & George, Mark. Biological Psychiatry. 3rd ed. 2010. (ENG., Illus.). 432p. 110.95 *(978-0-470-68894-6(7),* Wiley) Wiley, John & Sons, Inc.

Weissman, Sidney, et al. Integrating Psychological & Biological Therapies. 2008. (Psychotherapy in Clinical Practice Ser.). (ENG., Illus.). 176p. pap. 49.99 *(978-0-7817-5102-5(0))* Lippincott Williams & Wilkins.

BIOLOGICAL PSYCHOLOGY

see Psychobiology

BIOLOGICAL RESEARCH

see Biology—Research

BIOLOGICAL RHEOLOGY

see Rheology (Biology)

BIOLOGICAL RHYTHMS

see also Circadian Rhythms; Photoperiodism; Sexual Cycle

Aguda, Baltazar & Friedman, Avner. Models of Cellular Regulation. 2008. (Oxford Graduate Texts). (ENG., Illus.). 200p. 99.00 *(978-0-19-857091-2(0))* Oxford Univ. Pr., Inc.

Banfalvi, Gaspar, ed. Cell Cycle Synchronization: Methods & Protocols. 2011. (Methods in Molecular Biology Ser.). (Illus.). xii, 300p. 139.00 *(978-1-61779-181-9(4),* 1617791814) Humana Pr.

Brody, Stuart. The Genetics of Circadian Rhythms. 2011. (ENG., Illus.). 264p. 161.00 ***(978-0-12-387690-4(7),*** Academic Pr.) Elsevier Science & Technology Bks.

Buzsaki, Gyorgy. Rhythms of the Brain, 1 vol. 2011. (ENG., Illus.). 464p. pap. 39.99 *(978-0-19-982823-4(7))* Oxford Univ. Pr., Inc.

Dai, Wei, ed. Checkpoint Responses in Cancer Therapy. 2010. (Cancer Drug Discovery & Development Ser.). (Illus.). xiv, 314p. pap. 219.00 *(978-1-61737-847-8(X),* 161737847X) Humana Pr.

Edwards, Kasey. Thirty-Something & the Clock Is Ticking: What Happens When You Can No Longer Ignore the Baby Issue. 2011. (ENG.). 208p. pap. 14.95 ***(978-1-84596-734-5(8))*** Mainstream Publishing Co., Ltd. GBR. Dist: Independent Pubs. Group.

Foster, Russell G. & Kreitzman, Leon. Seasons of Life: The Biological Rhythms That Enable Living Things to Thrive & Survive. 2010. (Illus.). 320p. pap. 20.00 *(978-0-300-16786-3(5))* Yale Univ. Pr.

Giordano, Antonio & Soprano, Kenneth J., eds. Cell Cycle Inhibitors in Cancer Therapy. 2010. (Cancer Drug Discovery & Development Ser.). (Illus.). 326p. pap. 179.00 *(978-1-61737-257-5(9),* 1617372579) Humana Pr.

Green, Simon R. Biological Rhythms, Sleep & Hypnosis. 2011. (Palgrave Insights in Psychology Ser.). (ENG., Illus.). 200p. pap. 16.00 *(978-0-230-25265-3(6))* Palgrave Macmillan.

Griffiths, Dilwyn J. Microalgal Cell Cycles. 2010. (Cell Biology Research Progress Ser.). (Illus.). viii, 116p. pap. 49.00 *(978-1-60876-787-8(6),* Nova Novinka) Nova Science Pubs., Inc.

K, Pushkala & D Gupta, P. Dark Side of the Night Light. 2011. 136p. pap. ***(978-3-8443-1272-0(2))*** Lambert Academic Publishing.

Kubiak, Jacek Z., ed. Cell Cycle in Development. 2011. (Results & Problems in Cell Differentiation Ser.). (Illus.). xv, 588p. 239.00 *(978-3-642-19064-3(2),* 3642190642) Springer.

Lieberman, Howard B., ed. Cell Cycle Checkpoint Control Protocols. 2010. (Methods in Molecular Biology Ser.). (Illus.). 392p. pap. 119.00 *(978-1-61737-369-5(9),* 1617373699) Humana Pr.

Lloyd, David & Rossi, Ernest, eds. Ultradian Rhythms from Molecules to Mind: A New Vision of Life. 2010. x, 454p. pap. 229.00 *(978-90-481-7852-0(5),* 9048178525) Springer.

Lloyd, David & Rossi, Ernest Lawrence. Ultradian Rhythms from Molecules to Mind: A New Vision of Life. 2008. (Illus.). x, 450p. 229.00 *(978-1-4020-8351-8(3),* 1402083513) Springer.

Mancuso, S. & Shabala, S., eds. Rhythms in Plants: Phenomenology, Mechanisms, & Adaptive Significance. 2007. (ENG., Illus.). xx, 362p. 289.00 *(978-3-540-68069-7(1),* 3540680691) Springer.

Mancuso, Stefano & Shabala, Sergey, eds. Rhythms in Plants: Phenomenology, Mechanisms, & Adaptive Significance. 2010. (ENG., Illus.). xx, 362p. pap. 289.00 *(978-3-642-08774-5(4),* 3642087744) Springer.

Maroto, Miguel & Monk, Nick, eds. Cellular Oscillatory Mechanisms. 2010. (Advances in Experimental Medicine & Biology Ser.). (Illus.). viii, 153p. pap. 199.00 *(978-1-4419-1888-8(4),* 1441918884) Springer.

Melmed, Shlomo, et al. Hormonal Control of Cell Cycle. (Research & Perspectives in Endocrine Interactions Ser.). (Illus.). 2010. xii, 141p. pap. 169.00 *(978-3-642-09310-4(8),* 3642093108) 2007. 186p. 169.00 *(978-3-540-73854-1(1))* Springer.

Pardee, Joel D. & Brown, A. M. C. The Cell Cycle & Cell Division. 2011. (Colloquium Series on the Cell Biology of Medicine Ser.). 100p. pap. 35.00 *(978-1-61504-261-6(X))* Morgan & Claypool Life Science Publishers.

Salvenmoser, Oktav & Meklau, Brigitta, eds. Biological Clocks: Effects on Behavior, Health & Outlook. 2010. (Public Health in the 21st Century Ser.). 221p. 79.00 *(978-1-60741-251-9(9))* Nova Science Pubs., Inc.

Spaan, J. A. E., et al, eds. Biopacemaking. 2010. (Series in Biomedical Engineering Ser.). viii, 182p. pap. 159.00 *(978-3-642-09127-8(X),* 364209127X) Springer.

Spaan, Jos A. E., et al, eds. Biopacemaking. 2007. (Series in Biomedical Engineering Ser.). viii, 182p. 159.00 *(978-3-540-72109-3(6))* Springer.

Stillman, Bruce & Stewart, David, eds. Clocks & Rhythms, Vol. LXXII. 2008. (ENG., Illus.). 674p. 310.00 *(978-0-87969-822-5(5));* pap. 126.00 *(978-0-87969-823-2(3))* Cold Spring Harbor Laboratory Pr.

Tsuji, Masatsugu & Kuchiki, Akifumi, eds. From Agglomeration to Innovation: Upgrading Industrial Clusters in Emerging Economies. 2009. (ENG., Illus.). 288p. 121.00 *(978-0-230-23310-2(4))* Palgrave Macmillan.

Winfree, Arthur T. The Geometry of Biological Time. 2nd ed. 2010. (Interdisciplinary Applied Mathematics Ser.). (Illus.). xxvi, 777p. pap. 105.00 *(978-1-4419-3196-2(1),* 1441931961) Springer.

BIOLOGICAL SPECIMENS—COLLECTION AND PRESERVATION

Baust, John M., ed. Advances in Biopreservation. 2006. (ENG., Illus.). 426p. 226.95 *(978-0-8493-2772-8(5),* 2772, CRC Press) Taylor & Francis Group GBR. Dist: Taylor & Francis Group.

Biobanking: How the Lack of a Coherent Policy Allowed the Veterans Administration to Destroy an Irreplaceable Collection of Legionella Samples: Hearing Before the Subcommittee on Investigations & Oversight, Committee on Science & Technology, One Hundred Tenth Congress, Second Session, September 9, 2008. 2008. (Illus.). iv, 514p. *(978-0-16-082631-3(4),* 552-070-38649-1) United States Government Printing Office.

Borry, Pascal & Dierickx, Kris, eds. New Challenges for Biobanks: Ethics, Law & Governance. 2009. 277p. pap. 86.95 *(978-90-5095-974-2(1))* Intersentia Uitgevers N.V. BEL. Dist: International Specialized Bk. Services.

Caboux, E., et al. International Network of Biological Resource Centres for Cancer Research. Recommendations on Minimum Technical Standards: IARC Working Group Report, No. 2. 2007. (IARC Nonserial Publication). (ENG.). 56p. pap. 25.00 *(978-92-832-2442-6(6))* World Health Organization.

Guder, Walter G., et al. Diagnostic Samples: From the Patient to the Laboratory - The Impact of Preanalytical Variables on the Quality of Laboratory Results. 4th ed. 2009. (ENG., Illus.). 124p. 83.95 *(978-3-527-32307-4(4),* Wiley-VCH) Wiley, John & Sons, Inc.

Jenkins, Amanda J., ed. Drug Testing in Alternate Biological Specimens. 2010. (Forensic Science & Medicine Ser.). (Illus.). xxi, 186p. pap. 149.00 *(978-1-61737-732-7(5),* 1617377325) Humana Pr.

Kaye, Jane & Stranger, Mark. Principles & Practice in Biobank Governance. 2009. (Illus.). 316p. 124.95 *(978-0-7546-7825-0(3))* Ashgate Publishing Co.

Kohler, Robert E. All Creatures: Naturalists, Collectors & Biodiversity 1850-1950. 2006. (ENG., Illus.). 380p. (C). 46.95 *(978-0-691-12539-8(2))* Princeton Univ. Pr.

Migdalski, Edward C. Lure of the Wild: The Global Adventures of a Museum Naturalist. 2006. (Illus.). xxv, 294p. *(978-0-912532-74-5(2))* Peabody Museum of Natural History, Yale Univ.

Panel on Collecting, Storing, Accessing, and Protecting Biological Specimens and Biodata in Social Surveys & National Research Council. Conducting Biosocial Surveys: Collecting, Storing, Accessing, & Protecting Biospecimens & Biodata. 2010. (ENG.). 124p. pap. 31.75 *(978-0-309-15706-3(4))* National Academies Pr.

Solbakk, Jan Helge, et al, eds. The Ethics of Research Biobanking. 2009. (ENG., Illus.). xviii, 358p. 217.00 *(978-0-387-93871-4(0),* 0387938710) Springer.

BIOLOGICAL STRUCTURE

see Morphology

BIOLOGICAL SURFACES

see Biological Interfaces

BIOLOGICAL TELEMETRY

see Biotelemetry

BIOLOGICAL TIME

see Chronobiology

BIOLOGICAL TOLERANCE

see Biocompatibility

BIOLOGICAL TRANSPORT

see also Plant Translocation; Secretion

Amidon, Gordon L. & Lee, Ping I. Transport Processes in Pharmaceutical Systems. Date not set. (Drugs & the Pharmaceutical Sciences Ser.). *(978-0-8247-9374-6(9))* Dekker, Marcel Inc.

Appert-Rolland, Cécile. Traffic & Granular Flow '07. 2009. (Illus.). 700p. 219.00 *(978-3-540-77073-2(9))* Springer.

Appert-Rolland, Cécile, et al, eds. Traffic & Granular Flow ' 07. 2012. (ENG., Illus.). xvi, 758p. pap. 219.00 ***(978-3-642-09580-1(1),*** 3642095801) Springer.

Bernhardt, Ingolf & Ellory, J. Clive, eds. Red Cell Membrane Transport in Health & Disease. 2010. (ENG., Illus.). xxviii, 748p. pap. 199.00 *(978-3-642-07920-7(2),* 3642079202) Springer.

Borka, D., et al. Channeling of Protons Through Carbon Nanotubes. 2011. pap. *(978-1-61122-050-6(5))* Nova Science Pubs., Inc.

Conn, P. Michael, ed. Essential Ion Channel Methods. 2010. (Reliable Lab Solutions Ser.). (ENG., Illus.). 632p. pap. 77.95 *(978-0-12-382204-8(1),* Academic Pr.) Elsevier Science & Technology Bks.

Dhanoa Dale S Staff. Pharmacogenomics in Drug Discovery & Development. 2009. 1000p. 169.95 *(978-1-57444-507-7(3))* CRC Pr. LLC.

Douglas, Mark. Retrograde Cellular Transport of Herpes Simplex Virus. 2008. 180p. pap. *(978-3-639-02865-2(1))* VDM Verlag Dr. Mueller e.K.

Evans, David H., ed. Osmotic & Ionic Regulation: Cells & Animals. 2008. (ENG., Illus.). 606p. 129.95 *(978-0-8493-8030-3(8),* CRC Press) Taylor & Francis Group GBR. Dist: Taylor & Francis Group.

Figgins, Mark R. Calcium Channels: Properties, Functions & Regulation. 2012. (Cerebrovascular Research & Disorders Ser.). 201p. 95.00 ***(978-1-61470-232-0(2))*** Nova Science Pubs., Inc.

Fonseca, Danielle S., ed. Potassium Channels: Types, Structure & Blockers. 2012. (Cell Biology Research Progress Ser.). 157p. 95.00 ***(978-1-61324-880-5(6))*** Nova Science Pubs., Inc.

Fournier, Ronald L. Basic Transport Phenomena in Biomedical Engineering. 3rd rev. ed. 2011. (ENG., Illus.). 483p. (C). 89.95 *(978-1-4398-2670-6(6),* CRC Press) Taylor & Francis Group GBR. Dist: Taylor & Francis Group.

Friedman, Morton H. Principles & Models of Biological Transport. 2nd ed. (ENG., Illus.). xviii, 510p. 2010. pap. 149.00 *(978-1-4419-2715-6(8),* 1441927158) 2008. 149.00 *(978-0-387-79239-2(2),* 0387792392) Springer.

Gerencser, George A., ed. Epithelial Transport Physiology. 2009. (ENG., Illus.). xii, 488p. 269.00 *(978-1-60327-228-5(3),* 1603272283) Humana Pr.

Gupta, Satya Prakash, ed. Ion Channels & Their Inhibitors. 2011. (ENG., Illus.). xiii, 300p. 129.00 *(978-3-642-19921-9(6),* 3642199216) Springer.

Herchuelz, André. Sodium-Calcium Exchange & the Plasma Membrane Ca2+-ATPase in Cell Function: Fifth International Conference. Blaustein, Mordecai P. et al, eds. 2007. (Annals of the New York Academy of Sciences Ser.: Vol. 1096). (ENG., Illus.). 400p. pap. 169.95 *(978-1-57331-649-1(0),* Wiley-Blackwell) Wiley, John & Sons, Inc.

Horspool. Drg Del Tech. 2009. 600p. 199.95 *(978-1-57444-809-2(9),* Informa Healthcare) Taylor & Francis Group GBR. Dist: Taylor & Francis Group.

Junk, Matthias. Assessing the Functional Structure of Molecular Transporters by EPR Spectroscopy. 2012. (Springer Theses Ser.). (ENG., Illus.). xvi, 212p. 129.00 ***(978-3-642-25134-4(X),*** 364225134X) Springer.

Kamkin, Andre & Kiseleva, Irina, eds. Mechanosensitive Ion Channels. 2007. (Mechanosensitivity in Cells & Tissues Ser.). (Illus.). 381p. 189.00 *(978-1-4020-6425-8(X))* Springer.

—Mechanosensitive Ion Channels. 2010. (Mechanosensitivity in Cells & Tissues Ser.). xxii, 382p. pap. 189.00 *(978-90-481-7638-0(7),* 9048176387) Springer.

Kehlenbach, Ralph H., ed. Nuclear Transport. 2009. (Molecular Biology Intelligence Unit Ser.). *(978-1-58706-333-6(6))* Landes Bioscience.

Keränen, Sirkka & Jäntti, Jussi, eds. Regulatory Mechanisms of Intracellular Membrane Transport. 2010. (Topics in Current Genetics Ser.). (Illus.). x, 214p. pap. 169.00 *(978-3-642-06095-3(1),* 3642060951) Springer.

Krishnamurthy, Vikram, et al. Introductory Membrane Biophysics: A Stochastic Dynamical Approach to Biological Nano-Tubes. 2014. (IEEE Press Series on Biomedical Engineering Ser.). (ENG., Illus.). 256p. 89.95 *(978-0-470-08889-0(3),* Wiley-IEEE Pr.) Wiley, John & Sons, Inc.

Lash, Lawrence H., ed. Drug Metabolism & Transport: Molecular Methods & Mechanisms. 2010. (Methods in Pharmacology & Toxicology Ser.). (Illus.). 400p. pap. 179.00 *(978-1-61737-494-4(6),* 1617374946) Humana Pr.

Layton, Harold E. & Weinstein, Alan M., eds. Membrane Transport & Renal Physiology. 2010. (IMA Volumes in Mathematics & its Applications Ser.). (Illus.). xv, 394p. pap. 109.00 *(978-1-4419-3020-0(5),* 1441930205) Springer.

Leuchtag, H. Richard. Voltage-Sensitive Ion Channels: Biophysics of Molecular Excitability. (ENG.). xxiv, 532p. 2010. pap. 279.00 *(978-90-481-7384-6(1)*, 9048173841) 2008. 279.00 *(978-1-4020-5524-9(2)*, 1402055242) Springer.

Li, Haowen. Nonlinear Optical Properties of Potential-Sensitive Dyes. 2010. 156p. pap. *(978-3-639-12718-8(8))* VDM Verlag Dr. Mueller e.K.

Linke, H. & Mansson, Alf. Controlled Nanoscale Motion. 2007. (Lecture Notes in Physics Ser.: Vol. 711). (Illus.). XX, 412p. 159.00 *(978-3-540-49521-5(5)*, 3540495215) Springer.

Lippiat, Jonathan D. Potassium Channels: Methods & Protocols. 2008. (Methods in Molecular Biology Ser.). (Illus.). 296p. 119.00 *(978-1-934115-65-7(7))*; x, 300p. *(978-1-59745-526-8(1))* Humana Pr.

Lippiat, Jonathan D., ed. Potassium Channels: Methods & Protocols. 2010. (Methods in Molecular Biology Ser.). (Illus.). x, 302p. pap. 119.00 *(978-1-61737-940-6(9)*, 1617379409) Humana Pr.

Lopatin, Anatoli & Nichols, Colin G., eds. Ion Channel Localization. 2010. (Methods in Pharmacology & Toxicology Ser.). (Illus.). 496p. pap. 169.00 *(978-1-61737-211-7(0)*, 1617372110) Humana Pr.

Maguire, David, et al, eds. Oxygen Transport to Tissue XXVIII. 2007. (Illus.). 226p. 179.00 ***(978-0-387-71763-0(3)***, 0387717633) Springer.

Marsh, Mark. Membrane Trafficking in Viral Replication. 2010. (Current Topics in Microbiology & Immunology Ser.). (Illus.). ix, 259p. pap. 159.00 *(978-3-642-05981-0(3)*, 3642059813) Springer.

Martinac, Boris, ed. Sensing with Ion Channels. 2007. (Springer Series in Biophysics Ser.). (Illus.). 317p. 219.00 *(978-3-540-72683-8(7)*, 3540726837) Springer.

Mikoshiba, Katsuhiko, ed. Handbook of Neurochemistry & Molecular Neurobiology: Neural Signaling Mechanisms. 3rd ed. 2009. (ENG., Illus.). xvi, 632p. 249.00 *(978-0-387-30338-3(3)*, 0387303383) Springer.

Morimoto, Richard I., et al. Protein Homeostasis. 2011. 135.00 ***(978-1-936113-06-4(6))*** Cold Spring Harbor Laboratory Pr.

Napier, Susan & Bingham, Matilda. Transporters As Targets for Drugs. 2009. (Topics in Medicinal Chemistry Ser.). 400p. 199.00 *(978-3-540-87911-4(0))* Springer.

Okunieff, Paul, et al, eds. Oxygen Transport to Tissue XXVI. 2010. (Advances in Experimental Medicine & Biology Ser.). (Illus.). xiv, 407p. pap. 219.00 *(978-1-4419-3770-4(6)*, 1441937706) Springer.

Op den Kamp, J. A., ed. Protein, Lipid & Membrane Traffic: Pathways & Targeting. (NATO Science Ser.: Vol. A322). (Illus.). 277p. 139.00 *(978-1-58603-008-7(6))* IOS Pr., Inc.

Pasterkamp, Gerard, ed. Semaphorins: Receptor & Intracellular Signaling Mechanisms: Receptor & Intracellular Signaling Mechanisms. 2010. (Advances in Experimental Medicine & Biology Ser.). (Illus.). xiv, 147p. pap. 179.00 *(978-1-4419-2427-8(2)*, 1441924272) Springer.

Pittman, Roland. Regulation of Tissue Oxygenation. 2011. (Colloquium Series on Integrated Systems Physiology: from Molecule to Function Ser.). 100p. pap. 35.00 *(978-1-61504-177-0(X))* Morgan & Claypool Life Science Publishers.

Ponte-Sucre, Alicia. ABC Transporters in Microorganisms: Research, Innovation & Value as Targets against Drug Resistance. Ponte-Sucre, Alicia, ed. 2009. (Illus.). 260p. 319.00 *(978-1-904455-49-3(2))* Caister Academic Pr. GBR. Dist: International Specialized Bk. Services.

Poyner, David & Wheatley, Mark, eds. G Protein-Coupled Receptors: Essential Methods. 2010. (ENG., Illus.). 310p. 109.95 *(978-0-470-74914-2(8)*, Wiley) Wiley, John & Sons, Inc.

Reith, Maarten E. A., ed. Neurotransmitter Transporters: Structure, Function, & Regulation. 2nd ed. 2010. (Contemporary Neuroscience Ser.). (Illus.). 532p. pap. 179.00 *(978-1-61737-267-4(6)*, 1617372676) Humana Pr.

Rouleau, Guy & Gaspar, Claudia. Ion Channel Diseases. 2008. (ENG., Illus.). 168p. 161.00 *(978-0-12-374527-9(6)*, Academic Pr.) Elsevier Science & Technology Bks.

Sadhal, S. S. Interdisciplinary Transport Phenomena No. 5: Fluid, Thermal, Biological, Materials, & Space Sciences. 2009. (Annals of the New York Academy of Sciences Ser.: 19). (ENG., Illus.). 452p. pap. 159.95 *(978-1-57331-712-2(8)*, Wiley-Blackwell) Wiley, John & Sons, Inc.

Saier, M. H., Jr., ed. The Bioinformatic Study of Transmembrane Molecular Transport. (Illus.). 84p. pap. *(978-3-8055-8213-1(7))* Karger, S. AG.

Schmidt-Nielsen, Knut & Bolis, Liana. Comparative Physiology: Water, Ions & Fluid Mechanics. 2011. (ENG.). 376p. pap. 60.00 ***(978-0-521-10629-0(X))*** Cambridge Univ. Pr.

Sepulveda, Francisco & Bezanilla, Francisco, eds. Pumps, Transporters, & Ion Channels. 2010. (Series of the Centro de Estudios Cientificos Ser.). (Illus.). xvii, 165p. pap. 179.00 *(978-1-4419-3464-2(2)*, 1441934642) Springer.

Sharma, Kal. Transport Phenomena in Biomedical Engineering: Artifical organ Design & Development, & Tissue Engineering. 2010. (ENG., Illus.). 512p. 150.00 *(978-0-07-166397-7(5)*, 0071663975) McGraw-Hill Professional Publishing.

Sideman, Samuel, et al, eds. Control & Regulation of Transport Phenomena in the Cardiac System. 2008. (Annals of the New York Academy of Sciences Ser.: Vol. 1420). (ENG., Illus.). 300p. pap. 139.95 *(978-1-57331-706-1(3)*, Wiley-Blackwell) Wiley, John & Sons, Inc.

Stockand, James D. & Shapiro, Mark S., eds. Ion Channels: Methods & Protocols. 2010. (Methods in Molecular Biology Ser.). (Illus.). 224p. pap. 119.00 *(978-1-61737-652-8(3)*, 1617376523) Humana Pr.

Tettamanti, Guido & Sonnino, Sandro, eds. Handbook of Neurochemistry & Molecular Neurobiology: Neural Glycoconjugates. 3rd ed. 2008. (Illus.). 500p. 249.00 *(978-0-387-30355-0(3))* Springer.

Tombran-Tink, Joyce & Barnstable, Colin J., eds. Ocular Transporters in Ophthalmic Diseases & Drug Delivery. 2008. (Ophthalmology Research Ser.). (Illus.). 467p. 259.00 incl. cd-rom *(978-1-58829-958-1(9))* Springer.

Truskey, George A., et al. Transport Phenomena in Biological Systems. 2nd ed. 2008. (ENG.). 888p. (C). 191.00 *(978-0-13-156988-1(0)*, Prentice Hall) Prentice Hall PTR.

Tsaneva-Atanasova, Krasimira. A Mathematical Study of Calcium Oscillations & Waves. 2009. 176p. pap. *(978-3-639-13651-7(9))* VDM Verlag Dr. Mueller e.K.

Tzfira, Tzvi & Citovsky, Vitaly. Nuclear Import & Export in Plants & Animals. 2010. (Molecular Biology Intelligence Unit Ser.). xi, 229p. pap. 179.00 *(978-1-4419-3440-6(5)*, 1441934405) Springer.

Vancura, Ales. Membrane Trafficking. Vancura, Ales, ed. 2008. (Methods in Molecular Biology Ser.). (Illus.). 566p. 129.00 *(978-1-58829-925-3(2)*, 1588299252) Springer.

Vogel, Hans J., ed. Calcium-Binding Protein Protocols: Volume 1: Reviews & Case Studies. 2010. (Methods in Molecular Biology Ser.). (Illus.). 360p. pap. 119.00 *(978-1-61737-135-6(1)*, 1617371351) Humana Pr.

—Calcium-Binding Protein Protocols: Volume 2: Methods & Techniques. 2010. (Methods in Molecular Biology Ser.). (Illus.). 436p. pap. 119.00 *(978-1-61737-136-3(X)*, 161737136X) Humana Pr.

XI Zhu, Michael, ed. Trp Channels. 2011. (Methods in Signal Transduction Ser.). (ENG., Illus.). 499p. 149.95 *(978-1-4398-1860-2(6)*, CRC Press) Taylor & Francis Group GBR. Dist: Taylor & Francis Group.

Yan, Qing, ed. Membrane Transporters: Methods & Protocols. 2010. (Methods in Molecular Biology Ser.). (Illus.). 384p. pap. 119.00 *(978-1-61737-359-6(1)*, 1617373591) Humana Pr.

You, Guofeng & Morris, Marilyn E., eds. Drug Transporters: Molecular Characterization & Role in Drug Disposition. 2007. (Wiley Series in Drug Discovery & Development Ser.: 4). (ENG., Illus.). 897p. 195.00 *(978-0-471-78491-3(5)*, Wiley-Interscience) Wiley, John & Sons, Inc.

Yuan, Jason X. -J & Ward, Jeremy P. T., eds. Membrane Receptors, Channels & Transporters in Pulmonary Circulation. 2010. (Advances in Experimental Medicine & Biology Ser.). (Illus.). xv, 966p. 399.00 *(978-1-60761-499-9(5)*, 1607614995) Humana Pr.

Zamponi, Gerald Werner, ed. Voltage-Gated Calcium Channels. 2010. (Molecular Biology Intelligence Unit Ser.). (Illus.). xiv, 377p. pap. 229.00 *(978-1-4419-3411-6(1)*, 1441934111) Springer.

BIOLOGICAL WARFARE

ABBE Scientist Research Division Staff. Biologic Weapons for Warfare: Index, Reference & Medical Analysis of New Research Information. 2008. (Illus.). 160p. ring bd. 69.95 *(978-0-7883-3833-5(1))* ABBE Pubs. Assn. of Washington, D.C.

—Bioterrorism & Virus Warfare: Index, Reference & Medical Analysis of New Clinical & Research Information. 2008. (Illus.). 160p. ring bd. 69.95 *(978-0-7883-3836-6(6))* ABBE Pubs. Assn. of Washington, D.C.

Antosia, Robert & Cahill, John D., eds. Handbook of Bioterrorism & Disaster Medicine. 2010. (ENG., Illus.). xviii, 492p. pap. 109.00 *(978-1-4419-3731-5(5)*, 1441937315) Springer.

Armstrong, Robert E., et al, eds. Bio-Inspired Innovation & National Security. 2010. (ENG.). 351p. pap. 32.00 *(978-0-16-085501-6(2)*, Dept. of the Army) United States Government Printing Office.

Balmer, Brian. Secrecy & Science: A Historical Sociology of Biological & Chemical Warfare. 2012. 180p. 99.95 ***(978-1-4094-3057-5(X))*** Ashgate Publishing Co.

Bertolli, E. R. Shields Against Terror: the Field Guide: Guarding Against Weapons of Mass Destruction & Other Unconventional Threats. 2008. (ENG.). 96p. pap. 18.95 *(978-0-943599-45-8(8))* Optometric Extension Program Fndtn.

Biodetection Technologies, 4th Edition: Technological Responses to Biological Threats. 2007. 529p. pap. 299.00 *(978-1-59430-126-1(3))* Knowledge Pr.

Borden Institute, Walter Reed Army Medical Center, compiled by. Medical Aspects of Biological Warfare. 2008. (Textbooks of Military Medicine Ser.). (ENG., Illus.). 694p. 72.00 *(978-0-16-079731-6(4)*, Dept. of the Army) United States Government Printing Office.

Bravata, Dena M., ed. Regionalization of Bioterrorism Preparedness & Response. 2006. (Illus.). 166p. (C). reprint ed. pap. 35.00 *(978-1-4223-0646-8(1))* DIANE Publishing Co.

Cashman, John R. Emergency Response Handbook for Chemical & Biologica Agents & Weapons. 2nd rev. ed. 2008. (ENG., Illus.). 528p. 115.95 *(978-1-4200-5265-7(9)*, CRC Press) Taylor & Francis Group GBR. Dist: Taylor & Francis Group.

Clark, William R. Bracing for Armageddon? The Science & Politics of Bioterrorism in America. 2008. (ENG., Illus.). 176p. 21.95 *(978-0-19-533621-4(6))* Oxford Univ. Pr., Inc.

Coen, Bob & Nadler, Eric. Anthrax War: Dead Silence... Fear & Terror on the Anthrax Trail. 2010. (ENG.). 272p. pap. 15.95 *(978-1-58243-587-9(1)*, Counterpoint Pr.) Basic Bks. GBR. Dist: Perseus-PGW.

—Dead Silence: Fear & Terror on the Anthrax Trail. 2009. (ENG.). 256p. 25.00 *(978-1-58243-509-1(X)*, Counterpoint Pr.) Basic Bks. GBR. Dist: Perseus-PGW.

Cole, Leonard A. The Anthrax Letters: A Leading Expert on Bioterrorism Explains the Science Behind the Anthrax Attacks. 2009. (ENG.). 304p. pap. 14.95 *(978-1-60239-715-6(5)*, 239715) Skyhorse Publishing Co., Inc.

Committee on Improving Metrics for the Department of Defense, et al. Improving Metrics for the Department of Defense Cooperative Threat Reduction Program. 2012. (ENG.). 118p. pap. 38.00 ***(978-0-309-22255-6(9))*** National Academies Pr.

Committee on International Outreach Activities on Biosecurity, et al. The 2nd International Forum on Biosecurity: Summary of an International Meeting, Budapest, Hungary, March 30 to April 2 2008. 2009. (ENG.). 158p. pap. 37.50 *(978-0-309-12829-2(3))* National Academies Pr.

Committee on Protecting Occupants of DOD Buildings from Chemical and Biological Release & National Research Council Staff. Protecting Building Occupants & Operations from Biological & Chemical Airborne Threats: A Framework for Decision Making. 2007. (ENG.). 152p. pap. 36.50 *(978-0-309-10955-0(8))* National Academies Pr.

Committee on Special Immunizations Program for Laboratory Personnel Engaged in Research on Countermeasures for Select Agents & National Research Council. Protecting the Frontline in Biodefense Research: The Special Immunizations Program. 2011. (ENG.). 194p. pap. 39.00 ***(978-0-309-20924-3(2))*** National Academies Pr.

Committee on Test and Evaluation of Biological Standoff Detection Systems & National Research Council. Test & Evaluation of Biological Standoff Detection Systems. 2008. (ENG.). 42p. pap. 15.00 *(978-0-309-11443-1(8))* National Academies Pr.

Committee on the Evaluation of a Site-Specific Risk Assessment for the Department of Homeland Security's Planned National Bio-and Agro-Defense Facility in Manhattan, Kansas & National Research Council. Evaluation of a Site-Specific Risk Assessment for the Department of Homeland Security's Planned National Bio- & Agro-Defense Facility in Manhattan, Kansas. 2010. (ENG.). 146p. pap. 35.50 *(978-0-309-16281-4(5))* National Academies Pr.

Coverdell, Donald. Terror in the Air. 2008. 160p. pap. 19.50 *(978-1-4357-5957-2(5))* Lulu Enterprises Inc.

Dando, Malcolm. Bioterror & Biowarfare. 2009. lib. bdg. 33.25 *(978-1-4358-5166-5(8))* Rosen Publishing Group, Inc., The.

Defending Against Public Health Threats: Hearing Before a Subcommittee of the Committee on Appropriations, United States Senate, One Hundred Eleventh Congress, Second Session, Special Hearing, September 29, 2010, Washington, DC. 2011. iv, 45p. ***(978-0-16-088810-6(7)***, 552-070-42944-1) United States Government Printing Office.

Dishovsky, Christophor & Pivovarov, Alexander, eds. Counteraction to Chemical & Biological Terrorism in East European Countries. 2009. (NATO Science for Peace & Security Series A: Chemistry & Biology Ser.). (ENG., Illus.). xxiv, 324p. 319.00 *(978-90-481-2340-7(2))*; pap. 99.00 *(978-90-481-2341-4(0))* Springer.

Edwards, Mark. Biowar I: Hunger. 2007. 244p. pap. 26.96 *(978-1-4357-0019-2(8))* Lulu Enterprises Inc.

Ellison, D. Hank. Handbook of Chemical & Biological Warfare Agents. 2nd rev. ed. 2007. (ENG., Illus.). 800p. 149.95 *(978-0-8493-1434-6(8)*, CRC Press) Taylor & Francis Group GBR. Dist: Taylor & Francis Group.

Enemark, Christian. Disease & Security: Natural Plagues & Biological Weapons in East Asia. 2009. 230p. pap. 39.95 *(978-0-415-56989-7(3))* 2007. (Illus.). 229p. 160.00 *(978-0-415-42234-5(5))* Routledge.

Fidler, David P. & Gostin, Lawrence O. Biosecurity in the Global Age: Biological Weapons, Public Health, & the Rule of Law. 2007. (ENG., Illus.). 320p. 29.95 *(978-0-8047-5029-5(7)*, Stanford Law & Politics) Stanford Univ. Pr.

Fountain, Augustus W. Chemical & Biological Sensing VIII: 11-12 April 2007, Orlando, Florida, USA. 2007. (Proceedings of SPIE Ser.). (Illus.). 284p. pap. 80.00 *(978-0-8194-6676-1(X))* SPIE.

Freney, Jean & Renaud, François. Bacteriological Warfare: From ancient times To 9-11. 2012. 220p. pap. 24.95 *(978-2-7472-1547-3(4))* Eska, Editions FRA. Dist: International Publishers Marketing.

Gerstein, Daniel. Bioterror in 21St Century. 2009. 288p. pap. 25.95 *(978-1-59114-313-0(6))*; (Illus.). 49.95 *(978-1-59114-312-3(8))* Naval Institute Pr.

Harris, Larry. Bacteriological Warfare: A Threat to North America. Date not set. 28.50 *(978-0-9647860-5-9(2))* Virtue International Publishing Co.

Hoffman, David. Dead Hand: The Untold Story of the Cold War Arms Race & Its Dangerous Legacy. 2009. (ENG., Illus.). 592p. 35.00 *(978-0-385-52437-7(4)*, Doubleday) Knopf Doubleday Publishing Group.

Katona. Global Biosecurity: Threats & Responses. Sullivan, John P., ed. 2009. (Contemporary Security Studies). (Illus.). 272p. 130.00 *(978-0-415-46053-8(0))* Routledge.

Katona, Peter, et al, eds. Global Biosecurity. 2011. (ENG., Illus.). 344p. (C). pap. 44.95 ***(978-0-415-67059-3(4))*** Routledge.

Katz, Rebecca & Zilinskas, Raymond A., eds. Encyclopedia of Bioterrorism Defense. 2nd ed. 2011. (ENG., Illus.). 688p. 399.95 *(978-0-470-50893-0(0)*, Wiley-Blackwell) Wiley, John & Sons, Inc.

Kiesbye, Stefan. Biological & Chemical Weapons. 2010. (At Issue Ser.). (ENG.). 104p. 31.80 *(978-0-7377-4870-3(2))*; pap. 22.50 *(978-0-7377-4871-0(0))* Cengage Gale. (Greenhaven Pr., Inc.).

King, Kenneth. Germs Gone Wild: How the Unchecked Development of Domestic Bio-Defense Threatens America. 2011. (ENG.). 384p. pap. 16.95 *(978-1-60598-268-7(7)*, 605268) Pegasus Bks.

Klotz, Lynn C. & Sylvester, Edward J. Breeding Bio Insecurity: How U. S. Biodefense Is Exporting Fear, Globalizing Risk, & Making Us All Less Secure. 2009. (ENG., Illus.). 272p. 27.50 *(978-0-226-44405-5(8))* Univ. of Chicago Pr.

Koblentz, Gregory D. Living Weapons: Biological Warfare & International Security. (Cornell Studies in Security Affairs Ser.). (Illus.). 2011. 272p. pap. 22.95 ***(978-0-8014-7752-2(2))*** 2009. 256p. 36.95 *(978-0-8014-4768-6(2))* Cornell Univ. Pr.

Koenig, Robert. The Fourth Horseman: One Man's Secret Campaign to Fight the Great War in America. 2007. (ENG., Illus.). 376p. 26.00 *(978-1-58648-372-2(2))* PublicAffairs.

Leikin, Jerrold B. & McFee, Robin B. Toxico-Terrorism: Emergency Response & Clinical Approach to Chemical, Biological, & Radiological Agents. 2007. (ENG., Illus.). 622p. (C). per. 72.00 *(978-0-07-147186-2(3)*, 0071471863) McGraw-Hill Professional Publishing.

Leitenberg, Milton & Zilinskas, Raymond A. The Soviet Biological Weapons Program. 2012. (ENG., Illus.). 800p. 55.00 ***(978-0-674-04770-9(2))*** Harvard Univ. Pr.

Lele, Ajay. Bio-Weapons. 2007. 190p. 26.95 *(978-81-7062-272-7(7))* Lancer International, Lancer Pr. IND. Dist: Casemate Pubs. & Bk. Distributors, LLC.

Lockwood, Jeffrey A. Six-Legged Soldiers: Using Insects as Weapons of War, 1 vol. 2010. (ENG., Illus.). 384p. pap. 17.95 *(978-0-19-973353-8(8))* Oxford Univ. Pr., Inc.

Manolescu, Nicolae & Roberts, Guy B., eds. Bioterrorism: Impact on Civilian Society: Impact on Civilian Society. 2009. (NATO Science for Peace & Security Series B: Physics & Biophysics Ser.). (ENG.). 176p. 189.00 *(978-90-481-3267-6(3)*, 9048132673); pap. 89.95 *(978-90-481-3268-3(1)*, 9048132681) Springer.

Marmiroli, Nelson, et al, eds. Advanced Science & Technology for Biological Decontamination of Sites Affected by Chemical & Radiological Nuclear Agents. 2006. (Nato Science Series: IV: Earth & Environmental Sciences Ser.). (Illus.). xviii, 266p. 189.00 *(978-1-4020-5518-8(8)*, 1402055188); pap. 79.95 *(978-1-4020-5519-5(6)*, 1402055196) Springer.

Martinez, Coleen K. Biodefense Research Supporting the DoD: A New Strategic Vision. 2007. pap. *(978-1-58487-288-7(8))* Strategic Studies Institute, U.S. Army War College Commandant (AWCC-DSI/Pubns.).

Mauroni, Al. Chemical & Biological Warfare: A Reference Handbook. 2nd rev. ed. 2006. (Contemporary World Issues Ser.). 319p. 55.00 *(978-1-59884-027-8(4))* ABC-CLIO, LLC.

McCamley, N. J. Secret Biological Warfare. 2007. (Illus.). 216p. 39.95 *(978-1-84415-521-7(8))* Pen & Sword Bks. Ltd. GBR. Dist: Casemate Pubs. & Bk. Distributors, LLC.

Miller, Seumas & Selgelid, Michael. Ethical & Philosophical Consideration of the Dual-Use Dilemma in the Biological Sciences. 2008. VIII, 76p. (C). pap. 49.95 *(978-1-4020-8311-2(4)*, 1402083114) Springer.

Nano, Francis, et al, eds. Francisella Tularensis: Biology, Pathogenicity, Epidemiology, & Biodefense. 2007. (Annals of the New York Academy of Sciences Ser.). (ENG., Illus.). 352p. per. 159.95 *(978-1-57331-691-0(1)*, Wiley-Blackwell) Wiley, John & Sons, Inc.

National Research Council. Considerations for Ensuring Safety & Efficacy of Vaccines & Therapeutic Proteins Manufactured by Using Platform Approaches: Summary of a Workshop. 2010. (ENG.). 38p. pap. 15.00 *(978-0-309-15321-8(2))* National Academies Pr.

National Research Council (U.S.), Committee on Prevention of Proliferation of Biological Weapons Staff, contrib. by. The Biological Threat Reduction Program of the Department of Defense: From Foreign Assistance to Sustainable Partnerships. 2007. (ENG.). 120p. pap. 31.00 *(978-0-309-11158-4(7))* National Academies Pr.

Nuclear, Biological & Chemical Defence: Get Equipped to Meet the NBC Threat. 495.00 *(978-0-7106-2325-6(9))* Jane's Information Group, Inc.

Page, William Frank, et al. Long-Term Health Effects of Participation in Project SHAD (Shipboard Hazard & Defense) 2007. (ENG., Illus.). 142p. pap. 34.75 *(978-0-309-10210-0(3))* National Academies Pr.

Parker. Killing Factory. Date not set. (Illus.). vii, 230p. *(978-1-85685-121-3(4))* Robert Smith Literary Agency.

Potts, Malcolm & Hayden, Thomas. Sex & War: How Biology Explains Warfare & Terrorism & Offers a Path to a Safer World. (ENG.). 2010. 464p. pap. 16.95 *(978-1-935251-70-5(8))* 2008. (Illus.). 457p. 24.95 *(978-1-933771-57-1(7))* BenBella Bks.

Preston, Thomas. From Lambs to Lions: Future Security Relationships in a World of Biological & Nuclear Weapons. (ENG.). 2009. 450p. pap. 33.00 *(978-0-7425-5503-7(8))* 2007. (Illus.). 448p. 100.00 *(978-0-7425-5502-0(X))* Rowman & Littlefield Publishers, Inc.

Rega, Paul P. Bio-Terry. 2nd rev. ed. (Illus.). ring bd. 74.95 *(978-0-9716301-1-6(9))* MASCAP, Inc.

Richardt, Andre & Blum, Marc-Michael, eds. Decontamination of Warfare Agents: Enzymatic Methods for the Removal of B/C Weapons. 2008. (ENG., Illus.). 311p. 195.00 *(978-3-527-31756-1(2)*, Wiley-VCH) Wiley, John & Sons, Inc.

Ryan, Jeffrey R. & Glarum, Jan F. Biosecurity & Bioterrorism: Containing & Preventing Biological Threats. 2008. (Butterworth-Heinemann Homeland Security Ser.). (ENG., Illus.). 352p. 72.95 *(978-0-7506-8489-7(5)*, Butterworth-Heinemann) Elsevier Science & Technology Bks.

Schram, Martin. Avoiding Armageddon: Our Future, Our Choice. 2006. (Illus.). 356p. reprint ed. 26.00 *(978-1-4223-5459-9(8))* DIANE Publishing Co.

Sooryadas, Daya I. Biomimetic Sensor for Invivo Applications. 2008. 92p. pap. *(978-3-639-06946-4(3))* VDM Verlag Dr. Mueller e.K.

Stopa, Peter J. & Bartoszcze, Michael A., eds. Rapid Methods for Analysis of Biological Materials in the Environment. 2012. (NATO Science Partnership Sub-Series: 1: Ser.). (ENG.). 324p. pap. 171.00 *(978-90-481-5455-5(3)*, 9048154553) Springer.

Sweet, Muriel J. No Stoppin' Them Preachin' Women, 1 vol. 2009. 138p. pap. 24.95 *(978-1-61546-879-9(X))* PublishAmerica, Inc.

United States, Congress House Committee on Homeland Security Subcommittee on the Prevention of Nuclear and Biological Attack Staff, contrib. by.

Implementing the National Defense Strategy: Hearing Before the Subcommittee on [the] Prevention of Nuclear & Biological Attack of the Committee on Homeland Security, House of Representatives, One Hundred Ninth Congress, First Session, July 28, 2005. 2007. (Illus.). iv, 81p. (978-0-16-078383-8(6), 552-070-35688-6) United States Government Printing Office.

Wenger, Andreas & Wollenmann, Reto, eds. Bioterrorism: Confronting a Complex Threat. 2007. 245p. lib. bdg. 55.00 (978-1-58826-525-8(0)) Rienner, Lynne Pubs.

Zalloua, Zahi. Contagion: Health, Fear, Sovereignty, 1 vol. Magnusson, Bruce, ed. 2012. (ENG.). 184p. 70.00 (978-0-295-99174-0(7)) Univ. of Washington Pr.

Zeng, Daniel, et al. Biosurveillance & Biosecurity: International Workshop, BioSecure 2008, Raleigh, NC, USA, December 2, 2008. Proceedings. 2008. (Lecture Notes in Computer Science / Security & Cryptology Ser.). x, 183p. pap. 69.95 (978-3-540-89745-3(3)) Springer.

BIOLOGICALS

Here are entered works on substances derived from living organisms used in the diagnosis, prevention, or treatment of disease.

see also Antitoxins; Blood Products; Vaccines

Assessing the Impact of a Safe & Equitable Biosimilar Policy in the United States: Hearing Before the Subcommittee on Health of the Committee on Energy & Commerce, House of Representatives, One Hundred Tenth Congress, First Session, May 2, 2007. 2008. (Illus.). vi, 184p. (978-0-16-080887-6(1), 552-070-37432-9) United States Government Printing Office.

Ben Greenstein Daniel Brook Staff. Biological Therapeutics. 2011. (Illus.). 160p. pap. 49.99 (978-0-85369-843-2(0)) Pharmaceutical Pr. GBR. Dist: Smith Fulfillment Services.

How Can NIST Better Serve the Needs of the Biomedical Research Community in the 21st Century? Hearing Before the Subcommittee on Technology & Innovation, Committee on Science & Technology, House of Representatives, One Hundred Eleventh Congress, Second Session, February 24, 2010. 2010. (Illus.). iii, 41p. (978-0-16-086622-7(7), 552-070-41600-5) United States Government Printing Office.

The Potential Need for Measurement Standards to Facilitate the Research & Development of Biologic Drugs: Hearing Before the Subcommittee on Technology & Innovation, Committee on Science & Technology, House of Representatives, One Hundred Eleventh Congress, First Session, September 24, 2009. 2009. (Illus.). iv, 112p. (978-0-16-084956-5(X), 552-070-40346-9) United States Government Printing Office.

Safe & Affordable Biotech Drugs: The Need for a Generic Pathway: Hearing Before the Committee on Oversight & Government Reform, House of Representatives, One Hundred Tenth Congress, First Session, March 26, 2007. 2008. (Illus.). iv, 274p. (978-0-16-080781-7(6), 552-070-37399-3) United States Government Printing Office.

Termini & Termini, Roseann B. Life Sciences Law: Federal Regulation of Drugs, Biologics, Medical Devices, Foods, & Dietary Supplements. 4th ed. 2010. (Illus.). 524p. pap. (978-0-9729891-9-0(6)) Forti Pubns.

Valverde, J. L. & Valverde, José Luis. Key Issues in Pharmaceuticals Law. 2008. (Illus.). pap. 84.00 (978-1-58603-840-3(0)) IOS Pr., Inc.

BIOLOGISTS

see also Ecologists; Geneticists

Alcock, John. When the Rains Come: A Naturalist's Year in the Sonoran Desert. 2009. (ENG., Illus.). 336p. (C). 45.00 (978-0-8165-2835-6(7)); 288p. pap. 21.95 (978-0-8165-2762-5(8)) Univ. of Arizona Pr.

Alverson. Race to the Se: The Autobiography of a Marine Biologist. 2008. 568p. 42.95 (978-0-595-48778-3(5)); pap. 32.95 (978-0-595-48680-9(0)) iUniverse, Inc.

American Men & Women of Science, 8.0. 29th ed. 2011. 1368.00 (978-1-4144-7203-4(X)) Cengage Gale.

Aydon, Cyril. Charles Darwin. 2009. (ENG.). 326p. pap. 14.00 (978-1-4379-6343-4(9)) DIANE Publishing Co.

Balinska, Marta A. & Schneider, William H., eds. Ludwik Hirszfeld: The Story of One Life. Balinska, Marta A., tr. from POL. 2010. (Rochester Studies in Medical History Ser.: Volume 16). (Illus.). 508p. 49.95 (978-1-58046-338-6(X)) Univ. of Rochester Pr.

Barry, Susan R. Fixing My Gaze: A Scientist's Journey into Seeing in Three Dimensions. 2010. (ENG., Illus.). 272p. (gr. 9). pap. 15.95 (978-0-465-02073-7(9)) Basic Bks.

Bertoloni Meli, Domenico. Mechanism, Experiment, Disease: Marcello Malpighi & Seventeenth-Century Anatomy. 2011. (ENG., Illus.). 456p. (gr. 17). 90.00 (978-0-8018-9903-4(6)) Johns Hopkins Univ. Pr.

—Mechanism, Experiment, Disease: Marcello Malpighi & Seventeenth-Century Anatomy. 2011. (ENG., Illus.). 456p. (gr. 17). pap. 45.00 (978-0-8018-9904-1(4)) Johns Hopkins Univ. Pr.

Bondrup-Nielsen, Soren. A Sound Like Water Dripping: In Search of the Boreal Owl. 2009. (ENG.). 240p. pap. (978-1-55447-074-7(9)) Gaspereau Pr.

Brush, Stephen G. Choosing Selection: The Revival of Natural Selection in Anglo-American Evolutionary Biology, 1930-1970. 2009. (978-1-60618-993-1(X)) American Philosophical Society.

Cairns, John. Phage & the Origins of Molecular Biology. Stent, Gunther S. & Watson, James D., eds. 2nd ed. 2007. (ENG., Illus.). 394p. 30.00 (978-0-87969-800-3(4)) Cold Spring Harbor Laboratory Pr.

Chandler, C. Ray, et al. The Chicago Guide to Landing a Job in Academic Biology. 2007. (Chicago Guides to Academic Life Ser.). (Illus.). 176p. 37.50 (978-0-226-10129-3(0)); per. 14.00 (978-0-226-10130-9(4)) Univ. of Chicago Pr.

Clark, Ronald. J. B. S: The Life & Work of J. B. S Haldane. 2012. 293p. pap. (978-1-4482-0078-8(4), 143280, Bloomsbury Reader) Bloomsbury Publishing Plc.

Clinton, George Perkins & Thaxter, Roland. Biographical Memoir of Roland Thaxter, 1858-1932: National Academy of Sciences Biographical Memoirs, V17, Third Memoir. 2011. 22p. 35.95 (978-1-258-06845-5(1)) Literary Licensing, LLC.

Cooper, Ross Gordon. Termites: Terry & his Colony. 2010. 63p. pap. 29.95 (978-0-557-41924-1(7)) Lulu Enterprises Inc.

Crow, Richard. A Man of the Woods: Experiences Collecting 7,000 Woods of the World. 2009. (978-1-892529-54-1(8)) Forest Products Society.

Degueurce, Christophe. Fragonard Museum: the Ecorches. 2011. (ENG.). 160p. 50.00 (978-0-922233-39-7(X)) Blast Bks.

Fandel, Jennifer, et al. Louis Pasteur & Pasteurization. 2010. (Inventions & Discovery Ser.). 32p. 34.65 (978-1-4296-5224-7(1)) Capstone Digital.

Ferry, Georgina. Max Perutz & the Secret of Life. 2007. (ENG., Illus.). 352p. 40.00 (978-0-87969-785-3(7)) Cold Spring Harbor Laboratory Pr.

Friedberg, Errol C. Sydney Brenner: A Biography. 2010. (ENG., Illus.). 350p. 40.00 (978-0-87969-947-5(7)) Cold Spring Harbor Laboratory Pr.

Gilliland, Kurt O. & Montgomery, Royce L. Anatomists & Eponyms: An Illustrated History of Anatomy. 2011. 126p. pap. 40.00 (978-1-904761-73-0(9)) Nottingham Univ. Pr. GBR. Dist: Independent Pubs. Group.

Glynn, Jenifer. My Sister Rosalind Franklin: A Family Memoir. 2012. (ENG., Illus.). 160p. 27.95 (978-0-19-969962-9(3)) Oxford Univ. Pr., Inc.

Gould, Stephen Jay. I Have Landed: The End of a Beginning in Natural History. 2011. (ENG., Illus.). 432p. pap. 19.95 (978-0-674-06162-0(4), Belknap Pr.) Harvard Univ. Pr.

Grandin, Temple. Thinking in Pictures: My Life with Autism. exp. movie tie-in ed. 2010. (Vintage Ser.). (ENG.). 304p. pap. 15.00 (978-0-307-73958-2(9), Vintage) Knopf Doubleday Publishing Group.

Haffer, Jürgen. Ornithology, Evolution, & Philosophy: The Life & Science of Ernst Mayr 1904-2005. 2007. (ENG., Illus.). x, 474p. pap. 69.95 (978-3-540-71778-2(1), 3540717781) Springer.

Hargittai, István. The DNA Doctor: Candid Conversations with James D. Watson. 2007. xii, 220p. (978-981-270-796-3(4)) World Scientific Publishing Co., Inc.

Harman, Oren Solomon & Dietrich, Michael, eds. Rebels, Mavericks, & Heretics in Biology. 2009. (Illus.). 416p. pap. 23.00 (978-0-300-15845-8(9)) Yale Univ. Pr.

Heinrich, Bernd. The Snoring Bird: My Family's Journey Through a Century of Biology. 2008. (P. S. Ser.). (ENG.). 512p. pap. 15.95 (978-0-06-074216-4(X), HarperPerennial) HarperCollins Pubs.

Helmreich, Stefan. Alien Ocean: Anthropological Voyages in Microbial Seas. 2009. (Illus.). (ENG.). 464p. 60.00 (978-0-520-25061-0(3)); 336p. pap. 26.95 (978-0-520-25062-8(1)) Univ. of California Pr.

Herrick, C. Judson & Herrick, C. Judson. Biographical Memoir of George Ellett Coghill, 1872-1941: National Academy of Sciences, Biographical Memoirs V22, Twelfth Memoir. 2011. 30p. 35.95 (978-1-258-06670-3(X)) Literary Licensing, LLC.

Hirashi, Akemi & Fujimoto, Haruto, eds. Microbiology & Molecular Biology Researcher Biographical Sketches & Research Summaries. 2012. (978-1-61942-172-1(0)) Nova Science Pubs., Inc.

Holt, Sidney. Southern Ocean Sanctuary, 1 vol. 2011. 144p. 22.95 (978-1-907112-23-2(5)) Trolley GBR. Dist: Innovative Logistics.

Impey, Chris, ed. Talking about Life: Conversations on Astrobiology. 2010. (ENG., Illus.). 418p. 29.99 (978-0-521-51492-7(4)) Cambridge Univ. Pr.

James, Ioan. Remarkable Biologists: From Ray to Hamilton. 2009. (ENG., Illus.). 196p. 102.00 (978-0-521-87589-9(7)); pap. 48.99 (978-0-521-69918-1(5)) Cambridge Univ. Pr.

Johnson, Kristin. Jordan's Ark: One Man's Quest to Catalog the Living World. 2012. (978-1-4214-0600-8(4)); E-Book (978-1-4214-0650-3(0)) Johns Hopkins Univ. Pr.

Katchadourian, Herant. The Way It Turned Out: A Memoir. 2012. (ENG.). 350p. 29.95 (978-981-4364-75-1(4)) Pan Stanford Publishing SGP. Dist: Taylor & Francis Group.

Lakha, Shamim. 'What Mad Pursuit' The quest to breed Superman. 2011. 80p. pap. (978-3-8443-2676-5(6)) Lambert Academic Publishing.

Li, Judy & Barbour, Michael T. Wading for Bugs: Exploring Streams with the Experts. 2011. E-Book (978-0-87071-643-0(3)) Oregon State Univ. Pr.

Lourie, Peter. The Polar Bear Scientists. 2012. (Scientists in the Field Ser.). (ENG., Illus.). 80p. (J). (gr. 4-7). 18.99 (978-0-547-28305-0(9), Houghton Mifflin Bks. for Children) Houghton Mifflin Harcourt Trade & Reference Pubs.

Lytle, Mark H. The Gentle Subversive: Rachel Carson, Silent Spring, & the Rise of the Environmental Movement. 2007. (New Narratives in American History Ser.). (ENG., Illus.). 288p. (C). per. 19.95 (978-0-19-517247-8(7)) Oxford Univ. Pr., Inc.

Matthiessen, Peter. The Snow Leopard. rev. ed. 2008. (ENG., Illus.). 368p. (gr. 12-18). 16.00 (978-0-14-310551-0(5), Penguin Classics) Penguin Group (USA) Inc.

Messbarger, Rebecca Marie. The Lady Anatomist: The Life & Work of Anna Morandi Manzolini. 2010. (ENG., Illus.). 248p. 35.00 (978-0-226-52081-0(1)) Univ. of Chicago Pr.

Murray, Barbara Kauffmann. From Sorrento to Lossiemouth: A Record of Another Journey from Letters & Notes. 2011. 72p. 36.95 (978-1-258-02914-2(6)) Literary Licensing, LLC.

Neba, Funwi-Gabga. Spatial Point Pattern Analysis of Gorilla Nest Sites. 2011. 64p. pap. (978-3-8443-3089-2(5)) Lambert Academic Publishing.

O'Brien, Stacey. Wesley the Owl: The Remarkable Love Story of an Owl & His Girl. 2009. (ENG., Illus.). 256p. pap. 15.00 (978-1-4165-5177-5(8), Free Pr.) Free Pr.

—Wesley the Owl: The Remarkable Love Story of an Owl & His Girl. l.t. ed. 2009. 337p. 30.95 (978-1-4104-1310-9(1)) Thorndike Pr.

Olby, Robert. Francis Crick: Hunter of Life's Secrets. 2009. (ENG., Illus.). 538p. 46.00 (978-0-87969-798-3(9)) Cold Spring Harbor Laboratory Pr.

Osterhout, Winthrop John Vanleuven & Osterhout, Winthrop John VanLeuven. Biographical Memoir of Jacques Loeb, 1859-1924: Biographical Memoirs V13, Fourth Memoir. 2011. 94p. 38.95 (978-1-258-06786-1(2)) Literary Licensing, LLC.

Pearson, Karl. Walter Frank Raphael Weldon 1860-1906: A Memoir reprinted from Biometrika. 2011. (ENG.). 66p. pap. 19.99 (978-1-107-60122-2(3)) Cambridge Univ. Pr.

Peluso, Charles Tiggie & MacFarlane, Sandy. Tiggie: The Lure & Lore of Commercial Fishing in New England. 2007. (Illus.). 292p. per. 19.95 (978-1-60008-039-5(1), Rooftop Publishing) AuthorHouse.

Pietsch, Theodore W. Trees of Life: A Visual History of Evolution. 2012. (ENG., Illus.). 376p. (gr. 17). 69.95 (978-1-4214-0479-0(6)) Johns Hopkins Univ. Pr.

Quaratiello, Arlene R. Rachel Carson: A Biography. 2010. (ENG.). 152p. pap. 18.00 (978-1-61614-187-5(5)) Prometheus Bks., Pubs.

Raff, Rudolf A. Once We All Had Gills: Growing up Evolutionist in an Evolving World. 2012. (ENG., Illus.). 320p. 35.00 (978-0-253-00235-8(4), 0253002354) Indiana Univ. Pr.

Richards, Robert J. The Tragic Sense of Life: Ernst Haeckel & the Struggle over Evolutionary Thought. (ENG., Illus.). 2009. 576p. pap. 25.00 (978-0-226-71216-1(8)) 2008. 512p. 39.00 (978-0-226-71214-7(1)) Univ. of Chicago Pr.

Robinson, J. V. A. The making of a microbe Hunter. 2009. 265p. pap. 25.50 (978-1-4092-9243-2(6)) Lulu Enterprises Inc.

Roslytskyi, IEvhen. Serhii Vynohradskyi — Peredovyi Mikrobioloh Svitu. 2008. (UKR., Illus.). 66p. (978-966-360-092-5(6)) Akademperiodyka.

Scientific American Editors, creator. Germ Wars: Battling Killer Bacteria & Microbes. 2008. (Scientific American Cutting-Edge Science Ser.). (Illus.). 128p. (YA). (gr. 9-12). lib. bdg. 31.95 (978-1-4042-1405-7(4)) Rosen Publishing Group, Inc., The.

Scientific American Staff. Germ Wars: Battling Killer Bacteria & Microbes. 2009. (Scientific American Cutting-Edge Science Ser.). 128p. (gr. 9-9). 63.90 (978-1-60853-078-6(7)) Rosen Publishing Group, Inc., The.

Segre, Gino. Ordinary Geniuses: Max Delbruck, George Gamow, & the Origins of Genomics & Big Bang Cosmology. 2011. (ENG.). 352p. (gr. 12). 27.95 (978-0-670-02276-2(4), Viking Adult) Penguin Group (USA) Inc.

Sloan, Phillip R. & Brandon, Fogel, eds. Creating a Physical Biology: The Three-Man Paper & Early Molecular Biology. 2011. (ENG., Illus.). 320p. pap. 35.00 (978-0-226-76783-3(3)) Univ. of Chicago Pr.

Souder, William. On a Farther Shore: The Life & Legacy of Rachel Carson. 2012. (ENG., Illus.). 544p. 30.00 (978-0-307-46220-6(X), Crown) Crown Publishing Group.

Speroff, Leon. A Good Man: Gregory Goodwin Pincus the Man, His Story, the Birth Control Pill. 2009. (ENG., Illus.). 359p. 29.95 (978-0-9801942-9-6(6)) Amica Publishing, Inc.

Spotte, Stephen. The Smoking Horse: A Memoir in Pieces. 2010. (Excelsior Editions Ser.). 144p. 19.95 (978-1-4384-3139-0(2), Suny Pr.) State Univ. of New York Pr.

Staple, Joan Lorch. Change & Challenge, My Life after Thirty. 2009. 258p. pap. 20.00 (978-0-557-08292-6(7)) Lulu Enterprises Inc.

Stephens, Lester D. & Calder, Dale R. Seafaring Scientist: Alfred Goldsborough Mayor, Pioneer in Marine Biology. 2006. (Illus.). 220p. 54.95 (978-1-57003-641-5(1)); per. 29.95 (978-1-57003-642-2(X)) Univ. of South Carolina Pr.

Sykes, James E. Follow the Coastline. 2008. 132p. (ENG.). 29.99 (978-1-4257-9402-6(5)); per. 19.99 (978-1-4257-9378-4(9)) Xlibris Corp.

Teer, James G. It's a Long Way from Llano: The Journey of a Wildlife Biologist. 2008. (ENG., Illus.). 168p. 29.95 (978-1-60344-068-4(2)) Texas A&M Univ. Pr.

Transplanting Life: From mainland China to Taiwan to American. 2009. pap. (978-1-61584-115-8(6)) Independent Pub.

Trauth, Joy & Romero, Aldemaro, eds. Adventures in the Wild: Tales from Biologists of the Natural State. 2008. (Illus.). 182p. pap. 22.50 (978-1-55728-872-1(0)) Univ. of Arkansas Pr.

Troyer, Will. Bear Wrangler: The Memoirs of an Alaska Pioneer Biologist. (ENG., Illus.). 2010. 256p. pap. 19.95 (978-1-60223-044-6(7)) 2008. 250p. 26.95 (978-1-60223-043-9(9)) Univ. of Alaska Pr.

Waters, C. Kenneth & Helden, Albert Van, eds. Julian Huxley: Biologist & Statesman of Science. 2010. (ENG., Illus.). 358p. pap. 29.95 (978-1-60344-160-5(3)) Texas A&M Univ. Pr.

Watson, James D. Avoid Boring People: Lessons from a Life in Science. 2010. (Vintage Ser.). (ENG., Illus.). 368p. pap. 16.95 (978-0-375-72714-6(0), Vintage) Knopf Doubleday Publishing Group.

Wenkel, Simone & Deichmann, Ute, eds. Max Delbruck & Cologne: An Early Chapter of German Molecular Biology. 2007. (GER & ENG., Illus.). 318p. 98.00 (978-981-270-547-1(3)) World Scientific Publishing Co., Inc.

Williamson, Michael A. Trail of the Snake: From Big Bend to Baja. 2010. (Illus.). 172p. pap. 19.95 (978-0-86534-752-6(2)) Sunstone Pr.

BIOLOGY

see also Acclimatization; Adaptation (Biology); Anatomy; Aquatic Biology; Biochemistry; Biodiversity; Bioengineering; Biolinguistics; Biology, Experimental; Biomass; Biomathematics; Biophysics; Botany; Cells; Chronobiology; Convergence (Biology); Cryobiology; Cytology; Death (Biology); Desert Biology; Developmental Biology; Ecology; Electronics in Biology; Embryology; Evolution; Exobiology; Extinction (Biology); Fertilization (Biology); Genetics; Geobiology; Heredity; Human Biology; Hybridization; Information Theory in Biology; Karyokinesis; Life (Biology); Living Fossils; Marine Biology; Microbiology; Mimicry (Biology); Natural History; Ontogeny; Parasitology; Photobiology; Phylogeny; Physiology; Population Biology; Psychobiology; Radiobiology; Regeneration (Biology); Reproduction; Sex (Biology); Soil Biology; Space Biology; Spontaneous Generation; Symbiosis; Variation (Biology); Zoology

also headings beginning with the word Biological

Alon, Uri. An Introduction to Systems Biology: Design Principles of Biological Circuits. 2006. (CH/CRC Mathematical & Computational Biology Ser.: Vol. 10). (ENG., Illus.). 320p. (C). per. 59.95 (978-1-58488-642-6(0), Chapman & Hall/CRC) CRC Pr. LLC.

Alters, Sandra. Biology: Understanding Life. 2007. (Wiley Desktop Editions Ser.). 120.95 (978-0-470-24060-1(1)) Wiley, John & Sons, Inc.

Appalachian State University. Explorations in General Biology I. 2nd rev. ed. 2012. (ENG.). spiral bd. 34.00 (978-0-7575-9977-4(X)) Kendall Hunt Publishing Co.

Appalachian State University, Biology Department Staff. Explorations in General Biology II. 2nd rev. ed. 2010. (ENG.). 148p. spiral bd. 33.04 (978-0-7575-1554-5(1)) Kendall Hunt Publishing Co.

Arlott, Norman. Birds of the West Indies: 2010. (Princeton Illustrated Checklists Ser.). (ENG., Illus.). 240p. pap. 24.95 (978-0-691-14780-2(9)) Princeton Univ. Pr.

Arrison, Sonia. 100 Plus: How the Coming Age of Longevity Will Change Everything, from Careers & Relationships to Family & Faith. 2011. (ENG.). 272p. (gr. 9). 25.99 (978-0-465-01966-3(8)) Basic Bks.

Audesirk, et al. Books a la Carte for Biology: Life on Earth with Physiology. 9th ed. 2010. (ENG.). 1008p. (C). ring bd. 107.13 (978-0-321-61540-4(9)) Benjamin-Cummings Publishing Co.

Audesirk, Gerald, et al. Biology: Life on Earth. 9th ed. 2010. (ENG.). 696p. (C). 174.47 (978-0-321-68152-2(5)); (Illus.). 174.47 (978-0-321-59847-9(4)) Benjamin-Cummings Publishing Co.

—Biology: Life on Earth & Life on Earth with Physiology. 8th ed. 2007. (ENG.). 416p. (C). stu. ed., per., pupil's gde. ed. 28.47 (978-0-13-195769-5(4)) Benjamin-Cummings Publishing Co.

—Biology: Life on Earth & with Physiology. 9th ed. 2010. (ENG.). 528p. (C). pap. 34.20 (978-0-321-61179-6(9)) Benjamin-Cummings Publishing Co.

—Biology: Life on Earth with Physiology. 9th ed. 2010. (ENG.). (C). 1008p. 178.53 (978-0-321-68151-5(7)); (Illus.). 1008p. 178.53 (978-0-321-59846-2(6)); 57.20 (978-0-321-68247-5(5)) Benjamin-Cummings Publishing Co.

—Biology: Life on Earth with Physiology. 8th ed. 2008. (Illus.). 1024p. pap. (978-0-13-203882-9(X)) Prentice Hall PTR.

—Biology: Life on Earth with Physiology, Books a la Carte Plus MasteringBiologyreg; 9th ed. 2010. (ENG.). (C). ring bd. 117.13 (978-0-321-74222-3(2)) Benjamin-Cummings Publishing Co.

—WebCT Student Access Kit for Biology: Life on Earth. 9th ed. 2010. (ENG.). (C). 23.40 (978-0-321-61184-0(5)) Benjamin-Cummings Publishing Co.

Ball, Philip. Branches: Nature's Patterns, 3 vols. 2011. (ENG., Illus.). 240p. pap. 18.95 (978-0-19-960488-3(6)) Oxford Univ. Pr., Inc.

—Flow: Nature's Patterns - A Tapestry in Three Parts, 3 vols. 2011. (ENG., Illus.). 208p. pap. 18.95 (978-0-19-960487-6(8)) Oxford Univ. Pr., Inc.

—Shapes: Nature's Patterns - A Tapestry in Three Parts, 3 vols. 2011. (ENG., Illus.). 320p. pap. 18.95 (978-0-19-960486-9(X)) Oxford Univ. Pr., Inc.

Barbieri, Marcello, ed. The Codes of Life: The Rules of Macroevolution. 2010. (Biosemiotics Ser.). (Illus.). xx, 440p. pap. 219.00 (978-90-481-7611-3(5), 9048176115) Springer.

—Introduction to Biosemiotics: The New Biological Synthesis. 2008. (ENG.). xii, 532p. pap. 109.00 (978-1-4020-8344-0(0), 1402083440) Springer.

BarCharts Inc., Staff. Science Fundamentals. 2009. (ENG.). 4p. 4.95 (978-1-4232-0869-3(2)) Barcharts, Inc.

—Science Fundamentals 2. 2009. (ENG.). 4p. 4.95 (978-1-4232-0867-9(6)) Barcharts, Inc.

—Science Fundamentals 3 Physical Science. 2009. (ENG.). 4p. 4.95 (978-1-4232-0868-6(4)) Barcharts, Inc.

—Science Fundamentals Cells-Plants-Animals, No. 1. 2009. (ENG.). 4p. 4.95 (978-1-4232-0866-2(8)) Barcharts, Inc.

Bartlett, Douglas H., ed. High-Pressure Bioscience & Biotechnology. 2010. (Annals of the New York Academy of Sciences Ser.: 45). (ENG.). 352p. pap. 130.00 (978-1-57331-771-9(3), Wiley-Blackwell) Wiley, John & Sons, Inc.

Belk, Colleen & Borden Maier, Virginia. Biology: Science for Life. (ENG.). (C). 3rd ed. 2010. Illus.). 419p. pap. 141.53 (978-0-321-74229-2(X)) 3rd ed. 2009. 419p. pap. 141.47 (978-0-321-55959-3(2)) 4th rev. ed. 2012. (Illus.). 496p. pap. 141.53 (978-0-321-76782-0(9)) Benjamin-Cummings Publishing Co.

—Biology: Science for Life, Books a la Carte Edition. 4th ed. 2012. (ENG.). 496p. (C). ring bd. 84.93 (978-0-321-78733-0(1)) Benjamin-Cummings Publishing Co.

—Biology: Science for Life, Books a la Carte Plus MasteringBiologyreg; 4th ed. 2012. (ENG.). 496p. (C). ring bd. 94.93 (978-0-321-78734-7(X)) Benjamin-Cummings Publishing Co.

—Biology: Science for Life with Physiology. (ENG.). 720p. (C). 3rd ed. 2010. pap. 149.73 (978-0-321-74227-8(3)) 3rd ed. 2010. ring bd. 89.87

(978-0-321-59594-2(7)) 3rd ed. 2009. pap. 149.73 *(978-0-321-55958-6(4))* 4th ed. 2012. ring bd. 99.87 ***(978-0-321-77432-3(9))*** 4th rev. ed. 2012. pap. 149.73 ***(978-0-321-76758-5(6))*** 4th rev. ed. 2011. (Illus.). pap. 149.73 ***(978-0-321-76783-7(7))*** Benjamin-Cummings Publishing Co.

—Biology: Science for Life with Physiology, Books a la Carte Edition. 4th ed. 2012. (ENG.). 720p. (C). ring bd. 89.87 ***(978-0-321-77433-0(7))*** Benjamin-Cummings Publishing Co.

—Biology: Science for Life with Physiology, Books a la Carte Plus Masteringbiology. 3rd ed. 2011. (ENG.). (C). ring bd. 99.87 ***(978-0-321-73188-3(3))*** Benjamin-Cummings Publishing Co.

—Books a la Carte for Biology: Science for Life. 3rd ed. 2010. (ENG.). 512p. (C). ring bd. 84.93 *(978-0-321-59554-6(8))* Benjamin-Cummings Publishing Co.

—Books a la Carte Plus for Biology: Science for Life. 3rd ed. 2009. (ENG.). 496p. (C). ring bd. 84.93 *(978-0-321-59593-5(9))* Benjamin-Cummings Publishing Co.

—Books a la Carte Plus for Biology: Science for Life with Physiology. 3rd ed. 2009. (ENG.). 720p. (C). ring bd. 89.87 *(978-0-321-59595-9(5))* Benjamin-Cummings Publishing Co.

Belk, Colleen & Borden Maier, Virginia. For Biology: Science for Life with Physiology. 4th ed. 2012. (ENG.). 720p. (C). E-Book, E-Book 96.00 ***(978-0-321-77422-4(1))*** Benjamin-Cummings Publishing Co.

Bell, Agrippa Nelson. A Knowledge of Living Things, with the Laws of Their Existence. 2006. 336p. per. 23.99 *(978-1-4255-3437-0(6))* MPublishing.

Bentley, Peter J. Digital Biology: How Nature Is Transforming Our Technology & Our Lives. 2007. (ENG.). 272p. pap. 18.95 *(978-1-4165-7714-0(9))* Simon & Schuster.

Berg, Linda, et al. Biology, Vol. 1. 8th ed. 2006. (ENG.). 1p. (C). pap. 122.95 *(978-0-495-30978-9(8))* Brooks/Cole.

Berhardt, Leon V. Advances in Medicine & Biology. (Series: Advances in Medicine & Biology Ser.). 2012. 343p. 185.00 *(978-1-61324-359-6(6))* 2012. 330p. 185.00 *(978-1-61324-381-7(2))* 2011. 95.00 ***(978-1-61470-009-8(5)***, Nova Biomedical Bks.) 2011. 245p. 129.00 ***(978-1-61209-539-4(9))*** 2011. 129.00 *(978-1-61209-135-8(0))* 22nd rev. ed. 2011. 246p. 89.00 *(978-1-61209-565-3(8))* Vol. 16. 2011. 388p. 165.00 *(978-1-61122-731-4(3))* Vol. 23. 2011. 259p. 129.00 *(978-1-61209-703-9(0))* Nova Science Pubs., Inc.

—Advances in Medicine & Biology. Volume 17. 2011. (Advances in Medicine & Biology Ser.). 129.00 *(978-1-61122-790-1(9)*, Nova Biomedical Bks.) Nova Science Pubs., Inc.

—Advances in Medicine & Biology. Volume 18. 2011. (Advances in Medicine & Biology Ser.). 175.00 *(978-1-61122-791-8(7)*, Nova Biomedical Bks.) Nova Science Pubs., Inc.

—Advances in Medicine & Biology. Volume 19. 2011. (Advances in Medicine & Biology Ser.). 129.00 *(978-1-61122-798-7(4)*, Nova Biomedical Bks.) Nova Science Pubs., Inc.

Berhardt, Leon V., ed. Advances in Medicine & Biology. (Series: Advances in Medicine & Biology Ser.). 2012. 282p. 140.00 *(978-1-61324-714-3(1))* 2012. 236p. 95.00 ***(978-1-61470-476-8(7))*** 2012. 600p. 95.00 *(978-1-61324-494-4(0))* 2011. 185.00 *(978-1-61324-361-9(8)*, Nova Biomedical Bks.) Vol. 10. 2010. 235.00 *(978-1-61728-755-8(5)*, Nova Biomedical Bks.) Vol. 11. 2010. 155.00 *(978-1-61728-775-6(X))* Vol. 12. 2010. 89.00 *(978-1-61728-994-1(9))* Vol. 26. 2011. 329p. 140.00 *(978-1-61324-065-6(1))* Nova Science Pubs., Inc.

—Advances in Medicine & Biology: Volume 27. 2011. (Advances in Medicine & Biology Ser.). 305p. 140.00 *(978-1-61324-068-7(6))* Nova Science Pubs., Inc.

Bhushan, Bharat, ed. Nanotribology & Nanomechanics I: Measurement Techniques & Nanomechanics. 2011. (Illus.). xviii, 623p. 139.00 ***(978-3-642-15282-5(1)***, 3642152821) Springer.

—Nanotribology & Nanomechanics II: Nanotribology, Biomimetics, & Industrial Applications. 3rd ed. 2011. (Illus.). xvi, 1017p. 139.00 ***(978-3-642-15262-7(7)***, 3642152627) Springer.

Biggs, Alton, et al. Glencoe Biology. 2nd ed. 2008. (ENG.). 1248p. (C). stu. ed. 112.56 *(978-0-07-880284-3(9)*, 0078802849) McGraw-Hill Higher Education.

Die Biologie (Biology) (Schulerduden Ser.). (ENG & GER.). 27.95 *(978-3-411-02207-6(8)*, B2207) Bibliographisches Institut & F. A. Brockhaus AG DEU. Dist: Continental Bk. Co., Inc.

Biology Tutor. 3rd ed. 2007. 282p. 20.00 *(978-1-885380-64-7(X))* Suspended Animations.

Birkhead, Tim R., et al, eds. Sperm Biology: An Evolutionary Perspective. 2008. (ENG., Illus.). 674p. 83.95 *(978-0-12-372568-4(2)*, Academic Pr.) Elsevier Science & Technology Bks.

Bjorklund, Gustaf. Death & Resurrection from the Point of View of the Cell Theory. 2007. (ENG.). 228p. 41.95 *(978-0-548-03751-5(5))* Kessinger Publishing, LLC.

Boniolo, Giovanni & De Anna, Gabriele, eds. Evolutionary Ethics & Contemporary Biology. 2009. (Cambridge Studies in Philosophy & Biology Ser.). (ENG.). 224p. pap. 32.99 *(978-0-521-12270-2(8))* Cambridge Univ. Pr.

Bowler, Peter J. Monkey Trials & Gorilla Sermons: Evolution & Christianity from Darwin to Intelligent Design. 2009. (New Histories of Science, Technology, & Medicine Ser.). 272p. pap. 19.00 *(978-0-674-03220-0(9))* Harvard Univ. Pr.

Bradley & Calvert. Catch up Biology: For the Medical Sciences. 2006. (ENG., Illus.). 200p. pap. 28.99 *(978-1-904842-32-3(1))* Scion Publishing Ltd. GBR. Dist: Chicago Distribution Ctr.

Brigham Young University College of Humanities Staff. Genetics. 2010. (ENG.). 150p. (C). lab manual ed. 16.00 *(978-0-321-72622-3(7))* Benjamin-Cummings Publishing Co.

—Masteringbiology. 2010. (ENG.). (C). lab manual ed. 17.40 *(978-0-321-72278-2(7))*; 150p. lab manual ed. 16.00 *(978-0-321-72068-9(7))*; 150p. lab manual ed. 16.00 *(978-0-321-72272-0(8))* Benjamin-Cummings Publishing Co.

—Systematics. 2010. (ENG.). (C). 16.00 *(978-0-321-72279-9(5))* Benjamin-Cummings Publishing Co.

Brigham Young University Department of Communications Staff. MasteringBiology Virtual Labs. 2010. (ENG.). 150p. (C). lab manual ed. 73.33 *(978-0-321-69465-9(X))* Benjamin-Cummings Publishing Co.

Brooker, Rob. Biology. 2nd ed. 2010. (ENG.). (C). 223.66 *(978-0-07-740316-4(9)*, 0077403169, McGraw-Hill Science, Engineering & Mathematics) McGraw-Hill Higher Education.

Brooker, Robert. Biology - Plants & Animals, Vol. 3. 2nd ed. 2010. (ENG.). (C). pap. 90.67 *(978-0-07-740589-2(7)*, 0077405897, McGraw-Hill Science, Engineering & Mathematics) McGraw-Hill Higher Education.

—Loose-leaf Biology. 2nd ed. 2010. (ENG.). (C). 150.33 *(978-0-07-740382-9(7)*, 0077403827, McGraw-Hill Science, Engineering & Mathematics) McGraw-Hill Higher Education.

Brooker, Robert, et al. Biology: Evolution, Diversity & Ecology. 2nd ed. 2010. (ENG.). (C). pap. 113.00 *(978-0-07-749274-8(9)*, 0077492749, McGraw-Hill Science, Engineering & Mathematics) McGraw-Hill Higher Education.

Brooker, Robert J. Biology. (Illus.). 2006. xxxii, 1392p. *(978-0-07-295620-7(8))* 2nd ed. 2010. *(978-0-07-353221-9(5))* McGraw-Hill Cos., The.

—Biology (Reinforced NASTA Binding for Secondary Market) 2008. (ENG.). (C). 181.28 *(978-0-07-334983-1(6)*, 0073349836) McGraw-Hill Higher Education.

Brooker, Robert J., et al. Biology. (ENG., (C). 2007. Illus.). 1488p. 214.67 *(978-0-07-326807-1(0)*, 0073268070) 2nd ed. 2010. 1440p. 214.67 *(978-0-07-734996-7(2)*, 0077349962) McGraw-Hill Higher Education. (McGraw-Hill Science, Engineering & Mathematics).

Brooks, Randy & BarCharts Inc., Staff. Biology. 2006. (Quickstudy Bks.). (ENG., Illus.). 144p. pap. 6.95 *(978-1-4232-0256-1(2))* Barcharts, Inc.

Byers, Bruce, et al. Biology: Life on Earth with Physiology. 8th rev. ed. 2007. (ENG., Illus.). 1008p. (C). 178.53 *(978-0-13-195766-4(X))* Benjamin-Cummings Publishing Co.

Cabej, Nelson R. Epigenetic Principles of Evolution. 2011. (ENG.). 846p. 150.00 ***(978-0-12-415831-3(5))*** Elsevier Science & Technology Bks.

Cain. Discover Biology. 4th ed. 2009. (ENG.). 314p. (C). pap. 18.00 net. *(978-0-393-93310-9(5)*, 93310) Norton, W. W. & Co., Inc.

Cain, et al. Discover Biology. (ENG.). (C). 4th ed. 2009. 590p. pap. 86.50 net. *(978-0-393-93161-7(7)*, 93161) 4th ed. 2009. (Illus.). 1000p. pap. 96.50 net. *(978-0-393-93160-0(9)*, 93160) 5th ed. 2011. 795p. pap. 96.50 net. ***(978-0-393-93570-7(1)***, 93570) Norton, W. W. & Co., Inc.

Cain, M. L., et al. Study Guide to Accompany Discover Biology: Core Topics. 3rd ed. 2006. 203p. (C). pap., stu. ed. 24.00 *(978-0-393-92845-7(4))* Norton, W. W. & Co., Inc.

Cain, Michael & Singh-Cundy, Anu. Discover Biology. 5th ed. 2011. (ENG.). 654p. (C). pap. 86.50 net. ***(978-0-393-91814-4(9)***, 91814) Norton, W. W. & Co., Inc.

Cain, Michael L. Discover Biology 4E Core Topics Art Notebook. 2009. (ENG.). 216p. (C). pap. 15.00 net. *(978-0-393-93311-6(3)*, 93311) Norton, W. W. & Co., Inc.

Calder, Muffy & Gilmore, Stephen. Computational Methods in Systems Biology: International Conference CMSB 2007, Edinburgh, Scotland, September 20-21, 2007, Proceedings. 2007. (Lecture Notes in Computer Science / Lecture Notes in Bioinformatics Ser.). x, 249p. pap. 69.95 *(978-3-540-75139-7(4))* Springer.

Campbell, Neil A. & Reece, Jane B. Biology. 8th ed. 2008. (ENG., Illus.). 1393p. (C). 202.67 *(978-0-8053-6844-4(2))* Benjamin-Cummings Publishing Co.

—Practicing Biology: A Student Workbook: Biology Eighth Edition by Jean Heitz & Cynthia Giffen. 3rd ed. 2007. (ENG., Illus.). 360p. (C). per. 19.00 *(978-0-321-52293-1(1))* Benjamin-Cummings Publishing Co.

Campbell, Neil A., et al. Biology. (ENG.). (C). 8th ed. 2007. 128p. pap. 18.20 *(978-0-321-53659-4(2))* 8th ed. 2007. 1393p. 202.67 *(978-0-321-54325-7(4))* 9th ed. 2010. 1464p. E-Book, E-Book 126.67 *(978-0-321-68651-0(9))* Benjamin-Cummings Publishing Co.

—Biology: Concepts & Connections. (ENG., (C). 5th rev. ed. 2007. Illus.). 781p. 178.53 *(978-0-321-51244-4(8))* 6th ed. 2010. 928p. 178.53 *(978-0-321-74231-5(1))* Benjamin-Cummings Publishing Co.

—Biology: Concepts & Connections. 6th ed. 2010. (ENG.). (C). E-Book, E-Book 114.67 *(978-0-321-73650-5(8))* Benjamin-Cummings Publishing Co.

—Study Guide for Biology: Concepts & Connections. 6th ed. 2008. (ENG.). 504p. (C). pap. 61.80 *(978-0-321-54825-2(6))* Benjamin-Cummings Publishing Co.

Carolina Biological Staff, compiled by. Cell Bundle. 2009. (Inquiries in Science Biology Ser.). *(978-1-4350-0376-7(4))* Carolina Biological Supply Co.

—Classifying Across Kingdoms. 2009. (Inquiries in Science Biology Ser.). *(978-1-4350-0368-2(3))*; tchr. ed., spiral bd. *(978-1-4350-0367-5(5))* Carolina Biological Supply Co.

—Complete Biology Series Bundle. 2009. (Inquiries in Science Biology Ser.). *(978-1-4350-0375-0(6))* Carolina Biological Supply Co.

—Energizing Cells. 2009. (Inquiries in Science Biology Ser.). *(978-1-4350-0346-0(2))* Carolina Biological Supply Co.

—Evolution Bundle. 2009. (Inquiries in Science Biology Ser.). *(978-1-4350-0379-8(9))* Carolina Biological Supply Co.

—Examining Cellular Transport. 2009. (Inquiries in Science Biology Ser.). *(978-1-4350-0342-2(X))* Carolina Biological Supply Co.

Chikazawa-Nelson. Risk & Resilience. 2010. 204p. pap. *(978-3-8383-8556-3(X))* Lambert Academic Publishing.

Choi, Sangdun, ed. Introduction to Systems Biology. 2010. (Illus.). xvi, 542p. pap. 134.00 *(978-1-61737-729-7(5)*, 1617377295) Humana Pr.

Clamp, Alan & Jones, Mary. Biology: Energy, Exercise & Coordination. 2009. 112p. pap., instr.'s gde. ed. 22.50 *(978-0-340-94832-3(9))* Hodder Education GBR. Dist: Trans-Atlantic Pubns., Inc.

Clavien, Christine, et al. Morale et évolution Biologique: Entre Déterminisme et Liberté. 2007. (FRE., Illus.). x, 338p. *(978-2-88074-719-0(8))* Presses Polytechniques et Universitaires Romandes.

Clemente Gallardo, Jesús, et al, eds. Large Scale Simulations of Complex Systems, Condensed Matter & Fusion Plasma: Proceedings of the BIFI2008 International Conference. 2008. (AIP Conference Proceedings / Plasma Physics Ser.). 138p. 109.00 *(978-0-7354-0602-5(2))* American Institute of Physics.

Clemente-Gallardo, Jésus, et al, eds. From Physisc to Biology: The Interface between Experiment & Computation: Bifi 2006 II International Congress. 2006. (AIP Conference Proceedings Ser.). (Illus.). xi, 204p. 128.00 *(978-0-7354-0350-5(3)*, 0735403503) American Institute of Physics.

Cohen, Alix. Kant & the Human Sciences: Biology, Anthropology & History. 2009. (ENG., Illus.). 256p. 95.00 *(978-0-230-22432-2(6))* Palgrave Macmillan.

Comings, David E. Did Man Create God? Is Your Spiritual Brain at Peace with Your Thinking Brain? 2008. (ENG., Illus.). 694p. 29.95 *(978-1-878267-73-3(6))* Hope Pr.

Conn, H. W. The Story of the Living MacHine. 2007. (Illus.). 160p. per. *(978-1-4065-1481-0(0))* Dodo Pr.

Conn, Herbert William. The Story of the Living Machine: A Review of the Conclusions of Modern Biology... 2007. (ENG.). 158p. pap. 19.99 *(978-1-4346-0079-0(3))*; 176p. pap. 21.99 *(978-1-4346-0164-3(1))* BiblioBazaar.

Consumer Dummies Staff, et al. Biology for Dummies. 2nd ed. 2010. (ENG., Illus.). 384p. pap. 19.99 *(978-0-470-59875-7(1)*, For Dummies) Wiley, John & Sons, Inc.

Cook, Joseph. Boston Monday Lectures Biology. 2009. (Cambridge Library Collection - Religion Ser.). (ENG.). 168p. pap. 19.99 *(978-1-108-00419-0(9))* Cambridge Univ. Pr.

—Lectures on Biology, Transcendentalism & Orthodoxy - with the Preludes on Current Events & Analytical Indices. 2007. 488p. per. *(978-1-4067-8787-0(6)*, Pomona Pr.) Read Bks.

Corbellini, Giovanni. Bioreboot: The Architecture of R & Sie(N) 2010. (ENG.). 228p. pap. 40.00 *(978-1-56898-869-6(9))* Princeton Architectural Pr.

Cord Biology Grades 6-12: Science in Context. annot. ed. Date not set. tchr. ed. 88.95 *(978-0-538-68167-4(5))* Globe Fearon Educational Publishing.

Covert, Markus. The Systems Biology Workbook: A Hands-On Introduction to a Revolution in Biology. 2010. pap. 79.95 *(978-1-4200-8410-8(0))* CRC Pr. LLC.

Crampton, Henry Edward. Coming & Evolution of Life How Living. 2006. pap. 19.95 *(978-1-4286-3713-9(3))* Kessinger Publishing, LLC.

Cram101 Textbook Reviews. Outlines & Highlights for Cell Biology & Genetics: 9780495125785 0495125784. 2011. 408p. pap. 35.95 ***(978-1-61812-626-9(1))*** Cram101 Inc.

Cram101 Textbook Reviews Staff. Outlines & Highlights for a Brief Guide to Biology by David Krogh, Isbn: 9780131859654. 2009. 218p. pap. 30.95 *(978-1-4288-8246-1(4))* Cram101 Inc.

—Outlines & Highlights for Biological Science: Evolution, Diversity, & Ecology, Vol. 2 by Freeman, ISBN. 2008. 592p. pap. 22.95 *(978-1-4288-6114-5(9))* Cram101 Inc.

—Outlines & Highlights for Concepts in Biology by Enger Isbn: 9780077229962. 2008. 224p. pap. 13.95 *(978-1-4288-6078-0(9))* Cram101 Inc.

—Outlines & Highlights for Concepts of Biology by Mader, Isbn: 9780077229979. 2008. 524p. pap. 20.95 *(978-1-4288-6028-5(2))* Cram101 Inc.

—Outlines & Highlights for Essential Biology with Physiology by Campbell Isbn: 0805368418. 2008. 292p. pap. 15.95 *(978-1-4288-6056-8(8))* Cram101 Inc.

—Outlines & Highlights for Evolution & Ecology of the Organism by Rose, Isbn: 0130104043. 2008. 168p. pap. 12.95 *(978-1-4288-6439-9(3))* Cram101 Inc.

—Outlines & Highlights for Evolution, Diversity, & Ecology: Volume III by Raven, Johnson, Losos, Mason, & Singer, ISBN. 2009. 120p. pap. 28.95 *(978-1-4288-7657-6(X))* Cram101 Inc.

Crooks, Kevin & Sanjayan, M., eds. Connectivity Conservation. 2006. (Conservation Biology Ser.: Vol. 14). (ENG., Illus.). 732p. pap. 95.00 *(978-0-521-67381-5(X))* Cambridge Univ. Pr.

Darwin, Charles. The Annotated Origin. fac. ed. 2011. (Illus.). 576p. pap. 22.95 *(978-0-674-06017-3(2)*, Belknap Pr.) Harvard Univ. Pr.

Davim, J. Paulo, ed. Tribology for Engineers: A Practical Guide. 2011. (Woodhead Publishing in Mechanical Engineering Ser.). (ENG., Illus.). 320p. 220.00 *(978-0-85709-114-7(X))* Woodhead Publishing Ltd. GBR. Dist: Ingram Pub. Services.

Dejong-Lambert, William. The New Biology. 2008. 200p. pap. *(978-3-8364-8567-8(2))* VDM Verlag Dr. Mueller e.K.

Detwiler, Paul & Jester, Rozalind. Discovering the Living Ocean. rev. ed. 2010. (ENG.). 96p. spiral bd., lab manual ed. 34.05 *(978-0-7575-7226-5(X))* Kendall Hunt Publishing Co.

Diaz, Luis. Cuba: Sierra de Cubitas. Alverson, William S., ed. 2007. (Field Museum - Rapid Biological Inventories Ser.). (SPA.). 230p. pap. 30.00 *(978-0-914868-60-6(8))* Field Museum of Natural History, Div. of Pubns.

Dieckmann, Ulf & Couvet, Denis. Evolutionary Conservation Biology. Ferriére, Régis & Dieckmann, Ulf, eds. Couvet, Denis, ed. 2009. (Cambridge Studies in Adaptive Dynamics Ser.). (ENG., Illus.). 448p. pap. 58.00 *(978-0-521-11608-4(2))* Cambridge Univ. Pr.

Distefano, Matthew. Homework Helpers: Biology. 2nd rev. ed. 2011. (Homework Helpers Ser.). (ENG.). 1p. pap. 17.99 *(978-1-60163-164-0(2))* Career Pr., Inc.

Donohue, Kathleen, ed. Darwin's Finches: Readings in the Evolution of a Scientific Paradigm. 2011. (ENG., Illus.). 512p. 120.00 *(978-0-226-15770-2(9))*; pap. 45.00 *(978-0-226-15771-9(7))* Univ. of Chicago Pr.

Downes, Barbara J., et al. Monitoring Ecological Impacts: Concepts & Practice in Flowing Waters. 2008. (ENG., Illus.). 452p. pap. 79.00 *(978-0-521-06529-0(1))* Cambridge Univ. Pr.

Dutton, Denis. The Art Instinct: Beauty, Pleasure, & Human Evolution. 2008. (ENG.). 288p. 25.00 *(978-1-59691-401-8(7))* Bloomsbury Publishing.

Ebert, David A. & Sulikowski, James, eds. Biology of Skates. 2010. (Developments in Environmental Biology of Fishes Ser.). (ENG.). vi, 246p. pap. 179.00 *(978-90-481-8188-9(7)*, 9048181887) Springer.

Ebert, David A. & Sulikowski, James A., eds. Biology of Skates. 2009. (Developments in Environmental Biology of Fishes Ser.). (ENG., Illus.). vi, 246p. 179.00 *(978-1-4020-9702-7(6))* Springer.

Edwards, Gabrielle I. & Pfirrmann, Cynthia. E-Z Biology. 4th rev. ed. 2009. (Barron's E-Z Ser.). (ENG., Illus.). 496p. pap. 18.99 *(978-0-7641-4134-8(1))* Barron's Educational Series, Inc.

Enger, et al. Concepts in Biology. 13th ed. 2008. *(978-0-07-340343-4(1))* McGraw-Hill Cos., The.

—Concepts in Biology. 14th ed. 2011. (ENG., Illus.). 704p. (C). pap. 143.67 *(978-0-07-340346-5(6)*, 0073403466, McGraw-Hill Science, Engineering & Mathematics) McGraw-Hill Higher Education.

Enger, Eldon. Concepts in Biology w/ Connect Plus Access Card. 14th ed. 2011. (ENG.). (C). pap. 152.66 *(978-0-07-750230-0(2)*, 0077502302, McGraw-Hill Science, Engineering & Mathematics) McGraw-Hill Higher Education.

Enger, Eldon, et al. Loose Leaf Version for Concepts in Biology. 14th ed. 2011. (ENG.). (C). ring bd. 100.67 *(978-0-07-748957-1(8)*, 0077489578, McGraw-Hill Science, Engineering & Mathematics) McGraw-Hill Higher Education.

Evans, Ann S., et al. Introductory Biology 101. 2nd rev. ed. 2012. (ENG.). 172p. spiral bd., lab manual ed. 33.00 ***(978-0-7575-9534-9(0))*** Kendall Hunt Publishing Co.

Felix, Robert W. Magnetic Reversals & Evolutionary Leaps: The True Origin of Species. 2009. (Illus.). 192p. pap. 15.95 *(978-0-9648746-7-1(9))* Sugarhouse Publishing.

Fiore, Lisa B. LifeSmart. 2010. (ENG., Illus.). 368p. (C). pap. 87.33 *(978-0-07-803524-1(4)*, 0078035244) McGraw-Hill Cos., The.

Fisher. Biological Perspectives Text. rev. ed. 2011. (ENG.). 662p. pap. 146.00 ***(978-0-7575-9318-5(6))*** Kendall Hunt Publishing Co.

Fredericks, Anthony D. How Long Things Live: And How They Live As Long as They Do. 2010. (Illus.). 176p. pap. 16.95 *(978-0-8117-3622-0(9))* Stackpole Bks.

Freeman, Scott. Biological Science. 3rd ed. 2009. (ENG.). 1392p. (C). 202.67 *(978-0-13-224950-8(2))* 3rd ed. 2007. (ENG., Illus.). 1392p. (C). 202.67 *(978-0-321-54327-1(0))* 3rd ed. 2007. *(978-0-13-224985-0(5))* 4th ed. 2012. (ENG.). (C). ring bd. 131.60 ***(978-0-321-84024-0(0))*** 4th ed. 2010. (ENG.). 1320p. (C). 202.67 *(978-0-321-59820-2(2))* 4th ed. 2009. *(978-0-321-59819-6(9))* 4th ed. 2010. (ENG.). (C). 30.00 *(978-0-321-61349-3(X))* 4th ed. 2010. (ENG.). 1392p. (C). E-Book, E-Book 126.67 *(978-0-321-70396-5(0))* Vol. 2. 4th ed. 2010. (ENG.). 624p. (C). pap. 71.40 *(978-0-321-60531-3(4))* Vol. 3. 4th ed. 2010. (ENG.). 504p. (C). pap. 67.20 *(978-0-321-60947-2(6))* Benjamin-Cummings Publishing Co.

—Biological Science Vol. 1: The Cell, Genetics, & Development. 3rd ed. 2007. (ENG.). 600p. (C). pap. 79.80 *(978-0-13-225308-6(9))* Benjamin-Cummings Publishing Co.

—Biological Science Vol. 2: Evolution, Diversity, & Ecology. 3rd ed. 2007. (ENG.). 576p. (C). pap. 71.40 *(978-0-13-232543-1(8))* Benjamin-Cummings Publishing Co.

—Biological Science, Books a la Carte Edition. 4th ed. 2012. (ENG.). 1320p. (C). ring bd. 121.60 ***(978-0-321-84023-3(2))*** Benjamin-Cummings Publishing Co.

—Biological Science Volume 1. 4th ed. 2010. (ENG., Illus.). 608p. (C). pap. 79.80 *(978-0-321-61347-9(3))* Benjamin-Cummings Publishing Co.

—Biological Science Volume 2. 4th ed. 2010. (ENG., Illus.). 624p. (C). pap. 71.40 *(978-0-321-60530-6(6))* Benjamin-Cummings Publishing Co.

—Biological Science Volume 3. 4th ed. 2010. (ENG., Illus.). 504p. (C). pap. 67.20 *(978-0-321-57676-7(4))* Benjamin-Cummings Publishing Co.

—Blackboard Student Access Kit for Biological Science. 4th ed. 2010. (ENG.). (C). 23.40 *(978-0-321-60532-0(2))* Benjamin-Cummings Publishing Co.

—Study Guide for Biological Science. 3rd ed. 2008. (ENG.). 464p. (C). pap. 53.60 *(978-0-13-224984-3(7))* Benjamin-Cummings Publishing Co.

Freeman, Scott & Burggren, Warren. Study Guide for Biological Science. 4th ed. 2010. (ENG.). 480p. (C). pap. 53.80 *(978-0-321-56168-8(6))* Benjamin-Cummings Publishing Co.

Freeman, Scott, et al. Practicing Biology: A Student Workbook for Biological Science. 2nd ed. 2010. (ENG.). 420p. (C). pap. 20.00 *(978-0-321-61264-9(7))* Benjamin-Cummings Publishing Co.

—Practicing Biology: A Student Workbook for Freeman Biological Science. 3rd ed. 2008. (ENG.). 416p. (C). pap. 15.80 *(978-0-321-53682-2(7))* Benjamin-Cummings Publishing Co.

Fridman, Alexander A. Plasma Assisted Decontamination of Biological & Chemical Agents. Güçeri, Selçuk I., ed. 2008. (NATO Science for Peace & Security Series A: Chemistry & Biology Ser.). (ENG., Illus.). xiii, 311p. pap. 109.00 *(978-1-4020-8440-9(4)*, 1402084404) Springer.

B

Fukuda, Minoru, ed. Functional Glycomics. 2006. (ENG., Illus.). 488p. 187.00 *(978-0-12-182822-6(0),* Academic Pr.) Elsevier Science & Technology Bks.
—Glycobiology. 2006. (Methods in Enzymology Ser.). (ENG., Illus.). 424p. 187.00 *(978-0-12-182820-2(4));* Vol. 416. 456p. 187.00 *(978-0-12-182821-9(2))* Elsevier Science & Technology Bks. (Academic Pr.).
Furse, Mike T., et al. The Ecological Status of European Rivers: Evaluation & Intercalibration of Assessment Methods: Evaluation & Intercalibration of Assessment Methods. 2010. (Developments in Hydrobiology Ser.). viii, 555p. pap. 269.00 *(978-90-481-7298-6(5),* 9048172985) Springer.
Futuyma, Douglas J. Evolution: Easy Reading Edition. 2007. (Illus.). 607p. *(978-3-8274-1816-6(X))* Spektrum Akademischer Verlag GmbH.
Gardingen, P. R. van, et al, eds. Scaling-up: From Cell to Landscape. 2011. (Society for Experimental Biology Seminar Ser.). (ENG.). 402p. pap. 36.99 *(978-0-521-18775-6(3))* Cambridge Univ. Pr.
Garrett, Lori K. & Benjamin-Cummings Publishing Company Inc. Staff. Get Ready for Biology. 2006. (ENG., Illus.). 258p. (C). per. 46.67 *(978-0-321-50057-1(1))* Benjamin-Cummings Publishing Co.
General Biology Quick Reference Guide. 2007. *(978-1-934529-16-4(8))* Innovative Academic Solutions.
General Biology Workbook. 2007. *(978-1-934529-15-7(X))* Innovative Academic Solutions.
Gerhardt, Volker & Nida-Ramelin, Julian, eds. Evolution in Natur und Kultur. 2010. (Humanprojekt Ser.).Tr. of Evolution in Nature & Culture. (GER.). VIII, 303p. 154.00 ***(978-3-11-173318-0(1))*** De Gruyter, Walter Inc.
Gerhardt, Volker & Nida-Rümelin, Julian, eds. Evolution in Natur und Kultur. 2010. (Humanprojekt Ser.).Tr. of Evolution in Nature & Culture. (GER.). VIII, 303p. 98.00 *(978-3-11-021350-8(8))* De Gruyter, Walter Inc.
Gerhart, Karen & Karengerhart, Karen. Introduction to Biology. 2010. (ENG.). 324p. ring bd. 51.99 *(978-0-7575-7036-0(4))* Kendall Hunt Publishing Co.
Gevona, James T. Synthetic & Integrative Biology: Parts & Systems, Design Theory & Applications. 2010. (Biotechnology in Agriculture, Industry & Medicine Ser.). 243p. 79.00 *(978-1-60876-678-9(0))* Nova Science Pubs., Inc.
Giberson, Karl. Saving Darwin: How to Be a Christian & Believe in Evolution. 2009. 256p. pap. 14.99 *(978-0-06-144173-8(2),* HarperOne) HarperCollins Pubs.
Gladon, Richard J., et al. Getting Published in the Life Sciences. 2011. (ENG.). 368p. pap. 29.95 *(978-1-118-01716-6(1),* Wiley-Blackwell) Wiley, John & Sons, Inc.
Glass, David J. Experimental Design for Biologists. 2006. (ENG., Illus.). 206p. 37.00 *(978-0-87969-735-8(0))* Cold Spring Harbor Laboratory Pr.
Glencoe & Raven, Peter. Raven, Biology, 9e NASTA. 9th ed. 2010. (ENG.). (C). 170.01 *(978-0-07-893649-4(7),* 0078936497) McGraw-Hill Higher Education.
Globe-Fearon Staff. Fearon's Biology Critical Thinking. wbk. ed. 80.95 *(978-0-8359-3149-6(8),* 0872-1C01) Globe Fearon Educational Publishing.
Gonzalez, Juan, et al, eds. Nature Inspired Cooperative Strategies for Optimization (NICSO 2010) 2010. (Studies in Computational Intelligence Ser.). (ENG.). 420p. 199.00 *(978-3-642-12537-9(9),* 3642125379) Springer.
Gould, Stephen Jay. Leonardo's Mountain of the Clams & the Diet of Worms: Essays on Natural History. 2011. (ENG., Illus.). 432p. pap. 19.95 *(978-0-674-06163-7(2),* Belknap Pr.) Harvard Univ. Pr.
Grady, Wayne. Bringing Back the Dodo: Lessons in Natural & Unnatural History. 2007. (ENG.). 240p. pap. 19.95 *(978-0-7710-3505-0(5),* McClelland & Stewart) McClelland & Stewart CAN. Dist: Random Hse., Inc.
Greenwood, Tracey, et al. Skills in Biology. 2nd ed. 2007. (Illus.). 124p. (YA). pap. *(978-1-877462-14-6(4))* BIOZONE International, Ltd.
Gruber, Petra. Biomimetics in Architecture: Architecture of Life & Buildings. 2010. (ENG., Illus.). 280p. pap. 89.95 *(978-3-7091-0331-9(2),* 3709103312) Springer Wien AUT. Dist: Springer.
Güçeri, Selçuk I. Plasma Assisted Decontamination of Biological & Chemical Agents. Fridman, Alexander A., ed. 2008. (NATO Science for Peace & Security Series A: Chemistry & Biology Ser.). (Illus.). XIII, 311p. 249.00 *(978-1-4020-8438-6(2),* 1402084382) Springer.
Hassan, Yasoob & Hafiz, Azhar Ali Khan. Peach Fruit Fly, Bactrocera Zonata (Saunders) (Diptera: Tephritidae) Population Dynamics & Management with Different Tactics. 2011. 100p. pap. ***(978-3-639-34431-8(6))*** VDM Verlag Dr. Mueller e.K.
He, Jiankui. Modularity. 2011. 132p. pap. ***(978-3-8443-1141-9(6))*** Lambert Academic Publishing.
Heath, Lenwood S. & Ramakrishnan, Naren, eds. Problem Solving Handbook for Computational Biology & Bioinformatics. 2010. (ENG., Illus.). xvii, 347p. 129.00 *(978-0-387-09759-6(7),* 0387097597) Springer.
Hedges, S. Blair & Kumar, Sudhir, eds. The Timetree of Life. 2009. (ENG., Illus.). 576p. 200.00 *(978-0-19-953503-3(5))* Oxford Univ. Pr., Inc.
Heisterkamp, Alexander. Frontiers in Ultrafast Optics: Biomedical, Scientific, & Industrial Applications X: 24-26 January 2010, San Francisco, California, United States. 2010. (Proceedings of SPIE Ser.). (Illus.). 248p. pap. 105.00 ***(978-0-8194-7985-3(3))*** SPIE.
Heschl, Adolf. Darwins Traum: Die Entstehung des menschlichen Bewusstseins. 2010. (GER., Illus.). 442p. pap. 26.50 ***(978-3-527-32433-0(X),*** Wiley-VCH) Wiley, John & Sons, Inc.
Hillis, David M., et al. Principles of Life. 2010. (ENG., Illus.). 915p. (C). 112.95 *(978-1-4292-5721-3(0))* Freeman, W. H. & Co.
Hillis, David M., et al. Principles of Life (High School Edition) 2011. (ENG.). 915p. 112.95 ***(978-1-4292-9117-0(6))*** Freeman, W. H. & Co.
Hoefnagels. Biology: Concepts & Investigations. 2012. pap. ***(978-0-07-131554-8(3))*** McGraw-Hill Cos., The.
Hoefnagels, Mariëlle. Biology: Concepts & Investigations. (ENG., Illus.). (C). 2008. 944p. 183.00 *(978-0-07-334252-8(1),* 0073342521) 2nd ed. 2011. 912p. 183.00 *(978-0-07-340347-2(4),* 0073403474) McGraw-Hill Higher Education. (McGraw-Hill Science, Engineering & Mathematics).
—Biology: the Essentials with Connect Plus 1 Semester Access Card. 2012. (ENG.). (C). pap. 156.00 ***(978-0-07-758312-5(4),*** 0077583124, McGraw-Hill Science, Engineering & Mathematics) McGraw-Hill Higher Education.
Hoefnagels, Mariëlle. Loose Leaf Version for Biology: Concepts & Investigations. 2nd ed. 2011. (ENG.). (C). ring bd. 128.33 *(978-0-07-743123-5(5),* 0077431235, McGraw-Hill Science, Engineering & Mathematics) McGraw-Hill Higher Education.
Hoefnagels, Mariëlle, et al. Looseleaf for Biology: Concepts & Investigations. 2010. (ENG.). (C). ring bd. 128.33 *(978-0-07-744991-9(6),* 0077449916, McGraw-Hill Science, Engineering & Mathematics) McGraw-Hill Higher Education.
Hoefnagels, Marille. Biology: Concepts & Investigations. 2008. *(978-0-07-291690-4(7))* McGraw-Hill Cos., The.
Hoffmeyer, Jesper. Biosemiotics: An Examination into the Signs of Life & the Life of Signs. Favareau, Donald, ed. 2009. (USP-Approaches to Postmodernity Ser.). (Illus.). 300p. 45.00 *(978-1-58966-169-1(9))* Univ. of Scranton Pr.
Holt Rinehart & Winston, creator. Holt Biology: Photosynthesis & Cellular Respiration, Chapter 9 Resource File. 2008. (Illus.). 74p. pap. 10.60 *(978-0-03-093182-6(7))* Holt McDougal.
Holt, Rinehart and Winston Staff. Modern Biology: Premier Online Edition. 6th ed. Date not set. 83.93 *(978-0-03-036751-9(4))* Holt McDougal.
Horning, Ned, et al. Remote Sensing for Ecology & Conservation: A Handbook of Techniques. 2010. (Techniques in Ecology & Conservation Ser.). (ENG., Illus.). 448p. 125.00 *(978-0-19-921994-0(X));* pap. 60.00 *(978-0-19-921995-7(8))* Oxford Univ. Pr., Inc.
Horwitz, Jim. Biology for Non Majors Bsc 1005L. rev. ed. 2008. (ENG.). 86p. spiral bd. 50.03 *(978-0-7575-5354-7(0))* Kendall Hunt Publishing Co.
Houghton, Toby & Woodward, Christine. AQA GCSE Biology Student's Book. 2010. 238p. pap. 56.00 *(978-1-4441-2080-6(8))* Hodder Education GBR. Dist: Trans-Atlantic Pubns., Inc.
—AQA GCSE Science Biology. 2007. (Illus.). 240p. pap., stu. ed. 47.50 *(978-0-340-92797-7(6),* Hodder Murray) Hodder Education GBR. Dist: Trans-Atlantic Pubns., Inc.
Humphery-Smith, Ian & Hecker, Michael, eds. Microbial Proteomics: Functional Biology of Whole Organisms. 2006. (Methods of Biochemical Analysis Ser.: 48). (ENG., Illus.). 538p. 189.95 *(978-0-471-69975-0(6),* Wiley-Interscience) Wiley, John & Sons, Inc.
Huxley, Julian. Evolution: The Modern Synthesis. 2009. (ENG., Illus.). 784p. (gr. 17). pap. 35.00 *(978-0-262-51366-1(8))* MIT Pr.
Huxley, Thomas Henry. Discourses. 2008. 284p. 28.99 *(978-0-554-23194-5(8));* 25.99 *(978-0-554-32497-5(0))* BiblioBazaar.
—Discourses: Biological & Geological Essays. l.t. ed. 2007. (ENG.). 250p. pap. 20.99 *(978-1-4264-3917-9(2))* 2006. 280p. pap. 32.99 *(978-1-4264-3975-9(X))* BiblioBazaar.
—Discourses Biological & Geological. 2009. 182p. pap. *(978-0-217-70863-0(3))* Books LLC.
Hyde, Kenneth M. Selected Topics in Biology. rev. ed. 2011. (ENG.). 98p. pap. 64.95 *(978-0-7575-8838-9(7))* Kendall Hunt Publishing Co.
Ikram, Abarrul. Neutron & X-Ray Scattering. 2008. (AIP Conference Proceedings Ser.). 149.00 *(978-0-7354-0508-0(5))* American Institute of Physics.
Intro to Biology of Marine Life 10E International Ed. 10th rev. ed. 2011. pap. 143.95 *(978-0-7637-9276-3(4))* Jones & Bartlett Learning, LLC.
Jeffery, William R. Evolution & Development. 2009. (ENG., Illus.). 464p. 198.00 *(978-0-12-374455-5(5),* Academic Pr.) Elsevier Science & Technology Bks.
Jennings, Jason B. Introduction to Biology I & II. rev. ed. 2011. (ENG.). 240p. spiral bd. 77.95 *(978-0-7575-7667-6(2))* Kendall Hunt Publishing Co.
John Wiley and Sons Staff. Encyclopedia of Life Sciences, 6 vols., Set. 2007. (ENG., Illus.). 4060p. suppl. ed. 2000.00 *(978-0-470-06141-1(3),* Wiley) Wiley, John & Sons, Inc.
Johnson. Essentials of the Living World. 4th ed. 2012. pap. ***(978-0-07-352547-1(2))*** McGraw-Hill Cos., The.
Johnson & Johnson, George. The Living World. 7th ed. 2011. (ENG., Illus.). 880p. (C). 183.00 *(978-0-07-802417-7(X),* 007802417X, McGraw-Hill Science, Engineering & Mathematics) McGraw-Hill Higher Education.
Johnson, Dirk R. Nietzsche's Anti-Darwinism. 2010. (ENG.). 250p. 85.00 *(978-0-521-19678-9(7))* Cambridge Univ. Pr.
Johnson, George B. Essentials of the Living World. 2nd ed. 2007. *(978-0-07-352542-6(1))* 3rd ed. 2009. *(978-0-07-337793-3(7))* McGraw-Hill Cos., The.
—The Living World with Connect Plus Access Card. 7th ed. 2011. (ENG.). (C). 192.00 *(978-0-07-747485-0(6),* 0077474856, McGraw-Hill Science, Engineering & Mathematics) McGraw-Hill Higher Education.
Johnson, George B. & Losos, Jonathan. Essentials of the Living World. 3rd ed. 2010. (Illus.). xviii, 686p. pap. *(978-0-07-016776-6(1))* McGraw-Hill Cos., The.
—Essentials of the Living World. 3rd ed. 2009. (ENG., Illus.). 704p. (C). pap., pap. 135.00 *(978-0-07-728007-9(5),* 0077280075, McGraw-Hill Science, Engineering & Mathematics) McGraw-Hill Higher Education.
Johnson, George B. & Losos, Jonathan B. Essentials of the Living World. 2nd rev. ed. 2006. (Illus.). 704p. per. 107.50 *(978-0-07-330935-4(4),* 9780073309354, McGraw-Hill Science, Engineering & Mathematics) McGraw-Hill Higher Education.
—The Living World. 5th ed. 2007. (Illus.). *(978-0-07-298667-9(0))* 6th ed. 2009. *(978-0-07-337797-1(X))* McGraw-Hill Cos., The.
—The Living World. 5th rev. ed. 2007. (Illus.). 812p. 149.06 *(978-0-07-325653-5(6),* 9780073256535, McGraw-Hill Science, Engineering & Mathematics) McGraw-Hill Higher Education.
Jones, Mary & Jones, Geoff. Cambridge IGCSE Biology Coursebook with CD-ROM. 2nd rev. ed. 2009. (Cambridge International Examinations Ser.). (ENG., Illus.). 264p. pap. 30.00 incl. cd-rom *(978-0-521-14779-8(4))* Cambridge Univ. Pr.
Judkins, Aaron. The Global Phenomenon of Human Fossil Footprints in Rock. 2010. 426p. pap. 29.95 *(978-0-557-03507-6(4))* Lulu Enterprises Inc.
Kandeel, Fouad R., ed. Islets: Biology, Immunology, & Clinical Transplantation: Biology, Immunology, & Clinical Transplantation. 2009. (ENG., Illus.). 800p. 200.00 *(978-0-387-79577-5(4),* 0387795774) Springer.
Keynes, Randal. Creation: Darwin, His Daughter & Human Evolution. movie tie-in ed. 2009. (ENG.). 448p. (gr. 12). 16.00 *(978-1-59448-474-2(0),* Riverhead Trade (Paperbacks)) Penguin Group (USA) Inc.
Kimble, Michele. Femtochemistry VII: Fundamental Ultrafast Processes in Chemistry, Physics, & Biology. Castleman, Welford A., Jr., ed. 2006. (ENG., Illus.). 610p. 255.00 *(978-0-444-52821-6(0),* Elsevier Science) Elsevier Science & Technology Bks.
Kimmel, Marek & Axelrod, David E. Branching Processes in Biology. 2010. (Interdisciplinary Applied Mathematics Ser.). (Illus.). xviii, 230p. pap. 109.00 *(978-1-4419-2958-7(4),* 1441929584) Springer.
King, Stephen M., ed. Dyneins: Structure, Biology & Disease. 2011. (ENG.). 656p. 199.95 ***(978-0-12-382004-4(9),*** Academic Pr.) Elsevier Science & Technology Bks.
Kirkland, Kyle. Biological Sciences: Notable Research & Discoveries. 2010. (Frontiers of Science Ser.). (Illus.). 240p. (C). (gr. 9-18). 39.50 *(978-0-8160-7439-6(9))* Facts On File, Inc.
Klein, Gunter & Becker, Peter. Farewell to the Internal Clock: A Contribution in the Field of Chronobiology. 2007. (Illus.). xxiv, 116p. 44.95 *(978-0-387-40315-1(9),* 0387403159) Springer.
Knahr, Karl, ed. Tribology in Total Hip Arthroplasty. 2011. (ENG., Illus.). viii, 233p. pap. 99.00 *(978-3-642-19428-3(1),* 3642194281) Springer.
Knight, Celia, et al, eds. The Moss Physcomitrella Patens, Volume 36. 2009. (Annual Plant Reviews Ser.: 41). (ENG., Illus.). 368p. 229.95 *(978-1-4051-8189-1(3),* Wiley-Blackwell) Wiley, John & Sons, Inc.
Knisely, Karin. A Student Handbook for Writing in Biology. 3rd ed. 2009. (ENG., Illus.). 224p. (C). pap. 21.95 *(978-1-4292-3491-7(1))* Freeman, W. H. & Co.
Koeppl, Heinz. Design & Analysis of Biomolecular Circuits: Engineering Approaches to Systems & Synthetic Biology. Koeppl, Heinz et al, eds. 2011. (ENG., Illus.). xiii, 402p. 179.00 *(978-1-4419-6765-7(6),* 1441967656) Springer.
Konopka, Andrzej K., ed. Systems Biology: Principles, Methods, & Concepts. 2006. (ENG., Illus.). 256p. 79.95 *(978-0-8247-2520-4(4),* CRC Press) Taylor & Francis Group GBR. Dist: Taylor & Francis Group.
Kratz, Rene Fester. Biology Workbook for Dummies. 2012. (ENG.). 312p. pap. 19.99 ***(978-1-118-15840-1(7),*** For Dummies) Wiley, John & Sons, Inc.
Kratz, Rene Fester & Siegfried, Donna Rae. Biology Essentials for Dummies. 2011. (ENG., Illus.). 192p. pap. 9.99 *(978-1-118-07267-7(7),* For Dummies) Wiley, John & Sons, Inc.
Krogh. Biology: A Guide to the Natural World. 5th ed. 2010. (ENG.). (C). 30.00 *(978-0-321-68279-6(3));* (Illus.). 880p. pap. 178.53 *(978-0-321-61639-5(1))* Benjamin-Cummings Publishing Co.
Krogh & Krogh, David. Biology: A Guide to the Natural World, Books a la Carte Plus MasteringBiology. 4th ed. 2010. (ENG.). (C). ring bd. 132.20 *(978-0-321-74437-1(3))* Benjamin-Cummings Publishing Co.
Krogh, David. Biology: A Guide to the Natural World. 5th ed. 2010. (ENG.). 880p. (C). pap. 178.53 *(978-0-321-61655-5(3))* Benjamin-Cummings Publishing Co.
—Biology: A Guide to the Natural World. 5th ed. 2010. (ENG.). (C). 57.20 *(978-0-321-69663-2(8))* Benjamin-Cummings Publishing Co.
—Biology: A Guide to the Natural World, Books a la Carte Edition. 5th ed. 2010. (ENG.). 816p. (C). ring bd. 107.13 *(978-0-321-71594-4(2))* Benjamin-Cummings Publishing Co.
—Biology: A Guide to the Natural World, Books a la Carte Plus MasteringBiologyreg; 5th ed. 2010. (ENG.). (C). ring bd. 117.13 *(978-0-321-74027-4(0))* Benjamin-Cummings Publishing Co.
—A Brief Guide to Biology with Physiology. 2006. pap. *(978-0-13-612617-1(0))* Pearson Education Canada.
—Study Guide for Biology: A Guide to the Natural World. 5th rev. ed. 2010. (ENG.). 288p. (C). pap. 35.47 *(978-0-321-68303-8(X))* Benjamin-Cummings Publishing Co.
Krogh, David & Pearson Staff. Biology: A Guide to the Natural World. 5th ed. 2010. (ENG.). 880p. (C). E-Book, E-Book 96.00 *(978-0-321-69662-5(X))* Benjamin-Cummings Publishing Co.
Kull, Kalevi. Towards a Semiotic Biology: Life Is the Action of Signs. 2011. 300p. 110.00 *(978-1-84816-687-5(7))* Imperial College Pr. GBR. Dist: World Scientific Publishing Co., Inc.
Lang, Florian, ed. Encyclopedia of Molecular Mechanisms of Disease, 3 vols., Set. 2008. (Illus.). 1200p. 1200.00 *(978-3-540-67136-7(6),* 3540671366) Springer.
Lavers, Chris. The Natural History of Unicorns. 2010. (ENG.). 272p. pap. 13.99 *(978-0-06-087415-5(5),* HarperPerennial) HarperCollins Pubs.
Le Fanu, James. Why Us? How Science Rediscovered the Mystery of Ourselves. 2010. (Vintage Ser.). (ENG., Illus.). 336p. pap. 16.00 *(978-1-4000-3054-5(4),* Vintage) Knopf Doubleday Publishing Group.
Leather, Harry & Leather, Jan. Cambridge Checkpoints VCE Biology Unit 3 2007. 2006. (Cambridge Checkpoints Ser.). pap. 15.95 *(978-0-521-69792-7(1))* Cambridge Univ. Pr.
Lecca, Paola & Laurenzi, Ian. Deterministic Versus Stochastic Modelling in Biochemistry & Systems Biology. 2012. 250p. 165.00 ***(978-1-907568-62-6(X))*** Woodhead Publishing Ltd. GBR. Dist: Ingram Pub. Services.
Leddra, Michael J. Time Matters: Geology's Legacy to Scientific Thought. 2010. (ENG., Illus.). 288p. 159.95 *(978-1-4051-9908-7(3),* Wiley-Blackwell) Wiley, John & Sons, Inc.
Lee, Eva K. & Lim, Gino J., eds. Optimization in Medicine & Biology. 2008. (ENG., Illus.). 592p. 162.95 *(978-0-8493-0563-4(2))* Auerbach Pubs., Inc.
Leon V. Berhardt. Advances in Medicine & Biology. Volume 15. 2011. (Series: Advances in Biology & Medicine Ser.). 165.00 *(978-1-61122-467-2(5),* Nova Biomedical Bks.) Nova Science Pubs., Inc.
Lewis, Michael A., et al. Biologie und Epidemiologie der HormonersatztherapieBiology & Epidemiology of Hormone Replacement Therapy: Diskussionen zur Postmenopausalen GesundheitDiscussions on Post-Menopausal Health. 2006. (Ernst Schering Foundation Symposium Proceedings / Schering Foundation Symposium Proceedings Supplements Ser.). (Illus.). XVI, 174p. 79.95 *(978-3-540-32341-9(4),* 3540323414) Springer.
Light, William & Willingham, Emily Jane. College Biology - The Complete Idiot's Guide. 2010. (Complete Idiot's Guide Ser.). (ENG.). 400p. (gr. 12). 19.95 *(978-1-59257-848-1(9),* Alpha Bks.) Penguin Group (USA) Inc.
Liu, Limin Angela & Wei, Dongqing, eds. Interdisciplinary Research & Applications in Bioinformatics, Computational Biology, & Environmental Sciences. 2010. (Illus.). 350p. 245.00 *(978-1-60960-064-8(9),* Medical Information Science Reference) IGI Global.
Loomis, William F. Life As It Is: Biology for the Public Sphere. 2008. (Illus.). 247p. 40.00 *(978-0-520-25357-5(4))* Univ. of California Pr.
Losos, Jonathan B., et al. Biology. 8th ed. 2007. (ENG., Illus.). xxxii, 1259p. (C). 175.10 *(978-0-07-334982-4(8),* 0073349828) McGraw-Hill Higher Education.
Luisi, P. L., et al. Mind & Life: Discussions with the Dalai Lama on the Nature of Reality. 2008. (Columbia Series in Science & Religion Ser.). (ENG., Illus.). 232p. (gr. 17). 24.95 *(978-0-231-14550-3(0))* Columbia Univ. Pr.
Luisi, Pier Luigi. Mind & Life: Discussions with the Dalai Lama on the Nature of Reality. 2010. (Columbia Series in Science & Religion Ser.). (ENG., Illus.). 232p. (gr. 17). pap. 17.95 *(978-0-231-14551-0(9))* Columbia Univ. Pr.
Luisi, Pier Luigi & Chiarabelli, Cristiano, eds. Chemical Synthetic Biology. 2011. (ENG., Illus.). 384p. 155.00 *(978-0-470-71397-6(6),* Wiley) Wiley, John & Sons, Inc.
Lyons, Sherrie. Evolution: The Basics. 2011. (Basics Ser.). (ENG., Illus.). 208p. (C). 90.00 *(978-0-415-59225-3(9));* pap. 19.95 *(978-0-415-59226-0(7))* Routledge.
MacKintosh, Robert. From Comte to Benjamin Kidd: The Appeal to Biology or Evolution for Human Guidance. 2009. (Cambridge Library Collection - Religion Ser.). (ENG.). 316p. pap. 26.00 *(978-1-108-00453-4(9))* Cambridge Univ. Pr.
Mader & Windelspecht. Biology. 11th ed. 2012. 1024p. ***(978-0-07-352550-1(2))*** McGraw-Hill Cos., The.
Mader, Eric, et al. Managing Alternative Pollinators: A Handbook for Beekeepers, Growers, & Conservationists. 2009. *(978-1-933395-20-3(6))* Natural Resource, Agricultural, & Engineering Service.
Mader, Sylvia. Biology. 10th ed. 2009. (ENG.). 1024p. (C). 203.33 *(978-0-07-727433-7(4),* 0077274334, McGraw-Hill Science, Engineering & Mathematics) McGraw-Hill Higher Education.
—Biology. 10th ed. 2009. (ENG.). (C). 212.33 *(978-0-07-740321-8(5),* 0077403215, McGraw-Hill Science, Engineering & Mathematics) McGraw-Hill Higher Education.
—Biology w/connect access Card. 10th ed. 2009. (C). 164.06 *(978-0-07-738831-7(3),* 0077388313, McGraw-Hill Science, Engineering & Mathematics) McGraw-Hill Higher Education.
—Biology with 2-Semester Connect Plus Access Card. 11th ed. 2012. (ENG.). (C). 212.33 ***(978-0-07-758313-2(2),*** 0077583132, McGraw-Hill Science, Engineering & Mathematics) McGraw-Hill Higher Education.
—Inquiry into Life. 13th ed. 2010. (ENG.). (C). 192.00 *(978-0-07-740320-1(7),* 0077403207, McGraw-Hill Science, Engineering & Mathematics) McGraw-Hill Higher Education.
—Lab Manual for Essentials of Biology. 3rd ed. 2011. (ENG., Illus.). 352p. (C). pap. 72.00 *(978-0-07-740215-0(4),* 0077402154, McGraw-Hill Science, Engineering & Mathematics) McGraw-Hill Higher Education.
—Loose-leaf concepts of Biology. 2nd ed. 2010. (C). ring bd. 109.69 *(978-0-07-740034-7(8),* 0077400348, McGraw-Hill Science, Engineering & Mathematics) McGraw-Hill Higher Education.
—Loose-Leaf Concepts of Biology. 2nd ed. 2010. (ENG.). (C). ring bd., ring bd. 128.33 *(978-0-07-740261-7(8),* 0077402618, McGraw-Hill Science, Engineering & Mathematics) McGraw-Hill Higher Education.
—Loose Leaf Version for Biology. 10th ed. 2009. (ENG.). (C). ring bd. 112.81 *(978-0-07-734395-8(6),* 0077343956, McGraw-Hill Science, Engineering & Mathematics) McGraw-Hill Higher Education.
—Loose Leaf Version for Essentials of Biology. 2nd ed. 2009. (ENG.). (C). ring bd. 82.81 *(978-0-07-734394-1(8),* 0077343948, McGraw-Hill Science, Engineering & Mathematics) McGraw-Hill Higher Education.
—Loose Leaf Version for Inquiry. 13th ed. 2010. (ENG.). (C). ring bd. 128.33 *(978-0-07-740259-4(6),* 0077402596, McGraw-Hill Science, Engineering & Mathematics) McGraw-Hill Higher Education.

Mader, Sylvia. Mader, Biology, AP Edition. 11th ed. 2012. (ENG., Illus.). 1040p. (C). (gr. 9-12). 180.00 (978-0-07-662004-3(2), 0076620042) McGraw-Hill Higher Education.

Mader, Sylvia & Windelspecht, Michael. Loose Leaf Version for Essentials of Biology. 3rd ed. 2011. (ENG.). (C). ring bd. 103.00 (978-0-07-748956-4(X), 007748956X, McGraw-Hill Science, Engineering & Mathematics) McGraw-Hill Higher Education.

Mader, Sylvia S. Concepts of Biology. 2008. (978-0-07-340345-8(8)) 2nd ed. 2010. (978-0-07-340348-9(2)) McGraw-Hill Cos., The.

—Concepts of Biology. (ENG., Illus.). (C). 2008. 896p. 183.00 (978-0-07-722997-9(5), 0077229975) 2nd ed. 2010. 928p. 183.00 (978-0-07-735014-7(6), 0077350146) McGraw-Hill Higher Education. (McGraw-Hill Science, Engineering & Mathematics)

—Essentials of Biology. 2nd ed. 2009. (978-0-07-340342-7(3)) McGraw-Hill Cos., The.

—Essentials of Biology. 2006. (Illus.). 645p. per. 119.38 (978-0-07-330323-9(2), 9780073303239, McGraw-Hill Science, Engineering & Mathematics) McGraw-Hill Higher Education.

—Essentials of Biology with Connect Plus Access Card. 3rd ed. 2011. (ENG.). (C). pap., pap. 156.00 (978-0-07-747484-3(8), 0077474848, McGraw-Hill Science, Engineering & Mathematics) McGraw-Hill Higher Education.

—Inquiry into Life. 12th ed. 2007. (Illus.). (978-0-07-298675-4(1)) 13th ed. 2010. (978-0-07-340344-1(X)) McGraw-Hill Cos., The.

—Inquiry into Life. 13th ed. 2010. (ENG., Illus.). 832p. (C). 183.00 (978-0-07-728010-9(5), 0077280105, McGraw-Hill Science, Engineering & Mathematics) McGraw-Hill Higher Education.

Mader, Sylvia S. & Windelspecht, Michael. Essentials of Biology. 3rd ed. 2011. (ENG., Illus.). 736p. (C). pap. 147.00 (978-0-07-352551-8(0), 0073525510, McGraw-Hill Science, Engineering & Mathematics) McGraw-Hill Higher Education.

Mandoiu, Ion & Zelikovsky, Alexander. Bioinformatics Research & Applications: Third International Symposium,ISBRA 2007, Atlanta, GA, USA, May 7-10, 2007, Proceedings. 2007. (Lecture Notes in Computer Science / Lecture Notes in Bioinformatics Ser.). xv, 653p. pap. 119.00 (978-3-540-72030-0(8)) Springer.

Manteuffel. Introductory Biology Laboratory Manual. rev. ed. 2011. (ENG.). 98p. spiral bd. 29.95 (978-0-7575-9619-3(3)) Kendall Hunt Publishing Co.

Manzoor, M. Nauman & I. Sultan, Javed. Nutritional Evaluation of Irrigated Grasses. 2011. 92p. pap. (978-3-8443-0118-2(6)) Lambert Academic Publishing.

Maran, Timo, et al, eds. Readings in Zoosemiotics. (Semiotics, Communication & Cognition Ser.). (ENG., 2012. Illus.). 752p. (gr. 17). pap. 56.00 (978-3-11-025342-9(9)) 2011. 321.00 (978-3-11-026218-6(5)) 2011. VII, 438p. 210.00 (978-3-11-025320-7(8)) De Gruyter, Mouton DEU. Dist: de Gruyter, Walter GmbH & Co. KG.

Marchal, G. & Spincer, Michael. Living in Groups. Date not set. (Longman Biology Topics Ser.). (Illus.). 32p. pap. 35.67 (978-0-582-32302-5(9)) Addison-Wesley Longman, Ltd. GBR. Dist: Trans-Atlantic Pubns., Inc.

Marshall, Logvin. Discovering the Concepts of Life: A Biological Lab Manual with Inquiry Lab Experiences. rev. ed. 2010. (ENG.). 170p. spiral bd. 34.86 (978-0-7575-7832-8(2)) Kendall Hunt Publishing Co.

Martin, Diana W., et al. Biology. 8th ed. 2007. (ENG., Illus.). 1376p. (C). 241.95 (978-0-495-31714-2(4)) Brooks/Cole.

Martin, Jonathan B. & White, William B., eds. Frontiers of karst Resesarch: Proceedings & recommendations of the workshop held May 3 through 5, 2007 in San Antonio, Texas, USA. 2008. (Illus.). 118p. pap. 38.00 (978-0-9789976-2-5(X)) Karst Waters Institute.

McCalman, Iain. Darwin's Armada: Four Voyages & the Battle for the Theory of Evolution. 2010. (ENG., Illus.). 423p. pap. 18.95 (978-0-393-33877-5(0), 33877) Norton, W. W. & Co., Inc.

McCarthy, Dennis. Here Be Dragons: How the Study of Animal & Plant Distributions Revolutionized Our Views of Life & Earth. (ENG., Illus.). 2011. 240p. pap. 18.95 (978-0-19-959566-2(6)) 2009. 256p. 29.95 (978-0-19-954246-8(5)) Oxford Univ. Pr., Inc.

McDowall, S. A. Biology & Mankind. 2012. (ENG.). 254p. pap. 36.00 (978-1-107-60503-9(2)) Cambridge Univ. Pr.

McGuire, Betty, et al. Study Guide to Accompany Principles of Life. 2011. (Illus.). 405p. pap. 28.00 (978-1-4292-7930-7(3)) Freeman, W. H. & Co.

McMillan, Paul F. & Meersman, Filip. High Pressure Chemistry. 2011. (ENG.). 300p. 139.00 (978-90-481-3868-5(X), 904813868X) Springer.

McMillan, Victoria E. Writing Papers in the Biological Sciences. 5th ed. 2011. (ENG., Illus.). 256p. (C). spiral bd. 30.95 (978-0-312-64971-5(1)) Bedford/Saint Martin's.

Mekios, Constantinos. Systems Biology & Its Methodology. 2007. 236p. per. (978-3-8364-2830-9(X)) VDM Verlag Dr. Mueller e.K.

Midgley, Mary. The Solitary Self: Darwin & the Selfish Gene. 2010. (Heretics Ser.). (ENG.). 160p. (C). pap. (978-1-84465-253-2(X)) McGill-Queen's Univ. Pr.

Miller, David, et al, eds. Karl Popper: A Centenary Assessment Vol. 3: Science, 3 vols. 2006. (GER & ENG., Illus.). 300p. 130.00 (978-0-7546-5712-5(4)) Ashgate Publishing Co.

Minch, John, et al. Roadside Geology & Biology of Baja California. Date not set. (Illus.). 194p. 19.95 (978-0-9631090-1-9(4)) Minch, John & Assocs., Inc.

Minelli, Alessandro. Perspectives in Animal Phylogeny & Evolution. 2009. (ENG., Illus.). 336p. 165.00 (978-0-19-856620-5(4)); pap. 75.00 (978-0-19-856621-2(2)) Oxford Univ. Pr., Inc.

Minkoff, Eli C. Biology. 2nd rev. ed. 2008. (EZ-101 Study Keys Ser.). (ENG.). 160p. pap. 8.99 (978-0-7641-3920-8(7)) Barron's Educational Series, Inc.

Mohite, Swapnaja. Biology, Ecology & Culture of Paphia Malabaric. 2010. 276p. pap. (978-3-8383-6128-4(8)) Lambert Academic Publishing.

Moore, Kenneth A. & Reay, William G. The Chesapeake Bay NERR in Virginia: A Profile of the York River Ecosystem. 2009. (Illus.). iv, 125p. pap. (978-0-615-29219-9(4)) Coastal Education & Research Foundation, Inc.

Moore, R. Biology. Date not set. pap., lab manual ed. 32.25 net. (978-0-697-29269-8(X)) McGraw-Hill Cos., The.

Morris, Douglas W. & Lundberg, Per. Pillars of Evolution: Fundamental principles of the eco-evolutionary Process. 2011. (ENG., Illus.). 280p. 117.00 (978-0-19-856879-7(7)) Oxford Univ. Pr., Inc.

—Pillars of Evolution: Fundamental Principles of the Eco-Evolutionary Process. 2011. (ENG., Illus.). 280p. pap. 52.95 (978-0-19-856880-3(0)) Oxford Univ. Pr., Inc.

Morris, Victor J., et al. Atomic Force Microscopy for Biologists. 2nd ed. 2009. (Illus.). 420p. 65.00 (978-1-84816-467-3(X)) Imperial College Pr. GBR. Dist: World Scientific Publishing Co., Inc.

Müller, Gerd B. Evolution: The Extended Synthesis. Pigliucci, Massimo, ed. 2010. (ENG., Illus.). 504p. (gr. 17). pap. 37.00 (978-0-262-51367-8(6)) MIT Pr.

Mylonakis, Eleftherios, et al, eds. Recent Advances on Model Hosts. 2011. (Advances in Experimental Medicine & Biology Ser.). (ENG., Illus.). 300p. 189.00 (978-1-4419-5637-8(9), 1441956379) Springer.

Myrsky, Essi. Vascular Biology in Coeliac Disease. 2010. (Acta Universitatis Tamperensis Ser.). (Illus.). 144p. pap. 82.50 (978-951-44-8116-1(X)) Tampere Univ. Pr. FIN. Dist: Coronet Bks.

Nåsell, Ingemar. Extinction & Quasi-Stationarity in the Stochastic Logistic SIS Model. 2011. (Lecture Notes in Mathematics / Mathematical Biosciences Subseries Ser.). (Illus.). xi, 199p. pap. 59.95 (978-3-642-20529-3(1), 3642205291) Springer.

Naskrecki, Piotr. Relics: Travels in Nature's Time Machine. 2011. (Illus.). 384p. 45.00 (978-0-226-56870-6(9)) Univ. of Chicago Pr.

National Academies (U.S.) Staff, et al. Science, Evolution, & Creationism. 2008. (ENG., Illus.). 88p. per. 12.95 (978-0-309-10586-6(2)) National Academies Pr.

National Academies Keck Futures Initiatives Staff & National Academies. The National Academies Keck Futures Initiative: Complex Systems - Task Group Summaries. 2009. (ENG.). 122p. pap. 31.25 (978-0-309-13725-6(X)) National Academies Pr.

National Academy of Sciences. In the Light of Evolution IV: The Human Condition. Avise, John C. & Ayala, Francisco J., eds. 2010. (ENG.). 428p. 59.00 (978-0-309-15657-8(2)) National Academies Pr.

National Research Council. In the Light of Evolution Vol. II: Biodiversity & Extinction. Avise, John C. et al, eds. 2008. (ENG.). 432p. 59.00 (978-0-309-12743-1(2)) National Academies Pr.

National Research Council (U.S.), Committee on Defining and Advancing the Conceptual Basis of Biological Sciences in the 21st Century Staff, et al, contrib. by. The Role of Theory in Advancing 21st Century Biology: Catalyzing Transformative Research. 2008. (ENG., Illus.). 208p. pap. 45.00 (978-0-309-11249-9(4)) National Academies Pr.

Nevin, Norman Cummings. Should Christians Embrace Evolution? Biblical & Scientific Responses. 2011. pap. (978-1-59638-230-5(9)) P & R Publishing.

Newton, Silvia. Biology: Bullet Guides. 2012. (Bullet Guides). (ENG.). 128p. pap. 6.95 (978-1-4441-3504-6(X), Hodder & Stoughton) Hodder General Publishing Div. GBR. Dist: Independent Pubs. Group.

Nicholson, Henry Alleyne. Introduction to the Study of Biology; by H Alleyne Nicholson. 2006. 180p. per. 18.99 (978-1-4255-1437-2(5)) MPublishing.

Niehoff, Debra. The Language of Life: How Cells Communicate in Health & Disease. 2006. (ENG., Illus.). 336p. per. 17.95 (978-0-309-10201-8(4)) National Academies Pr.

Nunn, Charles L. The Comparative Approach in Evolutionary Anthropology & Biology. 2011. (ENG., Illus.). 424p. 120.00 (978-0-226-60898-3(0)); 392p. pap. 35.00 (978-0-226-60899-0(9)) Univ. of Chicago Pr.

OAS General Secretariat, Department of Scientific Research Staff. A Vida da Celula. (Serie de Biologia: No. 5). (Illus.). 117p. (Orig.). (C). reprint ed. 3.50 (978-0-8270-1141-0(5)) Organization of American States.

Ochoa, George. Science 101: Biology. 2007. (Science 101 Ser.). (ENG., Illus.). 224p. pap. 15.99 (978-0-06-089135-0(1), HarperPerennial) HarperCollins Pubs.

Ochoa, Sebastian Rios, et al, eds. Peru: Maijuna. 2010. (Field Museum - Rapid Biological & Social Inventories Ser.). 328p. pap. 30.00 (978-0-9828419-0-7(6)) Field Museum of Natural History, Div. of Pubns.

O'Connor, Linda. Biology Explorations Part 2. rev. ed. 2008. (ENG.). 172p. spiral bd. 46.56 (978-0-7872-9441-0(1)) Kendall Hunt Publishing Co.

—Biology Explorations Part I. rev. ed. 2010. (ENG.). 208p. spiral bd. 46.56 (978-0-7575-0176-0(1)) Kendall Hunt Publishing Co.

Olsen, Bruce D. Understanding Biology through Evolution - Fourth Edition. 2009. 267p. pap. 27.51 (978-0-557-09539-1(5)) Lulu Enterprises Inc.

Orians, Gordon H., et al. Supplement Sampler for Life: The Science of Biology. 2006. (C). pap. 3.00 net. (978-0-7167-7892-9(0)) Freeman, W. H. & Co.

Orry, Andrew J. W. & Abagyan, Ruben, eds. Homology Modeling: Methods & Protocols. 2012. (Methods in Molecular Biology Ser.). (ENG., Illus.). xi, 419p. 139.00 (978-1-61779-587-9(9), 1617795879) Humana Pr.

Osterman, Andrei L. & Gerdes, Svetlana Y., eds. Microbial Gene Essentiality: Protocols & Bioinformatics: Protocols & Bioinformatics. 2010. (Methods in Molecular Biology Ser.). xiv, 486p. pap. 139.00 (978-1-61737-529-3(2), 1617375292) Humana Pr.

Ostfeld, Richard S. & Schlesinger, William H. Year in Ecology & Conservation Biology 2008. 2008. (Annals of the New York Academy of Sciences Ser.). (ENG., Illus.). 452p. pap. 139.95 (978-1-57331-725-2(X), Wiley-Blackwell) Wiley, John & Sons, Inc.

Overhead Transparencies. (Illus.). 250.00 (978-0-7167-5818-1(0)) Freeman, W. H. & Co.

Panno, Joseph. The New Biology Set, 6 vols. 2010. (New Biology Ser.). (gr. 6-12). 240.00 (978-0-8160-8348-0(7)) Facts On File, Inc.

Pechenik, Jan A. Pechenik: Shor Guid Writ abou Biol_8. 8th rev. ed. 2012. (ENG., Illus.). 288p. (C). pap. 48.60 (978-0-205-07507-2(X)) Addison Wesley.

Pechenik, Jan A. A Short Guide to Writing about Biology. 7th ed. 2009. (Short Guides Ser.). (ENG., Illus.). 304p. (C). pap. 48.60 (978-0-205-66727-7(9)) Longman Publishing Group.

Perry, Chris. Biology. Date not set. (Adaptable Courseware-Hardside Ser.). pap., lab manual ed. 28.50 net. (978-0-534-16003-6(4)); Vol. 1. lab manual ed. 15.50 (978-0-534-15893-4(5)); Vol. 2. lab manual ed. 15.50 (978-0-534-15911-5(7)) Wadsworth.

Perry, Chris & Morton. Biology. Date not set. (Adaptable Courseware-Hardside Ser.). lab manual ed. 25.00 net. (978-0-534-55479-8(2)) Wadsworth.

Pfluger-Hall. Introductory Biology: A Laboratory Exploration of Life. rev. ed. 2011. (ENG.). 148p. ring bd. 35.00 (978-0-7575-8972-0(3)) Kendall Hunt Publishing Co.

Phelan, Jay. Student Success Guide for What Is Life? 2nd ed. 2011. (ENG.). 525p. (C). 18.95 (978-1-4641-0677-4(0)) Freeman, W. H. & Co.

Phelan, Jay. What Is Life? A Guide to Biology W/Prep-U. 2009. (ENG.). 610p. (C). pap. 107.95 (978-1-4292-2318-8(9)) Freeman, W. H. & Co.

Phelan, Jay, et al. Student Success Guide for What Is Life? A Guide to Biology. 2009. (ENG.). 525p. (C). pap. 18.95 (978-1-4292-3216-6(1)) Freeman, W. H. & Co.

Pierotti, Raymond. Indigenous Knowledge Ecology & Evolutionary Biology. 2010. (Indigenous Peoples & Politics Ser.). (ENG., Illus.). 528p. (C). 125.00 (978-0-415-87924-8(8)) Routledge.

Pittack, Richard. The Archaeopteryx Controversy. 2008. 239p. pap. 16.96 (978-0-615-18232-2(1)) Waldens Computer Services.

Plantinga, Alvin. Where the Conflict Really Lies: Science, Religion, & Naturalism, 1 vol. 2011. (ENG.). 376p. 27.95 (978-0-19-981209-7(8)) Oxford Univ. Pr., Inc.

Pocock, Gillian & Richards, Chris. Biological Science for the Biomedical & Healthcare Sciences. 2009. (ENG., Illus.). 813p. pap. 74.00 (978-0-19-928907-3(7)) Oxford Univ. Pr., Inc.

Polster, Burkard, et al. Sciencia: Mathematics, Physics, Chemistry, Biology, & Astronomy for All. 2011. (Wooden Bks.). (ENG., Illus.). 416p. 20.00 (978-0-8027-7899-4(2)) Walker & Co.

Pontarotti, Pierre, ed. Evolutionary Biology from Concept to Application. 2010. (ENG., Illus.). xii, 220p. pap. 159.00 (978-3-642-09781-2(2), 3642097812) Springer.

Porter, R. Birds of the Middle East - Second Edition. 2010. (Princeton Field Guides). (ENG., Illus.). 400p. pap. 39.50 (978-0-691-14844-1(9)) Princeton Univ. Pr.

Presson, Joelle C. & Jenner, Janann V. Biology: Dimensions of Life. 2007. (Illus.). (978-0-07-295267-4(9)) McGraw-Hill Cos., The.

—Biology: Dimensions of Life. 2007. (ENG., Illus.). 710p. (C). pap., per. 140.33 (978-0-07-322736-8(6), 0073227366, McGraw-Hill Science, Engineering & Mathematics) McGraw-Hill Higher Education.

Primack, Richard B. Essentials of Conservation Biology. 5th rev. ed. 2010. (Illus.). 535p. (978-0-87893-640-3(8)) Sinauer Assocs., Inc.

Pruitt, Nancy L. (WCS)BioInquiry 3rd Edition Flex Format. 2006. (ENG.). 668p. (C). ring bd. 92.95 (978-0-471-75238-7(X), Wiley) Wiley, John & Sons, Inc.

Purves, William K., et al. Life: The Science of Biology. 8th rev. ed. 2006. (ENG., Illus.). 500p. (C). pap., stu. ed. 36.95 (978-0-7167-7893-6(9)) Freeman, W. H. & Co.

Rahnejat, H., ed. Tribology & Dynamics of Engine & Powertrain: Fundamentals, Applications & Future Trends. 2010. (ENG., Illus.). 1048p. 380.00 (978-1-84569-361-9(2)) Woodhead Publishing Ltd. GBR. Dist: Ingram Pub. Services.

Ranjan, Ashish. Neuronal Differentiation of Embryonic Carcinoma Cells. 2011. 60p. pap. (978-3-8443-9036-0(7)) Lambert Academic Publishing.

Raoult, D., ed. Mimivirus & Other Giant Viruses. 2010. (Illus.). 134p. pap. (978-3-8055-9505-6(0)) Karger, S. AG.

Rasco, Jane & Lackey, Kim. Biology: The Study of Life. 2nd rev. ed. 2008. 200p. spiral bd. 49.00 (978-0-7575-5643-2(4)) Kendall Hunt Publishing Co.

Raven, Peter. Biology. 9th ed. 2010. (ENG., Illus.). (C). 223.66 (978-0-07-740317-1(7), 0077403177, McGraw-Hill Science, Engineering & Mathematics) McGraw-Hill Higher Education.

—Loose-leaf Biology. 9th ed. 2010. (ENG.). (C). ring bd. 150.33 (978-0-07-740258-7(8), 0077402588, McGraw-Hill Science, Engineering & Mathematics) McGraw-Hill Higher Education.

Raven, Peter, et al. Evolution, Diversity & Ecology Units 4, 5 & 8. 9th ed. 2010. (ENG.). (C). pap. 113.00 (978-0-07-749276-2(5), 0077492765, McGraw-Hill Science, Engineering & Mathematics) McGraw-Hill Higher Education.

—Foundations of Life Vol. 1: Chemistry, Cell Biology, & Genetics. 9th ed. 2010. (ENG.). (C). pap. 113.00 (978-0-07-749277-9(3), 0077492773, McGraw-Hill Science, Engineering & Mathematics) McGraw-Hill Higher Education.

—Laboratory Manual to accompany Stern's Introductory Plant Biology. 12th ed. 2010. (ENG., Illus.). 256p. (C). spiral bd. 82.33 (978-0-07-304053-0(3), 0073040533, McGraw-Hill Science, Engineering & Mathematics) McGraw-Hill Higher Education.

—Plant & Animal Biology, Vol. 3. 9th ed. 2010. (ENG.). (C). pap. 90.67 (978-0-07-739751-7(7), 0077397517, McGraw-Hill Science, Engineering & Mathematics) McGraw-Hill Higher Education.

Ray, Charles & Feser, Cathy. The Conifer & Broadleaf Trees of the South. 2011. 148p. pap. 36.95 (978-1-936343-65-2(7)) Peppertree Pr., The.

Reading, Anthony. Meaningful Information: The Bridge Between Biology, Brain, & Behavior. 2011. (SpringerBriefs in Biology Ser.). (ENG., Illus.). xiv, 158p. pap. 49.95 (978-1-4614-0157-5(7), 1461401577) Springer.

Reece, Jane B., et al. Biological Inquiry: A Workbook of Investigative Cases. 3rd ed. 2010. (ENG., Illus.). 192p. (C). pap. 24.60 (978-0-321-68320-5(X)) Benjamin-Cummings Publishing Co.

—Campbell Biology. 9th ed. (ENG.). (C). 2012. ring bd. 121.60 (978-0-321-83155-2(1)) 2010. 64.67 (978-0-321-68652-7(7)) 2010. 1464p. 202.67 (978-0-321-55814-5(6)) 2010. (Illus.). 1464p. 202.67 (978-0-321-55823-7(5)) Benjamin-Cummings Publishing Co.

—Campbell Biology: Concepts & Connections. 7th ed. 2011. (ENG.). (C). pap., pap. 178.53 (978-0-321-80878-3(9)); 928p. 178.53 (978-0-321-69648-9(4)); 928p. 178.53 (978-0-321-69681-6(6)); ring bd. 117.13 (978-0-321-78346-2(8)) Benjamin-Cummings Publishing Co.

—Campbell Biology: Concepts & Connections & Study Guide. 7th ed. 2011. (ENG.). (C). pap. 216.40 (978-0-321-79918-0(6)) Benjamin-Cummings Publishing Co.

—Campbell Biology: Concepts & Connections, Books a la Carte Edition. 7th ed. 2011. (ENG.). 928p. (C). ring bd. 107.13 (978-0-321-74203-2(6)) Benjamin-Cummings Publishing Co.

—Campbell Biology, Books a la Carte Edition. 9th ed. 2012. (ENG.). 1464p. (C). ring bd. 121.60 (978-0-321-83154-5(3)) Benjamin-Cummings Publishing Co.

—Inquiry in Action: Intrepreting Scientific Papers. 2nd ed. 2010. (ENG.). 128p. (C). pap. 17.20 (978-0-321-68336-6(6)) Benjamin-Cummings Publishing Co.

—Mastering Biology: Concepts & Connections. 7th ed. 2011. (ENG.). 928p. (C). E-Book, E-Book 96.00 (978-0-321-70925-7(X)) Benjamin-Cummings Publishing Co.

—Practicing Biology for Campbell Biology. 4th ed. 2010. (ENG.). 360p. (C). pap. 18.00 (978-0-321-68328-1(5)) Benjamin-Cummings Publishing Co.

—Spanish Glossary for Campbell Biology. 9th ed. 2010. (ENG.). 48p. (C). pap. 20.40 (978-0-321-68321-2(8)) Benjamin-Cummings Publishing Co.

—Study Guide for Campbell Biology. 9th ed. 2010. (ENG., Illus.). 544p. (C). pap. 60.60 (978-0-321-62992-0(2)) Benjamin-Cummings Publishing Co.

—Study Guide for Campbell Biology: Concepts & Connections. 7th rev. ed. 2011. (ENG., Illus.). 576p. (C). pap. 61.80 (978-0-321-74258-2(3)) Benjamin-Cummings Publishing Co.

Regents of California-Davis Staff. Introductory Biology: Bis 2B Laboratory Manual. 2nd rev. ed. 2012. (ENG.). 216p. ring bd. 36.76 (978-0-7575-9288-1(0)) Kendall Hunt Publishing Co.

Reguera, D., et al, eds. Statistical Mechanics of Biocomplexity: Proceedings of the XV Sitges Conference, Held at Sitges, Barcelona, Spain, 8-12 June 1998. 2010. (Lecture Notes in Physics Ser.). xi, 318p. pap. 109.00 (978-3-642-08553-6(9), 3642085539) Springer.

Reiher, Markus. Atomistic Approaches in Modern Biology: From Quantum Chemistry to Molecular Simulations. 2007. (Topics in Current Chemistry Ser.). (Illus.). xii, 361p. 419.00 (978-3-540-38082-5(5), 3540380825) Springer.

Renema, Willem, ed. Biogeography, Time & Place: Distributions, Barriers & Islands: Distributions, Barriers & Islands. 2010. (Topics in Geobiology Ser.). (Illus.). xii, 416p. pap. 239.00 (978-90-481-7618-2(2), 9048176182) Springer.

Rice, Stanley. Biology for a New Century. 2007. pap. 44.95 (978-0-471-73829-9(8)); 672p. pap. 83.95 (978-0-471-65065-2(X), Wiley-Interscience) Wiley, John & Sons, Inc.

Richards, Robert J., et al, eds. Evolution: The First Four Billion Years. 2009. (Illus.). 1008p. 44.00 (978-0-674-03175-3(X), Belknap Pr.) Harvard Univ. Pr.

Rieppel, Olivier. Evolutionary Theory & the Creation Controversy. 2010. (ENG.). x, 204p. 189.00 (978-3-642-14895-8(6), 3642148956) Springer.

Ritter, Bob, et al. Nelson Biology-Blue: Teacher's Resource Guide. (Illus.). 288p. (Orig.). pap., tchr. ed. 49.75 net. (978-0-17-603871-7(X)) CENGAGE Learning.

Ritter, William Emerson. The Probable Infinity of Nature & Life. 2009. 90p. pap. (978-0-217-60561-8(3)) Books LLC.

—The Probable Infinity of Nature & Life. 2007. (ENG.). 162p. 36.95 (978-0-548-03700-3(0)) Kessinger Publishing, LLC.

Roff, Derek A. Modeling Evolution: An Introduction to Numerical Methods. 2010. (ENG., Illus.). 352p. pap. 75.00 (978-0-19-957114-7(7)) Oxford Univ. Pr., Inc.

Rogers, Alan R. The Evidence for Evolution. 2011. (ENG., Illus.). 128p. 45.00 (978-0-226-72380-8(1)); pap. 18.00 (978-0-226-72382-2(8)) Univ. of Chicago Pr.

Rogers, Kara, ed. Fungi, Algae, & Protists. 2011. (Biochemistry, Cells, & Life Ser.). (Illus.). 232p. (YA). 80.00 (978-1-61530-464-6(9)) Rosen Publishing Group, Inc., The.

Roget, Peter Mark. Animal & Vegetable Physiology: Considered with Reference to Natural Theology. 2009. (Cambridge Library Collection - Religion Ser.). (ENG.). 636p. pap. 43.00 (978-1-108-00006-2(1)); 676p. pap. 45.00 (978-1-108-00007-9(X)) Cambridge Univ. Pr.

Rosenberg, Michael S. Sequence Alignment: Methods, Models, Concepts, & Strategies. Rosenberg, Michael S., ed. 2009. (ENG., Illus.). 288p. 60.00 (978-0-520-25697-2(2)) Univ. of California Pr.

Rowland, T. G. S., et al. Vital Things for Lively Youngsters. 2010. (ENG., Illus.). 192p. pap. 32.95 (978-1-84868-264-1(6)) Amberley Publishing GBR. Dist: Casemate Pubs. & Bk. Distributors, LLC.

Runtz, Michael. Algonquin Souvenir. 2007. (ENG., Illus.). 96p. 19.95 (978-1-55046-494-8(9)) Boston Mills Pr. CAN. Dist: Firefly Bks., Ltd.

Russe, Alona S., ed. Computational Biology: New Research. 2008. (Illus.). 441p. 129.00 (978-1-60692-040-4(5)) Nova Science Pubs., Inc.

Russell, Peter J. & Hertz, Paul E. Cengage Advantage Books: Biology: The Dynamic Science. 2nd ed. 2011. (ENG.). 1456p. (C). pap. 178.95 (978-0-538-49418-2(2)) Brooks/Cole.

Russell, Peter J., et al. Biology: The Dynamic Science. 2007. (Available Titles CengageNOW Ser.). (ENG.). 1456p. (C). 238.95 (978-0-534-24966-3(3)) Brooks/Cole.

Ryan, Frank P. The Mystery of Metamorphosis: A Scientific Detective Story. 2011. 320p. 26.95 (978-1-60358-341-1(6)) Chelsea Green Publishing.

Sadava. Life: The Science of Biology. 9th ed. 2011. (Illus.). (978-1-4292-4646-0(4)) Sinauer Assocs., Inc.

Sadava, David, et al. Life: The Science of Biology. (ENG., Illus.). (C). 8th ed. 2006. 1121p. 123.95 (978-1-4292-0459-0(1)) 9th ed. 2009. 1121p. 123.95 (978-1-4292-3253-1(6)) 9th ed. 2009. 1267p. 189.95 (978-1-4292-1962-4(9)) Freeman, W. H. & Co.

Sadava, David E., et al. Life Vol. 1: The Science of Biology. 9th ed. 2009. (ENG., Illus.). 389p. (C). pap. 74.95 (978-1-4292-4645-3(6)) Freeman, W. H. & Co.

—Life Vol. 3: The Science of Biology. 9th ed. 2009. (ENG., Illus.). 413p. (C). pap. 74.95 (978-1-4292-4647-7(2)) Freeman, W. H. & Co.

—Life - The Science of Biology Vol. 2, Vol. 2. 9th ed. 2009. (ENG., Illus.). 389p. (C). pap. 74.95 (978-1-4292-4644-6(8)) Freeman, W. H. & Co.

Sagot, Marie-France & Walter, Maria Emilia M. T. Advances in Bioinformatics & Computational Biology: Second Brazilian Symposium on Bioinformatics, BSB 2007, Angra dos Reis, Brazil, August 29-31, 2007, Proceedings. 2007. (Lecture Notes in Computer Science / Lecture Notes in Bioinformatics Ser.). xii, 177p. pap. 79.95 (978-3-540-73730-8(8)) Springer.

Salthe, Stanley N. Development & Evolution: Complexity & Change in Biology. 2009. (ENG., Illus.). 373p. (gr. 17). pap. 33.00 (978-0-262-51383-8(8)) MIT Pr.

Sattler, Paul W., et al. General Biology Laboratory Studies in Biology. 2nd rev. ed. 2006. (ENG., Illus.). 140p. pap. 58.78 (978-0-7575-3434-8(1)) Kendall Hunt Publishing Co.

Savitsky, Alexander P. & Wang, Yingxiao. Fluorescence in Vivo Imaging Based on Genetically Engineered Probes: From Living Cells to Whole Body Imaging IV: 25-26 January 2009, San Jose, California, United States. 2009. (Proceedings of SPIE Ser.). (Illus.). 96p. pap. 70.00 **(978-0-8194-7437-7(1))** SPIE.

Scharer. Biology Study of Life. 194.97 (978-0-13-085663-0(0)) Prentice Hall (Schl. Div.).

Schnell, Santiago, et al. Multiscale Modeling of Developmental Systems. 2007. (Current Topics in Developmental Biology Ser.). (ENG., Illus.). 604p. 198.00 (978-0-12-374253-7(6), Academic Pr.) Elsevier Science & Technology Bks.

Schön, Isa, et al, eds. Lost Sex: The Evolutionary Biology of Parthenogenesis. 2009. (ENG., Illus.). xvii, 615p. 209.00 (978-90-481-2769-6(6), 9048127696) Springer.

Schraer. Biology: Study of Life. 4th ed. stu. ed. 8.97 (978-0-13-083411-9(4)) 5th ed. 194.97 (978-0-13-085648-7(7)) 5th ed. 38.97 (978-0-13-085390-5(9)) 5th ed. tchr. ed. 59.47 (978-0-13-085408-7(5)) Prentice Hall (Schl. Div.).

Scientific American Editors. Current Issues in Biology, Vol. 4. 2007. (ENG.). (C). pap. 35.07 (978-0-8053-3566-8(8)) Benjamin-Cummings Publishing Co.

Scientific American Staff. Current Issues in Biology, Vol. 6. 2009. (ENG.). 76p. (C). pap. 34.00 (978-0-321-59849-3(0)) Benjamin-Cummings Publishing Co.

Scientific American Staff, et al. Current Issues in Biology, Vol. 5. 2008. (ENG.). 76p. (C). pap. 35.07 (978-0-321-54187-1(1)) Benjamin-Cummings Publishing Co.

Seckbach, Joseph & Rubin, Eitan, eds. The New Avenues in Bioinformatics. 2010. (Cellular Origin, Life in Extreme Habitats & Astrobiology Ser.). xxvi, 281p. pap. 269.00 (978-90-481-6694-7(2), 9048166942) Springer.

Secord, Mark. Principles of Biology. 2007. (Illus.). 250p. (C). spiral bd. (978-0-9799730-0-0(7)) Petmecky Custom Publishing.

Seethaler, Sherry. Curious Folks Ask 2: 188 Real Answers on Our Fellow Creatures, Our Planet, & Beyond. rev. ed. 2011. (FT Press Science Ser.). (ENG.). 240p. pap. 19.99 (978-0-13-705739-9(3)) FT Press.

Sewell, Dennis. The Political Gene: How Darwin's Ideas Changed Politics. 2009. (ENG.). 270p. 26.95 (978-0-330-42744-9(X)) Macmillan Pubs., Ltd. GBR. Dist: Independent Pubs. Group.

Sharma, V. P., ed. Nature at Work - the Ongoing Saga of Evolution. 2011. (ENG., Illus.). 400p. 99.00 (978-81-8489-991-7(2), 8184899912) Springer (India) Private Ltd. IND. Dist: Springer.

Sharples, Robert W., ed. Pseudo-Aristoteles (Pseudo-Alexander), Supplementa Problematorum. 2006. (Peripatoi Ser.: Vol. 20). (GEC & ENG.). V, 301p. 140.00 (978-3-11-019140-0(7)) De Gruyter, Walter Inc.

Shelp & Perry, Chris. Biology. Date not set. (Adaptable Courseware-Hardside Ser.). pap., lab manual ed. 15.00 net. (978-0-534-16091-3(3)) Wadsworth.

Shelp, et al. Biology. Date not set. (Adaptable Courseware-Hardside Ser.). lab manual ed. 17.50 net. (978-0-534-56571-8(9)) Wadsworth.

Shuch, H. Paul. Searching for Extraterrestrial Intelligence: SETI Past, Present, & Future. 2011. (Frontiers Collection). (Illus.). xxi, 320p. 79.95 (978-3-642-13195-0(6), 3642131956) Springer.

Sigmund, Karl. The Calculus of Selfishness. 2010. (Princeton Series in Theoretical & Computational Biology Ser.). (ENG., Illus.). 192p. (C). 37.50 (978-0-691-14275-3(0)) Princeton Univ. Pr.

Silvius, John E. Biology: Principles & Perspectives. 4th rev. ed. 2010. (ENG.). 468p. pap. 100.65 (978-0-7872-7679-9(0)) Kendall Hunt Publishing Co.

Simon, Eric J., et al. Biology. 5th ed. 2012. (ENG.). (C). 57.20 **(978-0-321-79170-2(3))** Benjamin-Cummings Publishing Co.

—Campbell Essential Biology. (ENG.). 544p. (C). 4th ed. 2009. pap. 141.47 (978-0-321-65289-8(4)) 4th ed. 2009. pap. 141.47 (978-0-321-60206-0(4)) 5th rev. ed. 2012. (Illus.). pap. 141.47 **(978-0-321-77259-6(8))** Benjamin-Cummings Publishing Co.

—Campbell Essential Biology, Books a la Carte Edition. 5th ed. 2012. (ENG.). 544p. (C). ring bd. 84.93 **(978-0-321-78823-8(0))** Benjamin-Cummings Publishing Co.

—Campbell Essential Biology, Books a la Carte Plus MasteringBiologyreg; 5th ed. 2012. (ENG.). 544p. (C). ring bd. 94.93 **(978-0-321-78824-5(9))** Benjamin-Cummings Publishing Co.

—Campbell Essential Biology with MasteringBiology & Reg; 5th rev. ed. 2012. (ENG., Illus.). 544p. (C). pap. 141.47 **(978-0-321-76333-4(5))** Benjamin-Cummings Publishing Co.

—Campbell Essential Biology with Physiology. (ENG.). 752p. (C). 3rd ed. 2009. pap. 150.00 (978-0-321-60207-7(2)) 3rd ed. 2009. pap. 149.47 (978-0-321-64954-6(0)) 4th rev. ed. 2012. pap. 149.47 **(978-0-321-76332-7(7))** 4th rev. ed. 2012. (Illus.). pap. 149.47 **(978-0-321-77260-2(1))** Benjamin-Cummings Publishing Co.

—Campbell Essential Biology with Physiology, Books a la Carte Edition. 4th ed. 2012. (ENG.). 752p. (C). ring bd. 89.73 **(978-0-321-78825-2(7))** Benjamin-Cummings Publishing Co.

—Campbell Essential Biology with Physiology, Books a la Carte Plus MasteringBiologyreg; 4th ed. 2012. (ENG.). 752p. (C). ring bd. 99.73 **(978-0-321-78822-1(2))** Benjamin-Cummings Publishing Co.

—Campbell Essential Biology (With Physiology Chapters) 5th ed. 2012. (ENG.). (C). E-Book 114.67 **(978-0-321-79200-6(9))**; 752p. E-Book, E-Book 96.00 **(978-0-321-79169-6(X))** Benjamin-Cummings Publishing Co.

Singham, Mano. God vs. Darwin: The War between Evolution & Creationism in the Classroom. 2010. (ENG.). 192p. pap. 22.95 (978-1-60709-170-7(4)) Rowman & Littlefield Education.

Smallwood & Green, Ken. Biologia. (SPA.). 756p. 39.95 (978-968-439-055-3(6), PC010) Publicaciones Cultural, S.A. de C.V. MEX. Dist: Continental Bk. Co., Inc.

Sober, Elliott. Did Darwin Write the Origin Backwards? 2010. (ENG., Illus.). 241p. pap. 21.00 (978-1-61614-230-8(8)) Prometheus Bks., Pubs.

Sodhi, Navjot S., et al. Tropical Conservation Biology. 2007. (ENG., Illus.). 344p. pap. 79.95 (978-1-4051-5073-6(4), Wiley-Blackwell) Wiley, John & Sons, Inc.

Soerhus, Elin. Studies on Minispectrins. 2009. 84p. pap. (978-3-639-15735-2(4)) VDM Verlag Dr. Mueller e.K.

Solomon, et al. Biology, Volume 2. 8th ed. 2006. (ENG.). 864p. (C). pap. 95.95 (978-0-495-30979-6(6)) Brooks/Cole.

Solomon, Eldra, et al. Biology. 2010. (ENG.). (C). 8th rev. ed. 1376p. 254.95 (978-0-8400-6824-8(7)) 9th ed. 1408p. 254.95 (978-0-538-74125-5(2)) Brooks/Cole.

—Cengage Advantage Books: Biology. 9th ed. 2010. (ENG., Illus.). 1408p. (C). pap. 184.95 (978-0-538-49419-9(0)) Brooks/Cole.

Somervill, Barbara A. How Life Changes. 2007. (Gareth Stevens Vital Science-Life Science Ser.). 48p. (gr. 5-12). pap. 14.05 (978-0-8368-8449-4(3), Stevens, Gareth Secondary Library) Stevens, Gareth Publishing LLLP.

Sorensen, Kathryn & Mccormac, Gregory. Biology Activity Workbook. rev. ed. 2010. (ENG.). 116p. spiral bd. 37.04 (978-0-7575-5662-3(0)) Kendall Hunt Publishing Co.

Sorenson, John L. & Johannessen, Carl L. World Trade & Biological Exchanges Before 1492. 2009. (Illus.). viii, 593p. E-Book (978-0-595-62495-9(2)) iUniverse, Inc.

Sparknotes 101. 2008. (978-1-4114-0337-6(1)) Spark Publishing Group.

Spellman, Frank R. & Price-Bayer, Joni. The Handbook of Nature. 2011. **(978-1-60590-774-1(X))**; (ENG.). 482p. 75.00 **(978-1-60590-773-4(1))** Government Institutes.

Spohn, Bryan. Introductory Biology Word Puzzles. 2007. (ENG.). (C). pap. 37.60 (978-0-536-36085-4(5)) Pearson Learning Solutions.

Srinivasan, Ashwin. Donald Michie: Machine Intelligence, Biology & More. 2009. (ENG., Illus.). 352p. 45.00 (978-0-19-957304-2(2)) Oxford Univ. Pr., Inc.

Stanfield, Cindy L. Principles of Human Physiology. 4th ed. 2010. (ENG.). 800p. (C). ring bd. 112.00 (978-0-321-68153-9(3)) Benjamin-Cummings Publishing Co.

Starr. Biology. Date not set. (Adaptable Courseware-Hardside Ser.). pap. 47.00 (978-0-534-15928-3(1)); pap. 45.00 net. (978-0-534-15946-7(X)); pap. 45.75 (978-0-534-15931-3(1)); pap. 68.85 (978-0-534-16000-5(X)) Wadsworth.

—Biology: Chapter 1. Date not set. (Adaptable Courseware-Hardside Ser.). mass mkt. 5.00 (978-0-534-15904-7(4)) Wadsworth.

Starr, Cecie. Biology: Concepts & Applications. 7th ed. 2007. (ENG.). 480p. (C). pap., wbk. ed. 84.95 (978-0-495-11971-5(7)) Brooks/Cole.

—Biology: Concepts & Applications, Enhanced Homework Edition. 6th ed. 2007. (C). pap. 125.95 (978-0-495-10272-4(5)) Brooks/Cole.

—Biology: Today & Tomorrow, Enhanced Homework Edition. 2nd ed. 2007. (C). pap. 108.95 (978-0-495-10286-1(5)) Brooks/Cole.

—High School Level 1 Biology Co. 2010. 195.95 (978-0-538-75717-1(5)) Brooks/Cole.

—Student Interactive Workbook for Starr's Biology: Concepts & Applications, 8th. 8th ed. 2010. (ENG.). 496p. (C). pap. 89.95 (978-0-8400-4816-5(5)) Brooks/Cole.

—Telecourse Student Guide for Cycles of Life: Exploring Biology. 8th ed. 2010. (ENG.). 384p. (C). pap. 85.95 (978-0-8400-4822-6(X)) Brooks/Cole.

Starr, Cecie & Evers. Biology: Today & Tomorrow Without Physiology. 2nd ed. 2007. (ENG.). 456p. (C). pap. 147.95 (978-0-495-10273-1(3)) Brooks/Cole.

Starr, Cecie & Taggart, Ralph. Biology: The Unity & Diversity of Life. 11th ed. 2007. (ENG.). 1056p. (C). 228.95 (978-0-495-10284-7(9)) Brooks/Cole.

—Biology: The Unity & Diversity of Life, Enhanced Homework Edition. 11th ed. 2007. (C). 131.95 (978-0-495-10283-0(0)) Brooks/Cole.

Starr, Cecie, et al. Biology: Concepts & Applications. (ENG., (C). 7th ed. 2007. Illus.). 912p. 246.95 (978-0-495-11997-5(0)) 8th ed. 2010. 864p. pap. 189.95 (978-1-4390-4673-9(5)) Brooks/Cole.

—Biology: Concepts & Applications without Physiology. 8th ed. 2010. (ENG.). 576p. (C). pap. 180.95 (978-0-538-73925-2(8)) Brooks/Cole.

—Biology: Today & Tomorrow without Physiology. 3rd ed. 2009. (ENG.). (C). 656p. 207.95 (978-0-495-82753-5(3)); 448p. pap. 151.95 (978-0-495-82752-8(5)); 656p. pap. 169.95 (978-0-495-56157-6(6)) Brooks/Cole.

—Cengage Advantage Books: Biology: Concepts & Applications. 8th ed. 2010. (ENG.). 864p. (C). ring bd. 148.95 (978-0-538-49389-5(5)) Brooks/Cole.

Stewart, Ian. The Mathematics of Life. 2011. (ENG.). 368p. (gr. 9). 27.99 (978-0-465-02238-0(3)) Basic Bks.

Strete, Dennis & Vodopich, Darrell S. Photo Atlas for General Biology. (ENG., Illus.). 288p. (C). 2nd ed. 2006. spiral bd. 64.67 (978-0-07-284610-2(0), 0072846100) 3rd ed. 2011. pap. 64.67 (978-0-07-352555-6(3), 0073525553) McGraw-Hill Higher Education. (McGraw-Hill Science, Engineering & Mathematics).

Strong, Brett. Principles of Biology Lab Manual. 2nd rev. ed. 2011. (ENG.). 232p. spiral bd. 63.43 (978-0-7575-6164-1(0)) Kendall Hunt Publishing Co.

Sundberg, Marshall. College Biology. 2007. (Collins College Outlines Ser.). (ENG., Illus.). 528p. per. 15.95 (978-0-06-088161-0(5)) HarperCollins Pubs.

Surowiec. Biology. Date not set. (C). pap. 26.75 (978-0-03-072787-0(1)); pap., tchr. ed. 26.75 (978-0-03-072782-5(0)); pap., lab manual ed. 26.75 (978-0-03-072786-3(3)); trans. 199.50 (978-0-03-072792-4(8)) Harcourt College Pubs.

Tannier, Eric. Comparative Genomics: International Workshop, RECOMB-CG 2010, Ottawa, Canada, October 9-11, 2010, Proceedings. 2010. (Lecture Notes in Computer Science / Lecture Notes in Bioinformatics Ser.). xii, 303p. pap. 83.00 (978-3-642-16180-3(4), 3642161804) Springer.

Tarasenko, Olga, ed. Biology, Nanotechnology, Toxicology & Applications: 4th BioNanoTox (Biology, Nanotechnology, Toxicology) & Applications. 2010. (AIP Conference Proceedings Ser.). 190p. pap. 99.00 (978-0-7354-0773-2(8), 0735407738, AIP Pr.) Springer.

Taylor, D. Lansing, ed. High Content Screening. 2010. (Methods in Molecular Biology Ser.). (Illus.). 464p. pap. 209.00 (978-1-61737-746-4(5), 1617377465) Humana Pr.

Temme, David H. Life Is Loopy: Exploring the Principles of Biology. rev. ed. (ENG.). 744p. 2010. spiral bd. 68.25 (978-0-7575-7004-9(6)) 2008. spiral bd. 70.90 (978-0-7575-5798-9(8)) Kendall Hunt Publishing Co.

Thatikunta, Ramesh & Prasadini, Prabhu. Sewage & Effluent Water in Musi River Bed. 2010. 88p. pap. (978-3-8383-2143-1(X)) Lambert Academic Publishing.

Thompson, Ruthanne, et al. The Scope of Biology: From Cells to Ecosystems. rev. ed. 2010. (ENG.). 162p. spiral bd. 40.57 (978-0-7575-4428-6(2)) Kendall Hunt Publishing Co.

Thomson, J. Arthur. The Bible of Nature. 2009. 264p. 30.99 (978-1-110-64630-2(5)); pap. 26.75 (978-1-110-64628-9(3)) BiblioBazaar.

—The Bible of Nature. 2007. (ENG.). 260p. 42.95 (978-0-548-06794-9(5)) Kessinger Publishing, LLC.

Tohamy, Ameer. What Drives Regeneration? 2010. 72p. pap. (978-3-8383-7701-8(X)) Lambert Academic Publishing.

Tomita, M. & Nishioka, T., eds. Metabolomics: The Frontier of Systems Biology. 2010. (ENG., Illus.). xiv, 256p. pap. 139.00 (978-4-431-99808-2(X), 443199808X) Springer.

Townshend, Emma. Darwin's Dogs: How Darwin's Pets Helped Form a World-Changing Theory of Evolution. 2009. (ENG., Illus.). 144p. pap. 14.95 (978-0-7112-3065-1(X)) Lincoln, Frances Ltd. GBR. Dist: Perseus-PGW.

Trevathan, Wenda. Ancient Bodies, Modern Lives: How Evolution Has Shaped Women's Health, 1 vol. 2010. (ENG., Illus.). 320p. 34.95 (978-0-19-538888-6(7)) Oxford Univ. Pr., Inc.

Turner, John Alan, et al. The Biology of Coral Reefs. 2009. (Biology of Habitats Ser.). (ENG., Illus.). 352p. pap. 55.00 (978-0-19-856636-6(0)) Oxford Univ. Pr., Inc.

Tweedie-Cullen, Ry. Quantitative Proteomics. 2010. 124p. pap. (978-3-639-26221-6(2)) VDM Verlag Dr. Mueller e.K.

Urry, Lisa A., et al. Biology. 8th ed. 2010. (ENG.). 1464p. (C). ring bd. 121.60 (978-0-321-69207-8(1)) Benjamin-Cummings Publishing Co.

Vaidyanath, K. Introduction to Biology & Biotechnology, Second Edition. 2nd ed. 2009. (ENG., Illus.). 625p. 82.95 (978-1-4398-0724-8(8), CRC Press) Taylor & Francis Group GBR. Dist: Taylor & Francis Group.

Vasseur, D. A. & McCann, K. S. The Impact of Environmental Variability on Ecological Systems. 2010. (Peter Yodzis Fundamental Ecology Ser.). xiii, 231p. pap. 139.00 (978-90-481-7457-7(0), 9048174570) Springer.

Vincent, Karla & Thazhath, Rupal. Biology 1520: An Introduction to Organismal Biology. rev. ed. 2010. (ENG.). 70p. spiral bd. 35.70 (978-0-7575-4915-1(2)) Kendall Hunt Publishing Co.

Vincent, P., et al. Mastering the Air. Date not set. (Longman Biology Topics Ser.). (Illus.). 32p. pap. 35.67 (978-0-582-32300-1(2)) Addison-Wesley Longman, Ltd. GBR. Dist: Trans-Atlantic Pubns., Inc.

Vines. Plant & Animal Biology. 4th ed. Date not set. (Illus.). Vol. 1. x, 1345p. pap. 11.25 (978-0-582-35598-9(2)) Vol. 2. x, 1092p. pap. 11.25 (978-0-582-35599-6(0)) Addison-Wesley Longman, Ltd. GBR. Dist: Trans-Atlantic Pubns., Inc.

Vinicius, Lucio. Modular Evolution: How Natural Selection Produces Biological Complexity. 2010. (ENG., Illus.). 248p. 99.00 (978-0-521-42964-1(1)); pap. 48.00 (978-0-521-72877-5(0)) Cambridge Univ. Pr.

Vivion, Nichole. Easy Biology Step-by-Step. 2012. (Easy Step-by-Step Ser.). (ENG., Illus.). 224p. (C). pap. 14.00 **(978-0-07-176779-8(7)**, 0071767797) McGraw-Hill Cos., The.

Vivion, Nichole. Practice Makes Perfect Biology. 2011. (Practice Makes Perfect Ser.). (ENG., Illus.). 240p. (C). pap. 13.00 (978-0-07-174551-2(3), 0071745513) McGraw-Hill Cos., The.

Voeikov, V. L., et al, eds. Biophotonics & Coherent Systems in Biology. 2006. (ENG., Illus.). xi, 306p. 149.00 (978-0-387-28378-4(1), 0387283781) Springer.

Vogel, Thomas. Fear & Loathing in Introductory Biology. rev. ed. 2012. (ENG.). 288p. pap. 55.00 (978-0-7575-6539-7(5)) Kendall Hunt Publishing Co.

Wagner, Andreas. The Origins of Evolutionary Innovations: A Theory of Transformative Change in Living Systems. 2011. (ENG., Illus.). 272p. 117.00 (978-0-19-969259-0(9)); pap. 52.95 (978-0-19-969260-6(2)) Oxford Univ. Pr., Inc.

Wasser, Solomon P., ed. Evolutionary Theory & Processes: Modern Horizons: Papers in Honour of Eviator Nevo. 2012. (ENG.). 495p. pap. 239.00 (978-90-481-6457-8(5), 9048164575) Springer.

Waterman, Margaret & Stanley, Ethel. Biological Inquiry: A Workbook of Investigative Case Studies for Campbell/Reece Biology Eighth Edition. 2nd ed. 2007. (ENG., Illus.). 192p. (C). per. 25.80 (978-0-321-51320-5(7)) Benjamin-Cummings Publishing Co.

Webley, Wilmore. Biology of Aids. 2nd rev. ed. 2011. (ENG., Illus.). 98p. pap. 25.32 (978-0-7575-5531-2(4)) Kendall Hunt Publishing Co.

Wei, Hsin-Lin. Food Digestion & Thermal Preference of Toad. 2009. 56p. pap. (978-3-639-13142-0(8)) VDM Verlag Dr. Mueller e.K.

Weiss, Kenneth M. & Buchanan, Anne V. The Mermaid's Tale: Four Billion Years of Cooperation in the Making of Living Things. 2009. (Illus.). 336p. 38.50 (978-0-674-03193-7(8)) Harvard Univ. Pr.

Wells, Marion R., et al. Investigations in Biology. 5th rev. ed. 2011. (ENG.). 174p. spiral bd. 34.72 (978-0-7575-5652-4(3)) Kendall Hunt Publishing Co.

Williams, Gareth. New Biology for You. 2nd rev. ed. 2011. (ENG., Illus.). 400p. pap. 62.50 **(978-1-4085-0920-3(2))** Nelson Thornes Ltd. GBR. Dist: Trans-Atlantic Pubns., Inc.

Wilson, E. O. The Creation: An Appeal to Save Life on Earth. 2007. (ENG., Illus.). 192p. per. 14.95 (978-0-393-33048-9(6), 33048) Norton, W. W. & Co., Inc.

Wilson, Joan. Reading Links: Nursing & Biology. 2nd rev. ed. 2009. (ENG.). 310p. pap. 49.20 (978-0-7575-7133-6(6)) Kendall Hunt Publishing Co.

Windelspecht. Biology 1801. rev. ed. 2011. (ENG.). 152p. spiral bd. 35.00 **(978-0-7575-9391-8(7))** Kendall Hunt Publishing Co.

Windelspecht, Michael & Harris, Betsy. Explorations in General Biology. 2nd rev. ed. 2011. (ENG.). 76p. spiral bd. 24.00 **(978-0-7575-9334-5(8))** Kendall Hunt Publishing Co.

—Explorations in General Biology II. 2nd rev. abr. ed. 2011. (ENG.). 88p. spiral bd. 24.00 **(978-0-7575-9336-9(4))** Kendall Hunt Publishing Co.

Windelspecht, Michael, et al. Biology 1802. rev. ed. 2012. (ENG.). 118p. spiral bd. 35.00 **(978-0-7575-9392-5(5))** Kendall Hunt Publishing Co.

Witzany, Ganther, ed. Biocommunication in Soil Microorganisms. 2010. (Soil Biology Ser.). (Illus.). xx, 474p. 209.00 (978-3-642-14511-7(6), 3642145116) Springer.

Wolfe, Stephen, et al. Biology: The Dynamic Science. 2007. (ENG.). 512p. (C). pap., pupil's gde. ed. 59.95 (978-0-534-40321-8(2)) Brooks/Cole.

Wood, Piers. As Biology, pACK. 2010. (ENG.). 336p. (YA). cd-rom 700.00 (978-0-19-915269-8(1)) Oxford Univ. Pr., Inc.

Wood, Todd Charles, ed. Genesis Kinds: Creationism & the Origin of Species. 2009. (Center for Origins Research Issues in Creation Ser.). 202p. pap. 22.00 (978-1-60608-490-8(9), Wipf and Stock) Wipf & Stock Pubs.

Xu, Ying, et al, eds. Computational Methods for Protein Structure Prediction & Modeling: Volume 1: Basic Characterization. 2010. (Biological & Medical Physics, Biomedical Engineering Ser.). (Illus.). xx, 394p. pap. 209.00 (978-1-4419-2205-2(9), 1441922059) Springer.

Yanofsky, Charles S. Beyond Biology: Metaphysical Brain Science. 2010. 670p. pap. 30.95 (978-1-4327-5401-3(7)) Outskirts Pr., Inc.

Yasmin, Shahla. Ecology & Biology of the Indian Peafowl, Pavo Cristatus. 2011. 68p. pap. **(978-3-8433-5980-1(6))** Lambert Academic Publishing.

Zhirnov, Victor V. & Cavin III, Ralph K. Microsystems for Bioelectronics: The Nanomorphic Cell. 2010. (Micro & Nano Technologies Ser.). (ENG., Illus.). 204p. 200.00 (978-1-4377-7840-3(2)) William Andrew, Inc.

Zimmer, Carl. The Tangled Bank: An Introduction to Evolution. 2009. (ENG., Illus.). 394p. (C). 59.95 (978-0-9815194-7-0(4)) Roberts & Co.

Zinn, Stephanie. McGraw-Hill's SAT Subject Test Biology E/M, 3rd Edition. 3rd ed. 2011. (ENG., Illus.). 352p. (C). pap. 18.00 **(978-0-07-176333-2(3)**, 0071763333) McGraw-Hill Cos., The.

BIOLOGY—APPARATUS AND SUPPLIES

see Biological Apparatus and Supplies

BIOLOGY—BIBLIOGRAPHY

see also Biological Literature

van Wyhe, John. Charles Darwin's Shorter Publications, 1829-1883. 2009. (ENG., Illus.). 556p. 144.00 (978-0-521-88809-7(3)) Cambridge Univ. Pr.

Walters, LeRoy, et al, eds. Bibliography of Bioethics. (ENG.). Vol. 33. 2007. 848p. *(978-1-883913-14-4(4))* Vol. 34. 2008. *(978-1-883913-15-1(2))* Vol. 35. 2009. 80.00 *(978-1-883913-16-8(0))* Georgetown Univ., Kennedy Institute of Ethics.

BIOLOGY—CLASSIFICATION

see also Species

also subdivision Classification under individual animals and groups of animals and individual plants and groups of plants, e.g. Fishes—Classification; Plants—Classification

Annual Review of Ecology, Evolution & Systematics. 2006. 80.00 *(978-0-8243-1437-6(9))* Annual Reviews, Inc.

Bauman, Robert W. Microbiology with Diseases by Taxonomy, Kit. 3rd ed. 2010. (ENG.). (C). 57.20 *(978-0-321-67237-7(2))* Benjamin-Cummings Publishing Co.

Bonucci, Ermanno. Biological Calcification: Normal & Pathological Processes in the Early Stages. 2006. (ENG., Illus.). xxii, 592p. 295.00 *(978-3-540-36012-4(3)*, 3540360123) Springer.

Dunn, Rob. Every Living Thing: Man's Obsessive Quest to Catalog Life, from Nanobacteria to New Monkeys. 2010. (ENG.). 288p. pap. 14.99 *(978-0-06-143031-2(5)*, Harper Paperbacks) HarperCollins Pubs.

Ereshefsky, Marc. The Poverty of the Linnaean Hierarchy: A Philosophical Study of Biological Taxonomy. 2007. (Cambridge Studies in Philosophy & Biology Ser.). (ENG., Illus.). 328p. pap. 72.00 *(978-0-521-03883-6(9))* Cambridge Univ. Pr.

Freedman, Jeri, ed. The Applications & Limitations of Taxonomy (in Classification of Organisms) An Anthology of Current Thought. 2009. (Contemporary Discourse in the Field of Biology Ser.). 224p. (gr. 10-12). 63.90 *(978-1-61511-912-7(4))* Rosen Publishing Group, Inc., The.

Golovatch, Sergei I. & Mesibov, Robert, eds. Advances in the Systematics of Diplopoda III. 2011. (ZooKeys Ser.). (Illus.). 65p. pap. 49.50 ***(978-954-642-586-7(9))*** Pensoft Pubs. BGR. Dist: Coronet Bks.

Heads, Michael J. Molecular Panbiogeography of the Tropics. 2012. (Species & Systematics Ser.). (ENG., Illus.). 566p. 75.00 ***(978-0-520-27196-8(3))*** Univ. of California Pr.

Hine, Christine. Systematics as Cyberscience: Computers, Change, & Continuity in Science. 2008. (Inside Technology Ser.). (ENG., Illus.). 320p. (gr. 17). 35.00 *(978-0-262-08371-3(X))* MIT Pr.

Johnson, Kristin. Jordan's Ark: One Man's Quest to Catalog the Living World. 2012. ***(978-1-4214-0600-8(4))***; E-Book ***(978-1-4214-0650-3(0))*** Johns Hopkins Univ. Pr.

Khan, Kiran Yasmin, et al. The Genus Ficus. 2011. 100p. pap. ***(978-3-8454-0073-0(0))*** Lambert Academic Publishing.

Lecointre, Guillaume & Le Guyader, Herve. The Tree of Life: A Phylogenetic Classification. McCoy, Karen, tr. from FRE. 2007. (Harvard University Press Reference Library). Orig. Title: Classification phylogenetique du Vivant. (Illus.). 560p. 39.95 *(978-0-674-02183-9(5)*, Belknap Pr.) Harvard Univ. Pr.

Lewis, D. Richard. Time Trip on a Moebius Strip. 2007. (ENG.). 256p. per. 13.95 *(978-0-7414-3797-6(X))* Infinity Publishing.

MacLeod, Norman. Automated Taxon Identification in Systematics: Theory, Approaches & Applications. Macleod, Norman, ed. 2007. (Systematics Association Special Volume Ser.). (ENG., Illus.). 368p. 99.95 *(978-0-8493-8205-5(X)*, CRC Press) Taylor & Francis Group GBR. Dist: Taylor & Francis Group.

Margulis, Lynn, et al. Kingdoms & Domains: An Illustrated Guide to the Phyla of Life on Earth. 4th ed. 2009. (ENG., Illus.). 864p. 82.95 *(978-0-12-373621-5(8)*, Academic Pr.) Elsevier Science & Technology Bks.

Marty, Daniel, et al, eds. Proceedings of the 5th International Symposium on Lithographic Limestone & Plattenkalk. 2012. (Swiss Journal of Geosciences Supplement Ser.). (ENG.). iv, 178p. pap. 199.00 ***(978-3-0348-0299-4(4)***, 3034802994) Birkhauser Verlag AG CHE. Dist: Springer.

Penev, Lyubomir, ed. Taxonomy Shifts up a Gear: New Publishing Tools to Accelerate Biodiversity Research. 2010. (ZooKeys Ser.). (Illus.). 126p. pap. 67.50 *(978-954-642-556-0(7))* Pensoft Pubs. BGR. Dist: Coronet Bks.

Rodland, K.D., ed. Systems Biology of Biomarkers: Book Edition of Disease Markers. 2010. pap. 130.00 *(978-1-60750-584-6(3))* IOS Pr., Inc.

Sapp, Jan. The New Foundations of Evolution: On the Tree of Life. 2009. (ENG., Illus.). 400p. pap. 39.95 *(978-0-19-538850-3(X))* Oxford Univ. Pr., Inc.

Schuh, Randall T. & Brower, Andrew V. Z. Biological Systematics. 2nd rev. ed. 2009. (Illus.). 320p. 59.95 *(978-0-8014-4799-0(2))* Cornell Univ. Pr.

Scott-Ram, N. R. Transformed Cladistics, Taxonomy & Evolution. 2008. (ENG.). 252p. pap. 53.00 *(978-0-521-05513-0(X))* Cambridge Univ. Pr.

Slaughter, M. M. Universal Languages & Scientific Taxonomy in the Seventeenth Century. 2010. (ENG.). 288p. pap. 30.99 *(978-0-521-13544-3(3))* Cambridge Univ. Pr.

Stille, Darlene R. Classifying Living Things. 2007. (Gareth Stevens Vital Science-Life Science Ser.). 48p. (gr. 5-12). pap. 14.05 *(978-0-8368-8447-0(7)*, Stevens, Gareth Secondary Library) Stevens, Gareth Publishing LLLP.

Wheeler, Ward C. Systematics: A Course of Lectures. 2012. (ENG.). 448p. 149.95 ***(978-0-470-67170-2(X))***; pap. 99.95 ***(978-0-470-67169-6(6))*** Wiley, John & Sons, Inc. (Wiley-Blackwell).

Wiley, E. O. & Lieberman, Bruce S. Phylogenetics: Theory & Practice of Phylogenetic Systematics. 2nd ed. 2011. (ENG., Illus.). 432p. 99.95 *(978-0-470-90596-8(4)*, Wiley-Blackwell) Wiley, John & Sons, Inc.

Williams, D. M. & Knapp, Sandra. Beyond Cladistics: The Branching of a Paradigm. 2010. E-Book 65.00 *(978-0-520-94799-3(1))* Univ. of California Pr.

Williams, David M. & Ebach, Malte C. Foundations of Systematics & Biogeography. (ENG., Illus.). xviii, 310p. 2010. pap. 89.95 *(978-1-4419-4445-0(1)*, 1441944451) 2007. 89.95 *(978-0-387-72728-8(0)*, 0387727280) Springer.

Yeh, Esther. UCBSO Second Year: Pharm & Systemics. 2010. 598p. pap. 33.90 *(978-0-557-65109-2(3))* Lulu Enterprises Inc.

Yoon, Carol Kaesuk. Naming Nature: The Clash Between Instinct & Science. (ENG., Illus.). 2010. 341p. pap. 16.95 *(978-0-393-33871-3(1)*, 33871) 2009. 352p. 27.95 *(978-0-393-06197-0(3)*, 6197) Norton, W. W. & Co., Inc.

BIOLOGY—COMPUTER-ASSISTED INSTRUCTION

Altman, Russ B. Biocomputing 2011 - Proceedings of the Pacific Symposium. 2010. 500p. 168.00 *(978-981-4335-04-1(5))* World Scientific Publishing Co., Inc.

Anai, Hirokazu, et al. Algebraic Biology: Second International Conference, AB 2007. 2007. (Lecture Notes in Computer Science Ser.). (Illus.). 377p. per. 79.95 *(978-3-540-73432-1(5))* Springer.

Barnes, David J. & Chu, Dominique. Introduction to Modeling for Biosciences. 2010. (ENG., Illus.). xii, 322p. 89.95 *(978-1-84996-325-1(8)*, 1849963258) Springer.

Donaldson, Mindi. Virtual Destinations & Student Learning in Middle School: A Case Study of a Biology Museum Online. 2006. (ENG., Illus.). 288p. (C). 104.95 *(978-1-934043-27-1(3))* Cambria Pr.

Helms, Volkhard. Principles of Computational Cell Biology: From Protein Complexes to Cellular Networks. 2008. (ENG.). 289p. pap. 89.95 *(978-3-527-31555-0(1)*, Wiley-VCH) Wiley, John & Sons, Inc.

Ladunga, Istvan, ed. Computational Biology of Transcription Factor Binding. 2010. (Methods in Molecular Biology Ser.). (Illus.). xi, 454p. 159.00 *(978-1-60761-853-9(2)*, 1607618532) Humana Pr.

Wood, Piers. A2 Biology Planning & Resource Pack with Oxbox CD-ROM. 2009. (ENG.). 304p. (YA). cd-rom 900.00 *(978-0-19-915272-8(1))* Oxford Univ. Pr., Inc.

BIOLOGY—CONGRESSES

Arena, Paolo, et al. Bioengineered & Bioinspired Systems III: 2-4 May 2007 Maspalomas, Gran Canaria, Spain. 2007. (Proceedings of SPIE Ser.). (Illus.). 376p. pap. 90.00 *(978-0-8194-6720-1(0))* SPIE.

Brebbia, Carlos A., ed. Modelling in Medicine & Biology VII. 2007. (Transactions in Biomedicine & Health: 12). (Illus.). 352p. 232.00 *(978-1-84564-089-7(6))* WIT Pr GBR. Dist: WIT Pr.

De Mattei, Roberto. Evoluzionismo: Il Tramonto Di una Ipotesi. 2009. (ITA., Illus.). 258p. *(978-88-8272-500-6(6))* Cantagalli.

Huang, De-Shuang, et al, eds. Advanced Intelligent Computing. Theories & Applications: 6th International Conference on Intelligent Computing, Changsha, China, August 18-21, 2010. Proceedings. 2010. (Communications in Computer & Information Science Ser.). xvi, 580p. pap. 129.00 *(978-3-642-14830-9(1)*, 3642148301) Springer.

—Advanced Intelligent Computing Theories & Applications: 6th International Conference on Intelligent Computing, ICIC 2010, Changsha, China, August 18-21, 2010, Proceedings. 2010. (Lecture Notes in Computer Science / Theoretical Computer Science & General Issues Ser.). xix, 689p. pap. 139.00 *(978-3-642-14921-4(9)*, 3642149219) Springer.

—Advanced Intelligent Computing Theories & Applications: with Aspects of Artificial Intelligence: 6th International Conference on Intelligent Computing, ICIC 2010, Changsha, China, August 18-21, 2010, Proceedings. 2010. (Lecture Notes in Computer Science / Lecture Notes in Artificial Intelligence Ser.). xviii, 685p. pap. 139.00 *(978-3-642-14931-3(6)*, 3642149316) Springer.

Rodríguez-Vázquez, Ángel, et al. Bioengineered & Bioinspired Systems IV: 4-6 May 2009, Dresden, Germany. 2009. (Proceedings of SPIE Ser.). (Illus.). 236p. pap. 70.00 *(978-0-8194-7639-5(0))* SPIE.

Tarasenko, Olga, et al, eds. Biology, Nanotechnology, Toxicology, & Applications: Proceedings of the 5th BioNano Tox & Applicatons International Research Conference. 2011. (AIP Conference Proceedings / Materials Physics & Applications Ser.). (ENG., Illus.). 200p. pap. 148.00 ***(978-0-7354-0910-1(2)***, 0735409102, AIP Pr.) Springer.

Waddington, C. H., ed. Biological Processes in Living Systems. 2012. (ENG., Illus.). 299p. pap. 49.95 ***(978-1-4128-4276-1(X))*** Transaction Pubs.

Waddington, C. H., ed. The Origin of Life Vol. 1: Toward a Theoretical Biology. 2008. (ENG., Illus.). 254p. pap. 89.95 *(978-0-202-36302-8(3))* Aldine Transaction.

2009 International Workshop on High Performance Computational Systems Biology: HiBi 2009, 14-16 October 2009, Trento, Italy. 2009. (Illus.). xii, 129p. pap. ***(978-0-7695-3809-9(6))*** IEEE Computer Society Pr.

BIOLOGY—DATA PROCESSING

see also Bioinformatics

Accardi, Luigi, et al. Quantum Bioinformatics IV: From Quantum Information to Bio-Informatics - Tokyo University of Science, Japan, 10-13 March 2010. 2011. (Illus.). 504p. 190.00 *(978-981-4343-75-6(7))* World Scientific Publishing Co., Inc.

Alterovitz, Gil & Ramoni, Marco, eds. Knowledge-Based Bioinformatics: From Analysis to Interpretation. 2010. (ENG., Illus.). 396p. 80.00 *(978-0-470-74831-2(1)*, Wiley) Wiley, John & Sons, Inc.

Beckerman, Andrew P. & Petchey, Owen L. Getting Started with R: An Introduction for Biologists. 2012. (ENG.). 160p. 99.99 ***(978-0-19-960161-5(5))***; pap. 37.99 ***(978-0-19-960162-2(3))*** Oxford Univ. Pr., Inc.

Berman, Jules J. Ruby Programming for Medicine & Biology. 2007. 378p. (C). pap. 69.95 *(978-0-7637-5090-9(5))* Jones & Bartlett Learning, LLC.

Bleasby, Alan J., et al. EMBOSS Administrator's Guide: Bioinformatics Software Management. 2011. (ENG., Illus.). 184p. pap. 65.00 ***(978-0-521-18815-9(6))*** Cambridge Univ. Pr.

Bloomfield, Victor. Computer Simulation & Data Analysis in Molecular Biology & Biophysics: An Introduction Using R. 2009. (Biological & Medical Physics, Biomedical Engineering Ser.). (ENG., Illus.). xvi, 321p. 109.00 *(978-1-4419-0084-5(5)*, 1441900845) Springer.

Bourgine, P., et al, eds. Complex Systems [Bibliography & Price not Definite.]: European Conference, Paris, November 2005: Selected Papers, Part 1: Special Issue: Complexus 2004/2005, Vol. 2, No. 3-4. (Illus.). 130p. pap. *(978-3-8055-8168-4(8))* Karger, S. AG.

—Complex Systems [Bibliography & Price not Definite.]: European Conference, Paris, November 2005: Selected Papers, Part 2: Special Issue: Complexus 2006, Vol. 3, No. 1-3. (Illus.). 184p. pap. *(978-3-8055-8169-1(6))* Karger, S. AG.

Condon, Anne, et al, eds. Algorithmic Bioprocesses. 2009. (Natural Computing Ser.). (ENG., Illus.). xx, 742p. 219.00 *(978-3-540-88868-0(3)*, 3540888683) Springer.

Cristianini, Nello & Hahn, Matthew W. Introduction to Computational Genomics: A Case Studies Approach. 2007. (ENG., Illus.). 200p. per. 62.00 *(978-0-521-67191-0(4))* Cambridge Univ. Pr.

Feng, Jianfeng, et al, eds. Frontiers in Computational & System Biology. 2010. (Computational Biology Ser.). (ENG., Illus.). xxv, 24p. 139.00 *(978-1-84996-195-0(6)*, 1849961956) Springer.

Fisher, Jasmin. Formal Methods in Systems Biology. 2008. (Lecture Notes in Computer Science / Lecture Notes in Bioinformatics Ser.). 139p. spiral bd. 69.95 *(978-3-540-68410-7(7)*, 3540684107) Springer.

Haddock, Steven H. D. & Dunn, Casey W. Practical Computing for Biologists. 2011. (Illus.). 538p. pap. ***(978-0-87893-391-4(3))*** Sinauer Assocs., Inc.

Hetherington, Alistair & Grierson, Claire, eds. Practical Systems Biology, Vol. 61. 2008. (Society for Experimental Biology Ser.). (Illus.). CCCp. 234.00 *(978-0-415-40780-9(X))* Taylor & Francis Group.

Hochreiter, Sepp & Wagner, Roland. Bioinformatics Research & Development. 2007. (Lecture Notes in Computer Science Ser.). (Illus.). XVI, 482p. pap. 109.00 *(978-3-540-71232-9(1)*, 3540712321) Springer.

Ison, Jon C., et al. EMBOSS Developer's Guide: Bioinformatics Programming. 2011. (ENG., Illus.). 652p. pap. 90.00 ***(978-0-521-60724-7(8))*** Cambridge Univ. Pr.

Jhoti, Harren & Leach, Andrew R., eds. Structure-based Drug Discovery. 2010. (ENG.). xii, 252p. pap. 219.00 *(978-90-481-7123-1(7)*, 9048171237) Springer.

Junker, Björn H. & Schreiber, Falk. Analysis of Biological Networks. 2008. (Wiley Series in Bioinformatics Ser.: 2). (ENG., Illus.). 368p. 111.00 *(978-0-470-04144-4(7)*, Wiley-Interscience) Wiley, John & Sons, Inc.

Khatree, Ravindra. Computational Methods in Biomedical Research. Naik, Dayanand N., ed. 2007. (Biostatistics Ser.). (ENG., Illus.). 432p. 109.95 *(978-1-58488-577-1(7)*, Chapman & Hall/CRC) CRC Pr. LLC.

Lamm, Ehud & Unger, Ron. Biological Computation. 2011. (Chapman & Hall/CRC Mathematical & Computational Biology Ser.). (ENG., Illus.). 343p. (C). 79.95 *(978-1-4200-8795-6(9)*, Chapman & Hall/CRC) CRC Pr. LLC.

LeBlanc, Mark D. & Dyer, Betsey Dexter. Perl for Exploring DNA. 2007. (ENG., Illus.). 288p. per. 34.99 *(978-0-19-530589-0(2))* Oxford Univ. Pr., Inc.

Lecca, Paola, et al. Systemic Approaches in Bioinformatics & Computational Systems Biology: Recent Advances. 2011. ***(978-1-61350-437-6(3))***; ***(978-1-61350-435-2(7))***; E-Book ***(978-1-61350-436-9(5))*** IGI Global.

Leser, Ulf, et al. Data Integration in the Life Sciences: Third International Workshop, DILS 2006, Hinxton, UK, July 20-22, 2006: Proceedings. 2006. (Lecture Notes in Computer Science Ser.). (Illus.). XI, 298p. pap. 74.95 *(978-3-540-36593-8(1)*, 3540365931) Springer.

Li, Kang, et al, eds. Life System Modeling & Intelligent Computing: International Conference on Life System Modeling & Simulation, LSMS 2010, & International Conference on Intelligent Computing for Sustainable Energy & Environment, ICSEE 2010, Wuxi, China, September 17-20, 2010. Proceedings. 2010. (Lecture Notes in Computer Science / Lecture Notes in Bioinformatics Ser.). xviii, 719p. pap. 131.00 *(978-3-642-15614-4(2)*, 3642156142) Springer.

—Life System Modeling & Intelligent Computing: International Conference on Life System Modeling & Simulation, LSMS 2010, & International Conference on Intelligent Computing for Sustainable Energy & Environment, ICSEE 2010, Wuxi, China, September 17-20, 2010, Proceedings, Part I. 2010. (Communications in Computer & Information Science Ser.). xviii, 261p. pap. 84.00 *(978-3-642-15852-0(8)*, 3642158528) Springer.

Lonardi, Stefano & Chen, Jake Y., eds. Biological Data Mining. 2009. (Chapman & Hall/CRC Data Mining & Knowledge Discovery Ser.). (ENG., Illus.). 733p. 99.95 *(978-1-4200-8684-3(7)*, Chapman & Hall/CRC) CRC Pr. LLC.

Ma, Zongmin & Chen, Jake, eds. Database Modeling in Biology: Practices & Challenges. 2007. (Illus.). 400p. 99.00 *(978-0-387-30238-6(7)*, 0387302387) Springer.

MacLeod, Norman. Automated Taxon Identification in Systematics: Theory, Approaches & Applications. Macleod, Norman, ed. 2007. (Systematics Association Special Volume Ser.). (ENG., Illus.). 368p. 99.95 *(978-0-8493-8205-5(X)*, CRC Press) Taylor & Francis Group GBR. Dist: Taylor & Francis Group.

Maglaveras, Nicos, et al, eds. Biological & Medical Data Analysis: 7th International Symposium, ISBMDA 2006 Thessaloniki, Greece, December 7-8, 2006: Proceedings. 2007. (Lecture Notes in Computer Science Ser.). (Illus.). XIII, 496p. pap. 89.00 *(978-3-540-68063-5(2)*, 3540680632) Springer.

Marchiori, Elena & Rajapakse, Jagath C., eds. Evolutionary Computation, Machine Learning & Data Mining in Bioinformatics: 5th European Conference, EvoBIO 2007, Valencia, Spain, April 11-13, 2007: Proceedings. 2007. (Lecture Notes in Computer Science Ser.: Vol. 4447). (Illus.). 302p. 79.95 *(978-3-540-71782-9(X)*, 354071782X) Springer.

McDermott, Jason, et al, eds. Computational Systems Biology. 2009. (Methods in Molecular Biology Ser.). (Illus.). 300p. 159.00 *(978-1-58829-905-5(8))* Humana Pr.

Najarian, Kayvan. Systems Biology & Bioinformatics: A Computational Approach - Solutions Manual. 2008. *(978-1-4398-0508-4(3))* CRC Pr. LLC.

Noble, Denis, et al. The Selected Papers of Denis Noble CBE FRS. 2012. 644p. 168.00 ***(978-1-84816-842-8(X))*** Imperial College Pr. GBR. Dist: World Scientific Publishing Co., Inc.

Palsson, Bernhard. Systems Biology: Simulation of Dynamic Network States. 2011. (ENG., Illus.). 332p. 75.00 *(978-1-107-00159-6(5))* Cambridge Univ. Pr.

Pardalos, Panos M., et al, eds. Data Mining in Biomedicine. 2010. (Springer Optimization & Its Applications Ser.). (Illus.). xviii, 580p. pap. 149.00 *(978-1-4419-4343-9(9)*, 1441943439) Springer.

Pardalos, Panos M., et al. Data Mining in Biomedicine. 2007. (Springer Optimization & Its Applications Ser.: Vol. 7). (Illus.). xviii, 580p. 149.00 *(978-0-387-69318-7(1))* Springer.

Penev, Lyubomir, ed. Taxonomy Shifts up a Gear: New Publishing Tools to Accelerate Biodiversity Research. 2010. (ZooKeys Ser.). (Illus.). 126p. pap. 67.50 *(978-954-642-556-0(7))* Pensoft Pubs. BGR. Dist: Coronet Bks.

Pham, Tuan D., et al, eds. 2011 International Symposium on Computational Models for Life Sciences (CMLS-11) 2011. (AIP Conference Proceedings / Mathematical & Statistical Physics Ser.). 356p. pap. 163.00 ***(978-0-7354-0931-6(5)***, 0735409315, AIP Pr.) Springer.

Pizzuti, Clara, et al, eds. Evolutionary Computation, Machine Learning & Data Mining in Bioinformatics: 9th European Conference, EvoBIO 2011, Torino, Italy, April 27-29, 2011, Proceedings. 2011. (Lecture Notes in Computer Science / Theoretical Computer Science & General Issues Ser.). (Illus.). xii, 188p. pap. 72.00 *(978-3-642-20388-6(4)*, 3642203884) Springer.

Rajapakse, Jagath Chandana, et al. Pattern Recognition in Bioinformatics: International Workshop, PRIB 2006, Hong Kong, China, August 20, 2006, Proceedings. 2006. (Lecture Notes in Computer Science Ser.). (Illus.). 186p. pap. 69.95 *(978-3-540-37446-6(9)*, 3540374469) Springer.

Rao, A. Ravishankar & Cecchi, Guillermo A. High-Throughput Image Reconstruction & Analysis. 2009. (Illus.). 380p. 139.00 *(978-1-59693-295-1(3))* Artech Hse., Inc.

Raval, Alpan & Ray, Animesh. Robust Networks: From Graphs to Systems Biology. 2012. (Chapman & Hall/CRC Mathematical & Computational Biology Ser.). (ENG., Illus.). 306p. 79.95 *(978-1-58488-463-7(0)*, Chapman & Hall/CRC) CRC Pr. LLC.

Reinert Knut Staff & Gogol-Döring, Andreas. Biological Sequence Analysis Using the Seqan C++ Library. 2009. (Chapman & Hall/CRC Mathematical & Computational Biology Ser.). (ENG., Illus.). 329p. 92.95 *(978-1-4200-7623-3(X)*, CRC Press) Taylor & Francis Group GBR. Dist: Taylor & Francis Group.

Revett, Kenneth. Bioinformatics for Computer Science: Foundations in Molecular Biology. 2012. 270p. pap. ***(978-1-907568-22-0(0)***, Biohealthcare Publishing (Oxford) Limited) Woodhead Publishing Ltd.

Rosyara, Umesh. R for Data Analysis in Biological Sciences. 2011. 444p. pap. ***(978-3-8443-2841-7(6))*** Lambert Academic Publishing.

Salzberg, Steven L. & Warnow, Tandy. Algorithms in Bioinformatics: 9th International Workshop, WABI 2009, Philadelphia, USA, September 12-13, 2009. Proceedings. 2009. (Lecture Notes in Computer Science / Lecture Notes in Bioinformatics Ser.). (Illus.). xi, 430p. pap. 99.00 *(978-3-642-04240-9(6)*, 3642042406) Springer.

Seref, Onur. Data Mining, Systems Analysis & Optimization in Biomedicine. 2007. (AIP Conference Proceedings Ser.). (Illus.). ix, 318p. 146.00 *(978-0-7354-0467-0(4))* American Institute of Physics.

Shin, Yong-Jun. Digital Microfluidics for Systems Biology: With an Introduction to State Machine-based Gene Regulation Network Modeling. 2008. 76p. pap. *(978-3-639-09376-6(3))* VDM Verlag Dr. Mueller e.K.

Swofford, David L. PAUP 4.0: Phylogenetic Analysis Using Parsimony. Date not set. (C). pap. 40.00 *(978-0-87893-801-8(X))* Sinauer Assocs., Inc.

Tagore, Somnath. Issues in Mining Skills: Application to computational biology Domain. 2010. 132p. pap. *(978-3-639-26563-7(7))* VDM Verlag Dr. Mueller e.K.

Transactions on Computational Systems Biology VIII. 2007. (Lecture Notes in Bioinformatics Ser.). (Illus.). 101p. pap. 79.95 *(978-3-540-76638-4(3))* Springer.

Zhu, Yangyong & Xiong, Yun. Sheng Wu Shu Ju Zheng He Yu Wa Jue. 2009. (CHI., Illus.). *(978-7-309-06614-2(6))* Fudan Univ. Pr.

BIOLOGY—DICTIONARIES

Abercrombie, M., et al. A Dictionary of Biology. 2008. (ENG.). 254p. pap. 39.95 *(978-0-202-36219-9(1))* Aldine Transaction.

Allaby, Michael. A Dictionary of Ecology. 4th ed. 2010. (ENG., Illus.). 480p. (Orig.). pap. 18.95 *(978-0-19-956766-9(2))* Oxford Univ. Pr., Inc.

Campbell, Neil A. & Reece, Jane B. Biology. 8th ed. (ENG.). (C). 2008. 30.00 *(978-0-321-53693-8(2))* 2008. 48p. pap. 20.40 *(978-0-321-49434-4(2))*Kit. 2009. E-Book, E-Book 126.67 *(978-0-321-63393-4(8))* Benjamin-Cummings Publishing Co.

Campbell, Neil A., et al. Biology. 8th ed. (ENG.). (C). 2010. E-Book, E-Book 126.67 *(978-0-321-73662-8(1))* 2007. 544p. pap. 63.20 *(978-0-321-50156-1(X))*Kit. 2008. 23.40 *(978-0-321-54260-1(6))* Benjamin-Cummings Publishing Co.

Clark & Hemsley, William. The Rosen Comprehensive Dictionary of Biology. John, O. E., ed. 2009. (Rosen Comprehensive Student Dictionaries Ser.). 272p. (gr. 9-9). 93.00 *(978-1-60852-504-1(X))* Rosen Publishing Group, Inc., The.

Clark, John O. E. & Hemsley, William, eds. The Rosen Comprehensive Dictionary of Biology. 2007. (Rosen Comprehensive Student Dictionaries Ser.). (Illus.). 271p. (YA). (gr. 9-12). lib. bdg. 46.50 *(978-1-4042-0701-1(5))* Rosen Publishing Group, Inc., The.

Hine, Robert S. & Martin, Elizabeth, eds. A Dictionary of Biology. 6th ed. 2008. (Oxford Paperback Reference Ser.). (ENG., Illus.). 704p. per. 17.95 *(978-0-19-920462-5(4))* Oxford Univ. Pr., Inc.

Holland, Carol A. & Farkas, Daniel H. DNA from A to Z & Back Again: A Primer on Genomics & Molecular Medicine For...everyone. 2008. *(978-1-59425-088-0(X)*, AACC Pr.) American Assn. for Clinical Chemistry, Inc.

Indge, Bill. A-Z Biology Handbook. 4th ed. 2010. (Illus.). 320p. 22.99 *(978-0-340-99099-5(6))* Hodder Education GBR. Dist: Oxford Univ. Pr., Inc.

Lackie, John M., ed. Dictionary of Cell & Molecular Biology. 4th ed. 2007. (ENG.). 472p. pap. 81.95 *(978-0-12-373986-5(1)*, Academic Pr.) Elsevier Science & Technology Bks.

Lawrence, Eleanor. Henderson's Dictionary of Biology. (ENG., Illus.). 776p. (C). 14th ed. 2008. pap. 41.60 *(978-0-321-50579-8(4))* 15th rev. ed. 2011. pap. 60.67 *(978-1-4082-3430-3(0))* Benjamin-Cummings Publishing Co.

Moore, Randy & Decker, Mark D. More Than Darwin: An Encyclopedia of the People & Places of the Evolution-Creationism Controversy, 1 vol. 2008. (Illus.). 448p. 85.00 *(978-0-313-34155-7(9)*, GR4155, Greenwood Pr.) Greenwood Publishing Group, Inc.

Patargias. English-Greek Dictionary of Biology & Medical Terms. (ENG & GRE.). 413p. pap. 95.00 *(978-0-7859-9051-2(8))* French & European Pubns., Inc.

BIOLOGY—ECOLOGY

see Ecology

BIOLOGY—EXAMINATIONS, QUESTIONS, ETC.

Allott, Andrew. Biology for the IB Diploma. 2nd ed. 2007. (International Baccalaureate Course Companions Ser.). (ENG., Illus.). 224p. (YA). pupil's gde. ed. 42.00 *(978-0-19-915143-1(1))* Oxford Univ. Pr., Inc.

Allott, Andrew & Mindorff, David. Biology. 2nd ed. 2010. (International Baccalaureate Ser.). (ENG., Illus.). 448p. (YA). pap. 42.00 *(978-0-19-913956-9(3))* Oxford Univ. Pr., Inc.

Anestis, Mark. AP Biology 2012. 4th ed. 2011. (5 Steps to a 5 on the Advanced Placement Examinations Ser.). (ENG.). pap. 27.95 incl. cd-rom *(978-0-07-175183-4(1)*, 0071751831) McGraw-Hill Cos., The.

—AP Biology 2012-2013. 4th ed. 2011. (5 Steps to a 5 on the Advanced Placement Examinations Ser.). (ENG., Illus.). 384p. (C). pap. 18.95 *(978-0-07-175179-7(3)*, 0071751793) McGraw-Hill Cos., The.

Biology. Date not set. (Advanced Placement Test Ser.). pap. 29.95 *(978-0-8373-6202-1(4)*, AP-2) National Learning Corp.

Boyle, Mike. AQA GCSE Biology. 2011. (My Revision Notes Ser.). 94p. pap. 19.95 ***(978-1-4441-2083-7(2))*** Hodder Education GBR. Dist: Trans-Atlantic Pubns., Inc.

Callihan, Laurie Ann. CLEP Biology w/CD-ROM. 2nd ed. 2011. (CLEP Test Preparation Ser.). (ENG.). 304p. (C). pap. 34.95 *(978-0-7386-0890-7(4))* Research & Education Assn.

Callihan, Laurie Ann, et al. AP Biology. 8th ed. 2009. (Advanced Placement (AP) Test Preparation Ser.). (ENG.). 496p. (gr. 12-12). pap. 24.95 *(978-0-7386-0786-3(X))* Research & Education Assn.

Campton, John. Biology: Molecules & Cells. 2010. (Illus.). 110p. (gr. 10-12). pap. 27.50 *(978-0-340-99193-0(3))* Hodder Education GBR. Dist: Trans-Atlantic Pubns., Inc.

Clamp, Alan. A2 Biology. 2009. (Illus.). 204p. pap. 13.95 *(978-0-340-99231-9(X))* Hodder Education GBR. Dist: Trans-Atlantic Pubns., Inc.

Clamp, Alan & Jones, Mary. Biology: The Natural Environment & Species Survival. 2009. 96p. pap., stu. ed. 22.50 *(978-0-340-94831-6(0))* Hodder Education GBR. Dist: Trans-Atlantic Pubns., Inc.

—Edexcel AS Biology: Development, Plants & the Environment. 2009. 80p. pap., stu. ed., instr.'s gde. ed. 22.50 *(978-0-340-94830-9(2))* Hodder Education GBR. Dist: Trans-Atlantic Pubns., Inc.

—Edexcel As Biology Unit 1: Lifestyle, Transport, Genes & Health. 2009. 96p. pap., stu. ed., instr.'s gde. ed. 22.50 *(978-0-340-94829-3(9))* Hodder Education GBR. Dist: Trans-Atlantic Pubns., Inc.

Clegg, C. J. IB Diploma Biology. 2007. (Illus.). 448p. pap. 92.50 *(978-0-340-92652-9(X)*, Hodder Murray) Hodder Education GBR. Dist: Trans-Atlantic Pubns., Inc.

Demers, David, et al. Biology: Core Tips. 4th ed. 2009. (ENG.). 208p. (C). pap., pupil's gde. ed. 15.00 net. *(978-0-393-93308-6(3)*, 93308) Norton, W. W. & Co., Inc.

Doltar, Robert, et al. Preparing for the AP Biology Examination: Fast Track to A 5. 2012. (ENG.). 339p. pap. 18.99 ***(978-1-4354-6124-6(X))*** Course Technology.

Fosbery, Richard. Biology: Communication, Homeostasis & Energy. 2009. (Illus.). 112p. pap., stu. ed. 22.50 *(978-0-340-95813-1(8))* Hodder Education GBR. Dist: Trans-Atlantic Pubns., Inc.

—Biology: Control, Genomes & Environment. 2010. (Illus.). 112p. pap. 22.50 *(978-0-340-95814-8(6))* Hodder Education GBR. Dist: Trans-Atlantic Pubns., Inc.

—OCR AS Biology. 2008. pap. 22.50 *(978-0-340-95811-7(1))* Hodder Education GBR. Dist: Trans-Atlantic Pubns., Inc.

—OCR as Biology: Molecules Biodiversity Food & Health. 2009. 112p. pap. 22.50 *(978-0-340-95812-4(X))* Hodder Education GBR. Dist: Trans-Atlantic Pubns., Inc.

Gilman, Michelle Rose, et al. AP Biology for Dummies. 2008. (ENG., Illus.). 362p. per. 16.99 *(978-0-470-22487-8(8)*, For Dummies) Wiley, John & Sons, Inc.

Goldberg, Deborah T. Barron's AP Biology. 3rd rev. ed. 2010. (ENG.). 576p. pap. 18.99 *(978-0-7641-4051-8(5))* Barron's Educational Series, Inc.

—Barron's AP Biology with CD-ROM. 3rd rev. ed. 2010. (ENG.). 576p. 29.99 *(978-0-7641-9524-2(7))* Barron's Educational Series, Inc.

Goldberg M.S., Deborah T. Barron's AP Biology: 500 Flash Cards. 2nd rev. ed. 2011. (ENG.). 492p. 18.99 *(978-0-7641-6265-7(9))* Barron's Educational Series, Inc.

—Barron's SAT Subject Test: Biology E/M with CD-ROM, 3rd Edition. 3rd rev. ed. 2011. (ENG.). 408p. pap. 24.99 *(978-1-4380-7079-7(9))* Barron's Educational Series, Inc.

—Barron's SAT Subject Test: Biology E/M, 3rd Edition. 3rd rev. ed. 2011. (ENG.). 408p. pap. 16.99 *(978-0-7641-4614-5(9))* Barron's Educational Series, Inc.

Gorlin, Alan. Preparing for the Georgia End of Course Test in Biology. 2007. (YA). pap. *(978-1-56765-912-2(8)*, R579W) AMSCO Schl. Pubns., Inc.

GRE Subject Exam Secrets Test Prep Staff, ed. GRE Biology Test Flashcard Study System: GRE Subject Exam Practice Questions & Review for the Graduate Record Examination. 2011. (C). 62.99 *(978-1-61403-554-1(7))* Mometrix Media LLC.

Gregory, Linda & Research and Education Association Staff. GRE Biology with TestWare. 6th ed. 2010. (GRE Test Preparation Ser.). 400p. (C). pap. 29.95 *(978-0-7386-0835-8(1))* Research & Education Assn.

Gross, Lauren. SAT Biology E/M Crash Course (REA) 2012. (SAT PSAT ACT (College Admission) Prep Ser.). 224p. (YA). (gr. 11-12). pap. 12.95 ***(978-0-7386-1033-7(X))*** Research & Education Assn.

Hunter, G. Scott. Biology, the Living Environment. 5th rev. ed. 2009. (Let's Review Ser.). (ENG.). 480p. pap. 13.99 *(978-0-7641-4018-1(3))* Barron's Educational Series, Inc.

Indge, Bill & Clamp, Alan. As/A-Level Biology. 2nd ed. 2009. (Exam Revision Notes Ser.). (Illus.). 144p. pap. 32.50 *(978-0-340-95860-5(X))* Hodder Education GBR. Dist: Trans-Atlantic Pubns., Inc.

Johnson, A. Daniel. 40 Inquiry Exercises for the College Biology Lab. 2009. (ENG., Illus.). 514p. pap. 34.95 *(978-1-933531-39-7(8))* National Science Teachers Assn.

Jones, Mary. As/A Level Biology. 2nd rev. ed. 2007. (Cambridge International Examinations Ser.). (ENG., Illus.). 424p. pap. 41.00 *(978-0-521-70306-2(9))* Cambridge Univ. Pr.

—Biology. rev. ed. 2010. 256p. pap. 42.50 *(978-1-4441-1267-2(8))* Hodder Education GBR. Dist: Trans-Atlantic Pubns., Inc.

Jones, Mary & Jones, Geoff. Cambridge IGCSE Biology Workbook. 2nd rev. ed. 2010. (Cambridge International Examinations Ser.). (ENG., Illus.). 96p. pap. 17.00 *(978-0-521-12443-0(3))* Cambridge Univ. Pr.

Kaplan. Kaplan SAT Subject Test Biology E/M 2011-2012. 2011. (Kaplan SAT Subject Test Ser.). (ENG.). 384p. pap. 18.99 *(978-1-60714-868-5(4))* Kaplan Publishing.

—KTPA MCAT Biology. 2010. (ENG.). 464p. pap. 45.00 *(978-1-60714-823-4(4))* Kaplan Publishing.

Kaplan Higher Education Staff. Kaplan MCAT Biology Review. 2010. (ENG.). 560p. pap. 45.00 *(978-1-60714-643-8(6))* Kaplan Publishing.

Kaplan Publishing Staff, ed. Biology. 5th ed. 2010. (ENG.). 456p. pap. 20.00 *(978-1-4195-5000-3(4))* Kaplan Publishing.

Kaplan Testprep, Neil A., et al. MCAT/GRE Kaplan Biology Test Preparation Guide for Biology. 2nd ed. 2008. (ENG.). 72p. (C). pap. 29.60 *(978-0-321-53463-7(8))* Benjamin-Cummings Publishing Co.

Kettering, James D. Microbiology PreTest Self-Assessment & Review 13th Edition. 13th ed. 2010. (PreTest Basic Science Ser.). (ENG., Illus.). 400p. pap. 33.00 *(978-0-07-162335-3(3)*, 0071623353) McGraw-Hill Medical Publishing Div.

Leather, Harry & Leather, Jan. Cambridge Checkpoints VCE Biology Unit 4 2007. 2006. (Cambridge Checkpoints Ser.). pap. 21.95 *(978-0-521-69793-4(X))* Cambridge Univ. Pr.

—Cambridge Checkpoints VCE Biology Unit 4 2008. 2007. (Cambridge Checkpoints Ser.). pap. 19.95 *(978-0-521-71710-6(8))* Cambridge Univ. Pr.

Lebitz, Mina & Evangelist, Thomas A. AP Biology Questions to Know by Test Day. 2010. (5 Steps to a 5 on the Advanced Placement Examinations Ser.). (ENG., Illus.). 176p. (C). pap. 14.00 *(978-0-07-174201-6(8)*, 0071742018) McGraw-Hill Cos., The.

Lebsack, Stephen, et al. Discover Biology. 4th ed. 2009. (ENG.). 304p. (C). pap., pupil's gde. ed. 21.00 net. *(978-0-393-93307-9(5)*, 93307) Norton, W. W. & Co., Inc.

LinguaForum Research Center Staff. Biology, Archeology, & Anthropology Vol. 3, Vol. 3. 2007. (TOEFL Practice Test Ser.). (ENG., Illus.). 159p. pap. *(978-89-556-3091-6(3))* Linguaforum Co., Ltd.

Mader, Sylvia S. Biology. 10th ed. 2009. *(978-0-07-352543-3(X))* McGraw-Hill Cos., The.

Miller, Toby & Levin. Biology Optical Data Correlation. pap. *(978-0-13-084211-4(7))* Prentice Hall (Schl. Div.).

Moulton, Glen E. CliffsNotes Praxis II: Biology Content Knowledge (0235) 2012. (ENG.). 240p. pap. 26.99 ***(978-1-118-07497-8(1)***, Cliff Notes) Wiley, John & Sons, Inc.

ORELA Exam Secrets Test Prep Staff, ed. ORELA Biology Flashcard Study System: ORELA Test Practice Questions & Exam Review for the Oregon Educator Licensure Assessments. 2011. (C). 62.99 *(978-1-61403-632-6(2))* Mometrix Media LLC.

—ORELA Biology Secrets Study Guide: ORELA Test Review for the Oregon Educator Licensure Assessments. 2011. (C). 62.99 *(978-1-61403-631-9(4))* Mometrix Media LLC.

Pack, Phillip E. Biology. 3rd ed. 2009. (ENG., Illus.). 360p. pap. 29.99 *(978-0-470-40035-7(8)*, Cliff Notes) Wiley, John & Sons, Inc.

—CliffsAP 5 Biology Practice Exams. 2006. (ENG., Illus.). 192p. pap. 16.99 *(978-0-471-77027-5(2)*, Cliff Notes) Wiley, John & Sons, Inc.

—CliffsAP Biology. 3rd rev. ed. 2007. (ENG., Illus.). 360p. pap. 16.99 *(978-0-470-09764-9(7)*, Cliff Notes) Wiley, John & Sons, Inc.

Passing the Georgia End of Course Test in Biology. 2007. per. 23.00 *(978-1-59807-134-4(3))* American Bk. Co.

Passing the Tennessee Gateway in Biology. 2007. per. 23.00 *(978-1-59807-122-1(X))* American Bk. Co.

Pfirrmann, Cynthia. Barron's New Jersey Biology Competency Test. 2012. (ENG.). 400p. pap. 16.99 *(978-0-7641-4378-6(6))* Barron's Educational Series, Inc.

Potter, S. AQA (A) A2 Biology. 2009. (Illus.). 312p. pap. 59.50 *(978-1-84489-218-1(2))* Hodder Education GBR. Dist: Trans-Atlantic Pubns., Inc.

Potter, Steve. Aqa As Biology. 2008. pap., stu. ed., instr.'s gde. ed. 22.50 *(978-0-340-94950-4(3))* Hodder Education GBR. Dist: Trans-Atlantic Pubns., Inc.

—AQA AS Biology: The Variety of Living Organisms. 2009. 96p. pap., stu. ed., instr.'s gde. ed. 22.50 *(978-0-340-94951-1(1))* Hodder Education GBR. Dist: Trans-Atlantic Pubns., Inc.

—Biology. 2008. 312p. pap. 59.50 *(978-0-340-95764-6(6))*; (Illus.). 113p. tchr. ed., spiral bd. 159.50 *(978-0-340-95765-3(4))* Hodder Education GBR. Dist: Trans-Atlantic Pubns., Inc.

Princeton Review. Cracking the AP Biology Exam, 2013 Edition. 2012. (College Test Preparation Ser.). (ENG.). 384p. pap. 18.99 ***(978-0-307-94508-2(1)***, Princeton Review) Random Hse. Information Group.

Princeton Review Staff. Cracking the AP Biology Exam, 2012 Edition. 2011. (College Test Preparation Ser.). (ENG.). 384p. pap. 18.99 *(978-0-375-42725-1(2)*, Princeton Review) Random Hse. Information Group.

—Cracking the SAT Biology E/M Subject Test, 2011-2012 Edition. 2011. (College Test Preparation Ser.). (ENG.). 480p. pap. 19.99 *(978-0-375-42810-4(0)*, Princeton Review) Random Hse. Information Group.

—Essential AP Biology (flashcards) 2010. (College Test Preparation Ser.). (ENG.). 450p. 18.99 *(978-0-375-42803-6(8)*, Princeton Review) Random Hse. Information Group.

Printed Test File. 108.20 *(978-0-7167-5815-0(6))* Freeman, W. H. & Co.

Ramesar, Myda, et al. Biology Unit 1 for CAPE Examinations. 2011. (ENG.). 288p. pap. 50.00 *(978-0-521-17690-3(5))* Cambridge Univ. Pr.

—Biology Unit 2 for CAPE(r) Examinations. 2011. (ENG., Illus.). 320p. pap. 36.00 *(978-0-521-17691-0(3))* Cambridge Univ. Pr.

REA Staff, et al. Praxis II Biology 0235 with TestWare. 2010. (PRAXIS Teacher Certification Test Prep Ser.). (ENG.). 272p. (C). pap. 39.95 *(978-0-7386-0774-0(6))* Research & Education Assn.

Redshaw, Nick & Bethan. 123 - PSYA3 Biological Rhythms, Perception & Relationships. 2010. 119p. pap. 27.50 *(978-1-4457-7368-1(6))* Lulu Enterprises Inc.

—124 - PSYA3 Biological Rhythms, Perception & Aggression. 2010. 120p. pap. 27.50 *(978-1-4457-7343-8(0))* Lulu Enterprises Inc.

—125 - PSYA3 Biological Rhythms, Perception & Eating Behaviour. 2010. 109p. pap. 27.50 *(978-1-4457-7397-1(X))* Lulu Enterprises Inc.

—126 - PSYA3 Biological Rhythms, Perception & Gender. 2010. 108p. pap. 27.50 *(978-1-4457-8989-7(2))* Lulu Enterprises Inc.

—134 - PSYA3 Biological Rhythms, Relationships & Aggression. 2010. 131p. pap. 27.50 *(978-1-4457-7475-6(5))* Lulu Enterprises Inc.

—135 - PSYA3 Biological Rhythms, Relationships & Eating Behaviour. 2010. 122p. pap. 27.50 *(978-1-4457-7759-7(2))* Lulu Enterprises Inc.

—138 - PSYA3 Biological Rhythms, Relationships, Cognition & Development. 2010. 125p. pap. 27.50 *(978-1-4461-4260-8(4))* Lulu Enterprises Inc.

—145 PSYA 3 - Biological Rhythms, Aggression & Eating Behaviour. 2010. 121p. pap. 27.50 *(978-1-4457-7363-6(5))* Lulu Enterprises Inc.

—146 - PSYA3 Biological Rhythms, Aggression & Gender. 2010. 121p. pap. 27.50 *(978-1-4457-7349-0(X))* Lulu Enterprises Inc.

—148 - PSYA3 Biological Rhythms, Aggression, Cognition & Development. 2010. 124p. pap. 27.50 *(978-1-4461-4255-4(8))* Lulu Enterprises Inc.

Research & Education Association, creator. The Best Test Preparation for the GRE Biology Test. 5th ed. 2007. (Test Preps Ser.). (ENG., Illus.). 400p. (C). pap. 32.95 *(978-0-7386-0361-2(9))* Research & Education Assn.

Roberts, Anna & Sinclair, Maria. Biology Workbook AME Scholarship Year 13. 2007. (YA). per. *(978-1-877401-91-6(9))* ESA Pubns. (NZ), Ltd.

Rudman, Jack. Area Examination - Biological Sciences. (Graduate Record Examination Ser.: Vol. 41). 49.95 *(978-0-8373-5291-6(6))* National Learning Corp.

—Biology. (Graduate Record Examination Ser.: Vol. 1). 49.95 *(978-0-8373-5251-0(7))*; (Undergraduate Program Field Tests Ser.: Vol. 2). 49.95 *(978-0-8373-6052-2(8)*, Passbooks); (Regents College Proficiency Examination Ser.: Vol. 5). (C). 49.95 *(978-0-8373-5455-2(2)*, Passbooks) National Learning Corp.

—General Biology. (College Level Examination Ser.: Vol. 5). (C). 49.95 *(978-0-8373-5355-5(6)*, Passbooks) National Learning Corp.

Sadava. Life: The Science of Biology. 9th ed. 2009. (ENG.). ring bd. 118.25 ***(978-1-4641-0124-3(8))*** Worth Pubs., Inc.

Sadava & Sadava, David E. Life: The Science of Biology, 2 vols. 9th ed. 3911. (Illus.). *(978-1-4292-3590-7(X)*, Branch Line Video) Freeman, W. H. & Co.

Sadava, et al. Life: The Science of Biology. 2010. (ENG.). pap. 214.75 *(978-1-4292-7765-5(3))*; 9th ed. pap. 197.25 *(978-1-4292-7768-6(8))* Freeman, W. H. & Co.

Sadava, David, et al. Student Study Guide for Life: The Science of Biology, 2 vols. 9th rev. ed. (Illus.). 500p. pap. *(978-1-4292-3569-3(1)*, Conran Octopus) Freeman, W. H. & Co.

SAT Subject Exam Secrets Test Prep Staff, ed. SAT Biology E/M Subject Test Flashcard Study System: SAT Subject Exam Practice Questions & Review for the SAT Subject Test. 2011. 62.99 *(978-1-61403-723-1(X))* Mometrix Media LLC.

Simon, Eric J., et al. Study Guide for Campbell Essential Biology (with Physiology Chapters) 4th ed. 2009. (ENG.). 480p. (C). pap. 57.07 *(978-0-321-64253-0(8))* Benjamin-Cummings Publishing Co.

Solomon, Eldra, et al. Study Guide for Solomon/Berg/Martin's Biology, 9th. 9th ed. 2010. (ENG.). 592p. (C). pap. 80.95 *(978-0-538-73167-6(2))* Brooks/Cole.

Spark Publishing Staff, contrib. by. SparkNotes AP Biology. 2008. (Illus.). xi, 452p. *(978-1-4114-0927-9(2))* Spark Publishing Group.

Stabler, Linda Brooke, et al. Kaplan AP Biology 2012. 2011. (Kaplan AP Ser.). (ENG.). 336p. pap. 17.99 *(978-1-60978-061-6(2))* Kaplan Publishing.

Stewart, Robert. McGraw-Hill's 500 MCAT Biology Questions to Know by Test Day. 2012. (ENG., Illus.). 192p. (C). pap. 25.00 ***(978-0-07-178273-9(7)***, 0071782737) McGraw-Hill Cos., The.

Stewart, Robert. My Max Score AP Biology: Maximize Your Score in Less Time. 2012. (My Max Score Ser.). (ENG.). 432p. pap. 14.99 *(978-1-4022-4315-8(4))* Sourcebooks, Inc.

The DeaNeil Institute. SAT II in Biology E/M, Math IIC & Writing. 2007. 276p. pap. 24.95 *(978-1-4303-1051-8(0))* Lulu Enterprises Inc.

—SAT II in Math Level I, Biology E/M & Writing. 2007. 272p. pap. 24.95 *(978-1-4303-1123-2(1))* Lulu Enterprises Inc.

Thompson, Liz A. Passing the North Carolina End of Course Test for Biology. 2007. per. 23.00 *(978-1-59807-139-9(4))* American Bk. Co.

Vivion, Nichole. AP Biology Flashcards. 2008. (ENG.). 1000p. pap. 19.99 *(978-0-470-28281-6(9)*, Cliff Notes) Wiley, John & Sons, Inc.

—CliffsNotes AP Biology Flashcards. 2008. 14.99 *(978-0-470-39260-7(6)*, Cliff Notes) Wiley, John & Sons, Inc.

W. W. Norton. Study Guide: For Discover Biology, Fifth Core Edition. 2012. (ENG.). 162p. (C). pap. 18.00 net. ***(978-0-393-91854-0(8)***, 91854) Norton, W. W. & Co., Inc.

—Study Guide: For Discover Biology, Fifth Edition. 2012. (ENG.). 240p. (C). pap. 24.00 net. ***(978-0-393-91851-9(3)***, 91851) Norton, W. W. & Co., Inc.

Walpole, Brenda, et al. Biology for the IB Diploma Coursebook. 2011. (Ib Ser.). (ENG.). 608p. pap. 50.00 *(978-0-521-17178-6(4))* Cambridge Univ. Pr.

Williams, Gareth. Top Biology Grades for You: GCSE Revision Guide for AQA. 2006. (ENG., Illus.). 120p. pap. 17.95 *(978-0-7487-8378-6(4))* Nelson Thomes Ltd. GBR. Dist: Trans-Atlantic Pubns., Inc.

Wynne, Sharon. GACE Biology 026, 027. 2008. (Xam Gace Ser.). (ENG.). 202p. pap., pupil's gde. ed. 64.95 *(978-1-58197-773-8(5))* XAMonline, Inc.

—Mtel Biology. 2008. (Xam Mtel Ser.). (ENG.). 192p. pap. 64.95 *(978-1-58197-687-8(9))* XAMonline, Inc.

Wynne, Sharon A. Praxis Biology 0231, 0233 0235. 3rd rev. ed. 2010. (Xam Praxis Ser.). (ENG.). 246p. pap. 38.45 *(978-1-60787-066-1(5))* XAMonline, Inc.

BIOLOGY—EXPERIMENTS

see also Biology, Experimental

Bablanian, Gayne. Biological Investigations. rev. ed. 2010. (ENG.). 212p. spiral bd. 83.14 *(978-0-7575-0337-5(3))* Kendall Hunt Publishing Co.

Biology with Vernier. 2007. spiral bd. 45.00 *(978-1-929075-43-0(X))* Vernier Software & Technology.

Camden County College Staff. Exploring Biology in the Lab. rev. ed. 2010. (ENG.). 238p. spiral bd. 42.58 *(978-0-7575-3553-6(4))* Kendall Hunt Publishing Co.

Devine, Edward & Bernard, Gretchen. Biological Investigations I: Lab Exercises for General Biology I. 13th rev. ed. 2011. (ENG.). 166p. spiral bd. 29.99 ***(978-0-7575-8950-8(2))*** Kendall Hunt Publishing Co.

—Biological Investigations Ii: Lab Exercises for General Biology. 13th rev. ed. 2011. (ENG.). 166p. spiral bd. 29.99 ***(978-0-7575-8951-5(0))*** Kendall Hunt Publishing Co.

Eversman, Sharon & Johnson, Carol. Molecular & Cellular Biology: Laboratory Observations in Biology 102. 4th rev. ed. 2011. (ENG.). 86p. spiral bd. 38.01 *(978-0-7575-1321-3(2))* Kendall Hunt Publishing Co.

Fcas-Mst, et al. Lab Experiments for Introductory Biology. Keith, ed. rev. ed. 2010. (ENG.). 224p. spiral bd. 54.95 *(978-0-7575-7895-3(0))* Kendall Hunt Publishing Co.

Katoch, Rajan. Analytical Techniques in Biochemistry & Molecular Biology. 2011. (ENG., Illus.). xviii, 441p. 209.00 *(978-1-4419-9784-5(9)*, 1441997849) Springer.

Lacey, Lawrence A. & Kaya, Harry K. Field Manual of Techniques in Invertebrate Pathology: Application & Evaluation of Pathogens for Control of Insects & Other Invertebrate Pests. 2nd ed. 2007. (Illus.). 868p. pap. 129.00 *(978-1-4020-5932-2(9))* Springer.

Montgomery College. Bio 107 Laboratory Exercises: Principles of Biology I. 3rd rev. ed. 2008. (ENG.). 182p. pap. 20.61 (978-0-7575-1752-5(8), 0757517528) Kendall Hunt Publishing Co.

Thompson, Robert Bruce & Thompson, Barbara Fritchman. Illustrated Guide to Home Biology Experiments: All Lab, No Lecture. 2012. (ENG., Illus.). 384p. pap. 34.99 (978-1-4493-9659-6(3)) O'Reilly Media, Inc.

Whitcher, Monlux & Carrer, L. Hands-on Hortscience Practical Investigations & Experimental Designs in Agriculture & Biology. rev. ed. 2010. (ENG., Illus.). ix, 153p. pap. 63.93 (978-0-7575-5296-0(X)) Kendall Hunt Publishing Co.

Wisconsin Fast Plants Program Staff. Bottle Biology. 2nd rev. ed. 2010. (ENG.). 136p. spiral bd. 40.57 (978-0-7575-0094-7(3)) Kendall Hunt Publishing Co.

BIOLOGY—FIELDWORK

see also Nature Study

Peckham, Irvin. Going North Thinking West: The INtersections of Social Class, Critical Thinking, & Politicized Writing Instruction. 2010. (ENG.). 184p. (gr. 14). pap. 24.95 (978-0-87421-804-6(7), Utah State Univ. Pr.) Univ. Pr. of Colorado.

Smith, Bruce L. Wildlife on the Wind: A Field Biologist's Journey & an Indian Reservation's Renewal. 2011. (Illus.). xii, 227p. pap. (978-0-87421-808-4(X)) 2010. (ENG.). 186p. (gr. 14). 29.95 (978-0-87421-791-9(1)) Univ. Pr. of Colorado. (Utah State Univ. Pr.).

BIOLOGY—HISTORY

Agutter, Paul S. & Wheatley, D. N. Thinking about Life: The History & Philosophy of Biology & Other Sciences. 2008. (Illus.). xiv, 274p. 54.95 (978-1-4020-8865-0(5)) Springer.

Bell, P. R., ed. Darwin's Biological Work: Some Aspects Reconsidered. 2012. (ENG.). 368p. pap. 47.99 (978-1-107-69715-7(8)) Cambridge Univ. Pr.

Bowler, Peter J. The Mendelian Revolution. (ENG., Illus.). 216p. 65.00 (978-0-485-11375-4(9)) Continuum International Publishing Group, Ltd. GBR. Dist: National Bk. Network.

Buican, Denis. Biologie: Histoire et Philosophie. 2010. (FRE.). 231p. (978-2-271-07022-7(3)) Editions du Centre National de la Recherche Scientifique.

Cain, Joe, et al. Descended from Darwin: Insights into the History of Evolutionary Studies, 1900-1970. 2009. (Illus.). xii, 360p. (978-1-60618-991-7(3)) American Philosophical Society.

Cairns, John. Phage & the Origins of Molecular Biology. Stent, Gunther S. & Watson, James D., eds. 2nd ed. 2007. (ENG., Illus.). 394p. 30.00 (978-0-87969-800-3(4)) Cold Spring Harbor Laboratory Pr.

Carroll, Sean B. Remarkable Creatures: Epic Adventures in the Search for the Origins of Species. 2009. (ENG., Illus.). 352p. pap. 14.95 (978-0-547-24778-6(8), Mariner Bks.); 26.00 (978-0-15-101485-9(X)) Houghton Mifflin Harcourt Trade & Reference Pubs.

Carroll, Sean B., et al. Into the Jungle: Great Adventures in the Search for Evolution. 2008. (ENG., Illus.). 224p. (C). pap. 24.60 (978-0-321-55671-4(2)) Benjamin-Cummings Publishing Co.

Committee on a New Biology for the 21st Century: Ensuring the United States Leads the Coming Biology Revolution & National Research Council. A New Biology for the 21st Century. 2009. (ENG.). 112p. pap. 29.75 (978-0-309-14488-9(4)) National Academies Pr.

Cosans, Christopher Ernest. Owen's Ape & Darwin's Bulldog: Beyond Darwinism & Creationism. 2009. (ENG., Illus.). 192p. 21.95 (978-0-253-35272-9(X), 025335272X) Indiana Univ. Pr.

Cosans, Christopher Ernest & Cosans, Christopher E. Owen's Ape & Darwin's Bulldog: Beyond Darwinism & Creationism. 2009. (ENG., Illus.). 192p. pap. 21.95 (978-0-253-22051-6(3), 0253220513) Indiana Univ. Pr.

Endersby, Jim. A Guinea Pig's History of Biology. 2009. Orig. Title: A Guinea Pig's History of Biology: the Plants & Animals Who Taught Us the Facts of Life. (Illus.). 544p. pap. 20.00 (978-0-674-03227-9(6)) Harvard Univ. Pr.

Harman, Oren Solomon & Dietrich, Michael, eds. Rebels, Mavericks, & Heretics in Biology. 2009. (Illus.). 416p. pap. 23.00 (978-0-300-15845-8(9)) Yale Univ. Pr.

James, Ioan. Remarkable Biologists: From Ray to Hamilton. 2009. (ENG., Illus.). 196p. 102.00 (978-0-521-87589-9(7)); pap. 48.99 (978-0-521-69918-1(5)) Cambridge Univ. Pr.

Kolchinskii, E. I. Biologiia Germanii I Rossii-SSSR V Usloviiakh Sotsialno-Politicheskikh Krizisov Pervoi Poloviny XX Veka: Mezhdu Liberalizmom, Kommunizmom I Natsional-Sotsializmom. 2007. (RUS., Illus.). 636p. (978-5-98187-172-6(5)) Nestor-Istorija, Izdatel'stvo Sankt-Peterburgskogo Instituta Istorii RAN.

Krementsov, Nikolai. A Martian Stranded on Earth: Alexander Bogdanov, Blood Transfusions, & Proletarian Science. 2011. (ENG., Illus.). 192p. 35.00 (978-0-226-45412-2(6)) Univ. of Chicago Pr.

Miller, Jonathan. Introducing Darwin. 2009. (ENG.). 176p. pap. 13.00 (978-1-4379-6572-8(5)) DIANE Publishing Co.

Pagel, W. William Harvey's Biological Ideas: Selected Aspects & Historical Background. (Illus.). 360p. (978-3-8055-0962-6(6)) Karger, S. AG.

Pietsch, Theodore W. Trees of Life: A Visual History of Evolution. 2012. (ENG., Illus.). 376p. (gr. 17). 69.95 (978-1-4214-0479-0(6)) Johns Hopkins Univ. Pr.

Rheinberger, Hans-Jörg. An Epistemology of the Concrete: Twentieth-Century Histories of Life. 2010. (ENG., Illus.). 352p. 89.95 (978-0-8223-4560-2(9)); pap. 24.95 (978-0-8223-4575-6(7)) Duke Univ. Pr.

Riedl, Rupert. Riedls Kulturgeschichte der Evolutionstheorie: Die Helden, ihre Irrungen und Einsichten. 2007. (GER., Illus.). XI, 236p. 59.95 (978-3-540-43668-3(5), 3540436685) Springer.

Seitler, Dana. Atavistic Tendencies: The Culture of Science in American Modernity. 2008. (Illus.). 320p. pap. 22.50 (978-0-8166-5124-5(8)) Univ. of Minnesota Pr.

Seitler, Dana & Seitler. Atavistic Tendencies: The Culture of Science in American Modernity. 2008. (Illus.). 320p. 67.50 (978-0-8166-5123-8(X)) Univ. of Minnesota Pr.

Vignais, Pierre V. & Vignais, Paulette. Discovering Life, Manufacturing Life: How the Experimental Method Shaped the Course of Life Sciences. 2010. Orig. Title: Science Expé(c)Rimentale et Connaissance du Vivant. la Mé(c)Thode et les Concepts. (ENG., Illus.). x, 418p. 159.00 (978-90-481-3766-4(7), 9048137667) Springer.

Williams, David M. & Ebach, Malte C. Foundations of Systematics & Biogeography. 2010. (ENG., Illus.). xviii, 310p. pap. 89.95 (978-1-4419-4445-0(1), 1441944451) Springer.

BIOLOGY—JUVENILE LITERATURE

Metz, Lorijo. What Can We Do about Invasive Species? 2009. (Protecting Our Planet Ser.). (Illus.). 24p. (YA). (gr. 2-5). 21.25 (978-1-4042-8084-7(7)) Rosen Publishing Group, Inc., The.

Meyers Taschenlexikon Biologie, 3 Baenden. (978-3-411-12003-1(7)) Bibliographisches Institut & F. A. Brockhaus AG DEU. Dist: I. b. d., Ltd.

Slade, Suzanne. Elements in Living Organisms. 2006. 28p. (gr. 3-7). pap. 21.25 (978-1-4358-3822-2(X), PowerKids Pr.) Rosen Publishing Group, Inc., The.

Snedden, Robert. Adaptation & Survival. 1 vol. 2012. (Web of Life Ser.). (ENG., Illus.). 48p. (gr. 6-10). pap. 8.99 (978-1-4109-4408-5(5), Raintree Freestyle) Heinemann-Raintree.

World Book, Inc Staff, contrib. by. What Living Things Need. 2010. (J). (978-0-7166-7744-4(X)) World Bk., Inc.

BIOLOGY—LABORATORIES

see Biological Laboratories

BIOLOGY—LABORATORY MANUALS

Abramoff. Lab Manual. pap., lab manual ed. 16.00 (978-0-7167-2634-0(3)) Freeman, W. H. & Co.

Allred, Sylvester & Benenati, Emma P. Principles of Biology: Biology 100 Laboratory Manual. 2nd rev. ed. 2011. (ENG.). 108p. spiral bd. 30.00 (978-0-7575-8667-5(8)) Kendall Hunt Publishing Co.

Audesirk, Gerald, et al. Biology: Life on Earth with Physiology. 9th ed. 2010. (ENG.). (C). E-Book, E-Book 114.67 (978-0-321-73655-0(9)) Benjamin-Cummings Publishing Co.

Awong-Taylor, Judy. Investigations in Biology: Lab Manual. 4th ed. 2009. (Illus.). iii, 140p. (978-1-4240-7464-8(9)) Course Technology.

Awua, Adolf Kofi. Preparation & Description of Solutions: In the Laboratory. 2011. 92p. pap. 11.95 (978-1-4502-7444-9(7)) iUniverse, Inc.

Barnby, Mark, et al. Introductory Biology Laboratory Manual. 3rd rev. ed. 2010. (ENG.). 220p. ring bd. 55.74 (978-0-7575-0852-3(9)) Kendall Hunt Publishing Co.

Biological Sciences Curriculum Studies Staff. Biological Perspectives: Thinking Biologically. 3rd rev. ed. 2010. (ENG.). 146p. pap., lab manua ed. 46.47 (978-0-7575-2573-5(3)) Kendall Hunt Publishing Co.

Biology Lab Book. 3rd ed. 2007. 412p. 26.50 (978-1-885380-61-6(5)) Suspended Animations.

Biology with Vernier. 2007. spiral bd. 45.00 (978-1-929075-43-0(X)) Vernier Software & Technology.

Biology Workshop Vol. 1: Living Things. 15.95 (978-1-55675-700-6(X)) Globe Fearon Educational Publishing.

Boise State University Biology Staff. Concepts of Biology Laboratory Manual. 5th rev. ed. 2011. (ENG.). 204p. ring bd. 31.16 (978-0-7575-6925-8(0)) Kendall Hunt Publishing Co.

Bonner, Philip & Hargreaves, Alan. Basic Bioscience Laboratory Techniques: A Pocket Guide. 2011. (ENG., Illus.). 232p. pap. 39.95 (978-0-470-74309-6(3), Wiley) Wiley, John & Sons, Inc.

Brader, Robert E. & Brader, Andrew B. Biology 185: Laboratory Manual & Student Study Guide. rev. ed. 2011. (ENG.). 140p. spiral bd. 54.99 (978-0-7575-7920-2(5)) Kendall Hunt Publishing Co.

Bres, Mimi & Weisshaar, Arnold. Thinking about Biology: An Introductory Laboratory Manual. (ENG., (C). 3rd ed. 2007. Illus.). 448p. per. 97.67 (978-0-13-230736-9(7)) 4th rev. ed. 2012. 456p. pap. 97.67 (978-0-321-79195-5(9)) Benjamin-Cummings Publishing Co.

Carluccio & Central Connecticut State Univ. General Biology. rev. ed. 2010. (ENG.). 130p. spiral bd., lab manual ed. 26.25 (978-1-60250-174-4(2)) Kendall Hunt Publishing Co.

Cates, Cathryn, et al. Laboratory Manual for Introductory Biology Human Biology & Zoology. 6th rev. ed. 2010. (ENG.). 316p. spiral bd. 58.50 (978-0-7575-7908-0(6)) Kendall Hunt Publishing Co.

Clark, Neil. Introduction to Biology: Lab Manual for Non-Majors. rev. ed. 2011. (ENG.). 49.70 (978-0-7575-7967-7(1)) Kendall Hunt Publishing Co.

Collin County Community College Staff. Biology 1406 & 1408 Lab Manual. rev. ed. 2010. (ENG.). 268p. spiral bd. 11.25 (978-0-7575-6510-6(7)) Kendall Hunt Publishing Co.

Crandall-Stotler, Barbara & Jacobson, Katherine. Bios: Process & Diversity: A Laboratory Manual for Biology. 5th rev. ed. 2010. (ENG.). 208p. spiral bd. 45.27 (978-0-7575-4897-0(0)) Kendall Hunt Publishing Co.

Cressey, Hillary. Introductory Biology I. rev. ed. 2007. (ENG.). 184p. spiral bd. 48.53 (978-0-7575-2155-3(X), 075752155X) Kendall Hunt Publishing Co.

Cunningham, Keith. Biology Laboratory Manual. 7th rev. ed. 2010. (ENG.). 366p. 46.70 (978-0-7575-8157-1(9)) Kendall Hunt Publishing Co.

Cunningham, Keith G. Biology Laboratory Manual. 6th rev. ed. 2010. (ENG.). 366p. spiral bd. 44.06 (978-0-7575-6154-2(3)) Kendall Hunt Publishing Co.

Davis Regents of the University of California Staff. Introductory Biology: Bis 2C Laboratory Manual. 2nd rev. ed. 2011. 296p. ring bd. 38.76 (978-0-7575-8769-6(0)) Kendall Hunt Publishing Co.

Davison, Paul G., et al. Introductory Biology Laboratory Manual. 3rd rev. ed. 2010. (ENG.). 124p. spiral bd. 45.22 (978-0-7575-0778-6(6)) Kendall Hunt Publishing Co.

Dearing, Stuart, et al. The Biology Experience: Laboratory Manual. 7th rev. ed. 2011. (ENG.). 334p. spiral bd. 51.36 (978-0-7872-1063-2(3)) Kendall Hunt Publishing Co.

Dept, Bio & Jayant. Laboratory Manual for Biology I. rev. ed. 2011. (ENG.). 262p. spiral bd. 38.95 (978-0-7575-9498-4(0)) Kendall Hunt Publishing Co.

Deschweinitz, Jean. Majors Biology Lab Manual. 2nd rev. ed. 2011. (ENG.). 302p. spiral bd. 61.95 (978-0-7575-7960-8(4)) Kendall Hunt Publishing Co.

Deschweinitz, Jean, et al. General College Biology Laboratory Manual. 2nd rev. ed. 2011. (ENG.). 286p. spiral bd. 57.00 (978-0-7575-8707-8(0)) Kendall Hunt Publishing Co.

Devine, Edward. Biological Investigations: Lab Exercises for General Biology. 12th rev. ed. 2010. (ENG.). 338p. spiral bd. 60.10 (978-0-7575-5298-4(6)) Kendall Hunt Publishing Co.

DiBartolomeis, Susan & Dept. of Biology, compiled by. Biology 100 - General Biology Laboratory Exercises, 5th Ed. 2011. (C). spiral bd. (978-1-60036-478-5(0)) Academx Publishing Services, Inc.

Dickson, Leon A., Jr. & Gordon, William. Biology 102 Lab Manual. rev. ed. 2012. (ENG.). 252p. spiral bd. 65.00 (978-0-7575-9051-1(9)) Kendall Hunt Publishing Co.

Dolphin, Warren, et al. Biological Investigations Lab Manual. 9th ed. 2010. (ENG., Illus.). 480p. (C). spiral bd. 132.33 (978-0-07-338305-7(8), 0073383058, McGraw-Hill Science, Engineering & Mathematics) McGraw-Hill Higher Education.

Egremy, Jose. Biology 1411 Lab Manual. rev. ed. 2008. (ENG.). 124p. spiral bd. 96.66 (978-0-7575-5206-9(4)) Kendall Hunt Publishing Co.

Eisenbach, Jamin & Winning, Robert S. BIOL 110 Laboratory Manual. 2008. (C). spiral bd. 19.73 (978-1-933377-15-5(1)) Huron Valley Printing & Imaging.

Elawad, et al. General Biology Laboratory Manual. rev. ed. 2009. (ENG.). 416p. spiral bd. 69.50 (978-1-60250-173-7(4)) Kendall Hunt Publishing Co.

Enger, Eldon & Ross, Frederick. Laboratory Manual Concepts in Biology. 14th ed. 2011. (ENG., Illus.). 304p. (C). spiral bd. 77.00 (978-0-07-729525-7(0), 0077295250, McGraw-Hill Science, Engineering & Mathematics) McGraw-Hill Higher Education.

Fisher. Biological Perspectives Lab Manual. rev. ed. 2011. (ENG.). 226p. spiral bd. 81.00 (978-0-7575-8955-3(3)) Kendall Hunt Publishing Co.

Fleckenstein, Stephen. Introduction to Biology Lab Manual. 2nd rev. ed. 2011. (ENG.). 114p. spiral bd. 37.51 (978-0-7575-8256-1(7)) Kendall Hunt Publishing Co.

Fleckenstein, Steven. Introduction to Biology Lab Manual Revised Printing. 2nd rev. ed. 2009. (ENG.). 114p. spiral bd. 37.00 (978-0-7575-5603-6(5)) Kendall Hunt Publishing Co.

Florence-Florence. Investigating Biology: The Unity of Life Lab Manual. rev. ed. 2011. (ENG.). 116p. spiral bd. 42.00 (978-0-7575-9144-0(2)) Kendall Hunt Publishing Co.

Florence, Paul. Exploring Biology: A Laboratory Manual for Introductory Biology. rev. ed. 2011. (ENG.). 58p. spiral bd. 40.00 (978-0-7575-9143-3(4)) Kendall Hunt Publishing Co.

Gamboa, George J. Experience Biology: Laboratory Manual. 3rd rev. ed. 2010. (ENG.). 106p. spiral bd. 43.13 (978-0-7575-3874-2(6)) Kendall Hunt Publishing Co.

Ghent, Cynthia & Gasparich, Gail. Biology: The Science of Life Laboratory Manual. rev. ed. 2011. (ENG.). 138p. spiral bd. 30.89 (978-0-7575-8141-0(2)) Kendall Hunt Publishing Co.

Gordon-Dickson. Biology 101 Lab Manual. rev. ed. 2011. (ENG.). 118p. spiral bd. 45.00 (978-0-7575-8985-0(5)) Kendall Hunt Publishing Co.

Grand Rapids Community College Staff. Experiencing Biology: A Laboratory Manual for Introductory Biology. 9th rev. ed. 2010. (ENG.). 208p. spiral bd. 43.13 (978-0-7575-6882-4(3)) Kendall Hunt Publishing Co.

Gunstream, Stanley E. Explorations in Basic Biology. 12th ed. 2011. (ENG., Illus.). 544p. (C). pap. 106.13 (978-0-321-72294-2(9)) Benjamin-Cummings Publishing Co.

—Explorations in Basic Biology. 11th ed. 2007. (ENG.). 528p. (C). pap. 103.00 (978-0-13-222913-5(7)) Prentice Hall PTR.

James, Roxie. Biology Concepts Lab Manual. 2nd rev. ed. 2008. (ENG.). 70p. spiral bd. 37.38 (978-0-7575-5415-5(6)) Kendall Hunt Publishing Co.

Jubenville, Robert B. & Thomas, Richard G. General Biology, Vols. I & II. 3rd rev. ed. 2010. (ENG.). 284p. spiral bd., lab manual ed. 60.37 (978-0-7575-5681-4(7)) Kendall Hunt Publishing Co.

Jubenville, Robert B., et al. Human Life Science Laboratory Manual: Biology 103. 2nd rev. ed. 2010. (ENG.). 152p. spiral bd. 45.33 (978-0-7575-0365-8(9)) Kendall Hunt Publishing Co.

Keeton, Robert, et al. Fundamentals of Biology. 2nd rev. ed. 2010. (ENG.). 120p. pap., lab manual ed. 65.49 (978-0-7575-3324-2(8)) Kendall Hunt Publishing Co.

Kilbourne, Jennifer & Montgomery, Laurie. Biology 110. 2nd rev. ed. 2011. (ENG.). 230p. spiral bd., lab manual ed. 37.00 (978-0-7575-8814-3(X)) Kendall Hunt Publishing Co.

Krilowicz, Beverly L. & Henter, Heather J. Laboratory Exercises in Animal Biology. rev. ed. 2010. (ENG.). 172p. spiral bd. 51.61 (978-0-7872-6503-8(9)) Kendall Hunt Publishing Co.

Krogh, David & Brigham Young University. Biology: A Guide to the Natural World. 5th ed. 2010. (ENG.). (C). E-Book, E-Book 114.67 (978-0-321-73644-4(3)) Benjamin-Cummings Publishing Co.

Lab Manual for Muskavitch/Roche's Biology. 2009. (C). pap. 33.95 (978-0-534-99887-5(9)) Brooks/Cole.

Laboratory Investigations. 2nd ed. 2007. 368p. 33.00 (978-1-885380-63-0(1)) Suspended Animations.

Lawson, Anton. Biology: An Inquiry Approach Laboratory Manual. rev. ed. 2010. (ENG.). 144p. spiral bd. 35.38 (978-0-7575-6441-3(0)) Kendall Hunt Publishing Co.

Lisenbee, Cayle & Olson, John. Biology: Exploring Its Applications Lab Manual. rev. ed. 2011. (ENG.). 98p. spiral bd., lab manual ed. 35.00 (978-0-7575-6624-0(3)) Kendall Hunt Publishing Co.

Littlejohn, Robert O., et al. Foundations of Biology: Laboratory Studies in Biology. 2nd rev. ed. 2010. (ENG.). 116p. pap. 55.34 (978-0-7575-2324-3(2), 0757523242) Kendall Hunt Publishing Co.

Lynn, Les M. Environmental Biology & Ecology Laboratory Manual. 5th rev. ed. 2010. (ENG.). 144p. spiral bd. 64.54 (978-0-7575-7728-4(8)) Kendall Hunt Publishing Co.

Mader, Sylvia. Lab manual Biology. 10th ed. 2009. (ENG., Illus.). 544p. (C). spiral bd. 120.33 (978-0-07-722617-6(8), 0077226178, McGraw-Hill Science, Engineering & Mathematics) McGraw-Hill Higher Education.

—Lab Manual Concepts of Biology. 2nd ed. 2010. (ENG., Illus.). 392p. (C). spiral bd. 108.00 (978-0-07-729733-6(4), 0077297334, McGraw-Hill Science, Engineering & Mathematics) McGraw-Hill Higher Education.

Mader, Sylvia S. Lab Manual t/a Concepts of Biology. 2008. (ENG., Illus.). 392p. (C). spiral bd. 108.00 (978-0-07-329200-7(1), 0073292001, McGraw-Hill Science, Engineering & Mathematics) McGraw-Hill Higher Education.

Maly, Ivan. Systems Biology. Maly, Ivan V., ed. 2009. (Methods in Molecular Biology Ser.). (ENG., Illus.). xii, 500p. 129.00 (978-1-934115-64-0(9)) Humana Pr.

Martin, Jim & Lawrence, Linda. Biology 101 Laboratory Manual. rev. ed. 2010. (ENG.). 118p. spiral bd. 29.83 (978-0-7575-5752-1(X)) Kendall Hunt Publishing Co.

Minocha, Subhash. Principles of Biology Laboratory Manual. 2nd rev. ed. 2009. (ENG.). 76p. spiral bd. 37.00 (978-0-7575-4577-1(7)) Kendall Hunt Publishing Co.

Mollick, Ronald S. Biological Sciences in the Laboratory. 2006. (C). spiral bd. (978-1-60036-014-5(9)) Academx Publishing Services, Inc.

Montgomery College. Biology 101 Lab Manual. 2nd rev. ed. 2010. (ENG.). 190p. pap. 36.56 (978-0-7575-4689-1(7)) Kendall Hunt Publishing Co.

Morgan, Judith Giles & Carter, M. Eloise Brown. Investigating Biology Laboratory Manual. 7th ed. 2010. 162.00 (978-0-321-67668-9(8)) Benjamin-Cummings Publishing Co.

Morgan, Judith Giles, et al. Investigating Biology Lab Manual. 6th ed. 2007. (ENG.). 816p. (C). spiral bd. 123.60 (978-0-321-53660-0(6)) Benjamin-Cummings Publishing Co.

Newell, Carrie. General Biology Bi 102C: Marine Biology Lecture/Lab Book. 2008. (ENG.). 482p. spiral bd. 158.58 (978-0-7575-5813-9(5)) Kendall Hunt Publishing Co.

Newsome, Joe. Biology 100 Laboratory Manual. 2nd rev. ed. 2009. (ENG.). 244p. spiral bd. 35.00 (978-0-7575-7007-0(0)) Kendall Hunt Publishing Co.

Ng, Kee Woei & Schantz, Jan-Thorsten. Manual for Primary Human Cell Culture, Vol. 1. 2nd ed. 2010. 212p. pap. 48.00 (978-981-283-477-5(X)) World Scientific Publishing Co., Inc.

North Carolina A and T State University Staff. Laboratory Manual for Biology 100. 2nd rev. ed. 2008. (ENG.). 164p. spiral bd. 45.27 (978-0-7575-3065-4(6)) Kendall Hunt Publishing Co.

North Carolina; University of. Laboratory Manual for Human Physiology: A Laboratory Manual for Students in Biology 277. 2nd rev. ed. 2011. (ENG.). 166p. spiral bd. 31.55 (978-0-7575-9265-2(1)) Kendall Hunt Publishing Co.

Parker, Bruce D. & Robbins, Robert. Experiences in Biology: Biology 1015 Laboratory Manual. 2nd rev. ed. 2010. (ENG.). 98p. spiral bd. 31.99 (978-0-7575-8047-5(5)) Kendall Hunt Publishing Co.

Paul, Florence & Florence, Annisa. Investigating Biology: The Diversity of Life Lab Manual. rev. ed. 2011. (ENG.). 178p. spiral bd. 45.00 (978-0-7575-9145-7(0)) Kendall Hunt Publishing Co.

Pentz, Lundy H. Cell Biology Laboratory Manual. rev. ed. 2009. (ENG.). 114p. spiral bd. 25.13 (978-1-60250-172-0(6)) Kendall Hunt Publishing Co.

Perry, Chris. Lab Manual for Biology 121. Date not set. pap., lab manual ed. 20.50 net. (978-0-534-32037-9(6)) Wadsworth.

Perry, James W., et al. Essentials Laboratory Exercises for General Biology: For Starr's Biology Texts. 5th ed. 2006. (ENG., Illus.). 408p. (C). spiral bd. 64.95 (978-0-495-31005-1(0)) Brooks/Cole.

—Laboratory Manual for General Biology. 5th rev. ed. 2006. (ENG.). 768p. (C). pap. 141.95 (978-0-534-38025-0(5)) Brooks/Cole.

Pfluger, Stacy & Hall, Taylor. Introductory Biology: A Laboratory Exploration of Life. 2011. (ENG.). 108p. ring bd. 37.00 (978-0-7575-9106-8(X)) Kendall Hunt Publishing Co.

Pilgrim, Judith A. & Pilgrim, Larry M. Laboratory Manual for Biology Majors. 3rd rev. ed. 2010. (ENG.). 182p. spiral bd. 68.73 (978-0-7575-6749-0(5)) Kendall Hunt Publishing Co.

Pratt, Catherine & Cressey, Hillary. Introductory Biology I Lab Manual. rev. ed. 2010. (ENG.). 164p. spiral bd. 51.88 (978-0-7575-4292-3(1)) Kendall Hunt Publishing Co.

B

—Introductory Biology II. rev. ed. 2010. (ENG.). 186p. spiral bd., lab manual ed. 48.64 *(978-0-7575-4921-2(7))* Kendall Hunt Publishing Co.

Priano, Michael, et al. Bio Logic: A Laboratory Manual for the Biological Sciences. 2nd rev. ed. (ENG.). 152p. 2011. spiral bd. 29.99 *(978-0-7575-7868-7(3))* 2009. spiral bd. 27.51 *(978-0-7575-5602-9(7))* Kendall Hunt Publishing Co.

Pu, Rongsun & Reid, H. Bruce. Principles of Biology: Laboratory Manual. 5th rev. ed. 2010. (ENG.). 174p. spiral bd. 41.70 *(978-0-7575-4622-8(6))* Kendall Hunt Publishing Co.

Ramsey, Jed J., et al. Laboratory Investigations in Biology. 5th rev. ed. 2010. (ENG.). 188p. spiral bd. 53.45 *(978-0-7872-1086-1(2))* Kendall Hunt Publishing Co.

Reece, Jane B., et al. Campbell Biology. 9th ed. 2010. (ENG.). (C). E-Book, E-Book 126.67 *(978-0-321-76600-7(8))* Benjamin-Cummings Publishing Co.

—Investigating Biology Lab Manual. 7th ed. 2010. (ENG., Illus.). 828p. (C). spiral bd. 120.80 *(978-0-321-66821-9(9))* Benjamin-Cummings Publishing Co.

Regents of U. of Cal, Davis. Introductory Biology: Bis 2C Laboratory Manual. 2nd rev. ed. 2012. (ENG.). 312p. ring bd. 36.76 ***(978-0-7575-9290-4(2))*** Kendall Hunt Publishing Co.

Regents of University of California Staff. Introductory Biology: Bis 2B Laboratory Manual. 2nd rev. ed. 2011. 208p. ring bd. 38.76 *(978-0-7575-8770-2(4))* Kendall Hunt Publishing Co.

Robbins, Laurie R. Field & Lab Biology for Elementary Teaching Majors. 2nd rev. ed. 2010. (ENG.). 258p. ring bd. 64.00 *(978-0-7575-5199-4(8))* Kendall Hunt Publishing Co.

Royt, Paulette W. & Andrykovitch, George. Biology of Microorganisms. 2nd rev. ed. 2010. (ENG.). 154p. spiral bd., lab manual ed. 55.81 *(978-0-7575-1650-4(5)*, 0757516505) Kendall Hunt Publishing Co.

Sagasti, Alessandra. Environmental Biology Laboratory Manual. rev. ed. 2011. (ENG.). 106p. spiral bd. 14.50 *(978-0-7575-7056-8(9))* Kendall Hunt Publishing Co.

Sharpe, James & Wong, Rachel, eds. Imaging in Developmental Biology: A Laboratory Manual. 2010. (Illus.). 888p. 246.00 *(978-0-87969-939-0(6))*; pap. 169.00 *(978-0-87969-940-6(X))* Cold Spring Harbor Laboratory Pr.

Solomon, et al. Laboratory Manual for Majors General Biology. 2008. (ENG.). 720p. (C). spiral bd. 141.95 *(978-0-495-11505-2(3))* Brooks/Cole.

Stein, Gary S., et al, eds. Human Stem Cell Technology & Biology: A Research Guide & Laboratory Manual. 2011. (ENG., Illus.). 419p. 146.95 *(978-0-470-59545-9(0)*, Wiley-Blackwell) Wiley, John & Sons, Inc.

Thazhath, Rupal. Biological Principles 1510 Lab Manual. rev. ed. 2009. (ENG.). 116p. spiral bd. 35.89 *(978-0-7575-5479-7(2))* Kendall Hunt Publishing Co.

Tschunko, Almuth. Plant Biology. 2006. (ENG.). 272p. (C). pap., lab manual ed. 65.80 *(978-0-13-143508-7(6)*, Prentice Hall) Prentice Hall PTR.

University of North Carolina Staff. Major Concepts of Biology Lab Manual. rev. ed. 2008. (ENG.). 156p. ring bd. 22.54 *(978-0-7575-4400-2(2))* Kendall Hunt Publishing Co.

University Of Texas Pan Am Staff. General Biology Laboratory Manual. 3rd rev. ed. 2010. (ENG.). 164p. spiral bd. 43.86 *(978-0-7575-3457-7(0))* Kendall Hunt Publishing Co.

Vodopich, Darrell. Biology Laboratory Manual. 9th ed. 2010. (Illus.). 608p. (C). spiral bd. 119.06 *(978-0-07-338306-4(6)*, 0073383066, McGraw-Hill Science, Engineering & Mathematics) McGraw-Hill Higher Education.

Vodopich, Darrell S. & Moore, Randy. Biology Laboratory Manual. 9th ed. 2010. (ENG.). (C). spiral bd., spiral bd. 140.00 *(978-0-07-738969-7(7)*, 0077389697, McGraw-Hill Science, Engineering & Mathematics) McGraw-Hill Higher Education.

Wade, Charles A. General Biology: Lecture & Laboratory Manual. 2nd rev. ed. 2010. (ENG.). 260p. spiral bd. 54.75 *(978-0-7575-2092-1(8)*, 0757520928) Kendall Hunt Publishing Co.

Walsh, et al. Organismal Biology 1108 Laboratory Manual. (ENG.). 134p. 2012. spiral bd. 34.00 ***(978-0-7575-9252-2(X))*** 2010. spiral bd. 32.21 *(978-0-7575-7099-5(2))* Kendall Hunt Publishing Co.

Walsh, Eileen. Explorations in General Biology Laboratory. rev. ed. 2012. (ENG.). 356p. spiral bd. 69.99 ***(978-0-7575-8927-0(8))*** Kendall Hunt Publishing Co.

Walsh, Eileen, et al. Laboratory Studies in General Biology. 3rd rev. ed. 366p. 2010. spiral bd. 73.50 *(978-0-7575-7870-0(5))* 2008. (ENG.). spiral bd. 66.97 *(978-0-7575-1907-9(5))* Kendall Hunt Publishing Co.

Walters, Holly, et al. Investigating Life: Biology Laboratory. rev. ed. 2011. (ENG.). 94p. spiral bd. 37.00 *(978-0-7575-8587-6(6))* Kendall Hunt Publishing Co.

Ward, Chelsea, et al. Principles of Biology 2 Lab Manual. rev. ed. (ENG.). 2011. 158p. spiral bd. 55.00 ***(978-0-7575-9283-6(X))*** 2010. 156p. spiral bd. 54.59 *(978-0-7575-5160-4(2))* Kendall Hunt Publishing Co.

Warren, Michael E. Focus on Biology: A Laboratory Manual. rev. ed. 2010. (ENG.). 64p. spiral bd. 36.06 *(978-0-7872-4469-9(4))* Kendall Hunt Publishing Co.

Weiner, Michael P., et al, eds. Genetic Variation: A Laboratory Manual. 2007. (ENG., Illus.). 472p. per. 165.00 *(978-0-87969-780-8(6))* Cold Spring Harbor Laboratory Pr.

—Genetic Variation: A Laboratory Manual. 2007. (ENG., Illus.). 472p. 240.00 *(978-0-87969-779-2(2))* Cold Spring Harbor Laboratory Pr.

Weinheimer, Ted. A Laboratory Guide for Biology 100: Perspectives in Biology. rev. ed. 2010. (ENG.). 150p. spiral bd. 46.47 *(978-0-7575-1396-1(4))* Kendall Hunt Publishing Co.

Westermeier, Reiner, et al. Proteomics in Practice: A Guide to Successful Experimental Design. 2nd ed. 2008. (ENG., Illus.). 502p. 149.95 *(978-3-527-31941-1(7)*, Wiley-VCH) Wiley, John & Sons, Inc.

Wiley, Emily A. & Gallagher, Sean, eds. Current Protocols Essential Laboratory Techniques. 2008. (ENG., Illus.). 806p. pap. 89.95 *(978-0-470-08993-4(8)*, Current Protocols) Wiley, John & Sons, Inc.

Wu, Cathy H. & Chen, Chuming. Bioinformatics for Comparative Proteomics. 2011. (Illus.). xiii, 387p. E-Book ***(978-1-60761-977-2(6))*** Humana Pr.

Zahn, et al. Explorations in Organismal Biology. rev. ed. 2011. (ENG.). 162p. spiral bd. 67.00 *(978-0-7575-8677-4(5))* Kendall Hunt Publishing Co.

Zhang, Bing, et al. Drosophila Neurobiology: A Laboratory Manual. 2010. (ENG., Illus.). 550p. 256.00 *(978-0-87969-904-8(3))*; pap. 154.00 *(978-0-87969-905-5(1))* Cold Spring Harbor Laboratory Pr.

BIOLOGY—MATHEMATICAL MODELS

Aletti, G., et al, eds. Math Everywhere: Deterministic & Stochastic Modelling in Biomedicine, Economics & Industry. 2010. (ENG., Illus.). xviii, 343p. pap. 129.00 *(978-3-642-07941-2(5)*, 3642079415) Springer.

Allen, Linda J. S. An Introduction to Mathematical Biology. 2006. (ENG., Illus.). 368p. (C). pap. 88.00 *(978-0-13-035216-3(0)*, Prentice Hall) Prentice Hall PTR.

Alon, Uri. An Introduction to Systems Biology. 2nd ed. 2013. (Illus.). 356p. (C). 59.95 ***(978-1-4398-3718-4(X)***, Chapman & Hall/CRC) CRC Pr. LLC.

Altman, Russ B. Biocomputing 2011 - Proceedings of the Pacific Symposium. 2010. 500p. 168.00 *(978-981-4335-04-1(5))* World Scientific Publishing Co., Inc.

Alves, Carlos J. S., et al, eds. Optimization in Medicine. 2008. (Springer Series in Optimization & Its Applications Ser.). (Illus.). 195p. 119.00 *(978-0-387-73298-5(5))* Springer.

AniÃ£a, Sebastian, et al. An Introduction to Optimal Control Problems in Life Sciences & Economics: From Mathematical Models to Numerical Simulation with MATLAB(r). 2010. (Modeling & Simulation in Science, Engineering & Technology Ser.). (ENG., Illus.). xii, 232p. 59.95 *(978-0-8176-8097-8(7)*, 0817680977) Birkhauser Verlag AG CHE. Dist: Springer.

Balakin, Konstantin V. Pharmaceutical Data Mining: Approaches & Applications for Drug Discovery. 2009. (Wiley Series on Technologies for the Pharmaceutical Industry Ser.: 7). (ENG., Illus.). 565p. 139.00 *(978-0-470-19608-3(4)*, Wiley) Wiley, John & Sons, Inc.

Bilotta, Eleonora & Pantano, Pietro. Cellular Automata & Complex Systems: Methods for Modeling Biological Phenomena. 2010. (Illus.). 361p. 245.00 *(978-1-61520-787-9(2))* IGI Global.

Boccaletti, Stefano. Handbook on Biological Networks. 2009. (Illus.). 450p. 135.00 *(978-981-283-879-7(1))* World Scientific Publishing Co., Inc.

Brabazon, Anthony & O'Neill, Michael. Biologically Inspired Algorithms for Financial Modelling. 2010. (Natural Computing Ser.). (Illus.). xvi, 275p. pap. 139.00 *(978-3-642-06573-6(2)*, 3642065732) Springer.

Brauer, Fred & Kribs-Zaleta, Christopher. An Introduction to Dynamical Systems for Biological Modeling. 2010. (Illus.). 480p. 89.95 *(978-1-4200-6641-8(2)*, Chapman & Hall/CRC) CRC Pr. LLC.

Brebbia, C. A., ed. Modelling in Medicine & Biology. 2011. (Illus.). 220p. lib. bdg. 190.00 *(978-1-84564-572-4(3))* WIT Pr GBR. Dist: WIT Pr.

—Modelling in Medicine & Biology VIII. 2009. (Transactions in Biomedicine & Health: 13). (Illus.). 352p. 239.00 *(978-1-84564-183-2(3))* WIT Pr GBR. Dist: WIT Pr.

Brebbia, Carlos A., ed. Modelling in Medicine & Biology VII. 2007. (Transactions in Biomedicine & Health: 12). (Illus.). 352p. 232.00 *(978-1-84564-089-7(6))* WIT Pr GBR. Dist: WIT Pr.

Burton, Richard. Biomedical Calculations: Principles & Practice. 2008. (ENG., Illus.). 310p. 169.95 *(978-0-470-51910-3(X))*; pap. 55.00 *(978-0-470-51911-0(8))* Wiley, John & Sons, Inc. (Wiley).

Cabada, Alberto, et al, eds. Mathematical Models in Engineering, Biology & Medicine: International Conference on Boundary Value Problems: Mathematical Models in Engineering, Biology & Medicine. 2009. (AIP Conference Proceedings Ser.). (Illus.). 370p. 166.00 *(978-0-7354-0660-5(X))* American Institute of Physics.

Calvo, Borja. Positive Unlabeled Learning with Applications in Computational Biology. 2010. 324p. pap. *(978-3-8383-7123-8(2))* Lambert Academic Publishing.

Cars & Stumpf, Michael P. H. Statistical & Evolutionary Analysis of Biological Networks. 2009. (Illus.). 180p. 81.00 *(978-1-84816-433-8(5))* Imperial College Pr. GBR. Dist: World Scientific Publishing Co., Inc.

Cassman, Marvin, et al. Systems Biology: International Research & Development. 2007. (ENG., Illus.). xvii, 262p. 159.00 *(978-1-4020-5467-9(X)*, 140205467X) Springer.

Chaitin, Gregory. Proving Darwin: Making Biology Mathematical. 2012. (ENG., Illus.). 144p. 24.00 ***(978-0-375-42314-7(1)***, Pantheon) Knopf Doubleday Publishing Group.

Chakraborty, Asprina. Numerical Study of Biological Problems in a Predator-Prey System: Mathematical biology. 2008. 164p. pap. *(978-3-639-09835-8(8))* VDM Verlag Dr. Mueller e.K.

Chaplain, Mark A. J., et al, eds. Mathematical Biology. 2009. (IAS/Park City Mathematics Ser.). (Illus.). 398p. 79.00 *(978-0-8218-4765-7(1))* American Mathematical Society.

Chauviere, Arnaud & Claude, Verdier. Cell Mechanics: From Single Scale-Based Models to Multiscale Modeling. Preziosi, Luigi & Verdier, Claude, eds. 2010. (Chapman & Hall/CRC Mathematical & Computational Biology Ser.). (ENG., Illus.). 482p. 119.95 *(978-1-4200-9454-1(8)*, Chapman & Hall/CRC) CRC Pr. LLC.

Cozzens, Margaret B. & Roberts, Fred S., eds. Biomath in the Schools. 2011. (DIMACS: Ser. in Discrete Mathematics & Theoretical Computer Science Ser.). (Illus.). 245p. 52.00 *(978-0-8218-4295-9(1))* American Mathematical Society.

Cram101 Textbook Reviews. Outlines & Highlights for an Introduction to Mathematical Biology by James Dickson Murray. 2011. 148p. pap. 29.95 ***(978-1-61905-797-5(2))*** Cram101 Inc.

—Outlines & Highlights for an Introduction to Mathematical Statistics & Its Applications by Richard J Larsen. 2011. 290p. pap. 32.95 ***(978-1-61905-235-2(0))*** Cram101 Inc.

Cram101 Textbook Reviews & Cram101 Textbook Reviews. Outlines & Highlights for Mathematical Biology by James D Murray, Isbn: 9780387952284 0387952284. 2011. 214p. pap. 30.95 ***(978-1-61812-030-4(1))*** Cram101 Inc.

Demin, Oleg & Goryanin, Igor. Kinetic Modelling in Systems Biology. 2008. (Chapman & Hall/CRC Mathematical & Computational Biology Ser.). (ENG., Illus.). 360p. 85.95 *(978-1-58488-667-9(6)*, C6676, Chapman & Hall/CRC) CRC Pr. LLC.

Deutsch, Andreas. Mathematical Modeling of Biological Systems: Epidemiology, Evolution & Ecology, Immunology, Neural Systems & the Brain, & Innovative Mathematical Methods. Deutsch, Andreas et al, eds. 2007. (Modeling & Simulation in Science, Engineering & Technology Ser.). (Illus.). 386p. 109.00 *(978-0-8176-4555-7(1))* Birkhauser Boston.

Deutsch, Andreas & Brusch, Lutz, eds. Mathematical Modeling of Biological Systems. 2007. (Modeling & Simulation in Science, Engineering & Technology Ser.). (ENG., Illus.). xviii, 382p. 134.00 *(978-0-8176-4557-1(8)*, 0817645578) Springer.

Di. Biomat 2007. 2008. 187.00 *(978-981-281-232-2(6))* World Scientific Publishing Co., Inc.

Dieckmann, Ulf, et al, eds. Adaptive Speciation. 2012. (Cambridge Studies in Adaptive Dynamics Ser.: 3). (ENG., Illus.). 275p. pap. 71.00 ***(978-1-107-40418-2(5))*** Cambridge Univ. Pr.

Ehresmann, Andrée C. & Vanbremeersch, Jean-Paul. Memory Evolutive Systems: Hierarchy, Emergence, Cognition. 2007. (Studies in Multidisciplinarity Ser.: 4). (ENG., Illus.). 402p. 185.00 *(978-0-444-52244-3(1)*, Elsevier Science) Elsevier Science & Technology Bks.

Elliston. Systems Biology Modeling: Approach & Application. 2010. 300p. 79.95 *(978-0-470-18782-1(4)*, Wiley-Interscience) Wiley, John & Sons, Inc.

Gascuel, Olivier & Steel, Mike, eds. Reconstructing Evolution: New Mathematical & Computational Advances. 2007. (ENG., Illus.). 352p. 99.00 *(978-0-19-920822-7(0))* Oxford Univ. Pr., Inc.

Ghergu, Marius & Rdulescu, Viceniu D. Nonlinear PDEs: Mathematical Models in Biology, Chemistry & Population Genetics. 2011. (Springer Monographs in Mathematics Ser.). (ENG., Illus.). xviii, 391p. 124.00 ***(978-3-642-22663-2(9)***, 3642226639) Springer.

Gilbert Robert P Staff. Homogenization Applications to the Biological & Physical Scienc. 2009. (Illus.). 352p. 99.95 *(978-1-58488-791-1(5)*, Chapman & Hall/CRC) CRC Pr. LLC.

Goldstein, Larry. College Algebra for Management, Social, & Biological Sciences. Date not set. (C). 88p. pap., stu. ed. 15.00 *(978-1-891304-18-7(6))*; (Illus.). 668p. 44.50 *(978-1-891304-15-6(1))* Mobius Communications, Ltd.

—College Algebra for Management, Social, & Biological Sciences: Instructor's Edition. Date not set. (Illus.). 708p. (C). pap., tchr. ed. *(978-1-891304-17-0(8))* Mobius Communications, Ltd.

—College Algebra for Management, Social, & Biological Sciences: Instructor's Solutions Manual. Date not set. 318p. (C). pap., tchr. ed. *(978-1-891304-16-3(X))* Mobius Communications, Ltd.

—College Algebra for Management, Social, & Biological Sciences: Test Item File. Date not set. 271p. (C). pap. *(978-1-891304-19-4(4))* Mobius Communications, Ltd.

Horimoto, Katsuhisa, et al, eds. Algebraic & Numeric Biology: 4th International Conference, ANB 2010, Hagenberg, Austria, July 31-August 2, 2010, Revised Selected Papers. 2012. (Lecture Notes in Computer Science / Theoretical Computer Science & General Issues Ser.). (ENG., Illus.). x, 185p. pap. 72.00 ***(978-3-642-28066-5(8)***, 3642280668) Springer.

Kooijman, Bas. Dynamic Energy Budget Theory for Metabolic Organisation. 3rd rev. ed. 2009. (ENG., Illus.). 532p. (C). pap. 72.00 *(978-0-521-13191-9(X))* Cambridge Univ. Pr.

Krabs, Werner & Pickl, Stefan. Modelling, Analysis & Optimization of Biosystems. 2010. (ENG., Illus.). xii, 203p. pap. 139.00 *(978-3-642-09066-0(4)*, 3642090664) Springer.

Laubenbacher, Reinhard. Modeling & Simulation of Biological Networks. 2007. (Proceedings of Symposia in Applied Mathematics Ser.). 151p. 40.00 *(978-0-8218-3964-5(0))* American Mathematical Society.

Laubichler, Manfred D. & Müller, Gerd B., eds. Modeling Biology: Structures, Behaviors, Evolution. 2007. (Vienna Series in Theoretical Biology Ser.). (ENG., Illus.). 408p. (gr. 17). 50.00 *(978-0-262-12291-7(X))* MIT Pr.

Lee, E. Stanley, ed. Emerging Developments in Autonomous Systems Technologies: Artificial Life Innovations. 2012. 455p. 245.00 ***(978-1-4666-0273-1(2)***, Medical Information Science Reference) IGI Global.

Lee, E. Stanley & Chang, Ping-Teng. Emerging Developments in Autonomous Systems Technologies: Artificial Life Innovations. 2012. ***(978-1-4666-0275-5(9))*** IGI Global.

Lestrel, Pete E., ed. Fourier Descriptors & their Applications in Biology. 2008. (ENG., Illus.). 484p. pap. 95.00 *(978-0-521-05573-4(3))* Cambridge Univ. Pr.

Martinez, Andre & Sordoni, Vania. Twisted Pseudodifferential Calculus & Application to the Quantum Evolution of Molecules. 2009. (Memoirs of the American Mathematical Society Ser.). 82p. pap. 62.00 *(978-0-8218-4296-6(X))* American Mathematical Society.

Mondaini, Rubem P. Biomat 2008: International Symposium on Mathematical & Computational Biology. 2009. 408p. 156.00 *(978-981-4271-81-3(0))* World Scientific Publishing Co., Inc.

—Biomat 2009 - International Symposium on Mathematical & Computational Biology. 2010. (Illus.). 408p. 156.00 *(978-981-4304-89-4(1))* World Scientific Publishing Co., Inc.

—Biomat 2010 - International Symposium on Mathematical & Computational Biology. 2011. 412p. 148.00 ***(978-981-4343-42-8(0))*** World Scientific Publishing Co., Inc.

Mondaini, Rubem P. Mathematical Modelling of Biosystems. 2008. (Applied Optimization Ser.). 159.00 *(978-3-540-76783-1(5))* Springer.

Mondaini, Rubem P., ed. Biomat 2006: International Symposium on Mathematical & Computational Biology. (Illus.). 400p. 188.00 *(978-981-270-768-0(9))* World Scientific Publishing Co., Inc.

Nowak, Martin. Evolutionary Dynamics: Exploring the Equations of Life. 2006. (Illus.). 384p. 47.50 *(978-0-674-02338-3(2)*, Belknap Pr.) Harvard Univ. Pr.

Pugesek, Bruce H., et al, eds. Structural Equation Modeling: Applications in Ecological & Evolutionary Biology. 2009. (ENG., Illus.). 424p. pap. 74.00 *(978-0-521-10402-9(5))* Cambridge Univ. Pr.

Schwartz, Russell. Biological Modeling & Simulation: A Survey of Practical Models, Algorithms, & Numerical Methods. 2008. (Computational Molecular Biology Ser.). (ENG., Illus.). 408p. 47.00 *(978-0-262-19584-3(4))* MIT Pr.

Sinclair, Robert Michael & Stiefel, Klaus M., eds. Multiscale Phenomena in Biology: Proceedings of the 2nd Conference on Mathematics & Biology. 2009. (AIP Conference Proceedings / Mathematical & Statistical Phsyics Ser.). (ENG.). 132p. 89.00 *(978-0-7354-0704-6(5)*, 0735407045) American Institute of Physics.

Smith, Hal L. & Thieme, Horst R. Dynamical Systems & Population Persistence. 2010. (Graduate Studies in Mathematics Ser.). (Illus.). 405p. 75.00 *(978-0-8218-4945-3(X))* American Mathematical Society.

Stephens, Christopher R. & Poli, Riccardo. Taming the Complexity of Evolutionary Dynamics: From Microscopic Models to Schema Theory & Beyond. 2012. (ENG.). x, 480p. 109.00 *(978-3-642-17360-8(8)*, 3642173608) Springer.

Stolovitzky, Gustavo & Califano, Andrea, eds. Reverse Engineering Biological Networks: Opportunities & Challenges in Computational Methods for Pathway Inference. 2008. (Annals of the New York Academy of Sciences Ser.: 5). (ENG., Illus.). 452p. pap. 139.95 *(978-1-57331-689-7(X)*, Wiley-Blackwell) Wiley, John & Sons, Inc.

van den Berg, Hugo. Mathematical Models of Biological Systems. 2011. (ENG., Illus.). 256p. 117.00 *(978-0-19-958219-8(X))*; pap. 49.50 *(978-0-19-958218-1(1))* Oxford Univ. Pr., Inc.

Waddington, C. H., ed. Sketching Theoretical Biology Vol. 2: Toward a Theoretical Biology. 2010. (Illus.). 351p. pap. 69.95 *(978-0-202-36319-6(8))* Aldine Transaction.

Wynn, James. Evolution by the Numbers: The Origins of Mathematical Argument in Biology. 2011. ***(978-1-60235-217-9(8))***; ***(978-1-60235-219-3(4))***; pap. ***(978-1-60235-216-2(X))*** Parlor Pr.

BIOLOGY—METHODOLOGY

Barnard, Chris, et al. Asking Questions in Biology: A Guide to Hypothesis Testing, Experimental Design & Presentation in Practical Work & Research Projects. 4th rev. ed. 2011. (ENG., Illus.). 264p. (C). pap. 48.40 *(978-0-273-73468-0(7))* Benjamin-Cummings Publishing Co.

Benestad, Haakon Breien & Laake, Petter. Research Methodology in the Medical & Biological Sciences. Olsen, Bjorn Reino, ed. 2007. (ENG., Illus.). 512p. per. 50.95 *(978-0-12-373874-5(1)*, Academic Pr.) Elsevier Science & Technology Bks.

Committee on a New Biology for the 21st Century: Ensuring the United States Leads the Coming Biology Revolution & National Research Council. A New Biology for the 21st Century. 2009. (ENG.). 112p. pap. 29.75 *(978-0-309-14488-9(4))* National Academies Pr.

Greene, James & Castora, Frank J. Handbook of Biological Research Methodology. 2009. (Illus.). 139.95 *(978-0-8493-7616-0(5))* CRC Pr. LLC.

Jones, Allan, et al. Practical Skills in Biology. 4th rev. ed. 2010. (Practical Skills Ser.). (ENG., Illus.). 496p. (C). pap. 89.35 *(978-0-13-175509-3(9))* Benjamin-Cummings Publishing Co.

Rheinberger, Hans-Jörg. An Epistemology of the Concrete: Twentieth-Century Histories of Life. 2010. (ENG., Illus.). 352p. 89.95 *(978-0-8223-4560-2(9))*; pap. 24.95 *(978-0-8223-4575-6(7))* Duke Univ. Pr.

Sharma, Kal Renganathan. Bioinformatics: Sequence Alignment & Markov Models. 2008. (ENG., Illus.). 320p. (C). 115.00 *(978-0-07-159306-9(3)*, 0071593063) McGraw-Hill Professional Publishing.

Vignais, Pierre V. & Vignais, Paulette. Discovering Life, Manufacturing Life: How the Experimental Method Shaped the Course of Life Sciences. 2010. Orig. Title: Science Expã(c)Rimentale et Connaissance du Vivant. la Mã(c)Thode et les Concepts. (ENG., Illus.). x, 418p. 159.00 *(978-90-481-3766-4(7)*, 9048137667) Springer.

Young, D. C., et al. Computational Drug Design: A Guide for Computational & Medicinal Chemists. 2009. (ENG., Illus.). 307p. 117.00 *(978-0-470-12685-1(X)*, Wiley-Interscience) Wiley, John & Sons, Inc.

BIOLOGY—MORAL AND ETHICAL ASPECTS

see Bioethics

BIOLOGY—NOMENCLATURE

see also subdivision Nomenclature under individual animals and groups of animals and individual plants and groups of plants, e.g. Birds—Nomenclature

Yoon, Carol Kaesuk. Naming Nature: The Clash Between Instinct & Science. (ENG., Illus.). 2010. 341p. pap. 16.95 *(978-0-393-33871-3(1),* 33871) 2009. 352p. 27.95 *(978-0-393-06197-0(3),* 6197) Norton, W. W. & Co., Inc.

BIOLOGY—OUTLINES, SYLLABI, ETC.

Cram101 Textbook Reviews. Outlines & Highlights for a Brief Guide to Biology by David Krogh, Isbn: 9780131859654. 2010. 258p. pap. 31.95 *(978-1-61698-625-4(5))* Cram101 Inc.

—Outlines & Highlights for Biological Science, Volume 3 by Scott Freeman, Isbn: 9780321543295 0321543297 9780131568167. 2011. 458p. pap. 37.95 ***(978-1-61490-424-3(3))*** Cram101 Inc.

—Outlines & Highlights for Biology: Chemistry, Cell Biology & Genetics. 2011. 714p. pap. 43.95 ***(978-1-61812-483-8(8))*** Cram101 Inc.

—Outlines & Highlights for Biology: Concepts & Conn. Media Update by Neil A. Campbell. 2011. 704p. pap. 43.95 ***(978-1-61812-321-3(1))*** Cram101 Inc.

—Outlines & Highlights for Biology: CONCEPTS & INVESTIGATIONS BRIEF by HOEFNAGELS, ISBN. 2010. 338p. pap. 33.95 *(978-1-61698-624-7(7))* Cram101 Inc.

—Outlines & Highlights for Biology: Dynamic Science, Volume 3, Units 5 & 6 by Peter J. Russell, ISBN. 2010. 520p. pap. 38.95 *(978-1-61698-030-6(3))* Cram101 Inc.

—Outlines & Highlights for Biology: Science for Life with Physiology by Colleen Belk, Virginia Borden Maier, ISBN. 2010. 334p. pap. 33.95 *(978-1-61698-623-0(9))* Cram101 Inc.

—Outlines & Highlights for Biology: The Dynamic Science, Volume 1, Units 1 & 2 by Peter J. Russell, ISBN. 2010. 478p. pap. 37.95 *(978-1-61698-031-3(1))* Cram101 Inc.

—Outlines & Highlights for Biology: The Dynamic Science, Volume 2, Units 3, 4 & 7 by Peter J. Russell, ISBN. 2010. 370p. pap. 34.95 *(978-1-61654-460-7(0))* Cram101 Inc.

—Outlines & Highlights for Biology: Today & Tomorrow with Physiology by Cecie Starr. 2011. 454p. pap. 36.95 ***(978-1-61490-997-2(0))***; 460p. pap. 36.95 ***(978-1-61812-022-9(0))*** Cram101 Inc.

—Outlines & Highlights for Biology: Today & Tomorrow Without Physiology by Cecie Starr, ISBN. 2011. 388p. pap. 34.95 ***(978-1-61812-158-5(8))*** Cram101 Inc.

—Outlines & Highlights for Discover Biology by Michael L Cain, Isbn: 9780393931617 0393931617 9780393931600. 2011. 686p. pap. 42.95 ***(978-1-61490-281-2(X))*** Cram101 Inc.

—Outlines & Highlights for Discover Biology, Core Topics by Michael L Cain, Carol Kaesuk Yoon, Hans Damman, Robert a Lue, Isbn: 9780393928433. 2010. 410p. pap. 35.95 *(978-1-61698-621-6(2))* Cram101 Inc.

—Outlines & Highlights for Essentials of the Living World by George Johnson, Isbn: 9780077280079 0077280075 9780073377933. 2011. 470p. pap. 37.95 ***(978-1-61490-239-3(9))*** Cram101 Inc.

Cram101 Textbook Reviews. Outlines & Highlights for Human Reproductive Biology by Richard E Jones, Kristin H Lopez, Isbn: 9780120884650. 2010. 136p. pap. 28.95 *(978-1-61698-620-9(4))* Cram101 Inc.

Cram101 Textbook Reviews & Cram101 Textbook Reviews. Outlines & Highlights for Biology: Understanding Life Custom by Alters. 2011. 788p. pap. 44.95 ***(978-1-61830-719-4(3))*** Cram101 Inc.

—Outlines & Highlights for Bryophyte Biology by Bernard Goffinet, Isbn: 9780521693226. 2011. 342p. pap. 33.95 ***(978-1-61461-836-2(4))*** Cram101 Inc.

—Outlines & Highlights for Introduction to Biological Evolution by Kenneth V Kardong, Isbn: 9780073050775 0073050776. 2011. 308p. pap. 32.95 ***(978-1-61490-824-1(9))*** Cram101 Inc.

Cram101 Textbook Reviews Staff. Outlines & Highlights for Biological Science by Freeman, Isbn: 0132187469. 2008. 576p. pap. 22.95 *(978-1-4288-6027-8(4))* Cram101 Inc.

—Outlines & Highlights for Biological Science Volume 1 by Freeman, Isbn: 0132187477. 2008. 592p. pap. 22.95 *(978-1-4288-6112-1(2))* Cram101 Inc.

—Outlines & Highlights for Biological Science with Masteringbiology+ by Freeman, Isbn: 0321543270. 2008. 572p. pap. 22.95 *(978-1-4288-6115-2(7))* Cram101 Inc.

—Outlines & Highlights for Biology: Concepts & Applications by Starr ISBN. 2008. 672p. pap. 24.95 *(978-1-4288-6259-3(5))* Cram101 Inc.

—Outlines & Highlights for Biology: CONCEPTS & INVESTIGATIONS BRIEF by HOEFNAGELS, ISBN. 2009. 298p. pap. 32.95 *(978-1-4288-8258-4(8))* Cram101 Inc.

—Outlines & Highlights for Biology: Concepts & Investigations by Hoefnagels, ISBN. 2008. 392p. pap. 17.95 *(978-1-4288-6118-3(1))* Cram101 Inc.

—Outlines & Highlights for Biology: Dimensions of Life by Presson, ISBN. 2008. 240p. pap. 14.95 *(978-1-4288-6117-6(3))* Cram101 Inc.

—Outlines & Highlights for Biology: Life on Earth by Audesirk, ISBN. 2008. 396p. pap. 17.95 *(978-1-4288-6260-9(9))* Cram101 Inc.

—Outlines & Highlights for Biology: Science for Life by Belk, ISBN. 2008. 140p. pap. 11.95 *(978-1-4288-6263-0(3))* Cram101 Inc.

—Outlines & Highlights for Biology: Science for Life by Colleen Belk, ISBN. 2009. 178p. pap. 29.95 *(978-1-4288-9591-1(4))* Cram101 Inc.

—Outlines & Highlights for Biology: Science for Life with Physiology by Belk, ISBN. 2008. 220p. pap. 13.95 *(978-1-4288-6256-2(0))* Cram101 Inc.

—Outlines & Highlights for Biology: The Dynamic Science by Russell ISBN. 2008. 564p. pap. 21.95 *(978-1-4288-5944-9(6))* Cram101 Inc.

—Outlines & Highlights for Biology by Brooker, Isbn: 0072956208. 2008. 472p. per. 19.95 *(978-1-4288-5794-0(X))* Cram101 Inc.

—Outlines & Highlights for Biology by Campbell, Isbn: 0321543254. 2008. 772p. pap. 26.95 *(978-1-4288-6305-7(2))* Cram101 Inc.

—Outlines & Highlights for Biology by Mader, Isbn: 9780072464634. 2008. 716p. pap. 25.95 *(978-1-4288-6582-2(9))* Cram101 Inc.

—Outlines & Highlights for Biology by Raven, Isbn: 0072965819. 2008. 576p. per. 22.95 *(978-1-4288-5796-4(6))* Cram101 Inc.

—Outlines & Highlights for Biology by Solomon Isbn: 0495107050. 2008. 356p. pap. 16.95 *(978-1-4288-6055-1(X))* Cram101 Inc.

—Outlines & Highlights for Biology by Sylvia Mader, Isbn: 9780077274337. 2009. 790p. pap. 44.95 *(978-1-4288-9129-6(3))* Cram101 Inc.

—Outlines & Highlights for Biology Concepts & Connections by Campbell, Isbn: 0321489845. 2008. 492p. pap. 20.95 *(978-1-4288-6583-9(7))* Cram101 Inc.

—Outlines & Highlights for Biology Today & Tomorrow with Physiology by Starr Isbn: 0495016543. 2008. 668p. pap. 24.95 *(978-1-4288-6254-8(4))* Cram101 Inc.

—Outlines & Highlights for Biology Volume II Plants & Animals by Brooker, Isbn: 9780073353319. 2008. 216p. pap. 13.95 *(978-1-4288-5946-3(2))* Cram101 Inc.

—Outlines & Highlights for Concepts in Biology by Enger, Isbn: 0072986573. 2007. 356p. per. 16.95 *(978-1-4288-5707-0(9))* Cram101 Inc.

—Outlines & Highlights for Essential Biology by Campbell Isbn: 0805368426. 2008. 244p. pap. 14.95 *(978-1-4288-6309-5(5))* Cram101 Inc.

—Outlines & Highlights for Essentials of Biology by Mader, Isbn. 2008. 284p. pap. 15.95 *(978-1-4288-5818-3(0))* Cram101 Inc.

—Outlines & Highlights for Essentials of Biology by Sylvia S Mader, Isbn: 9780077280093. 2009. 350p. pap. 33.95 *(978-1-4288-9153-1(6))* Cram101 Inc.

—Outlines & Highlights for Essentials of the Living World by Johnson, Isbn: 0073525421. 2008. 208p. per. 13.95 *(978-1-4288-5791-9(5))* Cram101 Inc.

—Outlines & Highlights for Foundations in Microbiology by Kathleen Park Talaro, Isbn: 9780077260576. 2009. 84p. pap. 27.95 *(978-1-4288-9643-7(0))* Cram101 Inc.

—Outlines & Highlights for Inquiry into Life by Mader, Isbn: 0072986751. 2008. 396p. per. 17.95 *(978-1-4288-5795-7(8))* Cram101 Inc.

—Outlines & Highlights for Life on Earth by Teresa Audesirk, Isbn: 9780131755352. 2009. 172p. pap. 29.95 *(978-1-4288-9112-8(9))* Cram101 Inc.

—Outlines & Highlights for Microbiology: A Human Perspective by Nester ISBN. 2008. 452p. pap. 19.95 *(978-1-4288-5940-1(3))* Cram101 Inc.

—Outlines & Highlights for Microbiology: A Systems Approach by Cowan, ISBN. 2008. 560p. pap. 21.95 *(978-1-4288-6306-4(0))* Cram101 Inc.

—Outlines & Highlights for Microbiology: An Introduction Brief Edition by Tortora ISBN. 2008. 244p. pap. 14.95 *(978-1-4288-6307-1(9))* Cram101 Inc.

—Outlines & Highlights for Microbiology Experiments: A Health Science Perspective by Kleyn, ISBN. 2008. 128p. pap. 11.95 *(978-1-4288-6261-6(7))* Cram101 Inc.

—Outlines & Highlights for Molecular Biology by Weaver, Isbn: 9780072846119. 2008. 188p. pap. 12.95 *(978-1-4288-5910-4(1))* Cram101 Inc.

—Outlines & Highlights for Molecular Biology by Weaver, Isbn: 9780073319940. 2008. 244p. pap. 14.95 *(978-1-4288-5912-8(8))* Cram101 Inc.

—Outlines & Highlights for Plant & Animal Biology: Volume II by Raven ISBN. 2009. 442p. pap. 36.95 *(978-1-4288-6797-0(X))* Cram101 Inc.

—Outlines & Highlights for Prescott Ó S Principles of Microbiology by Willey Isbn: 9780077213411. 2008. 620p. pap. 23.95 *(978-1-4288-6310-1(9))* Cram101 Inc.

—Outlines & Highlights for the Living World Basic Concepts by Johnson, Isbn: 9780073215815. 2009. 380p. pap. 30.95 *(978-1-4288-6691-1(4))* Cram101 Inc.

—Outlines & Highlights for the Living World by Johnson, Isbn: 0072986670. 2008. 236p. per. 14.95 *(978-1-4288-5790-2(7))* Cram101 Inc.

D'Alessio, Michael. AP Biology Crash Course (REA) 2009. (Advanced Placement (AP) Crash Course Ser.). (ENG.). 224p. (gr. 10-12). pap. 11.95 *(978-0-7386-0662-0(6))* Research & Education Assn.

Fried, George & Hademenos, George J. Biology. 2nd ed. 2010. (Schaum's Easy Outlines Ser.). (ENG., Illus.). 160p. (C). pap. 11.00 *(978-0-07-174654-0(4),* 0071746544) McGraw-Hill Cos., The.

Fried, George, et al. Schaum's Outline of Biology Third Edition. 3rd ed. 2009. (Schaum's Outline Ser.). (ENG., Illus.). 480p. (C). pap. 20.00 *(978-0-07-162561-6(5),* 0071625615) McGraw-Hill Cos., The.

Hunter, G. Scott. Biology, the Living Environment. 5th rev. ed. 2009. (Let's Review Ser.). (ENG.). 480p. pap. 13.99 *(978-0-7641-4018-1(3))* Barron's Educational Series, Inc.

Mader, Sylvia S. Biology. 10th ed. 2009. *(978-0-07-352543-3(X))* McGraw-Hill Cos., The.

Stansfield, William, et al. Schaum's Easy Outline Molecular & Cell Biology, Revised Edition. 2011. (Schaum's Easy Outlines Ser.). (ENG.). 128p. (C). pap. 11.00 ***(978-0-07-177749-0(0),*** 0071777490) McGraw-Hill Cos., The.

BIOLOGY—PERIODICITY

see Biological Rhythms

BIOLOGY—PHILOSOPHY

Agutter, Paul S. & Wheatley, D. N. Thinking about Life: The History & Philosophy of Biology & Other Sciences. 2008. (Illus.). xv, 274p. 54.95 *(978-1-4020-8865-0(5))* Springer.

Alexander, Denis R. & Numbers, Ronald L., eds. Biology & Ideology from Descartes to Dawkins. 2010. (ENG., Illus.). 448p. 95.00 *(978-0-226-60840-2(9))*; pap. 35.00 *(978-0-226-60841-9(7))* Univ. of Chicago Pr.

Asher, Robert J. Evolution & Belief: Confessions of a Religious Paleontologist. 2012. (ENG., Illus.). 324p. 24.99 ***(978-0-521-19383-2(4))*** Cambridge Univ. Pr.

Atlan, Henri. Sparks of Randomness Vol. 1: Spermatic Knowledge. Schramm, Lenn, tr. from FRE. 2010. (Cultural Memory in the Present Ser.). (ENG & HEB.). 352p. 65.00 *(978-0-8047-7357-7(2))*; pap. 24.95 *(978-0-8047-6027-0(6))* Stanford Univ. Pr.

Auletta, Gennaro. Cognitive Biology: Dealing with Information from Bacteria to Minds. 2011. (Illus.). 944p. 179.00 *(978-0-19-960848-5(2))* Oxford Univ. Pr., Inc.

Ayala, Francisco J. & Arp, Robert, eds. Contemporary Debates in Philosophy of Biology. 2009. (Contemporary Debates in Philosophy Ser.). (ENG., Illus.). 440p. 99.95 *(978-1-4051-5998-2(7))*; pap. 42.95 *(978-1-4051-5999-9(5))* Wiley, John & Sons, Inc. (Wiley-Blackwell).

Bachem, Albert. Beyond Matter & Mind: Natural Sciences Synthesized into Philosophy. 2011. 182p. 42.95 ***(978-1-258-06664-2(5))*** Literary Licensing, LLC.

Barberousse, Anouk, et al, eds. Mapping the Future of Biology: Evolving Concepts & Theories. 2009. (Boston Studies in the Philosophy of Science Ser.). (ENG., Illus.). xii, 184p. 129.00 *(978-1-4020-9635-8(6))* Springer.

Buican, Denis. Biologie: Histoire et Philosophie. 2010. (FRE.). 231p. *(978-2-271-07022-7(8))* Editions du Centre National de la Recherche Scientifique.

Carlson, Robert H., et al. Biology Is Technology: The Promise, Peril, & New Business of Engineering Life. 2011. (ENG., Illus.). 288p. pap. 21.95 *(978-0-674-06015-9(6))* Harvard Univ. Pr.

Chaitin, Gregory. Proving Darwin: Making Biology Mathematical. 2012. (ENG., Illus.). 144p. 24.00 ***(978-0-375-42314-7(1),*** Pantheon) Knopf Doubleday Publishing Group.

Chapin, III, F. Stuart, FStuart, et al. Principles of Terrestrial Ecosystem Ecology. 2nd ed. 2011. (ENG., Illus.). xv, 529p. pap. 69.95 ***(978-1-4419-9502-5(1),*** 1441995021) Springer.

Creager, Angela N. H., et al, eds. Science Without Laws: Model Systems, Cases, Exemplary Narratives. 2007. (Science & Cultural Theory Ser.). (ENG., Illus.). 296p. (C). 89.95 *(978-0-8223-4046-1(1))*; per. 24.95 *(978-0-8223-4068-3(2))* Duke Univ. Pr.

Darden, Lindley. Reasoning in Biological Discoveries: Essays on Mechanisms, Interfield Relations, & Anomaly Resolution. 2009. (Cambridge Studies in Philosophy & Biology Ser.). (ENG., Illus.). 372p. pap. 42.00 *(978-0-521-11727-2(5))* Cambridge Univ. Pr.

Dokholyan, Nikolay V., ed. Computational Modeling of Biological Systems: From Molecules to Pathways. 2012. (Biological & Medical Physics, Biomedical Engineering Ser.). (ENG., Illus.). vi, 364p. 129.00 ***(978-1-4614-2145-0(4),*** 1461421454) Springer.

Dougherty, Edward R. & Bittner, Michael L. Epistemology of the Cell: A Systems Perspective on Biological Knowledge. 2011. (Illus.). xii, 201p. ***(978-1-118-10486-6(2))*** IEEE Computer Society Pr.

—Epistemology of the Cell: A Systems Perspective on Biological Knowledge. 2011. (IEEE Press Series on Biomedical Engineering Ser.: 34). (ENG., Illus.). 216p. 110.00 *(978-1-118-02779-0(5),* Wiley-IEEE Pr.) Wiley, John & Sons, Inc.

Driesch, Hans. Science & Philosophy of the Organism. 2006. pap. 31.95 *(978-1-4286-4092-4(4))* Kessinger Publishing, LLC.

Dupré, John. Processes of Life: Essays in the Philosophy of Biology. 2012. (ENG.). 320p. 55.00 ***(978-0-19-969198-2(3),)*** Oxford Univ. Pr., Inc.

Dyson, Freeman J. A Many-Colored Glass: Reflections on the Place of Life in the Universe. (Page Barbour Lectures). (ENG.) 176p. 2010. pap. 14.95 *(978-0-8139-2973-6(3))* 2007. 21.95 *(978-0-8139-2663-6(7))* Univ. Pr. of Virginia.

Eastham, Scott. Biotech Time-Bomb: The Side-Effects Are the Main Effects. 2009. *(978-1-57273-904-8(5))* Hampton Pr., Inc.

Fletcher, Angus. Evolving Hamlet: Seventeenth-Century English Tragedy & the Ethics of Natural Selection. 2011. (Cognitive Studies in Literature & Performance Ser.). (ENG.). 208p. 80.00 *(978-0-230-11168-4(8))* Palgrave Macmillan.

Fodor, Jerry & Piattelli-Palmarini, Massimo. What Darwin Got Wrong. 2010. (ENG., Illus.). 288p. 26.00 *(978-0-374-28879-2(8))* Farrar, Straus & Giroux.

—What Darwin Got Wrong. 2011. (ENG., Illus.). 320p. pap. 16.00 *(978-0-312-68066-4(X))* Picador.

Follinger, Sabine, ed. Was Ist Leben? Aristoteles Anschauungen zur Entstehung und Funktionsweise von Leben. Akten der Tagung vom 23. 26. August 2006 in Bamberg. 2009. (Philosophie der Antike (PhA) Ser.). (GER.). 432p. (C). 98.00 *(978-3-515-09244-9(7))* Steiner, Franz Verlag Wiesbaden GmbH DEU. Dist: Brown, David Bk. Co., The.

Frost, G. Howard. The Reason Why. 2011. 58p. 36.95 ***(978-1-253-07634-4(9))*** Literary Licensing, LLC.

Gabbay, Dov M., et al, contrib. by. Philosophy of Biology. 2007. (Handbook of the Philosophy of Science Ser.). (ENG., Illus.). 638p. 185.00 *(978-0-444-51543-8(7),* North Holland) Elsevier Science & Technology Bks.

Gamsjaeger, Roland. AFM & SPR on Biological Systems: Applying Atomic Force Microscopy (AFM) & Surface Plasmon Resonance (SPR) to Biologically Important Systems. 2008. 72p. pap. *(978-3-8364-8854-9(X),* VDM Verlag Dr. Mueller e.K.

Garvey, Brian. Philosophy of Biology. 2007. (Philosophy & Science Ser.). (ENG.). 288p. (C). *(978-0-7735-3342-4(7))*; (Illus.). per. *(978-0-7735-3343-1(5))* McGill-Queen's Univ. Pr.

Gessert, George. Green Light: Toward an Art of Evolution. (Leonardo Book Ser.). (ENG., Illus.). 264p. (gr. 17). 2012. pap. 12.95 ***(978-0-262-51730-0(2))*** 2010. 24.95 *(978-0-262-01414-4(9))* MIT Pr.

Gilson, Étienne. From Aristotle to Darwin & Back Again: A Journey in Final Causality, Species & Evolution. 2009. 250p. pap. 16.95 *(978-1-58617-169-8(0))* Ignatius Pr.

Glick, Thomas F. What about Darwin? All Species of Opinion from Scientists, Sages, Friends, & Enemies Who Met, Read, & Discussed the Naturalist Who Changed the World. 2010. (ENG.). 552p. pap. 29.95 *(978-0-8018-9462-6(X))* Johns Hopkins Univ. Pr.

Gotthelf, Allan. Teleology, First Principles, & Scientific Method in Aristotle's Biology. 2012. (Oxford Aristotle Studies Ser.). (ENG.). 464p. 99.00 ***(978-0-19-928795-6(3))*** Oxford Univ. Pr., Inc.

Goy, Ina, ed. Kant's Theory on Biology. 2013. (ENG.). 400p. (gr. 17). 140.00 *(978-3-11-022578-5(6))* De Gruyter, Walter Inc.

Griffiths, P. E., ed. Trees of Life: Essays in Philosophy of Biology. 2010. (Studies in History & Philosophy of Science Ser.). 292p. pap. 159.00 *(978-90-481-4153-1(2),* 9048141532) Springer.

Haeckel, Ernst. The Wonders of Life: A Popular Study of Biological Philosophy. McCabe, Joseph, tr. 2007. (ENG.). 488p. 53.95 *(978-0-548-10588-7(X))* Kessinger Publishing, LLC.

Ho & Ho, Mae-Wan. The Rainbow & the Worm: The Physics of Organisms. 3rd ed. 2008. 58.00 *(978-981-283-259-7(9))* World Scientific Publishing Co., Inc.

Ho, Mae-Wan. The Rainbow & the Worm: The Physics of Organisms. 3rd ed. 2008. pap. 34.00 *(978-981-283-260-3(2))* World Scientific Publishing Co., Inc.

Hoffmeyer, Jesper. A Legacy for Living Systems: Gregory Bateson As Precursor to Biosemiotics. 2008. (Biosemiotics Ser.). (Illus.). 464p. 239.00 *(978-1-4020-6705-1(4),* 1402067054) Springer.

Hoffmeyer, Jesper, ed. A Legacy for Living Systems: Gregory Bateson as Precursor to Biosemiotics. 2010. (Biosemiotics Ser.). x, 290p. pap. 239.00 *(978-90-481-7703-5(0),* 9048177030) Springer.

Humanity: The Chimpanzees Who Would Be Ants. 2007. (Illus.). 215p. 24.95 *(978-0-9788441-0-3(6))* Collins Foundation Pr.

Huneman, Philippe, ed. Understanding Purpose: Kant & the Philosophy of Biology. 2007. (North American Kant Society Studies in Philosophy Ser.: Volume 8). (Illus.). 202p. per. 29.95 *(978-1-58046-265-5(0))* Univ. of Rochester Pr.

Igamberdiev, Abir. Physics & Logic of Life. 2012. ***(978-1-61942-664-1(1))*** Nova Science Pubs., Inc.

Kerr, Gordon. Contribution to the Theory of the Living. 2006. 212p. per. *(978-1-4067-1735-8(5),* Hesperides Pr.) Read Bks.

—Riddle of Life. 2006. 80p. per. *(978-1-4067-1989-5(7),* Hesperides Pr.) Read Bks.

Krohs, Ulrich. Eine Theorie biologischer Theorien: Status und Gehalt von Funktionsaussagen und informationstheoretischen Modellen. 2006. (Illus.). X, 268p. 99.00 *(978-3-540-22258-3(8),* 3540222588) Springer.

Krohs, Ulrich & Kroes, Peter, eds. Functions in Biological & Artificial Worlds: Comparative Philosophical Perspectives. 2009. (Vienna Series in Theoretical Biology Ser.). (ENG., Illus.). 312p. (gr. 17). 50.00 *(978-0-262-11321-2(X))* MIT Pr.

LaPorte, Joseph. Natural Kinds & Conceptual Change. 2009. (Cambridge Studies in Philosophy & Biology Ser.). (ENG., Illus.). 232p. pap. 34.99 *(978-0-521-10810-2(1))* Cambridge Univ. Pr.

Levins, Richard & Lewontin, Richard C. Biology under the Influence: Dialectical Essays on the Coevolution of Nature & Society. 2007. (ENG., Illus.). 304p. 79.00 *(978-1-58367-158-0(7))* Monthly Review Pr.

Looijen, Rick C. Holism & Reductionism in Biology & Ecology: The Mutual Dependence of Higher & Lower Level Research Programmes. 2010. (Episteme Ser.). 372p. pap. 239.00 *(978-90-481-5364-0(6),* 9048153646) Springer.

Lovelock, James. The Vanishing Face of Gaia: A Final Warning. 2010. (ENG.). 304p. (gr. 9). pap. 15.00 *(978-0-465-01907-6(2))* Basic Bks.

Mahner, Martin & Bunge, Mario. Foundations of Biophilosophy. 2010. (Illus.). xviii, 423p. pap. 129.00 *(978-3-642-08276-4(9),* 3642082769) Springer.

May, Hope & May. Aristotle's Ethics: Moral Development & Human Nature. rev. ed. 2010. (Continuum Studies in Ancient Philosophy Ser.). (ENG., Illus.). 208p. 120.00 *(978-0-8264-9110-7(3))* Continuum International Publishing Group, Ltd. GBR. Dist: National Bk. Network.

Mayr, Ernst. What Makes Biology Unique? Considerations on the Autonomy of a Scientific Discipline. 2007. (ENG.). 246p. per. 19.99 *(978-0-521-70034-4(5))* Cambridge Univ. Pr.

McDougall, William. Riddle of Life. 2006. 300p. per. *(978-1-4067-0910-0(7),* Hesperides Pr.) Read Bks.

McLaughlin, Peter. What Functions Explain: Functional Explanation & Self-Reproducing Systems. 2007. (Cambridge Studies in Philosophy & Biology Ser.). (ENG.). 272p. pap. 58.00 *(978-0-521-03885-0(5))* Cambridge Univ. Pr.

McShea, Daniel W. & Brandon, Robert N. Biology's First Law: The Tendency for Diversity & Complexity to Increase in Evolutionary Systems. 2010. (ENG., Illus.). 184p. 55.00 *(978-0-226-56225-4(5))*; pap. 20.00 *(978-0-226-56226-1(3))* Univ. of Chicago Pr.

Millett, Stephan. Aristotle's Powers & Responsibility for Nature. 2011. (Berner Reihe philosophischer Studien Ser.). (ENG.). 304p. pap. ***(978-3-0343-0679-9(2))*** Lang, Peter.

Moinat, Frederic. Le vivant et sa Naturalisation: Le problème du naturalisme en biologie chez Husserl et le jeune Merleau-Ponty. 2011. (Phaenomenologica Ser.). (FRE.). 200p. 139.00 (978-94-007-1813-5(6), 9400718136) Springer.

Mondaini, Rubem P. & Pardalos, Panos M., eds. Mathematical Modelling of Biosystems. 2010. (Applied Optimization Ser.). xii, 305p. pap. 159.00 (978-3-642-09546-7(1), 3642095461) Springer.

Morange, Michel. Life Explained. Cobb, Matthew & DeBevoise, Malcolm, trs. from FRE. (Odile Jacob Book Ser.). (ENG.). 224p. 2009. pap. 16.00 (978-0-300-15850-2(5)) 2008. (Illus.). 25.00 (978-0-300-13732-3(X)) Yale Univ. Pr.

—Life Explained. 2008. 284p. pap. 35.00 (978-0-300-15083-4(0)) Yale Univ. Pr.

Okasha, Samir. Evolution & the Levels of Selection. 2009. (ENG., Illus.). 288p. pap. 39.95 (978-0-19-955671-7(7)) Oxford Univ. Pr., Inc.

Oksanen, Markku & Pietarinen, Juhani, eds. Philosophy & Biodiversity. 2007. (Cambridge Studies in Philosophy & Biology Ser.). (ENG.). 280p. pap. 62.00 (978-0-521-03914-7(2)) Cambridge Univ. Pr.

Plaisance, Kathryn S. & Reydon, Thomas A. C., eds. Philosophy of Behavioral Biology. 2011. (Boston Studies in the Philosophy of Science Ser.). (ENG., Illus.). viii, 373p. 189.00 (978-94-007-1950-7(7), 9400719507) Springer.

Plotkin, Henry. Evolutionary Worlds without End. 2010. (ENG.). 224p. 59.95 (978-0-19-954495-0(6)) Oxford Univ. Pr., Inc.

Preston, Christopher J. & Ouderkirk, Wayne, eds. Nature, Value, Duty: Life on Earth with Holmes Rolston, III. 2010. (International Library of Environmental, Agricultural & Food Ethics Ser.). xx, 281p. pap. 219.00 (978-90-481-7215-3(2), 9048172152) Springer.

Regis, Ed. What Is Life? Investigating the Nature of Life in the Age of Synthetic Biology. 2009. (ENG.). 208p. pap. 13.95 (978-0-19-538341-6(9)) Oxford Univ. Pr., Inc.

Rheinberger, Hans-Jörg. An Epistemology of the Concrete: Twentieth-Century Histories of Life. 2010. (ENG., Illus.). 352p. 89.95 (978-0-8223-4560-2(9)); pap. 24.95 (978-0-8223-4575-6(7)) Duke Univ. Pr.

Richards, Robert J. Philosophy of Biology, 2nd Edition. 2nd rev. ed. 2007. (ENG., Illus.). 1p. pap. 24.98 (978-1-59102-527-6(3)) Prometheus Bks., Pubs.

Richards, Robert J., ed. The Philosophy of Biology. 2008. (Oxford Handbooks Ser.). (ENG., Illus.). 656p. 150.00 (978-0-19-518205-7(7)) Oxford Univ. Pr., Inc.

Richards, Robert J. & Hull, David L., eds. The Cambridge Companion to the Philosophy of Biology. 2007. (Cambridge Companions to Philosophy Ser.). (ENG.). 552p. per. 38.99 (978-0-521-61671-3(9)) Cambridge Univ. Pr.

—The Cambridge Companion to the Philosophy of Biology. 2007. (Cambridge Companions to Philosophy Ser.). (ENG., Illus.). 544p. 105.00 (978-0-521-85128-2(9)) Cambridge Univ. Pr.

Riedl, Rupert. Riedls Kulturgeschichte der Evolutionstheorie: Die Helden, ihre Irrungen und Einsichten. 2007. (GER., Illus.). XI, 236p. 59.95 (978-3-540-43668-3(5), 3540436685) Springer.

Ritchie, David George. Darwinism & Politics: With Two Additional Essays on Human Evolution. 3rd ed. 2010. (Illus.). 536p. pap. 40.75 (978-1-147-74094-3(1)) BiblioBazaar.

Rosenberg, Alex & Arp, Robert. Philosophy of Biology: An Anthology. Rosenberg, Alex & Arp, Robert, eds. 2009. (Blackwell Philosophy Anthologies Ser.). (ENG., Illus.). 464p. 116.95 (978-1-4051-8317-8(9), Wiley-Blackwell) Wiley, John & Sons, Inc.

Rosenberg, Alex & Arp, Robert, eds. Philosophy of Biology: An Anthology. 2009. (Blackwell Philosophy Anthologies Ser.). (ENG., Illus.). 464p. pap. 59.95 (978-1-4051-8316-1(0), Wiley-Blackwell) Wiley, John & Sons, Inc.

Rosenberg, Alex & McShea, Daniel W. Philosophy of Biology: A Contemporary Introduction. 2007. (Routledge Contemporary Introductions to Philosophy Ser.). (ENG., Illus.). 256p. 120.00 (978-0-415-31592-0(1)); per. 35.95 (978-0-415-31593-7(X)) Routledge.

Rosenberg, Alexander. Darwinian Reductionism: Or, How to Stop Worrying & Love Molecular Biology. 2006. (Illus.). 272p. 42.50 (978-0-226-72729-5(7)) Univ. of Chicago Pr.

Ruse, Michael. The Oxford Handbook of Philosophy of Biology, 1 vol. 2010. (Oxford Handbooks Ser.). (ENG., Illus.). 656p. pap. 49.95 (978-0-19-973726-0(6)) Oxford Univ. Pr., Inc.

Sarkar, Sahotra. Molecular Models of Life: Philosophical Papers on Molecular Biology. 2007. (Life & Mind: Philosophical Issues in Biology & Psychology Ser.). (ENG., Illus.). 352p. (gr. 17). per. 25.00 (978-0-262-69350-9(X)) MIT Pr.

Sarkar, Sahotra & Plutynksi, Anya, eds. A Companion to the Philosophy of Biology. 2008. (Blackwell Companions to Philosophy Ser.: 49). (ENG.). 616p. 209.95 (978-1-4051-2572-7(1), Wiley-Blackwell) Wiley, John & Sons, Inc.

Sarkar, Sahotra & Plutynski, Anya, eds. A Companion to the Philosophy of Biology. 2010. (Blackwell Companions to Philosophy Ser.: 90). (ENG., Illus.). 616p. pap. 49.95 (978-1-4443-3785-3(8), Wiley-Blackwell) Wiley, John & Sons, Inc.

Schatz, G. A Matter of Wonder: What Biology Reveals about Us, Our World, & Our Dreams. 2011. (Illus.). 190p. (978-3-8055-9744-9(4)) Karger, S. AG.

Schifellite, Carmen James. Biology after the Sociobiology Debate: What Introductory Textbooks Say about the Nature of Science & Organisms. 2011. xxiv, 252p. (C). 82.95 (978-1-4331-0018-5(5)) Lang, Peter Publishing, Inc.

Smith, Justin E. H. & Nachtomy, Ohad, eds. Machines of Nature & Corporeal Substances in Leibniz. 2011. (New Synthese Historical Library). (Illus.). xv, 200p. 139.00 (978-94-007-0040-6(7), 9400700407) Springer.

Sober, Elliott, ed. Conceptual Issues in Evolutionary Biology. 3rd ed. 2006. (ENG., Illus.). 624p. (gr. 17). 88.00 (978-0-262-19549-2(6)); per. 48.00 (978-0-262-69338-7(0)) MIT Pr.

Steel, Daniel. Across the Boundaries: Extrapolation in Biology & Social Science. 2007. (Environmental Ethics & Science Policy Ser.). (ENG., Illus.). 256p. 65.00 (978-0-19-533144-8(3)) Oxford Univ. Pr., Inc.

Stewart-Williams, Steve. Darwin, God, & the Meaning of Life: How Evolutionary Theory Undermines Everything You Thought You Knew. 2010. (ENG.). 352p. 28.00 (978-0-521-76278-6(2)) Cambridge Univ. Pr.

Waddington, C. H., ed. Biological Processes in Living Systems. 2012. (ENG., Illus.). 299p. pap. 49.95 (978-1-4128-4276-1(X)) Transaction Pubs.

Waddington, C. H., ed. The Origin of Life Vol. 1: Toward a Theoretical Biology. 2008. (ENG., Illus.). 254p. pap. 89.95 (978-0-202-36302-8(3)) Aldine Transaction.

Wagner, Andreas. Paradoxical Life: Meaning, Matter, & the Power of Human Choice. 272p. 2011. (ENG.). pap. 20.00 (978-0-300-17152-5(8)) 2009. 28.00 (978-0-300-14923-4(9)) Yale Univ. Pr.

Wilson, Jack. Biological Individuality: The Identity & Persistence of Living Entities. 2007. (Cambridge Studies in Philosophy & Biology Ser.). (ENG.). 152p. pap. 32.00 (978-0-521-03688-7(7)) Cambridge Univ. Pr.

Wonders of Organic Life. 2006. 196p. per. 18.99 (978-1-4255-1575-1(4)) MPublishing.

Woodley, Michael. The Limits of Ecology: New Perspectives from a Theoretical Borderland. 2006. (Illus.). 128p. per. (978-1-84549-166-6(1)) arima publishing.

BIOLOGY—PROGRAMMED INSTRUCTION

Muwanga-Zake, Johnnie Wycliffe Frank, ed. Playing to Learn: Experiences in Virtual Biology Environments. 2010. (Progress in Education Ser.). pap. 43.00 (978-1-60876-862-2(7)) Nova Science Pubs., Inc.

BIOLOGY—RESEARCH

Aisner, Dara & McGinnis, J. Michael. The Learning Healthcare System: Workshop Summary (IOM Roundtable on Evidence-Based Medicine) Olsen, LeighAnne, ed. 2007. (ENG.). 374p. pap. 59.00 (978-0-309-10300-8(2)) National Academies Pr.

Ali, Syed Abid & Atiya, Abbasi. Scorpion Hemocyanin: The Blue Blood. 2011. 160p. pap. (978-3-639-33725-9(5)) VDM Verlag Dr. Mueller e.K.

Barbieri, Marcello, ed. Biosemiotics Research Trends. 2007. 283p. 79.00 (978-1-60021-574-2(2)) Nova Science Pubs., Inc.

Barnard, Chris, et al. Asking Questions in Biology: A Guide to Hypothesis Testing, Experimental Design & Presentation in Practical Work & Research Projects. 4th rev. ed. 2011. (ENG., Illus.). 264p. (C). pap. 48.40 (978-0-273-73468-0(7)) Benjamin-Cummings Publishing Co.

Barnbaum, Deborah R. The Ethics of Autism: Among Them, but Not of Them. 2008. (Bioethics & the Humanities Ser.). (ENG., Illus.). 248p. pap. 21.95 (978-0-253-22013-4(0), 0253220130) Indiana Univ. Pr.

Barthold, Stephen W., et al. The Mouse in Biomedical Research: Immunology, 4. 2nd ed. 2006. (American College of Laboratory Animal Medicine Ser.: 4). (ENG., Illus.). 392p. 136.00 (978-0-12-369458-4(2), Academic Pr.) Elsevier Science & Technology Bks.

Bauer, Henry H. The Origin, Persistence & Failings of HIV/AIDS Theory. 2007. (ENG., Illus.). 296p. per. 35.00 (978-0-7864-3048-2(6)) McFarland & Co., Inc. Pubs.

Benestad, Haakon Breien & Laake, Petter. Research Methodology in the Medical & Biological Sciences. Olsen, Bjorn Reino, ed. 2007. (ENG., Illus.). 512p. per. 50.95 (978-0-12-373874-5(1), Academic Pr.) Elsevier Science & Technology Bks.

Berger, Martijn P. F., et al. An Introduction to Optimal Designs for Social & Biomedical Research. 2009. (Statistics in Practice Ser.). (ENG., Illus.). 346p. 90.00 (978-0-470-69450-3(5), Wiley) Wiley, John & Sons, Inc.

Berhardt, Leon V. Advances in Medicine & Biology. 2011. (Advances in Medicine & Biology Ser.). 140.00 (978-1-61470-980-0(7), Nova Biomedical Bks.) Nova Science Pubs., Inc.

Berhardt, Leon V. Advances in Medicine & Biology Research. 2011. (Series: Advances in Biology & Medicine Ser.). 129.00 (978-1-61761-930-4(2)) Nova Science Pubs., Inc.

Berhardt, Leon V., ed. Advances in Medicine & Biology. (Advances in Biology & Medicine Ser.). 2012. 161p. 95.00 (978-1-61470-702-8(2)) Vol. 6. 2010. 129.00 (978-1-61668-970-4(6)) Vol. 24. 2011. 368p. 165.00 (978-1-61209-796-1(0)) Nova Science Pubs., Inc.

—Advances in Medicine & Biology: Volume 25. 2011. (Advances in Medicine & Biology Ser.). 339p. 129.00 (978-1-61209-797-8(9)) Nova Science Pubs., Inc.

—Advances in Medicine & Biology. Volume 1. 2010. (Advances in Biology & Medicine Ser.). (Illus.). xx, 460p. 195.00 (978-1-60876-863-9(5)) Nova Science Pubs., Inc.

—Advances in Medicine & Biology, Volume 2. 2010. (Advances in Biology & Medicine (Series Editor - Tsisana Shartava, M. D. - Tbilisi, Georgia) Ser.). 129.00 (978-1-60876-288-0(2)) Nova Science Pubs., Inc.

—Advances in Medicine & Biology. Volume 3. 2010. (Advances in Biology & Medicine Ser.). 98.00 (978-1-60876-015-2(4), Nova Biomedical Bks.) Nova Science Pubs., Inc.

—Advances in Medicine & Biology. Volume 4, 5 vols. 2010. (Illus.). 195.00 (978-1-60876-158-6(4)) Nova Science Pubs., Inc.

—Advances in Medicine & Biology. Volume 5, 5 vols. 2010. (Illus.). 129.00 (978-1-60456-557-7(8)) Nova Science Pubs., Inc.

—Advances in Medicine & Biology. Volume 7. 2010. (Series:Advances in Biology & Medicine Ser.). 98.00 (978-1-61728-008-5(9)) Nova Science Pubs., Inc.

—Advances in Medicine & Biology. Volume 8. 2010. (Advances in Biology & Medicine Ser.). 160.00 (978-1-61728-009-2(7)) Nova Science Pubs., Inc.

—Advances in Medicine & Biology. Volume 9. 2010. (Advances in Biology & Medicine Ser.). 129.00 (978-1-61728-026-9(7)) Nova Science Pubs., Inc.

Bielby, Philip. Competence & Vulnerability in Biomedical Research. 2008. (International Library of Ethics, Law, & the New Medicine Ser.). XIV, 238p. (C). 159.00 (978-1-4020-8603-8(2), 1402086032) Springer.

Biological Research for Energy & Medical Applications at the Department of Energy Office of Science: Hearing Before the Subcommittee on Energy & Environment, Committee on Science & Technology, House of Representatives, One Hundred Eleventh Congress, First Session, September 10, 2009. 2009. iv, 60p. (978-0-16-084982-4(9), 552-070-40361-2) United States Government Printing Office.

Biswas, Atanu, et al, eds. Statistical Advances in the Biomedical Sciences: Clinical Trials, Epidemiology, Survival Analysis, & Bioinformatics. 2008. (Wiley Series in Probability & Statistics Ser.: 630). (ENG., Illus.). 582p. 159.00 (978-0-471-94753-0(9), Wiley-Interscience) Wiley, John & Sons, Inc.

Bogdanske, John J., et al. Laboratory Mouse Procedural Techniques: Manual & DVD. 2010. (ENG., Illus.). 100p. pap. 59.95 (978-1-4398-5042-8(9), CRC Press) Taylor & Francis Group GBR. Dist: Taylor & Francis Group.

Bowers, David, et al. Getting Started in Health Research. 2011. (ENG., Illus.). 192p. pap. 41.95 (978-1-4051-9148-7(1)) Wiley, John & Sons, Inc.

Braggina, Josse R. Stem Cell Research Trends. 2007. 225.00 (978-1-60021-622-0(6)) Nova Science Pubs., Inc.

Braun, Louis & Lange, Maximilian, eds. Cancer Prevention Research Trends. 2008. (Illus.). xiv, 137p. 137.00 (978-1-60456-639-0(6)) Nova Science Pubs., Inc.

Carlson, Elof Axel. Times of Triumph, Times of Doubt: Science & the Battle for Public Trust. 2006. (ENG.). 227p. 39.00 (978-0-87969-805-8(5)) Cold Spring Harbor Laboratory Pr.

Clarke, Laura B. Migraine Disorders Research Trends. 2007. 129.00 (978-1-60021-553-7(X)) Nova Science Pubs., Inc.

Committee on a New Biology for the 21st Century: Ensuring the United States Leads the Coming Biology Revolution & National Research Council. A New Biology for the 21st Century. 2009. (ENG.). 112p. pap. 29.75 (978-0-309-14488-9(4)) National Academies Pr.

Committee on Assessing Fundamental Attitudes of Life Scientists as a Basis for Biosecurity Education & National Research Council Staff. A Survey of Attitudes & Actions on Dual Use Research in the Life Sciences: A Collaborative Effort of the National Research Council & the American Association for the Advancement of Science. 2009. (ENG.). 188p. pap. 87.00 (978-0-309-12510-9(3)) National Academies Pr.

Committee on Laboratory Security and Personnel Reliability Assurance Systems for Laboratories Conducting Research on Biological Select Agents and Toxins & National Research Council. Responsible Research with Biological Select Agents & Toxins. 2010. (ENG.). 188p. pap. 32.00 (978-0-309-14535-0(X)) National Academies Pr.

Conniff, Richard. The Species Seekers: Heroes, Fools, & the Mad Pursuit of Life on Earth. 2011. (ENG., Illus.). 480p. pap. 17.95 (978-0-393-34132-4(1), 34132) Norton, W. W. & Co., Inc.

Cram101 Textbook Reviews & Cram101 Textbook Reviews. Outlines & Highlights for Clinical & Translational Science: Principles of Human Research by David Robertson, ISBN. 2011. 354p. pap. 34.95 (978-1-61461-200-1(5)) Cram101 Inc.

—Outlines & Highlights for Culture of Human Stem Cells by R Freshney. 2011. 224p. pap. 30.95 (978-1-61830-591-6(3)) Cram101 Inc.

Dehmer, Matthias & Emmert-Streib, Frank, eds. Analysis of Complex Networks: From Biology to Linguistics. 2009. (ENG., Illus.). 480p. 232.00 (978-3-527-32345-6(7), Wiley-VCH) Wiley, John & Sons, Inc.

Dillner, Joakim, ed. Methods in Biobanking. 2010. (Methods in Molecular Biology Ser.). (Illus.). 300p. 139.00 (978-1-58829-995-6(3)) Humana Pr.

Ditmier, Lawrence F. New Developments in Obesity Research. 2006. (Illus.). 244p. 105.00 (978-1-60021-296-3(4)) Nova Science Pubs., Inc.

Doherty, Peter. The Beginner's Guide to Winning the Nobel Prize: Advice for Young Scientists. 2008. (ENG., Illus.). 320p. (gr. 17). pap. 22.95 (978-0-231-13897-0(0)) Columbia Univ. Pr.

Dummies Press Staff, et al. Stem Cells for Dummies. 2010. (ENG., Illus.). 384p. pap. 21.99 (978-0-470-25928-3(0), For Dummies) Wiley, John & Sons, Inc.

Dzeroski, Saso & Todorovski, Ljupco, eds. Computational Discovery of Scientific Knowledge: Introduction, Techniques, & Applications in Environmental & Life Sciences. 2007. (Lecture Notes in Artificial Intelligence Ser.). (Illus.). 326p. per. 79.95 (978-3-540-73919-7(X)) Springer.

Enna, S. J. & Williams, Michael. Contemporary Aspects of Biomedical Research: Drug Discovery. 2009. (ENG., Illus.). 520p. 241.00 (978-0-12-378642-5(8), Academic Pr.) Elsevier Science & Technology Bks.

Ereland, Wade T. Research Developments in Stem Cells. 2008. 129.00 (978-1-60456-455-6(5)) Nova Science Pubs., Inc.

Fong, Calvin A. Stem Cell Research Developments. 2007. (C). 225.00 (978-1-60021-601-5(3)) Nova Science Pubs., Inc.

Ford, Thomas D. New Cancer Research Developments. 2009. pap. 129.00 (978-1-60692-447-1(8)) Nova Science Pubs., Inc.

Forum on Neuroscience and Nervous System Disorders & Institute of Medicine. Autism & the Environment: Challenges & Opportunities for Research, Workshop Proceedings. 2008. (ENG.). 358p. pap. 71.50 (978-0-309-10881-2(0)) National Academies Pr.

Fox, Sherry C., et al. New Directions in the Skeletal Biology of Greece. 2009. (Occasional Wiener Laboratory Ser.). (ENG., Illus.). 304p. pap. 75.00 (978-0-87661-543-0(4)) American Schl. of Classical Studies at Athens.

Francis, Amy. Should the Government Fund Embryonic Stem Cell Research? 2009. (At Issue Ser.). (ENG.). 128p. (gr. 10-12). 22.50 (978-0-7377-4439-2(1)); (Illus.). pap. 31.80 (978-0-7377-4438-5(3)) Cengage Gale. (Greenhaven Pr., Inc.).

Freshney, R. Ian, et al. Culture of Human Stem Cells. 2007. (Culture of Specialized Cells Ser.: 12). (ENG., Illus.). 351p. 169.95 (978-0-470-05246-4(5), Wiley-Liss) Wiley, John & Sons, Inc.

Gallin, John I. & Ognibene, Frederick P., eds. Principles & Practice of Clinical Research. 2nd ed. 2007. (Principles & Practice of Clinical Research Ser.). (ENG., Illus.). 448p. 114.00 (978-0-12-369440-9(X), Academic Pr.) Elsevier Science & Technology Bks.

Germs, Viruses, & Secrets: Government Plans to Move Exotic Disease Research to the Mainland United States: Hearing Before the Subcommittee on Oversight & Investigations of the Committee on Energy & Commerce, House of Representatives, One Hundred Tenth Congress, Second Session, May 22, 2008. 2008. (Illus.). iii, 538p. (978-0-16-086822-1(X), 552-070-41738-9) United States Government Printing Office.

Germs, Viruses, & Secrets: The Silent Proliferation of Bio-Laboratories in the United States: Hearing Before the Subcommittee on Oversight & Investigations of the Committee on Energy & Commerce, House of Representatives, One Hundred Tenth Congress, First Session, October 4, 2007. 2008. (Illus.). v, 267p. (978-0-16-082525-5(3), 552-070-38560-6) United States Government Printing Office.

Greene, James & Castora, Frank J. Handbook of Biological Research Methodology. 2009. (Illus.). 139.95 (978-0-8493-7616-0(5)) CRC Pr. LLC.

Gunstream, Stanley E. Biological Explorations: A Human Approach. 6th ed. 2008. (ENG.). 448p. (C). pap. 102.00 (978-0-13-156072-7(7)) Benjamin-Cummings Publishing Co.

Hailman, Jack P. & Strier, Karen B. Planning, Proposing, & Presenting Science Effectively: A Guide for Graduate Students & Researchers in the Behavioral Sciences & Biology. 2nd rev. ed. 2006. (ENG., Illus.). 248p. per. 46.00 (978-0-521-53388-1(0)) Cambridge Univ. Pr.

Hannaway, C. Biomedicine in the Twentieth Century. 2008. (Illus.). pap. 182.00 (978-1-58603-832-8(X)) IOS Pr., Inc.

Hannes, Karin & Lockwood, Craig. Synthesizing Qualitative Research: Choosing the Right Approach. 2nd ed. 2012. (ENG., Illus.). 210p. pap. 54.95 (978-0-470-65638-9(7)) Wiley, John & Sons, Inc.

Häyry, Matti, et al, eds. Ethics in Biomedical Research: International Perspectives. 2007. (Value Inquiry Book Ser.: 186). 280p. per. 70.20 (978-90-420-2179-2(9)) Rodopi.

Hogan, Matthew T. & Altevogt, Bruce. From Molecules to Minds: Challenges for the 21st Century - Workshop Summary. 2008. (ENG.). 90p. pap. 23.00 (978-0-309-12092-0(6)) National Academies Pr.

Hulverscheidt, Marion & Laukötter, Anja. Infektion und Institution: Zur Wissenschaftsgeschichte des Robert Koch-Instituts im Nationalsozialismus. 2009. (GER & ENG., Illus.). 270p. pap. (978-3-8353-0507-6(7)) Wallstein-Verlag GmbH Verlag und Werbung.

Jones, James W., et al. The Ethics of Surgical Practice: Cases, Dilemmas, & Resolutions. 2008. (ENG.). 320p. 99.00 (978-0-19-532108-1(1)) Oxford Univ. Pr., Inc.

Kastor, John A. The National Institutes of Health, 1991-2008. 2010. (ENG., Illus.). 272p. 49.95 (978-0-19-973799-4(1)) Oxford Univ. Pr., Inc.

Kaye, Jane, et al. Governing Biobanks: Understanding the Interplay Between Law & Practice, 0 vols. 2012. (ENG.). 362p. pap. 90.00 (978-1-84113-905-0(X)) Hart Publishing Ltd. GBR. Dist: International Specialized Bk. Services.

Kellman, Barry. Bioviolence: Preventing Biological Terror & Crime. 2007. (ENG.). 390p. per. 32.99 (978-0-521-70969-9(5)); 88.99 (978-0-521-88325-2(3)) Cambridge Univ. Pr.

Khatree, Ravindra. Computational Methods in Biomedical Research. Naik, Dayanand N., ed. 2007. (Biostatistics Ser.). (ENG., Illus.). 432p. 109.95 (978-1-58488-577-1(7), Chapman & Hall/CRC) CRC Pr. LLC.

Kolo, Castulus, et al. Bioinformation: Problemlösungen für die Wissensgesellschaft. 2007. (Technik, Wirtschaft und Politik Ser.). (GER.). 192p. per. 39.49 (978-3-7908-1241-1(2)) Springer.

Lancelot, Gael. University Reorganisations in Biology. 2009. 286p. pap. (978-3-639-18320-7(7)) VDM Verlag Dr. Mueller e.K.

Larson, Pedro, et al. Tyrannosaurus rex, the Tyrant King. Carpenter, Kenneth & Larson, Peter L., eds. 2008. (Life of the Past Ser.). (ENG., Illus.). 456p. 49.95 (978-0-253-35087-9(5), 0253350875) Indiana Univ. Pr.

Lehr, H. -A., ed. Biobanking - an Essential Tool in Translational Research [Bibliography & Price not Definite.]. 2007. (Illus.). 84p. pap. (978-3-8055-8345-9(1)) Karger, S. AG.

Li, Shaoguang. Mouse Models of Human Blood Cancers: Basic Research & Pre-Clinical Applications. 2008. (Illus.). 256p. 169.00 (978-0-387-69130-5(8)) Springer.

Liang, Kung-Hao. Bioinformatics for Biomedical Science & Clinical Applications. 2012. 250p. 165.00 (978-1-907568-44-2(1)) Woodhead Publishing Ltd. GBR. Dist: Ingram Pub. Services.

Liu, Edison T. & Lauffenburger, Douglas A., eds. Systems Biomedicine: Concepts & Perspectives. 2009. (ENG., Illus.). 448p. (C). 103.00 (978-0-12-372550-9(X), Academic Pr.) Elsevier Science & Technology Bks.

Liu, Limin Angela, et al, eds. Handbook of Research on Computational & Systems Biology: Interdisciplinary Applications. 2011. (Illus.). 550p. 295.00 (978-1-60960-491-2(1), Medical Information Science Reference) IGI Global.

Mazur, Suzan. The Altenberg 16: An Exposé of the Evolution Industry. 2010. (ENG., Illus.). 376p. pap. 25.00 (978-1-55643-924-7(5)) North Atlantic Bks.

Mduluza, Takafira. A Gateway to Biomedical Research in Africa. 2006. 184p. 169.00 (978-1-60021-444-8(4)) Nova Science Pubs., Inc.

Meacci, Giovanni. Min Oscillations in Escherichia Coli. 2009. 164p. pap. *(978-3-639-07158-0(1))* VDM Verlag Dr. Mueller e.K.

Miller, Seumas & Selgelid, Michael. Ethical & Philosophical Consideration of the Dual-Use Dilemma in the Biological Sciences. 2008. VIII, 76p. (C). pap. 49.95 *(978-1-4020-8311-2(4)*, 1402083114) Springer.

Miura, Hina & Sasaki, Yuuto, eds. Angiotensin Research Progress. 2008. (Illus.). xii, 255p. (C). 185.00 *(978-1-60456-537-9(3))* Nova Science Pubs., Inc.

Moreno, Jonathan D., et al. Progress in Bioethics: Science, Policy, & Politics. 2011. (Basic Bioethics Ser.). (ENG., Illus.). 308p. (gr. 17). pap. 15.00 ***(978-0-262-51742-3(6))*** MIT Pr.

Morrison, Adrian R. An Odyssey with Animals: A Veterinarian's Reflections on the Animal Rights & Welfare Debate. 2009. (ENG., Illus.). 288p. 29.95 *(978-0-19-537444-5(4))* Oxford Univ. Pr., Inc.

Muñoz, Sebastián I., ed. Ecology Research Progress. 2008. (C). 129.00 *(978-1-60021-807-1(5))* Nova Science Pubs., Inc.

Nahmias, Yaakov. Methods in Bioengineering: Microdevices in Biology & Medicine. Nahmias, Yaakov & Bhatia, Sangeeta, eds. 2009. (Illus.). 274p. 129.00 *(978-1-59693-404-7(2))* Artech Hse., Inc.

National Research Council (U.S.)., Committee on Identification of Research Needs Relating to Potential Biological or Adverse Health Effects of Wireless Communications Devices Staff, contrib. by. Identification of Research Needs Relating to Potential Biological or Adverse Health Effects of Wireless Communication. 2008. (ENG.). 78p. pap. 21.00 *(978-0-309-11294-9(X))* National Academies Pr.

Overturf, Ken. Molecular Research in Aquaculture. 2009. (ENG., Illus.). 408p. 232.00 *(978-0-8138-1851-1(6)*, Wiley-Blackwell) Wiley, John & Sons, Inc.

Panel on Handling Missing Data in Clinical Trials & National Research Council. The Prevention & Treatment of Missing Data in Clinical Trials. 2010. (ENG.). 162p. pap. 38.50 *(978-0-309-15814-5(1))* National Academies Pr.

Paterson, Barbara L., et al, eds. Translating Chronic Illness Research into Practice. 2010. (ENG., Illus.). 224p. pap. 47.99 *(978-1-4051-5965-4(0)*, Wiley-Blackwell) Wiley, John & Sons, Inc.

Penson, David F., ed. Clinical Research Methods for Surgeons. 2010. (ENG., Illus.). 350p. pap. 115.00 *(978-1-61737-496-8(2)*, 1617374962) Humana Pr.

Petersen, Melody. Our Daily Meds: How the Pharmaceutical Companies Transformed Themselves into Slick Marketing Machines & Hooked the Nation on Prescription Drugs. 2009. (ENG., Illus.). 448p. pap. 17.00 *(978-0-312-42825-9(1))* Picador.

Popescu, Mihail. Data Mining Applications Using Ontologies in Biomedicine. Xu, Dong, ed. 2009. (Illus.). 260p. 119.00 *(978-1-59693-370-5(4))* Artech Hse., Inc.

Rabinow, Paul & Bennett, Gaymon. Designing Human Practices: An Experiment with Synthetic Biology. 2012. (ENG.). 200p. pap. 25.00 ***(978-0-226-70314-5(2))***; (Illus.). 75.00 ***(978-0-226-70313-8(4))*** Univ. of Chicago Pr.

Richter, Felix W., ed. Biotechnology: Research, Technology & Applications. 2008. 139.00 *(978-1-60456-901-8(8))* Nova Science Pubs., Inc.

Russo, Jose. The Tools of Science: The Handbook for the Apprentice of Biomedical Research. 2010. 228p. 52.00 *(978-981-4293-16-7(4))* World Scientific Publishing Co., Inc.

Shanks, Niall & Greek, C. Ray. Animal Models in Light of Evolution. 2009. 444p. pap. 64.95 *(978-1-59942-502-3(5)*, Brown Walker Pr.) Universal Pubs.

Simonsen, Sigmund. Acceptable Risk in Biomedical Research: European Perspectives. 2012. (International Library of Ethics, Law, & the New Medicine Ser.). (ENG., Illus.). xv, 293p. 139.00 ***(978-94-007-2677-2(5)***, 9400726775) Springer.

Singh, M. P., et al. Recent Trends in Biotechnology. 2011. (Biotechnology in Agriculture, Industry & Medicine Ser.). (Illus.). 145.00 *(978-1-61761-797-3(0)*, Nova Biomedical Bks.) Nova Science Pubs., Inc.

Srivastava, Alok & Roy, Ipsita. Bio-Nano-Geo Sciences: The Future Challenge. 2011. (ENG., Illus.). 256p. 139.00 *(978-3-642-12925-4(0)*, 3642129250) Springer.

Statnikov, Alexander. Gentle Introduction to Support Vector Machines in Biomedicine Vol. 1: Theory & Methods. 2011. 200p. 78.00 *(978-981-4324-38-0(8))* World Scientific Publishing Co., Inc.

Steel, Daniel. Across the Boundaries: Extrapolation in Biology & Social Science. 2007. (Environmental Ethics & Science Policy Ser.). (ENG., Illus.). 256p. 65.00 *(978-0-19-533144-8(3))* Oxford Univ. Pr., Inc.

Tereskerz, Patricia M. Clinical Research & the Law. 2012. (ENG.). 280p. pap. 74.95 ***(978-1-4051-9567-6(3)***, Wiley-Blackwell) Wiley, John & Sons, Inc.

Tollefsen, Christopher O. Biomedical Research & Beyond: Expanding the Ethics of Inquiry. 2007. (Routledge Annals of Bioethics Ser.: Vol. 5). (ENG.). 242p. 125.00 *(978-0-415-96116-5(5)*, 0415961165) Routledge.

Tuniz, Claudio, et al. The Bone Readers: Science & Politics in Human Origins Research. 2009. (ENG., Illus.). 272p. (C). pap. 24.95 *(978-1-59874-475-0(5))* Left Coast Pr., Inc.

Unlu, Mehmet Zubeyir. A Deformable Finite Element Model for Breast Image Registration. 2009. 104p. pap. *(978-3-639-12703-4(X))* VDM Verlag Dr. Mueller e.K.

Urbano, Kevin V., ed. Advances in Genetics Research. Volume 3. 2010. (Advances in Genetics Research Ser.). 145.00 *(978-1-61668-543-0(3)*, Nova Biomedical Bks.) Nova Science Pubs., Inc.

Usher-Smith, Juliet A., et al. Research in Medicine: Planning a Project- Writing a Thesis. 3rd ed. 2010. (ENG., Illus.). 144p. (C). pap. 34.99 *(978-0-521-13228-2(2))* Cambridge Univ. Pr.

Wang, Hui-Zhong & Tian, Miao. Proteins Researcher Biographical Sketches & Research Summaries. 2012. pap. ***(978-1-62100-777-7(4))*** Nova Science Pubs., Inc.

Williams, Valerie L., et al. Demonstrating & Communicating Research Impact: Preparing NIOSH Programs for External Review. 2009. 102p. pap. 38.00 *(978-0-8330-4650-5(0)*, mg-809) RAND Corp., The.

Worthington, E. & Worthington, E. Barton. The Evolution of IBP. 2009. (International Biological Programme Synthesis Ser.). (ENG.). 300p. pap. 31.99 *(978-0-521-11611-4(2))* Cambridge Univ. Pr.

21st Century Biology: Hearing Before the Subcommittee on Research & Science Education, Committee on Science & Technology, House of Representatives, One Hundred Eleventh Congress, Second Session, June 29, 2010. 2010. iv, 71p. *(978-0-16-086892-4(0)*, 552-070-41802-4) United States Government Printing Office.

BIOLOGY—SOCIAL ASPECTS

da Costa, Beatriz & Philip, Kavita, eds. Tactical Biopolitics: Art, Activism, & Technoscience. (Leonardo Bks.). (ENG., Illus.). 536p. (gr. 17). 2010. pap. 20.00 *(978-0-262-51491-0(5))* 2008. 42.00 *(978-0-262-04249-9(5))* MIT Pr.

Fenton, T. R. How Money Acts Like an Evolving Organism: Exploring Implications of the Biological Analogy of Money As Species. 2010. (Illus.). 179p. 99.95 *(978-0-7734-1409-9(6))* Mellen, Edwin Pr., The.

Graf, Dittmar. Evolutionstheorie - Akzeptanz und Vermittlung im europäischen Vergleich: Tagungsband Einstellung und Wissen zu Evolution und Wissenschaft in Europa. 2011. (GER., Illus.). xii, 164p. pap. 39.95 *(978-3-642-02227-2(8))* Springer.

Herron, John P. Science & the Social Good: Nature, Culture, & Community, 1865-1965. 2009. (ENG., Illus.). 288p. 49.95 *(978-0-19-538354-6(0))* Oxford Univ. Pr., Inc.

Hibbing, John, et al, eds. The Biology of Political Behavior. 2007. (ANNALS of the American Academy of Political & Social Science Ser.: 614). (Illus.). 228p. per. 34.00 *(978-1-4129-6404-3(0)*, 295614P) SAGE Pubns., Inc.

Hibbing, John & Smith, Kevin B., eds. The Biology of Political Behavior. 2007. (ANNALS of the American Academy of Political & Social Science Ser.: 614). (Illus.). 228p. 47.00 *(978-1-4129-6405-0(9)*, 295614C) SAGE Pubns., Inc.

Lerner, Richard M. Final Solutions. 2008. pap. 25.95 *(978-0-271-02802-6(5))* Pennsylvania State Univ. Pr.

Levine, Alex & Novoa, Adriana. ¡Darwinistas! the Construction of Evolutionary Thought in Nineteenth Century Argentina. 2012. (History of Science & Medicine Library). (ENG., Illus.). xvii, 279p. ***(978-90-04-22136-9(0))*** BRILL.

Levins, Richard & Lewontin, Richard C. Biology under the Influence: Dialectical Essays on the Coevolution of Nature & Society. 2007. (ENG., Illus.). 304p. 79.00 *(978-1-58367-158-0(7))* Monthly Review Pr.

Loomis, William F. Life as It Is: Biology for the Public Sphere. 2009. (ENG., Illus.). 272p. pap. 17.95 *(978-0-520-26001-6(5))* Univ. of California Pr.

Mazur, Suzan. The Altenberg 16: An Exposé of the Evolution Industry. 2010. (ENG., Illus.). 376p. pap. 25.00 *(978-1-55643-924-7(5))* North Atlantic Bks.

Pilgrim, Sarah & Pretty, Jules, eds. Nature & Culture: Rebuilding Lost Connections. 2010. (ENG., Illus.). 296p. 84.95 *(978-1-84407-821-9(3))* Routledge.

Schifellite, Carmen James. Biology after the Sociobiology Debate: What Introductory Textbooks Say about the Nature of Science & Organisms. 2011. xxiv, 252p. (C). 82.95 ***(978-1-4331-0018-5(5))*** Lang, Peter Publishing, Inc.

Starr, Cecie, et al. Cengage Advantage Books: Biology Today & Tomorrow without Physiology. 4th ed. 2012. (ENG.). 250p. (C). pap. 151.95 ***(978-1-133-36536-5(1))*** Brooks/Cole.

Watson, Fuller. The Social Impact of Modern Biology. 2012. (ENG.). 272p. (C). pap. 42.95 ***(978-0-415-61179-4(2))*** Routledge.

BIOLOGY—STATISTICAL MODELS

see Biometry

BIOLOGY—STUDY AND TEACHING

Amodeo, Vincent, et al. CliffsTestPrep Regents Living Environment Workbook. 2008. (ENG., Illus.). 284p. pap., wbk. ed. 9.99 *(978-0-470-16783-0(1)*, Cliff Notes) Wiley, John & Sons, Inc.

Audesirk, Gerald, et al. Books a la Carte for Biology: Life on Earth. 9th ed. 2010. (ENG.). 696p. (C). ring bd. 104.73 *(978-0-321-61541-1(7))* Benjamin-Cummings Publishing Co.

Bablanian, Gayne. Biological Investigations. rev. ed. 2010. (ENG.). 212p. spiral bd. 83.14 *(978-0-7575-0337-5(3))* Kendall Hunt Publishing Co.

Batdorf, Brad R. & Lacy, Elizabeth A. Biology. 4th ed. 2011. (Illus.). xiii, 674p. ***(978-1-60682-017-9(6))*** BJU Pr.

Belk, Colleen & Borden Maier, Virginia. Study Guide for Biology: Science for Life. 3rd ed. 2009. (ENG.). 408p. (C). pap. 43.73 *(978-0-321-58743-5(X))* Benjamin-Cummings Publishing Co.

Biological Sciences Curriculum Study Staff, compiled by. The Biology Teacher's Handbook. 4th ed. 2009. (ENG.). 338p. 29.95 *(978-0-87355-244-8(X))* National Science Teachers Assn.

Carolina Biological Staff, compiled by. Analyzing Population Growth. 2009. (Inquiries in Science Biology Ser.). *(978-1-4350-0362-0(4))*; tchr. ed., spiral bd. *(978-1-4350-0361-3(6))* Carolina Biological Supply Co.

—Changing over Time. 2009. (Inquiries in Science Biology Ser.). *(978-1-4350-0366-8(7))*; tchr. ed., spiral bd. *(978-1-4350-0365-1(9))* Carolina Biological Supply Co.

—Energizing Cells. 2009. (Inquiries in Science Biology Ser.). tchr. ed., spiral bd. *(978-1-4350-0345-3(4))* Carolina Biological Supply Co.

—Examining Cellular Transport. 2009. (Inquiries in Science Biology Ser.). tchr. ed., spiral bd. *(978-1-4350-0341-5(1))* Carolina Biological Supply Co.

—Observing Form & Function. 2009. (Inquiries in Science Biology Ser.). *(978-1-4350-0370-5(5))*; tchr. ed., spiral bd. *(978-1-4350-0369-9(1))* Carolina Biological Supply Co.

—Physiology Bundle. 2009. (Inquiries in Science Biology Ser.). *(978-1-4350-0380-4(2))* Carolina Biological Supply Co.

—Simulating the Darwinian Theory. 2009. (Inquiries in Science Biology Ser.). *(978-1-4350-0364-4(0))*; tchr. ed., spiral bd. *(978-1-4350-0363-7(2))* Carolina Biological Supply Co.

—Understanding Reproduction & Chromosomes. 2009. (Inquiries in Science Biology Ser.). *(978-1-4350-0352-1(7))*; tchr. ed., spiral bd. *(978-1-4350-0351-4(9))* Carolina Biological Supply Co.

Committee on Conceptual Framework for the New K-12 Science Education Standards & National Research Council. A Framework for K-12 Science Education: Practices, Crosscutting Concepts, & Core Ideas. 2012. (ENG.). 400p. pap. 39.95 ***(978-0-309-21742-2(3))*** National Academies Pr.

Cram101 Textbook Reviews. Outlines & Highlights for Marketing Intelligent Design: Law & the Creationist Agenda by Frank Ravitch, ISBN. 2011. 114p. pap. 28.95 ***(978-1-61654-551-2(8))*** Cram101 Inc.

—Outlines & Highlights for Prentice Hall Biology by Kenneth R Miller. 2011. 620p. pap. 40.95 ***(978-1-61905-708-1(5))*** Cram101 Inc.

Devine, Edward & Bernard, Gretchen. Biological Investigations I: Lab Exercises for General Biology I. 13th rev. ed. 2011. (ENG.). 166p. spiral bd. 29.99 ***(978-0-7575-8950-8(2))*** Kendall Hunt Publishing Co.

—Biological Investigations II: Lab Exercises for General Biology. 13th rev. ed. 2011. (ENG.). 166p. spiral bd. 29.99 ***(978-0-7575-8951-5(0))*** Kendall Hunt Publishing Co.

Doltar, Robert, et al. Preparing for the AP Biology Examination: Fast Track to A 5. 2012. (ENG.). 339p. pap. 18.99 ***(978-1-4354-6124-6(X))*** Course Technology.

Donaldson, Mindi. Virtual Destinations & Student Learning in Middle School: A Case Study of a Biology Museum Online. 2006. (ENG., Illus.). 288p. (C). 104.95 *(978-1-934043-27-1(3))* Cambria Pr.

Elawad. The Biology Study Mate. 4th rev. ed. 2011. (ENG.). 478p. spiral bd. 47.50 ***(978-0-7575-9373-4(9))*** Kendall Hunt Publishing Co.

Fleckenstein, Steven. Introduction to Biology Lab Manual Revised Printing. 2nd rev. ed. 2009. (ENG.). 114p. spiral bd. 37.00 *(978-0-7575-5603-6(5))* Kendall Hunt Publishing Co.

Freeman, Scott. Biological Science. 4th ed. 2010. (ENG.). 1320p. (C). 202.67 *(978-0-321-59796-0(6))* Benjamin-Cummings Publishing Co.

Hairston, Robert. Biology 221: Student Study Guide & Laboratory Manual. rev. ed. 2010. (ENG.). 224p. spiral bd. 49.58 *(978-0-7872-6430-7(X))* Kendall Hunt Publishing Co.

Hart, Lynette A., et al. Why Dissection? Animal Use in Education, 1 vol. 2008. (Illus.). 240p. 49.95 *(978-0-313-32390-4(9)*, GR2390) Greenwood Publishing Group, Inc.

Healan, Tammy. I Live Inside Your Head. 2011. 28p. pap. 12.49 *(978-1-4343-6832-4(7))* AuthorHouse.

Hoefnagels. Biology: The Essentials. 2012. 672p. pap. ***(978-0-07-809692-1(8))*** McGraw-Hill Cos., The.

Hoefnagels, Marielle. Biology: Concepts & Investigations. 2nd ed. 2011. (ENG.). (C). 192.00 *(978-0-07-747483-6(X)*, 007747483X, McGraw-Hill Science, Engineering & Mathematics) McGraw-Hill Higher Education.

Holt, Rinehart and Winston Staff. Modern Biology: Teaching Resources. 6th ed. Date not set. pap. 224.33 *(978-0-03-036662-8(3))* Holt McDougal.

Humes, Edward. Monkey Girl: Evolution, Education, Religion, & the Battle for America's Soul. 400p. 2008. (ENG.). pap. 15.99 *(978-0-06-088549-6(1)*, HarperPerennial) 2007. 25.95 *(978-0-06-088548-9(3)*, Ecco) HarperCollins Pubs.

Hutchins, Michael, ed. Grzimek's Animal Life Encyclopedia: Evolution. 2011. 380p. 205.00 *(978-1-4144-8669-7(3))* Cengage Gale.

Huxley, Henry Thomas. Lectures on Evolution. 2007. 56p. per. 87.99 *(978-1-4280-7666-2(2))* IndyPublish.com.

Huxley, Thomas Henry. American Addresses: With a Lecture on the Study of Biology. 2006. (ENG.). 184p. per. 22.95 *(978-1-4286-3745-0(1))* Kessinger Publishing, LLC.

Jensen, Judy Elgin. NSTA Tool Kit for Teaching Evolution. 2008. (ENG.). 73p. pap. 9.95 *(978-1-933531-46-5(0))* National Science Teachers Assn.

Johnson, George. Loose Leaf Version for the Living World. 7th ed. 2011. (ENG.). (C). ring bd. 128.33 *(978-0-07-743124-2(3)*, 0077431243, McGraw-Hill Science, Engineering & Mathematics) McGraw-Hill Higher Education.

Jones, Mary & Jones, Geoff. CSEC Biology: A Foundation Course Teacher's Resource. 2008. tchr. ed. incl. cd-rom *(978-0-521-70350-5(6))* Cambridge Univ. Pr.

Keller, R W. Biology Connects to Language. 2006. (Real Science-4-Kids Ser.). (Illus.). 77p. per. 21.95 *(978-0-9765097-6-9(8))* Gravitas Pubns., Inc.

—Biology Level I Teacher's Manual. 2006. (Real Science-4-Kids Ser.). (Illus.). 86p. per. 21.95 *(978-0-9749149-9-2(1))* Gravitas Pubns., Inc.

Keller, Rebecca W. Real Science-4-Kids PreLevel I Biology Teacher's Manual. 2008. 23.95 *(978-0-9799459-2-2(5))* Gravitas Pubns., Inc.

Kinney, Cyndi. Apologia Exploring Creation with Biology 2nd Edition Lapbook Journal. 2010. (YA). (ENG.). pap. 64.99 *(978-1-61625-136-9(0))*; cd-rom 36.99 *(978-1-61625-135-2(2))* Knowledge Box Central.

Koba, Susan & Tweed, Anne. Hard-to-Teach Biology Concepts: A Framework to Deepen Student Understanding. 2009. 260p. pap. 32.95 *(978-1-933531-41-0(X))* National Science Teachers Assn.

Krogh, David. Biology: A Guide to the Natural World. 5th ed. 2011. (ENG.). (C). 23.40 *(978-0-321-68308-3(0))* Benjamin-Cummings Publishing Co.

Krüger, Dirk & Vogt, Helmut. Handbuch der Theorien in der biologiedidaktischen Forschung: Ein Handbuch für Lehramtsstudenten und Doktoranden. 2009. (Illus.). xiv, 272p. pap. *(978-3-540-68165-6(5))* Springer Singapore Pte. Ltd.

Larson, Sue C. Academic Literacy Instruction. 2011. 664p. pap. ***(978-3-8443-3363-3(0))*** Lambert Academic Publishing.

Lebo, Lauri. The Devil in Dover: An Insider's Story of Dogma V. Darwin in Small-Town America. 2008. (ENG.). 238p. 24.95 *(978-1-59558-208-9(8)*, New Pr., The.

Meadows, Lee. The Missing Link: Teaching Evolution as a Unifying Concept. 2009. 152p. pap. 22.50 *(978-0-325-01749-5(2)*, E01749) Heinemann.

Miller, Kenneth & Levine, Joseph. Biology. (YA). (gr. 9-10). tchr. ed. 85.97 *(978-0-13-166288-9(0))*; stu. ed. 65.47 *(978-0-13-166255-1(4))* Prentice Hall (Schl. Div.).

Muwanga-Zake, Johnnie Wycliffe Frank, ed. Playing to Learn: Experiences in Virtual Biology Environments. 2010. (Progress in Education Ser.). pap. 43.00 *(978-1-60876-862-2(7))* Nova Science Pubs., Inc.

Orians, Gordon H., et al. Evolution, Diversity & Ecology, Vol. 2. 8th rev. ed. 2006. (ENG., Illus.). 389p. (C). pap. 70.95 *(978-0-7167-7674-1(X))* Freeman, W. H. & Co.

Pack, Phillip E. & Wiley Publications Staff. CliffsNotes Biology Bundle. 2009. (ENG.). 24.99 *(978-0-470-44525-9(4)*, Cliff Notes) Wiley, John & Sons, Inc.

Peterson's. Graduate Programs in the Biological Sciences. 45th ed. 2010. (ENG.). 550p. (YA). 54.95 *(978-0-7689-2854-9(0))* Peterson's.

—Graduate Programs in the Biological Sciences 2010: More Than 2,800 Gradute Programs in 56 Disciplines. Schwartz, Jill, ed. 44th ed. 2009. (ENG.). 1152p. (YA). 54.95 *(978-0-7689-2710-8(2))* Peterson's.

Peterson's. Graduate Programs in the Biological Sciences 2012 (Grad 3) 46th ed. 2011. (ENG.). 668p. (YA). (gr. 7-17). 54.95 ***(978-0-7689-3282-9(3))*** Peterson's.

Peterson's Guides Staff, creator. Peterson's Graduate Programs in the Biological Sciences: Book 3. 41st ed. 2006. (ENG., Illus.). 1320p. 54.00 *(978-0-7689-2159-5(7))* Peterson's.

Pike, Nathan. Exploring Teaching & Learning in the Graduate Biosciences. 2009. 84p. pap. *(978-3-639-15526-6(2))* VDM Verlag Dr. Mueller e.K.

Postlethwait, John H. & Hopson, Janet L. Life. 2010. (Available Titles CourseMate Ser.). (ENG.). 320p. pap. 83.00 *(978-0-538-74134-7(1))* Brooks/Cole.

Potter, Steve. Biology. 2008. (Illus.). 113p. tchr. ed., spiral bd. 159.50 *(978-0-340-95765-3(4))* Hodder Education GBR. Dist: Trans-Atlantic Pubns., Inc.

Purves, William K., et al. Life Lecture Notebook. 8th ed. 2006. (ENG.). 552p. (C). pap. 31.95 *(978-0-7167-7894-3(7))* Freeman, W. H. & Co.

Ravitch, Frank S. Marketing Intelligent Design: Law & the Creationist Agenda. 2010. (ENG.). 360p. 85.00 *(978-0-521-19153-1(X))* Cambridge Univ. Pr.

Read, Graham. Case Studies in Classification, Evolution & Biodiversity, Pack. 2009. (Illus.). 189p. spiral bd. 225.00 *(978-0-340-97247-2(5))* Hodder Education GBR. Dist: Trans-Atlantic Pubns., Inc.

Reece, Jane B., et al. Blackboard Student Access Kit for Campbell Biology. 9th ed. 2011. (ENG.). (C). 23.40 *(978-0-321-68333-5(1))* Benjamin-Cummings Publishing Co.

Reiss, Michael, ed. Teaching Secondary Biology. 2nd ed. 2012. (Illus.). 318p. pap., pap. 57.50 ***(978-1-4441-2431-6(5))*** Hodder Education GBR. Dist: Trans-Atlantic Pubns., Inc.

Robbins, Laurie R. Field & Lab Biology for Elementary Teaching Majors. 2nd rev. ed. 2010. (ENG.). 258p. ring bd. 64.00 *(978-0-7575-5199-4(8))* Kendall Hunt Publishing Co.

Rosenblatt, Betty & Warrington, Sarah. Explorations in General Biology. rev. ed. 2011. (ENG.). 336p. spiral bd. 97.35 *(978-0-7575-8005-5(X))* Kendall Hunt Publishing Co.

Russell, Peter J., et al. Biology: The Dynamic Science. 2nd ed. 2011. (Available Titles CourseMate Ser.). (ENG.). (C). 1456p. 208.95 *(978-0-538-74124-8(4))*; 496p. pap. 97.95 *(978-0-538-47631-7(1))*; 496p. pap. 96.95 *(978-0-538-49372-7(0))*; 480p. pap. 96.95 *(978-0-538-49374-1(7))*; 560p. pap. 96.95 *(978-0-538-49373-4(9))* Brooks/Cole.

—Biology: The Dynamic Science Study Guide. 2nd ed. 2011. (ENG.). 496p. (C). pap. 59.95 *(978-0-538-49366-6(6))* Brooks/Cole.

Sadava, et al. Life: The Science of Biology. 8th rev. ed. 2006. (ENG., Illus.). 1121p. (C). 189.95 *(978-0-7167-7671-0(5))* Freeman, W. H. & Co.

Sadava, David, et al. Cell & Heredity Vol. 1, Vol. 1. 8th rev. ed. 2006. (ENG., Illus.). 389p. (C). pap. 74.95 *(978-0-7167-7673-4(1))* Freeman, W. H. & Co.

—Plants & Animals, Vol. 3. 8th rev. ed. 2006. (ENG., Illus.). 332p. (C). pap. 70.95 *(978-0-7167-7675-8(8))* Freeman, W. H. & Co.

Shelp, et al. Biology. Date not set. (Adaptable Courseware-Hardside Ser.). lab manual ed. 17.50 net. *(978-0-534-56571-8(9))* Wadsworth.

Singham, Mano & Russo, Charles J. God vs. Darwin: The War Between Evolution & Creationism in the Classroom. 2009. (ENG.). 192p. 40.00 *(978-1-60709-169-1(0))* Rowman & Littlefield Education.

Starkey, Walter. Evolution Exposed & Intelligent Designed Explained. 2011. 110p. 29.99 ***(978-1-4628-7225-1(5))*** Xlibris Corp.

Starr, Cecie, et al. Student Interactive Workbook for Starr/Evers.Starr's Biology: Today & Tomorrow with Physiology, 3rd. 3rd ed. 2009. (ENG.). 336p. (C). pap. 63.95 *(978-0-495-82762-7(2))* Brooks/Cole.

Study Guide for Muskavitch/Roche's Biology. 2009. (C). pap. 29.95 *(978-0-534-99884-4(4))* Brooks/Cole.

Taggart, Robert. Introduction to Life Science. 256p. tchr. ed. 25.95 *(978-0-8251-4308-3(X)*, 0-4308X) Walch Education.

Tiner, John Hudson. Exploring the World of Biology: From Mushrooms to Complex Life Forms. 2009. pap. 13.99 *(978-0-89051-552-5(2))* Master Bks.

Walch Publishing Staff. Real-Life Science: Biology. 2007. (gr. 9-12). pap., tchr. ed. 21.00 *(978-0-8251-6402-6(8))* Walch Education.

Web of Life. 4.50 *(978-0-687-07608-6(0))* Abingdon Pr.

Wheeler, Ward C. Systematics: A Course of Lectures. 2012. (ENG.). 448p. 149.95 ***(978-0-470-67170-2(X))***; pap. 99.95 ***(978-0-470-67169-6(6))*** Wiley, John & Sons, Inc. (Wiley-Blackwell).

Wood, Piers. A2 Biology Planning & Resource Pack with Oxbox CD-ROM. 2009. (ENG.). 304p. (YA). cd-rom 900.00 *(978-0-19-915272-8(1))* Oxford Univ. Pr., Inc.

Wymer, Carol. Inquiry Biology for K-8 Teachers. 2nd ed. 2011. (ENG.). 338p. (C). pap. 37.00 ***(978-1-256-31849-1(3))*** Pearson Learning Solutions.

Wynne, Sharon. FTCE Biology 6-12. 2006. (Xam Ftce Ser.). (ENG., Illus.). 194p. per. 59.95 *(978-1-58197-801-8(4))* XAMonline, Inc.

—GACE Biology 026, 027. 2008. (Xam Gace Ser.). (ENG.). 202p. pap., pupil's gde. ed. 64.95 *(978-1-58197-773-8(5))* XAMonline, Inc.

Wynne, Sharon & Xamonline Staff. FTCE Biology 6-12. 2008. (ENG.). 236p. pap., pupil's gde. ed. 64.95 *(978-1-58197-689-2(5))* XAMonline, Inc.

Xamonline Staff, creator. CSET Biology-Life Science 120, 124. 2008. (ENG.). 196p. pap. 64.95 *(978-1-58197-585-7(6))* XAMonline, Inc.

BIOLOGY—TERMINOLOGY

see also Botany—Terminology

Badziong, Hans-Jurgen. Semantische Strukturen Wissenschaftlicher Wirklichkeitskonstruktionen: Eine Qualitative Deskription Am Beispiel der Fachsprache der Biologie. (GER., Illus.). XII, 344p. pap. 68.95 *(978-3-631-56444-8(9))* Lang, Peter GmbH, Europaischer Verlag der Wissenschaften DEU. Dist: Lang, Peter Publishing, Inc.

BIOLOGY—VOCATIONAL GUIDANCE

Hailman, Jack P. & Strier, Karen B. Planning, Proposing, & Presenting Science Effectively: A Guide for Graduate Students & Researchers in the Behavioral Sciences & Biology. 2nd rev. ed. 2006. (ENG., Illus.). 248p. per. 46.00 *(978-0-521-53388-1(0))* Cambridge Univ. Pr.

Longson, Sally. Life after... Biological Sciences: A Practical Guide to Life after Your Degree. 2007. (Illus.). 178p. per. 21.95 *(978-0-415-41249-0(8))* Routledge.

BIOLOGY, ECONOMIC

see also Botany, Economic; Ethnobiology; Zoology, Economic

Clark, Colin W. Mathematical Bioeconomics: The Mathematics of Conservation. 3rd ed. 2010. (Pure & Applied Mathematics: a Wiley Series of Texts, Monographs & Tracts Ser.: 91). (ENG., Illus.). 368p. 111.00 *(978-0-470-37299-9(0)*, Wiley) Wiley, John & Sons, Inc.

Rodriguez-Labajos, Beatriz, ed. Assessing Biodiversity Risks with Socio-Economic Methods: The ALARM Experience (Illustrated) 2009. 366p. pap. 147.50 *(978-954-642-490-7(0))* Pensoft Pubs. BGR. Dist: Coronet Bks.

BIOLOGY, ELECTRONICS IN

see Electronics in Biology

BIOLOGY, EXPERIMENTAL

see also Biology—Experiments; Ovum Implantation

Dahm, Ralf. Modellorganismen. 2007. pap. *(978-3-7643-6770-1(9)*, 3764367709) Birkhauser Boston.

Lambris, J. D., ed. Current Topics in Complement. 2006. (Advances in Experimental Medicine & Biology Ser.: Vol. 586). (Illus.). xxii, 406p. 229.00 *(978-0-387-32231-5(0)*, 0387322310) Springer.

Lutz, Peter L. The Rise of Experimental Biology: An Illustrated History. 2010. (Illus.). 216p. pap. 79.95 *(978-1-61737-213-1(7)*, 1617372137) Humana Pr.

Petersen, John E. Enclosed Experimental Ecosystems & Scale: Tools for Understanding & Managing Coastal Ecosystems. 2009. (Illus.). x, 221p. pap. 49.95 *(978-0-387-76768-0(1)*, 0387767681) Springer.

Weber, Marcel. Philosophy of Experimental Biology. 2010. (Cambridge Studies in Philosophy & Biology Ser.). (ENG., Illus.). 376p. pap. 36.99 *(978-0-521-14344-8(6))* Cambridge Univ. Pr.

BIOLOGY, MOLECULAR

see Molecular Biology

BIOLOGY AS A PROFESSION

see Biology—Vocational Guidance

BIOLOGY IN ART

Clark, Andrew H. Diderot's Part: Aesthetics & Physiology. 2008. (Illus.). 242p. 99.95 *(978-0-7546-5438-4(9))* Ashgate Publishing Co.

Kunz, Sabine, ed. Observing Beast, Time, Evolution: Art & Natural Science. 2009. (ENG., Illus.). 128p. pap. 28.50 *(978-3-86678-206-8(3))* Kerber Verlag DEU. Dist: D.A.P./Distributed Art Pubs.

Mitchell, Robert & Mitchell, Robert E. Bioart & the Vitality of Media. 2010. (In Vivo Ser.). (ENG., Illus.). 224p. pap. 30.00 *(978-0-295-99008-8(2))* Univ. of Washington Pr.

Mitchell, Robert E. Bioart & the Vitality of Media. 2010. (In Vivo Ser.). (ENG., Illus.). 224p. 60.00 *(978-0-295-99007-1(4))* Univ. of Washington Pr.

Rhoades, Jason, illus. Jason Rhoades' Black Pussy Cocktail Coffee Table Book, 1 vol. 2008. (ENG.). 306p. 80.00 *(978-3-86521-631-1(5))* Steidl, Gerhard Druckerei und Verlag DEU. Dist: Innovative Logistics.

Rickli, Hannes, ed. Videograms. 2011. (ENG & GER., Illus.). 368p. 110.00 *(978-3-85881-325-1(7))* Scheidegger und Spiess AG, Verlag CHE. Dist: Chicago Distribution Ctr.

Ronell, Avital & Kac, Eduardo. Life Extreme: An Illustrated Guide to New Life, 1 vol. 2007. (ENG., Illus.). 128p. per. 39.95 *(978-2-914563-34-5(5))* Dis Voir Editions FRA. Dist: D.A.P./Distributed Art Pubs.

Rush, Michael, ed. Alexis Rockman: the Weight of Air. 2009. (ENG., Illus.). 135p. 45.00 *(978-0-9761593-6-0(8))* Brandeis Univ., Rose Art Museum.

Yu, Peng & Yuan, Sun. Sun Yuan & Peng Yu: Can't Have it All. 2010. (ENG., Illus.). 250p. pap. 50.00 *(978-988-18033-8-2(1))* Timezone 8 Ltd. HKG. Dist: D.A.P./Distributed Art Pubs.

BIOLUMINESCENCE

Brovko, Lubov. Bioluminescence for Food & Environmental Microbiological Safety. 2007. (Tutorial Texts in Optical Engineering Ser.: Vol. 74). (Illus.). 88p. pap. 48.00 *(978-0-8194-6643-3(3))* SPIE.

—Cells Illuminated: In Vivo Optical Imaging. 2010. (Tutorial Text Ser.). (Illus.). 162p. pap. 61.00 *(978-0-8194-8247-1(1))* SPIE.

Corey, Michael J. Coupled Bioluminescent Assays: Methods, Evaluations, & Applications. 2008. (ENG., Illus.). 308p. 139.00 *(978-0-470-10883-3(5)*, Wiley) Wiley, John & Sons, Inc.

Creath, Katherine. The Nature of Light: Light in Nature: 16 August 2006, San Diego, California, USA. 2006. (Proceedings of SPIE Ser.). (Illus.). 88p. pap. 60.00 *(978-0-8194-6364-7(7))* SPIE.

—The Nature of Light: Light in Nature II: 10-11 August 2008, San Diego, California, USA. 2008. (Proceedings of SPIE Ser.). (Illus.). 120p. pap. 60.00 *(978-0-8194-7277-9(8))* SPIE.

Creath, Katherine & Shaw, Joseph. The Nature of Light: Light in Nature III. 2010. (Proceedings of SPIE Ser.). 96p. pap. 60.00 ***(978-0-8194-8278-5(1))*** SPIE.

Herring, Peter J., et al, eds. Light & Life in the Sea. 2009. (ENG., Illus.). 368p. pap. 48.00 *(978-0-521-10548-4(X))* Cambridge Univ. Pr.

Jiin-Ju Chang, et al, eds. Biophotons. 2010. 428p. pap. 289.00 *(978-90-481-5033-5(7)*, 9048150337) Springer.

Jung, Gregor, ed. Fluorescent Proteins I: From Understanding to Design. 2011. (Springer Series on Fluorescence Ser.). (ENG., Illus.). xii, 268p. 309.00 ***(978-3-642-23371-5(6)***, 3642233716) Springer.

Love, John. The Secrets of Western & Eastern Occultism & Mysticism: The essential methods for billions bioluminescences with scientific Explanations. 2011. 36p. pap. 16.95 ***(978-1-4626-1262-8(8))*** PublishAmerica, Inc.

Mader, Kevin. Towards Clearer Imaging of Luminescent & Bioluminescent Samples. 2011. 68p. pap. ***(978-3-8443-8796-4(X))*** Lambert Academic Publishing.

Phipson, T. L. Phosphorescence - or, the Emission of Light by Minerals, Plants, & Animals. 2009. 228p. pap. 28.45 *(978-1-4446-0658-4(1))* Barclay Pr., Inc.

Roda, A. Chemiluminescence & Bioluminescence: Past, Present & Future. 2010. (ENG., Illus.). 608p. (C). 192.00 ***(978-1-84755-812-1(7))*** Royal Society of Chemistry, The GBR. Dist: Ingram Pub. Services.

Rodgerson, David J., ed. Bioluminescence: Characteristics, Adaptations & Biotechnology. 2011. (Biochemistry Research Trends Ser.). (Illus.). 189p. 89.00 *(978-1-61209-747-3(2))* Nova Science Pubs., Inc.

Roshchina. Fluorescing World Plant Secret Cells: Fluorescing World of Plant Secretory Cells. 2008. (ENG.). 356p. 99.95 *(978-1-57808-515-6(2))* BIOS Scientific Publishers Ltd. GBR. Dist: Taylor & Francis Group.

Shimomura, Osamu. Bioluminescence: Chemical Principles & Methods. 2011. 500p. 120.00 ***(978-981-4366-08-3(0))*** 2006. (Illus.). 470p. 111.00 *(978-981-256-801-4(8))* World Scientific Publishing Co., Inc.

Szalay, Aladar A., et al, eds. Bioluminescence & Chemiluminescence: Chemistry, Biology & Applications: Proceedings of the 14th International Symposium. 2007. (Illus.). 283p. 124.00 *(978-981-270-816-8(2))* World Scientific Publishing Co., Inc.

BIOMAGNETISM

see also Animal Magnetism; Magnetic Fields—Physiological Effect

Cheyne, Douglas, et al, eds. New Frontiers in Biomagnetism: Proceedings of the 15th International Conference on Biomagnetism, Vancouver, BC, Canada, August 21-25 2006. 2007. (International Congress Ser.: 1300). (ENG., Illus.). 816p. 275.00 *(978-0-444-52885-8(7)*, Elsevier) Elsevier - Health Sciences Div.

Häfeli, Urs, et al, eds. Scientific & Clinical Applications of Magnetic Carriers. 2010. (ENG.). 652p. pap. 389.00 *(978-1-4419-3283-9(6)*, 1441932836) Springer.

Ionescu, Adrian M. & Bland, J. A. C. Biomagnetism & Magnetic Biosystems Based on Molecular Recognition Processes. 2008. (AIP Conference Proceedings Ser.). (Illus.). 216p. 112.00 *(978-0-7354-0547-9(6))* American Institute of Physics.

Supek, Selma & Sušac, Ana, eds. 17th International Conference on Biomagnetism: Biomag March 28 - April 1 2010. 2010. (IFMBE Proceedings Ser.). (ENG.). xx, 458p. pap. 299.00 *(978-3-642-12196-8(9)*, 3642121969) Springer.

BIOMARKERS

see Biochemical Markers

BIOMASS

see also Biology

Amin Salehi, Farnaz. Bagasse As a Fuel for Combined Heat & Power. 2011. 132p. pap. ***(978-3-8454-1483-6(9))*** Lambert Academic Publishing.

Babu, Mohammed. Effects of Algal Biofilms & Operational Conditions on Nitrogen Transformations & Removal in Waste Stabilization Ponds. 2011. (ENG.). 140p. pap. 59.95 *(978-0-415-66946-7(4)*, CRC Press) Taylor & Francis Group GBR. Dist: Taylor & Francis Group.

Badeau, Jean-Pierre & Levi, Albrecht. Biomass Gasification: Chemistry, Processes & Applications. 2009. (Renewable Energy: Research, Development & Policies Ser.). (Illus.). xiv, 474p. 129.00 *(978-1-60741-461-2(9))* Nova Science Pubs., Inc.

Basu, Prabir. Biomass Gasification & Pyrolysis: Practical Design & Theory. 2010. (ENG., Illus.). 376p. 140.00 *(978-0-12-374988-8(3)*, Academic Pr.) Elsevier Science & Technology Bks.

Bates, Albert K. The Biochar Solution: Carbon Farming & Climate Change. 2010. (ENG., Illus.). 208p. pap. 17.95 ***(978-0-86571-677-3(3)***, 9780865716773) New Society Pubs., Ltd. CAN. Dist: Consortium Bk. Sales & Distribution.

Demirbas, Ayhan. Biorefineries: For Biomass Upgrading Facilities. 2009. (Green Energy & Technology Ser.). (ENG., Illus.). ix, 240p. 199.00 *(978-1-84882-720-2(2)*, 1848827202) Springer.

Doshi, Veena. Investigation in Ash Issues During Co-Combustion of Coal & Biomass. 2010. 152p. pap. *(978-3-639-14418-5(X))* VDM Verlag Dr. Mueller e.K.

Dunford, Nurhan T., ed. Food & Industrial Bioproducts & Bioprocessing. 2012. (ENG., Illus.). 392p. 199.95 ***(978-0-8138-2105-4(3)***, Wiley-Blackwell) Wiley, John & Sons, Inc.

Eljamal, Osama. Solute Transport with Biological Processes in Porous Medi. 2010. 160p. pap. *(978-3-639-25924-7(6))* VDM Verlag Dr. Mueller e.K.

Gupta, Priti. Bioethanol Production from Saccharum Spontaneum Using Pichia Stipitis. 2011. 120p. pap. ***(978-3-8443-8515-1(0))*** Lambert Academic Publishing.

Hanumantharao, Bindumadhava, et al. Plant Isotope Signatures: For Crop Traits. 2011. 180p. pap. ***(978-3-8454-0216-1(4))*** Lambert Academic Publishing.

Himmel, Michael E., ed. Biomass Recalcitrance: Deconstructing the Plant Cell Wall for Bioenergy. 2008. (ENG., Illus.). 528p. 195.00 *(978-1-4051-6360-6(7)*, Wiley-Blackwell) Wiley, John & Sons, Inc.

Hood, Elizabeth E., et al, eds. Plant Biomass Conversion. 2011. (ENG., Illus.). 376p. 199.95 *(978-0-8138-1694-4(7)*, Wiley-Blackwell) Wiley, John & Sons, Inc.

Hoover, Coeli M., ed. Field Measurements for Forest Carbon Monitoring: A Landscape-Scale Approach. (ENG., Illus.). xviii, 240p. 2010. pap. 149.00 *(978-90-481-7896-4(7)*, 9048178967) 2008. 149.00 *(978-1-4020-8505-5(2)*, 1402085052) Springer.

Insam, Heribert & Knapp, Brigitte A., eds. Recycling of Biomass Ashes. 2011. (ENG., Illus.). viii, 164p. 189.00 *(978-3-642-19353-8(6)*, 3642193536) Springer.

Le Van, An. Sweet Potato Leaves for Pigs: Biomass Yield, Digestion & Nutritive Value. 2008. 172p. pap. *(978-3-639-09825-9(0))* VDM Verlag Dr. Mueller e.K.

Parker, Bismark Quarku. Biomass Burning in Ghan. 2011. 92p. pap. ***(978-3-8443-9205-0(X))*** Lambert Academic Publishing.

Rosenberg, Norman J. A Biomass Future for the North American Great Plains: Toward Sustainable Land Use & Mitigation of Greenhouse Warming. (Advances in Global Change Research Ser.). xviii, 198p. 2010. pap. 169.00 *(978-90-481-7405-8(8)*, 9048174058) 2007. (ENG.). 169.00 *(978-1-4020-5600-0(1)*, 1402056001) Springer.

Sermyagina, Ekaterina. Circulating Fluidized Bed Boiler Technology. 2011. 92p. pap. ***(978-3-8454-1643-4(2))*** Lambert Academic Publishing.

Willems, Louise E., ed. Wildfires, Fuels & Invasive Plants. 2010. (Environmental Science, Engineering & Technology Ser.). 235.00 *(978-1-61728-164-8(6))* Nova Science Pubs., Inc.

Zhang, Xinshi & Huang, Hongwen, eds. Science & Technology on Bio-hylic & Biomass Resources in China: A Roadmap To 2050: A Roadmap To 2050. 2010. (Illus.). 175p. pap. 99.00 *(978-3-642-05339-9(4)*, 3642053394) Springer.

BIOMASS CHEMICALS

see also Biogas; Single Cell Lipids; Single Cell Proteins

Adney, William S., et al, eds. Biotechnology for Fuels & Chemicals: The Twenty-Ninth Symposium. 2010. (ABAB Symposium Ser.). xvi, 812p. pap. 289.00 *(978-1-61737-904-8(2)*, 1617379042) Humana Pr.

Belgacem, Mohamed Naceur & Gandini, Alessandro, eds. Monomers, Polymers & Composites from Renewable Resources. 2008. (ENG., Illus.). 560p. 205.00 *(978-0-08-045316-3(3)*, Elsevier Science) Elsevier Science & Technology Bks.

Cao, Zhong, et al, eds. Application of Chemical Engineering. 2011. (Advanced Materials Research Ser.: Vol. 236-238). 3102p. pap. ***(978-3-03785-121-0(X))*** Trans Tech Pubns., Ltd.

Chen, Hongzhang. Process Engineering in Plant-Based Products. 2009. (Environmental Science, Engineering & Technology Ser.). 89.00 *(978-1-60741-962-4(9))* Nova Science Pubs., Inc.

Doppenberg, Jannes & van der Aar, Piet, eds. Biofuels: Implications for the feed Industry. 2007. (Illus.). 118p. pap. 51.00 *(978-90-8686-043-2(5))* Wageningen Academic Publishers NLD. Dist: Enfield Publishing & Distribution Co., Inc.

Ibarra, Michael L., et al. Biomass for Biopower: Feedstock Supply Assessments. 2012. ***(978-1-61942-575-0(0))*** Nova Science Pubs., Inc.

Mielenz, Jonathan R. Biotechnology for Fuels & Chemicals. 2008. (ABAB Symposium Ser.). (Illus.). 812p. 289.00 *(978-1-60327-525-5(8))* Humana Pr.

Mielenz, Jonathan R., et al, eds. Biotechnology for Fuels & Chemicals: The Thirtieth Symposium. 2010. (ABAB Symposium Ser.). (ENG.). 300p. 189.00 *(978-1-60761-298-8(4)*, 1607612984) Humana Pr.

—Biotechnology for Fuels & Chemicals: The Thirty-First Symposium. 2010. (ABAB Symposium Ser.). (ENG.). 984p. 189.00 *(978-1-4419-6233-1(6)*, 1441962336); (Illus.). 329.00 *(978-1-4419-6230-0(1)*, 1441962301) Springer.

—Biotechnology for Fuels & Chemicals: The Twenty-Ninth Symposium. 2008. (ABAB Symposium Ser.). 259.00 *(978-1-60327-528-6(2))* Humana Pr.

Rauter, Amélia P., et al, eds. Carbohydrates in Sustainable Development I, 2 vols. 2010. (Topics in Current Chemistry Ser.). (Illus.). xiv, 200p. 299.00 *(978-3-642-14836-1(0)*, 3642148360) Springer.

—Carbohydrates in Sustainable Development II, 2 vols. 2010. (Topics in Current Chemistry Ser.). (Illus.). xi, 201p. 299.00 *(978-3-642-15160-6(4)*, 3642151604) Springer.

Sengupta, Debalina & Pike, Ralph W. Chemicals from Biomass: Integrating Bioprocesses into Chemical Production Complexes. 2012. (Green Chemistry & Chemical Engineering Ser.). (ENG., Illus.). 496p. 149.95 *(978-1-4398-7814-9(5)*, CRC Press) Taylor & Francis Group GBR. Dist: Taylor & Francis Group.

Waldron, K., ed. Bioalcohol Production: Biochemical Conversion of Lignocellulosic Biomass. 2010. (Illus.). 496p. *(978-1-84569-510-1(0))* Woodhead Publishing Ltd.

BIOMASS ENERGY

see also Agriculture and Energy; Refuse As Fuel

Abbasi, Tasneem, et al. Biogas Energy. 2011. (SpringerBriefs in Environmental Science Ser.). (ENG., Illus.). xiii, 169p. pap. 49.95 ***(978-1-4614-1039-3(8)***, 1461410398) Springer.

ABBE Scientist Research Division Staff. Biofuels -Analysis, availability & modern developments including dissent & Controversy: Index of New Research Information for All Nations. 2006. (Illus.). 160p. ring bd. 75.50 *(978-0-7883-4492-3(7)*, 07883-44927) ABBE Pubs. Assn. of Washington, D.C.

Adney, William S., et al, eds. Biotechnology for Fuels & Chemicals: The Twenty-Ninth Symposium. 2010. (ABAB Symposium Ser.). xvi, 812p. pap. 289.00 *(978-1-61737-904-8(2)*, 1617379042) Humana Pr.

Adouane, Belkacem. Towards a Clean Combustion of Lcv Gas. 2009. 160p. pap. *(978-3-639-10172-0(3))* VDM Verlag Dr. Mueller e.K.

Afionis, Stavros. Brazil's Ethanol Fuel Program. 2010. 64p. pap. *(978-3-8383-1442-6(5))* Lambert Academic Publishing.

Ahiduzzaman. Production & Use of Biomass Briquette Fuel in Bangladesh. 2011. 124p. pap. ***(978-3-8433-9159-7(9))*** Lambert Academic Publishing.

Almeida Monteiro, Gabriela. The Biodiesel Program & Sustainable Livelihoods. 2010. 80p. pap. *(978-3-8383-8770-3(8))* Lambert Academic Publishing.

Alonso, Stefania & Ortega, Maria Regina, eds. Biofuel Use in the U. S. Impact & Challenges. 2012. ***(978-1-62100-441-7(4))*** Nova Science Pubs., Inc.

Aluya, Joseph & Garraway, Ossian L. Disruptive Technology Meets the Biofuels Industry: Biofuels Global Implications. 2009. 116p. pap. 34.95 *(978-1-4490-2253-2(7))* AuthorHouse.

Alves Finco, Marcus Vinicius. Biofuels & Sustainable Development. 2011. 116p. pap. ***(978-3-8443-0066-6(X))*** Lambert Academic Publishing.

America's Energy Future Panel on Alternative Liquid Transportation Fuels Staff, et al. Liquid Transportation Fuels from Coal & Biomass: Technological Status, Costs, & Environmental Impacts. National Academy of Engineering Staff, ed. 2009. (ENG.). 388p. pap. 49.95 *(978-0-309-13712-6(8))* National Academies Pr.

Aviation & the Emerging Use of Biofuels: Hearing Before the Subcommittee on Space & Aeronautics, Committee on Science & Technology, House of Representatives, One Hundred Eleventh Congress, First Session, March 26, 2009. 2009. (Illus.). iv, 101p. *(978-0-16-084483-6(5)*, 552-070-40006-1) United States Government Printing Office.

Bain, R. L., ed. Worldwide Biomass Potential: Technology Characterizations. 2010. (Energy Policies, Politics & Prices Ser.). 167p. 79.00 *(978-1-60741-267-0(5))* Nova Science Pubs., Inc.

Barnes, Douglas F., et al. Cleaner Hearths, Better Homes: New Stoves for India & the Developing World. 2012. (ENG., Illus.). 176p. 40.00 ***(978-0-19-807836-4(6))*** Oxford Univ. Pr., Inc.

Bastos Vasconcelos Bomfim, Diana. The Eu & Its Sustainability Certification for Biofuels. 2010. 60p. pap. *(978-3-639-24745-9(0))* VDM Verlag Dr. Mueller e.K.

Basualdo, Marta S., et al, eds. PEM Fuel Cells with Bio-Ethanol Processor Systems: A Multidisciplinary Study of Modelling, Simulation, Fault Diagnosis & Advanced Control. 2011. (Green Energy & Technology Ser.). (ENG., Illus.). xxix, 461p. 179.00 *(978-1-84996-183-7(2)*, 1849961832) Springer.

BCC Staff. Biorefinery Technologies & Products. 2007. per. 4250.00 *(978-1-59623-307-2(9))* BCC Research.

Becek, Kazimierz. Biomass Representation in Synthetic Aperture Radar Data Sets. 2011. 284p. pap. ***(978-3-8443-2342-9(2))*** Lambert Academic Publishing.

Bessou, Cécile. Greenhouse Gas Emissions of Biofuels. 2010. 260p. pap. *(978-3-8383-7343-0(X))* Lambert Academic Publishing.

Biofuels for Energy Security & Transportation ACT of 2007: Hearing Before the Committee on Energy & Natural Resources, United States Senate, One Hundred Tenth Congress, First Session, on S. 987 ... April 12, 2007. 2007. iii, 71p. *(978-0-16-079071-3(9)*, 552-070-36173-1) United States Government Printing Office.

Biofuels for Transport: Global Potential & Implications for Sustainable Energy & Agriculture. 2007. (ENG., Illus.). 336p. 95.00 *(978-1-84407-422-8(6))* Routledge.

Biofuels Impact on Food Prices: Hearing Before the Committee on Energy & Natural Resources, United States Senate, One Hundred Tenth Congress, Second Session, to Receive Testimony on the Relationship Between the United States' Renewable Fuels Policy & Food Prices, June 12, 2008. 2008.

iii, 98p. (978-0-16-081941-4(5), 552-070-38114-7) United States Government Printing Office.

Biogas Volume 3: A Chinese Biogas Manual. 2007. per. 24.95 (978-1-60322-039-2(9)) Knowledge Pubns. Corp.

Biomass for Thermal Energy & Electricity: A Research & Development Portfolio for the Future: Hearing Before the Subcommittee on Energy & Environment, Committee on Science & Technology, House of Representatives, One Hundred Eleventh Congress, First Session, October 21, 2009. 2010. (Illus.). iv, 70p. (978-0-16-085772-0(4), 552-070-40990-4) United States Government Printing Office.

Borras Jr., Saturnino M., et al, eds. The Politics of Biofuels, Land & Agrarian Change. 2011. (Critical Agrarian Studies). (ENG., Illus.). 408p. (C). 158.00 (978-0-415-61320-0(5)) Routledge.

Bovair, Jennifer L. & Arent, Douglas Jay. Alternative Transportation Fuels & Vehicle Technologies: Challenges & Opportunities: A Report of the CSIS Energy & National Security Program, CSIS Global Strategy Institute, & National Renewable Energy Laboratory. 2008. pap. (978-0-89206-542-4(7)) Ctr. for Strategic & International Studies.

Brown, Kate. Biorenewable Resources Ep. (978-1-4051-2510-9(1), Wiley-Blackwell) Wiley, John & Sons, Inc.

Brown, Robert C., ed. Thermochemical Processing of Biomass: Conversion into Fuels, Chemicals & Power. 2011. (Wiley Series in Renewable Resource Ser.: 11). (ENG., Illus.). 348p. 145.00 (978-0-470-72111-7(1), Wiley) Wiley, John & Sons, Inc.

Brune, Michael. Coming Clean: Breaking America's Addiction to Oil & Coal. 2nd ed. 2010. (ENG.). 288p. pap. 15.95 (978-1-57805-190-8(8)) Sierra Club Bks.

Buckeridge, Marcos Silveira & Goldman, Gustavo H., eds. Routes to Cellulosic Ethanol. 2011. 284p. (978-0-387-92739-8(5)) Springer London, Ltd.

Burkin, Robert M. & Riley, Alex C. Cellulosic Biofuels: Feedstock, Technology & Policy Options. 2011. (Energy Science, Engineering & Technology Ser.). 89.00 (978-1-61209-509-7(7)) Nova Science Pubs., Inc.

Carolan, Michael S., ed. A Sociological Look at Biofuels: Understanding the Past/Prospects for the Future. 2010. (Energy Science, Engineering & Technology Ser.). 43.00 (978-1-60876-708-3(6)) Nova Science Pubs., Inc.

Carrier, Danielle Julie, et al. Biorefinery Co-Products: Phytochemicals, Primary Metabolites & Value-Added Biomass Processing. 2012. (Wiley Series in Renewable Resource Ser.). (ENG.). 382p. 140.00 (978-0-470-97357-8(9), Wiley) Wiley, John & Sons, Inc.

Chaurasia, Ashish, et al. Key Challenges in Biomass Gasification Processes. 2010. 256p. pap. (978-3-8383-7370-6(7)) Lambert Academic Publishing.

Chemical Sciences Roundtable & National Research Council. Bioinspired Chemistry for Energy: A Workshop Summary to the Chemical Sciences Roundtable. 2008. (ENG.). 68p. pap. 21.00 (978-0-309-11487-5(X)) National Academies Pr.

Chen, Hongzhang. Process Engineering in Plant-Based Products. 2009. (Environmental Science, Engineering & Technology Ser.). 89.00 (978-1-60741-962-4(9)) Nova Science Pubs., Inc.

Cheng, Jay, ed. Biomass to Renewable Energy Processes. 2009. (ENG., Illus.). 517p. (C). 107.95 (978-1-4200-9517-3(X), CRC Press) Taylor & Francis Group GBR. Dist: Taylor & Francis Group.

Cheng, Jay J. Biomass to Renewable Energy Processes. 2009. (ENG., Illus.). 400p. 109.95 (978-1-59169-044-3(7)) Taylor & Francis Group.

Clancy, Joy & Lovett, Jon C. Biofuels & Rural Poverty. 2012. (ENG., Illus.). 192p. 79.95 (978-1-84407-719-9(5)) Routledge.

Colince, Nguelo. Biofuel Impacts on Food Crisis. 2010. 116p. pap. (978-3-8383-6247-2(0)) Lambert Academic Publishing.

Committee on Economic and Environmental Impacts of Increasing Biofuels Production & National Research Council. Renewable Fuel Standard: Potential Economic & Environmental Effects of U. S. Biofuel Policy. 2011. (ENG.). 250p. pap. 68.00 (978-0-309-18751-0(6)) National Academies Pr.

Committee on Research Frontiers in Bioinspired Energy & National Research Council. Research Frontiers in Bioinspired Energy: Molecular-Level Learning from Natural Systems: A Workshop. 2012. (ENG.). 82p. pap. 36.00 (978-0-309-22044-6(0)) National Academies Pr.

Committee on U.S.-China Cooperation on Electricity from Renewable Resources, et al. The Power of Renewables: Opportunities & Challenges for China & the United States. 2010. (ENG.). 256p. pap. 36.00 (978-0-309-16000-1(6)) National Academies Pr.

Committee on Water Implications of Biofuels Production in the United States & National Research Council. Water Implications of Biofuels Production in the United States. 2008. (ENG.). 88p. pap. 30.00 (978-0-309-11361-8(X)) National Academies Pr.

Cram101 Textbook Reviews. Outlines & Highlights for Biofuels by Wim Soetaert. 2011. 92p. pap. 27.95 (978-1-61490-054-2(X)) Cram101 Inc.

Cram101 Textbook Reviews & Cram101 Textbook Reviews. Outlines & Highlights for Biofuels Engineering Process Technology by Caye Drapcho, Isbn: 0071487492 9780071487498. 2011. 66p. pap. 27.95 (978-1-61461-597-2(7)) Cram101 Inc.

Crowe, Daniel T., ed. Renewable Fuel Standard Issues. 2009. (Series: Renewable Energy: Research, Development & Policies Ser.). 79.00 (978-1-60692-289-7(0)) Nova Science Pubs., Inc.

Dahlquist, Erik, ed. Biomass as Energy Source: Resources, Systems & Applications. 2012. (Sustainable Energy Developments Ser.). (ENG.). 400p. 129.95 (978-0-415-62087-1(2), CRC Press) Taylor & Francis Group GBR. Dist: Taylor & Francis Group.

—Technologies for Converting Biomass to Useful Energy. 2012. (Sustainable Energy Developments Ser.). (ENG.). 400p. 129.95 (978-0-415-62088-8(0), CRC Press) Taylor & Francis Group GBR. Dist: Taylor & Francis Group.

Demirbas, Ayhan. Biodiesel: A Realistic Fuel Alternative for Diesel Engines. 2008. (ENG., Illus.). x, 208p. 109.00 (978-1-84628-994-1(7), 1846289947) Springer.

—Biofuels: Securing the Planet's Future Energy Needs. 2008. (Green Energy & Technology Ser.). (Illus.). x, 336p. 159.00 (978-1-84882-010-4(0)) Springer.

—Biohydrogen: For Future Engine Fuel Demands. 2009. (Green Energy & Technology Ser.). (ENG., Illus.). xii, 275p. 239.00 (978-1-84882-510-9(2), 1848825102) Springer.

Deublein, Dieter & Steinhauser, Angelika. Biogas from Waste & Renewable Resources: An Introduction. 2nd ed. 2010. (ENG., Illus.). 578p. 155.00 (978-3-527-32798-0(3), Wiley-VCH) Wiley, John & Sons, Inc.

Donovan, Jeremy B. Biofuel Lifecycle Issues & Research. 2010. (Illus.). 163p. 130.00 (978-1-61728-657-5(5)) Nova Science Pubs., Inc.

Doppenberg, Jannes & van der Aar, Piet, eds. Biofuels: Implications for the feed Industry. 2007. (Illus.). 118p. pap. 51.00 (978-90-8686-043-2(5)) Wageningen Academic Publishers NLD. Dist: Enfield Publishing & Distribution Co., Inc.

Doyle, Alisha M. & Bell, Jayden A., eds. Algal Biofuels: Where We've Been, Where We're Going (with DVD) 2011. (Energy Science, Engineering & Technology Ser.). 207p. 229.00 (978-1-61209-502-8(X)) Nova Science Pubs., Inc.

Drapcho, Caye, et al. Biofuels Engineering Process Technology. 2008. (ENG., Illus.). 371p. 125.00 (978-0-07-148749-8(2), 0071487492) McGraw-Hill Professional Publishing.

DuBois, Edgard & Mercier, Arthur. Energy Recovery. 2009. 89.00 (978-1-60741-065-2(6)) Nova Science Pubs., Inc.

Edwards, James B. There Is a Silver Bullet: PLUG-INS & BIOFUELS. 2007. 112p. per. 10.95 (978-1-59330-513-0(3)) Aventine Pr.

Egg Drop Vehicles GS Guide. 2007. spiral bd. 24.95 (978-1-58651-931-5(X)) Pitsco/Pitsco LEGO Dacta.

El Bassam, N. Bioenergy Crops: A Development Guide & Species Reference. 2nd ed. 2009. (Illus.). 352p. 117.00 (978-1-84407-540-9(0)) Earthscan GBR. Dist: Stylus Publishing, LLC.

EL-HALWAGI, Mahmoud M., et al. Design for Energy & the Environment: Proceedings of the Seventh International Conference on the Foundations of Computer-Aided Process Design. El-halwagi, Mahmoud M. & Linninger, Andreas A., eds. 2009. (ENG., Illus.). 1126p. 185.95 (978-1-4398-0912-9(7), CRC Press) Taylor & Francis Group GBR. Dist: Taylor & Francis Group.

El-Hawagi, Mahmoud. Integrated Biorefineries: Design, Analysis, & Optimization. 2012. (Green Chemistry & Chemical Engineering Ser.). (ENG., Illus.). 816p. 139.95 (978-1-4398-0346-2(3), CRC Press) Taylor & Francis Group GBR. Dist: Taylor & Francis Group.

Energy in the Americas: Hearing Before the Subcommittee on the Western Hemisphere of the Committee on Foreign Affairs, House of Representatives, One Hundred Tenth Congress, Second Session, July 31, 2008. 2008. iii, 75p. (978-0-16-081899-8(0), 552-070-38072-8) United States Government Printing Office.

Energy Market Effects on Recently Passed RFS: Hearing Before the Committee on Energy & Natural Resources, United States Senate, One Hundred Tenth Congress, Second Session, to Receive Testimony on the Energy Market Effects on Recently-Passed Renewable Fuel Standard, February 7, 2008. 2008. iii, 93p. (978-0-16-081360-3(3), 552-070-37738-7) United States Government Printing Office.

Erbaum, Jason B. Bioethanol: Production, Benefits & Economics. 2009. (Energy Science, Engineering & Technology Ser.). 135.00 (978-1-60741-697-5(2)) Nova Science Pubs., Inc.

Expanding the Role of Biofuels for America: Field Hearing Before the Committee on Agriculture, Nutrition, & Forestry, United States Senate, One Hundred Eleventh Congress, First Session, September 1, 2009. 2011. (Illus.). iii, 106p. (978-0-16-088026-1(2), 552-070-42450-4) United States Government Printing Office.

Ezeji, Thaddeus, et al. Biofuels from Agricultural Wastes & Byproducts. 2010. (ENG., Illus.). 276p. 209.95 (978-0-8138-0252-7(0), Wiley-Blackwell) Wiley, John & Sons, Inc.

Federal Renewable Fuels Programs: Hearing Before the Committee on Environment & Public Works, United States Senate, One Hundred Ninth Congress, Second Session, September 6, 2006. 2009. iii, 58p. (978-0-16-084853-7(9), 552-070-40254-3) United States Government Printing Office.

Ferraro, Douglas A., ed. Effects & Challenges of Increased Biofuel Production & Use. 2010. (Energy Science, Engineering & Technology Ser.). (Illus.). xi, 259p. 235.00 (978-1-61728-658-2(3)) Nova Science Pubs., Inc.

Fuel from Farms: A Guide to Small-Scale Ethanol Production. 2007. per. 29.95 (978-1-60322-036-1(4)) Knowledge Pubns. Corp.

Full Committee Hearing on the State of the Renewable Fuels Industry in the Current Economy: Hearing Before the Committee on Small Business, United States House of Representatives, One Hundred Eleventh Congress, First Session, Hearing Held March 4, 2009. 2009. (Illus.). v, 68p. (978-0-16-083032-7(X), 552-070-38927-0) United States Government Printing Office.

Furfari, Antonino. Biofuels: Illusion or Reality? - The European Experience. 2008. 137p. pap. 19.00 (978-2-7108-0920-3(6)) Editions Technip FRA. Dist: AtlasBooks Distribution.

Future Bioenergy & Sustainable Land Use. 2009. (ENG., Illus.). 392p. 146.00 (978-1-84407-841-7(8)) Routledge.

The Gas Is Greener: The Future of Biofuels: Hearing Before the Select Committee on Energy Independence & Global Warming, House of Representatives, One Hundred Tenth Congress, First Session, October 24, 2007. 2010. (Illus.). iii, 138p. (978-0-16-086897-9(1), 552-070-41807-5) United States Government Printing Office.

Gasparatos, Alexandros & Stromberg, Per, eds. Socioeconomic & Environmental Impacts of Biofuels: Evidence from Developing Nations. 2012. (ENG., Illus.). 200p. 120.00 (978-1-107-00935-6(9)) Cambridge Univ. Pr.

Giampietro, Mario & Mayumi, Kozo. Biofuel Delusion: The Fallacy of Large Scale Agro-Biofuels Production. 2009. (ENG., Illus.). 336p. 79.95 (978-1-84407-681-9(4)) Routledge.

Goettemoeller, Jeffrey & Goettemoeller, Adrian. Sustainable Ethanol: Biofuels, Biorefineries, Cellulosic Biomass, Flex-fuel Vehicles, & Sustainable Farming for Energy Independence. 2007. 196p. per. 17.00 (978-0-9786293-0-4(2)) Prairie Oak Publishing.

Gopalakrishnan, Kasthurirangan, et al, eds. Sustainable Bioenergy & Bioproducts: Value Added Engineering Applications. 2011. (Green Energy & Technology Ser.). (ENG., Illus.). x, 228p. 139.00 (978-1-4471-2323-1(9), 1447123239) Springer.

Gouveia, Luisa. Microalgae as a Feedstock for Biofuels. 2011. (SpringerBriefs in Microbiology Ser.). (ENG., Illus.). v, 68p. pap. 49.95 (978-3-642-17996-9(7), 3642179967) Springer.

Grammelis, Panagiotis. Solid Biofuels for Energy: A Lower Greenhouse Gas Alternative. 2010. (Green Energy & Technology Ser.). (Illus.). xiv, 242p. 129.00 (978-1-84996-392-3(4), 1849963924) Springer.

Graver, Lauren S. & Kriss, Matthew R., eds. Biofuel Sustainability: Research Areas & Knowledge Gaps. 2012. (Energy Science, Engineering & Technology Against Issues & Policies Ser.). 131p. 95.00 (978-1-62100-320-5(5)) Nova Science Pubs., Inc.

Gupta, Ram B. & Demirbas, Ayhan. Gasoline, Diesel & Ethanol Biofuels from Grasses & Plants. 2010. (ENG., Illus.). 244p. (C). 79.00 (978-0-521-76399-8(1)) Cambridge Univ. Pr.

Haas, Bratt P., ed. Ethanol Biofuel Production. 2010. (Energy Science, Engineering & Technology Ser.). 115.00 (978-1-60876-086-2(3)) Nova Science Pubs., Inc.

Haerens, Margaret, ed. Biofuels. 2012. (At Issue Ser.). (ENG.). 128p. (gr. 10-12). pap. 23.85 (978-0-7377-5553-4(9)); lib. bdg. 33.70 (978-0-7377-5552-7(0)) Cengage Gale. (Greenhaven Pr., Inc.).

Haggerty, Alfred P. Biomass Crops: Production, Energy & the Environment. 2011. (Environmental Science, Engineering & Technology Ser.). (Illus.). x, 232p. 165.00 (978-1-61209-398-7(1)) Nova Science Pubs., Inc.

Halinen, Dmitry S. The Potential for Wood Energy & Biomass Fuels in Alaska. 2012. (Energy Science, Engineering & Technology Ser.). 137p. 95.00 (978-1-61470-990-9(4)) Nova Science Pubs., Inc.

Hallenbeck, Patrick C., ed. Microbial Technologies in Advanced Biofuels Production. 2011. (ENG., Illus.). x, 272p. 189.00 (978-1-4614-1207-6(2), 1461412072) Springer.

Hauler, Thorsten. Emissions & Processes in Biomass Combustion. 2008. 220p. pap. (978-3-639-04931-2(4)) VDM Verlag Dr. Mueller e.K.

Hayworth, James M., ed. Methane Digesters & Biogas Recovery. 2011. (Agriculture Issues & Policies Ser.). (Illus.). 92p. pap. 47.00 (978-1-61324-594-1(7)) Nova Science Pubs., Inc.

Hearing to Review Renewable Fuels Standard Implementation & Agriculture Producer Eligibility: Hearing Before the Subcommittee on Conservation, Credit, Energy, & Research of the Committee on Agriculture, House of Representatives, One Hundred Tenth Congress, Second Session, Thursday, July 24, 2008. 2009. (Illus.). iv, 135p. (978-0-16-083941-2(6), 552-070-39630-6) United States Government Printing Office.

Hearing to Review the Future of Next Generation Biofuels: Hearing Before the Subcommittee on Conservation, Credit, Energy, & Research of the Committee on Agriculture, House of Representatives, One Hundred Eleventh Congress, First Session, October 29, 2009. 2009. (Illus.). v, 75p. (978-0-16-084838-4(5), 552-070-40239-0) United States Government Printing Office.

Hearing to Review the Implementation of the 2008 Farm Bill Energy Title: Hearing Before the Subcommittee on Conservation, Credit, Energy, & Research of the Committee on Agriculture, House of Representatives, One Hundred Eleventh Congress, Second Session, June 9, 2010. 2010. v, 52p. (978-0-16-087388-1(6), 552-070-42081-9) United States Government Printing Office.

Hemelt, Kevin C., ed. Biomass: Energy Data, Multi-Year Plan, & Legislative Definitions. 2010. (Energy Science, Engineering & Technology Ser.). 235.00 (978-1-61728-681-0(8)) Nova Science Pubs., Inc.

Henderson, Oscar P. Biomass for Energy. 2011. (Renewable Energy: Research, Development & Policies Ser.). 89.00 (978-1-61209-503-5(8)) Nova Science Pubs., Inc.

Hetemäki, Lauri, et al. Forest Products & Bioenergy: Future Opportunities in Nordic Countries & North America. 2009. (World Forests Ser.). 300p. 179.00 (978-1-4020-6346-6(6)) Springer.

Himmel, Michael E., ed. Biomass Recalcitrance: Deconstructing the Plant Cell Wall for Bioenergy. 2008. (ENG., Illus.). 528p. 195.00 (978-1-4051-6360-6(7), Wiley-Blackwell) Wiley, John & Sons, Inc.

Honary, Lou & Conconi, Charles, eds. Biofuels, Journ of ASTM International Selected Technical Papers. 2011. 623p. pap. 146.00 (978-0-8031-3411-9(8)) American Society for Testing & Materials.

Horn, Svein Jarle. Seaweed Biofuels. 2009. 104p. pap. (978-3-639-15307-1(3)) VDM Verlag Dr. Mueller e.K.

Hou, C. T. & Shaw, Jei-Fu. Biocatalysis & Bioenergy. 2008. (ENG., Illus.). 608p. 178.00 (978-0-470-13404-7(6), Wiley-Interscience) Wiley, John & Sons, Inc.

Houtart, Francois. Agrofuels: Big Profits, Ruined Lives & Ecological Destruction. 1 vol. Bawtree, Victoria, tr. from FRE. 2010. (ENG.). 280p. 95.00 (978-0-7453-3013-6(4)); pap. 30.00 (978-0-7453-3012-9(6)) Pluto Pr. GBR. Dist: Macmillan.

H.R. 547, the Advanced Fuels Infrastructure Research & Development ACT: Hearing Before the Subcommittee on Energy & Environment, Committee on Science & Technology, House of Representatives, One Hundred Tenth Congress, First Session, January 30, 2007. 2007. (Illus.). iv, 67p. (978-0-16-079261-8(4), 552-070-36365-3) United States Government Printing Office.

Ibarra, Michael L., et al. Biomass for Biopower: Feedstock Supply Assessments. 2012. (978-1-61942-575-0(0)) Nova Science Pubs., Inc.

Indarto, Antonius & Palguandi, Jelliarko. Syngas: Production, Applications, & Environmental Impact. 2012. (978-1-62100-870-5(3)) Nova Science Pubs., Inc.

Jadhav, Shailesh, et al. Production of Bioethanol from Mahua Flower. 2011. 84p. pap. (978-3-8433-9150-4(5)) Lambert Academic Publishing.

Jain, Siddharth & SHARMA, M. P. Biodiesel from High Ffa Oils. 2010. 136p. pap. (978-3-639-25587-4(9)) VDM Verlag Dr. Mueller e.K.

Janssen, Rainer & Rutz, Dominik, eds. Bioenergy for Sustainable Development in Africa. 2011. (ENG., Illus.). xxix, 413p. 179.00 (978-94-007-2180-7(3), 9400721803) Springer.

Johansen, Melanie N. Microalgae: Biotechnology, Microbiology & Energy. 2011. (Marine Biology Ser.). (Illus.). 489p. 185.00 (978-1-61324-625-2(0)) Nova Science Pubs., Inc.

Johnson, Francis X. & Seebaluck, Vikram, eds. Bioenergy for Sustainable Development & International Competitiveness: The Role of Sugar Cane in Africa. 2012. (ENG., Illus.). 472p. (C). 99.95 (978-1-84971-103-6(8)) Routledge.

Juergen, Wiegel. Incredible Anaerobes: From Physiology to Genomics to Fuels. Maier, Robert et al, eds. 2008. (Annals of the New York Academy of Sciences Ser.). (ENG., Illus.). 452p. pap. 159.95 (978-1-57331-705-4(5), Wiley-Blackwell) Wiley, John & Sons, Inc.

Kaliyan, Nalladurai & Morey, R. Vance. Densification of Biomass. 2008. 360p. pap. (978-3-639-05185-8(8)) VDM Verlag Dr. Mueller e.K.

Karmakar, Malay, et al. Biomass Gasification. 2011. 160p. pap. (978-3-8433-7557-3(7)) Lambert Academic Publishing.

Khanal, Samir. Anaerobic Biotechnology for Bioenergy Production: Principles & Applications. 2008. (ENG., Illus.). 320p. 237.00 (978-0-8138-2346-1(3), Wiley-Blackwell) Wiley, John & Sons, Inc.

Khanal, Samir K., et al, eds. Bioenergy & Biofuel from Biowastes & Biomass. 2010. (ENG., Illus.). 522p. pap. 140.00 (978-0-7844-1089-9(5)) American Society of Civil Engineers.

Khanna, Madhu, et al, eds. Handbook of Bioenergy Economics & Policy. 2009. (Natural Resource Management & Policy Ser.). (ENG., Illus.). xiv, 439p. 179.00 (978-1-4419-0368-6(2), 1441903682) Springer.

Koppejan, Jaap & van Loo, Sjaak. Biomass Combustion & Co-Firing. 2010. (ENG., Illus.). 464p. pap., instr.'s hndbk. ed. 84.95 (978-1-84971-104-3(6)) Routledge.

Koppejan, Jaap & Van Loo, Sjaak, eds. The Handbook of Biomass Combustion & Co-Firing. 2007. (ENG., Illus.). 464p. 146.00 (978-1-84407-249-1(5)) Routledge.

Korres, Nicholas, et al, eds. Bioenergy Production by Anaerobic Digestion: Using Agricultural Biomass & Organic Wastes. 2012. (ENG., Illus.). 352p. 85.95 (978-0-415-69840-5(5)) Earthscan LLC.

Kozlowski, Ryszard, et al, eds. Renewable Resources: Obtaining, Processing & Applying. 2008. 129.00 (978-1-60692-534-8(2)) Nova Science Pubs., Inc.

Krylova, L., et al. Molecular & Nanoscale Systems for Energy Conversion. Varfolomeev, Sergei D. & Krylova, L., eds. 2008. (Illus.). x, 192p. 120.00 (978-1-60456-682-6(5)) Nova Science Pubs., Inc.

Kulshreshtha, Priyanka & Khare, Mukesh. Indoor Air Pollution & Health. 2010. 376p. pap. (978-3-639-26093-9(7)) VDM Verlag Dr. Mueller e.K.

Kurucz, Adorjan & Bencik, Izsak, eds. Syngas: Production Methods, Post Treatment & Economics. 2009. (Environmental Science, Engineering & Technology Ser.). 129.00 (978-1-60741-841-2(X)) Nova Science Pubs., Inc.

Lal, Rattan. Soil Quality & Biofuel Production. 2009. (Advances in Soil Science Ser.). (ENG., Illus.). 222p. 133.95 (978-1-4398-0073-7(1), CRC Press) Taylor & Francis Group GBR. Dist: Taylor & Francis Group.

Lan, Christopher. Microalgae for Biofuel Production & CO2 Sequestration. Wang, Bei et al, eds. 2010. (Energy Science, Engineering & Technology Ser.). 180p. pap. 69.00 (978-1-61668-151-7(9)) Nova Science Pubs., Inc.

Langeveld, Hans & Meeusen, Marieke. The Biobased Economy: Biofuels, Materials & Chemicals in the Post-oil Era. Sanders, Johan, ed. 2012. (ENG., Illus.). 416p. pap. 47.95 (978-0-415-63132-7(7)) Routledge.

Latourette, et al. Supplying Biomass to Power Plants: A Model of the Costs of Utilising Agricultural Biomass in Co-Fired Power. 2011. (ENG.). 74p. (C). pap. 20.00 (978-0-8330-5218-6(7)) RAND Corp., The.

Lee, Sunggyu & Shah, Y. T. Biofuels & Bioenergy: Processes & Technologies. 2012. (Green Chemistry & Chemical Engineering Ser.: 14). (ENG., Illus.). 336p. 149.95 (978-1-4200-8955-4(2), CRC Press) Taylor & Francis Group GBR. Dist: Taylor & Francis Group.

Leland, Wesley P., ed. Ethanol & Biofuels: Production, Standards & Potential. 2009. pap. 69.00 (978-1-60692-224-8(6)) Nova Science Pubs., Inc.

Levy, Sarah L., ed. Biofuels, Biorefinery & Renewable Energy: Issues & Developments. 2010. (Energy Science, Engineering & Technology Ser.). (Illus.). ix, 192p. 137.00 (978-1-61728-678-0(8)) Nova Science Pubs., Inc.

Li, Zhengqi, ed. Corn Straw & Biomass Blends: Combustion Characteristics & NO Formation. 2010. (Energy Science, Engineering & Technology Ser.). 43.00 (978-1-60876-578-2(4)) Nova Science Pubs., Inc.

Lichtfouse, Eric. Biodiversity, Biofuels, Agroforestry & Conservation Agriculture. Lichtfouse, Eric, ed. 2010. (Sustainable Agriculture Reviews Ser.). (Illus.). x, 390p. 209.00 (978-90-481-9512-1(8), 9048195128) Springer.

Lindorfer, Johannes. Biodiesel Production. 2010. 156p. pap. (978-3-639-25504-1(6)) VDM Verlag Dr. Mueller e.K.

Liu, Zonglin Lewis, ed. Microbial Stress Tolerance for Biofuels: Systems Biology. 2011. (Microbiology Monographs). (ENG., Illus.). x, 307p. 189.00 **(978-3-642-21466-0(5)**, 3642214665) Springer.

Logan, Bruce E. Microbial Fuel Cells. 2008. (ENG., Illus.). 216p. 105.00 (978-0-470-23948-3(4), Wiley-Interscience) Wiley, John & Sons, Inc.

Lorenzini, Giulio, et al. Solar Thermal & Biomass Energy. 2010. (Illus.). 224p. 170.00 (978-1-84564-147-4(7)) WIT Pr GBR. Dist: WIT Pr.

MacDonald, Mary, et al. The Environmental Management of Low-Grade Fuels. 2009. (Energy & Infrastructure Set Ser.). (ENG., Illus.). 300p. 110.00 (978-1-84407-977-3(5)) Routledge.

Mainali, Kalidas. Catalytic Trasnesterification for Production of Alternative Biofuel. 2011. 116p. pap. **(978-3-8433-9376-8(1))** Lambert Academic Publishing.

Makanjuola, Abimbola. Upgrading of the Biofuels Value Chain in Nigeri. 2011. 84p. pap. **(978-3-8443-2551-5(4))** Lambert Academic Publishing.

Marchetti, Jorge Mario & Fang, Zhen, eds. Biodiesel: Blends, Properties & Applications. 2011. (Energy Science, Engineering & Technology Renewable Energy: Research, Development & Policies Ser.). (Illus.). 393p. 185.00 **(978-1-61324-660-3(9))** Nova Science Pubs., Inc.

Martijn, Vis & Matthias, Dees, eds. Biomass Resource Assessment Handbook: Harmonisation of Biomass Resource Assessments, Best Practices & Methods Handbook. 2011. 256p. pap. **(978-3-639-29018-9(6))** VDM Verlag Dr. Mueller e.K.

Marzouk, Abdelkrim. Time Series Analysis of Environmental Ecosystems: Case of Morocco. 2009. 116p. pap. (978-3-639-13872-6(4)) VDM Verlag Dr. Mueller e.K.

Mascia, Peter N., et al, eds. Plant Biotechnology for Sustainable Production of Energy & Co-products. 2010. (Biotechnology in Agriculture & Forestry Ser.). (Illus.). xvi, 458p. 239.00 (978-3-642-13439-5(4), 3642134394) Springer.

McGowan, Thomas. Biomass & Alternate Fuel Systems: An Engineering & Economic Guide. McGowan, Thomas F., ed. 2009. (ENG., Illus.). 280p. 99.95 (978-0-470-41028-8(0)) American Institute of Chemical Engineers.

Meijer, Gerwin, et al, eds. The Biobased Economy: Biofuels, Materials & Chemicals in the Post-Oil Era. 2010. (ENG., Illus.). 416p. 99.95 (978-1-84407-770-0(5)) Routledge.

Mielenz, Jonathan R. Biotechnology for Fuels & Chemicals. 2008. (ABAB Symposium Ser.). (Illus.). 812p. 289.00 (978-1-60327-525-5(8)) Humana Pr.

Mielenz, Jonathan R., ed. Biofuels: Methods & Protocols. 2009. (Methods in Molecular Biology Ser.). (ENG., Illus.). xiv, 293p. 119.00 (978-1-60761-213-1(5), 1607612135) Humana Pr.

Mielenz, Jonathan R., et al, eds. Biotechnology for Fuels & Chemicals: The Thirtieth Symposium. 2010. (ABAB Symposium Ser.). (ENG.). 300p. 189.00 (978-1-60761-298-8(4), 1607612984) Humana Pr.

—Biotechnology for Fuels & Chemicals: The Thirty-First Symposium. 2010. (ABAB Symposium Ser.). (ENG.). 984p. 189.00 (978-1-4419-6233-1(6), 1441962336); (Illus.). 329.00 (978-1-4419-6230-0(1), 1441962301) Springer.

—Biotechnology for Fuels & Chemicals: The Twenty-Ninth Symposium. 2008. (ABAB Symposium Ser.). 259.00 (978-1-60327-528-6(2)) Humana Pr.

Millington, Andrew & Townsend, John. Biomass Assessment. 2009. (Energy & Infrastructure Set Ser.). (ENG., Illus.). 292p. 110.00 (978-1-84407-978-0(3)) Routledge.

Mitchell, Donald. Biofuels in Africa: Opportunities, Prospects, & Challenges. 2010. (Illus.). xxxii, 184p. (978-0-8213-8517-3(8)); (ENG., 216p. pap. 30.00 (978-0-8213-8516-6(X), 9780821385166) World Bank Pubns.

Mousdale, David M. Biofuels: Biotechnology, Chemistry, & Sustainable Development. 2008. (ENG., Illus.). 424p. 129.95 (978-1-4200-5124-7(5), CRC Press) Taylor & Francis Group GBR. Dist: Taylor & Francis Group.

—Introduction to Biofuels. 2010. (Mechanical Engineering Ser.). (ENG., Illus.). 455p. 125.95 (978-1-4398-1207-5(1), CRC Press) Taylor & Francis Group GBR. Dist: Taylor & Francis Group.

Nag, Ahindra. Biofuels Refining & Performance. 2007. (ENG., Illus.). 312p. (C). 125.00 (978-0-07-148970-6(3), 0071489703) McGraw-Hill Professional Publishing.

National Research Council. Expanding Biofuel Production: Sustainability & the Transition to Advanced Biofuels: Summary of a Workshop. 2010. (ENG.). 178p. pap. 41.00 (978-0-309-14714-9(X)) National Academies Pr.

—Transitioning to Sustainability Through Research & Development on Ecosystem Services & Biofuels: Workshop Summary. 2008. (ENG.). 130p. pap. 31.75 (978-0-309-11982-5(0)) National Academies Pr.

Nelson, Willie. On the Clean Road Again: Biodiesel & the Future of the Family Farm. 2007. (Speaker's Corner Books). (ENG.). 96p. pap. 9.95 (978-1-55591-624-4(4)) Fulcrum Publishing.

The Next Generation of Biofuels: Cellulosic Ethanol & the 2007 Farm Bill: Hearing Before the Subcommittee on Energy, Science, & Technology of the Committee on Agriculture, Nutrition, & Forestry, United States Senate, One Hundred Tenth Congress, First Session, April 4, 2007. 2007. (Illus.). iii, 123p. (978-0-16-079621-0(0), 552-070-36578-8) United States Government Printing Office.

Nimlos, Mark R. & Crowley, Michael F. Computational Modeling in Lignocellulosic Biofuel Production. 2010. (ENG., Illus.). 352p. (978-0-8412-2571-8(0)) American Chemical Society.

NSTI, Contact. Nanotechnology 2009: Biofuels, Renewable Energy, Coatings, Fluidics & Compact Modeling Technical Proceedings of the 2009 NSTI Nanotechnology Conference & Expo, Volume 3. 2009. 692p. 179.95 (978-1-4398-1784-1(7)) CRC Pr. LLC.

O'Connery, Bryan D. Biodiesel Handling & Use Guide. 2010. (Energy Science, Engineering & Technology Ser.). pap. 43.00 (978-1-60876-138-8(X)) Nova Science Pubs., Inc.

Olsson, Lisbeth. Biofuels. (Advances in Biochemical Engineering Biotechnology Ser.). (Illus.). 2010. xii, 368p. pap. 449.00 (978-3-642-09282-4(9), 3642092829) 2007. 350p. 449.00 (978-3-540-73650-9(6), 3540736506) Springer.

Organisation for Economic Co-operation and Development Staff. Biofuel Support Policies: An Economic Assessment. 2008. pap. 63.00 (978-92-64-04922-2(3)) Organization for Economic Cooperation & Development.

—Ecmt Round Tables No. 138 Biofuels: Linking Support to Performance. 2008. pap. 4.00 (978-92-821-0179-7(7)) Organization for Economic Cooperation & Development.

Ortiz, David S., et al. Near-Term Opportunities for Integrating Biomass into the U. S. Electricity Supply: Technical Considerations, 1 vol. 2011. (Illus.). 186p. (C). pap. 38.50 **(978-0-8330-5835-5(5))** RAND Corp., The.

Pandey, Ashok. Handbook of Plant-Based Biofuels. 2008. (ENG., Illus.). 312p. 129.95 (978-1-56022-175-3(5), CRC Press) Taylor & Francis Group GBR. Dist: Taylor & Francis Group.

Pandey, Ashok, et al, eds. Biofuels: Alternative Feedstocks & Conversion Processes. 2011. (ENG., Illus.). 642p. 129.95 (978-0-12-385099-7(1), Academic Pr.) Elsevier Science & Technology Bks.

A Path Toward the Broader Use of Biofuels: Enhancing the Federal Commitment to Research & Development to Meet the Growing Need: Hearing Before the Subcommittee on Energy & Environment, Committee on Science & Technology, House of Representatives, One Hundred Tenth Congress, First Session, June 14, 2007. 2008. (Illus.). iv, 88p. (978-0-16-080544-8(9), 552-070-37205-9) United States Government Printing Office.

Pathiyamattom, Joseph Sebastian, et al. Biofuel Production from Organic Waste. 2010. 92p. pap. (978-3-8383-6443-8(0)) Lambert Academic Publishing.

Pena, Antonio. La Energia y la Vida Bioenergia. (Ciencia para Todos Ser.). (SPA.). pap. 6.99 (978-968-16-3479-7(9)) Fondo de Cultura Economica USA.

Pimentel, D., ed. Biofuels, Solar & Wind as Renewable Energy Systems: Benefits & Risks. 2010. (ENG., Illus.). xxii, 506p. pap. 89.95 (978-90-481-7945-9(9), 9048179459) Springer.

Pimentel, David, ed. Biofuels, Solar & Wind As Renewable Energy Systems: Benefits & Risks. 2008. (ENG., Illus.). xxii, 506p. 89.95 (978-1-4020-8653-3(9), 1402086539) Springer.

Pimentel, David, ed. Global Economic & Environmental Aspects of Biofuels. 2012. (Advances in Agroecology Ser.). (ENG., Illus.). 453p. 99.95 **(978-1-4398-3463-3(6)**, CRC Press) Taylor & Francis Group GBR. Dist: Taylor & Francis Group.

Political Economy Research Institute Staff. Biomass Technologies Industry Report. 2010. (ENG.). 1250.00 (978-0-470-62601-6(1), Wiley-Scrivener) Wiley, John & Sons, Inc.

Ponterio, Claude. Jatropha Curcas As a Premier Biofuel: Cost, Growing & Management. Ferra, Costanza, ed. 2010. (Energy Science, Engineering & Technology Ser.). (Illus.). 210p. 129.00 (978-1-60876-300-9(5)) Nova Science Pubs., Inc.

Prins, Mark Jan. Thermodynamic analysis of biomass gasification: Including torrefaction as a thermal pre-treatment. 2008. 160p. pap. (978-3-639-10006-8(9)) VDM Verlag Dr. Mueller e.K.

Purcella, Guy. Do It Yourself Guide to Biodiesel: Your Alternative Fuel Solution for Saving Money, Reducing Oil Dependency, Helping the Planet. 2007. (ENG., Illus.). 176p. per. 15.95 (978-1-56975-624-9(4)) Ulysses Pr.

Rajagopal, Deepak & Zilberman, David. Environmental, Economic & Policy Aspects of Biofuels. 2008. (Illus.). 128p. pap. 85.00 net. (978-1-60198-174-5(0)) Now Pubs.

Raven, Rob. Strategic Niche Management for Biomass: A Comparative Study on the Experimental Introduction of Bioenergy Technologies in the Netherlands & Denmark. 2008. 340p. pap. (978-3-639-09239-4(2)) VDM Verlag Dr. Mueller e.K.

Reijnders, Lucas, et al. Biofuels for Road Transport: A Seed to Wheel Perspective. 2009. (Green Energy & Technology Ser.). (Illus.). viii, 170p. 129.00 (978-1-84882-137-8(9)) Springer.

Review the Financial Structure of Renewable Energy Sources: Hearing Before the Subcommittee on Conservation, Credit, Energy, & Research of the Committee on Agriculture, House of Representatives, One Hundred Tenth Congress, First Session, March 7, 2007. 2007. (Illus.). iii, 143p. (978-0-16-079757-6(8), 552-070-36675-0) United States Government Printing Office.

Richardson, J, et al, eds. Bioenergy from Sustainable Forestry: Guiding Principles & Practice. 2010. (Forestry Sciences Ser.). 364p. pap. 279.00 (978-90-481-6043-3(X), 904816043X) Springer.

Rojas, S. Biofuels from Fischer-Tropsch Synthesis. Ojeda, M., ed. 2010. (Energy Science, Engineering & Technology Ser.). (Illus.). 73p. pap. 43.00 (978-1-61668-366-5(X)) Nova Science Pubs., Inc.

Rommer, Thomas E. World Biofuels Production Potential. 2010. (Energy Policies, Politics & Prices Ser.). 131p. pap. 43.00 (978-1-61668-663-5(4)) Nova Science Pubs., Inc.

Röser, Dominik, et al, eds. Sustainable Use of Forest Biomass for Energy: A Synthesis with Focus on the Baltic & Nordic Region. 2008. (Managing Forest Ecosystems Ser.). 250p. 179.00 (978-1-4020-5053-4(4)) Springer.

Rosillo-Calle, Ed. Food Versus Fuel: An Informed Introduction to Biofuels. Johnson, Francis X. & Rosillo-Calle, Frank, eds. 2010. (ENG., Illus.). 208p. 116.95 (978-1-84813-382-2(0)) Zed Bks., Ltd. GBR. Dist: Macmillan.

Rosillo-Calle, Frank. The Biomass Assessment Handbook: Bioenergy for a Sustainable Environment. Hemstock, Sarah et al, eds. 2006. (ENG., Illus.). 296p. 135.00 (978-1-84407-285-9(1)) Routledge.

Rosillo-Calle, Frank, et al, eds. The Biomass Assessment Handbook: Bioenergy for a Sustainable Environment. 2008. (ENG., Illus.). 296p. pap. 77.95 (978-1-84407-526-3(5)) Routledge.

Rosillo-Calle, Frank & Johnson, Francis X., eds. Food Versus Fuel: An Informed Introduction to Biofuels. 2010. (ENG., Illus.). 208p. pap. 26.95 (978-1-84813-383-9(9)) Zed Bks., Ltd. GBR. Dist: Macmillan.

Roy, Smarajit. Understanding Waste = Bioenergy. 2011. 60p. pap. 12.10 **(978-1-4567-8354-9(8))** AuthorHouse.

Royal Society of Chemistry Staff. Advanced Oil Crop Biorefineries. Kazmi, Abbas, ed. 2011. (RSC Green Chemistry Ser.). (ENG., Illus.). 336p. (C). 195.00 (978-1-84973-135-5(7)) Royal Society of Chemistry, The GBR. Dist: Ingram Pub. Services.

—The Biofuels Handbook, 3 vols., Set. Speight, James G., ed. 2011. (RSC Energy Ser.). (ENG., Illus.). 574p. 448.00 **(978-1-84973-026-6(1))** Royal Society of Chemistry, The GBR. Dist: Ingram Pub. Services.

—Chemical & Biochemical Catalysis for Next Generation Biofuels. Simmons, Blake A., ed. 2011. (RSC Energy & Environment Ser.). (ENG., Illus.). 206p. 202.00 **(978-1-84973-030-3(X))** Royal Society of Chemistry, The GBR. Dist: Ingram Pub. Services.

Royal Society of Chemistry Staff. Thermochemical Conversion of Biomass to Liquid Fuels & Chemicals. Crocker, Mark, ed. 2010. (RSC Energy & Environment Ser.). (ENG., Illus.). 552p. 224.00 (978-1-84973-035-8(0)) Royal Society of Chemistry, The GBR. Dist: Ingram Pub. Services.

Salas, Benjamin M. Hypoxia in the Northern Gulf of Mexico. 2011. (Environmental Science, Engineering & Technology Ser.). 195.00 (978-1-61209-318-5(3)) Nova Science Pubs., Inc.

Samuelson, Sheila. The Feel Good Heat: Pioneers in Corn & Biomass Energy. 2007. (Illus.). 150p. per. 16.95 (978-1-888160-29-1(2)) Ice Cube Pr.

Schwedt, Georg, et al. Bioprocessing Technologies in Integrated Biorefinery for Production of Biofuels, Biochemicals, & Biopolymers from Biomass. 2013. (ENG.). 368p. 99.95 (978-0-470-54195-1(4), Wiley) Wiley, John & Sons, Inc.

Scragg, Alan. Biofuels: Production, Application & Development. 2010. (Illus.). 256p. pap. 75.00 (978-1-84593-592-4(6)) CABI GBR. Dist: Stylus Publishing, LLC.

Singh, Om V. & Steven, Harvey P., eds. Sustainable Biotechnology: Sources of Renewable Energy. 2009. (ENG., Illus.). xviii, 323p. 199.00 (978-90-481-3294-2(0), 9048132940) Springer.

Smith, James. Biofuels & Globalisation of Risk: The Biggest Change in North-South Relationships since Colonialism? 2010. (ENG.). 170p. pap. 29.95 (978-1-84813-572-7(6)) Zed Bks., Ltd. GBR. Dist: Macmillan.

—Biofuels & the Globalisation of Risk: The Biggest Change in North-South Relationships since Colonialism? 2010. (ENG.). 170p. 126.95 (978-1-84813-571-0(8)) Zed Bks., Ltd. GBR. Dist: Macmillan.

Soetaert, Wim & Vandamme, Erik, eds. Biofuels. 2009. (Wiley Series in Renewable Resource Ser.). (ENG., Illus.). 256p. 130.00 (978-0-470-02674-8(X), Wiley) Wiley, John & Sons, Inc.

Solomon, Barry D. Renewable Energy from Forest Resources in the United States. Luzadis, Valerie A., ed. 2008. (Routledge Explorations in Environmental Economics Ser.). (Illus.). 352p. 170.00 (978-0-415-77600-4(7)) Routledge.

Solway, Andrew. Biofuels. 2007. (Energy for the Future & Global Warming Ser.). (Illus.). 32p. (gr. 5-8). pap. 11.70 (978-0-8368-8407-4(8)) Stevens, Gareth Publishing LLLP.

Spellman, Frank. Forest-Based Biomass Energy: Concepts & Applications. 2011. (ENG., Illus.). 514p. 159.95 (978-1-4398-6019-9(X), CRC Press) Taylor & Francis Group GBR. Dist: Taylor & Francis Group.

Stampfl, Paul. Miscanthus Bioenergy. 2008. 92p. pap. (978-3-8364-9331-4(4)) VDM Verlag Dr. Mueller e.K.

Starbuck, Jon & Harper, Gavin D. J. Run Your Diesel Vehicle on Biofuels: A Do-It-Yourself Manual. 2008. (ENG., Illus.). 248p. pap. 24.95 (978-0-07-160043-9(4), 0071600434, TAB/Electronics) McGraw-Hill Professional Publishing.

Subcommittee Hearing on Impacts of Outstanding Regulatory Policy on Small Biofuels Producers & Family Farmers: Hearing Before the Committee on Small Business, United States House of Representatives, One Hundred Eleventh Congress, First Session, Hearing Held May 20, 2009. 2009. v, 86p. (978-0-16-083908-5(4), 552-070-39597-1) United States Government Printing Office.

Subcommittee Hearing on Meeting the Workforce Demands of Small Bio-Energy Businesses. 2007. (Illus.). iii, 80p. (978-0-16-079939-6(2), 552-070-36766-7) United States Government Printing Office.

Subcommittee Hearing on Second Generation Biofuels: The New Frontier for Small Businesses. 2008. iii, 61p. (978-0-16-081344-3(1), 552-070-37724-7) United States Government Printing Office.

Suttie, Ed. Biomass Energy. 2012. (ENG., Illus.). 32p. pap. 39.95 **(978-1-84806-198-9(6))** Building Research Establishment GBR. Dist: Taylor & Francis Group.

Taylor C. Monahan. Biofuels: Developments & Issues. 2011. (Series: Energy Science, Engineering & Technology Ser.). (Illus.). viii, 166p. 89.00 (978-1-61761-935-9(3)) Nova Science Pubs., Inc.

Tillman, David, et al. Solid Fuel Blending: Principles, Practices, & Problems. 2012. (ENG., Illus.). 352p. 99.95 **(978-0-12-380932-2(0)**, Butterworth-Heinemann) Elsevier Science & Technology Bks.

Tomes, Dwight. Biofuels: Global Impact on Renewable Energy, Production Agriculture, & Technological Advancements. Tomes, Dwight et al, eds. 2010. (ENG., Illus.). viii, 357p. 189.00 (978-1-4419-7144-9(0), 1441971440) Springer.

Townsend, Amy, et al. Exploring Sustainable Biodiesel. 2008. (Illus.). 320p. pap. 29.95 (978-0-7643-2908-1(1)) Schiffer Publishing, Ltd.

Transforming Forest Waste to Biofuels & the Renewable Fuels Standard: Field Hearing Before the Committee on Agriculture, Nutrition, & Forestry, United States Senate, One Hundred Tenth Congress, Second Session, August 18, 2008. 2009. iii, 46p. (978-0-16-082724-2(8), 552-070-38734-0) United States Government Printing Office.

Travaglini, Irene. An Integrated Assessment of the European Policy on Biofuels. 2010. 60p. pap. (978-3-639-22441-2(8)) VDM Verlag Dr. Mueller e.K.

United Nations. The Bioenergy & Water Nexus. 2011. (ENG.). 40p. pap. 20.00 **(978-92-807-3157-6(2))** United Nations Pubns.

United Nations Environment Programme Staff. Towards Sustainable Production & Use of Resources: Assessing Biofuels. 2010. (ENG.). 36p. pap. 30.00 incl. lp (978-92-807-3052-4(5)) United Nations Environment Programme KEN. Dist: National Bk. Network.

United States, Congress Senate Committee on Energy and Natural Resources Staff, contrib. by. Accelerated Biofuels Diversity: Hearing Before the Committee on Energy & Natural Resources, United States Senate, One Hundred Tenth Congress, First Session, to Discuss Accelerated Biofuels Diversity, February 1, 2007. 2007. iii, 93p. (978-0-16-078644-0(4), 552-070-35886-2) United States Government Printing Office.

Venables, Mark. Biofuels. 2010. 200p. pap. 58.00 (978-0-86341-959-1(3)) Institution of Engineering & Technology GBR. Dist: Books International, Inc.

Vermerris, Wilfred, ed. Genetic Improvement of Bioenergy Crops. (ENG., Illus.). xxii, 450p. 2010. pap. 169.00 (978-1-4419-2422-3(1), 1441924221) 2008. 169.00 (978-0-387-70804-1(9), 0387708049) Springer.

Vertès, Alain, et al, eds. Biomass to Biofuels: Strategies for Global Industries. 2010. (ENG., Illus.). 584p. 90.00 (978-0-470-51312-5(8), Wiley) Wiley, John & Sons, Inc.

Viramuthu, Vijaianath. The Potential Usage of Oil Palm Biomass for the Production of Energy. 2010. 72p. pap. (978-3-8383-4706-6(4)) Lambert Academic Publishing.

Vogt, K. A., et al, eds. Bio Resource-Based Energy for Sustainable Societies. 2010. (Energy Science, Engineering & Technology Ser.). pap. 43.00 (978-1-60876-803-5(1)) Nova Science Pubs., Inc.

Waldron, K. Bioalcohol Production: Biochemical conversion of lignocellulosic Biomass. 2010. (ENG.). 496p. 249.95 (978-1-4398-0171-0(1)) Taylor & Francis Group GBR. Dist: Taylor & Francis Group.

Walker, G. M. & Hughes, P. H., eds. Distilled Spirits: New Horizons: Energy, Environmental & Enlightenment. 3rd ed. 2010. (ENG., Illus.). 400p. 82.00 (978-1-907284-45-8(1)) Nottingham Univ. Pr. GBR. Dist: Independent Pubs. Group.

Wang, Ting. Blending Petrodiesel with Biodiesel to Produce Ultra-Low Sulfur Diesel. 2010. 144p. pap. (978-3-8383-7988-3(8)) Lambert Academic Publishing.

Wammer, Steven F. Progress in Biomass & Bioenergy Research. 2006. (Illus.). 217p. (C). 225.00 (978-1-60021-328-1(6)) Nova Science Pubs., Inc.

Westhoff, Patrick. The Economics of Food: How Feeding & Fueling the Planet Affects Food Prices. 2010. (ENG., Illus.). 256p. 25.99 (978-0-13-700610-6(1)) FT Press.

Williamson, Meredith A. U. S. Biobased Products Market Potential & Projections Through 2025. 2009. (Agriculture Issues & Politics Ser.). 79.00 (978-1-60741-033-1(8)) Nova Science Pubs., Inc.

World Bank Staff, et al. Bioenergy Development: Issues & Impacts for Poverty & Natural Resource Management. 2009. (Agriculture & Rural Development Ser.). (ENG., Illus.). 232p. pap. 35.00 (978-0-8213-7629-4(2), 9780821376294) World Bank Pubns.

Wright, James H. & Evans, Daniel A. New Research on Biofuels. 2008. 87.00 (978-1-60456-828-8(3)) Nova Science Pubs., Inc.

Zaikov, G. E., et al. Renewable Resources & Biotechnology for Material Applications. 2011. (Materials Science & Technologies Ser.). (Illus.). 426p. 195.00 (978-1-61209-521-9(6)) Nova Science Pubs., Inc.

Zuurbier, Peter & van de Vooren, Jos, eds. Sugarcane Ethanol: Contributions to climate change mitigation & the Environment. 2008. (Illus.). 256p. pap. 47.00 (978-90-8686-090-6(7)) Wageningen Academic Publishers NLD. Dist: Enfield Publishing & Distribution Co., Inc.

BIOMATERIALS

see Biomedical Materials

BIOMATHEMATICS

see also Biology—Mathematical Models; Biometry; Genetics—Mathematical Models; Information Theory in Biology

Aletti, G., et al, eds. Math Everywhere: Deterministic & Stochastic Modelling in Biomedicine, Economics & Industry. 2010. (ENG., Illus.). xviii, 343p. pap. 129.00 *(978-3-642-07941-2(5)*, 3642079415) Springer.

Allen, Linda J. S. An Introduction to Stochastic Processes with Applications to Biology. 2nd rev. ed. 2010. (ENG., Illus.). 490p. 89.95 *(978-1-4398-1882-4(7)*, Chapman & Hall/CRC) CRC Pr. LLC.

Ammari, Habib. Mathematical Modeling in Biomedical Imaging I: Electrical & Ultrasound Tomographies, Anomaly Detection, & Brain Imaging. 2009. (Lecture Notes in Mathematics / Mathematical Biosciences Subseries Ser.). (ENG., Illus.). xvi, 234p. pap. 89.95 *(978-3-642-03443-5(8)*, 3642034438) Springer.

Anai, Hirokazu, et al. Algebraic Biology: Second International Conference, AB 2007. 2007. (Lecture Notes in Computer Science Ser.). (Illus.). 377p. per. 79.95 *(978-3-540-73432-1(5))* Springer.

Atan, Kamel Ariffin Mohd. International Conference on Mathematical Biology. 2008. (AIP Conference Proceedings Ser.). 139.00 *(978-0-7354-0489-2(5))* American Institute of Physics.

Barnet, et al. Finite Mathematics for Business, Economics, Life Sciences & Social Sciences, A la Carte with MML/MSL Student Access Kit (adhoc for Valuepacks) 12th ed. 2010. (ENG.). (C). ring bd. 104.67 *(978-0-321-70609-6(9))* Addison Wesley.

Barnett. Calculus F/Bus., Econ, Lifescience plus Acc. 12th ed. 2010. (ENG.). (C). pap. 167.33 *(978-0-321-70901-1(2))* Addison Wesley.

Barnett, et al. Finite Mathematics for Business, Economics, Life Sciences & Social Sciences plus MyMathLab/MyStatLab Student Access Code Card. 12th ed. 2010. (ENG.). (C). pap. 167.33 *(978-0-321-70903-5(9))* Addison Wesley.

Barnett & Ziegler & Byleen & Cram101 Textbook Reviews Staff. Calculus for Business, Economics, Life Sciences, & Social Sciences. 2007. 124p. per. 11.95 *(978-1-4288-3354-8(4))* Cram101 Inc.

Barnett, Raymond A., et al. Calculus for Business, Economics, Life Sciences & Social Sciences. 11th ed. 2008. (Illus.). 704p. pap. *(978-0-13-206974-8(1))* 12th ed. 2010. (ENG.). 704p. (C). 157.33 *(978-0-321-61399-8(6)*, Prentice Hall) 12th ed. 2010. (ENG.). 576p. (C). pap. 36.67 *(978-0-321-65498-4(6)*, Prentice Hall) Prentice Hall PTR.

—College Mathematics for Business, Economics, Life Sciences & Social Sciences. 12th ed. 2010. (Barnett Ser.). (ENG.). 1032p. (C). 174.67 *(978-0-321-61400-1(3)*, Prentice Hall) Prentice Hall PTR.

—College Mathematics for Business, Economics, Life Sciences & Social Sciences, Books a la Carte Edition. 12th ed. 2010. (ENG.). (C). ring bd. 104.80 *(978-0-321-69181-1(4))* Addison Wesley.

—Finite Mathematics for Business, Economics, Life Sciences & Social Sciences. 12th ed. 2010. (Barnett Ser.). (ENG.). 744p. (C). 157.33 *(978-0-321-61401-8(1)*, Prentice Hall) Prentice Hall PTR.

—Finite Mathematics for Business, Economics, Life Sciences & Social Sciences, Books a la Carte Edition. 12th ed. 2010. (ENG.). (C). ring bd. 94.40 *(978-0-321-69155-2(5))* Addison Wesley.

—Student Solutions Manual for College Mathematics for Business, Economics, Life Sciences & Social Sciences. 12th ed. 2010. (ENG.). 960p. (C). pap. 36.67 *(978-0-321-65497-7(8)*, Prentice Hall) Prentice Hall PTR.

—Student Worksheets for Calculus for Business, Economics, Life Sciences, & Social Sciences. 12th ed. 2010. 288p. (C). pap. 26.67 *(978-0-321-65398-7(X))* Addison-Wesley Longman, Inc.

—Student's Solutions Manual for Finite Mathematics for Business, Economics, Life Sciences & Social Sciences. 12th ed. 2010. (ENG.). 624p. (C). pap. 36.67 *(978-0-321-65511-0(7)*, Prentice Hall) Prentice Hall PTR.

—Worksheets for Classroom & Lab Practice for Finite Mathematics for Business, Economics, Life Sciences, & Social Sciences. 12th ed. 2010. 304p. (C). pap. 26.67 *(978-0-321-65397-0(1))* Addison-Wesley Longman, Inc.

Barnett, Raymong A., et al. Finite Mathematics: For Business, Economics, Life Sciences, & Social Sciences. 11th ed. 2007. (Illus.). 657p. incl. cd-rom *(978-0-13-513152-7(9))* Pearson Education Canada.

Barnett, Ziegler & Cram101 Textbook Reviews Staff. Finite Mathematics for Business, Economics, Life Sciences, & Social Sciences. 2007. 132p. per. 11.95 *(978-1-4288-3662-4(4))* Cram101 Inc.

Bellomo, N. & Bianca, Concetta. Towards a Mathematical Theory of Complex Biological Systems. 2011. 228p. 88.00 *(978-981-4340-53-3(7))* World Scientific Publishing Co., Inc.

Berestycki, Henri & Hamel, Francois. Reaction-Diffusion Equations & Propagation Phenomena. 2007. 410p. 69.95 *(978-0-387-34158-3(7)*, 0387341587) Springer.

Bruni, Renato, ed. Mathematical Approaches to Polymer Sequence Analysis & Related Problems. 2010. (ENG., Illus.). x, 248p. 189.00 *(978-1-4419-6793-2(0)*, 1441967990) Springer.

Byleen, Karl E., et al. Calculus: For Business, Economics, Life Sciences, & Social Sciences. 11th ed. 2007. (ENG., Illus.). 704p. (C). 153.33 *(978-0-13-232813-0(6)*, Prentice Hall) Prentice Hall PTR.

Chaitin, Gregory. Proving Darwin: Making Biology Mathematical. 2012. (ENG., Illus.). 144p. 24.00 ***(978-0-375-42314-7(1)***, Pantheon) Knopf Doubleday Publishing Group.

Chalub, Fabio & Rodrigues, José Francisco, eds. The Mathematics of Darwin's Legacy. 2011. (Mathematics & Biosciences in Interaction Ser.). (ENG., Illus.). viii, 293p. 124.00 ***(978-3-0348-0121-8(1)***, 3034801211) Birkhauser Verlag AG CHE. Dist: Springer.

Cozzens, Margaret B. & Roberts, Fred S., eds. Biomath in the Schools. 2011. (DIMACS: Ser. in Discrete Mathematics & Theoretical Computer Science Ser.). (Illus.). 245p. 52.00 *(978-0-8218-4295-9(1))* American Mathematical Society.

Cram101 Textbook Reviews & Cram101 Textbook Reviews. Outlines & Highlights for an Invitation to Biomathematics by Raina Stefanova Robeva, Isbn: 9780120887712 0120887711. 2011. 88p. pap. 27.95 ***(978-1-61490-052-8(3))*** Cram101 Inc.

Cram101 Textbook Reviews Staff. Outlines & Highlights for Calculus for Life Sciences by Marvin L Bittinger, Isbn: 9780321279354. 2009. 88p. pap. 27.95 *(978-1-4288-3683-9(7))* Cram101 Inc.

—Outlines & Highlights for College Math for Business, Economics, Life Sciences & Social Sciences by Barnett Isbn: 0131572253. 2008. 60p. per. 9.95 *(978-1-4288-5768-1(0))* Cram101 Inc.

—Outlines & Highlights for Finite Mathematics: For Business, Economics, Life Sciences, & Social Sciences by Barnett, Ziegler, & Byleen, ISBN. 2009. 152p. pap. 29.95 *(978-1-4288-3824-6(4))* Cram101 Inc.

Di. Biomat 2007. 2008. 187.00 *(978-981-281-232-2(6))* World Scientific Publishing Co., Inc.

Dobryshin, R. L. Locally Interacting Systems & Their Application in Biology: Proceedings of the School-Seminar on Markov Processes in Biology, Held in Pushchino, Moscow Region, March, 1976. 2008. (Lecture Notes in Mathematics Ser.). pap. 46.00 *(978-3-540-08450-1(9))* Springer.

Finney, David. Probit Analysis. 2009. (ENG.). 272p. pap. 28.99 *(978-0-521-13590-0(7))* Cambridge Univ. Pr.

Gardingen, P. R. van, et al, eds. Scaling-up: From Cell to Landscape. 2011. (Society for Experimental Biology Seminar Ser.). (ENG.). 402p. pap. 36.99 *(978-0-521-18775-6(3))* Cambridge Univ. Pr.

Hladky, Stephen B., et al. Mathematics for Biological Scientists. 2009. (ENG., Illus.). 450p. pap. 60.00 *(978-0-8153-4136-9(9))* BIOS Scientific Publishers Ltd. GBR. Dist: Taylor & Francis Group.

Hoppensteadt, Frank C. Mathematical Methods for Analysis of a Complex Disease. 2011. (Courant Lecture Notes Ser.). (Illus.). 149p. pap. 31.00 ***(978-0-8218-7286-4(9))*** American Mathematical Society.

Hoppensteadt, Frank C. & Peskin, Charles S. Modeling & Simulation in Medicine & the Life Sciences. 2nd ed. 2010. (Texts in Applied Mathematics Ser.). (Illus.). xiv, 376p. pap. 79.95 *(978-1-4419-2871-9(5)*, 1441928715) Springer.

Iannelli, Mimmo. Mathematics of Biology: Lectures given at the Centro Internazionale Matematico Estivo (C. I. M. E.) held in Cortona (Arezzo), Italy, June 18-30 1979. 2010. (CIME Summer Schools Ser.). 370p. pap. 49.95 *(978-3-642-11068-9(1)*, 3642110681) Springer.

Kelly, James T., ed. Progress in Mathematical Biology Research. 2008. 347p. (C). 129.00 *(978-1-60456-171-5(8))* Nova Science Pubs., Inc.

Kirkwood, James R., et al. Laboratory Manual of Biomathematics. 2007. (ENG., Illus.). 192p. (C). per. 25.95 *(978-0-12-374022-9(3)*, Academic Pr.) Elsevier Science & Technology Bks.

Kizilova. Optimal Transport Networks in Nature. 2011. 77.00 *(978-981-283-873-5(2))* World Scientific Publishing Co., Inc.

Leondes, Cornelius T., ed. Computational Methods in Biophysics, Biomaterials, Biotechnology & Medical Systems: Algorithm Development, Mathematical Analysis & DiagnosticsVolume I: Algorithm TechniquesVolume II: Computational MethodsVolume III: Mathematical Analysis MethodsVolume IV: Diagnostic Methods. 2006. 1461p. 1506.00 *(978-0-387-33630-5(3)*, 0387336303) Springer.

Logan, J. David & Wolesensky, William. Mathematical Methods in Biology. 2009. (Pure & Applied Mathematics: a Wiley Series of Texts, Monographs & Tracts Ser.: 96). (ENG., Illus.). 436p. pap. 89.95 *(978-0-470-52587-6(8)*, Wiley) Wiley, John & Sons, Inc.

Longo, Giuseppe. Mathematics & the Natural Sciences: The Physical Singularity of Life. 2011. 336p. 95.00 ***(978-1-84816-693-6(1))*** Imperial College Pr. GBR. Dist: World Scientific Publishing Co., Inc.

Mahdavi. Current Developments in Mathema.... (V38) (Illus.). 107.00 *(978-981-270-015-5(3))* World Scientific Publishing Co., Inc.

Misra. Topics in Biomathematics. 2011. 111.00 *(978-981-283-659-5(4))* World Scientific Publishing Co., Inc.

Mondaini, Rubem P. Biomat 2008: International Symposium on Mathematical & Computational Biology. 2009. 408p. 156.00 *(978-981-4271-81-3(0))* World Scientific Publishing Co., Inc.

—Biomat 2009 - International Symposium on Mathematical & Computational Biology. 2010. (Illus.). 408p. 156.00 *(978-981-4304-89-4(1))* World Scientific Publishing Co., Inc.

Mondaini, Rubem P. Biomat 2010 - International Symposium on Mathematical & Computational Biology. 2011. 412p. 148.00 ***(978-981-4343-42-8(0))*** World Scientific Publishing Co., Inc.

Morgenthaler, Stephan. Génétique Statistique. 2008. (Statistique et probabilités Appliquées Ser.). XI, 150p. pap. 49.95 *(978-2-287-33910-3(8)*, 2287339108) Springer.

Neuhauser & Cram101 Textbook Reviews Staff. Calculus for Biology & Medicine. 2007. 144p. per. 11.95 *(978-1-4288-3448-4(6))* Cram101 Inc.

Neuhauser, Claudia. Calculus for Biology & Medicine. 3rd ed. 2010. (ENG.). (C). ring bd. 100.00 *(978-0-321-67591-0(6))* Addison Wesley.

—Calculus for Biology & Medicine. 3rd ed. (ENG., 840p. 2011. Illus.). pap. *(978-0-321-67317-6(4))* 2010. (C). 166.67 *(978-0-321-64468-8(9)*, Prentice Hall) Prentice Hall PTR.

—Student Solutions Manual for Calculus for Biology & Medicine. 3rd ed. 2010. (ENG.). 624p. (C). pap. 36.67 *(978-0-321-64492-3(1)*, Prentice Hall) Prentice Hall PTR.

Plank, Michael & Sleeman, B. D. Differential Equations & Mathematical Biology. 2nd rev. ed. 2009. (Chapman & Hall/CRC Mathematical & Computational Biology Ser.). (ENG., Illus.). 462p. (C). 82.95 *(978-1-4200-8357-6(0)*, Chapman & Hall/CRC) CRC Pr. LLC.

Reed, Martin. Core Maths for the Biosciences. 2011. (ENG., Illus.). 368p. 39.95 *(978-0-19-921634-5(7))* Oxford Univ. Pr., Inc.

Robeva, Raina Stefanova, et al. An Invitation to Biomathematics. 2007. (ENG., Illus.). 480p. (C). 67.95 *(978-0-12-088771-2(1)*, Academic Pr.) Elsevier Science & Technology Bks.

—An Invitation to Biomathematics (Textbook & Manual Set) 2007. 384p. (C). pap. 74.95 *(978-0-12-374029-8(0)*, Academic Pr.) Elsevier Science & Technology Bks.

Rothe, F. Global Solutions of Reaction - Diffusion Systems. 2008. (Lecture Notes in Mathematics Ser.). pap. 59.95 *(978-3-540-13365-0(8))* Springer.

Shonkwiler, Ronald W. Mathematical Biology: An Introduction with Maple & Matlab. 2nd rev. ed. 2009. (Undergraduate Texts in Mathematics Ser.). (Illus.). 428p. 69.95 *(978-0-387-70983-3(5))* Springer.

Sivaloganathan, Siv, ed. New Perspectives in Mathematical Biology. 2010. (Fields Institute Communications Ser.). (Illus.). 134p. 79.00 *(978-0-8218-4845-6(3))* American Mathematical Society.

Steel, Robert George Douglas, et al. Principles & Procedures of Statistics. 2006. pap. 10.95 *(978-1-4288-1422-6(1))* Cram101 Inc.

Stephenson, Frank H. Calculations for Molecular Biology & Biotechnology: A Guide to Mathematics in the Laboratory 2e. 2nd ed. 2010. (ENG., Illus.). 460p. pap. 72.95 *(978-0-12-375690-9(1)*, Academic Pr.) Elsevier Science & Technology Bks.

Stewart, Ian. The Mathematics of Life. 2011. (ENG.). 368p. (gr. 9). 27.99 *(978-0-465-02238-0(3))* Basic Bks.

Takeuchi, Yasuhiro, et al, eds. Mathematics for Life Science & Medicine. 2010. (Biological & Medical Physics, Biomedical Engineering Ser.). (Illus.). x, 227p. pap. 189.00 *(978-3-642-07077-8(9)*, 3642070779) Springer.

Tan, Soo T. Student Solutions Manual for Tan's Finite Mathematics for the Managerial, Life, & Social Sciences, 10th. 10th ed. 2011. (ENG.). 256p. (C). pap. 62.95 *(978-0-8400-4904-9(8))* Brooks/Cole.

Taubes, Clifford Henry. Modeling Differential Equations in Biology. 2nd ed. 2008. (ENG., Illus.). 524p. (C). pap. 62.00 *(978-0-521-70843-2(5))* Cambridge Univ. Pr.

Triolo. Diffusion, Propagation & Growth in Biomedical Systems. 2011. 89.00 *(978-1-84816-341-6(X))* World Scientific Publishing Co., Inc.

Wilson, Caroline L., ed. Clustering Algorithms & Mathematical Modeling. 2009. (Mathematics Research Developments Ser.). 116.10 *(978-1-61668-581-9(2))* Nova Science Pubs., Inc.

Wilson, Lachlan B. Mathematical Biology Research Trends. Wilson, Lachlan B., ed. 2008. (Illus.). xii, 312p. 129.00 *(978-1-60456-141-8(6))* Nova Science Pubs., Inc.

BIOMECHANICS

see also Animal Mechanics; Human Engineering; Joints—Range of Motion

American Society of Mechanical Engineers, Bioengineering Division Staff, contrib. by. Proceedings of the ASME Summer Bioengineering Conference — 2009: Presented at 2009 ASME Summer Bioengineering Conference, June 17-21, 2009, Lake Tahoe, California, USA, 2 vols. 2009. (Illus.). lx, 1348p. pap. *(978-0-7918-4891-3(4))* American Society of Mechanical Engineers, The.

—Proceedings of the ASME Summer Bioengineering Conference — 2008: Presented at 2008 ASME Summer Bioengineering Conference, June 25-29, 2008, Marco Island, Florida, USA, 2 vols. 2009. (Illus.). lx, 1128p. *(978-0-7918-4321-5(1))* American Society of Mechanical Engineers, The.

—Proceedings of the ASME Summer Bioengineering Conference — 2010: Presented at 2010 ASME Summer Bioengineering Conference, June 16-19, 2010, Naples, Florida, USA. 2010. (Illus.). liii, 1018p. pap. ***(978-0-7918-4403-8(X))*** American Society of Mechanical Engineers, The.

American Society of Mechanical Engineers, Bioengineering Division Staff, contrib. by. Proceedings of the ASME Summer Bioengineering Conference, 2007: Presented at 2007 ASME Summer Bioengineering Conference, June 28-24 [sic], 2007, Keystone, Colorado: Sponsored by ASME Bioengineering Division. 2007. (Illus.). li, 1075p. pap. *(978-0-7918-4798-5(5))* American Society of Mechanical Engineers, The.

American Society of Mechanical Engineers Staff, ed. Biomechanics in Sport. (Illus.). 68p. 64.00 *(978-0-85298-647-9(5))* Professional Engineering Publishing GBR. Dist: SAE Intl.

Athanasiou, Kyriacos & Natoli, Roman. Introduction to Continuum Biomechanics. 2008. (Synthesis Lectures on Biomedical Engineering Ser.) 100p. pap. 40.00 *(978-1-59829-617-4(5))* Morgan & Claypool Pubs.

Bangash, M. Y. H., et al. Trauma: An Engineering Analysis with Medical Case Studies Investigation. 2007. (Illus.). xxvi, 844p. 379.00 *(978-3-540-36305-7(X)*, 354036305X) Springer.

Bao, Gang. Engineering Biomechanics. 2007. 672p. (C). 100.00 *(978-0-13-142403-6(3)*, Prentice Hall) Prentice Hall PTR.

Bhuyan, Bipul Chandra & Gopal Ch. Hazarika. Magnetic Effect on Blood Flow. 2011. 248p. pap. ***(978-3-639-32292-7(4))*** VDM Verlag Dr. Mueller e.K.

Blanchard, Jeff. The Physician's Golf Injury Desk Reference. 2006. (Illus.). 182p. (C). pap. 142.95 *(978-0-7637-4613-1(4))* Jones & Bartlett Learning, LLC.

Carter, Dennis R. & Beaupré, Gary S. Skeletal Function & Form: Mechanobiology of Skeletal Development, Aging, & Regeneration. 2007. (ENG., Illus.). 332p. pap. 69.00 *(978-0-521-71475-4(3))* Cambridge Univ. Pr.

Çehreli, Murat. Biomechanics of Dental Implants: Handbook of Researchers. 2012. ***(978-1-62100-780-7(4))*** Nova Science Pubs., Inc.

Challis, John H. Biomechanics Lecture Notes. rev. ed. 2010. (ENG.). 128p. spiral bd. 45.22 *(978-0-7872-8842-6(X))* Kendall Hunt Publishing Co.

Cheng, Robert & Sun, Wei. Biofabrication of 3d Liver Tissue Constructs As Drug Metabolism Models. 2010. 140p. pap. *(978-3-8383-2150-9(2))* Lambert Academic Publishing.

Chapman, Arthur E. Biomechanical Analysis of Fundamental Human Movements. 2008. (ENG., Illus.). 320p. (C). 86.00 *(978-0-7360-6402-6(8))* Human Kinetics Pubs.

Chauviere, Arnaud & Claude, Verdier. Cell Mechanics: From Single Scale-Based Models to Multiscale Modeling. Preziosi, Luigi & Verdier, Claude, eds. 2010. (Chapman & Hall/CRC Mathematical & Computational Biology Ser.). (ENG., Illus.). 482p. 119.95 *(978-1-4200-9454-1(8)*, Chapman & Hall/CRC) CRC Pr. LLC.

Chien, Shu. Tributes to Yuan-cheng Fung on His 90th Birthday: Biomechanics: from Molecules to Man. 2009. (Illus.). 364p. 88.00 *(978-981-4289-87-0(6))* World Scientific Publishing Co., Inc.

Cotterell, Brian. Fracture & Life. 2010. (Illus.). 500p. 111.00 *(978-1-84816-282-2(0))* Imperial College Pr. GBR. Dist: World Scientific Publishing Co., Inc.

Cowin, Stephen C. & Humphrey, Jay D., eds. Cardiovascular Soft Tissue Mechanics. 2010. 246p. pap. 139.00 *(978-90-481-5917-8(2)*, 9048159172) Springer.

Cram101 Textbook Reviews. Outlines & Highlights for Applied Biomechanics: Concepts & Connections by John Mclester, ISBN. 2010. 74p. pap. 27.95 *(978-1-61698-039-9(7))* Cram101 Inc.

—Outlines & Highlights for Biomechanical Basis of Human Movement by Joseph Hamill, Kathleen M Knutzen, Isbn: 9780781791281. 2010. 80p. pap. 27.95 *(978-1-61698-448-9(1))* Cram101 Inc.

Cram101 Textbook Reviews & Cram101 Textbook Reviews. Outlines & Highlights for Biomechanics in Ergonomics by Shrawan Kumar. 2011. 408p. pap. 35.95 ***(978-1-61830-367-7(8))*** Cram101 Inc.

—Outlines & Highlights for Clinical Decisions in Therapeutic Exercises: Planning & Implementation by John Nyland, ISBN. 2011. 426p. pap. 35.95 ***(978-1-61461-521-7(7))*** Cram101 Inc.

—Outlines & Highlights for Introductory Biomechanics by C Ross Ethier, Isbn: 9780521841122 0521841127. 2011. 264p. pap. 30.95 ***(978-1-61490-040-5(X))*** Cram101 Inc.

—Outlines & Highlights for Kinesiology: Scientific Basis of Human Motion (Cloth) by Nancy Hamilton, ISBN. 2011. 310p. pap. 32.95 ***(978-1-61490-840-1(0))*** Cram101 Inc.

—Outlines & Highlights for Kinesiology of the Musculoskeletal System by Donald a Neumann, Isbn: 9780323039895 9780323039895. 2011. 278p. pap. 32.95 ***(978-1-61461-380-0(X))*** Cram101 Inc.

Crompton, R. H., ed. Biomechanics, Vol. 75. (Illus.). 112p. pap. *(978-3-8055-7796-0(6))* Karger, S. AG.

Davies, Craig & DiSaia, Vince. Golf Anatomy. 2010. (ENG., Illus.). 200p. pap. 19.95 *(978-0-7360-8434-5(7))* Human Kinetics Pubs.

Davim, J. Paulo, ed. Biotribology. 2010. (Iste Ser.: 544). (ENG., Illus.). 224p. 99.95 *(978-1-84821-275-6(5)*, Wiley-ISTE) Wiley, John & Sons, Inc.

Davis, Paul O. & Sharkey, Brian J. Hard Work: Defining Physical Work Performance Requirements. 2008. (ENG., Illus.). 256p. 68.00 *(978-0-7360-5536-8(9))* Human Kinetics Pubs.

Day, Melissa, et al. Sport & Exercise Science. 2009. (Active Learning in Sport Ser.). (Illus.). 233p. pap. *(978-1-84445-187-6(9))* Learning Matters Ltd.

De Ste Croix, Mark & Korff, Thomas, eds. Paediatric Biomechanics & Motor Control. 2011. (Routledge Research in Sport & Exercise Science Ser.). (ENG., Illus.). 336p. (C). 145.00 *(978-0-415-58018-2(8))* Routledge.

De, Suvranu, et al, eds. Computational Modeling in Biomechanics. 2010. (ENG., Illus.). viii, 581p. 129.00 *(978-90-481-3574-5(5)*, 9048135745) Springer.

Di Silvio, L., ed. Cellular response to Biomaterials. 2009. (ENG., Illus.). 500p. 289.95 *(978-1-4200-9373-5(8))* CRC Pr. LLC.

Diehl, Moritz & Mombaur, Katja, eds. Fast Motions in Biomechanics & Robotics: Optimization & Feedback Control. 2006. (Lecture Notes in Control & Information Sciences Ser.). (Illus.). xiii, 443p. 259.00 *(978-3-540-36118-3(9)*, 3540361189) Springer.

Drummond, Heather. Vascular Mechanotranduction. 2012. (Colloquium Series on Integrated Systems Physiology: from Molecule to Function Ser.). 100p. pap. 35.00 *(978-1-61504-186-2(9))* Morgan & Claypool Life Science Publishers.

Elsheikh, Ahmed, ed. Understanding Corneal Biomechanics through Experimental Assessment & Numerical Simulation. 2010. (Eye & Vision Research Developments Ser.). 73p. pap. 43.00 *(978-1-60876-694-9(2))* Nova Science Pubs., Inc.

Ennos, R. Solid Biomechanics. 2011. (ENG., Illus.). 264p. (C). 65.00 ***(978-0-691-13550-2(9))*** Princeton Univ. Pr.

Enoka, Roger M. Neuromechanics of Human Movement. 4th ed. 2008. (ENG., Illus.). 560p. (C). 84.00 *(978-0-7360-6679-2(9))* Human Kinetics Pubs.

Ethier, C. Ross & Simmons, Craig A. Introductory Biomechanics: From Cells to Organisms. 2007. (Cambridge Texts in Biomedical Engineering Ser.). (ENG., Illus.). 528p. 110.00 *(978-0-521-84112-2(7))* Cambridge Univ. Pr.

Fung, Y. C. Biomechanics: Mechanical Properties of Living Tissues. 2nd ed. 2010. (ENG., Illus.). 592p. pap. 99.00 *(978-1-4419-3104-7(X)*, 144193104X) Springer.

Ghista, Dhanjoo N. Applied Biomedical Engineering Mechanics. 2008. (ENG., Illus.). 552p. 144.95 *(978-0-8247-5831-8(5)*, CRC Press) Taylor & Francis Group GBR. Dist: Taylor & Francis Group.

Giger, H. R. H. R. Giger's Biomechanics Limited Edition. 2007. (ENG., Illus.). 100p. lthr. 195.00 *(978-1-883398-69-9(X))* Morpheus International.

Gilchrist, M. D., ed. IUTAM Symposium on Impact Biomechanics: from Fundamental Insights to Applications: From Fundamental Insights to Applications. 2010. (Solid Mechanics & Its Applications Ser.). xv, 489p. pap. 239.00 *(978-90-481-6968-9(2)*, 9048169682) Springer.

Goh Cho Hong, James & Lim, Chwee Teck, eds. 6th World Congress of Biomechanics (WCB 2010), 1 - 6 August 2010, Singapore: In Conjunction with 14th International Conference on Biomedical Engineering (ICBME) & 5th Asia Pacific Conference on Biomechanics (APBiomech) 2010. (IFMBE Proceedings Ser.). 1700p. pap. 539.00 *(978-3-642-14514-8(0)*, 3642145140) Springer.

Goldmann, Tomas. Mechanical Properties of Cortical Bones. 2010. 124p. pap. *(978-3-8383-4413-3(8))* Lambert Academic Publishing.

Gough, Richard, et al, eds. The Meyerhold Companion. 2008. *(978-0-415-42616-9(2)*, Routledge) Taylor & Francis Group.

Gregersen, Hans. Biomechanics of the Gastrointestinal Tract: New Perspectives in Motility Research & Diagnostics. 2010. (ENG.). xv, 268p. pap. 159.00 *(978-1-84996-880-5(2)*, 1849968802) Springer.

Haake, Steven & Moritz, Eckehard Fozzy, eds. The Engineering of Sport 6: Developments for Innovation, 3 vols., Vol. 3. 2006. (Engineering of Sport 6 Ser.). (ENG., Illus.). xliv, 440p. 149.00 *(978-0-387-34680-9(5)*, 0387346805) Springer.

Hall, Susan. Package: Hall Basic Biomechanics with MaxTraq Software. 6th ed. 2011. (ENG.). (C). pap. 161.33 ***(978-0-07-756803-0(6)***, 0077568036) McGraw-Hill Cos., The.

Hall, Susan J. Basic Biomechanics. 6th ed. 2011. (ENG., Illus.). 560p. (C). pap. 158.67 *(978-0-07-337644-8(2)*, 0073376442) McGraw-Hill Cos., The.

Hammer, Joachim, et al. Medicine Meets Engineering: Proceedings of the 2nd Conference on Applied Biomechanics, Regensburg. 2008. (Illus.). x, 247p. 161.00 *(978-1-58603-828-1(1))* IOS Pr., Inc.

Hazelwood, Vikki, et al. Biomedical Engineering Principles. 2nd rev. ed. 2011. (ENG., Illus.). 540p. (C). 99.95 *(978-1-4398-1232-7(2)*, CRC Press) Taylor & Francis Group GBR. Dist: Taylor & Francis Group.

Holzapfel, Gerhard A. & Ogden, Ray W. Biomechanical Modelling at the Molecular, Cellular & Tissue Levels. 2009. (CISM International Centre for Mechanical Sciences Ser.). (Illus.). 352p. 229.00 *(978-3-211-95873-5(8))* Springer.

Hong, Youlian & Bartlett, Roger. Routledge Handbook of Biomechanics & Human Movement Science. 2nd ed. 2010. (Routledge International Handbooks Ser.). (ENG., Illus.). 420p. (C). pap. 59.95 *(978-0-415-57693-2(8))* Routledge.

Hong, Youlian & Bartlett, Roger, eds. Routledge Handbook of Biomechanics & Human Movement Science. 2008. (Routledge International Handbooks Ser.). (ENG., Illus.). 420p. (C). 270.00 *(978-0-415-40881-3(4))* Routledge.

Hsu, John D., et al. AAOS Atlas of Orthoses & Assistive Devices. 4th ed. 2008. (ENG., Illus.). 672p. 240.00 *(978-0-323-03931-4(6)*, Mosby) Elsevier - Health Sciences Div.

Humphrey, Jay D. & DeLange, Sherry. An Introduction to Biomechanics: Solids & Fluids, Analysis & Design. 2010. (ENG., Illus.). xvii, 631p. pap. 109.00 *(978-1-4419-2318-9(7)*, 1441923187) Springer.

Huston, Ronald L. & Huston, Ronald. Principles of Biomechanics. 2008. (Dekker Mechanical Engineering Ser.). (ENG., Illus.). 442p. 109.95 *(978-0-8493-3494-8(2)*, CRC Press) Taylor & Francis Group GBR. Dist: Taylor & Francis Group.

Iacoviello, Daniela & Andreaus, Ugo, eds. Biomedical Imaging & Computational Modeling in Biomechanics. 2012. (Lecture Notes in Computational Vision & Biomechanics Ser.: 4). (ENG., Illus.). viii, 214p. 129.00 ***(978-94-007-4269-7(X)***, 940074269X) Springer.

Ikai, Atsushi. The World of Nano-Biomechanics: Mechanical Imaging & Measurement by Atomic Force Microscopy. 2007. (ENG., Illus.). 300p. 165.00 *(978-0-444-52777-6(X)*, Elsevier Science) Elsevier Science & Technology Bks.

Ivancevic, Tijana T., et al. Complex Sports Biodynamics: With Practical Applications in Tennis. 2009. (Cognitive Systems Monographs). (ENG., Illus.). xii, 326p. 159.00 *(978-3-540-89970-9(7))* Springer.

Ivancevic, Vladimir G. & Ivancevic, Tijana T. Human-Like Biomechanics: A Unified Mathematical Approach to Human Biomechanics & Humanoid Robotics. 2010. (Intelligent Systems, Control & Automation: Science & Engineering Ser.). xiv, 468p. pap. 209.00 *(978-90-481-7047-0(8)*, 9048170478) Springer.

Johnson, Arthur T. Biomechanics & Exercise Physiology: Quantitative Modeling. 2nd ed. 2007. (ENG., Illus.). 688p. (C). 135.95 *(978-1-57444-906-8(0)*, DK5813, CRC Press) Taylor & Francis Group GBR. Dist: Taylor & Francis Group.

Kamkin, Andre & Kiseleva, Irina, eds. Mechanical Stretch & Cytokines. 2011. (Mechanosensitivity in Cells & Tissues Ser.). (ENG., Illus.). xv, 236p. 189.00 ***(978-94-007-2003-9(3)***, 9400720033) Springer.

Kanellopoulos, Asimakis. Hand & Wrist Biomechanics. 2010. 92p. pap. *(978-3-8383-1698-7(3))* Lambert Academic Publishing.

Kato, Naomi & Kamimura, Shinji, eds. Bio-mechanisms of Swimming & Flying: Fluid Dynamics, Biomimetic Robots, & Sports Science. 2010. (ENG., Illus.). xiv, 403p. pap. 189.00 *(978-4-431-99829-7(2)*, 4431998292) Springer.

Kerr, Andrew. Introductory Biomechanics. 2010. (ENG., Illus.). 166p. (C). pap. 48.95 *(978-0-443-06944-4(1)*, Churchill Livingstone) Elsevier - Health Sciences Div.

Kerr, Andrew. Introductory BiomechanicsText & Evolve eBooks Package. 2012. (ENG.). 166p. (C). 73.95 ***(978-0-7020-4473-1(3)***, Churchill Livingstone) Elsevier - Health Sciences Div.

Kisailus, D., et al, eds. Structure-Property Relationships in Biomineralized & Biomimetic Composites: Volume 1187. 2009. (MRS Proceedings Ser.). (ENG.). 195p. (C). 113.00 *(978-1-60511-160-5(0))* Cambridge Univ. Pr.

Kleinstreuer/Clement. Solutions Manual for Biofluid Dynamics. 2006. 209p. (C). *(978-0-8493-8747-0(7))* CRC Pr. LLC.

Knudson, Duane. Fundamentals of Biomechanics. 2nd ed. (ENG., Illus.). xii, 356p. 2011. pap. 109.00 *(978-1-4419-6497-7(5)*, 1441964975) 2007. 109.00 *(978-0-387-49311-4(5)*, 0387493115) Springer.

Kumar, Shrawan, ed. Biomechanics in Ergonomics. 2nd rev. ed. 2007. (ENG., Illus.). 744p. (C). 109.95 *(978-0-8493-7908-6(3)*, CRC Press) Taylor & Francis Group GBR. Dist: Taylor & Francis Group.

Kutz, Myer. Biomedical Engineering & Design, Vols. 1 & 2. 2nd ed. 2009. (ENG., Illus.). 1600p. 250.00 *(978-0-07-149840-1(0)*, 0071498400) McGraw-Hill Professional Publishing.

Latash, Mark L. Synergy. 2008. (ENG., Illus.). 432p. 67.95 *(978-0-19-533316-9(0))* Oxford Univ. Pr., Inc.

Latinovic, Olga. Micromechanics & Structure of Soft & Biological Materials. 2010. 136p. pap. *(978-3-639-23050-5(7))* VDM Verlag Dr. Mueller e.K.

Leondes. Biomechanical Systems Technology (Set) 2007. 544.00 *(978-981-270-798-7(0))* World Scientific Publishing Co., Inc.

—Biomechanical Systems Technology (V1) 2007. 155.00 *(978-981-270-981-3(9))* World Scientific Publishing Co., Inc.

—Biomechanical Systems Technology (V2) 2007. 139.00 *(978-981-270-982-0(7))* World Scientific Publishing Co., Inc.

—Biomechanical Systems Technology (V3) 2009. 155.00 *(978-981-270-983-7(5))* World Scientific Publishing Co., Inc.

—Biomechanical Systems Technology (V4) 2007. 155.00 *(978-981-270-984-4(3))* World Scientific Publishing Co., Inc.

LeVeau, Barney F. Biomechanics of Human Motion: Basics & Beyond for the Health Professions. 2010. (ENG., Illus.). 208p. (C). 43.95 *(978-1-55642-905-7(3))* SLACK, Inc.

Levy, Jerrod H., ed. Biomechanics: Principles, Trends & Applications. 2010. (Biomechanics - Theory & Applications Ser.). (Illus.). 414p. 145.00 *(978-1-60741-394-3(9))* Nova Science Pubs., Inc.

Li, Shaofan & Sun, Bohua, eds. Advances in Cell Mechanics. 2011. (ENG., Illus.). 475p. 179.00 *(978-3-642-17589-3(9)*, 3642175899) Springer.

Lyall, F. & El Haj, Alicia. Biomechanics & Cells. Lyall, Fiona & Haj, A. J. El, eds. 2009. (Society for Experimental Biology Seminar Ser.). (ENG., Illus.). 288p. pap. 58.00 *(978-0-521-11454-7(3))* Cambridge Univ. Pr.

Mandenius, Carl-Fredrik & Björkman, Mats. Biomechatronic Design in Biotechnology: A Methodology for Development of Biotechnological Products. 2011. (ENG., Illus.). 304p. 89.95 *(978-0-470-57334-1(1)*, Wiley) Wiley, John & Sons, Inc.

Marras, William S. The Working Back: A Systems View. 2008. (ENG., Illus.). 309p. 111.00 *(978-0-470-13405-4(4)*, Wiley-Interscience) Wiley, John & Sons, Inc.

Materials Research Society ( ) Staff, compiled by. Mechanics of Biological & Bio-Inspired Materials. 2007. (Materials Research Society Symposium Proceedings Ser.). 185p. pap. 115.00 *(978-1-60423-423-7(7))* Curran Assocs., Inc.

McGoron, Anthony, et al, eds. 25th Southern Biomedical Engineering Conference 2009;15 - 17 May, 2009, Miami, Florida, USA. 2009. (IFMBE Proceedings Ser.). (ENG., Illus.). xxii, 386p. pap. 239.00 *(978-3-642-01696-7(0)*, 3642016960) Springer.

McLester, John & St. Pierre, Peter. Applied Biomechanics: Concepts & Connections. 12th ed. 2007. (ENG.). 432p. (C). pap. 174.95 *(978-0-495-10586-2(4))* Brooks/Cole.

Miftahof, Roustem & Nam, Hong. Mathematical Foundations & Biomechanics of the Digestive System. 2010. (ENG., Illus.). 240p. 120.00 *(978-0-521-11662-6(7))* Cambridge Univ. Pr.

Millington, P. F. & Wilkinson, R. Skin. 2009. (Biological Structure & Function Bks.). (ENG.). 240p. pap. 51.00 *(978-0-521-10681-8(8))* Cambridge Univ. Pr.

Mollica, Francesco, et al, eds. Modeling of Biological Materials. 2007. (Modeling & Simulation in Science, Engineering & Technology Ser.). (ENG., Illus.). xv, 357p. 139.00 *(978-0-8176-4410-9(5)*, 0817644105) Birkhauser Boston.

Moritz, Eckehard Fozzy & Haake, Steve, eds. Developments for Sports, 3 vols. 2006. (Engineering of Sport 6 Ser.). (ENG., Illus.). xliv, 445p. 159.00 *(978-0-387-31773-1(2)*, 0387317732) Springer.

—The Engineering of Sport 6 Vol. 2: Developments for Disciplines, Vol. 2. 2006. (Engineering of Sport 6 Ser.). (ENG., Illus.). xl, 329p. 139.00 *(978-0-387-34678-6(3)*, 0387346783) Springer.

Mughal, Asif Mahmood. Analytical Biomechanics. 2009. 172p. pap. *(978-3-639-15921-9(7))* VDM Verlag Dr. Mueller e.K.

Munzir, Said. Biomechanical System Modeling & Smoothing. 2011. 140p. pap. ***(978-3-8443-9678-2(0))*** Lambert Academic Publishing.

Muscolino, Joseph E. Kinesiology: The Skeletal System & Muscle Function. 2nd ed. 2010. (ENG., Illus.). 704p. (C). pap. 67.95 *(978-0-323-06944-1(4)*, Mosby) Elsevier - Health Sciences Div.

Mwachaka, Philip, et al. The Human Rectus Sheath. 2010. 84p. pap. *(978-3-8383-7686-8(2))* Lambert Academic Publishing.

Nanda, Ram S. & Tosun, Yahya. Biomechanics in Orthodontics: Principles & Practice. 2010. (Illus.). vii, 160p. *(978-0-86715-505-1(1))* Quintessence Publishing Co., Inc.

Nedoma, Jirí & Stehlík, Jiri. Mathematical & Computational Methods & Algorithms in Biomechanics: Human Skeletal Systems. 2011. (Wiley Series in Bioinformatics Ser.: 12). (ENG., Illus.). 592p. 115.00 *(978-0-470-40824-7(3)*, Wiley-Interscience) Wiley, John & Sons, Inc.

Neumann, Donald A. Kinesiology of the Musculoskeletal System: Foundations for Rehabilitation. 2nd ed. 2009. (ENG., Illus.). 752p. (C). 88.95 *(978-0-323-03989-5(8)*, Mosby) Elsevier - Health Sciences Div.

Nigg, Benno M. & Herzog, Walter, eds. Biomechanics of the Musculo-Skeletal System. 3rd rev. ed. 2007. (ENG., Illus.). 686p. 139.95 *(978-0-470-01767-8(8)*, Wiley) Wiley, John & Sons, Inc.

Noda, Masaki, ed. Mechanosensing Biology. 2011. (ENG., Illus.). xiv, 218p. 189.00 *(978-4-431-89756-9(9)*, 4431897569) Springer.

Nordin. Basic Biomechanics Muscul (Us Ed) Pb. 4th rev. ed. 2012. (ENG., Illus.). 472p. pap. 76.95 ***(978-1-60913-335-1(8))*** Lippincott Williams & Wilkins.

Oatis. Kinesiology Mechanic Path (Int Ed) 2nd rev. ed. 2009. ***(978-1-4511-0898-9(2))*** Lippincott Williams & Wilkins.

Oatis, Carol A. Kinesiology: The Mechanics & Pathomechanics of Human Movement. 2nd rev. ed. 2008. (Recall Ser.). (ENG., Illus.). 960p. 91.99 *(978-0-7817-7422-2(5))* Lippincott Williams & Wilkins.

Öchsner, Andreas, et al, eds. Analysis & Design of Biological Materials & Structures. 2012. (Advanced Structured Materials Ser.). (ENG., Illus.). ix, 221p. 129.00 ***(978-3-642-22130-9(0)***, 3642221300) Springer.

Öchsner, Andreas & Ahmed, Waqar, eds. Biomechanics of Hard Tissues: Modeling, Testing, & Materials. 2011. (ENG., Illus.). 322p. 160.00 *(978-3-527-32431-6(3)*, Wiley-VCH) Wiley, John & Sons, Inc.

Pedersen, Pauli & Bendsøe, Martin P., eds. IUTAM Symposium on Synthesis in Bio Solid Mechanics. 2010. (Solid Mechanics & Its Applications Ser.). (Illus.). 420p. pap. 309.00 *(978-90-481-5179-0(1)*, 9048151791) Springer.

Peterson, Donald R. & Bronzino, Joseph D., eds. Biomechanics: Principles & Applications. 2nd rev. ed. 2007. (ENG., Illus.). 352p. 104.95 *(978-0-8493-8534-6(2)*, CRC Press) Taylor & Francis Group GBR. Dist: Taylor & Francis Group.

Pike, Jeffrey A. Neck Injury Biomechanics. 2009. 595p. pap. 99.95 *(978-0-7680-2163-9(4))* SAE Intl.

Pitkin, Mark R. Biomechanics of Lower Limb Prosthetics. 2009. (ENG., Illus.). xix, 141p. 189.00 *(978-3-642-03015-4(7)*, 3642030157) Springer.

Proulx, Tom, ed. Mechanics of Biological Systems & Materials, Volume 2: Proceedings of the 2011 Annual Conference on Experimental & Applied Mechanics. 2011. (Conference Proceedings of the Society for Experimental Mechanics Ser.). (ENG., Illus.). ix, 224p. 199.00 *(978-1-4614-0218-3(2)*, 1461402182) Springer.

Redfern. Human Movement Biomechanics. 2007. (Synthesis Lectures on Biomedical Engineering Ser.). 40.00 *(978-1-59829-288-6(9))* Morgan & Claypool Pubs.

Richards, Jim. Biomechanics in Clinic & Research: An Interactive Teaching & Learning Course. 2008. (ENG., Illus.). 232p. 155.00 *(978-0-443-10170-0(1)*, Churchill Livingstone) Elsevier - Health Sciences Div.

Rosman, Matthew. Biomechanical Integration Approach (tm) Level One: The Golfing Machine-Human Machine Partnership. 2009. spiral bd. 54.95 *(978-0-9826786-0-2(6))* Rosman, Dr. Matthew M. GSEM.

—Biomechanical Integration Approach (tm) Level Two: The Science of Exercise, Nutrition, & Performance. 2009. spiral bd. 54.95 *(978-0-9826786-1-9(4))* Rosman, Dr. Matthew M. GSEM.

Secher, Niels. Rowing. Volianitis, Stefanos, ed. 2007. (Olympic Handbook of Sports Medicine Ser.: 7). (ENG., Illus.). 184p. pap. 75.95 *(978-1-4051-5373-7(3)*, Wiley-Blackwell) Wiley, John & Sons, Inc.

Segel, Lee A., ed. Biological Kinetics. 2008. (Cambridge Studies in Mathematical Biology Ser.). (ENG.). 232p. pap. 53.00 *(978-0-521-06409-5(0))* Cambridge Univ. Pr.

Seifert, Ludovic. Motor Coordination & Expertise. 2011. 124p. pap. ***(978-3-8443-0875-4(X))*** Lambert Academic Publishing.

Seo, Na Jin. Biomechanical Models of Hand Coupling for Axial Torque & Push Exertions. 2008. 188p. per. *(978-3-8364-6431-4(4))* VDM Verlag Dr. Mueller e.K.

Shera, Christopher A. & Olson, Elizabeth S., eds. What Fire Is in Mine Ears: Progress in Auditory Biomechanics: Proceedings of the 11th International Mechanics of Hearing Workshop. 2012. (AIP Conference Proceedings Ser.: 1403). (ENG.). 742p. pap. 210.00 ***(978-0-7354-0975-0(7)***, 0735409757, AIP Pr.) Springer.

Silber, Gerhard & Then, Christophe. Preventive Biomechanics: Optimizing Support Systems for the Human Body in the Lying & Sitting Position. 2012. (ENG., Illus.). xii, 374p. 179.00 ***(978-3-642-29002-2(7)***, 3642290027) Springer.

Soh, Chee-Kiong, et al, eds. Smart Materials in Structural Health Monitoring, Control & Biomechanics. 2012. (Advanced Topics in Science & Technology in China Ser.). (ENG., Illus.). 400p. 179.00 ***(978-3-642-24462-9(9)***, 3642244629) Springer.

Sternad, Dagmar. Progress in Motor Control: A Multidisciplinary Perspective. 2009. (Advances in Experimental Medicine & Biology Ser.). (Illus.). 750p. 169.00 *(978-0-387-77063-5(1))* Springer.

Stoica, Adrian. AT-EQUAL 2009: 2009 ECSIS Symposium on Advanced Technologies for Enhanced Quality of Life (LAB-RS & ARTIPED 2009): Proceedings, 22-26 July 2009, Iasi, Romania. 2009. (Illus.). xi, 172p. pap. ***(978-0-7695-3753-5(7))*** IEEE Computer Society Pr.

Tanaka, Masao, et al. Computational Biomechanics: Theoretical Background & Biological/Biomedical Problems. 2012. (First Course in in Silico Medicine Ser.). (ENG.). xii, 196p. pap. 79.95 ***(978-4-431-54072-4(5)***, 4431540725) Springer.

Thomas, Adrian & Taylor, Graham. Evolutionary Biomechanics. 2011. (Oxford Series in Ecology & Evolution Ser.). 240p. pap. 49.95 *(978-0-19-856638-0(7))*; (ENG., Illus.). 110.00 *(978-0-19-856637-3(9))* Oxford Univ. Pr., Inc.

Thubrikar, Mano J. Vascular Mechanics & Pathology. 2007. (ENG., Illus.). xxiv, 496p. 124.00 *(978-0-387-33816-3(0)*, 0387338160) Springer.

Todd, Mabel E. The Thinking Body: A Study of the Balancing Forces of Dynamic Man. 2008. pap. 50.00 *(978-0-939266-54-8(7))* Gestalt Journal Pr.

Wada. Biomechanics at Micro- Nanoscale. . Vii. (Illus.). 107.00 *(978-981-256-746-8(1))* World Scientific Publishing Co., Inc.

—Biomechanics at Micro- Nanoscale... (V3) 2007. 84.00 *(978-981-270-814-4(6))* World Scientific Publishing Co., Inc.

Wada, Hiroshi, ed. Biomechanics at Micro- & Nanoscale Levels: Volume IV. 2007. (Biomechanics at Micro- & Nanoscale Levels Ser.). (Illus.). 172p. 104.00 *(978-981-277-131-5(X))* World Scientific Publishing Co., Inc.

Wang, Xiaodu, et al. Biomechanics in Bone Tissue Engineering. 2010. (Synthesis Lectures on Tissue Engineering Ser.). 225p. pap. 40.00 *(978-1-60845-169-2(0))* Morgan & Claypool Pubs.

Wang, Yu-Li & Discher, Dennis E., eds. Cell Mechanics. 2007. (ENG., Illus.). 632p. 161.00 *(978-0-12-370500-6(2)*, Academic Pr.) Elsevier Science & Technology Bks.

Watkins, James. Functional Anatomy. 2009. (Pocket Podiatry Ser.). (ENG., Illus.). 336p. (C). pap. 54.95 *(978-0-7020-3032-1(5)*, Churchill Livingstone) Elsevier - Health Sciences Div.

Wendlova, Jaroslava. Biomechanical Variables in Assessment of Fracture Risk. 2012. (Biomechanics - Theory & Applications Ser.). (Illus.). 155p. pap. 47.00 ***(978-1-61470-184-2(9))*** Nova Science Pubs., Inc.

Whiting, William, et al. Biomechanics of Musculoskeletal Injury. 2nd ed. 2008. (ENG., Illus.). 360p. (C). 79.00 *(978-0-7360-5442-3(1))* Human Kinetics Pubs.

Zaman, Muhammad H., ed. Statistical Mechanics of Cellular Systems & Processes. 2009. (ENG., Illus.). 228p. 80.00 *(978-0-521-88608-6(2))* Cambridge Univ. Pr.

BIOMEDICAL COMPATIBILITY

see Biocompatibility

BIOMEDICAL ENGINEERING

see also Biomedical Materials; Electronics in Biology; Medical Electronics; Medical Instruments and Apparatus; Physiological Apparatus

Abdou, Mohamed. Biomedical Engineering. 2010. 220p. pap. *(978-3-639-24018-4(9))* VDM Verlag Dr. Mueller e.K.

Abraham, David, et al, eds. Vascular Complications in Human Disease: Mechanisms & Consequences. 2010. (ENG., Illus.). xiv, 258p. pap. 179.00 *(978-1-84996-676-4(1)*, 1849966761) Springer.

Abu-Faraj, Ziad O. Biomedical Engineering Education & Advanced Bioengineering Learning: Interdisciplinary Concepts. 2012. (Illus.). ***(978-1-4666-0124-6(8))***; ***(978-1-4666-0122-2(1))***; E-Book ***(978-1-4666-0123-9(X))*** IGI Global.

Abu Osman, N. A. 4th Kuala Lumpur International Conference on Biomedical Engineering, 2 vols. 2008. (IFMBE Proceedings Ser.). (Illus.). 920p. pap. 439.00 *(978-3-540-69138-9(3))* Springer.

Akay, Metin, ed. Handbook of Neural Engineering. 2007. (IEEE Press Series on Biomedical Engineering Ser.: 21). (ENG., Illus.). 662p. 199.00 *(978-0-470-05669-1(X)*, Wiley-IEEE Pr.) Wiley, John & Sons, Inc.

—Wiley Encyclopedia of Biomedical Engineering, 6-Volume Set. 2006. 4500p. 1650.00 *(978-0-470-04968-6(5)*, Wiley-Interscience) Wiley, John & Sons, Inc.

Al. Topics in Scattering & Biomedical Engi. . 2008. 196.00 *(978-981-281-484-5(1))* World Scientific Publishing Co., Inc.

Al-Jumaily, Ahmed & Reddy, Prasika I. Medical Devices for Respiratory Dysfunctions: Principles & Modeling of Continuous Positive Airway Pressure (CPAP) Devices. 2011. ***(978-0-7918-5977-3(0))*** American Society of Mechanical Engineers, The.

American Society of Mechanical Engineers, Bioengineering Division Staff, contrib. by. Proceedings of the ASME Summer Bioengineering Conference — 2009: Presented at 2009 ASME Summer Bioengineering Conference, June 17-21, 2009, Lake Tahoe, California, USA, 2 vols. 2009. (Illus.). lx, 1348p. pap. *(978-0-7918-4891-3(4))* American Society of Mechanical Engineers, The.

—Proceedings of the ASME Summer Bioengineering Conference — 2008: Presented at 2008 ASME Summer Bioengineering Conference, June 25-29, 2008, Marco Island, Florida, USA, 2 vols. 2009. (Illus.). lx, 1128p. *(978-0-7918-4321-5(1))* American Society of Mechanical Engineers, The.

—Proceedings of the ASME Summer Bioengineering Conference — 2010: Presented at 2010 ASME Summer Bioengineering Conference, June 16-19, 2010, Naples, Florida, USA. 2010. (Illus.). lii, 1018p. pap. ***(978-0-7918-4403-8(X))*** American Society of Mechanical Engineers, The.

American Society of Mechanical Engineers, Bioengineering Division Staff, contrib. by. Proceedings of the ASME Summer Bioengineering Conference, 2007: Presented at 2007 ASME Summer Bioengineering Conference, June 28-24 [sic], 2007, Keystone, Colorado: Sponsored by ASME Bioengineering Division. 2007. (Illus.). li, 1075p. pap. *(978-0-7918-4798-5(5))* American Society of Mechanical Engineers, The.

American Society of Mechanical Engineers Staff, contrib. by. Proceedings of the 7th International Conference on Nanochannels, Microchannels & Minichannels, 2009: Presented at 7th International Conference on

Nanochannels, Microchannels & Minichannels, June 22-24, 2009, Pohang, South Korea, 2 vols. 2009. (Illus.). xxvi, 1457p. pap. *(978-0-7918-4349-9(1))* American Society of Mechanical Engineers, The.

—Proceedings of the 8th International Conference on Nanochannels, Microchannels & Minichannels — 2010: Presented at 8th International Conference on Nanochannels, Microchannels & Minichannels, August 1-5, 2010, Montreal, Canada, 2 vols. 2011. (Illus.). xxvi, 1784p. pap. *(978-0-7918-5450-1(7))* American Society of Mechanical Engineers, The.

Ammari, Habib. An Introduction to Mathematics of Emerging Biomedical Imaging. 2008. (Mathématiques et Applications Ser.). (ENG., Illus.). x, 198p. pap. 69.95 *(978-3-540-79552-0(9))*, 3540795529) Springer.

Ammari, Habib, ed. Mathematical Modeling in Biomedical Imaging II: Optical, Ultrasound, & Opto-Acoustic Tomographies. 2011. (Lecture Notes in Mathematics / Mathematical Biosciences Subseries Ser.). (ENG., Illus.). ix, 160p. pap. 49.95 ***(978-3-642-22989-3(1)***, 3642229891) Springer.

Annual Review of Biomedical Engineering. 2006. 75.00 *(978-0-8243-3508-3(2))* Annual Reviews, Inc.

ASME Nanotechnology Institute Staff, contrib. by. Proceedings of the ASME First Global Congress on NanoEngineering for Medicine & Biology: Presented at the ASME 2010 First Global Congress on NanoEngineering for Medicine & Biology, February 7-10, 2010, Houston, Texas, USA. 2010. (Illus.). xxii, 374p. pap. *(978-0-7918-4392-5(0))* American Society of Mechanical Engineers, The.

Astakhov, Vadim, ed. Biomedical Informatics. 2009. (Methods in Molecular Biology Ser.). (ENG., Illus.). x, 270p. 149.00 *(978-1-934115-63-3(0)*, 1934115630) Humana Pr.

Astolfi, Laura & Babiloni, Fabio. Advanced Signal Processing Techniques for the Estimation of Cortical Connectivity in Humans. Enderle, John D., ed. 2007. (Synthesis Lectures on Biomedical Engineering Ser.). 100p. pap. 40.00 *(978-1-59829-532-0(2))* Morgan & Claypool Pubs.

Athanasiou, Kyriacos, et al. Synthesis Series in Biomedical Engineering Vol. 5. 2012. (Synthesis Series in Biomedical Engineering Ser.). 500p. 85.00 *(978-1-60845-188-3(7))* Morgan & Claypool Pubs.

Atherton, Mark A., et al, eds. Repair & Redesign of Physiological Systems. 2008. (Design & Nature Ser.: 9). (Illus.). 304p. 190.00 *(978-1-84564-096-5(9))* WIT Pr GBR. Dist: WIT Pr.

Ayres, Fabio, et al. Analysis of Oriented Texture. 2010. (Synthesis Lectures on Biomedical Engineering Ser.). 162p. pap. 45.00 *(978-1-60845-029-9(5))* Morgan & Claypool Pubs.

Azhari, Haim & Azhari. Basics of Biomedical Ultrasound for Engineers. 2010. (ENG., Illus.). 371p. 110.00 *(978-0-470-46547-9(6)*, Wiley-IEEE Pr.) Wiley, John & Sons, Inc.

Ba. Dendrimer-Based Nanomedicine. Majoros, Istvan & Baker, Jr., James, eds. 320p. 88.00 *(978-981-270-642-3(9))* World Scientific Publishing Co., Inc.

Badylak, S. F., et al, eds. Cells Tissues Organs Vol. 195, No. 1-2: Cardiovascular Regenerative Biology. 2011. (ENG., Illus.). 184p. pap. ***(978-3-8055-9872-9(6))*** Karger, S. AG.

Baine, Celeste. Is There a Biomedical Engineer Inside You? A Student's Guide to Exploring Careers in Biomedical Engineering & Biomedical Engineering Technology. 2nd ed. 2006. (YA). 7.95 *(978-0-9664763-3-0(6)*, Engineering Education Service Ctr.) Bonamy Publishing.

Baker, James R. Dendrimer-Based Nanomedicine. Majoros, Istvan, ed. 2008. (ENG., Illus.). 440p. pap. 219.95 *(978-981-4241-04-5(0))* Pan Stanford Publishing SGP. Dist: Taylor & Francis Group.

Bal, Harshawardhan & Hujol, Johnny. Java for Bioinformatics & Biomedical Applications. 2010. (ENG., Illus.). xviii, 342p. pap. 115.00 *(978-1-4419-4245-6(9)*, 1441942459) Springer.

Barth, A. & Haris, P. I., eds. Biological & Biomedical Infrared Spectroscopy. 2009. (Illus.). 448p. 218.00 *(978-1-60750-045-2(0))* IOS Pr., Inc.

Bártolo, Paulo & Bidanda, Bopaya, eds. Bio-Materials & Prototyping Applications in Medicine. 2010. (ENG., Illus.). xi, 216p. pap. 149.00 *(978-1-4419-4296-8(3)*, 1441942963) Springer.

Bauer, Elizabeth & Fleming, Anthony H. Inside the Photon: A Journey to Health. 2011. 300p. 149.00 *(978-981-4241-40-3(7))* Pan Stanford Publishing SGP. Dist: Independent Pubs. Group.

Baura, Gail. A biosystems approach industrial Pati. 2011. (Synthesis Lectures on Biomedical Engineering Ser.). 100p. pap. 40.00 *(978-1-59829-294-7(3))* Morgan & Claypool Pubs.

Baxter, Walt & Lee, Abraham P. Proceedings of the 2nd Frontiers in Biomedical Devices Conference — 2007: Presented at the Frontiers in Biomedical Devices Conference, June 7-8, 2007, Irvine, California, USA. 2007. (Illus.). xiii, 160p. pap. *(978-0-7918-4266-9(5))* American Society of Mechanical Engineers, The.

Böhm, Christian, et al, eds. Information Technology in Bio- And Medical Informatics: Second International Conference, Itbam 2011, Toulouse, France, August - September, Proceedings. 2011. (Lecture Notes in Computer Science / Information Systems & Applications, incl. Internet/Web, & HCI Ser.). (ENG., Illus.). xii, 188p. pap. 72.00 ***(978-3-642-23207-7(8)***, 3642232078) Springer.

Beckingsworth, Robert H., ed. Hand Surgery: Preoperative Expectations, Techniques & Results. 2010. (Surgery - Procedures, Complications, & Results Ser.). 179p. 129.00 *(978-1-60876-280-4(7)*, Nova Biomedical Bks.) Nova Science Pubs., Inc.

Ben-Tzvi, Pinhas. A Dispensing System for Microdrops Generation in Medical Applications. 2010. 148p. pap. *(978-3-8383-6000-3(1))* Lambert Academic Publishing.

Berman, Jules J. Biomedical Informatics. 2006. (Illus.). 459p. per. 90.95 *(978-0-7637-4135-8(3))* Jones & Bartlett Learning, LLC.

—Pearl Programming for Medicine & Biology. 2007. 407p. per. 69.95 *(978-0-7637-4333-8(X))* Jones & Bartlett Learning, LLC.

Berthiaume, Francois & Morgan, Jeffrey. Methods in Bioengineering: 3D Tissue Engineering. 2010. (Illus.). 280p. 139.00 *(978-1-59693-458-0(1))* Artech Hse., Inc.

Bharath, A. A., et al. Synthesis Series in Biomedical Engineering Vol. 7. 2011. (Synthesis Series in Biomedical Engineering Ser.). 500p. 85.00 *(978-1-60845-190-5(9))* Morgan & Claypool Pubs.

Bidanda, Bopaya & Bártolo, Paulo, eds. Bio-Materials & Prototyping Applications in Medicine. 2008. (ENG., Illus.). xi, 216p. 149.00 *(978-0-387-47682-7(2)*, 0387476822) Springer.

Biomedical Engineering Entrepreneurship. 2010. 77.00 *(978-981-4295-60-4(4))* World Scientific Publishing Co., Inc.

Biomedical Engineering Principles. 2nd rev. ed. 2011. (C). 99.95 ***(978-1-4398-1233-4(0)***, CRC Press) Taylor & Francis Group GBR. Dist: Taylor & Francis Group.

Biomedical Microsystems. 2011. (C). 89.95 ***(978-1-4200-5123-0(7)***, CRC Press) Taylor & Francis Group GBR. Dist: Taylor & Francis Group.

Biomems. 2011. 99.95 ***(978-1-4398-1700-1(6)***, CRC Press) Taylor & Francis Group GBR. Dist: Taylor & Francis Group.

Blobel, B. EHealth: Combining Health Telematics, Telemedicine, Biomedical Engineering & Bioinformatics to the Edge. 2008. pap. 111.00 *(978-1-58603-834-2(6))* IOS Pr., Inc.

Boag, Graham, et al. Synthesis Series in Biomedical EngineeringVolume 9. 2012. (Synthesis Series in Biomedical Engineering Ser.). 500p. 85.00 *(978-1-60845-302-3(2))* Morgan & Claypool Pubs.

Boccaccini, Aldo R. & Gough, Julie E, eds. Tissue Engineering Using Ceramics & Polymers. 2007. (Illus.). 604p. 354.95 *(978-1-4200-4454-6(0))* CRC Pr. LLC.

Boccaccini, Aldo R. & Harding, Sian E., eds. Myocardial Tissue Engineering. 2010. (Studies in Mechanobiology, Tissue Engineering & Biomaterials Ser.). 350p. 179.00 *(978-3-642-18055-2(8)*, 3642180558) Springer.

Bonfiglio, Annalisa & Rossi, Danilo Emilio de, eds. Wearable Monitoring Systems. 2010. (ENG., Illus.). x, 290p. 129.00 *(978-1-4419-7383-2(4)*, 1441973834) Springer.

Borenstein, Jeffrey, ed. Micro & Nanoengineering of the Cell Microenvironment: Technologies & Applications. 2008. (Engineering in Medicine & Biology Ser.). (Illus.). 627p. 179.00 *(978-1-59693-148-0(5))* Artech Hse., Inc.

Bos, Lodewijk, et al, eds. Handbook of Digital Homecare: Successes & Failures. 2011. (Communications in Medical & Care Compunetics Ser.). (ENG., Illus.). vi, 245p. 179.00 *(978-3-642-19646-1(2)*, 3642196462) Springer.

Braddock, Martin, ed. Biomedical Imaging: The Chemistry of Labels, Probes & Contrast Agents. 2011. (RSC Drug Discovery Ser.). (ENG., Illus.). 552p. 232.00 ***(978-1-84973-014-3(8))*** Royal Society of Chemistry, The GBR. Dist: Ingram Pub. Services.

Brebbia, C. A., et al, eds. Environmental Health & Biomedicine. 2011. (Transactions in Biomedicine & Health: 15). (Illus.). 512p. lib. bdg. 440.00 *(978-1-84564-524-3(3))* WIT Pr GBR. Dist: WIT Pr.

Bronzino, Joseph D. & Reisner, David Evans. Bionanotechnology: Global Prospects. Reisner, David E., ed. 2008. (ENG., Illus.). 368p. 97.95 *(978-0-8493-7528-6(2)*, CRC Press) Taylor & Francis Group GBR. Dist: Taylor & Francis Group.

Brooker, Graham. Introduction to Biomechatronics. 2012. (ENG.). 616p. 135.00 ***(978-1-891121-27-2(8))*** SciTech Publishing, Inc.

Browning, Jaclyn E. & McMann, Alexander K. Computational Engineering: Design, Development & Applications. 2011. (Engineering Tools, Techniques & Tables Ser.). 89.00 *(978-1-61122-806-9(9))* Nova Science Pubs., Inc.

Burdick, Jason A. & Mauck, Robert L., eds. Biomaterials for Tissue Engineering Applications: A Review of the Past & Future Trends. 2010. (Illus.). 10p. 219.00 *(978-3-7091-0384-5(3)*, 3709103843) Springer.

Burg, Karen J. L., et al. Introduction to Biofabrication. 2008. (Synthesis Lectures on Biomedical Engineering Ser.). pap. 40.00 *(978-1-59829-632-7(9))* Morgan & Claypool Pubs.

Buzug, Thorsten M. Advances in Medical Engineering. 2007. (Springer Proceedings in Physics Ser.: Vol. 210). (Illus.). XVIII, 476p. 349.00 *(978-3-540-68763-4(7)*, 3540687637) Springer.

Buzug, Thorsten M., ed. Advances in Medical Engineering. 2010. (Springer Proceedings in Physics Ser.). (Illus.). xviii, 476p. pap. 349.00 *(978-3-642-08827-8(9)*, 3642088279) Springer.

Cai, Yang. Digital Human Modeling: Trends in Human Algorithms. 2008. (Lecture Notes in Computer Science / Lecture Notes in Artificial Intelligence Ser.). ix, 207p. pap. 69.95 *(978-3-540-89429-2(2))* Springer.

Cao, Hengchu, et al. Proceedings of the 3rd Frontiers in Biomedical Devices Conference — 2008: Presented at the 3rd Frontiers in Biomedical Devices Conference & Exhibition, June 18-20, 2008, Irvine, California, USA. 2008. (Illus.). xi, 126p. pap. *(978-0-7918-4833-3(7))* American Society of Mechanical Engineers, The.

Cao, Hua. Automated Fusion of Multi-Modality Biomedical Images. 2008. 164p. pap. *(978-3-639-06622-7(7))* VDM Verlag Dr. Mueller e.K.

Cees, Oomens, et al. Biomechanics: Concepts & Computation. 2010. (Cambridge Texts in Biomedical Engineering Ser.). (ENG.). 348p. (C). pap. 39.99 *(978-0-521-17296-7(9))* Cambridge Univ. Pr.

Chan, Anthony Y. K. Biomedical device Technology: Principles & Design. 2008. 594p. 0.00 *(978-0-398-07699-3(5))*; pap. 0.00 *(978-0-398-07700-6(2))* Thomas, Charles C. Pub., Ltd.

Chan, Warren C. W., ed. Bio-Applications of Nanoparticles. 2010. (Advances in Experimental Medicine & Biology Ser.). (Illus.). xx, 207p. pap. 209.00 *(978-1-4419-2633-3(X)*, 144192633X) Springer.

Chandran, Krishnan B., et al, eds. Image-Based Computational Modeling of the Human Circulatory & Pulmonary Systems: Methods & Applications. 2010. (ENG., Illus.). xx, 465p. 229.00 *(978-1-4419-7349-8(4)*, 1441973494) Springer.

Chatterjee, Shakti & Miller, Aubert. Biomedical Instrumentation Systems. 2010. (ENG.). 704p. (C). 98.95 *(978-1-4180-1866-5(X))* Delmar Cengage Learning.

Chau, Tom & Fairley, Jillian, eds. Pediatric Rehabilitation Engineering: From Disability to Possibility. 2010. (CRC Press Series in Rehabilitation Science in Practice Ser.). (ENG., Illus.). 366p. 145.95 *(978-1-4398-0842-9(2)*, CRC Press) Taylor & Francis Group GBR. Dist: Taylor & Francis Group.

Chaudhuri, Julian & Al-Rubeai, Mohamed, eds. Bioreactors for Tissue Engineering: Principles, Design & Operation. 2010. viii, 375p. pap. 219.00 *(978-90-481-6949-8(6)*, 9048169496) Springer.

Chirila, T. V. Biomaterials & Regenerative Medicine in Ophthalmology. 2010. (Illus.). 560p. 244.99 *(978-1-4398-0215-1(7))* CRC Pr. LLC.

Christe, Barbara. Introduction to Biomedical Instrumentation: The Technology of Patient Care. 2009. (ENG., Illus.). 248p. (C). 68.00 *(978-0-521-51512-2(2))* Cambridge Univ. Pr.

Christenser, Douglas & Athanasiou, K. A. Synthesis Series in Biomedical EngineeringVolume 10. 2012. (Synthesis Series in Biomedical Engineering Ser.). 500p. 85.00 *(978-1-60845-436-5(3))* Morgan & Claypool Pubs.

Cierniak, Robert. X-Ray Computed Tomography in Biomedical Engineering. 2011. (ENG., Illus.). xii, 319p. 179.00 *(978-0-85729-026-7(6)*, 0857290266) Springer.

Cieslak-Blinowska, Katarzyna & Zygierewicz, Jaroslaw. Practical Biomedical Signal Analysis. 2011. (Series in Medical Physics & Biomedical Engineering Ser.). (ENG., Illus.). 324p. 99.95 *(978-1-4398-1202-0(0)*, CRC Press) Taylor & Francis Group GBR. Dist: Taylor & Francis Group.

Clarkson, P. John, et al, eds. Designing Accessible Technology. 2010. (ENG., Illus.). xiv, 250p. pap. 209.00 *(978-1-84996-588-0(9)*, 1849965889) Springer.

Coates Jr., Thomas, et al. Synthesis Series in Biomedical Engineering Vol. 6. 2012. (Synthesis Series in Biomedical Engineering Ser.). 500p. 85.00 *(978-1-60845-189-0(5))* Morgan & Claypool Pubs.

Cohen, Smadar & Amitay-Shafrut, Sigalit. Cardiac Tissue Engineering. 2011. (Synthesis Lectures on Tissue Engineering Ser.). 100p. pap. 40.00 *(978-1-60845-204-0(2))* Morgan & Claypool Pubs.

Cooper, Rory A. An Introduction to Rehabilitation Engineering. 2006. (Series in Medical Physics & Biomedical Engineering Ser.). (ENG., Illus.). 472p. (C). 81.95 *(978-0-8493-7222-3(4)*, Taylor & Francis) Taylor & Francis Group GBR. Dist: Taylor & Francis Group.

Cram101 Textbook Reviews. Outlines & Highlights for Biomedical Engineering: Bridging Medicine & Technology by W. Mark Saltzman, ISBN. 2011. 508p. pap. 37.95 ***(978-1-61490-433-5(2))*** Cram101 Inc.

Cram101 Textbook Reviews & Cram101 Textbook Reviews. Outlines & Highlights for Design of Biomedical Devices & Systems by Donner. 2011. 76p. pap. 27.95 ***(978-1-61830-636-4(7))*** Cram101 Inc.

—Outlines & Highlights for Physics of the Human Body by Irving P Herman. 2011. 298p. pap. 32.95 ***(978-1-61830-781-1(9))*** Cram101 Inc.

Cullum, Brian & Mclamore, Eric. Smart Biomedical & Physiological Sensor Technology VIII. 2011. (Proceedings of SPIE Ser.). pap. 70.00 ***(978-0-8194-8599-1(3))*** SPIE.

Cullum, Brian M. & Carter, J. Chance. Smart Medical & Biomedical Sensor Technology IV: 3-4 October 2006, Boston, Massachusetts, USA. 2006. (Progress in Biomedical Optics & Imaging Ser.: No. 7). (Illus.). 250p. pap. 80.00 *(978-0-8194-6478-1(3))* SPIE.

Cullum, Brian M. & Porterfield, D. M. Smart Biomedical & Physiological Sensor Technology V: 10-11 September 2007, Boston, Massachusetts, USA. 2007. (Proceedings of SPIE Ser.). (Illus.). 172p. pap. 80.00 *(978-0-8194-6919-9(X))* SPIE.

—Smart Biomedical & Physiological Sensor Technology VI: 16-17 April 2009, Orlando, Florida, United States. 2009. (Proceedings of SPIE Ser.). (Illus.). 210p. pap. 70.00 *(978-0-8194-7579-4(3))* SPIE.

Denstedt, J. & Atala, A., eds. Biomaterials & Tissue Engineering in Urology. 2009. (Illus.). 560p. *(978-1-84569-402-9(3))* Woodhead Publishing Ltd.

Depeursinge, Christian D. & Vitkin, Ilya Alex. Novel Optical Instrumentation for Biomedical Applications IV: 14-17 June 2009, Munich, Germany. 2009. (Proceedings of SPIE Ser.). (Illus.). 220p. pap. 120.00 *(978-0-8194-7647-0(1))* SPIE.

Desai, Tejal & Bhatia, Sangeeta N. BioMEMS & Biomedical Nanotechnology: Volume III: Therapeutic Micro/Nanotechnology. 2010. (Illus.). xxiv, 376p. pap. 199.00 *(978-1-4419-3805-3(2)*, 1441938052) Springer.

DiLorenzo, Daniel J. & Bronzino, Joseph D., eds. Neuroengineering. 2007. (ENG., Illus.). 408p. 99.95 *(978-0-8493-8174-4(6)*, CRC Press) Taylor & Francis Group GBR. Dist: Taylor & Francis Group.

Dochain, Denis, ed. Automatic Control of Bioprocesses. 2008. (Iste Ser.: 305). (ENG., Illus.). 288p. 174.00 *(978-1-84821-025-7(6)*, Wiley-ISTE) Wiley, John & Sons, Inc.

Dodla, Mahesh Chandra. Tissue Engineered Scaffolds for Nerve Regeneration. 2008. 164p. per. *(978-3-8364-5763-7(6))* VDM Verlag Dr. Mueller e.K.

Dogramatzis, Dimitris. Healthcare Biotechnology. 2010. (ENG., Illus.). 689p. 104.95 *(978-1-4398-4746-6(0)*, CRC Press) Taylor & Francis Group GBR. Dist: Taylor & Francis Group.

Domach, Michael M. Introduction to Biomedical Engineering. 2nd ed. 2009. (ENG., Illus.). 312p. (C). 144.00 *(978-0-13-602003-5(8)*, Prentice Hall) Prentice Hall PTR.

Dominique. Stem Cell Microenvironments & Tissue Engineering. Prakash, Satya & Shum-Tim, Dominique, eds. 2010. 572p. 102.00 *(978-981-283-788-2(4))* World Scientific Publishing Co., Inc.

Dössel, Olaf & Becks, Thomas, eds. World Congress on Medical Physics & Biomedical Engineering, September 7-12, 2009 Munich, Germany, 13 vols., Set. 2009. (IFMBE Proceedings Ser.). (ENG., Illus.). xxix, 1083p. pap. 469.00 *(978-3-642-03472-5(1)*, 3642034721) Springer.

—World Congress on Medical Physics & Biomedical Engineering, September 7-12, 2009 Munich, Germany: Biomaterials, Cellular & Tussue Engineering, Artificial Organs, Vol. 25/X 2009. (IFMBE Proceedings Ser.). (Illus.). xiv, 314p. pap. 299.00 *(978-3-642-03899-0(9)*, 3642038999) Springer.

—World Congress on Medical Physics & Biomedical Engineering, September 7-12, 2009 Munich, Germany: Biomedical Engineering for Audiology, Ophthalmology, Emergency & Dental Medicine, Vol. 25/XI. 2009. (IFMBE Proceedings Ser.). (Illus.). xiii, 352p. pap. 299.00 *(978-3-642-03890-7(5)*, 3642038905) Springer.

—World Congress on Medical Physics & Biomedical Engineering, September 7-12, 2009 Munich, Germany: Diagnostic & Therapeutic Instrumentation, Clinical Engineering, Vol. 25/VII 2009. (IFMBE Proceedings Ser.). (Illus.). xxiv, 946p. pap. 469.00 *(978-3-642-03884-6(0)*, 3642038840) Springer.

—World Congress on Medical Physics & Biomedical Engineering, September 7-12, 2009 Munich, Germany: Diagnostic Imaging, Vol. 25/2. 2009. (IFMBE Proceedings Ser.). (Illus.). xxvi, 950p. pap. 469.00 *(978-3-642-03878-5(6)*, 3642038786) Springer.

—World Congress on Medical Physics & Biomedical Engineering, September 7-12, 2009 Munich, Germany: General Subjects, Vol. 25/XII 2009. (IFMBE Proceedings Ser.). (Illus.). xvi, 448p. pap. 299.00 *(978-3-642-03892-1(1)*, 3642038921) Springer.

—World Congress on Medical Physics & Biomedical Engineering, September 7-12, 2009 Munich, Germany: Image Processing, Biosignal Processing, Modelling & Simulation, Biomechanics, Vol. 25/IV. 2009. (IFMBE Proceedings Ser.). (Illus.). xlvii, 2365p. pap. 779.00 *(978-3-642-03881-5(6)*, 3642038816) Springer.

—World Congress on Medical Physics & Biomedical Engineering, September 7-12, 2009 Munich, Germany: Information & Communication in Medicine, Telemedicine & E-Health, Vol. 25/V 2009. (IFMBE Proceedings Ser.). (Illus.). xv, 388p. pap. 299.00 *(978-3-642-03903-4(0)*, 3642039030) Springer.

—World Congress on Medical Physics & Biomedical Engineering, September 7-12, 2009 Munich, Germany: Micro- & Nanosystems in Medicine, Active Implants, Biosensors, Vol. 25/VIII 2010. (IFMBE Proceedings Ser.). (Illus.). xv, 389p. pap. 299.00 *(978-3-642-03886-0(7)*, 3642038867) Springer.

—World Congress on Medical Physics & Biomedical Engineering, September 7-12, 2009 Munich, Germany: Neuroengineering, Neural Systems, Rehabilitation & Prosthetics, Vol. 25/IX 2009. (IFMBE Proceedings Ser.). (Illus.). xviii, 600p. pap. 389.00 *(978-3-642-03888-4(3)*, 3642038883) Springer.

—World Congress on Medical Physics & Biomedical Engineering, September 7-12, 2009 Munich, Germany: Radiation Protection & Dosimetry, Biological Effects of Radiation, Vol. 25/III 2009. (IFMBE Proceedings Ser.). (Illus.). xxii, 694p. pap. 389.00 *(978-3-642-03901-0(4)*, 3642039014) Springer.

—World Congress on Medical Physics & Biomedical Engineering, September 7-12, 2009 Munich, Germany: Special Topics & Workshops, Vol. 25/XIII 2009. (IFMBE Proceedings Ser.). (Illus.). xii, 225p. pap. 219.00 *(978-3-642-03894-5(8)*, 3642038948) Springer.

—World Congress on Medical Physics & Biomedical Engineering, September 7-12, 2009 Munich, Germany: Surgery, Nimimal Invasive Interventions, Endoscopy & Image Guided Therapy, Vol. 25/VI. 2009. (IFMBE Proceedings Ser.). (Illus.). xv, 371p. pap. 299.00 *(978-3-642-03905-8(7)*, 3642039057) Springer.

Dremstrup, Kim, et al, eds. 15th Nordic-Baltic Conference on Biomedical Engineering & Medical Physics: NBC 2011. 14-17 June 2011. Aalborg, Denmark. 2011. (IFMBE Proceedings Ser.). (Illus.). xvi, 280p. pap. 259.00 ***(978-3-642-21682-4(X)***, 364221682X) Springer.

Duarte, Andreia. Mobile Acquisition Platform for Sleep Assessment. 2011. 88p. pap. ***(978-3-8433-9111-5(4))*** Lambert Academic Publishing.

Duffy, Vincent D. Digital Human Modeling: First International Conference, DHM 2007, Held as Part of HCI International 2007, Beijing, China, July 22-27, 2007, Proceedings. 2007. (Lecture Notes in Computer Science / Information Systems & Applications, incl. Internet/Web, & HCI Ser.). xxiii, 1068p. pap. 169.00 *(978-3-540-73318-8(3))* Springer.

Editore, Patron & Cerutti. Advanced Methods of Biomedical Signal Processing. Cerutti, Sergio & Marchesi, Carlo, eds. 2011. (IEEE Press Series on Biomedical Engineering Ser.: 27). (ENG., Illus.). 608p. 110.00 *(978-0-470-42214-4(9)*, Wiley-IEEE Pr.) Wiley, John & Sons, Inc.

Eibl, Regine. Cell & Tissue Reaction Engineering. 2008. (Principles & Practice Ser.). (Illus.). 350p. 209.00 *(978-3-540-68175-5(2))* Springer.

el Haj, Alicia & Bader, Dan, eds. 8th International Conference on Cell & Stem Cell Engineering: Icce. 2011. (IFMBE Proceedings Ser.). (Illus.). x, 58p. pap. 199.00 *(978-3-642-19043-8(X)*, 364219043X) Springer.

Ellis, Warren. Crooked Little Vein. 2008. (P. S. Ser.). (ENG.). 304p. pap. 13.99 *(978-0-06-125205-1(0)*, William Morrow Paperbacks) HarperCollins Pubs.

Emami, Shahriar Hojjati. Polyethylene Oxide Hydrogels: Synthesis & Characterization. 2008. 104p. pap. *(978-3-639-10665-7(2))* VDM Verlag Dr. Mueller e.K.

Emiliani, P. L. & Burzagli, L., eds. Assistive Technology from Adapted Equipment to Inclusive Environments. 2009. (Assistive Technology Research Ser.). (Illus.). 924p. 232.00 *(978-1-60750-042-1(6))* IOS Pr., Inc.
Enderle, John. Bioinstrumentation. 2006. (Synthesis Lectures on Biomedical Engineering Ser.). 220p. pap. 40.00 *(978-1-59829-132-2(7))* Morgan & Claypool Pubs.
Enderle, John & Bronzino, Joseph. Introduction to Biomedical Engineering. 3rd ed. 2011. (Biomedical Engineering Ser.). (ENG., Illus.). 1272p. (C). 129.95 *(978-0-12-374979-6(4)*, Academic Pr.) Elsevier Science & Technology Bks.
Enderle, John, et al. Basic Probability Theory for Biomedical Engineers. 2006. (Synthesis Lectures on Biomedical Engineering Ser.). 136p. pap. 40.00 *(978-1-59829-060-8(6))* Morgan & Claypool Pubs.
Enderle, John D., et al. Advanced Probability Theory for Biomedical Engineers. 2006. (Synthesis Lectures on Biomedical Engineering Ser.). (Illus.). 108p. per. 40.00 *(978-1-59829-150-6(5))* Morgan & Claypool Pubs.
—Intermediate Probability Theory for Biomedical Engineers. 2006. (Synthesis Lectures on Biomedical Engineering Ser.). (Illus.). 114p. per. 40.00 *(978-1-59829-140-7(8))* Morgan & Claypool Pubs.
Farina, Dario, et al. Introduction to Neural Engineering for Motor Rehabilitation. 2012. (IEEE Press Series on Biomedical Engineering Ser.). (ENG., Illus.). 384p. 135.00 ***(978-0-470-91673-5(7)***, Wiley-IEEE Pr.) Wiley, John & Sons, Inc.
Feng, David Dagan, ed. Biomedical Information Technology. 2007. (Biomedical Engineering Ser.). (ENG., Illus.). 552p. 114.00 *(978-0-12-373583-6(1)*, Academic Pr.) Elsevier Science & Technology Bks.
Fernandes, Paulo R. & Bártolo, Paulo Jorge, eds. Advances on Modeling in Tissue Engineering. 2011. (Computational Methods in Applied Sciences Ser.). (ENG., Illus.). vii, 176p. 129.00 *(978-94-007-1253-9(7)*, 9400712537) Springer.
Ferri, Jöel & Hunziker, Ernst J., eds. Preprosthetic & Maxillofacial Surgery: Biomaterials, Bone Grafting & Tissue Engineering. 2011. (Woodhead Publishing in Materials Ser.). (ENG., Illus.). 400p. 240.00 *(978-1-84569-589-7(5))* Woodhead Publishing Ltd. GBR. Dist: Ingram Pub. Services.
Fielder. Biomedical Engineering Ethics. 2007. (Synthesis Lectures on Biomedical Engineering Ser.). 40.00 *(978-1-59829-286-2(2))* Morgan & Claypool Pubs.
Fisher, John P., ed. Tissue Engineering. (Advances in Experimental Medicine & Biology Ser.). (Illus.). xx, 463p. 2010. pap. 199.00 *(978-1-4419-4092-6(8)*, 1441940928) 2nd ed. 2006. 199.00 *(978-0-387-32664-1(2)*, 0387326642) Springer.
Flynne, William G., ed. Biotechnology & Bioengineering. 2008. (Illus.). xii, 272p. 129.00 *(978-1-60456-067-1(3)*, Nova Biomedical Bks.) Nova Science Pubs., Inc.
Fotiadis, Dimitrios I. Advanced Topics in Scattering Theory & Biomedical Engineering - Proceedings of the 9Th International Workshop on Mathematical Methods in Scattering Theory & Biomedical Engineering. 2010. 436p. 166.00 *(978-981-4322-02-7(4))* World Scientific Publishing Co., Inc.
Fournier, Ronald L. Basic Transport Phenomena in Biomedical Engineering. 3rd rev. ed. 2011. (ENG., Illus.). 483p. (C). 89.95 *(978-1-4398-2670-6(6)*, CRC Press) Taylor & Francis Group GBR. Dist: Taylor & Francis Group.
Fred, Ana, et al. Biomedical Engineering Systems & Technologies: International Joint Conference, BIOSTEC 2008 Funchal, Madeira, Portugal, January 28-31, 2008, Revised Selected Papers. 2008. (Communications in Computer & Information Science Ser.). xiv, 542p. pap. 129.00 *(978-3-540-92218-6(0))* Springer.
—Biomedical Engineering Systems & Technologies: International Joint Conference, BIOSTEC 2009, Porto, Portugal, January 14-17, 2009, Revised Selected Papers. 2010. (Communications in Computer & Information Science Ser.). 420p. pap. 109.00 *(978-3-642-11720-6(1)*, 3642117201) Springer.
Fred, Ana, et al, eds. Biomedical Engineering Systems & Technologies: Third International Joint Conference, BIOSTEC 2010, Valencia, Spain, January 20-23, 2010, Revised Selected Papers. 2011. (Communications in Computer & Information Science Ser.). xiii, 408p. pap. 107.00 *(978-3-642-18471-0(5)*, 3642184715) Springer.
Frize, Monique. Ethics, Research Methods & Standards in Biomedical Engineering. Enderle, John, ed. 2012. (Synthesis Lectures on Biomedical Engineering Ser.). 100p. pap. 40.00 *(978-1-60845-369-6(3))* Morgan & Claypool Pubs.
Fukuda, Toshio & Tercero, Carlos, eds. Microsurgery: Advances, Simulations & Applications. 2012. (ENG., Illus.). 300p. 179.95 ***(978-981-4364-69-0(X))*** Pan Stanford Publishing SGP. Dist: Taylor & Francis Group.
Functional Materials & Biomaterials. (Advances in Polymer Science Ser.). (Illus.). x, 232p. 2010. pap. 329.00 *(978-3-642-09072-1(9)*, 3642090729) 2007. 329.00 *(978-3-540-71508-5(8))* Springer.
Gaggioli, A. & Keshner, E. A., eds. Advanced Technologies in Rehabilitation: Empowering Cognitive, Physical, Social & Communicative Skills Through Virtual Reality, Robots, Wearable Systems & Brain-Computer Interfaces. 2009. (Studies in Health Technology & Informatics Ser.). (Illus.). 304p. 167.00 *(978-1-60750-018-6(3))* IOS Pr., Inc.
Garcia, Audric & Durand, Ciel, eds. Bioengineering: Principles, Methodologies & Applications. 2010. (Biotechnology in Agriculture, Industry & Medicine Ser.). (Illus.). xi, 218p. 129.00 *(978-1-60741-762-0(6))* Nova Science Pubs., Inc.
Gefen, Amit, ed. Bioengineering Research of Chronic Wounds: A Multidisciplinary Study Approach. 2009. (Studies in Mechanobiology, Tissue Engineering & Biomaterials Ser.). (ENG., Illus.). x, 454p. 209.00 *(978-3-642-00533-6(0)*, 3642005330) Springer.
Glasner, Peter, et al, eds. New Genetics, New Indentities. 2007. XII, 196p. 160.00 *(978-0-415-39407-9(4))* Routledge.
Glowacki, Julie & Bueno, Ericka. Biological Principles Underlying Approaches to Skeletal Tissue Engineering. 2012. (Synthesis Lectures on Tissue Engineering Ser.). 220p. pap. 40.00 *(978-1-60845-172-2(0))* Morgan & Claypool Pubs.
Goldberg, Jay. Introduction Biomedical Engineering D. 2007. (Synthesis Lectures on Biomedical Engineering Ser.). 100p. pap. 35.00 *(978-1-59829-292-3(7))* Morgan & Claypool Pubs.
Goldberg, Jay, et al. Synthesis Series in Biomedical Engineering Vol. 3. 2012. (Synthesis Series in Biomedical Engineering Ser.). 500p. 85.00 *(978-1-60845-186-9(0))* Morgan & Claypool Pubs.
Gonsalves, Kenneth, et al, eds. Biomedical Nanostructures. 2007. (ENG., Illus.). 515p. 166.00 *(978-0-471-92552-1(7)*, Wiley-Interscience) Wiley, John & Sons, Inc.
Good, Phillip I. Analyzing the Large Number of Variables in Biomedical & Satellite Imagery: Microarrays & Images. 2011. (ENG., Illus.). 200p. pap. 68.95 *(978-0-470-92714-4(3)*, Wiley) Wiley, John & Sons, Inc.
Grad, Sibylle, et al. Cells & Biomaterials for Intervetebral Disc Regeneration. 2010. (Synthesis Series on Tissue Engineering Ser.). 104p. pap. 35.00 *(978-1-60845-464-8(9))* Morgan & Claypool Pubs.
Grodzinsky, Ala. Fields, Forces, & Flows in Biological Systems. 2008. 90.00 *(978-0-8153-4154-3(7)*, Garland Science) Taylor & Francis Group.
Guliato, Denise & Rangayyan, Rangaraj. Modeling & Analysis of Shape. 2011. (Synthesis Lectures on Biomedical Engineering Ser.). 95p. pap. 40.00 *(978-1-60845-032-9(5))* Morgan & Claypool Pubs.
Guo, Yi, ed. Micro/Nano-robotics for Biomedical Applications. 2011. 300p. 129.00 *(978-1-4419-8410-4(0)*, 1441984100) Springer.
Hadjileontiadis, Leontios J. Lung Sounds: An Advanced Signal Processing Perspective. 2009. (Synthesis Lectures on Biomedical Engineering Ser.). 100p. pap. 40.00 *(978-1-59829-710-2(4))* Morgan & Claypool Pubs.
Haghi, A. K. & Zaikov, G. E. Electrospinning Process & Nanofiber Research. 2011. (Nanotechnology Science & Technology Ser.). (Illus.). 204p. 69.00 *(978-1-61209-330-7(2))* Nova Science Pubs., Inc.
Hammer, Joachim, et al. Medicine Meets Engineering: Proceedings of the 2nd Conference on Applied Biomechanics, Regensburg. 2008. (Illus.). x, 247p. 161.00 *(978-1-58603-828-1(1))* IOS Pr., Inc.
Harding, S. E., ed. Biotechnology & Genetic Engineering Reviews, Vol. 26. 2010. (Biotechnology & Genetic Engineering Reviews Ser.). (ENG.). 464p. 147.00 *(978-1-904761-91-4(7))* Nottingham Univ. Pr. GBR. Dist: Independent Pubs. Group.
Hauser, Hansjörg & Fussenegger, Martin M., eds. Tissue Engineering. 2nd ed. 2010. (Methods in Molecular Medicine Ser.). (Illus.). xii, 336p. pap. 69.95 *(978-1-61737-759-4(7)*, 1617377597) Humana Pr.
Hazelwood, Vikki, et al. Biomedical Engineering Principles. 2nd rev. ed. 2011. (ENG., Illus.). 540p. (C). 99.95 *(978-1-4398-1232-7(2)*, CRC Press) Taylor & Francis Group GBR. Dist: Taylor & Francis Group.
He, Bin, ed. Reviews in Neural Engineering 2006. 2007. 150.00 *(978-0-387-34062-3(9)*, 0387340629) Springer.
Hélix-Nielsen, Claus, ed. Biomimetic Membranes for Sensor & Separation Applications. 2012. (Biological & Medical Physics, Biomedical Engineering Ser.). (ENG., Illus.). xv, 284p. 169.00 ***(978-94-007-2183-8(8)***, 9400721838) Springer.
Helsen, Jozef A. & Missirlis, Yannis. Biomaterials: A Tantalizing Experience. 2010. (Biological & Medical Physics, Biomedical Engineering Ser.). (Illus.). xvi, 340p. 169.00 *(978-3-642-12531-7(X)*, 364212531X) Springer.
Herold, Keith E., et al, eds. 26th Southern Biomedical Engineering ConferenceSBEC 2010 April 30 - May 2, 2010 College Park, Maryland, USA. 2010. (IFMBE Proceedings Ser.). 1000p. pap. 469.00 *(978-3-642-14997-9(9)*, 3642149979) Springer.
Hettiarachchy, Navam S., et al, eds. Bioactive Food Proteins & Peptides: Applications in Human Health. 2011. (ENG., Illus.). 368p. 159.95 *(978-1-4200-9314-8(2)*, CRC Press) Taylor & Francis Group GBR. Dist: Taylor & Francis Group.
Hewitt, Charles W. & Lee, W. P. Andrew, eds. Transplantation of Composite Tissue Allografts. 2008. (ENG., Illus.). xx, 483p. 194.00 *(978-0-387-74681-4(1)*, 0387746811) Springer.
Hickey, Anthony J. & Ganderton, David, eds. Pharmaceutical Process Engineering: Second Edition. 2nd rev. ed. 2009. (ENG., Illus.). 236p. 300.00 *(978-1-4200-8475-7(5)*, Informa Healthcare) Taylor & Francis Group GBR. Dist: Taylor & Francis Group.
Ho, Chih-Ming. Micro/Nano Technology Systems for Biomedical Applications: Microfluidics, Optics, & Surface Chemistry. 2010. (ENG., Illus.). 496p. 125.00 *(978-0-19-921969-8(9))* Oxford Univ. Pr., Inc.
Hoffmann, Klaus-Peter, ed. Neural Engineering: Basics, Methods, Devices & Applications. 2012. (ENG.). 350p. 129.00 *(978-3-540-76273-7(6)*, 3540762736) Springer.
Hollander, Anthony P. & Hatton, Paul V., eds. Biopolymer Methods in Tissue Engineering. 2010. (Methods in Molecular Biology Ser.). (Illus.). 280p. pap. 139.00 *(978-1-61737-280-3(3)*, 1617372803) Humana Pr.
Holmes, Jeffrey & Humphrey, Jay D. Communication & Ethics Iin Biomedical. 2008. (Synthesis Lectures on Biomedical Engineering Ser.). 140p. pap. 30.00 *(978-1-59829-298-5(6))* Morgan & Claypool Pubs.
Hoque, Muhammad Enamul. Tissue Engineering Scaffold & Rapid Prototyping Technology. 2010. 228p. pap. *(978-3-8383-4929-9(6))* Lambert Academic Publishing.
Hu, Hai & Liebman, Michael. Biomedical Informatics in Translational Research. 2008. (Illus.). 364p. 95.00 *(978-1-59693-038-4(1))* Artech Hse., Inc.
Humayun, Mark S., et al, eds. Artificial Sight: Basic Research, Biomedical Engineering, & Clinical Advances. 2007. (Biological & Medical Physics, Biomedical Engineering Ser.). (Illus.). 394p. 139.00 *(978-0-387-49329-9(8))* Springer.
Hung, George K. Biomedical Engineering Principles of the Bionic Man, Vol. 3. 2009. 400p. 98.00 *(978-981-277-977-9(9))*; (Illus.). pap. 68.00 *(978-981-277-978-6(7))* World Scientific Publishing Co., Inc.
Huopalahti, Rainer, et al, eds. Bioactive Egg Compounds. 2010. (ENG., Illus.). xx, 298p. pap. 189.00 *(978-3-642-07238-3(0)*, 3642072380) Springer.
Hurst, Sarah J., ed. Biomedical Nanotechnology: Methods & Protocols. 2011. (Methods in Molecular Biology Ser.). (ENG., Illus.). xii, 436p. 139.00 *(978-1-61779-051-5(6)*, 1617790516) Humana Pr.
Hwang, Ned H. C., et al, eds. Advances in Cardiovascular Engineering. 2010. (Nato Science Series: A: Ser.). 452p. pap. 349.00 *(978-1-4419-3228-0(3)*, 1441932283) Springer.
Ibrahim, F. 3rd Kuala Lumpur International Conference on Biomedical Engineering 2006. 2007. (IFMBE Proceedings Ser.). (Illus.). 736p. per. 319.00 *(978-3-540-68016-1(0))* Springer.
IEEE Computer Society Staff. Third International Conference on Medical Information Visualisation (MediVis 2006) 05-07 July 2006/London, United Kingdom. 2006. (Illus.). 126p. pap. 167.00 *(978-0-7695-2603-4(9)*, P2603) IEEE Computer Society Pr.
IEEE Staff. 2007 IEEE Biomedical Circuits & Systems Conference. 2007. pap. 234.00 *(978-1-4244-1524-3(1))* IEEE.
—2007 IEEE Dallas Engineering in Medicine & Biology Workshop. 2007. pap. 200.00 *(978-1-4244-1626-4(4))* IEEE.
—2008 8th IEEE International Symposium on BioInformatics & BioEngineering. 2008. pap. 376.00 *(978-1-4244-2844-1(0))* IEEE.
—2008 IEEE International Conference on Bioinformatics & Biomedicine Workshops. 2008. pap. 222.00 *(978-1-4244-2890-8(4))* IEEE.
Ikada, Yoshito. Tissue Engineering: Fundamentals & Applications. 2006. (Interface Science & Technology Ser.: 8). (ENG., Illus.). 490p. 205.00 *(978-0-12-370582-2(7)*, Academic Pr.) Elsevier Science & Technology Bks.
Iniewski, Krzysztof, ed. Biological & Medical Sensor Technologies. 2012. (Devices, Circuits, & Systems Ser.). (ENG., Illus.). 412p. 149.95 ***(978-1-4398-8267-2(3)***, CRC Press) Taylor & Francis Group GBR. Dist: Taylor & Francis Group.
Institute of Electrical and Electronics Engineers, Inc. Staff. 2007 IEEE International Confernece on Bioinformatics & Biomedicine Workshops. 2007. pap. 214.00 *(978-1-4244-1604-2(3))* IEEE.
Institution of Engineering and Technology (IET) Staff, compiled by. 3rd International Conference on Advances in Medical, Signal & Information Processing (MEDSIP 2006) 2008. (IET Conference Publications Ser.). 256p. pap. 195.00 *(978-1-60423-982-9(4))* Curran Assocs., Inc.
Irudayaraj, Joseph, ed. Biomedical Nanosensors. 2012. (Pan Stanford Series on Biomedical Nanotechnology Ser.). (ENG.). 400p. 149.95 *(978-981-4303-03-3(8))* Pan Stanford Publishing SGP. Dist: Taylor & Francis Group.
Jabbari, Esmaiel. Biologically-responsive Hybrid Biomaterials: A Reference for Material Scientists & Bioengineers. 2010. (Illus.). 432p. 135.00 *(978-981-4295-67-3(1))* World Scientific Publishing Co., Inc.
Jain, Kewal K. Applications of Biotechnology in Cardiovascular Therapeutics. 2011. (Illus.). xxviii, 350p. ***(978-1-61779-240-3(3))*** Humana Pr.
Jarm, Tomaz, et al, eds. 11th Mediterranean Conference on Medical & Biological Engineering & Computing 2007: MEDICON 2007, 26-30 June 2007, Ljubljana, Slovenia. 2007. (IFMBE Proceedings Ser.). 1206p. pap. 389.00 *(978-3-540-73043-9(5)*, 3540730435) Springer.
Jayaraman, Arul & Hahn, Juergen. Methods in Bioengineering: Systems Analysis of Biological Networks. 2009. (Illus.). 330p. 129.00 *(978-1-59693-406-1(9))* Artech Hse., Inc.
Jobbágy, Ákos, ed. 5th European Conference of the International Federation for Medical & Biological Engineering 14 - 18 September 2011, Budapest, Hungary. 2011. (IFMBE Proceedings Ser.). (ENG., Illus.). xxxviii, 1446p. pap. 539.00 ***(978-3-642-23507-8(7)***, 3642235077) Springer.
Johnson, Arthur T. Biology for Engineers. 2010. (ENG., Illus.). 775p. (C). 104.95 *(978-1-4200-7763-6(5)*, CRC Press) Taylor & Francis Group GBR. Dist: Taylor & Francis Group.
Johnson, Michael L. & Brand, Ludwig. Computer Methods, Pt. A. 2009. (ENG., Illus.). 488p. 187.00 *(978-0-12-374552-1(7)*, Academic Pr.) Elsevier Science & Technology Bks.
—Computer Methods Part B. 2009. (ENG., Illus.). 712p. 187.00 *(978-0-12-375023-5(7)*, Academic Pr.) Elsevier Science & Technology Bks.
Jue, Thomas. Biomedical Applications of Biophysics. 2010. (Illus.). xi, 237p. E-Book ***(978-1-60327-233-9(X))*** Humana Pr.
Jue, Thomas, et al, eds. Biomembrane Frontiers: Nanostructures, Models, & the Design of Life. 2009. (Handbook of Modern Biophysics Ser.). (ENG., Illus.). xvi, 324p. 259.00 *(978-1-60761-313-8(1)*, 1607613131) Humana Pr.
Kakar, Manish. Intelligent & Adaptive Systems in Cancer Biomedicine. 2010. 116p. pap. *(978-3-8383-6923-5(8))* Lambert Academic Publishing.
Kalet, Ira J. Principles of Biomedical Informatics. 2008. (ENG., Illus.). 504p. 82.95 *(978-0-12-369438-6(8)*, Academic Pr.) Elsevier Science & Technology Bks.
Kasper, Cornelia, et al. Bioreactor Systems for Tissue Engineering. 2009. (Advances in Biochemical Engineering / Biotechnology Ser.). (ENG., Illus.). xii, 271p. 299.00 *(978-3-540-69356-7(4))* Springer.
Katashev, Alexei. Nbc - 14th Nordic-Baltic Conference on Biomedical Engineering & Medical Physics 16-20 June 2008; Riga, Latvia. 2008. (IFMBE Proceedings Ser.). (ENG.). xx, 647p. pap. 319.00 *(978-3-540-69366-6(1)*, 3540693661) Springer.
Katti, Kattesh V. Textbook of Nanomedicine. 2007. (Methods of Biochemical Analysis Ser.). 400p. 89.95 *(978-0-471-78716-7(7)*, Wiley-Interscience) Wiley, John & Sons, Inc.
Katz, B. Neuroengineering the Future: Virtual Minds & the Creation of Immortality. 2008. (ENG., Illus.). 400p. 63.95 *(978-1-934015-18-6(0))* Jones & Bartlett Learning, LLC.
Kausch, Henning, ed. Radiation Effects on Polymers for Biological Use. 2010. (Advances in Polymer Science Ser.). (Illus.). xi, 173p. pap. 279.00 *(978-3-642-07891-0(5)*, 3642078915) Springer.
Kayabasi, Oguz & Ekici, Bülent. Analysis of a Kayabasi_Ekici Type Hip Prosthesis. 2011. 176p. pap. ***(978-3-8454-1569-7(X))*** Lambert Academic Publishing.
Kendall, Jason B., ed. Biomaterials Research Advances. 2008. 129.00 *(978-1-60021-892-7(X))* Nova Science Pubs., Inc.
Khoo, M. C. K., ed. Bioengineering Approaches to Pulmonary Physiology & Medicine. 2010. (ENG.). 253p. pap. 199.00 *(978-1-4419-3260-0(7)*, 1441932607) Springer.
Khudyakov, Yury E. Medicinal Protein Engineering. Khudyakov, Yury E., ed. 2008. (ENG., Illus.). 584p. 195.95 *(978-0-8493-7368-8(9)*, CRC Press) Taylor & Francis Group GBR. Dist: Taylor & Francis Group.
Khuri, Sami, et al. Information, Technology in Bio- & Medical Informatics, ITBAM 2010: First International Conference, Bilbao, Spain, September 1-2, 2010, Proceedings. 2010. (Monographs in Contemporary Mathematics Ser.). xii, 236p. pap. 72.00 *(978-3-642-15019-7(5)*, 3642150195) Springer.
Kien Hui, Chua, et al. Growing Human Chondrocytes & Cartilage Tissue Engineering. 2010. 156p. pap. *(978-3-639-26246-9(8))* VDM Verlag Dr. Mueller e.K.
Kim, Kelly Y. R. 2010. 212p. pap. *(978-3-8383-5643-3(8))* Lambert Academic Publishing.
King, Paul & Fries, Richard C. Design of Biomedical Devices & Systems, Second Edition. 2nd rev. ed. 2008. (ENG., Illus.). 424p. (C). 124.95 *(978-1-4200-6179-6(8)*, CRC Press) Taylor & Francis Group GBR. Dist: Taylor & Francis Group.
Kirkpatrick, Sean & Wang, R. K. Optics in Tissue Engineering & Regenerative Medicine II: 20-21 January 2008, San Jose, California, USA. 2008. (Proceedings of SPIE Ser.). (Illus.). 138p. pap. 70.00 *(978-0-8194-7033-1(3))* SPIE.
Klingeler, Radiger & Sim, Robert B., eds. Carbon Nanotubes for Biomedical Applications. 2011. (Carbon Nanostructures Ser.). (Illus.). xx, 280p. 129.00 *(978-3-642-14801-9(8)*, 3642148018) Springer.
Kobayashi, Takeshi. Recent Progress of Biochemical & Biomedical Engineering in Japan II. 2010. (Advances in Biochemical Engineering Biotechnology Ser.). (Illus.). xii, 239p. pap. 289.00 *(978-3-642-05801-1(9)*, 3642058019) Springer.
Kondraske, George. Human Performance Modeling & Measurement. 2012. (Synthesis Lectures on Biomedical Engineering Ser.). 100p. pap. 40.00 *(978-1-59829-683-9(3))* Morgan & Claypool Pubs.
Kong, Hyunjoon. Stem Cells & Tissue Engineering. 2011. (Biotechnology & Bioprocessing Ser.). (ENG., Illus.). 342p. 149.95 *(978-1-4398-0323-3(4)*, CRC Press) Taylor & Francis Group GBR. Dist: Taylor & Francis Group.
Koprowski, Gene. Nanotechnology in Medicine: Emerging Applications. 2011. 198p. pap. 59.95 *(978-1-60650-248-8(4))* Momentum Pr.
Korobkin, Russell, et al. Stem Cell Century: Law & Policy for a Breakthrough Technology. 2009. (ENG.). 336p. pap. 23.00 *(978-0-300-14323-2(0))* Yale Univ. Pr.
Kranz, C., ed. Biomedical & Clinical Sensors. 2008. (ECS Transactions Ser.). 13p. pap. 28.00 *(978-1-60423-916-4(6))* Curran Assocs., Inc.
Kurtz, Steven M. PEEK Biomaterials Handbook. 2011. (Plastics Design Library). (ENG., Illus.). 306p. 199.00 ***(978-1-4377-4463-7(X))*** William Andrew, Inc.
Kutz, Myer. Biomedical Engineering & Design, Vols. 1 & 2. 2nd ed. 2009. (ENG., Illus.). 1600p. 250.00 *(978-0-07-149840-1(0)*, 0071498400) McGraw-Hill Professional Publishing.
—Biomedical Engineering & Design Vol. 1: Fundamentals, 2 vols. 2nd ed. 2009. (ENG., Illus.). 688p. instr.'s hndbk. ed. 150.00 *(978-0-07-149838-8(9)*, 0071498389) McGraw-Hill Professional Publishing.
—Biomedical Engineering & Design Vol. 2: Applications, 2 vols. 2nd ed. 2009. (ENG., Illus.). 816p. instr.'s hndbk. ed. 150.00 *(978-0-07-149839-5(7)*, 0071498397) McGraw-Hill Professional Publishing.
Labhasetwar, Vinod & Leslie-Pelecky, Diandra L., eds. Biomedical Applications of Nanotechnology. 2007. (ENG., Illus.). 257p. 128.00 *(978-0-471-72242-7(1)*, Wiley-Interscience) Wiley, John & Sons, Inc.
Lackie, John. A Dictionary of Biomedicine. 2010. (ENG.). 608p. 18.95 *(978-0-19-954935-1(4))* Oxford Univ. Pr., Inc.
Lam, Wilbur. Cell Mechanics of Leukostasis in Acute Leukemi. 2009. 164p. pap. *(978-3-639-13181-9(9))* VDM Verlag Dr. Mueller e.K.
Landaker, Mark. Mark the Biomed Troubleshooting Guide. 2008. 96p. pap. 25.00 *(978-0-9776860-6-3(X))* Pochette Bks.
Landheer, D., ed. Bioelectronics, Biointerfaces, & Biomedical Applications 2. 2007. (ECS Transactions Ser.). 41p. pap. 36.00 *(978-1-60423-378-0(8))* Curran Assocs., Inc.
Lay-Ekuakille, Aimé & Mukhopadhyay, Subhas Chandra, eds. Wearable & Autonomous Biomedical Devices & Systems for Smart Environment: Issues

& Characterization. 2010. (Lecture Notes in Electrical Engineering Ser.). (Illus.). 345p. pap. 179.00 *(978-3-642-15686-1(X), 364215686X)* Springer.

Lee, III, William E., William E. Biomedical Engineering Principles: An Introduction to Fluid, Heat & Mass Transport Processes, Second Edition. 2nd ed. 2010. (Illus.). 500p. 99.95 *(978-1-4200-8463-4(1))* CRC Pr. LLC.

Lee, Keekok. The Philosophical Foundations of Modern Medicine. 2012. (ENG., Illus.). 248p. 85.00 ***(978-0-230-34829-5(7))*** Palgrave Macmillan.

Lee, Kyongbum & Kaplan, David. Tissue Engineering 1: Scaffold Systems for Tissue Engineering, 2 vols. 2006. (Advances in Biochemical Engineering / Biotechnology Ser.). (Illus.). 243p. 359.00 *(978-3-540-31944-3(1), 3540319441)* Springer.

Lee, Kyongbum & Kaplan, David L. Tissue Engineering II: Basics of Tissue Engineering & Tissue Applications. 2010. (Advances in Biochemical Engineering Biotechnology Ser.). (Illus.). xiv, 335p. pap. 409.00 *(978-3-642-07161-4(9), 3642071619)* Springer.

Lee, T. C. & Niederer, P. F., eds. Basic Engineering for Medics & Biologists: An ESEM Primer. 2010. 380p. 94.00 *(978-1-60750-526-6(6))* IOS Pr., Inc.

Lee, Thay, et al. Proceedings of the 4th Frontiers in Biomedical Devices Conference & Exposition — 2009: Presented at 4th Frontiers in Biomedical Devices Conference & Exposition, June 6-8, 2009, Irvine, California, USA. 2009. (Illus.). xiii, 112p. pap. *(978-0-7918-4348-2(3))* American Society of Mechanical Engineers, The.

Lee, Thay, et al. Proceedings of the 5th Frontiers in Biomedical Devices Conference & Exposition — 2010: Presented at 5th Frontiers in Biomedical Devices Conference & Exposition, September 20-21, 2010, Newport Beach, California, USA. 2010. (Illus.). xiii, 106p. pap. ***(978-0-7918-4945-3(7))*** American Society of Mechanical Engineers, The.

Legard, Vincent & Schluter, Rémi, eds. Bone Regeneration: Growth Factors, Augmentation Procedures & Tissue Engineering Applications. 2010. (Human Anatomy & Physiology Ser.). (Illus.). xiv, 351p. 129.00 *(978-1-60876-621-5(7),* Nova Biomedical Bks.) Nova Science Pubs., Inc.

Lenaerts, Bert & Puers, Robert. Omnidirectional Inductive Powering for Biomedical Implants. (Analog Circuits & Signal Processing Ser.). xvi, 224p. 2010. pap. 159.00 *(978-90-481-8062-2(7), 9048180627)* 2008. (ENG., Illus.). 159.00 *(978-1-4020-9074-5(9), 1402090749)* Springer.

Lenhardt, Martin. Intellectual Property for Biomedical Engineers. 2011. (Synthesis Lectures on Biomedical Engineering Ser.). 100p. pap. 40.00 *(978-1-59829-869-7(0))* Morgan & Claypool Pubs.

Lenk, Christian, et al. Human Tissue Research: A European perspective on the ethical & legal Challenges. 2011. (ENG., Illus.). 240p. 98.50 *(978-0-19-958755-1(8))* Oxford Univ. Pr., Inc.

Lessard, Charles & Fernandez, Fidel. Introduction to Biomedical Engineering. rev. ed. 2009. (ENG.). 128p. pap. 47.00 *(978-0-7575-5234-2(X))* Kendall Hunt Publishing Co.

Lessard, Charles, et al. Synthesis Series in Biomedical Engineering Vol. 8. 2012. (Synthesis Series in Biomedical Engineering Ser.). 500p. 85.00 *(978-1-60845-191-3(7))* Morgan & Claypool Pubs.

Levy, Jerrod H., ed. Biomechanics: Principles, Trends & Applications. 2010. (Biomechanics - Theory & Applications Ser.). (Illus.). 414p. 145.00 *(978-1-60741-394-3(9))* Nova Science Pubs., Inc.

Li, Hua. Smart Hydrogel Modeling. 2009. (ENG., Illus.). xiii, 356p. 199.00 *(978-3-642-02367-5(3), 3642023673)* Springer.

Li, Qi (Peter). Speaker Authentication. 2011. (Signals & Communication Technology Ser.). (ENG., Illus.). xxv, 237p. 129.00 ***(978-3-642-23730-0(4),*** 3642237304) Springer.

Li, Song. Stem Cell & Tissue Engineering. 2011. 472p. 145.00 *(978-981-4317-05-4(5))* World Scientific Publishing Co., Inc.

Lim, Chwee Teck & Goh, James C. H., eds. ICBME2008 - 13th International Conference on Biomedical EngineeringDecember 3 - 6, 2008, Singapore, 3 vols. 2009. (IFMBE Proceedings Ser.). li, 2303p. pap. 539.00 *(978-3-540-92840-9(5))* Springer.

Liu, Shu Q. Bioregenerative Engineering: Principles & Applications. 2007. (ENG., Illus.). 1104p. 174.00 *(978-0-471-70907-7(7),* Wiley-Interscience) Wiley, John & Sons, Inc.

Luna-Bárcenas, G., et al. Chitosan-Based Hydrogels for Tissue Engineering Applications. 2011. (Biotechnology in Agriculture, Industry & Medicine Ser.). pap. 43.00 *(978-1-61761-312-8(6))* Nova Science Pubs., Inc.

Madihally, Sundararajan V. Principles of Biomedical Engineering. 2010. (Illus.). 464p. 139.00 *(978-1-60807-055-8(7))* Artech Hse., Inc.

Magjarevic, Ratko, et al, eds. World Congress of Medical Physics & Biomedical Engineering 2006. 2007. (IFMBE Proceedings Ser.). cxlviii, 4220p. 1709.00 *(978-3-540-36839-7(6), 3540368396)* Springer.

Mandenius, Carl-Fredrik & Björkman, Mats. Biomechatronic Design in Biotechnology: A Methodology for Development of Biotechnological Products. 2011. (ENG., Illus.). 304p. 89.95 *(978-0-470-57334-1(1),* Wiley) Wiley, John & Sons, Inc.

Mao, Jeremy J., et al, eds. Translational Approaches in Tissue Engineering & Regenerative Medicine. 2007. (Engineering in Medicine & Biology Ser.). (Illus.). 516p. 159.00 incl. cd-rom *(978-1-59693-111-4(6))* Artech Hse., Inc.

Mao, Jeremy J., et al. Translational Approaches in Tissue Engineering & Regenerative Medicine. 2007. 514p. 149.00 *(978-1-58693-111-7(3))* Artech Hse., Inc.

Martín-Palma, R. J. & Lakhtakia, A. Biomimetics & Bioinspiration: 2-3 August 2009, San Diego, California, United States. 2009. (Proceedings of SPIE Ser.). (Illus.). 196p. pap. 70.00 *(978-0-8194-7691-3(9))* SPIE.

MartíN-Palma, RaúL & Lakhtakia, Akhlesh. Bioinspiration, Biomimetics, & Bioreplication. 2011. (Proceedings of SPIE Ser.). 310p. pap. 90.00 ***(978-0-8194-8537-3(3))*** SPIE.

Martinez-Ramon, Manel, ed. Kernel Methods in Bioengineering, Signal & Image Processing. 2006. (Illus.). 415p. 99.95 *(978-1-59904-042-4(5))* IGI Global.

Masayoshi, Esashi, et al, eds. Future Medical Engineering Based on Bionanotechnology: Proceedings of the Final Symposium of the Tohoku University: 21st Century Center of Excellence Program. 2006. (Illus.). 1115p. 265.00 *(978-1-86094-710-0(7))* Imperial College Pr. GBR. Dist: World Scientific Publishing Co., Inc.

Mauck, Robert & Elliott, Dawn. Fibrocartilage Tissue Engineering. 2011. (Synthesis Lectures on Tissue Engineering Ser.). 100p. pap. 40.00 *(978-1-60845-166-1(6))* Morgan & Claypool Pubs.

Maurits, Natasha. From Neurology to Methodology & Back: An Introduction to Clinical Neuroengineering. 2011. (ENG., Illus.). xv, 235p. 79.95 ***(978-1-4614-1131-4(9),*** 1461411319) Springer.

McEachron, Donald. Applied Evolution: Integrating Evolutionary Perspectives in Medicine & Engineering. 2011. (Synthesis Lectures on Biomedical Engineering Ser.). 100p. pap. 40.00 *(978-1-59829-647-1(7))* Morgan & Claypool Pubs.

—Chronobioengineering: Introduction to Biological Rhythms with Applications. 2011. (Synthesis Lectures on Biomedical Engineering Ser.). 100p. pap. 40.00 *(978-1-59829-635-8(3))* Morgan & Claypool Pubs.

McGoron, Anthony, et al, eds. 25th Southern Biomedical Engineering Conference 2009;15 - 17 May, 2009, Miami, Florida, USA. 2009. (IFMBE Proceedings Ser.). (ENG., Illus.). xxii, 386p. pap. 299.00 *(978-3-642-01696-7(0), 3642016960)* Springer.

McIsaac, Joseph H. Hospital Preparation for Bioterror: A Medical & Biomedical Systems Approach. 2006. (Biomedical Engineering Ser.). (ENG., Illus.). 464p. 124.00 *(978-0-12-088440-7(2),* Academic Pr.) Elsevier Science & Technology Bks.

Medintz, Igor L. Methods in Bioengineering: Nanoscale Bioengineering & Nanomedicine. Rege, Kaushal, ed. 2009. (Illus.). 388p. 129.00 *(978-1-59693-410-8(7))* Artech Hse., Inc.

Mehta, Shreefal S. Commercializing Successful Biomedical Technologies: Basic Principles for the Development of Drugs, Diagnostics & Devices. 2011 (ENG.). 360p. pap. 45.00 *(978-0-521-20585-6(9))* Cambridge Univ. Pr.

Meng, Ellis. Biomedical Microsystems. 2010. (ENG., Illus.). 408p. (C). 94.95 *(978-1-4200-5122-3(9),* CRC Press) Taylor & Francis Group GBR. Dist: Taylor & Francis Group.

Mercanzini, Andre & Renaud, Philippe, eds. Microfabricated Cortical Neuroprostheses. 2011. (ENG., Illus.). 250p. 89.95 *(978-1-4398-3754-2(6),* CRC Pr. LLC.

Merkl, Brandon. The Future of the Operating Room. 2010. 252p. pap. *(978-3-8383-6197-0(0))* Lambert Academic Publishing.

Meyer, Ulrich & Wiesmann, Hans Peter. Bone & Cartilage Engineering. 2010. (ENG., Illus.). xiv, 264p. pap. 249.00 *(978-3-642-06468-5(X), 364206468X)* Springer.

Meyers, Arlen D., et al. Nanotechnology for the Life Sciences: Fundamentals & Applications. 2010. (Illus.). 450p. 139.95 *(978-1-4398-1122-1(9),* CRC Press) Taylor & Francis Group GBR. Dist: Taylor & Francis Group.

Mikhalovsky, Sergey & Khajibaev, Abdukhakim, eds. Biodefence: Advanced Materials & Methods for Health Protection. 2011. (NATO Science for Peace & Security Series A: Chemistry & Biology Ser.). xv, 325p. 229.00 *(978-94-007-0216-5(7), 9400702167)*; (ENG.). pap. 119.00 *(978-94-007-0219-6(1), 9400702191)* Springer.

Mikos, Antonios G. & Johnson, Peter C. Advances in Tissue Engineering Angiogenesis. 2010. *(978-1-934854-16-7(6))* Liebert, Mary Ann Inc.

Miller, Gerald. Introduction to Transport Processes. 2010. (Synthesis Lectures on Biomedical Engineering Ser.). 75p. pap. 30.00 *(978-1-59829-866-6(6))* Morgan & Claypool Pubs.

Miller, Gerald, et al. Synthesis Series in Biomedical Engineering Vol. 1. 2010. (Synthesis Series in Biomedical Engineering Ser.). 500p. 85.00 *(978-1-60845-184-5(4))* Morgan & Claypool Pubs.

Miller, Karol & Nielsen, Poul M. F. Computational Biomechanics for Medicine. 2010. (Illus.). 144p. pap. 24.95 *(978-1-4419-5894-5(0))* Springer.

Miller, Karol & Nielsen, Poul M. F., eds. Computational Biomechanics for Medicine: Workshop Proceedings. 2010. (ENG., Illus.). xii, 146p. 189.00 *(978-1-4419-5873-0(8), 1441958738)* Springer.

Moussavi, Zahra. Fundamentals of Respiratory Sounds & Analysis. 2007 (Synthesis Lectures on Biomedical Engineering Ser.). 100p. pap. 35.00 *(978-1-59829-096-7(7))* Morgan & Claypool Pubs.

Moussavi, Zahra, et al. Synthesis Series in Biomedical Engineering Vol. 2. 2010. (Synthesis Series in Biomedical Engineering Ser.). 500p. 85.00 *(978-1-60845-185-2(2))* Morgan & Claypool Pubs.

Mukhopadhyay, Subhas Chandra & Lay-Ekuakille, Aimé, eds. Advances in Biomedical Sensing, Measurements, Instrumentation & Systems. 2009. (Lecture Notes in Electrical Engineering Ser.). (ENG., Illus.). x, 358p. 199.00 *(978-3-642-05166-1(9), 3642051669)* Springer.

Müller, Hans Peter, et al. Synthesis Series in Biomedical Engineering Vol. 4. 2011. (Synthesis Series in Biomedical Engineering Ser.). 500p. 85.00 *(978-1-60845-187-6(9))* Morgan & Claypool Pubs.

Müller-Karger, Carmen, et al, eds. IV Latin American Congress on Biomedical Engineering 2007, Bioengineering Solution for Latin America Health September 24th-28th, 2007, Margarita Island, Venezuela: IV Congreso Latinoamericano de Ingeniería Biomédica, CLAIB 2007 Soluciones de Bioingeniería para la salud en Latina Isla de Margarita, Venezuela, 26 al 28 de Septiembre De 2007. 2007. (IFMBE Proceedings Ser.). 1200p. 459.00 *(978-3-540-74470-2(3))* Springer.

Nag, Ahindra. Biosystems Engineering. 2009. (ENG., Illus.). 544p. 150.00 *(978-0-07-160628-8(9), 0071606289)* McGraw-Hill Professional Publishing.

Nahmias, Yaakov. Methods in Bioengineering: Microdevices in Biology & Medicine. Nahmias, Yaakov & Bhatia, Sangaeta, eds. 2009. (Illus.). 274p. 129.00 *(978-1-59693-404-7(2))* Artech Hse., Inc.

Nahum, A. Neural Engineering. Kim, Yong I. & Thakor, Nitish V., eds. 2007. 350p. 79.95 *(978-0-387-94305-3(6), 0387943056)* Springer.

Najarian, Siamak, et al. Artificial Tactile Sensing in Biomedical Engineering. 2009. (ENG., Illus.). 260p. 125.00 *(978-0-07-160151-1(1), 0071601511)* McGraw-Hill Professional Publishing.

Najarian, Siamak, et al. Mechatronics in Medicine A Biomedical Engineering Approach. 2011. (ENG., Illus.). 208p. 125.00 ***(978-0-07-176896-2(3),*** 0071768963) McGraw-Hill Professional Publishing.

National Academies Keck Futures Initiative Healthspan Steering Committee. The National Academies Keck Futures Initiative: The Future of Human Healthspan - Demography, Evolution, Medicine, & Bioengineering, Task Group Summaries. 2008. (ENG.). 140p. pap. 34.50 *(978-0-309-11559-9(0))* National Academies Pr.

National Research Council (U.S.), Committee on Biomolecular Materials and Processes Staff, contrib. by. Inspired by Biology: From Molecules to Materials to Machines. 2008. (ENG.). 170p. pap. 59.00 *(978-0-309-11704-3(6))* National Academies Pr.

Navarro, Melba & Planell, Josep A., eds. Nanotechnology in Regenerative Medicine: Methods & Protocols. 2011. (Methods in Molecular Biology Ser.). (ENG., Illus.). xi, 319p. 139.00 ***(978-1-61779-387-5(6),*** 1617793876) Humana Pr.

Nicolau, Dan V. & Metcalfe, Guy. Biomedical Applications of Micro- & Nanoengineering IV & Complex Systems: 10-12 December 2008, Melbourne, Australia. 2008. (Proceedings of SPIE Ser.). (Illus.). 356p. pap. 105.00 *(978-0-8194-7522-0(X))* SPIE.

Nolta, Jan A., ed. Genetic Engineering of Mesenchymal Stem Cells. 2010. (ENG.). vi, 169p. pap. 169.00 *(978-90-481-6999-3(2), 9048169992)* Springer.

Northrop, Robert B. Analysis & Application of Analog Electronic Circuits to Biomedical Instrumentation. 2nd rev. ed. 2012. (Biomedical Engineering Ser.). (ENG., Illus.). 578p. 119.95 *(978-1-4398-6669-6(4),* CRC Press) Taylor & Francis Group GBR. Dist: Taylor & Francis Group.

—Signals & Systems Analysis in Biomedical Engineering, Second Edition. 2nd rev. ed. 2010. (Biomedical Engineering Ser.). (ENG., Illus.). 654p. (C). 104.95 *(978-1-4398-1251-8(9),* CRC Press) Taylor & Francis Group GBR. Dist: Taylor & Francis Group.

Ohnabe, H. & Kubo, M., eds. Selected Papers from the Japanese Conference on the Advancement of Assistive & Rehabilitation Technology: 23rd JCAART 2008, Niigata - Assistive Technology Research Series. 2011. 224p. 160.00 ***(978-1-60750-757-4(9))*** IOS Pr., Inc.

Palladino, Joseph. Physiological Modeling. 2011. (Synthesis Lectures on Biomedical Engineering Ser.). 100p. pap. 35.00 *(978-1-60845-622-2(6))* Morgan & Claypool Pubs.

Pallikarakis, Nicolas & Bamidis, Panagiotis D., eds. XII Mediterranean Conference on Medical & Biological Engineering & Computing 2010: MEDICON 2010, 27-30 May 2010, Chalkidiki, Greece. 2010. (IFMBE Proceedings Ser.). 1000p. pap. 399.00 *(978-3-642-13038-0(C), 3642130380)* Springer.

Pallua, Norbert & Suscheck, Christoph V., eds. Tissue Engineering: From Lab to Clinic. 2011. (ENG., Illus.). ix, 634p. 239.00 *(978-3-642-02823-6(3), 3642028233)* Springer.

Palmer, Ella, ed. Cell-Based Microarrays: Methods & Protocols. 2010. (Methods in Molecular Biology Ser.). (ENG., Illus.). x, 209p. 119.00 *(978-1-61737-969-7(7), 1617379697)* Humana Pr.

Papazoglou, Elisabeth & Parthasarathy, Aravind. Bionanotechnology. 2007. (Synthesis Lectures on Biomedical Engineering Ser.). 100p. pap. 40.00 *(978-1-59829-138-4(6))* Morgan & Claypool Pubs.

Paulson, Daryl S., ed. Handbook of Applied Biomedical Microbiology a Biofilms Approach: A Biofilms Approach. 2009. (ENG., Illus.). 176p. 133.95 *(978-0-8493-7569-9(X),* CRC Press) Taylor & Francis Group GBR. Dist: Taylor & Francis Group.

Peng, Yi. 7th Asian-Pacific Conference on Medical & Biological Engineering. 2008. (IFMBE Proceedings Ser.). (ENG.). xxii, 770p. pap. 399.00 *(978-3-540-79038-9(1), 3540790381)* Springer.

Petersen, Richard. Micromechanics & Fiber-Reinforced Composites in Biomedical Research - Advanced Bone Implant & Reconstruction Device Materials, Free Radicals in Comp. 2008. 304p. pap. *(978-3-639-07962-3(0))* VDM Verlag Dr. Mueller e.K.

Peterson, Donald R. & Bronzino, Joseph D., eds. Biomechanics: Principles & Applications. 2nd rev. ed. 2007. (ENG., Illus.). 352p. 104.95 *(978-0-8493-8534-6(2),* CRC Press) Taylor & Francis Group GBR. Dist: Taylor & Francis Group.

Podgorsak, Ervin B. Radiation Physics for Medical Physicists. 2nd ed. 2010. (Biological & Medical Physics, Biomedical Engineering Ser.). (ENG., Illus.). xxxiii, 745p. 169.00 *(978-3-642-00874-0(7), 3642008747)* Springer.

Popat, Ketul, ed. Nanotechnology in Tissue Engineering & Regenerative Medicine. 2010. (ENG., Illus.). 302p. 119.95 *(978-1-4398-0141-3(X),* CRC Press) Taylor & Francis Group GBR. Dist: Taylor & Francis Group.

Popp, Jürgen, et al, eds. Handbook of Biophotonics, 3 vols., Set. 2012. (ENG.). 2350p. 785.00 ***(978-3-527-40728-6(6),*** Wiley-VCH) Wiley, John & Sons, Inc.

—Handbook of Biophotonics: Vol. 3: Photonics in Pharmaceutics, Bioanalysis & Environmental Research. 2012. (ENG.). 320p. 210.00 ***(978-3-527-41049-1(X),*** Wiley-VCH) Wiley, John & Sons, Inc.

—Handbook of Biophotonics Vol. 1: Basics & Techniques, 3 vols. 2011. (ENG., Illus.). 686p. 330.00 ***(978-3-527-41047-7(3),*** Wiley-VCH) Wiley, John & Sons, Inc.

Popp, Jürgen & Bally, G. von. Biophotonics 2007: Optics in Life Science: 18-20 June 2007, Munich, Germany. 2007. (Proceedings of SPIE Ser.). (Illus.). 536p. pap. 140.00 ***(978-0-8194-6777-5(4))*** SPIE.

Porterfield, D. Marshall. Biological & Physiological Sensing, HB. 2010. 159.95 *(978-1-4200-8426-9(7))* CRC Pr. LLC.

Prager, Gary. Practical Pharmaceutical Engineering. 2010. (ENG.). 500p. 110.00 *(978-0-470-41032-5(9),* Wiley-Interscience) Wiley, John & Sons, Inc.

Prescott, Catherine & Polak, Dame Julia, eds. The Delivery of Regenerative Medicines & Their Impact on Healthcare. 2010. (ENG., Illus.). 400p. 169.95 *(978-1-4398-3606-4(X),* CRC Press) Taylor & Francis Group GBR. Dist: Taylor & Francis Group.

Principe, José & Sanchez, Justin C. Brain-Machine Interface Engineering. 2007. (Synthesis Lectures on Biomedical Engineering Ser.). 234p. pap. 50.00 *(978-1-59829-034-9(7))* Morgan & Claypool Pubs.

Puleo, David A. & Bizios, Rena. Biological Interactions on Materials Surfaces: Understanding & Controlling Protein, Cell, & Tissue Responses. Puleo, David A. & Bizios, Rena, eds. 2009. (ENG., Illus.). xx, 429p. 229.00 *(978-0-387-98160-4(8), 0387981608)* Springer.

Pullar, Christine E., ed. The Physiology of Bioelectricity in Development, Tissue Regeneration & Cancer. 2011. (ENG., Illus.). 342p. 119.95 *(978-1-4398-3723-8(6),* CRC Press) Taylor & Francis Group GBR. Dist: Taylor & Francis Group.

Quarteroni, A., et al, eds. Complex Systems in Biomedicine. 2010. (ENG., Illus.). xiv, 292p. pap. 109.00 *(978-88-470-1555-5(3), 8847015553)* Springer.

Raghavachari, Ramesh & Liang, Rongguang. Design & Quality for Biomedical Technologies: 21 January 2008, San Jose, California, USA. 2008. (Proceedings of SPIE Ser.). (Illus.). 142p. pap. 70.00 ***(978-0-8194-7024-9(4))*** SPIE.

—Design & Quality for Biomedical Technologies II: 26 January 2009, San Jose, California, United States. 2009. (Proceedings of SPIE Ser.). (Illus.). 166p. pap. 70.00 ***(978-0-8194-7416-2(9))*** SPIE.

Ramalingam, Murugan, et al, eds. Biomaterials & Stem Cells in Regenerative Medicine. 2012. (ENG., Illus.). 552p. 149.95 ***(978-1-4398-7925-2(7),*** CRC Press) Taylor & Francis Group GBR. Dist: Taylor & Francis Group.

Rao, A. Ravishankar & Cecchi, Guillermo A. High-Throughput Image Reconstruction & Analysis. 2009. (Illus.). 380p. 139.00 *(978-1-59693-295-1(3))* Artech Hse., Inc.

Ratner, Buddy D., et al. Biomedical Engineering Desk Reference. Tooley, Mike, ed. 2009. (ENG., Illus.). 816p. 103.00 *(978-0-12-374646-7(9),* Academic Pr.) Elsevier Science & Technology Bks.

Rhodes, Catherine. International Governance of Biotechnology. 2012. (ENG.). 256p. 90.00 *(978-1-84966-065-5(4),* Hodder Arnold) Bloomsbury Publishing.

Richards-Kortum, Rebecca. Biomedical Engineering for Global Health. 2009. (Cambridge Texts in Biomedical Engineering Ser.). (ENG., Illus.). 416p. (C). 87.00 *(978-0-521-87797-8(0))* Cambridge Univ. Pr.

Rigler, Rudolf & Vogel, H. Single Molecules & Nanotechnology. 2008. (Springer Series in Biophysics Ser.). (Illus.). 318p. 289.00 *(978-3-540-73923-4(8))* Springer.

Rigler, Rudolf & Vogel, H., eds. Single Molecules & Nanotechnology. 2010. (Springer Series in Biophysics Ser.). (Illus.). xiv, 318p. pap. 289.00 *(978-3-642-09316-6(7), 3642093167)* Springer.

Rittscher, Jens, et al. Microscopic Image Analysis for Life Science Applications. 2008. (Artech House Bioinformatics & Biomedical Imaging Ser.). (Illus.). 432p. 169.00 *(978-1-59693-236-4(8))* Artech Hse., Inc.

Rosen, Yitzhak. Biomaterials Science: An Integrated Clinical & Engineering Approach. 2012. (ENG., Illus.). 328p. 149.95 *(978-1-4398-0404-9(4),* CRC Press) Taylor & Francis Group GBR. Dist: Taylor & Francis Group.

Roy, Michael J. Biotechnology Operations: Principles & Practices. 2011. (ENG., Illus.). 416p. 99.95 *(978-1-4398-3027-7(4),* CRC Press) Taylor & Francis Group GBR. Dist: Taylor & Francis Group.

Royal Society of Chemistry Staff. Biomedical Applications of Synchrotron Infrared Microspectroscopy: A Practical Approach. Moss, David, ed. 2010. (RSC Analytical Spectroscopy Ser.). (ENG., Illus.). 400p. (C). 224.00 *(978-0-85404-154-1(0))* Royal Society of Chemistry, The GBR. Dist: Ingram Pub. Services.

—Soft Nanotechnology: Faraday Discussions No 143. 2009. (Faraday Discussions Ser.). (ENG.). 394p. (C). 318.00 *(978-1-84755-838-1(0))* Royal Society of Chemistry, The GBR. Dist: Ingram Pub. Services.

Rubenstein, David, et al. BioFluid Mechanics: An Introduction to Fluid Mechanics, Macrocirculation, & Microcirculation. 2011. (Biomedical Engineering Ser.). (ENG., Illus.). 410p. 119.95 ***(978-0-12-381383-1(2),*** Academic Pr.) Elsevier Science & Technology Bks.

Ruiz, Susana Beatriz Llanusa, et al, eds. V Latin American Congress on Biomedical Engineering CLAIB 2011May 16th-21st, 2011, Habana, Cuba: Sustainable Technologies for the Health of All. 2011. (IFMBE Proceedings Ser.). 800p. pap. 399.00 *(978-3-642-21197-3(6), 3642211976)* Springer.

Russomano, Thais. Hypergravity & Microgravity Effects on Biomedical Experiments. 2007. (Synthesis Lectures on Biomedical Engineering Ser.). 100p. pap. 35.00 *(978-1-59829-578-8(0))* Morgan & Claypool Pubs.

S, Poornachandra. Wavelet Shrinkage Models for Denoising of Biomedical Signals. 2010. 288p. pap. *(978-3-8383-7708-7(7))* Lambert Academic Publishing.

Saltzman, W. Mark & Tran, Veronique. Biomedical Engineering: Bridging Medicine & Technology. 2009. (Cambridge Texts in Biomedical Engineering Ser.). (ENG., Illus.). 656p. 104.00 *(978-0-521-84099-6(6))* Cambridge Univ. Pr.

Salzer, Reiner. Biomedical Imaging: Principles & Applications. 2008. 400p. 229.99 *(978-0-8138-1678-4(5)*, Wiley-Interscience) Wiley, John & Sons, Inc.

Sarbadhikari, S. N. A Short Introduction to Biomedical Engineering. 2007. (ENG.). 276p. 45.95 *(978-1-4200-6011-9(2)*, CRC Press) Taylor & Francis Group GBR. Dist: Taylor & Francis Group.

Savulescu, Julian & Bostrom, Nick, eds. Human Enhancement. 2009. (ENG.). 432p. 60.00 *(978-0-19-929972-0(2))* Oxford Univ. Pr., Inc.

Schiesser, William. Partial Differential Equation Analysis in Biomedical Engineering. 2012. (ENG., Illus.). 448p. 105.00 ***(978-1-107-02280-5(0))*** Cambridge Univ. Pr.

Schügerl, Karl & Zeng, A. P., eds. Tools & Applications of Biochemical Engineering Science. 2010. (Advances in Biochemical Engineering Biotechnology Ser.). (Illus.). xviii, 274p. pap. 349.00 *(978-3-642-07598-8(3)*, 3642075983) Springer.

Semmlow, John. Signals & Systems for Bioengineers: A MATLAB-Based Introduction. 2nd ed. 2011. (Biomedical Engineering Ser.). (ENG., Illus.). 604p. 119.95 ***(978-0-12-384982-3(9)**,* Academic Pr.) Elsevier Science & Technology Bks.

Sharma, Kal. Transport Phenomena in Biomedical Engineering: Artifical organ Design & Development, & Tissue Engineering. 2010. (ENG., Illus.). 512p. 150.00 *(978-0-07-166397-7(5)*, 0071663975) McGraw-Hill Professional Publishing.

Shi, D. Biomedical Devices & Their Applications. 2010. (Biological & Medical Physics, Biomedical Engineering Ser.). (Illus.). xiv, 201p. pap. 259.00 *(978-3-642-06068-7(4)*, 3642060684) Springer.

Shi, Donglu, ed. Biomaterials & Tissue Engineering. 2010. (Biological & Medical Physics, Biomedical Engineering Ser.). (Illus.). xi, 246p. pap. 289.00 *(978-3-642-06067-0(6)*, 3642060676) Springer.

Shukla, Anupam & Tiwari, Ritu, eds. Biomedical Engineering & Information Systems: Technologies, Tools, & Applications. 2010. (Illus.). 350p. 245.00 *(978-1-61692-004-3(1))* IGI Global.

—Intelligent Medical Technologies & Biomedical Engineering: Tools & Applications. 2010. (Illus.). 350p. 245.00 *(978-1-61520-977-4(8))* IGI Global.

Signals & Systems Analysis in Biomedical Engineering Second Ed. 2011. (C). 99.95 ***(978-1-4398-1253-2(5)**,* CRC Press) Taylor & Francis Group GBR. Dist: Taylor & Francis Group.

Simon, Matthew. Emergent Computation: Emphasizing Bioinformatics. 2010. (Biological & Medical Physics, Biomedical Engineering Ser.). (Illus.). xiv, 423p. pap. 139.00 *(978-1-4419-1963-2(5)*, 1441919635) Springer.

Simon, Melvin I. Computer Methods, Part C. 2011. (ENG., Illus.). 696p. 187.00 *(978-0-12-381270-4(4)*, Academic Pr.) Elsevier Science & Technology Bks.

Sloten, Jos van der. 4th European Congress for Medical & Biological Engineering23 - 27 November 2008, Antwerpen, Belgium. 2008. (IFMBE Proceedings Ser.). cxliv, 2808p. pap. 899.00 *(978-3-540-89207-6(9))* Springer.

Smolke, Christina D., ed. The Metabolic Pathway Engineering Handbook, 2 vols., Vol. 2. 2009. (ENG., Illus.). 581p. 164.95 *(978-1-4200-7765-0(1)*, CRC Press) Taylor & Francis Group GBR. Dist: Taylor & Francis Group.

Splinter, Robert. Physics in Medicine & Biology. 2010. (ENG., Illus.). 548p. instr.'s hndbk. ed. 149.95 *(978-1-4200-7524-3(1)*, CRC Press) Taylor & Francis Group GBR. Dist: Taylor & Francis Group.

Splinter, Robert & Hooper, Brett A. An Introduction to Biomedical Optics. 2006. (Series in Optics & Optoelectronics Ser.). (ENG., Illus.). 632p. (C). 92.95 *(978-0-7503-0938-7(5)*, Taylor & Francis) Taylor & Francis Group GBR. Dist: Taylor & Francis Group.

Starly, Binil. Biomimetic Design & Fabrication of Tissue Scaffolds: Using Computer Aided Engineering. 2007. pap. *(978-3-8364-2464-6(9))* VDM Verlag Dr. Mueller e.K.

Steinhoff, Gustav, ed. Regenerative Medicine. 2010. (Illus.). 300p. 279.00 *(978-90-481-9074-4(6)*, 9048190746) Springer.

Strahler, Alan H. Handbook of Biophotonics Vol. 2: Photonics for Health Care. Chiou, Arthur et al, eds. 2011. (ENG.). 1184p. 315.00 ***(978-3-527-41048-4(1)**,* Wiley-VCH) Wiley, John & Sons, Inc.

Street, Laurence. Introduction to Biomedical Engineering Technology. 2nd rev. ed. 2011. (ENG., Illus.). 391p. (C). 89.95 *(978-1-4398-6058-8(0)*, CRC Press) Taylor & Francis Group GBR. Dist: Taylor & Francis Group.

Sucosky, Philippe. Flow Transport Phenomena in Tissue Engineering. 2009. 136p. pap. *(978-3-639-16226-4(9))* VDM Verlag Dr. Mueller e.K.

Suh, Sang, et al, eds. Biomedical Engineering: Health Care Systems, Technology & Techniques. 2011. (ENG., Illus.). xiii, 285p. 189.00 *(978-1-4614-0115-5(1)*, 1461401151) Springer.

Suh, Sang C., et al. Biomedical Engineering: Health Care Systems, Technology & Techniques. 2011. (Illus.). xiii, 285p. E-Book ***(978-1-4614-0116-2(X))*** Springer.

Surfaces in Biomaterials Foundation Staff, compiled by. Biointerface Conference 2006. 2007. 50p. pap. 85.00 *(978-1-60423-979-9(4))* Curran Assocs., Inc.

Suri, Jasjit S. & Farag, Aly. Deformable Models, 2 vols. 2007. (Topics in Biomedical Engineering International Book Ser.). 400p. 269.00 *(978-0-387-72149-1(5))* Springer.

Swiegers, Gerhard. Bioinspiration & Biomimicry in Chemistry. 2012. (ENG.). 504p. 139.95 ***(978-0-470-56667-1(1)**,* Wiley) Wiley, John & Sons, Inc.

Tü, et al. A Computerized System for Tracking Clinical Engineering Outcomes. 2011. 96p. pap. ***(978-3-8454-0766-1(2))*** Lambert Academic Publishing.

Tagawa, Tatsuo, et al. Biomedical Sensors & Instruments. 2nd rev. ed. 2011. (ENG., Illus.). 423p. 139.95 *(978-1-4200-9078-9(X)*, CRC Press) Taylor & Francis Group GBR. Dist: Taylor & Francis Group.

Talpasanu, Ilie & Yih, Tachung, eds. Micro & Nano Manipulations for Biomedical Applications. 2007. (Illus.). 295p. 139.00 *(978-1-59693-254-8(6))* Artech Hse., Inc.

Thanh, Nguyen Thi Kim, ed. Magnetic Particles. 2012. (ENG., Illus.). 616p. 189.95 ***(978-1-4398-6932-1(4)**,* CRC Press) Taylor & Francis Group GBR. Dist: Taylor & Francis Group.

Ting, Hua-Nong, ed. 5th Kuala Lumpur International Conference on Biomedical Engineering 2011: BIOMED 2011, 20-23 June 2011, Kuala Lumpur, Malaysia. 2011. (IFMBE Proceedings Ser.). (ENG., Illus.). xxvi, 870p. pap. 399.00 ***(978-3-642-21728-9(1)**,* 3642217281) Springer.

Urban, Gerald, ed. BioMEMS. 2010. (Microsystems Ser.). xix, 372p. pap. 189.00 *(978-1-4419-3951-7(2)*, 1441939512) Springer.

Valentinuzzi, Max E. Cardiac Fibrillation-Defibrillation: Clinical & Engineering Aspects. 2010. (Illus.). 304p. 119.00 *(978-981-4293-63-1(6))* World Scientific Publishing Co., Inc.

Vallet-Regi, M. & Vila, M., eds. Advanced Bioceramics in Nanomedicine & Tissue Engineering: Special Topic Volume with Invited Peer Reviewed Papers Only, Vol.441. 2010. (Key Engineering Materials Ser.). (Illus.). 392p. pap. *(978-0-87849-270-1(4))* Trans Tech Pubns., Ltd.

van Meurs, Willem L. Modeling & Simulation in Biomedical Engineering: Applications in Cardiorespitory Physiology. 2011. (ENG., Illus.). 224p. 100.00 *(978-0-07-171445-7(6)*, 0071714456) McGraw-Hill Professional Publishing.

Van Schuylenbergh, Koenraad & Puers, Robert. Inductive Powering: Basic Theory & Application to Biomedical Systems. 2009. (Analog Circuits & Signal Processing Ser.). (Illus.). xvi, 224p. 159.00 *(978-90-481-2411-4(5))* Springer.

Van Toi, Vo & Khoa, Truong Quang Dang. The Third International Conference on the Development of Biomedical Engineering in Vietnam: BME2010 January 11 - 14th, 2010 Ho Chi Minh City, Vietnam. 2010. (IFMBE Proceedings Ser.). (Illus.). 350p. pap. 299.00 *(978-3-642-12019-0(9)*, 3642120199) Springer.

Verdonck, P. Advances in Biomedical Engineering. Verdonck, Pascal, ed. 2008. (ENG., Illus.). 320p. 250.00 *(978-0-444-53075-2(4)*, Elsevier Science) Elsevier Science & Technology Bks.

Verhaegh, Wim F. J., et al, eds. Intelligent Algorithms in Ambient & Biomedical Computing. 2006. (Philips Research Ser.: Vol. 7). (Illus.). xxi, 321p. 169.00 *(978-1-4020-4953-8(6)*, 1402049536) Springer.

Vlad, Simona, et al, eds. International Conference of Advancements of Medicine & Health Care through Technology; 23 - 26 September 2009 Cluj-Napoca, Romania. 2009. (IFMBE Proceedings Ser.). (Illus.). xvi, 432p. pap. 219.00 *(978-3-642-04291-1(0)*, 3642042910) Springer.

Vlad, Simona & Ciupa, Radu V., eds. International Conference on Advancements of Medicine & Health Care Through Technology 29th August - 2nd September 2011, Cluj-Napoca, Romania, Vol. 36. 2011. (IFMBE Proceedings Ser.). (ENG., Illus.). xiv, 406p. pap. 259.00 ***(978-3-642-22585-7(3)**,* 3642225853) Springer.

Vonta, Filia, et al, eds. Statistical Models & Methods for Biomedical & Technical Systems. 2008. (Statistics for Industry & Technology Ser.). (Illus.). 600p. 189.00 *(978-0-8176-4464-2(4))* Birkhauser Boston.

Wade, Eric. Biomedical Signal Processing: Devices, Methods, & Experimentation. 2011. (Synthesis Lectures on Biomedical Engineering Ser.). 100p. pap. 40.00 *(978-1-59829-553-5(5))* Morgan & Claypool Pubs.

Waite, Lee & Fine, Jerry. Applied Biofluid Mechanics. 2007. (ENG., Illus.). 314p. (C). 115.00 *(978-0-07-147217-3(7)*, 0071472177) McGraw-Hill Professional Publishing.

Wang, Xiaodu, et al. Biomechanics in Bone Tissue Engineering. 2010. (Synthesis Lectures on Tissue Engineering Ser.). 225p. pap. 40.00 *(978-1-60845-169-2(0))* Morgan & Claypool Pubs.

Webster, John G. Medical Instrumentation. 3rd ed. 2007. pap. 12.95 *(978-1-4288-1875-0(8))* Cram101 Inc.

—Medical Instrumentation Application & Design. 4th rev. ed. 2009. (ENG., Illus.). 713p. (C). 179.95 *(978-0-471-67600-3(4)*, Wiley) Wiley, John & Sons, Inc.

Webster, Thomas J., ed. Safety of Nanoparticles: From Manufacturing to Medical Applications. 2008. (Nanostructure Science & Technology Ser.). (Illus.). xii, 239p. 159.00 *(978-0-387-78607-0(4))* Springer.

Weinfurt, Philip. Biomedical Technology Assessment: The 3Q Method. 2010. (Synthesis Lectures on Biomedical Engineering Ser.). 101p. pap. 35.00 *(978-1-60845-160-9(7))* Morgan & Claypool Pubs.

Wiederhold, B. K. & Bouchard, S., eds. Annual Review of Cybertherapy & Telemedicine 2011: Advanced Technologies in Behavioral, Social & Neurosciences - Studies in Health Technology & Informatics. 2011. 220p. 152.00 ***(978-1-60750-765-9(X))*** IOS Pr., Inc.

Wilkinson, Ashley, et al. Central Nervous System Tissue Engineerng: Current Considerations & Strategies. 2011. (Synthesis Lectures on Tissue Engineering Ser.). pap. 35.00 ***(978-1-60845-786-1(9))*** Morgan & Claypool Pubs.

Winters, Jack. Muscle Tissue: Bioengineering Living Actuators. 2012. (Synthesis Lectures on Biomedical Engineering Ser.). 100p. pap. 35.00 *(978-1-59829-146-9(7))* Morgan & Claypool Pubs.

Wise, Donald L., et al, eds. Biomaterials Engineering & Devices: Human Applications: Vol 1: Fundamentals & Vascular & Carrier Applications. 2010. (Illus.). 368p. pap. 160.00 *(978-1-61737-226-1(9)*, 1617372269) Humana Pr.

—Biomaterials Engineering & Devices: Human Applications: Vol 2: Orthopedic, Dental, & Bone Graft Applications. 2010. (ENG., Illus.). 368p. pap. 160.00 *(978-1-61737-227-8(7)*, 1617372277) Humana Pr.

Wittek, Adam, et al, eds. Computational Biomechanics for Medicine: Soft Tissues & the Musculoskeletal System. 2011. (ENG., Illus.). xii, 155p. 199.00 *(978-1-4419-9618-3(4)*, 1441996184) Springer.

Wnek, Gary E. & Bowlin, Gary L. Encyclopedia of Biomaterials & Biomedical Engineering, 4 vols. 2nd ed. 2008. (Illus.). *(978-1-4200-7956-2(5))*; *(978-1-4200-7954-8(9))*; *(978-1-4200-7955-5(7))* Taylor & Francis Group. (Informa Healthcare).

Wnek, Gary E. & Bowlin, Gary L., eds. Encyclopedia of Biomaterials & Biomedical Engineering, 4 vols., Set. 2nd rev. ed. 2008. (Illus.). 3552p. 1800.00 *(978-1-4200-7802-2(X)*, Informa Healthcare) Taylor & Francis Group GBR. Dist: Taylor & Francis Group.

Woltman, Scott J., et al, eds. Liquid Crystals: Frontiers in Biomedical Engineering. 2007. (Illus.). 493p. 159.00 *(978-981-270-545-7(7))* World Scientific Publishing Co., Inc.

Wood, Andrew W. Physiology Biophysics & Biomedical Engineering. 2012. (Series in Medical Physics & Biomedical Engineering Ser.). (ENG., Illus.). 782p. (C). 99.95 *(978-1-4200-6513-8(0)*, Taylor & Francis) Taylor & Francis Group GBR. Dist: Taylor & Francis Group.

Wu, J. L., et al, eds. Complex Medical Engineering. 2010. (ENG., Illus.). xii, 619p. pap. 209.00 *(978-4-431-99816-7(0)*, 4431998160) Springer.

Wu, Jinglong, et al, eds. Complex Medical Engineering. 2007. (ENG., Illus.). xii, 619p. 209.00 *(978-4-431-30961-1(6)*, 4431309616) Springer.

Xi, Ning. Nanomedicine: A Systems Engineering Approach. Zhang, Mingjun, ed. 2009. (ENG., Illus.). 348p. 149.95 *(978-981-4241-36-6(9))* Pan Stanford Publishing SGP. Dist: Taylor & Francis Group.

Xu, Feng & Lu, Tianjian. Introduction to Skin Biothermomechanics & Thermal Pain. 2010. (ENG., Illus.). 400p. 179.00 *(978-3-642-13201-8(4)*, 3642132014) Springer.

Yamaguchi, T. Nano-Biomedical Engineering 2009: Proceedings of the Tohoku University Global Centre of Excellence Programme - Global Nano-Biomedical Engineering Education & Research Network Centre. 2009. (Illus.). 384p. 172.00 *(978-1-84816-352-2(5))* World Scientific Publishing Co., Inc.

Yang, Shengyuan. Micromachined Sensors to Study Cell Mechanical Response. 2008. 124p. pap. *(978-3-639-05857-4(7))* VDM Verlag Dr. Mueller e.K.

Yao, Kangde, et al, eds. Chitosan-Based Hydrogels. 2011. (ENG., Illus.). 521p. 189.95 *(978-1-4398-2114-5(3)*, CRC Press) Taylor & Francis Group GBR. Dist: Taylor & Francis Group.

Yarmush, Martin & Parekkadan, Biju. Methods in Bioengineering: Stem Cell Bioengineering. 2009. (Illus.). 228p. 129.00 *(978-1-59693-402-3(6))* Artech Hse., Inc.

Yarmush, Martin L. Annual Review of Biomedical Engineering, Vol. 9. 2007. 602p. pap. 181.00 *(978-0-8243-3509-0(0))* Annual Reviews, Inc.

Yarmush, Martin L., ed. Annual Review of Biomedical Engineering 2011. 2011. 556p. 202.00 ***(978-0-8243-3513-7(9))*** Annual Reviews, Inc.

Yazicioglu, Refet Firat, et al. Biopotential Readout Circuits for Portable Acquisition Systems. (Analog Circuits & Signal Processing Ser.). xvi, 164p. 2010. pap. 159.00 *(978-90-481-8070-7(8)*, 9048180708) 2008. (ENG., Illus.). 159.00 *(978-1-4020-9092-9(7)*, 1402090927) Springer.

Yin, Xiaoxia, et al. Terahertz Imaging for Biomedical Applications: Pattern Recognition & Tomographic Reconstruction. 2012. (ENG., Illus.). 332p. 179.00 ***(978-1-4614-1820-7(8)**,* 1461418208) Springer.

Zahavy, Eran, et al, eds. Nano-Biotechnology for Biomedical & Diagnostic Research. 2011. (Advances in Experimental Medicine & Biology Ser.). (ENG., Illus.). viii, 182p. 189.00 ***(978-94-007-2554-6(X)**,* 940072554X) Springer.

Zeng, Haishan, ed. Diagnostic Endoscopy. 2012. (Series in Medical Physics & Biomedical Engineering Ser.). (ENG., Illus.). 288p. 99.95 *(978-1-4200-8346-0(5)*, Chapman & Hall/CRC) CRC Pr. LLC.

Zhang, Changhong. Biodegradable Polyurethanes in Biomedical Engineering Field. 2010. 116p. pap. *(978-3-8383-7491-8(6))* Lambert Academic Publishing.

Zuccheri, Giampaolo & SamorÃ¬, Bruno, eds. DNA Nanotechnology: Methods & Protocols. 2011. (Methods in Molecular Biology Ser.). (ENG., Illus.). xii, 361p. 139.00 *(978-1-61779-141-3(5)*, 1617791415) Humana Pr.

2007 1st International Conference on Bioinformatics & Biomedical Engineering. 2007. pap. 340.00 *(978-1-4244-1119-1(X)*, 07EX1744) IEEE.

2007 Annual International Conference of the IEEE Engineering in Medicine & Biology Society. 2007. pap. 1852.00 *(978-1-4244-0787-3(7)*, 07CH37852) IEEE.

2007 IEEE 33rd Annual Northeast Bioengineering Conference. 2007. pap. 340.00 *(978-1-4244-1032-3(0)*, 07CH37883) IEEE.

2007 IEEE/ICME International Conference on Complex Medical Engineering. 2007. pap. 430.00 *(978-1-4244-1077-4(0)*, 07EX1719) IEEE.

2007 Joint Mtg of the 6th Intl Symp on Noninvasive Functional Source Imaging of the Brain & Heart & the Intl Conf on Functional Biomedical Imaging. 2007. pap. 296.00 *(978-1-4244-0948-8(9)*, 07EX1669) IEEE.

BIOMEDICAL ETHICS

see Bioethics

BIOMEDICAL MATERIALS

see also Biocompatibility; Ceramics in Medicine; Dental Materials; Implants, Artificial; Polymers in Medicine

Albu, Madalina Georgiana. Collagen Gels & Matrices for Biomedical Applications. 2011. 96p. pap. ***(978-3-8443-3057-1(7))*** Lambert Academic Publishing.

Alonso, Maria Jose & Csaba, Noemi S., eds. Nanostructured Biomaterials for Overcoming Biological Barriers. 2012. (ENG., Illus.). 336p. 230.00 ***(978-1-84973-363-2(5))*** Royal Society of Chemistry, The GBR. Dist: Ingram Pub. Services.

Alpa, Guido & Zenovich, Vincenzo. Italian Private Law. 2006. 312p. 150.00 *(978-1-84472-051-4(9)*, Routledge) Taylor & Francis Group GBR. Dist: Taylor & Francis Group.

Ambrosio, L. Biomedical Composites. Ambrosio, L., ed. 2009. 384p. 249.95 *(978-1-4398-0178-9(9))* CRC Pr. LLC.

An, Yuehuei H. & Friedman, Richard J., eds. Handbook of Bacterial Adhesion: Principles, Methods, & Applications. 2010. (ENG.). 672p. pap. 199.00 *(978-1-61737-192-9(0)*, 1617371920) Humana Pr.

Anand, Subhash. Medical & healthcare Textiles. Kennedy, J. F. et al, eds. 2010. (Illus.). 560p. *(978-1-84569-224-7(1))* Woodhead Publishing Ltd.

Anker, Jeffrey N. & Mefford, Thompson, eds. Biomedical Applications of Magnetic Particles. 2012. (ENG., Illus.). 456p. 139.95 ***(978-1-4398-3968-3(9)**,* CRC Press) Taylor & Francis Group GBR. Dist: Taylor & Francis Group.

Archer, C. Regenerative Medicine & Biomaterials for the Repair of Connective Issues. Archer, C. & Ralphs, J., eds. 2010. (ENG.). 600p. 249.95 *(978-1-4398-0110-9(X)*, CRC Press) Taylor & Francis Group GBR. Dist: Taylor & Francis Group.

Archer, C. & Ralphs, J., eds. Regenerative Medicine & Biomaterials for the Repair of Connective Tissues. 2010. (Illus.). 504p. *(978-1-84569-417-3(1))* Woodhead Publishing Ltd.

ASM International & Gilbert, Jeremy. Medical Device Materials IV: Proceedings of the Materials & Processes for Medical Devices Conference 2007, September 23-27, 2007, Palm Desert, California, USA. 2008. (Illus.). ix, 250p. *(978-0-87170-861-8(2))* ASM International, Inc.

ASM International Staff, contrib. by. Materials & Coatings for Medical Devices: Cardiovascular. 2009. (Illus.). viii, 444p. ***(978-1-61503-000-2(X))*** ASM International, Inc.

Atala, Anthony, ed. Foundations of Regenerative Medicine: Clinical & Therapeutic Applications. 2009. (ENG., Illus.). 824p. 103.00 *(978-0-12-375085-3(7)*, Academic Pr.) Elsevier Science & Technology Bks.

Baèákováá, L. Cell Colonization Control by Physical & Chemical Modification of Materials. 2008. pap. 29.00 *(978-1-60456-887-5(9))* Nova Science Pubs., Inc.

Barinov, Sergey & Komlev, Vladimir, eds. Calcium Phosphate Based Bioceramics for Bone Tissue Engineering. 2008. (Materials Science Foundations Ser.: Vol. 48). 170p. pap. *(978-0-87849-380-7(8))* Trans Tech Pubns., Ltd.

Barnes, Steven J. & Harris, Lawrence P. Tissue Engineering: Roles, Materials & Applications. 2008. 129.00 *(978-1-60456-293-4(5)*, Nova Biomedical Bks.) Nova Science Pubs., Inc.

Basu, Bikramjit, et al. Advanced Biomaterials: Fundamentals, Processing, & Applications. 2009. (ENG., Illus.). 776p. 166.00 *(978-0-470-19340-2(9)*, Wiley-American Ceramic Society) Wiley, John & Sons, Inc.

Baudis, Stefan. Vascular Tissue Regeneration. 2010. 108p. pap. *(978-3-639-25640-6(9))* VDM Verlag Dr. Mueller e.K.

Baxter, Walt & Lee, Abraham P. Proceedings of the 2nd Frontiers in Biomedical Devices Conference — 2007: Presented at the Frontiers in Biomedical Devices Conference, June 7-8, 2007, Irvine, California, USA. 2007. (Illus.). xiii, 160p. pap. *(978-0-7918-4266-9(5))* American Society of Mechanical Engineers, The.

Bhambhani, Akhilesh & Kumar, Chall V. Novel Enzyme/DNA/Inorganic Materials: A New Generation of Biomaterials. 2008. (Illus.). viii, 130p. pap. 39.00 *(978-1-60456-191-3(2)*, Nova Biomedical Bks.) Nova Science Pubs., Inc.

Bhatia, Sujata K. Biomaterials for Clinical Applications. 2010. (ENG., Illus.). xi, 275p. 129.00 *(978-1-4419-6919-4(5)*, 1441969195) Springer.

Bhatia, Sujata K., ed. Engineering Biomaterials for Regenerative Medicine: Novel Technologies for Clinical Applications. 2011. (ENG., Illus.). x, 352p. 169.00 ***(978-1-4614-1079-9(7)**,* 1461410797) Springer.

Biocompatible Materials for the Human Body. 2007. per. 4250.00 *(978-1-59623-277-8(3))* BCC Research.

Boomington, Denzel R. New Research on Biomaterials. 2006. 225.00 *(978-1-60021-360-1(X))* Nova Science Pubs., Inc.

Bourg, Henri & Lisle, Amaury, eds. Biomaterials Developments & Applications. 2010. (Advances in Biology & Medicine (Series Editor - Tsisana Shartava, M. D. - Tbilisi, Georgia) Ser.). (Illus.). xiii, 497p. 195.00 *(978-1-60876-476-1(1))* Nova Science Pubs., Inc.

Breme, Jürgen, et al, eds. Metallic Biomaterial Interfaces. 2008. (ENG.). 271p. 205.00 *(978-3-527-31860-5(7)*, Wiley-VCH) Wiley, John & Sons, Inc.

Buchanan, F. J., ed. Degradation Rate of Bioresorbable Materials: Prediction & Evaluation. 2008. (Illus.). 424p. *(978-1-84569-329-9(9))* Woodhead Publishing Ltd.

Burdick, Jason A. & Mauck, Robert L., eds. Biomaterials for Tissue Engineering Applications: A Review of the Past & Future Trends. 2010. (Illus.). 10p. 219.00 *(978-3-7091-0384-5(3)*, 3709103843) Springer.

Burghardt, Irene, et al, eds. Energy Transfer Dynamics in Biomaterial Systems. 2009. (Springer Series in Chemical Physics Ser.). (ENG., Illus.). xvi, 474p. 249.00 *(978-3-642-02305-7(3)*, 3642023053) Springer.

Campagna, Sebastiano, et al, eds. Designing Dendrimers. 2011. (ENG., Illus.). 616p. 149.95 *(978-0-470-43355-3(8)*, Wiley) Wiley, John & Sons, Inc.

Cao, Hengchu, et al. Proceedings of the 3rd Frontiers in Biomedical Devices Conference — 2008: Presented at the 3rd Frontiers in Biomedical Devices Conference & Exhibition, June 18-20, 2008, Irvine, California, USA. 2008. (Illus.). xi, 126p. pap. *(978-0-7918-4833-3(7))* American Society of Mechanical Engineers, The.

Chan, Warren C. W., ed. Bio-Applications of Nanoparticles. 2007. (Advances in Experimental Medicine & Biology Ser.: Vol. 620). (Illus.). 207p. 209.00 *(978-0-387-76712-3(6)*, 0387767126) Springer.

Cheng & Gross, Richard A., eds. Polymer Bicatalysis & Biomaterials II. 2008. (ACS Symposium Ser.). (ENG., Illus.). 506p. 195.00 *(978-0-8412-6970-5(X))* American Chemical Society.

Chiao, J. C. & Chiao, Mu, eds. Biomaterials for MEMS. 2011. (ENG., Illus.). 292p. 149.95 *(978-981-4241-46-5(6))* Pan Stanford Publishing SGP. Dist: Taylor & Francis Group.

Chirila, T. V. Biomaterials & Regenerative Medicine in Ophthalmology. 2010. (Illus.). 560p. 244.99 *(978-1-4398-0215-1(7))* CRC Pr. LLC.

Chirila, T. V., ed. Biomaterials & Regenerative Medicine in Ophthalmology. 2009. (Illus.). 560p. *(978-1-84569-443-2(0))* Woodhead Publishing Ltd.

Chu, Paul K. & Liu, Xuanyong, eds. Biomaterials Fabrication & Processing Handbook. 2008. (ENG., Illus.). 720p. 162.95 *(978-0-8493-7973-4(3)*, CRC Press) Taylor & Francis Group GBR. Dist: Taylor & Francis Group.

Cram101 Textbook Reviews. Outlines & Highlights for Biomaterials: Intro by Joon Park, ISBN. 2011. 432p. pap. 35.95 ***(978-1-61490-432-8(4))*** Cram101 Inc.

—Outlines & Highlights for Biomaterials Science: An Introduction to Materials in Medicine by Ratner, Buddy / Hoffman, Allan / Schoen, Frederick / Lemon. 2011. 128p. pap. 28.95 ***(978-1-61812-400-5(5))*** Cram101 Inc.

—Outlines & Highlights for Biomedical Materials by Roger Narayan. 2011. 132p. pap. 28.95 ***(978-1-61905-320-5(9))*** Cram101 Inc.

Cram101 Textbook Reviews & Cram101 Textbook Reviews. Outlines & Highlights for Biomaterials: The Intersection of Biology & Materials Science by Antonios G. Mikos; Johnna S. Temenoff, ISBN. 2011. 184p. pap. 29.95 ***(978-1-61461-750-1(3))*** Cram101 Inc.

—Outlines & Highlights for Design of Biomedical Devices & Systems by Donner. 2011. 76p. pap. 27.95 ***(978-1-61830-636-4(7))*** Cram101 Inc.

Curtis, R. V. & Watson, T. F., eds. Dental Biomaterials: Imaging, Testing & Modelling. 2008. (Illus.). xv, 512p. 299.95 *(978-1-4200-7209-9(9))* CRC Pr. LLC.

Dabrowiak, James C. Metals in Medicine. 2010. (ENG., Illus.). 334p. 174.00 *(978-0-470-68196-1(9))*; pap. 65.00 *(978-0-470-68197-8(7))* Wiley, John & Sons, Inc. (Wiley)

Decision Resources Inc Staff, ed. SAGE Sourcebook of Modern Biomedical Devices: Business Environments in a Global Market, 4 vols. 2007. (Illus.). 1680p. 895.00 *(978-1-4129-5054-1(6)*, B50546C) SAGE Pubns., Inc.

Dee, Kay C., et al. The Introduction to Tissue-Biomaterial Interactions. 2nd ed. 2008. 248p. 99.95 *(978-0-470-09630-7(6)*, Wiley-Liss) Wiley, John & Sons, Inc.

Denstedt, J. Biomaterials & tissue engineering in Urology. Denstedt, J. & Atala, A., eds. 2009. (ENG., Illus.). 500p. 247.95 *(978-1-4398-0177-2(0)*, CRC Press) Taylor & Francis Group GBR. Dist: Taylor & Francis Group.

Di Silvio, L., ed. Cellular response to Biomaterials. 2009. (ENG., Illus.). 500p. 289.95 *(978-1-4200-9373-5(8))* CRC Pr. LLC.

—Cellular Response to Biomaterials. 2008. (Illus.). 648p. *(978-1-84569-358-9(2))* Woodhead Publishing Ltd.

Dominique. Stem Cell Microenvironments & Tissue Engineering. Prakash, Satya & Shum-Tim, Dominique, eds. 2010. 572p. 102.00 *(978-981-283-788-2(4))* World Scientific Publishing Co., Inc.

Dorozhkin, Sergey V., ed. Calcium Orthophosphate-Based Biocomposites & Hybrid Biomaterials. 2010. (Biomaterials - Properties, Production & Devices Ser.). (Illus.). 177p. pap. 43.00 *(978-1-60876-941-4(0))* Nova Science Pubs., Inc.

Dössel, Olaf & Becks, Thomas, eds. World Congress on Medical Physics & Biomedical Engineering, September 7-12, 2009 Munich, Germany: Biomaterials, Cellular & Tussue Engineering, Artificial Organs, Vol. 25/X 2009. (IFMBE Proceedings Ser.). (Illus.). xiv, 314p. pap. 299.00 *(978-3-642-03899-0(9)*, 3642038999) Springer.

Dumitras, Dan C., et al. Advanced Laser Technologies 2006: 8-12 September, 2006, Brasov, Romania. 2007. (Proceedings of SPIE Ser.). (Illus.). 426p. pap. 90.00 *(978-0-8194-6744-7(8))* SPIE.

Dumitriu, Severian, ed. Polymeric Biomaterials Vol. 2: Medicinal & Pharmaceutical Applications. 2011. 249.95 *(978-1-4200-9468-8(8))* CRC Pr. LLC.

Edwards, Vincent, et al, eds. Modified Fibers with Medical & Specialty Applications. 2010. (ENG.). viii, 240p. pap. 269.00 *(978-90-481-6967-2(4)*, 9048169674) Springer.

Felton, Gary P. Biodegradable Polymers: Processing, Degradation & Applications. 2011. (Materials Science & Technologies Ser.). 295.00 *(978-1-61209-534-9(8))* Nova Science Pubs., Inc.

Ferguson, Arthur N. & O'Neill, Amy G., eds. Focus on Chitosan Research. 2011. (Series: Biotechnology in Agriculture, Industry & Medicine Ser.). (Illus.). 493p. 185.00 *(978-1-61324-454-8(1))* Nova Science Pubs., Inc.

Fitzpatrick, Michael. Defeating Autism: A Damaging Delusion. 2008. (Illus.). XVIII, 166p. pap. 39.95 *(978-0-415-44981-6(2))* Routledge.

Fratzl, Peter. Collagen: Structure & Mechanics. Fratzl, Peter, ed. 2008. (ENG., Illus.). xviii, 506p. 169.00 *(978-0-387-73905-2(X)*, 038773905X) Springer.

Fratzl, Peter, ed. Collagen: Structure & Mechanics. 2010. (ENG., Illus.). xviii, 506p. pap. 169.00 *(978-1-4419-4481-8(8)*, 1441944818) Springer.

Fred, Ana, et al, eds. Biomedical Engineering Systems & Technologies: Third International Joint Conference, BIOSTEC 2010, Valencia, Spain, January 20-23, 2010, Revised Selected Papers. 2011. (Communications in Computer & Information Science Ser.). xiii, 408p. pap. 107.00 *(978-3-642-18471-0(5)*, 3642184715) Springer.

Functional Materials & Biomaterials. (Advances in Polymer Science Ser.). (Illus.). x, 232p. 2010. pap. 329.00 *(978-3-642-09072-1(9)*, 3642090729) 2007. 329.00 *(978-3-540-71508-5(8))* Springer.

Galaev, Igor & Mattiasson, Bo, eds. Smart Polymers: Applications in Biotechnology & Biomedicine. 2nd rev. ed. 2007. (ENG., Illus.). 496p. 144.95 *(978-0-8493-9161-3(X)*, CRC Press) Taylor & Francis Group GBR. Dist: Taylor & Francis Group.

Gilbert, Jeremy. Medical Device Materials V: Proceedings of the Materials & Processes for Medical Devices Conference 2009, August 10-12, 2009, Minneapolis, MN, USA. 2010. (Illus.). x, 273p. ***(978-1-61503-039-2(5))*** ASM International, Inc.

Goldberg, Jay. Introduction Biomedical Engineering D. 2007. (Synthesis Lectures on Biomedical Engineering Ser.). 100p. pap. 35.00 *(978-1-59829-292-3(7))* Morgan & Claypool Pubs.

Gonsalves, Kenneth, et al, eds. Biomedical Nanostructures. 2007. (ENG., Illus.). 515p. 166.00 *(978-0-471-92552-1(7)*, Wiley-Interscience) Wiley, John & Sons, Inc.

Gourlay, T. & Black, R., eds. Biomaterials & Devices for the Circulatory System. 2010. (Woodhead Publishing Series in Biomaterials Ser.). (ENG., Illus.). 400p. 230.00 *(978-1-84569-464-7(3))* Woodhead Publishing Ltd. GBR. Dist: Ingram Pub. Services.

Greco, Giovanni N. Tissue Engineering Research Trends. 2008. (Illus.). (C). 129.00 *(978-1-60456-264-4(1)*, Nova Biomedical Bks.) Nova Science Pubs., Inc.

Gu, Zhongwei, et al, eds. Materials Research: Eco/Enviromental Materials, Energy Materials, Magnesium, Aerospace Materials & Biomaterials for Medical Application. 2009. (Materials Science Forum Ser.: Vol. 613). (Illus.). 1450p. pap. *(978-0-87849-340-1(9))* Trans Tech Pubns., Ltd.

Heckman, Emily M., et al. Nanobiotronics: 26-27 August 2007, San Diego, California, USA. 2007. (Proceedings of SPIE Ser.). (Illus.). 138p. pap. 70.00 *(978-0-8194-6794-2(4))* SPIE.

Helsen, Jozef A. & Missirlis, Yannis. Biomaterials: A Tantalizing Experience. 2010. (Biological & Medical Physics, Biomedical Engineering Ser.). (Illus.). xvi, 340p. 169.00 *(978-3-642-12531-7(X)*, 364212531X) Springer.

Herold, Keith E., et al, eds. 26th Southern Biomedical Engineering ConferenceSBEC 2010 April 30 - May 2, 2010 College Park, Maryland, USA. 2010. (IFMBE Proceedings Ser.). 1000p. pap. 469.00 *(978-3-642-14997-9(9)*, 3642149979) Springer.

Hipler, U. -C & Elsner, Peter. Biofunctional Textiles & the Skin. (Current Problems in Dermatology Ser.: Vol. 33). (Illus.). *(978-3-8055-8121-9(1))* Karger, S. AG.

Hollander, Anthony P. & Hatton, Paul V., eds. Biopolymer Methods in Tissue Engineering. 2010. (Methods in Molecular Biology Ser.). (Illus.). 280p. pap. 139.00 *(978-1-61737-280-3(3)*, 1617372803) Humana Pr.

Hollinger, Jeffrey O., ed. An Introduction to Biomaterials. 2nd rev. ed. 2011. (Biomedical Engineering Ser.). (ENG., Illus.). 644p. 119.95 *(978-1-4398-1256-3(X)*, CRC Press) Taylor & Francis Group GBR. Dist: Taylor & Francis Group.

Hong, Donglu Shi, et al. Nanomaterials & Biomedical Applications. 2009. (Illus.). 565p. 209.00 *(978-3-540-49660-1(2))* Springer.

Hsu, Jui-Mei. Encapsulation Materials for Neural Interface Devices. 2009. 184p. pap. *(978-3-639-14075-0(3))* VDM Verlag Dr. Mueller e.K.

Hutmacher, Dietmar W., et al, eds. Comprehensive Biomaterials, 6 vols., Set. 2011. (ENG.). 3672p. 3780.00 *(978-0-08-055302-3(8)*, Elsevier Science) Elsevier Science & Technology Bks.

Ionescu, Adrian M. & Bland, J. A. C. Biomagnetism & Magnetic Biosystems Based on Molecular Recognition Processes. 2008. (AIP Conference Proceedings Ser.). (Illus.). 216p. 112.00 *(978-0-7354-0547-9(6))* American Institute of Physics.

Jabbari, Esmaiel. Biologically-responsive Hybrid Biomaterials: A Reference for Material Scientists & Bioengineers. 2010. (Illus.). 432p. 135.00 *(978-981-4295-67-3(1))* World Scientific Publishing Co., Inc.

Jackson, Mark J. & Davim, J. Paulo, eds. Medical Device Manufacturing. 2012. (Materials & Manufacturing Technology Ser.). 213p. 69.00 *(978-1-61209-715-2(4))* Nova Science Pubs., Inc.

Jenkins M Staff. Biomedical Polymers. 2007. 224p. 309.95 *(978-1-4200-4451-5(6))* CRC Pr. LLC.

Kaminski, Haden D. & DuPois, Easton A. Dental Materials Research. 2009. (Dental Science, Materials & Technology Ser.). (Illus.). xi, 182p. 129.00 *(978-1-60741-104-8(0)*, Nova Biomedical Bks.) Nova Science Pubs., Inc.

Kausch, Henning, ed. Radiation Effects on Polymers for Biological Use. 2010. (Advances in Polymer Science Ser.). (Illus.). xi, 173p. pap. 279.00 *(978-3-642-07891-0(5)*, 3642078915) Springer.

Kendall, Jason B., ed. Biomaterials Research Advances. 2008. 129.00 *(978-1-60021-892-7(X))* Nova Science Pubs., Inc.

Kennedy, J. F., et al, eds. Medical Textiles 2007: Proceedings of the fourth international conference on healthcare & medical Textiles. 2008. (Illus.). 512p. 249.95 *(978-1-4200-7989-0(1))* CRC Pr. LLC.

Kennedy John F Staff. Medical Textiles 2007 Proceedings of the Fourth International con. 2008. 349.95 *(978-1-4200-4447-8(8))* CRC Pr. LLC.

Khang, Gilson, ed. Handbook of Intelligent Scaffold for Tissue Engineering & Regenerative Medicine. 2012. (ENG., Illus.). 974p. 499.95 *(978-981-4267-85-4(6))* Pan Stanford Publishing SGP. Dist: Taylor & Francis Group.

Khang, Gilson, et al. A Manual for Biomaterials/Scaffold Fabrication Technology. 2007. (Manuals in Biomedical Research Ser.). (Illus.). 258p. spiral bd. 45.00 *(978-981-270-595-2(3))* World Scientific Publishing Co., Inc.

Kim, Young-Ha, et al, eds. Advanced Biomaterials VII. 2007. (Illus.). 980p. *(978-0-87849-436-1(7))* Trans Tech Pubns., Ltd.

King, Paul & Fries, Richard C. Design of Biomedical Devices & Systems, Second Edition. 2nd rev. ed. 2008. (ENG., Illus.). 424p. (C). 124.95 *(978-1-4200-6179-6(8)*, CRC Press) Taylor & Francis Group GBR. Dist: Taylor & Francis Group.

Kisselev, Alexei M. Insights into Stimuli-Responsive Polymers. 2009. 136p. pap. *(978-3-639-16533-3(0))* VDM Verlag Dr. Mueller e.K.

Klajnert, Barbara & Bryszewska, Maria. Dendrimers in Medicine. 2007. 79.00 *(978-1-60021-664-0(1))* Nova Science Pubs., Inc.

Kobayashi, Norihisa, et al. Nanobiosystems: Processing, Characterization, & Applications III: 4-5 August 2010, San Diego, California, United States. 2010. (Proceedings of SPIE Ser.). (Illus.). 128p. pap. 80.00 ***(978-0-8194-8261-7(7))*** SPIE.

—Nanobiosystems: Processing, Characterization, & Applications IV. 2011. (Proceedings of SPIE Ser.). 138p. pap. 70.00 ***(978-0-8194-8713-1(9))*** SPIE.

Kossler, Wolffe & Fuchs, Jacob. Bioceramics: Properties, Preparation & Applications. 2009. 98.00 *(978-1-60741-056-0(7))* Nova Science Pubs., Inc.

Kumar, Challa S. S. R., ed. Nanomaterials for Medical Diagnosis & Therapy. 2007. (Nanotechnologies for the Life Sciences Ser.). (ENG., Illus.). 757p. 235.00 *(978-3-527-31390-7(7)*, Wiley-VCH) Wiley, John & Sons, Inc.

—Polymeric Nanomaterials. 2011. (Nanomaterials for Life Sciences (VCH) Ser.: 2). (ENG., Illus.). 544p. 210.00 *(978-3-527-32170-4(5)*, Wiley-VCH) Wiley, John & Sons, Inc.

Kumar, S. Ashok, et al, eds. Biocompatible Nanomaterials: Synthesis, Characterization & Applications. 2010. (Nanotechnology Science & Technology Ser.). 235.00 *(978-1-61668-677-2(4))* Nova Science Pubs., Inc.

Kurtz, Steven M. PEEK Biomaterials Handbook. 2011. (Plastics Design Library). (ENG., Illus.). 306p. 199.00 ***(978-1-4377-4463-7(X))*** William Andrew, Inc.

Kutz, Myer. Biomedical Engineering & Design, Vols. 1 & 2. 2nd ed. 2009. (ENG., Illus.). 1600p. 250.00 *(978-0-07-149840-1(0)*, 0071498400) McGraw-Hill Professional Publishing.

Langenhove, L. van. Smart textiles for medicine & Healthcare: Materials, systems & Applications. 2007. (Illus.). 336p. *(978-1-84569-027-4(3))* Woodhead Publishing Ltd.

Latinovic, Olga. Micromechanics & Structure of Soft & Biological Materials. 2010. 136p. pap. *(978-3-639-23050-5(7))* VDM Verlag Dr. Mueller e.K.

Laurent, Régis. Dendrimers: Towards Catalytic, Material & Biomedical Uses. Caminade, Anne-Marie et al, eds. 2011. (ENG., Illus.). 566p. 190.00 ***(978-0-470-74881-7(8)***, Wiley) Wiley, John & Sons, Inc.

Lee, Sunggyu & Henthorn, David, eds. Materials in Biology & Medicine. 2012. (Green Chemistry & Chemical Engineering Ser.). (ENG., Illus.). 260p. 169.95 ***(978-1-4398-8169-9(3)***, CRC Press) Taylor & Francis Group GBR. Dist: Taylor & Francis Group.

Lee, Thay, et al. Proceedings of the 4th Frontiers in Biomedical Devices Conference & Exposition — 2009: Presented at 4th Frontiers in Biomedical Devices Conference & Exposition, June 6-8, 2009, Irvine, California, USA. 2009. (Illus.). xiii, 112p. pap. *(978-0-7918-4348-2(3))* American Society of Mechanical Engineers, The.

Lee, Thay, et al. Proceedings of the 5th Frontiers in Biomedical Devices Conference & Exposition — 2010: Presented at 5th Frontiers in Biomedical Devices Conference & Exposition, September 20-21, 2010, Newport Beach, California, USA. 2010. (Illus.). xiii, 106p. pap. ***(978-0-7918-4945-3(7))*** American Society of Mechanical Engineers, The.

Lemm, W., ed. The Reference Materials of the European Communities: Results of Hemocompatibility Tests. 2010. (ENG., Illus.). 276p. pap. 224.00 *(978-90-481-4213-2(X)*, 904814213X) Springer.

Lima, Arturo H. Biomimetic & Supramolecular Systems Research. 2008. (Illus.). xiii, 358p. (C). 185.00 *(978-1-60456-405-1(9))* Nova Science Pubs., Inc.

Loh, Xian Jun. Smart Biomaterials. 2011. 224p. pap. ***(978-3-8443-9704-8(3))*** Lambert Academic Publishing.

Lysaght, Michael J. & Webster, Thomas. Biomaterials for Artificial Organs. 2011. (Woodhead Publishing Series in Biomaterials Ser.). (ENG., Illus.). 328p. 230.00 *(978-1-84569-653-5(0))* Woodhead Publishing Ltd. GBR. Dist: Ingram Pub. Services.

Martin, Colin R., et al, eds. Nanomedicine & the Nervous System. 2012. (ENG., Illus.). 380p. 129.95 ***(978-1-57808-728-0(7))*** BIOS Scientific Publishers Ltd. GBR. Dist: Taylor & Francis Group.

Martín-Palma, R. J. & Lakhtakia, A. Biomimetics & Bioinspiration: 2-3 August 2009, San Diego, California, United States. 2009. (Proceedings of SPIE Ser.). (Illus.). 196p. pap. 70.00 *(978-0-8194-7691-3(9))* SPIE.

MartíN-Palma, RaúL & Lakhtakia, Akhlesh. Bioinspiration, Biomimetics, & Bioreplication. 2011. (Proceedings of SPIE Ser.). 310p. pap. 90.00 ***(978-0-8194-8537-3(3))*** SPIE.

Materials Research Society ( ) Staff, compiled by. Biofilm-Material Interactions: New Tools, Technologies, & Opportunities. 2007. (Materials Research Society Symposium Proceedings Ser.). 31p. pap. 40.00 *(978-1-60423-410-7(5))* Curran Assocs., Inc.

—Biosurfaces & Biointerfaces. 2007. (Materials Research Society Symposium Proceedings Ser.). 240p. pap. 115.00 *(978-1-60423-406-0(7))* Curran Assocs., Inc.

—Mechanics of Biological & Bio-Inspired Materials. 2007. (Materials Research Society Symposium Proceedings Ser.). 185p. pap. 115.00 *(978-1-60423-423-7(7))* Curran Assocs., Inc.

McGoron, Anthony, et al, eds. 25th Southern Biomedical Engineering Conference 2009;15 - 17 May, 2009, Miami, Florida, USA. 2009. (IFMBE Proceedings Ser.). (ENG., Illus.). xxii, 386p. pap. 299.00 *(978-3-642-01696-7(0)*, 3642016960) Springer.

Menaa, Bouzid. Bioencapsulation in Silica-Based Nanoporous Sol-Gel Glasses. Menaa, Farid et al, eds. 2010. (Nanotechnology Science & Technology Ser.). 82p. pap. 43.00 *(978-1-60876-989-6(5))* Nova Science Pubs., Inc.

Merkoci, A., et al. Biosensing Using Nanomaterials. 2009. (Wiley Nanoscience & Nanotechnology Ser.). (ENG., Illus.). 499p. 170.00 *(978-0-470-18309-0(6)*, Wiley-Interscience) Wiley, John & Sons, Inc.

Merolli, Antonio & Joyce, Thomas J., eds. Biomaterials in Hand Surgery. 2009. (ENG., Illus.). xvi, 144p. 139.00 *(978-88-470-1194-6(9)*, 8847011949) Springer.

Meyer, Stefani. Building the Bionic Knee. 2011. 132p. pap. ***(978-3-8443-0654-5(4))*** Lambert Academic Publishing.

Michalek, J. Hydrogels in Biology & Medicine. 2010. (Polymer Science & Technology Ser.). pap. 49.00 *(978-1-61668-758-8(4)*, Nova Biomedical Bks.) Nova Science Pubs., Inc.

Mikos, Antonios G. & Temenoff, Johnna S. Biomaterials: The Intersection of Biology & Materials Science. 2008. (ENG.). 504p. (C). 180.00 *(978-0-13-009710-1(1)*, Prentice Hall) Prentice Hall PTR.

Moriarty, T. Fintan, et al, eds. Biomaterials Associated Infection: Immunological Aspects & Antimicrobial Strategies. 2012. (ENG., Illus.). 320p. 159.00 ***(978-1-4614-1030-0(4)***, 1461410304) Springer.

Mozafari, M. Reza, ed. Nanomaterials & Nanosystems for Biomedical Applications. 2010. xviii, 166p. pap. 169.00 *(978-90-481-7597-0(6)*, 9048175976) 2007. 235p. 169.00 *(978-1-4020-6288-9(5))* Springer.

N, Ram. Hydroxyapatite, a Wonder Biomaterial Synthesis & Characterization. 2011. 60p. pap. ***(978-3-8443-3092-2(5))*** Lambert Academic Publishing.

Narayan, Roger. Advances in Biomedical & Biomimetic Materials, Vol. 206. Kumta, P. N. & Wagner, W. R., eds. 2009. (Ceramic Transactions Ser.: 96). (ENG., Illus.). 204p. 111.00 *(978-0-470-40847-6(2)*, Wiley-American Ceramic Society) Wiley, John & Sons, Inc.

—Biomaterials: Processing, Characterization, & Applications. 2008. 650p. 75.00 *(978-0-521-83696-8(4))* Cambridge Univ. Pr.

Narayan, Roger, ed. Biomedical Materials. 2009. (Illus.). xx, 550p. 125.00 *(978-0-387-84871-6(1)*, 0387848711) Springer.

Narayan, Roger, et al, eds. Printed Biomaterials: Novel Processing & Modeling Techniques for Medicine & Surgery. 2009. (Biological & Medical Physics, Biomedical Engineering Ser.). (ENG., Illus.). xiv, 124p. 139.00 *(978-1-4419-1394-4(7)*, 1441913947) Springer.

Narayan, Roger & Colombo, Paolo, eds. Advances in Bioceramics & Porous Ceramics. 2009. (Ceramic Engineering & Science Proceedings Ser.: 510). (ENG., Illus.). 344p. 94.95 *(978-0-470-45756-6(2)*, Wiley-American Ceramic Society) Wiley, John & Sons, Inc.

Narayan, Roger, et al. Advances in Bioceramics & Biotechnologies. 2010. (Ceramic Transactions Ser.: 103). (ENG., Illus.). 244p. 105.00 *(978-0-470-90548-7(4)*, Wiley-American Ceramic Society) Wiley, John & Sons, Inc.

National Research Council (U.S.), Committee on Biomolecular Materials and Processes Staff, contrib. by. Inspired by Biology: From Molecules to Materials to Machines. 2008. (ENG.). 170p. pap. 59.00 *(978-0-309-11704-3(6))* National Academies Pr.

Nestor & Favret, Eduardo A. Functional Properties of Bio-Inspired Surfaces: Characterization & Technological Applications. 2009. 416p. 141.00 *(978-981-283-701-1(9))* World Scientific Publishing Co., Inc.

Nicolau, Dan V. BioMEMS & Nanotechnology III: 5-7 December 2007, Canberra, Australia. 2007. (Proceedings of SPIE Ser.). (Illus.). 400p. pap. 105.00 *(978-0-8194-6970-0(X))* SPIE.

Niinomi, M., ed. Metals for Biomedical Devices. 2010. (ENG., Illus.). 432p. 229.95 *(978-1-4398-3107-6(6)*, CRC Press) Taylor & Francis Group GBR. Dist: Taylor & Francis Group.

Nolta, Jan A., ed. Genetic Engineering of Mesenchymal Stem Cells. 2010. (ENG.). vi, 169p. pap. 169.00 *(978-90-481-6999-3(2)*, 9048169992) Springer.

Nolte, A. J., et al, eds. Soft Matter, Biological Materials & Biomedical Materials - Synthesis, Characterization & Applications: Volume 1301. 2011. (MRS Proceedings Ser.). (Illus.). 308p. 118.00 ***(978-1-60511-278-7(X))*** Cambridge Univ. Pr.

Orgill, D. & Blanco, C., eds. Biomaterials for Treating Skin Loss. 2009. (Illus.). 256p. *(978-1-84569-363-3(9))* Woodhead Publishing Ltd.

Pannone, Patrick J. Trends in Biomaterials Research. 2006. 244p. 225.00 *(978-1-60021-361-8(8))* Nova Science Pubs., Inc.

Papazoglou, Elisabeth & Parthasarathy, Aravind. Bionanotechnology. 2007. (Synthesis Lectures on Biomedical Engineering Ser.). 100p. pap. 40.00 *(978-1-59829-138-4(6))* Morgan & Claypool Pubs.

Parise, James. MOLECULAR INTERACTIONS AT THE CHEMISTRY-BIOLOGY INTERFACE: The Design of Interfacial Biomaterials & the Modulation of Galectin-3 Aggregation With Multivalent Saccharide Ligands. 2008. 160p. pap. *(978-3-639-09799-3(8))* VDM Verlag Dr. Mueller e.K.

Park, Joon. Biomaterials: An Introduction. 3rd rev. ed. 2007. (ENG., Illus.). xii, 564p. 109.00 *(978-0-387-37879-4(0)*, 0387378790) Springer.

Park, Joon & Lakes, R. S. Biomaterials: An Introduction. 3rd ed. 2010. (ENG., Illus.). xii, 564p. pap. 109.00 *(978-1-4419-2281-6(4)*, 1441922814) Springer.

Peer, Dan, ed. Handbook of Harnessing Biomaterials in Nanomedicine: Preparation, Toxicity, & Applications. 2012. (ENG., Illus.). 424p. 149.95 ***(978-981-4316-46-0(6))*** Pan Stanford Publishing SGP. Dist: Taylor & Francis Group.

Pietrzak, William S., ed. Musculoskeletal Tissue Regeneration: Biological Materials & Methods. 2007. (Orthopedic Biology & Medicine Ser.). (Illus.). 649p. 329.00 *(978-1-58829-909-3(0))* Springer.

Planell, J. A. Bone repair Biomaterials. Planell, J. A. et al, eds. 2009. (ENG., Illus.). 320p. 229.95 *(978-1-4398-0195-6(9))* CRC Pr. LLC.

Plant, Anne L., et al, eds. Architecture & Application of Biomaterials & Biomolecular Materials 1: 2003 MRS Fall Meeting — Extended Summary. 2009. (Materials Research Society Symposium Proceedings Ser.: EXS-1). 465p. 35.00 *(978-1-55899-745-5(8)*, EXS-1-C) Materials Research Society.

Pruitt, Lisa A. & Chakravartula, Ayyana M. Mechanics of Biomaterials: Fundamental Principles for Implant Design. 2011. (Cambridge Texts in Biomedical Engineering Ser.). (ENG., Illus.). 696p. 110.00 ***(978-0-521-76221-2(9))*** Cambridge Univ. Pr.

Puleo, David A. & Bizios, Rena. Biological Interactions on Materials Surfaces: Understanding & Controlling Protein, Cell, & Tissue Responses. Puleo, David A. & Bizios, Rena, eds. 2009. (ENG., Illus.). xx, 429p. 229.00 *(978-0-387-98160-4(8)*, 0387981608) Springer.

Qin, L., et al, eds. Advanced Bioimaging Technologies in Assessment of the Quality of Bone & Scaffold Materials: Techniques & Applications. 2010. (ENG., Illus.). xvi, 700p. pap. 299.00 *(978-3-642-07955-9(5)*, 3642079555) Springer.

Qin, Ling, et al, eds. Advanced Bioimaging Technologies in Assessment of the Quality of Bone & Scaffold Materials: Techniques & Applications. 2007. (ENG., Illus.). xvi, 700p. 299.00 *(978-3-540-45454-0(3)*, 3540454543) Springer.

Rakhorst, Gerhard & Ploeg, Rutger, eds. Biomaterials in Modern Medicine: The Groningen Perspective. 2008. (Illus.). 266p. 107.00 *(978-981-270-956-1(8))* World Scientific Publishing Co., Inc.

Ramakrishna Seeram Staff. Biomaterials a Nano Approach. 2010. (ENG., Illus.). 372p. (C). 99.95 *(978-1-4200-4781-3(7)*, CRC Press) Taylor & Francis Group GBR. Dist: Taylor & Francis Group.

Ramalingam, Murugan, et al, eds. Biomaterials & Stem Cells in Regenerative Medicine. 2012. (ENG., Illus.). 552p. 149.95 ***(978-1-4398-7925-2(7)***, CRC Press) Taylor & Francis Group GBR. Dist: Taylor & Francis Group.

Ramanujam, Vaibavi. In Vivo Biodegradation & Biocompatibility Studies of Biomaterial. 2011. 104p. pap. ***(978-3-8443-3433-3(5))*** Lambert Academic Publishing.

Ramsden, Jeremy. Biomedical Surfaces. 2008. (Engineering in Medicine & Biology Ser.). (Illus.). 270p. 99.00 *(978-1-59693-240-1(6))* Artech Hse., Inc.

Ratner, Buddy D., et al. Biomaterials Science: An Introduction to Materials in Medicine. 3rd ed. 2012. (ENG.). 1264p. (C). 129.95 *(978-0-12-374626-9(4)*, Academic Pr.) Elsevier Science & Technology Bks.

Rebelo Gomes, Lígia & Nicolson, John. Perfluorocarbon Compounds Used As Gas Carriers. 2010. 80p. pap. *(978-3-639-24585-1(7))* VDM Verlag Dr. Mueller e.K.

Rimmer, S., ed. Novel Biomedical Hydrogels: Biochemistry, Manufacture & Medical Implant Applications. 2011. (Woodhead Publishing in Materials Ser.). (ENG., Illus.). 288p. 210.00 *(978-1-84569-590-3(9))* Woodhead Publishing Ltd. GBR. Dist: Ingram Pub. Services.

Rodríguez-González, Federico Ángel. Biomaterials in Orthopaedic Surgery. 2009. (Illus.). xvii, 217p. ***(978-1-61503-009-5(3))*** ASM International, Inc.

Rosen, Yitzhak. Biomaterials Science: An Integrated Clinical & Engineering Approach. 2012. (ENG., Illus.). 328p. 149.95 *(978-1-4398-0404-9(4)*, CRC Press) Taylor & Francis Group GBR. Dist: Taylor & Francis Group.

Rossmann, T., et al. Bionics - Natural Technologies & Biomimetics. 2006. 350p. 89.95 *(978-3-540-33688-4(5)*, 3540336885) Springer.

Roy, Krishnendu, ed. Biomaterials as Stem Cell Niche. 2010. (Studies in Mechanobiology, Tissue Engineering & Biomaterials Ser.). viii, 309p. 179.00 *(978-3-642-13892-8(6)*, 3642138926) Springer.

Saner, Burcu. Fluorinated Biomaterials. 2009. 96p. pap. *(978-3-639-13053-9(7))* VDM Verlag Dr. Mueller e.K.

Santin, Matteo & Phillips, Gary J., eds. Biomimetic, Bioresponsive, & Bioactive Materials: An Introduction to Integrating Materials with Tissues. 2012. (ENG.). 248p. 99.95 *(978-0-470-05671-4(1)*, Wiley) Wiley, John & Sons, Inc.

Schmalz, Gottfried & Arenholt-Bindslev, Dorthe. Biocompatibility of Dental Materials. 2010. (ENG., Illus.). xvi, 380p. pap. 229.00 *(978-3-642-09650-1(6)*, 3642096506) Springer.

Shcherbakov, Ivan A. & Myllylä, Risto. Advanced Laser Technologies 2007: 3-7 September 2007, Levi, Finland. 2008. (Proceedings of SPIE Ser.). (Illus.). 440p. pap. 90.00 *(978-0-8194-7235-9(2))* SPIE.

Shi, Donglu, ed. Biomaterials & Tissue Engineering. 2010. (Biological & Medical Physics, Biomedical Engineering Ser.). (Illus.). xi, 246p. pap. 289.00 *(978-3-642-06067-0(6)*, 3642060676) Springer.

Srivastava, Shalini & Goyal, Pritee. Novel Biomaterials: Decontamination of Toxic Metals from Wastewater. 2010. (Environmental Science & Engineering / Environmental Science Ser.). (ENG., Illus.). x, 190p. 159.00 *(978-3-642-11328-4(1)*, 3642113281) Springer.

Sun, G. & Pan, N., eds. Functional Textiles for Improved Performance, Protection & Health. 2011. (Woodhead Publishing Series in Textiles Ser.). (ENG.). 560p. 265.00 *(978-1-84569-723-5(5))* Woodhead Publishing Ltd. GBR. Dist: Ingram Pub. Services.

Surfaces in Biomaterials Foundation Staff, compiled by. Biointerface Conference 2006. 2007. 50p. pap. 85.00 *(978-1-60423-979-9(4))* Curran Assocs., Inc.

—Role of the Government in the Biomaterials Industry Workshop & BioInterface 2004. 2007. 99p. pap. 137.00 *(978-1-60423-689-7(2))* Curran Assocs., Inc.

Suri, Jasjit S. & Farag, Aly A., eds. Deformable Models: Theory & Biomaterial Applications. 2007. (Topics in Biomedical Engineering. International Book Ser.). (Illus.). 581p. 171.00 incl. cd-rom *(978-0-387-31204-0(8)*, 0387312048) Springer.

Suzuki, Shuko & Ikada, Yoshito. Biomaterials for Surgical Operation. 2011. (ENG., Illus.). ix, 211p. 189.00 ***(978-1-61779-569-5(0)***, 1617795690) Humana Pr.

Swiegers, Gerhard. Bioinspiration & Biomimicry in Chemistry. 2012. (ENG.). 504p. 139.95 ***(978-0-470-56667-1(1)***, Wiley) Wiley, John & Sons, Inc.

Syed, Tofail, ed. Biological Interactions with Surface Charge Biomaterials. 2011. (RSC Nanoscience & Nanotechnology Ser.). (ENG., Illus.). 276p. (C). 195.00 ***(978-1-84973-185-0(3))*** Royal Society of Chemistry, The GBR. Dist: Ingram Pub. Services.

Talpasanu, Ilie & Yih, Tachung, eds. Micro & Nano Manipulations for Biomedical Applications. 2007. (Illus.). 295p. 139.00 *(978-1-59693-254-8(6))* Artech Hse., Inc.

Tateishi. Biomaterials in Asia: In Commemoration of the 1St Asian Biomaterials Congress. 2008. 175.00 *(978-981-283-574-1(1))* World Scientific Publishing Co., Inc.

Technology Research Editors, ed. Biocompatible Materials for Implants & Prosthetics, 2007 Ed. 2007. pap. 128.50 *(978-1-60030-207-7(6)*, Search-In-Print) CSA Journal Division.

Temenoff, Johnna S. & Mikos, Antonios G. Biomaterials: The Intersection of Biology & Materials Science: International Edition. 2008. (Pearson Prentice Hall Bioengineering Ser.). (Illus.). 504p. pap. *(978-0-13-235044-0(0))* Prentice Hall PTR.

Textor, Marcus & Grandin, H. Michelle, eds. Intelligent Surfaces in Biotechnology: Scientific & Engineering Concepts, Enabling Technologies, & Translation to Bio-Oriented Applications. 2012. (ENG., Illus.). 400p. 125.00 ***(978-0-470-53650-6(0)***, Wiley) Wiley, John & Sons, Inc.

Thian, Eng San. Nanostructured Biomedical Coatings. 2008. 116p. pap. *(978-3-639-03818-7(5))* VDM Verlag Dr. Mueller e.K.

Thomas, John G. & Kite, Peter, eds. Medical Biofilms: A Practical Guide to Pathogenesis, Detection, Treatment, & Prevention. 400p. 2008. 125.00 *(978-1-58829-371-8(8)*, 1588293718) 2006. 125.00 *(978-1-59745-265-6(3))* Humana Pr.

Thomas, John M., et al, eds. Annual Review of Materials Research 2007. 2007. 771p. 216.00 *(978-0-8243-1737-9(8))* Annual Reviews, Inc.

Tressaud, Alain & Haufe, Günter, eds. Fluorine & Health: Molecular Imaging, Biomedical Materials & Pharmaceuticals. 2008. (ENG.). 816p. 405.00 *(978-0-444-53086-8(X)*, Elsevier Science) Elsevier Science & Technology Bks.

Vallet-Regí, Maria, ed. Progress in Bioceramics. 2008. (Key Engineering Materials Ser.: Vol. 377). 284p. pap. *(978-0-87849-395-1(6))* Trans Tech Pubns., Ltd.

Van, Der Maarel Johan R. C. Introduction to Biopolymer Physics. 2007. (C). 65.00 *(978-981-277-603-7(6))* World Scientific Publishing Co., Inc.

Varadan, Vijay K., et al. Nanomedicine: Design & Applications of Magnetic Nanomaterials, Nanosensors & Nanosystems. 2008. (ENG., Illus.). 484p. 150.00 *(978-0-470-03351-7(7)*, Wiley) Wiley, John & Sons, Inc.

Vernon, B., ed. Injectable Biomaterials: Science & Applications. 2011. (Woodhead Publishing Series in Biomaterials Ser.). (ENG., Illus.). 432p. 245.00 *(978-1-84569-588-0(7))* Woodhead Publishing Ltd. GBR. Dist: Ingram Pub. Services.

Vincent, Julian. Structural Biomaterials. 3rd ed. 2012. (ENG., Illus.). 240p. (C). pap. 60.00 ***(978-0-691-15400-8(7))*** Princeton Univ. Pr.

Vincenzini, P. Medical Applications of Novel Biomaterials & Nano-Biotechnology: 5th Forum on New Materials Part E. 2011. (Illus.). 280p. pap. *(978-3-908158-59-2(1))* Trans Tech Pubns., Ltd.

Vincenzini, Pietro, ed. Complete Set of Forum of Cimtec 2010. 2011. 1500p. pap. *(978-3-908158-44-8(3))* Trans Tech Pubns., Ltd.

Wallace, Gordon G., et al. Organic Bionics. 2012. (ENG.). 238p. 170.00 ***(978-3-527-32882-6(3)***, Wiley-VCH) Wiley, John & Sons, Inc.

Wang, Meng-Jiy & Tsai, Wei-Bor, eds. Biomaterials in Blood-Contacting Devices: Complications & Solutions. 2010. (Biomaterials - Properties, Production & Devices Ser.). 87p. pap. 43.00 *(978-1-60876-784-7(1))* Nova Science Pubs., Inc.

Watanabe, M. & Okuno, O., eds. Interface Oral Health Science 2007: Proceedings of the 2nd International Symposium for Interface Oral Health Science, Held in Sendai, Japan, Between 18 & 19 February 2007. 2008. (ENG., Illus.). xvii, 385p. 179.00 *(978-4-431-76689-6(8)*, 4431766898) Springer.

—Interface Oral Health Science 2007: Proceedings of the 2nd International Symposium for Interface Oral Health Science, Held in Sendai, Japan, Between 18 & 19 February 2007. 2010. (ENG., Illus.). xvii, 385p. pap. 179.00 *(978-4-431-99840-2(3)*, 4431998403) Springer.

Williams, David F., ed. The Biomaterials Silver Jubilee Compendium: The Best Papers Published in Biomaterials, 1980-2004. 25th anniv. ed. 2007. (ENG., Illus.). 256p. 148.00 *(978-0-08-045154-1(3)*, Elsevier Science) Elsevier Science & Technology Bks.

Williams, R., ed. Surface Modification of Biomaterials: Methods Analysis & Applications. 2010. (Woodhead Publishing Series in Biomaterials Ser.). (ENG., Illus.). 436p. 245.00 *(978-1-84569-640-5(9))* Woodhead Publishing Ltd. GBR. Dist: Ingram Pub. Services.

Wise, Donald L., et al, eds. Biomaterials Engineering & Devices: Human Applications: Vol 1: Fundamentals & Vascular & Carrier Applications. 2010. (Illus.). 368p. pap. 160.00 *(978-1-61737-226-1(9)*, 1617372269) Humana Pr.

—Biomaterials Engineering & Devices: Human Applications: Vol 2: Orthopedic, Dental, & Bone Graft Applications. 2010. (ENG., Illus.). 368p. pap. 160.00 *(978-1-61737-227-8(7)*, 1617372277) Humana Pr.

—Human Biomaterials Applications. 2010. (ENG.). 472p. pap. 210.00 *(978-1-61737-012-0(6)*, 1617370126) Humana Pr.

Wnek, Gary E. & Bowlin, Gary L. Encyclopedia of Biomaterials & Biomedical Engineering, 4 vols. 2nd ed. 2008. (Illus.). *(978-1-4200-7956-2(5))*; *(978-1-4200-7955-5(7))*; *(978-1-4200-7954-8(9))* Taylor & Francis Group. (Informa Healthcare).

Wnek, Gary E. & Bowlin, Gary L., eds. Encyclopedia of Biomaterials & Biomedical Engineering, 4 vols., Set. 2nd rev. ed. 2008. (Illus.). 3552p. 1800.00 *(978-1-4200-7802-2(X)*, Informa Healthcare) Taylor & Francis Group GBR. Dist: Taylor & Francis Group.

Wong, Joyce Y. & Bronzino, Joseph D. Biomaterials. 2007. (ENG., Illus.). 296p. 99.95 *(978-0-8493-7888-1(5)*, CRC Press) Taylor & Francis Group GBR. Dist: Taylor & Francis Group.

Wong, Joyce Y., et al. Biomaterials. 2012. (ENG., Illus.). 350p. 99.95 ***(978-1-4398-7251-2(1)***, CRC Press) Taylor & Francis Group GBR. Dist: Taylor & Francis Group.

Xian Wujing Staff. A Laboratory Course in Biomaterials. 2009. (ENG., Illus.). 216p. (C). pap. 64.95 *(978-1-4200-7582-3(9)*, CRC Press) Taylor & Francis Group GBR. Dist: Taylor & Francis Group.

Yoneyama, T. & Mayazaki, S., eds. Shape Memory Alloys for Biomedical Applications. 2009. 320p. 219.95 *(978-1-4200-7966-1(2))* CRC Pr. LLC.

—Shape Memory Alloys for Biomedical Applications. 2008. (Illus.). 352p. *(978-1-84569-344-2(2))* Woodhead Publishing Ltd.

Zahavy, Eran, et al, eds. Nano-Biotechnology for Biomedical & Diagnostic Research. 2011. (Advances in Experimental Medicine & Biology Ser.). (ENG., Illus.). viii, 182p. 189.00 ***(978-94-007-2554-6(X)***, 940072554X) Springer.

Zhang, Sam, ed. Biological & Biomedical Coatings, 2 vols. 2011. (Advances in Materials Science & Engineering Ser.). (ENG., Illus.). 456p. 139.95 *(978-1-4398-4995-8(1))*; 520p. 139.95 *(978-1-4398-4996-5(X))* Taylor & Francis Group GBR. (CRC Press). Dist: Taylor & Francis Group.

—Biological & Biomedical Coatings Handbook, 2 vols. 2011. (Advances in Materials Science & Engineering Ser.). (ENG., Illus.). 976p. 249.95 *(978-1-4398-2125-1(9)*, CRC Press) Taylor & Francis Group GBR. Dist: Taylor & Francis Group.

Zhao, X., et al, eds. Bioactive Materials in Medicine: Design & Applications. 2011. (Woodhead Publishing Series in Biomaterials Ser.). (ENG., Illus.). 288p. 215.00 *(978-1-84569-624-5(7))* Woodhead Publishing Ltd. GBR. Dist: Ingram Pub. Services.

BIOMEDICAL POLYMERS

see Polymers in Medicine

BIOMEDICAL RESEARCH

see Biology—Research; Medicine—Research

BIOMEDICAL SCIENCES

see Medical Sciences

BIOMETEOROLOGY

see Bioclimatology

BIOMETRY

see also Biomathematics; Mathematical Statistics; Sampling (Statistics)

Ambrosius, Walter T., ed. Topics in Biostatistics. (Methods in Molecular Biology Ser.). (Illus.). 2010. xii, 528p. pap. 129.00 *(978-1-61737-623-8(X)*, 161737623X) 2007. 625p. 129.00 *(978-1-58829-531-6(1)*, 1588295311) Humana Pr.

Anbarjafari, Gholamreza & Demirel, Hasan. Face Recognition Using Colour Statistics. 2010. 80p. pap. *(978-3-639-24704-6(3))* VDM Verlag Dr. Mueller e.K.

Anderson, Iain A. & Vincent, Julian. Biomimetics & Ocean Organisms. 2013. (ENG., Illus.). 400p. 139.95 ***(978-1-4398-3762-7(7)***, CRC Press) Taylor & Francis Group GBR. Dist: Taylor & Francis Group.

Anderson Stewart Staff. Biostatistics: A Computing Approach. 2011. (Chapman & Hall/CRC Texts in Statistical Science Ser.). (ENG., Illus.). 326p. (C). 79.95 *(978-1-58488-834-5(2)*, Chapman & Hall/CRC) CRC Pr. LLC.

Anjum, Muhammad Almas & Javed, Younus. Face Recognition a Challenge in Biometrics. 2011. 188p. pap. ***(978-3-8443-0278-3(6))*** Lambert Academic Publishing.

Ashbourn, Julian. Guide to Biometrics for Large-Scale Systems: Technological, Operational, & User-Related Factors. 2011. (ENG., Illus.). xiv, 202p. 69.95 *(978-0-85729-466-1(0)*, 0857294660) Springer.

Barnette, J. Jackson, et al. Biostatistics: For the Biological & Health Sciences. 2006. (ENG., Illus.). 226p. (C). per. 36.67 *(978-0-321-28689-5(8))* Addison-Wesley Longman, Inc.

Basit, Abdul. Iris Recognition: An Identification Biometric System. 2010. 188p. pap. *(978-3-8383-8062-9(2))* Lambert Academic Publishing.

Bateson, Patrick & Gluckman, Peter. Plasticity, Robustness, Development & Evolution. 2011. (ENG., Illus.). 166p. (C). 115.00 *(978-0-521-51629-7(3))*; pap. 45.00 *(978-0-521-73620-6(X))* Cambridge Univ. Pr.

Beam, Craig, ed. Biostatistical Applications in Cancer Research. 2010. (Cancer Treatment & Research Ser.). 248p. pap. 199.00 *(978-1-4419-5310-0(8)*, 1441953108) Springer.

Bhanu, Bir & Chen, Hui. Human Ear Recognition by Computer. (Advances in Computer Vision & Pattern Recognition Ser.). (Illus.). 2010. xviii, 206p. pap. 119.00 *(978-1-84996-733-4(4)*, 1849967334) 2008. XVIII, 206p. 119.00 *(978-1-84800-128-2(2)*, 1848001282) Springer.

Bhanu, Bir & Han, Ju. Human Recognition at a Distance in Video. 2010. (Advances in Pattern Recognition Ser.). (Illus.). xxvi, 261p. 99.00 *(978-0-85729-123-3(8)*, 0857291238) Springer.

Bhattacharjee, Manish, et al. Recent Advances in Biostatistics: False Discovery Rates, Survival Analysis, & Related Topics. 2011. 312p. 90.00 *(978-981-4329-79-8(7))* World Scientific Publishing Co., Inc.

Bhowmik, Ujjal Kumar. Fingerprint Verification. 2010. 76p. pap. *(978-3-8383-1871-4(4))* Lambert Academic Publishing.

Biswas, Atanu, et al, eds. Statistical Advances in the Biomedical Sciences: Clinical Trials, Epidemiology, Survival Analysis, & Bioinformatics. 2008. (Wiley Series in Probability & Statistics Ser.: 630). (ENG., Illus.). 582p. 159.00 *(978-0-471-94753-0(9)*, Wiley-Interscience) Wiley, John & Sons, Inc.

Blanc-Talon, Jacques, et al. Advanced Concepts for Intelligent Vision Systems: 11th International Conference, ACIVS 2009 Bordeaux, France, September 28 — October 2, 2009 Proceedings. 2009. (Lecture Notes in Computer Science / Image Processing, Computer Vision, Pattern Recognition, & Graphics Ser.). (Illus.). xix, 743p. pap. 139.00 *(978-3-642-04696-4(7)*, 3642046967) Springer.

Bohnet, Alexandra. Using Biometrics in Customer Relationship Management. 2009. 176p. pap. *(978-3-639-00130-3(3))* VDM Verlag Dr. Mueller e.K.

Boutron, Isabelle, et al, eds. Randomized Clinical Trials of Nonpharmacologic Treatments. 2011. (Chapman & Hall/CRC Biostatistics Ser.). (ENG., Illus.). 403p. 99.95 *(978-1-4200-8801-4(7)*, Chapman & Hall/CRC) CRC Pr. LLC.

Bremer, Martina & Doerge, R. W. Statistics at the Bench: A Step-by-Step Handbook for Biologists. 2009. (ENG., Illus.). 200p. 61.00 *(978-0-87969-857-7(8))* Cold Spring Harbor Laboratory Pr.

Brimacombe, Michael. Biostatistics & Experimental Design for Medical & Health Researchers. 2009. 54.95 *(978-1-58829-839-3(6))* Humana Pr.

Brimacombe Michael Staff. Bayesian Likelihood Methods in Ecology & Biology. 2009. (Statistics: A Series of Textbooks & Monographs). (Illus.). 79.95 *(978-1-58488-788-1(5)*, Chapman & Hall/CRC) CRC Pr. LLC.

Broman, Karl W. & Sen, Saunak. A Guide to QTL Mapping with R/qtl. 2009. (Statistics for Biology & Health Ser.). (ENG., Illus.). xii, 400p. 119.00 *(978-0-387-92124-2(9)*, 0387921249) Springer.

Brown, Kate, et al. Statistics: A Biomedical Introduction. 2007. (Wiley Classics Library: 85). (ENG., Illus.). 482p. pap. 130.00 *(978-0-470-25161-4(1)*, Wiley-Interscience) Wiley, John & Sons, Inc.

Bush, Heather M. Biostatistics: An Applied Introduction for the Public Health Practitioner. 2011. (ENG.). 608p. (C). pap. 92.95 *(978-1-111-03514-3(8))* Delmar Cengage Learning.

Canovas Valles, Francisco, et al. Fingerpal: Biometric Payment System. 2010. 108p. pap. *(978-3-8383-8479-5(2))* Lambert Academic Publishing.

Carstensen, Bendix. Comparing Clinical Measurement Methods: A Practical Guide. 2010. (Statistics in Practice Ser.: 92). (ENG., Illus.). 172p. 90.00 *(978-0-470-69423-7(8)*, Wiley) Wiley, John & Sons, Inc.

Chang, Mark. Adaptive Design Theory & Implementation Using SAS & R. 2007. (Chapman & Hall/CRC Biostatistics Ser.: Vol. 22). (ENG., Illus.). 440p. 94.95 *(978-1-58488-962-5(4)*, Chapman & Hall/CRC) CRC Pr. LLC.

—Modern Issues & Methods in Biostatistics. 2011. (Statistics for Biology & Health Ser.). (ENG., Illus.). xiv, 307p. 89.95 *(978-1-4419-9841-5(1)*, 1441998411) Springer.

Chaudhary, Vivek & Kumar Singla, Sunil. Biometrics. 2011. 128p. pap. ***(978-3-8433-9022-4(3))*** Lambert Academic Publishing.

Chen, Xue-wen, et al. Computational & Statistical Methods in Bioinformatics. 2010. (Illus.). 329p. 79.95 *(978-1-4200-7054-5(1)*, Chapman & Hall/CRC) CRC Pr. LLC.

Chernick, Michael R. The Essentials of Biostatistics for Physicians, Nurses, & Clinicians. 2011. (ENG., Illus.). 224p. pap. 74.95 *(978-0-470-64185-9(1)*, Wiley) Wiley, John & Sons, Inc.

Cheung, Ying Kuen. Dose Finding by the Continual Reassessment Method. 2011. (Chapman & Hall/CRC Biostatistics Ser.). (ENG., Illus.). 200p. 79.95 *(978-1-4200-9151-9(4)*, Chapman & Hall/CRC) CRC Pr. LLC.

Chow, Shein-Chung. Sample Size Calculations in Clinical Research, Second Edition N-Solution bundle Version. 2nd rev. ed. 2009. (Chapman & Hall/CRC Biostatistics Ser.). (ENG.). 480p. 249.95 *(978-1-4398-1359-1(0)*, Chapman & Hall/CRC) CRC Pr. LLC.

Clarke, Nathan. Transparent User Authentication: Biometrics, RFID & Behavioural Profiling. 2011. (ENG., Illus.). xviii, 229p. 99.00 ***(978-0-85729-804-1(6)***, 0857298046) Springer.

Cleves, Mario, et al. An Introduction to Survival Analysis Using Stata, Third Edition. 3rd rev. ed. 2010. (ENG., Illus.). 412p. pap. 79.95 *(978-1-59718-074-0(2)*, Stata Pr.) StataCorp LP.

Collett, David & Kimber, Alan. Modelling Survival Data in Medical Research. 3rd rev. ed. 2011. (Illus.). 448p. 79.95 *(978-1-4398-5678-9(8)*, Chapman & Hall/CRC) CRC Pr. LLC.

Cook, Richard J. & Lawless, Jerald F. The Statistical Analysis of Recurrent Events. 2007. (Statistics for Biology & Health Ser.). (Illus.). 403p. 119.00 *(978-0-387-69809-0(4))* Springer.

Cowel, Jennifer K. Statistics Basics: A Resource Guide for Healthcare Managers. 2007. (Illus.). xvi, 145p. pap. *(978-1-57839-998-7(X))* Opus Communications.

—Statistics Basics Global Edition. 2008. 152p. pap. *(978-1-60146-188-9(7))* Opus Communications.

Cram101 Textbook Reviews. Outlines & Highlights for Basic & Clinical Biostatistics by Dawson & Trapp, Isbn: 9780071410175. 2010. 182p. pap. 29.95 *(978-1-61698-851-7(7))* Cram101 Inc.

—Outlines & Highlights for Basic Biostatistics: Statistics for Public Health Practice by Gerstman B. Burt, ISBN. 2010. 138p. pap. 28.95 *(978-1-61698-827-2(4))* Cram101 Inc.

—Outlines & Highlights for Biometric System & Data Analysis by Ted Dunstone. 2011. 74p. pap. 27.95 ***(978-1-61905-204-8(0))*** Cram101 Inc.

—Outlines & Highlights for Biostatistics: A Foundation for Analysis in the Health Sciences by Wayne W. Daniel, ISBN. 2010. 108p. pap. 28.95 *(978-1-61698-796-1(0))* Cram101 Inc.

—Outlines & Highlights for Epidemiology, Biostatistics & Preventive Medicine by Dorothea Wild, Isbn: 9781416034964 141603496x. 2011. 280p. pap. 32.95 ***(978-1-61490-249-2(6))*** Cram101 Inc.

—Outlines & Highlights for Fundamentals of Biostatistics by Bernard Rosner, Isbn: 9780534418205. 2010. 192p. pap. 30.95 *(978-1-61698-808-1(8))* Cram101 Inc.

—Outlines & Highlights for Statistics for Life Sciences by Jeffrey a Witmer, Isbn: 9780130413161. 2010. 128p. pap. 28.95 *(978-1-61698-834-0(7))* Cram101 Inc.

Cram101 Textbook Reviews Staff. Outlines & Highlights for Biostatistical Analysis by Jerrold H Zar, Isbn: 9780131008465. 2009. 56p. pap. 26.95 *(978-1-4288-1975-7(4))* Cram101 Inc.

—Outlines & Highlights for Biostatistics for the Biological & Health Sciences with Statdisk by Triola, Isbn: 0321194365. 2008. 88p. pap. 10.95 *(978-1-4288-5822-0(9))* Cram101 Inc.

—Outlines & Highlights for Biostatistics for the Health Sciences by Blair, Isbn. 2008. 72p. pap. 10.95 *(978-1-4288-5887-9(3))* Cram101 Inc.

Crimin, Kimberly & Vidmar, Thomas J. Non-Clinical Statistics in Drug Discovery. 2013. (Chapman & Hall/CRC Biostatistics Ser.). (ENG., Illus.). 270p. 79.95 *(978-1-4200-7935-7(2),* Chapman & Hall/CRC) CRC Pr. LLC.

Crowder, Martin J. Multivariate Survival Analysis & Competing Risks. 2012. (Chapman & Hall/CRC Texts in Statistical Science Ser.). (ENG., Illus.). 417p. 99.95 ***(978-1-4398-7521-6(9),*** Chapman & Hall/CRC) CRC Pr. LLC.

Daniel, Wayne W. Biostatistics: A Foundation for Analysis in the Health Sciences. 9th ed. (Wiley Series in Probability & Statistics Ser.). (ENG.). 2009. 168p. (C). pap., stu. ed. 56.95 *(978-0-470-10581-8(X),* Wiley) 2009. (Illus.). 177.25 incl. cd-rom *(978-0-470-50060-6(3))* 2008. 960p. (C). 195.95 *(978-0-470-10582-5(8))* Wiley, John & Sons, Inc.

—Biostatistics: A Foundation for Analysis in the Health Sciences 8th Edition with Minitab Student Release 14 SS Set. 2008. (Wiley Series in Probability & Statistics Ser.). (C). 190.95 *(978-0-470-40964-0(9))* Wiley, John & Sons, Inc.

—Biostatistics: A Foundation for Analysis in the Health Sciences with SPSS Student Software V14. 0. 8th ed. 2006. (Wiley Series in Probability & Statistics Ser.). 944p. 156.95 *(978-0-470-11796-5(6))* Wiley, John & Sons, Inc.

—Biostatistics: A Foundation for Analysis in the Health Sciences with SPSS Student Software Version 15. 0. 8th ed. 2007. (Wiley Series in Probability & Statistics Ser.). 93.00 net. *(978-0-470-19621-2(1))* Wiley, John & Sons, Inc.

Dawson, Gail F. Easy Interpretation of Biostatistics: The Vital Link to Applying Evidence in Medical Decisions. 2008. (ENG., Illus.). 208p. pap. 32.95 *(978-1-4160-3142-0(1),* Saunders) Elsevier - Health Sciences Div.

Dehert. Biometrics in EUrope: Legal Issues & Implications. 2010. 152.00 *(978-90-411-2833-1(6))* Wolters Kluwer Law & Business.

Dickman, P. Population-based Cancer Survival Analysis. 2008. (Statistics in Practice Ser.). (ENG.). 320p. 100.00 *(978-0-470-02859-9(9),* Wiley) Wiley, John & Sons, Inc.

Drahansky, Martin. Fingerprint Recognition Technology - Related Topics. 2011. 180p. pap. ***(978-3-8443-3007-6(0))*** Lambert Academic Publishing.

Drygajlo, Andrzej. Fundamentals of Biometrics. 2012. (ENG.). 320p. 95.00 *(978-1-4398-3515-9(2))* CRC Pr. LLC.

Du, Yingzi (Eliza), ed. Biometrics: From Fiction to Practice. 2012. (ENG.). 300p. 149.95 ***(978-981-4310-88-8(3))*** Pan Stanford Publishing SGP. Dist: Taylor & Francis Group.

Dunn, Olive Jean & Clark, Virginia A. Basic Statistics: A Primer for the Biomedical Sciences. 4th ed. 2009. (ENG., Illus.). 272p. 120.00 *(978-0-470-24879-9(3),* Wiley) Wiley, John & Sons, Inc.

Dunstone, Ted & Yager, Neil. Biometric System & Data Analysis: Design, Evaluation, & Data Mining. (ENG., Illus.). xx, 268p. 2010. pap. 99.00 *(978-1-4419-4595-2(4),* 1441945954) 2008. 99.00 *(978-0-387-77625-5(7),* 0387776257) Springer.

Dytham, Calvin. Choosing & Using Statistics: A Biologist's Guide. 3rd ed. 2011. (ENG., Illus.). 320p. 150.00 *(978-1-4051-9838-7(9))*; pap. 49.95 *(978-1-4051-9839-4(7))* Wiley, John & Sons, Inc. (Wiley-Blackwell).

Elston, Robert C., et al. Basic Biostatistics for Geneticists & Epidemiologists: A Practical Approach. 2008. (ENG., Illus.). 384p. 130.00 *(978-0-470-02489-8(5))*; pap. 50.00 *(978-0-470-02490-4(9))* Wiley, John & Sons, Inc. (Wiley).

Elsworth, John T. Design & Performance of Biometric System. 2010. (Computer Science, Technology & Applications Ser.). 124p. 79.00 *(978-1-60692-978-0(X))* Nova Science Pubs., Inc.

Ennos, Roland. Statistical & Data Handling Skills in Biology. (ENG., Illus.). 2nd rev. ed. 2007. 248p. (C). pap. 62.50 *(978-0-13-195584-4(5),* Prentice Hall) 3rd rev. ed. 2012. 271p. pap. 72.50 ***(978-0-273-72949-5(7))*** Pearson Education, Ltd. GBR. Dist: Trans-Atlantic Pubns., Inc.

Esposito, Anna. Fundamentals of Verbal & Nonverbal Communication & the Biometric Issue. 2007. (Illus.). xiii, 357p. 144.00 *(978-1-58603-733-8(1))* IOS Pr., Inc.

Fan, Jianqing. New Developments in Biostatistics & Bioinformatics, Vol. 21. 2009. 292p. 94.00 *(978-981-283-743-1(4))* World Scientific Publishing Co., Inc.

Ferrara, Matteo. Biometric Fingerprint Recognition Systems. 2010. 148p. pap. *(978-3-8383-6432-2(5))* Lambert Academic Publishing.

Feudale, Laura. Large Scale Extreme Events of Temperature During 1950-2003. 2008. 196p. pap. *(978-3-8364-8953-9(8))* VDM Verlag Dr. Mueller e.K.

Fierrez, Julian, et al. Biometric ID Management & Multimodal Communication: Joint COST 2101 & 2102 International Conference, BioID_MultiComm 2009, Madrid, Spain, September 16-18, 2009, Proceedings. 2009. (Lecture Notes in Computer Science / Image Processing, Computer Vision, Pattern Recognition, & Graphics Ser.). (Illus.). xiii, 358p. pap. 83.00 *(978-3-642-04390-1(9),* 3642043909) Springer.

Forthofer, Ronald N., et al. Biostatistics: A Guide to Design, Analysis & Discovery. 2nd ed. 2006. (ENG., Illus.). 528p. (C). 101.00 *(978-0-12-369492-8(2),* Academic Pr.) Elsevier Science & Technology Bks.

Foulkes, Andrea S. Applied Statistical Genetics with R: For Population-based Association Studies. 2009. (Use R Ser.). (ENG., Illus.). xxii, 252p. pap. 59.95 *(978-0-387-89553-6(1))* Springer.

Gaebelein, Claude J. & Gleason, Brenda L. Contemporary Drug Information: An Evidence-Based Approach. 2007. (Illus.). 370p. per. 62.99 *(978-0-7817-8280-7(5))* Lippincott Williams & Wilkins.

Gerstman, B. Burt. Basic Biostatistics: Statistics for Public Health Practice. 2007. (Illus.). 557p. per. 78.95 *(978-0-7637-3580-7(9))* Jones & Bartlett Learning, LLC.

Glantz, Stanton. Primer of Biostatistics. 7th ed. 2011. (ENG., Illus.). 320p. pap., pap. 65.00 incl. cd-rom ***(978-0-07-178150-3(1),*** 0071781501) McGraw-Hill Medical Publishing Div.

Glantz, Stanton A. Primer of Biostatistics. 7th ed. 2011. (Illus.). xiv, 306p. pap. ***(978-0-07-176800-9(9))*** McGraw-Hill Cos., The.

Glover, Thomas & Mitchell, Kevin. An Introduction to Biostatistics. 2nd ed. 2008. 487p. (C). pap. 58.95 *(978-1-57766-580-9(5))* Waveland Pr., Inc.

González Velasco, Miguel, et al, eds. Workshop on Branching Processes & Their Applications. 2010. (Lecture Notes in Statistics / Lecture Notes in Statistics - Proceedings Ser.). xx, 296p. pap. 129.00 *(978-3-642-11154-9(8),* 3642111548) Springer.

Gottweis, Herbert & Petersen, Alan, eds. Biobanks. 2007. (Illus.). 224p. 150.00 *(978-0-415-42737-1(1))* Routledge.

Govindaraju, Venu & Ratha, Nalini K., eds. Advances in Biometrics: Sensors, Algorithms & Systems. 2007. (ENG., Illus.). xx, 508p. 109.00 *(978-1-84628-920-0(3),* 1846289203) Springer.

Gregory, Peter & Simon, Michael A. Biometrics for Dummies. 2008. (ENG., Illus.). 292p. pap. 29.99 *(978-0-470-29288-4(1),* For Dummies) Wiley, John & Sons, Inc.

Hanagal, David D. Frailty Models for Survival Data Analysis. 2011. (ENG., Illus.). 334p. 89.95 *(978-1-4398-3667-5(1),* Chapman & Hall/CRC) CRC Pr. LLC.

Härdle, Wolfgang, et al, eds. Statistical Methods for Biostatistics & Related Fields. 2010. (ENG., Illus.). xvii, 370p. pap. 159.00 *(978-3-642-06921-5(5),* 3642069215) Springer.

Harkness, Gail A. & DeMarco, Rosanna. Community & Public Health Nursing: Evidence for Practice. 2011. (ENG., Illus.). 768p. pap. 107.99 *(978-0-7817-5851-2(3))* Lippincott Williams & Wilkins.

Harrington, David, ed. Designs for Clinical Trials: Perspectives on Current Issues. 2011. (Applied Bioinformatics & Biostatistics in Cancer Research Ser.). (ENG., Illus.). xiv, 204p. 189.00 *(978-1-4614-0139-1(9),* 1461401399) Springer.

Hart, Tom, et al. Introduction to Statistics for Biology. 3rd rev. ed. 2007. (ENG., Illus.). 296p. (C). 65.95 *(978-1-58488-652-5(8),* Chapman & Hall/CRC) CRC Pr. LLC.

Hawkins, Dawn. Biomeasurement: A student's guide to biological Statistics. 2nd ed. 2009. (ENG., Illus.). 320p. pap. 55.00 *(978-0-19-921999-5(0),)* Oxford Univ. Pr., Inc.

Heritier, Stephane, et al. Robust Methods in Biostatistics. 2009. (Wiley Series in Probability & Statistics Ser.: 838). (ENG., Illus.). 292p. 110.00 *(978-0-470-02726-4(6),* Wiley) Wiley, John & Sons, Inc.

Hoffer, Kenneth J. IOL Power. 2011. (ENG., Illus.). 288p. 99.95 *(978-1-55642-988-0(6))* SLACK, Inc.

Holmes, Larry. Basics of Public Health Core Competencies. 2008. 222p. pap. 91.95 *(978-0-7637-6537-8(6))* Jones & Bartlett Learning, LLC.

Huber, Catherine. Mathematical Methods in Survival Analysis, Reliability & Quality of Life. Mesbah, Mounir, ed. 2008. (Iste Ser.: 290). (ENG., Illus.). 420p. 205.00 *(978-1-84821-010-3(8),* Wiley-ISTE) Wiley, John & Sons, Inc.

IEEE Staff. 2007 Biometrics Symposium. 2007. pap. 188.00 *(978-1-4244-1548-9(9))* IEEE.

Indrayan, A. Medical Biostatistics. 2nd rev. ed. 2008. (Chapman & Hall/CRC Biostatistics Ser.: Vol. 25). (ENG., Illus.). 824p. (C). 104.95 *(978-1-58488-887-1(3),* Chapman & Hall/CRC) CRC Pr. LLC.

Indrayan, Abhaya. Medical Biostatistics. 3rd rev. ed. 2012. (Chapman & Hall/CRC Biostatistics Ser.). (ENG., Illus.). 1008p. 129.95 ***(978-1-4398-8414-0(5),*** Chapman & Hall/CRC) CRC Pr. LLC.

Islam, Rajibul. A Secure Personal Identification System. 2010. 196p. pap. *(978-3-8383-7028-6(7))* Lambert Academic Publishing.

Jain, Anil K., et al, eds. Handbook of Biometrics. 2007. (ENG., Illus.). x, 556p. 79.95 *(978-0-387-71040-2(X),* 038771040X) Springer.

Jain, Anil K. & Ross, Arun A. Introduction to Biometrics. 2010. (ENG., Illus.). 330p. 89.95 *(978-0-387-77325-4(8),* 0387773258) Springer.

Jefferson, Rachel B., ed. Biometrics, Privacy, Progress & Government. 2010. (Computer Science, Technology & Applications Ser.). 172p. 115.00 *(978-1-60741-098-0(2))* Nova Science Pubs., Inc.

Jekel, James F., et al. Epidemiology, Biostatistics & Preventive Medicine. 3rd rev. ed. 2007. (ENG., Illus.). 448p. (C). pap. 54.95 *(978-1-4160-3496-4(X),* Saunders) Elsevier - Health Sciences Div.

Jewell, Nicholas P., et al, eds. Lifetime Data: Models in Reliability & Survival Analysis: Models in Reliability & Survival Analysis. 2010. (ENG.). 424p. pap. 269.00 *(978-1-4419-4753-6(1),* 1441947531) Springer.

Johnson, Valen E. & Rosner, Gary L. An Introduction to Bayesian Biostatistics. 2012. (Chapman & Hall/CRC Texts in Statistical Science Ser.). (ENG., Illus.). 400p. 79.95 *(978-1-4398-0008-9(1),* Chapman & Hall/CRC) CRC Pr. LLC.

Källén, Anders. Understanding Biostatistics. 2011. (Statistics in Practice Ser.: 95). (ENG., Illus.). 388p. 96.00 *(978-0-470-66636-4(6),* Wiley) Wiley, John & Sons, Inc.

Kaps, Miroslav & Lamberson, William R. Biostatistics for Animal Science: An Introductory Text. 2nd ed. 2009. (Illus.). 520p. pap. 85.00 *(978-1-84593-540-5(3))* CABI GBR. Dist: Stylus Publishing, LLC.

Kaushik, Roy & Bhattacharya, Prabir. Iris Recognition: A Machine Learning Approach. 2008. (Illus.). 156p. pap. *(978-3-639-08259-3(1))* VDM Verlag Dr. Mueller e.K.

Keiding, Niels & Andersen, Per Kragh, eds. Survival & Event History Analysis. 2006. (Wiley Reference Series in Biostatistics Ser.). (ENG., Illus.). 550p. 289.00 *(978-0-470-05806-0(4),* Wiley) Wiley, John & Sons, Inc.

Kery, Marc. Introduction to WinBUGS for Ecologists: Bayesian Approach to Regression, ANOVA, Mixed Models & Related Analyses. 2010. (ENG., Illus.). 320p. pap. 51.95 *(978-0-12-378605-0(3),* Academic Pr.) Elsevier Science & Technology Bks.

Kholmatov, Alisher. Privacy Protecting Biometric Authentication Systems. 2009. 104p. pap. *(978-3-639-15104-6(6))* VDM Verlag Dr. Mueller e.K.

Kim, Jay S. & Dailey, Ronald J. Biostatistics for Oral Healthcare. 2008. (ENG., Illus.). 344p. 164.99 *(978-0-8138-2818-3(X),* Wiley-Blackwell) Wiley, John & Sons, Inc.

Klein, J. P. & Goel, P. K., eds. Survival Analysis: State of the Art: State of the Art. 2010. (NATO Science Series E: (closed) Ser.). 468p. pap. 299.00 *(978-90-481-4133-3(8),* 9048141338) Springer.

Klein, John P. & Moeschberger, Melvin L. Survival Analysis: Techniques for Censored & Truncated Data. 2nd ed. 2010. (Statistics for Biology & Health Ser.). (Illus.). xv, 536p. pap. 115.00 *(978-1-4419-2985-3(1),* 1441929851) Springer.

Kleinbaum, David G. & Klein, Mitchel. Survival Analysis: A Self-Learning Text, Third Edition. 3rd ed. 2011. (Statistics for Biology & Health Ser.). (ENG., Illus.). xv, 700p. 99.00 ***(978-1-4419-6645-2(5),*** 1441966455) Springer.

Korosteleva, Olga. Clinical Statistics: Introducing Clinical Trials, Survival Analysis & Longitudinal Data Analysis. 2008. 120p. spiral bd. 64.95 *(978-0-7637-5850-9(7))* Jones & Bartlett Learning, LLC.

Kumar, B.V.K.Vijaya, et al. Biometric Technology for Human Identification VII 5-6 April 2010, Orlando, Florida, United States. 2010. (Proceedings of SPIE Ser.). (Illus.). 340p. pap. 80.00 ***(978-0-8194-8131-3(9))*** SPIE.

Kupper Lawrence L Staff. Problems & Solutions in Biostatistical Theory. 2010. (Chapman & Hall/CRC Texts in Statistical Science Ser.). (ENG., Illus.). 420p. (C). 51.95 *(978-1-58488-722-5(2),* Chapman & Hall/CRC) CRC Pr. LLC.

Lai, Chin Diew & Xie, Min. Stochastic Ageing & Dependence for Reliability. 2010. (ENG., Illus.). xx, 420p. pap. 115.00 *(978-1-4419-2129-1(X),* 144192129X) Springer.

Laird, Nan M. & Lange, Christoph. The Fundamentals of Modern Statistical Genetics. 2011. (Illus.). xiv, 223p. E-Book ***(978-1-4419-7338-2(9))*** Springer.

Lam. Expect the Unexpected: A First Course in Biostatistics. 2011. 54.00 *(978-981-4291-32-3(3))* World Scientific Publishing Co., Inc.

Lawson, Andrew B. & Lesaffre, Emmanuel. Bayesian Methods in Biostatistics. 2012. (Statistics in Practice Ser.). (ENG.). 536p. 75.00 *(978-0-470-01823-1(2),* Wiley) Wiley, John & Sons, Inc.

Le, Chap T. Health & Numbers: A Problems-Based Introduction to Biostatistics. 3rd ed. 2009. (ENG., Illus.). 310p. pap. 99.95 *(978-0-470-18589-6(9),* Wiley-Blackwell) Wiley, John & Sons, Inc.

Lesne, Annick & Lagues, Michel, eds. Scale Invariance: From Phase Transitions to Turbulence. 2011. Orig. Title: Invariances D'échelle. (ENG., Illus.). xv, 395p. 99.00 *(978-3-642-15122-4(1),* 3642151221) Springer.

Lewis, Alvin E. Biostatistics. 2011. (ENG., Illus.). 320p. pap., tchr. ed. 24.95 *(978-0-07-160041-5(8),* 0071600418) McGraw-Hill Professional Publishing.

Li. Advanced Topics in Biometrics. 2011. (Illus.). 600p. 144.00 *(978-981-4287-84-5(9))* World Scientific Publishing Co., Inc.

Li, S. Z. Encyclopedia of Biometrics, 2 vols. 2009. (Illus.). 1000p. 559.00 *(978-0-387-73004-2(4),* 0387730044) Springer.

Li, Stan Z., ed. Encyclopedia of Biometrics, 2 vols. 2009. (Illus.). xxxi, 1433p. E-Book 449.00 *(978-0-387-73003-5(6))* Springer.

Li, Stan Z. (Chinese Academy of Sciences). Encyclopedia of Biometrics, 2 vols. 2009. (ENG., Illus.). xxxii, 1419p. 449.00 *(978-0-387-73002-8(8),* 0387730028) Springer.

Link, William & Barker, Richard J. Bayesian Inference: With Ecological Applications. 2009. (ENG., Illus.). 400p. 66.95 *(978-0-12-374854-6(2),* Academic Pr.) Elsevier Science & Technology Bks.

Liu, Yue. Bio-Privacy: Privacy Regulations & the Legal Challenge of Biometrics. 2011. (ENG & ACE., Illus.). 296p. 125.00 *(978-0-415-67790-5(4))* Routledge.

Logan, Murray. Biostatistical Design & Analysis Using R. 2010. (ENG., Illus.). 576p. 169.95 *(978-1-4443-3524-8(3),* Wiley-Blackwell) Wiley, John & Sons, Inc.

—Biostatistical Design & Analysis Using R: A Pratical Guide. 2010. (ENG., Illus.). 576p. pap. 69.95 *(978-1-4051-9008-4(6),* Wiley-Blackwell) Wiley, John & Sons, Inc.

Looney, Stephen W., ed. Biostatistical Methods. 2010. (Methods in Molecular Biology Ser.). (Illus.). 224p. pap. 149.00 *(978-1-61737-271-1(4),* 1617372714) Humana Pr.

Maalallah, Prof. Magid. Statistical Methodology. 2011. 128p. pap. ***(978-3-8443-0138-0(0))*** Lambert Academic Publishing.

Magnet, Shoshana Amielle. When Biometrics Fail: Gender, Race, & the Technology of Identity. 2011. (ENG., Illus.). 224p. pap. 22.95 ***(978-0-8223-5135-1(8))*** Duke Univ. Pr.

—When Biometrics Fail: Gender, Race, & the Technology of Identity. 2011. (ENG., Illus.). 224p. 79.95 ***(978-0-8223-5123-8(4))*** Duke Univ. Pr.

Malley, James D., et al. Statistical Learning for Biomedical Data. 2011. (Practical Guides to Biostatistics & Epidemiology Ser.). (Illus.). 298p. 105.00 *(978-0-521-87580-6(3))*; pap. 48.00 *(978-0-521-69909-9(6))* Cambridge Univ. Pr.

Martinussen, Torben & Scheike, Thomas H. Dynamic Regression Models for Survival Data. 2010. (Statistics for Biology & Health Ser.). (Illus.). xiv, 470p. pap. 115.00 *(978-1-4419-1904-5(X),* 144191904X) Springer.

Masulli, Francesco, et al. Computational Intelligence Methods for Bioinformatics & Biostatistics: 5th International Meeting, CIBB 2008 Vietri sul Mare, Italy, October 3-4, 2008 Revised Selected Papers. 2009. (Lecture Notes in Computer Science / Lecture Notes in Bioinformatics Ser.). (ENG.). xi, 294p. pap. 79.95 *(978-3-642-02503-7(X),* 364202503X) Springer.

Masulli, Francesco. Computational Intelligence Methods for Bioinformatics & Biostatistics: 6th International Meeting, CIBB 2009, Genoa, Italy, October 15-17, 2009, Revised Selected Papers. Masulli, Francesco et al, eds. 2010. (Lecture Notes in Computer Science / Lecture Notes in Bioinformatics Ser.). xiii, 320p. pap. 83.00 *(978-3-642-14570-4(1),* 3642145701) Springer.

Matthews, David E. & Farewell, Vernon T. Using & Understanding Medical Statistics. 4th ed. 2007. *(978-3-8055-8189-9(0))* Karger, S. AG.

Medical Biometrics. 2008. (Lecture Notes in Computer Science Ser.). (Illus.). 324p. pap. 79.95 *(978-3-540-77410-5(6))* Springer.

Medical Biostatistics Second Edition. 2011. (C). 99.95 ***(978-1-58488-888-8(1),*** Chapman & Hall/CRC) CRC Pr. LLC.

Menevidis, Z. & Schug, S. H., eds. Ethical Implications of the Global Use of Digitised Biomedical & Biometric Data Workshop Proceedings. 2011. 108p. pap. 58.00 ***(978-1-60750-720-8(X))*** IOS Pr., Inc.

Miettinen, O. S. Epidemiological Research: Terms & Concepts: Terms & Concepts. 2011. (ENG.). xvi, 175p. 59.95 *(978-94-007-1170-9(0),* 9400711700) Springer.

Mills, Melinda. Introducing Survival & Event History Analysis. 2011. (Illus.). 288p. (C). 125.00 *(978-1-84860-101-7(8),* B01017C); pap. 47.00 *(978-1-84860-102-4(6),* B01017P) SAGE Pubns., Ltd. GBR. Dist: SAGE Pubns., Inc.

Mohammad, Mohsin Khan. A Guide to Biostatistics: Health Care Research. 2011. 540p. pap. ***(978-3-639-32786-1(1))*** VDM Verlag Dr. Mueller e.K.

Mori, Yuichi, et al, eds. Statistical Methods for Biostatistics & Related Fields. 2006. (ENG., Illus.). xvii, 370p. 159.00 *(978-3-540-32690-8(1),* 3540326901) Springer.

Motulsky, Harvey. Intuitive Biostatistics: A Nonmathematical Guide to Statistical Thinking, 1 vol. 2nd ed. 2010. (ENG., Illus.). 512p. (C). pap. 64.95 *(978-0-19-973006-3(7))* Oxford Univ. Pr., Inc.

Mou, Dengpan. Machine-based Intelligent Face Recognition. 2010. (ENG., Illus.). 200p. 169.00 *(978-3-642-00750-7(3),* 3642007503) Springer.

Moyé, Lemuel A. Elementary Bayesian Biostatics. 2007. 88.95 *(978-1-58488-725-6(7),* CRC Press) Taylor & Francis Group GBR. Dist: Taylor & Francis Group.

—Elementary Bayesian Biostatistics. 2007. (Chapman & Hall/CRC Biostatistics Ser.). (ENG., Illus.). 400p. (C). 92.95 *(978-1-58488-724-9(9),* Chapman & Hall/CRC) CRC Pr. LLC.

—Statistical Reasoning in Medicine: The Intuitive P-Value Primer. 2nd rev. ed. 2006. (Illus.). 301p. per. 69.95 *(978-0-387-32913-0(7),* 0387329137) Springer.

Newman, Robert. Security & Access Control Using Biometric Technologies: Application, Technology & Management. 2009. (ENG.). 480p. pap. 84.95 *(978-1-4354-4105-7(2))* Course Technology.

Nichols, Ellen R., ed. Biometrics: Theory, Applications, & Issues. 2010. (Biotechnology in Agriculture, Industry & Medicine Ser.). 89.00 *(978-1-61728-765-7(2),* Nova Biomedical Bks.) Nova Science Pubs., Inc.

Olwell, David H., et al, eds. Statistical Methods in Counterterrorism: Game Theory, Modeling, Syndromic Surveillance, & Biometric Authentication. 2006. (Illus.). 292p. pap. 64.95 *(978-0-387-32904-8(8),* 0387329048) Springer.

O'Quigley, John. Proportional Hazards Regression. 2008. (Statistics for Biology & Health Ser.). (Illus.). 542p. 89.95 *(978-0-387-25148-6(0),* 0387251480) Springer.

Ortega Hortas, Marcos. Biometric Authentication Using the Retinal Vessel Tree. 2011. 184p. pap. ***(978-3-8443-1845-6(3))*** Lambert Academic Publishing.

Paulson, Daryl S. Biostatistics & Microbiology: A Survival Manual. 2008. (ENG., Illus.). x, 216p. pap. 89.95 *(978-0-387-77281-3(2),* 0387772812) Springer.

—Handbook of Regression & Modeling: Applications for the Clinical & Pharmaceutical Industries. 2006. (Biostatistics Ser.). (ENG., Illus.). 520p. 113.95 *(978-1-57444-610-4(X),* Chapman & Hall/CRC) CRC Pr. LLC.

Payton, Carl & Bartlett, Roger, eds. Biomechanical Evaluation of Movement in Sport & Exercise: The British Association of Sport & Exercise Sciences Guidelines. 2007. (Illus.). 232p. 64.95 *(978-0-415-43469-0(6))* Routledge.

Payton, Carl J. & Bartlett, Roger M., eds. Biomechanical Evaluation of Movement in Sport & Exercise: The British Association of Sport & Exercise Sciences Guidelines. 2008. (BASES Sport & Exercise Science Ser.). (Illus.). 218p. 200.00 *(978-0-415-43468-3(8))* Routledge.

Pejas, Jerzy & Piegat, Andrzej, eds. Enhanced Methods in Computer Security, Biometric & Artificial Intelligence Systems. 2010. (ENG., Illus.). xii, 396p. pap. 185.00 *(978-1-4419-5436-1(4)*, 1441954384) Springer.

Pesarin, Fortunato & Salmaso, Luigi. Permutation Tests for Complex Data: Theory, Applications & Software. 2010. (Wiley Series in Probability & Statistics Ser.). (ENG., Illus.). 448p. 130.00 *(978-0-470-51641-6(0)*, Wiley) Wiley, John & Sons, Inc.

Problems & Solutions in Biostatistical Theory. 2011. (C). 49.95 ***(978-1-58488-723-2(0)***, Chapman & Hall/CRC) CRC Pr. LLC.

Quarteroni, A., et al, eds. Complex Systems in Biomedicine. 2010. (ENG., Illus.). xiv, 292p. pap. 109.00 *(978-88-470-1555-5(3)*, 8847015553) Springer.

Reilly, Cavan. Statistics in Human Genetics & Molecular Biology. 2009. (Chapman & Hall/CRC Texts in Statistical Science Ser.). (ENG., Illus.). 280p. (C). 64.95 *(978-1-4200-7263-1(3)*, Chapman & Hall/CRC) CRC Pr. LLC.

Revett, Kenneth. Behavioral Biometrics: A Remote Access Approach. 2008. (ENG., Illus.). 250p. 130.00 *(978-0-470-51883-0(9)*, Wiley) Wiley, John & Sons, Inc.

Rocha, Miguel P., et al, eds. 5th International Conference on Practical Applications of Computational Biology & Bioinformatics. 2011. (Advances in Intelligent & Soft Computing Ser.). (Illus.). xvi, 400p. pap. 259.00 *(978-3-642-19913-4(5)*, 3642199135) Springer.

Rosenhahn, Bodo, et al, eds. Human Motion: Understanding, Modelling, Capture, & Animation. (Computational Imaging & Vision Ser.). 2010. x, 636p. pap. 129.00 *(978-90-481-7700-4(6)*, 9048177006) 2007. (Illus.). 633p. 129.00 *(978-1-4020-6692-4(9))* Springer.

Rosner, Bernard. Fundamentals of Biostatistics. 7th ed. 2010. (ENG.). 888p. (C). 222.95 *(978-0-538-73349-6(7))* Brooks/Cole.

Rossi, Richard J. Applied Biostatistics for the Health Sciences. 2009. (ENG., Illus.). 648p. 139.00 *(978-0-470-14764-1(4)*, Wiley) Wiley, John & Sons, Inc.

Rothmann Mark Staff. Design & Analysis of Non-Inferiority Trials. 2011. (Chapman & Hall/CRC Biostatistics Ser.). (ENG., Illus.). 454p. 89.95 *(978-1-58488-804-8(0)*, Chapman & Hall/CRC) CRC Pr. LLC.

Sada, Rajesh. Resource Assessment of Non-Timber Forest Products. 2010. 96p. pap. *(978-3-8383-4860-5(5))* Lambert Academic Publishing.

Saeed, Khalid, et al, eds. Biometrics, Computer Security Systems & Artificial Intelligence Applications. (ENG., Illus.). xii, 348p. 2010. pap. 175.00 *(978-1-4419-4212-8(2)*, 1441942122) 2006. 175.00 *(978-0-387-36232-8(0)*, 0387362320) Springer.

Salah, Albert Ali, et al, eds. Human Behavior Understanding: First International Workshop, HBU 2010, Istanbul, Turkey, August 22, 2010, Proceedings. 2010. (Lecture Notes in Computer Science / Image Processing, Computer Vision, Pattern Recognition, & Graphics Ser.). iv, 173p. pap. 72.00 *(978-3-642-14714-2(3)*, 3642147143) Springer.

Samuels, Myra L. & Witmer, Jeffrey A. Statistics for the Life Sciences. 3rd ed. 2006. pap. 9.95 *(978-1-4288-1445-5(0))* Cram101 Inc.

—Student Solutions Manual for Statistics for the Life Sciences. 4th ed. 2011. (ENG.). 96p. (C). pap. 36.67 *(978-0-321-69307-5(8))* Addison Wesley.

Samuels, Myra L., et al. Statistics for the Life Sciences. 4th rev. ed. 2010. (ENG.). 672p. (C). 146.67 *(978-0-321-65280-5(0))* Addison Wesley.

Sanderson, Conrad. Biometric Person Recognition. 2008. 156p. pap. *(978-3-639-02769-3(8))* VDM Verlag Dr. Mueller e.K.

Schuckers, Michael E. Computational Methods in Biometric Authentication: Statistical Methods for Performance Evaluation. 2010. (Information Science & Statistics Ser.). (ENG., Illus.). xxv, 317p. 139.00 *(978-1-84996-201-8(4)*, 1849962014) Springer.

Schuster, Harvey & Metzger, Wilfred. Biometrics: Methods, Applications & Analyses. 2010. (Computer Science, Technology & Applications Ser.). 145.00 *(978-1-60876-412-9(5))* Nova Science Pubs., Inc.

Selvin, Steve. Survival Analysis for Epidemiologic & Medical Research: A Practical Guide. 2008. (Practical Guides to Biostatistics & Epidemiology Ser.). (ENG., Illus.). 296p. 95.00 *(978-0-521-89519-4(7))*; pap. 41.99 *(978-0-521-71937-7(2))* Cambridge Univ. Pr.

Shahbaba, Babak. Biostatistics with R: An Introduction to Statistics Through Biological Data. 2011. (Use R Ser.). (ENG., Illus.). xvi, 352p. pap. 64.95 ***(978-1-4614-1301-1(X)***, 146141301X) Springer.

Shoniregun, Charles A. & Crosier, Stephen. Securing Biometrics Applications. 2010. (ENG., Illus.). xviii, 190p. pap. 109.00 *(978-1-4419-4350-7(1)*, 1441943501) Springer.

Sokal, Robert R. & Rohlf, F. James. Biometry. 4th ed. 2011. (ENG., Illus.). 937p. (C). 137.95 *(978-0-7167-8604-7(4))* Freeman, W. H. & Co.

—Introduction to Biostatistics. 2nd ed. 2009. (Dover Books on Mathematics Ser.). (ENG., Illus.). 384p. (C). pap. 19.95 *(978-0-486-46961-4(1))* Dover Pubns., Inc.

StataCorp LP, text. Stata Survival Analysis & Epidemiological Tables Reference Manual-Release 11. 2009. (Illus.). 548p. pap. 50.00 *(978-1-59718-061-0(0)*, Stata Pr.) StataCorp LP.

StataCorp LP, text. Stata Survival Analysis & Epidemiological Tables Reference Manual-Release 12. 2011. (Illus.). 554p. pap. 55.00 ***(978-1-59718-092-4(0)***, Stata Pr.) StataCorp LP.

Stiefelhagen, Rainer & Garofolo, John, eds. Multimodal Technologies for Perception of Humans: First International Evaluation Workshop on Classification of Events, Activities & Relationships, CLEAR 2006, Southampton, UK, April 6-7, 2006, Revised Selected Papers. 2007. (Lecture Notes in Computer Science / Image Processing, Computer Vision, Pattern Recognition, & Graphics Ser.). (Illus.). xii, 360p. pap. 99.00 *(978-3-540-69567-7(2)*, 3540695672) Springer.

Sullivan, Lisa M. & D'Agostino, Ralph B., Sr. Essentials of Biostatistics in Public Health. 2007. (Essential Public Health Ser.). 350p. (C). pap. 78.95 *(978-0-7637-3737-5(2))* Jones & Bartlett Learning, LLC.

Taylor, Richard & Blair, R. Clifford. Biostatistics for the Health Sciences. 2007. (ENG., Illus.). 552p. (C). pap. 88.00 *(978-0-13-117660-7(9)*, Prentice Hall) Prentice Hall PTR.

Thakur, Satyendra Singh & Manoria, Manish. Secure Cryptosystem for Biometric Information Using Rs. 2011. 92p. pap. ***(978-3-8443-8944-9(X))*** Lambert Academic Publishing.

Therneau, Terry M. & Grambsch, Patricia M. Modeling Survival Data: Extending the Cox Model: Extending the Cox Model. 2010. (Statistics for Biology & Health Ser.). (Illus.). xiii, 350p. pap. 139.00 *(978-1-4419-3161-0(9)*, 1441931619) Springer.

Tistarelli, Massimo & Nixon, Mark S. Advances in Biometrics: Third International Conferences, ICB 2009, Alghero, Italy, June 2-5, 2009, Proceedings. 2009. (Lecture Notes in Computer Science / Image Processing, Computer Vision, Pattern Recognition, & Graphics Ser.). xxi, 1302p. pap. 189.00 *(978-3-642-01792-6(4)*, 3642017924) Springer.

Transportation Worker Identification Credential (TWIC) Implementation: Hearing Before the Committee on Commerce, Science, & Transportation, United States Senate, One Hundred Tenth Congress, First Session, April 12, 2007. 2010. (Illus.). iv, 92p. *(978-0-16-086643-2(X)*, 552-070-41621-8) United States Government Printing Office.

Vacca, John R. Biometric Technologies & Verification Systems. 2007. (ENG., Illus.). 656p. per. 74.95 *(978-0-7506-7967-1(0)*, Butterworth-Heinemann) Elsevier Science & Technology Bks.

van Emden, Helmut. Statistics for Terrified Biologists. 2008. (ENG., Illus.). 360p. pap. 39.95 *(978-1-4051-4956-3(6)*, Wiley-Blackwell) Wiley, John & Sons, Inc.

van Houwelingen, Hans & Putter, Hein. Dynamic Prediction in Survival Analysis. 2011. (Chapman & Hall/CRC Monographs on Statistics & Applied Probability Ser.). (ENG., Illus.). 250p. 89.95 ***(978-1-4398-3533-3(0)***, CRC Press) Taylor & Francis Group GBR. Dist: Taylor & Francis Group.

Verbeke, Geert & Molenberghs, Geert. Linear Mixed Models for Longitudinal Data. 2009. (Springer Series in Statistics Ser.). (ENG., Illus.). xxii, 570p. pap. 79.95 *(978-1-4419-0299-3(6))* Springer.

Vicsek, Thomas. Fluctuations & Scaling in Biology. (Lecture Notes in Physics). 300p. (C). 55.80 *(978-3-540-66988-3(4))* Springer.

Vidal, Rene, ed. Dynamical Vision: ICCV 2005 & ECCV 2006 Workshops, WDV 2005 & WDV 2006, Beijing, China, October 21, 2005, Graz, Austria, May 13, 2006, Revised Papers. 2007. (Lecture Notes in Computer Science Ser.: Vol. 4358). (Illus.). 327p. per. 79.95 *(978-3-540-70931-2(2)*, 3540709312) Springer.

Vielhauer, Claus. Biometric User Authentication for IT Security: From Fundamentals to Handwriting. 2010. (Advances in Information Security Ser.). (Illus.). xii, 284p. pap. 149.00 *(978-1-4419-3873-2(7)*, 1441938737) Springer.

Vittinghoff, Eric, et al. Regression Methods in Biostatistics: Linear, Logistic, Survival, & Repeated Measures Models. 2007. (Statistics for Biology & Health Ser.). (Illus.). XVI, 344p. 129.00 *(978-0-387-20275-4(7)*, 0387202757) Springer.

Wall, Michael E. Quantitative Biology: From Molecular to Cellular Systems. 2012. (Chapman & Hall/CRC Mathematical & Computational Biology Ser.). (ENG., Illus.). 408p. 89.95 *(978-1-4398-2722-2(2)*, CRC Press) Taylor & Francis Group GBR. Dist: Taylor & Francis Group.

Wang, Hansheng, et al. Sample Size Calculations in Clinical Research. 2nd rev. ed. 2007. (Chapman & Hall/CRC Biostatistics Ser.: Vol. 20). (ENG., Illus.). 480p. 89.95 *(978-1-58488-982-3(9)*, Chapman & Hall/CRC) CRC Pr. LLC.

Wang, Liang & Geng, Xin, eds. Behavioral Biometrics for Human Identification: Intelligent Applications. 2009. (Illus.). 530p. 245.00 *(978-1-60566-725-6(0))* IGI Global.

Wang, Patrick S. P., ed. Pattern Recognition, Machine Intelligence & Biometrics. 2011. (ENG., Illus.). 800p. 219.00 ***(978-3-642-22406-5(7)***, 3642224067) Springer.

Whither Biometrics Committee & National Research Council. Biometric Recognition: Challenges & Opportunities. 2010. (ENG.). 182p. pap. 41.50 *(978-0-309-14207-6(5))* National Academies Pr.

Whitlock, Michael & Schluter, Dolph. The Analysis of Biological Data: From Mind to Molecules. 2008. (ENG., Illus.). 704p. (C). 99.50 *(978-0-9815194-0-1(7))* Roberts & Co.

Wienke, Andreas. Frailty Models in Survival Analysis. 2010. (Chapman & Hall/CRC Biostatistics Ser.). (ENG., Illus.). 312p. 104.95 *(978-1-4200-7388-1(5)*, Chapman & Hall/CRC) CRC Pr. LLC.

Wilson, Chuck. Vein Pattern Recognition: A Privacy-Enhancing Biometric. 2010. (ENG., Illus.). 307p. 79.95 *(978-1-4398-2137-4(2)*, CRC Press) Taylor & Francis Group GBR. Dist: Taylor & Francis Group.

Wit, Ernst, et al. Statistics for Biological Networks: How to Infer Networks from Data. 2011. (Illus.). 320p. 79.95 *(978-1-4398-4147-1(0)*, Chapman & Hall/CRC) CRC Pr. LLC.

Woodworth, George G. Biostatistics: Intermediate Bayesian Inference. 2013. (Wiley Series in Probability & Statistics Ser.). (ENG., Illus.). 416p. 99.95 *(978-0-470-17942-0(2)*, Wiley-Interscience) Wiley, John & Sons, Inc.

Wynn, James. Evolution by the Numbers: The Origins of Mathematical Argument in Biology. 2011. ***(978-1-60235-217-9(8))***; ***(978-1-60235-219-3(4))***; pap. ***(978-1-60235-216-2(X))*** Parlor Pr.

Zar, Jerrold H. Biostatistical Analysis. 5th ed. 2009. (ENG.). 960p. (C). 153.33 *(978-0-13-100846-5(3)*, Prentice Hall) Prentice Hall PTR.

—Biostatistical Analysis, Books a la Carte Edition. 5th ed. 2010. (ENG.). 960p. (C). ring bd. 92.00 *(978-0-321-65686-5(5)*, Prentice Hall) Prentice Hall PTR.

Zhang, David & Sonka, Milan, eds. Medical Biometrics: Second International Conference, ICMB 2010, Hong Kong, China, June 28-30, 2010. Proceedings. 2010. (Lecture Notes in Computer Science / Image Processing, Computer Vision, Pattern Recognition, & Graphics Ser.). xii, 424p. pap. 99.00 *(978-3-642-13922-2(1)*, 3642139221) Springer.

Zuur, Alain F., et al. Mixed Effects Models & Extensions in Ecology with R. 2011. (ENG.). xxii, 574p. pap. 84.95 *(978-1-4419-2764-4(6)*, 1441927646) Springer.

BIOMETRY—TABLES

Sokal, Robert R. & Rohlf, James. Statistical Tables. 4th rev. ed. 2012. (ENG.). 258p. (C). pap. 37.95 *(978-1-4292-4031-4(8))* Freeman, W. H. & Co.

BIOMICROSCOPY, OCULAR

see Ocular Biomicroscopy

BIOMOLECULES

Here are entered works on molecules produced by living systems or by biotechnological means and their synthetic analogs.

see also Biopolymers; Carbohydrates; Lipids; Microbial Metabolites; Molecular Biology; Nucleic Acids; Proteins

Anmala, Jagadeesh. Ing & Bimolecular Reactions in Heterogeneous Porous Media Flows. 2010. 196p. pap. *(978-3-8383-4383-9(2))* Lambert Academic Publishing.

Awizio, Ann-Katrin. From Lipid Bilayers to Synaptic Vesicles. 2008. 132p. pap. *(978-3-639-05411-8(3))* VDM Verlag Dr. Mueller e.K.

Bancia, Bogdan. Analysis of Selectively 15n Labelled ib, C-Peptide & Dnag-C by Nmr. 2010. 108p. pap. *(978-3-8383-2184-4(7))* Lambert Academic Publishing.

Bardhan, Jaydeep. Computational Methods for Molecular Analysis & Design. 2009. 196p. pap. *(978-3-639-14261-7(6))* VDM Verlag Dr. Mueller e.K.

Belgacem, Mohamed Naceur & Gandini, Alessandro, eds. Monomers, Polymers & Composites from Renewable Resources. 2008. (ENG., Illus.). 560p. 205.00 *(978-0-08-045316-3(3)*, Elsevier Science) Elsevier Science & Technology Bks.

Berrido, Christopher, et al. Stochastic & Quantum Dynamics of Biomolecular Systems: Proceedings of the 5th Jagna International Workshop, Jagna, Bohol, Philippines, 3-5 January 2008. 2008. (AIP Conference Proceedings Ser.). (Illus.). xi, 214p. 139.00 *(978-0-7354-0543-1(3))* American Institute of Physics.

Bertini, Ivano, et al, eds. NMR of Biomolecules: Towards Mechanistic Systems Biology. 2012. (ENG.). 650p. pap. 129.95 ***(978-3-527-32850-5(5)***, Wiley-VCH) Wiley, John & Sons, Inc.

Bhutani, S. P. Chemistry of Biomolecules. 2010. (ENG.). 300p. 99.95 *(978-1-4398-3929-4(8)*, CRC Press) Taylor & Francis Group GBR. Dist: Taylor & Francis Group.

Carré, Alain & Mittal, K. L. Surface & Interfacial Aspects of Cell Adhesion. 2011. (ENG., Illus.). 544p. 260.00 ***(978-90-04-19078-8(3)***, CRC Press) Taylor & Francis Group GBR. Dist: Taylor & Francis Group.

Chen, Luonan, et al. Modeling Biomolecular Networks: Structures & Dynamics. 2010. (Illus.). 330p. 179.00 *(978-1-84996-213-1(8)*, 1849962138) Springer.

Clarson, Stephen J., et al. New Approaches in Biomedical Spectroscopy. 2007. (ACS Symposium Ser.). (ENG., Illus.). 472p. 185.00 *(978-0-8412-7437-2(1))* American Chemical Society.

Cole, Richard B., ed. Electrospray & MALDI Mass Spectrometry: Fundamentals, Instrumentation, Practicalities, & Biological Applications. 2nd ed. 2010. (ENG., Illus.). 863p. 158.00 *(978-0-471-74107-7(8)*, Wiley) Wiley, John & Sons, Inc.

Coutts, Amanda S., ed. Adhesion Protein Protocols. 2nd ed. 2010. (Methods in Molecular Biology Ser.). (Illus.). x, 234p. pap. 149.00 *(978-1-61737-625-2(6)*, 1617376256) Humana Pr.

Cram101 Textbook Reviews & Cram101 Textbook Reviews. Outlines & Highlights for Statistical Physics of Biomolecules: An Introduction by Daniel M. Zuckerman. 2011. 118p. pap. 28.95 ***(978-1-61830-490-2(9))*** Cram101 Inc.

Dass, Chhabil. Fundamentals of Contemporary Mass Spectrometry. 2007. (Wiley - Interscience Series on Mass Spectrometry Ser.: 16). (ENG., Illus.). 608p. 139.00 *(978-0-471-68229-5(2)*, Wiley-Interscience) Wiley, John & Sons, Inc.

Deamer, David & Szostak, Jack W., eds. The Origins of Life. 2010. (ENG., Illus.). 318p. 135.00 *(978-1-936113-04-0(X))* Cold Spring Harbor Laboratory Pr.

Desai, Mohamed A., ed. Downstream Processing of Proteins: Methods & Protocols. 2010. (Methods in Biotechnology Ser.). (Illus.). 240p. pap. 189.00 *(978-1-61737-075-5(4)*, 1617370754) Humana Pr.

Dietrich, Heidi. Nanoassays for Biomolecular Research. 2010. 152p. pap. *(978-3-8383-5731-7(0))* Lambert Academic Publishing.

Ebbinghaus, Simon. Thz Spectroscopy of Biomolecules. 2008. 160p. pap. *(978-3-639-05513-9(6))* VDM Verlag Dr. Mueller e.K.

Eisenhaber, Frank, ed. Discovering Biomolecular Mechanisms with Computational Biology. 2010. (Molecular Biology Intelligence Unit Ser.). (Illus.). xi, 147p. pap. 179.00 *(978-1-4419-4177-0(0)*, 1441941770) Springer.

Enderlein, J. & Gryczynski, Zygmunt. Ultrasensitive & Single-Molecule Detection Technologies II: 20-21 & 23 January 2007, San Jose, California, USA. 2007. (Progress in Biomedical Optics & Imaging Ser.: No. 8). (Illus.). 162p. pap. 70.00 *(978-0-8194-6557-3(7))* SPIE.

Ens, W., et al, eds. New Methods for the Study of Biomolecular Complexes. 2010. (NATO Science Series C: (closed) Ser.). (ENG.). 368p. pap. 289.00 *(978-90-481-5017-5(5)*, 9048150175) Springer.

Fallon, Padraic G. Pathogen Derived Immunomodulatory Molecules. 2009. *(978-1-58706-334-3(4))* Landes Bioscience.

Farkas, Daniel, et al. Imaging, Manipulation, & Analysis of Biomolecules, Cells, & Tissues IX. 2011. (Proceedings of SPIE Ser.). 450p. pap. 140.00 ***(978-0-8194-8439-0(3))*** SPIE.

—Imaging, Manipulation, & Analysis of Biomolecules, Cells, & Tissues VI. 2008. (Proceedings of SPIE Ser.). 448p. pap. 130.00 ***(978-0-8194-7034-8(1))*** SPIE.

Farkas, Daniel L., et al. Imaging, Manipulation, & Analysis of Biomolecules, Cells, & Tissues V: 22-24 January 2007, San Jose, California, USA. 2007. (Proceedings of SPIE Ser.: No. 8). (Illus.). 514p. pap. 120.00 *(978-0-8194-6554-2(2))* SPIE.

—Imaging, Manipulation, & Analysis of Biomolecules, Cells, & Tissues VII: 26-28 January 2009, San Jose, California, United States. 2009. (Proceedings of SPIE Ser.). (Illus.). 450p. pap. 130.00 *(978-0-8194-7428-5(2))* SPIE.

Farkas, Daniel L., et al. Imaging, Manipulation, & Analysis of Biomolecules, Cells, & Tissues VIII: 23-25 January 2010, San Francisco, California, United States. 2010. (Proceedings of SPIE Ser.). (Illus.). 460p. pap. 140.00 ***(978-0-8194-7964-8(0))*** SPIE.

Fasman, G. D., ed. Circular Dichroism & the Conformational Analysis of Biomolecules. 2010. (ENG.). 695p. pap. 389.00 *(978-1-4419-3249-5(6)*, 1441932496) Springer.

Feig, Michael, ed. Modeling Solvent Environments: Applications to Simulations of Biomolecules. 2010. (ENG., Illus.). 334p. 190.00 *(978-3-527-32421-7(6)*, Wiley-VCH) Wiley, John & Sons, Inc.

Folkers, Gerd, et al. Molecular Modeling: Basic Principles & Applications. 3rd ed. 2008. (ENG., Illus.). 320p. pap. 90.00 *(978-3-527-31568-0(3)*, Wiley-VCH) Wiley, John & Sons, Inc.

Fontaine-Vive, F. From dynamics to structure & function of model bio-molecular Systems. 2007. pap. 63.00 *(978-1-58603-741-3(2)*, Delft University Pr) IOS Pr., Inc.

Forciniti, Daniel. Industrial Bioseparations: Principles & Practice. 2008. (ENG., Illus.). 376p. 134.00 *(978-0-8138-2085-9(5)*, Wiley-Blackwell) Wiley, John & Sons, Inc.

Gaines, Susan M., et al. Echoes of Life: What Fossil Molecules Reveal about Earth History. 2008. (ENG., Illus.). 376p. 35.00 *(978-0-19-517619-3(7))* Oxford Univ. Pr., Inc.

Galaev, Igor & Mattiasson, Bo, eds. Smart Polymers: Applications in Biotechnology & Biomedicine. 2nd rev. ed. 2007. (ENG., Illus.). 496p. 144.95 *(978-0-8493-9161-3(X)*, CRC Press) Taylor & Francis Group GBR. Dist: Taylor & Francis Group.

García Gómez-Tejedor, Gustavo & Fuss, Martina Christina, eds. Radiation Damage in Biomolecular Systems. 2012. (Biological & Medical Physics, Biomedical Engineering Ser.). (ENG., Illus.). x, 542p. 199.00 ***(978-94-007-2563-8(9)***, 9400725639) Springer.

Garikipati, Krishna & Arruda, Ellen M., eds. IUTAM Symposium on Cellular, Molecular & Tissue Mechanics: Proceedings of an IUTAM symposium held at Woods Hole, Mass., USA, June 18-21 2008. 2009. (IUTAM Bookseries Ser.). (ENG., Illus.). ix, 285p. 119.00 *(978-90-481-3347-5(5)*, 9048133475) Springer.

Gazit, Ehud. Plenty of Room for Biology at the Bottom: An Introduction to Bionanotechnology. 2007. (Illus.). 183p. 107.00 *(978-1-86094-677-6(1))* Imperial College Pr. GBR. Dist: World Scientific Publishing Co., Inc.

Ghosh, Raja. Principles of Bioseparations Engineering. 2006. (Illus.). 265p. 69.00 *(978-981-256-892-2(1))* World Scientific Publishing Co., Inc.

Griffiths, William J., ed. Metabolomics, Metabonomics & Metabolite Profiling. 2007. (RSC Biomolecular Sciences Ser.). (ENG., Illus.). 336p. 213.00 *(978-0-85404-299-9(7))* Royal Society of Chemistry, The GBR. Dist: Ingram Pub. Services.

Gunsteren, W. F. van, et al, eds. Computer Simulation of Biomolecular Systems: Theoretical & Experimental Applications Volume 3. 2010. (Computer Simulations of Biomolecular Systems Ser.). (ENG.). 644p. pap. 619.00 *(978-90-481-8528-3(9)*, 9048185289) Springer.

Gupta, Satya Prakash. QSAR & Molecular Modeling. 2008. 400p. 199.00 *(978-1-4020-5394-8(0)*, 1402053940) Springer.

Häfeli, Urs, et al, eds. Scientific & Clinical Applications of Magnetic Carriers. 2010. (ENG.). 652p. pap. 389.00 *(978-1-4419-3283-9(6)*, 1441932836) Springer.

Hagen, Wilfred Raymond. Biomolecular EPR Spectroscopy. 2008. (ENG., Illus.). 248p. 149.95 *(978-1-4200-5957-1(2)*, CRC Press) Taylor & Francis Group GBR. Dist: Taylor & Francis Group.

Hattesohl, Akira. Abstracting Properties of Biomolecules- about Averaging & Classification. 2007. 48p. per. *(978-3-8364-1360-2(4))* VDM Verlag Dr. Mueller e.K.

Herold, Keith.E., et al, eds. Lab on a Chip Technology: Biomolecular Separation & Analysis, 2 vols. 2009. (Illus.). 300p. 319.00 *(978-1-904455-47-9(6))* Caister Academic Pr. GBR. Dist: International Specialized Bk. Services.

Hinchliffe, Alan. Molecular Modelling for Beginners. 2nd ed. 2008. (ENG., Illus.). 428p. 190.00 *(978-0-470-51313-2(6)*, Wiley) Wiley, John & Sons, Inc.

Hinterdorfer, Peter & van Oijen, Antoine, eds. Handbook of Single-Molecule Biophysics. 2009. (ENG., Illus.). xxiv, 626p. 286.00 *(978-0-387-76496-2(8)*, 0387764968) Springer.

Iwamoto, Nancy, et al, eds. Molecular Modeling & Multiscaling Issues for Electronic Material Applications. 2011. (ENG., Illus.). xi, 258p. 129.00 ***(978-1-4614-1727-9(9)***, 1461417279) Springer.

Jelinek. Cellular & Biomolecular Recognition: Synthetic & Non-Biological Molecules. Jelinek, Raz, ed. 2009. (ENG.). 368p. 190.00 *(978-3-527-32265-7(5)*, Wiley-VCH) Wiley, John & Sons, Inc.

Kalkman, Ivo. Structure & Dynamics in Small Biomolecular Systems. 2009. 136p. pap. *(978-3-639-16658-3(2))* VDM Verlag Dr. Mueller e.K.

Kaltashov, Igor A. & Eyles, Stephen J. Mass Spectrometry in Structural Biology & Biophysics: Architecture, Dynamics, & Interaction of Biomolecules. 2nd ed. 2012. (Wiley - Interscience Series on Mass Spectrometry Ser.: 45). (ENG., Illus.). 316p. 140.00 ***(978-0-470-93779-2(3)***, Wiley) Wiley, John & Sons, Inc.

Karlovsky, Petr. Secondary Metabolites in Soil Ecology. 2010. (Soil Biology Ser.). (Illus.). xi, 294p. pap. 239.00 *(978-3-642-09394-4(9)*, 3642093949) Springer.

Khan, Mahmud T. H. Bioactive Heterocycles III. 2010. (Topics in Heterocyclic Chemistry Ser.). (Illus.). xvi, 287p. pap. 259.00 *(978-3-642-09244-2(6)*, 3642092446) Springer.

—Bioactive Heterocycles IV. 2010. (Topics in Heterocyclic Chemistry Ser.). (Illus.). xvi, 317p. pap. 289.00 *(978-3-642-09245-9(4)*, 3642092454) Springer.

Kiihne, S. R. & de Groot, H. J. M., eds. Perspectives on Solid State NMR in Biology. 2010. (Focus on Structural Biology Ser.). (Illus.). 248p. pap. 159.00 *(978-90-481-5744-0(7)*, 9048157447) Springer.

Kinghorn, A. Douglas, et al, eds. Progress in the Chemistry of Organic Natural Products Vol. 94. 2011. (Fortschritte der Chemie organischer Naturstoffe Progress in the Chemistry of Organic Natural Products Ser.). (ENG., Illus.). xviii, 253p. 259.00 *(978-3-7091-0747-8(4)*, 3709107474) Springer.

Koenig, Simone. Biomacromolecular Mass Spectrometry Research. 2008. (C). 69.00 *(978-1-60456-467-9(9))* Nova Science Pubs., Inc.

Koenig, Simone, ed. Biomacromolecular Mass Spectrometry, Vol. 1. 2010. (Biomacromolecular Mass Spectrometry Yearbook Ser.). 300p. 145.00 *(978-1-60876-167-8(3))* Nova Science Pubs., Inc.

Kuwajima, Kunihiro. Water & Biomolecules: Physical Chemistry of Life Phenomena. Kuwajima, Kunihiro et al, eds. 2009. (Biological & Medical Physics, Biomedical Engineering Ser.). (ENG., Illus.). xviii, 307p. 189.00 *(978-3-540-88786-7(5))* Springer.

Kyriakopoulos, A., et al, contrib. by. Reviews of Physiology, Biochemistry & Pharmacology 145. 2010. (Reviews of Physiology, Biochemistry & Pharmacology Ser.). (Illus.). vi, 222p. pap. 169.00 *(978-3-642-07805-7(2)*, 3642078052) Springer.

Lang, J. K. Handbook on Mass Spectrometry: Instrumentation, Data & Analysis, & Applications. 2009. (Advances in Chemistry Research Ser.). 195.00 *(978-1-60741-580-0(1))* Nova Science Pubs., Inc.

Lee, James Weifu & Foote, Robert S., eds. Biomolecule Analysis & Manipulation: Volume 1, Microfluidic & Physical Methods. 2009. (Methods in Molecular Biology Ser.). (ENG., Illus.). xx, 668p. 179.00 *(978-1-934115-40-4(1)*, 1934115401) Humana Pr.

—Biomolecule Analysis & Manipulation: Volume 2, Nanotechnologies for Biosystems. 2009. 272p. 110.00 *(978-1-60327-816-4(8))* Humana Pr.

Leeper, Finian J. & Vederas, John C. Biosynthesis: Aromatic Polyketides, Isoprenoids, Alkaloids. 2010. (Topics in Current Chemistry Ser.). (Illus.). x, 247p. pap. 259.00 *(978-3-642-08583-3(0)*, 3642085830) Springer.

Liang, Jie & DasGupta, Bhaskar. Models & Algorithms for Biomolecules & Molecular Networks. 2012. (IEEE Press Series on Biomedical Engineering Ser.). (ENG., Illus.). 400p. 110.00 *(978-0-470-60193-8(0)*, Wiley-IEEE Pr.) Wiley, John & Sons, Inc.

Lifshitz, Chava & Laskin, Julia, eds. Principles of Mass Spectrometry Applied to Biomolecules. 2006. (Wiley - Interscience Series on Mass Spectrometry Ser.: 10). (ENG., Illus.). 687p. 198.00 *(978-0-471-72184-0(0)*, Wiley-Interscience) Wiley, John & Sons, Inc.

Lindon, John C., et al, eds. The Handbook of Metabonomics & Metabolomics. 2006. (ENG., Illus.). 572p. 240.00 *(978-0-444-52841-4(5)*, Elsevier Science) Elsevier Science & Technology Bks.

Lindström, Sara & Andersson-Svahn, Helene, eds. Single-Cell Analysis: Methods & Protocols. 2012. (Methods in Molecular Biology Ser.). (ENG., Illus.). x, 238p. 139.00 ***(978-1-61779-566-4(6)***, 1617795666) Humana Pr.

Liu, Jian-Qin & Shimohara, Katsunori. Biomolecular Computation by Nanobiotechnology. 2007. (Illus.). 286p. 139.00 *(978-1-59693-014-8(4))* Artech Hse., Inc.

M Al Shargi, Hanan. Investigation of Statistical Characteristics of Biomolecules. 2010. 124p. pap. *(978-3-639-23674-3(2))* VDM Verlag Dr. Mueller e.K.

Manca, Paolo. 2-Methoxyestradiol Effectiveness on Glial & Neuronal Cells. 2011. 128p. pap. ***(978-3-8443-2025-1(3))*** Lambert Academic Publishing.

Mark, Sonny S., ed. Bioconjugation Protocols: Strategies & Methods. 2nd ed. 2011. (Methods in Molecular Biology Ser.). (ENG., Illus.). xvi, 605p. 159.00 *(978-1-61779-150-5(4)*, 1617791504) Humana Pr.

Mattiasson, B., ed. Expanded Bed Chromatography. 2010. 250p. pap. 199.00 *(978-90-481-5380-0(8)*, 9048153808) Springer.

Menkhaus, Todd J., et al, eds. Applications of Electrospun Nanofiber Membranes for Bio-separations. 2010. (Nanotechnology Science & Technology Ser.). (Illus.). 69p. pap. 43.00 *(978-1-60876-782-3(5))* Nova Science Pubs., Inc.

Messerschmidt, Albrecht. X-Ray Crystallography of Biomacromolecules: A Practical Guide. 2007. (ENG., Illus.). 318p. 209.95 *(978-3-527-31396-9(6)*, Wiley-VCH) Wiley, John & Sons, Inc.

Metz, Thomas O. Metabolic Profiling: Methods & Protocols. 2011. (Illus.). xi, 391p. E-Book ***(978-1-61737-985-7(9))*** Humana Pr.

Muhammad, Arshad. Role of Cd2 & Cd48 in Recruitment of Signaling Molecules in T Cells. 2010. 96p. pap. *(978-3-639-25894-3(0))* VDM Verlag Dr. Mueller e.K.

Nandi, Nilashis. Chirality in Biological Nanospaces: Reactions in Active Sites. 2011. (ENG., Illus.). 209p. 119.95 *(978-1-4398-4002-3(4)*, CRC Press) Taylor & Francis Group GBR. Dist: Taylor & Francis Group.

National Research Council (U.S.), Committee on Biomolecular Materials and Processes Staff, contrib. by. Inspired by Biology: From Molecules to Materials to Machines. 2008. (ENG.). 170p. pap. 59.00 *(978-0-309-11704-3(6))* National Academies Pr.

Neidle, S., et al, eds. Quadruplex Nucleic Acids. 2006. (Biomolecular Sciences Ser.). (ENG., Illus.). 316p. 149.00 *(978-0-85404-374-3(8)*, 0854043748) Royal Society of Chemistry, The GBR. Dist: Ingram Pub. Services.

Nicholson, Allen W., ed. Ribonucleases. 2011. (Nucleic Acids & Molecular Biology Ser.). (ENG., Illus.). xii, 403p. 209.00 *(978-3-642-21077-8(5)*, 3642210775) Springer.

Niemeyer, Christof M., ed. Bioconjugation Protocols: Strategies & Methods. 2010. (Methods in Molecular Biology Ser.). (Illus.). 344p. pap. 129.00 *(978-1-61737-354-1(0)*, 1617373540) Humana Pr.

O'Neil, Maryadele J., ed. The Merck Index: An Encyclopedia of Chemicals, Drugs, & Biologicals. 14th rev. ed. 2006. (ENG., Illus.). 2564p. 125.00 *(978-0-911910-00-1(X))* Merck & Co., Inc.

Pescatore, Fred. The Science of AHCC: Supplement for 21st Century Cancer Treatment, 1 vol. 2010. 128p. pap. 12.95 *(978-1-59120-280-6(9))* Basic Health Pubns., Inc.

Plant, Anne L., et al, eds. Architecture & Application of Biomaterials & Biomolecular Materials 1: 2003 MRS Fall Meeting — Extended Summary. 2009. (Materials Research Society Symposium Proceedings Ser.: EXS-1). 465p. 35.00 *(978-1-55899-745-5(8)*, EXS-1-C) Materials Research Society.

Principles & Practice of Bioanalysis Second Edition. 2011. 94.95 *(978-1-4200-0560-8(X)*, CRC Press) Taylor & Francis Group GBR. Dist: Taylor & Francis Group.

Rainer, Matthias. Mass Spectrometric Identification of Biomolecules: Employing Synthetic Polymers. 2008. 140p. pap. *(978-3-8364-6902-9(2))* VDM Verlag Dr. Mueller e.K.

Ramani, Prasanna. Peptide Nucleic Acids & Markers. 2011. 232p. pap. ***(978-3-8443-2805-9(X))*** Lambert Academic Publishing.

Ramawat, Kishan Gopal & Mérillon, Jean-Michel, eds. Bioactive Molecules & Medicinal Plants. (ENG., Illus.). xxiv, 380p. 2010. pap. 319.00 *(978-3-642-09405-7(8)*, 3642094058) 2008. 319.00 *(978-3-540-74600-3(5)*, 3540746005) Springer.

Rees, Douglas C., et al, eds. Annual Review of Biophysics & Biomolecular Structure. 2007. 507p. 197.00 *(978-0-8243-1836-9(6))* Annual Reviews, Inc.

Renugopalakrishnan, V. & Lewis, Randy V., eds. Bionanotechnology: Proteins to Nanodevices. 2010. (ENG.). xiv, 296p. pap. 229.00 *(978-90-481-7078-4(6)*, 9048170788) Springer.

Rogers, Kara. The Components of Life: From Nucleic Acids to Carbohydrates. 2011. (Biochemistry, Cells, & Life Ser.). (Illus.). 264p. (YA). lib. bdg. 40.00 *(978-1-61530-324-3(3))* Rosen Publishing Group, Inc., The.

Rogers, Kara, ed. The Components of Life: From Nucleic Acids to Carbohydrates. 2011. (Biochemistry, Cells, & Life Ser.). (Illus.). 264p. (YA). 80.00 *(978-1-61530-434-9(7))* Rosen Publishing Group, Inc., The.

Rupp, Bernhard & Kantardjieff, Katherine. Modern Biomolecular Crystallography. 2007. (Illus.). 1000p. 152.00 *(978-0-8153-4081-2(8))* Routledge.

Samori, Paolo. Stm & Afm Studies on (Bio)Molecular Systems. 2008. (Topics in Current Chemistry Ser.). 449.00 *(978-3-540-78394-7(6))* Springer.

Schlick, Tamar. Molecular Modeling & Simulation: an Interdisciplinary Guide: An Interdisciplinary Guide. 2nd ed. 2010. (Interdisciplinary Applied Mathematics Ser.). (ENG., Illus.). xlv, 723p. 84.95 *(978-1-4419-6350-5(2)*, 1441963502) Springer.

Schlick, Tamar, ed. Innovations in Biomolecular Modeling & Simulations, 2 vols. 2012. (ENG., Illus.). 734p. 416.00 ***(978-1-84973-410-3(0))*** Royal Society of Chemistry, The GBR. Dist: Ingram Pub. Services.

Schügerl, Karl. Solvent Extraction in Biotechnology: Recovery of Primary & Secondary Metabolites. 2010. (Illus.). viii, 213p. pap. 229.00 *(978-3-642-08190-3(8)*, 3642081908) Springer.

Schwarz, Siegfried. Molecules of Life & Mutations: Understanding Diseases by Understanding Proteins. (Illus.). *(978-3-8055-7395-5(2))* Karger, S. AG.

Semmar, Nabil. Computational Metabolomics. 2011. (Metabolic Diseases - Laboratory & Clinical Research Ser.). 69.00 *(978-1-61761-608-2(7)*, Nova Biomedical Bks.) Nova Science Pubs., Inc.

Sen, Ramkrishna, ed. Biosurfactants. 2010. (Advances in Experimental Medicine & Biology Ser.). (ENG., Illus.). xxviii, 330p. 229.00 *(978-1-4419-5978-2(5)*, 1441959785) Springer.

Sengupta, Anirvan M. Modeling Biomolecular Networks: An Introduction to Systems Biology. 2012. (ENG., Illus.). 208p. 69.50 *(978-0-19-856804-9(3))* Oxford Univ. Pr., Inc.

Sethi, Dalip, et al. Chemical Methods for Microarray Fabrication. 2011. 140p. pap. ***(978-3-8443-2808-0(4))*** Lambert Academic Publishing.

Shu Wenmiao & Shu, Wenmiao. Microcantilever-Based Sensors & Actuators. 2008. 164p. pap. *(978-3-639-07996-8(5))* VDM Verlag Dr. Mueller e.K.

Soberón-Chávez, Gloria, ed. Biosurfactants: From Genes to Applications. 2010. (Microbiology Monographs). (Illus.). vii, 216p. 219.00 *(978-3-642-14489-9(6)*, 3642144896) Springer.

Sussman, Joel L. & Spadon, Paola, eds. From Molecules to Medicines: Structure of Biological Macromolecules & Its Relevance in Combating New Diseases & Bioterrorism. 2009. (NATO Science for Peace & Security Series A: Chemistry & Biology Ser.). (ENG., Illus.). xv, 249p. 249.00 *(978-90-481-2337-7(2))*; pap. 129.00 *(978-90-481-2338-4(0))* Springer.

Teng, Quincy. Structural Biology: Practical NMR Applications. 2010. (ENG., Illus.). xii, 295p. pap. 115.00 *(978-1-4419-3730-8(7)*, 1441937307) Springer.

Thiele, Christoph & Miller, Lawrence W., eds. Probes & Tags to Study Biomolecular Function: For Proteins, RNA, & Membranes. 2008. (ENG., Illus.). 193p. 150.00 *(978-3-527-31566-6(7)*, Wiley-VCH) Wiley, John & Sons, Inc.

Tsai, C. Stan. Biomacromolecules: Introduction to Structure, Function & Informatics. 2006. (ENG., Illus.). 740p. 169.95 *(978-0-471-71397-5(X)*, Wiley-Liss) Wiley, John & Sons, Inc.

Uddin, Reaz, et al. In Silico Modeling & Its Applications on Biomolecules. 2011. 188p. pap. ***(978-3-8443-2823-3(8))*** Lambert Academic Publishing.

Van Overloop, Helena. Metabolism & Biological Activities of C(2)-Ceramide. 2006. (Acta Biomedica Lovaniensia: 377). (Illus.). 156p. (Orig.). pap. 99.50 *(978-90-5867-580-4(7))* Leuven Univ. Pr. BEL. Dist: Cornell Univ. Pr.

Venn, Richard F., ed. Principles & Practice of Bioanalysis. 2nd rev. ed. 2008. (ENG., Illus.). 344p. 99.95 *(978-0-8493-3857-1(3)*, CRC Press) Taylor & Francis Group GBR. Dist: Taylor & Francis Group.

Vogel, Viola, ed. Nanomedicine, 9 vols., Vol. 5. 2009. (Nanotechnology(VCH) Ser.: 5). (ENG., Illus.). 445p. 225.00 *(978-3-527-31736-3(8)*, Wiley-VCH) Wiley, John & Sons, Inc.

Vogel, Viola & Waser, Rainer, eds. Information Technology II, 9 vols., Vol. 2. 2008. (Nanotechnology(VCH) Ser.: 3). (ENG., Illus.). 414p. 220.00 *(978-3-527-31737-0(6)*, Wiley-VCH) Wiley, John & Sons, Inc.

Voth, Gregory A. Coarse-Graining of Condensed Phase & Biomolecular Systems. Voth, Gregory A, ed. 2008. (ENG., Illus.). 456p. 164.95 *(978-1-4200-5955-7(6)*, CRC Press) Taylor & Francis Group GBR. Dist: Taylor & Francis Group.

Watson, J. Throck & Sparkman, O. David. Introduction to Mass Spectrometry: Instrumentation, Applications & Strategies for Data Interpretation. 4th ed. 2007. (ENG., Illus.). 862p. 130.00 *(978-0-470-51634-8(8)*, Wiley) Wiley, John & Sons, Inc.

Williams, John R. & Clifford, Anthony A., eds. Supercritical Fluid Methods & Protocols. 2010. (Methods in Biotechnology Ser.). (Illus.). 272p. pap. 169.00 *(978-1-61737-079-3(7)*, 1617370797) Humana Pr.

Wong, J. Tze-Fei & Lazcano, Antonio. Prebiotic Evolution & Astrobiology. 2009. *(978-1-58706-330-5(1))* Landes Bioscience.

Wu, Ge. Assay Development: Fundamentals & Practice. 2010. (ENG., Illus.). 429p. 147.00 *(978-0-470-19115-6(5)*, Wiley) Wiley, John & Sons, Inc.

Zuckerman, Daniel M. Statistical Physics of Biomolecules: An Introduction. 2010. (ENG., Illus.). 356p. (C). 94.95 *(978-1-4200-7378-2(8)*, CRC Press) Taylor & Francis Group GBR. Dist: Taylor & Francis Group.

BION, WILFRED R. (WILFRED RUPRECHT), 1897-1979

Bion. All My Sins Remembered: Another Part: Of A Life & the Other Side of Genius: Family Letters. 2009. (Illus.). 252p. pap. 53.00 *(978-1-85575-845-2(8))* Karnac Bks. GBR. Dist: Stylus Publishing, LLC.

Brown, Lawrence. Intersubjective Processes & the Unconscious: An Integration of Freudian, Kleinian & Bionian Perspectives. 2011. (New Library of Psychoanalysis Ser.). (ENG., Illus.). 288p. pap. 36.95 *(978-0-415-60700-1(0))* Routledge.

—Intersubjectivity & Unconscious Processes. 2011. (New Library of Psychoanalysis Ser.). (ENG., Illus.). 288p. 99.00 *(978-0-415-60699-8(3))* Routledge.

De Cortinas, Lia Pistiner. The Aesthetic Dimension of the Mind: Variations on a Theme of Bion. 2009. (Illus.). 340p. pap. 42.95 *(978-1-85575-612-0(9))* Karnac Bks. GBR. Dist: Stylus Publishing, LLC.

Diem-Wille, Gertraud. The Early Years of Life: Psychoanalytical Development Theory According to Freud, Klein, & Bion. 2011. (Illus.). 310p. pap. 41.95 *(978-1-85575-710-3(9))* Karnac Bks. GBR. Dist: Stylus Publishing, LLC.

Egenfeldt-Nielsen, Fin. Attention & Creation: Growth Vertices. Maclean, Karen, tr. 2010. (Illus.). 176p. pap. 24.95 *(978-1-85575-653-3(6))* Karnac Bks. GBR. Dist: Stylus Publishing, LLC.

Grotstein, James. Beam of Intense Darkness. 2007. 395p. (C). pap. 52.95 *(978-1-85575-448-5(7))* Karnac Bks. GBR. Dist: Stylus Publishing, LLC.

Grotstein, James S. But at Same Time Another Level Vol 1: Psychoanalytic Theory & Technique in the Kleinian/Bionian Mode, 2 vols. 2009. 400p. pap. 53.00 *(978-1-85575-786-8(9))* Karnac Bks. GBR. Dist: Stylus Publishing, LLC.

Mawson, Chris, ed. Bion Today. 2010. (New Library of Psychoanalysis Ser.). (ENG., Illus.). 464p. 105.00 *(978-0-415-57071-8(9))*; pap. 37.95 *(978-0-415-57072-5(7))* Routledge.

Meltzer, Donald. Kleinian Development. 2008. (Harris Meltzer Trust Ser.). 256p. pap. 58.50 *(978-1-85575-678-6(1))* Karnac Bks. GBR. Dist: Stylus Publishing, LLC.

—Studies in Extended Metapsychology: Clinical Applications of Bion's Ideas. 2009. (Harris Meltzer Trust Ser.). 218p. pap. 39.95 *(978-1-85575-649-6(8))* Karnac Bks. GBR. Dist: Stylus Publishing, LLC.

Ross, Ciaran. Beckett's Art of Absence: Rethinking the Void. 2011. (ENG.). 248p. 80.00 *(978-0-230-57518-9(8))* Palgrave Macmillan.

Sandler. Clinical Application Bion's Concepts: Vol 2: Analytic Function & the Function of the Analyst. 2011. 246p. pap. 34.95 ***(978-1-78049-008-3(9))*** Karnac Bks. GBR. Dist: Stylus Publishing, LLC.

Sandler, Paulo & Menezes, Luis Carlos, eds. On the Clinical Application of the Work of Bion. 2009. 392p. pap. 53.00 *(978-1-85575-568-0(8))* Karnac Bks. GBR. Dist: Stylus Publishing, LLC.

Sandler, Paulo Cesar. The Language of Bion: A Dictionary of Concepts. 2010. 868p. pap. 65.00 *(978-1-85575-836-0(9))* Karnac Bks. GBR. Dist: Stylus Publishing, LLC.

Sullivan, Barbara Stevens. The Mystery of Analytical Work: Weavings from Jung & Bion. 2009. (ENG.). 280p. (C). 37.50 *(978-0-415-54776-5(8))*; 105.00 *(978-0-415-54775-8(X))* Routledge.

Williams, Harris. Bion's Dream: A Reading of the Autobiographies. 2010. 116p. pap. 21.95 *(978-1-85575-890-2(3))* Karnac Bks. GBR. Dist: Stylus Publishing, LLC.

Williams, Meg Harris. The Aesthetic Development: the Poetic Spirit of Psychoanalysis: Essays on Bion, Meltzer, Keats. 2010. 226p. pap. 36.95 *(978-1-85575-617-5(X))* Karnac Bks. GBR. Dist: Stylus Publishing, LLC.

BIONICS

see also Artificial Intelligence; Optical Data Processing

Abbott, A. & Ellison, M., eds. Biologically Inspired Textiles. 2009. (ENG., Illus.). 320p. 219.95 *(978-1-4200-7985-2(9)*, CRC Press) Taylor & Francis Group GBR. Dist: Taylor & Francis Group.

Aguilera, Christina. Christina Aguilera - Bionic. 2011. (ENG.). 104p. pap. 16.99 *(978-1-4234-9796-7(1)*, 1423497961) Leonard, Hal Corp.

Amos, Martyn. The Genesis Machine - The Coming Revolution in Biocomputation. 2007. (ENG., Illus.). 368p. pap. 15.95 *(978-1-84354-225-4(0))* Atlantic Bks., Ltd. GBR. Dist: Independent Pubs. Group.

Arena, Paolo. Dynamical Systems, Wave-Based Computation & Neuro-Inspired Robots. 2010. (CISM International Centre for Mechanical Sciences Ser.). (Illus.). ix, 255p. pap. 159.00 *(978-3-211-99930-1(2)*, 3211999302) Springer.

Arena, Paolo, ed. Dynamical Systems, Wave-Based Computation & Neuro-Inspired Robots. 2008. (CISM International Centre for Mechanical Sciences Ser.). (Illus.). 255p. 159.00 *(978-3-211-78774-8(7))* Springer.

Armstrong, Robert E., et al, eds. Bio-Inspired Innovation & National Security. 2010. (ENG.). 351p. pap. 32.00 *(978-0-16-085501-6(2)*, Dept. of the Army) United States Government Printing Office.

Bar-Cohen, Yoseph. Biomimetics. 2011. (ENG., Illus.). 788p. 159.95 *(978-1-4398-3476-3(8)*, CRC Press) Taylor & Francis Group GBR. Dist: Taylor & Francis Group.

Bionic, Team. Bionic - the Humanoid. 2011. 68p. pap. ***(978-3-8443-0474-9(6))*** Lambert Academic Publishing.

Blowers, Misty & Sisti, Alex F. Evolutionary & Bio-Inspired Computation: Theory & Applications II: 17-18 March 2008, Orlando, Florida, USA. 2008. (Proceedings of SPIE Ser.). (Illus.). 184p. pap. 60.00 *(978-0-8194-7155-0(0))* SPIE.

DeYoung, Donald & Hobbs, Derrik. Discovery of Design: Searching Out the Creator's Secrets. 2009. 160p. (YA). pap. 12.99 *(978-0-89051-574-7(3)*, Master Bks.

Frenay, Robert. Pulse: The Coming Age of Systems & Machines Inspired by Living Things. 2008. (ENG., Illus.). 576p. pap. 24.95 *(978-0-8032-1777-5(3)*, Bison Bks.) Univ. of Nebraska Pr.

Gookin, Dan. Droid Bionic for Dummies. 2011. (ENG., Illus.). 384p. pap. 24.99 *(978-1-118-08593-6(0)*, For Dummies) Wiley, John & Sons, Inc.

Guillot, Agnès & Meyer, Jean-Arcady. How to Catch a Robot Rat: When Biology Inspires Innovation. Emanuel, Susan, tr. from FRE. 2010. (ENG., Illus.). 240p. (gr. 17). 29.95 *(978-0-262-01452-6(1))* MIT Pr.

Hayel, Yezekael, et al, eds. Bioinspired Models of Network, Information, & Computing Systems: 4th International Conference, December 9-11, 2009, Revised Selected Papers. 2010. (Lecture Notes of the Institute for Computer Sciences, Social-Informatics & Telecommunications Engineering Ser.). x, 203p. pap. 72.00 *(978-3-642-12807-3(6)*, 3642128076) Springer.

Ishida, Yoshiteru. Immunity-Based Systems: A Design Perspective. 2010. (Advanced Information Processing Ser.). (Illus.). xii, 177p. pap. 159.00 *(978-3-642-05661-1(X)*, 364205661X) Springer.

Kahn, Peter H. Technological Nature: Adaptation & the Future of Human Life. 2011. (ENG., Illus.). 248p. (gr. 17). 24.95 *(978-0-262-11322-9(8))* MIT Pr.

Katz, Evgeny, ed. Information Processing, 2 vols., Set. 2012. (ENG.). 760p. 275.00 ***(978-3-527-33245-8(6)***, Wiley-VCH) Wiley, John & Sons, Inc.

Kefalas, Petros, et al, eds. Membrane Computing: 8th International Workshop, WMC 2007, Thessaloniki, Greece, June 25-28, 2007 Revised Selected & Invited Papers. 2008. (Lecture Notes in Computer Science Ser.). (Illus.). 452p. pap. 99.00 *(978-3-540-77311-5(8))* Springer.

Krasnogor, Natalio, et al, eds. Nature Inspired Cooperative Strategies for Optimization (NICSO 2007) 2010. (Studies in Computational Intelligence Ser.). (Illus.). xiv, 520p. pap. 199.00 *(978-3-642-09779-9(0)*, 3642097790) Springer.

Liò, Pietro, et al. Bio-Inspired Computing & Communication: First Workshop on Bio-Inspired Design of Networks, BIOWIRE 2007 Cambridge, UK, April 2-5, 2007, Revised Papers. 2008. (Lecture Notes in Computer Science / Theoretical Computer Science & General Issues Ser.). x, 428p. pap. 89.95 *(978-3-540-92190-5(7))* Springer.

Liò, Pietro & Verma, Dinesh. Biologically Inspired Networking & Sensing: Algorithms & Architectures. 2011. ***(978-1-61350-094-1(7))*** IGI Global.

Lio, Pietro & Verma, Dinesh, eds. Biologically Inspired Networking & Sensing: Algorithms & Architectures. 2011. 496p. 245.00 *(978-1-61350-092-7(0)*, Medical Information Science Reference) IGI Global.

Liu, Yunhui & Sun, Dong, eds. Biologically Inspired Robotics. 2011. (ENG., Illus.). 340p. 99.95 *(978-1-4398-5488-4(2)*, CRC Press) Taylor & Francis Group GBR. Dist: Taylor & Francis Group.

Lustig, B. A., et al, eds. Altering Nature: Volume I: Concepts of "Nature" & "the Natural" in Biotechnology Debates. 2010. (Philosophy & Medicine Ser.). (Illus.). viii, 332p. pap. 239.00 *(978-90-481-7763-9(4)*, 9048177634) Springer.

—Altering Nature: Volume II: Religion, Biotechnology, & Public Policy. 2010. (Philosophy & Medicine Ser.). x, 346p. pap. 239.00 *(978-90-481-7764-6(2)*, 9048177642) Springer.

B

Martín-Palma, R. J. & Lakhtakia, A. Biomimetics & Bioinspiration: 2-3 August 2009, San Diego, California, United States. 2009. (Proceedings of SPIE Ser.). (Illus.). 196p. pap. 70.00 *(978-0-8194-7691-3(9))* SPIE.

MartíN-Palma, RaúL & Lakhtakia, Akhlesh. Bioinspiration, Biomimetics, & Bioreplication. 2011. (Proceedings of SPIE Ser.). 310p. pap. 90.00 ***(978-0-8194-8537-3(3))*** SPIE.

Neumann, Frank & Witt, Carsten. Bioinspired Computation in Combinatorial Optimization: Algorithms & Their Computational Complexity. 2010. (Natural Computing Ser.). xii, 216p. 99.00 *(978-3-642-16543-6(5),* 3642165435) Springer.

Pan, Yi, et al, eds. Biologically Inspired Cooperative Computing: IFIP 19th World Computer Congress, TC 10: 1st IFIP International Conference on Biologically Inspired Cooperative Computing, August 21-24, 2006, Santiago, Chile. 2010. (IFIP Advances in Information & Communication Technology Ser.). x, 210p. pap. 139.00 *(978-1-4419-4184-8(3),* 1441941843) Springer.

Parikka, Jussi. Insect Media: An Archaeology of Animals & Technology. 2010. (Posthumanities Ser.). (ENG., Illus.). 320p. 75.00 *(978-0-8166-6739-0(X));* pap. 25.00 *(978-0-8166-6740-6(3))* Univ. of Minnesota Pr.

Pelta, David Alejandro, et al, eds. Nature Inspired Cooperative Strategies for Optimization (NICSO 2011) 2011. (Studies in Computational Intelligence Ser.). (ENG., Illus.). xxii, 350p. 179.00 ***(978-3-642-24093-5(3),*** 3642240933) Springer.

Rossmann, T., et al. Bionics - Natural Technologies & Biomimetics. 2006. 350p. 89.95 *(978-3-540-33688-4(5),* 3540336885) Springer.

Wallace, Gordon G., et al. Organic Bionics. 2012. (ENG.). 238p. 170.00 ***(978-3-527-32882-6(3),*** Wiley-VCH) Wiley, John & Sons, Inc.

Yu, Lean, et al. Bio-Inspired Credit Risk Analysis: Computational Intelligence with Support Vector Machines. 2010. (ENG., Illus.). xvi, 244p. pap. 139.00 *(978-3-642-09655-6(7),* 3642096557) Springer.

Zheng, George & Bouguettaya, Athman. Web Service Mining: Application to Discoveries of Biological Pathways. 2010. (ENG., Illus.). xvi, 152p. 99.00 *(978-1-4419-6538-7(6),* 1441965386) Springer.

2007 International Conference on Intelligent Engineering Systems. 2007. pap. 224.00 *(978-1-4244-1147-4(5),* 07EX1751) IEEE.

BIONOMICS

see Ecology

BIOORGANIC CHEMISTRY

Baldwin, Michael. Bioinorganic Chemistry: Cellular Systems & Synthetic Models. Long, Eric C., ed. 2009. (ACS Symposium Ser.). (Illus.). 264p. 150.00 *(978-0-8412-6975-0(0))* American Chemical Society.

Bonnet-Delpon, Daniele & Bégué, Jean-Pierre. Bioorganic & Medicinal Chemistry of Fluorine. Legros, Julien, tr. from FRE. 2008. (ENG., Illus.). 366p. 134.00 *(978-0-470-27830-7(7),* Wiley-Interscience) Wiley, John & Sons, Inc.

Burns, Jason H. Commodity Futures Trading Commision: Modern Tendencies in Organic & Bioorganic Chemistry: Today & Tomorrow. 2008. (Illus.). pap. 39.00 *(978-1-60456-296-5(X))* Nova Science Pubs., Inc.

Chemistry, Royal Society of, contrib. by. Spectroscopy, Theory & Mechanism in Bioinorganic Chemistry: Faraday Discussions No 148. 2011. (Faraday Discussions Ser.). (ENG.). 400p. (C). 240.00 ***(978-1-84973-232-1(9))*** Royal Society of Chemistry, The GBR. Dist: Ingram Pub. Services.

Ehrlich, Hermann. Biological Materials of Marine Origin. 2010. (Biologically-Inspired System Ser.). 450p. 239.00 *(978-90-481-9129-1(7),* 9048191297) Springer.

Huang, Pan Ming, et al. Biophysico-Chemical Processes Involving Natural Nonliving Organic Matter in Environmental Systems. 2009. (Wiley Series Sponsored by IUPAC in Biophysico-Chemical Processes in Environmental Systems Ser.: 2). (ENG., Illus.). 884p. 216.00 *(978-0-470-41300-5(X),* Wiley-Interscience) Wiley, John & Sons, Inc.

Jeromin, Günter E. & Bertau, Martin. Bioorganic Synthesis: Essentials of Biocatalysis for Chemists. 2009. 350p. pap. 39.50 *(978-3-527-32072-1(5),* Wiley-VCH) Wiley, John & Sons, Inc.

Kaim, Wolfgang & Schwederski, Brigitte. Bioinorganic Chemistry. 2nd ed. 2007. 400p. pap. 65.00 *(978-0-471-52187-7(6))* Wiley, John & Sons, Inc.

McMurry, John E. Organic Chemistry: With Biological Applications. 2nd ed. 2010. (ENG.). 704p. (C). pap., pupil's gde. ed. 108.95 *(978-0-495-39145-6(X))* Brooks/Cole.

Ojima, Iwao & Taguchi, Takeo. Fluorine in Medicinal Chemistry & Chemical Biology. Ojima, Iwao & Taguchi, Takeo, eds. 2009. (ENG., Illus.). 640p. 225.00 *(978-1-4051-6720-8(3),* Wiley-Blackwell) Wiley, John & Sons, Inc.

Reingold & Reingold, David. (Juniata PA) Organic Chemistry or the HAPPY CARBON, an Introductory Text Emphasizing Biological Connections. 2nd ed. 2011. (ENG.). 833p. (C). 165.00 ***(978-0-07-804324-6(7),*** 0078043247) McGraw-Hill Cos., The.

Simonneaux, Gerard, ed. Bioorganometallic Chemistry. 2006. (Topics in Organometallic Chemistry Ser.). (Illus.). x, 222p. 319.00 *(978-3-540-33047-9(X),* 354033047X) Springer.

University of Delaware Staff. Chem 106 Bioorganic Elementary Bioorganic Chemistry Laboratory Manual. rev. ed. 2011. (ENG.). 78p. spiral bd., lab manual ed. 28.98 *(978-0-7872-1887-4(1))* Kendall Hunt Publishing Co.

Waldmann, Herbert & Janning, Petra, eds. Chemical Biology: Learning Through Case Studies. 2009. (ENG., Illus.). 304p. pap. 60.00 *(978-3-527-32330-2(9),* Wiley-VCH) Wiley, John & Sons, Inc.

Xing, Baoshan, et al, eds. Biophysico-Chemical Processes of Anthropogenic Organic Compounds in Environmental Systems. 2011. (Wiley Series Sponsored by IUPAC in Biophysico-Chemical Processes in Environmental Systems Ser.: 3). (ENG., Illus.). 592p. 199.95 *(978-0-470-53963-7(1),* Wiley) Wiley, John & Sons, Inc.

BIOPHYSICS

see also Absorption (Physiology); Biological Control Systems; Biological Interfaces; Biomagnetism; Biomechanics; Biomedical Engineering; Bionics; Cells; Electronics in Biology; Fatigue; Homeostasis; Medical Electronics; Medical Physics; Molecular Biology; Radiobiology; Rheology (Biology)

Ahlborn, Boye K. Zoological Physics: Quantitative Models of Body Design, Actions, & Physical Limitations of Animals. 2010. (ENG., Illus.). xx, 428p. pap. 99.00 *(978-3-642-05877-6(9),* 3642058779) Springer.

Allen, James & Allen, James P. Biophysical Chemistry. 2008. (ENG., Illus.). 512p. 129.95 *(978-1-4051-2436-2(9),* Wiley-Blackwell) Wiley, John & Sons, Inc.

Arrondo, J. L. R & Alonso, Alicia. Advanced Techniques in Biophysics. 2006. (Springer Series in Biophysics: Vol. 10). (Illus.). xiv, 280p. 239.00 *(978-3-540-30700-6(1),* 3540307001) Springer.

Arrondo, José Luis R. & Alonso, Alicia. Advanced Techniques in Biophysics. 2010. (Springer Series in Biophysics Ser.). (Illus.). xiv, 280p. pap. 239.00 *(978-3-642-06798-3(0),* 3642067980) Springer.

Ashrafuzzaman & Tuszynski, Jack. Membrane Biophysics. 2012. (Biological & Medical Physics, Biomedical Engineering Ser.). (ENG., Illus.). x, 380p. 169.00 *(978-3-642-16104-9(9),* 3642161049) Springer.

Ball, John, et al. Ball & Moore's Essential Physics for Radiographers. 4th ed. 2008. (ENG., Illus.). 424p. pap. 60.99 *(978-1-4051-6101-5(9),* Wiley-Blackwell) Wiley, John & Sons, Inc.

Barnes, Frank S. & Greenebaum, Ben. Bioengineering & Biophysical Aspects of Electromagnetic Fields. 3rd ed. 2006. (Handbook of Biological Effects of Electromagnetic Fields, 3Ed Ser.). (ENG., Illus.). 440p. 124.95 *(978-0-8493-9539-0(9),* 9539, CRC Press) Taylor & Francis Group GBR. Dist: Taylor & Francis Group.

Beard, Daniel A. & Qian, Hong. Chemical Biophysics: Quantitative Analysis of Cellular Systems. 2008. (Cambridge Texts in Biomedical Engineering Ser.). (ENG., Illus.). 336p. (C). 94.00 *(978-0-521-87070-2(4))* Cambridge Univ. Pr.

Behari, Jitendra. Biophysical Bone Behaviour: Principles & Applications. 2009. (ENG., 416p. Illus.). 225.00 *(978-0-470-82400-9(X));* 210.00 *(978-0-470-82402-3(6))* Wiley, John & Sons, Inc. (Wiley).

beim Graben, Peter, et al, eds. Lectures in Supercomputational Neurosciences: Dynamics in Complex Brain Networks. 2007. (Understanding Complex Systems Ser.). (Illus.). 390p. 129.00 *(978-3-540-73158-0(X),* 354073158X) Springer.

Blomberg, Clas. Physics of Life: The Physicist's Road to Biology. 2007. (ENG., Illus.). 436p. 99.95 *(978-0-444-52798-1(2),* Elsevier Science) Elsevier Science & Technology Bks.

Bloomfield, Victor. Computer Simulation & Data Analysis in Molecular Biology & Biophysics: An Introduction Using R. 2009. (Biological & Medical Physics, Biomedical Engineering Ser.). (ENG., Illus.). xvi, 321p. 109.00 *(978-1-4419-0084-5(5),* 1441900845) Springer.

Boger, Erich. Mouse Myosin Xv. 2009. 208p. pap. *(978-3-639-16347-6(8))* VDM Verlag Dr. Mueller e.K.

Bok & Brochard-Wyart, Francoise. P. G. de Gennes' Impact on Science Vol. 1: Solid State & Liquid Crystals. 2009. 200p. 48.00 *(978-981-4273-80-0(5))* World Scientific Publishing Co., Inc.

—P. G. de Gennes' Impact on Science Vol. 2: Soft Matter & Biophysics. 2009. 180p. 48.00 *(978-981-4280-63-1(1))* World Scientific Publishing Co., Inc.

Brochard-Wyart, Francoise. P. G. de Gennes' Impact on Science Vol. 1: Solid State & Liquid Crystals. 2009. 200p. pap. 24.00 *(978-981-4291-03-3(X))* World Scientific Publishing Co., Inc.

—P. G. de Gennes' Impact on Science Vol. 2: Soft Matter & Biophysics. 2009. 180p. 86.00 *(978-981-4280-65-5(8));* pap. 24.00 *(978-981-4291-04-0(8));* pap. 43.00 *(978-981-4291-05-7(6))* World Scientific Publishing Co., Inc.

Bush, C. Allen, ed. Advances in Biophysical Chemistry, Vol. 7. Date not set. 112.50 *(978-0-7623-0343-4(3),* JAI Pr.) Elsevier Science & Technology Bks.

Buxbaum, Engelbert. Biophysical Chemistry of Proteins: An Introduction to Laboratory Methods. 2010. (ENG., Illus.). xvi, 510p. 209.00 *(978-1-4419-7250-7(1),* 1441972501) Springer.

Cantor & Schimmel. Biophysical Chemistry. 2nd ed. 2008. Pt. 2 *(978-0-7167-3861-9(9))*Pt. 3. *(978-0-7167-3862-6(7))* Freeman, W. H. & Co.

Carrington, Gerry, et al. Introduction to Biological Physics for the Health & Life Sciences. 2nd ed. 2010. (ENG., Illus.). 464p. 160.00 *(978-0-470-66592-3(0));* pap. 65.00 *(978-0-470-66593-0(9))* Wiley, John & Sons, Inc. (Wiley).

Claycomb, J. R. & Tran, Jonathan. Introductory Biophysics: Perspectives on the Living State. rev. ed. 2010. 364p. 110.95 *(978-0-7637-7998-6(9))* Jones & Bartlett Learning, LLC.

Committee on Forefronts of Science at the Interface of Physical and Life Sciences & National Research Council. Research at the Intersection of the Physical & Life Sciences. 2010. (ENG., Illus.). 124p. pap. 32.00 *(978-0-309-14751-4(4))* National Academies Pr.

Cooper, Nigel P. & Kemp, David T., eds. Mechanics of Hearing 2008. 2009. 600p. 200.00 *(978-981-283-377-8(3))* World Scientific Publishing Co., Inc.

Cotterill, Rodney & Bohr, Henrik G., eds. Molecular Biophysics: Methods & Applications. 2009. (Encyclopedia of Applied Physics Ser.). (ENG., Illus.). 1074p. instr.'s hndbk. ed. 379.00 *(978-3-527-40702-6(2),* Wiley-VCH) Wiley, John & Sons, Inc.

Cram101 Textbook Reviews. Outlines & Highlights for Physics in Biology & Medicine by Paul Davidovits, Isbn: 9780123694119 0123694116. 2011. 102p. pap. 27.95 ***(978-1-61812-365-7(3))*** Cram101 Inc.

—Outlines & Highlights for Physics of the Life Sciences by Jay Newman. 2011. 654p. pap. 41.95 ***(978-1-61905-736-4(0))*** Cram101 Inc.

Cram101 Textbook Reviews & Cram101 Textbook Reviews. Outlines & Highlights for Intermediate Physics for Medicine & Biology by Russel Hobbie, Isbn: 9780387309422 038730942x. 2011. 532p. pap. 38.95 ***(978-1-61490-101-3(5))*** Cram101 Inc.

—Outlines & Highlights for Physics of the Human Body by Irving P Herman. 2011. 298p. pap. 32.95 ***(978-1-61830-781-1(9))*** Cram101 Inc.

—Outlines & Highlights for Statistical Physics of Biomolecules: An Introduction by Daniel M. Zuckerman. 2011. 118p. pap. 28.95 ***(978-1-61830-490-2(9))*** Cram101 Inc.

—Outlines John Monteith, Isbn: 9780125051033. 2011. 114p. pap. 28.95 ***(978-1-61461-730-3(9))*** Cram101 Inc.

Cuyper, M. de & Bulte, Jeff W. M., eds. Physics & Chemistry Basis of Biotechnology. 2010. (Focus on Biotechnology Ser.). (Illus.). 340p. pap. 239.00 *(978-90-481-5741-9(2),* 9048157412) Springer.

Davidovits, Paul. Physics in Biology & Medicine. 3rd ed. 2007. (Complementary Science Ser.). (ENG., Illus.). 336p. (C). per. 51.95 *(978-0-12-369411-9(6),* Academic Pr.) Elsevier Science & Technology Bks.

Dillon, Patrick F. Biophysics: A Physiological Approach. 2012. (ENG., Illus.). 314p. (C). 130.00 ***(978-1-107-00144-2(7));*** pap. 65.00 ***(978-0-521-17216-5(0))*** Cambridge Univ. Pr.

Dössel, Olaf & Becks, Thomas, eds. World Congress on Medical Physics & Biomedical Engineering, September 7-12, 2009 Munich, Germany, 13 vols., Set. 2009. (IFMBE Proceedings Ser.). (ENG., Illus.). xxix, 1083p. pap. 469.00 *(978-3-642-03472-5(1),* 3642034721) Springer.

—World Congress on Medical Physics & Biomedical Engineering, September 7-12, 2009 Munich, Germany: Biomedical Engineering for Audiology, Ophthalmology, Emergency & Dental Medicine, Vol. 25/XI. 2009. (IFMBE Proceedings Ser.). (Illus.). xiii, 352p. pap. 299.00 *(978-3-642-03890-7(5),* 3642038905) Springer.

—World Congress on Medical Physics & Biomedical Engineering, September 7-12, 2009 Munich, Germany: Diagnostic & Therapeutic Instrumentation, Clinical Engineering, Vol. 25/VII 2009. (IFMBE Proceedings Ser.). (Illus.). xxiv, 946p. pap. 469.00 *(978-3-642-03884-6(0),* 3642038840) Springer.

—World Congress on Medical Physics & Biomedical Engineering, September 7-12, 2009 Munich, Germany: Diagnostic Imaging, Vol. 25/2. 2009. (IFMBE Proceedings Ser.). (Illus.). xxvi, 950p. pap. 469.00 *(978-3-642-03878-5(6),* 3642038786) Springer.

—World Congress on Medical Physics & Biomedical Engineering, September 7-12, 2009 Munich, Germany: Image Processing, Biosignal Processing, Modelling & Simulation, Biomechanics, Vol. 25/IV. 2009. (IFMBE Proceedings Ser.). (Illus.). xlvii, 2365p. pap. 779.00 *(978-3-642-03881-5(6),* 3642038816) Springer.

—World Congress on Medical Physics & Biomedical Engineering, September 7-12, 2009 Munich, Germany: Micro- & Nanosystems in Medicine, Active Implants, Biosensors, Vol. 25/VIII 2010. (IFMBE Proceedings Ser.). (Illus.). xv, 389p. pap. 299.00 *(978-3-642-03886-0(7),* 3642038867) Springer.

—World Congress on Medical Physics & Biomedical Engineering, September 7-12, 2009 Munich, Germany: Neuroengineering, Neural Systems, Rehabilitation & Prosthetics, Vol. 25/IX 2009. (IFMBE Proceedings Ser.). (Illus.). xviii, 600p. pap. 389.00 *(978-3-642-03888-4(3),* 3642038883) Springer.

—World Congress on Medical Physics & Biomedical Engineering, September 7-12, 2009 Munich, Germany: Radiation Protection & Dosimetry, Biological Effects of Radiation, Vol. 25/III 2009. (IFMBE Proceedings Ser.). (Illus.). xxii, 694p. pap. 389.00 *(978-3-642-03901-0(4),* 3642039014) Springer.

—World Congress on Medical Physics & Biomedical Engineering, September 7-12, 2009 Munich, Germany: Special Topics & Workshops, Vol. 25/XIII 2009. (IFMBE Proceedings Ser.). (Illus.). xii, 225p. pap. 219.00 *(978-3-642-03894-5(8),* 3642038948) Springer.

Duplantier, Bertrand & Rivasseau, Vincent, eds. Bio-Physics: Poincaré Seminar 2009. 2010. (Progress in Mathematical Physics Ser.). (Illus.). 150p. 99.00 *(978-3-0346-0427-7(0),* 3034604270) Birkhauser Verlag AG CHE. Dist: Springer.

Dusenbery, David B. Living at Micro Scale: The Unexpected Physics of Being Small. 2011. (Illus.). 448p. pap. 22.95 *(978-0-674-06021-0(0))* Harvard Univ. Pr.

Egelman, Edward. Comprehensive Biophysics. 2012. (ENG.). 3524p. 1995.00 ***(978-0-12-374920-8(4),*** Academic Pr.) Elsevier Science & Technology Bks.

Elber, Ron. Protein Modeling with Bioinformatics & Biophysics. 2007. (Illus.). 350p. 89.95 *(978-0-387-32988-8(9),* 0387329889) Springer.

Ferreira, H. G. & Marshall, M. W. The Biophysical Basis of Excitability. 2008. (ENG.). 512p. pap. 61.00 *(978-0-521-06727-0(8))* Cambridge Univ. Pr.

Franzese, Giancarlo. Aspects of Physical Biology. 2008. (Lecture Notes in Physics Ser.). (ENG., Illus.). x, 234p. 99.00 *(978-3-540-78764-8(X),* 354078764X) Springer.

Franzese, Giancarlo & Rubi, Miguel, eds. Aspects of Physical Biology: Biological Water, Protein Solutions, Transport & Replication. 2010. (Lecture Notes in Physics Ser.). (Illus.). x, 234p. pap. 99.00 *(978-3-642-09757-7(X),* 364209757X) Springer.

Garay, Oscar J. Curvature & Variational Modeling in Physics & Biophysics: Santiago de Compostela, Spain, 17-28 September 2007. 2008. (AIP Conference Proceedings Ser.). (Illus.). 266p. 152.00 *(978-0-7354-0521-9(2))* American Institute of Physics.

Glaser, Roland. Biophysics: An Introduction. 2010. (ENG., Illus.). xvi, 362p. pap. 89.95 *(978-3-642-08639-7(X),* 364208639X) Springer.

Goldfarb, Daniel. Biophysics DeMYSTiFied. 2010. (Demystified Ser.). (ENG., Illus.). 400p. pap. 24.95 *(978-0-07-163364-2(2),* 0071633642) McGraw-Hill Professional Publishing.

Graben, Peter, et al, eds. Lectures in Supercomputational Neuroscience: Dynamics in Complex Brain Networks. 2010. (Understanding Complex Systems Ser.). (Illus.). x; 378p. pap. 129.00 *(978-3-642-09216-9(0),* 3642092160) Springer.

Grimm, Bernhard, et al, eds. Chlorophylls & Bacteriochlorophylls: Biochemistry, Biophysics, Functions & Applications. (Advances in Photosynthesis & Respiration Ser.). (Illus.). 2010. xxix, 603p. pap. 449.00 *(978-90-481-7140-8(7),* 9048171407) 2006. 603p. 449.00 *(978-1-4020-4515-8(8),* 1402045158) Springer.

Grodzinsky, Alan J. Fields, Forces, & Flows in Biological Systems. 2011. (ENG., Illus.). 308p. 120.00 *(978-0-8153-4212-0(8),* Garland Science) Taylor & Francis Group.

Guardiani, Carlo. An Adaptive Evolution Strategy for Protein Folding. 2010. 232p. pap. *(978-3-8383-7425-3(8))* Lambert Academic Publishing.

Gupta. Remembering Sir J C Bose. 2009. 51.00 *(978-981-4271-61-5(6))* World Scientific Publishing Co., Inc.

Heimburg, Thomas. Thermal Biophysics of Membranes. 2007. (Tutorials in Biophysics Ser.). (ENG., Illus.). 378p. 220.00 *(978-3-527-40471-1(6),* Wiley-VCH) Wiley, John & Sons, Inc.

Hinterdorfer, Peter & van Oijen, Antoine, eds. Handbook of Single-Molecule Biophysics. 2009. (ENG., Illus.). xxiv, 626p. 286.00 *(978-0-387-76496-2(8),* 0387764968) Springer.

Ho & Ho, Mae-Wan. The Rainbow & the Worm: The Physics of Organisms. 3rd ed. 2008. 58.00 *(978-981-283-259-7(9))* World Scientific Publishing Co., Inc.

Ho, Mae-Wan. The Rainbow & the Worm: The Physics of Organisms. 3rd ed. 2008. pap. 34.00 *(978-981-283-260-3(2))* World Scientific Publishing Co., Inc.

Hobbie, Russell K. & Roth, Bradley J. Intermediate Physics for Medicine & Biology. 4th ed. (Illus.). 2010. xx, 620p. pap. 109.00 *(978-1-4419-2167-3(2),* 1441921672) 2007. 616p. 109.00 *(978-0-387-30942-2(X),* 038730942X) Springer.

Introduction to Experimental Biophysics: Biological Methods for Physical Scientists. 2011. 89.95 ***(978-1-4398-2954-7(3),*** CRC Press) Taylor & Francis Group GBR. Dist: Taylor & Francis Group.

Ishiwata. Physics of Self-Organization Systems. 2008. 124.00 *(978-981-279-336-2(4))* World Scientific Publishing Co., Inc.

Jue, Thomas. Biomedical Applications of Biophysics. 2010. (Illus.). xi, 237p. E-Book ***(978-1-60327-233-9(X))*** Humana Pr.

—Fundamental Concepts in Biophysics. 2009. (Illus.). xi, 240p. E-Book ***(978-1-59745-397-4(8))*** Humana Pr.

Jue, Thomas, ed. Fundamental Concepts in Biophysics: Volume 1. 2009. (Handbook of Modern Biophysics Ser.). (ENG., Illus.). viii, 248p. 149.00 *(978-1-58829-973-4(2))* Humana Pr.

Jue, Thomas, et al, eds. Biomembrane Frontiers: Nanostructures, Models, & the Design of Life. 2009. (Handbook of Modern Biophysics Ser.). (ENG., Illus.). xvi, 324p. 259.00 *(978-1-60761-313-8(1),* 1607613131) Humana Pr.

Kaltashov, Igor A. & Eyles, Stephen J. Mass Spectrometry in Structural Biology & Biophysics: Architecture, Dynamics, & Interaction of Biomolecules. 2nd ed. 2012. (Wiley - Interscience Series on Mass Spectrometry Ser.: 45). (ENG., Illus.). 316p. 140.00 ***(978-0-470-93779-2(3),*** Wiley) Wiley, John & Sons, Inc.

Khan, Faiz M. The Physics of Radiation Therapy. 4th rev. ed. 2009. (ENG., Illus.). 592p. 225.99 *(978-0-7817-8856-4(0))* Lippincott Williams & Wilkins.

Kim, Minjun. Bacterial Microfluidics. 2008. 116p. per. *(978-3-8364-3592-5(6))* VDM Verlag Dr. Mueller e.K.

Koenig, Simone. Biomacromolecular Mass Spectrometry Research. 2008. (C). 69.00 *(978-1-60456-467-9(9))* Nova Science Pubs., Inc.

Kozlov, Michael & Chernomordik, Leonid. Biophysics of Membrane Fusion & Fission. 2007. 330p. 165.00 *(978-3-527-40472-8(4),* Wiley-VCH) Wiley, John & Sons, Inc.

Krishnamurthy, Vikram, et al. Introductory Membrane Biophysics: A Stochastic Dynamical Approach to Biological Nano-Tubes. 2014. (IEEE Press Series on Biomedical Engineering Ser.). (ENG., Illus.). 256p. 89.95 *(978-0-470-08889-0(3),* Wiley-IEEE Pr.) Wiley, John & Sons, Inc.

Kuman, Maria & Narten, Stan Kuman. Quantum Biophysics. Date not set. pap. 20.00 *(978-1-893637-13-9(1))* Health & Happiness Bks.

Laws, Kenneth. Physics & the Art of Dance: Understanding Movement. 2nd ed. 2008. (ENG., Illus.). 288p. pap. 39.95 *(978-0-19-534101-0(5))* Oxford Univ. Pr., Inc.

Maltsev, Valeri P. & Semyanov, Konstantin A. Characterisation of Bio-Particles from Light Scattering. (Inverse & Ill-Posed Problems Ser.). (ENG.). X, 133p. 238.00 ***(978-3-11-182649-3(X))*** De Gruyter, Walter Inc.

Mitra, Ananya. Gating Nanodomains of the Acetylcholine Receptor. 2009. 172p. pap. *(978-3-639-16473-2(3))* VDM Verlag Dr. Mueller e.K.

Monteith, John. Principles of Environmental Physics. 4th ed. 2013. (ENG.). 432p. 92.95 *(978-0-12-386910-4(2),* Academic Pr.) Elsevier Science & Technology Bks.

Nadeau, Jay. Introduction to Experimental Biophysics: Biological Methods for Physical Scientists. 2011. (ENG., Illus.). 672p. pap. 89.95 *(978-1-4398-2953-0(5),* CRC Press) Taylor & Francis Group GBR. Dist: Taylor & Francis Group.

Nölting, Bengt. Methods in Modern Biophysics. 3rd ed. 2009. (ENG., Illus.). xvi, 273p. pap. 69.95 *(978-3-642-03021-5(1),* 3642030211) Springer.

Nelson, Philip. Biological Physics (Updated Edition) 2007. (ENG.). 600p. (C). pap. 114.95 *(978-0-7167-9897-2(2))* Freeman, W. H. & Co.

Newman, Jay. Physics of the Life Sciences. 2008. (Illus.). 760p. 99.00 *(978-0-387-77258-5(8))* Springer.

Nordlund, Thomas M. Quantitative Understanding of Biosystems: An Introduction to Biophysics. 2011. (ENG., Illus.). 583p. (C). 89.95 *(978-1-4200-8972-1(2)*, CRC Press) Taylor & Francis Group GBR. Dist: Taylor & Francis Group.

Parson, William W. Modern Optical Spectroscopy: With Exercises & Examples from Biophysics & Biochemistry. 2009. (ENG., Illus.). xii, 530p. pap. 89.95 *(978-3-540-95895-6(9)*, 3540958959) Springer.

Popp, Fritz Albert & Beloussov, L. V., eds. Integrative Biophysics: Biophotonics. 2010. 512p. pap. 299.00 *(978-90-481-6228-4(9)*, 9048162289) Springer.

Puglisi, Joseph, ed. Structure & Biophysics - New Technologies for Current Challenges in Biology & Beyond. 2007. (NATO Science for Peace & Security Series / NATO Science for Peace & Security Series B: Physics & Biophysics Ser.). vi, 155p. pap. 99.00 *(978-1-4020-5899-8(3)*, 1402058993) Springer London, Ltd. GBR. Dist: Springer.

Puglisi, Joseph D. Structure & Biophysics. 2007. (NATO Science for Peace & Security Series / NATO Science for Peace & Security Series B: Physics & Biophysics Ser.). 168p. 189.00 *(978-1-4020-5898-1(5))* Springer.

Puglisi, Joseph D., ed. Biophysics & the Challenges of Emerging Threats. 2009. (NATO Science for Peace & Security Series B: Physics & Biophysics Ser.). (ENG., Illus.). viii, 180p. 249.00 *(978-90-481-2366-7(6)*, 9048123666); pap. 89.95 *(978-90-481-2367-4(4)*, 9048123674) Springer.

Pylkkänen, Paavo T. I. Mind, Matter & the Implicate Order. 2010. (Frontiers Collection). (Illus.). xx, 271p. pap. 99.00 *(978-3-642-06286-5(5)*, 3642062865) Springer.

Quantitative Understanding of Biosystems. 2011. (C). 89.95 ***(978-1-4200-8973-8(0)***, CRC Press) Taylor & Francis Group GBR. Dist: Taylor & Francis Group.

Quaye, Amos. Biophysical Analysis of Agricultural Production in Ghan. 2010. 92p. pap. *(978-3-8383-3900-9(2))* Lambert Academic Publishing.

Raicu, Valerica & Popescu, Aurel. Integrated Molecular & Cellular Biophysics. (ENG.). xii, 252p. 2010. pap. 209.00 *(978-90-481-7825-4(8)*, 9048178258) 2008. (Illus.). 209.00 *(978-1-4020-8267-2(3)*, 1402082673) Springer.

Rees, Douglas C., et al, eds. Annual Review of Biophysics & Biomolecular Structure. 2007. 507p. 197.00 *(978-0-8243-1836-9(6))* Annual Reviews, Inc.

Rees, Douglas C. Ed, ed. Annual Review of Biophysics 2011. 2011. 411p. pap. 86.00 ***(978-0-8243-1840-6(4))*** Annual Reviews, Inc.

Schulten, Klaus. Computational Biophysics: Methods, & Applicationswith VMD & NAMD. 2012. (ENG., Illus.). 824p. 139.95 *(978-0-12-386978-4(1)*, Elsevier Science) Elsevier Science & Technology Bks.

Shishkina, Ludmila N., et al. Handbook of Chemistry, Biochemistry & Biology: New Frontiers. 2009. 195.00 *(978-1-60741-861-0(4))* Nova Science Pubs., Inc.

Splinter, Robert. Physics in Medicine & Biology. 2010. (ENG., Illus.). 548p. instr.'s hndbk. ed. 149.95 *(978-1-4200-7524-3(1)*, CRC Press) Taylor & Francis Group GBR. Dist: Taylor & Francis Group.

Stavroulakis, Peter, ed. Biological Effects of Electromagnetic Fields: Mechanisms, Modeling, Biological Effects, Therapeutic Effects, International Standards, Exposure Criteria. 2010. (Illus.). xv, 793p. pap. 319.00 *(978-3-642-07697-8(1)*, 3642076971) Springer.

Sten-Knudsen, Ove. Biological Membranes: Theory of Transport, Potentials & Electric Impulses. 2007. (ENG., Illus.). 696p. pap. 95.00 *(978-0-521-03635-1(6))* Cambridge Univ. Pr.

Sugiharto, PhD Toto & Sugiharto. Economic Analysis of Grazing Management Practices. 2011. 268p. pap. ***(978-3-8454-1325-9(5))*** Lambert Academic Publishing.

Taylor, Graham, et al, eds. Animal Locomotion. 2010. (ENG., Illus.). 350p. 169.00 *(978-3-642-11632-2(9)*, 3642116329) Springer.

Tuszynski, J. A. The Emerging Physics of Consciousness. 2010. (Frontiers Collection). (Illus.). xvi, 487p. pap. 89.95 *(978-3-642-06285-8(7)*, 3642062857) Springer.

Unsworth, Mike & Monteith, John. Principles of Environmental Physics. 3rd ed. 2007. (ENG., Illus.). 440p. (C). 54.95 *(978-0-12-505103-3(4)*, Academic Pr.) Elsevier Science & Technology Bks.

Varfolomeev, Sergei Dmitrievich. New Trends in Biochemical Physics Research. 2006. (Illus.). 128p. (C). 225.00 *(978-1-60021-463-9(0))* Nova Science Pubs., Inc.

Vicsek, Thomas. Fluctuations & Scaling in Biology. (Lecture Notes in Physics). 300p. (C). 55.80 *(978-3-540-66988-3(4))* Springer.

Vogel, Steven. Glimpses of Creatures in Their Physical Worlds. 2009. (ENG., Illus.). 328p. (C). 78.50 *(978-0-691-13806-0(0))*; pap. 37.50 *(978-0-691-13807-7(9))* Princeton Univ. Pr.

Volobuev, A. N. Biophysical Principles of Hemodynamics. V.I., Koshev & E.S., Petrov, eds. 2010. (Cardiology Research & Clinical Developments Ser.). 229p. pap. 43.00 *(978-1-61668-280-4(9))* Nova Science Pubs., Inc.

Waigh, Tom. Applied Biophysics: A Molecular Approach for Physical Scientists. 2007. (ENG., Illus.). 436p. per. 69.00 *(978-0-470-01718-0(X)*, Wiley-Interscience) Wiley, John & Sons, Inc.

Waigh, Tom A. & Waigh, Tom. Applied Biophysics: A Molecular Approach for Physical Scientists. 2007. (ENG., Illus.). 436p. 185.00 *(978-0-470-01717-3(1)*, Wiley-Interscience) Wiley, John & Sons, Inc.

Williamson, Michael. How Proteins Work. 2011. (ENG., Illus.). 464p. pap. 105.00 *(978-0-8153-4446-9(5)*, Garland Science) Taylor & Francis Group.

Wood, Andrew W. Physiology Biophysics & Biomedical Engineering. 2012. (Series in Medical Physics & Biomedical Engineering Ser.). (ENG., Illus.). 782p. (C). 99.95 *(978-1-4200-6513-8(0)*, Taylor & Francis) Taylor & Francis Group GBR. Dist: Taylor & Francis Group.

Yakubo, Kousuke, et al, eds. Topological Aspects of Critical Systems & Networks: Proceedings of the International Symposium. 2007. 280p. 124.00 incl. cd-rom *(978-981-270-736-9(0))* World Scientific Publishing Co., Inc.

Yang, Shengyuan. Micromachined Sensors to Study Cell Mechanical Response. 2008. 124p. pap. *(978-3-639-05857-4(7))* VDM Verlag Dr. Mueller e.K.

Young, Martin Ferrier. Essential Physics for Manual Medicine. 2009. (ENG., Illus.). 272p. pap. 50.95 *(978-0-443-10342-1(9)*, Churchill Livingstone) Elsevier - Health Sciences Div.

Yunus, Saheed O., et al. Analytical Methods Using Instrumental Neutron Activation Analysis. 2010. 84p. pap. *(978-3-639-24321-5(8))* VDM Verlag Dr. Mueller e.K.

Zaro, Fouad & Abido, Mohammad. Multi-Objective Optimal Power Flow. 2010. 104p. pap. *(978-3-8383-7996-8(9))* Lambert Academic Publishing.

Zewail. Physical Biology. 2008. (Illus.). 450p. (C). 177.00 *(978-1-84816-199-3(9))*; pap. 88.00 *(978-1-84816-200-6(6))* Imperial College Pr. GBR. Dist: World Scientific Publishing Co., Inc.

Zuckerman, Daniel M. Statistical Physics of Biomolecules: An Introduction. 2010. (ENG., Illus.). 356p. (C). 94.95 *(978-1-4200-7378-2(8)*, CRC Press) Taylor & Francis Group GBR. Dist: Taylor & Francis Group.

BIOPOLITICS

Agostino, Ana & Ashton, Glenn, eds. A Patented World? Privatisation of Life & Knowledge. 2007. (ENG., Illus.). 240p. pap. 18.00 *(978-1-77009-229-7(3))* Jacana Media ZAF. Dist: Independent Pubs. Group.

Amendola, Adalgiso. Biopolitica, Bioeconomia e Processi Di Soggettivazione. 2008. (ITA.). 431p. *(978-88-7462-231-3(7))* Quodlibet.

Blencowe, Claire. Biopolitical Experience: Foucault, Power & Positive Critique. 2012. (ENG., Illus.). 232p. 85.00 ***(978-0-230-30329-4(3))*** Palgrave Macmillan.

Brotherton, P. Sean. Revolutionary Medicine: Health & the Body in Post-Soviet Cuba. 2012. (Experimental Futures Ser.). (ENG., Illus.). 296p. 89.95 ***(978-0-8223-5194-8(3))*** Duke Univ. Pr.

—Revolutionary Medicine: Health & the Body in Post-Soviet Cuba. 2012. (Experimental Futures Ser.). (ENG., Illus.). 296p. pap. 24.95 ***(978-0-8223-5205-1(2))*** Duke Univ. Pr.

Bygrave, Stephen & Morton, Stephen, eds. Foucault in an Age of Terror: Essays on Biopolitics & the Defence of Society. 2008. (ENG.). 248p. 89.00 *(978-0-230-57433-5(5))* Palgrave Macmillan.

Campbell, Timothy C. Improper Life: Technology & Biopolitics from Heidegger to Agamben. 2011. (Posthumanities Ser.). (ENG.). 232p. 75.00 ***(978-0-8166-7464-0(7))***; pap. 25.00 ***(978-0-8166-7465-7(5))*** Univ. of Minnesota Pr.

Cárdenas, Micha & Fornssler, Barbara. Trans Desire/Affective Cyborgs. Schirmacher, Wolfgang, ed. 2010. (Illus.). 150p. pap. 16.95 *(978-0-9825309-3-4(4))* Atropos Pr.

Chiesa, Lorenzo & Toscano, Alberto, eds. The Italian Difference: Contemporary Italian Thought. 2009. (Transmission Ser.). 159p. pap. 25.00 *(978-0-9805440-7-7(6))* re.press AUS. Dist: Lightning Source, Inc.

Clough, Patricia Ticineto & Willse, Craig, eds. Beyond Biopolitics: Essays on the Governance of Life & Death. 2011. (ENG., Illus.). 400p. 99.95 *(978-0-8223-5003-3(3))*; pap. 26.95 *(978-0-8223-5017-0(3))* Duke Univ. Pr.

Cohen, Ed. A Body Worth Defending: Immunity, Biopolitics, & the Apotheosis of the Modern Body. 2009. (ENG., Illus.). 384p. 94.95 *(978-0-8223-4518-3(8))*; pap. 26.95 *(978-0-8223-4535-0(8))* Duke Univ. Pr.

Collier, Stephen J. Post Soviet Social - Neoliberalism, Social Modernity, Biopolitics. 2011. (ENG., Illus.). 320p. (C). 70.00 *(978-0-691-14830-4(9))*; pap. 26.95 *(978-0-691-14831-1(7))* Princeton Univ. Pr.

da Costa, Beatriz & Philip, Kavita, eds. Tactical Biopolitics: Art, Activism, & Technoscience. (Leonardo Bks.). (ENG., Illus.). 536p. (gr. 17). 2010. pap. 20.00 *(978-0-262-51491-0(5))* 2008. 42.00 *(978-0-262-04249-5(5))* MIT Pr.

Debrix, Francois & Barder, Alexander D. Beyond Biopolitics: Theory & Violence in World Politics. 2011. (Interventions Ser.). (ENG.). 184p. (C). 130.00 *(978-0-415-78059-9(4))* Routledge.

Dillon. The Liberal Way of War: The Martial Face of Global Biopolitics. 2007. 224p. 135.00 *(978-0-415-95299-6(9))* Routledge.

—The Liberal Way of War: The Martial Face of Global Biopolitics. 2007. 224p. 41.95 *(978-0-415-95300-9(6))* Taylor & Francis Group.

Dillon, Michael. Biopolitics of Security in the 21st Century: The Political Economy of Security after Foucault. 2013. (PRIO New Security Studies). (ENG.). 240p. (C). 39.95 *(978-0-415-48433-6(2))*; 145.00 *(978-0-415-48432-9(4))* Routledge.

Dillon, Michael & Neal, Andrew, eds. Foucault on Politics, Security & War. 2008. (ENG.). 256p. 95.00 *(978-1-4039-9904-7(X))* Palgrave Macmillan.

Esposito, Roberto. Bios: Biopolitics & Philosophy. Campbell, Timothy, tr. from ITA. 2008. (Posthumanities Ser.). 304p. pap. 22.50 *(978-0-8166-4990-7(1))*; 67.50 *(978-0-8166-4989-1(8))* Univ. of Minnesota Pr.

Foucault, Michel. The Birth of Biopolitics: Lectures at the College de France, 1978-1979. Senellart, Michel et al, eds. Burchell, Graham, tr. from FRE. 2008. (ENG.). 368p. 28.95 *(978-1-4039-8654-2(1))* Palgrave Macmillan.

—The Birth of Biopolitics: Lectures at the Collège de France, 1978-1979. 2010. (Lectures at the College de France Ser.). (FRE & ENG.). 368p. pap. 19.00 *(978-0-312-20341-2(1))* Picador.

Grzinic, Marina & Tatlic, Sefik Seki. From Biopolitics to Necropolitics: The Metastasis of Democracy, Communications & the Mass Intellect. 2011. 256p. pap. 15.95 ***(978-1-57027-222-6(0))*** Autonomedia.

Hanson, Clare. Eugenics, Literature, & Culture in Post-War Britain. 2012. (Routledge Interdisciplinary Perspectives on Literature Ser.). (ENG., Illus.). 200p. (C). 125.00 ***(978-0-415-80698-5(4))*** Routledge.

Hatemi, Peter K. Man Is by Nature a Political Animal: Evolution, Biology, & Politics. McDermott, Rose, ed. 2011. (ENG., Illus.). 352p. 80.00 *(978-0-226-31909-4(1))* Univ. of Chicago Pr.

Hatemi, Peter K. & McDermott, Rose, eds. Man Is by Nature a Political Animal: Evolution, Biology, & Politics. 2011. (ENG., Illus.). 352p. pap. 27.50 *(978-0-226-31910-0(5))* Univ. of Chicago Pr.

Hepner, Tricia Redeker & O'Kane, David, eds. Biopolitics, Militarism, & Development: Eritrea in the Twenty-First Century. (DISL Ser.). 236p. 2011. 25.00 *(978-0-85745-289-4(4))* 2009. 80.00 *(978-1-84545-567-5(3))* Berghahn Bks., Inc.

Hibbing, John, et al, eds. The Biology of Political Behavior. 2007. (ANNALS of the American Academy of Political & Social Science Ser.: 614). (Illus.). 228p. per. 34.00 *(978-1-4129-6404-3(0)*, 295614P) SAGE Pubns., Inc.

Hibbing, John & Smith, Kevin B., eds. The Biology of Political Behavior. 2007. (ANNALS of the American Academy of Political & Social Science Ser.: 614). (Illus.). 228p. 47.00 *(978-1-4129-6405-0(9)*, 295614C) SAGE Pubns., Inc.

Hull, Gordon & Hull. Hobbes & the Making of Modern Political Thought. 2010. (Continuum Studies in British Philosophy Ser.). (ENG.). 224p. 120.00 *(978-1-4411-4002-9(6))* Continuum International Publishing Group, Ltd. GBR. Dist: National Bk. Network.

Kiersey, Nicholas J. & Stokes, Doug, eds. Foucault & International Relations. 2010. (Interventions Ser.). (ENG.). 216p. (C). 125.00 *(978-0-415-57983-4(X)*, Routledge) Taylor & Francis Group GBR. Dist: Taylor & Francis Group.

Klawiter, Maren. The Biopolitics of Breast Cancer: Changing Cultures of Disease & Activism. 2008. (Illus.). 384p. 75.00 *(978-0-8166-5107-8(8))*; pap. 25.00 *(978-0-8166-5108-5(6))* Univ. of Minnesota Pr.

Lavine, Howard, ed. Political Psychology, 4 vols. 2010. (SAGE Library of Political Science Ser.). (Illus.). 1656p. 995.00 *(978-1-84860-709-5(1)*, B07095C) SAGE Pubns., Ltd. GBR. Dist: SAGE Pubns., Inc.

Lemke, Thomas, et al. Biopolitics: An Advanced Introduction. 2011. (ENG.). 158p. 60.00 *(978-0-8147-5241-8(1))*; pap. 20.00 *(978-0-8147-5242-5(X))* New York Univ. Pr.

Lu, Sheldon H. Chinese Modernity & Global Biopolitics: Studies in Literature & Visual Culture. 2007. (Illus.). 264p. (C). 58.00 *(978-0-8248-3111-0(X))*; per. 27.00 *(978-0-8248-3177-6(2))* Univ. of Hawaii Pr.

Masters, Cristina. The Logics of Biopower & the War on Terror: Living, Dying, Surviving. Masters, Cristina & Dauphinée, Elizabeth, eds. 2006. (ENG., Illus.). 272p. 89.00 *(978-1-4039-7465-5(9))* Palgrave Macmillan.

—Militarism Gender And (in)Security. 2012. (PRIO New Security Studies). (ENG.). 208p. (C). 135.00 *(978-0-415-57775-5(6))* Routledge.

Morra, Mike. Dawn of Bio/Politics: Governing the 12 DNA/Tribes of America. 2008. 572p. pap. 23.49 *(978-1-4389-3227-9(8))* AuthorHouse.

Murray, Alex, et al. The Work of Giorgio Agamben: Law, Literature, Life. 2009. (ENG.). 224p. (gr. 17). 95.00 *(978-0-7486-3462-0(2))* Edinburgh Univ. Pr. GBR. Dist: Columbia Univ. Pr.

Nadesan, Majia. Governmentality, Biopower, & Everyday Life. 2008. (Routledge Studies in Social & Political Thought). (ENG., Illus.). 258p. 125.00 *(978-0-415-95854-7(7))* Routledge.

Nadesan, Majia Holmer. Governing Childhood into the 21st Century: Biopolitical Technologies of Childhood Management & Education. 2010. (Critical Cultural Studies of Childhood Ser.). (ENG.). 256p. 89.00 *(978-0-230-61321-8(7))* Palgrave Macmillan.

Nichter, Jim & Nichter, Mark. Global Health: Why Cultural Perceptions, Social Representations, & Biopolitics Matter. 2008. (ENG., Illus.). 320p. (C). 65.00 *(978-0-8165-2573-7(0))* Univ. of Arizona Pr.

Nichter, Mark. Global Health: Why Cultural Perceptions, Social Representations, & Biopolitics Matter. 2008. (ENG., Illus.). 320p. pap. 29.95 *(978-0-8165-2574-4(9))* Univ. of Arizona Pr.

Oleskin, A. V. Biopolitics: The Political Potential of the Life Sciences. 2012. ***(978-1-62081-088-0(3))*** Nova Science Pubs., Inc.

Reid, Julian. The Biopolitics of the War on Terror: Life Struggles, Liberal Modernity & the Defence of Logistical Societies. (Reappraising the Political Ser.). (ENG.). 160p. 2009. pap. 29.95 *(978-0-7190-7406-6(1))* 2007. 84.00 *(978-0-7190-7405-9(3))* Manchester Univ. Pr. GBR. Dist: Macmillan.

Righi, Andrea. Biopolitics & Social Change in Italy: From Gramsci to Pasolini to Negri. 2011. (ENG., Illus.). 224p. 85.00 *(978-0-230-11503-3(9))* Palgrave Macmillan.

Roberts, David. Global Governance & Biopolitics: Regulating Human Security. 2009. (ENG., Illus.). 224p. pap. 29.95 *(978-1-84813-217-7(4))* Zed Bks., Ltd. GBR. Dist: Macmillan.

Ross, Alison. The Agamben Effect. 2008. (ENG., Illus.). 220p. per. 14.00 *(978-0-8223-6684-3(3))* Duke Univ. Pr.

Smith, Mick. Against Ecological Sovereignty: Ethics, Biopolitics, & Saving the Natural World. 2011. (Posthumanities Ser.). (ENG., Illus.). 320p. 75.00 *(978-0-8166-7028-4(5))*; pap. 25.00 *(978-0-8166-7029-1(3))* Univ. of Minnesota Pr.

Solo, Pam & Pressburg, Gail. The Promise & Politics of Stem Cell Research, 1 vol. 2006. 192p. 39.95 *(978-0-275-99038-1(9)*, C9038, Praeger Pubs.) Greenwood Publishing Group, Inc.

Somit, Albert & Peterson, Steven, eds. Biology & Politics: Where It Has Been & Where It Is Going. 2012. 150p. pap. 29.95 *(978-3-86649-274-5(X))* Budrich-Esser, Barbara DEU. Dist: International Specialized Bk. Services.

Somit, Albert & Peterson, Steven A., eds. Biology & Political Behavior: The Brain, Genes & Politics - the Cutting Edge. 2011. (Research in Biopolitics Ser.). (Illus.). 264p. *(978-0-85724-579-3(1))* Emerald Group Publishing Ltd.

Swiffen, Amy. Law, Ethics & the Biopolitical. 2012. (ENG.). pap. 42.79 ***(978-0-415-62870-9(9))*** 2011. 128p. 120.00 *(978-0-415-57844-8(2))* Routledge.

Takeshita, Chikako. The Global Biopolitics of the Iud: How Science Constructs Contraceptive Users & Women′s Bodies. 2011. (Inside Technology Ser.). (ENG., Illus.). 216p. (gr. 17). 30.00 ***(978-0-262-01658-2(3))*** MIT Pr.

Weir, Lorna. Pregnancy, Risk, & Biopolitics: On the Threshold of the Living Subject. 2006. (Illus.). 241p. 53.95 *(978-0-415-39257-0(8))* Routledge.

—Pregnancy, Risk & Biopolitics: On the Threshold of the Living Subject. annot. ed. 2006. (Transformations: Thinking Through Feminism Ser.). (ENG., Illus.). 256p. (C). 180.00 *(978-0-415-39258-7(6))* Routledge.

Wolfe, Cary. Before the Law: Humans & Other Animals in a Biopolitical Frame. 2012. 152p. 60.00 ***(978-0-226-92240-9(5))***; pap. 20.00 ***(978-0-226-92241-6(3))*** Univ. of Chicago Pr.

Wright, Jan & Harwood, Valerie. Biopolitics & the 'obesity Epidemic' Governing Bodies. 2008. (Routledge Studies in Health & Social Welfare Ser.). (Illus.). vi, 223p. 110.00 *(978-0-203-88206-1(7))* Routledge.

—Biopolitics & the 'obesity Epidemic' Governing Bodies. Harwood, Valerie, ed. 2008. (Routledge Studies in Health & Social Welfare Ser.: Vol. 3). (ENG., Illus.). 232p. 145.00 *(978-0-415-99188-9(9))* Routledge.

Wright, Jan & Harwood, Valerie, eds. Biopolitics & the 'Obesity Epidemic' Governing Bodies. 2012. (Routledge Studies in Health & Social Welfare Ser.). (ENG., Illus.). 232p. pap. 42.95 ***(978-0-415-54094-0(1))*** Routledge.

Ycude, Jeremy R. Biopolitical Surveillance & Public Health in International Politics. 2009. (ENG., Illus.). 260p. 95.00 *(978-0-230-61995-1(9))* Palgrave Macmillan.

BIOPOLYMERS

see also Polypeptides; Polysaccharides

Ahmed, Jasim, et al, eds. Starch-Based Polymeric Materials & Nanocomposites: Chemistry, Processing, & Applications. 2012. (ENG., Illus.). 416p. 169.95 ***(978-1-4398-5116-6(6)***, CRC Press) Taylor & Francis Group GBR. Dist: Taylor & Francis Group.

Ando, Isao, et al. Solid State NMR Spectroscopy for Biopolymers: Principles & Applications. 2006. (ENG., Illus.). xiii, 464p. 179.00 *(978-1-4020-4302-4(3)*, 1402043023) Springer.

Bastioli, Catia, ed. Handbook of Biodegradable Polymers. (Illus.). 520p. pap. *(978-1-85957-389-1(4))* iSmithers Rapra Publishing.

Bruni, Renato, ed. Mathematical Approaches to Polymer Sequence Analysis & Related Problems. 2010. (ENG., Illus.). x, 248p. 189.00 *(978-1-4419-6799-2(0)*, 1441967990) Springer.

Cadwallader, Keith R. & Chang, Sam, eds. Chemistry, Texture, & Flavor of Soy, 1 vol. 2011. (ACS Symposium Ser.). (ENG., Illus.). 424p. 175.00 *(978-0-8412-2561-9(3))* American Chemical Society.

Caldwell, Karin D. & Williams, S. Kim R., eds. Field-Flow Fractionation in Biopolymer Analysis. 2011. (ENG., Illus.). x, 305p. 189.00 ***(978-3-7091-0153-7(0)***, 3709101530) Springer.

Celina, Mathew C., et al, eds. Polymer Degradation & Performance. 2009. (ACS Symposium Ser.). (ENG., Illus.). 344p. 150.00 *(978-0-8412-6978-1(5))* American Chemical Society.

Chiellini, Emo, et al, eds. Biorelated Polymers: Sustainable Polymer Science & Technology. 2010. (ENG.). 400p. pap. 129.00 *(978-1-4419-3369-0(7)*, 1441933697) Springer.

Endres, Hans-Josef & Siebert-Raths, Andrea. Engineering Biopolymers: Markets, Manufacturing, Properties, & Applications. 2011. ***(978-1-56990-461-9(3))***; ***(978-3-446-42403-6(2))*** Hanser Pubns.

Fakirov, Stoiko & Bhattacharya, Debes. Handbook of Engineering Biopolymers: Homopolymers, Blends, & Composites. 2007. (Illus.). *(978-1-56990-405-3(7))* Hanser, Carl GmbH & Co.

Fishman, Marshall L., et al, eds. Advances in Biopolymers: Molecules, Clusters, Networks, & Interactions. 2006. (ACS Symposium Ser.: Vol. 935). (ENG., Illus.). 332p. (C). 179.50 *(978-0-8412-3959-3(2))* American Chemical Society.

Guenet, Jean-Michel. Polymer-Solvent Molecular Compounds. 2008. (ENG., Illus.). 315p. 165.00 *(978-0-08-045144-2(6)*, Elsevier Science) Elsevier Science & Technology Bks.

Hamano, Yoshimitsu, ed. Amino-Acid Homopolymers Occurring in Nature. 2010. (Microbiology Monographs). (Illus.). vii, 250p. 219.00 *(978-3-642-12452-5(6)*, 3642124526) Springer.

Hanipah, Suhaiza & Verbeek, Johan. A process for melt grafting itaconic anhydride onto polyethylene: Extrusion. 2008. 100p. pap. *(978-3-639-10574-2(5))* VDM Verlag Dr. Mueller e.K.

Heckman, Emily M., et al. Nanobiotronics: 26-27 August 2007, San Diego, California, USA. 2007. (Proceedings of SPIE Ser.). (Illus.). 138p. pap. 70.00 *(978-0-8194-6794-2(4))* SPIE.

Hollander, Anthony P. & Hatton, Paul V., eds. Biopolymer Methods in Tissue Engineering. 2010. (Methods in Molecular Biology Ser.). (Illus.). 280p. pap. 139.00 *(978-1-61737-280-3(3)*, 1617372803) Humana Pr.

Jimenez, Alfonso & Zaikov, Gennadii Efremovich, eds. Recent Advances in Research on Biodegradable Polymers & Sustainable Composites (Volume 2) 2008. 135.00 *(978-1-60692-094-7(4))* Nova Science Pubs., Inc.

Kalia, Susheel & Avérous, Luc. Biopolymers: Biomedical & Environmental Applications. 2011. (Wiley-Scrivener Ser.: 70). (ENG., Illus.). 642p. 195.00 *(978-0-470-63923-8(7)*, Wiley-Scrivener) Wiley, John & Sons, Inc.

Kaplan, David L., ed. Biopolymers from Renewable Resources. 2010. (Macromolecular Systems - Materials Approach Ser.). (ENG., Illus.). xix, 417p. pap. 335.00 *(978-3-642-08341-9(2)*, 3642083412) Springer.

Kobayashi, Norihisa, et al. Nanobiosystems: Processing, Characterization, & Applications III: 4-5 August 2010, San Diego, California, United States. 2010. (Proceedings of SPIE Ser.). (Illus.). 128p. pap. 80.00 (978-0-8194-8261-7(7)) SPIE.

—Nanobiosystems: Processing, Characterization, & Applications IV. 2011. (Proceedings of SPIE Ser.). 138p. pap. 70.00 (978-0-8194-8713-1(9)) SPIE.

Kobayashi, Shiro. Biopolymers: Lignin, Proteins, Bioactive Nanocomposites. Kobayashi, Shiro et al, eds. 2010. (Advances in Polymer Science Ser.). (Illus.). xii, 210p. 299.00 (978-3-642-13629-0(X), 364213629X) Springer.

Lundblad, Roger L. Chemical Modification of Biological Polymers. 2011. (ENG., Illus.). 426p. 149.95 (978-1-4398-4898-2(X), CRC Press) Taylor & Francis Group GBR. Dist: Taylor & Francis Group.

McDermott, Anne E. & Polenova, Tatyana, eds. Solid State NMR Studies of Biopolymers. 2010. (ENG., Illus.). 592p. 165.00 (978-0-470-72122-3(7), Wiley) Wiley, John & Sons, Inc.

Németh, Tamás S., ed. Biopolymer Research Trends. 2008. 185.00 (978-1-60021-983-2(7)) Nova Science Pubs., Inc.

Pearce, Eli M., et al, eds. New Steps in Chemical & Biochemical Physics. Pure & Applied Science. 2010. (Physics Research & Technology Ser.). 235.00 (978-1-61668-923-0(4)) Nova Science Pubs., Inc.

Plackett, David, ed. Biopolymers: New Materials for Sustainable Films & Coatings. 2011. (ENG., Illus.). 352p. 130.00 (978-0-470-68341-5(4), Wiley) Wiley, John & Sons, Inc.

Pogaku, Ravindra & Upender, Kallu. Rheology of Biopolymers. 2010. 64p. pap. (978-3-639-24103-7(7)) VDM Verlag Dr. Mueller e.K.

Przybylski, Michael. (Bio)Polymer Mass Spectrometry: Methods - Applications - Chemistry - Life Science. 2011. (ENG.). 400p. 165.00 (978-3-527-32955-7(2), Wiley-VCH) Wiley, John & Sons, Inc.

Rahmo, Abdulkader. The Case for Monomeric Enzyme with Intersubsite Cooperativity. 2010. 96p. pap. (978-3-639-24703-9(5)) VDM Verlag Dr. Mueller e.K.

Rigler, Rudolf & Vogel, H., eds. Single Molecules & Nanotechnology. 2010. (Springer Series in Biophysics Ser.). (Illus.). xiv, 318p. pap. 289.00 (978-3-642-09316-6(7), 3642093167) Springer.

Royal Society of Chemistry Staff. A Handbook of Applied Biopolymer Technology: Synthesis, Degradation & Applications. Sharma, Sanjay K. & Mudhoo, Ackmez, eds. 2011. (RSC Green Chemistry Ser.). (ENG., Illus.). 500p. (C). 240.00 (978-1-84973-151-5(9)) Royal Society of Chemistry, The GBR. Dist: Ingram Pub. Services.

—Renewable Resources for Functional Polymers & Biomaterials: Polysaccharides, Proteins & Polyesters. Williams, Peter A., ed. 2011. (ENG., Illus.). 456p. 224.00 (978-1-84973-245-1(0)) Royal Society of Chemistry, The GBR. Dist: Ingram Pub. Services.

Rudnik, Ewa. Compostable Polymer Materials. 2008. (ENG., Illus.). 224p. 170.00 (978-0-08-045371-2(6), Elsevier Science) Elsevier Science & Technology Bks.

Saitô, Hazime, et al. Solid State NMR Spectroscopy for Biopolymers: Principles & Applications. 2010. (ENG.). xiii, 464p. pap. 179.00 (978-90-481-7100-2(8), 9048171008) Springer.

Schmidt, M. New Developments in Polymer Analytics I. 2010. (Advances in Polymer Science Ser.). (Illus.). x, 233p. pap. 329.00 (978-3-642-08535-2(0), 3642085350) Springer.

Semenova, Maria Germanovna & Dickinson, Eric. Biopolymers in Food Colloids: Thermodynamics & Molecular Interactions. 2010. (ENG., Illus.). 384p. 250.00 (978-90-04-17186-2(X), CRC Press) Taylor & Francis Group GBR. Dist: Taylor & Francis Group.

Steinbüchel, Alexander. Biopolymers with Index: General Aspects & Special Applications, 10 vols. 2006. (ENG.). 5924p. 4150.00 (978-3-527-30290-1(5), Wiley-VCH) Wiley, John & Sons, Inc.

Telis, Vania Regina Nicoletti, ed. Biopolymer Engineering in Food Processing. 2012. (Contemporary Food Engineering Ser.: 25). (ENG., Illus.). 416p. 169.95 (978-1-4398-4494-6(1), CRC Press) Taylor & Francis Group GBR. Dist: Taylor & Francis Group.

Tsuji, Hideto. Degradation of Poly (Lactide) — Based Biodegradable Materials. 2008. (Illus.). 76p. (C). 50.00 (978-1-60456-502-7(0)) Nova Science Pubs., Inc.

van der Maarel, Johan R. C. Introduction to Biopolymer Physics. 2008. (Illus.). 247p. pap. 51.00 (978-981-277-604-4(4)) World Scientific Publishing Co., Inc.

Vasile, Cornelia & Zaikov, Gennadii Efremovich. Environmentally Degradable Materials Based on Multicomponent Polymeric Systems. 2009. (ENG.). 660p. 250.00 (978-90-04-16410-9(3), CRC Press) Taylor & Francis Group GBR. Dist: Taylor & Francis Group.

Vekshin, Nikolai L. Photonics of Biopolymers. 2010. (Biological & Medical Physics, Biomedical Engineering Ser.). (ENG., Illus.). x, 229p. pap. 149.00 (978-3-642-07855-2(9), 3642078559) Springer.

Vincent, Julian. Structural Biomaterials. 3rd ed. 2012. (ENG., Illus.). 240p. (C). pap. 60.00 (978-0-691-15400-8(7)) Princeton Univ. Pr.

Yang, Hongshun, ed. Polymer Morphology. 2011. (Polymer Science & Technology Ser.). 165.00 (978-1-61470-880-3(0)) Nova Science Pubs., Inc.

Zaikov, Gennadii Efremovich. Radiation Chemistry of Biopolymers. 2006. (ENG., Illus.). 376p. 184.00 (978-90-04-15425-4(6), CRC Press) Taylor & Francis Group GBR. Dist: Taylor & Francis Group.

Zaikov, Gennadii Efremovich, ed. Polymer & Biopolymer Analysis & Characterization. 2007. (Illus.). 253p. 210.00 (978-1-60021-608-4(0)) Nova Science Pubs., Inc.

BIOPSY

see also Needle Biopsy

Boerner, Scott L. & Asa, Sylvia L. Biopsy Interpretation of the Thyroid. 2009. (Biopsy Interpretation Ser.). (ENG., Illus.). 288p. 163.95 (978-0-7817-7204-4(4)) Lippincott Williams & Wilkins.

Brat, Daniel J. & Schniederjan, Matthew. Biopsy Interpretation of the Central Nervous System. 2011. (Biopsy Interpretation Ser.). (ENG., Illus.). 360p. 163.99 (978-0-7817-9993-5(7)) Lippincott Williams & Wilkins.

Cagle, Philip T. Transbronchial & Endobronchial Biopsies. Allen, Timothy C., ed. 2008. (ENG., Illus.). 256p. 237.99 (978-0-7817-8517-4(0)) Lippincott Williams & Wilkins.

Crowson, A. Neil, et al. The Skin: Primary Non-Lymphoid Neoplasms of the Skin. 2010. (Biopsy Interpretation Ser.). (ENG., Illus.). 464p. 163.95 (978-0-7817-7205-1(2)) Lippincott Williams & Wilkins.

Deavers, Michael T., et al. Biopsy Interpretation of the Uterine Cervix & Corpus. 2009. (Biopsy Interpretation Ser.). (ENG., Illus.). 304p. 163.95 (978-0-7817-8779-6(3)) Lippincott Williams & Wilkins.

Gervais, Debra A. & Sabharwal, Tarun, eds. Interventional Radiology Procedures in Biopsy & Drainage. 2010. (Techniques in Interventional Radiology Ser.). (ENG., Illus.). 250p. pap. 49.95 (978-1-84800-898-4(8), 1848008988) Springer.

Mills, Stacey E. & Stelow, Edward B. Biopsy Interpretation of the Upper Aerodigestive Tract & Ear. 2007. (Biopsy Interpretation Ser.). (ENG., Illus.). 375p. 163.95 (978-0-7817-9310-0(6)) Lippincott Williams & Wilkins.

Montgomery, Elizabeth & Fisher, Cyril. Biopsy Interpretation of Soft Tissue Tumors. 2010. (Biopsy Interpretation Ser.). (ENG., Illus.). 562p. 163.95 (978-0-7817-9559-3(1)) Lippincott Williams & Wilkins.

Mooi, Walter & Krausz, Thomas. Pathology of Melanocytic Disorders. 2nd ed. 2007. (ENG., Illus.). 500p. 345.00 (978-0-340-80968-6(X)) Hodder Arnold Pubs.

Schnitt, Stuart J. & Collins, Laura C. Biopsy Interpretation of the Breast. 2008. (Biopsy Interpretation Ser.). (ENG., Illus.). 496p. 164.95 (978-0-7817-9146-5(4)) Lippincott Williams & Wilkins.

Stelow. Biopsy Interp Upper Aero Tract Ear Cb. 2nd rev. ed. 2012. (978-1-4511-1063-0(4)) Lippincott Williams & Wilkins.

Suster. Biopsy Interpretation of the Lung. 2011. 149.00 (978-0-7817-8467-2(0)) Lippincott Williams & Wilkins.

Taxy, Jerome B., et al. The Frozen Section. 2009. (Biopsy Interpretation Ser.). (ENG., Illus.). 368p. 163.95 (978-0-7817-6779-8(2)) Lippincott Williams & Wilkins.

Zhou, Ming & Shah, Rajal B. Prostate Biopsy Interpretation: an Illustrated Guide: An Illustrated Guide. 2011. (ENG., Illus.). xvi, 185p. 139.00 (978-3-642-21368-7(5), 3642213685) Springer.

Zhou, Xin J., et al, eds. Silva's Diagnostic Renal Pathology. 2009. (ENG., Illus.). 636p. 184.00 (978-0-521-87702-2(4)) Cambridge Univ. Pr.

BIOPSY, NEEDLE

see Needle Biopsy

BIOPSYCHIATRY

see Biological Psychiatry

BIOPSYCHOLOGY

see Psychobiology

BIOREACTORS

Ajbar, Abdelhamid & Alhumaizi, Khalid. Dynamics of the Chemostat. 2011. (ENG., Illus.). 368p. 99.95 (978-1-4398-6714-3(3), Chapman & Hall/CRC) CRC Pr. LLC.

American Institute of Chemical Engineers (AIChE) Staff, compiled by. Topical Conference on Applications of Micro-Reactor Engineering 2007. 2007. 206p. pap. 118.00 (978-1-60423-350-6(8)) Curran Assocs., Inc.

Antolli, Paolo G. & Liu, Zhiming. Bioreactors: Design, Properties, & Applications. 2012. (Biotechnology in Agriculture, Industry & Medicine Ser.). 237p. 140.00 (978-1-62100-164-5(4)) Nova Science Pubs., Inc.

Basile, Angelo & Gallucci, Fausto. Simulation of Membrane Reactors. 2009. (Illus.). 472p. 89.00 (978-1-60692-425-9(7)) Nova Science Pubs., Inc.

Basile, Angelo & Gallucci, Fausto, eds. Membranes for Membrane Reactors: Preparation, Optimization & Selection. 2011. (ENG., Illus.). 640p. 195.00 (978-0-470-74652-3(1), Wiley) Wiley, John & Sons, Inc.

Batra, Aman. Microarrays. 2010. 64p. pap. (978-3-639-25757-1(X)) VDM Verlag Dr. Mueller e.K.

Bentem, A. G. N van. Membrane Bioreactors: Operation & Results of an MBR Wastewater Treatment Plant. 2007. (STOWA Report Ser.). 100p. (C). pap. (978-1-84339-173-9(2)) IWA Publishing.

Bilgen, Bahar. A Novel Bioreactor for Tissue Engineering. 2011. 280p. pap. (978-3-8443-9215-9(7)) Lambert Academic Publishing.

Brepols, Christoph. Operating Large Scale Membrane Bioreactors for Municipal Wastewater Treatment. 2010. (Illus.). 156p. (C). pap. (978-1-84339-305-4(0)) IWA Publishing.

Brownstein, Michael J. & Khodursky, Arkady, eds. Functional Genomics. 2010. (Methods in Molecular Biology Ser.). (Illus.). 272p. pap. 119.00 (978-1-61737-474-6(1), 1617374741) Humana Pr.

Butterfield, D. A., ed. Biofunctional Membranes. 2010. (ENG.). 306p. pap. 179.00 (978-1-4419-3254-9(2), 1441932542) Springer.

Campbell, Marissa J., ed. DNA Microarrays, Synthesis & Synthetic DNA. 2011. (Microbiology Research Advances Ser.). (Illus.). xi, 402p. 165.00 (978-1-61209-823-4(1)) Nova Science Pubs., Inc.

Cartwright, Terence. Animal Cells as Bioreactors. 2009. (Cambridge Studies in Biotechnology Ser.). (ENG., Illus.). 196p. pap. 39.99 (978-0-521-10310-7(X)) Cambridge Univ. Pr.

Chakrabarty, Krishnendu & Xu, Tao. Digital Microfluidic Biochips: Design Automation & Optimization. 2010. (ENG., Illus.). 213p. 139.95 (978-1-4398-1915-9(7), CRC Press) Taylor & Francis Group GBR. Dist: Taylor & Francis Group.

Chaudhuri, Julian & Al-Rubeai, Mohamed, eds. Bioreactors for Tissue Engineering: Principles, Design & Operation. 2010. viii, 375p. pap. 219.00 (978-90-481-6949-8(6), 9048169496) Springer.

Cheng, Ya, et al, eds. Microbiochips Monolithically Integrated with Microfluidics, Micromechanics, Photonics, & Electronics by 3D Femtosecond Laser Direct Writing. 2010. (Lasers & Electro-Optics Research & Technology Ser.). pap. 49.00 (978-1-61728-279-9(0), Nova Novinka) Nova Science Pubs., Inc.

Chevolot, Yann, ed. Carbohydrate Microarrays: Methods & Protocols. 2011. (Methods in Molecular Biology Ser.). (ENG., Illus.). xvi, 427p. 139.00 (978-1-61779-372-1(8), 1617793728) Humana Pr.

De Falco, Marcello, et al, eds. Membrane Reactors for Hydrogen Production Processes. 2011. (Illus.). xii, 235p. 179.00 (978-0-85729-150-9(5), 0857291505) Springer.

de Lemos Chernicharo, C. A. Anaerobic Reactors. 2007. (Biological Wastewater Treatment Ser.). (Illus.). 184p. (C). pap. (978-1-84339-164-7(3)) IWA Publishing.

Dochain, Denis, ed. Automatic Control of Bioprocesses. 2008. (Iste Ser.: 305). (ENG., Illus.). 288p. 174.00 (978-1-84821-025-7(6), Wiley-ISTE) Wiley, John & Sons, Inc.

Draghici, Sorin. Data Analysis Tools for DNA Microarrays using MATLAB, 2nd Edition. 2nd rev. ed. 2013. (Chapman & Hall/CRC Mathematical & Computational Biology Ser.). (ENG., Illus.). 706p. (C). 89.95 (978-1-4398-0977-8(1), Chapman & Hall/CRC) CRC Pr. LLC.

Dufva, Martin. DNA Microarrays for Biomedical Research: Methods & Protocols. 2009. (Methods in Molecular Biology Ser.). (Illus.). (ENG.). xii, 252p. 99.00 (978-1-934115-69-5(X)); ix, 304p. (978-1-59745-538-1(5)) Humana Pr.

Eibl, Regine & Eibl, Dieter. Disposable Bioreactors. 2009. (Advances in Biochemical Engineering / Biotechnology Ser.). (ENG., Illus.). xiii, 223p. 299.00 (978-3-642-01871-8(8), 3642018718) Springer.

Floriano, Pierre N. Microchip-Based Assay Systems: Methods & Applications. 2007. (Methods in Molecular Biology Ser.). (Illus.). 229p. 119.00 (978-1-58829-588-0(5), 1588295885) Humana Pr.

Floriano, Pierre N., ed. Microchip-Based Assay Systems: Methods & Applications. 2010. (Methods in Molecular Biology Ser.). (Illus.). xi, 229p. pap. 119.00 (978-1-61737-662-7(0), 1617376620) Humana Pr.

Fung, Eric, ed. Protein Arrays: Methods & Protocols. 2010. (Methods in Molecular Biology Ser.). (Illus.). 304p. pap. 99.50 (978-1-61737-456-2(3), 1617374563) Humana Pr.

Goel, Sanket. Opto-Biochips for Microcytometry. 2010. 156p. pap. (978-3-8383-8959-2(X)) Lambert Academic Publishing.

Hall, E. R. Membrane Bioreactors for Anaerobic Treatment of Wastewaters (Phase II) Wastewater Treatment & Reuse. 2006. (WERF Report 02-CTS-4a Ser.). 100p. (C). pap. (978-1-84339-760-1(9)) IWA Publishing.

Halvarsson, Bjorn. Interaction Analysis in Multivariable Control Systems: Applications to Bioreactors for Nitrogen Removal. 2010. (Uppsala Dissertations from the Faculty of Science & Technology Ser.). (Illus.). 162p. pap. 52.50 (978-91-554-7781-3(X)) Uppsala Universitet/Acta Universitatis Uppsaliensis SWE. Dist: Coronet Bks.

Hardt, Steffen & Schönfeld, Friedhelm, eds. Microfluidic Technologies for Miniaturized Analysis Systems. 2010. (MEMS Reference Shelf Ser.). xxi, 616p. pap. 179.00 (978-1-4419-3948-7(2), 1441939482) Springer.

Judd, Simon. The MBR Book: Principles & Applications of Membrane Bioreactors for Water & Wastewater Treatment. 2nd ed. 2011. (ENG., Illus.). 536p. 200.00 (978-0-08-096682-3(9), Butterworth-Heinemann) Elsevier Science & Technology Bks.

—MBR Book: Principles & Applications of Membrane Bioreactors for Water & Wastewater Treatment. 2nd rev. ed. 2010. (Elsevier Co-Pub Ser.). 528p. (C). (978-1-84339-518-8(5)) IWA Publishing.

Karagiannidis, Symeon. Catalytic Microreactors for Portable Power Generation. 2011. (Springer Theses Ser.). (Illus.). xvi, 112p. 129.00 (978-3-642-17667-8(4), 3642176674) Springer.

Kasper, Cornelia, et al, eds. Bioreactor Systems for Tissue Engineering II: Strategies for the Expansion & Directed Differentiation of Stem Cells. 2010. (Advances in Biochemical Engineering Biotechnology Ser.). (Illus.). xii, 310p. 309.00 (978-3-642-16050-9(6), 3642160506) Springer.

Kasper, Cornelia, et al. Bioreactor Systems for Tissue Engineering. 2009. (Advances in Biochemical Engineering / Biotechnology Ser.). (ENG., Illus.). xii, 271p. 299.00 (978-3-540-69356-7(4)) Springer.

Kennes, C. & Veiga, M. C., eds. Bioreactors for Waste Gas Treatment. 2010. (Environmental Pollution Ser.). 320p. pap. 179.00 (978-90-481-5772-3(2), 9048157722) Springer.

Koch, Joachim & Mahler, Michael, eds. Peptide Arrays on Membrane Supports: Synthesis & Applications. 2010. (Springer Lab Manuals Ser.). (Illus.). x, 173p. pap. 189.00 (978-3-642-07639-8(4), 3642076394) Springer.

Korf, Ulrike, ed. Protein Microarrays: Methods & Protocols. 2011. (Methods in Molecular Biology Ser.). (ENG., Illus.). xi, 398p. 139.00 (978-1-61779-285-4(3), 1617792853) Humana Pr.

Leon, Rosa, et al, eds. Transgenic Microalgae as Green Cell Factories. 2007. (Advances in Experimental Medicine & Biology Ser.). (ENG., Illus.). 600p. 159.00 (978-0-387-75531-1(4), 0387755314) Springer.

Li, Paul C. H. Fundamentals of Microfluidics & Lab on a Chip for Biological Analysis & Discovery. 2010. (ENG., Illus.). 418p. pap. 99.95 (978-1-4398-1855-8(X), CRC Press) Taylor & Francis Group GBR. Dist: Taylor & Francis Group.

Liu, Robin & Lee, Abraham P., eds. Integrated Biochips for DNA Analysis. 2010. (Biotechnology Intelligence Unit Ser.). (Illus.). xvi, 202p. pap. 199.00 (978-1-4419-2637-1(2), 1441926372) Springer.

Liu, Robin Hui & Lee, Abraham P. Integrated Biochips for DNA Analysis. 2008. (Biotechnology Intelligence Unit Ser.). (ENG., Illus.). 218p. 199.00 (978-0-387-76758-1(4), 0387767584) Springer.

Mahmood, Qaisar. Anoxic Sulfide Biooxidation Using Nitrite As Electron Acceptor. 2010. 220p. pap. (978-3-8383-3405-9(1)) Lambert Academic Publishing.

Matthiesen, Ulrich. DNA: Fingerprinting, Sequencing & Chips. Ovesen, Kresten, ed. 2010. (DNA: Properties & Modifications, Functions & Interactions, Recombination & Applications Ser.). 268p. 129.00 (978-1-60741-814-6(2), Nova Biomedical Bks.) Nova Science Pubs., Inc.

McConnell, Patrick, et al. Methods of Microarray Data Analysis V. 2010. (ENG., Illus.). xiv, 176p. pap. 109.00 (978-1-4419-4179-4(7), 1441941797) Springer.

Minteer, Shelley D., ed. Microfluidic Techniques: Reviews & Protocols. 2010. (Methods in Molecular Biology Ser.). (Illus.). x, 247p. pap. 119.00 (978-1-61737-613-9(2), 1617376132) Humana Pr.

Mitchell, David A., et al, eds. Solid-State Fermentation Bioreactors: Fundamentals of Design & Operation. 2010. (ENG., Illus.). xxxviii, 447p. pap. 219.00 (978-3-642-06839-3(1), 3642068391) Springer.

Mocellin, Simone, ed. Microarray Technology & Cancer Gene Profiling. 2010. (Advances in Experimental Medicine & Biology Ser.). (Illus.). xviii, 159p. pap. 159.00 (978-1-4419-2298-4(9), 1441922989) Springer.

Müller, Uwe R. & Nicolau, Dan V. Microarray Technology & Its Applications. 2010. (Biological & Medical Physics, Biomedical Engineering Ser.). (Illus.). xxii, 400p. pap. 189.00 (978-3-642-06182-0(6), 3642061826) Springer.

Palmer, Ella, ed. Cell-Based Microarrays: Methods & Protocols. 2010. (Methods in Molecular Biology Ser.). (ENG., Illus.). x, 209p. 119.00 (978-1-61737-969-7(7), 1617379697) Humana Pr.

Ray, Anamika. Application of Microarray Technology. 2010. 68p. pap. (978-3-8383-6406-3(6)) Lambert Academic Publishing.

Russell, Steve, et al. Microarray Technology in Practice. 2008. (ENG., Illus.). 464p. pap. 61.95 (978-0-12-372516-5(X), Academic Pr.) Elsevier Science & Technology Bks.

Shi, Cao Ye, et al. Biological Nitrogen Removal Activated Sludge Process in Warm Climates: Full-Scale Process Investigation, Laboratory Experimentation & Mathematical Modeling. 2008. 168p. (C). pap. (978-1-84339-187-6(2)) IWA Publishing.

Simon, Richard M., et al. Design & Analysis of DNA Microarray Investigations. 2012. (Statistics for Biology & Health Ser.). (ENG., Illus.). x, 199p. pap. 89.95 (978-1-4419-1802-4(7), 1441918027) Springer.

Stettler, Matthieu. Bioreactor Processes Based on Disposable Materials. 2009. 152p. pap. (978-3-639-15028-5(7)) VDM Verlag Dr. Mueller e.K.

Sunkel, Vanessa. Marine Bioprospecting & Natural Product Research. 2010. 220p. pap. (978-3-8383-4767-7(6)) Lambert Academic Publishing.

Valencia Vazquez, Roberto. Enhanced Stabilisation of Municipal Solid Waste in Bioreactor Landfills: UNESCO-IHE PhD Thesis. 2008. (ENG., Illus.). 158p. pap. 75.95 (978-0-415-47831-1(6), CRC Press) Taylor & Francis Group GBR. Dist: Taylor & Francis Group.

Villadsen, John, et al. Bioreaction Engineering Principles. 3rd ed. 2011. (ENG., Illus.). xxx, 561p. 89.95 (978-1-4419-9687-9(7), 1441996877) Springer.

Villela Filho, Murillo. Enantioselective Reduction of Hydrophobic Keto Compounds in Multiphase Bioreactor. 2007. (Schriften des Forschungszentrums Jülich: Vol. 34). 194p. pap. (978-3-89336-470-1(6)) Forschungszentrum Julich GmbH - Zentralbibliothek, Verlag.

Von Sperling, M. Activated Sludge & Aerobic Biofilm Reactors. 2007. (Biological Wastewater Treatment Ser.). (Illus.). 328p. (C). pap. (978-1-84339-165-4(1)) IWA Publishing.

—Waste Stabilisation Ponds. 2007. (Biological Wastewater Treatment Ser.). 168p. (C). pap. (978-1-84339-163-0(5)) IWA Publishing.

Water Environment Federation. Membrane Bio Reactors No. 36. 2011. (ENG., Illus.). 262p. (C). 125.00 (978-0-07-175366-1(4), 0071753664) McGraw-Hill Professional Publishing.

Xing, Wan-Li & Cheng, Jing. Biochips: Technology & Applications. 2010. (Biological & Medical Physics, Biomedical Engineering Ser.). (Illus.). vii, 134p. pap. 139.00 (978-3-642-05585-0(0), 3642055850) Springer.

Xing, Wan-Li & Cheng, Jing, eds. Frontiers in Biochip Technology. 2010. (ENG., Illus.). ix, 357p. pap. 149.00 (978-1-4419-3806-0(0), 1441938060) Springer.

Zhao, Yang & Chakrabarty, Krishnendu. Design & Testing of Digital Microfluidic Biochips. 2012. (ENG., Illus.). xii, 262p. 129.00 (978-1-4614-0369-2(3), 1461403693) Springer.

Zimmer, Gerald. Development of a CellChip based Multi-Well-Type Bioreactor: A multi-purpose platform for three dimensional cultivation of cells. 2008. 92p. pap. (978-3-639-10541-4(9)) VDM Verlag Dr. Mueller e.K.

BIOREMEDIATION

see also In Situ Bioremediation; Pollution

Aellon, Marjorie C. Env Isot Bioremed Biodegrad. 2009. (ENG., Illus.). 464p. 133.95 (978-1-56670-661-2(0), CRC Press) Taylor & Francis Group GBR. Dist: Taylor & Francis Group.

Agathos, Spiros & Reineke, W., eds. Biotechnology for the Environment: Soil Remediation: Soil Remediation. 2010. (Focus on Biotechnology Ser.). 148p. pap. 149.00 (978-90-481-6188-1(6), 9048161886) Springer.

—Biotechnology for the Environment: Wastewater Treatment & Modeling, Waste Gas Handling: Wastewater Treatment & Modeling, Waste Gas Handling. 2010. (Focus on Biotechnology Ser.). 288p. pap. 2`9.00 (978-90-481-6224-6(6), 9048162246) Springer.

Ahmad, Wan Azlina, et al, eds. Bacteria in Environmental Biotechnology: The Malaysian Case Study-Analysis, Waste Utilization & Wastewater Remediation. 2010. (Bacteriology Research Developments Environmental Science, Engineering & Technology Ser.). pap. 75.00 (978-1-61728-350-5(9), Nova Novinka) Nova Science Pubs., Inc.

Arora, Kalpana & Satyawati Sharma. Bioremediation of Heavy Metals. 2011. 100p. pap. (978-3-8433-8992-1(6)) Lambert Academic Publishing.

Ashraf, M., et al, eds. Plant Adaptation & Phytoremediation. 2010. (ENG., Illus.). x, 481p. 209.00 (978-90-481-9369-1(9), 9048193699) Springer.

Bartacek, Jan, et al, eds. Biotechniques for Air Pollution Control: Proceedings of the 3rd International Congress on Biotechniques for Air Pollution Control, Delft, the Netherlands, September 28-30 2009. 2010. (ENG., Illus.). 350p. 104.95 (978-0-415-58270-4(9), CRC Press) Taylor & Francis Group GBR. Dist: Taylor & Francis Group.

Battelle Press Staff, compiled by. 9th International in Situ & on-Site Bioremediation Symposium 2007. 2008. 1548p. pap. 350.00 (978-1-60423-948-5(4)) Curran Assocs., Inc.

Baveye, P., et al, eds. Bioavailability of Organic Xenobiotics in the Environment: Practical Consequences for the Environment. 2011. (NATO Science Partnership Sub-Series: 2: Ser.). (ENG., Illus.). 520p. pap. 379.00 (978-90-481-5311-4(5), 9048153115) Springer.

Bhattacharyya & Banerjee, Rintu. Environmental Biotechnology. 2008. (ENG.). 400p. pap. 45.00 (978-0-19-568782-8(5)) Oxford Univ. Pr., Inc.

Bini, Claudio, ed. Soil Contamination to Land Restoration. 2010. (Air, Water & Soil Pollution Science & Technology Ser.). pap. 43.00 (978-1-60876-853-0(8)) Nova Science Pubs., Inc.

Borah, Debajit. Ecologically Important Microbes in Automobile Engines. 2011. 76p. pap. (978-3-8443-0091-8(0)) Lambert Academic Publishing.

Chaudhry, G. Rasul. Biological Degradation & Bioremediation of Toxic Chemicals. 2010. (ENG.). 516p. pap. 69.95 (978-1-60469-204-4(9), 1604692049) Timber Pr., Inc.

EL-Sersy, Nermeen & El-Sersy, Nermeen. Microbial Catabolism of Some Marine Organic Pollutants: The Developmnt. 2011. 116p. pap. (978-3-8433-9456-7(3)) Lambert Academic Publishing.

Eljamal, Osama. Solute Transport with Biological Processes in Porous Medi. 2010. 160p. pap. (978-3-639-25924-7(6)) VDM Verlag Dr. Mueller e.K.

Evans, Gareth G. & Furlong, Judy. Environmental Biotechnology: Theory & Application. 2nd ed. 2011. (ENG & ABK., Illus.). 290p. pap. 89.95 (978-0-470-68417-7(8), Wiley) Wiley, John & Sons, Inc.

Filler, Dennis, et al, eds. Bioremediation of Petroleum Hydrocarbons in Cold Regions. 2008. (ENG., Illus.). 288p. 126.00 (978-0-521-86970-6(6)) Cambridge Univ. Pr.

Fulekar, M. H. Environmental Biotechnology. 2010. (ENG., Illus.). 620p. pap. 89.95 (978-1-57808-582-8(9)) BIOS Scientific Publishers Ltd. GBR. Dist: Taylor & Francis Group.

—Environmental Biotechnology. 2010. (978-1-57808-573-6(X)) Science Pubs.

Fulekar, M. H., ed. Bioremediation Technology: Recent Advances. 2010. (ENG., Illus.). x, 280p. 129.00 (978-90-481-3677-3(6), 9048136776) Springer.

Furlong, Judy & Evans, Gareth G. Environmental Biotechnology: Theory & Application. 2nd ed. 2011. (ENG., Illus.). 290p. 149.95 (978-0-470-68418-4(6), Wiley) Wiley, John & Sons, Inc.

Gad, Amber. Environmental Bio Remediation of Heavy Metals. 2011. 56p. pap. (978-3-8443-2595-9(6)) Lambert Academic Publishing.

Gadd, G. M., ed. Fungi in Bioremediation. 2008. (British Mycological Society Symposia Ser.). (ENG., Illus.). 496p. pap. 100.00 (978-0-521-06531-3(3)) Cambridge Univ. Pr.

Golubev, Ivan A., ed. Handbook of Phytoremediation. 2011. (Environmental Science, Engineering & Technology Ser.). 839p. 295.00 (978-1-61728-753-4(9)) Nova Science Pubs., Inc.

Gujarathi, Ninad. Phytoremediation of Antibiotics from Wastes of Animal Feedlots. 2009. (Illus.). 152p. pap. (978-3-639-13576-3(8)) VDM Verlag Dr. Mueller e.K.

Heipieper, Hermann. Bioremediation of Soils Contaminated with Aromatic Compounds: Proceedings of the NATO Advanced Research Workshop on Bioremediation of Soils Contaminated with Aromatic Compounds, Tartu, Estonia, 1-3 July 2004. (Nato Science Series: IV: Earth & Environmental Sciences Ser.). (ENG.). xxvi, 130p. (C). 2007. pap. 79.95 (978-1-4020-5692-5(3), 1402056923) 2006. 219.00 (978-1-4020-5691-8(5), 1402056915) Springer London, Ltd. GBR. Dist: Springer.

Ike, Michihiko, et al, eds. Handbook of Metal Biotechnology: Applications for Environmental Conservation & Sustainability. 2011. (ENG., Illus.). 264p. 249.95 (978-981-4267-98-4(8)) Pan Stanford Publishing SGP. Dist: Taylor & Francis Group.

Ikhajiagbe, Beckley. Synergism in Bioremediation. 2011. 284p. pap. (978-3-8433-6491-1(5)) Lambert Academic Publishing.

Jain, Pankaj Kumar, et al. Recent Advances in Environmental Biotechnology. 2011. 228p. pap. (978-3-8443-0687-3(0)) Lambert Academic Publishing.

Johnson, A. & Singhal, Naresh. Amendment-Enhanced Phytoextraction of Soil Contaminants. 2010. (Environmental Remediation Technologies, Regulations & Safety Ser.). pap. 43.00 (978-1-60876-275-1(5)) Nova Science Pubs., Inc.

Kaushish Lily, Dr. Madhuri, et al. Benzo-A-Pyrene Degradation by Bacillus Subtilis Bmt4i. 2011. 160p. pap. (978-3-8443-2455-6(0)) Lambert Academic Publishing.

Ke, Lin & Tam, Nora F. Y. Phytoremediation Using Constructed Mangrove Wetlands: Mechanisms & Application Potential. 2011. (Environmental Science, Engineering & Technology Ser.). pap. 43.00 (978-1-61761-925-0(6), Nova Novinka) Nova Science Pubs., Inc.

Koukkou, Anna-Irini, ed. Microbial Bioremediation of Non-Metals: Current Research. 2011. (Illus.). 290p. 319.00 (978-1-904455-83-7(2)) Caister Academic Pr. GBR. Dist: International Specialized Bk. Services.

Kriipsalu, Mait. Biotreatment of Oily Sludge & Sediments. 2009. 84p. pap. (978-3-639-16403-9(2)) VDM Verlag Dr. Mueller e.K.

Kulakow, Peter A. & Pidlisnyuk, Valentina V., eds. Application of Phytotechnologies for Cleanup of Industrial, Agricultural & Wastewater Contamination. 2009. (NATO Science for Peace & Security Series C: Environmental Security Ser.). (Illus.). vii, 202p. 219.00 (978-90-481-3590-5(7), 9048135907); (ENG., xiv, 198p. pap. 109.00 (978-90-481-3591-2(5), 9048135915) Springer.

Kvesitadze, George, et al. Biochemical Mechanisms of Detoxification in Higher Plants: Basis of Phytoremediation. 2010. (ENG., Illus.). x, 256p. pap. 239.00 (978-3-642-06702-0(6), 3642067026) Springer.

Landmeyer, James E. Introduction to Phytoremediation of Contaminated Groundwater: Historical Foundation, Hydrologic Control, & Contaminant Remediation. 2011. (ENG., Illus.). xxi, 415p. 179.00 (978-94-007-1956-9(6), 9400719566) Springer.

Liang, Yanna. Pyrene Degradation by Mycobacterium Sp Kms: Biochemical Pathway, Enzymatic Mechanisms, & Humic Acid Effect. 2010. 184p. pap. 25.95 (978-1-59942-717-1(6), Dissertation.com) Universal Pubs.

López, Eric S. Ecological Revitalization & Green Remediation of Contaminated Sites. 2011. (Series: Environmental Science, Engineering & Technology Ser.). 89.00 (978-1-61122-520-4(5)) Nova Science Pubs., Inc.

Lynch, James M. & Wiseman, Alan, eds. Environmental Biomonitoring: The Biotechnology Ecotoxicology Interface. 2011. (Biotechnology Research Ser.). (ENG., Illus.). 317p. pap. 39.99 (978-0-521-18773-2(7)) Cambridge Univ. Pr.

Mackova, Martina, et al, eds. Phytoremediation & Rhizoremediation. 2010. (Focus on Biotechnology Ser.). vi, 300p. pap. 289.00 (978-90-481-7238-2(1), 9048172381) Springer.

Margesin, Rosa & Schinner, Franz. Manual for Soil Analysis - Monitoring & Assessing Soil Bioremediation. 2010. (Soil Biology Ser.). (Illus.). xvi, 366p pap. 259.00 (978-3-642-06467-8(1), 3642064671) Springer.

Mason, Alexander C. Bioremediation: Biotechnology, Engineering & Environmental Management. 2011. (Series: Biotechnology in Agriculture, Industry & Medicine Ser.). 165.00 (978-1-61122-730-7(5)) Nova Science Pubs., Inc.

Mohee, Romeela & Mudhoo, Ackmez. Bioremediation & Sustainability: Research & Applications. 2012. (ENG.). 438p. 195.00 (978-1-118-06284-5(1), Wiley-Scrivener) Wiley, John & Sons, Inc.

Moo-Young, M., et al, eds. Environmental Biotechnology: Principles & Applications: Principles & Applications. 2010. 780p. pap. 329.00 (978-90-481-4657-4(7), 9048146577) Springer.

Pal, B. P. Search for New Genes. Bhat, S. R. et al, eds. 2007. (ENG., Illus.). 500p. 79.95 (978-81-7188-632-6(9)) Academic Foundation IND. Dist: Independent Pubs. Group.

Polinek, Jiri. Fermentative Production of Recombinant Haloalkane Dehalogenases. 2010. 76p. pap. (978-3-8383-6539-8(9)) Lambert Academic Publishing.

Popp, Nicole. Microflora in Bioremediation Systems Treating Contaminated Soils. 2008. 116p. pap. (978-3-639-06524-4(7)) VDM Verlag Dr. Mueller e.K.

Rai, Prabhat Kumar. Heavy Metal Pollution & Its Phytoremediation Through Wetland Plants. 2011. (Environmental Remediation Technologies, Regulations & Safety Air, Water & Soil Pollution Science & Technology Ser.) 221p. 69.00 (978-1-61209-938-5(6)) Nova Science Pubs., Inc.

Rawlings, Douglas E. & Johnson, D. Barrie, eds. Biomining. 2006. (ENG., Illus.). xx, 314p. 219.00 (978-3-540-34909-9(X), 354034909X) Springer.

Sadasivam, Senthil Kumar. Bioremediation of Textile Dyes & Effluent. 2011. 252p. pap. (978-3-8433-7885-7(1)) Lambert Academic Publishing.

Sanderson, John Craig. Bioremediation Using Seaweed Culture. 2009. 288p. pap. (978-3-639-13534-3(2)) VDM Verlag Dr. Mueller e.K.

Sengupta, Mritunjoy. Bioremediation Engineering for Mining & Mineral Processing Wastes Second Edition: Second Edition. 2008. (Illus.). 330p. ring bd. 85.00 (978-0-9653025-5-5(5)) Northwest Academic Publishing.

Sheehan, David, ed. Bioremediation Protocols. 2010. (Methods in Biotechnology Ser.). (Illus.). 352p. pap. 149.00 (978-1-61737-036-6(3), 1617370363) Humana Pr.

Singh, Ajay, et al. Advances in Applied Bioremediation. 2009. (Soil Biology Ser.). (ENG., Illus.). xiii, 361p. 269.00 (978-3-540-89620-3(1), 3540896201) Springer.

Singh, Ajay & Ward, Owen P. Biodegradation & Bioremediation. 2010. (Soil Biology Ser.). (Illus.). xvii, 309p. pap. 249.00 (978-3-642-05929-2(5), 3642059295) Springer.

Singh, Ajay & Ward, Owen P., eds. Applied Bioremediation & Phytoremediation. 2011. (Soil Biology Ser.). (ENG., Illus.). xix, 281p. pap. 289.00 (978-3-642-05908-7(2), 3642059082) Springer.

Singh, S. N. & Tripathi, R. D., eds. Environmental Bioremediation Technologies. (ENG., Illus.). xx, 518p. 2010. pap. 249.00 (978-3-642-07111-9(2), 3642071112) 2006. 249.00 (978-3-540-34790-3(9), 3540347909) Springer.

Sinha, Rajiv K., et al, eds. Microremediation, Phytoremediation & Vermiremediation Biotechnologies for Contaminated Lands & Soil. 2010. (Environmental Remediation Technologies, Regulations & Safety Ser.). 123p. pap. 43.00 (978-1-61668-148-7(9)) Nova Science Pubs., Inc.

Speight, James G. Bioremediation of Refined Petroleum Fractions. 2012. (ENG.). 185.00 (978-0-470-93849-2(8), Wiley-Scrivener) Wiley, John & Sons, Inc.

Srivastava, Sarvesh Kumar & Joshi, Namrata. Biosurfactant Production & Characterization. 2010. 96p. pap. (978-3-8383-6022-5(2)) Lambert Academic Publishing.

Thakur, Indu Shekhar. Environmental Biotechnology: Basic Concepts & Applications. 2nd rev. ed. 2011. 534p. (C). pap. (978-93-80578-47-7(4)) I.K. International Publishing House Pvt. Ltd.

Tsao, G. T., et al, eds. Biotechnology in China II: Chemicals, Energy & Environment. 2010. (Advances in Biochemical Engineering Biotechnology Ser.). (Illus.). xiv, 264p. 359.00 (978-3-642-14994-8(4), 3642149944) Springer.

Valdes, J. J., ed. Bioremediation. 2010. 184p. pap. 179.00 (978-90-481-5519-4(3), 9048155193) Springer.

Vallero, Daniel. Environmental Biotechnology: A Biosystems Approach. 2010. (ENG., Illus.). 750p. 129.00 (978-0-12-375089-1(X), Academic Pr.) Elsevier Science & Technology Bks.

Venkata Ramanaiah, Sudarsu. Bioremediation of Fluoride by Biosorption. 2010. 252p. pap. (978-3-639-24680-3(2)) VDM Verlag Dr. Mueller e.K.

Vimala, Yapadinna, et al. Bioremediation of Toxic Pollutants Using Microorganisms. 2011. 204p. pap. (978-3-8443-1556-1(X)) Lambert Academic Publishing.

Vuppu, Dr. Suneetha & Vuppu, Suneetha. Screening of Keratinolytic Bacteria from Poultry Waste. 2011. 108p. pap. (978-3-8443-2787-8(8)) Lambert Academic Publishing.

Vuppu, Suneetha. Screening, Characterization of Xylanase Producing Microorganisms. 2011. 88p. pap. (978-3-8443-1519-6(5)) Lambert Academic Publishing.

Wang, Lawrence K., et al, eds. Environmental Bioengineering, Vol. 11. 2007. (Handbook of Environmental Engineering Ser.). (Illus.). 465p. 209.00 (978-1-58829-493-7(5), 1588294935) Humana Pr.

—Environmental Biotechnology, Vol. 10. 2007. (Handbook of Environmental Engineering Ser.). (Illus.). 400p. 209.00 (978-1-58829-166-0(9), 1588291669) Humana Pr.

Wani, Parvaze Ahmad & Khan, Mohd. Saghir. Heavy Metal Toxicity & Their Remediation by Soil Microbes. 2011. 332p. pap. (978-3-8454-0447-9(7)) Lambert Academic Publishing.

Willey, Neil, ed. Phytoremediation: Methods & Reviews. (Methods in Biotechnology Ser.). (Illus.). 2010. xvi, 478p. pap. 199.00 (978-1-61737-631-3(0), 1617376310) 2007. XVI, 478p. 199.00 (978-1-58829-541-5(9), 1588295419) Humana Pr.

Wise, D. L., ed. Global Environmental Biotechnology. 2010. 640p. pap. 579.00 (978-90-481-4836-3(7), 9048148367) Springer.

Wolicka, Dorota, ed. Sulphate-Reducing Bacteria in Biological Treatment Wastewaters. 2010. (Air, Water & Soil Pollution Science & Technology Ser.). pap. 43.00 (978-1-60876-931-5(3)) Nova Science Pubs., Inc.

Wolverton, Bill. Plants: Why We Can't Live Without Them. 2010. (Roli Bks.). (ENG.). 144p. pap. 24.95 (978-81-7436-751-8(9)) Roli Bks. Private, Ltd. IND. Dist: Ingram Pub. Services.

Wypych, George, et al. Handbook of Material Biodegradation, Biodeterioration, & Biostablization. 2010. (ENG.). 250p. instr.'s hndbk. ed. 275.00 (978-1-895198-44-7(5)) ChemTec Publishing CAN. Dist: Elsevier Science & Technology Bks.

Yin, Xuebin. Phytoremediation of Heavy Metals & Organic Pollutants. 2012. (SpringerBriefs in Molecular Science / Green Chemistry for Sustainability Ser.). (ENG.). 125p. pap. 49.95 (978-94-007-1438-0(6), 9400714386) Springer.

Zaidi, Almas, et al, eds. Toxicity of Heavy Metals to Legumes & Bioremediation. 2012. (ENG., Illus.). xii, 248p. 189.00 (978-3-7091-0729-4(6), 3709107296) Springer.

Zhong, J. J., et al. Biotechnology in China I. 2009. (Advances in Biochemical Engineering / Biotechnology Ser.). (ENG., Illus.). xiii, 322p. 389.00 (978-3-540-88414-9(9), 3540884149) Springer.

BIORHYTHMS

see Biological Rhythms

BIOSCIENCES

see Life Sciences

BIOSCOPE

see Motion Picture Projection

BIOSENSORS

Achilefu, Samuel I. Genetically Engineered & Optical Probes for Biomedical Applications IV: 23-24 January 2007, San Jose, California, USA. 2007. (Progress in Biomedical Optics & Imaging Ser.: No. 8). (Illus.). 278p. pap. 90.00 (978-0-8194-6552-7(3)) SPIE.

Achilefu, Samuel I., et al. Molecular Probes for Biomedical Applications II: 21-22 January 2008, San Jose, California, USA. 2008. (Proceedings of SPIE Ser.). (Illus.). 156p. pap. 70.00 (978-0-8194-7042-3(2)) SPIE.

Al-Hilli, Safaa & Willander, Magnus, eds. ZnO Nano-Structures for Biosensing Applications: Molecular Dynamic Simulations. 2009. (Nanotechnology Science & Technology Ser.). pap. 43.00 (978-1-61728-280-5(4), Nova Novinka) Nova Science Pubs., Inc.

Alegret, Salvador & Merkoci, Arben, eds. Electrochemical Sensor Analysis. 2007. (Comprehensive Analytical Chemistry Ser.: 49). (ENG., Illus.). 1028p. 325.00 (978-0-444-53053-0(3), Elsevier Science) Elsevier Science & Technology Bks.

Anslyn, Eric V. & Wang, Binghe, eds. Chemosensors: Principles, Strategies, & Applications. 2011. (Wiley Series in Drug Discovery & Development Ser.: 15). (ENG., Illus.). 540p. 149.95 (978-0-470-59206-9(0), Wiley) Wiley, John & Sons, Inc.

Baldrich, Eva. Pathogen Detection Methods: Biosensor Development. Garcia-Aljaro, Cristina, ed. 2010. (Biotechnology in Agriculture, Industry & Medicine Ser.). 154p. pap. 43.00 (978-1-61668-298-9(1)) Nova Science Pubs., Inc.

Baronas, Romas, et al. Mathematical Modeling of Biosensors: An Introduction for Chemists & Mathematicians. 2009. (Springer Series on Chemical Sensors & Biosensors Ser.). (ENG., Illus.). xix, 334p. 189.00 (978-90-481-3242-3(8), 9048132428) Springer.

Barth, Friedrich, et al, eds. Frontiers in Sensing: From Biology to Engineering. 2011. (ENG., Illus.). x, 438p. 209.00 (978-3-211-99748-2(2), 3211997482) Springer.

Becker, H. & Gray, Bonnie Lynne. Microfluidics, BioMEMS, & Medical Microsystems IX: 23-25 January 2011, San Francisco, California, United States. 2011. (Proceedings of SPIE Ser.). (Illus.). 288p. pap. 80.00 (978-0-8194-8466-6(0)) SPIE.

Belkin, Shimshon & Gu, Man Bock, eds. Whole Cell Sensing System II: Applications, 2 vols. 2010. (Advances in Biochemical Engineering Biotechnology Ser.). (Illus.). xii, 220p. 299.00 (978-3-642-12852-3(1), 3642128521) Springer.

Belyanin, Alexey, et al. Infrared, Mid-IR, & Terahertz Technologies for Health & the Environment II. 2007. (Proceedings of SPIE Ser.). 80p. pap. 60.00 (978-0-8194-6920-5(3)) SPIE.

Biggins, Peter, et al. Bio-Inspired Materials & Sensing Systems. 2011. (ENG., Illus.). 164p. 120.00 (978-1-84973-121-8(7)) Royal Society of Chemistry, The GBR. Dist: Ingram Pub. Services.

Billah, Morsaline. Electrochemical Impedimetric Immunosensors for Cardiac Pathology. 2011. 284p. pap. (978-3-8443-1572-1(1)) Lambert Academic Publishing.

Bock, Wojtek J., et al. Optical Waveguide Sensing & Imaging: [proceedings of the NATO Advanced Study Institute on Optical Waveguide Sensing & Imaging in Medicine, Environment, Security & Defence, Gatineau, Québec, Canada, 12-21 October 2006]. Bock, Wojtek J. et al, eds. 2007. (NATO Science for Peace & Security Series B: Physics & Biophysics Ser.). (Illus.). VIII, 269p. 249.00 (978-1-4020-6950-5(2), 1402069502) Springer.

Brongersma, Mark L. & Kik, Pieter G., eds. Surface Plasmon Nanophotonics. 2010. (Springer Series in Optical Sciences Ser.). vi, 271p. pap. 189.00 (978-90-481-7113-2(X), 904817113X) Springer.

Carapezza, Edward M. Unmanned/Unattended Sensors & Sensor Networks III: 11-12 September, 2006, Stockholm, Sweden. 2006. (Proceedings of SPIE Ser.). (Illus.). 184p. pap. 80.00 (978-0-8194-6492-7(9)) SPIE.

—Unmanned/Unattended Sensors & Sensor Networks V: 16-18 September 2008, Cardiff, Wales, United Kingdom. 2008. (Proceedings of SPIE Ser.). (Illus.). 306p. pap. 90.00 (978-0-8194-7344-8(8)) SPIE.

—Unmanned/Unattended Sensors & Sensor Networks VI: 1-3 September 2009, Berlin, Germany. 2009. (Proceedings of SPIE Ser.). (Illus.). 298p. pap. 90.00 (978-0-8194-7786-6(9)) SPIE.

Carapezza, Edward M. Unmanned/Unattended Sensors & Sensor Networks VII: 20-22 September 2010, Toulouse, France. 2010. (Proceedings of SPIE Ser.). (Illus.). 256p. pap. 90.00 (978-0-8194-8351-5(6)) SPIE.

Carloni, Adolfo. A Novel Optical Biochip Based on Fluorescence Anisotropy. 2010. 236p. pap. (978-3-639-22368-2(3), VDM Verlag Dr. Mueller e.K.

Carrano, John C. & Collins, Charles J. Optically Based Biological & Chemical Detection for Defence V: 1 September 2009, Berlin, Germany. 2009. (Proceedings of SPIE Ser.). (Illus.). 172p. pap. 70.00 (978-0-8194-7790-3(7)) SPIE.

Carrano, John C. & Zukauskas, Arturas. Optically Based Biological & Chemical Detection for Defence III: 11-13 September 2006, Stockholm, Sweden. 2006. (Proceedings of SPIE Ser.). (Illus.). 248p. pap. 90.00 (978-0-8194-6496-5(1)) SPIE.

Carrara, Sandro, ed. Nano-Bio-Sensing. 2010. (ENG., Illus.). x, 248p. 129.00 (978-1-4419-6168-6(2), 1441961682) Springer.

Cartwright, Alexander N. & Nicolau, Dan V. Nanoscale Imaging, Spectroscopy, Sensing, & Actuation for Biomedical Applications IV: 23-24 January 2007, San Jose, California, USA. 2007. (Progress in Biomedical Optics & Imaging Ser.: No. 8). (Illus.). 174p. pap. 70.00 (978-0-8194-6560-2(7)) SPIE.

Chang, Huan-Tsung & Chau, Lai-Kwan, eds. From Bioimaging to Biosensors: Noble Metal Nanoparticles in Biodetection. 2012. (ENG., Illus.). 400p. 149.95 (978-981-4267-24-3(4)) Pan Stanford Publishing SGP. Dist: Taylor & Francis Group.

Cheng, Xiaoyang. Capacitive Micromachined Ultrasonic Transducers. 2009. 124p. pap. (978-3-639-18633-8(8)) VDM Verlag Dr. Mueller e.K.

Christesen, Steven Dale. Chemical & Biological Sensors for Industrial & Environmental Monitoring II: 3-4 October, 2006, Boston, Massachusetts,

USA. 2006. (Progress in Biomedical Optics & Imaging Ser.: No. 7). (Illus.). 372p. pap. 105.00 *(978-0-8194-6476-7(7))* SPIE.

Colomer-Farrarons, Jordi & Miribel-Catala, Pere Luis. A CMOS Self-Powered Front-End Architecture for Subcutaneous Event-Detector Devices: Three-Electrodes Amperometric Biosensor Approach. 2011. (ENG., Illus.). xi, 200p. 129.00 *(978-94-007-0685-9(5)*, 9400706855) Springer.

Comeaux, Rafael & Novotny, Pablo. Biosensors: Properties, Materials & Applications. 2009. (Biotechnology in Agriculture, Industry & Medicine Ser.). 129.00 *(978-1-60741-617-3(4))* Nova Science Pubs., Inc.

Cooper, M. A. Label-Free Biosensors: Techniques & Applications. 2009. (ENG., Illus.). 300p. 158.00 *(978-0-521-88453-2(5))*; pap. 72.99 *(978-0-521-71151-7(7))* Cambridge Univ. Pr.

Cullen, David C., et al, eds. Handbook of Biosensors & Biochips. 2007. (ENG.). 1500p. 990.00 *(978-0-470-01905-4(0)*, Wiley-Interscience) Wiley, John & Sons, Inc.

Cullum, Brian & Mclamore, Eric. Smart Biomedical & Physiological Sensor Technology VIII. 2011. (Proceedings of SPIE Ser.). pap. 70.00 ***(978-0-8194-8599-1(3))*** SPIE.

Cullum, Brian M. & Carter, J. Chance. Smart Medical & Biomedical Sensor Technology IV: 3-4 October 2006, Boston, Massachusetts, USA. 2006. (Progress in Biomedical Optics & Imaging Ser.: No. 7). (Illus.). 250p. pap. 80.00 *(978-0-8194-6478-1(3))* SPIE.

Cullum, Brian M. & Porterfield, D. M. Smart Biomedical & Physiological Sensor Technology V: 10-11 September 2007, Boston, Massachusetts, USA. 2007. (Proceedings of SPIE Ser.). (Illus.). 172p. pap. 80.00 *(978-0-8194-6919-9(X))* SPIE.

—Smart Biomedical & Physiological Sensor Technology VI: 16-17 April 2009, Orlando, Florida, United States. 2009. (Proceedings of SPIE Ser.). (Illus.). 210p. pap. 70.00 *(978-0-8194-7579-4(3))* SPIE.

Defense, Security, & Sensing 2011: Imaging & Sensing. 2011. (Proceedings of SPIE Ser.). cd-rom 665.00 ***(978-0-8194-8641-7(8))*** SPIE.

Dishongh, Terrance J., et al. Wireless Sensor Networks for Healthcare Applications. 2008. (Illus.). 430p. 109.00 *(978-1-59693-305-7(4))* Artech Hse., Inc.

Dugas, V., et al, eds. Use of Organosilanes in Biosensors. 2010. (Biotechnology in Agriculture, Industry & Medicine Ser.). pap. 43.00 *(978-1-61668-029-9(6))* Nova Science Pubs., Inc.

Ewing, Kenneth J. Chemical & Biological Sensors for Industrial & Environmental Monitoring III: 11-12 September 2007, Boston, Massachusetts, USA. 2007. (Proceedings of SPIE Ser.). (Illus.). 146p. pap. 70.00 ***(978-0-8194-6916-8(5))*** SPIE.

Fabry, Pierre & Fouletier, Jacques. Chemical & Biological Microsensors: Applications in Fluid Media. 2010. (Iste Ser.: 422). (ENG., Illus.). 320p. 158.00 *(978-1-84821-142-1(2)*, Wiley-ISTE) Wiley, John & Sons, Inc.

Falck, Thomas & Mahonen, Petri, eds. 4th International Workshop on Wearable & Implantable Body Sensor Networks (BSN 2007) March 26-28, 2007 RWTH Aachen University, Germany. 2007. (Ifmbe Proceedings Ser.). (Illus.). 298p. pap. 219.00 *(978-3-540-70993-0(2))* Springer.

Fan, Xudong, ed. Advanced Photonic Structure for Biological & Chemical Detection. 2009. (Integrated Analytical Systems Ser.). (ENG., Illus.). xx, 540p. 229.00 *(978-0-387-98060-7(1)*, 0387980601) Springer.

Fountain, Augustus & Gardner, Patrick. Chemical, Biological, Radiological, Nuclear, & Explosives (CBRNE) Sensing XII. 2011. (Proceedings of SPIE Ser.). 568p. pap. 130.00 ***(978-0-8194-8592-2(6))*** SPIE.

Fountain, Augustus W. Chemical & Biological Sensing VIII: 11-12 April 2007, Orlando, Florida, USA. 2007. (Proceedings of SPIE Ser.). (Illus.). 284p. pap. 80.00 *(978-0-8194-6676-1(X))* SPIE.

Fountain, Augustus W. & Gardner, Patrick J. Chemical, Biological, Radiological, Nuclear, & Explosives (CBRNE) Sensing IX: 18-20 March 2008, Orlando, Florida, USA. 2008. (Proceedings of SPIE Ser.). (Illus.). 354p. pap. 90.00 *(978-0-8194-7145-1(3))* SPIE.

—Chemical, Biological, Radiological, Nuclear, & Explosives (CBRNE) Sensing X: 14-16 April 2009, Orlando, Florida, United States. 2009. (Proceedings of SPIE Ser.). (Illus.). 416p. pap. 120.00 *(978-0-8194-7570-1(X))* SPIE.

Francesca, Berti. Towards Nanobiosensors: New Micro- & Nano-Technologies for Biosensors Development. 2011. 168p. pap. ***(978-3-639-24406-9(0))*** VDM Verlag Dr. Mueller e.K.

Francia. Sensors & Microsystems. Di, Francia G., ed. 2008. 187.00 *(978-981-283-358-7(7))* World Scientific Publishing Co., Inc.

Garnsjaeger, Roland. AFM & SPR on Biological Systems: Applying Atomic Force Microscopy (AFM) & Surface Plasmon Resonance (SPR) to Biologically Important Systems. 2008. 72p. pap. *(978-3-8364-8854-9(X))* VDM Verlag Dr. Mueller e.K.

Gannot, Israel. Optical Fibers & Sensors for Medical Diagnostics & Treatment Applications IX: 24-25 January 2009, San Jose, [Calif.], United States. 2009. (Proceedings of SPIE Ser.). (Illus.). 196p. pap. 80.00 *(978-0-8194-7419-3(3))* SPIE.

—Optical Fibers & Sensors for Medical Diagnostics & Treatment Applications VII: 20-21 January 2007, San Jose, California, USA. 2007. (Proceedings of SPIE Ser.: No. 8). (Illus.). 172p. pap. 70.00 *(978-0-8194-6546-7(1))* SPIE.

—Optical Fibers & Sensors for Medical Diagnostics & Treatment Applications VIII: 19-21 January 2008, San Jose, California, USA. 2008. (Proceedings of SPIE Ser.). (Illus.). 224p. pap. 80.00 *(978-0-8194-7027-0(9))* SPIE.

—Optical Fibers & Sensors for Medical Diagnostics & Treatment Applications X: 23-24 January 2010, San Francisco, California, United States. 2010. (Proceedings of SPIE Ser.). (Illus.). 184p. pap. 80.00 ***(978-0-8194-7955-6(1))*** SPIE.

—Optical Fibers, Sensors, & Devices for Biomedical Diagnostics & Treatment XI. 2011. (Proceedings of SPIE Ser.). 260p. pap. 90.00 ***(978-0-8194-8431-4(8))*** SPIE.

Genzer, Jan, ed. Soft Matter Gradient Surfaces: Methods & Applications. 2012. (ENG., Illus.). 458p. 135.00 *(978-0-470-52265-3(8)*, Wiley) Wiley, John & Sons, Inc.

Ghafar-Zadeh, Ebrahim & Sawan, Mohamad. CMOS Capacitive Sensors for Lab-on-Chip Applications: A Multidisciplinary Approach. 2010. (Analog Circuits & Signal Processing Ser.). (ENG., Illus.). 250p. 159.00 *(978-90-481-3726-8(8)*, 9048137268) Springer.

Giardi, Maria Teresa & Piletska, Elena. Biotechnological Applications of Photosynthetic Proteins: Biochips, Biosensors & Biodevices. 2010. (Biotechnology Intelligence Unit Ser.). xiv, 218p. pap. 209.00 *(978-1-4419-4110-7(X)*, 144194110X) Springer.

Giardi, Maria Teresa, et al. Bio-Farms for Nutraceuticals: Functional Food & Safety Control by Biosensors. 2011. (Advances in Experimental Medicine & Biology Ser.). (ENG., Illus.). xxviii, 332p. 209.00 *(978-1-4419-7346-7(X)*, 144197346X) Springer.

Govindaraju, Venu & Ratha, Nalini K., eds. Advances in Biometrics: Sensors, Algorithms & Systems. 2007. (ENG., Illus.). xx, 508p. 109.00 *(978-1-84628-920-0(3)*, 1846289203) Springer.

Hélix-Nielsen, Claus, ed. Biomimetic Membranes for Sensor & Separation Applications. 2012. (Biological & Medical Physics, Biomedical Engineering Ser.). (ENG., Illus.). xv, 284p. 169.00 ***(978-94-007-2183-8(8)***, 9400721838) Springer.

Hepel, Maria & Stobiecka, Magdalena. Interactions of Herbicide Atrazine with DNA. 2010. pap. *(978-1-61728-908-8(6))* Nova Publishing Co.

Herold, Keith E. & Rasooly, Avraham, eds. Biosensors for Cancer Diagnostics. 2012. (Series in Sensors Ser.). (ENG., Illus.). 844p. 169.95 *(978-1-4398-4165-5(9)*, Taylor & Francis) Taylor & Francis Group GBR. Dist: Taylor & Francis Group.

Hesketh, Peter J., ed. BioNanoFluidic MEMS. 2010. (MEMS Reference Shelf Ser.). (Illus.). x, 295p. pap. 179.00 *(978-1-4419-4279-1(3)*, 1441942793) Springer.

—Bionanofluidic Mems. 2008. (Mems Reference Shelf Ser.). (Illus.). 295p. 179.00 *(978-0-387-46281-3(3))* Springer.

Homola, Jiri, ed. Surface Plasmon Resonance Based Sensors. 2006. (Springer Series on Chemical Sensors & Biosensors Ser.). (Illus.). xii, 251p. 199.00 *(978-3-540-33918-2(3)*, 3540339183) Springer.

IEEE Staff. 2008 IEEE 14th International Mixed-Signals, Sensors, & Systems Test Workshop. 2008. pap. 224.00 *(978-1-4244-2395-8(3))* IEEE.

Iniewski, Krzysztof, ed. Biological & Medical Sensor Technologies. 2012. (Devices, Circuits, & Systems Ser.). (ENG., Illus.). 412p. 149.95 ***(978-1-4398-8267-2(3)***, CRC Press) Taylor & Francis Group GBR. Dist: Taylor & Francis Group.

Ionescu, Adrian M. & Bland, J. A. C. Biomagnetism & Magnetic Biosystems Based on Molecular Recognition Processes. 2008. (AIP Conference Proceedings Ser.). (Illus.). 216p. 112.00 *(978-0-7354-0547-9(6))* American Institute of Physics.

Iqbal, Samir. Bionanosensors. 2008. (Synthesis Lectures on Biomedical Engineering Ser.). pap. 40.00 *(978-1-59829-707-2(4))* Morgan & Claypool Pubs.

Ju, Huangxian, et al. NanoBiosensing: Principles, Development & Application. 2011. (Biological & Medical Physics, Biomedical Engineering Ser.). (ENG., Illus.). xv, 586p. 199.00 *(978-1-4419-9621-3(4)*, 1441996214) Springer.

Kalyankar, Nikhil. Novel Biosensors Using Intact Liposome Microarrays. 2009. 112p. pap. *(978-3-639-18938-4(8))* VDM Verlag Dr. Mueller e.K.

Kamerman, Gary, et al. Electro-Optical Remote Sensing, Photonic Technologies, & Applications III. 2009. (Proceedings of SPIE Ser.). 264p. pap. 70.00 ***(978-0-8194-7788-0(5))*** SPIE.

Kamerman, Gary W. Electro-Optical Remote Sensing, Detection, & Photonic Technologies & Their Applications: 18-20 September 2007, Florence, Italy. 2007. (Proceedings of SPIE Ser.). (Illus.). 414p. pap. 105.00 *(978-0-8194-6897-0(5))* SPIE.

—Electro-Optical Remote Sensing, Photonic Technologies, & Applications II: 15-16 September 2008, Cardiff, Wales, United Kingdom. 2008. (Proceedings of SPIE Ser.). (Illus.). 206p. pap. 80.00 *(978-0-8194-7346-2(4))* SPIE.

Kamerman, Gary W. Electro-Optical Remote Sensing, Photonic Technologies, & Applications IV: 20 & 22-23 September 2010, Toulouse, France. 2010. (Proceedings of SPIE Ser.). (Illus.). 322p. pap. 80.00 ***(978-0-8194-8353-9(2))*** SPIE.

Kaniusas, Eugenijus. Biomedical Signals & Sensors I: Linking Physiological Phenomena & Biosignals. 2012. (Biological & Medical Physics, Biomedical Engineering Ser.). (ENG., Illus.). xv, 293p. 139.00 ***(978-3-642-24842-9(X)***, 364224842X) Springer.

Kasry, Amal. New Aspects in Surface Plasmon Fluorescence Spectroscopy. 2008. 120p. pap. *(978-3-639-04442-3(8))* VDM Verlag Dr. Mueller e.K.

Kisaalita, William S. 3-D Cell-Based Biosensors in Drug Discovery Programs. 2010. (ENG., Illus.). 404p. 129.95 *(978-1-4200-7349-2(4)*, CRC Press) Taylor & Francis Group GBR. Dist: Taylor & Francis Group.

Knopf George K Staff. Smart Biosensor Technology. 2006. (Optical Science & Engineering Ser.). (ENG., Illus.). 664p. 167.95 *(978-0-8493-3759-8(3)*, CRC Press) Taylor & Francis Group GBR. Dist: Taylor & Francis Group.

Konry, Tali (Tania). Development of Ito-Coated Fiber Optic Immunosensors & Bio-Devices. 2011. 88p. pap. ***(978-3-8433-7282-4(9))*** Lambert Academic Publishing.

Kranz, C., ed. Biomedical & Clinical Sensors. 2008. (ECS Transactions Ser.). 13p. pap. 28.00 *(978-1-60423-916-4(6))* Curran Assocs., Inc.

Kumar, C. S. S R. Nanomaterials for Biosensors. Kumar, Challa S. S. R., ed. 2007. (Nanotechnologies for the Life Sciences Ser.: 9). (ENG., Illus.). 430p. 235.00 *(978-3-527-31388-4(5)*, Wiley-VCH) Wiley, John & Sons, Inc.

Lechuga, Laura M. Commercial & Pre-Commercial Cell Detection Technologies for Defence Against Bioterror: Technology, Market & Society. 2008. (Illus.). x, 165p. 161.00 *(978-1-58603-858-8(3))* IOS Pr., Inc.

Li, Changzhi & Lin, Jenshan. Microwave Noncontact Motion Sensing & Analysis. 2012. (Wiley Series in Microwave & Optical Engineering Ser.: 230). (ENG.). 220p. 94.95 *(978-0-470-64214-6(9)*, Wiley) Wiley, John & Sons, Inc.

Li, Songjun, et al, eds. Biosensor Nanomaterials. 2011. (ENG., Illus.). 296p. 185.00 *(978-3-527-32841-3(6)*, Wiley-VCH) Wiley, John & Sons, Inc.

Li, Xingde, et al. Optics in Health Care & Biomedical Optics III: 12-15 November 2007, Beijing, China. 2007. (Proceedings of SPIE Ser.). (Illus.). 620p. pap. 160.00 *(978-0-8194-7001-0(5))* SPIE.

Lieber, Charles & Royal Society of Chemistry Staff. Nano & Microsensors for Chemical & Biological Terrorism Surveillance. Tok, Jeffrey B-H, ed. 2008. (ENG., Illus.). 224p. 160.00 ***(978-0-85404-140-4(0))*** Royal Society of Chemistry, The GBR. Dist: Ingram Pub. Services.

Ligler, Frances S. & Taitt, Chris Rowe, eds. Optical Biosensors: Today & Tomorrow. 2nd ed. 2008. (ENG., Illus.). 712p. 205.00 *(978-0-444-53125-4(4)*, Elsevier Science) Elsevier Science & Technology Bks.

Lisdat, Fred. Biosensing for the 21st Century. 2010. (Advances in Biochemical Engineering Biotechnology Ser.). (Illus.). xvi, 504p. pap. 599.00 *(978-3-642-09444-6(9)*, 3642094449) Springer.

Lo, Benny K. C. & Mitcheson, Paul. Proceedings: Sixth International Workshop on Wearable & Implantable Body Sensor Networks: Berkeley, CA 3-5 June 2009. 2009. (Illus.). xii, 348p. *(978-0-7695-3644-6(1))* IEEE Computer Society Pr.

Luo, Qingming. Fifth International Conference on Photonics & Imaging in Biology & Medicine: 1-3 September 2006, Wuhan, China, 2 vols. 2007. (Proceedings of SPIE — The International Society for Optical Engineering Ser.: No. 8). (Illus.). 1002p. pap. 170.00 *(978-0-8194-6656-3(5))* SPIE.

Luo, Qingming, et al. Seventh International Conference on Photonics & Imaging in Biology & Medicine: 24-27 November 2008, Wuhan, China. 2009. (Proceedings of SPIE Ser.). (Illus.). 758p. pap. 140.00 *(978-0-8194-7539-8(4))* SPIE.

Materials Research Society ( ) Staff, compiled by. Nanofunctional Materials, Nanostructures, & Novel Devices for Biological & Chemical Detection. 2007. (Materials Research Society Symposium Proceedings Ser.). 306p. pap. 115.00 *(978-1-60423-407-7(5))* Curran Assocs., Inc.

Mattoussi, Hedi, et al. Inorganic Nanoprobes for Biological Sensing & Imaging. Cheon, Jinwoo, ed. 2009. (Illus.). 360p. 139.00 *(978-1-59693-196-1(5))* Artech Hse., Inc.

Mir, Monica. Dna & Aptamer Biosensors. 2009. 204p. pap. *(978-3-639-16675-0(2))* VDM Verlag Dr. Mueller e.K.

Mirsky, Vladimir M., ed. Ultrathin Electrochemical Chemo- & Biosensors: Technology & Performance. 2010. (Springer Series on Chemical Sensors & Biosensors Ser.). (Illus.). xx, 358p. pap. 199.00 *(978-3-642-05961-2(9)*, 3642059619) Springer.

Mohseni, Hooman & Razeghi, M. Biosensing III: 1-3 August 2010, San Diego, California, United States. 2010. (Proceedings of SPIE Ser.). (Illus.). 150p. pap. 90.00 ***(978-0-8194-8255-6(2))*** SPIE.

Mohseni, Hooman, et al. Biosensing & Nanomedicine IV. 2011. (Proceedings of SPIE Ser.). 184p. pap. 80.00 ***(978-0-8194-8709-4(0))*** SPIE.

Mol, Nico J. de & Fischer, Marcel J. E., eds. Surface Plasmon Resonance: Methods & Protocols. 2010. (Methods in Molecular Biology Ser.). (Illus.). x, 255p. 139.00 *(978-1-60761-669-6(6)*, 1607616696) Humana Pr.

Mulchandani, Ashok & Rogers, Kim, eds. Enzyme & Microbial Biosensors: Techniques & Protocols. 2010. (Methods in Biotechnology Ser.). 284p. pap. 159.00 *(978-1-61737-028-1(2)*, 1617370282) Humana Pr.

Mutlu, Mehmet, ed. Biosensors in Food Processing, Safety, & Quality Control. 2010. (Contemporary Food Engineering Ser.). (ENG., Illus.). 358p. 159.95 *(978-1-4398-1985-2(8)*, CRC Press) Taylor & Francis Group GBR. Dist: Taylor & Francis Group.

Nait-Ali, Amine. Advanced Biosignal Processing. 2009. (ENG., Illus.). xvi, 374p. 159.00 *(978-3-540-89505-3(1)*, 3540895051) Springer.

Natale C., Di. Sensors & Microsystems. 2008. (Illus.). xix, 544p. 187.00 *(978-981-283-597-0(0))* World Scientific Publishing Co., Inc.

Nicolau, Dan V. Biomedical Applications of Micro- & Nanoengineering III: 11-13 December 2006, Adelaide, Australia. 2006. (Proceedings of SPIE Ser.). (Illus.). 320p. pap. 90.00 *(978-0-8194-6524-5(0))* SPIE.

—BioMEMS & Nanotechnology III: 5-7 December 2007, Canberra, Australia. 2007. (Proceedings of SPIE Ser.). (Illus.). 400p. pap. 105.00 *(978-0-8194-6970-0(X))* SPIE.

Nicolau, Dan V. & Metcalfe, Guy. Biomedical Applications of Micro- & Nanoengineering IV & Complex Systems: 10-12 December 2008, Melbourne, Australia. 2008. (Proceedings of SPIE Ser.). (Illus.). 356p. pap. 105.00 *(978-0-8194-7522-0(X))* SPIE.

Nikolelis, D. P., et al, eds. Biosensors for Direct Monitoring of Environmental Pollutants in Field. 2010. (Nato Science Partnership Subseries: 2 (closed) Ser.). 400p. pap. 389.00 *(978-90-481-4959-9(2)*, 9048149592) Springer.

Noda, Masaki, ed. Mechanosensing Biology. 2011. (ENG., Illus.). xiv, 218p. 189.00 *(978-4-431-89756-9(9)*, 4431897569) Springer.

Nsiah, Francis & McDermott, Mark T. Probing Protein Adsorption on Model Surfaces: Sensitive Spectroscopic Approach. 2008. 124p. pap. *(978-3-639-10059-4(X))* VDM Verlag Dr. Mueller e.K.

Oraevsky, Alexander & Wang, Lihong. Photons Plus Ultrasound: Imaging & Sensing 2011. 2011. (Proceedings of SPIE Ser.). pap. 210.00 ***(978-0-8194-8436-9(9))*** SPIE.

Oraevsky, Alexander A. & Wang, Lihong V. Photons Plus Ultrasound: Imaging & Sensing 2007: The Eighth Conference on Biomedical Thermoacoustics, Optoacoustics, & Acousto-Optics: 21-24 January 2007, San Jose, California, USA. 2007. (Proceedings of SPIE Ser.: No. 8). (Illus.). 602p. pap. 140.00 *(978-0-8194-6550-4(X))* SPIE.

—Photons Plus Ultrasound: Imaging & Sensing 2008: The Ninth Conference on Biomedical Thermoacoustics, Optoacoustics, & Acousto-Optics: 20-23 January 2008, San Jose, California, USA. 2008. (Proceedings of SPIE Ser.). (Illus.). 690p. pap. 140.00 *(978-0-8194-7031-7(7))* SPIE.

—Photons Plus Ultrasound: Imaging & Sensing 2009: 25-28 January 2009, San Jose, California, United States. 2009. (Proceedings of SPIE Ser.). (Illus.). 708p. pap. 160.00 *(978-0-8194-7423-0(1))* SPIE.

Orellana, Guillermo & Moreno-Bondi, Maria Cruz. Frontiers in Chemical Sensors: Novel Principles & Techniques. 2010. (Springer Series on Chemical Sensors & Biosensors Ser.). (Illus.). xii, 370p. pap. 269.00 *(978-3-642-06612-2(7)*, 3642066127) Springer.

Osinski, Marek, et al. Colloidal Quantum Dots for Biomedical Applications II: 20-21, 23 January 2007, San Jose, California, USA. 2007. (Progress in Biomedical Optics & Imaging Ser.: No. 8). (Illus.). 226p. pap. 80.00 *(978-0-8194-6561-0(5))* SPIE.

Panchenko, Vladislav IAkovlevich, et al. International Conference on Lasers, Applications, & Technologies 2007: Laser Technologies for Medicine: 28 May-1 June 2007, Minsk, Belarus. 2007. (Proceedings of SPIE Ser.). (Illus.). 260p. pap. 70.00 *(978-0-8194-6892-5(4))*; 426p. pap. 90.00 *(978-0-8194-6891-8(6))* SPIE.

Papautsky, Ian & Wang, Wanjun. Microfluidics, BioMEMS, & Medical Microsystems V: 22-24 January 2007, San Jose, California, USA. 2007. (Proceedings of SPIE Ser.). (Illus.). 320p. pap. 80.00 *(978-0-8194-6578-8(X))* SPIE.

Pingarron, Jose M. & Luong, John H., eds. Biosensor Technology. 2013. (Biotechnology & Bioprocessing Ser.). (ENG., Illus.). 520p. 139.95 ***(978-1-4398-4141-9(1)***, CRC Press) Taylor & Francis Group GBR. Dist: Taylor & Francis Group.

Prabhakar, Nirmal, et al. Development of Conductng Polymer Based Nucleic Acid Biosensors. 2010. 196p. pap. *(978-3-8383-8051-3(7))* Lambert Academic Publishing.

Premanode, Bhusana. Cmos Biosensor for Peritoneal Dialysis. 2011. 316p. pap. ***(978-3-8443-0947-8(0))*** Lambert Academic Publishing.

Rasooly, Avraham & Herold, K. E. Biosensors & Biodetection: Methods & Protocols, 2 vols. 2009. (Illus.). E-Book *(978-1-60327-567-5(3))* Humana Pr.

Rasooly, Avraham & Herold, Keith E., eds. Biosensors & Biodetection: Methods & Protocols, Volume 1: Optical-Based Detectors. 2009. (Methods in Molecular Biology Ser.). (Illus.). xviii, 454p. 129.00 *(978-1-60327-566-8(5))* Humana Pr.

—Biosensors & Biodetection: Methods & Protocols, Volume 2: Electrochemical & Mechanical Detectors, Lateral Flow & Ligands for Biosensors. 2009. (Methods in Molecular Biology Ser.). (Illus.). xviii, 470p. 129.00 *(978-1-60327-568-2(1))* Humana Pr.

Razeghi, M. & Mohseni, Hooman. Biosensing: 12-14 August 2008, San Diego, California, USA. 2008. (Proceedings of SPIE Ser.). (Illus.). 254p. pap. 90.00 *(978-0-8194-7255-7(7))* SPIE.

—Biosensing II: 4-6 August 2009, San Diego, California, United States. 2009. (Proceedings of SPIE Ser.). (Illus.). 256p. pap. 90.00 *(978-0-8194-7687-6(0))* SPIE.

Ren, Fan & Pearton, Stephen J., eds. Semiconductor Device-Based Sensors for Gas Chemical & Bio App. 2011. (ENG., Illus.). 324p. 149.95 *(978-1-4398-1387-4(6)*, CRC Press) Taylor & Francis Group GBR. Dist: Taylor & Francis Group.

Renneberg, Reinhard, et al, eds. Biosensing for the 21st Century. 2008. (Advances in Biochemical Engineering & Biotechnology Ser.). (Illus.). 504p. 599.00 *(978-3-540-75200-4(5))* Springer.

Rich, Preston B. & Douillet, Christelle, eds. Bioluminescence: Methods & Protocols, Second Edition. 2nd ed. 2009. (Methods in Molecular Biology Ser.). (ENG., Illus.). x, 257p. 149.00 *(978-1-60327-320-6(4)*, 1603273204) Humana Pr.

Rinken, Toonika. Modelling of Biosensors. 2011. 56p. pap. ***(978-3-8443-2768-7(1))*** Lambert Academic Publishing.

Roelof van der Meer, Jan. Concepts & Engineering in Synthetic Biosensing. 2010. (Synthesis Lectures on Synthetic Biology Ser.). 100p. pap. 40.00 *(978-1-59829-911-3(5))* Morgan & Claypool Pubs.

Rogers, Kim & Mulchandani, Ashok, eds. Affinity Biosensors: Techniques & Protocols. 2010. (Methods in Biotechnology Ser.). 264p. pap. 139.00 *(978-1-61737-066-3(5)*, 1617370665) Humana Pr.

Royal Society of Chemistry Staff. Engineering the Bioelectronic Interface: Applications to Analyte Biosensing & Protein Detection. Davis, Jason, ed. 2009. (ENG., Illus.). 270p. 141.00 *(978-0-85404-165-7(6))* Royal Society of Chemistry, The GBR. Dist: Ingram Pub. Services.

—Handbook of Surface Plasmon Resonance. Schasfoort, Richard B. M. & Tudos, Anna J., eds. 2008. (ENG., Illus.). 426p. 232.00 *(978-0-85404-267-8(9))* Royal Society of Chemistry, The GBR. Dist: Ingram Pub. Services.

—Nucleic Acid Biosensors for Environmental Pollution Monitoring. Mascini, Marco & Palchetti, Ilaria, eds. 2011. (ENG., Illus.). 186p. (C). 195.00 *(978-1-84973-131-7(4))* Royal Society of Chemistry, The GBR. Dist: Ingram Pub. Services.

Sadana, Ajit. Binding & Dissociation Kinetics for Different Biosensor Applications Using Fractals. 2006. (ENG., Illus.). 384p. 350.00 *(978-0-444-52784-4(2),* Elsevier Science) Elsevier Science & Technology Bks.

Sadana, Ajit & Sadana, Neeti. Fractal Analysis of the Binding & Dissociation Kinetics for Different Analytes on Biosensor Surfaces. 2007. (ENG., Illus.). 372p. 215.00 *(978-0-444-53010-3(X),* Elsevier Science) Elsevier Science & Technology Bks.

—Handbook of Biosensors & Biosensor Kinetics. 2010. (ENG.). 536p. 590.00 *(978-0-444-53262-6(5),* Elsevier Science) Elsevier Science & Technology Bks.

Samudrala, Pavan. Waveguide Characterization & Biosensor Modeling. 2009. 100p. pap. *(978-3-639-12270-1(4))* VDM Verlag Dr. Mueller e.K.

Schultz, Jerome, et al, eds. Biosensing: International Research & Development. 2010. (Illus.). xxix, 387p. pap. 189.00 *(978-90-481-7026-5(5),* 9048170265) Springer.

Schweitzer, Dietrich & Fitzmaurice, Maryann. Diagnostic Optical Spectroscopy in Biomedicine IV: 19-21 June 2007, Munich, Germany. 2007. (Proceedings of SPIE Ser.). (Illus.). 382p. pap. 130.00 *(978-0-8194-6772-0(3))* SPIE.

Semmlow, John L. Biosignal & Medical Image Processing: MATLAB-Based Applications. 2nd rev. ed. 2008. (Signal Processing & Communications Ser.). (ENG., Illus.). 472p. (C). 102.95 *(978-1-4200-6230-4(1),* CRC Press) Taylor & Francis Group GBR. Dist: Taylor & Francis Group.

Shaikh Anwar, Mohd. Sadique. Modeling of Evanescent Wave Optical Fiber Biosensor. 2011. 60p. pap. ***(978-3-8443-1718-3(X))*** Lambert Academic Publishing.

Shinar, Ruth & Kymissis, Ioannis. Organic Semiconductors in Sensors & Bioelectronics III: 4-5 August 2010, San Diego, California, United States. 2010. (Proceedings of SPIE Ser.). (Illus.). 106p. pap. 70.00 ***(978-0-8194-8275-4(7))*** SPIE.

Shinar, Ruth & Malliaras, George G. Organic-Based Chemical & Biological Sensors: 28 August 2007, San Diego, California, USA. 2007. (Proceedings of SPIE Ser.). (Illus.). 86p. pap. 60.00 ***(978-0-8194-6807-9(X))*** SPIE.

Shinar, Ruth & Malliaras, George G. Organic Semiconductors in Sensors & Bioelectronics II: 4-6 August 2009, San Diego, California, United States. 2009. (Proceedings of SPIE Ser.). (Illus.). 136p. pap. 70.00 *(978-0-8194-7708-8(7))* SPIE.

Siciliano, P. Sensors & Microsystems: Proceedings of the 11Th Italian Conference. 2008. 211.00 *(978-981-279-338-6(0))* World Scientific Publishing Co., Inc.

Silverman, Scott K., ed. Nucleic Acid Switches & Sensors. (Illus.). 2010. ix, 125p. pap. 139.00 *(978-1-4419-4248-7(3),* 1441942483) 2006. 125p. 139.00 *(978-0-387-37491-8(4))* Springer.

Soledad Rodriguez, Beatriz Elena. Biosensores en la Industria. 2009. (SPA.). 54p. pap. 15.16 *(978-0-557-07084-8(8))* Lulu Enterprises Inc.

Somerset, Vernon. Mercaptobenzothiazole on Gold Biosensor Systems For. 2010. 548p. pap. *(978-3-639-25898-1(3))* VDM Verlag Dr. Mueller e.K.

Sooryadas, Daya I. Biomimetic Sensor for Invivo Applications. 2008. 92p. pap. *(978-3-639-06946-4(3),* VDM Verlag Dr. Mueller e.K.

Stepanov, Andrey L. Surface Plasmon Polariton Nanooptics. 2012. 230p. pap. ***(978-1-61942-352-7(9))*** Nova Science Pubs., Inc.

Stepanova, Maria & Dew, Steven, eds. Nanofabrication: Techniques & Principles. 2011. (ENG., Illus.). viii, 344p. 189.00 *(978-3-7091-0423-1(8),* 3709104238) Springer.

Tao, Junhua, et al. Biocatalysis for the Pharmaceutical Industry: Discovery, Development & Manufacturing. 2008. (ENG., Illus.). 250p. 140.00 *(978-0-470-82314-9(3),* Wiley) Wiley, John & Sons, Inc.

Tominaga, Junji & Nakano, Takashi. Optical near-Field Recording: Science & Technology. 2010. (ENG., Illus.). viii, 124p. pap. 104.00 *(978-3-642-06049-6(8),* 3642060498) Springer.

Tuchin, V. V. Complex Dynamics & Fluctuations in Biomedical Photonics IV: 20 & 23 January 2007, San Jose, California, USA. 2007. (Proceedings of SPIE Ser.: No. 8). (Illus.). 236p. pap. 80.00 *(978-0-8194-6549-8(6))* SPIE.

—Saratov Fall Meeting: Optical Technologies in Biophysics & Medicine VII. 2006. (Progress in Biomedical Optics & Imaging Ser.: No. 7). (Illus.). 602p. pap. 120.00 *(978-0-8194-6215-2(2))* SPIE.

—Saratov Fall Meeting 2006: Optical Technologies in Biophysics & Medicine VIII. 2007. (Progress in Biomedical Optics & Imaging Ser.: No. 8). (Illus.). 658p. pap. 130.00 *(978-0-8194-6657-0(3))* SPIE.

—Saratov Fall Meeting 2007: Optical Technologies in Biophysics & Medicine IX: 25-28 September 2007, Saratov, Russia. 2008. (Proceedings of SPIE Ser.). (Illus.). 284p. pap. 80.00 *(978-0-8194-6955-7(6))* SPIE.

Tuchin, V. V. & Wang, Lihong V. Complex Dynamics & Fluctuations in Biomedical Photonics V: 19, 21 January 2008, San Jose, California, USA. 2008. (Proceedings of SPIE Ser.). (Illus.). 154p. pap. 70.00 ***(978-0-8194-7030-0(9))*** SPIE.

Tuchin, Valery & Genina, Elina. Saratov Fall Meeting 2010: Optical Technologies in Biophysics & Medicine XII. 2011. (Proceedings of SPIE Ser.). 206p. pap. 70.00 ***(978-0-8194-8572-4(1))*** SPIE.

Tuchin, Valery, et al. Dynamics & Fluctuations in Biomedical Photonics VIII. 2011. (Proceedings of SPIE Ser.). 252p. pap. 90.00 ***(978-0-8194-8435-2(0))*** SPIE.

Tuchin, Valery V., ed. Optical Sensing of Glucose in Biological Fluids & Tissues. 2008. (Series in Medical Physics & Biomedical Engineering). (ENG., Illus.). 744p. instr.'s hndbk. ed. 139.95 *(978-1-58488-974-8(8),* Taylor & Francis) Taylor & Francis Group GBR. Dist: Taylor & Francis Group.

Varshney, Upkar. Pervasive Healthcare Computing: EMR/EHR, Wireless & Health Monitoring. (ENG., Illus.). vii, 288p. 2010. pap. 99.00 ***(978-1-4419-5496-1(1),*** 1441954961) 2009. 99.00 *(978-1-4419-0214-6(7),* 1441902147) Springer.

Vo-Dinh, Tuan. Biomedical Diagnostics, Vol. 2. 2nd ed. 2010. pap. 149.95 *(978-1-4200-8514-3(X))* CRC Pr. LLC.

—Biomedical Photonics Handbook, 3 vols. 2nd ed. 2010. (ENG., Illus.). 3000p. 249.95 *(978-1-4398-0444-5(3))* CRC Pr. LLC.

Vo-Dinh, Tuan, ed. The Biomedical Photonics Handbook Vol. 1: Fundamentals, Devices, & Techniques. 2nd ed. 2010. pap. 149.95 *(978-1-4200-8512-9(3))* CRC Pr. LLC.

—Therapeutic & Advanced Biophotonics, No. 3. 2nd ed. 2010. (Illus.). 800p. pap. 149.95 *(978-1-4200-8516-7(6))* CRC Pr. LLC.

Vo-Dinh, Tuan & Lakowicz, Joseph. Plasmonics in Biology & Medicine VIII. 2011. (Proceedings of SPIE Ser.). 192p. pap. 105.00 ***(978-0-8194-8448-2(2))*** SPIE.

Vo-Dinh, Tuan & Lakowicz, Joseph R. Plasmonics in Biology & Medicine IV: 23 January 2007, San Jose, California, USA. 2007. (Progress in Biomedical Optics & Imaging Ser.: No. 8). (Illus.). 182p. pap. 70.00 *(978-0-8194-6563-4(1))* SPIE.

—Plasmonics in Biology & Medicine V: 21-22 January 2008, San Jose, California, USA. 2008. (Proceedings of SPIE Ser.). (Illus.). 166p. pap. 80.00 *(978-0-8194-7044-7(9))* SPIE.

—Plasmonics in Biology & Medicine VI: 26-27 January 2009, San Jose, California, United States. 2009. (Proceedings of SPIE Ser.). (Illus.). 190p. pap. 80.00 *(978-0-8194-7438-4(X))* SPIE.

Vo-Dinh, Tuan & Lakowicz, Joseph R. Plasmonics in Biology & Medicine VII: 25 & 27-28 January 2010, San Francisco, California, United States. 2010. (Proceedings of SPIE Ser.). (Illus.). 184p. pap. 90.00 ***(978-0-8194-7973-0(X))*** SPIE.

Vo-Dinh, Tuan, et al. Advanced Environmental, Chemical, & Biological Sensing Technologies IV: 1-3 October 2006, Boston, Massachusetts, USA. 2006. (Progress in Biomedical Optics & Imaging Ser.: No. 7). (Illus.). 220p. pap. 80.00 *(978-0-8194-6475-0(9))* SPIE.

—Advanced Environmental, Chemical, & Biological Sensing Technologies V: 10-11 September 2007, Boston, Massachusetts, USA. 2007. (Proceedings of SPIE Ser.). (Illus.). 156p. pap. 80.00 *(978-0-8194-6915-1(7))* SPIE.

—Advanced Environmental, Chemical, & Biological Sensing Technologies VI: 13-14 April 2009, Orlando, Florida, United States. 2009. (Proceedings of SPIE Ser.). (Illus.). 210p. pap. 80.00 *(978-0-8194-7578-7(5))* SPIE.

Vo-Dinh, Tuan, et al. Advanced Environmental, Chemical, & Biological Sensing Technologies VIII. 2011. (Proceedings of SPIE Ser.). pap. 80.00 ***(978-0-8194-8598-4(5))*** SPIE.

Wang, Ping & Liu, Qingjun. Biomedical Sensors & Measurement. 2011. (Advanced Topics in Science & Technology in China Ser.). (Illus.). 300p. 129.00 *(978-3-642-19524-2(5),* 3642195245) Springer.

Wang, Ping, et al. Cell-Based Biosensors: Principles & Applications. 2009. (Illus.). 310p. 129.00 *(978-1-59693-439-9(5))* Artech Hse., Inc.

Wang, Wanjun. Microfluidics, BioMEMS, & Medical Microsystems VII: 26-28 January 2009, San Jose, California, United States. 2009. (Proceedings of SPIE Ser.). (Illus.). 156p. pap. 80.00 *(978-0-8194-7453-7(3))* SPIE.

Wang, Wanjun & Vauchier, Claude. Microfluidics, BioMEMS, & Medical Microsystems VI: 21-22 January 2008, San Jose, California, USA. 2008. (Proceedings of SPIE Ser.). (Illus.). 298p. pap. 80.00 *(978-0-8194-7061-4(9))* SPIE.

Weigl, Bernhard, et al. Microfluidics & Microsensors: Applications for Life Sciences, Drug Discovery & Medical Diagnostics. 2008. (RSP Bird Ser.). 400p. 130.00 *(978-0-470-03187-2(5))* Wiley, John & Sons, Inc.

Westerink, Joyce H. D. M., et al, eds. Probing Experience: From Assessment of User Emotions & Behaviour to Development of Products. 2010. (Philips Research Book Ser.). xii, 245p. pap. 129.00 *(978-90-481-7675-5(1),* 9048176751) Springer.

Williams, Shaun. The Infrared Enhanced Transmission of Metallic Subwavelength Arrays. 2009. 252p. pap. *(978-3-639-16441-1(5))* VDM Verlag Dr. Mueller e.K.

Wojtek J., Bock, et al, eds. Optical Waveguide Sensing & Imaging. 2007. (NATO Science for Peace & Security Series B: Physics & Biophysics Ser.). (Illus.). VIII, 269p. pap. 109.00 *(978-1-4020-6951-2(0),* 1402069510) Springer.

Wolfbeis, Otto S., ed. Fluorescence Methods & Applications: Spectroscopy, Imaging, & Probes. 2008. (Annals of the New York Academy of Sciences Ser.: Vol. 1130). (ENG., Illus.). 452p. pap. 159.95 *(978-1-57331-716-0(0),* Wiley-Blackwell) Wiley, John & Sons, Inc.

Wriedt, Thomas & Hergert, Wolfram, eds. The Mie Theory: Basics & Applications. 2012. (Springer Series in Optical Sciences Ser.). (ENG., Illus.). x, 259p. 179.00 ***(978-3-642-28737-4(9),*** 3642287379) Springer.

Xiao, Hai, et al. Photonic Microdevices/Microstructures for Sensing III. 2011. (Proceedings of SPIE Ser.). 158p. pap. 70.00 ***(978-0-8194-8608-0(6))*** SPIE.

Xu, Kexin. Fourth International Conference on Photonics & Imaging in Biology & Medicine: 3-6 September, 2005, Tianjin, China, 2 vols. 2006. (Progress in Biomedical Optics & Imaging Ser.: No. 7). (Illus.). 992p. pap. 170.00 *(978-0-8194-6080-6(X))* SPIE.

Yang, Guang-Zhong, ed. Body Sensor Networks. 2010. (ENG., Illus.). xxviii, 500p. pap. 99.00 *(978-1-84996-569-9(2),* 1849965692) Springer.

Yogeswaran, Umasankar, et al. Nanostructured Materials for Electrochemical Biosensors. 2009. (Nanotechnology Science & Technology Ser.). 89.00 *(978-1-60741-706-4(5))* Nova Science Pubs., Inc.

Yoon, Jeong-Yeol & Lucas, Lonnie J. Biosensors: From Electric Circuits to Immunosensors. 2010. (ENG.). xx, 330p. 89.00 *(978-1-4419-6021-4(X),* 144196021X) Springer.

Zhang, Xueji, et al, eds. Electrochemical Sensors, Biosensors & Their Biomedical Applications. 2007. (ENG., Illus.). 616p. 140.00 *(978-0-12-373738-0(9),* Academic Pr.) Elsevier Science & Technology Bks.

Zourob, Mohammed, et al, eds. Recognition Receptors in Biosensors. 2010. (ENG., Illus.). xiv, 849p. 209.00 *(978-1-4419-0918-3(4),* 1441909184) Springer.

Zourob, Mohammed & Lakhtakia, A. Optical Guided-Wave Chemical & Biosensors, 2 vols. 2010. (Springer Series on Chemical Sensors & Biosensors Ser.). (ENG., Illus.). x, 250p. 249.00 *(978-3-540-88241-1(3),* 3540882413) Springer.

Zourob, Mohammed & Lakhtakia, Akhlesh, eds. Optical Guided-wave Chemical & Biosensors II, 2 vols. 2010. (Springer Series on Chemical Sensors & Biosensors Ser.). (ENG., Illus.). x, 316p. 359.00 *(978-3-642-02826-7(8),* 3642028268) Springer.

Zourob, Mohammed, et al. Principles of Bacterial Detection: Biosensors, Recognition Receptors & Microsystems. 2008. (ENG., Illus.). xxxii, 970p. 137.00 *(978-0-387-75112-2(2),* 0387751122) Springer.

2007 4th IEEE/EMBS International Summer School & Symposium on Medical Devices & Biosensors. 2007. pap. 198.00 *(978-1-4244-1345-4(1),* 07EX1837) IEEE.

BIOSPHERE

see also Gaia Hypothesis; Geobiology

Abram, David. Becoming Animal: An Earthly Cosmology. 2011. (Vintage Ser.). (ENG.). 336p. pap. 16.95 *(978-0-375-71369-9(7),* Vintage) Knopf Doubleday Publishing Group.

Allen, John. Me & the Biospheres: A Memoir by the Inventor of Biosphere 2. 2008. 336p. 39.95 *(978-0-907791-37-9(9))* Synergetic Pr.

Babiadelis, Paul. Developing Institutional Options for Watershed Management - the Sixaola Binational Watershed and. 2008. 276p. pap. *(978-3-8364-6312-6(1))* VDM Verlag Dr. Mueller e.K.

Dobretsov, Nikolay, et al, eds. Biosphere Origin & Evolution. 2010. (ENG., Illus.). xx, 428p. pap. 169.00 *(978-1-4419-4329-3(3),* 1441943293) Springer.

Fikseaunet, Torhild Holen. Four Scenarios of Fish Finger Production from a Life Cycle Perspective. 2011. 100p. pap. ***(978-3-8433-5955-9(5))*** Lambert Academic Publishing.

Florinsky, Igor V., ed. Man & the Geosphere. 2010. (Earth Sciences in the 21st Century Ser.). 399p. 145.00 *(978-1-60876-387-0(0))* Nova Science Pubs., Inc.

Huggett, Richard John. The Natural History of the Earth: Debating Long-Term Change in the Geosphere & Biosphere. 2006. (Routledge Studies in Physical Geography & Environment). (Illus.). 203p. 218.00 *(978-0-415-35802-6(7))* Routledge.

Jorgensen, Sven Erik, ed. Global Ecology. 2010. (ENG.). 480p. 83.95 *(978-0-444-53626-6(4),* Academic Pr.) Elsevier Science & Technology Bks.

Keller, Michael. Amazonia & Global Change. 2009. (Illus.). ix, 565p. *(978-0-87590-476-4(9))* American Geophysical Union.

Lovelock, James. The Vanishing Face of Gaia: A Final Warning. 2010. (ENG.). 304p. (gr. 9). pap. 15.00 *(978-0-465-01907-6(2))* Basic Bks.

MacKenzie, Fred T., ed. Carbon in the Geobiosphere: Earth's Outer Shell. 2006. (Topics in Geobiology Ser.). (Illus.). 402p. 269.00 *(978-1-4020-4044-3(X),* 140204044X) Springer.

Mackenzie, Fred T. & Lerman, Abraham. Carbon in the Geobiosphere: - Earth's Outer Shell - 2010. (Topics in Geobiology Ser.). (Illus.). xxi, 402p. pap. 269.00 *(978-90-481-7022-7(2),* 9048170222) Springer.

Midgley, Mary. Earthy Realism: The Meaning of Gaia. 2007. (Societas Ser.). (ENG., Illus.). 111p. per. 17.90 *(978-1-84540-080-4(1),* Societas) Imprint Academic GBR. Dist: Ingram Pub. Services.

Poynter, Jane. The Human Experiment: Two Years & Twenty Minutes Inside Biosphere 2. 2006. (ENG., Illus.). 384p. 26.95 *(978-1-56025-775-2(X))* Basic Bks.

Reider, Rebecca. Dreaming the Biosphere: The Theater of All Possibilities. 2010. (ENG., Illus.). 326p. pap. 29.95 *(978-0-8263-4674-2(X))* Univ. of New Mexico Pr.

Sadler, Guy Albert. Outline for a Viable Techno Sphere. 2010. 188p. 29.99 *(978-1-4535-1157-2(1));* pap. 19.99 *(978-1-4535-1156-5(3))* Xlibris Corp.

Sefcik, Lesley T. Biosphere-Atmosphere Interactions: Northern Hardwood Seedling Responses to Anthropogenic Atmospheric Resource Alteration. 2008. 144p. pap. *(978-3-8364-8143-4(X))* VDM Verlag Dr. Mueller e.K.

BIOSTATISTICS

see Biometry

BIOSURFACES

see Biological Interfaces

BIOSYNTHESIS

see also Genetic Regulation; Proteins—Synthesis

Ankamwar, Balaprasad. Biosynthesis: An Eco-Friendly Approach of Nanomaterials Synthesis. 2010. 68p. pap. *(978-3-639-28228-3(0))* VDM Verlag Dr. Mueller e.K.

Cohen. Biosynthesis. 2008. *(978-0-412-99331-2(7))* Springer Singapore Pte. Ltd.

Dewick, Paul M. Medicinal Natural Products: A Biosynthetic Approach. 3rd ed. 2009. (ENG., Illus.). 550p. pap. 70.00 *(978-0-470-74167-2(8),* Wiley) Wiley, John & Sons, Inc.

Dewick, Paul M. & Dewick. Medicinal Natural Products: A Biosynthetic Approach. 3rd ed. 2009. (ENG., Illus.). 550p. 180.00 *(978-0-470-74168-9(6),* Wiley) Wiley, John & Sons, Inc.

Dragutan, Valerian, et al, eds. Green Metathesis Chemistry: Great Challenges in Synthesis, Catalysis & Nanotechnology. 2009. (NATO Science for Peace & Security Series A: Chemistry & Biology Ser.). (Illus.). xix, 425p. 269.00 *(978-90-481-3431-1(5),* 9048134315); (ENG.), pap. 139.00 *(978-90-481-3432-8(3),* 9048134323) Springer.

Grogan, Gideon. Practical Biotransformations: A Beginner's Guide. 2009. (ENG., Illus.). 344p. instr.'s gde. ed. 160.00 *(978-1-4051-9367-2(0),* Wiley-Blackwell) Wiley, John & Sons, Inc.

Hopwood, David A. Complex Enzymes in Microbial Natural Product Biosynthesis Pt. A: Overview Articles & Peptides, 2 vols. 2009. (ENG., Illus.). 350p. 187.00 *(978-0-12-374588-0(8),* Academic Pr.) Elsevier Science & Technology Bks.

—Complex Enzymes in Microbial Natural Product Biosynthesis Pt. B: Polyketides, Aminocoumarins & Carbohydrates, 2 vols. 2009. (ENG., Illus.). 398p. 187.00 *(978-0-12-374591-0(8),* Academic Pr.) Elsevier Science & Technology Bks.

Hudlicky, Tomas & Reed, Josephine W. The Way of Synthesis: Evolution of Design & Methods for Natural Products. 2007. (ENG.). 1018p. pap. 110.00 *(978-3-527-31444-7(X),* Wiley-VCH) Wiley, John & Sons, Inc.

Ibrahim, Ahmed. Salicylic Acid Biosynthetic Genes Expressed in Rhizobium. 2010. 164p. pap. *(978-3-639-26969-7(1))* VDM Verlag Dr. Mueller e.K.

Morgan, E. David. Biosynthesis in Insects. 2nd rev. ed. 2010. (ENG., Illus.). 380p. (C). 72.00 ***(978-1-84755-808-4(9))*** Royal Society of Chemistry, The GBR. Dist: Ingram Pub. Services.

Piel, Jö, ed. Natural Products via Enzymatic Reactions. 2010. (Topics in Current Chemistry Ser.). (Illus.). xiv, 200p. 259.00 *(978-3-642-16426-2(9),* 3642164269) Springer.

Rebeille, Fabrice & Douce, Roland. Biosynthesis of Vitamins in Plants Pt. A: Vitamins A, B1, B2, B3, B5. 2011. (ENG.). 322p. 193.00 ***(978-0-12-386479-6(8),*** Academic Pr.) Elsevier Science & Technology Bks.

Salomons, Gajja S. & Wyss, Markus, eds. Creatine & Creatine Kinase in Health & Disease. 2010. (Subcellular Biochemistry Ser.). xviii, 352p. pap. 319.00 *(978-90-481-7652-6(2),* 9048176522) Springer.

Shah, Muhammad Ghani, et al. A Central Asaian Medicenal Plant Primula MacRophylla D Don. 2010. 164p. pap. *(978-3-639-26393-0(6))* VDM Verlag Dr. Mueller e.K.

Smolke, Christina D. The Metabolic Pathway Engineering Handbook: Fundamentals, 2 vols. Smolke, Christina D., ed. 2009. (ENG., Illus.). 678p. 164.95 *(978-1-4398-0296-0(3),* CRC Press) Taylor & Francis Group GBR. Dist: Taylor & Francis Group.

Walde, Peter. Prebiotic Chemistry: From Simple Amphiphiles to Protocell Models. 2010. (Topics in Current Chemistry Ser.). xii, 221p. pap. 249.00 *(978-3-642-06614-6(3),* 3642066143) Springer.

Wendisch, Volker F. Amino Acid Biosynthesis - Pathways, Regulation & Metabolic Engineering. 2007. (Microbiology Monographs). (Illus.). x, 413p. 319.00 *(978-3-540-48595-7(3))* Springer.

Yasmeen, Shazia. Isolation & Synthesis of Biologicaly Active Natural Products. 2010. 240p. pap. *(978-3-639-23020-8(5))* VDM Verlag Dr. Mueller e.K.

Zhang, Sharon S. Regulation of Insulin Biosynthesis. 2010. 160p. pap. *(978-3-639-13508-4(3))* VDM Verlag Dr. Mueller e.K.

BIOSYSTEMATICS

see Biology—Classification

BIOTECHNOLOGICAL MICROORGANISMS

Ahmad, Iqbal, et al, eds. Microbes & Microbial Technology: Agricultural & Environmental Applications. 2011. (ENG.). xvi, 516p. 179.00 *(978-1-4419-7930-8(1),* 1441979301) Springer.

Du Plessis, Kamila. Bacterial P450s & Steroid Transformations. 2011. 156p. pap. ***(978-3-8443-3077-9(1))*** Lambert Academic Publishing.

Kim, Minjun, et al, eds. Microbiorobotics: Biologically Inspired Microscale Robotic Systems. 2012. (Micro & Nano Technologies Ser.). (ENG.). 328p. 169.00 ***(978-1-4557-7891-1(5))*** William Andrew, Inc.

Kotrba, Pavel, et al, eds. Microbial Biosorption of Metals. 2011. (ENG., Illus.). x, 390p. 209.00 *(978-94-007-0442-8(9),* 9400704429) Springer.

Nikaido, Hiroshi & Glazer, Alexander N. Microbial Biotechnology: Fundamentals of Applied Microbiology. 2nd unexpurg. ed. 2007. (ENG., Illus.). 576p. 80.00 *(978-0-521-84210-5(7))* Cambridge Univ. Pr.

Ray, R. C. Microbial Biotechnology in Horticulture. 2008. (ENG.). 366p. 99.95 *(978-1-57808-517-0(9))* BIOS Scientific Publishers Ltd. GBR. Dist: Taylor & Francis Group.

Satyanarayana, T., et al, eds. Microorganisms in Environmental Management: Microbes & Environment. 2012. (ENG., Illus.). xxi, 819p. 279.00 ***(978-94-007-2228-6(1),*** 9400722281) Springer.

BIOTECHNOLOGY

Here are entered works on the application of living organisms or their biological systems or processes to the manufacture of useful products.

see also Agricultural Biotechnology; Food—Biotechnology; Pharmaceutical Biotechnology; Reproductive Technology

Abbott, A. & Ellison, M., eds. Biologically Inspired Textiles. 2008. (ENG.). 244p. *(978-1-84569-247-6(0))* Woodhead Publishing Ltd.

Abdur Rab, Faiza. Solving a Biological Problem. 2010. 52p. pap. *(978-3-639-24749-7(3))* VDM Verlag Dr. Mueller e.K.

Ach, Johann S., et al. Nano-Bio-Ethics: Ethical Dimensions of Nanobiotechnology. Siep, Ludwig & Ach, Johann, eds. 2007. (ENG.). 120p. (gr. 11). pap. 39.95 *(978-3-8258-9058-2(9))* Lit Verlag DEU. Dist: Transaction Pubs.

Adebowale, Boladale Abiola. Innovation Biotechnology & Organizational Change in Nigeri. 2010. 56p. pap. *(978-3-8383-7462-8(2))* Lambert Academic Publishing.

Agostino, Ana & Ashton, Glenn, eds. A Patented World? Privatisation of Life & Knowledge. 2007. (ENG., Illus.). 240p. pap. 18.00 *(978-1-77009-229-7(3))* Jacana Media ZAF. Dist: Independent Pubs. Group.

Aheto, Denis Worlanyo. Implication Analysis for Biotechnology Regulation & Management in Africa: Baseline Studies for Assessment of Potential Effects of Genetically Modified Maize (Zea mays L.) Cultivation in Ghanaian Agriculture. 2009. (Theorie in der Ökologie Ser.). 240p. pap. 61.95 *(978-3-631-59450-6(X))* Lang, Peter GmbH, Europaischer Verlag der Wissenschaften DEU. Dist: Lang, Peter.

Ahmad, Wan Azlina, et al, eds. Bacteria in Environmental Biotechnology: The Malaysian Case Study-Analysis, Waste Utilization & Wastewater Remediation. 2010. (Bacteriology Research Developments Environmental Science, Engineering & Technology Ser.). pap. 75.00 *(978-1-61728-350-5(9),* Nova Novinka) Nova Science Pubs., Inc.

Ahn, Mark J., et al, eds. Building the case for Biotechnology: Management case studies in science, laws, regulations, politics, & Business. 2010. 416p. 99.95 *(978-1-934899-16-8(X))*; pap. 79.95 *(978-1-934899-15-1(1))* ThinkBiotech, LLC. (Logos Pr.).

Akbar, Sadiq. Molecular Detection Tecchniques. 2011. 88p. pap. ***(978-3-8443-2061-9(X))*** Lambert Academic Publishing.

Al-Khayri, Jameel, et al, eds. Date Palm Biotechnology. 2011. (ENG., Illus.). xviii, 743p. 239.00 *(978-94-007-1317-8(7),* 9400713177) Springer.

Alcamo, E. I., et al. DNA & Biotechnology. 3rd ed. 2009. (ENG.). 400p. (C). 103.00 *(978-0-12-048930-5(9),* Academic Pr.) Elsevier Science & Technology Bks.

Alon Uri Staff. Solutions Manual - Introduction to Systems Biology: Simplicity in Biology. 2006. (C). *(978-1-58488-645-7(5),* Chapman & Hall/CRC) CRC Pr. LLC.

Amani, Bita. State Agency & the Patenting of Life in Interntaional Law: Merchants & Missionaries in a Global Society. 2009. (Globalization & Law Ser.). 394p. 144.95 *(978-0-7546-7438-2(X))* Ashgate Publishing Co.

Amendola, Vincenzo & Meneghetti, Moreno, eds. Self-Healing at the Nanoscale: Mechanisms & Key Concepts of Natural & Artificial Systems. 2011. (ENG., Illus.). 463p. 129.95 *(978-1-4398-5473-0(4),* CRC Press) Taylor & Francis Group GBR. Dist: Taylor & Francis Group.

American Health Lawyers Association. AHLA the Fundamentals of Life Sciences Law: Drugs, Devices, & Biotech (AHLA Members) 2007. pap. 119.00 *(978-1-4224-3974-6(7))* American Health Lawyers Assn.

Amsel, Louis & Hirsch, Lena, eds. Food Science & Security. 2009. 98.00 *(978-1-60692-977-3(1))* Nova Science Pubs., Inc.

Anderson, Rebecca J. Career Opportunities in Clinical Drug Research. 2010. (ENG., Illus.). 279p. 61.00 *(978-1-936113-05-7(8))* Cold Spring Harbor Laboratory Pr.

Andersson, Helene & Van Den Berg, Albert. Lab-on-Chips for Cellomics: Micro & Nanotechnologies for Life Science. 2007. (Illus.). 363p. per. 79.95 *(978-1-4020-6562-0(0))* Springer.

Aoki-Kinoshita, Kiyoko F. Glycome Informatics: Methods & Applications. 2009. (Chapman & Hall/CRC Mathematical & Computational Biology Ser.). (ENG., Illus.). 256p. 96.95 *(978-1-4200-8334-7(1),* Chapman & Hall/CRC) CRC Pr. LLC.

Aranoff, Shara L., et al. Industrial Biotechnology. 2009. 69.00 *(978-1-60692-256-9(4))* Nova Science Pubs., Inc.

Arezzo, Emanuela & Ghidini, Gustavo. Biotechnology & Software Patent Law: A Comparative Review of New Developments. 2012. (New Directions in Patent Law Ser.). 392p. 160.00 ***(978-1-84980-040-2(5))*** Elgar, Edward Publishing, Inc.

Arora, Himanshu. Illustrated Dictionary of Biotechnology. 2009. (ENG.). 450p. pap. 61.95 *(978-1-4398-0173-4(8),* CRC Press) Taylor & Francis Group GBR. Dist: Taylor & Francis Group.

Austin, Martin. Business Development for the Biotechnology & Pharmaceutical Industry. 2008. (Illus.). 202p. 124.95 *(978-0-566-08781-3(2),* Gower Publishing Co., Ltd.) Ashgate Publishing, Ltd. GBR. Dist: Ashgate Publishing Co.

Bainbridge, William Sims. Nanoconvergence: The Unity of Nanoscience, Biotechnology, Information Technology & Cognitive Science. 2007. (ENG., Illus.). 272p. per. 36.99 *(978-0-13-244643-3(X))* Prentice Hall PTR.

Bainbridge, William Sims & Roco, Mihail C., eds. Managing Nano-Bio-Info-Cogno Innovations: Converging Technologies in Society. 2010. (ENG.). vi, 390p. pap. 159.00 *(978-90-481-7044-9(3),* 9048170443) Springer.

Bains, William. Venture Capital & the European Biotechnology Industry. 2009. (ENG., Illus.). 232p. 110.00 *(978-0-230-21719-5(2))* Palgrave Macmillan.

Bajaj, Y.P.S. Trees II. 2008. (Biotechnology in Agriculture & Forestry Ser.). (Illus.). xviii, 622p. 589.00 *(978-3-540-19158-2(5))* Springer.

Bamford, Sandra C. Biology Unmoored: Melanesian Reflections on Life & Biotechnology. 2007. (Illus.). 230p. 50.00 *(978-0-520-24712-3(4))*; per. 24.95 *(978-0-520-24713-0(2))* Univ. of California Pr.

Banerjee, Debadyuti. Impact of Genetically Modified Organisms on International Trade. 2011. 56p. pap. ***(978-3-8443-0762-7(1))*** Lambert Academic Publishing.

Barbarisi, Alfonso, et al. Biotechnology in Surgery. 2010. (Updates in Surgery Ser.). (ENG., Illus.). 200p. 189.00 *(978-88-470-1657-6(6),* 8847016576) Springer.

Barfield, Claude E. Biotechnology & the Patent System: Balancing Innovation & Property Rights. Calfee, John E., ed. 2007. (ENG.). 132p. per. 25.00 *(978-0-8447-4256-4(2),* AEI Pr.) American Enterprise Institute for Public Policy Research.

Barh, Debmalya, ed. Omics. 2011. (ENG., Illus.). 613p. 139.95 ***(978-1-4398-5008-4(9),*** CRC Press) Taylor & Francis Group GBR. Dist: Taylor & Francis Group.

Barredo, José-Luis, ed. Microbial Processes & Products. 2010. (Methods in Biotechnology Ser.). (Illus.). 536p. pap. 179.00 *(978-1-61737-635-1(3),* 1617376353) Humana Pr.

Barredo, Jose Luis, ed. Microbial Enzymes & Biotransformations. 2010. (Methods in Biotechnology Ser.). (Illus.). 336p. pap. 149.00 *(978-1-61737-454-8(7),* 1617374547) Humana Pr.

Bartlett, Douglas H., ed. High-Pressure Bioscience & Biotechnology. 2010. (Annals of the New York Academy of Sciences Ser.: 45). (ENG.). 352p. pap. 130.00 *(978-1-57331-771-9(3),* Wiley-Blackwell) Wiley, John & Sons, Inc.

Baxter, Walt & Lee, Abraham P. Proceedings of the 2nd Frontiers in Biomedical Devices Conference — 2007: Presented at the Frontiers in Biomedical Devices Conference, June 7-8, 2007, Irvine, California, USA. 2007. (Illus.). xiii, 160p. pap. *(978-0-7918-4266-9(5))* American Society of Mechanical Engineers, The.

BCC Staff. Biorefinery Technologies & Products. 2007. per. 4250.00 *(978-1-59623-307-2(9))* BCC Research.

Becker, E. W. Microalgae: Biotechnology & Microbiology. 2008. (Cambridge Studies in Biotechnology Ser.). (ENG., Illus.). 304p. pap. 61.00 *(978-0-521-06113-1(X))* Cambridge Univ. Pr.

Bedau, Mark A. & Parke, Emily C., eds. The Ethics of Protocells: Moral & Social Implications of Creating Life in the Laboratory. 2009. (Basic Bioethics Ser.). (ENG., Illus.). 384p. (gr. 17). 55.00 *(978-0-262-01262-1(6))*; pap. 29.00 *(978-0-262-51269-5(6))* MIT Pr.

Bellucci, S. Nanoparticles & Nanodevices in Biological Applications Vol. 1: The INFN Lectures. 2008. (Lecture Notes in Nanoscale Science & Technology Ser.). (Illus.). xii, 198p. 159.00 *(978-3-540-70943-5(6))* Springer.

Bellucci, Stefano, ed. Nanoparticles & Nanodevices in Biological Applications: The INFN Lectures - Vol I. 2010. (Lecture Notes in Nanoscale Science & Technology Ser.). (Illus.). xii, 198p. pap. 159.00 *(978-3-642-08993-0(3),* 3642089933) Springer.

Berthier, Jean. Micro-Drops & Digital Microfluidics. (Micro & Nano Technologies Ser.). (ENG., 2008. Illus.). 350p. 180.00 *(978-0-8155-1544-9(8))* 2nd ed. 2013. 480p. 169.00 ***(978-1-4557-2550-2(1))*** William Andrew, Inc.

Berthier, Jean & Silberzan, Pascal. Microfluidics for Biotechnology, Second Edition. 2nd rev. ed. 2010. (Illus.). 525p. 169.00 *(978-1-59693-443-6(3))* Artech Hse., Inc.

Bhargava, Atul & Srivastava, Shilpi. Biotechnology: New Ideas, New Developments. 2012. ***(978-1-62100-539-1(9))*** Nova Science Pubs., Inc.

Bhattacharya, Sanjoy K., ed. Enzyme Mixtures & Complex Biosynthesis. 2007. (Illus.). 136p. 129.00 *(978-1-58706-216-2(X))* Landes Bioscience.

Biehl, Joâo. Will to Live: AIDS Therapies & the Politics of Survival. 2009. (In-Formation Ser.). (ENG., Illus.). 480p. (C). pap. 39.95 *(978-0-691-14385-9(4))* Princeton Univ. Pr.

Bin Mohamed, Abdul Aziz, ed. Neutron & X-Ray Scattering in Advancing Materials Research: Proceedings of the International Conference on Neutron & X-Ray Scattering - 2009. 2010. (AIP Conference Proceedings Ser.). 262p. 147.00 *(978-0-7354-0739-8(8),* 0735407398, AIP Pr.) Springer.

Bin, Roberto, et al, eds. Biotech Innovations & Fundamental Rights. 2011. (ENG.). x, 290p. 139.00 *(978-88-470-2031-3(X),* 884702031X) Springer.

Binder, Gordon & Bashe, Philip. Science Lessons: What the Business of Biotech Taught Me about Management. 2008. (ENG., Illus.). 292p. 29.95 *(978-1-59139-861-5(4))* Harvard Business Review Pr.

Biocompatible Materials for the Human Body. 2007. per. 4250.00 *(978-1-59623-277-8(3))* BCC Research.

Biotechnology. 2011. 89.95 ***(978-1-4398-2010-0(4),*** CRC Press) Taylor & Francis Group GBR. Dist: Taylor & Francis Group.

Biotechnology in Cosmetics: Concepts, Tools & Techniques. 2007. (ENG.). 423p. pap. 149.00 *(978-1-932633-24-5(3))* Allured Business Media.

BioWorld Biotechnology State of the Industry Report 2007. 2007. per. *(978-1-933040-71-4(8))* AHC Media, LLC.

BioWorld Top 25 Biotechnology Drugs Report 2007. 2007. per. *(978-1-933040-72-1(6))* AHC Media, LLC.

Birenbaum-Carmeli, Daphna & Inhorn, Marcia Claire, eds. Assisting Reproduction, Testing Genes: Global Encounters with New Biotechnologies. 2009. 304p. 90.00 *(978-1-84545-625-2(4))* Berghahn Bks., Inc.

Blaschek-Miller, Travis, ed. BayBio: Translating Science into Better Health. 2008. (Illus.). 177p. per. *(978-0-9789300-0-4(2))* BayBio.

—California Cures: Translating Opportunity into California¿s Success. 2008. (Illus.). cd-rom *(978-0-9789300-2-8(9))* BayBio.

Bloch, David J. The Fundamentals of Life Sciences Law: Drugs, Devices, & Biotech. 2007. xx, 502p. pap. 155.00 *(978-1-4224-3975-3(5))* American Health Lawyers Assn.

Boas, David A., et al, eds. Handbook of Biomedical Optics. 2011. (ENG., Illus.). 831p. 149.95 *(978-1-4200-9036-9(4),* CRC Press) Taylor & Francis Group GBR. Dist: Taylor & Francis Group.

Bodiguel, Luc & Cardwell, Michael, eds. The Regulation of Genetically Modified Organisms: Comparative Approaches. 2010. (ENG., Illus.). 430p. 143.00 *(978-0-19-954248-2(1))* Oxford Univ. Pr., Inc.

Bohrer, Robert A. A Guide to Biotechnology Law & Business. 2007. (ENG.). 362p. 60.00 *(978-1-59460-087-6(2))* Carolina Academic Pr.

Boisseau, Patrick, et al, eds. Nanoscience: Nanobiotechnology & Nanobiology. 2009. Orig. Title: Les Nanosciences III - Nanobiotechnologies et Nanobiologie. (ENG., Illus.). xxxviii, 1200p. 309.00 *(978-3-540-88632-7(X),* 354088632X) Springer.

Bonner, Philip & Palmer, Trevor. Enzymes: Biochemistry, Biotechnology, Clinical Chemistry. 2nd rev. ed. 2007. (ENG.). 432p. pap. 75.00 *(978-1-904275-27-5(3),* Horwood Publishing, Ltd.) Woodhead Publishing Ltd. GBR. Dist: Ingram Pub. Services.

Borbye, Lisbeth, et al. Industry Immersion Learning: Real-Life Industry Case-Studies in Biotechnology & Business. 2009. (ENG., Illus.). 220p. 110.95 *(978-3-527-32408-8(9),* Wiley-VCH) Wiley, John & Sons, Inc.

Bourgaize. Biotechnology 2E: Demystifying the Concepts. 2nd rev. ed. 2011. pap. 105.95 *(978-0-7637-8551-2(2))* Jones & Bartlett Learning, LLC.

Bovenkerk, Bernice. The Biotechnology Debate: Democracy in the Face of Intractable Disagreement. 2012. (Library of Ethics & Applied Philosophy Ser.). (ENG., Illus.). xix, 334p. 139.00 ***(978-94-007-2690-1(2),*** 9400726902) Springer.

Brahma, Nitosh Kumar. Microbes, Microbial Engineering & Technology. 2011. (Microbiology Research Advances Ser.). 145.00 *(978-1-61209-331-4(0))* Nova Science Pubs., Inc.

Braidotti, Rosi. Posthuman. 2012. (ENG.). 180p. 69.95 ***(978-0-7456-4157-7(1))***; pap. 19.95 ***(978-0-7456-4158-4(X))*** Polity Pr. GBR. Dist: Wiley, John & Sons, Inc.

Brand, Stewart. Whole Earth Discipline: Why Dense Cities, Nuclear Power, Transgenic Crops, Restored Wildlands, & Geoengineering Are Necessary. 2010. (ENG.). 352p. (gr. 12). 16.00 *(978-0-14-311828-2(5),* Penguin (Non-Classics)) Penguin Group (USA) Inc.

Bronzino, Joseph D. & Reisner, David Evans. Bionanotechnology: Global Prospects. Reisner, David E., ed. 2008. (ENG., Illus.). 368p. 97.95 *(978-0-8493-7528-6(2),* CRC Press) Taylor & Francis Group GBR. Dist: Taylor & Francis Group.

Brossard, Dominique, et al. The Public, the Media & Agricultural Biotechnology. 2007. (Illus.). 405p. 160.00 *(978-1-84593-204-6(8))* CABI GBR. Dist: Stylus Publishing, LLC.

Brown, F., et al, eds. Biologics 2000 - Comparability of Biotechnology Products: Hyatt Washington Hotel, Washington, D. C., June 2000, Vol. 109. (Developments in Biologicals Ser.). (Illus.). *(978-3-8055-7427-3(4))* Karger, S. AG.

Brown, F. & Lubiniecki, A. S., eds. Process Validation for Manufacturing of Biologics & Biotechnology Products Vol. 113: Conference, Berlin, September 2001: Proceedings, (Developments in Biologicals Ser.: Vol. 113). (Illus.). *(978-3-8055-7576-8(9))* Karger, S. AG.

Brown, Sheldon S. Opportunities in Biotech Careers. 2007. (Opportunities In... Ser.). (ENG.). 160p. per. 13.95 *(978-0-07-147605-8(9),* 0071476059) McGraw-Hill Cos., The.

Buchner, Thomas B. & Ewingen, Nicolas H., eds. Photosynthesis: Theory & Applications in Energy, Biotechnology & Nanotechnology. 2009. (Illus.). xi, 255p. 98.00 *(978-1-60692-719-9(1))* Nova Science Pubs., Inc.

Bucke, Christopher, ed. Carbohydrate Biotechnology Protocols. 2010. (Methods in Biotechnology Ser.). (Illus.). 352p. pap. 149.00 *(978-1-61737-074-8(6),* 1617370746) Humana Pr.

Burchfiel, Kenneth J. Biotechnology & the Federal Circuit. 2nd ed. 2009. xxxvii, 1113p. *(978-1-57018-738-4(X))*; *(978-0-87179-738-4(0))* BNA Bks.

Burnstein, Leonid. Matlab in Bioscience & Biotechnology. 2011. (Woodhead Publishing Series in Biomedicine Ser.). (ENG., Illus.). 248p. 140.00 ***(978-1-907568-04-6(2),*** Biohealthcare Publishing (Oxford) Limited) Woodhead Publishing Ltd. GBR. Dist: Ingram Pub. Services.

Butler, Michael, et al, eds. Comprehensive Biotechnology, 6 vols. 2nd ed. 2011. (ENG.). 5320p. 1900.00 *(978-0-444-53352-4(4),* Pergamon) Elsevier Science & Technology Bks.

Cao, Hengchu, et al. Proceedings of the 3rd Frontiers in Biomedical Devices Conference — 2008: Presented at the 3rd Frontiers in Biomedical Devices Conference & Exhibition, June 18-20, 2008, Irvine, California, USA. 2008. (Illus.). xi, 126p. pap. *(978-0-7918-4833-3(7))* American Society of Mechanical Engineers, The.

Cao, Zhong, et al, eds. Application of Chemical Engineering. 2011. (Advanced Materials Research Ser.: Vol. 236-238). 3102p. pap. ***(978-3-03785-121-0(X))*** Trans Tech Pubns., Ltd.

Carlson, Robert H., et al. Biology Is Technology: The Promise, Peril, & New Business of Engineering Life. 2011. (ENG., Illus.). 288p. pap. 21.95 *(978-0-674-06015-9(6))* Harvard Univ. Pr.

Carnazza, Santina. Phage Display as a Tool for Synthetic Biology. Guglielmino, Salvatore, ed. 2010. (Nanotechnology Science & Technology Ser.). 93p. pap. 43.00 *(978-1-60876-987-2(9))* Nova Science Pubs., Inc.

Carolan, Michael. Decentering Biotechnology: Assemblages Built Assemblages Masked. 2010. (Theory, Technology & Society Ser.). (Illus.). 200p. 89.95 *(978-1-4094-1005-8(6))* Ashgate Publishing Co.

Carolina Biological Staff, compiled by. Introduction to Biotechnology. 2009. (Inquiries in Science Biology Ser.). *(978-1-4350-0354-5(3))*; tchr. ed., spiral bd. *(978-1-4350-0353-8(5))* Carolina Biological Supply Co.

Caruso, Denise. Intervention: Confronting the Real Risks. 2006. 270p. pap. 17.95 *(978-0-615-13553-3(6))* Hybrid Vigor Institute, The.

Castle, D., ed. The Role of Intellectual Property Rights in Biotechnology Innovation. 2009. (Illus.). 480p. 200.00 *(978-1-84720-980-1(7))* Elgar, Edward Publishing, Inc.

Castle, David, ed. The Role of Intellectual Property Rights in Biotechnology Innovation. 2011. (Illus.). 480p. pap. 59.95 *(978-1-84844-788-2(4))* Elgar, Edward Publishing, Inc.

Caulfield, Sean, et al, eds. Perceptions of Promise: Biotechnology, Society & Art. 2011. (ENG., Illus.). 98p. (C). pap. 35.00 *(978-0-9699898-4-4(9))* Univ .of Alberta, Dept. of Art and Design CAN. Dist: Univ. of Washington Pr.

Cerda, Joan, ed. The Fish Oocyte: From Basic Studies to Biotechnological Applications. 2007. (Illus.). 508p. 239.00 *(978-1-4020-6233-9(8))* Springer.

Chan, Warren C. W., ed. Bio-Applications of Nanoparticles. 2010. (Advances in Experimental Medicine & Biology Ser.). (Illus.). xx, 207p. pap. 209.00 *(978-1-4419-2633-3(X),* 144192633X) Springer.

Chandler, Alfred D., Jr. Shaping the Industrial Century: The Remarkable Story of the Evolution of the Modern Chemical & Pharmaceutical Industries. 2009. (Harvard Studies in Business History Ser.: 46). (Illus.). 384p. pap. 23.50 *(978-0-674-03221-7(7))* Harvard Univ. Pr.

Chandrasekaran, M., ed. Valorization of Food Processing By-Products. 2012. (Fermented Foods & Beverages Ser.). (ENG., Illus.). 624p. 169.95 ***(978-1-4398-4885-2(8),*** CRC Press) Taylor & Francis Group GBR. Dist: Taylor & Francis Group.

Chang, Thomas Ming Swi. Artificial Cells: Biotechnology, Nanomedicine, Regenerative Medicine, Blood Substitutes, Bioencapsulation, & Cell/Stem Cell Therapy. 2007. (Regenerative Medicine, Artificial Cells & Nanomedicine Ser.: Vol. 1). (Illus.). 455p. pap. 98.00 *(978-981-270-778-9(6))* World Scientific Publishing Co., Inc.

—Artificial Cells: Biotechnology, Nanomedicine, Regenerative Medicine, Blood Substitutes, Bioencapsulation, Cell/Stem Cell Therapy. 2007. (Regenerative Medicine, Artificial Cells & Nanomedicine Ser.: Vol. 1). (Illus.). 455p. 197.00 *(978-981-270-576-1(7))* World Scientific Publishing Co., Inc.

Channarayappa & Channarayappa. Molecular Biotechnology: Principles & Practices. 2007. (ENG., Illus.). 1228p. (C). 119.95 *(978-1-4200-5157-5(1),* CRC Press) Taylor & Francis Group GBR. Dist: Taylor & Francis Group.

Charcosset, Catherine. Membrane Processes in Biotechnologies & Pharmaceutics. 2012. (ENG.). 350p. 225.00 ***(978-0-444-56334-7(2))*** Elsevier Science & Technology Bks.

Chawla. Introduction to Plant Biotechnology 3Ed. 3rd rev. ed. 2009. (ENG., Illus.). 730p. pap. 69.95 *(978-1-57808-636-8(1))* BIOS Scientific Publishers Ltd. GBR. Dist: Taylor & Francis Group.

Chen, Jake & Sidhu, Amandeep S. Biological Database Modeling. 2007. (Illus.). 224p. 123.00 *(978-1-59693-258-6(9))* Artech Hse., Inc.

Chen, Lei Zhi, et al. Modelling & Optimization of Biotechnological Processes: Artificial Intelligence Approaches. 2010. (Studies in Computational Intelligence Ser.). (Illus.). viii, 123p. pap. 189.00 *(978-3-642-06792-1(1),* 3642067921) Springer.

Clark, David P. & Pazdernik, Nanette J. Biotechnology. rev. ed. 2010. (ENG., Illus.). 768p. (C). 109.95 *(978-0-12-385063-8(0),* Academic Cell) Elsevier Science & Technology Bks.

Clarke, Adele. Biomedicalization: Technoscience, Health, & Illness in the U.S. Fishman, Jennifer R. et al, eds. 2010. (ENG., Illus.). 512p. 99.95 *(978-0-8223-4553-4(6))* Duke Univ. Pr.

Clarke, Adele E., et al, eds. Biomedicalization: Technoscience, Health, & Illness in the U.S. 2010. (ENG., Illus.). 512p. pap. 28.95 *(978-0-8223-4570-1(6))* Duke Univ. Pr.

The Clinical Trials Business. 2006. per. 4250.00 *(978-1-59623-223-5(4))* BCC Research.

Clinton, Steven V. & Kelly, Michael F. Clostridia: Biotechnology, Medicinal Applications, & Implications. 2012. ***(978-1-62100-761-6(8))*** Nova Science Pubs., Inc.

Cobb, Allan B. Scientifically Engineered Food: The Debate over What's on Your Plate. 2009. (Focus on Science & Society Ser.). 64p. (gr. 5-6). 58.50 *(978-1-61512-623-1(6))* Rosen Publishing Group, Inc., The.

Cole-Turner, Ronald, ed. Transhumanism & Transcendence: Christian Hope in an Age of Technological Enhancement. 2011. (Illus.). 232p. pap. 32.95 *(978-1-58901-780-1(3))* Georgetown Univ. Pr.

Commercial Biotech Agriculture & Aquaculture. *(978-81-204-0827-2(6))* Science Pubs.

Comstive, Layla, et al, eds. Major Pharmaceutical & Biotechnology Companies of the World 2011. 14th ed. 2011. (Major Pharmaceutical & Biotechnology Companies of the World Ser.). (ENG.). 558p. pap. 1350.00 ***(978-1-86099-686-3(8),*** Graham & Whiteside Ltd) Cengage Gale.

Conference, Arnold and Mabel Beckman Center, Irvine California, November 20-22, 2009 & The National Academies. NAKFI Synthetic Biology: Building a Nation's Inspiration: Interdisciplinary Research Team Summaries. 2010. (ENG.). 120p. pap. 31.00 *(978-0-309-14942-6(8))* National Academies Pr.

Conlisk, A. Terrence. Essentials of Micro & Nano Fluidics: With Applications to the Biological & Chemical Sciences. 2012. (ENG., Illus.). 548p. (C). 130.00 ***(978-0-521-88168-5(4))*** Cambridge Univ. Pr.

Cooke. Growth Cultures. 2007. (Genetics & Society Ser.). (Illus.). XVIII, 286p. 190.00 *(978-0-415-39223-5(3))* Routledge.

Cooley, Dennis R. Technology, Transgenics & a Practical Moral Code. 2009. (International Library of Ethics, Law & Technology Ser.). xxiv, 271p. 159.00 *(978-90-481-3020-7(4),* 9048130204) Springer.

Cooper, Melinda. Life as Surplus: Biotechnology & Capitalism in the Neoliberal Era. 2008. (In Vivo Ser.). (ENG.). 208p. pap. 25.00 *(978-0-295-98791-0(X))* Univ. of Washington Pr.

Cordonier Segger, Marie-Claire, et al, eds. Legal Aspects of Implementing the Cartagena Protocol on Biosafety. 2012. (ENG., Illus.). 525p. 125.00 ***(978-1-107-00438-2(1))*** Cambridge Univ. Pr.

Cram101 Textbook Reviews. Outlines & Highlights for Drug & Biological Development by Ronald Evens, Isbn: 9780387329789 0387329781. 2011. 226p. pap. 30.95 ***(978-1-61490-259-1(3))*** Cram101 Inc.

—Outlines & Highlights for Microbial Biotechnology: Fundamentals of Applied Microbiology by Alexander N. Glazer. 2011. 634p. pap. 40.95 ***(978-1-61905-794-4(8))*** Cram101 Inc.

Cram101 Textbook Reviews. Outlines & Highlights for Molecular Biotechnology: Principles & Applications of Recombinant DNA by Glick, Bernard R. / Pasternak, Jack J. , ISBN. 2010. 206p. pap. 30.95 *(978-1-61698-545-5(3))* Cram101 Inc.

CRC Press Staff, creator. NSTI Nanotech: Technical Proceedings: Volume 2. 2007. (Illus.). 814p. per. 139.95 *(978-1-4200-6183-3(6))* CRC Pr. LLC.

—NSTI Nanotech: Technical Proceedings: Volume 3. 2007. (Illus.). 710p. per. 139.95 *(978-1-4200-6184-0(4))* CRC Pr. LLC.

Cullen, David C., et al, eds. Handbook of Biosensors & Biochips. 2007. (ENG.). 1500p. 990.00 *(978-0-470-01905-4(0)*, Wiley-Interscience) Wiley, John & Sons, Inc.

Cummings, Stephen P., ed. Bioremediation: Methods & Protocols. 2009. (Methods in Molecular Biology Ser.). (ENG., Illus.). x, 235p. 119.00 *(978-1-60761-438-8(3)*, 1607614383) Humana Pr.

Cunningham, Charles & Porter, Andrew J. R., eds. Recombinant Proteins from Plants. 2010. (Methods in Biotechnology Ser.). 308p. pap. 149.00 *(978-1-61737-021-2(5)*, 1617370215) Humana Pr.

Cuyper, M. de & Bulte, Jeff W. M., eds. Physics & Chemistry Basis of Biotechnology. 2010. (Focus on Biotechnology Ser.). (Illus.). 340p. pap. 239.00 *(978-90-481-5741-9(2)*, 9048157412) Springer.

da Costa, Beatriz & Philip, Kavita, eds. Tactical Biopolitics: Art, Activism, & Technoscience. (Leonardo Bks.). (ENG., Illus.). 536p. (gr. 17). 2010. pap. 20.00 *(978-0-262-51491-0(5))* 2008. 42.00 *(978-0-262-04249-9(5))* MIT Pr.

Daniel F. Robinson. Confronting Biopiracy. 2011. (ENG.). 208p. pap. 39.95 ***(978-1-84971-432-7(0))*** Routledge.

Danielski, Leandro. Supercritical Processing of Plant Materials. 2008. 200p. pap. *(978-3-639-02458-6(3))* VDM Verlag Dr. Mueller e.K.

Dasgupta, Anjan K. & Datta, Asit K. Nanobiotechnology & Nanomedicine: Trends & Applications. 2011. 300p. 149.00 *(978-981-4267-07-6(4))* Pan Stanford Publishing SGP. Dist: Independent Pubs. Group.

DaSilva, E. J., et al, eds. Biotechnology: Economic & Social Aspects: Issues for Developing Countries. 2009. (ENG., Illus.). 404p. pap. 55.00 *(978-0-521-12228-3(7))* Cambridge Univ. Pr.

David, Kenneth & Thompson, Paul B., eds. What Can Nanotechnology Learn from Biotechnology? Social & Ethical Lessons for Nanoscience from the Debate over Agrifood Biotechnology & GMOs. 2008. (Food Science & Technology Ser.). (ENG., Illus.). 360p. 80.95 *(978-0-12-373990-2(X)*, Academic Pr.) Elsevier Science & Technology Bks.

Davidberg, Joshua. Biotechnology Applications, Facts & Discoveries: Biotechnology in the Millenium, Vol. 11. 2009. (C). pap., tchr. ed., stu. ed. 175.20 *(978-1-933844-15-2(9))* BioVoyage Institute, Inc.

—Biotechnology Applications, Facts & Discoveries: Biotechnology in the Millenium; College. 2009. (C). pap., tchr. ed., stu. ed. 175.25 *(978-1-933844-14-5(0))* BioVoyage Institute, Inc.

—Exploring Scinece & Biotechnology, Kindergarten; Teacher's Manual: BioScience-BioTech Education Program. 2009. pap., tchr. ed., suppl. ed. 200.00 *(978-1-933844-17-6(5))* BioVoyage Institute, Inc.

Daviter, Falk. Policy Framing in the European Union. 2011. (ENG., Illus.). 208p. 85.00 ***(978-0-230-27778-6(0))*** Palgrave Macmillan.

de Grey, Aubrey, et al. Ending Aging: The Rejuvenation Breakthroughs That Could Reverse Human Aging in Our Lifetime. 2008. (ENG., Illus.). 448p. pap. 16.99 *(978-0-312-36707-7(4)*, St. Martin's Griffin) St. Martin's Pr.

Decision Resources Inc Staff, ed. SAGE Sourcebook of Modern Biomedical Devices: Business Environments in a Global Market, 4 vols. 2007. (Illus.). 1680p. 895.00 *(978-1-4129-5054-1(6)*, B50546C) SAGE Pubns., Inc.

Delrue, Iris. Development of a New Inactivated Virus Vaccine. 2011. 172p. pap. ***(978-3-8454-0282-6(2))*** Lambert Academic Publishing.

Demirbas, Ayhan. Biorefineries: For Biomass Upgrading Facilities. 2009. (Green Energy & Technology Ser.). (ENG., Illus.). ix, 240p. 199.00 *(978-1-84882-720-2(2)*, 1848827202) Springer.

Desai, Mohamed A., ed. Downstream Processing of Proteins: Methods & Protocols. 2010. (Methods in Biotechnology Ser.). (Illus.). 240p. pap. 189.00 *(978-1-61737-075-5(4)*, 1617370754) Humana Pr

Desai, Tejal & Bhatia, Sangeeta N. BioMEMS & Biomedical Nanotechnology: Volume III: Therapeutic Micro/Nanotechnology. 2010. (Illus.). xxiv, 376p. pap. 199.00 *(978-1-4419-3805-3(2)*, 1441938052) Springer.

Deutscher, J., ed. Ser/Thr/Tyr Protein Phosphorylation in Bacteria: A Written Symposium, Vol. 9. (Illus.). 118p. pap. *(978-3-8055-8073-1(8))* Karger, S. AG.

Dhingra, Harish Kumar, et al. Current Topics in Biotechnology & Microbiology. 2011. 336p. pap. ***(978-3-8443-2975-9(7))*** Lambert Academic Publishing.

Dickenson, Donna. Body Shopping: The Economy Fuelled by Flesh & Blood. (ENG.). 2009. 240p. pap. 14.95 *(978-1-85168-623-0(1))* 2008. 320p. 27.95 *(978-1-85168-591-2(X))* Oneworld Pubns. GBR. Dist: National Bk. Network.

—Property in the Body: Feminist Perspectives. 2007. (Cambridge Law, Medicine & Ethics Ser.). (ENG.). 222p. per. 50.99 *(978-0-521-68732-4(2))* Cambridge Univ. Pr.

Dochain, Denis. Automatic Control of Bioprocesses. 2007. 256p. 150.00 *(978-1-905209-36-1(3))* ISTE/Hermes Science Publishing GBR. Dist: Independent Pubs. Group.

Dochain, Denis, ed. Automatic Control of Bioprocesses. 2008. (Iste Ser.: 305). (ENG., Illus.). 288p. 174.00 *(978-1-84821-025-7(6)*, Wiley-ISTE) Wiley, John & Sons, Inc.

Donati, Edgardo R. & Sand, Wolfgang, eds. Microbial Processing of Metal Sulfides. (ENG.). xi, 314p. 2010. pap. 239.00 *(978-90-481-7402-7(3)*, 9048174023) 2007. 239.00 *(978-1-4020-5588-1(9)*, 1402055889) Springer.

Doran, Pauline M. Bioprocess Engineering Principles. 2nd ed. 2012. (ENG.). 928p. pap. 119.95 ***(978-0-12-220851-5(X)***, Academic Pr.) Elsevier Science & Technology Bks.

Dragoman, Daniela & Dragoman, Mircea. Bionanoelectronics: Bioinquiring & Bioinspired Devices. 2012. (NanoScience & Technology Ser.). (ENG., Illus.). x, 254p. 169.00 ***(978-3-642-25571-7(X)***, 364225571X) Springer.

Dronamraju. Biotechnology & Biodiversity. 2008. 73.00 *(978-981-277-500-9(5))* World Scientific Publishing Co., Inc.

Dübel, Stefan, ed. Handbook of Therapeutic Antibodies: Technologies, Emerging Developments & Approved Therapeutics. 2010. (ENG., Illus.). 1250p. pap. 262.95 *(978-3-527-32902-1(1)*, Wiley-VCH) Wiley, John & Sons, Inc.

Dunford, Nurhan T., ed. Food & Industrial Bioproducts & Bioprocessing. 2012. (ENG., Illus.). 392p. 199.95 ***(978-0-8138-2105-4(3)***, Wiley-Blackwell) Wiley, John & Sons, Inc.

Dungs, Susanne & Gerber, Uwe, eds. Biotechnologie in Kontexten der Sozial- und Gesundheitsberufe: Professionelle Praxen - Disziplinäre Nachbarschaften - Gesellschaftliche Leitbilder. 2009. (GER.). 414p. pap. 42.95 *(978-3-631-57779-0(6))* Lang, Peter GmbH, Europaischer Verlag der Wissenschaften DEU. Dist: Lang, Peter.

Durieux, A. & Simon, J. P., eds. Applied Microbiology. 2010. (Focus on Biotechnology Ser.). 288p. pap. 199.00 *(978-90-481-5669-6(6)*, 9048156696) Springer.

Dürre, P., ed. Biotech Genomics: Genome-Based Analysis of Biotechnologically Relevant Prokaryotes. 2008. (Illus.). 136p. pap. *(978-3-8055-8963-5(8))* Karger, S. AG.

Dutta, N.N., et al, contrib. by. History & Trends in Bioprocessing & Biotransformation. 2010. (Advances in Biochemical Engineering Biotechnology Ser.). (Illus.). ix, 258p. pap. 319.00 *(978-3-642-07616-9(5)*, 3642076165) Springer.

The Dynamic Media, Sera & Reagent Market in Biotechnology. 2007. per. 4250.00 *(978-1-59623-274-7(9))* BCC Research.

Edwards, David, ed. Plant Bioinformatics: Methods & Protocols. (Methods in Molecular Biology Ser.). (Illus.). 2010. xv, 552p. pap. 189.00 *(978-1-61737-697-9(3)*, 1617376973) 2008. 552p. 189.00 *(978-1-58829-653-5(9))* Humana Pr.

Eggleston, Gillian & Vercellotti, John R. Industrial Application of Enzymes on Carbohydrate Based Materials. 2007. (ACS Symposium Ser.). (ENG., Illus.). 260p. (C). 135.00 *(978-0-8412-7406-8(1))* American Chemical Society.

Egorov, Alexei M. & Zaikov, Gennadii Efremovich. New Aspects in Biotechnology & Medicine. 2006. (Illus.). 189p. 225.00 *(978-1-60021-465-3(7))* Nova Science Pubs., Inc.

Einsiedel, Edna F., ed. Emerging Technologies: From Hindsight to Foresight. 2009. (ENG.). 328p. pap. 32.95 *(978-0-7748-1549-9(3))* UBC Pr. CAN. Dist: Univ. of Washington Pr.

El-Gewely, M. Raafat. Biotechnology Annual Review. (Biotechnology Annual Review Ser.: 14). (ENG.). 2008. 492p. 250.00 *(978-0-444-53226-8(9))* 2007. 378p. 250.00 *(978-0-444-53032-5(0))* Elsevier Science & Technology Bks. (Elsevier Science).

—Biotechnology Annual Review, Vol. 12. 2006. (Biotechnology Annual Review Ser.: 12). (ENG., Illus.). 422p. 250.00 *(978-0-444-52724-0(9)*, Elsevier Science) Elsevier Science & Technology Bks.

El-Kadi, Sherif. Bioplastic Production from Inexpensive Sources. 2010. 152p. pap. *(978-3-639-26372-5(3))* VDM Verlag Dr. Mueller e.K.

El-Mansi, E. M. T., et al, eds. Fermentation Microbiology & Biotechnology, Third Edition. 3rd rev. ed. 2011. (ENG., Illus.). 555p. 129.95 *(978-1-4398-5579-9(X)*, CRC Press) Taylor & Francis Group GBR. Dist: Taylor & Francis Group

Enderle, John. Bioinstrumentation. 2006. (Synthesis Lectures on Biomedical Engineering Ser.). 220p. pap. 40.00 *(978-1-59829-132-2(7))* Morgan & Claypool Pubs.

Endo, Isao & Nagamune, Teruyuki, eds. Nano/Micro Biotechnology. 2010. (Advances in Biochemical Engineering Biotechnology Ser.). (Illus.). xvi, 270p. 359.00 *(978-3-642-14946-7(4)*, 3642149464) Springer.

Endo, M., et al, eds. Endoglycosidases: Biochemistry, Biotechnology, Application. 2010. (ENG., Illus.). xv, 272p. pap. 209.00 *(978-3-642-07085-3(X)*, 364207085X) Springer.

Endo, Masahiko, et al, eds. Endoglycosidases: Biochemistry, Biotechnology, Application. 2006. (ENG., Illus.). xv, 272p. 209.00 *(978-3-540-34494-0(2)*, 3540344942) Springer.

Engelhard, Margret, et al, eds. Genetic Engineering in Livestock: New Applications & Interdisciplinary Perspectives. 2010. (Ethics of Science & Technology Assessment Ser.). (Illus.). xvi, 146p. pap. 79.95 *(978-3-642-09937-3(8)*, 3642099378) Springer.

Eom, Kilho. Simulations in Nanobiotechnology. 2011. (ENG., Illus.). 562p. 139.95 *(978-1-4398-3504-3(7)*, CRC Press) Taylor & Francis Group GBR. Dist: Taylor & Francis Group.

Ewing, Eileen Smith, et al. Biotechnology & the Law. 2007. (ENG.). 921p. per. 189.95 *(978-1-59031-761-7(0))* American Bar Assn.

Ewing, W. N. The Living Gut. 2nd ed. 2009. (ENG., Illus.). 168p. 52.95 *(978-1-904761-57-0(7))* Nottingham Univ. Pr. GBR. Dist: Independent Pubs. Group.

Farid, Hadi & Daud Silong, Abu. Biotechnology Adoption: Correlate of university-company Perspectives. 2011. 204p. pap. ***(978-3-8443-9685-0(3))*** Lambert Academic Publishing.

Faurie, Robert & Thommel, Jargen. Microbial Production of L-Amino Acids. 2010. (Advances in Biochemical Engineering Biotechnology Ser.). (Illus.). xiii, 185p. pap. 159.00 *(978-3-642-07775-3(7)*, 3642077757) Springer.

Fialho, Arsenio & Chakrabarty, Ananda M., eds. Emerging Cancer Therapy: Microbial Approaches & Biotechnological Tools. 2010. (Wiley Series in Biotechnology & Bioengineering Ser.: 2). (ENG., Illus.). 432p. 132.00 *(978-0-470-44467-2(3)*, Wiley) Wiley, John & Sons, Inc.

Flemming, Hans-C. Marine & Industrial Biofouling. 2008. (Springer Series on Biofilms Ser.). (Illus.). 330p. 239.00 *(978-3-540-69794-7(2))* Springer.

Flynne, William G., ed. Biotechnology & Bioengineering. 2008. (Illus.). xii, 272p. 129.00 *(978-1-60456-067-1(3)*, Nova Biomedical Bks.) Nova Science Pubs., Inc.

Förch, Renate, et al, eds. Surface Design: Applications in Bioscience & Nanotechnology. 2009. (ENG., Illus.). 532p. 171.00 *(978-3-527-40789-7(8)*, Wiley-VCH) Wiley, John & Sons, Inc.

Fournier, Ronald L. Basic Transport Phenomena in Biomedical Engineering. 3rd rev. ed. 2011. (ENG., Illus.). 483p. (C). 89.95 *(978-1-4398-2670-6(6)*, CRC Press) Taylor & Francis Group GBR. Dist: Taylor & Francis Group.

Francioni, Francesco, ed. Biotechnologies & International Human Rights. 2007. (ENG.). 401p. 130.00 *(978-1-84113-703-2(0))* Hart Publishing Ltd. GBR. Dist: International Specialized Bk. Services.

Franklin, Sarah H. & Lock, Margaret M., eds. Remaking Life & Death: Toward an Anthropology of the Biosciences. (School of American Research Advanced Seminar Ser.). (Illus.). 396p. 34.95 *(978-1-930618-19-0(0))*; pap. 29.95 *(978-1-930618-20-6(4))* School for Advanced Research Pr./SAR Pr.

Freedman, Toby. Career Opportunities in Biotechnology & Drug Development. (Illus.). 409p. 2009. (ENG.). pap. 40.00 *(978-0-87969-880-5(2))* 2007. 59.00 *(978-0-87969-725-9(3))* Cold Spring Harbor Laboratory Pr.

Friedman, Yali. Building Biotechnology: Business, Regulations, Patents, Law, Politics, Science. 3rd ed. 2008. 460p. 89.95 *(978-0-9734676-5-9(7))*; (Illus.). pap. 64.95 *(978-0-9734676-6-6(5))* ThinkBiotech, LLC. (Logos Pr.).

—The Business of Biotechnology: Profit from the expanding influence of Biotechnology. 2008. (ENG.). 252p. pap. 34.95 *(978-1-934899-00-7(3)*, Logos Pr.) ThinkBiotech, LLC.

Friedman, Yali, ed. Best Practices in Biotechnology Business Development: Valuation, Licensing, Cash Flow, Pharmacoeconomics, Market Selection, Communication, & Intellectual Property. 2008. 186p. pap. 67.95 *(978-0-9734676-0-4(6)*, Logos Pr.) ThinkBiotech, LLC.

—Best Practices in Biotechnology Education: 22 Chapters Covering International Best Practices in: K-12, College, Certificate, Master's, Doctoral, MBA programs, & Student Groups. 2008. (Illus.). 342p. pap. 74.95 *(978-0-9734676-7-3(3)*, Logos Pr.) ThinkBiotech, LLC.

Friend, Tim. The Third Domain: The Untold Story of Archea & the Future of Biotechnology. 2007. (ENG., Illus.). 312p. 27.95 *(978-0-309-10237-7(5)*, Joseph Henry Pr.) National Academies Pr.

Fuchs, Harald & Bhushan, Bharat, eds. Biosystems - Investigated by Scanning Probe Microscopy. 2010. (ENG., Illus.). xxxii, 834p. 299.00 *(978-3-642-02404-7(1)*, 3642024041) Springer.

Fulekar, M. H. Dictionary of Biotechnology. 2009. (Dictionary Ser.). 200p. (C). pap. *(978-81-907462-9-8(4))* I.K. International Publishing House Pvt. Ltd.

—Environmental Biotechnology. 2010. (ENG., Illus.). 620p. pap. 89.95 *(978-1-57808-582-8(9))* BIOS Scientific Publishers Ltd. GBR. Dist: Taylor & Francis Group.

—Environmental Biotechnology. 2010. *(978-1-57808-573-6(X))* Science Pubs.

Fusetani, Nobuhiro & Clare, Anthony S. Antifouling Compounds. 2010. (Progress in Molecular & Subcellular Biology Ser.). (Illus.). xiv, 225p. pap. 249.00 *(978-3-642-06758-7(1)*, 3642067581) Springer.

Gad, Shayne Cox, ed. Handbook of Pharmaceutical Biotechnology. 2007. (Pharmaceutical Development Ser.: 2). (ENG.). 1680p. 205.00 *(978-0-471-21386-4(1)*, Wiley-Interscience) Wiley, John & Sons, Inc.

Gale. Biotechnology in Context, 2 vols. 2012. (Biotechnology in Context Ser.). (ENG., Illus.). 1000p. lib. bdg. 270.00 ***(978-1-4144-9082-3(8))*** Cengage Gale.

Ganguli, Prabuddha, et al, eds. Technology Transfer in Biotechnology: A Global Perspective. 2009. (ENG., Illus.). 232p. 165.00 *(978-3-527-31645-8(0)*, Wiley-VCH) Wiley, John & Sons, Inc.

Garg, Neha, et al. Xylanase: Applications & Biotechnological Aspects. 2010. 60p. pap. *(978-3-8383-7504-5(1))* Lambert Academic Publishing.

Gault, Percy M. & Marler, Harris J. Handbook on Cyanobacteria: Biochemistry, Biotechnology & Applications. 2009. (Bacteriology Research Developments Ser.). pap. 195.00 *(978-1-60741-092-8(3))* Nova Science Pubs., Inc.

Gaur, Rajarshi Kumar. Recent Trends in Biotechnology & Microbiology. 2010. 98.00 *(978-1-60876-666-6(7))* Nova Science Pubs., Inc.

Gazit, Ehud. Plenty of Room for Biology at the Bottom: An Introduction to Bionanotechnology. 2007. (Illus.). 183p. 107.00 *(978-1-86094-677-6(1))* Imperial College Pr. GBR. Dist: World Scientific Publishing Co., Inc.

Gerlach, Neil, et al. Becoming Biosubjects: Bodies. Systems. Technology. 2010. 224p. (ENG.). *(978-0-8020-9983-9(1))*; pap. *(978-0-8020-9683-8(2))* Univ. of Toronto Pr.

Glasner, Peter, et al. Local Cells, Global Science: The Rise of Embryonic Stem Cell Research in India. 2009. (Genetics & Society Ser.). 160p. 170.00 *(978-0-415-39609-7(3))* Routledge.

Glycoscience - Chemistry & Chemical Biology I-III. 2008. 1689.00 *(978-3-540-36157-2(X)*, 354036157X); 1349.00 *(978-3-540-30429-6(0))* Springer.

Gnanamanickam, Samuel S., ed. Plant-Associated Bacteria. (Illus.). 2007. 712p. pap. 129.00 *(978-1-4020-4537-0(9))* 2006. ix, 724p. 319.00 *(978-1-4020-4536-3(0)*, 1402045360) Springer.

Godden, Danielle A. & Andrews, Mason C. Technology Policies & Issues for the U. S. Government. 2011. (Government Procedures & Operations Ser.). 115.00 *(978-1-61209-501-1(1))* Nova Science Pubs., Inc.

Golan, Adam E. Cellulase: Types & Action, Mechanism, & Uses. 2011. (Series: Biotechnology in Agriculture, Industry & Medicine Ser.). 129.00 *(978-1-61761-983-0(3))* Nova Science Pubs., Inc.

Golden James Staff. Nanobiotechnology. 2008. 400p. 139.95 *(978-1-57444-495-7(6)*, DK3301) Taylor & Francis Group.

Goldys, Ewa M. & Hibbs, Alan R. Fluorescence Applications in Biotechnology & Life Sciences. 2009. (ENG., Illus.). 367p. 146.95 *(978-0-470-08370-3(0)*, Wiley-Blackwell) Wiley, John & Sons, Inc.

Gomase, Virendra & Gomase, Shruti. Mass Spectrometric Biotechnology. 2010. (Illus.). 216p. pap. *(978-3-639-17925-5(0))* VDM Verlag Dr. Mueller e.K.

—Microscopy in Biotechnology. 2010. (Illus.). 256p. pap. *(978-3-639-24549-3(0))* VDM Verlag Dr. Mueller e.K.

Göransson, B. & Pålsson, C. M., eds. Biotechnology & Innovation Systems: The Role of Public Policy. 2012. 424p. 185.00 ***(978-1-78100-138-7(3))*** Elgar, Edward Publishing, Inc.

Gottinger, Hans & Umali, Celia, eds. Strategic Alliances in Biotechnology & Pharmaceuticals. 2010. (Biotechnology in Agriculture, Industry & Medicine Ser.). 89.00 *(978-1-60876-997-1(6))* Nova Science Pubs., Inc.

Gouma, Perena. Nanomaterials for Chemical Sensors & Biotechnology. 2009. (ENG., Illus.). 159p. 129.95 *(978-981-4267-11-3(2))* Pan Stanford Publishing SGP. Dist: Taylor & Francis Group.

Graaf, E. S. van de, contrib. by. Patent Law & Modern Biotechnology: A Comparative Study about the Requirements & the Scope of Protection. xii, 447p. *(978-90-387-0577-4(8))* Wolters Kluwer nv.

Grace, Eric S. Biotechnology Unzipped: Promises & Realities. 2nd rev. ed. 2006. (ENG., Illus.). 241p. per. 19.95 *(978-0-309-09621-8(9)*, Joseph Henry Pr.) National Academies Pr.

Graimann, Bernhard, et al, eds. Brain-Computer Interfaces: Non-Invasive & Invasive Technologies. 2010. (Frontiers Collection). (ENG., Illus.). xiv, 393p. 99.00 *(978-3-642-02090-2(9)*, 3642020909) Springer.

Greenwood, Tracey, et al. Microbiology & Biotechnology. 2nd ed. 2007. (Illus.). 108p. pap. *(978-1-877462-12-2(8))* BIOZONE International, Ltd.

Gregg. Seed Conditioning Vol 1: Management. 2009. (ENG.). 497p. 149.95 *(978-1-57808-572-9(1))* BIOS Scientific Publishers Ltd. GBR. Dist: Taylor & Francis Group.

Grogan, Gideon. Practical Biotransformations: A Beginner's Guide. 2009. (ENG., Illus.). 344p. instr.'s gde. ed. 160.00 *(978-1-4051-9367-2(0))*; (Postgraduate Chemistry Ser.: 2). pap. 75.00 *(978-1-4051-7125-0(1))* Wiley, John & Sons, Inc. (Wiley-Blackwell).

Gruber, Alexandra Carina. Biotech Funding Trends: Insights from Entrepreneurs & Investors. 2009. (ENG., Illus.). 210p. 136.95 *(978-3-527-32435-4(6)*, Wiley-VCH) Wiley, John & Sons, Inc.

Grunwald, Armin. Responsible Nanobiotechnology: Philosophy & Ethics. 2012. (ENG.). 300p. 149.95 ***(978-981-4316-80-4(6))*** Pan Stanford Publishing SGP. Dist: Taylor & Francis Group.

Guebitz, Georg M., et al, eds. Biotechnology in Textile Processing. 2006. (ENG., Illus.). 246p. 59.95 *(978-1-56022-142-5(9))*; 254p. per. 35.95 *(978-1-56022-143-2(7))* Taylor & Francis Group GBR. (CRC Press). Dist: Taylor & Francis Group.

Gupta, Vijai Kumar & Ayyachamy, Manimaran. Biotechnology of Microbial Enzymes. 2011. ***(978-1-62100-131-7(8))*** Nova Science Pubs., Inc.

Gupta, Vijai Kumar, et al. Fungal Biochemistry & Biotechnology. 2011. 230p. pap. ***(978-3-8433-5800-2(1))*** Lambert Academic Publishing.

Haider, Syed Imtiaz & Ashok, Anika. Biotechnology: A Comprehensive Training Guide for the Biotechnology Industry. 2009. (ENG., Illus.). 868p. pap. 107.95 *(978-1-4200-8448-1(8)*, CRC Press) Taylor & Francis Group GBR. Dist: Taylor & Francis Group.

Haider, Syed Imtiaz & Syed Asif, Erfan. Quality Operations Procedures for Pharmaceutical, API & Biotechnology. 2012. (ENG., Illus.). 592p. 129.95 ***(978-1-4398-8690-8(3)***, CRC Press) Taylor & Francis Group GBR. Dist: Taylor & Francis Group.

Hamaker, B. R., ed. Technology of Functional Cereal Products. 2007. 568p. *(978-1-84569-177-6(6))* Woodhead Publishing Ltd.

Hancock, William S., et al. Introduction to Analytical Biotechnology. 2009. (Illus.). 384p. 139.95 *(978-1-4200-5115-5(6))* CRC Pr. LLC.

Hansen, Janus. Biotechnology & Public Engagement in Europe. 2010. (ENG., Illus.). 240p. 89.00 *(978-0-230-24212-8(X))* Palgrave Macmillan.

Harding, S. E., ed. Biotechnology & Genetic Engineering Reviews, Vol. 26. 2010. (Biotechnology & Genetic Engineering Reviews Ser.). (ENG.). 464p. 147.00 *(978-1-904761-91-4(7))* Nottingham Univ. Pr. GBR. Dist: Independent Pubs. Group.

Harding, Stephen. Biotechnology & Genetic Engineering Reviews, Vol. 25. 25th ed. 2009. (Biotechnology & Genetic Engineering Reviews Ser.). (ENG., Illus.). 464p. 147.00 *(978-1-904761-66-2(6))* Nottingham Univ. Pr. GBR. Dist: Independent Pubs. Group.

Harding, Stephen E., ed. Biotechnology & Genetic Engineering Reviews. (Biotechnology & Genetic Engineering Reviews Ser.). (ENG., 24th ed. 2008. Illus.). 384p. 150.00 *(978-1-904761-62-4(3))* Vol. 27. 27th ed. 2011. 400p.

pap. 130.00 (978-1-907284-55-7(9)) Nottingham Univ. Pr. GBR. Dist: Independent Pubs. Group.

Harisha, S. Biotechnology Procedures & Experiments Handbook. 2007. (Illus.). 694p. 109.95 incl. cd-rom (978-1-934015-11-7(3)) Jones & Bartlett Learning, LLC.

Harvey, Mark & McMeekin, A. Public or Private Economies of Knowledge? Turbulence in the Biological Sciences. 2009. 224p. pap. 50.00 (978-1-84844-701-1(9)) Elgar, Edward Publishing, Inc.

Hatti-Kaul, Rajni, ed. Aqueous Two-Phase Systems: Methods & Protocols. 2010. (Methods in Biotechnology Ser.). 468p. pap. 149.00 (978-1-61737-067-0(3), 1617370673) Humana Pr.

Hauskeller, Michael. Biotechnology & the Integrity of Life: Taking Public Fears Seriously. 2007. (Ashgate Studies in Applied Ethics Ser.). 174p. 99.95 (978-0-7546-6044-6(3)) Ashgate Publishing Co.

Healey, Peter & Rayner, Steve, eds. Unnatural Selection: The Challenges of Engineering Tomorrow's People. 2008. (ENG., Illus.). 224p. 74.95 (978-1-84407-622-2(9)) Routledge.

Healy, M., et al, eds. Environmental Monitoring & Biodiagnostics of Hazardous Contaminants. 2010. 352p. pap. 239.00 (978-90-481-5674-0(2), 9048156742) Springer.

Hench, L. L., et al. New Materials & Technologies for Healthcare. 2011. (Illus.). 300p. 168.00 (978-1-84816-558-8(7)) World Scientific Publishing Co., Inc.

Henco, A. International Biotechnology - Economics & Policy. 2007. 548p. per. (978-0-7552-0293-5(7)) Authors OnLine, Ltd.

Hermanson, Greg T. Bioconjugate Techniques. 2nd ed. 2008. (ENG., Illus.). 1323p. 103.00 (978-0-12-370501-3(0), Academic Pr.) Elsevier Science & Technology Bks.

Herold, Keith E., et al, eds. Lab on a Chip Technology: Biomolecular Separation & Analysis, 2 vols. 2009. (Illus.). 300p. 319.00 (978-1-904455-47-9(6)) Caister Academic Pr. GBR. Dist: International Specialized Bk. Services.

Herren, Ray V. Introduction to Biotechnology. 2nd ed. 2012. (ENG.). 432p. (C). 123.95 (978-1-4354-9837-2(2)) Delmar Cengage Learning.

Hesham, Abd El-Latif & Yang, Min. Biodegradation of Petroleum Compounds & Environmental Meta-Genomics. 2010. 180p. pap. (978-3-8383-9341-4(4)) Lambert Academic Publishing.

Hesketh, Peter J., ed. BioNanoFluidic MEMS. 2010. (MEMS Reference Shelf Ser.). (Illus.). x, 295p. pap. 179.00 (978-1-4419-4279-1(3), 1441942793) Springer.

Hindmarsh, Richard. Edging Towards Bioutopia: A New Politics of Reordering Life & the Democratic Challenge. 2008. 347p. (C). pap. 32.00 (978-0-9802965-8-7(7)) UWA Publishing AUS. Dist: International Specialized Bk. Services.

Hirai, Atsushi, et al. Rice Biology in the Genomics Era. 2008. (Biotechnology in Agriculture & Forestry Ser.). (Illus.). 380p. 359.00 (978-3-540-74248-7(4), 3540742484) Springer.

Hofman, M. & Thonart, P., eds. Engineering & Manufacturing for Biotechnology. 2010. (Focus on Biotechnology Ser.). 496p. pap. 359.00 (978-90-481-5689-4(0), 9048156890) Springer.

Hondermarck, Hubert, ed. Proteomics: Biomedical & Pharmaceutical Applications: Biomedical & Pharmaceutical Applications. 2010. xii, 396p. pap. 239.00 (978-90-481-6637-4(3), 9048166373) Springer.

Hope, Janet. Biobazaar: The Open Source Revolution & Biotechnology. 2008. 448p. 27.95 (978-0-674-02635-3(7)) Harvard Univ. Pr.

Hórvölgyi, Zoltán D. & Kiss, Eva. Colloids for Nano- & Biotechnology. 2008. (Progress in Colloid & Polymer Science Ser.). (Illus.). viii, 234p. 299.00 (978-3-540-85133-2(X)) Springer.

Hórvölgyi, Zoltán & Kiss, Eva. Colloids for Nano- & Biotechnology. 2010. (Progress in Colloid & Polymer Science Ser.). (Illus.). viii, 234p. pap. 299.00 (978-3-642-09886-4(X), 364209886X) Springer.

Hou, C. T. & Shaw, Jei-Fu. Biocatalysis & Bioenergy. 2008. (ENG., Illus.). 608p. 178.00 (978-0-470-13404-7(6), Wiley-Interscience) Wiley, John & Sons, Inc.

Hou, Ching T. & Shaw, Jei-Fu, eds. Biocatalysis & Biomolecular Engineering. 2010. (ENG., Illus.). 490p. 142.00 (978-0-470-48759-4(3), Wiley) Wiley, John & Sons, Inc.

Hou Ching T Staff. Biocatalysis & Biotechnology for Functional Foods & Industria. 2006. (ENG., Illus.). 563p. 205.95 (978-0-8493-9282-5(9), CRC Press) Taylor & Francis Group GBR. Dist: Taylor & Francis Group.

Houdebine, Louis Marie & Fan, Jianglin, eds. Rabbit Biotechnology: Rabbit genomics, transgenesis, cloning & Models. 2009. (ENG., Illus.). viii, 136p. 159.00 (978-90-481-2226-4(0), 9048122260) Springer.

Hsieh, Wen-Kuo. The Novel Fabrication of Lithographic Platform for Microfluidic System: Lab-on-A-Cd. 2011. 64p. pap. (978-3-639-33508-8(2)) VDM Verlag Dr. Mueller e.K.

Hu, Wei-Shu. Cell Culture Engineering. (Advances in Biochemical Engineering Biotechnology Ser.). xii, 168p. 2010. pap. 279.00 (978-3-642-07051-8(5), 3642070515) 2006. (Illus.). 279.00 (978-3-540-34006-5(8), 3540340068) Springer.

Huang, Xuefei & Barchi, Joseph J. Petite & Sweet: Glyco-Nanotechnology As a Bridge to New Medicines. 2012. (ACS Symposium Ser.: 1091). (ENG.). 240p. 150.00 **(978-0-8412-2688-3(1))** American Chemical Society.

Hübel, Andreas, et al. Biopatent Law: Patent Strategies & Patent Management: Patent Strategies & Patent Management. 2012. (SpringerBriefs in Biotech Patents Ser.). (Illus.). xii, 44p. pap. 49.95 **(978-3-642-24845-0(4),** 3642248454) Springer.

Hughes, Sally Smith. Genentech: The Beginnings of Biotech. 2011. (Synthesis Ser.). (ENG., Illus.). 232p. 25.00 (978-0-226-35918-2(2)) Univ. of Chicago Pr.

Hughes, William, ed. Microengineering in Biotechnology. 2008. (Methods in Molecular Biology Ser.). (Illus.). 375p. 119.00 (978-1-58829-381-7(5), 1588293815) Humana Pr.

Huopalahti, Rainer, et al, eds. Bioactive Egg Compounds. 2007. (ENG., Illus.). xx, 298p. 189.00 (978-3-540-37883-9(9), 3540378839) Springer.

Hussain, Mir Abid, et al. Population Genetic Structure of Rhizomatous Picrorhiza Kurrooa Royle. 2011. 108p. pap. **(978-3-8443-1456-4(3))** Lambert Academic Publishing.

Ignatova, Maya & Lyubenova, Velislava. Control of Biotechnological Processes: New formalization of Kinetics. 2011. 120p. pap. **(978-3-8443-2623-9(5))** Lambert Academic Publishing.

Ike, Michihiko, et al, eds. Handbook of Metal Biotechnology: Applications for Environmental Conservation & Sustainability. 2011. (ENG., Illus.). 264p. 249.95 (978-981-4267-98-4(8)) Pan Stanford Publishing SGP. Dist: Taylor & Francis Group.

Impe, J. F. van, et al, eds. Advanced Instrumentation, Data Interpretation, & Control of Biotechnological Processes. 2010. 484p. pap. 214.00 (978-90-481-4954-4(1), 9048149541) Springer.

Iniewski, Krzysztof. Semiconductor Radiation Detection Systems. 2010. (Devices, Circuits, & Systems Ser.). (ENG., Illus.). 400p. 149.95 (978-1-4398-0385-1(4), CRC Press) Taylor & Francis Group GBR. Dist: Taylor & Francis Group.

Islam, Rafiqul. Focus on Information, Intelligence, & Knowledge. 2011. (978-1-61209-979-8(3)) Nova Science Pubs., Inc.

Jaafari, Deema, et al. Aragen Biotechnology: From Innovation to Prosperity. 2011. 128p. pap. **(978-3-8443-9910-3(0))** Lambert Academic Publishing.

Jain, Kewal K. Applications of Biotechnology in Cardiovascular Therapeutics. 2011. (Illus.). xxviii, 350p. 209.00 (978-1-61779-239-7(X), 161779239X) Humana Pr.

Jain, Shri Mohan & Ochatt, Sergio J., eds. Protocols for in Vitro Propagation of Ornamental Plants. 2009. (Methods in Molecular Biology Ser.). (ENG., Illus.). xiv, 400p. 129.00 (978-1-60327-390-9(5), 1603273905) Humana Pr.

Jasmuheen. Biofields & Bliss Trilogy. 2008. 242p. pap. 22.00 (978-1-4092-0523-4(1)) Lulu Enterprises Inc.

Jayakumar, R., et al, eds. Chitosan for Biomaterials I, 2 vols. 2011. (Advances in Polymer Science Ser.). (ENG., Illus.). xi, 236p. 259.00 **(978-3-642-23113-1(6),** 3642231136) Springer.

Jayakumar, Rangasamy, et al, eds. Chitosan for Biomaterials II, 2 vols. 2011. (Advances in Polymer Science Ser.). (ENG., Illus.). xi, 212p. 259.00 **(978-3-642-24060-7(7),** 3642240607) Springer.

Johnson, Don Hanlon. The Meaning of Life in the 21st Century: Tensions among Science, Religion, & Experience. 2008. 356p. 33.95 (978-0-595-49509-2(5)); pap. 23.95 (978-0-595-45188-3(8)) iUniverse, Inc.

Johnson, Terry D. & Kurpinski, Kyle. How to Defeat Your Own Clone: And Other Tips for Surviving the Biotech Revolution. 2010. (ENG., Illus.). 192p. pap. 14.00 (978-0-553-38578-6(X)) Random House Publishing Group.

Jotterand, Fabrice, ed. Emerging Conceptual, Ethical & Policy Issues in Bionanotechnology. 2010. (Philosophy & Medicine Ser.). vi, 266p. pap. 159.00 (978-90-481-7943-5(2), 9048179432) Springer.

Jurczyk, Mieczyslaw, ed. Bionanomaterials for Dental Applications. 2012. (ENG.). 350p. 149.95 **(978-981-4303-83-5(6))** Pan Stanford Publishing SGP. Dist: Taylor & Francis Group.

Kahl, Guenter & Kahl. The Dictionary of Genomics, Transcriptomics & Proteomics, 3 vols., Set. 4th ed. 2009. (ENG., Illus.). 1916p. 740.00 (978-3-527-32073-8(3), Wiley-VCH) Wiley, John & Sons, Inc.

Kamau, Evanson C. & Winter, Gerd, eds. Genetic Resources, Traditional Knowledge & the Law: Solutions for Access & Benefit Sharing. 2009. (ENG., Illus.). 528p. 128.00 (978-1-84407-793-9(4)) Routledge.

Kamm, Birgit, et al, eds. Biorefineries - Industrial Processes & Products: Status Quo & Future Directions. 2010. (ENG., Illus.). 949p. pap. 175.00 (978-3-527-32953-3(6), Wiley-VCH) Wiley, John & Sons, Inc.

Katdare, Ashok & Chaubal, Mahesh V., eds. Excipient Development for Pharmaceutical, Biotechnology, & Drug Delivery Systems. 2006. (ENG., Illus.). 452p. 230.00 (978-0-8493-2706-3(7)) CRC Pr. LLC.

Katona, Peter, et al, eds. Global Biosecurity. 2011. (ENG., Illus.). 344p. (C). pap. 44.95 **(978-0-415-67059-3(4))** Routledge.

Kaufman, Peter B. & Kirakosyan, Ara. Recent Advances in Plant Biotechnology. 2009. (ENG., Illus.). xvi, 412p. 194.00 (978-1-4419-0193-4(0), 1441901930) Springer.

Kayser, Oliver & Quax, Wim J., eds. Medicinal Plant Biotechnology: From Basic Research to Industrial Applications, 2 vols. 2007. (ENG., Illus.). 618p. 390.00 (978-3-527-31443-0(1), Wiley-VCH) Wiley, John & Sons, Inc.

Keating, Peter & Cambrosio, Alberto. Biomedical Platforms: Realigning the Normal & the Pathological in Late-Twentieth-Century Medicine. 2006. (Inside Technology Ser.). (ENG., Illus.). 560p. (gr. 17). per. 29.00 (978-0-262-61215-9(1)) MIT Pr.

Keegan, Karl. Biotechnology Valuation: An Introductory Guide. 2009. (Wiley Finance Ser.). (ENG., Illus.). 216p. instr.'s gde. ed. 90.00 (978-0-470-51178-7(8), Wiley) Wiley, John & Sons, Inc.

Kent, James A., ed. Handbook of Industrial Chemistry & Biotechnology. 11th rev. ed. 2007. (Illus.). 1400p. 199.00 (978-0-387-27842-1(7), 0387278427) Springer.

Khan, Firdos Alam. Biotechnology. 2011. (ENG., Illus.). 608p. 89.95 (978-1-4398-2009-4(0), CRC Press) Taylor & Francis Group GBR. Dist: Taylor & Francis Group.

Khan, Firdos Alam, ed. Medical Biotechnology. 2012. (ENG.). 368p. 99.95 **(978-0-12-385542-8(X),** Academic Pr.) Elsevier Science & Technology Bks.

Khan, Haseena. Bengali-English English-Bengali Biotechnology Glossary. 2007. 109p. (978-1-931546-36-2(3)) Dunwoody Pr.

Kholmurodov, Kholmirzo, ed. Molecular Dynamics of Nanobiostructures. 2012. (Series: Nanotechnology Science & Technology Ser.). 230p. 75.00 (978-1-61324-320-6(0)) Nova Science Pubs., Inc.

Kim, Hyungjun. Multiscale & Multiphysics Computational Frameworks for Nano- & Bio-Systems. 2010. (Springer Theses Ser.). (ENG., Illus.). xxviii, 170p. 129.00 (978-1-4419-7600-0(0), 1441976000) Springer.

Kim, Kelly Y. R. 2010. 212p. pap. (978-3-8383-5643-3(8)) Lambert Academic Publishing.

Kim, Minjun, et al, eds. Microbiorobotics: Biologically Inspired Microscale Robotic Systems. 2012. (Micro & Nano Technologies Ser.). (ENG.). 328p. 169.00 **(978-1-4557-7891-1(5))** William Andrew, Inc.

Kim, Seong H. Biomolecular Catalysis: Nanoscale Science & Technology. Kim, Jungbae & Wang, Ping, eds. 2008. (ACS Symposium Ser.). (ENG., Illus.). 440p. 195.00 (978-0-8412-7415-0(0)) American Chemical Society.

Kim, Tai-hoon, et al, eds. Database Theory & Application, Bio-Science & Bio-Technology: International Conferences, DTA & BSBT 2011, Held as Part of the Future Generation Information Technology Conference, FGIT 2011, in Conjunction with GDC 2011, Jeju Island, Korea, December 8-10, 2011. Proceedings. 2011. (Communications in Computer & Information Science Ser.). (ENG., Illus.). xiv, 197p. pap. 84.00 **(978-3-642-27156-4(1),** 3642271561) Springer.

King, Michael & Gee, David. Multiscale Modeling of Particle Interactions: Applications in Biology & Nanotechnology. 2010. (ENG., Illus.). 388p. 139.00 (978-0-470-24235-3(3), Wiley) Wiley, John & Sons, Inc.

King, Nancy M. P. & Hyde, Michael J., eds. Bioethics Public Moral Argument & Social Responsibility. 2011. (Routledge Annals of Bioethics Ser.). (ENG.). 196p. (C). 125.00 (978-0-415-89855-3(2)) Routledge.

King, Paul & Fries, Richard C. Design of Biomedical Devices & Systems, Second Edition. 2nd rev. ed. 2008. (ENG., Illus.). 424p. (C). 124.95 (978-1-4200-6179-6(8), CRC Press) Taylor & Francis Group GBR. Dist: Taylor & Francis Group.

Kopec, Jolanta. Dna Relaxases, the Key Enzymes of Bacterial Conjugation. 2008. 104p. pap. (978-3-639-06950-1(1)) VDM Verlag Dr. Mueller e.K.

Kornprobst, Jean-Michel. Encyclopedia of Marine Natural Products, 3 vols., Set. 2010. (ENG., Illus.). 1680p. 795.00 (978-3-527-32703-4(7), Wiley-VCH) Wiley, John & Sons, Inc.

Kragl, Udo. Technology Transfer in Biotechnology: From Lab to Industry to Production. 2010. (Advances in Biochemical Engineering Biotechnology Ser.). (Illus.). xii, 340p. pap. 369.00 (978-3-642-06122-6(2), 3642061222) Springer.

Krishnan, Hari, ed. Modification of Seed Composition to Promote Health & Nutrition: Agronomy Monograph, Vol. 51. 2009. (Agronomy Ser.: 51). lib. bdg. 105.00 (978-0-89118-169-9(5)) ASA-CSSA-SSSA.

Kulys, Juozas. Bioinzinerija Ir Bioinformatika (2008 M. Balandzio 3 D.) Fizika Ir Fizine Kompiuterija (2008 M. Balandzio 4 D.): 11-Osios Lietuvos Jaunuju Mokslininku Konferencijos "Mokslas — Lietuvos Ateitis" 2008 Metu Teminiu Konferenciju Straipsniu Rinkinys. 2008. (LIT., Illus.). 192p. (978-9955-28-301-0(7)) Technika.

Kumar, Challa S. S. R., ed. Biomimetic & Bioinspired Nanomaterials. 2010. (Nanomaterials for Life Sciences (VCH) Ser.: 3). (ENG., Illus.). 586p. 205.00 (978-3-527-32167-4(5), Wiley-VCH) Wiley, John & Sons, Inc.

Kumar, S. Ashok, et al, eds. Biocompatible Nanomaterials: Synthesis, Characterization & Applications. 2010. (Nanotechnology Science & Technology Ser.). 235.00 (978-1-61668-677-2(4)) Nova Science Pubs., Inc.

Kun, Lee Yuan, ed. Microbial Biotechnology: Principles & Applications. 2nd ed. 2006. (Illus.). 794p. 167.00 (978-981-256-676-8(7)); per. 82.00 (978-981-256-677-5(5)) World Scientific Publishing Co., Inc.

Kurtz, Steven M. & Edidin, Avram Allan. Spine Technology Handbook. 2006. (ENG., Illus.). 560p. 86.95 (978-0-12-369390-7(X), Academic Pr.) Elsevier Science & Technology Bks.

Lab-Volt Staff. Biotechnology: Tech-Design ESeries. 2010. 121p. 13.00 (978-1-60533-160-7(0)); 76p. ring bd. 9.00 (978-1-60533-161-4(9)) Lab-Volt Systems, Inc.

LaBaer, Joshua & Nicolini, Claudio, eds. Functional Proteomics & Nanotechnology-Based Microarrays. 2010. (Pan Stanford Series on Nanobiotechnology Ser.). (ENG., Illus.). 308p. 159.95 (978-981-4267-76-2(7)) Pan Stanford Publishing SGP. Dist: Taylor & Francis Group.

Laboratory Research Notebook. 2007. (ENG., Illus.). 50p. pap. 12.00 (978-0-87969-760-0(1)) Cold Spring Harbor Laboratory Pr.

Lackie, John. A Dictionary of Biomedicine. 2010. (ENG.). 608p. 18.95 (978-0-19-954935-1(4)) Oxford Univ. Pr., Inc.

Lahann, Joerg, ed. Click Chemistry for Biotechnology & Materials Science. 2009. (ENG., Illus.). 432p. 165.00 (978-0-470-69970-6(1), Wiley) Wiley, John & Sons, Inc.

Landecker, Hannah. Culturing Life: How Cells Became Technologies. 2010. (Illus.). 288p. pap. 20.00 (978-0-674-03476-1(7)) Harvard Univ. Pr.

Laudon, Matthew & Romanowicz, Bart, eds. NSTI Nanotech: Technical Proceedings: Volume 1. 2007. (Illus.). 850p. per. 119.95 (978-0-9767985-6-9(5)) Taylor & Francis Group.

—NSTI Nanotech: Technical Proceedings: Volume 2. 2007. (Illus.). 872p. per. 119.95 (978-0-9767985-7-6(3)) Taylor & Francis Group.

Lawler, Peter Augustine. Modern & american Dignity: Who We Are as Persons, & What That Means for Our Future. 2010. (ENG.). 288p. 26.95 (978-1-935191-89-6(6)) ISI Bks.

Le Gal, Yves & Ulber, Roland. Marine Biotechnology I. 2010. (Advances in Biochemical Engineering Biotechnology Ser.). xii, 288p. pap. 349.00 (978-3-642-06506-4(6), 3642065066) Springer.

—Marine Biotechnology II. 2010. (Advances in Biochemical Engineering Biotechnology Ser.). xii, 261p. pap. 299.00 (978-3-642-06510-1(4), 3642065104) Springer.

Lee, Abraham P. & Ferrari, Mauro. BioMEMS & Biomedical Nanotechnology, 4 vols. 2006. (Illus.). LXXX, 1856p. 499.00 (978-0-387-25561-3(3), 0387255613) Springer.

Lee, Hakho, et al, eds. CMOS Biotechnology. 2010. (Integrated Circuits & Systems Ser.). xv, 385p. pap. 159.00 (978-1-4419-4230-2(0), 1441942300) Springer.

Lee, Shui Chuen, ed. The Family, Medical Decision-Making, & Biotechnology: Critical Reflections on Asian Moral Perspectives. 2007. (Philosophy & Medicine Ser.). xii, 220p. (C). 139.00 (978-1-4020-5219-4(7), 1402052197) Springer.

Lee, Thay, et al. Proceedings of the 4th Frontiers in Biomedical Devices Conference & Exposition — 2009: Presented at 4th Frontiers in Biomedical Devices Conference & Exposition, June 6-8, 2009, Irvine, California, USA. 2009. (Illus.). xiii, 112p. pap. (978-0-7918-4348-2(3)) American Society of Mechanical Engineers, The.

Lee, Thay, et al. Proceedings of the 5th Frontiers in Biomedical Devices Conference & Exposition — 2010: Presented at 5th Frontiers in Biomedical Devices Conference & Exposition, September 20-21, 2010, Newport Beach, California, USA. 2010. (Illus.). xiii, 106p. pap. **(978-0-7918-4945-3(7))** American Society of Mechanical Engineers, The.

Leon, Rosa, et al, eds. Transgenic Microalgae as Green Cell Factories. 2007. (Advances in Experimental Medicine & Biology Ser.). (ENG., Illus.). 600p. 159.00 (978-0-387-75531-1(4), 0387755314) Springer.

Lerner, Brenda Wilmoth & Lerner, K. Lee. Biotechnology. 2012. **(978-1-4144-9084-7(4)); (978-1-4144-9083-0(6))** Cengage Gale.

Li, Yahong. Imitation to Innovation in China: The Role of Patents in Biotechnology & Pharmaceutical Industries. 2010. (New Horizons in Intellectual Property Ser.). 208p. 112.00 (978-1-84844-206-1(8)) Elgar, Edward Publishing, Inc.

Linton, Katherine, et al. Industrial Biotechnology: Patenting Trends & Innovation. 2009. (Biotechnology in Agriculture, Industry & Medicine Ser.). (Illus.). 84p. 43.00 (978-1-60741-032-4(X)) Nova Science Pubs., Inc.

Liong, Min-Tze. Bioprocess Sciences & Technology. 2011. (Biochemistry Research Trends Ser.). (Illus.). 526p. 195.00 (978-1-61122-950-9(2)) Nova Science Pubs., Inc.

Lippert-Rasmussen, Kasper, ed. The Posthuman Condition: Ethics,Aesthetics & Politics of Biotechnological Challenges. 2011. (ENG., Illus.). 304p. (C). pap. 48.00 **(978-87-7934-570-6(0))** Aarhus Universitetsforlag DNK. Dist: ISD.

Liu, Jian-Qin & Shimohara, Katsunori. Biomolecular Computation by Nanobiotechnology. 2007. (Illus.). 286p. 139.00 (978-1-59693-014-8(4)) Artech Hse., Inc.

Liu, Yu & Wang, Jianlong, eds. Fundamentals & Applications of Biosorption Isotherms, Kinetics & Thermodynamics. 2009. (Illus.). vii, 294p. 89.00 (978-1-60741-169-7(5)) Nova Science Pubs., Inc.

Loos, Katja, ed. Biocatalysis in Polymer Chemistry. 2011. (ENG., Illus.). 463p. 210.00 (978-3-527-32618-1(9), Wiley-VCH) Wiley, John & Sons, Inc.

Luisi, Pier Luigi & Chiarabelli, Cristiano, eds. Chemical Synthetic Biology. 2011. (ENG., Illus.). 384p. 155.00 (978-0-470-71397-6(6), Wiley) Wiley, John & Sons, Inc.

Lustig, B. A., et al, eds. Altering Nature: Volume I: Concepts of "Nature" & "the Natural" in Biotechnology Debates. 2010. (Philosophy & Medicine Ser.). (Illus.). viii, 332p. pap. 239.00 (978-90-481-7763-9(4), 9048177634) Springer.

—Altering Nature: Volume II: Religion, Biotechnology, & Public Policy. 2010. (Philosophy & Medicine Ser.). x, 346p. pap. 239.00 (978-90-481-7764-6(2), 9048177642) Springer.

Lustig, B. Andrew, et al. Altering Nature, 2 vols. 2008. (Philosophy & Medicine Ser.). (Illus.). 330p. 239.00 (978-1-4020-6920-8(0)); 322p. 239.00 (978-1-4020-6922-2(7)) Springer.

Lutwick, Larry I. & Lutwick, Suzanne M., eds. Beyond Anthrax: The Weaponization of Infectious Diseases. 2008. 350p. 149.00 (978-1-58829-438-8(2), 1588294382) Springer.

Macek, Tomas, et al, eds. Phytoremediation & Rhizoremediation: Theoretical Background. 2006. (Focus on Biotechnology Ser.: Vol. 9). (ENG., Illus.). vi, 300p. 289.00 (978-1-4020-4952-1(8), 1402049528) Springer.

MACKLER. Cleanro Tech Phar Biotec. 2009. 500p. 199.95 (978-0-8247-5836-3(6), Informa Healthcare) Taylor & Francis Group GBR. Dist: Taylor & Francis Group.

Mackova, Martina, et al, eds. Phytoremediation & Rhizoremediation. 2010. (Focus on Biotechnology Ser.). vi, 300p. pap. 289.00 (978-90-481-7238-2(1), 9048172381) Springer.

Madhavan, Guruprasad, et al, eds. Career Development in Bioengineering & Biotechnology. 2008. (Series in Biomedical Engineering Ser.). (Illus.). XLVIII, 536p. pap. 59.95 (978-0-387-76494-8(1), 0387764941) Springer.

Maheshwari, Priti. Exploitation of Medicinal Plant Species. 2009. 240p. pap. (978-3-639-18754-0(7)) VDM Verlag Dr. Mueller e.K.

Malik, C. P. & Verma, Aman. Biotechnology: Cracking New Pastures. 2010. 363p. 87.50 (978-81-7533-233-1(6)) M. D. Pubns. Pvt. Ltd. IND. Dist: Coronet Bks.

Manchester, Marianne & Steinmetz, Nicole F. Viruses & Nanotechnology. 2010. (Current Topics in Microbiology & Immunology Ser.). (Illus.). x, 150p. pap. 159.00 (978-3-642-08888-9(0), 3642088880) Springer.

Mandenius, Carl-Fredrik & Björkman, Mats. Biomechatronic Design in Biotechnology: A Methodology for Development of Biotechnological Products. 2011. (ENG., Illus.). 304p. 89.95 (978-0-470-57334-1(1), Wiley) Wiley, John & Sons, Inc.

María, Pablo Domínguez De. Ionic Liquids in Biotransformations & Organocatalysis: Solvents & Beyond. 2012. (ENG.). 456p. 149.95 (978-0-470-56904-7(2), Wiley) Wiley, John & Sons, Inc.

María, Pablo Domínguez De, et al. Redox Biocatalysis: Fundamentals & Applications. 2012. (ENG.). 526p. 149.95 (978-0-470-87420-2(1), Wiley) Wiley, John & Sons, Inc.

Martin, Donald, ed. Nanobiotechnology of Biomimetic Membranes. (Fundamental Biomedical Technologies Ser.). (Illus.). xii, 174p. 2010. pap. 179.00 (978-1-4419-4251-7(3), 1441942513) 2006. 179.00 (978-0-387-37738-4(7), 0387377387) Springer.

Masayoshi, Esashi, et al, eds. Future Medical Engineering Based on Bionanotechnology: Proceedings of the Final Symposium of the Tohoku University: 21st Century Center of Excellence Program. 2006. (Illus.). 1115p. 265.00 (978-1-86094-710-0(7)) Imperial College Pr. GBR. Dist: World Scientific Publishing Co., Inc.

Mascia, Peter N., et al, eds. Plant Biotechnology for Sustainable Production of Energy & Co-products. 2010. (Biotechnology in Agriculture & Forestry Ser.). (Illus.). xvii, 458p. 239.00 (978-3-642-13439-5(4), 3642134394) Springer.

Mascini, M. Aptamers in Bioanalysis. 2009. (ENG., Illus.). 325p. 150.00 (978-0-470-14830-3(6), Wiley-Interscience) Wiley, John & Sons, Inc.

Matamá, Teresa. Surface Functionalization of Acrylic & Cellulose Acetate Fibres. 2009. 140p. pap. (978-3-639-20376-9(3)) VDM Verlag Dr. Mueller e.K.

Matsuda, Tomoko, ed. Future Directions in Biocatalysis. 2007. (ENG., Illus.). 364p. 240.00 (978-0-444-53059-2(2), Elsevier Science) Elsevier Science & Technology Bks.

Mattiasson, B., ed. Expanded Bed Chromatography. 2010. 250p. pap. 199.00 (978-90-481-5380-0(8), 9048153808) Springer.

Mazzucato, Mariana & Dosi, Giovanni, eds. Knowledge Accumulation & Industry Evolution: The Case of Pharma-Biotech. 2009. (ENG., Illus.). 468p. pap. 42.00 (978-0-521-12400-3(X)) Cambridge Univ. Pr.

McClements, D. J., ed. Understanding & controlling the microstructure of complex Foods. 2007. 792p. (978-1-84569-151-6(2)) Woodhead Publishing Ltd.

McManis, Charles R., ed. Biodiversity & the Law: Intellectual Property, Biotechnology & Traditional Knowledge. 2007. (ENG., Illus.). 520p. 152.00 (978-1-84407-349-8(1)) Routledge.

McManis, Charles R. & Busch, Lawrence, eds. Biodiversity & the Law: Intellectual Property, Biotechnology & Traditional Knowledge. 2009. (ENG., Illus.). 520p. pap. 72.00 (978-1-84407-816-5(7)) Routledge.

Meireles, M. Angela A. Extracting Bioactive Compounds for Food Products: Theory & Applications. Meireles, M. Angela A., ed. 2008. (Contemporary Food Engineering Ser.: Vol. 5). (ENG., Illus.). 464p. 185.95 (978-1-4200-6237-3(9), CRC Press) Taylor & Francis Group GBR. Dist: Taylor & Francis Group.

Mellon, Jim & Chalabi, Al. Cracking the Code: Understand & Profit from the Biotech Revolution That Will Transform Our Lives & Generate Fortunes. 2nd ed. 2012. (ENG.). 360p. 27.95 (978-1-119-96318-9(4), Wiley) Wiley, John & Sons, Inc.

Mendez-Vilas, Antonio. Microorganisms in Industry & Environment: From Scientific & Industrial Research to Consumer Products - Proceedings of the III International Conference on Environmental, Industrial & Applied Microbiology (Biomicroworld2009) 2010. (Illus.). 736p. 188.00 (978-981-4322-10-2(5)) World Scientific Publishing Co., Inc.

Mendez-Vilas, Antonio, ed. Current Research Topics in Applied Microbiology & Microbial Biotechnology. 2009. (Illus.). 780p. 228.00 (978-981-283-754-7(X)) World Scientific Publishing Co., Inc.

Mensolson, Mel I. Learning Bio-Micro-Nanotechnology. 2009. (ENG., Illus.). 600p. 89.95 (978-1-4200-8203-6(5)) CRC Pr. LLC.

Mertens, Gilbert. A Future with Immense Opportunity. 2008. 460p. pap. 50.00 (978-1-934350-48-4(1)) Raider Publishing International.

Meyer, Ulrich, et al, eds. Fundamentals of Tissue Engineering & Regenerative Medicine. 2009. (Illus.). 820p. 289.00 (978-3-540-77754-0(7)) Springer.

Mgbeoji, Ikechi. Global Biopiracy: Patents, Plants, & Indigenous Knowledge. 2006. 311p. per. 24.95 (978-0-8014-7311-1(X)) Cornell Univ. Pr.

Microbiology. Microbial Production of Industrial Chemicals [Bibliography & Price Not Definite.]. Gosset Lagarda, G., ed. 2008. (Illus.). 66p. pap. (978-3-8055-8444-9(X)) Karger, S. AG.

Mielenz, Jonathan R. Biotechnology for Fuels & Chemicals. 2008. (ABAB Symposium Ser.). (Illus.). 812p. 289.00 (978-1-60327-525-5(8)) Humana Pr.

Mielenz, Jonathan R., et al, eds. Biotechnology for Fuels & Chemicals: The Thirty-First Symposium. 2010. (ABAB Symposium Ser.). (ENG.). 984p. 189.00 (978-1-4419-6233-1(6), 1441962336); (Illus.). 329.00 (978-1-4419-6230-0(1), 1441962301) Springer.

—Biotechnology for Fuels & Chemicals: The Twenty-Ninth Symposium. 2008. (ABAB Symposium Ser.). 259.00 (978-1-60327-528-6(2)) Humana Pr.

Miller, Gerald. Introduction to Transport Processes. 2010. (Synthesis Lectures on Biomedical Engineering Ser.). 75p. pap. 30.00 (978-1-59829-866-6(6)) Morgan & Claypool Pubs.

Miller, Kenneth & Levine, Joseph. Biology. 3rd ed. wbk. ed. (978-0-13-804899-0(1)); wbk. ed. (978-0-13-803008-7(1)) Prentice Hall (Schl. Div.).

Mine, Yoshinori. Egg Bioscience & Biotechnology. Mine, Yoshinori, ed. 2008. (ENG., Illus.). 366p. 117.00 (978-0-470-03998-4(1), Wiley-Interscience) Wiley, John & Sons, Inc.

Mishra, Neeraj. Bioseparation Technology. 2011. (ENG.). 300p. pap. 49.95 (978-1-4398-0172-7(X), CRC Press) Taylor & Francis Group GBR. Dist: Taylor & Francis Group.

Mitchell, C. Ben, et al. Biotechnology & the Human Good. annot. ed. 2007. (ENG.). 224p. pap. 29.95 (978-1-58901-138-0(4)) Georgetown Univ. Pr.

Molfino, Francesca & Zucco, Flavia. Women in Biotechnology: Creating Interfaces. 2008. 273p. 189.00 (978-1-4020-8610-6(5)) Springer.

Molfino, Francesca & Zucco, Flavia, eds. Women in Biotechnology: Creating Interfaces. 2010. xxiv, 352p. pap. 189.00 (978-90-481-7933-6(5), 9048179335) Springer.

Montet, Didier & Ray, Ramesh C. Aquaculture Microbiology & Biotechnology, Vol. 1. 2009. (ENG., Illus.). 286p. 99.95 (978-1-57808-574-3(8)) BIOS Scientific Publishers Ltd. GBR. Dist: Taylor & Francis Group.

Montet, Didier & Ray, Ramesh C., eds. Aquaculture Microbiology & Biotechnology, Vol. 2. 2011. (ENG., Illus.). 295p. 119.95 (978-1-57808-711-2(2)) BIOS Scientific Publishers Ltd. GBR. Dist: Taylor & Francis Group.

Montgomery, Douglas C., et al, eds. Statistical Methods for Bioprocess Development & Commercializaton. 2011. (Illus.). 400p. 129.95 (978-1-4398-3074-1(6)); 129.95 (978-1-4398-3073-4(8)) Taylor & Francis Group GBR. (CRC Press). Dist: Taylor & Francis Group.

Montpetit, Eric. The Politics of Biotechnology in North America & Europe: Policy Networks, Institutions & Internationalization. 2006. (ENG.). 304p. 94.50 (978-0-7391-1247-2(3)) Lexington Bks.

Morgan, Gareth E. Patent Litigation in the Pharmaceutical & Biotechnology Industries. 2013. 270p. (978-1-907568-20-6(4)) Woodhead Publishing Ltd.

Mosier, Nathan S. & Ladisch, Michael R. Modern Biotechnology: Connecting Innovations in Microbiology & Biochemistry to Engineering Fundamentals. 2009. (ENG., Illus.). 464p. 111.00 (978-0-470-11485-8(1)) American Institute of Chemical Engineers.

Mousdale, David M. Biofuels: Biotechnology, Chemistry, & Sustainable Development. 2008. (ENG., Illus.). 424p. 129.95 (978-1-4200-5124-7(5), CRC Press) Taylor & Francis Group GBR. Dist: Taylor & Francis Group.

Mozafari, M. Reza, ed. Nanocarrier Technologies: Frontiers of Nanotherapy. 2010. (ENG.). xvii, 225p. pap. 169.00 (978-90-481-7262-7(4), 9048172624) Springer.

Mozzi, Fernanda, et al, eds. Biotechnology of Lactic Acid Bacteria: Novel Applications. 2010. (ENG., Illus.). 408p. 229.95 (978-0-8138-1583-1(5), Wiley-Blackwell) Wiley, John & Sons, Inc.

Mugwagwa, Julius. To Harmonise or Not to Harmonise? 2011. 276p. pap. (978-3-8383-5796-6(5)) Lambert Academic Publishing.

Mulchandani, Ashok & Rogers, Kim, eds. Enzyme & Microbial Biosensors: Techniques & Protocols. 2010. (Methods in Biotechnology Ser.). 284p. pap. 159.00 (978-1-61737-028-1(2), 1617370282) Humana Pr.

Müller, Susanne & Bley, Thomas, eds. High Resolution Microbial Single Cell Analytics. 2011. (Advances in Biochemical Engineering Biotechnology Ser.). (ENG., Illus.). xiv, 233p. 259.00 (978-3-642-16886-4(8), 3642168868) Springer.

Murphy, Denis. The Great Biotech Disaster. 2007. (ENG.). 452p. 155.00 (978-0-521-82389-0(7)) Cambridge Univ. Pr.

Murphy, Denis J. Plant Breeding & Biotechnology: Societal Context & the Future of Agriculture. 2007. (ENG., Illus.). 440p. per. 67.99 (978-0-521-53088-0(1)) Cambridge Univ. Pr.

Murphy, Thérèse, ed. New Technologies & Human Rights. 2009. (Collected Courses of the Academy of European Law Ser.). (ENG.). 288p. 120.00 (978-0-19-956257-2(1)) Oxford Univ. Pr., Inc.

Murthy, S., et al, eds. Materials & Strategies for Lab-on-a-Chip - Biological Analysis, Cell-Material Interfaces & Fluidic Assembly: Volume 1191. 2009. (MRS Proceedings Ser.). (ENG.). 149p. (C). 113.00 (978-1-60511-164-3(3)) Cambridge Univ. Pr.

Myers, Chris J. Engineering Genetic Circuits. 2009. (Chapman & Hall/CRC Mathematical & Computational Biology Ser.). (ENG., Illus.). 306p. (C). 75.95 (978-1-4200-8324-8(4), Chapman & Hall/CRC) CRC Pr. LLC.

Nag, Ahindra. Biosystems Engineering. 2009. (ENG., Illus.). 544p. 150.00 (978-0-07-160628-8(9), 0071606289) McGraw-Hill Professional Publishing.

Nag, Debapriyo. Strategic Synergy Between Alliances, Collaboration & Innovation. 2011. 56p. pap. (978-3-8443-0822-8(9)) Lambert Academic Publishing.

Naidu, David. Biotechnology & Nanotechnology: Regulation under Environmental, Health, & Safety Laws. 2009. (ENG.). 352p. 247.50 (978-0-19-534008-2(6)) Oxford Univ. Pr., Inc.

Nair. Intro Biotechnology & Genetic Engineering W/Cd. rev. ed. 2010. 82.95 (978-0-7637-7375-5(1)) Jones & Bartlett Learning, LLC.

Nair, A. /J. Introduction to Biotechnology & Genetic Engineering. 2007. 1000p. 109.95 (978-1-934015-16-2(4)) Jones & Bartlett Learning, LLC.

Najafpour, Ghasem. Biochemical Engineering & Biotechnology. 2006. (ENG., Illus.). 438p. 215.00 (978-0-444-52845-2(8), Elsevier Science) Elsevier Science & Technology Bks.

Naka, Kensuke. Biomineralization I: Crystallization & Self-Organization Process, 2 vols. 2006. (Topics in Current Chemistry Ser.). (Illus.). xii, 199p. 259.00 (978-3-540-46379-5(8), 3540463798) Springer.

Nallari, Pratibha & Rao, V. V. Medical Biotechnology. 2010. (ENG., Illus.). 376p. 22.95 (978-0-19-569960-9(2)) Oxford Univ. Pr., Inc.

Nano Science &, Tech Inst., ed. Technical Proceedings of the 2004 NSTI Nanotechnology Conference & Trade Show, Volume 3. 2007. 79.95 (978-0-9728422-9-7(2)) Taylor & Francis Group.

—Technical Proceedings of the 2005 NSTI Nanotechnology Conference & Trade Show, Volume 1. 2007. 109.95 (978-0-9767985-0-7(6)) Taylor & Francis Group.

—Technical Proceedings of the 2006, 2005, & 2004 Nanotechnology Conferences & Trade Shows. 2007. 950.00 (978-1-4200-6369-1(3)) Taylor & Francis Group.

—Technical Proceedings of the 2006, 2005, & 2004 Nanotechnology Conferences & Trade Shows CD-ROMs. 2007. 750.00 (978-1-4200-6370-7(7)) Taylor & Francis Group.

—Technical Proceedings of the 2006 NSTI Nanotechnology Conference & Trade Show on CD-ROM. 2007. ring bd. 299.95 (978-0-9767985-9-0(X)) Taylor & Francis Group.

—Technical Proceedings of the 2006 NSTI Nanotechnology Conference & Trade Show, Volume 3. 2007. 119.95 (978-0-9767985-8-3(1)) Taylor & Francis Group.

—Technical Proceedings of the 2007 Nanotechnology Conference & Trade Show, Nanotech 2007, Volume 4. 2007. 199.95 (978-1-4200-6457-5(6)) Taylor & Francis Group.

Nano Science and Technology Institute, creator. NSTI Nanotech: Technical Proceedings: Volume 2. 2007. (Illus.). 788p. per. 109.95 (978-0-9767985-1-4(4)) Taylor & Francis Group.

—NSTI Nanotech: Technical Proceedings: Volume 3. 2007. (Illus.). 766p. per. 109.95 (978-0-9767985-2-1(2)) Taylor & Francis Group.

—NSTI Nanotech: Technical Proceedings, Volume 1: The Nanotechnology Conference & Trade Show: Boston, March 7-11 2004. 2007. (Illus.). 501p. per. 79.95 (978-0-9728422-7-3(6)) Taylor & Francis Group.

—Nsti Nanotech: Technical Proceedings, Volume 2. 2007. (Illus.). 501p. per. 79.95 (978-0-9728422-8-0(4)) Taylor & Francis Group.

Neumann, Karl-Hermann, et al. Plant Cell & Tissue Culture - A Tool in Biotechnology: Basics & Application. 2009. (Principles & Practice Ser.). (ENG., Illus.). ix, 333p. 239.00 (978-3-540-93882-8(6), 3540938826) Springer.

Newell-McGloughlin, Martina & Re, Edward. The Evolution of Biotechnology: From Natufians to Nanotechnology. 2007. (ENG., Illus.). xiv, 262p. 159.00 (978-1-4020-5148-7(4), 1402051484) Springer.

—The Evolution of Biotechnology: From Natufians to Nanotechnology. 2010. (ENG.). xiv, 262p. pap. 159.00 (978-90-481-7296-2(9), 9048172969) Springer.

Newton, David E. DNA Technology: A Reference Handbook, 1 vol. 2009. (Contemporary World Issues Ser.). 311p. 65.00 (978-1-59884-328-6(1), A2214C) ABC-CLIO, LLC.

Nicolau, Dan V. BioMEMS & Nanotechnology III: 5-7 December 2007, Canberra, Australia. 2007. (Proceedings of SPIE Ser.). (Illus.). 400p. pap. 105.00 (978-0-8194-6970-0(X)) SPIE.

Nicolini, Claudio. Nanobiotechnology & Nanobiosciences. 2008. (Pan Stanford Series on Nanobiotechnology Ser.). (ENG., Illus.). 367p. 119.95 (978-981-4241-38-0(5)) Pan Stanford Publishing SGP. Dist: Taylor & Francis Group.

Niekerk, Alvin van, ed. Ethics in Agriculture - an African Perspective. 2010. (ENG.). viii, 167p. pap. 149.00 (978-90-481-6761-6(2), 9048167612) Springer.

Nielsen, Jens. Biotechnology for the Future. 2010. (Advances in Biochemical Engineering Biotechnology Ser.). (Illus.). xiv, 229p. pap. 279.00 (978-3-642-06527-9(9), 3642065279) Springer.

Niemeyer, Christof M. & Mirkin, Chad A., eds. Nanobiotechnology II: More Concepts & Applications. 2007. (ENG., Illus.). 459p. 249.00 (978-3-527-31673-1(6), Wiley-VCH) Wiley, John & Sons, Inc.

Niknejad, Azadeh. Genetic Relationship & in Vitro Propagation of Phalaenopsis Gigante. 2011. 136p. pap. (978-3-8443-8660-8(2)) Lambert Academic Publishing.

Ninfa, Alexander J., et al. Fundamental Laboratory Approaches for Biochemistry & Biotechnology. 2nd ed. 2009. (ENG., Illus.). 480p. (C). pap. 93.95 (978-0-470-08766-4(8), Wiley) Wiley, John & Sons, Inc.

NSTI, Contact. Nanotechnology 2009: Fabrication, Particles, Characterization, MEMS, Electronics & Photonics Technical Proceedings of the 2009 NSTI Nanotechnology Conference & Expo, Volume 1. 2009. 698p. 179.95 (978-1-4398-1782-7(0)) CRC Pr. LLC.

—Nanotechnology 2009: Life Sciences, Medicine, Diagnostics, Bio Materials & Composites Technical Proceedings of the 2009 NSTI Nanotechnology Conference & Expo, Volume 2. 2009. (ENG.). 586p. 179.95 (978-1-4398-1783-4(9), CRC Press) Taylor & Francis Group GBR. Dist: Taylor & Francis Group.

Nwankwo, Uche M. Sustainable Biotechnology Adoption in Nigeria to Reduce Food Insecurity: Involving Cooperatives in the Process. 2010. 282p. 79.95 (978-3-631-60266-9(9)) Lang, Peter GmbH, Europaischer Verlag der Wissenschaften DEU. Dist: Lang, Peter.

Offenhäusser, Andreas & Rinaldi, Ross, eds. Nanobioelectronics: For Electronics, Biology, & Medicine. 2009. (Nanostructure Science & Technology Ser.). (ENG., Illus.). xiv, 338p. 99.00 (978-0-387-09458-8(X), 038709458X) Springer.

Office of Technology Assessment Staff. Patenting Life New Developments in Biote. 2006. 204p. per. 29.50 (978-1-4102-2567-2(4)) Univ. Pr. of the Pacific.

Ohshima, Hiroyuki. Electrical Phenomena at Interfaces & Biointerfaces: Fundamentals & Applications in Nano-, Bio-, & Environmental Sciences. 2012. (ENG., Illus.). 872p. 175.00 (978-0-470-58255-8(3), Wiley) Wiley, John & Sons, Inc.

Okafor, Nduka. Modern Industrial Microbiology & Biotechnology. 2007. (ENG., Illus.). 550p. pap. 69.95 (978-1-57808-513-2(6)) BIOS Scientific Publishers Ltd. GBR. Dist: Taylor & Francis Group.

—Modern Industrial Microbiology & Biotechnology. 2007. 548p. 85.00 (978-1-57808-434-0(2)) Science Pubs.

Okafor, Nduka. Modern Industrial Microbiology & Biotechnology. 2007. (Illus.). xx, 530p. (978-1-57808-939-0(5)) Science Pubs.

Oliver, Amalya Lumerman. Networks for Learning & Knowledge Creation in Biotechnology. (ENG.). 2011. 272p. pap. 50.00 (978-0-521-18877-7(6)) 2009. (Illus.). 270p. 99.00 (978-0-521-87248-5(0)) Cambridge Univ. Pr.

Ong, Aihwa & Chen, Nancy N., eds. Asian Biotech: Ethics & Communities of Fate. 2010. (Experimental Futures Ser.). (ENG., Illus.). 344p. 84.95 (978-0-8223-4793-4(8)); pap. 23.95 (978-0-8223-4809-2(8)) Duke Univ. Pr.

Organisation for Economic Co-operation and Development Staff. The Bioeconomy to 2030: Designing a Policy Agenda. 2009. pap. 63.00 (978-92-64-03853-0(1)) Organization for Economic Cooperation & Development.

Orsenigo, Luigi. The World of Biotechnology. (Illus.). 288p. (978-0-86187-702-7(0), Burns & Oates) Continuum International Publishing Group, Ltd.

Owen, Tim. Social Theory & Human Biotechnology. 2009. xiv, 193p. 79.00 (978-1-60692-531-7(8)) Nova Science Pubs., Inc.

Palombi, Luigi. Gene Cartels: Biotech Patents in the Age of Free Trade. 416p. 2010. pap. 69.00 (978-1-84980-245-1(9)) 2009. 158.00 (978-1-84720-836-1(3)) Elgar, Edward Publishing, Inc.

Palsson, Gisli. Anthropology & the New Genetics. 2007. (New Departures in Anthropology Ser.). (ENG., Illus.). 282p. 102.99 (978-0-521-85572-3(1)); 280p. per. 38.00 (978-0-521-67174-3(4)) Cambridge Univ. Pr.

Pandey, Ashwani. Identification of Best Substrate for the Production of Phytase Enzyme. 2011. 64p. pap. (978-3-8443-9012-4(X)) Lambert Academic Publishing.

Paschall, Christopher D. Biomimicking Leukocytes to Design Drug Delivery Vehicles. 2008. 200p. per. (978-3-8364-6576-2(0)) VDM Verlag Dr. Mueller e.K.

Pasupuleti, Vijai K., ed. Protein Hydrolysates in Biotechnology. 2010. (ENG., Illus.). xiii, 229p. 189.00 (978-1-4020-6673-3(2), 1402066732) Springer.

Patel, Charles W. Biotechnology: Global Policies, Perspectives & Issues. 2011. (Biotechnology in Agriculture, Industry & Medicine Ser.). 195.00 (978-1-61209-208-9(X)) Nova Science Pubs., Inc.

Patel, Ramesh N. Biocatalysts in the Pharmaceutical & Biotechnology Industries. 2006. (ENG., Illus.). 893p. 189.95 (978-0-8493-3732-1(1), CRC Press) Taylor & Francis Group GBR. Dist: Taylor & Francis Group.

Patzelt, Holger & Brenner, Thomas, eds. Handbook of Bioentrepreneurship. 2010. (International Handbook Series on Entrepreneurship Ser.). (Illus.). xiii, 296p. pap. 189.00 (978-1-4419-2372-1(1), 1441923721) Springer.

Paun, Gheorghe, et al. Membrane Computing: 10th International Workshop, WMC 2009, Curtea de Arges, Romania, August 24-27, 2009, Revised, Selected & Invited Papers. 2010. (Lecture Notes in Computer Science / Theoretical Computer Science & General Issues Ser.). ix, 487p. pap. 99.00 (978-3-642-11466-3(0), 3642114660) Springer.

Peacock, Kathy Wilson. Biotechnology & Genetic Engineering. 2010. (Global Issues Ser.). (Illus.). 368p. (C). (gr. 9-18). 45.00 (978-0-8160-7784-7(3)) Facts On File, Inc.

Pechlaner, Gabriela. Corporate Crops: Biotechnology, Agriculture, & the Struggle for Control. 2012. (ENG., Illus.). 294p. 55.00 (978-0-292-73945-1(1)) Univ. of Texas Pr.

Peinemann, Klaus-Viktor & Nunes, Suzana Pereira, eds. Membranes for Life Sciences, Vol. 1. 2007. (Membranes Ser.: 5). (ENG.). 343p. 245.00 (978-3-527-31480-5(6), Wiley-VCH) Wiley, John & Sons, Inc.

Petrenko, Valery & Smith, George P., eds. Phage Bionanotechnology. 2011. (RSC Nanoscience & Nanotechnology Ser.). (ENG., Illus.). 288p. 195.00 (978-0-85404-184-8(2)) Royal Society of Chemistry, The GBR. Dist: Ingram Pub. Services.

Pietka, Ewa. Information Technologies in Biomedicine. 2008. (Advances in Intelligent & Soft Computing Ser.). (Illus.). 588p. spiral bd. 289.00 (978-3-540-68167-0(1), 3540681671) Springer.

Pietka, Ewa & Kawa, Jacek, eds. Information Technologies in Biomedicine: Volume 2. 2010. (Advances in Intelligent & Soft Computing Ser.). 640p. pap. 389.00 (978-3-642-13104-2(2), 3642131042) Springer.

Pingarron, Jose M. & Luong, John H., eds. Biosensor Technology. 2013. (Biotechnology & Bioprocessing Ser.). (ENG., Illus.). 520p. 139.95 (978-1-4398-4141-9(1), CRC Press) Taylor & Francis Group GBR. Dist: Taylor & Francis Group.

Pisano, Gary P. Science Business: The Promise, the Reality, & the Future of Biotech. 2006. (ENG., Illus.). 256p. 32.00 (978-1-59139-840-0(1)) Harvard Business Review Pr.

Plunkett, Jack. E-Book Plunkett's Biotech & Genetics Industry Almanac 2008: Biotech & Genetics Industry Market Research, Statistics, Trends & Leading Companies. annuals Plunkett, Jack, ed. 2007. 590p. E-Book 299.99 incl. cd-rom (978-1-59392-430-0(5)) Plunkett Research, Ltd.

Plunkett, Jack W. Plunkett's Biotech & Genetics Industry Almanac 2007: Biotech & Genetics Industry Market Research, Statistics, Trends & Leading Companies. Plunkett, Jack W., ed. 2006. 552p. pap. 299.99 incl. cd-rom (978-1-59392-058-6(X)) Plunkett Research, Ltd.

—Plunkett's Biotech & Genetics Industry Almanac 2007 (E-Book) Biotech & Genetics Industry Market Research, Statistics, Trends & Leading Companies.

Plunkett, Jack W., ed. 2006. 574p. E-Book 499.99 incl. cd-rom *(978-1-59392-400-3(3))* Plunkett Research, Ltd.

—Plunkett's Biotech & Genetics Industry Almanac 2008: Biotech & Genetics Industry Market Research, Statistics, Trends & Leading Companies. annuals Plunkett, Jack W., ed. 2007. 579p. pap. 299.99 incl. cd-rom *(978-1-59392-087-6(3))* Plunkett Research, Ltd.

Prager, Gary. Practical Pharmaceutical Engineering. 2010. (ENG.). 500p. 110.00 *(978-0-470-41032-5(9)*, Wiley-Interscience) Wiley, John & Sons, Inc.

Prince, Violaine & Roche, Mathieu, eds. Information Retrieval in Biomedicine: Natural Language Processing for Knowledge Integration. 2009. (Illus.). 460p. 225.00 *(978-1-60566-274-9(7))* IGI Global.

Pritchett Thomas J Staff. Quality Assurance & Control in Biotechnology. 2009. 500p. 169.95 *(978-1-57444-519-0(7))* CRC Pr. LLC.

Prokop, Ales & Michelson, Seth. Systems Biology in Biotech & Pharma: A Changing Paradigm. 2012. (SpringerBriefs in Pharmaceutical Science & Drug Development Ser.). (ENG., Illus.). xviii, 127p. pap. 49.95 ***(978-94-007-2848-6(4)***, 9400728484) Springer.

Putri, Tuflikha Primi. Potential Use of Edible Fruits & Australian Native Plants. 2010. 104p. pap. *(978-3-8383-8708-6(2))* Lambert Academic Publishing.

Qian, Shizhi & Ai, Ye. Electrokinetic Particle Transport in Micro/Nano-fluidics: Direct Numerical Simulation Analysis. 2012. (Surfactant Science Ser.). (ENG., Illus.). 398p. 129.95 *(978-1-4398-5438-9(6)*, CRC Press) Taylor & Francis Group GBR. Dist: Taylor & Francis Group.

Qiu, Xujian. Use of Natural Ingredients to Control Foodborne Pathogens. 2010. 148p. pap. *(978-3-639-18748-9(2))* VDM Verlag Dr. Mueller e.K.

Qureshi, Abdul Sattar. Proteolytic Enzyme of Bacteri. 2011. 240p. pap. ***(978-3-8454-1302-0(6))*** Lambert Academic Publishing.

Rabaey, Korneel. Bio-electrochemical Systems: From Extracellular Electron Transfer to Biotechnological Application. 2009. (Integrated Environmental Technology Ser.). (Illus.). 524p. (C). *(978-1-84339-233-0(X))* IWA Publishing.

Raghavachari, Ramesh & Liang, Rongguang. Design & Quality for Biomedical Technologies IV. 2011. (Proceedings of SPIE Ser.). 160p. pap. 80.00 ***(978-0-8194-8428-4(8))*** SPIE.

Rai, Arti & Latty, Elvin R., eds. Intellectual Property & Biotechnology. 2011. (Critical Concepts in Intellectual Property Law Ser.). (Illus.). 584p. 310.00 ***(978-1-84844-261-0(0))*** Elgar, Edward Publishing, Inc.

Rajan, Kaushik Sunder, ed. Lively Capital: Biotechnologies, Ethics, & Governance in Global Markets. 2012. (Experimental Futures Ser.). (ENG., Illus.). 512p. pap. 29.95 ***(978-0-8223-4831-3(4))*** Duke Univ. Pr.

Ramachandran Kb Staff. Process Engineering in Biotechnology. 2009. 600p. 169.95 *(978-1-57444-515-2(4))* CRC Pr. LLC.

Ramakrishna, Seeram. Polymer Membranes in Biotechnology: Preparation, Functionalization & Application. 2009. (Illus.). 300p. 88.00 *(978-1-84816-379-9(7))*; pap. 45.00 *(978-1-84816-380-5(0))* Imperial College Pr. GBR. Dist: World Scientific Publishing Co., Inc.

Ramos, Christian G. Unveiling Novel Virulence Factors from Burkholderia Cepacia Complex. 2011. 128p. pap. ***(978-3-8454-2283-1(1))*** Lambert Academic Publishing.

Rao, Govind, ed. Optical Sensor Systems in Biotechnology. 2009. (Advances in Biochemical Engineering / Biotechnology Ser.). (ENG.). xiii, 161p. 219.00 *(978-3-642-03469-5(1)*, 3642034691) Springer.

Rappert, Brian. Biotechnology, Security & the Search for Limits: An Inquiry into Research & Methods. 2007. (New Security Challenges Ser.). (ENG., Illus.). 208p. 100.00 *(978-0-230-00248-7(X))* Palgrave Macmillan.

—Experimental Secrets: International Security, Codes, & the Future of Research. 2009. (ENG.). 250p. pap. 36.99 *(978-0-7618-4475-4(9))* Univ. Pr. of America, Inc.

Rashed, Mortagy. Methods & Advances in Biotech. 2010. (Illus.). 58p. 12.00 *(978-1-4251-5390-8(9))* Trafford Publishing.

Rashid, Bushra, et al. Gene Pyramiding: An Approach Towards Sustainable Insect Resistance. 2010. 172p. pap. *(978-3-639-25629-1(8))* VDM Verlag Dr. Mueller e.K.

Rastall, R., ed. Novel enzyme technology for food Applications. 2007. (Illus.). 336p. *(978-1-84569-132-5(6))* Woodhead Publishing Ltd.

Rastall Robert Staff. Novel Enzyme Technology for Food Applications. 2007. (ENG., Illus.). 320p. 269.95 *(978-1-4200-4396-9(X)*, CRC Press) Taylor & Francis Group GBR. Dist: Taylor & Francis Group.

Rathore, Anurag, compiled by. Elements of Bipharmaceutical Production Series. 2007. 130p. spiral bd. 49.95 net. *(978-0-9794343-0-3(0))* Advanstar Communications Inc.

Rauter, Amélia Pilar, et al, eds. Natural Products in the New Millennium: Prospects & Industrial Application: Prospects & Industrial Application. 2010. (Proceedings of the Phytochemical Society of Europe Ser.). 540p. pap. 329.00 *(978-90-481-6186-7(X)*, 904816186X) Springer.

Rawlings, Douglas E. & Johnson, D. Barrie, eds. Biomining. 2006. (ENG., Illus.). xx, 314p. 219.00 *(978-3-540-34909-9(X)*, 354034909X) Springer.

Rees, Andy. Genetically Modified Food: A Short Guide for the Confused. 2006. (ENG.). 240p. 74.00 *(978-0-7453-2440-1(1))*; per. 19.95 *(978-0-7453-2439-5(8))* Pluto Pr. GBR. Dist: Macmillan.

Reid-Henry, S. M. The Cuban Cure: Reason & Resistance in Global Science. 2010. 216p. 39.00 *(978-0-226-70917-8(5))* Univ. of Chicago Pr.

Reisner, David E. Bionanotechnology II: Global Prospects. 2011. (ENG., Illus.). 583p. 99.95 *(978-1-4398-0463-6(X)*, CRC Press) Taylor & Francis Group GBR. Dist: Taylor & Francis Group.

Renneberg, Reinhard. Biotechnology for Beginners. Demain, Arnold L., ed. FitzRoy, Renate & Jones, Jackie, trs. 2007. (ENG., Illus.). 360p. pap. 61.95 *(978-0-12-373581-2(5)*, Academic Pr.) Elsevier Science & Technology Bks.

—Who Cloned My Cat? Fun Adventures in Biotechnology. 2010. (ENG., Illus.). 178p. 29.95 *(978-981-4267-65-6(1))* Pan Stanford Publishing SGP. Dist: Taylor & Francis Group.

Renugopalakrishnan, V. & Lewis, Randy V., eds. Bionanotechnology: Proteins to Nanodevices. 2010. (ENG.). xiv, 296p. pap. 229.00 *(978-90-481-7078-4(8)*, 9048170788) Springer.

Restrepo Orrego, Carlos Ernesto. Apropiación Indebida de Recursos Genéticos, Biodiversidad y Conocimientos Tradicionales: "Biopiratería" 2006. (SPA.). 302p. pap. 25.00 *(978-958-710-140-9(5))* Universidad Externado de Colombia COL. Dist: Siglo del Hombre.

Rhodes, Catherine. International Governance of Biotechnology. 2012. (ENG.). 256p. 90.00 *(978-1-84966-065-5(4)*, Hodder Arnold) Bloomsbury Publishing.

Richter, Felix W., ed. Biotechnology: Research, Technology & Applications. 2008. 139.00 *(978-1-60456-901-8(8))* Nova Science Pubs., Inc.

Rimmer, M. Intellectual Property & Biotechnology: Biological Inventions. 2008. 400p. 160.00 *(978-1-84572-947-9(1))* Elgar, Edward Publishing, Inc.

Rimmer, Matthew. Intellectual Property & Biotechnology: Biological Inventions. 392p. 2011. pap. 59.95 *(978-0-85793-370-6(1))* 2008. 167.00 ***(978-1-84542-947-8(8))*** Elgar, Edward Publishing, Inc.

Ringeisen, Bradley R., et al, eds. Cell & Organ Printing. 2010. (ENG.). xiv, 300p. 189.00 *(978-90-481-9144-4(0)*, 9048191440) Springer.

Ripp, Steven & Henry, Theodore B., eds. Biotechnology & Nanotechnology Risk Assessment: Minding & Managing the Potential Threats Around Us. 2012. (ACS Symposium Ser.: 1079). (ENG.). 200p. 150.00 ***(978-0-8412-2660-9(1))*** American Chemical Society.

Robbins, Peter T. & Huzair, Farah, eds. Exploring Central & Eastern Europe's Biotechnology Landscape. 2011. (International Library of Ethics, Law & Technology Ser.). (ENG., Illus.). xi, 228p. 139.00 *(978-90-481-9783-5(X)*, 904819783X) Springer.

Robinson, Daniel F. Confronting Biopiracy: Challenges, Cases & International Debates. 2010. (ENG., Illus.). 208p. 96.00 *(978-1-84407-722-9(5))* Routledge.

Roco, Mihail C. & Bainbridge, William Sims, eds. Progress in Convergence: Technologies for Human Wellbeing. 2007. (Annals of the New York Academy of Sciences Ser.: 17). (ENG., Illus.). 300p. pap. 139.95 *(978-1-57331-665-1(2)*, Wiley-Blackwell) Wiley, John & Sons, Inc.

Roelof van der Meer, Jan. Concepts & Engineering in Synthetic Biosensing. 2010. (Synthesis Lectures on Synthetic Biology Ser.). 100p. pap. 40.00 *(978-1-59829-911-3(5))* Morgan & Claypool Pubs.

Rogers, Kim & Mulchandani, Ashok, eds. Affinity Biosensors: Techniques & Protocols. 2010. (Methods in Biotechnology Ser.). 264p. pap. 139.00 *(978-1-61737-066-3(5)*, 1617370665) Humana Pr.

Ronald, Pamela C. & Adamchak, Raoul W. Tomorrow's Table: Organic Farming, Genetics, & the Future of Food. (ENG., Illus.). 232p. 2010. pap. 16.95 *(978-0-19-539357-6(0))* 2008. 29.95 *(978-0-19-530175-5(7))* Oxford Univ. Pr., Inc.

Rose, Hilary & Rose, Steven. Genes, Cells & Brains: Bioscience's Promethean Promises. 2012. (ENG.). 224p. 24.95 ***(978-1-84467-881-5(4)***, 844881) Verso Bks. GBR. Dist: Norton, W. W. & Co., Inc.

Rothmayr, Christine & Varone, Frederic, eds. The Politics of Biotechnology in North America & Europe: Policy Networks, Institutions, & Internationalization. 2006. (Studies in Public Policy Ser.). (ENG.). 304p. per. 34.99 *(978-0-7391-1248-9(1))* Lexington Bks.

Roussos, S., et al, eds. New Horizons in Biotechnology. 2010. 496p. pap. 215.00 *(978-90-481-6468-4(0)*, 9048164680) Springer.

Roy, Michael J. Biotechnology Operations. 2011. (Illus.). 416p. 99.95 *(978-1-4398-3028-4(2)*, CRC Press) Taylor & Francis Group GBR. Dist: Taylor & Francis Group.

—Biotechnology Operations: Principles & Practices. 2011. (ENG., Illus.). 416p. 99.95 *(978-1-4398-3027-7(4)*, CRC Press) Taylor & Francis Group GBR. Dist: Taylor & Francis Group.

Royal Society of Chemistry Staff. Thermochemical Conversion of Biomass to Liquid Fuels & Chemicals. Crocker, Mark, ed. 2010. (RSC Energy & Environment Ser.). (ENG., Illus.). 552p. 224.00 *(978-1-84973-035-8(0))* Royal Society of Chemistry, The GBR. Dist: Ingram Pub. Services.

Rubinsky, Boris, ed. Irreversible Electroporation. 2009. (Series in Biomedical Engineering Ser.). (ENG., Illus.). xiv, 314p. 169.00 *(978-3-642-05419-8(6)*, 3642054196) Springer.

Ruivenkamp, Guido, et al, eds. Reconstructing Biotechnologies: Critical social Analyses. 2008. 250p. 90.00 *(978-90-8686-062-3(1))* Wageningen Academic Publishers NLD. Dist: Enfield Publishing & Distribution Co., Inc.

Ryadnov, Maxim. Bionanodesign: Following Nature's Touch. 2009. (RSC Nanoscience & Nanotechnology Ser.). (ENG., Illus.). 250p. (C). 160.00 ***(978-0-85404-162-6(1))*** Royal Society of Chemistry, The GBR. Dist: Ingram Pub. Services.

Saier Jr., M. H., ed. Active Transport in Communication, Protection & Nutrition. 2007. (Illus.). 124p. pap. *(978-3-8055-8291-9(9))* Karger, S. AG.

Saier, M. H., Jr., ed. The Bioinformatic Study of Transmembrane Molecular Transport. (Illus.). 84p. pap. *(978-3-8055-8213-1(7))* Karger, S. AG.

Saier, Milton H., Jr., ed. Accelerating Evolutionary Change through Adaptive & Directed Mutation Vol. 21, No. 1: Special Topic Issue - 'Journal of Molecular Microbiology & Biotechnology 2011. 2012. (ENG., Illus.). 82p. pap. ***(978-3-8055-9920-7(X))*** Karger, S. AG.

Sampath, Padmashree Gehl & Oyelaran-Oyeyinka, Banji. The Gene Revolution & Global Food Security: Biotechnology Innovation in Latecomers. 2010. (ENG., Illus.). 288p. 105.00 *(978-0-230-22882-5(8))* Palgrave Macmillan.

Samuels, Damon S., ed. Biosafety & Biosecurity Issues in High-Containment Laboratories. 2010. (Defense, Security & Strategies Ser.). (Illus.). ix, 288p. 195.00 *(978-1-61668-706-9(1))* Nova Science Pubs., Inc.

Sandana-Mala, J. Geraldine & Takeuchi, Satoru, eds. Perspectives on Lipase Enzyme Technology. 2009. (Biotechnology in Agriculture, Industry & Medicine Ser.). 89.00 *(978-1-60741-977-8(7))* Nova Science Pubs., Inc.

Sanderson. Understanding Genes & Gmos. 2007. (C). 79.00 *(978-981-270-375-0(6))* World Scientific Publishing Co., Inc.

Sanderson, Colin J. Understanding Genes & Gmos. 2007. (Illus.). 345p. pap. 49.00 *(978-981-270-376-7(4))* World Scientific Publishing Co., Inc.

Satyanarayana, T., et al, eds. Microorganisms in Environmental Management: Microbes & Environment. 2012. (ENG., Illus.). xxi, 819p. 279.00 ***(978-94-007-2228-6(1)***, 9400722281) Springer.

Satyanarayana, T. & Kunze, Gotthard. Yeast Biotechnology: Diversity & Applications. 2009. (ENG., Illus.). xxii, 744p. 379.00 *(978-1-4020-8291-7(6)*, 1402082916) Springer.

Schaefer, Richard T. & Zellner, William W. Extraordinary Groups: An Examination of Unconventional Lifestyles. 8th ed. 2007. (ENG.). 378p. (C). pap. 47.95 *(978-0-7167-7034-3(2))* Worth Pubs., Inc.

Scharfetter, Hermann & Merwa, Robert, eds. 13th International Conference on Electrical Bioimpedance & the 8th Conference on Electrical Impedance Tomography: ICEBI 2007, August 29th - September 2nd 2007, Graz, Austria. 2007. (IFMBE Proceedings Ser.). 846p. pap. 499.00 *(978-3-540-73840-4(1)*, 3540738401) Springer.

Schmidt, Markus, et al, eds. Synthetic Biology: The technoscience & its societal Consequences. 2009. (ENG., Illus.). viii, 186p. 159.00 *(978-90-481-2677-4(0)*, 9048126770) Springer.

Schmidt, Stanley. The Coming Convergence: The Surprising Ways Diverse Technologies Interact to Shape Our World & Change the Future. 2008. (ENG., Illus.). 336p. 28.98 *(978-1-59102-613-6(X))* Prometheus Bks., Pubs.

Schoemaker, Joyce A. & Schoemaker, Paul J. H. Chips, Clones, & Living Beyond 100: How Far Will the Biosciences Take Us? 2009. (FT Press Science Ser.). (ENG., Illus.). 240p. 24.99 *(978-0-13-715385-5(6))* FT Press.

Scholer, Kaye. Pharmaceutical & Biotech Patent Law. 2007. (ENG.). 919p. 275.00 *(978-1-4024-0899-1(4))* Practising Law Institute.

Schügerl, Karl. Solvent Extraction in Biotechnology: Recovery of Primary & Secondary Metabolites. 2010. (Illus.). viii, 213p. pap. 229.00 *(978-3-642-08190-3(8)*, 3642081908) Springer.

Schügerl, Karl & Zeng, A. P., eds. Tools & Applications of Biochemical Engineering Science. 2010. (Advances in Biochemical Engineering Biotechnology Ser.). (Illus.). xviii, 274p. pap. 349.00 *(978-3-642-07598-8(3)*, 3642075983) Springer.

Schulz, Mark J. & Shanov, Vesselin N., eds. Nanomedicine Design of Particles, Sensors, Motors, Implants, Robots, & Devices. 2009. (Illus.). 560p. 159.00 *(978-1-59693-279-1(1))* Artech Hse., Inc.

Schurman, Rachel & Munro, William A. Fighting for the Future of Food: Activists versus Agribusiness in the Struggle over Biotechnology. 2010. (Social Movements, Protest & Contention Ser.). (ENG., Illus.). 280p. pap. 22.50 *(978-0-8166-4762-0(3))* Univ. of Minnesota Pr.

Scientific and Humane Issues in the Use of Random Source Dogs and Cats for Research Committee. Scientific & Humane Issues in the Use of Random Source Dogs & Cats in Research. National Research Council Staff, ed. 2009. (ENG.). 118p. pap. 35.00 *(978-0-309-13807-9(8))* National Academies Pr.

Seidman, Lisa. Basic Laboratory Calculations for Biotechnology. 2007. (ENG.). 504p. (C). pap. 62.13 *(978-0-13-223810-6(1))* Benjamin-Cummings Publishing Co.

Seidman, Lisa A. & Moore, Cynthia J. Basic Laboratory Methods for Biotechnology: Textbook & Laboratory Reference. 2nd ed. 2008. (ENG., Illus.). 450p. (C). spiral bd. 93.40 *(978-0-321-57014-7(6))* Benjamin-Cummings Publishing Co.

Seidman, Lisa A., et al. Laboratory Manual for Biotechnology & Laboratory Science: The Basics. 2010. (ENG.). 464p. (C). spiral bd. 64.20 *(978-0-321-64402-2(6))* Benjamin-Cummings Publishing Co.

Semenova, Maria Germanovna & Dickinson, Eric. Biopolymers in Food Colloids: Thermodynamics & Molecular Interactions. 2010. (ENG., Illus.). 384p. 250.00 *(978-90-04-17186-2(X)*, CRC Press) Taylor & Francis Group GBR. Dist: Taylor & Francis Group.

Shahi (Editor), Director Gurinder S. BioBusiness Perspectives. 2008. 147p. pap. 19.98 *(978-0-557-02336-3(X))* Lulu Enterprises Inc.

Shareefdeen, Zarook & Singh, Ajay K., eds. Biotechnology for Odor & Air Pollution Control. 2007. (ENG., Illus.). xviii, 409p. per. 119.00 *(978-3-540-74049-0(X)*, 354074049X) Springer.

Sharma, Naveen & Rathore, Madhu. Emerging Trends: Applied Biotechnology. 2011. 184p. pap. ***(978-3-8443-9630-0(6))*** Lambert Academic Publishing.

Sharma, Vinay & Nath Tripathi, Bhumi. Molecular Biology & Biotechnology. 2011. 252p. pap. ***(978-3-8433-6029-6(4))*** Lambert Academic Publishing.

Sharon, Maheshwar & Sharon, Madhuri. Bionanotechnology. 2012. (ENG., Illus.). 300p. 79.95 *(978-1-4398-5214-9(6)*, CRC Press) Taylor & Francis Group GBR. Dist: Taylor & Francis Group.

Shi, D. Biomedical Devices & Their Applications. 2010. (Biological & Medical Physics, Biomedical Engineering Ser.). (Illus.). xiv, 201p. pap. 259.00 *(978-3-642-06068-7(4)*, 3642060684) Springer.

Shimasaki, Craig D. The Business of Bioscience: What Goes into Making a Biotechnology Product. 2009. (ENG., Illus.). xiii, 269p. 159.00 *(978-1-4419-0063-0(2)*, 1441900632) Springer.

Shiva, Vandana. Biopiratería: El Saqueo de la Naturaleza y del Conocimiento. 2010. (SPA & ENG.). 152p. pap. 15.00 *(978-0-89608-791-0(3))* South End Pr.

Shmaefsky, Brian R. & Calhoun, Yael. Medicine in the News. 2007. (Science News Flash Ser.). 144p. (YA). (gr. 7-12). 31.95 *(978-0-7910-9256-9(9))* Facts On File, Inc.

Shmaefsky, Brian Robert. Biotechnology 101, 1 vol. 2006. (Science 101 Ser.). (Illus.). 272p. 49.95 *(978-0-313-33528-0(1)*, GR3528, Greenwood Pr.) Greenwood Publishing Group, Inc.

Shoseyov, Oded & Levy, Ilan, eds. NanoBioTechnology: BioInspired Devices & Materials of the Future. (Illus.). 2010. xi, 485p. pap. 149.00 *(978-1-61737-830-0(5)*, 1617378305) 2007. 485p. 149.00 *(978-1-58829-894-2(9)*, 1588298949) Humana Pr.

Sigmund Wolfgang Staff & Sigmund, Wolfgang. Particulate Systems in Nano- & Biotechnologies. 2008. (ENG., Illus.). 385p. 162.95 *(978-0-8493-7436-4(7)*, CRC Press) Taylor & Francis Group GBR. Dist: Taylor & Francis Group.

Silver, Lee M. Challenging Nature: The Clash Between Biotechnology & Spirituality. 2007. (Ecco Ser.). (ENG.). 464p. pap. 15.99 *(978-0-06-058268-5(5)*, HarperPerennial) HarperCollins Pubs.

Simon?i?, Barbara, et al, eds. Biodegradation of Cellulose Fibers. 2010. (Bacteriology Research Developments Ser.). pap. 43.00 *(978-1-61668-154-8(3))* Nova Science Pubs., Inc.

Singh, M. P., ed. Recent Trends in Biotechnology. Volume 1. 2009. (Recent Trends in Biotechnology Ser.). (Illus.). 145.00 *(978-1-60876-148-7(7)*, Nova Biomedical Bks.) Nova Science Pubs., Inc.

Singh, M. P., et al. Recent Trends in Biotechnology. 2011. (Biotechnology in Agriculture, Industry & Medicine Ser.). (Illus.). 145.00 *(978-1-61761-797-3(0)*, Nova Biomedical Bks.) Nova Science Pubs., Inc.

Singh-Nee Nigam, Poonam & Pandey, Ashok, eds. Biotechnology for Agro-Industrial Residues Utilisation: Utilisation of Agro-Residues. 2009. (ENG., Illus.). xviii, 470p. 219.00 *(978-1-4020-9941-0(X)*, 140209941X) Springer.

Sitharaman, Balaji, ed. Nanobiomaterials Handbook. 2011. (ENG., Illus.). 737p. 169.95 *(978-1-4200-9466-4(1)*, CRC Press) Taylor & Francis Group GBR. Dist: Taylor & Francis Group.

Sleator, Roy & Hill, Colin. Patho-Biotechnology. Sleator, Roy & Hill, Colin, eds. 2008. *(978-1-58706-304-6(2))* Landes Bioscience.

Slezak, Dominik, et al. Bio-Science & Bio-Technology: International Conference, BSBT 2009 Held as Part of the Future Generation Information Technology Conference, FGIT 2009 Jeju Island, Korea, December 10-12, 2009 Proceedings. 2009. (Communications in Computer & Information Science Ser.). xii, 151p. pap. 89.95 *(978-3-642-10615-6(3)*, 3642106153) Springer.

Small, Michael. Dynamics of Biological Systems. 2011. (Chapman & Hall/CRC Mathematical & Computational Biology Ser.). (ENG., Illus.). 284p. 79.95 *(978-1-4398-5336-8(3)*, Chapman & Hall/CRC) CRC Pr. LLC.

Smith, George P. The Christian Religion & Biotechnology: A Search for Principled Decision-making. 2010. (International Library of Ethics, Law, & the New Medicine Ser.). xx, 254p. pap. 219.00 *(978-90-481-6808-8(2)*, 9048168082) Springer.

Smith, John E. Biotechnology. 5th ed. 2009. (ENG., Illus.). 278p. (C). pap. 44.00 *(978-0-521-71193-7(2))* Cambridge Univ. Pr.

Smith, Wesley J. Consumer's Guide to a Brave New World. 2010. (ENG.). 240p. pap. 15.95 *(978-1-59403-492-3(3))* Encounter Bks.

Smolke, Christina D. The Metabolic Pathway Engineering Handbook: Fundamentals, 2 vols. Smolke, Christina D., ed. 2009. (ENG., Illus.). 678p. 164.95 *(978-1-4398-0296-0(3)*, CRC Press) Taylor & Francis Group GBR. Dist: Taylor & Francis Group.

Sobti, R. C. & Pachouri, Suparna S. Essentials of Biotechnology. 2008. (ENG., Illus.). 750p. 129.95 *(978-1-4200-8284-5(1)*, CRC Press) Taylor & Francis Group GBR. Dist: Taylor & Francis Group.

Soetaert, Wim & Vandamme, Erick J., eds. Industrial Biotechnology: Sustainable Growth & Economic Success. 2010. (ENG., Illus.). 522p. 230.00 *(978-3-527-31442-3(3)*, Wiley-VCH) Wiley, John & Sons, Inc.

Somsen. The Regulatory Challenge of Biotechnology Human Genetics, Food & Patents. 2007. (Biotechnology Regulation Ser.). (Illus.). 296p. (C). 137.00 *(978-1-84542-489-3(1))* Elgar, Edward Publishing, Inc.

Speece & Speece, Richard E. Anaerobic Biotechnology & Odor/Corrosion Control for Municipalities & Industries: Corrosion Control. 2008. (Illus.). xxx, 586p. *(978-1-57843-052-9(6))* Fields Publishing, Inc.

Spencer, Joshua. Contemporary Issues. 2008. 108p. per. 19.99 *(978-1-4257-8512-3(3))* Xlibris Corp.

Srivastava, Chandan. Support Vector Data Description. 2011. 72p. pap. ***(978-3-8443-8521-2(5))*** Lambert Academic Publishing.

Steinberg, Mark L. & Cosloy, Sharon D. The Facts on File Dictionary of Biotechnology & Genetic Engineering. 3rd rev. ed. 2006. (Science Dictionaries Ser.). (Illus.). 288p. (C). (gr. 9). 49.50 *(978-0-8160-6351-2(6))* Facts On File, Inc.

Steinhoff, Gustav, ed. Regenerative Medicine. 2010. (Illus.). 300p. 279.00 *(978-90-481-9074-4(6)*, 9048190746) Springer.

Stephenson, Frank H. Calculations for Molecular Biology & Biotechnology: A Guide to Mathematics in the Laboratory 2e. 2nd ed. 2010. (ENG., Illus.). 460p. pap. 72.95 *(978-0-12-375690-9(1)*, Academic Pr.) Elsevier Science & Technology Bks.

—DNA: How the Biotech Revolution Is Changing the Way We Fight Disease. 2007. (ENG.). 1p. 26.98 *(978-1-59102-482-8(X))* Prometheus Bks., Pubs.

Stewart, J. M. Biotechnology in Cotton Research & Production. 2006. 120p. (C). pap. 55.00 *(978-0-85199-526-7(8))* Oxford Univ. Pr., Inc.

Stifling or Stimulating: The Role of Gene Patents in Research & Genetic Testing: Hearing Before the Subcommittee on Courts, the Internet, & Intellectual Property of the Committee on the Judiciary, House of Representatives, One Hundred Tenth Congress, First Session, October 30, 2007. 2008. (Illus.). iv, 125p. *(978-0-16-080797-8(2)*, 552-070-37386-1) United States Government Printing Office

Styhre, Alexander. Organizations & the Bioeconomy. 2012. (Routledge Studies in Management, Organizations & Society Ser.). (ENG., Illus.). 208p. (C). 125.00 ***(978-0-415-52926-6(3))*** Routledge.

Sun, RunCang. Cereal Straw As a Resource for Sustainable Biomaterials & Biofuels: Chemistry, Extractives, Lignins, Hemicelluloses & Cellulose. 2010. (ENG., Illus.). 300p. 275.00 *(978-0-444-53234-3(X)*, Elsevier Science & Technology Bks.

Sunder Rajan, Kaushik, ed. Lively Capital: Biotechnologies, Ethics, & Governance in Global Markets. 2012. (Experimental Futures Ser.). (ENG., Illus.). 512p. 99.95 ***(978-0-8223-4820-7(9))*** Duke Univ. Pr.

Sunderland, Naomi, et al, eds. Towards Humane Technologies: Biotechnology, New Media & Ethics. 2008. 216p. *(978-90-8790-445-6(2))*; (Illus.). pap. *(978-90-8790-444-9(4))* Sense Pubs.

Sutton, Sean D. Biotechnology: Our Future as Human Beings & Citizens. 2009. (SUNY series in Philosophy & Biology Ser.). 224p. 74.50 *(978-1-4384-2685-3(2))*; pap. 24.95 *(978-1-4384-2686-0(0))* State Univ. of New York Pr.

Swati, Zahoor A. Urdu-English English-Urdu Biotechnology Glossary. 2009. 254p. *(978-1-931545-58-4(4))* Dunwoody Pr.

Swiegers, Gerhard. Mechanical Catalysis: Methods of Enzymatic, Homogeneous, & Heterogeneous Catalysis. 2008. (ENG., Illus.). 352p. 117.00 *(978-0-470-26202-3(8)*, Wiley-Interscience) Wiley, John & Sons, Inc.

Talens, Pau, et al, eds. Edible Polysaccharide Films & Coatings. 2010. (Biotechnology in Agriculture, Industry & Medicine Ser.). pap. 43.00 *(978-1-61668-191-3(8))* Nova Science Pubs., Inc.

Tang, K. S., et al. Multiobjective Optimization Methodology: A Jumping Gene Approach. 2012. (Industrial Electronics Ser.). (ENG., Illus.). 279p. 139.95 ***(978-1-4398-9919-9(3)***, CRC Press) Taylor & Francis Group GBR. Dist: Taylor & Francis Group.

Taylor, John G. Bioengineering for Pollution Prevention. 2009. (Illus.). 189p. 79.00 *(978-1-60692-900-1(3))* Nova Science Pubs., Inc.

Taylor, Mark. Genetic Data & the Law: A Critical Perspective on Privacy Protection. 2012. (Cambridge Bioethics & Law Ser. 16). (ENG.). 246p. 99.00 ***(978-1-107-00711-6(9))*** Cambridge Univ. Pr.

Teng. Bioscience Entrepreneurship in Asia. 2008. 320p. 60.00 *(978-981-270-020-9(X))* World Scientific Publishing Co., Inc.

Textor, Marcus & Grandin, H. Michelle, eds. Intelligent Surfaces in Biotechnology: Scientific & Engineering Concepts, Enabling Technologies, & Translation to Bio-Oriented Applications. 2012. (ENG., Illus.). 400p. 125.00 ***(978-0-470-53650-6(0)***, Wiley) Wiley, John & Sons, Inc.

Thacker, Eugene. The Global Genome: Biotechnology, Politics, & Culture. 2006. (Leonardo Bks.). (ENG., Illus.). 464p. (gr. 17). per. 27.95 *(978-0-262-70116-7(2))* MIT Pr.

Thakur, Indu Shekhar. Environmental Biotechnology: Basic Concepts & Applications. 2nd rev. ed. 2011. 534p. (C). pap. *(978-93-80578-47-7(4))* I.K. International Publishing House Pvt. Ltd.

Thieman, William J. & Palladino, Michael A. Introduction to Biotechnology. (ENG.) 408p. (C). 2nd ed. 2008. pap. 123.07 *(978-0-321-49145-9(9))* 3rd rev. ed. 2012. (Illus.). pap. 123.07 ***(978-0-321-76611-3(3))*** Benjamin-Cummings Publishing Co.

Thomson Gale Staff. Biotechnology: Changing Life Through Science, 3 vols., Set. Lerner, Lee & Lerner, Brenda, eds. rev. ed. 2007. (ENG., Illus.). 878p. 225.00 *(978-1-4144-0151-5(5)*, UXL) Cengage Gale.

Tokar, Brian. Redesigning Life: The Worldwide Challenge to Genetic Engineering. 448p. pap. 45.00 *(978-0-908011-60-5(1))* Scribe Pubns. AUS. Dist: Independent Pubs. Group.

Tonye Mahop, Marcelin. Intellectual Property Community Rights & Human Rights. 2010. (Routledge Research in Intellectual Property Ser.). (ENG.). 216p. 125.00 *(978-0-415-47942-4(8))* Routledge.

Tonye Mahop, Marcelin. Intellectual Property, Community Rights & Human Rights: The Biological & Genetic Resources of Developing Countries. 2012. (ENG.). 200p. pap. 44.95 ***(978-0-415-63138-9(6))*** Routledge.

Tsao, David, ed. Phytoremediation. 2010. (Advances in Biochemical Engineering Biotechnology Ser.). (Illus.). xi, 206p. pap. 269.00 *(978-3-642-07776-0(5)*, 3642077765) Springer.

Tsao, G. T., et al, eds. Biotechnology in China II: Chemicals, Energy & Environment. 2010. (Advances in Biochemical Engineering Biotechnology Ser.). (Illus.). xiv, 264p. 359.00 *(978-3-642-14994-8(4)*, 3642149944) Springer.

Tucker, Jonathan B. & Danzig, Richard. Innovation, Dual Use, & Security: Managing the Risks of Emerging Biological & Chemical Technologies. 2012. (ENG., Illus.). 352p. (gr. 17). pap. 27.00 ***(978-0-262-51696-9(9))***; 54.00 ***(978-0-262-01717-6(2))*** MIT Pr.

Twine, Richard. Animals as Biotechnology: Ethics, Sustainability & Critical Animal Studies. 2010. (Science in Society Ser.). (ENG., Illus.). 232p. 84.95 *(978-1-84407-830-1(2))* Routledge.

Ulber, Roland & Sell, Dieter. White Biotechnology. (Advances in Biochemical Engineering Biotechnology Ser.). (Illus.). 2010. xii, 301p. pap. 359.00 *(978-3-642-07956-6(3)*, 3642079563) 2007. XII, 301p. 359.00 *(978-3-540-45695-7(3)*, 3540456953) Springer.

Useche, Pilar. Demand for Innovations. 2008. 224p. pap. *(978-3-8364-9250-8(4))* VDM Verlag Dr. Mueller e.K.

Vaidyanath, K. Introduction to Biology & Biotechnology, Second Edition. 2nd ed. 2009. (ENG., Illus.). 625p. 82.95 *(978-1-4398-0724-8(8)*, CRC Press) Taylor & Francis Group GBR. Dist: Taylor & Francis Group.

Valikhov, A. F. Russian-English English-Russian Biotechnology Glossary. 2007. (RUS & ENG.). 179p. *(978-1-931546-29-4(0))* Dunwoody Pr.

Vallero, Daniel. Environmental Biotechnology: A Biosystems Approach. 2010. (ENG., Illus.). 750p. 129.00 *(978-0-12-375089-1(X)*, Academic Pr.) Elsevier Science & Technology Bks.

Vanston, John & Elliott, Henry. Biotechnology: A Technology Forecast. 2006. 180p. per. 24.95 *(978-0-9786773-1-2(5))* Texas State Technical College Publishing.

Varfolomeev, Sergey D., et al, eds. Biochemistry & Biotechnology: Research & Development. 2012. ***(978-1-62100-452-3(X))*** Nova Science Pubs., Inc.

Varfolomeev, Sergey D., et al, eds. Biotechnology in Medicine, Foodstuffs, Biocatalysis, Environment & Biogeotechnology. 2010. (Biotechnology in Agriculture, Industry & Medicine Ser.). 245.00 *(978-1-60876-902-5(X))* Nova Science Pubs., Inc.

Varfolomeev, Sergey D., et al. Biotechnology & the Ecology of Big Cities. 2011. (Biotechnology in Agriculture, Industry & Medicine Ser.). pap. 43.00 *(978-1-61122-641-6(4)*, Nova Novinka) Nova Science Pubs., Inc.

Varshney, Rajeev K. & Tuberosa, Roberto, eds. Genomics-Assisted Crop Improvement: Vol 2: Genomics Applications in Crops. 2010. xx, 509p. pap. 259.00 *(978-90-481-7600-7(X)*, 904817600X) Springer.

Vasantha Kandasamy, W. B. & Smarandache, Florentin. Methods in Industrial Biotechnology for Chemical Engineers. 2008. 125p. *(978-1-59973-034-9(0))*, Multimedia Larga.

Velazquez, E. & Rodriguez-Barrueco, C., eds. First International Meeting on Microbial Phosphate Solubilization. 2010. (Developments in Plant & Soil Sciences Ser.). x, 362p. pap. 349.00 *(978-90-481-7013-5(3)*, 9048170133) Springer.

Villadsen, John, et al. Bioreaction Engineering Principles. 3rd ed. 2011. (ENG., Illus.). xxx, 561p. 89.95 ***(978-1-4419-9687-9(7)***, 1441996877) Springer.

Vincenzini, P. Medical Applications of Novel Biomaterials & Nano-Biotechnology: 5th Forum on New Materials Part E. 2011. (Illus.). 280p. pap. *(978-3-908158-59-2(1))* Trans Tech Pubns., Ltd.

Vinci, Victor A. & Parekh, Sarad R., eds. Handbook of Industrial Cell Culture: Mammalian, Microbial, & Plant Cells. 2010. (Illus.). 546p. pap. 239.00 *(978-1-61737-315-2(X)*, 161737315X) Humana Pr.

Vivero-Escoto, Juan, ed. Silica Nanoparticles: Preparation, Properties & Uses. 2011. (Illus.). xi, 288p. ***(978-1-61324-452-4(5))*** Nova Science Pubs., Inc.

Vogel, Joseph Henry, ed. The Museum of Bioprospecting, Intellectual Property, & the Public Domain: A Place, A Process, A Philosophy. (Environmental Conventions: Transdisciplinary Approaches Ser.). 174p. 2011. pap. 40.00 *(978-0-85728-416-7(9))* 2010. (ENG., Illus.). 99.00 *(978-1-84331-862-0(8))* Anthem Pr. GBR. Dist: Books International, Inc.

Vogel, Viola, ed. Nanomedicine 9 vols., Vol. 5. 2009. (Nanotechnology(VCH) Ser.: 5). (ENG., Illus.). 445p. 225.00 *(978-3-527-31736-3(8)*, Wiley-VCH) Wiley, John & Sons, Inc.

Vogel, Viola & Waser, Rainer, eds. Information Technology II, 9 vols., Vol. 2. 2008. (Nanotechnology(VCH) Ser.: 3). (ENG., Illus.). 414p. 220.00 *(978-3-527-31737-0(6)*, Wiley-VCH) Wiley, John & Sons, Inc.

Volova, Tatiana G. Hydrogen-Based Biosynthesis. 2009. 145.00 *(978-1-60876-053-4(7))* Nova Science Pubs., Inc.

Voss, Jon. Cleaning & Cleaning Validation: A Biotechnology Perspective. 192p. 145.00 *(978-0-939459-50-5(7))* PDA.

Vurro, Maurizio & Gressel, Jonathan, eds. Novel Biotechnologies for Biocontrol Agent Enhancement & Management. 2007. (NATO Security through Science Series A: Chemistry & Biology Ser.). x, 425p. 249.00 *(978-1-4020-5797-7(0))* Springer.

—Novel Biotechnologies for Biocontrol Agent Enhancement & Management. 2007. (NATO Science for Peace & Security Series / NATO Science for Peace & Security Series A: Chemistry & Biology Ser.). x, 374p. pap. 129.00 *(978-1-4020-5798-4(9)*, 1402057989) Springer London, Ltd. GBR. Dist: Springer.

Walker, John, et al. Molecular Biology & Biotechnology. Walker, John et al, eds. 5th rev. ed. 2009. (ENG., Illus.). 524p. (C). 80.00 *(978-0-85404-125-1(7))* Royal Society of Chemistry, The GBR. Dist: Ingram Pub. Services.

Walker, Sharon. Biotechnology. 2006. (Demystified Ser.). (ENG., Illus.). 276p. per. 21.95 *(978-0-07-144812-3(8)*, 0071448128) McGraw-Hill Professional Publishing.

Walters. Crime Political Economy & Genetically Modified Food. 2006. 200p. 57.95 *(978-0-415-42037-2(7)*, Routledge Cavendish) Taylor & Francis Group GBR. Dist: Taylor & Francis Group.

Walters, Reece. Crime, Political Economy & Gentically Modified Food. 2010. (ENG.). 176p. (C). 115.00 *(978-1-904385-22-6(2)*, Routledge Cavendish) Taylor & Francis Group GBR. Dist: Taylor & Francis Group.

Ward, Robin. A Manual for Laboratory Animal Mana. . V5. 2008. (Manuals in Biomedical Research Ser.). pap. 61.00 *(978-981-277-958-8(2))* World Scientific Publishing Co., Inc.

Welch, Ashley J. & Gemert, Martin J. C. van, eds. Optical-Thermal Response of Laser-Irradiated Tissue. 2nd ed. 2011. (ENG., Illus.). xiii, 958p. 229.00 *(978-90-481-8830-7(X)*, 904818830X) Springer.

West, Darrell M. Biotechnology Policy across National Boundaries: The Science-Industrial Complex. 2007. (ENG.). 208p. 89.00 *(978-1-4039-7251-4(6))* Palgrave Macmillan.

Westerlund. Patent Rights in Biotechnology & Other Emerging Life Sciences. 2008. *(978-90-411-2383-1(0))* Kluwer Law International.

WetFeet Editorial Staff, ed. Careers in Biotech & Pharmaceuticals. 2007. 134p. pap. 24.95 *(978-1-58207-550-6(2))* WetFeet, Inc.

Whitby, Corinne, ed. Applied Microbiology & Molecular Biology in Oil Field Systems: Proceedings from the International Symposium on Applied Microbiology & Molecular Biology in Oil Systems (ISMOS-2) 2009. 2010. (ENG., Illus.). xvi, 279p. 199.00 *(978-90-481-9251-9(X)*, 904819251X) Springer.

Whittall, John & Sutton, Peter. Practical Methods for Biocatalysis & Biotransformations. 2010. (ENG., Illus.). 432p. 175.00 *(978-0-470-51927-1(4)*, Wiley) Wiley, John & Sons, Inc.

Whittall, John & Sutton, Peter, eds. Practical Methods for Biocatalysis & Biotransformations, No. 2. 2012. (ENG.). 392p. 160.00 ***(978-1-119-99139-7(0)***, Wiley) Wiley, John & Sons, Inc.

Wiederhold, B. K., ed. Annual Review of Cybertherapy & Telemedicine 2010. 2010. 167.00 *(978-1-60750-560-0(6))* IOS Pr., Inc.

Wiesman, Zeev. Desert Olive Oil Cultivation: Advanced Bio Technologies. 2009. (ENG.). 416p. 78.95 *(978-0-12-374257-5(9)*, Academic Pr.) Elsevier Science & Technology Bks.

Wiley-VCH Staff, ed. Ullmann's Biotechnology & Biochemical Engineering, 2 vols. 2007. (ENG., Illus.). 874p. 570.00 *(978-3-527-31603-8(5)*, Wiley-VCH) Wiley, John & Sons, Inc.

Williams, James A. Strain Engineering: Methods & Protocols. 2011. (Illus.). xi, 480p. E-Book ***(978-1-61779-197-0(0))*** Humana Pr.

Willner, Itamar & Katz, Eugenii. Bionanomaterials: Synthesis & Applications for Sensors, Electronics & Medicine. 2008. 500p. 230.00 *(978-3-527-31454-6(7))* Wiley, John & Sons, Inc.

Wink, Michael, ed. An Introduction to Molecular Biotechnology: Fundamentals, Methods & Applications. 2nd ed. 2011. (ENG., Illus.). 636p. pap. 99.95 *(978-3-527-32637-2(5)*, Wiley-VCH) Wiley, John & Sons, Inc.

Winter, Peter, ed. Biotech 2008: Life Sciences: A 20/20 Vision For 2020. 2008. 500p. per. 395.00 *(978-0-9801800-0-8(7))* Burrill & Co.

Wiwanitkit, Viroj. Advanced Nanomedicine & Nanobiotechnology. 2008. (Illus.). 232p. 120.00 *(978-1-60456-435-8(0))* Nova Science Pubs., Inc.

Wohlsen, Marcus. Biopunk: Kitchen-Counter Scientists Hack the Software of Life. 2011. (ENG.). 256p. (gr. 12). 25.95 *(978-1-61723-002-8(2)*, Current) Penguin Group (USA) Inc.

Woon-Fong Leung, Wallace. Centrifugal Separations in Biotechnology. 2007. (ENG., Illus.). 312p. 205.00 *(978-1-85617-477-0(8)*, Academic Pr.) Elsevier Science & Technology Bks.

Wüger, Daniel & Cottier, Thomas, eds. Genetic Engineering & the World Trade System: World Trade Forum. 2008. (ENG.). 366p. 110.00 *(978-0-521-88360-3(1))* Cambridge Univ. Pr.

Xu, Xiao-Hong Nancy, ed. New Frontiers in Ultrasensitive Bioanalysis: Advanced Analytical Chemistry Applications in Nanobiotechnology, Single Molecule Detection, & Single Cell Analysis. 2007. (Chemical Analysis: a Series of Monographs on Analytical Chemistry & Its Applications Ser.: 250). (ENG., Illus.). 324p. 139.00 *(978-0-471-74660-7(6)*, Wiley-Interscience) Wiley, John & Sons, Inc.

Yang, Shang-Tian, ed. Bioprocessing for Value-Added Products from Renewable Resources: New Technologies & Applications. 2006. (ENG., Illus.). 684p. 260.00 *(978-0-444-52114-9(3)*, Elsevier Science) Elsevier Science & Technology Bks.

Yen. Biotechnology for Environmental Engineering. 2011. 98.00 *(978-1-84816-511-3(0))*; pap. 65.00 *(978-1-84816-512-0(9))* World Scientific Publishing Co., Inc.

Yount, Lisa. Biotechnology & Genetic Engineering. 3rd rev. ed. 2008. (Library in a Book). 368p. (C). (gr. 9). 45.00 *(978-0-8160-7217-0(5))* Facts On File, Inc.

Zaikov, G. E., et al. Renewable Resources & Biotechnology for Material Applications. 2011. (Materials Science & Technologies Ser.). (Illus.). 426p. 195.00 *(978-1-61209-521-9(6))* Nova Science Pubs., Inc.

Zaikov, Gennadii Efremovich. Biotechnology: State of the Art & Prospects for Development. 2008. (Illus.). (C). 129.00 *(978-1-60456-015-2(0)*, Nova Biomedical Bks.) Nova Science Pubs., Inc.

—Research Progress in Biotechnology. 2008. (Illus.). (C). 129.00 *(978-1-60456-000-8(2)*, Nova Biomedical Bks.) Nova Science Pubs., Inc.

Zaikov, Gennadii Efremovich & Krylova, Larisa Petrivna, eds. Biotechnology, Biodegradation, Water & Foodstuffs. 2008. 145.00 *(978-1-60692-097-8(9))* Nova Science Pubs., Inc.

Zamboni, Alessandro. Protection of the Photosynthetic Apparatus. 2011. 92p. pap. ***(978-3-8443-9189-3(4))*** Lambert Academic Publishing.

Zesiewicz, Theresa A., et al. Parkinson's Disease. 5th ed. 2010. (Illus.). 280p. per. 34.95 *(978-1-873413-63-0(7))* Merit Publishing International, Inc.

Zhang, Man. The Measurement & Imaging of Soft Tissue Viscoelastic Properties. 2008. 144p. pap. *(978-3-639-07792-6(X))* VDM Verlag Dr. Mueller e.K.

Zhang, Yanchun, et al, eds. Database Theory & Application, Bio-Science & Bio-Technology: International Conferences, DTA / BSBT 2010, Held as Part of the Future Generation Information Technology Conference, FGIT 2010, Jeju Island, Korea, December 13-15, 2010. Proceedings. 2010. (Communications in Computer & Information Science Ser.). xiv, 310p. pap. 95.00 *(978-3-642-17621-0(6)*, 3642176216) Springer.

Zhong, J. J., et al. Biotechnology in China I. 2009. (Advances in Biochemical Engineering / Biotechnology Ser.). (ENG., Illus.). xiii, 322p. 389.00 *(978-3-540-88414-9(9)*, 3540884149) Springer.

Zhou, Yong, ed. Bio-Inspired Nanomaterials & Nanotechnology. 2009. (Nanotechnology Science & Technology Ser.). (Illus.). x, 301p. 89.00 *(978-1-60876-105-0(3)*, Nova Biomedical Bks.) Nova Science Pubs., Inc.

Zimmer, Gerald. Development of a CellChip based Multi-Well-Type Bioreactor: A multi-purpose platform for three dimensional cultivation of cells. 2008. 92p. pap. *(978-3-639-10541-4(9))* VDM Verlag Dr. Mueller e.K.

Zuccheri, Giampaolo & Samoriapos, B. DNA Nanotechnology: Methods & Protocols. 2011. (Illus.). xii, 361p. E-Book ***(978-1-61779-142-0(3))*** Humana Pr.

BIOTELEMETRY

see also Animal Radio Tracking

Barculo, Diana & Daniels, Julia, eds. Telemetry: Research, Technology & Applications. 2009. 239p. 129.00 *(978-1-60692-509-6(1))* Nova Science Pubs., Inc.

BIOTIC COMMUNITIES

see also Animal Societies; Ecosystem Management

Adey, Walter H. & Loveland, Karen. Dynamic Aquaria: Building Living Ecosystems. 3rd ed. 2007. (ENG., Illus.). 528p. 91.95 *(978-0-12-370641-6(6)*, Academic Pr.) Elsevier Science & Technology Bks.

Amiard-Triquet, Claude & Rainbow, Philip S., eds. Environmental Assessment of Estuarine Ecosystems: A Case Study. 2009. (Environmental & Ecological Risk Assessment Ser.). (ENG., Illus.). 368p. 133.95 *(978-1-4200-6260-1(3)*, CRC Press) Taylor & Francis Group GBR. Dist: Taylor & Francis Group.

Aoki, Ichiro. Entropy Principle for the Development of Complex Biotic Systems: Organisms, Ecosystems, the Earth. 2012. (ENG.). 122p. 99.95 ***(978-0-12-391493-4(0))*** Elsevier Science & Technology Bks.

Auken, Oscar van, ed. Western North American Juniperus Communities: A Dynamic Vegetation Type. 2010. (Ecological Studies). (Illus.). xx, 316p. pap. 129.00 *(978-1-4419-2227-4(X)*, 144192227X) Springer.

Bachev, Hrabrin. Governing of Agro-Ecosystem Services. 2009. 88p. pap. *(978-3-639-20773-6(4))* VDM Verlag Dr. Mueller e.K.

Bailey, Bailey. Ecosystem Geography: From Ecoregions to Sites. Zyryanova, Zyryanova, ed. 2nd ed. 2009. (ENG., Illus.). xii, 243p. 129.00 *(978-0-387-89515-4(9)*, 0387895159) Springer.

Bailey, Robert G. Ecosystem Geography: Second Edition. 2nd ed. 2009. (ENG., Illus.). xii, 243p. pap. 49.95 *(978-1-4419-0391-4(7)*, 1441903917) Springer.

Baker, William L. & Paulson, Deborah D. The Nature of Southwest Colorado: Recognizing Human Legacies & Restoring Natural Places. 2006. (ENG., Illus.). 386p. 80.00 *(978-0-87081-848-6(1))* Univ. Pr. of Colorado.

Bakus, Gerald J. Quantitative Analysis of Marine Biological Communities: Field Biology & Environment. 2007. (ENG., Illus.). 435p. 139.00 *(978-0-470-04440-7(3)*, Wiley-Interscience) Wiley, John & Sons, Inc.

Bardgett, Richard D. & Wardle, David A. Aboveground-Belowground Linkages: Biotic Interactions, Ecosystem Processes, & Global Change. 2010. (Oxford Series in Ecology & Evolution Ser.). (ENG., Illus.). 320p. 108.50 *(978-0-19-954687-9(8))*; pap. 52.95 *(978-0-19-954688-6(6))* Oxford Univ. Pr., Inc.

Barkley, Allen L. Ecosystems in Modern Conditions & the Environment with Index & Medical Analysis of New Research Information for All Nations. 2006. (Illus.). 160p. 69.95 *(978-0-7883-4251-6(7)*, 07883-42517) ABBE Pubs. Assn. of Washington, D.C.

Bell, Elanor. Life at Extremes: Environments, Organisms, & Strategies for Survival. 2012. 576p. 180.00 ***(978-1-84593-814-7(3))*** CABI GBR. Dist: Stylus Publishing, LLC.

Blevins, David & Schafale, Michael Paul. Wild North Carolina: Discovering the Wonders of Our State's Natural Communities. 2011. (ENG., Illus.). 176p. 30.00 *(978-0-8078-3467-1(X))* Univ. of North Carolina Pr.

Bossel, Hartmut. System Zoo 2 Simulation Models Climate, Ecosystems, Resources. 2007. 204p. per. *(978-3-8334-8423-0(3))* Books on Demand GmbH.

Boucot, A. J. & Lawson, J. D., eds. Paleocommunities: A Case Study from the Silurian & Lower Devonian, 2 vols. 2009. (World & Regional Geology Ser.). (ENG., Illus.). 911p. pap. 116.00 *(978-0-521-11531-5(0))* Cambridge Univ. Pr.

Bowling, Tim. The Lost Coast: Salmon, Memory & the Death of Wild Culture. unabr. ed. 2007. (ENG., Illus.). 255p. 29.95 *(978-0-88971-211-9(5))* Harbour Publishing Co., Ltd. CAN. Dist: Ingram Pub. Services.

Brebbia, C. A., ed. Ecodynamics: The Prigogine Legacy. 2011. (ENG., Illus.). 368p. lib. bdg. 316.00 ***(978-1-84564-654-7(1))*** WIT Pr GBR. Dist: WIT Pr.

Brebbia, C. A. & Tiezzi, E., eds. Ecosytems & Sustainable Development VII. 2009. (WIT Transactions on Ecology & the Environment Ser.: 122). (Illus.). 640p. 437.00 *(978-1-84564-194-8(9))* WIT Pr GBR. Dist: WIT Pr.

Brebbia, C. A. & Villacampa Esteve, Y., eds. Ecosystems & Sustainable Development, Vol. 8. 2011. (WIT Transactions on Ecology & the Environment Ser.: 144). (Illus.). 544p. lib. bdg. 468.00 *(978-1-84564-510-6(3))* WIT Pr GBR. Dist: WIT Pr.

Broadhead, Geoffrey D. & Davis, Walter E. Ecological Task Analysis & Movement. 2007. (ENG., Illus.). 344p. (C). 81.00 *(978-0-7360-5185-9(6))* Human Kinetics Pubs.

Brokaw, Nicholas, et al, eds. A Caribbean Forest Tapestry: The Multidimensional Nature of Disturbance & Response, 1 vol. 2012. (Long-Term Ecological Research Network Ser.). (ENG.). 464p. 74.99 ***(978-0-19-533469-2(8))*** Oxford Univ. Pr., Inc.

B

Bruce, Scott G. Ecologies & Economies in Medieval & Early Modern Europe: Studies in Environmental History for Richard C. Hoffmann. 2009. (978-90-04-18007-9(9)) BRILL.

Buffetaut, E., et al, eds. Late Palaeozoic & Mesozoic Ecosystems in SE Asia. 2009. (Illus.). vi, 306p. (978-1-86239-275-5(7)) Geological Society Publishing Hse.

Carran, R. Andrew, et al, eds. Agroecosystems in a Changing Climate. 2006. (Advances in Agroecology Ser.). (ENG., Illus.). 364p. 133.95 (978-0-8493-2088-0(7), 2088, CRC Press) Taylor & Francis Group GBR. Dist: Taylor & Francis Group.

Carson. Tropical Forest Community Ecology. Carson, Walter & Schnitzer, Stefan, eds. 2008. (ENG., Illus.). 536p. 229.95 (978-1-4051-8952-1(5), Wiley-Blackwell) Wiley, John & Sons, Inc.

Carson, Walter & Schnitzer, Stefan, eds. Tropical Forest Community Ecology. 2008. (ENG., Illus.). 536p. pap. 99.95 (978-1-4051-1897-2(0), Wiley-Blackwell) Wiley, John & Sons, Inc.

Caskey, B. J. & Frey, Jeffrey W. Biological-Community Composition in Small Streams & Its Relations to Habitat, Nutrients, & Land Use in Agriculturally Dominated Landscapes in Indiana & Ohio, 2004, & Implications for Assessing Nutrient Conditions in Midwest Streams. 2009. (Illus.). vi, 21p. (978-1-4113-2412-1(9)) United States Geological Survey.

Chaturvedi, Ravi & Raghubanshi, Akhilesh. Plant Functional Traits in a Tropical Deciduous Forest. 2011. 260p. pap. (978-3-8443-8059-0(0)) Lambert Academic Publishing.

Chuvieco, Emilio, ed. Earth Observation of Wildland Fires in Mediterranean Ecosystems. 2009. (ENG., Illus.). x, 251p. 169.00 (978-3-642-01753-7(3), 3642017533) Springer.

Ciuffa, Daniele & Ciccotti, Eleonora. Nutrients & Fish Effects on Plankton Community in Shallow Lakes. 2011. 220p. pap. (978-3-8433-8846-7(6)) Lambert Academic Publishing.

Coleman, David C. Big Ecology: The Emergence of Ecosystem Science. 2010. (ENG., Illus.). 248p. 45.00 (978-0-520-26475-5(4)) Univ. of California Pr.

Committee for the Workshop on Frontiers in Understanding Climate Change and Polar Ecosystems & National Research Council. Frontiers in Understanding Climate Change & Polar Ecosystems: Summary of a Workshop. 2011. (ENG.). 86p. pap. 21.00 (978-0-309-21087-4(9)) National Academies Pr.

Cook, William A. Issues in Bioethics & the Concept of Scale. 2008. (American University Studies V: Philosophy Ser.: Vol. 202). 146p. (C). 58.95 (978-1-4331-0199-1(8)) Lang, Peter Publishing, Inc.

Cooper, Ross Gordon. Termites: Terry & his Colony. 2010. 63p. pap. 29.95 (978-0-557-41924-1(7)) Lulu Enterprises Inc.

Davies, Bryan R. & Walker, Keith F., eds. The Ecology of River Systems. 2010. (Monographiae Biologicae Ser.). 816p. pap. 529.00 (978-90-481-8515-3(7), 9048185157) Springer.

Dawson, Allen. Ecological Values & Ecosystem Services of Natural Forests. 2010. 92p. pap. (978-3-639-25814-1(2)) VDM Verlag Dr. Mueller e.K.

DeClerck, Fabrice, et al, eds. Ecosystem Services from Agriculture & Agroforestry: Measurement & Payment. 2011. (ENG., Illus.). 448p. 99.95 (978-1-84971-147-0(X)) Routledge.

Demas, Gregory E. & Nelson, Randy F., eds. Eco-Immunology. 2011. (ENG., Illus.). 576p. 89.95 (978-0-19-973734-5(7)) Oxford Univ. Pr., Inc.

Dennison, William C. Enclosed Experimental Ecosystems & Scale: Tools for Understanding & Managing Coastal Ecosystems. Petersen, John E., ed. 2009. (Illus.). 250p. 129.00 (978-0-387-76766-6(5)) Springer.

Dickinson, Gordon & Murphy, Kevin. Ecosystems. 2nd rev. ed. 2006. (Routledge Introductions to Environment Ser.). (Illus.). XVIII, 206p. 155.00 (978-0-415-33278-1(8), RU3278X); 205p. per. 47.95 (978-0-415-33279-8(6), RU3279X) Routledge.

Dodds, W. K. & Dodds, Walter. Laws, Theories, & Patterns in Ecology. 2009. (ENG., Illus.). 256p. 50.00 (978-0-520-26040-5(6)) Univ. of California Pr.

Dodds, Walter. Laws, Theories, & Patterns in Ecology. 2009. (ENG., Illus.). 256p. pap. 22.95 (978-0-520-26041-2(4)) Univ. of California Pr.

Dogra, Kuldip Singh, et al. Impact of Invasive Plant Species. 2010. 388p. pap. (978-3-8383-6686-9(7)) Lambert Academic Publishing.

Doran, Peter T., et al, eds. Life in Antarctic Deserts & Other Cold Dry Environments: Astrobiological Analogues. 2010. (Cambridge Astrobiology Ser.). (ENG., Illus.). 320p. 112.00 (978-0-521-88919-3(7)) Cambridge Univ. Pr.

Drew, Patrick. 100 Places to Go Before They Disappear. 2011. (ENG., Illus.). 256p. 24.95 (978-1-4197-0003-3(0)) Abrams.

Driver, Patrick. Carp Ecosystem Impacts. 2008. 192p. pap. (978-3-639-07284-6(7)) VDM Verlag Dr. Mueller e.K.

Elias, Peter. Floodplains, Soils & Land Use. 2010. 168p. pap. (978-3-8383-4909-1(1)) Lambert Academic Publishing.

Evelpidou, Niki, et al, eds. Natural Heritage from East to West: Case studies from 6 EU-Countries. 2010. (ENG., Illus.). xiii, 363p. 129.00 (978-3-642-01576-2(X), 364201576X) Springer.

Fairless, Caroline. The Space Between Church & Not-Church: A Sacramental Vision for the Healing of Our Planet. 2010. (ENG.). 182p. pap. 27.99 (978-0-7618-5407-4(X)) Hamilton Bks.

Few, Roger. The Atlas of Wild Places: In Search of Earth's Last Wildernesses. (Illus.). 240p. 19.95 (978-0-89599-047-1(4), KD0003) Smithsonian Bks.

Fränzle, Otto. Ecosystem Organization of a Complex Landscape: Long-Term Research in the Bornhöved Lake District, Germany. 2008. (Ecological Studies). (Illus.). 400p. 249.00 (978-3-540-75810-5(0)) Springer.

Fraser, Nicholas C. & Sues, Hans-Dieter. Triassic Life on Land: The Great Transition. 2010. (Critical Moments & Perspectives in Earth History & Paleobiology Ser.). (ENG., Illus.). 224p. (gr. 17). 65.00 (978-0-231-13522-1(X)) Columbia Univ. Pr.

Frid, Christopher L. J. & Raffaelli, David G., eds. Ecosystem Ecology: A New Synthesis. 2010. (Ecological Reviews Ser.). (ENG., Illus.). 172p. pap. 54.99 (978-0-521-73503-2(3)) Cambridge Univ. Pr.

Gallardo, Belinda. The Mediterranean Middle Ebro Floodplain. 2010. 132p. pap. (978-3-8383-6114-7(8)) Lambert Academic Publishing.

Gange, A. C. & Brown, Vernon K. Multitrophic Interactions in Terrestrial Systems: The 36th Symposium of the British Ecological Society Royal Holloway College University of London 1995. Gange, A. C. & Brown, V. K., eds. 2009. (Symposia of the British Ecological Society Ser.). (ENG., Illus.). 460p. pap. 58.00 (978-0-521-10055-7(0)) Cambridge Univ. Pr.

Gao, Wei & Jackson, T. J. Remote Sensing & Modeling of Ecosystems for Sustainability VI: 5-6 August 2009, San Diego, California, United States. 2009. (Proceedings of SPIE Ser.). (Illus.). 346p. pap. 120.00 (978-0-8194-7744-6(3)) SPIE.

Gao, Wei & Jackson, Thomas. Remote Sensing & Modeling of Ecosystems for Sustainability VIII. 2011. (Proceedings of SPIE Ser.). 278p. pap. 90.00 (978-0-8194-8766-7(X)) SPIE.

Gao, Wei & Ustin, Susan L. Remote Sensing & Modeling of Ecosystems for Sustainability III: 14-16 August 2006, San Diego, California, USA. 2006. (Proceedings of SPIE Ser.). (Illus.). 722p. pap. 165.00 (978-0-8194-6377-7(9)) SPIE.

—Remote Sensing & Modeling of Ecosystems for Sustainability IV: 28-29 August 2007, San Diego, California, USA. 2007. (Proceedings of SPIE Ser.). (Illus.). 558p. pap. 120.00 (978-0-8194-6827-7(4)) SPIE.

Gao, Wei & Wang, Hao. Remote Sensing & Modeling of Ecosystems for Sustainability V: 13 August 2008, San Diego, California, USA. 2008. (Proceedings of SPIE Ser.). (Illus.). 354p. pap. 120.00 (978-0-8194-7303-5(0)) SPIE.

Gao, Wei, et al. Remote Sensing & Modeling of Ecosystems for Sustainability VII: 2-4 August 2010, San Diego, California, United States. 2010. (Proceedings of SPIE Ser.). (Illus.). 182p. pap. 90.00 (978-0-8194-8305-8(2)) SPIE.

Gaucher, Claudio, et al, eds. Neoproterozoic-Cambrian Tectonics, Global Change & Evolution: A Focus on South Western Gondwana. 2009. (Developments in Precambrian Geology Ser.: 16). (ENG.). 498p. 170.00 (978-0-444-53249-7(8), Elsevier Science) Elsevier Science & Technology Bks.

Gayton, Don. Okanagan Odyssey: Journeys through Terrain, Terroir & Culture, 1 vol. 2010. (ENG.). 176p. pap. (978-1-897522-81-3(9)) Rocky Mountain Bks.

Germanno, Denise M. Steppe Ecosystems: Dynamics, Land Use & Conservation. 2012. (Environmental Science, Engineering & Technology Ser.). 231p. 89.00 (978-1-61122-765-9(8)) Nova Science Pubs., Inc.

Gleason, Robert A. Literature Review & Database of Relations Between Salinity & Aquatic Biota: Applications to Bowdoin National Wildlife Refuge, Montana. 2009. (Illus.). vi, 76p. (978-1-4113-2426-8(9)) United States Geological Survey.

Greenwood, Tracey, et al. Environmental Science. 2008. (Illus.). 140p. (YA). pap. (978-1-877462-15-3(2)) BIOZONE International, Ltd.

Grime, J. Philip & Pierce, Simon. The Evolutionary Strategies That Shape Ecosystems. 7th ed. 2012. (ENG.). 264p. 149.95 (978-0-470-67481-9(4)); pap. 79.95 (978-0-470-67482-6(2)) Wiley, John & Sons, Inc. (Wiley-Blackwell).

Gunawardena, E. R. N., et al, eds. Ecosystems & Integrated Water Resources Management in South Asia. 2012. (ENG., Illus.). 320p. (C). 95.00 (978-0-415-69305-9(5), Routledge India) Taylor & Francis Group GBR. Dist: Taylor & Francis Group.

Hailemelekot, Abraham & Legesse, Dagnachew. Determination of Spatio-Temporal Differences of Water Hyacinth. 2010. 92p. pap. (978-3-639-08868-7(9)) VDM Verlag Dr. Mueller e.K.

Harris. Evolution & Paleoecology of Continental Ecosystems. 2008. 480p. pap. 85.00 (978-0-471-39303-0(7), Wiley-Liss) Wiley, John & Sons, Inc.

Hatcher, Melanie J. & Dunn, Alison M. Parasites in Ecological Communities: From Interactions to Ecosystems. 2011. (Ecology, Biodiversity & Conservation Ser.). (ENG., Illus.). 464p. 125.00 (978-0-521-88970-4(7)); pap. 60.00 (978-0-521-71822-6(8)) Cambridge Univ. Pr.

Higashi, M. & Burns, Thomas P., eds. Theoretical Studies of Ecosystems: The Network Perspective. 2009. (ENG.). 376p. pap. 51.00 (978-0-521-10583-5(8)) Cambridge Univ. Pr.

Himberg, Nina. Community-Based Ecotourism As a Sustainable Development Option. 2008. 152p. pap. (978-3-639-08839-7(5)) VDM Verlag Dr. Mueller e.K.

Hogg, Alan J., Jr., et al, eds. The Changing Environment of Northern Michigan: A Century of Science & Nature at the University of Michigan Biological Station. 2009. (ENG., Illus.). 224p. 65.00 (978-0-472-07075-6(4)); pap. 26.95 (978-0-472-05075-8(3)) Univ. of Michigan Pr.

Holt, Rinehart and Winston Staff. Environmental Science Chptr. 5: How Ecosystems Work. 4th ed. Date not set. pap. 11.20 (978-0-03-066604-9(X)) Holt McDougal.

—Environmental Science Chptr. 6: Biomes. 4th ed. Date not set. pap. 11.20 (978-0-03-066607-0(4)) Holt McDougal.

Hone, Jim. Applied Population & Community Ecology: The Case of Feral Pigs in Australia. 2012. (Conservation Science & Practice Ser.). (ENG.). 256p. 129.95 (978-0-470-65864-2(9), Wiley-Blackwell) Wiley, John & Sons, Inc.

Hornung, Thomas. The Carnian Crisis in the Tethys Realm. 2008. 252p. pap. (978-3-639-00035-1(8)) VDM Verlag Dr. Mueller e.K.

Hughes, J. Donal & Hughes, J. Donald. An Environmental History of the World: Humankind's Changing Role in the Community of Life. 2nd ed. 2009. (Illus.). 320p. 130.00 (978-0-415-48149-6(X)) Routledge.

Hughes, J. Donald. An Environmental History of the World: Humankind's Changing Role in the Community of Life. 2nd ed. 2009. (ENG., Illus.). 320p. (C). 46.95 (978-0-415-48150-2(3)) Routledge.

Jaiteh, Malanding S. Land Cover Dynamics in Miombo Ecosystems. 2008. 92p. pap. (978-3-639-03737-1(5)) VDM Verlag Dr. Mueller e.K.

Jandl, Robert, et al, eds. Soil Carbon in Sensitive European Ecosystems: From Science to Land Management. 2012. (ENG., Illus.). 296p. 129.95 (978-1-119-97001-9(6), Wiley) Wiley, John & Sons, Inc.

Jax, Kurt. Ecosystem Functioning. 2010. (Ecology, Biodiversity & Conservation Ser.). (ENG., Illus.). 286p. 120.00 (978-0-521-87953-8(1)); pap. 60.00 (978-0-521-70523-3(1)) Cambridge Univ. Pr.

Jorgensen, Erik, ed. Ecotoxicology. 2010. (ENG.). 402p. 83.95 (978-0-444-53628-0(0), Academic Pr.) Elsevier Science & Technology Bks.

Jorgensen, Sven Erik. Introduction to Systems Ecology. 2012. (Applied Ecology & Environmental Management Ser.). (ENG., Illus.). 360p. 99.95 (978-1-4398-5501-0(3), CRC Press) Taylor & Francis Group GBR. Dist: Taylor & Francis Group.

Jorgensen, Sven Erik, ed. Ecosystem Ecology. 2009. (ENG., Illus.). xi, 520p. 83.95 (978-0-444-53466-8(0), Academic Pr.) Elsevier Science & Technology Bks.

Karau, Gordon. Thinking Like an Ecosystem. 2007. 88p. per. (978-3-8364-2533-9(5)) VDM Verlag Dr. Mueller e.K.

Karem, Joseph. Native Bees & Wasps in Maine, Us. 2008. 96p. pap. (978-3-639-05624-2(8)) VDM Verlag Dr. Mueller e.K.

Kato, Sakura Y. Archaea: Structure, Habitats & Ecological Significance. 2011. (Microbiology Research Advances Ser.). 98.00 (978-1-61761-932-8(9), Nova Biomedical Bks.) Nova Science Pubs., Inc.

Klijn, Frans, ed. Ecosystem Classification for Environmental Management. 2011. (Ecology & Environment Ser.). (ENG., Illus.). 329p. pap. 389.00 (978-90-481-4420-4(5), 9048144205) Springer.

Knox, George A. Biology of the Southern Ocean. 2nd ed. 2006. (Marine Biology Ser.). (ENG., Illus.). 640p. 199.95 (978-0-8493-3394-1(6), 3394, CRC Press) Taylor & Francis Group GBR. Dist: Taylor & Francis Group.

Kozlov, Mikhail, et al. Impacts of Point Polluters on Terrestrial Biota: Comparative analysis of 18 contaminated Areas. 2009. (Environmental Pollution Ser.). (ENG.). xvii, 466p. 209.00 (978-90-481-2466-4(2), 9048124662) Springer.

Kumar, Pushpam, ed. The Economics of Ecosystems & Biodiversity: Ecological & Economic Foundations. (ENG.). 456p. (C). 2012. pap. 59.95 (978-0-415-50108-8(3)) 2010. (Illus.). 79.95 (978-1-84971-212-5(3)) Routledge.

Leeuwe, M. A. van, et al. Phaeocystis, major link in the biogeochemical cycling of climate-relevant Elements. 2011. (ENG.). vi, 330p. pap. 109.00 (978-90-481-7569-7(0), 9048175690) Springer.

Line, Mommies. ECO ACTS for Mommies. 2009. 96p. pap. 12.95 (978-0-557-05408-4(7)) Lulu Enterprises Inc.

Lisagor, Kimberly & Hansen, Heather. Disappearing Destinations: 37 Places in Peril & What Can Be Done to Help Save Them. 2008. (Vintage Departures Original Ser.). (ENG., Illus.). 400p. pap. 15.95 (978-0-307-27736-7(4), Vintage) Knopf Doubleday Publishing Group.

Lynas, Mark. The God Species: Saving the Planet in the Age of Humans. 2011. (ENG.). 288p. 25.00 (978-1-4262-0891-1(X), National Geographic) National Geographic Society.

Mackay, Richard. The Atlas of Endangered Species. rev. ed. 2008. 128p. pap. 21.95 (978-0-520-25862-4(2)) Univ. of California Pr.

MacNally, Ralph C. Ecological Versatility & Community Ecology. 2009. (Cambridge Studies in Ecology Ser.). (ENG., Illus.). 456p. pap. 48.00 (978-0-521-11926-9(X)) Cambridge Univ. Pr.

Manzoor, M. Nauman & I. Sultan, Javed. Nutritional Evaluation of Irrigated Grasses. 2011. 92p. pap. (978-3-8443-0118-2(6)) Lambert Academic Publishing.

Mayr, Floyd B., ed. Marine Protected Areas. 2010. (Oceanography & Ocean Engineering Ser.). 153p. 69.00 (978-1-60741-549-7(6)) Nova Science Pubs., Inc.

McCann, K. S., ed. From Energetics to Ecosystems: The Dynamics & Structure of Ecological Systems. 2006. (Peter Yodzis Fundamental Ecology Ser.). (ENG., Illus.). xix, 265p. 139.00 (978-1-4020-5336-8(3), 1402053363) Springer.

—The Impact of Environmental Variability on Ecological Systems. 2007. (Peter Yodzis Fundamental Ecology Ser.). (Illus.). 231p. 139.00 (978-1-4020-5850-9(0)) Springer.

McCann, Kevin. Food Webs. 2011. (Monographs in Population Biology Ser.). (ENG., Illus.). 250p. (C). 99.50 (978-0-691-13417-8(0)) Princeton Univ. Pr.

—Food Webs - A New Synthesis. 2011. (Monographs in Population Biology Ser.). (ENG., Illus.). 250p. (C). pap. 45.00 (978-0-691-13418-5(9)) Princeton Univ. Pr.

McDonald, Alison. The Historical Ecology of Some Unimproved Alluvial Grassland in the Upper Thames Valley. 2007. (ENG., Illus.). 161p. (C). pap. 95.00 (978-1-4073-0122-8(5)) British Archaeological Reports Ltd. GBR. Dist: Brown, David Bk. Co., The.

Melis, Theodore S. Effects of Three High-Flow Experiments on the Colorado River Ecosystem Downstream from Glen Canyon Dam, Arizona. 2011. (Illus.). v, 147p. (978-1-4113-3009-2(9)) United States Geological Survey.

Menezes, Ronaldo, et al, eds. Complex Networks: Results of the 1st International Workshop on Complex Networks (CompleNet 2009) 2009. (Studies in Computational Intelligence Ser.). (ENG., Illus.). xviii, 226p. 159.00 (978-3-642-01205-1(1), 3642012051) Springer.

Molosiwa, Kgomotso. Payment for Ecosystem Services. 2011. 124p. pap. (978-3-8433-8046-1(5)) Lambert Academic Publishing.

Montaggioni, Lucien F. & Braithwaite, Colin J. R. Quaternary Coral Reef Systems: History, development processes & controlling Factors. 2009. (Developments in Marine Geology Ser.: 5). (ENG.). 550p. 140.00 (978-0-444-53247-3(1), Elsevier Science) Elsevier Science & Technology Bks.

Moore, John C. & de Ruiter, Peter C. Energetic Food Webs: An analysis of real & model Ecosystems. 2012. (ENG., Illus.). 352p. 125.00 (978-0-19-856618-2(2)); pap. 59.99 (978-0-19-856619-9(0)) Oxford Univ. Pr., Inc.

Morin, Peter J. Community Ecology. 2nd ed. 2011. (ENG., Illus.). 424p. 149.95 (978-1-4443-3821-8(8)); pap. 89.95 (978-1-4051-2411-9(3)) Wiley, John & Sons, Inc. (Wiley-Blackwell).

Murray, Kim. Humanity: Threatened: 100 Species on the Verge of Extinction. 2010. (Humanity Ser.). (ENG.). 260p. pap. 19.95 (978-1-926654-08-9(0)) Patrick Bonneville Society CAN. Dist: Independent Pubs. Group.

Naeem, Shahid, et al, eds. Biodiversity, Ecosystem Functioning, & Human Wellbeing: An Ecological & Economic Perspective. 2009. (ENG., Illus.). 384p. pap. 85.00 (978-0-19-954796-8(3)) Oxford Univ. Pr., Inc.

Nagelkerken, Ivan. Ecological Connectivity among Tropical Coastal Ecosystems. 2009. (ENG., Illus.). xiii, 615p. 229.00 (978-90-481-2405-3(0), 9048124050) Springer.

National Research Council (U.S.), Committee on Earth-Atmosphere Interactions: Understanding and Responding to Multiple Environmental Stresses Staff, contrib. by. Understanding Multiple Environmental Stresses: Report of a Workshop. 2007. (ENG., Illus.). 154p. pap. 36.75 (978-0-309-10331-2(2)) National Academies Pr.

Neale, Christopher M. U. & Maltese, Antonino. Remote Sensing for Agriculture, Ecosystems, & Hydrology XI: 1-3 September 2009, Berlin, Germany. 2009. (Proceedings of SPIE Ser.). (Illus.). 476p. pap. 160.00 (978-0-8194-7777-4(X)) SPIE.

Niamir, Aidin, et al. Distribution Modelling of the Short-Toed Eagle. 2010. 80p. pap. (978-3-8383-7565-6(3)) Lambert Academic Publishing.

Ninan, K. N., ed. Conserving & Valuing Ecosystem Services & Biodiversity: Economic, Institutional & Social Challenges. (ENG., Illus.). 432p. 2010. pap. 49.95 (978-1-84971-173-9(9)) 2008. 136.50 (978-1-84407-651-2(2)) Routledge.

Noormets, Asko. Phenology of Ecosystem Processes: Applications in Global Change Research. 2009. (ENG., Illus.). x, 299p. 79.95 (978-1-4419-0025-8(X), 144190025X) Springer.

Nyhart, Lynn K. & Nyhart, L. K. Modern Nature: The Rise of the Biological Perspective in Germany. 2009. (ENG., Illus.). 440p. 45.00 (978-0-226-61089-4(6)) Univ. of Chicago Pr.

Okamoto, Ariel Rubissow & Wong, Kathleen M. Natural History of San Francisco Bay. 2011. (California Natural History Guides). (ENG., Illus.). 368p. 65.00 (978-0-520-26825-8(3)) Univ. of California Pr.

—Natural History of San Francisco Bay. 2011. (California Natural History Guides). (ENG., Illus.). 368p. pap. 24.95 (978-0-520-26826-5(1)) Univ. of California Pr.

O'Malley, Robin & H. John Heinz III Center for Science, Economics, and the Environment Staff. The State of the Nation's Ecosystems 2008: Measuring the Land, Waters, & Living Resources of the United States. 2008. (ENG., Illus.). 368p. pap. 37.50 (978-1-59726-471-6(7)) Island Pr.

—The State of the Nation's Ecosystems 2008: Measuring the Lands, Waters, & Living Resources of the United States. 2008. (ENG., Illus.). 368p. 75.00 (978-1-59726-441-9(5)) Island Pr.

Osaki, Mitsuru, et al, eds. Designing Our Future: Perspectives on Bioproduction, Ecosystems, & Humanity. 2011. (ENG., Illus.). 425p. pap. 39.00 (978-92-808-1183-4(5)) United Nations Univ. Pr. JPN. Dist: Brookings Institution Pr.

Osawa, Akira, et al, eds. Permafrost Ecosystems: Siberian Larch Forests. 2010. (Ecological Studies). (ENG., Illus.). xxvi, 502p. 249.00 (978-1-4020-9692-1(5), 1402096925) Springer.

Ostfeld, Richard S., et al, eds. Infectious Disease Ecology: Effects of Ecosystems on Disease & of Disease on Ecosystems. 2008. (ENG., Illus.). 504p. (C). 120.00 (978-0-691-12484-1(1)); per. 59.95 (978-0-691-12485-8(X)) Princeton Univ. Pr.

Ottich, Indra & Barth, Uwe. Natur vor der Haustür - Stadtnatur in Frankfurt am Main: Ergebnisse der Biotopkartierung. 2009. (GER., Illus.). 204p. (978-3-510-61393-9(7)) Schweizerbartsche, E. Verlagsbuchhandlung.

Owe, Manfred. Remote Sensing for Agriculture, Ecosystems, & Hydrology VIII: 11-13 September, 2006, Stockholm, Sweden. 2006. (Proceedings of SPIE Ser.). (Illus.). 364p. pap. 120.00 (978-0-8194-6454-5(6)) SPIE.

Owe, Manfred, et al. Remote Sensing for Agriculture, Ecosystems, & Hydrology IX: 18-20 September 2007, Florence, Italy. 2007. (Proceedings of SPIE Ser.). (Illus.). 354p. pap. 120.00 (978-0-8194-6900-7(9)) SPIE.

Owe, Manfred, et al. Remote Sensing for Agriculture, Ecosystems, & Hydrology X: 16-18 September 2008, Cardiff, Wales, United Kingdom. 2008. (Proceedings of SPIE Ser.). (Illus.). 390p. pap. 90.00 (978-0-8194-7335-6(9)) SPIE.

Pachur, Hans-Joachim & Altmann, Norbert. Die Ostsahara im Spätquartär: Ökosystemwandel im größten hyperariden Raum der Erde. 2006. (Illus.). XII, 662p. 279.00 (978-3-540-20445-9(8), 3540204458) Springer.

Paine, Timothy D., ed. Invasive Forest Insects, Introduced Forest Trees, & Altered Ecosystems: Ecological Pest Management in Global Forests of a Changing

World. 2006. (ENG., Illus.). x, 190p. 139.00 *(978-1-4020-5161-6(1)*, 1402051611) Springer.

Panel to Review California's Draft Bay Delta Conservation Plan & National Research Council. A Review of the Use of Science & Adaptive Management in California's Draft Bay Delta Conservation Plan. 2011. (ENG.). 100p. pap. 26.00 ***(978-0-309-21231-1(6))*** National Academies Pr.

Paulson, Deborah D. & Baker, William L. The Nature of Southwestern Colorado: Recognizing Human Legacies & Restoring Natural Places. 2006. (ENG., Illus.). 386p. per. 32.95 *(978-0-87081-849-3(X))* Univ. Pr. of Colorado.

Perillo, Gerardo M. E., et al, eds. Coastal Wetlands: An Integrated Ecosystem Approach. 2009. (ENG., Illus.). 974p. 170.00 *(978-0-444-53103-2(3)*, Elsevier Science) Elsevier Science & Technology Bks.

Petersen, Christine. Preserving the Living Earth. 2011. (Environment at Risk 2 Ser.). 112p. (gr. 7). 39.93 *(978-1-60870-480-4(7))* Marshall Cavendish Corp.

Petersen, John E. Enclosed Experimental Ecosystems & Scale: Tools for Understanding & Managing Coastal Ecosystems. 2009. (Illus.). x, 221p. pap. 49.95 *(978-0-387-76766-0(1)*, 0387767681) Springer.

Peterson, David A. Assessment of Ecological Conditions & Potential Effects of Water Produced from Coalbed Natural Gas Development on Biological Communities in Streams of the Powder River Structural Basin, Wyoming & Montana, 2005-08. 2010. (Illus.). vii, 64p. ***(978-1-4113-2936-2(8))*** United States Geological Survey.

Polgar, G. & Sasekumar, A., eds. Ecotourism & Flagship Species: Holistic Approaches & Higher Levels of Connectivity for Endangered Tropical Mudflats & Coastal Swamps. 2010. (Hospitality, Tourism & Marketing Studies). pap. 43.00 *(978-1-60876-691-8(8))* Nova Science Pubs., Inc.

Postali Parra, José Roberto, et al, eds. Egg Parasitoids in Agroecosystems with emphasis on Trichogramma. 2010. (Progress in Biological Control Ser.). (ENG., Illus.). 450p. 199.00 *(978-1-4020-9109-4(5)*, 1402091095) Springer.

Putnam, R. Community Ecology. 2010. (ENG.). 196p. pap. 125.00 *(978-90-481-4011-4(0)*, 9048140110) Springer.

Raffaelli, David G. & Frid, Christopher L. J., eds. Ecosystem Ecology: A New Synthesis. 2010. (Ecological Reviews Ser.). (ENG., Illus.). 172p. 130.00 *(978-0-521-51349-4(9))* Cambridge Univ. Pr.

Rafferty, John P., ed. Biomes & Ecosystems. 2011. (Living Earth Ser.). (Illus.). 240p. (YA). 103.40 *(978-1-61530-422-6(3))* Rosen Publishing Group, Inc., The.

Rakhimov, Ilgizar. Birds of Anthropogenous Landscapes. 2010. 280p. pap. *(978-3-639-23745-0(5))* VDM Verlag Dr. Mueller e.K.

Reed, Sasha. Scaling from Molecules to Ecosystems. 2009. 128p. pap. *(978-3-639-16851-8(8))* VDM Verlag Dr. Mueller e.K.

Ritchie, M. E. Scale, Heterogeneity, & the Structure & Diversity of Ecological Communities. 2009. (Monographs in Population Biology Ser.). (ENG., Illus.). 232p. (C). 78.50 *(978-0-691-09069-6(6))* Princeton Univ. Pr.

Ritchie, Mark E. Scale, Heterogeneity, & the Structure & Diversity of Ecological Communities. 2009. (Monographs in Population Biology Ser.). (ENG., Illus.). 232p. (C). pap. 37.50 *(978-0-691-09070-2(X))* Princeton Univ. Pr.

Robbins, Kalyani, ed. The Laws of Nature: Managing Ecosystems for a Sustainable Future. 2012. 250p. pap. 22.95 ***(978-1-935603-63-4(9))*** Univ. of Akron Pr., The.

Rogers, Alex D., et al, eds. Antarctic Ecosystems: An Extreme Environment in a Changing World. 2012. (ENG., Illus.). 564p. 159.95 ***(978-1-4051-9840-0(0)***, Wiley-Blackwell) Wiley, John & Sons, Inc.

Rohwer, et al. Coral Reefs in the Microbial Seas. 2010. (Illus.). 201p. pap. *(978-0-9827012-0-1(9))* Plaid Productions.

Rooney, N., et al. From Energetics to Ecosystems: the Dynamics & Structure of Ecological Systems: The Dynamics & Structure of Ecological Systems. 2010. (Peter Yodzis Fundamental Ecology Ser.). xix, 265p. pap. 139.00 *(978-90-481-7347-1(7)*, 9048173477) Springer.

Rundel, Philip W., et al, eds. Landscape Disturbance & Biodiversity in Mediterranean-Type Ecosystems. 2010. (Ecological Studies). (Illus.). xxv, 447p. pap. 319.00 *(978-3-642-08416-4(8)*, 3642084168) Springer.

Ruth, Matthias & Davidsdottir, Brynhildur, eds. Changing Stocks, Flows & Behaviors in Industrial Ecosystems. 2009. (Illus.). 168p. 119.00 *(978-1-84720-740-1(5))* Elgar, Edward Publishing, Inc.

Ryan, James M. Adirondack Wildlife: A Field Guide. 2009. (ENG., Illus.). 296p. pap. 24.95 *(978-1-58465-749-1(9))* Univ. Pr. of New England.

Sabater, Marlowe & Tulafono, Ray. American Samoa Archipelagic Fishery Ecosystem Report. 2011. (Illus.). 31p. 0.00 net. ***(978-1-934061-49-7(2))*** Western Pacific Fishery Management Council.

Salman, Aneel. A Coastal Ecosystem & a People in Peril. 2011. 232p. pap. ***(978-3-8454-0056-3(0))*** Lambert Academic Publishing.

Sangster, Alan J. Warming to Ecocide: A Thermodynamic Diagnosis. 2011. (ENG., Illus.). xvii, 338p. 169.00 ***(978-0-85729-925-3(5)***, 0857299255) Springer.

Sayre, Roger. A New Map of Standardized Terrestrial Ecosystems of the Conterminous United States. 2009. (Illus.). iv, 17p. *(978-1-4113-2432-9(3))* United States Geological Survey.

Scheffer, M. & Scheffer, Marten. Critical Transitions in Nature & Society. 2009. (Princeton Studies in Complexity Ser.). (ENG., Illus.). 400p. (C). 99.50 *(978-0-691-12203-8(2))*; pap. 46.95 *(978-0-691-12204-5(0))* Princeton Univ. Pr.

Schilthuizen, Menno. The Loom of Life: Unravelling Ecosystems. 2008. (Illus.). 220p. 79.95 *(978-3-540-68051-2(9))* Springer.

Schmitz, Oswald J. Resolving Ecosystem Complexity. 2010. (Monographs in Population Biology Ser.). (ENG., Illus.). 176p. (C). pap. 35.00 *(978-0-691-12649-8(9))* Princeton Univ. Pr.

Schmitz, Roger. Ecological Models & Dynamics: An Interactive Textbook. 2008. (Illus.). cd-rom 55.00 *(978-0-8153-4426-1(0)*, Garland Science) Taylor & Francis Group.

Seth, C. S. Mechanisms of Cadmium Phtoextraction in Indian Mustard. 2011. 124p. pap. ***(978-3-8443-2384-9(8))*** Lambert Academic Publishing.

Shanmuganathan, Subana. Soft Systems. 2008. 284p. pap. *(978-3-639-06754-5(1))* VDM Verlag Dr. Mueller e.K.

Shattuck, Terri. The Influence of Bioirrigation. 2010. 120p. pap. *(978-3-8383-6768-2(5))* Lambert Academic Publishing.

Sivaperuman, C. Faunal Ecology & Conservation of the Great Indian Desert. 2008. (ENG., Illus.). xviii, 222p. 199.00 *(978-3-540-87408-9(9)*, 3540874089) Springer.

Sodhi, Navjot S., et al. Conservation of Tropical Birds. 2011. (ENG., Illus.). 312p. 134.95 *(978-1-4443-3482-1(4)*, Wiley-Blackwell) Wiley, John & Sons, Inc.

Sperduto, Daniel D. & Kimball, Ben. The Nature of New Hampshire: Natural Communities of the Granite State. 2011. (Illus.). 360p. pap. 29.95 *(978-1-58465-898-6(3))* Univ. Pr. of New England.

Stefels, J., et al, eds. Phaeocystis, major link in the biogeochemical cycling of climate-relevant Elements. 2007. (ENG.). vi, 330p. 109.00 *(978-1-4020-6213-1(3)*, 1402062133) Springer.

Stolzenburg, William. Where the Wild Things Were: Life, Death, & Ecological Wreckage in a Land of Vanishing Predators. (ENG.). 304p. 2009. pap. 16.00 *(978-1-59691-624-1(9))* 2008. 24.99 *(978-1-59691-299-1(5))* Bloomsbury Publishing.

Sukhovolski, V. G., et al. Optmizatsionnye Modeli Mezhpopuliatsionnykh Vzaimodeistvii. 2008. (RUS., Illus.). 161p. *(978-5-02-023260-0(2))* Nauka.

Thompson, Ruthanne, et al. The Scope of Biology: From Cells to Ecosystems. rev. ed. 2010. (ENG.). 162p. spiral bd. 40.57 *(978-0-7575-4428-6(2))* Kendall Hunt Publishing Co.

Tiezzi, E., et al, eds. Ecosytems & Sustainable Development VI. 2007. (WIT Transactions on Ecology & the Environment Ser.: 106). (Illus.). 592p. 385.00 *(978-1-84564-088-0(8))* WIT Pr GBR. Dist: WIT Pr.

Van Auken, O W, ed. Western North American Juniperus Communities: A Dynamic Vegetation Type. 2007. (Ecological Studies: Vol. 196). (Illus.). 311p. 129.00 *(978-0-387-34002-9(5))* Springer.

Vasseur, D. A. & McCann, K. S. The Impact of Environmental Variability on Ecological Systems. 2010. (Peter Yodzis Fundamental Ecology Ser.). xiii, 231p. pap. 139.00 *(978-90-481-7457-7(0)*, 9048174570) Springer.

Verde, Cinzia & di Prisco, Guido, eds. Adaptation & Evolution in Marine Environments Vol. 1: The Impacts of Global Change on Biodiversity. 2012. (From Pole to Pole Ser.). (ENG., Illus.). xxiv, 222p. 129.00 ***(978-3-642-27351-3(3)***, 3642273513) Springer.

—Adaptation & Evolution in Marine Environments, Vol 2: The Impacts of Global Change on Biodiversity. 2012. (From Pole to Pole Ser.). (ENG.). 200p. 139.00 ***(978-3-642-27348-3(3)***, 3642273483) Springer.

Verhoef, Herman A. & Morin, Peter J., eds. Community Ecology: Processes, Models, & Applications. 2010. (ENG., Illus.). 288p. 104.95 *(978-0-19-922897-3(3))*; pap. 59.95 *(978-0-19-922898-0(1))* Oxford Univ. Pr., Inc.

Wahl, Martin. Marine Hard Bottom Communities: Patterns, Dynamics, Diversity, & Change. 2009. (Ecological Studies). (ENG., Illus.). xxiv, 445p. 269.00 *(978-3-540-92703-7(4)*, 3540927034) Springer.

Wantzen, Karl M., et al, eds. Ecological Effects of Water-level Fluctuations in Lakes. 2010. (Developments in Hydrobiology Ser.). (ACE.). 184p. pap. 189.00 *(978-90-481-8088-2(0)*, 9048180880) Springer.

Wantzen, Karl Matthias. Ecological Effects of Water-Level Fluctuations in Lakes. 2008. (Developments in Hydrobiology Ser.). (Illus.). vi, 184p. 189.00 *(978-1-4020-9191-9(5))* Springer.

Weathers, Kathie C., et al, eds. Fundamentals of Ecosystem Science. 2012. (ENG.). 464p. (C). pap. 69.95 *(978-0-12-088774-3(6)*, Academic Pr.) Elsevier Science & Technology Bks.

Webb, Robert H., et al, eds. The Mojave Desert: Ecosystem Processes & Sustainability. 2009. (ENG., Illus.). 528p. 65.00 *(978-0-87417-776-3(6))* Univ. of Nevada Pr.

Weisser, Wolfgang W. & Siemann, Evan, eds. Insects & Ecosystem Function. 2007. (Ecological Studies). (Illus.). 413p. per. 119.00 *(978-3-540-74003-2(1))* Springer.

Wells, Troth & Henderson, Caspar. Our Fragile World: The Beauty of a Planet under Pressure. 2006. (ENG., Illus.). 192p. 39.95 *(978-1-904456-21-6(9))* New Internationalist Pubns., Ltd. GBR. Dist: Consortium Bk. Sales & Distribution.

Whitaker, John O., Jr., et al, eds. Habitats & Ecological Communities of Indiana: Pre-settlement to Present. 2012. (Indiana Natural Science Ser.). (ENG., Illus.). 448p. 35.00 *(978-0-253-35602-4(4)*, 0253356024) Indiana Univ. Pr.

Whitefield, Patrick. The Living Landscape: How to Read It & Understand It. 2010. (ENG., Illus.). 360p. pap. 37.95 *(978-1-85623-043-8(0))* Permanent Pubns. GBR. Dist: Chelsea Green Publishing.

Wieder, R. Kelman & Vitt, Dale H. Boreal Peatland Ecosystems. 2006. (Ecological Studies). (Illus.). xx, 444p. 249.00 *(978-3-540-31912-2(3)*, 3540319123) Springer.

Williams, Gina S. Mediterranean Ecosystems: Dynamics, Management & Conservation. 2011. (Earth Sciences in the 21st Century Ser.). 129.00 *(978-1-61209-146-4(6))* Nova Science Pubs., Inc.

World Resources Institute Staff, contrib. by. Nature's Benefits in Kenya: An Atlas of Ecosystems & Human Well-Being. 2007. (Illus.). xii, 148p. *(978-1-56973-642-5(1))* World Resources Institute.

Wright, Harold D. National Coastal Conditions & Estuary Reports (with DVD) 2011. (Series: Environmental Science, Engineering & Technology Ser.). 295.00 *(978-1-61122-468-9(3))* Nova Science Pubs., Inc.

Yanick Jr. Nd Cnc Cqm, Paul. Quorum Superhealing. 2009. 240p. 34.95 *(978-1-4269-1681-6(7))* Trafford Publishing.

Yin, Runsheng, ed. An Integrated Assessment of China's Ecological Restoration Programs. 2009. (ENG., Illus.). xvi, 471p. 169.00 *(978-90-481-2654-5(1)*, 9048126541) Springer.

BIOTIC DIVERSITY
see Biodiversity

BIOTITE-GRANITE
see Mica

BIOTOLERANCE
see Biocompatibility

BIPOLAR DISORDER
see Manic-Depressive Illness

BIRACIAL CHILDREN
see Children of Interracial Marriage

BIRACIAL MINORITIES
see Racially Mixed People

BIRCH-BARK CANOES
see Indians of North America—Boats

BIRD, ISABELLA L. (ISABELLA LUCY), 1831-1904

Bird, Isabella. Among the Tibetans. 2010. (Cambridge Library Collection - Travel & Exploration Ser.). (ENG.). 168p. pap. 19.99 *(978-1-108-01472-4(0))* Cambridge Univ. Pr.

—Lady's Life in the Rocky Mountains. 2009. (Stanfords Travel Classics Ser.). 192p. pap. 10.95 *(978-1-906780-08-1(0))* Beaufoy, John Publishing GBR. Dist: Midpoint Trade Bks., Inc.

Bird, Isabella L. Among the Tibetans. 2008. (Illus.). 84p. pap. *(978-1-4099-1426-6(7))*; (ENG.). 68p. per. *(978-1-4065-9203-0(X))* Dodo Pr.

—Among the Tibetans. 2008. (ENG.). 72p. pap. 7.45 *(978-1-4385-0382-0(2))*; pap. 7.95 *(978-1-4385-0888-7(3))* Standard Pubns., Inc. (Book Jungle).

—The Englishwoman in America. 2009. (Cambridge Library Collection - History Ser.). 476p. pap. 35.99 *(978-1-108-00384-1(2))* Cambridge Univ. Pr.

—The Englishwoman in America. 2008. (ENG.). 312p. per. *(978-1-4065-9204-7(8))* Dodo Pr.

—A Lady's Life in the Rocky Mountains. 2009. 328p. 25.99 *(978-1-103-72779-7(6))*; pap. 19.99 *(978-1-103-72778-0(8))* BiblioBazaar.

—A Lady's Life in the Rocky Mountains. 2009. (Cambridge Library Collection - History Ser.). (ENG.). 328p. pap. 28.99 *(978-1-108-00383-4(4))* Cambridge Univ. Pr.

—A Lady's Life in the Rocky Mountains. 2008. (ENG.). 176p. per. *(978-1-4065-9207-8(2))* Dodo Pr.

—A Lady's Life in the Rocky Mountains. 2009. 180p. pap. 12.95 *(978-1-4385-2834-2(5)*, Book Jungle) Standard Pubns., Inc.

—My First Travels in North America. 2010. (ENG.). 400p. pap. 14.95 *(978-0-486-47309-3(0))* Dover Pubns., Inc.

—Unbeaten Tracks in Japan. 2008. (ENG.). 292p. per. *(978-1-4065-9205-4(6))* Dodo Pr.

—Unbeaten Tracks in Japan. 2008. (ENG.). 300p. pap. 13.95 *(978-1-4385-1262-4(7)*, Book Jungle) Standard Pubns., Inc.

Bird, Isabella Lucy. Unbeaten Tracks in Japan. 2008. 356p. 29.99 *(978-0-554-36081-2(0))*; 31.99 *(978-0-554-26778-4(0))* BiblioBazaar.

—Unbeaten Tracks in Japan. 2009. 298p. pap. *(978-0-217-41340-4(4))* Books LLC.

—Unbeaten Tracks in Japan: An Account of Travels in the Interior, Including Visits to the Aborigines of Yezo & the Shrines of Nikka & Isè. 2010. (Cambridge Library Collection - Travel & Exploration Ser.). (ENG., Illus.). 404p. pap. 31.99 *(978-1-108-01463-2(1))* Cambridge Univ. Pr.

—Unbeaten Tracks in Japan: Volume 1: An Account of Travels in the Interior, Including Visits to the Aborigines of Yezo & the Shrines of Nikka & Isè. 2010. (Cambridge Library Collection - Travel & Exploration Ser.). (ENG., Illus.). 432p. pap. 32.99 *(978-1-108-01462-5(3))* Cambridge Univ. Pr.

Mayhan, Maggie. Isabella Bird: Liminal Performances. 2009. 88p. pap. *(978-3-639-16640-8(X))* VDM Verlag Dr. Mueller e.K.

Root, Robert L. Following Isabella: Travels in Colorado Then & Now. 2009. (ENG.). 288p. pap. 19.95 *(978-0-8061-4018-6(6))* Univ. of Oklahoma Pr.

Stoddart, Anna M. The Life of Isabella Bird. 2011. (Cambridge Library Collection - Travel & Exploration Ser.). (ENG., Illus.). 516p. pap. 37.99 *(978-1-108-02896-7(9))* Cambridge Univ. Pr.

BIRD, LARRY, 1956-

Bird, Larry, et al. When the Game Was Ours. (ENG., Illus.). 2010. 368p. pap. 15.95 *(978-0-547-39458-9(6)*, Mariner Bks.) 2009. 352p. 26.00 *(978-0-547-22547-0(4))* Houghton Mifflin Harcourt Trade & Reference Pubs.

Connelly, Michael P. Rebound! Basketball, Busing, Larry Bird, & the Rebirth of Boston. 2008. (ENG., Illus.). 304p. 25.00 *(978-0-7603-3501-7(X)*, 076033501X, MVP Bks.) MBI Publishing Co. LLC.

May, Peter. The Big Three. 2007. (ENG., Illus.). 288p. pap. 19.95 *(978-1-4165-5207-9(3))* Simon & Schuster.

BIRD, ROBERT MONTGOMERY, 1806-1854

Foust, Clement E. The Life & Dramatic Works of Robert Montgomery Bird. 2007. (ENG.). 744p. per. 51.95 *(978-0-548-64530-7(2))* Kessinger Publishing, LLC.

BIRD ATTRACTING
see also Bird Feeders

Baker, Jerry. Jerry Baker's Backyard Bird Feeding Bonanza: 1,487 Tips, Tricks, & Treats for Attracting Your Fine-Feathered Friends. 2006. (Jerry Baker's Good Gardening Ser.). (ENG., Illus.). 384p. 29.95 *(978-0-922433-57-5(7))* Baker, Jerry.

—Jerry Baker's Backyard Birdscaping Bonanza: 1,046 Quick-and-Easy Ways to Make Your Yard Absolutely Irresistible to Birds. 2008. (Jerry Baker Good Flower Gardening & Birding Ser.). (ENG., Illus.). 384p. 29.95 *(978-0-922433-88-9(7))* Baker, Jerry.

Burton, Robert & Dorling Kindersley Publishing Staff. Audubon North American Birdfeeder Guide. 2009. (ENG.). 224p. (gr. 12). pap. 14.95 *(978-0-7566-5883-0(7))* Dorling Kindersley Publishing, Inc.

Fenimore, Bill. Backyard Birds of North Carolina: How to Identify & Attract the Top 25 Birds. 2009. *(978-1-4236-0644-4(2))* Gibbs Smith, Publisher.

—Backyard Birds of Ohio: How to Identify & Attract the Top 25 Birds. 2009. *(978-1-4236-0645-1(0))* Gibbs Smith, Publisher.

—Backyard Birds of Wisconsin: How to Identify & Attract the Top 25 Birds. 2009. *(978-1-4236-0646-8(9))* Gibbs Smith, Publisher.

Frischmann, Carol. Attracting & Feeding Backyard Birds, 1 vol. 2007. (Animal Planet Pet Care Library). (ENG., Illus.). 112p. 11.95 *(978-0-7938-3786-1(3))* TFH Pubns., Inc.

Green, Jen. The Illustrated Practical Guide to Attracting & Feeding Backyard Birds: The Complete Book of Bird Feeders, Bird Tables, Birdbaths, Nest Boxes & Backyard Birdwatching. 2009. (ENG.). 256p. 35.00 *(978-0-7548-1989-9(2))* Anness Publishing GBR. Dist: National Bk. Network.

Loggins, George & Cool Springs Press Publications Staff. Build Your Own Backyard Birdhouses & Feeders. 2011. (Backyard Birding Ser.). (ENG., Illus.). 96p. pap. 12.99 *(978-1-59186-011-2(3)*, 1591860113) Cool Springs Pr.

Martin, Deborah L. The Secrets of Backyard Bird-Feeding Success: Hundreds of Surefire Tips for Attracting & Feeding Your Favorite Birds. 2011. (ENG., Illus.). 320p. pap. 22.99 *(978-1-60529-130-7(7))* Rodale Pr., Inc.

Martin, Deborah L. & Koch, Arlene. Secrets of Backyard Bird-Feeding Success: Hundreds of Surefire Tips for Attracting & Feeding Your Favorite Birds. 2011. *(978-1-60529-131-4(5))* Rodale Pr., Inc.

Martin, Deborah L. & Rodale Garden Books Editors. Best-Ever Backyard Birding Tips: Hundreds of Easy Ways to Attract the Birds You Love to Watch. 2008. (ENG., Illus.). 384p. pap. 21.99 *(978-1-59486-831-3(X))* Rodale Pr., Inc.

O'Sullivan, Oran & Wilson, Jim. Ireland's Garden Birds: How to Identify, Attract, & Garden for Birds. 2009. (ENG., Illus.). 192p. pap. 31.95 *(978-1-905172-73-3(7))* Collins Pr., The IRL. Dist: Dufour Editions, Inc.

Petersen, C. J. Popular Mechanics How to Charm a Bird: Create a Backyard Haven with Bird Houses, Baths, & Feeders. Popular Mechanics Press Editors, ed. 2010. (ENG., Illus.). 176p. pap. 9.95 *(978-1-58816-720-0(8))* Hearst Communications, Inc.

Roth, Sally. Attracting Songbirds to Your Backyard. 2012. (ENG., Illus.). 352p. pap. 22.99 ***(978-1-60961-754-7(1))*** Rodale Pr., Inc.

—Attracting Songbirds to Your Backyard: Hundreds of Easy Ways to Bring the Music & Beauty of Songbirds to Your Yard. 2012. ***(978-1-60961-753-0(3))*** Rodale Pr., Inc.

—The Backyard Bird Lover's Field Guide: Secrets to Attracting, Identifying, & Enjoying Birds of Your Region. 2007. (ENG., Illus.). 352p. pap. 21.99 *(978-1-59486-602-9(3))* Rodale Pr., Inc.

—Backyard Bird Secrets for Every Season: Attract a Variety of Nesting, Feeding, & Singing Birds Year-Round. 2009. (ENG.). pap. 15.50 *(978-1-60529-666-1(X))*; (ENG., Illus.). 352p. pap. 21.95 *(978-1-59486-911-2(1))*; *(978-1-59486-910-5(3))* Rodale Pr., Inc.

—Bird-by-Bird Gardening: The Ultimate Guide to Bringing in Your Favorite Birds — Year after Year. 2009. (ENG., Illus.). 384p. pap. 19.95 *(978-1-60529-825-2(5))* Rodale Pr., Inc.

Rowinski, Kate. The Joy of Birding: A Beginner's Guide. 2011. (Joy of Ser.). (ENG., Illus.). 256p. pap. 14.95 *(978-1-61608-122-5(8)*, 608122) Skyhorse Publishing Co., Inc.

Schmauss, Anne, et al. For the Birds: A Month-by-Month Guide to Attracting Birds to Your Backyard. 2008. (ENG., Illus.). 224p. pap. 21.95 *(978-1-58479-717-3(7))* Stewart, Tabori & Chang.

Thompson III, Bill. Identifying & Feeding Birds. 2010. (Peterson Field Guides/Bird Watcher's Digest Backyard Bird Guides). (ENG., Illus.). 256p. pap. 14.95 *(978-0-618-90444-0(1))* Houghton Mifflin Harcourt Trade & Reference Pubs.

Wild about Birds: The DNR Bird Feeding Guide. 278p. pap. 40.00 *(978-0-7881-2921-6(X))* DIANE Publishing Co.

Zemaitis, Louise, et al. National Geographic Backyard Guide to the Birds of North America. 2011. (National Geographic Backyard Guides). (ENG., Illus.). 256p. pap. 18.95 *(978-1-4262-0720-4(4)*, National Geographic) National Geographic Society.

Zickefoose, Julie & Bird Watcher's Digest Staff. Backyard Birding: Using Natural Gardening to Attract Birds. 2011. (ENG., Illus.). 256p. pap. 14.95 *(978-1-61608-266-6(6)*, 608266) Skyhorse Publishing Co., Inc.

BIRD BANDING

Schmidt, Paul R. Report of the Federal Advisory Committee on the Bird Banding Laboratory. 2008. *(978-1-4113-2032-1(8))* United States Geological Survey.

Smith, Walter Post. Kiptopeke Chronicles. 2009. 228p. pap. 14.50 *(978-1-59330-571-0(0))* Aventine Pr.

BIRD CALLS
see Birdsongs

BIRD CONTROL
Sanger, Margaret. The Selected Papers of Margaret Sanger: Volume 2: Birth Control Comes of Age, 1928-1939. Katz, Esther et al, eds. 2007. (Illus.). 592p. 67.00 *(978-0-252-03137-3(7))* Univ. of Illinois Pr.

BIRD CULTURE
see Aviculture

BIRD DOGS
see also Pointing Dogs; Retrievers
Brown, William F. & Hochwalt, Albert Frederick. Albert Frederick: A Biography. 2011. 430p. 56.95 ***(978-1-258-06355-9(7))*** Literary Licensing, LLC.
Eckhoff, Christopher. Following the Scent: Bird Dogs, Their Handlers, & Field Trialing. 2010. 200p. (ENG.). 24.99 *(978-1-4490-8701-2(9))*; pap. 14.49 *(978-1-4490-8700-5(0))* AuthorHouse.
Falk, John R. The Complete Guide to Bird Dog Training. 2006. (ENG., Illus.). 288p. per. 16.95 *(978-1-59228-855-7(3)*, Lyons Pr.) Globe Pequot Pr., The.
Sansom, Andrew. Scout, the Christmas Dog. 2006. (ENG., Illus.). 32p. 12.95 *(978-1-58544-562-2(2))* Texas A&M Univ. Pr.

BIRD FEEDERS
Baker, Jerry. Jerry Baker's Backyard Bird Feeding Bonanza: 1,487 Tips, Tricks, & Treats for Attracting Your Fine-Feathered Friends. 2006. (Jerry Baker's Good Gardening Ser.). (ENG., Illus.). 384p. 29.95 *(978-0-922433-57-5(7))* Baker, Jerry.
Barquest, G., et al. Birdhouses & Feeders. 2007. (Dover Woodworking Ser.). (ENG., Illus.). 48p. per. 5.95 *(978-0-486-46046-8(0))* Dover Pubns., Inc.
Birds and Blooms Editors. For the Birds: Easy-to-Make Recipes for Your Feathered Friends. 2010. (ENG.). 120p. (gr. 12). spiral bd. 9.95 *(978-1-60652-131-1(4))* Reader's Digest Assn., Inc., The.
Burton, Robert & Kress, Stephen. The Audubon Backyard Birdwatcher: Birdfeeders & Bird Gardens. 2012. (ENG., Illus.). 384p. pap. 19.95 ***(978-1-60710-404-9(0)**, Thunder Bay Pr.)* Advantage Pubs. Group.
Craven, Scott, et al. Bird Feeding — Tips for Beginners & Veterans. 2008. (Illus.). 12p. pap. 5.00 *(978-0-9801401-2-5(9))* Univ. of Wisconsin-Extension.
Green, Jen. How to Make 40 Beautiful Bird Boxes, Feeders & Birdbaths: Attract Birds to Your Farden by Creating Nesting Sites & Feeding Stations, Illustrated with 380 Photographs. 2010. (ENG., Illus.). 128p. pap. 17.99 *(978-1-84476-915-5(1))* Anness Publishing GBR. Dist: National Bk. Network.
Loggins, George & Cool Springs Press Publications Staff. Build Your Own Backyard Birdhouses & Feeders. 2011. (Backyard Birding Ser.). (ENG., Illus.). 96p. pap. 12.99 *(978-1-59186-011-2(3)*, 1591860113) Cool Springs Pr.
Martin, Deborah L. The Secrets of Backyard Bird-Feeding Success: Hundreds of Surefire Tips for Attracting & Feeding Your Favorite Birds. 2011. (ENG., Illus.). 320p. pap. 22.99 *(978-1-60529-130-7(7))* Rodale Pr., Inc.
Martin, Deborah L. & Koch, Arlene. Secrets of Backyard Bird-Feeding Success: Hundreds of Surefire Tips for Attracting & Feeding Your Favorite Birds. 2011. *(978-1-60529-131-4(5))* Rodale Pr., Inc.
Meisel, Paul. Bird-Friendly Nest Boxes & Feeders: 12 Easy-to-Build Designs that Attract Birds to Your Yard. 2012. (ENG., Illus.). 112p. pap. 14.95 ***(978-1-56523-692-9(0))*** Fox Chapel Publishing Co., Inc.
—Wild & Wacky Birdhouses & Feeders. 2012. (ENG., Illus.). 152p. pap. 19.95 ***(978-1-56523-679-0(3))*** Fox Chapel Publishing Co., Inc.
Roth, Sally. The Backyard Bird: More Than 200 Easy Ideas & Projects for Attracting & Feeding Your Favorite Birds. 2010. *(978-1-60529-520-6(5))* Rodale Pr., Inc.
—The Backyard Bird Lover's Ultimate How-to Guide: More Than 200 Easy Ideas & Projects for Attracting & Feeding Your Favorite Birds. 2010. (ENG., Illus.). 320p. pap. 21.99 *(978-1-60529-519-0(1))* Rodale Pr., Inc.
—Backyard Bird Secrets for Every Season: Attract a Variety of Nesting, Feeding, & Singing Birds Year-Round. 2009. (ENG.). pap. 15.50 *(978-1-60529-666-1(X))*; (ENG., Illus.). 352p. pap. 21.95 *(978-1-59486-911-2(1))*; *(978-1-59486-910-5(3))* Rodale Pr., Inc.
Wild about Birds: The DNR Bird Feeding Guide. 278p. pap. 40.00 *(978-0-7881-2921-6(X))* DIANE Publishing Co.
Zickefoose, Julie & Bird Watcher's Digest Staff. Backyard Birding: Using Natural Gardening to Attract Birds. 2011. (ENG., Illus.). 256p. pap. 14.95 *(978-1-61608-266-6(6)*, 608266) Skyhorse Publishing Co., Inc.

BIRD FLIGHT
see Birds—Flight

BIRD-HOUSES
see Birdhouses

BIRD HUNTING
see Fowling

BIRD NAMES
see Birds—Nomenclature

BIRD NAVIGATION
Stratton-Porter, Gene. Homing with the Birds: The History of a Lifetime of Personal Experience with the Birds. 32.95 *(978-0-8488-1449-6(5))* Amereon LTD.
—Homing with the Birds: The History of a Lifetime of Personal Experience with the Birds. 2008. 398p. 49.95 *(978-1-4365-9180-5(5))* 2007. 400p. per. 34.95 *(978-0-548-80308-0(0))* Kessinger Publishing, LLC.
Wallraff, Hans G. Avian Navigation: Pigeon Homing as a Paradigm: Pigeon Homing as a Paradigm. 2010. (ENG., Illus.). xii, 229p. pap. 189.00 *(978-3-642-06118-9(4)*, 3642061184) Springer.

BIRD PESTS
see also Birds of Prey
Scoones, Ian. Avian Influenza: Science, Policy & Politics. 2010. (Pathways to Sustainability Ser.). (ENG., Illus.). 288p. 125.00 *(978-1-84971-095-4(3))* Routledge.
Scoones, Ian, ed. Avian Influenza: Science, Policy & Politics. 2010. (Pathways to Sustainability Ser.). (ENG., Illus.). 288p. pap. 39.95 *(978-1-84971-096-1(1))* Routledge.
Wild, Dennis. The Double-Crested Cormorant: Symbol of Ecological Conflict. 2012. E-Book ***(978-0-472-02812-2(X))***; (ENG.). 274p. 27.95 ***(978-0-472-11763-5(7))*** Univ. of Michigan Pr.

BIRD PHOTOGRAPHY
see Photography of Birds

BIRD POPULATIONS
Beyond Mayfield: Studies in Avian Biology No. 34. 2007. (Studies in Avian Biology: 34). per. 18.00 *(978-0-943610-76-4(1))* American Ornithologists Union.
Bildstein, Keith L. Migrating Raptors of the World: Their Ecology & Conservation. 2006. (Illus.). 320p. 35.00 *(978-0-8014-4179-0(X))* Cornell Univ. Pr.
Bradley, Patricia E. & Norton, Robert L. An Inventory of Breeding Seabirds of the Caribbean. 2009. (ENG., Illus.). 448p. 75.00 *(978-0-8130-3329-7(2))* Univ. Pr. of Florida.
Cadman, Michael D. Atlas of the Breeding Birds of Ontario, 2001-2005. 2009. (ENG., Illus.). 728p. 92.50 *(978-1-896059-15-0(5))* Federation of Ontario Naturalists CAN. Dist: Firefly Bks., Ltd.
Ellison, Walter G., ed. Second Atlas of the Breeding Birds of Maryland & the District of Columbia. 2010. (ENG., Illus.). 520p. (gr. 17). 75.00 *(978-0-8018-9576-0(6))* Johns Hopkins Univ. Pr.
Forsman, Eric D. Population Demography of Northern Spotted Owls: Published for the Cooper Ornithological Society. 2011. (Studies in Avian Biology Ser.). (ENG., Illus.). 118p. 39.95 *(978-0-520-27008-4(8))* Univ. of California Pr.
Griesser, Michael & Barnaby, Jonathan, eds. The Role of Nepotism, Cooperation & Competition in the Avian Families. 2010. (Birds - Evolution, Behavior & Ecology Ser.). pap. 43.00 *(978-1-60876-867-7(8))* Nova Science Pubs., Inc.
Kirkpatrick, Roy L. Comparative Influence of Nutrition on Reproduction & Survival of Wild Birds & Mammals - An Overview. 60p. pap. 5.50 *(978-0-912229-17-1(9))* Kleberg, Caesar Wildlife Research Institute.
Payevsky, Vladimir. Songbird Demography: Demographic structure, survival rates, & population dynamics of songbirds with particular reference to the birds of the Eastern Baltic. Griffiths, Martin, ed. 2009. 260p. 147.50 *(978-954-642-470-9(6))* Pensoft Pubs. BGR. Dist: Coronet Bks.
Ribic, Christine A., et al. Video Surveillance of Nesting Birds. 2012. ***(978-0-520-27313-9(3))*** Univ. of California Pr.
Schneider, Todd M., et al, eds. The Breeding Bird Atlas of Georgia. 2010. (ENG., Illus.). 520p. 64.95 *(978-0-8203-2893-5(6))* Univ. of Georgia Pr.

BIRD-SONG
see Birdsongs

BIRD SONGS
see Birdsongs

BIRD WATCHING
Alderfer, Jonathan, et al. National Geographic Birding Essentials: All the Tools, Techniques, & Tips You Need to Begin & Become a Better Birder. 2007. (ENG., Illus.). 224p. pap. 15.95 *(978-1-4262-0135-6(4)*, National Geographic) National Geographic Society.
Anderson, Ora E. Out of the Woods: A Bird Watcher's Year. Griffith, Deborah, ed. 2007. (Illus.). 184p. 28.95 *(978-0-8214-1741-6(X))*; per. 16.95 *(978-0-8214-1742-3(8))* Ohio Univ. Pr.
Arbour, Claude. Choosing Wildness: My Life among the Ospreys, 1 vol. Irving, Joan, tr. from FRE. 2008. (ENG.). 256p. pap. 22.95 *(978-1-55365-297-7(5)*, Greystone Bks.) D&M Pubs. Inc. CAN. Dist: Perseus-PGW.
Arlott, Norman & Taylor, Moss. Identifying Birds by Colour. 2008. (ENG., Illus.). 256p. pap. 29.95 *(978-0-00-720679-7(8))* HarperCollins Pubs. Ltd. GBR. Dist: Independent Pubs. Group.
Audubon Minnesota, creator. The Great River Birding Trail Guide: A Guide to Great Birding on the Mississippi River from the Headwaters Tp the Iowa Border. 2007. (Audubon Field Guide Ser.). (Illus.). 103p. per. 12.95 *(978-0-9787908-2-0(0))* Audubon Minnesota.
—The Minnesota River Valley Birding Trail: A Guide to Great Birding along the Minnesota River. 2007. (Audubon Birding Guides). (Illus.). 142p. per. 12.95 *(978-0-9787908-1-3(2))* Audubon Minnesota.
—The North Shore Birding Trail: A Guide to Birding Minnesota's North Shore of Lake Superior from Duluth to Grand Portage. 2007. (Illus.). 64p. per. 9.95 *(978-0-9787908-0-6(4))* Audubon Minnesota.
Baker, Jerry. Jerry Baker's Backyard Bird Feeding Bonanza: 1,487 Tips, Tricks, & Treats for Attracting Your Fine-Feathered Friends. 2006. (Jerry Baker's Good Gardening Ser.). (ENG., Illus.). 384p. 29.95 *(978-0-922433-57-5(7))* Baker, Jerry.
Barber, Lynn E. Extreme Birder: One Woman's Big Year. 2011. (Illus.). 288p. pap. 29.95 *(978-1-60344-261-9(8))* Texas A&M Univ. Pr.
Beletsky, Les. Global Birding: Traveling the World in Search of Birds. 2010. (Illus.). 320p. 35.00 *(978-1-4262-0640-5(2)*, National Geographic) National Geographic Society.
Booth, Anita K. Find 'em Fast Birding Guide. 2006. 80p. 7.95 *(978-0-9748702-3-6(4))* AKB Design.
Boyle, William J. The Birds of New Jersey: Status & Distribution. 2011. (ENG., Illus.). 320p. (C). 55.00 *(978-0-691-14409-2(5))*; pap. 24.95 *(978-0-691-14410-8(9))* Princeton Univ. Pr.
Buff, Sheila. Birding for Beginners: A Comprehensive Introduction to the Art of Birdwatching. 2nd ed. 2010. 224p. pap. 19.95 *(978-1-59921-914-1(X))* Globe Pequot Pr., The.
Burrows, Roger. Birding in New Brunswick. 2010. (ENG.). 372p. pap. 24.95 *(978-0-86492-618-0(9))* Goose Lane Editions CAN. Dist: Univ. of Toronto Pr.
Cannings, Richard. Birds of Interior BC & the Rockies, 1 vol. 2009. (ENG., Illus.). 448p. pap. *(978-1-894974-59-2(X))* Heritage Hse.
—An Enchantment of Birds: Memories from a Birder's Life, 1 vol. 2007. (ENG., Illus.). 208p. 24.95 *(978-1-55365-235-9(5)*, Greystone Bks.) D&M Pubs. Inc. CAN. Dist: Perseus-PGW.
—Flights of Imagination: Extraordinary Writing about Birds, 1 vol. 2010. (ENG.). 280p. pap. 16.95 *(978-1-55365-535-0(4)*, Greystone Bks.) D&M Pubs. Inc. CAN. Dist: Perseus-PGW.
Chandler, David & Couzens, Dominic. 100 Birds to See Before You Die: The Ultimate Wish-List for Birders Everywhere. 2009. (ENG., Illus.). 224p. pap. 19.95 *(978-1-59223-958-0(7)*, Thunder Bay Pr.) Advantage Pubs. Group.
Chepaitis, Barbara. Feathers of Hope: Pete Dubacher, the Berkshire Bird Paradise, & the Human Connection with Birds. 2010. (Excelsior Editions Ser.). (Illus.). 128p. 19.95 *(978-1-4384-3291-5(7))* State Univ. of New York Pr.
Chu, Miyoko. Songbird Journeys: Four Seasons in the Lives of Migratory Birds. 2007. (ENG., Illus.). 1p. per. 13.95 *(978-0-8027-1518-0(4))* Walker & Co.
Chu, Miyoko & Erickson, Laura. The Bird Watching Answer Book: Everything You Need to Know to Enjoy Birds in Your Backyard & Beyond. 2009. (ENG., Illus.). 400p. pap. 14.95 *(978-1-60342-452-3(0)*, 1603424520) Workman Publishing Co., Inc.
Cohen, Callan, et al. Southern African Birdfinder: Where to Find 1,400 Bird Species in Southern Africa & Madagascar. 2007. (Illus.). 448p. pap. 29.95 *(978-1-86872-725-4(4))* Struik Pubs. ZAF. Dist: International Publishers Marketing.
Contreras, Alan. Afield: Forty Years of Birding the American West. 2009. (ENG., Illus.). 176p. pap. 18.95 *(978-0-87071-420-7(1))* Oregon State Univ. Pr.
Contreras, Alan, ed. Birds of Lane County, Oregon. 2006. (Illus.). 366p. per. 20.00 *(978-0-87071-180-0(6))* Oregon State Univ. Pr.
Couzens, Dominic. Top 100 Birding Sites of the World. 2009. (ENG.). 320p. 50.00 *(978-0-520-25932-4(7))* Univ. of California Pr.
Davies, Alan & Miller, Ruth. The Biggest Twitch: Around the World in 4,000 Birds. 2012. (ENG., Illus.). 320p. pap. 19.95 ***(978-1-4081-2387-4(8))*** A & C Black GBR. Dist: Macmillan.
Dee, Tim. A Year on the Wing: Journeys with Birds in Flight. 2010. (ENG.). 240p. pap. 15.00 *(978-1-4165-5934-4(5)*, Free Pr.) Free Pr.
Dempsey, Luke. A Supremely Bad Idea: Three Mad Birders & Their Quest to See It All. 2009. (ENG., Illus.). 272p. pap. 15.00 *(978-1-59691-634-0(6))* Bloomsbury Publishing.
Dickerman, R. W. Birds of the Southern Pacific Lowlands of Guatemala; with a Review of Icterus Gularis. 2007. 45p. pap. 10.00 *(978-0-9794517-1-3(X))* Museum of Southwest Biology Pubn. Series.
Domm, Jeffrey C. Lorimer Field Guide to 225 Ontario Birds. 2012. (ENG., Illus.). 288p. pap. 19.95 ***(978-1-4594-0041-2(0))*** Lorimer, James & Co., Ltd., Pubs. CAN. Dist: Casemate Pubs. & Bk. Distributors, LLC.
—Nova Scotia Birds - Formac Field Guide. 3rd ed. 2012. (ENG., Illus.). 224p. pap. 24.95 ***(978-1-4595-0049-5(0))*** Formac Publishing Co., Ltd. CAN. Dist: Casemate Pubs. & Bk. Distributors, LLC.
Dooley, Sean. The Big Twitch: One Man, One Continent, a Race Against Time - A True Story about Birdwatching. 2006. (ENG., Illus.). 320p. pap. 16.95 *(978-1-74114-528-1(7))* Allen & Unwin AUS. Dist: Independent Pubs. Group.
Duchesne, Bob. Maine Birding Trail: The Official Guide to More Than 260 Accessible Sites. 2009. (ENG., Illus.). 272p. pap. 15.95 *(978-0-89272-783-4(7))* Down East Bks.
Dunlap, Thomas R. In the Field, among the Feathered: A History of Birders & Their Guides, 1 vol. 2011. (ENG., Illus.). 240p. 34.95 *(978-0-19-973459-7(3))* Oxford Univ. Pr., Inc.
Dunne, Pete. The Art of Bird Finding. 2011. (Illus.). 80p. pap. 14.95 *(978-0-8117-0896-8(9))* Stackpole Bks.
Elwins, Dannie. Bird Watching for Beginners: Learn Bird Watching Simply & Easily. 2009. 32p. pap. 16.99 *(978-0-557-15526-2(6))* Lulu Enterprises Inc.
—How to Become A Birdwatcher & Learn the Hobby of Bird Watching. 2009. 32p. pap. 16.99 *(978-0-557-15524-8(X))* Lulu Enterprises Inc.
Engleman, Dodge, et al. A Bird-Finding Guide to Panama. 2008. (Illus.). 391p. per. 29.95 *(978-0-8014-7423-1(X)*, Comstock Publishing Assocs.) Cornell Univ. Pr.
—A Bird-Finding Guide to Panama. 2008. (Illus.). 391p. 75.50 *(978-0-8014-4650-4(3)*, Comstock Publishing Assocs.) Cornell Univ. Pr.
Erritzoe, Johannes. The Ornithologist's Dictionary. 2007. 289p. pap. *(978-84-96553-43-9(4))* LYNX, ED.
Eubanks, Ted Lee, Jr., et al. Finding Birds on the Great Texas Coastal Birding Trail: Houston, Galveston, & the Upper Texas Coast. 2008. (Texas A&M Nature Guides). (ENG., Illus.). 258p. pap. 23.00 *(978-1-58544-534-9(7))* Texas A&M Univ. Pr.
Foster, Mike F. The Ties That Bind: Birds, Nature & Us. 2010. 152p. 22.49 *(978-1-4520-7617-1(0))*; pap. 13.99 *(978-1-4520-7618-8(9))* AuthorHouse.
Fried, Natasha Tabori & Tabori, Lena, eds. The Little Big Book of Birds. 2007. (ENG., Illus.). 352p. 24.95 *(978-1-59962-023-7(5)*, Welcome Bks.) Welcome Enterprises, Inc.
Fulton, Robert. Swamp Drifter: Nature Tales, Photographs, Reminiscences, & Rants. 2007. (Illus.). 168p. per. *(978-1-933678-15-3(1))* Palmland Publishing.
Gallagher, Tim. In Search of Birds & Wild Places: A Naturalist's Journey into Parts Unknown. 2006. (ENG., Illus.). 256p. per. 14.95 *(978-1-59921-006-3(1)*, Lyons Pr.) Globe Pequot Pr., The.
Garrett, Kimball L., et al. Birds of the Los Angeles Region. 2006. (ENG., Illus.). 486p. 15.95 *(978-0-9640810-5-5(9))* Morse, R.W. Co.
Garrigues, Richard. The Birds of Costa Rica: A Field Guide. 2007. pap. 29.95 *(978-0-9705678-5-7(5))* Zona Tropical Pubns.
Gentile, Olivia. Life List: A Woman's Quest for the World's Most Amazing Birds. (ENG.). 352p. 2010. pap. 15.00 *(978-1-59691-170-3(0))* 2009. (Illus.). 26.00 *(978-1-59691-169-7(7))* Bloomsbury Publishing.
Gilbert, Suzie. Flyaway: How a Wild Bird Rehabber Sought Adventure & Found Her Wings. l.t. ed. 2009. 496p. pap. 25.99 *(978-0-06-172009-3(7)*, HarperLuxe) HarperCollins Pubs.
Glassberg, Jeffrey. Birds of North America. 2011. (ENG., Illus.). 240p. pap. 12.95 *(978-1-4027-8276-3(4))* Sterling Publishing Co., Inc.
Gress, Bob & Janzen, Pete. The Guide to Kansas Birds & Birding Hot Spots. 2008. (Illus.). 354p. pap. 19.95 *(978-0-7006-1565-0(2))* Univ. Pr. of Kansas.
Guttman, Burton S. Finding Your Wings: A Workbook for Beginning Bird Watchers. 2008. (Peterson Field Guide Workbook Ser.). (ENG., Illus.). 224p. pap. 14.95 *(978-0-618-78216-1(8))* Houghton Mifflin Harcourt Trade & Reference Pubs.
Haynes, Patricia Meehan. A Hummingbird Miracle. 2010. 36p. pap. 18.95 *(978-1-4269-2807-9(6))* Trafford Publishing.
Hilbers, Dirk. The Nature Guide to the Hortobagy & Tisza River Floodplain, Hungary. 2011. (Illus.). 191p. pap. 47.50 *(978-90-5011-276-5(5))* Koninklijke Nederlandse Natuurhistorische Vereniging, Stichting Uitgeverij NLD. Dist: Trans-Atlantic Pubns., Inc.
Humphries, Courtney. Superdove: How the Pigeon Took Manhattan... & the World. 2008. 208p. 24.95 *(978-0-06-125916-6(0))* Smithsonian Institution Pr.
Jacquelyn M. Howard. Tale Feathers: A Celebration of Birds, Birders & Bird Watching. 2009. 300p. pap. 21.95 *(978-1-4401-7333-2(8))* iUniverse, Inc.
James, Charlie Hamilton. Kingfisher: Tales from the Halcyon River. 2009. (ENG.). 168p. 34.95 *(978-1-901268-38-6(1)*, 1901268381) Evans Mitchell Bks. GBR. Dist: MBI Distribution Services/Quayside Distribution.
Johnson, Kenneth J. Amazing, Incredible Birds. 2007. 367p. per. 14.95 *(978-0-9744610-9-0(1))* Printers Inc., The.
Kaufman, Kenn. Kaufman Field Guide to Advanced Birding. 2011. (Kaufman Field Guides). (ENG., Illus.). 448p. 21.00 *(978-0-547-24832-5(6))* Houghton Mifflin Harcourt Trade & Reference Pubs.
Kaufman, Kenn, frwd. Birding for Everyone: Encouraging People of Color to Become Birdwatchers. 2008. (Illus.). 168p. (YA). per. 18.95 *(978-0-9679338-3-2(8)*, Wings-on-Disk) PassionQuest Technologies, LLC.
Keane, Gwen. Swan Wait. 2011. (ENG.). 33p. 24.95 ***(978-0-615-32598-9(X))*** Keane Writers Publishing.
Kee, Sheila N. Backyard Birds of the Inland Empire. 2010. pap. *(978-1-59714-132-1(1))* Heyday.
King, Alicia. Bird Watching. 2008. (Orvis Guides). (ENG., Illus.). 240p. pap. 19.95 *(978-1-58923-349-2(2)*, 1589233492, Creative Publishing International) Quayside.
Kingery, Hugh E. Birding Colorado: Over 180 Premier Birding Sites at 93 Locations. 2007. (Birding Ser.). (ENG., Illus.). 336p. per. 19.95 *(978-0-7627-3960-8(6)*, Falcon Guides) Globe Pequot Pr., The.
Knight, Richard L. The Birds of Northeast Tennessee: An Annotated Checklist for Carter, Johnson, Sullivan, Unicoi, & Washington Counties. 2nd ed. 2008. (Illus.). 127p. pap. *(978-0-615-23756-5(8))* Knight, Richard L.
Kress, Steve & Audubon Historical Society Staff. Audubon Pocket Backyard Birdwatch. rev. ed. 2010. (ENG.). 96p. pap. 9.95 *(978-0-7566-5864-9(0))* Dorling Kindersley Publishing, Inc.
Kroodsma, Donald. Western North America: A Guide to Listening. 2008. (ENG., Illus.). 192p. 29.95 *(978-0-8118-6397-1(2))* Chronicle Bks. LLC.
Lawson, Barrett. A Bird-Finding Guide to Costa Rica. 2009. (Illus.). 360p. pap. 29.95 *(978-0-8014-7584-9(8)*, Comstock Publishing Assocs.) Cornell Univ. Pr.
Leahy, C. W. Birdwatcher's Companion to North American Birdlife. 2006. (ENG., Illus.). 1072p. pap. 19.95 *(978-0-691-11388-3(2))* Princeton Univ. Pr.
Leslie, Scott. Sea & Coastal Birds of North America: A Guide to Observation, Understanding, & Conservation. 2008. (ENG., Illus.). 248p. pap. 19.95 *(978-1-55470-045-5(0))* Key Porter Bks. CAN. Dist: Perseus-PGW.
—Wetland Birds of North America: A Guide to Observation, Understanding & Conservation. rev. ed. 2007. (ENG., Illus.). 304p. pap. 19.95 *(978-1-55263-722-7(0))* Key Porter Bks. CAN. Dist: Perseus-PGW.
—Woodland Birds of North America: A Guide to Observing, Understanding & Conservation. rev. ed. 2007. (ENG., Illus.). 312p. pap. 19.95 *(978-1-55263-922-1(3))* Key Porter Bks. CAN. Dist: Perseus-PGW.
Levy, Bob. Club George: The Diary of a Central Park Birdwatcher. pap. 12.95 *(978-0-312-34168-8(7)*, St. Martin's Paperbacks) St. Martin's Pr.
Liddell, Judith & Hussey, Barbara. Birding Hot Spots of Central New Mexico. 2011. (W. L. Moody Jr. Natural History Ser.). (Illus.). 224p. pap. 24.95 *(978-1-60344-426-2(2))* Texas A&M Univ. Pr.
Lindo, David. The Urban Birder. 2012. (ENG., Illus.). 224p. 14.95 ***(978-1-84773-950-6(4))*** New Holland Pubs., Ltd. GBR. Dist: Sterling Publishing Co., Inc.
Lockwood, Mark. A Birder's Guide to the Rio Grande Valley. 4th ed. 2008. *(978-1-878788-49-8(3))* American Birding Assn., Inc.

Lovitch, Derek. How to Be a Better Birder. 2012. (ENG., Illus.). 208p. pap. 19.95 ***(978-0-691-14448-1(6))*** Princeton Univ. Pr.

Lukas, David. Watchable Birds of the Great Basin. (Watchable Birds Ser.: No. 3). (Illus.). 174p. pap. 16.00 *(978-0-87842-397-2(4),* 439) Mountain Pr. Publishing Co., Inc.

Marshall, David B., et al, eds. Birds of Oregon: A General Reference. 2006. (Illus.). 752p. per. 45.00 *(978-0-87071-182-4(2))* Oregon State Univ. Pr.

Martin, Deborah L. Best-Ever Backyard Birding Tips: Hundreds of Easy Ways to Attract the Birds You Love to Watch. 2008. (Illus.). xi, 356p. *(978-1-59486-830-6(1))* Rodale Pr., Inc.

MARTINET, Francois Nicolas. Histoire des Oiseaux: A history of Birds, 1 vol. 2011. (ENG.). 440p. 69.99 *(978-3-8331-6178-0(7))* h.f.ullmann DEU. Dist: Innovative Logistics.

Maslowski, Steve & Maslowski, Dave, photos by. Time Flies Journal: A Bird Lover's Daybook. 2006. (ENG., Illus.). 128p. 19.50 *(978-1-59543-421-0(6),* 4210) Willow Creek Pr., Inc.

McGrath, Rory. Bearded Tit: A Love Story with Feathers. 2008. (ENG.). 352p. 24.95 *(978-0-09-192269-6(0))* Ebury Publishing GBR. Dist: Independent Pubs. Group.

—Bearded Tit: When It Comes to Love & Life, We're All Winging It. 2009. (ENG.). 352p. pap. 15.95 *(978-0-09-192460-7(X))* Ebury Publishing GBR. Dist: Independent Pubs. Group.

Merrell, Patrick. Bird Brain-Teasers: Puzzles, Games & Avian Trivia. 2008. (ENG., Illus.). 224p. pap. 9.95 *(978-1-60342-080-8(0),* 1603420800) Storey Publishing, LLC.

Milne, Paul. Where to Watch Birds in World Cities. 2007. (ENG., Illus.). 496p. pap. 30.00 *(978-0-300-11691-5(8))* Yale Univ. Pr.

Minetor, Randi. Backyard Birding: A Guide to Attracting & Identifying Birds. 2011. (ENG., Illus.). 256p. pap. 19.95 *(978-0-7627-7166-0(6),* Lyons Pr.) Globe Pequot Pr., The.

Moss, Stephen. The Birder's Companion. 2007. (ENG., Illus.). 208p. pap. 16.95 *(978-1-55407-212-5(3))* Firefly Bks., Ltd.

Mynott, Jeremy. Birdscapes: Birds in Our Imagination & Experience. 2009. (ENG., Illus.). 392p. (C). 29.95 *(978-0-691-13539-7(8))* Princeton Univ. Pr.

Mynott, Jeremy. Birdscapes - Birds in Our Imagination & Experience. 2012. (ENG., Illus.). 392p. (C). pap. 19.95 ***(978-0-691-15428-2(7))*** Princeton Univ. Pr.

Nelson, Ronald R., ed. Birding in the Northern Plains: The Ornithological Writings of Herbert Krause. 2008. (Prairie Plains Ser.). 200p. pap. 27.50 *(978-0-931170-87-4(7))* Ctr. for Western Studies.

North Carolina Birding Trail. The North Carolina Birding Trail: Mountain Trail Guide. 2009. (Distributed for the North Carolina Birding Trail Ser.). (ENG.). 180p. pap. 19.95 *(978-0-8078-5965-0(6))* Univ. of North Carolina Pr.

O'Beirne, Kathleen P. Birds of a Feather: Lessons from the Sea. 2006. (Illus.). 206p. pap. 19.95 *(978-1-879979-02-4(0))* Lifescape Enterprises.

Obmascik, Mark. The Big Year: A Tale of Man, Nature, & Fowl Obsession. 2011. (ENG.) 288p. pap. 15.00 ***(978-1-4516-4860-7(X),*** Free Pr.) Free Pr.

Oddie, Bill. Bill Oddie's Little Black Bird Book. 2011. (ENG., Illus.). 144p. pap. 15.95 *(978-1-907554-27-8(0))* Anova Bks. GBR. Dist: Independent Pubs. Group.

O'Neill, Henrietta. Birding at Point Pelee. 2006. (ENG., Illus.). 224p. pap. *(978-1-55028-933-6(0))* Lorimer, James & Co., Ltd., Pubs. CAN. Dist: Casemate Pubs. & Bk. Distributors, LLC.

Ostling, Brutus & Akesson, Susanne. Penguins. 2007. (ENG., Illus.). 192p. 29.95 *(978-0-06-119858-8(7))* HarperCollins Pubs.

Pepperberg, Irene. Alex & Me: How a Scientist & a Parrot Discovered a Hidden World of Animal Intelligence - And Formed a Deep Bond in the Process. 2009. (ENG.). 288p. pap. 13.99 *(978-0-06-167398-6(6),* HarperPerennial) HarperCollins Pubs.

Petersen, C. J. Popular Mechanics How to Charm a Bird: Create a Backyard Haven with Bird Houses, Baths, & Feeders. Popular Mechanics Press Editors, ed. 2010. (ENG., Illus.). 176p. pap. 9.95 *(978-1-58816-720-0(8))* Hearst Communications, Inc.

Peterson, John M. C. & Lee, Gary. Adirondack Birding. 2008. (Illus.). pap. *(978-0-9789254-3-7(2))* Lost Pond Pr.

Peterson, Roger Tory. All Things Reconsidered: My Birding Adventures. Thompson, Bill, III & Thompson III, Bill, eds. 2007. (ENG., Illus.). 368p. pap. 14.95 *(978-0-618-92615-2(1))* Houghton Mifflin Harcourt Trade & Reference Pubs.

Piedmont Trail Guide Staff, contrib. by. North Carolina Birding Trail: Piedmont Trail Guide. 2008. (Illus.). 176p. spiral bd. 19.95 *(978-0-8078-5917-9(6))* Univ. of North Carolina Pr.

Pope, Richard. The Reluctant Twitcher: A Quite Truthful Account of My Big Birding Year. 2009. (ENG., Illus.). 216p. 35.00 *(978-1-55488-458-2(6))* Dundurn CAN. Dist: Ingram Pub. Services.

Rapoza, Brian. Birding Florida: Over 200 Prime Birding Sites at 54 Locations. 2007. (Falcon Guide Ser.). (ENG., Illus.). 304p. per. 22.95 *(978-0-7627-3914-1(2),* Falcon Guides) Globe Pequot Pr., The.

Richard, Modlin. Chasing Wings: Birding Exploits & Encounters. 2007. pap. 16.95 *(978-0-9800473-0-1(7))* Hartside Publishing.

Ritter, Jamie. Birding Corpus Christi & the Coastal Bend: More Than 75 Prime Birding Sites. 2007. (Falcon Guide Ser.). (ENG., Illus.). 264p. per. 17.95 *(978-0-7627-3915-8(0),* Falcon Guides) Globe Pequot Pr., The.

Rogers, Dennis W. Site Guides: Costa Rica - A Guide to the Best Birding Locations. 3rd ed. 2006. pap. 19.95 *(978-0-9637765-7-0(6))* Cinclus Pubns.

Rosen, Jonathan. The Life of the Skies: Birding at the End of Nature. 2008. (ENG., Illus.). 336p. pap. 16.00 *(978-0-312-42819-8(7))* Picador.

Rosenthal, Elizabeth J. Birdwatcher: The Life of Roger Tory Peterson. 2008. (ENG., Illus.). 464p. 29.95 *(978-1-59921-294-4(3),* Lyons Pr.) Globe Pequot Pr., The.

Roth, Sally. Attracting Songbirds to Your Backyard. 2012. (ENG., Illus.). 352p. pap. 22.99 ***(978-1-60961-754-7(1))*** Rodale Pr., Inc.

—Attracting Songbirds to Your Backyard: Hundreds of Easy Ways to Bring the Music & Beauty of Songbirds to Your Yard. 2012. ***(978-1-60961-753-0(3))*** Rodale Pr., Inc.

—The Backyard Bird: More Than 200 Easy Ideas & Projects for Attracting & Feeding Your Favorite Birds. 2010. *(978-1-60529-520-6(5))* Rodale Pr., Inc.

—The Backyard Bird Lover's Field Guide: Secrets to Attracting, Identifying, & Enjoying Birds of Your Region. 2007. (ENG., Illus.). 352p. pap. 21.99 *(978-1-59486-602-9(3))* Rodale Pr., Inc.

—The Backyard Bird Lover's Ultimate How-to Guide: More Than 200 Easy Ideas & Projects for Attracting & Feeding Your Favorite Birds. 2010. (ENG., Illus.). 320p. pap. 21.99 *(978-1-60529-519-0(1))* Rodale Pr., Inc.

Rowinski, Kate. The Joy of Birding: A Beginner's Guide. 2011. (Joy of Ser.). (ENG., Illus.). 256p. pap. 14.95 *(978-1-61608-122-5(8),* 608122) Skyhorse Publishing Co., Inc.

Santella, Chris. Fifty Places to Go Birding Before You Die: Birding Experts Share the World's Greatest Destinations. 2007. (ENG., Illus.). 224p. 24.95 *(978-1-58479-629-9(4))* Abrams.

Schaffner, Spencer. Binocular Vision: The Politics of Representation in Birdwatching Field Guides. 2011. (Illus.). 224p. (ENG.). pap. 24.95 *(978-1-55849-886-0(9));* lib. bdg. 80.00 *(978-1-55849-885-3(0))* Univ. of Massachusetts Pr.

Scott Shupe & Shupe, Scott. North American Bird I. D. Checklist: A Journal for Backyard Bird Enthusiasts. 2009. (ENG.). 96p. pap. 9.95 *(978-1-59186-460-8(7),* 1591864607) Cool Springs Pr.

Seymour, Tom. Maine: Over 90 Prime Birding Sites at 40 Locations. 2008. (Falcon Guides Birding Ser.). (ENG., Illus.). 144p. per. 18.95 *(978-0-7627-4224-0(0),* Falcon Guides) Globe Pequot Pr., The.

Sheldon, Pj M. M. Feathers & Gifts: A Heartwarming True Story. 2011. 152p. 29.99 ***(978-1-4568-9960-8(0));*** pap. 19.99 ***(978-1-4568-9959-2(7))*** Xlibris Corp.

Sterry, Paul & AA Publishing Staff. Birds of Britain & Europe: The Identification Guide to the Birds of Britain & Europe. 3rd ed. 2009. (ENG., Illus.). 320p. 50.00 *(978-0-7495-5862-8(8))* Automobile Assn. GBR. Dist: Independent Pubs. Group.

Stirling, David. Birds, Beasts & a Bike under the Southern Cross: Two Canadian Naturalists Camping Rough in New Zealand & Australia in The 1950s. 2008. 192p. pap. *(978-1-897435-19-9(3))* Agio Publishing Hse.

Sutton, Clay & Sutton, Patricia. Birds & Birding at Cape May. 2006. (ENG., Illus.). 568p. per. 26.95 *(978-0-8117-3134-8(0))* Stackpole Bks.

Tait, Malcolm. Birdwatcher's Pocket Companion. 2008. (Pocket Companion Ser.). (ENG., Illus.). 160p. 13.95 *(978-1-86205-797-5(4),* Pavilion Bks., Ltd.) Anova Bks. GBR. Dist: Independent Pubs. Group.

Taylor, Richard Cachor. Birds of Southeastern Arizona. Bickel, Barbara, ed. 2010. (Illus.). 440p. 19.95 *(978-0-9640910-7-9(5))* Morse, R.W. Co.

Tekiela, Stan. Birds of Prey of the Midwest Field Guide. 2010. 188p. pap. 14.95 *(978-1-59193-247-5(5))* Adventure Pubns., Inc.

Walsh, Roger L. The Invasion of the Crow. 2009. 28p. pap. 15.99 *(978-1-4415-1603-9(4))* Xlibris Corp.

Warhol, Tom & Schneck, Marcus. Birdwatcher's Daily Companion: 365 Days of Advice, Insight, & Information for Enthusiastic Birders. 2010. (ENG., Illus.). 320p. 19.99 *(978-1-59253-650-4(6),* 1592536506) Quayside.

Washington, Audubon, ed. WA Birding Trail Cascade Loop. 2007. pap. *(978-0-930698-03-4(7))* National Audubon Society.

—WA Birding Trail Coulee Corridor. 2007. pap. *(978-0-930698-06-5(1))* National Audubon Society.

—WA Birding Trail Olympic Loop. 2007. pap. *(978-0-930698-02-7(9))* National Audubon Society.

—WA Birding Trail Southwest Loop. 2007. pap. *(978-0-930698-05-8(3))* National Audubon Society.

Wassink, Jan. Watchable Birds of the Black Hills, Badlands, & Northern Great Plains. 2006. (Watchable Birds Ser.). (Illus.). 231p. pap. 22.00 *(978-0-87842-526-6(8))* Mountain Pr. Publishing Co., Inc.

Weidensaul, Scott. Of a Feather: A Brief History of American Birding. (ENG., Illus.). 368p. 2008. pap. 15.00 *(978-0-15-603355-8(0),* Mariner Bks.) 2007. 25.00 *(978-0-15-101247-3(4))* Houghton Mifflin Harcourt Trade & Reference Pubs.

West, George C. A Birder's Guide to Alaska. 2nd ed. 2008. (Illus.). x, 662p. pap. *(978-1-878788-48-1(5))* American Birding Assn., Inc.

White, David M. Zen Birding. 2010. (ENG., Illus.). 184p. pap. 16.95 *(978-1-84694-389-8(2))* O Bks., John Hunt.

White, Lisa, ed. Good Birders Don't Wear White: 50 Tips from North America's Top Birders. 2007. (ENG., Illus.). 288p. pap. 9.95 *(978-0-618-75642-1(6))* Houghton Mifflin Harcourt Publishing Co.

Williams, Peggy. Friends in the Meadow: Birds. 2009. 40p. pap. 18.49 *(978-1-4389-3386-3(X))* AuthorHouse.

Winter, Stuart. The Birdman Abroad. 2012. (ENG., Illus.). 224p. pap. 12.95 ***(978-1-84773-692-5(0))*** New Holland Pubs., Ltd. GBR. Dist: Sterling Publishing Co., Inc.

Wroth, Katherine, ed. The Zen of Watching Birds: Wit, Wisdom, & Inspiration. 2009. (ENG.). 112p. pap. 12.95 *(978-1-59485-272-5(3),* Skipstone) Mountaineers Bks., The.

Young, Jon. What the Robin Knows: How Birds Reveal the Secrets of the Natural World. 2012. (ENG., Illus.). 272p. 22.00 ***(978-0-547-45125-1(3))*** Houghton Mifflin Harcourt Trade & Reference Pubs.

Yow, John. The Armchair Birder Goes Coastal: The Secret Lives of Birds of the Southeastern Shore. 2012. (ENG., Illus.). 256p. 26.00 ***(978-0-8078-3561-6(7))*** Univ. of North Carolina Pr.

Zaleksy, Phil. Birding in Snohomish County. 2007. (Illus.). 104p. 9.95 *(978-0-9793333-2-3(6))* Northwest Wild Bks.

Zickefoose, Julie. Letters from Eden: A Year at Home, in the Woods. 2006. (ENG., Illus.). 240p. 26.00 *(978-0-618-57308-0(9))* Houghton Mifflin Harcourt Publishing Co.

BIRDBANDING

see Bird Banding

BIRDFEEDERS

see Bird Feeders

BIRDHOUSES

Barnard, Susan M., ed. Bats in Captivity: Biological & Medical Aspects. 2009. 600p. 99.95 *(978-1-934899-02-1(X));* pap. 74.95 *(978-1-934899-03-8(8))* ThinkBiotech, LLC. (Logos Pr.).

Barquest, G., et al. Birdhouses & Feeders. 2007. (Dover Woodworking Ser.). (ENG., Illus.). 48p. per. 5.95 *(978-0-486-46046-8(0))* Dover Pubns., Inc.

Birds of the National Aviary. 2006. (Illus.). 100p. per. 24.95 *(978-0-615-13269-3(3))* West, Doug.

Black, Robert G. Building an Aviary. 2006. 115p. pap. 19.95 *(978-0-910335-03-4(6))* Avian Pubns.

Green, Jen. How to Make 40 Beautiful Bird Boxes, Feeders & Birdbaths: Attract Birds to Your Farden by Creating Nesting Sites & Feeding Stations, Illustrated with 380 Photographs. 2010. (ENG., Illus.). 128p. pap. 17.99 *(978-1-84476-915-5(1))* Anness Publishing GBR. Dist: National Bk. Network.

Hamler, A. J. Easy to Build Birdhouses - A Natural Approach: Must Know Info to Attract & Keep the Birds You Want. 2010. (ENG., Illus.). 144p. pap. 24.99 *(978-1-4403-0220-6(0),* Popular Woodworking Bks.) F&W Media, Inc.

Henderson, Carrol L. Woodworking for Wildlife: Homes for Birds & Animals. 2010. (ENG., Illus.). 164p. pap. 19.95 *(978-0-9754338-3-6(0))* Minnesota's Bookstore.

Homes for Rent-Cheep! 7 Painted Gourd Birdhouses. 2006. 52p. 11.95 *(978-1-60140-259-2(7))* Leisure Arts, Inc.

Jones, Derek. Bird, Bee & Bug Houses: Simple Projects for Your Garden. 2011. (ENG., Illus.). 160p. pap. 17.95 *(978-1-86108-644-0(X))* Guild of Master Craftsman Pubns., Ltd. GBR. Dist: Sterling Publishing Co., Inc.

Loggins, George & Cool Springs Press Publications Staff. Build Your Own Backyard Birdhouses & Feeders. 2011. (Backyard Birding Ser.). (ENG., Illus.). 96p. pap. 12.99 *(978-1-59186-011-2(3),* 1591860113) Cool Springs Pr.

Meisel, Paul. Bird-Friendly Nest Boxes & Feeders: 12 Easy-to-Build Designs that Attract Birds to Your Yard. 2012. (ENG., Illus.). 112p. pap. 14.95 ***(978-1-56523-692-9(0))*** Fox Chapel Publishing Co., Inc.

—Wild & Wacky Birdhouses & Feeders. 2012. (ENG., Illus.). 152p. pap. 19.95 ***(978-1-56523-679-0(3))*** Fox Chapel Publishing Co., Inc.

Norman, H. Aviaries, Bird-Rooms & Cages - Their Construction & Furnishing. 2007. 116p. per. *(978-1-4067-8934-3(4),* Pierides Pr.) Read Bks.

Perkins, John. Build Your Own Birdhouses & Feeders: From Simple, Natural Designs to Spectacular, Customized Houses & Feeders. 2008. (ENG., Illus.). 144p. pap. 19.95 *(978-1-55209-135-7(X))* Firefly Bks., Ltd.

Ramuz, Mark & Delicata, Frank. Birdhouses: 20 Unique Woodworking Projects for Houses & Feeders. 2011. (ENG., Illus.). 128p. (Orig.). pap. 12.95 *(978-1-61608-307-6(7),* 608307) Skyhorse Publishing Co., Inc.

Self, Charles. Easy-to-Build Birdhouses. 2007. (Dover Woodworking Ser.). (ENG., Illus.). 112p. per. 8.95 *(978-0-486-45182-4(8))* Dover Pubns., Inc.

BIRDS

see also Bird Pests; Cage Birds; Game and Game-Birds; Ornithology; Water Birds also names of particular birds, e.g. Robins

Alderton, David. The Complete Illustrated Encyclopedia of Birds of the World: The ultimate reference source & identifier for 1600 birds, profiling habitat, plumage, nesting & Food. 2012. (ENG., Illus.). 512p. 22.50 ***(978-0-7548-2166-3(8))*** Anness Publishing GBR. Dist: National Bk. Network.

Allison, Sandy, ed. Backyard Birds & Bird Feeding: 100 Things to Know. 2007. (ENG., Illus.). 80p. per. 9.95 *(978-0-8117-3431-8(5))* Stackpole Bks.

Altum, Bernard. Der Vogel und Sein Leben. 2009. 302p. 30.99 *(978-1-110-15143-1(8));* pap. 28.75 *(978-1-110-15140-0(3))* BiblioBazaar.

Andrews, Ted. Feathered Omens Book & Tarot. 2009. 128p. 24.95 *(978-1-888767-56-8(1))* Dragonhawk Publishing.

Arnott, W. Geoffrey. Birds in the Ancient World from A to Z. 2007. (Ancient World from a to Z Ser.). (ENG & GEC., Illus.). 304p. 130.00 *(978-0-415-23851-9(X))* Routledge.

Askins, Robert A. Conservation of Grassland Birds in North America: Ornithological Monographs, No. 64. 2007. (Ornithological Monographs). 48p. per. 19.95 *(978-0-943610-78-8(8))* American Ornithologists Union.

Audubon, John James. 120 Audubon Bird Prints. 2008. (Dover Electronic Clip Art Ser.). (ENG., Illus.). 64p. pap. 22.95 *(978-0-486-99854-1(1))* Dover Pubns., Inc.

Beehler, Bruce M. Lost Worlds: Adventures in the Tropical Rainforest. 2009. (ENG., Illus.). 272p. pap. 17.00 *(978-0-300-15833-5(5))* Yale Univ. Pr.

Belding, Lyman. Land Birds of the Pacific District. 2009. 280p. pap. 28.75 *(978-1-115-63897-5(1));* 34.99 *(978-1-115-63895-1(5));* 30.99 *(978-1-115-63896-8(3));* pap. 27.75 *(978-1-115-63898-2(X))* BiblioBazaar.

—Land Birds of the Pacific District. 2009. 162p. pap. 19.99 *(978-1-150-67496-9(2))* General Bks. LLC.

Birds and Blooms Editors. Name That Bird: A Simple Approach to Identifying Your Backyard Friends. 2011. (ENG.). 120p. (gr. 12). 9.95 *(978-1-60652-335-3(X))* Reader's Digest Assn., Inc., The.

Birds Gotta Fly. (Illus.). 192p. *(978-0-9653945-2-9(2))* Shepard, Nancy Arts Ensemble.

Birkhead, Tim. The Wisdom of Birds: An Illustrated History of Ornithology. 2008. (ENG., Illus.). 448p. 45.00 *(978-1-59691-541-1(2))* Bloomsbury Publishing.

Blackburn, Tim M., et al. Avian Invasions: The Ecology & Evolution of Exotic Birds. 2009. (Oxford Avian Biology Ser.). (ENG., Illus.). 320p. 135.00 *(978-0-19-923254-3(7));* pap. 60.00 *(978-0-19-923255-0(5))* Oxford Univ. Pr., Inc.

Brush, Alan H. & Clark, George A., Jr., eds. Perspectives in Ornithology: Essays Presented for the Centennial of the American Ornithologists' Union. 2009. (ENG.). 572p. pap. 69.00 *(978-0-521-11304-5(0))* Cambridge Univ. Pr.

Burnett, Charles, ed. Adelard of Bath, Conversations with His Nephew: On the Same & the Different, Questions on Natural Science & on Birds. 2006. (Cambridge Medieval Classics Ser.: Vol. 9). (LAT & ENG., Illus.). 293p. pap. 55.00 *(978-0-521-39775-9(8))* Cambridge Univ. Pr.

Burroughs, John. Riverby. 2010. (ENG.). 340p. pap. 31.75 *(978-1-176-95288-1(9))* 2010. 348p. pap. 32.75 *(978-1-143-80195-2(4))* 2010. 392p. pap. 33.75 *(978-1-142-23075-3(9))* 2010. 318p. pap. 30.75 *(978-1-142-86738-6(2))* 2010. 398p. pap. 33.75 *(978-1-142-10916-5(X))* 2009. (ENG.). 333p. pap. 23.99 *(978-1-113-88283-7(2),* BiblioLife) 2009. 336p. 25.99 *(978-1-103-79918-3(5))* 2009. 336p. pap. 19.99 *(978-1-103-79914-5(2))* 2009. 336p. 25.99 *(978-0-559-95549-5(9))* 2009. 336p. pap. 19.99 *(978-0-559-95546-4(4))* BiblioBazaar.

—Riverby. 2009. 152p. pap. *(978-1-150-75413-5(3));* 200p. pap. *(978-0-217-86822-8(3));* 198p. pap. *(978-0-217-86820-4(7));* 198p. pap. *(978-0-217-79109-0(3))* Books LLC.

—Riverby. 2008. 332p. per. *(978-1-4086-4076-0(7))* Read Bks.

—Riverby. 2008. 388p. 39.95 *(978-1-4344-9788-8(7));* per. 24.95 *(978-1-4344-9787-1(9))* Wildside Pr., LLC.

—Riverby: The Writings of John Burroughs V9. 2007. 372p. 48.95 *(978-0-548-03364-7(1))* Kessinger Publishing, LLC.

Cannings, Richard. Flights of Imagination: Extraordinary Writing about Birds, 1 vol. 2010. (ENG.). 280p. pap. 16.95 *(978-1-55365-535-0(4),* Greystone Bks.) D&M Pubs. Inc. CAN. Dist: Perseus-PGW.

Cecil Smith. Birds of Guernsey: And the Neighbouring Islands: Alderney Sark Jeth. I.t. ed. 2007. (ENG.). 166p. pap. 21.99 *(978-1-4264-8075-1(X))* BiblioBazaar.

Chandler, David, et al. Birds. 2007. (Facts at Your Fingertips Ser.). (Illus.). 64p. (YA). (gr. 7-12). lib. bdg. 35.65 *(978-1-933834-00-9(5))* Brown Bear Books.

Chronicle Books Staff. Birds. 2009. (ENG., Illus.). 96p. 16.95 *(978-0-8118-6234-9(8))* Chronicle Bks. LLC.

Clements, James F. The Clements Checklist of Birds of the World. 6th rev. ed. 2007. (Illus.). 855p. 59.95 *(978-0-8014-4501-9(9),* Comstock Publishing Assocs.) Cornell Univ. Pr.

Colver, Kevin, et al. The Calls of Ducks & Geese. 2008. (ENG., Illus.). 103p. pap. 19.95 *(978-0-8117-3490-5(0))* Stackpole Bks.

Contreras, Alan. Afield: Forty Years of Birding the American West. 2009. (ENG., Illus.). 176p. pap. 18.95 *(978-0-87071-420-7(1))* Oregon State Univ. Pr.

Coues, Elliott, et al. Audubon & His Journals. 2010. (ENG.). 618p. pap. 45.75 *(978-1-171-61603-0(1));* 598p. pap. 44.75 *(978-1-144-90368-6(8));* 598p. pap. 44.75 *(978-1-144-68190-4(1));* 638p. pap. 45.75 *(978-1-145-67102-7(0));* 600p. pap. 44.75 *(978-1-145-99192-7(0))* BiblioBazaar.

Couzens, Dominic. Extreme Birds: The World's Most Extraordinary & Bizarre Birds. 2008. (ENG., Illus.). 320p. 45.00 *(978-1-55407-423-5(1))* Firefly Bks., Ltd.

Cox, George W. Bird Migration & Global Change. 2010. (ENG.). 304p. 90.00 *(978-1-59726-687-1(6));* pap. 45.00 *(978-1-59726-688-8(4))* Island Pr.

Dey, Amanda, et al. Predicting Occurrence of Area-Sensitive Forest Birds. 2008. 108p. pap. *(978-3-639-01538-6(X))* VDM Verlag Dr. Mueller e.K.

Diamond, Anthony William, ed. Studies of Mascarene Island Birds. 2009. (ENG.). 468p. pap. 61.00 *(978-0-521-11331-1(8))* Cambridge Univ. Pr.

Dorling Kindersley Publishing Staff. Nature Handbooks Birds. 2012. (ENG.). 352p. pap. 14.95 ***(978-0-7566-9041-0(2))*** Dorling Kindersley Publishing, Inc.

Dubkin, Leonard. The Murmur of Wings. 2007. (ENG.). 174p. 37.95 *(978-0-548-07042-0(3))* Kessinger Publishing, LLC.

Dunning, John B., Jr. CRC Handbook of Avian Body Masses. 2nd rev. ed. 2007. (ENG., Illus.). 672p. 125.95 *(978-1-4200-6444-5(4),* CRC Press) Taylor & Francis Group GBR. Dist: Taylor & Francis Group.

Fiedler, Wolfgang & Berthod, Peter. Effects of Climate Change on Birds. Moller, Anders Pape, ed. 2010. (ENG., Illus.). 344p. 117.00 *(978-0-19-956974-3(6));* pap. 62.95 *(978-0-19-956975-5(4))* Oxford Univ. Pr., Inc.

Frischmann, Carol. Attracting & Feeding Backyard Birds, 1 vol. 2007. (Animal Planet Pet Care Library). (ENG., Illus.). 112p. 11.95 *(978-0-7938-3786-1(3))* TFH Pubns., Inc.

B

Glomski, Chester A. & Pica, Alessandra. The Avian Erythrocyte. 2nd ed. 2011. (ENG.). 650p. 179.95 *(978-1-57808-718-1(X))* BIOS Scientific Publishers Ltd. GBR. Dist: Taylor & Francis Group.

Gooddie, Chris. The Jewel Hunter: A Journey Through the Rainforest. 2011. (Illus.). 364p. pap. 47.50 *(978-1-903657-16-4(4))* Trans-Atlantic Pubns., Inc.

Grant, Joan. The Cuckoo on the Kettle. (Illus.). 125p. 28.95 *(978-1-873580-05-9(3))* Whittet Bks., Ltd. GBR. Dist: Diamond Farm Bk. Pubs.

Hanson, Thor. Feathers: The Evolution of a Natural Miracle. 2011. (ENG., Illus.). 352p. (gr. 9). 25.99 *(978-0-465-02013-3(5))* Basic Bks.

Hausman, Leon Augustus. Field Guide for Birds, Wildflowers & Nature Study: Grosset's Library of Practical Handbooks. 2011. 118p. 39.95 ***(978-1-258-07551-4(2))*** Literary Licensing, LLC.

Hilbers, Dirk. The Nature Guide to the Hortobagy & Tisza River Floodplain, Hungary. 2011. (Illus.). 191p. pap. 47.50 *(978-90-5011-276-5(5))* Koninklijke Nederlandse Natuurhistorische Vereniging, Stichting Uitgeverij NLD. Dist: Trans-Atlantic Pubns., Inc.

Howitt, Mary. Birds & Flowers. 2007. (ENG.). 200p. 39.95 *(978-0-548-04448-3(1))* Kessinger Publishing, LLC.

H.R. 1054, H.R. 2213, H.R. 3433, & H.R. 3537: Legislative Hearing Before the Subcommittee on Insular Affairs, Oceans, & Wildlife of the Committee on Natural Resources, U.S. House of Representatives, One Hundred Eleventh Congress, First Session, Tuesday, September 22, 2009. 2010. iv, 94p. ***(978-0-16-086368-4(6)***, 552-070-41447-9) United States Government Printing Office.

Hudson, W. H. Adventures among Birds. reprint ed. 64.50 *(978-0-404-03407-8(1))* AMS Pr., Inc.

—Birds & Man. reprint ed. 64.50 *(978-0-404-03399-6(7))* AMS Pr., Inc.

—Birds & Man. 2009. 146p. pap. *(978-0-217-44707-2(4))* Books LLC.

—Birds & Man. 2008. 316p. pap. *(978-1-4097-8575-0(0))* 2007. (ENG.). 252p. per. *(978-1-4067-8936-2(4)*, Pierides Pr.) Read Bks.

—Birds in Town & Village. reprint ed. 64.50 *(978-0-404-03409-2(8))* AMS Pr., Inc.

—Dead Man's Plack, an Old Thorn & Miscellanea. reprint ed. 75.00 *(978-0-404-03414-6(4))* AMS Pr., Inc.

Ingersoll, Ernest. Birds in Legend, Fable & Folklore. 2010. 148p. pap. 23.56 *(978-1-153-29714-1(0))* General Bks. LLC.

Jacquelyn M. Howard. Tale Feathers: A Celebration of Birds, Birders & Bird Watching. 2009. 300p. pap. 21.95 *(978-1-4401-7333-2(8))* iUniverse, Inc.

Jamieson, Barrie G. M. Reproductive Biology & Phylogeny of Birds. 2007. (ENG., Illus.). 516p. 119.95 *(978-1-57808-444-9(X))* BIOS Scientific Publishers Ltd. GBR. Dist: Taylor & Francis Group.

Keen, Sam. Sightings: Extraordinary Encounters with Ordinary Birds. 2007. (ENG., Illus.). 120p. 14.95 *(978-0-8118-5976-9(2))* Chronicle Bks. LLC.

Kirwan, Guy M. & Greenhaigh, Graeme. Cotingas & Manakins. 2012. (ENG., Illus.). 624p. 55.00 ***(978-0-691-15352-0(3))*** Princeton Univ. Pr.

McNaughton, Frances. Sugar Birds. 2011. (Twenty to Make Ser.). (ENG., Illus.). 48p. pap. 9.95 *(978-1-84448-672-4(9))* Search Pr., Ltd. GBR. Dist: Independent Pubs. Group.

Michelet, Jules. The Bird. 2008. 342p. 46.95 *(978-1-4366-5194-3(8))*; 344p. pap. 31.95 *(978-0-548-87562-9(6))* Kessinger Publishing, LLC.

Mindlin, Gabriel B. & Laje, Rodrigo. The Physics of Birdsong. 2010. (Biological & Medical Physics, Biomedical Engineering Ser.). (Illus.). x, 157p. pap. 109.00 *(978-3-642-06480-7(9)*, 3642064809) Springer.

Mine, Yoshinori. Egg Bioscience & Biotechnology. Mine, Yoshinori, ed. 2008. (ENG., Illus.). 366p. 117.00 *(978-0-470-03998-4(1)*, Wiley-Interscience) Wiley, John & Sons, Inc.

Mitigating Bird Collisions. pap. 40.00 *(978-0-931032-33-2(4))* Edison Electric Institute.

Montgomery, Sy. Birdology: Adventures with a Pack of Hens, a Peck of Pigeons, Cantankerous Crows, Fierce Falcons, Hip Hop Parrots, Baby Hummingbirds, & One Murderously Big Living Dinosaur. 2010. (ENG., Illus.). 272p. 25.00 *(978-1-4165-6984-8(7)*, Free Pr.) Free Pr.

—Birdology: Adventures with a Pack of Hens, a Peck of Pigeons, Cantankerous Crows, Fierce Falcons, Hip Hop Parrots, Baby Hummingbirds, & One Murderously Big Living Dinosaur. l.t. ed. 2010. 458p. 31.99 *(978-1-4104-3122-6(3))* Thorndike Pr.

Morrison, Lesley. The Healing Wisdom of Birds: An Everyday Guide to Their Spiritual Songs & Symbolism. 2011. (ENG.). 240p. pap. 15.95 *(978-0-7387-1882-8(3))* Llewellyn Pubns.

Moss, Steven & BirdLife International Staff. Remarkable Birds: 100 of the World's Most Notable Birds. 2008. 208p. 24.95 *(978-0-06-162664-7(3))* Smithsonian Institution Pr.

El Mundo Maravilloso de las Aves. (SPA.). 10.00 *(978-84-241-5403-5(7))* Torres, Eliseo & Sons.

Murphy-Hiscock, Arin. Birds: Explore the Symbology & Significance of These Divine Winged Messengers. 2012. (ENG., Illus.). 240p. pap. 19.95 ***(978-1-4405-2688-6(5))*** Adams Media Corp.

Nahmad, Claire. Angel Messages: The Oracle of the Birds. 2010. (ENG.). 224p. pap. 19.95 *(978-1-906787-51-6(4)*, Watkins Publishing) Duncan Baird Pubs. GBR. Dist: Sterling Publishing Co., Inc.

Naldo, Jesus L. & Samour, Jaime, eds. Anatomical & Clinical Radiology of Birds of Prey: Including Interactive Advanced Anatomical Imaging. 2007. (ENG., Illus.). 300p. 215.00 *(978-0-7020-2802-1(9)*, Saunders) Elsevier - Health Sciences Div.

Nasira, Khatoon & Bilqees, F. M. Acanthocephala of Vertebrates a World Record. 2011. 576p. pap. ***(978-3-639-32875-2(2))*** VDM Verlag Dr. Mueller e.K.

National Geographic Society Staff. National Geographic Complete Birds of the World. Harris, Tim, ed. 2009. (ENG., Illus.). 384p. 35.00 *(978-1-4262-0403-6(5)*, National Geographic) National Geographic Society.

Nelson, Ronald R., ed. Birding in the Northern Plains: The Ornithological Writings of Herbert Krause. 2008. (Prairie Plains Ser.). 200p. pap. 27.50 *(978-0-931170-87-4(7))* Ctr. for Western Studies.

Nozedar, Adele. The Secret Language of Birds Tarot. 2011. (Illus.). 192p. 39.99 ***(978-0-7643-3900-4(1)***, Schiffer Publishing Ltd) Schiffer Publishing, Ltd.

Ober, Frederick A. Crusoe's Island - a Bird-Hunter's Story. 2011. 302p. pap. 30.45 ***(978-1-4460-7568-5(0))*** Research Pr.

O'Connor, Mike. Why Don't Woodpeckers Get Headaches? And Other Answers to Bird Questions You Know You Want to Ask. Miller, Olivia, ed. 2007. (ENG., Illus.). 224p. per. 14.95 *(978-0-8070-8574-5(X))* Beacon Pr.

Onley, Derek & Scofield, Paul. Albatrosses, Petrels & Shearwaters of the World. 2007. (Princeton Field Guides). (ENG., Illus.). 256p. pap. 29.95 *(978-0-691-13132-0(5))* Princeton Univ. Pr.

Ostling, Brutus & Ullman, Magnus. Between the Wingtips: The Secret Life of Birds. 2006. 208p. 34.95 *(978-0-06-113685-6(9))* HarperCollins Pubs.

Pearson, T. Gilbert. The Bird Study Book. 2008. (Illus.). 116p. pap. *(978-1-84830-937-1(6)*, Wildhern Pr.) Echo Library.

Pease, Shirley & Lois, Carlos, eds. Mammalian & Avian Transgenesis - New Approaches. 2010. (Principles & Practice Ser.). (ENG., Illus.). xx, 281p. pap. 269.00 *(978-3-642-06665-8(8)*, 3642066658) Springer.

Perrins, Christopher, ed. The Princeton Encyclopedia of Birds. 2009. (ENG., Illus.). 656p. pap. 35.00 *(978-0-691-14070-4(7))* Princeton Univ. Pr.

Pinowski, Jan & Kendeigh, S. Charles, eds. Granivorous Birds in Ecosystems: Their Evolution, Populations, Energetics, Adaptations, Impact & Control. 2012. (International Biological Programme Synthesis Ser.). (ENG.). 454p. pap. 55.00 ***(978-1-107-40383-3(9))*** Cambridge Univ. Pr.

Powell, Alvin. The Race to Save the World's Rarest Bird: The Discovery & Death of the Po'ouli. 2008. (ENG., Illus.). 304p. 24.95 *(978-0-8117-3448-6(X))* Stackpole Magazines.

Pratt, H. Douglas & Etpison, Mandy. Birds & Bats of Palau. 2008. 290p. pap. 29.95 *(978-1-56647-871-7(5))* Mutual Publishing LLC.

Price, Trevor. Speciation in Birds. 2007. (ENG., Illus.). 480p. pap. 59.95 *(978-0-9747077-8-5(3))* Roberts & Co.

Rakhimov, Ilgizar. Birds of Anthropogenous Landscapes. 2010. 280p. pap. *(978-3-639-23745-0(5))* VDM Verlag Dr. Mueller e.K.

Riddle, Gordon. Kestrels for Company. 2011. (Illus.). 208p. pap. *(978-1-84995-029-9(6))* Whittles Publishing.

Roosevelt, Theodore. A Book Lover's Holidays in the Open. 2007. (ENG.). 390p. 48.95 *(978-0-548-02284-9(4))* Kessinger Publishing, LLC.

—A Book Lover's Holidays in the Open. 373p. reprint ed. 98.00 *(978-0-7222-9563-2(4))* Library Reprints, Inc.

Roots, Clive. Flightless Birds, 1 vol. 2006. (Greenwood Guides to the Animal World). (Illus.). 248p. 65.00 *(978-0-313-33545-7(1)*, GR3545, Greenwood Pr.) Greenwood Publishing Group, Inc.

Routledge, Chapman, Hall Inc. Staff. Gulls & Plovers the Ecology of Mixed-Species Feeding Groups. (Illus.). xii, 302p. (C). *(978-0-7099-3230-7(8))* Croom Helm, Ltd.

Sample, Geoff. Collins Bird Songs & Calls, 3 vols. 2nd ed. 2010. (ENG., Illus.). 192p. 44.95 *(978-0-00-733976-1(3))* HarperCollins Pubs. Ltd. GBR. Dist: Independent Pubs. Group.

Scott, Graham. Essential Ornithology. 2010. (ENG., Illus.). 208p. pap. 55.00 *(978-0-19-856997-8(1))* Oxford Univ. Pr., Inc.

Serjeantson, Dale & Serjeantson, D. Birds. 2009. (Cambridge Manuals in Archaeology Ser.). (ENG., Illus.). 512p. (C). 95.00 *(978-0-521-86617-0(0))*; pap. 44.00 *(978-0-521-75858-1(0))* Cambridge Univ. Pr.

Sheehan, Larry, et al. The Birding Life: A Passion for Birds at Home & Afield. 2011. (ENG., Illus.). 240p. 50.00 *(978-0-307-71635-4(X)*, Clarkson Potter) Crown Publishing Group.

Sinclair, Ian, et al, trs. Birds of Africa: A Complete Illustrated Field Guide to the Birds of the Sahara. 2009. (Illus.). 760p. pap. 47.95 *(978-1-86872-857-2(9))* Struik Pubs. ZAF. Dist: International Publishers Marketing.

Smith, Malcolm. Life with Birds: A Story of Mutual Exploitation. 2011. (Illus.). 208p. pap. *(978-1-84995-028-2(8))* Whittles Publishing.

Sodhi, Navjot S., et al. Conservation of Tropical Birds. 2011. (ENG., Illus.). 312p. 134.95 *(978-1-4443-3482-1(4)*, Wiley-Blackwell) Wiley, John & Sons, Inc.

Stap, Don. Birdsong: A Natural History. 2006. 261p. reprint ed. 24.00 *(978-1-4223-5498-8(9))* DIANE Publishing Co.

Stockland, Jonathan & Watkins, Peter. Winged Wonders: A Celebration of Birds in Human History. 2010. (ENG.). 224p. pap. 12.95 *(978-1-933346-29-8(9))* BlueBridge.

Stratton-Porter, Gene. Friends in Feathers: Character Studies of Native American Birds, Which Through Friendly Advances, I Induced to Pose for Me (1917) 2008. 354p. 46.95 *(978-0-548-98859-6(5))* 2007. (ENG.). 356p. per. 31.95 *(978-0-548-65872-7(2))* Kessinger Publishing, LLC.

Street, J. Fletcher. Brief Bird Biographies: A Guide to Birds Through Habitat Associations. 2011. 160p. 41.95 ***(978-1-258-06723-6(4))*** Literary Licensing, LLC.

Tait, Malcolm. Birdwatcher's Pocket Companion. 2008. (Pocket Companion Ser.). (ENG., Illus.). 160p. 13.95 *(978-1-86205-797-5(4)*, Pavilion Bks., Ltd.) Anova Bks. GBR. Dist: Independent Pubs. Group.

Taylor, Barbara. Atlas Visual de las Aves.Tr. of Bird Atlas. (SPA.). 13.98 *(978-968-13-2743-9(8))* Editorial Diana, S.A. MEX. Dist: Continental Bk. Co., Inc.

Thompson, Max, et al. Birds of Kansas. 2011. (Illus.). 544p. 39.95 *(978-0-7006-1782-1(5))* Univ. Pr. of Kansas.

Toerien, Jane & Van Dobben, Joyce. Bird Cards: The Healing Power of the Bird Kingdom. 2007. (ENG.). 1p. 12.47 *(978-90-6963-748-8(0))* Binkey Kok NLD. Dist: Red Wheel/Weiser.

Torrey, Bradford. Birds in the Bush. 2009. 310p. 32.99 *(978-1-116-11407-2(0))*; 36.99 *(978-1-116-11406-5(2))*; pap. 28.75 *(978-1-116-11409-6(7))*; pap. 29.75 *(978-1-116-11408-9(9))*; 32.99 *(978-1-113-62636-3(4))*; pap. 28.75 *(978-1-113-62634-9(8))*; pap. 29.75 *(978-1-113-62635-6(6))* BiblioBazaar.

—Birds in the Bush. 2009. 128p. pap. *(978-0-217-18196-9(1))* Books LLC.

—Birds in the Bush. 2008. 152p. pap. *(978-1-4099-1069-5(5))* Dodo Pr.

—Birds in the Bush. 2008. 304p. 43.95 *(978-1-4366-1010-0(9))*; (ENG.). 308p. per. 28.95 *(978-0-548-81483-3(X))* Kessinger Publishing, LLC.

—Field Days in California. 2009. 268p. 42.95 *(978-1-120-23725-5(4))*; pap. 27.95 *(978-1-120-19597-5(7))* Kessinger Publishing, LLC.

—The Foot-Path Way. 2009. 104p. pap. *(978-0-217-95139-5(2))*; 106p. pap. *(978-0-217-95141-8(4))* Books LLC.

—The Foot-Path Way. 2008. 116p. pap. *(978-1-4099-1077-0(6))* Dodo Pr.

—The Foot-Path Way. 2009. 96p. pap. *(978-1-4068-9436-3(2))* Echo Library.

Turner, David. Was Beethoven A Birdwatcher?? 2012. (ENG., Illus.). 288p. 19.95 ***(978-1-84953-145-0(5))*** Summerdale Pubs. GBR. Dist: Independent Pubs. Group.

Unwin, Mike. The Atlas of Birds: Diversity, Behavior & Conservation. 2011. (ENG.). 144p. pap. 22.95 *(978-0-691-14949-3(6))* Princeton Univ. Pr.

Vriends, Matthew & Vriends, Tanya M. Raising Companion Birds. (Illus.). *(978-0-88839-564-1(7))* Hancock Hse. Pubs.

Walters, Martin. Bird Watch: A Survey of Planet Earth's Changing Ecosystems. 2011. (Illus.). 256p. 45.00 *(978-0-226-87226-1(2))* Univ. of Chicago Pr.

Wansbury, Andrea. Birds: Divine Messengers - Transform Your Life with Their Guidance & Wisdom. 2006. (ENG., Illus.). 156p. per. 16.95 *(978-1-84409-074-7(4))* Findhorn Pr. GBR. Dist: Independent Pubs. Group.

Watkins, Peter & Stockland, Jonathan. Winged Wonders: A Celebration of Birds in Human History. 2007. (ENG., Illus.). 224p. 22.00 *(978-1-933346-07-6(8))* BlueBridge.

Whitefield. Longman World Guide: Birds. Date not set. (Illus.). 228p. pap. 4.95 *(978-0-582-89354-2(2))* Addison-Wesley Longman, Ltd. GBR. Dist: Trans-Atlantic Pubns., Inc.

Williams, Peggy. Friends in the Meadow: Birds. 2009. 40p. pap. 18.49 *(978-1-4389-3386-3(X))* AuthorHouse.

Wilson, Jeremy D., et al. Bird Conservation & Agriculture: The Bird Life of Farmland, Grassland & Heathland. 2009. (Ecology, Biodiversity & Conservation Ser.). (ENG., Illus.). 404p. pap. 68.00 *(978-0-521-73472-1(X))* Cambridge Univ. Pr.

Wood, Douglas. The Thing with Feathers. 2007. 56p. 9.95 *(978-1-59193-176-8(2))* Adventure Pubns., Inc.

Zickefoose, Julie. The Bluebird Effect: Uncommon Bonds with Common Birds. 2012. (ENG., Illus.). 384p. 28.00 *(978-0-547-00309-2(9))* Houghton Mifflin Harcourt Trade & Reference Pubs.

BIRDS—ANATOMY

Kaiser, Gary W. The Inner Bird: Anatomy & Evolution. 2007. (Illus.). 386p. 85.00 *(978-0-7748-1343-3(1))* UBC Pr. CAN. Dist: Univ. of Washington Pr.

Maina, John N. The Lung-Air Sac System of Birds: Development, Structure, & Function. 2010. (ENG., Illus.). xv, 210p. pap. 159.00 *(978-3-642-06501-9(5)*, 3642065015) Springer.

Peaker, M. & Linzell, J. L. Salt Glands in Birds & Reptiles. 2009. (ENG.). 336p. pap. 48.00 *(978-0-521-11203-1(6))* Cambridge Univ. Pr.

Silverman, Sam & Tell, Lisa A. Radiology of Birds: An Atlas of Normal Anatomy & Positioning. 2009. (ENG., Illus.). 299p. 145.00 *(978-0-7216-0635-4(0)*, Saunders) Elsevier - Health Sciences Div.

BIRDS—BANDING

see Bird Banding

BIRDS—BEHAVIOR

Athan, Mattie Sue. Guide to Companion Parrot Behavior. 2nd rev. ed. 2010. (ENG., Illus.). 248p. pap. 16.99 *(978-0-7641-4213-0(5))* Barron's Educational Series, Inc.

Birkhead, Tim & Swainson, Bill. Bird Sense: What It's Like to Be a Bird. 2012. (ENG.). 288p. 25.00 ***(978-0-8027-7966-3(2))*** Walker & Co.

Bradford, Walter. Michigan Bird Life. (Illus.). reprint ed. lib. bdg. 125.00 *(978-0-7222-0082-7(X))* Library Reprints, Inc.

Burroughs, John. Birds & Bees: Sharp Eyes & Other Papers. 2009. 196p. 22.99 *(978-1-103-08529-3(8))*; pap. 16.99 *(978-1-103-08526-2(3))* BiblioBazaar.

—Birds & Bees: Sharp Eyes, & Other Papers. 2011. 198p. pap. 23.75 ***(978-1-245-39671-4(4))*** BiblioBazaar.

—Birds & Bees, Sharp Eyes, & Other Papers. 2008. 136p. per. *(978-1-4065-9007-4(X))* Dodo Pr.

—Birds & Bees, Sharp Eyes & Other Papers. 2007. 104p. per. *(978-1-4068-2363-9(5))* Echo Library.

—Birds & Bees, Sharp Eyes & Other Papers. 2010. 90p. pap. 20.00 *(978-1-153-59228-4(2))* General Bks. LLC.

—Birds & Bees, Sharp Eyes & Other Papers. 2010. 114p. pap. 15.96 *(978-1-162-65557-4(7))*; 27.96 ***(978-1-169-24726-0(1))***; 34.95 *(978-1-161-42422-5(9))* Kessinger Publishing, LLC.

—Birds & Bees Sharp Eyes & Other Papers. 2008. 164p. 25.99 *(978-0-554-28420-0(0))*; 22.99 *(978-0-554-37723-0(3))* BiblioBazaar.

Burroughs, John & A Biographical Sketch. Birds & Bees Sharp Eyes & Other Papers. 2007. (ENG.). 162p. pap. 21.99 *(978-1-4346-5368-0(4))*; 148p. pap. 18.99 *(978-1-4346-5367-3(6))* BiblioBazaar.

Burton, Robert & Dorling Kindersley Publishing Staff. Audubon North American Birdfeeder Guide. 2009. (ENG.). 224p. (gr. 12). pap. 14.95 *(978-0-7566-5883-0(7))* Dorling Kindersley Publishing, Inc.

Carrick, Doug. The Eagles of Hornby Island: My Tree-Top Neighbours. 2007. (Illus.). 112p. pap. 14.95 ***(978-0-88839-649-5(X))*** Hancock Hse. Pubs.

Catchpole, Clive & Slater, Peter. Bird Song: Biological Themes & Variations. 2nd rev. ed. 2008. (ENG., Illus.). 348p. 80.00 *(978-0-521-87242-3(1))* Cambridge Univ. Pr.

Coster, Bill. Creative Bird Photography: Essential Tips & Techniques, 1 vol. 2010. (ENG., Illus.). 160p. pap. 17.95 *(978-1-55365-545-9(1)*, Greystone Bks.) D&M Pubs. Inc. CAN. Dist: Perseus-PGW.

Dee, Tim. A Year on the Wing: Journeys with Birds in Flight. 2010. (ENG.). 240p. pap. 15.00 *(978-1-4165-5934-4(5)*, Free Pr.) Free Pr.

Dhondt, Andre A. Interspecific Competition in Birds. 2012. (ENG., Illus.). 296p. 117.00 ***(978-0-19-958901-2(1))***; pap. 59.99 ***(978-0-19-958902-9(X))*** Oxford Univ. Pr., Inc.

Elphick, Jonathan, ed. Atlas of Bird Migration: Tracing the Great Journeys of the World's Birds. 2011. (ENG., Illus.). 176p. pap. 24.95 *(978-1-55407-971-1(3))* Firefly Bks., Ltd.

Goodfellow, Peter. Avian Architecture: How Birds Design, Engineer & Build. 2011. (ENG., Illus.). 160p. 27.95 *(978-0-691-14849-6(X))* Princeton Univ. Pr.

Griesser, Michael & Barnaby, Jonathan, eds. The Role of Nepotism, Cooperation & Competition in the Avian Families. 2010. (Birds - Evolution, Behavior & Ecology Ser.). pap. 43.00 *(978-1-60876-867-7(8))* Nova Science Pubs., Inc.

Griffith, George. Musical Birds of Nevad: Silence! Meadowlark Singing. 2009. 100p. pap. 11.95 *(978-1-4401-1508-0(7))* iUniverse, Inc.

Heinrich, Bernd. Mind of the Raven: Investigations & Adventures with Wolf-Birds. 2007. (P. S. Ser.). (ENG., Illus.). 336p. pap. 14.99 *(978-0-06-113605-4(0)*, HarperPerennial) HarperCollins Pubs.

—The Nesting Season: Cuckoos, Cuckolds, & the Invention of Monogamy. (Illus.). 352p. 2011. (ENG.). pap. 17.95 *(978-0-674-06193-4(4))* 2010. 29.95 *(978-0-674-04877-5(6))* Harvard Univ. Pr. (Belknap Pr.).

Low, Rosemary. Why Does My Parrot ... ? rev. ed. 2009. (ENG., Illus.). 208p. pap. 16.95 *(978-0-285-63840-2(8))* Souvenir Pr. Ltd. GBR. Dist: Independent Pubs. Group.

Mancini, Julie Rach. Why Does My Bird Do That: A Guide to Parrot Behavior. 2nd rev. ed. 2006. (ENG., Illus.). 256p. pap. 19.99 *(978-0-470-03971-7(X)*, Howell Bk. Hse.) Wiley, John & Sons, Inc.

Marzluff, John & Angell, Tony. The Gift of the Crow. 2012. (ENG., Illus.). 304p. 25.00 ***(978-1-4391-9873-5(X)***, Free Pr.) Free Pr.

Morrone, Marc & Fernandez, Amy. Ask the Bird Keeper. 2009. (ENG., Illus.). 128p. pap. 14.95 *(978-1-933958-31-6(6))* BowTie Pr.

Moustaki, Nikki. Boredom Busters for Birds: 40 Fun & Feather-Friendly Toys & Activities. 2010. (ENG.). 64p. (gr. 6). pap. 6.95 *(978-1-935484-19-6(2))* BowTie Pr.

O'Beirne, Kathleen P. Birds of a Feather: Lessons from the Sea. 2006. (Illus.). 206p. pap. 19.95 *(978-1-879979-02-4(0))* Lifescape Enterprises.

Otter, Ken A., ed. The Ecology & Behavior of Chickadees & Titmice. 2007. (ENG., Illus.). 352p. 125.00 *(978-0-19-856999-2(8))* Oxford Univ. Pr., Inc.

Patterson, I. J. The Shelduck: A Study in Behavioural Ecology. 2009. (ENG., Illus.). 288p. pap. 42.00 *(978-0-521-11335-9(0))* Cambridge Univ. Pr.

Pepperberg, Irene. Alex & Me: How a Scientist & a Parrot Discovered a Hidden World of Animal Intelligence - And Formed a Deep Bond in the Process. l.t. ed. 2008. 240p. pap. 23.95 *(978-0-06-173484-7(5)*, HarperLuxe) HarperCollins Pubs.

Pepperberg, Irene & Lewin, Roger. Alex & Me: How a Scientist & a Parrot Discovered a Hidden World of Animal Intelligence - And Formed a Deep Bond in the Process. 2008. (ENG., Illus.). 256p. 23.95 *(978-0-06-167247-7(5))* HarperCollins Pubs.

Regan, Patrick & Chester, Jonathan. Flipping Brilliant: A Penguin's Guide to a Happy Life. 2008. (ENG., Illus.). 64p. 9.99 *(978-0-7407-7229-0(5))* Andrews McMeel Publishing.

Ribic, Christine A., et al. Video Surveillance of Nesting Birds. 2012. ***(978-0-520-27313-9(3))*** Univ. of California Pr.

Rowinski, Kate. The Joy of Birding: A Beginner's Guide. 2011. (Joy of Ser.). (ENG., Illus.). 256p. pap. 14.95 *(978-1-61608-122-5(8)*, 608122) Skyhorse Publishing Co., Inc.

Schmauss, Anne, et al. For the Birds: A Month-by-Month Guide to Attracting Birds to Your Backyard. 2008. (ENG., Illus.). 224p. pap. 21.95 *(978-1-58479-717-3(7))* Stewart, Tabori & Chang.

Sibley, David Allen. The Sibley Guide to Bird Life & Behavior. 2009. (ENG., Illus.). 608p. 39.95 *(978-1-4000-4386-6(7)*, Knopf) Knopf Doubleday Publishing Group.

Stutchbury, Bridget. The Private Lives of Birds: A Scientist Reveals the Intricacies of Avian Social Life. 2010. (ENG., Illus.). 272p. 25.00 *(978-0-8027-1746-7(2))* Walker & Co.

Vallarino, Adriana. Sibling Rivalry in Black-Legged Kittiwakes. 2009. 172p. pap. *(978-3-639-21989-0(9))* VDM Verlag Dr. Mueller e.K.

Van Nieuwenhuyse, Dries, et al. The Little Owl: Conservation, Ecology & Behavior of Athene Noctua. (ENG.). 628p. 2011. pap. 39.99 *(978-0-521-71420-4(6))* 2008. (Illus.). 84.00 *(978-0-521-88678-9(3))* Cambridge Univ. Pr.

Watson, Jeff, et al. The Golden Eagle: Second Edition. 2nd ed. 2011. (Illus.). 400p. 65.00 *(978-0-300-17019-1(X))* Yale Univ. Pr.

Webb, A. C. Some Birds & Their Ways. (Illus.). 144p. reprint ed. lib. bdg. 88.00 *(978-0-7222-4846-1(6))* Library Reprints, Inc.
Wright, J. & Leonard, Marty L., eds. The Evolution of Begging: Competition, Cooperation & Communication. 2010. 508p. pap. 299.00 *(978-90-481-5997-0(0),* 9048159970) Springer.

BIRDS—BIBLIOGRAPHY

Anker, Jean. Bird Books & Bird Art: An Outline of the Literary History & Iconography of Descriptive Ornithology Based Principally on the Collection of Books Containing Plates with Figures of Birds & Their Eggs Now in the University Library at Copenhagen & Including a Catalogue of These Works. 2008. (Illus.). 90.00 *(978-1-57898-657-6(5))* Martino Publishing.
Audubon, John James. Audubon: Early Drawings. 2008. (Illus.). 288p. 125.00 *(978-0-674-03102-9(4),* Belknap Pr.) Harvard Univ. Pr.
Batchelder, Charles Foster. A Bibliography of the Published Writings of William Brewster. 2011. 56p. 36.95 ***(978-1-258-06491-4(X))*** Literary Licensing, LLC.
—A Bibliography of the Published Writings of William Brewster: Memoirs of the Nuttall Ornithological Club, No. 10. 2011. 56p. 36.95 ***(978-1-258-06057-2(4))*** Literary Licensing, LLC.

BIRDS—BREEDING

Black, Robert G. Cockatiels: Overcoming Problems in Their Care Feeding & Breeding. 2007. 168p. pap. 21.95 *(978-0-910335-06-5(0))* Avian Pubns.
—Parrot Nutrition. 2007. 270p. 49.95 *(978-0-910335-07-2(9))* Avian Pubns.
Bostic, Gregg. Aviary Breeding Exotic Birds: The Ultimate Way to Breed Birds. 2011. 62p. pap. 19.95 ***(978-1-4560-6925-4(X))*** PublishAmerica, Inc.
Demaine, A. F. Roller Canary Its History Breeding Trai. 2006. 92p. per. *(978-1-4067-9555-0(X),* Hesperides Pr.) Read Bks.
Firman, D. & Firman, Jeffrey. Commercial Turkey Production. 2008. (Illus.). 544p. 69.99 *(978-0-8138-0413-2(2),* Wiley-Blackwell) Wiley, John & Sons, Inc.
Gage, Laurie J. & Duerr, Rebecca S., eds. Hand-Rearing Birds. 2007. (ENG., Illus.). 456p. 99.99 *(978-0-8138-0666-2(6),* Wiley-Blackwell) Wiley, John & Sons, Inc.
Green, Jen. The Illustrated Practical Guide to Attracting & Feeding Backyard Birds: The Complete Book of Bird Feeders, Bird Tables, Birdbaths, Nest Boxes & Backyard Birdwatching. 2009. (ENG.). 256p. 35.00 *(978-0-7548-1989-9(2))* Anness Publishing GBR. Dist: National Bk. Network.
Griesser, Michael & Barnaby, Jonathan, eds. The Role of Nepotism, Cooperation & Competition in the Avian Families. 2010. (Birds - Evolution, Behavior & Ecology Ser.). pap. 43.00 *(978-1-60876-867-7(8))* Nova Science Pubs., Inc.
Jones, Alan. Keeping Parrots: Understanding Their Care & Breeding. 2011. (ENG., Illus.). 208p. 34.95 *(978-1-84797-263-7(2))* Crowood Pr., Ltd. GBR. Dist: Independent Pubs. Group.
Karsten, Peter. Pekin Robins & Small Softbills: Management & Breeding. 2007. (ENG., Illus.). 252p. 49.95 *(978-0-88839-606-8(6))* Hancock Hse. Pubs.
Mcdonald, Jodi. A Closer Look at Button-Quail. 2009. pap. *(978-1-61584-456-2(2))* Independent Pub.
Peck, George K. & James, Ross D. Breeding Birds of Ontario, Nidiology & Distribution: Nonpasserines. (Illus.). 709p. pap. *(978-0-88854-288-5(7))* BRILL.
Perveen, Farzana. Captive Crane, Its Breeding, Diet & Diseases in N-Wfp, Pakistan. 2010. 200p. pap. *(978-3-639-24737-4(X))* VDM Verlag Dr. Mueller e.K.
Renwick, E. S. Thermostatic Incubator: Raising Chickens by Hand. 98p. pap. 15.00 *(978-0-87556-360-2(0))* Saifer, Albert Pub.
Villier, Danny. The Bird Ringing Scheme. 2010. 200p. pap. *(978-3-639-18851-6(9))* VDM Verlag Dr. Mueller e.K.
Woginrich, Jenna. Chick Days: An Absolute Beginner's Guide to Raising Chickens from Hatching to Laying. Manalo, Paula, ed. 2011. (ENG., Illus.). 128p. pap. 14.95 *(978-1-60342-584-1(5),* 1603425845) Storey Publishing, LLC.
Woods, Judith A. Those Crazy Caiques. 2007. 56p. pap. 19.95 *(978-0-910335-05-8(2))* Avian Pubns.

BIRDS—CARE AND HYGIENE

Black, Robert G. Cockatiels: Overcoming Problems in Their Care Feeding & Breeding. 2007. 168p. pap. 21.95 *(978-0-910335-06-5(0))* Avian Pubns.
—Parrot Nutrition. 2007. 270p. 49.95 *(978-0-910335-07-2(9))* Avian Pubns.
Gilbert, Suzie. Flyaway: How a Wild Bird Rehabber Sought Adventure & Found Her Wings. 2010. (ENG.). 352p. pap. 14.99 *(978-0-06-156313-3(7),* HarperPerennial) HarperCollins Pubs.
Haupt, Thomas. Canaries. 2010. (Complete Pet Owner's Manuals Ser.). (ENG., Illus.). 64p. pap. 8.99 *(978-0-7641-4430-1(8))* Barron's Educational Series, Inc.
King, Doreen. First Aid & Nursing for Wild Birds. (Illus.). 96p. pap. 19.95 *(978-1-873580-15-8(0))* Whittet Bks., Ltd. GBR. Dist: Diamond Farm Bk. Pubs.
Mcdonald, Jodi. A Closer Look at Button-Quail. 2009. pap. *(978-1-61584-456-2(2))* Independent Pub.
Woods, Judith A. Those Crazy Caiques. 2007. 56p. pap. 19.95 *(978-0-910335-05-8(2))* Avian Pubns.

BIRDS—CLASSIFICATION

Blanchan, Nellie. Bird Neighbors. 2009. 350p. 36.99 *(978-1-117-51646-2(6));* (ENG.). 348p. pap. 23.99 *(978-1-117-51648-6(2),* BiblioLife); 350p. pap. 31.75 *(978-1-117-51647-9(4))* BiblioBazaar.
Blanchan, Neltje. Bird Neighbors. 2009. 350p. 36.99 *(978-1-116-07247-1(5))* 2009. 350p. 32.99 *(978-1-116-07248-8(3))* 2009. 350p. pap. 32.75 *(978-1-116-07249-5(1))* 2009. (ENG.). 349p. pap. 24.99 *(978-1-116-07251-8(3),* BiblioLife) 2009. (ENG.). 349p. pap. 23.99 *(978-1-116-07252-5(1),* BiblioLife) 2008. (ENG.). 307p. pap. 29.75 *(978-1-4264-0135-0(3))* 2008. (ENG.). 321p. pap. 23.99 *(978-1-4264-0006-3(3))* BiblioBazaar.
—Bird Neighbors. 2010. (Illus.). 146p. pap. 23.37 *(978-1-153-59227-7(4))* General Bks. LLC.
—Bird Neighbors. 2010. 262p. 34.36 *(978-1-163-34100-1(2))* 2010. 262p. pap. 22.36 *(978-1-162-78460-1(1))* 2007. (ENG.). 260p. 42.95 *(978-0-548-02945-9(8))* Kessinger Publishing, LLC.
Christidis, Les & Boles, Walter. Systematics & Taxonomy of Australian Birds. 2009. 288p. pap. 44.00 *(978-0-643-09602-8(7))* CSIRO Publishing AUS. Dist: Stylus Publishing, LLC.
Kenefick, Martyn, et al. Field Guide to the Birds of Trinidad & Tobago. 2008. (ENG., Illus.). 288p. pap. 40.00 *(978-0-300-13557-2(2))* Yale Univ. Pr.

BIRDS—COLLECTION AND PRESERVATION

see also Zoological Specimens—Collection and Preservation

burdge, les, l. Celebration of Birds: By les Burdge. 2007. (Illus.). 80p. 31.95 *(978-0-9801815-3-0(1))* Burdge, Les Photography.
Gibb, Andy. Build a British Bird List. 2010. 32p. pap. 10.50 *(978-1-4461-5017-7(8))* Lulu Enterprises Inc.
Metzler, Sally. Theatres of Nature: Dioramas at the Field Museum. 2008. (Illus.). 68p. pap. 9.95 *(978-0-914868-25-5(X))* Field Museum of Natural History, Div. of Pubns.
Tingay, Ruth E. & Katzner, Todd E., eds. The Eagle Watchers: Observing & Conserving Raptors around the World. 2010. (Illus.). 296p. 29.95 *(978-0-8014-4873-7(5),* Comstock Publishing Assocs.) Cornell Univ. Pr.

BIRDS—COLLISIONS WITH AIRPLANES

see Aircraft Accidents

BIRDS—COLOR

Hill, Geoffrey E. National Geographic Bird Coloration. 2010. (ENG., Illus.). 256p. 27.50 *(978-1-4262-0571-2(6),* National Geographic) National Geographic Society.

BIRDS—CONTROL

see Bird Control

BIRDS—DISEASES

see also specific diseases of birds, e.g. Ornithosis

Allegra, Ernesto P. Avian Influenza Research Progress. 2008. (C). 137.00 *(978-1-60021-617-6(X))* Nova Science Pubs., Inc.
Atkinson, Carter T., et al, eds. Parasitic Diseases of Wild Birds. 2009. (ENG., Illus.). 592p. 115.99 *(978-0-8138-2081-1(2),* Wiley-Blackwell) Wiley, John & Sons, Inc.
Avilcino, A. A. Bird Flu: What We Need to Know, 1 vol. 2010. (ENG., Illus.). 224p. per. *(978-1-394974-15-8(8))* Heritage Hse.
Brown, Charles. Are Wild Birds Important in the Transport of Arthropod-Borne. 2011. 76p. pap. 19.95 ***(978-0-9436*10-90-0(7))** Univ. of California Pr.
Campbell, Terry W. & Grant, Krystan. Clinical Cases in Avian & Exotic Animal Hematology & Cytology. 2010. (ENG., Illus.). 392p. 136.99 *(978-0-8138-1661-6(0),* Wiley-Blackwell) Wiley, John & Sons, Inc.
Chatterjee, Samrat. Migratory Birds & Spread of Disease. 2010. 140p. pap. *(978-3-639-26825-6(3))* VDM Verlag Dr. Mueller e.K.
Chitty, John & Lierz, Michael. BSAVA Manual of Raptors, Pigeons & Passerine Birds. 2008. (BSAVA British Small Animal Veterinary Association Ser.: 5). (ENG., Illus.). 420p. pap. 167.99 *(978-1-905319-04-6(5))* British Small Animal Veterinary Assn. (BSAVA) GBR. Dist: Wiley, John & Sons, Inc.
Clark, Phillip, et al. Atlas of Clinical Avian Hematology. 2009. (ENG., Illus.). 200p. 173.99 *(978-1-4051-9248-4(8),* Wiley-Blackwell) Wiley, John & Sons, Inc.
Coles, Brian H., ed. Essentials of Avian Medicine & Surgery. 3rd rev. ed. 2007. (ENG., Illus.). 392p. per. 99.99 *(978-1-4051-5755-1(0),* Wiley-Blackwell) Wiley, John & Sons, Inc.
Davis, Mike. The Monster at Our Door: The Global Threat of Avian Flu. rev. exp. ed. 2006. (ENG., Illus.). 240p. pap. 16.00 *(978-0-8050-8191-6(7),* Owl Bks.) Holt, Henry & Co.
Doneley, Robert & Doneley, Bob. Avian Medicine & Surgery in Practice: Companion & Aviary Birds. 2010. (ENG., Illus.). 336p. 120.00 *(978-1-84076-112-2(1))* Manson Publishing, Ltd. GBR. Dist: Thieme Medical Pubs., Inc.
Haugan, Salomon & Bjornson, Walter. Avian Influenza: Etiology, Pathogenesis & Interventions. 2009. (Public Health in the 21st Century Ser.). 129.00 *(978-1-60741-846-7(0),* Nova Biomedical Bks.) Nova Science Pubs., Inc.
Krautwald-Junghanns, Maria-Elisabeth, et al. Diagnostic Imaging of Exotic Pets: Birds, Small Mammals, Reptiles. 2010. (ENG., Illus.). 460p. *(978-3-89993-049-8(5))* schlütersche.
Marx, Keath L. & Roston, Margaret, eds. Proceedings of the 29th annual conference, Avian Medicine & Surgery: Mid-Atlantic States Association of Avian Veterinarians: Williamsburg, Virginia, USA, 27-20 April 2008. 2008. (Illus.). 304p. spiral bd. 50.00 incl. DVD *(978-0-9788405-1-8(8))* Mid-Atlantic States Assoc. of Avian Veterinarians.
Mercola, Joseph. The Great Bird Flu Hoax, 0 vols. 2009. 256p. pap. 13.99 *(978-0-7852-9733-8(2))* Nelson, Thomas Inc.
Muzaffar, Sabir B. Diseases & Parasites of Birds. 2009. 132p. pap. *(978-3-639-20926-6(5))* VDM Verlag Dr. Mueller e.K.
Nagle, Jeanne. Frequently Asked Questions about Avian Flu. 2008. (FAQ Ser.). (Illus.). 64p. (YA). (gr. 7-12). lib. bdg. 29.25 *(978-1-4042-1810-9(6))* Rosen Publishing Group, Inc., The.
Paul, Ellen, ed. Emerging Avian Disease. 2012. (Studies in Avian Biology Ser.). (ENG.). 125p. 39.95 ***(978-0-520-27237-8(4))*** Univ. of California Pr.
Phillips, Brendanne. What You Must Do to Escape the Bird Flu. 2007. per. 19.95 *(978-0-9774513-8-8(0))* Changing Lives Publishing.
Samour, Jaime, ed. Avian Medicine. 2nd rev. ed. 2008. (ENG., Illus.). 540p. 206.00 *(978-0-7234-3401-6(8),* Mosby) Elsevier - Health Sciences Div.
Schat, Karel A. Avian Immunology. Davison, Fred et al, eds. 2008. (ENG., Illus.). 496p. 170.00 *(978-0-12-370634-8(3),* Academic Pr.) Elsevier Science & Technology Bks.
Schudel, Alejandro & Lombard, Michel. OIE/FAO International Scientific Conference on Avian Influenza: Paris, France, 7-8 April 2005, Vol. 124. (Developments in Biologicals Ser.: Vol. 124). (Illus.). 278p. pap. *(978-3-8055-8031-1(2))* Karger, S. AG.
Selzer, Michael I. How to stay safe during the coming avian flu Pandemic: A guide for every Household. 2006. pap. 14.95 *(978-0-9789089-0-4(2))* Farshaw Publishing.
St. John, Clauce. Bird Ailments & Accidents - Their Trea. 2006. 128p. per. *(978-1-4067-9594-3(1),* Hesperides Pr.) Read Bks.
Stroud, Robert. Diseases of Canaries. 2008. 256p. *(978-1-4437-3505-6(1),* Home Farm Bks.) Read Bks.
Thomas, Nancy J., et al, eds. Infectious Diseases of Wild Birds. 2007. (ENG., Illus.). 496p. 110.99 *(978-0-8138-2812-1(0),* Wiley-Blackwell) Wiley, John & Sons, Inc.
Wells, H. Bird Flu, Are You Prepared? 2007. 120p. per. *(978-1-899820-29-0(9))* Paragon Publishing, Rothersthorpe.
Young, Robert W., ed. Animal & Plant Health Inspection Service Oversight of Avian Influenza: Audit Report. 2006. 51p. (C). pap. 15.00 *(978-1-4223-0766-3(2))* DIANE Publishing Co.

BIRDS—EGGS

Black, J. G. Birds Nesting & Egg Collecting. 2008. (Illus.). 288p. *(978-1-4437-3727-2(5),* Home Farm Bks.) Read Bks.
Bosiger, E. & Guilcher, J. M. A Bird Is Born. 2011. 90p. 38.95 ***(978-1-258-06247-7(X))*** Literary Licensing, LLC.
Henderson, Carrol L. Oology & Ralph's Talking Eggs: Bird Conservation Comes Out of Its Shell. 2007. (Mildred Wyatt-Wold Series in Ornithology). (ENG., Illus.). 200p. 29.95 *(978-0-292-71451-9(3))* Univ. of Texas Pr.
Hosking, Eric & Reade, W. Winwood. Nesting Birds: Eggs & Fledglings. 3rd ed. (Illus.). 275p. *(978-0-7137-0444-0(6))* Blandford Pr.
Purcell, Rosamond, et al. Egg & Nest. 2008. (Illus.). 232p. 39.95 *(978-0-674-03172-2(5),* Belknap Pr.) Harvard Univ. Pr.

BIRDS—EMBRYOLOGY

see Embryology—Birds

BIRDS—EVOLUTION

Chiappe, Luis. The Glorified Dinosaurs: Origins & Early Evolution of Birds. 2007. 192p. 69.95 *(978-0-470-07508-1(2),* Wiley-Liss) Wiley, John & Sons, Inc.
Cicero, Carla & Remsen Jr., J. V., eds. Festschrift for Ned K. Johnson: Geographic Variation & Evolution in Birds. 2011. (Ornithological Monographs). 126p. pap. 24.95 *(978-0-943610-75-7(3))* Univ. of California Pr.
Czerkas, Stephen & Czerkas, Sylvia Massey. Feathered Dinosaurs. 2008. (Illus.). 46p. (J). *(978-1-932075-03-8(8))* Dinosaur Museum, The.
Dyke, Gareth & Kaiser, Gary, eds. Living Dinosaurs: The Evolutionary History of Modern Birds. 2011. (ENG., Illus.). 440p. 134.95 *(978-0-470-65666-2(2),* Wiley-Blackwell) Wiley, John & Sons, Inc.
James, Frances C. & Pourtless, John A., IV. Cladistics & the Origin of Birds: A Review & Two New Analyses. 2010. (Ornithological Monographs). 88p. pap. 19.95 *(978-0-943610-85-6(0))* Univ. of California Pr.
Kaiser, Gary W. The Inner Bird: Anatomy & Evolution. 2007. (Illus.). 386p. 85.00 *(978-0-7748-1343-3(1))* UBC Pr. CAN. Dist: Univ. of Washington Pr.
Lima-de-Faria, Antonio. Molecular Geometry of Body Pattern in Birds. 2012. (ENG., Illus.). xi, 162p. 189.00 ***(978-3-642-25300-3(8),*** 3642253008) Springer.
O'Donald, Peter. The Arctic Skua: A study of the ecology & evolution of a Seabird. 2009. (ENG., Illus.). 344p. pap. 48.00 *(978-0-521-11334-2(2))* Cambridge Univ. Pr.
Smith, J. & Nanda, I., eds. Avian Genomics in Evolution, Agriculture & Health [Bibliography & Price not Definite.]. 2007. (Illus.). 404p. *(978-3-8055-8338-1(9))* Karger, S. AG.
Tudge, Colin. The Bird: A Natural History of Who Birds Are, Where They Came from, & How They Live. 2010. (ENG., Illus.). 480p. pap. 17.00 *(978-0-307-34205-8(0),* Three Rivers Pr.) Crown Publishing Group.
Winker, Kevin & Haig, Susan, eds. Avian Subspecies. 2010. (Ornithological Monographs). 210p. pap. 40.00 *(978-0-943610-86-3(9))* Univ. of California Pr.

BIRDS—FLIGHT

Alexander, David E. Why Don't Jumbo Jets Flap Their Wings? Flying Animals, Flying Machines, & How They Are Different. 2009. (ENG., Illus.). 296p. 26.95 *(978-0-8135-4479-3(3))* Rutgers Univ. Pr.
Ettlinger, Richard. On Feathered Wings: Birds in Flight. 2008. (ENG., Illus.). 192p. 42.00 *(978-0-8109-9525-3(5))* Abrams.
Henderson, Carrol L. Birds in Flight: The Art & Science of How Birds Fly. 2008. (ENG., Illus.). 160p. 25.00 *(978-0-7603-3392-1(0),* 0760333920, Voyageur Pr) MBI Publishing Co. LLC.
Liguori, Jerry. Hawks at a Distance: Identification of Migrant Raptors. 2011. (ENG., Illus.). 216p. (C). 49.50 *(978-0-691-13558-8(4));* pap. 19.95 *(978-0-691-13559-5(2))* Princeton Univ. Pr.
Pennycuick, C. J. Modelling the Flying Bird. 2008. (Theoretical Ecology Ser.: 5). (ENG., Illus.). 496p. 86.95 *(978-0-12-374299-5(4),* Academic Pr.) Elsevier Science & Technology Bks.
Shyy, Wei, et al. Aerodynamics of Low Reynolds Number Flyers. 2011. (Cambridge Aerospace Ser.). (ENG.). 212p. pap. 45.00 *(978-0-521-20401-9(1))* Cambridge Univ. Pr.

BIRDS—FOLKLORE

Anderson, Glynn. Birds of Ireland: Facts, Folklore & History. 2009. (ENG., Illus.). 375p. 48.95 *(978-1-905172-72-6(9))* Collins Pr., The IRL. Dist: Dufour Editions, Inc.
Ingersoll, Ernest. Birds in Legend, Fable & Folklore. 2010. 148p. pap. 23.56 *(978-1-153-29714-1(0))* General Bks. LLC.
Kroll, Jennifer L. Wings & Tales: Learning about Birds Through Folklore, Facts, & Fun Activities. 2011. E-Book *(978-1-59884-598-3(5))* Libraries Unlimited, Inc.
—Wings & Tales: Learning about Birds Through Folklore, Facts, and Fun Activities, 1 vol. (Illus.). 170p. pap. 30.00 *(978-1-59884-597-6(7),* A3130P) Libraries Unlimited, Inc.
Moss, Stephen. Birds Britannia. 2011. (ENG.). 320p. 29.95 ***(978-0-00-741344-7(0))*** HarperCollins Pubs. Ltd. GBR. Dist: Independent Pubs. Group.
Nozedar, Adele. The Secret Language of Birds: A Treasury of Myths, Folklore & Inspirational True Stories. 2007. (Illus.). 534p. 29.00 *(978-1-4223-9010-8(1))* DIANE Publishing Co.
Rea, Amadeo M. Wings in the Desert: A Folk Ornithology of the Northern Pimans. 2008. (ENG.). 320p. 70.00 *(978-0-8165-2459-4(9))* Univ. of Arizona Pr.
Stratton-Porter, Gene. Wings. 2011. 128p. 40.95 ***(978-1-258-06088-6(4))*** Literary Licensing, LLC.
Tate, Peter. Flights of Fancy: Birds in Myth, Legend, & Superstition. 2008. (ENG., Illus.). 192p. 19.95 *(978-0-385-34248-3(9),* Delacorte Pr) Random House Publishing Group.
Waterbury, Florence. Bird Deities in China. 2007. *(978-1-57898-678-1(8))* Martino Publishing.

BIRDS—FOOD

Baker, Jerry. Jerry Baker's Backyard Bird Feeding Bonanza: 1,487 Tips, Tricks, & Treats for Attracting Your Fine-Feathered Friends. 2006. (Jerry Baker's Good Gardening Ser.). (ENG., Illus.). 384p. 29.95 *(978-0-922433-57-5(7))* Baker, Jerry.
Birds and Blooms Editors. For the Birds: Easy-to-Make Recipes for Your Feathered Friends. 2010. (ENG.). 120p. (gr. 12). spiral bd. 9.95 *(978-1-60652-131-1(4))* Reader's Digest Assn., Inc., The.
Black, Robert G. Parrot Nutrition. 2007. 270p. 49.95 *(978-0-910335-07-2(9))* Avian Pubns.
Craven, Scott, et al. Bird Feeding — Tips for Beginners & Veterans. 2008. (Illus.). 12p. pap. 5.00 *(978-0-9801401-2-5(9))* Univ. of Wisconsin-Extension.
Croxall, J. P., ed. Seabirds: Feeding Ecology & Role in Marine Ecosystems. 2009. (ENG.). 420p. pap. 53.00 *(978-0-521-10510-1(2))* Cambridge Univ. Pr.
Niles, Lawrence, et al. Status of the Red Knot (Calidris canutus rufa) in the Western Hemisphere: Studies in Avian Biology, No. 36. 2008. (Studies in Avian Biology). 186p. mass mkt. 20.00 *(978-0-943610-83-2(4))* American Ornithologists Union.
Schmauss, Anne, et al. For the Birds: A Month-by-Month Guide to Attracting Birds to Your Backyard. 2008. (ENG., Illus.). 224p. pap. 21.95 *(978-1-58479-717-3(7))* Stewart, Tabori & Chang.
Wright, J. & Leonard, Marty L., eds. The Evolution of Begging: Competition, Cooperation & Communication. 2010. 508p. pap. 299.00 *(978-90-481-5997-0(0),* 9048159970) Springer.
Zickefoose, Julie & Bird Watcher's Digest Staff. Backyard Birding: Using Natural Gardening to Attract Birds. 2011. (ENG., Illus.). 256p. pap. 14.95 *(978-1-61608-266-6(6),* 608266) Skyhorse Publishing Co., Inc.

BIRDS—GEOGRAPHICAL DISTRIBUTION

Beletsky, Les. Global Birding: Traveling the World in Search of Birds. 2010. (Illus.). 320p. 35.00 *(978-1-4262-0640-5(2),* National Geographic) National Geographic Society.
Cadman, Michael D. Atlas of the Breeding Birds of Ontario, 2001-2005. 2009. (ENG., Illus.). 728p. 92.50 *(978-1-896059-15-0(5))* Federation of Ontario Naturalists CAN. Dist: Firefly Bks., Ltd.
Cicero, Carla & Remsen Jr., J. V., eds. Festschrift for Ned K. Johnson: Geographic Variation & Evolution in Birds. 2011. (Ornithological Monographs). 126p. pap. 24.95 *(978-0-943610-75-7(3))* Univ. of California Pr.
Cleere, N. Nightjars, Potoos, Frogmouths, Oilbird, & Owlet-Nightjars of the World. 2010. (ENG., Illus.). 464p. (C). 45.00 *(978-0-691-14857-1(0))* Princeton Univ. Pr.
Ellison, Walter G., ed. Second Atlas of the Breeding Birds of Maryland & the District of Columbia. 2010. (ENG., Illus.). 520p. (gr. 17). 75.00 *(978-0-8018-9576-0(6))* Johns Hopkins Univ. Pr.
Harrison, John & Worfolk, Tim. A Field Guide to the Birds of Sri Lanka. 2nd ed. 2011. (ENG., Illus.). 224p. pap. 49.50 *(978-0-19-958567-0(9))* Oxford Univ. Pr., Inc.
Niles, Lawrence, et al. Status of the Red Knot (Calidris canutus rufa) in the Western Hemisphere: Studies in Avian Biology, No. 36. 2008. (Studies in Avian Biology). 186p. mass mkt. 20.00 *(978-0-943610-83-2(4))* American Ornithologists Union.
Norman, David. Birds in Cheshire & Wirral: A Breeding & Wintering Atlas. 2009. (ENG., Illus.). 704p. 90.00 *(978-1-84631-152-9(7))* Liverpool Univ. Pr. GBR. Dist: Chicago Distribution Ctr.

Schneider, Todd M., et al, eds. The Breeding Bird Atlas of Georgia. 2010. (ENG., Illus.). 520p. 64.95 *(978-0-8203-2893-5(6))* Univ. of Georgia Pr.
Winker, Kevin & Haig, Susan, eds. Avian Subspecies. 2010. (Ornithological Monographs). 210p. pap. 40.00 *(978-0-943610-86-3(9))* Univ. of California Pr.
Wormworth, Janice & Sekercioglu, Cagan H. Winged Sentinels: Birds & Climate Change, 1 vol. 2011. (ENG., Illus.). 296p. pap. 40.00 *(978-0-521-12682-3(7))* Cambridge Univ. Pr.

BIRDS—JUVENILE LITERATURE

Burgess. The Burgess Bird Book for Children. 2010. 142p. pap. 13.85 *(978-1-152-50820-0(2))* General Bks. LLC.
Burgess, Thornton W. The Burgess Bird Book for Children. 2009. 436p. 34.99 *(978-1-113-14339-6(8))*; (ENG.). 434p. pap. 28.99 *(978-1-113-14334-1(7)*, BiblioLife); (ENG.). 434p. pap. 26.99 *(978-1-113-14333-4(9)*, BiblioLife); 436p. pap. 34.75 *(978-1-113-14336-5(3))* BiblioBazaar.
—The Burgess Bird Book for Children. 2010. 188p. pap. 18.36 *(978-1-162-69001-8(1))*; (gr. -1-7). 30.36 ***(978-1-169-28041-0(2))***; 37.95 *(978-1-161-45866-4(2))* Kessinger Publishing, LLC.
—Burgess Bird Book for Children. 2010. 128p. pap. 21.70 *(978-1-153-59343-4(2))* General Bks. LLC.
Burgess, Thornton W. 1874-1965 & Fuertes, Louis Agassiz. The Burgess Bird Book for Children. 2011. 444p. pap. 36.75 ***(978-1-172-92743-2(X))*** 2010. (ENG.). 440p. pap. 35.75 *(978-1-171-57747-8(8))* 2010. (ENG.). 444p. pap. 36.75 *(978-1-171-53821-9(9))* 2010. (ENG.). 444p. pap. 36.75 *(978-1-171-74347-7(5))* 2010. (ENG.). 444p. pap. 36.75 *(978-1-176-23714-8(4))* BiblioBazaar.
Hancock, David. Story of Eagle. 2007. (Illus.). 24p. (J). pap. 5.95 ***(978-0-88839-641-9(4))*** Hancock Hse. Pubs.
Hess, Deborah. The Bald Eagle. 2007. (J). pap. 6.99 *(978-0-7614-3371-2(6))* Marshall Cavendish Corp.
Rafferty, John P., ed. Meat Eaters: Raptors, Sharks, & Crocodiles. 2011. (Britannica Guide to Predators & Prey Ser.). (Illus.). 208p. (YA). 103.40 *(978-1-61530-451-6(7))* Rosen Publishing Group, Inc., The.
Thornton W. Burgess, Junr. The Burgess Bird Book for Children. 2009. (CAM.). 182p. pap. 13.45 *(978-1-4385-7319-9(7*, Book Jungle) Standard Pubns., Inc.

BIRDS—MIGRATION

Berthold, Peter, et al, eds. Avian Migration. 2010. (ENG., Illus.). xvi, 610p. pap. 279.00 *(978-3-642-07780-7(3)*, 3642077803) Springer.
Bildstein, Keith L. Migrating Raptors of the World: Their Ecology & Conservation. 2006. (Illus.). 320p. 35.00 *(978-0-8014-4179-0(X))* Cornell Univ. Pr.
Chu, Miyoko. Songbird Journeys: Four Seasons in the Lives of Migratory Birds. 2007. (ENG., Illus.). 1p. per. 13.95 *(978-0-8027-1518-0(4))* Walker & Co.
Coward, T. A. The Migration of Birds. 3rd rev. ed. 2012. (ENG.). 156p. pap. 19.99 ***(978-1-107-60609-8(8))*** Cambridge Univ. Pr.
Dean, W. Richard J. Nomadic Desert Birds. 2010. (Adaptations of Desert Organisms Ser.). (Illus.). x, 185p. pap. 219.00 *(978-3-642-07325-0(5)*, 3642073255) Springer.
Elphick, Jonathan, ed. Atlas of Bird Migration: Tracing the Great Journeys of the World's Birds. 2011. (ENG., Illus.). 176p. pap. 24.95 *(978-1-55407-971-1(3))* Firefly Bks., Ltd.
Gibb, Andy. The British Birding Year. 2010. 53p. pap. 21.50 *(978-1-4457-7242-4(6))* Lulu Enterprises Inc.
Hochbaum, H. Albert 1911-. Travels & Traditions of Waterfowl. 2011. 320p. pap. 30.75 ***(978-1-245-51406-4(7))*** BiblioBazaar.
Hughes, Janice M. The Migration of Birds: Seasons on the Wing. 2009. (ENG., Illus.). 208p. 40.00 *(978-1-55407-432-7(0))* Firefly Bks., Ltd.
Kempthorne, Dirk & Myers, Mark D. Radar Technology Applied to Migratory Conservation & Management. 2009. pap. 43.00 *(978-1-60692-935-3(6))* Nova Science Pubs., Inc.
Kerlinger, Paul. How Birds Migrate. 2nd rev. ed. 2008. (ENG., Illus.). 272p. pap. 21.95 *(978-0-8117-3230-7(4))* Stackpole Bks.
Liguori, Jerry. Hawks at a Distance: Identification of Migrant Raptors. 2011. (ENG., Illus.). 216p. (C). 49.50 *(978-0-691-13558-8(4))*; pap. 19.95 *(978-0-691-13559-5(2))* Princeton Univ. Pr.
McCarthy, Michael. Say Goodbye to the Cuckoo: Migratory Birds & the Impending Ecological Catastrophe. 2010. (ENG.). 288p. 26.95 *(978-1-56663-856-2(9))* Dee, Ivan R. Pub.
Newton, Ian. The Migration Ecology of Birds. 2007. (ENG.). 984p. 142.00 *(978-0-12-517367-4(9)*, Academic Pr.) Elsevier Science & Technology Bks.
Niles, Lawrence, et al. Status of the Red Knot (Calidris canutus rufa) in the Western Hemisphere: Studies in Avian Biology, No. 36. 2008. (Studies in Avian Biology). 186p. mass mkt. 20.00 *(978-0-943610-83-2(4))* American Ornithologists Union.
Wallraff, Hans G. Avian Navigation: Pigeon Homing as a Paradigm: Pigeon Homing as a Paradigm. 2010. (ENG., Illus.). xii, 229p. pap. 189.00 *(978-3-642-06118-9(4)*, 3642061184) Springer.

BIRDS—NAVIGATION

see Bird Navigation

BIRDS—NESTS

Black, J. G. Birds Nesting & Egg Collecting. 2008. (Illus.). 288p. *(978-1-4437-3727-2(5)*, Home Farm Bks.) Read Bks.
Bosiger, E. & Guilcher, J. M. A Bird Is Born. 2011. 90p. 38.95 ***(978-1-258-06247-7(X))*** Literary Licensing, LLC.
Braun, Bjorn. Björn Braun: Nest. 2010. (ENG., Illus.). 112p. 37.50 *(978-3-86678-369-0(8))* Kerber Verlag DEU. Dist: D.A.P./Distributed Art Pubs.
Dyes, John C. Nesting Birds of the Coastal Islands: A Naturalist's Year on Galveston Bay. 2011. (ENG., Illus.). 163p. pap. 19.95 ***(978-0-292-72973-5(1))*** Univ. of Texas Pr.
Flannery, Maureen. Nests: Fifty Nests & the Birds That Built Them. 2011. (ENG., Illus.). 120p. 29.95 *(978-0-8118-7758-9(2))* Chronicle Bks. LLC.
Goodfellow, Peter. Avian Architecture: How Birds Design, Engineer & Build. 2011. (ENG., Illus.). 160p. 27.95 *(978-0-691-14849-6(X))* Princeton Univ. Pr.
Heinrich, Bernd. The Nesting Season: Cuckoos, Cuckolds, & the Invention of Monogamy. 2010. (Illus.). 352p. 29.95 *(978-0-674-04877-5(6)*, Belknap Pr.) Harvard Univ. Pr.
Macnamara, Peggy. Architecture by Birds & Insects: A Natural Art. 2008. (ENG., Illus.). 164p. 25.00 *(978-0-226-50097-3(7))* Univ. of Chicago Pr.
Purcell, Rosamond, et al. Egg & Nest. 2008. (Illus.). 232p. 39.95 *(978-0-674-03172-2(5)*, Belknap Pr.) Harvard Univ. Pr.
Ribic, Christine A., et al. Video Surveillance of Nesting Birds. 2012. ***(978-0-520-27313-9(3))*** Univ. of California Pr.
Schmauss, Anne, et al. For the Birds: A Month-by-Month Guide to Attracting Birds to Your Backyard. 2008. (ENG., Illus.). 224p. pap. 21.95 *(978-1-58479-717-3(7))* Stewart, Tabori & Chang.

BIRDS—NOMENCLATURE

Burridge, John T. Burridge's Multilingual Dictionary of Birds of the World. 2008. (LAT, ENG & MUL.). 325p. *(978-1-84718-515-0(0))*; (MUL & ENG.). 260p. *(978-1-84718-517-4(7))*; (GER, ENG & MUL.). 260p. *(978-1-84718-525-9(8))*; (DUT, ENG & MUL.). 325p. *(978-1-84718-529-7(0))*; (CAT, BAQ, SPA, ENG & MUL.). 305p. *(978-1-4438-0119-5(4))* Cambridge Scholars Pub.
—Burridge's Multilingual Dictionary of Birds of the World: Volume VI - Danish (Dansk) & Volume VII - Faroese (Færosk) 2008. (DAN, ENG & MUL.). 290p. *(978-1-84718-869-4(9))* Cambridge Scholars Pub.
—Burridge's Multilingual Dictionary of Birds of the World: Volume VIII - Norwegian (Norsk) & Volume IX - Icelandic (slandsk) 2008. (NOR, ICE, ENG & MUL.). 328p. ***(978-1-4438-0055-6(4))*** Cambridge Scholars Pub.
—Burridge's Multilingual Dictionary of Birds of the World: Volume X Swedish (Svensk) 2008. (SWE, ENG & MUL.). 259p. *(978-1-4438-1741-7(4))* Cambridge Scholars Pub.
—Burridge's Multilingual Dictionary of Birds of the World: Volume XI French (Français) 2008. (DUT, ENG & MUL.). 261p. *(978-1-84718-644-7(0))* Cambridge Scholars Pub.
—Burridge's Multilingual Dictionary of Birds of the World: Volume XIX Czech (Aumi;OElig;eAring;iexcl;tina) & Volume XX Slovak (Slovenskagrave;) 2008. (MUL & ENG.). *(978-1-4438-1320-4(6))* Cambridge Scholars Pub.
—Burridge's Multilingual Dictionary of Birds of the World: Volume XV - Portuguese (Portuguecirc;s) 2008. (POR, ENG & MUL.). 260p. *(978-1-4438-0604-6(8))* Cambridge Scholars Pub.
—Burridge's Multilingual Dictionary of Birds of the World: Volume XXI - Polish (Polski) 2008. (POL, ENG & MUL.). 260p. *(978-1-4438-1262-7(5))* Cambridge Scholars Pub.
—Burridge's Multilingual Dictionary of Birds of the World: Volume XXII Russian (ETH; Ntilde;fnof;NuNuETH;ordm;ETH;cedil;ETH;) 2008. (MUL & ENG.). *(978-1-4438-1427-0(X))* Cambridge Scholars Pub.
—Burridge's Multilingual Dictionary of Birds of the World: Volume XXXVII Finnish (Suomi) 2008. (FIN, ENG & MUL.). 261p. *(978-1-4438-1753-0(8))* Cambridge Scholars Pub.
—Burridge's Multilingual Dictionary of Birds of the World: Volume XXXVIII Estonian (Eesti) 2008. (EST, ENG & MUL.). 261p. *(978-1-4438-1756-1(2))* Cambridge Scholars Pub.
—Burridge's Multilingual Dictionary of Birds of the World: Volumes XXIII Bulgarian; Volume XXIV Ukranian; Volume XXV Belarusian. 2008. (BUL, UKR, BEL, ENG & MUL.). 230p. *(978-1-4438-2112-4(8))* Cambridge Scholars Pub.
Gill, Frank & Wright, Minturn. Birds of the World: Recommended English Names. 2006. 259p. pap. 19.95 incl. audio compact disk *(978-0-691-12827-6(8))* Princeton Univ. Pr.
Holloway, Joel Ellis. Dictionary of Birds of the United States. 2009. (ENG.). 224p. pap. 22.95 *(978-1-60469-174-0(3)*, 1604691743) Timber Pr., Inc.
Rozzi, Ricardo. Multi-Ethnic Bird Guide of the Subantarctic Forests of South America. 2nd ed. 2010. (SPA, ENG & SAI., Illus.). 236p. 34.95 *(978-1-57441-282-6(5))* Univ. of North Texas Pr.

BIRDS—PARASITES

Atkinson, Carter T., et al, eds. Parasitic Diseases of Wild Birds. 2009. (ENG., Illus.). 592p. 115.99 *(978-0-8138-2081-1(2)*, Wiley-Blackwell) Wiley, John & Sons, Inc.
Muzaffar, Sabir B. Diseases & Parasites of Birds. 2009. 132p. pap. *(978-3-639-20926-6(5))* VDM Verlag Dr. Mueller e.K.

BIRDS—PHYSIOLOGY

Bicudo, J. Eduardo P. W., et al. Ecological & Environmental Physiology of Birds. 2010. (Ecological & Environmental Physiology Ser.). (ENG., Illus.). 328p. 125.00 *(978-0-19-922844-7(2))*; pap. 65.00 *(978-0-19-922845-4(0))* Oxford Univ. Pr., Inc.
Birkhead, Tim & Swainson, Bill. Bird Sense: What It's Like to Be a Bird. 2012. (ENG.). 288p. 25.00 ***(978-0-8027-7966-3(2))*** Walker & Co.
Norris, David O. & Lopez, Kristin H., eds. Hormones & Reproduction of Vertebrates - Vol 4: Birds, 5 vols. 2010. (ENG., Illus.). 286p. 119.95 *(978-0-12-374929-1(8)*, Academic Pr.) Elsevier Science & Technology Bks.
Williams, Tony. Physiological Adaptations for Breeding in Birds. 2012. (ENG., Illus.). 392p. (C). 65.00 ***(978-0-691-13982-1(2))*** Princeton Univ. Pr.
Zeigler, H. Philip & Marler, Peter, eds. Neuroscience of Birdsong. 2008. (ENG., Illus.). 542p. 148.00 *(978-0-521-86915-7(3))* Cambridge Univ. Pr.

BIRDS—PICTORIAL WORKS

Anker, Jean. Bird Books & Bird Art: An Outline of the Literary History & Iconography of Descriptive Ornithology Based Principally on the Collection of Books Containing Plates with Figures of Birds & Their Eggs Now in the University Library at Copenhagen & Including a Catalogue of These Works. 2008. (Illus.). 90.00 *(978-1-57898-657-6(5))* Martino Publishing.
Audubon, John James. Audubon: Early Drawings. 2008. (Illus.). 288p. 125.00 *(978-0-674-03102-9(4)*, Belknap Pr.) Harvard Univ. Pr.
Audubon, John James. Eighteen Best Loved Bird Paintings. 2011. 24p. pap. 35.95 ***(978-1-258-01999-0(X))*** Literary Licensing, LLC.
Audubon, John James & Oppenheimer, Joel. The Birds of America: The Bien Chromolithographic Edition. 2012. (ENG., Illus.). 256p. 350.00 ***(978-0-393-08865-6(0)**, 8865)* Norton, W. W. & Co., Inc.
Audubon Society Staff, et al. Bird: The Definitive Visual Guide. 2009. (ENG.). 512p. (gr. 12). pap. 27.95 *(978-0-7566-5574-7(9))* Dorling Kindersley Publishing, Inc.
Beletsky, Les. Birds of the World. 2006. (ENG., Illus.). 528p. 59.95 *(978-0-7748-1358-7(X))* Univ. of British Columbia Pr. CAN. Dist: Univ. of Toronto Pr.
Birds of the National Aviary. 2006. (Illus.). 100p. per. 24.95 *(978-0-615-13269-3(3))* West, Doug.
Blocksma, Mary. Whats in the Woods. 2008. pap. 12.50 *(978-0-9708575-7-6(8))* Beaver Island Arts.
Boyle, William J. The Birds of New Jersey: Status & Distribution. 2011. (ENG., Illus.). 320p. (C). 55.00 *(978-0-691-14409-2(5))*; pap. 24.95 *(978-0-691-14410-8(9))* Princeton Univ. Pr.
Brady, Alan. Atlantic Seabird Photo Journal. 2009. 202p. 29.99 *(978-1-4363-9319-5(1))*; pap. 19.99 *(978-1-4363-9318-8(3))* Xlibris Corp.
Branch, Susan. Birdies. 20p. pap. 29.70 *(978-0-7683-2207-1(3))* CEDCO Publishing.
Braun, Bjorn. Björn Braun: Nest. 2010. (ENG., Illus.). 112p. 37.50 *(978-3-86678-369-0(8))* Kerber Verlag DEU. Dist: D.A.P./Distributed Art Pubs.
Bryan, Denver. A Portrait of North American Waterfowling. 2006. (Illus.). 96p. tchr. ed. 19.50 *(978-1-59543-051-9(2))* Willow Creek Pr., Inc.
Buffon, Comte de, Georges Louis Leclerc, Comte de. The Natural History of Birds: From the French of the Count de Buffon; Illustrated with Engravings, & a Preface, Notes, & Additions, by the Translator. 2010. (Cambridge Library Collection - Life Sciences Ser.). (ENG.). 534p. pap. 39.99 *(978-1-108-02300-9(2))*; 558p. pap. 39.99 *(978-1-108-02299-6(5))*; 654p. pap. 45.00 *(978-1-108-02303-0(7))*; 618p. pap. 43.00 *(978-1-108-02306-1(1))*; 554p. pap. 39.99 *(978-1-108-02301-6(0))*; 596p. pap. 43.00 *(978-1-108-02302-3(9))*; 492p. pap. 35.99 *(978-1-108-02298-9(7))*; 540p. pap. 39.99 *(978-1-108-02305-4(3))*; (Illus.). 610p. pap. 43.00 *(978-1-108-02304-7(5))* Cambridge Univ. Pr.
burdge, les, III. Celebration of Birds: By les Burdge. 2007. (Illus.). 80p. 31.95 *(978-0-9801816-3-0(1))* Burdge, Les Photography.
Burdge, Lester James, 3rd. Wild Florida by les Burdge. 2007. (Illus.). 80p. 75.00 *(978-0-9801816-0-9(7))* Burdge, Les Photography.
burdge, lester james, III. Wild Florida by les Burdge. 2007. (Illus.). 80p. 45.00 *(978-0-9801816-1-6(5))* Burdge, Les Photography.
Byland, Steve. North American Birds in Photographs CD-ROM & Book. 2011. (Dover Electronic Clip Art Ser.). (ENG., Illus.). 48p. pap. 19.95 *(978-0-486-99007-1(9))* Dover Pubns., Inc.
Catherine E., Clark. The Birds We Live With. 2009. (Illus.). 112p. 24.99 *(978-0-7643-3260-9(0))* Schiffer Publishing, Ltd.
Chandler, Richard. Shorebirds of North America, Europe & Asia: A Photographic Guide. 2009. (ENG., Illus.). 448p. pap. 35.00 *(978-0-691-14281-4(5))* Princeton Univ. Pr.
Cillie, Burger, et al. Pocket Guide to Birds of Southern Africa: With New English Names. 4th ed. 2009. (Illus.). 160p. pap. 12.00 *(978-1-919938-97-4(4))* Sunbird Publishing ZAF. Dist: International Publishers Marketing.
Cook, Katrina. Birds. 2007. (Illus.). 223p. *(978-1-84724-200-6(6))* Quercus.
Couzens, Dominic. Extreme Birds: The World's Most Extraordinary & Bizarre Birds. 2011. (ENG., Illus.). 288p. pap. 24.95 *(978-1-55407-952-0(7))* Firefly Bks., Ltd.
Cross, Theodore. Waterbirds. 2009. (ENG., Illus.). 344p. 150.00 *(978-0-393-07226-6(6)*, 7226) Norton, W. W. & Co., Inc.
Crossley, Richard. The Crossley ID Guide: Eastern Birds. 2011. (ENG., Illus.). 544p. 35.00 *(978-0-691-14778-9(7))* Princeton Univ. Pr.
de la Harpe, Jean Paul. Chile, Shelter of Life. 2007. 157p. *(978-956-310-766-1(7))* Abtao Ediciones.
Dorling Kindersley Publishing Staff. What's That Bird. 2012. (ENG., Illus.). 128p. 9.95 *(978-0-7566-8968-1(6))* Dorling Kindersley Publishing, Inc.
Dorling Kindersley Publishing Staff, et al. Bird: The Definitive Visual Guide. 2007. (Illus.). 512p. pap. *(978-1-4053-0633-1(5))* Dorling Kindersley Publishing, Inc.
Dover. Detmolds' Birds. 2011. (Dover Postcards Ser.). (ENG., Illus.). 24p. pap. 6.95 *(978-0-486-48017-6(8))* Dover Pubns., Inc.
Downer, John. EarthFight: Breathtaking Photographs from a Bird's-Eye View of the World. 2011. (ENG., Illus.). 240p. 49.95 ***(978-1-77085-039-2(2))*** Firefly Bks., Ltd.
Dyes, John C. Nesting Birds of the Coastal Islands: A Naturalist's Year on Galveston Bay. 2011. (ENG., Illus.). 163p. pap. 19.95 ***(978-0-292-72973-5(1))*** Univ. of Texas Pr.
Erize, Francisco, et al. Birds of South America: Non-Passerines: Rheas to Woodpeckers. 2006. (Princeton Illustrated Checklists Ser.). (ENG., Illus.). 376p. pap. 29.95 *(978-0-691-12688-3(7))* Princeton Univ. Pr.
Ettlinger, Richard. On Feathered Wings: Birds in Flight. 2008. (ENG., Illus.). 192p. 42.00 *(978-0-8109-9525-3(5))* Abrams.
Evans, Middleton. Rhapsody in Blue: A Celebration of North American Waterbirds. 2007. (Illus.). 272p. per. 60.00 *(978-0-9778055-1-8(4))* Ravenwood Pr., Inc.
Everett, Roger S. Birds of Coastal South Carolina. 2008. (Illus.). 144p. bds. 29.95 *(978-0-7643-2845-9(X))* Schiffer Publishing, Ltd.
Fenimore, Bill. Backyard Birds of California: How to Identify & Attract the Top 25 Birds, 1 vol. 2008. (ENG., Illus.). 96p. spiral bd. 9.99 *(978-1-4236-0348-1(6))* Gibbs Smith, Publisher.
—Backyard Birds of Georgia: How to Identify & Attract the Top 25 Birds, 1 vol. 2009. (ENG., Illus.). 96p. pap. 9.99 *(978-1-4236-0567-6(5))* Gibbs Smith, Publisher.
—Backyard Birds of Maryland: How to Identify & Attract the Top 25 Birds, 1 vol. 2008. (ENG., Illus.). 96p. spiral bd. 9.95 *(978-1-4236-0354-2(0))* Gibbs Smith, Publisher.
—Backyard Birds of Michigan: How to Identify & Attract the Top 25 Birds. 2009. *(978-1-4236-0569-0(1))* Gibbs Smith, Publisher.
—Backyard Birds of New York: How to Identify & Attract the Top 25 Birds, 1 vol. 2008. (ENG., Illus.). 96p. pap. 9.95 *(978-1-4236-0349-8(4))* Gibbs Smith, Publisher.
—Backyard Birds of Utah: How to Identify & Attract the Top 25 Birds, 1 vol. 2008. (ENG., Illus.). 96p. spiral bd. 9.99 *(978-1-4236-0353-5(2))* Gibbs Smith, Publisher.
—Backyard Birds of Washington: How to Identify & Attract the Top 25 Birds, 1 vol. 2009. (ENG., Illus.). 96p. pap. 9.99 *(978-1-4236-0568-3(3))* Gibbs Smith, Publisher.
Fennimore, Bill. Backyard Birds of Florida: How to Identify & Attract the Top 25 Birds, 1 vol. 2008. (ENG., Illus.). 96p. pap. 9.99 *(978-1-4236-0352-8(4))* Gibbs Smith, Publisher.
—Backyard Birds of Illinois: How to Identify & Attract the Top 25 Birds, 1 vol. 2008. (ENG., Illus.). 96p. pap. 9.99 *(978-1-4236-0357-3(5))* Gibbs Smith, Publisher.
—Backyard Birds of New Jersey: How to Identify & Attract the Top 25 Birds, 1 vol. 2009. (ENG., Illus.). 96p. pap. 9.99 *(978-1-4236-0355-9(9))* Gibbs Smith, Publisher.
Flannery, Maureen. Nests: Fifty Nests & the Birds That Built Them. 2011. (ENG., Illus.). 120p. 29.95 *(978-0-8118-7758-9(2))* Chronicle Bks. LLC.
Floyd, Madeleine. Birdsong. 2011. (ENG., Illus.). 128p. 12.95 *(978-1-905400-97-3(7))* National Trust, Aylesbury GBR. Dist: Independent Pubs. Group.
Forget D. Sc, Gilles & Forget D.Sc., Gilles. Oiseaux du Sénégal / Birds of Senegal. 2011. 148p. pap. 58.51 ***(978-0-557-19327-1(3))*** Lulu Enterprises Inc.
Gosler, Andrew, ed. Birds of the World: A Photographic Guide. 2007. (ENG., Illus.). 384p. 39.95 *(978-1-55407-241-5(7))* Firefly Bks., Ltd.
Grimmett, Richard. Birds of India - Pakistan, Nepal, Bangladesh, Bhutan, Sri Lanka, & the Maldives 2e. 2012. (Princeton Field Guides). (ENG., Illus.). 528p. pap. 39.50 ***(978-0-691-15349-0(3))*** Princeton Univ. Pr.
Hackett, Mundy. Missouri in Flight: The Bird Photography of Mundy Hackett. 2007. (ENG., Illus.). 152p. (gr. 9). 34.95 *(978-0-8262-1706-6(0))* Univ. of Missouri Pr.
Heinrich, Bernd. The Nesting Season: Cuckoos, Cuckolds, & the Invention of Monogamy. 2010. (Illus.). 352p. 29.95 *(978-0-674-04877-5(6)*, Belknap Pr.) Harvard Univ. Pr.
Henderson, Carrol L. Birds in Flight: The Art & Science of How Birds Fly. 2008. (ENG., Illus.). 160p. 25.00 *(978-0-7603-3392-1(0)*, 0760333920, Voyageur Pr) MBI Publishing Co. LLC.
Hohorst, Charlie, photos by. Wings of Paradise: Birds of the Louisiana Wetlands. 2009. (Illus.). 144p. 39.95 *(978-0-8071-3450-4(3))* Louisiana State Univ. Pr.
Howell, Steve N. G. Petrels, Albatrosses & Storm-Petrels of North America: A Photographic Guide. 2012. (ENG., Illus.). 520p. 45.00 *(978-0-691-14211-1(4))* Princeton Univ. Pr.
Hunt, Lynn Bogue. An Artist's Game Bag. 2011. 106p. 39.95 ***(978-1-258-01366-0(5))*** Literary Licensing, LLC.
John, Audubon James. Birds of America. 2011. (ENG., Illus.). 448p. 80.00 *(978-1-4027-8947-2(5))* Sterling Publishing Co., Inc.
Kiser, Joy M. America's Other Audubon. 2012. (ENG., Illus.). 144p. 45.00 ***(978-1-61689-059-9(2))*** Princeton Architectural Pr.
Koch, MaryJo. Flight Plans: A Bird's Eye View of Life. 2007. (ENG., Illus.). 96p. 9.99 *(978-0-7407-6432-5(2))* Andrews McMeel Publishing.
Leclerc De Buffon, Georges-Louis. Birds. 2011. (ENG., Illus.). 288p. pap. 22.99 *(978-0-06-203956-9(3)*, Collins Design) HarperCollins Pubs.
Leclerc, Georges-Louis. The Natural History of Birds from the French of the Count de Buffon Illustrated with Engravings; & a Preface, Notes, & Additions, by the Transl. 2010. (Illus.). 536p. pap. 40.75 *(978-1-170-36495-6(0))*; 474p. pap. 37.75 *(978-1-170-36492-5(6))*; 538p. pap. 40.75 *(978-1-170-36493-2(4))*; 508p. pap. 39.75 *(978-1-170-36095-8(5))*; 510p. pap. 39.75 *(978-1-170-36494-9(2))*; 582p. pap. 43.75 *(978-1-170-36496-3(9))*; 630p. pap. 45.75 *(978-1-170-36497-0(7))*; 592p. pap. 44.75 *(978-1-170-36498-7(5))*; 498p. pap. 38.75 *(978-1-170-36499-4(3))*; 592p. pap. 44.75 *(978-1-170-36500-7(0))* BiblioBazaar. (Gale ECCO, Print Editions).
Lukas, David. Watchable Birds of the Great Basin. (Watchable Birds Ser.: No. 3). (Illus.). 174p. pap. 16.00 *(978-0-87842-397-2(4)*, 439) Mountain Pr. Publishing Co., Inc.

Macnamara, Peggy. Architecture by Birds & Insects: A Natural Art. 2008. (ENG., Illus.). 164p. 25.00 *(978-0-226-50097-3(7))* Univ. of Chicago Pr.
Martin, James & Martin, Joyce. Images of North American Big Game. 2007. 108p. pap. 41.50 *(978-1-4357-0076-5(7))* Lulu Enterprises Inc.
—The Rookery at Noxubee Wildlife Refuge. 2007. 100p. pap. 39.50 *(978-1-4303-2356-3(6))* Lulu Enterprises Inc.
McCartney, Paula, et al. Bird Watching. 2010. (ENG., Illus.). 120p. 50.00 *(978-1-56898-855-9(9))* Princeton Architectural Pr.
McDonald, John. Nothin' but Puffins: And Other Silly Observations. 2010. (ENG.). 64p. 12.95 *(978-0-89272-547-2(8))* Down East Bks.
Mobley, Jason A. Birds of the World. 2008. 571.36 *(978-0-7614-7775-4(6))* Marshall Cavendish Corp.
Mylane, Jean Luc, photos by. Jean Luc Mylane. 2007. (Illus.). 136p. 60.00 *(978-1-931885-67-6(2))* Twin Palms Pubs.
Nigge, Klaus. Whooping Crane: Images from the Wild. 2010. (Illus.). 228p. 45.00 *(978-1-60344-209-1(X))* Texas A&M Univ. Pr.
Nolley, John 2nd. On the Wing: A Photographic Journey of John's First Year of Birding. rev. ed. 2006. (Illus.). 112p. per. 34.95 *(978-0-9801571-0-9(2))* Exerda Pubns.
—Taking to the Skies: A Photologue of Birds across the United States. 2007. (Illus.). 120p. per. 34.95 *(978-0-9801571-1-6(0))* Exerda Pubns.
Otto, John R. & Otto, Jason. An Otto Brothers Collection of Waterfowl Reference. 2007. (Illus.). 83p. 39.99 *(978-1-4257-6385-5(5))* Xlibris Corp.
Porter, Adele. Birds in Our Backyard: Say Hello to Minnesota's Feathered Friends. 2011. (ENG., Illus.). 42p. (J). (gr. -1-2). 16.95 ***(978-0-87351-836-9(5))*** Minnesota Historical Society Pr.
Pratt, Douglas. Birds. 2007. 48p. 8.95 *(978-1-56647-795-6(6))* Mutual Publishing LLC.
Purcell, Rosamond, et al. Egg & Nest. 2008. (Illus.). 232p. 39.95 *(978-0-674-03172-2(5))*, Belknap Pr.) Harvard Univ. Pr.
Regan, Patrick & Chester, Jonathan. Flipping Brilliant: A Penguin's Guide to a Happy Life. 2008. (ENG., Illus.). 64p. 9.99 *(978-0-7407-7229-0(5))* Andrews McMeel Publishing.
Rodabaugh, Steven, et al. Birds of the World, Vol. 1. 2009. (Rod & Staff Nature Library Ser.). (Illus.). 400p. (YA). (gr. 7). 29.50 *(978-0-7399-2800-4(7))* Rod & Staff Pubs., Inc.
Rogers, Denny & Corbett, Lori. The Illustrated Owl: Barn, Barred, & Great Horned: The Ultimate Reference Guide for Bird Lovers, Artists, & Woodcarvers. 2008. (Denny Rogers Visual Reference Ser.). (ENG.). 248p. pap. 29.95 *(978-1-56523-313-3(1))* Fox Chapel Publishing Co., Inc.
Rugoff, Ralph & Sultan, Terrie. Jean-Luc Mylayne: English-French Edition. 2010. (ENG., Illus.). 120p. 45.00 *(978-88-7439-530-9(2))* 5 Continents ITA. Dist: Hachette Bk. Group.
Shallenberger, Robert J. Hawaiian Birds of the Sea: Na Manu Kai. 2009. pap. 21.99 *(978-0-8248-3403-6(8))* Univ. of Hawaii Pr.
Small, Brian E. & Sterry, Paul. Birds of Eastern North America: A Photographic Guide. 2009. (Princeton Field Guides). (ENG., Illus.). 336p. (C). 46.95 *(978-0-691-13425-3(1))* Princeton Univ. Pr.
—Birds of Western North America: A Photographic Guide. 2009. (Princeton Field Guides). (ENG., Illus.). 416p. (C). 46.95 *(978-0-691-13427-7(8))*; pap. 18.95 *(978-0-691-13428-4(6))* Princeton Univ. Pr.
Snead, Bobbie & Irish, Terry. Owl Grove. 2009. pap. *(978-1-61623-344-0(3))* Independent Pub.
Sterry, Paul & Small, Brian E. Birds of Eastern North America: A Photographic Guide. 2009. (Princeton Field Guides). (ENG., Illus.). 336p. pap. 18.95 *(978-0-691-13426-0(X))* Princeton Univ. Pr.
Svensson, Lars & Dan, Zetterström. Birds of Europe. 2nd ed. 2010. (Princeton Field Guides). (ENG., Illus.). 448p. pap. 29.95 *(978-0-691-14392-7(7))* Princeton Univ. Pr.
Taylor, Richard Cachor. Birds of Southeastern Arizona. Bickel, Barbara, ed. 2010. (Illus.). 440p. 19.95 *(978-0-9640810-7-9(5))* Morse, R.W. Co.
Vermeer, Jan & Essen, Frieda van. Antarctica. 2009. (ENG., Illus.). 300p. *(978-90-78964-10-0(3))*, Thieme Art (Acc)) Antique Collectors' Club.
Wassink, Jan. Watchable Birds of the Black Hills, Badlands, & Northern Great Plains. 2006. (Watchable Birds Ser.). (Illus.). 231p. pap. 22.00 *(978-0-87842-526-6(8))* Mountain Pr. Publishing Co., Inc.
Weller, Alan. Birds. 2011. (Dover Pictura Electronic Clip Art Ser.). (ENG., Illus.). 128p. pap. 39.95 *(978-0-486-99158-0(X))* Dover Pubns., Inc.
Zuckerman, Andrew, photos by. Bird. 2009. (ENG., Illus.). 300p. 60.00 *(978-0-8118-7098-6(7))* Chronicle Bks. LLC.

BIRDS—POETRY

Collier, Michael. Dark Wild Realm. 2007. (ENG.). 80p. pap. 13.95 *(978-0-618-91991-8(0))*, Mariner Bks.) Houghton Mifflin Harcourt Trade & Reference Pubs.
Collins, Billy, ed. Bright Wings: An Illustrated Anthology of Poems about Birds. 2009. (ENG., Illus.). 288p. (gr. 17). 22.95 *(978-0-231-15084-2(9))* Columbia Univ. Pr.
Crawford, Tom. The Names of Birds: Poems, 1 vol. 2011. (ENG.). 128p. pap. 14.95 ***(978-1-890932-40-4(X))*** Sherman Asher Publishing.
Dickinson, Emily. A Spicing of Birds. Schuman, Jo Miles & Hodgman, Joanna Bailey, eds. 2010. (Driftless Ser.). (ENG., Illus.). 112p. 22.95 *(978-0-8195-7069-7(9))* Wesleyan Univ. Pr.
Goodman, Mae W. & Scheele, William E. In Time of Swallows. (Illus.). 6.95 *(978-0-8159-5808-5(0))* Devin-Adair Pubs., Inc.
Houchin, Ron. Museum Crows. 2010. (ENG.). 80p. pap. 22.95 *(978-1-907056-17-3(3))* Salmon Publishing IRL. Dist: Dufour Editions, Inc.
Lawrence, D. H. Birds, Beasts & Flowers. 2011. 178p. pap. ***(978-1-84861-157-3(9))*** Shearsman Bks.
Monkton, Edward. The Penguin of Death. 2008. (ENG.). 32p. 9.99 *(978-0-7407-7383-9(6))* Andrews McMeel Publishing.
Sharma, Ravi. A Collection of Poems Pankhuri. 2009. 136p. 21.49 *(978-1-4490-2990-6(6))*; pap. 10.99 *(978-1-4490-2975-3(2))* AuthorHouse.
Simms, Colin. Gyrfalcon Poems. 2007. (Illus.). 112p. per. *(978-1-905700-35-6(0))* Shearsman Bks.

BIRDS—PROTECTION

see also Game Protection

Bildstein, Keith L. Migrating Raptors of the World: Their Ecology & Conservation. 2006. (Illus.). 320p. 35.00 *(978-0-8014-4179-0(X))* Cornell Univ. Pr.
Chatterjee, Samrat. Migratory Birds & Spread of Disease. 2010. 140p. pap. *(978-3-639-26825-6(3))* VDM Verlag Dr. Mueller e.K.
Elliott, Douglas. Oc Honkers: The Corona & Big Guy Story. 2008. 216p. pap. 12.95 *(978-1-4327-1947-0(5))* Outskirts Pr., Inc.
McCasland, Bebe. The Scoop from Bird Poop: 35 Years of Wild Bird Rescues. 2010. (ENG., Illus.). 207p. 35.00 *(978-1-933979-52-6(6))*, Bright Sky Pr.
Moir, John. Return of the Condor: The Race to Save Our Largest Bird from Extinction. 2006. (ENG., Illus.). 272p. 24.95 *(978-1-59228-949-3(5))*, Lyons Pr.) Globe Pequot Pr., The.
Smith, Walter Post. Kiptopeke Chronicles. 2009. 228p. pap. 14.50 *(978-1-59330-571-0(0))* Aventine Pr.
Wilson, Robert M. Seeking Refuge: Birds & Landscapes of the Pacific Flyway. 2012. (ENG., Illus.). 320p. (C). pap. 25.00 ***(978-0-295-99211-2(5))*** Univ. of Washington Pr.

BIRDS—AFRICA

Alderton, David. The Illustrated Encyclopedia of Birds of Britain, Europe & Africa: A Fine Visual Guide to over 400 Birds Inhabiting These Continents. 2012. (ENG., Illus.). 264p. pap. 18.99 *(978-1-78019-004-4(2))* Anness Publishing GBR. Dist: National Bk. Network.
Carnaby, Trevor. Beat about the Bush - Birds. 2009. (Beat about the Bush Ser.). (ENG.). 768p. pap. 43.95 *(978-1-77009-241-9(2))* Jacana Media ZAF. Dist: Independent Pubs. Group.
—Beat about the Bush: Mammals. 2008. (Beat about the Bush Ser.). (ENG., Illus.). 376p. pap. 40.00 *(978-1-77009-240-2(4))* Jacana Media ZAF. Dist: Independent Pubs. Group.
Chittenden, Hugh. Roberts Voelgids. 2010. (ENG.). 264p. pap. 23.00 *(978-1-77009-715-5(5))* Jacana Media ZAF. Dist: Independent Pubs. Group.
Chittenden, Hugh & Whyte, Ian. Roberts Bird Guide: Kruger National Park & Adjacent Lowveld - A Guide to More than 420 Birds in the Region. 2009. (ENG.). 264p. pap. 18.95 *(978-1-77009-638-7(8))* Jacana Media ZAF. Dist: Independent Pubs. Group.
Cillie, Burger. Pocket Guide to Southern African Birds: Revised Third Edition. 2009. (Illus.). 160p. pap. 11.95 *(978-1-919938-65-3(6))* International Publishers Marketing.
Cillie, Burger, et al. Pocket Guide to Birds of Southern Africa: With New English Names. 4th ed. 2009. (Illus.). 160p. pap. 12.00 *(978-1-919938-97-4(4))* Sunbird Publishing ZAF. Dist: International Publishers Marketing.
Forget D. Sc, Gilles & Forget D.Sc., Gilles. Oiseaux du Sénégal / Birds of Senegal. 2011. 148p. pap. 58.51 ***(978-0-557-19327-1(3))*** Lulu Enterprises Inc.
Luft, Stefan. Parrots of Afric. 2007. 200p. per. *(978-3-8334-8445-2(4))* Books on Demand GmbH.
Milstein, Peter. Remarkable Birds of South Africa. 2012. (Illus.). 208p. pap. 29.95 ***(978-1-875093-58-8(3))*** International Publishers Marketing.
Newman, Kenneth. Newman's Birds of Southern Africa. 2011. (Illus.). 528p. pap. 26.00 *(978-1-77007-876-5(2))* Random Hse. Struik (Pty.), Ltd. ZAF. Dist: International Publishers Marketing.
Redman, Nigel, et al. Birds of the Horn of Africa: Ethiopia, Eritrea, Djibouti, Somalia, & Socotra. 2009. (Princeton Field Guides). (ENG., Illus.). 488p. pap. 40.00 *(978-0-691-14345-3(5))* Princeton Univ. Pr.
Sinclair, Ian. Birds of Southern Africa. 2011. (Illus.). 144p. pap., instr.'s gde. ed. 12.95 *(978-1-77007-769-0(3))* Struik Pubs. ZAF. Dist: International Publishers Marketing.
Sinclair, Ian & Ryan, Peter. Birds of Africa, South of the Sahara: A Comprehensive Illustrated Field Guide. 2nd ed. 2011. (Illus.). 768p. pap. 47.00 *(978-1-77007-623-5(9))* Random Hse. Struik (Pty.), Ltd. ZAF. Dist: International Publishers Marketing.
—Birds of Southern Africa: The Complete Photographic Guide. 2009. (Illus.). 440p. pap. 35.95 *(978-1-77007-388-3(4))* Struik Pubs. ZAF. Dist: International Publishers Marketing.
Sinclair, Ian, et al. Birds of Southern Africa: Fourth Edition. 2011. (Princeton Field Guides). (ENG., Illus.). 448p. pap. 35.00 ***(978-0-691-15225-7(X))*** Princeton Univ. Pr.
Sinclair, Ian, et al. The Larger Illustrated Guide to Birds of Southern Africa. 2nd ed. 2007. (Illus.). 448p. pap. 32.95 *(978-1-77007-243-5(8))* Struik Pubs. ZAF. Dist: International Publishers Marketing.
Steyn, Peter. A Delight of Owls: African Owls Observed. 2nd ed. 2010. (ENG.). 176p. pap. 28.00 *(978-1-77009-740-7(6))* Jacana Media ZAF. Dist: Independent Pubs. Group.
Van Perlo, Ber. Birds of Eastern Africa. 2009. (Princeton Illustrated Checklists Ser.). (ENG., Illus.). 304p. pap. 29.95 *(978-0-691-14170-1(3))* Princeton Univ. Pr.
—Birds of Southern Africa. 2009. (Princeton Illustrated Checklists Ser.). (ENG., Illus.). 320p. pap. 29.95 *(978-0-691-14169-5(X))* Princeton Univ. Pr.
Witherby, Harry F. Bird Hunting on the White Nile - a Naturalist's Experience in the Soudan. 2009. 116p. pap. 26.45 *(978-1-4437-8791-8(4))* Harrison House Pubs.

BIRDS—ALASKA

Armstrong, Robert H. Guide to the Birds of Alaska. 5th ed. 2008. (ENG., Illus.). 360p. pap. 27.95 *(978-0-88240-729-6(5))*, Alaska Northwest Bks.) Graphic Arts Ctr. Publishing Co.
Bart, Jonathan & Johnston, Victoria Helen. Arctic Shorebirds in North America: A Decade of Monitoring. 2012. ***(978-0-520-27310-8(9))*** Univ. of California Pr.
Gibson, Daniel D. & Byrd, G. Vernon. Birds of the Aleutian Islands, Alaska: Series in Ornithology, No. 1. 2007. (Series in Ornithology: 1). 40.00 *(978-0-943610-73-3(7))* American Ornithologists Union.
King, James Gore. Attending Alaska's Birds: A Wildlife Pilot's Story. 2nd ed. 2010. (Illus.). 474p. pap. 29.95 ***(978-0-88839-656-3(2))*** Hancock Hse. Pubs.
Schempf, Philip F. & Wright, Bruce A. Bald Eagles in Alaska. 2010. 438p. pap. 29.95 ***(978-0-88839-695-2(3))*** Hancock Hse. Pubs.

BIRDS—AMERICA

see also Birds—Latin America; Birds—North America; Birds—United States

Hamlen, Peggy. Foxy & Her Forest Friends. 2011. 32p. pap. 14.39 *(978-1-4567-0109-3(6))* AuthorHouse.
Martinez-Sanchez, Juan C. & Will, Tom, eds. Thomas R. Howell's Check-list of the Birds of Nicaragua as Of 1993. 2010. (Ornithological Monographs). 125p. pap. 24.95 *(978-0-943610-87-0(7))* Univ. of California Pr.
Spear, Larry B. & Ainley, David G. Storm-petrels of the Eastern Pacific Ocean: Species Assembly & Diversity along Marine Habitat Gradients. 2007. (Ornithological Monographs: 62). per. 10.00 *(978-0-943610-71-9(0))* American Ornithologists Union.
Stutchbury, Bridget. Silence of the Songbirds. 2009. (ENG., Illus.). 272p. pap. 16.00 *(978-0-8027-1691-0(1))* Walker & Co.

BIRDS—ANTARCTICA

Lovegrove, Roger. Islands Beyond the Horizon: The life of twenty of the world's most remote Places. 2012. (ENG., Illus.). 224p. 29.95 ***(978-0-19-960649-8(8))*** Oxford Univ. Pr., Inc.
Lowen, James. Antarctic Wildlife: A Visitor's Guide. 2011. (ENG., Illus.). 240p. pap. 22.95 *(978-0-691-15033-8(8))* Princeton Univ. Pr.
Shirihai, Hadoram. The Complete Guide to Antarctic Wildlife: Birds & Marine Mammals of the Antarctic Continent & the Southern Ocean. 2nd ed. 2008. (ENG., Illus.). 544p. 55.00 *(978-0-691-13666-0(1))* Princeton Univ. Pr.

BIRDS—ARCTIC REGIONS

Korte, Jacobus de, et al. A Passion for the Pole: Ethological Research in Polar Regions. 2008. (Circumpolar Studies). (ENG., Illus.). x, 149p. (C). pap. 21.00 ***(978-90-77922-40-8(7))*** Barkhuis Publishing NLD. Dist: Brown, David Bk. Co., The.
Lovegrove, Roger. Islands Beyond the Horizon: The life of twenty of the world's most remote Places. 2012. (ENG., Illus.). 224p. 29.95 ***(978-0-19-960649-8(8))*** Oxford Univ. Pr., Inc.

BIRDS—ASIA

Brazil, Mark. Birds of East Asia: China, Taiwan, Korea, Japan, & Russia. 2009. (Princeton Field Guides). (ENG.). 528p. pap. 39.95 *(978-0-691-13926-5(1))* (Illus.). (C). 85.00 *(978-0-691-13925-8(3))* Princeton Univ. Pr.
Chandler, Richard. Shorebirds of North America, Europe & Asia: A Photographic Guide. 2009. (ENG., Illus.). 448p. pap. 35.00 *(978-0-691-14281-4(5))* Princeton Univ. Pr.
Davison, G. W. H. & Aik, Yeap Chin. A Naturalist's Guide to the Birds of Malaysia & Singapore: Including Sabah & Sarawak. 2010. (Naturalists' Guides). 176p. pap. 14.95 *(978-1-906780-21-0(8))* Beaufoy, John Publishing GBR. Dist: Midpoint Trade Bks., Inc.
Gombobaatar, Sundev, et al. Birds of Mongolia. 2013. (Princeton Field Guides). (ENG., Illus.). 224p. pap. 35.00 *(978-0-691-13882-4(6))* Princeton Univ. Pr.
Grimmett, Richard, et al. Birds of Pakistan. 2009. (ENG., Illus.). 288p. pap. 40.00 *(978-0-300-15249-4(3))* Yale Univ. Pr.
Jeyarajasingam, Allen. A Field Guide to the Birds of Peninsular Malaysia & Singapore. 2nd ed. 2012. (ENG., Illus.). 641p. 108.00 ***(978-0-19-963942-7(6))***; pap. 62.95 ***(978-0-19-963943-4(4))*** Oxford Univ. Pr., Inc.
Kinnaird, Margaret F. & O'Brien, Timothy G. The Ecology & Conservation of Asian Hornbills: Farmers of the Forest. 2008. (Illus.). 352p. 47.50 *(978-0-226-43712-5(4))* Univ. of Chicago Pr.
Koerkamp, G. Groot & Golovach, S. I., eds. Atlas: Birds of Moscow City & the Moscow Region. 2006. (Faunistica Ser.: Vol. 54). (RUS., Illus.). 149.50 *(978-954-642-262-0(2))* Pensoft Pubs. BGR. Dist: Coronet Bks.
Manakadan, Ranjit, et al. Birds of the Indian Subcontinent: A Field Guide. 2012. (ENG., Illus.). 400p. 34.99 ***(978-0-19-807723-7(8))*** Oxford Univ. Pr., Inc.
Myers, Susan. Birds of Borneo: Brunei, Sabah, Sarawak, & Kalimantan. 2009. (Princeton Field Guides). (ENG., Illus.). 272p. pap. 29.95 *(978-0-691-14350-7(1))* Princeton Univ. Pr.
Renner, Swen C. Avifauna of the Eastern Himalayas & Southeastern Sub-Himalayan Mountains: Center of Endemism or Many Species in Marginal Habitats? Rappole, John H., ed. 2011. (Ornithological Monographs). (ENG.). 176p. pap. 24.95 *(978-0-943610-89-4(3))* Univ. of California Pr.
Schweizer, Manuel, et al. Birds of Central Asia - Kazakhstan, Turkmenistan, Uzbekistan. 2012. (Princeton Field Guides). (ENG., Illus.). 336p. pap. 39.50 ***(978-0-691-15337-7(X))*** Princeton Univ. Pr.
Shimba, Tadao. A Photographic Guide to the Birds of Japan & North-East Asia. 2008. (ENG., Illus.). 504p. pap. 40.00 *(978-0-300-13556-5(4))* Yale Univ. Pr.
Sibley, David Allen. Sibleys Backyard Birds of Southeast. 2009. pap. 7.95 *(978-1-935380-10-8(9))* Lewers, Steven & Assocs.
Urf, A. J. The Painted Stork: Ecology & Conservation. 2011. (ENG., Illus.). xviii, 166p. 129.00 *(978-1-4419-8467-8(4))*, 1441984674) Springer.
Wijesundara, Chaminda. Foraging Ecology of Selected Birds in a Hill Forest in Sri Lanka. 2010. 72p. pap. *(978-3-639-26035-9(X))* VDM Verlag Dr. Mueller e.K.

BIRDS—ATLANTIC OCEAN

Brady, Alan. Atlantic Seabird Photo Journal. 2009. 202p. 29.99 *(978-1-4363-9319-5(1))*; pap. 19.99 *(978-1-4363-9318-8(3))* Xlibris Corp.

BIRDS—AUSTRALIA

Christidis, Les & Boles, Walter. Systematics & Taxonomy of Australian Birds. 2009. 288p. pap. 44.00 *(978-0-643-09602-8(7))* CSIRO Publishing AUS. Dist: Stylus Publishing, LLC.
Geering, Andrew, et al. Shorebirds of Australia. 2007. (Illus.). 256p. pap. 43.95 *(978-0-643-09226-6(9))* CSIRO Publishing AUS. Dist: Stylus Publishing, LLC.
Jones, Darryl & Göth, Ann. Mound-Builders: Mallee Fowl, Brush Turkeys & Scrubfowl. 2009. (Australian Natural History Ser.). 130p. pap. 35.00 *(978-0-643-09345-4(1))* CSIRO Publishing AUS. Dist: Stylus Publishing, LLC.
Kaplan, Gisela T. Tawny Frogmouth. 2007. (Australian Natural History Ser.). 158p. pap. 35.95 *(978-0-643-09239-6(0))* CSIRO Publishing AUS. Dist: Stylus Publishing, LLC.
Moise, Dragos. Ecology of Red-Lored & Gilbert's Whistler in South Australi. 2010. 256p. pap. *(978-3-8383-4802-5(8))* Lambert Academic Publishing.
Morris, Frank T. Finches of Australia: A Folio. (Illus.). 124p. 65.00 *(978-0-7018-1000-9(9))* Eastview Editions.
Pizzey, Graham. The Field Guide to the Birds of Australia. Menkhorst, Peter, ed. 8th rev. ed. 2007. (Illus.). 592p. *(978-0-207-19935-6(3))* HarperCollins Pubs. Australia.
Rowland, Peter. Bowerbirds. 2008. (Australian Natural History Ser.). 144p. (C) pap. 35.00 *(978-0-643-09420-8(2))* CSIRO Publishing AUS. Dist: Stylus Publishing, LLC.
Simpson, Ken & Day, Nicolas. Birds of Australia. 8th ed. 2010. (Princeton Field Guides). (ENG., Illus.). 392p. 39.50 *(978-0-691-14692-8(6))*, Princeton Univ. Pr.
Villier, Danny. The Bird Ringing Scheme. 2010. 200p. pap. *(978-3-639-18851-6(9))* VDM Verlag Dr. Mueller e.K.

BIRDS—CANADA

Alderfer, Jonathan & Dunn, Jon L., eds. The Birds of Western North America. 2008. (ENG., Illus.). 448p. instr.'s gde. ed. 19.95 *(978-1-4262-0331-2(4))*, National Geographic) National Geographic Society.
Austin Jr., Oliver Luther. The Birds of Newfoundland Labrador: Memoirs of the Nuttall Ornithological Club, No. 7. 2011. 236p. 46.95 ***(978-1-258-10420-7(2))*** Literary Licensing, LLC.
Barber, Lynn E. Extreme Birder: One Woman's Big Year. 2011. (Illus.). 288p. pap. 29.95 *(978-1-60344-261-9(8))* Texas A&M Univ. Pr.
Bart, Jonathan & Johnston, Victoria Helen. Arctic Shorebirds in North America: A Decade of Monitoring. 2012. ***(978-0-520-27310-8(9))*** Univ. of California Pr.
Bull, John, et al. The Easy Bird Guide: Eastern Region: A Quick Identification Guide for All Birders. 2006. (Falcon Guide Ser.). (ENG., Illus.). 160p. pap. 14.95 *(978-0-7627-3741-3(7))*, Falcon Guides) Globe Pequot Pr., The.
Burrows, Roger. Birding in New Brunswick. 2010. (ENG.). 372p. pap. 24.95 *(978-0-86492-618-0(9))* Goose Lane Editions CAN. Dist: Univ. of Toronto Pr.
Cadman, Michael D. Atlas of the Breeding Birds of Ontario, 2001-2005. 2009. (ENG., Illus.). 728p. 92.50 *(978-1-896059-15-0(5))* Federation of Ontario Naturalists CAN. Dist: Firefly Bks., Ltd.
Cannings, Richard. Birds of Interior BC & the Rockies, 1 vol. 2009. (ENG., Illus.). 448p. pap. *(978-1-894974-59-2(X))* Heritage Hse.
Cannings, Richard, et al. Birds of Southwestern British Columbia, 1 vol. 2010. (ENG., Illus.). 432p. pap. *(978-1-894384-96-4(2))* Heritage Hse.
Carrick, Doug. The Eagles of Hornby Island: My Tree-Top Neighbours. 2007. (Illus.). 112p. pap. 14.95 ***(978-0-88839-649-5(X))*** Hancock Hse. Pubs.
Domm, Jeffrey C. Formac Pocketguide to Nature: Animals, plants & birds in New Brunswick, Nova Scotia & Prince Edward Island. 2nd ed. 2012. (ENG., Illus.). 128p. (gr. 3-8). pap. 9.95 ***(978-1-4595-0061-7(X))*** Formac Publishing Co., Ltd. CAN. Dist: Casemate Pubs. & Bk. Distributors, LLC.
—Lorimer Field Guide to 225 Ontario Birds. 2012. (ENG., Illus.). 288p. pap. 19.95 ***(978-1-4594-0041-2(0))*** Lorimer, James & Co., Ltd., Pubs. CAN. Dist: Casemate Pubs. & Bk. Distributors, LLC.
—Nova Scotia Birds - Formac Field Guide. 3rd ed. 2012. (ENG., Illus.). 224p. pap. 24.95 ***(978-1-4595-0049-5(0))*** Formac Publishing Co., Ltd. CAN. Dist: Casemate Pubs. & Bk. Distributors, LLC.
Dorling Kindersley Publishing Staff. American Museum of Natural History Birds of Western North America. 2011. (ENG.). 480p. (gr. 12). pap. 19.95 *(978-0-7566-5868-7(3))* Dorling Kindersley Publishing, Inc.
Earley, Chris G. Hawks & Owls of Eastern North America. 2nd rev. ed. 2012. (ENG., Illus.). 144p. pap. 19.95 ***(978-1-55407-999-5(3))*** Firefly Bks., Ltd.
Elliott, Douglas. Oc Honkers: The Corona & Big Guy Story. 2008. 216p. pap. 12.95 *(978-1-4327-1947-0(5))* Outskirts Pr., Inc.
Gibson, Merritt & Bondrup-Nielsen, Soren. Winter Nature: Common Mammals, Birds, Trees & Shrubs of the Maritimes. 2008. (ENG., Illus.). 224p. pap. *(978-1-55447-059-4(5))* Gaspereau Pr.

B

Kavanagh, James. Calgary Birds: An Introduction to Familiar Species. 2010. (Pocket Naturalist Guide Ser.). (ENG.). 2p. 5.95 *(978-1-58355-548-4(X))* Waterford Pr., Inc.

—Vancouver Birds: An Introduction to Familiar Species. 2010. (Pocket Naturalist Guide Ser.). (ENG.). 2p. 5.95 *(978-1-58355-549-1(8))* Waterford Pr., Inc.

Kermode, Francis. Catalogue of British Columbia Birds. 2008. 132p. 24.99 *(978-0-554-30401-4(5))* 2008. 132p. 21.99 *(978-0-554-39704-7(8))* 2007. (ENG.). 128p. pap. 20.75 *(978-1-4375-0175-9(3))* 2007. (ENG.). 102p. pap. 18.75 *(978-1-4375-0174-2(5))* BiblioBazaar.

—Catalogue of British Columbia Birds. 2007. 88p. per. *(978-1-4065-1904-4(9))* Dodo Pr.

—Catalogue of British Columbia Birds. 2008. 88p. pap. *(978-1-4068-7608-6(9))* Echo Library.

Lehman, Paul. National Geographic Field Guide to the Birds of Eastern North America. Alderfer, Jonathan & Dunn, Jon L., eds. 2008. (ENG., Illus.). 432p. 19.95 *(978-1-4262-0330-5(6))* National Geographic Society.

Mair, Charles. Through the MacKenzie Basin. 2009. 148p. 21.99 *(978-0-559-05263-7(4))*; 24.99 *(978-0-559-05247-7(2))*; pap. 20.75 *(978-0-559-05258-3(8))*; pap. 21.75 *(978-0-559-05253-8(7))* BiblioBazaar.

—Through the MacKenzie Basin. 2007. (ENG.). 124p. per. *(978-1-4065-8240-6(9))* Dodo Pr.

Peck, George K. & James, Ross D. Breeding Birds of Ontario, Nidiology & Distribution: Nonpasserines. (Illus.). 709p. pap. *(978-0-88854-288-5(7))* BRILL.

Peterson, Roger Tory. Peterson Field Guide to Birds of Western North America. 4th ed. 2010. (Peterson Field Guides). (ENG., Illus.). 512p. 19.95 *(978-0-547-15270-7(1))* Houghton Mifflin Harcourt Trade & Reference Pubs.

Pope, Richard. The Reluctant Twitcher: A Quite Truthful Account of My Big Birding Year. 2009. (ENG., Illus.). 216p. 35.00 *(978-1-55488-458-2(6))* Dundurn CAN. Dist: Ingram Pub. Services.

Roy, Kayo J. & Black, John E. Niagara Birds: A Compendium of Articles & Species Accounts of the Birds of the Niagara Region in Ontario. 2010. (Illus.). 703p. *(978-0-9811489-0-8(5))* Black, John E. & Kayo J. Roy.

Small, Brian E. & Sterry, Paul. Birds of Eastern North America: A Photographic Guide: 2009. (Princeton Field Guides). (ENG., Illus.). 336p. (C). 46.95 *(978-0-691-13425-3(1))* Princeton Univ. Pr.

Sterry, Paul & Small, Brian E. Birds of Eastern North America: A Photographic Guide. 2009. (Princeton Field Guides). (ENG., Illus.). 336p. pap. 18.95 *(978-0-691-13426-0(X))* Princeton Univ. Pr.

Wassink, Jan. Watchable Birds of the Black Hills, Badlands, & Northern Great Plains. 2006. (Watchable Birds Ser.). (Illus.). 231p. pap. 22.00 *(978-0-87842-526-6(8))* Mountain Pr. Publishing Co., Inc.

Wheeler, Brian K., photos by. Raptors of Eastern North America: The Wheeler Guide. 2007. (Illus.). 439p. per. 29.95 *(978-0-691-13476-5(6))* Princeton Univ. Pr.

—Raptors of Western North America: The Wheeler Guide. 2007. (Illus.). 544p. per. 29.95 *(978-0-691-13477-2(4))* Princeton Univ. Pr.

BIRDS—CARIBBEAN AREA

Arlott, Norman. Birds of the West Indies: 2010. (Princeton Illustrated Checklists Ser.). (ENG., Illus.). 240p. pap. 24.95 *(978-0-691-14780-2(9))* Princeton Univ. Pr.

Arnette, Edgar. Bahamian & Caribbean Birds. 32p. *(978-976-610-214-2(7))* Creative Links.

—Jamaican & Caribbean Birds. 32p. *(978-976-610-213-5(9))* Creative Links.

Barbour, Thomas. Cuban Ornithology: Memoirs of the Nuttall Ornithological Club, No. 9. 2011. 150p. 40.95 ***(978-1-258-07151-6(7))*** Literary Licensing, LLC.

Birds of the Caribbean. 2010. pap. 7.95 *(978-1-893770-90-4(7))* Lewers, Steven & Assocs.

Birds of the Caribbean, Vol 2. 2nd ed. 2008. (Illus.). 248p. *(978-1-929440-17-7(0))* Nautilus Publishing Co.

Bradley, Patricia E. & Norton, Robert L. An Inventory of Breeding Seabirds of the Caribbean. 2009. (ENG., Illus.). 448p. 75.00 *(978-0-8130-3329-7(2))* Univ. Pr. of Florida.

De Boer, Bart, et al. Birds of Aruba, Bonaire & Curacao. 2012. (Princeton Field Guides). (ENG., Illus.). 192p. pap. 27.95 ***(978-0-691-15336-0(1))*** Princeton Univ. Pr.

Garrido, Orlando H. & Kirkconnell, Arturo. Aves de Cuba: Field Guide to the Birds of Cuba, Spanish-Language Edition. 2011. (SPA., Illus.). 376p. pap. 35.00 *(978-0-8014-7691-4(7)*, Comstock Publishing Assocs.) Cornell Univ. Pr.

Hallett, Bruce. Birds of the Bahamas & the Turks & Caicos Islands. 2006. (Caribbean Pocket Natural History Ser.). (Illus.). 245p. pap. 15.95 *(978-0-333-93744-0(9))* Macmillan Pubs., Ltd. GBR. Dist: Trafalgar Square Publishing.

Kenefick, Martyn, et al. Field Guide to the Birds of Trinidad & Tobago. 2008. (ENG., Illus.). 288p. pap. 40.00 *(978-0-300-13557-2(2))* Yale Univ. Pr.

Kirkconnell, Arturo. Cuba: Cienaga de Zapata. Stotz, Douglas F., ed. 2007. (Field Museum - Rapid Biological Inventories Ser.). (SPA & ENG.). 230p. pap. 30.00 *(978-0-914868-61-3(6))* Field Museum of Natural History, Div. of Pubns.

Waring, Rob. Birds in Paradise (US) 2008. (ENG.). 24p. (C). pap. 10.95 *(978-1-4240-4405-4(7))* Cengage Heinle.

BIRDS—CENTRAL AMERICA

Barcott, Bruce. The Last Flight of the Scarlet Macaw: One Woman's Fight to Save the World's Most Beautiful Bird. 2009. (ENG., Illus.). 336p. pap. 16.00 *(978-0-8129-7313-6(5)*, Random Hse. Trade Paperbacks) Random House Publishing Group.

Garrigues, Richard. The Birds of Costa Rica: A Field Guide. 2007. (Illus.). 387p. 82.95 *(978-0-8014-4587-3(6))* Cornell Univ. Pr.

—The Birds of Costa Rica: A Field Guide. 2007. pap. 29.95 *(978-0-9705678-5-7(5))* Zona Tropical Pubns.

Kavanagh, James. Costa Rica Birds: An Introduction to Familiar Species. 2007. (Pocket Naturalist - Waterford Press Ser.). (ENG., Illus.). 1p. 5.95 *(978-1-58355-339-8(8))* Waterford Pr., Inc.

—Monteverde Birds: An Introduction to Familiar Species in Costa Rica's Monteverde Region. 2007. (Pocket Naturalist - Waterford Press Ser.). (ENG., Illus.). 1p. 5.95 *(978-1-58355-343-5(6))* Waterford Pr., Inc.

Lawson, Barrett. A Bird-Finding Guide to Costa Rica. 2009. (Illus.). 360p. pap. 29.95 *(978-0-8014-7584-9(8)*, Comstock Publishing Assocs.) Cornell Univ. Pr.

Lewis, Hunter, ed. Alexander Skutch: An Appreciation. 2007. (ENG.). 293p. per. 12.00 *(978-0-9661908-7-8(4))* Axios Pr.

Redondo-Brenes, Alvaro & Montagnini, Florencia, eds. Forested Habitats & Human-Modified Land-Use Effects on Avian Diversity. 2010. (Birds - Evolution, Behavior & Ecology Ser.). pap. 43.00 *(978-1-60876-879-0(1))* Nova Science Pubs., Inc.

Spear, Larry B. Foraging Dynamics of Seabirds in the Eastern Tropical Pacific Ocean: Studies in Avian Biology No. 35. 2007. (Studies in Avian Biology). 100p. per. 15.00 *(978-0-943610-79-5(6))* American Ornithologists Union.

Van Perlo, Ber. Birds of Mexico & Central America. 2006. (Princeton Illustrated Checklists Ser.). (ENG., Illus.). 336p. pap. 29.95 *(978-0-691-12070-6(6))* Princeton Univ. Pr.

Whitacre, D. Raptors of Maya Forest. 2012. (Published in Association with the Peregrine Fund Ser.). (ENG., Illus.). 560p. 75.00 *(978-0-8014-4079-3(3))* Cornell Univ. Pr.

BIRDS—CHILE

Rozzi, Ricardo. Multi-Ethnic Bird Guide of the Subantarctic Forests of South America. 2nd ed. 2010. (SPA, ENG & SAI., Illus.). 236p. 34.95 *(978-1-57441-282-6(5))* Univ. of North Texas Pr.

BIRDS—CHINA

Arlott, Norman. Birds of Europe, Russia, China, & Japan: Non-Passerines - Loons to Woodpeckers. 2009. (Princeton Illustrated Checklists Ser.). (ENG., Illus.). 256p. pap. 29.95 *(978-0-691-13685-1(8))* Princeton Univ. Pr.

—Birds of Europe, Russia, China, & Japan: Passerines: Tyrant Flycatchers to Buntings. 2007. (Princeton Illustrated Checklists Ser.). (ENG., Illus.). 240p. per. 29.95 *(978-0-691-13372-0(7))* Princeton Univ. Pr.

Feduccia, Alan. Riddle of the Feathered Dragons: Hidden Birds of China. 2012. (ENG., Illus.). 368p. 55.00 *(978-0-300-16435-0(1))* Yale Univ. Pr.

Ptak, Roderich. Birds & Beasts in Chinese Texts & Trade: Lectures Related to South China & the Overseas World. 2011. (Maritime Asia Ser.). (ENG., Illus.). 140p. (C). 57.00 ***(978-3-447-06449-1(8))*** Harrassowitz, Otto Verlag DEU. Dist: ISD.

BIRDS—EUROPE

Alderton, David. The Illustrated Encyclopedia of Birds of Britain, Europe & Africa: A Fine Visual Guide to over 400 Birds Inhabiting These Continents. 2012. (ENG., Illus.). 264p. pap. 18.99 *(978-1-78019-004-4(2))* Anness Publishing GBR. Dist: National Bk. Network.

Arlott, Norman. Birds of Europe, Russia, China, & Japan: Non-Passerines - Loons to Woodpeckers. 2009. (Princeton Illustrated Checklists Ser.). (ENG., Illus.). 256p. pap. 29.95 *(978-0-691-13685-1(8))* Princeton Univ. Pr.

—Birds of Europe, Russia, China, & Japan: Passerines: Tyrant Flycatchers to Buntings. 2007. (Princeton Illustrated Checklists Ser.). (ENG., Illus.). 240p. per. 29.95 *(978-0-691-13372-0(7))* Princeton Univ. Pr.

Bevis, John, et al. Aaaaw to Zzzzzd: The Words of Birds - North America, Britain, & Northern Europe. 2010. (ENG., Illus.). 160p. (gr. 17). 14.95 *(978-0-262-01429-8(7))* MIT Pr.

Burridge, John T. Burridge's Multilingual Dictionary of Birds of the World: Volumes XXIII Bulgarian; Volume XXIV Ukranian; Volume XXV Belarusian. 2008. (BUL, UKR, BEL, ENG & MUL.). 230p. *(978-1-4438-2112-4(8))* Cambridge Scholors Pub.

Chandler, Richard. Shorebirds of North America, Europe & Asia: A Photographic Guide. 2009. (ENG., Illus.). 448p. pap. 35.00 *(978-0-691-14281-4(5))* Princeton Univ. Pr.

De Boer, Bart, et al. Birds of Aruba, Bonaire & Curacao. 2012. (Princeton Field Guides). (ENG., Illus.). 192p. pap. 27.95 ***(978-0-691-15336-0(1))*** Princeton Univ. Pr.

Dutson, Guy. Birds of Melanesia - Bismarcks, Solomons, Vanuatu, & New Caledonia. 2012. (Princeton Field Guides). (ENG., Illus.). 448p. pap. 49.95 ***(978-0-691-15350-6(7))*** Princeton Univ. Pr.

Farrow, Dave. A Guide to the Garden Birds of Britain & Northern Europe. 2011. (ENG., Illus.). 200p. pap. 16.95 *(978-1-84732-744-4(3))* Carlton Bks., Ltd. GBR. Dist: Independent Pubs. Group.

Goodfellow, Peter. A Naturalist's Guide to the Birds of Britain & Northern Europe. 2010. (Naturalists' Guides). (Illus.). 160p. pap. 14.95 *(978-1-906780-12-8(9))* Beaufoy, John Publishing GBR. Dist: Midpoint Trade Bks., Inc.

Grant, Peter & Grant, Rosemary. How & Why Species Multiply: The Radiation of Darwin's Finches. 2011. (Princeton Series in Evolutionary Biology Ser.). (ENG., Illus.). 256p. (C). pap. 24.95 *(978-0-691-14999-8(2))* Princeton Univ. Pr.

Hosking, Eric & Reade, W. Winwood. Nesting Birds: Eggs & Fledglings. 3rd ed. (Illus.). 275p. *(978-0-7137-0444-0(6))* Blandford Pr.

Kavanagh, James. European Backyard Birds: An Introduction to Familiar Species. 2010. (Pocket Naturalist Guide Ser.). (ENG.). 2p. 5.95 *(978-1-58355-550-7(1))* Waterford Pr., Inc.

Payevsky, Vladimir. Songbird Demography: Demographic structure, survival rates, & population dynamics of songbirds with particular reference to the birds of the Eastern Baltic. Griffiths, Martin, ed. 2009. 260p. 147.50 *(978-954-642-470-9(6))* Pensoft Pubs. BGR. Dist: Coronet Bks.

Sterry, Paul & AA Publishing Staff. Birds of Britain & Europe: The Identification Guide to the Birds of Britain & Europe. 3rd ed. 2009. (ENG., Illus.). 320p. 50.00 *(978-0-7495-5862-8(8))* Automobile Assn. GBR. Dist: Independent Pubs. Group.

Svensson, Lars & Dan, Zetterström. Birds of Europe. 2nd ed. 2010. (Princeton Field Guides). (ENG., Illus.). 448p. pap. 29.95 *(978-0-691-14392-7(7))* Princeton Univ. Pr.

BIRDS—GALAPAGOS ISLANDS

Apanius, Victor, et al. Reproduction & Immune Homeostasis in a Long-lived Seabird, the Nazca Booby (Sula Granti) Ornithological Monographs, No. 65. 2008. 46p. 10.00 *(978-0-943610-80-1(X))* American Ornithologists Union.

BIRDS—GREAT BRITAIN

Bircham, P. M. M. The Birds of Cambridgeshire. 2009. (ENG., Illus.). 296p. pap. 31.99 *(978-0-521-11172-0(2))* Cambridge Univ. Pr.

Bowmer, Roger. British Orchids. 2008. (ENG., Illus.). 128p. pap. 34.95 *(978-1-84797-002-2(8))* Crowood Pr., Ltd. GBR. Dist: Independent Pubs. Group.

Cabot, David. Wildfowl of Britain & Ireland. 2009. (Collins New Naturalist Ser.). (ENG., Illus.). 320p. 85.00 *(978-0-00-714658-1(2))* HarperCollins Pubs. Ltd. GBR. Dist: Independent Pubs. Group.

Farrow, Dave. A Guide to the Garden Birds of Britain & Northern Europe. 2011. (ENG., Illus.). 200p. pap. 16.95 *(978-1-84732-744-4(3))* Carlton Bks., Ltd. GBR. Dist: Independent Pubs. Group.

Gibb, Andy. The British Birding Year. 2010. 53p. pap. 21.50 *(978-1-4457-7242-4(6))* Lulu Enterprises Inc.

—Build a British Bird List. 2010. 32p. pap. 10.50 *(978-1-4461-5017-7(8))* Lulu Enterprises Inc.

Goodfellow, Peter. A Naturalist's Guide to the Birds of Britain & Northern Europe. 2010. (Naturalists' Guides). (Illus.). 160p. pap. 14.95 *(978-1-906780-12-8(9))* Beaufoy, John Publishing GBR. Dist: Midpoint Trade Bks., Inc.

Hudson, W. H. Birds in London. reprint ed. 64.50 *(978-0-404-03397-2(0))* AMS Pr., Inc.

—Birds in London. 2009. 202p. pap. *(978-1-150-65169-4(5))* Books LLC.

—Birds in London. 2008. 388p. 48.95 *(978-1-4366-5873-7(X))*; pap. 33.95 *(978-0-548-88160-6(X))* Kessinger Publishing, LLC.

—Birds in Town & Village. 2008. 176p. 22.99 *(978-0-554-31733-5(8))* 2008. 176p. 25.99 *(978-0-554-22430-5(5))* 2007. (ENG.). 160p. pap. 19.99 *(978-1-4264-2331-4(4))* 2006. 172p. pap. 21.99 *(978-1-4264-2379-6(9))* BiblioBazaar.

—Birds in Town & Village. 2007. (ENG., Illus.). 168p. per. *(978-1-4065-6013-8(8))* Dodo Pr.

—Birds in Town & Village. 2008. 300p. pap. *(978-1-4097-8574-3(2))* Read Bks.

—British Birds. reprint ed. 64.50 *(978-0-404-03396-5(2))* AMS Pr., Inc.

Hudson, W. H. & Beddard, Frank Evers. British Birds. 2010. 444p. pap. 35.75 *(978-1-145-09298-3(5))* BiblioBazaar.

Hudson, William Henry, et al. British Birds. 2010. 442p. pap. 35.75 *(978-1-148-15279-0(2))* BiblioBazaar.

Jackson, Tom. The Illustrated World Encyclopedia of Animals, Birds & Fish of the British Isles: A Natural History & Identification Guide with over 450 Native Species from England, Ireland, Scotland & Wales. 2011. (ENG., Illus.). 256p. 29.99 *(978-0-7548-1968-4(X))* Anness Publishing GBR. Dist: National Bk. Network.

Main, Iain, et al. Birds of the Cotswolds. 2009. (ENG., Illus.). 248p. 95.00 *(978-1-84631-210-6(8))* Liverpool Univ. Pr. GBR. Dist: Chicago Distribution Ctr.

Moss, Stephen. Birds Britannia. 2011. (ENG.). 320p. 29.95 ***(978-0-00-741344-7(0))*** HarperCollins Pubs. Ltd. GBR. Dist: Independent Pubs. Group.

Niles, Lawrence, et al. Status of the Red Knot (Calidris canutus rufa) in the Western Hemisphere: Studies in Avian Biology, No. 36. 2008. (Studies in Avian Biology). 186p. mass mkt. 20.00 *(978-0-943610-83-2(4))* American Ornithologists Union.

Norman, David. Birds in Cheshire & Wirral: A Breeding & Wintering Atlas. 2009. (ENG., Illus.). 704p. 90.00 *(978-1-84631-152-9(7))* Liverpool Univ. Pr. GBR. Dist: Chicago Distribution Ctr.

Oddie, Bill. Bill Oddie's Little Black Bird Book. 2011. (ENG., Illus.). 144p. pap. 15.95 *(978-1-907554-27-8(0))* Anova Bks. GBR. Dist: Independent Pubs. Group.

Owen, Richard. A History of British Fossil Mammals, & Birds. 2011. (Cambridge Library Collection - Life Sciences Ser.). (ENG., Illus.). 616p. pap. 43.00 ***(978-1-108-03816-4(6))*** Cambridge Univ. Pr.

Ratcliffe, D. A. Bird Life of Mountain & Upland. 2010. (Bird Life Ser.). (ENG.). 272p. pap. 23.99 *(978-0-521-14259-5(8))* Cambridge Univ. Pr.

Sample, Geoff. Garden Bird Songs & Calls. 2009. (ENG., Illus.). 32p. 23.95 *(978-0-00-731329-7(2))* HarperCollins Pubs. Ltd. GBR. Dist: Independent Pubs. Group.

Scott, Don. The Hen Harrier: In the Shadow of Slemish. 2010. (Illus.). 192p. pap. *(978-1-904445-93-7(4))* Whittles Publishing.

Sharpe, Christopher Martyn, et al, eds. Manx Bird Atlas. 2007. (ENG., Illus.). 416p. 95.00 *(978-1-84631-039-3(3))* Liverpool Univ. Pr. GBR. Dist: Chicago Distribution Ctr.

Smith, Cecil. Birds of Guernsey. 2008. 168p. 22.99 *(978-0-554-34322-8(3))*; 25.99 *(978-0-554-25019-9(5))* BiblioBazaar.

—Birds of Guernsey. 2006. pap. *(978-1-84702-482-4(3))* Echo Library.

Sterry, Paul. British Birds: A Photographic Guide to Every Common Species. 2008. (Collins Complete Photo Guides). (ENG., Illus.). 288p. pap. 31.95 *(978-0-00-723686-2(7))* HarperCollins Pubs. Ltd. GBR. Dist: Independent Pubs. Group.

Sterry, Paul & AA Publishing Staff. Birds of Britain & Europe: The Identification Guide to the Birds of Britain & Europe. 3rd ed. 2009. (ENG., Illus.). 320p. 50.00 *(978-0-7495-5862-8(8))* Automobile Assn. GBR. Dist: Independent Pubs. Group.

Stevens, Ronald. Laggard. 2010. 312p. 34.95 ***(978-0-88839-699-0(6))*** Hancock Hse. Pubs.

Swainson, Charles. Provincial Names & Folk Lore of British Birds. 256p. 2009. 34.99 *(978-1-115-37395-1(1))* 2009. 30.99 *(978-1-115-37392-0(7))* 2009. pap. 26.75 *(978-1-115-37390-6(0))* 2009. 24.99 *(978-1-103-48456-0(7))* 2009. pap. 18.99 *(978-1-103-48451-5(6))* 2008. 25.99 *(978-0-559-53114-9(1))* 2008. pap. 25.75 *(978-0-559-53110-1(9))* BiblioBazaar.

Thorn, Valerie. Collins Scottish Birds. 2nd ed. 2008. (ENG., Illus.). 256p. pap. 19.95 *(978-0-00-727068-2(2))* HarperCollins Pubs. Ltd. GBR. Dist: Independent Pubs. Group.

Walker, David. Call of the Eagle. 2009. (Illus.). 224p. pap. *(978-1-904445-82-1(9))* Whittles Publishing.

Yalden, Derek & Albarella, Umberto. The History of British Birds. (ENG., Illus.). 2010. 272p. 55.00 *(978-0-19-958116-0(9))* 2009. 288p. 125.00 *(978-0-19-921751-9(3))* Oxford Univ. Pr., Inc.

BIRDS—GREECE

Arnott, W. Geoffrey. Birds in the Ancient World from A to Z. 2012. (Ancient World from a to Z Ser.). (ENG & GEC., Illus.). 304p. pap. 42.95 ***(978-0-415-54088-9(7))*** Routledge.

BIRDS—GUATEMALA

Dickerman, R. W. Birds of the Southern Pacific Lowlands of Guatemala; with a Review of Icterus Gularis. 2007. 45p. pap. 10.00 *(978-0-9794517-1-3(X))* Museum of Southwest Biology Pubn. Series.

BIRDS—HAWAII

Hearne, Margo. Birds at Risk: A Haida Gwaii Introduction. 2011. 40p. pap. ***(978-1-77067-571-1(X))*** FriesenPress.

Pratt, Douglas. Birds. 2007. 48p. 8.95 *(978-1-56647-795-6(6))* Mutual Publishing LLC.

Pratt, Thane K., et al, eds. Conservation Biology of Hawaiian Forest Birds: Implications for Island Avifauna. 2009. (ENG., Illus.). 728p. 85.00 *(978-0-300-14108-5(4))* Yale Univ. Pr.

Shallenberger, Robert J. Hawaiian Birds of the Sea: Na Manu Kai. 2009. pap. 21.99 *(978-0-8248-3403-6(8))* Univ. of Hawaii Pr.

van Perlo, Ber. Birds of Hawaii, New Zealand, & the Central & West Pacific: 2011. (Princeton Illustrated Checklists Ser.). (ENG., Illus.). 256p. pap. 29.95 ***(978-0-691-15188-5(1))*** Princeton Univ. Pr.

BIRDS—INDIA

Dave, Sanjay. Piscivorous Birds in Natural Habitats. 2010. 140p. pap. *(978-3-639-23649-1(1))* VDM Verlag Dr. Mueller e.K.

Dewar, Douglas. A Bird Calendar for Northern India. 2008. 128p. 24.99 *(978-0-554-26160-7(X))* 2007. (ENG.). 114p. pap. 18.99 *(978-1-4346-0630-3(9))* 2007. (ENG.). 124p. pap. 19.99 *(978-1-4346-0631-0(7))* BiblioBazaar.

—A Bird Calendar for Northern India. 2009. 132p. pap. *(978-1-4099-6687-6(9))* Dodo Pr.

—Birds of the Plains. 2008. 294p. 43.95 *(978-1-4365-6003-0(9))* 2007. (ENG.). 296p. per. 28.95 *(978-0-548-76212-7(0))* Kessinger Publishing, LLC.

Grewal, Bikram. Birds of the Indian Subcontinent. (Illustrated Travel Guides). (Illus.). *(978-962-8711-07-9(5))* Local Colour, Ltd. HKG. Dist: 7 Hills Bk. Distributors.

Grimmett, Richard. Birds of India - Pakistan, Nepal, Bangladesh, Bhutan, Sri Lanka, & the Maldives 2e. 2012. (Princeton Field Guides). (ENG., Illus.). 528p. pap. 39.50 ***(978-0-691-15349-0(3))*** Princeton Univ. Pr.

Jathar, Girish & Rahmani, Asad. Ecology of the Forest Owlet. 2011. 204p. pap. ***(978-3-8443-0572-2(6))*** Lambert Academic Publishing.

Mackintosh, L. J. Birds of Darjeeling & India. 2009. (ENG.). 321p. pap. 24.99 *(978-1-116-11400-3(3))*; pap. 23.99 *(978-1-116-11401-0(1))* BiblioBazaar. (BiblioLife).

Sinclair, Ian, et al. Birds of the Indian Ocean Islands: Madagascar, Mauritius, Seychelles, Reunion & the Comoros. 2011. (Illus.). 184p. pap. 26.00 *(978-1-86872-956-2(7))* Struik Pubs. ZAF. Dist: International Publishers Marketing.

—A Photographic Guide to the Birds of the Indian Ocean Islands: Madagascar, Mauritius, Seychelles, Reunion & the Comoros. 2011. (Illus.). 128p. per. 12.00 *(978-1-77007-175-9(X))* Struik Pubs. ZAF. Dist: International Publishers Marketing.

Urfi, Abdul Jamil. Birds of India: A Literary Anthology. 2011. (ENG., Illus.). 414p. pap. 26.50 *(978-0-19-806939-3(1))* Oxford Univ. Pr., Inc.

—Birds of India: A Literary Anthology. Urfi, Abdul Jamil, ed. 2008. (ENG., Illus.). 504p. 49.95 *(978-0-19-568945-7(3))* Oxford Univ. Pr., Inc.

BIRDS—IRELAND

Anderson, Glynn. Birds of Ireland: Facts, Folklore & History. 2009. (ENG., Illus.). 375p. 43.95 *(978-1-905172-72-6(9))* Collins Pr., The IRL. Dist: Dufour Editions, Inc.

Cabot, David. Wildfowl of Britain & Ireland. 2009. (Collins New Naturalist Ser.). (ENG., Illus.). 320p. 85.00 *(978-0-00-714658-1(2))* HarperCollins Pubs. Ltd. GBR. Dist: Independent Pubs. Group.

Kavanagh, James. Birds of Ireland: An Introduction to Familiar Species. 2007. (Pocket Naturalist - Waterford Press Ser.). (ENG., Illus.). 1p. 5.95 *(978-1-58355-338-1(X))* Waterford Pr., Inc.

Nairn, Richard & O'Halloran, John L., eds. Bird Habitats in Ireland. 2012. (ENG., Illus.). 232p. 59.95 ***(978-1-84889-138-8(5))*** Collins Pr., The IRL. Dist: Dufour Editions, Inc.

O'Sullivan, Oran & Wilson, Jim. Ireland's Garden Birds: How to Identify, Attract, & Garden for Birds. 2009. (ENG., Illus.). 192p. pap. 31.95 *(978-1-905172-73-3(7))* Collins Pr., The IRL. Dist: Dufour Editions, Inc.

Wilson, Jim. The Shorebirds of Ireland. 2010. (ENG., Illus.). 208p. pap. 37.95 *(978-1-84889-017-6(6))* Collins Pr., The IRL. Dist: Dufour Editions, Inc.

BIRDS—ISLANDS OF THE ATLANTIC

Ferns, P. N. Bird Life of Coasts & Estuaries. 2009. (Bird Life Ser.). (ENG.). 352p. pap. 36.99 *(978-0-521-11449-3(7))* Cambridge Univ. Pr.

BIRDS—ISLANDS OF THE PACIFIC

DuPont, John Eleuthère & Sandström, George F. South Pacific Birds. 2010. *(978-0-89803-165-9(4))* Jameson Bks., Inc.

Steadman, David W. Extinction & Biogeography of Tropical Pacific Birds. 2006. (Illus.). 480p. 120.00 *(978-0-226-77141-0(5))*; per. 47.50 *(978-0-226-77142-7(3))* Univ. of Chicago Pr.

van Perlo, Ber. Birds of Hawaii, New Zealand, & the Central & West Pacific. 2011. (Princeton Illustrated Checklists Ser.). (ENG., Illus.). 256p. pap. 29.95 ***(978-0-691-15188-5(1))*** Princeton Univ. Pr.

BIRDS—JAPAN

Arlott, Norman. Birds of Europe, Russia, China, & Japan: Non-Passerines - Loons to Woodpeckers. 2009. (Princeton Illustrated Checklists Ser.). (ENG., Illus.). 256p. pap. 29.95 *(978-0-691-13685-1(8))* Princeton Univ. Pr.

—Birds of Europe, Russia, China, & Japan: Passerines: Tyrant Flycatchers to Buntings. 2007. (Princeton Illustrated Checklists Ser.). (ENG., Illus.). 240p. per. 29.95 *(978-0-691-13372-0(7))* Princeton Univ. Pr.

Carroll, Julie C. & Takahashi, Carol. Takahashi Bird Pins. 2010. (ENG., Illus.). 176p. 39.95 *(978-1-57432-686-4(4)*, 1574326864) Collector Bks.

Shimba, Tadao. A Photographic Guide to the Birds of Japan & North-East Asia. 2008. (ENG., Illus.). 504p. pap. 40.00 *(978-0-300-13556-5(4))* Yale Univ. Pr.

BIRDS—LATIN AMERICA

Garrigues, Richard. The Birds of Costa Rica: A Field Guide. 2007. (Illus.). 387p. pap. 29.95 *(978-0-8014-7373-9(X)*, Comstock Publishing Assocs.) Cornell Univ. Pr.

Taylor, W. Thomas, et al, contrib. by. Aves: A Survey of the Literature of Neotropical Ornithology. 2011. (Illus.). xv, 156p. ***(978-0-615-45363-7(5))*** Resource Assocs. Corp.

BIRDS—MALTA

Fenech, Natalino. A Complete Guide to Birds of Malta. 2010. (ENG., Illus.). 448p. (C). 75.00 *(978-99932-7-310-3(4))* Midsea Bks. Ltd. MLT. Dist: Brown, David Bk. Co., The.

BIRDS—MEXICO

Kavanagh, James. Mexico Birds: An Introduction to Familiar Species. 2009. (International Nature Guides). (ENG., Illus.). 1p. 5.95 *(978-1-58355-480-7(7))* Waterford Pr., Inc.

Paynter Jr., Raymond A. The Ornithogeography of the Yucatan Peninsula: Peabody Museum of Natural History, Yale University, Bulletin 9. 2011. 360p. 51.95 ***(978-1-258-08644-2(1))*** Literary Licensing, LLC.

Ruth, Janet M., et al. Birds of the US-Mexico Borderlands: Distribution, Ecology, & Conservation. 2008. (Illus.). vi, 165p. *(978-0-943610-84-9(2))* Allen Pr., Inc.

Saunders, Dorothy Chapman. Chico, George, the Birds, & Me: The Mexican Travelogue of a Woman Naturalist, 1948-1949. Reeves, Henry M. & Tomlinson, Roy E., eds. 2008. (Louise Lindsey Merrick Natural Environment Ser.: No. 43). (Illus.). 248p. 34.00 *(978-1-60344-061-5(5))* Texas A&M Univ. Pr.

Van Perlo, Ber. Birds of Mexico & Central America. 2006. (Princeton Illustrated Checklists Ser.). (ENG., Illus.). 336p. pap. 29.95 *(978-0-691-12070-6(6))* Princeton Univ. Pr.

BIRDS—MIDDLE EAST

Kavanagh, James. Middle East Wildlife: An Introduction to Familiar & Dangerous Species in Iraq, Iran, Afghanistan & the Middle East. 2010. (Duraguide Ser.). (ENG.). 2p. 7.95 *(978-1-58355-555-2(2))* Waterford Pr., Inc.

Porter, R. Birds of the Middle East - Second Edition. 2010. (Princeton Field Guides). (ENG., Illus.). 400p. pap. 39.50 *(978-0-691-14644-1(9))* Princeton Univ. Pr.

BIRDS—NEW ZEALAND

Dowding, J. E. & Davis, Alison M. New Zealand Dotterel (Charadrius Obscurus) Recovery Plan, 2004-14. 2007. 28p. pap. *(978-0-478-14145-0(9))* New Zealand Govt. - Dept. of Conservation.

Fitter, Julian. Birds of New Zealand. 2012. (Princeton Pocket Guides). (ENG., Illus.). 320p. pap. 24.95 ***(978-0-691-15351-3(5))*** Princeton Univ. Pr.

Hutton, Frederick Wollaston & Drummond, James. The Animals of New Zealand: An Account of the Dominion's Air-Breathing Vertebrates. 2011. (Cambridge Library Collection - Life Sciences Ser.). (ENG., Illus.). 440p. pap. 32.99 ***(978-1-108-04002-0(0))*** Cambridge Univ. Pr.

O'Connor, S. M., et al. Pateke (Anas Chlorotis) Recovery Plan, 2005-10. 2007. 33p. pap. *(978-0-478-14146-7(7))* New Zealand Govt. - Dept. of Conservation.

Peat, Neville. Kiwi. 2006. (Illus.). 176p. pap. 45.00 *(978-1-877372-36-0(6))* Otago University Pr. NZL. Dist: International Specialized Bk. Services.

van Perlo, Ber. Birds of Hawaii, New Zealand, & the Central & West Pacific. 2011. (Princeton Illustrated Checklists Ser.). (ENG., Illus.). 256p. pap. 29.95 ***(978-0-691-15188-5(1))*** Princeton Univ. Pr.

BIRDS—NORTH AMERICA

see also Birds—Canada; Birds—Mexico; Birds—United States

Arlott, Norman. Birds of North America & Greenland. 2011. (Princeton Illustrated Checklists Ser.). (ENG., Illus.). 224p. pap. 15.95 ***(978-0-691-15140-3(7))*** Princeton Univ. Pr.

Audubon, John James. The Birds of America. unabr. ed. (Illus.). reprint ed. 17.75 *(978-0-8446-7095-9(2))*; Vol. 5. 17.75 *(978-0-8446-7099-7(5))*; Vol. 7. 17.75 *(978-0-8446-7101-7(0))* Smith, Peter Pub., Inc.

Audubon, John James & Oppenheimer, Joel. The Birds of America: The Bien Chromolithographic Edition. 2012. (ENG., Illus.). 256p. 350.00 ***(978-0-393-08865-6(8)***, 8865) Norton, W. W. & Co., Inc.

Bannick, Paul. The Owl & the Woodpecker: Encounters with North America's Most Iconic Birds. 2008. (ENG.). 128p. 24.95 *(978-1-59485-095-0(X))* Mountaineers Bks., The.

Beletsky, Les. Bird Songs: 250 North American Birds in Song. 2007. 45.00 *(978-1-932855-75-3(0))* 2006. 368p. 360.00 *(978-1-932855-54-8(8))* becker&mayer! books.

—The Bird Songs Anthology. 2007. 45.00 *(978-1-932855-88-3(2))* becker&mayer! books.

Beletsky, Les, ed. Bird Songs Bible: The Complete, Illustrated Reference for North American Birds. 2010. (ENG., Illus.). 536p. 125.00 *(978-0-8118-7138-9(X))* Chronicle Bks. LLC.

Bevis, John, et al. Aaaaw to Zzzzzd: The Words of Birds - North America, Britain, & Northern Europe. 2010. (ENG., Illus.). 160p. (gr. 17). 14.95 *(978-0-262-01429-8(7))* MIT Pr.

Bildstein, Keith L. State of North America's Birds of Prey. 2008. (Illus.). 466p. *(978-0-943610-81-8(8))* American Ornithologists Union.

Brinkley, Edward S. National Wildlife Federation Field Guide to Birds of North America. 2007. (National Wildlife Federation Field Guide Ser.). (ENG., Illus.). 528p. pap. 19.95 *(978-1-4027-3874-6(9))* Sterling Publishing Co., Inc.

Bryan, Denver. A Portrait of North American Waterfowling. 2006. (Illus.). 96p. tchr. ed. 19.50 *(978-1-59543-051-9(2))* Willow Creek Pr., Inc.

Burton, Robert & Dorling Kindersley Publishing Staff. Audubon North American Birdfeeder Guide. 2009. (ENG.). 224p. (gr. 12). pap. 14.95 *(978-0-7566-5883-0(7))* Dorling Kindersley Publishing, Inc.

Burton, Robert & Kress, Stephen. The Audubon Backyard Birdwatcher: Birdfeeders & Bird Gardens. 2012. (ENG., Illus.). 384p. pap. 19.95 ***(978-1-60710-404-9(0)***, Thunder Bay Pr.) Advantage Pubs. Group.

Byland, Steve. North American Birds in Photographs CD-ROM & Book. 2011. (Dover Electronic Clip Art Ser.). (ENG., Illus.). 48p. pap. 19.95 *(978-0-486-99007-1(9))* Dover Pubns., Inc.

Chandler, Richard. Shorebirds of North America, Europe & Asia: A Photographic Guide. 2009. (ENG., Illus.). 448p. pap. 35.00 *(978-0-691-14281-4(5))* Princeton Univ. Pr.

Couzens, Dominic. Color Yourself Smart: Birds of North America. 2011. (ENG., Illus.). 128p. 19.95 *(978-1-60710-218-2(6)*, Thunder Bay Pr.) Advantage Pubs. Group.

Davis, Kate. Falcons of North America. 2008. pap. *(978-0-87842-553-2(5))* Mountain Pr. Publishing Co., Inc.

Dorling Kindersley Publishing Staff. American Museum of Natural History Birds of Eastern North America. 2011. (ENG.). 480p. (gr. 12). pap. 19.95 *(978-0-7566-5867-0(5))* Dorling Kindersley Publishing, Inc.

—American Museum of Natural History Birds of Western North America. 2011. (ENG.). 480p. (gr. 12). pap. 19.95 *(978-0-7566-5868-7(3))* Dorling Kindersley Publishing, Inc.

—What's That Bird. 2012. (ENG., Illus.). 128p. 9.95 *(978-0-7566-8968-1(6))* Dorling Kindersley Publishing, Inc.

Dunn, Jon & Alderfer, Jonathan K. Birds of North America. 2009. (Illus.). 502p. *(978-1-4262-0577-4(5))* National Geographic Society.

Dunn, Jon L. & Alderfer, Jonathan. Birds of North America. 2009. (ENG., Illus.). 504p. 50.00 *(978-1-4262-0525-5(2)*, National Geographic) National Geographic Society.

—National Geographic Field Guide to the Birds of North America, Sixth Edition. 6th ed. 2011. (ENG., Illus.). 576p. pap. 27.95 *(978-1-4262-0828-7(6)*, National Geographic) National Geographic Society.

Earley, Chris. The Great Lakes Birds Collection. 2009. (ENG.). pap. 19.95 *(978-1-55407-471-6(1))* Firefly Bks., Ltd.

Ellwood, Nancy. American Museum of Natural History Birds of North America. 2010. (ENG.). 744p. 34.95 *(978-0-7566-6588-3(4))* Dorling Kindersley Publishing, Inc.

Encyclopedia of North American Birds. 2008. 384p. *(978-1-4075-2436-8(4))* Parragon, Inc.

Evans, Middleton. Rhapsody in Blue: A Celebration of North American Waterbirds. 2007. (Illus.). 272p. per. 60.00 *(978-0-9778055-1-8(4))* Ravenwood Pr., Inc.

Floyd, Ted. Smithsonian Field Guide to the Birds of North America. Hess, Paul & Scott, George, eds. 2008. (ENG., Illus.). 528p. pap. 24.95 *(978-0-06-112040-4(5)*, HarperPerennial) HarperCollins Pubs.

Gates, Larry & Gates, Terrie. Enjoying Hummingbirds: In the Wild & in Your Yard. 2007. (ENG., Illus.). 144p. per. 24.95 *(978-0-8117-3421-9(8))* Stackpole Bks.

Glassberg, Jeffrey. Birds of North America. 2011. (ENG., Illus.). 240p. pap. 12.95 *(978-1-4027-8276-3(4))* Sterling Publishing Co., Inc.

Hook, Patrick. North American Birds. 2007. (Illus.). 255p. 29.99 *(978-0-7858-2219-6(4)*, Chartwell) Book Sales, Inc.

Howell, Steve N. G. Peterson Reference Guide to Molt in North American Birds. 2010. (Peterson Reference Guides). (ENG., Illus.). 280p. 35.00 *(978-0-547-15235-6(3))* Houghton Mifflin Harcourt Trade & Reference Pubs.

Jackson, Tom. The Illustrated Encyclopedia of Animals, Birds & Fish of North America: A Natural History & Identification Guide with More Than 420 Native Species from the United States of America & Canada. 2012. (ENG., Illus.). 256p. 35.00 *(978-0-7548-1987-5(6))* Anness Publishing GBR. Dist: National Bk. Network.

John, Audubon James. Birds of America. 2011. (ENG., Illus.). 448p. 80.00 *(978-1-4027-8947-2(5))* Sterling Publishing Co., Inc.

Kaufman, Kenn. Kaufman Field Guide to Advanced Birding. 2011. (Kaufman Field Guides). (ENG., Illus.). 448p. 21.00 *(978-0-547-24832-5(6))* Houghton Mifflin Harcourt Trade & Reference Pubs.

Kiser, Joy M. America's Other Audubon. 2012. (ENG., Illus.). 144p. 45.00 ***(978-1-61689-059-9(2))*** Princeton Architectural Pr.

Knick, Steven & Connelly, John. Greater Sage-Grouse: Ecology & Conservation of a Landscape Species & Its Habitats. 2011. (Studies in Avian Biology Ser.). (ENG., Illus.). 664p. 95.00 *(978-0-520-26711-4(7))* Univ. of California Pr.

Kroodsma, Donald. The Backyard Birdsong Guide (East & Central North America Edition: A Cornell Lab of Ornithology Audio Field Guide. 2008. 24.95 *(978-1-932855-90-6(4))* becker&mayer! books.

—The Backyard Birdsong Guide (West North America Edition) A Cornell Lab of Ornithology Audio Field Guide. 2008. 24.95 *(978-1-932855-91-3(2))* becker&mayer! books.

Leahy, C. W. Birdwatcher's Companion to North American Birdlife. 2006. (ENG., Illus.). 1072p. pap. 19.95 *(978-0-691-11388-3(2))* Princeton Univ. Pr.

Lebbin, Daniel J., et al. The American Bird Conservancy Guide to Bird Conservation. 2010. (ENG., Illus.). 456p. 45.00 *(978-0-226-64727-2(7))* Univ. of Chicago Pr.

Leslie, Scott. Sea & Coastal Birds of North America: A Guide to Observation, Understanding, & Conservation. 2008. (ENG., Illus.). 248p. pap. 19.95 *(978-1-55470-045-5(0))* Key Porter Bks. CAN. Dist: Perseus-PGW.

Liguori, Jerry. Hawks at a Distance: Identification of Migrant Raptors. 2011. (ENG., Illus.). 216p. (C). 49.50 *(978-0-691-13558-8(4))*; pap. 19.95 *(978-0-691-13559-5(2))* Princeton Univ. Pr.

Maslowski, Steve & Maslowski, Dave, photos by. Time Flies Journal: A Bird Lover's Daybook. 2006. (ENG., Illus.). 128p. 19.50 *(978-1-59543-421-0(6)*, 4210) Willow Creek Pr., Inc.

Mega Square, ed. Audubons Birds Mega Sq. 2006. (Mega Squares Ser.). (Illus.). 256p. pap. 10.95 *(978-1-84013-942-6(0))* New Line Bks.

Nehrling, Henry. Our Native Birds of Song & Beauty Set, 2 vols. (Illus.). reprint ed. lib. bdg. 250.00 *(978-0-7222-0350-7(0))* Library Reprints, Inc.

North Carolina Birding Trail. The North Carolina Birding Trail: Mountain Trail Guide. 2009. (Distributed for the North Carolina Birding Trail Ser.). (ENG.). 180p. pap. 19.95 *(978-0-8078-5965-0(6))* Univ. of North Carolina Pr.

Peterson, Roger Tory. Peterson Field Guide to Birds of Eastern & Central North America. 6th rev. ed. 2010. (Peterson Field Guides). (ENG., Illus.). 464p. 19.95 *(978-0-547-15246-2(9))* Houghton Mifflin Harcourt Trade & Reference Pubs.

—Peterson Field Guide to Birds of North America. 11th ed. 2008. (Peterson Field Guides). (ENG., Illus.). 544p. 26.00 *(978-0-618-96614-1(5))* Houghton Mifflin Harcourt Trade & Reference Pubs.

Reed, Chester A. The Bird Book: Illustrating More than Seven Hundred North American Birds, Also Several Hundred Photographs of Their Nests & Eggs. 2008. 476p. pap. 19.99 *(978-1-60459-577-2(9))* Wilder Pubns., Ltd.

Roetzel, Jim, photos by. Birds of North America. 2007. (ENG., Illus.). 160p. 26.95 *(978-1-885435-80-4(0))* Twin Lights Pubs., Inc.

Romano, Tom. Birds of Prey. Strozier, M. Stefan & Torke, Kyle, eds. 2010. 54p. 16.00 *(978-1-935444-44-2(1))*; 48p. pap. 15.00 *(978-1-935444-56-5(5))* World Audience Pubs.

Schmauss, Anne, et al. For the Birds: A Month-by-Month Guide to Attracting Birds to Your Backyard. 2008. (ENG., Illus.). 224p. pap. 21.95 *(978-1-58479-717-3(7))* Stewart, Tabori & Chang.

Scott, S. & McFarland, Casey. Bird Feathers: A Guide to North American Species. 2010. (ENG., Illus.). 400p. pap. 34.95 *(978-0-8117-3618-3(0))* Stackpole Bks.

Scott Shupe & Shupe, Scott. North American Bird I. D. Checklist: A Journal for Backyard Bird Enthusiasts. 2009. (ENG.). 96p. pap. 9.95 *(978-1-59186-460-8(7)*, 1591864607) Cool Springs Pr.

Sibley, David Allen. Sibley Backyard Birding Flashcards: 100 Common Birds of Eastern & Western North America. 2012. (ENG.). 100p. 14.99 ***(978-0-307-88897-6(5)***, Potter Style) Crown Publishing Group.

—The Sibley Guide to Bird Life & Behavior. 2009. (ENG., Illus.). 608p. 39.95 *(978-1-4000-4386-6(7)*, Knopf) Knopf Doubleday Publishing Group.

—Sibleys Ducks Geese & Swans E N Amer. 2009. pap. 7.95 *(978-1-935380-13-9(3))* Lewers, Steven & Assocs.

—Sibleys Owls of N Amer. 2009. pap. 7.95 *(978-1-935380-16-0(8))* Lewers, Steven & Assocs.

—Sibleys Raptors of E N Amer. 2009. pap. 7.95 *(978-1-935380-17-7(6))* Lewers, Steven & Assocs.

Snyder, Noel & Snyder, Helen. Raptors of North America: Natural History & Conservation. rev. ed. 2006. (ENG., Illus.). 320p. 50.00 *(978-0-7603-2582-7(0)*, 0760325820, Voyageur Pr) MBI Publishing Co. LLC.

Snyder, Noel F. R. & Snyder, Helen. Raptors of North America: Natural History & Conservation. 2006. (Illus.). 320p. *(978-0-89658-659-8(6)*, Voyageur Pr) MBI Publishing Co. LLC.

Snyder, Noel F. R., et al. The Travails of Two Woodpeckers: Ivory-Bills & Imperials. 2009. (ENG., Illus.). 184p. 34.95 *(978-0-8263-4664-3(2))* Univ. of New Mexico Pr.

Stokes, Donald & Stokes, Lillian. The Stokes Field Guide to the Birds of North America. 2010. (ENG., Illus.). 816p. pap. 24.99 *(978-0-316-01050-4(2))* Little Brown & Co.

Stratton-Porter, Gene. Homing with the Birds: The History of a Lifetime of Personal Experience with the Birds. 32.95 *(978-0-8488-1449-6(5))* Amereon LTD.

—Homing with the Birds: The History of a Lifetime of Personal Experience with the Birds. 2008. 398p. 49.95 *(978-1-4365-9180-5(5))* 2007. 400p. per. 34.95 *(978-0-548-80308-0(0))* Kessinger Publishing, LLC.

Thompson III, Bill. Identifying & Feeding Birds. 2010. (Peterson Field Guides/Bird Watcher's Digest Backyard Bird Guides). (ENG., Illus.). 256p. pap. 14.95 *(978-0-618-90444-0(1))* Houghton Mifflin Harcourt Trade & Reference Pubs.

Waddell, Gene, ed. John Bachman: Selected Writings on Science, Race, & Religion. 2011. (Publications of the Southern Texts Society Ser.). (ENG., Illus.). 400p. 39.95 *(978-0-8203-3818-7(4))* Univ. of Georgia Pr.

Wells, Jeffrey. Boreal Birds of North America: A Hemispheric View of Their Conservation Links & Significance. 2011. (Studies in Avian Biology Ser.). (ENG., Illus.). 160p. 39.95 *(978-0-520-27100-5(9))* Univ. of California Pr.

Wells, Jeffrey V. Birder's Conservation Handbook: 100 North American Birds at Risk. 2007. (Illus.). 452p. 79.50 *(978-0-691-12322-6(5))*; (ENG., 464p. per. 35.00 *(978-0-691-12323-3(3))* Princeton Univ. Pr.

Wild, Dennis. The Double-Crested Cormorant: Symbol of Ecological Conflict. 2012. E-Book ***(978-0-472-02812-2(X))***; (ENG.). 274p. 27.95 ***(978-0-472-11763-5(7))*** Univ. of Michigan Pr.

Zemaitis, Louise, et al. National Geographic Backyard Guide to the Birds of North America. 2011. (National Geographic Backyard Guides). (ENG., Illus.). 256p. pap. 18.95 *(978-1-4262-0720-4(4)*, National Geographic) National Geographic Society.

BIRDS—PAKISTAN

Nadeem, Muhammed. Ecology of Houbara Bustard in Punjab & Nag Valley. 2010. 280p. pap. *(978-3-639-20031-7(4))* VDM Verlag Dr. Mueller e.K.

Perveen, Farzana. Captive Crane, Its Breeding, Diet & Diseases in N-Wfp, Pakistan. 2010. 200p. pap. *(978-3-639-24737-4(X))* VDM Verlag Dr. Mueller e.K.

BIRDS—PANAMA

Angehr, George R. & Dean, Robert. The Birds of Panama: A Field Guide. 2010. (Zona Tropical Publication Ser.). (Illus.). 464p. pap. 35.00 *(978-0-8014-7674-7(7)*, Comstock Publishing Assocs.) Cornell Univ. Pr.

Angehr, George Richard & Dean, Robert. The Birds of Panama: A Field Guide. 2010. ***(978-0-9798804-5-2(9))***; ***(978-0-8014-4960-4(X))*** Cornell Univ. Pr. (Comstock Publishing Assocs.).

BIRDS—PERU

Byers, Clive. Photographic Guide to the Birds of Peru. 2007. (ENG., Illus.). 144p. pap. *(978-0-88359-062-1(X)*, 0621, Curtis, Ralph Bk.) Curtis, Ralph Publishing.

Lane, Daniel F., et al. Birds of Peru. 2007. (Princeton Field Guides). (Illus.). 656p. 49.50 *(978-0-691-04915-1(7))* Princeton Univ. Pr.

Schulenberg, Thomas S. Birds of Peru. 2010. (Princeton Field Guides). (ENG., Illus.). 664p. pap. 39.50 *(978-0-691-13023-1(X))* Princeton Univ. Pr.

BIRDS—SOUTH AMERICA

Canaday, Chris & Jost, Lou. Common Birds of Amazonian Ecuador: A Guide for the Wide-Eyed Ecotourist (with Special Reference to the Cuyabeno Reserve) (Illus.). 132p. *(978-9978-40-028-9(1))* Autores-Editores.

Erize, Francisco, et al. Birds of South America: Non-Passerines: Rheas to Woodpeckers. 2006. (Princeton Illustrated Checklists Ser.). (ENG., Illus.). 376p. pap. 29.95 *(978-0-691-12688-3(7))* Princeton Univ. Pr.

Gwynne, John A., et al. Wildlife Conservation Society Birds of Brazil: The Pantanal & Cerrado of Central Brazil. 2010. (Illus.). 336p. pap. 35.00 *(978-0-8014-7646-4(1)*, Comstock Publishing Assocs.) Cornell Univ. Pr.

Rain Forest Birds: An Educational Coloring Book. pap. 1.99 *(978-0-86545-211-4(3))* Spizzirri Pr., Inc.

Restall, Robin, et al. Birds of Northern South America, 2 vols., Set. 2007. (ENG., Illus.). 1536p. pap. 160.00 *(978-0-300-12504-7(6))* Yale Univ. Pr.

—Birds of Northern South America Vol. 1: An Identification Guide - Species Accounts. 2007. (ENG., Illus.). 880p. pap. 100.00 *(978-0-300-10862-0(1))* Yale Univ. Pr.

—Birds of Northern South America Vol. 2: An Identification Guide - Plates & Maps. 2007. (ENG., Illus.). 656p. per. 70.00 *(978-0-300-12415-6(5))* Yale Univ. Pr.

Ridgely, Robert S. & Tudor, Guy. Field Guide to the Songbirds of South America: The Passerines. 2009. (ENG.). 736p. pap. 49.95 *(978-0-292-71979-8(5))*; (Illus.). 125.00 *(978-0-292-71748-0(2))* Univ. of Texas Pr.

Spear, Larry B. Foraging Dynamics of Seabirds in the Eastern Tropical Pacific Ocean: Studies in Avian Biology No. 35. 2007. (Studies in Avian Biology). 100p. per. 15.00 *(978-0-943610-79-5(6))* American Ornithologists Union.

B

Van Perlo, Ber. A Field Guide to the Birds of Brazil. 2009. (Illus.). 480p. instr.'s gde. ed. 149.00 *(978-0-19-530154-0(4))*; (ENG., 496p. pap. 39.95 *(978-0-19-530155-7(2))* Oxford Univ. Pr., Inc.

BIRDS—SOVIET UNION

Arlott, Norman. Birds of Europe, Russia, China, & Japan: Passerines: Tyrant Flycatchers to Buntings. 2007. (Princeton Illustrated Checklists Ser.). (ENG., Illus.). 240p. per. 29.95 *(978-0-691-13372-0(7))* Princeton Univ. Pr.

Seebohm, Henry. The Birds of Siberia: A Record of a Naturalist's Visits to the Valleys of the Petchora & Yenesei. 2011. (Cambridge Library Collection - Life Sciences Ser.). (ENG., Illus.). 544p. pap. 39.99 ***(978-1-108-03795-2(X))*** Cambridge Univ. Pr.

BIRDS—SRI LANKA

Harrison, John & Worfolk, Tim. A Field Guide to the Birds of Sri Lanka. 2nd ed. 2011. (ENG., Illus.). 224p. 98.50 *(978-0-19-958566-3(0))*; pap. 49.50 *(978-0-19-958567-0(9))* Oxford Univ. Pr., Inc.

BIRDS—TEXAS

Dyes, John C. Nesting Birds of the Coastal Islands: A Naturalist's Year on Galveston Bay. 2011. (ENG., Illus.). 163p. pap. 19.95 ***(978-0-292-72973-5(1))*** Univ. of Texas Pr.

Eubanks, Ted L., et al. Birdlife of Houston, Galveston, & the Upper Texas Coast. 2006. (Gulf Coast Studies: No. 10). (ENG., Illus.). 328p. 45.00 *(978-1-58544-510-3(X))* Texas A&M Univ. Pr.

Eubanks, Ted Lee, Jr., et al. Finding Birds on the Great Texas Coastal Birding Trail: Houston, Galveston, & the Upper Texas Coast. 2008. (Texas A&M Nature Guides). (ENG., Illus.). 258p. pap. 23.00 *(978-1-58544-534-9(7))* Texas A&M Univ. Pr.

Hernández, Fidel & Guthery, Fred S. Beef, Brush, & Bobwhites: Quail Management in Cattle Country. 2012. (Perspectives on South Texas, sponsored by Texas A&M University-Kingsville Ser.). (Illus.). 286p. pap. 24.95 ***(978-1-60344-475-0(0))*** Texas A&M Univ. Pr.

Kirkwood-Hatchett, Queen. From romise to Fulfillment. 2010. pap. 129.00 *(978-0-578-05767-5(0))* Hatchett, Queen Kirkwood.

Quick Reference Publishing, Inc. Staff. Birds of North Texas: A Guide to Common & Notable Species. 2010. 7.95 *(978-0-9826211-7-2(5))* Quick Reference Publishing, Inc.

Sibley, David Allen. Sibleys Backyard Birds of Eastern Texas. 2009. pap. 7.95 *(978-1-935380-12-2(5))* Lewers, Steven & Assocs.

BIRDS—UNITED STATES

see also Birds—Alaska; Birds—Hawaii; Birds—Texas

Alderfer, Jonathan. National Geographic Field Guide to Birds: Pennsylvania. 2006. (Ng Field Guide to Birds Ser.). (ENG., Illus.). 272p. per. 14.95 *(978-0-7922-5562-8(3)*, National Geographic) National Geographic Society.

Alderfer, Jonathan, ed. National Geographic Field Guide to Birds: Colorado. 2006. (Ng Field Guide to Birds Ser.). (ENG., Illus.). 272p. per. 14.95 *(978-0-7922-5561-1(5)*, National Geographic) National Geographic Society.

Alderfer, Jonathan & Dunn, Jon L., eds. The Birds of Western North America. 2008. (ENG., Illus.). 448p. instr.'s gde. ed. 19.95 *(978-1-4262-0331-2(4)*, National Geographic) National Geographic Society.

Anderson, Ora E. Out of the Woods: A Bird Watcher's Year. Griffith, Deborah, ed. 2007. (Illus.). 184p. 28.95 *(978-0-8214-1741-6(X))*; per. 16.95 *(978-0-8214-1742-3(8))* Ohio Univ. Pr.

Audubon Minnesota, creator. The North Shore Birding Trail: A Guide to Birding Minnesota's North Shore of Lake Superior from Duluth to Grand Portage. 2007. (Illus.). 64p. per. 9.95 *(978-0-9787908-0-6(4))* Audubon Minnesota.

Bailey, Harold H. Birds of Virginia Field Guide. (Illus.). 362p. reprint ed. lib. bdg. 98.00 *(978-0-7222-4656-6(0))* Library Reprints, Inc.

Bailey, Vernon. Wild Animals of Glacier National Park Th. 2006. pap. 27.95 *(978-1-4286-5182-1(9))* Kessinger Publishing, LLC.

Barber, Lynn E. Extreme Birder: One Woman's Big Year. 2011. (Illus.). 288p. pap. 29.95 *(978-1-60344-261-9(8))* Texas A&M Univ. Pr.

Behle, William H. Utah Birds: Historical Perspective & Bibliography. 25.00 *(978-0-940378-11-7(6))* Utah Museum of Natural History.

Beston, Henry. The Outermost House: A Year of Life on the Great Beach of Cape Cod. 2007. 34.99 *(978-1-60252-776-8(8))* Findaway World, LLC.

Bildstein, Keith L. Migrating Raptors of the World: Their Ecology & Conservation. 2006. (Illus.). 320p. 35.00 *(978-0-8014-4179-0(X))* Cornell Univ. Pr.

Birds of the National Aviary. 2006. (Illus.). 100p. per. 24.95 *(978-0-615-13269-3(3))* West, Doug.

The Birds Without Borders-Aves Sin Fronteras Recommendations for Landowners: How to Manage Your Land to Help Birds (Wisconsin, Midwest & eastern United States Edition) 2008. (Illus.). 125p. spiral bd. *(978-0-9794151-1-1(X))* Zoological Society of Milwaukee.

Bosakowski, Thomas & Smith, Dwight G. Raptors of the Northeast. 2010. 202p. pap. 27.95 *(978-1-930585-95-9(0))* Coachwhip Pubns.

Bousman, William G. Breeding Bird Atlas of Santa Clara County, California. 2007. pap. *(978-0-9796038-0-8(3))* Santa Clara Valley Audubon Society.

Boyle, William J. The Birds of New Jersey: Status & Distribution. 2011. (ENG., Illus.). 320p. (C). 55.00 *(978-0-691-14409-2(5))*; pap. 24.95 *(978-0-691-14410-8(9))* Princeton Univ. Pr.

Bradford, Walter. Michigan Bird Life. (Illus.). reprint ed. lib. bdg. 125.00 *(978-0-7222-0082-7(X))* Library Reprints, Inc.

Bull, John, et al. The Easy Bird Guide: Eastern Region: A Quick Identification Guide for All Birders. 2006. (Falcon Guide Ser.). (ENG., Illus.). 160p. pap. 14.95 *(978-0-7627-3741-3(7)*, Falcon Guides) Globe Pequot Pr., The.

—The Easy Bird Guide: Western Region: A Quick Identification Guide for All Birders. 2006. (Falcon Guide Ser.). (ENG., Illus.). 160p. pap. 14.95 *(978-0-7627-3742-0(5)*, Falcon Guides) Globe Pequot Pr., The.

Burns, Jim. Jim Burns' Arizona Birds: From the Backyard to the Backwoods. 2008. (ENG., Illus.). 256p. pap. 16.95 *(978-0-8165-2644-4(3))* Univ. of Arizona Pr.

Chepaitis, Barbara. Feathers of Hope: Pete Dubacher, the Berkshire Bird Paradise, & the Human Connection with Birds. 2010. (Excelsior Editions Ser.). (Illus.). 128p. 19.95 *(978-1-4384-3291-5(7))* State Univ. of New York Pr.

Colver, Kevin & Elliott, Lang. Know Your Bird Sounds: Common Western Species. 2008. (Lang Elliott Audio Library). (ENG., Illus.). 96p. pap. 19.95 *(978-0-8117-3446-2(3))* Stackpole Bks.

Conner, Richard, et al. The Red-cockaded Woodpecker: Surviving in a Fire-Maintained Ecosystem. 2010. (ENG., Illus.). 400p. pap. 35.00 *(978-0-292-72627-7(9))* Univ. of Texas Pr.

Contreras, Alan, ed. Birds of Lane County, Oregon. 2006. (Illus.). 366p. per. 20.00 *(978-0-87071-180-0(6))* Oregon State Univ. Pr.

Cory, Charles B. Hunting & Fishing in Florida, Including a Key to the Water Birds. (Illus.). 304p. reprint ed. lib. bdg. 98.00 *(978-0-7222-0214-2(8))* Library Reprints, Inc.

Coues, Elliott. Birds of the Colorado Valley: A Repository of Scientific & Popular Information Concerning North American Ornithology. 2010. 832p. pap. 56.75 *(978-1-174-52213-0(5))*; 822p. pap. 55.75 *(978-1-147-09831-0(X))* BiblioBazaar.

—Birds of the Northwest: A Handbook of the Ornithology of the Region Drained by the Missouri River & Its Tributaries. 2010. 806p. 55.96 *(978-1-169-37731-8(9))* 2010. 806p. pap. 43.96 *(978-1-163-31257-5(6))* 2010. 806p. 69.95 *(978-1-161-65668-8(5))* 2007. (ENG.). 804p. per. 54.95 *(978-1-4325-4931-2(6))* Kessinger Publishing, LLC.

Culver, Craig. My San Diego & Her Falconry. 2007. (Illus.). 136p. 34.95 *(978-0-9798405-0-0(3))* Culver Publishing.

Dawson, William L. & Bowles, J. N. Birds of Washington Set, 2 vols. (Illus.). reprint ed. lib. bdg. 250.00 *(978-0-7222-4708-2(7))* Library Reprints, Inc.

Dawson, William Leon. Dawson's Avian Kingdom. 2007. (California Legacy Book Ser.). 285p. per. 16.95 *(978-1-59714-062-1(7))* Heyday.

Dean, Blanche E. Birds. (Southern Regional Nature Ser.). (Illus.). pap. 4.95 *(978-0-87651-018-6(7))* Southern Univ. Pr.

DeForbes, Donna M., ed. Save The Bay's Uncommon Guide to Common Life of Narragansett Bay & Rhode Island Coastal Waters. 2nd exp. ed. 2008. (Illus.). pap. 20.00 *(978-0-615-22901-0(8))* Save The Bay, Inc.

Dempsey, Luke. A Supremely Bad Idea: Three Mad Birders & Their Quest to See It All. 2009. (ENG., Illus.). 272p. pap. 15.00 *(978-1-59691-634-0(6))* Bloomsbury Publishing.

DuMond, F. L. Introduction to the Birds of Michigan. (Illus.). reprint ed. lib. bdg. 125.00 *(978-0-7222-0087-2(0))* Library Reprints, Inc.

Dunlap, Thomas R. In the Field, among the Feathered: A History of Birders & Their Guides, 1 vol. 2011. (ENG., Illus.). 240p. 34.95 *(978-0-19-973459-7(3))* Oxford Univ. Pr., Inc.

Ellison, Walter G., ed. Second Atlas of the Breeding Birds of Maryland & the District of Columbia. 2010. (ENG., Illus.). 520p. (gr. 17). 75.00 *(978-0-8018-9576-0(6))* Johns Hopkins Univ. Pr.

Erickson, Laura. Twelve Owls. 2011. (ENG., Illus.). 64p. 19.95 ***(978-0-8166-7758-0(1))*** Univ. of Minnesota Pr.

Everett, Roger S. Birds of Coastal South Carolina. 2008. (Illus.). 144p. bds. 29.95 *(978-0-7643-2845-9(X))* Schiffer Publishing, Ltd.

Fallon, Katie. Cerulean Blues: A Personal Search for a Vanishing Songbird. 2011. (ENG.). 224p. pap. 17.95 ***(978-0-9830111-1-8(7))*** Ruka Pr.

Faulkner, Douglas. Birds of Wyoming. 2010. (ENG., Illus.). 404p. 45.00 *(978-1-936221-02-8(0))* Roberts & Co.

Fenimore, Bill. Backyard Birds of California: How to Identify & Attract the Top 25 Birds, 1 vol. 2008. (ENG., Illus.). 96p. spiral bd. 9.99 *(978-1-4236-0348-1(6))* Gibbs Smith, Publisher.

—Backyard Birds of Maryland: How to Identify & Attract the Top 25 Birds, 1 vol. 2008. (ENG., Illus.). 96p. spiral bd. 9.95 *(978-1-4236-0354-2(0))* Gibbs Smith, Publisher.

—Backyard Birds of New York: How to Identify & Attract the Top 25 Birds, 1 vol. 2008. (ENG., Illus.). 96p. pap. 9.95 *(978-1-4236-0349-8(4))* Gibbs Smith, Publisher.

—Backyard Birds of North Carolina: How to Identify & Attract the Top 25 Birds. 2009. *(978-1-4236-0644-4(2))* Gibbs Smith, Publisher.

—Backyard Birds of Ohio: How to Identify & Attract the Top 25 Birds. 2009. *(978-1-4236-0645-1(0))* Gibbs Smith, Publisher.

—Backyard Birds of Utah: How to Identify & Attract the Top 25 Birds, 1 vol. 2008. (ENG., Illus.). 96p. spiral bd. 9.99 *(978-1-4236-0353-5(2))* Gibbs Smith, Publisher.

—Backyard Birds of Washington: How to Identify & Attract the Top 25 Birds, 1 vol. 2009. (ENG., Illus.). 96p. pap. 9.99 *(978-1-4236-0568-3(3))* Gibbs Smith, Publisher.

—Backyard Birds of Wisconsin: How to Identify & Attract the Top 25 Birds. 2009. *(978-1-4236-0646-8(9))* Gibbs Smith, Publisher.

Fennimore, Bill. Backyard Birds of Florida: How to Identify & Attract the Top 25 Birds, 1 vol. 2008. (ENG., Illus.). 96p. pap. 9.99 *(978-1-4236-0352-8(4))* Gibbs Smith, Publisher.

—Backyard Birds of Illinois: How to Identify & Attract the Top 25 Birds, 1 vol. 2008. (ENG., Illus.). 96p. pap. 9.99 *(978-1-4236-0357-3(5))* Gibbs Smith, Publisher.

—Backyard Birds of New Jersey: How to Identify & Attract the Top 25 Birds, 1 vol. 2009. (ENG., Illus.). 96p. pap. 9.99 *(978-1-4236-0355-9(9))* Gibbs Smith, Publisher.

Fisher, Chris. Birds of Washington, D. C. rev. ed. Date not set. (City Bird Guides). (ENG., Illus.). 160p. pap. 9.95 *(978-1-55105-169-7(9))* Lone Pine Publishing USA.

Floyd, Ted, et al. Atlas of the Breeding Birds of Nevada. 2007. (ENG., Illus.). 608p. 60.00 *(978-0-87417-695-7(6))* Univ. of Nevada Pr.

Gabrielson, Ira N. & Jewett, Stanley G. Birds of Oregon. 2010. 684p. pap. 35.95 *(978-0-557-68649-0(0))* Lulu Enterprises Inc.

Gardner, Dana, illus. Fifty Uncommon Birds of the Upper Midwest. 2007. (Bur Oak Book Ser.). (ENG.). 132p. 34.95 *(978-1-58729-590-4(3))* Univ. of Iowa Pr.

Garrett, Kimball L., et al. Birds of the Los Angeles Region. 2006. (ENG., Illus.). 486p. 15.95 *(978-0-9640810-5-5(9))* Morse, R.W. Co.

Georgia Department of Education Staff. Natural Resources of Georgia. 222p. reprint ed. lib. bdg. 98.00 *(978-0-7222-0422-1(1))* Library Reprints, Inc.

Gone with the Wind: Impacts of Wind Turbines on Birds & Bats: Oversight Hearing Before the Subcommittee on Fisheries, Wildlife, & Oceans of the Committee on Natural Resources, U.S. House of Representatives, One Hundred Tenth Congress, First Session, Tuesday, May 1, 2007. 2007. iii, 82p. *(978-0-16-079595-4(8)*, 552-070-36555-9) United States Government Printing Office.

Goss, N. S. History of the Birds of Kansas. (Illus.). 692p. reprint ed. lib. bdg. 128.00 *(978-0-7222-4882-9(2))* Library Reprints, Inc.

Gress, Bob & Janzen, Pete. The Guide to Kansas Birds & Birding Hot Spots. 2008. (Illus.). 354p. pap. 19.95 *(978-0-7006-1565-0(2))* Univ. Pr. of Kansas.

Griffith, George. Musical Birds of Nevad: Silence! Meadowlark Singing. 2009. 100p. pap. 11.95 *(978-1-4401-1508-0(7))* iUniverse, Inc.

Hackett, Mundy. Missouri in Flight: The Bird Photography of Mundy Hackett. 2007. (ENG., Illus.). 152p. (gr. 9). 34.95 *(978-0-8262-1706-6(0))* Univ. of Missouri Pr.

Hausman, Leon Augustus. The Book of Songbirds. 2011. 44p. pap. 35.95 ***(978-1-258-10405-4(9))*** Literary Licensing, LLC.

Heinzel, Hermann. Birds of Napa County. 2007. (Illus.). 132p. pap. 12.95 *(978-1-59714-030-0(9))* Heyday.

Herlyn, Hendrik G. & Contreras, Alan L. Handbook of Oregon Birds: A Field Companion to Birds of Oregon. 2009. (ENG.). 328p. pap. 22.95 *(978-0-87071-571-6(2))* Oregon State Univ. Pr.

Hohorst, Charlie, photos by. Wings of Paradise: Birds of the Louisiana Wetlands. 2009. (Illus.). 144p. 39.95 *(978-0-8071-3450-4(3))* Louisiana State Univ. Pr.

Holloway, Joel Ellis. Dictionary of Birds of the United States. 2009. (ENG.). 224p. pap. 22.95 *(978-1-60469-174-0(3)*, 1604691743) Timber Pr., Inc.

Horn, Evelyn. Still Following the Feathered & Flowered: Quiet Adventures in the Realm of Birds & Flowers. 2007. pap. 17.95 *(978-0-9779965-9-9(X))* Lifetime Chronicle Pr.

Howell, Steve N. G. & Dunn, Jon. Peterson Reference Guides: Gulls of the Americas. 2007. (Peterson Reference Guides Ser.). (ENG., Illus.). 528p. 35.00 *(978-0-618-72641-7(1))* Houghton Mifflin Harcourt Publishing Co.

Hudson, W. H. Birds of la Plata. reprint ed. 64.50 *(978-0-404-03411-5(X))* AMS Pr., Inc.

—Birds of la Plata. 2009. 174p. pap. *(978-0-217-18199-0(6))* Books LLC.

Karlson, Kevin T. Birds of Cape May, New Jersey. 2010. (Illus.). 256p. 49.99 *(978-0-7643-3534-1(0))* Schiffer Publishing, Ltd.

Kaufman, Kenn & Kaufman, Kimberly. Kaufman Field Guide to Nature of New England. 2012. (Kaufman Field Guides). (ENG., Illus.). 416p. 20.00 ***(978-0-618-45697-0(X))*** Houghton Mifflin Harcourt Trade & Reference Pubs.

Kavanagh, James. Cape May Birds: An Introduction to Familiar Species in Cape May County. 2007. (Pocket Naturalist - Waterford Press Ser.). (ENG., Illus.). 1p. 5.95 *(978-1-58355-334-3(7))* Waterford Pr., Inc.

—Everglades Birds: An Introduction to Familiar Species. 2007. (Pocket Naturalist - Waterford Press Ser.). (ENG., Illus.). 1p. 5.95 *(978-1-58355-335-0(5))* Waterford Pr., Inc.

—Great Smoky Mountain Birds: An Introduction to Familiar Species. 2008. (Pocket Naturalist - Waterford Press Ser.). (ENG., Illus.). 1p. 5.95 *(978-1-58355-422-7(X))* Waterford Pr., Inc.

—New Jersey Wildlife: An Introduction to Familiar Species. 2009. (State Nature Guides). (ENG., Illus.). 1p. 5.95 *(978-1-58355-481-4(5))* Waterford Pr., Inc.

—Ohio Wildlife: An Introduction to Familiar Species. 2009. (State Nature Guides). (ENG., Illus.). 1p. 5.95 *(978-1-58355-482-1(3))* Waterford Pr., Inc.

—Vancouver Birds: An Introduction to Familiar Species. 2010. (Pocket Naturalist Guide Ser.). (ENG.). 2p. 5.95 *(978-1-58355-549-1(8))* Waterford Pr., Inc.

Kee, Sheila N. Backyard Birds of the Inland Empire. 2010. pap. *(978-1-59714-132-1(1))* Heyday.

Kemper, Charles. Birds of Chippewa Land. 2007. 360p. per. 66.95 *(978-1-4327-0305-9(6))* Outskirts Pr., Inc.

Kingery, Hugh E. Birding Colorado: Over 180 Premier Birding Sites at 93 Locations. 2007. (Birding Ser.). (ENG., Illus.). 336p. per. 19.95 *(978-0-7627-3960-8(6)*, Falcon Guides) Globe Pequot Pr., The.

Krech, Shepard, 3rd. Spirits of the Air: Birds & American Indians in the South. 2009. (Environmental History & the American South Ser.). (ENG., Illus.). 264p. 44.95 *(978-0-8203-2815-7(4))* Univ. of Georgia Pr.

Kroodsma, Donald. Birdsong by the Seasons: A Year of Listening to Birds. 2009. (ENG., Illus.). 384p. 28.00 *(978-0-618-75336-9(2))* Houghton Mifflin Harcourt Trade & Reference Pubs.

Kumlien, Ludwig & Hollister, N. Birds of Wisconsin. (Illus.). 143p. reprint ed. lib. bdg. 88.00 *(978-0-7222-0349-1(7))* Library Reprints, Inc.

Lebbin, Daniel J., et al. The American Bird Conservancy Guide to Bird Conservation. 2010. (ENG., Illus.). 456p. 45.00 *(978-0-226-64727-2(7))* Univ. of Chicago Pr.

Lehman, Paul. National Geographic Field Guide to the Birds of Eastern North America. Alderfer, Jonathan & Dunn, Jon L., eds. 2008. (ENG., Illus.). 432p. 19.95 *(978-1-4262-0330-5(6))* National Geographic Society.

Local, Birds. Local Birds South California. 2011. pap. 8.95 *(978-1-886403-62-8(7))* Local Birds, Inc.

Lockwood, Mark W. Basic Texas Birds: A Field Guide. 2007. (Texas Natural History Guides). (ENG., Illus.). 419p. pap. 22.95 *(978-0-292-71349-9(5))* Univ. of Texas Pr.

Loggins, George. Backyard Birds of the Mid-Atlantic. Cool Springs Press Publications Staff, ed. 2008. (Field-Guide to Backyard Birds Ser.). (ENG., Illus.). 90p. pap. 9.95 *(978-1-59186-010-5(5)*, 1591860105) Cool Springs Pr.

—Backyard Birds of the Northeast. Cool Springs Press Publications Staff, ed. 2008. (Field-Guide to Backyard Birds Ser.). (ENG., Illus.). 90p. pap. 9.95 *(978-1-59186-008-2(3)*, 1591860083) Cool Springs Pr.

—Backyard Birds of the South. Cool Springs Press Publications Staff, ed. 2008. (Field-Guide to Backyard Birds Ser.). (ENG., Illus.). 90p. pap. 9.95 *(978-1-59186-006-8(7)*, 1591860067) Cool Springs Pr.

—Backyard Birds of the West. Cool Springs Press Publications Staff, ed. 2008. (Field-Guide to Backyard Birds Ser.). (ENG., Illus.). 90p. pap. 9.95 *(978-1-59186-009-9(1)*, 1591860091) Cool Springs Pr.

—Field Guide to Backyard Birds of the Midwest. Cool Springs Press Publications Staff, ed. 2008. (Field-Guide to Backyard Birds Ser.). (ENG., Illus.). 90p. pap. 9.95 *(978-1-59186-007-5(5)*, 1591860075) Cool Springs Pr.

Lukas, David. Watchable Birds of the Great Basin. (Watchable Birds Ser.: No. 3). (Illus.). 174p. pap. 16.00 *(978-0-87842-397-2(4)*, 439) Mountain Pr. Publishing Co., Inc.

Lynch, Wayne. Owls of the United States & Canada: A Complete Guide to Their Biology & Behavior. 2007. (ENG., Illus.). 264p. 39.95 *(978-0-8018-8687-4(2))* Johns Hopkins Univ. Pr.

Marshall, David B., et al, eds. Birds of Oregon: A General Reference. 2006. (Illus.). 752p. per. 45.00 *(978-0-87071-182-4(2))* Oregon State Univ. Pr.

Martin, James & Martin, Joyce. The Rookery at Noxubee Wildlife Refuge. 2007. 100p. pap. 39.50 *(978-1-4303-2356-3(6))* Lulu Enterprises Inc.

Mason, John W. At-Sea Distribution & Abundance of Seabirds off Southern California: Studies in Avian Biology No. 33. 2007. (Studies in Avian Biology: 33). per. 15.00 *(978-0-943610-72-6(9))* American Ornithologists Union.

McGowan, Kevin J. & Corwin, Kimberley, eds. The Second Atlas of Breeding Birds in New York State. 2008. (Illus.). 696p. 62.95 *(978-0-8014-4716-7(X))* Cornell Univ. Pr.

McKenny, Margaret. Birds in the Garden & How to Attract Them. 2009. (ENG.). 347p. pap. 60.00 *(978-0-8166-5960-9(5))* Univ. of Minnesota Pr.

Minetor, Randi. Backyard Birding: A Guide to Attracting & Identifying Birds. 2011. (ENG., Illus.). 256p. pap. 19.95 *(978-0-7627-7166-0(6)*, Lyons Pr) Globe Pequot Pr., The.

Mollenhauer, Jeff. Birding South Carolina: A Guide to 40 Premier Birding Sites. 2009. (Birding Ser.). (ENG., Illus.). 224p. pap. 21.95 *(978-0-7627-4579-1(7)*, Falcon Guides) Globe Pequot Pr., The.

Nolley, John, 2nd. Taking to the Skies: A Photologue of Birds across the United States. 2007. (Illus.). 120p. per. 34.95 *(978-0-9801571-1-6(0))* Exerda Pubns.

North Carolina Birding Trail, compiled by. The North Carolina Birding Trail: Coastal Plain Trail Guide. 2008. (Illus.). 172p. spiral bd. 19.95 *(978-0-9794468-0-1(5))* Univ. of North Carolina Pr.

O'Beirne, Kathleen P. Birds of a Feather: Lessons from the Sea. 2006. (Illus.). 206p. pap. 19.95 *(978-1-879979-02-4(0))* Lifescape Enterprises.

O'Brien, Stacey. Wesley the Owl: The Remarkable Love Story of an Owl & His Girl. 2009. (ENG., Illus.). 256p. pap. 15.00 *(978-1-4165-5177-5(8)*, Free Pr.) Free Pr.

Peeters, Hans J. Field Guide to Owls of California & the West. 2007. (California Natural History Guides Ser.). (Illus.). 346p. 55.00 *(978-0-520-24741-3(8))*; 326p. pap. 21.95 *(978-0-520-25280-6(2))* Univ. of California Pr.

Peterson, Roger Tory. Peterson Field Guide to Birds of Western North America. 4th ed. 2010. (Peterson Field Guides). (ENG., Illus.). 512p. 19.95 *(978-0-547-15270-7(1))* Houghton Mifflin Harcourt Trade & Reference Pubs.

Piedmont Trail Guide Staff, contrib. by. North Carolina Birding Trail: Piedmont Trail Guide. 2008. (Illus.). 176p. spiral bd. 19.95 *(978-0-8078-5917-9(6))* Univ. of North Carolina Pr.

Porter, Adele. Birds in Our Backyard: Say Hello to Minnesota's Feathered Friends. 2011. (ENG., Illus.). 42p. (J). (gr. -1-2). 16.95 ***(978-0-87351-836-9(5))*** Minnesota Historical Society Pr.

Porter, Adele. Wild about Minnesota Birds: A Youth's Guide to the Birds of Minnesota. 2007. (Illus.). 200p. (J). (gr. 4-7). pap. 17.95 *(978-1-59193-052-5(9))* Adventure Pubns., Inc.

Rea, Amadeo M. Wings in the Desert: A Folk Ornithology of the Northern Pimans. 2008. (ENG.). 320p. 70.00 *(978-0-8165-2459-4(9))* Univ. of Arizona Pr.

Richie Oberbillig, Deborah. Bird Feats of Montana: Including Yellowstone & Glacier National Parks. 2008. (Farcountry Explorer Bks.). (Illus.). 48p. pap. 14.95 *(978-1-56037-463-3(2))* Farcountry Pr.

Rosen, Jonathan. The Life of the Skies: Birding at the End of Nature. 2008. (ENG., Illus.). 336p. pap. 16.00 *(978-0-312-42819-8(7))* Picador.

Roth, Sally. The Backyard Bird Lover's Field Guide: Secrets to Attracting, Identifying, & Enjoying Birds of Your Region. 2007. (Rodale Organic Gardening Book Ser.). (Illus.). xiii, 336p. *(978-1-59486-603-6(1))* Rodale Pr., Inc.

Rowinski, Kate. The Joy of Birding: A Beginner's Guide. 2011. (Joy of Ser.). (ENG., Illus.). 256p. pap. 14.95 *(978-1-61608-122-5(8)*, 608122) Skyhorse Publishing Co., Inc.

Sage, John Hall. The Birds of Connecticut. 2009. 192p. pap. *(978-0-217-29144-6(9))* Books LLC.

—The Birds of Connecticut. (Illus.). reprint ed. lib. bdg. 98.00 *(978-0-7222-4979-6(9))* Library Reprints, Inc.

Scee, Trudy I. A Bird for the Bonnet: Gender, Class & Culture in American Birdkeeping ,1776 - 2000. 2010. (Illus.). 264p. 74.95 *(978-1-930901-93-3(3))* Academica Pr., LLC.

Schneider, Todd M., et al, eds. The Breeding Bird Atlas of Georgia. 2010. (ENG., Illus.). 520p. 64.95 *(978-0-8203-2893-5(6))* Univ. of Georgia Pr.

Shaw, Harley G. & Weisenberger, Mara E. Twelve Hundred Miles by Horse & Burro: J. Stokely Ligon & New Mexico's First Breeding Bird Survey, 1 vol. 2011. (ENG., Illus.). 264p. pap. 26.95 *(978-0-8165-2861-5(6))* Univ. of Arizona Pr.

Sibley, David Allen. Sibleys Backyard Birds New England. 2009. pap. 7.95 *(978-1-935380-08-5(7))* Lewers, Steven & Assocs.

—Sibleys Backyard Birds of Florida. 2009. pap. 7.95 *(978-1-935380-11-5(7))* Lewers, Steven & Assocs.

—Sibleys Backyard Birds of Mid Atlantic. 2009. pap. 7.95 *(978-1-935380-09-2(5))* Lewers, Steven & Assocs.

Simmons, Albert Dixon. Wing Shots A Series of Camera Studies of. 2006. pap. 22.95 *(978-1-4286-5438-9(0))* Kessinger Publishing, LLC.

Small, Brian E. & Sterry, Paul. Birds of Eastern North America: A Photographic Guide. 2009. (Princeton Field Guides). (ENG., Illus.). 336p. (C). 46.95 *(978-0-691-13425-3(1))* Princeton Univ. Pr.

—Birds of Western North America: A Photographic Guide. 2009. (Princeton Field Guides). (ENG., Illus.). 416p. (C). 46.95 *(978-0-691-13427-7(8))*; pap. 18.95 *(978-0-691-13428-4(6))* Princeton Univ. Pr.

Stebbins, Cyril A. & Stebbins, Robert C. Birds of Yosemite National Park: Yosemite Nature Notes V33, No. 8, August 1954. 2011. 82p. 37.95 ***(978-1-258-06445-7(6))*** Literary Licensing, LLC.

Sterry, Paul & Small, Brian E. Birds of Eastern North America: A Photographic Guide. 2009. (Princeton Field Guides). (ENG., Illus.). 336p. pap. 18.95 *(978-0-691-13426-0(X))* Princeton Univ. Pr.

Stockslager, Rebecca. Birds of a Feather. 2009. 61p. pap. 40.00 *(978-0-557-12829-7(3))* Lulu Enterprises Inc.

Stone, Witmer. The Birds of Eastern Pennsylvania & New Jersey: With Introductory Chapters on Geographical Distribution & Migration. 2010. 200p. reprint ed. pap. 24.95 *(978-1-120-87169-5(7))* Kessinger Publishing, LLC.

Sutton, Clay & Sutton, Patricia. Birds & Birding at Cape May. 2006. (ENG., Illus.). 568p. per. 26.95 *(978-0-8117-3134-8(0))* Stackpole Bks.

Taylor, Richard Cachor. Birds of Southeastern Arizona. Bickel, Barbara, ed. 2010. (Illus.). 440p. 19.95 *(978-0-9640810-7-9(5))* Morse, R.W. Co.

Tekiela, Stan. Birds of Prey of the Midwest Field Guide. 2010. 188p. pap. 14.95 *(978-1-59193-247-5(5))* Adventure Pubns., Inc.

—Birds of Yellowstone & the Tetons Field Guide. 2007. 148p. pap. 9.95 *(978-1-59193-160-7(6))* Adventure Pubns., Inc.

Telander, Todd. Birds of Arizona: A Falcon Field Guide [tm]. 2012. (Falcon Field Guide Ser.). (ENG., Illus.). 104p. pap. 9.95 ***(978-0-7627-7416-6(9)***, Falcon Guides) Globe Pequot Pr., The.

—Birds of California: A Falcon Field Guide [tm]. 2012. (Falcon Field Guide Ser.). (ENG., Illus.). 104p. pap. 9.95 *(978-0-7627-7417-3(7)*, Falcon Guides) Globe Pequot Pr., The.

—Birds of Colorado. 2012. (Falcon Field Guide Ser.). (ENG., Illus.). 104p. pap. 9.95 *(978-0-7627-7418-0(5)*, Falcon Guides) Globe Pequot Pr., The.

—Birds of Florida: A Falcon Field Guide [tm]. 2012. (Falcon Field Guide Ser.). (ENG., Illus.). 104p. pap. 9.95 *(978-0-7627-7419-7(3)*, Falcon Guides) Globe Pequot Pr., The.

Torrey, Bradford. Field-Days in California. 2008. (Illus.). 148p. pap. *(978-1-4099-1076-3(8))* Dodo Pr.

—Field-Days in California. reprint ed. lib. bdg. *(978-0-7222-3072-5(9))* Library Reprints, Inc.

—Spring Notes from Tennessee. 2008. 112p. pap. *(978-1-4099-1070-1(9))* Dodo Pr.

—Spring Notes from Tennessee. 2009. 86p. pap. 14.14 *(978-1-151-32752-9(2))* General Bks. LLC.

Trull, Peter. An Illustrated Guide to the Common Birds of Cape Cod. 2011. (Illus.). 176p. pap. 19.99 ***(978-0-7643-3877-9(3)***, Schiffer Publishing Ltd) Schiffer Publishing, Ltd.

Unitt, Philip. Birds of San Diego County. 39.95 *(978-0-916251-60-4(8))*; pap. 24.95 *(978-0-916251-61-1(6))* Sunbelt Pubns., Inc.

Washington, Audubon, ed. WA Birding Trail Cascade Loop. 2007. pap. *(978-0-930698-03-4(7))* National Audubon Society.

—WA Birding Trail Coulee Corridor. 2007. pap. *(978-0-930698-06-5(1))* National Audubon Society.

—WA Birding Trail Olympic Loop. 2007. pap. *(978-0-930698-02-7(9))* National Audubon Society.

—WA Birding Trail Southwest Loop. 2007. pap. *(978-0-930698-05-8(3))* National Audubon Society.

Wetmore, Ralph H. Bosque Del Apache National Wildlife Refuge: A Photographer's & Visitor's Guide. 2009. (Illus.). 104p. *(978-0-9825662-0-6(4))* Runnin' Iron.

Wheeler, Brian K., photos by. Raptors of Eastern North America: The Wheeler Guide. 2007. (Illus.). 439p. per. 29.95 *(978-0-691-13476-5(6))* Princeton Univ. Pr.

—Raptors of Western North America: The Wheeler Guide. 2007. (Illus.). 544p. per. 29.95 *(978-0-691-13477-2(4))* Princeton Univ. Pr.

Whiting, Susan B. & Pesch, Barbara B. Vineyard Birds II: Where & What to See on Martha's Vineyard. 2007. (Illus.). xiii, 151p. *(978-0-9771384-6-3(1))* Vineyard Stories.

Wild, Cole & Komar, Nicholas. Wild Birding Colorado: The Big Year Of 2010. 2011. 150p. pap. 19.95 ***(978-1-4327-7103-4(5))*** Outskirts Pr., Inc.

Wilson, Jim. Common Birds of Coastal Georgia. 2011. (ENG., Illus.). 240p. pap. 16.95 *(978-0-8203-3828-6(1))* Univ. of Georgia Pr.

Wilson, Jim & Atkins, Anselm. Common Birds of Greater Atlanta. 2011. (ENG., Illus.). 160p. pap. 14.95 *(978-0-8203-3825-5(7))* Univ. of Georgia Pr.

Wilson, Robert M. Seeking Refuge: Birds & Landscapes of the Pacific Flyway. (ENG., Illus.). 320p. 2012. (C). pap. 25.00 ***(978-0-295-99211-2(5))*** 2010. 35.00 *(978-0-295-99002-6(3))* Univ. of Washington Pr.

BIRDS, AQUATIC
see Water Birds

BIRDS, ATTRACTING OF
see Bird Attracting

BIRDS, EXTINCT
see Extinct Birds

BIRDS, FOLKLORE OF
see Birds—Folklore

BIRDS, FOSSIL

Campbell, Kenneth E., Jr. The Non-Passerine Pleistocene Avifauna of the Talara Tar Seeps, Northwestern Peru. (Illus.). 454p. pap. *(978-0-88854-230-4(5))* BRILL.

Chiappe, Luis. The Glorified Dinosaurs: Origins & Early Evolution of Birds. 2007. 192p. 69.95 *(978-0-470-07508-1(2)*, Wiley-Liss) Wiley, John & Sons, Inc.

Czerkas, Stephen & Czerkas, Sylvia Massey. Feathered Dinosaurs. 2008. (Illus.). 46p. (J). *(978-1-932075-03-8(8))* Dinosaur Museum, The.

Feduccia, Alan. Riddle of the Feathered Dragons: Hidden Birds of China. 2012. (ENG., Illus.). 368p. 55.00 *(978-0-300-16435-0(1))* Yale Univ. Pr.

James, Frances C. & Pourtless, John A., IV. Cladistics & the Origin of Birds: A Review & Two New Analyses. 2010. (Ornithological Monographs). 88p. pap. 19.95 *(978-0-943610-85-6(0))* Univ. of California Pr.

Long, John A. Feathered Dinosaurs: The Origin of Birds. 2008. (ENG., Illus.). 208p. 39.95 *(978-0-19-537266-3(2))* Oxford Univ. Pr., Inc.

Mayr, Gerald. Paleogene Fossil Birds. 2009. (ENG., Illus.). xiii, 262p. 189.00 *(978-3-540-89627-2(9))* Springer.

Owen, Richard. A History of British Fossil Mammals, & Birds. 2011. (Cambridge Library Collection - Life Sciences Ser.). (ENG., Illus.). 616p. pap. 43.00 ***(978-1-108-03816-4(6))*** Cambridge Univ. Pr.

Owen, Richard. A History of British Fossil Mammals & Birds. Von Krosigk, Esther, ed. 2007. 616p. per. *(978-3-8364-2791-3(5))* VDM Verlag Dr. Mueller e.K.

Smith, N. Adam. Taxonomic Revision & Phylogenetic Analysis of the Flightless Mancallinae (Aves, Pan-Alcidae) 2011. (ZooKeys Ser.). (Illus.). 116p. pap. 77.50 ***(978-954-642-585-0(0))*** Pensoft Pubs. BGR. Dist: Coronet Bks.

Stewart, John R. An Evolutionary Study of Some Archaeologically Significant Avian Taxa in the Quaternary of the Western Palaearctic. 2007. (Bar S Ser.). (ENG., Illus.). 272p. (C). pap. 95.00 *(978-1-4073-0089-4(X))* British Archaeological Reports Ltd. GBR. Dist: Brown, David Bk. Co., The

Yalden, Derek & Albarella, Umberto. The History of British Birds. 2010. (ENG., Illus.). 272p. 55.00 *(978-0-19-958116-0(9))* Oxford Univ. Pr., Inc.

BIRDS, INJURIOUS AND BENEFICIAL
see Bird Pests

BIRDS, ORNAMENTAL
see Ornamental Birds

BIRDS, PHOTOGRAPHY OF
see Photography of Birds

BIRDS, PROTECTION OF
see Birds—Protection

BIRDS, RARE
see Rare Birds

BIRDS, TROPICAL
see Tropical Birds

BIRDS AS PETS
see Cage Birds; Ornamental Birds

BIRDS IN ART

Albus, Anita. On Rare Birds. Chapple, Gerald, tr. from GER. 2011. (ENG., Illus.). 288p. 24.95 *(978-0-7627-6987-2(4)*, Lyons Pr) Globe Pequot Pr., The.

Audubon, John James. Audubon: Early Drawings. 2008. (Illus.). 288p. 125.00 *(978-0-674-03102-9(4)*, Belknap Pr.) Harvard Univ. Pr.

—The Birds of America. unabr. ed. (Illus.). reprint ed. 17.75 *(978-0-8446-7095-9(2))*; Vol. 5. 17.75 *(978-0-8446-7099-7(5))*; Vol. 7. 17.75 *(978-0-8446-7101-7(0))* Smith, Peter Pub., Inc.

Bairei, Kono. The Birds & Flowers of Kono Bairei: An Album of Japanese Woodblock Prints. 2011. (Dover Fine Art, History of Art Ser.). (ENG., Illus.). 160p. pap. 24.95 *(978-0-486-47050-4(4))* Dover Pubns., Inc.

Basile, Kenneth. The Sculpture of Grainger Mckoy. 2011. pap. ***(978-1-932543-43-8(0))*** High Museum of Art.

Bateman, Robert, illus. Birds. 2010. (ENG.). 176p. 40.00 *(978-1-897330-48-7(0))* Madison Pr. Bks. CAN. Dist: Independent Pubs. Group.

Bluchel, Kurt G. Game & Hunting. 2008. (Hobbies & Nature Ser.). (Illus.). 653p. 59.95 *(978-0-8416-0175-8(5))* American Map Corp.

Brown, David. Draw Birds. 4th rev. ed. 2007. (ENG., Illus.). 48p. pap. 9.95 *(978-0-7136-8322-6(8))* A & C Black GBR. Dist: Macmillan.

C&T Publishing's Design Collective. Little Birds: 26 Handmade Projects to Sew, Stitch, Quilt & Love. 2010. (ENG., Illus.). 112p. pap. 15.95 *(978-1-60705-003-2(X))* C & T Publishing.

Carroll, Julie C. & Takahashi, Carol. Takahashi Bird Pins. 2010. (ENG., Illus.). 176p. 39.95 *(978-1-57432-686-4(4)*, 1574326864) Collector Bks.

Cook, Katrina. Birds. 2011. (ENG., Illus.). 224p. 39.95 *(978-1-84724-199-3(9))* Quercus GBR. Dist: Independent Pubs. Group.

Cooper, William T. Capturing the Essence: Techniques for Bird Artists. 2011. (ENG., Illus.). 128p. pap. 42.00 *(978-0-300-17626-1(0))* Yale Univ. Pr.

Djurberg, Nathalie. The Parade: Nathalie Djurberg with Music by Hans Berg. 2011. (ENG., Illus.). 192p. pap. 24.99 ***(978-1-935963-04-2(X))*** Walker Art Ctr.

Eiche, Sabine. Presenting the Turkey: The Fabulous Story of a Flamboyant & Flavourful Bird. 2006. (Bird Ser.). (ENG., Illus.). 128p. 35.00 *(978-88-7038-414-7(4))* Centro Di ITA. Dist: National Bk. Network.

Ellis, Joseph H. Birds in Wood & Paint: American Miniature Bird Carvings & Their Carvers, 1900-1970. 2009. (ENG., Illus.). 204p. 60.00 *(978-1-58465-785-9(5))* Univ. Pr. of New England.

Elphick, Jonathan. Birds: The Art of Ornithology. 2008. (ENG., Illus.). 336p. 19.95 *(978-0-8478-3134-0(5))* Rizzoli International Pubns., Inc.

Elphick, Jonathan. John Gould - Family of Toucans. 2011. (ENG.). 118p. pap. 99.99 ***(978-3-8365-0524-6(X))*** TASCHEN DEU. Dist: Ingram Pub. Services.

Erickson, Laura. Twelve Owls. 2011. (ENG., Illus.). 64p. 19.95 ***(978-0-8166-7758-0(1))*** Univ. of Minnesota Pr.

Flynn, Ron. The Audubon Price Guide Book. 2008. 252p. pap. 59.95 *(978-1-4357-0809-9(1))* Lulu Enterprises Inc.

Glassenberg, Abigail Patner. The Artful Bird: Feathered Friends to Make & Sew. 2011. (ENG., Illus.). 160p. pap. 24.95 *(978-1-59668-238-2(8))* Interweave Pr., LLC.

Harper, Charley. Birds & Words. 2008. (ENG., Illus.). 151p. 50.00 *(978-1-934429-20-4(1))*; 152p. 50.00 *(978-1-934429-17-4(1))* AMMO Bks., LLC.

Jackson, Patrick Thaddeus. Great Bird Paintings. 45.00 *(978-1-85149-200-8(3))*; Vol. 4. 45.00 *(978-1-85149-201-5(1))* Antique Collectors' Club.

Jonsson, Lars. Lars Jonsson's Birds: Paintings from a Near Horizon. 2009. (ENG., Illus.). 192p. 55.00 *(978-0-691-14151-0(7))* Princeton Univ. Pr.

Jordan, Al. Half-Size Osprey. 2008. (Workbench Projects Ser.). (Illus.). 32p. 24.95 *(978-1-881982-64-7(5))* Stackpole Bks.

Kiser, Joy M. America's Other Audubon. 2012. (ENG., Illus.). 144p. 45.00 ***(978-1-61689-059-9(2))*** Princeton Architectural Pr.

Koch, MaryJo & Jennifer Barry Designs Staff. Nesting Instincts: A Bird's-Eye View. 2010. (ENG.). 64p. 9.99 *(978-0-7407-8128-5(6))* Andrews McMeel Publishing.

Laws, John Muir, illus. The Laws Guide to Drawing Birds. 2012. pap. ***(978-1-59714-195-6(X))*** Heyday.

Leclerc, Georges-Louis. All the World's Birds: Buffon's Illustrated Natural History General & Particular of Birds. 2008. (ENG., Illus.). 672p. 350.00 *(978-0-8478-3091-6(8))* Rizzoli International Pubns., Inc.

Lippit, Yukio. Colorful Realm: Japanese Bird-and-Flower Paintings by Ito Jakuchu. 2012. (ENG., Illus.). 224p. 50.00 ***(978-0-226-48460-0(2))*** Univ. of Chicago Pr.

Longabaugh, Rick & Longabaugh, Karen. Birds of North America for the Scroll Saw: 25 Projects from the Berry Basket Collection. 2006. (ENG., Illus.). 120p. pap. 16.95 *(978-1-56523-312-6(3))* Fox Chapel Publishing Co., Inc.

Lucio, Laura. Eastern Bluebird. 2007. (ENG., Illus.). 44p. spiral bd. 24.95 *(978-1-881982-54-8(8))* Stackpole Magazines.

Morris, Desmond. Owl. 2009. (Reaktion Books - Animal Ser.). (ENG., Illus.). 224p. pap. 19.95 *(978-1-86189-525-7(9))* Reaktion Bks., Ltd. GBR. Dist: Chicago Distribution Ctr.

Murphy-Hiscock, Arin. Birds: Explore the Symbology & Significance of These Divine Winged Messengers. 2012. (ENG., Illus.). 240p. pap. 19.95 ***(978-1-4405-2688-6(5))*** Adams Media Corp.

Nelson, Sherry C. Painting Songbirds with Sherry C. Nelson: 15 Beautiful Birds in Oil. 2007. (ENG., Illus.). 144p. pap. 24.99 *(978-1-58180-876-6(3)*, North Light Bks.) F&W Media, Inc.

Nielsen, Jette Norregaard. Feathered Friends: 18 Paper-Pieced Blocks for Bird Lovers. 2008. (ENG., Illus.). 72p. pap. 21.95 *(978-1-57120-537-7(3))* C & T Publishing.

North Light Books Staff, contrib. by. Painter's Quick Reference: Birds & Butterflies. 2008. *(978-1-60061-032-5(3)*, North Light Bks.) F&W Media, Inc.

North Light Books Staff, ed. Painter's Quick Reference Birds & Butterflies. 2008. (ENG., Illus.). 128p. pap. 24.99 *(978-1-60061-031-8(5))* F&W Media, Inc.

Nye, Sally & David. ... more FAN-CARVING: ... more History & more Patterns with Step-by-Step Instructions. 2007. (Illus.). 144p. per. *(978-0-9744464-1-7(6))* Fan Carver's World.

Ogden Museum of Southern Art Staff. One World, Two Artists: John Alexander & Walter Anderson. Strachan, Sue, ed. 2011. (ENG., Illus.). 90p. 55.00 *(978-0-9833707-0-3(2)*, Univ. Pr. of Mississippi/Ogden Museum of Southern Art) Univ. Pr. of Mississippi.

Ono, Mari & Ono, Roshin. Fly Origami Fly! 2006. (ENG., Illus.). 128p. pap. 19.95 *(978-1-907030-59-8(X))* CICO Bks. GBR. Dist: Ryland Peters & Small.

Pinder, Polly. Birds: In Simple Steps. 2009. (How to Draw Ser.). (ENG., Illus.). 32p. pap. 9.95 *(978-1-84448-354-9(1))* Search Pr., Ltd. GBR. Dist: Independent Pubs. Group.

Poole, Kaaren. Drawing Birds with Colored Pencils. 2008. (ENG., Illus.). 144p. pap. 14.95 *(978-1-4027-5263-6(6))* Sterling Publishing Co., Inc.

Rogers, Denny. The Illustrated Birds of Prey - Red-Tailed Hawk, American Kestrel & Peregrine Falcon: The Ultimate Reference Guide for Bird Lovers, Woodcarvers, & Artists. 2007. (Denny Rogers Visual Reference Ser.). (ENG., Illus.). 237p. pap. 34.95 *(978-1-56523-310-2(7))* Fox Chapel Publishing Co., Inc.

—The Illustrated Owl: Screech & Snowy: The Ultimate Reference Guide for Bird Lovers, Woodcarvers, & Artists. 2006. (Denny Rogers Visual Reference Ser.). (ENG., Illus.). 237p. pap. 29.95 *(978-1-56523-285-3(2)*, 1264460) Fox Chapel Publishing Co., Inc.

Ruo, Mei. Birds & Insects: The Beginner's Guide to Chinese Painting. Lee, Yawtsong, tr. 2010. (Beginner's Guide To Ser.). (ENG., Illus.). 56p. pap. 12.95 *(978-1-60220-108-8(0))* BetterLink Pr., Inc.

Sakai, Masako & Sahara, Michie. Rokoan Origami: The Art of Connecting Cranes. 2007. (Heian Origami Favorites Ser.). 72p. pap. 24.95 *(978-0-89346-954-2(8))* Stone Bridge Pr.

Scholz, Floyd. The Golden Eagle: A Behind-the-Scenes Look at the Art of Bird Carving, 1 vol. 2007. (ENG., Illus.). 106p. 34.95 *(978-0-8117-0232-4(4))* Stackpole Bks.

Seder, Anton, ed. Dragons, Birds & Incredible Sea Creatures. 2012. (Dover Pictorial Archive Ser.). (ENG., Illus.). 96p. pap. 19.95 ***(978-0-486-48447-1(5))*** Dover Pubns., Inc.

Sharp, Laurie & Sharp, Kevin. Felted Feathered Friends: Techniques & Projects for Needle-felted Birds. 2012. (ENG., Illus.). 128p. 19.99 ***(978-1-58923-694-3(7)***, 1589236947) Quayside.

Shaw, Robert. Bird Decoys of North America: Nature, History, & Art. 2010. (ENG., Illus.). 304p. 40.00 *(978-1-4027-4772-4(1))* Sterling Publishing Co., Inc.

Solinas, Francesco, et al. The Parrots. 2009. (ENG., Illus.). 128p. pap. 39.99 *(978-3-8228-5274-3(0))* TASCHEN DEU. Dist: Ingram Pub. Services.

Sykes, Keith, et al, illus. The Grouse: Artists' Impressions. 2007. (ENG.). 148p. 49.95 *(978-1-84689-019-2(5))* Swan Hill Pr. GBR. Dist: Stackpole Bks.

Tanimoto, Ichiro, ed. Animals, Birds & Butterflies. 2008. (Shikosha Design Library). (Illus.). 120p. pap. 16.95 *(978-1-933330-77-8(5))* Stone Bridge Pr.

Toikka, Oiva, et al. Birds by Toikka. 2008. (FIN & ENG., Illus.). 159p. pap. *(978-951-0-34905-2(4))* Osakeyhtio, Werner Soderstrom.

Tompkins, Robert David, et al. The Life & Art of Ralph Ray, Jr. 2009. (Illus.). 124p. 71.99 *(978-1-4415-2914-5(4))* Xlibris Corp.

Turner, David. Was Beethoven A Birdwatcher?? 2012. (ENG., Illus.). 288p. 19.95 ***(978-1-84953-145-0(5))*** Summersdale Pubs. GBR. Dist: Independent Pubs. Group.

Wentzler, Theresa, des. Teresa Wentzler's Brilliant Plumage. 2006. (ENG.). 12p. pap. 6.95 *(978-1-60140-136-6(1))* Leisure Arts, Inc.

Wheye, Darryl & Kennedy, Donald. Humans, Nature, & Birds: Science Art from Cave Walls to Computer Screens. (ENG., Illus.). 240p. 2009. pap. 22.00 *(978-0-300-15862-5(9))* 2008. 37.50 *(978-0-300-12368-3(4))* Yale Univ. Pr.

Wolfe, Willow. Painting Wildlife & Birds. 2009. (ENG., Illus.). 130p. pap. 19.95 *(978-0-9789513-9-9(5)*, 0978951395) All American Crafts.

Wootton, Tim. Drawing & Painting Birds, 1 vol. 2011. (ENG., Illus.). 160p. 29.95 *(978-1-84797-224-8(1))* Crowood Pr., Ltd. GBR. Dist: Independent Pubs. Group.

Wright, Jody. Birds, Flowers & Friends Stained Glass Pattern Book. 2007. (Dover Stained Glass Instruction Ser.). (ENG., Illus.). 64p. per. 8.95 *(978-0-486-45437-5(1))* Dover Pubns., Inc.

Wright, Lewis, illus. Poultry. 2009. (ENG.). 56p. pap. 19.95 *(978-1-60889-800-8(8))* Applewood Bks.

Yahgulanaas, Michael Nicoll, et al. Flight of the Hummingbird: A Parable for the Environment, 1 vol. 2008. (ENG., Illus.). 64p. 16.00 *(978-1-55365-372-1(6)*, Greystone Bks.) D&M Pubs. Inc. CAN. Dist: Perseus-PGW.

BIRDS IN LITERATURE

Allen, Barbara. Pigeon. 2009. (Reaktion Books - Animal Ser.). (ENG., Illus.). 224p. pap. 19.95 *(978-1-86189-513-4(5))* Reaktion Bks., Ltd. GBR. Dist: Chicago Distribution Ctr.

Carter, Steven. Judgement of the Crows: Parables & Fables. 2009. (ENG.). 154p. pap. 26.50 *(978-0-7618-4820-2(7))* Univ. Pr. of America, Inc.

Churchill, Abby P. Birds in Literature. 2007. (ENG.). 180p. 37.95 *(978-0-548-04173-4(3))* Kessinger Publishing, LLC.

Courtney, Julia & James, Julia, eds. The Role of the Parrot in Selected Texts from Ovid to Jean Rhys: Telling a Story from an Alternative Viewpoint. 2006. (Illus.). 240p. *(978-0-7734-5574-0(4))* Mellen, Edwin Pr., The.

Gannon, Thomas C. Skylark Meets Meadowlark: Reimagining the Bird in British Romantic & Contemporary Native American Literature. 2009. (ENG.). 436p. 50.00 *(978-0-8032-2057-7(X))* Univ. of Nebraska Pr.

Kordecki, Lesley. Ecofeminist Subjectivities: Chaucer's Talking Birds. 2011. (New Middle Ages Ser.). (ENG., Illus.). 224p. 85.00 *(978-0-230-11527-9(6))* Palgrave Macmillan.

Morris, Desmond. Owl. 2009. (Reaktion Books - Animal Ser.). (ENG., Illus.). 224p. pap. 19.95 *(978-1-86189-525-7(9))* Reaktion Bks., Ltd. GBR. Dist: Chicago Distribution Ctr.

Todd, Kim. Sparrow. 2012. (Reaktion Books - Animal Ser.). (Illus.). 192p. pap. 19.95 *(978-1-86189-875-3(4))* Reaktion Bks., Ltd. GBR. Dist: Chicago Distribution Ctr.

Turner, David. Was Beethoven A Birdwatcher?? 2012. (ENG., Illus.). 288p. 19.95 ***(978-1-84953-145-0(5))*** Summersdale Pubs. GBR. Dist: Independent Pubs. Group.

Urfi, Abdul Jamil. Birds of India: A Literary Anthology. Urfi, Abdul Jamil, ed. 2008. (ENG., Illus.). 504p. 49.95 *(978-0-19-568945-7(3))* Oxford Univ. Pr., Inc.

BIRDS' NESTS
see Birds—Nests

B

BIRDS OF PARADISE

Von Teese, Dita & Nields, Sheryl. Dita: Stripteese. 2009. (ENG., Illus.). 256p. 30.00 *(978-0-06-176311-3(X))* HarperCollins Pubs.

BIRDS OF PREY

see also Owls

Arent, Lori. Care & Management of Captive Raptors II: A Guide to Caring for Permanently Disabled Birds of Prey. 2007. 304p. 49.95 ***(978-0-88839-613-6(9))*** Hancock Hse. Pubs.

Bildstein, Keith L. Migrating Raptors of the World: Their Ecology & Conservation. 2006. (Illus.). 320p. 35.00 *(978-0-8014-4179-0(X))* Cornell Univ. Pr.

—State of North America's Birds of Prey. 2008. (Illus.). 466p. *(978-0-943610-81-8(8))* American Ornithologists Union.

Bird, David M. Raptor Research & Management Techniques. 2007. (Illus.). 464p. pap. 70.00 ***(978-0-88839-639-6(2))*** Hancock Hse. Pubs.

Birds of Prey. 96p. *(978-1-4054-7131-2(X))* Parragon, Inc.

Bosakowski, Thomas & Smith, Dwight G. Raptors of the Northeast. 2010. 202p. pap. 27.95 *(978-1-930585-95-9(0))* Coachwhip Pubns.

Capainolo, Peter & Butler, Carol A. How Fast Can a Falcon Dive? Fascinating Answers to Questions about Birds of Prey. 2010. (Rutgers Animal Q & A Ser.). (ENG., Illus.). 248p. pap. 21.95 *(978-0-8135-4790-9(3))* Rutgers Univ. Pr.

Cartron, Jean-Luc, ed. Raptors of New Mexico. 2010. (ENG., Illus.). 728p. 50.00 *(978-0-8263-4145-7(4))* Univ. of New Mexico Pr.

Chitty, John & Lierz, Michael. BSAVA Manual of Raptors, Pigeons & Passerine Birds. 2008. (BSAVA British Small Animal Veterinary Association Ser.: 5). (ENG., Illus.). 420p. pap. 167.99 *(978-1-905319-04-6(5))* British Small Animal Veterinary Assn. (BSAVA) GBR. Dist: Wiley, John & Sons, Inc.

Davis, Kate. Raptors of the West: Captured in Photographs. 2011. (Illus.). 224p. pap. 30.00 *(978-0-87842-575-4(6))* Mountain Pr. Publishing Co., Inc.

Earley, Chris G. Hawks & Owls of Eastern North America. 2nd rev. ed. 2012. (ENG., Illus.). 144p. pap. 19.95 ***(978-1-55407-999-5(3))*** Firefly Bks., Ltd.

Houle, Marcy. The Prairie Keepers: Secrets of the Zumwalt. 2nd ed. 2007. 274p. per. 19.95 *(978-0-87071-186-2(5))* Oregon State Univ. Pr.

Jance, J. A. Birds of Prey. 2012. (ENG.). 432p. mass mkt. 9.99 ***(978-0-06-208812-3(2))*** HarperCollins Pubs.

O'Brien, Dan. Equinox: Life, Love, & Birds of Prey. 2010. (ENG., Illus.). 232p. pap. 19.95 *(978-0-8032-3459-8(7)*, Bison Bks.) Univ. of Nebraska Pr.

Petersen, Michael. Birds of Prey: Winged Masters of the Sky. 2008. (Illus.). 160p. 12.99 *(978-0-7858-2425-1(1))* Book Sales, Inc.

Romano, Tom. Birds of Prey. Strozier, M. Stefan & Torke, Kyle, eds. 2010. 54p. 16.00 *(978-1-935444-44-2(1))*; 48p. pap. 15.00 *(978-1-935444-56-5(5))* World Audience Pubs.

Snyder, Noel & Snyder, Helen. Raptors of North America: Natural History & Conservation. rev. ed. 2006. (ENG., Illus.). 320p. 50.00 *(978-0-7603-2582-7(0)*, 0760325820, Voyageur Pr) MBI Publishing Co. LLC.

Snyder, Noel F. R. & Snyder, Helen. Raptors of North America: Natural History & Conservation. 2006. (Illus.). 320p. *(978-0-89658-659-8(6)*, Voyageur Pr) MBI Publishing Co. LLC.

Watson, Kevin, photos by. Hawk Mountain: The World's First Raptor Sanctuary. 2009. *(978-1-933822-12-9(0))* Camino Bks., Inc.

Wheeler, Brian K., photos by. Raptors of Eastern North America: The Wheeler Guide. 2007. (Illus.). 439p. per. 29.95 *(978-0-691-13476-5(6))* Princeton Univ. Pr.

—Raptors of Western North America: The Wheeler Guide. 2007. (Illus.). 544p. per. 29.95 *(978-0-691-13477-2(4))* Princeton Univ. Pr.

Whitacre, D. Raptors of Maya Forest. 2012. (Published in Association with the Peregrine Fund Ser.). (ENG., Illus.). 560p. 75.00 *(978-0-8014-4079-3(3))* Cornell Univ. Pr.

BIRDSONGS

Beletsky, Les. Bird Songs: 250 North American Birds in Song. 2007. 45.00 *(978-1-932855-75-3(0))* 2006. 368p. 360.00 *(978-1-932855-54-8(8))* becker&mayer! books.

—The Bird Songs Anthology. 2007. 45.00 *(978-1-932855-88-3(2))* becker&mayer! books.

Beletsky, Les, ed. Bird Songs Bible: The Complete, Illustrated Reference for North American Birds. 2010. (ENG., Illus.). 536p. 125.00 *(978-0-8118-7138-9(X))* Chronicle Bks. LLC.

Bevis, John, et al. Aaaaw to Zzzzzd: The Words of Birds - North America, Britain, & Northern Europe. 2010. (ENG., Illus.). 160p. (gr. 17). 14.95 *(978-0-262-01429-8(7))* MIT Pr.

Catchpole, Clive & Slater, Peter. Bird Song: Biological Themes & Variations. 2nd rev. ed. 2008. (ENG., Illus.). 348p. 80.00 *(978-0-521-87242-3(1))* Cambridge Univ. Pr.

Colver, Kevin & Elliott, Lang. Know Your Bird Sounds: Common Western Species. 2008. (Lang Elliott Audio Library). (ENG., Illus.). 96p. pap. 19.95 *(978-0-8117-3446-2(3))* Stackpole Bks.

Elliott, Lang. The Songs of Wild Birds. 2006. (ENG., Illus.). 128p. 19.95 *(978-0-618-66398-9(3))* Houghton Mifflin Harcourt Trade & Reference Pubs.

Floyd, Madeleine. Birdsong. 2011. (ENG., Illus.). 128p. 12.95 *(978-1-905400-97-3(7))* National Trust, Aylesbury GBR. Dist: Independent Pubs. Group.

Hausman, Leon Augustus. The Book of Songbirds. 2011. 44p. pap. 35.95 ***(978-1-258-10405-4(9))*** Literary Licensing, LLC.

Konig, Claus, et al. Owls of the World. 2009. (ENG., Illus.). 528p. 75.00 *(978-0-300-14227-3(7))* Yale Univ. Pr.

Kroodsma, Donald. Birdsong by the Seasons: A Year of Listening to Birds. 2009. (ENG., Illus.). 384p. 28.00 *(978-0-618-75336-9(2))* Houghton Mifflin Harcourt Trade & Reference Pubs.

—The Singing Life of Birds: The Art & Science of Listening to Birdsong. 2007. (ENG., Illus.). 496p. 16.95 *(978-0-618-84076-2(1))* Houghton Mifflin Harcourt Trade & Reference Pubs.

—Western North America: A Guide to Listening. 2008. (ENG., Illus.). 192p. 29.95 *(978-0-8118-6397-1(2))* Chronicle Bks. LLC.

Leach, Elizabeth Eva. Sung Birds: Music, Nature, & Poetry in the Later Middle Ages. 2006. (Illus.). 345p. 59.95 *(978-0-8014-4491-3(8))* Cornell Univ. Pr.

Rozzi, Ricardo. Multi-Ethnic Bird Guide of the Subantarctic Forests of South America. 2nd ed. 2010. (SPA, ENG & SAI., Illus.). 236p. 34.95 *(978-1-57441-282-6(5))* Univ. of North Texas Pr.

Sample, Geoff. Collins Bird Songs & Calls, 3 vols. 2nd ed. 2010. (ENG., Illus.). 192p. 44.95 *(978-0-00-733976-1(3))* HarperCollins Pubs. Ltd. GBR. Dist: Independent Pubs. Group.

Stap, Don. Birdsong. 2010. (ENG.). 272p. pap. 17.99 *(978-1-4516-1297-4(4)*, Scribner) Scribner.

Whitney, Stephen R. & Stewart, Martyn. Birdsongs of the Pacific Northwest. 2006. (ENG., Illus.). 80p. 21.95 *(978-0-89886-821-0(1))* Mountaineers Bks., The.

Young, Jon. What the Robin Knows: How Birds Reveal the Secrets of the Natural World. 2012. (ENG., Illus.). 272p. 22.00 ***(978-0-547-45125-1(3))*** Houghton Mifflin Harcourt Trade & Reference Pubs.

Zeigler, H. Philip & Marler, Peter, eds. Neuroscience of Birdsong. 2008. (ENG., Illus.). 542p. 148.00 *(978-0-521-86915-7(3))* Cambridge Univ. Pr.

BIRDWATCHING

see Bird Watching

BIREFRINGENCE

see Refraction, Double

BIRMINGHAM (ALA.)

American Map. Birmingham. 2008. 200p. 17.95 *(978-0-8416-0874-0(1))* American Map Corp.

Bartpm, Jessica. Historic Photos of Birmingham in the 50s, 60s, And 70s. 2010. (Historic Photos Ser.). (ENG., Illus.). 206p. 39.95 *(978-1-59652-752-2(8))* Turner Publishing Co.

Bennett, James R. Historic Birmingham & Jefferson County. 2008. (Illus.). 202p. pap. *(978-1-893619-91-3(5))* Historical Publishing Network.

—Historic Birmingham & Jefferson County: An Illustrated History. 2008. (Illus.). 312p. *(978-1-893619-83-8(4))* Historical Publishing Network.

Caldwell, H. M. History of the Elyton Land Company & Birmingham, Ala. The Origin & Development of an American City. reprint ed. pap. 3.75 *(978-0-87651-988-2(5))* Southern Univ. Pr.

Crawford, Sr Donald. Wheels of Birmingham Civil Rights Movement. 2007. 100p. pap. 18.95 *(978-1-60008-025-8(1)*, Rooftop Publishing) AuthorHouse.

Dabney, Richard. Birmingham's Highland Park. 2006. (Images of America Ser.). (ENG., Illus.). 128p. per. 21.99 *(978-0-7385-4343-7(8))* Arcadia Publishing.

Dorsey, Mignette Y. Patrick. Speak Truth to Power: The Story of Charles Patrick, a Civil Rights Pioneer. 2nd ed. 2010. (Alabama Fire Ant Ser.). (ENG., Illus.). 152p. pap. 16.00 *(978-0-8173-5556-2(1))* Univ. of Alabama Pr.

Hamilton, Virginia Van der Veer. Teddy's Child: Growing up in the Anxious Southern Gentry Between the Great Wars: A Family Memoir. 2009. *(978-1-58838-195-8(1)*, NewSouth Bks.) NewSouth, Inc.

Hollis, Tim. Vintage Birmingham Signs. 2008. (Images of America Ser.). (Illus.). 127p. pap. 21.99 *(978-0-7385-5376-4(X))* Arcadia Publishing.

Keith, Todd. Insiders' Guide to Birmingham. 2011. (Insiders' Guide Ser.). (ENG.). 304p. pap. 18.95 *(978-0-7627-6467-9(8)*, Insiders' Guide) Globe Pequot Pr., The.

Lewis, W. David. Sloss Furnaces & the Rise of the Birmingham District: An Industrial Epic. 2011. (History Amer Science & Technol Ser.). (ENG.). 672p. pap. 59.50 *(978-0-8173-5668-2(1))* Univ. of Alabama Pr.

Rand McNally, creator. Rand Mcnally Birmingham Street Guide. 5th ed. 2007. (Rand Mcnally Birmingham Street Guide Ser.). (Illus.). pap. 17.95 *(978-0-528-86793-4(8))* Rand McNally.

BIRMINGHAM (ALA.)—RACE RELATIONS

Huntley, Horace & McKerley, John W., eds. Foot Soldiers for Democracy: The Men, Women, & Children of the Birmingham Civil Rights Movement. 2009. (ENG., Illus.). 264p. 75.00 *(978-0-252-03478-7(3))*; pap. 25.00 *(978-0-252-07668-8(0))* Univ. of Illinois Pr.

King, Martin Luther. Why We Can't Wait. 2011. (King Legacy Ser.). 24.95 *(978-0-8070-0114-1(7))*; (ENG., Illus.). 256p. pap. 14.00 *(978-0-8070-0112-7(0))* Beacon Pr.

BIRMINGHAM (ENGLAND)

AA Publishing Staff. Birmingham: Britain's Clearest Mapping - Dudley, Solihull, Stourbridge, Walsall, West Bromwich. 3rd ed. 2008. (ENG., Illus.). 312p. pap. 9.95 *(978-0-7495-5144-5(5))* Automobile Assn. GBR. Dist: Independent Pubs. Group.

—Birmingham Wolverhampton Street by Stree: Dudley, Solihull, Stourbridge, Walsall, West Bromwich. 3rd ed. 2007. (ENG., Illus.). 312p. spiral bd. 10.95 *(978-0-7495-5145-2(3))* Automobile Assn. GBR. Dist: Independent Pubs. Group.

Anderton, Thomas. A Tale of One City: The New Birmingham. 2009. 100p. pap. *(978-1-4099-6367-7(5))* Dodo Pr.

Armstrong, Eric. Birmingham's Horse Transport. 2007. (ENG., Illus.). 128p. pap. 29.95 *(978-0-7524-4613-4(4))* History Pr. Ltd.,The GBR. Dist: Independent Pubs. Group.

Birmingham Royal Ballet Staff, contrib. by. Birmingham Royal Ballet: A Cinderella Story. 2011. (ENG., Illus.). 150p. 50.00 ***(978-1-84943-097-5(7))*** Oberon Bks., Ltd. GBR. Dist: Consortium Bk. Sales & Distribution.

Blackman, Robert. King's Heath. 2008. (Images of England Ser.). (ENG.). 128p. pap. 30.95 *(978-0-7524-4481-9(6))* History Pr. Ltd.,The GBR. Dist: Independent Pubs. Group.

Drake, Peter. Birmingham & the Chamberlains. 2007. (Images of England Ser.). (ENG.). 128p. pap. 29.95 *(978-0-7524-4492-5(1))* History Pr. Ltd.,The GBR. Dist: Independent Pubs. Group.

Drake, Peter & Maxam, Andrew. Birmingham Shops & Shopping. 2008. (Images of England Ser.). (ENG.). 128p. pap. 29.95 *(978-0-7524-4493-2(X))* History Pr. Ltd.,The GBR. Dist: Independent Pubs. Group.

Edwards, Eliezer E. Personal Recollections of Birmingham & Birmingham Men. 2007. (ENG.). 184p. pap. 19.99 *(978-1-4264-9459-8(9))*; 204p. pap. 22.99 *(978-1-4264-9840-4(3))* BiblioBazaar.

—Personal Recollections of Birmingham & Birmingham Men. 2007. (Illus.). 244p. per. *(978-1-4065-1770-5(4))* Dodo Pr.

George T. Noszlopy Staff, et al. Birmingham Public Sculpture Trails. 2008. (ENG., Illus.). 224p. pap. 20.00 *(978-1-84631-134-5(9))* Liverpool Univ. Pr. GBR. Dist: Chicago Distribution Ctr.

Harvey, David. Hockley. 2009. (Images of England Ser.). (ENG., Illus.). 128p. pap. 24.95 *(978-0-7524-4721-6(1))* History Pr. Ltd.,The GBR. Dist: Independent Pubs. Group.

Hilton, R. H. A Medieval Society: The West Midlands at the End of the Thirteenth Century. 2008. (Past & Present Publications). (ENG.). 320p. pap. 42.00 *(978-0-521-08155-9(6))* Cambridge Univ. Pr.

Hutton, William. An History of Birmingham. 2009. 324p. 28.99 *(978-0-559-10669-9(6))*; 29.99 *(978-0-559-10653-8(X))*; pap. 30.75 *(978-0-559-10656-9(4))*; pap. 29.75 *(978-0-559-10664-4(5))* BiblioBazaar.

Jenkins, Lyndon & Fraser, Fiona. Town Hall Birmingham: A History in Pictures. 2007. (Illus.). 128p. per. 19.99 *(978-1-84383-349-9(2)*, Boydell Press) Boydell & Brewer, Ltd. GBR. Dist: Boydell & Brewer, Inc.

Moran, James. Irish Birmingham: A History. 2010. (ENG., Illus.). 256p. 95.00 *(978-1-84631-474-2(7))*; pap. 29.95 *(978-1-84631-475-9(5))* Liverpool Univ. Pr. GBR. Dist: Chicago Distribution Ctr.

Norton, Mark. Birmingham Then & Now. 2010. (Then & Now Ser.). (ENG., Illus.). 96p. pap. 23.95 *(978-0-7524-5722-2(5))* History Pr. Ltd.,The GBR. Dist: Independent Pubs. Group.

Pye, Charles. A Description of Modern Birmingham. 2008. 172p. 22.99 *(978-0-554-32874-4(7))*; 25.99 *(978-0-554-23571-4(4))* BiblioBazaar.

—A Description of Modern Birmingham. 2008. (ENG.). 156p. per. *(978-1-4065-6662-8(4))* Dodo Pr.

—A Description of Modern Birmingham: Whereunto Are Annexed Observations Made during an Excursion Round the Town, in the Summer of 1818, Including Warwick & Leamington. 2007. (ENG.). 150p. pap. 18.99 *(978-1-4264-4688-7(8))*; 168p. pap. 21.99 *(978-1-4264-4719-8(1))* BiblioBazaar.

Showell, Walter. Showells Dictionary of Birmingham. 2006. pap. *(978-1-4068-0555-0(6))* Echo Library.

Watkins, Bill. A Celtic Childhood. 2011. (ENG.). 312p. pap. 14.95 *(978-0-9765201-8-4(4))* Scarletta Pr.

Woodhall, Dave. Little Book of Aston Villa. 2012. (ENG.). 192p. pap. 4.95 ***(978-1-84732-938-7(1))*** Carlton Bks., Ltd. GBR. Dist: Independent Pubs. Group.

BIRMINGHAM UNIVERSITY

see University of Birmingham

BIRNEY, JAMES GILLESPIE, 1792-1857

Rogers, D. Laurence. Apostles of Equality: The Birneys, the Republicans, & the Civil War. 2011. (ENG., Illus.). 250p. 39.95 *(978-1-61186-015-3(6))* Michigan State Univ. Pr.

BIRTH

see Childbirth; Labor (Obstetrics)

BIRTH (IN RELIGION, FOLK-LORE, ETC.)

see Childbirth—Religious Aspects

BIRTH, MULTIPLE

see Multiple Birth

BIRTH, PREMATURE

see Infants (Premature)

BIRTH CONTROL

see also Abortion; Abortion Counseling; Contraception; Family Size; Intrauterine Contraceptives; Natural Family Planning

Baker, Jean H. Margaret Sanger: A Life of Passion, 1 vol. (ENG.). 368p. 2012. pap. 16.00 ***(978-0-8090-6757-2(9))*** 2011. (Illus.). 35.00 *(978-0-8090-9498-1(3))* Farrar, Straus & Giroux. (Hill & Wang).

Barth, Richard P. Reducing the Risk 5th Edition (TG & Wkbk) (359) Building Skills to Prevent Pregnancy, STD & HIV. 2011. (ENG.). 236p. pap. 49.99 *(978-1-56071-714-0(9))* ETR Assocs.

Bringle, Jennifer. Reproductive Rights: Making the Right Choices. 2010. (Young Woman's Guide to Contemporary Issues Ser.). 112p. (YA). (gr. 9-12). lib. bdg., E-Book 63.90 *(978-1-61532-909-0(9))* Rosen Publishing Group, Inc., The.

Browning, Jill S. & James-Enger, Kelly. The Belated Baby: Healing Yourself after the Long Journey of Infertility. 2008. (ENG.). 242p. pap. 16.95 *(978-1-58182-610-4(9))* Turner Publishing Co.

Carlson, Allan C. Godly Seed: American Evangelicals Confront Birth Control, 1873-1973. 2011. (ENG.). 172p. 29.95 ***(978-1-4128-4261-7(1))*** Transaction Pubs.

Caron, Sandra L. Sex Around the World: Cross-Cultural Perspectives on Human Sexuality. 2nd ed. 2007. (Illus.). x, 217p. *(978-0-536-30726-2(1))* Pearson Learning Solutions.

Caron, Simone M. Who Chooses? American Reproductive History Since 1830. (ENG.). 2010. 384p. pap. 29.95 *(978-0-8130-3504-8(X))* 2008. (Illus.). 416p. 69.95 *(978-0-8130-3199-6(0))* Univ. Pr. of Florida.

Chaulagai, Ganesh. Media Exposure to Family Planning Messages. 2010. 100p. pap. *(978-3-639-26495-1(9))* VDM Verlag Dr. Mueller e.K.

Coates, Patricia Walsh. Margaret Sanger & the Origin of the Birth Control Movement, 1910-1930: The Concept of Women's Sexual Autonomy. 2008. (Illus.). 232p. 109.95 *(978-0-7734-5099-8(8))* Mellen, Edwin Pr., The.

Connelly, Matthew. Fatal Misconception: The Struggle to Control World Population. 2010. (Illus.). 544p. pap. 21.00 *(978-0-674-03460-0(0)*, Belknap Pr.) Harvard Univ. Pr.

Craven, Christa. Pushing for Midwives: Homebirth Mothers & the Reproductive Rights Movement. 2010. (ENG.). 232p. 81.50 *(978-1-4399-0219-6(4))* Temple Univ. Pr.

—Pushing for Midwives: Reproductive Rights in a Consumer Era. 2010. (ENG.). 208p. pap. 26.95 *(978-1-4399-0220-2(8))* Temple Univ. Pr.

Daly, Sunny. Changing Images of the Birth Control Pill, 1960-1973. 2008. 104p. pap. *(978-3-639-01052-7(3))* VDM Verlag Dr. Mueller e.K.

Day-Sclater, Shelley, et al, eds. Regulating Autonomy: Sex, Reproduction & Family. 2009. (ENG.). 267p. pap. 72.00 *(978-1-84113-946-3(7))* Hart Publishing Ltd. GBR. Dist: International Specialized Bk. Services.

Devereux, George. A Study of Abortion in Primitive Societies. 2011. 406p. 54.95 ***(978-1-258-01802-3(0))*** Literary Licensing, LLC.

Doh, Emmanuel. Analysis of Changing Rural Women's Reproduction Behavior Patterns in South Africa. 2008. 136p. pap. 24.95 *(978-99944-55-34-8(6))* African Bks. Collective, Ltd. GBR. Dist: Lightning Source, Inc.

Drysdale, George. The Elements of Social Science: Physical, Sexual, & Natural Religion. Darby, Robert, ed. 2010. (Great Mind Ser.). (ENG.). 365p. pap. 16.00 *(978-1-61614-179-0(4))* Prometheus Bks., Pubs.

Engelman, Peter. A History of the Birth Control Movement in America. 2011. E-Book *(978-0-313-36510-2(5)*, Praeger Pubs.) Greenwood Publishing Group, Inc.

Engelman, Peter C. A History of the Birth Control Movement in America, 1 vol. 2011. (Healing Society: Disease, Medicine, & History Ser.). (Illus.). 231p. 44.95 *(978-0-313-36509-6(1)*, C36509) Greenwood Publishing Group, Inc.

Fisher, Terri D., et al. Handbook of Sexuality-Related Measures. 3rd ed. 2010. (ENG., Illus.). 680p. instr.'s hndbk. ed. 158.00 *(978-0-415-80174-4(5))* Routledge.

—Sexuality-Related Measures. 3rd ed. 2010. (ENG., Illus.). 680p. pap., instr.'s hndbk. ed. 95.00 *(978-0-415-80175-1(3))* Routledge.

Fontain, Mario. Are You Having Sex for Fun & Babies? 2008. (ENG.). 82p. pap. 8.95 *(978-0-533-15721-1(8))* Vantage Pr., Inc.

Friedman, Lauri S. Birth Control. 2009. (Introducing Issues with Opposing Viewpoints Ser.). (ENG.). 144p. (gr. 7-10). 35.75 *(978-0-7377-4334-0(4)*, Greenhaven Pr., Inc.) Cengage Gale.

Glasier, Anna & Gebbie, Ailsa. Handbook of Family Planning & Reproductive Healthcare. 5th ed. 2008. (ENG., Illus.). 448p. pap. 64.95 *(978-0-443-06887-4(9)*, Churchill Livingstone) Elsevier - Health Sciences Div.

Goodwin, Michele. Baby Markets: Money & the New Politics of Creating Families. 2010. (ENG., Illus.). 336p. 94.99 *(978-0-521-51373-9(1))* Cambridge Univ. Pr.

Goodwin, Michele Bratcher. Baby Markets: Money & the New Politics of Creating Families. 2010. (ENG., Illus.). 336p. pap. 28.99 *(978-0-521-73510-0(6))* Cambridge Univ. Pr.

Gordon, Linda. The Moral Property of Women: A History of Birth Control Politics in America. 3rd annot. ed. 2007. 464p. per. 26.00 *(978-0-252-07459-2(9))* Univ. of Illinois Pr.

Haerens, Margaret & Zott, Lynn M. Birth Control. Zott, Lynn, ed. 2012. (Opposing Viewpoints Ser.). (ENG., Illus.). 240p. (gr. 10-12). 41.70 ***(978-0-7377-6044-6(3))***; pap. 28.90 ***(978-0-7377-6045-3(1))*** Cengage Gale. (Greenhaven Pr., Inc.).

Hajo, Cathy Moran. Birth Control on Main Street: Organizing Clinics in the United States, 1916-1939. 2010. (ENG., Illus.). 264p. 75.00 *(978-0-252-03536-4(4))*; pap. 25.00 *(978-0-252-07725-8(3))* Univ. of Illinois Pr.

Halfon, Saul. The Cairo Consensus: Demographic Surveys, Women's Empowerment, & Regime Change in Population Policy. 2006. (ENG., Illus.). 282p. 62.99 *(978-0-7391-1176-5(0))* Lexington Bks.

Holz, Rose. The Birth Control Clinic in a Marketplace World. 2012. (Rochester Studies in Medical History Ser.: Volume 21). 238p. 80.00 ***(978-1-58046-399-7(1))*** Univ. of Rochester Pr.

Janssens, Angélique. Gendering the Fertility Decline in the Western World. (Population, Family, & Society Ser.: Vol. 7). 306p. pap. 73.95 *(978-3-03911-311-8(9))* Lang, Peter Publishing, Inc.

Johnsen, Jennifer. Is the Ring Right for You? 2007. *(978-1-930996-98-4(5))* Planned Parenthood Federation of America, Inc.

Jütte, Robert. Contraception: A History. Russell, Vicky, tr. from GER. 2008. (ENG., Illus.). 288p. 69.95 *(978-0-7456-3270-4(X))* Polity Pr. GBR. Dist: Wiley, John & Sons, Inc.

—Contraception: A History. Russell, V. Jean, tr. from GER. 2008. (ENG., Illus.). 288p. pap. 28.95 *(978-0-7456-3271-1(8))* Polity Pr. GBR. Dist: Wiley, John & Sons, Inc.

Kane, Shelli. Student's Quick Guide to STI's & Birth Control. 2007. (ENG.). (C). pap. 8.40 *(978-0-536-48607-3(7))* Pearson Learning Solutions.
Katz, Esther, et al, eds. The Selected Papers of Margaret Sanger: Volume 1: the Woman Rebel, 1900-1928. 2007. (Illus.). 576p. per. 37.00 *(978-0-252-07460-8(2))* Univ. of Illinois Pr.
Katz, Esther, et al. The Selected Papers of Margaret Sanger, Volume 3: The Politics of Planned Parenthood, 1939-1966. 2010. (ENG., Illus.). 592p. 80.00 *(978-0-252-03372-8(8))* Univ. of Illinois Pr.
Kennedy, David M. Birth Control in Americ: The Career of Margaret Sanger. 2008. 344p. pap. 34.00 *(978-1-59740-427-3(6))* ACLS Humanities E-Book.
King, Martin Luther, Jr. Family Planning, A Special & Urgent Concern: Upon Accepting he Planned parenthood Federation of America Margaret Sanger Award - May 5 1966. 2007. *(978-1-930996-97-7(7))* Planned Parenthood Federation of America, Inc.
Kluchin, Rebecca M. Fit to Be Tied: Sterilization & Reproductive Rights in America, 1950-1980. (Critical Issues in Health & Medicine Ser.). (ENG., 288p. 2011. Illus.). pap. 26.95 *(978-0-8135-4999-6(X))* 2009. 45.95 *(978-0-8135-4527-1(7))* Rutgers Univ. Pr.
Knopf, S. Adolphus. The Medical, Social, Economic, Moral & Religious Aspects of Birth Control. 2011. 70p. 36.95 ***(978-1-258-05159-4(1))*** Literary Licensing, LLC.
MacKay, Jennifer. Teen Pregnancy. 2011. (Hot Topics Ser.). 128p. lib. bdg. 33.45 *(978-1-4205-0479-8(7)*. Lucent Bks.) Cengage Gale.
Margaret Sanger. Woman & the New Race. 2007. 132p. pap. 18.99 *(978-1-4346-3948-6(7))*; (ENG.). 144p. pap. 19.99 *(978-1-4346-3949-3(5))* BiblioBazaar.
Marlow, Florence. Maternal Control of Development: My Mother Made Me Do It. Kessler, Daniel, ed. 2011. (Colloquium Series on Developmental Biology Ser.). 196p. pap. 50.00 *(978-1-61504-051-3(X))* Morgan & Claypool Life Science Publishers.
May, Elaine Tyler. America & the Pill: A History of Promise, Peril, & Liberation. 2011. (ENG.). 232p. (gr. 9). pap. 15.99 *(978-0-465-02459-9(9))* Basic Bks.
McVeigh, Enda, et al. Oxford Handbook of Reproductive Medicine & Family Planning. 2008. (Oxford Handbooks Ser.). (ENG., Illus.). 456p. pap. 49.95 *(978-0-19-920380-2(6))* Oxford Univ. Pr., Inc.
Mosher, Steven W. & Mosher, Steven. Population Control: Real Costs, Illusory Benefits. 2008. (ENG., Illus.). 310p. (gr. 11). pap. 29.95 *(978-1-4128-0713-5(1))* Transaction Pubs.
Mosher, William D. & Jones, Jo. Use of Contraception in the United States: 1982-2008. 2010. *(978-0-8406-0640-2(0))* National Ctr. for Health Statistics.
Muller, Connie. Hello-Goodbye My Precious Child: A Mother's True Story of Her Special Child's Journey from Heaven to Earth & Back to Heaven. 2011. (Illus.). 272p. pap. 15.95 ***(978-1-4327-7498-1(0))*** Outskirts Pr., Inc.
Newman, Susan. The Case for the Only Child: What You Need to Know about the Single-Child Decision. 2011. (ENG.). 264p. pap. 14.95 *(978-0-7573-1551-0(8))* Health Communications, Inc.
Pathfinder International. Courageous Pioneers: Celebrating Pathfinder International¿s impact on reproductive health around the World. Suttenfield, Linda J. et al, eds. 2007. (Illus.). 84p. pap. 30.00 *(978-0-9799712-0-4(9))* Pathfinder International.
Pius XI. On Christian Marriage. 2007. 88p. per. 10.95 *(978-0-9782985-6-2(X))* Catholic Authors Pr.
Prescott, Heather Munro. The Morning After: A History of Emergency Contraception in the United States. 2011. (Critical Issues in Health & Medicine Ser.). (ENG.). 256p. pap. 22.95 ***(978-0-8135-5163-0(3))***; (Illus.). 184p. 69.00 ***(978-0-8135-5162-3(5))*** Rutgers Univ. Pr.
Robinson, William J. Birth Control, or, the Limitation of Offspring. 2007. 260p. 29.95 *(978-1-4344-9620-1(1))*; per. 19.95 *(978-1-4344-9619-5(8))* Wildside Pr., LLC.
Rout, Ettie A. Safe Marriage: A Return to Sanity. 2009. (Illus.). 68p. pap. *(978-1-4099-5700-3(4))* Dodo Pr.
—Safe Marriage: A Return to Sanity. 2007. 56p. per. *(978-1-4068-4058-2(0))* Echo Library.
Russell, Bertrand. A Liberal View of Divorce. Haldeman-Julius, E., ed. 2011. 32p. 35.95 ***(978-1-258-01479-7(3))*** Literary Licensing, LLC.
Sanger, Margaret. Birth Control Review. 2009. 100p. pap. 20.00 *(978-1-151-42810-3(8))* General Bks. LLC.
—The Pivot of Civilization. 2011. 312p. pap. 29.75 ***(978-1-179-97983-0(4))*** 2011. 306p. pap. 29.75 ***(978-1-178-94849-3(8))*** 2008. 176p. 25.99 *(978-0-554-26656-5(3))* 2008. 176p. 22.99 *(978-0-554-35959-5(6))* 2007. (ENG.). 156p. pap. 19.99 *(978-1-4346-1515-2(4))* 2007. (ENG.). 172p. pap. 21.99 *(978-1-4346-1609-8(6))* BiblioBazaar.
—The Pivot of Civilization. 2007. (ENG.). 144p. per. *(978-1-4065-3860-1(4))* Dodo Pr.
—The Pivot of Civilization. 2010. (Illus.). 98p. pap. 7.85 *(978-1-4432-3032-2(4))* 2009. 114p. pap. 7.85 *(978-1-150-18955-5(X))* General Bks. LLC.
—The Pivot of Civilization. 2010. 124p. pap. 16.76 *(978-1-162-70488-3(8))*; 28.76 ***(978-1-169-25234-9(6))***; 35.95 *(978-1-161-47352-0(1))* Kessinger Publishing, LLC.
—The Pivot of Civilization. 2011. 284p. pap. 28.00 ***(978-1-878465-75-7(9))*** Scott-Townsend Pubs.
—The Pivot of Civilization. 2008. (ENG.). 148p. pap. 11.45 *(978-1-60597-693-8(8)*, Book Jungle) Standard Pubns., Inc.
—Woman & the New Race. 2010. 256p. pap. 26.75 *(978-1-141-08996-3(3))* 2008. 148p. 21.99 *(978-0-554-37067-5(0))* 2008. 148p. 24.99 *(978-0-554-27764-6(6))* BiblioBazaar.
—Woman & the New Race. 2007. (ENG.). 128p. per. *(978-1-4065-3867-0(1))* Dodo Pr.
—Woman & the New Race. 2009. 104p. pap. 20.00 *(978-1-4589-9444-8(9))* General Bks. LLC.
Schwartz, Timothy T. Fewer Men, More Babies: Sex, Family, & Fertility in Haiti. 2009. (ENG., Illus.). 290p. 78.99 *(978-0-7391-2867-1(1))* Lexington Bks.
Singer, Alan. Creating Your Perfect Family Size: How to Make an Informed Decision about Having a Baby. 2011. (ENG., Illus.). 192p. pap. 16.95 *(978-0-470-90031-4(8)*, Jossey-Bass) Wiley, John & Sons, Inc.
Solinger, Rickie. Pregnancy & Power: A Short History of Reproductive Politics in America. 2007. (ENG., Illus.). 312p. pap. 23.00 *(978-0-8147-9828-7(4))* New York Univ. Pr.
Solinger, Rickie. Reproductive Politics, 1 vol. 2013. (What Everyone Needs to Know Ser.). (ENG.). 192p. pap. 16.95 ***(978-0-19-981141-0(5))*** Oxford Univ. Pr., Inc.
United Nations. Asia-Pacific population journal, April 2006. 2007. (ENG.). 110p. pap. 12.50 *(978-92-1-120472-8(0))* United Nations Pubns.
—Asia-Pacific Population Journal, April 2007. 2007. (ENG.). 76p. pap. 12.50 *(978-92-1-120508-4(5))* United Nations Pubns.
—Asia-Pacific Population Journal, August 2006. 2007. (ENG.). 84p. pap. 12.50 *(978-92-1-120483-4(6))* United Nations Pubns.
—Asia-Pacific Population Journal, December 2006. 2007. (Air Pollution Studies). (ENG.). 140p. pap. 12.50 *(978-92-1-120498-8(4))* United Nations Pubns.
United Nations: Department of Economic and Social Affairs. Population Division. World Fertility Report 2007. 2011. (ENG., Illus.). 88p. pap. 26.00 incl. cd-rom ***(978-92-1-151473-5(8))*** United Nations Pubns.
Virtala, Aira. Family Planning among University Students in Finland. 2009. 96p. pap. *(978-3-639-13002-7(2))* VDM Verlag Dr. Mueller e.K.
Vong, Sreytouch. Female Education & Family Planning. 2011. 112p. pap. ***(978-3-8443-3028-1(3))*** Lambert Academic Publishing.
Wendt, Ralph. Birth Control & the Sovereignty of God. 2010. 85p. pap. 11.49 *(978-0-557-16552-0(0))* Lulu Enterprises Inc.
World Bank Group & World Bank. The Little Data Book on Gender 2009. 2009. (World Development Indicators Ser.). (ENG., Illus.). 240p. pap. 15.00 *(978-0-8213-7872-4(4)*, 9780821378724) World Bank Pubns.
World Health Organization. WHO Medical Eligibility Criteria Wheel for Contraceptive Use 2008, 20, Pack. 2010. (Nonserial Publication Ser.). (ENG.). 72.00 *(978-92-4-154771-0(5))* World Health Organization.
Xiang, Debao. From Propaganda to Persuasion. 2010. 288p. pap. *(978-3-639-24405-2(2))* VDM Verlag Dr. Mueller e.K.
Zlidar, Vera, et al. Family Planning: A global handbook for Providers. 2007. (Illus.). 372p. per. 24.99 *(978-0-9788563-0-4(9))* Johns Hopkins CCP.
Zonderman, Jon & Shader, Laurel. Birth Control Pills. Triggle, David J., ed. 2006. (Drugs Ser.). (Illus.). 96p. (YA). (gr. 9-12). lib. bdg. 30.00 *(978-0-7910-8553-0(8))* Facts On File, Inc.
Zorea, Aharon W. Birth Control. 2012. E-Book ***(978-0-313-36255-2(6)***, Greenwood Pr.); 216p. 58.00 *(978-0-313-36254-5(8)*, GR6254) Greenwood Publishing Group, Inc.

BIRTH CONTROL—LAW AND LEGISLATION

Ehrenreich, Nancy, ed. The Reproductive Rights Reader: Law, Medicine, & the Construction of Motherhood. 2008. (ENG.). 448p. 85.00 *(978-0-8147-2230-5(X))*; per. 28.00 *(978-0-8147-2231-2(8))* New York Univ. Pr.
Lombardo, Paul A. Three Generations, No Imbeciles: Eugenics, the Supreme Court, & Buck V. Bell. 2010. (ENG., Illus.). 384p. (gr. 17). pap. 25.00 *(978-0-8018-9824-2(2))* Johns Hopkins Univ. Pr.
Merino, Noël. Birth Control. 2010. (Issues on Trial Ser.). (ENG.). 240p. 39.70 *(978-0-7377-4947-2(4)*, Greenhaven Pr., Inc.) Cengage Gale.
Panu, Mihnea. Contextualizing Family Planning: Truth, Subject, & the Other in the U. S. Government. 2009. (ENG.). 256p. 95.00 *(978-0-230-60798-9(5))* Palgrave Macmillan.
Scott, Charles C. Bridging the Abortion Divide. 2008. 224p. per. 10.95 *(978-1-4327-0888-7(0))* Outskirts Pr., Inc.

BIRTH CONTROL—MORAL AND ETHICAL ASPECTS

see also Pro-Choice Movement; Pro-Life Movement

Acevedo Nieves, Juan Antonio. Sobrepoblacion: Pobreza o riqueza de Puerto Rico. 2010. (SPA., Illus.). 232p. pap. 16.99 *(978-1-61505-024-6(8))* Publicaciones Gaviota.
Page, Christina. How the Pro-Choice Movement Saved America: Freedom, Politics, & the War on Sex. 2006. (ENG.). 256p. per. 15.00 *(978-0-465-05490-9(0))* Basic Bks.

BIRTH CONTROL—PUBLIC OPINION

Soloway, Richard A. Birth Control & the Population Question in England, 1877-1930. 2011. (ENG.). 438p. pap. 50.00 *(978-0-8078-9783-6(3))* Univ. of North Carolina Pr.

BIRTH CONTROL—RELIGIOUS ASPECTS

see also Pro-Choice Movement; Pro-Life Movement

Acevedo Nieves, Juan Antonio. Sobrepoblacion: Pobreza o riqueza de Puerto Rico. 2010. (SPA., Illus.). 232p. pap. 16.99 *(978-1-61505-024-6(8))* Publicaciones Gaviota.
Al-Kawthari, Muhammad ibn Adam. Birth Control & Abortion in Islam, 1. 2nd enl. ed. 2006. 88p. per. 9.95 *(978-1-933764-00-9(7))* White Thread Pr.
Allen, Paul. Condom. 2008. (Trigger Issues Ser.). (ENG., Illus.). 128p. pap. 9.00 *(978-1-904456-76-6(6))* New Internationalist Pubns., Ltd. GBR. Dist: Consortium Bk. Sales & Distribution.
Baron, Mary Lee. Natural Family Planning: A Catholic Approach. 2009. 48p. pap. 4.95 *(978-0-7648-1833-2(3))* Liguori Pubns.
Brosens, I. A. The Challenge of Reproductive Medicine at Catholic Universities: Time to Leave the Catacombs. Brosens, I., ed. 2006. (Illus.). 263p. (C). pap. 57.00 *(978-90-429-1762-0(8))* Peeters Pubs. & Booksellers BEL. Dist: Brown, David Bk. Co., The.
Davis, Tom. Sacred Work: Planned Parenthood & Its Clergy Alliances. 2006. (ENG., Illus.). 264p. per. 18.95 *(978-0-8135-3950-8(1))* Rutgers Univ. Pr.
Endow - Humanae Vitae. 2007. spiral bd. 19.95 *(978-1-932927-82-5(4))* Ascension Pr.
Hillstrom, Kevin, ed. Religion & Sexuality. 2007. (Opposing Viewpoints Ser.). (ENG., Illus.). 226p. (YA). (gr. 8-12). 27.50 *(978-0-7377-3750-9(6)*, 1271460); pap. 39.70 *(978-0-7377-3749-3(2)*, 1271460) Cengage Gale. (Greenhaven Pr., Inc.).
Hodge, Bryan C. The Christian Case Against Contraception. 2009. 310p. pap. 34.00 *(978-1-60899-010-8(9)*, Wipf and Stock) Wipf & Stock Pubs.
Houghton, Craig. Family UNplanning. 2006. pap. 9.99 *(978-1-60034-851-8(3))* Xulon Pr., Inc.
Maguire, Daniel C., ed. Sacred Rights: The Case for Contraception & Abortion in World Religions. 2007. 295p. reprint ed. pap. 25.00 *(978-1-4223-6831-2(9))* DIANE Publishing Co.
Ramirez De Arellano, Annette B., et al. Colonialism, Catholicism, & Contraception: A History of Birth Control in Puerto Rico. 2011. (ENG.). 233p. pap. 40.00 *(978-0-8078-9757-7(4))* Univ. of North Carolina Pr.
Tentler, Leslie Woodcock. Catholics & Contraception: An American History. 2009. (Cushwa Center Studies of Catholicism in Twentieth-Century America). (Illus.). 352p. pap. 21.95 *(978-0-8014-7494-1(9))* Cornell Univ. Pr.
Twomey, Vincent. Moral Theology after Humanae Vitae - Fundamental Issues in Moral Theology & Sexual Ethics. 2010. 226p. 45.00 *(978-1-84682-201-8(7))* Four Courts Pr. IRL. Dist: International Specialized Bk. Services.
Watters, Steve, et al. Start Your Family: Inspiration for Having Babies 2009. (ENG.). 176p. pap. 13.99 *(978-0-8024-5830-8(0))* Moody Pubs.
Zubizzarreta, Eduardo. Manual del Metodo Billings.Tr. of Manual of the Billings' Method. (SPA.). 40p. pap. 1.95 *(978-980-350-105-1(4))* Sociedad de San Pablo VEN. Dist: St Pauls/Alba Hse. Pubs.

BIRTH CONTROL—AFRICA

Abdella, Yetmgeta. Socio-Cultural Factors Related to Fertility in Suri Ethnic Group. 2009. 80p. pap. *(978-3-639-20775-0(0))* VDM Verlag Dr. Mueller e.K.
Bekele, Biruhtesfa. Standard Days Method in Expanding Family Planning Method Choice. 2009. 64p. pap. *(978-3-639-21724-7(1))* VDM Verlag Dr. Mueller e.K.
Benaya, Kabwe. Contraceptive Choices. 2010. 352p. pap. *(978-3-639-21879-4(5))* VDM Verlag Dr. Mueller e.K.
Krause, Sandra & Bader, Laetitia. We Want Birth Control: Reproductive Health Findings in Northern Uganda. 2007. *(978-1-58030-060-5(X))* Women's Commission For Refugee Women & Children, The.

BIRTH CONTROL—ASIA

Khaniya, Rina. Family Planning in Nepalese Context. 2010. 84p. pap. *(978-3-8383-7974-6(8))* Lambert Academic Publishing.
Sunil, T. S. & Pillai, Vijayan K. Women's Reproductive Health in Yemen. 2010. 242p. *(978-1-60497-662-5(4))* Cambria Pr.
United Nations. Asia-Pacific Population Journal: 20th Anniversary Special. 2007. (ENG.). 112p. pap. 12.50 *(978-92-1-120489-6(5))* United Nations Pubns.
—Asia-Pacific Population Journal, April 2008. 2009. (ENG.). 116p. pap. 12.50 *(978-92-1-120549-7(2))* United Nations Pubns.
—Asia-Pacific Population Journal, August 2007. 2008. (ENG.). 132p. pap. 12.50 *(978-92-1-120527-5(1))* United Nations Pubns.
—Asia-Pacific Population Journal, August 2008. 2009. (ENG.). 108p. pap. 12.50 *(978-92-1-120558-9(1))* United Nations Pubns.
—Asia-Pacific Population Journal, December 2007. 2008. (ENG.). 96p. pap. 12.50 *(978-92-1-120543-5(3))* United Nations Pubns.
—Asia-Pacific Population Journal, December 2008. 2009. (ENG.). 120p. pap. 12.50 *(978-92-1-120566-4(2))* United Nations Pubns.
United Nations. Asia-Pacific Population Journal, December 2010. 2012. (ENG.). 142p. pap. 15.00 ***(978-92-1-120627-2(8))*** United Nations Pubns.

BIRTH CONTROL—BANGLADESH

Islam, Mohammad Amirul. Male Involvement in Reproductive Health in Bangladesh: A Multilevel Analysis. 2008. 176p. pap. *(978-3-639-10225-3(8))* VDM Verlag Dr. Mueller e.K.
Khatun, Mahmuda. Encountering Men's Unmet Need for Family Planning. 2010. 232p. pap. *(978-3-8383-5493-4(1))* Lambert Academic Publishing.

BIRTH CONTROL—CHINA

Cheng, Chiung-Fang. Minority Fertility in Contemporary Chin. 2009. 128p. pap. *(978-3-639-13482-7(6))* VDM Verlag Dr. Mueller e.K.
Childs, G. Tibetan Transitions: Historical & Contemporary Perspectives on Fertility, Family Planning, & Demographic Change. 2008. (Illus.). 300p. *(978-90-04-16808-4(7))* BRILL.
Greenhalgh, Susan. Just One Child: Science & Policy in Deng's China. 2008. (Illus.). 440p. 55.00 *(978-0-520-25338-4(8))*; 403p. per. 26.95 *(978-0-520-25339-1(6))* Univ. of California Pr.
Hvistendahl, Mara. Unnatural Selection: Choosing Boys over Girls, & the Consequences of a World Full of Men. 2011. (ENG., Illus.). 336p. 26.99 *(978-1-58648-850-5(3))* PublicAffairs.
Poston, Dudley L., ed. Fertility,Family Planning, & Population Policy in Chin. 2009. 212p. pap. 39.95 *(978-0-415-49738-1(8))* Routledge.
White, Tyrene. China's Longest Campaign: Birth Planning in the People's Republic, 1949-2005. 2009. (Illus.). 320p. pap. 24.95 *(978-0-8014-7539-9(2))* Cornell Univ. Pr.
Wu, Hongda Harry & Shen, Kuo. Zui Zai Dang Dai Yi Huo Qian Qiu: Zhongguo Ji Hua Sheng Yü Zheng Ce Shi Shi San Shi Zhou Nian Yan Jiu Bao Gao. 2010. (CHI., Illus.). 222p. *(978-1-931550-57-4(3))* Laogai Research Foundation, The.
Yang, Juhua. Beyond Birth Control. 2008. 392p. per. *(978-3-8364-3925-1(5))* VDM Verlag Dr. Mueller e.K.

BIRTH CONTROL—DEVELOPING COUNTRIES

Ahlburg, Dennis A., et al, eds. The Impact of Population Growth on Well-being in Developing Countries. 2010. (Population Economics Ser.). (Illus.). ix, 360p. pap. 199.00 *(978-3-642-08235-1(1)*, 3642082351) Springer.
Goldberg, Michelle. The Means of Reproduction: Sex, Power, & the Future of the World. 2010. (ENG.). 272p. (gr. 12-18). 16.00 *(978-0-14-311688-2(6)*, Penguin (Non-Classics)) Penguin Group (USA) Inc.
The Mexico City Policy/Global Gag Rule: Its Impact on Family Planning & Reproductive Health: Hearing Before the Committee on Foreign Affairs, House of Representatives, One Hundred Tenth Congress, First Session, October 31, 2007. 2008. (Illus.). iii, 132p. *(978-0-16-080141-9(9)*, 552-070-36881-7) United States Government Printing Office.
Robinson, Warren C. & Ross, John A., eds. The Global Family Planning Revolution: Three Decades of Population Policies & Programs. 2007. (Moving Out of Poverty Ser.). (ENG., Illus.). 490p. per. 45.00 *(978-0-8213-6951-7(2)*, 9780821369517) World Bank Pubns.
Smith, T. E., ed. The Politics of Family Planning in the Third World. 2011. (ENG.). 352p. 120.00 *(978-0-415-59291-8(7))* Routledge.

BIRTH CONTROL—FRANCE

Accampo, Elinor Ann. Blessed Motherhood, Bitter Fruit: Nelly Roussel & the Politics of Female Pain in Third Republic France. 2006. (ENG., Illus.). 336p. (gr. 17). 52.00 *(978-0-8018-8404-7(1))* Johns Hopkins Univ. Pr.
McLaren, Angus. Sexuality & Social Order: The Debate over the Fertility of Women & Workers in France, 1770-1920. 2008. 244p. pap. 24.00 *(978-1-59740-608-6(2))* ACLS Humanities E-Book.

BIRTH CONTROL—GREAT BRITAIN

Askham, Janet. Fertility & Deprivation: A Study of Differential Fertility Amongst Working-Class Families in Aberdeen. 2010. (Cambridge Papers in Sociology Ser.). 196p. pap. 19.99 *(978-0-521-13437-8(4))* Cambridge Univ. Pr.
Busfield, Joan & Paddon, Michael. Thinking about Children: Sociology & Fertility in Post-War England. 2010. (ENG.). 328p. pap. 25.99 *(978-0-521-13447-7(1)*, Cambridge Univ. Pr.
Cartwright, Ann. Parents & Family Planning Services. 2009. (ENG.). 303p. pap. 34.95 *(978-0-202-36320-2(1))* Aldine Transaction.
Farmer, Ann. By Their Fruits: Eugenics, Population Control, & the Abortion Campaign. 2008. 448p. (C). pap. 79.95 *(978-0-8132-1530-3(7))* Catholic Univ. of America Pr.
Fisher Kate. Birth Control, Sex, & Marriage in Britain 1918-1960. 2008. (ENG.). 304p. pap. 55.00 *(978-0-19-954460-8(3))* Oxford Univ. Pr., Inc.
Reynolds, Moira Davison. Women Advocates of Reproductive Rights: Eleven Who Led the Struggle in the United States & Great Britain. alt. ed. 2012. (ENG.). 179p. pap. 20.00 ***(978-0-7864-6739-6(8))*** McFarland & Co., Inc. Pubs.
Soloway, Richard A. Birth Control & the Population Question in England, 1877-1930. 2011. (ENG.). 438p. pap. 50.00 *(978-0-8078-9783-6(3))* Univ. of North Carolina Pr.

BIRTH CONTROL—INDIA

Ahluwalia, Sanjam. Reproductive Restraints: Birth Control in India, 1877-1947. 272p. 2008. 62.00 *(978-0-252-03240-0(3))* 2007. per. 26.00 *(978-0-252-07480-6(7))* Univ. of Illinois Pr.
Arokiasamy, P., contrib. by. Poverty, Nutrition, & Fertility: A Micro Study. xiv, 322p. *(978-81-7018-856-8(3))* B.R. Publishing Corp. IND. Dist: Asia Bk. Corp. of America.
Barthakur, Jitendra Kumar. Think India: Age Table. 2009. 456p. *(978-81-89392-00-0(X))* Kumud Bks.
Chandrasekhar, S. Infant Mortality, Population Growth, & Family Planning in India. 2011. (ENG.). 410p. pap. 50.00 *(978-0-8078-9635-8(7))* Univ. of North Carolina Pr.
Chandrasekhar, S., ed. Infant Mortality Population Growth & Family Planning in India: An Essay on Population Problems & International Tensions. 2011. (ENG.). 408p. 120.00 *(978-0-415-59544-5(4))* Routledge.
Hodges, Sarah E. International Birth Control: The South Indian Experience 1921-1951. 2008. (History of Medicine in Context Ser.). 188p. 114.95 *(978-0-7546-3809-4(X))* Ashgate Publishing Co.
Kar, Suparna Majumdar. Planning the Family in Indi. 2011. 88p. pap. ***(978-3-8443-9390-3(0))*** Lambert Academic Publishing.
Pandya, Rameshwari, ed. Health, Family Planning & Nutrition in India: First Five Year Plan (1951-56) to Eleventh Five Year Plan (2007-12) 2009. 547p. 109.50 *(978-81-7708-200-5(0))* New Century Publications IND. Dist: International Specialized Bk. Services.
Rawat, Nand Kishore & Jagdish Prasad, Prof. Statistical Techniques for Family Planning Measures. 2011. 284p. pap. ***(978-3-8443-2983-4(8))*** Lambert Academic Publishing.

BIRTH CONTROL—JAMAICA

Mitchell, Madeleine E., compiled by. Selected Vital Records from the Jamaican Daily Gleaner: Life on the Island of Jamaica As Seen Through Newspaper Extracts. 2009. 44.00 *(978-0-7884-4497-5(2))* Heritage Bks.

BIRTH CONTROL—PACIFIC AREA

United Nations. Asia-Pacific Population Journal, December 2010. 2012. (ENG.). 142p. pap. 15.00 ***(978-92-1-120627-2(8))*** United Nations Pubns.

BIRTH CONTROL—PUERTO RICO

Acevedo Nieves, Juan Antonio. Sobrepoblacion: Pobreza o riqueza de Puerto Rico. 2010. (SPA., Illus.). 232p. pap. 16.99 *(978-1-61505-024-6(8))* Publicaciones Gaviota.

López, Iris Ofelia. Matters of Choice: Puerto Rican Women's Struggle for Reproductive Freedom. 2008. (ENG.). 208p. 65.00 *(978-0-8135-4372-7(X))*; pap. 25.95 *(978-0-8135-4373-4(8))* Rutgers Univ. Pr.

BIRTH CONTROL CLINICS

see also Abortion Services

Bluestone, Julia, et al, eds. IUD Guidelines for Family Planning Service Programs: A Problem-Solving Reference Manual. 3rd ed. 2006. 138p. 15.00 *(978-0-929817-90-3(7))* JHPIEGO Corp.

Engelman, Peter C. A History of the Birth Control Movement in America, 1 vol. 2011. (Healing Society: Disease, Medicine, & History Ser.). (Illus.). 231p. 44.95 *(978-0-313-36509-6(1), C36509)* Greenwood Publishing Group, Inc.

Faundes, Anibal & Barzelatto, Jose S. The Human Drama of Abortion: A Global Search for Consensus. 2006. (Illus.). 216p. (ENG.). 59.95 *(978-0-8265-1525-4(8))*; (POR, SPA & ENG., per. 24.95 *(978-0-8265-1526-1(6))* Vanderbilt Univ. Pr.

Guillebaud, John. Contraception. 5th ed. 2008. (Your Questions Answered Ser.). (ENG., Illus.). 618p. (Orig.). (C). pap. 64.95 *(978-0-443-06908-6(5),* Churchill Livingstone) Elsevier - Health Sciences Div.

Hajo, Cathy Moran. Birth Control on Main Street: Organizing Clinics in the United States, 1916-1939. 2010. (ENG., Illus.). 264p. 75.00 *(978-0-252-03536-4(4))*; pap. 25.00 *(978-0-252-07725-8(3))* Univ. of Illinois Pr.

Holz, Rose. The Birth Control Clinic in a Marketplace World. 2012. (Rochester Studies in Medical History Ser.: Volume 21). 238p. 80.00 ***(978-1-58046-399-7(1))*** Univ. of Rochester Pr.

Institute of Medicine Staff & Committee on a Comprehensive Review of the HHS Office of Family Planning Title X Program. A Review of the HHS Family Planning Program: Mission, Management, & Measurement of Results. Butler, Adrienne Stith & Clayton, Ellen Wright, eds. 2009. (ENG.). 192p. pap. 50.00 *(978-0-309-13117-9(0))* National Academies Pr.

Kar, Supama Majumdar. Planning the Family in Indi. 2011. 88p. pap. ***(978-3-8443-9390-3(0))*** Lambert Academic Publishing.

McIntosh, Noel, et al, eds. Procedimentos DIU para Programas de Servicos de Planejamento Familiar: Un Manual de Referencia para la Solucion de Problemas. 2nd ed. Date not set. (POR., Illus.). pap. 15.00 *(978-0-929817-37-8(0))* JHPIEGO Corp.

McLaren, Angus. Sexuality & Social Order: The Debate over the Fertility of Women & Workers in France, 1770-1920. 2008. 244p. pap. 24.00 *(978-1-59740-608-6(2))* ACLS Humanities E-Book.

National Center for Health Statistics (U.S.) Staff, contrib. by. Adoption Experiences of Women & Men, & Demand for Children to Adopt by Women Ages 18-44 in the United States: Data from Cycle 6 (2002) of the National Survey of Family Growth. 2008. (DHHS Publication Ser.: Nos. 2008-1979). (Illus.). v, 36p. *(978-0-8406-0624-2(9))* National Ctr. for Health Statistics.

Perrucci, Alissa C. Decision Assessment & Counseling in Abortion Care: Philosophy & Practice. 2012. (ENG.). 208p. (gr. 17). 59.95 ***(978-1-4422-1456-9(2))*** Rowman & Littlefield Publishers, Inc.

Ruff, Robert. Aborting Planned Parenthood. 189p. (C). reprint ed. pap. 9.95 *(978-0-919225-32-9(2))* Life Cycle Bks.

Taylor, Hugh S., et al. Oxford American Handbook of Reproductive Medicine, 1 vol. 2012. (Oxford American Handbooks in Medicine Ser.). (ENG.). 336p. pap. 49.99 ***(978-0-19-973576-1(X))*** Oxford Univ. Pr., Inc.

World Health Organization. Frequently Asked Clinical Questions about Medical Abortion: Conclusions of an International Consensus Conference on Medical Abortion in Early First Trimester, Bellagio, Italy. 2006. (Nonserial Publication). (ENG.). 35p. pap. 12.00 *(978-92-4-159484-4(5))* World Health Organization.

—WHO Medical Eligibility Criteria Wheel for Contraceptive Use 2008, 20, Pack. 2010. (Nonserial Publication Ser.). (ENG.). 72.00 *(978-92-4-154771-0(5))* World Health Organization.

BIRTH CUSTOMS

Caron, Lisa. Bearing Witness: Childbirth Stories Told by Doulas. Doran, Lisa, ed. 2010. 240p. pap. 19.95 *(978-1-894997-16-4(6))* Fox Music Bks. CAN. Dist: SCB Distributors.

Gonzales, Patrisia. Red Medicine: Traditional Indigenous Rites of Birthing & Healing. 2012. (First Peoples: New Directions in Indigenous Studies). (ENG., Illus.). 272p. pap. 35.00 ***(978-0-8165-2956-8(6))*** Univ. of Arizona Pr.

Hodari, Askhari Johnson. The African Book of Names: 5,000+ Common & Uncommon Names from the African Continent. 2009. (ENG.). 343p. pap. 14.95 *(978-0-7573-0779-9(5))* Health Communications, Inc.

Hubbell Maiden, Anne, et al. The Tibetan Art of Parenting: From Before Conception Through Early Childhood. rev. ed. 2008. (ENG., Illus.). 204p. pap. 16.95 *(978-0-86171-579-4(9))* Wisdom Pubns.

Hungrywolf, Adolf. Tribal Childhood: Growning up in Traditional Native America. 2008. (ENG., Illus.). 224p. pap. *(978-1-57067-213-2(X))* Book Publishing Co.

Levine, Peg. Love & Dread in Cambodia. 2010. (Illus.). 260p. pap. 28.00 *(978-9971-69-472-2(7))* National Univ. of Singapore Pr. SGP. Dist: Univ. of Hawaii Pr.

Odent, Michel. Childbirth in the Age of Plastics. 2011. 208p. pap. 17.95 *(978-1-905177-54-7(2))* Pinter & Martin Ltd. GBR. Dist: National Bk. Network.

Poulsen. Childbirth & Tradition in Northeast Thailand. 2006. (Illus.). 240p. (C). 35.00 *(978-87-7694-003-4(9))* Nordic Institute of Asian Studies DNK. Dist: Univ. of Hawaii Pr.

Randall, Ronne. Birth. 2009. (Illus.). 48p. 70.50 *(978-1-4358-5453-6(5))*; pap. 11.75 *(978-1-4358-5452-9(7))* Rosen Publishing Group, Inc., The. (Rosen Central).

BIRTH DEFECTS

see Abnormalities, Human

BIRTH INJURIES

Ancheta, Ruth S. & Simkin, Penny. The Labor Progress Handbook: Early Interventions to Prevent & Treat Dystocia. 3rd ed. 2011. (ENG., Illus.). 424p. pap. 41.99 *(978-1-4443-3771-6(8),* Wiley-Blackwell) Wiley, John & Sons, Inc.

Graham, John M. Smith's Recognizable Patterns of Human Deformation. 3rd rev. ed. 2007. (ENG., Illus.). 384p. 110.00 *(978-0-7216-1489-2(2),* Saunders) Elsevier - Health Sciences Div.

Griffiths, Paul D., et al. Atlas of Fetal & Neonatal Brain Mr Imaging. 2009. (ENG., Illus.). 272p. 174.00 *(978-0-323-05296-2(7),* Mosby) Elsevier - Health Sciences Div.

BIRTH MOTHERS

see Birthmothers

BIRTH OF A NATION (MOTION PICTURE)

Stokes, Melvyn. D. W. Griffith's the Birth of a Nation: A History of the Most Controversial Motion Picture of All Time. 2008. (ENG., Illus.). 416p. per. 24.95 *(978-0-19-533679-5(8))* Oxford Univ. Pr., Inc.

BIRTH ORDER

see also Children, First-Born

Leman, Kevin. The Birth Order Book: Why You Are the Way You Are. rev. ed. 2009. (Illus.). 368p. pap. 15.99 *(978-0-8007-3406-0(8))* Revell.

—Born to Win: Keeping Your Firstborn Edge Without Losing Your Balance. 2009. 288p. pap. 13.99 *(978-0-8007-3262-2(6))* Revell.

—The First Born Advantage: Making Your Birth Order Work for You. 2008. 288p. pap. 12.99 *(978-0-8007-3337-7(1))* Baker Publishing Group.

—The Firstborn Advantage: Making Your Birth Order Work for You. 2008. 288p. 19.99 *(978-0-8007-1911-1(5))* Revell.

Liebermeister, Svagi. The Roots of Love. 2006. xii, 322p. pap. *(978-1-905399-23-9(5))* Perfect Pubs.

Milevsky, Avidan. Sibling Relationships in Childhood & Adolescence: Predictors & Outcomes. 2011. (ENG.). 176p. (gr. 17). pap. 29.50 *(978-0-231-15709-4(6))*; (Illus.). 89.50 *(978-0-231-15708-7(8))* Columbia Univ. Pr.

Payton, Michelle A. Birth Mix Patterns & Loving Relationships: Using Astrology, Numerology & Birth Order. 2007. 134p. pap. 12.95 *(978-0-9719804-4-0(6))* Left Side, The.

Salmon, Catherine & Schumann, Katrin. The Secret Power of Middle Children: How Middleborns Can Harness Their Unexpected & Remarkable Abilities. (ENG.). (gr. 12). 2012. 304p. pap. 16.00 ***(978-0-452-29793-7(1),*** Plume) 2011. 288p. 25.95 *(978-1-59463-080-4(1),* Hudson Street Pr.) Penguin Group (USA) Inc.

BIRTH PARENTS

see Birthparents

BIRTH-RATE

see Population

BIRTH RECORDS

see Registers of Births, etc.

BIRTH-STONES

see Birthstones

BIRTH WEIGHT

Kroelinger, Charlan. Biological & Psychosocial Determinants of Problematic Birth Outcomes. 2008. 252p. pap. *(978-3-639-03158-4(X))* VDM Verlag Dr. Mueller e.K.

Nik Hussain, Nik Hazlina, et al. Newborn Weight & Large for Gestational Age Newborns. 2011. 88p. pap. ***(978-3-8454-0809-5(X))*** Lambert Academic Publishing.

BIRTH WEIGHT, LOW

Adamkin, David H. Nutritional Strategies for the Very Low Birthweight Infant. 2009. (ENG., Illus.). 208p. pap. 44.99 *(978-0-521-73246-8(8))* Cambridge Univ. Pr.

Czernichow, P., et al, eds. Understanding the Biology & Therapeutic Consequences of Being Born SGA: Proceedings of SGA 2005, Vol. 65. (Hormone Research Ser.). (Illus.). 162p. pap. *(978-3-8055-8117-2(3))* Karger, S. AG.

Fortes Filho, Joã, et al. Low Weight Gain As a Predictor of Retinopathy of Prematurity. 2010. 72p. pap. *(978-3-8383-0407-6(1))* Lambert Academic Publishing.

Linden, Dana Wechsler, et al. Preemies - Second Edition: The Essential Guide for Parents of Premature Babies. 2010. (ENG., Illus.). 656p. pap. 25.99 *(978-1-4165-7232-9(5))* Gallery Pr., The IRL. Dist: Simon & Schuster, Inc.

Newnham, J. P. & Ross, M. G., eds. Early Life Origins of Human Health & Disease. 2009. (ENG., Illus.). 224p. *(978-3-8055-9139-3(X))* Karger, S. AG.

Singh, Manjari. Introducing & Reviewing Preterm Delivery & Low Birth Weight. 2011. 72p. pap. ***(978-3-8443-9002-5(2))*** Lambert Academic Publishing.

BIRTHDAY BOOKS

Beilenson, Laurence, compiled by. Happy Birthday. 2007. 5.95 *(978-1-59359-856-3(4))* Peter Pauper Pr. Inc.

Crawford, Rebekah. Musical Messages. 2007. (ENG.). 420p. 49.95 *(978-0-548-06430-6(X))* Kessinger Publishing, LLC.

Emerson, Ralph Waldo. Emerson Birthday Book. 2006. pap. 36.95 *(978-1-4286-4615-5(9))* Kessinger Publishing, LLC.

Happy Birthday. 2.00 *(978-0-687-06546-2(1))*; 2.00 *(978-0-687-06556-1(9))* Abingdon Pr.

Nelson, Julia. My Book of Birthdays. Date not set. *(978-0-9673230-1-5(0))* Allyn Group Pubns.

Nowlan, Robert A. Born This Day: A Book of Birthdays & Quotations of Prominent People Through the Centuries. 2nd alt. ed. 2011. (ENG., Illus.). 519p. pap. 45.00 *(978-0-7864-6435-7(6))* McFarland & Co., Inc. Pubs.

Zerner, Amy & Farber, Monte. The Enchanted Birthday Book: Discover the Meaning & Magic of Your Birthday. 2011. (ENG.). 376p. pap. 19.95 *(978-1-4027-8121-6(0))* Sterling Publishing Co., Inc.

BIRTHDAYS

see also Birthday Books; Birthstones

Branch, Susan. Happy Birthday. (Illus.). 20p. pap. *(978-0-7683-2208-8(1))* CEDCO Publishing.

Brown, Debbie. Gorgeous & Gruesome Cakes for Children: 30 Original & Fun Designs for Every Occasion. 2010. (ENG., Illus.). 128p. 19.95 *(978-1-84773-646-8(7))* New Holland Pubs., Ltd. GBR. Dist: Sterling Publishing Co., Inc.

Chase's Calendar of Events Editors. The Teachers Calendar 2011-2012. 2011. (ENG.). 1125p. (C). pap. 25.00 *(978-0-07-176108-6(X),* 007176108X) McGraw-Hill Cos., The.

Colville, W. J. Significance of Birthdays. 2007. (ENG.). 160p. 36.95 *(978-0-548-28136-9(X))* Kessinger Publishing, LLC.

Cragin, Sally. Astrology on the Cusp: Birthdays on the Edge of Two Signs. 2012. (ENG., Illus.). 240p. pap. 17.95 ***(978-0-7387-3154-4(4))*** Llewellyn Pubns.

De Lima, Heber S. Feliz Cumpleanos. 128p. 6.95 *(978-958-607-725-5(X))* Sociedad de San Pablo COL. Dist: St Pauls/Alba Hse. Pubs.

Fyke, Nancy, et al. The Icing on the Cake: A Party Planning Book for Survivors & Their Kids. 120p. pap. 14.95 *(978-0-9633564-0-6(2))* Fyke, Nejam, Overstreet.

Koelmeyer, Neil & Kolecki, Ursula. The Secret Language of Your Name: Unlock the Mysteries of Your Name & Birth Date Through the Science of Numerology. 2012. (ENG., Illus.). 288p. pap. 16.00 ***(978-1-58270-350-3(7),*** Beyond Words/Atria Bks.) Atria Bks.

Michael O'Mara Books UK. A Gift for Your Birthday. 2010. (ENG.). 64p. 4.95 *(978-1-84317-409-7(X))* O'Mara, Michael Bks., Ltd. GBR. Dist: Independent Pubs. Group.

Parent, Rene G. Those Birthdays In-Between. 2011. 224p. pap. 19.59 ***(978-1-4269-7195-2(8))*** Trafford Publishing.

Regan, Patrick. Age Is Irrelevant (until You Hit 40!) Coupons to Make Your Birthday Brighter. 2011. (ENG.). 104p. pap. 8.99 *(978-1-4494-0067-5(1))* Andrews McMeel Publishing.

—Getting Old Sucks!.. but It Beats the Alternative! Coupons to Make Your Birthday Livelier. 2011. (ENG.). 104p. pap. 8.99 *(978-1-4494-0066-8(3))* Andrews McMeel Publishing.

—60 & Still Rolling (Downhill Fast) Birthday Coupons to Enjoy on the Ride. 2011. (ENG.). 104p. pap. 8.99 *(978-1-4494-0070-5(1))* Andrews McMeel Publishing.

Richmond, Marianne. Having a Happy Birthday. 2008. (ENG., Illus.). 40p. 5.95 *(978-1-934082-39-3(2),* Sourcebooks Jabberwocky) Sourcebooks, Inc.

Rupp, Joyce. May You Rejoice: A Blessing for Your Birthday. 2010. (Illus.). 32p. 4.50 *(978-1-59471-257-9(3))* Ave Maria Pr.

Ryland Peters & Small Staff, creator. Birthdays. 2007. (ENG., Illus.). 112p. *(978-1-84597-407-7(7))* Ryland Peters & Small.

Thompson, Alicia, et al. The Secret Language of Birthdays. 10th ed. 2010. (ENG.). 416p. (YA). (gr. 5-18). 19.99 *(978-1-59514-232-0(0),* Razorbill) Penguin Group (USA) Inc.

Vega, Phyllis. What Your Birthday Reveals about You: 366 Days of Astonishingly Accurate Revelations about Your Future, Your Secrets, & Your Strengths. 2009. (ENG., Illus.). 480p. 12.99 *(978-0-7858-2238-7(0),* 0785822380, Castle Bks., Inc.) Book Sales, Inc.

Wybranietz, Kris & Wybranietz, Volk. Feliz Cumpleaños/ Happy Birthday. 2008. 48p. 9.95 *(978-987-9338-74-2(X))* Vergara & Riba ARG. Dist: Baker & Taylor Bks.

Zadra, Dan. Happy Birthday. 2010. 48p. pap. 4.95 *(978-1-932319-89-7(1))* Compendium, Inc., Publishing & Communications.

BIRTHMOTHERS

Bennett, Susan. Late Discoveries: An Adoptee's Quest for Truth. 2011. (ENG.). 176p. pap. 14.95 *(978-1-56474-513-2(9),* Fithian Pr) Daniel & Daniel, Pubs., Inc.

Coppinger, Maureen. Annie's Girl: How an Abandoned Orphan Finally Discovered the Truth about Her Mother. 2010. (ENG., Illus.). 432p. pap. 14.95 *(978-1-84596-579-2(5))* Mainstream Publishing Co., Ltd. GBR. Dist: Independent Pubs. Group.

—Annie's Girl: How an Abandoned Orphan Finally Found the Truth about Her Mother. 2009. (ENG., Illus.). 432p. pap. 22.95 *(978-1-84596-493-1(4))* Mainstream Publishing Co., Ltd. GBR. Dist: Independent Pubs. Group.

Coulter, Myrl. The House with the Broken Two: A Birthmother Remembers. 2011. (ENG., Illus.). 160p. pap. 18.00 *(978-1-897535-72-1(4))* Anvil Pr. CAN. Dist: Univ. of Toronto Pr.

Crumpacker, Bunny & Picariello, Jil. Jessica Lost: A Story of Birth & Adoption. 2011. (ENG., Illus.). 224p. 24.95 *(978-1-4027-7570-3(9))* Union Square Pr.

Ellerby, Janet Mason. Following the Tambourine Man: A Birthmother's Memoir. 2007. (Writing American Women Ser.). (Illus.), 289p. *(978-0-8156-0889-9(6))* Syracuse Univ. Pr.

Fessler, Ann. The Girls Who Went Away: The Hidden History of Women Who Surrendered Children for Adoption in the Decades Before Roe V. Wade. 2007. (ENG.). 368p. (gr. 12-18). 16.00 *(978-0-14-303897-9(4),* Penguin (Non-Classics)) Penguin Group (USA) Inc.

Homes, A. M. The Mistress's Daughter. 2008. (ENG., Illus.). 256p. (gr. 12-18). 14.00 *(978-0-14-311331-7(3),* Penguin (Non-Classics)) Penguin Group (USA) Inc.

Meyers, Julia I. Coffee & Cake: An Adoptee in Search of Her Past. 2010. ***(978-1-935001-57-7(4))*** Acclaim Pr., Inc.

BIRTHPARENTS

Here are entered works on natural, i.e. biological, parents who relinquished their children for adoption.

see also Birthmothers

Adams, Teresa. God Wanted Me! God Created Me! 2010. pap. 10.99 *(978-1-60799-957-7(9))* Tate Publishing & Enterprises, LLC.

Briccetti, Katherine A. Blood Strangers: A Memoir. 2010. 300p. pap. 16.95 *(978-1-59714-130-7(5))* Heyday.

Carangelo, Lori. The Ultimate Search Book 2011 Edition Worldwide Adpotion, Genealogy & Other Search Secrets from the Files of Americans for Open Records. 2011. 306p. pap. 39.95 ***(978-0-8063-5515-3(8))*** Clearfield Co.

Cashin, Claire. Will You Be Here When I Get Home? 2006. (ENG.). 222p. pap. 24.95 *(978-1-85635-521-6(7))* Mercier Pr., Ltd., The IRL. Dist: Dufour Editions, Inc.

Gritter, James L. Hospitious Adoption. 2009. pap. *(978-1-58760-123-1(0),* CWLA Pr.) Child Welfare League of America, Inc.

Holloway, Sara, ed. Family Wanted: Stories of Adoption. 2006. (ENG.). 320p. per. 14.95 *(978-0-8129-7547-5(2),* Random Hse. Trade Paperbacks) Random House Publishing Group.

Holman, William Roger. The Orphans' Nine Commandments. 2009. (ENG., Illus.). 246p. pap. 19.95 *(978-0-87565-403-4(7))* Texas Christian Univ. Pr.

Hopgood, Mei-Ling. Lucky Girl. (ENG.). 2010. 272p. pap. 13.95 *(978-1-56512-982-5(2),* 1565129822) 2009. 244p. 23.95 *(978-1-56512-600-8(9),* 1565126009) Algonquin Bks. of Chapel Hill.

Kay, Jackie. Red Dust Road: An Autobiographical Journey. 2011. (ENG.). 304p. 24.00 *(978-1-935633-34-1(1),* 935634) Atlas & Co.

Lauck, Jennifer. Found: A Memoir. (ENG.). 2012. 280p. pap. 17.00 ***(978-1-58005-395-2(5))*** 2011. 272p. 24.95 *(978-1-58005-367-9(X))* Seal Pr.

Oakwater, Helen. Bubble Wrapped Children: How social networking Is transforming the face of 21st century Adoption. 2012. 202p. pap. ***(978-1-78092-097-9(0))*** MX Publishing, Ltd.

Slaton, Pamela & Marshall, Samantha. Reunited: An Investigative Genealogist Unlocks Some of Life's Greatest Family Mysteries. 2012. (ENG.). 272p. pap. 14.99 ***(978-0-312-61732-5(1),*** St. Martin's Griffin) St. Martin's Pr.

Sutton, Maria. The Night Sky: A Journey from Dachua to Denver & Back: A Memoir: A Journey from Dachua to Denver & Back. 2011. 240p. 24.95 ***(978-1-55566-446-6(6))*** Johnson Bks.

Toelle, Kaylene. The Southernmost Point: Searching for Them; Finding Me. 2011. 114p. pap. 19.99 ***(978-1-4653-4263-8(X))*** Xlibris Corp.

Ward, Margaret E. Missing Mila, Finding Family: An International Adoption in the Shadow of the Salvadoran Civil War. 2011. (ENG., Illus.). 294p. pap. 24.95 *(978-0-292-72908-7(1))* Univ. of Texas Pr.

BIRTHS, REGISTERS OF

see Registers of Births, etc.

BIRTHSTONES

see also Birthdays

Hall, Judy. The Crystal Zodiac: Use Birthstones to Enhance Your Life. 2006. (ENG., Illus.). 320p. pap. 17.95 *(978-1-84181-241-0(2),* Godsfield Press) Octopus Publishing Group GBR. Dist: Hachette Bk. Group.

Jenkins, Victoria. Bejeweled Weddings: Find Wedding Inspirations through Gemstones. 2009. 32p. pap. 15.95 *(978-1-4490-0623-5(X))* AuthorHouse.

BIRTHWEIGHT

see Birth Weight

BIRUNI, MUHAMMAD IBN AHMAD, 973?-1048

Ataman, Kemal. Understanding Other Religions: Al-Biruni's & Gadamer's "Fusion of Horizons" 2008. pap. *(978-1-56518-252-3(9))* Council for Research in Values & Philosophy.

Kamiar, Mohammad S. Brilliant Biruni: A Life Story of Abu Rayhan Mohammad Ibn Ahmad. 2008. (ENG.). 200p. pap. 50.00 *(978-0-8108-6243-2(3))* Scarecrow Pr., Inc.

BISAYA LANGUAGE

see Cebuano Language

BISBEE (ARIZ.)

Rosok, Ingwald Andreas. Retrospect: An Autobiography. Norlie, O. M., ed. 2011. 346p. 51.95 ***(978-1-258-10085-8(1))*** Literary Licensing, LLC.

BISCAYANS

see Basques

BISCHOF, WERNER
Bischof, Werner. WernerBischofPictures, 1 vol. Bischof, Marco et al, eds. 2008. (ENG., Illus.). 464p. 75.00 *(978-3-86521-265-8(4))* Steidl, Gerhard Druckerei und Verlag DEU. Dist: Innovative Logistics.

BISCUITS
Australian Women's Weekly Staff. Biscuits & Slices. Coleman, Mary, ed. (Illus.). 64p. pap. 5.95 *(978-1-86396-182-0(8))* ACP Publishing Pty, Ltd. AUS. Dist: Graphic Arts Ctr. Publishing Co.

—Quick-Mix Biscuits & Slices. Blacker, Maryanne, ed. (Illus.). 120p. pap. 12.95 *(978-1-86396-029-8(5))* ACP Publishing Pty, Ltd. AUS. Dist: Graphic Arts Ctr. Publishing Co.

Dupree, Nathalie & Graubart, Cynthia Stevens. Southern Biscuits, 1 vol. 2011. (ENG., Illus.). 216p. 21.99 *(978-1-4236-2176-8(X))* Gibbs Smith, Publisher.

Hanley, Linda O'Brien. Better World Scones: Enjoy tea & scones with dairy & eggs & with fair trade & organic ingredients. 2007. per. 14.00 *(978-1-59872-784-5(2))* Instant Pub.

Knights, Genevieve. Scones. 2010. (ENG., Illus.). 128p. pap. 11.95 ***(978-1-907016-47-9(3))*** Accent Pr. Ltd. GBR. Dist: SCB Distributors.

Pare, Jean. Mostly Muffins. 2007. (Company's Coming Ser.). (Illus.). 156p. spiral bd. *(978-1-897069-03-5(0))* Company's Coming Publishing, Ltd.

Patrick, Toni. 101 Things to Do with Canned Biscuits. 2008. (ENG., Illus.). 128p. spiral bd. 9.99 *(978-1-4236-0463-1(6))* Gibbs Smith, Publisher.

Pepkin, Karen. The Best 50 Scones. 2007. (ENG.). 80p. pap. 5.95 *(978-1-55867-338-0(5))* Bristol Publishing Enterprises.

Santinoceto, Phyllis. Biscotti Are Not Just a Dessert Cookie but Also Something More. 2011. 108p. pap. 51.99 ***(978-1-4568-3627-6(7))*** Xlibris Corp.

BISCUITS, ENGLISH
see Cookies

BISEXUALITY
see also Homosexuality

Alexander, Jonathan & Anderlini-D'Onofrio, Serena, eds. Bisexuality & Queer Theory: Intersections Connections & Challenges. 2011. (ENG.). 288p. (C). 125.00 *(978-0-415-68671-6(7))* Routledge.

Arndt, Marlene. Attitudes Towards Bisexual Men & Women. 2010. 260p. pap. *(978-3-8383-5562-7(8))* Lambert Academic Publishing.

Baird, Vanessa. The No-Nonsense Guide to Sexual Diversity. 2007. (No-Nonsense Guides). (ENG., Illus.). 144p. per. 11.95 *(978-1-904456-64-3(2))* New Internationalist Pubns., Ltd. GBR. Dist: Consortium Bk. Sales & Distribution.

Barker, Meg & Langdridge, Darren. Understanding Non-Monogamies. 2009. (Illus.). x, 312p. 95.00 *(978-0-203-86980-2(X))* Routledge.

Bi Academic Intervention Staff, contrib. by. The Bisexual Imaginary: Representation, Identity & Desire. (Illus.). 256p. *(978-0-304-33744-6(7),* Burns & Oates) Continuum International Publishing Group, Ltd.

Chantler. Bi-Sexual Revolution, 1 vol. 2010. 48p. pap. 16.95 *(978-1-4489-5436-0(3))* PublishAmerica, Inc.

Des Esseintes, Pierre. Dare... to Try Bisexuality. 2010. (Positively Sexual Ser.). (ENG., Illus.). 144p. pap. 10.95 *(978-0-89793-523-4(3))* Hunter Hse., Inc.

Diamond, Lisa M. Sexual Fluidity: Understanding Women's Love & Desire. 2009. 352p. pap. 19.00 *(978-0-674-03226-2(8))* Harvard Univ. Pr.

Fruhauf, Christine A. & Mahoney, Dan. Older Gay,Lesbian,Bisexual, & Transgender Family & Community Life: Contempo. 2009. 285p. 45.95 *(978-1-55023-754-9(6))*; 125.00 *(978-1-56023-753-2(8))* Routledge.

Galupo, M. Paz. Bisexuality & Same-Sex Marriage. 2008. (Illus.). X, 214p. pap. 150.00 *(978-0-415-99632-7(5))*; 230p. 45.95 *(978-1-56023-776-1(7))* Routledge.

Galz. Unspoken Facts. 2008. 272p. pap. 29.95 *(978-0-7974-3407-3(0))* GALZ ZWE. Dist: Michigan State Univ. Pr.

Grever & Bowman. When Your Spouse Comes Out: A Straight Mate's Recovery Manual. 2008. (ENG., Illus.). 170p. 125.00 *(978-0-7890-3628-5(2))* Routledge.

Grever, Carol & Bowman, Deborah. When Your Spouse Comes Out: A Straight Mate's Recovery Manual. 2008. (ENG., Illus.). 170p. per. 27.95 *(978-0-7890-3629-2(0))* Routledge.

Kaye, Bonnie. Bonnie Kaye's Straight Talk: A Collection of Her Best Newsletters about Gay Husbands. 2008. 248p. pap. *(978-1-926585-04-8(6),* CCB Publishing) CCB Publishing.

—How I Made My Husband Gay: Myths about Straight Wives. 2007. 188p. pap. *(978-0-9784388-4-5(1),* CCB Publishing) CCB Publishing.

Kaye, Bonnie, compiled by. Straight Wives Shattered Lives Volume 2: True Stories of Women Married to Gay & Bisexual Men. 2011. (ENG.). 238p. pap. ***(978-1-926918-83-9(5),*** CCB Publishing) CCB Publishing.

Meyer, Ilan H. & Northridge, Mary E., eds. The Health of Sexual Minorities: Public Health Perspectives on Lesbian, Gay, Bisexual & Transgender Populations. 2010. (ENG., Illus.). xx, 732p. pap. 109.00 *(978-1-4419-3959-3(8),* 1441939598) Springer.

Nectoux, Tracy, ed. Out Behind the Desk: Workplace Issues for LGBTQ Librarians. 2011. pap. 30.00 *(978-1-936117-03-1(7),* Library Juice Pr.) Litwin Bks., LLC.

Stekel, Wilhelm. Bi-Sexual Love. 2009. 176p. pap. *(978-1-4588-2317-5(2))* Books LLC.

Stobie, Cheryl. Somewhere in the Double Rainbow: Representations of Bisexuality in Post-Apartheid Novels. 2007. 323p. (C). pap. 39.95 *(978-1-86914-130-1(X))* University of Kwazulu-Natal Press ZAF. Dist: International Specialized Bk. Services.

Waldner, Katharina. Geburt und Hochzeit des Kriegers: Geschlechterdifferenz und Initiation in Mythos und Ritual der griechischen Polis. (Religionsgeschichtliche Versuche und Vorarbeiten Ser.). (GER.). IX, 281p. 210.00 ***(978-3-11-176113-8(4))*** De Gruyter, Walter Inc.

Walsh, Candace & Andre, Laura, eds. Dear John, I Love Jane: Women Write about Leaving Men for Women. 2010. (ENG.). 272p. pap. 16.95 *(978-1-58005-339-6(4))* Seal Pr.

Whitby, Fred. Adventures of a Pinko Commie Bisexual in The 1980s. 2010. 110p. pap. 16.00 *(978-0-557-66781-9(X))* Lulu Enterprises Inc.

Witten, Tarynn M. & Eyler, A. Evan, eds. Gay, Lesbian, Bisexual, & Transgender Aging: Challenges in Research, Practice, & Policy. 2012. (ENG.). 360p. (C). (gr. 13-17). 60.00 ***(978-1-4214-0319-9(6))***; pap. 30.00 ***(978-1-4214-0320-5(X))*** Johns Hopkins Univ. Pr.

BISEXUALITY (BIOLOGY)
see Intersexuality

BISEXUALS
Alexander, Jonathan F., et al. Finding Out: An Introduction to LGBT Studies. 2009. (Illus.). 480p. (C). 97.00 *(978-1-4129-3864-8(3),* B38643C); pap. 57.00 *(978-1-4129-3865-5(1),* B38643P) SAGE Pubns., Inc.

Anderlini-D'Onofrio, Serena. Eros: A Journey of Multiple Loves. 2006. (ENG.). 240p. 125.00 *(978-1-56023-571-2(3))*; per. 37.95 *(978-1-56023-572-9(1))* Routledge.

Arndt, Marlene. Attitudes Towards Bisexual Men & Women. 2010. 260p. pap. *(978-3-8383-5562-7(8))* Lambert Academic Publishing.

Baumgardner, Jennifer. Look Both Ways. 2008. (ENG., Illus.). 256p. pap. 14.00 *(978-0-374-53108-9(0))* Farrar, Straus & Giroux.

Beemyn, Brett. Queer Capital. 2010. 320p. 95.00 *(978-0-415-92172-5(4))* Routledge.

Bisexual Women: Friendship & Social Organization. 2007. (ENG.). 168p. 125.00 *(978-1-56023-702-0(3))*; per. 54.50 *(978-1-56023-703-7(1))* Routledge.

Black, Amy. Objectification or Liberation- Bisexual & Lesbian Women's Experiences with Physical Appearance. 2007. 256p. per. *(978-3-8364-2591-9(2))* VDM Verlag Dr. Mueller e.K.

Choudhuri, Devika Dibya & Santiago-Rivera, Azara. Counseling & Diversity: Counseling LGBTQ Americans. 2011. (SW 360K Confronting LGBTQ Oppression Ser.). (ENG.). 112p. (C). pap. 13.95 *(978-1-111-15667-8(7))* Wadsworth.

Coffey, Kevin. Risk & Protective Factors for Gay, Lesbian, & Bisexual Youth. 2008. 180p. pap. *(978-3-639-07205-1(7))* VDM Verlag Dr. Mueller e.K.

Committee on Lesbian, Gay, Bisexual, and Transgender Health Issues and Research Gaps and Opportunities, et al. The Health of Lesbian, Gay, Bisexual, & Transgender People: Building a Foundation for Better Understanding. 2011. (ENG.). 368p. 59.95 *(978-0-309-21061-4(5))* National Academies Pr.

Current Issues in Lesbian, Gay, Bisexual, & Transgender Health. 2006. (ENG., Illus.). 230p. (C). 125.00 *(978-1-56023-659-7(0))* Routledge.

Dean, Terrance. Hiding in Hip Hop: On the down Low in the Entertainment Industry — from Music to Hollywood. 2009. (ENG.). 320p. pap. 15.00 *(978-1-4165-5340-3(1),* Beyond Words/Atria Bks.) Atria Bks.

Dees, Abby. Queer Questions Straight Talk: 108 Frank, Provocative Questions It's OK to Ask Your Lesbian, Gay or Bi Loved One. 2010. (ENG.). 128p. pap. 9.95 *(978-0-9819615-2-1(5))* St. Lynn's Pr.

Dworkin, Sari H. & Pope, Mark. Casebook for Counseling Lesbian, Gay, Bisexual, & Transgender Persons & Their Families. 2012. ***(978-1-55620-306-0(3))*** American Counseling Assn.

Eaklor, Vicki L. Queer America: A GLBT History of the 20th Century. 2008. (Illus.). 312p. 65.00 *(978-0-313-33749-9(7),* GR3749) Greenwood Publishing Group, Inc.

—Queer America: A People's GLBT History of the United States. 2011. (ENG., Illus.). 304p. pap. 17.95 *(978-1-59558-636-0(9))* New Pr., The.

Eischen, Donald F. Love Against Hate: As It Relates to Gays, Lesbians, Bisexuals, & Transgenders as Reflected in the Twenty-First Century, Book 2. 2007. (Illus.). 135p. per. 13.95 *(978-1-60002-050-6(X))* Mountain Valley Publishing, LLC.

Firestein, Beth A. & Firestein, Beth. Becoming Visible: Counseling Bisexuals Across the Lifespan. 2007. (ENG., Illus.). 472p. (gr. 17). 65.00 *(978-0-231-13724-9(9))* Columbia Univ. Pr.

Fox, Ronald C., ed. Affirmative Psychotherapy with Bisexual Women & Bisexual Men. 2006. (ENG.). 214p. 44.95 *(978-1-56023-298-8(6))*; per. 28.95 *(978-1-56023-299-5(4))* Routledge.

Galz. Unspoken Facts. 2008. 272p. pap. 29.95 *(978-0-7974-3407-3(0))* GALZ ZWE. Dist: Michigan State Univ. Pr.

Gambone, Philip. Travels in a Gay Nation: Portraits of LGBTQ Americans. 2010. (Living Out: Gay & Lesbian Autobiog Ser.). (ENG.). 308p. pap. 26.95 *(978-0-299-23684-7(6))* Univ. of Wisconsin Pr.

Haggerty, George E. & McGarry, Molly, eds. A Companion to Lesbian, Gay, Bisexual, Transgender, & Queer Studies. 2007. (Blackwell Companions in Cultural Studies: 13). (ENG., Illus.). 496p. 209.95 *(978-1-4051-1329-8(4),* Wiley-Blackwell) Wiley, John & Sons, Inc.

Human Rights Watch (Organization) Staff, contrib. by. We Need a Law for Liberation: Gender, Sexuality, & Human Rights in Changing Turkey. 2008. 123p. ***(978-1-56432-316-3(1))*** Human Rights Watch.

An Introduction to GLBT Family Studies. 2006. (ENG., Illus.). 330p. 128.00 *(978-0-7890-2496-1(9))* Routledge.

Kelly, Gary. Green Room. 2008. 390p. pap. 34.50 *(978-1-4092-0754-2(4))* Lulu Enterprises Inc.

Lovaas, Karen, et al. LGBT Studies & Queer Theory: New Conflicts, Collaborations, & Contested Terrain. 2007. (ENG.). 372p. 125.00 *(978-1-56023-316-9(8))* Routledge.

Lovaas, Karen E., ed. LGBT Studies & Queer Theory: New Conflicts, Collaborations, & Contested Terrain. 2007. (ENG.). 372p. per. 54.50 *(978-1-56023-317-6(6))* Routledge.

Mallon, Gerald P. Social Work Practice with Lesbian, Gay, Bisexual, & Transgender People. 2nd ed. 2008. (Illus.). 464p. pap. 175.00 *(978-0-7890-3357-4(7))* Routledge.

Mallon, Gerald P., ed. Social Work Practice with Lesbian, Gay, Bisexual, & Transgender People. 2nd ed. 2008. (Illus.). 413p. pap. 56.95 *(978-0-7890-3358-1(5))* Routledge.

Martin, James I. Handbook of Research with Lesbian, Gay, Bisexual, & Transgender Populations. Meezan, William, ed. 2008. (ENG., Illus.). 472p. pap. 87.95 *(978-1-56023-531-6(4))* Routledge.

Meezan, William & Martin, James I. Handbook of Research with Lesbian, Gay, Bisexual, & Transgender Populations. 2008. (ENG., Illus.). 472p. 158.00 *(978-1-56023-530-9(6))* Routledge.

Meyer, Ilan H. & Northridge, Mary E., eds. The Health of Sexual Minorities: Public Health Perspectives on Lesbian, Gay, Bisexual & Transgender Populations. 2006. (ENG., Illus.). xx, 732p. 109.00 *(978-0-387-28871-0(6),* 0387288716) Springer.

Miner, Anthony & Limberg, Beth. Coming Out Effects on Religious Practices of Urban Gays & Bisexuals. 2010. 84p. pap. *(978-3-8383-6640-1(9))* Lambert Academic Publishing.

Peel, Elizabeth, et al, eds. British Lesbian, Gay, & Bisexual Psychologies: Theory, Research, & Practice. 2007. 183p. per. 16.00 *(978-0-7890-3252-2(X),* Informa Healthcare) Taylor & Francis Group.

Royal, Katharine L. Between Two Worlds. 2007. 52p. per. 9.95 *(978-0-595-45939-1(0))* iUniverse, Inc.

Schenkar, Joan. The Talented Miss Highsmith: The Secret Life & Serious Art of Patricia Highsmith. 2011. (ENG., Illus.). 704p. pap. 24.00 *(978-0-312-36381-9(8))* Picador.

Stern, Jessica. These Everyday Humiliations: Violence Against Lesbians, Bisexual Women, & Transgender Men in Kyrgyzstan. 2008. 45p. *(978-1-56432-381-1(1))* Human Rights Watch.

Stern, Keith. Queers in History: The Comprehensive Encyclopedia of Historical Gays, Lesbians & Bisexuals. 2009. (ENG.). 608p. pap. 19.95 *(978-1-933771-87-8(9))* BenBella Bks.

Stewart, Chuck, ed. The Greenwood Encyclopedia of LGBT Issues Worldwide, 3 vols. 2009. (Illus.). 1282p. 280.00 *(978-0-313-34231-8(8),* GR4231) Greenwood Publishing Group, Inc.

Zepezauer, Mark, ed. Bi Men's Lives: Bisexual Men Tell Their Stories. Date not set. 288p. pap. 14.95 *(978-1-884365-11-9(6))* See Sharp Pr.

BISHOP, CHARLES REED, 1822-1915
Galuteria, Peter. Heart of a Hero: Charles Reed Bishop. 2009. (Illus.). xiv, 176p. (J). pap. *(978-1-58178-094-9(X))* Bishop Museum Pr.

BISHOP, ELIZABETH, 1911-1979
Barry, Sandra. Elizabeth Bishop: Nova Scotia's "Home-Made" Poet, 1 vol. 2011. (ENG., Illus.). 122p. pap. 15.95 ***(978-1-55109-823-4(7))*** Down East Bks.

Bishop, Elizabeth. Elizabeth Bishop & the New Yorker: The Complete Correspondence, 1 vol. Biele, Joelle, ed. 2011. (ENG., Illus.). 496p. 35.00 *(978-0-374-28138-0(6))* Farrar, Straus & Giroux.

Bishop, Elizabeth. Exchanging Hats: Paintings, 1 vol. Benton, William, ed. 2011. (ENG., Illus.). 136p. pap. 35.00 ***(978-0-374-53343-4(1))*** Farrar, Straus & Giroux.

Bishop, Elizabeth & Lowell, Robert. Words in Air: The Complete Correspondence Between Elizabeth Bishop & Robert Lowell. Travisano, Thomas & Hamilton, Saskia, eds. (ENG.). 928p. 2010. pap. 26.00 *(978-0-374-53189-8(7))* 2008. (Illus.). 45.00 *(978-0-374-18543-5(3))* Farrar, Straus & Giroux.

Blasing, Mutlu Konuk. Politics & Form in Postmodern Poetry: O'Hara, Bishop, Ashbery, & Merrill. 2009. (Cambridge Studies in American Literature & Culture Ser.). (ENG.). 236p. pap. 36.00 *(978-0-521-10613-9(3))* Cambridge Univ. Pr.

Boschman, Robert. In the Way of Nature: Ecology & Westward Expansion in the Poetry of Anne Bradstreet, Elizabeth Bishop & Amy Clampitt. 2009. (ENG.). 236p. pap. 39.95 *(978-0-7864-3356-8(6))* McFarland & Co., Inc. Pubs.

Corelle, Laurel Snow. A Poet's High Argument: Elizabeth Bishop & Christianity. 2008. (Illus.). 152p. 34.95 *(978-1-57003-762-7(0))* Univ. of South Carolina Pr.

Cucinella, Catherine. Poetics of the Body: Edna St. Vincent Millay, Elizabeth Bishop, Marilyn Chin, & Marilyn Hacker. 2010. (ENG.). 190p. 79.00 *(978-0-230-62088-9(4))* Palgrave Macmillan.

Ellis, Jonathan. Art & Memory in the Work of Elizabeth Bishop. 2006. (Illus.). 218p. 110.00 *(978-0-7546-3566-6(X))* Ashgate Publishing Co.

Harrison, Victoria. Elizabeth Bishop's Poetics of Intimacy. 2008. (Cambridge Studies in American Literature & Culture Ser.). (ENG.). 272p. (C). pap. 37.99 *(978-0-521-06212-1(8))* Cambridge Univ. Pr.

Hicok, Bethany. Degrees of Freedom: American Women Poets & the Women's College, 1905-1955. 2008. (Illus.). 224p. (C). 51.50 *(978-0-8387-5693-5(X))* Bucknell Univ. Pr.

Phillips, Siobhan. The Poetics of the Everyday: Creative Repetition in Modern American Verse. 2010. 304p. E-Book *(978-0-231-52029-4(8))* 2009. (ENG., Illus.). 336p. (gr. 17). 45.00 *(978-0-231-14930-3(1))* Columbia Univ. Pr.

Pickard, Zachariah. Elizabeth Bishop's Poetics of Description. 2009. (ENG.). 220p. (C). *(978-0-7735-3505-3(5))* McGill-Queen's Univ. Pr.

Samuels, Peggy. Deep Skin: Elizabeth Bishop & Visual Art. 2010. (Illus.). 256p. 39.95 *(978-0-8014-4826-3(3))* Cornell Univ. Pr.

Snediker, Michael D. Queer Optimism: Lyric Personhood & Other Felicitous Persuasions. 2008. 288p. 75.00 *(978-0-8166-4999-0(5))*; pap. 25.00 *(978-0-8166-5000-2(4))* Univ. of Minnesota Pr.

Stevenson, Anne. Five Looks at Elizabeth Bishop. annot. ed. 2006. (ENG., Illus.). 176p. pap. 26.95 *(978-1-85224-725-6(8))* Bloodaxe Bks. GBR. Dist: Dufour Editions, Inc.

Von Der Heydt, James E. At the Brink of Infinity: Poetic Humility in Boundless American Space. 2008. (ENG.). 262p. 42.50 *(978-1-58729-628-4(4))* Univ. of Iowa Pr.

Wójcik-Leese, Elzbieta. Cognitive Poetic Readings in Elizabeth Bishop: Portrait of a Mind Thinking. 2010. (Applications of Cognitive Linguistics [ACL] Ser.). (ENG.). VIII, 317p. 140.00 *(978-3-11-018610-9(1))* De Gruyter, Mouton DEU. Dist: de Gruyter, Walter GmbH & Co. KG.

BISHOP, WILLIAM AVERY, 1894-1956
Bishop, William A. Winged Warfare: The Experiences of a Canadian 'Ace' of the RFC During the First World War. 2011. 160p. ***(978-0-85706-511-7(4))***; pap. ***(978-0-85706-512-4(2))*** Leonaur Ltd.

BISHOPRICS
see Dioceses

BISHOPS
see also Apostolic Succession; Church Polity; Conciliar Theory; Dioceses; Episcopacy; Investiture; Ordination; Popes—Primacy; Vicars-General

Adams, Elizabeth. Going to Heaven: The Life & Election of Bishop Gene Robinson. 2006. (ENG., Illus.). 256p. per. 14.95 *(978-1-933368-22-1(5))* Counterpoint LLC.

Adeuyan, Jacob Oluwatayo. The Journey of the First Black Bishop: Bishop Samuel Ajayi Crowther 1806 - 1891. 2011. 364p. 28.49 ***(978-1-4634-0733-9(5))***; pap. 17.72 ***(978-1-4634-0734-6(3))*** AuthorHouse.

Alberti, Leon Battista & Piccardi, Andrea. Leonis Baptiste Alberti Pontifex. 2007. (Edizione nazionale opere di leon battista Alberti Ser.). (LAT & ITA.). 316p. (C). 58.00 *(978-88-596-0363-4(3))* Edizioni Polistampa ITA. Dist: Brown, David Bk. Co., The.

Allen, Anne Beiser. And the Wilderness Shall Blossom: Henry Benjamin Whipple: Bishop, Educator, Advocate for the Indians. 2007. (ENG., Illus.). 45.00 *(978-1-890434-75-5(2))* Afton Historical Society Pr.

Allen, John. Desmond Tutu: Rabble-Rouser for Peace - The Authorized Biography. 2008. (ENG.). 496p. pap. 16.95 *(978-1-55652-798-2(5),* Hill, Lawrence Bks.) Chicago Review Pr., Inc.

Archbishops Diary a Year with John Habgood. 4.00 *(978-0-687-85020-4(7))* Abingdon Pr.

Augustine, Saint. Confessions. Wills, Garry, tr. 2008. (ENG.). 368p. (gr. 12-18) 16.00 *(978-0-14-310570-1(1),* Penguin Classics) Penguin Group (USA) Inc.

Augustine, Saint, text. Confessions. 2007. (ENG.). 380p. 48.95 *(978-0-548-00423-4(4))* Kessinger Publishing, LLC.

Auslander, Mark. The Accidental Slaveowner: Revisiting a Myth of Race & Finding an American Family. 2011. (ENG.). 376p. pap. 24.95 *(978-0-8203-4043-2(X))*; (Illus.). 69.95 *(978-0-8203-4042-5(1))* Univ. of Georgia Pr.

Bates, John Condliffe & Bothe, William. The Register of William Bothe, Bishop of Coventry & Lichfield, 1447-1452. Bates, John Condliffe, ed. 2008. (Canterbury & York Society Ser.: Volume 98). 228p. 45.00 *(978-0-907239-70-3(6))* Canterbury & York Society GBR. Dist: Boydell & Brewer, Inc.

Baudry. A Warrior Bishop of the Twelfth Century: The Deeds of Albero of Trier. Pavlac, Brian A., tr. from LAT. 2008. (Mediaeval Sources in Translation Ser.). (ENG.). pap. 15.95 *(978-0-88844-294-9(7))* Pontifical Institute of Mediaeval Studies, Dept. of Pubns. CAN. Dist: Univ. of Toronto Pr.

Benson, Arthur Christopher. The Life of Edward White Benson, Sometime Archbishop of Canterbury. 2009. 564p. pap. *(978-0-217-94282-9(2))* Books LLC.

Berger, Albrecht, ed. Life & Works of Saint Gregentios, Archbishop of Taphar: Introduction, Critical Edition & Translation with a Contribution by Gianfranco Fiaccadori. 2006. (Millennium-Studien / Millennium Studies). (ENG & GRE.). IX, 915p. 189.00 *(978-3-11-018445-7(1))* De Gruyter, Walter Inc.

Bishop's Journey. 2011. 54p. pap. 15.99 ***(978-1-4568-4982-5(4))*** Xlibris Corp.

Boece, Hector. Hectoris Boetii Murthlacensium Et Aberdonensium Episcoporum Vitae, Iterum in Lucem Editae. (Bannatyne Club, Edinburgh Publications: No. 11). reprint ed. 44.50 *(978-0-404-52711-2(6))* AMS Pr., Inc.

Bonner, Jeremy. The Road to Renewal: Victor Joseph Reed & Oklahoma Catholicism, 1905-1971. 2007. (ENG.). 425p. 34.95 *(978-0-8132-1507-5(2))* Catholic Univ. of America Pr.

Boresky, Theodosia. Life of St Josaphat: Martyr of the Union. 2011. 388p. 53.95 ***(978-1-258-03017-9(9))*** Literary Licensing, LLC.

Breck, Charles, ed. The Life of the Reverend James Lloyd Breck, D. D., Chiefly Letters Written by Himself. 557p. reprint ed. lib. bdg. 98.00 *(978-0-7222-0310-1(1))* Library Reprints, Inc.

Brehmer, Karl. Wilhelm Emmanuel von Ketteler (1811-1877) Arbeiterbischof und Sozialethiker: Auf den Spuren einer zeitlosen Modernität. 2009. (GER., Illus.). 165p. *(978-3-7954-2135-9(7))* Schnell und Steiner GmbH, Verlag.

Brent, Allen & Brent. Ignatius of Antioch: A Martyr Bishop & the Origin of Episcopacy. 2007. (ENG.). 192p. 130.00 *(978-0-567-03200-3(0),* T&T Clark Int'l) Continuum International Publishing Group, Ltd. GBR. Dist: National Bk. Network.

B

Brice, A. H. M. (Arthur Hallam Montefior, creator. Reginald Heber, Bishop of Calcutta, Scholar & Evangelist. 2010. 164p. pap. 21.75 ***(978-1-172-52883-7(7))*** BiblioBazaar.

Brice, Arthur Hallam Montefiore. Reginald Heber, Bishop of Calcutta, Scholar & Evangelist. 2009. 94p. pap. 14.14 *(978-1-151-67225-4(4))* General Bks. LLC.

Broadley, Martin John, ed. Bishop Herbert Vaughan & the Jesuits: Education & Authority. 2010. (Catholic Record Society: Records Ser.: Volume 82). (Illus.). 286p. 80.00 *(978-0-902832-25-1(5))* Catholic Record Society GBR. Dist: Boydell & Brewer, Inc.

Brumath, Adrien Leblond de. The Makers of Canada: Bishop Laval. 2007. (ENG.). 164p. pap. 19.99 *(978-1-4346-0731-7(3))*; 184p. pap. 21.99 *(978-1-4346-0791-1(7))* BiblioBazaar.

Buchanan, Colin, ed. The Bishop in Liturgy. 2009. 88.00 *(978-1-60724-361-8(X))* Gorgias Pr., LLC.

Buck, Mark. Politics, Finance & the Church in the Reign of Edward II. 2008. (Cambridge Studies in Medieval Life & Thought: Third Ser.). (ENG.). 264p. pap. 37.99 *(978-0-521-09119-0(5))* Cambridge Univ. Pr.

Bulman, Jan K. The Court Book of Mende & the Secular Lordship of the Bishop: Recollecting the Past in Thirteenth-Century Gévaudan. 2008. (ENG., Illus.). 176p. *(978-0-8020-9337-0(X))* Univ. of Toronto Pr.

Byford, Jovan. Denial & Repression of Anti-Semitism: Post-Communist Rehabilitation of the Serbian Bishop Nikolaj Velimirovic. 2008. (ENG.). 200p. 35.00 *(978-963-9776-15-9(7))* Central European Univ. Pr.

Camper, Catherine A. As God Would Have It: The Life & Ministry of Catherine A. Camper. 2007. per. 24.99 *(978-1-886068-29-2(1))* Fruitbearer Publishing, LLC.

Carty, Francis X. Hold Firm: John Charles Mcquaid & the Second Vatican Council. 2008. (ENG.). 181p. pap. 23.95 *(978-1-85607-585-5(0))* Columba Pr. IRL. Dist: Dufour Editions, Inc.

Castinei, Manuel. Compostela & Europe: The Story of Diego Gelmirez. 2010. (ENG., Illus.). 432p. 90.00 *(978-88-572-0493-2(6))* Skira Editore ITA. Dist: Random Hse., Inc.

Chandler, Andrew & Hein, David. Archbishop Fisher. 2012. (Archbishops of Canterbury Ser.). 256p. 99.95 ***(978-1-4094-1232-8(6))***; pap. 39.95 ***(978-1-4094-1233-5(4))*** Ashgate Publishing Co.

Comiskey, John P. In My Heart's Best Wishes for You: A biography of Archbishop John Walsh. 2012. (McGill-Queen's Studies in the History of Religion Ser.). (ENG., Illus.). 304p. (C). ***(978-0-7735-4013-2(X))*** McGill-Queen's Univ. Pr.

Congregation for Institutes of Consecrated Life and Societies of Apostolic Life Staff & Societies of Apostolic Life Staff. Directives for Mutual Relations Between Bishops & Religious in the Church: Mutuae Relationes. 65p. pap. 0.50 *(978-0-8198-1860-7(7))* Pauline Bks. & Media.

Corcuera de Mancera, Sonia. De Picaros y Malqueridos. 2010. (Historia Ser.). (SPA.). 278p. pap. 14.99 *(978-607-02-1180-5(4))* Fondo de Cultura Económcia.

Curley, Michael J. John Neumann, a Biography: Fourth Bishop of Philadelphia. 2011. 568p. 63.95 ***(978-1-258-08953-5(X))*** Literary Licensing, LLC.

Daly, Edward. A Troubled See: Memoirs of a Derry Bishop. 2011. (Illus.). 298p. pap. 19.95 ***(978-1-84682-312-1(9))*** Four Courts Pr. IRL. Dist: International Specialized Bk. Services.

D'Ambra, Sebastiano. Building the Culture of Dialogue, Path to Peace. 2011. 228p. pap. ***(978-3-8443-2997-1(8))*** Lambert Academic Publishing.

Daniels, Louis E. William Andrew Leonard A Beloved Prelate. 2006. pap. 20.95 *(978-1-4286-5663-5(4))* Kessinger Publishing, LLC.

Danilo, et al. Zivoti Kraljeva I Arhiepiskopa Srpskih: Sluzbe. 2008. 421p. *(978-86-07-01798-0(5))* Prosveta, Izdavacko preduzece.

Davis, Adam Jeffrey. The Holy Bureaucrat: Eudes Rigaud & Religious Reform in Thirteenth-Century Normandy. 2006. (Illus.). 268p. 52.50 *(978-0-8014-4474-6(8))* Cornell Univ. Pr.

Dean, Kevan N. & Brown, Terry L. Ezekiel, Yuma's Native Son: A Journey through the eyes of a Centenarian: Bishop Herman E. Dean. 2011. 208p. 29.99 *(978-1-4567-1245-7(4))*; pap. 19.99 *(978-1-4567-1246-4(2))* AuthorHouse.

Diaz Vara Calderon, Gabriel. A 17th Century Letter of Gabriel Diaz Vara Calderon, Bishop of Cuba, Describing the Indian Missions of Florida. Wenhold, Lucy L., tr. reprint ed. lib. bdg. 88.00 *(978-0-7222-0208-1(3))* Library Reprints, Inc.

Dudley, Geoffrey V. Prayer Answers Guaranteed! Learn How to Ask God ... & Receive It! 2009. 106p. pap. 13.95 *(978-1-4327-3207-3(2))* Outskirts Pr., Inc.

Duggan, Anne J. Thomas Becket: Friends Networks Texts & Cult. 2007. (Variorum Collected Studies). (Illus.). 368p. 170.00 *(978-0-7546-5922-8(4))* Ashgate Publishing Co.

Dunning, Robert, ed. Jocelin of Wells: Bishop, Builder, Courtier. 2010. (Studies in the History of Medieval Religion Ser.: Volume 36). (Illus.). 236p. 90.00 *(978-1-84383-556-1(8)*, Boydell Press) Boydell & Brewer, Ltd. GBR. Dist: Boydell & Brewer, Inc.

Dziwisz, Stanislaw. A Life with Karol: My Forty-Year Friendship with the Man Who Became Pope. Walker, Adrian J., tr. from ITA. 2008. (ENG., Illus.). 272p. 25.00 *(978-0-385-52374-5(2)*, Doubleday) Doubleday Religious Publishing Group, The.

Eames, Robin. Finding Common Ground: The Search for a Way Forward. 2012. (ENG.). 42.95 *(978-1-85607-666-1(0))* Columba Pr. IRL. Dist: Dufour Editions, Inc.

Ennodius, Magnus Felix & Gioanni, Stéphane. Lettres. 2010. (Collection des universites de France Serie Latine Ser.). (LAT & FRE.). 207p. (C). pap. 68.00 ***(978-2-251-01456-2(X))*** Societe d'edition Les Belles lettres FRA. Dist: ISD.

Fallows, Alice Katharine. Everybody's Bishop: Being the Life & Times of Samuel Fallows. 2011. 526p. 60.95 ***(978-1-258-02643-1(0))*** Literary Licensing, LLC.

Fernández Gracia, Ricardo. Varia Palafoxiana: Doce Estudios en Torno a Don Juan de Palafox y Mendoza. 2010. (SPA.). 380p. *(978-84-235-3236-0(4))* Navarra, Comunidad Autonoma, Servicio de Prensa, Publicaciones y Relaciones Sociales.

Gavrilin, A. V. Pod Pokrovom Tikhvinskoi Ikony: Arkhipastorskii Put Ioanna (Garklavsa) 2009. (RUS., Illus.). 462p. *(978-5-86983-031-9(1))* Ljubavic, ICP Rumjanceva M.P.

Gibbs, Marion E. Bishops & Reform. 2006. 228p. per. *(978-1-4067-1232-2(9)*, Hesperides Pr.) Read Bks.

Goldman, Francisco. Art of Political Murder: Who Killed the Bishop? 2008. (ENG.). 416p. pap. 15.00 *(978-0-8021-4385-3(7)*, Grove Pr.) Grove/Atlantic, Inc.

Gribble, Richard. An Archbishop for the People: The Life of Edward J. Hanna. 2006. (Illus.). 416p. per. 24.95 *(978-0-8091-4405-1(0)*, 4405-0) Paulist Pr.

Hendrix, John Shannon. Robert Grosseteste: Philosophy of Intellect & Vision. 2010. (ENG.). 260p. (C). pap. *(978-3-89665-524-0(8))* Academia Verlag Richarz GmbH.

Hodges, George. Henry Codman Potter, Seventh Bishop of New York. 2009. 416p. pap. 33.75 *(978-1-115-57634-5(8))* BiblioBazaar.

—Henry Codman Potter, Seventh Bishop of New York. 2009. 276p. pap. *(978-0-217-48215-8(5))* Books LLC.

Hübner, Reinhard M. Die Schrift des Apolinarius von Laodicea gegen Photin (Pseudo-Athanasius, Contra Sabellianos) und Basilius von Caesarea. (Patristische Texte und Studien Ser.). (GER., Illus.). VIII, 322p. 270.00 ***(978-3-11-180738-6(X))*** De Gruyter, Walter Inc.

Jenkins, Janice F. Bishop Reo Jenkins. 2011. 124p. pap. 19.99 ***(978-1-4415-7118-2(3))*** Xlibris Corp.

Jestice, Phyllis & Sherry, Matthew, trs. from FRE. A Life Poured Out: Pierre Claverie of Algeria. 2007. Orig. Title: Pierre claverie: un Algerien par Alliance. (FRE., Illus.). 286p. per. 30.00 *(978-1-57075-706-8(2))* Orbis Bks.

Jewell, F. Little Abe: Or- the Bishop of Berry Brow. 2007. (ENG.). 132p. pap. 18.99 *(978-1-4346-3434-4(5))*; 142p. pap. 19.99 *(978-1-4346-3435-1(3))* BiblioBazaar.

—Little Abe; or, the Bishop of Berry Brow. 2007. 136p. per. *(978-1-4065-3474-0(9))* Dodo Pr.

Johnston, Araminta Stone. And One Was a Priest: The Life & Times of Duncan M. Gray Jr. 2010. (ENG.). 320p. 40.00 *(978-1-60473-828-5(6))* Univ. Pr. of Mississippi.

Karmann, Thomas R. Meletius von Antiochien: Studien zur Geschichte des trinitätstheologischen Streits in den Jahren 360-364 N. Chr. 2009. (Regensburger Studien zur Theologie Ser.). (GRE.). 550p. pap. 124.95 *(978-3-631-56284-0(5))* Lang, Peter GmbH, Europaischer Verlag der Wissenschaften DEU. Dist: Lang, Peter.

Katos, Demetrios S. Palladius of Helenopolis: The Origenist Advocate. 2012. (Oxford Early Christian Studies). (ENG.). 288p. 135.00 ***(978-0-19-969696-3(9))*** Oxford Univ. Pr., Inc.

Kearney, Patrick & Kearney. Guardian of the Light: Archbishop Denis Hurley, a Life Against Apartheid. 2009. (ENG., Illus.). 400p. 34.95 *(978-0-8264-1875-3(9))* Continuum International Publishing Group, Ltd. GBR. Dist: National Bk. Network.

Keith, Robert & Spottiswoode, John. An Historical Catalogue of the Scottish Bishops down to the Year 1688. 2011. pap. 101.56 *(978-1-61143-896-3(9))*; pap. 101.56 *(978-1-61143-861-1(6))* Gorgias Pr., LLC.

Knowles, David. The Episcopal Colleagues of Archbishop Thomas Becket: Being the Ford Lectures delivered in the University of Oxford in Hilary Term 1949. 2008. (ENG.). 204p. pap. 42.00 *(978-0-521-07967-9(5))* Cambridge Univ. Pr.

Kolbet, Paul R. Augustine & the Cure of Souls: Revising a Classical Ideal. 2009. (ND Christianity & Judaism Anitqui Ser.). (ENG.). 416p. pap. 45.00 *(978-0-268-03321-7(8))* Univ. of Notre Dame Pr.

Kravchenko, Iryna. The Role of Bishops in Icelandic Society Political & Social Aspects of Activities. 2009. 92p. pap. *(978-3-639-10688-6(1))* VDM Verlag Dr. Mueller e.K.

Lange, Dietz. Nathan Soderblom: Brcv - Lettres - Briefe - Letters. A Selection from his Correspondence. 2006. (ENG, FRE & GER.). 528p. (C). 158.00 *(978-3-525-60005-4(4))* Vandenhoeck & Ruprecht GmbH & Co. KG DEU. Dist: ISD.

Leblond de Brumath, A. Bishop Laval. 2007. 172p. per. *(978-1-4065-3648-5(2))* Dodo Pr.

Leemans, Johan, et al, eds. Episcopal Elections in Late Antiquity. 2011. (Arbeiten zur Kirchengeschichte Ser.). XII, 606p. (ENG., Illus.). E-Book 280.00 ***(978-3-11-026861-4(2))***; (FRE, GER & ENG.). 182.00 ***(978-3-11-026855-3(8))*** De Gruyter, Walter Inc.

MacAulay, Ambrose. Patrick Mcalister, Bishop of down & Connor, 1886-95. 2006. (Illus.). 182p. 65.00 *(978-1-85182-997-2(0))* Four Courts Pr. IRL. Dist: International Specialized Bk. Services.

Marshall, Paul V. The Bishop Is Coming! A Practical Guide for Bishops & Congregations. 2007. (Illus.). 128p. per. 12.00 *(978-0-89869-542-7(2))* Church Publishing, Inc.

Marshall, Peter. Mother Leakey & the Bishop: A Ghost Story. 2007. (ENG., Illus.). 352p. 35.00 *(978-0-19-927371-3(5))* Oxford Univ. Pr., Inc.

McAnally, Thomas S. Bishop with a Pastor's Heart: Kenneth W. Copeland. 2006. (Illus.). 240p. 24.95 *(978-1-57736-378-1(7))* Providence Hse Pubs.

McGowan, Mark G. Michael Power: The Struggle to Build the Catholic Church on the Canadian Frontier. 2007. (McGill-Queen's Studies in the History of Religion Ser.). (ENG., Illus.). 392p. (C). per. *(978-0-7735-3248-9(X))* McGill-Queen's Univ. Pr.

Mcnally, Paddy & Milne, Kenneth, eds. The Boulter Letters. 2012. 320p. 74.50 *(978-1-84682-290-2(4))* Four Courts Pr. IRL. Dist: International Specialized Bk. Services.

McPheters, Mike. Agent Bishop. 2009. pap. 17.99 *(978-1-59955-317-7(1))* Cedar Fort, Inc./CFI Distribution.

Millard, Mary Weeks. Emmanuel Kolini: The Unlikely Archbishop of Rwanda. 2009. (ENG.). 251p. pap. 16.99 *(978-1-934068-65-6(9))* Authentic Media.

Moore, Honor & Moore, H. The Bishop's Daughter: A Memoir. 2009. (ENG., Illus.). 384p. pap. 16.95 *(978-0-393-33536-1(4)*, 33536) Norton, W. W. & Co., Inc.

Moore, Michael Edward. A Sacred Kingdom: Bishops & the Rise of Frankish Kingship, 300-850. 2011. 456p. 69.95 ***(978-0-8132-1877-9(2))*** Catholic Univ. of America Pr.

Morey, Dom Adrian & Brooke, C. N. L. Gilbert Foliot & His Letters. 2008. (Cambridge Studies in Medieval Life & Thought: New Ser.). (ENG.). 636p. pap. 48.00 *(978-0-521-07288-5(3))* Cambridge Univ. Pr.

Morrissey, Thomas J. Edward J. Byrne, 1872-1941: The Forgotten Archbishop of Dublin. 2011. (ENG., Illus.). 312p. 35.95 *(978-1-85607-703-3(9))* Columba Pr. IRL. Dist: Dufour Editions, Inc.

Myine, Alexander. Vitae Dunkeldensis Ecclesiae Episcoporum, a Prima Sedis Foundatione, Ad Annum MDXV Ab Alexandro Myln, Eiusdem Ecclesiae Canonica Conscriptae, Repr. Of 1823 Ed. Thomson, Thomas, ed. 20.00 *(978-0-404-52701-3(9))* AMS Pr., Inc.

Newman, Richard. Freedom's Prophet: Bishop Richard Allen, the AME Church, & the Black Founding Fathers. 2009. (ENG., Illus.). 368p. pap. 23.00 *(978-0-8147-5857-1(6))* New York Univ. Pr.

Norton, John Nicholas. Life of Archbishop Laud by John N Norton. 2006. 276p. per. 23.99 *(978-1-4255-2523-1(7))* MPublishing.

Nwachukwu, Amaechi. When the Cup Is Found in Your Possession. 2009. 124p. 29.99 *(978-1-4415-4608-1(1))*; pap. 19.99 *(978-1-4415-4607-4(3))* Xlibris Corp.

Oldfield, John. El Obispo del Barrio: Una Biografico del Obispo Alphonso Gallegos, OAR. Alvarez, Beatriz O., tr. from ENG. 2007. (SPA., Illus.). 101p. per. 12.95 *(978-0-8091-4431-0(X)*, 4431-x) Paulist Pr.

Page, Jesse. The Black Bishop: Samuel Adjai Crowther. 2010. 494p. pap. 38.75 *(978-1-142-98420-5(6))* BiblioBazaar.

Pavlov, Plamen & Temelski, Khristo. Bulgari Svettsi. 2010. (BUL., Illus.). 271p. *(978-954-378-064-8(1))* Tangra TanNakRa.

Peart-Binns, John S. & Peart-Binns. A Heart in My Head: A Biography of Richard Harries. 2007. (ENG., Illus.). 288p. 39.95 *(978-0-8264-8154-2(X))* Continuum International Publishing Group, Ltd. GBR. Dist: National Bk. Network.

Petot, Patrick. Alain de Solminihac (1593-1659), Prélat Réformateur: De L'abbaye de Chancelade à L'évêché de Cahors, 2 vols. 2009. (Bibliotheca Victorina Ser.). (FRE & ENG., Illus.). 1091p. (C). 203.00 ***(978-2-503-53278-3(0))*** Brepols Pubs. BEL. Dist: ISD.

Preus, David W. Pastor & President: Reflections of a Lutheran Churchman. 2012. (ENG., Illus.). 192p. pap. 18.00 ***(978-1-932688-64-1(1)***, Lutheran Univ. Pr.) Kirk Hse. Pubs.

Pruter, Bishop. Blue Jellybean Hedy Lamarr & We Dont E. 2006. 172p. per. 14.95 *(978-0-912134-23-9(2)*, Borgo Pr.) Wildside Pr., LLC.

Rammelt, Claudia. Ibas von Edessa: Rekonstruktion einer Biographie und dogmatischen Position zwischen den Fronten. 2008. (Arbeiten zur Kirchengeschichte Ser.).Tr. of Ibas of Edessa. Reconstruction of a Biography & Dogmatic Position between the Fronts. (GER.). X, 344p. 147.00 *(978-3-11-020218-2(2))*; 224.00 ***(978-3-11-916661-4(8))*** De Gruyter, Walter Inc.

Ravitch, Norman. Sword & Mitre: Government & episcopate in France & England in the age of Aristocracy. (Studies in European History Ser.). (ENG.). 246p. 210.00 ***(978-3-11-210727-0(6))***; 135.00 ***(978-3-11-100221-7(7))*** De Gruyter, Mouton DEU. Dist: de Gruyter, Walter GmbH & Co. KG.

Roberts, Apostle J. Rodney. Son of Destiny. 2011. 192p. pap. 14.99 ***(978-1-61379-155-4(0))*** Xulon Pr., Inc.

Robins, Glenn. The Bishop of the Old South: The Ministry & Civil War Legacy of Leonidas Polk. 2006. (Illus.). 243p. 35.00 *(978-0-88146-038-4(9))* Mercer Univ. Pr.

Romberg, Winfried. Die Würzburger Bischöfe Von 1617 Bis 1684. 2011. (GER., Illus.). XIV, 599p. 210.00 *(978-3-11-025183-8(3))* De Gruyter, Walter Inc.

Ryan, Patrick. Archbishop Patrick John Ryan His Life & Times: Ireland - St. Louis - Philadelphia 1831-1911. 2010. (Illus.). 372p. 28.49 *(978-1-4389-9823-7(6))* AuthorHouse.

Scammell, G. V. Hugh du Puiset: A Biography of the Twelfth-Century Bishop of Durham. 2011. (ENG.). 365p. pap. 29.99 *(978-0-521-17985-0(8))* Cambridge Univ. Pr.

Schmitt, Oskar. Ein würdiger Verwalter im Weinberg unseres Herrn Jesus Christus: Bischof Pierre Martin Ngo-dinh-Thuc. 2006. 206p. pap. 17.90 *(978-3-8334-5385-4(0))* Bks. on Demand.

Schneider, Nicholas A. Joseph Elmer Cardinal Ritter: His Life & Times. 2008. (Illus.). 188p. pap. 19.95 *(978-0-7648-1701-4(9))* Liguori Pubns.

Shusherin, Ioann. From Peasant to Patriarch: Account of the Birth, Upbringing, & Life of His Holiness Nikon, Patriarch of Moscow & All Russia. Kain, Kevin & Levintova, Katia, trs. 2007. (ENG.). 214p. per. 27.50 *(978-0-7391-1580-0(4))* Lexington Bks.

Shusherin, Ivan Kornilevich. From Peasant to Patriarch: Account of the Birth, Upbringing, & Life of His Holiness Nikon, Patriarch of Moscow & All Russia. Kain, Kevin, tr. from RUS. annot. ed. 2007. (ENG.). 214p. 62.99 *(978-0-7391-1579-4(0))* Lexington Bks.

Siemens, James. The Christology of Theodore of Tarsus. 2010. (Studia Traditionis Theologiae Ser.). (ENG.). 211p. (C). pap. 102.00 *(978-2-503-53385-8(X))* Brepols Pubs. BEL. Dist: ISD.

Skórzewska, Joanna A. Constructing a Cult: The Life & Veneration of Guðmundr Arason (1161-1237) in the Icelandic Written Sources. 2011. XIV, 312p. *(978-90-04-19496-0(7))* BRILL.

Smith, D. Guide to Bishops' Registers. xvi, 286p. 27.00 *(978-0-901050-72-4(5))* Brown, David Bk. Co., The.

Sneddon, Andrew. Witchcraft & Whigs: The Life of Bishop Francis Hutchinson, 1660-1739. 2008. (ENG., Illus.). 232p. 84.00 *(978-0-7190-7612-1(9))* Manchester Univ. Pr. GBR. Dist: Macmillan.

Sot, Michel & Lobrichon, Guy. Les Gestes des évêques D'Auxerre. 2006. (LAT & FRE., Illus.). 374p. (C). pap. 62.00 ***(978-2-251-34054-8(8))*** Societe d'edition Les Belles lettres FRA. Dist: ISD.

Spencer, Stephen. William Temple: A Calling to Prophecy. 132p. 12.00 *(978-0-281-05437-4(1))* SPCK Publishing GBR. Dist: Pilgrim Pr., The/United Church Pr.

Stewart, Jon. Hans Lassen Martensen: Theologian, Philosopher & Social Critic. 2012. (Museum Tusculanum Press - Danish Golden Age Studies). (ENG., Illus.). 369p. 70.00 *(978-87-635-3169-6(0))* Museum Tusculanum Pr. DNK. Dist: Chicago Distribution Ctr.

Stringfellow, William & Towne, Anthony. The Death & Life of Bishop Pike: An Utterly Candid Biography of America's Most Controversial Clergyman. 2007. 480p. pap. 53.00 *(978-1-55635-327-7(8)*, Wipf and Stock) Wipf & Stock Pubs.

Stults, Donald Le Roy. Grasping Truth & Reality: Lesslie Newbigin's Theology of Mission to the Western World. 2008. 308p. pap. 34.00 *(978-1-55635-723-7(0)*, Wipf and Stock) Wipf & Stock Pubs.

Sykes, Norman. William Wake: Archbishop of Canterbury ,1657-1757, 2 vols. 2008. (ENG., Illus.). 681p. (C). pap. 90.00 *(978-0-521-74328-0(1))* Cambridge Univ. Pr.

Taylor, Maurice. Being a Bishop in Scotland. 2006. (ENG.). 141p. per. 18.95 *(978-1-85607-529-9(X))* Columba Pr. IRL. Dist: Dufour Editions, Inc.

Teal, Jane. Shaping a Colonial Church: Bishop Harper & the Anglican Diocese of Christchurch, 1856-1890. Brown, Colin & Peters, Marie, eds. 2006. (ENG., Illus.). 316p. pap. 27.99 *(978-1-877257-44-5(3))* Canterbury Univ. Pr. NZL. Dist: Independent Pubs. Group.

Thaler, Manfred Josef. Das Salzburger Domkapitel in der Frühen Neuzeit (1514 Bis 1806) Verfassung und Zusammensetzung. 2011. (Wissenschaft und Religion Ser.). (GER.). 688p. 115.95 *(978-3-631-60601-8(X))* Lang, Peter GmbH, Europaischer Verlag der Wissenschaften DEU. Dist: Lang, Peter.

Trumbore Jones, A. Noble Lord, Good Shepherd: Episcopal Power & Piety in Aquitaine, 877-1050. 2009. (Brill's Ser. on the Early Middle Ages Ser.). 288p. *(978-90-04-17786-4(8))* BRILL.

Turner, Henry McNeal. An African American Pastor Before & During the American Civil War. 2010. 109.95 *(978-0-7734-1429-7(0))* Mellen, Edwin Pr., The.

Weakland, Rembert G. A Pilgrim in a Pilgrim Church: Memoirs of a Catholic Archbishop. 2009. (Illus.). 450p. 35.00 *(978-0-8028-6382-9(5))* Eerdmans, William B. Publishing Co.

Weber, Christoph. Episcopus et Princeps: Italienische Bischöfe als Fürsten, Grafen und Barone vom 17. bis zum 20. Jahrhundert. 2010. (Beiträge zur Kirchen- und Kulturgeschichte Ser.). (GER.). 218p. 64.95 *(978-3-631-60242-3(1))* Lang, Peter GmbH, Europaischer Verlag der Wissenschaften DEU. Dist: Lang, Peter.

Weller, John. The Flying Bishop. 2008. (Illus.). 100p. per. *(978-1-84748-225-9(2))* Athena Pr.

Williams, Hirron Ignatius. The Church & the Kingdom. 2009. 64p. pap. 11.18 *(978-1-4269-1387-7(7))* Trafford Publishing.

Woolgar, C. M., ed. Testamentary Records of the English & Welsh Episcopate, 1200-1413: Wills, Executors' Accounts & Inventories, & the Probate Process. 2011. (Canterbury & York Society Ser.: Volume 102). 418p. 45.00 *(978-0-907239-74-1(9))* Canterbury & York Society GBR. Dist: Boydell & Brewer, Inc.

Yates, Nigel. Bishop Burgess & His World: Culture, Religion & Society in Britain, Europe & North America in the Eighteenth & Nineteenth Centuries. 2007. 288p. (C). 90.00 *(978-0-7083-2075-4(9))* Univ. of Wales Pr. GBR. Dist: Chicago Distribution Ctr.

Zwierlein, Frederick James. Letters of Archbishop Corrigan to Bishop Mcquaid & Allied Documents. 2011. 250p. 46.95 ***(978-1-258-03347-7(X))*** Literary Licensing, LLC.

BISHOPS—ROME

see Popes

BISLAMA LANGUAGE

Churchill, William. Beach-la-Mar. 2009. 80p. pap. 14.14 *(978-1-151-67724-2(8))* General Bks. LLC.

—Beach-la-Mar: The Jargon or Trade Speech of the Western Pacific. 2010. 66p. pap. 17.75 *(978-1-147-98794-2(7))* 2009. 60p. pap. 16.75 *(978-1-110-06729-9(1))* BiblioBazaar.

—Beach-la-Mar: The Jargon or Trade Speech of the Western Pacific (1911) 2008. 60p. pap. 16.95 *(978-1-4367-8619-5(3))* Kessinger Publishing, LLC.

—Beach-la-Mar; the Jargon or Trade Speech of the Western Pacific. 2010. 62p. pap. 11.66 *(978-1-152-74172-0(1))* General Bks. LLC.

—Beach la mar: the Jargon or Trade Speech of the Western Pacific. 2009. 59p. pap. 18.99 *(978-1-110-06727-5(5))*; (ENG.). pap. 16.99 *(978-1-110-06726-8(7))* BiblioBazaar. (BiblioLife).

—Beach-la-Mar, the Jargon or Trade Speech of the Western Pacific. 2010. (Illus.). 62p. pap. 11.66 *(978-1-154-63589-8(9))* General Bks. LLC.

BISMARCK, OTTO, FURST VON, 1815-1898

Aydelotte, William Osgood. Bismarck & British Colonial Policy: The Problem of South West Africa, 1883-1885. 2011. 198p. 44.95 *(978-1-258-01927-3(2))* Literary Licensing, LLC.

Beran, Michael Knox. Forge of Empires: Three Revolutionary Statesmen & the World They Made, 1861-1871. 2011. (ENG.). 496p. pap. 28.99 *(978-0-7432-7070-0(3)*, Free Pr.) Free Pr.

Bismarck, Prince Herbert Von, ed. The Love Letters of Bismarck: Being Letters to His Fiancee & Wife. Lewis, Charlton T., tr. 2007. pap. 36.95 *(978-1-4304-5077-1(0))* Kessinger Publishing, LLC.

Busch, Moritz. Bismarck in the Franco-German War, 1870-1871. 2010. 370p. pap. 32.75 *(978-1-177-79451-0(9))*; (ENG.). 380p. pap. 33.75 *(978-1-176-46919-8(3))* BiblioBazaar.

—Bismarck in the Franco-German War, 1870-1871. 2010. 200p. pap. *(978-1-152-87355-1(5))* Books LLC.

—Bismarck in the Franco-German War, 1870-1871. 2010. 190p. pap. 16.95 *(978-1-153-30153-4(9))* 2009. 388p. pap. 29.59 *(978-1-150-74216-3(X))* General Bks. LLC.

Crankshaw, Edward. Bismark. 2012. 463p. pap. ***(978-1-4482-0531-8(X)**, 146533, Bloomsbury Reacer)* Bloomsbury Publishing Plc.

Darmstaedter, Friedrich. Bismarck & the Creation of the Second Reich. 2008. (ENG.). 452p. pap. 34.95 *(978-1-4128-0783-8(2))* Transaction Pubs.

Fuller, Joseph Vincent. Bismarck's Diplomacy at Its Zenith. 2009. 382p. 48.95 *(978-1-104-70414-8(5))*; 382p. pap. 33.95 *(978-1-104-62570-2(9))*; 384p. 48.95 *(978-1-104-07276-6(9))*; 384p. pap. 33.95 *(978-1-104-04092-5(1))* Kessinger Publishing, LLC.

—Bismarck's Diplomacy at Its Zenith. 368p. reprint ed. 98.00 *(978-0-7222-7286-2(3))* Library Reprints, Inc.

Headlam, James Wycliffe. Bismarck & the Foundation of the German Empire. 2008. 376p. 29.99 *(978-0-554-33550-6(6))* 2008. 376p. 31.99 *(978-0-554-24247-7(8))* 2007. (ENG.). 340p. pap. 23.99 *(978-1-4264-6041-8(4))* 2007. (ENG.). 372p. pap. 26.99 *(978-1-4264-6112-5(7))* BiblioBazaar.

—Bismarck & the Foundation of the German Empire. 2009. 258p. pap. *(978-0-217-18244-7(5))* Books LLC.

—Bismarck & the Foundation of the German Empire. Abbott, Evelyn, ed. 2007. 340p. per. *(978-1-4065-4424-4(8))* Dodo Pr.

—Bismarck & the Foundation of the German Empire. 2007. (ENG.). 528p. per. 40.95 *(978-1-4326-3474-2(7))* Kessinger Publishing, LLC.

Headlam-Morley, James. Bismarck & the Foundation of the German Empire. (Heroes of the Nations Ser.). reprint ed. 30.00 *(978-0-404-58265-4(6))* AMS Pr., Inc.

Hesekiel, George. Bismarck His Authentic Biography. 2007. (ENG.). 604p. 59.95 *(978-0-548-01048-8(X))* Kessinger Publishing, LLC.

Robertson, C. Grant. Bismarck. 2010. 534p. 43.99 *(978-1-140-17641-1(2))* 2009. 532p. 36.99 *(978-1-113-67431-9(8))* 2009. 532p. 43.99 *(978-1-113-67433-3(4))* 2009. 532p. pap. 39.75 *(978-1-113-67427-2(X))* 2009. 532p. pap. 40.75 *(978-1-113-67429-6(6))* 2009. (ENG.). 530p. pap. 31.99 *(978-1-113-67425-8(3)*, BiblioLife) 2009. (ENG.). 530p. pap. 30.99 *(978-1-113-67423-4(7)*, BiblioLife) BiblioBazaar.

Steefel, Lawrence Dinkelspiel. Bismarck, the Hohenzollern Candidacy, & the Origins of the Franco-German War Of 1870. 2011. 296p. 48.95 ***(978-1-258-01717-0(2))*** Literary Licensing, LLC.

Steinberg, Jonathan. Bismarck: A Life, 1 vol. 2011. (Illus.). 592p. 34.95 *(978-0-19-978252-9(0))* Oxford Univ. Pr., Inc.

—Bismarck: A Life. 2011. E-Book 24.95 ***(978-0-19-984543-9(3))*** Oxford University Press.

Ullrich, Volker. Bismarck: The Iron Chancellor. 2008. (Life & Times Ser.). (ENG., Illus.). 170p. pap. 15.95 *(978-1-904950-84-4(1))* Haus Publishing GBR. Dist: Consortium Bk. Sales & Distribution.

Von Bismarck, Otto. Bismarck: The Man & the Statesman,Volume 2. 2007. 388p. 33.95 *(978-1-60206-695-3(7))* Cosimo, Inc.

White, Andrew Dickson. Seven Great Statesmen in the Warfare of Humanity with Unreason. 2009. 338p. pap. 25.23 *(978-1-4589-7315-3(8))* General Bks. LLC.

—Seven Great Statesmen in the Warfare of Humanity with Unreason. 2007. (ENG.). 562p. 58.95 *(978-0-548-01978-8(9))* Kessinger Publishing, LLC.

Williamson, David G. Bismarck & Germany: 1862-1890. 3rd ed. 2010. (Seminar Studies in History Ser.). (ENG., Illus.). 224p. (C). pap. 28.20 *(978-1-4082-2318-5(X))* Longman Publishing Group.

BISMARCK (BATTLESHIP)

Ballantyne, Iain. Killing the Bismarck: Destroying the Pride of Hitler's Fleet. 2010. (Illus.). 288p. 50.00 *(978-1-84415-983-3(3))* Pen & Sword Bks. Ltd. GBR. Dist: Casemate Pubs. & Bk. Distributors, LLC.

Ballard, Robert. Robert Ballard's Bismarck. 2007. (Illus.). 231p. 17.99 *(978-0-7858-2205-9(4)*, Chartwell) Book Sales, Inc.

Grenfell, Russell. The Bismarck Episode. 2010. (ENG., Illus.). 232p. pap. 14.95 *(978-1-59416-110-0(0))* Westholme Publishing.

Konstam, Angus. The Bismarck 1941: Hunting Germany's greatest Battleship. 2011. (Campaign Ser.). (ENG., Illus.). 96p. pap. 19.95 *(978-1-84908-383-6(5))* Osprey Publishing, Ltd. GBR. Dist: Random Hse., Inc.

Zetterling, Niklas. Bismarck: A Minute by Minute Account of the Final Hours of Germany's Greatest Battleship. 2009. (Illus.). 320p. 32.95 *(978-1-935149-04-0(0))* Casemate Pubs. & Bk. Distributors, LLC.

Zetterling, Niklas & Tamelander, Michael. Bismarck: The Final Days of Germany's Greatest Battleship. 2011. (Illus.). 320p. pap. 16.95 ***(978-1-61200-075-6(4)**,* Casemate) Casemate Pubs. & Bk. Distributors, LLC.

BISMUTH

Ghatak, Kamakhya Prasad & Bhattacharya, Sitangshu. Bismuth: Characteristics, Production & Applications. 2011. (Materials Science & Technologies Ser.). 140.00 ***(978-1-61470-640-3(9))*** Nova Science Pubs., Inc.

Sun, Hongzhe, ed. Biological Chemistry of Arsenic, Antimony & Bismuth. 2011. (ENG., Illus.). 400p. 175.00 *(978-0-470-71390-7(9)*, Wiley) Wiley, John & Sons, Inc.

BISON

see also American Bison

Braun, Sebastian Felix. Buffalo Inc: American Indians & Economic Development. 2008. (ENG., Illus.). 280p. (C). 39.95 *(978-0-8061-3904-3(8))* Univ. of Oklahoma Pr.

BISON, AMERICAN

see American Bison

BITS (BRIDLES)

see Bridle

BITUMEN

see also Asphalt; Bituminous Materials

Ancheyta, Jorge, et al. Asphaltenes: Chemical Transformation During Hydroprocessing of Heavy Oils. 2010. (Chemical Industries Ser.). (ENG., Illus.). 461p. 169.95 *(978-1-4200-6630-2(7)*, CRC Press) Taylor & Francis Group GBR. Dist: Taylor & Francis Group.

British Standards Institute Staff. Bitumen & bituminous binders. Specifications for hard paving grade Bitumens. 30p. pap. 99.00 *(978-0-580-53487-4(1))* Artech Hse., Inc.

Duncan, Jeremy A. Asphaltenes: Characterization, Properties & Applications. 2010. (Chemical Engineering Methods & Technology Ser.). 181p. 59.00 *(978-1-60741-453-7(8))* Nova Science Pubs., Inc.

Johnston, Merrick. Temperature & Frequency Dependence of Viscoelasticity in Bitumen. 2010. 180p. pap. *(978-3-8383-8760-4(0))* Lambert Academic Publishing.

Mullins, Oliver C., et al. Asphaltenes, Heavy Oils, & Petroleomics. 2010. (ENG., Illus.). xxi, 669p. pap. 139.00 *(978-1-4419-2176-5(1)*, 1441921761) Springer.

Tarun, Cynthia. Economical Hydrogen Production with Co2 Capture in Oil Sands Industry. 2008. 136p. per. *(978-3-8364-5471-1(8))* VDM Verlag Dr. Mueller e.K.

BITUMINOUS MATERIALS

see also Asphalt; Asphalt Emulsion Mixtures; Coal-Tar

British Standards Institute Staff. Bitumen & bituminous binders. Specifications for hard paving grade Bitumens. 30p. pap. 99.00 *(978-0-580-53487-4(1))* Artech Hse., Inc.

Hunter, Robert N., ed. Bituminous Mixtures in Road Construction. (Illus.). 441p. 115.00 *(978-0-7277-1683-5(2))* Telford, Thomas Ltd. GBR. Dist: Routledge, Chapman & Hall, Inc.

Solaimanian, Mansour, et al. Improved Conditioning & Testing Procedures for HMA Moisture Susceptibility. 2007. (Illus.). 69p. 41.00 *(978-0-309-09906-6(4))* Transportation Research Board.

BIVALVES

see Bivalvia

BIVALVIA

see also Oysters; Pearls

Claudi, Renata & Mackie, Gerry. Monitoring & Control of Macrofouling Mollusks in Fresh Water Systems. 2nd rev. ed. 2009. (ENG., Illus.). 550p. 144.95 *(978-1-4398-0050-8(2)*, CRC Press) Taylor & Francis Group GBR. Dist: Taylor & Francis Group.

Committee on Best Practices for Shellfish Mariculture and the Effects of Commercial Activities in Drakes Estero, Pt. Reyes National Seashore, California. Ecosystem Concepts for Sustainable Bivalve Mariculture. 2010. (ENG.). 190p. pap. 43.00 *(978-0-309-14695-1(X))* National Academies Pr.

Mcalester, A. Lee. Upper Devonian Pelecypods of the New York Chemung Stage. 2011. 166p. 41.95 ***(978-1-258-08756-2(1))*** Literary Licensing, LLC.

McGevin, Lauren E. Mussels: Anatomy, Habitat & Environmental Impact. 2011. *(978-1-61761-763-8(6))* Nova Science Pubs., Inc.

BIZET, GEORGES, 1838-1875

Bizet. Bizet - L'Arlesienne Suites 1-2. 2008. (ENG.). 176p. pap. 17.99 incl. audio compact disk *(978-3-7957-6505-7(6)*, 3795765056) Schott Musik International GmbH & Co. KG DEU. Dist: Leonard, Hal Corp.

Deininger, Tina & Jaugstetter, Gerhard, photos by. Carmen's Dance: A Fantasy of Spanish Flamenco. 2006. (Ear Books Mini Ser.). (ENG., Illus.). 14.95 incl. lp *(978-3-937406-51-0(4))* Edel Classica Gmbh.

Lawrence, Robert, ed. Carmen: The Story of Bizet's Opera. 2011. 42p. 35.95 ***(978-1-258-06941-4(5))*** Literary Licensing, LLC.

BLACK, HUGO LAFAYETTE, 1886-1971

Feldman, Noah. Scorpions: The Battles & Triumphs of FDR's Great Supreme Court Justices. (ENG., Illus.). 528p. 2011. pap. 16.99 *(978-0-446-69928-0(4))* 2010. 30.00 *(978-0-446-58057-1(0))* Grand Central Publishing. (Twelve).

Freyer, Tony A. Hugo L. Black & the Dilemma of American Liberalism. 2nd ed. 2007. (ENG.). 256p. (C). per. 25.20 *(978-0-205-59078-0(0))* Longman Publishing Group.

BLACK

Jogig, Laura & Leong, Roger. Black in Fashion: Mourning to Night. 2008. (ENG., Illus.). 88p. pap. 29.95 *(978-0-7241-0293-8(0))* National Gallery of Victoria AUS. Dist: National Bk. Network.

Mavor, Carol. Black & Blue: The Bruised Passion of Camera Lucida, la Jetée, Sans Soleil, & Hiroshima Mon Amour. 2012. (ENG.). 200p. pap. 24.95 ***(978-0-8223-5271-6(0))***; (Illus.). 89.95 ***(978-0-8223-5252-5(4))*** Duke Univ. Pr.

Standish, Jules. How Not to Wear Black. 2011. (ENG., Illus.). 131p. pap. 13.95 ***(978-1-84694-561-8(5))*** Hunt, John Publishing Ltd. GBR. Dist: National Bk. Network.

BLACK AFRICANS

see Blacks

BLACK AMERICANA

see African Americans—Collectibles

BLACK AMERICANS

see African Americans

BLACK ART (WITCHCRAFT)

see Witchcraft

BLACK ARTISTS

Brownlee, Andrea Barnwell & Oliver, Valerie Cassel. Cinema Remixed & Reloaded: Black Women & the Moving Image Since 1970. 2008. (ENG., Illus.). 82p. (C). *(978-0-295-98864-1(9))* Contemporary Arts Museum, Houston.

Carman, Jillian. Steven Cohen. (TAXI Art Bks.: Bk. 8). (Illus.). 16p. (C). pap., tchr. ed., suppl. ed. *(978-0-9584688-1-7(8))* Krut, David Publishing.

Croucamp, Andre. David Koloane. (TAXI Art Bks.: Bk. 6). (Illus.). 16p. (C). pap., tchr. ed., suppl. ed. *(978-0-9584496-4-9(3))* Krut, David Publishing.

Dube, Prince Mbusi. Dumile Feni: The Story of a Great Artist. 2011. 286p. 61.95 ***(978-0-9869833-0-6(6))*** STE Pubs. ZAF. Dist: Independent Pubs. Group.

Hobbs, Philippa. Jeremy Wafer. (TAXI Art Bks.: Bk. 3). (Illus.). 20p. (C). pap., tchr. ed., suppl. ed. *(978-0-620-27381-7(X))* Krut, David Publishing.

—Pat Mautloa. (TAXI Art Bks.: Bk. 9). (Illus.). 16p. (C). pap., tchr. ed., suppl. ed. *(978-0-9584496-8-7(6))* Krut, David Publishing.

—Samson Mudzunga. (TAXI Art Bks.: Bk. 2). (Illus.). 20p. (C). pap., tchr. ed., suppl. ed. *(978-0-620-27079-3(9))* Krut, David Publishing.

Miles, Elza. Land & Lives: A Story of Early Black Artists. (Illus.). 190p. *(978-0-7981-3658-7(8))* Human & Rousseau.

Wylie, Diana. Art & Revolution: The Life & Death of Thami Mnyele, South African Artist. 2008. (Reconsiderations in Southern African History Ser.). (ENG., Illus.). 264p. (C). (gr. 13-17). pap. 25.00 *(978-0-8139-2764-0(1))* Univ. Pr. of Virginia.

BLACK BASEBALL LEAGUES

see Negro Leagues

BLACK BEAR

Anderson, Margaret, et al. Discovering Black Bears. 2007. (ENG., Illus.). 40p. (J). per. 8.95 *(978-0-941042-37-6(5))* Dog-Eared Pubns.

Brewer, Gabriele. Pawprints in My Soul. 2009. 162p. pap. 19.48 *(978-0-557-11964-6(2))* Lulu Enterprises Inc.

Lewis, Gary & Van Tassel, Lee. Black Bear Hunting: Expert Strategies for Success. 2007. (Complete Hunter Ser.). (ENG., Illus.). 128p. 21.95 *(978-1-58923-315-7(8)*, 1589233158, Creative Publishing International) Quayside.

Poulsen, Else. Smiling Bears: A Zookeeper Explores the Behavior & Emotional Life of Bears, 1 vol. 2011. (ENG.). 264p. pap. 17.95 *(978-1-55365-805-4(1)*, Greystone Bks.) D&M Pubs. Inc. CAN. Dist: Perseus-PGW.

Reed, Tom & Gookin, John. Bear Essentials: Hiking & Camping in Bear Country. 2009. (Nols Ser.). (ENG., Illus.). 112p. pap. 9.95 *(978-0-8117-3549-0(4))* Stackpole Bks.

Smith, Dave. Backcountry Bear Basics: The Definitive Guide to Avoiding Unpleasant Encounters. 2nd rev. ed. 2006. (Mountaineers Outdoor Basics Ser.). (ENG., Illus.). 175p. per. 15.95 *(978-1-59485-028-8(3))* Mountaineers Bks., The.

Smith, Richard P. Black Bear Hunting. 2007. (ENG., Illus.). 384p. 32.95 *(978-0-8117-0269-0(3))* Stackpole Bks.

Taylor, Dave. Black Bears: A Natural History, 1 vol. 2006. (ENG., Illus.). 188p. pap. 29.95 *(978-1-55041-849-1(1))* Fitzhenry & Whiteside, Ltd. CAN. Dist: Ingram Pub. Services.

BLACK BODY RADIATION

see Blackbody Radiation

BLACK BRIGADE OF CINCINNATI

Clark. The Black Brigade of Cincinnati; Being a Report of Its Labors & a Muster-Roll of Its Members; Toge. 2009. 36p. pap. 15.75 *(978-1-115-22521-2(9))* BiblioBazaar.

Clark,, Peter H., Peter H. The Black brigade of Cincinnati; being a report of its labors & a muster-roll of its members; Toge. 2009. 33p. pap. 16.99 *(978-1-115-22519-9(7)*, BiblioLife) BiblioBazaar.

BLACK CANADIANS

see Blacks—Canada

BLACK CARIB INDIANS

see Indians of Central America; Indians of the West Indies

BLACK CORPS (GERMANY)

see Nationalsozialistische Deutsche Arbeiter-Partei—Schutzstaffel

BLACK COUNTRY (ENGLAND)

Here are entered works on the region that comprises South Staffordshire, North Worcestershire, and North West Warwickshire.

Dovey, Zillah. Black Country. (Illus.). 160p. *(978-0-7509-1938-8(8))* Sutton Publishing.

Larkin, Tom. Black Country Chronicles. 2009. (ENG.). 96p. pap. 18.95 *(978-0-7509-5084-8(5))* History Pr. Ltd.,The GBR. Dist: Independent Pubs. Group.

Solomon, Philip. Haunted Black Country. 2009. (Haunted Ser.). (ENG., Illus.). 96p. pap. 19.95 *(978-0-7524-4882-4(X))* History Pr. Ltd.,The GBR. Dist: Independent Pubs. Group.

Williams, Ned. Black Country Chapels: A Third Selection. 2008. (ENG., Illus.). 128p. pap. 29.95 *(978-0-7509-4665-0(2))* History Pr. Ltd.,The GBR. Dist: Independent Pubs. Group.

BLACK DEATH

Here are entered works on the outbreak of the plague that swept parts of Asia and Europe in the fourteenth century.

Aberth, John. From the Brink of the Apocalypse: Confronting Famine, War, Plague & Death in the Later Middle Ages. 2nd rev. ed. 2009. (ENG., Illus.). 352p. 35.95 *(978-0-415-77797-1(6))*; 115.00 *(978-0-415-77796-4(8))* Routledge.

Baillie, Mike. New Light on the Black Death. 2006. (ENG., Illus.). 192p. pap. 39.95 *(978-0-7524-3598-5(1))* History Pr. Ltd.,The GBR. Dist: Independent Pubs. Group.

Benedictow, Ole J. The Black Death, 1346-1353: The Complete History. 2008. (Illus.). 454p. per. 45.00 *(978-1-84383-214-0(3))* Boydell & Brewer, Inc.

Bisgaard, Lars & Sondergaard, Leif. Living with the Black Death. 2009. (Illus.). 233p. pap. 30.00 *(978-87-7674-389-5(6))* Univ. Pr. of Southern Denmark DNK. Dist: International Specialized Bk. Services.

Borsch, Stuart J. The Black Death in Egypt & England: A Comparative Study. 2009. (ENG.). 207p. pap. 19.95 *(978-0-292-72213-2(3))* Univ. of Texas Pr.

Byrne, Joseph P. Daily Life During the Black Death. 2006. (Greenwood Press Daily Life Through History Ser.). (Illus.). 344p. 49.95 *(978-0-313-33297-5(5)*, GR3297, Greenwood Pr.) Greenwood Publishing Group, Inc.

Byrne, Joseph P. Encyclopedia of the Black Death, 1 vol. 2012. (Illus.). 429p. 89.00 ***(978-1-59884-253-1(6)**,* BLKDC) ABC-CLIO, LLC.

Byrne, Joseph Patrick. Encyclopedia of the Black Death. 2012. (Illus.). xxii, 429p. E-Book ***(978-1-59884-254-8(4))*** ABC-CLIO, LLC.

Campbell, Anna Montgomery. The Black Death & Men of Learning. 2011. 222p. 44.95 ***(978-1-258-04730-6(6))*** Literary Licensing, LLC.

Christakos, George, et al. Interdisciplinary Public Health Reasoning & Epidemic Modelling: the Case of Black Death: The Case of Black Death. 2010. (ENG., Illus.). xvi, 320p. pap. 159.00 *(978-3-642-06518-7(X)*, 364206518X) Springer.

French, Katherine L. The Good Women of the Parish: Gender & Religion after the Black Death. 2007. (Middle Ages Ser.). (Illus.). 352p. (C). 69.95 *(978-0-8122-4053-5(7))* Univ. of Pennsylvania Pr.

Hecker, Justus Fried. The Dancing Mania & the Black Death. 2006. pap. *(978-1-4068-1239-8(0))* Echo Library.

Hecker, Justus Friedrich Carl. The Black Death: The Dancing Mania. l.t. ed. 2007. (ENG.). 128p. pap. 18.99 *(978-1-4346-1629-6(0))*; 140p. pap. 19.99 *(978-1-4346-1798-9(X))* BiblioBazaar.

Martin, Sean. The Black Death. 2009. (ENG.). 160p. 8.99 *(978-0-7858-2289-9(5)*, 0785822895, Chartwell) Book Sales, Inc.

Sloane, Barnie. History of the Black Death in London. 2011. (ENG., Illus.). 224p. pap. 24.95 ***(978-0-7524-2829-1(2))*** History Pr. Ltd.,The GBR. Dist: Independent Pubs. Group.

Wray, Shona Kelly. Communities & Crisis: Bologna During the Black Death. 2009. 312p. *(978-90-04-17634-8(9))* BRILL.

Ziegler, Philip. The Black Death. 2006. (Illus.). 281p. reprint ed. 26.00 *(978-1-4223-5357-8(5))* DIANE Publishing Co.

—The Black Death. 2009. (P. S. Ser.). 336p. pap. 14.99 *(978-0-06-171898-4(X)*, HarperPerennial) HarperCollins Pubs.

BLACK DIASPORA

see African Diaspora

BLACK DRAMA (AFRICAN)

see African Drama

BLACK DRAMA (AMERICAN)

see American Drama—African American Authors

BLACK ELK, 1863-1950

Neihardt, John G. Black Elk Speaks: Being the Life Story of a Holy Man of the Oglala Sioux, the Premier Edition. 2008. (Illus.). xxviii, 334p. pap. 19.95 *(978-1-4384-2540-5(6))* State Univ. of New York Pr.

Stampoulos, Linda L. Black Elks Vermachtnis. 2006. (GER., Illus.). 178p. per. 14.95 *(978-1-60002-240-1(5)*, 4344) Mountain Valley Publishing, LLC.

—Black Elks Vermächtnis: Ein alter Pfad zu innerer Kraft Auf den Fußspuren eines heiligen Mannes der Lakota. Höh, Rainer, tr. from ENG. 2nd ed. 2010.Tr. of Redemption of Black Elk. (GER., Illus.). 176p. pap. *(978-1-926585-93-2(3)*, CCB Publishing) CCB Publishing.

—The Redemption of Black Elk: An Ancient Path to Inner Strength Following the Footprints of the Lakota Holy Man. 2nd ed. 2010.Tr. of Black Elks Vermächtnis. (Illus.). 152p. pap. *(978-1-926585-91-8(7)*, CCB Publishing) CCB Publishing.

Steltenkamp, Michael F. Nicholas Black Elk: Medicine Man, Missionary, Mystic. 2009. (ENG., Illus.). 256p. 24.95 *(978-0-8061-4063-6(1))* Univ. of Oklahoma Pr.

BLACK ENGLISH

Alim, H. Samy & Baugh, John, eds. Talkin Black Talk: Language, Education, & Social Change. (Multicultural Education Ser.). (ENG., Illus.). 192p. 2007. pap. 26.95 *(978-0-8077-4746-9(7))* 2006. 60.00 *(978-0-8077-4747-6(5))* Teachers College Pr., Teachers College, Columbia Univ.

Bailey, Joseph A., 2nd. Afrocentric English & Critical Thinking. 2006. xi, 319p. per. 19.95 *(978-1-59594-073-5(1))* WingSpan Publishing.

Banks, Adam J. Digital Griots: African American Rhetoric in a Multimedia Age. 2011. 192p. E-Book *(978-0-8093-8619-2(4))*; 208p. pap. 32.00 *(978-0-8093-3020-1(2))* Southern Illinois Univ. Pr.

Carroll-Flowers, Joan. The Ebonic Plague: A Little Book of Mentoring Wisdom. 2009. pap. 12.99 *(978-1-881223-21-4(3))* Zulema Enterprises.

Foster, Herbert L. The First Yiddish & Jive Dictionary: A Lexicon of the Yiddish & Jive Words in Common Usage. Date not set. (Orig.). pap. *(978-0-9624847-1-1(7))* Foster, Herbert L. Assocs., Inc.

Githiora, Christopher. Attitudes of Us African Immigrants' Toward African American English. 2009. 172p. pap. *(978-3-639-16111-3(4))* VDM Verlag Dr. Mueller e.K.

Green, Lisa J. Language & the African American Child. 2010. (ENG., Illus.). 284p. 99.00 *(978-0-521-85309-5(5))*; 288p. pap. 32.99 *(978-0-521-61817-5(7))* Cambridge Univ. Pr.

Gundaker, Grey. Signs of Diaspora/Diaspora of Signs. Date not set. (Commonwealth Center Studies in American Culture). (Illus.). 288p. reprint ed. pap. 18.95 *(978-0-19-510770-8(5))* Oxford Univ. Pr., Inc.

Herskovits, Melville Jean & Herskovits, Frances S. Suriname Folk-Lore. (Columbia University, Contributions to Anthropology Ser.: No. 27). (Illus.). reprint ed. 67.50 *(978-0-404-50577-6(5))* AMS Pr., Inc.

Kautzsch, Alexander. The Historical Evolution of Earlier African American English: An Empirical Comparison of Early Sources. (Topics in English Linguistics [TiEL] Ser.). (ENG.). XV, 335p. 180.00 ***(978-3-11-179679-6(5))*** De Gruyter, Mouton DEU. Dist: de Gruyter, Walter GmbH & Co. KG.

Meier, Terry. Black Communications & Learning to Read: Building on Children's Linguistic & Cultural Strengths. 2007. (Illus.). 335p. 110.00 *(978-0-8058-5759-7(1))*; per. 45.95 *(978-0-8058-5760-3(5))* Erlbaum, Lawrence Assocs., Inc.

Richardson, Elaine. Hiphop Literacies. 2006. (Literacies Ser.). (Illus.). 142p. 120.00 *(978-0-415-32928-6(0))*; (ENG., 160p. per. 39.95 *(978-0-415-32927-9(2))* Routledge.

Richardson, Elaine B. & Jackson, Ronald L. African Amer Rhetorics. 2007. (ENG.). 328p. pap. 30.00 *(978-0-8093-2745-4(7))* Southern Illinois Univ. Pr.

Rickford. African American English & Other Vernaculars in Education. pap. 150.00 *(978-0-8058-6051-1(7))* Erlbaum, Lawrence Assocs., Inc.

Rickford & Sweetland. African American English & Other Vernaculars in Education. 2012. (NCTE-Routledge Research Ser.). (ENG.). 336p. 135.00 *(978-0-8058-6050-4(9))* Routledge.

Yaeger-Dror, Malcah & Thomas, Erik R. African American English Speakers & Their Participation in Local Sound Changes: A Comparative Study. 2010. *(978-0-8223-6732-1(7))* Duke Univ. Pr.

BLACK EXPLORERS

see Explorers, Black

BLACK FAMILY

Carroll, William. On the Shoulders of Our Ancestors. 2010. pap. 14.95 *(978-0-7414-6102-5(1))* Infinity Publishing.

Craig, Robert. A Civil War Family: The Battling Blacks of Butler County, Pennsylvania. 2011. (ENG.). 45.00 *(978-0-615-46005-5(4))* CRAIG, Robert Scott S Craig.

BLACK FICTION (AFRICAN)

see African Fiction

BLACK FICTION (AMERICAN)

see American Fiction—African American Authors

BLACK FOREST (GERMANY)

Kaeflein, Achim & Philipp, Dorothee. Schwarzwald /Black Forest. 2006. 144p. 32.95 *(978-3-9810093-5-4(5))* edition-kaeflein.de DEU. Dist: Perseus-PGW.

Locken, E. Travel Journal the Black Forest. 2010. 192p. pap. 19.99 *(978-0-557-34031-6(4))* Lulu Enterprises Inc.

Meisen, Annette. Journey Through the Black Forest. 2011. (Journey Through Ser.). (ENG., Illus.). 140p. 29.95 *(978-3-8003-4078-1(X))* Verlagshaus Wurzburg GmbH & Co. KG DEU. Dist: Independent Pubs. Group.

Ruff, Thomas, photos by. Thomas Ruff: Schwarzwald - Landschaft. 2010. (GER & ENG., Illus.). 80p. 45.00 *(978-3-941185-51-7(9))* Verlag fur Moderne Kunst DEU. Dist: D.A.P./Distributed Art Pubs.

Schulte-Peevers, Andrea, et al. Munich, Bavaria & the Black Forest. 3rd rev. ed. 2008. (Lonely Planet Munich, Bavaria, & the Black Forest Ser.). (ENG., Illus.). 324p. pap. 19.99 *(978-1-74104-671-7(6))* Lonely Planet Pubns.

BLACK FRIARS

see Dominicans

BLACK HAIRDRESSING

see Hairdressing of Blacks

BLACK HAWK, SAUK CHIEF, 1767-1838

Black, Hawk. Autobiography of Ma-ka-tai-me-she-kia-kiak: Or Black Hawk. 2007. (ENG.). 180p. pap. 19.99 *(978-1-4264-6755-4(9))*; 198p. pap. 21.99 *(978-1-4264-6818-6(0))* BiblioBazaar.

Black Hawk, Chief Sauk. Life of Black Hawk. 2009. (Native American Ser.). (ENG.). 212p. pap. 15.95 *(978-1-4290-2231-6(0))* Applewood Bks.

Cole, Cyrenus. I Am a Man: The Indian Black Hawk. 316p. 2008. 45.95 *(978-1-4366-9766-8(2))* 2007. (ENG.). per. 30.95 *(978-1-4325-7040-8(4))* Kessinger Publishing, LLC.

—I Am a Man: The Indian Black Hawk. 312p. reprint ed. lib. bdg. 98.00 *(978-0-7222-0395-8(0))* Library Reprints, Inc.

Drake, Benjamin. The Great Indian Chief of the West: Or, Life & Adventures of Black Hawk. 2006. 194p. pap. 19.99 *(978-1-4264-5155-3(5))* 2007. (ENG.). 218p. pap. 22.99 *(978-1-4264-5456-1(2))* BiblioBazaar.

Hall, John W. Uncommon Defense: Indian Allies in the Black Hawk War. 2009. (Illus.). 384p. 31.50 *(978-0-674-03518-8(6))* Harvard Univ. Pr.

Hawk, Black. The Autobiography of Black Hawk. Patterson, J. B., ed. 2007. 160p. per. 12.75 *(978-1-60206-761-5(9))* Cosimo, Inc.

—Black Hawk: An Autobiography. 2006. pap. 7.99 *(978-1-59986-961-2(6))* Filiquarian Publishing, LLC.

Jung, Patrick. Thunder on the Wisconsin: The Battle of Wisconsin Heights. 2011. 128p. pap. 19.99 *(978-1-60949-052-2(5))* History Pr., The.

BLACK HAWK WAR, 1832

Army, Department of the. Uh-60 Black Hawk Pilot's Flight Operating Manual. 2011. 586p. pap. 49.95 ***(978-1-935700-61-6(8))*** Periscope Film, LLC.

Black Hawk, Chief Sauk. Life of Black Hawk. 2009. (Native American Ser.). (ENG.). 212p. pap. 15.95 *(978-1-4290-2231-6(0))* Applewood Bks.

Black Hawk Staff & Black Hawk. Life of Black Hawk, or Ma-ka-tai-me-she-kia-kiak: Dictated by Himself. 2008. (ENG., Illus.). 144p. (gr. 12-18). 14.00 *(978-0-14-310539-8(6),* Penguin Classics) Penguin Group (USA) Inc.

Cole, Cyrenus. I Am a Man: The Indian Black Hawk. 316p. 2008. 45.95 *(978-1-4366-9766-8(2))* 2007. (ENG.). per. 30.95 *(978-1-4325-7040-8(4))* Kessinger Publishing, LLC.

—I Am a Man: The Indian Black Hawk. 312p. reprint ed. lib. bdg. 98.00 *(978-0-7222-0395-8(0))* Library Reprints, Inc.

Cooke, Philip St George. Scenes & Adventures in the Army: Or, Romance of Military Life. by P. St. G. Cooke ... 2006. 436p. per. 26.99 *(978-1-4255-4813-1(X))* MPublishing.

Deeter, Robert. Bullseye: Journal of a Black Hawk Pilot. 2009. (ENG.). 192p. 25.99 *(978-1-4490-1463-6(1))*; pap. 16.99 *(978-1-4490-1462-9(3))* AuthorHouse.

Hall, John W. Uncommon Defense: Indian Allies in the Black Hawk War. 2009. (Illus.). 384p. 31.50 *(978-0-674-03518-8(6))* Harvard Univ. Pr.

Hawk, Black. The Autobiography of Black Hawk. Patterson, J. B., ed. 2007. 160p. per. 12.75 *(978-1-60206-761-5(9))* Cosimo, Inc.

—Black Hawk: An Autobiography. 2006. pap. 7.99 *(978-1-59986-961-2(6))* Filiquarian Publishing, LLC.

Jung, Patrick J. The Black Hawk War of 1832. 2008. (Campaigns & Commanders Ser.). (ENG.). 288p. pap. 19.95 *(978-0-8061-3994-4(3))* Univ. of Oklahoma Pr.

Stevens, Eugene C. Last Stand at Old Man's Creek: The True & Correct Story of the Battle of Stillman's Run, Black Hawk War 1832. 2008. 80p. pap. 16.95 *(978-1-60703-287-8(2))* PublishAmerica, Inc.

Thwaites, Reuben Gold. How George Rogers Clark Won the Northwest, & Other Essays in Western History. 2010. 156p. pap. *(978-1-152-96474-7(7))* Books LLC.

BLACK HEBREWS

Here are entered works on those groups (or individuals belonging to those groups) of African Americans or blacks who consider themselves Jewish or Hebrew in religion and ethnicity, but are not recognized as such by the Jewish community in general. Works on African Americans who are Jewish and are recognized as such by other Jews are entered under African American Jews.

Brinson, John. The Jewish Masquerade: The Relationship Between Modern Jews & Ancient Hebrew-Israelites. 2010. (Illus.). 158p. pap. 14.95 *(978-1-4327-6228-5(1))* Outskirts Pr., Inc.

Hayes, Stefanie. Identity in Contemporary Black-Jewish Fiction. 2010. 116p. pap. *(978-3-639-26514-9(9))* VDM Verlag Dr. Mueller e.K.

Könighofer, Martina. The New Ship of Zion: Dynamic Diaspora Dimensions of the African Hebrew Israelites of Jerusalem. 2011. (ENG.). 144p. pap. 29.50 *(978-3-8258-1055-9(0))* Lit Verlag DEU. Dist: Transaction Pubs.

Sherron, Fred Gilbert. The Spirituality of Black Hebrew Pentecostals: A Study of Two Religious Communities. 2010. vii, 217p. *(978-1-920383-03-9(4))* Sun Media.

BLACK HILLS (S.D. AND WYO.)

Bidwell, Laural A. Moon Mount Rushmore & the Black Hills: Including the Badlands. 2010. (Moon Handbooks Ser.). (ENG., Illus.). 236p. pap. 16.95 *(978-1-59880-365-5(4))* Avalon Travel Publishing.

Bryan, Jerry. An Illinois Gold Hunter in the Black Hills: The Diary of Jerry Bryan, March 13, 1876 to August 20 1876. 2011. 42p. 35.95 ***(978-1-258-06176-0(7))*** Literary Licensing, LLC.

Casey, Robert J. The Black Hills & Their Incredible Characters: A Chronicle & A Guide. 2011. 412p. 54.95 ***(978-1-258-08098-3(2))*** Literary Licensing, LLC.

Cerney, Jan, et al. Black Hills Gold Rush Towns. 2010. (Images of America Ser.). (ENG., Illus.). 128p. pap. 21.99 *(978-0-7385-7749-4(9))* Arcadia Publishing.

Dodge, Richard Irving. The Black Hills a Minute Description of the Routes. 2006. 188p. per. 18.99 *(978-1-4255-1498-3(7))* MPublishing.

Griffith, T. D. Insiders' Guide to South Dakota's Black Hills & Badlands. 6th ed. 2011. (Insiders' Guide Ser.). (ENG., Illus.). 368p. pap. 18.95 *(978-0-7627-6476-1(7),* Insiders' Guide) Globe Pequot Pr., The.

—Mount Rushmore: Black Hills & Badlands. 2011. (Illus.). 64p. pap. 9.95 *(978-1-933855-50-9(9))* Rio Nuevo Pubs.

Haber Stanton, Ann. Jewish Pioneers of the Black Hills Gold Rush. 2011. (Images of America Ser.). (Illus.). 128p. pap. 21.99 *(978-0-7385-7781-4(2))* Arcadia Publishing.

Horsted, Paul. The Black Hills Yesterday & Today. 2006. (Illus.). 304p. 65.00 *(978-0-9718053-3-0(4))* Golden Valley Pr.

Horsted, Paul, et al. Crossing the Plains with Custer. 2009. (Illus.). 336p. pap. 45.00 *(978-0-9718053-5-4(0))* Golden Valley Pr.

Howe, Craig Phillip, et al. He Sapa Woihanble: Black Hills Dream. 2011.Tr. of Black Hills Dream. (DAK., Illus.). pap. 20.00 ***(978-0-9721886-9-2(X))*** Living Justice Pr.

Kirschenmann, Jay. Black Hills: A Guide to South Dakota's Classic American Frontier. 2nd ed. 2011. (Tourist Town Guides). 216p. pap. 14.95 *(978-1-935455-10-3(9))* Channel Lake, Inc.

Kopco, Mary A., ed. Beyond Mount Rushmore: Other Black Hills Faces. 2010. (Illus.). pap. 19.95 *(978-0-9822749-6-5(3))* South Dakota State Historical Society.

Luschei, Martin. The Black Hills & the Indians. 2007. 25.00 *(978-1-930401-56-3(6))*; pap. 18.00 *(978-1-930401-55-6(8))* Central Coast Pr.

National Geographic Society Staff. Black Hills North: Trails Illustrated Map. 2010. 11.95 *(978-1-56695-379-5(0))* National Geographic Maps.

Orenczak, Zach & Lynn, Rachael. The Needles: A Climber's Guide to the Black Hills Needles. 2007. per. 35.00 *(978-0-9746532-8-0(4))* Extreme Angles.

Ostler, Jeffrey. The Lakotas & the Black Hills: The Struggle for Sacred Ground. (ENG.). 256p. (gr. 12). 2011. 14.00 *(978-0-14-311920-3(6),* Penguin (Non-Classics)) 2010. 22.95 *(978-0-670-02195-6(4),* Viking Adult) Penguin Group (USA) Inc.

Owen, Luella Agnes. Cave Regions of the Ozarks & Black Hills. 2008. 172p. 22.99 *(978-0-554-35613-6(9))* 2008. 172p. 25.99 *(978-0-554-26310-6(6))* 2007. (ENG.). 156p. pap. 19.99 *(978-1-4346-0844-4(1))* 2007. (ENG.). 170p. pap. 21.99 *(978-1-4346-0918-2(9))* BiblioBazaar.

—Cave Regions of the Ozarks & Black Hills. 2009. (Illus.). 160p. pap. *(978-1-4099-6036-2(6))* Dodo Pr.

Pengra, Lilah. Sarah Campbell: The first white woman in the Black Hills was African American. 2009. (Illus.). 136p. pap. 18.95 *(978-0-615-28873-4(1))* Lune Hse. Publishing.

Price, S. Goodale. Black Hills: The Land of Legend. 2011. 138p. 40.95 ***(978-1-258-01491-9(2))*** Literary Licensing, LLC.

Putnam, Larry D., et al. Water-Quality Effects & Characterization of Indicators of Onsite Wastewater Disposal Systems in the East-Central Black Hills Area, South Dakota, 2006-08. 2008. (Illus.). viii, 115p. pap. *(978-1-4113-2342-1(4))* United States Geological Survey.

Sanders, Jerry & Baskett, Tom, Jr. An Introduction to Custer State Park & the Southern Black Hills. (Illus.). 48p. pap. 5.95 *(978-0-9629549-1-7(8))* Three-Mile Creek Publishing Co.

Spring, Agnes Wright. The Cheyenne & the Black Hills Stage & Express Routes. 2011. 418p. 54.95 ***(978-1-258-04688-0(1))*** Literary Licensing, LLC.

United States. Army. Corps Of Engineers. Report of a Reconnaissance of the Black Hills of Dakota, Made in the Summer of 1874 by William Ludlow, Captain of Engineers, Bvt Lieut Colonel, U S. 2011. 128p. pap. 16.99 ***(978-1-4255-0886-9(3))*** MPublishing.

BLACK HOLES (ASTRONOMY)

Abramowicz, Marek A., et al, eds. Theory of Black Hole Accretion Discs. 2010. (Cambridge Contemporary Astrophysics Ser.). (ENG., Illus.). 308p. pap. 39.99 *(978-0-521-15295-2(X))* Cambridge Univ. Pr.

Axelsson, Magnus. Cool Discs, Hot Flows. 2008. (AIP Conference Proceedings / Astronomy & Astrophysics Space Ser.). spiral bd. 145.00 *(978-0-7354-0584-4(0),* 0735405840) American Institute of Physics.

Barger, A. J., ed. Supermassive Black Holes in the Distant Universe. 2010. (Astrophysics & Space Science Library). x, 302p. pap. 189.00 *(978-90-481-6662-6(4),* 9048166624) Springer.

Begelman, Mitchell C. & Rees, Martin. Gravity's Fatal Attraction: Black Holes in the Universe. 2nd ed. 2009. (ENG., Illus.). 312p. pap. 38.99 *(978-0-521-71793-9(0))* Cambridge Univ. Pr.

Bellucci, Stefano, ed. Supersymmetric Mechanics Vol. 1: Supersymmetry, Noncommutativity & Matrix Models, 2 vols. 2006. (Lecture Notes in Physics Ser.: Vol. 698). (Illus.). xiv, 229p. 89.95 *(978-3-540-33313-5(4),* 3540333134) Springer.

Beskin, Vasily. MHD Flows in Compact Astrophysical Objects: Accretion, Winds & Jets. 2009. (Astronomy & Astrophysics Library). (ENG., Illus.). xviii, 425p. 129.00 *(978-3-642-01289-1(2),* 3642012892) Springer.

Black Holes Expanded: The Unified Theory. 2008. (Illus.). 128p. pap. 9.95 net. *(978-0-912175-01-0(X))* Quality Pr.

Blaha, Stephen. Physics Beyond the Light Barrier: The Source of Parity Violation, Tachyons, & a Derivation of Standard Model Features. 2007. (ENG., Illus.). 124p. pap. 17.95 *(978-0-9746958-7-7(4))* Pingree-Hill Publishing.

Chow, Tai L. Gravity, Black Holes, & the Very Early Universe: An Introduction to General Relativity & Cosmology. (ENG., Illus.). xv, 280p. 2010. pap. 99.00 *(978-1-4419-2525-1(2),* 1441925252) 2007. 99.00 *(978-0-387-73629-7(8),* 0387736298) Springer.

Constantin, Anca. Supermassive Black Hole Accretion Across the Age of the Universe. 2011. 184p. pap. ***(978-3-8443-2477-8(1))*** Lambert Academic Publishing.

Debattista, Victor P. & Popescu, Cristina C., eds. Hunting for the Dark: The Hidden Side of Galaxy Formation. 2010. (AIP Conference Proceedings / Astronomy & Astrophysics Ser.). (Illus.). 472p. 236.00 *(978-0-7354-0786-2(X),* 073540786X, AIP Pr.) Springer.

Dermer, C. D. High-Energy Radiation from Black Holes - Gamma Rays, Cosmic Rays, & Neutrinos. 2009. (Princeton Series in Astrophysics Ser.). (ENG., Illus.). 568p. (C). 125.00 *(978-0-691-13795-7(1))*; pap. 78.50 *(978-0-691-14408-5(7))* Princeton Univ. Pr.

Frolov, Valeri P. & Zelnikov, Andrei. Introduction to Black Hole Physics. 2011. (ENG., Illus.). 504p. 98.50 ***(978-0-19-969229-3(7))*** Oxford Univ. Pr., Inc.

Futterman, J. A. H., et al. Scattering from Black Holes. 2009. (Cambridge Monographs on Mathematical Physics Ser.). (ENG.). 204p. pap. 48.00 *(978-0-521-11210-9(9))* Cambridge Univ. Pr.

G, Ersin, et al, eds. Astrophysics of Neutron Stars 2010: A Conference in Honor of M. Ali Alpar. 2012. (AIP Conference Proceedings / Astronomy & Astrophysics Ser.). (ENG.). 242p. pap. 144.00 ***(978-0-7354-0939-2(0),*** 073540939O, AIP Pr.) Springer.

Garfinkle, David & Garfinkle, Richard. Three Steps to the Universe: From the Sun to Black Holes to the Mystery of Dark Matter. 280p. 2010. (ENG.). pap. 16.00 *(978-0-226-28348-7(8))* 2008. (Illus.). 25.00 *(978-0-226-28346-3(1))* Univ. of Chicago Pr.

Garrison, David. Testing Binary Black Hole Codes in Strong Field Regimes. 2011. 128p. pap. ***(978-3-8443-1445-8(8))*** Lambert Academic Publishing.

Glendenning, Norman K. Special & General Relativity: With Applications to White Dwarfs, Neutron Stars & Black Holes. (Astronomy & Astrophysics Library). (Illus.). 2010. xii, 228p. pap. 99.00 *(978-1-4419-2366-0(7),* 1441923667) 2007. XII, 228p. (C). 99.00 *(978-0-387-47106-8(5),* 0387471065) Springer.

Hacyan, Shahen. Los Hoyos Negros y la Curvatura del Espacio. (Ciencia para Todos Ser.). (SPA.). pap. 6.99 *(978-968-16-2797-3(0))* Fondo de Cultura Economica USA.

Hawking, Stephen W. & Israel, W., eds. General Relativity: An Einstein Centenary Survey, 2 vols. 2010. 919p. pap. 86.00 ***(978-0-521-13798-0(5))*** Cambridge Univ. Pr.

Ho, Luis C., ed. Coevolution of Black Holes & Galaxies. 2010. (ENG., Illus.). 500p. pap. 60.00 *(978-0-521-14156-7(7))* Cambridge Univ. Pr.

Horowitz, Gary T., ed. Black Holes in Higher Dimensions. 2012. (ENG., Illus.). 436p. 99.00 ***(978-1-107-01345-2(3))*** Cambridge Univ. Pr.

Iyer, B. R. & Bhawal, B., eds. Black Holes, Gravitational Radiation & the Universe: Essays in Honor of C. V. Vishveshwara. 2010. (Fundamental Theories of Physics Ser.). 588p. pap. 419.00 *(978-90-481-5121-9(X),* 904815121X) Springer.

Jamil, Mubasher. Black Holes in an Accelerated Universe. 2011. 132p. pap. ***(978-3-8454-1789-9(7))*** Lambert Academic Publishing.

Joshi, Pankaj S. Gravitational Collapse & Spacetime Singularities. 2007. (Cambridge Monographs on Mathematical Physics). (ENG., Illus.). 284p. 123.00 *(978-0-521-87104-4(2))* Cambridge Univ. Pr.

Karas, Vladimir & Matt, Giorgio. Black Holes from Stars to Galaxies: Across the Range of Masses: Proceedings of the 238th Symposium of the International Astronomical Union Held in Prague, Czech Republic, August 21-25, 2006.

Karas, Vladimir & Matt, Giorgio, eds. 2007. (Proceedings of the International Astronomical Union Symposia & Colloquia Ser.). (ENG., Illus.). 504p. 141.99 *(978-0-521-86347-6(3))* Cambridge Univ. Pr.

Kawaler, S.D., et al. Stellar Remnants: Saas-Fee Advanced Course 25. Lecture Notes 1995. Swiss Society for Astrophysics & Astronomy. Meynet, Georges & Schaerer, Daniel, eds. 2010. (Saas-Fee Advanced Courses Ser.). (Illus.). xii, 340p. pap. 89.95 *(978-3-642-08264-1(5),* 3642082645) Springer.

Kubeka, Amos. Linear Perturbations of a Schwarzschild Black Hole. 2010. 184p. pap. *(978-3-8383-4435-5(9))* Lambert Academic Publishing.

Livio, Mario & Koekemoer, Anton M., eds. Black Holes. 2011. (Space Telescope Science Institute Symposium Ser.). (ENG., Illus.). 332p. 115.00 *(978-1-107-00553-2(1))* Cambridge Univ. Pr.

Maccarone, Thomas J., et al, eds. From X-ray Binaries to Quasars: Black Holes on All Mass Scales: Black Holes on All Mass Scales. 2010. (Illus.). vi, 288p. pap. 149.00 *(978-90-481-7037-1(0),* 9048170370) Springer.

Mao, Jirong. Coevolution Between Supermassive Black Holes & Their Host Galaxies. 2010. 200p. pap. *(978-3-8383-6756-9(1))* Lambert Academic Publishing.

Meier, David L. Black Hole Astrophysics: The Engine Paradigm. 2012. (Springer Praxis Books / Astronomy & Planetary Sciences Ser.). (ENG., Illus.). 850p. 139.00 *(978-3-642-01935-7(8),* 3642019358) Springer.

Melia, Fulvio. Cracking the Einstein Code: Relativity & the Birth of Black Hole Physics. 2009. (ENG., Illus.). 150p. 25.00 *(978-0-226-51951-7(1))* Univ. of Chicago Pr.

—The Galactic Supermassive Black Hole. 2007. (Illus.). 320p. (C). (ENG.). per. 59.95 *(978-0-691-13129-0(5))*;Bk. 2. 110.00 *(978-0-691-09535-6(3))* Princeton Univ. Pr.

Merloni, Andrea, et al, eds. Growing Black Holes: Accretion in a Cosmological Context: Proceedings of the MPA/ESO/MPE/USM Joint Astronomy Conference Held at Garching, Germany, 21-25 June 2004. 2010. (ESO Astrophysics Symposia Ser.). xiv, 506p. pap. 99.95 *(978-3-642-06447-0(7),* 3642064477) Springer.

Metzger, Lenard. Common Sense Cosmology. 2010. 104p. pap. 10.98 *(978-0-557-51848-7(2))* Lulu Enterprises Inc.

Michelle, Harley. Radiation Recoil from Spinning Black Hole Mergers. 2010. 88p. pap. *(978-3-8383-4008-1(6))* Lambert Academic Publishing.

Morris, Mark, et al. The Galactic Center: A Window to the Nuclear Environment of Disk Galaxies: Proceedings of a Workshop Held at Shanghai, China, 19-23

October 2009. 2011. (Illus.). xix, 494p. E-Book ***(978-1-58381-759-9(X))*** Astronomical Society of the Pacific, The.

Morris, Mark R., ed. Galactic Center: A Window to the Nuclear Environment of Disk Galaxies, Proceedings. 2011. 494p. 77.00 ***(978-1-58381-758-2(1))*** Astronomical Society of the Pacific, The.

Novikov, I. & Frolov, V. Physics of Black Holes. Kisin, V. I. & Yankovsky, E. M., trs. 2010. (Fundamental Theories of Physics Ser.). 360p. pap. 379.00 *(978-90-481-8448-4(7)*, 9048184487) Springer.

Ottersbach, John Philip. Micro Black Holes at the Lhc. 2010. 96p. pap. *(978-3-8383-7273-0(5))* Lambert Academic Publishing.

Papantonopoulos, Lefteris. Physics of Black Holes. 2009. (Lecture Notes in Physics Ser.). (ENG., Illus.). xvi, 511p. 129.00 *(978-3-540-88459-0(9))* Springer.

Peterson, Bradley M., et al, eds. Co-evolution of Central Black Holes & Galaxies (IAU S267) 2010. (Proceedings of the International Astronomical Union Symposia & Colloquia Ser.). (Illus.). 494p. 125.00 *(978-0-521-76502-2(1))* Cambridge Univ. Pr.

Poisson, Eric. A Relativist's Toolkit: The Mathematics of Black-Hole Mechanics. 2007. (ENG., Illus.). 252p. pap. 54.00 *(978-0-521-53790-3(0))* Cambridge Univ. Pr.

Propst, Raphael J. Black Holes & Galaxy Formation. Wachter, Adonis D., ed. 2010. (Space Science, Exploration & Policies Ser.). 413p. 145.00 *(978-1-60741-703-3(0))* Nova Science Pubs., Inc.

Punsly, Brian. Black Hole Gravitohydromagnetics. 2nd ed. (Astrophysics & Space Science Library). (Illus.). 2010. xiv, 399p. pap. 179.00 *(978-3-642-09563-4(1)*, 3642095631) 2008. 440p. 179.00 *(978-3-540-76955-2(2)*, 3540769552) Springer.

Ralf, Schützhold & Unruh, William, eds. Quantum Analogues: From Phase Transitions to Black Holes & Cosmology. 2007. (Lecture Notes in Physics Ser.). (Illus.). xiv, 300p. (C). 129.00 *(978-3-540-70658-2(8)*, 3540708588) Springer.

Scharf, Caleb. Gravity's Engines: How Bubble-Blowing Black Holes Rule Galaxies, Stars, & Life in the Cosmos. 2012. (ENG., Illus.). 272p. 26.00 ***(978-0-374-11412-1(9)***, Scientific American Bk., A) Farrar, Straus & Giroux.

Slezakova, Gabriela & Kalnins, Ernie. Geodesic Geometry of Black Holes. 2008. 368p. pap. *(978-3-639-07042-2(9))* VDM Verlag Dr. Mueller e.K.

Susskind, Leonard. The Black Hole War: My Battle with Stephen Hawking to Make the World Safe for Quantum Mechanics. (ENG., Illus.). 480p. 2009. pap. 15.99 *(978-0-316-01641-4(1)*, Back Bay Bks.) 2008. 27.99 *(978-0-316-01640-7(3))* Little Brown & Co.

Thomas, Edwin & Raine, Derek. Black Holes: An Introduction. 2nd ed. 2009. (Illus.). 212p. 58.00 *(978-1-84816-382-9(7))* Imperial College Pr. GBR. Dist: World Scientific Publishing Co., Inc.

Tiwari, Bhupendra Nath. Correlations, Stabilities & Black Holes in String Theory & M-Theory. 2011. 240p. pap. ***(978-3-8443-9521-1(0))*** Lambert Academic Publishing.

Tyson, Neil deGrasse. Death by Black Hole: And Other Cosmic Quandaries. 2007. (ENG., Illus.). 384p. pap. 15.95 *(978-0-393-33016-8(8)*, 33016); 320p. 24.95 *(978-0-393-06224-3(4)*, 6224) Norton, W. W. & Co., Inc.

Unruh, William & Schatzhold, Ralf, eds. Quantum Analogues: from Phase Transitions to Black Holes & Cosmology: From Phase Transitions to Black Holes & Cosmology. 2010. (Lecture Notes in Physics Ser.). (Illus.). xiv, 300p. pap. 129.00 *(978-3-642-08984-8(4)*, 3642089844) Springer.

Uruchurtu, Linda. Exploring the Gauge/Gravity Correspondence. 2009. 228p. pap. *(978-3-639-17716-9(9))* VDM Verlag Dr. Mueller e.K.

Vishveshwara, C. V. Einstein's Enigma or Black Holes in My Bubble Bath. (ENG.). x, 360p. 2010. pap. 39.95 *(978-3-642-06973-4(8)*, 3642069738) 2006. (Illus.). 39.95 *(978-3-540-33199-5(9)*, 3540331999) Springer.

Wiltshire, David L., et al. The Kerr Spacetime: Rotating Black Holes in General Relativity. Wiltshire, David L. et al, eds. 2009. (ENG., Illus.). 378p. 108.00 *(978-0-521-88512-6(4))* Cambridge Univ. Pr.

Zhang, Mimi. Loss Cone Refilling by Flyby Encounters. 2009. 140p. pap. *(978-3-639-16455-8(5))* VDM Verlag Dr. Mueller e.K.

Zink, Burkhard. Ray-tracing Black Holes: Theory & Implementation. 2008. 136p. pap. *(978-3-639-02902-4(X))* VDM Verlag Dr. Mueller e.K.

BLACK HUMOR (AFRICAN AMERICAN HUMOR)
see African American Wit and Humor

BLACK JACK (GAME)
see Blackjack (Game)

BLACK JEWS (AFRICAN AMERICAN RELIGIOUS SECTS)
see Black Hebrews

BLACK JUDAISM
see Black Hebrews

BLACK LABRADOR RETRIEVER
see Labrador Retriever

BLACK-LEAD
see Graphite

BLACK LIGHT
see Ultraviolet Radiation

BLACK LITERATURE
see Literature—Black Authors

BLACK LITERATURE (AFRICAN)
see African Literature

BLACK LITERATURE (AMERICAN)
see American Literature—African American Authors

BLACK MADONNA (ICON)
see Our Lady of Czestochowa (Icon)

BLACK MARKET

Andreas, Peter. Blue Helmets & Black Markets: The Business of Survival in the Siege of Sarajevo. 2008. (Illus.). 240p. 25.00 *(978-0-8014-4355-8(5))* Cornell Univ. Pr.

Drugs and Crime Prevention Committee Staff. Transnational Trafficking & the Rule of Law in West Africa: A Threat Assessment. 2012. (ENG.). 100p. pap. 25.00 ***(978-92-1-130284-4(6))*** United Nations Pubns.

Gilman, Nils, et al. Deviant Globalization. Gilman, Nils et al, eds. 2011. (ENG., Illus.). 320p. 110.00 *(978-1-4411-9312-4(X))* Continuum International Publishing Group, Ltd. GBR. Dist: National Bk. Network.

—Deviant Globalization: Black Market Economy in the 21st Century. Gilman, Nils et al, eds. 2011. (ENG., Illus.). 320p. pap. 32.95 *(978-1-4411-7810-7(4))* Continuum International Publishing Group, Ltd. GBR. Dist: National Bk. Network.

Naylor, R. T. Wages of Crime: Black Markets, Illegal Finance & the Underworld Economy. (ENG.). 270p. *(978-0-7735-2417-0(7))* McGill-Queen's Univ. Pr.

Potter, Matt. The Outlaws Inc: Under the Radar & on the Black Market with the World's Most Dangerous Smugglers. 2011. (Illus.). 336p. 27.00 *(978-1-60819-530-5(9))* Bloomsbury Publishing.

Rachlin, Andrew & Dimitrova, Dessislava, eds. Marshaling Every Resource: State & Local Responses to Human Trafficking. 2007. 150p. pap. 13.95 *(978-0-9789595-0-0(7))* Policy Research Institute for the Region.

Zierenberg, Malte. Stadt der Schieber: Der Berliner Schwarzmarkt 1939 - 1950. Kritische Studien zur Geschichtswissenschaft Bd.179. 2008. (Kritische Studien Zur Geschichtswissenschaft Ser.). (GER., Illus.). 349p. (C). pap. 54.00 *(978-3-525-35111-6(9))* Vandenhoeck & Ruprecht GmbH & Co. KG DEU. Dist: ISD.

BLACK MARKET—INFANTS
see Adoption—Corrupt Practices

BLACK MASS
see Satanism

BLACK MILITANT ORGANIZATIONS

Alliez, Eric & Kerslake, Christian, eds. The Guattari Effect. 2011. (ENG., Illus.). 320p. 130.00 *(978-1-4411-3680-0(0))* Continuum International Publishing Group, Ltd. GBR. Dist: National Bk. Network.

Jeffries, Judson L., ed. Black Power in the Belly of the Beast. 2006. 336p. 67.00 *(978-0-252-03148-9(2))*; per. 26.00 *(978-0-252-07394-6(0))* Univ. of Illinois Pr.

Muntaqim, Jalil A. We Are Our Own Liberators: Selected Prison Writings. 2010. (ENG.). 304p. pap. 16.95 *(978-0-9742884-6-8(2))* Arissa Media Group.

BLACK MONKS
see Benedictines

BLACK MOUNTAIN COLLEGE (BLACK MOUNTAIN, N.C.)

Alexander, Lincoln. Go to School, You're a Little Black Boy: The Honourable Lincoln M. Alexander - A Memoir. 2010. (ENG., Illus.). 256p. pap. 26.99 *(978-1-55488-733-0(X))* Dundurn CAN. Dist: Ingram Pub. Services.

Duberman, Martin B. Black Mountain: An Exploration in Community. 2009. (ENG., Illus.). 616p. pap. 24.95 *(978-0-8101-2594-0(3))* Northwestern Univ. Pr.

BLACK MUSIC
see Blacks—Music

BLACK MUSLIMS
Here are entered works on the movement known as the Nation of Islam or Black Muslims.

Berg, Herbert. Elijah Muhammad & Islam. 2009. (ENG.). 208p. 39.00 *(978-0-8147-9113-4(1))* New York Univ. Pr.

Curtis, Edward E., IV. Black Muslim Religion in the Nation of Islam, 1960-1975. 2006. (ENG., Illus.). 256p. per. 22.00 *(978-0-8078-5771-7(8))* Univ. of North Carolina Pr.

Doctor, Bernard Aquina. Malcolm X for Beginners. 2007. (For Beginners Ser.). (ENG., Illus.). 192p. per. 14.95 *(978-1-934389-04-1(8)*, For Beginners) Steerforth Pr.

Gibson, Dawn-Marie. A History of the Nation of Islam: Race, Islam, & the Quest for Freedom, 1 vol. 2012. 239p. 48.00 ***(978-0-313-39807-0(0)***, A3607C) Greenwood Publishing Group, Inc.

The History of Masjid Muhammad And: The Early Muslims in the Washington, DC Area. 2009. 74p. pap. 12.00 *(978-0-9742868-4-6(2))* FreeMan Pubns.

Jackson, Sherman A. Islam & the Problem of Black Suffering. 2009. (ENG.). 232p. 29.95 *(978-0-19-538206-8(4))* Oxford Univ. Pr., Inc.

Jarvis, Malcolm Shorty & Nichols, Paul D. The Other Malcolm- Shorty Jarvis: His Memoir. West, Cornel, ed. alt. ed. 2008. (ENG., Illus.). 179p. pap. 35.00 *(978-0-7864-4057-3(0))* McFarland & Co., Inc. Pubs.

Levinsohn, Florence H. & Levinsohn, Florence. Looking for Farrakhan. 2009. (ENG.). 320p. pap. 26.00 *(978-1-56663-784-8(8))* Dee, Ivan R. Pub.

Malcolm X. End of White World Supremacy: Four Speeches. 2011. (ENG.). 160p. pap. 12.95 *(978-1-61145-016-3(0)*, 611016, Arcade Publishing) Skyhorse Publishing Co., Inc.

Marable, Manning. Malcolm X: A Life of Reinvention. 2011. (ENG.). 608p. (gr. 12). 18.00 ***(978-0-14-312032-2(8)***, Penguin (Non-Classics)); (Illus.). 30.00 *(978-0-670-02220-5(9)*, Viking Adult) Penguin Group (USA) Inc.

Marable, Manning & Aidi, Hishaam D., eds. Black Routes to Islam. 2009. (Critical Black Studies). (ENG.). 336p. 105.00 *(978-1-4039-8400-5(X))*; pap. 32.00 *(978-1-4039-7781-6(X))* Palgrave Macmillan.

McCloud, Aminah Beverly. Transnational Muslims in American Society. 2006. (ENG.). 176p. 39.95 *(978-0-8130-2971-9(6))* Univ. Pr. of Florida.

Muhammad, Elijah. How to Eat to Live, Bk. I. 123p. reprint ed. pap. 8.95 *(978-1-56411-019-0(2))* UBUS Communications Systems.

Muhammad, Jabril, compiled by. Closing the Gap: Inner Views of the Heart, Mind & Soul of the Honorable Minister Louis Farrakhan. 2006. per. 20.00 *(978-1-929594-99-3(2))* FCN Publishing Co.

Nash, Michael. Islam among Urban Blacks: Muslims in Newark, New Jersey: A Social History. 2008. (ENG., Illus.). 154p. 57.99 *(978-0-7618-3865-4(1))*; per. 31.50 *(978-0-7618-3866-1(X))* Univ. Pr. of America, Inc.

Peele, Thomas. Killing the Messenger: A Story of Radical Faith, Racism's Backlash, & the Assassination of a Journalist. 2012. (ENG.). 464p. 26.00 ***(978-0-307-71755-9(0)***, Crown) Crown Publishing Group.

Pitre, Abul. The Educational Philosophy of Elijah Muhammad: Education for a New World. 2nd ed. 2008. (ENG.). 132p. 57.99 *(978-0-7618-4082-4(6))* Univ. Pr. of America, Inc.

—Elijah Muhammad Ideas for Black Education. 2007. pap. 15.00 *(978-1-56411-544-7(5)*, YBBG#0509, UBUS Communications Systems) UBUS Communications Systems.

—An Introduction to Elijah Muhammad Studies: The New Educational Paradigm. 2010. (Elijah Muhammad Studies: Interdisciplinary, Educational, & Islamic Studies Ser.). (ENG.). 100p. 41.99 *(978-0-7618-5080-9(5))* Univ Pr. of America, Inc.

Pitre, Abul & Pahl, Ray. The Educational Philosophy of Elijah Muhammad: Education for a New World. 2nd ed. 2008. (ENG.). 132p. pap. 28.50 *(978-0-7618-4083-1(4))* Univ. Pr. of America, Inc.

Sherwood, Marika. Malcolm X: Visits Abroad. 2011. 256p. pap. 24.95 ***(978-1-59907-050-6(2))*** Tsehai Pubs. & Distributors.

Wainstock, Dennis. Malcolm X, African American Revolutionary. 2008. (ENG., Illus.). 229p. pap. 35.00 *(978-0-7864-3934-8(3))* McFarland & Co., Inc. Pubs.

BLACK NATIONALISM
see also Black Muslims

Boyce Davies, Carole, ed. Claudia Jones: Beyond Containment. 2011. (Illus.). 240p. pap. 24.95 *(978-0-9562401-6-3(X))* Clarke, Ayebia Publishing, Ltd. GBR. Dist: Rienner, Lynne Pubs.

Bush, Rod. The End of White World Supremacy: Black Internationalism & the Problem of the Color Line. 2009. (ENG.). 264p. 81.50 *(978-1-59213-572-1(2))*; pap. 29.95 *(978-1-59213-573-8(0))* Temple Univ. Pr.

Cruse, Harold. Rebellion or Revolution? 2009. (ENG.). 280p. pap. 18.50 *(978-0-8166-5901-2(X))* Univ. of Minnesota Pr.

Curtis, Edward E., IV. Black Muslim Religion in the Nation of Islam, 1960-1975. 2006. (ENG., Illus.). 256p. per. 22.00 *(978-0-8078-5771-7(8))* Univ. of North Carolina Pr.

Davidson, Harry X. Somebody's Trying to Kill You Vol. I: Psychodynamics of White Racism & Black Pathology. 2nd rev. ed. 137p. pap. *(978-0-9644417-1-2(3))* Davidson, Harry R.

Davidson, Harry X., et al. Somebody's Trying to Kill You Vol. II: The Economics of Death. Lewis, R. H., ed. 158p. pap. 15.00 *(978-0-9644417-0-5(5))* Davidson, Harry R.

Delany, Martin Robison. The Condition Elevation Emigration & Destiny of the Colored People of the United States. 2008. 184p. 25.99 *(978-0-554-26249-9(5))* 2008. 184p. 22.99 *(978-0-554-35552-8(3))* 2007. (ENG.). 162p. pap. 19.99 *(978-1-4346-0724-9(0))* 2007. (ENG.). 182p. pap. 21.99 *(978-1-4346-0784-3(4))* BiblioBazaar.

Doctor, Bernard Aquina. Malcolm X for Beginners. 2007. (For Beginners Ser.). (ENG., Illus.). 192p. per. 14.95 *(978-1-934389-04-1(8)*, For Beginners) Steerforth Pr.

Dodson, Howard & Palmer, Colin, eds. Ideology, Identity, & Assumptions. 2007. (Schomburg Studies on the Black Experience). (ENG., Illus.). 205p. per. 19.95 *(978-0-87013-795-2(6))* Michigan State Univ. Pr.

Dossett, Kate. Bridging Race Divides: Black Nationalism, Feminism, & Integration in the United States, 1896-1935. 2009. (ENG., Illus.). 280p. pap. 29.95 *(978-0-8130-3495-9(7))* Univ. Pr. of Florida.

Duse Mohamed & Abdelwahid, Mustafa A. Dusé Mohamed Ali (1866-1945) 2011. 218p. *(978-1-56902-343-3(3))*; pap. *(978-1-56902-344-0(1))* Red Sea Pr.

Fergus, Devin. Liberalism, Black Power, & the Making of American Politics, 1965-1980. 2009. (Politics & Culture in the Twentieth-Century South Ser.). (ENG., Illus.). 376p. pap. 26.95 *(978-0-8203-3324-3(7))*; lib. bdg. 69.95 *(978-0-8203-3323-6(9))* Univ. of Georgia Pr.

Foley, Barbara. Spectres Of 1919: Class & Nation in the Making of the New Negro. 2008. (ENG., Illus.). 328p. pap. 26.00 *(978-0-252-07585-8(4))* Univ. of Illinois Pr.

Harold, Claudrena N. The Rise & Fall of the Garvey Movement in the Urban South, 1918-1942. 2007. (Studies in African American History & Culture). (Illus.). 171p. 120.00 *(978-0-415-95619-2(6))* Routledge.

Harris-Lacewell, Melissa Victoria. Barbershops, Bibles, & Bet: Everyday Talk & Black Political Thought. annot. ed. 2006. (ENG., Illus.). 368p. (C). per. 26.95 *(978-0-691-12609-8(7))* Princeton Univ. Pr.

Hucks, Tracey E. Yoruba Traditions & African American Religious Nationalism. 2012. ***(978-0-8263-5077-0(1))***; (ENG., Illus.). 456p. (C). 60.00 ***(978-0-8263-5075-6(5))*** Univ. of New Mexico Pr.

Hughes, Heather. The First President: A Life of John L. Dube, Founding President of the ANC. 2011. (ENG., Illus.). 288p. pap. 35.95 ***(978-1-77009-813-8(5))*** Jacana Media ZAF. Dist: Independent Pubs. Group.

Jackson, Maurice & Bacon, Jacqueline, eds. African Americans & the Haitian Revolution. 2009. (ENG., Illus.). 272p. (C). 150.00 *(978-0-415-80375-5(6))*; pap. 39.95 *(978-0-415-80376-2(4))* Routledge.

Jackson, Sherman A. Islam & the Blackamerican: Looking Toward the Third Resurrection, 1 vol. 2011. (ENG.). 246p. pap. 24.95 *(978-0-19-978238-3(5))* Oxford Univ. Pr., Inc.

James, C. Boyd. Garvey, Garveyism, & the Problem of Black Redemption. 2008. *(978-1-59221-654-3(4))*; 416p. pap. *(978-1-59221-655-0(2))* Africa World Pr.

Kly, Yussuf Naim. The Black Book II: From Hajji Malik Al-Shabazz to Barack Obama, 30 vols. 2010. (ENG.). 140p. pap. 14.95 *(978-0-932863-88-1(4))* Clarity Pr., Inc.

Konadu, Kwasi B. A View from the East: Black Cultural Nationalism & Education in New York City. 2nd ed. 2009. (Illus.). 232p. 29.95 *(978-0-8156-3206-1(1))* Syracuse Univ. Pr.

Magaziner, Daniel R. The Law & the Prophets: Black Consciousness in South Africa, 1968-1977. 2010. (New African Histories Ser.). (ENG., Illus.). 280p. 59.95 *(978-0-8214-1917-5(X))* Ohio Univ. Pr.

—The Law & the Prophets: Faith, Hope, & Politics in South Africa, 1968-1977. 2010. (New African Histories Ser.). (ENG., Illus.). 280p. pap. 26.95 *(978-0-8214-1918-2(8))* Ohio Univ. Pr.

Marable, Manning & Agard-Jones, Vanessa, eds. Transnational Blackness: Navigating the Global Color Line. 2008. (Critical Black Studies). (ENG.). 384p. 100.00 *(978-0-230-60267-0(3))*; pap. 31.00 *(978-0-230-60268-7(1))* Palgrave Macmillan.

Oltman, Adele. Sacred Mission, Worldly Ambition: Black Christian Nationalism in the Age of Jim Crow. (ENG.). 264p. 2012. pap. 24.95 ***(978-0-8203-4126-2(6))*** 2008. 44.95 *(978-0-8203-3036-5(1))* Univ. of Georgia Pr.

Ongiri, Amy Abugo. Spectacular Blackness: The Cultural Politics of the Black Power Movement & the Search for a Black Aesthetic. 2009. (ENG.). 240p. (C). (gr. 13-17). pap. 22.50 *(978-0-8139-2860-9(5))*; (gr. 17). 55.00 *(978-0-8139-2859-3(1))* Univ. Pr. of Virginia.

Peller, Gary. Critical Race Consciousness: Reconsidering American Ideologies of Racial Justice. 2012. 256p. pap. 29.95 *(978-1-59451-905-5(6))* Paradigm Pubs.

Pettersburgh, Fitz. The Royal Parchment Scroll of Black Supremacy. 2007. 72p. per. 10.99 *(978-1-59547-831-3(0))* NuVision Pubns., LLC.

Price, Melanye. Dreaming Blackness: Black Nationalism & African American Public Opinion. 2009. (ENG.). 240p. pap. 22.00 *(978-0-8147-6745-0(1))* New York Univ. Pr.

Rolinson, Mary G. Grassroots Garveyism: The Universal Negro Improvement Association in the Rural South, 1920-1927. 2007. (John Hope Franklin Series in African American History & Culture Ser.). (ENG., Illus.). 296p. (C). pap. 24.95 *(978-0-8078-5795-3(5))* Univ. of North Carolina Pr.

Shelby, Tommie. We Who Are Dark: The Philosophical Foundations of Black Solidarity. 2007. 336p. pap. 20.00 *(978-0-674-02571-4(7)*, Belknap Pr.) Harvard Univ. Pr.

Sidbury, James. Becoming African in America: Race & Nation in the Early Black Atlantic. (ENG., Illus.). 2009. 304p. pap. 19.95 *(978-0-19-538294-5(3))* 2007. 320p. 99.00 *(978-0-19-532010-7(7))* Oxford Univ. Pr., Inc.

Simeon-Jones, Kersuze. Literary & Socio-Political Writings of the Black Diaspora in the Nineteenth & Twentieth Centuries. 2010. (ENG.). 252p. 73.50 *(978-0-7391-2253-2(3))* Lexington Bks.

Smith, Matthew J. Red & Black in Haiti: Radicalism, Conflict, & Political Change, 1934-1957. 2009. (ENG., Illus.). 304p. 62.95 *(978-0-8078-3265-3(0))*; pap. 26.95 *(978-0-8078-5937-7(0))* Univ. of North Carolina Pr.

Stanford, Karin. If We Must Die: African American Voices on War & Peace. 2009. (ENG.). 384p. pap. 37.50 *(978-0-7425-4114-6(2))* Rowman & Littlefield Publishers, Inc.

Stanford, Karin L., ed. If We Must Die: African American Voices on War & Peace. 2008. (ENG.). 384p. 63.95 *(978-0-7425-4113-9(4))* Rowman & Littlefield Publishers, Inc.

Taylor, James Lance. Black Nationalism in the United States: From Malcolm X to Barack Obama. 2011. (Illus.). 410p. 68.50 *(978-1-58826-778-8(4))* Rienner, Lynne Pubs.

Thompson, Mark Christian. Black Fascisms: African American Literature & Culture Between the Wars. 2007. (ENG.). 240p. (gr. 17). 57.50 *(978-0-8139-2670-4(X))*; per. 19.50 *(978-0-8139-2671-1(8))* Univ. Pr. of Virginia.

Toure, Ahati N. N. John Henrik Clarke & the Power of Africana History: Africalogical Quest for Decolonization & Sovereignty. 2008. xi, 356p. *(978-1-59221-626-0(9))*; 256p. pap. *(978-1-59221-627-7(7))* Africa World Pr.

Van Wyk, Chris, ed. Celebrating Steve Biko: We Write What We Like. 2011. (Columbia/Hurst Ser.). (ENG.). 224p. (gr. 17). 50.00 *(978-0-231-15430-7(5))*; pap. 19.50 *(978-0-231-15431-4(3))* Columbia Univ. Pr.

BLACK PANTHER PARTY

Abu-Jamal, Mumia. We Want Freedom: A Life in the Black Panther Party. 2008. (ENG., Illus.). 176p. pap. 20.00 *(978-0-89608-718-7(2))* South End Pr.

Alkebulan, Paul. Survival Pending Revolution: The History of the Black Panther Party. 2nd ed. 2007. (ENG.). 200p. 29.95 *(978-0-8173-1549-8(7))* Univ. of Alabama Pr.

Arend, Orissa. Showdown in Desire: The Black Panthers Take a Stand in New Orleans. 2010. (ENG., Illus.). 294p. pap. 19.95 *(978-1-55728-896-7(8))* Univ. of Arkansas Pr.

Austin, Curtis J. Up Against the Wall: Violence in the Making & Unmaking of the Black Panther Party. 2008. (ENG., Illus.). 456p. per. 22.50 *(978-1-55728-875-2(5))* Univ. of Arkansas Pr.

B

Bingham, Howard. Black Panthers 1968. Crist, Steve, ed. 2009. (ENG., Illus.). 192p. 100.00 *(978-1-934429-15-0(5))*; 44.95 *(978-1-934429-14-3(7))* AMMO Bks., LLC.

Blake, J. Herman & Newton, Huey P. Revolutionary Suicide. 2009. (Penguin Classics Deluxe Edition Ser.). (ENG.). 384p. (gr. 12). 16.00 *(978-0-14-310532-9(9))*, Penguin Classics) Penguin Group (USA) Inc.

Bukhari, Safiya. The War Before: The True Life Story of Becoming a Black Panther, Keeping the Faith in Prison, & Fighting for Those Left Behind. Whitehorn, Laura, ed. 2010. (ENG.). 320p. pap. 15.95 *(978-1-55861-610-3(1))* Feminist Pr. at The City Univ. of New York.

Conway, Marshall Eddie. Marshall Law: The Life & Times of a Baltimore Black Panther. 2011. (ENG.). 200p. pap. 15.95 ***(978-1-84935-022-8(1))*** AK Pr. GBR. Dist: Consortium Bk. Sales & Distribution.

Freed, Donald. Agony in New Haven: The Trial of Bobby Seale, Ericka Huggins & the Black Panther Party. 2008. 362p. pap. 27.00 *(978-1-932800-32-6(8))* Figueroa Pr.

Fujino, Diane C. Samurai among Panthers: Richard Aoki on Race, Resistance, & a Paradoxical Life. 2012. (Critical American Studies). 496p. 75.00 ***(978-0-8166-7786-3(7))***; pap. 24.95 ***(978-0-8166-7787-0(5))*** Univ. of Minnesota Pr.

Haas, Jeffrey. The Assassination of Fred Hampton: How the FBI & the Chicago Police Murdered a Black Panther. 2011. (ENG.). 384p. pap. 16.95 *(978-1-56976-709-2(2))* 2009. (Illus.). 424p. 26.95 *(978-1-55652-765-4(9))* Chicago Review Pr., Inc. (Hill, Lawrence Bks.).

Hilliard, David. Huey: Spirit of the Panther. 2006. (ENG., Illus.). 320p. per. 16.95 *(978-1-56025-897-1(7))* Basic Bks.

Hilliard, David, ed. & selected by. The Black Panther: Intercommunal News Service, 1967-1980. 2007. (ENG., Illus.). 192p. pap. 25.00 *(978-1-4165-3259-0(5)*, Beyond Words/Atria Bks.) Atria Bks.

Huey P. Newton Foundation Staff. The Black Panther Party: Service to the People Programs. Hilliard, David & The Huey P. Newton Foundation, eds. 2008. (ENG., Illus.). 170p. pap. 21.95 *(978-0-8263-4394-9(5))* Univ. of New Mexico Pr.

Jeffries, Judson L. Huey P. Newton: The Radical Theorist. 2006. 176p. 36.00 *(978-1-57806-432-8(5))* Univ. Pr. of Mississippi.

Jeffries, Judson L., ed. Black Power in the Belly of the Beast. 2006. 336p. 67.00 *(978-0-252-03148-9(2))*; per. 26.00 *(978-0-252-07394-6(0))* Univ. of Illinois Pr.

—Comrades: A Local History of the Black Panther Party. 2007. (Blacks in the Diaspora Ser.). (ENG., Illus.). 336p. per. 24.95 *(978-0-253-21930-5(2)*, 0253219302) Indiana Univ. Pr.

Jeffries, Judson L., ed. On the Ground: The Black Panther Party in Communities Across America. (ENG.). 304p. 2011. pap. 30.00 ***(978-1-61703-200-4(X))*** 2010. 50.00 *(978-1-60473-492-8(2))* Univ. Pr. of Mississippi.

Joseph, Jamal. Panther Baby. 2012. (ENG.). 272p. 23.95 *(978-1-56512-950-4(4)*, 1565129504) Algonquin Bks. of Chapel Hill.

Lazerow, Jama, et al, eds. In Search of the Black Panther Party: New Perspectives on a Revolutionary Movement. annot. ed. 2006. (ENG.). 408p. per. 26.95 *(978-0-8223-3890-1(4))* Duke Univ. Pr.

Lazerow, Jama & Williams, Yohuru, eds. In Search of the Black Panther Party: New Perspectives on a Revolutionary Movement. 2006. (ENG., Illus.). 408p. 94.95 *(978-0-8223-3837-6(8))* Duke Univ. Pr.

Major, Reginald. Panther Is a Black Cat: An Account of the Early Years of the Black Panther Party - Its Origins, Its Goals, & Its Struggle for Survival. 2007. (ENG.). 310p. pap. 16.95 *(978-1-57478-037-6(9))* Black Classic Pr.

McCutchen, Steve D. We Were Free for a While. 2008. 232p. pap. 24.95 *(978-1-60441-675-6(0))* PublishAmerica, Inc.

Murch, Donna. Living for the City: Migration, Education, & the Rise of the Black Panther Party in Oakland, California. 2010. (John Hope Franklin Series in African American History & Culture Ser.). (ENG., Illus.). 344p. 65.00 *(978-0-8078-3376-6(2))*; pap. 22.95 *(978-0-8078-7113-3(3))* Univ. of North Carolina Pr.

Nelson, Alondra. The Black Panther Party & the Fight Against Medical Discrimination. 2011. pap. ***(978-0-8166-7649-1(6))*** Univ. of Minnesota Pr.

Newton, Huey. To Die for the People. Morrison, Toni, ed. 2009. (ENG., Illus.). 248p. pap. 16.95 *(978-0-87286-529-7(0))* City Lights Bks.

Ongiri, Amy Abugo. Spectacular Blackness: The Cultural Politics of the Black Power Movement & the Search for a Black Aesthetic. 2009. (ENG.). 240p. (C). (gr. 13-17). pap. 22.50 *(978-0-8139-2860-9(5))*; (gr. 17). 55.00 *(978-0-8139-2859-3(1))* Univ. Pr. of Virginia.

Rae, Douglas W. & Bass, Paul. Murder in the Model City: The Black Panthers, Yale, & the Redemption of a Killer. 2006. (ENG., Illus.). 352p. 26.00 *(978-0-465-06902-6(9))* Basic Bks.

Shames, Stephen, photos by. The Black Panthers, 1 vol. 2006. (ENG., Illus.). 152p. 35.00 *(978-1-59711-024-2(8))* Aperture Foundation, Inc.

Williams, Yohuru & Lazerow, Jama, eds. Liberated Territory: Untold Local Perspectives on the Black Panther Party. 2009. (ENG.). 312p. 89.95 *(978-0-8223-4343-1(6))*; pap. 24.95 *(978-0-8223-4326-4(6))* Duke Univ. Pr.

Witt, Andrew. The Black Panthers in the Midwest: The Community Programs & Services of the Black Panther Party in Milwaukee, 1966-1977. 2007. (Studies in African American History & Culture). 152p. 126.00 *(978-0-415-98148-4(4))* Routledge.

Wolfe, Tom. Radical Chic & Mau-Mauing the Flak Catchers. 2009. (ENG.). 144p. pap. 15.00 *(978-0-312-42913-3(4))* Picador.

BLACK POETRY
see Poetry—Black Authors

BLACK POETRY (AFRICAN)
see African Poetry

BLACK POETRY (AMERICAN)
see American Poetry—African American Authors

BLACK POTTERY

Roth, Roman. Styling Romanisation: Pottery & Society in Central Italy. 2011. (Cambridge Classical Studies). (ENG.). 254p. pap. 50.00 *(978-0-521-34951-2(6))* Cambridge Univ. Pr.

BLACK POWER
see also Black Militant Organizations

Austin, Curtis J. Up Against the Wall: Violence in the Making & Unmaking of the Black Panther Party. 2008. (ENG., Illus.). 456p. per. 22.50 *(978-1-55728-875-2(5))* Univ. of Arkansas Pr.

Barnes, Jack. Malcolm X, Black Liberation, & the Road to Workers Power. Clark, Steve & Waters, Mary-Alice, eds. 2009. (Illus.). 413p. pap. 20.00 *(978-1-60488-021-2(X))* Pathfinder Pr.

Blake, J. Herman & Newton, Huey P. Revolutionary Suicide. 2009. (Penguin Classics Deluxe Edition Ser.). (ENG.). 384p. (gr. 12). 16.00 *(978-0-14-310532-9(9))*, Penguin Classics) Penguin Group (USA) Inc.

Bradley, Anthony B. Liberating Black Theology: The Bible & the Black Experience in America. 2010. 208p. pap. 17.99 *(978-1-4335-1147-9(9))* Crossway.

Bradley, Stefan M. Harlem vs. Columbia University: Black Student Power in the Late 1960s. 2009. (ENG., Illus.). 272p. 40.00 *(978-0-252-03452-7(X))* Univ. of Illinois Pr.

Buhring, Kurt. Conceptions of God, Freedom, & Ethics in African American & Jewish Theology. 2008. (Black Religion/Womanist Thought/Social Justice Ser.). (ENG.). 272p. 95.00 *(978-1-4039-8479-1(4))* Palgrave Macmillan.

Conyers, James L., Jr., ed. Engines of the Black Power Movement: Essays on the Influence of Civil Rights Actions, Arts, & Islam. 2006. (ENG., Illus.). 296p. per. 39.95 *(978-0-7864-2540-2(7))* McFarland & Co., Inc. Pubs.

Countryman, Matthew J. Up South: Civil Rights & Black Power in Philadelphia. 2007. (Politics & Culture in Modern America Ser.). (Illus.). 432p. (C). per. 24.95 *(978-0-8122-2002-5(1))* Univ. of Pennsylvania Pr.

Fergus, Devin. Liberalism, Black Power, & the Making of American Politics, 1965-1980. 2009. (Politics & Culture in the Twentieth-Century South Ser.). (ENG., Illus.). 376p. pap. 26.95 *(978-0-8203-3324-3(7))*; lib. bdg. 69.95 *(978-0-8203-3323-6(9))* Univ. of Georgia Pr.

Garvey, Marcus. The Marcus Garvey & Universal Negro Improvement Association Papers: Africa for the Africans, 1923-1945. Hill, Robert A. et al, eds. 2006. (Marcus Garvey & Universal Negro Improvement Association Papers). (Illus.). 805p. 95.00 *(978-0-520-24732-1(9))* Univ. of California Pr.

Jeffries, Judson L., ed. Black Power in the Belly of the Beast. 2006. 336p. 67.00 *(978-0-252-03148-9(2))*; per. 26.00 *(978-0-252-07394-6(0))* Univ. of Illinois Pr.

Johnson, Cedric. Revolutionaries to Race Leaders: Black Power & the Making of African American Politics. 2007. 320p. 60.00 *(978-0-8166-4477-3(2))*; per. 20.00 *(978-0-8166-4478-0(0))* Univ. of Minnesota Pr.

Jolly, Kenneth. Black Liberation in the Midwest: The Struggle in St. Louis, Missouri, 1964-1970. 2006. (Studies in African American History & Culture). 232p. 136.00 *(978-0-415-97969-6(2))* Routledge.

Joseph, Peniel E. Dark Days, Bright Nights: From Black Power to Barack Obama. 2010. (ENG.). 288p. (gr. 13). 26.00 *(978-0-465-01366-1(X)*, Basic Civitas Bks.) Basic Bks.

—Waiting 'Til the Midnight Hour: A Narrative History of Black Power in America. 2007. (ENG., Illus.). 432p. pap. 17.99 *(978-0-8050-8335-4(9)*, Owl Bks.) Holt, Henry & Co.

Joseph, Peniel E., ed. Neighborhood Rebels: Black Power at the Local Level. 2009. (Contemporary Black History Ser.). (ENG.). 264p. pap. 32.00 *(978-0-230-62077-3(9))* Palgrave Macmillan.

Mayes, Keith. Civil Rights & Black Power: The Struggle for Black Equality in the United States, 1945-1975. 2009. (ENG., Illus.). 352p. 36.95 *(978-0-415-99129-2(3))*; 125.00 *(978-0-415-99128-5(5))* Routledge.

Mayes, Keith & Mayes, Keith A. Kwanzaa: Black Power & the Making of the African-American Holiday Tradition. 2009. (ENG., Illus.). 312p. 130.00 *(978-0-415-99854-3(9))* Routledge.

McTaggart, Ursula. Guerrillas in the Industrial Jungle: Radicalism's Primitive & Industrial Rhetoric. 2012. (ENG.). 224p. 75.00 ***(978-1-4384-3903-7(2))***; pap. 24.95 ***(978-1-4384-3904-4(0))*** State Univ. of New York Pr.

Muntaqim, Jalil A. We Are Our Own Liberators: Selected Prison Writings. 2010. (ENG.). 304p. pap. 16.95 *(978-0-9742884-6-8(2))* Arissa Media Group.

Murray, Rolland. Our Living Manhood: Literature, Black Power, & Masculine Ideology. 2006. 160p. (C). 49.95 *(978-0-8122-3972-0(5))* Univ. of Pennsylvania Pr.

Olsson, Göran, ed. The Black Power Mixtape 1967-1975. 2012. (ENG., Illus.). 192p. 27.95 ***(978-1-60846-173-8(4))*** Haymarket Bks.

Oltman, Adele. Sacred Mission, Worldly Ambition: Black Christian Nationalism in the Age of Jim Crow. (ENG.). 264p. 2012. pap. 24.95 ***(978-0-8203-4126-2(6))*** 2008. 44.95 *(978-0-8203-3036-5(1))* Univ. of Georgia Pr.

Ongiri, Amy Abugo. Spectacular Blackness: The Cultural Politics of the Black Power Movement & the Search for a Black Aesthetic. 2009. (ENG.). 240p. (C). (gr. 13-17). pap. 22.50 *(978-0-8139-2860-9(5))*; (gr. 17). 55.00 *(978-0-8139-2859-3(1))* Univ. Pr. of Virginia.

Rafalko, Frank J. MH/Chaos: The CIA's Campaign Against the Radical New Left & the Black Panthers. 2011. (Illus.). 336p. 35.95 ***(978-1-61251-045-3(0))*** Naval Institute Pr.

Shelby, Tommie. We Who Are Dark: The Philosophical Foundations of Black Solidarity. 2007. 336p. pap. 20.00 *(978-0-674-02571-4(7)*, Belknap Pr.) Harvard Univ. Pr.

Sullivan, Denise. Keep on Pushing: Black Power Music from Blues to Hip-hop. 2011. (ENG., Illus.). 224p. pap. 16.95 *(978-1-55652-817-0(5)*, Hill, Lawrence Bks.) Chicago Review Pr., Inc.

Swan, Quito. Black Power in Bermuda: The Struggle for Decolonization. 2009. (Contemporary Black History Ser.). (ENG., Illus.). 264p. 89.00 *(978-0-230-61906-7(1))* Palgrave Macmillan.

Taylor, James Lance. Black Nationalism in the United States: From Malcolm X to Barack Obama. 2011. (Illus.). 410p. 68.50 *(978-1-58826-778-8(4))* Rienner, Lynne Pubs.

Theoharis, Jeanne & Woodard, Komozi. Want to Start a Revolution? Radical Women in the Black Freedom Struggle. Gore, Dayo, ed. 2009. (ENG., Illus.). 368p. pap. 25.00 *(978-0-8147-8314-6(7))* New York Univ. Pr.

Ward, Stephen, ed. Pages from a Black Radical's Notebook: A James Boggs Reader. 2010. 488p. pap. 27.95 *(978-0-8143-3256-6(0))* Wayne State Univ. Pr.

Warren Hill, Laura & Rabig, Julia, eds. The Business of Black Power: Community Development, Capitalism, & Corporate Responsibility in Postwar America. 2012. (Illus.). 336p. 85.00 ***(978-1-58046-403-1(3))*** Univ. of Rochester Pr.

Watkins, Rychetta. Black Power, Yellow Power, & the Making of Revolutionary Identities. 2012. (ENG.). 176p. 55.00 ***(978-1-61703-161-8(5))*** Univ. Pr. of Mississippi.

West, Michael O., et al, eds. From Toussaint to Tupac: The Black International since the Age of Revolution. 2009. (ENG., Illus.). 336p. 62.95 *(978-0-8078-3309-4(6))*; pap. 23.95 *(978-0-8078-5972-8(9))* Univ. of North Carolina Pr.

Williams, Hettie V. We Shall Overcome to We Shall Overrun: The Collapse of the Civil Rights Movement & the Black Power Revolt (1962-1968) 2008. (ENG.). 124p. pap. 27.50 *(978-0-7618-4353-5(1))* Univ. Pr. of America, Inc.

Williams, Yohuru & Lazerow, Jama, eds. Liberated Territory: Untold Local Perspectives on the Black Panther Party. 2009. (ENG.). 312p. 89.95 *(978-0-8223-4343-1(6))*; pap. 24.95 *(978-0-8223-4326-4(6))* Duke Univ. Pr.

Witt, Andrew. The Black Panthers in the Midwest: The Community Programs & Services of the Black Panther Party in Milwaukee, 1966-1977. 2007. (Studies in African American History & Culture). 152p. 126.00 *(978-0-415-98148-4(4))* Routledge.

BLACK PRINCE, 1330-1376
see Edward, Prince of Wales, 1330-1376

BLACK RACE

Here are entered theoretical works discussing the Black race from an anthropological point of view. Works on blacks as an element in the population are entered under Blacks.

Ariel. The Negro: What Is His Ethnological Status? 2007. pap. 15.95 *(978-1-4304-6950-6(1))* Kessinger Publishing, LLC.

Bauval, Robert & Brophy, Thomas. Black Genesis: The Prehistoric Origins of Ancient Egypt. 2011. 384p. pap. 20.00 *(978-1-59143-114-5(X))* Bear & Co.

Burton, Richard F. A Mission to Gelele, King of Dahome. 2011. (Cambridge Library Collection - Travel & Exploration Ser.). (ENG.). 424p. pap. 31.99 *(978-1-108-03032-8(7))*; (Illus.). 406p. pap. 31.99 *(978-1-108-03031-1(9))* Cambridge Univ. Pr.

—A Mission to Gelele, King of Dahome. (ENG.). 384p. 2007. 48.95 *(978-0-548-13941-7(5))* 2006. per. 33.95 *(978-1-4286-5121-0(7))* Kessinger Publishing, LLC.

Clarke, Kamari Maxine & Thomas, Deborah A., eds. Globalization & Race: Transformations in the Cultural Production of Blackness. 2006. (ENG., Illus.). 424p. (C). 99.95 *(978-0-8223-3759-1(2))* Duke Univ. Pr.

Du Bois, W. E. B. The Negro. 2009. 168p. 25.00 *(978-1-59740-364-1(4))*; 166p. pap. 17.00 *(978-1-59740-365-8(2))* ACLS Humanities E-Book.

—The Negro. 2008. 188p. 22.99 *(978-0-554-38912-7(6))* 2008. 184p. 22.99 *(978-0-554-34581-9(1))* 2008. 188p. 25.99 *(978-0-554-29609-8(8))* 2008. 184p. 25.99 *(978-0-554-25278-0(3))* 2007. (ENG.). 170p. pap. 19.99 *(978-1-4346-8014-3(2))* 2007. (ENG.). 186p. pap. 21.99 *(978-1-4346-8015-0(0))* 2007. (ENG.). 162p. pap. 19.99 *(978-1-4264-8576-3(X))* 2007. (ENG.). 182p. pap. 21.99 *(978-1-4264-8633-3(2))* BiblioBazaar.

—The Negro. 2007. (ENG.). 156p. per. 11.95 *(978-1-60206-814-8(3))* Cosimo, Inc.

—The Negro. 2006. (Illus.). pap. *(978-1-4065-1121-5(8))* Dodo Pr.

—The Negro. 2007. *(978-0-19-532576-8(1))* Oxford Univ. Pr., Inc.

—The Negro. 2009. 160p. pap. 11.95 *(978-1-4385-1906-7(0))*; (ENG.). pap. 14.45 *(978-1-4385-1287-7(2))* Standard Pubns., Inc. (Book Jungle).

—The Negro. 2008. 120p. pap. 7.99 *(978-1-60459-371-6(7))* Wilder Pubns., Ltd.

Durham, Frederick A. The Lone Star of Liberia: The Outcome of Reflections on Our Own People. 331p. reprint ed. 98.00 *(978-0-7222-9816-9(1))* Library Reprints, Inc.

Fanon, Frantz. Black Skin, White Masks. Philcox, Richard, tr. from FRE. rev. ed. 2008. (ENG.). 240p. pap. 14.95 *(978-0-8021-4300-6(8)*, Grove Pr.) Grove/Atlantic, Inc.

—Peau Noir Masques Blancs. (FRE.). pap. 16.95 *(978-2-02-000601-9(4))* Editions du Seuil FRA. Dist: Distribooks, Inc.

Hall, Bruce S. A History of Race in Muslim West Africa, 1600-1960. 2011. (African Studies). (ENG., Illus.). 358p. 90.00 *(978-1-107-00287-6(7))* Cambridge Univ. Pr.

Horton, James Africanus Beale. West African Countries & Peoples, British & Native: And a Vindication of the African Race. 2011. (Cambridge Library Collection - Slavery & Abolition Ser.). (ENG., Illus.). 312p. pap. 24.99 *(978-1-108-02859-2(4))* Cambridge Univ. Pr.

Johnson, Guy B. & Du Bois, W. E. B. Encyclopedia of the Negro. Provenzo, Eugene F., ed. 2008. (ENG., Illus.). 253p. (C). 89.00 *(978-1-59874-301-2(5))* Left Coast Pr., Inc.

—Encyclopedia of the Negro, a Prospectus. Provenzo, Eugene F., ed. 2008. (ENG., Illus.). 253p. pap. 39.95 *(978-1-59874-302-9(3))* Left Coast Pr., Inc.

Marriott, David. Haunted Life: Visual Culture & Black Modernity. 2007. (ENG., Illus.). 312p. (C). 70.00 *(978-0-8135-4027-6(5))*; per. 24.95 *(978-0-8135-4028-3(3))* Rutgers Univ. Pr.

Maxwell, Joseph R. The Negro Question. 188p. reprint ed. 88.00 *(978-0-7222-9818-3(8))* Library Reprints, Inc.

Myers-El, Noble Timothy. The Unknown Lore of Amexem's Indigenous People: An Aboriginal Treatise. 2008. 300p. pap. 18.00 *(978-1-4343-2767-3(1))* AuthorHouse.

Nardal, Paulette. Beyond Negritude: Essays from Woman in the City. Sharpley-Whiting, T. Denean, tr. from FRE. 2009. (SUNY series, Philosophy & Race Ser.). (FRE & ENG., Illus.). 100p. 45.00 *(978-1-4384-2947-2(9))*; pap. 14.95 *(978-1-4384-2946-5(0))* State Univ. of New York Pr.

Perry, Rufus L. The Cushite: or The Children of Ham. 49p. pap. 5.95 *(978-0-916157-20-3(2))* African Islamic Mission Pubns.

Simon-Aaron, Charles. The Atlantic Slave Trade: Empire, Enlightenment, & the Cult of the Unthinking Negro. 2008. 680p. 139.95 *(978-0-7734-5197-1(8))* Mellen, Edwin Pr., The.

Simpson, Bertram L. The Conflict of Colour: A Detailed Examination of Racial Problems Throughout the World with Special Reference to the English-Speaking Peoples. 340p. reprint ed. 98.00 *(978-0-7222-9702-5(5))* Library Reprints, Inc.

Smedley, Audrey & Smedley, Brian. Race in North America: Origin & Evolution of a Worldview. 4th ed. 2011. (ENG.). 400p. pap. 45.00 *(978-0-8133-4554-3(5))* Westview Pr.

Thomas, Deborah A. & Clarke, Kamari Maxine, eds. Globalization & Race: Transformations in the Cultural Production of Blackness. 2006. (ENG.). 424p. per. 27.95 *(978-0-8223-3772-0(X))* Duke Univ. Pr.

Work, Monroe N., ed. A Bibliography of the Negro in Africa & America. 2007. (ENG.). 720p. per. 50.95 *(978-1-4325-8864-9(8))* Kessinger Publishing, LLC.

BLACK SEA

Ataç, Metin. Istiklal Harbi'nde Bahriyemiz. 2008. (TUR., Illus.). 217p. *(978-975-409-239-4(7))* Genelkurmay Baakanl.

Ban, Ioana. Black Sea Region: A Nascent Security Community? 2010. 68p. pap. *(978-3-8383-5537-5(7))* Lambert Academic Publishing.

Beller-Hann, Ildiko & Hann, Chris. Turkish Region: State, Market & Social Identities on the East Black Sea Coast. (World Anthropology Ser.). (Illus.). 256p. 65.00 *(978-0-933452-70-1(5))*; pap. 29.95 *(978-0-933452-71-8(3))* School for Advanced Research Pr./SAR Pr.

Bilde, Pia Guldager & Petersen, Jane Hjarl, eds. Meetings of Cultures in the Black Sea Region: Between Conflict & Coexistence. 2008. (Black Sea Studies). (ENG., Illus.). 422p. (C). 60.00 *(978-87-7934-419-8(4))* Aarhus Universitetsforlag DNK. Dist: ISD.

Buynevich, Ilya V. Geology & Geoarchaeology of the Black Sea Region: Beyond the Flood Hypothesis. 2011. (Illus.). vii, 196p. pap. *(978-0-8137-2473-7(2))* Geological Society of America, Inc.

Dimitrov, Dimitar. Geology & Non-Traditional Resources of the Black Sea. 2010. 244p. pap. *(978-3-8383-8639-3(6))* Lambert Academic Publishing.

Erkut, Gulden & Mitchell, Stephen, eds. The Black Sea: Past, Present & Future. 2007. (British Institute at Ankara Monogrpah Ser.). (Illus.). 172p. 60.00 *(978-1-898249-21-4(0))* British Institute of Archaeology at Ankara GBR. Dist: Brown, David Bk. Co., The.

Hamilton, Daniel S. Wider Black Sea Region in the 21st Century. Mangott, Gerhard, ed. 2008. (ENG., Illus.). 200p. pap. 25.00 *(978-0-9801871-3-7(3))* Ctr. for Transatlantic Relations.

Henderson, Karen & Weaver, Carol. The Black Sea Region & EU Policy: The Challenge of Divergent Agendas. 2010. (Illus.). 196p. 99.95 *(978-1-4094-1201-4(6))* Ashgate Publishing Co.

Ivanov, Leonid I. & Ogammauz, Temel, eds. Ecosystem Modeling as a Management Tool for the Black Sea. 2011. (NATO Science Partnership Sub-Series: 2: Ser.). (ENG.). 774p. pap. 629.00 *(978-90-481-5097-7(3)*, 9048150973) Springer.

Leskov, Aleksandr Mikhailovich. The Maikop Treasure. 2008. (Illus.). 304p. (C). 75.00 *(978-1-934536-04-9(0)*, Univ. of Pennsylvania Museum of Archaeology & Anthropology) Univ. Museum Pubns.

Manoli, Panagiota. Dynamics of Black Sea Subregionalism. 2012. (Illus.). 256p. 99.95 ***(978-0-7546-7991-2(8))*** Ashgate Publishing Co.

Posamentir, Richard. Chersonesan Studies 1: The Polychrome Grave Stelai from the Early Hellenistic Necropolis. 2010. (ENG., Illus.). 510p. 75.00 *(978-0-292-72312-2(1))* Univ. of Texas Pr.

Seydi, Süleyman. The Turkish Straits & the Great Powers. 2010. 110.36 *(978-1-61719-095-7(0))* Gorgias Pr., LLC.

Triantaphyllou, Dimitrios, ed. The Security Context in the Black Sea Region. 2010. (ENG., Illus.). 172p. 125.00 *(978-0-415-56088-7(8)*, Routledge) Taylor & Francis Group GBR. Dist: Taylor & Francis Group.

Trofimova, Anna A., ed. Greeks on the Black Sea: Ancient Art from the Hermitage. 2007. (Illus.). 384p. 70.00 (978-0-89236-883-9(7)) Oxford Univ. Pr., Inc.

BLACK-TAILED DEER
see Mule Deer

BLACK THEOLOGY
Alastair Kee Staff. Reclaiming Liberation Theology: The Rise & Demise of Black Theology. 2011. pap. (978-0-334-04164-1(3), SCM Pr.) Hymns Ancient & Modern Ltd.

Alexander, Willie J. Entering the Promised Land. 2007. (Illus.). 190p. spiral bd. 24.95 (978-0-9798779-0-2(3)) Entering The Promised Land.

Allah, Jihad. The Immortal Birth. 2007. pap. 25.00 (978-1-56411-487-7(2), YBBG#0476) UBUS Communications Systems.

Anyabwile, Thabiti M. The Decline of African American Theology: From Biblical Faith to Cultural Captivity. 2007. (ENG., Illus.). 255p. per. 20.00 (978-0-8308-2827-2(3), IVP Acad.) InterVarsity Pr.

Baker-Fletcher, Garth Kasimu & Baker-Fletcher, Garth. Bible Witness in Black Churches. 2009. (Black Religion/Womanist Thought/Social Justice Ser.). (ENG.). 208p. 84.00 (978-0-230-61771-1(9)) Palgrave Macmillan.

Beckford, Robert. Dread & Pentecostal: A Political Theology for the Black Church in Britain. 2011. 230p. pap. 25.00 (978-1-61097-513-1(8), Wipf and Stock) Wipf & Stock Pubs.

Bradley, Anthony B. Liberating Black Theology: The Bible & the Black Experience in America. 2010. 208p. pap. 17.99 (978-1-4335-1147-9(9)) Crossway.

Bridgeman, Valerie & Page, Hugh. The Africana Bible: Reading Israel's Scriptures from Africa & the African Diaspora. 2009. 512p. 39.00 (978-0-8006-2125-4(5), Fortress Pr.) Augsburg Fortress, Pubs.

Brinson Mdiv, John D. The Black Presence in the Biblical Exodus: The Exodus Revisited. 2008. 160p. per. 18.95 (978-1-4327-2087-2(2)) Outskirts Pr., Inc.

Buhring, Kurt. Conceptions of God, Freedom, & Ethics in African American & Jewish Theology. 2008. (Black Religion/Womanist Thought/Social Justice Ser.). (ENG.). 272p. 95.00 (978-1-4039-8479-1(4)) Palgrave Macmillan.

Cone, James H. A Black Theology of Liberation: Fortieth Anniversary Edition. 40th ed. 2010. 192p. pap. 20.00 (978-1-57075-895-9(6)) Orbis Bks.

Davis, Reginald F. The Black Church: Relevant or Irrelevant in the 21st Century? 2010. pap. (978-1-57312-557-4(1)) Smyth & Helwys Publishing, Inc.

Douglas, Kelly Brown. Black Bodies & the Black Church: A Blues Slant. 2012. (Black Religion/Womanist Thought/Social Justice Ser.). (ENG., Illus.). 224p. 85.00 (978-0-230-11681-8(7)) Palgrave Macmillan.

Erskine, Noel Leo. Black Theology & Pedagogy. 2008. (Black Religion/Womanist Thought/Social Justice Ser.). (ENG.). 196p. 84.00 (978-1-4039-7740-3(2)) Palgrave Macmillan.

Evans, Curtis J. The Burden of Black Religion. 2008. (ENG.). 392p. pap. 24.95 (978-0-19-532931-5(7)) Oxford Univ. Pr., Inc.

Evans, James H. & Ray, Stephen G. We Have Been Believers: An African American Systematic Theology. 2nd rev. ed. 2012. 256p. (C). pap. 27.00 (978-0-8006-9878-2(9), Fortress Pr.) Augsburg Fortress, Pubs.

Gilbreath, Edward. Reconciliation Blues: A Black Evangelical's Inside View of White Christianity. 2008. (ENG.). 207p. pap. 16.00 (978-0-8308-3362-7(5), IVP Bks.) InterVarsity Pr.

Gonzalez, Michelle A. Afro-Cuban Theology: Religion, Race, Culture, & Identity. 208p. 2011. (Illus.). 34.95 (978-0-8130-3715-8(8)) 2009. (ENG., Illus.). pap. 29.95 (978-0-8130-3416-4(7)) 2006. (ENG.). 59.95 (978-0-8130-2997-9(X)) Univ. Pr. of Florida.

Hart, William David. Black Religion: Malcolm X, Julius Lester, & Jan Willis. 2008. (ENG.). 244p. 89.00 (978-0-230-60537-4(0)) Palgrave Macmillan.

Hopkins, Dwight N. Black Faith & Public Talk: Critical Essays on James H. Cone's Black Theology & Black Power. 2007. 262p. per. 29.95 (978-1-60258-013-8(8)) Baylor Univ. Pr.

Hopkins, Dwight N. & Antonio, Edward P., eds. The Cambridge Companion to Black Theology. 2012. (ENG.). 368p. (C). 90.00 (978-0-521-87986-6(8)); pap. 29.99 (978-0-521-70569-1(X)) Cambridge Univ. Pr.

Hopkins, Dwight N. & Thomas, Linda E., eds. Walk Together Children. 2009. 444p. pap. 48.00 (978-1-60608-987-3(0), Cascade Bks.) Wipf & Stock Pubs.

Jackson, Sherman A. Islam & the Problem of Black Suffering. 2009. (ENG.). 232p. 29.95 (978-0-19-538206-8(4)) Oxford Univ. Pr., Inc.

Jagessar, Michael N. & Reddie, Anthony, eds. Black Theology in Britain. 2007. (Cross Cultural Theologies Ser.). (ENG., Illus.). 288p. (C). 34.95 (978-1-84553-059-4(4)) Equinox Publishing Ltd. GBR. Dist: ISD.

Jihad, Allah. The Immortal Birth. 2007. (Illus.). 406p. pap. 35.00 (978-1-56411-486-0(4), 0476, United Brothers Bks.) UBUS Communications Systems.

Lucas, Jeremy D. The Segregated Hour: A Layman's Guide to the History of Black Liberation Theology. 2009. 98p. pap. 14.00 (978-1-60608-396-3(1), Wipf and Stock) Wipf & Stock Pubs.

Magaziner, Daniel R. The Law & the Prophets: Black Consciousness in South Africa, 1968-1977. 2010. (New African Histories Ser.). (ENG., Illus.). 280p. 59.95 (978-0-8214-1917-5(X)) Ohio Univ. Pr.

—The Law & the Prophets: Faith, Hope, & Politics in South Africa, 1968-1977. 2010. (New African Histories Ser.). (ENG., Illus.). 280p. pap. 26.95 (978-0-8214-1918-2(8)) Ohio Univ. Pr.

Motlhabi, Mokgethi B. G. African Theology/Black Theology in South Africa: Looking Back, Moving On. 2008. 162p. pap. 29.00 (978-1-86888-433-9(3)) Unisa Press / Uitgewers GBR. Dist: International Specialized Bk. Services.

Nawls, Alexander. Praising God: The Way Home for So-Called African Americans. 2012. (978-1-58982-672-4(8)) American Bk. Publishing Group.

Pinn, Anthony. Embodiment & the New Shape of Black Theological Thought. 2010. (ENG.). 232p. 65.00 (978-0-8147-6774-0(5)); pap. 22.00 (978-0-8147-6775-7(3)) New York Univ. Pr.

Pinn, Anthony B. Understanding & Transforming the Black Church. 2009. 166p. pap. 19.00 (978-1-55635-301-7(4), Cascade Bks.) Wipf & Stock Pubs.

Powe, F. Douglas. Just Us or Justice? Moving Toward a Pan-Methodist Theology. 2009. pap. 19.00 (978-0-687-46553-8(2)) Abingdon Pr.

Reddie, Anthony. Black Theology. 2012. (SCM Core Text Ser.). 288p. pap. 40.00 (978-0-334-04156-6(2), SCM Pr.) Hymns Ancient & Modern Ltd GBR. Dist: Westminster John Knox Pr.

Reddie, Anthony. Working Against the Grain: Black Theology in the 21st Century. 2008. (Cross Cultural Theologies Ser.). (ENG.). 292p. (C). 99.95 (978-1-84553-385-4(2)); pap. 34.95 (978-1-84553-386-1(0)) Equinox Publishing Ltd. GBR. Dist: ISD.

Reddie, Anthony G. Black Theology, Slavery & Contemporary Christianity: 200 Years & No Apology. 2010. (Illus.). 242p. 99.95 (978-0-7546-6727-8(8)) Ashgate Publishing Co.

Reid-Salmon, Delroy A. Home Away from Home: The Caribbean Diasporan Church in the Black Atlantic Tradition. 2008. (Cross Cultural Theologies Ser.). (ENG.). 256p. (C). 99.95 (978-1-84553-383-0(6)) Equinox Publishing Ltd. GBR. Dist: ISD.

—Home Away from Home: The Caribeean Diasporan Church in the Black Atlantic Tradition. 2008. (Cross Cultural Theologies Ser.). (ENG.). 256p. (C). pap. 34.95 (978-1-84553-384-7(4)) Equinox Publishing Ltd. GBR. Dist: ISD.

Riggs, Marcia Y. Plenty Good Room: Women Versus Male Power in the Black Church. 2008. 160p. pap. 18.00 (978-1-60608-213-3(2), Wipf and Stock) Wipf & Stock Pubs.

Rogers, Robert. The Holy Piby - the Blackman's Bible. 2007. 72p. per. 10.99 (978-1-59547-822-1(1)) NuVision Pubns., LLC.

Sheppard, Phillis Isabella. Self, Culture, & Others in Womanist Practical Theology. 2011. (Black Religion/Womanist Thought/Social Justice Ser.). (ENG.). 240p. 89.00 (978-0-230-10288-0(3)) Palgrave Macmillan.

Sneed, Roger A. Representations of Homosexuality: Black Liberation Theology & Cultural Criticism. 2010. (Black Religion/Womanist Thought/Social Justice Ser.). (ENG.). 236p. 89.00 (978-0-230-60824-5(8)) Palgrave Macmillan.

Thistlethwaite, Susan Brooks. Sex, Race, & God: Christian Feminism in Black & White. 2009. 192p. pap. 22.00 (978-1-60608-569-1(7), Wipf and Stock) Wipf & Stock Pubs.

Ukpong, Justin S. African Interpretation of the Bible: A Reader. 2006. (978-90-04-15114-7(1)) BRILL.

—African Interpretation of the Bible: A Reader. 2006. (978-1-58983-242-8(6)) Society of Biblical Literature.

Ware, Frederick L. Methodologies of Black Theology. 2008. 192p. pap. 22.00 (978-1-55635-736-7(2)) Wipf & Stock Pubs.

Weaver, J. Denny. The Nonviolent Atonement, Second Edition. 2nd ed. 2011. 376p. pap. 28.00 (978-0-8028-6437-6(6)) Eerdmans, William B. Publishing Co.

Westfield, Nancy Lynne. Being Black, Teaching Black: Politics & Pedagogy in Religious Studies. 2008. 211p. pap. 28.00 (978-0-687-46503-3(6)) Abingdon Pr.

Wills, Richard W. Martin Luther King, Jr. , & the Image of God, 1 vol. 2011. 260p. pap. 24.95 (978-0-19-984396-1(1)) Oxford Univ. Pr., Inc.

BLACK WOMEN
see Women, Black

BLACKBERRY (SMARTPHONE)
Allen, Sarah, et al. Pro Smartphone Cross-Platform Development: iPhone, Blackberry, Windows Mobile & Android Development & Distribution. 2010. (ENG.). 288p. pap. 49.99 (978-1-4302-2868-4(7)) Apress L. P.

Davis, Leon. Turn off your bloody blackberry!!! 7 highly effective habits to help achieve the perfect work/life Balance. 2010. 83p. pap. 14.99 (978-1-4457-7286-8(8)) Lulu Enterprises Inc.

Giguere, Eric, et al. BlackBerry PlayBook Companion. 2011. 320p. pap. 19.99 (978-1-118-02648-9(9), Wiley) Wiley, John & Sons, Inc.

Harner, Carol & Davison, Andrew. Learn BlackBerry Games Development. 2010. (ENG., Illus.). 504p. pap. 49.99 (978-1-4302-2718-2(4)) Apress L. P.

Hoffman, Daniel V. Blackjacking: Security Threats to BlackBerry Devices, PDAs, & Cell Phones in the Enterprise. 2007. (ENG., Illus.). 312p. per. 39.99 (978-0-470-12754-4(6), Wiley) Wiley, John & Sons, Inc.

Johnston, Craig James. My BlackBerry Curve. 2009. (My... Ser.). (ENG., Illus.). 384p. pap. 24.99 (978-0-7897-4285-8(3)) Que.

—My BlackBerry PlayBook. 2013. (My... Ser.). (ENG.). 432p. pap. 24 99 (978-0-7897-4117-2(2)) Que.

—My BlackBerry Torch. 2013. (My... Ser.). (ENG., Illus.). 432p. pap. 24.99 (978-0-7897-4118-9(0)) Que.

Kac, Robert & Sarigumba, Dante. BlackBerry Curve for Dummies. 2009. (ENG., Illus.). 360p. pap. 24.99 (978-0-470-58744-7(X), For Dummies) Wiley, John & Sons, Inc.

Kaplan, Dean. BlackBerry Application Sketch Book. 2011. (ENG.). 160p. pap. 14.99 (978-1-4302-4239-0(6)) Apress L. P.

King, Chris. Advanced BlackBerry 6 Development. 2nd ed. 2011. (ENG.). 528p. pap. 49.99 (978-1-4302-3210-0(2)) Apress L. P.

—Advanced BlackBerry Development. 2009. (ENG.). 350p. pap. 39.99 (978-1-4302-2656-7(0)) Apress L. P.

McQueen, Rod. The BlackBerry: The Inside Story of Research in Motion. 2010. (ENG.). 320p. 26.95 (978-1-55263-940-5(1)) Key Porter Bks. CAN. Dist: Perseus-PGW.

Michaluk, Kevin, et al. CrackBerry: True Tales of BlackBerry Use & Abuse. 2010. (ENG.). 160p. pap. 19.99 (978-1-4302-3180-6(7)) Apress L. P.

Mittal, Kunal & Gupta, Shikha. BlackBerry for Work: Productivity for Professionals. 2010. (ENG.). 288p. pap. 29.99 (978-1-4302-2626-0(9)) Apress L. P.

Moore, M. Blackberry Fully Loaded. 2010. (ENG.). 272p. pap. 24.99 (978-0-470-54904-9(1), Wiley) Wiley, John & Sons, Inc.

Rizk, Anthony. Beginning BlackBerry Development. 2009. (ENG.). 300p. pap. 39.99 (978-1-4302-7225-0(2)) Apress L. P.

Rizk, Anthony, et al. Beginning BlackBerry 7 Development. 2nd ed. 2011. (ENG., Illus.). 280p. pap. 39.99 (978-1-4302-3015-1(0)) Apress L. P.

Sarigumba, Dante & Kao, Robert. BlackBerry Bold for Dummies. 2009. (ENG., Illus.). 360p. pap. 24.99 (978-0-470-52540-1(1), For Dummies) Wiley, John & Sons, Inc.

Sarigumba, Dante, et al. Blackberry All-in-One for Dummies. 2010. (ENG., Illus.). 672p. pap. 34.99 (978-0-470-53120-4(7), For Dummies) Wiley, John & Sons, Inc.

Sweeny, Alastair. BlackBerry Planet: The Story of Research in Motion & the Little Device That Took the World by Storm. 2009. (ENG.). 304p. 28.95 (978-0-470-15940-8(5), Wiley) Wiley, John & Sons, Inc.

Thompson, David. The Magic Blackberry. 2010. 256p. pap. 13.95 (978-1-905736-43-0(6)) Marshall Cavendish GBR. Dist: Midpoint Trade Bks., Inc.

Trautschold, Martin & Mazo, Gary. BlackBerry Bold Made Simple. 2010. (For the BlackBerry Bold 9700 Ser.). (ENG.). 436p. pap. 29.99 (978-1-4302-3117-2(3)) Apress L. P.

—BlackBerry Curve Made Simple. 2nd ed. 2010. (For the BlackBerry Curve 8500 Ser.). (ENG.). 600p. pap. 29.99 (978-1-4302-3123-3(8)) Apress L. P.

—BlackBerry Storm2 Made Simple. 2010. (ENG.). 640p. pap. 29.99 (978-1-4302-3120-2(3)) Apress L. P.

Wargo, John M. BlackBerry Development Fundamentals. 2009. (ENG., Illus.). 480p. pap. 39.99 (978-0-321-64742-9(4)) Addison Wesley Professional.

BLACKBIRDS
Air Force, United States & Aircraft, Lockheed, creators. Lockheed Sr-71 Blackbird Pilot's Flight Operating Instructions. 2010. 354p. pap. 34.95 (978-1-935327-84-4(4)) Periscope Film, LLC.

BLACKBODY RADIATION
Fuhrmann-Lieker, T., et al, contrib. by. Emissive Materials - Nanomaterials. 2010. (Advances in Polymer Science Ser.). x, 289p. pap. 359.00 (978-3-642-06837-9(5), 3642068375) Springer.

BLACKBURN (ENGLAND)
Woodruff, William. Nab End & Beyond: The Road to Nab End & Beyond Nab End. 2006. (Abacus Ser.). (ENG., Illus.). 736p. per. 18.95 (978-0-349-11987-8(2), Warner Books) Little, Brown Bk. Group Ltd. GBR. Dist: Independent Pubs. Group.

BLACKFEET INDIANS
see Indians of North America—Northwest, Pacific

BLACKFOOT LANGUAGE
see Siksika Language

BLACKJACK (GAME)
Axelrad, Josh. Repeat until Rich: A Professional Card Counter's Chronicle of the Blackjack Wars. 2011. (ENG.). 272p. (gr. 12). 15.00 (978-0-14-311885-5(4), Penguin (Non-Classics)) Penguin Group (USA) Inc.

Baldwin, Roger, et al. Playing Blackjack to Win: A New Strategy for the Game Of 21. 2008. (ENG.). 160p. pap. 14.95 (978-1-58042-251-2(9)) Cardoza Publishing.

BSH Designs. Whack 'Em Blackjack: Card counting made Easy. 2007. 60p. pap. 13.95 (978-0-9754099-0-9(5)) Run21 Pubs.

Bukofsky, John. Blackjack: Play Like the Pros. 2006. (ENG., Illus.). 240p. 14.95 (978-0-8184-0656-0(9), Stuart, Lyle) Kensington Publishing Corp.

Cardoza, Avery. Winning Casino BlackJack for the Non-Counter. 2010. (ENG.). 160p. pap. 12.95 (978-1-58042-243-7(8)) Cardoza Publishing.

Costantino, Doug. Blackjack Made Easy. 2009. 52p. pap. 15.99 (978-1-4415-5432-1(7)) Xlibris Corp.

Dare, Mervyn. London to Las Vegas Playing Roulette. 2010. (Illus.). 188p. pap. 15.99 (978-1-4490-9164-4(4)) AuthorHouse.

Dunki-Jacobs, Frits. Betting on Blackjack: A Non-Counter's Breakthrough Guide to Making Profits at the Tables. 2006. (Illus.). 214p. reprint ed. pap. 13.00 (978-1-4223-5572-5(1)) DIANE Publishing Co.

Elwins, Dannie. Blackjack for Beginners: Learn How to Win at Blackjack. 2009. 32p. pap. 16.99 (978-0-557-15527-9(4)) Lulu Enterprises Inc.

Fayolle, H. Pierre J. F. Yes We Can: Win at the Blackjack Table. 2010. 204p. pap. 14.49 (978-1-4520-2083-9(3)) AuthorHouse.

Gollehon, John. Blackjack Mania. 2008. pap. 5.99 (978-0-914839-82-8(9)) Gollehon Pr.

—Commando Craps & Blackjack. 2012. (ENG.). 176p. pap. 12.95 (978-1-58042-299-4(3)) Cardoza Publishing.

Hagen, Tom & Weiss, Sonia. 101 Ways to Win Blackjack: Includes Tips to Win at the Casino & Online. 2009. (ENG.). 192p. pap. 10.95 (978-1-4405-0005-3(3)) Adams Media Corp.

Harvey, Richard. Blackjack the SMART Way: Gold (Fourth) Edition. 4th ed. 2009. Orig. Title: Blackjack the Smart Way. (ENG., Illus.). 290p. pap. 21.95 (978-0-9742845-1-4(3)) Mystic Ridge Bks.

—Cutting Edge Blackjack. 3rd ed. 2009. (ENG., Illus.). 376p. pap. 21.95 (978-0-9742845-2-1(1)) Mystic Ridge Bks.

Hornik, Joshua. The Double-down Guide to Blackjack. 2010. (ENG.). 128p. pap. 12.95 (978-1-4027-7307-5(2), Puzzlewright) Sterling Publishing Co., Inc.

James, Grosjean. Exhibit CAA Beyond Counting. 2009. 250.00 (978-0-9790061-4-2(7)) South Side Advantage Pr.

Lohner, Henry. Poker, Blackjack, Faro: Internationale Bibliographie des Kartenglücksspiels; International Bibliograpy of Gambler's Card Games. 2010. 246p. pap. 49.50 (978-3-8391-2508-3(1)) Bks. on Demand.

McCaulay, Philip Martin. Blackjack Card Counting. 2009. 48p. pap. 14.95 (978-0-557-17893-3(2)) Lulu Enterprises Inc.

Moore, Jay. Blackjack Secrets: A Handbook for Beginners. 2011. (ENG.). 160p. pap. 12.95 (978-1-61608-314-4(X), 608314) Skyhorse Publishing Co., Inc.

Patrick, John. John Patrick's Advanced Blackjack. 2006. (ENG.). 336p. 14.95 (978-0-8184-0705-5(0), Stuart, Lyle) Kensington Publishing Corp.

Perry, Ronald. MASTER 21 How to Play Winning Blackjack Full Color Edition. 2010. 121p. pap. 50.00 (978-0-557-27995-1(X)) Lulu Enterprises Inc.

Purdy, Dennis. The Illustrated Guide to Blackjack: 150 Situations & Solutions to Make Winners Out of Beginners! 2007. (ENG., Illus.). 336p. 15.95 (978-0-8184-0708-6(5), Stuart, Lyle) Kensington Publishing Corp.

Revere, Lawrence. Playing Blackjack as a Business. 2011. (ENG.). 202p. pap. 19.95 (978-4-87187-607-0(1)) Ishi Pr. International.

Sampson, Carl. Princes of Darkness: The World of High Stakes Blackjack. 2006. (ENG.). 208p. per. 17.95 (978-1-904468-34-9(9)) D & B Publishing GBR. Dist: Globe Pequot Pr., The.

Schlesinger, Don. Blackjack Attack: Playing the Pros' Way. 3rd exp. ed. 2008. (Illus.). 533p. per. 24.99 (978-0-910575-20-1(7), B9105) RGE Publishing, Ltd.

Scoblete, Frank. Beat Blackjack Now! The Easiest Way to Get the Edge! 2010. (ENG.). 192p. pap. 16.95 (978-1-60078-333-3(3)) Triumph Bks.

Silberstang, Edwin. Winning Blackjack for the Serious Player. 2011. (ENG.). 288p. pap. 16.95 (978-1-58042-284-0(5)) Cardoza Publishing.

Simon, Al. Count Me In: A Professional's Guide to Blackjack. 2011. 356p. pap. 19.99 (978-1-4269-7590-5(2)) Trafford Publishing.

Snyder, Arnold. Radical Blackjack. 2012. (ENG.). 256p. pap. 16.95 (978-1-58042-296-3(9)) Cardoza Publishing.

Stann, Dave. Hollywood Blackjack: An Uncensored Guide to Doing It Like a Pro. 2008. 170p. per. 19.99 (978-0-910575-26-3(6)) RGE Publishing, Ltd.

Uston, Ken. The Big Player How a Team of Blackjack Players Made a Million Dollars. 2011. (ENG., Illus.). 262p. pap. (978-4-87187-604-9(7)) Ishi Pr. International.

—Ken Uston on Blackjack. 2011. (ENG.). 224p. pap. 25.95 (978-4-87187-606-3(3)) Ishi Pr. International.

—Million Dollar Blackjack. 2011. (ENG.). 424p. pap. 29.95 (978-4-87187-605-6(5)) Ishi Pr. International.

Wattenberger, Norm. Modern Blackjack Second Edition Volume I. 2010. 316p. pap. 19.00 (978-0-557-47416-5(7)) Lulu Enterprises Inc.

—Modern Blackjack Second Edition Volume II. 2010. 370p. pap. 22.00 (978-0-557-47443-1(4)) Lulu Enterprises Inc.

Werthamer, N. Richard. Risk & Reward: The Science of Casino Blackjack. 2009. (ENG., Illus.). xviii, 134p. 54.95 (978-1-4419-0252-8(X), 144190252X) Springer.

BLACKLISTING OF AUTHORS
Barranger, Milly S. Unfriendly Witnesses: Gender, Theater, & Film in the Mccarthy Era. 2008. (Theater in the Americas Ser.). (ENG., Illus.). 224p. pap. 37.50 (978-0-8093-2876-5(3)) Southern Illinois Univ. Pr.

Casty, Alan. Communism in Hollywood: The Moral Paradoxes of Testimony, Silence, & Betrayal. 2009. (ENG.). 376p. 55.00 (978-0-8108-6948-6(9)) Scarecrow Pr., Inc.

Edwards, Anne. Leaving Home: A Hollywood Blacklisted Writer's Years Abroad. 2012. (ENG., Illus.). 248p. 29.95 (978-0-8108-8199-0(3)); E-Book (978-0-8108-8200-3(0)) Scarecrow Pr., Inc.

Falk, Andrew J. Upstaging the Cold War: American Dissent & Cultural Diplomacy, 1940-1960. 2010. (Illus.). 264p. 34.95 net. (978-1-55849-728-3(5)) Univ. of Massachusetts Pr.

Horne, Gerald. The Final Victim of the Blacklist: John Howard Lawson, Dean of the Hollywood Ten. 2006. (Illus.). 360p. 60.00 (978-0-520-24372-9(2)); per. 27.95 (978-0-520-24860-1(0)) Univ. of California Pr.

Humphries, Reynold. Hollywood's Blacklists: A Political & Cultural History. (ENG.). 192p. 2010. (gr. 17). pap. 35.00 (978-0-7486-2456-0(2)) 2009. 95.00 (978-0-7486-2455-3(4)) Edinburgh Univ. Pr. GBR. Dist: Columbia Univ. Pr.

BLACKLISTING OF ENTERTAINERS
Barranger, Milly S. Unfriendly Witnesses: Gender, Theater, & Film in the Mccarthy Era. 2008. (Theater in the Americas Ser.). (ENG., Illus.). 224p. pap. 37.50 (978-0-8093-2876-5(3)) Southern Illinois Univ. Pr.

Casty, Alan. Communism in Hollywood: The Moral Paradoxes of Testimony, Silence, & Betrayal. 2009. (ENG.). 376p. 55.00 (978-0-8108-6948-6(9)) Scarecrow Pr., Inc.

Ceplair, Larry. The Marxist & the Movies: A Biography of Paul Jarrico. 2007. (Screen Classics Ser.). (ENG., Illus.). 352p. 50.00 (978-0-8131-2453-7(0)) Univ. Pr. of Kentucky.

Dick, Bernard F. Radical Innocence: A Critical Study of the Hollywood Ten. 2009. (ENG.). 280p. pap. 30.00 (978-0-8131-9328-1(1)) Univ. Pr. of Kentucky.

Everitt, David. A Shadow of Red: Communism & the Blacklist in Radio & Television. 2007. (ENG., Illus.). 432p. 27.50 (978-1-56663-575-2(6)) Dee, Ivan R. Pub.

Humphries, Reynold. Hollywood's Blacklists: A Political & Cultural History. (ENG.). 192p. 2010. (gr. 17). pap. 35.00 *(978-0-7486-2456-0(2))* 2009. 95.00 *(978-0-7486-2455-3(4))* Edinburgh Univ. Pr. GBR. Dist: Columbia Univ. Pr.

Neve, Brian & Krutnik, Frank, eds. Un-American Hollywood: Politics & Film in the Blacklist Era. 2007. (ENG., Illus.). 368p. 75.00 *(978-0-8135-4197-6(2))* Rutgers Univ. Pr.

—Un-American Hollywood: Politics & Film in the Blacklist Era. 2008. (ENG., Illus.). 368p. per. 27.95 *(978-0-8135-4198-3(0))* Rutgers Univ. Pr.

BLACKMAIL

see Extortion

BLACKMAN, CHARLES

Smith, Geoffrey. Charles Blackman. 2009. (ENG.). 144p. 34.95 *(978-0-7241-0274-7(4))* National Gallery of Victoria AUS. Dist: National Bk. Network.

Smith, Geoffrey & St John Moore, Felicity. Charles Blackman: Alice in Wonderland. 2007. (ENG., Illus.). 144p. pap. 26.50 *(978-0-7241-0272-3(8))* National Gallery of Victoria AUS. Dist: National Bk. Network.

BLACKS

Here are entered works on blacks as an element in the population. Theoretical works discussing the Black race from an anthropological point of view are entered under Black Race. Works on black people in countries whose racial composition is predominantly black are assigned headings appropriate for the country as a whole without the use of the heading Blacks. The heading Blacks is assigned to works on such countries only if the work discusses blacks apart from other groups in the country.

Aldridge, Delores P. & James, E. Lincoln. Africana Studies: Philosophical Perspectives & Theoretical Paradigms. 2008. (Illus.). 338p. per. 24.95 *(978-0-87422-294-4(X))* Washington State Univ. Pr.

Asante, Molefi K. Cheikh Anta Diop: An Intellectual Portrait. 2006. *(978-0-943412-26-9(9))* Univ. of Sankore Pr., The.

Blyden, Edward W. Christianity, Islam, & the Negro Race. 423p. reprint ed. 98.00 *(978-0-7222-9808-4(0))* Library Reprints, Inc.

Camara, Babacar. Marxist Theory, Black/African Specificities, & Racism. 2008. (ENG.). 146p. 62.99 *(978-0-7391-1056-0(X))* Lexington Bks.

De Gregoire, Abbe Henri. An Enquiry Concerning the Intellectual & Moral Faculties & Literature of Negroes. Warden, D. B., tr. (B. E. Ser.: No. 70, Pt. 2). 65.00 *(978-0-8115-3020-0(5))* Periodicals Service Co.

de Sandoval, Alonso. Treatise on Slavery: Selections from de Instauranda Aethiopum Salute. von Germeten, Nicole, ed. & tr. by. from SPA. 2008. (Illus.). 232p. (C). 42.00 *(978-0-87220-930-5(X))*; pap. 14.95 *(978-0-87220-929-9(6))* Hackett Publishing Co., Inc.

Du Bois, W. E. B. The Relation of the Negroes to Whites in the South. reprint ed. 150.00 *(978-0-7222-9719-3(X))* Library Reprints, Inc.

Dudly, Studly. Stud Bourne. 2008. 56p. pap. 11.99 *(978-1-4357-1260-7(9))* Lulu Enterprises Inc.

Escobar, Arturo. Territories of Difference: Place, Movements, Life, Redes. 2008. (John Hope Franklin Center Book Ser.). (ENG., Illus.). 456p. (C). 99.95 *(978-0-8223-4344-8(4))*; pap. 27.95 *(978-0-8223-4327-1(4))* Duke Univ. Pr.

Hall, Bruce S. A History of Race in Muslim West Africa, 1600-1960. 2011. (African Studies). (ENG., Illus.). 358p. 90.00 *(978-1-107-00287-6(7))* Cambridge Univ. Pr.

Hilliard, Constance. Straightening the Bell Curve: How Stereotypes about Black Masculinity Drive Research on Race & Intelligence. 2012. 160p. 24.95 ***(978-1-61234-191-0(8))*** Potomac Bks., Inc.

Hilliard, Constance B. Straightening the Bell Curve: How Stereotypes about Black Masculinity Drive Research on Race & Intelligence. 2012. ***(978-1-61234-192-7(6))*** Potomac Bks., Inc., Pubs.

Houston, Drusilla. Wonderful Ethiopians of the Ancient Cushite Empire. 2007. 160p. per. 15.99 *(978-1-59547-852-8(3))* NuVision Pubns., LLC.

—Wonderful Ethiopians of the Ancient Cushite Empire: Origin of the Civilization from the Cushites. Brooks-Bertram, Peggy, ed. 2009. (Uncrowned Queens Institute Ser.). (Illus.). 293p. (C). pap. 24.95 *(978-0-9722977-3-8(1))* Uncrowned Queens Institute for Research & Education On Women, Inc.

Houston, Drusilla Dunjee. Wonderful Ethiopians of the Ancient Cushite Empire. 2009. 158p. 32.99 *(978-1-59547-090-4(5))* NuVision Pubns., LLC.

Hudson-Weems, Clenora, ed. Contemporary Africana Theory & Thought: A Guide to Africana Studies. 2007. 420p. 99.95 *(978-1-59221-309-2(X))* Africa World Pr.

Irele, Abiola. The Négritude Moment: Explorations in Francophone African & Caribbean Literature & Thought. 2010. xv, 259p. *(978-1-59221-797-7(4))*; 256p. pap. *(978-1-59221-798-4(2))* Africa World Pr.

Irele, F. Abiola & Jeyifo, Biodun, eds. The Oxford Encyclopedia of African Thought, 2 vols., Set. 2010. (ENG., Illus.). 992p. 315.00 *(978-0-19-533473-9(6))* Oxford Univ. Pr., Inc.

Ivan Hugh Walters. Education & Cultural Politics: Interrogating Idiotic Education. 2010. 320p. 32.95 *(978-1-4401-7695-1(7))*; pap. 22.95 *(978-1-4401-7696-8(5))* iUniverse, Inc.

Jankowsky, Richard C. Stambeli: Music, Trance, & Alterity in Tunisia. 2010. (Chicago Studies in Ethnomusicology Ser.). (ENG., Illus.). 256p. 27.50 *(978-0-226-39219-6(8))* Univ. of Chicago Pr.

Johnson, Edward A. History of Negro Soldiers in the Spanish-American War, & Other Items of Interest. 2009. (Illus.). 116p. pap. *(978-1-4068-2966-2(8))* Echo Library.

—History of Negro Soldiers in the Spanish-American War, & Other Items of Interest. 2010. (Illus.). 84p. pap. 19.11 *(978-1-153-62818-1(X))* General Bks. LLC.

—History of Negro Soldiers in the Spanish-American War, & Other Items of Interest. 2010. 100p. pap. *(978-1-4076-1158-7(5))* HardPr.

—The History of Negro Soldiers in the Spanish American War & Other Items of Interest. 2010. 116p. pap. 15.96 *(978-1-162-66616-7(1))*; 27.96 ***(978-1-169-24761-1(X))***; 34.95 *(978-1-161-43481-1(X))* Kessinger Publishing, LLC.

Johnson, Edward Austin. History of Negro Soldiers in the Spanish-American War: And Other Items of Interest. 2010. 234p. pap. 25.75 *(978-1-141-49917-5(7))* BiblioBazaar.

Jolivette, Andrew J. Louisiana Creoles: Cultural Recovery & Mixed-Race Native American Identity. (ENG., Illus.). 144p. 2007. per. 26.50 *(978-0-7391-1897-9(8))* 2006. 62.99 *(978-0-7391-1896-2(X))* Lexington Bks.

Lamothe, Daphne. Inventing the New Negro: Narrative, Culture, & Ethnography. 2008. 240p. (C). 59.95 *(978-0-8122-4093-1(6))* Univ. of Pennsylvania Pr.

Lee, A. Robert, ed. African American Writing, 5 vols. 2012. (ENG.). 1736p. (C). 1425.00 ***(978-0-415-68048-6(4))*** Routledge.

Mandell, Daniel R. Tribe, Race, History: Native Americans in Southern New England, 1780-1880. 2011. (Johns Hopkins University Studies in Historical & Political Science Ser.: 125). (ENG., Illus.). 344p. (gr. 17). pap. 35.00 *(978-0-8018-9819-8(5))* Johns Hopkins Univ. Pr.

Miles, Tiya & Holland, Sharon Patricia, eds. Crossing Waters, Crossing Worlds: The African Diaspora in Indian Country. 2006. (ENG., Illus.). 392p. 94.95 *(978-0-8223-3812-3(2))*; pap. 26.95 *(978-0-8223-3865-9(3))* Duke Univ. Pr.

Nobles, Wade W. Seeking the Sakhu: Foundational Writings for an African Psychology. 2006. (ENG., Illus.). 470p. per. 27.95 *(978-0-88378-276-7(6))* Third World Press.

Okpewho, Isidore & Nzegwu, Nkiru, eds. The New African Diaspora: The New African Immigrant Experience. 2009. (ENG., Illus.). 544p. 75.00 *(978-0-253-35337-5(8))*, 0253353378); pap. 29.95 *(978-0-253-22095-0(5))*, 0253220955) Indiana Univ. Pr.

Person-Lynn, Kwaku. First Word: Black Scholars — Thinkers — Warriors. 2nd ed. 2011. (ENG.). 320p. pap. 21.95 *(978-0-88378-307-8(X))* Third World Press.

Pullen-Burry, Bessie. Ethiopia in Exile: Jamaica Revisited. 292p. 2010. pap. 28.75 *(978-1-141-53853-9(9))* 2009. 24.99 *(978-1-103-69112-8(0))* 2009. pap. 18.99 *(978-1-103-69109-8(0))* BiblioBazaar.

—Ethiopia in Exile: Jamaica Revisited. 2007. (ENG.). 288p. 43.95 *(978-0-548-36973-9(9))*; per. 28.95 *(978-0-548-31279-7(6))* Kessinger Publishing, LLC.

Riggs, Marcia C. & Logan, James Samuel, eds. Ethics That Matters: African, Caribbean, & African American Sources. 2011. 288p. (C). pap. 29.00 *(978-0-8006-1976-3(5)*, Fortress Pr.) Augsburg Fortress, Pubs.

Rojas, Fabio. From Black Power to Black Studies: How a Radical Social Movement Became an Academic Discipline. 2010. (ENG., Illus.). 304p. (gr. 17). pap. 26.00 *(978-0-8018-9825-9(0))* Johns Hopkins Univ. Pr.

Sachs, Wulf. Black Anger. 2011. 334p. 50.95 ***(978-1-258-06887-5(7))*** Literary Licensing, LLC.

Talton, Benjamin. Black Subjects in the African Diaspora. Mills, Quincy, ed. 2011. (ENG.). 224p. 85.00 *(978-0-230-11587-3(X))* Palgrave Macmillan.

Tasew, Yilma Tafere. Outcast: The Plight of Black African Refugees. 2011. (Illus.). 235p. pap. *(978-1-56902-349-5(2))* Red Sea Pr.

Tillinghast, Joseph A. The Negro in Africa & America. 231p. reprint ed. 98.00 *(978-0-7222-9820-6(X))* Library Reprints, Inc.

Woodard, Colin. American Nations: A History of the Eleven Rival Regional Cultures of North America. 2011. (ENG., Illus.). 384p. (gr. 12). 30.00 *(978-0-670-02296-0(9)*, Viking Adult) Penguin Group (USA) Inc.

BLACKS—BIBLIOGRAPHY

Kamara, Saysay S. Blackman: Too Hard for You. 2008. 180p. pap. 15.95 *(978-0-595-48486-7(7))* iUniverse, Inc.

BLACKS—BIOGRAPHY

Al-Bilali, Shahid. A Mirror for My Children. 2010. 352p. pap. 32.95 *(978-1-4502-5825-8(5))* iUniverse, Inc.

Ayaba, Cho Lucas. Not Guilty: We Versus Them, the Experience of an African Refugee. 2006. 186p. pap. 24.95 *(978-1-4241-2796-2(3))* PublishAmerica, Inc.

Batrell, Ricardo. A Black Soldier's Story: The Narrative of Ricardo Batrell & the Cuban War of Independence. Sanders, Mark A., ed. 2010. (ENG., Illus.). 288p. 75.00 *(978-0-8166-5008-8(X))*; pap. 24.95 *(978-0-8166-5009-5(8))* Univ. of Minnesota Pr.

Benjamin, Richard. Searching for Whitopia: An Improbable Journey to the Heart of White America. 2009. (ENG.). 368p. 24.99 *(978-1-4013-2268-7(9))* Hyperion Pr.

Britton, Annette. 5 Black Women Inc. Silva-Travers, Eva & Blake, Corey, eds. 2009. 134p. pap. 17.95 *(978-0-9822206-6-5(9))* Writer of the Round Table Pr.

Brooks, Nevia. He Wouldn't Let It Be So. 2008. 53p. pap. 16.95 *(978-1-60563-628-3(2))* PublishAmerica, Inc.

Burgess, Dave. A Tale of Two Brothers (trade Softcover) 2010. 212p. pap. 19.95 *(978-0-557-56095-0(0))* Lulu Enterprises Inc.

Carter, Tomeiko Ashford. Powers Divine: Spiritual Autobiography & Black Women's Writing. 2008. (ENG.). 194p. pap. 36.99 *(978-0-7618-4184-5(9))* Univ. Pr. of America, Inc.

Colley, Leroy. Born to Make A Difference. 2010. 124p. 23.99 *(978-1-4490-9293-1(4))*; pap. 13.99 *(978-1-4490-9292-4(6))* AuthorHouse.

Contemporary Black Biography. (Contemporary Black Biography Ser.). (ENG.). 2008. 304p. 150.00 *(978-1-4144-3276-2(3))* 2008. 304p. 150.00 *(978-1-4144-3275-5(5))* 2008. 296p. 150.00 *(978-0-7876-9544-6(0))* 2008. 288p. 150.00 *(978-0-7876-9543-9(2))* 2008. 304p. 150.00 *(978-0-7876-9541-5(6))* 2007. 288p. 150.00 *(978-0-7876-7934-7(8))* 2007. 304p. 150.00 *(978-0-7876-7933-0(X))*70. 2008. 304p. 150.00 *(978-1-4144-3277-9(1))*71. 2009. 288p. 150.00 *(978-1-4144-1928-2(7))* Vol. 77. 2010. 304p. 150.00 *(978-1-4144-3970-9(9))* Vol. 78. 2010. 304p. 150.00 *(978-1-4144-3971-6(7))* Vol. 79. 2010. 150.00 *(978-1-4144-3972-3(5))* Vol. 80. 2010. 150.00 *(978-1-4144-4601-1(2))* Cengage Gale.

Contemporary Black Biography: Profiles from the International Black Community. 2011. 150.00 *(978-1-4144-5852-6(5))*; 150.00 *(978-1-4144-5851-9(7))* Cengage Gale.

Douglass II, Frederick. Facing America: The Arrival of a Black Man to His Native Land, 1 vol. 2010. 242p. pap. 24.95 *(978-1-60610-383-8(0))* PublishAmerica, Inc.

Draper, Adrienne & Foundation, The Utafiti, eds. A Father's Fight. 2011. 108p. pap. 13.95 ***(978-0-615-47267-6(2))*** AS&J Publishing Group.

Durangowalt. Hiz-Story. 2009. 304p. pap. 15.49 *(978-1-4490-1555-8(7))* AuthorHouse.

Farr, Stacie. Black Girl in America: A Memoir. 2010. 84p. pap. 12.99 *(978-1-4269-2871-0(8))* Trafford Publishing.

Franklin, Marlow Curtis. Lyrical Thesis: Who I Am. 2007. (ENG.). 184p. per. 24.95 *(978-1-4241-6500-1(8))* PublishAmerica, Inc.

Fraser, Fil. Running Uphill: The Fast, Short Life of Harry Jerome. 2007. (ENG.). 240p. pap. *(978-1-896124-13-1(5))* Dragon Hill Publishing CAN. Dist: Lone Pine Publishing.

Gale Cengage Publishing, creator. Contemporary Black Biography: Volume 65. 2008. (Contemporary Black Biography Ser.). (ENG., Illus.). 304p. 150.00 *(978-0-7876-9542-2(4))* Cengage Gale.

Gale Editor, ed. Contemporary Black Biography: Profiles from the International Black Community. 2011. 264p. (ENG.). lib. bdg. 150.00 *(978-1-4144-7173-0(4))*; (ENG.). lib. bdg. 150.00 *(978-1-4144-7172-3(6))*; (ENG.). lib. bdg. 150.00 *(978-1-4144-7171-6(8))*; 150.00 *(978-1-4144-7169-3(6))*; (ENG.). 150.00 *(978-1-4144-7168-6(8))*; (ENG.). lib. bdg. 150.00 *(978-1-4144-7170-9(X))* Cengage Gale.

Gaskin, J. M. & Perry, E. W. A Prophet in Ebony: The Life Story of E. W. Perry. 2011. 126p. 40.95 ***(978-1-258-02794-0(1))*** Literary Licensing, LLC.

Goodwin, Robert. Crossing the Continent, 1527-1540: The Story of the First African-American Explorer of the American South. 2009. (ENG.). 432p. pap. 14.99 *(978-0-06-114045-7(7)*, Harper Paperbacks) HarperCollins Pubs.

Gracie L. Ansley & Melanie J. Ansley. Gracie. 2009. 196p. pap. 25.00 *(978-1-4389-4532-3(9))* AuthorHouse.

Grigsby, Daryl. In Their Footsteps: Inspirational Reflections on Black History for Every Day of the Year. 2007. (Illus.). 384p. per. 14.95 *(978-0-87946-336-6(8))* ACTA Pubns.

Haidari, Benn. Letters to my Children. 2009. (Illus.). 68p. pap. *(978-1-84748-436-9(0))* Athena Pr.

Henson, Josiah. Uncle Tom's Story of His Life: An Autobiography of the Reverend Josiah Henson. Lobb, John, ed. 2011. (ENG., Illus.). 180p. pap. 25.00 ***(978-0-8078-6961-1(9))*** Univ. of North Carolina Pr.

Hollis, John. Life in the Paint: The Story of a Black Man Fighting for His Identity. 2009. 114p. 22.50 *(978-1-60860-545-3(0)*, Eloquent Bks.) AEG Literary Publishing Services, Inc.

Hurley, Jon. Tom Cribb: The Life of the Black Diamond. 2009. (ENG., Illus.). 288p. 36.95 *(978-0-7524-4751-3(3))* History Pr. Ltd.,The GBR. Dist: Independent Pubs. Group.

Johnson, William Jerome. The Upstart. 2008. 256p. pap. 21.49 *(978-1-4343-8180-4(3))* AuthorHouse.

Kambalu, Samson. The Jive Talker: An Artist's Genesis. 2008. (ENG.). 336p. 24.00 *(978-1-4165-5931-3(0)*, Free Pr.) Free Pr.

Kimoni, Shombay. A Black College Nightmare. Dixon, Christopher, ed. 2007. 150p. per. 13.99 *(978-0-9793796-7-3(9))* Strategic Publishing Group.

Larry, Natasha. Grey Girl A Memoir of Blackness. 2007. 132p. 24.95 *(978-1-4241-4828-8(6))* PublishAmerica, Inc.

Lee, George L. Inspiring African Americans: Black History Makers in the United States, 1750-1980. alt. ed. 2012. (ENG.). 144p. pap. 19.99 ***(978-0-7864-6765-5(7))*** McFarland & Co., Inc. Pubs.

—Interesting People: Black American History Makers. alt. ed. 2012. (ENG., Illus.). 224p. pap. 19.99 ***(978-0-7864-6767-9(3))*** McFarland & Co., Inc. Pubs.

Lennon, Frankie. The Mee Street Chronicles: Straight up Stories of a Black Woman's Life. 2007. 248p. pap. 14.95 *(978-0-9788777-4-3(8))* Kerlak Publishing.

Love, Deborah Sharon. Blue Moon. 2011. 268p. 28.99 ***(978-1-4670-2627-7(1))***; pap. 19.95 ***(978-1-4670-2624-6(7))*** AuthorHouse.

Lynch, Fiona. From Darkness to Light. 2008. 304p. pap. 25.50 *(978-1-4092-1218-8(1))* Lulu Enterprises Inc.

Mamigonian, Beatriz G. & Racine. The Human Tradition in the Black Atlantic, 1500 D 2000. 2009. (Human Tradition around the World Ser.). (ENG.). 236p. pap. 27.50 *(978-0-7425-6730-6(3))* Rowman & Littlefield Publishers, Inc.

Mamigonian, Beatriz G. & Racine, Karen. The Human Tradition in the Black Atlantic, 1500-2000. 2009. (Human Tradition around the World Ser.). (ENG.). 236p. 79.00 *(978-0-7425-6729-0(X))* Rowman & Littlefield Publishers, Inc.

Marsh. Getting Out of Dodge City, Heading for L a on the Atchison, Topeka, & Santa Fe. 2011. 144p. pap. 24.95 ***(978-1-4560-8943-6(9))*** PublishAmerica, Inc.

Mathis, Carrie A. Overcoming Shattered Dreams: Ouch! That Hurt! 2009. 276p. pap. 25.00 *(978-1-4251-9072-9(3))* Trafford Publishing.

Millner, Derrick K. From the Projects to the Pulpit: God's Grace Is Sufficient. 2009. 68p. pap. 16.95 *(978-1-4389-7711-9(5))* AuthorHouse.

Morse, Stan. But for the Grace of God: One Man's Spiritual Walk from Self Destruction to Salvation. 2010. 332p. pap. 17.99 *(978-1-4490-6509-6(0))*; (ENG.). 28.49 *(978-1-4490-6510-2(4))* AuthorHouse.

Odum, Howard W. Wings on My Feet: Black Ulysses at the Wars. 2007. (ENG.). 360p. pap. 22.95 *(978-0-253-21923-7(X)*, 025321923X) Indiana Univ. Pr.

Okonkwo, Rudolf Ogoo. Children of a Retired God. 2006. per. *(978-0-9768354-3-1(6))* Iroko Productions & Pubns. LLC.

Parks, Gregory S. & Hughey, Matthew, eds. 12 Angry Men: True Stories of Being a Black Man in America Today. 2011. (ENG.). 208p. 24.95 *(978-1-59558-538-7(9))* New Pr., The.

Pendergast, Sara & Pendergast, Tom. Contemporary Black Biography: Profiles from the International Black Community, Vol. 59. 2007. (Contemporary Black Biography Ser.). (ENG., Illus.). 300p. 150.00 *(978-0-7876-7931-6(3))* Cengage Gale.

Pendergast, Tom, ed. Contemporary Black Biography: Profiles from the International Black Community. 2007. (Contemporary Black Biography Ser.: Vol. 63). (ENG., Illus.). 288p. 150.00 *(978-0-7876-7935-4(6))* Cengage Gale.

Purnell/Mangum, Shawn. Why Am I Black: The Beginning of Healing. 2010. 136p. 22.99 *(978-1-4389-4111-0(0))*; pap. 15.99 *(978-1-4389-4110-3(2))* AuthorHouse.

Randolph, Robert H. Rich White Folks: Growing up Black in America. 2011. (ENG.). 154p. pap. 13.95 ***(978-1-4327-5203-3(0))*** Outskirts Pr., Inc.

Rawlings, Ronald Kaye. A Black Cop in the South: In Spite of Everything. 2007. 116p. pap. 12.95 *(978-0-9724586-6-5(2))* PearlStone Publishing, Inc.

Reid, James. So, What's Wrong, Black Man? 2010. 92p. pap. 12.00 *(978-1-4269-3585-5(4))* Trafford Publishing.

Scott, Rebecca J. & Hébrard, Jean M. Freedom Papers: An Atlantic Odyssey in the Age of Emancipation. 2012. (ENG., Illus.). 288p. 35.00 ***(978-0-674-04774-7(5))*** Harvard Univ. Pr.

Selzer, Steven Michael. Meet the Real Joe Black: An Inspiring Life - Baseball, Teaching, Business, Giving. 2010. 172p. 25.95 *(978-1-4401-7120-8(3))*; (ENG.). pap. 15.95 *(978-1-4401-7119-2(X))* iUniverse, Inc.

Shephard, Timothy. Can We Help Us? Growing up Bi-Racial in America. 2011. 220p. 24.59 ***(978-1-4567-5462-4(9))***; pap. 14.03 ***(978-1-4567-5888-2(8))*** AuthorHouse.

Sithole, Michael Mbheki. The Incredible Journey. 2009. 144p. pap. 19.95 *(978-1-61546-616-0(9))* PublishAmerica, Inc.

Strickland, James W. A Charge to Keep - I Have: A Promise Kept. 2010. 105p. pap. 19.95 *(978-1-4327-5115-9(8))* Outskirts Pr., Inc.

Stringer, Lee. White People: Stories from the Heart of the Suburbs. 2010. 224p. 23.95 *(978-1-58322-908-8(6))* Seven Stories Pr.

Thomson Gale, creator. Contemporary Black Biography: Profiles from the International Black Community. (Contemporary Black Biography Ser.). (ENG., Illus.). Vol. 56. 2006. 288p. 150.00 *(978-0-7876-7928-6(3))* Vol. 60. 2007. 300p. 150.00 *(978-0-7876-7932-3(1))* Cengage Gale.

—Contemporary Black Biography, Volume 57, Vol. 57. 2006. (Contemporary Black Biography Ser.). (ENG., Illus.). 288p. 150.00 *(978-0-7876-7929-3(1))* Cengage Gale.

—Contemporary Black Biography, Volume 58: Profiles from the International Black Community, Vol. 58. 2007. (Contemporary Black Biography Ser.). (ENG., Illus.). 288p. 150.00 *(978-0-7876-7930-9(5))* Cengage Gale.

Tsolo, Donald A. The Promise: Black Youth Confront the Cauldron of Apartheid. 2009. 208p. 27.95 *(978-1-4401-4542-1(3))*; pap. 17.95 *(978-1-4401-4540-7(7))* iUniverse, Inc.

Turner, Morrie. Black Sports Heroes: Past & Present. 2011. 148p. pap. 15.00 ***(978-1-4269-7652-0(6))*** Trafford Publishing.

Willis, Vivian. Mom Suse: Matriarch of the Preston area Black Communities. 2010. 216p. 27.99 *(978-1-4490-5202-7(9))* AuthorHouse.

Wright, Roberta. Blessings in the Storm: Samuel Wesley Gathing: A Closer Look. 2011. 100p. pap. 11.65 ***(978-1-4269-3770-5(9))*** Trafford Publishing.

Zenzelle, Kalifa Obioma. God Is, That Is Why I Am! 2011. 230p. pap. 24.95 ***(978-1-4512-7535-3(8))*** PublishAmerica, Inc.

BLACKS—CIVIL RIGHTS

see also Blacks—Politics and Government

Asher, Kiran. Black & Green: Afro-Colombians, Development, & Nature in the Pacific Lowlands. 2009. (ENG., Illus.). 272p. 84.95 *(978-0-8223-4487-2(4))*; pap. 23.95 *(978-0-8223-4483-4(1))* Duke Univ. Pr.

Connell, Dan. Old Wrongs, New Rights: Student Views of the New South Africa. 2008. *(978-1-59221-628-4(5))*; 168p. pap. *(978-1-59221-629-1(3))* Africa World Pr.

Grimes, Erik K. & Slaughter, Butch. Why Our Children Hate Us: How Black Adults Betray Black Children. 2006. 72p. per. 10.95 *(978-0-9777013-9-1(5))* Ulysses Slaughter.

Mamigonian, Beatriz G. & Racine. The Human Tradition in the Black Atlantic, 1500 D 2000. 2009. (Human Tradition around the World Ser.). (ENG.). 236p. pap. 27.50 *(978-0-7425-6730-6(3))* Rowman & Littlefield Publishers, Inc.

Mamigonian, Beatriz G. & Racine, Karen. The Human Tradition in the Black Atlantic, 1500-2000. 2009. (Human Tradition around the World Ser.). (ENG.). 236p. 79.00 *(978-0-7425-6729-0(X))* Rowman & Littlefield Publishers, Inc.

Swan, Quito. Black Power in Bermuda: The Struggle for Decolonization. (Contemporary Black History Ser.). (ENG., Illus.). 2010. 262p. pap. 31.00 *(978-0-230-10958-2(6))* 2009. 264p. 89.00 *(978-0-230-61906-7(1))* Palgrave Macmillan.

Thorburn, Ryan. Black: The Rise, Fall & Rebirth of Wyoming Football. 2009. 164p. pap. 22.00 *(978-0-9777318-9-3(8)*, Burning Daylight) Pearn & Assocs. Inc.

Tutu, Desmond, intro. Believe: The Words & Inspiration of Desmond Tutu. 2007. (Illus.). 95p. 14.95 *(978-1-59842-241-2(3)*, Blue Mountain Pr.) Blue Mountain Arts Inc.

BLACKS—ECONOMIC CONDITIONS

Clingman, James. Black Empowerment with an Attitude! You Got a Problem with That? 2007. 318p. per. 17.95 *(978-0-9799308-4-3(7))* Milligan Bks.

Haygood, Marsha, et al. The Little Black Book of Success: Laws of Leadership for Black Women. 2010. (ENG.). 176p. 20.00 *(978-0-345-51848-4(9)*, One World/Ballantine) Random House Publishing Group.

Jordaan, B., et al, eds. Understanding Broad-Based Black Economic Empowerment. 2010. 190p. pap. 17.50 *(978-0-7021-8187-0(0))* Gaunt, Inc.

Kamlana, Unathi. The Taxation of Black Economic Empowerment Transactions. 2010. 100p. pap. *(978-3-8383-4493-5(6))* Lambert Academic Publishing.

MacDonald, Michael. Why Race Matters in South Africa. 2012. (ENG., Illus.). 256p. pap. 19.95 ***(978-0-674-06389-1(9))*** Harvard Univ. Pr.

Marais, Hein. South Africa Pushed to the Limit: The Political Economy of Change. 2011. (ENG., Illus.). 544p. 126.00 *(978-1-84813-860-5(1))*; pap. 45.00 *(978-1-84813-859-9(8))* Zed Bks., Ltd. GBR. Dist: Macmillan.

Model, Suzanne. West Indian Blacks: An Immigrant Success Story? 2008. (C). *(978-0-87154-631-9(0))* Russell Sage Foundation.

Thompson, Bankole. A Matter of Black Transformation. 2007. 180p. per. 15.00 *(978-0-9760755-7-8(1)*, Read4Life Bks.) Christian Bk. Outreach, Inc.

BLACKS—EDUCATION

Badat, Saleem. Black Man, You Are on Your Own. 2010. 168p. pap. 24.95 *(978-1-920222-39-0(1))* STE Pubs. ZAF. Dist: Independent Pubs. Group.

Bhopal, Kalwant & Preston, John, eds. Intersectionality & Race in Education. 2011. (Routledge Research in Education Ser.). (ENG., Illus.). 238p. (C). 125.00 *(978-0-415-88877-6(8))* Routledge.

Christie, Ron. Acting White: The Curious History of a Racial Slur. 2010. (ENG.). 304p. 25.99 *(978-0-312-59946-1(3)*, Dunne, Thomas Bks.) St. Martin's Pr.

Ernest H. Johnson, Ph. D. & Champions. The Secrets for Motivating, Educating, & Lifting the Spirit of African American Males. 2011. 496p. 39.95 ***(978-1-4620-4644-7(4))***; pap. 29.95 ***(978-1-4620-4642-3(8))*** iUniverse, Inc.

Fairclough, Adam. A Class of Their Own: Black Teachers in the Segregated South. 2007. (Illus.). 552p. 29.95 *(978-0-674-02307-9(2)*, Belknap Pr.) Harvard Univ. Pr.

Freeman, Kassie & Johnson, Ethan, eds. Education in the Black Diaspora. 2011. (Routledge Research in Education Ser.). (ENG., Illus.). 214p. (C). 125.00 *(978-0-415-89034-2(9))* Routledge.

Gasman, Marybeth. Envisioning Black Colleges: A History of the United Negro College Fund. 2007. (ENG., Illus.). 288p. (gr. 17). 48.00 *(978-0-8018-8604-1(X))* Johns Hopkins Univ. Pr.

Glenn, Charles. African-American/Afro-Canadian Schooling: From the Colonial Period to the Present. 2011. (ENG., Illus.). 216p. 85.00 *(978-0-230-11416-6(4))* Palgrave Macmillan.

Hitchens, Ed . D. Why Black Boys Fail in Public Schools. 2009. 124p. pap. 12.99 *(978-1-4490-1269-4(8))* AuthorHouse.

Kim, Jason J., et al. HBCU-up Academic Indicator Report 2005, 1 vol. 2006. (Illus.). 209p. per. *(978-0-9761402-2-1(5))* Systemic Research, Inc.

Kimoni, Shombay. A Black College Nightmare. Dixon, Christopher, ed. 2007. 150p. per. 13.99 *(978-0-9793796-7-3(9))* Strategic Publishing Group.

Maylor, Uvanney. Teacher Training & the Education of Black Children: Bringing Color into Difference. 2012. (Routledge Research in Education Ser.). (ENG.). 192p. (C). 125.00 *(978-0-415-89762-4(9))* Routledge.

Mills, Robin. They Didn't Tell Us That. 2009. 80p. pap. *(978-3-639-16248-6(X))* VDM Verlag Dr. Mueller e.K.

Mocombe, Paul. Oppositional Culture Theory. 2010. (ENG.). 176p. pap. 28.00 *(978-0-7618-5013-7(9))* Univ. Pr. of America, Inc.

Nafeo. The State of America's Black Colleges 2008. 2008. 156p. per. 14.95 *(978-0-9802380-4-4(6))* Beckham Pubns. Group, Inc.

Paik, Susan J. & Walberg, Herbert J., eds. Narrowing the Achievement Gap: Strategies for Educating Latino, Black, & Asian Students. 2007. (Issues in Children's & Families' Lives Ser.). (Illus.). 210p. 89.95 *(978-0-387-44609-7(5)*, 0387446095) Springer.

Robinson, Michael. Educating the Endangered Species - the Black Male. 2007. per. 20.00 *(978-0-9794135-0-6(8))* Strategic Achievement, LLC.

Sherer, Robert G. Black Education in Alabama, 1865-1901. 2009. (Library Alabama Classics Ser.). 224p. pap. 31.50 *(978-0-8173-5145-8(0))* Univ. of Alabama Pr.

Shockley, Kmt G. The Miseducation of Black Children. 2008. (ENG.). 120p. pap. 12.95 *(978-1-934155-12-7(8))* African American Images.

Tennant, Noah. Black Students, White Schools- Caught Between Two Worlds. 2007. 152p. per. *(978-3-8364-2867-5(9))* VDM Verlag Dr. Mueller e.K.

Winkle-Wagner, Rachelle. The Unchosen Me: Race, Gender, & Identity among Black Women in College. 2009. (ENG., Illus.). 248p. (gr. 17). 57.00 *(978-0-8018-9354-4(2))* Johns Hopkins Univ. Pr.

Wright, Cecile, et al. Black Youth Matters: Transitions from School to Success. 2009. (Critical Youth Studies). (ENG.). 176p. 130.00 *(978-0-415-99510-8(8))* Routledge.

BLACKS—EMPLOYMENT

Bressey, Caroline, ed. Belonging in Europe - the African Diaspora & Work. 2009. 192p. 150.00 *(978-0-415-48870-9(2))* Routledge.

Jenkins, Richard. Racism & Recruitment: Managers, Organisations, & Equal Opportunity in the Labour Market. 2010. (Comparative Ethnic & Race Relations Ser.). 296p. pap. 42.00 *(978-0-521-12576-5(6))* Cambridge Univ. Pr.

Turrell, Robert Vicat. Capital & Labour on the Kimberley Diamond Fields, 1871-1890. 2008. (African Studies). (ENG.). 316p. pap. 42.00 *(978-0-521-07179-6(8))* Cambridge Univ. Pr.

BLACKS—HAIRDRESSING

see Hairdressing of Blacks

BLACKS—HISTORY

see also Free Blacks

Ahmad, Muhammad. We Will Return in the Whirlwind: Black Radical Organizations 1960-1975. 2007. (Illus.). 332p. per. 15.00 *(978-0-88286-314-6(2))* Kerr, Charles H. Publishing Co.

Ahmad, Muhammad & Stanford, Maxwell, Jr. We Will Return in the Whirlwind: Black Radical Organizations 1960-1975. 2007. 340p. 26.00 *(978-0-88286-315-3(0))* Kerr, Charles H. Publishing Co.

Andre, Jean-Max. Window into the Eyes of A Lone Black Nation. 2008. 158p. pap. 14.97 *(978-1-4357-3873-7(X))* Lulu Enterprises Inc.

Andrews, George Reid. Blackness in the White Nation: A History of Afro-Uruguay. 2010. (ENG., Illus.). 272p. 59.95 *(978-0-8078-3417-6(3))*; pap. 22.95 *(978-0-8078-7158-4(3))* Univ. of North Carolina Pr.

Andujar, Carlos. The African Presence in Santo Domingo. 2012. (African Diaspora Research Project Ser.). (ENG., Illus.). 100p. pap. 19.95 ***(978-1-61186-042-9(3))*** Michigan State Univ. Pr.

Barkhuizen, Pieter Erens. Fleey: The Beloved Country - A South African Tragedy. 2009. 94p. pap. 16.95 *(978-1-60749-374-7(8))* PublishAmerica, Inc.

Black History II: Martin Luther King, Jr. & the Civil Rights Movement, South Africa, Maroons, Escaped Slave Communities, Haiti, the Yoruba People, Nigeria & Beyond... tchr. ed. 41.95 *(978-0-382-40660-7(5))* Cobblestone Publishing Co.

Bonnett, Aubrey W. Continuing Perspectives on the Black Diaspora. Holder, Calvin B., ed. 2009. (ENG.). 286p. pap. 39.99 *(978-0-7618-4662-8(X))* Univ. Pr. of America, Inc.

Bonnett, Aubrey W. & Holder, Calvin B. Continuing Perspectives on the Black Diaspora. 2009. xxi, 263p. *(978-0-7618-4663-5(8))* Univ. Pr. of America, Inc.

Bowser, Frederick P. The African Slave in Colonial Peru, 1524-1650. 460p. 2009. 22.00 *(978-1-59740-337-5(7))* 2008. pap. 46.00 *(978-1-59740-704-5(6))* ACLS Humanities E-Book.

Briggs-Dehorney, Jun & Louise. Just the Typical American Negro. 2009. 232p. pap. 14.49 *(978-1-4389-9381-2(1))* AuthorHouse.

Bryant, Sherwin K., et al, eds. Africans to Spanish America: Expanding the Diaspora. 2012. (New Black Studies Ser.). (ENG., Illus.). 288p. 50.00 ***(978-0-252-03663-7(8))*** Univ. of Illinois Pr.

Byrd, Alexander X. Captives & Voyagers: Black Migrants Across the Eighteenth-Century British Atlantic World. 2009. (Illus.). xi, 346p. *(978-0-8071-3359-0(0))* Louisiana State Univ. Pr.

Chamberlain, Mary. Family Love in the Diaspora: Migration & the Anglo-Caribbean Experience. 2009. (ENG.). 260p. pap. 24.95 *(978-1-4128-0855-2(3))* Transaction Pubs.

Chater, Kathleen. Untold Histories: Black People in England & Wales During the Period of the British Slave Trade, C. 1660-1807. 2010. (ENG., Ilus.). 320p. 90.00 *(978-0-7190-8013-5(4))* Manchester Univ. Pr. GBR. Dist: Macmillan.

Cram101 Textbook Reviews. Outlines & Highlights for Africana Studies: A Survey of Africa & the African Diaspora by Azevedo, ISBN. 2011. 122p. pap. 28.95 ***(978-1-61812-813-3(2))*** Cram101 Inc.

—Outlines & Highlights for Africana Studies: Survey of Africa & the African Diaspora by Azevedo, Mario, ISBN. 2011. 254p. pap. 31.95 ***(978-1-61812-522-4(2))*** Cram101 Inc.

Curry, Dawne Y., et al, eds. Extending the Diaspora: New Histories of Black People. 2009. (New Black Studies Ser.). (ENG., Illus.). 312p. 75.00 *(978-0-252-03459-6(7))*; 328p. pap. 30.00 *(978-0-252-07652-7(4))* Univ. of Illinois Pr.

Dabydeen, David, et al, eds. The Oxford Companion to Black British History. 2007. (ENG.). 592p. 65.00 *(978-0-19-280439-6(1))* Oxford Univ. Pr., Inc.

Dabydeen, David, et al. The Oxford Companion to Black British History. 2010. (ENG., Illus.). 592p. pap. 21.95 *(978-0-19-957877-1(X))* Oxford Univ. Pr., Inc.

Demissie, Fassil, ed. African Diaspora & the Metropolis: Reading the African, African American & Caribbean Experience. 2009. (ENG.). 118p. 125.00 *(978-0-415-56034-4(9))* Routledge.

Dennis, Denise. Black History for Beginners. 2007. (For Beginners Ser.). (ENG., Illus.). 192p. per. 16.99 *(978-1-934389-19-5(6)*, For Beginners) Steerforth Pr.

Duffield, Ian. Across Many Boundaries. 224p. *(978-0-7185-0096-2(2)*, Burns & Oates) Continuum International Publishing Group, Ltd.

Filostrat, Christian. Negritude Agonistes, Assimilation Against Nationalism in the French-Speaking Caribbean & Guyane. 2008. (Illus.). 240p. 50.00 *(978-0-9818939-2-1(9))* Africana Homestead Legacy Pubs., Inc.

Grégoire, Henri-Baptiste. An Enquiry Concerning the Intellectual & Moral Faculties & Literature of Negroes: Followed with an Account of the Life & Works of Fifteen Negroes & Mulattoes, Distinguished in Science, Literature, & the Arts. 2012. (AccessAble Bks.). (ENG.). 268p. pap. 19.95 *(978-1-57003-895-2(3))* Univ. of South Carolina Pr.

Grigsby, Daryl. In Their Footsteps: Inspirational Reflections on Black History for Every Day of the Year. 2007. (Illus.). 384p. per. 14.95 *(978-0-87946-336-6(8))* ACTA Pubns.

Gudmundson, Lowell & Wolfe, Justin, eds. Blacks & Blackness in Central America: Between Race & Place. 2010. (ENG., Illus.). 416p. 89.95 *(978-0-8223-4787-3(3))*; pap. 24.95 *(978-0-8223-4803-0(9))* Duke Univ. Pr.

Habib, Imtiaz. Black Lives in the English Archives 1500-1677: Imprints of the Invisible. 2008. (Illus.). 432p. 124.95 *(978-0-7546-5695-1(0))* Ashgate Publishing Co.

Hall, John H. Dancing & Crying to be Free. 2009. 148p. pap. 16.98 *(978-1-4269-1230-6(7))* Trafford Publishing.

Hamilton, Ginetta V. Black History: Someone Forgot to Teach the Children: Lord, I dun bin through someum yah, But... 2010. 76p. pap. 24.99 *(978-1-4490-7384-8(0))* AuthorHouse.

Hudson, James. The Rising of Black America with the Assistance of White Americ. 2009. 284p. 27.50 *(978-1-60860-142-4(0)*, Eloquent Bks.) AEG Literary Publishing Services, Inc.

Jenkins, Everett. Pan-African Chronology II: A Comprehensive Reference to the Black Quest for Freedom in Africa, the Americas, Europe & Asia, 1865-1915, 2 vols. alt. ed. 2011. (Pan-African Chronologies Ser.). (ENG., Illus.). 582p. pap. 75.00 *(978-0-7864-4506-6(8))* McFarland & Co., Inc. Pubs.

—Pan-African Chronology III: A Comprehensive Reference to the Black Quest for Freedom in Africa, the Americas, Europe & Asia, 1914-1929, 2 vols. alt. ed. 2011. (Pan-African Chronologies Ser.). (ENG., Illus.). 640p. pap. 75.00 *(978-0-7864-4507-3(6))* McFarland & Co., Inc. Pubs.

Jenkins, Everett Jr. & Jenkins, Everett. Pan-African Chronology I: A Comprehensive Reference to the Black Quest for Freedom in Africa, the Americas, Europe & Asia, 1400-1865. alt. ed. 2011. (Pan-African Chronologies Ser.). (ENG., Illus.). 448p. pap. 75.00 *(978-0-7864-4505-9(X))* McFarland & Co., Inc. Pubs.

Johnson, Violet Showers & Johnson, Violet M. The Other Black Bostonians: West Indians in Boston, 1900-1950. 2006. (Blacks in the Diaspora Ser.). (ENG., Illus.). 200p. 24.95 *(978-0-253-34752-7(1)*, 0253347521) Indiana Univ. Pr.

King, Sleetie. Longview: Black History Lived & Written. 2006. 13.00 *(978-0-8059-8353-1(8))* Dorrance Publishing Co., Inc.

Landers, Jane G. Atlantic Creoles in the Age of Revolutions. 2010. (Illus.). 352p. 31.50 *(978-0-674-03591-1(7))* Harvard Univ. Pr.

Manning, Patrick. The African Diaspora: A History Through Culture. (Columbia Studies in International & Global History Ser.). (ENG., Illus.). 424p. (gr. 17). 2010. pap. 24.50 *(978-0-231-14471-1(7))* 2009. 29.95 *(978-0-231-14470-4(9))* Columbia Univ. Pr.

Martone, Eric. Encyclopedia of Blacks in European History & Culture, 2 vols. 2008. (Illus.). 712p. 199.95 *(978-0-313-34448-0(5)*, GR4448, Greenwood Pr.) Greenwood Publishing Group, Inc.

McKittrick, Katherine & Woods, Clyde, eds. Black Geographies & the Politics of Place. 2007. (ENG., Illus.). 288p. per. 20.00 *(978-0-89608-773-6(5))* South End Pr.

Millette, James & contrib. by. Freedom Road. 2007. 264p. pap. *(978-976-8189-89-9(4))* Arawak Pubns.

Moore, Lois Merriweather, ed. The Dispersion of Africans & African Culture Throughout the World: Essays on the African Diaspora. 2007. 225p. *(978-0-7734-5309-8(1))* Mellen, Edwin Pr., The.

Moore, Richard B. The Name "Negro" (African Studies). reprint ed. 18.00 *(978-0-938818-97-7(X))* ECA Assocs.

Mumford, Clarence J. American Crucible: Black Enslavement, White Capitalism, & Imperial Globalization: An Interpretation of Western Civilization since 1441. 2009. *(978-1-59221-670-3(6))*; 426p. pap. *(978-1-59221-671-0(4))* Africa World Pr.

Naro, Nancy Priscilla, et al, eds. Cultures of the Lusophone Black Atlantic. 2007. (Studies of the Americas Ser.). (ENG., Illus.). 272p. 95.00 *(978-0-230-60047-8(0))* Palgrave Macmillan.

Nelson, Jennifer J. Razing Africville: A Geography of Racism. 2009. (ENG.). 192p. pap. *(978-1-4426-1028-6(X))* Univ. of Toronto Pr.

Nwachuku, Levi, ed. Exploring the African-American Experience, Fourth Edition. 2008. (C). pap. *(978-0-9798711-0-8(7))* Lincoln Univ. Pr.

Poosson, Sylvain B. La historia Silenciada: Los afroargentinos protagonistas de un drama Social. 2007. (SPA.). 248p. 109.95 *(978-0-7734-5633-4(3))* Mellen, Edwin Pr., The.

Redford, Donald B. From Slave to Pharaoh: The Black Experience of Ancient Egypt. 2006. (ENG., Illus.). 232p. (gr. 17). per. 27.00 *(978-0-8018-8544-0(2))* Johns Hopkins Univ. Pr.

Restall, Matthew. The Black Middle: Africans, Mayas, & Spaniards in Colonial Yucatan. 2009. (ENG., Illus.). 456p. 65.00 *(978-0-8047-4983-1(3))* Stanford Univ. Pr.

Robart-Johnson, Sharon. Africa's Children: A History of Blacks in Yarmouth, Nova Scotia. 2009. (ENG., Illus.). 240p. pap. 28.99 *(978-1-55002-862-1(6))* Dundurn CAN. Dist: Ingram Pub. Services.

Robinson, Carey. Fight for Freedom: The Destruction of Slavery in Jamaica. 2007. 196p. per. *(978-976-8202-42-0(4))* LMH Publishing, Ltd.

Robinson, Devin A. & Roper, Vernon. Blacks: from the Plantation to the Prison: The Move, the Mockery, the Mental Slavery. 2008. (Illus.). 160p. pap. *(978-978-8174-51-6(5))* Loretta Davis.

Rogers, J. A. One Hundred Amazing Facts about the Negro with Complete Proof: A Short Cut to the World History of the Negro. 2011. 68p. 36.95 ***(978-1-258-03077-3(2))*** Literary Licensing, LLC.

Rosen, Hannah. Terror in the Heart of Freedom: Citizenship, Sexual Violence, & the Meaning of Race in the Postemancipation South. 2008. (Gender & American Culture Ser.). (ENG., Illus.). 424p. 69.95 *(978-0-8078-3202-8(2))* Univ. of North Carolina Pr.

Schomburg, Arthur A. Racial Integrity - A Plea for the Establishment of a Chair of Negro History in Our Schools & Colleges, Etc. (African Studies). reprint ed. 10.00 *(978-0-938818-42-7(2))* ECA Assocs.

Shadd, Adrienne. The Journey from Tollgate to Parkway: African Canadians in Hamilton. 2010. (ENG., Illus.). 368p. pap. 35.00 *(978-1-55488-394-3(6))* Dundurn CAN. Dist: Ingram Pub. Services.

Simanga, Michael. The Congress of African People: History, Memory, & an Ideological Journey. 2012. (Contemporary Black History Ser.). (ENG.). 224p. 75.00 ***(978-0-230-11215-5(3))*** Palgrave Macmillan.

Tardieu, Jean-Pierre. Cimarrones de Panamá: La Forja de une Identidad Afroamericana en el Siglo XVI. 2009. (SPA., Illus.). 288p. pap. 36.00 *(978-84-8489-456-8(8))* Iberoamericana Vervuert Publishing Corp.

White, Derrick E. The Challenge of Blackness: The Institute of the Black World & Political Activism in The 1970s. 2011. (Southern Dissent Ser.). (ENG., Illus.). 288p. 69.95 *(978-0-8130-3735-6(2))* Univ. Pr. of Florida.

Wilson, Francille Rusan. The Segregated Scholars: Black Social Scientists & the Creation of Black Labor Studies, 1890-1950. 2006. (Carter G. Woodson Institute Ser.). (ENG., Illus.). 352p. (gr. 17). 37.50 *(978-0-8139-2550-9(9))* Univ. Pr. of Virginia.

Wilson, Maloyd Ben. Black Chronicle Teacher's Guide. 2008. 120p. pap. 50.00 *(978-0-9753210-1-0(3))* Wilson Group Network, Inc.

Wyatt, Don J. The Blacks of Premodern China. 2009. (Encounters with Asia Ser.). (Illus.). 208p. (C). 65.00 *(978-0-8122-4193-8(2))* Univ. of Pennsylvania Pr.

BLACKS—LANGUAGES

English, Parker. What We Say, Who We Are: Leopold Senghor, Zora Neale Hurston, & the Philosophy of Language. 2009. (ENG.). 134p. 57.99 *(978-0-7391-2651-6(2))* Lexington Bks.

Kleifgen, Jo Anne & Bond, George C. The Languages of Africa & the Diaspora: Educating for Language Awareness. Kleifgen, Jo Anne & Bond, George C., eds. 2009. (New Perspectives on Language & Education Ser.). (ENG., Illus.). 256p. 54.95 *(978-1-84769-133-0(1))* Multilingual Matters GBR. Dist: Univ. of Toronto Pr.

Kleifgen, Jo Anne & Bond, George C., eds. The Languages of Africa & the Diaspora: Educating for Language Awareness. 2009. (New Perspectives on Language & Education Ser.). (ENG., Illus.). 256p. 139.95 *(978-1-84769-134-7(X))* Multilingual Matters GBR. Dist: Univ. of Toronto Pr.

BLACKS—MUSIC

Barnett, Lashonda. I Got Thunder: Black Women Songwriters & Their Craft. 2007. (ENG.). 352p. per. 16.95 *(978-1-56858-331-0(1))* Da Capo Pr., Inc.

Brennan, Timothy. Secular Devotion: Afro-Latin Music & Imperial Jazz. 2008. (ENG., Illus.). 290p. pap. 29.95 *(978-1-84467-291-2(3)*, 844291) Verso Bks. GBR. Dist: Norton, W. W. & Co., Inc.

de Jong, Nanette. Tambú: Curaçao's African-Caribbean Ritual & the Politics of Memory. 2012. (Ethnomusicology Multimedia Ser.). (ENG., Illus.). 182p. 70.00 *(978-0-253-35654-3(7)*, 0253356547); pap. 25.00 *(978-0-253-22337-1(7)*, 0253223377) Indiana Univ. Pr.

Dearling, Alan & Kigongo, Denis. The Youth Africa Music Experience. 2008. (Illus.). 80p. pap. 35.95 incl. audio compact disk *(978-1-903855-94-2(2))* Russell Hse. Publishing Ltd. GBR. Dist: International Specialized Bk. Services.

Diouf, Mamadou & Nwankwo, Ifeoma Kiddoe. Rhythms of the Afro-Atlantic World: Rituals & Remembrances. 2010. *(978-0-472-05096-3(6))* Univ. of Michigan Pr.

Eshun, Kodwo & Sagar, Anjalika, eds. The Ghosts of Songs: The Art of the Black Audio Film Collective. 2007. (ENG., Illus.). 240p. 35.00 *(978-1-84631-014-0(8))* Liverpool Univ. Pr. GBR. Dist: Chicago Distribution Ctr.

Feldman, Heidi Carolyn & Feldman, Heidi. Black Rhythms of Peru: Reviving African Musical Heritage in the Black Pacific. 2007. (Music Culture Ser.). (ENG., Illus.). 328p. pap. 25.95 *(978-0-8195-6815-1(5))* Wesleyan Univ. Pr.

Jong, Nanette de. Tambú: Curaçao's African-Caribbean Ritual & the Politics of Memory. 2012. ***(978-0-253-00572-4(8))*** Indiana Univ. Pr.

Nwankwo, Ifeoma C. K. & Diouf, Mamadou, eds. Rhythms of the Afro-Atlantic World: Rituals & Remembrances. 2010. (ENG., Illus.). 298p. (C). 70.00 *(978-0-472-07096-1(7))* Univ. of Michigan Pr.

Sullivan, Denise. Keep on Pushing: Black Power Music from Blues to Hip-hop. 2011. (ENG., Illus.). 224p. pap. 16.95 *(978-1-55652-817-0(5)*, Hill, Lawrence Bks.) Chicago Review Pr., Inc.

BLACKS—POLITICS AND GOVERNMENT

see also Black Nationalism

Alexander, Amanda & Mngxitama, Andile. Biko Lives! Contesting the Legacies of Steve Biko. Gibson, Nigel, ed. 2008. (Contemporary Black History Ser.). (ENG.). 304p. pap. 31.00 *(978-0-230-60649-4(0))* Palgrave Macmillan.

Alexander-Floyd, Nikol G. & Alexander-floyd, Nikol G. Gender, Race, & Nationalism in Contemporary Black Politics. 2007. (Comparative Feminist Studies). (ENG.). 256p. 89.00 *(978-1-4039-7966-7(9))* Palgrave Macmillan.

Dash, Heather. Negative Perceptions & Low Opinions. 2008. 56p. pap. *(978-3-639-07821-3(7))* VDM Verlag Dr. Mueller e.K.

Duse Mohamed & Abdelwahid, Mustafa A. Dusé Mohamed Ali (1866-1945) 2011. 218p. *(978-1-56902-343-3(3))*; pap. *(978-1-56902-344-0(1))* Red Sea Pr.

Eze, Michael Onyebuchi. Intellectual History in Contemporary South Africa. 2010. (ENG.). 234p. 89.00 *(978-0-230-62299-9(2))* Palgrave Macmillan.

Jacobs, Brian D. Black Politics & Urban Crisis in Britain. 2009. (ENG.). 236p. pap. 36.99 *(978-0-521-12552-9(9))* Cambridge Univ. Pr.

James, C. Boyd. Garvey, Garveyism, & the Problem of Black Redemption. 2008. *(978-1-59221-654-3(4))*; 418p. pap. *(978-1-59221-655-0(2))* Africa World Pr.

Mandela, Nelson. Let Freedom Reign: The Words of Nelson Mandela. Russell, Henry, ed. 2010. (ENG.). 144p. 14.95 *(978-1-56656-800-5(5)*, Interlink Bks.) Interlink Publishing Group, Inc.

Mngxitama, Andile, et al. Biko Lives! Contesting the Legacies of Steve Biko. Alexander, Amanda et al, eds. 2008. (Contemporary Black History Ser.). (ENG.). 304p. 95.00 *(978-0-230-60519-0(2))* Palgrave Macmillan.

Nascimento, Elisa Larkin. The Sorcery of Color: Identity, Race, & Gender in Brazil. 2nd ed. 2009. (ENG.). 336p. pap. 30.95 *(978-1-59213-351-2(7))* Temple Univ. Pr.

Ng'weno, Bettina. Turf Wars: Territory & Citizenship in the Contemporary State. 2007. (ENG., Illus.). 312p. 50.00 *(978-0-8047-5596-2(5))* Stanford Univ. Pr.

Pappademos, Melina. Black Political Activism & the Cuban Republic. 2011. (Envisioning Cuba Ser.). (ENG., Illus.). 368p. 39.95 *(978-0-8078-3490-9(4))* Univ. of North Carolina Pr.

Pohlandt-McCormick, Helena. I Saw a Nightmare: Doing Violence to Memory - The Soweto Uprising, June 16, 1976. 2008. (Gutenberg-e Ser.). (ENG.). 655p. 60.00 *(978-0-231-12220-7(9))* Columbia Univ. Pr.

Polsgrove, Carol. Ending British Rule in Africa: Writers in a Common Cause. 2009. (Studies in Imperialism Ser.). (ENG.). 240p. 89.95 *(978-0-7190-7767-8(2))* Manchester Univ. Pr. GBR. Dist: Macmillan.

Rahier, Jean Muteba, ed. Black Social Movements in Latin America: From Monocultural Mestizaje to Multiculturalism. 2012. (ENG., Illus.). 272p. 90.00 ***(978-0-230-39360-8(8))*** Palgrave Macmillan.

Redding, Sean. Sorcery & Sovereignty: Taxation, Power, & Rebellion in South Africa, 1880-1963. 2006. (Illus.). 304p. 55.00 *(978-0-8214-1704-1(5))*; per. 29.95 *(978-0-8214-1705-8(3))* Ohio Univ. Pr.

Romo, Anadelia A. Brazil's Living Museum: Race, Reform, & Tradition in Bahia. 2010. (ENG., Illus.). 272p. 59.95 *(978-0-8078-3382-7(7))*; 240p. pap. 24.95 *(978-0-8078-7115-7(X))* Univ. of North Carolina Pr.

Thompson, Bankole. A Matter of Black Transformation. 2007. 180p. per. 15.00 *(978-0-9760755-7-8(1)*, Read4Life Bks.) Christian Bk. Outreach, Inc.

Turok, Ben, ed. The Historical Roots of the ANC. 2011. (Understanding the ANC Today Ser.). (ENG., Illus.). 144p. pap. 15.95 *(978-1-77009-965-4(4))* Jacana Media ZAF. Dist: Independent Pubs. Group.

Tymowski, Michal. The Origins & Structures of Political Institutions in Pre-Colonial Black Africa: Dynastic Monarchy, Taxes & Tributes, War & Slavery, Kinship & Territory. 2009. (Illus.). 240p. 109.95 *(978-0-7734-4718-9(0))* Mellen, Edwin Pr., The.

West, Michael O., et al, eds. From Toussaint to Tupac: The Black International since the Age of Revolution. 2009. (ENG., Illus.). 336p. 62.95 *(978-0-8078-3309-4(6))*; pap. 23.95 *(978-0-8078-5972-8(9))* Univ. of North Carolina Pr.

BLACKS—RACE IDENTITY

see also Black Nationalism

Adeleke, Tunde. The Case Against Afrocentrism. 2009. (ENG.). 224p. 50.00 *(978-1-60473-293-1(8))* Univ. Pr. of Mississippi.

Alexander-Floyd, Nikol G. & Alexander-floyd, Nikol G. Gender, Race, & Nationalism in Contemporary Black Politics. 2007. (Comparative Feminist Studies). (ENG.). 256p. 89.00 *(978-1-4039-7966-7(9))* Palgrave Macmillan.

Asher, Kiran. Black & Green: Afro-Colombians, Development, & Nature in the Pacific Lowlands. 2009. (ENG., Illus.). 272p. 84.95 *(978-0-8223-4487-2(4))*; pap. 23.95 *(978-0-8223-4483-4(1))* Duke Univ. Pr.

Ashimolowo, Matthew. What Is Wrong with Being Black? Celebrating Our Heritage, Confronting Our Challenges. 2008. (Illus.). 348p. pap. 16.99 *(978-0-7684-2638-0(3))* Destiny Image Pubs.

Badiane, Mamadou. The Changing Face of Afro-Caribbean Cultural Identity: Negrismo & NZgritude. 2009. (ENG.). 198p. 68.50 *(978-0-7391-2553-3(2))* Lexington Bks.

Bailey, Julius. Race Patriotism: Protest & Print Culture in the A.M.E. Church. 2012. (ENG., Illus.). 192p. 47.00 ***(978-1-57233-845-6(8))*** Univ. of Tennessee Pr.

Bailey, Stanley R. Legacies of Race: Identities, Attitudes, & Politics in Brazil. 2009. (ENG., Illus.). 304p. 70.00 *(978-0-8047-6277-9(5))*; pap. 24.95 *(978-0-8047-6278-6(3))* Stanford Univ. Pr.

Barry, Boubacar, et al. Africa, Brazil, & the Construction of Trans-Atlantic Black Identities. 2007. *(978-1-59221-526-3(2))*; x, 346p. pap. *(978-1-59221-527-0(0))* Africa World Pr.

Bashkow, Ira. The Meaning of Whitemen: Race & Modernity in the Orokaiva Cultural World. 2006. (Illus.). 328p. per. 30.00 *(978-0-226-03891-9(2))*; 70.00 *(978-0-226-03890-2(4))* Univ. of Chicago Pr.

Bird, S. R. & Bird, Stephanie Rose. Light, Bright, & Damned near White: Biracial & Triracial Culture in America, 1 vol. 2009. (Race & Ethnicity in Psychology Ser.). 168p. 39.95 *(978-0-275-98954-5(2)*, C8954, Praeger Pubs.) Greenwood Publishing Group, Inc.

Bornstein, George. The Colors of Zion: Blacks, Jews, & Irish from 1845 To 1945. 2011. (ENG., Illus.). 272p. 27.95 *(978-0-674-05701-2(5))* Harvard Univ. Pr.

Bryant, Sherwin K., et al, eds. Africans to Spanish America: Expanding the Diaspora. 2012. (New Black Studies Ser.). (ENG., Illus.). 288p. 50.00 ***(978-0-252-03663-7(8))*** Univ. of Illinois Pr.

Caldwell, Kia Lilly. Negras in Brazil: Re-Envisioning Black Women, Citizenship, & the Politics of Identity. 2006. (ENG., Illus.). 252p. per. 24.95 *(978-0-8135-3957-7(9))* Rutgers Univ. Pr.

Camba Ludlow, Úrsula. Imaginarios Ambiguos, Realidades Contradictorias: Conductas y Representaciones de Los Negros y Mulatos Novohispanos: Siglos XVI y XVII. 2008. (Estudios Históricos Ser.). (SPA., Illus.). 227p. pap. 23.99 *(978-968-12-1374-9(2))* El Colegio de México, A.C., Biblioteca Miguel Cosio Villegas MEX. Dist: Fondo de Cultura Economica USA.

Cathialam, Aam'pah-Katoh BaNtump'l. The African Remedy. 2008. 160p. 33.49 *(978-1-4389-0993-6(4))*; pap. 17.99 *(978-1-4389-0994-3(2))* AuthorHouse.

Clarke, Kamari Maxine & Thomas, Deborah A., eds. Globalization & Race: Transformations in the Cultural Production of Blackness. 2006. (ENG., Illus.). 424p. (C). 99.95 *(978-0-8223-3759-1(2))* Duke Univ. Pr.

Coates, Rodney D., ed. Race & Ethnicity: Across Time, Space & Discipline. 2009. (Studies in Critical Social Sciences Ser.). (ENG., Illus.). 506p. pap. 36.00 *(978-1-60846-045-8(2))* Haymarket Bks.

Coates, Rodney D. & Dennis, Rutledge M. The 'new Black' Alternative Paradigms & Strategies for the 21st Century. Coates, Rodney & Dennis, Rutledge, eds. 2007. 372p. 111.95 *(978-0-7623-0985-6(7))* Emerald Group Publishing Ltd. GBR. Dist: Turpin Distribution Services Ltd.

Cunha Júnior, Henrique Antunes, et al. Espaço Urbano e Afrodescendência: Estudos Da Espacialidade Negra Urbana para o Debate das Políticas Públicas. 2007. (POR., Illus.). 206p. *(978-85-7282-259-6(3))* Universidade Federal do Ceara. Editora.

Curran, Andrew S. The Anatomy of Blackness: Science & Slavery in an Age of Enlightenment. 2011. (ENG., Illus.). 328p. (gr. 17). 75.00 *(978-1-4214-0150-8(9))* Johns Hopkins Univ. Pr.

DaCosta, Kahlil. My People. 2008. 205p. pap. 19.95 *(978-1-4092-0518-0(5))* Lulu Enterprises Inc.

Davidson, Marianne. Critical Perspectives on Bell Hooks. 2009. (ENG.). 242p. 145.00 *(978-0-415-98980-0(9))* Routledge.

Davis, Darien J. Beyond Slavery: The Multilayered Legacy of Africans in Latin America & the Caribbean. 2006. (Jaguar Books on Latin America Ser.). (ENG., Illus.). 298p. 92.00 *(978-0-7425-4130-6(4))*; per. 34.95 *(978-0-7425-4131-3(2))* Rowman & Littlefield Publishers, Inc.

Dillard, Cynthia B. Learning to (Re)member the Things We've Learned to Forget: Endarkened Feminisms, Spirituality, & the Sacred Nature of (Re)search & Teaching. 2012. ***(978-1-4331-1282-9(5))***; pap. ***(978-1-4331-1281-2(7))***; E-Book ***(978-1-4539-0243-1(0))*** Lang, Peter Publishing, Inc.

Duncan, Carol B. This Spot of Ground: Spiritual Baptists in Toronto. 2008. (ENG.). 304p. 85.00 *(978-1-55458-017-0(X))* Wilfrid Laurier Univ. Pr. CAN. Dist: Univ. of Toronto Pr.

Egar, Emmanuel Edame. The Crisis of Negritude: A Study of the Black Movement Against Intellectual Oppression in the Early 20th Century. 2008. pap. 17.95 *(978-1-59942-472-9(X)*, Brown Walker Pr.) Universal Pubs.

Eggens, Laura. Never 100% Black. 2010. 108p. pap. *(978-3-8383-6036-2(2))* Lambert Academic Publishing.

Ehlers, Nadine. Racial Imperatives: Discipline, Performativity, & Struggles against Subjection. 2012. (ENG.). 200p. 70.00 *(978-0-253-35656-7(3)*, 0253356563); pap. 25.00 *(978-0-253-22336-4(9)*, 0253223369) Indiana Univ. Pr.

Evelyn White. Untold Stalking Story. 2009. 76p. pap. 10.95 *(978-1-4401-8749-0(5))* iUniverse, Inc.

Filostrat, Christian. Negritude Agonistes, Assimilation Against Nationalism in the French-Speaking Caribbean & Guyane. 2008. (Illus.). 240p. 50.00 *(978-0-9818939-2-1(9))* Africana Homestead Legacy Pubs., Inc.

Fleetwood, Nicole R. Troubling Vision: Performance, Visuality, & Blackness. 2011. (ENG., Illus.). 296p. 75.00 *(978-0-226-25302-2(3))*; pap. 25.00 *(978-0-226-25303-9(1))* Univ. of Chicago Pr.

Folan, Karyn Langhorne. Don't Bring Home a White Boy: And Other Notions That Keep Black Women from Dating Out. 2010. (ENG.). 256p. 24.99 *(978-1-4391-5475-5(9)*, Gallery Books/Karen Hunter Publishing) Gallery Books/Karen Hunter Publishing.

François, Anne M. Rewriting the Return of Africa: Voices of Francophone Caribbean Women Writers. 2011. (ENG.). 146p. 60.00 *(978-0-7391-4826-6(5))* Lexington Bks.

François, Anne M. Rewriting the Return to Africa: Voices of Francophone Caribbean Women Writers. 2011. xxxiii, 111p. E-Book ***(978-0-7391-4828-0(1))*** Lexington Bks.

Franks, Pamela & Steele, Robert E. Embodied: Black Identities in American Art from the Yale University Art Gallery. 2010. *(978-0-89467-977-3(5))* Yale Univ. Art Gallery.

Frazier, John W., et al, eds. The African Diaspora in the United State & Canada at the Dawn of the 21st Century. 2010. (Global Academic Publishing Ser.). (Illus.). 383p. pap. 49.00 *(978-1-4384-3684-5(X)*, Suny Pr.) State Univ. of New York Pr.

—The African Diaspora in the United States & Canada at the Dawn of the 21st Century. 2009. pap. *(978-1-58684-271-0(4))* Global Academic Publishing.

Frindéthié, K. Martial. The Black Renaissance in Francophone African & Caribbean Literatures. 2008. (ENG., Illus.). 215p. pap. 39.95 *(978-0-7864-3663-7(8))* McFarland & Co., Inc. Pubs.

Gates, Henry Louis, Jr. Black in Latin America. 2011. (ENG.). 270p. 26.95 *(978-0-8147-3298-4(4))*; E-Book *(978-0-8147-3342-4(5))* New York Univ. Pr.

Gibson, Nigel. Fanonian Practices in South Africa: From Steve Biko to Abahlali BaseMjondolo. 2011. (ENG.). 320p. 85.00 *(978-0-230-11784-6(8))* Palgrave Macmillan.

Githiora, Chege J. Afro-Mexicans: Discourse of Race & Identity on the African Diaspora. 2008. *(978-1-59221-646-8(3))*; 276p. pap. *(978-1-59221-647-5(1))* Africa World Pr.

Golash-Boza, Tanya Maria. Yo Soy Negro: Blackness in Peru. 2011. (New World Diasporas Ser.). (ENG., Illus.). 208p. 74.95 *(978-0-8130-3574-1(0))* Univ. Pr. of Florida.

Gonzalez, Nancie L. Sojourners of the Caribbean: Ethnogenesis & Ethnohistory of the Garifuna. 2009. 292p. 41.00 *(978-1-59740-289-7(3))* ACLS Humanities E-Book.

Gonzalez, Nancie L. & Conrad, Earl. Sojourners of the Caribbean: Ethnogenesis & Ethnohistory of the Garifuna. 2008. 292p. pap. 27.00 *(978-1-59740-662-8(7))* ACLS Humanities E-Book.

Guridy, Frank Andre. Forging Diaspora: Afro-Cubans & African Americans in a World of Empire & Jim Crow. 2010. (Envisioning Cuba Ser.). (ENG., Illus.). 288p. 59.95 *(978-0-8078-3361-2(4))*; pap. 22.95 *(978-0-8078-7103-4(6))* Univ. of North Carolina Pr.

Habib, Imtiaz. Black Lives in the English Archives 1500-1677: Imprints of the Invisible. 2008. (Illus.). 432p. 124.95 *(978-0-7546-5695-0(4))* Ashgate Publishing Co.

Hamblet, Wendy C. Savage Constructions: The Myth of African Savagery. 2008. (ENG.). 274p. 78.99 *(978-0-7391-2280-8(0))*; pap. 31.50 *(978-0-7391-2281-5(9))* Lexington Bks.

Harris, Dwight. American Nigger: Black Beyond King. 2007. 148p. per. 15.95 *(978-0-9767575-3-5(2))* Topos Bks.

Hartigan, John, Jr. Race in the 21st Century: Ethnographic Approaches, 1 vol. 2009. 240p. (C). 64.95 *(978-0-19-537561-9(0))*; (ENG., Illus.). pap. 34.95 *(978-0-19-537560-2(2))* Oxford Univ. Pr., Inc.

Hine, Darlene Clark, et al, eds. Black Europe & the African Diaspora. 2009. (New Black Studies Ser.). (ENG., Illus.). 376p. 75.00 *(978-0-252-03467-1(8))*; pap. 30.00 *(978-0-252-07657-2(5))* Univ. of Illinois Pr.

Irele, Abiola. The Négritude Moment: Explorations in Francophone African & Caribbean Literature & Thought. 2010. xv, 259p. *(978-1-59221-797-7(4))*; 256p. pap. *(978-1-59221-798-4(2))* Africa World Pr.

Jackson, Sandra & Moody-Freeman, Julie E. The Black Imagination, Science Fiction, Futurism & the Speculative. 2011. (Black Studies & Critical Thinking Ser.). (C). 129.95 *(978-1-4331-1242-3(6))*; pap. 32.95 *(978-1-4331-1241-6(8))* Lang, Peter Publishing, Inc.

Japtok, Martin. Authentic Blackness/ Real Blackness: Essays on the Meaning of Blackness in Culture & Literature (CB) 2011. (C). 129.95 *(978-1-4331-1509-7(3))* Lang, Peter Publishing, Inc.

—Authentic Blackness/ Real Blackness: Essays on the Meaning of Blackness in Literature & Culture. 2011. (C). pap. 34.95 *(978-1-4331-1508-0(5))* Lang, Peter Publishing, Inc.

Khalifah, H. Khalif. Melanin: Conscious Attunement & the God in I. (Orig.). reprint ed. pap. 10.00 *(978-1-56411-133-3(4))* UBUS Communications Systems.

Kitch, Sally. The Specter of Sex: Gendered Foundations of Racial Formation in the United States. 2009. 288p. 70.00 *(978-1-4384-2753-9(0))*; pap. 29.95 *(978-1-4384-2754-6(9))* State Univ. of New York Pr.

Lewis, Laura A. Chocolate & Corn Flour: History, Race, & Place in the Making of "Black" Mexico. 2012. (ENG., Illus.). 400p. pap. 25.95 ***(978-0-8223-5132-0(3))*** Duke Univ. Pr.

—Chocolate & Corn Flour: History, Race, & Place in the Making of ldquo;Blackrdquo; Mexico. 2012. (ENG., Illus.). 400p. 94.95 ***(978-0-8223-5121-4(8))*** Duke Univ. Pr.

Magaziner, Daniel R. The Law & the Prophets: Black Consciousness in South Africa, 1968-1977. 2010. (New African Histories Ser.). (ENG., Illus.). 280p. 59.95 *(978-0-8214-1917-5(X))* Ohio Univ. Pr.

—The Law & the Prophets: Faith, Hope, & Politics in South Africa, 1968-1977. 2010. (New African Histories Ser.). (ENG., Illus.). 280p. pap. 26.95 *(978-0-8214-1918-2(8))* Ohio Univ. Pr.

Marriott, David. Haunted Life: Visual Culture & Black Modernity. 2007. (ENG., Illus.). 312p. (C). 70.00 *(978-0-8135-4027-6(5))*; per. 24.95 *(978-0-8135-4028-3(3))* Rutgers Univ. Pr.

M'Baye, Babacar. The Trickster Comes West: Pan-African Influence in Early Black Diasporan Narratives. (ENG.). 272p. 2011. pap. 30.00 ***(978-1-61703-210-3(7))*** 2009. 50.00 *(978-1-60473-233-7(4))* Univ. Pr. of Mississippi.

Mccusker, Peter J. Barry Barack Hussein Soetoro Obama: Identity & Racial Hypocrisy in America Double Standards, Double Speak, & Double Binds. 2011. 404p. 32.95 ***(978-1-4620-3262-4(1))***; pap. 22.95 ***(978-1-4620-3260-0(5))*** iUniverse, Inc.

Miyeni, Eric. O'Mandingo! Before Mandela was Mandela. 2008. (ENG.). 144p. pap. 20.95 *(978-1-77009-345-4(1))* Jacana Media ZAF. Dist: Independent Pubs. Group.

—O'Mandingo! The Only Black at a Dinner Party. 2007. (ENG.). 276p. per. 18.95 *(978-1-77009-187-0(4))* Jacana Media ZAF. Dist: Independent Pubs. Group.

Moorehead, Monica, ed. Marxism, Reparations & the Black Freedom Struggle. 2007. (ENG.). 197p. pap. 19.95 *(978-0-89567-137-0(9))* World View Forum.

Morris, Edward W. Learning the Hard Way: Masculinity, Place, & the Gender Gap in Education. 2012. (Rutgers Series in Childhood Studies). 224p. (C). pap. 26.95 ***(978-0-8135-5369-6(5))***; (ENG.). 72.00 ***(978-0-8135-5368-9(7))*** Rutgers Univ. Pr.

Mullins, Victor. African American Students in College. 2009. 144p. pap. *(978-3-639-17694-0(4))* VDM Verlag Dr. Mueller e.K.

Mutua. Progressive Black Masculinities. 2006. 320p. (ENG.). 36.95 *(978-0-415-97687-9(1))*; 125.00 *(978-0-415-97686-2(3))* Routledge.

Nelson, Jennifer J. Razing Africville: A Geography of Racism. (ENG.). 192p. 2009. pap. *(978-1-4426-1028-6(X))* 2008. *(978-0-8020-9252-6(7))* Univ. of Toronto Pr.

Ntarangwi, Mwenda. East African Hip Hop: Youth Culture & Globalization. 2009. (Interp Culture New Millennium Ser.). (ENG.). 176p. 60.00 *(978-0-252-03457-2(0))*; pap. 20.00 *(978-0-252-07653-4(2))* Univ. of Illinois Pr.

Nunes, Zita. Cannibal Democracy: Race & Representation in the Literature of the Americas. 2008. (Critical American Studies). (Illus.). 240p. 67.50 *(978-0-8166-4840-5(9))*; pap. 22.50 *(978-0-8166-4841-2(7))* Univ. of Minnesota Pr.

Ojara, Pius. Toward a Fuller Human Identity: A Phenomenology of Family Life, Social Harmony, & the Recovery of the Black Self, Vol. 825. 2006. xiv,477p. pap. 68.95 *(978-0-8204-8360-3(5))* Lang, Peter Publishing, Inc.

Owens, Michael Eric. A New Philosophy of Black Identity: Yes I Am Who I Am. 2009. 183p. pap. 16.99 *(978-0-88144-323-3(9))* Yorkshire Publishing Group.

Peters, Christabelle. Cuban Identity & the Angolan Experience. 2012. (New Directions in Latino American Culture Ser.). (ENG., Illus.). 256p. 85.00 ***(978-0-230-34093-0(8))*** Palgrave Macmillan.

Pierre, Jemima. The Predicament of Blackness: Postcolonial Ghana & the Politics of Race. 2012. 280p. pap. 30.00 ***(978-0-226-92303-1(7))***; (Illus.). 90.00 ***(978-0-226-92302-4(9))*** Univ. of Chicago Pr.

Pinho, Patricia de Santana. Mama Africa: Reinventing Blackness in Bahia. Langdon, Elena, tr. from POR. 2010. (ENG., Illus.). 280p. 84.95 *(978-0-8223-4654-8(0))*; pap. 23.95 *(978-0-8223-4646-3(X))* Duke Univ. Pr.

Price, Charles. Becoming Rasta: Origins of Rastafari Identity in Jamaica. 2009. (ENG., Illus.). 288p. pap. 22.00 *(978-0-8147-6747-4(8))* New York Univ. Pr.

Proctor, Frank. Damned Notions of Liberty: Slavery, Culture, & Power in Colonial Mexico, 1640-1769. 2010. (Diálogos Ser.). (ENG., Illus.). 296p. (C). pap. 27.95 *(978-0-8263-4966-8(8))* Univ. of New Mexico Pr.

Rahier, Jean. Global Circuits of Blackness: Interrogating the African Diaspora. Hintzen, Percy C. & Smith, Felipe, eds. 2010. (ENG., Illus.). 288p. pap. 30.00 *(978-0-252-07753-1(9))* Univ. of Illinois Pr.

Rahier, Jean Muteba, et al, eds. Global Circuits of Blackness: Interrogating the African Diaspora. 2010. (ENG., Illus.). 288p. 80.00 *(978-0-252-03562-3(3))* Univ. of Illinois Pr.

Reiter, Bernd & Eison Simmons, Kimberly, eds. Afro-Descendants, Identity, & the Struggle for Development in the Americas. 2012. (African Diaspora Research Project Ser.). (ENG.). 344p. pap. 34.95 ***(978-1-61186-040-5(7))*** Michigan State Univ. Pr.

Romo, Anadelia A. Brazil's Living Museum: Race, Reform, & Tradition in Bahia. 2010. (ENG., Illus.). 272p. 59.95 *(978-0-8078-3382-7(7))*; 240p. pap. 24.95 *(978-0-8078-7115-7(X))* Univ. of North Carolina Pr.

Seltzer, Richard & Johnson. Experiencing Racism: Exploring Discrimination through the Eyes of College Students. 2009. (ENG.). 390p. pap. 34.99 *(978-0-7391-3432-0(9))* Lexington Bks.

Seltzer, Richard & Johnson, Nicole E. Experiencing Racism: Exploring Discrimination through the Eyes of College Students. 2009. (ENG.). 326p. 83.99 *(978-0-7391-3431-3(0))* Lexington Bks.

Senghor, Leopold S. Les Fondements de l'Africanite ou Negritude et Arabite. (FRE.). pap. 17.95 *(978-0-7859-5307-4(8))* French & European Pubns., Inc.

—Negritude & Humanism. Jeanpierre, Wendell A., tr. from FRE. *(978-0-89388-197-9(X))* Okpaku Communications Corp.

Shotwell, Alexis. Knowing Otherwise: Race, Gender, & Implicit Understanding. 2011. 200p. 54.95 *(978-0-271-03763-9(6))* Pennsylvania State Univ. Pr.

Simmons, Kimberly Eison. Reconstructing Racial Identity & the African Past in the Dominican Republic. 2011. (New World Diasporas Ser.). (ENG., Illus.). 176p. pap. 24.95 *(978-0-8130-3675-5(5))* Univ. Pr. of Florida.

Smith, Faith Lois, et al. Gendering the African Diaspora: Women, Culture, & Historical Change in the Caribbean & Nigerian Hinterland. Byfield, Judith A. et al, eds. 2010. (Blacks in the Diaspora Ser.). (ENG., Illus.). 344p. 65.00 *(978-0-253-35416-7(1)*, 0253354161); pap. 24.95 *(978-0-253-22153-7(6)*, 0253221536) Indiana Univ. Pr.

Telles, Edward E. Race in Another America: The Significance of Skin Color in Brazil. 2006. (ENG., Illus.). 336p. (C). per. 25.95 *(978-0-691-12792-7(1))* Princeton Univ. Pr.

Thomas, Deborah A. & Clarke, Kamari Maxine, eds. Globalization & Race: Transformations in the Cultural Production of Blackness. 2006. (ENG.). 424p. per. 27.95 *(978-0-8223-3772-0(X))* Duke Univ. Pr.

Tillis, Antonio D. (Re)Considering Blackness in Contemporary Afro-Brazilian (con)Texts. 2011. (C). 139.95 ***(978-1-4331-0787-0(2))***; pap. 34.95 ***(978-1-4331-0786-3(4))*** Lang, Peter Publishing, Inc.

Vinson, Ben. Black Mexico: Race & Society from Colonial to Modern Times. Restall, Matthew, ed. 2009. (Diálogos Ser.). (ENG., Illus.). 296p. (C). pap. 29.95 *(978-0-8263-4701-5(0))* Univ. of New Mexico Pr.

Wildgen, Quirin. Aimé Césaire Zwischen Poesie und Politik: Identität und Gesellschaft Auf Martinique. 2010. (GER.). 120p. *(978-3-631-60185-3(9))* Lang, Peter Publishing, Inc.

Yancy, George. Look, A White! Philosophical Essays on Whiteness. 2012. (ENG.). 228p. 84.50 ***(978-1-4399-0853-2(2))***; pap. 26.95 ***(978-1-4399-0854-9(0))*** Temple Univ. Pr.

—Look, a White! Philosophical Essays on Whiteness. 2012. E-Book ***(978-1-4399-0855-6(9))*** Temple Univ. Pr.

Zeleza, Paul Tiyambe. In Search of African Diasporas: Testimonies & Encounters. 2012. 592p. 65.00 ***(978-1-61163-056-5(8))*** Carolina Academic Pr.

BLACKS—RELIGION

see also Black Theology; Rastafari Movement

Bastide, Roger. The African Religions of Brazil: Toward a Sociology of the Interpenetration of Civilizations. Sebba, Helen, tr. from FRE. 2007. (Johns Hopkins Studies in Atlantic History & Culture Ser.). (ENG.). 494p. (gr. 17). pap. 26.00 *(978-0-8018-8624-9(4))* Johns Hopkins Univ. Pr.

Capone, Stefania. Searching for Africa in Brazil: Power & Tradition in Candomblé. Grant, Lucy Lyall, tr. from FRE. 2010. (ENG., Illus.). 336p. 84.95 (978-0-8223-4625-8(7)); pap. 23.95 (978-0-8223-4636-4(2)) Duke Univ. Pr.

Caronia, Anthony & Alonso, Ania Rodríguez. Afro-Cuba. Mystik und Magie der afro-kubanischen Religion. 2011. (Illus.). 176p. 60.00 (978-3-7165-1624-9(4)) Benteli Verlag CHE. Dist: Antique Collectors' Club.

Cole, Steve. The Black Church: The Root of the Problems in the Black Community. 2006. 149p. 21.95 (978-0-9786272-0-1(2)) Cole, Steve.

Finley, Stephen C. & Alexander, Torin. African American Religious Cultures, 2 vols. Pinn, Anthony B., ed. 2009. (American Religious Cultures Ser.). (Illus.). 739p. 195.00 (978-1-57607-470-1(6), AFRCC) ABC-CLIO, LLC.

Gonzalez, Michelle A. Afro-Cuban Theology: Religion, Race, Culture, & Identity. (ENG., 208p. 2009. Illus.). pap. 29.95 (978-0-8130-3416-4(7)) 2006. 59.95 (978-0-8130-2997-9(X)) Univ. Pr. of Florida.

Hopkins, Dwight N. Another World Is Possible: Spiritualities & Religions of Global Darker Peoples. 2009. (Cross Cultural Theologies Ser.). (ENG.). 386p. (C). pap. 39.95 (978-1-84553-393-9(3)) Equinox Publishing Ltd. GBR. Dist: ISD.

Hopkins, Dwight N. & Lewis, Marjorie, eds. Another World Is Possible: Spiritualities & Religions of Global Darker Peoples. 2009. (Cross Cultural Theologies Ser.). (ENG.). 386p. (C). 120.00 (978-1-84553-392-2(5)) Equinox Publishing Ltd. GBR. Dist: ISD.

Jagessar, Michael N. & Reddie, Anthony, eds. Black Theology in Britain. 2007. (Cross Cultural Theologies Ser.). (ENG., Illus.). 288p. (C). 34.95 (978-1-84553-059-4(4)) Equinox Publishing Ltd. GBR. Dist: ISD.

Jam, John Hawkins. Divine Prophecy & Blackman. 2009. 204p. pap. 15.99 (978-1-4389-3442-6(4)) AuthorHouse.

Johnston, Ruby F. The Development of Negro Religion. (African Studies). reprint ed. 20.00 (978-0-938818-69-4(4)) ECA Assocs.

Ludwig, Frieder & Asamoah-Gyadu, J. Kwabena. African Christian Presence in the West: New Immigrant Congregations & Transnational Networks in North America & Europe. 2011. (978-1-59221-807-3(5)); 238p. pap. (978-1-59221-808-0(3)) Africa World Pr.

Motlhabi, Mokgethi B. G. African Theology/Black Theology in South Africa: Looking Back, Moving On. 2008. 162p. pap. 29.00 (978-1-86888-433-9(3)) Unisa Press / Uitgewers GBR. Dist: International Specialized Bk. Services.

Ngoma, Samuel. Why Is God Silent on Mandela? The Unspoken Question about a World Icon in Relation to Christ. 2009. (ENG.). 112p. pap. 14.99 (978-1-59979-777-9(1), Creation Hse.) Charisma Media.

Nisbett, J. Mastine. A Journey to the Promised Land: The Struggle of a Suburban Church to Build an Edifice. 2011. 184p. 24.99 (978-1-4520-9232-4(X)) AuthorHouse.

Noel, James A. Black Religion & the Imagination of Matter in the Atlantic World. 2009. (Black Religion/Womanist Thought/Social Justice Ser.). (ENG., Illus.). 256p. 95.00 (978-0-230-61506-9(6)) Palgrave Macmillan.

Ugba, Abel. Shades of Belonging: African Pentecostals in Twenty-First Century Ireland. 2008. (Illus.). xii, 284p. (978-1-59221-658-1(7)); 302p. pap. (978-1-59221-659-8(5)) Africa World Pr.

Yisrael, Navee Yaacov. Biblical Heritage Awakening. 2011. 116p. 24.95 (978-1-4269-4883-1(2)); pap. 14.95 (978-1-4269-4881-7(6)) Trafford Publishing.

BLACKS—SEGREGATION

Brownlow, Alec. A Political Ecology of Neglect. 2008. 232p. pap. (978-3-639-09269-1(4)) VDM Verlag Dr. Mueller e.K.

Bullard, Robert D. The Black Metropolis in the Twenty-First Century: Race, Power, & Politics of Place. 2007. (ENG., Illus.). 294p. 89.00 (978-0-7425-4328-7(5)); pap. 31.95 (978-0-7425-4329-4(3)) Rowman & Littlefield Publishers, Inc.

Cram101 Textbook Reviews & Cram101 Textbook Reviews. Outlines & Highlights for the Black Metropolis in the Twenty-First Century: Race, Power, & Politics of Place by Robert Bullard, ISBN. 2011. 216p. pap. 30.95 (978-1-61461-858-4(5)) Cram101 Inc.

BLACKS—SOCIAL CONDITIONS

see also Blacks—Segregation

Adderley, Rosanne Marion. New Negroes from Africa: Slave Trade Abolition & Free African Settlement in the Nineteenth-Century Caribbean. 2006. (Blacks in the Diaspora Ser.). (Illus.). (ENG.). 360p. pap. 24.95 (978-0-253-21827-8(6), 0253218276); 337p. 65.00 (978-0-253-34703-9(3)) Indiana Univ. Pr.

Alberto, Paulina. Terms of Inclusion: Black Intellectuals in Twentieth-Century Brazil. 2011. (ENG., Illus.). 432p. 69.95 (978-0-8078-3437-4(8)); pap. 29.95 (978-0-8078-7171-3(0)) Univ. of North Carolina Pr.

Alcena, Valiere. Black People & Medical Diseases. 2012. 49.95 (978-0-7414-7009-6(8)); pap. 39.95 (978-0-7414-7008-9(X)) Infinity Publishing.

Alexander, Amy. Uncovering Race: A Black Journalist's Story of Reporting & Reinvention. 2011. 240p. 28.95 (978-0-8070-6100-8(X)) Beacon Pr.

Amin, Muhammad. The Healing of the Black Family. 2011. 176p. pap. 17.00 (978-1-4389-4284-1(2)) AuthorHouse.

Andrews, George Reid. Blackness in the White Nation: A History of Afro-Uruguay. 2010. (ENG., Illus.). 272p. 59.95 (978-0-8078-3417-6(3)); pap. 22.95 (978-0-8078-7158-4(3)) Univ. of North Carolina Pr.

Atwater, Deborah. The Rhetoric of Black Mayors: In Their Own Words. 2010. (ENG.). 78p. pap. 14.95 (978-0-7618-5076-2(7)) Univ. Pr. of America, Inc.

Bennett, Herman L. Colonial Blackness: A History of Afro-Mexico. 2010. (Blacks in the Diaspora Ser.). (ENG., Illus.). 248p. pap. 24.95 (978-0-253-22331-9(8), 0253223318) Indiana Univ. Pr.

Bhopal, Kalwant & Preston, John, eds. Intersectionality & Race in Education. 2011. (Routledge Research in Education Ser.). (ENG., Illus.). 238p. (C). 125.00 (978-0-415-88877-6(8)) Routledge.

Bressey, Caroline, ed. Belonging in Europe - the African Diaspora & Work. 2009. 192p. 150.00 (978-0-415-48870-9(2)) Routledge.

Bristol, Joan Cameron. Christians, Blasphemers, & Witches: Afro-Mexican Ritual Practice in the Seventeenth Century. 2007. (Dialogos Ser.). (ENG., Illus.). 297p. (C). pap. 29.95 (978-0-8263-3799-3(6)) Univ. of New Mexico Pr.

Campt, Tina M. Image Matters: Archive, Photography, & the African Diaspora in Europe. 2012. (ENG., Illus.). 256p. 89.95 (978-0-8223-5056-9(4)); pap. 24.95 (978-0-8223-5074-3(2)) Duke Univ. Pr.

Cathialam, Aam'pah-Katoh BaNtump'l. The African Remedy. 2008. 160p. 33.49 (978-1-4389-0993-6(4)); pap. 17.99 (978-1-4389-0994-3(2)) AuthorHouse.

Chamberlain, Mary. Family Love in the Diaspora: Migration & the Anglo-Caribbean Experience. 2009. (ENG.). 260p. pap. 24.95 (978-1-4128-0855-2(3)) Transaction Pubs.

Colemon, Kobie. To Kill & Die: Dark Man of Violence. 2008. 188p. pap. 15.95 (978-1-4327-3284-4(6)) Outskirts Pr., Inc.

Creese, Gillian Laura. The New African Diaspora in Vancouver: Migration, Exclusion, & Belonging. 2011. (ENG.). 288p. (978-1-4426-4295-9(5)); pap. (978-1-4426-1159-7(6)) Univ. of Toronto Pr.

Cuffee, Sallie M. Manchild Dying in the Promised Land: Strategies to Save Black Males. 2009. (ENG.). 150p. pap. 15.95 (978-1-934155-13-4(6)) African American Images.

Cunha Júnior, Henrique Antunes, et al. Espaço Urbano e Afrodescendência: Estudos Da Espacialidade Negra Urbana para o Debate das Políticas Públicas. 2007. (POR., Illus.). 206p. (978-85-7282-259-6(3)) Universidade Federal do Ceara. Editora.

Davidson, Harry X. Somebody's Trying to Kill You Vol. I: Psychodynamics of White Racism & Black Pathology. 2nd rev. ed. 137p. pap. (978-0-9644417-1-2(3)) Davidson, Harry R.

Davidson, Harry X., et al. Somebody's Trying to Kill You Vol. II: The Economics of Death. Lewis, R. H., ed. 158p. pap. 15.00 (978-0-9644417-0-5(5)) Davidson, Harry R.

Dennis, Christopher. Afro-Colombian Hip-Hop: Globalization, Transcultural Music, & Ethnic Identities. 2011. (ENG.). 190p. (gr. 17). 60.00 (978-0-7391-5056-6(1)) Lexington Bks.

Duru, Eddy. Europe: A Mission Misunderstood. 2010. 88p. pap. 11.49 (978-1-4520-7703-1(7)) AuthorHouse.

Emeka, Amon. New Blacks, New Whites, & the New Day. 2008. 168p. pap. (978-3-639-07803-9(9)) VDM Verlag Dr. Mueller e.K.

Evelyn White. Untold Stalking Story. 2009. 76p. pap. 10.95 (978-1-4401-8749-0(5)) iUniverse, Inc.

Falola, Toyin, et al. Migrations & Creative Expressions in Africa & the African Diaspora. 2008. 510p. pap. 55.00 (978-1-59460-460-7(6)) Carolina Academic Pr.

Fanon, Frantz. Black Skin, White Masks. Philcox, Richard, tr. from FRE. rev. ed. 2008. (ENG.). 240p. pap. 14.95 (978-0-8021-4300-6(8), Grove Pr.) Grove/Atlantic, Inc.

Fennell, Christopher C. Crossroads & Cosmologies: Diasporas & Ethnogenesis in the New World. 2010. (Cultural Heritage Studies). (ENG., Illus.). 192p. pap. 29.95 (978-0-8130-3496-6(5)) Univ. Pr. of Florida.

Fitzgerald, Terence D. White Prescriptions? The Dangerous Social Potential for Ritalin & Other Psychotropic Drugs to Harm Black Males. 2009. 210p. 125.00 (978-1-59451-689-4(8)) Paradigm Pubs.

Frazier, John W., et al, eds. The African Diaspora in the United States & Canada at the Dawn of the 21st Century. 2009. pap. (978-1-58684-271-0(4)) Global Academic Publishing.

Gilroy, Paul. Black Britain: A Photographic History. 2008. (ENG., Illus.). 320p. pap. 35.00 (978-0-86356-540-3(9)) Saqi Bks. GBR. Dist: Consortium Bk. Sales & Distribution.

Graham, Mekada. Black Issues in Social Work & Social Care. 2007. 208p. (C). pap. 29.95 (978-1-86134-845-6(2)) Policy Pr. GBR. Dist: Chicago Distribution Ctr.

Grimes, Erik K. & Slaughter, Butch. Why Our Children Hate Us: How Black Adults Betray Black Children. 2006. 72p. per. 10.95 (978-0-9777013-9-1(5)) Ulysses Slaughter.

Guridy, Frank Andre. Forging Diaspora: Afro-Cubans & African Americans in a World of Empire & Jim Crow. 2010. (Envisioning Cuba Ser.). (ENG., Illus.). 288p. 59.95 (978-0-8078-3361-2(4)); pap. 22.95 (978-0-8078-7103-4(6)) Univ. of North Carolina Pr.

Haji-Kella, Mohamed. What's Culture Got to Do with It? 2009. 76p. pap. (978-3-639-14815-2(0)) VDM Verlag Dr. Mueller e.K.

Hine, Darlene Clark, et al, eds. Black Europe & the African Diaspora. 2009. (New Black Studies Ser.). (ENG., Illus.). 376p. 75.00 (978-0-252-03467-1(8)); pap. 30.00 (978-0-252-07657-2(5)) Univ. of Illinois Pr.

Horne, Victor Carter. A Black Patriot: The Real American. 2011. 136p. pap. 12.87 (978-1-4269-6144-1(8)) Trafford Publishing.

Jackson, James S., et al. Researching Black Communities: A Methodological Guide. 2012. E-Book (978-0-472-02618-0(6)) Univ. of Michigan Pr.

Jenkins, Jennifer. West Africans in Paris. 2008. 180p. pap. (978-3-8364-9726-8(3)) VDM Verlag Dr. Mueller e.K.

Johnson, Violet Showers & Johnson, Violet M. The Other Black Bostonians: West Indians in Boston, 1900-1950. 2006. (Blacks in the Diaspora Ser.). (ENG., Illus.). 200p. 24.95 (978-0-253-34752-7(1), 0253347521) Indiana Univ. Pr.

Johnson, Whittington B. Post-Emancipation Race Relations in the Bahamas. 2006. (ENG., Illus.). 192p. 59.95 (978-0-8130-2994-8(5)) Univ. Pr. of Florida.

Kamara, Saysay S. Blackman: Too Hard for You. 2008. 180p. pap. 15.95 (978-0-595-48486-7(7)) iUniverse, Inc.

Kinchlow, Ben. Black Yellow Dogs: The Most Dangerous Citizen Is Not Armed, but Uninformed. 2008. (ENG.). 26.95 (978-1-60037-285-8(6)) Morgan James Publishing.

Love, Deborah Sharon. Blue Moon. 2011. 268p. 28.99 (978-1-4670-2627-7(1)); pap. 19.95 (978-1-4670-2624-6(7)) AuthorHouse.

Mackey, Frank. Done with Slavery: The Black Fact in Montreal, 1760-1840. 2010. (Studies on the History of Quebec/Études d'histoire du Quebec Ser.). (ENG & FRE., Illus.). 568p. (C). (978-0-7735-3578-7(0)) McGill-Queen's Univ. Pr.

Madibbo, Amal Ibrahim. Minority Within a Minority: Black Francophone Immigrants & the Dynamics of Power & Resistance. 2006. (New Approaches in Sociology Ser.). (Illus.). 256p. 138.00 (978-0-415-97911-5(0)) Routledge.

Mamatu, Tsepo. Laughing at Blackness: Leon schuster & the colonizing Laughter. 2010. 64p. pap. (978-3-8383-4346-4(8)) Lambert Academic Publishing.

Mamigonian, Beatriz G. & Racine. The Human Tradition in the Black Atlantic, 1500 D 2000. 2009. (Human Tradition around the World Ser.). (ENG.). 236p. pap. 27.50 (978-0-7425-6730-6(3)) Rowman & Littlefield Publishers, Inc.

Mamigonian, Beatriz G. & Racine, Karen. The Human Tradition in the Black Atlantic, 1500-2000. 2009. (Human Tradition around the World Ser.). (ENG.). 236p. 79.00 (978-0-7425-6729-0(X)) Rowman & Littlefield Publishers, Inc.

Marais, Hein. South Africa Pushed to the Limit: The Political Economy of Change. 2011. (ENG., Illus.). 544p. 126.00 (978-1-84813-860-5(1)); pap. 45.00 (978-1-84813-859-9(8)) Zed Bks., Ltd. GBR. Dist: Macmillan.

Marie, Deborah. Reparations Now!, Restoring Truth, Balance, & Harmony to the World. 2009. 124p. 22.50 (978-1-60693-910-9(6), Eloquent Bks.) AEG Literary Publishing Services, Inc.

Mathews, Lawrence. A Black Man, My Point of View. 2007. 184p. per. 13.99 (978-0-9786346-1-2(6)) Mathews, Lawrence.

Mathieu, Sarah-Jane. North of the Color Line: Migration & Black Resistance in Canada, 1870-1955. 2010. (John Hope Franklin Series in African American History & Culture Ser.). (ENG., Illus.). 320p. 65.00 (978-0-8078-3429-9(7)); pap. 22.95 (978-0-8078-7166-9(4)) Univ. of North Carolina Pr.

Mintsa, Joe. What Is Wrong with Black People? - How Post-slave Psychology & Afrocentricity are joining with Colonialism to undermine Black Africa's Cultural Integrity. 2008. 700p. pap. 48.50 (978-1-84799-323-6(0)) Lulu Enterprises Inc.

Mirza, Heidi Safia. Race, Gender & Educational Desire: Why Black Women Succeed & Fail. 2008. (ENG., Illus.). 224p. 150.00 (978-0-415-44875-8(1)); pap. 42.95 (978-0-415-44876-5(X)) Routledge.

Mirza, Heidi Safia & Joseph, Cynthia, eds. Black & Postcolonial Feminisms in New Times: Researching Educational Inequalities. 2010. (ENG.). 152p. (C). 125.00 (978-0-415-57168-5(5)) Routledge.

Model, Suzanne. West Indian Blacks: An Immigrant Success Story? 2008. (C). (978-0-87154-631-9(0)) Russell Sage Foundation.

Moorehead, Monica, ed. Marxism, Reparations & the Black Freedom Struggle. 2007. (ENG.). 197p. pap. 19.95 (978-0-89567-137-0(9)) World View Forum.

Nascimento, Elisa Larkin. The Sorcery of Color: Identity, Race, & Gender in Brazil. 2006. (Illus.). 272p. 55.50 (978-1-59213-350-5(9)) 2nd ed. 2009. (ENG.). 336p. pap. 30.95 (978-1-59213-351-2(7)) Temple Univ. Pr.

Neate, Patrick & Platt, Damian. Culture Is Our Weapon: Making Music & Changing Lives in Rio de Janeiro. 2010. (ENG.). 224p. (gr. 12-18). 14.00 (978-0-14-311674-5(6), Penguin (Non-Classics)) Penguin Group (USA) Inc.

Nelson, David W. Black Men & Responsibility. 2006. 68p. per. 8.95 (978-1-59824-342-0(X)) E-BookTime LLC.

Okonkwo, Rudolf Ogoo. Children of a Retired God. 2006. per. (978-0-9768354-3-1(6)) Iroko Productions & Pubns. LLC.

Oliveira Sobrinho, Reinaldo de. O Negro Açucarou o Nordeste. 2007. (POR., Illus.). 166p. (978-85-7539-349-9(9)) Ideia Personalizadora e Editora Ltda.

O'Toole, Therese & Gale, Richard. Political Engagement Amongst Ethnic Minority Young People: Making a Difference. 2013. (ENG.). 256p. 85.00 (978-0-230-20273-3(X)) Palgrave Macmillan.

Padmore, George. The Life & Struggles of Negro Toilers. 2007. 128p. per. 19.95 (978-1-877880-04-9(3), Borgo Pr.) Wildside Pr., LLC.

Parks, Gregory S. & Hughey, Matthew, eds. 12 Angry Men: True Stories of Being a Black Man in America Today. 2011. (ENG.). 208p. 24.95 (978-1-59558-538-7(9)) New Pr., The.

Proctor, Frank. Damned Notions of Liberty: Slavery, Culture, & Power in Colonial Mexico, 1640-1769. 2010. (Dialogos Ser.). (ENG., Illus.). 296p. (C). pap. 27.95 (978-0-8263-4966-8(8)) Univ. of New Mexico Pr.

Provenzo, Jr, Eugene F, Eugene F & Abaka, Edmund, eds. W. E. B. du Bois on Africa. 2012. (ENG.). 200p. 94.00 (978-1-61132-180-7(8)); pap. 34.95 (978-1-61132-181-4(6)) Left Coast Pr., Inc.

Rahier, Jean. Global Circuits of Blackness: Interrogating the African Diaspora. Hintzen, Percy C. & Smith, Felipe, eds. 2010. (ENG., Illus.). 288p. pap. 30.00 (978-0-252-07753-1(9)) Univ. of Illinois Pr.

Rahier, Jean Muteba, ed. Black Social Movements in Latin America: From Monocultural Mestizaje to Multiculturalism. 2012. (ENG., Illus.). 272p. 90.00 (978-0-230-39360-8(8)) Palgrave Macmillan.

Rahier, Jean Muteba, et al, eds. Global Circuits of Blackness: Interrogating the African Diaspora. 2010. (ENG., Illus.). 288p. 80.00 (978-0-252-03562-3(3)) Univ. of Illinois Pr.

Reid, James. So, What's Wrong, Black Man? 2010. 92p. pap. 12.00 (978-1-4269-3585-5(4)) Trafford Publishing.

Robinson, Barry M., ed. Slaves, Subjects, & Subversives: Blacks in Colonial Latin America. 2006. (Dialogos Ser.). (ENG., Illus.). 328p. (C). pap. 29.95 (978-0-8263-2397-2(9)) Univ. of New Mexico Pr.

Rosenbloom, Lucky. Black Man with a Gun: Justifiable Force Is a Constitutional Right. 2011. 152p. pap. 14.95 (978-1-4502-9212-2(7)) iUniverse, Inc.

Rousseau, Nicole. Black Woman's Burden: Commodifying Black Reproduction. 2009. (ENG.). 240p. 84.00 (978-0-230-61530-4(9)) Palgrave Macmillan.

Saunders, A. A Social History of Black Slaves & Freedmen in Portugal, 1441-1555. 2010. (Cambridge Iberian & Latin American Studies). (ENG.). 308p. pap. 42.00 (978-0-521-13003-5(4)) Cambridge Univ. Pr.

Scott, Rebecca J. & Hébrard, Jean M. Freedom Papers: An Atlantic Odyssey in the Age of Emancipation. 2012. (ENG., Illus.). 288p. 35.00 (978-0-674-04774-7(5)) Harvard Univ. Pr.

Shilgba, Leonard Karshima. From My Heart the Black Race: Myths, Realities, & Complexes. 2011. 510p. 34.95 (978-1-60911-049-9(8), Eloquent Bks.) AEG Literary Publishing Services, Inc.

Slatton, Brittany C. Mythologizing Black Women: Unveiling White Men's Racist & Sexist Deep Frame, 1 vol. 2011. 176p. 91.00 (978-1-61205-049-2(2)) Paradigm Pubs.

Squier, Susan Erica. People Aren't Black: People Are Human. 2007. per. 8.95 (978-1-59872-802-6(4)) Instant Pub.

Swift, Sally. Experiences of Violent Victimisation & Attitudes to Knife Crime. 2011. 68p. pap. (978-3-8443-2809-7(2)) Lambert Academic Publishing.

Temple, Catherine. Undercurrents in America. 2011. 52p. pap. 19.95 (978-1-4634-0699-8(1)) AuthorHouse.

Tennant, Noah. Black Students, White Schools- Caught Between Two Worlds. 2007. 152p. per. (978-3-8364-2867-5(9)) VDM Verlag Dr. Mueller e.K.

Terrell, Keino. Us vs. Them: Black Peoples' Battle for Mentality. 2010. 128p. (ENG.). 21.49 (978-1-4490-9419-5(8)); pap. 10.99 (978-1-4490-9418-8(X)) AuthorHouse.

Thomas, Greg. The Sexual Demon of Colonial Power: Pan-African Embodiment & Erotic Schemes of Empire. 2007. (ENG.). 224p. 50.00 (978-0-253-34841-8(2), 0253348412); pap. 21.95 (978-0-253-21894-0(2), 0253218942) Indiana Univ. Pr.

Thompson, Bankole. A Matter of Black Transformation. 2007. 180p. per. 15.00 (978-0-9760755-7-8(1), Read4Life Bks.) Christian Bk. Outreach, Inc.

Vargas, Joao H. Costa. Never Meant to Survive: Genocide & Utopias in Black Diaspora Communities. 2008. (Transformative Politics Ser.). (ENG.). 262p. 85.00 (978-0-7425-4101-6(0)) Rowman & Littlefield Publishers, Inc.

Vinson, Ben. Black Mexico: Race & Society from Colonial to Modern Times. Restall, Matthew, ed. 2009. (Dialogos Ser.). (ENG., Illus.). 296p. (C). pap. 29.95 (978-0-8263-4701-5(0)) Univ. of New Mexico Pr.

Vinzant, Jeremy. Does Race Matter for Black Educational Leaders? 2010. 204p. pap. (978-3-8383-5059-2(6)) Lambert Academic Publishing.

Walker, Barrington. Race on Trial. 2010. (Osgoode Society for Canadian Legal History Ser.). (978-0-8020-9909-9(2)) Univ. of Toronto Pr.

—Race on Trial: Black Defendants in Ontario's Criminal Courts, 1858-1958. 2011. (ENG., Illus.). xii, 256p. pap. (978-0-8020-9610-4(7)) Univ. of Toronto Pr.

Walters, Ronald. The Price of Racial Reconciliation. 2009. (Politics of Race & Ethnicity Ser.). (ENG., Illus.). 264p. pap. 25.95 (978-0-472-03380-5(8)) Univ. of Michigan Pr.

Watts, Jerome L., ed. The Power of Resilience: Factors that Influence Black Males to Reenroll & Complete Their High School Diploma or GED. 2011. pap. 12.99 (978-1-61777-138-5(4)) Tate Publishing & Enterprises, LLC.

White, Elisa Joy. Modernity, Freedom, & the African Diaspora: Dublin, New Orleans, Paris. 2012. (Blacks in the Diaspora Ser.). (ENG.). 356p. pap. 30.00 (978-0-253-00125-2(0), 0253001250); (Illus.). 80.00 (978-0-253-00115-3(3), 0253001153) Indiana Univ. Pr.

Willis, Jay Thomas. Over the Celestial Wireless. 2007. 208p. pap. 14.95 (978-0-7414-4160-7(8)) Infinity Publishing.

Worsley, Shawan M. Audience, Agency & Identity in Black Popular Culture. 2009. (Studies in African American History & Culture Ser.). (ENG., Illus.). 158p. 125.00 (978-0-415-80486-8(8)) Routledge.

Wright, Cecile, et al. Black Youth Matters: Transitions from School to Success. 2009. (Critical Youth Studies). (ENG.). 176p. 130.00 (978-0-415-99510-8(8)); pap. 38.95 (978-0-415-99512-2(4)) Routledge.

Wright, Donald R. The Only Prayer I'll Ever Pray: Let My People Go. 2009. 96p. pap. 13.95 (978-1-60844-291-1(8)) Dog Ear Publishing, LLC.

Zeleza, Paul Tiyambe. In Search of African Diasporas: Testimonies & Encounters. 2012. 592p. 65.00 (978-1-61163-056-5(8)) Carolina Academic Pr.

BLACKS—SUFFRAGE

see Blacks—Politics and Government

BLACKS—AMERICA

Afolabi, Niyi & Falola, Toyin, eds. African Minorities in the New World. 2007. (African Studies: History, Politics, Economics & Culture Ser.). (ENG.). 290p. 125.00 (978-0-415-96092-2(4)) Routledge.

Anderson, Mark. Black & Indigenous: Garifuna Activism & Consumer Culture in Honduras. 2009. (ENG., Illus.). 304p. 75.00 (978-0-8166-6101-5(4)); pap. 25.00 (978-0-8166-6102-2(2)) Univ. of Minnesota Pr.

Carney, Judith A. & Rosomoff, Richard Nicholas. In the Shadow of Slavery: Africa's Botanical Legacy in the Atlantic World. 2010. (Illus.). 238p. 50.00 (978-0-520-25750-4(2)) Univ. of California Pr.

Chambers, Glenn Anthony. Race, Nation, & West Indian Immigration to Honduras, 1890-1940. 2010. 232p. 35.00 (978-0-8071-3557-0(7)) Louisiana State Univ. Pr.

Fennell, Christopher C. Crossroads & Cosmologies: Diasporas & Ethnogenesis in the New World. 2010. (Cultural Heritage Studies). (ENG., Illus.). 192p. pap. 29.95 *(978-0-8130-3496-6(5))* Univ. Pr. of Florida.

Finley, Stephen C. & Alexander, Torin. African American Religious Cultures, 2 vols. Pinn, Anthony B., ed. 2009. (American Religious Cultures Ser.). (Illus.). 739p. 195.00 *(978-1-57607-470-1(6),* AFRCC) ABC-CLIO, LLC.

Gonzalez, Nancie L. Sojourners of the Caribbean: Ethnogenesis & Ethnohistory of the Garifuna. 2009. 292p. 41.00 *(978-1-59740-289-7(3))* ACLS Humanities E-Book.

Gonzalez, Nancie L. & Conrad, Earl. Sojourners of the Caribbean: Ethnogenesis & Ethnohistory of the Garifuna. 2008. 292p. pap. 27.00 *(978-1-59740-662-8(7))* ACLS Humanities E-Book.

Hartnell, Anna. Rewriting Exodus: American Futures from du Bois to Obama, 1 vol. 2011. (Decolonial Studies, Postcolonial Horizons Ser.). (ENG.). 240p. 95.00 *(978-0-7453-2956-7(X))* Pluto Pr. GBR. Dist: Macmillan.

Johnston, Harry Hamilton. The Negro in the New World. 499p. reprint ed. 98.00 *(978-0-7222-9730-8(0))* Library Reprints, Inc.

King, Stewart R. Encyclopedia of Free Blacks & People of Color in the Americas, 2 vols., Set. 2012. 1034p. (C). (gr. 9-18). 185.00 *(978-0-8160-7212-5(4))* Facts On File, Inc.

Knight, Frederick. Working the Diaspora: The Impact of African Labor on the Anglo-American World, 1650-1850. 2010. (ENG., Illus.). 240p. 48.00 *(978-0-8147-4818-3(X))* New York Univ. Pr.

Nelson, Charles A. Back to Africa? 2009. 168p. 29.99 *(978-1-4415-1210-9(1))*; pap. 19.99 *(978-1-4415-1209-3(8))* Xlibris Corp.

Opie, Frederick Douglass. Hog & Hominy: Soul Food from Africa to America. 2010. (Arts & Traditions of the Table: Perspectives on Culinary History Ser.). (ENG., Illus.). 256p. (gr. 17). pap. 17.95 *(978-0-231-14639-5(6))* Columbia Univ. Pr.

Rawlings, Ronald Kaye. A Black Cop in the South: In Spite of Everything. 2007. 116p. pap. 12.95 *(978-0-9724586-6-5(2))* PearlStone Publishing, Inc.

Salvatore, Frank. The Arduous Road from Slavery to Barack Obama. 2010. pap. 10.95 *(978-0-7414-6178-0(1))* Infinity Publishing.

Steen, Shannon, et al. AfroAsian Encounters: Culture, History, Politics. Raphael-Hernandez, Heike, ed. 2006. (ENG., Illus.). 336p. pap. 24.00 *(978-0-8147-7581-3(0))*; 75.00 *(978-0-8147-7580-6(2))* New York Univ. Pr.

Thornton, John, et al. Central Africans, Atlantic Creoles, & the Foundation of the Americas, 1585-1660. 2007. (ENG., Illus.). 384p. (C). pap. 25.99 *(978-0-521-77922-7(7))*; 88.00 *(978-0-521-77065-1(3))* Cambridge Univ. Pr.

Valencia Chala, Santiago. Blacks in Central America. 2006. (SPA., Illus.). 112p. (C). 99.95 *(978-0-7734-5762-1(3))* Mellen, Edwin Pr., The.

Vargas, Joao H. Cost. Never Meant to Survive: Genocide & Utopias in Black Diaspora Communities. 2010. (Transformative Politics Series, ed. Joy James Ser.). (ENG.). 262p. pap. 27.50 *(978-0-7425-4102-3(9))* Rowman & Littlefield Publishers, Inc.

Vargas, Joao H. Costa. Never Meant to Survive: Genocide & Utopias in Black Diaspora Communities. 2008. (Transformative Politics Ser.). (ENG.). 262p. 85.00 *(978-0-7425-4101-6(0))* Rowman & Littlefield Publishers, Inc.

BLACKS—BRAZIL

Afolabi, Niyi. Afro-Brazilians: Cultural Production in a Racial Democracy. 2009. (Rochester Studies in African History & the Diaspora Ser.: Volume 39). 443p. 90.00 *(978-1-58046-262-4(6))* Univ. of Rochester Pr.

Afolabi, Niyi, et al. Cadernos Negros: Literatura Afro-Brasileira Contemporânea = Black Notebooks: Contemporary Afro-Brazilian Literature. 2006. (POR & ENG.). *(978-1-59221-383-2(9))*; pap. *(978-1-59221-384-9(7))* Africa World Pr.

—Cadernos Negros: Movimento Literário Afro-Brasileiro Contemporâneo = Black Notebooks: Contemporary Afro-Brazilian Literary Movement. 2006. (POR & ENG.). *(978-1-59221-454-9(1))*; pap. *(978-1-59221-455-6(X))* Africa World Pr.

Barbosa, José Carlos. Slavery & Protestant Missions in Imperial Brazil: The Black Does Not Enter the Church, He Peeks in from Outside. Danford, Richard K. & MacHaffie, Fraser G., trs. 2008. (ENG.). 190p. pap. 35.99 *(978-0-7618-4300-9(0))* Univ. Pr. of America, Inc.

Bastide, Roger. The African Religions of Brazil: Toward a Sociology of the Interpenetration of Civilizations. Sebba, Helen, tr. from FRE. 2007. (Johns Hopkins Studies in Atlantic History & Culture Ser.). (ENG.). 494p. (gr. 17). pap. 26.00 *(978-0-8018-8624-9(4))* Johns Hopkins Univ. Pr.

Capone, Stefania. Searching for Africa in Brazil: Power & Tradition in Candomblé. Grant, Lucy Lyall, tr. from FRE. 2010. (ENG., Illus.). 336p. 84.95 *(978-0-8223-4625-8(7))*; pap. 23.95 *(978-0-8223-4636-4(2))* Duke Univ. Pr.

Covin, David. The Unified Black Movement in Brazil, 1978-2002. 2006. (ENG., Illus.). 266p. per. 45.00 *(978-0-7864-2438-2(9))* McFarland & Co., Inc. Pubs.

Cunha Júnior, Henrique Antunes, et al. Espaço Urbano e Afrodescendência: Estudos Da Espacialidade Negra Urbana para o Debate das Políticas Públicas. 2007. (POR., Illus.). 206p. *(978-85-7282-259-6(3))* Universidade Federal do Ceara. Editora.

Eduardo, Octavio D. The Negro in Northern Brazil. (African Heritage Classical Research Studies). 131p. reprint ed. 20.00 *(978-0-938818-53-3(8))* ECA Assocs.

Kiddy, Elizabeth W. Blacks of the Rosary: Memory & History in Minas Gerais, Brazil. 2007. (ENG., Illus.). 328p. pap. 27.00 *(978-0-271-02694-7(4))* Pennsylvania State Univ. Pr.

Klein, Herbert S. & Luna, Francisco Vidal. Slavery in Brazil. 2009. (ENG., Illus.). 376p. (C). 97.00 *(978-0-521-19398-6(2))*; pap. 29.99 *(978-0-521-14192-5(3))* Cambridge Univ. Pr.

Langfur, Hal. The Forbidden Lands: Colonial Identity, Frontier Violence, & the Persistence of Brazil's Eastern Indians, 1750-1830. (ENG., Illus.). 432p. 2008. pap. 27.95 *(978-0-8047-6338-7(0))* 2006. 70.00 *(978-0-8047-5180-3(3))* Stanford Univ. Pr.

Nascimento, Elisa Larkin. The Sorcery of Color: Identity, Race, & Gender in Brazil. 2006. (Illus.). 272p. 55.50 *(978-1-59213-350-5(9))* 2nd ed. 2009. (ENG.). 336p. pap. 30.95 *(978-1-59213-351-2(7))* Temple Univ. Pr.

Neate, Patrick & Platt, Damian. Culture Is Our Weapon: Making Music & Changing Lives in Rio de Janeiro. 2010. (ENG.). 224p. (gr. 12-18). 14.00 *(978-0-14-311674-5(6),* Penguin (Non-Classics)) Penguin Group (USA) Inc.

Oliveira Sobrinho, Reinaldo de. O Negro Açucarou o Nordeste. 2007. (POR., Illus.). 166p. *(978-85-7539-349-9(9))* Ideia Personalizadora e Editora Ltda.

Phaf-Rheinberger, Ineke & Pinto, Tiago de Oliveira. AfricAmericas: Itineraries, Dialogues, & Sounds. 2008. (Illus.). 224p. pap. 29.80 *(978-84-8489-380-6(4))* Iberoamericana Vervuert Publishing Corp.

Pinho, Patricia de Santana. Mama Africa: Reinventing Blackness in Bahia. Langdon, Elena, tr. from POR. 2010. (ENG., Illus.). 280p. 84.95 *(978-0-8223-4654-8(0))*; pap. 23.95 *(978-0-8223-4646-3(X))* Duke Univ. Pr.

Romo, Anadelia A. Brazil's Living Museum: Race, Reform, & Tradition in Bahia. 2010. (ENG., Illus.). 272p. 59.95 *(978-0-8078-3382-7(7))*; 240p. pap. 24.95 *(978-0-8078-7115-7(X))* Univ. of North Carolina Pr.

Sansi & Sansi-Roca, Roger. Fetishes & Monuments: Afro-Brazilian Art & Culture in the Twentieth Century. 2007. (Remapping Cultural History Ser.: Vol. 6). (Illus.). 224p. 90.00 *(978-1-84545-363-3(8))* Berghahn Bks., Inc.

Sansi, Roger. Fetishes & Monuments: Afro-Brazilian Art & Culture in the 20th Century. 2009. (Illus.). 224p. 24.50 *(978-1-84545-711-2(0))* Berghahn Bks., Inc.

Selka, Stephen. Religion & the Politics of Ethnic Identity in Bahia, Brazil. 2009. (New World Diasporas Ser.). (ENG., Illus.). 192p. pap. 29.95 *(978-0-8130-3387-7(X))* Univ. Pr. of Florida.

Telles, Edward E. Race in Another America: The Significance of Skin Color in Brazil. 2006. (ENG., Illus.). 336p. (C). per. 25.95 *(978-0-691-12792-7(1))* Princeton Univ. Pr.

Tillis, Antonio D. (Re)Considering Blackness in Contemporary Afro-Brazilian (con)Texts. 2011. (C). 139.95 ***(978-1-4331-0787-0(2))***; pap. 34.95 ***(978-1-4331-0786-3(4))*** Lang, Peter Publishing, Inc.

Vargas, Joao H. Cost. Never Meant to Survive: Genocide & Utopias in Black Diaspora Communities. 2010. (Transformative Politics Series, ed. Joy James Ser.). (ENG.). 262p. pap. 27.50 *(978-0-7425-4102-3(9))* Rowman & Littlefield Publishers, Inc.

Vargas, Joao H. Costa. Never Meant to Survive: Genocide & Utopias in Black Diaspora Communities. 2008. (Transformative Politics Ser.). (ENG.). 262p. 85.00 *(978-0-7425-4101-6(0))* Rowman & Littlefield Publishers, Inc.

BLACKS—CANADA

Africville Genealogy Society Staff. The Spirit of Africville. 2nd rev. ed. 2010. (ENG., Illus.). 128p. (C). pap. 29.95 *(978-0-88780-925-5(1))* Lorimer, James & Co., Ltd., Pubs. CAN. Dist: Casemate Pubs. & Bk. Distributors, LLC.

Alexander, Lincoln. Go to School, You're a Little Black Boy: The Honourable Lincoln M. Alexander - A Memoir. 2010. (ENG., Illus.). 256p. pap. 26.99 *(978-1-55488-733-0(X))* Dundurn CAN. Dist: Ingram Pub. Services.

Armstrong, Frederick H., et al, eds. Ontario's African-Canadian Heritage: Collected Writings by Fred Landon, 1919-1974. 2009. (ENG., Illus.). 368p. pap. 28.99 *(978-1-55002-814-0(6))* Dundurn CAN. Dist: Ingram Pub. Services.

Creese, Gillian Laura. The New African Diaspora in Vancouver: Migration, Exclusion, & Belonging. 2011. (ENG.). 288p. ***(978-1-4426-4295-9(5))***; pap. ***(978-1-4426-1159-7(6))*** Univ. of Toronto Pr.

Drew, Benjamin. The Refugee: Narratives of Fugitive Slaves in Canada. 2008. (ENG.). 384p. pap. 29.99 *(978-1-55002-801-0(4),* Dundurn Pr.) Dundurn CAN. Dist: Ingram Pub. Services.

Foster, Cecil. Blackness & Modernity: The Colour of Humanity & the Quest for Freedom. 2007. (ENG.). 656p. (C). *(978-0-7735-3105-5(X))*; pap. *(978-0-7735-3247-2(1))* McGill-Queen's Univ. Pr.

Fraser, Fil. Running Uphill: The Fast, Short Life of Harry Jerome. 2007. (ENG.). 240p. pap. *(978-1-896124-13-1(5))* Dragon Hill Publishing CAN. Dist: Lone Pine Publishing.

Frazier, John W., et al, eds. The African Diaspora in the United State & Canada at the Dawn of the 21st Century. 2010. (Global Academic Publishing Ser.). (Illus.). 383p. pap. 49.00 *(978-1-4384-3684-5(X),* Suny Pr.) State Univ. of New York Pr.

—The African Diaspora in the United States & Canada at the Dawn of the 21st Century. 2009. pap. *(978-1-58684-271-0(4))* Global Academic Publishing.

Freyer, Tony & Campbell, Lyndsay, eds. Freedom's Conditions in the U. S. -Canadian Borderlands in the Age of Emancipation. 2011. 344p. 45.00 *(978-1-59460-772-1(9))* Carolina Academic Pr.

Frost, John. Broken Shackles: Old Man Henson from Slavery to Freedom. Meyler, Peter, ed. 2007. (ENG., Illus.). 240p. reprint ed. pap. 16.95 *(978-1-896219-57-8(8),* Natural Heritage Bks.) Natural Heritage/Natural History, Inc. CAN. Dist: Ingram Pub. Services.

Henry, Natasha L. Emancipation Day: Celebrating Freedom in Canada. 2010. (ENG., Illus.). 288p. pap. 28.99 *(978-1-55488-717-0(8))* Dundurn CAN. Dist: Ingram Pub. Services.

Henson, Josiah. Uncle Tom's Story of His Life: An Autobiography of the Reverend Josiah Henson. Lobb, John, ed. 2011. (ENG., Illus.). 180p. pap. 25.00 ***(978-0-8078-6961-1(9))*** Univ. of North Carolina Pr.

Hornby, Jim. Black Islanders No. 3: Prince Edward Island's Historical Black Community. (Illus.). 136p. pap. 9.95 *(978-0-919013-14-8(7))* Univ. of Prince Edward Island, Institute of Island Studies CAN. Dist: Goose Lane Editions.

Howe, S. G. (Samuel Gridley). The Refugees from Slavery in Canada West Report to the Freedmen's Inquiry Commission, by S G Howe. 2006. 116p. per. 16.99 *(978-1-4255-0743-5(3))* MPublishing.

James, Carl, et al. Race & Well-Being: The Lives, Hopes & Activism of African Canadians. 2010. (ENG.). 160p. pap. 22.95 *(978-1-55266-354-7(X))* Fernwood Publishing Co., Ltd. CAN. Dist: Independent Pubs. Group.

Mackey, Frank. Done with Slavery: The Black Fact in Montreal, 1760-1840. 2010. (Studies on the History of Quebec/Études d'histoire du Quebec Ser.). (ENG & FRE., Illus.). 568p. (C). *(978-0-7735-3578-7(0))* McGill-Queen's Univ. Pr.

Madden, Paula C. African Nova Scotian: Mi'Kmaw Relations. 2010. (Fernwood Basics Ser.). (ENG.). 128p. pap. 15.95 *(978-1-55266-323-3(X))* Fernwood Publishing Co., Ltd. CAN. Dist: Independent Pubs. Group.

Madibbo, Amal Ibrahim. Minority Within a Minority: Black Francophone Immigrants & the Dynamics of Power & Resistance. 2006. (New Approaches in Sociology Ser.). (Illus.). 256p. 138.00 *(978-0-415-97911-5(0))* Routledge.

Mathieu, Sarah-Jane. North of the Color Line: Migration & Black Resistance in Canada, 1870-1955. 2010. (John Hope Franklin Series in African American History & Culture Ser.). (ENG., Illus.). 320p. 65.00 *(978-0-8078-3429-9(7))*; pap. 22.95 *(978-0-8078-7166-9(4))* Univ. of North Carolina Pr.

Mensah, Joseph. Black Canadians: History, Experience, Social Conditions. 2nd ed. 2010. (ENG.). 3495p. pap. 34.95 *(978-1-55266-345-5(0))* Fernwood Publishing Co., Ltd. CAN. Dist: Independent Pubs. Group.

Montague, Kenneth, intro. Position As Desired: Exploring African Canadian Identity: Photographs from the Wedge Collection. 2011. (ENG., Illus.). 80p. pap. 25.00 *(978-0-9783370-1-8(8))* Wedge Curatorial Projects CAN. Dist: D.A.P./Distributed Art Pubs.

Nelson, Jennifer J. Razing Africville: A Geography of Racism. (ENG.). 192p. 2009. pap. *(978-1-4426-1028-6(X))* 2008. *(978-0-8020-9252-6(7))* Univ. of Toronto Pr.

Pachai, Bridglal. Accidental Opportunities: A Journey Though Many Doors - An Autobiography. 2008. (ENG., Illus.). 192p. pap. 22.95 *(978-1-55266-236-6(5))* Fernwood Publishing Co., Ltd. CAN. Dist: Independent Pubs. Group.

Shadd, Adrienne. The Journey from Tollgate to Parkway: African Canadians in Hamilton. 2010. (ENG., Illus.). 368p. pap. 35.00 *(978-1-55488-394-3(6))* Dundurn CAN. Dist: Ingram Pub. Services.

Shadd, Adrienne, et al. The Underground Railroad: Next Stop, Toronto! 3rd ed. 2009. (ENG.). 104p. pap. 16.99 *(978-1-55488-429-2(2))* Dundurn CAN. Dist: Ingram Pub. Services.

Tobin, Jacqueline L. From Midnight to Dawn: The Last Tracks of the Underground Railroad. 2008. (ENG., Illus.). 304p. per. 14.00 *(978-1-4000-7936-0(5),* Anchor) Knopf Doubleday Publishing Group.

Walker, Barrington. Race on Trial. 2010. (Osgoode Society for Canadian Legal History Ser.). ***(978-0-8020-9909-9(2))*** Univ. of Toronto Pr.

—Race on Trial: Black Defendants in Ontario's Criminal Courts, 1858-1958. 2011. (ENG., Illus.). xii, 256p. pap. ***(978-0-8020-9610-4(7))*** Univ. of Toronto Pr.

Wane, Njoki Nathani & Massaquoi, Notisha, eds. Theorizing Empowerment: Canadian Perspectives on Black Feminist Thought. 2008. (ENG., Illus.). 314p. pap. 29.95 *(978-0-9782233-4-2(9))* Inanna Pubns. & Education, Inc. CAN. Dist: SPD-Small Pr. Distribution.

BLACKS—CHINA

Bodomo, Adams. Africans in China: A Sociocultural Study & Its Implications on Africa-China Relations. 2012. 14.99 ***(978-1-60497-790-5(6))*** Cambria Pr.

Wyatt, Don J. The Blacks of Premodern China. 2009. (Encounters with Asia Ser.). (Illus.). 208p. (C). 65.00 *(978-0-8122-4193-8(2))* Univ. of Pennsylvania Pr.

BLACKS—COLOMBIA

Asher, Kiran. Black & Green: Afro-Colombians, Development, & Nature in the Pacific Lowlands. 2009. (ENG., Illus.). 272p. 84.95 *(978-0-8223-4487-2(4))*; pap. 23.95 *(978-0-8223-4483-4(1))* Duke Univ. Pr.

Dennis, Christopher. Afro-Colombian Hip-Hop: Globalization, Transcultural Music, & Ethnic Identities. 2012. E-Book ***(978-0-7391-5058-0(8))*** 2011. (ENG.). 190p. (gr. 17). 60.00 ***(978-0-7391-5056-6(1))*** Lexington Bks.

Friedemann, Nina. African Sag: Cultural Heritage & Contributions to Colombia. Joseph, Ron, tr. from SPA. 2007. 200p. 36.95 *(978-0-9777514-4-0(9))* World Arts Pr.

Hinestroza Cuesta, Lisneider. Declaración de áreas Protegidas en Territorios Colectivos de Comunidades Negras en Colombia. 2008. (SPA.). 349p. pap. 16.00 *(978-958-710-346-5(7))* Universidad Externado de Colombia COL. Dist: Siglo del Hombre.

Ng'weno, Bettina. Turf Wars: Territory & Citizenship in the Contemporary State. 2007. (ENG., Illus.). 312p. 50.00 *(978-0-8047-5596-2(5))* Stanford Univ. Pr.

BLACKS—CUBA

Allen, Jafari S. Venceremos? The Erotics of Black Self-Making in Cuba. 2011. (Perverse Modernities Ser.). (ENG., Illus.). 256p. 84.95 *(978-0-8223-4932-7(9))*; pap. 23.95 *(978-0-8223-4950-1(7))* Duke Univ. Pr.

Batrell, Ricardo. A Black Soldier's Story: The Narrative of Ricardo Batrell & the Cuban War of Independence. Sanders, Mark A., ed. 2010. (ENG., Illus.). 288p. 75.00 *(978-0-8166-5008-8(X))*; pap. 24.95 *(978-0-8166-5009-5(8))* Univ. of Minnesota Pr.

Caronia, Anthony. Afro-Cuba. Mystik und Magie der afro-kubanischen Religion. 2011. 176p. 60.00 *(978-3-7165-1661-4(9),* Benteli Verlags Ag Dist) Antique Collectors' Club GBR. Dist: National Bk. Network.

Caronia, Anthony & Alonso, Ania Rodríguez. Afro-Cuba. Mystik und Magie der afro-kubanischen Religion. 2011. (Illus.). 176p. 60.00 ***(978-3-7165-1624-9(4))*** Benteli Verlag CHE. Dist: Antique Collectors' Club.

García Martínez, Orlando. Esclavitud y Colonización en Cienfuegos, 1819-1879. 2008. (SPA.). 87p. *(978-959-220-226-9(5))* Mecenas, Ediciones.

Garoutte, Claire & Wambaugh, Anneke. Crossing the Water: A Photographic Path to the Afro-Cuban Spirit World. 2007. (ENG., Illus.). 280p. lib. bdg. 94.95 *(978-0-8223-4020-1(8))*; per. 25.95 *(978-0-8223-4039-3(9))* Duke Univ. Pr.

Gonzalez, Michelle A. Afro-Cuban Theology: Religion, Race, Culture, & Identity. 208p. 2011. (Illus.). 34.95 *(978-0-8130-3715-8(8))* 2009. (ENG., Illus.). pap. 29.95 *(978-0-8130-3416-4(7))* 2006. (ENG.). 59.95 *(978-0-8130-2997-9(X))* Univ. Pr. of Florida.

Guridy, Frank Andre. Forging Diaspora: Afro-Cubans & African Americans in a World of Empire & Jim Crow. 2010. (Envisioning Cuba Ser.). (ENG., Illus.). 288p. 59.95 *(978-0-8078-3361-2(4))*; pap. 22.95 *(978-0-8078-7103-4(6))* Univ. of North Carolina Pr.

Gutiérrez, Mariela. An Ethnological Interpretation of the Afro-Cuban World of Lydia Cabrera (1900-1991) Gutierrez, Mariela A., ed. & tr. by. Wedel-Carballo, Julio, ed. Kergoat, Catherine, tr. 2008. (Illus.). 250p. 109.95 *(978-0-7734-5042-4(4))* Mellen, Edwin Pr., The.

Hay, Michelle A. I've Been Black in Two Countries: Black Cuban Views on Race in the US. 2009. (New Americans). 258p. *(978-1-59332-335-6(2))* LFB Scholarly Publishing LLC.

Maguire, Emily A. Racial Experiments in Cuban Literature & Ethnography. 2011. (ENG., Illus.). 192p. 74.95 *(978-0-8130-3747-9(6))* Univ. Pr. of Florida.

Miller, Ivor L. & Miller, Ivor. Voice of the Leopard: African Secret Societies & Cuba. 2009. (Caribbean Studies Ser.). (ENG., Illus.). 432p. 55.00 *(978-1-934110-83-6(3))* Univ. Pr. of Mississippi.

Reid-Vazquez, Michele. The Year of the Lash: Free People of Color in Cuba & the Nineteenth-Century Atlantic World. 2011. (Early American Places Ser.). (ENG.). 208p. pap. 24.95 *(978-0-8203-4068-5(5))*; (Illus.). 59.95 *(978-0-8203-3575-9(4))* Univ. of Georgia Pr.

BLACKS—EGYPT

Bauval, Robert & Brophy, Thomas. Black Genesis: The Prehistoric Origins of Ancient Egypt. 2011. 384p. pap. 20.00 *(978-1-59143-114-5(X))* Bear & Co.

Redford, Donald B. From Slave to Pharaoh: The Black Experience of Ancient Egypt. 2006. (ENG., Illus.). 232p. (gr. 17). per. 27.00 *(978-0-8018-8544-0(2))* Johns Hopkins Univ. Pr.

BLACKS—EUROPE

Bressey, Caroline, ed. Belonging in Europe - the African Diaspora & Work. 2009. 192p. 150.00 *(978-0-415-48870-9(2))* Routledge.

Duru, Eddy. Europe: A Mission Misunderstood. 2010. 88p. pap. 11.49 *(978-1-4520-7703-1(7))* AuthorHouse.

Fonseca, Jorge. Escravos e Senhores Na Lisboa Quinhentista. 2010. (POR., Illus.). 504p. *(978-989-689-041-4(2))* Colibri, Edicoes.

Fumo, Raffaele. Intra-Cultural Theater: Performing the Life of Black Migrants to Italy. 2010. 208p. pap. *(978-3-639-25019-0(2))* VDM Verlag Dr. Mueller e.K.

Hine, Darlene Clark, et al, eds. Black Europe & the African Diaspora. 2009. (New Black Studies Ser.). (ENG., Illus.). 376p. 75.00 *(978-0-252-03467-1(8))*; pap. 30.00 *(978-0-252-07657-2(5))* Univ. of Illinois Pr.

Ludwig, Frieder & Asamoah-Gyadu, J. Kwabena. African Christian Presence in the West: New Immigrant Congregations & Transnational Networks in North America & Europe. 2011. *(978-1-59221-807-3(5))*; 238p. pap. *(978-1-59221-808-0(3))* Africa World Pr.

Martone, Eric. Encyclopedia of Blacks in European History & Culture, 2 vols. 2008. (Illus.). 712p. 199.95 *(978-0-313-34448-0(5),* GR4448, Greenwood Pr.) Greenwood Publishing Group, Inc.

Onyejelem, Chinedu & Onyejelem, Chinedu Nnadozie. News in Black & White. 2010. 88p. pap. *(978-3-8383-4125-5(2))* Lambert Academic Publishing.

Sandberg, Sveinung & Pedersen, Willy. Street Capital: Black Cannabis Dealers in a White Welfare State. 2009. (Illus.). 200p. pap. 42.95 *(978-1-84742-901-8(7))* Policy Pr. GBR. Dist: Chicago Distribution Ctr.

Ugba, Abel. Shades of Belonging: African Pentecostals in Twenty-First Century Ireland. 2008. (Illus.). xii, 284p. *(978-1-59221-658-1(7))* Africa World Pr.

BLACKS—FRANCE

Jenkins, Jennifer. West Africans in Paris. 2008. 180p. pap. *(978-3-8364-9726-8(3))* VDM Verlag Dr. Mueller e.K.

Keaton, Trica Danielle, et al, eds. Black France-France Noire: The History & Politics of Blackness. 2012. (ENG., Illus.). 328p. 89.95 ***(978-0-8223-5247-1(8))***; pap. 24.95 ***(978-0-8223-5262-4(1))*** Duke Univ. Pr.

Thomas, Dominic. Black France: Colonialism, Immigration, & Transnationalism. 2006. (ENG.). 328p. pap. 27.95 *(978-0-253-21881-0(0),* 0253218810) Indiana Univ. Pr.

White, Elisa Joy. Modernity, Freedom, & the African Diaspora: Dublin, New Orleans, Paris. 2012. (Blacks in the Diaspora Ser.). (ENG.). 356p. pap. 30.00 ***(978-0-253-00125-2(0),*** 0253001250); (Illus.). 80.00 ***(978-0-253-00115-3(3),*** 0253001153) Indiana Univ. Pr.

BLACKS—GERMANY

Campt, Tina M. Image Matters: Archive, Photography, & the African Diaspora in Europe. 2012. (ENG., Illus.). 256p. 89.95 ***(978-0-8223-5056-9(4))***; pap. 24.95 ***(978-0-8223-5074-3(2))*** Duke Univ. Pr.

BLACKS—GREAT BRITAIN

Arana, R. Victoria & Ramey, Lauri. Black British Writing. Arana, R. Victoria & Ramey, Lauri, eds. 2009. (ENG.). 192p. pap. 33.00 *(978-0-230-61705-6(0))* Palgrave Macmillan.

Black British Writers, 347. 2009. (Dictionary of Literary Biography Ser.). (ENG.). 496p. 315.00 (978-0-7876-8165-4(2)) Cengage Gale.

Bourne, Stephen. Mother Country: Britain's Black Community on the Home Front, 1939-45. 2010. (ENG., Illus.). 160p. pap. 22.95 (978-0-7524-5610-2(5)) History Pr. Ltd.,The GBR. Dist: Independent Pubs. Group.

Byrd, Alexander X. Captives & Voyagers: Black Migrants Across the Eighteenth-Century British Atlantic World. 2009. (Illus.). xi, 346p. (978-0-8071-3359-0(0)) Louisiana State Univ. Pr.

—Captives & Voyagers: Black Migrants across the Eighteenth-Century British Atlantic World. 2010. (Antislavery, Abolition, & the Atlantic World Ser.). (Illus.). 360p. pap. 24.95 (978-0-8071-3710-9(3)) Louisiana State Univ. Pr.

Campt, Tina M. Image Matters: Archive, Photography, & the African Diaspora in Europe. 2012. (ENG., Illus.). 256p. 89.95 **(978-0-8223-5056-9(4))**; pap. 24.95 **(978-0-8223-5074-3(2))** Duke Univ. Pr.

Chamberlain, Mary. Family Love in the Diaspora: Migration & the Anglo-Caribbean Experience. 2009. (ENG.). 260p. pap. 24.95 (978-1-4128-0855-2(3)) Transaction Pubs.

Chambers. Black & Asian Theatre in Britain. 2011. (ENG., Illus.). 304p. pap. 39.95 (978-0-415-37598-6(3)) Routledge.

Chater, Kathleen. Untold Histories: Black People in England & Wales During the Period of the British Slave Trade, C. 1660-1807. (ENG.). 2011. 288p. pap. 30.95 **(978-0-7190-8597-0(7))** 2010. (Illus.). 320p. 90.00 (978-0-7190-8013-5(4)) Manchester Univ. Pr. GBR. Dist: Macmillan.

Dabydeen, David, et al, eds. The Oxford Companion to Black British History. (ENG., 592p. 2008. Illus.). pap. 21.95 (978-0-19-923894-1(4)) 2007. 65.00 (978-0-19-280439-6(1)) Oxford Univ. Pr., Inc.

Dabydeen, David, et al. The Oxford Companion to Black British History. 2010. (ENG., Illus.). 592p. pap. 21.95 (978-0-19-957877-1(X)) Oxford Univ. Pr., Inc.

Davis, Mary. Comrade or Brother? The History of the British Labour Movement. 2nd ed. 2009. (ENG.). 256p. 80.00 (978-0-7453-2577-4(7)); pap. 26.00 (978-0-7453-2576-7(9)) Pluto Pr. GBR. Dist: Macmillan.

Fisch, Audrey A. American Slaves in Victorian England: Abolitionist Politics in Popular Literature & Culture. 2009. (ENG.). 152p. pap. 30.00 (978-0-521-12165-1(5)) Cambridge Univ. Pr.

Fryer, Peter. Staying Power: The History of Black People in Britain, Second Edition, 1 vol. 2nd ed. 2010. (Get Political Ser.). (ENG.). 656p. 95.00 (978-0-7453-3073-0(8)); pap. 30.00 (978-0-7453-3072-3(X)) Pluto Pr. GBR. Dist: Macmillan.

Gerloff, Roswith I. H. A Plea for British Black Theologies, 2 Volumes: The Black Church Movement in Britain in Its Transatlantic Cultural & Theological Interaction with Special Reference to the Pentecostal Oneness (Apostolic) & Sabbatarian Movements. 2010. 1130p. pap. 135.00 (978-1-60899-667-4(0), Wipf and Stock) Wipf & Stock Pubs.

—A Plea for British Black Theologies, Volume 1: The Black Church Movement in Britain in Its Transatlantic Cultural & Theological Interaction with Special Reference to the Pentecostal Oneness (Apostolic) & Sabbatarian Movements. 2010. 466p. pap. 61.00 (978-1-60899-665-0(4), Wipf and Stock) Wipf & Stock Pubs.

—A Plea for British Black Theologies, Volume 2: The Black Church Movement in Britain in Its Transatlantic Cultural & Theological Interaction with Special Reference to the Pentecostal Oneness (Apostolic) & Sabbatarian Movements. 2010. 678p. pap. 75.00 (978-1-60899-666-7(2), Wipf and Stock) Wipf & Stock Pubs.

Gilroy, Paul. Black Britain: A Photographic History. 2008. (ENG., Illus.). 320p. pap. 35.00 (978-0-86356-540-3(9)) Saqi Bks. GBR. Dist: Consortium Bk. Sales & Distribution.

Habib, Imtiaz. Black Lives in the English Archives 1500-1677: Imprints of the Invisible. 2008. (Illus.). 432p. 124.95 (978-0-7546-5695-1(0)) Ashgate Publishing Co.

Haji-Kella, Mohamed. What's Culture Got to Do with It? 2009. 76p. pap. (978-3-639-14815-2(0)) VDM Verlag Dr. Mueller e.K.

Hurley, Jon. Tom Cribb: The Life of the Black Diamond. 2009. (ENG., Illus.). 288p. 36.95 (978-0-7524-4751-3(3)) History Pr. Ltd.,The GBR. Dist: Independent Pubs. Group.

Husbands, Christopher T. Race in Britain. (Conflict & Change in Britain Ser.). 240p. (C). (978-0-485-80004-3(7)); pap. (978-0-485-80104-0(3)) Continuum International Publishing Group, Ltd. (Burns & Oates).

Hylton, Ochieng. Black Families in Britain as the Site of Struggle. Ochieng, Bertha & Hylton, Carl, eds. 2010. (ENG., Illus.). 304p. 90.00 (978-0-7190-7686-2(2)) Manchester Univ. Pr. GBR. Dist: Macmillan.

Innes, C. L. A History of Black & Asian Writing in Britain. 2nd ed. 2008. (ENG., Illus.). 330p. pap. 28.99 (978-0-521-71968-1(2)) Cambridge Univ. Pr.

Jacobs, Brian D. Black Politics & Urban Crisis in Britain. 2009. (ENG.). 236p. pap. 36.99 (978-0-521-12552-9(9)) Cambridge Univ. Pr.

Jagessar, Michael N. & Reddie, Anthony, eds. Black Theology in Britain. 2007. (Cross Cultural Theologies Ser.). (ENG., Illus.). 288p. (C). 34.95 (978-1-84553-059-4(4)) Equinox Publishing Ltd. GBR. Dist: ISD.

Jenkinson, Jacqueline. Black 1919: Riots, Racism & Resistance in Imperial Britain. 2009. (Liverpool University Press - Postcolonialism Across Disciplines Ser.). (ENG., Illus.). 256p. 95.00 (978-1-84631-200-7(0)) Liverpool Univ. Pr. GBR. Dist: Chicago Distribution Ctr.

King-Dorset, Rodreguez. Black Dance in London, 1730-1850: Innovation, Tradition & Resistance. 2008. (ENG., Illus.). 204p. pap. 39.95 (978-0-7864-3850-1(9)) McFarland & Co., Inc. Pubs.

Makalani, Minkah. In the Cause of Freedom: Radical Black Internationalism from Harlem to London, 1917-1939. 2011. (ENG., Illus.). 384p. 39.95 (978-0-8078-3504-3(8)) Univ. of North Carolina Pr.

Molineux, Catherine. Faces of Perfect Ebony: Encountering Atlantic Slavery in Imperial Britain. 2012. (Harvard Historical Studies: 175). (ENG., Illus.). 374p. 49.95 (978-0-674-05008-2(8)) Harvard Univ. Pr.

Ord, Jon. Youth Work Process, Product & Practice: Creating an Authentic Curriculum in Work with Young People. 2007. 144p. pap. 33.95 (978-1-905541-11-9(2)) Russell Hse. Publishing Ltd. GBR. Dist: International Specialized Bk. Services.

Pennybacker, Susan D. From Scottsboro to Munich: Race & Political Culture in 1930s Britain. 2009. (ENG., Illus.). 400p. (C). pap. 28.95 (978-0-691-14186-2(X)) Princeton Univ. Pr.

Pirker, Eva Ulrike. Narrative Projections of A Black British History. 2011. (Routledge Approaches to History Ser.). (ENG & ABK., Illus.). 336p. (C). 125.00 (978-0-415-89375-6(5)) Routledge.

Polsgrove, Carol. Ending British Rule in Africa: Writers in a Common Cause. 2009. (Studies in Imperialism Ser.). (ENG.). 240p. 89.95 (978-0-7190-7767-8(2)) Manchester Univ. Pr. GBR. Dist: Macmillan.

Robinson, Amanda. Psychology for Social Workers: Black Perspectives on Human Development & Behaviour. 2nd ed. 2009. 224p. 140.00 (978-0-415-36912-1(6)) Routledge.

Rowe, Michael, ed. Policing Beyond Macpherson: Issues in Policing, Race & Society. 2007. (Illus.). 220p. (C). pap. 47.50 (978-1-84392-212-4(6)) Willan Publishing GBR. Dist: Taylor & Francis Group.

Sallah, Momodou & Howson, Carlton, eds. Working with Black Young People. 2007. 256p. pap. 49.95 (978-1-905541-14-0(7)) Russell Hse. Publishing Ltd. GBR. Dist: International Specialized Bk. Services.

Schama, Simon. Rough Crossings: The Slaves, the British, & the American Revolution. 2007. (Illus.). 496p. per. 16.95 (978-0-06-053917-7(8), HarperPerennial) HarperCollins Pubs.

Sparks, Randy J. The Two Princes of Calabar: An Eighteenth-Century Atlantic Odyssey. 2009. (Illus.). 208p. pap. 16.50 (978-0-674-03205-7(5)) Harvard Univ. Pr.

Stein, Mark & Osborne, Deidre. Black British Fiction. 2011. (Writers & Their Work Ser.). (ENG.). 128p. (C). 80.00 (978-0-7463-1039-7(0)) Northcote Hse. Publishers, Ltd. GBR. Dist: Brown, David Bk. Co., The.

—Black British Literature. 2012. (Writers & Their Work Ser.). (ENG.). 128p. (C). pap. 26.00 (978-0-7463-1044-1(7)) Northcote Hse. Publishers, Ltd. GBR. Dist: Brown, David Bk. Co., The.

Wright, Cecile, et al. Black Youth Matters: Transitions from School to Success. 2009. (Critical Youth Studies). (ENG.). 176p. 130.00 (978-0-415-99510-8(8)); pap. 38.95 (978-0-415-99512-2(4)) Routledge.

Wynne-Davies, Marion & Low, Gail, eds. A Black British Canon? 2006. (ENG., Illus.). 256p. 84.00 (978-1-4039-4268-5(4)) Palgrave Macmillan.

BLACKS—HAITI

Garrett, Mitchell Bennett. The French Colonial Question 1789-1791. 167p. reprint ed. 88.00 (978-0-7222-9501-4(4)) Library Reprints, Inc.

Garrigus, John D. Before Haiti: Race & Citizenship in French Saint-Domingue. 2010. (Americas in the Early Modern Atlantic World Ser.). (ENG., Illus.). 410p. pap. 33.00 (978-0-230-10837-0(7)) Palgrave Macmillan.

Weaver, Karol K. Medical Revolutionaries: The Enslaved Healers of Eighteenth-Century Saint Domingue. 2006. (Illus.). 184p. 52.00 (978-0-252-03085-7(0)) Univ. of Illinois Pr.

BLACKS—JAMAICA

see also Maroons

Bigelow, John. Jamaica In 1850. 2006. 228p. per. 20.99 (978-1-4255-1961-2(X)) MPublishing.

Dallas, Robert Charles. The History of the Maroons: From their Origin to the Establishment of their Chief Tribe at Sierra Leone. 2010. (Cambridge Library Collection - Slavery & Abolition Ser.). (ENG.). 542p. pap. 39.99 (978-1-108-02415-0(7)); (Illus.). 498p. pap. 35.99 (978-1-108-02414-3(9)) Cambridge Univ. Pr.

Diptee, Audra A. From Africa to Jamaica: The Making of an Atlantic Slave Society, 1775-1807. 2010. (ENG., Illus.). 176p. 69.95 (978-0-8130-3482-9(5)) Univ. Pr. of Florida.

Livingstone, William P. Black Jamaica: A Study in Evolution. 298p. reprint ed. 98.00 (978-0-7222-9804-6(8)) Library Reprints, Inc.

Pim, Bedford. The Negro & Jamaica. 2007. pap. 17.95 (978-1-4304-6945-2(5)) Kessinger Publishing, LLC.

Pullen-Burry, Bessie. Ethiopia in Exile: Jamaica Revisited. 292p. 2010. pap. 28.75 (978-1-141-53853-9(9)) 2009. 24.99 (978-1-103-69112-8(0)) 2009. pap. 18.99 (978-1-103-69109-8(0)) BiblioBazaar.

—Ethiopia in Exile: Jamaica Revisited. 2007. (ENG.). 288p. 43.95 (978-0-548-36973-9(9)); per. 28.95 (978-0-548-31279-7(6)) Kessinger Publishing, LLC.

Robinson, Carey. Fight for Freedom: The Destruction of Slavery in Jamaica. 2007. 196p. per. (978-976-8202-42-0(4)) LMH Publishing, Ltd.

Seacole, Mary. Wonderful Adventures of Mrs. Seacole in Many Lands. RUSSELL, W. H., ed. 2007. (ENG.). 186p. per. 21.99 (978-1-4346-9382-2(1)); 170p. per. 19.99 (978-1-4346-9381-5(3)) BiblioBazaar.

—Wonderful Adventures of Mrs. Seacole in Many Lands. 2008. (ENG.). 160p. pap. 11.95 (978-1-4385-0336-3(9), Book Jungle) Standard Pubns., Inc.

BLACKS—LATIN AMERICA

Brennan, Timothy. Secular Devotion: Afro-Latin Music & Imperial Jazz. 2008. (ENG., Illus.). 290p. pap. 29.95 (978-1-84467-291-2(3), 844291) Verso Bks. GBR. Dist: Norton, W. W. & Co., Inc.

—Secular Devotion Afro-Latin Music & Imp. 2008. (ENG., Illus.). 290p. 110.00 (978-1-84467-290-5(5), 844290) Verso Bks. GBR. Dist: Norton, W. W. & Co., Inc.

Davis, Darien J. Beyond Slavery: The Multilayered Legacy of Africans in Latin America & the Caribbean. 2006. (Jaguar Books on Latin America Ser.). (ENG., Illus.). 298p. 92.00 (978-0-7425-4130-6(4)); per. 34.95 (978-0-7425-4131-3(2)) Rowman & Littlefield Publishers, Inc.

Dixon, Kwame & Burdick, John, eds. Comparative Perspectives on Afro-Latin America. 2012. (ENG., Illus.). 382p. 74.95 **(978-0-8130-3756-1(5))** Univ. Pr. of Florida.

Foote, Nicola & Harder Horst, Rene D., eds. Military Struggle & Identity Formation in Latin America: Race, Nation, & Community during the Liberal Period. 2010. (ENG., Illus.). 336p. 69.95 (978-0-8130-3487-4(6)) Univ. Pr. of Florida.

Gates, Henry Louis, Jr. Black in Latin America. 2011. (ENG.). 270p. 26.95 (978-0-8147-3298-4(4)); E-Book (978-0-8147-3342-4(5)) New York Univ. Pr.

Liennard, Martin. Disidentes, Rebeldes, Insurgentes: Resistencia Indígena y Negra en América Latina: Ensayos de Historia Testimonial. 2008. (SPA., Illus.). 163p. pap. 24.80 (978-84-8489-349-3(9)) Iberoamericana Vervuert Publishing Corp.

Rahier, Jean Muteba, ed. Black Social Movements in Latin America: From Monocultural Mestizaje to Multiculturalism. 2012. (ENG., Illus.). 272p. 90.00 **(978-0-230-39360-8(8))** Palgrave Macmillan.

Reiter, Bernd & Eison Simmons, Kimberly, eds. Afro-Descendants, Identity, & the Struggle for Development in the Americas. 2012. (African Diaspora Research Project Ser.). (ENG.). 344p. pap. 34.95 **(978-1-61186-040-5(7))** Michigan State Univ. Pr.

Robinson, Barry M., ed. Slaves, Subjects, & Subversives: Blacks in Colonial Latin America. 2006. (Dialogos Ser.). (ENG., Illus.). 328p. (C). pap. 29.95 (978-0-8263-2397-2(9)) Univ. of New Mexico Pr.

Tillis, Antonio D., ed. Critical Perspectives on Afro-Latin American Literature. 2011. (Routledge Studies on African & Black Diaspora Ser.). (ENG.). 272p. (C). 125.00 (978-0-415-89627-6(4)) Routledge.

BLACKS—MEXICO

Bennett, Herman L. Colonial Blackness: A History of Afro-Mexico. 2010. (Blacks in the Diaspora Ser.). (ENG., Illus.). 248p. pap. 24.95 (978-0-253-22331-9(8), 0253223318) Indiana Univ. Pr.

Bristol, Joan Cameron. Christians, Blasphemers, & Witches: Afro-Mexican Ritual Practice in the Seventeenth Century. 2007. (Dialogos Ser.). (ENG., Illus.). 297p. (C). pap. 29.95 (978-0-8263-3799-3(6)) Univ. of New Mexico Pr.

Camba Ludlow, Úrsula. Imaginarios Ambiguos, Realidades Contradictorias: Conductas y Representaciones de Los Negros y Mulatos Novohispanos: Siglos XVI y XVII. 2008. (Estudios Históricos Ser.). (SPA., Illus.). 227p. pap. 23.99 (978-968-12-1374-9(2)) El Colegio de México, A.C., Biblioteca Miguel Cosio Villegas MEX. Dist: Fondo de Cultura Economica USA.

Githiora, Chege J. Afro-Mexicans: Discourse of Race & Identity on the African Diaspora. 2008. (978-1-59221-646-8(3)); 276p. pap. (978-1-59221-647-5(1)) Africa World Pr.

González, Anita. Afro-Mexico: Dancing Between Myth & Reality. 2010. (ENG., Illus.). 183p. 55.00 (978-0-292-72324-5(5)) Univ. of Texas Pr.

González, Anita. Afro-Mexico: Dancing between Myth & Reality. 2011. (ENG., Illus.). 183p. pap. 25.00 **(978-0-292-73744-0(0))** Univ. of Texas Pr.

Hall, Raymond A. An Ethnographic Study of Afro-Mexicans in Mexico's Gulf Coast: Fishing, Festivals, & Foodways. 2008. 152p. 99.95 (978-0-7734-4929-9(9)) Mellen, Edwin Pr., The.

Hernandez Cuevas, Marco Polo. Africa en Mexico: Una Herencia Repudiada. (SPA.). 140p. 99.95 (978-0-7734-5216-9(8)) Mellen, Edwin Pr., The.

—Africa Late en la Mexicanidad. 2007. (SPA.). 140p. 99.95 (978-0-7734-5399-9(7)) Mellen, Edwin Pr., The.

Hernández Cuevas, Marco Polo. The Africanization of Mexico from the Sixteenth Century Onward: A Review of the Evidence. 2010. v, 189p. 109.95 (978-0-7734-3781-4(9)) Mellen, Edwin Pr., The.

Lewis, Laura A. Chocolate & Corn Flour: History, Race, & Place in the Making of "Black" Mexico. 2012. (ENG., Illus.). 400p. pap. 25.95 **(978-0-8223-5132-0(3))** Duke Univ. Pr.

—Chocolate & Corn Flour: History, Race, & Place in the Making of ldquo;Blackrdquo; Mexico. 2012. (ENG., Illus.). 400p. 94.95 **(978-0-8223-5121-4(8))** Duke Univ. Pr.

Proctor, Frank. Damned Notions of Liberty: Slavery, Culture, & Power in Colonial Mexico, 1640-1769. 2010. (Dialogos Ser.). (ENG., Illus.). 296p. (C). pap. 27.95 (978-0-8263-4966-8(8)) Univ. of New Mexico Pr.

Vinson, Ben. Black Mexico: Race & Society from Colonial to Modern Times. Restall, Matthew, ed. 2009. (Dialogos Ser.). (ENG., Illus.). 296p. (C). pap. 29.95 (978-0-8263-4701-5(0)) Univ. of New Mexico Pr.

BLACKS—SOUTH AFRICA

Alexander, Amanda & Mngxitama, Andile. Biko Lives! Contesting the Legacies of Steve Biko. Gibson, Nigel, ed. 2008. (Contemporary Black History Ser.). (ENG.). 304p. pap. 31.00 (978-0-230-60649-4(0)) Palgrave Macmillan.

Cargill, Jenny. Trick or Treat: Perspectives on Black Economic. 2010. (ENG.). 280p. pap. 24.00 (978-1-77009-830-5(5)) Jacana Media ZAF. Dist: Independent Pubs. Group.

Connell, Dan. Old Wrongs, New Rights: Student Views of the New South Africa. 2008. (978-1-59221-628-4(5)); 168p. pap. (978-1-59221-629-1(3)) Africa World Pr.

Coplan, David B. In Township Tonight! South Africa's Black City Music & Theatre. 2nd ed. 2008. (Chicago Studies in Ethnomusicology Ser.). (Illus.). 496p. 72.50 (978-0-226-11566-5(6)); pap. 27.50 (978-0-226-11567-2(4)) Univ. of Chicago Pr.

Eggens, Laura. Never 100% Black. 2010. 108p. pap. (978-3-8383-6036-2(2)) Lambert Academic Publishing.

Elizabeth A. Eldredge And Fred Morton. Slavery in South Afric: Captive Labor on the Dutch Frontier. 2010. 340p. pap. 22.95 (978-1-4401-2500-3(7)) iUniverse, Inc.

Eze, Michael Onyebuchi. Intellectual History in Contemporary South Africa. 2010. (ENG.). 234p. 89.00 (978-0-230-62299-9(2)) Palgrave Macmillan.

Gevisser, Mark. A Legacy of Liberation: Thabo Mbeki & the Future of the South African Dream. (ENG., Illus.). 400p. 2010. pap. 20.00 (978-0-230-61999-9(1)) 2009. 29.95 (978-0-230-61100-9(1)) Palgrave Macmillan.

Hummel, Philip. My Life Growing up White during Apartheid in South Africa. 2011. 100p. pap. 9.99 (978-1-4567-1800-8(2)) AuthorHouse.

Jordaan, B., et al, eds. Understanding Broad-Based Black Economic Empowerment. 2010. 190p. pap. 17.50 (978-0-7021-8187-0(0)) Gaunt, Inc.

Kamlana, Unathi. The Taxation of Black Economic Empowernment Transactions. 2010. 100p. pap. (978-3-8383-4493-5(6)) Lambert Academic Publishing.

Lindfors, Bernth. Early Black South African Writing in English. 2011. **(978-1-59221-840-0(7))**; (Illus.). 236p. pap. **(978-1-59221-841-7(5))** Africa World Pr.

MacDonald, Michael. Why Race Matters in South Africa. 2012. (ENG., Illus.). 256p. pap. 19.95 **(978-0-674-06389-1(9))** Harvard Univ. Pr.

—Why Race Matters in South Africa. 256p. pap. (978-1-86914-093-9(1)) University of Kwazulu-Natal Press ZAF. Dist: International Specialized Bk. Services.

Mandela, Nelson. Let Freedom Reign: The Words of Nelson Mandela. Russell, Henry, ed. 2010. (ENG.). 144p. 14.95 (978-1-56656-800-5(5), Interlink Bks.) Interlink Publishing Group, Inc.

—Selected Speeches & Writings of Nelson Mandela: The End of Apartheid in South Africa. 2010. 290p. pap. (978-1-934941-78-2(6)) Red & Black Pubs.

Marais, Hein. South Africa Pushed to the Limit: The Political Economy of Change. 2011. (ENG., Illus.). 544p. 126.00 (978-1-84813-860-5(1)); pap. 45.00 (978-1-84813-859-9(8)) Zed Bks., Ltd. GBR. Dist: Macmillan.

Matsinhe, David M. Apartheid Vertigo: South African & African Outsiders. 2011. (Interdisciplinary Research Ser. in Ethnic, Gender & Class Relations Ser.). (Illus.). 230p. 99.95 **(978-1-4094-2619-6(X))** Ashgate Publishing Co.

Minow, Verena. Variation in the Grammar of Black South African English. 2010. (Europäische Hochschulschriften. Reihe 21: Linguistik Ser.). (GER.). 278p. pap. 72.95 (978-3-631-60148-8(4)) Lang, Peter GmbH, Europaischer Verlag der Wissenschaften DEU. Dist: Lang, Peter.

Miyeni, Eric. O'Mandingo! Before Mandela was Mandela. 2008. (ENG.). 144p. pap. 20.95 (978-1-77009-345-4(1)) Jacana Media ZAF. Dist: Independent Pubs. Group.

—O'Mandingo! The Only Black at a Dinner Party. 2007. (ENG.). 276p. per. 18.95 (978-1-77009-187-0(4)) Jacana Media ZAF. Dist: Independent Pubs. Group.

Mngxitama, Andile, et al. Biko Lives! Contesting the Legacies of Steve Biko. Alexander, Amanda et al, eds. 2008. (Contemporary Black History Ser.). (ENG.). 304p. 95.00 (978-0-230-60519-0(2)) Palgrave Macmillan.

Mojapelo, John Seakalala. The Corner People of Lady Selborne. 2009. 295p. pap. 59.00 (978-1-86888-560-2(7)) Unisa Press / Uitgewers GBR. Dist: International Specialized Bk. Services.

Motlhabi, Mokgethi B. G. African Theology/Black Theology in South Africa: Looking Back, Moving On. 2008. 162p. pap. 29.00 (978-1-86888-433-9(3)) Unisa Press / Uitgewers GBR. Dist: International Specialized Bk. Services.

Ngoma, Samuel. Why Is God Silent on Mandela? The Unspoken Question about a World Icon in Relation to Christ. 2009. (ENG.). 112p. pap. 14.99 (978-1-59979-777-9(1), Creation Hse.) Charisma Media.

Nielsen, Peter. The Black Man's Place in South Africa. 2007. 80p. per. (978-1-4065-4954-6(1)) Dodo Pr.

Pohlandt-McCormick, Helena. I Saw a Nightmare: Doing Violence to Memory - The Soweto Uprising, June 16, 1976. 2008. (Gutenberg-e Ser.). (ENG.). 655p. 60.00 (978-0-231-12220-7(9)) Columbia Univ. Pr.

Redding, Sean. Sorcery & Sovereignty: Taxation, Power, & Rebellion in South Africa, 1880-1963. 2006. (Illus.). 304p. 55.00 (978-0-8214-1704-1(5)); per. 29.95 (978-0-8214-1705-8(3)) Ohio Univ. Pr.

Tsolo, Donald A. The Promise: Black Youth Confront the Cauldron of Apartheid. 2009. 208p. 27.95 (978-1-4401-4542-1(3)); pap. 17.95 (978-1-4401-4540-7(7)) iUniverse, Inc.

Turok, Ben, ed. The Historical Roots of the ANC. 2011. (Understanding the ANC Today Ser.). (ENG., Illus.). 144p. pap. 15.95 (978-1-77009-965-4(4)) Jacana Media ZAF. Dist: Independent Pubs. Group.

Tutu, Desmond, intro. Believe: The Words & Inspiration of Desmond Tutu. 2007. (Illus.). 95p. 14.95 (978-1-59842-241-2(3), Blue Mountain Pr.) Blue Mountain Arts Inc.

BLACKS—SOUTH AMERICA

Andrews, George Reid. Blackness in the White Nation: A History of Afro-Uruguay. 2010. (ENG., Illus.). 272p. 59.95 (978-0-8078-3417-6(3)); pap. 22.95 (978-0-8078-7158-4(3)) Univ. of North Carolina Pr.

Blanchard, Peter. Under the Flags of Freedom: Slave Soldiers & the Wars of Independence in Spanish South America. 2008. (Pitt Latin American Studies). (ENG., Illus.). 312p. (C). 60.00 (978-0-8229-4347-1(6)); pap. 26.95 (978-0-8229-5992-2(5)) Univ. of Pittsburgh Pr.

Bowser, Frederick P. The African Slave in Colonial Peru, 1524-1650. 460p. 2009. 22.00 (978-1-59740-337-5(7)) 2008. pap. 46.00 (978-1-59740-704-5(6)) ACLS Humanities E-Book.

Brockington, Lolita Gutierrez. Blacks, Indians, & Spaniards in the Eastern Andes: Reclaiming the Forgotten in Colonial Mizque, 1550-1782. 2009. (ENG.). 360p. pap. 24.95 *(978-0-8032-2484-1(2))* Univ. of Nebraska Pr.

Johnson, Whittington B. Post-Emancipation Race Relations in the Bahamas. 2006. (ENG., Illus.). 192p. 59.95 *(978-0-8130-2994-8(5))* Univ. Pr. of Florida.

Lasso, Marixa. Myths of Harmony: Race & Republicanism During the Age of Revolution, Colombia 1795-1831. 2007. (Pitt Latin Amercian Studies). 248p. per. 24.95 *(978-0-8229-5965-6(8))* Univ. of Pittsburgh Pr.

Poosson, Sylvain B. La historia Silenciada: Los afroargentinos protagonistas de un drama Social. 2007. (SPA.). 248p. 109.95 *(978-0-7734-5633-4(3))* Mellen, Edwin Pr., The.

BLACKS—SURINAM

Herskovits, Melville Jean & Herskovits, Frances S. Suriname Folk-Lore. (Columbia University, Contributions to Anthropology Ser.: No. 27). (Illus.). reprint ed. 67.50 *(978-0-404-50577-6(5))* AMS Pr., Inc.

BLACKS—TRINIDAD AND TOBAGO

Adderley, Rosanne Marion. New Negroes from Africa: Slave Trade Abolition & Free African Settlement in the Nineteenth-Century Caribbean. 2006. (Blacks in the Diaspora Ser.). (Illus.). (ENG.). 360p. pap. 24.95 *(978-0-253-21827-8(6),* 0253218276); 337p. 65.00 *(978-0-253-34703-9(3))* Indiana Univ. Pr.

Carmichael, A. C. Five Years in Trinidad & St Vincent V1: a View of the Social. 2007. pap. 31.95 *(978-1-4304-6954-4(4))* Kessinger Publishing, LLC.

BLACKS—UNITED STATES

Here are entered works on blacks who temporarily reside in the United States, such as aliens, students from abroad, etc. Works on citizens of the United States of black African descent are entered under African Americans.

see also African Americans

Adams, Grace, ed. 2010-11 Black Authors & Published Writers Directory: A Writers Guide for Students & Teachers. 2010. 142p. pap. 24.95 *(978-1-877807-36-7(2),* Black Authors & Published Writers Directory) Grace Publishing Co.

Benjamin, Richard. Searching for Whitopia: An Improbable Journey to the Heart of White America. 2009. (ENG.). 368p. 24.99 *(978-1-4013-2268-7(9))* Hyperion Pr.

Bhopal, Kalwant & Preston, John, eds. Intersectionality & Race in Education. 2011. (Routledge Research in Education Ser.). (ENG., Illus.). 238p. (C). 125.00 *(978-0-415-88877-6(8))* Routledge.

Bradley, Michael. Dawn Voyage: The Black African Discovery of America. 2011. (Illus.). 193p. pap. 14.95 ***(978-1-61759-003-0(7))*** EWorld, Inc.

Brandwein, Pamela. Rethinking the Judicial Settlement of Reconstruction. 2011. (Cambridge Studies on the American Constitution Ser.). (ENG.). 288p. 90.00 *(978-0-521-88771-7(2))* Cambridge Univ. Pr.

Bullard, Robert D. The Black Metropolis in the Twenty-First Century: Race, Power, & Politics of Place. 2007. (ENG., Illus.). 294p. 89.00 *(978-0-7425-4328-7(5));* pap. 31.95 *(978-0-7425-4329-4(3))* Rowman & Littlefield Publishers, Inc.

Carney, Judith & Rosomoff, Richard Nicholas. In the Shadow of Slavery: Africa's Botanical Legacy in the Atlantic World. 2011. (ENG., Illus.). 296p. pap. 18.95 *(978-0-520-26996-5(9))* Univ. of California Pr.

Christie, Ron. Acting White: The Curious History of a Racial Slur. 2010. (ENG.). 304p. 25.99 *(978-0-312-59946-1(3),* Dunne, Thomas Bks.) St. Martin's Pr.

Christie, Ron. Blacklash: How Black Leadership Is Returning America to the Days of Separate but Equal. 2012. (ENG.). 304p. 25.99 ***(978-0-312-59147-2(0),*** Dunne, Thomas Bks.) St. Martin's Pr.

D-Kha'd. The Transformation Process of a People: From BC Africa up to 1619 America, with reference to modernity for comparative Analysis. 2011. 216p. 29.99 ***(978-1-4535-4911-7(0));*** pap. 19.99 ***(978-1-4535-4910-0(2))*** Xlibris Corp.

Dickerson, Gregory B. Steven. 2009. 116p. pap. 10.49 *(978-1-4389-7328-9(4))* AuthorHouse.

Durangowalt. Hiz-Story. 2009. 304p. pap. 15.49 *(978-1-4490-1555-8(7))* AuthorHouse.

Edd., John Lee Peterson Jr. Managing the Storms of Inner & Outer Conflicts. 2011. 96p. 24.99 ***(978-1-4568-5665-6(0));*** pap. 15.99 ***(978-1-4568-5664-9(2))*** Xlibris Corp.

Emeka, Amon. New Blacks, New Whites, & the New Day. 2008. 168p. pap. *(978-3-639-07803-9(9))* VDM Verlag Dr. Mueller e.K.

Farr, Stacie. Black Girl in America: A Memoir. 2010. 84p. pap. 12.99 *(978-1-4269-2871-0(8))* Trafford Publishing.

Franks, Pamela & Steele, Robert E. Embodied: Black Identities in American Art from the Yale University Art Gallery. 2010. *(978-0-89467-977-3(5))* Yale Univ. Art Gallery.

Hamilton, Ginetta V. Black History: Someone Forgot to Teach the Children: Lord, I dun bin through someum yah, But... 2010. 76p. pap. 24.99 *(978-1-4490-7384-8(0))* AuthorHouse.

Haynes, Stephen R. The Last Segregated Hour: The Memphis Kneel-Ins & the Campaign for Southern Church Desegregation. 2012. (ENG., Illus.). 352p. 29.95 ***(978-0-19-539505-1(0))*** Oxford Univ. Pr., Inc.

Horne, Victor Carter. A Black Patriot: The Real American. 2011. 136p. pap. 12.87 ***(978-1-4269-6144-1(8))*** Trafford Publishing.

Ifedi, Rosaire Ifeyinwa. African-Born Women Faculty in the United States: Lives in Contradiction. 2008. (Illus.). 256p. 109.95 *(978-0-7734-5114-8(5))* Mellen, Edwin Pr., The.

Johnson, George D. Profiles in Hue. 2011. 386p. pap. 19.99 ***(978-1-4568-5119-4(5))*** Xlibris Corp.

Johnson, Violet Showers & Johnson, Violet M. The Other Black Bostonians: West Indians in Boston, 1900-1950. 2006. (Blacks in the Diaspora Ser.). (ENG., Illus.). 200p. 24.95 *(978-0-253-34752-7(1),* 0253347521) Indiana Univ. Pr.

Lynn, Scott. Thornridge: The Perfect Season in Black & White. 2009. 316p. 27.95 *(978-1-4490-4090-1(X));* pap. 22.95 *(978-1-4490-4089-5(6))* AuthorHouse.

Metzler, Christoper J. The construction & rearticulation of race in a post-racial America. 2008. 189p. pap. 49.96 *(978-0-615-21670-6(6))* Aberdeen Univ. Pr. Services.

Mocombe, Paul C. The Liberal Black Protestant Heterosexual Bourgeois Male: From W. E. B. du Bois to Barack Obama. 2009. (ENG.). 180p. 57.99 *(978-0-7618-4801-1(0));* pap. 33.99 *(978-0-7618-4757-1(X))* Univ. Pr. of America, Inc.

Model, Suzanne. West Indian Blacks: An Immigrant Success Story? 2008. (C). *(978-0-87154-631-9(0))* Russell Sage Foundation.

Morris, Edward W. Learning the Hard Way: Masculinity, Place, & the Gender Gap in Education. 2012. (Rutgers Series in Childhood Studies). 224p. (C). pap. 26.95 ***(978-0-8135-5369-6(5));*** (ENG.). 72.00 ***(978-0-8135-5368-9(7))*** Rutgers Univ. Pr.

Nash, Michael & Lewis, David Levering, eds. Red Activists & Black Freedom: James & Esther Jackson & the Long Civil Rights Revolution. 2009. (ENG., Illus.). 136p. (C). 125.00 *(978-0-415-47255-5(5))* Routledge.

Naylor, Celia E. African Cherokees in Indian Territory: From Chattel to Citizens. (ENG., Illus.). 376p. 2009. pap. 49.95 *(978-0-8078-5883-7(8))* 2008. 62.95 *(978-0-8078-3203-5(0))* Univ. of North Carolina Pr.

Odhoji, Benjamin M. O. Restoying the Margins. 2011. 252p. pap. ***(978-3-8443-8212-9(7))*** Lambert Academic Publishing.

Randolph, Robert H. Rich White Folks: Growing up Black in America. 2011. (ENG.). 154p. pap. 13.95 ***(978-1-4327-5203-3(0))*** Outskirts Pr., Inc.

Rebelo, Marcia. Acculturation Influences on the Self Concept of the Black Adolescent. 2009. 140p. pap. *(978-3-639-16237-0(4))* VDM Verlag Dr. Mueller e.K.

Saunders, Bernard W. My Encounter with Ordinary Women Who Led Extraordinary Lives: As Torchbearers of Culture, Way Showers of Self-Determination & Freedom. 2011. 58p. pap. 15.99 ***(978-1-4568-9231-9(2))*** Xlibris Corp.

Saunt, Claudio. Black, White, & Indian: Race & the Unmaking of an American Family. 2006. (ENG., Illus.). 312p. per. 25.00 *(978-0-19-531310-9(0))* Oxford Univ. Pr., Inc.

Temple, Catherine. Undercurrents in America. 2011. 52p. pap. 19.95 ***(978-1-4634-0699-8(1))*** AuthorHouse.

Terrell, Keino. Us vs. Them: Black Peoples' Battle for Mentality. 2010. 128p. (ENG.). 21.49 *(978-1-4490-9419-5(8));* pap. 10.99 *(978-1-4490-9418-8(X))* AuthorHouse.

Valdez, Rhonda. Tried by Fire. 2009. 392p. 29.99 *(978-1-4415-2562-8(9))* Xlibris Corp.

Wright, Donald R. The Only Prayer I'll Ever Pray: Let My People Go. 2009. 96p. pap. 13.95 *(978-1-60844-291-1(8))* Dog Ear Publishing, LLC.

Zellar, Gary. African Creeks: Estelvste & the Creek Nation. 2007. (Race & Culture in the American West Ser.: Vol. 1). (ENG., Illus.). 368p. (C). 34.95 *(978-0-8061-3815-2(7))* Univ. of Oklahoma Pr.

BLACKS—WEST INDIES

see also Maroons

Candelario, Ginetta E. B. Black Behind the Ears: Dominican Racial Identity from Museums to Beauty Shops. 2007. (ENG., Illus.). 360p. 94.95 *(978-0-8223-4018-8(6));* per. 25.95 *(978-0-8223-4037-9(2))* Duke Univ. Pr.

Carmichael, A. C. Five Years in Trinidad & St Vincent V1: a View of the Social. 2007. pap. 31.95 *(978-1-4304-6954-4(4))* Kessinger Publishing, LLC.

Chamberlain, Mary. Family Love in the Diaspora: Migration & the Anglo-Caribbean Experience. 2009. (ENG.). 260p. pap. 24.95 *(978-1-4128-0855-2(3))* Transaction Pubs.

Dixon, Kwame & Burdick, John, eds. Comparative Perspectives on Afro-Latin America. 2012. (ENG., Illus.). 382p. 74.95 ***(978-0-8130-3756-1(5))*** Univ. Pr. of Florida.

Landers, Jane G. Atlantic Creoles in the Age of Revolutions. 2011. (ENG., Illus.). 352p. pap. 19.95 *(978-0-674-06204-7(3))* Harvard Univ. Pr.

Mintz, Sidney Wilfred & Rouse, Irving, eds. Papers in Caribbean Anthropology: Yale University Publications in Anthropology, No. 57-64. 2011. 270p. 47.95 ***(978-1-258-09117-0(8))*** Literary Licensing, LLC.

Munro, Martin. Different Drummers: Rhythm & Race in the Americas. 2010. (Music of the African Diaspora Ser.). (ENG.). 296p. 65.00 *(978-0-520-26282-9(4));* pap. 27.50 *(978-0-520-26283-6(2))* Univ. of California Pr.

Stephen, James. The Crisis of the Sugar Colonies: Or, an Enquiry into the Objects & Probable Effects of the French Expedition to the West Indies. 2010. (Cambridge Library Collection - History Ser.). 234p. pap. 22.99 *(978-1-108-02047-3(X))* Cambridge Univ. Pr.

BLACKS—WEST INDIES, BRITISH

Mill, John Stuart. The Nigger Question. reprint ed. lib. bdg. 98.00 *(978-0-7426-2413-9(1))* Classic Bks.

Sheridan, Richard B. Doctors & Slaves: A Medical & Demographic History of Slavery in the British West Indies, 1680-1834. 2009. (ENG., Illus.). 444p. pap. 55.00 *(978-0-521-10238-4(3))* Cambridge Univ. Pr.

Sturge, Joseph & Harvey, Thomas. The West Indies In 1837. 2007. 496p. per. 19.95 *(978-1-60206-132-3(7))* Cosimo, Inc.

—The West Indies In 1837: Being the Journal of a Visit to Antigua, Montserrat, Dominica, St. Lucia, Barbados, & Jamaica. 2010. (Cambridge Library Collection - Slavery & Abolition Ser.). (ENG., Illus.). 512p. pap. 35.99 *(978-1-108-02431-0(9))* Cambridge Univ. Pr.

—The West Indies in 1837: Being the Journal of a Visit to Antigua. 2007. pap. 38.95 *(978-1-4304-6960-5(9))* Kessinger Publishing, LLC.

BLACKS—WEST INDIES, FRENCH

Filostrat, Christian. Negritude Agonistes, Assimilation Against Nationalism in the French-Speaking Caribbean & Guyane. 2008. (Illus.). 240p. 50.00 *(978-0-9818939-2-1(9))* Africana Homestead Legacy Pubs., Inc.

BLACKS IN ART

Amadiume, Ifi. Black Womanhood: Images, Icons, & Ideologies of the African Body. Thompson, Barbara, ed. 2008. (ENG., Illus.). 376p. (C). *(978-0-295-98770-5(7))* Hood Museum of Art.

Arnold, Peter, photos by. Black & Beautiful. 2012. (Illus.). 128p. 87.99 ***(978-3-86787-235-5(X))*** Bruno Gmunder Verlag GmbH DEU. Dist: Bookazine Co., Inc.

Bindman, David. The Image of the Black in Western Art Vol. 2: From the Early Christian Era to the Age of Discovery - From the Demonic Threat to the Incarnation of Sainthood, Part 1. Gates, Henry Louis, Jr., ed. 2010. (ENG., Illus.). 336p. 95.00 *(978-0-674-05256-7(0),* Belknap Pr.) Harvard Univ. Pr.

Bindman, David & Gates, Henry Louis, Jr., eds. The Image of the Black in Western Art Pt. 2: From the Early Christian Era to the Age of Discovery - Africans in the Christian Ordinance of the World, Part 2. 2010. (ENG., Illus.). 400p. 95.00 *(978-0-674-05258-1(7),* Belknap Pr.) Harvard Univ. Pr.

—The Image of the Black in Western Art Vol. 3, Part 3: From the Age of Discovery to the Age of Abolition: The Eighteenth Century, Part 3. 2011. (ENG., Illus.). 400p. 95.00 *(978-0-674-05263-5(3),* Belknap Pr.) Harvard Univ. Pr.

Bindman, David, et al. The Image of the Black in Western Art: From the American Revolution to World War I - Black Models & White Myths, Part 2. 2012. (ENG., Illus.). 384p. 95.00 ***(978-0-674-05260-4(9),*** Belknap Pr.) Harvard Univ. Pr.

—The Image of the Black in Western Art Vol. 1: From the Pharaohs to the Fall of the Roman Empire, Volume I. 2010. (ENG., Illus.). 416p. 95.00 *(978-0-674-05271-0(4),* Belknap Pr.) Harvard Univ. Pr.

—The Image of the Black in Western Art Vol. 3: From the Age of Discovery to the Age of Abolition, Part 2: Europe & the World Beyond, Part 2. 2011. (ENG., Illus.). 528p. 95.00 *(978-0-674-05262-8(5),* Belknap Pr.) Harvard Univ. Pr.

—The Image of the Black in Western Art Vol. 3, Pt. 1: From the Age of Discovery to the Age of Abolition - Artists of the Renaissance & Baroque, Part 1. 2010. (Illus.). 432p. 95.00 *(978-0-674-05261-1(7),* Belknap Pr.) Harvard Univ. Pr.

Bindman, David, et al. The Image of the Black in Western Art Vol. 4: From the American Revolution to World War I - Slaves & Liberators, Part 1. 2012. (ENG., Illus.). 384p. 95.00 ***(978-0-674-05259-8(5),*** Belknap Pr.) Harvard Univ. Pr.

Bonvicini, Monica & Bidner, Stefan. Cut. 2008. (ENG., Illus.). 52p. 38.00 *(978-3-86560-378-4(5))* Verlag der Buchhandlung Walther Konig DEU. Dist: D.A.P./Distributed Art Pubs.

Braziel, Jana Evans. Artists, Performers, & Black Masculinity in the Haitian Diaspora. 2008. (Blacks in the Diaspora Ser.). (ENG., Illus.). 312p. 65.00 *(978-0-253-35139-5(1),* 0253351391); pap. 24.95 *(978-0-253-21978-7(7),* 0253219787) Indiana Univ. Pr.

Bryant, Tisa. Unexplained Presence. 2007. 159p. per. 15.95 *(978-0-9765820-1-4(5))* Leon Works.

Colored People. 100th ltd. ed. 2008. (Illus.). 50p. *(978-0-9792486-2-7(0))* C & C Pr.

Cross, Kay Capps. Quilted Panels in Black & White: Fast & Friendly Techniques for Using Fabric Panels & Large Prints. 2010. (ENG., Illus.). 128p. pap. 24.99 *(978-1-4402-1133-1(7))* Krause Pubns.

Cross, Larry Jean. Vibrant Energy: Black Men Revealed Contemporary Edgy Images. 2007. (Illus.). 174p. pap. 59.95 *(978-0-615-15636-1(3))* Tree of Life Pr.

Garcia, S. L. Colour Design Black, 1 vol. 2009. (DUT, FRE & ENG., Illus.). 180p. pap. 39.95 *(978-90-79761-17-3(6))* Tectum B.V.B.A. BEL. Dist: Innovative Logistics.

Henderson. America & the Black Body. 2009. 69.50 *(978-0-8386-4132-3(6))* Fairleigh Dickinson Univ. Pr.

Jager, Jim. Mr. Long: The Models of Third World Studio: Chicago 1976-1981. 2007. (Illus.). 111p. pap. 59.95 *(978-1-919901-35-0(3))* Janssen Pubs. ZAF. Dist: Perseus-PGW.

Katlan, Alexander. The Black & White Exhibitions of the Salmagundi Sketch Club 1878 to 1887: A Guide to Etchings, Engravings, Drawings, Sculpture, Ceramics, Oils, & Monotypes. 2007. (Illus.). 273p. *(978-0-9791290-0-1(1))* Katlan, Alexander Conservator, Inc.

Kriz, Kay Dian. Slavery, Sugar, & the Culture of Refinement: Picturing the British West Indies, 1700-1840. 2008. (ENG., Illus.). 288p. 75.00 *(978-0-300-14062-0(2))* Yale Univ. Pr.

McEvilley, Thomas & Venet, Bernar. Bernar Venet. 2006. (Illus.). 45.00 *(978-2-84845-006-3(1))* Hard Pr. Editions.

Moriceau, Benoît-Marie, et al. Psycho: [conversation Avec Benoît-Marie Moriceau]. 2010. (FRE & ENG., Illus.). 66p. *(978-2-36008-025-0(3))* Archibooks.

Pastoureau, Michel. Black: The History of a Color. 2008. (ENG., Illus.). 216p. 35.00 *(978-0-691-13930-2(X))* Princeton Univ. Pr.

Stromberg, Fredrik. Black Images in the Comics. 2012. (ENG., Illus.). 296p. pap. 19.99 ***(978-1-60699-562-4(6),*** 699562) Fantagraphics Bks.

Thompson, Barbara, ed. Black Womanhood: Images, Icons, & Ideologies of the African Body. 2008. (ENG., Illus.). 376p. pap. 50.00 *(978-0-295-98771-2(5))* Hood Museum of Art.

Waanders Editors. Black Is Beautiful: Rubens to Dumas. 2008. (ENG., Illus.). 336p. 45.00 *(978-90-400-8497-3(1))* Waanders B.V., Uitgeverij NLD. Dist: National Bk. Network.

Warhol, Andy. Andy Warhol: Ladies & Gentlemen. 2010. (ENG., Illus.). 80p. 30.00 *(978-1-61623-717-2(1))* Skarstedt Fine Art.

Zett, Leonard. Bongani. 2008. (ENG., Illus.). 96p. 19.95 *(978-1-919901-41-1(8),* Art Stock Bks. Ltd/Csi) Continental Sales, Inc.

BLACKS IN LITERATURE

Afolabi, Niyi, et al. The Afro-Brazilian Mind: Contemporary Afro-Brazilian Literary & Cultural Criticism. 2006. (POR & ENG.). *(978-1-59221-385-6(5));* 320p. pap. *(978-1-59221-386-3(3))* Africa World Pr.

—Cadernos Negros: Literatura Afro-Brasileira Contemporânea = Black Notebooks: Contemporary Afro-Brazilian Literature. 2006. (POR & ENG.). *(978-1-59221-383-2(9));* pap. *(978-1-59221-384-9(7))* Africa World Pr.

Anderson, Thomas F. Carnival & National Identity in the Poetry of Afrocubanismo. 2011. (ENG., Illus.). 288p. 74.95 *(978-0-8130-3558-1(9))* Univ. Pr. of Florida.

Arana, R. Victoria & Ramey, Lauri. Black British Writing. Arana, R. Victoria & Ramey, Lauri, eds. 2009. (ENG.). 192p. pap. 33.00 *(978-0-230-61705-6(0))* Palgrave Macmillan.

Arnedo-Gómez, Miguel. Writing Rumba: The Afrocubanista Movement in Poetry. 2006. (New World Studies). (ENG.). 256p. (gr. 17). 55.00 *(978-0-8139-2541-7(X))* Univ. Pr. of Virginia.

—Writing Rumba: The Afrocubanista Movement in Poetry. annot. ed. 2006. (New World Studies). (ENG.). 256p. (gr. 17). per. 21.50 *(978-0-8139-2542-4(8))* Univ. Pr. of Virginia.

Bartels, Emily C. Speaking of the Moor: From Alcazar to Othello. 2009. 264p. (C). pap. 22.50 *(978-0-8122-2101-5(X))* Univ. of Pennsylvania Pr.

Black British Writers, 347. 2009. (Dictionary of Literary Biography Ser.). (ENG.). 496p. 315.00 *(978-0-7876-8165-4(2))* Cengage Gale.

Black Literature Criticism: Classic & Emerging Authors since 1950, 3 vols., Set. 2nd rev. ed. 2008. (ENG.). 544p. 552.00 *(978-1-4144-3170-3(8))* Cengage Gale.

Brown, Caroline. The Black Female Body in American Literature & Art. 2011. (Routledge Interdisciplinary Perspectives on Literature Ser.). (ENG., Illus.). 308p. (C). 125.00 *(978-0-415-89550-7(2))* Routledge.

Bryant, Tisa. Unexplained Presence. 2007. 159p. per. 15.95 *(978-0-9765820-1-4(5))* Leon Works.

Chambers. Black & Asian Theatre in Britain: A History. 2011. (ENG., Illus.). 304p. 120.00 *(978-0-415-36513-0(9))* Routledge.

Curran, Andrew S. The Anatomy of Blackness: Science & Slavery in an Age of Enlightenment. 2011. (ENG., Illus.). 328p. (gr. 17). 75.00 *(978-1-4214-0150-8(9))* Johns Hopkins Univ. Pr.

Decosta-Willis, Miriam. Blacks in Hispanic Literature: Critical Essays. 2011. (ENG.). 173p. pap. 18.95 *(978-1-58073-044-0(2))* Black Classic Pr.

Easley Morris, Andrea. Afro-Cuban Identity in Post-Revolutionary Novel & Film: Inclusion, Loss, & Cultural Resistance. 2011. (ENG.). 204p. (gr. 17). 65.00 ***(978-1-61148-422-9(7))*** Bucknell Univ. Pr.

Edwards, Erica R. Black Charisma: Fictions of Political Leadership. 2012. (Difference Incorporated Ser.). (Illus.). 288p. 75.00 ***(978-0-8166-7545-6(7))*** Univ. of Minnesota Pr.

—Charisma & the Fictions of Black Leadership. 2012. (Difference Incorporated Ser.). (Illus.). 288p. pap. 25.00 ***(978-0-8166-7546-3(5))*** Univ. of Minnesota Pr.

Egar, Emmanuel Edame. The Crisis of Negritude: A Study of the Black Movement Against Intellectual Oppression in the Early 20th Century. 2008. pap. 17.95 *(978-1-59942-472-9(X),* Brown Walker Pr.) Universal Pubs.

Egejuru, Phanuel Akubueze. Womanbeing & Womanself: Characters in Black Women's Novels. 2011. 208p. pap. 17.95 ***(978-1-4502-6520-1(0))*** iUniverse, Inc.

Finney, Nikky, ed. The Ringing Ear: Black Poets Lean South. 2007. (ENG.). 432p. 69.95 *(978-0-8203-2925-3(8));* per. 22.95 *(978-0-8203-2926-0(6))* Univ. of Georgia Pr.

Frindéthié, K. Martial. The Black Renaissance in Francophone African & Caribbean Literatures. 2008. (ENG., Illus.). 215p. pap. 39.95 *(978-0-7864-3663-7(8))* McFarland & Co., Inc. Pubs.

Greene, J. Lee. The Diasporan Self: Unbreaking the Circle in Western Black Novels. 2008. (ENG.). 264p. (C). (gr. 13-17). pap. 19.50 *(978-0-8139-2740-4(4));* (gr. 17). 55.00 *(978-0-8139-2739-8(0))* Univ. Pr. of Virginia.

Gutiérrez, Mariela. An Ethnological Interpretation of the Afro-Cuban World of Lydia Cabrera (1900-1991) Gutierrez, Mariela A., ed. & tr. by. Wedel-Carballo, Julio, ed. Kergoat, Catherine, tr. 2008. (Illus.). 250p. 109.95 *(978-0-7734-5042-4(4))* Mellen, Edwin Pr., The.

Holcomb, Gary Edward. Claude Mckay, Code Name Sasha: Queer Black Marxism & the Harlem Renaissance. 2009. (ENG., Illus.). 288p. pap. 29.95 *(978-0-8130-3450-8(7))* Univ. Pr. of Florida.

Jackson, Richard L. Black Literature & Humanism in Latin America. 2008. (ENG.). 184p. pap. 22.95 *(978-0-8203-3312-0(3))* Univ. of Georgia Pr.

Jackson, Sandra & Moody Freeman, Julie, eds. The Black Imagination, Science Fiction & the Speculative. 2010. (ENG.). 176p. (C). 125.00 *(978-0-415-61482-5(1))* Routledge.

Jackson, Sandra & Moody-Freeman, Julie E. The Black Imagination, Science Fiction, Futurism & the Speculative. 2011. (Black Studies & Critical Thinking Ser.). (C). 129.95 (978-1-4331-1242-3(6)); pap. 32.95 (978-1-4331-1241-6(8)) Lang, Peter Publishing, Inc.

King, Nicole. C. L. R. James & Creolization: Circles of Influence. 2007. (ENG.). 192p. per. 25.00 (978-1-934110-49-2(3)) Univ. Pr. of Mississippi.

Knadler, Stephen & Knadler, Stephen P. Remapping Citizenship & the Nation in African-American Literature. 2009. (Routledge Transnational Perspectives on American Literature Ser.). (ENG.). 248p. (C). 125.00 (978-0-415-99631-0(7)) Routledge.

Krstovic, Jelena O. Black Literature Criticism: Classic & Emerging Authors since 1950, 3 vols. 2008. (Illus.). (978-1-4144-3171-0(6)); (978-1-4144-3172-7(4)); (978-1-4144-3173-4(2)) Cengage Gale.

Lewis, Shireen K. Race, Culture, & Identity: Francophone West African & Caribbean Literature & Theory from Negritude to Creolite. 2006. (Caribbean Studies (Lexington Books) Ser.). (ENG.). 188p. per. 27.50 (978-0-7391-1473-5(5)) Lexington Bks.

Luis, William. Literary Bondage: Slavery in Cuban Narrative. 2012. (ENG.). 326p. pap. 30.00 (978-0-292-74132-4(4)) Univ. of Texas Pr.

Morton, Gerald W. Phyllis Wheatley: Slave & Poet. 2008. 80p. pap. 16.95 (978-1-60474-855-0(9)) PublishAmerica, Inc.

Ojo-Ade, Femi. Configuring the African World: Continental & Diasporic Literatures & Cultures. 2006. (978-1-59221-447-1(9)); 312p. pap. (978-1-59221-448-8(7)) Africa World Pr.

Olliz-Boyd, Antonio. The Latin American Identity & the African Diaspora: Ethnogenesis in Context. 2010. (978-1-60497-704-2(3)) Cambria Pr.

Ortiz, Lucia. "Chambacú, la Historia la Escribes Tú" Ensayos Sobre Cultura Afrocolombiana. 2007. (Illus.). 404p. pap. 44.00 (978-84-8489-266-3(2)) Iberoamericana Vervuert Publishing Corp.

Pirker, Eva Ulrike. Narrative Projections of A Black British History. 2011. (Routledge Approaches to History Ser.). (ENG & ABK., Illus.). 336p. (C). 125.00 (978-0-415-89375-6(5)) Routledge.

Poosson, Sylvain B. La historia Silenciada: Los afroargentinos protagonistas de un drama Social. 2007. (SPA.). 248p. 109.95 (978-0-7734-5633-4(3)) Mellen, Edwin Pr., The.

Stromberg, Fredrik. Black Images in the Comics. 2012. (ENG., Illus.). 296p. pap. 19.99 (978-1-60699-562-4(6), 699562) Fantagraphics Bks.

Vaughan, Virginia Mason. Performing Blackness on English Stages, 1500-1800. 2008. (ENG., Illus.). 208p. pap. 33.00 (978-0-521-10226-1(X)) Cambridge Univ. Pr.

Walrond, Eric. In Search of Asylum: The Later Writings of Eric Walrond. Parascandola, Louis J. & Wade, Carl A., eds. 2011. (ENG., Illus.). 224p. 74.95 (978-0-8130-3560-4(0)) Univ. Pr. of Florida.

Yenika-Agbaw, Vivian. African & African-American Children's & Adolescent Literature in the Classroom: A Critical Guide. 2011. (Black Studies & Critical Thinking Ser.). 318p. (C). 129.95 (978-1-4331-1196-9(9)) Lang, Peter Publishing, Inc.

—African & African American Children's & Adolescent Literature in the Classroom: A Critical Guide. 2011. (Black Studies & Critical Thinking Ser.). 320p. (C). pap. 32.95 (978-1-4331-1195-2(0)) Lang, Peter Publishing, Inc.

Zauchner, Sabine, et al. African Diasporas: Afro-German Literature in the Context of the African American Experience. 2007. (ENG.). 144p. (gr. 11). pap. 39.95 (978-3-8258-9612-6(9)) Lit Verlag DEU. Dist: Transaction Pubs.

BLACKS IN MOTION PICTURES

Here are entered works on the portrayal of Blacks in motion pictures. Works on all aspects of Black involvement in motion pictures are entered under Blacks in the Motion Picture Industry. Works on specific aspects of Black involvement are entered under the particular subject, e.g. Actors, Black.

Bryant, Tisa. Unexplained Presence. 2007. 159p. per. 15.95 (978-0-9765820-1-4(5)) Leon Works.

Dacosta, Charles. Framing Invisibility. 2010. 212p. pap. (978-3-8383-4683-0(1)) Lambert Academic Publishing.

Greene, Shelleen. Equivocal Subjects: Mixed-Race Identity in the Italian Cinema. 2012. (ENG., Illus.). 328p. 120.00 (978-1-4411-9043-7(0)) Continuum International Publishing Group, Ltd. GBR. Dist: National Bk. Network.

Jackson, Sandra & Moody Freeman, Julie, eds. The Black Imagination, Science Fiction & the Speculative. 2010. (ENG.). 176p. (C). 125.00 (978-0-415-61482-5(1)) Routledge.

Jones, Peter. Teaching Black Cinema. 2006. (ENG., Illus.). 92p. pap. 42.95 (978-1-84457-156-7(4)) BFI Publishing GBR. Dist: Macmillan.

Lehman, Christopher P. The Colored Cartoon: Black Representation in American Animated Short Films, 1907-1954. 2007. 137p. 29.95 net. (978-1-55849-613-2(0)) Univ. of Massachusetts Pr.

Marriott, David. Haunted Life: Visual Culture & Black Modernity. 2007. (ENG., Illus.). 312p. (C). 70.00 (978-0-8135-4027-6(5)); per. 24.95 (978-0-8135-4028-3(3)) Rutgers Univ. Pr.

McCluskey, Audrey Thomas, ed. Frame by Frame III: A Filmography of the African Diasporan Image, 1994-2004. 2007. (ENG.). 1112p. 75.00 (978-0-253-34829-6(3), 0253348293) Indiana Univ. Pr.

Nama, Adilifu. Black Space: Imagining Race in Science Fiction Film. 2008. (ENG., Illus.). 212p. pap. 24.95 (978-0-292-71745-9(8)) Univ. of Texas Pr.

Petty, Sheila J. Contact Zones: Memory, Origin, & Discourse in Black Diasporic Cinema. 2008. (Contemporary Approaches to Film & Television Ser.). (Illus.). 295p. per. 29.95 (978-0-8143-3099-9(1)) Wayne State Univ. Pr.

BLACKS IN THE BIBLE

Alexander, Willie J. Entering the Promised Land. 2007. (Illus.). 190p. spiral bd. 24.95 (978-0-9796779-0-2(3)) Entering The Promised Land.

Ben, Bro. A Griot's Journal. 2008. 48p. pap. 16.95 (978-1-60441-432-5(4)) PublishAmerica, Inc.

Burton, Keith Augustus. The Blessing of Africa: The Bible & African Christianity. 2007. (ENG.). 294p. per. 22.00 (978-0-8308-2762-6(5), IVP Acad.) InterVarsity Pr.

Davis, Stacy. This Strange Story: Jewish & Christian Interpretation of the Curse of Canaan from Antiquity To 1865. 2008. (ENG.). 250p. per. 40.99 (978-0-7618-3879-1(1)) Univ. Pr. of America, Inc.

Felder, Cain Hope. The Original African Heritage Study Bible. 2007. (Illus.). 2200p. lm. lthr. 50.00 (978-0-8170-1512-1(4)) Judson Pr.

Felder, Cain Hope, ed. Original African Heritage Study Bible-KJV. l.t. ed. 2007. (Illus.). 1893p. per. 34.00 (978-0-8170-1511-4(6)) Judson Pr.

Hobbs, Antony O. Food for the Power of Thinking, Book II: The Roots of the Races. 2007. 58p. pap. 9.00 (978-0-8059-7503-1(9)) Dorrance Publishing Co., Inc.

McCray, Walter. The Black Presence & the Passion: A Christ-Centered Historical Identity Response of a Gospelizer. 2008. 100p. pap. 9.95 (978-0-933176-53-9(8)) Black Light Fellowship.

Melekin, Embaye. The African Bible: The Records of the Abyssinian Prophets. 2011. 730p. pap. 23.99 (978-1-4628-6191-0(1)) Xlibris Corp.

Sadler, Rodney S., Jr. Can a Cushite Change His Skin? An Examination of Race, Ethnicity, & Othering in the Hebrew Bible. 2009. (Library Hebrew Bible/Old Testament Studies). (ENG.). 192p. pap. 49.95 (978-0-567-02765-8(1), T&T Clark Int'l) Continuum International Publishing Group, Ltd. GBR. Dist: National Bk. Network.

Yamauchi, Edwin M. Africa & the Bible. 2006. (Illus.). 304p. (C). pap. 26.00 (978-0-8010-3119-9(2)) Baker Academic.

Yisrael, Bethuel. A Discussion of Biblical Scripture Translation: That Pertains to African-American History. 2007. pap. 14.00 (978-0-8059-8425-5(9)) Dorrance Publishing Co., Inc.

Yisrael, Navee Yaacov. Biblical Heritage Awakening. 2011. 116p. 24.95 (978-1-4269-4883-1(2)); pap. 14.95 (978-1-4269-4881-7(6)) Trafford Publishing.

BLACKSMITHING

see also Carriage and Wagon Making; Forging; Horseshoeing; Ironwork; Welding

Ares, Jose Antonio. Blacksmithing: Hot Techniques & Striking Projects. 2008. (ENG., Illus.). 144p. pap. 22.95 (978-1-60059-384-0(4)) Lark Bks.

Blandford, Percy W. Blacksmithing Projects. 2006. (ENG., Illus.). 144p. per. 12.95 (978-0-486-45276-0(X)) Dover Pubns., Inc.

Clarke, Mathew S. From Fire to Form Metalsmith: Sculpture from the Modern Blacksmith & Metalsmith. 2009. (Illus.). 256p. bds. 50.00 (978-0-7643-3247-0(3)) Schiffer Publishing, Ltd.

DeLaRonde, Joe. Blacksmithing Basics for the Homestead. 2008. (ENG., Illus.). 136p. pap. 18.99 (978-1-58685-706-6(1)) Gibbs Smith, Publisher.

Doyle, Eamon. Tales of the Anvil: The Forges & Blacksmiths of Wexford. 2008. (ENG., Illus.). 160p. pap. 24.95 (978-1-84588-919-7(3)) History Pr. Ltd.,The GBR. Dist: Independent Pubs. Group.

Dunham, S. Ann & Dewey, Alice G. Surviving Against the Odds: Village Industry in Indonesia. Cooper, Nancy I., ed. 2009. (John Hope Franklin Center Book Ser.). (ENG., Illus.). 440p. 29.95 (978-0-8223-4687-6(7)) Duke Univ. Pr.

Esau, Cecyl. Saul Januarie. 2011. 92p. pap. (978-3-8443-2292-7(2)) Lambert Academic Publishing.

Friese, John Frank. Farm Blacksmithing - a Textbook & Problem Book for Students in Agricultural Schools & Colleges, Technical Schools, & for Farmers. 2011. 94p. pap. 26.45 (978-1-4460-7836-5(1)) Audubon Pr. & Christian Bk. Service.

Holmstrom, J. G. Traditional Blacksmithing: The Fine Art of Horseshoeing & Wagon Making. 2012. (ENG., Illus.). 204p. pap. 12.95 (978-1-61608-551-3(7), 608551) Skyhorse Publishing Co., Inc.

Hrisoulas, Jim. Master Bladesmith: Advanced Studies in Steel. 2010. (Illus.). 296p. pap. (978-1-58160-543-3(9)) Paladin Pr.

Keller, Charles M. & Keller, Janet Dixon. Cognition & Tool Use: The Blacksmith at Work. 2008. (ENG., Illus.). 220p. pap. 29.99 (978-0-521-05648-9(9)) Cambridge Univ. Pr.

McDaniel, Randy. A Blacksmithing Primer: A Course in Basic & Intermediate Blacksmithing. pap. 25.00 (978-0-9662589-1-2(6)) Dragonfly Enterprises.

Richardson, Grover, Jr. Impressions. Blacksmithing made Easy. 2006. (Illus.). 120p. per. (978-1-905524-05-1(6)) Twin Serpents, Ltd.

Richardson, M. T. Practical Blacksmithing. 2010. 88p. pap. (978-1-151-79452-9(X)); 104p. pap. (978-1-151-79454-3(6)) Books LLC.

Ruddel, David-Thiery & Tremblay, Robert. By Hammer & Hand, All Acts Do Stand: Blacksmithing in Canada Before 1950. 2010. (Illus.). xx, 82p. (978-0-660-19960-3(2)) Canadian Government Publishing.

Simmons, Marc & Turley, Frank. Southwestern Colonial Ironwork: The Spanish Blacksmithing Tradition. 2008. (ENG., Illus.). 199p. per. 39.95 (978-0-86534-601-7(1)) Sunstone Pr.

Sims, Lorelei. The Backyard Blacksmith: Traditional Techniques for the Modern Smith. 2009. (ENG., Illus.). 174p. 12.99 (978-0-7858-2567-8(3), 0785825673, Crestline) MBI Publishing Co. LLC.

BLACKSMITHS

Bear, John W. The Life & Travels of John W Bear, the Buckeye Blacksmith Written by Himself. 2006. 300p. per. 23.99 (978-1-4255-2812-6(0)) MPublishing.

David, Nicholas. Metals in Mandara Mountains' Society & Culture. 2012. (978-1-59221-889-9(X)); pap. (978-1-59221-890-5(3)) Africa World Pr.

Doyle, Eamon. Tales of the Anvil: The Forges & Blacksmiths of Wexford. 2008. (ENG., Illus.). 160p. pap. 24.95 (978-1-84588-919-7(3)) History Pr. Ltd.,The GBR. Dist: Independent Pubs. Group.

Gamache Thomas, Kodji. Traditional Beliefs in Modern Society. 2009. 92p. pap. (978-3-639-19305-3(9)) VDM Verlag Dr. Mueller e.K.

Pattie, Jane. Cowboy Spurs & Their Makers. 2012. (Centennial Series of the Association of Former Students, Texas A&M University Ser.). (Illus.). 192p. pap. 29.95 (978-1-60344-521-4(8)) Texas A&M Univ. Pr.

Pattie, Jane & Kelly, Tom. Cowboy Spur Maker: The Story of Ed Blanchard. 2008. (ENG.). 160p. pap. 17.95 (978-1-60344-050-9(X)) Texas A&M Univ. Pr.

BLACKSTONE, WILLIAM, SIR, 1723-1780

Field, Barron & Blackstone, William. An Analysis of Blackstone's Commentaries on the Laws of England: In a Series of Questions, to Which the Student Is to Frame His Own Answers, by Reading That Work. 2008. 297p. 125.00 (978-1-58477-899-8(7)) Lawbook Exchange, Ltd., The.

Prest, Wilfrid. William Blackstone: Law & Letters in the Eighteenth Century. 2008. (ENG., Illus.). 284p. 71.50 (978-0-19-955029-6(8)) Oxford Univ. Pr., Inc.

Prest, Wilfrid, ed. Blackstone & his Commentaries: Biography, Law, History. 2009. (ENG., Illus.). 254p. 104.00 (978-1-84113-796-4(0)) Hart Publishing Ltd. GBR. Dist: International Specialized Bk. Services.

Prest, Wilfrid R. William Blackstone: Law & Letters in the Eighteenth Century. 2012. (ENG.). 376p. pap. 40.00 (978-0-19-965201-3(5)) Oxford Univ. Pr., Inc.

BLACKWATER RIVER (W. VA.)

Kennedy, Philip Pendleton. The Blackwater Chronicle: A Narrative of an Expedition into the Land of Canaan. 2007. (ENG.). 226p. 41.95 (978-0-548-18701-2(0)); 228p. per. 26.95 (978-1-4304-9059-3(4)) Kessinger Publishing, LLC.

[Kennedy, Philip Pendleton]. The Blackwater Chronicle, a Narrative of an Expedition into the Land of Canaan, in Randolph County, Virginia by the Clerke of Oxenforde with Il. 2006. 244p. per. 20.99 (978-1-4255-2046-5(4)) MPublishing.

Zimmerman, W. Frederick. Liveblogging Blackwater by Jeremy Scahill: Unauthorized Color Commentary, Maps, & Images. 2007. 40p. per. 20.51 (978-1-934840-05-4(X)) Nimble Bks. LLC.

BLACKWELL, ELIZABETH, 1821-1910

Blackwell, Elizabeth. Pioneer Work in Opening the Medical Profession to Women: Autobiographical Sketches. 2009. 280p. 24.99 (978-1-103-69781-6(1)); pap. 18.99 (978-1-103-69774-8(9)); 24.99 (978-1-103-45649-0(0)); pap. 18.99 (978-1-103-45648-2(2)) BiblioBazaar.

—Pioneer Work in Opening the Medical Profession to Women: Autobiographical Sketches. 2007. (ENG.). 276p. 42.95 (978-0-548-36578-6(4)); per. 27.95 (978-0-548-30873-8(X)) Kessinger Publishing, LLC.

—Pioneer Work in Opening the Medical Profession to Women: Autobiographical Sketches. 265p. reprint ed. 98.00 (978-0-7222-1612-5(2)) Library Reprints, Inc.

World Book, Inc. Staff, ed. Biographical Connections. 2007. 896p. 299.00 (978-0-7166-1325-1(5)) World Bk., Inc.

BLACKWOOD, WILLIAM, 1776-1834

Oliphant, Margaret O. Annals of a Publishing House. 2010. (Cambridge Library Collection - Printing & Publishing History Ser.). (Illus.). 544p. pap. 39.99 (978-1-108-02139-5(5)) Cambridge Univ. Pr.

—Annals of a Publishing House: Volume 2, William Blackwood & his Sons, their Magazine & Friends. 2010. (Cambridge Library Collection - Printing & Publishing History Ser.). (Illus.). 534p. pap. 39.99 (978-1-108-02140-1(9)) Cambridge Univ. Pr.

Porter, Mary Blackwood. Annals of a Publishing House: Volume 3, John Blackwood. 2010. (Cambridge Library Collection - Printing & Publishing History Ser.). (Illus.). 460p. pap. 34.99 (978-1-108-02141-8(7)) Cambridge Univ. Pr.

BLADDER

American Cancer Society Staff. Bladder Cancer: What You Need to Know — Now. 2010. (ACS Quick Facts Ser.). 160p. pap. 8.95 (978-0-944235-77-5(8), 0944235778) American Cancer Society, Inc.

Bassi, Pierfrancesco & Pagano, Francesco, eds. Invasive Bladder Cancer. 2006. (Illus.). 303p. 119.00 (978-1-84628-376-5(0), 1846283760) Springer.

Beyer, Julie. Confident Choices: A Cookbook for Interstitial Cystitis & Overactive Bladder. 2006. (Illus.). 212p. pap. (978-0-9767246-2-9(6)) NutraConsults.

Blaivas, Jerry G. & Purohit, Rajveer S. Diagnosis & Treatment of Overactive Bladder, 1 vol. 2011. (Oxford American Pocket Notes Ser.). (ENG., Illus.). 72p. pap. 14.95 (978-0-19-975372-7(5)) Oxford Univ. Pr., Inc.

Cardozo, Linda & Robinson, Dudley. Overactive Bladder Pocket Guide. 2010. (Illus.). pap. (978-1-84184-736-8(4)) Informa Healthcare.

Chapple, Christopher C. R. & Wein, Alan J. Overactive Bladder in Clinical Practice. 2010. (Illus.). 192p. pap. 39.95 (978-1-84628-830-2(4), 1846288304) Springer.

Cheng, Liang, et al. Bladder Pathology. 2012. (ENG., Illus.). 768p. 199.95 (978-0-470-57108-8(X), Wiley-Blackwell) Wiley, John & Sons, Inc.

Cohan, Wendy. The Better Bladder Book: A Holistic Approach to Healing Interstitial Cystitis & Chronic Pelvic Pain. 2010. (ENG.). 288p. pap. 17.95 (978-0-89793-555-5(1)) Hunter Hse., Inc.

Consortium for Spinal Cord Medicine, text. Bladder Management for Adults with Spinal Cord Injury: A Clinical Practice Guideline for Health-Care Providers. 2006. 19.95 (978-0-929819-19-8(5)) Paralyzed Veterans of America.

Corcos, Jacques & Schick, Erik, eds. Neurogenic Bladder: Adults & Children. 2nd rev. ed. 2008. (ENG., Illus.). 928p. 750.00 (978-0-415-42316-8(3), Informa Healthcare) Taylor & Francis Group GBR. Dist: Taylor & Francis Group.

Droller, Michael J., ed. Bladder Cancer: Current Diagnosis & Treatment. 2010. (Current Clinical Urology Ser.). (Illus.). 472p. pap. 169.00 (978-1-61737-202-5(1), 1617372021) Humana Pr.

Dwyer, Peter L., ed. Atlas of Urogynecological Endoscopy. 2007. (Atlas Of... Ser.). (ENG., Illus.). 232p. 210.00 (978-1-84184-540-1(X)) Taylor & Francis Group.

Ellsworth. 100 Questions & Answers about Bladder Cancer. 2nd rev. ed. 2010. 154p. pap. 22.95 (978-0-7637-9587-0(9)) Jones & Bartlett Learning, LLC.

Ellsworth, Pamela J & B Clinical Card: Overactive Bladder. 2009. 12.95 (978-0-7637-7586-5(X)) Jones & Bartlett Learning, LLC.

Ellsworth, Pamela, et al. Overactive Bladder. 2nd rev. ed. 2009. (ENG.). 136p. pap. 22.95 (978-0-7637-7198-0(8)) Jones & Bartlett Learning, LLC.

Epstein, Jonathan I., et al. Biopsy Interpretation of the Bladder. 2nd rev. ed. 2010. (Biopsy Interpretation Ser.). (ENG., Illus.). 368p. 163.95 (978-1-60547-335-2(9)) Lippincott Williams & Wilkins.

Galsky. Dx/Rx: Genitourinary Oncology 2E: Cancer of Kidney, Bladder. 2nd rev. ed. 2011. 314p. pap. 49.95 (978-0-7637-9298-5(5)) Jones & Bartlett Learning, LLC.

Galsky, Matthew D. Dx/Rx: Genitourinary Oncology: Cancer of the Kidney, Bladder, & Testis. 2008. 142p. pap. 49.95 (978-0-7637-5484-6(6)) Jones & Bartlett Learning, LLC.

Gontard, Alexander von & Nevéus, Tryggve. The Management of Disorders of Bladder & Bowel Control in Children. 2006. (Clinics in Developmental Medicine Ser.). (ENG., Illus.). 368p. 125.95 (978-1-898683-45-2(X)) Mac Keith Pr. GBR. Dist: Wiley, John & Sons, Inc.

Hashim, Hashim & Abrams, Paul, eds. Overactive Bladder Syndrome & Urinary Incontinence. 2012. (ENG., Illus.). 128p. pap. 24.95 (978-0-19-959939-4(4)) Oxford Univ. Pr., Inc.

Kolvin, I., et al. Bladder Control & Enuresis. 328p. (C). (978-0-901260-42-0(8)) Mac Keith Pr. GBR. Dist: Cambridge Univ. Pr.

Kreder, Karl J., III & Dmochowski, Roger R., eds. The Overactive Bladder: Evaluation & Management. 2007. (ENG., Illus.). 448p. 269.95 (978-1-84184-630-9(9), Informa Healthcare) Taylor & Francis Group GBR. Dist: Taylor & Francis Group.

Lacey, Sandra, et al. People Like Us: Life with Rob Lacey, 1 vol. 2011. (ENG.). 272p. pap. 14.99 (978-0-310-31904-7(8)) Zondervan.

Lee, Cheryl & Wood, David P. Bladder Cancer: Diagnosis, Therapeutics, & Management. 2010. (Illus.). xv, 330p. E-Book (978-1-59745-417-9(6)) Humana Pr.

Lee, Cheryl T. & Wood, David P. Bladder Cancer: Diagnosis, Therapeutics, & Management. 2009. (Current Clinical Urology Ser.). (ENG., Illus.). xvi, 332p. 149.00 (978-1-58829-988-8(0), 1588299880) Humana Pr.

Lerner, Seth P., et al, eds. Treatment & Management of Bladder Cancer. 2008. (ENG., Illus.). 256p. 197.95 (978-0-415-46217-4(7), Informa Healthcare) Taylor & Francis Group GBR. Dist: Taylor & Francis Group.

Litlekalsoy, Jorunn. Molecular Investigations on Archival Tissues. 2009. 104p. pap. (978-3-639-16847-1(X)) VDM Verlag Dr. Mueller e.K.

Lokeshwar, Vinata B., et al, eds. Bladder Tumors: Molecular Aspects & Clinical Management. 2010. (Cancer Drug Discovery & Development Ser.). (ENG., Illus.). v, 350p. 209.00 (978-1-60761-927-7(X), 160761927X) Humana Pr.

Lokeshwar, Vinata B., et al. Bladder Tumors: Molecular Aspects & Clinical Management. 2011. (Illus.). xv, 466p. E-Book (978-1-60761-928-4(8)) Humana Pr.

MacVicar, David, ed. Carcinoma of the Bladder. 2008. (Contemporary Issues in Cancer Imaging Ser.). (ENG., Illus.). 194p. 87.00 (978-0-521-88456-3(X)) Cambridge Univ. Pr.

Nilsson, William E., ed. Bladder Cancer: Etymology, Diagnosis, & Treatments. 2010. (Cancer Etiology, Diagnosis & Treatments Ser.). 160.00 (978-1-61728-002-3(X)) Nova Science Pubs., Inc.

Nordling, J., et al, eds. Bladder Pain Syndrome: A Guide for Clinicians. 2012. (ENG., Illus.). 250p. 189.00 (978-1-4419-6928-6(4), 1441969284) Springer.

Rabin, Jill Maura & Stein, Gail. Mind over Bladder: I Never Met a Bathroom I Didn't Like! 2008. 244p. pap. 19.95 (978-0-595-43238-7(7)) iUniverse, Inc.

Raghavan, M D, et al. Bladder Cancer: A Cleveland Clinic Guide. 2008. (Cleveland Clinic Guide Ser.). (ENG.). 187p. pap. 14.95 (978-1-59624-060-5(1)) Cleveland Clinic Pr.

Rosette, Jean J. M C. H de la, et al, eds. Imaging in Oncological Urology. 2008. (Illus.). 936p. 169.00 (978-1-84628-514-1(3), 1846285143) Springer.

Sharma, Arun K. & Cheng, Earl Y. Pediatric Urinary Bladder Tissue Engineering. 2011. pap. (978-1-61209-624-7(7)) Nova Science Pubs., Inc.

Slack, Alex, et al. Fast Facts: Fast Facts: Bladder Disorders. 2nd rev. ed. 2011. (Illus.). 126p. pap. 25.00 (978-1-905832-96-5(6)) Health Pr., Ltd. GBR. Dist: BookMasters Distribution Services (BDS).

Staskin, David. Atlas of Bladder Disease. Staskin, David, ed. 2009. (ENG., Illus.). 256p. 149.00 (978-1-57340-307-8(5)) Current Medicine Group LLC.

Stoffel, John & McGuire, Edward J. Treating the Adult Neurogenic Bladder, an Issue of Urologic Clinics. 2010. (Clinics: Internal Medicine Ser.: 37-4). (ENG., Illus.). xii, 488p. 105.00 (978-1-4377-2535-3(X), Saunders) Elsevier - Health Sciences Div.

Weiss, , FACS, FACS, Jeffrey P., Jeffrey P, et al, eds. Nocturia: Causes, Consequences & Clinical Approaches. 2011. (ENG., Illus.). xii, 172p. 139.00 (978-1-4614-1155-0(6), 1461411556) Springer.

BLADDERY FEVER

see Pemphigus

BLAINE, JAMES GILLESPIE, 1830-1893

Beale, Harriet S. Bla. Letters of Mrs James G Blaine V1. 2006. pap. 30.95 *(978-1-4286-5461-7(5))* Kessinger Publishing, LLC.

—Letters of Mrs James G Blaine V2. 2006. pap. 30.95 *(978-1-4286-5460-0(7))* Kessinger Publishing, LLC.

Conwell, Russell H. Life & Public Services of James G Blai. 2006. pap. 40.95 *(978-1-4286-5661-1(8))* Kessinger Publishing, LLC.

Crawford, Theron Clark. James G. Blaine. 644p. reprint ed. 128.00 *(978-0-7222-8992-1(8))* Library Reprints, Inc.

Dodge, Mary Abigail. A Biography of James G. Blaine. 722p. reprint ed. 148.00 *(978-0-7222-8993-8(6))* Library Reprints, Inc.

Johnson, Willis Fletcher. The Life of James G. Blaine, "The Plumed Knight," Editor, Representative, Speaker, Senator, Cabinet Minister, Diplomat & True Patriot: A Graphic Record of His Whole Illustrious Career. 578p. reprint ed. 98.00 *(978-0-7222-8994-5(4))* Library Reprints, Inc.

Rolde, Neil. Continental Liar from the State of Maine: James G. Blaine. 2010. (Illus.). 368p. per. 20.00 *(978-0-88448-286-4(3))* Tilbury Hse. Pubs.

Stanwood, Edward. James Gillespie Blaine. 2009. 396p. 29.99 *(978-1-113-78047-8(9))*; 388p. 26.99 *(978-1-103-25011-0(6))*; 388p. 26.99 *(978-1-103-35612-6(7))*; 388p. pap. 20.99 *(978-1-103-35608-9(9))*; 388p. pap. 20.99 *(978-1-103-25008-0(6))* BiblioBazaar.

—James Gillespie Blaine. 2009. 170p. pap. 19.99 *(978-1-150-56250-1(1))* General Bks. LLC.

—James Gillespie Blaine. (American Statesmen Ser.). 377p. reprint ed. 98.00 *(978-0-7222-8995-2(2))*; 98.00 *(978-0-7222-8508-4(6))* Library Reprints, Inc.

BLAIR, FRANCIS PRESTON, 1821-1875

Croly, David G. Seymour & Blair Their Lives & Servic. 2006. pap. 28.95 *(978-1-4286-4773-2(2))* Kessinger Publishing, LLC.

McCabe, James Dabney. The Life & Public Services of Horatio Seymour: Together with A Complete & Authentic Life of Francis P. Blair, Jr. by James D. Mccabe, Jr. 2006. 508p. per. 29.99 *(978-1-4255-5656-3(6))* MPublishing.

BLAIR, TONY, 1953-

Bennister, Mark. Prime Ministers in Power: Political Leadership in Britain & Australia. 2012. (Palgrave Studies in Political Leadership Ser.). (ENG., Illus.). 240p. 85.00 ***(978-0-230-27321-4(1))*** Palgrave Macmillan.

Blair, Tony. A Journey: My Political Life. (Vintage Ser.). (Illus.). 2011. 784p. pap. 19.00 *(978-0-307-39063-9(2)*, Vintage) 2010. (ENG.). 720p. 35.00 *(978-0-307-26983-6(3)*, Knopf) Knopf Doubleday Publishing Group.

—A Journey: My Political Life. l.t. ed. 2010. (ENG.). 1280p. pap. 35.00 *(978-0-7393-7796-3(5))* Random Hse. Large Print.

Burton, John & McCabe, Eileen. We Don't Do God: Blair's Religious Belief & its Consequences. 2009. (ENG., Illus.). 256p. 22.95 *(978-1-84706-352-6(7))* Continuum International Publishing Group, Ltd. GBR. Dist: National Bk. Network.

Campbell, Alastair. Prelude to Power Vol. 1. 2010. (ENG.). 774p. pap. 32.95 *(978-0-09-193702-7(7))* Random Hse. GBR. Dist: Independent Pubs. Group.

Casey, Terrence, ed. The Blair Legacy: Politics, Policy, Governance, & Foreign Affairs. 2009. (ENG., Illus.). 384p. 110.00 *(978-0-230-21661-7(7))*; pap. 41.00 *(978-0-230-21662-4(5))* Palgrave Macmillan.

Cecar, Sonja. Blatcherism - How Much Thatcherism Is in Blairism. 2007. 88p. per. *(978-3-8364-4454-5(2))* VDM Verlag Dr. Mueller e.K.

Coates, Ken. War Crimes: Indicting Tony Blair. 2007. (Illus.). 86p. pap. 16.50 *(978-0-85124-745-8(8))* Spokesman Bks. GBR. Dist: Coronet Bks.

Dorman, Andrew. Blair's Successful War: British Military Intervention in Sierra Leone. 2009. (Military Strategy & Operational Art Ser.). (Illus.). 170p. 99.95 *(978-0-7546-7299-9(9))* Ashgate Publishing Co.

Dyson, Stephen Benedict. The Blair Identity: Leadership & Foreign Policy. 2009. (ENG.). 160p. 84.95 *(978-0-7190-7999-3(3))* Manchester Univ. Pr. GBR. Dist: Macmillan.

Faucher-King, Florence & Le Galès, Patrick. The New Labour Experiment: Change & Reform under Blair & Brown. Elliott, Gregory, tr. from FRE. 2010. (ENG.). 200p. 60.00 *(978-0-8047-6234-2(1))*; pap. 21.95 *(978-0-8047-6235-9(X))* Stanford Univ. Pr.

Gallagher, Julia. Britain & Africa under Blair: In Pursuit of the Good State. 2011. (ENG.). 240p. 100.00 *(978-0-7190-8500-0(4))* Manchester Univ. Pr. GBR. Dist: Macmillan.

Heinzl, Karin Christine. George W Bush & Tony Blair's Leadership During the War in Iraq. 2010. 104p. pap. *(978-3-639-22269-2(5))* VDM Verlag Dr. Mueller e.K.

Lee, Peter. Blair's Just War: Iraq & the Illusion of Morality. 2011. (ENG., Illus.). 224p. 85.00 ***(978-0-230-31927-1(0))***; pap. 28.00 ***(978-0-230-35570-5(6))*** Palgrave Macmillan.

O'Driscoll, Cian & O'driscoll, Cian. The Renegotiation of the Just War Tradition & the Right to War in the Twenty-First Century. 2008. (ENG.). 244p. 95.00 *(978-0-230-60583-1(4))* Palgrave Macmillan.

O'Reilly, David & O'reilly, David. The New Progressive Dilemma: Australia & Tony Blair's Legacy. 2007. (ENG., Illus.). 272p. 110.00 *(978-0-230-00655-3(8))* Palgrave Macmillan.

Powell, Jonathan. The New Machiavelli: How to Wield Power in the Modern World. (ENG.). 2011. 320p. pap. 15.95 ***(978-0-09-954609-2(4))*** 2010. 352p. 34.95 *(978-1-84792-122-2(1))* Random Hse. GBR. Dist: Independent Pubs. Group.

Radice, Giles. Trio: Inside the Blair, Brown, Mandelson Project. 2010. (ENG., Illus.). 288p. 40.00 *(978-1-84885-445-1(5))* I. B. Tauris & Co., Ltd. GBR. Dist: Macmillan.

Riddell, Peter. The Unfulfilled Prime Minister: Tony Blair's Quest for a Legacy. 2006. 238p. per. 15.95 *(978-1-84275-168-8(9))* Politico's Publishing Ltd. GBR. Dist: Consortium Bk. Sales & Distribution.

Scott, Paul. Tony & Cherie: Behind the Scenes in Downing Street. 2007. (ENG., Illus.). 320p. mass mkt. 13.95 *(978-0-330-44006-6(3))* Macmillan Pubs., Ltd. GBR. Dist: Independent Pubs. Group.

Seldon, Anthony, ed. Blair's Britain, 1997-2007. 2007. (ENG., Illus.). 708p. pap. 40.00 *(978-0-521-70946-0(6))*; 712p. 95.00 *(978-0-521-88293-4(1))* Cambridge Univ. Pr.

Seldon, Anthony, et al. Blair Unbound. 2008. (ENG., Illus.). 688p. 35.00 *(978-1-84737-078-5(0))* Simon & Schuster, Ltd. GBR. Dist: Independent Pubs. Group.

Shaw, Eric. Losing Labour's Soul? New Labour & the Blair Government 1997-2007. 2008. (ENG.). 264p. 49.95 *(978-0-415-35500-1(1))*; 168.00 *(978-0-415-35499-8(4))* Routledge.

Snowdon, Peter, et al. Blair Unbound. 2009. (ENG., Illus.). 688p. pap. 14.95 *(978-1-84739-090-5(0))* Simon & Schuster, Ltd. GBR. Dist: Independent Pubs. Group.

Stachan, Hew, et al. British Generals in Blair's Wars. 2012. (Military Strategy & Operational Art Ser.). (Illus.). 457p. pap. 59.95 ***(978-1-4094-3736-9(1))*** Ashgate Publishing Co.

Strachan, Hew, et al. British Generals in Blair's Wars. 2012. (Military Strategy & Operational Art Ser.). (Illus.). 457p. 59.95 ***(978-1-4094-3737-6(X))***; 460p. 124.95 ***(978-1-4094-3735-2(3))*** Ashgate Publishing Co.

Temple, Mick. Blair. 2006. (British Prime Ministers of the 20th Century Ser.). (ENG., Illus.). 160p. pap. 16.95 *(978-1-904950-73-8(6))* Haus Publishing GBR. Dist: Consortium Bk. Sales & Distribution.

Utton, Norman. Living in a Dictatorship: (The Blair Years) 2006. 388p. per. 24.80 *(978-1-4120-9621-8(9))* Trafford Publishing.

Walford, Geoffre & Walford, Geoffrey. Blair's Educational Legacy? 2009. (ENG.). 160p. (C). 125.00 *(978-0-415-48305-6(0))* Routledge.

BLAKE, WILLIAM, 1757-1827

Adams, Hazard. Blake's Margins: An Interpretive Study of the Annotations. 2009. (ENG., Illus.). 212p. pap. 39.95 *(978-0-7864-4536-3(X))* McFarland & Co., Inc. Pubs.

—William Blake on His Poetry & Painting: A Study of A Descriptive Catalogue, Other Prose Writings & Jerusalem. 2010. (ENG., Illus.). 199p. pap. 55.00 *(978-0-7864-4986-6(1))* McFarland & Co., Inc. Pubs.

Ankarsjö, Magnus. William Blake & Religion: A New Critical View. 2009. (ENG.). 171p. pap. 39.95 *(978-0-7864-4559-2(9))* McFarland & Co., Inc. Pubs.

Beer, John. William Blake: A Literary Life. 2007. (Literary Lives Ser.). (ENG., Illus.). 264p. pap. 39.00 *(978-0-230-54682-0(X))* Palgrave Macmillan.

Bentley, G. E. William Blake's Conversations: A Compilation, Concordance, & Rhetorical Analysis. 2008. (Illus.). xlix, 297p. *(978-0-7734-4848-3(9))* Mellen, Edwin Pr., The.

Bentley, G. E., Jr. & Nurmi, Martin K. A Blake Bibliography: Annotated Lists of Works, Studies, & Blakeana. 2009. 416p. pap. 60.00 *(978-0-8166-5706-3(8))* Univ. of Minnesota Pr.

Bentley Jnr., G. E. William Blake: The Critical Heritage. 2009. 294p. pap. 45.00 *(978-0-415-56889-0(7))* Routledge.

Bindman, David. Mind Forg'd Manacles William Blake, 1 vol. 2007. (ENG., Illus.). 148p. pap. 30.00 *(978-1-85332-259-4(8))* Hayward Gallery Publishing GBR. Dist: D.A.P./Distributed Art Pubs.

Blake, William. Blake's Poetry & Designs. Johnson, Mary Lynn & Grant, John E., eds. 2nd rev. ed. 2007. (Norton Critical Editions Ser.). (ENG., Illus.). 704p. (C). per. 27.03 *(978-0-393-92498-5(X)*, 92498) Norton, W. W. & Co., Inc.

—Illustrations of the Book of Job. 2006. pap. 15.95 *(978-1-4286-4375-8(3))* Kessinger Publishing, LLC.

—Life of William Blake Pictor Ignotus V1. 2006. pap. 36.95 *(978-1-4286-4776-3(7))* Kessinger Publishing, LLC.

—Life of William Blake Pictor Ignotus V2. 2006. pap. 31.95 *(978-1-4286-4783-1(X))* Kessinger Publishing, LLC.

—Songs of Innocence. 2011. (ENG., Illus.). 80p. 15.00 *(978-0-486-47604-9(9))* Dover Pubns., Inc.

—William Blake's Divine Comedy Illustrations: 102 Full-Color Plates. 2008. (Dover Fine Art, History of Art Ser.). (ENG., Illus.). 112p. pap. 19.95 *(978-0-486-46429-9(6))* Dover Pubns., Inc.

Blake, William, et al. Genesis: William Blake's Last Illuminated Work. 2012. (ENG., Illus.). 100p. 80.00 ***(978-0-87328-247-5(7))*** Huntington Library Pr.

Bruder, Helen P. Women Read William Blake: Opposition Is True Friendship. Bruder, Helen P., ed. 2007. (ENG., Illus.). 304p. 95.00 *(978-1-4039-9704-3(7))* Palgrave Macmillan.

Bruder, Helen P. & Connolly, Tristanne J., eds. Queer Blake. 2010. (ENG., Illus.). 280p. 84.00 *(978-0-230-21836-9(9))* Palgrave Macmillan.

Burdett, Osbert. William Blake. 2009. (Temporis Ser.). (GER, FRE & ENG., Illus.). 256p. 39.95 *(978-1-84484-649-8(0))* Parkstone International GBR. Dist: Ingram Pub. Services.

—William Blake's Apprenticeship & Marriage. 2006. pap. 15.95 *(978-1-4286-7597-1(3))* Kessinger Publishing, LLC.

Chesterton, G. K. William Blake. reprint ed. lib. bdg. 98.00 *(978-0-7426-3020-8(X))* Classic Bks.

Clark, Lorraine. Blake, Kierkegaard, & the Spectre of Dialectic. 2009. (ENG.). 252p. pap. 36.99 *(978-0-521-11047-1(5))* Cambridge Univ. Pr.

Clark, Steve. Reception of Blake in the Orient. Suzuki, Masashi, ed. 2009. (Continuum Reception Studies). (ENG.). 360p. 65.00 *(978-0-8264-3805-8(9))* Continuum International Publishing Group, Ltd. GBR. Dist: National Bk. Network.

Clark, Steve, et al, eds. Blake 2. 0: William Blake in Twentieth-Century Art, Music & Culture. 2012. (ENG., Illus.). 328p. 85.00 ***(978-0-230-28033-5(1))*** Palgrave Macmillan.

Clark, Steve & Whittaker, Jason, eds. Blake, Modernity & Popular Culture. 2007. (ENG.). 256p. 95.00 *(978-0-230-00844-1(5))* Palgrave Macmillan.

Colebrook, Claire. Blake, Deleuzian Aesthetics & the Digital. 2012. (Continuum Literary Studies). (ENG.). 200p. 120.00 *(978-1-4411-5533-7(3))* Continuum International Publishing Group, Ltd. GBR. Dist: National Bk. Network.

Crosby, Mark, et al, eds. Re-envisioning Blake. 2012. (ENG., Illus.). 280p. 85.00 ***(978-0-230-27551-5(6))*** Palgrave Macmillan.

Csikos, Dora Janzer. Four Mighty Ones Are in Every Man: The Development of the Fourfold in Blake. Siptar, Peter, ed. (Philosophiae Doctores Ser.: Vol. 15). (Illus.). 135p. pap. *(978-963-05-7936-0(7))* Akademiai Kiado.

De Selincourt, Basil. William Blake. 2007. (ENG.). 388p. 48.95 *(978-0-548-10811-6(0))* Kessinger Publishing, LLC.

—William Blake. 2007. (ENG.). 384p. per. *(978-1-4067-7628-7(9))* Read Bks.

Ellis, Edwin J. The Real Blake: A Portrait Biography. 2007. (ENG.). 480p. 53.95 *(978-0-548-09660-4(0))* Kessinger Publishing, LLC.

Gardner, Charles. William Blake, the Man. 2010. 102p. pap. 20.00 *(978-1-152-11859-1(5))* General Bks. LLC.

Gardner, Stanley. Blake's "Innocence & Experience" Retraced. (Illus.). 230p. *(978-0-485-11285-6(X))* Continuum International Publishing Group, Ltd.

Gilchrist, Alexander. Life of William Blake. 2008. 436p. *(978-1-4437-3606-0(6)*, Hesperides Pr.) Read Bks.

—Life of William Blake: With Selections from his Poems & Other Writings. Rossetti, Dante Gabriel & Rossetti, William, eds. 2010. (Cambridge Library Collection - Printing & Publishing History Ser.). (ENG., Illus.). 480p. pap. 35.99 *(978-1-108-01368-0(6))*; 508p. pap. 37.99 *(978-1-108-01367-3(8))* Cambridge Univ. Pr.

Gillham, Bill. Blake's Contrary States: The 'Songs of Innocence & Experience' as Dramatic Poems. 2010. (ENG.). 268p. pap. 38.99 *(978-0-521-12986-2(9))* Cambridge Univ. Pr.

Hahn, Daniel. Blake. 2012. (Poetic Lives Ser.). (ENG.). 112p. pap. 12.95 *(978-1-84391-304-7(6))* Hesperus Pr. GBR. Dist: Independent Pubs. Group.

Hamblen, Emily S. William Blake & His Structural Plan in the Book of the Dead - 2006. pap. 12.95 *(978-1-4286-8958-9(3))* Kessinger Publishing, LLC.

Hamilton, Gail. Skirmishes & Sketches. 2009. 222p. pap. *(978-0-217-04812-5(9))* Books LLC.

—Skirmishes & Sketches. 2007. 456p. 52.95 *(978-0-548-55725-9(X))*; (ENG.). per. 37.95 *(978-0-548-46165-5(1))* Kessinger Publishing, LLC.

—Skirmishes & Sketches. 2006. 464p. per. 29.99 *(978-1-4255-5111-7(4))* MPublishing.

Jackson, Noel. Science & Sensation in Romantic Poetry. 2011. (Cambridge Studies in Romanticism Ser.). (ENG., Illus.). 308p. pap. 39.99 *(978-0-521-18869-2(5))* Cambridge Univ. Pr.

Jones, John H. Blake on Language, Power, & Self-Annihilation. 2010. (ENG.). 250p. 84.00 *(978-0-230-62235-7(6))* Palgrave Macmillan.

Larrissy, Edward & Larrissy, Ed. Blake & Modern Literature. annot. ed. 2006. (ENG.). 200p. 84.00 *(978-1-4039-4176-3(9))* Palgrave Macmillan.

Linnell, David. Blake, Palmer, Linnell & Co. Life of John Linnell. 2010. (ENG., Illus.). 416p. 60.00 *(978-0-86332-917-3(9))* Antique Collectors' Club.

Lussier, Mark. Blake & Lacan. 2008. *(978-0-8204-9507-1(7))* Lang, Peter Publishing, Inc.

MacDonald, Greville. The Sanity of William Blake. 2007. (ENG.). 68p. pap. 16.95 *(978-0-548-60416-8(9))* Kessinger Publishing, LLC.

Marsh, Nicholas. William Blake: the Poems. 2nd rev. ed. 2012. (Analysing Texts). (ENG., Illus.). 288p. (C). 80.00 ***(978-0-230-34807-3(6))***; pap. 25.00 ***(978-0-230-34808-0(4))*** Palgrave Macmillan.

Matthews, Susan. Blake, Sexuality & Bourgeois Politeness. 2011. (Cambridge Studies in Romanticism Ser.). (ENG., Illus.). 286p. 90.00 *(978-0-521-51357-9(X))* Cambridge Univ. Pr.

Michael, Jennifer D. Blake & the City. 2006. (ENG.). 50.00 *(978-1-61148-254-6(2))* Bucknell Univ. Pr.

Michael, Jennifer Davis. Blake & the City. 2006. (Illus.). 240p. 50.00 *(978-0-8387-5646-1(8))* Bucknell Univ. Pr.

Miner, Paul. The Tyger: Genesis & Evolution in the Poetry of William Blake. 2011. 18p. 35.95 ***(978-1-258-01224-3(3))*** Literary Licensing, LLC.

Mounsey, Chris. Understanding the Poetry of William Blake Through a Dialectic of Contraries: A Study of the Philosophical Contexts within which Blake Developed His Ideas. 2011. 368p. ***(978-0-7734-1605-5(6))*** Mellen, Edwin Pr., The.

Myrone, Martin. The Blake Book. 2008. (ENG., Illus.). 224p. pap. 29.95 *(978-1-85437-727-2(2))* Tate Publishing, Ltd. GBR. Dist: Hachette Bk. Group.

Paley, Morton D. The Traveller in the Evening - the Last Works of William Blake: The Last Works of William Blake. 2008. (ENG., Illus.). 352p. pap. 55.00 *(978-0-19-922761-7(6))* Oxford Univ. Pr., Inc.

Parker, Fred. The Devil as Muse: Blake, Byron, & the Adversary. 2011. (Making of the Christian Imagination Ser.). (ENG., Illus.). 215p. 29.95 *(978-1-60258-269-9(6))* Baylor Univ. Pr.

Plowman, Max. An Introduction to the Study of Blake. 2009. (ENG.). 180p. pap. 19.99 *(978-1-113-43270-4(5)*, BiblioLife); (ENG.). 180p. pap. 21.99 *(978-1-113-43272-8(1)*, BiblioLife); 182p. pap. 21.75 *(978-1-113-43274-2(8))* BiblioBazaar.

—An Introduction to the Study of Blake. 2010. 52p. pap. *(978-1-152-97916-1(7))* Books LLC.

—An Introduction to the Study of Blake. 2007. (ENG.). 180p. per. *(978-1-4067-1940-6(4))* Read Bks.

Quinney, Laura. William Blake on Self & Soul. 2010. 216p. 42.00 *(978-0-674-03524-9(0))* Harvard Univ. Pr.

Rix, Robert. William Blake & the Culture of Radical Christianity. 2007. 192p. 114.95 *(978-0-7546-5600-5(4))* Ashgate Publishing Co.

Roberts, Jonathan. Blake. Wordsworth. Religion. 2011. (New Directions in Religion & Literature Ser.). (ENG., Illus.). 144p. 27.95 *(978-0-8264-2502-7(X))*; 90.00 *(978-0-8264-2233-0(0))* Continuum International Publishing Group, Ltd. GBR. Dist: National Bk. Network.

Roberts, Jonathan & Roberts. William Blake's Poetry. 2007. (Reader's Guides). (ENG.). 144p. 19.95 *(978-0-8264-8860-2(9))* Continuum International Publishing Group, Ltd. GBR. Dist: National Bk. Network.

Roberts, Victoria. William Blake's Poetry. 2007. (Reader's Guides). (ENG.). 144p. 110.00 *(978-0-8264-8859-6(5))* Continuum International Publishing Group, Ltd. GBR. Dist: National Bk. Network.

Robertson, W. Graham. Letters to Frances White Emerson from W Graham Robertson. 2011. 64p. 36.95 ***(978-1-258-09079-1(1))*** Literary Licensing, LLC.

Robinson, Henry C. Blake, Coleridge, Wordsworth, Lamb, Etc., Being Selections from the Remains of Henry Crabb Robinson. Morley, Edith J., ed. reprint ed. 24.50 *(978-0-404-05364-2(5))* AMS Pr., Inc.

Rossetti, William Michael. Letters of William Michael Rossetti: Concerning Whitman, Blake & Shelley. Gohdes, Clarence & Baum, Paul Franklin, eds. 2011. 210p. 44.95 ***(978-1-258-03012-4(8))*** Literary Licensing, LLC.

Rovira, James. Blake & Kierkegaard: Creation & Anxiety. 2010. (Continuum Literary Studies). (ENG.). 208p. 110.00 *(978-1-4411-3559-9(6))* Continuum International Publishing Group, Ltd. GBR. Dist: National Bk. Network.

Rowland, Christopher. Blake & the Bible. 2011. (ENG., Illus.). 320p. 50.00 *(978-0-300-11260-3(2))* Yale Univ. Pr.

—"Wheels Within Wheels" William Blake & the Ezekiel's Merkabah in Text & Image. 2007. (C). *(978-0-87462-587-5(4))* Marquette Univ. Pr.

Schneider, Matthew. The Long & Winding Road from Blake to the Beatles. 2008. (Nineteenth-Century Major Lives & Letters Ser.). (ENG.). 240p. 89.00 *(978-1-4039-8489-0(1))* Palgrave Macmillan.

Schuchard, Marsha Keith. William Blake's Sexual Path to Spiritual Vision. 2nd ed. 2008. (Illus.). 398p. pap. 19.95 *(978-1-59477-211-5(8))* Inner Traditions International, Ltd.

Sklar, Suzanne M. Blake's 'Jerusalem' As Visionary Theatre: Entering the Divine Body. 2011. (ENG., Illus.). 320p. 135.00 *(978-0-19-960314-5(6))* Oxford Univ. Pr., Inc.

Smith, John & Raine, Kathleen. Blake & the New Age (Routledge Revivals) 2011. (Routledge Revivals Ser.). (ENG.). 190p. 110.00 *(978-0-415-67636-6(3))* Routledge.

Snart, Jason Allen. The Torn Book: Unreading William Blake's Marginalia. 2006. (ENG., Illus.). 213p. 46.50 *(978-1-57591-109-0(4))* Susquehanna Univ. Pr.

Sung, Mei-Ying. William Blake & the Art of Engraving, 1 vol. 2009. (History of the Book Ser.). (ENG., Illus.). 240p. 99.00 *(978-1-85196-958-6(6))* Pickering & Chatto Pubs., Ltd. GBR. Dist: Ashgate Publishing Co.

Symons, Arthur. William Blake. 2009. 84p. pap. 19.99 *(978-1-4589-9034-1(6))* General Bks. LLC.

—William Blake. 2007. (ENG.). 452p. 52.95 *(978-0-548-28098-0(3))* Kessinger Publishing, LLC.

—William Blake. 2008. 456p. pap. *(978-1-4097-9062-4(2))* Read Bks.

Symons, Arthur, et al. William Blake. 2010. 450p. pap. 36.75 *(978-1-142-45232-2(8))* BiblioBazaar.

Tatham, Frederick. The Letters of William Blake. Russell, Archibald G., ed. (ENG.). 364p. 2007. 46.95 *(978-0-548-13915-8(6))* 2006. per. 31.95 *(978-1-4286-5092-3(X))* Kessinger Publishing, LLC.

Trodd, Colin. Visions of Blake: William Blake in the Art World, 1830-1930. (Liverpool University Press - Value-Art-Politics Ser.). (ENG., 2010. Illus.). 520p. 85.00 *(978-1-84631-111-6(X))* 2009. 256p. pap. 29.00 *(978-1-84631-112-3(8))* Liverpool Univ. Pr. GBR. Dist: Chicago Distribution Ctr.

Van Sinderen, Adrian. Blake: The Mystic Genius. 120p. 2008. 34.95 *(978-1-4367-1646-8(2))* 2007. (ENG.). per. 19.95 *(978-1-4325-3398-4(3))* Kessinger Publishing, LLC.

Vine, Steven. William Blake. 2006. (Writers & Their Work Ser.). (ENG.). 128p. (C). 80.00 *(978-0-7463-1041-0(2))*; pap. 26.00 *(978-0-7463-0980-3(5))* Northcote Hse. Publishers, Ltd. GBR. Dist: Brown, David Bk. Co., The.

White, Helen C. The Mysticism of William Blake. 280p. 2008. 42.95 *(978-1-4366-8052-3(2))* 2007. (ENG.). per. 27.95 *(978-1-4325-9750-4(7))* Kessinger Publishing, LLC.

Williams, Nicholas. Ideology & Utopia in the Poetry of William Blake. 2006. (Cambridge Studies in Romanticism Ser.). (ENG., Illus.). 272p. pap. 50.00 *(978-0-521-02684-0(9))* Cambridge Univ. Pr.

Wilson, Eric G. My Business Is to Create: Blake's Infinite Writing. 2011. (Muse Bks.). (ENG.). 112p. 19.95 *(978-1-58729-990-2(9))* Univ. of Iowa Pr.

Woodman, Ross Greig. Sanity, Madness, Transformation: The Psyche in Romanticism. Faflak, Joel, ed. 2009. (ENG.). 270p. pap. *(978-1-4426-1029-3(8))* Univ. of Toronto Pr.

Worrall, David & Clark, Steve, eds. Blake, Nation & Empire. 2006. (ENG., Illus.). 256p. 84.00 *(978-0-333-99314-9(4))* Palgrave Macmillan.

Yoder, R. Paul. The Narrative Structure of William Blake's Poem Jerusalem: A Revisionist Interpretation. 2010. (Illus.). v, 179p. *(978-0-7734-3640-4(5))* Mellen, Edwin Pr., The.

BLAKE, WILLIAM, 1757-1827—MUSICAL SETTINGS

De Selincourt, Basil. William Blake. 2007. (ENG.). 388p. 48.95 *(978-0-548-10811-6(0))* Kessinger Publishing, LLC.

—William Blake. 2007. (ENG.). 384p. per. *(978-1-4067-7628-7(9))* Read Bks.

BLAME

Alasko, Carl, PhD. Beyond Blame: Freeing Yourself from the Most Toxic Form of Emotional Bullsh*t. 2011. (ENG.). 336p. (gr. 12). 15.95 *(978-1-58542-876-2(0)*, Tarcher) Penguin Group (USA) Inc.

Coleman, Joshua. When Parents Hurt: Compassionate Strategies When You & Your Grown Child Don't Get Along. 2008. (ENG.). 32p. pap. 15.95 *(978-0-06-114843-9(1)*, Harper Paperbacks) HarperCollins Pubs.

Cunningham, Geof. Office of Blame Accountability. 2010. (ENG.). 192p. pap. 19.95 *(978-0-615-28909-0(6))* Loud Mouth Pr.

Dattner, Ben. The Blame Game: How the Hidden Rules of Credit & Blame Determine Our Success or Failure. 2012. (ENG.). 256p. pap. 16.00 *(978-1-4391-6957-5(8)*, Free Pr.) Free Pr.

Dattner, Ben & Dattner, Ben. The Blame Game: How the Hidden Rules of Credit & Blame Determine Our Success or Failure. 2011. (ENG., Illus.). 256p. 26.00 *(978-1-4391-6956-8(X)*, Free Pr.) Free Pr.

Hood, C. The Blame Game: Spin, Bureaucracy & Self-Preservation in Government. 2010. (ENG., Illus.). 242p. (C). 39.95 *(978-0-691-12995-2(9))* Princeton Univ. Pr.

Hughes, Gerard J. Is God to Blame? The Problem of Evil Revisited. 2008. (ENG.). 128p. pap. 23.95 *(978-1-84730-029-4(4))* Veritas Pubns. IRL. Dist: Dufour Editions, Inc.

Klemm, W. R. (Bill). Blame Game: How to Win It. 2008. (Illus.). 194p. pap. 14.95 *(978-0-9755225-3-0(1))* Benecton Pr.

Nash, David, et al, eds. Crime, Violence, & the Modern State, 1600-1900: Shame, Blame, & Culpability. 2012. (Routledge Studies in Modern History Ser.). (ENG., Illus.). 256p. (C). 180.00 ***(978-0-415-53722-3(3))*** Routledge.

Preston, Thomas. Pandora's Trap: Presidential Decision Making & Blame Avoidance in Vietnam & Iraq. 2011. x, 264p. E-Book ***(978-1-4422-1215-2(2))***; (ENG.). 252p. (gr. 17). 75.00 ***(978-0-7425-6263-9(8))*** Rowman & Littlefield Publishers, Inc.

Scanlon, T. M. Moral Dimensions: Permissibility, Meaning, Blame. 2010. (ENG.). 264p. pap. 17.95 *(978-0-674-05745-6(7)*, Belknap Pr.) Harvard Univ. Pr.

Schlessinger, Laura & Schlessinger, L. Bad Childhood — Good Life: How to Blossom & Thrive in Spite of an Unhappy Childhood. 2007. (ENG.). 272p. pap. 13.95 *(978-0-06-057787-2(8)*, HarperPerennial) HarperCollins Pubs.

Tilly, Charles. Credit & Blame. 2008. (ENG., Illus.). 196p. (C). 24.95 *(978-0-691-13578-6(9))* Princeton Univ. Pr.

BLANC, MONT (FRANCE AND ITALY)

Manthorpe, Jim. Tour de Mont Blanc. 2008. (ENG., Illus.). 256p. pap. 22.95 *(978-1-905864-12-6(4))* Trailblazer Pubns. GBR. Dist: Globe Pequot Pr., The.

Reynolds, Kev. Tour of Mont Blanc: Complete two-way trekking Guide. 3rd ed. 2012. (ENG.). n/ap. pap. 24.95 ***(978-1-85284-672-5(0))*** Cicerone Pr. GBR. Dist: Midpoint Trade Bks., Inc.

Sharp, Hilary. Mont Blanc Walks: 50 Walks & 4 Short Treks. 2nd ed. 2010. (Illus.). 288p. pap. 24.95 *(978-1-85284-597-1(X))* Cicerone Pr. GBR. Dist: Midpoint Trade Bks., Inc.

BLANCHING

see Bleaching

BLAND, EDITH NESBIT, 1858-1924

see Nesbit, E. (Edith), 1858-1924

BLAND COUNTY (VA.)

Archer, William R. "Bill". Bland County. 2011. (Images of America Ser.). (Illus.). 128p. pap. 21.99 *(978-0-7385-8733-2(8))* Arcadia Publishing.

BLANKETS

see also Afghans (Coverlets); Indian Textile Fabrics

Gott Warner, Kara, ed. Baby Nouveau: Stylish Blankets for Baby. 2011. (ENG., Illus.). 48p. pap. 12.95 ***(978-1-59217-339-6(X)***, House of White Birches, Inc.) Annie's Publishing, LLC.

Mondragon, Rick & Rowley, Elaine, eds. The Great American Afghan Collection: Knit Tradition & Innovation-One Square at a Time. 2012. (Illus.). 208p. pap. 24.95 *(978-1-933064-22-2(6)*, XRX Bks.) XRX, Inc.

BLASCO IBANEZ, VICENTE, 1867-1928

Ibáñez, Vicente Blasco. The Shadow of the Cathedral. 2007. (ENG.). 270p. pap. 21.99 *(978-1-4264-5773-9(1))*; 300p. pap. 23.99 *(978-1-4264-5833-0(9))* BiblioBazaar.

BLASKET ISLANDS (IRELAND)

Lucchitti, Irene. The Islandman: The Hidden Life of Tomás O'Crohan. 2008. (Reimagining Ireland Ser.). (ENG.). 232p. pap. 64.95 *(978-3-03911-837-3(4))* Lang, Peter AG GBR. Dist: Lang, Peter.

BLASKET ISLANDS (IRELAND)—DESCRIPTION AND TRAVEL

Stagles, Ray & Redican, Sue. The Blasket Island Guide. 2011. (ENG., Illus.). 96p. pap. 9.95 ***(978-1-84717-216-7(4))*** O'Brien Pr., Ltd., The IRL. Dist: Dufour Editions, Inc.

BLASPHEMY

Here are entered works on blasphemy in the legal and theological sense of maliciously reviling God or religion. Works on profane language are entered under Swearing. Works on judicial or official oaths are entered under Oaths.

Asad, T. Is Critique Secular? - Blasphemy, Injury & Free Speech. 2009. (Townsend Papers in the Humanities Ser.). 96p. pap. 16.95 *(978-0-9823294-1-2(5))* Townsend Ctr. For The Humanities.

BISIKAY. The cosmic god, you & I. 2010. 293p. pap. 27.50 *(978-1-4461-3662-1(0))* Lulu Enterprises Inc.

Brown, Peter D. G. Oskar Panizza & the Love Council: A History of the Scandalous Play on Stage & in Court, with the Complete Text in English & a Biography of the Author. 2010. (ENG., Illus.). 292p. pap. 49.95 *(978-0-7864-4273-7(5))* McFarland & Co., Inc. Pubs.

Craun, Edwin D. The Hands of the Tongue: Essays on Deviant Speech. 2006. (Studies in Medieval Culture). 20.00 *(978-1-58044-115-5(7))*; 40.00 *(978-1-58044-114-8(9))* Medieval Institute Pubns.

Dacey, Austin. The Future of Blasphemy: Democracy, Faith & Freedom of Expression. 2012. (ENG.). 208p. 80.00 *(978-1-4411-0737-4(1))*; pap. 19.95 *(978-1-4411-8392-7(2))* Continuum International Publishing Group, Ltd. GBR. Dist: National Bk. Network.

Graham, Michael F. The Blasphemies of Thomas Aikenhead: Boundaries of Belief on the Eve of the Enlightenment. 2008. (ENG., Illus.). 224p. (gr. 17). 110.00 *(978-0-7486-3426-2(6))* Edinburgh Univ. Pr. GBR. Dist: Columbia Univ. Pr.

Hille, Iris. Der Teufelspakt in frühneuzeitlichen Verhörprotokollen: Standardisierung und Regionalisierung im Frühneuhochdeutschen. 2009. (Studia Linguistica Germanica Ser.).Tr. of Pact with the Devil in Early Modern Interrogation Records. (GER., Illus.). X, 394p. 140.00 *(978-3-11-021894-7(1))* De Gruyter, Walter Inc.

Hille, Iris. Der Teufelspakt in frahneuzeitlichen Verhörprotokollen: Standardisierung und Regionalisierung im Frahneuhochdeutschen. 2009. (Studia Linguistica Germanica Ser.).Tr. of Pact with the Devil in Early Modern Interrogation Records. (GER.). X, 394p. 210.00 ***(978-3-11-173438-5(2))*** De Gruyter, Walter Inc.

Lindorfer, Bettina. Bestraftes Sprechen: Zur historischen Pragmatik des Mittelalters. 2009. (LAT, FRE & GER., Illus.). 364p. *(978-3-7705-4700-5(4))* Wilhelm/Fink#GmbH & Co. Verlags-KG.

Loetz, Francisca. Dealings with God: From Blasphemers in Early Modern Zurich to Cultural History of Religiousness. 2009. (St Andrews Studies in Reformation History Ser.). (Illus.). 342p. 134.95 *(978-0-7546-6883-1(5))* Ashgate Publishing Co.

Nash, David. Blasphemy in the Christian World: A History. (ENG., Illus.). 2010. 286p. 37.95 *(978-0-19-957075-1(2))* 2007. 288p. 85.00 *(978-0-19-925516-0(4))* Oxford Univ. Pr., Inc.

Nash, David, ed. Blasphemy in Britain & America, 1800-1930, 4 vols. 2010. (ENG., Illus.). 1184p. 625.00 *(978-1-85196-996-8(9))* Pickering & Chatto Pubs., Ltd. GBR. Dist: Ashgate Publishing Co.

Plate, Brent S. Blasphemy: Art That Offends. 2006. (ENG., Illus.). 189p. 45.00 *(978-1-904772-53-8(6))* Black Dog Publishing Ltd. GBR. Dist: Perseus Distribution.

Villa-Flores, Javier. Dangerous Speech: A Social History of Blasphemy in Colonial Mexico. 2006. (ENG., Illus.). 248p. pap. 24.95 *(978-0-8165-2563-8(3))*; (C). 50.00 *(978-0-8165-2556-0(0))* Univ. of Arizona Pr.

BLAST EFFECT

see also Buildings—War Damage; Impact

Lo, Shi Wei, et al. Numerical Investigations in the Propagations & Interactions of Blast Waves. 2008. 112p. pap. *(978-3-639-00080-1(3))* VDM Verlag Dr. Mueller e.K.

Needham, Charles E. Blast Waves. 2010. (Shock Wave & High Pressure Phenomena Ser.). (ENG., Illus.). x, 320p. 159.00 *(978-3-642-05287-3(8)*, 3642052878) Springer.

Spathis, Alex T. Vibrations from Blasting: Workshop Hosted by Fragblast 9 - The 9th International Symposium on Rock Fragmentation by Blasting. 2009. (ENG., Illus.). 144p. (C). 107.95 *(978-0-415-48295-0(X)*, CRC Press) Taylor & Francis Group GBR. Dist: Taylor & Francis Group.

Usmani, Zeeshan-Ul-Hassan. Modeling & Simulation of Explosion Effectiveness. 2009. 168p. pap. *(978-3-639-08956-1(1))* VDM Verlag Dr. Mueller e.K.

Williamson, Eric B. Blast-Resistant Highway Bridges: Design & Detailing Guidelines. 2010. (Illus.). 142p. pap. ***(978-0-309-11819-4(0))*** Transportation Research Board.

Zhang, F. Shock Wave Science & Technology Reference Library Vol. 4: Heterogeneous Detonation. 2009. (Shock Waves Science & Technology Reference Library). (ENG., Illus.). xiv, 394p. 229.00 *(978-3-540-88446-0(7)*, 3540884467) Springer.

BLAST FURNACES

Bennett, James R. & Utz, Karen R. Iron & Steel: A Driving Guide to the Birmingham Area Industrial Heritage. 2010. (Alabama the Forge of History Ser.). (ENG., Illus.). 144p. pap. 19.95 *(978-0-8173-5611-8(8))* Univ. of Alabama Pr.

—Iron & Steel: A Guide to Birmingham Area Industrial Heritage Sites. 2010. *(978-0-8173-8398-5(0))* Univ. of Alabama Pr.

Duru Gölalmis, Kevser. Sulfate Resistance of Blended Cements. 2010. 112p. pap. *(978-3-8383-7187-0(9))* Lambert Academic Publishing.

Forsythe, Robert. The Blast Furnace & the Manufacture of Pig Iron. 2007. 368p. 84.95 *(978-1-4276-1461-2(6))* Wexford College Pr.

Technology Research Editors, ed. Blast Furnace Simulation: Mathematical Models, 2007 Ed. 2007. pap. 128.50 *(978-1-60030-564-1(4)*, Search-In-Print) CSA Journal Division.

Wiesner, Robert A. & Sadler, Lynn Veach. The Men of Endor: Their Works & Times, 1861-1876. 2006. *(978-0-9647954-1-9(8))* Railroad Hse. Historical Assn., Inc.

Woodward, Joseph H., III & Woodward, Joseph H. Alabama Blast Furnaces. 2nd ed. 2006. (Library Alabama Classics Ser.). (ENG., Illus.). 176p. per. 19.95 *(978-0-8173-5432-9(8))* Univ. of Alabama Pr.

BLASTING

see also Explosives; Nuclear Excavation

Awuah-Offei, Kwame. Dynamic Modeling of Cable Shovel-Formation Interactions. 2010. 168p. pap. *(978-3-8383-1876-9(5))* Lambert Academic Publishing.

Ding, Wen, et al. Bao Po Cai Liao Yu Qi Bao Ji Shu. 2008. (CHI., Illus.). xiii, 378p. *(978-7-118-05860-4(2))* National Defence Industry Pr.

Massawe, Antipas. Drilling & Blasting Part I. 2010. 204p. pap. *(978-3-8383-7231-0(X))* Lambert Academic Publishing.

Massawe, Antipas & Maronga, Savinus. Drilling & Blasting Part II. 2010. 116p. pap. *(978-3-8383-7454-3(1))* Lambert Academic Publishing.

Petushkov, Vladimir G. Explosion & Its Applications in Metalworking. 2008. 315.00 *(978-1-60456-926-1(3))* Nova Science Pubs., Inc.

Practicas de Seguridad Para el Chorreado con Abrasivo. Date not set. (SPA.). *(978-0-9675287-2-4(0))* Clemco Industries Corp.

Ramulu, More & G. Sitharam, T. Blast Induced Rock Mass Damage in Underground Excavations. 2011. 208p. pap. ***(978-3-8433-9318-8(4))*** Lambert Academic Publishing.

Rossmanith. Mechanics & Physics of Electronic Blasting with Applications to Mining & Quarrying. 2011. instr.'s hndbk. ed. 110.00 *(978-1-84816-345-4(2))* World Scientific Publishing Co., Inc.

Rustan, Agne, et al, eds. Mining & Rock Construction Technology: Rock Mechanics, Drilling & Blasting. 2010. (ENG., Illus.). 466p. (C). 119.95 *(978-0-415-60043-9(X)*, CRC Press) Taylor & Francis Group GBR. Dist: Taylor & Francis Group.

Sanchidrian Blanco, Jose A. Fragblast 9: Proceedings of the 9th Int. Symp. on Rock Fragmentation by Blasting. 2009. (ENG., Illus.). 872p. (C). 259.95 *(978-0-415-48296-7(8)*, CRC Press) Taylor & Francis Group GBR. Dist: Taylor & Francis Group.

Sharma, Partha. Mining & Blasting Techniques. 2010. 136p. pap. *(978-3-8383-7439-0(8))* Lambert Academic Publishing.

Spathis, Alex T. Vibrations from Blasting: Workshop Hosted by Fragblast 9 - The 9th International Symposium on Rock Fragmentation by Blasting. 2009. (ENG., Illus.). 144p. (C). 107.95 *(978-0-415-48295-0(X)*, CRC Press) Taylor & Francis Group GBR. Dist: Taylor & Francis Group.

Twitty, Eric. Blown to Bits in the Mine. 2009. 220p. pap. 25.95 *(978-1-932738-82-7(7))* Western Reflections Publishing Co.

Zhao, Gen. Shui Gong Wei Yan Chai Chu Bao Po. 2009. (CHI., Illus.). 202p. *(978-7-5084-7127-3(X))* Zhongguo Shuili Shuidian Chubanshe.

BLAUROCK, GEORGE

Chen, Katherine K. Enabling Creative Chaos: The Organization Behind the Burning Man Event. 2009. (ENG., Illus.). 272p. 75.00 *(978-0-226-10237-5(8))*; pap. 25.00 *(978-0-226-10238-2(6))* Univ. of Chicago Pr.

BLAVATSKY, H. P. (HELENA PETROVNA), 1831-1891

Blavatsky, H. P. The Deluge & Noah. 2006. pap. 12.95 *(978-1-4286-7257-4(5))* Kessinger Publishing, LLC.

—From the Caves & Jungles of Hindostan. 2009. (ENG.). 325p. 36.99 *(978-1-117-08710-8(7))*; pap. 23.99 *(978-1-117-08712-2(3)*, BiblioLife); pap. 30.75 *(978-1-117-08711-5(5))* BiblioBazaar.

—From the Caves & Jungles of Hindostan. 2008. 236p. pap. *(978-1-4099-5553-5(2))* Dodo Pr.

—From the Caves & Jungles of Hindostan. 2010. 324p. 36.76 ***(978-1-169-32068-0(6))***; pap. 24.76 ***(978-1-162-59415-6(2))*** Kessinger Publishing, LLC.

—Post-Christian Adepts & Their Doctrines. 2006. pap. 9.95 *(978-1-4286-7183-6(8))* Kessinger Publishing, LLC.

—Post Christian Adepts & Their Doctrines & the Two Eternal. 2006. pap. 9.95 *(978-1-4286-7174-4(9))* Kessinger Publishing, LLC.

—Post Christian Successors to the Mysteries. 2006. pap. 12.95 *(978-1-4286-7262-8(1))* Kessinger Publishing, LLC.

—The Post Christian Successors to the Mysteries. 2006. pap. 12.95 *(978-1-4286-7265-9(6))* Kessinger Publishing, LLC.

Blavatsky, H. P. (Helena Petrovna). From the Caves & Jungles of Hindostan. 2011. 246p. pap. ***(978-3-8424-6402-5(9))*** Tredition GmbH.

—Isis Unveiled, Vol. I. 2010. 684p. pap. 34.95 *(978-0-557-35694-2(6))* Lulu Enterprises Inc.

—Isis Unveiled, Vol. II. 2010. 708p. pap. 34.95 *(978-0-557-35703-1(9))* Lulu Enterprises Inc.

Blavatsky, H. p. 1831-1891. From the Caves & Jungles of Hindostan. 2010. (ENG.). 340p. pap. 31.75 *(978-1-171-76003-0(5))*; 326p. pap. 31.75 *(978-1-176-63148-9(9))* BiblioBazaar.

Blavatsky, Helena. The Secret Doctrine, 3. 2006. reprint ed. per. 16.95 *(978-0-9753093-9-1(0))* Ancient Wisdom Pubns.

Blavatsky, Helena Petrovna. From the Caves & Jungles of Hindostan. 2010. 340p. pap. 31.75 *(978-1-146-39901-2(4))* 2008. 276p. 28.99 *(978-0-554-23740-4(7))* 2008. 276p. 25.99 *(978-0-554-33043-3(1))* 2007. (ENG.). 250p. pap. 20.99 *(978-1-4264-4973-4(9))* 2007. (ENG.). 274p. pap. 23.99 *(978-1-4264-5274-1(8))* BiblioBazaar.

—From the Caves & Jungles of Hindostan. 2009. 178p. pap. *(978-1-150-66602-5(1))* Books LLC.

—From the Caves & Jungles of Hindostan. 2008. 212p. pap. 16.99 *(978-1-59547-701-9(2))* NuVision Pubns., LLC.

Blavatsky, Helena Pretrovna. From the Caves & Jungles of Hindostan. 2008. (ENG.). 240p. pap. 14.45 *(978-1-4385-1133-7(7)*, Book Jungle) Standard Pubns., Inc.

Blavatsky, Helena Petrovna & Blavatsky, H. P. From the Caves & Jungles of Hindostan. 2010. (Illus.). 162p. pap. 24.86 *(978-1-153-62360-5(9))* General Bks. LLC.

—From the Caves & Jungles of Hindostan. 2010. 324p. 45.95 *(978-1-161-37745-3(X))* Kessinger Publishing, LLC.

Bragdon, Claude. Episodes from an Unwritten History. 2007. (ENG.). 108p. 34.95 *(978-0-548-28198-7(X))* Kessinger Publishing, LLC.

Carrithers Jr., Walter A. The Truth about Madame Blavatsky. 2011. 32p. 35.95 ***(978-1-258-00916-8(1))*** Literary Licensing, LLC.

Cleather, Alice Leighton. H P Blavatsky & Her Inner Group. 2006. pap. 9.95 *(978-1-4286-7853-8(0))* Kessinger Publishing, LLC.

Heindel, Max. Blavatsky & the Secret Doctrine. 2008. pap. 14.95 *(978-0-9815971-5-7(7))* Ancient Wisdom Pubns.

Maroney, Tim. The Book of Dzyan: Being a Manuscript Curiously Received by Helena Petrovna Blavatsky with Diverse & Rare Texts of Related Interest. 2008. (Call of Cthulhu Ser.). (ENG., Illus.). 272p. pap. 15.95 *(978-1-56882-259-4(6))* Chaosium, Inc.

Mills, Joy. Reflections on an Ageless Wisdom: A Commentary on the Mahatma Letters to A. P. Sinnett. 2010. (ENG.). 750p. pap. 39.95 *(978-0-8356-0885-5(9)*, Quest Bks.) Theosophical Publishing Hse.

Olcott, Henry S. Count de Saint Germain & H P B Two Mes. 2006. pap. 15.95 *(978-1-4286-4384-0(2))* Kessinger Publishing, LLC.

Plummer, L. Gordon & Ryan, Charles J. Star Habits & Orbits: Astronomy for Theosophical Students. 2011. 172p. 42.95 ***(978-1-258-03986-8(9))*** Literary Licensing, LLC.

Ransom, Josephine. Studies in the Secret Doctrine. 2007. (ENG.). 182p. 37.95 *(978-0-548-00696-2(2))* Kessinger Publishing, LLC.

Ryan, Charles J. H P Blavatsky & the Theosophical Movement: A Brief Historical Sketch. 2011. 408p. 54.95 ***(978-1-258-02482-6(9))*** Literary Licensing, LLC.

Solovyov, Vladimir Sergeyevich. A Modern Priestess of Isis. 2011. (Cambridge Library Collection - Spiritualism & Esoteric Knowlege Ser.). (ENG.). 392p. pap. 31.99 *(978-1-108-07303-5(4))* Cambridge Univ. Pr.

Tingley, Katherine. Helena Petrovna Blavatsky 1921. 2007. (ENG.). 108p. 33.95 *(978-0-548-05391-1(X))* Kessinger Publishing, LLC.

Wachtmeister, Constance. Reminiscences of H P Blavatsky & the Secret Doctrine. 2009. 100p. pap. *(978-0-217-25412-0(8))* Books LLC.

BLAZONRY

see Heraldry

BLEACHING

see also Dyes and Dyeing

Goddard-Clark, Lorri. The Hair Color Mix: More Than 150 Recipes for Salon-Perfect Color at Home. 2008. (ENG., Illus.). 320p. pap. 19.99 *(978-0-06-114790-6(7)*, Harper Paperbacks) HarperCollins Pubs.

Haywood, Van B. Tooth Whitening: Indications & Outcomes of Nightguard Vital Bleaching. 2007. (Illus.). 144p. *(978-0-86715-450-4(0))* Quintessence Publishing Co., Inc.

Marsh, J. t. & Marsh, J. T. An Introduction to Textile Bleaching. 2011. 556p. pap. 33.95 ***(978-1-4474-0078-3(X))*** Research Pr.

Patterson, H. B W. Bleaching & Purifying Fats & Oils: Theory & Practice. 2nd rev. ed. 2010. (ENG.). 285p. 205.00 *(978-1-893997-91-2(X))* American Oil Chemists' Society.

Suess, Hans Ulrich. Pulp Bleaching Today. 2010. (ENG.). IX, 310p. 252.00 ***(978-3-11-173638-9(5))*** De Gruyter, Walter Inc.

Suess, Ulrich. Pulp Bleaching Today. 2010. (ENG., Illus.). IX, 310p. 165.00 *(978-3-11-020737-8(0))* De Gruyter, Walter Inc.

BLEEDING

see Hemorrhage

BLENDERS (COOKING)

Brown, Ellen & Konopelski, Karen. Supercharge Your Immune System: 100 Ways to Help Your Body Fight Illness - One Glass at a Time. 2008. (ENG., Illus.). 208p. 14.95 *(978-1-59233-328-8(1)*, 1592333281) Quayside.

Cookbook Resources, ed. Cool Smoothies. 2010. 176p. pap. *(978-1-59769-042-3(2))* Cookbook Resources, LLC.

Crocker, Pat. The Smoothies Bible. 2nd ed. 2010. (ENG., Illus.). 384p. pap. 24.95 *(978-0-7788-0241-9(8))* Rose, Robert Inc. CAN. Dist: Firefly Bks., Ltd.

Foley, Ray. The Ultimate Little Frozen Drinks Book. 2nd ed. 2011. (ENG.). 480p. pap. 11.99 *(978-1-4022-5406-2(7))* Sourcebooks, Inc.

Good Housekeeping Editors. Good Housekeeping Blend It! 150 Sensational Recipes to Make in Your Blender - Frappes, Smoothies, Soups, Pancakes, Frozen Cocktails & More. 2010. (Favorite Good Housekeeping Recipes Ser.). (ENG., Illus.). 176p. spiral bd. 14.95 *(978-1-58816-807-8(7))* Hearst Communications, Inc.

Haasarud, Kim. 101 Blender Drinks. 2010. (ENG., Illus.). 128p. 16.95 *(978-0-470-50513-7(3)*, Wiley) Wiley, John & Sons, Inc.

Madani, Catherine. Blender: Krups Cookbook, 50 Recipes. 2007. (ENG., Illus.). 128p. 19.95 *(978-2-84123-122-5(4))* Stewart, Tabori & Chang.

Patrick, Toni. 101 Things to Do with a Blender, 1 vol. 2010. (ENG.). 128p. spiral bd. 9.99 *(978-1-4236-0690-1(6))* Gibbs Smith, Publisher.

Pickford, Louise. Smoothies: Over 100 Fabulous Blended Drinks from Breakfast Boosters to Indulgent Treats. 2008. (ENG., Illus.). 96p. *(978-1-84597-594-4(4))* CICO Bks.

B

Publications International Staff. Concealed Spiral Oster Creative Entertaining. 2008. (Illus.). 160p. spiral bd. 10.98 *(978-1-4127-9941-6(4))* Publications International, Ltd.

Shomron, Leah & Borowski, Hanny. Smoothies, Smoothies & More Smoothies! (Illus.). 144p. 2011. 1895.00 *(978-1-936140-24-4(1))* 2010. (ENG., 18.95 *(978-1-936140-12-1(8)*, Imagine Publishing) Charlesbridge Publishing, Inc.

Suzanne, Kristen. Kristen Suzanne's Easy Raw Vegan Smoothies, Juices, Elixirs, & Drinks: The Definitive Raw Fooder's Book of Beverage Recipes for Boosting Energy, Getting Healthy, Losing Weight, Having Fun, or Cutting Loose ... Including Wine Drinks! 2008. 96p. pap. *(978-0-9817556-7-0(4))* Green Butterfly Pr.

Young, Nicole & Day, Nadine. Blender Baby Food: Over 175 Recipes for Healthy Homemade Meals. 2nd ed. 2011. (ENG., Illus.). 216p. pap. 19.95 *(978-0-7788-0262-4(0))* Rose, Robert Inc. CAN. Dist: Firefly Bks., Ltd.

BLENDING

see Mixing

BLEPHAROPTOSIS

Cohen, Adam J. & Weinberg, David A., eds. Blepharoptosis: Diagnosis & Management. 2010. (Illus.). 180p. 159.00 *(978-0-387-92854-8(5)*, 0387928545) Springer.

BLESSED VIRGIN MARY, SAINT

see Mary, Blessed Virgin, Saint

BLESSING AND CURSING

see also Exorcism

Agrippa, Henry Cornelius. Of the Virtue of Writing & of Making Imprecations & Inscriptions. 2006. pap. 9.95 *(978-1-4286-6455-5(6))* Kessinger Publishing, LLC.

Aitken, J. K. The Semantics of Blessing & Cursing in Ancient Hebrew. 2007. (Ancient near Eastern Studies Supplement Ser.). (ENG.). 306p. (C). 124.00 *(978-90-429-1896-2(9))* Peeters Pubs. & Booksellers BEL. Dist: Brown, David Bk. Co., The.

Ashley, Leonard R. N. The Complete Book of Spells, Curses, & Magical Recipes. 2010. (ENG., Illus.). 384p. pap. 14.95 *(978-1-61608-098-3(1)*, 608098) Skyhorse Publishing Co., Inc.

Brezsny, Rob. Pronoia Is the Antidote for Paranoia: How the Whole World Is Conspiring to Shower You with Blessings. rev. exp. ed. 2009. (ENG., Illus.). 400p. pap. 21.00 *(978-1-55643-818-9(4))* North Atlantic Bks.

Britt, Brian. Biblical Curses & the Displacement of Tradition. 2011. 322p. ***(978-1-907534-11-9(3))*** Sheffield Phoenix Pr.

Buck, Robert. The Book of Blessing: Speaking God's Word & Blessing into People's Lives. 2009. 19.99 *(978-1-60791-632-1(0))*; pap. 11.99 *(978-1-60791-631-4(2))* Xulon Pr., Inc.

Cowins, Sr. & Blackshear-Cowins, Harriet. The Art of Good Cursing. 2011. 68p. pap. 19.95 ***(978-1-4626-2115-6(5))*** PublishAmerica, Inc.

Donahou, Michael. A Comparison of the Egyptian Execration Ritual to Exodus 32: 19 & Jeremiah 19. 2010. 110.12 *(978-1-61143-546-7(3))* Gorgias Pr., LLC.

Dowton, Dawn Rae. The Little Book of Curses & Maledictions for Everyday Use: Dawn Rae Downton. 2009. (ENG., Illus.). 192p. 12.95 *(978-1-60239-741-5(4)*, 239741) Skyhorse Publishing Co., Inc.

Doyle, Tsarina & Doyle, Brian. Words with Teeth: Metaphors & the Psalms of Imprecation. 2014. (Library of Hebrew Bible/Old Testament Studies, the Ser.). (ENG., Illus.). 144p. 105.00 *(978-0-567-02772-6(4)*, T&T Clark Int'l) Continuum International Publishing Group, Ltd. GBR. Dist: National Bk. Network.

Eckhardt, John. Prayers That Activate Blessings. 2011. E-Book *(978-1-61638-427-2(1)*, Charisma Hse.) Charisma Media.

—Prayers That Break Curses: Prayers for Breaking the Power of Curses So You Can Walk in God's Promises. 2009. (ENG.). 128p. pap. 9.99 *(978-1-59979-944-5(8)*, Charisma Hse.) Charisma Media.

Eckhardt, John J. Identifying & Breaking Curses. pap. 5.00 *(978-1-883927-00-4(5))* Crusaders Ministries.

Eidinow, Esther. Oracles, Curses, & Risk among the Ancient Greeks. 2007. (ENG., Illus.). 480p. 199.00 *(978-0-19-927778-0(8))* Oxford Univ. Pr., Inc.

Fox, William Sherwood. The Johns Hopkins Tabellae Defixionum. 2009. pap. 26.08 *(978-1-60724-652-7(X))* Gorgias Pr., LLC.

Garner, The Greatest Painful Blessings Scott. The Greatest PAINFUL Blessings. 2010. 71p. pap. 10.60 *(978-0-557-10981-4(7))* Lulu Enterprises Inc.

Huch, Larry. The 7 Places Jesus Shed His Blood. 2012. pap. ***(978-1-60374-246-7(8))*** Whitaker Hse.

James, G. A. N. The Myth of the Generational Curse. 2007. 96p. per. 9.99 *(978-1-60477-292-0(1))* Xulon Pr., Inc.

McKenna, Megan. Luke: The Book of Blessings & Woes. 2009. (ENG.). 240p. pap. 19.95 *(978-1-56548-323-1(5))* New City Pr.

Mees, Bernard. Celtic Curses. 2009. (Illus.). 238p. 99.00 *(978-1-84383-457-1(X)*, Boydell Press) Boydell & Brewer, Ltd. GBR. Dist: Boydell & Brewer, Inc.

Minor, Vernon Hyde & Curran, Brian A., eds. Memoirs of the American Academy in Rome Vol. 55. 2011. (Memoirs of the American Academy in Rome Ser.). (ENG., Illus.). 338p. 70.00 ***(978-1-879549-19-7(0))*** American Academy in Rome.

Odukoya, Taiwo. Get All You Want. 2010. 76p. pap. 10.99 *(978-1-61579-740-0(8))* Xulon Pr., Inc.

Popoola, Abi. The Tell-Tale Signs of Spiritual Growth. 2008. 108p. 18.99 *(978-1-60647-196-8(1))*; pap. 10.99 *(978-1-60647-195-1(3))* Xulon Pr., Inc.

Prince, Derek. Blessing or Curse: You Can Choose. 3rd ed. 2006. 304p. pap. 14.99 *(978-0-8007-9408-8(7))* Chosen Bks.

Quainoo, Vanessa Wynder. Speak Life. 2011. 218p. pap. 15.99 ***(978-1-61215-918-8(4))*** Xulon Pr., Inc.

Rochelle-Levy, Paulette. And You Shall Be a Blessing: Inspirations. 2006. *(978-0-9719063-1-0(9))* Rochelle-Levy, Paulette.

Seavey, Wm. G., Sr. Waves of Blessings. 2007. 200p. (YA). pap. 22.95 *(978-0-9800126-0-6(0))* Seavey, Bill Ministries International.

Sharpe, Van. The Blessings of Rejection. 2008. 156p. (ENG.). 21.99 *(978-1-60477-430-6(4))*; per. 13.99 *(978-1-60477-429-0(0))* Xulon Pr., Inc.

Versnel, H. S. Fluch und Gebet: Magische Manipulation versus religio¨ses Flehen? Religionsgeschichtliche und hermeneutische Betrachtungen u¨ber antike Fluchtafeln. 2009. (Hans-Lietzmann-Vorlesungen Ser.).Tr. of Curse & Prayer: Magic Manipulation versus Religious Supplication? (GER.). X, 54p. pap. 21.00 *(978-3-11-022635-5(9))* De Gruyter, Walter Inc.

Vienne-Guerrin, Nathalie. The Unruly Tongue in Early Modern England: Three Treatises. 2012. (ENG.). 300p. 75.00 ***(978-1-61147-469-5(8))*** Fairleigh Dickinson Univ. Pr.

Watkins, Peter, compiled by. A Little Book of House Blessings. 2007. 70p. 15.99 *(978-1-85311-829-6(X))* Canterbury Pr.

Weathersby, Melissa. Are You Arresting Your Blessing? 2011. 132p. pap. 14.99 ***(978-1-61379-538-5(6))*** Xulon Pr., Inc.

Wiersbe, Warren W. Bless You: Receiving & Sharing the Blessings of the Lord. 2008. (ENG.). 192p. pap. 12.99 *(978-1-57293-235-7(X))* Discovery Hse. Pubs.

Wise, Gayla. The Power of Your Patriarchal Blessing. 2007. 182p. per. 14.95 *(978-1-932898-75-0(1))* Spring Creek Bk. Co.

BLESSINGS, TABLE

see Grace at Meals

BLESSINGTON, MARGUERITE, COUNTESS OF, 1789-1849

Avram, Foteini. Lady Blessington. 2010. 72p. pap. *(978-3-639-27429-5(6))* VDM Verlag Dr. Mueller e.K.

Madden, R. R. The Literary Life & Correspondence of the Countess of Blessington V1. 2008. 558p. 57.95 *(978-1-4365-4784-0(9))* 2007. 560p. per. 42.95 *(978-0-548-68945-5(8))* Kessinger Publishing, LLC.

Madden, Richard Robert. The Literary Life & Correspondence of the Countess of Blessington R R Madden. 2006. 564p. per. 32.99 *(978-1-4255-6174-1(8))*; 608p. per. 34.99 *(978-1-4255-6483-4(6))* MPublishing.

—The Literary Life & Correspondence of the Countess of Blessington V3. 2007. (ENG.). 522p. 55.95 *(978-0-548-17257-5(9))*; 524p. per. 40.95 *(978-1-4304-7084-7(4))* Kessinger Publishing, LLC.

Molloy, J. Fitzgerald. Lady Blessington. 2008. 474p. 52.95 *(978-1-4365-9562-9(2))* 2007. (ENG.). 476p. per. 37.95 *(978-0-548-80082-9(0))* Kessinger Publishing, LLC.

Stoddard, Richard Henry. Personal Recollections of Lamb, Hazlitt, & Others. 2009. 158p. pap. 20.03 *(978-1-4588-4056-1(5))* General Bks. LLC.

Stoddard, Richard Henry, ed. The Personal Recollections of Lamb, Hazlitt & Others. 2007. 354p. 46.95 *(978-0-548-03338-8(2))* Kessinger Publishing, LLC.

BLIGH, WILLIAM, 1754-1817

Barrow, John. Eventful History of the Mutiny & Pirat. 2006. pap. *(978-1-4065-1084-3(X))* Dodo Pr.

Bligh, William. The Mutiny on Board H. M. S. Bounty. Laurel Associates Inc Staff, ed. 2008. (Graphic Novels Ser.). (ENG., Illus.). 16p. (YA). (gr. 9-12). tchr. ed., pupil's gde. ed. 7.95 incl. cd-rom *(978-1-59905-306-6(3))* Saddleback Educational Publishing.

—The Mutiny on Board H. M. S. Bounty. 2010. (Saddleback's Illustrated Classics Ser.). (ENG., Illus.). 64p. (YA). (gr. 9-12). lib. bdg. 19.95 *(978-1-59905-911-2(8))* Saddleback Educational Publishing.

—Mutiny on the Bounty. 2010. (ENG.). 224p. pap. 8.95 *(978-0-486-47257-7(4))* Dover Pubns., Inc.

—Mutiny on the Bounty. 2006. (Adventure Classics Ser.). (ENG., Illus.). 432p. (gr. 3-6). 12.95 *(978-88-544-0123-5(4)*, White Star) Rizzoli International Pubns., Inc.

—Mutiny on the H. M. S. Bounty. 24.95 *(978-0-8488-1278-2(6))* Amereon LTD.

Salmond, Anne. Bligh: William Bligh in the South Seas. 2011. (ENG., Illus.). 528p. 39.95 *(978-0-520-27056-5(8))* Univ. of California Pr.

Schreiber, Roy, ed. Captain Bligh's Second Chance: An Eyewitness Account of His Return to the South Seas. 2007. (Illus.). 184p. 34.95 *(978-1-86176-280-1(1))* Duckworth Publishers GBR. Dist: Naval Institute Pr.

Souhami, Diana. Coconut Chaos: Pitcairn, Mutiny & A Seduction at Sea ... 2007. (ENG., Illus.). 272p. 32.95 *(978-0-297-84787-8(2))* Orion Publishing Group, Ltd. GBR. Dist: Independent Pubs. Group.

—Coconut Chaos: Pitcairn, Mutiny & a Seduction at Sea ... 2008. (ENG., Illus.). 272p. pap. 16.95 *(978-0-7538-2367-5(5)*, Phoenix) Orion Publishing Group, Ltd. GBR. Dist: Independent Pubs. Group.

BLIMPS

see Airships

BLIND

see also Children, Blind; Deafblind People

Artman, William. Beauties & Achievements of the Blind by Wm Artman & L V Hall. 2006. 396p. per. 26.99 *(978-1-4255-4236-8(0))*; 392p. per. 26.99 *(978-1-4255-4133-0(X))* MPublishing.

Brown, Eleanor Gertrude. Milton's Blindness. 2011. 178p. 42.95 ***(978-1-258-03796-3(3))*** Literary Licensing, LLC.

California State Department of Health Staff. Leisure Time Activities for Deaf-Blind Children. 24.95 *(978-0-917002-06-9(7))* Joyce Media, Inc.

Carrington, Hereward. The Psychology of the Blind: Helps for Those Who Have Lost Their Sight, & for Those Associated with Them. Haldeman-Julius, E., ed. 2011. 34p. 35.95 ***(978-1-258-05036-8(6))*** Literary Licensing, LLC.

Chevigny, Hector & Braverman, Sydell. The Adjustment of the Blind. 2011. 338p. 50.95 ***(978-1-258-08628-2(X))*** Literary Licensing, LLC.

Devlieger, Patrick, ed. Blindness & the Multi-Sensorial City. 2006. (Illus.). 372p. (C). pap. 89.50 *(978-90-441-1739-4(4))* Garant Uitgevers N.V. BEL. Dist: Coronet Bks.

Eze, Smart. My Four Worlds. 2010. 268p. pap. 14.49 *(978-1-4520-5077-5(5))* AuthorHouse.

Friedman, Dan. Sound Advice: Voiceover from an Audio Engineer's Perspective. 2010. 84p. pap. 34.95 *(978-1-4520-3790-5(6))* AuthorHouse.

Latimer, Henry Randolph. The Conquest of Blindness: An Autobiographical Review of the Life & Work of Henry Randolph Latimer. 2011. 414p. 54.95 ***(978-1-258-05226-3(1))*** Literary Licensing, LLC.

Montalembert, Hugues de. Invisible: A Memoir. 2011. (ENG., Illus.). 144p. pap. 13.00 *(978-1-4165-9367-6(5)*, Beyond Words/Atria Bks.) Atria Bks.

Omansky, Beth. Borderlands of Blindness. 2011. 175p. 55.00 *(978-1-58826-780-1(6))* Rienner, Lynne Pubs.

Weiskrantz, Lawrence. Blindsight: A case study spanning 35 years & new Developments. 2nd ed. 2009. (Oxford Portraits in Science Ser.). (ENG., Illus.). 256p. pap. 64.95 *(978-0-19-956721-8(2))* Oxford Univ. Pr., Inc.

Weygand, Zina. The Blind in French Society from the Middle Ages to the Century of Louis Braille. Cohen, Emily-Jane, tr. from FRE. 2009. (ENG.). 424p. 60.00 *(978-0-8047-5768-3(2))* Stanford Univ. Pr.

Wheatley, Edward. Stumbling Blocks Before the Blind: Medieval Constructions of a Disability. 2010. (Corporealities: Discourses of Disability Ser.). (ENG., Illus.). 298p. 75.00 *(978-0-472-11720-8(3))* Univ. of Michigan Pr.

BLIND—BIOGRAPHY

Allen-King, Jill. Just Jill: The AUTOB of Jill Allen-King MBE. 2010. (Illus.). 200p. 19.95 *(978-1-906358-76-1(1))* Apex Publishing Ltd., Essex GBR. Dist: APG Sales & Distribution Services.

Bagayoko, Amadou, et al. Away from the Light of Day. 2011. (ENG.). 176p. pap. 16.95 *(978-1-901927-45-0(8))* Route GBR. Dist: Dufour Editions, Inc.

Buchanan, William J. Running Toward the Light: The George Mendoza Story. 2006. (ENG., Illus.). 175p. pap. 14.95 *(978-0-8263-3751-1(1))* Univ. of New Mexico Pr.

Crosby, Fanny J. Fanny J Crosby: An Autobiography. 2008. 240p. 14.95 *(978-1-59856-281-1(9))* Hendrickson Pubs. Marketing, LLC.

Eadie, Doug & Jacko, Virginia. The Blind Visionary: Practical Lessons for Meeting Challenges on the Way to a More Fulfilling Life & Career. 2010. 176p. 29.95 *(978-0-9798894-3-1(X)*, Governance Edge Pubns.) Governance Edge.

Freeman, James A. Clarence Hawkes: America's Blind Naturalist & the World He Lived In. 2009. pap. *(978-1-935052-21-0(7))* White River Pr.

Giles, Tony. Seeing the World My Way. 2010. (Illus.). 224p. pap. ***(978-1-906236-38-0(0))*** SilverWood Bks.

Giovanelli, Joe. Let There Be Light: The Inspirational Achievements of a Man Born Blind. 2010. 340p. pap. 23.95 *(978-1-4502-6211-8(2))* iUniverse, Inc.

Harris, Helen J. How to Survive Losing Vision: Managing & Overcoming Progressive Blindness Because of Retinal Disease. 2011. 200p. pap. 16.95 ***(978-1-4567-4801-2(7))*** AuthorHouse.

Harvey, Christopher Howell. Until My Blindfold Comes Off. 2008. 196p. pap. 14.99 *(978-1-60647-909-4(1))* Xulon Pr., Inc.

Hingson, Michael. Thunder Dog: The True Story of a Blind Man, His Guide Dog, & the Triumph of Trust at Ground Zero. 2011. 256p. 22.99 *(978-1-4002-0304-8(X))* Nelson, Thomas Inc.

Hingson, Michael & Flor, Susy. Thunder Dog: The True Story of a Blind Man, His Guide Dog, & the Triumph of Trust at Ground Zero. l.t. ed. 2011. 322p. 32.99 ***(978-1-4104-4130-0(X))*** Thorndike Pr.

Jernigan-Carter, Earlene. The TASTE of SURVIVAL, the Larry Cox Story. 2010. 73p. pap. 15.50 *(978-0-557-15345-9(X))* Lulu Enterprises Inc.

Jordan, Pamela. Racing in the Slow Lane, 1 vol. 2009. 263p. pap. 21.95 *(978-1-61582-855-5(9))* PublishAmerica, Inc.

Keller, Helen. The Story of My Life. 2007. (ENG.). 240p. per. *(978-1-4068-1984-7(0))* Echo Library.

—The Story of My Life. 2006. (Twelve-Point Ser.). lib. bdg. 25.00 *(978-1-58287-392-3(5))*; lib. bdg. 26.00 *(978-1-58287-883-6(8))* North Bks.

—The World I Live In. 2009. 220p. 23.99 *(978-1-103-51533-2(0))*; pap. 17.99 *(978-1-103-51531-8(4))* BiblioBazaar.

—The World I Live In. 2009. 76p. pap. *(978-0-217-89780-8(0))* Books LLC.

—The World I Live In. 2009. 90p. pap. *(978-1-4099-6339-4(X))* Dodo Pr.

—The World I Live In. 2009. 104p. pap. 11.45 *(978-1-4385-1920-3(6))*; (ENG.). pap. 12.95 *(978-1-4385-1304-1(6))* Standard Pubns., Inc. (Book Jungle).

—The World I Live In. 2009. 64p. pap. 9.95 *(978-1-4344-0400-8(5))* Wildside Pr., LLC.

Keller, Helen & Sullivan, Anne Mansfield. The Story of My Life. Macy, John Albert, ed. 2007. (ENG.). 332p. per. *(978-1-4065-1873-3(5))* Dodo Pr.

Keller, Helen & Sullivan, Macy. Valiant Companions. 224p. 21.95 *(978-0-8488-2631-4(0))* Amereon LTD.

Knighton, Ryan. Cockeyed. 2007. (ENG.). 288p. per. 12.95 *(978-1-58648-440-8(0))* PublicAffairs.

Kurson, Robert. Crashing Through: The Extraordinary True Story of the Man Who Dared to See. 2008. (ENG., Illus.). 320p. pap. 16.00 *(978-0-8129-7368-6(2)*, Random Hse. Trade Paperbacks) Random House Publishing Group.

Kuusisto, Stephen. Eavesdropping: A Life by Ear. 2006. (ENG.). 208p. 23.95 *(978-0-393-05892-5(1)*, 5892) Norton, W. W. & Co., Inc.

Lucas, David. Stepping into the Dark: A lad from Jarrow battles with sight Loss. 2010. (Illus.). 228p. pap. 28.00 *(978-1-906619-17-6(4))* Fresh Heart Publishing GBR. Dist: Lightning Source, Inc.

Martin, Frances. Elizabeth Gilbert & Her Work for the Blind. 2011. 164p. pap. 14.99 ***(978-1-61203-073-9(4))*** Bottom of the Hill Publishing.

Maurer, Marc. Freedom. Maurer, Marc, ed. 2006. (Kernel Book Ser.). 96p. pap. 3.00 *(978-1-885218-33-9(8))* National Federation of the Blind.

—Revolution. Maurer, Marc, ed. l.t. ed. 2006. (Kernel Book Ser.: Vol. 31). (Illus.). 96p. pap. 3.00 *(978-1-885218-34-6(6))* National Federation of the Blind.

McWilliams, Carey. Guide Dogs & Guns: America's First Blind Marksman Fires Back. 2007. (Illus.). 248p. per. 12.95 *(978-1-60002-295-1(2)*, 4267) Mountain Valley Publishing, LLC.

Mehta, Ved & Johnson, Beth. The Stolen Light. 2009. 410p. pap. *(978-1-59194-095-1(8))* Townsend Pr. - Sunday Schl. Publishing Board.

Montalembert, Hugues de. Invisible: A Memoir. 2010. (ENG., Illus.). 144p. 21.99 *(978-1-4165-9366-9(7)*, Beyond Words/Atria Bks.) Atria Bks.

Neill, Sharon. Second Sight: The Inspirational Autobiography of the UK's Only Blind Medium. 2008. (Illus.). 231p. 19.95 *(978-0-7528-8612-1(6))* Orion Bks. Ltd. GBR. Dist: Sterling Publishing Co., Inc.

Ockelford, Adam. In the Key of Genius: The Extraordinary Life of Derek Paravicini. 2010. (ENG., Illus.). 288p. pap. 15.95 *(978-0-09-951358-2(7))* Random Hse. GBR. Dist: Independent Pubs. Group.

O'Rourke, Angela L. A Long Walk to a Guide Dog. 2006. 399p. pap. 25.35 *(978-1-4120-9022-3(9))* Trafford Publishing.

Out of Sight Living: The story of Blake Lindsay: A Sightless Man with Perfect Vision. 2006. per. 12.00 *(978-0-9787268-2-9(0))* Power Publishing.

Perlman, Rosalind. The Blind Doctor: The Jacob Bolotin Story. 2007. (Illus.). 256p. per. 19.95 *(978-1-883423-13-1(9))*; 416p. pap. 24.95 *(978-1-883423-14-8(7))* Blue Point Bks.

Rothschild, Jennifer. Fingerprints of God: Recognizing God's Touch on Your Life. 2006. (ENG.). 160p. pap. 14.99 *(978-1-60142-037-4(4)*, Multnomah) Doubleday Religious Publishing Group, The.

Scotto, Robert. Moondog, the Viking of 6th Avenue: The Authorized Biography. 2007. (ENG., Illus.). 280p. 24.95 *(978-0-9760822-8-6(4)*, Process) Process Packaging.

Seamans, Art. I See, Said the Blind Man. 2010. 136p. pap. 13.95 *(978-1-4490-9837-7(1))* AuthorHouse.

Sullivan, Tom. Adventures in Darkness: Memoirs of an Eleven-Year-Old Blind Boy, 0 vols. 2008. 224p. pap. 14.99 *(978-0-8499-2910-6(5))* 2007. 240p. 24.99 *(978-0-7852-2081-7(X))* Nelson, Thomas Inc.

Sullivan, Tom. As I See It. 2012. (ENG.). 256p. 22.99 ***(978-1-4516-6351-8(X)***, Howard Bks.) Howard Books.

Wessler, D. J. & McDaniel, Adam Dawson. Chasing Echoes Through the Dark. 2011. (ENG.). *(978-0-9719919-2-7(8))* Aisling Eye Bks.

BLIND—BOOKS AND READING

Library of Congress, National Library Service for the Blind and Physically Handicapped Staff, contrib. by. Westerns, 2011. 2011. ***(978-0-8444-9524-8(7))*** Library of Congress.

Walker, Charles. Blind but Now I See. 2009. pap. 19.99 *(978-1-61623-345-7(1))* Independent Pub.

BLIND—EDUCATION

see also Deafblind People—Education

Akanji, David Oyebamiji. A Study of Blind Education in Three States of Nigeria. 2009. 216p. pap. 23.65 *(978-1-4269-1471-3(7))* Trafford Publishing.

Eaton, Allen H. Beauty for the Sighted & the Blind. 2011. 268p. 47.95 ***(978-1-258-00201-5(9))*** Literary Licensing, LLC.

Ferrell, Kay Alicyn. Reach Out & Teach: Helping Your Child Who Is Visually Impaired Learn & Grow. 2nd ed. 2011. ***(978-0-89128-484-0(2))***; ***(978-0-89128-457-4(5))*** American Foundation for the Blind Pr.

French, Sally, et al. An Oral History of the Education of Visually Impaired People: Telling Stories for Inclusive Futures. 2006. (Illus.). 448p. 129.95 *(978-0-7734-5706-5(2))* Mellen, Edwin Pr., The.

Hayhoe, Simon. God, Money, & Politics: English Attitudes to Blindness & Touch, from the Enlightenment to Integration. 2008. 136p. (C). pap. *(978-1-59311-913-3(5))* Information Age Publishing, Inc.

—God, Money, & Politics: English Attitudes to Blindness & Touch, from the Enlightenment to Integration (HC) 2008. 136p. (C). 84.99 *(978-1-59311-914-0(3))* Information Age Publishing, Inc.

Kinash, S. & Paszuk, A. Accessible education for blind Learners. 2007. 40p. per. 39.99 *(978-1-59311-649-1(7))* Information Age Publishing, Inc.

Mann, Horace. Twelve Sermons: Delivered at Antioch College. 2006. 316p. per. 23.99 *(978-1-4255-3044-0(3))* MPublishing.

Martin, Frances. Elizabeth Gilbert & Her Work for the Blind. 2011. 164p. pap. 14.99 ***(978-1-61203-073-9(4))*** Bottom of the Hill Publishing.

Oliphant, John. The Early Education of the Blind in Britain C. 1790-1900: Institutional Experience in England & Scotland. 2007. 200p. *(978-0-7734-5247-3(8))* Mellen, Edwin Pr., The.

Region IV Education Service Center. Psychoeducational Assessment of Students who are Visually Impaired or Blind: Infancy through High School. 2007. spiral bd. *(978-1-933521-71-8(6))* Region IV Education Service Ctr.

Tunstall, Kate E. Blindness & Enlightenment: An Essay - With a New Translation of Diderots Letter on the Blind. 2011. (ENG., Illus.). 256p. pap. 29.95 *(978-1-4411-1932-2(9))* Continuum International Publishing Group, Ltd. GBR. Dist: National Bk. Network.

—Blindness & Enlightenment: Diderot's 'Letter on the Blind': an Essay with a New Translation. 2011. (ENG., Illus.). 256p. 100.00 *(978-1-4411-5803-1(0))* Continuum International Publishing Group, Ltd. GBR. Dist: National Bk. Network.

Were, Charles M. The Relationship Between Self-Concept & Achievement in Maths. 2010. 76p. pap. *(978-3-639-27496-7(2))* VDM Verlag Dr. Mueller e.K.

Willoughby, Edith. Overbrook School for the Blind. 2007. (College History Ser.). (Illus.). 128p. per. 19.99 *(978-0-7385-4916-3(9))* Arcadia Publishing.

BLIND—JUVENILE LITERATURE

Marilyn Maple, Ph. D. & Marilyn Maple. I Can't Hear the Walls. 2010. 52p. pap. *(978-1-4269-2892-5(0))* Trafford Publishing (UK) Ltd.

Schaefer, Lola M. Algunos Niños Son Ciegos. 2010. (Comprendiendo las diferencias/Understanding Differences Ser.).Tr. of Some Kids Are Blind. (MUL & SPA.). 24p. (gr. k-1). lib. bdg. 21.32 *(978-1-4296-4590-4(3))* Capstone Pr., Inc.

BLIND—LIFE SKILLS GUIDES

Seamans, Art. I See, Said the Blind Man. 2010. 136p. pap. 13.95 *(978-1-4490-9837-7(1))* AuthorHouse.

BLIND—ORIENTATION AND MOBILITY

Ferguson, Ronald J. The Blind Need Not Apply: A History of Overcoming Prejudice in the Orientation & Mobility Profession. 2006. (Critical Concerns in Blindness Ser.). (ENG.). 164p. (C). *(978-1-59311-575-3(X))*; per. *(978-1-59311-574-6(1))* Information Age Publishing, Inc.

Penrod, William. Spatial Organization Skills of the Blind in Large Outdoor Places. 2009. 180p. pap. *(978-3-639-14408-6(2))* VDM Verlag Dr. Mueller e.K.

Warren, D. H. & Strelow, Edward R., eds. Electronic Spatial Sensing for the Blind: Contributions from Perception, Rehabilitation, & Computer Vision. 2010. (NATO Science Series E: (closed) Ser.). 544p. pap. 469.00 *(978-90-481-8293-0(X)*, 904818293X) Springer.

Wiener, William R., et al. Foundations of Orientation & Mobility. 3rd ed. 2010. *(978-0-89128-448-2(6))*; *(978-0-89128-462-8(1))* American Foundation for the Blind Pr.

BLIND—PERSONAL NARRATIVES

see Blind—Biography

BLIND—PRINTING AND WRITING SYSTEMS

Risjord, Constance. Instruction Manual for Braille Transcribing. 5th ed. 2009. *(978-0-8444-1227-6(9))* Library of Congress.

BLIND—REHABILITATION

Crandell, John M. & Robinson, Lee W. Living with low vision & Blindness: Guidelines That Help Professionals & Individuals Understand Vision Impairments. 2007. 220p. pap. 49.95 *(978-0-398-07741-9(X))*; pap. 34.95 *(978-0-398-07742-6(8))* Thomas, Charles C. Pub., Ltd.

Kurson, Robert. Crashing Through: The Extraordinary True Story of the Man Who Dared to See. 2008. (ENG., Illus.). 320p. pap. 16.00 *(978-0-8129-7368-6(2)*, Random Hse. Trade Paperbacks) Random House Publishing Group.

La Grow, Steve & Long, Richard. Orientation & Mobility: Techniques for Independence. 2nd ed. 2011. (Illus.). pap. 44.95 ***(978-0-9821792-4-6(3))*** Assn. for Education & Rehab of Blind & Visually Impaired.

Tenberken, Sabriye. My Path Leads to Tibet: The Inspiring Story of How One Young Blind Woman Brought Hope to the Blind Children of Tibet. l.t. ed. 2007. 368p. 32.50 *(978-1-84617-941-9(6))* Ulverscroft Large Print Bks., Ltd.

Wiener, William R., et al. Foundations of Orientation & Mobility. 3rd ed. 2010. *(978-0-89128-448-2(6))*; *(978-0-89128-462-8(1))* American Foundation for the Blind Pr.

BLIND—SERVICES FOR

see also Blind—Rehabilitation

Durflinger, Serge Marc. Veterans with a Vision: Canada's War Blinded in Peace & War. 2010. (ENG., Illus.). 484p. (C). pap. 29.95 *(978-0-7748-1856-8(5))* UBC Pr. CAN. Dist: Univ. of Washington Pr.

Ferguson, Ronald J. The Blind Need Not Apply: A History of Overcoming Prejudice in the Orientation & Mobility Profession. 2006. (Critical Concerns in Blindness Ser.). (ENG.). 164p. (C). *(978-1-59311-575-3(X))*; per. *(978-1-59311-574-6(1))* Information Age Publishing, Inc.

Fogg, Laura. Traveling Blind: Life Lessons from Unlikely Teachers. 2007. (Illus.). 280p. pap. 16.00 *(978-0-9797152-0-4(2))* Medusa's Muse.

Lucas, David. Stepping into the Dark: A lad from Jarrow battles with sight Loss. 2010. (Illus.). 228p. pap. 28.00 *(978-1-906619-17-6(4))* Fresh Heart Publishing GBR. Dist: Lightning Source, Inc.

Norman, Andrew. Father of the Blind. 2009. (ENG., Illus.). 160p. 32.95 *(978-0-7524-5182-4(0))* History Pr. Ltd.,The GBR. Dist: Independent Pubs. Group.

Tenberken, Sabriye. My Path Leads to Tibet: The Inspiring Story of How One Young Blind Woman Brought Hope to the Blind Children of Tibet. l.t. ed. 2007. 368p. 32.50 *(978-1-84617-941-9(6))* Ulverscroft Large Print Bks., Ltd.

Tobe, Carol Brenner. History in the Making: The Story of the American Printing House for the Blind 1858-2008. 2008. (Illus.). 178p. 39.95 *(978-1-884532-96-2(9))* Butler Bk. Publishing.

BLIND—TRAVEL

see also Guide Dogs

Naylor, Nicola. Jasmine & Arnica. 2010. (Eye Classics Ser.). (ENG.). 250p. pap. 12.95 *(978-1-903070-76-5(7))* Eye Bks. GBR. Dist: Independent Pubs. Group.

BLIND, BOOKS FOR THE

see Blind—Books and Reading

BLIND, SERVICES FOR THE

see Blind—Services for

BLIND CHILDREN

see Children, Blind

BLIND-DEAF

see Deafblind People

BLIND FLYING

see Instrument Flying

BLIND SERVICES

see Blind—Services for

BLINDNESS

see also Color Blindness

Afshan, Yasmeen. Childhood Blindness: Genetic & Molecular Basis of Hereditary Congenital Cataract. 2011. 144p. pap. ***(978-3-639-32133-3(2))*** VDM Verlag Dr. Mueller e.K.

Ashmead, Daniel H., et al, eds. Blindness & Brain Plasticity in Navigation & Object Perception. 2007. (ENG., Illus.). 448p. 120.00 *(978-0-8058-5551-7(3)*, Psychology Press) Taylor & Francis Group GBR. Dist: Taylor & Francis Group.

Brown, Eleanor Gertrude. Milton's Blindness. 2011. 178p. 42.95 ***(978-1-258-03796-3(3))*** Literary Licensing, LLC.

Cattaneo, Zaira & Vecchi, Tomaso. Blind Vision: The Neuroscience of Visual Impairment. 2011. (ENG., Illus.). 280p. (gr. 17). 36.00 *(978-0-262-01503-5(X))* MIT Pr.

Dagnelie, Gislin, ed. Visual Prosthetics: Physiology, Bioengineering, Rehabilitation. 2011. (ENG., Illus.). xviii, 453p. 179.00 *(978-1-4419-0753-0(X)*, 144190753X) Springer.

Fisichella, David. Seven-Tenths: Love, Piracy, & Science at Sea. 2010. (LeapSci Ser.). (ENG.). 232p. pap. 15.95 *(978-1-935248-10-1(3))* Leapfrog Pr.

Goodwin, Harper W. Blind, Blindness & Visual Capacities with Index & Medical Analysis of New Research Information for All Nations. 2006. (Illus.). 160p. 69.95 *(978-0-7883-4450-3(1)*, 07883-44501) ABBE Pubs. Assn. of Washington, D.C.

Harris, Helen J. How to Survive Losing Vision: Managing & Overcoming Progressive Blindness Because of Retinal Disease. 2011. 200p. pap. 16.95 ***(978-1-4567-4801-2(7))*** AuthorHouse.

Hartsock, Chad. Sight & Blindness in Luke-Acts: The Use of Physical Features in Characterization. 2008. (Biblical Interpretation Ser.). 232p. *(978-90-04-16535-9(5))* BRILL.

Hayhoe, Simon. God, Money, & Politics: English Attitudes to Blindness & Touch, from the Enlightenment to Integration. 2008. 136p. (C). pap. *(978-1-59311-913-3(5))* Information Age Publishing, Inc.

—God, Money, & Politics: English Attitudes to Blindness & Touch, from the Enlightenment to Integration (HC) 2008. 136p. (C). 84.99 *(978-1-59311-914-0(3))* Information Age Publishing, Inc.

Higgins, Jeffrey & Truax, Dominique, eds. Eye Infections, Blindness & Myopia. 2009. (Illus.). 274p. 129.00 *(978-1-60692-630-7(6))* Nova Science Pubs., Inc.

Hopkins, Lloyd F. Training Manual for Sight Without Eyes - Through Mind Sight & Perception. 2008. 116p. pap. 12.95 *(978-1-884979-01-9(7))* Clear Springs Pr.

Horsky, Nicole. My Dog Is Blind: But Lives Life to the Full! 2010. (ENG., Illus.). 80p. pap. 19.95 *(978-1-84584-291-8(X)*, 184584291X, Hubble & Hattie) Veloce Publishing Ltd. GBR. Dist: MBI Distribution Services/Quayside Distribution.

Humayun, Mark S., et al, eds. Artificial Sight: Basic Research, Biomedical Engineering, & Clinical Advances. 2010. (Biological & Medical Physics, Biomedical Engineering Ser.). (Illus.). xxiv, 400p. pap. 139.00 *(978-1-4419-2382-0(9)*, 1441923829) Springer.

Jabeen, Farhat. Inheritance of Congenital Blindness. 2009. 108p. pap. *(978-3-639-21474-1(9))* VDM Verlag Dr. Mueller e.K.

Langdell, Cheri Colby & Langdell, Tim. Coping with Vision Loss: Understanding the Psychological, Social, & Spiritual Effects, 1 vol. 2010. 177p. 34.95 *(978-0-313-34664-4(X)*, C34664); *(978-0-313-34665-1(8))* Greenwood Publishing Group, Inc. (Praeger Pubs.).

Lucas, David. Stepping into the Dark: A lad from Jarrow battles with sight Loss. 2010. (Illus.). 228p. pap. 28.00 *(978-1-906619-17-6(4))* Fresh Heart Publishing GBR. Dist: Lightning Source, Inc.

McWilliam, Candia. What to Look for in Winter: A Memoir in Blindness. 2012. (ENG.). 464p. 27.99 ***(978-0-06-209450-6(5))*** HarperCollins Pubs.

Montalembert, Hugues de. Invisible: A Memoir. (ENG., Illus.). 144p. 2011. pap. 13.00 *(978-1-4165-9367-6(5))* 2010. 21.99 *(978-1-4165-9366-9(7))* Atria Bks. (Beyond Words/Atria Bks.).

Omansky, Beth. Borderlands of Blindness. 2011. 175p. 55.00 *(978-1-58826-780-1(6))* Rienner, Lynne Pubs.

Rieser, John J., et al, eds. Blindness, Brain Plasticity, & Spatial Function. 2007. (Illus.). 448p. 55.00 *(978-0-8058-6294-2(3))* Erlbaum, Lawrence Assocs., Inc.

Sullivan, Tom. As I See It. 2012. (ENG.). 256p. 22.99 ***(978-1-4516-6351-8(X)***, Howard Bks.) Howard Books.

Tunstall, Kate E. Blindness & Enlightenment: An Essay - With a New Translation of Diderots Letter on the Blind. 2011. (ENG., Illus.). 256p. pap. 29.95 *(978-1-4411-1932-2(9))* Continuum International Publishing Group, Ltd. GBR. Dist: National Bk. Network.

—Blindness & Enlightenment: Diderot's 'Letter on the Blind': an Essay with a New Translation. 2011. (ENG., Illus.). 256p. 100.00 *(978-1-4411-5803-1(0))* Continuum International Publishing Group, Ltd. GBR. Dist: National Bk. Network.

Varughese, Sara. A Situation Analysis of Retinopathy of Prematurity in South Afric. 2010. 64p. pap. *(978-3-8383-6793-4(6))* Lambert Academic Publishing.

Wyman, Frank. An Intellectual History of Blindness: The Enlightenment to the Present. 2012. (Routledge Studies in Cultural History Ser.). (ENG.). 168p. (C). 125.00 *(978-0-415-89620-7(7))* Routledge.

BLISS, TASKER HOWARD, 1853-1930

Palmer, Frederick. Bliss, Peacemaker: The Life & Letters of General Tasker Howard Bliss. 520p. 2010. 44.76 *(978-1-163-36877-0(6))* 2010. pap. 32.76 *(978-1-162-76817-5(7))* 2007. (ENG.). 55.95 *(978-0-548-05658-9(X))* Kessinger Publishing, LLC.

BLITZKRIEG

see Lightning War

BLIXEN, KAREN, 1885-1962

see Dinesen, Isak, 1885-1962

BLIZZARDS

Adamson, Heather. Surviving a Blizzard. 2011. (Amicus Readers: Be Prepared (Level 2) Ser.). 24p. (J). (gr. 1-4). 16.95 *(978-1-60753-147-0(X))* Amicus Publishing.

Earls, Alan R. Greater Boston's Blizzard Of 1978. 2008. (Images of America Ser.). (ENG., Illus.). 128p. per. 21.99 *(978-0-7385-5519-5(3))* Arcadia Publishing.

Light, Japheth J. Blizzard Sudoku. 2011. (ENG., Illus.). 240p. pap. 7.95 *(978-1-4027-8007-3(9)*, Puzzlewright) Sterling Publishing Co., Inc.

Rice, William. Forces in Nature Floods & Blizzards: Geology & Weather. 2009. (Science Readers Ser.). 32p. (gr. 2-3). pap. 8.99 *(978-1-4333-0313-5(2))* Teacher Created Materials, Inc.

Snow Disasters for Local, State & Federal Governments in the National Capital Region: Response & Recovery Partnerships with FEMA: Hearing Before the Subcommittee on Economic Development, Public Buildings, & Emergency Management of the Committee on Transportation & Infrastructure, House of Representatives, One Hundred Eleventh Congress, Second Session, March 23, 2010. 2010. xiii, 172p. *(978-0-16-086391-2(0)*, 552-070-41470-3) United States Government Printing Office.

Taylor. Humbled by the Devastator. 2007. 192p. pap. 18.75 *(978-0-9796963-4-3(8))* Taylor, Carol Bks.

BLMC AUTOMOBILES

see also Austin Automobile; Austin-Healey Automobile; M.G. Automobile; Mini Automobiles

Mort, Norm & Fox, Tony. Triumph Stag, 1970-1977. 2010. (Essential Buyer's Guide Ser.). (ENG., Illus.). 64p. pap. 19.95 *(978-1-84584-270-3(7)*, 1845842707) Veloce Publishing Ltd. GBR. Dist: MBI Distribution Services/Quayside Distribution.

Robson, Graham. The A-Series Engine: Its First Sixty Years. 2011. (ENG., Illus.). 256p. 49.95 *(978-0-85733-083-3(7)*, 0857330837) Haynes Publishing PLC GBR. Dist: MBI Distribution Services/Quayside Distribution.

BLOCH, ERNEST, 1880-1959

Móricz, Klára. Jewish Identities: Nationalism, Racism, & Utopianism in Twentieth-Century Music. 2008. (California Studies in 20th-Century Music). (Illus.). 436p. 60.00 *(978-0-520-25088-8(5))* Univ. of California Pr.

BLOCH, ERNST, 1885-1977

Korstvedt, Benjamin M. Listening for Utopia in Ernst Bloch's Musical Philosophy. 2010. (ENG., Illus.). 234p. 99.00 *(978-0-521-89615-3(0))* Cambridge Univ. Pr.

Richter, Gerhard. Thought-Images: Frankfurt School Writers' Reflections from Damaged Life. 2007. (Cultural Memory in the Present Ser.). (ENG., Illus.). 256p. 65.00 *(978-0-8047-5616-7(3))*; per. 24.95 *(978-0-8047-5617-4(1))* Stanford Univ. Pr.

BLOCH, ROBERT, 1917-1994

Bilstad, T. Allan. The Lovecraft Necronomicon Primer: A Guide to the Cthulhu Mythos. 2009. (ENG.). 288p. pap. 11.95 *(978-0-7387-1379-3(1))* Llewellyn Pubns.

Szumskyj, Benjamin, ed. The Man Who Collected Psychos: Critical Essays on Robert Bloch. 2009. (ENG., Illus.). 262p. pap. 35.00 *(978-0-7864-4208-9(5))* McFarland & Co., Inc. Pubs.

BLOCK ANESTHESIA

see Conduction Anesthesia

BLOCK BOOKS

see also Wood-Engraving

Schwieger, Peter, ed. Tibetische Handschriften und Blockdrucke: Teil 13: (Die mTshur-phu-Ausgabe der Sammlung Rin-chen gter-mdzod chen-mo, nach dem Exemplar der Orientabteilung, Staatsbibliothek zu Berlin Preussischer Kulturbesitz, Hs or 778, Bande 4052) 2009. (Verzeichnis der Orientalischen Handschriften in Deutschland (VOHD) Ser.). (GER & TIB.). 474p. (C). 117.00 *(978-3-515-07347-9(7))* Steiner, Franz Verlag Wiesbaden GmbH DEU. Dist: Brown, David Bk. Co., The.

BLOCK BOOKS—FACSIMILES

see also Incunabula—Facsimiles

Biblia Pauperum. 195.00 *(978-0-9633632-0-6(4))* Ebory, Inc.

BLOCK COPOLYMERS

Abetz, Volker. Block Copolymers I. 2010. (Advances in Polymer Science Ser.). xii, 238p. pap. 239.00 *(978-3-642-06589-7(9)*, 3642065899) Springer.

—Block Copolymers II. 2010. (Advances in Polymer Science Ser.). xii, 252p. pap. 279.00 *(978-3-642-06595-8(3)*, 3642065953) Springer.

Gorzolnik, Blazej. Block Copolymer Nanostructuring: Amphiphilic Block Copolymers as Templates for Particle Formation & Positioning. 2008. 188p. pap. *(978-3-639-08625-6(2))* VDM Verlag Dr. Mueller e.K.

Lazzari, Massimo, et al, eds. Block Copolymers in Nanoscience. 2007. (ENG., Illus.). 447p. 225.00 *(978-3-527-31309-9(5)*, Wiley-VCH) Wiley, John & Sons, Inc.

Lee, Kwang-Sup. Polymer Materials: Block-Copolymers, Nanocomposites, Organic/Inorganic Hybrids, Polymethylenes. Lee, Kwang-Sup & Kobayashi, Shiro, eds. 2010. (Advances in Polymer Science Ser.). (Illus.). ix, 235p. 359.00 *(978-3-642-13626-9(5)*, 3642136265) Springer.

Müller, Axel & Schmidt, Hans-Werner, eds. Complex Macromolecular Systems I, 2 vols. 2010. (Advances in Polymer Science Ser.). (Illus.). xii, 220p. 299.00 *(978-3-642-12875-2(0)*, 3642128750) Springer.

—Complex Macromolecular Systems II, 2 vols. 2010. (Advances in Polymer Science Ser.). (Illus.). xii, 220p. 259.00 *(978-3-642-12911-7(0)*, 3642129110) Springer.

Müller, Axel H. E. & Borisov, Oleg, eds. Self Organized Nanostructures of Amphiphilic Block Copolymers I, 2 vols. 2011. (Advances in Polymer Science Ser.). (Illus.). xiii, 253p. 309.00 ***(978-3-642-22485-0(7)***, 3642224857) Springer.

Peeters, Marloes. Biohybrid Nanocomposites. 2010. 120p. pap. *(978-3-8383-7873-2(3))* Lambert Academic Publishing.

Schmidt, Kristin. Orientation & Phase Behavior of Block Copolymers in External Electric Fields. 2008. 152p. pap. *(978-3-639-00929-3(0))* VDM Verlag Dr. Mueller e.K.

Scruggs, Neal. Block Copolymers in Liquid Crystal Solvents. 2009. 336p. pap. *(978-3-639-13224-3(6))* VDM Verlag Dr. Mueller e.K.

Segewicz, Liudvikas & Petrowsky, Marijus. Polymer Aging, Stabilizers & Amphiphilic Block Copolymers. 2010. (Polymer Science & Technology Ser.). 145.00 *(978-1-60692-928-5(3))* Nova Science Pubs., Inc.

Theato, Patrick, et al, eds. Non-Conventional Functional Block Copolymers, 1 vol. 2012. (ACS Symposium Ser.). (ENG., Illus.). 160p. 150.00 ***(978-0-8412-2614-2(8))*** American Chemical Society.

Tsui, Ophelia K. C. Polymer Thin Films. 2008. (Illus.). 350p. 117.00 *(978-981-281-881-2(2))* World Scientific Publishing Co., Inc.

BLOCK FLUTE

see Recorder (Musical Instrument)

BLOCK POLYMERS

see Block Copolymers

BLOCK-PRINTING, LINOLEUM

see Linoleum Block-Printing

BLOCKADE

see also Continental System of Napoleon

Bayoumi, Moustafa, ed. Midnight on the Mavi Marmara: The Attack on the Gaza Freedom Flotilla & How It Changed the Course of the Israel/Palestine Conflict. 2010. (ENG.). 280p. pap. 16.00 *(978-1-60846-121-9(1))* Haymarket Bks.

Copeland, Thomas E., et al. Drawing a Line in the Sea: The 2010 Gaza Flotilla Incident & the Israeli-Palestinian Conflict. 2011. E-Book ***(978-0-7391-6955-1(6))*** Lexington Bks.

Davis, Lance & Engerman, Stanley L. Naval Blockades in Peace & War: An Economic History Since 1750. 2006. (ENG., Illus.). 464p. 110.00 *(978-0-521-85749-9(X))* Cambridge Univ. Pr.

Elleman, Bruce Allen & Paine, Sarah C. M., eds. Naval Blockades & Seapower. 2007. 39.95 *(978-0-415-43871-1(3))* Routledge.

Hobart-Hampden, Augustus. Never Caught. 2008. (Civil War Ser.). (ENG.). 72p. pap. 9.95 *(978-1-4290-1528-8(4))* Applewood Bks.

Hogan, Albert E. Pacific Blockade. 2007. (ENG.). 188p. 37.95 *(978-0-548-20875-5(1))*; 192p. per. 22.95 *(978-1-4325-2716-7(9))* Kessinger Publishing, LLC.

Kaserman, James & Kaserman, Sarah. Florida Pirates: From the Southern Gulf Coast to the Keys & Beyond. 2011. 144p. pap. 16.99 ***(978-1-60949-419-3(9))*** History Pr., The.

Underwood, Rodman L. Waters of Discord: The Union Blockade of Texas During the Civil War. alt. ed. 2008. (ENG., Illus.). 208p. pap. 35.00 *(978-0-7864-3776-4(6))* McFarland & Co., Inc. Pubs.

Wiche, Glen N., ed. Dispatches from Bermuda: The Civil War Letters of Charles Maxwell Allen, U. S. Consul at Bermuda, 1861-1888. 2008. (Civil War in the North Ser.). (Illus.). 160p. 32.00 *(978-0-87338-938-9(7))* Kent State Univ. Pr.

BLOGGING

see Blogs

BLOGS

Albert, Susan Wittig. An Extraordinary Year of Ordinary Days. 2010. (ENG.). 240p. 24.95 *(978-0-292-72306-1(7))* Univ. of Texas Pr.

Armstrong, Jerome, et al. Crashing the Gate: Netroots, Grassroots, & the Rise of People-Powered Politics. 2006. (ENG.). 216p. pap. 12.95 *(978-1-933392-41-7(X))* Chelsea Green Publishing.

Aryon Weblog Authors. Aryon's Spanking Stories. 2011. 174p. pap. 18.96 ***(978-1-4466-9051-2(2))*** Lulu Enterprises Inc.

Bailey, Brian. The Blogging Church: Sharing the Story of Your Church Through Blogs. 2007. (Jossey-Bass Leadership Network Ser.: 24). (ENG.). 224p. per. 19.95 *(978-0-7879-8487-8(6)*, Jossey-Bass) Wiley, John & Sons, Inc.

Balakina, Julia. Anglicisms in Russian & German Blogs: A Comparative Analysis. 2011. (Hallesche Sprach- und Textforschung Ser.). 262p. 76.95 *(978-3-631-61517-1(5))* Lang, Peter GmbH, Europaischer Verlag der Wissenschaften DEU. Dist: Lang, Peter.

B

Balijepalli, Sandeep. Information Retrieval based on Sentiment Analysis: Blogvox2: Modular Domain Independent Approach. 2008. 72p. pap. (978-3-639-10151-5(0)) VDM Verlag Dr. Mueller e.K.

Banks, Michael A. Blogging Heroes: Interviews with 30 of the World's Top Bloggers. 2007. (ENG., Illus.). 298p. 24.99 (978-0-470-19739-4(0), Wiley) Wiley, John & Sons, Inc.

Barlow, Aaron. Blogging America: The New Public Sphere, 1 vol. 2007. (New Directions in Media Ser.). 200p. 49.95 (978-0-275-99872-1(X), C9872, Praeger Pubs.) Greenwood Publishing Group, Inc.

—The Rise of the Blogosphere, 1 vol. 2007. 232p. 49.95 (978-0-275-98996-5(8), C8996, Praeger Pubs.) Greenwood Publishing Group, Inc.

Beck, Jessica Neuman & Beck, Matt. WordPress: Visual QuickStart Guide. 2009. (Visual QuickStart Guide Ser.). (ENG., Illus.). 288p. pap. 29.99 (978-0-321-67921-5(0)) Peachpit Pr.

Beck, Matt & Beck, Jessica Neuman. Wordpress. 2nd rev. ed. 2011. (Visual QuickStart Guide Ser.). (ENG., Illus.). 288p. pap. 29.99 **(978-0-321-79266-2(1))** Peachpit Pr.

Becker, Gary S. & Posner, Richard A. Uncommon Sense: Economic Insights, from Marriage to Terrorism. 2009. (ENG.). 384p. 29.00 (978-0-226-04101-8(8)) Univ. of Chicago Pr.

Bly, Robert W. Blog Schmog: The Truth about What Blogs Can (and Can't) Do for Your Business, 0 vols. 2007. (Illus.). 256p. 19.99 (978-0-7852-1576-9(X)) Nelson, Thomas Inc.

Boehlert, Eric. Bloggers on the Bus: How the Internet Changed Politics & the Press. (ENG.). 304p. 2010. pap. 15.00 (978-1-4165-6011-1(4)) 2009. (Illus.). 26.00 (978-1-4165-6010-4(6)) Free Pr. (Free Pr.).

Boxer, Sarah. Ultimate Blogs: Masterworks from the Wild Web. 2008. (Vintage Original Ser.). (ENG., Illus.). 368p. pap. 14.95 (978-0-307-27806-7(9), Vintage) Knopf Doubleday Publishing Group.

Brazell, Aaron. WordPress Bible. (Bible Ser.: 634). (ENG., Illus.). 2010. 672p. pap. 49.99 (978-0-470-56813-2(5)) 2nd ed. 2011. 744p. pap. 49.99 (978-0-470-93781-5(5)) Wiley, John & Sons, Inc. (Wiley).

Brogan, Molly. All about Living: Book 1. 2010. 128p. pap. 14.99 (978-0-557-26574-9(6)) Lulu Enterprises Inc.

Brown, Bruce C. The Secret Power of Blogging: How to Promote & Market Your Business, Organization, or Cause with Free Blogs. 2007. (ENG., Illus.). 288p. per. 24.95 (978-1-60138-009-8(7)) Atlantic Publishing Co.

Bruns, Axel. Blogs, Wikipedia, Second Life, & Beyond: From Production to Produsage. 2008. (Digital Formations Ser.). 432p. (C). 119.95 (978-0-8204-8867-7(4)); pap. 34.95 (978-0-8204-8866-0(6)) Lang, Peter Publishing, Inc.

Bruns, Axel & Jacobs, Joanne. Uses of Blogs. 2006. (Digital Formations Ser.: Vol. 38). vi, 267p. (C). pap. 32.95 (978-0-8204-8124-1(6)) Lang, Peter Publishing, Inc.

Bryant, Brantley L. Geoffrey Chaucer Hath a Blog: Medieval Studies & New Media. 2010. (New Middle Ages Ser.). (ENG.). 212p. 89.00 (978-0-230-10506-5(8)); pap. 26.00 (978-0-230-10507-2(6)) Palgrave Macmillan.

Bryant, Stephanie Cottrell. Videoblogging for Dummies. 2006. (ENG., Illus.). 386p. pap. 29.99 (978-0-471-97177-1(4), For Dummies) Wiley, John & Sons, Inc.

Buckley, James F. Blogs on God: A Unique Collection of Brief, High-Impact, This & Thats on God, the Bible, & the Human Race. 2007. (ENG.). 144p. per. 7.99 (978-1-59979-255-2(9), Creation Hse.) Charisma Media.

Burrows, Terry. Blogs, Wikis, Myspace, & More: Everything You Want to Know about Using Web 2. 0 but Are Afraid to Ask. 2008. (ENG., Illus.). 224p. pap. 14.95 (978-1-55652-756-2(X)) Chicago Review Pr., Inc.

Butow, Eric & Bollwitt, Rebecca. Blogging to Drive Business: Create & Maintain Valuable Customer Connections. 2010. (Que Biz-Tech Ser.). (ENG., Illus.). 192p. pap. 21.99 (978-0-7897-4256-8(X)) Que.

Cartwright, Reed, Editor & Zivkovic, Bora, Series Editor. The Open Laboratory: the Best Science Writing on Blogs 2007. 2008. 324p. per. 29.96 (978-1-4357-0832-7(6)) Lulu Enterprises Inc.

Cass, John. Strategies & Tools for Corporate Blogging. 2007. (ENG., Illus.). 240p. per. 32.95 (978-0-7506-8416-3(X)) Routledge.

Castro, Elizabeth. Publishing a Blog with Blogger. 2nd ed. 2009. (Visual QuickProject Guide Ser.). (ENG., Illus.). 192p. pap. 19.99 (978-0-321-63752-9(6)) Peachpit Pr.

Cho, Joy Deangdeelert & Ilasco, Meg Mateo. Blog, Inc: Blogging for Passion, Profit, & to Create Community. Ilasco, Meg Mateo, ed. 2012. (ENG.). 184p. pap. 16.95 **(978-1-4521-0720-2(3))** Chronicle Bks. LLC.

Chow, John. Make Money Online: Roadmap of a Dot Com Mogul. 2010. (ENG.). 160p. pap. 15.95 (978-1-60037-673-3(8)) Morgan James Publishing.

Cleger, Osvaldo. Narrar en la ERA de Las Blogoficciones: Literatura, Cultura y Sociedad de Las Redes en el Siglo XXI. 2010. (SPA.). 478p. 129.95 (978-0-7734-3599-5(9)) Mellen, Edwin Pr., The.

Cole, Allan, et al. Build Your Own Wicked Wordpress Themes. 2010. (ENG., Illus.). 250p. pap. 39.95 (978-0-9804552-9-8(4)) SitePoint Pty, Ltd. AUS. Dist: Ingram Pub. Services.

Coombs, Karen A. & Griffey, Jason. Library Blogging. 2008. (Illus.). 151p. pap. 39.95 (978-1-58683-331-2(6)) Linworth Publishing, Inc.

Cooper, Stephen D. Watching the Watchdog: Bloggers as the Fifth Estate. 2006. 385p. per. 39.95 (978-0-922993-47-5(5)) Marquette Bks., LLC.

Crockett, Lee, et al. The Digital Diet: Today's Digital Tools in Small Bytes. 2010. (21st Century Fluency Ser.). (Illus.). 196p. pap. 32.95 (978-1-4129-8236-8(7), B82368P) Corwin Pr.

Crosby, Connie. Effective Blogging for Libraries. 2010. (Tech Set Ser.: Vol. 10). (Illus.). 138p. 55.00 (978-1-55570-713-2(0)) Neal-Schuman Pubs., Inc.

Cross, Mary. Bloggerati, Twitterati: How Blogs & Twitter Are Transforming Popular Culture, 1 vol. 2011. (Illus.). 190p. 34.95 (978-0-313-38484-4(3), A2935C) Greenwood Publishing Group, Inc.

Davis, Richard Harding. Typing Politics: The Role of Blogs in American Politics. 2009. (ENG.). 256p. pap. 19.95 (978-0-19-537375-2(8)) Oxford Univ. Pr., Inc.

Day-MacLeod, Deirdre. Career Building Through Blogging. 2009. (Digital Career Building Ser.). 64p. (gr. 6-6). 58.50 (978-1-61512-163-2(3)) Rosen Publishing Group, Inc., The.

Dean, Jodi. Blog Theory: Feedback & Capture in the Circuits of Drive. 2010. (ENG.). 140p. 64.95 (978-0-7456-4969-6(6)); pap. 19.95 (978-0-7456-4970-2(X)) Polity Pr. GBR. Dist: Wiley, John & Sons, Inc.

Demopoulos, Ted. Secrets of Successful Blogging: 101+ Tips for Blogging more Efficiently, Effectively, & Profitably. 2007. 40p. 7.00 (978-0-9788060-0-2(X)) Demopoulos Assocs.

—Secrets of Successful Blogging System: 101+ Tips for Blogging More Efficiently, Effectively, & Profitably, 3 Audio CDs & 1 Booklet. 2007. 40p. audio compact disk 97.00 (978-0-9788060-1-9(8)) Demopoulos Assocs.

Diamond, Lisa M. & Plumley, George. WordPress 24-Hour Trainer. 2nd ed. 2011. (ENG., Illus.). 408p. pap. 34.99 (978-1-118-06690-4(1), Wrox) Wiley, John & Sons, Inc.

Douglas, Nick. Twitter Wit: Brilliance in 140 Characters or Less. 2009. (ENG.). 240p. pap. 12.99 (978-0-06-189727-6(2)) HarperCollins Pubs.

Dumova, Tatyana & Fiordo, Richard. Blogging in the Global Society: Cultural, Political & Geographical Aspects. 2011. xv, 285p. **(978-1-60960-746-3(5))** IGI Global.

Dumova, Tatyana & Fiordo, Richard, eds. Blogging in the Global Society: Cultural, Political & Geographical Aspects. 2011. 415p. 195.00 (978-1-60960-744-9(9), Information Science Reference) IGI Global.

Duncan, Donna, et al. The New ISearch, You Search, We All Learn to Research: A How-To-Do-It Manual for Teaching Research Using Web 2.0 Tools & Digital Resources. 2011. (Illus.). 175p. 60.00 **(978-1-55570-758-3(0))** Neal-Schuman Pubs., Inc.

Elzer, Christoph. Watchblogs. 2010. 76p. pap. (978-3-639-24602-5(0)) VDM Verlag Dr. Mueller e.K.

Entrepreneur Press Staff & Rich, Jason R. Start Your Own Blogging Business. 2nd ed. 2010. (ENG.). 240p. pap. 19.95 (978-1-59918-376-3(5), 1599183765) Entrepreneur Pr. dba Entrepreneur Media, Inc.

Evans, Cassie M., ed. Internet Issues: Blogging, the Digital Divide & Digital Libraries. 2010. (Internet Policies & Issues Ser.). 129.00 (978-1-60741-824-5(X)) Nova Science Pubs., Inc.

Farkas, Meredith. Social Software in Libraries: Building Collaboration, Communication, & Community Online. 2007. (Illus.). xxiv, 320p. pap. 39.50 (978-1-57387-275-1(X)) Information Today, Inc.

Fitzgibbon, Kathleen. Teaching with Wikis, Blogs, Podcasts & More: Dozens of Easy Ideas for Using Technology to Get Kids Excited about Learning. 2010. (ENG.). 48p. (gr. 3). pap. 10.99 (978-0-545-16834-2(1), Teaching Resources) Scholastic, Inc.

Forrester, Duane & Powell, Gavin. How to Make Money with Your Blog: The Ultimate Reference Guide for Building, Optimizing, & Monetizing Your Blog. 2007. (ENG., Illus.). 256p. per. 21.95 (978-0-07-150857-5(0), 0071508570) McGraw-Hill Cos., The.

Frey, Tara. Blogging for Bliss: Crafting Your Own Online Journal: A Guide for Crafters, Artists & Creatives of all Kinds. 2009. (ENG., Illus.). 156p. pap. 14.95 (978-1-60059-511-0(1)) Lark Bks.

Fuller, Mati H. A Step by Step Wordpress Tutorial for Beginners. 2009. 120p. pap. 19.95 (978-0-578-02270-3(2)) Bigger Vision Bks.

The Future of Journalism: Hearing Before the Subcommittee on Communications, Technology, & the Internet of the Committee on Commerce, Science, & Transportation, United States Senate, One Hundred Eleventh Congress, First Session, May 6, 2009. 2010. iv, 120p. (978-0-16-086100-0(4), 552-070-41210-7) United States Government Printing Office.

Galapon, Clarence. Creating Unique Websites with Blogger. 2009. 121p. pap. 17.99 (978-0-557-06645-2(X)) Lulu Enterprises Inc.

Gardner, Susannah & Birley, Shane. Blogging for Dummies. 4th ed. 2012. (ENG., Illus.). 408p. pap. 24.99 **(978-1-118-15194-5(1),** For Dummies) Wiley, John & Sons, Inc.

Getgood, Susan J. Professional Blogging for Dummies. 2010. (ENG., Illus.). 384p. pap. 24.99 (978-0-470-60179-2(5), For Dummies) Wiley, John & Sons, Inc.

Gillieron, Rebecca, et al. The Bookaholic's Guide to Book Blogs. 2007. (ENG.). 288p. pap. 17.95 (978-0-7145-3151-9(0)) Boyars, Marion Pubs., Inc.

Gillin, Paul. The New Influencers: A Marketer's Guide to the New Social Media. 2009. (Books to Build Your Career By Ser.). (ENG.). 236p. pap. 16.95 (978-1-884956-94-2(7)) Linden Publishing Co., Inc.

Godin, Seth. Everyone Is an Expert. 2007. 52p. per. (978-956-291-214-3(0)) Editorial Benei Noaj.

—Everyone's an Expert. 2007. 52p. per. (978-956-291-986-9(2)) Editorial Benei Noaj.

Guerin, Lisa. Smart Policies for Workplace Technologies: Email, Blogs, Cell Phones & More. 2nd ed. 2011. E-Book (978-1-4133-1352-9(3)) NOLO.

—Smart Policies for Workplace Technology: Email, Blogs, Cell Phones & More, 2 vols. 2nd rev. ed. 2011. (ENG.). 240p. pap. 34.99 (978-1-4133-1326-0(4)) NOLO.

Gunelius, Susan. Blogging All-in-One for Dummies. (ENG., 720p. 2010. Illus.). pap. 34.99 (978-0-470-57377-8(5)) 2nd ed. 2012. pap. 34.99 **(978-1-118-29944-9(2))** Wiley, John & Sons, Inc. (For Dummies).

—The Complete Idiot's Guide to WordPress. 2011. (Complete Idiot's Guide Ser.). (ENG.). 464p. (gr. 12). 24.95 (978-1-61564-072-0(X), Alpha Bks.) Penguin Group (USA) Inc.

—Google Blogger for Dummies. 2009. (ENG., Illus.). 384p. pap. 26.99 (978-0-470-40742-4(5), For Dummies) Wiley, John & Sons, Inc.

Gupta, Sulakshana. Blog Journalism As an Online Public Sphere. 2011. 96p. pap. **(978-3-8433-8893-1(8))** Lambert Academic Publishing.

Haas, Tanni. Making It in the Political Blogosphere: The World's Top Political Bloggers Share the Secret. 2011. (ENG.). 182p. (C). pap. 20.25 **(978-0-7188-9277-7(1))** Lutherworth Pr., The GBR. Dist: Printondemand-worldwide.com.

Hangen, Nathan. Beyond Blogging. 2010. 232p. pap. 14.99 (978-0-557-27681-3(0)); (ENG.). pap. 22.00 (978-0-557-42315-6(5)) Lulu Enterprises Inc.

Hanson, Kathlene & Cervone, H. Frank. Using Interactive Technologies in Libraries: A LITA Guide. 2007. (Illus.). 59.95 (978-1-55570-612-8(6)) Neal-Schuman Pubs., Inc.

Hastings, Robin M. Microblogging & Lifestreaming in Libraries. 2010. (Tech Set Ser.: Vol. 3). (Illus.). ix, 103p. 55.00 (978-1-55570-707-1(6)) Neal-Schuman Pubs., Inc.

Hayder, Hasin. WordPress Complete: A Comprehensive, Step-by-Step Guide on How to Set up, Customize & Market Your Blog Using WordPress. 2006. pap. (978-1-904811-89-3(2)) Packt Publishing, Ltd.

Hayslip, Michael. WordPress Quickstart Guide. 2009. 124p. pap. 24.95 (978-0-557-17758-5(8)) Lulu Enterprises Inc.

Heaton, Gavin. The Dialup Guide to Blogging. 2009. 43p. pap. 9.97 (978-1-4092-8445-1(X)) Lulu Enterprises Inc.

Hedengren, Thord Daniel. Smashing WordPress: Beyond the Blog. (Smashing Magazine Book Ser.: 18). (ENG., 2nd ed. 2011. Illus.). 352p. pap. 39.99 (978-1-119-99596-8(5)) 3rd ed. 2012. 382p. pap. 44.99 **(978-1-119-94271-9(3))** Wiley, John & Sons, Inc. (Wiley).

—Smashing WordPress Themes: Making WordPress Beautiful. 2011. (Smashing Magazine Book Ser.: 2). (ENG.). 368p. pap. 39.99 (978-0-470-66990-7(X), Wiley) Wiley, John & Sons, Inc.

Hedengren, Thord Daniel. Tackling Tumblr: Web Publishing Made Simple. 2011. (ENG., Illus.). 272p. pap. 29.99 **(978-1-119-95015-8(5),** Wiley) Wiley, John & Sons, Inc.

Henderson Smith, Margaret. A Flight of Fancy. 2010. 150p. pap. (978-1-84549-418-6(0), Swirl) arima publishing.

Higginson, Simon. A Case Study on the Impact of Weblogs on the Writing of Low-Level Learners in the University of Chile. 2011. 102p. pap. 25.95 **(978-1-61233-756-2(2),** Dissertation.com) Universal Pubs.

Hogbin, Emma Jane & Kafer, Konstantin. Drupal Fundamentals. 2012. (ENG.). 69.99 (978-0-13-704036-0(9)) Prentice Hall PTR.

Hsiao, Kuo-Lun. Studies on the Behaviors of Internet Users in Web 2 0 Environment. 2011. 84p. pap. **(978-3-8443-1985-9(9))** Lambert Academic Publishing.

Huang, Eugene. Learner Perceptions of Using Blogs in English Learning - Instructional Technology-on Line Journal. 2008. 144p. pap. (978-3-8364-8650-7(4)) VDM Verlag Dr. Mueller e.K.

Hudson, David L. Blogging. 2nd rev. ed. 2011. (Point/Counterpoint Ser.). (Illus.). 116p. (C). (gr. 9). 35.00 (978-1-60413-749-1(5), Chelsea Hse.) Facts On File, Inc.

Huffington Post Editors. The Huffington Post Complete Guide to Blogging. 2008. (ENG., Illus.). 240p. pap. 15.00 (978-1-4391-0500-9(6)) Simon & Schuster.

Hussey, Tris. Create Your Own Blog: 6 Easy Projects to Start Blogging Like a Pro. (Create Your Own Ser.). (ENG., Illus.). 288p. 2009. pap. 24.99 (978-0-672-33065-0(2)) 2nd rev. ed. 2012. pap. 24.99 **(978-0-672-33597-6(2))** Sams.

Hussey, Tris. Using WordPress. (Using Ser.). (ENG., Illus.). 368p. 2011. pap. 24.99 **(978-0-7897-4907-9(6))** 2010. pap. 24.99 (978-0-7897-4634-4(4)) Que.

Ingram, Leah. Suddenly Frugal: How to Live Happier & Healthier for Less. 2010. (ENG.). 256p. pap. 12.95 (978-1-4405-0182-1(3)) Adams Media Corp.

Jansen, Bernard J. Handbook of Research on Web Log Analysis. 2008. (Illus.). 628p. 265.00 (978-1-59904-974-8(0), Information Science Publishing) IGI Global.

Johnson, Paul William. Creative Blogging: For Personal or Business Improvement How You Do Dat? 2009. 108p. 21.49 (978-1-4389-4993-2(6)); pap. 11.49 (978-1-4389-4994-9(4)) AuthorHouse.

Jones, Kyle M. L. & Farrington, Polly-Alida. Using Wordpress As a Library Content Management System. 2011. 66p. pap. 43.00 **(978-0-8389-5831-5(1))** American Library Assn.

Jordan, Lee. Blogger: Beyond the Basics. 2008. 356p. pap. (978-1-84719-317-9(X)) Packt Publishing, Ltd.

Joseph, Mary T. All You Need Is Food. 2009. pap. (978-1-61623-085-2(1)) Independent Pub.

Junli, Feng. Grassroots Blogging Practice in America & China- Studies on 60 American & 60 Chinese Bloggers. 2007. 136p. per. (978-3-8364-1773-0(1)) VDM Verlag Dr. Mueller e.K.

Kaminsky, Michael Sean. Naked Lens - Video Blogging & Video Journaling to Reclaim the YOU in YouTube: How to use Online Video to Increase Self Expression, Enhance Creativity, & Join the Video Regeneration. 2010. 224p. pap. (978-0-9813188-0-6(0)) Organik Media, Inc.

Karpf, David. The MoveOn Effect: The Unexpected Transformation of American Political Advocacy, 1 vol. 2012. (Oxford Studies in Digital Politics Ser.). (ENG.). 256p. pap. 27.95 **(978-0-19-989838-1(3))** Oxford Univ. Pr., Inc.

Karr, Douglas & Flannery, Chantelle. Corporate Blogging for Dummies. 2010. (ENG., Illus.). 432p. pap. 24.99 (978-0-470-60457-1(3), For Dummies) Wiley, John & Sons, Inc.

Keen, Andrew. The Cult of the Amateur: How Blogs, Myspace, Youtube, & the Rest of Today's User-Generated Media Are Destroying Our Economy, Our Culture, & Our Values. 2008. (ENG.). 256p. pap. 14.00 (978-0-385-52081-2(6), Broadway Business) Knopf Doubleday Publishing Group.

Kelsey, Todd. Social Networking Spaces: From Facebook to Twitter & Everything in Between. 2010. (ENG.). 536p. pap. 29.99 (978-1-4302-2596-6(3)) Apress L. P.

Kerbel, Matthew R. & Kerbel, Matthew Robert. Netroots: Online Progressives & the Transformation of American Politics. 2009. (Media & Power Ser.). 224p. pap. 28.95 (978-1-59451-495-1(X)) Paradigm Pubs.

Keren, Michael. Blogosphere: The New Political Arena. 2006. (ENG.). 176p. 83.99 (978-0-7391-1671-5(1)); per. 28.50 (978-0-7391-1672-2(X)) Lexington Bks.

Khan, Kashif. Marketing Communication Phenomenon Within Social Networks & Blogs. 2011. 200p. pap. **(978-3-8443-3087-8(9))** Lambert Academic Publishing.

Kill, Josh & Black, Kris. Squarespace for Dummies. 2012. (Illus.). 224p. pap. 24.99 **(978-0-470-92325-2(3),** For Dummies) Wiley, John & Sons, Inc.

Kimmig, Sarah. Blooks - Weblogs in Buchform: Eine Analyse unter Berücksichtigung der Medienspezifika. 2010. 128p. pap. (978-3-639-23527-2(4)) VDM Verlag Dr. Mueller e.K.

Kobayashi-Hillary, Mark. Talking Outsourcing. 2009. 402p. pap. 25.50 (978-1-4092-8568-7(5)) Lulu Enterprises Inc.

Krakoff, Patsi & Wakeman, Denise. Build a Better Blog: The Ultimate Guide to Boosting Your Business with a Professional Blog. 2nd ed. 2006. (978-0-9765153-2-6(6)) Customized Newsletter Services.

Laws, Angel. Angel's Laws of Blogging: What You Need to Know If You Want to Have a Successful & Profitable Blog. 2011. (ENG., Illus.). 160p. pap. 14.95 (978-1-61608-268-0(2), 608268) Skyhorse Publishing Co., Inc.

Leary, Stephanie. Beginning WordPress 3. 2010. (ENG.). 432p. pap. 39.99 (978-1-4302-2895-0(4)) Apress L. P.

Lewis, Richart Drake. All My Internet Blogs. 2011. 162p. 32.73 **(978-0-557-09028-0(8))** Lulu Enterprises Inc.

Lima, Manuel. Blogviz. 2009. 84p. pap. (978-3-639-20902-0(8)) VDM Verlag Dr. Mueller e.K.

Liu, Huan & Agarwal, Nitin. Modeling & Data Mining Blogs. 2009. (Synthesis Lectures on Data Mining & Knowledge Discovery Ser.). 109p. pap. 30.00 (978-1-59829-908-3(5)) Morgan & Claypool Pubs.

Lock, Sharyn & Irving, Sarah. Gaza: Beneath the Bombs. 2010. (ENG., Illus.). 240p. pap. 20.00 (978-0-7453-3024-2(X)) Pluto Pr. GBR. Dist: Macmillan.

Loewenstein, Antony. The Blogging Revolution. 2008. (ENG.). 336p. pap. 27.00 (978-0-522-85490-9(7)) Melbourne Univ. Publishing AUS. Dist: Independent Pubs. Group.

Ludrovska, Katarina. Blogs in Slovaki. 2011. 76p. pap. **(978-3-8433-8332-5(4))** Lambert Academic Publishing.

Luehmann, April. Blogging As Change: Transforming Science & Math Education Through New Media Literacies. 2011. (Illus.). x, 356p. (C). 149.95 (978-1-4331-0558-6(6)); pap. 36.95 (978-1-4331-0559-3(4)) Lang, Peter Publishing, Inc.

Majure, Janet. WordPress. 2010. (ENG., Illus.). 304p. pap. 29.99 (978-0-470-57092-0(X), Visual) Wiley, John & Sons, Inc.

Makice, Kevin. Twitter API: Up & Running. 2009. (ENG., Illus.). 416p. pap. 34.99 (978-0-596-15461-5(5)) O'Reilly Media, Inc.

Marc, Kürsten. Blended Learning with Wordpress Blogging Software: Case Study in an Undergraduate Course on Business Information Systems. 2011. 140p. pap. **(978-3-639-31450-2(6))** VDM Verlag Dr. Mueller e.K.

Martin, Gail. 30 Days to Social Media Success: The 30 Day Results Guide to Making the Most of Twitter, Blogging, LinkedIN, & Facebook. 2010. (ENG.). 1p. pap. 13.99 (978-1-60163-130-5(8)) Career Pr., Inc.

Martin, Steve. The Ten, Make That Nine, Habits of Very Organized People. Make That Ten: The Tweets of Steve Martin. 2012. (ENG.). 112p. 15.99 **(978-1-4555-1247-8(8))** Grand Central Publishing.

Mason, Margaret. No One Cares What You Had for Lunch: 100 Ideas for Your Blog. 2006. (ENG., Illus.). 144p. per. 19.99 (978-0-321-44972-6(X)) Peachpit Pr.

Masters, Tom. Blogging Quick & Easy: A Planned Approach to Blogging Success. 2007. 150p. per. 18.95 (978-0-9794614-0-8(5)) Orion Wellspring, Inc.

McFedries, Paul. Twitter Tips, Tricks, & Tweets. 2nd ed. 2010. (ENG., Illus.). 288p. pap. 19.99 (978-0-470-62466-1(3), Wiley) Wiley, John & Sons, Inc.

McNeal, Natalie. The Frugalista Files: How One Woman Got Out of Debt Without Giving up the Fabulous Life. 2010. (ENG.). 192p. pap. 14.95 (978-0-373-89229-7(2)) Harlequin Enterprises, Ltd. CAN. Dist: Simon & Schuster, Inc.

McNulty, Scott. Building a TypePad Blog People Want to Read. rev. ed. 2010. (ENG., Illus.). 272p. pap. 29.99 (978-0-321-62451-2(3)) Peachpit Pr.

—Building a Wordpress Blog: People Want to Read. 2nd ed. 2010. (ENG., Illus.). 312p. pap. 29.99 (978-0-321-74957-4(X)) Peachpit Pr.

—Building a WordPress Blog People Want to Read. 2008. (ENG., Illus.). 272p. pap. 29.99 (978-0-321-59193-7(3)) New Riders Publishing.

MECHENTEL, Pierre. Blogs et Entreprises. 2008. 111p. 41.95 (978-1-4092-0420-6(0)) Lulu Enterprises Inc.

Mehrotra, Dheeraj. Blogs Towards Excellence in Education. 2011. 88p. pap. **(978-3-8443-2875-2(0))** Lambert Academic Publishing.

Micek, John-Paul, et al. Business Blogging Secrets Revealed. 2006. (ENG.). 332p. per. 18.95 *(978-1-60037-029-8(2)*, 1600370292) Morgan James Publishing.
Michels, Ulrike. Communicating News Via Weblogs: An Innovative Strategy in Readership Bonding. 2007. 148p. per. *(978-3-86550-795-2(6))* VDM Verlag Dr. Mueller e.K.
Morrell, Matthew W. Leukemia & Key Lime Pie. 2006. pap. 10.95 *(978-1-890768-77-5(4))* Johnson Bks.
Morris, Tee. All a Twitter: A Personal & Professional Guide to Social Networking with Twitter. 2009. (ENG., Illus.). 312p. pap. 19.99 *(978-0-7897-4228-5(4))* Que.
—Sams Teach Yourself Twitter in 10 Minutes. 2009. (Sams Teach Yourself Ser.). (ENG., Illus.). 192p. pap. 14.99 *(978-0-672-33124-4(1))* Sams.
Myers, Greg. The Discourse of Blogs & Wikis. 2010. (Continuum Discourse Ser.). (ENG., Illus.). 192p. 150.00 *(978-1-84706-413-4(2))* Continuum International Publishing Group, Ltd. GBR. Dist: National Bk. Network.
Nesheba. What's It All about Nesheba? 2008. 120p. 25.75 *(978-0-615-24029-9(1))* Essential Spirit Enterprises, Inc.
Niemann, Christoph. Abstract City. 2012. (ENG., Illus.). 256p. 24.95 ***(978-1-4197-0207-5(6))*** Abrams.
Oppenheimer, Elizabeth, Ed. Writing Cheerfully on the Web: A Quaker Blog Reader. 2009. 277p. pap. 19.98 *(978-0-557-07541-6(6))* Lulu Enterprises Inc.
O'Reilly, Tim & Milstein, Sarah. The Twitter Book. 2nd ed. 2011. (ENG., Illus.). 256p. pap. 19.99 ***(978-1-4493-1420-0(1))*** O'Reilly Media, Inc.
Papakyriakou, Beba. GET-THIS Series I/2010/3 Selected Works House of Bee Sting Landa's Haven. 2010. 54p. pap. 11.99 *(978-1-4461-5660-5(5))* Lulu Enterprises Inc.
Parisi, Lisa & Crosby, Brian. Making Connections with Blogging: Authentic Learning for Today's Classrooms. 2012. pap. ***(978-1-56484-312-8(2))*** International Society for Technology in Education.
Pasqua, Mike "Mfp". Mfp: 16. 2009. 216p. pap. 24.95 *(978-1-4401-4838-5(4))* iUniverse, Inc.
Patten, Justin, et al. Blogging & Other Social Media: Exploiting the Technology & Protecting the Enterprise. 2008. (Illus.). 202p. 114.95 *(978-0-566-08789-9(8)*, Gower Publishing Co., Ltd.) Ashgate Publishing, Ltd. GBR. Dist: Ashgate Publishing Co.
Pearson Education Staff & Edward, Mark. Professional Growth Course in Teaching Writing Through Blogs & Wikis. 2010. (ENG.). (C). 53.33 *(978-0-13-704710-9(X))* Allyn & Bacon, Inc.
Pedersen, Sarah. Why Blog? Motivations for Blogging. 2010. (Illus.). 162p. pap. 70.00 *(978-1-84334-583-1(8)*, Chandos Publishing) Woodhead Publishing Ltd. GBR. Dist: Neal-Schuman Pubs., Inc.
Peng, Chi Yuan. Online Journal Writing. 2008. 112p. pap. *(978-3-8364-8924-9(4))* VDM Verlag Dr. Mueller e.K.
Piersall, Wendy. Mom Blogging for Dummies. 2011. (ENG., Illus.). 384p. pap. 24.99 *(978-1-118-03843-7(6)*, For Dummies) Wiley, John & Sons, Inc.
Piontek, Jeff. Blogs, Wikis, & Podcasts, Oh, My! Electronic Media in the Classroom. 2009. (Primary Source Fluency Activities Ser.). 88p. (gr. k-12). pap. 19.99 *(978-1-4258-0112-0(9))* Shell Educational Publishing.
PK. BibliOdyssey: Archival Images from the Internet, 1 vol. 2007. (ENG., Illus.). 160p. 34.95 *(978-0-9550061-6-6(3))* FUEL Publishing GBR. Dist: D.A.P./Distributed Art Pubs.
Plumley, George. WordPress 24-Hour Trainer: Watch, Read, & Learn How to Create & Customize WordPress Sites. 2009. (ENG., Illus.). 336p. pap. 44.99 *(978-0-470-55458-6(4)*, Wrox) Wiley, John & Sons, Inc.
Pole, Antoinette. Blogging the Political: Political Participation in a Networked Society. 2009. (ENG., Illus.). 176p. 138.00 *(978-0-415-96341-1(9))* Routledge.
Powell, Gavin, et al. WordPress. 2010. (In Depth Ser.). (ENG., Illus.). 432p. pap. 29.99 *(978-0-7897-4275-9(6))* Que.
Reagan, Dusty. Twitter Application Development for Dummies. 2010. (ENG., Illus.). 456p. pap. 29.99 *(978-0-470-56862-0(3)*, For Dummies) Wiley, John & Sons, Inc.
Rettberg, Jill Walker. Blogging. 2008. (DMS - Digital Media & Society Ser.). (ENG., Illus.). 184p. pap. 19.95 *(978-0-7456-4134-8(2))*; 59.95 *(978-0-7456-4133-1(4))* Polity Pr. GBR. Dist: Wiley, John & Sons, Inc.
Rich, Jason R. R., et al. Blogging for Fame & Fortune: Includes Exclusive Interviews with Celebrity Gossip Blogger Perez Hilton & Other World-Famous Bloggers. 2009. (ENG.). x, 284p. 21.95 *(978-1-59918-342-8(0)*, 1599183420) Entrepreneur Pr. dba Entrepreneur Media, Inc.
Richardson, Willard. Learning on the Blog: Collected Posts for Educators & Parents. 2011. 144p. pap. 28.95 ***(978-1-4129-9570-2(1)***, B95702P) Corwin Pr.
Rosen, Larry D. Me, Myspace, & I: Parenting the Net Generation. 2007. (ENG., Illus.). 272p. pap. 16.95 *(978-0-230-60003-4(4))* Palgrave Macmillan.
Rosenberg, Scott. Say Everything: How Blogging Began, What It's Becoming, & Why It Matters. 2010. (ENG.). 416p. pap. 15.00 *(978-0-307-45137-8(2)*, Three Rivers Pr.) Crown Publishing Group.
Ross, Michael E. American Bandwidth: Weblogs & Essays. 2009. 440p. pap. 20.49 *(978-1-4490-1899-3(8))*; xi, 427p. *(978-1-4490-1898-6(X))* AuthorHouse.
Rowse, Darren & Garrett, Chris. ProBlogger: Secrets for Blogging Your Way to a Six-Figure Income. 3rd ed. 2012. (ENG.). 336p. pap. 24.99 ***(978-1-118-19955-8(3)***, Wiley) Wiley, John & Sons, Inc.
Russell, Adrienne & Echchaibi, Nabil. International Blogging: Identity, Politics & Networked Publics. 2008. (Digital Formations Ser.). pap. 32.95 *(978-1-4331-0233-2(1))* Lang, Peter Publishing, Inc.
Sabin-Wilson, Lisa. WordPress for Dummies. 4th ed. 2011. (ENG., Illus.). 432p. pap. 24.99 *(978-1-118-07342-1(8)*, For Dummies) Wiley, John & Sons, Inc.
Sabin-Wilson, Lisa, et al. TypePad for Dummies. 2010. (ENG., Illus.). 432p. pap. 24.99 *(978-0-470-55094-6(5)*, For Dummies) Wiley, John & Sons, Inc.
—WordPress All-in-One for Dummies. 2011. (ENG., Illus.). 912p. pap. 34.99 *(978-0-470-87701-2(4)*, For Dummies) Wiley, John & Sons, Inc.
San Martín, Macarena. Blogs Mad about Design. 2009. 530p. *(978-981-245-715-8(1))* Page One Publishing.
Sánchez, Yoani. Cuba Libre: Vivir y Escribir en la Habana. 2010. (SPA.). 344p. pap. *(979-987-1307-27-2(6))* Marea S.R.L., Editorial.
Sanderson, Catherine. Petite Anglaise. 2009. (ENG.). 352p. pap. 15.00 *(978-0-385-52281-6(9))* Spiegel & Grau.
Sanique, Isha. Blog: Barely the Beginning. 2011. 100p. pap. 14.99 *(978-1-4567-5239-2(1))* AuthorHouse.
Scalzi, John. Your Hate Mail Will Be Graded: A Decade of Whatever, 1998-2008. 2010. (ENG.). 368p. pap. 14.99 *(978-0-7653-2711-6(2)*, Tor Bks.) Doherty, Tom Assocs., LLC.
—Your Hate Mail Will Be Graded: A Decade of Whatever, 1998-2008. 2008. 368p. 35.00 *(978-1-59606-211-5(8))* Subterranean Pr.
Schuman, Scott. The Sartorialist. 2009. (ENG.). 512p. (gr. 12-18). 25.00 *(978-0-14-311637-0(1)*, Penguin (Non-Classics)) Penguin Group (USA) Inc.
Senyei, Kelly. Food Blogging for Dummies. 2012. (ENG.). 320p. pap. 24.99 ***(978-1-118-15769-5(9)***, For Dummies) Wiley, John & Sons, Inc.
Shetterly, Caitlin. Made for You & Me: Going West, Going Broke, Finding Home. 2011. 256p. 23.99 *(978-1-4013-4146-6(2))* Hyperion Pr.
Siarto, Jeff. Head First WordPress. 2010. (ENG., Illus.). 370p. pap. 34.99 *(978-0-596-80628-6(0))* O'Reilly Media, Inc.
Silver, Tessa Blakeley. WordPress 2.8 Theme Design. 2009. 310p. pap. *(978-1-84951-008-0(3))* Summerdale Pubs.
—WordPress Theme Design. 2008. (Illus.). 220p. per. *(978-1-84719-309-4(9))* Packt Publishing, Ltd.
Sirota, David. The Uprising: An Unauthorized Tour of the Populist Revolt Scaring Wall Street & Washington. 2009. (ENG., Illus.). 400p. pap. 14.95 *(978-0-307-39564-1(2)*, Three Rivers Pr.) Crown Publishing Group.
Smith, Bud. Sams Teach Yourself Tumblr in 10 Minutes. 2010. (Sams Teach Yourself — Minutes Ser.). (ENG., Illus.). 216p. pap. 14.99 *(978-0-672-33116-9(0))* Sams.
Smith, Bud E. & McCallister, Michael. WordPress in Depth. 2nd rev. ed. 2011. (In Depth Ser.). (ENG., Illus.). 600p. pap. 34.99 *(978-0-7897-4107-3(5))* Que.
Smith, Xander. Letters to an Angel. 2007. 80p. pap. 16.50 *(978-0-615-15332-2(1))* Smith, Wilma.
Spaanjaars, Imar. A Blogging Application in ASP. NET 2. 0. 2007. (Wrox Briefs Ser.). 52p. 6.99 *(978-0-470-26121-7(8)*, Wrox) Wiley, John & Sons, Inc.
Stauffer, Todd. How to Do Everything with Your Web 2. 0 Blog. 2007. (How to Do Everything Ser.). (ENG., Illus.). 460p. per. 24.99 *(978-0-07-149218-8(6)*, 0071492186) McGraw-Hill Osborne.
Stefanac, Suzanne. Dispatches from Blogistan: A Travel Guide for the Modern Blogger. 2006. (Voices Ser.). (ENG., Illus.). 256p. per. 24.99 *(978-0-321-39555-9(7))* New Riders Publishing.
Stern, Hal, et al. Professional WordPress: Design & Development. 2010. (ENG., Illus.). 412p. pap. 44.99 *(978-0-470-56054-9(1)*, Wrox) Wiley, John & Sons, Inc.
Stock, Mark J. The School Administrator's Guide to Blogging: A New Way to Connect with the Community. (ENG.). 120p. 2009. 55.00 *(978-1-57886-919-0(6))* 2008. pap. 19.95 *(978-1-57886-920-6(X))* Rowman & Littlefield Education.
Tao, Terence. Structure & Randomness: Pages from Year One of a Mathematical Blog. 2008. (Illus.). 298p. pap. 36.00 *(978-0-8218-4695-7(7))* American Mathematical Society.
Taprial, Varinder & Kanwar, Priya. A Beginner's Guide to Blogging & Making Money Online. 2010. 240p. pap. *(978-81-223-1110-5(5))* Mahal, Pustak Pubs., Booksellers & Order Suppliers.
Teacher Created Resources Staff & Heskett, Tracie. Blogging in the Classroom. 2009. (ENG.). 96p. pap. 14.99 *(978-1-4206-2167-9(X))* Teacher Created Resources, Inc.
The Teen's Ultimate Guide to Making Money When You Can't Get a Job: 199 Ideas for Earning Cash on Your Own Terms. 2012. (ENG.). 288p. pap. 24.95 *(978-1-60138-611-3(7))* Atlantic Publishing Co.
Theimer, Kate. A Different Kind of Web: New Connections Between Archives & Our Users. 2011. ***(978-1-931666-39-8(3))*** Scarecrow Pr., Inc.
Thewlis, Paul. WordPress for Business Bloggers. 2008. (Illus.). 300p. pap. *(978-1-84719-532-6(6))* Packt Publishing, Ltd.
Tomasi, Chuck & Steppe, Kreg. Sams Teach Yourself WordPress 3 in 10 Minutes. 2010. (Sams Teach Yourself — Minutes Ser.). (ENG.). 240p. pap. 16.99 *(978-0-672-33546-4(8))* Sams.
—WordPress in 10 Minutes. 2010. (Sams Teach Yourself — Minutes Ser.). (ENG., Illus.). 240p. pap. 14.99 *(978-0-672-33120-6(9))* Sams.
Tremayne, Mark, ed. Blogging, Citizenship, & the Future of Media. 2006. (ENG., Illus.). 240p. 125.00 *(978-0-415-97939-9(0))*; per. 37.95 *(978-0-415-97940-5(4))* Routledge.
Walsh, Bob. Clear Blogging: How People Blogging Are Changing the World & How You Can Join Them. 2007. (ENG., Illus.). 351p. per. 24.99 *(978-1-59059-691-3(9))* Apress L. P.
Warlick, David. Classroom Blogging: 2nd Edition. 2nd ed. 2007. (Illus.). 188p. pap. 20.95 *(978-1-4303-2676-2(X))* Lulu Enterprises Inc.
Wasik, Bill. And Then There's This: How Stories Live & Die in Viral Culture. 2010. (ENG.). 208p. (gr. 12). 15.00 *(978-0-14-311761-2(0)*, Penguin (Non-Classics)) Penguin Group (USA) Inc.
White, Charlie & Biggs, John. Blogger's Boot Camp: Learning How to Build, Write, & Run a Successful Blog. 2011. (ENG.). 224p. pap. 29.95 ***(978-0-240-81917-4(9)***, Focal Pr.) Elsevier Science & Technology Bks.
Whitlock, Warren & Micek, Deborah. Twitter Revolution: How Social Media & Mobile Marketing Is Changing the Way We Do Business & Market Online. 2008. (Illus.). 277p. pap. 18.97 *(978-1-934275-07-8(7))* Xeno Pr.
Williams, Brad, et al. Professional WordPress Plugin Development. 2011. (ENG., Illus.). 552p. pap. 44.99 *(978-0-470-91622-3(2)*, Wrox) Wiley, John & Sons, Inc.
Williams, Doug. Biz Blog Marketing: The Secrets of Business Blog Marketing. 2008. (Illus.). 208p. per. 24.95 *(978-0-9801307-0-6(0))* Williams Business Services, Inc.
Winograd, Morley. Millennial Makeover: My Space, YouTube, & the Future of American Politics. 2008. (ENG.). 360p. (C). pap. 22.95 *(978-0-8135-4504-2(8))* Rutgers Univ. Pr.
—Millennial Makeover: MySpace, YouTube, & the Future of American Politics. 2008. (ENG.). 336p. 24.95 *(978-0-8135-4301-7(0))* Rutgers Univ. Pr.
Wißotzki, Matthias. Electronic Commerce & Web 2.0: A Managerial Approach for Start-up Businesses in the 'new' Internet. 2008. 184p. pap. *(978-3-639-09452-7(2))* VDM Verlag Dr. Mueller e.K.
Wodtke, Larissa. Does NME Even Know What a Music Blog Is? The Rhetoric & Social Meaning of MP3 Blogs. 2008. (Illus.). 120p. pap. *(978-3-639-09509-8(X))* VDM Verlag Dr. Mueller e.K.
WordPress For Dummies, 3e + Professional Blogging For Dummies - Book Bundle. 2011. pap. 30.00 *(978-1-118-01203-1(8)*, For Dummies) Wiley, John & Sons, Inc.
Wright-Porto, Heather. Beginning Google Blogger. 2010. (ENG.). 192p. pap. 24.99 *(978-1-4302-3012-0(6))* Apress L. P.
—Creative Blogging: Your First Steps to a Successful Blog. 2011. (ENG.). 336p. pap. 34.99 *(978-1-4302-3428-9(8))* Apress L. P.
Xposed, Night. Dear Fantasy Girl... 2009. 220p. pap. 19.99 *(978-0-578-01038-0(0))* Night Xposed.
Zafiropoulos, Kostas & Vrana, Vasiliki. Hyperlink Analysis of Political Blogs Communication Patterns. 2010. (Media & Communications - Technologies, Policies & Challenges Ser.). pap. 43.00 *(978-1-61728-922-4(1)*, Nova Novinka) Nova Science Pubs., Inc.
Zivkovic, Bora, Series Editor. The Open Laboratory 2008. 2010. 186p. pap. 15.50 *(978-0-557-05317-9(X))* Lulu Enterprises Inc.
Zivkovic, Bora. The Open Laboratory 2009. 2010. 222p. pap. 15.50 *(978-0-557-33450-6(0))* Lulu Enterprises Inc.
Zuniga, Markos Moulitsas. Taking on the System: Rules for Change in a Digital Era. 2009. (ENG.). 304p. (gr. 12-18). pap. 16.00 *(978-0-451-22806-2(5)*, Celebra) Penguin Group (USA) Inc.

BLOK, ALEKSANDR ALEKSANDROVICH, 1880-1921

Goldberg, Stuart. Mandelstam, Blok, & the Boundaries of Mythopoetic Symbolism. 2011. 336p. 51.95 ***(978-0-8142-1159-5(3))***; cd-rom 14.95 ***(978-0-8142-9260-0(7))*** Ohio State Univ. Pr.
Presto, Jenifer. Beyond the Flesh: Alexander Blok, Zinaida Gippius, & the Symbolist Sublimation of Sex. 2008. (ENG., Illus.). 352p. 60.00 *(978-0-299-22950-4(5))* Univ. of Wisconsin Pr.

BLONDEL, MAURICE, 1861-1949

Bernardi, Peter J., ed. Maurice Blondel, Social Catholicism, & Action Francaise: The Clash over the Church's Role in Society During the Modernist Era. 2008. 320p. 79.95 *(978-0-8132-1542-6(0))* Catholic Univ. of America Pr.
Blanchette, Oliva. Maurice Blondel: A Philosophical Life. 2009. 836p. pap. 45.00 *(978-0-8028-6365-2(5))* Eerdmans, William B. Publishing Co.
English, Adam C. The Possibility of Christian Philosophy: Maurice Blondel at the Intersection of Theology & Philosophy. (Routledge Radical Orthodoxy Ser.). 2012. (ENG.). 160p. (C). pap. 42.95 ***(978-0-415-54196-1(4))*** 2007. 144p. 145.00 *(978-0-415-77041-5(6))* Routledge.
Kennedy, Matthew. Joan Blondell: A Life Between Takes. 2007. (ENG., Illus.). 300p. 30.00 *(978-1-57806-961-3(0))* Univ. Pr. of Mississippi.
Leclercq, J., ed. La raison par quatre Chemins: En hommage a Claude Troisfontaines. 2007. (Bibliotheque Philosophique de Louvain Ser.). (FRE.). 532p. (C). pap. 70.00 *(978-90-429-1970-9(1))* Peeters Pubs. & Booksellers BEL. Dist: Brown, David Bk. Co., The.
Mulhern, Kathleen A. Beyond the Contingent: Epistemological Authority, a Pascalian Revival, & the Religious Imagination in Third Republic France. 2011. 230p. pap. 25.00 ***(978-1-60899-370-3(1)***, Pickwick Pubns.) Wipf & Stock Pubs.

BLOOD

see also Blood Plasma; Hematopoiesis; Hemolysis and Hemolysins; Hemorrhage

Baskurt, Oguz K. Handbook of hemorheology & Hemodynamics. 2007. 250.00 *(978-1-58603-771-0(4))* IOS Pr., Inc.
Bechamp, Antoine. The Blood & Its Third Anatomical Element. reprint ed. 98.00 *(978-0-7222-9869-5(2))* Library Reprints, Inc.
Blann, Andrew, et al. Haematology. 2010. (Fundamentals of Biomedical Science Ser.). (ENG., Illus.). 384p. pap. 45.00 *(978-0-19-956883-3(9))* Oxford Univ. Pr., Inc.
Bunn, Howard Franklin & Aster, Jon C. Pathophysiology of Blood Disorders. 2010. (ENG., Illus.). 342p. (C). pap. 58.00 *(978-0-07-171378-8(6)*, 0071713786) McGraw-Hill Medical Publishing Div.
Caughey, Aaron B. Pathophysiology Review. 2nd rev. ed. 2009. (ENG., Illus.). 376p. pap. 45.50 *(978-0-7817-8254-8(6))* Lippincott Williams & Wilkins.
Cokelet, Giles. Hemorheology & Hemodynamics. 2011. (Colloquium Series on Integrated Systems Physiology: from Molecule to Function Ser.). 100p. pap. 45.00 *(978-1-61504-162-6(1))* Morgan & Claypool Life Science Publishers.
Englert, Rod & Pessero, Kathy. Blood Secrets: Chronicles of a Crime Scene Reconstructionist. 2010. (ENG., Illus.). 304p. 25.99 *(978-0-312-56400-1(7)*, Dunne, Thomas Bks.) St. Martin's Pr.
Kawanishi, H. & Yamashita, A. C., eds. Hemodiafiltration: A New Era. 2010. (Contributions to Nephrology Ser.). (Illus.). 218p. *(978-3-8055-9560-5(3))* Karger, S. AG.
Kawanishi, Hideki & Yamashita, Akihiro C. Hemodiafiltration: A New ERA. 2011. (Illus.). x, 218p. E-Book *(978-3-8055-9561-2(1))* Karger, S. AG.
Lemm, W., ed. The Reference Materials of the European Communities: Results of Hemocompatibility Tests. 2010. (ENG., Illus.). 276p. pap. 224.00 *(978-90-481-4213-2(X)*, 904814213X) Springer.
Lempa, Heikki. Beyond the Gymnasium: Educating the Middle-Class Bodies in Classical Germany. 2007. (ENG.). 306p. 83.99 *(978-0-7391-2089-7(1))*; pap. 40.99 *(978-0-7391-2090-3(5))* Lexington Bks.
Mehta, R. L., ed. Crrt 2005 - a Multimedia Conference Compilation: Including Abstracts of the 1st to 10th International Conferences on Continuous Renal Replacement Therapies, San Diego, Calif., 1995-2005. cd-rom *(978-3-8055-7929-2(2))* Karger, S. AG.
Oliver, George. Friend Earthworm. 2007. (ENG.). 170p. pap. *(978-0-9802976-1-4(3))* dminoz.
Osselaer, J. C., ed. Meeting the Challenges of Blood Safety in the 21st Century. (Illus.). *(978-3-8055-7725-0(7))* Karger, S. AG.
Ronco, C., et al. Hemodiafiltration. 2007. (Contributions to Nephrology Ser.: Vol. 158). (Illus.). 238p. *(978-3-8055-8288-9(9))* Karger, S. AG.
Suzuki, H. & Hirasawa, H., eds. Acute Blood Purification. 2010. (Contributions to Nephrology Ser.). (ENG., Illus.). 196p. *(978-3-8055-9478-3(X))* Karger, S. AG.
Transfusion - Think about It. 2010. (Health Care Issues, Costs & Access Ser.). 160.00 *(978-1-61668-969-8(2))* Nova Science Pubs., Inc.

BLOOD—ANALYSIS

Here are entered works on the physicochemical analysis of serum or plasma, and on the diagnostic significance of the results. Works on the examination of the formed elements of the blood by microscopic and other techniques, and on the diagnostic significance of the results, are entered under Blood—Examination.

Aabb, creator. Standards for Molecular Testing for Red Cell, Platelet, & Neutrophil Antigens. 2010. (Illus.). 50p. pap. 134.25 *(978-1-56395-275-3(0))* American Assn. of Blood Banks.
ABBE Scientist Research Division Staff. AIDS & HIV in Blood: Index & Medical Analysis of New Clinical & Research Information. 2007. (ENG., Illus.). 160p. ring bd. 69.95 *(978-0-7883-4777-1(2))* ABBE Pubs. Assn. of Washington, D.C.
Ashford, Paul, ed. ISBT 128 an Introduction. 3rd ed. 2006. *(978-1-933243-01-6(5))* ICCBBA Inc.
—ISBT 128 for Cellular Therapy an Intoduction. 2006. *(978-1-933243-02-3(3))* ICCBBA Inc.
—ISBT 128 for Tissues, an Introduction. 2007. *(978-1-933243-05-4(8))* ICCBBA Inc.
Bain, Barbara J., et al. Dacie & Lewis Practical Haematology. 11th ed. 2011. (ENG., Illus.) 668p. pap. 130.00 ***(978-0-7020-3408-4(8)***, Churchill Livingstone) Elsevier - Health Sciences Div.
Bugert, Peter. DNA & RNA Profiling in Human Blood: Methods & Protocols. 2008. (Methods in Molecular Biology Ser.). (ENG., Illus.). xii, 344p. 139.00 *(978-1-934115-93-0(2))* Humana Pr.
Cram101 Textbook Reviews & Cram101 Textbook Reviews. Outlines & Highlights for Hematology: Clinical Principles & Applications by Bernadette Rodak, ISBN. 2011. 386p. pap. 42.95 ***(978-1-61461-952-9(2))*** Cram101 Inc.
—Outlines & Highlights for Hematology by Bernadette F Rodak, Isbn: 9781416030065 1416030069. 2011. 168p. pap. 28.95 ***(978-1-61490-147-1(3))*** Cram101 Inc.
CRRT 2007 - a multimedia conference Compilation. 2007. pap. *(978-3-8055-8293-3(5))* Karger, S. AG.
Gahan, Peter B., ed. Circulating Nucleic Acids in Plasma & Serum: Proceedings of the 6th international conference on circulating nucleic acids in plasma & serum held on 9-11 November 2009 in Hong Kong. 2010. (ENG., Illus.). xx, 285p. 189.00 *(978-90-481-9381-3(8)*, 9048193818) Springer.
Kitchen, Steve, et al, eds. Quality in Laboratory Hemostasis & Thrombosis. 2009. (ENG., Illus.). 232p. 152.95 *(978-1-4051-5803-8(X)*, Wiley-Blackwell) Wiley, John & Sons, Inc.
Kottke-Marchant, Kandice, et al, eds. Laboratory Hematology Practice. 2012. (ENG.). 776p. 299.00 ***(978-1-4051-6218-0(X)***, Wiley-Blackwell) Wiley, John & Sons, Inc.
The Science Behind the Skill of Vein Access for the Blood Donation Tech. 2008. ring bd. *(978-0-9723656-6-4(4))* Vein Access Technologies.
Swaminathan, R., et al, eds. Annals of the New York Academy of Sciences, Circulating Nucleic Acids in Plasma & Serum, Vol. 1075. 2006. (Annals of the New York Academy of Sciences Ser.: Vol. 1074). (ENG., Illus.). 352p. per. 139.95 *(978-1-57331-627-9(X)*, Wiley-Blackwell) Wiley, John & Sons, Inc.

B

Wray, Bruce. ISBT 128 an Introduction to Bar Coding. 2nd ed. 2007. *(978-1-933243-04-7(X))* ICCBBA Inc.

BLOOD—CHEMISTRY
see Blood—Analysis

BLOOD—CIRCULATION
see also Aorta; Arteries; Blood Flow; Blood Pressure; Blood-Vessels; Blood Volume; Cardiac Catheterization; Cardiovascular System; Collateral Circulation; Heart; Hemodynamics; Microcirculation; Peripheral Circulation; Plethysmography; Pulmonary Circulation; Pulse; Veins

Booth, Kathy, et al. Phlebotomy for Health Care Personnel. 2009. (Illus.). xviii, 254p. *(978-0-07-351097-2(1))* McGraw-Hill Cos., The.

Butler, Jon. Control Coordinatn Respiration. 319p. *(978-0-521-25348-2(9))* Cambridge Univ. Pr.

Caro, C. G., et al. The Mechanics of the Circulation. 2nd rev. ed. 2011. (ENG., Illus.). 550p. pap. 49.00 ***(978-0-521-15177-1(5))*** Cambridge Univ. Pr.

Cipolla, Marilyn J. The Cerebral Circulation. Granger, D. Neil & Granger, Joey, eds. 2010. (Colloquium Series on Integrated Systems Physiology: from Molecule to Function Ser.). 59p. (C). pap., pap. 30.00 *(978-1-61504-012-4(9))* Morgan & Claypool Life Science Publishers.

Flourens, P. (Pierre). A History of the Discovery of the Circulation of the Blood. 2006. 176p. per. 18.99 *(978-1-4255-1431-0(6))* MPublishing.

Harvey, William. Works of William Harvey Physician to the. 2006. pap. 50.95 *(978-1-4286-3445-9(2))* Kessinger Publishing, LLC.

Koller, A., ed. European Society for Microcirculation: 25th Conference, Budapest, August 2008: 379 AbstractsIntegrating Vascular Biology & Medicine: Basic & Clinical Science. 2008. 200p. pap. *(978-3-8055-8635-1(3))* Karger, S. AG.

Korthuis, Ronald. Skeletal Muscle Circulation. 2011. (Colloquium Series on Integrated Systems Physiology: from Molecule to Function Ser.). 100p. pap. 45.00 *(978-1-61504-183-1(4))* Morgan & Claypool Life Science Publishers.

Rogers, Kara, ed. Blood: Physiology & Circulation. 2010. (Human Body Ser.). 240p. (YA). (ENG.). lib. bdg. 45.00 *(978-1-61530-121-8(6))*; (Illus.). 90.00 *(978-1-61530-259-8(X))* Rosen Publishing Group, Inc., The.

Satchell, Geoffrey H. Physiology & Form of Fish Circulation. 2008. (ENG.). 256p. pap. 56.00 *(978-0-521-06554-2(2))* Cambridge Univ. Pr.

Singer, Charles J. The Discovery of the Circulation of the Blood. (Illus.). x, 80p. reprint ed. lib. bdg. 88.00 *(978-0-7222-3086-2(9))* Library Reprints, Inc.

Thiriet, Marc. Cell & Tissue Organization in the Circulatory & Ventilatory Systems. 2011. (Biomathematical & Biomechanical Modeling of the Circulatory & Ventilatory Systems Ser.). (ENG., Illus.). xii, 735p. 199.00 *(978-1-4419-9757-9(1)*, 1441997571) Springer.

Zamir, M. The Physics of Coronary Blood Flow. 2010. (Biological & Medical Physics, Biomedical Engineering Ser.). (Illus.). xviii, 410p. pap. 169.00 *(978-1-4419-3782-7(X)*, 144193782X) Springer.

BLOOD—CIRCULATION, ARTIFICIAL
see also Cardiopulmonary Bypass; Heart, Artificial; Heart, Mechanical

Deng, Mario C. & Naka, Yoshifumi. Mechanical Circulatory Support Therapy in Advanced Heart Failure. 2007. (Illus.). 404p. pap. 51.00 *(978-1-86094-773-5(5))* Imperial College Pr. GBR. Dist: World Scientific Publishing Co., Inc.

Joyce, David, et al. Mechanical Circulatory Support: Principles & Applications. 2011. (ENG., Illus.). 253p. 99.00 *(978-0-07-175344-9(3)*, 0071753443) McGraw-Hill Professional Publishing.

Yoshifumi. Mechanical Circulatory Support Therapy. . 2007. (Illus.). 300p. 98.00 *(978-1-86094-728-5(X))* Imperial College Pr. GBR. Dist: World Scientific Publishing Co., Inc.

BLOOD—CIRCULATION, DISORDERS OF
see Blood Circulation Disorders

BLOOD—COAGULATION
see also Anticoagulants (Medicine); Fibrinolysis; Hemophilia

Blomback, Margareta & Antovic, Jovan, eds. Essential Guide to Blood Coagulation. 2010. (ENG., Illus.). 192p. pap. 78.95 *(978-1-4051-9627-7(0)*, Wiley-Blackwell) Wiley, John & Sons, Inc.

Coagulation. ring bd. 250.00 *(978-1-56238-236-0(5)*, SC12-L) NCCLC.

Fang, Margaret C. Inpatient Anticoagulation. 2011. (Hospital Medicine: Current Concepts Ser.: 4). (ENG., Illus.). 448p. pap. 69.95 *(978-0-470-60211-9(2)*, Wiley-Blackwell) Wiley, John & Sons, Inc.

Federici, Augusto B., et al, eds. Von Willebrand Disease: Basic & Clinical Aspects. 2011. (ENG., Illus.). 268p. 131.95 *(978-1-4051-9512-6(6)*, Wiley-Blackwell) Wiley, John & Sons, Inc.

Ferguson, John H. Lipoids & Blood Platelets with Reference to Blood Coagulation & the Hemorrhagic Diseases. 2011. (ENG.). 298p. pap. 40.00 ***(978-0-8078-6864-5(7))*** Univ. of North Carolina Pr.

Halkier, Torben. Mechanisms in Blood Coagulation, Fibrinolysis & the Complement System. Woolley, Paul, tr. from DAN. 2008. (ENG., Illus.). 484p. pap. 90.00 *(978-0-521-07183-3(6))* Cambridge Univ. Pr.

Kini, R. Manjunatha, et al, eds. Toxins & Hemostasis: From Bench to Bedside. 2010. (ENG., Illus.). xxiii, 600p. 239.00 *(978-90-481-9294-6(3)*, 9048192943) Springer.

Rumbaut, Rolando. Platelet-Vessel Wall Interactions in Hemostasis & Thrombosis. Granger, Neil & Granger, Joey, eds. 2010. (Colloquium Series on Integrated Systems Physiology: from Molecule to Function Ser.). 75p. pap. 30.00 *(978-1-61504-039-1(0))* Morgan & Claypool Life Science Publishers.

Wang, Meng-Jiy & Tsai, Wei-Bor, eds. Biomaterials in Blood-Contacting Devices: Complications & Solutions. 2010. (Biomaterials - Properties, Production & Devices Ser.). 87p. pap. 43.00 *(978-1-60876-784-7(1))* Nova Science Pubs., Inc.

BLOOD—COAGULATION, DISORDERS OF
see Blood Coagulation Disorders

BLOOD—COLLECTION AND PRESERVATION
see also Phlebotomy

American Association of Blood Banks Staff. Standards for Perioperative Autologous Blood Collection & Administration. 2007. pap. ***(978-3-8055-8408-1(3))*** Karger, S. AG.

American Association of Blood Banks Staff, contrib. by. Standards for Perioperative Autologous Blood Collection & Administration. 3rd ed. 2007. (Illus.). xv, 52p. pap. *(978-1-56395-248-7(3)*, AABB Pr.) American Assn. of Blood Banks.

Ashford, Paul, ed. ISBT 128 an Introduction. 3rd ed. 2006. *(978-1-933243-01-6(5))* ICCBBA Inc.

—ISBT 128 for Cellular Therapy an Intoduction. 2006. *(978-1-933243-02-3(3))* ICCBBA Inc.

—ISBT 128 for Tissues, an Introduction. 2007. *(978-1-933243-05-4(8))* ICCBBA Inc.

AuBuchon, James P. & Prowse, Christopher V. Pathogen Inactivation: The Penultimate Paradigm Shift. 2010. *(978-1-56395-309-5(9)*, AABB Pr.) American Assn. of Blood Banks.

Bennett, Jeffrey A. Banning Queer Blood: Rhetorics of Citizenship, Contagion, & Resistance. 2009. (Rhetoric Culture & Social Critique Ser.). (ENG.). 256p. 44.00 *(978-0-8173-1664-8(7))* Univ. of Alabama Pr.

Blood Collection Centers. (Specialty Collections). ring bd. 250.00 *(978-1-56238-297-1(7)*, SC20-L) NCCLC.

Copeman, Jacob. Veins of Devotion: Blood Donation & Religious Experience in North India. 2008. (Studies in Medical Anthropology Ser.). (ENG., Illus.). 264p. 72.00 *(978-0-8135-4448-9(3))*; 256p. pap. 25.95 *(978-0-8135-4449-6(1))* Rutgers Univ. Pr.

Dax, Elizabeth M., et al. Advances in Transfusion Safety: Sydney, Australia, 11-13th October 2005: Proceedings of an International Conference Organized by the International Association for Biologicals (IABS), the National Serology Reference Laboratory, Australia, & the Therapeutics Goods Administration. 2007. (Developments in Biologicals Ser.: Vol. 127). (Illus.). xiv, 271p. *(978-3-8055-8239-1(0))* Karger, S. AG.

Di Lorenzo, et al. Blood Collection: A Short Course. 2nd rev. ed. 2009. (Illus.). 192p. pap. 31.95 *(978-0-8036-1699-8(6))* Davis, F. A. Co.

Petrides, Marian & Stack, Gary. Practical Guide to Transfusion Medicine. 2nd ed. 2007. *(978-1-56395-243-2(2)*, AABB Pr.) American Assn. of Blood Banks.

Vyas, Girish N. & Williams, A. E. Advances in Transfusion Safety Vol. 120: Natcher Auditorium, National Institutes of Health (NIH), Bethesda, MD, USA, June 4-6, 2003. (Developments in Biologicals Ser.: Vol. 120). (Illus.). *(978-3-8055-7935-3(7))* Karger, S. AG.

WHO Regional Office for the Western Pacific. Design Guidelines for Blood Centres. 2012. (WPRO Nonserial Publication Ser.). (ENG.). 110p. pap. 24.00 ***(978-92-9061-319-0(X))*** World Health Organization.

Winters, Jeffrey L. & Crookston, Kendall P. Therapeutic Apheresis: A Physician's Handbook. 2nd ed. 2008. (Illus.). ix, 245p. ***(978-1-56395-271-5(8)***, AABB Pr.) American Assn. of Blood Banks.

Wray, Bruce. ISBT 128 an Introduction to Bar Coding. 2nd ed. 2007. *(978-1-933243-04-7(X))* ICCBBA Inc.

BLOOD—CORPUSCLES AND PLATELETS
see Blood Cells

BLOOD—DIALYSIS
see Artificial Kidney

BLOOD—DISEASES
see also Anemia; Hemochromatosis; Hemophilia; Hyperlipidemia; Pediatric Hematology; Septicemia

ABBE Scientist Research Division Staff. AIDS & HIV in Blood: Index & Medical Analysis of New Clinical & Research Information. 2007. (ENG., Illus.). 160p. ring bd. 69.95 *(978-0-7883-4777-1(2))* ABBE Pubs. Assn. of Washington, D.C.

Armitage, James O. Atlas of Clinical Hematology. Armitage, James O., ed. 2nd ed. 2008. (Illus.). 226p. 169.00 *(978-1-57340-284-2(2))* Current Medicine Group LLC.

Bain, Barbara Jane. Haematology: A Core Curriculum. 2010. (Illus.). 348p. 99.00 *(978-1-84816-710-0(5))* Imperial College Pr. GBR. Dist: World Scientific Publishing Co., Inc.

—Haematology: A Core Curriculum. 2010. (Illus.). 348p. pap. 65.00 *(978-1-84816-499-4(8))* World Scientific Publishing Co., Inc.

Balducci, Lodovico, et al, eds. Blood Disorders in the Elderly. 2008. (ENG., Illus.). 496p. 120.00 *(978-0-521-87573-8(0))* Cambridge Univ. Pr.

Ballantyne, Christie M., et al. Dyslipidemia Essentials 2008. 4th ed. 2008. (Illus.). 208p. pap. 31.95 *(978-0-7637-6609-2(7))* Jones & Bartlett Learning, LLC.

Beck, Norman. Diagnostic Hematology. 2009. (Illus.). 752p. pap. 109.00 *(978-1-84800-282-1(3))* Springer.

Berger, Dietmar P., et al, eds. Concise Manual of Hematology & Oncology. 2008. (Illus.). xii, 1058p. 189.00 *(978-3-540-73276-1(4))* Springer.

Bick, Rodger L., et al, eds. Hematological Complications in Obstetrics, Pregnancy, & Gynecology. 2009. (ENG., Illus.). 620p. pap. 104.00 *(978-0-521-10869-0(1))* Cambridge Univ. Pr.

Boyiadzis, Michael, et al. Hematology-Oncology Therapy, Second Edition. 2nd ed. 2012. (ENG.). 1008p. pap. 99.00 *(978-0-07-163789-3(3)*, 0071637893) McGraw-Hill Professional Publishing.

Brown, Marvelle & Cutler, Tracey, eds. Haematology Nursing. 2012. (ENG.). 336p. pap. 50.00 ***(978-1-4051-6996-7(6)***, Wiley-Blackwell) Wiley, John & Sons, Inc.

Bruserud, Oystein, ed. The Chemokine System in Experimental & Clinical Hematology. 2010. (Current Topics in Microbiology & Immunology Ser.). (Illus.). xii, 210p. 219.00 *(978-3-642-12638-3(3)*, 3642126383) Springer.

Bunn, Howard Franklin & Aster, Jon C. Pathophysiology of Blood Disorders. 2010. (ENG., Illus.). 342p. (C). pap. 58.00 *(978-0-07-171378-8(6)*, 0071713786) McGraw-Hill Medical Publishing Div.

Carr, Jacqueline H. & Rodak, Bernadette F. Clinical Hematology Atlas. 3rd ed. 2008. (ENG., Illus.). 280p. spiral bd. 63.95 *(978-1-4160-5039-1(6)*, Saunders) Elsevier - Health Sciences Div.

Ciesla, Betty. Hematology in Practice. 2nd rev. ed. 2011. (Illus.). 384p. 79.95 *(978-0-8036-2561-7(8))* Davis, F. A. Co.

Connors, Jean. Hematologic Disorders in Pregnancy,an Issue of Hematology/Oncology Clinics of North America. 2011. (Clinics: Internal Medicine Ser.: 25-2). (ENG., Illus.). 232p. 104.00 *(978-1-4557-0459-0(8)*, Saunders) Elsevier - Health Sciences Div.

Coppes, Max J., et al. An Update on Pediatric Oncology & Hematology: Hematology - Oncology Clinics of North America. 2010. (Clinics: Internal Medicine Ser.: 24-1). (ENG.). 99.00 *(978-1-4377-2202-4(4)*, Saunders) Elsevier - Health Sciences Div.

Cram101 Textbook Reviews & Cram101 Textbook Reviews. Outlines & Highlights for Clinical Malignant Hematology by Mikkael a Sekeres, Isbn: 9780071436502. 2011. 514p. pap. 37.95 ***(978-1-61461-339-8(7))*** Cram101 Inc.

—Outlines & Highlights for Hematology in Clinical Practice by Robert S Hillman, Isbn: 9780071440356 9780071440356 0071440356. 2011. 96p. pap. 27.95 ***(978-1-61461-522-4(5))*** Cram101 Inc.

—Outlines & Highlights for Wintrobes Clinical Hematology by John P Greer, Isbn: 9780781765077. 2011. 162p. pap. 29.95 ***(978-1-61812-043-4(3))*** Cram101 Inc.

Crisan, Domnita. Hematopathology: Genomic Mechanisms of Neoplastic Diseases. 2010. (Illus.). xii, 358p. E-Book ***(978-1-60761-262-9(3))*** Humana Pr.

Crisan, Domnita, ed. Hematopathology: Genomic Mechanisms of Neoplastic Diseases. 2010. (Molecular & Translational Medicine Ser.). (Illus.). xii, 358p. 259.00 *(978-1-60761-261-2(5)*, 1607612615) Humana Pr.

Crowther, Mark A., et al, eds. Evidence-Based Hematology. 2008. (Evidence-Based Medicine Ser.: 21). (ENG., Illus.). 440p. 284.00 *(978-1-4051-5747-6(X))* Wiley, John & Sons, Inc.

Cualing, Hernani, et al. Non-Neoplastic Hematopathology & Infections. 2012. (ENG., Illus.). 608p. 189.95 ***(978-0-470-64600-7(4)***, Wiley-Blackwell) Wiley, John & Sons, Inc.

Descotes, Jacques. Toxicology of the Blood & Bone Marrow, Second Edition. 2nd ed. 2009. 169.95 *(978-1-4200-7846-6(1))* CRC Pr. LLC.

Diamond, Lawrence W., et al. Flow Cytometry in Hematopathology: A Visual Approach to Data Analysis & Interpretation. 2nd ed. 2007. (Illus.). 344p. 199.00 incl. cd-rom *(978-1-58829-855-3(8))* Humana Pr.

Dunphy, Cherie H., ed. Molecular Pathology of Hematolymphoid Diseases. 2010. (Molecular Pathology Library). (ENG., Illus.). xix, 620p. 199.00 *(978-1-4419-5697-2(2)*, 1441956972) Springer.

Estlin, Eddy. Pediatric Hematology & Oncology: Scientific Principles & Clinical Practice. Gilbertson, Richard et al, eds. 2010. (ENG., Illus.). 448p. 225.95 *(978-1-4051-5350-8(4)*, Wiley-Blackwell) Wiley, John & Sons, Inc.

Fashoro, Gabriel A. Some Blood & Heart Related Diseases. 2008. 148p. pap. 14.95 *(978-0-595-51407-6(3))* iUniverse, Inc.

Foucar, Kathy. Blood & Bone Marrow. 2011. (ENG.). 800p. 299.00 *(978-1-931884-27-3(7))* Lippincott Williams & Wilkins.

Gadisseur, A. & Michiels, J. J., eds. Advances in the Diagnosis & Classification of von Willebrand Disease. 2009. (Illus.). 120p. pap. *(978-3-8055-9208-6(6))* Karger, S. AG.

Green, Anthony R. Postgraduate Haematology. Hoffbrand, A. Victor et al, eds. 6th ed. 2010. (ENG., Illus.). 1076p. 315.00 *(978-1-4051-9180-7(5)*, Wiley-Blackwell) Wiley, John & Sons, Inc.

Harmening, Denise M. Clinical Hematology & Fundamentals of Hemostasis. 5th rev. ed. 2008. (Illus.). 960p. 124.00 *(978-0-8036-1732-2(1))* Davis, F. A. Co.

Hasserjian, Robert Paul. Current Concepts in Hematopathology: Applications in Clinical Practice, an Issue of Surgical Pathology Clinics. 2010. (Clinics: Internal Medicine Ser.: 3-4). (ENG.). 57.00 *(978-1-4377-2499-8(X)*, Saunders) Elsevier - Health Sciences Div.

Hastings, Caroline A., et al. Handbook of Pediatric Hematology & Oncology: Children's Hospital & Research Center Oakland. 2nd ed. 2012. (ENG.). 390p. pap. 65.95 ***(978-0-470-67088-0(6)***, Wiley-Blackwell) Wiley, John & Sons, Inc.

Hillman, Robert, et al. Hematology in Clinical Practice, Fifth Edition. 5th ed. 2010. (LANGE Clinical Medicine Ser.). (ENG., Illus.). 512p. pap. 73.00 *(978-0-07-162699-6(9)*, 0071626999) McGraw-Hill Professional Publishing.

Hoffbrand, Victor & Moss, Paul. Essential Haematology. 6th ed. 2011. (Essentials Ser.: 15). (ENG., Illus.). 468p. pap. 64.95 *(978-1-4051-9890-5(7)*, Wiley-Blackwell) Wiley, John & Sons, Inc.

Hoffman, Ronald, et al. Hematology: Basic Principles & Practice. 5th ed. 2008. (ENG., Illus.). 2640p. 425.00 *(978-0-443-06713-6(9))*; 2560p. 314.00 *(978-0-443-06715-0(5))* Elsevier - Health Sciences Div. (Churchill Livingstone).

—Hoffman, Hematology, Expert Consult Premium Edition - Enhanced Online Features & Print, 5e & Hoffbrand, Color Atlas of Clinical Hematology, Expert Consult - Online & Print, 4e Package. 2009. (ENG.). 595.00 *(978-1-4377-0647-5(9)*, Saunders) Elsevier - Health Sciences Div.

Howard, Martin R. & Hamilton, Peter J. Haematology: An Illustrated Colour Text. 3rd rev. ed. 2007. (Illustrated Colour Text Ser.). (ENG., Illus.). 124p. pap. 54.95 *(978-0-443-10362-9(3)*, Churchill Livingstone) Elsevier - Health Sciences Div.

Hsi, Eric D. Hematopathology. 2nd ed. 2012. (Foundations in Diagnostic Pathology Ser.). (ENG., Illus.). 760p. 179.00 ***(978-1-4377-2606-0(2)***, Saunders) Elsevier - Health Sciences Div.

Hughes-Jones, N. C., et al. Haematology. 8th ed. 2008. (Lecture Notes Ser.). (ENG., Illus.). 216p. pap. 45.95 *(978-1-4051-8050-4(1)*, Wiley-Blackwell) Wiley, John & Sons, Inc.

Jones, Daniel, ed. Neoplastic Hematopathology: Experimental & Clinical Approaches. 2010. (Contemporary Hematology Ser.). (ENG., Illus.). xiii, 622p. 279.00 *(978-1-60761-383-1(2)*, 1607613832) Humana Pr.

Kaushansky, Kenneth & Williams, William J. Williams Hematology. 8th ed. 2010. *(978-0-07-162144-1(X))* McGraw-Hill Medical Publishing Div.

Kaushansky, Kenneth, et al. Williams Hematology, Eighth Edition. 8th ed. 2010. (ENG., Illus.). 2460p. 286.00 *(978-0-07-162151-9(2)*, 0071621512) McGraw-Hill Professional Publishing.

Kini, R. Manjunatha, et al, eds. Toxins & Hemostasis: From Bench to Bedside. 2010. (ENG., Illus.). xxiii, 600p. 239.00 *(978-90-481-9294-6(3)*, 9048192943) Springer.

Kitchen, Gareth. Immunology & Haematology. 3rd rev. ed. 2007. (Crash Course Ser.). (Illus.). 204p. pap. *(978-0-7234-3418-4(2))* Mosby GBR. Dist: Elsevier - Health Sciences Div.

Lazarus, Hillard & Laughlin, Mary, eds. Allogeneic Stem Cell Transplantation. 2nd ed. 2010. (Contemporary Hematology Ser.). (ENG., Illus.). 881p. 239.00 *(978-1-934115-33-6(9)*, 1934115339) Humana Pr.

Lazarus, Hillard M. & Schmaier, Alvin H., eds. Concise Guide to Hematology. 2011. (ENG.). 432p. 74.95 ***(978-1-4051-9666-6(1)***, Wiley-Blackwell) Wiley, John & Sons, Inc.

Löffler, Helmut, et al, eds. Atlas of Clinical Hematology. 6th ed. 2010. (Illus.). xiii, 429p. pap. 399.00 *(978-3-642-05906-3(6)*, 3642059066) Springer.

Lichtman, Marshall A. Williams Manual of Hematology. 8th ed. 2011. (ENG., Illus.). 756p. pap. 73.00 *(978-0-07-162242-4(X)*, 007162242X) McGraw-Hill Professional Publishing.

Limpon, Bora. Beta-Thalassaemia: Arms Pcr Technique: Arms Pcr Technique. 2011. 124p. pap. ***(978-3-639-34536-0(3))*** VDM Verlag Dr. Mueller e.K.

Longo, Dan L. & Harrison, Tinsley Randolph. Hematology & Oncology. 2010. (ENG., Illus.). 788p. pap. 82.00 *(978-0-07-166335-9(5)*, 0071663355) McGraw-Hill Professional Publishing.

McCann, Shaun, et al. Haematology. 2nd ed. 2009. (Clinical Cases Ser.: 30). (ENG., Illus.). 200p. pap. 50.95 *(978-1-4051-8322-2(5)*, Wiley-Blackwell) Wiley, John & Sons, Inc.

Mehta, Atul B. & Hoffbrand, Victor. Haematology at a Glance. 3rd ed. 2009. (At a Glance Ser.: 5). (ENG., Illus.). 128p. pap. 45.95 *(978-1-4051-7970-6(8)*, Wiley-Blackwell) Wiley, John & Sons, Inc.

Munker, Reinhold, et al, eds. Modern Hematology: Biology & Clinical Management. 2nd ed. 2010. (Contemporary Hematology Ser.). (Illus.). 498p. pap. 179.00 *(978-1-61737-640-5(X)*, 161737640X) Humana Pr.

Naeim, Faramarz, et al. Hematopathology: Morphology, Immunophenotype, Cytogenetics, & Molecular Approaches. 2008. (ENG., Illus.). 612p. 155.00 *(978-0-12-370607-2(6)*, Academic Pr.) Elsevier Science & Technology Bks.

Neeb, Gunter R. Blood Stasis: China's Classical Concept in Modern Medicine. Beer, Maximilian & Kaiser, Julia, trs. 2006. (ENG., Illus.). 384p. 93.95 *(978-0-443-10165-4(X)*, Churchill Livingstone) Elsevier - Health Sciences Div.

Pereira, Irma, et al. Atlas of Peripheral Blood: The Primary Diagnostic Tool. 2011. (ENG., Illus.). 304p. 154.99 ***(978-0-7817-7780-3(1))*** Lippincott Williams & Wilkins.

Porwit, Anna, et al, eds. Blood & Bone Marrow Pathology. 2nd ed. 2011. (ENG., Illus.). 722p. 319.95 ***(978-0-7020-3147-2(X)***, Churchill Livingstone) Elsevier - Health Sciences Div.

Provan, Drew & Gribben, John, eds. Molecular Hematology. 3rd ed. 2010. (ENG., Illus.). 428p. 236.00 *(978-1-4051-8231-7(8)*, Wiley-Blackwell) Wiley, John & Sons, Inc.

Provan, Drew, et al. Oxford Handbook of Clinical Haematology. 3rd ed. 2009. (Oxford Handbooks Ser.). (ENG., Illus.). 920p. pap. 59.95 *(978-0-19-922739-6(X))* Oxford Univ. Pr., Inc.

Proytcheva, Maria, ed. Diagnostic Pediatric Hematopathology. 2011. (ENG., Illus.). 588p. 225.00 *(978-0-521-88160-9(9))* Cambridge Univ. Pr.

Raanani, P. & Skoetz, N., eds. The Role of Systematic Reviews & Meta-Analyses in the Management of Hemato-Oncological Disorders Vol. 125, Nos. 1-2: Special Issue - Acta Haematologica 2011. 2010. (Illus.). 102p. pap. *(978-3-8055-9666-4(9))* Karger, S. AG.

Reagan, William J., et al. Veterinary Hematology: Atlas of Common Domestic & Non-Domestic Species. 2nd ed. 2008. (ENG., Illus.). 128p. 69.99 *(978-0-8138-2809-1(0)*, Wiley-Blackwell) Wiley, John & Sons, Inc.

Rodak, Bernadette F. & Carr, Jacqueline H. Clinical Hematology Atlas. 4th ed. 2012. (ENG., Illus.). 296p. spiral bd. 66.95 ***(978-1-4557-0830-7(5)***, Saunders) Elsevier - Health Sciences Div.

Rodak, Bernadette F., et al. Hematology: Clinical Principles & Applications. 4th ed. 2011. (ENG., Illus.). 880p. (C). 105.00 *(978-1-4377-0692-5(4)*, Saunders) Elsevier - Health Sciences Div.

Rozenberg, Gillian. Cases in Microscopic Haematology. 2011. (ENG.). (C). spiral bd. 54.95 *(978-0-7295-4092-6(8)*, Churchill Livingstone) Elsevier - Health Sciences Div.
Schiffman, Fred & Mega, Anthony. Consultative Hematology, an Issue of Hematology/Oncology Clinics of North America. 2012. (Clinics: Internal Medicine Ser.: 26-2). (ENG.). 1440p. 109.00 ***(978-1-4557-3875-5(1)***, Saunders) Elsevier - Health Sciences Div.
Steinberg, Martin H., et al. Disorders of Hemoglobin: Genetics, Pathophysiology, & Clinical Management. 2nd ed. 2009. (ENG., Illus.). 846p. 399.00 *(978-0-521-87519-6(6))* Cambridge Univ. Pr.
Tefferi, Ayalew, ed. Primary Hematology. 2010. (ENG., Illus.). 488p. pap. 135.00 *(978-1-61737-122-6(X)*, 161737122X) Humana Pr.
Valverde, J. L., ed. Rare Diseases: Focus on Rare Plasma Related Disorders. 2009. (Pharmaceuticals Policy & Law Ser.). (Illus.). 330p. pap. 174.00 *(978-1-60750-055-1(8))* IOS Pr., Inc.
van der Walt, J. & Borisch, B., eds. Haematological Malignancy & the Bone Marrow Trephine Biopsy. 2007. (Illus.). 88p. pap. *(978-3-8055-8297-1(8))* Karger, S. AG.
Weitzman, Sheila & Egeler, R. Maarten, eds. Histiocytic Disorders of Children & Adults: Basic Science, Clinical Features & Therapy. 2011. (ENG., Illus.). 456p. pap. 80.00 *(978-0-521-18416-8(9))* Cambridge Univ. Pr.
Wintrobe, Maxwell M. Wintrobe's Clinical Hematology, 2 vols., Set. Greer, John P. et al, eds. 12th rev. ed. 2008. (ENG., Illus.). 3232p. 369.99 *(978-0-7817-6507-7(2))* Lippincott Williams & Wilkins.
Zaidi, Syed Z. A. HEMATOLOGY - an updated review through Extended Matching Questions. 2009. 344p. pap. 23.95 *(978-1-4327-2380-4(4))* Outskirts Pr., Inc.

BLOOD—EXAMINATION

Here are entered works on the examination of the formed elements of the blood by microscope and other techniques, and on the diagnostic significance of the results. Works on the physicochemical analysis of serum or plasma and on the diagnostic significance of the results are entered under Blood—Analysis.
see also Blood Groups; Glycolysis

Bain, Barbara J., et al. Dacie & Lewis Practical Haematology. 11th ed. 2011. (ENG., Illus.). 668p. pap. 130.00 ***(978-0-7020-3408-4(8)***, Churchill Livingstone) Elsevier - Health Sciences Div.
Blackall, Douglas P., et al. Transfusion Medicine: Self-Assessment & Review. 2nd ed. 2009. *(978-1-56395-280-7(7)*, AABB Pr.) American Assn. of Blood Banks.
Gulati, Gene L. Blood Cell Morphology Grading Guide. 2009. 88p. spiral bd. 74.25 *(978-0-89189-569-5(8))* American Society for Clinical Pathology.
Kohut, George. Blood Test as Proof of Kinship in Jewish Folklore. 2010. pap. 17.92 *(978-1-61143-014-1(3))* Gorgias Pr., LLC.
LaValle, James B. Your Blood Never Lies: How to Read a Blood Test for a Longer, Healthier Life. 2010. (ENG.). 208p. pap. 14.95 *(978-0-7570-0350-9(8))* Square One Pubs.
Löffler, Helmut, et al, eds. Atlas of Clinical Hematology. 6th ed. 2010. (Illus.). xiii, 429p. pap. 399.00 *(978-3-642-05906-3(6)*, 3642059066) Springer.
Lippi, Giuseppe. Hemolysis: An Unresolved Dispute in Laboratory Medicine. 2012. (Patient Safety Ser.). (ENG., Illus.). 205p. 91.00 ***(978-3-11-024613-1(9))*** De Gruyter, Walter Inc.
Reddy, Vishnu, et al. Hematology Testing. 2007. 131p. spiral bd. 20.00 *(978-1-59425-072-9(3))* American Assn. for Clinical Chemistry, Inc.
—Quick Guide to Hematology Testing. 2007. *(978-1-59425-074-3(X)*, AACC Pr.) American Assn. for Clinical Chemistry, Inc.

BLOOD—FLOW

see Blood Flow

BLOOD—FOLKLORE

Pollack, Andrew J. The Blood of Christ in Christian Greek Literature till the Year 444 a D. 2011. 180p. 42.95 ***(978-1-258-04828-0(0))*** Literary Licensing, LLC.
Seeman, Bernard. The River of Life: The Story of Man's Blood from Magic to Science. 2011. 264p. 47.95 ***(978-1-258-05124-2(9))*** Literary Licensing, LLC.

BLOOD—GAS CONTENT

see Blood Gases

BLOOD—GROUPS

see Blood Groups

BLOOD—JURISPRUDENCE

see Forensic Hematology

BLOOD—PLASMA

see Blood Plasma

BLOOD—PRESSURE

see Blood Pressure

BLOOD—RELIGIOUS ASPECTS

see also Blood Accusation

Biale, David. Blood & Belief: The Circulation of a Symbol Between Jews & Christians. (Illus.). 2008. 316p. pap. 25.95 *(978-0-520-25798-6(7))* 2007. 299p. 55.00 *(978-0-520-25304-9(3))* Univ. of California Pr.
Clivaz, C. L' Ange et la Sueur de Sang (Lc 22,43-44) Ou Comment on Pourrait Bien Encore Ecrire l'Histoire. 2010. (Biblical Tools & Studies). (FRE.). 733p. (C). 124.00 *(978-90-429-2278-5(8))* Peeters Pubs. & Booksellers BEL. Dist: Brown, David Bk. Co., The.
Copeman, Jacob. Veins of Devotion: Blood Donation & Religious Experience in North India. 2008. (Studies in Medical Anthropology Ser.). (ENG., Illus.). 264p. 72.00 *(978-0-8135-4448-9(3))*; 256p. pap. 25.95 *(978-0-8135-4449-6(1))* Rutgers Univ. Pr.
Feder, Yitzhaq. Blood Expiation in Hittite & Biblical Ritual: Origins, Context, & Meaning. 2011. 310p. ***(978-90-04-20259-7(5))*** BRILL.
—Blood Expiation in Hittite & Biblical Ritual: Origins, Context, & Meaning. 2011. ***(978-1-58983-555-9(7))***; ***(978-1-58983-554-2(9))*** Society of Biblical Literature.
Ford, Juanita. Life in the Blood. 2009. 36p. pap. 16.99 *(978-1-4490-3843-4(3))* AuthorHouse.
Hart, Mitchell. Jewish Blood: Reality & metaphor in history, religion & Culture. Hart, Mitchell, ed. 2009. (Routledge Jewish Studies Ser.). (ENG., Illus.). 240p. (C). 120.00 *(978-0-415-47749-9(2))* Routledge.
Hurt, Connie M. His Sacred Blood. 2009. 108p. pap. 11.99 *(978-1-61579-000-5(4))* Xulon Pr., Inc.
Pollack, Andrew J. The Blood of Christ in Christian Greek Literature till the Year 444 a D. 2011. 180p. 42.95 ***(978-1-258-04828-0(0))*** Literary Licensing, LLC.
Seeman, Bernard. The River of Life: The Story of Man's Blood from Magic to Science. 2011. 264p. 47.95 ***(978-1-258-05124-2(9))*** Literary Licensing, LLC.

BLOOD—SEMIOLOGY

see Blood—Examination

BLOOD—TRANSFUSION

see also Blood Banks; Blood Groups; Blood Plasma Substitutes

American Association of Blood Banks, creator. Technical Manual 12th - 16th Editions & Standards 1st - 25th Editions. 2008. cd-rom 376.50 *(978-1-56395-272-2(6))* American Assn. of Blood Banks.
American Association of Blood Banks Staff. Standards for Perioperative Autologous Blood Collection & Administration. 2007. pap. ***(978-3-8055-8408-1(3))*** Karger, S. AG.
American Association of Blood Banks Staff, contrib. by. Standards for Perioperative Autologous Blood Collection & Administration. 3rd ed. 2007. (Illus.). xv, 52p. pap. *(978-1-56395-248-7(3)*, AABB Pr.) American Assn. of Blood Banks.
Ashford, Paul, ed. ISBT 128 an Introduction. 3rd ed. 2006. *(978-1-933243-01-6(5))* ICCBBA Inc.
—ISBT 128 for Tissues, an Introduction. 2007. *(978-1-933243-05-4(8))* ICCBBA Inc.
AuBuchon, James P. & Prowse, Christopher V. Pathogen Inactivation: The Penultimate Paradigm Shift. 2010. *(978-1-56395-309-5(9)*, AABB Pr.) American Assn. of Blood Banks.
Bein, G., ed. German Society for Transfusion Medicine & Immunohematology (DGTI) 40th Annual Meeting, Friedrichshafen, September 2007: Abstracts: Supplement Issue: Transfusion Medicine & Hemotherapy 2007, Vol. 34, Suppl. 1. 2007. 80p. pap. *(978-3-8055-8417-3(2))* Karger, S. AG.
Berte, Lucia M. Quality Manual Preparation Workbook for Perioperative Autologous Blood Collection & Administration. 2007. (Illus.). 51p. spiral bd. 196.50 incl. cd-rom *(978-1-56395-246-3(7))* American Assn. of Blood Banks.
Blackall, Douglas P., et al. Transfusion Medicine: Self-Assessment & Review. 2nd ed. 2009. *(978-1-56395-280-7(7)*, AABB Pr.) American Assn. of Blood Banks.
Blaney, Kathy D. & Howard, Paula R. Basic & Applied Concepts of Immunohematology. 2nd ed. 2008. (ENG., Illus.). 400p. (C). 75.95 *(978-0-323-04805-7(6)*, Mosby) Elsevier - Health Sciences Div.
Blasczyk, R., ed. German Society for Transfusion Medicine & Immunohematology (DGTI) 44th Annual Meeting, Hannover, September 2011: Abstracts. Supplement Issue:'Transfusion Medicine & Hemotherapy 2011, Vol. 38, Suppl. 1' 2011. (ENG.). 76p. pap. ***(978-3-8055-9880-4(7))*** Karger, S. AG.
Brown, F. & Seitz, R., eds. Advances in Transfusion Safety 2001: International Symposium, Langen, June 2001, Vol. 108. (Developments in Biologicals Ser.: Vol. 108). (Illus.). *(978-3-8055-7426-6(6))* Karger, S. AG.
Contreras, Marcela. ABC of Transfusion. 4th ed. 2009. (ABC Ser.). (ENG., Illus.). 128p. pap. 55.95 *(978-1-4051-5646-2(5))* Wiley, John & Sons, Inc.
Dax, Elizabeth M., et al. Advances in Transfusion Safety: Sydney, Australia, 11-13th October 2005: Proceedings of an International Conference Organized by the International Association for Biologicals (IABS), the National Serology Reference Laboratory, Australia, & the Therapeutics Goods Administration. 2007. (Developments in Biologicals Ser.: Vol. 127). (Illus.). xiv, 271p. *(978-3-8055-8239-1(0))* Karger, S. AG.
Eder, Anne & Bianco, Celso. Screening Blood Donors: Science, Reason, & the Donor History Questionnaire. 2007. *(978-1-56395-247-0(5))*; *(978-1-56395-252-4(1))* American Assn. of Blood Banks. (AABB Pr.).
Harmening, Denise. Modern Blood Banking & Transfusion Practices. 6th rev. ed. 2012. (Illus.). 608p. 89.95 ***(978-0-8036-2682-9(7))*** Davis, F. A. Co.
Hillyer, Christopher D., et al, eds. Transfusion Medicine & Hemostasis: Clinical & Laboratory Aspects. 2009. (ENG., Illus.). 775p. pap. 56.95 *(978-0-12-374432-6(6)*, Elsevier Science) Elsevier Science & Technology Bks.
Hillyer, Christopher D., et al. Blood Banking & Transfusion Medicine: Basic Principles & Practice. 2nd rev. ed. 2006. (ENG., Illus.). 912p. 240.00 *(978-0-443-06981-9(6)*, Churchill Livingstone) Elsevier - Health Sciences Div.
Jeter, Elaine K. & Spivey, Mary Ann. Introduction to Transfusion Medicine: A Case Study Approach. (Illus.). (Orig.). pap. ***(978-3-8055-6472-4(4))*** Karger, S. AG.
Kiefel, V. & Eckstein, R., eds. German Society for Transfusion Medicine & Immunohematology (DGTI) 42nd Annual Meeting, Rostock, September 2009: Abstracts. 2009. 76p. pap. *(978-3-8055-9325-0(2))* Karger, S. AG.
Klein, Harvey G. & Anstee, David J. Mollison's Blood Transfusion in Clinical Medicine. 12th ed. 2013. (ENG.). 912p. 199.95 *(978-1-4051-9940-7(7)*, Wiley-Blackwell) Wiley, John & Sons, Inc.
Kleinman, Steven & Popovsky, Mark A. TRALI: Mechanisms, Management, & Prevention. 2008. *(978-1-56395-267-8(X)*, AABB Pr.) American Assn. of Blood Banks.
Knight, Robin, ed. Transfusion & Transplantation Science. 2011. (Fundamentals of Biomedical Science Ser.). (ENG., Illus.). 336p. pap. 44.95 *(978-0-19-953328-2(8))* Oxford Univ. Pr., Inc.
Krementsov, Nikolai. A Martian Stranded on Earth: Alexander Bogdanov, Blood Transfusions, & Proletarian Science. 2011. (ENG., Illus.). 192p. 35.00 *(978-0-226-45412-2(6))* Univ. of Chicago Pr.
Lecerer, Susan E. Flesh & Blood: Organ Transplantation & Blood Transfusion in Twentieth-Century America. 2008. (ENG., Illus.). 256p. 35.00 *(978-0-19-516150-2(5))* Oxford Univ. Pr., Inc.
Lippert, Hans-Dieter & Flegel, Willy A. Kommentar Zum Transfusionsgesetz (Tfg) Und Den Hamotherapie-Richtlinien. 2nd ed. 2008. 550p. 129.00 *(978-3-540-36739-0(X)*, 354036739X) Springer.
Maniatis, Alice, et al, eds. Alternatives to Blood Transfusion in Transfusion Medicine. 2nd ed. 2010. (ENG., Illus.). 608p. 167.95 *(978-1-4051-6321-7(6)*, Wiley-Blackwell) Wiley, John & Sons, Inc.
Marques, Marisa B. & Fritsma, Margaret G. Quick Guide to Transfusion Medicine. 2007. *(978-1-59425-073-6(1)*, AACC Pr.) American Assn. for Clinical Chemistry, Inc.
Massie, Bob. A Song in the Night: A Memoir of Resilience. 2012. (ENG., Illus.). 304p. 24.00 ***(978-0-385-53575-5(9)***, Talese, Nan A.) Knopf Doubleday Publishing Group.
McCullough, Jeff. Transfusion Medicine. 3rd ed. 2012. (ENG., Illus.). 608p. pap. 84.95 ***(978-1-4443-3705-1(X)***, Wiley-Blackwell) Wiley, John & Sons, Inc.
McLeod, Bruce C. Apheresis: Principles & Practice. 3rd ed. 2010. *(978-1-56395-305-7(6)*, AABB Pr.) American Assn. of Blood Banks.
Mijovic, Aleksandar. Transfusion Medicine: Case Studies & Clinical Management. 2011. (ENG., Illus.). xix, 111p. pap. 39.95 ***(978-1-4471-2181-7(3)***, 1447121813) Springer.
Mintz, Paul D. Transfusion Therapy: Clinical Principles & Practice. 3rd ed. 2010. *(978-1-56395-307-1(2)*, AABB Pr.) American Assn. of Blood Banks.
Murphy, Michael F., et al. Practical Transfusion Medicine. 3rd ed. 2009. (ENG., Illus.). 576p. 173.95 *(978-1-4051-8196-9(6)*, Wiley-Blackwell) Wiley, John & Sons, Inc.
Norris, Jane. Regulation & Licensure of Whole Blood, Blood Components, & Source Plasma. 2009. (Illus.). xiii, 175p. pap. *(978-1-56395-301-9(3)*, AABB Pr.) American Assn. of Blood Banks.
Overall Blood Supply Strategy with Regard to Variant Creutzfeldt-Jakob Disease (vCJD) Report of the Working Group Commissioned by the German Federal Ministry of Health April 2006 (Update of the Report from August 2001): Supplement Issue: Transfusion Medicine & Hemotherapy 2006, Vol. 33, Suppl. 2. (Illus.). 40p. pap. *(978-3-8055-8238-4(2))* Karger, S. AG.
Pan American Health Organization. Eligibility for Blood Donation: Recommendations for Education & Selection of Prospective Blood Donors. 2009. (PAHO Occasional Publication Ser.). 95p. pap. 20.00 *(978-92-75-12939-5(8))* Pan American Health Organization (PAHO).
Pemberton, Stephen Gregory. The Bleeding Disease: Hemophilia & the Unintended Consequences of Medical Progress. 2011. (ENG., Illus.). 400p. (gr. 17). 50.00 *(978-1-4214-0115-7(0))* Johns Hopkins Univ. Pr.
Perioperative Blood Management: A Physician's Handbook. 2nd ed. 2009. xi, 259p. *(978-1-56395-292-0(0)*, AABB Pr.) American Assn. of Blood Banks.
Petrides, Marian & Stack, Gary. Practical Guide to Transfusion Medicine. 2nd ed. 2007. *(978-1-56395-243-2(2)*, AABB Pr.) American Assn. of Blood Banks.
Popovsky, Mark A. Transfusion Reactions. 3rd ed. 2007. *(978-1-56395-244-9(0)*, AABB Pr.) American Assn. of Blood Banks.
Quinley, Eva D. Immunohematology: Principles & Practice. 3rd rev. ed. 2010. (ENG., Illus.). 432p. 86.99 *(978-0-7817-8204-3(X))* Lippincott Williams & Wilkins.
Rahman, Shibley, et al. Basics of Blood Management. 2007. (ENG., Illus.). 400p. 122.95 *(978-1-4051-5131-3(5)*, Wiley-Blackwell) Wiley, John & Sons, Inc.
Reesink, H. W., ed. Hepatitis C Virus, Vol. 62. 2nd rev. enl. ed. (Current Studies in Hematology & Blood Transfusion: Vol. 62, 1997). (Illus.). *(978-3-8055-5542-4(9))* Karger, S. AG.
Roseff, Susan D. Pediatric Transfusion: A Physician's Handbook. 3rd ed. 2009. (Illus.). viii, 228p. *(978-1-56395-291-3(2)*, AABB Pr.) American Assn. of Blood Banks.
Saxena, Sunita. The Transfusion Committee: Putting Patient Safety First. Shulman, Ira A., ed. 2006. (Illus.). xvi, 155p. *(978-1-56395-223-4(8)*, AABB Pr.) American Assn. of Blood Banks.
Scharf, R. E., ed. Progress & Challenges in Transfusion Medicine, Hemostasis, & Hemotherapy: State of the Art 41st Congress of the German Society for Transfusion Medicine & Immunohematology, Düsseldorf, September 2008. 2008. (Illus.). 408p. pap. *(978-3-8055-8659-7(0))* Karger, S. AG.
Scharf, R. E. & Moog, R., eds. German Society for Transfusion Medicine & Immunohematology (DGTI) / Interdisciplinary European Society for Haemapheresis & Haemotherapy (ESFH), in Cooperation with the Société Française de Transfusion Sanguine (SFTS) Joint Annual Congress, Düsseldorf, September 2008: Abstracts. 2008. 100p. pap. *(978-3-8055-9013-6(X))* Karger, S. AG.
Schexneider, Katherine I. Transfusion Medicine: A Clinical Guide. 2008. (Vademecum Ser.). *(978-1-57059-703-9(0))* Landes Bioscience.
Schonewille, H. Red Blood Cell Alloimmunization after Blood Transfusion. 2008. (LUP Dissertaties Ser.). 180p. per. *(978-90-8728-031-4(9)*, Leiden Univ. Pr.) Amsterdam Univ. Pr.
Select Committee on Quality Assurance in Blood Transfusion. Guide to the preparation, use & quality assurance of blood components - 13th Edition (2007) 13th ed. 2007. 300p. pap. 42.00 *(978-92-871-6137-6(2))* Council of Europe FRA. Dist: Manhattan Publishing Co.
Silva, Marianne A. & Vengelen-Tyler, Virginia. Quality Toolkit & Case Studies: Solutions for Common Problems. 2011. ***(978-1-56395-317-0(X)***, AABB Pr.) American Assn. of Blood Banks.
Simon, Toby L., et al, eds. Rossi's Principles of Transfusion Medicine. 4th ed. 2009. (ENG., Illus.). 1112p. 330.95 *(978-1-4051-7588-3(5)*, Wiley-Blackwell) Wiley, John & Sons, Inc.
Singbartl, G. & Schleinzer, W., eds. Autologous Transfusion - from Euphoria to Reason: Clinical Practice Based on Scientific Knowledge - 3rd International Symposium, Nottwil, January 2004: Proceedings, Vol. 31. (Illus.). 104p. pap. *(978-3-8055-7818-9(0))* Karger, S. AG.
—Autologous Transfusion - from Euphoria to Reason: Clinical Practice Based on Scientific Knowledge [Bibliography & Price not Definite.]: Concept Autologe Transfusion - 4th International Symposium, Nottwil, January 2006: Proceedings: Special Issue: Transfusion Medicine & Hemotherapy 2006, Vol. 33, No. 4. (Illus.). 68p. pap. *(978-3-8055-8188-2(2))* Karger, S. AG.
Smit-Sibinga, C. Th. Neonatology & Blood Transfusion. 2010. (Developments in Hematology & Immunology Ser.). xv, 294p. pap. 229.00 *(978-1-4419-3641-7(6)*, 1441936416) Springer.
Smit Sibinga, C. Th., et al, eds. Automation in Blood Transfusion. 2010. (Developments in Hematology & Immunology Ser.). 252p. pap. 329.00 *(978-1-4419-4744-4(2)*, 1441947442) Springer.
Smit Sibinga, C. Th. & Alter, H. J., eds. Risk Management in Blood Transfusion: the Virtue of Reality: The Virtue of Reality. 2010. (Developments in Hematology & Immunology Ser.). 226p. pap. 329.00 *(978-1-4419-4822-9(8)*, 1441948228) Springer.
Smit Sibinga, C. Th. & de Leij, L. F. M. H., eds. Cellular Engineering & Cellular Therapies. 2010. (Developments in Hematology & Immunology Ser.). 232p. pap. 139.00 *(978-1-4419-5250-9(0)*, 1441952500) Springer.
Smit Sibinga, C. Th. & Dodd, Roger Y., eds. Transmissible Diseases & Transfusion. 2010. (Developments in Hematology & Immunology Ser.). 232p. pap. 199.00 *(978-1-4419-5233-2(0)*, 1441952330) Springer.
Smit Sibinga, C. Th. & Klein, Harvey G., eds. Molecular Biology in Blood Transfusion. 2010. (Developments in Hematology & Immunology Ser.). 296p. pap. 239.00 *(978-1-4419-4837-3(6)*, 1441948376) Springer.
Stowell, Christopher P., ed. Informed Consent for Blood Transfusion. (Illus.). pap. ***(978-3-8055-6706-0(5))*** Karger, S. AG.
Stowell, Christopher P. & Sazama, Kathleen. Informed Consent in Blood Transfusion & Cellular Therapies: Patients, Donors, & Research Subjects. 2007. *(978-1-56395-254-8(8)*, AABB Pr.) American Assn. of Blood Banks.
Tefferi, Ayalew, ed. Primary Hematology. 2010. (ENG., Illus.). 488p. pap. 135.00 *(978-1-61737-122-6(X)*, 161737122X) Humana Pr.
Transfusion - Think about It. 2010. (Health Care Issues, Costs & Access Ser.). 160.00 *(978-1-61668-969-8(2))* Nova Science Pubs., Inc.
Tucker, Holly. Blood Work: A Tale of Medicine & Murder in the Scientific Revolution. (ENG.). 2012. 336p. pap. 15.95 ***(978-0-393-34223-9(9)***, 34223) 2011. (Illus.). 304p. 25.95 *(978-0-393-07055-2(7)*, 7055) Norton, W. W. & Co., Inc.
Vyas, Girish N. & Williams, A. E. Advances in Transfusion Safety Vol. 120: Natcher Auditorium, National Institutes of Health (NIH), Bethesda, MD, USA, June 4-6, 2003. (Developments in Biologicals Ser.: Vol. 120). (Illus.). *(978-3-8055-7935-3(7))* Karger, S. AG.
Wailoo, Keith, et al, eds. A Death Retold: Jesica Santillan, the Bungled Transplant, & Paradoxes of Medical Citizenship. 2006. (Studies in Social Medicine). (ENG., Illus.). 392p. per. 23.95 *(978-0-8078-5773-1(4))* Univ. of North Carolina Pr.
Walters, Lisa M. & Badley, Jacquelyn K. Carpenter. S3: Simple Six Sigma for Blood Banking, Transfusion, & Cellular Therapy. 2007. *(978-1-56395-249-4(1)*, AABB Pr.) American Assn. of Blood Banks.
Waters, Jonathan H. Blood Management: Options for Better Patient Care. 2008. xviii, 461p. *(978-1-56395-253-1(X)*, AABB Pr.) American Assn. of Blood Banks.
WHO Regional Office for the Western Pacific. Design Guidelines for Blood Centres. 2012. (WPRO Nonserial Publication Ser.). (ENG.). 110p. pap. 24.00 ***(978-92-9061-319-0(X))*** World Health Organization.
World Health Organization. Screening donated blood for transfusion-transmissible Infections: Recommendations. 2010. (Nonserial Publication Ser.). 67p. pap. 36.00 *(978-92-4-154788-8(X))* World Health Organization.
Yazer, Mark. Tranfusion in the Year 2020: The Future of Blood Transfusion - Clinics in Laboratory Medicine. 2010. (Clinics: Internal Medicine Ser.: 30-2). (ENG.). 105.00 *(978-1-4377-1832-4(9)*, Saunders) Elsevier - Health Sciences Div.

BLOOD, GASES IN

see Blood Gases

BLOOD ACCUSATION

Biale, David. Blood & Belief: The Circulation of a Symbol Between Jews & Christians. (Illus.). 2008. 316p. pap. 25.95 *(978-0-520-25798-6(7))* 2007. 299p. 55.00 *(978-0-520-25304-9(3))* Univ. of California Pr.
Birnbaum, Pierre & Goldhammer, Arthur. A Tale of Ritual Murder in the Age of Louis XIV: The Trial of Raphaël Lévy, 1669. 2012. (Stanford Studies in Jewish History & C Ser.). (ENG.). 192p. 60.00 ***(978-0-8047-7404-8(8))*** Stanford Univ. Pr.
Hart, Mitchell. Jewish Blood: Reality & metaphor in history, religion & Culture. Hart, Mitchell, ed. 2009. (Routledge Jewish Studies Ser.). (ENG., Illus.). 240p. (C). 120.00 *(978-0-415-47749-9(2))* Routledge.

B

Israeli, Raphael. Blood Libel & Its Derivatives: The Scourge of Anti-Semitism. 2011. (ENG.). 298p. 39.95 ***(978-1-4128-4271-6(9))*** Transaction Pubs.

Johnson, Hannah. Blood Libel: The Ritual Murder Accusation at the Limit of Jewish History. 2012. (ENG.). 250p. (C). 70.00 ***(978-0-472-11835-9(8))*** Univ. of Michigan Pr.

Perry, Marvin B., et al, eds. Antisemitic Myths: A Historical & Contemporary Anthology. 2008. (ENG.). 384p. pap. 27.00 *(978-0-253-21950-3(7),* 0253219507) Indiana Univ. Pr.

Rosenberg, Yudl. The Golem & the Wondrous Deeds of the Maharal of Prague. Leviant, Curt, tr. from HEB. 2008. (ENG., Illus.). 256p. pap. 18.00 *(978-0-300-14320-1(6))* Yale Univ. Pr.

BLOOD ALCOHOL LEVEL

see Alcohol in the Body

BLOOD BANKS

see also Blood—Collection and Preservation

Aabb, creator. Standards for Molecular Testing for Red Cell, Platelet, & Neutrophil Antigens. 2010. (Illus.). 50p. pap. 134.25 *(978-1-56395-275-3(0))* American Assn. of Blood Banks.

American Association of Blood Banks, creator. Technical Manual 12th - 16th Editions & Standards 1st - 25th Editions. 2008. cd-rom 376.50 *(978-1-56395-272-2(6))* American Assn. of Blood Banks.

American Association of Blood Banks Staff, contrib. by. Standards for Cellular Therapy Product Services. 3rd ed. 2008. *(978-1-56395-273-9(4),* AABB Pr.) American Assn. of Blood Banks.

—Standards for Immunohematology Reference Laboratories. xv, 50p. 5th ed. 2007. *(978-1-56395-250-0(5))* 6th ed. 2009. ***(978-1-56395-287-6(4))*** American Assn. of Blood Banks. (AABB Pr.).

Berte, Lucia M. Quality Manual Preparation Workbook for Perioperative Autologous Blood Collection & Administration. 2007. (Illus.). 51p. spiral bd. 196.50 incl. cd-rom *(978-1-56395-246-3(7))* American Assn. of Blood Banks.

Blaney, Kathy D. & Howard, Paula R. Basic & Applied Concepts of Immunohematology. 2nd ed. 2008. (ENG., Illus.). 400p. (C). 75.95 *(978-0-323-04805-7(6),* Mosby) Elsevier - Health Sciences Div.

Broxmeyer, Hal E. Cord Blood: Biology, Transplantation, Banking, & Regulation. 2011. ***(978-1-56395-318-7(8),*** AABB Pr.) American Assn. of Blood Banks.

Dax, Elizabeth M., et al. Advances in Transfusion Safety: Sydney, Australia, 11-13th October 2005: Proceedings of an International Conference Organized by the International Association for Biologicals (IABS), the National Serology Reference Laboratory, Australia, & the Therapeutics Goods Administration. 2007. (Developments in Biologicals Ser.: Vol. 127). (Illus.). xiv, 271p. *(978-3-8055-8239-1(0))* Karger, S. AG.

Eder, Anne & Bianco, Celso. Screening Blood Donors: Science, Reason, & the Donor History Questionnaire. 2007. *(978-1-56395-252-4(1)); (978-1-56395-247-0(5))* American Assn. of Blood Banks. (AABB Pr.).

Eder, Anne & Goldman, Mindy. Blood Donor Health & Safety. 2009. *(978-1-56395-281-4(5),* AABB Pr.) American Assn. of Blood Banks.

Farrell, Anne-Maree. The Politics of Blood: Ethics, Innovation & the Regulation of Risk. 2012. (Cambridge Bioethics & Law Ser.: 17). (ENG., Illus.). 288p. 99.00 ***(978-0-521-19318-4(4))*** Cambridge Univ. Pr.

Harmening, Denise. Modern Blood Banking & Transfusion Practices. 6th rev. ed. 2012. (Illus.). 608p. 89.95 ***(978-0-8036-2682-9(7))*** Davis, F. A. Co.

Hassan, Fathelrahman. Immunohematology & Blood Bank. 2010. 236p. pap. *(978-3-8383-8090-2(8))* Lambert Academic Publishing.

Hillyer, Christopher D., et al. Blood Banking & Transfusion Medicine: Basic Principles & Practice. 2nd rev. ed. 2006. (ENG., Illus.). 912p. 240.00 *(978-0-443-06981-9(6),* Churchill Livingstone) Elsevier - Health Sciences Div.

Knight, Robin, ed. Transfusion & Transplantation Science. 2011. (Fundamentals of Biomedical Science Ser.). (ENG., Illus.). 336p. pap. 44.95 *(978-0-19-953328-2(8))* Oxford Univ. Pr., Inc.

McCullough, Jeff. Transfusion Medicine. 3rd ed. 2012. (ENG., Illus.). 608p. pap. 84.95 ***(978-1-4443-3705-1(X),*** Wiley-Blackwell) Wiley, John & Sons, Inc.

Norris, Jane. Regulation & Licensure of Whole Blood, Blood Components, & Source Plasma. 2009. (Illus.). xiii, 175p. pap. *(978-1-56395-301-9(3),* AABB Pr.) American Assn. of Blood Banks.

Pan American Health Organization. Eligibility for Blood Donation: Recommendations for Education & Selection of Prospective Blood Donors. 2009. (PAHO Occasional Publication Ser.). 95p. pap. 20.00 *(978-92-75-12939-5(8))* Pan American Health Organization (PAHO).

Perioperative Blood Management: A Physician's Handbook. 2nd ed. 2009. xi, 259p. *(978-1-56395-292-0(0),* AABB Pr.) American Assn. of Blood Banks.

Quinley, Eva D. Immunohematology: Principles & Practice. 3rd rev. ed. 2010. (ENG., Illus.). 432p. 86.99 *(978-0-7817-8204-3(X))* Lippincott Williams & Wilkins.

Rahman, Shibley, et al. Basics of Blood Management. 2007. (ENG., Illus.). 400p. 122.95 *(978-1-4051-5131-3(5),* Wiley-Blackwell) Wiley, John & Sons, Inc.

Select Committee on Quality Assurance in Blood Transfusion. Guide to the preparation, use & quality assurance of blood components - 13th Edition (2007) 13th ed. 2007. 300p. pap. 42.00 *(978-92-871-6137-6(2))* Council of Europe FRA. Dist: Manhattan Publishing Co.

Sezdi, Mana. The Quality of Stored Human Blood. 2011. 112p. pap. ***(978-3-8383-9658-3(8))*** Lambert Academic Publishing.

Silva, Marianne A. & Vengelen-Tyler, Virginia. Quality Toolkit & Case Studies: Solutions for Common Problems. 2011. ***(978-1-56395-317-0(X),*** AABB Pr.) American Assn. of Blood Banks.

Simon, Toby L., et al, eds. Rossi's Principles of Transfusion Medicine. 4th ed. 2009. (ENG., Illus.). 1112p. 330.95 *(978-1-4051-7588-3(5),* Wiley-Blackwell) Wiley, John & Sons, Inc.

Smit Sibinga, C. Th., et al, eds. Automation in Blood Transfusion. 2010. (Developments in Hematology & Immunology Ser.). 252p. pap. 329.00 *(978-1-4419-4744-4(2),* 1441947442) Springer.

Smit Sibinga, C. Th. & Alter, H. J., eds. Risk Management in Blood Transfusion: the Virtue of Reality: The Virtue of Reality. 2010. (Developments in Hematology & Immunology Ser.). 226p. pap. 329.00 *(978-1-4419-4822-9(8),* 1441948228) Springer.

Turner, Marc L. Creutz feld-Jakob Disease Managing the Risk of Transmission by Blood, Plasma & Tissues. 2006. xvi, 319p. *(978-1-56395-224-1(6),* AABB Pr.) American Assn. of Blood Banks.

Vyas, Girish N. & Williams, A. E. Advances in Transfusion Safety Vol. 120: Natcher Auditorium, National Institutes of Health (NIH), Bethesda, MD, USA, June 4-6, 2003. (Developments in Biologicals Ser.: Vol. 120). (Illus.). *(978-3-8055-7935-3(7))* Karger, S. AG.

Walters, Lisa M. & Badley, Jacquelyn K. Carpenter. S3: Simple Six Sigma for Blood Banking, Transfusion, & Cellular Therapy. 2007. *(978-1-56395-249-4(1),* AABB Pr.) American Assn. of Blood Banks.

Waters, Jonathan H. Blood Management: Options for Better Patient Care. 2008. xviii, 461p. *(978-1-56395-253-1(X),* AABB Pr.) American Assn. of Blood Banks.

WHO Regional Office for the Western Pacific. Design Guidelines for Blood Centres. 2012. (WPRO Nonserial Publication Ser.). (ENG.). 110p. pap. 24.00 ***(978-92-9061-319-0(X))*** World Health Organization.

BLOOD BANKS—DATA PROCESSING

Ashford, Paul, ed. ISBT 128 an Introduction. 3rd ed. 2006. *(978-1-933243-01-6(5))* ICCBBA Inc.

—ISBT 128 for Cellular Therapy an Intoduction. 2006. *(978-1-933243-02-3(3))* ICCBBA Inc.

—ISBT 128 for Tissues, an Introduction. 2007. *(978-1-933243-05-4(8))* ICCBBA Inc.

Wray, Bruce. ISBT 128 an Introduction to Bar Coding. 2nd ed. 2007. *(978-1-933243-04-7(X))* ICCBBA Inc.

BLOOD-BORNE DISEASES

see Bloodborne Infections

BLOOD-BORNE INFECTIONS

see Bloodborne Infections

BLOOD-BRAIN BARRIER

Baehr, Carsten H. Choroid Plexus Pharmacology. 2008. 148p. pap. *(978-3-639-05740-9(6))* VDM Verlag Dr. Mueller e.K.

Helio, Tomas R., ed. The Blood Brain Barrier. 2008. 129.00 *(978-1-60456-894-3(1))* Nova Science Pubs., Inc.

Mikoshiba, Katsuhiko, ed. Handbook of Neurochemistry & Molecular Neurobiology: Neural Signaling Mechanisms. 3rd ed. 2009. (ENG., Illus.). xvi, 632p. 249.00 *(978-0-387-30338-3(3),* 0387303383) Springer.

Montenegro, Pedro A. & Juárez, Stefanee M. The Blood-Brain Barrier: New Research. 2012. ***(978-1-62100-766-1(9))*** Nova Science Pubs., Inc.

Nag, Sukriti. The Blood-Brain & Other Neural Barriers: Reviews & Protocols. 2011. (Illus.). xiv, 502p. E-Book ***(978-1-60761-938-3(5))*** Humana Pr.

Nag, Sukriti, ed. The Blood-Brain & Other Neural Barriers: Reviews & Protocols. 2010. (Methods in Molecular Biology Ser.). (ENG., Illus.). xiv, 502p. 139.00 *(978-1-60761-937-6(7),* 1607619377) Humana Pr.

—Blood'Brain Barrier: Biology & Research Protocols. 2010. (Methods in Molecular Medicine Ser.). (Illus.). 572p. pap. 209.00 *(978-1-61737-339-8(7),* 1617373397) Humana Pr.

Pardridge, William M. Brain Drug Targeting: The Future of Brain Drug Development. 2010. (ENG.). 376p. pap. 50.00 *(978-0-521-15446-8(4))* Cambridge Univ. Pr.

Pardridge, William M., ed. Introduction to the Blood-Brain Barrier: Methodology, Biology & Pathology. 2006. (ENG.). 504p. pap. 110.00 *(978-0-521-03427-2(2))* Cambridge Univ. Pr.

Rahman, Shafiqur, ed. The Brain as a Drug Target. 2011. (ENG.). 468p. 161.00 *(978-0-12-385506-0(3),* Academic Pr.) Elsevier Science & Technology Bks.

Rosenberg, Gary A. Molecular Physiology & Metabolism of the Nervous System: A Clinical Perspective. 2012. (Contemporary Neurology Ser.: 82). (ENG.). 240p. 99.99 ***(978-0-19-539427-6(5))*** Oxford Univ. Pr., Inc.

Tettamanti, Guido & Sonnino, Sandro, eds. Handbook of Neurochemistry & Molecular Neurobiology: Neural Glycoconjugates. 3rd ed. 2008. (Illus.). 500p. 249.00 *(978-0-387-30355-0(3))* Springer.

Walz, Wolfgang, ed. The Neuronal Environment: Brain Homeostasis in Health & Disease. 2010. (Contemporary Neuroscience Ser.). (Illus.). 428p. pap. 179.00 *(978-1-61737-235-3(8),* 1617372358) Humana Pr.

Watanabe, Akiyama. Dopamine Research Advances. 2007. (C). 185.00 *(978-1-60021-820-0(2))* Nova Science Pubs., Inc.

BLOOD CELL COUNT

Bain, Barbara J. Blood Cells: A Practical Guide. 4th rev. ed. 2006. (ENG., Illus.). 488p. 187.95 *(978-1-4051-4265-6(0),* Wiley-Blackwell) Wiley, John & Sons, Inc.

BLOOD CELLS

see also Blood Cell Count; Erythrocytes; Hematopoietic Stem Cells; Leucocytes

Ackerman, G. Adolph, et al. Work: Promoting Participation & Productivity Through Occupational Therapy. 2011. (Illus.). 480p. (C). 59.95 *(978-0-8036-0016-4(X))* Davis, F. A. Co.

Bain, Barbara J. Blood Cells: A Practical Guide. 4th rev. ed. 2006. (ENG., Illus.). 488p. 187.95 *(978-1-4051-4265-6(0),* Wiley-Blackwell) Wiley, John & Sons, Inc.

Baskurt, Oguz, et al. Red Blood Cell Aggregation. 2011. (ENG., Illus.). 318p. 119.95 *(978-1-4398-4180-8(2),* CRC Press) Taylor & Francis Group GBR. Dist: Taylor & Francis Group.

Bhatia Sujata K. & Bhatia, Sujata K. Selectin-mediated Leukocyte Adhesion During the Immune Response: Experimental & computational studies of white blood cell recruitment to the vascular wall. 2008. 220p. pap. *(978-3-639-09454-1(9))* VDM Verlag Dr. Mueller e.K.

Cram101 Textbook Reviews & Cram101 Textbook Reviews. Outlines & Highlights for Hematology by Bernadette F Rodak, Isbn: 9781416030065 1416030069. 2011. 168p. pap. 28.95 ***(978-1-61490-147-1(3))*** Cram101 Inc.

Descotes, Jacques. Toxicology of the Blood & Bone Marrow, Second Edition. 2nd ed. 2009. 169.95 *(978-1-4200-7846-6(1))* CRC Pr. LLC.

El Hage, Rabih. Lipopolysaccharide Effect on Rbc Volume in an in-Vitro Model. 2010. 88p. pap. *(978-3-639-27925-2(5))* VDM Verlag Dr. Mueller e.K.

Farhi, Diane C. Pathology of Bone Marrow & Blood Cells. 2nd rev. ed. 2008. (ENG., Illus.). 432p. 254.99 *(978-0-7817-7093-4(9))* Lippincott Williams & Wilkins.

Gulati, Gene L. Blood Cell Morphology Grading Guide. 2009. 88p. spiral bd. 74.25 *(978-0-89189-569-5(8))* American Society for Clinical Pathology.

Gupta, A. P. Insect Hemocytes: Developement, Forms, Functions & Techniques. 2009. (ENG.). 628p. pap. 79.00 *(978-0-521-11303-8(2))* Cambridge Univ. Pr.

Harmening, Denise M. Clinical Hematology & Fundamentals of Hemostasis. 5th rev. ed. 2008. (Illus.). 960p. 124.00 *(978-0-8036-1732-2(1))* Davis, F. A. Co.

Kitchen, Gareth. Immunology & Haematology. 3rd rev. ed. 2007. (Crash Course Ser.). (Illus.). 204p. pap. *(978-0-7234-3418-4(2))* Mosby GBR. Dist: Elsevier - Health Sciences Div.

Koller, F., et al, eds. Human Cell Culture: Volume IV: Primary Hematopoietic Cells. 2010. (Human Cell Culture Ser.). 352p. pap. 359.00 *(978-90-481-5264-3(X),* 904815264X) Springer.

Mehta, Atul B. & Hoffbrand, Victor. Haematology at a Glance. 3rd ed. 2009. (At a Glance Ser.: 5). (ENG., Illus.). 128p. pap. 45.95 *(978-1-4051-7970-6(8),* Wiley-Blackwell) Wiley, John & Sons, Inc.

Rowley, A. F., ed. Vertebrate Blood Cells. 2009. (ENG.). 456p. pap. 84.00 *(978-0-521-10366-4(5))* Cambridge Univ. Pr.

van der Walt, J. & Borisch, B., eds. Haematological Malignancy & the Bone Marrow Trephine Biopsy. 2007. (Illus.). 88p. pap. *(978-3-8055-8297-1(8))* Karger, S. AG.

BLOOD CHEMISTRY

see Blood—Analysis

BLOOD CIRCULATION DISORDERS

see also Hypertension; Hypotension; Ischemia

Thiriet, Marc. Biology & Mechanics of Blood Flows: Part I: Biology, 2 vols. 2007. (CRM Series in Mathematical Physics Ser.). (Illus.). XIII, 657p. 149.00 *(978-0-387-74846-7(6),* 0387748466) Springer.

—Biology & Mechanics of Blood Flows: Part II: Mechanics & Medical Aspects, 2 vols. 2007. (CRM Series in Mathematical Physics Ser.). (Illus.). XII, 467p. 129.00 *(978-0-387-74848-1(2),* 0387748482) Springer.

'vestková, Sabina. Examinations of Venous System Diseases. 2011. 96p. pap. ***(978-3-8383-7039-2(2))*** Lambert Academic Publishing.

Yim, Peter J. Vascular Hemodynamics: Bioengineering & Clinical Perspectives. 2008. (ENG., Illus.). 354p. 148.00 *(978-0-470-08947-7(4),* Wiley-Blackwell) Wiley, John & Sons, Inc.

BLOOD COAGULATION DISORDERS

see also Hemophilia

Ataullakhanov, F. I. & Panteleev, M. A., eds. Mathematical Modelling & Computer Simulation in Blood Coagulation. (Illus.). 94p. pap. *(978-3-8055-8080-9(0))* Karger, S. AG.

Berlot, Giorgio, ed. Hemocoagulative Problems in the Critically Ill Patient. 2012. (ENG., Illus.). xiii, 238p. 189.00 ***(978-88-470-2447-2(1),*** 8847024471) Springer.

Blomback, Margareta & Antovic, Jovan, eds. Essential Guide to Blood Coagulation. 2010. (ENG., Illus.). 192p. pap. 78.95 *(978-1-4051-9627-7(0),* Wiley-Blackwell) Wiley, John & Sons, Inc.

Crowther, Mark & Donadini, Marco. Hypercoagulable States & New Anticoagulants, an Issue of Hematology/Oncology Clinics of North America. 2010. (Clinics: Internal Medicine Ser.: 24-4). (ENG., Illus.). xiv, 670p. 99.00 *(978-1-4377-2529-2(5),* Saunders) Elsevier - Health Sciences Div.

Gadisseur, A. & Michiels, J. J., eds. Advances in the Diagnosis & Classification of von Willebrand Disease. 2009. (Illus.). 120p. pap. *(978-3-8055-9208-6(6))* Karger, S. AG.

Green, David & Kwaan, Hau C., eds. Coagulation in Cancer. 2009. (Cancer Treatment & Research Ser.). (ENG., Illus.). x, 310p. 169.00 *(978-0-387-79961-2(3))* Springer.

James, Andra H. 100 Questions & Answers about Von Willebrand Disease. 2008. 127p. pap. 22.95 *(978-0-7637-5767-0(5))* Jones & Bartlett Learning, LLC.

Key, Nigel, et al, eds. Practical Hemostasis & Thrombosis. 2nd ed. 2009. (ENG., Illus.). 328p. 165.95 *(978-1-4051-8460-1(4),* Wiley-Blackwell) Wiley, John & Sons, Inc.

Kitchen, Steve, et al, eds. Quality in Laboratory Hemostasis & Thrombosis. 2009. (ENG., Illus.). 232p. 152.95 *(978-1-4051-6803-8(X),* Wiley-Blackwell) Wiley, John & Sons, Inc.

Laposata, Michael. Coagulation Disorders: Quality in Laboratory Diagnosis. 2010. *(978-1-933864-82-2(6))* Demos Medical Publishing, LLC.

Lee, Christine, et al. Inherited Bleeding Disorders in Women. Kadir, Rezan et al, eds. 2009. (ENG., Illus.). 208p. 152.95 *(978-1-4051-6915-8(X),* Wiley-Blackwell) Wiley, John & Sons, Inc.

Lipinski, Boguslaw. Significance of Free Radical-Modified Fibrinogen in Thrombosis & Related Diseases. 2010. (Cardiology Research & Clinical Developments Ser.). pap. 43.00 *(978-1-61668-859-2(9),* Nova Biomedical Bks.) Nova Science Pubs., Inc.

Lockwood, Charles J., et al. Hemostasis & Thrombosis in Obstetrics & Gynecology. 2010. (ENG., Illus.). 232p. 125.95 *(978-1-4051-8399-4(3),* Wiley-Blackwell) Wiley, John & Sons, Inc.

Marques, Marisa B. & Fritsma, George A. Quick Guide to Coagulation Testing. 2nd ed. 2009. *(978-1-59425-095-8(2))* American Assn. for Clinical Chemistry, Inc.

Mousa, Shaker A., ed. Anticoagulants, Antiplatelets, & Thrombolytics. 2nd ed. 2010. (Methods in Molecular Biology Ser.). (Illus.). xi, 316p. 159.00 *(978-1-60761-802-7(8),* 1607618028) Humana Pr.

Raabe, Michelle. Hemophilia. 2008. (Genes & Disease Ser.). (Illus.). 136p. (YA). (gr. 7-12). 35.00 *(978-0-7910-9648-2(3))* Facts On File, Inc.

Regulation of Tissue Factor. 24.50 *(978-91-554-4966-7(2))* Almqvist & Wiksell International SWE. Dist: Coronet Bks.

Roberts, Harold Ross, ed. Haemophilia & Haemostasis: A Case-Based Approach to Management. 2007. (ENG., Illus.). 256p. 128.95 *(978-1-4051-6716-1(5),* Wiley-Blackwell) Wiley, John & Sons, Inc.

Rodriguez-Merchan, E. Carlos & Valentino, Leonard A., eds. Current & Future Issues in Haemophilia Care. 2nd ed. 2011. (ENG., Illus.). 192p. 98.95 *(978-0-470-67057-6(6),* Wiley-Blackwell) Wiley, John & Sons, Inc.

Sanyal, Arun J. & Caldwell, Stephen H. Coagulation & Hemostasis in Liver Disease: Controversies & Advances - An Issue of Clinics in Liver Disease. 2009. (Clinics: Internal Medicine Ser.: 13-1). (ENG., Illus.). 240p. 99.00 *(978-1-4377-0495-2(6),* Saunders) Elsevier - Health Sciences Div.

Taloyan, Anett M. & Bankiewicz, David S., eds. Coagulation: Kinetics, Structure Formation & Disorders. 2012. ***(978-1-62100-331-1(0))*** Nova Science Pubs., Inc.

Viroj Wiwanitkit. Advances in Thrombohemostatic Diseases. 2006. 202p. 225.00 *(978-1-60021-323-6(5))* Nova Science Pubs., Inc.

—New Developments in Thrombohemostatic Diseases. 2007. 89.00 *(978-1-60021-495-0(9))* Nova Science Pubs., Inc.

Wiwanitkit, Viroj. Advances in Neonatal Hematology. 2007. (Illus.). 201p. 129.00 *(978-1-60021-889-7(X))* Nova Science Pubs., Inc.

BLOOD COLLECTION

see Blood—Collection and Preservation

BLOOD COMPONENTS

see Blood Products

BLOOD CORPUSCLES

see Blood Cells

BLOOD-FEUDS

see Vendetta

BLOOD FLOW

see also Plethysmography

Bhuyan, Bipul Chandra & Gopal Ch. Hazarika. Magnetic Effect on Blood Flow. 2011. 248p. pap. ***(978-3-639-32292-7(4))*** VDM Verlag Dr. Mueller e.K.

Breitstein, Jacob. Mirf. 2010. 32p. pap. 21.99 *(978-1-4500-6510-8(4))* Xlibris Corp.

Chandran, Krishnan B., et al. Biofluid Mechanics. 2nd rev. ed. 2012. (ENG., Illus.). 451p. (C). 104.95 ***(978-1-4398-4516-5(6),*** CRC Press) Taylor & Francis Group GBR. Dist: Taylor & Francis Group.

Cowley, Allen. Renal Medullary Circulation. 2012. (Colloquium Series on Integrated Systems Physiology: from Molecule to Function Ser.). 100p. pap. 35.00 *(978-1-61504-228-9(8))* Morgan & Claypool Life Science Publishers.

Fusenig, Norbert & Marme, Dieter, eds. Tumor Angiogenesis: Basic Mechanisms & Cancer Therapy. 2007. (Illus.). 845p. 409.00 *(978-3-540-33176-6(X))* Springer.

Harris, Alon, ed. Atlas of Ocular Blood Flow: Vascular Anatomy, Pathophysiology, & Metabolism. 2nd ed. 2010. (ENG., Illus.). 160p. 99.00 *(978-1-4377-1737-2(3),* Butterworth-Heinemann) Elsevier - Health Sciences Div.

Jamshed, Shamoon, et al. Blood Flow Analysis Through Blocked Artery. 2010. 112p. pap. *(978-3-8383-4396-9(4))* Lambert Academic Publishing.

Langheim, Lisa. Effects of Stress - Cerebral Blood Flow Velocity, Salivary Cortisol, & Subjective State. 2008. 72p. pap. *(978-3-639-03290-1(X))* VDM Verlag Dr. Mueller e.K.

McDonald's Blood Flow in Arteries. 3rd ed. *(978-0-340-52944-7(X),* Hodder Arnold) Hodder Education.

Nichols, Wilmer W., et al. McDonald's Blood Flow in Arteries: Theoretical, Experimental & Clinical Principles. 6th rev. ed. 2011. (ENG., Illus.). 768p. 198.50 *(978-0-340-98501-4(1))* Hodder Arnold Pubs.

Shepherd, A. P. & Öberg, P. Ã...., eds. Laser-Doppler Blood Flowmetry. 2010. (Developments in Cardiovascular Medicine Ser.). 420p. pap. 509.00 *(978-1-4419-4745-1(0),* 1441947450) Springer.

SHUNG. Diag Ultra Imag Blood Flow. 2010. 350p. 199.95 *(978-0-8247-2840-3(8),* Informa Healthcare) Taylor & Francis Group GBR. Dist: Taylor & Francis Group.

Spurrell, Brian. Cellular Mechanisms Underlying Arteriolar Myogenic Tone. 2010. 200p. pap. *(978-3-8383-8081-0(9))* Lambert Academic Publishing.

Sut, Dusmanta Kumar & Hazarika, G. C. Mathematical Studies of Certain Second Order Blood Flow Problems: A Computer Oriented Numerical Approach. 2011. 132p. pap. **(978-3-639-31605-6(3))** VDM Verlag Dr. Mueller e.K.
Thiriet, Marc. Biology & Mechanics of Blood Flows: Part I: Biology. (CRM Series in Mathematical Physics Ser.). (Illus.). 2010. xiii, 657p. pap. 149.00 *(978-1-4419-2575-6(9)*, 1441925759) 2007. XIII, 657p. 149.00 *(978-0-387-74846-7(6)*, 0387748466) Springer.
—Biology & Mechanics of Blood Flows: Part II: Mechanics & Medical Aspects. (CRM Series in Mathematical Physics Ser.). (Illus.). 2010. xii, 467p. pap. 129.00 *(978-1-4419-2576-3(7)*, 1441925767) 2007. XII, 467p. 129.00 *(978-0-387-74848-1(2)*, 0387748482) Springer.
Thrush, Abigail & Hartshorne, Timothy. Vascular Ultrasound: How, Why & When. Thrush, Abigail & Hartshorne, Timothy, eds. 3rd ed. 2009. (How, Why & When Ser.). (ENG., Illus.). 320p. (C). 85.95 *(978-0-443-06918-5(2)*, Churchill Livingstone) Elsevier - Health Sciences Div.
Volobuev, A. N. Biophysical Principles of Hemodynamics. V.I., Koshev & E.S., Petrov, eds. 2010. (Cardiology Research & Clinical Developments Ser.). 229p. pap. 43.00 *(978-1-61668-280-4(9))* Nova Science Pubs., Inc.
Zamir, M. The Physics of Coronary Blood Flow. 2010. (Biological & Medical Physics, Biomedical Engineering Ser.). (Illus.). xviii, 410p. pap. 169.00 *(978-1-4419-3782-7(X)*, 144193782X) Springer.

BLOOD FORMATION
see Hematopoiesis

BLOOD GASES
Cram101 Textbook Reviews Staff. Outlines & Highlights for Clinical Application of Blood Gases by Shapiro Isbn: 0801678390. 2007. 516p. pap. 14.95 *(978-1-4288-1928-3(2))* Cram101 Inc.
Hasan, Ashfaq. Handbook of Blood Gas/Acid-Base Interpretation. 2009. (ENG., Illus.). x, 320p. pap. 69.95 *(978-1-84800-333-0(1)*, 1848003331) Springer.
Hennessey, Iain & Japp, Alan. Arterial Blood Gases Made Easy. 2007. (Made Easy Ser.). (ENG., Illus.). 152p. (C). pap. 32.95 *(978-0-443-10414-5(X)*, Churchill Livingstone) Elsevier - Health Sciences Div.
Külpmann, Wolf-Rüdiger, et al. Electrolytes, Acid-Base Balance & Blood Gases: Clinical Aspects & Laboratory. 2nd rev. ed. 2007. (Illus.). VIII, 192p. pap. 49.95 *(978-3-211-33127-9(1)*, 3211331271) Springer.
Oakes, Dana. Oakes' ABG Instructional Guide. 2008. pap., pap. 26.25 *(978-0-932887-37-5(6))* Health Educator Pubns., Inc.
PH & Blood Gas. ring bd. 200.00 *(978-1-56238-247-6(0)*, SC5-L) NCCLC.
Thompson, Donald A. Blood Gases Made Simple, Easy & Quick. 2007. 55p. pap. 15.95 *(978-0-615-16555-4(9))* MicroHealth Software & Publishing.
Toffaletti, John G. & American Association for Clinical Chemistry Staff. Blood Gases & Electrolytes. 2nd ed. 2009. *(978-1-59425-097-2(9))* American Assn. for Clinical Chemistry, Inc.
Yoshikawa, Toshikazu & Naito, Yuji, eds. Gas Biology Research in Clinical Practice. 2011. (ENG., Illus.). 148p. *(978-3-8055-9664-0(2))* Karger, S. AG.

BLOOD GLUCOSE
see Blood Sugar

BLOOD GROUPS
see also Blood—Transfusion
Balinska, Marta A. & Schneider, William H., eds. Ludwik Hirszfeld: The Story of One Life. Balinska, Marta A., tr. from POL. 2010. (Rochester Studies in Medical History Ser.: Volume 16). (Illus.). 508p. 49.95 *(978-1-58046-338-6(X))* Univ. of Rochester Pr.
Blackall, Douglas P., et al. Transfusion Medicine: Self-Assessment & Review. 2nd ed. 2009. *(978-1-56395-280-7(7)*, AABB Pr.) American Assn. of Blood Banks.
Christiano, Joseph. Blood Types, Body Types & You: Why Your Unique Genetic Code Is the Key to Losing Weight for Life. rev. exp. ed. 2008. (ENG., Illus.). 336p. pap. 17.99 *(978-1-59979-290-3(7)*, Siloam Pr.) Charisma Media.
—Bloodtype Diet: A Custom Eating Plan for Losing Weight, Fighting Disease, & Staying Healthy for People with Type a Blood. 2010. (ENG.). 192p. pap. 12.99 *(978-1-61638-000-7(4)*, Siloam Pr.) Charisma Media.
—Bloodtype Diet: A Custom Eating Plan for Losing Weight, Fighting Disease, & Staying Healthy for People with Type O Blood. 2010. (ENG., Illus.). 192p. pap. 12.99 *(978-1-59979-962-9(6)*, Siloam Pr.) Charisma Media.
—Joseph Christiano's Bloodtype Diet AB: A Custom Eating Plan for Losing Weight, Fighting Disease, & Staying Healthy for People with Type AB Blood. 2010. (ENG.). 192p. pap. 12.99 *(978-1-59979-982-7(0)*, Siloam Pr.) Charisma Media.
—Joseph Christiano's Bloodtype Diet, Type B: A Custom Eating Plan for Losing Weight, Fighting Disease, & Staying Healthy for People with Type B Blood. 2010. (ENG., Illus.). 192p. pap. 12.99 *(978-1-59979-999-5(5)*, Siloam Pr.) Charisma Media.
D'Adamo, James L. Just an Ounce of Prevention... Is Worth a Pound of Cure: A Modern Guide to Healthful Living from the Originator of the Blood-Type Diet. 2010. (ENG., Illus.). 256p. 24.95 *(978-1-4019-2719-5(X))* Hay Hse., Inc.
D'Adamo, James L. & Richards, Allan. Just an Ounce of Prevention... Is Worth a Pound or Cure. 2011. (ENG.). pap. 14.95 *(978-1-4019-2720-2(3))* Hay Hse., Inc.
D'Adamo, Peter J. & Whitney, Catherine. Aging: Fight It with the Blood Type Diet - The Individualized Plan for Preventing & Treating Brain Impairment, Hormonal Deficiency, & the Loss of Vitality Associated with Advancing Years. 2007. (ENG.). 256p. (gr. 12-18). 6.99 *(978-0-425-21341-4(2)*, Berkley) Penguin Group (USA) Inc.
—The GenoType Diet: Change Your Genetic Destiny to Live the Longest, Fullest, & Healthiest Life Possible. 2007. (ENG., Illus.). 352p. 24.95 *(978-0-7679-2524-2(6)*, Morgan Road Bks.) Broadway Bks.
Daniels, Geoff & Bromilow, Imelda. Essential Guide to Blood Groups. 2nd ed. 2010. (ENG., Illus.). 128p. pap. 47.95 *(978-1-4443-3530-9(8)*, Wiley-Blackwell) Wiley, John & Sons, Inc.
Judd, W. John, et al. Judd's Methods in Immunohematology. 3rd ed. 2008. *(978-1-56395-266-1(1)*, AABB Pr.) American Assn. of Blood Banks.
Lomas-Francis, Christine & Reid, Marion E. Blood Group Antigens & Antibodies: A Guide to Clinical Relevance & Technical Tips. 2007. (Illus.). 214p. per. 25.00 *(978-1-59572-103-7(7))* Star Bright Bks., Inc.
McCullough, Jeff. Transfusion Medicine. 3rd ed. 2012. (ENG., Illus.). 608p. pap. 84.95 **(978-1-4443-3705-1(X)**, Wiley-Blackwell) Wiley, John & Sons, Inc.
Petrides, Marian & Stack, Gary. Practical Guide to Transfusion Medicine. 2nd ed. 2007. *(978-1-56395-243-2(2)*, AABB Pr.) American Assn. of Blood Banks.
Reid, Marion E. & Shine, Ian. The Discovery & Significance of the Blood Groups. 2012. (Illus.). 214p. 36.00 **(978-1-59572-422-9(2))** Star Bright Bks., Inc.
Takahashi, Kota, ed. ABO-Incompatible Organ Transplantation from Japan: Invited Papers from the International Meeting at the 41st Annual Meeting of the Japan Society for Transplantation Held in Niigata on 29 October 2005. 2006. (International Congress Ser.). (Illus.). 131p. 169.00 *(978-0-444-52165-1(8)*, Elsevier) Elsevier - Health Sciences Div.

BLOOD LIBEL
see Blood Accusation

BLOOD PLASMA
see also Blood Banks; Blood Plasma Substitutes; Blood Proteins; Serum
Schaller, Johann, et al. Human Blood Plasma Proteins: Structure & Function. 2008. (ENG., Illus.). 538p. 190.00 *(978-0-470-01674-9(4)*, Wiley) Wiley, John & Sons, Inc.
Simpson, Richard J. & Greening, David W., eds. Serum/Plasma Proteomics: Methods & Protocols. 2011. (Methods in Molecular Biology Ser.). (Illus.). xiv, 397p. 139.00 *(978-1-61779-067-6(2)*, 1617790672) Humana Pr.

BLOOD PLASMA SUBSTITUTES
see also Dextran
Bühler, Volker. Polyvinylpyrrolidone Excipients for Pharmaceuticals: Povidone, Crospovidone & Copovidone. 2010. (ENG., Illus.). vii, 254p. pap. 319.00 *(978-3-642-06243-8(1)*, 3642062431) Springer.

BLOOD PLATELETS
AuBuchon, James P. & Prowse, Christopher V. Pathogen Inactivation: The Penultimate Paradigm Shift. 2010. *(978-1-56395-309-5(9)*, AABB Pr.) American Assn. of Blood Banks.
Baskurt, Oguz, et al. Red Blood Cell Aggregation. 2011. (ENG., Illus.). 318p. 119.95 *(978-1-4398-4180-8(2)*, CRC Press) Taylor & Francis Group GBR. Dist: Taylor & Francis Group.
Bhatt, Deepak L., ed. Platelets in Cardiovascular Disease. 2008. (Illus.). 218p. 124.00 *(978-1-86094-826-8(X))* Imperial College Pr. GBR. Dist: World Scientific Publishing Co., Inc.
Ferguson, John H. Lipoids & Blood Platelets with Reference to Blood Coagulation & the Hemorrhagic Diseases. 2011. (ENG.). 298p. pap. 40.00 **(978-0-8078-6864-5(7))** Univ. of North Carolina Pr.
García-Alonso, Ángel. Platelet Proteomics: Principles, Analysis, & Applications. Senis, Yotis, ed. 2011. (Wiley - Interscience Series on Mass Spectrometry Ser.: 37). (ENG., Illus.). 424p. 99.95 *(978-0-470-46337-6(6)*, Wiley) Wiley, John & Sons, Inc.
Gawaz, Meinrad, ed. Blood Platelets — Clinical Relevance. 2010. (ENG., Illus.). 100p. pap. 6.95 *(978-3-13-146211-4(6))* Thieme Medical Pubs., Inc.
Gibbins, Jonathan M. & Mahaut-Smith, Martyn P., eds. Platelets & Megakaryocytes: Volume 1: Functional Assays. 2010. (Methods in Molecular Biology Ser.). (Illus.). 408p. pap. 179.00 *(978-1-61737-356-5(7)*, 1617373567) Humana Pr.
—Platelets & Megakaryocytes: Volume 2: Perspectives & Techniques. 2010. (Methods in Molecular Biology Ser.). (Illus.). 500p. pap. 199.00 *(978-1-61737-305-3(2)*, 1617373052) Humana Pr.
Gibbins, Jonathan M. & Mahaut-Smith, Martyn P., eds. Platelets & Megakaryocytes: Volume 3, Additional Protocols & Perspectives. 2011. (Methods in Molecular Biology Ser.). (ENG., Illus.). xiv, 409p. 139.00 **(978-1-61779-306-6(X)**, 161779306X) Humana Pr.
Gresele, Paolo, et al, eds. Platelets in Hematologic & Cardiovascular Disorders: A Clinical Handbook. 2007. (ENG., Illus.). 526p. 163.00 *(978-0-521-88115-9(3))* Cambridge Univ. Pr.
Gutierrez, Rosa Martha Perez. Handbook of Compounds with Anti-Inflammatory & Anti-Platelet Aggregation Activities Isolated from Plants. 2008. (Illus.). 296p. 98.00 *(978-1-60456-607-9(8))* Nova Science Pubs., Inc.
Michelson, Alan D. Platelets. Michelson, Alan D, ed. 2nd ed. 2006. (ENG., Illus.). 1376p. 375.00 *(978-0-12-369367-9(5)*, Academic Pr.) Elsevier Science & Technology Bks.
Michelson, Alan D, ed. Platelets. 3rd ed. 2012. (ENG.). 1712p. 250.00 **(978-0-12-387837-3(3)**, Academic Pr.) Elsevier Science & Technology Bks.
Quinn, Martin, et al, eds. Platelet Function: Assessment, Diagnosis, & Treatment. 2010. (Contemporary Cardiology Ser.). (Illus.). xi, 397p. pap. 159.00 *(978-1-61737-447-0(4)*, 1617374474) Humana Pr.
Rumbaut, Rolando. Platelet-Vessel Wall Interactions in Hemostasis & Thrombosis. Granger, Neil & Granger, Joey, eds. 2010. (Colloquium Series on Integrated Systems Physiology: from Molecule to Function Ser.). 75p. pap. 30.00 *(978-1-61504-039-1(0))* Morgan & Claypool Life Science Publishers.
Shrivastava, Siddhartha. Signaling Mechanism in Blood Platelets & Effect of Nanosilver. 2011. 220p. pap. **(978-3-8443-2927-8(7))** Lambert Academic Publishing.
Warkentin, Theodore & Greinacher, Andreas, eds. Heparin-Induced Thrombocytopenia, Fourth Edition: Abridged, Special Edition. 4th ed. 2007. 112p. 11.50 *(978-1-4200-6897-9(0)*, Informa Healthcare) Taylor & Francis Group GBR. Dist: Taylor & Francis Group.
Wiviott, Stephen D. Antiplatelet Therapy in Ischemic Heart Disease. 2008. (American Heart Association Clinical Ser.: 4). (ENG., Illus.). 312p. 138.95 *(978-1-4051-7626-2(1)*, Wiley-Blackwell) Wiley, John & Sons, Inc.

BLOOD POISONING
see Septicemia

BLOOD PRESSURE
see also Blood—Circulation; Hypotension
Arfi, Robert A. Systolic Blood Pressure: Influences, Associations & Management. 2011. (Public Health in the 21st Century Ser.). 89.00 *(978-1-61209-263-8(2))* Nova Science Pubs., Inc.
Barst, Robyn, ed. Pulmonary Arterial Hypertension: Diagnosis & Evidence-Based Treatment. 2008. (ENG., Illus.). 270p. 118.00 *(978-0-470-05972-2(9)*, Wiley) Wiley, John & Sons, Inc.
Cong, Peng. Wireless Batteryless Blood Pressure Sensing Microsystem. 2009. 176p. pap. *(978-3-639-16699-6(X))* VDM Verlag Dr. Mueller e.K.
Gayler, Paul. Healthy Eating for Lower Blood Pressure: 100 Delicious Recipes from an Expert Team of Chef & Nutritionist. 2011. 160p. pap. 16.95 *(978-1-906868-28-4(X))* Cathie, Kyle Ltd. GBR. Dist: National Bk. Network.
Granger, Joey. Regulation of Arterial Pressure. 2011. (Colloquium Series on Integrated Systems Physiology: from Molecule to Function Ser.). 100p. pap. 35.00 *(978-1-61504-171-8(0))* Morgan & Claypool Life Science Publishers.
Javorka, Michal, et al, eds. Cardiovascular Signals in Diabetes Mellitus: A New Tool to Detect Autonomic Neuropathy. 2010. (Cardiology Research & Clinical Developments Ser.). 115p. pap. 43.00 *(978-1-60876-788-5(4)*, Nova Biomedical Bks.) Nova Science Pubs., Inc.
Mangano, Frank. The Blood Pressure Miracle. 2008. 120p. 23.50 *(978-1-60693-042-7(7)*, Strategic Bk. Publishing) AEG Literary Publishing Services, Inc.
Pijls, N. H. & Bruyne, B. de. Coronary Pressure. 2nd ed. 2010. (Developments in Cardiovascular Medicine Ser.). 448p. pap. 259.00 *(978-90-481-5398-5(0)*, 9048153980) Springer.
Semple, Jane. Blood Pressure: A Naturopathic Approach. 2008. (Woodland Publishing Ser.). 32p. pap. 4.95 *(978-1-58054-107-7(0))* Woodland Publishing, Inc.
Shaaban, Juwita, et al. Ambulatory Blood Pressure Monitoring. 2011. 80p. pap. **(978-3-8443-0201-1(8))** Lambert Academic Publishing.
Suzuki, H. & Saruta, T., eds. Kidney & Blood Pressure Regulation [Bibliography & Price Not Definite]. Vol. 143. (Contributions to Nephrology Ser.: Vol. 143). (Illus.). 8;72p. *(978-3-8055-7751-9(6))* Karger, S. AG.
Tesar, V., ed. Opportunities & Challenges with Biosimilars. 2007. (Illus.). 22p. pap. *(978-3-8055-8396-1(6))* Karger, S. AG.
Tesar, V., et al, eds. Trends in Kidney Research: Era-Edta Meeting, Prague, June 2011. Special Topic Issue: 'Kidney & Blood Pressure Research 2011, Vol. 34, No. 4' 2011. (Illus.) 108p. pap. *(978-3-8055-9769-2(X))* Karger, S. AG.
White, William B., ed. Blood Pressure Monitoring in Cardiovascular Medicine & Therapeutics. 2nd ed. 2007. (Clinical Hypertension & Vascular Diseases Ser.). (Illus.). 494p. 119.00 *(978-1-58829-512-5(5)*, 1588295125) Humana Pr.

BLOOD PRESSURE, HIGH
see Hypertension

BLOOD PRESSURE, LOW
see Hypotension

BLOOD PRODUCTS
see also Blood Substitutes
Ashford, Paul, ed. ISBT 128 an Introducton. 3rd ed. 2006. *(978-1-933243-01-6(5))* ICCBBA Inc.
—ISBT 128 for Cellular Therapy an Intoduction. 2006. *(978-1-933243-02-3(3))* ICCBBA Inc.
—ISBT 128 for Tissues, an Introduction. 2007. *(978-1-933243-05-4(8))* ICCBBA Inc.
Cross-Sectional Guidelines for Therapy with Blood Components & Plasma Derivatives: The Board of the German Medical Association on the Recommendation of the Scientific Advisory Board (Bundesaerztekammer) 4th ed. 2009. (Illus.). 148p. pap. *(978-3-8055-9392-2(9))* Karger, S. AG.
Fridey, Joy L., et al, eds. Component Selection: Polemics & Politics. (Illus.). pap. **(978-3-8055-6660-5(3))** Karger, S. AG.
Mintz, Paul D. Transfusion Therapy: Clinical Principles & Practice. 3rd ed. 2010. *(978-1-56395-307-1(2)*, AABB Pr.) American Assn. of Blood Banks.
Penfield, Linda R. & Nelson, Rachel T., eds. Apoprotein Research. 2009. 98.00 *(978-1-60692-632-1(2))* Nova Science Pubs., Inc.
Select Committee on Quality Assurance in Blood Transfusion. Guide to the preparation, use & quality assurance of blood components - 13th Edition (2007) 13th ed. 2007. 300p. pap. 42.00 *(978-92-871-6137-6(2))* Council of Europe FRA. Dist: Manhattan Publishing Co.
Wray, Bruce. ISBT 128 an Introduction to Bar Coding. 2nd ed. 2007. *(978-1-933243-04-7(X))* ICCBBA Inc.

BLOOD PROTEINS
see also Complement (Immunology); Fibronectins; Hemoglobin; Immunoglobulins; Prothrombin
Alekseev, Robert J. & Rebane, Alisa L. Serum Albumin: Structure, Functions, & Health Impact. 2012. **(978-1-62100-231-4(4))** Nova Science Pubs., Inc.
Andreeva, Alla Michailovna. Structural & Functional Organization of Fish Blood Proteins. 2012. (Marine Biology Fish, Fishing & Fisheries Ser.). 196p. 47.00 **(978-1-62100-264-2(0))** Nova Science Pubs., Inc.
Dammacco, Franco, ed. HCV Infection & Cryoglobulinemia. 2011. (Illus.). 350p. 219.00 *(978-88-470-1704-7(1)*, 8847017041) Springer.
Faye, Farba Balle Khodia. Malaria Resistance or Susceptibility in Red Cells Disorders. 2009. pap. 37.00 *(978-1-60692-943-8(7))* Nova Science Pubs., Inc.
Ghosh, Abhik, ed. The Smallest Biomolecules: Diatomics & Their Interactions with Heme Proteins. 2007. (ENG., Illus.) 614p. 250.00 *(978-0-444-52839-1(3)*, Elsevier Science) Elsevier Science & Technology Bks.
Misciagna, Giovanni. Glycemic Index of Food & Non Enzymatic Glycation of Blood Proteins. 2009. 152p. pap. *(978-3-639-16792-4(9))* VDM Verlag Dr. Mueller e.K.
Pagano, Irwin S. & Strait, Nathan B. HDL & LDL Cholesterol: Physiology & Clinical Significance. 2009. (Biochemistry Research Trends Ser.). 129.00 *(978-1-60741-767-5(7)*, Nova Biomedical Bks.) Nova Science Pubs., Inc.
Penfield, Linda R. & Nelson, Rachel T., eds. Apoprotein Research. 2009. 98.00 *(978-1-60692-632-1(2))* Nova Science Pubs., Inc.
Perera, Rohan F. & Liyanage, Vijayantha. Spectroscopic Methods in Ligand Protein Interactions. 2010. 136p. pap. *(978-3-8383-9046-8(6))* Lambert Academic Publishing.
Petersen, John R. & Mohammad, Amin A., eds. Clinical & Forensic Applications of Capillary Electrophoresis. 2010. (Pathology & Laboratory Medicine Ser.). (Illus.). 456p. pap. 169.00 *(978-1-61737-113-4(0)*, 1617371130) Humana Pr.
Schaller, Johann, et al. Human Blood Plasma Proteins: Structure & Function. 2008. (ENG., Illus.). 538p. 190.00 *(978-0-470-01674-9(4)*, Wiley) Wiley, John & Sons, Inc.
Serum Proteins in Clinical Medicine Vol. II: Clinical Section. Date not set. (Illus.). 420p. ring bd. 125.00 *(978-0-9653655-2-9(2))* Foundation for Blood Research.
Winter, William. Multiple Myeloma & Related Serum Protein Disorders: An Electrophoretic Guide. 2012. 184p. 90.00 **(978-1-933864-75-4(3))** Demos Medical Publishing, LLC.

BLOOD SERUM
see Serum

BLOOD SUBSTITUTES
see also Blood Products
Chang, Thomas Ming Swi. Artificial Cells: Biotechnology, Nanomedicine, Regenerative Medicine, Blood Substitutes, Bioencapsulation, & Cell/Stem Cell Therapy. 2007. (Regenerative Medicine, Artificial Cells & Nanomedicine Ser.: Vol. 1). (Illus.). 455p. pap. 98.00 *(978-981-270-778-9(6))* World Scientific Publishing Co., Inc.
—Artificial Cells: Biotechnology, Nanomedicine, Regenerative Medicine, Blood Substitutes, Bioencapsulation, Cell/Stem Cell Therapy. 2007. (Regenerative Medicine, Artificial Cells & Nanomedicine Ser.: Vol. 1). (Illus.). 455p. 197.00 *(978-981-270-576-1(7))* World Scientific Publishing Co., Inc.
Maniatis, Alice, et al, eds. Alternatives to Blood Transfusion in Transfusion Medicine. 2nd ed. 2010. (ENG., Illus.). 608p. 167.95 *(978-1-4051-6321-7(6)*, Wiley-Blackwell) Wiley, John & Sons, Inc.
Messmer, K., et al, eds. Microcirculatory Effects of Hemoglobin Solutions: 17th Bodensee Symposium on Microcirculation, Lindau, September 21-22, 2002, Vol. 25. (Progress in Applied Microcirculation Ser.: Vol. 25). (Illus.). *(978-3-8055-7719-9(2))* Karger, S. AG.
Rahman, Shibley, et al. Basics of Blood Management. 2007. (ENG., Illus.). 400p. 122.95 *(978-1-4051-5131-3(5)*, Wiley-Blackwell) Wiley, John & Sons, Inc.

BLOOD SUGAR
see also Hyperglycemia; Hypoglycemia
Bernstein, Richard K. Dr. Bernstein's Diabetes Solution: A Complete Guide to Achieving Normal Blood Sugars. 4th rev. ed. 2011. (ENG., Illus.). 560p. 29.99 *(978-0-316-18269-0(9))* Little Brown & Co.
Chee, Frederick & Fernando, Tyrone. Closed-Loop Control of Blood Glucose. 2007. (Lecture Notes in Control & Information Sciences Ser.). (Illus.). 157p. pap. 129.00 *(978-3-540-74030-8(9))* Springer.
Coté, Gerard Laurence & Priezzhev, Aleksandr Vasil'evich. Optical Diagnostics & Sensing VII: 23-24 January 2007, San Jose, California, USA. 2007. (Progress in Biomedical Optics & Imaging Ser.: No. 8). (Illus.). 198p. pap. 80.00 *(978-0-8194-6558-0(5))* SPIE.
Elwins, Dannie. Secrets to Handling & Controlling Your Glycemic Index. 2009. 36p. pap. 16.99 *(978-0-557-15749-5(8))* Lulu Enterprises Inc.
Fittante, Ann. Prevention's the Sugar Solution: Your Symptoms Are Real — & Your Solution Is Here. 2007. (Illus.). vi, 426p. *(978-1-59486-693-7(7))* Rodale Pr., Inc.
Fittante, Ann & Prevention Magazine Editors. The Sugar Solution: Your Symptoms Are Real — And Your Solution Is Here. 2007. (ENG.). 400p. per. 15.99 *(978-0-446-17833-4(0))* Grand Central Publishing.
Harrar, Sari, et al. The Ganele a la Glucosa: Aprenda como Controlar el Azucar en Sangre Naturalmente para Vencer Enfermedades, Bajar de Peso y Mejorar su Salud en Grande. 2006. (SPA & ENG.). 480p. pap. 17.95 *(978-1-59486-138-3(2))* Rodale Pr., Inc.
Hyman, Mark. The Blood Sugar Solution: The UltraHealthy Program for Losing Weight, Preventing Disease, & Feeling Great Now! 2012. (ENG.). 448p.

27.99 *(978-0-316-12737-0(X))*; 656p. 28.99 *(978-0-316-19617-8(7))* Little Brown & Co.

Illa. The Illa Protocol: A Systematic & Safe Method of Controlling Diabetes Mellitus While Avoiding Hypoglycemia. 2010. 204p. pap. 66.99 *(978-1-4490-6872-1(3))* AuthorHouse.

Jackson, Gram & Reader's Digest Editors. Reverse Diabetes Forever: Your Ultimate Guide to Controlling Your Blood Sugar. 2011. (ENG.). 304p. (gr. 12). 17.99 ***(978-1-60652-425-1(9))*** Reader's Digest Assn., Inc., The.

Kaufman, Francine R. Insulin Pumps & Continuous Glucose Monitoring: A User's Guide to Effective Diabetes Management. 2012. (ENG.). 120p. pap. 18.95 ***(978-1-58040-461-7(8))*** American Diabetes Assn.

Lidman, Leonida. Controlling Fluctuations of Diabetes Blood Glucose, Healing & Preventing Nerve Damage with Baby's Milk. 2nd ed. 2009. 112p. pap. *(978-1-926585-63-5(1)*, CCB Publishing) CCB Publishing.

Misciagna, Giovanni. Glycemic Index of Food & Non Enzymatic Glycation of Blood Proteins. 2009. 152p. pap. *(978-3-639-16792-4(9))* VDM Verlag Dr. Mueller e.K.

Polakof, Sergio. Brain Glucosensing: Physiological Implications. 2011. (Neurology - Laboratory & Clinical Research Developments Ser.). 43.00 *(978-1-61761-334-0(7))* Nova Science Pubs., Inc.

Publications International Staff, ed. Get Control of Your Blood Sugar. 2010. 144p. spiral bd. 10.98 *(978-1-4508-0800-2(X))* Publications International, Ltd.

Ruhl, Jenny. Blood Sugar 101: What They Don't Tell You about Diabetes. 2008. 200p. per. 14.95 *(978-0-9647116-1-7(3))* Technion Bks.

Scheiner, Gary. Get Control of Your Blood Sugar. 2010. 192p. 6.98 *(978-1-4127-4626-7(4))* Publications International, Ltd.

Tuchin, Valery V., ed. Optical Sensing of Glucose in Biological Fluids & Tissues. 2008. (Series in Medical Physics & Biomedical Engineering). (ENG., Illus.). 744p. instr.'s hndbk. ed. 139.95 *(978-1-58488-974-8(8)*, Taylor & Francis) Taylor & Francis Group GBR. Dist: Taylor & Francis Group.

Wait, Marianne. Magic Foods for Better Blood Sugar. 2006. (Illus.). 304p. *(978-0-7621-0755-1(3))* Reader's Digest Assn., Inc., The.

BLOOD TESTS

see Blood—Analysis; Blood—Examination

BLOOD TRANSFUSION

see Blood—Transfusion

BLOOD-VESSELS

see also Arteries; Blood—Circulation; Capillaries; Veins

also names of organs and regions of the body, with or without the subdivision Blood Vessels

Baert, Albert L., frwd. MR Angiography of the Body: Technique & Clinical Applications. 2009. (Medical Radiology / Diagnostic Imaging Ser.). (Illus.). 310p. 239.00 *(978-3-540-79716-6(5))* Springer.

Belanger, Ann C. Vascular Anatomy & Physiology: An Introductory Text. 2nd ed. Date not set. pap. 39.95 *(978-0-941022-40-8(4))* Davies Publishing, Inc.

Carr, James C. & Carroll, Timothy J., eds. Magnetic Resonance Angiography: Principles & Applications. 2012. (ENG., Illus.). xvii, 412p. 179.00 ***(978-1-4419-1685-3(7)*****,** 1441916857) Springer.

Chenevert, Thomas L. & Weadock, William J. Emerging Concepts in MR Angiography, an Issue of Magnetic Resonance Imaging Clinics. 2009. (Clinics: Radiology Ser.: 17-1). (ENG., Illus.). 240p. 99.00 *(978-1-4377-0497-6(2)*, Saunders) Elsevier - Health Sciences Div.

Cheresh, David A. Angiogenesis Pt. B,Vol. 445: In Vivo Systems, 2 vols. 2008. (ENG., Illus.). 464p. 187.00 *(978-0-12-374314-5(1)*, Academic Pr.) Elsevier Science & Technology Bks.

Cheresh, David A., ed. Angiogenesis Vol. 443: In Vitro Systems. 2008. (ENG., Illus.). 432p. 187.00 *(978-0-12-374315-2(X)*, Academic Pr.) Elsevier Science & Technology Bks.

Deindl, Elisabeth & Kupatt, Christian, eds. Therapeutic Neovascularization: Quo Vadis? 2010. (ENG.). x, 262p. pap. 159.00 *(978-90-481-7488-1(0)*, 9048174880) Springer.

Dougherty, Lisa. Central Venous Access Devices: Care & Management. 2007. (Essential Clinical Skills for Nurses Ser.). (ENG., Illus.). 216p. pap. 48.99 *(978-1-4051-1952-8(7)*, Wiley-Blackwell) Wiley, John & Sons, Inc.

Figg, William D. & Folkman, M. Judah. Angiogenesis: An Integrative Approach from Science to Medicine. 2008. (ENG., Illus.). x, 601p. 194.00 ***(978-0-387-71517-9(7)*****,** 0387715177) Springer.

Gao, Bulang. Endovascular Embolization for Hyperthyroidism in Graves' Disease. 2011. (Endocrinology Research & Clinical Developments Ser.). pap. 43.00 *(978-1-61122-972-1(3))* Nova Science Pubs., Inc.

Halpern, William, et al. The Resistance Arteries: Integration of the Regulatory Pathways. 2010. (Experimental Biology & Medicine Ser.). 384p. pap. 179.00 *(978-1-61737-008-3(8)*, 1617370088) Humana Pr.

Hobson, Robert W., et al. Endovascular Surgery. 2007. 119.95 *(978-0-8493-9894-0(0)*, Informa Healthcare) Taylor & Francis Group.

Klagsbrun, Michael & D'Amore, Patricia A. Angiogenesis: Biology & Pathology. 2011. 135.00 ***(978-1-936113-43-9(0))*** Cold Spring Harbor Laboratory Pr.

Leiner, Tim, et al, eds. Clinical Blood Pool MR Imaging. 2010. xviii, 262p. pap. 79.95 *(978-3-642-09666-2(2)*, 3642096662) Springer.

—Vasovist Monography. 2008. (Illus.). 260p. 79.95 *(978-3-540-77860-8(8))* Springer.

Leong, Stanley P. L. From Local Invasion to Metastatic Cancer: Involvement of Distant Sites Through the Lymphovascular System. 2009. (Illus.). xxviii, 637p. ***(978-1-60327-087-8(6))*** Humana Pr.

Lewis, Thomas J. & Robinson, James, eds. Angiogenesis Research Progress. 2008. (Illus.). x, 218p. pap. 39.00 *(978-1-60456-620-8(5))* Nova Science Pubs., Inc.

Markland, Francis S., Jr., et al, eds. Tumor Angiogenesis: From Molecular Mechanisms to Targeted Therapy. 2010. (ENG., Illus.). 351p. 179.95 *(978-3-527-32091-2(1)*, Wiley-VCH) Wiley, John & Sons, Inc.

Martin, Stewart & Murray, J. Clifford. Angiogenesis Protocols. 2nd ed. (Illus.). 2009. xi, 358p. *(978-1-59745-241-0(6))* 2008. 348p. 119.00 *(978-1-58829-907-9(4))* Humana Pr.

Middleton, William D. General & Vascular Ultrasound. 2nd rev. ed. 2007. (Case Review Ser.). (ENG., Illus.). 288p. pap. 54.95 *(978-1-4160-3989-1(9)*, Mosby) Elsevier - Health Sciences Div.

Moncada, Salvador & Higgs, Annie. The Vascular Endothelium I. 2010. (Handbook of Experimental Pharmacology Ser.). (Illus.). x, 339p. pap. 439.00 *(978-3-642-06951-2(7)*, 3642069517) Springer.

—The Vascular Endothelium II. 2010. (Handbook of Experimental Pharmacology Ser.). (Illus.). x, 356p. pap. 489.00 *(978-3-642-07156-0(2)*, 3642071562) Springer.

Moneta, Gregory L. Year Book of Vascular Surgery 2011. 2011. (Year Bks.: 2011). (ENG.). 384p. 159.00 ***(978-0-323-08429-1(X)*****,** Mosby) Elsevier - Health Sciences Div.

Moores, Carl & Nimmo, Alastair, eds. Core Topics in Vascular Anesthesia. 2012. (ENG., Illus.). 224p. 80.00 ***(978-1-107-00181-7(1))*** Cambridge Univ. Pr.

Neri, Emanuele, et al, eds. MR Angiography of the Body: Technique & Clinical Applications. 2011. (Medical Radiology / Diagnostic Imaging Ser.). (ENG., Illus.). x, 178p. pap. 109.00 ***(978-3-642-23590-0(5)*****,** 3642235905) Springer.

Novartis Foundation Staff, ed. Vascular Development. 2007. (Novartis Foundation Symposia Ser.). (ENG., Illus.). 260p. 195.00 *(978-0-470-03428-6(9)*, Wiley-Interscience) Wiley, John & Sons, Inc.

Pedley, T. J. The Fluid Mechanics of Large Blood Vessels. 2008. (Cambridge Monographs on Mechanics Ser.). (ENG., Illus.). 464p. pap. 58.00 *(978-0-521-08956-2(5))* Cambridge Univ. Pr.

Ribatti, Domenico. The Chick Embryo Chorioallantoic Membrane in the Study of Angiogenesis & Metastasis: The CAM assay in the study of angiogenesis & Metastasis. 2010. (ENG., Illus.). x, 119p. 129.00 *(978-90-481-3843-2(4)*, 9048138434) Springer.

—History of Research on Tumor Angiogenesis. (ENG.). x, 126p. 2010. pap. 159.00 *(978-90-481-8156-8(9)*, 9048181569) 2009. (Illus.). 159.00 *(978-1-4020-9559-7(7)*, 1402095597) Springer.

Rubens, Deborah J. & Grant, Edward G. Vascular Ultrasound, an Issue of Ultrasound Clinics. 2011. (Clinics: Radiology Ser.: 6-4). (ENG., Illus.). vii, 422p. 83.00 ***(978-1-4557-1160-4(8)*****,** Saunders) Elsevier - Health Sciences Div.

Ruhrberg, Christiana. VEGF in Development. 2008. (Molecular Biology Intelligence Unit Ser.). (Illus.). 106p. (C). 189.00 *(978-0-387-78631-5(7))* Springer.

Ruhrberg, Christiana, ed. VEGF in Development. 2010. (Molecular Biology Intelligence Unit Ser.). (Illus.). xi, 106p. pap. 189.00 *(978-1-4419-2693-7(3)*, 1441926933) Springer.

Sadick, Neil S., et al. Practical Phlebology: Venous Ultrasound. 2013. (ENG., Illus.). 208p. 125.00 *(978-1-85315-948-0(4))* Hodder Arnold Pubs.

Sangaeza, Omar P. & Requena, Luis. Pathology of Vascular Skin Lesions. 2010. (Current Clinical Pathology Ser.). (Illus.). 336p. pap. 199.00 *(978-1-61737-407-4(5)*, 1617374075) Humana Pr.

The Science Behind the Skill of Vein Access for the RN. 2008. ring bd. *(978-0-9723656-3-5(X))* Vein Access Technologies.

The Science Behind the Skill of Vein Access for the X-ray Tech. 2008. ring bd. *(978-0-9723656-5-9(6))* Vein Access Technologies.

Seed, Michael P. & Walsh, David A., eds. Angiogenesis in Inflammation: Mechanisms & Clinical Correlates. 2008. (Progress in Inflammation Research Ser.). (Illus.). 250p. 189.00 ***(978-3-7643-7626-0(0)*****,** 3764376260) Birkhauser Verlag AG CHE. Dist: Springer.

Shahidi, Fereidoon, et al, eds. Anti-Angiogenic Functional & Medicinal Foods. 2007. (Nutraceutical Science & Technology Ser.: Vol. 6). (ENG., Illus.). 736p. 199.95 *(978-1-57444-445-2(X)*, DK3217, CRC Press) Taylor & Francis Group GBR. Dist: Taylor & Francis Group.

Simons, Michael & Rubanyi, Gabor M., eds. Modern Concepts in Angiogenesis. 2007. (Illus.). 430p. 239.00 *(978-1-86094-763-6(8))* Imperial College Pr. GBR. Dist: World Scientific Publishing Co., Inc.

Skinard, Elmer T. New Research on Angiogenesis Inhibitors. 2006. 225.00 *(978-1-60021-473-8(8))* Nova Science Pubs., Inc.

Staton, Carolyn A., et al, eds. Angiogenesis Assays: A Critical Appraisal of Current Techniques. 2007. (ENG., Illus.). 410p. 209.95 *(978-0-470-01600-8(0)*, Wiley) Wiley, John & Sons, Inc.

stotler, M. Gail S. T. O. T. L. E. R. The Science Behind the Skill of Vein Access for the Phlebotomist. 2006. (Illus.). 170p. pap. 59.95 net. *(978-0-9723656-1-1(3))* Vein Access Technologies.

Thrush, Abigail & Hartshorne, Timothy. Vascular Ultrasound: How, Why & When. Thrush, Abigail & Hartshorne, Timothy, eds. 3rd ed. 2009. (How, Why & When Ser.). (ENG., Illus.). 320p. (C). 85.95 *(978-0-443-06918-5(2)*, Churchill Livingstone) Elsevier - Health Sciences Div.

Tracy, R. E. The Role of Aging in Atherosclerosis: The Sequestration Hypothesis. 2010. 288p. pap. 124.00 *(978-90-481-6265-9(3)*, 9048162653) Springer.

Uflacker, Renan. Atlas of Vascular Anatomy: An Angiographic Approach. 2nd rev. ed. 2006. (ENG., Illus.). 928p. 278.99 *(978-0-7817-6081-2(X))* Lippincott Williams & Wilkins.

Voelkel, Norbert & Rounds, Sharon. The Pulmonary Endothelium: Function in Health & Disease. 2009. (ENG., Illus.). 532p. 266.00 *(978-0-470-72361-6(0)*, Wiley) Wiley, John & Sons, Inc.

Wilson, Chuck. Vein Pattern Recognition: A Privacy-Enhancing Biometric. 2010. (ENG., Illus.). 307p. 79.95 *(978-1-4398-2137-4(2)*, CRC Press) Taylor & Francis Group GBR. Dist: Taylor & Francis Group.

Wilson, Samuel Eric. Vascular Access: Principles & Practice. 5th rev. ed. 2009. (ENG.). 328p. 169.99 *(978-1-60547-203-4(4))* Lippincott Williams & Wilkins.

BLOOD-VESSELS—DISEASES

see also Aneurysms; Angiocardiography; Peripheral Vascular Diseases; Systemic Lupus Erythematosus

Abraham, David, et al, eds. Vascular Complications in Human Disease: Mechanisms & Consequences. 2010. (ENG., Illus.). xiv, 258p. pap. 179.00 *(978-1-84996-676-4(1)*, 1849966761) Springer.

Akuthota, Venu & Herring, Stanley A., eds. Nerve & Vascular Injuries in Sports Medicine. 2009. (ENG., Illus.). x, 290p. 114.00 *(978-0-387-76599-0(9)*, 0387765999) Springer.

Al-Wabil, Linda Moh'd. ABC of Vascular Laboratory in King Khalid University Hospital (K. K. U. H.) 2009. 84p. pap. 15.00 *(978-1-4269-0024-2(4))* Trafford Publishing.

Baker, Andrew H., ed. Vascular Disease: Molecular Biology & Gene Transfer Protocols. 2010. (Methods in Molecular Medicine Ser.). 456p. pap. 149.00 *(978-1-61737-155-4(6)*, 1617371556) Humana Pr.

Bandello, F., et al, eds. Anti-VEGF. 2010. (Developments in Ophthalmology Ser.). (Illus.). 144p. *(978-3-8055-9529-2(8))* Karger, S. AG.

Bergan, John J. & Aburahma, Ali F., eds. Noninvasive Vascular Diagnosis: A Practical Guide to Therapy. 2nd rev. ed. 2006. (Illus.). 561p. 279.00 *(978-1-84628-446-5(5)*, 1846284465) Springer.

Bhattacharya, Jahar, ed. Cell Signaling in Vascular Inflammation. 2010. (ENG., Illus.). 240p. pap. 135.00 *(978-1-61737-619-1(1)*, 1617376191) Humana Pr.

Bismuth, Jean & Garami, Zsolt, eds. Vascular Imaging: A Practical Approach. 2013. (ENG., Illus.). 350p. 179.95 *(978-1-4419-7697-0(3)*, 1441976973) Springer.

Bluth, Edward I., et al. Ultrasonography in Vascular Diseases: A Practical Approach to Clinical Problems. 2nd ed. 2007. (ENG., Illus.). 144p. pap. 69.99 *(978-1-58890-610-6(8))* Thieme Medical Pubs., Inc.

Borer, J. S., et al, eds. Vascular Biology & Medicine Vol. 42: 3rd European Meeting, Hamburg, September 2005: Abstracts. (Advances in Cardiology Ser.). *(978-3-8055-8035-9(5))* Karger, S. AG.

Bosevski, Marijan, ed. Diabeto-Angiology. 2009. (Metabolic Diseases - Laboratory & Clinical Research Ser.). 145.00 *(978-1-61668-926-1(9)*, Nova Biomedical Bks.) Nova Science Pubs., Inc.

Caralis, Dennis G. & Bakris, George L., eds. Lower Extremity Arterial Disease. 2010. (Clinical Hypertension & Vascular Diseases Ser.). (Illus.). 320p. pap. 119.00 *(978-1-61737-639-9(6)*, 1617376396) Humana Pr.

Cassidy, James T., et al. Pediatric Rheumatology. 6th ed. 2010. (ENG., Illus.). 800p. (C). 218.00 *(978-1-4160-6581-4(4)*, Saunders) Elsevier - Health Sciences Div.

Cheresh, David A., ed. Angiogenesis Pt. A, Vol. 444: In Vivo Systems, 2 vols. 2008. (ENG., Illus.). 400p. 187.00 *(978-0-12-374313-8(3)*, Academic Pr.) Elsevier Science & Technology Bks.

Cissarek, Thomas, et al. Vascular Medicine: Therapy & Practice. 2010. (ENG., Illus.). 432p. 139.00 *(978-0-07-175092-9(4)*, 0071750924) McGraw-Hill Professional Publishing.

Civas, Ekrem, et al. ND: Yag Laser Treatment for Various Vascular Lesions. 2010. pap. 47.00 *(978-1-61761-099-8(2))* Nova Science Pubs., Inc.

Creager, Mark, ed. Atlas of Vascular Disease. 3rd ed. 2009. (ENG.). cd-rom 99.00 *(978-1-57340-318-4(0)*, 1573403180) Current Medicine Group LLC.

Creager, Mark A. Atlas of Vascular Disease. Creager, Mark, ed. 3rd ed. 2008. (ENG., Illus.). vii, 296p. 199.00 *(978-1-57340-269-9(9)*, 1573402699) Current Medicine Group LLC.

Daigle, Robert J., Jr. Techniques in Noninvasive Vascular Diagnosis: An Encyclopedia of Vascular Testing. 3rd ed. 2008. (ENG., Illus.). 380p. spiral bd. 79.95 *(978-0-9720653-6-8(9))* Summer Publishing, LLC.

Diehm, C., et al. Color Atlas of Vascular Diseases. Burgdorf, W. H. C., tr. from GER. 2012. (ENG., Illus.). xi, 396p. pap. 419.00 *(978-3-642-08296-2(3)*, 3642082963) Springer.

Dieter, Robert & Dieter, Raymond A., Jr. Venous & Lymphatic Diseases. 2010. (ENG., Illus.). 688p. 207.00 *(978-0-07-160158-0(9)*, 0071601589) McGraw-Hill Professional Publishing.

Donnelly, Richard W. & London, Nick J. M., eds. Arterial & Venous Disease. 2nd ed. 2009. (ABC Ser.: 101). (ENG., Illus.). 120p. pap. 54.95 *(978-1-4051-7889-1(2))* Wiley, John & Sons, Inc.

Enjolras, Odile, et al. Color Atlas of Vascular Tumors & Vascular Malformations. 2006. (ENG., Illus.). 310p. 179.00 *(978-0-521-84851-0(2))* Cambridge Univ. Pr.

Festa, Joanne & Lazar, Ronald, eds. Neurovascular Neuropsychology. 2010. (ENG., Illus.). xvi, 315p. pap. 79.95 *(978-1-4419-6541-7(6)*, 1441965416) Springer.

Fisher, Miles. Diabetes & Heart Disease. 2009. (Oxford Drama Library). (ENG., Illus.). 160p. pap. 24.95 *(978-0-19-954372-4(0))* Oxford Univ. Pr., Inc.

Fitridge, Robert & Thompson, Matthew, eds. Mechanisms of Vascular Disease: A reference book for vascular Specialists. 2011. (Illus.). 582p. pap. ***(978-0-9871718-2-5(8))*** Univ. of Adelaide Pr.

Garbani, Nathalie. Practical Vascular Technology: A Comprehensive Laboratory Text. 2010. (ENG., Illus.). 336p. spiral bd. 81.95 *(978-1-58255-809-7(4))* Lippincott Williams & Wilkins.

Gloviczki, Peter. Handbook of Venous Disorders: Guidelines of the American Venous Forum. 3rd ed. 2009. (ENG., Illus.). 624p. 199.00 *(978-0-340-93880-5(3)*, Hodder Arnold) Hodder Education GBR. Dist: Oxford Univ. Pr., Inc.

Greer, Ian A., et al. Women's Vascular Health. 2007. (ENG., Illus.). 496p. 179.50 *(978-0-340-80997-6(3))* Hodder Arnold Pubs.

Hallett, John W., Jr., et al. Comprehensive Vascular & Endovascular Surgery. 2nd ed. 2009. (ENG., Illus.). 932p. 295.00 *(978-0-323-05726-4(8)*, Mosby) Elsevier - Health Sciences Div.

Handler, Clive, et al, eds. Vascular Complications in Human Disease: Mechanisms & Consequences. 2008. (ENG., Illus.). xiv, 258p. 179.00 *(978-1-84628-918-7(1)*, 1846289181) Springer.

Hoffman, Gary S., et al, eds. Inflammatory Diseases of Blood Vessels. 2nd ed. 2012. (ENG.). 600p. 239.95 ***(978-1-4443-3822-5(6)*****,** Wiley-Blackwell) Wiley, John & Sons, Inc.

Humbert, M., et al, eds. Pulmonary Vascular Disorders. 2012. (Progress in Respiratory Research Ser.). (ENG., Illus.). 290p. ***(978-3-8055-9914-6(5))*** Karger, S. AG.

Jackson, Trachette L., ed. Modeling Tumor Vasculature: Molecular, Cellular, & Tissue Level Aspects & Implications. 2011. (ENG., Illus.). xi, 409p. 189.00 *(978-1-4614-0051-6(1)*, 1461400511) Springer.

Jaff, Michael R. & White, Christopher J., eds. Vascular Disease: Diagnostic & Therapeutic Approaches. 2011. (ENG., Illus.). 600p. 99.00 *(978-1-935395-16-4(5))* Cardiotext Publishing.

Johnstone, Michael T. & Veves, Aristidis, eds. Diabetes & Cardiovascular Disease. 2nd ed. 2010. (Contemporary Cardiology Ser.). (Illus.). 672p. pap. 189.00 *(978-1-61737-549-1(7)*, 1617375497) Humana Pr.

Joussen, A M, et al, eds. Retinal Vascular Disease. 2007. (Illus.). 778p. 219.00 *(978-3-540-29541-9(0)*, 3540295410) Springer.

Judd, Sandra, ed. Blood & Circulatory Disorders Sourcebook. 3rd rev. ed. 2010. (Health Reference Ser.). lib. bdg. 93.00 *(978-0-7808-1081-5(3))* Omnigraphics, Inc.

Macdonald, R. Loch, ed. Vascular Neurosurgery. 2nd ed. 2008. (Neurosurgical Operative Atlas Ser.). (ENG., Illus.). 296p. 269.99 *(978-1-60406-034-8(4))* Thieme Medical Pubs., Inc.

Mattassi, Raúl, et al. Vascular Malformations & Hemangiomas: An Atlas of Diagnosis & Treatment. 2009. (Illus.). 210p. 169.00 *(978-88-470-0568-6(X))* Springer.

Mohler, Emile R. Atlas of Vascular Medicine: Case-Based Approach to Current Management. 2012. 256p. ***(978-1-936287-29-1(3))*** Demos Medical Publishing, LLC.

Mohler, Emile R. & Litt, Harold. Atlas of Vascular Medicine: A Case-Based Approach to Current Management. 2012. E-Book ***(978-1-61705-059-6(8))*** Demos Medical Publishing, LLC.

Moncada, Salvador & Higgs, Annie. The Vascular Endothelium, 2 vols., Vol. 1. 2006. (Handbook of Experimental Pharmacology Ser.). (Illus.). x, 339p. 439.00 *(978-3-540-32966-4(8)*, 3540329668) Springer.

—The Vascular Endothelium II, 2 vols. 2006. (Handbook of Experimental Pharmacology Ser.). (Illus.). x, 356p. 489.00 *(978-3-540-36027-8(1)*, 3540360271) Springer.

Moore, Wesley S. & Jimenez, Juan Carlos. A Handbook of Vascular Disease Management. 2011. 500p. 108.00 *(978-981-4317-77-1(2))* World Scientific Publishing Co., Inc.

Peacock, Andrew J., et al. Pulmonary Circulation. 3rd ed. 2011. (ENG., Illus.). 728p. 225.00 *(978-0-340-98192-4(X))* Hodder Arnold Pubs.

Pellerito, John. Introduction to Vascular Ultrasonography: Expert Consult - Online & Print. 6th ed. 2012. (ENG., Illus.). 704p. 119.00 ***(978-1-4377-1417-3(X)*****,** Saunders) Elsevier - Health Sciences Div.

Penn, J. S., ed. Retinal & Choroidal Angiogenesis. 2008. (Illus.). 557p. 179.00 *(978-1-4020-6779-2(8))* Springer.

Rajagopalan, Sanjay, et al, eds. Manual of Vascular Diseases. 2nd rev. ed. 2011. (ENG., Illus.). 640p. pap. 82.99 *(978-1-60913-422-8(2))* Lippincott Williams & Wilkins.

Rasmussen, Todd E., et al. Handbook of Patient Care in Vascular Diseases. 5th rev. ed. 2008. (Lippincott Williams & Wilkins Handbook Ser.). (ENG., Illus.). 352p. pap. 64.99 *(978-0-7817-8135-0(3))* Lippincott Williams & Wilkins.

Robinson, K., ed. Homocysteine & Vascular Disease. 2010. (Developments in Cardiovascular Medicine Ser.). 468p. pap. 319.00 *(978-90-481-5431-9(6)*, 9048154316) Springer.

Rooke, Thom. Vascular Medicine & Endovascular Interventions. Sullivan, Timothy M. & Jaff, Michael R., eds. 2007. (ENG., Illus.). 352p. 115.95 *(978-1-4051-5827-5(1)*, Wiley-Blackwell) Wiley, John & Sons, Inc.

Schäberle, Wilhelm. Ultrasonography in Vascular Diagnosis: A Therapy-Oriented Textbook & Atlas. Herwig, B., tr. from GER. 2nd ed. 2011. (ENG., Illus.). xx, 520p. 219.00 *(978-3-642-02508-2(0)*, 3642025080) Springer.

Simon, Daniel I. & Rogers, Campbell, eds. Vascular Disease & Injury: Preclinical Research. 2010. (Contemporary Cardiology Ser.). (Illus.). 368p. pap. 169.00 *(978-1-61737-169-1(6)*, 1617371696) Humana Pr.

Slevin, Mark, ed. Therapeutic Angiogenesis for Vascular Diseases: Molecular Mechanisms & Targeted Clinical Approaches for the Treatment of Angiogenic Disease. 2010. (ENG., Illus.). xvi, 430p. 239.00 *(978-90-481-9494-0(6)*, 9048194946) Springer.

Sreejayan, Nair & Ren, Jun, eds. Vascular Biology Protocols. 2010. (Methods in Molecular Medicine Ser.). xii, 372p. pap. 179.00 (978-1-61737-650-4(7), 1617376507) Humana Pr.
Thompson, Ralph, ed. Microcirculation: Function, Malfunction & Measurement. 2008. 129.00 (978-1-60692-721-2(3)) Nova Science Pubs., Inc.
Vascular Biology Protocols. 2008. (Methods in Molecular Medicine Ser.). 179.00 (978-1-58829-574-3(5)) Humana Pr.
Wahlberg, Eric, et al. Emergency Vascular Surgery: A Practical Guide. 2010. (Illus.). viii, 202p. pap. 29.00 (978-3-642-07938-2(5), 3642079385) Springer.
Watts, Richard A. & Scott, David G. I. Vasculitis in Clinical Practice. 2010. (Illus.). 120p. pap. 39.95 (978-1-84996-246-9(4), 1849962464) Springer.
White, Rodney A. & Fogarty, Thomas J., eds. Peripheral Endovascular Interventions. 3rd ed. 2010. (ENG., Illus.). xix, 746p. 199.00 (978-1-4419-1386-9(6), 1441913866) Springer.
Wolf, Karl-Jurgen, et al. Vascular Imaging. 2009. (Direct Diagnosis in Radiology Ser.). (ENG., Illus.). 303p. pap. 64.99 (978-3-13-145181-1(5)) Thieme Medical Pubs., Inc.
Yuan, Jason X. -J, et al, eds. Textbook of Pulmonary Vascular Disease. 2009. (ENG., Illus.). 2000p. 249.00 (978-0-387-87428-9(3), 0387874283) Springer.
Yuan, Jason X. -J & Ward, Jeremy P. T., eds. Membrane Receptors, Channels & Transporters in Pulmonary Circulation. 2010. (Advances in Experimental Medicine & Biology Ser.). (Illus.). xv, 966p. 399.00 (978-1-60761-499-9(5), 1607614995) Humana Pr.
Zierler, R. Eugene & Meissner, Mark. Strandness's Duplex Scanning in Vascular Disorders. Zierler, R. Eugene, ed. 4th rev. ed. 2009. (ENG., Illus.). 528p. 189.99 (978-0-7817-9838-9(8)) Lippincott Williams & Wilkins.

BLOOD-VESSELS—GRAFTS
see Arterial Grafts; Vascular Grafts

BLOOD-VESSELS—RADIOGRAPHY
see Angiography

BLOOD-VESSELS—SURGERY
see also Angioplasty
Balzer, K., et al, eds. Vascular Surgery. 2007. (European Manual of Medicine Ser.). (Illus.). 674p. per. 159.00 (978-3-540-30955-0(1), 3540309551) Springer.
Beard, Jonathan D. & Gaines, Peter A. Vascular & Endovascular Surgery. 4th ed. 2009. (Companion to Specialist Surgical Practice Ser.). (ENG., Illus.). 408p. 140.00 (978-0-7020-3011-6(2), Saunders) Elsevier - Health Sciences Div.
Bhattacharya, Vish & Stansby, Gerard, eds. Postgraduate Vascular Surgery: The Candidate's Guide to the FRCS. 2011. (ENG., Illus.). 338p. pap. 65.00 (978-0-521-13352-4(1)) Cambridge Univ. Pr.
Butler, Paul, ed. Endovascular Neurosurgery: A Multidisciplinary Approach. 2010. (ENG.). x, 160p. pap. 259.00 (978-1-84996-890-4(X), 184996890X) Springer.
Byrne, James Vincent. Tutorials in Endovascular Neurosurgery & Interventional Neuroradiology. 2012. (ENG., Illus.). xvii, 361p. 139.00 (978-3-642-19153-4(3), 3642191533) Springer.
Civas, Ekrem, et al. ND: Yag Laser Treatment for Various Vascular Lesions. 2010. pap. 47.00 (978-1-61761-099-8(2)) Nova Science Pubs., Inc.
Coding Companion for Cardiology/Cardiothoracic Surgery/Vascular Surgery. 2007. per. 199.95 (978-1-56337-897-3(3)) Optuminsight, Inc.
Cronenwett, Jack L. & Johnston, Wayne, eds. Vascular Surgery, 2 vols., Set. 7th ed. 2010. (ENG., Illus.). 2448p. 389.00 (978-1-4160-5223-4(2), Saunders) Elsevier - Health Sciences Div.
Dale, W. Andrew, et al. eds. Band of Brothers: Creators of Modern Vascular Surgery. (Illus.). 172p. 59.95 (978-1-56757-000-7(3)) Appleton Communications, Inc.
Davies, Alun H. & Brophy, Colleen M., eds. Vascular Surgery. 2010. (Springer Specialist Surgery Ser.). (Illus.). x, 266p. pap. 149.00 (978-1-84996-860-7(8), 1849968608) Springer.
Earnshaw, J. J. & Murie, J. A. The Evidence for Vascular Surgery. 2nd ed. 2007. (Illus.). 278p. 115.00 (978-1-903378-45-8(1)) TFM Publishing Ltd. GBR. Dist: JAMCO Distribution.
Earnshaw, Jonathan J. & Wyatt, Michael G., eds. Complications in Vascular & Endovascular Surgery: How to Avoid Them & How to Get Out of Trouble. 2011. (Illus.). 400p. (978-1-903378-80-9(X)) TFM Publishing Ltd.
Eskandari, Mark K., et al. Modern Trends in Vascular Surgery: Endovascular Technology. 2010. (Illus.). 600p. (978-1-60795-053-0(7)) PMPH-USA. Ltd.
—Modern Trends in Vascular Surgery: Surgery of the Aorta & its Body Branches. 2009. 600p. (978-1-60795-054-7(5)) PMPH-USA. Ltd.
—New Findings in Vascular Surgery. 2nd ed. 2010. (Illus.). 448p. (978-1-60795-157-5(6)) PMPH-USA. Ltd.
Fogarty, Thomas J. & White, Rodney A. Peripheral Endovascular Interventions. 3rd ed. 2010. (Illus.). xix, 512p. E-Book (978-1-4419-1387-6(4)) Springer.
Geroulakos, George & Sumpio, Bauer, eds. Vascular Surgery: Cases, Questions & Commentaries. 3rd ed. 2011. (ENG., Illus.). x, 406p. 119.00 (978-1-84996-355-8(X), 184996355X) Springer.
Golzarian, Jafar, et al, eds. Vascular Embolotherapy: A Comprehensive Approach, Volume 2: Oncology, Trauma, Gene Therapy, Vascular Malformations, & Neck. 2012. (Medical Radiology / Diagnostic Imaging Ser.). (ENG., Illus.). xii, 338p. pap. 239.00 (978-3-642-05995-7(3), 3642059953) Springer.
Green, Richard M., et al. Atlas of Endovascular Surgery. Date not set. (Illus.). 368p. 150.00 (978-0-07-024292-0(5)) McGraw-Hill Medical Publishing Div.
Hallett, John W., Jr., et al. Comprehensive Vascular & Endovascular Surgery. 2nd ed. 2009. (ENG., Illus.). 932p. 295.00 (978-0-323-05726-4(8), Mosby) Elsevier - Health Sciences Div.
Heuser, Richard R. & Henry, Michel, eds. Textbook of Peripheral Vascular Interventions. 2nd rev. ed. 2008. (Illus.). XX, 930p. 300.00 (978-0-84184-643-9(0)) Taylor & Francis Group.
Hoballah, Jamal J., ed. Vascular Surgery. 2008. (Springer Surgery Atlas Ser.). (Illus.). 390p. 319.00 (978-3-540-41102-4(X), 354041102X) Springer.
Hoballah, Jamal J. & Scott-Conner,, Carol E. H., Carol EH, eds. Operative Dictations in General & Vascular Surgery. 2nd ed. 2011. (ENG.). xxxvi, 1062p. pap. 89.95 (978-1-4614-0450-7(9), 1461404509) Springer.
Hobson, Robert W. Endovascular Surgery Clinical. 2007. 119.95 (978-0-8493-3995-0(2)) Dekker, Marcel Inc.
Kandarpa, Krishna, ed. Peripheral Vascular Interventions. 2007. (ENG., Illus.). 720p. 215.99 (978-0-7817-8687-4(8)) Lippincott Williams & Wilkins.
Klimo, Paul, Jr., et al. Pediatric Vascular Neurosurgery, an Issue of Neurosurgery Clinics. 2010. (Clinics: Surgery Ser.: 21-3). (ENG., Illus.). xiv, 400p. 105.00 (978-1-4377-1840-9(X), Saunders) Elsevier - Health Sciences Div.
Lanzer, Peter, ed. Mastering Endovascular Techniques: A Guide to Excellence. 2006. (ENG., Illus.). 480p. 179.99 (978-1-58255-967-4(8)) Lippincott Williams & Wilkins.
Lumsden, Alan B., et al, eds. Advanced Endovascular Therapy of Aortic Disease. 2007. (ENG., Illus.). 240p. 162.95 (978-1-4051-5570-0(1), Wiley-Blackwell) Wiley, John & Sons, Inc.
Mattassi, Raúl, et al. Vascular Malformations & Hemangiomas: An Atlas of Diagnosis & Treatment. 2009. (Illus.). 210p. 169.00 (978-88-470-0568-6(X)) Springer.
Moneta, Gregory L. Year Book of Vascular Surgery 2010. 2010. (Year Bks.: 2010). (ENG.). 176.00 (978-0-323-06849-9(9), Mosby) Elsevier - Health Sciences Div.
Moore, Wesley S. Endovascular Surgery. 4th ed. 2010. (ENG., Illus.). 868p. 274.00 (978-1-4160-6208-0(4), Saunders) Elsevier - Health Sciences Div.
Pearce, William H. & Yao, James S. T. Vascular Surgery: A Manual for Survival. 2009. 600p. (978-1-60795-055-4(3)) PMPH-USA. Ltd.
Perlyn, Chad & Greene, Arin. Vascular Anomalies, an Issue of Clinics in Plastic Surgery. 2010. (Clinics: Surgery Ser.: 38-1). (ENG., Illus.). 176p. 110.00 (978-1-4557-0492-7(X), Saunders) Elsevier - Health Sciences Div.
Rooke, Thom. Vascular Medicine & Endovascular Interventions. Sullivan, Timothy M. & Jaff, Michael R., eds. 2007. (ENG., Illus.). 352p. 115.95 (978-1-4051-5827-5(1), Wiley-Blackwell) Wiley, John & Sons, Inc.
Sales. Hdbk Vascular Surg 2e. 2nd ed. 2010. 300p. 199.95 (978-0-8247-2852-6(1), Informa Healthcare) Taylor & Francis Group GBR. Dist: Taylor & Francis Group.
Schillinger, Martin & Minar, Erich, eds. Complications in Peripheral Vascular Interventions. 2007. (ENG., Illus.). 268p. 199.95 (978-1-84184-628-6(7), Informa Healthcare) Taylor & Francis Group GBR. Dist: Taylor & Francis Group.
Schneider, Peter. Endovascular Skills: Guidewire & Catheter Skills for Endovascular Surgery, Third Edition. 3rd rev. ed. 2008. (ENG., Illus.). 500p. 230.00 (978-1-4200-6937-2(3)) CRC Pr. LLC.
Sharp, Michael, ed. Vascular Surgery. 2007. (Oxford Specialist Handbooks series in Surgery Ser.). (ENG., Illus.). 504p. pap. 79.95 (978-0-19-920308-6(3)) Oxford Univ. Pr., Inc.
Sreejayan, Nair & Ren, Jun, eds. Vascular Biology Protocols. 2010. (Methods in Molecular Medicine Ser.). xii, 372p. pap. 179.00 (978-1-61737-650-4(7), 1617376507) Humana Pr.
Strauch, Berish & Yu, Han-Liang. Atlas of Microvascular Surgery: Anatomy & Operative Techniques. 2nd ed. (Illus.). 2008. 229.95 (978-3-13-783002-3(8)) 2006. (ENG., 712p. 239.99 (978-1-58890-466-9(0)) Thieme Medical Pubs., Inc.
Thompson, Matt M., et al, eds. Endovascular Intervention for Vascular Disease: Principles & Practice. 2007. (ENG., Illus.). 616p. 250.00 (978-0-8493-3979-0(0), Informa Healthcare) Taylor & Francis Group GBR. Dist: Taylor & Francis Group.
Vascular Biology Protocols. 2008. (Methods in Molecular Medicine Ser.). 179.00 (978-1-58829-574-3(5)) Humana Pr.
Wahlberg, Eric, et al. Emergency Vascular Surgery: A Practical Guide. 2007. (Illus.). 201p. 129.00 (978-3-540-44393-3(2), 3540443932) Springer.
Wax, Mark K. Microvascular Reconstructive Surgery of the Face, an Issue of Facial Plastic Surgery Clinics. 2009. (Clinics: Surgery Ser.: 17-2). (ENG.). 240p. 99.00 (978-1-4377-0474-7(3), Saunders) Elsevier - Health Sciences Div.
Wilmink Teun Staff, et al. Vascular Emergencies. 2006. 400p. 199.95 (978-0-8247-2922-6(6), Informa Healthcare) Taylor & Francis Group.

BLOOD VOLUME
Dorhout Mees, E. J., ed. Cardiovascular Aspects of Dialysis Treatment: The Importance of Volume Control. 2010. 160p. pap. 92.00 (978-90-481-5442-5(1), 9048154421) Springer.

BLOODBORNE DISEASES
see Bloodborne Infections

BLOODBORNE INFECTIONS
Assessment of Blood-Borne Pathogens. 2009. (Illus.). 100p. pap. (978-3-8055-9112-6(8)) Karger, S. AG.
AuBuchon, James P. & Prowse, Christopher V. Pathogen Inactivation: The Penultimate Paradigm Shift. 2010. (978-1-56395-309-5(9), AABB Pr.) American Assn. of Blood Banks.
Goetsch, David & LearnSomething Staff. Blood-Borne Pathogens for Healthcare. 2008. cd-rom 27.73 (978-0-13-500914-7(6)) Prentice Hall Pr.
Klennberg, Michael E., ed. Managing Infections in Patients with Hematological Malignancies. 2009. (Contemporary Hematology Ser.). 300p. 219.00 (978-1-58829-986-4(4)) Humana Pr.
Lindsey, Jeffery. Bloodborne Pathogens. Gulli, Benjamin & Krohmer, Jon R., eds. 5th rev. ed. 2007. (Illus.). 85p. pap. 10.95 (978-0-7637-4245-4(7)) Jones & Bartlett Learning, LLC.
National Safety Council (NSC) Staff. Bloodborne & Airborne Pathogens. 2nd ed. 2009. 64p. pap. (978-0-07-338288-3(4)) McGraw-Hill Cos., The.
Smit Sibinga, C. Th. & Dodd, Roger Y., eds. Transmissible Diseases & Transfusion. 2010. (Developments in Hematology & Immunology Ser.). 232p. pap. 199.00 (978-1-4419-5233-2(0), 1441952330) Springer.
Wiwanitkit, Viroj. Blood Infections: Scientific, Clinical & Public Health Aspects. 2007. 89.00 (978-1-60021-685-5(4)) Nova Science Pubs., Inc.
World Health Organization. Screening donated blood for transfusion-transmissible infections: Recommendations. 2010. (Nonserial Publication Ser.). 67p. pap. 36.00 (978-92-4-154788-8(X)) World Health Organization.

BLOODHOUND
Liebeck, Christiane. Man-Trailing: How to Train Your Bloodhound. 2008. (ENG., Illus.). 96p. pap. 24.95 (978-3-86127-929-7(0)) Cadmos Verlag GmbH DEU. Dist: Independent Pubs. Group.
Linzy, Jan, et al. Bloodhound Champions, 2005-2007. 2008. (Illus.). 101p. spiral bd. 46.95 (978-1-55893-236-4(4)) Camino E.E. & Bk. Co.
Schettler, Jeff. Red Dog Rising. 2009. (Illus.). 256p. pap. 12.95 (978-1-57779-104-1(5)) Alpine Pubns., Inc.

BLOODHOUNDS
see Bloodhound

BLOODLETTING
see Phlebotomy

BLOOMER, AMELIA JENKS, 1818-1894
Bloomer, D. C. Life & Writings of Amelia Bloomer. 2009. 402p. 33.99 (978-1-110-78848-4(7)); pap. 33.75 (978-1-110-78846-0(0)) BiblioBazaar.
—Life & Writings of Amelia Bloomer. 396p. 2008. 49.95 (978-1-4365-6656-8(8)) 2007. (ENG.). per. 34.95 (978-0-548-77408-3(0)) Kessinger Publishing, LLC.
—Life & Writings of Amelia Bloomer. (Illus.). reprint ed. lib. bdg. 98.00 (978-0-7222-4785-3(0)) Library Reprints, Inc.
—Life & Writings of Amelia Bloomer. 2007. (ENG.). 400p. per. (978-1-4067-3049-4(1)) Read Bks.

BLOOMINGDALE'S (FIRM)
Jones, Kevin & Johnson, Christina. High Style: Betsy Bloomingdale & the Haute Couture. 2009. (Illus.). 51p. pap. 24.95 (978-0-615-29814-6(1)) FIDM Museum & Library, Inc.

BLOOMSBERRIES
see Bloomsbury Group

BLOOMSBURY GROUP
Arnold, Anthea. Charleston Saved, 1979-1989. 2010. (ENG., Illus.). 144p. 39.95 (978-0-7090-9018-2(8)) Hale, Robert Ltd. GBR. Dist: Independent Pubs. Group.
Cauchi, Tiziana. The Bloomsbury Reform. 2009. 236p. pap. (978-3-639-11668-7(2)) VDM Verlag Dr. Mueller e.K.
Chisholm, Anne. Frances Partridge: The Biography. 2010. (ENG., Illus.). 404p. pap. 16.95 (978-0-7538-2699-7(2), Phoenix) Orion Publishing Group, Ltd. GBR. Dist: Independent Pubs. Group.
Cribb, Tim. Bloomsbury & British Theatre: The Marlowe Story. 2007. (ENG., Illus.). 204p. per. (978-1-84471-414-8(4)) Salt Publishing.
Curtis, Anthony. Virginia Woolf. 2008. (Illus.). 256p. 24.95 (978-1-905791-47-7(X)) Haus Publishing GBR. Dist: Consortium Bk. Sales & Distribution.
Diment, Galya. A Russian Jew of Bloomsbury: The Life & Times of Samuel Koteliansky. 2011. (ENG., Illus.). 456p. (C). **(978-0-7735-3899-3(2))** McGill-Queen's Univ. Pr.
Froula, Christine. Virginia Woolf & the Bloomsbury Avant-Garde: War, Civilization, Modernity. 2007. (Gender & Culture Ser.). (ENG.). 432p. (gr. 17). pap. 26.50 (978-0-231-13445-3(2)) Columbia Univ. Pr.
Hall, Sarah M. Bedside, Bathtub & Armchair Companion to Virginia Woolf & Bloomsbury. 2007. (Bedside, Bathtub & Armchair Companions Ser.). (ENG., Illus.). 224p. 90.00 (978-0-8264-8674-5(6)) Continuum International Publishing Group, Ltd. GBR. Dist: National Bk. Network.
Hall, Sarah M. & Hall. The Bedside, Bathtub & Armchair Companion to Virginia Woolf & Bloomsbury. 2007. (Bedside, Bathtub & Armchair Companions Ser.). (ENG., Illus.). 224p. 27.95 (978-0-8264-8675-2(4)) Continuum International Publishing Group, Ltd. GBR. Dist: National Bk. Network.
Hodson, Millicent & Archer, Kenneth. Nijinsky's Bloomsbury Ballet: Reconstruction of Dance & Design for Jeux. 2007. (Wendy Hilton Dance & Music Ser.). (C). (978-1-57647-042-8(3)) Pendragon Pr.
Holbrook Gerzina, Gretchen, et al. A Room of Their Own: The Bloomsbury Artists in American Collections. Green, Nancy E. & Reed, Christopher, eds. 2008. (Distributed for the Herbert F. Johnson Museum of Art, Cornell University Ser.). (Illus.). 272p. 35.00 (978-1-934260-05-0(3)) Cornell Univ., Herbert F. Johnson Museum of Art.
Light, Alison. Mrs. Woolf & the Servants: An Intimate History of Domestic Life in Bloomsbury. 2009. (ENG., Illus.). 400p. pap. 20.00 (978-1-59691-694-4(X)) Bloomsbury Publishing.
Potts, Gina & Shahriari, Lisa, eds. Virginia Woolf's Bloomsbury Pack, Vols. 1 & 2: Aesthetic Theory & Literary Practice - International Influence & Politics, 2 vols. 2010. (ENG.). 472p. 147.00 (978-0-230-24737-6(7)) Palgrave Macmillan.
—Virginia Woolf's Bloomsbury Vol. 2: International Influence & Politics, 2 vols. 2010. (ENG.). 256p. 84.00 (978-0-230-51767-7(6)) Palgrave Macmillan.
Rawlinson, Zsuzsanna. The Sphinx of Bloomsbury. 210p. (C). pap. (978-963-05-8351-0(8)) Akademiai Kiado.
Spalding, Frances. The Bloomsbury Group. 2006. (National Portrait Gallery Insights Ser.). (Illus.). 108p. 19.95 (978-1-85514-351-7(8)) National Portrait Gallery Pubns. GBR. Dist: Antique Collectors' Club.
Stansky, Peter & Abrahams, William Miller. Julian Bell: From Bloomsbury to the Spanish Civil War. 2012. (ENG.). 32p. 45.00 **(978-0-8047-7413-0(7))** Stanford Univ. Pr.
Wolfe, Jesse. Bloomsbury, Modernism, & the Reinvention of Intimacy. 2011. (ENG., Illus.). 272p. 90.00 (978-1-107-00604-1(X)) Cambridge Univ. Pr.

BLOWERS
see Compressors; Fans (Machinery)

BLOWING ENGINES
see Fans (Machinery)

BLOWING THE WHISTLE
see Whistle Blowing

BLOWOUTS, OILWELL
see Oil Well Blowouts

BLOWPIPE
see also Assaying; Chemistry, Analytic—Qualitative
Elderhorst, William. Elderhorst's Manual of Qualitative Blow-Pipe Analysis, & Determinative Mineralogy Edited by Henry B Nason & Charles F Chandler. 2006. 316p. per. 23.99 (978-1-4255-3045-7(1)) MPublishing.
—A Manual of Blow-Pipe Analysis & Determinative Mineralogy. 2008. 172p. 22.99 (978-0-559-45548-3(8)); pap. 20.75 (978-0-559-45546-9(1)) BiblioBazaar.
—A Manual of Blow-Pipe Analysis & Determinative Mineralogy. 2006. 180p. per. 18.99 (978-1-4255-1464-8(2)) MPublishing.
—A Manual of Blow-Pipe Analysis & Determinative Mineralogy by William Elderhorst. 2006. 180p. per. 18.99 (978-1-4255-1480-8(4)) MPublishing.
—A Manual of Blowpipe-Analysis, & Determinative Mineralogy by William Elderhorst. 2006. 184p. per. 18.99 (978-1-4255-1517-1(7)) MPublishing.
A System of Instruction in the Practical Use of the Blow Pipe Being a Graduated Course of Analysis for the Use of Students & All Those Engaged in T. 2006. 292p. per. 23.99 (978-1-4255-2708-2(6)) MPublishing.

BLOY, LEON, 1846-1917
Brady, M. Rosalie. Thought & Style in the Works of Leon Bloy. (Catholic University of America, Studies in Romance Languages & Literatures: No. 30). reprint ed. 37.50 (978-0-404-50330-7(6)) AMS Pr., Inc.

BLUE BABY
see Tetralogy of Fallot

BLUE COLLAR WORKERS
Bessard, Pierre, photos by. Pierre Bessard: Wuhan Boiler Company Workers. 2011. (ENG., Illus.). 170p. 60.00 (978-988-17144-5-9(1)) Timezone 8 Ltd. HKG. Dist: D.A.P./Distributed Art Pubs.
Booker, M. Keith. Blue-Collar Pop Culture: From NASCAR to the Jersey Shore. 2012. E-Book **(978-0-313-39199-6(8)**, Praeger Pubs.) Greenwood Publishing Group, Inc.
Booker, M. Keith, ed. Blue Collar Pop Culture: From NASCAR to the Jersey Shore, 2 vols. 2012. (Illus.). 714p. 131.00 **(978-0-313-39198-9(X)**, A3225C) Greenwood Publishing Group, Inc.
Challis, R. A. & Coon, Rose Ann. What Do You Mean Your Dog Ate Your Timecard? A Look at the Blue-Collar Worker. 2009. 57p. pap. 16.95 (978-1-60836-499-2(2)) PublishAmerica, Inc.
Davis, James J. Iron Puddler. 2006. 288p. per. (978-1-4067-2301-4(0), Hesperides Pr.) Read Bks.
—The Iron Puddler: My Life in the Rolling Mills & What Came of It. 2010. 122p. 27.96 **(978-1-169-25064-2(5))**; pap. 15.96 **(978-1-162-69850-2(0))**; 34.95 (978-1-161-46715-4(7)) Kessinger Publishing, LLC.
Davis, James J. The Iron Puddler My Life in the Rolling Mills & What Came of It. 2010. (Illus.). 86p. pap. 20.00 (978-1-153-70726-8(8)) General Bks. LLC.
Davis, James J. (James John), creator. The Iron Puddler; My Life in the Rolling Mills & What Came of It. 2011. 296p. pap. 28.75 **(978-1-178-64411-1(1))** BiblioBazaar.
Davis, James J. 1873-1947. The Iron Puddler: My life in the rolling mills & what came of it. 2010. (ENG.). 292p. pap. 28.75 (978-1-176-38749-2(9)) BiblioBazaar.
—The Iron Puddler; My Life in the Rolling Mills & What Came of It. 2010. (ENG.). 294p. pap. 28.75 (978-1-171-69120-4(3)); pap. 28.75 (978-1-176-48911-0(9)) BiblioBazaar.
Davis, James John. The Iron Puddler: My Life in the Rolling Mills & What Came of It. 2010. 296p. pap. 28.75 (978-1-149-08696-4(3)); 298p. pap. 28.75 (978-1-146-46508-0(0)) BiblioBazaar.
Davis, James John. The Iron Puddler: My Life in the Rolling Mills & What Came of It... 2012. 296p. pap. 28.75 **(978-1-273-95025-1(X))** BiblioBazaar.
Lamacchia, Joe & Samburg, Bridget. Blue Collar & Proud of It: The All-In-One Resource for Finding Freedom, Financial Success, & Security Outside the Cubicle. 2009. (ENG.). 432p. pap. 15.95 (978-0-7573-0778-2(7)) Health Communications, Inc.
Lepadatu/Janoski. Diversity at Kaizen Motors: Gender, Race, Age & Insecurity in a Japanese Auto Transplant. 2011. (ENG.). 160p. 65.00 **(978-0-7618-5594-1(7))**; pap. 26.95 **(978-0-7618-5593-4(9))** Univ. Pr. of America, Inc.

Palm. The Flight from Work. 2008. 232p. pap. 31.99 (978-0-521-06846-8(0)) Cambridge Univ. Pr.
Torlina, Jeff. Working Class: Challenging Myths about Blue-Collar Labor. 2011. 200p. 55.00 (978-1-58826-756-6(3)) Rienner, Lynne Pubs.
Wank, Rolf. Arbeiter und Angestellte: Zur Unterscheidung im Arbeits- und Sozialversicherungsrecht. (GER.). XLIV, 522p. 404.00 **(978-3-11-181009-6(7))** De Gruyter, Walter Inc.

BLUE-GLASS CURE
see Phototherapy

BLUE-GREEN ALGAE
see Cyanobacteria

BLUE-GREEN BACTERIA
see Cyanobacteria

BLUE JACKET (SHAWNEE CHIEF)
Calloway, Colin G. The Shawnees & the War for America. 2008. (ENG.). 256p. (gr. 12-18). 14.00 (978-0-14-311391-1(7), Penguin (Non-Classics)) Penguin Group (USA) Inc.

BLUE LAWS
see Sunday Legislation

BLUE MOUNTAIN LAKE (N.Y.)
Hochschild, Harold K. An Adirondack Resort in the Nineteenth Century: Blue Mountain Lake, 1870-1900, Stagecoaches & Luxury Hotels. rev. ed. 2010. (Township Thirty-Four Ser.). (Illus.). reprint ed. 8.95 (978-0-910020-07-7(8)) Adirondack Museum, The.

BLUE MOUNTAINS (N.S.W.)
Tredinnick, Mark. The Blue Plateau: An Australian Pastoral. 2009. (ENG.). 256p. pap. 16.00 (978-1-57131-320-1(6)) Milkweed Editions.

BLUE NILE RIVER (ETHIOPIA AND SUDAN)
Mekonnen, Amare, et al. Ecological Implications of River Flow Modification. 2010. 124p. pap. (978-3-639-26147-9(X)) VDM Verlag Dr. Mueller e.K.

BLUE-PRINTS
see Blueprints

BLUE RIDGE MOUNTAINS
Bernstein, Danny. Hiking the Carolina Mountains. 2007. (Illus.). 360p. pap. 19.95 (978-1-889596-19-8(1)) Milestone Pr., Inc.
Coffey, Lynn. Backroads, 3 vols. 2009. (Illus.). pap. **(978-0-615-49310-7(6))** Quartet Bks., Ltd.
First, Frederick Blair, Jr. Slow Road Home: A Blue Ridge Book of Days. 2006. (Illus.). 232p. per. 15.95 (978-0-9779395-0-3(2)) Goose Creek Pr.
Hesperides. Biographical Memoirs - National Academy of Science. 2007. 292p. per. (978-1-4067-5508-4(7), Hesperides Pr.) Read Bks.
Huso, Deborah. Moon Blue Ridge & Smoky Mountains. 2010. (Moon Handbooks Ser.). (ENG., Illus.). 328p. pap. 16.95 (978-1-59880-532-1(0)) Avalon Travel Publishing.
Maynard, Charles W. The Blue Ridge Ancient & Majestic: A Celebration of the World's Oldest Mountains. 2010. (ENG.). 192p. 39.95 (978-0-9821162-2-7(5)) Mountain Trail Pr. LLC.
McClellan, John Howard. Blue Ridge Summit, the Beginnings of a Resort Era: Colonial Counterfeiters of the Blue Ridge. 2007. (Illus.). 116p. per. 14.95 (978-0-9790983-1-4(9)) Copyquik Printing & Graphics LLC.
Roberts, Mark. Blue ridge High Country from Blowing Rock to Grandfather Mountain. 2009. pap. (978-1-61623-041-8(X)) Independent Pub.
Sheppard, Muriel E. Cabins in the Laurel. 313p. reprint ed. lib. bdg. 98.00 (978-0-7222-0511-2(2)) Library Reprints, Inc.
Simmons, Nye. Best of the Blue Ridge Parkway: The Ultimate Guide to the Parkway's Best Attractions. 2008. (ENG., Illus.). 160p. pap. 19.95 (978-0-9777933-9-6(7)) Mountain Trail Pr. LLC.
Straub, Rick. Along the Way Blue Ridge Scenic, Second Edition Color: Trip Guide. 2007. (Illus.). 96p. per. 8.00 (978-0-9793269-2-9(3)) Straub, Rick.
Thomas, Evelyn L. The Great Blue Ridge Manhunt: The Missing Pieces. 2008. (Illus.). vii, 99p. (978-1-931575-72-0(X)) Old Mountain Pr.
Thomas, Jean. Blue Ridge Country. 2007. 348p. per. (978-1-4067-5537-4(0)) Read Bks.

BLUE RIDGE PARKWAY (N.C. AND VA.)
Blackley, Pat & Blackley, Chuck. Blue Ridge Parkway Simply Beautiful. 2008. 120p. 32.95 (978-1-56037-447-3(0)) Farcountry Pr.
Hall, Karen J. & Friends of the Blue Ridge Parkway. Building the Blue Ridge Parkway. 2007. (Images of America Ser.). (ENG., Illus.). 128p. per. 21.99 (978-0-7385-5287-3(9)) Arcadia Publishing.
Hargan, Jim & Hargan, J. Blue Ridge Parkway: Where to Find Perfect Shots & How to Take Them. 2010. (Photographer's Guide Ser.). (ENG., Illus.). 96p. pap. 14.95 (978-0-88150-873-4(X), 150873) Countryman Pr.
Hunter, Elizabeth C. Blue Ridge Parkway Road to Discovery. 2010. 144p. 39.95 (978-1-890483-28-9(1)) Graham, J. Scott.
Johnson, Randy. Hiking the Blue Ridge Parkway: The Ultimate Travel Guide to America's Most Popular Scenic Roadway. 2nd ed. 2010. (Hiking Guide Ser.). (ENG., Illus.). 352p. pap. 18.95 (978-0-7627-5531-8(8), Falcon Guides) Globe Pequot Pr., The.
Logue, Frank, et al. Guide to the Blue Ridge Parkway. 3rd ed. 2010. (ENG., Illus.). 160p. pap. 16.95 (978-0-89732-908-8(2)) Menasha Ridge Pr., Inc.
Maynard, Charles W. Blue Ridge Parkway: An Extraordinary Journey along the World's Oldest Mountains. 2012. (ENG., Illus.). 120p. 24.95 (978-0-9844218-0-0(7)) Mountain Trail Pr. LLC.
Pegram, Tim. The Blue Ridge Parkway by Foot: A Park Ranger's Memoir. 2007. (Contributions to Southern Appalachian Studies). (ENG., Illus.). 324p. per. 29.95 (978-0-7864-3140-3(7)) McFarland & Co., Inc. Pubs.
Simmons, Nye. Best of the Blue Ridge Parkway: The Ultimate Guide to the Parkway's Best Attractions. 2008. (ENG., Illus.). 160p. pap. 19.95 (978-0-9777933-9-6(7)) Mountain Trail Pr. LLC.
Whisnant, Anne Mitchell. Super-Scenic Motorway: A Blue Ridge Parkway History. (ENG., Illus.). 464p. 2010. pap. 22.00 (978-0-8078-7126-3(5)) 2006. 38.95 (978-0-8078-3037-6(2)) Univ. of North Carolina Pr.
Wilkerson, Lyn. Slow Travels-Blue Ridge Parkway. 2010. 171p. pap. 16.99 (978-0-557-13223-2(1)) Lulu Enterprises Inc.

BLUE SKY LAWS
see Securities

BLUE TONGUE
see Bluetongue

BLUEBERRIES
Hancock, J. F. & Retamales, Jorge B. Blueberries. 2012. (Crop Production Science in Horticulture Ser.). (Illus.). 336p. pap. 85.00 **(978-1-84593-826-0(7))** CABI GBR. Dist: Stylus Publishing, LLC.
Keeler, Chelsey, compiled by. Peek-A-Blue berry farm. A collection of classic blueberry recipes from across the United States: A collection of classic blueberry recipes from across the United States. 2006. per. 24.95 (978-1-4276-0081-3(3)) Aardvark Global Publishing.
Nixon (Ahdanah), Leticia Roa. Blueberry Lady: The Story of Elizabeth Coleman White 1871-1954. 2009. 32p. pap. 12.99 (978-1-4389-9287-7(4)) AuthorHouse.
Trehane, Jennifer. Blueberries, Cranberries & Other Vacciniums. 2009. (ENG.). 272p. pap. 29.95 (978-1-60469-072-9(0), 1604690720) Timber Pr., Inc.
Wright, Virginia. The Wild Blueberry Book, 1 vol. 2011. (ENG.). 32p. 14.95 (978-0-89272-939-5(2)) Down East Bks.

BLUEGRASS MUSIC
Adler, Thomas A. Bean Blossom: The Brown County Jamboree & Bill Monroe's Bluegrass Festivals. 2011. (Music in American Life Ser.). (ENG., Illus.). 288p. 75.00 (978-0-252-03615-6(8)); pap. 24.95 (978-0-252-07810-1(1)) Univ. of Illinois Pr.
Anger, Darol. All-Star Bluegrass Jam-along: For Fiddle. 2009. (ENG.). 44p. pap. 19.95 incl. audio compact disk (978-1-59773-127-0(7), 1597731277) Homespun Video.
Bruce, Dix. Parking Lot Picker's Songbook: Guitar Edition, 1 vol. 2007. (ENG., Illus.). 304p. spiral bd. 29.95 (978-0-7866-7498-5(9)) Mel Bay Pubns., Inc.
—Parking Lot Picker's Songbook: Mandolin Edition, 1 vol. 2007. (ENG., Illus.). 304p. spiral bd. 29.95 (978-0-7866-7492-3(X)) Mel Bay Pubns., Inc.
Carr, Joe. Mel Bay's School of Mandolin: Bluegrass Classics. 2011. (ENG.). 32p. audio compact disk 14.99 **(978-0-7866-8261-4(2))** Mel Bay Pubns., Inc.
Claypool, James C. Kentucky's Bluegrass Music. 2010. (Images of America Ser.). (ENG., Illus.). 128p. pap. 21.99 (978-0-7385-8561-1(0)) Arcadia Publishing.
Collins, Eddie. ASAP Bluegrass Guitar: Learn How to Play the Bluegrass Way. 2011. (ENG.). 128p. pap. 22.99 incl. audio compact disk **(978-1-57424-275-1(X)**, 157424275X) Centerstream Publishing.
Collins, Eddie. Introduction to Bluegrass Banjo, 1 vol. 2007. (ENG., Illus.). 112p. spiral bd. 22.95 (978-0-7866-7290-5(0)) Mel Bay Pubns., Inc.
Collins, Todd. Classic Bluegrass Solos for Mandolin, 1 vol. 2007. (ENG.). 48p. pap. 17.95 (978-0-7866-7653-8(1), 20551) Mel Bay Pubns., Inc.
Crowley, Lisle. Flatpicking Bluegrass Guitar. 2010. (ENG.). 48p. pap. 12.99 incl. audio compact disk (978-1-4234-9769-1(4), 1423497694) Leonard, Hal Corp.
Dailey and Vincent. The Dailey & Vincent Songbook. 2010. (ENG.). 72p. pap. 16.99 (978-1-4234-9078-4(9), 1423490789) Leonard, Hal Corp.
Davis, Janet. Mel Bay's School of Banjo: Bluegrass Melodic Style. 2011. (ENG.). 94p. audio compact disk 19.99 **(978-0-7866-8270-6(1))** Mel Bay Pubns., Inc.
Erbsen, Wayne. The Bluegrass Gospel Songbook. 2007. (Illus.). 172p. per. (978-1-883206-52-9(9)) Native Ground Music, Inc.
Fleischhauer, Carl & Rosenberg, Neil V. Bluegrass Odyssey: A Documentary in Pictures & Words, 1966-86. 2006. (Music in American Life Ser.). (Illus.). 208p. per. 29.95 (978-0-252-07400-4(9)) Univ. of Illinois Pr.
Flinner, Matt. All-Star Bluegrass Jam-along: For Mandolin. 2012. (ENG.). 67p. pap. 19.95 incl. audio compact disk (978-1-59773-126-3(9), 1597731269) Homespun Video.
Fuhrman Bragg, Elizabeth. Vernon's Vault of Vintage Vinyl. 2008. 120p. pap. (978-3-639-02545-3(8)) VDM Verlag Dr. Mueller e.K.
Glazer, Matt. Vassar Clements Fiddle. 2008. (ENG.). 64p. pap. 17.95 (978-0-8256-0223-8(8), 0825602238) Music Sales Corp.
Grant, Bob. The Gig Bag Book of Mandolin Chords. 2009. (ENG.). 148p. pap. 14.99 (978-0-8256-3697-4(3), 0825636973) Music Sales Corp.
—Starting Bluegrass Mandolin. 2007. (Illus.). 48p. pap. 14.95 incl. audio compact disk (978-0-8256-0351-8(X), Oak Pubns.) Music Sales Corp.
Grier, David. All-Star Bluegrass Jam-along: For Guitar. 2008. (ENG.). 75p. pap. 19.95 incl. audio compact disk (978-1-59773-124-9(2), 1597731242) Homespun Video.
Hal Leonard Corp., creator. The Real Bluegrass Book: C Instruments. 2011. (ENG.). 432p. pap. 29.99 (978-0-634-04921-7(6), 0634049216) Leonard, Hal Corp.
Hal Leonard Corporation Staff, creator. The Big Book of Bluegrass Songs. 2008. (ENG.). 224p. pap. 19.95 (978-1-4234-5613-1(0), 1423456130) Leonard, Hal Corp.
—Bluegrass Classics: Violin Play-along Volume 11. 2011. (ENG.). 40p. pap. 14.99 incl. audio compact disk (978-1-4234-4734-4(4), 1423447344) Leonard, Hal Corp.
—Bluegrass Favorites: Violin Play-along Volume 10, 1 vol. 2010. (ENG.). 48p. pap. 14.99 incl. audio compact disk (978-1-4234-4733-7(6), 1423447336) Leonard, Hal Corp.
Hatfield, Jack, ed. Bluegrass Band Method, Bk. 2. l.t. ed. pap. 15.00 incl. audio compact disk (978-1-892531-05-6(4), CCD) Hatfield Music.
Kaufman, Steve. My First Bluegrass Guitar Picking Songs Book/CD Set, 1 vol. 2010. (ENG.). 36p. pap. 17.99 (978-0-7866-8213-3(2)) Mel Bay Pubns., Inc.
—Steve Kaufman's Four-Hour Bluegrass Workout - Series Two: Book/4-CD Pack. 2008. (ENG.). 105p. pap. 44.95 incl. audio compact disk (978-1-59773-239-0(7), 1597732397) Homespun Video.
Kaufman, Steve & Ottway, Conny. My First Fiddle Picking Songs. 2011. (ENG.). 39p. pap. 17.99 incl. audio compact disk **(978-0-7866-8298-0(1))** Mel Bay Pubns., Inc.
Ledgin, Stephanie P. Homegrown Music: Discovering Bluegrass. 2006. (Music in American Life Ser.). (Illus.). 224p. per. 20.95 (978-0-252-07376-2(2)) Univ. of Illinois Pr.
McCabe, Larry. 101 Three-Chord Country & Bluegrass Songs: For Guitar, Banjo & Uke, 1 vol. 2008. (ENG.). 144p. pap. 14.95 (978-0-7866-7708-5(2)) Mel Bay Pubns., Inc.
McGill, Terry. Alternate Tunings for Five-String Banjo Played Bluegrass Style, 1 vol. 2008. (ENG.). 72p. pap. 19.95 (978-0-7866-7438-1(5)) Mel Bay Pubns., Inc.
Munde, Alan. Getting into Bluegrass Banjo, 1 vol. 2007. (Getting Into Ser.). (ENG., Illus.). 96p. pap. 17.95 (978-0-7866-7557-9(8)) Mel Bay Pubns., Inc.
Noles, Randy. Fiddler's Curse: The Untold Story of Ervin T. Rouse, Chubby Wise, Johnny Cash & the Orange Blossom Special. 2007. (ENG., Illus.). 226p. per. 14.95 (978-1-57424-214-0(8), 1574242148) Centerstream Publishing.
Nygaard, Scott. Bluegrass Guitar Essentials: Learn to Play Bass Runs, Fiddle Tunes, Bluesy Solos, & More. 2007. (Acoustic Guitar's Private Lessons Ser.). (ENG., Illus.). 72p. pap. 19.95 incl. audio compact disk (978-1-4234-0841-3(1), 1423408411) String Letter Publishing.
Patton, Jeff. A Bluegrass State of Mind. 2011. 30p. pap. 16.95 **(978-1-4560-5619-3(0))** PublishAmerica, Inc.
Phillips, Todd. All-Star Bluegrass Jam-along: For Bass. 2007. (ENG.). 34p. pap. 19.95 incl. audio compact disk (978-1-59773-128-7(5), 1597731285) Homespun Video.
Piazza, Tom. True Adventures with the King of Bluegrass: Jimmy Martin. 2009. (ENG., Illus.). 112p. pap. 12.95 (978-0-8265-1680-0(7)) Vanderbilt Univ. Pr.
Roller, Robin. Starting Bluegrass Banjo: The Definitive Step-by-Step Guide to Playing 5-String Banjo. 2007. (Illus.). 47p. pap. 14.95 incl. audio compact disk (978-0-8256-0352-5(8), Oak Pubns.) Music Sales Corp.
Rubner-Peterson, Jasper. Mandolin Picker's Guide to Bluegrass Improvisation Book/CD Set, 1 vol. 2010. (ENG.). 200p. pap. 24.99 (978-0-7866-8237-9(X)) Mel Bay Pubns., Inc.
Schmid, Will, et al. Hal Leonard Banjo Method - Book 2: For 5-String Banjo. 2nd rev. ed. 2011. (ENG.). 64p. pap. 16.99 incl. audio compact disk **(978-1-4234-6318-4(8)**, 1423463188) Leonard, Hal Corp.
Senyak, Zhenya Gene. Banjo Camp! Learning, Picking & Jamming with Bluegrass & Old-Time Greats. 2008. (ENG., Illus.). 152p. 21.95 (978-1-60059-282-9(1)) Lark Bks.
Smith, Javonda. Bill Monroe & Friends (Inside the Life of Bill Monroe) 2008. pap. 12.95 (978-0-7414-4936-8(6)) Infinity Publishing.
Stanley, Ralph & Dean, Eddie. Man of Constant Sorrow: My Life & Times. 2010. (ENG.). 464p. (gr. 12). 18.00 (978-1-59240-584-8(3), Gotham) Penguin Group (USA) Inc.
Trischka, Tony. All-Star Bluegrass Jam-along: For Banjo. 2007. (ENG.). 43p. pap. 19.95 incl. audio compact disk (978-1-59773-125-6(0), 1597731250) Homespun Video.
Warlick, Tom & Warlick, Lucy. The WBT Briarhoppers: Eight Decades of a Bluegrass Band Made for Radio. 2007. (ENG., Illus.). 215p. per. 35.00 (978-0-7864-3144-1(X)) McFarland & Co., Inc. Pubs.

BLUEPRINTS
Bennett, A. E. & Siy, Louis J. Blueprint Reading for Welders. 8th ed. 2008. (ENG., Illus.). 432p. (C). spiral bd. 109.95 (978-1-4283-3528-8(5)) Delmar Cengage Learning.
Bisharat, Keith A. Construction Graphics: A Practical Guide to Interpreting Working Drawings. 2nd ed. 2008. (ENG., Illus.). 480p. 115.00 (978-0-470-13750-5(9), Wiley) Wiley, John & Sons, Inc.
Brown, Walter C. & Brown, Ryan K. Print Reading for Industry: Power Point Presentations, Site License. 2010. cd-rom 600.00 (978-1-60525-312-1(X)) Goodheart-Willcox Pub.
—Print Reading for Industry Electronic Prints-Classroom Network License. 2010. cd-rom 166.40 (978-1-60525-314-5(6)) Goodheart-Willcox Pub.
—Print Reading for Industry Electronic Prints-Individual License. 2010. cd-rom 33.28 (978-1-60525-313-8(8)) Goodheart-Willcox Pub.
—Print Reading for Industry ExamView Assessment Suite. 2010. cd-rom 240.00 (978-1-60525-310-7(3)) Goodheart-Willcox Pub.
—Print Reading for Industry Instructor's CD. 2010. cd-rom 98.00 (978-1-60525-309-1(X)) Goodheart-Willcox Pub.
—Print Reading for Industry PowerPoint Presentations-Individual License. 2010. cd-rom 240.00 (978-1-60525-311-4(1)) Goodheart-Willcox Pub.
Brown, Walter Charles & Brown, Ryan K. Print Reading for Industry. 9th ed. 2010. (ENG.). 523p. (gr. 9-14). pap. 88.00 (978-1-60525-308-4(1)) Goodheart-Willcox Pub.
Brown, Walter Charles & Dorfmueller, Daniel P. Print Reading for Construction: Residential & Commercial: Write-In Text with 130 Large Prints. 6th ed. 2012. **(978-1-60525-802-7(4))** Goodheart-Willcox Pub.
Corgan, Kevin. Print Reading for Welding & Fabrication. 2010. (ENG., Illus.). 304p. (C). pap. 109.80 (978-0-13-502817-9(5), Prentice Hall) Prentice Hall PTR.
Fowlie, Frank. Evaluating Ombudsman Operations. 2011. 476p. pap. **(978-3-8443-1448-9(2))** Lambert Academic Publishing.
Joyce, Michael A. Blueprint Reading & Drafting for Plumbers. 2nd ed. 2008. (ENG.). 208p. (C). pap. 116.95 (978-1-4283-3513-4(7)) Delmar Cengage Learning.
Kubba, Sam. Blueprint Reading: Construction Drawings for the Building Trades. 2008. (ENG., Illus.). 384p. pap. 49.95 (978-0-07-154986-8(2), 0071549862) McGraw-Hill Professional Publishing.
Lammey, W. Clyde. How to Read Blueprints. 2011. 98p. 38.95 **(978-1-258-07580-4(6))** Literary Licensing, LLC.
Madsen, David A., et al. Print Reading for Architecture & Construction Technology. 3rd ed. 2012. (ENG.). 416p. (C). pap. 157.95 **(978-1-133-12727-7(4))** Delmar Cengage Learning.
Miller, Frank & Moravek, Joseph. Blueprints & Plans for HVAC. 3rd ed. 2008. (ENG.). 320p. (C). pap. 149.95 (978-1-4283-3520-2(X)) Delmar Cengage Learning.
Miller, R. T. Printreading: Based on the 2002 NEC: Answer Key. 5.00 (978-0-8269-1564-1(7)) American Technical Pubs., Inc.
Olivo, Thomas P. & Olivo, C. Thomas. Basic Blueprint Reading & Sketching. 9th ed. 2010. (ENG.). 304p. (C). pap. 117.95 (978-1-4354-8378-1(2)) Delmar Cengage Learning.
Russell, Ron. Print & Specifications Reading for Construction. 2011. (ENG.). 240p. 95.00 **(978-0-470-87941-2(6)**, Wiley) Wiley, John & Sons, Inc.
Schultz, Russ & Smith, Larry. Blueprint Reading for Machine Trades. 7th rev. ed. 2011. (ENG.). 408p. (C). pap. 68.00 **(978-0-13-217220-2(8)**, Prentice Hall) Prentice Hall PTR.
Schultz, Russ & Smith, Larry. Blueprint Reading for the Machine Trades. 6th rev. ed. 2008. (ENG., Illus.). 408p. (C). pap. 73.60 (978-0-13-503878-9(2), Prentice Hall) Prentice Hall PTR.
Walsh, Harold VanDervoort, et al. Blueprint Reading Made Easy. 2011. 602p. 64.95 **(978-1-258-06403-7(0))** Literary Licensing, LLC.
Yamin, Edward. Blueprint Reading & Estimating: Ecmn 131 & Ecmn 132. rev. ed. 2009. (ENG.). 9p. ring bd. 63.00 (978-0-7575-6458-1(5)) Kendall Hunt Publishing Co.
Zachariason, Rob. Blueprint Reading for Electricians. 3rd ed. 2009. (ENG.). 464p. (C). 94.95 (978-1-4354-9119-9(X)) Delmar Cengage Learning.

BLUES (MUSIC)
see also Spirituals (Songs)
Alfred Publishing Staff. Blues Guitar Tracks: Book & mp3 CD. 2012. (Guitar Tracks Ser.). (ENG.). 80p. pap. 14.99 **(978-0-7390-8602-5(2))** Alfred Publishing Co., Inc.
—Blues Soloing Strategies for Guitar: Modern Ideas for All Styles, Book & CD. 2011. (Improv Ser.). (ENG.). 96p. pap. 19.99 **(978-0-7390-8253-9(1))** Alfred Publishing Co., Inc.
—Classical Jazz Rags & Blues, Bk 5. 2012. (Classical Jazz, Rags & Blues Ser.: Bk 5). (ENG.). 24p. pap. 6.99 **(978-0-7390-8921-7(8))** Alfred Publishing Co., Inc.
—Complete Blues Guitar Method: Complete, Book & CD. 2010. (ENG.). 312p. pap. 29.99 (978-0-7390-6636-2(6)) Alfred Publishing Co., Inc.
—Down & Out: Conductor Score & Parts. 2011. (Eighth Note Publications). (ENG.). 68p. pap. 45.00 **(978-1-55473-736-9(2))** Alfred Publishing Co., Inc.
—Guitar World — How to Play Blues & Blues Rock Guitar: The Ultimate DVD Guide, DVD. 2009. (Guitar World Ser.). (ENG.). 14.95 (978-0-7390-5904-3(1)) Alfred Publishing Co., Inc.
—PLAY Blues Guitar 1: The Ultimate Multimedia Instructor, DVD. 2009. (Play Ser.). (ENG.). 19.99 (978-0-7390-6572-3(6)) Alfred Publishing Co., Inc.
—Real Blues Guitar: Book & DVD. rev. ed. 2010. (ENG.). 80p. pap. 19.99 (978-0-7390-6517-4(3)) Alfred Publishing Co., Inc.
—Slow Dog Blues: Sheet. 2011. (Signature Ser.). (ENG.). 4p. pap. 2.99 **(978-0-7390-8712-1(6))** Alfred Publishing Co., Inc.
—Ultimate Beginner Blues Guitar Basics: Steps One & Two, Book & CD. rev. ed. 2011. (Ultimate Beginner Ser.). (ENG.). 48p. pap. 12.99 **(978-0-7390-8200-3(0))** Alfred Publishing Co., Inc.
Alfred Publishing Staff & Liston, Matthew. The Total Blues Bassist: A Fun & Comprehensive Overview of Blues Bass Playing, Book & CD. 2008. (Total Bassist Ser.). (ENG.). 128p. pap. 19.95 (978-0-7390-5267-9(5)) Alfred Publishing Co., Inc.
Alfred Publishing Staff & Natter, Frank. The Blues Guitar Experience: Your practical guide to the landmark styles of blues, Book & CD. 2009. (ENG.). 48p. pap. 16.95 (978-0-7390-6011-7(2)) Alfred Publishing Co., Inc.
All You Need Is Love. 2008. (ENG.). 99.95 (978-1-4234-5664-3(5), 1423456645) Leonard, Hal Corp.
B. B. King, Vol. 100. 2009. (ENG.). 56p. pap. 16.99 incl. audio compact disk (978-1-4234-5193-8(7), 1423451937) Leonard, Hal Corp.
B. B. King - Master Bluesman. deluxe ed. 2010. (ENG.). 80p. pap. 24.99 incl. audio compact disk (978-1-4234-2574-8(X), 142342574X) Leonard, Hal Corp.

Barrett, David. Blues Drums Play-along Trax, 1 vol. 2006. (School of the Blues Ser.). (ENG., Illus.). 24p. pap. 14.95 *(978-0-7866-7388-9(5)*, 21067BCD) Mel Bay Pubns., Inc.

—Blues Harmonica Method, Level 1, 1 vol. 2006. (School of the Blues Ser.). (ENG., Illus.). 32p. pap. 14.95 *(978-0-7866-7316-2(8)*, 21053bcd) Mel Bay Pubns., Inc.

—Blues Harmonica Play-along Trax: Play-along Tracks for Developing Your Rhythm & Lead Blues Harmonica Skills, 1 vol. 2006. (School of the Blues Ser.). (ENG., Illus.). 24p. pap. 14.95 *(978-0-7866-7393-3(1)*, 21055bcd) Mel Bay Pubns., Inc.

—Blues Keyboard Method, Level 1, 1 vol. 2006. (School of the Blues Ser.). (ENG., Illus.). 48p. pap. 14.95 *(978-0-7866-7532-6(2)*, 21060bcd) Mel Bay Pubns., Inc.

—Blues Keyboard Play-along Trax, 1 vol. 2006. (School of the Blues Ser.). (ENG., Illus.). 24p. pap. 14.95 *(978-0-7866-7391-9(5)*, 21062bcd) Mel Bay Pubns., Inc.

Barrett, David & Coggins, Kevin. Blues Drums Method: An Essential Study of Blues Drums for the Beginning to Advanced Player, 1 vol. 2006. (School of the Blues Ser.). (ENG., Illus.). 56p. pap. 14.95 *(978-0-7866-7614-9(0)*, 21066bcd) Mel Bay Pubns., Inc.

Barrett, David & De Rose, Frank. Blues Bass Method: An Essential Study of Blues Bass for the Beginning to Intermediate Player, 1 vol. 2006. (School of the Blues Ser.). (ENG.). 40p. pap. 14.95 *(978-0-7866-7531-9(4)*, 21063bcd) Mel Bay Pubns., Inc.

—Blues Bass Play-along Trax: Play-along Tracks for Developing Your Blues Bass Performance Skills, 1 vol. 2006. (School of the Blues Ser.). (ENG., Illus.). 24p. pap. 14.95 *(978-0-7866-7390-2(7)*, 21064bcd) Mel Bay Pubns., Inc.

Barrett, David & Garcia, John. Blues Guitar Method, Level 1: An Essential Study of Blues Accompaniment Guitar for All Skill-Level Players, 1 vol. 2006. (School of the Blues Ser.). (ENG., Illus.). 48p. pap. 14.95 *(978-0-7866-7530-2(6)*, 21057bcd) Mel Bay Pubns., Inc.

—Blues Guitar Method, Level 2, 1 vol. 2008. (ENG.). 40p. pap. 14.95 *(978-0-7866-7638-5(8))* Mel Bay Pubns., Inc.

—Improvising Blues Harmonica, 1 vol. 2008. (ENG.). 80p. pap. 19.95 *(978-0-7866-7321-6(4))* Mel Bay Pubns., Inc.

Bay, William. Modern Guitar Method, Grade 1: Blues Jam Play-along, 1 vol. 2007. (Modern Guitar Method (Mel Bay) Ser.). (ENG.). 16p. pap. 12.95 *(978-0-7866-7769-6(4))* Mel Bay Pubns., Inc.

Beston, Nick. Improvising Blues Saxophone. 2010. (ENG.). 140p. pap. 29.95 incl. audio compact disk *(978-1-84761-147-5(8)*, 1847611478) Schott Music Corp.

Blue Album. (Butterfly Bks.). (ARA., Illus.). 12.95 *(978-0-86685-713-0(3))* International Bk. Ctr., Inc.

Blues. (Easy Keyboard Library). (Illus.). 48p. 9.95 *(978-1-85909-315-3(9)*, Warner Bros. Pubns.) Alfred Publishing Co., Inc.

Blues & Rock Improvising Made Easy. pap. 6.95 *(978-0-918321-93-0(X))* Musical I Pr.

Bradley, David. The Blues Guitar Chord Deck. 2006. (ENG., Illus.). 46p. pap. 9.95 *(978-0-8256-3538-0(1)*, 0825635381) Music Sales Corp.

—The Blues Guitar Scale Deck. 2006. (ENG., Illus.). 96p. pap. 9.99 *(978-0-8256-3537-3(3)*, 0825635373) Music Sales Corp.

Bruce, Dix. Backup Trax: Basic Blues for Guitar, 1 vol. 2007. (Backup Trax Ser.). (ENG., Illus.). 48p. pap. 14.95 *(978-0-7866-7669-9(8))* Mel Bay Pubns., Inc.

Bruce, Jack, et al. Jack Bruce & Robin Trower - Seven Moons Live. 2009. (ENG.). 24.95 *(978-1-4234-9050-0(9)*, 1423490509) Leonard, Hal Corp.

Bruno Mars - Doo-Wops & Hooligans: Easy Piano. 2011. (ENG.). 72p. pap. 14.99 *(978-1-4584-0286-8(X)*, 145840286X) Leonard, Hal Corp.

Caldwell, Jennifer Shelton. The Abc's of the Mississippi Blues. 2009. 68p. pap. 25.49 *(978-1-4389-3211-8(1))* AuthorHouse.

Carter, Doug. Cool Fool: Blues Rockin' in the Hammer. 2010. (ENG., Illus.). 171p. pap. 22.95 *(978-0-9808879-8-3(4))* Seraphim Editions CAN. Dist: Univ. of Toronto Pr.

Cartwright, Joan. Joan Cartwright Song Book. 2009. 156p. pap. 24.99 *(978-0-557-04454-2(5))* Lulu Enterprises Inc.

Chiarello, Gianni. Contemporary Blues Soloing. 2010. 68p. pap. 31.50 *(978-1-4452-5888-1(9))* Lulu Enterprises Inc.

Cohen, David. Learn to Play Blues Piano. 2008. (ENG.). 89.95 *(978-1-59773-245-1(1)*, 1597732451) Homespun Video.

Cohen, John. The High & Lonesome Sound. 2012. (ENG., Illus.). 270p. pap. 58.00 *(978-3-86930-254-6(2))* Steidl, Gerhard Druckerei und Verlag DEU. Dist: Innovative Logistics.

Collins, Albert. Albert Collins: Blues Play-along Volume 9. 2011. (ENG.). 72p. pap. 12.99 incl. audio compact disk *(978-1-4234-8707-4(9)*, 1423487079) Leonard, Hal Corp.

—Albert Collins - in Concert. 2008. (ENG.). 19.95 *(978-1-4234-4356-8(X)*, 142344356X) Leonard, Hal Corp.

DelGrosso, Rich. Blues Guitar Lesson Anthology: A Guide to Playing Genuine Houserockin' Music. 2010. (ENG.). 104p. pap. 19.99 incl. audio compact disk *(978-1-4234-8165-2(8)*, 1423481658) Leonard, Hal Corp.

Derek Trucks - Already Free. 2010. (ENG.). 168p. pap. 24.99 *(978-1-60378-188-6(9)*, 1603781889) Cherry Lane Music Co.

Douglas, Kelly Brown. Black Bodies & the Black Church: A Blues Slant. 2012. (Black Religion/Womanist Thought/Social Justice Ser.). (ENG., Illus.). 224p. 85.00 ***(978-0-230-11681-8(7))*** Palgrave Macmillan.

Dowling, Mike. Bottleneck Blues & Beyond. 2008. 49.95 *(978-1-59773-248-2(6)*, 1597732486) Homespun Video.

Dutkanicz, David. A First Book of Blues: 16 Arrangements for the Beginning Pianist. 2011. (Dover Music for Piano Ser.). (ENG.). 48p. pap. 5.95 *(978-0-486-48129-6(8))* Dover Pubns., Inc.

Ek, Al. Beginning Blues Guitar: Rhythm & Solos. 2011. (ENG.). 32p. pap. 19.99 ***(978-1-60378-376-7(8)***, 1603783768) Cherry Lane Music Co.

Felten, Buzz. Blues by the Bar - Master Class with Buzz Felten. 2011. (ENG.). 48p. pap. 12.99 incl. audio compact disk ***(978-1-60378-262-3(1)***, 1603782621) Cherry Lane Music Co.

Felten, Buzz, et al. Join the Jam: With Buzz Felten, Reggie Mcbride, John JT Thomas, & Steve Ferrone. 2011. (ENG.). 24p. pap. 9.99 incl. audio compact disk *(978-1-60378-287-6(7)*, 1603782877) Cherry Lane Music Co.

Ford, Robert. Blues Bibliography. 2nd rev. ed. 2007. 800p. 210.00 *(978-0-415-97887-3(4))* Routledge.

Foster Stovel, Nora, ed. Jane Austen Sings the Blues. 2009. (ENG., Illus.). 304p. pap. 26.95 *(978-0-88864-510-4(4))* Univ. of Alberta Pr. CAN. Dist: Michigan State Univ. Pr.

Friedland, Ed. Blues Jam: 40 Progressions & Grooves. 2008. (ENG.). 24p. pap. 19.99 incl. audio compact disk *(978-1-4234-4680-4(1)*, 1423446801) Leonard, Hal Corp.

Gallagher, Rory. The Essential Rory Gallagher - Vol. 1. 2009. (ENG.). pap. 22.99 *(978-1-4234-8906-1(3)*, 1423489063) Music Sales Corp.

—Essential Rory Gallagher Tab, Vol. 1. 2009. (ENG.). 128p. pap. 22.99 *(978-1-84772-381-9(0)*, 1847723810) Music Sales Corp.

—The Essential Rory Gallagher: the Complete Taste. 2010. (ENG.). 152p. pap. 24.99 *(978-1-84938-514-5(9)*, 1849385149) Music Sales Corp.

Garcia John, contrib. by. Blues Guitar Play-along Trax, 1 vol. 2006. (School of the Blues Ser.). (ENG., Illus.). 24p. pap. 14.95 *(978-0-7866-7392-6(3)*, 21059bcd) Mel Bay Pubns., Inc.

Garwood, Donald. The Masters of Instrumental Blues Guitar. (Illus.). 78p. pap. *(978-0-8256-0001-2(4)*, OK61960) Omnibus Pr.

Gelling, Peter. Beginner Blues Guitar: For Beginners. 2008. 80p. pap. incl. audio compact disk *(978-1-86469-380-5(0))* Koala Music Publications.

Gindick, Jon. Country & Blues Harmonica for the Musically Hopeless: Revised Book & 73-Minute CD. 2011. (ENG.). 112p. pap. 19.95 incl. audio compact disk ***(978-0-930948-18-4(1)***, 0930948181) Cross Harp Pr.

Gleason, David. Total* the Total Blues Keyboardist: A Fun & Comprehensive Overview of Blues Keyboard Playing, Book & CD. 2011. (Total Keyboardist Ser.). (ENG.). 128p. pap. 19.99 *(978-0-7390-7524-1(1))* Alfred Publishing Co., Inc.

Glover, Tony. The Blues Harp. 2008. (ENG., Illus.). 72p. (Orig.). pap. 21.95 *(978-0-8256-0018-0(9)*, 0825600189) Music Sales Corp.

Gress, Jesse. Blues Lick Factory: Building Great Blues Riffs. 2007. (ENG.). 144p. pap. 19.99 incl. disk *(978-0-87930-913-8(X)*, 087930913X, Backbeat Books) Leonard, Hal Corp.

Grossman, Stefan, ed. Anthology of Country Blues Guitar: Authentic Guitar Tab. 2007. (Stefan Grossman's Early Masters of American Blues Guitar Ser.). (ENG., Illus.). 88p. pap. 19.95 *(978-0-7390-4328-8(5))* Alfred Publishing Co., Inc.

—Mississippi John Hurt. 2007. (Stefan Grossman's Early Masters of American Blues Guitar Ser.). (ENG., Illus.). 96p. pap. 21.95 *(978-0-7390-4330-1(7))* Alfred Publishing Co., Inc.

Guy, Buddy. Buddy Guy Anthology. 2010. (ENG.). 208p. pap. 24.99 *(978-1-4234-7573-6(9)*, 1423475739) Leonard, Hal Corp.

Hal Leonard Corp. Blue Classics: Guitar Play-along Volume 95. 2011. (ENG.). 56p. pap. 14.99 incl. audio compact disk ***(978-1-4234-5346-8(8)***, 1423453468) Leonard, Hal Corp.

Hal Leonard Corp., creator. Blues Classics: Violin Play-along Volume 14. 2010. (ENG.). 24p. pap. 14.99 incl. audio compact disk *(978-1-4234-8646-6(3)*, 1423486463) Leonard, Hal Corp.

—Blues Classics - Harmonica Play-along Volume 10 Book/cd (diatonic Harmonica) 2011. (ENG.). pap. 14.99 incl. audio compact disk *(978-1-4234-2614-1(2)*, 1423426142) Leonard, Hal Corp.

—Blues Instrumentals: Guitar Play-along Volume 91. 2010. (ENG.). 56p. pap. 14.99 incl. audio compact disk *(978-1-4234-5342-0(5)*, 1423453425) Leonard, Hal Corp.

—Blues Rock: Bass Play-along Volume 18. 2010. (ENG.). 72p. pap. 14.99 incl. audio compact disk *(978-1-4234-1451-3(9)*, 1423414519) Leonard, Hal Corp.

—Chicken Soup for the Soul Piano Songbook: 40 Inspirational & Heartwarming Songs. 2010. (ENG.). 240p. pap. 19.99 *(978-1-4234-8549-0(1)*, 1423485491) Leonard, Hal Corp.

—Christmas Blues: Blues Play-along Volume 11. 2010. (ENG.). 72p. pap. 12.99 incl. audio compact disk *(978-1-4234-9471-3(7)*, 1423494717) Leonard, Hal Corp.

—The Real Blues Book: C Instruments. 2011. (ENG.). 480p. pap. 34.99 *(978-1-4234-0451-4(3)*, 1423404513) Leonard, Hal Corp.

Hal Leonard Corporation Staff. Blues Rock: Boss eBand Guitar Play-along Volume 4. 2010. (ENG.). 96p. pap. 29.99 *(978-1-4234-9409-6(1)*, 1423494091) Leonard, Hal Corp.

—Chicago Blues: Harmonica Play-along Volume 9. 2012. (ENG.). 56p. pap. 14.99 incl. audio compact disk *(978-1-4234-2613-4(4)*, 1423426134) Leonard, Hal Corp.

Hal Leonard Corporation Staff, creator. Best Blues Guitar Songs Ever. 2007. (ENG.). 184p. per. 19.95 *(978-1-4234-5180-8(5)*, 1423451805) Leonard, Hal Corp.

—Blues, Vol. 9. 2007. (ENG., Illus.). 56p. pap. 14.99 incl. audio compact disk *(978-1-4234-1422-3(5)*, 1423414225) Leonard, Hal Corp.

—Blues & Soul Christmas. 2008. (ENG.). 112p. pap. 12.95 *(978-1-4234-5682-7(3)*, 1423456823) Leonard, Hal Corp.

—Blues Classics: Blues Play-along Volume 8. 2011. (ENG.). 72p. pap. 12.99 incl. audio compact disk *(978-1-4234-8703-6(6)*, 1423487036) Leonard, Hal Corp.

—Blues Guitar Tab White Pages. 2008. (ENG.). 1,104p. per. 29.99 *(978-1-4234-2771-1(8)*, 1423427718) Leonard, Hal Corp.

—Blues Songs: Budget Books. 2008. (ENG.). 352p. pap. 12.95 *(978-1-4234-3619-5(9)*, 1423436199) Leonard, Hal Corp.

—Blues/Rock: Harmonica Play-along Volume 3. 2009. (ENG.). 64p. pap. 14.99 incl. audio compact disk *(978-1-4234-2347-8(X)*, 142342347X) Leonard, Hal Corp.

—Bluesy Rock: Guitar Play-along Volume 73. 2010. (ENG.). 88p. pap. 16.99 incl. audio compact disk *(978-1-4234-1452-0(7)*, 1423414527) Leonard, Hal Corp.

—Chicago Blues: Blues Play-along Volume 1. 2010. (ENG.). 72p. pap. 12.99 incl. audio compact disk *(978-1-4234-5347-5(6)*, 1423453476) Leonard, Hal Corp.

—Clapton: Complete Clapton. 2008. (Guitar Recorded Versions Ser.). (ENG.). 344p. pap. 29.99 *(978-1-4234-3437-5(4)*, 1423434374) Leonard, Hal Corp.

—Jazz Blues: Blues Play-along Volume 6. 2010. (ENG.). 40p. pap. 12.99 incl. audio compact disk *(978-1-4234-8697-8(8)*, 1423486978) Leonard, Hal Corp.

—Maiden Voyage/All Blues: Jazz Play-along Volume 1A. 2010. (ENG.). 80p. pap. 15.99 incl. audio compact disk *(978-1-4234-7099-1(0)*, 1423470990) Leonard, Hal Corp.

—Shuffle Blues: Blues Play-along Volume 4. 2011. (ENG.). 72p. pap. 12.99 incl. audio compact disk *(978-1-4234-8669-5(2)*, 1423486692) Leonard, Hal Corp.

—Slow Blues: Blues Play-along Volume 3. 2010. (ENG.). 72p. pap. 12.99 incl. audio compact disk *(978-1-4234-5349-9(2)*, 1423453492) Leonard, Hal Corp.

—Texas Blues: Blues Play-along Volume 2. 2011. (ENG.). 72p. pap. 12.99 incl. audio compact disk *(978-1-4234-5348-2(4)*, 1423453484) Leonard, Hal Corp.

—Torch Songs: Women's Edition. 2008. (Hal Leonard Pro Vocal Ser.). (ENG.). 40p. pap. 14.95 incl. audio compact disk *(978-1-4234-3192-3(8)*, 1423431928) Leonard, Hal Corp.

—Torch Songs, Volume 29: Men's Edition. 2008. (Hal Leonard Pro Vocal Ser.: Vol. 29). (ENG.). 32p. pap. 14.95 incl. audio compact disk *(978-1-4234-3193-0(6)*, 1423431936) Leonard, Hal Corp.

—Uptempo Blues: Blues Play-along Volume 10. 2010. pap. 12.99 incl. audio compact disk *(978-1-4234-8708-1(7)*, 1423487087) Leonard, Hal Corp.

Hal Leonard Music Books Staff. B. B. King: Blues Play-along Volume 5, 1 vol. 2010. (ENG.). 72p. pap. 14.99 incl. audio compact disk *(978-1-4234-8670-1(6)*, 1423486706) Leonard, Hal Corp.

Hal Leonard Publications Staff. The Big Book of Blues. 2009. (ENG.). 312p. pap. 19.99 *(978-1-4234-6787-8(6)*, 1423467876) Leonard, Hal Corp.

—The Gargantuan Guitar Songbook, 1 vol. 2009. (ENG.). 432p. pap. 24.99 *(978-1-4234-8392-2(8)*, 1423483928) Leonard, Hal Corp.

Hanson, Karen. Today's Chicago Blues. 2007. (Illus.). 238p. per. 15.95 *(978-1-893121-19-5(4))* Everything Goes Media, LLC.

Harp, David. Three Minutes to Blues, Rock, & Folk Harmonica. 3rd ed. 2009. (ENG.). 96p. pap. 16.95 *(978-0-918321-89-3(1))* Musical I Pr.

—3 Minutes to Blues, Rock & Folk Harmonica. 2007. (ENG.). 96p. pap. 12.95 incl. audio compact disk *(978-0-918321-88-6(3)*, 0918321883) Music Sales Corp.

Herriges, Greg P. Blues Guitar Songs for Dummies. 2008. (For Dummies Ser.). (ENG., Illus.). 272p. per. 22.95 *(978-1-4234-2623-3(1)*, 1423426231) Leonard, Hal Corp.

Hiland, Johnny. Licks & Tricks, Volume 2, 1 vol. 2006. (ENG., Illus.). 16p. pap. 19.95 *(978-0-7866-7148-9(3)*, 20378bcd) Mel Bay Pubns., Inc.

Hogarth, Thaddeus. Funk/R&B Guitar: Creative Solos, Grooves & Sounds. 2008. (ENG., Illus.). 96p. pap. 19.95 incl. audio compact disk *(978-0-87639-091-7(2)*, 0876390912, Berklee Pr.) Leonard, Hal Corp.

Jam with the Blues Masters. 21.95 incl. audio compact disk *(978-1-85909-679-6(4)*, Warner Bros. Pubns.) Alfred Publishing Co., Inc.

James, Steve. Roots & Blues Mandolin. 2010. (ENG., Illus.). 48p. pap. 19.99 incl. audio compact disk *(978-1-890490-79-9(2)*, 1890490792) String Letter Publishing.

Joe Bonamassa - Blues Deluxe, 1 vol. 2009. (ENG.). 136p. pap. 22.99 *(978-1-60378-102-2(1)*, 1603781021) Cherry Lane Music Co.

John Mayer - Strum & Sing. 2011. (ENG.). 80p. pap. 10.99 ***(978-1-60378-330-9(X)***, 160378330X) Cherry Lane Music Co.

Jones, Stacy Holman. Torch Singing: Performing Resistance & Desire from Billie Holiday to Edith Piaf. 2007. (Ethnographic Alternatives Book Ser.). (ENG.). 228p. 80.00 *(978-0-7591-0658-1(4))* per. 26.95 *(978-0-7591-0659-8(2))* AltaMira Pr.

Laster, Marty. Getting into... Blues Violin, 1 vol. 2007. (Getting Into Ser.). (ENG., Illus.). 88p. pap. 17.95 *(978-0-7866-7588-3(8))* Mel Bay Pubns., Inc.

Latarski, Don. The Guitar Scale Picture Book. 2008. (ENG.). 156p. pap. 16.95 *(978-0-7390-5352-2(3))* Alfred Publishing Co., Inc.

Lehmann, Theo. Blues Music & Gospel Proclamation: The Extraordinary Life of a Courageous East German Pastor. Pierard, Richard V., ed. Arnold, Edwin P., tr. 2008. (Illus.). 264p. pap. 29.00 *(978-1-55635-544-8(0))* Wipf & Stock Pubs.

Little Walter. Little Walter, Vol. 13. 2010. (ENG.). 56p. pap. 14.99 incl. audio compact disk *(978-1-4234-7535-4(6)*, 1423475356) Leonard, Hal Corp.

Lock, Graham & Murray, David. The Hearing Eye: Jazz & Blues Influences in African American Visual Art. Lock, Graham & Murray, David, eds. 2009. (ENG., Illus.). 288p. 99.00 *(978-0-19-534050-1(7))* Oxford Univ. Pr., Inc.

Lock, Graham & Murray, David, eds. The Hearing Eye: Jazz & Blues Influences in African American Visual Art. 2009. (ENG., Illus.). 288p. pap. 24.95 *(978-0-19-534051-8(5))* Oxford Univ. Pr., Inc.

Mayall, John. John Mayall's Bluesbreakers: Live at Iowa State University. 2008. (ENG.). 14.95 *(978-1-4234-6660-4(3)*, 1423466608) Leonard, Hal Corp.

McCarthy, John. Blues Guitar Course: Everything You Need to Start Playing Blues Guitar. Gorenburg, Steve, ed. 2007. (ENG., Illus.). 96p. pap. 29.99 incl. audio compact disk *(978-0-9789832-9-1(7)*, 0978983297, Rock Hse. Method, The) Russell, Fred Publishing.

—Electric Guitar Course: Everything You Need to Start Playing Electric Guitar. Gorenburg, Steve & Palombo, Joe, eds. 2007. (House of Blues Ser.). (ENG., Illus.). 80p. pap. 29.99 incl. audio compact disk *(978-0-9789832-7-7(0)*, 097898327O, Rock Hse. Method, The) Russell, Fred Publishing.

McCumber, Dennis. The Total Blues Guitarist. 2007. (Total Guitarist Ser.). (ENG.). 128p. pap. 19.95 *(978-0-7390-3849-9(4))* Alfred Publishing Co., Inc.

McLoughlin, Shirley Wade. A Pedagogy of the Blues. 2008. 136p. *(978-90-8790-692-4(7))*; pap. *(978-90-8790-691-7(9))* Sense Pubs.

Meadows, Blues: A Research & Information Guide. 2010. (Routledge Music Bibliographies Ser.). (ENG.). 416p. 155.00 *(978-0-415-97319-9(8))* Routledge.

Mier, Martha. Classical Jazz Rags & Blues, Bk 3: 10 Classical Melodies Arranged in Jazz Styles for Intermediate to Late Intermediate Pianists. 2008. (Classical Jazz, Rags & Blues Ser.). (ENG.). 24p. pap. 6.95 *(978-0-7390-5708-7(1))* Alfred Publishing Co., Inc.

—Classical Jazz Rags & Blues, Bk 4: 10 Classical Melodies Arranged in Jazz Styles for Early Intermediate Pianists. 2008. (Classical Jazz, Rags & Blues Ser.). (ENG.). 24p. pap. 6.95 *(978-0-7390-5709-4(X))* Alfred Publishing Co., Inc.

Mier, Martha. Jazz, Rags & Blues for Two, Bk 5. 2011. (Jazz, Rags & Blues for Two Ser.). (ENG.). 24p. pap. 6.99 ***(978-0-7390-8470-0(4))*** Alfred Publishing Co., Inc.

Mock, Don, contrib. by. The Blues from Rock to Jazz. 2007. (Alfred's Artist Ser.). (ENG.). 29.95 *(978-0-7390-4509-1(1))* Alfred Publishing Co., Inc.

Moore, Andrew & Pappas, Paul, contrib. by. Best of Joe Bonamassa. 2007. (ENG.). 116p. per. 22.95 *(978-1-57560-894-5(4)*, 1575608944) Cherry Lane Music Co.

Morritt, Robert. Recording the Blues. 2011. 164p. pap. ***(978-3-8443-1766-4(X))*** Lambert Academic Publishing.

Mumford, Mark. What Jazz & Blues Can I Play - Piano. 32p. 6.95 *(978-1-85909-394-8(9)*, Warner Bros. Pubns.) Alfred Publishing Co., Inc.

Music Sales. Blues Double Deck (Chord & S. 2007. 192p. pap. 19.99 *(978-0-8256-3540-3(3))* Music Sales Corp.

Neeley, Blake. Blues Licks for Piano. 2011. (ENG.). 40p. pap. 8.99 ***(978-1-57560-165-6(6)***, 1575601656) Cherry Lane Music Co.

Neely, Blake & Downing, Doug. FastTrack Mini Harmonica Method - Book 1 with Hohner Blues Harmonica. 2006. (ENG.). 16p. (J). pap. 12.95 incl. audio compact disk *(978-1-4234-1975-4(8)*, 1423419758) Leonard, Hal Corp.

Nichols, Stephen J. Getting the Blues: What Blues Music Teaches Us about Suffering & Salvation. 2008. (Illus.). 192p. pap. 20.00 *(978-1-58743-212-5(9))* Brazos Pr.

Paul, Alan. Big in China: My Unlikely Adventures Raising a Family, Playing the Blues, & Becoming a Star in Beijing. 2011. (ENG.). 256p. 25.99 *(978-0-06-199315-2(8))* HarperCollins Pubs.

Pearl, David. Bob Dylan: Together Through Life. 2008. (ENG.). 48p. pap. 17.95 *(978-0-8256-3721-6(X)*, 082563721X) Music Sales Corp.

Petty, Tom. Tom Petty & the Heartbreakers - Mojo. 2010. (ENG.). 80p. pap. 16.99 *(978-1-4234-9866-7(6)*, 1423498666) Leonard, Hal Corp.

Phillips, Mark. 70 Bach Chorales for Easy Classical Guitar. 2011. (ENG.). 76p. pap. 16.99 incl. audio compact disk ***(978-1-60378-380-4(6)***, 1603783806) Cherry Lane Music Co.

Reed, Jimmy. Jimmy Reed: Blues Play-along Volume 12. 2011. (ENG.). 72p. pap. 12.99 incl. audio compact disk ***(978-1-4234-9647-2(7)***, 1423496477) Leonard, Hal Corp.

Robillard, Duke. Duke Robillard - Guitar Method, Vol. 1. 2009. (ENG.). 19.95 *(978-1-4234-9046-3(0)*, 1423490460) Leonard, Hal Corp.

Rockin Blues Solos. 17.95 *(978-0-89524-848-0(4)*, 02503460) Cherry Lane Music Co.

Rubin, Dave. B. B. King - Blues Legend: A Step-by-Step Breakdown of His Guitar Styles & Techniques. 2010. (ENG.). 48p. pap. 22.99 incl. audio compact disk *(978-1-4234-5792-3(7)*, 1423457927) Leonard, Hal Corp.

—Beginning Blues Guitar: A Guide to the Essential Chords, Licks, Techniques & Concepts. 2007. (ENG., Illus.). 48p. pap. 9.95 incl. audio compact disk *(978-1-4234-0457-6(2)*, 1423404572) Leonard, Hal Corp.

—Blues. deluxe ed. 2009. (ENG.). 120p. pap. 24.99 incl. audio compact disk *(978-1-4234-2492-5(1)*, 1423424921) Leonard, Hal Corp.

—Blues Cruise: 10 Original Songs with Bluesy Chords, Rhythms, & Riffs. 2007. (ENG.). 32p. pap. 9.95 incl. audio compact disk *(978-1-4234-1913-6(8)*, 1423419138) Leonard, Hal Corp.

—Blues/Rock Guitar Heroes: A Step-by-Step Breakdown of the Guitar Styles & Techniques of the Blues/Rock Greats. 2010. (ENG.). 88p. pap. 19.99 incl. audio compact disk *(978-1-4234-5455-4(X)*, 142345455X) Leonard, Hal Corp.

—12-Bar Blues - All-in-One Combo Pack. 2011. (ENG.). 88p. pap. 24.99 incl. audio compact disk *(978-1-4584-0261-5(4)*, 1458402614) Leonard, Hal Corp.

—12-Bar Blues Solos: 25 Authentic Leads Arranged for Guitar in Standard Notation & Tablature. 2006. (ENG., Illus.). 32p. pap. 12.95 *(978-1-4234-0742-3(3)*, 1423407423) Leonard, Hal Corp.

Scaggs, Boz. Boz Scaggs: Hits! 2007. (ENG., Illus.). 66p. per. 16.95 *(978-1-57560-909-6(6)*, 1575609096) Cherry Lane Music Co.

Scott, Michelle R. Blues Empress in Black Chattanooga: Bessie Smith & the Emerging Urban South. 2008. (ENG., Illus.). 216p. 60.00

B

(978-0-252-03338-4(8)); pap. 26.00 (978-0-252-07545-2(5)) Univ. of Illinois Pr.

Seales, Lennox G. Praying the Blues. 2009. 108p. pap. 10.99 (978-1-4389-7762-1(X)) AuthorHouse.

Sebastian, John. John Sebastian - Harmonica Bundle Pack: John Sebastian Teaches Blues Harmonica (Book/CD) with John Sebastian Teaches Blues Harmonica (DVD) 2009. (ENG.). 32p. spiral bd. 44.95 (978-1-4234-3665-2(2), 1423436652) Homespun Video.

Smit, Jeroen. Essential Rory Gallagher, Vol. 2. 2009. (ENG.). 128p. pap. 22.99 (978-1-84938-116-1(X), 184938116X) Music Sales Corp.

Smith, Scott A. Play Blues Guitar: Beginning Chords, Strums & Solos. 2007. (ENG.). pap. 19.95 (978-1-929395-94-1(9)) Workshop Arts, Inc.

Sokolow, Fred. Best of Blues Guitar, 1 vol. 2008. (ENG.). 44p. pap. 9.95 (978-0-87166-281-1(7)) Mel Bay Pubns., Inc.

—Blues Ukulele: A Jumpin' Jim's Ukulele Songbook. 2008. (ENG.). 40p. pap. 24.95 incl. audio compact disk (978-1-4234-6572-0(5), 1423465725) Leonard, Hal Corp.

—Classic Blues Licks for Electric Guitar, 1 vol. 2008. (ENG.). 32p. pap. 9.95 (978-0-7866-7859-4(3)) Mel Bay Pubns., Inc.

—Electric Blues & Rock Guitar: The 1930s, 40s And 50s, 1 vol. 2006. (Stefan Grossman's Guitar Workshop Ser.). (ENG., Illus.). 48p. pap. 24.95 (978-0-7866-7488-6(1), 21143bcd) Mel Bay Pubns., Inc.

—Electric Blues & Rock Guitar: The 1960s And 70s, 1 vol. 2006. (Stefan Grossman's Guitar Workshop Ser.). (ENG., Illus.). 56p. pap. 24.95 (978-0-7866-7487-9(3)) Mel Bay Pubns., Inc.

St. James, Adam. The Blues Guitar Handbook: A Complete Course in Techniques & Styles. 2011. (ENG.). 256p. 29.99 incl. audio compact disk (978-1-61713-011-3(7), 1617130117, Backbeat Books) Leonard, Hal Corp.

Starr, Eric. The Everything Rock & Blues Piano Book: Master Riffs, Licks, & Blues Styles from New Orleans to New City. 2007. (ENG., Illus.). 288p. pap. 19.95 (978-1-59869-260-0(7)) Adams Media Corp.

Steinberg, Jesse R. & Fairweather, Abrol, eds. Blues - Philosophy for Everyone: Thinking Deep about Feeling Low. 2012. (Philosophy for Everyone Ser.: 49). (ENG.). 248p. pap. 19.95 **(978-0-470-65680-8(8)**, Wiley-Blackwell) Wiley, John & Sons, Inc.

Taylor, Mark & Roberts, Jim, contrib. by. Jazz/Blues: 9 Favorite Tunes. 2008. (Jazz Play-along Ser.: Vol. 73). (ENG.). 56p. pap. 14.95 incl. audio compact disk (978-1-4234-2616-5(9), 1423426169) Leonard, Hal Corp.

Terrell & Terrell, Maurice. Blues & Jazz: American Music in a Strange Land. rev. ed. 2010. (ENG.). 132p. pap. 92.00 (978-0-7575-8305-6(9)) Kendall Hunt Publishing Co.

Theme Time Radio Hour Compendium: Themes, Dreams, Schemes. 2011. (Illus.). 176p. 30.00 (978-1-4165-9270-9(9)) Simon & Schuster.

Thiam, Pascal Bokar. From Timbuktu to the Mississippi Delta. 2010. (C). pap. 0.00 (978-1-60927-861-8(5)) Univ. Readers.

The Total Blues Drummer: A Fun & Comprehensive Overview of Blues Drumming. 2010. (Total Drummer Ser.). (ENG., Illus.). 128p. pap. 19.99 (978-0-7390-6645-4(5)) Alfred Publishing Co., Inc.

Traum, Happy. Happy Traum - Blues Guitar Bundle Pack: Happy Traum Teaches Blues Guitar (Book/CD Pack) with Easy Steps to Blues Guitar Jamming (DVD) 2009. (ENG.). 30p. pap. 44.95 incl. audio compact disk (978-1-4234-3661-4(X), 142343661X) Homespun Video.

Trovato, Steve. Steve Trovato's Beginning Blues Lead Guitar: Book & DVD. 2011. 64p. pap. 16.99 **(978-0-7390-7689-7(2))** Alfred Publishing Co., Inc.

Vogler, Leonard. The Compact Blues Guitar Chord Reference: Compact Reference Library. 2009. (ENG.). 48p. pap. 6.99 (978-0-8256-3689-9(2), 0825636892) Music Sales Corp.

Watts, Jennifer & Watts, Mike. Blues, Jazz, Rock & Rags - Book 1: 12 Original Piano Solos - Late Elementary Level. 2011. (ENG.). 32p. pap. 8.99 **(978-1-61780-662-9(5)**, 1617806625) Leonard, Hal Corp.

—Blues, Jazz, Rock & Rags - Book 2: 12 Original Piano Solos - Intermediate Level. 2011. (ENG.). 40p. pap. 8.99 **(978-1-61780-663-6(3)**, 1617806633) Leonard, Hal Corp.

Weissman, Dick. American Popular Music: Blues, Second Edition. 2nd rev. ed. 2012. (American Popular Music Ser.). 75.00 (978-0-8160-7918-6(8)) Facts On File, Inc.

White Stripes. The White Stripes: Icky Thump. 2007. (ENG.). 76p. per. 19.95 (978-1-60378-029-2(7), 1603780297) Cherry Lane Music Co.

Williams, Michael. Berklee Blues Guitar. 2010. (ENG.). 104p. pap. 24.99 incl. audio compact disk (978-0-87639-100-6(5), 0876391005, Berklee Pr.) Leonard, Hal Corp.

Wine, Toby. Blues Masters by the Bar. 2007. (ENG.). 88p. pap. 19.95 incl. audio compact disk (978-1-57560-863-1(4), 1575608634) Cherry Lane Music Co.

—Johnny Winter Plays the Blues. 2011. (ENG.). 48p. pap. 19.99 incl. audio compact disk (978-1-60378-149-7(8), 1603781498) Cherry Lane Music Co.

Wine, Toby & DoCampo, Michael. 75 Blues Turnarounds. 2011. (ENG.). 36p. pap. 12.99 incl. audio compact disk (978-1-57560-971-3(1), 1575609711) Leonard, Hal Corp.

Winter, Johnny. Johnny Winter - Live Through The '70s. 2009. (ENG.). 19.95 (978-1-4234-7405-0(8), 1423474058) Leonard, Hal Corp.

Wise Publications, creator. Corinne Bailey Rae. 2007. (Illus.). 60p. per. 19.95 (978-1-84609-510-8(7), Amsco Music) Music Sales Corp.

Wolf, Howlin'. Howlin' Wolf: Blues Play-along Volume 7. 2010. (ENG & ACH.). 72p. pap. 12.99 incl. audio compact disk (978-1-4234-8698-5(6), 1423486986) Leonard, Hal Corp.

Woods, Clyde. Development Arrested: From the Plantation Era to the Katrina Crisis in the Mississippi Delta. rev. ed. 2012. 352p. pap. 26.95 (978-1-84467-561-6(0), New Left Bks.) Verso Bks. GBR. Dist: Norton, W. W. & Co., Inc.

Wyatt, Keith. Blues Rhythm Guitar. 2008. (ENG.). 112p. pap. 19.95 incl. audio compact disk (978-0-7935-7128-4(6), 0793571286, Musicians Institute Pr.) Leonard, Hal Corp.

Wyatt, Keith, contrib. by. Rockin' the Blues. 2007. (Alfred's Artist Ser.). (ENG.). 29.95 (978-0-7390-4827-6(9)) Alfred Publishing Co., Inc.

Young, Michael Lloyd, photos by. Blues, Booze, & BBQ. 2009. (ENG., Illus.). 112p. 39.95 (978-1-57687-512-4(1), powerHouse Bks.) powerHouse Cultural Entertainment, Inc.

BLUES (MUSIC)—DISCOGRAPHY

Evans, David, ed. Ramblin' on My Mind: New Perspectives on the Blues. 2008. (African American Music in Culture Ser.). (Illus.). 440p. 78.00 (978-0-252-03203-5(9)); per. 28.00 (978-0-252-07448-6(3)) Univ. of Illinois Pr.

Musichound Blues. 2nd ed. Date not set. 24.95 (978-1-57859-082-7(5)) Music Sales Corp.

Oliver, Paul. Barrelhouse Blues: Location Recording & the Early Traditions of the Blues. 2009. (ENG., Illus.). 240p. 24.95 (978-0-465-00881-0(X), Basic Civitas Bks.) Basic Bks.

Rubin, Dave. 8-Bar Blues: Inside the Blues Series. 2008. (ENG.). 56p. pap. 14.99 incl. audio compact disk (978-1-4234-2311-9(9), 1423423119) Leonard, Hal Corp.

BLUES (MUSIC)—HISTORY AND CRITICISM

Adelt, Ulrich. Blues Music in the Sixties: A Story in Black & White. (ENG., Illus.). 204p. 2011. pap. 23.95 **(978-0-8135-5174-6(9))** 2010. 39.95 (978-0-8135-4750-3(4)) Rutgers Univ. Pr.

Barrow-Pryor, Erany. Motherin' the BluesLinda Hopkins: The Continuing Legacy of The Blues Woman. 2008. 196p. pap. (978-3-639-09649-1(5)) VDM Verlag Dr. Mueller e.K.

Bekker, Peter O. E., Jr. The Story of the Blues. (Musicbooks Ser.). (Illus.). 64p. 13.50 (978-1-56799-535-0(7), MetroBooks) Friedman, Michael Publishing Group, Inc.

Bell, Vince. One Man's Music: The Life & Times of Texas Songwriter Vince Bell. 2009. (North Texas Lives of Musicians Ser.: No. 3). (ENG.). 288p. pap. 14.95 (978-1-57441-267-3(1)); (Illus.). 29.95 (978-1-57441-266-6(3)) Univ. of North Texas Pr.

Bratcher, Melanie E. Words & Songs of Bessie Smith, Billie Holiday, & Nina Simone: Sound Motion, Blues Spirit, & African Memory. 2007. (Studies in African American History & Culture Ser.). (ENG., Illus.). 278p. 128.00 (978-0-415-98029-6(1)) Routledge.

Calt, Stephen. Barrelhouse Words: A Blues Dialect Dictionary. 2009. (ENG.). 320p. 75.00 (978-0-252-03347-6(7)); pap. 26.95 (978-0-252-07660-2(5)) Univ. of Illinois Pr.

—I'd Rather Be the Devil: Skip James & the Blues. 2008. (ENG., Illus.). 400p. (Orig.). pap. 16.95 (978-1-55652-746-3(2)) Chicago Review Pr., Inc.

Cheseborough, Steve. Blues Traveling: The Holy Sites of Delta Blues, Third Edition. 3rd rev. exp. ed. 2008. (ENG., Illus.). 256p. pap. 22.00 (978-1-60473-124-8(9)) Univ. Pr. of Mississippi.

Chicago Beau & Beauchamp, Lincoln T. BluesSpeak: The Best of the Original Chicago Blues Annual. 2010. (ENG., Illus.). 192p. 75.00 (978-0-252-03440-4(6)); pap. 24.95 (978-0-252-07692-3(3)) Univ. of Illinois Pr.

Coleman, Rick. Blue Monday: Fats Domino & the Lost Dawn of Rock 'n' Roll. 2007. (ENG., Illus.). 416p. per. 15.95 (978-0-306-81531-7(1)) Da Capo Pr., Inc.

—Blue Monday: Fats Domino & the Lost Dawn of Rock 'n' Roll. Date not set. pap. 15.95 (978-0-06-051362-7(4)) HarperCollins Pubs.

Elkington, John. Beale Street: Resurrecting the Home of the Blues. 2008. 25.99 (978-1-59629-492-9(2)) History Pr., The.

Erlewine, Michael. Blues in Black & White: The Landmark Ann Arbor Blues Festivals. 2010. (ENG., Illus.). 144p. pap. 29.95 (978-0-472-11695-9(9)) Univ. of Michigan Pr.

Ferris, William. Give My Poor Heart Ease: Voices of the Mississippi Blues. 2009. (ENG., Illus.). 312p. 36.95 (978-0-8078-3325-4(8)) Univ. of North Carolina Pr.

Gioia, Ted. Delta Blues: The Life & Times of the Mississippi Masters Who Revolutionized American Music. 2009. (ENG., Illus.). 482p. pap. 17.95 (978-0-393-33750-1(2), 33750) Norton, W. W. & Co., Inc.

Govenar, Alan. Texas Blues: The Rise of a Contemporary Sound. 2008. (John & Robin Dickson Series in Texas Music). (ENG., Illus.). 624p. 40.00 (978-1-58544-605-6(X)) Texas A&M Univ. Pr.

Gussow, Adam. Journeyman's Road: Modern Blues Lives from Faulkner's Mississippi to Post-9/11 New York. 2007. (ENG., Illus.). 208p. per. 21.95 (978-1-57233-625-4(0)) Univ. of Tennessee Pr.

Hamilton, Marybeth. In Search of the Blues. 2009. (ENG.). 320p. pap. 15.95 (978-0-465-01812-3(2)) Basic Bks.

Handy, W. C., ed. Blues, an Anthology: Complete Words & Music of 60 Great Songs from Memphis Blues to the Present Day. 2012. (Dover Song Collections). (ENG.). 304p. pap. 19.95 **(978-0-486-48619-2(2))** Dover Pubns., Inc.

Harper, Colin. Dazzling Stranger: Bert Jansch & the British Folk & Blues Revival. (Illus.). 384p. pap. 16.99 (978-0-7475-5330-4(0)); 2007. (ENG., 416p. per. 16.95 (978-0-7475-8725-5(6)) Bloomsbury Publishing Plc GBR. Dist: Trafalgar Square Publishing, Independent Pubs. Group.

Inaba, Mitsutoshi. Willie Dixon: Preacher of the Blues. 2011. (African American Cultural Theory & Heritage Ser.). (ENG., Illus.). 502p. 55.00 (978-0-8108-6993-6(4)) Scarecrow Pr., Inc.

Kay, George W. Those Fabulous Gennetts! the Life Story of a Remarkable Label. 2011. 12p. pap. 35.95 **(978-1-258-04565-4(6))** Literary Licensing, LLC.

King, Stephen A. I'm Feeling the Blues Right Now: Blues Tourism in the Mississippi Delta. 2011. (American Made Music Ser.). (ENG., Illus.). 256p. 55.00 (978-1-61703-010-9(4)) Univ. Pr. of Mississippi.

Kubik, Gerhard. Africa & the Blues. 2008. (ENG., Illus.). 260p. pap. 25.00 (978-1-57806-146-4(6)) Univ. Pr. of Mississippi.

Lawson, R. A. Jim Crow's Counterculture: The Blues & Black Southerners, 1890-1945. 2010. (Making the Modern South Ser.). (Illus.). 328p. 45.00 (978-0-8071-3680-5(8)) Louisiana State Univ. Pr.

Muir, Peter C. Long Lost Blues: Popular Blues in America, 1850-1920. (Music in American Life Ser.). (ENG., Illus.). 2010. 344p. 85.00 (978-0-252-03487-9(2)) 2009. 280p. pap. 35.00 (978-0-252-07676-3(1)) Univ. of Illinois Pr.

Oliver, Paul. Barrelhouse Blues: Location Recording & the Early Traditions of the Blues. 2009. (ENG., Illus.). 240p. 24.95 (978-0-465-00881-0(X), Basic Civitas Bks.) Basic Bks.

Olsson, Bengt. Memphis Blues. 2008. 256p. 18.95 (978-0-415-97337-3(6)); 85.00 (978-0-415-97336-6(8)) Routledge.

Reich, Howard. Let Freedom Swing: Collected Writings on Jazz, Blues, & Gospel. 2010. (ENG.). 416p. pap. 24.95 (978-0-8101-2705-0(9)) Northwestern Univ. Pr.

Rijn, Guido Van. Kennedy's Blues: African-American Blues & Gospel Songs on JFK. (ENG.). 2010. 248p. pap. 25.00 (978-1-60473-858-2(8)) 2007. (Illus.). 220p. 50.00 (978-1-57806-957-6(2)) Univ. Pr. of Mississippi.

Rolf, Julia. The Definitive Illustrated Encyclopedia of Jazz & Blues. 2011. (Illus.). 448p. 24.99 (978-1-57215-668-5(6), JG Pr.) World Pubns. Group, Inc.

Rubin, Dave. 8-Bar Blues: Inside the Blues Series. 2008. (ENG.). 56p. pap. 14.99 incl. audio compact disk (978-1-4234-2311-9(9), 1423423119) Leonard, Hal Corp.

Rudinow, Joel. Soul Music: Tracking the Spiritual Roots of Pop from Plato to Motown. 2010. xiii, 250p. E-Book 28.95 (978-0-472-02279-3(2)); (ENG.). 264p. pap. 28.95 (978-0-472-05108-3(3)) Univ. of Michigan Pr.

Schwartz, Roberta Freund. How Britain Got the Blues: The Transmission & Reception of American Blues Style in the United Kingdom. 2007. (Ashgate Popular & Folk Music Ser.). 282p. 114.95 (978-0-7546-5580-0(6)) Ashgate Publishing Co.

Springer, Robert, ed. Nobody Knows Where the Blues Come From: Lyrics & History. 2007. (ENG.). 303p. pap. 25.00 (978-1-934110-29-4(9)) Univ. Pr. of Mississippi.

Stolle, Roger. HH Mississippi Blues. 2011. pap. 19.99 (978-1-60949-219-9(6)) History Pr., The.

Terry, Jill & Wynn, Neil A., eds. Transatlantic Roots Music: Folk, Blues, & National Identities. 2012. (American Made Music Ser.). (ENG.). 256p. 60.00 **(978-1-61703-288-2(3))** Univ. Pr. of Mississippi.

Wald, Elijah. The Blues: A Very Short Introduction. 2010. (Very Short Int Ser.). (ENG., Illus.). 144p. pap. 11.95 (978-0-19-539893-9(9)) Oxford Univ. Pr., Inc.

Wright, Vickie, et al. Motown from the Background. 2007. 296p. per. (978-1-904408-29-1(X)) Bank House Bks.

BLUES (SONGS, ETC.)

see Blues (Music)

BLUES MUSICIANS

Bagayoko, Amadou, et al. Away from the Light of Day. 2011. (ENG.). 176p. pap. 16.95 (978-1-901927-45-0(8)) Route GBR. Dist: Dufour Editions, Inc.

B.B. King, David. Blues All Around Me: The Autobiography of B. B. King. 2011. 15.12 (978-0-7848-3591-3(8), Everbind) Marco Bk. Co.

Beaumont, Daniel E. Preachin' the Blues: The Life & Times of Son House, 1 vol. 2011. (ENG., Illus.). 224p. 24.95 (978-0-19-539557-0(3)) Oxford Univ. Pr., Inc.

Bell, Vince. One Man's Music: The Life & Times of Texas Songwriter Vince Bell. 2009. (North Texas Lives of Musicians Ser.: No. 3). (ENG.). 288p. pap. 14.95 (978-1-57441-267-3(1)); (Illus.). 29.95 (978-1-57441-266-6(3)) Univ. of North Texas Pr.

Burrows, Toby. I Remember When I Was Young: the Matt Taylor Story. 2009. 228p. pap. 18.99 (978-1-4092-9421-4(8)) Lulu Enterprises Inc.

Caldwell, Jennifer Shelton. The Abc's of the Mississippi Blues. 2009. 68p. pap. 25.49 (978-1-4389-3211-8(1)) AuthorHouse.

Carter, Doug. Cool Fool: Blues Rockin' in the Hammer. 2010. (ENG., Illus.). 171p. pap. 22.95 (978-0-9808879-8-3(4)) Seraphim Editions CAN. Dist: Univ. of Toronto Pr.

Cheseborough, Steve. Blues Traveling: The Holy Sites of Delta Blues, Third Edition. 3rd rev. exp. ed. 2008. (ENG., Illus.). 256p. pap. 22.00 (978-1-60473-124-8(9)) Univ. Pr. of Mississippi.

Chicago Beau & Beauchamp, Lincoln T. BluesSpeak: The Best of the Original Chicago Blues Annual. 2010. (ENG., Illus.). 192p. 75.00 (978-0-252-03440-4(6)); pap. 24.95 (978-0-252-07692-3(3)) Univ. of Illinois Pr.

Cohen, John. The High & Lonesome Sound. 2012. (ENG., Illus.). 270p. pap. 58.00 (978-3-86930-254-6(2)) Steidl, Gerhard Druckerei und Verlag DEU. Dist: Innovative Logistics.

Coleman, Rick. Blue Monday: Fats Domino & the Lost Dawn of Rock 'n' Roll. 2007. (ENG., Illus.). 416p. per. 15.95 (978-0-306-81531-7(1)) Da Capo Pr., Inc.

—Blue Monday: Fats Domino & the Lost Dawn of Rock 'n' Roll. Date not set. pap. 15.95 (978-0-06-051362-7(4)) HarperCollins Pubs.

Crumb, R. R. Crumb's Heroes of Blues, Jazz & Country. 2006. (ENG., Illus.). 240p. 21.95 (978-0-8109-3086-5(2)) Abrams.

Cushing, Steve. Blues Before Sunrise: The Radio Interviews. 2010. (ENG., Illus.). 264p. 75.00 (978-0-252-03301-8(9)); pap. 25.00 (978-0-252-07718-0(0)) Univ. of Illinois Pr.

Farley, Charles. Soul of the Man: Bobby Blue Bland. 2011. (American Made Music Ser.). (ENG., Illus.). 336p. 35.00 (978-1-60473-919-0(3)) Univ. Pr. of Mississippi.

Ferris, William. Give My Poor Heart Ease: Voices of the Mississippi Blues. 2009. (ENG., Illus.). 312p. 36.95 (978-0-8078-3325-4(8)) Univ. of North Carolina Pr.

Franklin, Benjamin, V. Jazz & Blues Musicians of South Carolina: Interviews with Jabbo, Dizzy, Drink, & Others. 2008. (Illus.). 296p. 29.95 (978-1-57003-743-6(4)) Univ. of South Carolina Pr.

Govenar, Alan. Lightnin' Hopkins: His Life & Blues. 2010. (ENG.). 352p. 28.95 (978-1-55652-962-7(7)) Chicago Review Pr., Inc.

—Texas Blues: The Rise of a Contemporary Sound. 2008. (John & Robin Dickson Series in Texas Music). (ENG., Illus.). 624p. 40.00 (978-1-58544-605-6(X)) Texas A&M Univ. Pr.

Gray, Michael. Hand Me My Travelin' Shoes: In Search of Blind Willie Mctell. 2009. (ENG.). 448p. 26.95 (978-1-55652-975-7(9)) Chicago Review Pr., Inc.

Grossman, Stefan, ed. Mississippi John Hurt. 2007. (Stefan Grossman's Early Masters of American Blues Guitar Ser.). (ENG., Illus.). 96p. pap. 21.95 (978-0-7390-4330-1(7)) Alfred Publishing Co., Inc.

Guitar World Magazine Editors & Tolinsky, Brad. Stevie Ray Vaughan. 2010. (ENG., Illus.). 258p. pap. 14.99 (978-0-87930-971-8(7), 0879309717, Backbeat Books) Leonard, Hal Corp.

Gulla, Bob, ed. Icons of R&B & Soul: An Encyclopedia of the Artists Who Revolutionized Rhythm, 2 vols. 2007. (Greenwood Icons Ser.). 552p. 175.00 (978-0-313-34044-4(7), GR4044, Greenwood Pr.) Greenwood Publishing Group, Inc.

Gussow, Adam. Journeyman's Road: Modern Blues Lives from Faulkner's Mississippi to Post-9/11 New York. 2007. (ENG., Illus.). 208p. per. 21.95 (978-1-57233-625-4(0)) Univ. of Tennessee Pr.

—Mister Satan's Apprentice: A Blues Memoir. 2009. (ENG., Illus.). 408p. pap. 18.95 (978-0-8166-6775-8(6)) Univ. of Minnesota Pr.

Guy, Buddy. When I Left Home: My Story. 2012. (ENG.). 320p. 26.00 **(978-0-306-81957-5(0))** Da Capo Pr., Inc.

Hopkins, Craig. Stevie Ray Vaughan: Day by Day, Night after Night. 2008. (Illus.). 432p. 75.00 (978-0-9654927-2-0(9)) Hopkins, Craig L.

Hopkins, Craig. Stevie Ray Vaughan - Day by Day, Night after Night: Deluxe Box Set. 2011. (ENG.). 624p. 75.00 **(978-1-61713-030-4(3)**, 1617130303, Backbeat Books) Leonard, Hal Corp.

House, Roger. Blue Smoke: The Recorded Journey of Big Bill Broonzy. 2010. (Illus.). 280p. pap. 19.95 (978-0-8071-3720-8(0)) Louisiana State Univ. Pr.

Joseph, Pleasant & Ottenheimer, Harriett J. Cousin Joe: Blues from New Orleans, 1 vol. 2012. (ENG., Illus.). 228p. pap. 19.95 **(978-1-4556-1543-8(9))** Pelican Publishing Co., Inc.

Merrill, John C. Call to Order: Plato's Legacy of Social Control. 2009. 160p. pap. 39.95 (978-0-922993-81-9(5)) Marquette Bks., LLC.

Morritt, Robert. Recording the Blues. 2011. 164p. pap. **(978-3-8443-1766-4(X))** Lambert Academic Publishing.

Morthland, John. Texas Music: Legends from the Lone Star State. 2010. (Texas Ser.). (ENG.). 112p. 33.32 (978-1-4296-6763-0(X)) Capstone Pr., Inc.

Paul, Alan. Big in China: My Unlikely Adventures Raising a Family, Playing the Blues, & Becoming a Star in Beijing. 2011. (ENG.). 256p. 25.99 (978-0-06-199315-2(8)) HarperCollins Pubs.

Pearson, Barry Lee & McCulloch, Bill. Robert Johnson: Lost & Found. 2008. (Music in American Life Ser.). (ENG., Illus.). 176p. pap. 26.00 (978-0-252-07528-5(5)) Univ. of Illinois Pr.

Ratcliffe, Philip R. Mississippi John Hurt: His Life, His Times, His Blues. 2011. (American Made Music Ser.). (ENG., Illus.). 272p. 35.00 (978-1-61703-008-6(2)) Univ. Pr. of Mississippi.

Reynolds, John & Robinson, Tiny. Lead Belly: A Life in Pictures, 1 vol. Reynolds, John & Robinson, Tiny, eds. 2008. (ENG., Illus.). 224p. 50.00 (978-3-86521-459-1(2)) Steidl, Gerhard Druckerei und Verlag DEU. Dist: Innovative Logistics.

Riesman. I Feel So Good. 2007. (Illus.). 306p. (978-0-415-97276-5(0), 0415972760, Routledge) Taylor & Francis Group.

Riesman, Robert & Riesman, Bob. I Feel So Good: The Life & Times of Big Bill Broonzy. 2011. (ENG., Illus.). 366p. 27.50 (978-0-226-71745-6(3)) Univ. of Chicago Pr.

Ritz, David. Blues All Around Me: The Autobiography of B. B. King. 2011. (ENG.). 352p. pap. 15.99 (978-0-06-206103-4(8)) HarperCollins Pubs.

Rodney, Dave. Usher. 2009. (Contemporary Musicians & Their Music Ser.). (ENG.). 48p. (gr. 6-6). 53.00 (978-1-61511-947-9(7)) Rosen Publishing Group, Inc., The.

Rubin, Dave. Inside the Blues, 1942-1982: Four Decades of the Greatest Electric Blues Guitarists. 2nd ed. 2007. (ENG., Illus.). 176p. pap. 24.95 incl. audio compact disk (978-1-4234-1666-1(X), 142341666X) Leonard, Hal Corp.

Taylor, Larry & McKeown, Bonni. Stepson of the Blues: A Chicago Song of Survival. 2010. (Illus.). 310p. (978-0-9621483-1-6(8)) Peaceful Patriot Pr.

Vande Kappelle, Robert P. Blue Notes: Profiles of Jazz Personalities. 2011. 492p. pap. 54.00 (978-1-61097-283-3(X), Resource Pubns.) Wipf & Stock Pubs.

Wald, Gayle F. Shout, Sister, Shout! The Untold Story of Rock-and-Roll Trailblazer Sister Rosetta Tharpe. 2008. (ENG., Illus.). 264p. per. 16.00 *(978-0-8070-0985-7(7))* Beacon Pr.

Wallace, Debby. Home of the Blues: 35 Years of the Double Door Inn. 2009. (Illus.). 108p. pap. 20.95 *(978-1-4327-2357-6(X))* Outskirts Pr., Inc.

Wanguri, Deloris McGee. Cases in Organizational Communication. 2009. 108p. (C). pap. 32.95 *(978-0-922993-82-6(3))* Marquette Bks., LLC.

Weissman, Dick. American Popular Music: Blues, Second Edition. 2nd rev. ed. 2012. (American Popular Music Ser.). 75.00 *(978-0-8160-7918-6(8))* Facts On File, Inc.

—Blues. 2006. (American Popular Music Ser.). (Illus.). 336p. (gr. 7-12). per. 21.95 *(978-0-8160-6926-2(3))*, Checkmark Bks.) Facts On File, Inc.

BLUETONGUE

Baylis, Matthew, et al. Bluetongue. Mertens, Peter & Baylis, Matthew, eds. Mellor, Philip, ed. 2008. (Biology of Animal Infections Ser.). (ENG., Illus.). 506p. 98.95 *(978-0-12-369368-6(3)*, Academic Pr.) Elsevier Science & Technology Bks.

BLUM, LEON, 1872-1950

Judt, Tony. The Burden of Responsibility: Blum, Camus, Aron, & the French Twentieth Century. 2007. (ENG., Illus.). 204p. per. 17.50 *(978-0-226-41419-5(1))* Univ. of Chicago Pr.

Stokes, Richar L. Leon Blum from Poet to Premier. 2006. 328p. per. *(978-1-4067-3172-9(2)*, Hesperides Pr.) Read Bks.

Stokes, Richard L. Leon Blum: From Poet to Premier. 2007. (ENG.). 306p. 43.95 *(978-0-548-06310-1(9))* Kessinger Publishing, LLC.

BLUMENSTOCK, DAVID IRVING, 1913-1963

Gagosian Gallery Staff, et al, contrib. by. Ferus. 2nd ed. 2009. (Illus.). 146p. 55.00 *(978-0-8478-3234-7(1))* Rizzoli International Pubns., Inc.

BLUMER, HERBERT, 1900-1987

Baugh, Kenneth, Jr. The Methodology of Herbert Blumer. 2006. (American Sociological Association Rose Monographs). (ENG.). 124p. (C). pap. 30.00 *(978-0-521-03035-9(8))* Cambridge Univ. Pr.

BLUMHARDT, CHRISTOPH, 1842-1919

Zahl, Simeon. Pneumatology & Theology of the Cross in the Preaching of Christoph Friedrich Blumhardt: The Holy Spirit Between Wittenberg & Azusa Street. 2012. (T&T Clark Studies in Systematic Theology Ser.). (ENG.). 224p. pap. 44.95 **(978-0-567-47240-3(X)**, T&T Clark Int'l) Continuum International Publishing Group, Ltd. GBR. Dist: National Bk. Network.

Zahl, Simeon. Pneumatology & Theology of the Cross in the Preaching of Christoph Friedrich Blumhardt: The Holy Spirit Between Wittenberg & Azuza Street. 2010. (T&T Clark Studies in Systematic Theology Ser.). (ENG.). 224p. 130.00 *(978-0-567-64591-3(6)*, T&T Clark Int'l) Continuum International Publishing Group, Ltd. GBR. Dist: National Bk. Network.

Zundel, Friedrich. Pastor Johann Christoph Blumhardt: An Account of His Life. Collins Winn, Christian T. & Moore, Charles E., eds. Brinkman, Hugo, tr. 2010. (Blumhardt Ser.). (Illus.). 556p. pap. 52.00 *(978-1-60899-406-9(6))* Wipf & Stock Pubs.

BLUNDEN, EDMUND, 1896-1974

Blunden, Edmund. Undertones of War. 3rd ed. (ENG., Illus.). 272p. pap. 14.95 *(978-0-14-118436-4(1))* Penguin Bks., Ltd. GBR. Dist: Trafalgar Square Publishing.

—Undertones of War. 2007. (ENG.). 252p. pap. 14.00 *(978-0-226-06176-4(0))* Univ. of Chicago Pr.

BLUNDERS

see Common Fallacies; Errors and Blunders, Literary

BLY, NELLIE, 1867-1922

Bly, Nellie. Ten Days in a Mad-House. 2008. (Illus.). 124p. pap. *(978-1-4099-1570-6(0))* Dodo Pr.

BMC AUTOMOBILES

see BLMC Automobiles

BMW AUTOMOBILES

Autobooks, creator. Bmw 2000 & 2002 1966-1976 Owners Workshop Manual. 2011. (Illus.). 202p. pap. 34.95 **(978-1-58850-162-2(0))** Veloce Enterprises, Inc.

—Bmw 2500, 2800, 3 0, 3 3 & Bavaria 1968-1977 Owners Workshop Manual. 2011. (Illus.). 172p. pap. 34.95 **(978-1-58850-163-9(9))** Veloce Enterprises, Inc.

Bentley Publishers. BMW 3 Series Service Manual (E90, E91, E92, E93) 2006, 2007, 2008, 2009 Service Manual: 325i, 325xi, 328i, 328xi, 330i, 330xi, 335i, 335xi: 2006, 2007, 2008 2009. 2009. (Illus.). 1256p. pap. 129.95 *(978-0-8376-1608-7(5))* Bentley Pubs.

—BMW 5 Series Service Manual: 525i, 528i, 530i, 535i, 545i, 550i: 2004, 2005, 2006, 2007, 2008, 2009 2010: 2004, 2005, 2006, 2007, 2008, 2009 2010. 2010. (Illus.). 1734p. 149.95 *(978-0-8376-1621-6(2))* Bentley Pubs.

Bentley Publishers, creator. BMW X5 Service Manual: 3 0i, 4. 4i, 4, 6is, 4. 8is. 2008. (Illus.). 1240p. per. 129.95 *(978-0-8376-1534-9(8))* Bentley Pubs.

Bentley Publishers Staff. BMW 3 Series Service Manual (E90, E91, E92, E93) 2006, 2007, 2008, 2009 Service Manual: 325i, 325xi, 328i, 328xi, 330i, 330xi, 335i, 335xi: 2006, 2007, 2008 2009. 2010. (Illus.). 1256p. 129.95 *(978-0-8376-1638-4(7))* Bentley Pubs.

Bentley, Robert. BMW 7 Series (E38) Service Manual: 1995-2001: 740i, 740il, 750il. 2007. (Illus.). 1300p. per. 129.95 *(978-0-8376-1531-8(3)*, B701) Bentley Pubs.

BMW. Bmw Motorcycles Factory Workshop Manual R26 R27. 2007. 164p. per. 29.95 *(978-1-58850-068-7(3))* Veloce Enterprises, Inc.

Clarke, R. M., compiled by. BMW 2002 Ultimate Portfolio 1968-1976. 2007. (Ultimate Portfolio Ser.). (ENG., Illus.). 208p. pap. 37.95 *(978-1-85520-737-0(0)*, 1855207370) Brooklands Bks. GBR. Dist: MBI Distribution Services/Quayside Distribution.

—BMW M3 Ultimate Portfolio, 1986-2006: M3. E30. E36. E46. Coupe. Convertible. Racing. Saloon. 2008. (Ultimate Portfolio Ser.). (ENG., Illus.). 200p. pap. 37.95 *(978-1-85520-750-9(8)*, 1855207508) Brooklands Bks. GBR. Dist: MBI Distribution Services/Quayside Distribution.

—Bmw M5 Gold Portfolio, 1980 - 2003: E12 M535i. E28 M535i & M5. E34 M5. E39 M5. 2008. (Gold Portfolio Ser.). (ENG., Illus.). 160p. pap. 32.95 *(978-1-85520-756-1(7)*, 1855207567) Brooklands Bks. GBR. Dist: MBI Distribution Services/Quayside Distribution.

Clymer, Floyd. Bmw Motorcycles Workshop Manual R50 R50s R60 R69s. 2007. (MUL.). 180p. per. 34.95 *(978-1-58850-067-0(5))* Veloce Enterprises, Inc.

Cranswick, Marc. The BMW 5 Series & X5: A History of Production Cars & Tuner Specials, 1972-2008. 2010. (ENG., Illus.). 293p. pap. 38.00 *(978-0-7864-4351-2(0))* McFarland & Co., Inc. Pubs.

Dempsey, Wayne R. 101 Performance Projects for Your BMW 3 Series 1982-2000. rev. ed. 2006. (Motorbooks Workshop Ser.). (ENG., Illus.). 272p. pap. 34.95 *(978-0-7603-2695-4(9)*, 0760326959, Motorbooks) MBI Publishing Co. LLC.

Eliasson, Olafur. The Climate Car: Your mobile expectations: BMW H2R Project. 2008. (Illus.). 320p. 44.95 *(978-3-03778-117-3(3)*, 303778117З) Springer.

Gannon, Todd. Zaha Hadid: BMW Central Building, Leipzig, Germany. 2006. (ENG., Illus.). 160p. pap. 29.95 *(978-1-56898-536-7(3))* Princeton Architectural Pr.

Gantris, Peter. The Art of BMW: 85 Years of Motorcycling Excellence. 2008. (Illus.). 192p. 40.00 *(978-0-7603-3315-0(7)*, 0760333157, Motorbooks) MBI Publishing Co. LLC.

Haynes Editors. BMW 3-Series,1999 Thru 2005. 2012. (Haynes Repair Manual Ser.). (ENG., Illus.). 336p. pap. 26.95 **(978-1-56392-966-3(X)**, 156392966X) Haynes Manuals, Inc.

Haynes Manuals Editors. BMW 3-Series 2006 Thru 2010: 325i, 325xi, 330i, 330xi (2006), 328i, 328xi (2007 Thru 2010) 2011. (Haynes Repair Manual Ser.). (ENG., Illus.). 304p. pap. 26.95 **(978-1-56392-914-4(7)**, 1563929147) Haynes Manuals, Inc.

Lehbrink, Hartmut & Von Osterroth, Jochen. Bmw. Schlegelmilch, Rainer W., ed. rev. ed. 2010. (ENG., Illus.). 480p. 49.95 **(978-3-8331-1059-7(7))** h.f.ullmann DEU. Dist: Innovative Logistics.

Lehbrink, Hartmut, et al. BMW, 1 vol. 2010. (ENG., Illus.). 384p. spiral bd. 19.99 *(978-3-8331-5291-7(5))* h.f.ullmann DEU. Dist: Innovative Logistics.

Ludvigsen, Karl. BMW Racing Cars: 328 to Racing V12. 2007. (Ludvigsen Library Ser.). (ENG., Illus.). 128p. pap. 29.95 *(978-1-58388-201-6(4)*, 1583882014) Iconografix, Inc.

Maddox, Robert & Hamilton, Joe L. BMW 3-Series/Z4 Repair Manual. 2006. (Chilton's Total Car Care Ser.). (ENG., Illus.). 400p. per. 29.95 *(978-1-56392-609-9(1)*, 18401) Haynes,Chilton.

Publishing Teneues Staff, ed. BMW from vision to Reality. 2008. 256p. 125.00 *(978-3-8327-9231-2(7))* teNeues Publishing Co.

Reverente, Jose & Cook, Joshua R. BMW E21 3 Series, 1975-1983. 2012. (Essential Buyer's Guide Ser.). (ENG., Illus.). 64p. pap. 19.95 *(978-1-84584-366-3(5)*, 1845843665) Veloce Publishing Ltd. GBR. Dist: MBI Distribution Services/Quayside Distribution.

Robson, Graham. Inside the BMW Factories: Building the Ultimate Driving Machine. 2008. (ENG., Illus.). 192p. 40.00 *(978-0-7603-3463-8(3)*, 0760334633, Motorbooks) MBI Publishing Co. LLC.

—Mini Cooper. 2009. (Rally Giants Ser.). (ENG., Illus.). 128p. pap. 29.95 *(978-1-84584-183-6(2)*, 1845841832) Veloce Publishing Ltd. GBR. Dist: MBI Distribution Services/Quayside Distribution.

Sannia, Alessandro. Bmw, 1 vol. 2011. (ENG & FRE., Illus.). 192p. 12.95 *(978-90-79761-90-6(7))* Tectum B.V.B.A. BEL. Dist: Innovative Logistics.

Schlegelmilch, Rainer W., et al. Bmw. 2008. (Transportation Ser.). (Illus.). 479p. 49.95 *(978-0-8416-0274-8(3))* American Map Corp.

Staud, René, photos by. Mercedes-Benz: 300SL Book. 2012. (GER, ENG & FRE., Illus.). 304p. 125.00 **(978-3-8327-9616-7(9))** teNeues Publishing Co.

Storer, Jay. BMW 3-series: 2006 Thru 2010. 2011. (Illus.). 368p. pap. 29.95 **(978-1-56392-930-4(9))** Haynes,Chilton.

Ultimate History of BMW. 192p. *(978-1-4054-5316-5(8))* Parragon, Inc.

Vivian, David. BMW - The Power of M. 2013. (ENG., Illus.). 224p. 69.95 *(978-1-84584-336-6(3)*, 1845843363) Veloce Publishing Ltd. GBR. Dist: MBI Distribution Services/Quayside Distribution.

BMW MOTORCYCLE

Allen, Laurel C. & Gardiner, Mark. BMW Racing Motorcycles: The Mastery of Speed. 2008. (ENG., Illus.). 176p. (J). 29.95 *(978-1-884313-65-3(5)*, 1884313655) Whitehorse Pr.

Ash, Kevin. BMW Motorcycles: The Evolution of Excellence. 2006. (ENG., Illus.). 174p. 29.95 *(978-1-884313-57-8(4)*, 1884313574) Whitehorse Pr.

Cloesen, Ulrich (Uli) Peter. BMW Custom Motorcycles: Choppers, Cruisers, Bobbers, Trikes & Quads. 2011. (ENG., Illus.). 128p. 39.95 *(978-1-84584-325-0(8)*, 1845843258) Veloce Publishing Ltd. GBR. Dist: MBI Distribution Services/Quayside Distribution.

Clymer Publications Staff. Bmw k1200rs, lt & Gt 1998-2008. 2008. pap. 51.95 *(978-1-59969-234-0(1))* Clymer Publishing.

—BMW R-Series, 1970-1994. 2nd ed. (Illus.). 792p. reprint ed. pap. 39.95 *(978-0-89287-624-2(7)*, M502) Penton Media, Inc.

—BMW R850, R1100, R1150 & R1200C 1993-2005. 2nd ed. 2006. (Illus.). xiv, 775p. pap. 47.95 *(978-1-59969-040-7(3))* Penton Media, Inc.

Clymer Staff. BMW K1200RS, GT & LT, 1998-2005. 2006. (Clymer Motorcycle Ser.). (Illus.). 625p. per. 49.95 *(978-0-89287-992-2(0))* Penton Media, Inc.

Coombs, Matthew. BMW R850, 1100 & 1150 4-Valve Twins '93 To '06. Haynes, Max, ed. 3rd ed. 2009. (ENG., Illus.). 320p. 45.45 *(978-1-84425-779-9(7)*, 1844257797) Haynes Manuals, Inc.

Falloon, Ian. The BMW Boxer Twins Bible: All Air-Cooled Models 1970-1996 (Except R45, R65, G/S & GS) 2009. (Bible Ser.). (ENG., Illus.). 160p. 59.95 *(978-1-84584-168-3(9)*, 1845841689) Veloce Publishing Ltd. GBR. Dist: MBI Distribution Services/Quayside Distribution.

Henshaw, Peter. Bmw Gs. 2008. (Essential Buyer's Guide Ser.). (ENG., Illus.). 64p. pap. 19.95 *(978-1-84584-135-5(2)*, 1845841352) Veloce Publishing Ltd. GBR. Dist: MBI Distribution Services/Quayside Distribution.

Holmstrom, Darwin. BMW Motorcycles. 2009. (ENG., Illus.). 192p. pap. 24.99 *(978-0-7603-3748-6(9)*, 0760337489, Motorbooks) MBI Publishing Co. LLC.

Stermer, Bill. Bmw R100rs. 2011. (Motorcycle Collector Ser.). (ENG., Illus.). 80p. pap. 17.95 **(978-1-884313-30-1(2)**, 1884313302) Whitehorse Pr.

B'NAI B'RITH

Foxman, Abraham H. The Deadliest Lies: The Israel Lobby & the Myth of Jewish Control. 2007. (ENG.). 256p. 24.95 *(978-1-4039-8492-0(1))* Palgrave Macmillan.

Wilhelm, Cornelia. Deutsche Juden in Amerika: Bürgerliches Selbstbewusstsein und jüdische Identität in den Orden B'nai B'rith und Treue Schwestern, 1843 - 1914. 2007. (Transatlantische Historische Studien (THS) Ser.). (GER & ENG., Illus.). 371p. (C). 72.00 *(978-3-515-08550-2(5))* Steiner, Franz Verlag Wiesbaden GmbH DEU. Dist: Brown, David Bk. Co., The.

BOADICEA, QUEEN, D. 62

Adler, Eric. Valorizing the Barbarians: Enemy Speeches in Roman Historiography. (ENG.). 2012. 283p. pap. 25.00 **(978-0-292-74403-6(X))** 2011. 300p. 55.00 *(978-0-292-72628-4(7))* Univ. of Texas Pr.

Aldhouse-Green, Miranda. Boudica Britannia. 2007. (ENG., Illus.). 320p. 52.95 *(978-1-4058-1100-2(5))* Longman Publishing Group.

Fields, Nic. Boudicca's Rebellion AD 60-61: The Britons Rise up Against Rome. 2011. (Campaign Ser.). (ENG., Illus.). 96p. pap. 19.95 *(978-1-84908-313-3(4))* Osprey Publishing, Ltd. GBR. Dist: Random Hse., Inc.

Hingley, Richard & Unwin, Christina. Boudica: Iron Age Warrior Queen. 2006. (ENG., Illus.). 256p. 24.95 *(978-1-85285-516-1(9)*, Hambledon Continuum) Continuum International Publishing Group, Ltd. GBR. Dist: National Bk. Network.

Sealey, Paul R. The Boudican Revolt Against Rome. 2nd ed. 2008. (Shire Archaeology Ser.). (Illus.). 64p. pap. 13.95 *(978-0-7478-0618-9(7))* Shire Pubns., Ltd. GBR. Dist: Random Hse., Inc.

Waite, John. Boudica's Last Stand: Britain's Revolt Against Rome, A. D. 60-61. 2011. (ENG., Illus.). 256p. pap. 16.95 *(978-0-7524-5909-7(0))* History Pr. Ltd., The GBR. Dist: Independent Pubs. Group.

Williams, Carolyn D. Boudica & Her Stories: Narrative Transformations of a Warrior Queen. 2009. (Illus.). 272p. 65.00 *(978-0-87413-079-9(4))*; (ENG.). 65.00 *(978-1-61149-134-0(7))* Univ. of Delaware Pr.

BOADICIA, QUEEN, D. 62

see Boadicea, Queen, D. 62

BOARD GAMES

see also Backgammon; Checkers; Chess; Go (Game); Monopoly (Game)

Adult Loaded Questions. 2007. mass mkt. 24.99 *(978-0-9779540-8-7(0))* All Things Equal, Inc.

Anspach, Ralph. The Billion Dollar Monopoly (r) Swindle. 2010. 312p. pap. 22.99 *(978-1-4500-9287-6(X))* Xlibris Corp.

Botermans, Jack. The Book of Games: Strategy, Tactics & History. 2008. (ENG., Illus.). 736p. 29.95 *(978-1-4027-4221-7(5))* Sterling Publishing Co., Inc.

Brisman, Andrew. Entertainment. 2009. (ENG.). 96p. pap. 5.95 *(978-1-4027-6505-6(3)*, Puzzlewright) Sterling Publishing Co., Inc.

—Sports. 2009. (ENG.). 96p. pap. 5.95 *(978-1-4027-6504-9(5)*, Puzzlewright) Sterling Publishing Co., Inc.

Cover, Jennifer Grouling. The Creation of Narrative in Tabletop Role-Playing Games. 2010. (ENG., Illus.). 215p. pap. 35.00 *(978-0-7864-4451-9(7))* McFarland & Co., Inc. Pubs.

Crist, Nancy & Sheedy, Rose. What do you say... What do you do... at School? A social Skills Game. 2007. (J). 54.95 *(978-1-58650-770-1(2))* Super Duper Pubns.

de Las Casas, Dianne. Stories on Board! Creating Board Games from Favorite Tales, 1 vol. 2010. 107p. pap. 30.00 *(978-1-59158-862-7(6)*, LU8862) Libraries Unlimited, Inc.

Dunn, Munita. Hands Off! 2010. 388p. pap. *(978-3-8383-5048-6(0))* Lambert Academic Publishing.

Finkel, I. L., ed. Ancient Board Games in Perspective: Papers from the 1990 British Museum Colloquium. 2007. (Illus.). 281p. 100.00 *(978-0-7141-1153-7(8))* British Museum Pr. GBR. Dist: Brown, David Bk. Co., The.

HASBRO, ed. The Ultimate TRIVIAL PURSUIT Question & Answer Book. 2009. (ENG., Illus.). 864p. pap. 14.95 *(978-1-4027-7065-4(0)*, Puzzlewright) Sterling Publishing Co., Inc.

Hasbro Staff, ed. Ouija Answer Book: Look into the Future. Have Fun! 2009. (ENG.). 784p. pap. 9.95 *(978-1-4027-6747-0(1)*, Sterling Innovation) Sterling Publishing Co., Inc.

Hinebaugh, Jeffrey P. A Board Game Education. 2009. (ENG.). 188p. 65.00 *(978-1-60709-259-9(X))*; pap. 16.95 *(978-1-60709-260-5(3))* Rowman & Littlefield Education.

Hollywood Shuffle. 2007. mass mkt. 24.99 *(978-0-9779540-7-0(2))* All Things Equal, Inc.

Hutson-Nechkash, Peg. Story Stunts. 2007. per. 34.95 *(978-1-58650-816-6(4))* Super Duper Pubns.

Imagination Station Board Game. 15.99 *(978-1-56179-836-0(3))* Focus on the Family Publishing.

Ken, Cliffe. Exalted Perfect Circle Boardgame. 2008. pap. 74.99 *(978-1-58846-614-3(0))* White Wolf Publishing, Inc.

Kill Doctor Lucky. 2006. (YA). 34.95 *(978-1-60125-005-6(3))* Paizo Publishing, LLC.

Kill Doctor Lucky.. & His Little Dog Too! 2007. (YA). 7.99 *(978-1-60125-054-4(1))* Paizo Publishing, LLC.

Knizia, Reiner. Genesis. 2007. (Reiner Knizia Ser.). 35.00 *(978-0-9761156-5-6(4))* Face 2 Face Games Publishing.

Mayer, Brian & Harris, Christopher. Libraries Got Game: Aligned Learning Through Modern Board Games. 2009. (Illus.). 134p. 45.00 *(978-0-8389-1009-2(2))* American Library Assn.

Mayfair Games Staff. Settlers of Catan. 2006. pap. 38.00 *(978-1-56905-091-0(0))* Mayfair Games, Inc.

Moffatt, Neil. Games of Go. 2009. 224p. pap. 31.50 *(978-0-9561562-1-1(5))* Moffatt, Neil GBR. Dist: Lulu Enterprises Inc.

Phillies, George & Vasel, Tom. Contemporary Perspectives on Game Design. 2006. pap. 19.89 *(978-1-932657-64-7(9))* Third Millennium Pubns.

Seidman, Glenn. Winning Monopoly. 2011. 52p. pap. 14.98 **(978-1-4634-4132-6(0))** AuthorHouse.

Steele, Bryan. Fighting Ships. 2009. 104p. pap. 24.95 *(978-1-906103-82-8(8))* Mongoose Publishing GBR. Dist: Diamond Bk. Distributors.

Topsfield, Andrew. The Art of Play: Board & Card Games of India. 2007. 168p. 66.00 *(978-81-502-6769-6(7))* Marg Pubns. IND. Dist: National Bk. Network.

BOARD OF GOVERNORS OF THE FEDERAL RESERVE SYSTEM (U.S.)

Auerbach, Robert D. Deception & Abuse at the Fed: Henry B. Gonzalez Battles Alan Greenspan's Bank. 2008. (ENG., Illus.). 285p. 24.95 *(978-0-292-71785-5(7))* Univ. of Texas Pr.

Axilrod, Stephen H. Inside the Fed: Monetary Policy & Its Management, Martin Through Greenspan to Bernanke. 2nd rev. ed. 2011. (ENG., Illus.). 240p. (gr. 17). 24.95 *(978-0-262-01562-2(5))* MIT Pr.

Bernanke, Ben, et al. Bernanke & Greenspan: A Decade of Speeches from Jackson Hole, Wyoming. 2012. pap. **(978-1-62100-912-2(2))** Nova Science Pubs., Inc.

Brave, Scott A. & Genay, Hesna. Federal Reserve Policies & Financial Market Conditions During the Crisis. 2011. 61p. (C). pap. 25.00 **(978-1-4379-8783-6(4))** DIANE Publishing Co.

Broz, J. Lawrence. The International Origins of the Federal Reserve System. 2009. (Illus.). 288p. pap. 28.95 *(978-0-8014-7595-5(3))* Cornell Univ. Pr.

Burns, Arthur F. & Ferrell, Robert H. Inside the Nixon Administration: The Secret Diary of Arthur Burns, 1969-1974. 2010. (Illus.). 144p. 24.95 *(978-0-7006-1730-2(2))* Univ. Pr. of Kansas.

Can Monetary Policy Really Create Jobs? Hearing Before the Subcommittee on Domestic Monetary Policy & Technology of the Committee on Financial Services, U.S. House of Representatives, One Hundred Twelfth Congress, First Session, February 9, 2011. 2011. (Illus.). v, 80p. **(978-0-16-088544-0(2)**, 552-070-42721-0) United States Government Printing Office.

Corder, J. Kevin. The Fed & the Credit Crisis. 2012. 160p. 49.95 **(978-1-58826-820-4(9))** Rienner, Lynne Pubs.

Dewey, C. E. The Feral State. 2010. pap. 14.95 *(978-0-7414-5930-5(2))* Infinity Publishing.

Examining the Link Between Fed Bank Supervision & Monetary Policy: Hearing Before the Committee on Financial Services, U.S. House of Representatives, One Hundred Eleventh Congress, Second Session, March 17, 2010. 2010. iii, 129p. *(978-0-16-086419-3(4)*, 552-070-41480-1) United States Government Printing Office.

Federal Reserve's First Monetary Policy Report for 2007: Hearing Before the Committee on Banking, Housing, & Urban Affairs, United States Senate, One Hundred Tenth Congress, First Session, on Oversight on the Monetary Policy Report to Congress Pursuant to the Full Employment & Balanced Growth ACT of 1978, February 14, 2007. 2007. (Illus.). iii, 102p. *(978-0-16-079964-8(3)*, 552-070-36789-6) United States Government Printing Office.

Federal Reserve's First Monetary Policy Report for 2010: Hearing Before the Committee on Banking, Housing, & Urban Affairs, United States Senate, One Hundred Eleventh Congress, Second Session, on Receiving the Federal Reserve's Semi-Annual Monetary Policy Report to the Congress & Discussing Monetary Policy & the Economic Outlook, February 25, 2010. 2010. (Illus.). iii, 130p. **(978-0-16-087950-0(7)**, 552-070-42382-6) United States Government Printing Office.

Federal Reserve's First Monetary Policy Report for 2011: Hearing Before the Committee on Banking, Housing, & Urban Affairs, United States Senate, One Hundred Twelfth Congress, First Session, on Oversight on the Monetary Policy Report to Congress Pursuant to the Full Employment & Balanced

Growth ACT of 1978, March 1, 2011. 2011. (Illus.). iii, 130p. ***(978-0-16-089092-5(6)***, 552-070-43115-2) United States Government Printing Office.

Federal Reserve's Second Monetary Policy Report for 2010: Hearing Before the Committee on Banking, Housing, & Urban Affairs, United States Senate, One Hundred Eleventh Congress, Second Session, on Oversight on the Monetary Policy Report to Congress Pursuant to the Full Employment & Balanced Growth ACT of 1978, July 21, 2010. 2010. (Illus.). iii, 131p. ***(978-0-16-087951-7(5)***, 552-070-42383-4) United States Government Printing Office.

Griffin, G. Edward. The Creature from Jekyll Island: A Second Look at the Federal Reserve. 5th ed. 2010. pap. 24.50 *(978-0-912986-45-6(X))* American Media.

Harris, Ethan S. Ben Bernanke's Fed: The Federal Reserve after Greenspan. 2008. (ENG., Illus.). 237p. 26.95 *(978-1-4221-2584-7(X))* Harvard Business Review Pr.

Hester, Donald D. The Evolution of Monetary Policy & Banking in the US. (ENG., Illus.). viii, 206p. 2010. pap. 129.00 *(978-3-642-09651-8(4)*, 3642096514) 2008. 129.00 *(978-3-540-77793-9(8)*, 3540777938) Springer.

Kelsey, Lindsay S. Monetary Policy & the Federal Reserve. 2010. 130.00 *(978-1-61728-867-8(5))* Nova Science Pubs., Inc.

Kudkinski, Jim. The Tarnished Fed: Behind Closed Doors: Forty Years of Successes, Failures, Mystique, & Humor. 2010. 250p. pap. 16.95 *(978-0-533-16318-2(8))* Vantage Pr., Inc.

Lorca-Susino, Maria. The Euro in the 21st Century: Economic Crisis & Financial Uproar. 2010. (International Political Economy of New Regionalisms Ser.). (Illus.). 334p. 119.95 *(978-1-4094-0418-7(8))* Ashgate Publishing Co.

Meltzer, Allan H. History Federal Reserve, 1951-1969, Vol. 2. 2007. pap. 25.00 *(978-0-226-52002-5(1))* Univ. of Chicago Pr.

—A History Federal Reserve, 1951-1969, Vol. 2, Bk. 1. 2010. (ENG., Illus.). 696p. 75.00 *(978-0-226-52001-8(3))* Univ. of Chicago Pr.

Monetary Policy & the Debt Ceiling: Examining the Relationship Between the Federal Reserve & Government Debt: Hearing Before the Subcommittee on Domestic Monetary Policy & Technology of the Committee on Financial Services, U.S. House of Representatives, One Hundred Twelfth Congress, First Session, May 11, 2011. 2011. (Illus.). iv, 69p. ***(978-0-16-089066-6(7)***, 552-070-43098-9) United States Government Printing Office.

Monetary Policy & the State of the Economy: Hearing Before the Committee on Financial Services, U.S. House of Representatives, One Hundred Tenth Congress, Second Session, July 16, 2008. 2008. (Illus.). iii, 121p. *(978-0-16-082207-0(6)*, 552-070-38342-5) United States Government Printing Office.

Moore, Carl H. The Federal Reserve System: A History of the First 75 Years. alt. ed. 2011. (ENG., Illus.). 280p. pap. 25.00 *(978-0-7864-6735-8(5))* McFarland & Co., Inc. Pubs.

Nominations of Edward P. Lazear, Randall S. Kroszner, & Kevin M. Warsh: Hearing Before the Committee on Banking, Housing, & Urban Affairs, United States Senate, One Hundred Ninth Congress, Second Session, on Nominations of Edward P. Lazear, of California, to Be Chairman of the Council of Economic Advisers: Randall S. Kroszner, of New Jersey, to Be a Member of the Board of Governors of the Federal Reserve System: Kevin M. Warsh, of New York, to Be a Member of the Boa. 2007. iii, 77p. *(978-0-16-079309-7(2)*, 552-070-36387-4) United States Government Printing Office.

Oversight of the Consumer Financial Protection Bureau: Hearing Before the Subcommittee on Financial Institutions & Consumer Credit of the Committee on Financial Services, U.S. House of Representatives, One Hundred Twelfth Congress, First Session, March 16, 2011. v, 100p. ***(978-0-16-089073-4(X)***, 552-070-43105-5) United States Government Printing Office.

Paul, Ron. End the Fed. (ENG.). 2010. 224p. pap. 14.99 *(978-0-446-54917-2(7))* 2009. 224p. 21.99 *(978-0-446-54919-6(3))* 2009. 336p. pap. 21.00 *(978-0-446-55997-3(0))* Grand Central Publishing.

Ranchett, John P., ed. Federal Reserve: Functions & Policies. 2012. ***(978-1-62100-528-5(3))*** Nova Science Pubs., Inc.

Regulatory Restructuring: Safeguarding Consumer Protection & the Role of the Federal Reserve: Hearing Before the Subcommittee on Domestic Monetary Policy & Technology of the Committee on Financial Services, U.S. House of Representatives, One Hundred Eleventh Congress, First Session, July 16, 2009. 2009. (Illus.). v, 247p. *(978-0-16-085145-2(9)*, 552-070-40499-6) United States Government Printing Office.

The Role of the International Monetary Fund & the Federal Reserve in Stabilizing Europe: Joint Hearing Before the Subcommittee on Domestic Monetary Policy & Technology & the Subcommittee on International Monetary Policy & Trade of the Committee on Financial Services, U.S. House of Representatives, One Hundred Eleventh Congress, Second Session, May 20, 2010. 2010. v, 80p. ***(978-0-16-086859-7(9)***, 552-070-41771-1) United States Government Printing Office.

Santow, Leonard J. Do They Walk on Water? Federal Reserve Chairmen & the Fed, 1 vol. 2008. 360p. 44.95 *(978-0-313-36033-6(2)*, C36033, Praeger Pubs.) Greenwood Publishing Group, Inc.

Silber, William L. Volcker: Central Banker. 2012. (ENG., Illus.). 464p. 30.00 ***(978-1-60819-070-6(6))*** Bloomsbury Publishing.

State of the Economy: View from the Federal Reserve: Hearing Before the Committee on the Budget, House of Representatives, One Hundred Eleventh Congress, Second Session, Hearing Held in Washington, DC, June 9, 2010. 2010. (Illus.). iii, 61p. ***(978-0-16-086811-5(4)***, 552-070-41727-3) United States Government Printing Office.

The State of the U.S. Economy: Hearing Before the Committee on the Budget, House of Representatives, One Hundred Twelfth Congress, First Session, Hearing Held in Washington, DC, February 9, 2011. 2011. iii, 72p. ***(978-0-16-088823-6(9)***, 552-070-42957-3) United States Government Printing Office.

Thomas, Lloyd B. The Financial Crisis & Federal Reserve Policy. 2011. (ENG., Illus.). 282p. 100.00 *(978-0-230-10846-2(6))* Palgrave Macmillan.

Van Overtveldt, Johan. Bernanke's Test: Ben Bernanke, Alan Greenspan, & the Drama of the Central Banker. 2010. (ENG.). 300p. pap. 19.95 *(978-1-932841-51-0(2))* Agate Publishing, Inc.

Wessel, David. In Fed We Trust: Ben Bernanke's War on the Great Panic. 2010. 352p. pap. 16.00 *(978-0-307-45969-5(1)*, Three Rivers Pr.) 2009. (ENG.). 336p. 26.99 *(978-0-307-45968-8(3)*, Crown Business) Crown Publishing Group.

Wood, John H. A History of Central Banking in Great Britain & the United States. 2008. (Studies in Macroeconomic History Ser.). (ENG., Illus.). 458p. pap. 36.99 *(978-0-521-74131-6(9))* Cambridge Univ. Pr.

BOARDING SCHOOLS

see also Private Schools

Arieli, M. Residential Settings & the Community: Congruence & Conflict. Kashti, Y., ed. *(978-965-294-026-1(7))* Freund Publishing Hse., Ltd.

Bollen, David. Up on the Hill: A History of St. Patrick's College, Goulburn. 2008. (ENG.). 640p. pap. 53.95 *(978-0-86840-967-2(7)*, UNSW Press) NewSouth Publishing AUS. Dist: Independent Pubs. Group.

Brewer, S. Grey. The Rabbit in the Moon. 2009. 232p. 25.99 *(978-1-60791-311-5(9))*; pap. 15.99 *(978-1-60791-388-7(7))* Xulon Pr., Inc.

Chalcraft, Edwin L. Assimilation's Agent: My Life as a Superintendent in the Indian Boarding School System. Collins, Cary C., ed. & intro. by. 2007. (ENG., Illus.). 368p. pap. 29.95 *(978-0-8032-2244-1(0))* Univ. of Nebraska Pr.

Chen, Yangbin. Muslim Uyghur Students in a Chinese Boarding School: Social Recapitalization as a Response to Ethnic Integration. 2008. (Emerging Perspectives on Education in China Ser.). (ENG., Illus.). 230p. 73.50 *(978-0-7391-2112-2(X))* Lexington Bks.

Downs, Jacqueline. Coping with Change. 2010. 456p. pap. *(978-3-8383-4679-3(3))* Lambert Academic Publishing.

Fortunate Eagle, Adam. Pipestone: My Life in an Indian Boarding School. 2010. (ENG., Illus.). 248p. pap. 19.95 *(978-0-8061-4114-5(X))* Univ. of Oklahoma Pr.

Gaztambide-Fernández, Rubén A. The Best of the Best: Becoming Elite at an American Boarding School. 2009. (Illus.). 312p. 31.50 *(978-0-674-03568-3(2))* Harvard Univ. Pr.

Greene, Howard R., et al. Boarding Schools. 2006. (ENG.). 300p. per. 19.00 *(978-0-7689-2241-7(0))* Peterson's.

Helfer, Celeste, ed. American Boarding Schools: The American Boarding School Experience. 2009. (ENG.). 205p. pap. 14.95 *(978-1-934159-02-6(6))* ThingsAsian Pr.

Howard, Adam. Educating Elites: Class Privilege & Educational Advantage. 2010. (ENG.). 220p. 95.00 *(978-1-60709-458-6(4))* Rowman & Littlefield Publishers, Inc.

Howard, Adam & Gaztambide-Fernandez, Ruben A. Educating Elites: Class Privilege & Educational Advantage. 2010. xii, 214p. 37.95 *(978-1-60709-460-9(6))* Rowman & Littlefield Publishers, Inc.

Howard/Gaztambid-Fer. Educating Elites: Class Privilege & Educational Advantage. 2010. (ENG.). 220p. per. 37.95 *(978-1-60709-459-3(2))* Rowman & Littlefield Publishers, Inc.

Humberg, Kerstin. Boarding School Education for Tribal Girls in Development Projects. 2008. 152p. per. *(978-3-8364-5357-8(6))* VDM Verlag Dr. Mueller e.K.

Katanski, Amelia V. Learning to Write Indian: The Boarding-School Experience & American Indian Literature. 2007. (ENG., Illus.). 288p. (C). per. 19.95 *(978-0-8061-3852-7(1))* Univ. of Oklahoma Pr.

Khan, Shamus Rahman. Privilege: The Making of an Adolescent Elite at St. Paul's School. 2010. (Princeton Studies in Cultural Sociology Ser.). (ENG.). 256p. (C). 29.95 *(978-0-691-14528-0(8))* Princeton Univ. Pr.

Lei, Christine. The History of a Catholic Girls Day & Boarding School, 1865-1970: The Religious & Educational Achievement of the Loretto Sisters. 2010. 268p. 109.95 *(978-0-7734-3861-3(0))* Mellen, Edwin Pr., The.

McConnell, Jess. Analysis of Documents Related to Residential Schools in Canad. 2010. 176p. pap. *(978-3-639-22283-8(0))* VDM Verlag Dr. Mueller e.K.

McLester, L. Gordon, III. The Oneida Indians in the Age of Allotment, 1860-1920. Hauptman, Laurence M., ed. 2006. (Civilization of the American Indian Ser.: 253). (ENG., Illus.). 368p. (C). 34.95 *(978-0-8061-3752-0(5))* Univ. of Oklahoma Pr.

Peterson's Guides Staff, creator. Peterson's American & Canadian Boarding Schools & Worldwide Enrichment Programs. 13th ed. 2006. (ENG., Illus.). 216p. pap. 18.00 *(978-0-7689-2332-2(8))* Peterson's.

Phillips, Winston J. The Grenada Boys Secondary School Hostel: Reminiscing on a Boarding School Life in Grenada. 2009. (Illus.). 200p. pap. 16.95 *(978-1-4327-4665-0(0))* Outskirts Pr., Inc.

Shillinger, Sarah. A Case Study of the American Indian Boarding School Movement: An Oral History of Saint Joseph's Indian Industrial School. 2008. 164p. 99.95 *(978-0-7734-5015-8(7))* Mellen, Edwin Pr., The.

Silvin, Richard Rene. I Survived Swiss Boarding Schools. 2006. pap. 14.95 *(978-0-9764052-9-0(6))* Thomas Max Publishing.

Snicket, Lemony, pseud. Das Internat des Schreckens. *(978-3-407-79823-7(7))* Beltz, Julius GmbH & Company KG.

Vuckovic, Myriam. Voices from Haskell: Indian Students Between Two Worlds, 1884-1927. 2008. (Illus.). 320p. (C). 34.95 *(978-0-7006-1617-6(9))* Univ. Pr. of Kansas.

Zhu, Zhiyong. State Schooling & Ethnic Identity: The Politics of a Tibetan Neidi Secondary School in China. Zhu, Zhiyong, ed. 2007. (Emerging Perspectives on Education in China Ser.). (ENG., Illus.). 378p. 78.99 *(978-0-7391-1539-8(1))* Lexington Bks.

BOARDINGHOUSES

see also Hotels

Davis, Roy. Crest Park: A Catskill Mountain Memoir. 2009. 472p. pap. 19.95 *(978-1-4327-1238-9(1))* Outskirts Pr., Inc.

Faflik, David. Boarding Out: Inhabiting the American Urban Literary Imagination, 1840-1860. 2012. (ENG., Illus.). 368p. pap. 29.95 ***(978-0-8101-2838-5(1))*** Northwestern Univ. Pr.

Fleming, Geoffrey K. & Folk, Amy Kasuga. Hotels & Inns of Long Island's North Fork. 2009. (Vintage Images Ser.). 160p. pap. 21.99 *(978-1-59629-725-8(5))* History Pr., The.

Gamber, Wendy. The Boardinghouse in Nineteenth-Century America. 2007. (ENG., Illus.). 232p. (gr. 17). 47.00 *(978-0-8018-8571-6(X))* Johns Hopkins Univ. Pr.

Gunn, Thomas. The Physiology of New York Boarding-Hous. 2009. (City Ser.). (ENG.). 302p. pap. 19.95 *(978-1-4290-2194-4(2))* Applewood Bks.

Gunn, Thomas Butler. The Physiology of New York Boarding-Houses. 2011. 308p. pap. 29.75 ***(978-1-179-97145-2(0))*** 2010. 312p. pap. 29.75 *(978-1-142-75634-5(3))* BiblioBazaar.

—The Physiology of New York Boarding-Houses. 2010. 128p. pap. *(978-1-151-78277-9(7))* Books LLC.

Gunn, Thomas Butler. The Physiology of New York Boarding Houses. 2010. 304p. pap. 23.16 *(978-1-163-97671-5(7))* 2010. 304p. 35.16 ***(978-1-164-33031-8(4))*** 2008. 302p. 43.95 *(978-0-548-98385-0(2))* 2007. (ENG.). 304p. per. 28.95 *(978-0-548-66363-9(7))* Kessinger Publishing, LLC.

Gunn, Thomas Butler & Faflik, David, eds. The Physiology of New York Boarding-Houses. 2008. (ENG., Illus.). 234p. 68.00 *(978-0-8135-4439-7(4))*; xxxiii, 200p. pap. 23.95 *(978-0-8135-4440-3(8))* Rutgers Univ. Pr.

Henning, R. & Henning, Ronelle. Effective Guest House Management. 3rd ed. 2008. (ENG., Illus.). 232p. spiral bd. 46.00 *(978-0-7021-7705-7(9))* Juta Academic ZAF. Dist: Independent Pubs. Group.

Kohl, Christiane. The Witness House: Nazis & Holocaust Survivors Sharing a Villa during the Nuremberg Trials. Bell, Anthea, tr. from GER. 2010. (ENG., Illus.). 272p. pap. 14.95 *(978-1-59051-379-8(7))* Other Pr., LLC.

Lynch, Paul & Tucker, Hazel. Commercial Homes in Tourism: An International Perspective. Lynch, Paul & McIntosh, Alison J., eds. 2009. (Routledge Critical Studies in Tourism, Business & Management Ser.). (ENG., Illus.). 288p. (C). 133.00 *(978-0-415-47018-6(8))* Routledge.

Marshall, Dan. Starting & Running a Guesthouse. 2nd ed. 2008. 191p. pap. 30.00 *(978-1-84528-203-5(5))* How To Books GBR. Dist: Parkwest Pubns., Inc.

Mathews, Gordon. Ghetto at the Center of the World: Chungking Mansions, Hong Kong. 2011. (Illus.). 256p. pap. ***(978-988-8083-36-7(8))*** Hong Kong Univ. Pr.

—Ghetto at the Center of the World: Chungking Mansions, Hong Kong. 2011. (ENG., Illus.). 256p. 62.00 *(978-0-226-51019-4(0))*; pap. 19.00 *(978-0-226-51020-0(4))* Univ. of Chicago Pr.

Michelin Guesthouses. Guesthouses in France. 2008. (Illus.). 400p. instr.'s gde. ed. 19.95 *(978-2-06-713599-4(6))* Michelin.

Parker, Ken. How to Buy & Run a Small Hotel: The Complete Guide to Setting up & Managing Your Own Hotel, Guesthouse or B&B. 5th rev. ed. 2007. (Illus.). 246p. per. 30.00 *(978-1-84528-168-7(3))* How To Books GBR. Dist: Parkwest Pubns., Inc.

Smith, Evelyn Eileen. Boardinghouse Stew: A Novel. 2011. (Illus.). 200p. 24.95 ***(978-0-9835615-1-4(6))*** Phoenix International, Inc.

Wright, Kevin J. Europe's Monastery & Convent Guesthouses: A Pilgrim's Travel Guide. 2008. (Illus.). xiv, 240p. 18.99 *(978-0-7648-1780-9(9))* Liguori Pubns.

BOARDS OF DIRECTORS

see Directors of Corporations

BOARDS OF EDUCATION

see School Boards

BOARDS OF SUPERVISION (CORPORATION LAW)

see Directors of Corporations

BOARDS OF TRADE

see also Industrial Promotion

Bennett, Robert J. Local Business Voice: The History of Chambers of Commerce in Britain, Ireland, & Revolutionary America, 1760-2011. 2012. (ENG., Illus.). 936p. 175.00 ***(978-0-19-958473-4(7))*** Oxford Univ. Pr., Inc.

Chen, Zhongping. Modern China's Network Revolution: Chambers of Commerce & Sociopolitical Change in the Early Twentieth Century. 2011. (ENG.). 312p. 55.00 *(978-0-8047-7409-3(9))* Stanford Univ. Pr.

Hertz, Thomas. Die Industrie- und Handelskammer zu Berlin: Ein Beitrag zur Wirtschaftsgeschichte Berlins. 2008.Tr. of Berlin Chamber of Industry & Commerce. (GER., XII, 488p. Illus.). 42.00 *(978-3-11-020669-2(2))*; 70.00 ***(978-3-11-916230-2(2))*** De Gruyter, Walter Inc.

Schmaltz, Jacqueline. Die Entwicklung der Industrie- und Handelskammern: Zwischen Pflicht und Kür. 2010. (Rechtshistorische Reihe Ser.). (GER.). 292p. 79.95 *(978-3-631-60330-7(4))* Lang, Peter GmbH, Europaischer Verlag der Wissenschaften DEU. Dist: Lang, Peter.

United Nations Publications Staff, contrib. by. World Directory of Trade Promotion Organizations & Other Support Institutions 2007. 2007. (Trade Information Ser.). (MUL.). 228p. pap. 50.00 *(978-92-1-015009-5(0))* United Nations Pubns.

Vesser, Cyrus & Kusserow, Karl. World Safe for Capitalism. 2011. (ENG.). 320p. (gr. 17). 60.00 *(978-0-231-12358-7(2))* Columbia Univ. Pr.

Visscher, Sikko. The Business of Politics & Ethnicity: A History of the Singapore Chinese Chamber of Commerce & Industry. 2007. (Illus.). 372p. per. 32.00 *(978-9971-69-365-7(8))* Univ. of Hawaii Pr.

World Chamber of Commerce, creator. World Chamber of Commerce Directory. (World Chamber of Commerce Directory Ser.). 2010. 413p. pap. 61.25 *(978-0-943581-23-1(0))* 2007. 422p. per. 56.25 *(978-0-943581-20-0(6))* World Wide Chamber of Commerce Directory.

World Directory to Chambers of Commerce. lib. bdg. *(978-92-842-0014-6(8))* Springer.

BOARS

Hagey, Thomas. Playboar. (Illus.). reprint ed. pap. 9.95 *(978-0-9628198-2-7(4))* Kent, William Inc.

Hainds, Mark J. Year of the Pig. 2011. (ENG., Illus.). 272p. pap. 16.95 ***(978-0-8173-5670-5(3))***; ***(978-0-8173-8563-7(0))*** Univ. of Alabama Pr.

BOAS, FRANZ, 1858-1942

Boas, Franz. Eskimo Story (Written for My Children) My Arctic Expedition 1883-1884. Boas, Norman F., ed. 2007. (Illus.). 56p. (YA). (gr. 1-12). pap. 6.00 *(978-0-9672626-3-5(1))* Boas & Meyer, Pubs.

Freed, Stanley A. Anthropology Unmasked: Museums, Science, & Politics in New York City. 2011. *(978-1-933197-84-5(6))*; 80.00 *(978-1-933197-83-8(8))* Orange Frazer Pr.

Gieseking, Bernd & Müller-Wile, Ludger. Inuit & Whalers on Baffin Islands Through German Eyes: Wilhelm Wieke's Arctic Journal & Letters (1883-1884) 2011. (ENG., Illus.). 270p. 29.95 ***(978-1-926824-11-6(3))*** Baraka Bks. CAN. Dist: Independent Pubs. Group.

Morris-Reich, Amos. The Quest for Jewish Assimilation in Modern Social Science. 2012. (Routledge Studies in Social & Political Thought Ser.). (ENG.). 206p. pap. 42.95 ***(978-0-415-54073-5(9))*** Routledge.

Willis, William Shedrick & Zumwalt, Rosemary Levy. Franz Boas & W.E.B. Du Bois at Atlanta University, 1906. 2008. *(978-0-87169-982-4(6))* American Philosophical Society.

BOAT HANDLING

see Boats and Boating

BOAT MODELS

see Ship Models

BOAT NAMES

Artof, Susan D. Boat Naming Made Simple: The Complete Book. 4th ed. 2008. *(978-1-889198-14-9(5))* Center Pr., The.

Churchman, Laurie. The Art of Boat Names: Inspiring Ideas for Names & Designs. 2008. (ENG.). 184p. pap. 24.95 *(978-0-07-159142-3(7)*, 0071591427, International Marine/Ragged Mountain Pr.) McGraw-Hill Professional Publishing.

BOAT RACING

see Motorboat Racing; Rowing; Sailboat Racing; Yacht Racing

BOAT TRADE

see Boating Industry

BOATBUILDING

see also Fiberglass Boats; Shipbuilding; Yacht Building

Atkin, Gavin. Ultrasimple Boatbuilding: 17 Plywood Boats Anyone Can Build. 2007. (ENG., Illus.). 192p. per. 24.95 *(978-0-07-147792-5(6)*, 0071477926, International Marine/Ragged Mountain Pr.) McGraw-Hill Professional Publishing.

Barry, James P. Hackercraft. 2009. (ENG., Illus.). 128p. pap. 24.99 *(978-0-7603-3632-8(6)*, 0760336326, Voyageur Pr) MBI Publishing Co. LLC.

Beard, Daniel. Boat-Building & Boating. 2006. (Dover Maritime Bks.). (ENG., Illus.). 208p. per. 9.95 *(978-0-486-45115-2(1))* Dover Pubns., Inc.

Blandford, Percy W. Build Your Own Boat. 2006. (Dover Books on Woodworking & Carving Ser.). (ENG., Illus.). 192p. per. 10.95 *(978-0-486-45289-0(1))* Dover Pubns., Inc.

Bray, Maynard. Mystic Seaport Watercraft. 2008. (Maritime Ser.). (ENG.). 420p. pap. 24.95 *(978-0-913372-95-1(1))* Mystic Seaport Museum, Inc.

Brown, J. D. & Pickett, Bob. A Boat Named Clancy: A Builder's Guide to a Superb Little Sailboat. rev. ed. Orig. Title: Build a Clancy. pap. 15.95 *(978-0-917436-04-8(0))* Tamal Vista Pubns.

Burke, John. Pete Culler on Wooden Boats: The Master Craftsman's Collected Teachings on Boat Design, Building, Repair, & Use. 2007. (ENG., Illus.). 400p. per. 29.95 *(978-0-07-148979-9(7)*, 0071489797, International Marine/Ragged Mountain Pr.) McGraw-Hill Professional Publishing.

California, Pa., 1849-1881: A History of a Boat Building Town. 2009. (Illus.). 466p. pap. 20.00 *(978-0-9630513-5-6(0))* Yohogania Pr.

Carolina Flare: Outer Banks Boatbuilding & Sportfishing Heritage. 2007. 60.00 *(978-0-9791177-0-1(4))* Carolina Flare, LLC.

Cheek, Lawrence W. The Year of the Boat: Beauty, Imperfection, & the Art of Doing It Yourself. 2008. (ENG., Illus.). 288p. 23.95 *(978-1-57061-544-3(6))* Sasquatch Bks.

—The Year of the Boat: Beauty, Imperfection, & the Art of Doing It Yourself. 2009. (ENG.). 288p. pap. 16.95 *(978-1-57061-614-3(0))* Sasquatch Bks.
Cramer, Carl & Steward, Robert. Boatbuilding Manual. 5th ed. 2010. (ENG., Illus.). 448p. 40.00 *(978-0-07-162834-1(7)*, 0071628347, International Marine/Ragged Mountain Pr.) McGraw-Hill Professional Publishing.
D Custom. MasterCraft: Setting a Higher Standard for 40 Years. 2007. 132p. pap. 39.95 *(978-0-9761697-1-0(1))* D Magazine Ltd. Partners.
Denny, Mark. Float Your Boat! The Evolution & Science of Sailing. 2008. (ENG., Illus.). 280p. 30.00 *(978-0-8018-9009-3(8))* Johns Hopkins Univ. Pr.
Desmond, Charles. Wooden Ship-Building. 2010. 226p. pap. 16.65 *(978-1-152-49141-0(5))* General Bks. LLC.
Dodds, Richard J. S. & Hurry, Robert J. Boats for Work, Boats for Pleasure: The Last ERA of Wooden Boatbuilding in Southern Maryland. 2009. (Illus.). xviii, 129p. pap. ***(978-0-941647-20-5(X))*** Calvert Marine Museum Pr.
Evans, Doug. Noah's Last Canoe: The Last Art of Cree Birch Bark Canoe Building. 2008. (ENG.). 104p. pap. 24.95 *(978-1-894283-82-3(1))* Great Plains Pubns. CAN. Dist: Univ. of Toronto Pr.
Gerr, Dave. Boat Mechanical Systems Handbook: How to Design, Install, & Recognize Proper Systems in Boats. 2nd ed. 2008. (ENG., Illus.). 448p. 39.95 *(978-0-07-144456-9(4)*, 0071444564, International Marine/Ragged Mountain Pr.) McGraw-Hill Professional Publishing.
Gilpatrick, Gil. Building a Strip Canoe: Full-Sized Plans & Instructions for Eight Easy-to-Build, Field-Tested Canoes. 2nd rev. expurg. ed. 2010. (Illus.). 112p. pap. 24.95 *(978-1-56523-483-3(9))* Fox Chapel Publishing Co., Inc.
Grijalva, Edward. Glasspar Boat Builder: Circa 1952-1962. 2008. 48p. pap. 16.95 *(978-1-60610-882-6(4))* PublishAmerica, Inc.
Hichborn, Philip. Standard Designs for Boats of the United States Navy: Specifications, Schedule of Material, Weights & Cost. 2007. *(978-1-57898-662-0(1))* United States Government Printing Office.
Hume, David D., illus. Blueberry: A Boat of the Connecticut Shoreline. 2007. (ENG.). 115p. per. 15.00 *(978-1-933002-54-5(9))* PublishingWorks.
Into, John & Price, Nancy. Fundamentals of Model Boat Building. 2011. (Illus.). 160p. 34.99 *(978-0-7643-3105-3(1))* Schiffer Publishing, Ltd.
Kapitan, Gerhard. Records of Traditional Watercraft from South & West Sri Lanka. 2009. (Illus.). 191p. (C). 112.50 *(978-1-4073-0413-7(5))* British Archaeological Reports Ltd. GBR. Dist: Brown, David Bk. Co., The.
Mallan, Lloyd. The Complete Book of Kit Boats. 2011. 148p. 40.95 ***(978-1-258-08133-1(4))*** Literary Licensing, LLC.
Máté, Ferenc. Best Boats to Build or Buy. 2006. (ENG., Illus.). 384p. pap. 29.95 *(978-0-920256-24-4(4)*, 25624) Albatross Publishing CAN. Dist: Norton, W. W. & Co., Inc.
Mellor, John. Logbook for Cruising under Sail. 2009. (ENG.). 96p. 29.95 *(978-0-470-74684-4(X)*, Wiley) Wiley, John & Sons, Inc.
Mollica Jr, Anthony & Savage, Jack. Chris-Craft Boats. 2009. (ENG., Illus.). 192p. pap. 24.99 *(978-0-7603-3631-1(8)*, 0760336318, Voyageur Pr) MBI Publishing Co. LLC.
Nelson, Adrian. Practical Boat Building for Amateurs: Full Instructions for Designing & Building Punts, Skiffs, Canoes, Sailing Boats, &c. 2008. (Illus.). 132p. pap. 9.99 *(978-1-929516-13-1(4))* Dixon-Price Publishing.
Nichols, David L. Building the Sea Eagles: A Pair of Safe & Seaworthy Beach & Coastal Cruisers. 2010. (ENG.). 160p. pap. 24.95 *(978-1-891369-87-2(3))* Breakaway Bks.
—Lapstrake Canoes: Everything You Need to Know to Build a Light, Strong, Beautiful Boat. 2007. (ENG., Illus.). 160p. pap. 21.95 *(978-1-891369-72-8(5))* Breakaway Bks.
Pardey, Lin. Bull Canyon: A Boatbuilder, a Writer & other Wildlife. 2011. (Illus.). 320p. 24.95 *(978-1-929214-67-9(7))* Pardey Bks.
Payson, Harold H. Instant Boatbuilding with Dynamite Payson: The Fastest, Easiest Way to Build 15 Boats for Power, Sail, Oar, & Paddle. 2007. (ENG., Illus.). 144p. per. 19.95 *(978-0-07-147264-7(9)*, 0071472649, International Marine/Ragged Mountain Pr.) McGraw-Hill Professional Publishing.
Pollard, Stephen F. Boatbuilding with Aluminum: A Complete Guide for the Amateur & Small Shop. 2nd rev. ed. 2006. (ENG., Illus.). 320p. 36.95 *(978-0-07-144318-0(5)*, 0071443185, International Marine/Ragged Mountain Pr.) McGraw-Hill Professional Publishing.
Rizzetta, Sam. Canoe & Kayak Building the Light & Easy Way: How to Build Tough, Super-Safe Boats in Kevlar, Carbon, or Fiberglass. 2009. (ENG., Illus.). 256p. pap. 24.95 *(978-0-07-159735-7(2)*, 0071597352, International Marine/Ragged Mountain Pr.) McGraw-Hill Professional Publishing.
Rossel, Greg. The Boatbuilder's Apprentice: The Ins & Outs of Building Lapstrake, Carvel, Stitch-and-Glue, Strip-Planked, & Other Wooden Boats. 2006. (ENG., Illus.). 352p. 39.95 *(978-0-07-146405-5(0)*, 0071464050, International Marine/Ragged Mountain Pr.) McGraw-Hill Professional Publishing.
Roy, Zoë S. Butterfly Tears. 2009. (ENG., Illus.). 17p. pap. 22.95 *(978-0-9782233-7-3(3))* Inanna Pubns. & Education, Inc. CAN. Dist: SPD-Small Pr. Distribution.
Schade, Nick. Building Strip-Planked Boats. 2009. (ENG., Illus.). 288p. pap. 22.95 *(978-0-07-147524-2(9)*, 0071475249, International Marine/Ragged Mountain Pr.) McGraw-Hill Professional Publishing.
Seymour, Martin. Clinker Boat Building: A guide to traditional Techniques, 1 vol. 2012. (ENG., Illus.). 160p. 45.00 ***(978-1-84797-334-4(5))*** Crowood Pr., Ltd. GBR. Dist: Independent Pubs. Group.
Sherriff, Clare. Boathouses. 2009. (ENG., Illus.). 168p. 75.00 *(978-0-906290-97-2(X))* Unicorn Pr., London GBR. Dist: National Bk. Network.
Simpson, Richard V. Herreshoff Yachts: Seven Generations of Industrialists, Inventors & Ingenuity in Bristol. 2007. (Illus.). 152p. pap., per. 21.99 *(978-1-59629-306-9(3))* History Pr., The.
Swinger, Patricia. Hard Work, Good People, & 100,000 Boats: 50 Years of Boat-Building with Zach McClendon. 2009. 152p. *(978-1-57864-576-3(X))* Donning Co. Pubs.
Taylor, David A. Boat Building in Winterton, Trinity Bay, Newfoundland. 2006. (Mercury Ser.: Vol. 80). (Illus.). 164p. per. 29.95 *(978-0-660-19599-5(2))* Canadian Museum of Civilization/Musee Canadien des Civilisations CAN. Dist: Univ. of Washington Pr.
Wahl, Ryan. Legacy in Wood: The Wahl Family Boat Builders. 2009. (ENG., Illus.). 240p. 32.95 *(978-1-55017-433-5(9))* Harbour Publishing Co., Ltd. CAN. Dist: Ingram Pub. Services.
Young, Dorothy & Stuff, Hal. A Full Plate of Retirement: Grandma Learns to Cook, Build Boats, Then Goes Cruising. 2011. 229p. pap. 18.95 ***(978-1-4327-7158-4(2))*** Outskirts Pr., Inc.

BOATING

see Boats and Boating

BOATING INDUSTRY

Brown, David G. Make Money with Your Captain's License: How to Get a Job or Run a Business on a Boat. 2007. (ENG., Illus.). 240p. 22.95 *(978-0-07-147523-5(0)*, 0071475230, International Marine/Ragged Mountain Pr.) McGraw-Hill Professional Publishing.
Mondadori Electa, ed. Wally. 2nd ed. 2009. (Illus.). 224p. 115.00 *(978-88-370-6008-4(4))* Electa ITA. Dist: Trans-Atlantic Pubns., Inc.
Rodengen, Jeffrey. Commanding the Waterways: The Story of Sea Ray. 2008. (Illus.). 192p. 39.95 *(978-1-932022-33-9(3)*, Write Stuff) Write Stuff Enterprises, Inc.
Strickler, Darryl. Rowable Classics: Wooden Single Sculling Boats & Oars. 2008. (Illus.). 144p. 29.95 *(978-0-937822-96-8(5))* WoodenBoat Pubns.
Swinger, Patricia. Hard Work, Good People, & 100,000 Boats: 50 Years of Boat-Building with Zach McClendon. 2009. 152p. *(978-1-57864-576-3(X))* Donning Co. Pubs.

BOATMEN

see also Shipping

Dimock, Brad. The Very Hard Way: Bert Loper & the Colorado River. 2007. (Illus.). 457p. per. 17.95 *(978-1-892327-69-7(4))*; 472p. 29.95 *(978-1-892327-49-9(X))* Fretwater Pr.
Fewster, Joseph M. The Keelmen of Tyneside: Labour Organisation & Conflict in the North-East Coal Industry, 1600-1830. 2011. (Regions & Regionalism in History Ser.: Volume 13). (Illus.). 232p. 99.00 *(978-1-84383-632-2(7)*, Boydell Press) Boydell & Brewer, Ltd. GBR. Dist: Boydell & Brewer, Inc.
Wood, George Randolph & Hammond, Theresa. A Young Virginia Boatman Navigates the Civil War: The Journals of George Randolph Wood. Molineux, Will, ed. 2010. (ENG., Illus.). 216p. (gr. 17). 30.00 *(978-0-8139-2903-3(2))* Univ. Pr. of Virginia.

BOATMEN'S SONGS

see Sea Songs

BOATS, SUBMARINE

see Submarines (Ships)

BOATS AND BOATING

see also Aquatic Sports; Boatbuilding; Boating Industry; Canoes and Canoeing; Catamarans; Fiberglass Boats; Fishing Boats; Houseboats; Hydrofoil Boats; Lifeboats; Motorboats; Rafting (Sports); Rowing; Sailboats; Sailing; Ships; Steamboats and Steamboat Lines; Submarines (Ships); Yachts and Yachting

Adams-Smith, Beth. Atlantic Cruising Club's Guide to Mid-Atlantic/ICW Marinas - Book with DVD: Hampton, Virginia to St. Mary's, Georgia (Including the Intra-Coastal Waterway, North Carolina Sounds & Bermuda) Smith, Richard Y., ed. 7th ed. 2010. (ENG., Illus.). 280p. pap. 39.95 incl. DVD *(978-0-9664028-6-5(3)*, Atlantic Cruising Club) Atlantic Cruising Club at Jerawyn Publishing.
Adney, Edwin Tappan & Chappelle, Howard I. Bark Canoes & Skin Boats of North America. 2007. (ENG., Illus.). 276p. pap. 19.95 *(978-1-60239-071-3(1)*, 239071) Skyhorse Publishing Co., Inc.
Agius, Dionisius A. Classic Ships of Islam: From Mesopotamia to the Indian Ocean. 2007. (Handbook of Oriental Studies). (Illus.). 440p. *(978-90-04-15863-4(4))* BRILL.
—In the Wake of the Dhow: The Arabian Gulf & Oman. 2010. 272p. pap. 34.95 *(978-0-86372-341-4(1)*, Ithaca Pr.) Garnet Publishing, Ltd. GBR. Dist: International Specialized Bk. Services.
Anderson, Brian, ed. Small Boats on Green Waters: A Treasury of Good Reading on Coastal & Inland Cruising. 2007. (ENG., Illus.). 304p. per. 15.00 *(978-1-891369-70-4(9))* Breakaway Bks.
Angers, Trent. An Airboat on the Streets of New Orleans: A Cajun Couple Lends a Hand after Hurricane Katrina Floods the City. 2008. pap. *(978-0-925417-88-5(2))* Acadian Hse. Publishing.
Angus, Julie. Rowboat in a Hurricane: My Amazing Journey Across a Changing Atlantic Ocean, 1 vol. 2009. (ENG., Illus.). 272p. pap. 17.95 *(978-1-55365-337-0(8)*, Greystone Bks.) D&M Pubs. Inc. CAN. Dist: Perseus-PGW.
Arbizzani, Ron. Living Aboard a Boat Named Farfetched: A Couple Tells Their Story of Eight Years Living & Traveling Aboard Their Boat. 2008. 224p. pap. 15.95 *(978-0-595-52973-5(9))* iUniverse, Inc.
Armstrong, Bob. Florida Cruising Directory 2007-2008. 2007. 208p. pap. 16.00 *(978-1-928864-07-3(4))* Waterways Etc., Inc.
Ask, Thomas. Handbook of Marine Surveying. 2nd ed. 2007. (ENG., Illus.). 272p. pap. 49.50 *(978-1-57409-249-3(9)*, 1268745) Sheridan Hse., Inc.
Bailey, Joanne I. & Nyberg, Carl O. Gunkholing in North Puget Sound: Complete Cruising Guide from Edmonds-Kingston North to the San Juans. Date not set. (Gunkholing Ser.: Vol. 5). (Illus.). 320p. (Orig.). pap. 27.50 *(973-0-944257-03-6(8))* San Juan Enterprises.
Ballantyne, Robert Michael. Man on the Ocean: A Book about Boats & Ships. 2007. (ENG.). 182p. pap. 19.99 *(978-1-4346-3752-9(2))*; 196p. pap. 21.99 *(978-1-4346-3766-6(2))* BiblioBazaar.
Barber, James Alden. Naval Shiphandler's Guide. (Illus.). 320p. 48.95 *(978-1-55750-435-7(0))* Naval Institute Pr.
Bartlett, Tim. The Book of Navigation: Traditional Navigation Techniques for Boating & Yachting. 2009. (ENG., Illus.). 176p. pap. 14.95 *(978-1-60239-621-0(3)*, 239621) Skyhorse Publishing Co., Inc.
Baughman, Michael. Boat: A Memoir of Friendship, Faith, Death, & Life Everlasting. 2012. (ENG., Illus.). 144p. 16.95 ***(978-1-61145-493-2(X)***, 611493, Arcade Publishing) Skyhorse Publishing Co., Inc.
Beard, Daniel. Boat-Building & Boating. 2006. (Dover Maritime Bks.). (ENG., Illus.). 208p. per. 9.95 *(978-0-486-45115-2(1))* Dover Pubns., Inc.
Beattie, Rob. The Boating Companion: All You Need to Know for Life on the Water. 2008. (ENG., Illus.). 144p. pap. 19.95 *(978-0-7624-3186-1(5))* Running Pr. Bk. Pubs.
—Boating Handbook: All You Need to Know for Life on the Water. 2008. (Illus.). 144p. pap. 24.95 *(978-0-470-99611-9(0)*, Wiley) Wiley, John & Sons, Inc.
Benford, Jay. Catboats: From the Boards of the Benford Design Group. 2009. (ENG.). 128p. pap. 19.95 *(978-1-888671-25-4(4))* Tiller Publishing.
Bishop, Nathaniel, abr. Four Months in a Sneak-box. 2009. (Transportation Ser.). (ENG.). 360p. pap. 22.95 *(978-1-4290-2006-0(7))* Applewood Bks.
Blanchet, M. Wylie. The Curve of Time. 50th ed. 2011. 178p. 24.95 *(978-1-77050-037-2(5))* Whitecap Bks., Ltd. CAN. Dist: Midpoint Trade Bks., Inc.
Boat Smart, 2001: Keeping Your Crew Safe & Well. (Illus.). 119p. pap. 25.00 *(978-1-891148-32-3(X))* United States Power Squadrons.
Bottenberg, Jeanna Rosembalm. Dory Fleet of Pacific City. 2008. (Images of America Ser.). (ENG., Illus.). 128p. pap. 19.99 *(978-0-7385-5813-4(3))* Arcadia Publishing.
Bray, Anne & Bray, Maynard. Boat Plans at Mystic Seaport. Date not set. (Illus.). 207p. pap. 24.95 *(978-0-913372-86-9(2))* Mystic Seaport Museum, Inc.
Bray, Maynard. Mystic Seaport Watercraft. 2008. (Maritime Ser.). (ENG.). 420p. pap. 24.95 *(978-0-913372-95-1(1))* Mystic Seaport Museum, Inc.
Bray, Maynard & Jackson, Tom. Worthy of the Sea: K. Aage Nielsen & His Legacy of Yacht Design. 2010. (Illus.). 302p. 59.95 *(978-0-88448-281-9(2))* Tilbury Hse. Pubs.
Breeding, Shawn & Bansmer, Heather. Pacific Mexico: A Cruiser's Guidebook. 2010. (Illus.). 226p. pap. ***(978-0-9800901-2-3(1))*** Blue Latitude Pr.
Brindley, Robert. Painting Boats & Coastal Scenery. 2010. (ENG., Illus.). 176p. pap. 34.95 *(978-1-84797-119-7(9))* Crowood Pr., Ltd. GBR. Dist: Independent Pubs. Group.
Brown, Ian. The Psychology of Sailing: How to Develop a Winning Mindset. 2011. (ENG.). 112p. pap. 22.95 *(978-1-4081-2447-5(5))* A & C Black GBR. Dist: Macmillan.
Brownlee, John. Bahamas Boating & Fishing Guide. 2007. (Illus.). 224p. pap. 19.95 *(978-1-60239-068-3(1))* Skyhorse Publishing Co., Inc.
Bryant, Betty. Here Comes the Showboat! 2010. (Ohio River Valley Ser.). (ENG., Illus.). 216p. pap. 25.00 *(978-0-8131-2967-9(2))* Univ. Pr. of Kentucky.
Buchan, Alistair. How to Sail on a Budget. 2011. (Sailmate Ser.). (ENG., Illus.). 144p. pap. 17.95 *(978-0-7136-8889-4(0))* A & C Black GBR. Dist: Macmillan.
Buckley, Michael. Voices of the Chesapeake Bay. 2008. (Illus.). 464p. pap. 19.95 *(978-0-9787278-5-7(1))*; 463p. *(978-0-9787278-8-8(6))* Geared Up LLC.
Burke, Michael D. & Burke, Michael. Same River Twice: A Boatman's Journey Home. 2006. (ENG., Illus.). 224p. pap. 16.95 *(978-0-8165-2531-7(5))* Univ. of Arizona Pr.
Calahan, H. a. & Calahan, H. A. Boats Anyone Can Build. Popular Science Monthly, ed. 2011. 258p. 47.95 ***(978-1-258-07046-5(4))*** Literary Licensing, LLC.
Calder, Nigel, et al. The Instant Handbook of Boat Handling, Navigation, & Seamanship: A Quick-Reference Guide for Sail & Power. 2007. (ENG., Illus.). 240p. per. 24.95 *(978-0-07-149910-1(5)*, 0071499105, International Marine/Ragged Mountain Pr.) McGraw-Hill Professional Publishing.
Campanella, Richard. Lincoln in New Orleans: The 1828-1831 Flatboat Voyages & Their Place in History. 2010. 592p. 35.00 *(978-1-935754-02-2(5))* Univ. of Louisiana at Lafayette Pr.
Carter, Robert A., et al, contrib. by. Maritime Interactions in the Arabian Neolithic: Evidence from H3, As-Sabiyah, an Ubaid-Related Site in Kuwait. 2010. (Illus.). 384p. *(978-90-04-16359-1(X))* BRILL.
Chapman, Christopher J. T. Dreamboats. 2011. 108p. pap. ***(978-1-907652-89-9(2))*** Grosvenor Hse. Publishing Ltd.
Chowning, Larry S. Deadrise & Cross-Planked. 2007. (Illus.). 177p. per. 34.95 *(978-0-87033-588-4(X)*, Cornell Maritime Pr./Tidewater Pubs.) Schiffer Publishing, Ltd.
Clinchy, Richard A. Emergency First Aid on Board: A Captain's Quick Guide. 2007. (ENG.). 16p. pap. 8.95 *(978-0-07-147393-4(9)*, 0071473939, International Marine/Ragged Mountain Pr.) McGraw-Hill Professional Publishing.
Cochran, Michael J. Invincible: History of the Duluth Boat Club. 2008. *(978-1-57864-496-4(8))* Donning Co. Pubs.
Colle, Jon. Adventures in the Ditch: A Memoir of Family, Navigation, & Discovery on the Intracoastal Waterway. 2011. 208p. pap. 14.95 *(978-1-936236-51-0(6))* iUniverse, Inc.
Coles, Bryony, ed. Journal of Wetland Archaeology 8 (2008), Vol. 8. 2009. (ENG.). 120p. (C). pap. 30.00 *(978-1-84217-328-2(6))* Oxbow Bks., Ltd. GBR. Dist: Brown, David Bk. Co., The.
Concept Systems Inc., contrib. by. Boat Diving Instructor Outline: German. 3rd ed. 2008. (GER.). tchr. ed., ring bd. *(978-1-59750-110-1(7))* Concept Systems, Inc.
—Boat Diving Student Manual: German. 2nd ed. 2008. (GER.). stu. ed., per. *(978-1-59750-061-6(5))* Concept Systems, Inc.
Conder, Tony. Canal Narrowboats & Barges. 2008. (Shire Library). (ENG., Illus.). 56p. pap. 12.95 *(978-0-7478-0587-8(3))* Shire Pubns., Ltd. GBR. Dist: Random Hse., Inc.
Connecticut River Watershed Council, et al. The Connecticut River Boating Guide: Source to Sea. 3rd ed. 2007. (Paddling Ser.). (ENG., Illus.). 256p. pap. 19.95 *(978-0-7627-4097-0(3)*, Falcon Guides) Globe Pequot Pr., The.
Cooking Aboard Your Yacht. (Orig.). pap. 17.95 *(978-0-937070-09-3(2))* Crabtree Publishing.
Cookson, Gary. A Home Afloat: Living Aboard Vessels of All Shapes & Sizes. 2nd ed. 2010. (ENG., Illus.). 128p. 29.95 *(978-0-7136-8877-1(7)*, Reed, Thomas Pubns.) A & C Black GBR. Dist: Macmillan.
Cornell, William E. Tales of a Great Lakes Sailor: (the Evolution of Landlubber) 2010. pap. 13.95 *(978-0-7414-5833-9(0))* Infinity Publishing.
Cotton, Les. Over 50 & Sailing Away. 2009. 332p. pap. 24.95 *(978-1-4269-0010-5(4))* Trafford Publishing.
Crooks, Richard. Skipper's Practical Handbook. 2007. (ENG., Illus.). 80p. pap. 14.95 *(978-0-470-05971-5(0)*, Wiley) Wiley, John & Sons, Inc.
Cruising Powerboat Certification Standards. 2007. 8.00 *(978-0-9762261-9-2(7))* U. S. Sailing Assn.
Cunliffe, Tom. Coastal & Offshore Navigation. 3rd ed. 2009. (ENG., Illus.). 160p. pap. 29.95 *(978-0-470-75390-3(0)*, Wiley) Wiley, John & Sons, Inc.
Dahl, Bonnie. Bonnie Dahl's Superior Way: The Cruising Guide to Lake Superior. 4th ed. 2008. (Illus.). 426p. spiral bd. 49.95 *(978-0-942235-92-0(4))* Lake Superior Port Cities, Inc.
Davies, Robert. Boats, Smoke, Steam & Folk. (ENG., Illus.). 128p. pap. 24.99 *(978-0-7524-1765-3(7))* History Pr. Ltd., The GBR. Dist: Trafalgar Square Publishing.
de Rothschild, David. Plastiki: Across the Pacific by Plastic - An Adventure to Save Our Oceans. 2011. (ENG., Illus.). 240p. 27.50 *(978-1-4521-0002-9(0))* Chronicle Bks. LLC.
Dean, Allan. Boat Dough: Boat Buying secrets Froman Insider. 2009. pap. 99.00 *(978-1-61623-776-9(7))* Independent Pub.
Desoutter, Denny. Boat Words. 2012. (Adlard Coles Book Of Ser.). (ENG., Illus.). 256p. pap. 19.95 ***(978-1-4081-2676-9(1))*** A & C Black GBR. Dist: Macmillan.
Di Piazza, Anne & Pearthree, Erik. Canoes of the Grand Ocean. 2008. (Bar S Ser.). (Illus.). 154p. (C). 92.50 *(978-1-4073-0289-8(2))* British Archaeological Reports Ltd. GBR. Dist: Brown, David Bk. Co., The.
Dimock, Brad. The Very Hard Way: Bert Loper & the Colorado River. 2007. (Illus.). 457p. per. 17.95 *(978-1-892327-69-7(4))*; 472p. 29.95 *(978-1-892327-49-9(X))* Fretwater Pr.
Doyle, Chris. The Cruising Guide to the Leeward Islands: Anguilla Through Dominica. 11th ed. 2010. (Cruising Guide to the Leeward Islands Ser.). (Illus.). spiral bd. 34.95 *(978-0-944428-87-0(8))* Cruising Guide Pubns., Inc.
Doyle, Mark Stephen & Doyle, Diana Richards. Managing the Waterway: An Enriched Cruising Guide for Florida Keys Travelers, 1. 2006. (Managing the Waterway Ser.: 2). (Illus.). 220p. spiral bd. 24.95 *(978-0-9758617-1-4(9))* Semi-Local Pubns.
Dummies Press Staff & Vance, Randy. Power Boating for Dummies. 2009. (ENG., Illus.). 392p. pap. 21.99 *(978-0-470-40956-5(8)*, For Dummies) Wiley, John & Sons, Inc.
Durham, Dick. Peyton: The World's Greatest Yachting Cartoonist. 2011. (ENG., Illus.). 176p. 25.95 *(978-1-4081-2440-6(8))* A & C Black GBR. Dist: Macmillan.
Dye, Margaret. Dinghy Cruising. 4th ed. 2011. (ENG., Illus.). 224p. pap. 22.95 *(978-1-4081-3289-0(3))* A & C Black GBR. Dist: Macmillan.
—Dinghy Cruising: The Enjoyment of Wandering Afloat. 3rd rev. ed. 2006. (ENG., Illus.). 224p. pap. 24.95 *(978-0-7136-7934-2(4))* A & C Black GBR. Dist: Macmillan.
Edwards, Fred. Making Money with Boats. 2nd rev. ed. 2011. 224p. pap. 19.99 ***(978-0-87033-627-0(4)***, Schiffer Publishing Ltd) Schiffer Publishing, Ltd.
Elements of Boat Design & Construction. Date not set. (Learning Guides Ser.). (Illus.). 38p. pap. 5.79 *(978-1-891148-04-0(4))* United States Power Squadrons.
Elfers, Jim. The Baja Bash II. 2006. (Illus.). 128p. per. 24.95 *(978-0-9538470-4-1(X))* Point Loma Publishing.
Elheddeny, Moataz. Shipping Quality Standard Assessment. 2010. 60p. pap. *(978-3-8383-7880-0(6))* Lambert Academic Publishing.
Ely, Kenneth E. The Family Regatta. 2009. pap. *(978-1-61623-343-3(5))* Independent Pub.
Fishwick, Mark. The West Country Cruising Companion. 7th ed. 2008. (ENG., Illus.). 256p. 49.95 *(978-0-470-98569-4(0)*, Wiley) Wiley, John & Sons, Inc.
Flemming, Anthony. Painting Boats & Harbours. 2006. (ENG., Illus.). 112p. pap. 39.95 *(978-0-7136-6745-5(1))* A & C Black GBR. Dist: Macmillan.

B

Fletcher, Rodger L. Drift Boats & River Dories: Their History, Design, Construction, & Use. 2007. (ENG., Illus.). 304p. 49.95 *(978-0-8117-0234-8(0))* Stackpole Bks.

Ford, Clyde W. Boat Green: 50 Steps Boaters Can Take to Save Our Waters. 2008. (ENG., Illus.). 224p. per. 17.95 *(978-0-86571-590-5(4), 9780865715905)* New Society Pubs., Ltd. CAN. Dist: Consortium Bk. Sales & Distribution.

Frankel, Michael L. Outfitting & Organizing Your Boat: For a Day, a Week, a Lifetime. 2nd rev. ed. 2007. per. 21.95 *(978-0-9789350-3-0(9))* Nautical Publishing Co.

Frazer, Neil. Boat Camping Haida Gwaii: A Small Vessel Guide. 2nd unabr. rev. ed. 2010. (ENG., Illus.). 176p. pap. *(978-1-55017-487-8(8))* Harbour Publishing Co., Ltd.

Fretz, Gerald. Insider Secrets to Boat Buying. 2007. 0.01 net. *(978-1-60402-016-8(4))* Independent Pub.

Garry, Jean-Francois. Wooden Boat Building. 2011. (ENG., Illus.). 128p. pap. 25.95 *(978-1-4081-2853-4(5))* A & C Black GBR. Dist: Macmillan.

Gelder, Paul & Fisher, Bob. A Legend Sails Again. 2008. (ENG., Illus.). 256p. 44.95 *(978-0-470-72443-9(9)*, Wiley) Wiley, John & Sons, Inc.

Giacon, Alfredo. The Magic of Turkey: A Guide to the Turkish Coast. 2008. (ENG., Illus.). 200p. pap. 19.95 *(978-1-57409-270-7(7))* Sheridan Hse., Inc.

Gibellini, Piero M. Carlo Riva, the Legend, the Myth, 2 vols., Set. UpMan Language Services Staff, tr. Incl. Vol. 1. 275p. *(978-0-9645548-4-9(4))*; Vol. 2. 269p. *(978-0-9645548-5-6(2))*; (Illus.). 1998. 186.00 *(978-0-9645548-3-2(6))* Classic Boating.

Goldman, Matthew. The Journals of Constant Waterman: Paddling, Poling, & Sailing for the Love of It. 2007. (ENG.). 336p. pap. 14.00 *(978-1-891369-73-5(3))* Breakaway Bks.

Gottlicher, Arvid. Fahren, Frachter, Fischerboote: Antike Kleinschiffe in Wort und Bild. 2009. (GER., Illus.). 207p. (C). 100.00 *(978-1-4073-0404-5(6))* British Archaeological Reports Ltd. GBR. Dist: Brown, David Bk. Co., The.

Gracq, Julien. The Narrow Waters. Kohn, Ingeborg, tr. from FRE. 2008.Tr. of Eaux Etroites. (ENG.). 64p. pap. 12.95 *(978-1-885586-97-1(3))* Turtle Point Pr.

Guirard, Greg & Brassieur, C. Ray. Inherit the Atchafalaya. 2007. *(978-1-887366-76-2(8))* Univ. of Louisiana at Lafayette Pr.

Hand Tools. Date not set. (Learning Guides Ser.). (Illus.). 76p. pap. 5.79 *(978-1-891148-06-4(0))* United States Power Squadrons.

Harrell, Alvin C. Compendium of State Certificates of Title Laws. 2009. *(978-1-60442-298-6(X))* American Bar Assn.

Harrison, Gaz. Teach Dinghy Sailing. 2008. (ENG., Illus.). 152p. pap. 29.95 *(978-0-470-72550-4(8)*, Wiley) Wiley, John & Sons, Inc.

Harsin, Ron & Farley, Fred. Vintage Hydroplane Heritage: B/W Edition. Harsin, Ron & Farley, Fred, eds. 2007. (ENG., Illus.). 128p. per. 19.95 *(978-0-9796203-1-7(7))* Deer Trail Publishing.

Havers, Richard. Classic Ships. 2010. (ENG., Illus.). 128p. 14.95 *(978-1-84425-708-9(8), 1844257088)* Haynes Publishing PLC GBR. Dist: MBI Distribution Services/Quayside Distribution.

Henry, Tom. Westcoasters: Boats That Built BC. 2nd unabr. ed. (ENG., Illus.). 192p. pap. 28.95 *(978-1-55017-233-1(6))* Harbour Publishing Co., Ltd. CAN. Dist: Ingram Pub. Services.

Hickman, Roy Scott, et al. Boat Accident Reconstruction & Litigation. 3rd ed. 2012. (Illus.). iv, 502p. ***(978-1-936360-02-4(0))*** Lawyers & Judges Publishing Co., Inc.

Husick, Charles B. Chapman Piloting & Seamanship 66th Edition. 66th ed. 2009. (ENG., Illus.). 192p. 59.95 *(978-1-58816-744-6(5))* Hearst Communications, Inc.

Introduction to Knots, Bends, Hitches: Marlinespike. Date not set. (Learning Guides Ser.). (Illus.). 53p. pap. 5.79 *(978-1-891148-07-1(9))* United States Power Squadrons.

Jacobs, W. W. Night Watches. 2008. 128p. 24.99 *(978-0-554-27002-9(1))* 2008. 128p. 21.99 *(978-0-554-36305-9(4))* 2007. (ENG.). 112p. pap. 18.99 *(978-1-4346-2298-3(3))* 2007. (ENG.). 126p. pap. 19.99 *(978-1-4346-2356-0(4))* BiblioBazaar.

—Night Watches. 2007. (ENG., Illus.). 128p. per. *(978-1-4065-1822-1(0))* Dodo Pr.

Jefferson, David. Through the French Canals. 11th ed. 2006. (ENG., Illus.). 320p. pap. 29.95 *(978-1-57409-233-2(2))* Sheridan Hse., Inc.

Jensen, Carol A. & The North Lake Tahoe Historical Society. Lake Tahoe's West Shore. 2012. (Images of America Ser.). (ENG., Illus.). 128p. pap. 21.99 ***(978-0-7385-8891-9(1))*** Arcadia Publishing.

Johnson, Bill. Essential Boat Radar. 2009. (ENG., Illus.). 110p. pap. 29.95 *(978-0-470-77811-1(3)*, Wiley) Wiley, John & Sons, Inc.

Jones, Tony. The Liveaboard Guide: Living afloat on the inland Waterways. 2012. (ENG., Illus.). 160p. pap. 22.95 ***(978-1-4081-4555-5(3))*** A & C Black GBR. Dist: Macmillan.

Kapitan, Gerhard. Records of Traditional Watercraft from South & West Sri Lanka. 2009. (Illus.). 191p. (C). 112.50 *(978-1-4073-0413-7(5))* British Archaeological Reports Ltd. GBR. Dist: Brown, David Bk. Co., The.

Karlshausen, C. L'iconographie de la barque processionnelle divine en Egypte au Nouvel Empire. 2009. (Orientalia Lovaniensia Analecta Ser.). (FRE.). 418p. (C). 109.00 *(978-90-429-2118-4(8))* Peeters Pubs. & Booksellers BEL. Dist: Brown, David Bk. Co., The.

Kavanagh, James. Boat & Water Safety: A Waterproof Reference to Safe Practices & Procedures. 2010. (Duraguide Ser.). (ENG.). 2p. 7.95 *(978-1-58355-519-4(6))* Waterford Pr., Inc.

Kelley, Clay. Boater's Checklist. 2nd ed. 2007. per. 21.95 *(978-0-9789350-5-4(5))* Nautical Publishing Co.

Kelley, Clay & Kelley, Marybeth. Florida Through the Islands: What Boaters Need to Know. 2nd ed. 2007. per. 21.95 *(978-0-9789350-4-7(7))* Nautical Publishing Co.

Kelsey, John, ed. Boating Disasters: How to Avoid, & Survive, the Most Common to Extreme Mishaps on the Water. 2011. (Essential Guide to Boating Ser.). (ENG., Illus.). 160p. pap. 14.95 *(978-1-56523-590-8(8))* Fox Chapel Publishing Co., Inc.

Kelsey, Michael R. Boater's Guide to Lake Powell: Featuring Hiking, Camping, Geology, History & Archaeology. 5th ed. 2008. (Illus.). 288p. pap. 19.95 *(978-0-944510-24-7(8))* Kelsey Publishing.

Kettlewell, John. The Intracoastal Waterway Chartbook: Norfolk, Virginia to Miami, Florida. Kettlewell, Leslie, ed. 5th ed. 2008. (ENG., Illus.). 288p. spiral bd. 69.95 *(978-0-07-154579-2(4), 0071545794*, International Marine/Ragged Mountain Pr.) McGraw-Hill Professional Publishing.

Kimantas, John. A Kayaking, Hiking & Recreation Guide for North & West Vancouver Island Vol. 1: The Wild Coast. 2nd ed. 2012. (Kayaking & Small Boat Atlas Series #1 Ser.). (Illus.). 64p. spiral bd. 29.95 *(978-1-77050-057-0(X))* Whitecap Bks., Ltd. CAN. Dist: Midpoint Trade Bks., Inc.

Knecht, G. Bruce. The Proving Ground: The Inside Story of the 1998 Sydney to Hobart, 0 vols. unabr. ed. 2011. (ENG.). 320p. pap. 14.95 ***(978-1-61218-143-1(0)***, 9781612181431) AmazonEncore.

Knuth, Barbara A. & Siemer, William F., eds. Aquatic Stewardship Education in Theory & Practice. 2007. (American Fisheries Society Symposium Ser.). 187p. 60.00 *(978-1-888569-90-2(5))* American Fisheries Society.

Kolb, Ellsworth L. Through the Grand Canyon from Wyoming to Mexico. 2007. (ENG., Illus.). 456p. pap. 16.95 *(978-0-938216-96-4(1))* Grand Canyon Assn.

Kolb, Ellsworth Leonardson. Through the Grand Canyon from Wyoming to Mexico. 2008. 248p. 27.99 *(978-0-554-25073-1(X))* 2008. 248p. 24.99 *(978-0-554-34376-1(2))* 2007. (ENG.). 218p. pap. 20.99 *(978-1-4264-8124-6(1))* 2007. (ENG.). 244p. pap. 22.99 *(978-1-4264-8196-3(9))* BiblioBazaar.

Kretschmer, John. At the Mercy of the Sea: The True Story of Three Sailors in a Caribbean Hurricane. 2007. (ENG., Illus.). 240p. per. 14.95 *(978-0-07-149887-6(7), 0071498877*, International Marine/Ragged Mountain Pr.) McGraw-Hill Professional Publishing.

Kretschmer, John & Krestschmer, John. At the Mercy of the Sea: The True Story of Three Sailors in a Caribbean Hurricane. 2006. (Illus.). 223p. 24.95 *(978-0-07-147507-5(9), 9780071475075*, International Marine/Ragged Mountain Pr.) McGraw-Hill Professional Publishing.

Kutz, David. Burgee Premier Marina Guidebook. 2011. pap. 26.95 *(978-0-9641934-8-2(5))* Pierside Publishing.

Lakeland Boating Ports O Call Lake Michigan: Lake Michigan. 5th rev. ed. 2007. (Lakeland Boating Ports O'Call Ser.). spiral bd. 39.95 *(978-1-890839-15-4(9))* O'Meara-Brown Pubns., Inc.

Langley-Price, Pat & Ouvry, Philip. Competent Crew. 5th rev. ed. 2007. (ENG., Illus.). 160p. pap. 24.95 *(978-0-7136-8262-5(0))* A & C Black GBR. Dist: Macmillan.

Larson, Ron. Mississippi Tenn-Tom River Cruise: Stipaul to Gulf of Mexico. 2008. (Illus.). 197p. 28.00 *(978-0-9640937-3-7(1))*; pap. 19.95 *(978-0-9640937-4-4(X))* Steamboat Pr.

Launer, Donald. The Galley: How Things Work. 2009. (ENG., Illus.). 102p. pap. 17.95 *(978-1-57409-288-2(X))* Sheridan Hse., Inc.

Lofenfeld, Leah. Boat & the Sea of Galilee. 2007. 104p. 24.95 *(978-965-229-402-9(0))* Gefen Publishing Hse., Ltd ISR. Dist: Gefen Bks.

Mallan, Lloyd. The New Complete Book of Small Boats. 2011. 148p. 40.95 ***(978-1-258-07811-9(2))*** Literary Licensing, LLC.

Maloney, Elbert S. The Boater's Handbook: The Indispensable Look-It-Up Book. 4th ed. 2008. (ENG., Illus.). 304p. instr.'s hndbk. ed. 12.95 *(978-1-58816-751-4(8))* Hearst Communications, Inc.

Manley, Pat. Electrics Companion. 2006. (ENG., Illus.). 24p. pap. 14.95 *(978-1-898660-95-8(6)*, Wiley) Wiley, John & Sons, Inc.

Marine University Staff, contrib. by. Boater101: A Full-Reference Guide to Boating Basics. 2006. (ENG., Illus.). 132p. pap. *(978-1-56825-111-0(4))* Rainbow Bks., Inc.

Mason, Jerry, ed. The Complete Book of Small Boats. 2011. 148p. 40.95 ***(978-1-258-08184-3(9))*** Literary Licensing, LLC.

Máté, Ferenc. Best Boats to Build or Buy. 2006. (ENG., Illus.). 384p. pap. 29.95 *(978-0-920256-24-4(4), 25624)* Albatross Publishing CAN. Dist: Norton, W. W. & Co., Inc.

McCarthy, Kevin. Hillsborough River Guidebook. 2011. (Illus.). 160p. pap. 14.95 *(978-1-56164-487-2(0))* Pineapple Pr., Inc.

McCarthy, Kevin M. Caloosahatchee River Guidebook. 2012. (ENG.). 256p. pap. 14.95 ***(978-1-56164-507-7(9))*** Pineapple Pr., Inc.

McGrail, Sean. Ancient Boats & Ships. 2nd ed. 2008. (Shire Archaeology Ser.). (ENG., Illus.). 72p. per. 13.95 *(978-0-7478-0645-5(4))* Shire Pubns., Ltd. GBR. Dist: Random Hse., Inc.

McKnew, Ed. 2008 PowerBoat Guide. 2007. 600p. per. 79.95 *(978-0-9773539-4-1(X))* American Marine Publishing, Inc.

McRonald, Malcolm. The Irish Boats Vol. 2: Liverpool to Cork & Waterford. 2006. (ENG., Illus.). 256p. per. 39.95 *(978-0-7524-3884-9(0))* History Pr. Ltd.,The GBR. Dist: Independent Pubs. Group.

—Liverpool - Belfast, 3 vols. 2008. (ENG., Illus.). 224p. pap. 45.95 *(978-0-7524-4235-8(X))* History Pr. Ltd.,The GBR. Dist: Independent Pubs. Group.

Mehaffy, Bob & Mehaffy, Carolyn. Cruising Guide to the Hawaiian Islands. 2010. 324p. pap. 29.95 *(978-93-983773-0-7(6))* Paradise Cay Pubns.

—Cruising Guide to the Hawaiian Islands. 2nd rev. ed. 2006. (Illus.). 313p. per. 29.95 *(978-0-939837-73-1(0))* Paradise Cay Pubns.

Mendlowitz, Benjamin & Bray, Maynard. The Book of Wooden Boats, Vol. 3. 2011. (ENG., Illus.). 192p. 60.00 *(978-0-393-08011-7(0), 8011)* Norton, W. W. & Co., Inc.

Missouri State Water Patrol 50th Anniversary Committee Staff, contrib. by. Missouri State Water Patrol 50th Anniversary: A Pictorial History. 2009. *(978-1-57864-570-1(0))* Donning Co. Pubs.

Moeller, Bill & Kettlewell, John J. The Intracoastal Waterway, Norfolk to Miami: The Complete Cockpit Cruising Guide. 6th ed. 2010. (ENG.). 256p. pap. 29.95 *(978-0-07-162376-6(0), 0071623760*, International Marine/Ragged Mountain Pr.) McGraw-Hill Professional Publishing.

Mollica Jr, Anthony & Savage, Jack. Chris-Craft Boats. 2009. (ENG., Illus.). 192p. pap. 24.99 *(978-0-7603-3631-1(8), 0760336318*, Voyageur Pr) MBI Publishing Co. LLC.

Morgan, Adrian. The Trouble with Old Boats. 2008. (ENG., Illus.). 96p. pap. 15.95 *(978-0-7136-8933-4(1))* A & C Black GBR. Dist: Macmillan.

Mosenthal, Basil. The Cockpit Companion. 2nd rev. ed. 2006. (ENG., Illus.). 24p. pap. 14.95 *(978-1-904475-08-8(6)*, Wiley) Wiley, John & Sons, Inc.

—Learning the Rule of the Road: A Guide for the Skippers & Crew of Small Craft. 4th ed. 2009. (ENG., Illus.). 40p. pap. 19.95 *(978-1-4081-0633-4(7))* A & C Black GBR. Dist: Macmillan.

—Learning to Sail: A No-Nonsense Guide for Beginners of All Ages. 2011. (ENG., Illus.). 74p. 24.95 *(978-1-55407-960-5(8))*; pap. 16.95 *(978-1-55407-921-6(7))* Firefly Bks., Ltd.

Newman, Lawrence William & Newman, Lawrence. The Apostle Islands: America's Wilderness in the Water: A Guide for Boaters, Kayakers & Beachcombers. 2009. (Illus.). 151p. pap. *(978-1-60743-040-7(1))* Independent Pub.

Nicholas, Mark. The Essentials of Living Aboard a Boat: The Definitive Guide for Liveaboards. 2010. (Illus.). 268p. per. 17.95 *(978-0-939837-66-3(8))* Paradise Cay Pubns.

Northwest Boat Travel, Vol. 22. (Illus.). 19.95 *(978-0-945989-11-0(3))* Anderson Publishing Co., Inc.

Olweiler, David B. Cowboy Boots in Africa. pap. *(978-1-882204-21-2(2))* Wilde Publishing.

Ostis, Nate. NOLS River Rescue: Essential Skills for Boaters. 2010. (Nols Ser.). (ENG., Illus.). 128p. pap. 9.95 *(978-0-8117-3352-6(1))* Stackpole Bks.

Outdoor Books & Maps. Colorado Lakes & Reservoirs: Fishing & Boating Guide. 2008. (Illus.). 216p. pap. 19.95 *(978-0-930657-54-3(3)*, Outdoor Books & Maps) Adler Publishing Co.

Papy, Frank M. Sailing Impressions, Ideas, Deeds. pap. 12.95 *(978-0-9619838-6-4(8))* Papy, Frank Cruising Guide to the Florida Keys.

Pardey, Lin & Pardey, Larry. Storm Tactics Handbook: Modern Methods of Heaving-To for Survival in Extreme Conditions. 3rd rev. ed. 2008. (Illus.). 256p. (Orig.). pap. 22.95 *(978-1-929214-47-1(2))* Pardey Bks.

Parrott, Daniel S. Bridge Resource Management for Small Ships. 2011. (ENG., Illus.). 192p. 50.00 *(978-0-07-155007-9(0), 0071550070*, International Marine/Ragged Mountain Pr.) McGraw-Hill Professional Publishing.

Pavitt, Trevor. Living the Dream. 2007. 343p. pap. 24.50 *(978-1-84753-757-7(X))* Lulu Enterprises Inc.

Pavlidis, Stephen J. A Cruising Guide to Puerto Rico: Including the Spanish Virgin Islands & Selected Ports along the Northern Coast of the Dominican Republic. 2010. pap. *(978-1-892399-32-8(6))* Seaworthy Pubns., Inc.

—A Cruising Guide to the Virgin Islands: Including the Spanish Virgin Islands, the United States Virgin Islands, & the British Virgin Islands. 2nd ed. 2011. pap. ***(978-1-892399-35-9(0))*** Seaworthy Pubns., Inc.

—Life at Sea Level: Tales of Island Adventures from a Travel Guide Author's Perspective. 2011. pap. *(978-1-892399-33-5(4))* Seaworthy Pubns., Inc.

—The Northern Bahamas Guide: From Grand Bahama & the Abacos South to Cat Island. 2009. pap. *(978-1-892399-28-1(8))* Seaworthy Pubns., Inc.

Payne, John C. Understanding Boat AC Power Systems: (Generators, Inverters, Shore Power) 2008. (ENG., Illus.). 106p. pap. 14.95 *(978-1-57409-262-2(6))* Sheridan Hse., Inc.

Pearson, Malcolm. Reeds Skipper's Handbook. 6th ed. 2010. (ENG., Illus.). 208p. pap. 12.95 *(978-1-4081-2477-2(7)*, Reed, Thomas Pubns.) A & C Black GBR. Dist: Macmillan.

Pelling, Sue. Sail for a Living: Find a Job, Start a Business, Change Your Life. 2011. (ENG., Illus.). 196p. pap. 24.95 ***(978-0-470-97564-0(4)***, Wiley) Wiley, John & Sons, Inc.

Predicted Log Contests. Date not set. (Learning Guides Ser.). (Illus.). 64p. pap. 5.79 *(978-1-891148-11-8(7))* United States Power Squadrons.

Price Digest Staff. Clymer Powersport Vehicle Blue Book Fall 2006. 2006. pap. 39.95 *(978-1-59969-070-4(5))* Penton Media, Inc.

Price Digests Staff. ABOS Marine Blue Book Vol 1 2007. 2006. pap. 164.95 *(978-1-59969-036-0(5))* Penton Media, Inc.

—ABOS Marine Blue Book Vol 2 2007. 2006. pap. 89.95 *(978-1-59969-037-7(3))* Penton Media, Inc.

Rains, Patricia. Cruising Ports: The Central American Route. 6th ed. 2006. (Illus.). 320p. per. 59.95 *(978-0-9638470-2-7(3))* Point Loma Publishing.

Randall, Ian. Spiritual Revolution: The Story of OM. 2008. (ENG.). 288p. 16.99 *(978-1-85078-766-2(2))* Authentic Media.

Rankin, Alan. Solo Round Scotland: The first single-handed circumnavigation by boat & Bike. 2010. (Illus.). 224p. pap. *(978-1-84995-003-9(2))* Whittles Publishing.

Reinhold, Danny. Der Schutz der Umwelt in der Binnenschifffahrt unter besonderer Berücksichtigung ausgewählter zukünftiger Handlungsansätze auf dem Weg zu einer ökologischen Binnenschifffahrtspolitik. 2009. (Studien zum Internationalen, Europäischen und Öffentlichen Recht Ser.). (GRE.). 282p. pap. 74.95 *(978-3-631-58145-2(9))* Lang, Peter GmbH, Europaischer Verlag der Wissenschaften DEU. Dist: Lang, Peter.

Rhodes, Rick. The Ohio River: In American History. Byrnes, Bill, ed. 2008. (Illus.). 224p. 29.95 *(978-0-9665866-4-0(6))* Heron Island Guides.

—The Ohio River: In American History & Voyaging on Today's River. Byrnes, Bill, ed. 2007. (Illus.). 320p. per. *(978-0-9665866-3-3(8))* Heron Island Guides.

Rich, Nancy & Spectre, Peter H. Afloat on the Tide: Wooden Dinghies, Prams, Skiffs & Other Rowboats. 2009. (ENG., Illus.). 192p. pap. 29.95 *(978-1-57409-285-1(5))* Sheridan Hse., Inc.

Robb, Daniel. Sloop: Restoring My Family's Wooden Sailboat — an Adventure in Old-Fashioned Values. 2009. (ENG.). 336p. pap. 22.95 *(978-0-7432-0251-0(1))* Simon & Schuster.

—Sloop: Restoring My Family's Wooden Sailboat- An Adventure in Old-Fashioned Values. 2008. (ENG., Illus.). 336p. 25.00 *(978-0-7432-0239-8(2))* Simon & Schuster.

Rodriguez, Andres, et al, compiled by. Maritime dictionary-Diccionario Maritimo. 2009. (ENG & SPA., Illus.). 200p. pap. 50.00 *(978-0-9801801-2-1(0))* Myths & Bks., Inc.

Rolt, L. T. C. Narrow Boat: Take a Trip down the Waterways of England During Their Hey-Day. 2009. (ENG., Illus.). 224p. pap. 29.95 *(978-0-7524-5109-1(X))* History Pr. Ltd.,The GBR. Dist: Independent Pubs. Group.

Russell, Joe & Bunzel, Mark J. Cruising the Virgin Islands, 1 vol. 2nd ed. 2009. (ENG.). 239p. pap. *(978-1-932310-29-0(0))* FineEdge.Com LLC.

Schuetz, Marlin & Schuetz, Joan. Extended Power Cruising. 2008. pap. *(978-1-892399-26-7(1))* Seaworthy Pubns., Inc.

SDI Wreck, Boat & Drift Diving Instructor Resouce CD-ROM. 2007. cd-rom *(978-1-931451-48-2(6))* International Training, Inc.

Seaver, Douglass J. Four Across the Atlantic: One Captain's Story of the Historic 2004 Nordhavn Atlantic Rally. 2007. per. 21.95 *(978-0-9789350-1-6(2))* Nautical Publishing Co.

Seidman, David & Hemmel, Jeff. The Anti-Pirate Potato Cannon: And 101 Other Things for Young Mariners to Build, Try, & Do on the Water. 2010. (ENG., Illus.). 272p. 24.95 *(978-0-07-162837-2(1), 0071628371*, International Marine/Ragged Mountain Pr.) McGraw-Hill Professional Publishing.

Seyfarth, Fritz. In Pursuit of Adventure & Freedom. 68p. 9.95 *(978-0-944428-16-0(9))* Papy, Frank Cruising Guide to the Florida Keys.

Sharp, Jim. With Reckless Abandon: Memoirs of a Boat-Obsessed Life. 2007. (ENG., Illus.). 272p. pap. 18.95 *(978-1-928862-12-3(8))* Devereux Bks.

Sheehy, Harry. Driftwood. 2009. 176p. pap. 16.24 *(978-1-4269-0056-3(2))* Trafford Publishing.

Skipper Saver: Basic Safety & Boat Handling in an Emergency. Date not set. (Learning Guides Ser.). (Illus.). 76p. reprint ed. pap. 5.79 *(978-1-891148-15-6(X))* United States Power Squadrons.

Slesinger, Jeff & Reid, George H. Shiphandling with Tugs: Second Edition. 2nd ed. 2008. (ENG.). 40.00 *(978-0-87033-598-3(7)*, Cornell Maritime Pr./Tidewater Pubs.) Schiffer Publishing, Ltd.

Sloan, Linda. The Frugal Yacht. 2009. 240p. 26.50 *(978-1-60693-952-9(1)*, Eloquent Bks.) AEG Literary Publishing Services, Inc.

Smith, Bruce W. The Complete Guide to Trailering Your Boat: How to Select, Use, Maintain, & Improve a Boat Trailer. 2007. (ENG., Illus.). 168p. per. 16.95 *(978-0-07-147164-0(2), 0071471642*, International Marine/Ragged Mountain Pr.) McGraw-Hill Professional Publishing.

Smith, Joy. The Perfect First Mate: A Woman's Guide to Recreational Boating. 2nd ed. 2009. (ENG., Illus.). 230p. pap. 19.95 *(978-1-57409-282-0(0))* Sheridan Hse., Inc.

South, Mary. The Cure for Anything Is Salt Water: How I Threw My Life Overboard & Found Happiness at Sea. 2008. (ENG.). 224p. pap. 13.95 *(978-0-06-074703-9(X)*, HarperPerennial) HarperCollins Pubs.

The Squadron Boating Course, 2001: Fundamental Boating Education for the Power & Sail Boater. (Illus.). 234p. pap. 25.00 *(978-1-891148-31-6(1))* United States Power Squadrons.

Stevens, Paul. Surveying Yachts & Small Craft. 2011. (ENG., Illus.). 208p. pap. 39.95 *(978-1-4081-1403-2(8))* A & C Black GBR. Dist: Macmillan.

Stewart, Chris. Three Ways to Capsize a Boat: An Optimist Afloat. 2010. 192p. pap. 12.99 *(978-0-307-59237-8(5))* Broadway Bks.

Stockard, Heather. A Cruising Cook's Guide to Mexico: Up-to-Date Information on Provisioning & Cooking in Pacific Mexico. 2007. (Illus.). 195p. pap. 24.95 *(978-1-892399-25-0(3))* Seaworthy Pubns., Inc.

Stoker, Simon. The Adventures of the Hebe. 2011. (Illus.). 192p. pap. 24.95 ***(978-1-4456-0221-9(0))*** Amberley Publishing GBR. Dist: Casemate Pubs. & Bk. Distributors, LLC.

Stone, Michel & Dishman, Lydia. Outdoor Adventures in the Upcountry. 2010. (Illus.). 168p. 19.95 *(978-1-891885-75-4(8))* Hub City Writers Project.

Streeks, Neale. Float-Fishing Strategies: Tactics & Techniques for Drift Boats, Rafts, & Personal Watercraft. 2nd ed. 2011. (ENG., Illus.). 304p. pap. 19.95 *(978-0-8117-0747-3(4))* Stackpole Bks.

Street, Donald M. Street's Guide to the Cape Verde Islands. 2011. pap. ***(978-1-892399-34-2(2))*** Seaworthy Pubns., Inc.

Strickler, Darryl. Rowable Classics: Wooden Single Sculling Boats & Oars. 2008. (Illus.). 144p. 29.95 *(978-0-937822-96-8(5))* WoodenBoat Pubns.

Sweet, Robert J. Powerboat Handling Illustrated: How to Make Your Boat Do Exactly What You Want It to Do. 13th ed. 2006. (ENG., Illus.). 192p. per.

22.95 *(978-0-07-146881-7(1),* 0071468811, International Marine/Ragged Mountain Pr.) McGraw-Hill Professional Publishing.

Taft, Hank, et al. A Cruising Guide to the Maine Coast, 5th edition Hardcover. 2008. 480p. 56.95 *(978-0-9649246-6-6(8))* Diamond Pass Publishing, Inc.

—A Cruising Guide to the Maine Coast, 5th edition Softcover. 2008. 480p. pap. 44.95 *(978-0-9649246-7-3(6))* Diamond Pass Publishing, Inc.

Taper, Jean. NYS Canal Reference. 2009. pap. 54.99 *(978-1-61623-688-5(4))* Independent Pub.

Tigner, James. St. Michaels, Oxford, & the Talbot County Bayside. 2007. (Illus.). 160p. pap. 39.95 *(978-0-7643-2708-7(9))* Schiffer Publishing, Ltd.

Tigner, James, Jr. Yesterday on the Chesapeake Bay. 2007. (Illus.). 160p. 39.95 *(978-0-7643-2597-7(3))* Schiffer Publishing, Ltd.

Travis, Georgia-Rose. C Hector: Behaviour in Response to Tour-Boat & Yacht Presence. 2008. 124p. pap. *(978-3-639-04394-5(4))* VDM Verlag Dr. Mueller e.K.

United States Coast Guard Auxiliary Staff. Boating Skills & Seamanship. 13th ed. 2006. (ENG., Illus.). 384p. per. 24.95 *(978-0-07-146729-2(7),* 0071467297, International Marine/Ragged Mountain Pr.) McGraw-Hill Professional Publishing.

USPS Glossary. Date not set. (Learning Guides Ser.). 58p. pap. 5.79 *(978-1-891148-16-3(8))* United States Power Squadrons.

Van Gaasbeek, Richard. A Practical Course in Wooden Boat & Ship Building: The Fundamental Principles & Practical Methods Described in Detail. 2007. pap. 11.99 *(978-1-929516-25-4(8))* Dixon-Price Publishing.

Van Leuven, Susan. Woodstrip Rowing Craft. 2007. (Illus.). 288p. 49.95 *(978-0-7643-2553-3(1))* Schiffer Publishing, Ltd.

Vigor, John. The Practical Encyclopedia of Boating: An A-Z Compendium of Seamanship, Boat Maintenance, Navigation, & Nautical Wisdom. 2007. (ENG., Illus.). 384p. per. 18.95 *(978-0-07-149888-3(5),* 0071498885, International Marine/Ragged Mountain Pr.) McGraw-Hill Professional Publishing.

Wagner, Craig, et al. Small Boats Big Adventures. 2007. per. *(978-0-9801439-1-1(8))* Town & Country Reprographics.

Walbrun, Richard. The Great Boat Race: History of the Winnebagoland Outboard Marathon. 2008. 252p. 25.95 *(978-1-4327-2829-8(6));* pap. 14.95 *(978-1-4327-2248-7(4))* Outskirts Pr., Inc.

Warren, Nigel. Metal Corrosion in Boats: The Prevention of Metal Corrosion in Hulls, Engines, Rigging & Fittings. 3rd rev. ed. 2006. (ENG., Illus.). 96p. pap. 29.95 *(978-1-57409-237-0(5))* Sheridan Hse., Inc.

Watson, Tom. Kids Gone Paddlin' The Young Paddler's Guide to Having More Fun Outdoors. 2008. (ENG., Illus.). 96p. (YA). (gr. 3-7). pap. 12.95 *(978-1-58923-371-3(9),* 1589233719) Quayside.

White, Peter & White. Powerboating: The RIB & Sportsboat Handbook. 3rd ed. 2009. (ENG., Illus.). 192p. pap. 29.95 *(978-0-470-69728-3(8),* Wiley) Wiley, John & Sons, Inc.

White, Robb. Flotsam & Jetsam: The Collected Adventures, Opinions, & Wisdom from a Life Spent Messing about in Boats. 2009. (ENG.). 568p. pap. 19.95 *(978-1-891369-83-4(0))* Breakaway Bks.

Whitis, Duwain & Vinson, Barbara. Guide to the Middle Fork & Main Salmon Rivers, Idaho. 2007. (Illus.). 72p. spiral bd. 23.95 *(978-0-9776749-7-8(5))* RiverMaps, LLC.

Wilkinson, William D. & Dring, Timothy R. American Coastal Rescue Craft: A Design History of Coastal Rescue Craft Used by the USLSS & USCG. 2009. (New Perspectives on Maritime History & Nautical Archaeology Ser.). (ENG., Illus.). 384p. 125.00 *(978-0-8130-3334-1(9))* Univ. Pr. of Florida.

Williams, John Page. Chesapeake: Exploring the Water Trail of Captain John Smith. (Illus.). 2007. (ENG.). 192p. per. 12.95 *(978-1-4262-0069-4(2),* National Geographic) 2006. 191p. *(978-0-7922-5557-4(7))* 2006. 191p. *(978-0-7922-5556-7(9))* National Geographic Society.

Williams, Margaret. The Boater's Weather Guide: Revised & Expanded. 2nd rev. ed. 2011. (Illus.). 160p. pap. 12.99 ***(978-0-87033-624-9(X),*** Schiffer Publishing Ltd) Schiffer Publishing, Ltd.

Williams, Rosemary. Maritime Annapolis: A History of Watermen, Sails, & Midshipmen. 2009. (American Chronicles Ser.). (ENG., Illus.). 128p. pap. 19.99 *(978-1-59629-659-6(3))* History Pr., The.

Winans, Forville. Cruise of the Pintail: A Journal. Winans, Robert L., ed. 2011. (Hill Collection: Holdings of the LSU Libraries Ser.). (Illus.). 216p. 35.00 ***(978-0-8071-3985-1(8))*** Louisiana State Univ. Pr.

Woods, Stuart. Blue Water, Green Skipper: A Memoir of Sailing Alone Across the Atlantic. 2012. (ENG., Illus.). 224p. (gr. 12). 26.95 ***(978-0-399-16111-7(2),*** Putnam Adult) Penguin Group (USA) Inc.

Yeadon-Jones, Anne & Yeadon-Jones, Laurence. Gulf Islands & Vancouver: A Dreamspeaker Cruising Guide, Volume 1. 2010. *(978-1-932310-43-6(6))* FineEdge.Com LLC.

—The West Coast of Vancouver Island. 2008. pap. *(978-1-932310-38-2(X))* FineEdge.Com LLC.

Yetman, David S. Without a Prop. 2010. 132p. pap. 14.95 *(978-1-60844-475-5(9))* Dog Ear Publishing, LLC.

Young, Claiborne. Cruising Guide to Eastern Florida. 6th ed. 2013. (Cruising Guide Ser.). (ENG., Illus.). 544p. pap. 34.95 *(978-1-58980-666-5(2))* Pelican Publishing Co., Inc.

Young, Claiborne S. Cruising Guide to Western Florida. 7th ed. 2008. (Cruising Guide to Western Florida Ser.). 560p. per. 34.95 *(978-1-58980-506-4(2))* Pelican Publishing Co., Inc.

Young, Mary E. Arizona Waterways: A pocket guide to boating & fishing in Arizona. 2007. *(978-0-9776524-1-9(6))* Angan Publishers LLC.

BOATS AND BOATING—ELECTRIC EQUIPMENT

Hopkinson, Sara. VHF Afloat. 3rd ed. 2009. (ENG., Illus.). 80p. pap. 24.95 *(978-0-470-75858-8(9),* Wiley Nautical) Wiley, John & Sons, Inc.

Manley, Pat. Essential Boat Electrics. 2007. (ENG., Illus.). 152p. 34.95 *(978-1-904475-17-0(5),* Wiley) Wiley, John & Sons, Inc.

Payne, John C. Understanding Boat Electrical Equipment, 1 vol. 2010. (ENG., Illus.). 85p. 16.95 *(978-1-57409-301-8(0))* Sheridan Hse., Inc.

—Understanding Boat Refridgeration & Air Conditioning Systems, 1 vol. 2010. (ENG., Illus.). 81p. pap. 16.95 *(978-1-57409-300-1(2))* Sheridan Hse., Inc.

Sherman, Edwin R. Advanced Marine Electrics & Electronics Troubleshooting. 2007. (ENG., Illus.). 192p. 34.95 *(978-0-07-146186-3(8),* 0071461868, International Marine/Ragged Mountain Pr.) McGraw-Hill Professional Publishing.

Sweet, Robert J. Weekend Navigator. 2nd ed. 2011. (ENG., Illus.). 288p. pap. 25.00 ***(978-0-07-175996-0(4),*** 0071759964, International Marine/Ragged Mountain Pr.) McGraw-Hill Professional Publishing.

United Nations. Standardized Vocabulary for Radio Connections in Inland Navigation. 2010. (MUL.). 104p. pap. 15.00 *(978-92-1-139137-4(7))* United Nations Pubns.

BOATS AND BOATING—MAINTENANCE AND REPAIR

Armstrong, Robert J. Your First Powerboat: How to Find, Buy, & Enjoy the Best Boat for You. 2008. (ENG., Illus.). 240p. pap. 18.95 *(978-0-07-149673-5(4),* 0071496734, International Marine/Ragged Mountain Pr.) McGraw-Hill Professional Publishing.

Brown, David G. The Pontoon & Deckboat Handbook: How to Buy, Maintain, Operate, & Enjoy the Ultimate Family Boats. 2007. (ENG., Illus.). 192p. per. 17.95 *(978-0-07-147263-0(0),* 0071472630, International Marine/Ragged Mountain Pr.) McGraw-Hill Professional Publishing.

Casey, Don. Sailboat Refinishing. 2007. (ENG., Illus.). 144p. 14.95 *(978-0-07-148658-3(5),* 0071486585, International Marine/Ragged Mountain Pr.) McGraw-Hill Professional Publishing.

—This Old Boat. 2nd rev. exp. ed. 2009. (ENG., Illus.). 576p. 49.95 *(978-0-07-147794-9(2),* 0071477942, International Marine/Ragged Mountain Pr.) McGraw-Hill Professional Publishing.

Clymer Publications Staff. OMC Cobra Stern Drive & Engine, 1994-2000. 2006. pap. 34.95 *(978-1-59969-107-7(8))* Penton Media, Inc.

Danenberg, Don. The Complete Wooden Runabout Restoration Guide, 2 vols. 2008. (ENG., Illus.). 432p. pap. 39.99 *(978-0-7603-3488-1(9),* 0760334889, Voyageur Pr) MBI Publishing Co. LLC.

Donat, Hans. Skipper's Outboard Motor Guide. 2011. (ENG., Illus.). 26p. pap. 16.95 *(978-1-4081-1418-6(6))* A & C Black GBR. Dist: Macmillan.

du Plessis, Hugo. Fibreglass Boats: Construction, Gel Coat, Stressing, Blistering, Repair, Maintenance. 5th ed. 2010. (ENG., Illus.). 304p. pap. 39.95 *(978-1-4081-2274-7(X))* A & C Black GBR. Dist: Macmillan.

Evridge, Ben L. Emergency Boat Mechanics: Commonsense Ways to Prevent, Diagnose, & Repair Engines & Mechanical Problems. 2009. (ENG., Illus.). 320p. pap. 26.95 *(978-0-07-144505-4(6),* 0071445056, International Marine/Ragged Mountain Pr.) McGraw-Hill Professional Publishing.

Gerr, Dave. Boat Mechanical Systems Handbook: How to Design, Install, & Recognize Proper Systems in Boats. 2nd ed. 2008. (ENG., Illus.). 448p. 39.95 *(978-0-07-144456-9(4),* 0071444564, International Marine/Ragged Mountain Pr.) McGraw-Hill Professional Publishing.

Kelsey, John, ed. Boat Maintenance: The Complete Guide to Keeping Your Boat Ship-Shape. 2011. (Essential Guide to Boating Ser.). (ENG., Illus.). 160p. pap. 19.95 *(978-1-56523-549-6(5))* Fox Chapel Publishing Co., Inc.

Lindsey, Sandy. Quick & Easy Boat Maintenance: 1,001 Time-Saving Tips. 2nd ed. 2012. (ENG., Illus.). 160p. pap. 18.00 ***(978-0-07-178997-4(9),*** 0071789979, International Marine/Ragged Mountain Pr.) McGraw-Hill Professional Publishing.

Manley, Pat. Simple Boat Maintenance. 2006. (ENG., Illus.). 160p. 34.95 *(978-1-904475-02-6(7),* Wiley) Wiley, John & Sons, Inc.

Manley, Pat & Holmes, Rupert. Essential Boat Maintenance: A Comprehensive Guide to Boat Improvement, Refitting, & Repair. 2011. (ENG.). 320p. 34.95 *(978-1-57409-305-6(3))* Sheridan Hse., Inc.

Mapes, Ed. Ready to Sail: A Captain's Guide to Boat Inspection & Repairs Preparations of Boat & Crew for Offshore Passagemaking. 2nd rev. ed. 2008. (ENG., Illus.). 207p. pap. 29.95 *(978-1-57409-271-4(5))* Sheridan Hse., Inc.

Marshall, Roger. Fiberglass Boat Repairs Illustrated. 2010. (ENG., Illus.). 192p. pap. 24.95 *(978-0-07-154992-9(7),* 0071549927, International Marine/Ragged Mountain Pr.) McGraw-Hill Professional Publishing.

Nestor, Gregg. The Trailer Sailer Owner's Manual. 2009. 340p. pap. 17.95 *(978-0-939837-82-3(X))* Paradise Cay Pubns.

Parsons, Kathy. Spanish for Cruisers: The Boater's Complete Language Guide for Spanish-Speaking Destination. 2nd rev. ed. 2008. (Illus.). 368p. spiral bd. 31.95 *(978-0-9675905-2-3(3))* Paradise Cay Pubns.

Payne, John C. Understanding Boat Plumbing & Water Systems. 2008. (ENG., Illus.). 96p. pap. 14.95 *(978-1-57409-263-9(4))* Sheridan Hse., Inc.

Sail Magazine Editors, compiled by. Boatworks: Sailboat Maintenance, Repair, & Improvement Advice You Can't Get Anywhere Else. 2007. (ENG., Illus.). 256p. 39.95 *(978-0-07-149707-7(2),* 0071497072, International Marine/Ragged Mountain Pr.) McGraw-Hill Professional Publishing.

Sears, Natalie. Boat Cleaning & Detailing: Professional Secrets to Make Your Sailboat or Powerboat Shine. 2009. (ENG., Illus.). 192p. pap. 22.00 *(978-0-07-159693-0(3),* 0071596933, International Marine/Ragged Mountain Pr.) McGraw-Hill Professional Publishing.

Seloc. Yamaha Personal Watercraft: All 4 Stroke Models From 2002 - 2011. 2011. (ENG.). pap. 38.95 ***(978-0-89330-082-1(9))*** Delmar Cengage Learning.

Seloc Publications Staff. Evinrude Outboards 2002-2006 Repair Manual. 2007. (ENG.). pap. 36.95 *(978-0-89330-071-5(3))* Delmar Cengage Learning.

Sherman, Edwin R. Advanced Marine Electrics & Electronics Troubleshooting. 2007. (ENG., Illus.). 192p. 34.95 *(978-0-07-146186-3(8),* 0071461868, International Marine/Ragged Mountain Pr.) McGraw-Hill Professional Publishing.

Watts, Dennis. Motor Boat Manual: Buying, using, improving, maintaining & Repairing. 2009. (ENG., Illus.). 176p. 35.95 *(978-1-84425-513-9(1),* 1844255131) Haynes Publishing PLC GBR. Dist: MBI Distribution Services/Quayside Distribution.

—Sailing Boat Manual: Buying, using, improving, maintaining & repairing yachts & small sailing Boats. 2008. (ENG., Illus.). 176p. 36.95 *(978-1-84425-484-2(4),* 1844254844) Haynes Publishing PLC GBR. Dist: MBI Distribution Services/Quayside Distribution.

BOBBIN LACE

Cummings, Patricia. Sweetheart & Mother Pillows, 1917-1945. 2011. (Illus.). 128p. pap. 24.99 ***(978-0-7643-3917-2(6),*** Schiffer Publishing Ltd) Schiffer Publishing, Ltd.

Dye, Gilian & Thunder, Adrienne. Beginner's Guide to Bobbin Lace. 2008. (Beginner's Guide To Ser.). (ENG., Illus.). 80p. pap. 19.95 *(978-1-84448-108-8(5))* Search Pr., Ltd. GBR. Dist: Independent Pubs. Group.

Scott, Michele. Bobbin Quiltin' & Fusin' Fun. 2011. (ENG., Illus.). 96p. 26.95 *(978-1-60460-006-3(3),* 1604600063, American Quilter's Society) Collector Bks.

Tregidgo, Jan. Torchon Lacemaking: A Step-by-Step Guide. 2011. (ENG., Illus.). 240p. 39.95 *(978-1-84797-201-9(2))* Crowood Pr., Ltd. GBR. Dist: Independent Pubs. Group.

BOBCAT

Hansen, Kevin. Bobcat: Master of Survival. 2006. (ENG., Illus.). 248p. 35.00 *(978-0-19-518303-0(7))* Oxford Univ. Pr., Inc.

BOBTAIL DOG

see Old English Sheepdog

BOBWHITES

see Quails

BOCCACCIO, GIOVANNI, 1313-1375

Baranski, Zygmunt & McLaughlin, Martin, eds. The Three Crowns: Reading Petrarch, Dante, Boccaccio. 2008. (ENG., Illus.). 128p. pap. 30.00 *(978-1-85124-301-3(1))* Bodleian Library GBR. Dist: Chicago Distribution Ctr.

Boccaccio, Giovanni. The Decameron. 2007. (ENG.). 408p. per. 19.95 *(978-1-60312-213-9(3));* 408p. 34.95 *(978-1-60312-791-2(7));* 344p. per. 15.95 *(978-1-60312-152-1(8));* 344p. 30.95 *(978-1-60312-834-6(4))* Aegypan.

—The Decameron. Nichols, J. G., tr. from ITA. 2008. (Oneworld Classics Ser.). (ENG., Illus.). 1072p. pap. 24.95 *(978-1-84749-057-5(3))* Alma Classics GBR. Dist: Independent Pubs. Group.

—The Decameron. 2010. 424p. pap. 35.75 *(978-1-142-83305-3(4))* 2009. 330p. 28.99 *(978-1-115-46298-3(9))* 2009. 330p. pap. 30.75 *(978-1-115-46300-3(4))* 2008. 464p. 31.99 *(978-0-554-35406-4(3))* 2008. 396p. 29.99 *(978-0-554-35405-7(5))* 2008. 468p. 31.99 *(978-0-554-35813-2(0))* 2008. 396p. 31.99 *(978-0-554-26102-7(2))* 2008. 464p. 33.99 *(978-0-554-26103-4(0))* 2008. 468p. 33.99 *(978-0-554-24510-2(8))*1. 2007. (ENG.). 392p. pap. 26.99 *(978-1-4346-0457-6(8))*2. 2006. (ENG.). 466p. pap. 30.99 *(978-1-4264-6822-3(9))* Vol. 2. 2007. (ENG.). 462p. pap. 30.99 *(978-1-4346-0456-3(6))* BiblioBazaar.

—The Decameron. 2010. 194p. pap. *(978-1-152-22842-9(0))* 2010. 248p. pap. *(978-1-152-22838-2(2))* 2010. 212p. pap. *(978-1-152-02027-6(7))* 2009. 318p. pap. *(978-0-217-58314-5(8))* 2009. 460p. pap. *(978-1-4588-6945-6(8))* 2009. 304p. pap. *(978-0-217-07829-0(X))* Books LLC.

—The Decameron. 2010. 148p. pap. 7.57 *(978-1-152-22840-5(4))* General Bks. LLC.

—The Decameron. Usher, Jonathan, ed. Waldman, Guido, tr. from ITA. 2008. (Oxford World's Classics Ser.). (ENG.). 752p. pap. 13.95 *(978-0-19-954041-9(1))* Oxford Univ. Pr., Inc.

—The Decameron. Musa, Mark & Bondanella, Peter, trs. 2010. (ENG.). 864p. (gr. 12). 8.95 *(978-0-451-53173-5(6),* Signet Classics) Penguin Group (USA) Inc.

—The Decameron, Volume II. 2007. 428p. pap. 26.99 *(978-1-4346-0385-2(7))* 2006. (ENG.). 422p. pap. 26.99 *(978-1-4264-6759-2(1))* BiblioBazaar.

Botti, Francesco Paolo. Alle Origini Della Modernità: Studi Su Petrarca e Boccaccio. 2009. (ITA.). 128p. *(978-88-207-4674-2(3))* Liguori.

Cerocchi, Marco. Funzioni Semantiche e Metatestuali Della Musica in Dante, Petrarca e Boccaccio. 2010. (ITA., Illus.). xii, 158p. *(978-88-222-5991-2(2))* Olschki.

Cervigni, Dino S. From Divine to Human: Dante's Circle vs. Boccaccio's Parodic Centers. 2009. (Bernardo Lecture Ser.). (ENG.). 43p. pap. 9.95 *(978-1-58684-279-6(X))* Global Academic Publishing.

Clarke, K. P. Chaucer & Italian Textuality. 2011. 256p. 110.00 *(978-0-19-960777-8(X))* Oxford Univ. Pr., Inc.

Daniels, Rhiannon. Boccaccio & the Book: Production & Reading in Italy 1340-1520. 2009. (Legenda Italian Perspectives Ser.). (ENG., Illus.). 240p. (C). 89.50 *(978-1-906540-49-4(7))* European Humanities Research Ctr. GBR. Dist: Brown, David Bk. Co., The.

Gittes, Tobias Foster. Boccaccio's Naked Muse: Eros, Culture, & the Mythopoeic Imagination. 2008. (Toronto Italian Studies). (LAT, ITA & ENG.). 304p. *(978-0-8020-9204-5(7))* Univ. of Toronto Pr.

Grudin, Robert, et al. Boccaccio's Decameron & the Ciceronian Renaissance. 2012. (New Middle Ages Ser.). (ENG., Illus.). 208p. 85.00 ***(978-0-230-34112-8(8))*** Palgrave Macmillan.

Hedeman, Anne D. Translating the Past: Laurent de Premierfait & Boccaccio's de Casibus. 2008. (Illus.). 240p. 60.00 *(978-0-89236-935-5(3))* Oxford Univ. Pr., Inc.

Hutton, Edward. Giovanni Boccaccio. 2009. 442p. pap. *(978-0-217-25659-9(7))* Books LLC.

—Some Aspects of the Genius of Giovanni Boccaccio. 2010. (ENG.). 24p. pap. 14.75 *(978-1-176-98494-3(2))* BiblioBazaar.

Morosini, Roberta, ed. Boccaccio Geografo: Un viaggio nel Mediterraneo tra le città, i giardini ea il 'mondo' di Giovanni Boccaccio. 2010. (Storie del Mondo Ser.). (ITA., Illus.). 272p. (C). pap. 40.00 *(978-88-564-0102-8(9))* Polistampa ITA. Dist: Brown, David Bk. Co., The.

Ricketts, Jill M. Visualizing Boccaccio: Studies on Illustrations of the Decameron, from Giotto to Pasolini. 2011. (Cambridge Studies in New Art History & Criticism Ser.). (ENG., Illus.). 226p. pap. 39.99 *(978-0-521-17454-1(6))* Cambridge Univ. Pr.

Sherberg, Michael. The Governance of Friendship: Law & Gender in the Decameron. 2011. 296p. 49.95 *(978-0-8142-1155-7(0));* cd-rom 14.95 *(978-0-8142-9253-2(4))* Ohio State Univ. Pr.

Symonds, John Addington. Giovanni Boccaccio As Man & Author. reprint ed. 24.50 *(978-0-404-06329-0(2))* AMS Pr., Inc.

Tournoy, G., ed. Boccaccio in Europe. 250p. 45.20 *(978-90-6186-054-9(7))* Leuven Univ. Pr. BEL. Dist: Cornell Univ. Pr.

University of Toronto Press Staff & Houston, Jason. Building a Monument to Dante: Boccaccio as Dantista. 2010. (Toronto Italian Studies). 272p. *(978-1-4426-4051-1(0))* Univ. of Toronto Pr.

BODENREFORM

see Physiocrats; Single Tax

BODHI

see Enlightenment (Buddhism)

BODICCA, QUEEN, D. 62

see Boadicea, Queen, D. 62

BODIE (CALIF.)

Discovering Bodie. 2010. (Illus.). 80p. pap. 21.99 *(978-0-9843634-0-7(8))* Gariaeff, Nick.

Sprague, Marguerite. Bodie's Gold: Tall Tales & True History from a California Mining Town. 2011. (Illus.). 248p. pap. 21.95 *(978-0-87417-856-2(8))* Univ. of Nevada Pr.

BODIN, JEAN, 1530-1596

Brown, John L. Methodus Ad Facilem Historiarum Cognitionem of Jean Bodin: A Critical Study. (Catholic University of America, Studies in Romance Languages & Literatures: No. 18). reprint ed. 37.50 *(978-0-404-50318-5(7))* AMS Pr., Inc.

Franklin, Julian H. Jean Bodin & the Rise of Absolutist Theory. 2009. (Cambridge Studies in the History & Theory of Politics Ser.). (ENG.). 136p. pap. 31.99 *(978-0-521-11014-3(9))* Cambridge Univ. Pr.

Franklin, Julian H., ed. Jean Bodin. 2006. (International Library of Essays in the History of Social & Political Thought). (Illus.). 472p. 280.00 *(978-0-7546-2545-2(1))* Ashgate Publishing Co.

Reynolds, Beatrice. Proponents of Limited Monarchy in Sixteenth Century France. (Columbia University, Studies in the Social Sciences: No. 334). reprint ed. 22.50 *(978-0-404-51334-4(4))* AMS Pr., Inc.

BODLEY, THOMAS, SIR, 1545-1613

Bodley, Thomas. The Autobiography of Sir Thomas Bodley. 2006. (Illus.). 70p. 10.00 *(978-1-85124-340-2(2))* Bodleian Library GBR. Dist: Chicago Distribution Ctr.

BODMER, JOHANN JAKOB, 1698-1783

Reiling, Jesko. Die Genese der idealen Gesellschaft: Studien zum literarischen Werk von Johann Jakob Bodmer (1698-1783) 2010. (Frühe Neuzeit Ser.). (GER.). VI, 322p. 126.00 *(978-3-11-023126-7(3))* De Gruyter, Walter Inc.

BODY, HUMAN

see Human Body

BODY, HUMAN (PHILOSOPHY)

see Human Body (Philosophy)

BODY AND MIND

see Mind and Body

BODY AND SOUL (PHILOSOPHY)

see Mind and Body

BODY AND SOUL (THEOLOGY)

see Theological Anthropolgy

BODY AND SOUL IN LITERATURE

Here are entered works dealing with the medieval legends and debates of the Body and Soul.

Pappa, Joseph. Carnal Reading. 2011. (ENG.). 160p. 60.00 *(978-1-61149-004-6(9))* Univ. of Delaware Pr.

—Carnal Reading: Early Modern Language & Bodies. 2011. *(978-0-87413-774-3(8))* Univ. of Delaware Pr.

Raskolnikov, Masha. Body Against Soul: Gender & Sowlehele in Middle English Allegory. 2009. (Interventions: New Studies Medieval Cult Ser.). (ENG.). 288p.

B

61.95 (978-0-8142-1102-1(X)); cd-rom 14.95 (978-0-8142-9200-6(3)) Ohio State Univ. Pr.
Targoff, Ramie. John Donne, Body & Soul. (ENG., Illus.). 2009. 232p. pap. 20.00 (978-0-226-78964-4(0)) 2008. 208p. 30.00 (978-0-226-78963-7(2)) Univ. of Chicago Pr.

BODY ART

Bizarre Magazine Staff. Body Art. 2011. (ENG., Illus.). 160p. pap. 14.95 (978-0-85768-080-8(3), Titan Bks.) Titan Bks. Ltd. GBR. Dist: Random Hse., Inc.
Clerk, Carol. Vintage Tattoos: The Book of Old-School Skin Art. 2009. (ENG., Illus.). 256p. pap. 29.95 (978-0-7893-1824-4(5)) Universe Publishing.
De Cuyper, Christa & Cotapos, Maria Luisa. Dermatologic Complications with Body Art: Tattoos, Piercings & Permanent Make-up. 2009. (ENG., Illus.). x, 110p. 99.00 (978-3-642-03291-2(5), 3642032915) Springer.
Ewart, Elizabeth & O'Hanlon, Michael, eds. Body Arts & Modernity. (ENG., Illus.). 2011. 194p. 37.50 (978-1-907774-04-1(1)) 2007. 208p. 99.50 (978-0-9545572-9-4(8)) Kingston, Sean Publishing GBR. Dist: Lightning Source, Inc.
Gair, Joanne. Body Painting. 2010. (ENG., Illus.). 156p. 17.98 (978-0-7893-2047-6(9), Rizzoli Universe Promotional Bks.) Rizzoli International Pubns., Inc.
Grazioli, Elio. Fotografia Europea: Umano Troppo Umano = European Photography: Human All Too Human. 2008. (ITA & ENG., Illus.). 384p. pap. 45.00 (978-88-6208-058-3(1)) Damiani ITA. Dist: D.A.P./Distributed Art Pubs.
Johnson, Dominic, ed. Franko B: Blinded by Love, 1 vol. 2007. (ENG., Illus.). 256p. 75.00 (978-88-89431-79-5(2)) Damiani ITA. Dist: D.A.P./Distributed Art Pubs.
Johnson, Jeff. Tattoo Machine: Tall Tales, True Stories, & My Life in Ink. 2010. (ENG., Illus.). 272p. pap. 15.00 (978-0-385-53072-9(2)) Spiegel & Grau.
Jones, A. Perform, Repeat, Record: Live Art in History. Heathfield, Adrian, ed. 2012. (ENG., Illus.). 700p. pap. 95.00 (978-1-84150-489-6(0)) Intellect, Ltd. GBR. Dist: Chicago Distribution Ctr.
Ketchum, Art. Painting the Body Beautiful: A Showcase of Expert Body Painting. 2009. (ENG., Illus.). 128p. per. 34.95 (978-1-60138-269-6(3)) Atlantic Publishing Co.
Khan, Farah. The First British Book of Henna Art. 2008. (Illus.). 64p. pap. 25.49 (978-1-4343-6759-4(2)) AuthorHouse.
Klanten, R., et al, eds. Doppelganger: Images of the Human Being. 2011. (Illus.). 240p. (978-3-89955-332-1(2)) Die Gestalten Verlag.
Kuppers, Petra. The Scar of Visibility: Medical Performances & Contemporary Art. 2007. (Illus.). 360p. 90.00 (978-0-8166-4652-4(X)); per. 29.95 (978-0-8166-4653-1(8)) Univ. of Minnesota Pr.
Mitchel, Doug. Body Painting. 2008. (ENG., Illus.). 144p. pap. 27.95 (978-1-929133-66-6(9), 1929133669) Wolfgang Pubns., Inc.
Orlan. Fabulous Harlequin: Orlan & the Patchwork Self. Veneciano, Jorge Daniel & Garelick, Rhonda K., eds. 2010. (Life in Performance Ser.). (ENG., Illus.). 176p. pap. 44.95 (978-0-8032-3475-8(9)) Univ. of Nebraska Pr.
Pabijanek, Katarzyna. Representation of the Body in Polish Art after 1989: Towards a history of Polish art after 1989. 2008. 88p. pap. (978-3-639-10610-7(5)) VDM Verlag Dr. Mueller e.K.
Sasabuchi, Fumie, illus. Fumie Sasabuchi, 1 vol. 2007. (ENG.). 104p. 35.00 (978-3-938821-65-7(5)) Verlag fur Moderne Kunst DEU. Dist: D.A.P./Distributed Art Pubs.
Shepherd, Simon & Donger, Simon, eds. Orlan: A Hybrid Body of Artworks. 2010. (ENG., Illus.). 240p. 115.00 (978-0-415-56233-1(3)); pap. 40.95 (978-0-415-56234-8(1)) Taylor & Francis Group GBR. (Routledge). Dist: Taylor & Francis Group.
Shukla, Pravina. The Grace of Four Moons: Dress, Adornment, & the Art of the Body in Modern India. 2008. (Material Culture Ser.). (ENG., Illus.). 528p. 34.95 (978-0-253-34911-8(7), 0253349117) Indiana Univ. Pr.
Silvester, Hans. Natural Fashion: Tribal Decoration from Africa. (ENG., Illus.). 168p. 2009. pap. 29.95 (978-0-500-28805-4(4), 528805) 2008. 45.00 (978-0-500-54358-0(5)) Thames & Hudson.
Sports Illustrated Editors. In the Paint: The Complete Body-Painting Collection from the SI Swimsuit Issue - The Art of Joanne Gair. 2007. (ENG., Illus.). 144p. 29.95 (978-1-933821-20-7(5)) Time Home Entertainment, Inc.
Thézé, Ariane. Le Corps à L'écran: La Mutation de L'image du Corps Par L'art écranique: Essai. (FRE., Illus.). 263p. (978-2-89024-165-7(3)) Editions de la Pleine lune.
Tilt. Fetish Bubblegirls: Babitches & graffitiTilt Worldwide. 2007. (FRE & ENG., Illus.). 112p. pap. 24.95 (978-3-939566-10-6(1)) Publikat Verlags- und Handels KG DEU. Dist: Gingko Pr., Inc.
Top Notch Tattoos By Brandon Notch. La Inked: Slinging Ink in the City of Angeles. 2008. 124p. pap. 39.99 (978-1-4389-1544-9(6)) AuthorHouse.
Warr, Tracey. Artist's Body. 2006. (SPA.). 49.95 (978-0-7148-9837-7(6)) Phaidon Pr., Inc.
Warr, Tracey, ed. The Artist's Body. 2012. (ENG., Illus.). 208p. pap. 19.95 (978-0-7148-6393-1(9)) Phaidon Pr., Inc.
Watson, Leonie. Collecting the Self. 2008. 52p. pap. (978-3-639-06114-7(4)) VDM Verlag Dr. Mueller e.K.
Webb, Spider. Dragon Flash. 2006. (Illus.). 79p. pap. 19.95 (978-0-7643-2504-5(3)) Schiffer Publishing, Ltd.
Weller, Alan. Asian Tattoo Flash CD-ROM & Book. 2009. (Dover Electronic Clip Art Ser.). (ENG., Illus.). 48p. pap. 22.95 (978-0-486-99015-6(X)) Dover Pubns., Inc.
Weller, Alan, ed. Wizards & Dragons Tattoo Flash CD-ROM & Book. 2009. (Dover Electronic Clip Art Ser.). (ENG., Illus.). 48p. pap. 19.95 (978-0-486-99051-4(6)) Dover Pubns., Inc.

BODY BUILDING

see Bodybuilding

BODY-CENTERED THERAPIES (PSYCHOTHERAPY)

see Mind and Body Therapies

BODY COMPOSITION

see also Alcohol in the Body; Carbohydrates in the Body; Iron in the Body; Metals in the Body; Minerals in the Body; Sugar in the Body

Applied Body Composition Assessment. 2nd ed. (C). instr.'s gde. ed. 24.00 (978-0-7360-5170-5(8)) Human Kinetics Pubs.
Bardocz, Susan & White, Ann, eds. Polyamines in Health & Nutrition. 2010. (ENG.). 352p. pap. 218.00 (978-1-4419-4735-2(3), 1441947353) Springer.
Bienertovaacute;-Vascaron;k?, Julie, ed. Body Fat: Composition, Measurements & Reduction Procedures. 2011. (Series: Nutrition & Diet Research Progress Ser.). (Illus.). 186p. 95.00 (978-1-61324-332-9(4)) Nova Science Pubs., Inc.
Davies, P. S. W. & Cole, T. J., eds. Body Composition Techniques in Health & Disease. 2006. (Society for the Study of Human Biology Symposium Ser.: Vol. 36). (ENG., Illus.). 296p. pap. 58.00 (978-0-521-03192-9(3)) Cambridge Univ. Pr.
Götherström, Galina. Growth Hormone Deficiency in Adults. 2009. 176p. pap. (978-3-639-20753-8(X)) VDM Verlag Dr. Mueller e.K.
Human Kinetics Staff. Assessing Body Composition. 78p. stu. ed. 99.00 (978-0-7360-0145-8(X)) Human Kinetics Pubs.
Lucas, A., et al, eds. Importance of Growth for Health & Development: 65th Nestlé Nutrition Institute Workshop, Pediatric Program, Kuala Lumpur, March 2009. 2010. (Nestlé Nutrition Institute Workshop Series: Clinical & Performance Program Ser.). (ENG., Illus.). 252p. (978-3-8055-9304-5(X)) Karger, S. AG.
Marfell-Jones, Michael, et al, eds. Kinanthropometry IX: Proceedings of the 9th International Conference of the International Society for the Advancement of Kinanthropometry. 2008. 168p. 49.95 (978-0-415-48493-0(6)) Routledge.
National Center for Health Statistics (U.S.) Staff & National Health and Nutrition Examination Survey (U.S.) Staff, contrib. by. Body Composition Data for Individuals Eight Years of Age & Older, U.S. Population, 1999-2004. 2010. (978-0-8406-0635-8(4)) National Ctr. for Health Statistics.
Speakman, John R., ed. Body Composition Analysis of Animals: A Handbook of Non-Destructive Methods. 2008. (ENG., Illus.). 260p. pap. 53.00 (978-0-521-08140-5(8)) Cambridge Univ. Pr.
Stewart, Arthur D. & Sutton, Laura, eds. Body Composition in Sport, Exercise & Health. 2012. (ENG., Illus.). 232p. (C). 160.00 (978-0-415-61497-9(X)); pap. 53.95 (978-0-415-61498-6(8)) Routledge.
Test Package for Applied Body Composition Assessment. 2nd ed. 24.00 (978-0-7360-5230-6(5)) Human Kinetics Pubs.
Wells, Jonathan. The Evolutionary Biology of Human Body Fatness: Thrift & Control. 2009. (Cambridge Studies in Biological & Evolutionary Anthropology Ser.). (ENG., Illus.). 394p. 108.00 (978-0-521-88420-4(9)) Cambridge Univ. Pr.

BODY CONSTITUTION, HUMAN

see Human Beings—Constitution

BODY FLUID DISORDERS

see also Edema

Baumberger-Henry, Mary. Quick Look Nursing: Fluids & Electrolytes. 2nd rev. ed. 2007. (ENG.). 287p. pap. 59.95 (978-0-7637-5133-3(2)) Jones & Bartlett Learning, LLC.
Cram101 Textbook Reviews & Cram101 Textbook Reviews. Outlines & Highlights for Portable Fluids & Electrolytes by Springhouse. 2011. 130p. pap. 28.95 (978-1-61830-770-5(3)) Cram101 Inc.
Donohoe, Charlotte. Fluid Therapy for Veterinary Technicians & Nurses. 2012. (ENG., Illus.). 248p. pap. 49.99 (978-0-8138-1484-1(7), Wiley-Blackwell) Wiley, John & Sons, Inc.
Feld, Leonard G. & Kaskel, Frederick. Fluid & Electrolytes in Pediatrics: A Comprehensive Handbook. 2010. (Nutrition & Health Ser.). (ENG., Illus.). xvi, 411p. 119.00 (978-1-60327-224-7(0), 1603272240) Humana Pr.
Feld, Leonard G. & Kaskel, Frederick J. Fluid & Electrolytes in Pediatrics: A Comprehensive Handbook. 2010. (Illus.). xviii, 408p. E-Book (978-1-60327-225-4(9)) Humana Pr.
Feld, Leonard G. & Kaskel, Frederick J., eds. Fluid & Electrolytes in Pediatrics: A Comprehensive Handbook. 2011. (Nutrition & Health Ser.). (ENG., Illus.). xviii, 411p. pap. 49.95 (978-1-61779-410-0(4), 1617794104) Humana Pr.
Hahn, Robert G., ed. Clinical Fluid Therapy in the Peri-Operative Setting. 2011. (ENG., Illus.). 218p. pap. 49.00 (978-1-107-00098-8(X)) Cambridge Univ. Pr.
Johnson, Joyce Y., et al. Fluids & Electrolytes Demystified. 2007. (Demystified Nursing Ser.). (ENG., Illus.). 304p. per. 24.95 (978-0-07-149624-7(6), 0071496246) McGraw-Hill Professional Publishing.
Kee, Joyce LeFever, et al. Fluids & Electrolytes with Clinical Applications. 8th ed. 2008. (ENG.). 576p. (C). pap. 67.95 (978-1-4354-5367-8(0)) Delmar Cengage Learning.
—Fluids, Electrolytes & Acid Base Imabalances. 3rd ed. 2009. (Nursing Reference Ser.). (ENG.). 432p. (C). pap., instr.'s hndbk. ed. 66.95 (978-1-4354-5368-5(9)) Delmar Cengage Learning.
Lippincott Williams and Wilkins Staff. Fluids & Electrolytes. Springhouse Publishing Company Staff, ed. 2nd rev. ed. 2009. (Incredibly Easy! Ser.). (ENG., Illus.). 256p. pap., instr.'s gde. ed. 32.99 (978-1-60547-252-2(2)) Lippincott Williams & Wilkins.
—Fluids & Electrolytes Made Incredibly Easy! 5th ed. 2010. (Incredibly Easy! Ser.). (ENG.). 384p. pap. 46.95 (978-1-60831-290-0(9)) Lippincott Williams & Wilkins.
Lippincott Williams and Wilkins Staff, creator. Straight A's in Fluids & Electrolytes. 2006. (Straight A's Ser.). (ENG., Illus.). 288p. pap. 44.95 (978-1-58255-659-8(8)) Lippincott Williams & Wilkins.
Metheny, Norma M. Fluid & Electrolyte Balance: Nursing Considerations. 5th rev. ed. 2010. 398p. pap. 51.95 (978-0-7637-8164-4(9)) Jones & Bartlett Learning, LLC.
Ronco, C., et al, eds. Fluid Overload: Diagnosis & Management. 2010. (Contributions to Nephrology Ser.). (ENG., Illus.). 244p. (978-3-8055-9416-5(X)) Karger, S. AG.
Springhouse Corporation Staff, contrib. by. Metabolic Problems. 2011. (NurseReview Ser.). ring bd. (978-0-87434-148-5(5), Springhouse Corp.) Lippincott Williams & Wilkins.
Toffaletti, John G. & American Association for Clinical Chemistry Staff. Blood Gases & Electrolytes. 2nd ed. 2009. (978-1-59425-097-2(9)) American Assn. for Clinical Chemistry, Inc.
Westgard, Elizabethe. Clinical Coach for Fluid & Electrolyte Balance. 2011. (Illus.). 512p. spiral bd. 39.95 (978-0-8036-2290-6(2)) Davis, F. A. Co.
Zerwekh, JoAnn, et al. Mosby's Fluids & Electrolytes Memory NoteCards: Visual, Mnemonic, & Memory Aids for Nurses. 2nd ed. 2009. (ENG.). 144p. spiral bd. 24.95 (978-0-323-06746-1(8), Mosby) Elsevier - Health Sciences Div.

BODY FLUID IMBALANCES

see Body Fluid Disorders

BODY FLUIDS

see also Biological Transport; Blood; Fluid Therapy; Gastric Juice; Homeostasis; Osmosis; Pancreas; Salivary Glands; Semen; Urine; Water in the Body

ABBE Scientist Research Division Staff. AIDS & HIV in Body Fluids: Index & Medical Analysis of New Clinical & Research Information. 2007. (ENG., Illus.). 160p. ring bd. 69.95 (978-0-7883-4778-8(0)) ABBE Pubs. Assn. of Washington, D.C.
Arikha, Noga. Passions & Tempers: A History of the Humours. 2008. (ENG.). 400p. pap. 14.95 (978-0-06-073117-5(6), HarperPerennial) HarperCollins Pubs.
Body Fluid & Tissue Specimen Collection. (Specialty Collections). ring bd. 250.00 (978-1-56238-295-7(0), SC18-L) NCCLC.
Brunzel, Nancy A. Fundamentals of Urine & Body Fluid Analysis. 3rd ed. 2012. (ENG.). 464p. (C). pap. 65.95 (978-1-4377-0989-6(3), Saunders) Elsevier - Health Sciences Div.
Coté, Gerard Laurence. Optical Diagnostics & Sensing IX: 26-27 January 2009, San Jose, California, United States. 2009. (Proceedings of SPIE Ser.). (Illus.). 150p. pap. 70.00 (978-0-8194-7432-2(0)) SPIE.
Coté, Gerard Laurence & Priezzhev, Aleksandr Vasil'evich. Optical Diagnostics & Sensing VII: 23-24 January 2007, San Jose, California, USA. 2007. (Progress in Biomedical Optics & Imaging Ser.: No. 8). (Illus.). 198p. pap. 80.00 (978-0-8194-6558-0(5)) SPIE.
—Optical Diagnostics & Sensing VIII: 21, 23 January 2008, San Jose, California, USA. 2008. (Proceedings of SPIE Ser.). (Illus.). 228p. pap. 80.00 (978-0-8194-7038-6(4)) SPIE.
Ganjei-Azar, Parvin, et al. Effusion Cytology: A Practical Guide toCancer Diagnosis. 2011. 192p. pap. 85.00 (978-1-933864-65-5(6)) Demos Medical Publishing, LLC.
Kee, Joyce LeFever, et al. Fluids & Electrolytes with Clinical Applications. 8th ed. 2008. (ENG.). 576p. (C). pap. 67.95 (978-1-4354-5367-8(0)) Delmar Cengage Learning.
—Fluids, Electrolytes & Acid Base Imabalances. 3rd ed. 2009. (Nursing Reference Ser.). (ENG.). 432p. (C). pap., instr.'s hndbk. ed. 66.95 (978-1-4354-5368-5(9)) Delmar Cengage Learning.
Lippincott Williams and Wilkins Staff, creator. Straight A's in Fluids & Electrolytes. 2006. (Straight A's Ser.). (ENG., Illus.). 288p. pap. 44.95 (978-1-58255-659-8(8)) Lippincott Williams & Wilkins.
Malamud, Daniel & Niedbala, R. Sam, eds. Oral-Based Diagnostics. 2007. (Annals of the New York Academy of Sciences Ser.: Vol. 1097). (ENG., Illus.). 352p. per. 149.95 (978-1-57331-661-3(X), Wiley-Blackwell) Wiley, John & Sons, Inc.
Nordstrom, Robert J. & Coté, Gerard Laurence. Optical Diagnostics & Sensing XI: Toward Point-Of-Care Diagnostics: And, Design & Performance Validation of Phantoms Used in Conjunction with Optical Measurement of Tissue III: 22, 24, & 26, January 2011, San Francisco, California, United States. 2011. (Proceedings of SPIE Ser.). (Illus.). pap. 90.00 (978-0-8194-8443-7(1)) SPIE.
Pinchuk, L. S. & Chernıakova, Yuliya Michailovna. Biophysics of Synovia. 2012. (978-1-61942-006-9(6)) Nova Science Pubs., Inc.
Pozrikidis, Constantine, ed. Computational Hydrodynamics of Capsules & Biological Cells. 2010. (Chapman & Hall/CRC Mathematical & Computational Biology Ser.). (ENG., Illus.). 327p. 135.95 (978-1-4398-2005-6(8), CRC Press) Taylor & Francis Group GBR. Dist: Taylor & Francis Group.
Ronco, C., et al, eds. Fluid Overload: Diagnosis & Management. 2010. (Contributions to Nephrology Ser.). (ENG., Illus.). 244p. (978-3-8055-9416-5(X)) Karger, S. AG.
Schmidt-Nielsen, Knut & Bolis, Liana. Comparative Physiology: Water, Ions & Fluid Mechanics. 2011. (ENG.). 376p. pap. 60.00 (978-0-521-10629-0(X)) Cambridge Univ. Pr.
Strasinger, Susan King, et al. Urinalysis & Body Fluids. 5th rev. ed. 2008. (Illus.). 624p. pap. 59.95 (978-0-8036-1697-4(X)) Davis, F. A. Co.
Thongboonkerd, Visith. Proteomics of Human Body Fluids: Principles, Methods, & Applications. 2007. (Illus.). 553p. 185.00 (978-1-58829-657-3(1), 1588296571) Humana Pr.
Thongboonkerd, Visith, ed. Proteomics of Human Body Fluids: Principles, Methods, & Applications. 2010. (Illus.). xiii, 533p. pap. 185.00 (978-1-61737-700-6(7), 1617377007) Humana Pr.
—Renal & Urinary Proteomics: Methods & Protocols. 2010. (ENG., Illus.). 422p. 239.95 (978-3-527-31974-9(3), Wiley-VCH) Wiley, John & Sons, Inc.
Vivanco, Jorge M. & Baluka, Frantiek, eds. Secretions & Exudates in Biological Systems. 2012. (Signaling & Communication in Plants Ser.). (ENG., Illus.). viii, 283p. 189.00 (978-3-642-23046-2(6), 3642230466) Springer.
Wheeler, Michael J., et al, eds. Hormone Assays in Biological Fluids. 2010. (Methods in Molecular Biology Ser.). (Illus.). 272p. pap. 139.00 (978-1-61737-299-5(4), 1617372994) Humana Pr.
Wong, Raphael C. & Tse, Harley Y., eds. Drugs of Abuse: Body Fluid Testing. 2010. (Forensic Science & Medicine Ser.). (Illus.). 320p. pap. 209.00 (978-1-61737-567-5(5), 1617375675) Humana Pr.

BODY FLUIDS—PROGRAMMED INSTRUCTION

Cram101 Textbook Reviews Staff. Outlines & Highlights for Urinalysis & Body Fluids by Susan King Strasinger, Isbn: 9780803616974. 2009. 60p. pap. 26.95 (978-1-4288-9966-7(9)) Cram101 Inc.

BODY FORM IN ANIMALS

see Morphology (Animals)

BODY HEAT

see Body Temperature

BODY IMAGE

Abraham, Christiana. Re-Reading the Savage Woman. 2011. 104p. pap. (978-3-8433-9178-8(5)) Lambert Academic Publishing.
Allegranti, Beatrice. Embodied Performances: Sexuality, Gender, Bodies. 2011. (ENG., Illus.). 256p. 85.00 (978-0-230-24593-8(5)) Palgrave Macmillan.
Allison, Maggie & Rocheron, Yvette, eds. The Resilient Female Body: Health & Malaise in Twentieth-Century France. 230p. pap. 57.95 (978-3-03910-521-2(3)) Lang, Peter Publishing, Inc.
Alvarez, Erick. Muscle Boys: Gay Gym Culture. 2008. (ENG., Illus.). 316p. pap. 29.95 (978-1-56023-404-3(0)) Routledge.
Anderson, Frances Sommer. Bodies in Treatment: The Unspoken Dimension. Anderson, Frances Sommer, ed. 2007. (Relational Perspectives Book Ser.: Vol. 36). (ENG., Illus.). 281p. 52.00 (978-0-88163-448-8(4)) Routledge.
Arnold, Rebecca. The American Look: Sportswear, Fashion & the Image of Women in 1930s & 1940s New York. 2008. (ENG., Illus.). 288p. 89.00 (978-1-84511-896-9(0)) I. B. Tauris & Co., Ltd. GBR. Dist: Macmillan.
Bailey, Eric J. Black America, Body Beautiful: How the African American Image Is Changing Fashion, Fitness, & Other Industries, 1 vol. 2008. 176p. 44.95 (978-0-275-99595-9(X), C9595, Praeger Pubs.) Greenwood Publishing Group, Inc.
Baistow, Karen & Treasure, Janet, eds. The Female Body in Mind: The Interface Between the Female Body & Mental Health. 2007. (ENG., Illus.). 304p. (C). 128.00 (978-0-415-38514-5(8)) Routledge.
Ballard, Pat. 10 Steps to Loving Your Body: (No Matter What Size You Are) 2008. 136p. pap. 14.95 (978-1-59719-014-5(4)) Pearlsong Pr.
Bea, Tahseen. Memory of Touch, for Love of the Other. 2008. (Global Academic Publishing Ser.). (ENG.). 211p. pap. 23.95 (978-1-58684-268-0(4)) Global Academic Publishing.
Bell, Lorraine & Rushforth, Jenny. Overcoming Body Image Disturbance: A Programme for People with Eating Disorders. 2008. (ENG., Illus.). 160p. pap. 42.50 (978-0-415-42330-4(9)) Routledge.
Berry, Bonnie. The Power of Looks: Social Stratification of Physical Appearance. 2008. (Illus.). 154p. 99.95 (978-0-7546-4758-4(7)) Ashgate Publishing Co.
Bevere, Lisa. You Are Not What You Weigh: End Your War with Food & Discover Your True Value. rev. ed. 2006. (ENG.). 192p. pap. 14.99 (978-1-59979-075-6(0), Siloam Pr.) Charisma Media.
Biali, Susan. Live a Life You Love: 7 Steps to a Healthier, Happier, More Passionate You. 2010. 208p. pap. 16.95 (978-0-8253-0599-3(3)) Beaufort Bks., Inc.
Black, Amy. Objectification or Liberation- Bisexual & Lesbian Women's Experiences with Physical Appearance. 2007. 256p. per. (978-3-8364-2591-9(2)) VDM Verlag Dr. Mueller e.K.
Boero, Natalie. Killer Fat: Media, Medicine, & Morals in the American "Obesity Epidemic" 2012. 192p. 32.95 (978-0-8135-5371-9(7)) Rutgers Univ. Pr.
Brewis, Alexandra A. Obesity: Cultural & Biocultural Perspectives. 2010. (Studies in Medical Anthropology Ser.). (ENG., Illus.). 208p. (C). pap. 24.95 (978-0-8135-4891-3(8)) Rutgers Univ. Pr.
Burt, Anne & Kline, Christina Baker, eds. About Face: Women Write about What They See When They Look in the Mirror. 2008. (ENG., Illus.). 256p. pap. 15.95 (978-1-58005-246-7(0)) Westview Pr.
Calogero, Rachel M. Self-Objectification in Women: Causes, Consequences, & Counteractions. Tantleff-Dunn, Stacey et al, eds. 2010. (Illus.). 248p. 59.95 (978-1-4338-0798-5(X)) American Psychological Assn.
Cash, Thomas F. The Body Image Workbook: An Eight-Step Program for Learning to Like Your Looks. 2nd rev. ed. 2008. (New Harbinger Self-Help Workbook Ser.). (ENG., Illus.). 240p. pap. 21.95 (978-1-57224-546-4(8)) New Harbinger Pubns.
Cash, Thomas F. Encyclopedia of Body Image & Human Appearance. 2012. (ENG.). 938p. 400.00 (978-0-12-384925-0(X), Academic Pr.) Elsevier Science & Technology Bks.

Cash, Thomas F. & Smolak, Linda, eds. Body Image: A Handbook of Science, Practice, & Prevention. 2nd rev. ed. 2011. (ENG., Illus.). 490p. 65.00 (978-1-60918-182-6(4)) Guilford Pubns., Inc.

Chadwick, Dara. You'd Be So Pretty If... Teaching Our Daughters to Love Their Bodies - Even When We Don't Love Our Own. 2009. (ENG.). 256p. pap. 15.95 (978-0-7382-1258-6(X)) Da Capo Pr., Inc.

Coleman, Rebecca. The Becoming of Bodies: Girls, Images, Experience. 2009. (ENG., Illus.). 256p. 90.00 (978-0-7190-7821-7(0)) Manchester Univ. Pr. GBR. Dist: Macmillan.

—Transforming Images: Screens, affect, Futures. 2012. (International Library of Sociology Ser.). (ENG.). 224p. (C). 135.00 (978-0-415-67884-1(6)) Routledge.

Craggs-Hinton, C. Eating Disorders & Body Image. 2007. 128p. pap. 13.95 (978-0-85969-966-2(6), Sheldon Press) SPCK Publishing GBR. Dist: Westminster John Knox Pr.

Creadick, Anna. Perfectly Average: The Pursuit of Normality in Postwar America. 2010. (Illus.). 240p. pap. 26.95 (978-1-55849-806-8(0)); (ENG., lib. bdg. 80.00 (978-1-55849-805-1(2)) Univ. of Massachusetts Pr.

Crompvoets, Samantha. Breast Cancer & the Post-Surgical Body: Recovering the Self. 2006. (ENG., Illus.). 224p. 100.00 (978-1-4039-9900-9(7)) Palgrave Macmillan.

Cserjesi, Renata. Being in or Out. 2009. 120p. pap. (978-3-639-09781-8(5)) VDM Verlag Dr. Mueller e.K.

Currie, Lachlan. Everybody's Guide to Cosmetic Plastic Surgery. 2008. 185p. pap. 31.50 (978-0-9556809-0-8(5)) Gladiator Publishing GBR. Dist: Lulu Enterprises Inc.

Dalley, Simon. Emotional Body. 2007. 192p. 69.95 (978-1-84169-356-9(1), RU3561X, Psychology Press) Taylor & Francis Group GBR. Dist: Taylor & Francis Group.

DasGupta, Sayantani & Hurst, Marsha, eds. Stories of Illness & Healing: Women Write Their Bodies. 2007. (Literature & Medicine Ser.). 329p. pap. 37.95 (978-0-87338-916-7(6)) Kent State Univ. Pr.

Davy, Zowie. Recognizing Transsexuals: Personal Political & Medicolegal Embodiment. 2011. 204p. 99.95 (978-1-4094-0565-8(6)) Ashgate Publishing Co.

Diller, Vivian & Muir-Sukenick, Jill. Face It: What Women Really Feel As Their Looks Change. Willens, Michele, ed. 2010. (ENG.). 224p. 24.95 (978-1-4019-2540-6(5)) Hay Hse., Inc.

—Face It: What Women Really Feel as Their Looks Change & What to Do about It. 2011. (ENG.). 202p. pap. 15.95 (978-1-4019-2541-3(3)) Hay Hse., Inc.

Dodd, Mikyla. The Fat Girl from Hollyoaks. 2007. (ENG., Illus.). 306p. 24.95 (978-0-340-93547-7(2)) Headline Bk. Publishing GBR. Dist: Independent Pubs. Group.

Ellis, Stella. Size Sexy: How to Look Good, Feel Good, & Be Happy - at Any Size. 2010. (ENG., Illus.). 216p. pap. 16.95 (978-1-60550-355-4(X)) Adams Media Corp.

F, Marks D. Image Body & Mind. 256p. (C). 0.01 (978-0-415-01366-6(6)); 0.01 (978-0-415-01367-3(4)) Routledge.

Farrell, Amy. Fat Shame: Stigma & the Fat Body in American Culture. 2011. (ENG., Illus.). 219p. pap. 21.00 (978-0-8147-2769-0(7)) New York Univ. Pr.

Farrell, Amy Erdman. Fat Shame: Stigma & the Fat Body in American Culture. 2011. (Illus.). x, 209p. E-Book (978-0-8147-2834-5(0)) New York Univ. Pr.

Feldenkrais, Moshe. Embodied Wisdom: The Collected Papers of Moshe Feldenkrais. Beringer, Elizabeth, ed. 2010. (ENG.). 256p. pap. 21.95 (978-1-55643-906-3(7)) North Atlantic Bks.

Fenske, Mindy. Tattoos in American Visual Culture. 2007. (ENG.). 224p. 89.00 (978-0-230-60027-0(1)) Palgrave Macmillan.

Foco, Zonya & Moss, Stephen. Water with Lemon: An Inspiring Story of Diet-Free, Guilt-Free Weight Loss. 2007. per. 16.95 (978-1-890926-10-6(8)) Z.H.I. Publishing.

Frankel, Valerie. Thin Is the New Happy. 2009. (ENG.). 272p. pap. 14.99 (978-0-312-37393-1(7), St. Martin's Griffin) St. Martin's Pr.

Franklin, Eric N. Dynamic Alignment Through Imagery. 2nd ed. 2012. (ENG., Illus.). 448p. (gr. 9-17). pap. 32.95 (978-0-7360-6789-8(2)) Human Kinetics Pubs.

French, Paul & Crabbe, Matthew. Fat China: How Expanding Waistlines are Changing a Nation. 2010. (China in the 21st Century Ser.). (Illus.). 250p. pap. 29.95 (978-0-85728-965-0(9)) Anthem Pr. GBR. Dist: Books International, Inc.

—Fat China: How Expanding Waistlines Are Changing a Nation. 2010. (China in the 21st Century Ser.). (ENG., Illus.). 250p. 99.00 (978-0-85728-978-0(0)) Anthem Pr. GBR. Dist: Books International, Inc.

Fryzowicz, Karolina. The Representation of the Female Body. 2010. 104p. pap. (978-3-639-27392-2(3)) VDM Verlag Dr. Mueller e.K.

Gilman, Sander L. & Budig, Gene A. Fat Boys: A Slim Book. 2011. (ENG.). 324p. pap. 19.95 (978-0-8032-7123-4(9), Bison Bks.) Univ. of Nebraska Pr.

Goins, Darren. Performing Masculinities. 2008. 264p. per. (978-3-8364-5695-1(8)) VDM Verlag Dr. Mueller e.K.

Goldman, Leslie. Locker Room Diaries: The Naked Truth about Women, Body Image, & Re-Imagining the Perfect Body. 2007. (ENG.). 264p. per. 14.95 (978-0-7382-1095-7(1)) Da Capo Pr., Inc.

Grand, David J., et al. Practical Body MRI: Protocols, Applications & Image Interpretation. 2012. (ENG., Illus.). 250p. 79.00 (978-1-107-01404-6(2)) Cambridge Univ. Pr.

Greene, Sophia B. Body Image: Perceptions, Interpretations & Attitudes. 2011. (Series: Psychology of Emotions, Motivations & Actions Ser.). 129.00 (978-1-61761-992-2(2)) Nova Science Pubs., Inc.

Grogan, Sarah. Body Image: Understanding Body Dissatisfaction in Men, Women, & Children. 2nd rev. ed. 2007. (ENG., Illus.). 264p. (C). 59.95 (978-0-415-35822-4(1)); per. 37.50 (978-0-415-35821-7(3)) Routledge.

Guislain, Museum. The Weighty Body: About Thick, Thin, Perfect or Deranged. 2011. (FRE, DUT & ENG., Illus.). 192p. pap. (978-90-209-9215-1(5), Lannoo Pubs. (Acc)) Antique Collectors' Club.

Hall, Stephen S. Size Matters: How Height Affects the Health, Happiness, & Success of Boys - & the Men They Become. 2006. (ENG.). 352p. 26.00 (978-0-618-47040-2(9)) Houghton Mifflin Harcourt Publishing Co.

Harpole, Heather & Heather, Harpole. Teasing & Its Long-Term Effects on Body Image: How Teasing Influences One's Body Perception. 2011. 72p. pap. (978-3-639-32055-8(7)) VDM Verlag Dr. Mueller e.K.

Hesse-Biber, Sharlene Nagy. The Cult of Thinness. 2nd rev. ed. 2006. (ENG., Illus.). 288p. (C). pap. 34.95 (978-0-19-517878-4(5)) Oxford Univ. Pr., Inc.

Hilbert, A., ed. The Burden of the Burden: Current Advances in Weight Stigma Research. 2010. (Illus.). 76p. pap. (978-3-8055-9458-5(5)) Karger, S. AG.

Holder, Christen & Robillard, Rachel. Self-Compassion, Self-Esteem, & Body Image. 2011. 68p. pap. (978-3-8443-9966-0(6)) Lambert Academic Publishing.

Holloway, Hannah. The Thin Ideal. 2010. 64p. pap. (978-3-639-23192-2(9)) VDM Verlag Dr. Mueller e.K.

Holt, Rinehart and Winston Staff. Decisions for Health Green Chptr. 4: Body Image. 4th ed. Date not set. pap. 11.20 (978-0-03-066831-9(X)) Holt McDougal.

Hot Talk-Starter Videos Series 4: Gay Rights/Palm Reading/Body Image/Homeless Teenagers. pap., tchr. ed. 19.99 incl. VHS (978-1-55945-276-2(5)) Group Publishing, Inc.

James, Judi. The Body Language Rules: A Savvy Guide to Understanding Who's Flirting, Who's Faking, & Who's Really Interested. 2009. (ENG.). 416p. pap. 16.99 (978-1-4022-2283-2(1)) Sourcebooks, Inc.

Jensen, Erik Norman. Body by Weimar: Athletes, Gender, & German Modernity. 1 vol. 2010. (ENG., Illus.). 256p. 50.00 (978-0-19-539564-8(6)) Oxford Univ. Pr., Inc.

Johnson, Kerri L. & Shiffrar, Maggie. People Watching: Social, Perceptual, & Neurophysiological Studies of Body Perception: Findings, Theory, & Practice. 2012. (978-0-19-539370-5(8)) Oxford Univ. Pr., Inc.

Johnson, M. W. Oops Things Not to Say to Your Teenager or Adolescent: Speaking to Your Teenager. 2009. 168p. pap. 18.95 (978-1-4327-4154-9(3)) Outskirts Pr., Inc.

Jones, Meredith & Heyes, Cressida J. Cosmetic Surgery: A Feminist Primer. 2009. (Illus.). 276p. 99.95 (978-0-7546-7699-7(4)) Ashgate Publishing Co.

Kanekoa, Maren. The Eating Attitudes Test & Body Shape Questionnaire. 2011. 56p. pap. (978-3-8443-8334-8(4)) Lambert Academic Publishing.

Kehler, Michael. Boys' Bodies: Speaking the Unspoken. 2010. (Adolescent Cultures, School & Society Ser.). 256p. (C). 129.95 (978-1-4331-0626-2(4)); pap. 33.95 (978-1-4331-0625-5(6)) Lang, Peter Publishing, Inc.

King, Desiret Capri. Body Image: Self-Acceptance vs. Imperfection. 2008. 82p. pap. 16.95 (978-1-60610-164-3(1)) PublishAmerica, Inc.

Kinzel, Lesley. Two Whole Cakes: How to Stop Dieting & Learn to Love Your Body. 2012. (ENG., Illus.). 164p. pap. 14.95 (978-1-55861-793-3(0)) Feminist Pr. at The City Univ. of New York.

Klaver, Elizabeth. The Body in Medical Culture. 2009. (Illus.). 256p. 74.50 (978-1-4384-2585-6(6)) State Univ. of New York Pr.

Klaver, Elizabeth & Klaver, E. The Body in Medical Culture. 2009. (Illus.). 256p. pap. 29.95 (978-1-4384-2586-3(4)) State Univ. of New York Pr.

Koide, Reiko & Tamaoka, Akira. Body Image Deviation in Chronic Schizophrenia. 2008. viii, 82p. pap. 39.00 (978-1-60456-655-0(8)) Nova Science Pubs., Inc.

Labrada, Lee. The Lean Body Promise: Burn Away Fat & Release the Leaner, Stronger Body Inside You. 2006. 208p. pap. 14.95 (978-0-06-059372-8(5)) HarperCollins Pubs.

Lankford, Ronnie D. Body Image. 2010. (Hot Topics Ser.). (Illus.). 128p. 32.45 (978-1-4205-0146-9(1), Lucent Bks.) Cengage Gale.

Lesnik-Oberstein, Karin. The Last Taboo: Women & Body Hair. (ENG., Illus.). 256p. 2010. pap. 24.95 (978-0-7190-8323-5(0)) 2007. 84.00 (978-0-7190-7500-1(9)) Manchester Univ. Pr. GBR. Dist: Macmillan.

Levin, Diane E. & Kilbourne, Jean. So Sexy So Soon: The New Sexualized Childhood & What Parents Can Do to Protect Their Kids. 2009. (ENG.). 240p. pap. 15.00 (978-0-345-50507-1(7), Ballantine Bks.) Random House Publishing Group.

Lewis, Vivienne. The Context of Body Image in Adults with & Without Eating Disorders. 2010. 296p. pap. (978-3-8383-6828-3(2)) Lambert Academic Publishing.

Lo, Vivienne, ed. Perfect Bodies: Sports, Medicine & Immortality Ancient & Modern. 2012. (British Museum Research Publication: 188). (ENG., Illus.). 240p. (C). pap. 70.00 (978-0-86159-188-6(7)) British Museum Pr. GBR. Dist: Brown, David Bk. Co., The.

Maizes, Sarah. Got Milf™ The Modern Mom's Guide to Feeling Fabulous, Looking Great, & Rocking A Minivan. 2011. (ENG.). 224p. (gr. 12). 14.00 (978-0-425-23904-9(7), Berkley Trade) Penguin Group (USA) Inc.

Malacrida, Claudia & Low, Jacqueline. Sociology of the Body: A Reader. 2008. (ENG.). 408p. (C). pap. 64.95 (978-0-19-542548-2(0)) Oxford Univ. Pr., Inc.

Manderson, Lenore. Surface Tensions: Surgery, Bodily Boundaries, & the Social Self. 2011. (ENG., Illus.). 295p. 89.00 (978-1-61132-097-8(6)); pap. 29.95 (978-1-61132-098-5(4)) Left Coast Pr., Inc.

Marcillo, Aurora G. Seduction of Modern Spain: The Female Body & the Francoist Body Politics. 2010. (ENG.). 338p. 69.50 (978-1-61148-343-7(3)) Bucknell Univ. Pr.

Maria, Sarah. Love Your Body, Love Your Life: 5 Steps to End Negative Body Obsession & Start Living Happily & Confidently. 2009. (ENG.). 256p. pap. 14.95 (978-1-60550-153-6(0)) Adams Media Corp.

Markula, Pirkko & Pringle, Richard. Focault, Sport & Exercise: Power, Knowledge & Transforming the Self. 2006. (Illus.). 250p. per. 51.95 (978-0-415-35863-7(9)); 200.00 (978-0-415-35862-0(0)) Routledge.

Martin, Courtney E. & Martin, Courtney. Perfect Girls, Starving Daughters: How the Quest for Perfection Is Harming Young Women. 2008. (ENG.). 400p. (gr. 12-18). 17.00 (978-0-425-22336-9(1), Berkley Trade) Penguin Group (USA) Inc.

McSharry, Majella. Schooled Bodies? Negotiating Adolescent Validation Through Press, Peers & Parents. 2009. 148p. pap. 32.50 (978-1-85856-429-6(8)) Trentham Bks. Ltd. GBR. Dist: Stylus Publishing, LLC.

Meléndez, Mariselle. Deviant & Useful Citizens: The Cultural Production of the Female Body in Eighteenth-Century Peru. 2011. (ENG., Illus.). 256p. 55.00 (978-0-8265-1768-5(4)) Vanderbilt Univ. Pr.

Metcalfe, David. Obsession: A Study of Male Body Obsession in the USA. 2007. 121p. pap. 14.95 (978-1-84799-860-6(7)) Lulu Enterprises Inc.

Metzler, Irina. Disability in Medieval Europe. 2010. (ENG., Illus.). 364p. (C). pap. 39.95 (978-0-415-58204-9(0)) Routledge.

Miller, Evonne. Media & Body Image. 2009. 140p. pap. (978-3-639-17183-9(7)) VDM Verlag Dr. Mueller e.K.

Miller, Laura. Beauty Up: Exploring Contemporary Japanese Body Aesthetics. 2006. (Illus.). 256p. 60.00 (978-0-520-24508-2(3)); per. 26.95 (978-0-520-24509-9(1)) Univ. of California Pr.

Miller, Mev & King, Kathleen P. Our Stories, Ourselves: The EmBODYment of Women's Learning in Literacy. 2012. 266p. (978-1-61735-639-1(5)); (Illus.). xx, 244p. E-Book (978-1-61735-640-7(9)) Information Age Publishing, Inc.

Miller, Mev & King, Kathleen P., eds. Our Stories, Ourselves: The EmBODYment of Women's Learning in Literacy. 2011. 266p. pap. 45.99 (978-1-61735-638-4(7)) Information Age Publishing, Inc.

Mirriam-Goldberg, Caryn. The Sky Begins at Your Feet. 2009. 242p. pap. 21.95 (978-1-888160-43-7(8)) Ice Cube Pr.

Monaghan, Lee F. Men & the War on Obesity: A Sociological Study. 2008. (Illus.). XIV, 218p. (ENG.) 45.95 (978-0-415-40712-0(5)); 160.00 (978-0-415-40711-3(7)) Routledge.

Mondry, Henrietta. Exemplary Bodies: Constructing the Jew in Russian Culture since The 1880s. 2009. (Borderlines: Russian & East European-Jewish Studies). (ENG., Illus.). 300p. 58.00 (978-1-934843-39-0(3)) Academic Studies Pr.

Morcillo, Aurora G. The Seduction of Modern Spain: The Female Body & the Francoist Body Politic. 2010. 69.50 (978-0-8387-5753-6(7)) Bucknell Univ. Pr.

Morgan, John F. The Invisible Man: A Self-Help Guide for Men with Eating Disorders, Compulsive Exercise & Bigorexia. 2008. (ENG., Illus.). 184p. pap. 24.95 (978-1-58391-150-1(2)) Routledge.

Muller, John P. & Tillman, Jane G., eds. The Embodied Subject: Minding the Body in Psychoanalysis. 2007. (Psychological Issues Ser.). (ENG., Illus.). 128p. per. 41.99 (978-0-7657-0528-0(1), Aronson, Jason) Rowman & Littlefield Publishers, Inc.

Muller/Tillman. Embodied Subject: Minding the Body in Psychoanalysis. 2007. (Psychological Issues Ser.). (ENG., Illus.). 128p. 83.99 (978-0-7657-0527-3(3), Aronson, Jason) Rowman & Littlefield Publishers, Inc.

Murray, Samantha. The 'Fat' Female Body. 2008. (ENG.). 224p. 100.00 (978-0-230-54258-7(1)) Palgrave Macmillan.

Nasser, Mervat. The Female Body in Mind: The Interface Between the Female Body & Mental Health. Baistow, Karen & Treasure, Janet, eds. 2007. (ENG., Illus.). 304p. (C). per. 42.50 (978-0-415-38515-2(6)) Routledge.

Natalia, Sira. Ecological View on Body Image: Relationship to Body Mass Index, Attachment Relationship & Dieting Behavior among College Students. 2011. 88p. pap. (978-3-639-10020-4(4)) VDM Verlag Dr. Mueller e.K.

Newman, Deborah. Comfortable in Your Own Skin: Making Peace with Your Body Image. 2007. (ENG.). 176p. per. 12.99 (978-1-58997-354-1(2)) Tyndale Hse. Pubs.

Northrop, Jane Megan. Reflecting on Cosmetic Surgery. 2012. (ENG.). 240p. (C). 135.00 (978-0-415-52139-0(4)) Routledge.

Oliver, Kristen. Reconstructing Normal. 2009. 96p. pap. (978-3-639-16909-6(3)) VDM Verlag Dr. Mueller e.K.

Orbach, Susie. Bodies: Big Ideas - Small Books. 2009. (ENG.). 224p. pap. 14.00 (978-0-312-42720-7(4)) Picador.

Palad, Thea. Mixed Messages: Interpreting Body Image & Social Norms. 2008. (Essential Health: Strong Beautiful Girls Ser.). 112p. (YA). (gr. 7-12). 34.22 (978-1-60453-102-2(9)) ABDO Publishing Co.

Parker, Brooke. Love Your Body: A Diet-Free Approach to Balanced Eating. 2009. (Illus.). 158p. pap. 14.95 (978-1-935217-37-4(2), Walnut Springs Press) Leatherwood Pr.

Paul, Angela. The Beauty of Aging: A Woman's Guide to Joyful Living. 2009. 172p. pap. 21.95 (978-0-595-44683-4(3)) iUniverse, Inc.

Pearson, Adria & Heffner, Michelle. Acceptance & Commitment Therapy for Body Image Dissatisfaction: A Practitioner's Guide to Using Mindfulness, Acceptance, & Values-Based Behavior Change Strategies. 2010. (Professional Ser.). (ENG.). 216p. 49.95 (978-1-57224-775-8(4)) New Harbinger Pubns.

B

Phillips, Katharine A. Understanding Body Dysmorphic Disorder. 2009. (ENG., Illus.). 304p. pap. 14.95 (978-0-19-537940-2(3)) Oxford Univ. Pr., Inc.

Pitts-Taylor, Victoria, ed. Cultural Encyclopedia of the Body, 2 vols. 2008. (Illus.). 632p. 175.00 (978-0-313-34145-8(1), GR4145) Greenwood Publishing Group, Inc.

Poretsky, Golda, HHC. Stop Dieting Now: 25 Reasons to Stop, 25 Ways to Heal. 2010. 94p. pap. 9.97 (978-0-578-05791-0(3)) Body Love Wellness.

Redd, Nancy Amanda. Diet Drama: Feed Your Body! Love Your Body! Move Your Body! 2010. (ENG.). 256p. (gr. 12). 22.50 (978-1-59240-602-9(5), Gotham) Penguin Group (USA) Inc.

Rhodes, Kimberly. Ophelia & Victorian Visual Culture: Representing Body Politics in the Nineteenth Century. 2008. (Illus.). 224p. 124.95 (978-0-7546-5876-4(7)) Ashgate Publishing Co.

Rimm, Sylvia & Rimm, Eric. Rescuing the Emotional Lives of Overweight Children: What Our Kids Go Through — & How We Can Help. 2007. (Illus.). 228p. reprint ed. pap. 14.00 (978-1-4223-6795-7(9)) DIANE Publishing Co.

Romero, M. S. & Scarpa, Angela. Women's Stress, Body Dissatisfaction, & Binge Eating. 2010. 88p. pap. (978-3-639-24057-3(X)) VDM Verlag Dr. Mueller e.K.

Rumsey, Nichola & Harcourt, Diana, eds. Oxford Handbook of the Psychology of Appearance. 2012. (ENG.). 670p. 135.00 (978-0-19-958052-1(9)) Oxford Univ. Pr., Inc.

Schaefer, Michael, ed. Body in Mind: A New Look at the Somatosensory Cortices. 2010. (Neurology - Laboratory & Clinical Research Developments Ser.). (Illus.). x, 85p. pap. 43.00 (978-1-60876-955-1(0)) Nova Science Pubs., Inc.

Schissel, Wendy. Home/Bodies: Geographies of Self, Place, & Space. 2006. (ENG.). 216p. per. 34.95 (978-1-55238-184-7(6)) Univ. of Calgary Pr. CAN. Dist: Chicago Distribution Ctr.

Schoech, Samantha & Taggart, Lisa, eds. The Bigger the Better, the Tighter the Sweater: 21 Funny Women on Beauty, Body Image, & Other Hazards of Being Female. 2007. (ENG., Illus.). 256p. per. 14.95 (978-1-58005-210-8(X)) Seal Pr.

Schultz, R. Louis. Out in the Open, Revised Edition: The Complete Male Pelvis. 2012. (ENG., Illus.). 176p. pap. 16.95 (978-1-58394-436-3(2)) North Atlantic Bks.

Scott, Renee Sum. What Is Eating Latin American Women Writers: Food, Weight, & Eating Disorders. 2009. 99.99 (978-1-60497-640-3(3)) Cambria Pr.

Shaw, Andrea Elizabeth. The Embodiment of Disobedience: Fat Black Women's Unruly Political Bodies. 2006. (ENG.). 162p. 78.99 (978-0-7391-1486-5(7)); per. 24.50 (978-0-7391-1487-2(5)) Lexington Bks.

Shimizu, Akiko. Lying Bodies: Survival & Subversion in the Field of Vision. 2008. (Gender, Sexuality, & Culture Ser.). (Illus.). 152p. (C). 61.95 (978-1-4331-0100-7(9)) Lang, Peter Publishing, Inc.

Shusterman, Richard. Body Consciousness: A Philosophy of Mindfulness & Somaesthetics. (ENG.). 256p. 2008. per. 25.99 (978-0-521-67587-1(1)) 2007. 94.00 (978-0-521-85890-8(9)) Cambridge Univ. Pr.

Sisgold, Steve. What's Your Body Telling You? Listening to Your Body's Signals to Stop Anxiety, Erase Self-Doubt & Achieve True Wellness. 2009. (ENG., Illus.). 240p. 21.95 (978-0-07-162457-2(0), 0071624570) McGraw-Hill Cos., The.

Skrypzak, Joann M. Sporting Modernity. 2008. 336p. pap. (978-3-8364-6533-5(7)) VDM Verlag Dr. Mueller e.K.

Slaughter, Virginia & Brownell, Celia, eds. Early Development of Body Representations. 2011. (Cambridge Studies in Cognitive & Perceptual Development Ser.). (ENG.). 300p. 99.00 (978-0-521-76382-0(7)) Cambridge Univ. Pr.

Smolak, Linda & Thompson, J. Kevin. Body Image, Eating Disorders, & Obesity in Youth: Assessment, Prevention, & Treatment. 2nd ed. 2008. (Illus.). 376p. 49.95 (978-1-4338-0405-2(0)) American Psychological Assn.

Spellers, Regina E. & Moffitt, Kimberly R. Blackberries & Redbones: Critical Articulations of Black Hair/Body Politics in Africana Communities. 2010. (Illus.). xii, 472p. (978-1-57273-880-5(4)); pap. (978-1-57273-881-2(2)) Hampton Pr., Inc.

Springgay, Stephanie. Body Knowledge & Curriculum: Pedagogies of Touch in Youth & Visual Culture. 2008. (Illus.). 168p. (C). pap. 32.95 (978-1-4331-0281-3(1)) Lang, Peter Publishing, Inc.

Springgay, Stephanie & Freedman, Debra, eds. Curriculum & the Cultural Body. 2007. (Complicated Conversation Ser.: Vol. 20). (Illus.). 269p. (C). pap. 32.95 (978-0-8204-8686-4(8)) Lang, Peter Publishing, Inc.

Starbuck, Margot. Unsqueezed: Springing Free from Skinny Jeans, Nose Jobs, Highlights & Stilettos. 2010. (ENG.). 237p. pap. 16.00 (978-0-8308-3616-1(0), IVP Bks.) InterVarsity Pr.

Stice, Eric & Presnell, Katherine. The Body Project: Promoting Body Acceptance & Preventing Eating Disorders. 2007. (Treatments That Work Ser.). (ENG., Illus.). 152p. (C). per., instr.'s gde. ed. 37.95 (978-0-19-531989-7(3)) Oxford Univ. Pr., Inc.

Swanson, Eric. Ideal Body. the New Science of Cosmetic Surgery. 2009. pap. 59.99 (978-0-578-03665-6(7)) Ideal Look, LLC.

Thomas, Helen. Body & Everyday Life. 2012. (New Sociology Ser.). (ENG., Illus.). 192p. (C). 31.95 (978-0-415-33112-8(9)); 118.00 (978-0-415-33111-1(0)) Routledge.

Thompson, J. Kevin & Cafri, Guy. The Muscular Ideal: Psychological, Social, & Medical Perspectives. 2007. (Illus.). 265p. 49.95 (978-1-59147-792-1(1)) American Psychological Assn.

Tilin, Andrew. The Doper Next Door: My Strange & Scandalous Year on Performance-Enhancing Drugs. 2011. (ENG.). 320p. 25.00 (978-1-58243-715-6(7), Counterpoint) Counterpoint LLC.

Tornambe, Robert. The Beauty Quotient Formula: How to Find Your Own Beauty Quotient to Look Your Best - No Matter What Your Age. 2010. (ENG.). 256p. 24.95 *(978-1-4019-2451-5(4))* Hay Hse., Inc.

Tornambe, Robert M. The Beauty Quotient Formula: How to Find Your Own Beauty Quotient to Look Your Best - No Matter What Your Age. 2011. (ENG.). 256p. pap. 14.95 *(978-1-4019-2452-2(2))* Hay Hse., Inc.

Veale, David & Neziroglu, Fugen. Body Dysmorphic Disorder: A Treatment Manual. 2010. (ENG., Illus.). 496p. 143.95 *(978-0-470-85120-3(1))*; 488p. pap. 72.95 *(978-0-470-85121-0(X))* Wiley, John & Sons, Inc. (Wiley).

Veale, David, et al. Overcoming Body Body Image Problems Including Body Dysmorphic Disorder: A Self-Help Guide Using Cognitive Behavioral Techniques. 2009. (Overcoming Ser.). (ENG.). 416p. pap. 16.95 *(978-0-465-01264-0(7))* Basic Bks.

Vincent, Susan J., , Susan J. The Anatomy of Fashion: Dressing the Body from the Renaissance to Today. 2010. (ENG., Illus.). 1p. pap. 34.95 *(978-1-84520-764-9(5))* Berg Pubs. GBR. Dist: Macmillan.

Vincent, Susan. The Anatomy of Fashion: Dressing the Body from the Renaissance to Today. 2010. (ENG., Illus.). 1p. 99.95 *(978-1-84520-763-2(7))* Berg Pubs. GBR. Dist: Macmillan.

Watson, Stephanie. This Is Me: Facing Physical Challenges. 2009. (Essential Health: Strong Beautiful Girls Ser.). (Illus.). 112p. (YA). (gr. 7-12). 34.22 *(978-1-60453-753-6(1))* ABDO Publishing Co.

Wegenstein, Bernadette. The Cosmetic Gaze: Body Modification & the Construction of Beauty. 2012. (ENG., Illus.). 240p. (gr. 17). 32.00 ***(978-0-262-23267-8(7))*** MIT Pr.

Wicker, Kate. Weightless: Making Peace with Your Body. 2011. ***(978-0-86716-971-3(0)***, Servant Bks.) Franciscan Media.

Winge, Theresa M. Body Style. 2012. (Subcultural Style Ser.). (ENG., Illus.). 192p. pap. 29.95 *(978-1-84788-023-9(1))* Berg Pubs. GBR. Dist: Bloomsbury Publishing Plc.

—Body Style. 2012. (Subcultural Style Ser.). (ENG., Illus.). 192p. 99.95 *(978-1-84788-001-7(0))* Berg Pubs. GBR. Dist: Bloomsbury Publishing Plc.

Young, Harvey. Embodying Black Experience: Stillness, Critical Memory, & the Black Body. 2010. (Theater: Theory/Text/Performance Ser.). (ENG., Illus.). 272p. 80.00 *(978-0-472-07111-1(4))*; pap. 32.50 *(978-0-472-05111-3(3))* Univ. of Michigan Pr.

Zackheim, Victoria, ed. For Keeps: Women Tell the Truth about Their Bodies, Growing Older, & Acceptance. 2007. (ENG.). 256p. per. 15.95 *(978-1-58005-204-7(5))* Seal Pr.

Zinczenko, David & Spiker, Ted. The New Abs Diet: The 6-Week Plan to Flatten Your Stomach & Keep You Lean for Life. 2010. (Illus.). xvii, 317p. ***(978-1-60529-276-2(1))*** Rodale Pr., Inc.

BODY LANGUAGE

Here are entered works on non-linguistic communication in interpersonal relations, conveying emotions, attitudes, social status, etc., by such means as eye contact, facial expression, use of personal space, gestures, or posture.

see also Facial Expression; Gesture

Assaiante, Julia Goesser. Body Language & the Body of Language: Corporeality, Subjectivity, & Language in Johann Georg Hamann. 2012. ix, 143p. E-Book ***(978-1-4539-0214-1(7))*** 2011. 156p. (C). 68.95 ***(978-1-4331-1596-7(4))*** Lang, Peter Publishing, Inc.

Atlantic Publishing Group. A Man's Guide to Understanding Female Body Language: How to Detect, Decipher, & Understand the Unspoken Language of Women. 2012. (ENG.). 288p. pap. 24.95 *(978-1-60138-588-8(9))* Atlantic Publishing Co.

Beall, Anne E. Reading the Hidden Communications Around You: A Guide to Reading Body Language in the Workplace. 2009. 120p. 22.95 *(978-0-595-49760-7(8))*; pap. 12.95 *(978-0-595-50250-9(4))* iUniverse, Inc.

Beattie, Geoff & Bear, Misery. Get the Edge: How Small Changes Will Transform Your Life. 2011. (ENG.). 320p. pap. 15.95 ***(978-0-7553-6038-3(9))*** Headline Bk. Publishing GBR. Dist: Independent Pubs. Group.

Beattie, Geoffrey. Get the Edge: How Simple Changes Will Transform Your Life. 2011. (ENG.). 244p. 23.95 *(978-0-7553-6037-6(0))* Headline Bk. Publishing GBR. Dist: Independent Pubs. Group.

Borg, James. Body Language: 7 Easy Lessons to Master the Silent Language. 2009. (ENG.). 256p. pap. 19.99 *(978-0-13-700260-3(2))* FT Press.

Borg, James. Body Language: How to Know What's Really Being Said. 2nd rev. ed. 2011. (ENG., Illus.). 280p. pap. 19.99 ***(978-0-273-75879-2(9))*** FT Press.

Bowden, Mark. Winning Body Language: Control the Conversation, Command Attention, & Convey the Right Message Without Saying a Word. 2010. (ENG., Illus.). 256p. pap. 18.95 *(978-0-07-170057-3(9)*, 0071700579) McGraw-Hill Cos., The.

Brehove, Aaron. Knack Body Language: Techniques on Interpreting Nonverbal Cues in the World & Workplace. 2011. (Knack: Make It Easy Ser.). (ENG., Illus.). 256p. pap. 19.95 *(978-1-59921-949-3(2)*, Knack) Globe Pequot Pr., The.

Burgoon, Judee K., et al. Nonverbal Communication. 2009. (ENG., Illus.). 480p. (C). pap. 88.40 *(978-0-205-52500-3(8))* Allyn & Bacon, Inc.

Burman, Sanjay. Reading People: The Body Language of Your Favorite Stars. 2011. (ENG.). 152p. pap. 14.95 *(978-1-897404-32-4(8))* Burman Books, Inc. CAN. Dist: Innovative Logistics.

Burton, Darren G. Dating & Mating: Reading the Body Language Signals. 2009. 80p. pap. 11.95 *(978-1-4092-6498-9(X))* Lulu Enterprises Inc.

Cram101 Textbook Reviews. Outlines & Highlights for Nonverbal Communication by Judee K Burgoon. 2011. 142p. pap. 28.95 ***(978-1-61905-780-7(8))*** Cram101 Inc.

Cram101 Textbook Reviews & Cram101 Textbook Reviews. Outlines & Highlights for Nonverbal Communication in Everyday Life by Martin S Remland, Isbn: 9780205582198. 2011. 102p. pap. 27.95 ***(978-1-61461-649-8(3))*** Cram101 Inc.

—Outlines & Highlights for Nonverbal Communication in Human Interaction by Mark L Knapp & Judith a Hall, Isbn: 9780495568698. 2011. 138p. pap. 28.95 ***(978-1-61461-650-4(7))*** Cram101 Inc.

—Outlines & Highlights for Successful Nonverbal Communication: Principles & Applications by Dale Leathers, ISBN. 2011. 326p. pap. 33.95 ***(978-1-61461-791-4(0))*** Cram101 Inc.

Driver, Janine. You Can't Lie to Me: The Revolutionary Program to Supercharge Your Inner Lie Detector & Get to the Truth. 2012. (ENG.). 288p. 26.99 ***(978-0-06-211253-8(8)***, HarperOne) HarperCollins Pubs.

Driver, Janine & van Aalst, Mariska. You Say More Than You Think: Use the New Body Language to Get What You Want!, the 7-Day Plan. 2011. (ENG., Illus.). 240p. pap. 15.00 *(978-0-307-45398-3(7)*, Three Rivers Pr.) Crown Publishing Group.

Eggert, Max. Brilliant Body Language: Impress, Persuade & Succeed with the Power of Body Language. rev. ed. 2010. (ENG., Illus.). 256p. (C). pap. 19.99 ***(978-0-273-74074-2(1))*** FT Press.

Elwins, Dannie. How to Learn & Use Body Language Achieve Huge Success in Life. 2009. 36p. pap. 16.99 *(978-0-557-15534-7(7))* Lulu Enterprises Inc.

Ford, Mark H. Body Language: And Behavioral Profiling. 2010. 344p. pap. 17.99 *(978-1-4520-4942-7(4))* AuthorHouse.

Frank, Mark G. Nonverbal Communication: Science & Applications. Matsumoto, David R. & Hwang, Hyi Sung, eds. 2012. 336p. (C). pap. 40.00 ***(978-1-4129-9930-4(8)***, B99304P) SAGE Pubns., Inc.

Furnham, Adrian & Petrova, Evgeniya. Body Language in Business: Decoding the Signals. 2010. (ENG., Illus.). 256p. 42.00 *(978-0-230-24146-6(8))* Palgrave Macmillan.

Garnett, Liz. Choral Conducting & the Construction of Meaning: Gesture, Voice, Identity. 2009. (Illus.). 242p. 99.95 *(978-0-7546-6379-9(5))* Ashgate Publishing Co.

Gertsman, Elina. Crying in the Middle Ages. 2011. (Routledge Studies in Medieval Religion & Culture Ser.). (ENG., Illus.). 350p. (C). 125.00 *(978-0-415-88985-8(5))* Routledge.

Givens, David. Crime Signals: How to Spot a Criminal Before You Become a Victim. 2008. (ENG.). 240p. 24.95 *(978-0-312-36261-4(7))* St. Martin's Pr.

—Love Signals: The Five Phases of Courtship. Date not set. mass mkt. *(978-0-312-98999-6(7)*, St. Martin's Paperbacks) St. Martin's Pr.

—Your Body at Work: A Guide to Sight-Reading the Body Language of Business, Bosses, & Boardrooms. 2010. (ENG., Illus.). 240p. pap. 16.99 *(978-0-312-57047-7(3)*, St. Martin's Griffin) St. Martin's Pr.

Givens, David & Givens, David B. Crime Signals: How to Spot a Criminal Before You Become a Victim. 2009. (ENG.). 240p. pap. 14.99 *(978-0-312-36219-5(6)*, St. Martin's Griffin) St. Martin's Pr.

Goman, Carol Kinsey. The Nonverbal Advantage: Secrets & Science of Body Language at Work. 2008. (Bk Business Ser.). (ENG., Illus.). 202p. pap. 21.95 *(978-1-57675-492-4(8))* Berrett-Koehler Pubs., Inc.

—The Silent Language of Leaders: How Body Language Can Help — Or Hurt — How You Lead. 2011. (ENG., Illus.). 288p. 24.95 *(978-0-470-87636-7(0)*, Jossey-Bass) Wiley, John & Sons, Inc.

Greenberg, Barbara R. & Powell-Lunder, Jennifer A. Teenage As a Second Language. 2010. E-Book *(978-1-4405-0916-2(6))* Adams Media Corp.

Gritten, Anthony & King, Elaine, eds. Music & Gesture: New Perspectives on Theory & Contemporary Practice. 2006. (Illus.). 258p. 120.00 *(978-0-7546-5298-4(X))* Ashgate Publishing Co.

Hagen, Shelly. Body Language Book: Master the Art of Nonverbal Communication to Succeed in Work, Love, & Life. 2008. (ENG., Illus.). 304p. per. 15.95 *(978-1-59869-419-2(7))* Adams Media Corp.

—The Everything Body Language Book: Succeed in work, love, & life - all without saying a Word! 2nd ed. 2011. (ENG.). 304p. pap. 16.95 *(978-1-4405-2583-4(8))* Adams Media Corp.

Hargrave and Associates Staff. Strictly Business: Body Language: Using Nonverbal Communication for Power & Success. 2nd rev. ed. 2009. (ENG.). 150p. pap. 22.95 *(978-0-7575-6014-9(8))* Kendall Hunt Publishing Co.

Harrigan, Jinni, et al, eds. New Handbook of Methods in Nonverbal Behavior Research. 2008. (ENG., Illus.). 536p. pap. 79.99 *(978-0-19-852962-0(7))* Oxford Univ. Pr., Inc.

Hartley, Gregory & Karinch, Maryann. The Body Language Handbook: How to Read Everyone's Hidden Thoughts & Intentions. 2009. (ENG., Illus.). 1p. pap. 15.99 *(978-1-60163-076-6(X))* Career Pr., Inc.

—Get People to Do What You Want: How to Use Body Language & Words to Attract People You Like & Avoid the Ones You Don't. 2008. (ENG.). 1p. pap. 15.99 *(978-1-56414-993-0(5))* Career Pr., Inc.

—I Can Read You Like a Book: How to Spot the Messages & Emotions People Are Really Sending with Their Body Language. 2007. (ENG., Illus.). 1p. pap. 15.99 *(978-1-56414-941-1(2))* Career Pr., Inc.

Hartley, Mary. Body Language at Work. 2007. (Illus.). 119p. reprint ed. pap. 20.00 *(978-1-4223-6820-6(3))* DIANE Publishing Co.

Hemmings, Robert. Jump-Start Your Career. 2011. (Illus.). 176p. pap. 19.95 *(978-1-933199-27-6(X))* Racom Communications.

Hogan. The Secret Language of Business: How to Read Anyone in 3 Seconds or Less. 2008. (ENG.). 256p. pap. 24.95 *(978-0-470-58029-5(1)*, Wiley) Wiley, John & Sons, Inc.

Hogan, Kevin. The Secret Language of Business: How to Read Anyone in 3 Seconds or Less. 2008. (ENG.). 256p. 24.95 *(978-0-470-22289-8(1)*, Wiley) Wiley, John & Sons, Inc.

Ivy, Diana K. & Wahl, Shawn T. The Nonverbal Self: Communication for a Lifetime. 2008. (ENG., Illus.). 456p. (C). pap. 91.60 *(978-0-205-47481-3(0))* Allyn & Bacon, Inc.

James, Judi. The Body Language Rules: A Savvy Guide to Understanding Who's Flirting, Who's Faking, & Who's Really Interested. 2009. (ENG.). 416p. pap. 16.99 *(978-1-4022-2283-2(1))* Sourcebooks, Inc.

—Poker Face: Mastering Body Language to Bluff, Read Tells & Win. 2007. (ENG.). 272p. per. 14.95 *(978-1-60094-051-4(X))* Da Capo Pr., Inc.

James, Judi & Moore, James. You Code: What Your Habits Say about You. 2012. (ENG.). xii, 324p. pap. 15.95 ***(978-0-09-192954-1(7))*** Random Hse. GBR. Dist: Independent Pubs. Group.

Krämer, Olaf. Nonverbale Seelsorge im Kontext stationärer Pflege: Analysen, Beobachtungen und Poimenische Postulate. 2011. (Europäische Hochschulschriften. Reihe 23: Theologie Ser.). (GER.). 414p. pap. 93.95 *(978-3-631-61831-8(X))* Lang, Peter GmbH, Europaischer Verlag der Wissenschaften DEU. Dist: Lang, Peter.

Kuhnke, Elizabeth. Body Language for Dummies. (ENG., Illus.). 2007. 338p. per. 19.99 *(978-0-470-51291-3(1))* 2nd ed. 2012. 380p. pap. 19.99 ***(978-1-119-95351-7(0))*** Wiley, John & Sons, Inc. (For Dummies).

LaFrance, Marianne. Lip Service: Smiles in Life, Death, Trust, Lies, Work, Memory, Sex, & Politics. 2011. (ENG., Illus.). 336p. 26.95 *(978-0-393-06004-1(7)*, 6004) Norton, W. W. & Co., Inc.

Lambert, David. Body Language 101: The Ultimate Guide to Knowing When People Are Lying, How They Are Feeling, What They Are Thinking, & More. 2008. (ENG., Illus.). 192p. pap. 12.95 *(978-1-60239-291-5(9)*, 239291) Skyhorse Publishing Co., Inc.

Leathers, Dale & Eaves, Michael H. Successful Nonverbal Communication: Principles & Applications. 4th ed. 2007. (ENG., Illus.). 416p. (C). per. 97.00 *(978-0-205-61742-5(5))* Allyn & Bacon, Inc.

Lumsden, Gay & Lumsden, Donald. Communicating with Credibility & Confidence: Diverse People, Diverse Settings. 2nd ed. 464p. pap. 42.95 *(978-0-534-50945-3(2))* Wadsworth.

Mazzarella, Mark C., et al. Reading People: How to Understand People & Predict Their Behavior — Anytime, Anyplace. 2008. (ENG.). 384p. pap. 16.00 *(978-0-345-50413-5(5)*, Ballantine Bks.) Random House Publishing Group.

McGowan, Jack & Carroll, Patrick. Rabies Mom. 2008. 208p. pap. 15.99 *(978-0-9801106-0-9(2))* Rabies Mom LLC.

Meyer, Pamela. Liespotting: Proven Techniques to Detect Deception. (ENG., Illus.). 256p. 2011. pap. 14.99 *(978-0-312-61173-6(0)*, St. Martin's Griffin) 2010. 24.99 *(978-0-312-60187-4(5))* St. Martin's Pr.

Morse, MaryKate. Making Room for Leadership: Power, Space & Influence. 2008. (ENG.). 215p. pap. 17.00 *(978-0-8308-3448-8(6)*, IVP Bks.) InterVarsity Pr.

Navarro, Joe & Karlins, Marvin. What Every Body Is Saying: An Ex-FBI Agent's Guide to Speed-Reading People. 2008. (ENG., Illus.). 272p. pap. 19.99 *(978-0-06-143829-5(4)*, William Morrow Paperbacks) HarperCollins Pubs.

Nelson, Maritza. Speaking Without Words: The language of the Body. 2011. 28p. pap. 18.99 ***(978-1-4634-1146-6(4))*** AuthorHouse.

Nierenberg, Gerard I., et al. How to Read a Person Like a Book: Observing Body Language to Know What People Are Thinking. 2009. (ENG.). 128p. pap. 15.95 *(978-0-7570-0314-1(1))* Square One Pubs.

Pease, Barbara & Pease, Allan. The Definitive Book of Body Language. 2006. (ENG., Illus.). 400p. 26.00 *(978-0-553-80472-0(3)*, Bantam) Random House Publishing Group.

Phipps, Robert G. Body Language: It's What You Don't Say That Matters. 2012. (ENG., Illus.). 238p. pap. 21.95 ***(978-0-85708-174-2(8)***, Capstone) Wiley, John & Sons, Inc.

Pozzer Ardenghi, Lilian & Roth, Wolff-Michael. Staging & Performing Scientific Concepts: Lecturing Is Thinking with Hands, Eyes, Body, & Signs. 2010. 186p. *(978-94-6091-191-0(9))*; pap. *(978-94-6091-190-3(0))* Sense Pubs.

Reiman, Tonya. The Body Language of Dating: Read His Signals, Send Your Own, & Get the Guy. 2012. (ENG., Illus.). 400p. 24.99 *(978-1-4516-2434-2(4))* Gallery Pr., The IRL. Dist: Simon & Schuster, Inc.

—The Power of Body Language: How to Succeed in Every Business & Social Encounter. 2008. (ENG., Illus.). 352p. pap. 16.00 *(978-1-4165-6109-5(9))* Gallery Pr., The IRL. Dist: Simon & Schuster, Inc.

Remland, Martin S. Nonverbal Communication in Everyday Life. 3rd ed. 2008. (ENG., Illus.). 432p. (C). pap. 88.40 *(978-0-205-58219-8(2))* Allyn & Bacon, Inc.

Ribbens, Geoff & Whitear, Greg. Body Language. 2009. (Instant Manager Ser.). (ENG., Illus.). 224p. pap. 19.95 *(978-0-340-94571-1(0)*, Hodder & Stoughton) Hodder General Publishing Div. GBR. Dist: Independent Pubs. Group.

Richmond, Virginia P., et al. Nonverbal Behavior in Interpersonal Relations. 7th ed. 2011. (ENG., Illus.). 368p. (C). pap. 79.40 *(978-0-205-04230-2(9))* Allyn & Bacon, Inc.

Rosenthal, Robert. Judgment Studies: Design, Analysis, & Meta-Analysis. 2008. (Studies in Emotion & Social Interaction Ser.). (ENG.). 268p. pap. 36.99 *(978-0-521-10147-9(6))* Cambridge Univ. Pr.

Rosetree, Rose. Read People Deeper: Body Language + Face Reading + Auras. 2008. (Illus.). 277p. pap. 14.95 *(978-0-9752538-3-0(2))* Women's Intuition Worldwide LLC.

Sayler, Sharon. What Your Body Says (And How to Master the Message) Inspire, Influence, Build Trust, & Create Lasting Business Relationships. 2010. (ENG., Illus.). 172p. 22.95 *(978-0-470-59916-7(2)*, Wiley) Wiley, John & Sons, Inc.

Sharifian, Farzad. Culture, Body, & Language: Conceptualizations of Internal Body Organs Across Cultures & Languages. 2008. (Applications of Cognitive Linguistics [ACL] Ser.). (ENG.). X, 431p. 147.00 *(978-3-11-019622-1(0))* De Gruyter, Mouton DEU. Dist: de Gruyter, Walter GmbH & Co. KG.

Sharifian, Farzad, et al, eds. Culture, Body, & Language: Conceptualizations of Internal Body Organs across Cultures & Languages. 2008. (Applications of Cognitive Linguistics [ACL] Ser.). (ENG.). X, 431p. 224.00 ***(978-3-11-173118-6(9))*** De Gruyter, Mouton DEU. Dist: de Gruyter, Walter GmbH & Co. KG.

Stalter, Harmony. Employee Body Language Revealed: How to Predict Behavior in the Workplace by Reading & Understanding Body Language. 2010. (ENG.). 288p. per. 21.95 *(978-1-60138-147-7(6))* Atlantic Publishing Co.

Wachsmuth, Ipke, et al. Embodied Communication in Humans & Machines. Wachsmuth, Ipke et al, eds. 2008. (ENG., Illus.). 416p. 110.00 *(978-0-19-923175-1(3))* Oxford Univ. Pr., Inc.

Wainright, Gordon. Teach Yourself Body Language, Third Edition. 3rd ed. 2009. (Teach Yourself: Health & New Age Ser.). (ENG.). 224p. pap. 14.95 *(978-0-07-162584-5(4)*, 0071625844) McGraw-Hill Cos., The.

Wainwright, Gordon. Understand Body Language. 2011. (Teach Yourself Ser.). (ENG.). 224p. pap. 15.95 ***(978-1-4441-0740-1(2)***, Hodder & Stoughton) Hodder General Publishing Div. GBR. Dist: Independent Pubs. Group.

Waisman, Orit Sônia. Body, Language & Meaning in Conflict Situations: A Semiotic Analysis of Gesture-Word Mismatches in Israeli-Jewish & Arab Discourse. 2010. (Illus.). viii, 188p. *(978-90-272-1572-7(3))*; *(978-90-272-8755-7(4))* Benjamins, John Publishing Co.

White, John & Gardner, John E. The Classroom X-Factor: The Role of Body Language & Non-Verbal Communication in Teaching. 2011. (ENG., Illus.). 208p. (C). 125.00 *(978-0-415-59314-4(X))*; pap. 41.95 *(978-0-415-59315-1(8))* Routledge.

Winthrop, Simon. How to Be a Mentalist: Master the Secrets Behind the Hit TV Show. 2011. (ENG.). 256p. (gr. 12). 15.00 *(978-0-425-23651-2(X)*, Berkley Trade) Penguin Group (USA) Inc.

Young, Stephen. Micromessaging: Why Great Leadership Is Beyond Words. 2006. (ENG.). 224p. 24.95 *(978-0-07-146757-5(2)*, 0071467572) McGraw-Hill Cos., The.

BODY MARKING

see also Tattooing

Abdoyan, Brenda. Teach Yourself Henna Tattoo: Easy-to-Follow Instructions, Patterns, & Projects for Making Mehndi Art. 2012. (ENG., Illus.). 128p. pap. 19.95 ***(978-1-56523-672-1(6))*** Fox Chapel Publishing Co., Inc.

Bennett, Margo E. & Lumbert, David E. A.S.C. Tattoo Directory 2007. 2007. (Illus.). 20.00 *(978-1-887080-20-0(1))* Active Publishing, Inc.

—A.S.C. Tattoo Directory 2008. 2008. 240p. pap. 20.00 *(978-1-887080-21-7(X))* Active Publishing, Inc.

DeMello, Margo. Encyclopedia of Body Adornment, 1 vol. 2007. (Illus.). 360p. 79.95 *(978-0-313-33695-9(4)*, GR3695, Greenwood Pr.) Greenwood Publishing Group, Inc.

Faulks, Philippa. Henna Magic: Crafting Charms & Rituals with Sacred Body Art. 2010. (ENG., Illus.). 288p. pap. 18.95 *(978-0-7387-1915-3(3))* Llewellyn Pubns.

Giansanti, Gianni, text. Last African Warriors. 2011. (ENG., Illus.). 216p. 60.00 *(978-88-544-0472-4(1))* White Star ITA. Dist: Sterling Publishing Co., Inc.

Hambly, Wilfrid Dyson. The History of Tattooing. 2009. (ENG., Illus.). 384p. pap. 14.95 *(978-0-486-46812-9(7))* Dover Pubns., Inc.

Kalman, Tibor & Kalman, Maira. Fashion. (Illus.). 224p. *(978-1-86154-144-4(9))* Booth-Clibborn Editions GBR. Dist: Hachette Bk. Group.

Mitchel, Doug. Body Painting. 2008. (ENG., Illus.). 144p. pap. 27.95 *(978-1-929133-66-6(9)*, 1929133669) Wolfgang Pubns., Inc.

Roleff, Tamara, ed. Body Piercing & Tattoos. 2007. (At Issue Ser.). (ENG.). 91p. (gr. 10-12). pap. 22.50 *(978-0-7377-3112-5(5)*, Greenhaven Pr., Inc.); (Illus.). 101p. (YA). (gr. 9-12). pap. 31.80 *(978-0-7377-3111-8(7))* Cengage Gale.

Silvester, Hans. Natural Fashion: Tribal Decoration from Africa. 2009. (ENG., Illus.). 168p. pap. 29.95 *(978-0-500-28805-4(4)*, 528805) Thames & Hudson.

Sports Illustrated Editors. In the Paint: The Complete Body-Painting Collection from the SI Swimsuit Issue - The Art of Joanne Gair. 2007. (ENG., Illus.). 144p. 29.95 *(978-1-933821-20-7(5))* Time Home Entertainment, Inc.

Vale, V., ed. Modern Primitives: An Investigation of Contemporary Adornment & Ritual. 2010. (ENG., Illus.). 228p. pap. 25.00 *(978-1-889307-26-8(2))* RE/Search.

BODY MECHANICS, ANIMAL

see Animal Mechanics

BODY MECHANICS, HUMAN

see Human Mechanics

BODY PIERCING

Angel, Elayne. Piercing Bible. 2009. (ENG., Illus.). 320p. pap. 20.00 *(978-1-58091-193-1(5)*, Crossing Pr.) Ten Speed Pr.

Bizarre Magazine. Body Art 3. 2012. (ENG., Illus.). 160p. pap. 16.95 ***(978-0-85768-082-2(X)***, Titan Bks.) Titan Bks. Ltd. GBR. Dist: Random Hse., Inc.

Bizarre Magazine Staff. Body Art. 2011. (ENG., Illus.). 160p. pap. 14.95 *(978-0-85768-080-8(3)*, Titan Bks.) Titan Bks. Ltd. GBR. Dist: Random Hse., Inc.

Book Sales, Inc. Staff. Body Piercing: The Body Art Manual. 2010. (ENG.). 224p. spiral bd. 14.99 (978-0-7858-2655-2(6), 0785826556, Chartwell) Book Sales, Inc.
DeMello, Margo. Encyclopedia of Body Adornment, 1 vol. 2007. (Illus.). 360p. 79.95 (978-0-313-33695-9(4), GR3695, Greenwood Pr.) Greenwood Publishing Group, Inc.
Hudson, Karen L. Living Canvas: Your Total Guide to Tattoos, Piercings, & Body Modification. 2009. (ENG.). 336p. pap. 17.95 (978-1-58005-288-7(6)) Seal Pr.
Lemma, Alessandra. Under the Skin: A Psychoanalytic Study of Body Modification. 2010. (New Library of Psychoanalysis 'Beyond the Couch' Ser.). (ENG.). 216p. (C). 105.00 (978-0-415-48569-2(X)); pap. 35.95 (978-0-415-48570-8(3)) Routledge.
Mueller, Kurtis & Howe, Tanya Lee. Start & Run a Tattoo & Body Piercing Business. 2011. (ENG., Illus.). 176p. pap. 22.95 incl. cd-rom (978-1-77040-070-2(2)) Self-Counsel Pr., Inc. CAN. Dist: National Bk. Network.
Roleff, Tamara, ed. Body Piercing & Tattoos. 2007. (At Issue Ser.). (ENG.). 91p. (gr. 10-12). pap. 22.50 (978-0-7377-3112-5(5), Greenhaven Pr., Inc.); (Illus.). 101p. (YA). (gr. 9-12). pap. 31.80 (978-0-7377-3111-8(7)) Cengage Gale.
Romanienko, Lisiunia A. & Romanienko, Lisa A. Body Piercing & Identity Construction: A Comparative Perspective - New York, New Orleans, Wroclaw. 2011. (ENG., Illus.). 280p. 89.00 (978-0-230-11032-8(0)) Palgrave Macmillan.
Trattner, Agnes. Piercing, Tattoo und Schönheitsoperationen: Jugendliche Protesthaltung oder psychopathologische Auffälligkeit? 2008. (Erziehung in Wissenschaft und Praxis Ser.). 156p. pap. 49.95 (978-3-631-57666-3(8)) Lang, Peter GmbH, Europaischer Verlag der Wissenschaften DEU. Dist: Lang, Peter.

BODY POSITION
see Posture

BODY SIZE
see also Anthropometry

Bonner, John Tyler. Why Size Matters: From Bacteria to Blue Whales. 2006. (ENG., Illus.). 176p. (C). 16.95 (978-0-691-12850-4(2)) Princeton Univ. Pr.
Bonner, John Tyler. Why Size Matters: From Bacteria to....... Blue Whales. 2011. (ENG., Illus.). 176p. pap. 12.95 **(978-0-691-15233-2(0))** Princeton Univ. Pr.
Cohen, Susan & Cosgrove, Christine. Normal at Any Cost: Tall Girls, Short Boys, & the Medical Industry's Quest to Manipulate Height. 2009. (ENG.). 416p. (gr. 12-18). 26.95 (978-1-58542-683-6(0), Tarcher) Penguin Group (USA) Inc.
Dunning, John B., Jr. CRC Handbook of Avian Body Masses. 2nd rev. ed. 2007. (ENG., Illus.). 672p. 125.95 (978-1-4200-6444-5(4), CRC Press) Taylor & Francis Group GBR. Dist: Taylor & Francis Group.
Fairbairn, Daphne J., et al, eds. Sex, Size, & Gender Roles: Evolutionary Studies of Sexual Size Dimorphism. 2007. (ENG., Illus.). 280p. 135.00 (978-0-19-920878-4(6)) Oxford Univ. Pr., Inc.
—Sex, Size & Gender Roles: Evolutionary Studies of Sexual Size Dimorphism. 2009. (ENG., Illus.). 280p. pap. 65.00 (978-0-19-954553-2(8)) Oxford Univ. Pr., Inc.
Hildrew, Alan, et al, eds. Body Size: The Structure & Function of Aquatic Ecosystems. 2007. (Ecological Reviews Ser.). (ENG., Illus.). 356p. per. 79.99 (978-0-521-67967-1(2)) Cambridge Univ. Pr.
Mironov, Boris Nikolaevich. The Standard of Living & Revolutions in Russia, 1700-1917. 2012. **(978-0-203-11944-0(4))** Routledge.
Samaras, Thomas T. Human Body Size: Scaling, Physiology, Aging, & Ecology. 2006. (Illus.). (C). 169.00 (978-1-60021-408-0(8)) Nova Science Pubs., Inc.
Silverman, Robyn. Good Girls Don't Get Fat: How Weight Obsession Is Messing up Our Girls & How We Can Help Them Thrive Despite It. 2010. (ENG.). 288p. pap. 16.95 (978-0-373-89220-4(9)) Harlequin Enterprises, Ltd. CAN. Dist: Simon & Schuster, Inc.
World Health Organization Staff & World Health Organization, Nutrition for Health and Development Staff, contrib. by. Who Child Growth Standards: Head Circumference-for-Age, Arm Circumference-For Age, Triceps Skinfold-for-Age & Subscapular Skinfold-For Age. 2007. (Nonserial Publication). (ENG.). 234p. pap. 48.00 (978-92-4-154718-5(9)) World Health Organization.

BODY SURFING
see Surfing

BODY TEMPERATURE
see also Fever; Hypothermia

Hopkins, Philip M. & Ellis, F. R., eds. Hyperthermic & Hypermetabolic Disorders: Exertional Heat-stroke, Malignant Hyperthermia & Related Syndromes. 2011. (ENG., Illus.). 302p. pap. 55.00 (978-0-521-28182-9(2)) Cambridge Univ. Pr.

BODY TEMPERATURE—MEASUREMENT
see also Medical Thermography

Wunderlich, C. A. & Seguin, Edward. Medical Thermometry & Human Temperature. 2007. 288p. 43.95 (978-0-548-19887-2(X),; 292p. per. 28.95 (978-1-4325-0754-1(0)) Kessinger Publishing, LLC.

BODY TEMPERATURE—REGULATION

Cisneros, Austin B. & Goins, Bryan L. Body Temperature Regulation. 2009. (Physiology - Laboratory & Clinical Research Ser.). (Illus.). xx, 392p. 129.00 (978-1-60741-282-3(9)) Nova Science Pubs., Inc.
Cooper, Keith E. Fever & Antipyresis: The Role of the Nervous System. 2008. (Illus.). 200p. pap. 42.00 (978-0-521-07203-8(4)) Cambridge Univ. Pr.
Dietz, Markus. Thermoregulation & Foraging Strategies of the Trawling Bat Myotis Daubentonii. 2008. 132p. pap. (978-3-639-03718-0(9)) VDM Verlag Dr. Mueller e.K.
Flouris, Andreas. On the Functional Architecture of the Human Thermoregulatory System. 2009. 280p. pap. (978-3-639-16818-1(6)) VDM Verlag Dr. Mueller e.K.
Gordon, Christopher J. Temperature Regulation in Laboratory Rodents. 2009. (Illus.). 296p. pap. 58.00 (978-0-521-10279-7(0)) Cambridge Univ. Pr.
Johnston, Ian A. & Bennett, Albert F., eds. Animals & Temperature: Phenotypic & Evolutionary Adaptation. 2008. (Society for Experimental Biology Seminar Ser.). (Illus.). 436p. pap. 79.00 (978-0-521-05061-6(8)) Cambridge Univ. Pr.
Marino, F. E., ed. Thermoregulation & Human Performance: Physiological & Biological Aspects. 2008. (Medicine & Sport Science Ser.). (Illus.). 134p. (978-3-8055-8648-1(5)) Karger, S. AG.
McNab, Brian K. Extreme Measures: The Ecological Energetics of Birds & Mammals. 2012. (ENG., Illus.). 336p. 100.00 **(978-0-226-56122-6(4))**; pap. 35.00 **(978-0-226-56123-3(2))** Univ. of Chicago Pr.

BODY THERAPIES (PSYCHOTHERAPY)
see Mind and Body Therapies

BODY WATER
see Water in the Body

BODY WEIGHT
see also Birth Weight; Body Composition; Obesity; Weight Loss

Bacon, Linda. Health at Every Size: The Surprising Truth about Your Weight. 2010. (ENG.). 400p. pap. 14.95 (978-1-935618-25-6(3)) BenBella Bks.
Committee on the Impact of Pregnancy Weight on Maternal and Child Health Staff, et al, contrib. by. Influence of Pregnancy Weight on Maternal & Child Health: Workshop Report. 2007. (ENG., Illus.). 116p. pap. 30.25 (978-0-309-10406-7(8)) National Academies Pr.
Cooper, Steven J. & Kirkham, Tim, eds. Appetite & Body Weight: Integrative Systems & the Development of Anti-Obesity Drugs. 2006. (ENG., Illus.). 384p. 131.00 (978-0-12-370633-1(5), Academic Pr.) Elsevier Science & Technology Bks.
Fitzgerald, Matt. Racing Weight Quick Start Guide: A 4-WeekWeight-Loss Plan for Endurance Athletes. 2011. (ENG., Illus.). 240p. (gr. 11). pap. 18.95 (978-1-934030-72-1(4)) VeloPress.
Gouveia, Camilo & Melo, Diego, eds. Weight Change: Patterns, Risks & Psychosocial Effects. 2012. (Public Health in the 21st Century Ser.). 191p. 95.00 **(978-1-61470-386-5(X))** Nova Science Pubs., Inc.
Gripp, Karen, et al. Handbook of Physical Measurements. 2nd ed. 2006. (ENG., Illus.). 520p. 65.00 (978-0-19-530149-6(8)) Oxford Univ. Pr., Inc.
hickombottom, leigh. Logistics of leanness Defined. 2010. 50p. pap. 15.00 (978-0-557-25442-2(6)) Lulu Enterprises Inc.
Holt, Rinehart and Winston Staff. Decisions for Health Red Chptr. 6: Healthy Body Weight. 4th ed. Date not set. pap. 11.20 (978-0-03-066839-5(5)) Holt McDougal.
Isaacs, Scott. Hormonal Balance: How to Lose Weight by Understanding Your Hormones & Metabolism. 3rd ed. 2012. (ENG.). 466p. pap. 17.95 **(978-1-936693-22-1(4))** Bull Publishing Co.
Karasu, Sylvia R. & Karasu, T. Byram. The Gravity of Weight: A Clinical Guide to Weight Loss & Maintenance. 2010. (ENG., Illus.). 518p. pap. 64.00 (978-1-58562-360-0(1)) American Psychiatric Publishing, Inc.
Langhans, W. & Geary, N., eds. Frontiers in Eating & Weight Regulation. 2009. (Forum of Nutrition Ser.). (Illus.). 208p. (978-3-8055-9300-7(7)) Karger, S. AG.
Libonati, Ms. What State Do You Live In? The Consequences of Weight Gain. 2008. 216p. pap. 24.95 (978-1-4389-3503-4(X)) AuthorHouse.
Marfell-Jones, Mike & Olds, Tim, eds. Kinanthropometry X: Proceedings of the 10th International Society for Advancement of Kinanthropometry Conference, Held in Conjunction with the 13th Commonwealth International Sport Conference. 2007. (ENG.). 272p. (C). 190.00 (978-0-415-43470-6(X)) Routledge.
McDowell, Margaret A., et al. Anthropometric Reference Data for Children & Adults: United States, 1988-1994. 2009. (978-0-8406-0631-0(1)) National Ctr. for Health Statistics.
McKenzie, Richard B. Heavy! The Surprising Reasons America Is the Land of the Free - And the Home of the Fat. 2011. (ENG., Illus.). xvi, 325p. pap. 27.95 (978-3-642-20134-9(2), 3642201342) Springer.
Paul, Fit by Fart: Toot Your Horn to Good Health Hope. Fit by Fart: Toot Your Horn to Good Health. 2010. 76p. pap. 13.54 (978-0-557-11446-7(2)) Lulu Enterprises Inc.
Tucci, ed. Phytochemicals for the Control of Human Appetite & Body Weight. 2010. (Nutrition & Diet Research Progress Ser.). 93p. pap. 43.00 (978-1-61668-676-5(6)) Nova Science Pubs., Inc.
Wells, Jonathan. The Evolutionary Biology of Human Body Fatness: Thrift & Control. 2009. (Cambridge Studies in Biological & Evolutionary Anthropology Ser.). (ENG., Illus.). 394p. 108.00 (978-0-521-88420-4(9)) Cambridge Univ. Pr.
Woods, Velinda D. The Slowly But Surely Solution. 2011. 278p. 19.95 (978-1-936183-26-5(9), Langdon Street Pr.) Hillcrest Publishing Group, Inc.

BODY WORKS (ART)
see Body Art

BODYBUILDING
see also Weight Lifting; Weight Training

Adams, Mark. Mr. America: How Muscular Millionaire Bernarr Macfadden Transformed the Nation Through Sex, Salad, & the Ultimate Starvation Diet. 2010. (ENG.). 320p. pap. 14.99 (978-0-06-059476-3(4)) HarperCollins Pubs.
Allsen, Philip E. Strength Training: Beginners, Body Builders, Athletes. 5th rev. ed. 2010. (ENG.). 236p. spiral bd. 42.02 (978-0-7575-5932-7(8)) Kendall Hunt Publishing Co.
Andrew Wilson, B. Sc. The Price: The Education of a Fast-Oxidizer. 2009. 556p. pap. 29.99 (978-1-4389-4144-8(7)) AuthorHouse.
Ballantyne, Craig. Just Say No to Cardio: Burn Belly Fat in Half the Time Using Research Proven Turbulence Training. 2008. (ENG.). 108p. pap. 11.99 (978-1-59932-081-6(9)) Advantage Media Group.
Bass, Clarence. Great Expectations: Health Fitness Leanness Without Suffering. 2007. (Illus.). 172p. (YA). pap. 24.95 (978-0-9747682-4-3(3)) Bass, Clarence Ripped Enterprises.
Body Sculpting Bible Team Staff, et al. Featuring the 21 Minute Body Sculpting Workout. 2009. (Body Sculpting Bible Ser.). (ENG., Illus.). 176p. pap. 15.95 (978-1-57826-295-3(X)) Hatherleigh Co., Ltd., The.
Breitenstein, Berend. Ultimate Pump! Bestform ohne Doping. 2009. 122p. pap. (978-3-8370-3327-4(9)) Books on Demand GmbH.
Cabral, Stephen. A Man's Guide to Muscle & Strength. 2011. (Illus.). 288p. pap. 19.95 **(978-1-4504-0220-0(8))** Human Kinetics Pubs.
Cardillo, Stephen. How a Champion Is Made. 2011. 106p. pap. 14.95 (978-0-9843845-1-8(0)) Sports Improper Pubns., LLC.
Cheeke, Robert. Vegan Bodybuilding & Fitness: Building Your Body on a Plant-Based Diet. 2010. (ENG.). 338p. pap. 19.95 (978-0-9843916-0-8(6)) Gaven Pr.
Clark, Joshua & Lauren, Mark. Body by You: The You Are Your Own Gym Guide to Total Women's Fitness. 2012. (ENG., Illus.). 208p. pap. 16.00 **(978-0-345-52897-1(2)**, Ballantine Bks.) Random House Publishing Group.
Coleman, Ronnie & Berg, Michael. Hard Core: Ronnie Coleman's Complete Guide to Weight Training. 2007. (ENG., Illus.). 176p. pap. 22.95 (978-1-57243-973-3(4)) Triumph Bks.
Dan Lurie & David Robson. Heart of Steel: The Dan Lurie Story. 2009. 416p. 44.95 (978-1-4343-8546-8(9)); pap. 34.95 (978-1-4343-8545-1(0)) AuthorHouse.
Daniel-Lemoine, Jo-Ann. How to Prepare Your Body for Biological & Chemical Warfare: Arm Yourself with Knowledge. 2009. 140p. pap. 18.95 (978-1-4327-3933-1(6)) Outskirts Pr., Inc.
dos Remedios, Robert. Cardio Strength Training: Torch Fat, Build Muscle, & Get Stronger Faster. 2009. (ENG., Illus.). 256p. pap. 19.99 (978-1-60529-655-5(4)) Rodale Pr., Inc.
Elwins, Dannie. How to Build Lean & Solid Muscle Mass in Less Than 60 Days. 2009. 48p. pap. 16.99 (978-0-557-15533-0(9)) Lulu Enterprises Inc.
—How to Build Muscle Quickly & Easily Even If That's Uncommon for You. 2009. 36p. pap. 16.99 (978-0-557-15739-6(0)) Lulu Enterprises Inc.
Endacott, Jan. Weights Work for Women: Create a Beautiful Body in Less Than an Hour a Week! 2008. (Illus.). 128p. pap. 14.95 (978-0-600-61637-5(1), Hamlyn) Octopus Publishing Group GBR. Dist: Jaguar Bk. Group.
Evans, Nick. Bodybuilding Anatomy. 2006. (ENG., Illus.). 200p. per. 19.95 (978-0-7360-5926-8(1)) Human Kinetics Pubs.
—Men's Body Sculpting. 2nd rev. ed. 2010. (ENG., Illus.). 256p. pap. 19.95 (978-0-7360-8321-8(9)) Human Kinetics Pubs.
Everts, Kellie. The Origin & Decline of Female Body Building. 2009. 350p. pap 24.95 (978-0-557-06850-0(9)) Lulu Enterprises Inc.
Fee, Alexander. Logical H I T: A Means to Fight for Your Greatest Value. 2009. 328p. pap. 22.95 (978-1-4401-3653-5(X)) iUniverse, Inc.
Fett, B. Michael. Beautiful Hardship: My Story. 2009. (978-1-58982-555-0(1)) American Bk. Publishing Group.
Frost, Neil. Abs for Life - the No. 1 Solution on How to Get Six Pack Abs. 2008. 261p. pap. 27.50 (978-0-9559879-0-8(3)) Elite Media Publishing GBR. Dist: Lulu Enterprises Inc.
Green, Nate. Built for Show: Four Body-Changing Workouts for Building Muscle, Losing Fat, & Looking Good Enough to Hook Up. 2008. (ENG.). 256p. (gr. 12-18). 19.95 (978-1-58333-319-8(3), Avery) Penguin Group (USA) Inc.
Hartman, Bill & Campbell, Adam. Total Body Plan: The Ultimate Guide to Building Muscle & Losing Fat. 2007. (ENG., Illus.). 192p. per. 14.95 (978-1-57243-971-9(8)) Triumph Bks.
Hofmekler, Ori. Maximum Muscle, Minimum Fat: The Secret Science Behind Physical Transformation. 2008. (ENG., Illus.). 176p. pap. 16.95 (978-1-55643-689-5(0)) North Atlantic Bks.
Incledon, Thomas & Hoffman, Matthew. Men's Health Maximum Muscle Plan: The High-Efficiency Workout Program to Increase Your Strength & Muscle Size in Just 12 Weeks. 2006. (ENG., Illus.). 416p. pap. 23.99 (978-1-59486-314-1(8)) Rodale Pr., Inc.
John, Dan. Mass Made Simple: A Six-Week Journey into Bulking. 2011. (Illus.). 163p. spiral bd. 19.95 (978-1-931046-02-2(6)) On Target Pubns.
—Never Let Go: A Philosophy of Lifting, Living & Learning. 2009. 416p. pap. 24.95 (978-1-931046-38-1(7)) On Target Pubns.
Joon, Jong Sze. HUMAN MOTION BASED ON ACTOR PHYSIQUE USING MOTION CAPTURE: A Case Study. 2008. 164p. pap. (978-3-639-09948-5(6)) VDM Verlag Dr. Mueller e.K.
Kelley, Ian. The Organic Body. 2008. 111p. pap. 24.96 (978-0-615-17237-8(7)) Kelley, Ian.
Kennedy, Robert. Encyclopedia of Bodybuilding: The Complete A-Z Book on Muscle Building. 21st ed. 2008. (ENG.). 800p. 39.95 (978-1-55210-051-6(0)) Kennedy, Robert Publishing CAN. Dist: National Bk. Network.
Kennedy Robert. 1001 Musclebuilding Tips. 2007. (ENG., Illus.). 144p. per. 16.95 (978-1-55210-040-0(5)) Kennedy, Robert Publishing CAN. Dist: National Bk. Network.
Kleiner, Susan & Greenwood-Robinson, Maggie. Power Eating. 3rd rev. ed. 2006. (ENG., Illus.). 328p. per. 16.95 (978-0-7360-6698-3(5)) Human Kinetics Pubs.
Kroger, William S. & Teufel, Trey. Felon Fitness: How to Get a Hard Body Without Doing Hard Time. 2011. (ENG.). 224p. pap. 15.95 **(978-1-4405-2659-6(1))** Adams Media Corp.
Ladefoged, Joachim. Mirror. 2008. (ENG.). 132p. 79.00 (978-87-92241-06-1(9), Art Stock Bks. Ltd/Csi) Continental Sales, Inc.
Lauren, Mark & Clark, Joshua. You Are Your Own Gym: The Bible of Bodyweight Exercises for Men & Women. 2010. (ENG.). 240p. pap. (978-0-9714076-1-9(4)) Light of New Orleans Publishing, LLC.
Lewis-McCormick, Irene. A Women's Guide to Muscle & Strength. 2012. (Illus.). 224p. pap. 19.95 **(978-0-7360-9035-3(5))** Human Kinetics Pubs.
Liederman, Earle E. Secrets of Strength. 2008. 194p. pap. 23.95 (978-1-4092-0475-6(8)) Lulu Enterprises Inc.
Lipowski, Michael. Pure Physique. 2nd ed. 2010. (ENG.). 224p. pap. 14.95 (978-0-9724102-7-4(9)) Price World Publishing.
Little, John R. Beginning Bodybuilding: Real Muscle/Real Fast. 2007. (ENG., Illus.). 220p. per. 18.95 (978-0-07-149576-9(2), 0071495762) McGraw-Hill Cos., The.
Little, John R. & McGuff, Doug. Body by Science: A Research-Based Program for Strength Training, Body Building, & Complete Fitness in 12 Minutes a Week. 2008. (ENG., Illus.). 288p. pap. 19.95 (978-0-07-159717-3(4), 0071597174) McGraw-Hill Cos., The.
LL Cool J, et al. LL Cool J's Platinum Workout: Sculpt Your Best Body Ever with Hollywood's Fittest Star. 2009. (ENG., Illus.). 256p. pap. 19.95 (978-1-60529-823-8(9)) Rodale Pr., Inc.
Locks, Adam & Richardson, Niall, eds. Critical Readings in Bodybuilding. 2011. (Routledge Research in Sport, Culture & Society Ser.). (ENG., Illus.). 272p. 125.00 (978-0-415-87852-4(7)) Routledge.
Mackenzie, Natalie Gingerich. Fastest Way to Sculpt! Get Firm Three Times Faster! with Our Revolutionary New Plan. 2012. **(978-1-60961-243-6(4))** Rodale Pr., Inc.
Mackenzie, Natalie Gingerich & Prevention Magazine Editors. Tone Every Inch: The Fastest Way to Sculpt Your Belly, Butt & Thighs. 2012. (ENG., Illus.). 336p. pap. 18.99 **(978-1-60961-742-4(8))** Rodale Pr., Inc.
Magazine, Flex. Huge: A Complete Workout Regimen from Bodybuilding's Superstars. 2010. (ENG.). 212p. pap. 24.95 (978-1-60078-432-3(1)) Triumph Bks.
Malley, Kevin S. Get Firefighter Fit: The Complete Workout from the Former Director of the New York City Fire Department Physical Training Program. 2008. (ENG., Illus.). 176p. pap. 15.95 (978-1-56975-626-3(0)) Ulysses Pr.
Marchante, Frank. Sergio Oliva the Myth: Building the Ultimate Physique. 2007. (ENG., Illus.). 350p. pap. 29.95 (978-0-9779040-1-3(6)) Gras Publishing.
Marguerre, K. & Wölfel, H. Mechanics of Vibrations. 2010. (Mechanics of Structural Systems Ser.). 288p. pap. 159.00 (978-90-481-8465-1(7), 9048184657) Springer.
McRobert, Stuart. Beyond Brawn: The Insider's Encyclopedia on How to Build Muscle & Might. 2nd ed. 2007. (Illus.). 509p. per. 29.95 (978-9963-9163-6-8(8)) CS Publishing, Ltd. CYP. Dist: Cardinal Pubs. Group.
—Brawn. 3rd ed. 2007. 230p. per. 19.95 (978-9963-9163-1-3(7)) CS Publishing, Ltd. CYP. Dist: Cardinal Pubs. Group.
—Build Muscle, Lose Fat, Look Great: Everything You Need to Know to Transform Your Body. 2007. (Illus.). 638p. per. (978-9963-9163-0-6(9)) CS Publishing.
Mejia, Michael. Men's Health Better Body Blueprint: The Start-Right, Stick-to-It Strength-Training Plan for Beginners of All Ages. 2006. (ENG., Illus.). 432p. pap. 19.95 (978-1-59486-332-5(6)) Rodale Pr., Inc.
Murphy, Myatt. Men's Health Ultimate Dumbbell Guide: More Than 21,000 Moves Designed to Build Muscle, Increase Strength & Burn Fat. 2007. (ENG., Illus.). 288p. pap. 19.99 (978-1-59486-487-2(X)) Rodale Pr., Inc.
Muscle & Fitness Magazine Hers Staff. 101 Strength Training Workouts for Men. 2011. (ENG.). 176p. pap. 14.95 **(978-1-60078-586-3(7))** Triumph Bks.
Nilsson, Nick. Muscle Explosion: 28 Days to Maximum Mass. 2011. (ENG., Illus.). 223p. pap. 14.95 (978-0-9724102-9-8(5)) Price World Publishing.
Price, Robert G. The Ultimate Guide to Weight Training for Skiing. 2nd ed. 2008. (Ultimate Guide to Weight Training for Sports Ser.). (Illus.). 168p. pap. 16.95 (978-1-932549-59-1(5)) Price World Publishing.
—The Ultimate Guide to Weight Training for Tennis. 4th ed. 2007. (Ultimate Guide to Weight Training Ser.). (Illus.). 168p. pap. 16.95 (978-1-932549-57-7(9)) Price World Publishing.
Ramsay, Craig. Anatomy of Muscle Building: A Trainer's Guide to Increasing Muscle Mass. 2011. (ENG., Illus.). 160p. 35.00 (978-1-55407-825-7(3)); pap. 24.95 (978-1-55407-816-5(4)) Firefly Bks., Ltd.
Randolph, Dave. The Ultimate Kettlebells Workbook: The Revolutionary Program to Tone, Sculpt & Strengthen Your Whole Body. 2011. (ENG., Illus.). 144p. pap. 15.95 (978-1-56975-874-8(3)) Ulysses Pr.
Ratamess, Nicholas A. & Hoffman, Jay R. A Practical Guide to Developing Resistance-Training Programs. 2nd ed. 2008. (Coaches Choice Ser.). (Illus.). 200p. pap. 24.95 (978-1-58518-081-3(5)) Coaches Choice.
The Resistance Band Workout. 96p. (978-1-4054-8953-9(7)) Parragon, Inc.
Resistance Band Workout Kit, the. (Health Ser.). 96p. (978-1-4075-1167-2(X)) Parragon, Inc.
Rivera, Hugo. The Weight Training Diary. 2nd ed. 2010. (ENG.). 160p. pap. 14.95 (978-0-470-60740-4(8), Wiley) Wiley, John & Sons, Inc.
Roach, Randy. Muscle, Smoke & Mirrors, Vol. 2. 2011. 728p. 79.95 **(978-1-4670-3840-9(7))**; pap. 69.95 **(978-1-4670-3841-6(5))** AuthorHouse.

Robert dos Remedios. Men's Health Power Training: Build Bigger, Stronger Muscles with Performance Secrets from Top Athletes. 2007. pap. 16.50 *(978-1-60529-759-0(3))* Rodale Pr., Inc.

Rona, Zoltan P. Supplements for Natural Body Building: Easy-to-Follow Steroid-Free Program. 2007. (ENG., Illus.). 64p. pap. 11.95 *(978-1-55312-021-6(3))* Books Alive.

Savacool, Julia. World Has Curves: The Global Quest for the Perfect Body. 2009. (ENG., Illus.). 224p. 24.99 *(978-1-60529-938-9(3))* Rodale Pr., Inc.

Schoenfeld, Brad. Sculpting Her Body Perfect. 3rd rev. ed. 2007. (ENG., Illus.). 256p. 19.95 *(978-0-7360-7388-2(4))* Human Kinetics Pubs.

—Women's Home Workout Bible. 2009. (Illus.). 336p. pap. 19.95 *(978-0-7360-7828-3(2))* Human Kinetics Pubs.

Schuler, Lou & Cosgrove, Alwyn. The New Rules of Lifting: Six Basic Moves for Maximum Muscle. 2008. (ENG., Illus.). 320p. (gr. 12-18). 18.00 *(978-1-58333-338-9(X)*, Avery) Penguin Group (USA) Inc.

Solotaroff, Paul. The Body Shop: Parties, Pills, & Pumping Iron - Or, My Life in the Age of Muscle. 2010. (ENG., Illus.). 304p. 24.99 *(978-0-316-01101-3(0))* Little Brown & Co.

Thorne, Gerard. Anabolic Primer: Ergogenic Enhancement for Hardcore Bodybuilders. 2009. (ENG.). 600p. pap. 29.95 *(978-1-55210-066-0(9))* Kennedy, Robert Publishing CAN. Dist: National Bk. Network.

—SuperSized! A Step-by-Step 12-Month Musclebuilding Course to Take You from Beginner to Advanced. 2011. (ENG.). 208p. pap. 22.95 *(978-1-55210-102-5(9))* Kennedy, Robert Publishing CAN. Dist: National Bk. Network.

Troccoli, Joseph. More Than Muscles: Mr. Usa-mind, Motives, Mentors. 2010. 236p. 28.95 *(978-1-4502-5243-0(5))*; pap. 18.95 *(978-1-4502-5241-6(9))* iUniverse, Inc.

Tsatsouline, Pavel. Enter the Kettlebell! Strength Secret of the Soviet Supermen. 2010. 200p. pap. 34.95 *(978-0-938045-69-4(5))* Dragon Door Pubns.

Vella, Mark. Women's Guide to Strength & Anatomy Training. 2008. (ENG., Illus.). 144p. pap. 19.95 *(978-0-07-149572-1(X)*, 007149572X) McGraw-Hill Cos., The.

Villepigue, James. The Body Sculpting Bible for Abs: The Way to Physical Perfection. deluxe ed. 2007. (Body Sculpting Bible Ser.). (ENG., Illus.). 160p. pap. 17.95 *(978-1-57826-264-9(X)*, Healthy Living Bks.) Hatherleigh Co., Ltd., The.

Villepigue, James & Mejia, Mike. The Body Sculpting Bible for Abs: The Way to Physical Perfection. deluxe ed. 2007. (Body Sculpting Bible Ser.). (ENG., Illus.). 160p. pap. 17.95 *(978-1-57826-265-6(8)*, Healthy Living Bks.) Hatherleigh Co., Ltd., The.

Villepigue, James & Rivera, Hugo. The Body Sculpting Bible for Men. 3rd ed. 2011. (Body Sculpting Bible Ser.). (ENG., Illus.). 480p. pap. 24.95 *(978-1-57826-400-1(6))* Hatherleigh Co., Ltd., The.

—The Body Sculpting Bible for Women. 3rd ed. 2011. (Body Sculpting Bible Ser.). (ENG., Illus.). 400p. pap. 24.95 *(978-1-57826-401-8(4))* Hatherleigh Co., Ltd., The.

Volek, Jeff & Campbell, Adam. Men's Health Targeted Nutrition Tactics(TNT) Diet: The Explosive New Plan to Blast Fat, Build Muscle, & Get Healthy in 12 Weeks. 2008. (ENG., Illus.). 288p. pap. 15.99 *(978-1-59486-976-1(6))* Rodale Pr., Inc.

Waterbury, Chad. Men's Health Huge in a Hurry: Get Bigger, Stronger, & Leaner in Record Time with the New Science of Building Muscle. 2008. (Illus.). xiii, 354p. *(978-1-59486-954-9(5))* Rodale Pr., Inc.

—Men's Health Huge in a Hurry: Get Bigger, Stronger, & Leaner in Record Time with the New Science of Strength Training. 2008. (ENG., Illus.). 368p. pap. 23.99 *(978-1-60529-934-1(0))* Rodale Pr., Inc.

Weider, Joe & Weider, Ben. Brothers of Iron: How the Weider Brothers Created the Fitness Movement & Built a Business Empire. 2006. (Illus.). 305p. 24.95 *(978-1-59670-124-3(2))* Sports Publishing, LLC.

Weis, Dennis & Kennedy, Robert. Huge & Freaky Muscle Mass & Strength Secrets: Build a Body Fortress Naturally. 2010. (ENG.). 500p. pap. 29.95 *(978-1-55210-083-7(9))* Kennedy, Robert Publishing CAN. Dist: National Bk. Network.

Willey, Warren. Better Than Steroids! 2007. (Illus.). 180p. per. 35.00 *(978-1-4251-0339-2(1))* Trafford Publishing.

Wuebben, Joseph & Stoppani, Jim. Stronger Arms & Upper Body. 2008. (ENG., Illus.). 264p. pap. 18.95 *(978-0-7360-7401-8(5))* Human Kinetics Pubs.

Yates, Dorian. A Potrait of Dorian Yates: The Life & Training Philosophy of the World's Best Bodybuilder. 2006. (Illus.). 146p. pap. 24.95 *(978-0-9534764-0-4(5))* Health 'n' Life Publishing GBR. Dist: Midpoint Trade Bks., Inc.

Zim, Steve & Steinberg, Steve. The 30-Minute Celebrity Makeover Miracle: Achieve the Body You've Always Wanted. 2008. (ENG., Illus.). 264p. 24.95 *(978-0-470-17403-6(X)*, Wiley) Wiley, John & Sons, Inc.

BODYGUARDS

Barratt, Robin. Bouncers & Bodyguards: Tales from a Twilight World. 2008. (ENG., Illus.). 272p. pap. 19.95 *(978-1-84596-302-6(4))* Mainstream Publishing Co., Ltd. GBR. Dist: Independent Pubs. Group.

Durant, Philippe. Haute Protection: La Protection des Hautes Personnalités de de Gaulle à Sarkozy. 2010. (FRE.). 364p. *(978-2-84736-544-3(3))* Nouveau Monde editions.

Hewerdine, Anita. The Yeomen of the Guard in the Early Tudor: The Formation of a Royal Bodyguard. 2012. (International Library of Historical Studies). (ENG., Illus.). 320p. 95.00 ***(978-1-84885-983-8(X))*** I. B. Tauris & Co., Ltd. GBR. Dist: Macmillan.

Holiday, Ivan. Sun Tzu & the Art of Bouncing. 2011. 166p. pap. 19.95 ***(978-1-4327-7093-8(4))*** Outskirts Pr., Inc.

Johnson, Graham & Owens, Joseph. The Nazi Assassin: The Double Life of Britain's Most Feared Gangland Hitman. 2006. (Illus.). 272p. pap. 22.95 *(978-1-84596-177-0(3))* Mainstream Publishing Co., Ltd. GBR. Dist: Trafalgar Square Publishing.

Kennedy, Michael & Winner, Pete. Soldier 'I' - the story of an SAS Hero: From Mirbat to the Iranian Embassy Siege & Beyond. 2010. (General Military Ser.). (ENG., Illus.). 408p. pap. 16.95 *(978-1-84603-995-9(9))* Osprey Publishing, Ltd. GBR. Dist: Random Hse., Inc.

Mullins, Larry. Bodyguard to the Prophets. 2010. pap. 10.99 *(978-1-59955-336-8(8))* Cedar Fort, Inc./CFI Distribution.

O'Keefe, Padraig & Riegel, Ralph. Hidden Soldier: An Irish Legionnaire's Wars from Bosnia to Iraq. 2007. (ENG., Illus.). 336p. pap. 15.95 ***(978-1-84717-032-3(3))*** O'Brien Pr., Ltd., The IRL. Dist: Dufour Editions, Inc.

Rockwell, John W., et al. Stories from the Life of Porter Rockwell. 2010. (Illus.). xxxv, 166p. 18.99 *(978-1-60861-005-1(5))* Covenant Communications, Inc.

Rogers, Christopher. Corporate Executive Protection: A Manual for Inspiring Corporate Bodyguards. 2008. (Illus.). 171p. 47.00 *(978-1-4251-3592-8(7))* Trafford Publishing.

Schneider, Gavriel. Beyond the Bodyguard: The Enigma Revealed: Proven Tactics & Dynamic Strategies for Protective Practices Success. 2009. 168p. pap. 27.95 *(978-1-59942-932-8(2))* Universal Pubs.

Sciacca, Frank, Jr. Bodyguard Principles. 2006. 292p. per. 19.95 *(978-0-7414-3167-7(X))* Infinity Publishing.

Snell, Roy. The Bodyguard. 2010. (ENG., Illus.). 288p. pap. 13.95 *(978-1-84454-838-5(4))* Blake, John Publishing, Ltd. GBR. Dist: Independent Pubs. Group.

Speidel, Micheal P. Riding for Caesar. 2011. (ENG.). pap. 42.95 ***(978-0-415-62005-5(8))*** Routledge.

Spin Committee Illustrations, illus. Shady Bizzness: Life as Eminem's Bodyguard in an Industry of Paper Gangsters. 2008. 170p. (YA). pap. 17.95 *(978-0-9703881-2-4(8))* Manage Me Productions, LLC.

Taylor, Thomas A. Mortal Shield. 2009. (ENG.). 224p. 22.95 *(978-1-59687-361-2(2))* IBks., Inc.

BOECK'S SARCOID

see Sarcoidosis

BOEHM FLUTE

see Flute

BOEHME, JAKOB, 1575-1624

see Bohme, Jakob, 1575-1624

BOEING AIRCRAFT COMPANY

Bauer, Eugene E. Boeing: The First Century & Beyond. 2nd ed. 2006. (Illus.). 424p. 29.50 *(978-1-879242-09-8(5))* TABA Publishing, Inc.

The Boeing Company Global Settlement Agreement: Hearing Before the Committee on Armed Services, United States Senate, One Hundred Ninth Congress, Second Session, August 1, 2006. 2007. iii, 64p. *(978-0-16-078979-3(6)*, 552-070-36094-8) United States Government Printing Office.

Corporate Campaigns & the NLRB: The Impact of Union Pressure on Job Creation: Hearing Before the Subcommittee on Health, Employment, Labor & Pensions, Committee on Education & the Workforce, U.S. House of Representatives, One Hundred Twelfth Congress, First Session, Hearing Held in Washington, DC, May 26, 2011. 2011. (Illus.). iii, 109p. ***(978-0-16-089683-5(5)***, 552-070-43567-1) United States Government Printing Office.

Dancey, Peter. BOEING Plane-makers of Distinction. 2010. 128p. pap. 30.50 *(978-1-4461-5917-0(5))* Lulu Enterprises Inc.

The Future of Border Security: Can SBInet Succeed?: Joint Hearing Before the Subcommittee on Border, Maritime, & Global Counterterrorism Joint with the Subcommittee on Management, Investigations, & Oversight of the Committee on Homeland Security, House of Representatives, One Hundred Tenth Congress, First Session, October 24, 2007. 2009. iv, 57p. *(978-0-16-084511-6(4)*, 552-070-40033-8) United States Government Printing Office.

Greenberg, Edward S., et al. Turbulence: Boeing & the State of American Workers & Managers. (Illus.). 256p. 2011. pap. 27.50 *(978-0-300-17756-5(9))* 2010. (ENG., 40.00 *(978-0-300-15461-0(5))* Yale Univ. Pr.

Pelletier, Alain J. Boeing: The Complete Story. 2010. (ENG., Illus.). 256p. 44.95 *(978-1-84425-703-4(7)*, 1844257037) Haynes Publishing PLC GBR. Dist: MBI Distribution Services/Quayside Distribution.

Redding, Robert & Yenne, Bill. Boeing: Planemaker to the World. rev. ed. 2006. (Illus.). 256p. reprint ed. 27.00 *(978-1-4223-5693-7(0))* DIANE Publishing Co.

Yenne, Bill. The Story of the Boeing Company, Updated Edition. rev. ed. 2010. (ENG., Illus.). 288p. 40.00 *(978-0-7603-4002-8(1)*, 0760340021, Zenith Pr.) MBI Publishing Co. LLC.

BOEING B-SEVENTEEN

see B-Seventeen Bomber

BOEING B-TWENTY-NINE

see B-Twenty-Nine Bomber

BOEING BOMBERS

see also B-Fifty-Two Bomber; B-Seventeen Bomber

Breffort, Dominique. Boeing 707 Kc-135: And Their Derivatives, from Dash 80 to the E-8 J-Stars. 2008. 212p. 49.95 *(978-2-35250-075-9(3))* Histoire et Collections FRA. Dist: Casemate Pubs. & Bk. Distributors, LLC.

Doyle, David. B-17 Flying Fortress in Action. 2010. (Illus.). 80p. pap. ***(978-0-89747-622-5(0))*** Squadron Signal Pubns.

Hasey, Casey. My Bombsight View of Wwii. 2011. 328p. 28.28 ***(978-1-4567-1315-7(9))*** AuthorHouse.

Lockett, Brian. Painting Guide for the Boeing Stratofortress Motherships. 2009. 96p. pap. 44.95 *(978-0-578-03110-1(8))* Lockett, Brian.

Natola, Mark. Boeing B-47 Stratojet: A Photographic History. 2011. (Illus.). 120p. pap. 19.99 *(978-0-7643-3758-1(0)*, Schiffer Publishing Ltd) Schiffer Publishing, Ltd.

Savage, Dennis M. & Greer, Don. B-29 Superfortress. 2008. (Illus.). 80p. pap. ***(978-0-89747-570-9(4))*** Squadron Signal Pubns.

Zichek, Jared A. The Boeing XF8B-1 Fighter: Last of the Line. 2007. (Schiffer Military History Ser.). (Illus.). 376p. pap. 69.95 *(978-0-7643-2587-8(6))* Schiffer Publishing, Ltd.

BOEING FORTRESSES (BOMBERS)

see Boeing Bombers

BOEING 707 (JET TRANSPORT)

Verhovek, Sam Howe. Jet Age: The Comet, the 707, & the Race to Shrink the World. 2011. (ENG., Illus.). 272p. (gr. 12). 16.00 *(978-1-58333-436-2(X)*, Avery) Penguin Group (USA) Inc.

BOEING 727 (JET TRANSPORT)

Shaw, Robbie. Baby Boeings: Boeing 7275 & 7375. 2006. (Illus.). 128p. reprint ed. pap. 22.00 *(978-1-4223-5519-0(5))* DIANE Publishing Co.

BOEING 747 (JET TRANSPORT)

Fitzgerald, Allistair. Air Crash Investigations: MASS MURDER in the SKY, the Bombing of Air India Flight 182. 2011. 356p. pap. 33.95 ***(978-0-557-98184-7(0))*** Lulu Enterprises Inc.

Griffioen, Hans. Air Crash Investigations: LOST PROPELLER BLADE KILLS 8, the Crash of Atlantic Southeast Airlines Flight 529. 2011. 156p. pap. 25.50 ***(978-1-257-07001-5(0))*** Lulu Enterprises Inc.

Korovin, Igor. AIR CRASH INVESTIGATIONS: HORROR in GUAM, the Crash of Korean Air Flight 801. 2010. 324p. pap. 31.95 *(978-0-557-32356-2(8))* Lulu Enterprises Inc.

March, Peter R. The Boeing 747 Story: The History of the World's Most Iconic Jumbo Jets. 2009. (Story Ser.). (ENG., Illus.). 128p. 19.95 *(978-0-7509-4485-4(4))* History Pr. Ltd., The GBR. Dist: Independent Pubs. Group.

Sutter, Joe & Spenser, Jay. 747: Creating the World's First Jumbo Jet & Other Adventures from a Life in Aviation. 2007. (ENG., Illus.). 288p. pap. 14.99 *(978-0-06-088242-6(5)*, HarperPerennial) HarperCollins Pubs.

Wilson, Stewart. Boeing 747. 2006. (Aviation Notebook Ser.). 51p. reprint ed. pap. 20.00 *(978-1-4223-5797-2(X))* DIANE Publishing Co.

BOELCKE, OSWALD, 1891-1916

Richthofen, Manfred Freiherr Von & Böelcke, Oswald. Richthofen & Böelcke in Their Own Words. 2011. 188p. ***(978-0-85706-647-3(1))***; pap. ***(978-0-85706-648-0(X))*** Leonaur Ltd.

Werner, Johannes. Knight of Germany. 2009. (Illus.). 256p. 29.95 *(978-1-935149-11-8(3))* Casemate Pubs. & Bk. Distributors, LLC.

—Knight of Germany: Oswald Boelcke - German Ace. (Illus.). 256p. pap. 19.95 *(978-1-85367-099-2(5)*, 5542) Stackpole Bks.

BOELL, HEINRICH, 1917-1985

see Boll, Heinrich, 1917-1985

BOEOTIA (GREECE)

see Voiotia (Greece)

BOER WAR, 1880-1881

see Transvaal (South Africa)—History—War of 1880-1881

BOER WAR, 1899-1902

see South African War, 1899-1902

BOERHAAVE, HERMAN, 1668-1738

Powers, John C. Inventing Chemistry: Herman Boerhaave & the Reform of the Chemical Arts. 2012. (Synthesis Ser.). (ENG., Illus.). 288p. 40.00 ***(978-0-226-67760-6(5))*** Univ. of Chicago Pr.

BOERS

see Afrikaners

BOETHIUS, D. 524

Aquinas, Thomas. The Trinity & the Unicity of the Intellect. Brennan, Rose Emmanuella, tr. 2009. 289p. pap. 25.00 *(978-1-60608-509-7(3)*, Wipf and Stock) Wipf & Stock Pubs.

Cooper, Lane. A Concordance of Boethius: The Five Theological Tractates & the Consolation of Philosophy. Cooper, Lane, ed. 2011. 478p. 58.95 ***(978-1-258-00971-7(4))*** Literary Licensing, LLC.

Harper, Henry Howard. Boethius & Dante: With Echoes & Love Laments of the Early Italian Renaissance. 2011. 62p. 36.95 ***(978-1-258-01636-4(2))*** Literary Licensing, LLC.

Heilmann, Anja. Boethius' Musiktheorie und das Quadrivium: Eine Einführung in Den Neuplatonischen Hintergrund Von "De Institutione Musica" 2007. (Hypomnemata Ser.). (GER.). 400p. (C). 110.00 *(978-3-525-25268-0(4))* Vandenhoeck & Ruprecht GmbH & Co. KG DEU. Dist: ISD.

Kaylor, Noel Harold, et al. New Directions in Boethian Studies. 2006. (Studies in Medieval Culture: Vol. 45). (ENM & ENG.). 45.00 *(978-1-58044-100-1(9))*; pap. 20.00 *(978-1-58044-101-8(7))* Medieval Institute Pubns.

Marenbon, John, ed. The Cambridge Companion to Boethius. 2009. (Cambridge Companions to Philosophy Ser.). (ENG.). 372p. (C). 93.00 *(978-0-521-87266-9(9))*; pap. 35.00 *(978-0-521-69425-4(6))* Cambridge Univ. Pr.

Metcalf, Allan A. Poetic diction in the Old English meters of Boethius. (De Proprietatibus Litterarum. Series Practica Ser.). (ENG.). 168p. 210.00 ***(978-3-11-193042-8(4))***; 135.00 ***(978-3-11-099164-2(0))*** De Gruyter, Mouton DEU. Dist: de Gruyter, Walter GmbH & Co. KG.

Relihan, Joel C. The Prisoner's Philosophy: Life & Death in Boethius's Consolation. 2006. 240p. per. 30.00 *(978-0-268-04024-6(9))* Univ. of Notre Dame Pr.

Stone-Davis, Fbdquo;rdia J. Musical Beauty: Negotiating the Boundary Between Subject & Object. 2010. 228p. pap. 25.00 *(978-1-60608-557-8(3)*, Cascade Bks.) Wipf & Stock Pubs.

Tax, Petrus W. Notker Latinus Zu Boethius, "De Consolatione Philosophiae", 3 vols. (Altdeutsche Textbibliothek Ser.). (LAT & GER.). 2009. VI, 82p. *(978-3-484-21222-0(5))* 2009. VI, 82p. pap. *(978-3-484-20222-1(X))* 2008. VI, 71p. *(978-3-484-21221-3(7))* 2008. VI, 71p. pap. *(978-3-484-20221-4(1))* 2008. XLIX, 95p. *(978-3-484-21220-6(9))* 2008. XLIX, 95p. pap. *(978-3-484-20220-7(3))* Verlag Max Niemeyer.

Vollmer, Matthias. Fortuna Diagrammatica: Das Rad der Fortuna als bildhafte Verschlüsselung der Schrift de consolatione philosophiae des Boethius. 2009. (Apeliotes. Studien zur Kulturgeschichte und Theologie Ser.). (GER., Illus.). 342p. pap. 74.95 *(978-3-631-57949-7(7))* Lang, Peter GmbH, Europäischer Verlag der Wissenschaften DEU. Dist: Lang, Peter.

BOG BODIES

Here are entered works on human remains preserved by the anaerobic conditions in bogs.

Asingh, Pauline. Grauballe Man: Portrait of a Bog Body. 2009. (Jutland arch Society Ser.). (ENG., Illus.). 244p. (C). 38.00 *(978-87-00-79655-3(7))* Aarhus Universitetsforlag DNK. Dist: ISD.

Grace, N. B. It Came from the Swamp! Was This Mummy Murdered? 2011. pap. *(978-0-545-32956-9(6))* Scholastic, Inc.

Sanders, Karin. Bodies in the Bog: And the Archaeological Imagination. 2009. (ENG., Illus.). 344p. 37.50 *(978-0-226-73404-0(8))* Univ. of Chicago Pr.

Sanders, Karin. Bodies in the Bog & the Archaeological Imagination. 2012. (ENG., Illus.). 344p. pap. 24.00 ***(978-0-226-73405-7(6))*** Univ. of Chicago Pr.

BOG MEN

see Bog Bodies

BOGARDE, DIRK, 1921-1999

Bogarde, Dirk. Ever, Dirk: The Bogarde Letters. Coldstream, John, ed. 2009. (ENG., Illus.). 664p. 23.95 *(978-0-7538-2589-1(9)*, Phoenix) Orion Publishing Group, Ltd. GBR. Dist: Independent Pubs. Group.

BOGART, HUMPHREY, 1899-1957

Goulart, Ron & Herman, Daniel. Humphrey Bogart: The Films from 1941 to 1956. 2012. (Illus.). 206p. pap. 39.99 *(978-1-932563-24-5(5))* Hermes Pr.

Kanfer, Stefan. Tough Without a Gun: The Life & Extraordinary Afterlife of Humphrey Bogart. (Vintage Ser.). (ENG., Illus.). 2012. 320p. pap. 15.95 ***(978-0-307-45581-9(5)***, Vintage) 2011. 304p. 26.95 *(978-0-307-27100-6(5)*, Knopf) Knopf Doubleday Publishing Group.

—Tough Without a Gun: The Life & Extraordinary Afterlife of Humphrey Bogart. l.t. ed. 2011. 527p. 31.99 *(978-1-4104-3704-4(3))* Thorndike Pr.

Nollen, Scott Allen. Warners Wiseguys: All 112 Films That Robinson, Cagney & Bogart Made for the Studio. 2007. (ENG., Illus.). 372p. 55.00 *(978-0-7864-3262-2(4))* McFarland & Co., Inc. Pubs.

Porter, Darwin. Humphrey Bogart: The Making of a Legend. 2010. (ENG., Illus.). 520p. 27.95 *(978-1-936003-14-3(7))* Blood Moon Productions, Ltd.

Schickel, Richard & Perry, George C. Bogie: A Celebration of the Life & Films of Humphrey Bogart. 2011. (ENG., Illus.). 192p. pap. 19.95 *(978-0-9564448-5-1(7))* Palazzo Editions, Ltd. GBR. Dist: Independent Pubs. Group.

Sperber, Ann. Bogart. 2011. (ENG.). 704p. pap. 16.99 *(978-0-06-210736-7(4))* HarperCollins Pubs.

Thomson, David. Humphrey Bogart. 2010. (ENG., Illus.). 144p. pap. 14.00 *(978-0-86547-933-3(X))* Faber & Faber, Inc.

Ursini, James & Duncan, Paul. ICONS Film - Humphrey Bogart. 2007. (Movie Icons Ser.). (FRE, GER & ENG., Illus.). 192p. per. 9.99 *(978-3-8228-2118-3(7))* TASCHEN DEU. Dist: Ingram Pub. Services.

BOGOMILES

Varzonovtseva, Milena. The Secret Books of the Bogomils. 2008. 84p. pap. *(978-3-639-06125-3(X))* VDM Verlag Dr. Mueller e.K.

BOGS

see also Fens; Marshes; Peat Bogs

Hurd, Barbara. Stirring the Mud: On Swamps, Bogs, & Human Imagination. 2008. (ENG.). 160p. pap. 17.95 *(978-0-8203-3152-2(X))* Univ. of Georgia Pr.

BOHEMIA (CZECH REPUBLIC)

Capková, Katerina. Czechs, Germans, Jews: National Identity of the Jews of Bohemia. 2012. (ENG.). 296p. 95.00 ***(978-0-85745-474-4(9))*** Berghahn Bks., Inc.

Charvát, Petr. The Emergence of the Bohemian State. 2010. (Illus.). 288p. *(978-90-04-18009-3(5))* BRILL.

Cosmas. The Chronicle of the Czechs. 2009. (Illus.). 288p. pap. 34.95 *(978-0-8132-1570-9(6))* Catholic Univ. of America Pr.

David, Zdenek V. Realism, Tolerance, & Liberalism in the Czech National Awakening: Legacies of the Bohemian Reformation. 2010. (ENG.). 504p. (gr. 17). 70.00 *(978-0-8018-9546-3(4))* Johns Hopkins Univ. Pr.

Demetz, Peter. Prague in Danger: The Years of German Occupation, 1939-45: Memories & History, Terror & Resistance, Theater & Jazz, Film & Poetry, Politics & War. 2009. (ENG., Illus.). 288p. pap. 15.00 *(978-0-374-53156-0(0))* Farrar, Straus & Giroux.

Denis, Ernest. Boheme Depuis la Montagne-Blanche, 2 vols. (FRE.). reprint ed. 59.00 *(978-0-403-00941-1(3))* Scholarly Pr., Inc.

Herben, Jan. Huss & His Followers. reprint ed. 30.00 *(978-0-404-19806-0(6))* AMS Pr., Inc.

Kerner, Robert J. Bohemia in the Eighteenth Century. reprint ed. 42.50 *(978-0-404-01948-8(X))* AMS Pr., Inc.

Klapste, Jan. The Czech Lands in Medieval Transformation. 2011. (East Central & Eastern Europe in the Middle Ages Ser.). (Illus.). 640p. ***(978-90-04-20347-1(8))*** BRILL.

Murdock, Caitlin. Changing Places: Society, Culture, & Territory in the Saxon-Bohemian Borderlands, 1870-1946. 2010. (Social History, Popular Culture, & Politics in Germany Ser.). (ENG., Illus.). 268p. (C). 75.00 *(978-0-472-11722-2(X))* Univ. of Michigan Pr.

Seton, Walter W. Some New Sources for the Life of Blessed Agnes of Bohemia: Including a Fourteenth-Century Latin Version (Bamberg, Misc. Hist. 146, E. VII, 19): & a Fifteenth-Century German Version (Berlin, Germ. Oct. 484) 2010. (Cambridge Library Collection - History Ser.). (Illus.). 200p. pap. 21.00 *(978-1-108-01750-2(6))* Cambridge Univ. Pr.

Thomas, Alfred. A Blessed Shore: England & Bohemia from Chaucer to Shakespeare. 2007. (Illus.). 239p. 52.50 *(978-0-8014-4568-2(X))* Cornell Univ. Pr.

Verney, Victor. Warrior of God. 2009. (Illus.). 256p. 39.99 *(978-1-84832-516-6(9)*, Frontline) Pen & Sword Bks. Ltd. GBR. Dist: Casemate Pubs. & Bk. Distributors, LLC.

Vyiny, Paul. Neo-Slavism & the Czechs, 1898-1914. 2010. (Cambridge Russian, Soviet & Post-Soviet Studies). (ENG.). 304p. pap. 25.99 *(978-0-521-13445-3(5))* Cambridge Univ. Pr.

Wiskemann, Elizabeth. Czechs & Germans: A Study of the Struggles in the Historic Provinces of Bohemia & Moravia. reprint ed. 28.50 *(978-0-404-16599-4(0))* AMS Pr., Inc.

Workman, Herbert B. Letters of John Hus. 2006. pap. 30.95 *(978-1-4286-3884-6(9))* Kessinger Publishing, LLC.

Wright, William E. Serf, Seigneur, & Sovereign: Agrarian Reform in Eighteenth-Century Bohemia. 2009. (ENG.). 232p. pap. 50.00 *(978-0-8166-5893-0(5))* Univ. of Minnesota Pr.

BOHEMIAN AUTHORS

see Authors, Czech

BOHEMIAN BRETHREN

see also Moravians

Atwood, Craig D. & Atwood, Craig. The Theology of the Czech Brethren from Hus to Comenius. 2009. (ENG.). 392p. 80.00 *(978-0-271-03532-1(3))* Pennsylvania State Univ. Pr.

Crews, C. Daniel & Starbuck, Richard W. Records of the Moravians among the Cherokees Pt. 1: The Anna Rosina Years, Success in School & Mission, 1805-1810, Pt. I, Vol. 3. 2011. (Records of the Moravians among the Cherokees Ser.). (ENG.). 624p. 50.00 *(978-0-9826907-4-1(6))* Cherokee National Pr.

Crews, C. Daniel & Starbuck, Richard W., eds. Records of the Moravians among the Cherokees Pt. 2: The Anna Rosina Years, Warfare on the Horizon, 1810-1816. 2012. (Records of the Moravians among the Cherokees Ser.). (ENG.). 618p. 50.00 *(978-0-9826907-5-8(4))* Cherokee National Pr.

De Schweinitz, E. The Moravian Manual; Containing an Account of the Protestant Church of the Moravian United Brethren, or Unitas Fratrum by E de Schweinitz Publis. 2006. 188p. per. 18.99 *(978-1-4255-1516-4(9))* MPublishing.

Heckewaelder, John Gottlieb Ernestus. A Canoe Journey from the Big Beaver to the Tuscarawas In 1773: A Travel Diary of John Heckewaelder. Mahr, August Carl, tr. 2011. 20p. 35.95 ***(978-1-258-06518-8(5))*** Literary Licensing, LLC.

Herben, Jan. Huss & His Followers. reprint ed. 30.00 *(978-0-404-19806-0(6))* AMS Pr., Inc.

Meyer, Dietrich, et al. Katechismen. 2008. (Texte Zur Geschichte des Pietismus Ser.). (GER., Illus.). 581p. (C). 128.00 *(978-3-525-55854-6(6))* Vandenhoeck & Ruprecht GmbH & Co. KG DEU. Dist: ISD.

Sessler, Jacob John. Communal Pietism among Early American Mo. 2006. pap. 28.95 *(978-1-4286-5318-4(X))* Kessinger Publishing, LLC.

Teigeler, Otto. Die Herrnhuter in Russland: Ziel, Umfang und Ertrag Ihrer Aktivitäten. 2006. (Arbeiten Zur Geschichte des Pietismus Ser.). (GER.). 726p. (C). 144.00 *(978-3-525-55837-9(6))* Vandenhoeck & Ruprecht GmbH & Co. KG DEU. Dist: ISD.

Thomas, Nancy Smith. Moravian Christmas in the South. 2007. (ENG., Illus.). 184p. 34.95 *(978-0-8078-3181-6(6))* Univ. of North Carolina Pr.

Zinzendorf, Nicholaus Ludwig Von. Christian Life & Witness: Count Zinzendorf's 1738 Berlin Speeches. Kinkel, Gary S., ed. 2010. (Princeton Theological Monographs). 164p. pap. 19.00 *(978-1-60608-617-9(0)*, Pickwick Pubns.) Wipf & Stock Pubs.

BOHEMIAN LANGUAGE

see Czech Language

BOHEMIANISM

see also Beat Generation; Hippies

Abrams, Brett L. Hollywood Bohemians: Transgressive Sexuality & the Selling of the Movieland Dream. 2008. (ENG., Illus.). 256p. pap. 39.95 *(978-0-7864-3929-4(7))* McFarland & Co., Inc. Pubs.

Brooker, Peter. Bohemia in London: The Social Scene of Early Modernism. 2007. (ENG., Illus.). 224p. pap. 31.00 *(978-0-230-54692-9(7))* Palgrave Macmillan.

Deener, Andrew. Venice: A Contested Bohemia in Los Angeles. 2012. (ENG., Illus.). 336p. 90.00 ***(978-0-226-14000-1(8))***; pap. 29.00 ***(978-0-226-14001-8(6))*** Univ. of Chicago Pr.

Feast or Famine: Growing up Bohemian in Provincetown. 2008. (Illus.). 144p. 50.00 *(978-0-9818755-0-7(5))* Kelly, Julia.

Field, Edward. The Man Who Would Marry Susan Sontag: And Other Intimate Literary Portraits of the Bohemian Era. 2007. (Living Out: Gay & Lesbian Autobiog Ser.). (ENG., Illus.). 302p. per. 21.95 *(978-0-299-21324-4(2))* Univ. of Wisconsin Pr.

Gair, Christopher. The Beat Generation: A Beginner's Guide. 2008. (Beginners Guide (Oneworld) Ser.). (ENG.). 192p. pap. 14.95 *(978-1-85168-542-4(1))* Oneworld Pubns. GBR. Dist: National Bk. Network.

Gluck, Mary. Popular Bohemia: Modernism & Urban Culture in Nineteenth-Century Paris. 2008. (Illus.). 238p. per. 25.50 *(978-0-674-02731-2(0))* Harvard Univ. Pr.

Gold, Herbert. Bohemia: Where Art, Angst, Love, & Strong Coffee Meet. 2007. (ENG.). 250p. per. 12.00 *(978-0-9753662-4-0(6))* Axios Pr.

—Still Alive! A Feisty Bohemian Explores the Art of Growing Old. 2011. (ENG.). 264p. pap. 12.95 *(978-1-61145-029-3(2)*, 611029, Arcade Publishing) Skyhorse Publishing Co., Inc.

Kotynek, Roy & Cohassey, John. American Cultural Rebels: Avant-Garde & Bohemian Artists, Writers & Musicians from the 1850s Through the 1960s. 2008. (ENG.). 262p. per. 39.95 *(978-0-7864-3709-2(X))* McFarland & Co., Inc. Pubs.

Lause, Mark A. The Antebellum Crisis & America's First Bohemians. 2011. 45.00 *(978-1-60635-033-1(1))* Kent State Univ. Pr.

Levin, Joanna. Bohemia in America, 1858-1920. 2009. (ENG., Illus.). 480p. 65.00 *(978-0-8047-6083-6(7))* Stanford Univ. Pr.

Lipton, Lawrence. The Holy Barbarians. 2009. pap. *(978-1-57898-752-8(0))*; 35.00 *(978-1-57898-751-1(2))* Martino Publishing.

Lloyd, Richard, ed. Neo-Bohemia: Art & Commerce in the Postindustrial City. 2nd rev. ed. 2010. (ENG., Illus.). 328p. 130.00 *(978-0-415-87096-2(8))*; pap. 34.95 *(978-0-415-87097-9(6))* Taylor & Francis Group GBR. (Routledge). Dist: Taylor & Francis Group.

Louthan, Howard. Converting Bohemia: Force & Persuasion in the Catholic Reformation. 2009. (New Studies in European History Ser.). (ENG., Illus.). 368p. 116.00 *(978-0-521-88929-2(4))* Cambridge Univ. Pr.

Murger, Henri. The Bohemians of the Latin Quarter. 2009. 224p. pap. *(978-0-217-88890-5(9))* Books LLC.

—The Bohemians of the Latin Quarter. 2007. (ENG.). 396p. per. 21.45 *(978-1-59462-584-8(0)*, 620, Book Jungle) Standard Pubns., Inc.

Parry, Albert. Garrets & Pretenders: Bohemian Life in America from Poe to Kerouac. 2012. (New York City Ser.). (ENG.). 480p. pap. 16.95 ***(978-0-486-48605-5(2))*** Dover Pubns., Inc.

Ryan, John. Remembering How We Stood: Bohemian Dublin at the Mid-Century. 2009. (ENG.). 168p. pap. 21.95 *(978-1-84351-142-7(8))* Lilliput Pr., Ltd., The IRL. Dist: Dufour Editions, Inc.

Sorel, Edward. The Mural at the Waverly Inn: A Portrait of Greenwich Village Bohemians. 2008. (Illus.). 56p. 15.95 *(978-0-307-37731-9(8)*, Pantheon) Knopf Doubleday Publishing Group.

Stansell, Christine. American Moderns: Bohemian New York & the Creation of a New Century. 2009. (ENG., Illus.). 432p. pap. 26.95 *(978-0-691-14283-8(1))* Princeton Univ. Pr.

Taylor, D. J. Bright Young People: The Lost Generation of London's Jazz Age. 2010. (ENG., Illus.). 384p. pap. 17.00 *(978-0-374-53211-6(7))* Farrar, Straus & Giroux.

Von Dewitz, Bodo, ed. La Bohème: Artists in the 19th & 20th century photography, 1 vol. 2010. (GER & ENG., Illus.). 280p. 75.00 *(978-3-86930-139-6(2))* Steidl, Gerhard Druckerei und Verlag DEU. Dist: Innovative Logistics.

BOHEMIANS

see Czechs

BOHEMOND I, PRINCE OF ANTIOCH, 1058?-1111

Bailey, Ralph Yewdale. Bohemond I, Prince of Antioch: A Norman Soldier of Fortune & Crusader 1050-1111. 2010. 140p. pap. *(978-0-85706-209-3(3))* Leonaur Ltd.

Duggan, Alfred. Count Bohemond: A Novel. 2007. (Cassell Military Paperbacks Ser.). 288p. pap. 9.95 *(978-0-304-36273-8(5))* Cassell P L C GBR. Dist: Sterling Publishing Co., Inc.

Yewdale, Ralph Bailey. Bohemond I, Prince of Antioch: A Norman Soldier of Fortune & Crusader 1050-1111. 2010. 140p. *(978-0-85706-210-9(7))* Leonaur Ltd.

BOHME, JAKOB, 1575-1624

Boehme, Jacob. Adam & Eve. 2006. pap. 9.95 *(978-1-4286-7345-8(8))* Kessinger Publishing, LLC.

—Adam's Fall. 2006. pap. 9.95 *(978-1-4286-7344-1(X))* Kessinger Publishing, LLC.

—The Confessions of Jacob Boehme. 2010. 182p. 30.36 *(978-1-169-27827-1(2))*; 37.95 *(978-1-161-34975-7(8))*; 37.95 *(978-1-161-60040-7(X))* Kessinger Publishing, LLC.

—The Created Universe. 2006. pap. 9.95 *(978-1-4286-7298-7(2))* Kessinger Publishing, LLC.

—The Fall of Lucifer. 2006. pap. 9.95 *(978-1-4286-7343-4(1))* Kessinger Publishing, LLC.

—The Seven Qualities. 2006. pap. 9.95 *(978-1-4286-7342-7(3))* Kessinger Publishing, LLC.

—The Threefold Life of Man. unabr. ed. 2007. (ENG.). 684p. per. *(978-1-897352-32-8(8))* Providence University.

Brinton, Howard H. Early Christianity & Ethics. 2006. pap. 9.95 *(978-1-4286-7480-6(2))* Kessinger Publishing, LLC.

—Greek Philosophy & Mysticism. 2006. pap. 9.95 *(978-1-4286-7479-0(9))* Kessinger Publishing, LLC.

—Protestant & Catholic Mysticism. 2006. pap. 9.95 *(978-1-4286-7481-3(0))* Kessinger Publishing, LLC.

—The Two Wills in Eastern & Western Philosophy. 2006. pap. 9.95 *(978-1-4286-7478-3(0))* Kessinger Publishing, LLC.

Isham, Thomas & Faas, Robert J. A Christian Spiritual Psychology: The Four Temperaments of Jacob Boehme. 2006. (ENG.). 132p. *(978-1-59650-006-8(9)*, New Grail) New Cultures Pr.

Madden, Kathryn Wood. Dark Light of the Soul. 2008. (Illus.). 272p. pap. 25.00 *(978-1-58420-065-9(0)*, Lindisfarne Bks.) SteinerBooks, Inc.

Muses, Charles A. Illumination on Jacob Boehme: The Work of Dionysius Andreas Freher. 2011. 224p. 44.95 ***(978-1-258-00845-7(6))*** Literary Licensing, LLC.

Penny, A. J. & Penny, A. J. Studies in Jacob Boehme. 2010. 504p. 53.95 *(978-1-161-35139-5(8))* Kessinger Publishing, LLC.

Rix, Robert. William Blake & the Culture of Radical Christianity. 2007. 192p. 114.95 *(978-0-7546-5600-5(4))* Ashgate Publishing Co.

Stoudt, John J. Sunrise to Eternity: A Study in Jacob Boehme's Life & Thought. reprint ed. 34.50 *(978-0-404-18492-6(8))* AMS Pr., Inc.

BOHR, NIELS, 1885-1962

Aaserud, Finn. Popularization & People (1911-1962), 12 vols. 2006. (Niels Bohr - Collected Works 12). (ENG, DAN & GER., Illus.). 610p. 215.00 *(978-0-444-52946-6(2)*, North Holland) Elsevier Science & Technology Bks.

Faye, J. & Folse, H., eds. Niels Bohr & Contemporary Philosophy. 2010. (Boston Studies in the Philosophy of Science Ser.). (Illus.). 420p. pap. 329.00 *(978-90-481-4299-6(7)*, 9048142997) Springer.

Garcia-Colin, Leopoldo. Niels Bohr: Cientifico, Filosofo. (Ciencia para Todos Ser.). (SPA.). pap. 6.99 *(978-968-16-2458-3(0))* Fondo de Cultura Economica USA.

Jacobsen, Anja Skaar. Between Bohr & Marx: Leon Rosenfeld in Physics & Ideology. 2011. 360p. 81.00 *(978-981-4307-81-9(5))* World Scientific Publishing Co., Inc.

Katsumori, Makoto. Niels Bohr's Complementarity: Its Structure, History, & Intersections with Hermeneutics & Deconstruction. 2011. (Boston Studies in the Philosophy of Science Ser.). (ENG., Illus.). xiv, 176p. 139.00 *(978-94-007-1747-3(4)*, 9400717474) Springer.

Kragh, Helge. Niels Bohr & the Quantum Atom: The Bohr Model of Atomic Structure 1913-1925. 2012. (ENG., Illus.). 416p. 62.99 ***(978-0-19-965498-7(0))*** Oxford Univ. Pr., Inc.

Kumar, Manjit. Quantum: Einstein, Bohr, & the Great Debate about the Nature of Reality. 2011. (ENG., Illus.). 448p. pap. 16.95 *(978-0-393-33988-8(2)*, 33988) Norton, W. W. & Co., Inc.

Petruccioli, Sandro. Atoms, Metaphors & Paradoxes: Niels Bohr & the Construction of a New Physics. McGilvray, Ian, tr. from ITA. 2006.Tr. of Atomi, Metafore, Paradossi. (ENG., Illus.). 252p. pap. 48.00 *(978-0-521-03188-2(5))* Cambridge Univ. Pr.

Plotnitsky, Arkady. Reading Bohr: Physics & Philosophy. 2007. (Fundamental Theories of Physics Ser.: Vol. 152). (Illus.). 222p. 249.00 *(978-1-4020-5253-8(7)*, 1402052537) Springer.

—Reading Bohr: Physics & Philosophy: Physics & Philosophy. 2010. (Fundamental Theories of Physics Ser.). xiii, 229p. pap. 249.00 *(978-90-481-7323-5(X)*, 904817323X) Springer.

Simeonov Kamenov, Pavel. Quantum Mechanical Initial Conditions & Gravity (Copenhagen's Illusions) 2011. (Physics Research & Technology Ser.). (Illus.). xxii, 215p. pap. 129.00 *(978-1-61209-549-3(6)*, Nova Novinka) Nova Science Pubs., Inc.

Stenholm, Stig. The Quest for Reality: Bohr & Wittgenstein - Two Complementary Views. 2011. 296p. 62.95 *(978-0-19-960358-9(8))* Oxford Univ. Pr., Inc.

Whitaker, Andrew. Einstein, Bohr & the Quantum Dilemma: From Quantum Theory to Quantum Information. 2nd rev. ed. 2006. (ENG., Illus.). 480p. per. 68.99 *(978-0-521-67102-6(7))* Cambridge Univ. Pr.

BOIARDO, MATTEO MARIA, 1440 OR 41-1494

DeCoste, Mary-Michelle. Hopeless Love: Boiardo, Ariosto, & Narratives of Queer Female Desire. 2009. (Toronto Italian Studies). (ENG & ITA.). 192p. *(978-0-8020-9684-5(0))* Univ. of Toronto Pr.

BOILEAU DESPREAUX, NICOLAS, 1636-1711

Pocock, Gordon. Boileau & the Nature of Neoclassicism. 2010. (Major European Authors Ser.). (ENG.). 224p. pap. 27.99 *(978-0-521-13675-4(X))* Cambridge Univ. Pr.

BOILER-SCALE

see Steam-Boilers

BOILER WATER

see Feed-Water

BOILERS

see also Autoclaves; Feed-Water; Heating; Pressure Vessels; Steam-Boilers

American Society of Mechanical Engineers Staff, ed. BPVC Code Cases: Boilers & Pressure Vessels. 376p. 250.00 *(978-0-7918-2423-8(3))*; 466p. 275.00 *(978-0-7918-2520-4(5))* ASME Pr.

—BPVC Section I - Power Boilers. 344p. 225.00 *(978-0-7918-2494-8(2))* ASME Pr.

—BPVC Section IV - Rules for Construction of Heating Boilers. 266p. 180.00 *(978-0-7918-2414-6(4))*; 328p. 195.00 *(978-0-7918-2510-5(8))* ASME Pr.

—BPVC Section VI - Recommended Rules for the Care & Operation of Heating Boilers. 102p. 110.00 *(978-0-7918-2416-0(0))*; 144p. 125.00 *(978-0-7918-2512-9(4))* ASME Pr.

—BPVC Section VII - Recommended Guidelines for the Care of Power Boilers. 192p. 145.00 *(978-0-7918-2513-6(2))*; 157p. 125.00 *(978-0-7918-2417-7(9))* ASME Pr.

—Consensus on Operating Practices for the Control of Feedwater & Boiler Water Chemistry in Modern Industrial Boilers. 48p. 10.00 *(978-0-7918-1204-4(9))* ASME Pr.

—Control & Safety Devices for Automatically Fired Boilers. 56p. 55.00 *(978-0-7918-2480-1(2))* ASME Pr.

—Criteria of the ASME Boiler & Pressure Vessel Code Section VIII, Division 3. 64p. 69.00 *(978-0-7918-2585-3(X))* ASME Pr.

Jawad, Maan H. & Jetter, R. I. Design & Analysis of Boiler & Pressure Vessel Components in the Creep Range. 2009. 90.00 *(978-0-7918-0284-7(1))* ASME Pr.

Jenkins, Dilwyn. Wood Pellet Heating Systems: The Earthscan Expert Handbook on Planning, Design & Installation. 2010. (Earthscan Expert Ser.). (ENG., Illus.). 144p. 59.95 *(978-1-84407-845-5(0))* Routledge.

Lai, George Y. High-Temperature Corrosion & Materials Applications. 2007. (Illus.). 461p. 188.00 *(978-0-87170-853-3(1))* ASM International.

Li, Zhengqi. Radial-Bias-Combustion & Central-Fuel-Rich Swirl Pulverized Coal Burners for Wall-Fired Boilers. 2010. (Energy Science, Engineering & Technology Ser.). pap. 47.00 *(978-1-60876-455-6(9))* Nova Science Pubs., Inc.

Malek, Mohammad A. Heating Boiler Operator's Manual: Maintenance, Operation, & Repair. 2006. (ENG., Illus.). 352p. 69.95 *(978-0-07-147522-8(2)*, 0071475222) McGraw-Hill Professional Publishing.

Miura, Taro. Tools. 7.98 *(978-1-56334-394-0(0))* Hampton-Brown Bks.

NCCER. Boilermaking Level 3 Trainee Guide. 2nd rev. ed. 2012. (ENG., Illus.). 436p. (C). pap. 125.33 ***(978-0-13-257824-0(7)***, Prentice Hall) Prentice Hall PTR.

Rayaprolu, Kumar. Boilers for Power & Process. 2009. (ENG., Illus.). 811p. 144.95 *(978-1-4200-7536-6(5)*, CRC Press) Taylor & Francis Group GBR. Dist: Taylor & Francis Group.

Sermyagina, Ekaterina. Circulating Fluidized Bed Boiler Technology. 2011. 92p. pap. ***(978-3-8454-1643-4(2))*** Lambert Academic Publishing.

Spitz, N., et al. Prediction of Performance & Pollutant Emission from Pulverized Coal Utility Boilers. 2009. pap. 37.00 *(978-1-60741-184-0(9))* Nova Science Pubs., Inc.

Steingress. Low Pressure Boilers. wbk. ed. 16.00 *(978-0-8269-4418-4(3))* American Technical Pubs., Inc.

Steingress, et al. High Pressure Boilers. 4th ed. 2009. (Illus.). *(978-0-8269-4309-5(8)*, Debolsillo) American Technical Pubs., Inc.

Steingress, Frederick M. Low Pressure Boilers Resource Guide. 395.00 net. *(978-0-8269-4419-1(1))* American Technical Pubs., Inc.

Technology Research Editors, ed. Corrosion Prevention for Boilers & Pressure Vessels, 2007 Ed. 2007. pap. 118.50 *(978-1-60030-394-4(3)*, Search-In-Print) CSA Journal Division.

—Nondestructive Testing of Pressure Vessels & Boilers, 2007 Ed. 2007. pap. 128.50 *(978-1-60030-596-2(2)*, Search-In-Print) CSA Journal Division.

—Welding of Pressure Vessel & Boiler Components, 2007 Ed. 2007. pap. 128.50 *(978-1-60030-626-6(8)*, Search-In-Print) CSA Journal Division.

BOILING

see Ebullition

BOJARDO, MATTEO MARIA, 1440 OR 41-1494

see Boiardo, Matteo Maria, 1440 or 41-1494

BOJER, JOHAN, 1872-1959

Gad, Carl. Johan Bojer, the Man & His Works. 2009. 94p. pap. 14.14 *(978-1-151-31873-2(6))* General Bks. LLC.

BOK, EDWARD WILLIAM, 1863-1930

Bok, Edward. Dutch Boy Fifty Years after. 2006. pap. *(978-1-4068-1104-9(1))* Echo Library.

Bok, Edward William. The Americanization. (Best Sellers of 1922 Ser.). reprint ed. lib. bdg. 48.00 *(978-0-7426-1389-8(5))* Classic Bks.

—The Americanization of Edward Bok. 28.95 *(978-0-8488-0199-1(7))* Amereon LTD.

—The Americanization of Edward Bok. 2009. 520p. 29.99 *(978-1-103-00342-6(9))*; pap. 23.99 *(978-1-103-00339-6(9))* BiblioBazaar.

—The Americanization of Edward Bok. 2009. 290p. pap. *(978-0-217-56772-5(X))* Books LLC.

—The Americanization of Edward Bok. 461p. reprint ed. 98.00 *(978-0-7222-8996-9(0))* Library Reprints, Inc.

—A Dutch Boy Fifty Years After. 2008. 220p. 27.99 *(978-0-554-27204-7(0))* 2008. 220p. 24.99 *(978-0-554-36507-7(3))* 2007. (ENG.). 192p. pap. 19.99

B

(978-1-4346-2727-8(6)) 2007. (ENG.). 218p. pap. 22.99 (978-1-4346-2760-5(8)) BiblioBazaar.

BOKER, GEORGE HENRY, 1823-1890

Bradley, Edward S. George Henry Boker, Poet & Patriot. (BCL Ser. I). (Illus.). reprint ed. 34.50 *(978-0-404-00928-1(X))* AMS Pr., Inc.

BOKHARA

Becker, Seymour. Russia's Protectorates in Central Asia: Bukhara & Khiva, 1865-1924. 2nd ed. 2009. 424p. pap. 39.95 *(978-0-415-54618-8(4))* Routledge.

Burnes, Alexander. Travels into Bokhara. 2009. 166p. pap. *(978-0-217-64733-5(2))* Books LLC.

—Travels into Bokhara. 2009. 172p. pap. 19.99 *(978-1-4589-8814-0(7))*; 216p. pap. 19.99 *(978-0-217-30157-2(6))* General Bks. LLC.

Narshakhi, Abu Bakr Muhammad ibn Jafar & Frye, Richard Nelson. The History of Bukhara. 2007. (Illus.). xix, 170p. pap. *(978-1-55876-419-4(4))* Wiener, Markus Pubs., Inc.

Wolff, Joseph. Narrative of a Mission to Bokhara, in the Years 1843-1845, to Ascertain the Fate of Colonel Stoddart & Captain Conolly. 2010. 322p. pap. *(978-1-151-74964-2(8))* 2010. 158p. pap. *(978-1-151-74968-0(0))* 2009. 176p. pap. *(978-1-150-74893-6(1))* Books LLC.

—Narrative of a Mission to Bokhara, in the Years 1843-1845, to Ascertain the Fate of Colonel Stoddart & Captain Conolly. 2008. 540p. pap. *(978-1-4086-8877-9(8))* Read Bks.

BOLAS

see Lasso

BOLDINI, GIOVANNI, 1845-1931

Lees, Sarah. Giovanni Boldini in Impressionist Paris. 2009. *(978-0-931102-83-7(9))* Clark, Sterling & Francine Art Institute.

BOLEYN, ANNE, 1507-1536

see Anne Boleyn, Queen, Consort of Henry VIII, King of England, 1507-1536

BOLEYN, JANE, VISCOUNTESS ROCHFORD, D. 1542

Fox, Julia. Jane Boleyn: The True Story of the Infamous Lady Rochford. 2009. (ENG., Illus.). 416p. pap. 16.00 *(978-0-345-51078-5(X))*, Ballantine Bks.) Random House Publishing Group.

BOLINGBROKE, HENRY ST. JOHN, VISCOUNT, 1678-1751

Hassall, Arthur. Life of Viscount Bolingbroke. 2007. (ENG.). 256p. 42.95 *(978-0-548-09183-8(8))* Kessinger Publishing, LLC.

Lashmore-Davies, Adrian, ed. The Unpublished Letters of Henry St John, 1st Viscount Bolingbroke, 5 vols. 2014. (Pickering Masters Ser.). (ENG.). 2000p. 795.00 *(978-1-85196-957-9(8))* Pickering & Chatto Pubs., Ltd. GBR. Dist: Ashgate Publishing Co.

Sichel, Walter. Bolingbroke & His Times. 2007. (ENG.). 564p. 58.95 *(978-0-548-08619-3(2))* Kessinger Publishing, LLC.

St. John, Henry Lord Viscount Bolingbro. Lord Bolingbroke's Works V1. 2007. pap. 40.95 *(978-1-4304-4872-3(5))* Kessinger Publishing, LLC.

BOLIVAR, SIMON, 1783-1830

Autores Varios Staff. Constituciones Fundacionales de Colombia Decreto Orgßnico de la Dictadura de Bolfvar. 2010. (SPA.). 20p. per. 4.00 *(978-84-9816-141-0(X))* Linkgua Ediciones, S.L. ESP. Dist: AtlasBooks Distribution.

Bates, Lindon Wallace. The Path of the Conquistadores: Trinidad & Venezuelan Guiana. 307p. reprint ed. 98.00 *(978-0-7222-9530-4(8))* Library Reprints, Inc.

—The Path of the Conquistadores, Trinidad & Venezuelan Guiana. 307p. reprint ed. 98.00 *(978-0-7222-9620-2(7))* Library Reprints, Inc.

Biographiq. Simon Bolivar - South American Leader (Biography) 2008. 52p. pap. 9.99 *(978-1-59986-072-5(4)*, Biographiq) Filiquarian Publishing, LLC.

Bolivar, Simon. Simón Bolívar. Chávez, Hugo, ed. & pref. by. 2009. (Revolutions Ser.). (ENG.). 160p. pap. 14.95 *(978-1-84467-381-0(2)*, 844381) Verso Bks. GBR. Dist: Norton, W. W. & Co., Inc.

Bushnell, David & Langley, Lester D., eds. Simon Bolivar: Essays on the Life & Legacy of the Liberator. 2008. (Latin American Silhouettes Ser.). (ENG., Illus.). 224p. 80.00 *(978-0-7425-5619-5(0))* Rowman & Littlefield Publishers, Inc.

Cheng, William Joaquin. La Reevaluacion de la Figura de Simón Bolívar en las Postrimerias del Siglo XX: Las Novelas Sobre el Libertador. 2007. (SPA.). 200p. *(978-0-7734-5377-7(6))* Mellen, Edwin Pr., The.

Cussen, Antonio. Bello & Bolívar: Poetry & Politics in the Spanish American Revolution. 2009. (Cambridge Studies in Latin American & Iberian Literature Ser.). (ENG.). 224p. (C). pap. 33.99 *(978-0-521-11139-3(0))* Cambridge Univ. Pr.

Harvey, Robert. Bolivar: The South America Liberator. 2011. (ENG., Illus.). 416p. 25.95 *(978-1-61608-316-8(6)*, 608316) Skyhorse Publishing Co., Inc.

Langley, Lester D. Simón Bolívar: Venezuelan Rebel, American Revolutionary. 2009. (Latin American Silhouettes Ser.). (ENG.). 168p. 35.00 *(978-0-7425-3752-1(8))* Rowman & Littlefield Publishers, Inc.

Lynch, John. Simon Bolivar: A Life. 2007. (ENG., Illus.). 368p. per. 20.00 *(978-0-300-12604-4(2))* Yale Univ. Pr.

Martinez Díaz, Nelson. Jose Marti: Cuban Revolutionist. (SPA., Illus.). 159p. 4.95 *(978-84-7679-024-3(4))* Informacion y Revistas ESP. Dist: AIMS International Bks., Inc.

Masur, Gerhard. Simon Bolivar. 2007. (ENG.). 760p. per. 52.95 *(978-1-4325-5973-1(7))* Kessinger Publishing, LLC.

Murray, Pamela S. For Glory & Bolívar: The Remarkable Life of Manuela Sáenz. 2010. (ENG., Illus.). 238p. pap. 25.00 *(978-0-292-72151-7(X))* Univ. of Texas Pr.

Petre, F. L. Simon Bolivar: The Liberator. reprint ed. 150.00 *(978-0-7222-9591-5(X))* Library Reprints, Inc.

Sherwell, Guillermo Antonio. Simon Bolivar, the Liberator. 2006. pap. *(978-1-4068-0550-5(5))* Echo Library.

—Simón Bolívar, the Liberator: Patriot, Warrior, Statesman Father of Five Nations. 2007. (ENG.). 166p. pap. 19.99 *(978-1-4264-3296-5(8))* 2006. 186p. pap. 21.99 *(978-1-4264-3351-1(4))* BiblioBazaar.

BOLIVIA

Andrews, Joseph D. Journey from Buenos Ayres Undertaken on Behalf of the Chilian & Peruvian Mining Assn., 1825-26, 2 vols. reprint ed. 82.50 *(978-0-404-00410-1(5))* AMS Pr., Inc.

Buechler, Hans C. The Masked Media: Aymara Fiestas & Social Interaction in the Bolivian Highlands. (Approaches to Semiotics [AS] Ser.). (ENG.). X, 399p. 196.00 ***(978-3-11-177061-1(3))*** De Gruyter, Mouton DEU. Dist: de Gruyter, Walter GmbH & Co. KG.

Parker, William B. Bolivians of Today. (Hispanic Notes & Monographs). 332p. reprint ed. 98.00 *(978-0-7222-9587-8(1))* Library Reprints, Inc.

Zulawski, Ann. Unequal Cures: Public Health & Political Change in Bolivia, 1900-1950. 2007. (ENG., Illus.). 264p. 84.95 *(978-0-8223-3900-7(5))*; per. 23.95 *(978-0-8223-3916-8(1))* Duke Univ. Pr.

BOLIVIA—ANTIQUITIES

Alconini, Sonia. El Inkario en Los Valles Del Sur Andino Boliviano: Los Yamparas Entre la Arqueología y Etnohistoria. 2008. (SPA & ENG., Illus.). iv, 143p. (C). pap. 102.50 *(978-1-4073-0235-5(3))* British Archaeological Reports Ltd. GBR. Dist: Brown, David Bk. Co., The.

Arkush, Elizabeth N. Hillforts of the Ancient Andes: Colla Warfare, Society, & Landscape. 2011. (ENG., Illus.). 320p. 69.95 *(978-0-8130-3526-0(0))* Univ. Pr. of Florida.

Bandelier, Adolph F. A. The Islands of Titicaca & Koati. 358p. reprint ed. 98.00 *(978-0-7222-9691-2(6))* Library Reprints, Inc.

Stanish, Charles. Lake Titicaca: Legend, Myth, & Science. 2011. (World heritage & monument Ser.). (ENG., Illus.). 224p. (C). pap. 45.00 *(978-1-931745-82-6(X))* Cotsen Institute of Archaeology at UCLA.

Young-Sanchez, Margaret, ed. Tiwanaku: Papers from the 2005 Mayer Center Symposium at the Denver Art Museum. 2009. (ENG.). 264p. (C). pap. 45.00 *(978-0-8061-9972-6(5))* Denver Art Museum.

BOLIVIA—DESCRIPTION AND TRAVEL

Atkinson, David. Bolivia: The Bradt Travel Guide. 2007. (Bradt Travel Guide Ser.). (ENG., Illus.). 288p. per. 22.95 *(978-1-84162-165-4(X))* Bradt Travel Guides GBR. Dist: Globe Pequot Pr., The.

Bolivia: The Essential Guide to Customs & Culture. 2009. (Culture Smart! Ser.). (ENG., Illus.). 168p. pap. 9.95 *(978-1-85733-485-2(X))* Kuperard Pubs. GBR. Dist: Random Hse., Inc.

Box, Ben. Bolivia. 2012. (Footprint Focus Ser.). (ENG., Illus.). 144p. pap. 12.95 ***(978-1-908206-72-5(1))*** Footprint Handbooks GBR. Dist: Globe Pequot Pr., The.

Box, Ben. Cuzco, la Paz & Lake Titicaca Footprint Focus. 2011. (Footprint Focus Ser.). (ENG., Illus.). 152p. pap. 12.95 *(978-1-908206-30-5(6))* Footprint Handbooks GBR. Dist: Globe Pequot Pr., The.

Box, Ben, et al. Peru, Bolivia & Ecuador Handbook. 3rd ed. 2011. (Footprint - Handbooks Ser.). (ENG., Illus.). 708p. 25.95 *(978-1-907263-23-1(3))* Footprint Handbooks GBR. Dist: Globe Pequot Pr., The.

Camacho, Guillermo. Bolivian Forever: Celebrating an Extraordinary Heritage & an Unforgettable People. 2011. 168p. pap. 47.00 *(978-1-4567-3626-2(4))* AuthorHouse.

Cherry, Brigid. Bolivia in Focus. Date not set. (In Focus Ser.). (Illus.). 80p. pap. 12.00 *(978-0-85345-899-9(5))* Latin America Bureau GBR. Dist: Monthly Review Pr.

Cramer, Mark. Cultureshock Bolivia, 1 vol. 2010. (ENG., Illus.). 240p. pap. 15.95 *(978-0-7614-5658-2(9))* Marshall Cavendish Corp.

Cramer, Mark & Cavendish, Marshall. CultureShock! Bolivia, 1 vol. 2007. (Cultureshock Bolivia: A Survival Guide to Customs & Etiquette Ser.). (ENG., Illus.). 32p. pap. 15.95 *(978-0-7614-2488-8(1))* Marshall Cavendish Corp.

De Bonelli, L. Hugh. Travels in Bolivia: A Tour Across the Pampas to Buenos Ayres, 2 Vols, Set. reprint ed. 250.00 *(978-0-7222-9588-5(X))* Library Reprints, Inc.

Duguid, Julian. Green Hell. 2008. 348p. *(978-1-4437-3470-7(5)*, Pomona Pr.) Read Bks.

Ericson, Libby. An Oil Geologist Abroad: Exploration with Family in Bolivia, Spain, & Nigeria, 1956-1966. 2011. 222p. pap. ***(978-0-86534-824-0(3))*** Sunstone Pr.

Ghinsberg, Yossi. Lost in the Jungle: A Harrowing True Story of Adventure & Survival. 2009. (ENG.). 320p. pap. 14.95 *(978-1-60239-370-7(2)*, 239370) Skyhorse Publishing Co., Inc.

Hayes, Don. Adventures of a First Year Teacher in a Third World Country. 2010. 112p. pap. 12.95 *(978-1-4502-7391-6(2))* iUniverse, Inc.

Herndon, William Lewis. Exploration of the Valley of the Amazon, Made under Direction of the Navy Department. 2006. 424p. per. 26.99 *(978-1-4255-4621-2(8))*; 428p. per. 26.99 *(978-1-4255-4704-2(4))* MPublishing.

Kunstaetter, Robert & Kunstaetter, Daisy. Bolivia: Tread Your Own Path. 5th ed. 2009. (ENG., Illus.). 464p. 24.95 *(978-1-906098-21-6(2))* Footprint Handbooks GBR. Dist: Globe Pequot Pr., The.

Locken, E. Travel Journal Bolivia. 2010. 192p. pap. 19.99 *(978-0-557-43273-8(1))* Lulu Enterprises Inc.

Lonely Planet Staff & Mutic, Anja. Bolivia. 7th ed. 2010. (Country Guide Ser.). (ENG., Illus.). 392p. pap. 25.99 *(978-1-74104-998-5(9))* Lonely Planet Pubns.

McLaughlin, Don. Bolivia: Looking Beyond Its Rocks. 2008. (ENG., Illus.). 132p. 39.00 *(978-0-9790597-1-1(2))* Fields Publishing.

Munan. Culture Shock! Bolivia. 2006. (Illus.). xi, 300p. pap. *(978-0-462-00002-2(8))* Marshall Cavendish.

Museum Im Bellpark Kriens Staff. Guido Baselgia. 2008. (GER & ENG., Illus.). 104p. lthr. 85.00 *(978-3-7757-2098-4(7))* Hatje Cantz Verlag GmbH & Co KG DEU. Dist: D.A.P./Distributed Art Pubs.

Ochoa, Carlos M. The Potatoes of South America: Bolivia. Ugent, Donald, tr. 2011. (ENG., Illus.). 570p. pap. 70.00 *(978-0-521-18990-3(X))* Cambridge Univ. Pr.

Post, Charles J. Across the Andes. 362p. reprint ed. 98.00 *(978-0-7222-9589-2(8))* Library Reprints, Inc.

—Across the Andes. 2008. 388p. pap. *(978-1-4097-7191-3(1))* Read Bks.

—Across the Andes. 362p. reprint ed. 98.00 *(978-0-7222-9561-8(8))* Library Reprints, Inc.

Post, Charles Johnso. Across the Andes A Tale of Wandering Day. 2006. pap. 33.95 *(978-1-4286-5708-3(8))* Kessinger Publishing, LLC.

Read, James. The Rough Guide to Bolivia. 3rd ed. 2012. (Rough Guide To... Ser.). (ENG., Illus.). 384p. 27.99 *(978-1-4053-8964-8(8))* Rough Guides, Ltd. GBR. Dist: Dorling Kindersley Publishing, Inc.

Rushenberger, William, abr. Three Years in the Pacific. 2009. (Military History Ser.). (ENG.). 463p. pap. 27.95 *(978-1-4290-2192-0(6))* Applewood Bks.

Stanish, Charles. Lake Titicaca: Legend, Myth, & Science. 2011. (World heritage & monument Ser.). (ENG., Illus.). 224p. (C). pap. 45.00 *(978-1-931745-82-6(X))* Cotsen Institute of Archaeology at UCLA.

Tomlinson, H. M. The Sea & the Jungle. 2010. 254p. pap. *(978-1-4099-7378-2(6))* Dodo Pr.

Tomlinson, Henry M. The Sea & the Jungle. 371p. reprint ed. 98.00 *(978-0-7222-9601-1(0))*; 98.00 *(978-0-7222-9568-7(5))* Library Reprints, Inc.

Wehner, Ross & del Gaudio, Renée. Moon Spotlight Lake Titicaca. 2011. (Moon Spotlight Ser.). (ENG.). 64p. pap. 6.95 *(978-1-59880-673-1(4))* Avalon Travel Publishing.

Werner, Robert J. Bolivia in Focus: A Guide to the People, Politics, & Culture. 2009. (In Focus Guides). (ENG., Illus.). 144p. pap. 17.00 *(978-1-56656-299-7(6))* Interlink Publishing Group, Inc.

Wigowsky, Paul John. Inka Pilgrimage: Hidden Treasures of Pachamama (Colombia, Ecuador, Peru, Bolivia) 2011. 324p. pap. 77.88 *(978-1-4634-3244-7(5))* AuthorHouse.

Woods, Josephine Hoeppner. High Spots in the Andes: Peruvian Letters of A Mining Engineer's Wife. 2011. 352p. 51.95 ***(978-1-258-02628-8(7))*** Literary Licensing, LLC.

BOLIVIA—ECONOMIC CONDITIONS

Adams, Alexander A. The Plateau Peoples of South America: An Essay in Ethnic Psychology. 134p. reprint ed. 88.00 *(978-0-7222-9586-1(3))*; 88.00 *(978-0-7222-6481-2(X))* Library Reprints, Inc.

Astaburuaga, Estibaliz & LAFUENTE, Oroitz. Bolivia'S External Debt Burden. 2010. 116p. pap. *(978-3-8383-8317-0(6))* Lambert Academic Publishing.

Bolivia: Commercial Law. 300p. (Orig.). pap. 295.00 *(978-0-7605-1230-2(2))* Rector Pr., Ltd.

Cherry, Brigid. Bolivia in Focus. Date not set. (In Focus Ser.). (Illus.). 80p. pap. 12.00 *(978-0-85345-899-9(5))* Latin America Bureau GBR. Dist: Monthly Review Pr.

Crabtree, John & Whitehead, Laurence, eds. Unresolved Tensions: Bolivia Past & Present. 2008. (Pitt Latin American Studies). (ENG., Illus.). 288p. (C). 65.00 *(978-0-8229-4355-6(7))*; pap. 26.95 *(978-0-8229-6006-5(0))* Univ. of Pittsburgh Pr.

Giugale, Marcelo M., et al, eds. Bolivia: Public Policy Options for the Well-Being of All. 2006. (Books Ser.). (ENG., Illus.). 568p. per. 50.00 *(978-0-8213-6662-2(9))*, 9780821366622) World Bank Pubns.

Grosse, Melanie. Measurement of Trends in Wellbeing, Poverty, & Inequality with Case Studies from Bolivia & Colombia. 2011. (Göttinger Studien zur Entwicklungsökonomik. Göttingen Studies in Development Economics Ser.). (Illus.). 246p. 72.95 *(978-3-631-61376-4(8))* Lang, Peter GmbH, Europaischer Verlag der Wissenschaften DEU. Dist: Lang, Peter.

Icon Group International, Inc. Staff, compiled by. The 2006 Economic & Product Market Databook for Cochabamba, Bolivia. 2006. 618p. ring bd. 95.00 *(978-0-497-80387-2(9))* Icon Group International, Inc.

—The 2006 Economic & Product Market Databook for la Paz, Bolivia. 2006. 618p. ring bd. 95.00 *(978-0-497-80802-0(1))* Icon Group International, Inc.

—The 2006 Economic & Product Market Databook for Oruro, Bolivia. 2006. 618p. ring bd. 95.00 *(978-0-497-81170-9(7))* Icon Group International, Inc.

—The 2006 Economic & Product Market Databook for Potosi, Bolivia. 2006. 618p. ring bd. 95.00 *(978-0-497-81285-0(1))* Icon Group International, Inc.

—The 2006 Economic & Product Market Databook for Santa Cruz, Bolivia. 2006. 618p. ring bd. 95.00 *(978-0-497-81445-8(5))* Icon Group International, Inc.

—The 2006 Economic & Product Market Databook for Sucre, Bolivia. 2006. 618p. ring bd. 95.00 *(978-0-497-81573-8(7))* Icon Group International, Inc.

—The 2006 Economic & Product Market Databook for Tarija, Bolivia. 2006. 618p. ring bd. 95.00 *(978-0-497-81648-3(2))* Icon Group International, Inc.

Lazar, Sian. El Alto, Rebel City: Self & Citizenship in Andean Bolivia. (Latin America Otherwise: Languages, Empires, Nations Ser.). (ENG., Illus.). 344p. 2008. per. 25.95 *(978-0-8223-4154-3(9))* 2007. (C). 94.95 *(978-0-8223-4129-1(8))* Duke Univ. Pr.

Lora, Guillermo. A History of the Bolivian Labour Movement, 1848-1971. 2009. (Cambridge Latin American Studies). 424p. pap. 53.00 *(978-0-521-10021-2(6))* Cambridge Univ. Pr.

Luff, Connie, et al, eds. Por el Bienestar de Todos Bolivia. 2006. (Books Ser.). (SPA., Illus.). 568p. per. 50.00 *(978-0-8213-6660-8(2)*, 9780821366608) World Bank Pubns.

Olivera, Oscar & Lewis, Tom. !Cochabamba! Water War in Bolivia. 2008. (ENG.). 208p. 40.00 *(978-0-89608-703-3(4))* South End Pr.

Poverty Reduction and Economic Management Staff. Bolivia: Policies for Increasing Firms' Formality & Productivity. 2009. (Country Studies). (ENG., Illus.). 160p. pap. 25.00 *(978-0-8213-8023-9(0)*, 9780821380239) World Bank Pubns.

—Strengthening Bolivian Competitiveness: Export Diversification & Inclusive Growth. 2009. (Country Studies). (ENG., Illus.). 249p. pap. 25.00 *(978-0-8213-8021-5(4)*, 9780821380215) World Bank Pubns.

Spatz, Julius. Poverty & Inequality in the Era of Structural Reforms: The Case of Bolivia. 2006. (Kieler Studien - Kiel Studies). (Illus.). xvii, 167p. 109.00 *(978-3-540-30894-2(6)*, 3540308946) Springer.

—Poverty & Inequality in the Era of Structural Reforms: the Case of Bolivia: The Case of Bolivia. 2010. (Kieler Studien - Kiel Studies). (Illus.). xvii, 167p. pap. 109.00 *(978-3-642-06811-9(1)*, 3642068111) Springer.

Tsolakis, Andreas. The Reform of the Bolivian State: Domestic Politics in the Context of Globalization. 2010. (Illus.). 275p. 79.95 *(978-1-935049-27-2(5))* FirstForumPress.

Werner, Robert J. Bolivia in Focus: A Guide to the People, Politics, & Culture. 2009. (In Focus Guides). (ENG., Illus.). 144p. pap. 17.00 *(978-1-56656-299-7(6))* Interlink Publishing Group, Inc.

BOLIVIA—HISTORY

see also Chaco War, 1932-1935

Berg, Hans van den. Con Los Yuracarees (Bolivia) Crónicas Misionales (1765-1825) Eichmann, Andrés, ed. 2010. (SPA., Illus.). 616p. pap. 64.00 *(978-84-8489-528-2(9))* Iberoamericana Vervuert Publishing Corp.

Brockington, Lolita Gutierrez. Blacks, Indians, & Spaniards in the Eastern Andes: Reclaiming the Forgotten in Colonial Mizque, 1550-1782. 2009. (ENG.). 360p. pap. 24.95 *(978-0-8032-2484-1(2))* Univ. of Nebraska Pr.

Camacho, Guillermo. Bolivian Forever: Celebrating an Extraordinary Heritage & an Unforgettable People. 2011. 168p. pap. 47.00 *(978-1-4567-3626-2(4))* AuthorHouse.

Cherry, Brigid. Bolivia in Focus. Date not set. (In Focus Ser.). (Illus.). 80p. pap. 12.00 *(978-0-85345-899-9(5))* Latin America Bureau GBR. Dist: Monthly Review Pr.

De Leon, Miriam Monica Montellano Ponce. Social Movements; Development Actors in Bolivia? A Case Study of How 'cocaleros' Movements Perceive Their Role in Bolivian Development Processes. 2011. 120p. pap. ***(978-3-639-33983-3(5))*** VDM Verlag Dr. Mueller e.K.

Dunkerley, James. Bolivia: Revolution & the Power of History in the Present. 2007. (ENG., Illus.). 224p. per. 30.00 *(978-1-900039-81-9(8))* Institute of Latin American Studies GBR. Dist: Brookings Institution Pr.

English, Adrian J. The Green Hell: A Concise History of the Chaco War Between Bolivia & Paraguay, 1932-35. 2008. (Spellmount Military Studies). (ENG., Illus.). 224p. pap. 32.95 *(978-1-86227-445-7(2))* History Pr. Ltd., The GBR. Dist: Independent Pubs. Group.

Estrada, Ulises. Tania: Undercover with Che Guevara in Bolivia. 2007. (Illus.). 327p. pap. 20.00 *(978-1-4223-6626-4(X))* DIANE Publishing Co.

Fifer, J. Valerie. Bolivia: Land, Location & Politics Since 1825. 2008. (Cambridge Latin American Studies). (ENG.). 328p. pap. 46.00 *(978-0-521-10170-7(0))* Cambridge Univ. Pr.

Gotkowitz, Laura. A Revolution for Our Rights: Indigenous Struggles for Land & Justice in Bolivia, 1880-1952. 2008. (ENG., Illus.). 416p. 94.95 *(978-0-8223-4049-2(6))* Duke Univ. Pr.

Hylton, Forrest & Thomson, Sinclair. Revolutionary Horizons: Past & Present in Bolivian Politics. 2007. (ENG., Illus.). 177p. per. 24.95 *(978-1-84467-097-0(X)*, 844097) Verso Bks. GBR. Dist: Norton, W. W. & Co., Inc.

John, S. Sándor. Bolivia's Radical Tradition: Permanent Revolution in the Andes. 2009. (ENG., Illus.). 320p. 55.00 *(978-0-8165-2764-9(4))* Univ. of Arizona Pr.

Klein, Herbert S. A Concise History of Bolivia. 2nd ed. 2011. (Cambridge Concise Histories Ser.). (ENG., Illus.). 376p. 85.00 *(978-1-107-00568-6(X))*; pap. 25.99 *(978-0-521-18372-7(3))* Cambridge Univ. Pr.

Larken, Meriel. The Ship, the Lady & the Lake: The Extraordinary Life of a Victorian Steamship in the Andes. 2012. (ENG.). 240p. 29.95 ***(978-1-903071-42-7(9))*** Bene Factum Publishing, Ltd. GBR. Dist: Independent Pubs. Group.

Lisle, Gerard de. The Royal Navy & the Peruvian-Chilean War 1879 - 1881: Rudolf de Lisle's Diaries & Watercolours. 2008. (Illus.). 192p. 50.00 *(978-1-84415-652-8(4))* Pen & Sword Bks. Ltd. GBR. Dist: Casemate Pubs. & Bk. Distributors, LLC.

Morales, Waltraud Q. Bolivia. 2nd rev. ed. 2010. (Brief History Ser.). 384p. (C). (gr. 9-18). 49.50 *(978-0-8160-7877-6(7))* Facts On File, Inc.

Munan. Culture Shock! Bolivia. 2006. (Illus.). xi, 300p. pap. *(978-0-462-00002-2(8))* Marshall Cavendish.

Perea, Natalia Sobrevilla. The Caudillo of the Andes: Andres de Santa Cruz. 2011. (New Approaches to the Americas Ser.). (ENG., Illus.). 256p. (C). 85.00 *(978-0-521-89567-5(7))* Cambridge Univ. Pr.

Ramirez, Rocio. Hip Hop: The response from the Streets? 2011. 76p. pap. **(978-3-8443-0432-9(0))** Lambert Academic Publishing.

Robins, Nicholas A. Mercury, Mining, & Empire: The Human & Ecological Cost of Colonial Silver Mining in the Andes. 2011. (ENG., Illus.). 320p. 45.00 *(978-0-253-35651-2(2)*, 0253356512) Indiana Univ. Pr.

—Priest-Indian Conflict in Upper Peru: A Generation of Rebellion, 1750-1780. 2007. (Religion & Politics Ser.). 272p. (C). 54.95 *(978-0-8156-3118-7(9))* Syracuse Univ. Pr.

—Priest-Indian Conflict in Upper Peru: The Generation of Rebellion, 1750-1780. 2007. (Religion & Politics Ser.). 315p. per. 29.95 *(978-0-8156-3142-2(1))* Syracuse Univ. Pr.

Rockefeller, Stuart Alexander. Starting from Quirpini: The Travels & Places of a Bolivian People. 2010. (ENG., Illus.). 320p. 65.00 *(978-0-253-35497-6(8)*, 0253354978); pap. 24.95 *(978-0-253-22210-7(9)*, 0253222109) Indiana Univ. Pr.

Sater, William F. Andean Tragedy: Fighting the War of the Pacific, 1879-1884. 2009. (Studies in War, Society, & the Militar Ser.). (ENG., Illus.). 456p. pap. 29.95 *(978-0-8032-2799-6(X))* Univ. of Nebraska Pr.

Walle, Paul. Bolivia: Its People & Its Resources, Its Railways, Mines, & Rubber Forests. 407p. reprint ed. 98.00 *(978-0-7222-9590-8(1))* Library Reprints, Inc.

Werner, Robert J. Bolivia in Focus: A Guide to the People, Politics, & Culture. 2009. (In Focus Guides). (ENG., Illus.). 144p. pap. 17.00 *(978-1-56656-299-7(6))* Interlink Publishing Group, Inc.

BOLIVIA—POLITICS AND GOVERNMENT

Adams, Alexander A. The Plateau Peoples of South America: An Essay in Ethnic Psychology. 134p. reprint ed. 88.00 *(978-0-7222-9586-1(3))*; 88.00 *(978-0-7222-6481-2(X))* Library Reprints, Inc.

Albro, Robert. Roosters at Midnight: Indigenous Signs & Stigma in Local Bolivian Politics. 2010. (ENG., Illus.). 264p. pap. 34.95 *(978-1-934691-18-2(6))* School for Advanced Research Pr./SAR Pr.

Andrade, Victor. My Missions for Revolutionary Bolivia, 1944-1962. 2009. (Pitt Latin American Studies). (ENG.). 218p. (C). pap. 25.95 *(978-0-8229-8456-6(3))* Univ. of Pittsburgh Pr.

Artaraz, Kepa. Bolivia: Refounding the Nation, 1 vol. 2012. (ENG.). 256p. 30.00 **(978-0-7453-3089-1(4))**; lib. bdg. 110.00 **(978-0-7453-3090-7(8))** Pluto Pr. GBR. Dist: Macmillan.

Autores Varios Staff. Constituciones Fundacionales de Bolivi. 2010. (SPA.). 140p. per. 10.00 *(978-84-9816-132-8(0))* Linkgua Ediciones, S.L. ESP. Dist: AtlasBooks Distribution.

Cherry, Brigid. Bolivia in Focus. Date not set. (In Focus Ser.). (Illus.). 80p. pap. 12.00 *(978-0-85345-899-9(5))* Latin America Bureau GBR. Dist: Monthly Review Pr.

Crabtree, John & Whitehead, Laurence, eds. Unresolved Tensions: Bolivia Past & Present. 2008. (Pitt Latin American Studies). (ENG., Illus.). 288p. (C). 65.00 *(978-0-8229-4355-6(7))*; pap. 26.95 *(978-0-8229-6006-5(0))* Univ. of Pittsburgh Pr.

Dangl, Benjamin. El Precio del Fuego: Resource Wars & Social Movements in Bolivia. 2010. (SPA & ENG.). 240p. pap. 18.00 *(978-1-60846-069-4(X))* Haymarket Bks.

—The Price of Fire: Resource Wars & Social Movements in Bolivia. 2007. (ENG., Illus.). 240p. per. 15.95 *(978-1-904859-33-8(X))* AK Pr. GBR. Dist: Consortium Bk. Sales & Distribution.

Dunkerley, James. Bolivia: Revolution & the Power of History in the Present. 2007. (ENG., Illus.). 224p. per. 30.00 *(978-1-900039-81-9(8))* Institute of Latin American Studies GBR. Dist: Brookings Institution Pr.

Fabricant, Nicole & Gustafson, Bret. Remapping Bolivia: Resources, Territory, & Indigeneity in a Plurinational State. 2011. (Illus.). viii, 251p. *(978-1-934691-51-9(8))* School for Advanced Research Pr./SAR Pr.

Fifer, J. Valerie. Bolivia: Land, Location & Politics Since 1825. 2008. (Cambridge Latin American Studies). (ENG.). 328p. pap. 46.00 *(978-0-521-10170-7(0))* Cambridge Univ. Pr.

Gamarra, Eduardo A. Bolivia on the Brink. 2007. (Council Special Report). 51p. per. 10.00 *(978-0-87609-374-0(8))* Council on Foreign Relations.

Gianotten, Vera. Bolivia, the Strength of Political Courage: 35 Years of CIPCA History. 2011. 256p. pap. 39.95 **(978-94-6022-096-8(7))** Royal Tropical Institute Pr. (KIT (Koninklijk Instituut voor de Tropen) NLD. Dist: Stylus Publishing, LLC.

Giugale, Marcelo M., et al, eds. Bolivia: Public Policy Options for the Well-Being of All. 2006. (Books Ser.). (ENG., Illus.). 568p. per. 50.00 *(978-0-8213-6662-2(9)*, 9780821366622) World Bank Pubns.

Goodale, Mark. Dilemmas of Modernity: Bolivian Encounters with Law & Liberalism. 2008. (ENG., Illus.). 264p. 65.00 *(978-0-8047-5981-6(2))*; pap. 24.95 *(978-0-8047-5982-3(0))* Stanford Univ. Pr.

Gotkowitz, Laura. A Revolution for Our Rights: Indigenous Struggles for Land & Justice in Bolivia, 1880-1952. 2008. (ENG., Illus.). 416p. per. 25.95 *(978-0-8223-4067-6(4))* Duke Univ. Pr.

Harten, Sven. The Rise of Evo Morales & the MAS. 2011. (ENG.). 256p. 116.95 *(978-1-84813-523-9(8))*; pap. 34.95 *(978-1-84813-524-6(6))* Zed Bks., Ltd. GBR. Dist: Macmillan.

Haymarket Books. Rebellion & Reform in Bolivia: Class Struggle, Indigenous Liberation, & the Politics of Evo Morales. 2011. (ENG., Illus.). 340p. pap. *(978-1-60846-106-6(8))* Pluto Pr.

Hylton, Forrest & Thomson, Sinclair. Revolutionary Horizons: Past & Present in Bolivian Politics. 2007. (ENG., Illus.). 177p. 90.00 *(978-1-84467-070-3(8)*, 844070); per. 24.95 *(978-1-84467-097-0(X)*, 844097) Verso Bks. GBR. Dist: Norton, W. W. & Co., Inc.

John, S. Sándor. Bolivia's Radical Tradition: Permanent Revolution in the Andes. 2009. (ENG., Illus.). 320p. 55.00 *(978-0-8165-2764-9(4))* Univ. of Arizona Pr.

Klein, Herbert S. Parties & Political Change in Bolivia: 1880-1952. 2008. (Cambridge Latin American Studies). (ENG.). 468p. pap. 58.00 *(978-0-521-10201-8(4))* Cambridge Univ. Pr.

Kohl, Benjamin & Farthing, Linda C. From the Mines to the Streets: A Bolivian Activist's Life. 2012. (ENG., Illus.). 263p. pap. 25.00 **(978-0-292-74392-2(0))** Univ. of Texas Pr.

Lazar, Sian. El Alto, Rebel City: Self & Citizenship in Andean Bolivia. (Latin America Otherwise: Languages, Empires, Nations Ser.). (ENG., Illus.). 344p. 2008. per. 25.95 *(978-0-8223-4154-3(9))* 2007. (C). 94.95 *(978-0-8223-4129-1(8))* Duke Univ. Pr.

Lucero, Jose Antonio. Struggles of Voice: The Politics of Indigenous Representation in the Andes. 2008. (Pitt Latin American Studies). (ENG., Illus.). 224p. (C). 65.00 *(978-0-8229-4352-5(2))* Univ. of Pittsburgh Pr.

Lucero, José Antonio. Struggles of Voice: The Politics of Indigenous Representation in the Andes. 2008. (Pitt Latin American Studies). (ENG., Illus.). 224p. (C). pap. 25.95 *(978-0-8229-5998-4(4))* Univ. of Pittsburgh Pr.

Manzaneda Medina, Jofat Julio Manuel. Probleme und Perspektiven kommunaler Bürgerbeteiligung in Bolivien: Unter Berücksichtigung der deutschen Erfahrungen mit der Bürgergesellschaft. 2008. (Speyerer Schriften zur Verwaltungswissenschaft Ser.). 482p. pap. 107.95 *(978-3-631-57660-1(9))* Lang, Peter GmbH, Europaischer Verlag der Wissenschaften DEU. Dist: Lang, Peter.

Mejia Silva, Carola. Assessment of Community-Based Forest Management in Bolivi. 2011. 72p. pap. **(978-3-8443-0738-2(9))** Lambert Academic Publishing.

Munoz-Pogossian, Betilde, et al. Electoral Rules & the Transformation of Bolivian Politics: The Rise of Evo Morales. 2008. (ENG., Illus.). 256p. 95.00 *(978-0-230-60819-1(1))* Palgrave Macmillan.

Oxhorn, Philip. Sustaining Civil Society: Economic Change, Democracy, & the Social Construction of Citizenship in Latin America. 2011. (ENG.). 280p. 74.95 *(978-0-271-04394-9(8))* Pennsylvania State Univ. Pr.

Pearce, Adrian, ed. Evo Morales & the Movimiento AL Socialismo in Bolivia: The First Term in Context 2005-2009. 2011. (ENG.). 300p. pap. 20.95 *(978-1-900039-99-4(0))* Institute of Latin American Studies GBR. Dist: Brookings Institution Pr.

Philip, George & Panizza, Francisco. The Triumph of Politics. 2011. (ENG.). 200p. 69.95 *(978-0-7456-4748-7(0))*; pap. 24.95 *(978-0-7456-4749-4(9))* Polity Pr. GBR. Dist: Wiley, John & Sons, Inc.

Postero, Nancy Grey. Now We Are Citizens: Indigenous Politics in Postmulticultural Bolivia. 2006. (ENG., Illus.). 312p. 70.00 *(978-0-8047-5519-1(1))*; per. 26.95 *(978-0-8047-5520-7(5))* Stanford Univ. Pr.

Romanowski, Arne. Pr Electoral Systems & Indigenous Representation. 2009. 128p. pap. *(978-3-639-15650-8(1))* VDM Verlag Dr. Mueller e.K.

Schildt, Janine. Evo Morales: Die Konstitution Einer Neuen Lateinamerikanischen Heldenfigur. 2007. (GER.). 59p. pap. *(978-3-86010-924-3(3))* Martin-Luther-Universitat Halle-Wittenberg, Universitats- und Landesbibliothek Sachsen-Anhalt.

Schiwy, Freya. Indianizing Film: Decolonization, the Andes, & the Question of Technology. 2009. (New Directions in International Studies). (ENG., Illus.). 296p. 72.00 *(978-0-8135-4539-4(0))*; pap. 24.95 *(978-0-8135-4540-0(4))* Rutgers Univ. Pr.

Siekmeier, James F. The Bolivian Revolution & the United States, 1952 to the Present. 2011. (ENG.). 224p. 64.95 *(978-0-271-03779-0(2))* Pennsylvania State Univ. Pr.

Sivak, Martin. Jefazo. 2009. (SPA.). 344p. pap. 16.95 *(978-0-307-39284-8(8))* Debate, Editorial ESP. Dist: Random Hse., Inc.

Soldal, Arild. The Water War? Coca, Structural Adjustments & Water in Cochabamba, Bolivi. 2008. 120p. pap. *(978-3-639-05961-8(1))* VDM Verlag Dr. Mueller e.K.

Spatz, Julius. Poverty & Inequality in the Era of Structural Reforms: the Case of Bolivia: The Case of Bolivia. 2010. (Kieler Studien - Kiel Studies). (Illus.). xvii, 167p. pap. 109.00 *(978-3-642-06811-9(1)*, 3642068111) Springer.

Tsolakis, Andreas. The Reform of the Bolivian State: Domestic Politics in the Context of Globalization. 2010. (Illus.). 275p. 79.95 *(978-1-935049-27-2(5))* FirstForumPress.

U.S.-Bolivia Relations: Looking Ahead: Hearing Before the Subcommittee on the Western Hemisphere of the Committee on Foreign Affairs, House of Representatives, One Hundred Eleventh Congress, First Session, March 3, 2009. 2009. iii, 86p. *(978-0-16-083056-3(7)*, 552-070-38951-2) United States Government Printing Office.

Werner, Robert J. Bolivia in Focus: A Guide to the People, Politics, & Culture. 2009. (In Focus Guides). (ENG., Illus.). 144p. pap. 17.00 *(978-1-56656-299-7(6))* Interlink Publishing Group, Inc.

Woll, Bettina. The Ownership Paradox. 2010. 220p. pap. *(978-3-8383-6557-0(8))* Lambert Academic Publishing.

Zibechi, Raúl. Dispersing Power: Social Movements As Anti-State Forces. Ryan, Ramor, tr. from SPA. 2010. (ENG.). 174p. pap. 15.95 *(978-1-84935-011-2(6))* AK Pr. GBR. Dist: Consortium Bk. Sales & Distribution.

BOLL, HEINRICH, 1917-1985

Boll, Heinrich. What's to Become of the Boy? Or, Something to Do with Books. Vennewitz, Leila, tr. from GER. 2011. (ENG.). 96p. pap. 14.95 *(978-1-61219-001-3(4))* Melville Hse. Publishing.

McDonald, Edward R. Daseinfunktion Von Heinrich Bolls Umstrittenem Helden: Wozu ist der Clown Da? 2007. (GER & ENG.). 148p. 99.95 *(978-0-7734-5394-4(6))* Mellen, Edwin Pr., The.

Stolz, Wolfgang. Der Begriff der Schuld im Werk von Heinrich Böll. 2008. (Kölner Studien zur Literaturwissenschaft Ser.). (GER.). 342p. pap. 81.95 *(978-3-631-57986-2(1))* Lang, Peter GmbH, Europaischer Verlag der Wissenschaften DEU. Dist: Lang, Peter.

BOLOGNA (ITALY)—DESCRIPTION AND TRAVEL

Breveglieri, Walter & Veronesi, Gilberto. Walter Breveglieri. 2008. (ITA., Illus.). 207p. *(978-88-7381-234-0(1))* Stewart, Tabori & Chang.

Thomas Cook Publishing Staff. Bologna Pocket Guide. 3rd ed. 2011. (Thomas Cook Pocket Guides). (ENG., Illus.). 160p. pap. 9.95 *(978-1-84848-349-1(X))* Cook, Thomas Publishing GBR. Dist: Globe Pequot Pr., The.

Wallpaper Magazine Editors, ed. Bologna - Wallpaper City Guide. 2008. (ENG., Illus.). 128p. pap. 9.95 *(978-0-7148-4894-5(8))* Phaidon Pr., Inc.

BOLSHEVISM

see Communism

BOLTON, HERBERT EUGENE, 1870-1953

Hurtado, Albert L. Herbert Eugene Bolton: Historian of the American Borderlands. 2012. (ENG., Illus.). 360p. 39.95 **(978-0-520-27216-3(1))** Univ. of California Pr.

BOLTS AND NUTS

American Society of Mechanical Engineers Staff, ed. Clearance Holes for Bolts Screws & Studs. 16p. 29.00 *(978-0-7918-2611-9(2))* ASME Pr.

—Metric Round Head Short Square Neck Bolts. 24p. 32.00 *(978-0-7918-2370-5(9))* ASME Pr.

—Plow Bolts. 20p. 32.00 *(978-0-7918-2377-4(6))* ASME Pr.

—Round Head Bolts. 15p. 30.00 *(978-0-7918-2114-5(5))* ASME Pr.

—Round Head Square Neck Bolts with Large Head Metric Series. 13p. 29.00 *(978-0-7918-2095-4(3))* ASME Pr.

—Square & Hex Bolts & Screws. 64p. 47.00 *(978-0-7918-2396-5(2))* ASME Pr.

—Square Head Bolts. 20p. 28.00 *(978-0-7918-2376-7(8))* ASME Pr.

C135.1-1999 IEEE Standard for Zinc-Coated Steel Bolts & Nuts for Overhead Line Construction. 54.00 *(978-0-7381-1841-3(9)*, SH94803-THT) IEEE.

C135.2-1999 IEEE Standard for Threaded Zinc-Coated Ferrous Strand-Eye Anchor Rods & Nuts for Overhead Line Construction. 53.00 *(978-0-7381-1843-7(5)*, SH94804-THT) IEEE.

Yu, Liang. Behavior of Bolted Connections During & after a Fire. 2009. 224p. pap. *(978-3-639-16565-2(3))* VDM Verlag Dr. Mueller e.K.

BOLTZMANN TRANSPORT EQUATION

see Transport Theory

BOLZANO, BERNARD, 1781-1848

Lapointe, Sandra. Bolzano's Theoretical Philosophy: An Introduction. 2011. (History of Analytic Philosophy Ser.). (ENG., Illus.). 208p. 80.00 *(978-0-230-20149-1(0))* Palgrave Macmillan.

Rojszczak, Artur. From the Act of Judging to the Sentence: The Problem of Truth Bearers from Bolzano to Tarski. Wolenski, Jan, ed. 2010. (Synthese Library). xv, 240p. pap. 159.00 *(978-90-481-6853-8(8)*, 9048168538) Springer.

BOMB-PROOF CONSTRUCTION

see Building, Bombproof

BOMB RECONNAISSANCE

Here are entered works on the location, identification, and application of safety measures as protection against unexploded bombs which have been set to detonate.

Basic Weapon Retention for Law Enforcement & Security Officers. 2007. 8.00 *(978-0-9793293-5-7(3))* Pro-Bushi Publishing.

BOMB SHELTERS

see Nuclear Bomb Shelters

BOMBARDMENT

Here are entered works on sustained military attacks on cities, military positions, etc., with bombs, shells, rockets, or other explosive missiles. Works on military bombardments by means of bombs dropped from the air are entered under Bombing, Aerial. Works on the use of explosive devices for the purposes of political terrorism, protest, etc., are entered under Bombings.

see also Bombers; Bombing, Aerial

Garlasco, Marc E. Precisely Wrong: Gaza Civilians Killed by Israeli Drone-Launched Missiles. 2009. (Illus.). 43p. pap. **(978-1-56432-492-4(3))** Human Rights Watch.

Grayling, A. C. Among the Dead Cities: The History & Moral Legacy of the WWII Bombing of Civilians in Germany & Japan. 2009. (ENG.). 361p. 26.00 *(978-1-4379-6720-3(5))* DIANE Publishing Co.

Human Rights Watch (Organization) Staff, contrib. by. Rain of Fire: Israel's Unlawful Use of White Phosphorus in Gaza. 2009. (Illus.). 71p. pap. *(978-1-56432-458-0(3))* Human Rights Watch.

McFarland, Stephen L. America's Pursuit of Precision Bombing, 1910-1945. 2nd ed. 2008. (ENG., Illus.). 332p. pap. 33.50 *(978-0-8173-5503-6(0))* Univ. of Alabama Pr.

Werrell, Kenneth. Death from Heavens. 2009. (Illus.). 400p. 49.95 *(978-1-59114-940-8(1))* Naval Institute Pr.

BOMBARDMENT, ION

see Ion Bombardment

BOMBARDMENTS WITH PARTICLES

see Collisions (Nuclear Physics)

BOMBAY (INDIA)

Basu, Anustup. Bollywood in the Age of New Media: The Geo-Televisual Aesthetic. 2010. (ENG., Illus.). 256p. (gr. 17). 110.00 *(978-0-7486-4102-4(5))* Edinburgh Univ. Pr. GBR. Dist: Columbia Univ. Pr.

Bilkha, Shubika. Stories of the Cities by the Se. 2010. 132p. pap. *(978-3-8383-8100-6(9))* Lambert Academic Publishing.

Boo, Katherine. Behind the Beautiful Forevers: Life, Death, & Hope in a Mumbai Undercity. 2012. (ENG.). 288p. 27.00 *(978-1-4000-6755-8(3)*, Random House) Random House Publishing Group.

—Behind the Beautiful Forevers: Life, Death, & Hope in a Mumbai Undercity. 2012. E-Book **(978-0-679-64550-4(0))** Random Hse., Inc.

—Behind the Beautiful Forevers: Life, Death, & Hope in a Mumbai Undercity. l.t. ed. 2012. (ENG.). 421p. 31.99 **(978-1-4104-4676-3(X))** Thorndike Pr.

Chandavarkar, Rajnayaran. Labour, Class & Culture: Essays on Indian History. 2009. (ENG.). 282p. 88.00 *(978-0-521-76871-9(3))* Cambridge Univ. Pr.

Dossal, Mariam. Theatre of Conflict, City of Hope: Mumbai - 1660 to Present Times. 2010. (ENG., Illus.). 344p. 110.00 *(978-0-19-806438-1(1))* Oxford Univ. Pr., Inc.

Edwardes, S. M. By-Ways of Bombay. 2007. 88p. per. *(978-1-4065-1767-5(4))* Dodo Pr.

—By-Ways of Bombay. 2009. 72p. pap. *(978-1-4068-5154-0(X))* Echo Library.

Edwardes, Stephen Meredyth. The Rise of Bombay: A Retrospect. 2011. (Cambridge Library Collection - History Ser.). (ENG., Illus.). 410p. pap. 31.99 *(978-1-108-14407-0(1))* Cambridge Univ. Pr.

Epstein, Mitch. Mitch Epstein: Work. 2008. (ENG., Illus.). 276p. 50.00 *(978-3-86521-281-8(6))* Steidl, Gerhard Druckerei und Verlag DEU. Dist: Innovative Logistics.

Gauldie, Robin. Goa & Mumbai. 3rd ed. 2009. (Globetrotter Travel Packs Ser.). (ENG., Illus.). 128p. pap. 14.95 *(978-1-84773-039-8(6)*, Globetrotter) New Holland Pubs., Ltd. GBR. Dist: Globe Pequot Pr., The.

Masselos, Jim. The City in Action: Bombay Struggles for Power in the 19th & 20th Century. 2007. (ENG.). 336p. 55.00 *(978-0-19-567929-8(6))* Oxford Univ. Pr., Inc.

Menon, Meena. Riots & after in Mumbai: Chronicles of Truth & Reconciliation. 2011. (C). 33.00 **(978-81-321-0700-2(4)**, B07002C) SAGE Pubns., Inc.

Narayan, Kirin. My Family & Other Saints. 2008. (Illus.). 246p. pap. 15.00 *(978-0-226-56821-8(0))* Univ. of Chicago Pr.

Prakash, Gyan. Mumbai Fables. (ENG., Illus.). 424p. 2011. pap. 19.95 **(978-0-691-15317-9(5))** 2010. (C). 29.95 *(978-0-691-14284-5(X))* Princeton Univ. Pr.

Ranganathan, Murali & Madagavakara, Govinda Narayana. Govind Narayan's Mumbai: An Urban Biography from 1863. Ranganathan, Murali, ed. 2008. (Anthem South Asian Studies). (ENG., Illus.). 407p. 80.00 *(978-1-84331-277-2(8))* Anthem Pr. GBR. Dist: Books International, Inc.

Rode, sanjay & Rode, Sanjay. Malnourishment among Children in Mumbai City. 2010. 196p. pap. *(978-3-8383-8001-8(0))* Lambert Academic Publishing.

Sanllorente, Jaume. Bombay Smiles: The Trip That Changed My Life. Gout, Gwendolyn & Dreesen, Robert, trs. from SPA. 2009. (ENG.). 225p. pap. 12.00 *(978-1-58988-055-9(2))* Dry, Paul Bks., Inc.

Sheppard, Samuel T., et al, eds. Bombay in the Days of Queen Anne, Being an Account of the Settlement Written by John Burnell. 2010. (Hakluyt Society, Second Ser.). 222p. 69.95 *(978-1-4094-1439-1(6))* Hakluyt Society GBR. Dist: Ashgate Publishing Co.

Sinha, Shalini. Discover Mumbai: The City's History & Culture Redefined. 2009. (Illus.). 160p. pap. 20.99 *(978-981-261-519-0(9))* Marshall Cavendish International (Asia) Private Ltd. SGP. Dist: Marshall Cavendish Corp.

Stott, David & McCulloch, Victoria. Mumbai & Gujarat Footprint Focus. 2011. (Footprint Focus Ser.). (ENG., Illus.). 136p. pap. 12.95 *(978-1-908206-41-1(1))* Footprint Handbooks GBR. Dist: Globe Pequot Pr., The.

Time Out Guides Staff. Time Out Mumbai & Goa. 3rd ed. 2011. (Time Out Guides). (ENG., Illus.). 256p. pap. 19.95 *(978-1-84670-212-9(7))* Time Out Guides Ltd. GBR. Dist: Perseus-PGW.

Wallpaper Magazine Editors, ed. Mumbai 2012 - Wallpaper City Guide. 2nd ed. 2012. (ENG., Illus.). 128p. pap. 9.95 **(978-0-7148-6305-4(X))** Phaidon Pr. Ltd. GBR. Dist: Hachette Bk. Group.

BOMBERS

see also B-Seventeen Bomber; B-Twenty-Four Bomber; Boeing Bombers; Bombing, Aerial; Heinkel One Hundred Seventy-Seven (Bombers); Kamikaze Airplanes; Lancaster (Bombers); Skyhawk Bomber; Stuka (Bombers)

Air Force, United States & Corporation, Convair, creators. Convair B-36 Peacemaker Pilot's Flight Operating Instructions. 2010. 500p. pap. 44.95 *(978-1-935327-87-5(9))* Periscope Film, LLC.

Alling, Chuck. A Mighty Fortress: Lead Bomber over Europe. Hildt, Elizabeth Alling, ed. 2006. (Illus.). 186p. per. 19.95 *(978-1-932033-59-5(9))* Casemate Pubs. & Bk. Distributors, LLC.

Army Air Force, United States. North American B-25 Mitchell Bomber Pilot's Flight Operating Manual. 2007. 183p. pap. 24.96 *(978-1-4303-2198-9(9))* Lulu Enterprises Inc.

Ayres, Travis L. The Bomber Boys: Heroes Who Flew the B-17s in World War II. 2009. (ENG., Illus.). 288p. (gr. 12-18). 16.00 *(978-0-451-22871-0(5)*, N A L Trade) Penguin Group (USA) Inc.

Barker, Ralph. Ship-Busters! A classic account of RAF torpedo-busters in WWII. 2009. (Illus.). 256p. 39.95 *(978-1-906502-29-4(3))* Grub Street GBR. Dist: Casemate Pubs. & Bk. Distributors, LLC, Littlehampton Bk Services, Ltd.

—Ship-Busters: British Torpedo-Bombers in World War II. 2010. (Stackpole Military History Ser.). (ENG., Illus.). 272p. pap. 18.95 *(978-0-8117-0644-5(3))* Stackpole Bks.

Berliner, Don. Surviving Bomber Aircraft of World War Two. 2011. (Illus.). 50.00 ***(978-1-84884-545-9(6))*** Pen & Sword Bks. Ltd. GBR. Dist: Casemate Pubs. & Bk. Distributors, LLC.

Birtles, Philip. The Avro Vulcan: Britain's Cold War Warrior. 2008. (Illus.). 128p. 32.95 *(978-1-85780-269-6(1))* Midland Publishing Ltd. GBR. Dist: Partners Pubs. Group, Inc.

Blackman, Tony. Vulcan Test Pilot: My Experiences in the Cockpit of a Cold War Icon. 2007. (Illus.). 218p. 39.95 *(978-1-904943-88-4(8))* Grub Street GBR. Dist: Casemate Pubs. & Bk. Distributors, LLC.

—Vulcan Test Pilot: My experiences in the cockpit of a Cold War Icon. 2009. (Illus.). 224p. pap. 26.95 *(978-1-906502-30-0(7))* Grub Street GBR. Dist: Casemate Pubs. & Bk. Distributors, LLC.

Bousquet, Gérard. French Wings No. 1: Latecoere 290&298. 2010. (French Wings Ser.). (Illus.). 80p. pap. 23.00 *(978-83-61421-20-7(3))* Stratus, Wydawnictwo, Juszczak, Artur POL. Dist: Casemate Pubs. & Bk. Distributors, LLC.

Bowman, Martin W. Achtung! Moskito! RAF & USAAF Mosquito Fighters, Fighter-Bombers, & Bombers over the Third Reich, 1941-1945. 2009. (Illus.). 352p. bds. 69.99 *(978-0-7643-3347-7(X))* Schiffer Publishing, Ltd.

—Bomber Bases of WW2 3rd Air Division, 8th Air Force USAAF 1942-45: Flying Fortress & Liberator Squadrons in Norfolk & Suffolk. 2009. (Illus.). 192p. pap. 25.99 *(978-1-84415-828-7(4))* Pen & Sword Bks. Ltd. GBR. Dist: Casemate Pubs. & Bk. Distributors, LLC.

Bowman, Martin W. The Wellington Bomber Story. 2011. (Story Ser.). (ENG., Illus.). 128p. 15.95 ***(978-0-7524-6193-9(1))*** History Pr. Ltd., The GBR. Dist: Independent Pubs. Group.

Brookes, Andrew. Victor Units of the Cold War. 2011. (Combat Aircraft Ser.). (ENG., Illus.). 96p. pap. 22.95 *(978-1-84908-339-3(8))* Osprey Publishing, Ltd. GBR. Dist: Random Hse., Inc.

Butler, Phil. Handley Page Victor: The Crescent-Winged V-Bomber. 2010. (ENG., Illus.). 143p. pap. 31.95 *(978-1-85780-311-2(6))* Allan, Ian Publishing GBR. Dist: BookMasters Distribution Services (BDS).

Butler, Phil & Buttler, Tony. Avro Vulcan: Britain's Famous Delta-Wing V-Bomber. 2008. (Aerofax Ser.). (Illus.). 144p. pap. 32.95 *(978-1-85780-256-6(X))* Midland Publishing Ltd. GBR. Dist: Partners Pubs. Group, Inc.

Caygill, Peter. Flying the Buccaneer: Britain's Cold War Warrior. 2008. (Illus.). 256p. 39.95 *(978-1-84415-669-6(9))* Pen & Sword Bks. Ltd. GBR. Dist: Casemate Pubs. & Bk. Distributors, LLC.

Cea, Eduardo. Bombers of the Imperial Japanese Army. (Illus.). 152p. pap. 42.95 *(978-84-96935-23-5(X))* Alcaniz y Fresnos, S.A. ESP. Dist: Casemate Pubs. & Bk. Distributors, LLC.

Centre of Excellence Defence Against Terrorism Staff, contrib. by. Suicide As a Weapon. 2007. (Illus.). xii, 185p. 150.00 *(978-1-58603-795-6(1))* IOS Pr., Inc.

Chant, Chris. Allied Bombers 1939-45. 2008. (Essential Aircraft Identification Guide Ser.). (ENG., Illus.). 192p. pap. 19.95 *(978-0-7603-3450-8(1), 0760334501, Zenith Pr.)* MBI Publishing Co. LLC.

Coastal Dawn: Blenheim's in action from the Phoney War through the Battle of Britain. 2010. (Illus.). 224p. 39.95 *(978-1-906502-69-0(2))* Grub Street GBR. Dist: Casemate Pubs. & Bk. Distributors, LLC.

Cole, Robert E., ed. The Incident That Could Have Killed Pittsburgh. 2008. (Illus.). 245p. pap. 19.95 *(978-1-55856-495-4(0))* Closson Pr.

Cox, Dale. Top Secret Flight. 2011. 436p. pap. 22.95 ***(978-1-257-12522-7(2))*** Lulu Enterprises Inc.

Craig, Bruce Galvin. Survival: Self & Country, WWII: Combat Adventures of a B24 Navigator. 2011. 272p. 28.99 ***(978-1-4670-3521-7(1))***; pap. 19.95 ***(978-1-4670-3519-4(X))*** AuthorHouse.

Crosby, Francis. The World Encyclopedia of Fighters & Bombers - An Illustrated History of the World's Greatest Military Aircraft, from the Pioneering Days of Air Fighting in World War I Through to the Jet Fighters & Stealth Bombers of the Present Day. 2010. (ENG., Illus.). 512p. pap. 24.99 *(978-1-84476-917-9(8))* Anness Publishing GBR. Dist: National Bk. Network.

Cunningham, Pat. Bomb on the Red Markers: Memories of Bomber Operations. 2010. (Memories Ser.). (ENG., Illus.). 192p. (C). pap. 29.95 *(978-1-84674-198-2(X))* Countryside Bks. GBR. Dist: Brown, David Bk. Co., The.

Darling, Kev. Avro Vulcan Part1. 2007. 132p. pap. 39.95 *(978-1-84799-237-6(4))* Lulu Enterprises Inc.

de Zeng, Henry L., IV & Stankey, Douglas G. Bomber Units of the Luftwaffe, 1933-1945 Vol. 2: A Reference Source. 2008. (ENG., Illus.). 208p. 56.95 *(978-1-903223-87-1(3))* Allan, Ian Publishing GBR. Dist: BookMasters Distribution Services (BDS).

Diez, Octavio. Fighters & Fighter Bombers. 2006. (Aircraft Ser.). (ENG., Illus.). 96p. pap. 24.95 *(978-84-933924-9-9(9))* Udyat, S.L. ESP. Dist: Independent Pubs. Group.

Dinan, Tim. He 177 Greif: Design, Production, Operations. 2011. (Tech Ser.). (ENG., Illus.). 386p. ***(978-91-85657-97-1(2))*** Leandoer & Ekholm Förlag.

Espejo, Roman. What Motivates Suicide Bombers? 2009. (At ISSUE Ser.). (ENG.). 128p. pap. 22.50 *(978-0-7377-4449-1(9))*; (Illus.). pap. 31.80 *(978-0-7377-4448-4(0))* Cengage Gale. (Greenhaven Pr., Inc.).

Fernando, Jeremy. The Suicide Bomber; & Her Gift of Death. Schirmacher, Wolfgang, ed. 2010. 290p. pap. 21.95 *(978-0-9825309-6-2(X))* Atropos Pr.

Fildes, David W. Avro Vulcan: Design & Development. 2011. (Illus.). 328p. 60.00 ***(978-1-84884-284-7(8))*** Pen & Sword Bks. Ltd. GBR. Dist: Casemate Pubs. & Bk. Distributors, LLC.

Film.com, Periscope. B-17 Bomber Pilot's Flight Operating Manual. 2007. 175p. pap. 24.95 *(978-1-4116-8725-7(6))* Lulu Enterprises Inc.

Forsyth, Robert. Fw 190 Sturmbock vs B-17: Europe 1944-45. 2009. (Duel Ser.). (ENG., Illus.). 80p. pap. 17.95 *(978-1-84603-941-6(X))* Osprey Publishing, Ltd. GBR. Dist: Random Hse., Inc.

Gardiner, Ian. Flatpack Bombers: The Royal Navy & the Zeppelin Menace. 2009. (Illus.). 176p. 39.99 *(978-1-84884-071-3(3))* Pen & Sword Bks. Ltd. GBR. Dist: Casemate Pubs. & Bk. Distributors, LLC.

Gibson, Chris. Vulcan's Hammer: V-Force Projects & Weapons Since 1945. 2011. (Illus.). 192p. ***(978-1-902109-17-6(1))*** Hikoki Pubns.

Gordon, Yefim. Tupolev Tu-95/142. 2010. (ENG., Illus.). 416p. 94.95 *(978-1-85780-310-5(8))* Allan, Ian Publishing GBR. Dist: BookMasters Distribution Services (BDS).

Gordon, Yefim & Buttler, Tony. Soviet Secret Projects Bombers Since 1945, Vol. 1. 2010. (ENG., Illus.). 176p. 44.95 *(978-1-85780-194-1(6))* Allan, Ian Publishing GBR. Dist: BookMasters Distribution Services (BDS).

Gordon, Yefim & Davison, Peter. Tupolev Tu-95 Bear, Vol. 43. 2006. (Warbird Tech Ser.: Vol. 43). (ENG., Illus.). 108p. pap. 16.95 *(978-1-58007-102-4(3), 1258145)* Specialty Pr. Pubs. & Wholesalers, Inc.

Gordon, Yefim & Dexter, Keith. Sukhoi Su-24 Fencer: Soviet Swing-Wing Bomber. 2010. (Aerofax Ser.). (ENG., Illus.). 159p. pap. 36.95 *(978-1-85780-202-3(0))* Allan, Ian Publishing GBR. Dist: BookMasters Distribution Services (BDS).

Greenburg, Michael M. The Mad Bomber of New York: The Extraordinary True Story of the Manhunt That Paralyzed a City. 2011. (Illus.). 336p. 22.95 *(978-1-4027-7434-8(6))* Union Square Pr.

Hassan, Riaz. Life As a Weapon: The Global Rise of Suicide Bombings. 2010. (ENG., Illus.). 288p. (C). 165.00 *(978-0-415-58885-0(5), Routledge)* Taylor & Francis Group GBR. Dist: Taylor & Francis Group.

Hoffman, Richard Alden. The Fighting Flying Boat: A History of the Martin PBM Mariner. (Illus.). 272p. 36.95 *(978-1-59114-375-8(6))* Naval Institute Pr.

Jenkins, Dennis R. Magnesium Overcast: The Story of the Convair B-36. rev. ed. 2008. (Illus.). 230p. pap. 28.95 *(978-1-58007-129-1(5))* Specialty Pr. Pubs. & Wholesalers, Inc.

Jenkins, Dennis R. & Landis, Tony R. Valkyrie: North American's Mach 3 Superbomber. rev. ed. 2008. (Illus.). 246p. pap. 28.95 *(978-1-58007-130-7(9))* Specialty Pr. Pubs. & Wholesalers, Inc.

Jones, Barry. V-Bombers. 2007. (Illus.). 200p. pap. 34.95 *(978-1-86126-945-4(5))* Crowood Pr., Ltd. GBR. Dist: MBI Distribution Services/Quayside Distribution.

Kobrin, Nancy Hartevelt. The Banality of Suicide Terrorism: The Naked Truth about the Psychology of Islamic Suicide Bombing. 2010. 192p. 24.95 *(978-1-59797-504-9(4))* Potomac Bks., Inc.

Kotelnikov, V. R. Krasnozvezdnye "Amerikantsy" Stalina: A-20 "Boston", Shturmoviki, Bombardirovshchiki, Torpedonostsy, Istrebiteli. 2010. (Illus.). 127p. *(978-5-699-45013-8(0))* Dksmo-Press, Izdatel'skaja firma.

Lake, Jon & Brookes, Andrew. Vulcan Units of the Cold War. 2009. (Combat Aircraft Ser.). (ENG., Illus.). 96p. pap. 22.95 *(978-1-84603-297-4(0))* Osprey Publishing, Ltd. GBR. Dist: Random Hse., Inc.

Langenfeld, Robert E. & Langenfeld, Robert. A Young Man's Letters from World War II: "More Than Becoming a Soldier" 2011. (Illus.). 234p. ***(978-0-944318-39-3(8))*** ELT Pr.

Lemay, Curtis E, et al. Superfortress: The Boeing B-29 & American Airpower in World War II. 2006. (Illus.). 224p. per. 19.95 *(978-1-59416-039-4(2))* Westholme Publishing.

Listemann, Phil. Martin Marauder Mk. I. 2008. pap. 20.95 *(978-2-9526381-6-6(0))* Listemann, Philippe FRA. Dist: Casemate Pubs. & Bk. Distributors, LLC.

LoCicero, Alice & Sinclair, Samuel J. Creating Young Martyrs: Conditions That Make Dying in a Terrorist Attack Seem Like a Good Idea, 1 vol. 2008. (Contemporary Psychology Ser.). 148p. 39.95 *(978-0-275-99690-1(5), C9690, Praeger Security International)* Greenwood Publishing Group, Inc.

Lockett, Brian. Flying Aircraft Carriers of the USAF: Mcdonnell XF-85 Goblin. 2009. 52p. pap. 16.95 *(978-0-578-03481-2(6))* Lockett, Brian.

—Flying Aircraft Carriers of the USAF: Wing Tip Coupling. 2009. 100p. pap. 21.95 *(978-0-578-03186-6(8))* Lockett, Brian.

Mann, Robert A. The B-29 Superfortress: A Comprehensive Registry of the Planes & Their Missions. alt. ed. 2009. (ENG.). 288p. pap. 39.95 *(978-0-7864-4458-8(4))* McFarland & Co., Inc. Pubs.

Marvasti, Jamshid A., ed. Psycho-Political Aspects of Suicide Warriors, Terrorism & Martyrdom: A Critical View from Both Sides in Regard to Cause & Cure. 2008. (American Series in Behavioral Science & Law). 374p. 73.95 *(978-0-398-07802-7(5))*; pap. 53.95 *(978-0-398-07803-4(3))* Thomas, Charles C. Pub., Ltd.

McDonough, James L. The Wars of Myron King: A B-17 Pilot Faces WWII & U.S.-Soviet Intrigue. 2009. (ENG.). 32.95 *(978-1-57233-675-9(7))* Univ. of Tennessee Pr.

McLelland, Tim. The Avro Vulcan. 2009. (Illus.). 336p. 49.95 *(978-0-85979-127-4(0))* Crecy Publishing GBR. Dist: Partners Pubs. Group, Inc.

McLelland, Tim. The Victor Story. 2012. (Story Ser.). (ENG., Illus.). 128p. 14.95 ***(978-0-7524-6314-8(4))*** History Pr. Ltd., The GBR. Dist: Independent Pubs. Group.

Merrick, K. A. Handley Page Halifax: From Hell to Victory & Beyond. 2009. (ENG., Illus.). 224p. 56.95 *(978-1-906537-06-7(2))* Allan, Ian Publishing GBR. Dist: BookMasters Distribution Services (BDS).

Miller, Debra A. Suicide Bombers. 2006. (Lucent Terrorism Library). (ENG., Illus.). 96p. (YA). (gr. 8-12). lib. bdg. 30.85 *(978-1-59018-748-7(2), Lucent Bks.)* Cengage Gale.

Mower, Mark. Zeppelin over Suffolk. 2009. pap. 25.99 *(978-1-84415-737-2(7))* Pen & Sword Bks. Ltd. GBR. Dist: Casemate Pubs. & Bk. Distributors, LLC.

Navy, United States & Aircraft, McDonnell. F-4 Phantom II Pilot's Flight Operating Manual. 2010. 602p. pap. 49.95 *(978-1-935700-41-8(3))* Periscope Film, LLC.

Norton, Bill. American Bomber Aircraft Development in World War 2. 2012. (ENG., Illus.). 224p. 39.95 *(978-1-85780-330-3(2))* Allan, Ian Publishing GBR. Dist: BookMasters Distribution Services (BDS).

Page, Charles. Wings of Destiny: Wing Commander Charles Learmonth DFC & Bar, & the Air War in New Guinea. 2008. (Illus.). 416p. pap. 35.00 *(978-1-877058-64-6(5))* Rosenberg Publishing Pty, Ltd. AUS. Dist: International Specialized Bk. Services.

Panek, Robert. Henschel Hs 123. 2012. (Illus.). 160p. pap. 38.00 ***(978-83-61421-48-1(3))*** Stratus, Wydawnictwo, Juszczak, Artur POL. Dist: Casemate Pubs. & Bk. Distributors, LLC.

Peczkowski, Robert. Douglas & Dauntless. 2007. (Illus.). 128p. pap. *(978-83-89450-39-5(9))* Stratus, Wydawnictwo, Juszczak, Artur.

Polmar, Norman & Norris, Robert S. The U. S. Nuclear Arsenal: A History of Weapons & Delivery Systems since 1945. 2009. (Illus.). 240p. 49.95 *(978-1-55750-681-8(7))* Naval Institute Pr.

Pyeatt, Don. B-36 Saving the Last Peacemaker Third Edition: An epic story of saving the last B-36. 3rd ed. 2006. cd-rom *(978-0-9677593-2-6(3))* ProWeb Fort Worth.

Pyeatt, Don & Jenkins, Dennis R. Convair B-36 Peacemaker. 2010. 228p. 32.95 *(978-1-58007-127-7(9))* Specialty Pr. Pubs. & Wholesalers, Inc.

Rehr, Louis S. & Rehr, Carleton R. Marauder: Memoir of a B-26 Pilot in Europe in World War II. alt. l.t. ed. 2009. (ENG.). 353p. pap. 39.95 *(978-0-7864-4367-3(7))* McFarland & Co., Inc. Pubs.

Reshetnikov, Vasily, et al. Bomber Pilot on the Eastern Front: 307 Missions Behind Enemy Lines. 2008. (Illus.). 224p. 39.95 *(978-1-84415-660-3(5))* Pen & Sword Bks. Ltd. GBR. Dist: Casemate Pubs. & Bk. Distributors, LLC.

Robinson, Ian. Home Is the Halifax: An Extraordinary Account of Re-Building a Classic Wwii Bomber & Creating the Yorkshire Air Museum to House It. 2010. (Illus.). 160p. 39.95 *(978-1-906502-77-5(3))* Grub Street GBR. Dist: Casemate Pubs. & Bk. Distributors, LLC.

Ryon, Edward L. Bombs Away! My Life & Training as a B-26 Pilot. 2007. (Illus.). 148p. 29.95 *(978-0-9793712-6-4(0))* Waldenhouse Pubs., Inc.

Samuel, Wolfgang W. E. Glory Days: The Untold Story of the Men who Flew the B-66 Destroyer into the Face of Fear. 2008. (Illus.). 464p. bds. 35.00 *(978-0-7643-3086-5(1))* Schiffer Publishing, Ltd.

Sandall, Howard J. We Wage War by Night: An Operational & Photographic History of No. 622 Squadron RAF Bomber Command. 2011. (Illus.). 336p. 69.99 *(978-0-7643-3814-4(5))* Schiffer Publishing, Ltd.

Semple, Clive. The Blazing Trail. 2012. (Illus.). 256p. 39.95 ***(978-1-84884-657-9(6))*** Pen & Sword Bks. Ltd. GBR. Dist: Casemate Pubs. & Bk. Distributors, LLC.

Semple, Clive & Mawby, Alan. Diary of a Night Bomber in World War I. 2008. (ENG., Illus.). 352p. 39.95 *(978-1-86227-452-5(5))* History Pr. Ltd., The GBR. Dist: Independent Pubs. Group.

Simons, Graham M. Valkyrie: The North American XB-70. 2011. (Illus.). 256p. 39.95 ***(978-1-84884-546-6(4))*** Pen & Sword Bks. Ltd. GBR. Dist: Casemate Pubs. & Bk. Distributors, LLC.

Slongo, Ludovico & Gustavsson, Hakan. Fiat CR. 42 Aces of World War 2. 2009. (Aircraft of the Aces Ser.). (ENG., Illus.). 96p. pap. 22.95 *(978-1-84603-427-5(2))* Osprey Publishing, Ltd. GBR. Dist: Random Hse., Inc.

Smith, Peter C. The History of Dive-Bombing: A Comprehensive History from 1911 Onward. 2007. (Illus.). 245p. 39.95 *(978-1-84415-592-7(7))* Pen & Sword Bks. Ltd. GBR. Dist: Casemate Pubs. & Bk. Distributors, LLC.

—Torpedo Bombers. 2007. (Illus.). 256p. 26.95 *(978-1-84415-607-8(9))* Pen & Sword Bks. Ltd. GBR. Dist: Casemate Pubs. & Bk. Distributors, LLC.

Stankey, Douglas G. & deZeng, Henry L., IV. Dive Bomber & Ground Attack Units of the Luftwaffe, 1933-1945, Vol. 2. 2012. (ENG., Illus.). 192p. 49.95 *(978-1-906537-09-8(7))* Classic Pubns. GBR. Dist: BookMasters Distribution Services (BDS).

Stapfer, Hans-Heiri. B-26 Marauder. 2008. (Illus.). 59p. *(978-0-89747-549-5(6))* Squadron Signal Pubns.

Thomas, Andrew. Defiant, Blenheim & Havoc Aces. 2012. (Aircraft of the Aces Ser.). (ENG., Illus.). 96p. pap. 22.95 ***(978-1-84908-666-0(4))*** Osprey Publishing, Ltd. GBR. Dist: Random Hse., Inc.

Thomason, Tommy H. Strike from the Sea: U. S. Navy Attack Aircraft from Skyraider to Super Hornet, 1948-Present. 2009. (Illus.). 228p. 46.95 *(978-1-58007-132-1(5))* Specialty Pr. Pubs. & Wholesalers, Inc.

Thorning, Arthur G. The Dambuster Who Cracked the Dam: The story of Melvin 'Dinghy' Young. 2008. (Illus.). 192p. 39.95 *(978-1-84415-667-2(2))* Pen & Sword Bks. Ltd. GBR. Dist: Casemate Pubs. & Bk. Distributors, LLC.

Vancata, Pavel. 311 Squadron RAF. 2011. (Illus.). 128p. pap. 27.00 ***(978-83-61421-43-6(2))*** Stratus, Wydawnictwo, Juszczak, Artur POL. Dist: Casemate Pubs. & Bk. Distributors, LLC.

Vilens, Alexander. Terror & Suicide. Sher, Leo, ed. 2010. (Terrorism, Hot Spots & Conflict-Related Issues Ser.). 175p. 79.00 *(978-1-60876-103-6(7))* Nova Science Pubs., Inc.

Walsh, Thomas L. Damnyankee: A WWII Story of Tragedy & Survival off the West of Ireland. 2008. 180p. pap. 17.95 *(978-1-4327-2910-3(1))* Outskirts Pr., Inc.

Warrick, Joby. The Triple Agent: The al-Qaeda Mole who Infiltrated the CIA. 2012. (ENG., Illus.). 288p. pap. 15.95 ***(978-0-307-74231-5(8)***, Vintage) Knopf Doubleday Publishing Group.

Weekley, Harold D. & Zazas, James B. The Last of Combat B-17 Drivers. 60th ed. 2006. (Illus.). 334p. 39.95 *(978-0-9785980-1-3(6))* Flying Fortress International.

Windle, Dave & Bowman, Martin. Profiles of Flight series: V Bombers: Vulcan, Valiant & Victor. 2009. (Illus.). 80p. 39.99 *(978-1-84415-827-0(6))* Pen & Sword Bks. Ltd. GBR. Dist: Casemate Pubs. & Bk. Distributors, LLC.

Wolf, William. Douglas B-18 Bolo: The Ultimate Look: from Drawing Board to U-Boat Hunter. 2007. (Illus.). 216p. 59.95 *(978-0-7643-2581-6(7))* Schiffer Publishing, Ltd.

—North American B-25 Mitchell: The Ultimate Look: from Drawing Board to Flying Arsenal. 2008. (Illus.). 336p. bds. 69.95 *(978-0-7643-2930-2(8))* Schiffer Publishing, Ltd.

Wragg, David. Bombers: From the First World War to Kosovo. 2010. (ENG., Illus.). 288p. pap. 39.95 *(978-0-7524-5202-9(9))* History Pr. Ltd., The GBR. Dist: Independent Pubs. Group.

Yancey, Diane. The Unabomber. 2007. (Crime Scene Investigations Ser.). (ENG., Illus.). 104p. (YA). (gr. 7-12). lib. bdg. 33.45 *(978-1-59018-992-4(2))* Cengage Gale.

Zeng, Henry & Stankey, Douglas G. Dive-Bomber & Ground-Attack Units of the Luftwaffe, 1933-1945, Vol. 1. 2010. (ENG., Illus.). 208p. 49.95 *(978-1-906537-08-1(9))* Allan, Ian Publishing GBR. Dist: BookMasters Distribution Services (BDS).

BOMBING, AERIAL

Here are entered works on military bombardments by means of bombs dropped from the air. Works on sustained military attacks on cities, military positions, etc., with bombs, shells, rockets, or other explosive missiles are entered under Bombardment. Works on the use of explosive devices for the purposes of political terrorism, protest, etc., are entered under Bombings.

see also subdivision Aerial Operations under individual wars, e.g. World War, 1939-1945—Aerial Operations

Arnold, Jörg. The Allied Air War & Urban Memory: The Legacy of Strategic Bombing in Germany. 2011. (Studies in the Social & Cultural History of Modern Warfare Ser.). (ENG., Illus.). 400p. 105.00 *(978-1-107-00496-2(9))* Cambridge Univ. Pr.

Baldoli, Claudia & Knapp, Andrew. Forgotten Blitzes: France & Italy under Allied Air Attack, 1940-1945. 2012. (ENG., Illus.). 312p. 120.00 *(978-1-4411-3109-6(4))*; pap. 34.95 *(978-1-4411-8581-5(X))* Continuum International Publishing Group, Ltd. GBR. Dist: National Bk. Network.

Bright, Paul. Air War over East Yorkshire in World War II. 2006. (ENG., Illus.). 176p. pap. 44.95 *(978-0-9545605-7-7(4))* Flight Recorder Pubns. Ltd. GBR. Dist: MBI Distribution Services/Quayside Distribution.

Call, Steve. Danger Close: Tactical Air Controllers in Afghanistan & Iraq. 2007. (Williams-Ford Texas A&M University Military History Ser.). (ENG., Illus.). 272p. 50.00 *(978-1-58544-624-7(6))* Texas A&M Univ. Pr.

Castle, Ian. London 1917-18: The Bomber Blitz. 2010. (Campaign Ser.). (ENG., Illus.). 96p. pap. 19.95 *(978-1-84603-682-8(8))* Osprey Publishing, Ltd. GBR. Dist: Random Hse., Inc.

Claringbould, Michael J., et al. Rampage of the Roarin' Twenties: The Illustrated History of the 312th Bombardment Group During WWII. 2009. (Eagles over the Pacific Ser.: Vol. 4). (ENG., Illus.). 408p. *(978-0-913511-03-9(X))*, International Historical Research Assocs.) Forty-Five LLC.

Clodfelter, Mark. Beneficial Bombing: The Progressive Foundations of American Air Power, 1917-1945. 2011. (Studies in War, Society, & the Militar Ser.). (ENG., Illus.). 392p. 40.00 *(978-0-8032-3398-0(1))* Univ. of Nebraska Pr.

Cotkin, George. Morality's Muddy Waters: Ethical Quandaries in Modern America. 2010. 304p. 29.95 *(978-0-8122-4227-0(0))* Univ. of Pennsylvania Pr.

De Decker, Cynrik & Roba, Jean-Louis. Doelwit Leuven: De Luchanvallen van 12 en 13 Mei 1944 en de Berging van een Halifax-Bommenwerper Bij Geraardsbergen. (DUT., Illus.). 224p. pap. 29.95 *(978-90-72547-61-3(6))* De Krijger BEL. Dist: Casemate Pubs. & Bk. Distributors, LLC.

Directing the Secretary of State to Transmit to the House of Representatives Copies of Any Document, Record, Memo, Correspondence, or Other Communication of the Department of State, or Any Portion of Such Communication, That Refers or Relates to Any Consultation with Congress Regarding Operation Odyssey Dawn or Military Actions in or Against Libya: Markup Before the Committee on Foreign Affairs, House of Representatives, One Hundred Twelfth Congress, First Session, on H. Res. 209, May 11, 2011. 2011. iii, 18p. ***(978-0-16-089215-8(5)***, 552-070-43212-4) United States Government Printing Office.

Ericson Wolke, Lars. "Bomba Och Bränn Dom" Taktik Och Terror under 100 år Av Flygkrig. 2009. (Illus.). 335p. *(978-91-85057-42-9(8))* Svenska Historiska media AB.

Friedrich, Jörg & Friedrich, Jorg. The Fire: The Bombing of Germany, 1940-1945. Brown, Allison, tr. from GER. 2008. (ENG., Illus.). 552p. (gr. 17). pap. 27.95 *(978-0-231-13381-4(2))* Columbia Univ. Pr.

Garlasco, Marc E. "Troops in Contact" Airstrikes & Civilian Deaths in Afghanistan. 2008. (Illus.). 40p. *(978-1-56432-362-0(5))* Human Rights Watch.

Grayzel, Susan R. At Home & under Fire: The Air Raid in Britain from the Great War to the Blitz. 2012. (ENG., Illus.). 334p. 99.00 ***(978-0-521-87494-6(7))*** Cambridge Univ. Pr.

Grosscup, Beau. Strategic Terror: The Politics & Ethics of Aerial Bombardment. 2006. (ENG.). 224p. 94.95 *(978-1-84277-542-4(1))*; per. 31.95 *(978-1-84277-543-1(X))* Zed Bks., Ltd. GBR. Dist: Macmillan.
Hansen, Randall. Fire & Fury: The Allied Bombing of Germany, 1942-1945. 2010. (ENG.). 368p. (gr. 12). 15.00 *(978-0-451-23008-9(6)*, N A L Trade) Penguin Group (USA) Inc.
Harmon, Christopher C. Are We Beasts? Churchill & the Moral Question of World War II Area Bombing. 2006. 35p. pap. 3.25 *(978-0-16-076995-5(7)*, Defense Dept.) United States Government Printing Office.
Hickey, James E. Precision-Guided Munitions & Human Suffering in War. 2012. ***(978-1-4094-2952-4(0))***; 200p. ***(978-1-4094-2951-7(2))*** Ashgate Publishing Co.
Iklé, Fred Charles. Annihilation from Within: The Ultimate Threat to Nations. 2006. (ENG.). 160p. (gr. 17). 27.50 *(978-0-231-13952-6(7))* Columbia Univ. Pr.
Irons, Roy. The Relentless Offensive: War & Bomber Command 1939 - 1945. 2009. (Illus.). 224p. 39.99 *(978-1-84415-819-5(5))* Pen & Sword Bks. Ltd. GBR. Dist: Casemate Pubs. & Bk. Distributors, LLC.
LaHurd, Christopher M. A Story of One: Walking the Path of a World War II Airman. 2009. 226p. 36.95 *(978-0-557-14713-7(1))*; pap. 21.95 *(978-0-557-14716-8(6))* Lulu Enterprises Inc.
Legacies of War: Unexploded Ordnance in Laos: Hearing Before the Subcommittee on Asia, the Pacific, & the Global Environment of the Committee on Foreign Affairs, House of Representatives, One Hundred Eleventh Congress, Second Session, April 22, 2010. 2010. (Illus.). iii, 127p. ***(978-0-16-087146-7(8)***, 552-070-41989-6) United States Government Printing Office.
Martel, Rene. French Strategic & Tactical Bombardment Forces of World War I. Suddaby, Allen, tr. from FRE. 2006. (ENG., Illus.). 504p. per. 70.00 *(978-0-8108-5662-2(X))* Scarecrow Pr., Inc.
McMahon, Sean. Bombs over Dublin. 2010. (ENG., Illus.). 128p. pap. 24.95 *(978-1-85607-983-9(X))* Curragh Pr. IRL. Dist: Dufour Editions, Inc.
Meurs, John, compiled by. Not Home for Christmas: A Day in the Life of the Mighty Eighth. 2009. *(978-1-934193-31-0(3))* Quail Ridge Pr., Inc.
Mrazek, Robert J. To Kingdom Come: An Epic Saga of Survival in the Air War over Germany. 2012. (ENG.). 400p. (gr. 12). 16.00 ***(978-0-451-23575-6(4)***, N A L Trade) Penguin Group (USA) Inc.
Nichol, John & Rennell, Tony. Tail-End Charlies: The Last Battles of the Bomber War, 1944-45. 2008. (ENG., Illus.). 440p. pap. 18.99 *(978-0-312-37806-6(8)*, St. Martin's Griffin) St. Martin's Pr.
No Foxholes in the Sky & Guns of Ploesti. 2006. (YA). per. *(978-1-59872-535-3(1))* Instant Pub.
O'Donnell, Joe. Japan 1945: A U. S. Marine's Photographs from Ground Zero. 2008. (ENG., Illus.). 104p. pap. 24.95 *(978-0-8265-1612-1(2))* Vanderbilt Univ. Pr.
Primoratz, Igor, ed. Terror from the Sky: The Bombing of German Cities in World War II. 2010. 256p. 90.00 *(978-1-84545-687-0(4))* Berghahn Bks., Inc.
Read, Simon. The Killing Skies. 2007. (ENG., Illus.). 256p. 35.00 *(978-1-86227-329-0(4)*, Spellmount, Limited Pubs.) History Pr. Ltd.,The GBR. Dist: Independent Pubs. Group.
Robert, Ehlers. Targeting the Third Reich. 2009. 432p. 39.95 *(978-0-7006-1682-4(9))* Univ. Pr. of Kansas.
Rowley, Esther & Folkes, John. Dogs, Goats, Bulbs & Bombs: An Exeter & Exmouth Wartime Diary. 2010. (ENG., Illus.). 224p. pap. 27.95 *(978-0-7524-4883-1(8))* History Pr. Ltd.,The GBR. Dist: Independent Pubs. Group.
Sion, Edward M. Through Blue Skies to Hell: America's Bloody 100th in the Air War over Germany. 2011. (Illus.). 256p. pap. 18.95 *(978-1-935149-87-3(3))* Casemate Pubs. & Bk. Distributors, LLC.
Steinbeck, John. Bombs Away: The Story of a Bomber Team. 2009. (ENG.). 192p. (gr. 12-18). 15.00 *(978-0-14-310591-6(4)*, Penguin Classics) Penguin Group (USA) Inc.
Tanaka, Yuki & Young, Marilyn B., eds. Bombing Civilians: A Twentieth-Century History. 2010. (ENG.). 304p. pap. 19.95 *(978-1-59558-547-9(8))* New Pr., The.
Todd, Walter C. Nozuru. 2011. 248p. pap. ***(978-3-8454-0746-3(8))*** Lambert Academic Publishing.
Torrie, Julia S. For Their Own Good: Civilian Evacuations in Germany & France, 1939-1945. 2010. (Illus.). 304p. 95.00 *(978-1-84545-725-9(0))* Berghahn Bks., Inc.
Turner Publishing Company Staff. 44th Bombardment Group: The Flying Eightballs. Date not set. 112p. 52.50 *(978-1-56311-271-3(X))* Turner Publishing Co.
Von Benda-Beckmann, Bas. A German Catastrophe? German historians & the Allied Bombings, 1945-2010. 2010. (UvA Proefschriften Ser.). 390p. pap. *(978-90-5629-653-7(1)*, Vossiupers UvA) Amsterdam Univ. Pr.
Wilson, Donald E. The Alabama Bomber Boys: Unlocking Memories of Alabamians Who Bombed the Third Reich. 2008. (Illus.). xvii, 162p. *(978-0-7884-7265-7(8))*; 180p. pap. 21.00 *(978-0-7884-4682-5(7))* Heritage Bks.
Wilson, Kevin. Bomber Boys: The Ruhr, the Dambusters & Bloody Berlin. 2006. (ENG., Illus.). 480p. pap. 12.95 *(978-0-304-36724-5(9))* Casemate Pubs. & Bk. Distributors, LLC.
Wolk, Herman S. Cataclysm: General Hap Arnold & the Defeat of Japan. 2010. (ENG., Illus.). 344p. 24.95 *(978-1-57441-281-9(7))* Univ. of North Texas Pr.
Wragg, David. Bombers: From the First World War to Kosovo. 2010. (ENG., Illus.). 288p. pap. 39.95 *(978-0-7524-5202-9(9))* History Pr. Ltd.,The GBR. Dist: Independent Pubs. Group.
Young, Marilyn B. & Tanaka, Yuki, eds. Bombing Civilians: A Twentieth-Century History. 2009. (ENG., Illus.). 291p. 30.00 *(978-1-59558-363-5(7)*, 955363) New Pr., The.

BOMBING INVESTIGATION

Basic Weapon Retention for Law Enforcement & Security Officers. 2007. 8.00 *(978-0-9793293-5-7(3))* Pro-Bushi Publishing.
Casil, Amy Sterling. Bomb Scares. 2008. (Violence & Society Ser.). (Illus.). 64p. (YA). (gr. 9-12). lib. bdg. 29.25 *(978-1-4042-1791-1(6))* Rosen Publishing Group, Inc., The.
Dornstein, Ken. The Boy Who Fell Out of the Sky: A True Story. 2007. (Vintage Ser.). (ENG.). 352p. pap. 13.95 *(978-0-375-70769-8(7)*, Vintage) Knopf Doubleday Publishing Group.
Ellis, John W. Police Analysis & Planning for Homicide Bombings: Prevention, Defense, & Response (2nd Ed.) 2nd ed. 2007. 372p. *(978-0-398-07719-8(3))*; pap. *(978-0-398-07720-4(7))* Thomas, Charles C. Pub., Ltd.
Ferguson, Amanda. The Attack on U. S. Servicemen in Saudi Arabia on June 25 1996. 2009. (Terrorist Attacks Ser.). 64p. (gr. 5-5). 58.50 *(978-1-60853-313-8(1))* Rosen Publishing Group, Inc., The.
Gerstein, Ted & Esposito, Richard. Bomb Squad: A Year Inside the Nation's Most Exclusive Police Unit. 2007. (Illus.). 352p. 24.95 *(978-1-4013-0152-1(5))* Hyperion Pr.
Gumbel, Andrew & Charles, Roger G. Oklahoma City: What the Investigation Missed — And Why It Still Matters. 2012. pap. ***(978-0-06-198645-1(3)***, Morrow, William & Co.); E-Book ***(978-0-06-210092-4(0)***, Morrow, William & Co.); (ENG.). 448p. pap. 27.99 ***(978-0-06-210710-7(0)***, HarperLuxe) HarperCollins Pubs.
Jamieson, Perry D. Khobar Towers: Tragedy & Response: Tragedy & Response. 2008. (ENG., Illus.). 302p. pap. 29.00 *(978-0-16-080701-5(8)*, Dept. of the Air Force) United States Government Printing Office.
Recent Inspector General Reports Concerning the FBI: Hearing Before the Subcommittee on Crime, Terrorism, & Homeland Security of the Committee on the Judiciary, House of Representatives, One Hundred Eleventh Congress, Second Session, February 24, 2010. 2010. (Illus.). iii, 447p. *(978-0-16-086752-1(5)*, 552-070-41674-9) United States Government Printing Office.
Spahr, Lisa L. Patrol-Level Response to a Suicide Bomb Threat: Guidelines for Consideration. 2007. 15.00 *(978-1-934485-01-9(2))* Police Executive Research Forum.
Thurman, James T. Practical Bomb Scene Investigation. 2nd rev. ed. 2011. (Practical Aspects of Criminal & Forensic Investigations Ser.). (ENG., Illus.). 519p. 99.95 *(978-1-4398-1959-3(9)*, Taylor & Francis) Taylor & Francis Group GBR. Dist: Taylor & Francis Group.
Vollers, Maryanne. Lone Wolf: Eric Rudolph & the Legacy of American Terror. 2007. (Illus.). 384p. per. 14.95 *(978-0-06-059863-1(8)*, HarperPerennial) HarperCollins Pubs.
—Lone Wolf: Eric Rudolph: Murder, Myth, & the Pursuit of an American Outlaw. 2006. (Illus.). 368p. 25.95 *(978-0-06-059862-4(X))* HarperCollins Pubs.
Whatley, Bruce, et al. Oklahoma City: What the Investigation Missed — And Why It Still Matters. 2012. (ENG.). 352p. 27.99 ***(978-0-06-198644-4(5)***, Morrow, William & Co.) HarperCollins Pubs.
Yancey, Diane. The Unabomber. 2007. (Crime Scene Investigations Ser.). (ENG., Illus.) 104p. (YA). (gr. 7-12). lib. bdg. 33.45 *(978-1-59018-992-4(2))* Cengage Gale.

BOMBING OF PAN AM FLIGHT 103, 1988

see Pan Am Flight 103 Bombing Incident, 1988

BOMBINGS

Here are entered works on the use of explosive devices for the purpose of political terrorism, protests, etc. Works on sustained military attacks on cities, military positions, etc., with bombs, shells, rockets or other explosive missiles are entered under Bombardment. Works on military bombardments by means of bombs dropped from the air are entered under Bombing, Aerial.

see also Bombs; Oklahoma City Federal Building Bombing, Oklahoma City, Okla., 1995, Pan Am Flight 103 Bombing Incident, 1988

Abufarha, Nasser. The Making of a Human Bomb: An Ethnography of Palestinian Resistance. 2009. (Cultures & Practice of Violence Ser.). (ENG., Illus.). 288p. 84.95 *(978-0-8223-4428-5(9))*; pap. 23.95 *(978-0-8223-4439-1(4))* Duke Univ. Pr.
Berger, Arthur Asa & Bukay, David. From Muhammad to Bin Laden: Religious & Ideological Sources of the Homicide Bombers Phenomenon. 2007. (ENG.) 377p. (gr. 11). 49.95 *(978-0-7658-0390-0(9))* Transaction Pubs.
Bernstein, Arnie. Bath Massacre: America's First School Bombing. 2009. (ENG., Illus.) 216p. pap. 18.95 *(978-0-472-03346-1(8))* Univ. of Michigan Pr.
Blum, Howard. American Lightning: Terror, Mystery, & the Birth of Hollywood. (ENG., Illus.). 352p. 2009. pap. 15.00 *(978-0-307-34695-7(1)*, Three Rivers Pr.) 2008. 24.95 *(978-0-307-34694-0(3)*, Crown) Crown Publishing Group.
Capan, Ergun, ed. Terror & Suicide Attacks: An Islamic Perspective. 2008. (FRE, GER, RUS & ENG.). 155p. pap. 11.50 *(978-1-932099-74-4(3))* Tughra Bks.
—Terrorismo y Ataques Suicidas: Una Perspectiva Islamica. Laraki, Ali, tr. 2007. (ENG.). 146p. per. 12.95 *(978-1-932099-82-9(4))* Tughra Bks.
Copeland, Thomas E. Fool Me Twice: Intelligence Failure & Mass Casualty Terrorism. 2007. 292p. *(978-90-04-15845-0(6))* BRILL.
Cornell, Svante E., et al. The August 2007 Bombing Incident in Georgia: Implications for the Euro-Atlantic Region. 2007. (Illus.). 81p. *(978-91-85473-43-4(X))* Indonesian Society for Democracy and Peace, ISDP.
Debnam, Aaron. One Morning in July: The Man Who Was First on the Scene Tells His Story about the Day That Changed London Forever. 2007. (ENG., Illus.). 273p. 24.95 *(978-1-84454-449-3(4))* Blake, John Publishing, Ltd. GBR. Dist: Independent Pubs. Group.
Dzikansky, Mordecai, et al. Terrorist Suicide Bombings. 2011. (ENG., Illus.). 342p. 79.95 ***(978-1-4398-7131-7(0)***, CRC Press) Taylor & Francis Group GBR. Dist: Taylor & Francis Group.
Edwards, Ruth Dudley. Aftermath: The Omagh Bombing & the Families' Pursuit of Justice. (ENG., Illus.). 2010. 400p. pap. 14.95 *(978-0-09-947217-9(1))* 2009. 384p. pap. 24.95 *(978-0-436-20599-6(8))* Random Hse. GBR. Dist: Independent Pubs. Group.
Fulton, Kevin. Unsung Hero: How I Saved Dozens of Lives as a Secret Agent Inside the IRA. 2008. (ENG., Illus.). 288p. pap. 15.95 *(978-1-84454-552-0(0))* Blake, John Publishing, Ltd. GBR. Dist: Independent Pubs. Group.
Golenbock, Peter & Curtis, Tony. American Prince: A Memoir. 2009. (ENG., Illus.). 384p. pap. 15.00 *(978-0-307-40856-3(6)*, Three Rivers Pr.) Crown Publishing Group.
Granot, Hayim & Levinson, Jay. Terror Bombing: The Global Urban Threat. 2009. 193p. pap. 50.00 *(978-0-9782526-1-8(6))* Key Publishing Hse., Inc., The CAN. Dist: AtlasBooks Distribution.
Greene, Melissa Fay. The Temple Bombing. 2006. (ENG., Illus.). 514p. per. 21.00 *(978-0-306-81518-8(4))* Da Capo Pr., Inc.
Gumbel, Andrew & Charles, Roger G. Oklahoma City: What the Investigation Missed — And Why It Still Matters. 2012. pap. ***(978-0-06-198645-1(3)***, Morrow, William & Co.); E-Book ***(978-0-06-210092-4(0)***, Morrow, William & Co.); (ENG.). 448p. pap. 27.99 ***(978-0-06-210710-7(0)***, HarperLuxe) HarperCollins Pubs.
Haerens, Margaret, ed. Suicide. 2011. (Global Viewpoints Ser.). (Illus.). 224p. (ENG.). pap. 26.50 *(978-0-7377-5665-4(9)*, Greenhaven Pr., Inc.); (YA). (gr. 9-12). 38.45 *(978-0-7377-5664-7(0))* Cengage Gale.
Hafez, Mohammed M. Suicide Bombers in Iraq: The Strategy & Ideology of Martyrdom. 2007. (Illus.). 285p. per. 17.50 *(978-1-60127-004-7(6))* U. S. Institute of Peace Pr. (USIP Pr.).
Hassan, Riaz. Life As a Weapon: The Global Rise of Suicide Bombings. 2010. (ENG., Illus.). 288p. (C). 165.00 *(978-0-415-58885-0(5)*, Routledge) Taylor & Francis Group GBR. Dist: Taylor & Francis Group.
—Suicide Bombings. 2011. (Short Cuts Ser.). (ENG., Illus.). 128p. (C). 104.00 *(978-0-415-58886-7(3))*; pap. 33.95 *(978-0-415-58887-4(1))* Routledge.
Henningfeld, Diane Andrews, ed. The Oklahoma City Bombing. 2012. (Perspectives on Modern World History Ser.). (ENG., Illus.). 224p. (gr. 10-12). lib. bdg. 41.70 ***(978-0-7377-5796-5(5)***, Greenhaven Pr., Inc.) Cengage Gale.
Hicks, Gill. One Unknown: A Powerful Account of Survival & One Woman's Inspirational Journey to a New Life. 2007. (ENG., Illus.). 244p. 27.95 *(978-1-4050-9989-9(5))* Macmillan Pubs., Ltd. GBR. Dist: Independent Pubs. Group.
—One Unknown: A powerful account of survival & one woman's inspirational journey to a new Life. 2008. (ENG., Illus.). 244p. pap. 15.95 *(978-1-905744-14-5(5))* Macmillan Pubs., Ltd. GBR. Dist: Independent Pubs. Group.
Inskeep, Steve. Instant City: Life & Death in Karachi. 2012. (ENG., Illus.). 304p. (gr. 12). pap. 16.00 ***(978-0-14-312216-6(9)***, Penguin (Non-Classics)) Penguin Group (USA) Inc.
Kobrin, Nancy Hartevelt. The Banality of Suicide Terrorism: The Naked Truth about the Psychology of Islamic Suicide Bombing. 2010. 192p. 24.95 *(978-1-59797-504-9(4))* Potomac Bks., Inc.
Kohler, Benjamin P. Dirty Bombs: Elements, Prevention & Response. 2012. ***(978-1-62100-234-5(9))*** Nova Science Pubs., Inc.
Kollerstrom, Nick. Terror on the Tube: Behind the Veil of 7/7, an Investigation. 2009. (Illus.). 292p. pap. 17.77 *(978-1-61577-007-6(0))* Progressive Pr.
Levitt, Matthew. Hamas: Politics, Charity, & Terrorism in the Service of Jihad. 2007. (ENG., Illus.). 336p. per. 18.00 *(978-0-300-12258-9(6))* Yale Univ. Pr.
Marvasti, Jamshid A., ed. Psycho-Political Aspects of Suicide Warriors, Terrorism & Martyrdom: A Critical View from Both Sides in Regard to Cause & Cure. 2008. (American Series in Behavioral Science & Law). 374p. 73.95 *(978-0-398-07802-7(5))*; pap. 53.95 *(978-0-398-07803-4(3))* Thomas, Charles C. Pub., Ltd.
Merriman, John. The Dynamite Club: How a Bombing in Fin-de-Siècle Paris Ignited the Age of Modern Terror. 2009. (ENG., Illus.). 224p. 26.00 *(978-0-618-55598-7(6))* Houghton Mifflin Harcourt Trade & Reference Pubs.
Miller, Debra A. Suicide Bombers. 2006. (Lucent Terrorism Library). (ENG., Illus.). 96p. (YA). (gr. 8-12). lib. bdg. 30.85 *(978-1-59018-748-7(2)*, Lucent Bks.) Cengage Gale.
Moghadam, Assaf. The Globalization of Martyrdom: Al Qaeda, Salafi Jihad, & the Diffusion of Suicide Attacks. (ENG., Illus.). 360p. (gr. 17). 2011. pap. 30.00 *(978-1-4214-0058-7(8))* 2008. 48.00 *(978-0-8018-9055-0(1))* Johns Hopkins Univ. Pr.
Mrazek, Robert J. To Kingdom Come: An Epic Saga of Survival in the Air War over Germany. 2011. (ENG.). 400p. (gr. 12). 25.95 *(978-0-451-23227-4(5)*, N A L Hardcover) Penguin Group (USA) Inc.
National Research Council (U.S.), Committee on Defeating Improvised Explosive Devices: basic research to interrupt the IED delivery chain Staff, et al, contrib. by. Countering the Threat of Improvised Explosive Devices: Basic Research Opportunities. 2007. (ENG., Illus.). 36p. pap. 21.00 *(978-0-309-10915-4(9))* National Academies Pr.
Newton, Michael. Bomb Squad. 2010. (Law Enforcement Agencies Ser.). 128p. (gr. 6-12). 35.00 *(978-1-60413-624-1(3)*, Chelsea Hse.) Facts On File, Inc.
Overy, Richard. Bombing, States & Peoples in Western Europe 1940-1945. Overy, Richard et al, eds. 2011. (ENG., Illus.). 376p. 120.00 *(978-1-4411-9254-7(9))*; pap. 34.95 *(978-1-4411-8568-6(2))* Continuum International Publishing Group, Ltd. GBR. Dist: National Bk. Network.
Pape, Robert A. & Feldman, James K. Cutting the Fuse: The Explosion of Global Suicide Terrorism & How to Stop It. (ENG.). 360p. 2012. pap. 20.00 ***(978-0-226-64565-0(7))*** 2010. (Illus.). 30.00 *(978-0-226-64560-5(6))* Univ. of Chicago Pr.
Pardoe, Blaine. Secret Witness: The Untold Story of the 1967 Bombing in Marshall, Michigan. 2012. (ENG.). 232p. 55.00 ***(978-0-472-11823-6(4))***; (Illus.). pap. 22.95 ***(978-0-472-03502-1(9))*** Univ. of Michigan Pr.
Pedahzur, Ami, ed. Root Causes of Suicide Terrorism: The Globalization of Martyrdom. 2006. (Political Violence Ser.). (Illus.). 202p. 170.00 *(978-0-415-77029-3(7))*; (ENG., 224p. per. 43.95 *(978-0-415-77030-9(0))* Routledge.
Read, Simon. The Killing Skies: RAF Bomber Command at War. 2009. (ENG., Illus.). 272p. pap. 29.95 *(978-1-86227-457-0(6))* History Pr. Ltd.,The GBR. Dist: Independent Pubs. Group.
Speirs, Dale. The History of Mail Bombs: A Philatelic & Historical Study. 2009. pap. *(978-1-61658-464-1(5))* Independent Pub.
Tanzilo, Robert. The Milwaukee Police Station Bombing of 1917. 2010. (True Crime Ser.). (ENG., Illus.). 160p. pap. 19.99 *(978-1-60949-067-6(3))* History Pr., The.
Tillman, Barrett. Whirlwind: The Air War Against Japan, 1942-1945. 2011. (ENG., Illus.). 336p. pap. 16.00 ***(978-1-4165-8441-4(2))*** Simon & Schuster.
United Nations. Report of the Ad Hoc Committee Established by General Assembly Resolution 51/210 of 17 December 1996 Fourteenth Session (12 to 16 April 2010) 2010. (ENG.). 20p. pap. 7.00 *(978-92-1-820164-5(6))* United Nations Pubns.
—Report of the Ad Hoc Committee Established by General Assembly Resolution 51/210 of 17 December 1996, Twelfth Session (25 & 26 February & 6 March 2008) 2008. (ENG.). 16p. pap. 5.00 *(978-92-1-820036-5(4))* United Nations Pubns.
Vollers, Maryanne. Lone Wolf: Eric Rudolph & the Legacy of American Terror. 2007. (Illus.). 384p. per. 14.95 *(978-0-06-059863-1(8)*, HarperPerennial) HarperCollins Pubs.
—Lone Wolf: Eric Rudolph: Murder, Myth, & the Pursuit of an American Outlaw. 2006. (Illus.). 368p. 25.95 *(978-0-06-059862-4(X))* HarperCollins Pubs.
Waring, Marilyn & Wakelam, Randall T. The Science of Bombing: Operational Research in RAF Bomber Command. 2009. (ENG.). 384p. *(978-0-8020-9936-5(X))* Univ. of Toronto Pr.
Whatley, Bruce, et al. Oklahoma City: What the Investigation Missed — And Why It Still Matters. 2012. (ENG.). 352p. 27.99 ***(978-0-06-198644-4(5)***, Morrow, William & Co.) HarperCollins Pubs.
White, Wayne. It Wasn't My Time. 2011. 112p. pap. 9.99 ***(978-1-257-11257-9(0))*** Lulu Enterprises Inc.
Williams, William A., et al. Preserving Range & Airspace Access for the Air Force Mission: Striving for a Strategic Vantage Point. 2011. (Illus.). 100p. pap. 29.50 *(978-0-8330-5140-0(7))* RAND Corp., The.
Yancey, Diane. The Unabomber. 2007. (Crime Scene Investigations Ser.). (ENG., Illus.). 104p. (YA). (gr. 7-12). lib. bdg. 33.45 *(978-1-59018-992-4(2))* Cengage Gale.
Yinon, Jehuda, ed. Counterterrorist Detection Techniques of Explosives. 2007. (ENG., Illus.). 454p. 107.00 *(978-0-444-52204-7(2)*, Elsevier Science) Elsevier Science & Technology Bks.

BOMBPROOF CONSTRUCTION

see Building, Bombproof

BOMBS

see also Atomic Bomb; Bomb Reconnaissance; Bombing, Aerial; Bombings; Guided Missiles; Hydrogen Bomb, Neutron Bomb

Ainslie, Graham M. Hand Grenades: A Handbook on Rifle & Hand Grenades. 1917. 2009. 68p. pap. *(978-1-84734-856-2(4))* Naval & Military Pr., The.
Breitegger, Alexander. Cluster Munitions & International Law. 2011. (Routledge Research in the Law of Armed Conflicts Ser.). (ENG., Illus.). 288p. (C). 135.00 *(978-0-415-66815-6(8))* Routledge.
Committee on Radiation Source Use and Replacement & National Research Council. Radiation Source Use & Replacement: Abbreviated Version. 2008. (ENG.). 232p. pap. 50.00 *(978-0-309-11014-3(9))* National Academies Pr.
Davis, Mike. Buda's Wagin. 2008. (ENG., Illus.). 224p. pap. 16.95 *(978-1-84467-294-3(8)*, 844294) Verso Bks. GBR. Dist: Norton, W. W. & Co., Inc.
Defeating the Improvised Explosive Device (IED) & Other Asymmetric Threats: Reviewing the Performance & Oversight of the Joint IED Defeat Organization (JIEDDO): Hearing Before the Oversight & Investigations Subcommittee of the Committee on Armed Services, House of Representatives, One Hundred Eleventh Congress, First Session, Hearing Held October 29, 2009. 2010. iii, 110p. *(978-0-16-085697-6(3)*, 552-070-40929-7) United States Government Printing Office.
Defeating the Improvised Explosive Device (IED) & Other Asymmetric Threats: Today's Efforts & Tomorrow's Requirements: Hearing Before the Oversight & Investigations Subcommittee of the Committee on Armed Services, House of Representatives, One Hundred Tenth Congress, Second Session, Hearing

Held September 16, 2008. 2009. iv, 67p. *(978-0-16-084904-6(7),* 552-070-40300-1) United States Government Printing Office.

Dirty Bomb Vulnerabilities: Fake Companies, Fake Licenses, Real Consequences: Hearing Before the Permanent Committee on Investigations of the Committee on Homeland Security & Governmental Affairs, United States Senate, One Hundred Tenth Congress, First Session, July 12, 2007. 2007. (Illus.). iii, 102p. *(978-0-16-079811-5(6),* 552-070-36716-1) United States Government Printing Office.

Flower, Stephen. Barnes Wallis' Bombs. 2010. (Illus.). 320p. pap. 34.95 *(978-1-84868-959-6(4))* Amberley Publishing GBR. Dist: Casemate Pubs. & Bk. Distributors, LLC.

Force Protection Equipment Programs for Operations in Iraq & Afghanistan: Joint Hearing Before the Seapower & Expeditionary Forces Subcommittee Meeting Jointly with Air & Land Forces Subcommittee of the Committee on Armed Services, House of Representatives, One Hundred Eleventh Congress, Second Session, Hearing Held March 17, 2010. 2010. (Illus.). iv, 97p. ***(978-0-16-087052-1(6),*** 552-070-41909-8) United States Government Printing Office.

Grenade Office, Home Guard. No 36 Grenade. 2009. 48p. pap. *(978-1-84734-861-6(0))* Naval & Military Pr., The.

Iraq: IEDs & Munitions, Are They Secured?: Hearing Before the Subcommittee on National Security & Foreign Affairs of the Committee on Oversight & Government Reform, House of Representatives, One Hundred Tenth Congress, First Session, March 22, 2007. 2007. iii, 54p. *(978-0-16-079267-0(3),* 552-070-36352-1) United States Government Printing Office.

Murray, Iain. Dam Buster Manual: A Guide to the Weapons Technology Used Against the Dams & Special Targets of Nazi-Occupied Europe. 2011. (ENG., Illus.). 160p. 29.95 *(978-0-85733-015-4(2),* 0857330152) Haynes Publishing PLC GBR. Dist: MBI Distribution Services/Quayside Distribution.

National Research Council (U.S.), Committee on Opportunities for U.S.-Russian Collaboration in Combating Radiological Terrorism Staff & National Academies Press (U.S.) Staff, contrib. by. U. S. -Russian Collaboration in Combating Radiological Terrorism. 2007. (ENG.). 124p. pap. 31.75 *(978-0-309-10410-4(6))* National Academies Pr.

Not a Matter of "If", but of "When" The Status of U.S. Response Following an RDD Attack: Joint Hearing Before the Oversight of Government Management, the Federal Workforce, & the District of Columbia Subcommittee & Ad Hoc Subcommittee on State, Local & Private Sector Preparedness & Integration of the Committee on Homeland Security & Governmental Affairs, United States Senate, One Hundred Tenth Congress, First Session, Nove. 2008. (Illus.). iv, 157p. *(978-0-16-080728-2(X),* 552-070-37336-5) United States Government Printing Office.

Nystuen, Gro & Casey-Maslen, Stuart. The Convention on Cluster Munitions: A Commentary. 2010. (ENG.). 708p. 198.50 *(978-0-19-959900-4(9))* Oxford Univ. Pr., Inc.

Smith, Jim. A Law Enforcement & Security Officers' Guide to Responding to Bomb Threats: Providing a Working Knowledge of Bombs, Preparing for Such Incidents & Performing Basic Analysis of Potential Threats. 2nd ed. 2009. 192p. 45.95 *(978-0-398-07870-6(X));* pap. 29.95 *(978-0-398-07871-3(8))* Thomas, Charles C. Pub., Ltd.

BOMBS, AERIAL

see Bombs

BON (TIBETAN RELIGION)

Chaoul, Alejandro. Chod Practice in the Bon Tradition. 2009. (ENG.). 118p. pap. 18.95 *(978-1-55939-292-1(4))* Snow Lion Pubns., Inc.

De Nebesky-Wojkowitz, Rene. Oracles & Demons of Tibet: The Cult & Iconography of the Tibetan Protective Dieties. (Illus.). 682p. *(978-81-7303-039-0(1))* Book Faith India.

Karmay, Samten G. & Watt, Jeff, eds. Bon: the Magic Word: The Indigenous Religion of Tibet. 2007. (ENG., Illus.). 240p. 79.00 *(978-0-85667-649-9(7))* Wilson, Philip Pubs., Ltd. GBR. Dist: Macmillan.

Karmay, Samten G. & Watt, Jeff. Bon, the Magic Word: The Indiginous Religion of Tibet. 2007. (Illus.). 231p. pap. *(978-0-9772131-2-2(9))* Serindia Pubns., Inc.

Snellgrove, David. The Nine Ways of Bon: Excerpts from GZi-brjid. 2010. (ENG.). 318p. pap. 40.00 *(978-974-524-111-4(3))* Orchid Pr. THA. Dist: National Bk. Network.

Wangyal Rinpoche, Tenzin. Tibetan Sound Healing: Seven Guided Practices to Clear Obstacles, Cultivate Positive Qualities, & Uncover Your Inherent Wisdom. unabr. ed. 2011. 120p. pap. 14.98 incl. audio compact disk *(978-1-60407-095-8(1))* Sounds True, Inc.

BON-SAI

see Bonsai

BONA FIDES (LAW)

see Good Faith (Law)

BONA VACANTIA

see also Treasure Troves

George Teke, Forbid. Sustainable Management of Automobile Waste. 2010. 148p. pap. *(978-3-639-25496-9(1))* VDM Verlag Dr. Mueller e.K.

Suhariningsih. Tanah Terlantar: Asas Dan Pembaharuan Konsep Menuju Penertiban. 2009. (IND.). xiv, 312p. *(978-602-8432-06-1(7))* Prestasi Pustaka.

BONAIRE

Brushaber, Susan & Greenberg, Arnold. Aruba, Bonaire & Curacao: Alive Guide. 2nd ed. (Illus.). 380p. pap. 18.99 *(978-1-58843-259-9(9))* Hunter Publishing, Inc.

Colón, Christina Paulette. Frommer's Portable Aruba, Bonaire & Curacao. 6th ed. 2011. (Frommer's Portable Ser.: 274). (ENG.). 216p. pap. 12.99 *(978-1-118-07472-5(6),* Frommers) Wiley, John & Sons, Inc.

Jackson, Jack. Dive Aruba, Bonaire & Curacao: Complete Guide to Diving & Snorkeling. 2007. (Dive Ser.). (ENG., Illus.). 176p. pap. 20.00 *(978-1-56656-707-7(6))* Interlink Publishing Group, Inc.

Sullivan, Lynne M. Adventure Guide to Aruba, Bonaire & Curacao. 2nd rev. ed. 2008. (Illus.). 285p. per. 18.99 *(978-1-58843-572-9(5))* Hunter Publishing, Inc.

BONALD, LOUIS GABRIEL AMBROISE, VICOMTE, 1754-1840

Bonald, Louis-Gabriel-Ambroise, et al. Lettres à Joseph de Maistre. (FRE.). 205p. *(978-2-912642-00-4(0))* Clovis, Editions.

BONAPARTE, ELIZABETH PATTERSON, 1785-1879

Boyer Lewis, Charlene M. Elizabeth Patterson Bonaparte: An American Aristocrat in the Early Republic. 2012. (Illus.). 312p. 34.95 ***(978-0-8122-4430-4(3))*** Univ. of Pennsylvania Pr.

Burn, Helen J. Betsy Bonaparte. 2010. (ENG., Illus.). 244p. (gr. 17). pap. 34.00 *(978-0-9842135-0-4(3))* Johns Hopkins Univ. Pr.

Didier, Eugene L. The Life & Letters of Madame Bonaparte. 2009. 282p. 30.99 *(978-1-115-29176-7(9));* 34.99 *(978-1-115-29177-4(7));* pap. 28.75 *(978-1-115-29175-0(0))* BiblioBazaar.

—The Life & Letters of Madame Bonaparte. 2007. (ENG.). 280p. 42.95 *(978-0-548-02146-0(5))* Kessinger Publishing, LLC.

BONAPARTE, LOUIS-NAPOLEON, EMPEROR OF THE FRENCH, 1808-1873

see Napoleon III, Emperor of the French, 1808-1873

BONAPARTE, NAPOLEON, 1769-1821

see Napoleon I, Emperor of the French, 1769-1821

BONAPARTE, PAOLINA, 1780-1825

Fleischmann, Hector. Pauline Bonaparte & Her Lovers. 2009. 300p. 34.99 *(978-1-113-86462-8(1))* BiblioBazaar.

—Pauline Bonaparte & Her Lovers. 2007. (ENG.). 298p. 43.95 *(978-0-548-04292-2(6))* Kessinger Publishing, LLC.

Fraser, Flora. Pauline Bonaparte: Venus of Empire. 2010. (ENG., Illus.). 320p. pap. 16.95 *(978-0-307-27793-0(3),* Anchor) Knopf Doubleday Publishing Group.

BONAPARTE, PAULINE, 1780-1825

see Bonaparte, Paolina, 1780-1825

BONAPARTE FAMILY

Burn, Helen J. Betsy Bonaparte. 2010. (ENG., Illus.). 244p. (gr. 17). pap. 34.00 *(978-0-9842135-0-4(3))* Johns Hopkins Univ. Pr.

Court & Camp of Bonaparte. 2006. pap. 34.95 *(978-1-4286-4964-4(6))* Kessinger Publishing, LLC.

Smith, William H. C. The Bonapartes: The History of a Dynasty. 2007. (Dynasties Ser.). (ENG., Illus.). 304p. per. 29.95 *(978-1-85285-578-9(9),* Hambledon Continuum) Continuum International Publishing Group, Ltd. GBR. Dist: National Bk. Network.

Williams, Hugh N. The Women Bonapartes, 2 Vols. reprint ed. 250.00 *(978-0-7222-1926-3(1))* Library Reprints, Inc.

BONAR LAW, ANDREW, 1858-1923

see Law, Andrew Bonar, 1858-1923

BONAVENTURA, SAINT, CARDINAL, CA. 1217-1274

see Bonaventure, Saint, Cardinal, ca. 1217-1274

BONAVENTURE, SAINT, CARDINAL, CA. 1217-1274

Bonaventure, et al. Such Is the Power of Love: Saint Francis as Seen by Bonaventure. 2007. 283p. per. 19.95 *(978-1-56548-257-9(3))* New City Pr.

Calisi, Maria. Trinitarian Perspectives in the Franciscan Theological Tradition. 2008. 91p. pap. *(978-1-57659-204-5(9))* Franciscan Institute Pubns.

Clairmont, David A. Moral Struggle & Religious Ethics: On the Person as Classic in Comparative Theological Contexts. 2011. (ENG.). 256p. 109.95 *(978-1-4443-3682-5(7),* Wiley-Blackwell) Wiley, John & Sons, Inc.

De Benedictis, Matthew M. The Social Thought of St Bonaventure: A Study in Social Philosophy, A Dissertation. 2011. 292p. 48.95 ***(978-1-258-05382-6(9))*** Literary Licensing, LLC.

Healy, Emma Therese. Woman: According to St. Bonaventure. 2011. 292p. 48.95 ***(978-1-258-01191-8(3))*** Literary Licensing, LLC.

Karnes, Michelle. Imagination, Meditation, & Cognition in the Middle Ages. 2011. (ENG., Illus.). 280p. 45.00 *(978-0-226-42531-3(2))* Univ. of Chicago Pr.

O'Leary, Conrad John. The Substantial Composition of Man According to St Bonaventure: A Dissertation. 2011. 116p. 39.95 ***(978-1-258-05748-0(4))*** Literary Licensing, LLC.

Prentice, Robert F. The Psychology of Love According to St Bonaventure. 2011. 156p. 41.95 ***(978-1-258-05120-4(6))*** Literary Licensing, LLC.

Quinn, Mary Bernetta. To God Alone the Glory: A Life of St. Bonaventure. 2011. 294p. 48.95 ***(978-1-258-02288-4(5))*** Literary Licensing, LLC.

BOND, JAMES (FICTITIOUS CHARACTER)

DeRose, Cristopher. You Know My Name - the World of James Bond, 007, in Film & Print. 2006. 197p. per. 19.95 *(978-0-9754300-0-2(9))* MensHourBooks.com.

Gardiner, Philip. The Bond Code: The Dark World of Ian Fleming & James Bond. 2008. (ENG., Illus.). 1p. pap. 16.99 *(978-1-60163-004-9(2),* New Page Bks.) Career Pr., Inc.

Gresh, Lois H. & Weinberg, Robert. The Science of James Bond: From Bullets to Bowler Hats to Boat Jumps, the Real Technology Behind 007's Fabulous Films. 2006. (ENG., Illus.). 224p. pap. 15.95 *(978-0-471-66195-5(3),* Wiley) Wiley, John & Sons, Inc.

Lindner, Christoph. James Bond Phenomenon: A Critical Reader. 2nd rev. ed. 2010. (ENG., Illus.). 272p. pap. 24.95 *(978-0-7190-8095-1(9))* Manchester Univ. Pr. GBR. Dist: Macmillan.

Mason, Mark. Bond. 2006. (Bluffer's Guides). (ENG.). 92p. pap. 7.95 *(978-1-903096-90-1(1))* Oval Bks. GBR. Dist: Independent Pubs. Group.

Paterson, Michael. Amazing & Extraordinary Facts - James Bond. 2012. (ENG., Illus.). 144p. 12.99 ***(978-1-4463-0195-1(8))*** David & Charles Pubs. GBR. Dist: F&W Media, Inc.

Porter, Alan J. James Bond: The History of the Illustrated 007. 2008. (Illus.). 240p. pap. 29.99 *(978-1-932563-18-4(0))* Hermes Pr.

Sellers, Robert. Battle for Bond. 2nd ed. 2008. (Illus.). 272p. pap. 21.95 *(978-0-9557670-0-5(8))* Tomahawk Pr. GBR. Dist: Midpoint Trade Bks., Inc.

West, Nigel. Historical Dictionary of Ian Fleming's World of Intelligence: Fact & Ficiton. 2009. (Historical Dictionaries of Intelligence & Counterintelligence Ser.). (ENG.). 308p. 84.00 *(978-0-8108-6190-9(9))* Scarecrow Pr., Inc.

Winder, Simon. The Man Who Saved Britain: A Personal Journey into the Disturbing World of James Bond. 2007. (ENG.). 312p. per. 14.00 *(978-0-312-42666-8(6))* Picador.

Yeffeth, Glenn. James Bond in the 21st Century: Why We Still Need 007. Wilson, Leah, ed. 2006. (Smart Pop Ser.). (ENG., Illus.). 199p. per. 17.95 *(978-1-933771-02-1(X))* BenBella Bks.

BOND GRAPHS

Borutzky, Wolfgang. Bond Graph Methodology: Development & Analysis of Multidisciplinary Dynamic System Models. 2010. (ENG., Illus.). xxii, 662p. 209.00 *(978-1-84882-881-0(0),* 1848828810) Springer.

Borutzky, Wolfgang & Margolis, Donald. Bond Graph Modelling of Engineering Systems: Theory, Applications & Software Support. 2011. (Illus.). xvi, 435p. ***(978-1-4419-9368-7(1))*** Springer.

Brown, Forbes T. Engineering System Dynamics. 2nd rev. ed. 2006. (ENG., Illus.). 1059p. (C). 135.95 *(978-0-8493-9648-9(4),* CRC Press) Taylor & Francis Group GBR. Dist: Taylor & Francis Group.

Das, Shuvra. Mechatronic Modeling & Simulation Using Bond Graphs. 2009. (ENG., Illus.). 504p. (C). 124.95 *(978-1-4200-7314-0(1),* CRC Press) Taylor & Francis Group GBR. Dist: Taylor & Francis Group.

Karnopp, Dean C., et al. System Dynamics: Modeling, Simulation, & Control of Mechatronic Systems. 5th ed. 2012. (ENG., Illus.). 648p. 155.00 ***(978-0-470-88908-4(X),*** Wiley) Wiley, John & Sons, Inc.

Onesmus, Muvengei & John, Kihiu. Using Bond Graphs in Simulating Hydro-Mechanical Systems: Case Study of an Excavator. 2011. 164p. pap. ***(978-3-639-32552-2(4))*** VDM Verlag Dr. Mueller e.K.

Samantaray, Arun K. & Bouamama, Belkacem Ould. Model-Based Process Supervision: A Bond Graph Approach. 2008. (Advances in Industrial Control Ser.). (ENG., Illus.). xx, 473p. 219.00 *(978-1-84800-158-9(4),* 1848001584) Springer.

Samantaray, Arun Kumar & Ould Bouamama, Belkacem. Model-based Process Supervision: A Bond Graph Approach. 2010. (Advances in Industrial Contro Ser.). (Illus.). xx, 473p. pap. 219.00 *(978-1-84996-739-6(3),* 1849967393) Springer.

Thoma, Jean & Mocellin, Gianni. Simulation with Entropy in Engineering Thermodynamics: Understanding Matter & Systems with Bondgraphs. 2010. (ENG., Illus.). xiii, 136p. pap. 149.00 *(978-3-642-06933-8(9),* 3642069339) Springer.

BONDHOLDERS

Weiss, Sandra. Shareholder Value Versus Bondholder Value. 2010. 104p. pap. *(978-3-639-26183-7(6))* VDM Verlag Dr. Mueller e.K.

BONDING (TECHNOLOGY)

see Sealing (Technology)

BONDING OF EMPLOYEES

see Surety and Fidelity Insurance

BONDS, BARRY, 1964-

Ezra, David. Asterisk: Home Runs, Steroids, & the Rush to Judgement. 2008. (ENG.). 256p. 24.95 *(978-1-60078-062-2(8))* Triumph Bks.

Fainaru-Wada, Mark & Williams, Lance. Game of Shadows: Barry Bonds, Balco, & the Steroids Scandal That Rocked Professional Sports. 2007. (ENG., Illus.). 368p. (gr. 12-18). 15.00 *(978-1-59240-268-7(2),* Gotham) Penguin Group (USA) Inc.

—Game of Shadows: Barry Bonds, Balco, & the Steroids Scandal That Rocked Professional Sports. l.t. ed. 2006. (Thorndike Nonfiction Ser.). (Illus.). 607p. 30.95 *(978-0-7862-8866-3(3))* Thorndike Pr.

Pearlman, Jeff. Love Me, Hate Me: Barry Bonds & the Making of an Antihero. 2007. (ENG., Illus.). 384p. pap. 14.99 *(978-0-06-079753-9(3))* HarperCollins Pubs.

BONDS

see also Bondholders; Convertible Bonds; Debts, Public; Government Securities; Municipal Bonds; Stocks

Allentuck, Andrew. Bonds for Canadians: How to Build Wealth & Lower Risk in Your Portfolio. 2007. (ENG., Illus.). 320p. 34.95 *(978-0-470-83691-0(1),* Wiley) Wiley, John & Sons, Inc.

Appel, Marvin. Higher Returns from Safe Investments: Using Bonds, Stocks, & Options to Generate Lifetime Income. 2010. (ENG., Illus.). 224p. 24.99 *(978-0-13-700335-8(8))* FT Press.

Bond Guide: Moody's. 200p. (Orig.). pap. 195.00 *(978-0-7605-1818-2(1))* Rector Pr., Ltd.

Bond Record Handbook: Moody's. 300p. (Orig.). pap. 595.00 *(978-0-7605-1811-3(4))* Rector Pr., Ltd.

Bond Survey: Moody's. 400p. (Orig.). pap. 1595.00 *(978-0-7605-1812-0(2))* Rector Pr., Ltd.

Byrnes, Tracy. Break down Your Money: How to Get Beyond the Noise to Profit in the Markets. 2008. (ENG., Illus.). 224p. 24.95 *(978-0-470-22680-3(3),* Wiley) Wiley, John & Sons, Inc.

Cagan, Michele. The Everything Investing Book: Smart strategies to secure your financial Future! 3rd ed. 2009. (ENG.). 304p. pap. 15.95 *(978-1-59869-829-9(X))* Adams Media Corp.

Carmona, Rene A. & Tehranchi, M. R. Interest Rate Models: an Infinite Dimensional Stochastic Analysis Perspective: An Infinite Dimensional Stochastic Analysis Perspective. 2010. (Springer Finance Ser.). xiv, 235p. pap. 89.95 *(978-3-642-06600-9(3),* 3642066003) Springer.

Chamberlain, Lawrence. The Work of the Bond House. 2009. 160p. 26.99 *(978-1-110-63719-5(5));* pap. 20.75 *(978-1-110-63716-4(0))* BiblioBazaar.

—The Work of the Bond House. 2009. 90p. pap. 14.14 *(978-0-217-64803-5(7))* General Bks. LLC.

Choudhry, Moorad. Bonds: A Concise Guide for Investors. 2006. (ENG., Illus.). 192p. 46.00 *(978-0-230-00649-2(3))* Palgrave Macmillan.

Cohen, Marilyn & Malburg, Christopher R. Surviving the Bond Bear Market: Bondland's Nuclear Winter. 2011. (ENG., Illus.). 224p. 39.95 *(978-0-470-93752-5(1),* Wiley) Wiley, John & Sons, Inc.

Cohen, Marilyn, et al. Bonds Now! Making Money in the New Fixed Income Landscape. 2009. (ENG., Illus.). 195p. 29.95 *(978-0-470-54700-7(6),* Wiley) Wiley, John & Sons, Inc.

Cook, Frank. 21 Things I Wish My Broker Had Told Me: Practical Advice for New Real Estate Professionals. 2nd ed. 2007. (ENG., Illus.). 240p. pap. 17.63 *(978-1-4277-5060-0(2))* Kaplan Publishing.

Covered Bonds: Potential Uses & Regulatory Issues: Hearing Before the Committee on Banking, Housing, & Urban Affairs, United States Senate, One Hundred Eleventh Congress, Second Session, on Examining Covered Bonds, Their Potential Uses, & Regulatory Issues, September 15, 2010. 2011. (Illus.). iii, 198p. ***(978-0-16-088600-3(7),*** 552-070-42776-7) United States Government Printing Office.

Covered Bonds: Prospects for a U.S. Market Going Forward: Hearing Before the Committee on Financial Services, U.S. House of Representatives, One Hundred Eleventh Congress, First Session, December 15, 2009. 2010. (Illus.). iii, 80p. *(978-0-16-085976-2(X),* 552-070-41167-4) United States Government Printing Office.

Cram101 Textbook Reviews Staff. Outlines & Highlights for Bond Markets, Analysis, & Strategies by Frank J Fabozzi, Isbn: 9780131986435. 2009. 176p. pap. 29.95 *(978-1-4288-9769-4(0))* Cram101 Inc.

Crescenzi, Anthony & El-Erian, Mohamed. The Strategic Bond Investor: Strategies & Tools to Unlock the Power of the Bond Market. 2nd ed. 2010. (ENG., Illus.). 432p. 39.95 *(978-0-07-166731-9(8),* 0071667318) McGraw-Hill Cos., The.

Cunningham, W. H. (Hank). In Your Best Interest: The Ultimate Guide to the Canadian Bond Market. 3rd ed. 2012. Orig. Title: English. (ENG., Illus.). 224p. pap. 28.99 *(978-1-55488-889-4(1))* Dundurn CAN. Dist: Ingram Pub. Services.

Doulis, Alex. The Bond's Revenge: A Guide to Thriving in the Bond Market. 2007. (ENG., Illus.). 152p. per. 19.95 *(978-1-55022-773-4(4))* ECW Pr. CAN. Dist: Independent Pubs. Group.

Dym, Steven. The Complete Practitioner's Guide to the Bond Market. 2009. (ENG.). 464p. 75.00 *(978-0-07-163714-5(1),* 0071637141) McGraw-Hill Cos., The.

Dynkin, Lev, et al. Quantitative Management of Bond Portfolios. 2006. (Advances in Financial Engineering Ser.). (ENG., Illus.). 1000p. (C). 115.00 *(978-0-691-12831-3(6))* Princeton Univ. Pr.

Fabozzi, Frank J. Bond Markets Analysis & Strategies. 2006. pap. 15.95 *(978-1-4288-0817-1(5))* Cram101 Inc.

—Bond Markets, Analysis, & Strategies. 7th ed. 2009. (ENG.). 792p. (C). pap. 220.00 *(978-0-13-607897-5(4),* Prentice Hall) Prentice Hall PTR.

—Bond Markets, Analysis & Strategies. 8th rev. ed. 2012. (ENG.). 744p. (C). 220.00 ***(978-0-13-274354-9(X),*** Prentice Hall) Prentice Hall PTR.

Fabozzi, Frank J. Handbook of Fixed Income Securities. 7th ed. 2006. pap. 25.95 *(978-1-4288-1279-6(2))* Cram101 Inc.

Fabozzi, Frank J. & Mann, Steven V. The Handbook of Fixed Income Securities. 8th rev. ed. 2011. (ENG., Illus.). 1536p. 150.00 ***(978-0-07-176846-7(7),*** 0071768467) McGraw-Hill Cos., The.

Faerber, Esme E. All about Bonds, Bond Mutual Funds, & Bond ETFs. 3rd ed. 2008. (ENG., Illus.). 336p. pap. 21.95 *(978-0-07-154427-6(5),* 0071544275) McGraw-Hill Cos., The.

Gaudestad, Jan Olaf. Norwegian Towns Investing in Tender Option Bonds. 2010. 88p. pap. *(978-3-8383-8579-2(9))* Lambert Academic Publishing.

Goble, Jeff. More Yield, Less Risk - Better Sleep! A common sense guide to managing your bank's bond Portfolio. 2007. (Illus.). 122p. pap. 49.00 *(978-0-9799077-4-6(8))* Financial Managers Society, Inc.

He, Qiang & Yu, Jie. Zhai Quan Shou Cang. 2009. (CHI., Illus.). *(978-7-300-11130-8(0))* China Renmin Univ.Pr.

Ibbotson Staff. Stocks, Bonds, Bills, & Inflation: Valuation Edition 2007 Yearbook. Harrington, James, ed. 2007. (Illus.). 120.00 *(978-0-9792402-1-8(2))* Morningstar, Inc.

—Stocks, Bonds, Bills, & Inflation 2007 Yearbook: Market Returns For 1926-2006. Harrington, James, ed. 2007. (Illus.). 370p. 120.00 *(978-0-9792402-0-1(4))* Morningstar, Inc.

Jha, Siddhartha. Interest Rate Markets: A Practical Approach to Fixed Income. 2011. (Wiley Trading Ser.: 501). (ENG., Illus.). 368p. 85.00 *(978-0-470-93220-9(1)*, Wiley) Wiley, John & Sons, Inc.

Johnson, R. Stafford. Bond Evaluation, Selection, & Management: + Website. 2nd ed. 2010. (Wiley Finance Ser.: 529). (ENG., Illus.). 881p. 125.00 *(978-0-470-47835-5(7)*, Wiley) Wiley, John & Sons, Inc.

Kenadjian, Patrick S., ed. Too Big To Fail - Brauchen wir ein Sonderinsolvenzrecht für Banken? 2011. (Institute for Law & Finance Ser.).Tr. of Too Big to Fail ndash; Do we need a Special Insolvency Law for Banks? (GER.). XIV, 236p. 98.00 ***(978-3-11-027220-8(2))*** De Gruyter, Walter Inc.

Kjellson, Fredrick. Private Activity, Tax-Exempt & Tax Credit Bonds. 2011. (American Political, Economic, & Security Issues Ser.). 104p. pap. 47.00 ***(978-1-61470-227-6(6))*** Nova Science Pubs., Inc.

Korn, Ralf, et al. Monte Carlo Methods & Models in Finance & Insurance. 2010. (Chapman & Hall/CRC Financial Mathematics Ser.). (ENG., Illus.). 484p. 94.95 *(978-1-4200-7618-9(3)*, CRC Press) Taylor & Francis Group GBR. Dist: Taylor & Francis Group.

Kristof, Kathy. Investing 101. 2nd exp. rev. ed. 2008. (Bloomberg Ser.: 27). (ENG.). 260p. pap. 16.95 *(978-1-57660-307-9(5)*, Bloomberg Pr.) Wiley, John & Sons, Inc.

Legislative Proposals to Create a Covered Bond Market in the United States: Hearing Before the Subcommittee on Capital Markets & Government Sponsored Enterprises of the Committee on Financial Services, U.S. House of Representatives, One Hundred Twelfth Congress, First Session, March 11, 2011. 2011. (Illus.). v, 146p. ***(978-0-16-089010-9(1)***, 552-070-43042-3) United States Government Printing Office.

Lewis, Michael. Liar's Poker. 2010. (ENG.). 310p. pap. 15.95 *(978-0-393-33869-0(X)*, 33869) Norton, W. W. & Co., Inc.

Livingston, Miles. Bonds & Bond Derivatives. 2nd rev. ed. 2008. (ENG., Illus.). 320p. pap. 65.00 *(978-1-4051-1912-2(8)*, Wiley-Blackwell) Wiley, John & Sons, Inc.

Locke, Natania. Aspects of Traditional Securitisation in South African Law. 2010. 416p. pap. *(978-3-8383-4814-8(1))* Lambert Academic Publishing.

Maeda, Martha. The Complete Guide to Investing in Bonds & Bond Funds: How to Earn High Rates of Return Safely. 2009. (ENG.). 336p. pap. 24.95 *(978-1-60138-293-1(6))* Atlantic Publishing Co.

National Quotation Bureau Staff. National Quotation Bureau Bond Summary. annuals. 115.00 *(978-1-57447-001-7(9))* National Quotation Bureau, LCC.

Parizek, Tomas. Death Bonds. 2010. 80p. pap. *(978-3-8383-5741-6(8))* Lambert Academic Publishing.

Puhle, Michael. Bond Portfolio Optimization. 2008. (Lecture Notes in Economics & Mathematical Systems Ser.). (Illus.). 136p. pap. 119.00 *(978-3-540-76592-9(1))* Springer.

Qi, Howard. Risky Bond Valuation. 2008. 112p. pap. *(978-3-639-05957-1(3))* VDM Verlag Dr. Mueller e.K.

Richelson, Hildy & Richelson, Stan. Bonds: The Unbeaten Path to Secure Investment Growth. 2nd ed. 2011. (Bloomberg Ser.: 145). (ENG., Illus.). 511p. 29.95 *(978-1-118-00446-3(9)*, Bloomberg Pr.) Wiley, John & Sons, Inc.

Sardehi, Nangi. Islamic Capital Markets. 2008. 80p. pap. *(978-3-639-00639-1(9))* VDM Verlag Dr. Mueller e.K.

Schmid, Bernd. Credit risk. Pricing models: Theory & practice. 2nd ed. 2011. (Springer Finance Ser.). (ENG., Illus.). xi, 383p. pap. 189.00 *(978-3-642-07335-9(2)*, 3642073352) Springer.

Sekhar, Aryasomayajula. Parametric Versus Non-Parametric Bond Pricing & Hedging Models. 2009. 196p. pap. *(978-3-639-14812-1(6))* VDM Verlag Dr. Mueller e.K.

Sinclair, Timothy J. The New Masters of Capital: American Bond Rating Agencies & the Politics of Creditworthiness. 2008. (Cornell Studies in Political Economy). (Illus.). 200p. pap. 21.00 *(978-0-8014-7491-0(4))* Cornell Univ. Pr.

Smith, Donald J. Bond Math: The Theory Behind the Formulas. 2011. (Wiley Finance Ser.: 106). (ENG., Illus.). 272p. 65.00 *(978-1-57660-306-2(7)*, Bloomberg Pr.) Wiley, John & Sons, Inc.

Sophastienphong, Kiatchai, et al. South Asian Bond Markets: Developing Long-Term Finance for Growth. 2008. (ENG.). 220p. 65.00 *(978-0-8213-7718-5(3)*, 9780821377185) World Bank Pubns.

Street.com Ratings, creator. TheStreet. com Ratings' Guide to Bond & Money Market Mutual Funds. 31st ed. 2007. (Street. com Ratings Guide to Bond & Money Markete Mutual Funds Ser.). (Illus.). 473p. per. 249.00 *(978-1-59237-247-8(3))* Grey Hse. Publishing.

Thau, Annette. The Bond Book: Everything Investors Need to Know about Treasuries, Municipals, Gnmas, Corporates, Zeros, Bond Funds, Money Market Funds, & More. 3rd ed. 2010. (ENG., Illus.). 400p. 35.00 *(978-0-07-166470-7(X)*, 007166470X) McGraw-Hill Cos., The.

Wild, Russell. Bond Investing for Dummies. 2007. (ENG., Illus.). 360p. per. 24.99 *(978-0-470-13459-7(3)*, For Dummies) Wiley, John & Sons, Inc.

Zhao, Wei & Li, Chan. Covered Bonds: Features & Proposals. 2011. (Congressional Policies, Practices & Procedures Ser.). 125.00 ***(978-1-61470-118-7(0))*** Nova Science Pubs., Inc.

BONDS—TAXATION

see Taxation of Bonds, Securities, etc.

BONDS, CHEMICAL

see Chemical Bonds

BONDS, FIDELITY

see Surety and Fidelity Insurance

BONDS, MUNICIPAL

see Municipal Bonds

BONDS, SURETY

see Surety and Fidelity Insurance

BONE

see also Bones; Calcification

Bronner, Felix & Farach-Carson, Mary C. Bone & Osteoarthritis. 2007. (Topics in Bone Biology Ser.). (Illus.). 215p. 399.00 *(978-1-84628-513-4(5))* Springer.

Bronner, Felix & Farach-Carson, Mary C., eds. Bone & Osteoarthritis. 2010. (Topics in Bone Biology Ser.). (Illus.). xiv, 218p. pap. 399.00 *(978-1-84996-617-7(6)*, 1849966176) Springer.

Goldmann, Tomas. Mechanical Properties of Cortical Bones. 2010. 124p. pap. *(978-3-8383-4413-3(8))* Lambert Academic Publishing.

Hochberg, Z. Endocrine Control of Skeletal Maturation: Annotation to Bone Age Readings. (Illus.). *(978-3-8055-7313-9(8))* Karger, S. AG.

Holick, Michael F. & Dawson-Hughes, Bess, eds. Nutrition & Bone Health. 2010. (Nutrition & Health Ser.). (Illus.). 720p. pap. 229.00 *(978-1-61737-451-7(2)*, 1617374512) Humana Pr.

Laugier, Pascal & Haïat, Guillaume, eds. Bone Quantitative Ultrasound. 2010. (ENG., Illus.). xii, 468p. 239.00 *(978-94-007-0016-1(4)*, 9400700164) Springer.

Pourquié, Olivier. The Skeletal System. Pourquie, Olivier & Pourqui_, Olivier, eds. 2009. (ENG., Illus.). 365p. 95.00 *(978-0-87969-825-6(X))* Cold Spring Harbor Laboratory Pr.

Qin, L., et al, eds. Advanced Bioimaging Technologies in Assessment of the Quality of Bone & Scaffold Materials: Techniques & Applications. 2010. (ENG., Illus.). xvi, 700p. pap. 299.00 *(978-3-642-07955-9(5)*, 3642079555) Springer.

Qin, Ling, et al, eds. Advanced Bioimaging Technologies in Assessment of the Quality of Bone & Scaffold Materials: Techniques & Applications. 2007. (ENG., Illus.). xvi, 700p. 299.00 *(978-3-540-45454-0(3)*, 3540454543) Springer.

Zaidi, Mone, ed. Osteoclast - Osteoblast, Vol. 1. Date not set. 128.50 *(978-0-7623-0396-0(4)*, JAI Pr.) Elsevier Science & Technology Bks.

BONE—GROWTH

see Bones—Growth

BONE DEVELOPMENT

see Bones—Growth

BONE CARVING

see also Scrimshaws

Auger, Emily E. The Way of Inuit Art: Aesthetics & History in & Beyond the Arctic. alt. ed. 2011. (ENG., Illus.). 304p. pap. 45.00 *(978-0-7864-6412-8(7))* McFarland & Co., Inc. Pubs.

Bouvry, Florence. Une Anthropologie des Manifestations Esthetiques Du Mesolithique Europeen De la Fin Du Tardiglaciaire et Durant le Postglaciaire. 2008. (Bar S Ser.). (FRE., Illus.). 643 p. (C). 175.00 *(978-1-4073-0255-3(8))* British Archaeological Reports Ltd. GBR. Dist: Brown, David Bk. Co., The.

Legrand-Pineau, Alexandra, et al, eds. Ancient & Modern Bone Artefacts from America to Russia. 2010. (Bar S Ser.). (ENG., Illus.). 324p. (C). pap. 132.50 *(978-1-4073-0677-3(4))* British Archaeological Reports Ltd. GBR. Dist: Brown, David Bk. Co., The.

Stevens, Jim. Scrimshaw Techniques. 2008. 176p. pap. 29.95 *(978-0-7643-2831-2(X))* Schiffer Publishing, Ltd.

Walrod, Dennis. Antlers: A Guide to Collecting, Scoring, Mounting, & Carving. 2nd ed. 2010. (ENG., Illus.). 224p. pap. 22.95 *(978-0-8117-0596-7(X))* Stackpole Bks.

BONE-GRAFTING

Alfaro, Federico Hernandez. Bone Grafting in Oral Implantology: Techniques & Clinical Applications. (Illus.). 234p. 110.00 *(978-1-85097-103-0(X))* Quintessence Publishing Co., Inc.

Ferri, Joël & Hunziker, Ernst J., eds. Preprosthetic & Maxillofacial Surgery: Biomaterials, Bone Grafting & Tissue Engineering. 2011. (Woodhead Publishing in Materials Ser.). (ENG., Illus.). 400p. 240.00 *(978-1-84569-589-7(5))* Woodhead Publishing Ltd. GBR. Dist: Ingram Pub. Services.

Giannoudis, Peter V., ed. Practical Procedures in Orthopaedic Surgery: Joint Aspiration/Injection, Bone Graft Harvesting & Lower Limb Amputations. 2011. (ENG., Illus.). vii, 103p. 139.00 ***(978-0-85729-816-4(X)***, 085729816X) Springer.

Jan, Ahmed. Effects of Hyberbaric Oxygen on Healing of Bone, Bone Grafts & Bone Graft Substitutes in Calvarial Defects. 2010. (Acta Universitatis Tamperensis Ser.). 118p. pap. 79.50 *(978-951-44-8065-2(1))* Tampere Univ. Pr. FIN. Dist: Coronet Bks.

Jensen, Ole T. The Osteoperiosteal Flap: A Simplified Approach to Alveolar Bone Reconstruction. 2010. 218.00 *(978-0-86715-418-4(7))* Quintessence Publishing Co., Inc.

Khoury, Fouad. Bone Augmentation in Oral Implantology. (Illus.). 448p. 298.00 *(978-1-85097-159-7(5))* Quintessence Publishing Co., Inc.

Marx, Robert E. & Stevens, Mark R. Atlas of Oral & Extraoral Bone Harvesting. 2010. *(978-0-86715-482-5(9))* Quintessence Publishing Co., Inc.

Nilesh, Kumar & Rao, B. H. Sripathi. Bone Graft in Regeneration of Alveolar Bone Following Tooth Extraction. 2010. 92p. pap. *(978-3-8383-7972-2(1))* Lambert Academic Publishing.

Pietrzak, William S., ed. Musculoskeletal Tissue Regeneration: Biological Materials & Methods. 2007. (Orthopedic Biology & Medicine Ser.). (Illus.). 649p. 329.00 *(978-1-58829-909-3(0))* Springer.

Sarment, David P., et al. Manual of Dental Implants: A Reference Guide for Diagnosis & Treatment. 2nd ed. 2009. (Lexi-Comp's Dental Reference Library). (Illus.). 122p. spiral bd. 64.95 *(978-1-59195-250-3(6))* Lexi-Comp, Inc.

Stone, Daniel. Specific Lithic Modification of Bone During Butchery. 2009. 148p. pap. *(978-3-639-18632-1(X))* VDM Verlag Dr. Mueller e.K.

Waite, Peter. Oral & Maxillofacial Surgery Clinics of North America: Alveolar Bone Grafting Techniques in Dental Implant Preparation. 2010. (Clinics: Dentistry Ser.: 22-3). (ENG.). 105.00 *(978-1-4377-2472-1(8)*, Saunders) Elsevier - Health Sciences Div.

BONE GROWTH

see Bones—Growth

BONE LACE

see Bobbin Lace

BONE MARROW

Abdel-Hamid, Emad, et al. Stem Cell Transplantation in Liver Diseases. 2010. 128p. pap. *(978-3-8383-7636-3(6))* Lambert Academic Publishing.

Chia, Mantak. Bone Marrow Nei Kung: Taoist Techniques for Rejuvenating the Blood & Bone. 2006. (ENG., Illus.). 1p. per. 18.95 *(978-1-59477-112-5(X))* Inner Traditions International, Ltd.

Clark, David M., et al. Bone Marrow Pathology. 4th ed. 2010. (ENG., Illus.). 640p. 236.95 *(978-1-4051-6825-0(0)*, Wiley-Blackwell) Wiley, John & Sons, Inc.

Farhi, Diane C. Pathology of Bone Marrow & Blood Cells. 2nd rev. ed. 2008. (ENG., Illus.). 432p. 254.99 *(978-0-7817-7093-4(9))* Lippincott Williams & Wilkins.

Koller, F., et al, eds. Human Cell Culture: Volume IV: Primary Hematopoietic Cells. 2010. (Human Cell Culture Ser.). 352p. pap. 359.00 *(978-90-481-5264-3(X)*, 904815264X) Springer.

Prentice, H. G., ed. Recent Advances in the Treatment of Multiple Myeloma: Proceedings European Expert Meeting, Vol. 114. (Acta Haematologica 2005, Vol. 114, Suppl. 1 Ser.). (Illus.). *(978-3-8055-8005-2(3))* Karger, S. AG.

Tomakovic, Emina Emilia, et al. Bone Marrow IHC. 2009. (Illus.). 274p. 261.25 *(978-0-89189-572-5(8))* American Society for Clinical Pathology.

BONE MARROW—DISEASES

Bain, Barbara J. & Matutes, Estella. Myeloid Malignancies. 2010. (Atlas of Investigation & Diagnosis Ser.). (Illus.). 138p. *(978-1-84692-055-4(8))* Clinical Publishing Services.

Barbui, Tiziano & Tefferi, Ayalew, eds. Myeloproliferative Neoplasms: Critical Concepts & Management. 2012. (Hematologic Malignancies Ser.). (ENG., Illus.). viii, 240p. 189.00 ***(978-3-642-24988-4(4)***, 3642249884) Springer.

Burke, John M. J & B Clinical Card: Myelodysplastic Syndromes Clinical Card. 2008. 12.95 *(978-0-7637-6267-4(9))* Jones & Bartlett Learning, LLC.

Cherry, Daniel A. & Jelic, Tomislav M. Bone Marrow: A Practical Manual. 2011. (ENG., Illus.). 210p. pap. 45.00 *(978-1-57059-708-4(1))* Landes Bioscience.

Clinical Trials for Patients with Bone Marrow Diseases Basic Explanations. 2006. 1.00 net. *(978-0-9755572-5-9(4))* Aplastic Anemia + MDS International Foundation.

Descotes, Jacques. Toxicology of the Blood & Bone Marrow, Second Edition. 2nd ed. 2009. 169.95 *(978-1-4200-7846-6(1))* CRC Pr. LLC.

Ebert, Benjamin L. Myelodysplastic Syndromes: Hematology/Oncology Clinics of North America. 2010. (Clinics: Internal Medicine Ser.: 24-2). (ENG., Illus.). xvi, 288p. 99.00 *(978-1-4377-2203-1(2)*, Saunders) Elsevier - Health Sciences Div.

Editorial Staff of Annals of the New York Academy of Sciences, ed. Annals Meeting Reports: Research Advances in Bipolar Disorder & Shwachman-Diamond Syndrome, Volume 1242. 2012. (Annals of the New York Academy of Sciences Ser.: 95). (ENG., Illus.). 96p. pap. 75.00 ***(978-1-57331-855-6(8)***, Wiley-Blackwell) Wiley, John & Sons, Inc.

Erber, Wendy N., ed. Diagnostic Techniques in Hematological Malignancies. 2010. (ENG., Illus.). 348p. 125.00 *(978-0-521-11121-8(8))* Cambridge Univ. Pr.

Gatter, Kevin, et al. Bone Marrow Diagnosis: An Illustrated Guide. 2nd rev. ed. 2006. (ENG., Illus.). 224p. 236.95 *(978-1-4051-3561-0(1)*, Wiley-Blackwell) Wiley, John & Sons, Inc.

Gorczyca, Wojciech. Cytogenetics, FISH & Molecular Testing in Hematologic Malignancies. 2008. (Illus.). 319p. 219.95 *(978-0-415-42009-9(1))* CRC Pr. LLC.

Gotlib, Jason R. & Fechler, Lenora. 100 QandA about Myelodysplastic Syndromes. 2007. 172p. pap. 22.95 *(978-0-7637-5333-7(5))* Jones & Bartlett Learning, LLC.

Greenberg, Peter L., ed. Myelodysplastic Syndromes: Clinical & Biological Advances. 2011. (ENG.). 336p. pap. 39.99 *(978-0-521-18228-7(X))* Cambridge Univ. Pr.

Greil, Richard. Chronic Myeloid Neoplasias & Clonal Overlap Syndromes. 2009. (Illus.). 200p. 229.00 *(978-3-211-79891-1(9))* Springer.

Ilaslan, Hakan & Sundaram, Murali. Pediatric & Adult MRI Atlas of Bone Marrow: Normal Appearances, Variants & Diffuse Disease States. 2013. (ENG., Illus.). 300p. 179.00 *(978-3-642-02739-0(3)*, 3642027393) Springer.

Karp, Judith E., ed. Acute Myelogenous Leukemia. 2010. (Contemporary Hematology Ser.). (Illus.). xiv, 426p. pap. 189.00 *(978-1-61737-675-7(2)*, 1617376752) Humana Pr.

Kauser, Katalin. Bone Marrow Derived Progenitors. 2007. (Handbook of Experimental Pharmacology Ser.). (Illus.). x, 290p. 419.00 *(978-3-540-68975-1(3)*, 3540689753) Springer.

Kauser, Katalin & Zeiher, Andreas Michael. Bone Marrow-Derived Progenitors. 2010. (Handbook of Experimental Pharmacology Ser.). (Illus.). x, 290p. pap. 419.00 *(978-3-642-08849-0(X)*, 364208849X) Springer.

Managing Treatment Decisions for Bone Marrow Failure Disease: Aplastic Anemia, Myelodysplastic Syndromes, Paroxysmal Nocturnal Hemoglobinuria. 2006. 1.00 net. *(978-0-9755572-6-6(2))* Aplastic Anemia + MDS International Foundation.

Melo, J. V. & Goldman, J. M., eds. Myeloproliferative Disorders. 2007. (Hematologic Malignancies Ser.). (Illus.). 354p. 209.00 *(978-3-540-34505-3(1)*, 3540345051) Springer.

Meyers, Gabrielle & Bagby, Grover C. Bone Marrow Failure Syndromes, an Issue of Hematology/Oncology Clinics. 2009. (Clinics: Internal Medicine Ser.: 23-2). (ENG., Illus.). 240p. 90.00 *(978-1-4377-0487-7(5)*, Saunders) Elsevier - Health Sciences Div.

Mufti, Ghulam J., ed. Myelodysplasias: Molecular Pathology & Treatment. 2012. (Contemporary Hematology Ser.). (ENG.). 350p. 189.00 *(978-1-60761-624-5(6)*, 1607615246) Humana Pr.

Mughal, Tariq I. & Goldman, John, eds. Chronic Myeloproliferative Disorders. 2008. (Illus.). 272p. 190.00 *(978-0-415-41598-9(5)*, Informa Healthcare) Taylor & Francis Group GBR. Dist: Taylor & Francis Group.

Multiple Myeloma: Translational & Emerging Therapies. 2007. (ENG., Illus.). 320p. 99.95 *(978-1-4200-7801-5(1)*, Informa Healthcare) Taylor & Francis Group GBR. Dist: Taylor & Francis Group.

Orazi, Attilio, et al. Illustrated Pathology of Bone Marrow. 2006. (ENG., Illus.). 160p. 174.00 *(978-0-521-81003-6(5))* Cambridge Univ. Pr.

Porwit, Anna, et al, eds. Blood & Bone Marrow Pathology. 2nd ed. 2011. (ENG., Illus.). 722p. 319.95 ***(978-0-7020-3147-2(X)***, Churchill Livingstone) Elsevier - Health Sciences Div.

Raab, Diana. Healing with Words: A Writer's Cancer Journey. 2010. pap. *(978-1-61599-010-8(C))* Loving Healing Pr., Inc.

Raab, Diana M. Healing with Words: A writer's cancer Journey. 2011. 204p. 32.95 ***(978-1-61599-110-5(7))*** Loving Healing Pr., Inc.

Silver, Richard T. & Tefferi, Ayalew, eds. Myeloproliferative Disorders: Biology & Management. 2008. (ENG., Illus.). 240p. 200.00 *(978-1-4200-6162-8(3)*, Informa Healthcare) Taylor & Francis Group GBR. Dist: Taylor & Francis Group.

Valli, Victor E. Veterinary Comparative Hematopathology. 2007. (ENG., Illus.). 576p. 230.99 *(978-0-8138-0924-3(X)*, Wiley-Blackwell) Wiley, John & Sons, Inc.

van der Walt, J. & Borisch, B., eds. Haematological Malignancy & the Bone Marrow Trephine Biopsy. 2007. (Illus.). 88p. pap. *(978-3-8055-8297-1(8))* Karger, S. AG.

Várkonyi, Judit, ed. The Myelodysplastic Syndromes. 2011. (ENG., Illus.). xiii, 286p. 209.00 *(978-94-007-0439-8(9)*, 9400704399) Springer.

Verstovsek, Srdan & Tefferi, Ayalew, eds. Myeloproliferative Neoplasms: Biology & Therapy. 2010. (Contemporary Hematology Ser.). (ENG., Illus.). x, 237p. 189.00 *(978-1-60761-265-0(8)*, 1607612658) Humana Pr.

BONE MARROW—TRANSPLANTATION

Beksac, Meral, ed. Bone Marrow & Stem Cell Transplantation. 2010. (Methods in Molecular Medicine Ser.). (Illus.). x, 234p. pap. 159.00 *(978-1-61737-667-2(1)*, 1617376671) Humana Pr.

—Bone Marrow & Stem Stell Transplantation. 2007. (Methods in Molecular Medicine Ser.: Vol. 134). (Illus.). 234p. 159.00 *(978-1-58829-595-8(6)*, 1588295958) Humana Pr.

Bone Marrow Transplantation: International Comparisons of Availability & Appropriateness of Use. 61p. pap. 35.00 *(978-0-7881-1598-1(7))* DIANE Publishing Co.

Coppes, Max J., et al. Hematopoietic Stem Cell Transplantation: Pediatric Clinics of North America. 2010. (Clinics: Internal Medicine Ser.: 57-1). (ENG., Illus.). xix, 352p. 84.00 *(978-1-4377-1852-2(3)*, Saunders) Elsevier - Health Sciences Div.

Keller, Steve. Lost in Amyloidosis. 2008. 173p. pap. 65.95 *(978-0-615-19244-4(0))* Keller, Steve.

Kline, Ronald M., ed. Pediatric Hematopoietic Stem Cell Transplantation. 2006. (ENG., Illus.). 640p. 300.00 *(978-0-8247-2445-0(3))* Taylor & Francis Group.

Martelli, Massimo F. & Reisner, Yair. Bone Marrow Transplantation Across Major Genetic Barriers, 2 vols. 2010. 400p. 118.00 *(978-981-4271-26-4(8))* World Scientific Publishing Co., Inc.

Marx, Robert E. & Stevens, Mark R. Atlas of Oral & Extraoral Bone Harvesting. 2010. *(978-0-86715-482-5(9))* Quintessence Publishing Co., Inc.

Munker, Reinhold, et al. The BMT Data Book. 2nd ed. 2009. (ENG., Illus.). 544p. pap. 99.00 *(978-0-521-71100-5(2))* Cambridge Univ. Pr.

Oh, Soo-Young. Autologous Bone Plugs Fusion: Treatment for Lumbar Instability. 2009. (Illus.). 100p. *(978-3-8055-9188-1(8))* Karger, S. AG.

Palmer, Joycelynne M., et al. Blood/Marrow Transplantation for Treatment of Chronic Myeloid Leukemi. 2008. 156p. pap. *(978-3-639-05743-0(0))* VDM Verlag Dr. Mueller e.K.

Slutsky, David & Slade, Joseph F., III, eds. The Scaphoid. 2010. (ENG., Illus.). 400p. 249.99 *(978-1-60406-237-3(1))* Thieme Medical Pubs., Inc.

University of Minnesota, Blood and Marrow Transplant Program Staff & University of Minnesota, Amplatz Children's Hospital Staff, contrib. by. Blood & Marrow Transplantation: A Patient's Guide. 2nd ed. 2010. *(978-1-57749-239-9(0))* Taylor Trade Publishing.

Wallace, W. H. B. & Kelnar, C. J. H., eds. Endocrinopathy after Childhood Cancer Treatment. 2009. (Endocrine Development Ser.). (ENG., Illus.). 186p. (978-3-8055-9037-2(7)) Karger, S. AG.

Wang, Xiaodu, et al. Biomechanics in Bone Tissue Engineering. 2010. (Synthesis Lectures on Tissue Engineering Ser.). 225p. pap. 40.00 (978-1-60845-169-2(0)) Morgan & Claypool Pubs.

Whitehouse, Beth. The Match: Savior Siblings & One Family's Battle to Heal Their Daughter. 2011. pap. 16.00 (978-0-8070-0121-9(X)) 2010. (ENG.). 272p. 24.95 (978-0-8070-7286-8(9)) Beacon Pr.

Williams, Riley J., III, ed. Cartilage Repair Strategies. 2007. (ENG., Illus.). xviii, 374p. 249.00 (978-1-58829-629-0(6), 1588296296) Humana Pr.

Yuxue, Jin. Regression Modeling of Competing Risks: Applications to Bone Marrow Transplantation Studies & Mortgage Prepayment & Default Analysis. 2011. 120p. pap. (978-3-639-34319-9(0)) VDM Verlag Dr. Mueller e.K.

BONE MARROW DERIVED CELLS

see B Cells

BONE PRODUCTS

see also Glue; Phosphates

Gates St. Pierre, Christian & Walker, Renee Beauchamp. Bones As Tools: Current Methods & Interpretations in Worked Bone Studies. 2007. (Bar S Ser.). (Illus.). iii, 182p. (C). 90.00 (978-1-4073-0034-4(2)) British Archaeological Reports Ltd. GBR. Dist: Brown, David Bk. Co., The.

BONEFISH

Ault, Jerald S. Biology & Management of the World Tarpon & Bonefish Fisheries. 2007. (Marine Biology Ser.). (ENG., Illus.). 472p. 129.95 (978-0-8493-2792-6(X), CRC Press) Taylor & Francis Group GBR. Dist: Taylor & Francis Group.

Brown, Dick. Fly Fishing for Bonefish. 2008. (ENG., Illus.). 368p. 39.95 (978-1-59921-046-9(0), Lyons Pr.) Globe Pequot Pr., The.

BONES

see also Animal Remains (Archaeology); Anthropometry; Bone; Callus; Cartilage; Extremities (Anatomy); Fractures; Joints; Ligaments; Pelvis; Skeleton; Skull; Spine

Adams, Bradley & Crabtree, Pam. Comparative Osteology: A Laboratory & Field Guide of Common North American Animals. 2011. (ENG., Illus.). 460p. spiral bd. 59.95 (978-0-12-388437-4(3), Academic Pr.) Elsevier Science & Technology Bks.

Afghani, Afrooz. Family History of Osteoporosis. 2009. (Public Health in the 21st Century Ser.). pap. 43.00 (978-1-60876-190-6(8), Nova Biomedical Bks.) Nova Science Pubs., Inc.

An, Yuehuei H. & Martin, Kylie L., eds. Handbook of Histology Methods for Bone & Cartilage. 2010. (ENG., Illus.). 588p. pap. 189.00 (978-1-61737-277-3(3), 1617372773) Humana Pr.

Behari, Jitendra. Biophysical Bone Behaviour: Principles & Applications. 2009. (ENG., 416p. Illus.). 225.00 (978-0-470-82400-9(X)); 210.00 (978-0-470-82402-3(6)) Wiley, John & Sons, Inc. (Wiley).

Bilezikian, John P., et al, eds. Principles of Bone Biology, 2 vols., Vols. 1-2; Set. 3rd ed. 2008. (ENG., Illus.). 1900p. 445.00 (978-0-12-373884-4(9), Academic Pr.) Elsevier Science & Technology Bks.

Bonewald, L. F. & Krebsbach, P. H., eds. Chemistry & Biology of Mineralized Tissues: 9th International Conference, Austin, Tex. , November 2007. 2008. (Illus.). 306p. pap. (978-3-8055-8624-5(8)) Karger, S. AG.

Brenner, Joni, et al. Life of Bone: Art Meets Science. 2011. (ENG., Illus.). 160p. 50.00 (978-1-86814-539-3(5)) Witwatersrand Univ. Pr. Pubns. ZAF. Dist: Transaction Pubs.

Brickley, Megan & Smith, Martin. Proceedings of the Eight Annual Conference of the British Association for Biological Anthropology & Osteoarchaeology. 2008. (Bar S Ser.). (Illus.). iv, 120p. (C). 67.50 (978-1-4073-0185-3(3)) British Archaeological Reports Ltd. GBR. Dist: Brown, David Bk. Co., The.

Bronner, Felix & Farach-Carson, Mary. Bone & Cancer. 2010. (Topics in Bone Biology Ser.). (Illus.). 256p. pap. 99.95 (978-1-84882-841-4(1)) Springer.

Chinsamy-Turan, Anusuya, ed. Forerunners of Mammals: Radiation - Histology - Biology. 2011. (Life of the Past Ser.). (ENG., Illus.). 352p. 60.00 (978-0-253-35697-0(0), 0253356970) Indiana Univ. Pr.

Currey, John D. Bones: Structure & Mechanics. 2nd ed. 2006. (ENG., Illus.). 456p. (C). per. 49.95 (978-0-691-12804-7(9)) Princeton Univ. Pr.

Davies, A. M., et al. Imaging of Bone Tumors. 2009. (Medical Radiology / Diagnostic Imaging Ser.). (Illus.). 410p. 239.00 (978-3-540-77982-7(5)) Springer.

Duhamel, Megan. Bones. 2010. 16p. (978-0-545-24798-6(5)) Scholastic, Inc.

Dunsworth, Holly. Proconsul Heseloni Feet from Rusinga Island, Kenya - Preservation, Anatomy, Ontogeny, & Cross-Sectional Geometry of the Metatarsals. 2008. 324p. pap. (978-3-639-10543-8(5)) VDM Verlag Dr. Mueller e.K.

Econs, Michael J., ed. The Genetics of Osteoporosis & Metabolic Bone Disease. 2010. (Illus.). 474p. pap. 150.00 (978-1-61737-142-4(4), 1617371424) Humana Pr.

Feiler, Bruce. The Council of Dads: A Story of Family, Friendship, & Learning How to Live. 2011. (ENG.). 256p. pap. 13.99 (978-0-06-177877-3(X), William Morrow Paperbacks) HarperCollins Pubs.

Fox, Sherry C., et al. New Directions in the Skeletal Biology of Greece. 2009. (Occasional Wiener Laboratory Ser.). (ENG., Illus.). 304p. pap. 75.00 (978-0-87661-543-0(4)) American Schl. of Classical Studies at Athens.

France, Diane L. Human & Nonhuman Bone Identification: A Color Atlas. 2008. (Illus.). cd-rom 195.95 (978-1-4200-6296-0(4)) CRC Pr. LLC.

—Human & Nonhuman Bone Identification: A Color Atlas. 2008. (ENG., Illus.). 584p. 309.95 (978-1-4200-6286-1(7), CRC Press) Taylor & Francis Group GBR. Dist: Taylor & Francis Group.

—Human & Nonhuman Bone Identification: A Concise Field Guide. 2010. (ENG., Illus.). 295p. pap. 69.95 (978-1-4398-2039-1(2), CRC Press) Taylor & Francis Group GBR. Dist: Taylor & Francis Group.

Goldberg, H. A., et al, eds. Advances in Chemistry & Biology of Mineralized Tissues: 10th International Conference on the Chemistry & Biology of Mineralized Tissues, Carefree, Ariz. , November 2010. Special Topic Issue: 'Cells Tissues Organs 2011, Vol. 194, No. 2-4' 2011. (ENG., Illus.). 264p. pap. (978-3-8055-9841-5(6)) Karger, S. AG.

Gunn, Christine. Bones & Joints: A Guide for Students. 6th ed. 2012. (ENG., Illus.). 270p. (C). pap. 54.95 (978-0-7020-4311-6(7), Churchill Livingstone) Elsevier - Health Sciences Div.

Helfrich, Miep H. & Ralston, Stuart H., eds. Bone Research Protocols. (Methods in Molecular Medicine Ser.). (Illus.). 2010. 468p. pap. 159.00 (978-1-61737-321-3(4), 1617373214) 2nd ed. 2011. (ENG., xiv, 643p. 159.00 (978-1-61779-414-8(7), 1617794147) Humana Pr.

Kardamakis, Dimitrios, et al, eds. Bone Metastases: A translational & clinical Approach. 2009. (Cancer Metastasis - Biology & Treatment Ser.). (ENG., Illus.). xvi, 400p. 219.00 (978-1-4020-9818-5(9), 1402098189) Springer.

Martin, R. Bruce, et al. Skeletal Tissue Mechanics. 2010. (ENG., Illus.). xiv, 392p. pap. 149.00 (978-1-4419-3128-3(7), 1441931287) Springer.

Mehta, Samir & Collinge, Cory. Orthobiologics: Improving Fracture Care Through Science. 2007. (Illus.). 70p. per. 45.99 (978-0-7817-6700-2(8)) Lippincott Williams & Wilkins.

Muscolino, Joseph E. The Muscle & Bone Palpation Manual with Trigger Points, Referral Patterns & Stretching. 2008. (ENG., Illus.). 544p. (C). pap. 61.95 (978-0-323-05171-2(5), Mosby) Elsevier - Health Sciences Div.

Owen, Richard. The Principal Forms of the Skeleton & of the Teeth by Professor R Owen. 2006. 352p. per. 26.99 (978-1-4255-3605-3(0)) MPublishing.

Pedersen, Pauli & Bendsøe, Martin P., eds. IUTAM Symposium on Synthesis in Bio Solid Mechanics. 2010. (Solid Mechanics & Its Applications Ser.). (Illus.). 420p. pap. 309.00 (978-90-481-5179-0(1), 9048151791) Springer.

Planell, J. A. Bone repair Biomaterials. Planell, J. A. et al, eds. 2009. (ENG., Illus.). 320p. 229.95 (978-1-4398-0195-6(9)) CRC Pr. LLC.

Seibel, Markus J., et al, eds. Dynamics of Bone & Cartilage Metabolism: Principles & Clinical Applications. 2nd rev. ed. 2006. (ENG., Illus.). 920p. 260.00 (978-0-12-088562-6(X), Academic Pr.) Elsevier Science & Technology Bks.

Stodder, Ann L. W. & Palkovich, Ann M., eds. The Bioarchaeology of Individuals. 2012. (Bioarchaeological Interpretations of the Human Past: Local, Regional, & Global Ser.). (ENG., Illus.). 256p. 74.95 (978-0-8130-3807-0(3)) Univ. Pr. of Florida.

Sun, Li, et al, eds. Molecular & Integrative Physiology of the Musculoskeletal System. 2010. (Annals of the New York Academy of Sciences Ser.: 67). (ENG., Illus.). 252p. pap. 130.00 (978-1-57331-831-0(0), Wiley-Blackwell) Wiley, John & Sons, Inc.

Weissman, Barbara N. W. Imaging of Arthritis & Metabolic Bone Disease: Expert Consult - Online & Print. 2009. (ENG., Illus.). 772p. 195.00 (978-0-323-04177-5(9), Mosby) Elsevier - Health Sciences Div.

Westendorf, Jennifer J., ed. Osteoporosis: Methods & Protocols. 2008. (Methods in Molecular Biology Ser.). (Illus.). 354p. 119.00 incl. cd-rom (978-1-58829-828-7(0)) Humana Pr.

White, Tim D., et al. Human Osteology. 3rd ed. 2011. (ENG., Illus.). 688p. (C). 99.95 (978-0-12-374134-9(3), Academic Pr.) Elsevier Science & Technology Bks.

BONES—ABNORMALITIES

Pape, Hans-Christian & Weber, Timothy G. Autologous Techniques to Fill Bone Defects for Acute Fractures & Nonunions, an Issue of Orthopedic Clinics. 2009. (Clinics: Orthopedics Ser.: 41-1). (ENG., Illus.). 105.00 (978-1-4377-1847-8(7), Saunders) Elsevier - Health Sciences Div.

Sahar, Nadder D. Exercise, Aging & Bone Tissue Quality. 2010. 136p. pap. (978-3-8383-6642-5(5)) Lambert Academic Publishing.

BONES—ABNORMITIES AND DEFORMITIES

see Bones—Abnormalities

BONES—DISEASES

see also Bones—Radiography; Necrosis; Osteomyelitis; Osteoporosis; Rickets; X-Rays

Abrams, Steven A. & Hawthorne, Keli M. Bone Health in Children. 2012. (ENG., Illus.). 241p. 119.95 (978-1-4398-4926-2(9), CRC Press) Taylor & Francis Group GBR. Dist: Taylor & Francis Group.

Adler, Claus-Peter. Bone Diseases: Macroscopic, Histological, & Radiological Diagnosis of Structural Changes in the Skeleton. Steel, F. & Steel, J., trs. from FRE. 2012. (ENG., Illus.). xxix, 589p. pap. 279.00 (978-3-642-08450-8(8), 3642084508) Springer.

Åkerman, M., et al. Fine Needle Aspiration of Bone Tumours: The Clinical, Radiological & Cytological Approach. 2009. (Monographs in Clinical Cytology Ser.). (ENG., Illus.). 92p. (978-3-8055-9214-7(0)) Karger, S. AG.

Alexander, Ivy M. & Knight, Karla A. 100 Questions & Answers about Osteoporosis & Osteopenia. 2nd rev. ed. 2009. 330p. pap. 24.95 (978-0-7637-7780-7(3)) Jones & Bartlett Learning, LLC.

Allgrove, J. & Shaw, N. J., eds. Calcium & Bone Disorders in Children & Adolescents. 2009. (Endocrine Development Ser.). (ENG., Illus.). 300p. (978-3-8055-9161-4(6)) Karger, S. AG.

American Cancer Society Staff, creator. QuickFacts Bone Metastases: What You Need to Now — Now. 2007. (ACS Quick Facts Ser.). (ENG.). 86p. per. 7.95 (978-0-944235-81-2(6), 9780944235812) American Cancer Society, Inc.

Anderson, John J. B., et al, eds. Diet, Nutrients, & Bone Health. 2011. (ENG., Illus.). 566p. 139.95 (978-1-4398-1955-5(6), CRC Press) Taylor & Francis Group GBR. Dist: Taylor & Francis Group.

Bartl, Christoph, et al. Bisphosphonates in Medical Practice: Actions - Side Effects - Indications - Strategies. 2007. (Illus.). 265p. per. 89.95 (978-3-540-69869-2(8)) Springer.

Bickels, Jacob. Operative Techniques in Orthopaedic Surgical Oncology. Malawer, Martin M. & Wittig, James C., eds. 2012. (ENG., Illus.). 416p. 279.00 (978-1-4511-7628-5(7)) Lippincott Williams & Wilkins.

Bonnick, Sydney Lou. Bone Densitometry in Clinical Practice: Application & Interpretation. 3rd ed. 2009. (Current Clinical Practice Ser.). (ENG., Illus.). 537p. 149.00 (978-1-60327-498-2(7), 1603274987) Humana Pr.

Brickley, Megan & Ives, Rachel. The Bioarchaeology of Metabolic Bone Disease. 2008. (ENG., Illus.). 350p. 86.95 (978-0-12-370486-3(3), Academic Pr.) Elsevier Science & Technology Bks.

Bullough, Peter G. Orthopaedic Pathology: Expert Consult - Online & Print. 5th ed. 2009. (ENG., Illus.). 576p. 285.00 (978-0-323-05471-3(4), Mosby) Elsevier - Health Sciences Div.

Camacho-Huebner, C., et al, eds. Cartilage & Bone Development & Its Disorders: 4th ESPE Advanced Seminar in Developmental Endocrinology, Stockholm, June-July 2010. 2011. (Endocrine Development Ser.). (ENG., Illus.). 120p. (978-3-8055-9792-0(4)) Karger, S. AG.

Catz, Sylvester L. Joints & Bones of Humans-Afflictions, Conditions & Treatments: Index of New Information. Date not set. 160p. 57.50 (978-0-7883-1936-5(1)); pap. 47.50 (978-0-7883-1937-2(X)) ABBE Pubs. Assn. of Washington, D.C.

Cavanagh, Peter R. & Rice, Andrea J. Bone Loss During Spaceflight: Etiology, Countermeasures, & Implications for Bone Health on Earth. 2007. (978-1-59624-093-3(8)) Cleveland Clinic Pr.

Chhem, R K & Brothwell, D. R. Paleoradiology: Imaging Mummies & Fossils. (Illus.). 2010. xx, 163p. pap. 209.00 (978-3-642-08024-1(3), 3642080243) 2008. 163p. 209.00 (978-3-540-48832-3(4)) Springer.

Chiappelli, Francesco. Osteoimmunopathology: Evidence-Based Perspectives from Molecular Biology to Systems Biology. 2011. (ENG., Illus.). xii, 137p. 139.00 (978-1-4419-9494-3(7), 1441994947) Springer.

Compston, Juliet E. & Lian, Jane B. Primer on the Metabolic Bone Diseases & Disorders of Mineral Metabolism. 7th ed. 2008. (ENG., Illus.). 537p. pap. 69.95 (978-0-9778882-1-4(5), Wiley) Wiley, John & Sons, Inc.

Conrad, Ernest U. Orthopaedic Oncology: Diagnosis & Treatment. 2008. 179.95 (978-3-13-124641-7(3)); (978-3-13-147861-0(6)) Thieme Medical Pubs., Inc.

Conrad, Ernest U., ed. Orthopaedic Oncology: Diagnosis & Treatment. 2008. (ENG.). 320p. 189.99 (978-1-58890-523-9(3)) Thieme Medical Pubs., Inc.

Davies, Andrew. Cancer-Related Bone Pain. 2008. (Oxford Pain Management Library Ser.). (ENG., Illus.). 128p. pap. 26.50 (978-0-19-921573-7(1)) Oxford Univ. Pr., Inc.

De Ponte, Francesco Saverio, ed. Bisphosphonates & Osteonecrosis of the Jaw: A Multidisciplinary Approach: A Multidisciplinary Approach. 2011. (ENG., Illus.). xiii, 181p. 139.00 (978-88-470-2082-5(4), 8847020824) Springer.

Dionne, Jean-Yves. S. O. S. Os: Des os solides a tout Age. 2008. (FRE., Illus.). 144p. pap. 24.95 (978-0-470-15443-4(8), Wiley) Wiley, John & Sons, Inc.

Evans, Ronald C. Instant Access to Orthopedic Physical Assessment. 2nd ed. 2009. (ENG., Illus.). 928p. pap. 55.95 (978-0-323-04533-9(2), Mosby) Elsevier - Health Sciences Div.

Feiler, Bruce. The Council of Dads: A Story of Family, Friendship, & Learning How to Live. 2010. (ENG.). 256p. 22.99 (978-0-06-177876-6(1), Morrow, William & Co.) HarperCollins Pubs.

Frassica, Frank J. Bone & Soft Tissue Tumors. 2009. (Core Knowledge in Orthopaedics Ser.). (Illus.). 480p. 79.95 (978-0-323-04366-3(6), Mosby) Elsevier - Health Sciences Div.

Hameed, Omar, et al. Frozen Section Library: Bone: Bone. 2011. (Frozen Section Library). (ENG., Illus.). xii, 136p. pap. 139.00 (978-1-4419-8375-6(9), 1441983759) Springer.

Hasan, Heather. Bone Cancer: Current & Emerging Trends in Detection & Treatment. 2009. (Cancer & Modern Science Ser.). 64p. (gr. 5-5). 58.50 (978-1-61511-769-7(5)) Rosen Publishing Group, Inc., The.

Heymann, Dominique, ed. Bone Cancer: Progression & Therapeutic Approaches. 2009. (ENG., Illus.). 504p. 145.00 (978-0-12-374895-9(X), Academic Pr.) Elsevier Science & Technology Bks.

Horvai, Andrew & Link, Thomas. Bone & Soft Tissue Pathology. 2012. (High Yield Pathology Ser.). (ENG., Illus.). 480p. 199.00 (978-1-4377-2520-9(1), Saunders) Elsevier - Health Sciences Div.

Howard, Larry M. & Payne, Anthony C. Health Benefits of Vitamin K2: A Revolutionary Natural Treatment for Heart Disease & Bone Loss. 2006. 92p. per. 9.95 (978-1-59120-184-7(5)) Basic Health Pubns., Inc.

Hukkanen, Mika V. J., et al, eds. Nitric Oxide in Bone & Joint Disease. 2011. (Postgraduate Medical Science Ser.). (ENG., Illus.). 208p. pap. 45.00 (978-0-521-17513-5(5)) Cambridge Univ. Pr.

Iwegbu, Godwin. A Patient & Carer's Guide to Bone Diseases & Fractures. 2010. 224p. pap. 19.99 (978-1-4520-2665-7(3)) AuthorHouse.

Jaffe, Norman, et al. Pediatric & Adolescent Osteosarcoma. 2009. (Illus.). xx, 591p. E-Book (978-1-4419-0284-9(8)) Springer.

Joerger, Markus & Gnant, Michael, eds. Prevention of Bone Metastases. 2012. (Recent Results in Cancer Research Ser.). (ENG., Illus.). ix, 233p. 219.00 (978-3-642-21891-0(1), 3642218911) Springer.

Khurana, Jasvir S., ed. Bone Pathology. 2nd ed. (Illus.). 600p. 2008. 189.00 (978-1-58829-766-2(7), 1588297667) 2006. 175.00 (978-1-59745-347-9(1)) Humana Pr.

Lanz, Ulrich & Schmitt, Rainer. Diagnostic Imaging of the Hand. 2007. (ENG.). 628p. 229.99 (978-1-58890-453-9(9)); 209.95 (978-3-13-140581-4(3)) Thieme Medical Pubs., Inc.

Layfield, Lester J., et al. Musculoskeletal Cytopathology. 2012. (Cytohistology of Small Tissue Samples Ser.). (ENG., Illus.). 326p. 175.00 incl. cd-rom (978-1-107-01405-3(0)) Cambridge Univ. Pr.

Lee, Diane, et al. The Pelvic Girdle: An Integration of Clinical Expertise & Research. 4th ed. 2010. (ENG., Illus.). 464p. 79.95 (978-0-443-06963-5(8), Churchill Livingstone) Elsevier - Health Sciences Div.

Magee, David J. Orthopedic Physical Assessment. 5th ed. 2007. (ENG., Illus.). 1152p. (C). 106.00 (978-0-7216-0571-5(0), Saunders) Elsevier - Health Sciences Div.

McCarthy, Edward F., et al. Essentials in Bone & Soft-Tissue Pathology. 2010. (ENG., Illus.). ix, 220p. pap. 89.95 (978-0-387-89844-5(1), 0387898441) Springer.

McCleane, Gary & Smith, Howard S. Clinical Management of Bone & Joint Pain. 2007. (ENG.). 424p. 90.00 (978-0-7890-3145-7(0)); (Illus.). 418p. per. 50.00 (978-0-7890-3146-4(9)) Taylor & Francis Group. (Informa Healthcare).

McRae, Ronald. Clinical Orthopaedic Examination. 6th ed. 2010. (ENG., Illus.). 344p. (C). pap. 74.95 (978-0-7020-3393-3(6), Churchill Livingstone) Elsevier - Health Sciences Div.

Meani, E., et al, eds. Infection & Local Treatment in Orthopedic Surgery. 2007. (Illus.). 395p. 149.00 (978-3-540-47998-7(8), 3540479988) Springer.

Meeks, Sara. Walk Tall! An Exercise Program for the Prevention & Treatment of Back Pain, Osteoporosis & the Postural Changes of Aging. 2010. (ENG., Illus.). 160p. spiral bd. 24.95 (978-0-937404-71-3(3)) Triad Publishing Co.

Nieden, Nicole I. zur, ed. Embryonic Stem Cell Therapy for Osteo-Degenerative Diseases: Methods & Protocols. 2010. (Methods in Molecular Biology Ser.). (Illus.). xii, 336p. 139.00 (978-1-60761-961-1(X), 160761961X) Humana Pr.

Oestreich, Alan Emil. Growth of the Pediatric Skeleton: A Primer for Radiologists. 2010. (ENG., Illus.). xi, 96p. pap. 69.95 (978-3-642-07234-5(8), 3642072348) Springer.

Pappo, Alberto S., ed. Pediatric Bone & Soft Tissue Sarcomas. 2010. (Pediatric Oncology Ser.). (Illus.). xiv, 242p. pap. 189.00 (978-3-642-07409-7(X), 364207409X) Springer.

Perkins, C. Gale. The Baby's Cross: A Tuberculosis Survivor's Memoir. 3rd ed. 2012. (ENG., Illus.). 186p. pap. (978-1-927360-14-9(5), CCB Publishing) CCB Publishing.

Peterson, Hamlet A. Physeal Injury Other Than Fracture. 2012. (ENG., Illus.). xxv, 428p. 219.00 (978-3-642-22562-8(4), 3642225624) Springer.

Pettifor, John M., et al, eds. Pediatric Bone: Biology & Diseases. 2nd ed. 2011. (ENG.). 868p. 199.95 (978-0-12-382040-2(5), Academic Pr.) Elsevier Science & Technology Bks.

Pietschmann, Peter, ed. Principles of Osteoimmunology: Molecular Mechanisms & Clinical Applications. 2011. (ENG., Illus.). xvi, 280p. 189.00 (978-3-7091-0519-1(6), 3709105196) Springer.

Reddy, Dr. D. Raja & Reddy, D. Raja. Endemic Skeletal Fluorosis. 2011. 180p. pap. (978-3-8454-1303-7(4)) Lambert Academic Publishing.

Reibel, Amélie. Clinical & Genetic Aspects of Hypophosphatasi. 2010. 104p. pap. (978-3-639-23673-6(4)) VDM Verlag Dr. Mueller e.K.

Reith, John D. Current Concepts in Bone Pathology, an Issue of Surgical Pathology Clinics. 2012. (Clinics: Internal Medicine Ser.: 5-1). (ENG.). 63.00 (978-1-4557-1156-7(X), Saunders) Elsevier - Health Sciences Div.

Robson-Brown, Kate & Roberts, Alice M. BABAO 2004: Proceedings of the 6th Annual Conference of the British Association for Biological Anthropology & Osteoarchaeology, University of Bristol. 2007. (Bar S Ser.). (Illus.). v, 81p. (C). 72.50 (978-1-4073-0035-1(0)) British Archaeological Reports Ltd. GBR. Dist: Brown, David Bk. Co., The.

Roodman, G. David, ed. Myeloma Bone Disease. 2010. (Current Clinical Oncology Ser.). (ENG., Illus.). x, 252p. 259.00 (978-1-60761-553-8(3), 1607615533) Humana Pr.

Rosenberg, Andrew E. & Nielsen, G. Petur. Diagnostic Pathology - Bone. 2012. (ENG., Illus.). 500p. 299.00 (978-1-931884-63-1(3)) Lippincott Williams & Wilkins.

Rothschild, Bruce M., et al. Herpetological Osteopathology: Annotated Bibliography of Amphibians & Reptiles. 2012. (ENG., Illus.). xi, 450p. 209.00 (978-1-4614-0823-9(7), 1461408237) Springer.

Scheuer, Louise, et al. Juvenile Osteology: A Laboratory & Field Manual. 2008. (ENG., Illus.). 384p. spiral bd. 51.95 (978-0-12-374635-1(3), Academic Pr.) Elsevier Science & Technology Bks.

Schnettler, Reinhard & Steinau, Hans-Ulrich. Septic Bone & Joint Surgery. 2010. (ENG., Illus.). 328p. 209.99 (978-3-13-149031-5(4)) Thieme Medical Pubs., Inc.

Shin, Alexander Y. Scaphoid Fractures. 2007. pap. (978-0-89203-435-2(1)) American Academy of Orthopaedic Surgeons.

Spranger, Jürgen W., et al. Bone Dysplasias: An Atlas of Genetic Disorders of Skeletal Development. 3rd ed. 2012. (ENG.). 1456p. 275.00 (978-0-19-539608-9(1)) Oxford Univ. Pr., Inc.

Stacy, Scott. Imaging of Bone & Soft Tissue Tumors, an Issue of Radiologic Clinics of North America. 2011. (Clinics: Radiology Ser.: 49-6). (ENG., Illus.). x, 1080p. 110.00 (978-1-4557-1152-9(7), Saunders) Elsevier - Health Sciences Div.

Thakker, Rajesh V., et al, eds. Genetics of Bone Biology & Skeletal Disease. 2012. (ENG.). 648p. 149.95 ***(978-0-12-387829-8(2)***, Academic Pr.) Elsevier Science & Technology Bks.

Throop, Brian. Stacy's Miracle. 2010. 160p. 25.95 *(978-1-4490-7177-6(5))*; pap. 19.95 *(978-1-4490-7176-9(7))* AuthorHouse.

Tunn, Per-Ulf. Treatment of Bone & Soft Tissue Sarcomas. 2008. (Recent Results in Cancer Research Ser.). (Illus.). 200p. 199.00 *(978-3-540-77959-9(0))* Springer.

Unni, K. Krishnan & Inwards, Carrie Y. Dahlin's Bone Tumors: General Aspects & Data on 10,165 Cases. 6th rev. ed. 2009. (ENG., Illus.). 416p. 225.99 *(978-0-7817-6242-7(1))* Lippincott Williams & Wilkins.

Vigorita, Vincent J., et al. Orthopaedic Pathology. 2nd rev. ed. 2007. (ENG., Illus.). 808p. 345.99 *(978-0-7817-9670-5(9))* Lippincott Williams & Wilkins.

Wodajo, Felasfa M., et al. Visual Guide to Musculoskeletal Tumors: A Clinical - Radiologic - Histologic Approach: Expert Consult: Online & Print. 2010. (ENG., Illus.). 256p. 142.00 *(978-1-4377-0303-0(8)*, Saunders) Elsevier - Health Sciences Div.

Wold, Lester E., et al. Atlas of Orthopedic Pathology. 3rd ed. 2008. (Atlas of Surgical Pathology Ser.). (ENG., Illus.). 560p. 262.00 *(978-1-4160-5328-6(X)*, Saunders) Elsevier - Health Sciences Div.

Wu, Jim S. & Hochman, Mary. Bone Tumors: A Practical Guide to Imaging. 2010. (ENG., Illus.). 250p. pap. 89.95 ***(978-1-4419-0807-0(2)***, 1441908072) Springer.

Yamaguchi, Masayoshi. Osteocalcin: Production, Regulation, & Disease. 2012. ***(978-1-61942-047-2(3))*** Nova Science Pubs., Inc.

Zaidi, Mone. Skeletal Biology & Medicine. 2008. (Annals of the New York Academy of Sciences Ser.: Vol. 1115). (ENG., Illus.). 500p. pap. 159.95 *(978-1-57331-728-3(4)*, Wiley-Blackwell) Wiley, John & Sons, Inc.

Zaidi, Mone. Skeletal Biology & Medicine II: Bone & Cartilage Homeostasis & Bone Disease. 2012. (Annals of the New York Academy of Sciences Ser.: 93). (ENG., Illus.). 252p. pap. 75.00 ***(978-1-57331-856-3(6)***, Wiley-Blackwell) Wiley, John & Sons, Inc.

Zur Nieden, Nicole I. Embryonic Stem Cell Therapy for Osteo-Degenerative Diseases: Methods & Protocols. 2011. (Illus.). xii, 336p. E-Book ***(978-1-60761-962-8(8))*** Humana Pr.

BONES—GROWTH

Abdelmagid, Samir, et al. Role of Osteoactivin in Bone Formation & Fracture Repair. 2010. 144p. pap. *(978-3-8383-5436-1(2))* Lambert Academic Publishing.

Bell, William H. & Guerrero, Cesar A. Distraction Osteogenesis of the Facial Skeleton. 2007. (Illus.). 609p. incl. cd-rom *(978-1-55009-344-5(4))* Decker Publishing.

Botelho, Claudia. Silicon-Substituted Hydroxyapatite. 2011. 200p. pap. ***(978-3-8454-0429-5(9))*** Lambert Academic Publishing.

Bronner, Felix, et al, eds. Bone & Development. 2010. (Topics in Bone Biology Ser.). (Illus.). xii, 300p. 219.00 *(978-1-84882-821-6(7)*, 1848828217) Springer.

Bronner, Felix & Farach-Carson, Mary C., eds. Bone Formation. 2010. (Topics in Bone Biology Ser.). (Illus.). xv, 160p. pap. 419.00 *(978-1-84996-900-0(0)*, 1849969000) Springer.

Burnstock, Geoffrey & Arnett, Timothy R., eds. Nucleotides & Regulation of Bone Cell Function. 2006. (ENG., Illus.). 207p. 199.95 *(978-0-8493-3368-2(7)*, CRC Press) Taylor & Francis Group GBR. Dist: Taylor & Francis Group.

Camacho-Huebner, C., et al, eds. Cartilage & Bone Development & Its Disorders: 4th ESPE Advanced Seminar in Developmental Endocrinology, Stockholm, June-July 2010. 2011. (Endocrine Development Ser.). (ENG., Illus.). 120p. ***(978-3-8055-9792-0(4))*** Karger, S. AG.

Carter, Dennis R. & Beaupré, Gary S. Skeletal Function & Form: Mechanobiology of Skeletal Development, Aging, & Regeneration. 2007. (ENG., Illus.). 332p. pap. 69.00 *(978-0-521-71475-4(3))* Cambridge Univ. Pr.

Cranney, Ann. Effectiveness & Safety of Vitamin D in Relation to Bone Health. 2007. (Evidence Report/Technology Assessment Ser.: No. 158). (Illus.). xii, 235p. *(978-1-58763-265-5(9))* Agency for Healthcare Research & Quality.

Daly, Robin M. & Petit, Moira A. Optimizing Bone Mass & Strength: The Role of Physical Activity & Nutrition During Growth. 2007. (Medicine & Sport Science Ser.: Vol. 51). (Illus.). 162p. *(978-3-8055-8275-9(7))* Karger, S. AG.

Donescu, Oana Smaranda. Osteoporosis & Biochemical Markers of Bone Turnover in Men. 2008. 176p. pap. *(978-3-639-01541-6(X))* VDM Verlag Dr. Mueller e.K.

Fuortes, Michelle. Bones: Growth, Strength, & Osteoporosis. 2011. (Colloquium Series on the Cell Biology of Medicine Ser.). 100p. pap. 35.00 *(978-1-61504-249-4(0))* Morgan & Claypool Life Science Publishers.

Gaskin, Cree M., et al. Skeletal Development of the Hand & Wrist: A Radiographic Atlas & Digital Bone Age Companion, 1 vol. 2011. (ENG., Illus.). 144p. 199.00 *(978-0-19-978205-5(9))* Oxford Univ. Pr., Inc.

—Skeletal Development of the Hand & Wrist Digital Bone Age Companion, 1 vol. 2011. (ENG., Illus.). xi, 131p. cd-rom 149.50 *(978-0-19-984361-9(9))* Oxford Univ. Pr., Inc.

Gerard, Karsenty. Skeletal Biology & Medicine: Aspects of Bone Morphogenesis & Remodeling, 2 vols. Zaidi, Mone, ed. 2008. (Annals of the New York Academy of Sciences Ser.: 3). (ENG.). 500p. pap. 164.95 *(978-1-57331-684-2(9)*, Wiley-Blackwell) Wiley, John & Sons, Inc.

Graci, Sam, et al. The Bone-Building Solution. 2006. (ENG., Illus.). 400p. per. 24.95 *(978-0-470-83891-4(4)*, Wiley) Wiley, John & Sons, Inc.

Holick, Michael F. & Dawson-Hughes, Bess, eds. Nutrition & Bone Health. 2010. (Nutrition & Health Ser.). (Illus.). 720p. pap. 229.00 *(978-1-61737-451-7(2)*, 1617374512) Humana Pr.

Kahn, S., et al. Radiographic Atlas of Skeletal Maturation. 2011. (ENG., Illus.). 620p. 249.99 ***(978-1-60406-571-8(0))*** Thieme Medical Pubs., Inc.

Lynch, Samuel E. Tissue Engineering: Applications in Oral & Maxillofacial Surgery & Periodontics. 2nd ed. 2008. *(978-0-86715-464-1(0))* Quintessence Publishing Co., Inc.

Massaro, Edward J. & Rogers, John M., eds. The Skeleton. 2010. (ENG., Illus.). 456p. pap. 150.00 *(978-1-61737-427-2(X)*, 161737427X) Humana Pr.

McCauley, Laurie K. & Somerman, Martha J., eds. Mineralized Tissues in Oral & Craniofacial Science: Biological Principles & Clinical Correlates. 2012. (ENG.). 392p. 149.99 ***(978-0-470-95833-9(2)***, Wiley-Blackwell) Wiley, John & Sons, Inc.

Oestreich, Alan Emil. Growth of the Pediatric Skeleton: A Primer for Radiologists. 2010. (ENG., Illus.). xi, 96p. pap. 69.95 *(978-3-642-07234-5(8)*, 3642072348) Springer.

Paschalides, Constantinos. Thyroid Function & Bone Health. 2010. 60p. pap. *(978-3-639-25969-8(6))* VDM Verlag Dr. Mueller e.K.

Pettifor, John M., et al, eds. Pediatric Bone: Biology & Diseases. 2nd ed. 2011. (ENG.). 868p. 199.95 ***(978-0-12-382040-2(5)***, Academic Pr.) Elsevier Science & Technology Bks.

Sawyer, Aenor, ed. Bone Densitometry in Growing Patients. 2010. (Current Clinical Practice Ser.). (Illus.). 350p. pap. 149.00 *(978-1-61737-685-6(X)*, 161737685X) Humana Pr.

Sawyer, Aenor J., et al, eds. Bone Densitometry in Growing Patients: Guidelines for Clinical Practice. 2006. (Current Clinical Practice Ser.). (Illus.). 226p. 149.00 *(978-1-58829-634-4(2)*, 1588296342) Humana Pr.

Schneider, Diane L. The Complete Book of Bone Health. 2011. (ENG., Illus.). 375p. pap. 21.00 *(978-1-61614-435-7(1))* Prometheus Bks., Pubs.

Snow, M. Elizabeth. Effects on Prenatal Alcohol Exposure on Long Bone Development. 2008. 176p. pap. *(978-3-639-04892-6(X))* VDM Verlag Dr. Mueller e.K.

Suryo Rahmanto, Yohan. Regulation of Smad6 Gene Expression Using Catalytic Rn. 2009. 96p. pap. *(978-3-639-09276-9(7))* VDM Verlag Dr. Mueller e.K.

Whitfield, James F. Growing Bone, Second Edition. 2nd ed. 2007. (Illus.). 272p. 159.00 *(978-1-58706-156-1(2))* Landes Bioscience.

Young, Marian F. & Krebsbach, Paul H., eds. Extra-Cellular Matrix in the Craniofacial Complex. (Cells Tissues Organs Ser.). (Illus.). 144p. pap. *(978-3-8055-8109-7(2))* Karger, S. AG.

Zaidi, Mone. Skeletal Biology & Medicine. 2008. (Annals of the New York Academy of Sciences Ser.: Vol. 1115). (ENG., Illus.). 500p. pap. 159.95 *(978-1-57331-728-3(4)*, Wiley-Blackwell) Wiley, John & Sons, Inc.

Zaidi, Mone, ed. Skeletal Biology & Medicine, Vol. 1192. 2010. (Annals of the New York Academy of Sciences Ser.: 32). (ENG., Illus.). 352p. pap. 130.00 *(978-1-57331-785-6(3)*, Wiley-Blackwell) Wiley, John & Sons, Inc.

—Skeletal Development & Remodeling in Health, Disease, & Aging, Volume 1068. 2006. (Annals of the New York Academy of Sciences Ser.: Vol. 1068). (ENG., Illus.). 452p. per. 164.95 *(978-1-57331-583-8(4)*, Wiley-Blackwell) Wiley, John & Sons, Inc.

BONES—RADIOGRAPHY

Bahk, Yong-Whee. Combined Scintigraphic & Radiographic Diagnosis of Bone & Joint Diseases. 3rd ed. 2010. (Illus.). xx, 538p. pap. 335.00 *(978-3-642-06170-7(2)*, 3642061702) Springer.

Bahk, Yong-Whee. Combined Scintigraphic & Radiographic Diagnosis of Bone & Joint Diseases: Including Gamma Correction Interpretation. 4th ed. 2012. (ENG., Illus.). xii, 550p. 339.00 ***(978-3-642-25143-6(9)***, 3642251439) Springer.

Bonnick, Sydney Lou & Lewis, Lori Ann. Bone Densitometry for Technologists. 2010. (Illus.). 344p. pap. 94.50 *(978-1-61737-309-1(5)*, 1617373095) Humana Pr.

Cassar-Pullicino, Victor N., et al, eds. Measurements on Orthopedic Radiology. 2011. (Medical Radiology / Diagnostic Imaging Ser.). (Illus.). 300p. 319.00 *(978-3-540-43853-3(X)*, 354043853X) Springer.

Chew, Felix S. Skeletal Radiology: The Bare Bones. 3rd rev. ed. 2010. (ENG., Illus.). 360p. 136.99 *(978-1-60831-706-6(4))* Lippincott Williams & Wilkins.

Gaskin, Cree M., et al. Skeletal Development of the Hand & Wrist: A Radiographic Atlas & Digital Bone Age Companion, 1 vol. 2011. (ENG., Illus.). 144p. 199.00 *(978-0-19-978205-5(9))* Oxford Univ. Pr., Inc.

Johnson, K. J. & Bache, E., eds. Imaging in Pediatric Skeletal Trauma: Techniques & Applications. 2007. (Medical Radiology / Diagnostic Imaging Ser.). (Illus.). 364p. 219.00 *(978-3-540-66196-2(4))* Springer.

Kahn, S., et al. Radiographic Atlas of Skeletal Maturation. 2011. (ENG., Illus.). 620p. 249.99 ***(978-1-60406-571-8(0))*** Thieme Medical Pubs., Inc.

Licata, Angelo A. Bone Densitometry: A Practical Case-Based Guide to Understanding & Interpreting DXA. 2010. 125.00 *(978-1-60761-027-4(2))* Humana Pr.

Lüdkovsky, Sergey V. Stochastic Processes in Non-Archimedean Banach Spaces, Manifolds & Topological Groups. 2010. (Public Health in the 21st Century Ser.). xi, 296p. 145.00 *(978-1-61668-787-8(8))* Nova Science Pubs., Inc.

Murray, James, et al. A-Z of Musculoskeletal & Trauma Radiology. 2008. (ENG., Illus.). 360p. pap. 77.00 *(978-0-521-70013-9(2))* Cambridge Univ. Pr.

Oestreich, Alan Emil. Growth of the Pediatric Skeleton: A Primer for Radiologists. 2010. (ENG., Illus.). xi, 96p. pap. 69.95 *(978-3-642-07234-5(8)*, 3642072348) Springer.

Sawyer, Aenor, ed. Bone Densitometry in Growing Patients. 2010. (Current Clinical Practice Ser.). (Illus.). 350p. pap. 149.00 *(978-1-61737-685-6(X)*, 161737685X) Humana Pr.

BONES—SURGERY

see also Osteotomy

Adunka, Oliver F. & Buchman, Craig A. Otology, Neurotology, & Lateral Skull Base Surgery: An Illustrated Handbook. 2010. (ENG., Illus.). 468p. 159.99 *(978-3-13-145021-0(5))* Thieme Medical Pubs., Inc.

Deb, S., ed. Orthopaedic Bone Cements. 2008. (Illus.). 424p. *(978-1-84569-376-3(0))* Woodhead Publishing Ltd.

Dines, David M., et al. Complex Upper Extremity Trauma: Acute & Reconstructive Solutions. 2008. 203p. 159.95 *(978-3-13-142241-5(6))* Thieme Medical Pubs., Inc.

Donescu, Oana Smaranda. Osteoporosis & Biochemical Markers of Bone Turnover in Men. 2008. 176p. pap. *(978-3-639-01541-6(X))* VDM Verlag Dr. Mueller e.K.

Gottarelli, Paolo. Modified Inferior Turbinoplasty: A new surgical Approach. 2012. (ENG., Illus.). xii 88p. pap. 49.95 ***(978-88-470-2441-0(2)***, 8847024412) Springer.

Lorich, Dean G., et al, eds. Solutions for Complex Upper Extremity Trauma. 2008. (ENG., Illus.). 272p. 169.99 *(978-1-58890-504-8(7))* Thieme Medical Pubs., Inc.

Niparko, John K. & Francis, Howard W. Temporal Bone Dissection Guide. 2011. (ENG., Illus.). 84p. 79.99 *(978-1-60406-409-4(9))* Thieme Medical Pubs., Inc.

Poblete-Michel, Marie G. & Michel, Jean-François. Clinical Success in Bone Surgery with Ultrasonic Devices. 2009. (Clinical Success Ser.). (Illus.). 95p. pap. 78.00 *(978-2-912550-64-4(5))* Quintessence Publishing Co., Inc.

Rodríguez-González, Federico Ángel. Biomaterials in Orthopaedic Surgery. 2009. (Illus.). xvii, 217p. ***(978-1-61503-009-5(3))*** ASM International, Inc.

Rozbruch, S. Robert & Ilizarov, Svetlana, eds. Limb Lengthening & Reconstruction Surgery. 2006. (ENG., Illus.). 696p. 330.00 *(978-0-8493-4051-2(9)*, Informa Healthcare) Taylor & Francis Group GBR. Dist: Taylor & Francis Group.

Scher, Susan, ed. Surgical Management of the Pediatric Long Bone. 2008. per. 55.00 *(978-0-89203-456-7(4))* American Academy of Orthopaedic Surgeons.

Schnettler, Reinhard & Steinau, Hans-Ulrich. Septic Bone & Joint Surgery. 2010. (ENG., Illus.). 328p. 209.99 *(978-3-13-149031-5(4))* Thieme Medical Pubs., Inc.

Slutsky, David & Slade, Joseph F., III, eds. The Scaphoid. 2010. (ENG., Illus.). 400p. 249.99 *(978-1-60406-237-3(1))* Thieme Medical Pubs., Inc.

Ulug, Tuncay. Atlas of Temporal Bone Surgery. 2010. (ENG., Illus.). 216p. 139.99 *(978-3-13-147151-2(4))* Thieme Medical Pubs., Inc.

Zaidi, Mone. Skeletal Biology & Medicine. 2008. (Annals of the New York Academy of Sciences Ser.: Vol. 1115). (ENG., Illus.). 500p. pap. 159.95 *(978-1-57331-728-3(4)*, Wiley-Blackwell) Wiley, John & Sons, Inc.

BONHOEFFER, DIETRICH, 1906-1945

Arnold, Matthieu. 15 Days of Prayer with Dietrich Bonhoeffer. McDonald, Jack, tr. from FRE. 2009. (15 Days of Prayer Ser.). 144p. pap. 12.95 *(978-1-56548-311-8(1))* New City Pr.

Bonhoeffer, Dietrich. Barcelona, Berlin, New York: 1928-1931: Dietrich Bonhoeffer Works. Green, Clifford J., ed. 2008. (Dietrich Bonhoeffer Works Ser.). 790p. (C). 60.00 *(978-0-8006-8330-6(7)*, Fortress Pr.) Augsburg Fortress, Pubs.

—Berlin 1932-1933. 2009. (Dietrich Bonhoeffer Works Ser.). 704p. 55.00 *(978-0-8006-8312-2(9)*, Fortress Pr.) Augsburg Fortress, Pubs.

—Letters & Papers from Prison: Dietrich Bonhoeffer Works. 2010. 800p. (C). 60.00 *(978-0-8006-9703-7(0)*, Fortress Pr.) Augsburg Fortress, Pubs.

—London, 1933-1935. Goedeking, Hans et al, eds. Best, Isabel, tr. from GER. 2007. (Dietrich Bonhoeffer Works). 550p. 50.00 *(978-0-8006-8313-9(7)*, Fortress Pr.) Augsburg Fortress, Pubs.

Burnell, Joel. Poetry, Providence, & Patriotism. 2009. (Princeton Theological Monographs). 320p. pap. 35.00 *(978-1-60608-042-9(3)*, Pickwick Pubns.) Wipf & Stock Pubs.

Busch Nielsen, Kirsten, et al. Mysteries in the Theology of Dietrich Bonhoeffer: A Copenhagen Bonhoeffer Symposium. 2007. (Forschungen Zur Systematischen und Okumenischen Theologie Ser.). (GER & ENG.). 186p. (C). 68.00 *(978-3-525-56347-2(7))* Vandenhoeck & Ruprecht GmbH & Co. KG DEU. Dist: ISD.

Clements, Keith. A Patriotism for Today: Love of Country in Dialogue with the Witness of Dietrich Bonhoeffer. 2011. 192p. pap. 22.00 ***(978-1-61097-127-0(2)***, Wipf and Stock) Wipf & Stock Pubs.

—What Freedom? The Persistent Challenge of Dietrich Bonhoeffer. 2011. 198p. pap. 23.00 ***(978-1-61097-126-3(4)***, Wipf and Stock) Wipf & Stock Pubs.

Dahill, Lisa E. Reading from the Underside of Selfhood: Bonhoeffer & Spiritual Formation. 2008. (Princeton Theological Monographs). 284p. pap. 33.00 *(978-1-55635-425-0(8)* Pickwick Pubns.) Wipf & Stock Pubs.

DeJonge, Michael P. Bonhoeffer's Theological Formation: Berlin, Barth, & Protestant Theology. 2012. (ENG.). 208p. 90.00 ***(978-0-19-963978-6(7))*** Oxford Univ. Pr., Inc.

Dramm, Sabine. Dietrich Bonhoeffer: An Introduction to His Thought. Rice, Thomas, tr. from GER. 2007. 253p. per. *(978-1-56563-762-7(3))* Hendrickson Pubs. Marketing, LLC.

—Dietrich Bonhoeffer & the Resistance. 2009. 304p. (C). 29.00 *(978-0-8006-6322-3(5)*, Fortress Pr.) Augsburg Fortress, Pubs.

Greggs, Tom. Theology against Religion: Constructive Dialogues with Bonhoeffer & Barth. 2011. (ENG.). 256p. 130.00 *(978-0-567-46279-4(X))*; pap. 34.95 *(978-0-567-10423-6(0))* Continuum International Publishing Group, Ltd. GBR. (T&T Clark Int'l). Dist: National Bk. Network.

Gregor, Brian E. & Zimmermann, Jens, eds. Bonhoeffer & Continental Thought: Cruciform Philosophy. 2009. (Indiana Ser. in the Philosophy of Religion Ser.). (ENG.). 264p. 65.00 *(978-0-253-35318-4(1)*, 0253353181); pap. 24.95 *(978-0-253-22084-4(X)*, 025322084X) Indiana Univ. Pr.

Grey, Mary. Dark Night Spirituality. 96p. 13.00 *(978-0-281-04884-7(3))* SPCK Publishing GBR. Dist: Pilgrim Pr., The/United Church Pr.

Haynes, Stephen R. & Hale, Lori Brandt. Bonhoeffer for Armchair Theologians. 2009. (Armchair Ser.). (ENG., Illus.). 192p. pap. 17.00 *(978-0-664-23010-4(5))* Westminster John Knox Pr.

Henley, Grant. Cultural Confessionalism: Literary Resistance & the Bekennende Kirche. 2007. (Studies in Modern German Literature Ser.: Vol. 102). 200p. (C). pap. 53.95 *(978-0-8204-7224-9(7))*; 49.95 *(978-3-03910-298-3(2))* Lang, Peter Publishing, Inc.

Hohne, David A. Spirit & Sonship: Colin Gunton's Theology of Particularity & the Holy Spirit. 2010. (New Critical Thinking in Religion, Theology & Biblical Studies). 194p. 89.95 *(978-0-7546-6911-1(4))* Ashgate Publishing Co.

Kelly, Geffrey B. Reading Bonhoeffer: A Guide to His Spiritual Classics & Selected Writings on Peace. 2008. (Cascade Companions: Ser.). 198p. pap. 23.00 *(978-1-55635-236-2(0))* Wipf & Stock Pubs.

Kirkpatrick, Matthew D. Attacks on Christendom in a World Come of Age: Kierkegaard, Bonhoeffer, & the Question of Religionless Christianity. 2011. (Princeton Theological Monographs). 258p. pap. 28.00 ***(978-1-60899-550-9(X)***, Pickwick Pubns.) Wipf & Stock Pubs.

Klug, Ron. 40-Day Journey with Dietrich Bonhoeffer. 2007. 144p. pap. 12.99 *(978-0-8066-5368-6(X)*, Augsburg Bks.) Augsburg Fortress, Pubs.

Lawrence, Joel. Bonhoeffer. 2010. (Guides for the Perplexed Ser.). (ENG.). 144p. 24.95 *(978-0-567-03238-6(8))*; 80.00 *(978-0-567-03237-9(X))* Continuum International Publishing Group, Ltd. GBR. (T&T Clark Int'l). Dist: National Bk. Network.

Martin, Michael. Dietrich Bonhoeffer. 2008. 196p. pap. *(978-3-8364-6619-6(8))* VDM Verlag Dr. Mueller e.K.

Marty, Martin E. Dietrich Bonhoeffer's Letters & Papers from Prison: A Biography. 2011. (Lives of Great Religious Bks.). (ENG., Illus.). 288p. 24.95 *(978-0-691-13921-0(0))* Princeton Univ. Pr.

Marty, Martin E., ed. The Place of Bonhoeffer. 2009. 224p. pap. 25.00 *(978-1-60608-983-5(8)*, Wipf and Stock) Wipf & Stock Pubs.

Matthews, John W. Bonhoeffer: A Brief Overview of the Life & Writings of Diedrich Bonhoeffer. 2011. (ENG.). 100p. pap. 15.00 ***(978-1-932688-65-8(X)***, Lutheran Univ. Pr.) Kirk Hse. Pubs.

McBride, Jennifer M. The Church for the World: A Theology of Public Witness, 1 vol. 2011. (ENG.). 352p. 74.00 ***(978-0-19-975568-4(X))*** Oxford Univ. Pr., Inc.

Metaxas, Eric. Bonhoeffer: Pastor, Martyr, Prophet, Spy. 2011. 624p. pap. 19.99 *(978-1-59555-246-4(4))* 2010. 608p. 29.99 *(978-1-59555-138-2(7))* Nelson, Thomas Inc.

Moses, John Anthony. The Reluctant Revolutionary: Dietrich Bonhoeffer's Collision with Prusso-German History. 2009. 320p. 90.00 *(978-1-84545-531-6(2))* Berghahn Bks., Inc.

Owens, L. Roger. The Shape of Participation: A Theology of Church Practices. 2010. 204p. pap. 22.00 *(978-1-60608-519-6(0)*, Cascade Bks.) Wipf & Stock Pubs.

Plant, Stephen & Wüstenberg, Ralf K., eds. Religion, Religionlessness & Contemporary Western Culture: Explorations in Dietrich Bonhoeffer's Theology. 2008. 134p. 39.95 *(978-3-631-57754-7(0))* Lang, Peter GmbH, Europaischer Verlag der Wissenschaften DEU. Dist: Lang, Peter.

Pugh, Jeffrey C. & Pugh. Religionless Christianity: Dietrich Bonhoeffer in Troubled Times. 2009. (ENG.). 190p. 29.95 *(978-0-567-03259-1(0))*; 192p. 120.00 *(978-0-567-03258-4(2))* Continuum International Publishing Group, Ltd. GBR. (T&T Clark Int'l). Dist: National Bk. Network.

Schliesser, Christine. Everyone Who Acts Responsibly Becomes Guilty: Bonhoeffer's Concept of Accepting Guilt. 2008. (ENG., Illus.). 224p. pap. 35.00 *(978-0-664-23216-0(7))* Westminster John Knox Pr.

Schlingensiepen, Ferdinand. Dietrich Bonhoeffer, 1906-1945: Martyr, Thinker, Man of Resistance. (ENG., Illus.). 472p. 2012. pap. 24.95 ***(978-0-567-49319-4(9))*** 2010. 29.95 *(978-0-567-03400-7(3))* Continuum International Publishing Group, Ltd. GBR. (T&T Clark Int'l). Dist: National Bk. Network.

Siemon-Netto, Uwe. The Acquittal of God: A Theology for Vietnam Veterans. 2008. 108p. (Orig.). pap. 13.00 *(978-1-60608-364-2(3)*, Wipf and Stock) Wipf & Stock Pubs.

Todt, Heinz Eduard. Authentic Faith: Bonhoeffer's Theological Ethics in Context. Scharffenorth, Ernst-Albert & Stassen, Glen Harold, eds. Stassen, David & Todt, Ilse, trs. from GER. 2007. 291p. per. 24.00 *(978-0-8028-0382-5(2))* Eerdmans, William B. Publishing Co.

Walker, Jon. Costly Grace: A Contemporary View of Bonhoeffer's the Cost of Discipleship. 2010. 224p. pap. 15.99 *(978-0-89112-676-8(7)*, Leafwood Pubs.) Abilene Christian Univ. Pr.

—Costly Grace 90-Day Devotional. 2010. 224p. pap. 13.99 *(978-0-89112-677-5(5)*, Leafwood Pubs.) Abilene Christian Univ. Pr.

Walker, Jon. In Visible Fellowship: A Contemporary View of Bonhoeffer's Classic Work Life Together. 2011. (ENG.). pap. 13.99 ***(978-0-89112-295-1(8)***, Leafwood Pubs.) Abilene Christian Univ. Pr.

Wannenwetsch. Who Am I? Bonhoeffer's Theology Through His Poetry. 2009. (ENG.). 272p. 120.00 *(978-0-567-03222-5(1)*, T&T Clark Int'l) Continuum International Publishing Group Ltd. GBR. Dist: National Bk. Network.

Wannenwetsch, Bernd, ed. Who am I? Bonhoeffer's Theology through his Poetry. 2012. (ENG.). 272p. pap. 49.95 ***(978-0-567-06783-8(1)***, T&T Clark Int'l)

Continuum International Publishing Group, Ltd. GBR. Dist: National Bk. Network.

Zimmerling, Peter. Bonhoeffer als Praktischer Theologe. 2006. (GER.). 231p. (C). 41.00 *(978-3-525-55451-7(6))* Vandenhoeck & Ruprecht GmbH & Co. KG DEU. Dist: ISD.

Zimmermann, Jens, ed. Being Human, Becoming Human: Dietrich Bonhoeffer & Social Thought. 2012. (ENG.). 258p. pap. 39.00 ***(978-0-227-68027-8(8))*** Clarke, James Co., Ltd. GBR. Dist: Brown, David Bk. Co., The.

Zimmermann, Jens & Gregor, Brian, eds. Being Human, Becoming Human: Dietrich Bonhoeffer & Social Thought. 2010. (Princeton Theological Monographs). 258p. pap. 28.00 *(978-1-60899-420-5(1)*, Pickwick Pubns.) Wipf & Stock Pubs.

BONHOMME RICHARD (SHIP)

Barnes, J. S. Logs Of "serapis," "alliance," "ariel", 1779-80. reprint ed. 150.00 *(978-0-7222-9423-9(9))* Library Reprints, Inc.

Barnes, John Sanford. The Logs of the Serapis — Alliance — Ariel, under The Command of John Paul Jones, 1779-1780: With Extracts from Public Documents, Unpublished Letters, & Narratives. (Publications of the Naval History Society Ser.). 138p. reprint ed. 88.00 *(978-0-7222-7702-7(4))* Library Reprints, Inc.

Lardas, Mark. Bonhomme Richard vs Serapis: Flamborough Head 1779. 2012. (Duel Ser.). (ENG., Illus.). 80p. pap. 18.95 ***(978-1-84908-785-8(7))*** Osprey Publishing, Ltd. GBR. Dist: Random Hse., Inc.

BONIFACE, SAINT, ARCHBISHOP OF MAINZ, CA. 675-754

Clay, J. -H. In the Shadow of Death: Saint Boniface & the Conversion of Hessia, 721-54. 2011. (Cultural Encounters in Late Antiquity & the Middle Ages Ser.). (ENG, GER & LAT., Illus.). 487p. (C). 152.00 *(978-2-503-53161-8(X))* Brepols Pubs. BEL. Dist: ISD.

Ernest, Brother. A Story of St Boniface. 2011. 28p. 35.95 ***(978-1-258-01193-2(X))*** Literary Licensing, LLC.

BONINGTON, RICHARD PARKES, 1801-1828

Noakes, Aubrey. Chaucer Catalogue 2004. 2007. (Illus.). 192p. 55.00 *(978-1-904449-43-0(3))* Chaucer Pr. GBR. Dist: International Publishers Marketing.

Noon, Patrick. Richard Parkes Bonington: The Complete Drawings. 2011. (Paul Mellon Centre for Studies in British Art Ser.). (ENG., Illus.). 224p. 85.00 *(978-0-300-17045-0(9))* Yale Univ. Pr.

Noon, Patrick J. & Bonington, Richard Parkes. Richard Parkes Bonington: The Complete Paintings. 2009. (ENG., Illus.). 472p. 125.00 *(978-0-300-13421-6(5))* Yale Univ. Pr.

BONKEI

Covello, Vincent T., et al. The Japanese Art of Stone Appreciation: Suiseki & Its Use with Bonsai. 2009. (Tuttle Classics Ser.). (ENG., Illus.). 160p. pap. 19.95 *(978-4-8053-1013-7(8))* Tuttle Publishing.

BONN (GERMANY)

Krüger, Jens. Die Finanzierung der Bundeshauptstadt Bonn. 2006. (Veröffentlichungen der Historischen Kommission zu Berlin Ser.). (GER., Illus.). X, 283p. 154.00 *(978-3-11-019090-8(7))* De Gruyter, Walter Inc.

BONN (GERMANY)—DESCRIPTION AND TRAVEL

Bredenbeck, Martin, et al. Beethovenhalle Bonn: Konzerthaus. Festsaal. Denkmal. 2010. (Illus.). 207p. *(978-3-938803-28-8(2))* Weidle Verlag GmbH.

BONNARD, PIERRE, 1867-1947

Amory, Dita, ed. & contrib. by. Pierre Bonnard: The Late Still Lifes & Interiors. 2009. (ENG., Illus.). 208p. 50.00 *(978-0-300-14889-3(5))* Yale Univ. Pr.

Bonnard, Pierre, et al. Pierre Bonnard: The Late Still Lifes & Interiors. 2009. 45.00 *(978-1-58839-308-1(9))* Metropolitan Museum of Art, The.

Kostenevitch, Albert. The Nabis. 2009. (Art of Century Ser.). (ENG., Illus.). 200p. 19.95 *(978-1-84484-623-8(7))* Parkstone International GBR. Dist: Ingram Pub. Services.

BONNEVILLE, BENJAMIN LOUIS EULALIE DE, 1796-1878

Adventures Captain Bonneville, U. S. A. 54.95 *(978-0-8488-0222-6(5)*, Carroll, J. M. Company) Amereon LTD.

Irving, Washington. The Adventures of Captain Bonneville: U. S. A.; in the Rocky Mountains & the Far West. 2007. (ENG.). 334p. pap. 23.99 *(978-1-4346-5257-7(2))*; 364p. pap. 26.99 *(978-1-4346-5258-4(0))* BiblioBazaar.

BONNEY, WILLIAM H., 1859-1881

see Billy, the Kid

BONNIE PRINCE CHARLIE, 1720-1788

see Charles Edward, Prince, Grandson of James II, King of England, 1720-1788

BONNY LANGUAGE

see Ijo Language

BONOBO

Benson, James D. & Greaves, William S., eds. Functional Dimensions of Ape-Human Discourse. 2010. (Functional Linguistics Ser.). (ENG.). 192p. (C). pap. 50.00 *(978-1-84553-653-4(3))* Equinox Publishing Ltd. GBR. Dist: ISD.

Bonobos: Encounters in Empathy. 2007. (Illus.). 109p. pap. 22.00 *(978-0-9794151-0-4(1))* Zoological Society of Milwaukee.

De Waal, Frans B. M. Our Inner Ape: The Best & Worst of Human Nature. 2008. 272p. 35.00 *(978-1-4223-9513-4(8))* DIANE Publishing Co.

Furuichi, Takeshi & Thompson, Jo, eds. The Bonobos: Behavior, Ecology, & Conservation. 2010. (Developments in Primatology: Progress & Prospects Ser.). (Illus.). xiv, 330p. pap. 199.00 *(978-1-4419-2572-5(4)*, 1441925724) Springer.

Furuichi, Takeshi, et al. The Bonobos: Ecology, Behavior, Genetics, & Conservation. Furuichi, Takeshi et al, eds. 2008. (Developments in Primatology Ser.). (Illus.). 288p. 199.00 *(978-0-387-74785-9(0))* Springer.

Nishida, Toshisada, et al. Chimpanzee Behavior in the Wild: An Audio-Visual Encyclopedia. 2010. (Illus.). 255p. 189.00 *(978-4-431-53894-3(1)*, 4431538941) Springer.

Woods, Vanessa. Bonobo Handshake: A Memoir of Love & Adventure in the Congo. 2011. (ENG.). 288p. (gr. 12). 16.00 *(978-1-59240-634-0(3)*, Gotham) Penguin Group (USA) Inc.

BONPLAND, AIME, 1773-1858

Bell, Stephen. A Life in Shadow: Aimé Bonpland in Southern South America, 1817-1858. 2010. (ENG., Illus.). 336p. 65.00 *(978-0-8047-5260-2(5))* Stanford Univ. Pr.

BONPO (SECT)

see Bon (Tibetan Religion)

BONS MOTS

see Wit and Humor

BONSAI

Adams, Peter. Bonsai with Japanese Maples. 2nd ed. 2006. (ENG., Illus.). 156p. 34.95 *(978-0-88192-809-9(7)*, 0881928097) Timber Pr., Inc.

Albek, Morten. Majesty in Miniature: Shohin Bonsai: Unlocking the Secrets of Small Trees. Schoech, Wayne, ed. 2008. (Illus.). 198p. pap. 24.95 *(978-0-9767550-6-7(8))* Stone Lantern Publishing.

Bonsai: 10 Jahre Noelanders Trophy. (Mini Lifestyle Kits Ser.). 32p. *(978-1-84510-596-9(6))* Top That! Publishing PLC.

Burrell, C. Colston, ed. Wildflower Gardens: 60 Spectacular Plants & How to Grow Them in Your Garden. 2007. (21st-Century Gardening Ser.). (ENG., Illus.). 112p. per. 9.95 *(978-1-889538-31-0(0))* Brooklyn Botanic Garden.

Chan, Peter. Choosing & Growing Bonsai. 2007. (ENG., Illus.). 192p. pap. 17.95 *(978-0-600-61442-5(5)*, Hamlyn) Octopus Publishing Group GBR. Dist: Hachette Bk. Group.

Chesshire, Charles. The Complete Illustrated Guide to Japanese Gardening & Growing Bonsai: Essential Advice, Step-by-Step Techniques & Projects, Plans, Plant Listings & over 1500 Photographs & Illustrations. 2012. (ENG., Illus.). 512p. 35.00 *(978-0-7548-2091-8(2))* Anness Publishing GBR. Dist: National Bk. Network.

Coussins, Craig. Bonsai Master Class. 2006. (ENG., Illus.). 256p. 24.95 *(978-1-4027-3547-9(2))* Sterling Publishing Co., Inc.

Covello, Vincent T., et al. The Japanese Art of Stone Appreciation: Suiseki & Its Use with Bonsai. 2009. (Tuttle Classics Ser.). (ENG., Illus.). 160p. pap. 19.95 *(978-4-8053-1013-7(8))* Tuttle Publishing.

Elwins, Dannie. Growing Bonsai Trees Made Simple & Easy. 2009. 32p. pap. 16.99 *(978-0-557-15536-1(3))* Lulu Enterprises Inc.

Freeman, Michael A. & Sakai, Noriko. Pocket Gardens: Contemporary Japanese Miniature Designs. 2008. (ENG., Illus.). 224p. 29.95 *(978-0-7893-1587-8(4))* Universe Publishing.

Harnett, Charles. Miniature Trees: Their Care & Maintenance. (Secrets of Bonsai Ser.). (Illus.). 190p. (Orig.). pap. 14.95 *(978-0-9630959-0-9(0))* Bonsai East.

Kobayashi, Kunio. Bonsai. 2011. (ENG., Illus.). 288p. pap. 39.95 *(978-4-7562-4094-1(1)*, PIE Bks.) Rizzoli International Pubns., Inc.

Kuo-cheng, Lin. Miniature Bonsai. (Illus.). 120p. pap. *(978-957-629-160-9(7))* Hilit Publishing Co., Ltd.

Levitt, Gerald M. The Sphagnum Moss Bonsai Method: An Illustrated Handbook. 2011. (ENG., Illus.). 199p. pap. 29.95 *(978-0-7864-6292-6(2))* McFarland & Co., Inc. Pubs.

Lewis, Colin. Bonsai Basics: A Comprehensive Guide to Care & Cultivation. 2009. (ENG., Illus.). 128p. pap. 9.95 *(978-0-600-61910-9(9)*, Hamlyn) Octopus Publishing Group GBR. Dist: Hachette Bk. Group.

Liang, Amy. The Art of Bonsai. (Illus.). 288p. *(978-957-629-037-4(6))* Hilit Publishing Co., Ltd.

Liew, Walter. The Living Art of Bonsai. 2007. (ENG., Illus.). 148p. *(978-1-59700-185-4(6))* Island Heritage Publishing.

Lucke Morris, Pat & Wolff Saphire, Sigrun, eds. Growing Bonsai Indoors. (BBG Guides for a Greener Planet Ser.). (ENG., Illus.). 120p. 2011. pap. 12.95 *(978-1-889538-79-2(5))* 2008. pap. 9.95 *(978-1-889538-42-6(6))* Brooklyn Botanic Garden.

Norman, Ken. The Complete Practical Encyclopedia of Bonsai: The Essential Step-by-step Guide to Creating, Growing, & Displaying Bonsai with over 800 Photographs. 2009. (ENG., Illus.). 264p. 21.99 *(978-0-7548-2180-9(3))* Anness Publishing GBR. Dist: National Bk. Network.

—Practical Bonsai Projects: Create 23 Superb Trees. 2007. (ENG., Illus.). 96p. pap. 14.99 *(978-1-84476-372-6(2))* Anness Publishing GBR. Dist: National Bk. Network.

Prescott, David. The Bonsai Handbook. Lewis, Colin, ed. 2011. (ENG., Illus.). 160p. pap. 17.95 *(978-1-84773-930-8(X))* New Holland Pubs., Ltd. GBR. Dist: Sterling Publishing Co., Inc.

Schoech, Joseph, adapted by. Bonsai Today's Pocket Bonsai Gallery. 2008. pap. 6.95 net. *(978-0-9767550-0-5(X))* Stone Lantern Publishing.

Schoech, Wayne, ed. The Bonsai Art of Kimura, Vol. 2. 2008. (Bonsai Today Masters' Ser.). (Illus.). 175p. pap. 29.95 net. *(978-0-9767550-4-3(1))* Stone Lantern Publishing.

Schoech, Wayne & Kimura, Masahiko. Junipers: GROWING & STYLING JUNIPER BONSAI. 2007. (Bonsai Today Masters' Ser.). (Illus.). 184p. pap. 29.95 *(978-0-9767550-3-6(3))* Stone Lantern Publishing.

Singer, Jonathan, photos by. Bonsai: Art in Nature. 2012. (ENG., Illus.). 416p. 225.00 ***(978-0-7892-1116-3(5))*** Abbeville Pr., Inc.

Singer, Jonathan M., photos by. Fine Bonsai: Art & Nature. 2012. (ENG., Illus.). 416p. 150.00 ***(978-0-7892-1112-5(2))*** Abbeville Pr., Inc.

Squire, David. Successful Bonsai: Raising Exotic Miniature Trees. 2011. (ENG., Illus.). 160p. pap. 19.95 *(978-1-55407-157-9(7))* Firefly Bks., Ltd.

Stichting Kunstboek. Bonsai: Noelanders Trophy 10 Years. 2010. (ENG., Illus.). 224p. *(978-90-5856-341-5(3)*, Stichting Kunstboak (Acc)) Antique Collectors' Club.

Tindale, Constance. Bonsai. (Illus.). 160p. 50.00 *(978-1-86126-418-3(6))* Crowood Pr., Ltd. GBR. Dist: Trafalgar Square Publishing.

Yamamoto, Junsun. The Beauty of Bonsai: A Guide to Displaying & Viewing Nature's Exquisite Sculpture, 1 vol. 2011. (ENG., Illus.). 96p. 29.95 *(978-4-7700-3126-6(2))* Kodansha America, Inc.

BONUS ARMY

see Bonus Expeditionary Forces

BONUS EXPEDITIONARY FORCES

Ortiz, Stephen. Beyond the Bonus March & GI Bill: How Veteran Politics Shaped the New Deal Era. 2009. (ENG., Illus.). 264p. 47.00 *(978-0-8147-6213-4(1))* New York Univ. Pr.

BONUS SYSTEM

see also Piecework

Cichelli, David J. Compensating the Sales Force: A Practical Guide to Designing Winning Sales Reward Programs. 2nd ed. 2010. (ENG., Illus.). 272p. 39.95 *(978-0-07-173902-3(5)*, 0071739025) McGraw-Hill Cos., The.

Compensation in the Financial Industry: Government Perspectives: Hearing Before the Committee on Financial Services, U.S. House of Representatives, One Hundred Eleventh Congress, Second Session, February 25, 2010. 2010. iii, 76p. *(978-0-16-086169-7(1)*, 552-070-41269-7) United States Government Printing Office.

Ederhof, Merle, et al. Discretion in Managerial Bonus Pools. 2011. 88p. pap. 65.00 ***(978-1-60198-454-8(5))*** Now Pubs.

Eliminating Wasteful Contractor Bonuses: Hearing Before the Federal Financial Management, Government Information, Federal Services, & International Security Subcommittee of the Committee on Homeland Security & Governmental Affairs, United States Senate of the One Hundred Eleventh Congress, First Session, August 3, 2009. 2010. iv, 167p. *(978-0-16-086232-8(9)*, 552-070-41323-5) United States Government Printing Office.

Kennedy, Van Dusen. Union Policy & Incentive Wage Methods. (Columbia University, Studies in the Social Sciences: No. 513). reprint ed. 29.50 *(978-0-404-51513-3(4))* AMS Pr., Inc.

Pabón Roca, Luis. El bono de Navidad: Guía para el Patrono. 2009. pap. *(978-1-59608-690-6(4))* Biblio Services, Inc.

Seltzer, Richard. Getting a Cut: A Contextual Understanding of Commission Systems. 2010. (ENG.). 164p. 60.00 *(978-0-7391-4439-8(1))* Lexington Bks.

Senior Executive Service Bonuses: Ensuring the U.S. Department of Veterans Affairs Process Works: Hearing Before the Subcommittee on Oversight & Investigations of the Committee on Veterans' Affairs, U.S. House of Representatives, One Hundred Tenth Congress, First Session, June 12, 2007. 2008. (Illus.). iii, 55p. *(978-0-16-080742-8(5)*, 552-070-37346-2) United States Government Printing Office.

Startz, Dick. Profit of Education. 2010. (Illus.). xxiii, 230p. E-Book *(978-0-313-39380-8(X)*, Praeger Pubs.) Greenwood Publishing Group, Inc.

Startz, Richard. Profit of Education. 1 vol. 2010. (Illus.). 230p. 44.95 *(978-0-313-39379-2(6)*, A3391C, Praeger Pubs.) Greenwood Publishing Group, Inc.

BOOBY TRAPS (MILITARY SCIENCE)

see Mines (Military Explosives)

BOOK AGENTS

see Booksellers and Bookselling—Colportage, Subscription Trade, etc.

BOOK ART

see Artists' Books

BOOK BUYING (LIBRARIES)

see also Books—Prices

Lattu, Brandon. Brandon Lattu: Office Gray Case, 1 vol. 2010. (ENG., Illus.). 88p. 55.00 *(978-3-86560-351-7(3))* Verlag der Buchhandlung Walther Konig DEU. Dist: D.A.P./Distributed Art Pubs.

Rose, Jonathan, ed. The Holocaust & the Book: Destruction & Preservation. 2008. (Studies in Print Culture & the History of the Book). (ENG., Illus.). 314p. pap. 29.95 *(978-1-55849-643-9(2))* Univ. of Massachusetts Pr.

BOOK CENSORSHIP

see Censorship

BOOK CLUBS (BOOKSELLING)

Collins, Jim. Bring on the Books for Everybody: How Literary Culture Became Popular Culture. 2010. (ENG., Illus.). 300p. 84.95 *(978-0-8223-4588-6(9))*; pap. 23.95 *(978-0-8223-4606-7(0))* Duke Univ. Pr.

Mead, Barbara Drummond Mead, ed. Reading Group Choices 2008: Selections for Lively Book Discussion, Volume 14. 2007. 160p. pap. 6.95 *(978-0-9759742-3-0(8))* Reading Group Choices.

BOOK CLUBS (DISCUSSION GROUPS)

see also Group Reading

Appleman, Deborah. Reading for Themselves: How to Transform Adolescents into Lifelong Readers Through Out-of-Class Book Clubs. 2006. (ENG., Illus.). 128p. pap. 21.25 *(978-0-325-00827-1(2)*, E00827) Heinemann.

Calkins, Lucy McCormick & Ehrenworth, Mary. Tackling Complex Texts: Historical Fiction in Book Clubs. 2010. *(978-0-325-03068-5(5))* Heinemann.

Collins, Jim. Bring on the Books for Everybody: How Literary Culture Became Popular Culture. 2010. (ENG., Illus.). 300p. 84.95 *(978-0-8223-4588-6(9))*; pap. 23.95 *(978-0-8223-4606-7(0))* Duke Univ. Pr.

Dodson, Shireen. The Mother-Daughter: How Ten Busy Mothers & Daughters Came Together to Talk, Laugh, & Learn Through Their Love of Reading. 10th rev. ed. 2007. 304p. pap. 13.95 *(978-0-06-089034-6(7)*, HarperPerennial) HarperCollins Pubs.

Farr, Cecilia Konchar & Harker, Jaime, eds. The Oprah Affect: Critical Essays on Oprah's Book Club. 2008. 336p. (C). 74.50 *(978-0-7914-7615-4(4))*; pap. 29.95 *(978-0-7914-7616-1(2))* State Univ. of New York Pr.

Farren, Donald & Imholtz, August A., eds. The Baltimore Bibliophiles at Fifty, 1954-2004. 2009. 55.00 *(978-1-58456-251-1(X))* Oak Knoll Pr.

Fish, Thomas R. & Rabidoux, Paula. Next Chapter Book Club: A Model Community Literacy Program for People with Intellectual Disabilities. 2009. (Illus.). 200p. 24.95 *(978-1-890627-79-9(8))* Woodbine Hse.

Hill, Nanci. Reading Women: A Book Club Guide for Women's Fiction, 1 vol. 2012. 221p. pap. 35.00 *(978-1-59158-802-3(2)*, LU8802) Libraries Unlimited, Inc.

Hill, Nanci Milone. Reading Women: A Book Club Guide for Women's Fiction. 2012. E-Book ***(978-1-59158-806-1(5))*** ABC-CLIO, LLC.

Hollands, Neil. Fellowship in a Ring: A Guide for Science Fiction & Fantasy Book Groups, 1 vol. 2010. 300p. pap. 40.00 *(978-1-59158-703-3(4)*, LU7034) Libraries Unlimited, Inc.

Hudson, Cindy. Book by Book: The Complete Guide to Creating Mother-Daughter Book Clubs. 2009. (ENG.). 312p. pap. 16.95 *(978-1-58005-299-3(1))* Seal Pr.

Kooy, Mary. Telling Stories in Book Clubs: Women Teachers & Professional Development. 2010. xii, 244p. pap. 109.00 *(978-1-4419-4158-9(4)*, 1441941584) Springer.

Lit 'n' Lattes: Adding Faith & Fun to Your Book Club. 2008. pap. *(978-0-7644-3714-4(3))* Group Publishing, Inc.

Loevy, Diana. The Book Club Companion: A Comprehensive Guide to the Reading Group Experience. 2006. (ENG.). 352p. (gr. 12). per. 23.00 *(978-0-425-21009-3(X)*, Berkley Trade) Penguin Group (USA) Inc.

Malin, Ginger. From Literature to Life. 2009. 218p. pap. *(978-3-639-18189-0(1))* VDM Verlag Dr. Mueller e.K.

McDowell, Josh, et al. O God: A Dialogue on Truth & Oprah's Spirituality. 2009. 128p. pap. 14.99 *(978-1-935071-17-4(3))* WND Bks, Inc.

Mead, Barbara, ed. Reading Group Choices 2009: Selections for Lively Book Discussions. 2008. 176p. pap. 6.95 net. *(978-0-9759742-4-7(6))* Reading Group Choices.

Mead, Barbara Drummond Mead, ed. Reading Group Choices 2008: Selections for Lively Book Discussion, Volume 14. 2007. 160p. pap. 6.95 *(978-0-9759742-3-0(8))* Reading Group Choices.

Moeller, Victor J. & Moeller, Marc V. Literature Circles That Engage Middle & High School Students. 2007. (ENG.). 208p. pap. 29.95 *(978-1-59667-062-4(2))* Eye On Education, Inc.

Morris, Marilyn K. The Story of the Young Women's Book Club & the Birth of the Scottboro Public Library. 2009. 56p. pap. 9.95 *(978-1-4401-3142-4(2))* iUniverse, Inc.

Niebuhr, Gary Warren. Read 'Em Their Writes: A Handbook for Mystery & Crime Fiction Book Discussions, 1 vol. 2006. (Illus.). 264p. per. 35.00 *(978-1-59158-303-5(9)*, LU3039) Libraries Unlimited, Inc.

O'Donnell-Allen, Cindy. The Book Club Companion: Fostering Strategic Readers in the Secondary Classroom. 2006. (ENG., Illus.). 192p. pap. 30.00 *(978-0-325-00829-5(9)*, E00829) Heinemann.

Patrick, Kathy L. The Pulpwood Queens' Tiara-Wearing, Book-Sharing Guide to Life. l.t. ed. 2008. 485p. (YA). 29.95 *(978-1-4104-0782-5(9))* Thorndike Pr.

Ramone, Jenni & Cousins, Helen. The Richard & Judy Book Club Reader: Popular Texts & the Practices of Reading. 2011. 224p. 99.95 ***(978-1-4094-0133-9(2))*** Ashgate Publishing Co.

Rooney, Kathleen. Reading with Oprah: The Book Club That Changed America. 2nd ed. 2008. 284p. per. 17.95 *(978-1-55728-873-8(9))* Univ. of Arkansas Pr.

Roth, Philip & Herbert, Marilyn. Plot Against America. 2007. 82p. pap. 19.95 *(978-1-897082-18-8(5))* Bookclub-in-a-Box CAN. Dist: AtlasBooks Distribution.

Sedo, DeNel Rehberg, ed. Reading Communities from Salons to Cyberspace. 2011. (ENG., Illus.). 240p. 85.00 *(978-0-230-29988-7(1))* Palgrave Macmillan.

Sprague, Marsha M. & Keeling, Kara K. Discovering Their Voices: Engaging Adolescent Girls with Young Adult Literature. 2007. (Illus.). xii, 211p. (gr. 7-12). pap. 23.95 net. *(978-0-87207-611-2(3))* International Reading Assn.

Toews, Miriam. Bookclub in A Box Discusses the Novel A Complicated Kindness. 2006. 80p. pap. 19.95 *(978-1-897082-27-0(4))* Bookclub-in-a-Box CAN. Dist: AtlasBooks Distribution.

BOOK COLLECTING

see also Antiquarian Booksellers; Bibliomania; Books—Owners' Marks

Baron, Robert C. & Wright, Conrad Edick. The Libraries, Leadership, & Legacy of John Adams & Thomas Jefferson. 2010. (ENG.). 304p. 35.00 *(978-1-936218-08-0(9))* Fulcrum Publishing.

Bartlett, Allison Hoover. The Man Who Loved Books Too Much: The True Story of a Thief, a Detective, & a World of Literary Obsession. 2010. (ENG.). 288p. (gr.

12). 15.00 *(978-1-59448-481-0(3)*, Riverhead Trade (Paperbacks)) Penguin Group (USA) Inc.
Bauman, David & Bauman, Natalie. Rare Finds. 2007. 106p. pap. 12.95 *(978-0-615-15316-2(X))* Bauman Rare Bks.
—Rare Finds: A Guide to Book Collecting. 2007. (Illus.). 106p. pap. 12.95 *(978-1-4243-2050-9(X))* Bauman Rare Bks.
Bennett, Arnold. Literary Taste: How to Form It. 2007. 84p. per. *(978-1-4065-4794-8(8))* Dodo Pr.
—Literary Taste — How to Form It: With detailed instructions for collecting a complete library of English Literature. 2010. (ENG.). 132p. pap. 20.75 *(978-1-178-03641-1(3))* BiblioBazaar.
—Literary Taste; How to Form It with Detailed Instructions for Collecting a Complete Library of English Literature. 2010. (Illus.). 50p. pap. 20.00 *(978-1-153-74417-1(1))* General Bks. LLC.
Bennett, Arnold & Swinnerton, Frank. Literary Taste; How to Form It, with Detailed Instructions for Collecting a Complete Library of English Literature. 2010. 138p. pap. 20.75 *(978-1-177-85195-4(4))* BiblioBazaar.
Bernhard, Tim & Loe, Tim. Collecting the New Naturalists. 2011. (ENG., Illus.). 320p. 95.00 ***(978-0-00-736715-3(5))*** HarperCollins Pubs. Ltd. GBR. Dist: Independent Pubs. Group.
Bond, W. H. Thomas Hollis of Lincoln's Inn: A Whig & His Books. 2009. (Sandars Lectures in Bibliography Ser.). (ENG.). 152p. pap. 28.99 *(978-0-521-11480-5(2))* Cambridge Univ. Pr.
Bury, Richard de. Love of Books the Philobiblon of Richa. 2006. pap. *(978-1-4068-0109-5(7))* Echo Library.
—Philobiblon. 2009. 48p. pap. *(978-1-4588-4123-0(5))* Books LLC.
—Philobiblon, a Treatise on the Love of Books. 2006. 268p. per. 23.99 *(978-1-4255-2424-1(9))* MPublishing.
The Changing Book: Transitions in Design, Production, & Preser. 2008. (ENG.). 270p. 75.00 *(978-0-7890-3460-1(3))* Routledge.
De Ricci, Seymour. English Collectors of Books & Manuscripts, 1530-1930: And Their Marks of Ownership. 2011. (ENG.). 228p. pap. 22.99 *(978-0-521-15646-2(7))* Cambridge Univ. Pr.
Dershowitz, Alan M. Finding Jefferson: A Lost Letter, a Remarkable Discovery, & the First Amendment in an Age of Terrorism. 2007. (ENG., Illus.). 256p. 25.95 *(978-0-470-15711-3(4)*, Wiley) Wiley, John & Sons, Inc.
Dibdin, Thomas Frognall. Reminiscences of a Literary Life. 2010. (Cambridge Library Collection - Printing & Publishing History Ser.). (Illus.). 444p. pap. 32.99 *(978-1-108-00934-8(4))*; (ENG.). 608p. pap. 43.00 *(978-1-108-00933-1(6))* Cambridge Univ. Pr.
Elton, Charles Isaac. The Great Book-Collectors. 2007. (ENG.). 158p. pap. 19.99 *(978-1-4264-9505-2(6))*; 170p. pap. 21.99 *(978-1-4264-9886-2(1))* BiblioBazaar.
Elton, Charles Isaac & Elton, Mary Augusta. The Great Book-Collectors. 2008. 172p. 25.99 *(978-0-554-25773-0(4))*; 22.99 *(978-0-554-35076-9(9))* BiblioBazaar.
—The Great Book-Collectors. 2009. 108p. pap. *(978-1-4068-5171-7(X))* Echo Library.
—The Great Book-Collectors. 2007. (ENG.). 234p. 41.95 *(978-0-548-23001-5(3))*; 236p. per. 26.95 *(978-1-4325-5312-8(7))* Kessinger Publishing, LLC.
Elton, Charles Issac & Elton, Mary Augusta. The Great Book-Collectors. 2007. (Illus.). 160p. per. *(978-1-4065-2505-2(7))* Dodo Pr.
Ferguson, John. Some Aspects of Bibliography. 2010. 128p. pap. 19.75 *(978-1-147-53780-2(1))*; 122p. pap. 19.75 *(978-1-141-12107-6(7))*; 122p. pap. 19.75 *(978-1-141-06195-2(3))* BiblioBazaar.
—Some Aspects of Bibliography. 2009. 68p. pap. *(978-0-217-99471-2(7))* Books LLC.
Field, Eugene. The Love Affairs of a Bibliomaniac. 2009. 102p. pap. *(978-0-217-59564-3(2))* Books LLC.
—The Love Affairs of a Bibliomaniac. 2007. (ENG.). 108p. per. *(978-1-4065-2392-8(5))* Dodo Pr.
—The Love Affairs of a Bibliomaniac. 2009. 88p. pap. *(978-1-4068-9353-3(6))* Echo Library.
—The Love Affairs of a Bibliomaniac. 2007. 270p. 42.95 *(978-0-548-07233-2(7))* Kessinger Publishing, LLC.
—The Love Affairs of a Bibliomaniac. 2011. (Series: Fine Arts, Music & Literature Ser.). 75.00 *(978-1-60456-626-0(4)*, Nova Snova) Nova Science Pubs., Inc.
Hazlitt, W. Carew. The Book Collector. 2009. 364p. 33.99 *(978-1-113-62896-1(0))*; pap. 31.75 *(978-1-113-62894-7(4))* BiblioBazaar.
Hinks, John & Day, Matthew, eds. From Compositors to Collectors: Essays on Book-Trade History. 2012. 75.00 ***(978-1-58456-301-3(X))*** Oak Knoll Pr.
Hobson, Anthony. Renaissance Book Collecting: Jean Grolier & Diego Hurtado de Mendoza, their Books & Bindings. 2012. (ENG., Illus.). 295p. pap. 36.00 ***(978-0-521-12617-5(7))*** Cambridge Univ. Pr.
Jensen, Kristian. Revolution & the Antiquarian Book: Reshaping the Past, 1780-1815. 2011. (ENG., Illus.). 328p. 90.00 *(978-1-107-00051-3(3))* Cambridge Univ. Pr.
Jones, Diane McClure & Jones, Rosemary. Encyclopedia of Collectible Children's Books. 2008. (ENG., Illus.). 344p. 29.95 *(978-1-57432-575-1(2)*, 1574325752) Collector Bks.
Lang, Andrew. Books & Bookmen. 2009. 166p. 22.99 *(978-1-110-00813-1(9))*; pap. 16.99 *(978-1-110-00811-7(2))* BiblioBazaar.
—Books & Bookmen. 2009. 66p. pap. *(978-0-217-44913-7(1))* Books LLC.
—Books & Bookmen. 2007. 92p. per. *(978-1-4065-2607-3(X))* Dodo Pr.
—Books & Bookmen. 2008. 160p. 36.95 *(978-1-4369-0470-4(6))*; pap. 21.95 *(978-1-4367-9121-2(9))* Kessinger Publishing, LLC.
—The Library. reprint ed. 40.00 *(978-0-404-03816-8(6))* AMS Pr., Inc.
—The Library. 2007. 92p. per. *(978-1-4065-2627-1(4))* Dodo Pr.
—The Library. 2007. (ENG.). 218p. 39.95 *(978-0-548-04543-5(7))* Kessinger Publishing, LLC.
Lang, Andrew & Dobson, Austin. The Library. 2nd enl. ed. reprint ed. 40.00 *(978-0-404-03844-1(1))* AMS Pr., Inc.
Luther, Farnham. A Glance at Private Libraries. 2010. 84p. pap. 9.95 *(978-1-4290-4276-5(1))* Applewood Bks.
Merryweather, Frederick Somner. Bibliomania in the Middle Ages. 2008. 264p. 25.99 *(978-0-554-39123-6(6))*; 28.99 *(978-0-554-29820-7(1))* BiblioBazaar.
Murphy, Lynda & Rugg, Julie. Buried in Books: A Reader's Anthology. 2010. (ENG.). 224p. pap. 16.95 *(978-0-7112-2923-5(6))* Lincoln, Frances Ltd. GBR. Dist: Perseus-PGW.
Myers, Robin, et al, eds. Books on the Move: Tracking Copies Through Collections & the Book Trade. 2007. (Publishing Pathways Ser.). (Illus.). 180p. 49.95 *(978-1-58456-219-1(6))* Oak Knoll Pr.
Myers, Robin & Harris, Michael, eds. Antiquaries, Book Collectors & the Circles of Learning. (Illus.). 165p. *(978-1-873040-29-4(6))* Bow Historical Bks.
Myers, Robin, et al. Owners, Annotators & the Signs of Reading. (Publishing Pathways Ser.). (Illus.). xv, 231p. (C). *(978-1-58456-171-2(8))* Oak Knoll Pr.
Prince, Richard. Richard Prince: American Prayer. 2011. (ENG., Illus.). 600p. pap. 65.00 *(978-0-8478-3649-9(5))* Rizzoli International Pubns., Inc.
Quentin-Bauchart, Ernest. Les Femmes Bibliophiles de France, 2 Vols. reprint ed. 250.00 *(978-0-7222-1916-4(4))* Library Reprints, Inc.
Ransom, Harry. A Renaissance Gentleman in Texas: Notes on the Life & Library of Swante Palm. Carroll, H. Bailey & Hackett, Charles W., eds. 2011. 16p. pap. 35.95 ***(978-1-258-05477-9(9))*** Literary Licensing, LLC.
Rasmussen, Eric. The Shakespeare Thefts: In Search of the First Folios. 2012. (ENG., Illus.). 240p. pap. 17.00 ***(978-0-230-34167-8(5))*** Palgrave Macmillan.
Russell, Richard. Antique Trader Book Collector's Price Guide. 3rd ed. 2009. (ENG.). 400p. pap. 24.99 *(978-1-4402-0372-5(5))* Krause Pubns.
Shannon, Mike. Baseball Books: A Collector's Guide. 2007. (ENG.). 257p. per. 29.95 *(978-0-7864-3139-7(3))* McFarland & Co., Inc. Pubs.
Shriver, Lionel, frwd. The Book Club Bible: The Definitive Guide That Every Book Club Member Needs. 2008. (ENG.). 224p. pap. 15.95 *(978-1-84317-269-7(0))* O'Mara, Michael Bks., Ltd. GBR. Dist: Independent Pubs. Group.
Silver, Joel. Dr. Rosenbach & Mr. Lilly: Book Collecting in a Golden Age. 2011. ***(978-1-58456-295-5(1))*** Oak Knoll Pr.
Stokes, Roy. Bibliographical Companion. 2011. (ENG.). 308p. pap. 40.00 *(978-0-8108-6047-6(3))* Scarecrow Pr., Inc.
Summit, Jennifer. Memory's Library: Medieval Books in Early Modern England. 2011. (Illus.). 354p. pap. 27.50 *(978-0-226-78170-9(4))* Univ. of Chicago Pr.
Thomas Frognall, Dibdin. Bibliophobia: Remarks on the Present Languid & Depressed State of Literature & the Book Trade. in a Letter Addressed to the Author of the Bibliomania. 2010. (Cambridge Library Collection - Printing & Publishing History Ser.). 108p. pap. 19.99 *(978-1-108-01559-2(X))* Cambridge Univ. Pr.
Wendorf, Richard. The Literature of Collecting & Other Essays. 2008. 49.95 *(978-1-58456-230-6(7))* Oak Knoll Pr.
Wheatley, Henry Benjamin. How to Form a Library. 2009. 256p. 24.99 *(978-1-103-31851-3(9))* 2009. 256p. pap. 18.99 *(978-1-103-31849-0(7))* 2008. 240p. 28.99 *(978-0-554-63324-4(8))* 2008. 167p. 25.99 *(978-0-554-63333-6(7))* 2008. 260p. 25.99 *(978-0-554-49806-5(5))* 2008. 260p. 28.99 *(978-0-554-49788-4(3))* 2008. 240p. pap. 26.75 *(978-0-554-63328-2(0))* 2008. 240p. pap. 25.75 *(978-0-554-63330-5(2))* 2008. 260p. pap. 26.75 *(978-0-554-49797-6(2))* 2008. 260p. pap. 25.75 *(978-0-554-49803-4(0))* BiblioBazaar.
—How to Form a Library. 2009. 94p. pap. *(978-0-217-93373-5(4))* Books LLC.
—How to Form a Library. 2010. (Cambridge Library Collection - Printing & Publishing History Ser.). 264p. pap. 23.99 *(978-1-108-02149-4(2))* Cambridge Univ. Pr.
Willes, Margaret. Reading Matters: Five Centuries of Discovering Books. 2010. (ENG., Illus.). 304p. pap. 22.00 *(978-0-300-16404-6(1))* Yale Univ. Pr.
Wilson, Robert A. Modern Book Collecting: A Basic Guide to All Aspects of Book Collecting - What to Collect, Who to Buy From, Auctions, Bibliographies, Care, Fakes & Forgeries, Investment, Donation, Definitions, & More. 2010. (ENG., Illus.). 276p. pap. 14.95 *(978-1-60239-985-3(9)*, 239985) Skyhorse Publishing Co., Inc.

BOOK COLLECTING—BIBLIOGRAPHY

MacDonald, Dorothy, compiled by. Cumulative Index to American Book Collector. 7.50 *(978-0-89679-008-7(8))* Moretus Pr., Inc., The.
Slater, J. Herbert. Library Manual. 2006. 128p. per. *(978-1-4067-1848-5(3)*, Hesperides Pr.) Read Bks.

BOOK COLLECTORS

see also Book Clubs (Discussion Groups); Private Libraries

Bartlett, Allison Hoover. The Man Who Loved Books Too Much: The True Story of a Thief, a Detective, & a World of Literary Obsession. 2010. (ENG.). 288p. (gr. 12). 15.00 *(978-1-59448-481-0(3)*, Riverhead Trade (Paperbacks)) Penguin Group (USA) Inc.
Bond, W. H. Thomas Hollis of Lincoln's Inn: A Whig & His Books. 2009. (Sandars Lectures in Bibliography Ser.). (ENG.). 152p. pap. 28.99 *(978-0-521-11480-5(2))* Cambridge Univ. Pr.
Bond, William H. & Bond, W. H. From the Great Desire of Promoting Learning: Thomas Hollis's Gifts to the Harvard College Library. 2010. (Harvard Library Bulletin Ser.: 19). (Illus.). 275p. 29.95 *(978-0-9765472-9-7(5))* Harvard Univ. Pr.
Booton, Diane E. Manuscripts, Market & the Transition to Print in Late Medieval Brittany. 2010. (Illus.). 490p. 144.95 *(978-0-7546-6623-3(9))* Ashgate Publishing Co.
De Ricci, Seymour. English Collectors of Books & Manuscripts, 1530-1930: And Their Marks of Ownership. 2011. (ENG.). 228p. pap. 22.99 *(978-0-521-15646-2(7))* Cambridge Univ. Pr.
Edwards, Edward. Free Town Libraries, their Formation, Management, & History: In Britain, France, Germany, & America. 2010. (Cambridge Library Collection - Printing & Publishing History Ser.). 676p. pap. 45.00 *(978-1-108-00936-2(0))* Cambridge Univ. Pr.
—Free Town Libraries, Their Formation, Management, & History; in Britain, France, Germany, & America. 2006. 684p. per. 36.99 *(978-1-4255-6830-6(0))* MPublishing.
—Libraries & Founders of Libraries. 2010. (Cambridge Library Collection - Printing & Publishing History Ser.). (ENG.). 540p. pap. 39.99 *(978-1-108-01052-8(0))* Cambridge Univ. Pr.
—Lives of the Founders of the British Museum: With Notices of its Chief Augmentors & Other Benefactors, 1570-1870. 2010. (Cambridge Library Collection - Printing & Publishing History Ser.). (ENG., Illus.). 436p. pap. 32.99 *(978-1-108-01495-3(X))*; 396p. pap. 31.99 *(978-1-108-01496-0(8))* Cambridge Univ. Pr.
Elton, Charles Isaac. The Great Book-Collectors. 2007. (ENG.). 158p. pap. 19.99 *(978-1-4264-9505-2(6))*; 170p. pap. 21.99 *(978-1-4264-9886-2(1))* BiblioBazaar.
Elton, Charles Isaac & Elton, Mary Augusta. The Great Book-Collectors. 2008. 172p. 22.99 *(978-0-554-35076-9(9))*; 25.99 *(978-0-554-25773-0(4))* BiblioBazaar.
—The Great Book-Collectors. 2009. 108p. pap. *(978-1-4068-5171-7(X))* Echo Library.
—The Great Book-Collectors. 2007. (ENG.). 234p. 41.95 *(978-0-548-23001-5(3))*; 236p. per. 26.95 *(978-1-4325-5312-8(7))* Kessinger Publishing, LLC.
Elton, Charles Issac & Elton, Mary Augusta. The Great Book-Collectors. 2007. (Illus.). 160p. per. *(978-1-4065-2505-2(7))* Dodo Pr.
Farren, Donald & Imholtz, August A., eds. The Baltimore Bibliophiles at Fifty, 1954-2004. 2009. 55.00 *(978-1-58456-251-1(X))* Oak Knoll Pr.
Fletcher, William Younger. English Book Collectors. 2009. 204p. pap. *(978-0-217-71638-3(5))* Books LLC.
—English Book Collectors. Pollard, Alfred, ed. 2008. (Illus.). 344p. pap. *(978-1-4099-0694-0(9))* Dodo Pr.
Hazlitt, W. Carew. The Book Collector. 2009. 364p. 33.99 *(978-1-113-62896-1(0))*; pap. 31.75 *(978-1-113-62894-7(4))* BiblioBazaar.
Hazlitt, William Carew. Confessions of A Collector. 2006. pap. 33.95 *(978-1-4286-3415-2(0))* Kessinger Publishing, LLC.
—The Confessions of a Collector. 2009. 372p. 33.99 *(978-1-115-25679-7(3))*; pap. 31.75 *(978-1-115-25677-3(7))* BiblioBazaar.
—The Confessions of a Collector. 2009. 164p. pap. 19.99 *(978-1-4589-7905-6(9))* General Bks. LLC.
—The Confessions of a Collector. 2007. (ENG.). 372p. 48.95 *(978-0-548-12455-0(8))* Kessinger Publishing, LLC.
Hinks, John & Day, Matthew, eds. From Compositors to Collectors: Essays on Book-Trade History. 2012. 75.00 ***(978-1-58456-301-3(X))*** Oak Knoll Pr.
Information Today Inc, creator. American Book Trade Directory. 55th ed. 2009. (American Book Trade Directory Ser.). (Illus.). 1632p. 375.00 *(978-1-57387-345-1(4))* Information Today, Inc.
Kerr, Donald Jackson. Amassing Treasures for All Times: Sir George Grey, Colonial Bookman & Collector. 2007. (Illus.). 351p. 49.95 *(978-1-58456-196-5(3))* Oak Knoll Pr.
MacDonald, Dorothy, compiled by. Cumulative Index to American Book Collector. 7.50 *(978-0-89679-008-7(8))* Moretus Pr., Inc., The.
Merryweather, F. Somner. Bibliomania in the Middle Ages. 2009. 250p. pap. *(978-1-4099-8324-8(2))* Dodo Pr.
Painter, Deborah. Forry: The Life of Forrest J Ackerman. 2010. (ENG., Illus.). 224p. 45.00 *(978-0-7864-4884-5(9))* McFarland & Co., Inc. Pubs.
Private Libraries Association Staff, contrib. by. A Modest Collection: Private Libraries Association, 1956-2006. 2007. (Illus.). 378p. 60.00 *(978-0-900002-67-0(0))*, Private Libraries Assn. GBR. Dist: Oak Knoll Pr.
Silverman, Willa Z. The New Bibliopolis: French Book Collectors & the Culture of Print, 1880-1914. 2008. (Studies in Book & Print Culture Ser.). (ENG., Illus.). 368p. *(978-0-8020-9211-3(X))* Univ. of Toronto Pr.
Smith, Carolyn L., ed. Members of the Grolier Club, 1884-2009. 2009. (ENG.). 240p. pap. 20.00 *(978-1-60583-022-3(4))* Grolier Club of New York, The.
Udoff, Alan, et al. The Companionship of Books: Essays in Honor of Laurence Berns. 2011. (ENG.). 308p. 80.00 ***(978-0-7391-5046-7(4))*** Lexington Bks.
Wendorf, Richard. The Literature of Collecting & Other Essays. 2008. 49.95 *(978-1-58456-230-6(7))* Oak Knoll Pr.
Willes, Margaret. Reading Matters: Five Centuries of Discovering Books. 2010. (ENG., Illus.). 304p. pap. 22.00 *(978-0-300-16404-6(1))* Yale Univ. Pr.

BOOK COVERS

see also Book Jackets

Altitude Associates. The Best of Cover Design: Books, Magazines, Catalogs, & More. 2011. (ENG., Illus.). 224p. 45.00 *(978-1-59253-689-4(1)*, 1592536891, Fair Winds Press) Quayside.
Beletsky, Misha. The Book Jackets of Ismar David: A Calligraphic Legacy. 2011. (Illus.). 48p. pap. 19.95 *(978-1-933360-51-5(8)*, RIT Cary Graphic Arts Pr.) Rochester Institute of Technology, Cary Graphic Arts Pr.
Brower, Steven. Breathless Homicidal Slime Mutants: The Art of the Paperback. 2010. (ENG., Illus.). 304p. pap. 24.95 *(978-0-7893-1804-6(0))* Universe Publishing.
Buckley, Paul, ed. & intro. Designers, Authors, Commentary (The Good, the Bad...) 2010. (ENG., Illus.). 256p. (gr. 12). pap. 25.00 *(978-0-14-311762-9(9)*, Penguin (Non-Classics)) Penguin Group (USA) Inc.
Cosmic Debris Etc., Inc. Staff, et al. Art of Mcsweeney's. 2010. (ENG., Illus.). 264p. 45.00 *(978-0-8118-6623-1(8))* Chronicle Bks. LLC.
Crane, Walter, illus. The Marquis of Carabas Picture Book. 2008. 36p. pap. *(978-1-84830-913-5(9)*, Wildhern Pr.) Echo Library.
Drew, Ned, et al. Purity of Aim: The Book Jackets of Alvin Lustig. 2010. (Illus.). 88p. 21.95 *(978-1-933360-48-5(8)*, RIT Cary Graphic Arts Pr.) Rochester Institute of Technology, Cary Graphic Arts Pr.
Dubansky, Mindell. The Proper Decoration of Book Covers: The Life & Work. 2008. (ENG., Illus.). 108p. pap. 35.00 *(978-0-910672-74-0(1))* Grolier Club of New York, The.
Foss, Chris. Hardware: The Definitive SF Works of Chris Foss. 2011. (ENG., Illus.). 240p. reprint ed. 34.95 *(978-1-84856-698-9(0)*, Titan Bks.) Titan Bks. Ltd. GBR. Dist: Random Hse., Inc.
Gertz, Stephen J. Dope Menace: The Sensational World of Drug Paperbacks, 1900-1975. 2008. (ENG., Illus.). 250p. pap. 24.95 *(978-1-932595-34-5(1))* Feral Hse.
Gill, Simryn, ed. Pearls. 2008. (Illus.). 204p. pap. *(978-0-9556674-0-4(2))* Actar Birkhauser Distribution.
Jean, James. Fables: Covers by James Jean. 2008. (Illus.). 208p. 49.99 *(978-1-4012-1576-7(9)*, Vertigo) DC Comics.
Larkin, Bob, illus. The Savage Art of Bob Larkin, Volume One. 2009. 64p. pap. 19.95 *(978-0-86562-175-6(6))* S.Q. Productions, Inc.
Lascault, Gilbert. In Folio: Gouaches et Aquarelles de Candida Romero. 2012. (FRE & ENG., Illus.). 112p. pap. 30.00 *(978-2-35340-025-6(6))* Gourcuff Gradenigo FRA. Dist: National Bk. Network.
Marren, Peter & Gillmor, Robert. The Art of the New Naturalists: A Complete History. 2009. (ENG., Illus.). 288p. 80.00 *(978-0-00-728471-9(3))* HarperCollins Pubs. Ltd. GBR. Dist: Independent Pubs. Group.
Matthews, Nicole & Moody, Nickianne, eds. Judging a Book by Its Cover: Fans, Publishers, Designers, & the Marketing of Fiction. 2007. (Illus.). 214p. 99.95 *(978-0-7546-5731-6(0)*, Ashgate Publishing Co.
Minskey, Robert & Minsky, Richard, eds. The Art of American Book Covers: 1875-1930. 2010. (ENG., Illus.). 136p. 34.95 *(978-0-8076-1602-4(8)*, 761602) Braziller, George Inc.
Puffin Books Staff. Postcards from Puffin: One Hundred Puffin Covers in One. 2012. (ENG., Illus.). 100p. (J). 25.00 ***(978-0-14-133337-3(5)***, Puffin) Penguin Group (USA) Inc.
Salvatore, R. A. The Comic Cover Art of Dungeons & Dragons, Vol. 1. 2008. (Illus.). 300p. (YA). 49.99 *(978-1-934692-19-6(0))* Devil's Due Publishing, Inc.
Suydam, Arthur. Marvel Zombies: The Covers. 2007. (ENG., Illus.). 104p. 19.99 *(978-0-7851-2908-0(1))* Marvel Worldwide, Inc.

BOOK DEDICATIONS

see Dedications

BOOK DESIGN

AIGA Staff. Designing Audiences. 2008. (ENG., Illus.). 112p. per. 16.95 *(978-1-56898-751-4(X))* Princeton Architectural Pr.
Barchas, Janine. Graphic Design, Print Culture, & the Eighteenth-Century Novel. 2008. (ENG., Illus.). 316p. pap. 42.00 *(978-0-521-09057-5(1))* Cambridge Univ. Pr.
Boot, Peter. Mesotext: Digitised Emblems, Modelled Annotations & Humanities Scholarship. 2009. (Pallas Proefschriften Ser.). pap. *(978-90-8964-187-8(4))*; (ENG.). 288p. pap. *(978-90-8555-052-5(1))* Amsterdam Univ. Pr. (Pallas Publications).
Bringhurst, Robert. The Surface of Meaning: Books & Book Design in Canada. 2009. (ENG.). 240p. 59.95 *(978-0-9738727-2-9(1)*, Canadian Centre for Studies in Publishing) CCSP Pr CAN. Dist: Perseus-PGW.
Capek, Josef. The Book Design of Josef Capek: Seeing the Book. 2011. (ENG., Illus.). 328p. 80.00 *(978-80-7437-014-4(3))* Kant CZE. Dist: D.A.P./Distributed Art Pubs.
Cosmic Debris Etc., Inc. Staff, et al. Art of Mcsweeney's. 2010. (ENG., Illus.). 264p. 45.00 *(978-0-8118-6623-1(8))* Chronicle Bks. LLC.
Cram101 Textbook Reviews. Outlines & Highlights for a History of Graphic Design by Meggs, Isbn: 0471291986. 2011. 512p. pap. 37.95 ***(978-1-61830-058-4(X))*** Cram101 Inc.
Cram101 Textbook Reviews. Outlines & Highlights for Meggs History of Graphic Design by Philip B Meggs, Alston W Purvis, Isbn: 9780471699026. 2010. 144p. pap. 28.95 *(978-1-61698-353-6(1))* Cram101 Inc.
Diehn, Gwen. Live & Learn: Real Life Journals - Designing & Using Handmade Books. 2010. (AARP Ser.). (ENG.). 180p. 24.95 *(978-1-60059-492-2(1))* Lark Bks.
Doubleday, Richard B. Jan Tschichold, Designer: The Penguin Years. 2006. (Illus.). 240p. 39.95 *(978-1-58456-178-1(5))* Oak Knoll Pr.
Feeding Your Wild Child. 2009. (ENG., Illus.). 419p. pap. *(978-0-9779098-2-7(4))* Everglades Publishing.
Frankel, Nicholas. Masking the Text: Essays on Literature & Mediation in the 1890s. 2009. (Illus.). 279p. *(978-1-904201-14-4(8))* Rivendale Pr.

Gaylord, Susan Kapuscinski. Handmade Books for a Healthy Planet: Sixteen Earth-Friendly Projects from Around the World. 2010. (ENG., Illus.). 130p. pap. 19.95 *(978-0-9842319-0-4(0))* makingbooks.com.

Golden, Alisa J. Making Handmade Books: 100+ Bindings, Structures & Forms. 2011. (ENG., Illus.). 256p. pap. 19.95 *(978-1-60059-587-5(1))* Lark Bks.

GROUP WORK, compiled by. Imprint: Innovative book & promo Design. 2011. (ENG., Illus.). 240p. *(978-84-92810-27-7(0))* Promotora de prensa internacional S.A.

Hamilton, April. The Indie Author Guide: Self-Publishing Strategies Anyone Can Use. 2nd ed. 2010. (ENG., Illus.). 304p. pap. 19.99 *(978-1-58297-994-6(4),* Writer's Digest Bks.) F&W Media, Inc.

Haslam, Andrew. Book Design. 2006. (ENG., Illus.). 256p. pap. 32.50 *(978-0-8109-9220-7(5))* Abrams.

Hemachandra, Ray. Lark Studio Series: Handmade Books. 2010. (ENG., Illus.). 204p. 12.95 *(978-1-60059-682-7(7))* Lark Bks.

Jury, David, ed. Book Art Object. 2010. (ENG., Illus.). 448p. 155.00 *(978-0-9817914-0-1(9))* Codex Foundation.

Kelly, Jerry. The Art of the Book in the Twentieth Century: A Study of Eleven Influential Book Designers from 1900 To 2000. 2011. (ENG., Illus.). 200p. 39.95 *(978-1-933360-46-1(1),* RIT Cary Graphic Arts Pr.) Rochester Institute of Technology, Cary Graphic Arts Pr.

—The First Flowering: Bruce Rogers at the Riverside Press, 1896-1912. 2008. (ENG., Illus.). 96p. 75.00 *(978-1-56792-374-2(7))* Boss, Thomas G. Fine Bks.

Kuhl, Nancy, ed. Erica Van Horn: the Book Remembers Everything. 2011. (ENG., Illus.). 122p. 20.00 *(978-1-887123-79-2(2))* Granary Bks., Inc.

Lark. 500 Handmade Books: Inspiring Interpretations of a Timeless Form. 2008. (500 Ser.). (ENG., Illus.). 420p. pap. 24.95 *(978-1-57990-877-5(2))* Lark Bks.

Lee, Marshall, et al. Bookmaking: Editing, Design, Production. 3rd ed. 2009. (ENG., Illus.). 494p. pap. 31.50 net. *(978-0-393-73296-2(7),* 73296) Norton, W. W. & Co., Inc.

Loxley, Simon. Printer's Devil: The Life & Work of Frederic Warde. 2012. (ENG., Illus.). 179p. 45.00 *(978-1-56792-367-4(4))* Godine, David R. Pub.

Lupton, Ellen. Indie Publishing: How to Design & Produce Your Own Book. Lupton, Ellen, ed. 2008. (ENG., Illus.). 112p. pap. 24.95 *(978-1-56898-760-6(9))* Princeton Architectural Pr.

Lynskey, Marie. Family Trees: A Manual for Their Design, Layout & Display. 2011. (ENG.). 112p. pap. 24.95 *(978-1-86077-596-3(9))* History Pr. Ltd.,The GBR. Dist: Independent Pubs. Group.

Martens, Karel, et al. Printed Matter - Drukwerk. 3rd ed. 2011. (DUT & ENG., Illus.). 256p. pap. 60.00 *(978-0-907259-41-1(3))* Hyphen Pr. GBR. Dist: Hachette Bk. Group.

McCafferty, Kathleen. Making Mini Books: Big Ideas for 30+ Little Projects. 2012. (ENG., Illus.). 144p. pap. 19.95 ***(978-1-4547-0200-9(1))*** Lark Bks.

Meggs, Philip B. & Purvis, Alston W. Meggs' History of Graphic Design. 5th ed. 2011. (ENG., Illus.). 624p. 85.00 ***(978-0-470-16873-8(0),*** Wiley) Wiley, John & Sons, Inc.

Michaels, Adam & Schnapp, Jeffrey T. The Electric Information Age Book: McLuhan/Agel/Fiore & the Experimental. 2012. (ENG., Illus.). 240p. pap. 22.95 ***(978-1-61689-034-6(7))*** Princeton Architectural Pr.

Miller, Abbott J. Open Book: Design & Content by Abbott Miller. 2008. 224p. 60.00 *(978-1-56898-726-2(9))* Princeton Architectural Pr.

Millidge, Gary & Gary Spencer, Millidge. Comic Book Design: The Essential Guide to Creating Great Comics & Graphic Novels. 2009. (ENG., Illus.). 160p. pap. 24.95 *(978-0-8230-9796-8(X))* Crown Publishing Group.

Newfeld, Frank. Drawing on Type. 2008. (ENG., Illus.). 336p. pap. 27.95 *(978-0-88984-304-2(X))* Porcupine's Quill, Inc. CAN. Dist: Univ. of Toronto Pr.

Rinehart, Benjamin D. Creating Books & Boxes: Fun & Unique Approaches to Handmade Structures. 2007. (ENG., Illus.). 128p. pap. 24.99 *(978-1-59253-291-9(8),* 1592532918) Quayside.

Rivers, Charlotte. Book-Art: Innovation in Book Design. 2010. (ENG., Illus.). 160p. pap. 19.99 *(978-2-88893-088-4(9),* 2888930889) RotoVision SA CHE. Dist: Quayside.

Roddis, Sue. Handmade Decorative Books. 2010. (Passion for Paper Ser.). (ENG., Illus.). 80p. pap. 19.95 *(978-1-84448-314-3(2))* Search Pr., Ltd. GBR. Dist: Independent Pubs. Group.

Shirley, Rodney. Courtiers & Cannibals, Angels & Amazons: The art of the decorative cartographic Titlepage. 2009. (Illus.). 272p. 89.00 *(978-90-6194-060-9(5))* HES & DE GRAAF Pubs. BV NLD. Dist: Oak Knoll Pr.

Tanselle, G. Thomas. Bibliographical Analysis: A Historical Introduction. 2009. (ENG.). 176p. (C). 77.00 *(978-0-521-76034-8(8));* pap. 27.99 *(978-0-521-75762-1(2))* Cambridge Univ. Pr.

Thomas, Peter & Thomas, Donna. More Making Books by Hand: Exploring Miniature Books, Alternative Structures, & Found Objects. 2007. (Illus.). 142p. pap. 19.00 *(978-1-4223-6592-2(1))* DIANE Publishing Co.

Toman, Jindrich, ed. Photo-Montage in Print. 2011. (ENG., Illus.). 376p. 75.00 *(978-80-86970-92-9(2))* Kant CZE. Dist: D.A.P./Distributed Art Pubs.

Vinegar, Aron. I Am a Monument: On Learning from Las Vegas. (ENG., Illus.). 248p. (gr. 17). 2012. pap. 16.95 ***(978-0-262-51752-2(3))*** 2008. 29.95 *(978-0-262-22082-8(2))* MIT Pr.

Wilde, Oscar & Ricketts, Charles S. The Sphinx. 2010. *(978-0-89263-034-9(5)); (978-0-89263-035-6(3)); (978-0-89263-033-2(7)); (978-0-89263-032-5(9))* Rice Univ. Pr.

Withers, Benjamin C. The Illustrated Old English Hexateuch, Cotton Claudius B.IV: The Frontier of Seeing & Reading in Anglo-Saxon England. 2007. (Studies in Book & Print Culture Ser.). (ENG., Illus.). 464p. *(978-0-8020-9104-8(0))* Univ. of Toronto Pr.

Wolff, Laetitia. Massin. 2007. (ENG., Illus.). 216p. 75.00 *(978-0-7148-4811-2(5))* Phaidon Pr., Inc.

BOOK DISCUSSION GROUPS

see Book Clubs (Discussion Groups)

BOOK FAIRS

see Book Industries and Trade—Exhibitions

BOOK ILLUSTRATION

see Illustration of Books

BOOK INDUSTRIES AND TRADE

see also Bookbinding; Booksellers and Bookselling; Paper Making and Trade; Printing; Publishers and Publishing

Acree Jr., William Garrett. Everyday Reading: Print Culture & Collective Identity in the Rio de la Plata, 1780-1910. 2011. (ENG., Illus.). 304p. 55.00 *(978-0-8265-1789-0(7))* Vanderbilt Univ. Pr.

Ashuntantang, Joyce B. Landscaping Postcoloniality: The Dissemination of Cameroon Anglophone Literature. 2009. 188p. pap. *(978-9956-558-29-2(X))* Langaa Research & Publishing Common Initiative Group CMR. Dist: Michigan State Univ. Pr.

Bancroft, Hubert Howe. Literary Industries. 2009. 550p. pap. *(978-0-217-50730-1(1));* 310p. pap. *(978-0-217-01555-4(7))* Books LLC.

BIA. Key Russian Manufacturers & Suppliers of Books & Publishing Materials. 6th rev. ed. 2006. 436p. (J). pap. 249.00 *(978-1-4187-4503-5(0))* Business Information Agency.

Borealis Centre for Environment and Trade Research, compiled by. Environmental Trends & Climate Impacts: Findings from the U. S. Book Industry. 2008. (Illus.). 73p. per. 195.00 net. *(978-0-940016-90-3(7))* Bk. Industry Study Group, Inc.

Bradley, Sue, ed. The British Book Trade: An Oral History. 2010. (ENG.). 320p. pap. 22.50 *(978-0-7123-5091-4(8))* British Library, The GBR. Dist: Chicago Distribution Ctr.

Brokaw, Cynthia J. Commerce in Culture: The Sibao Book Trade in the Qing & Republican Periods. 2007. (Harvard East Asian Monographs: 280). (Illus.). 673p. 44.95 *(978-0-674-02449-6(4))* Harvard Univ., Asia Ctr.

Bullock, Adrian. Book Production. 2012. (ENG., Illus.). 224p. (C). 125.00 ***(978-0-415-59379-3(4));*** pap. 44.95 ***(978-0-415-59380-9(8))*** Routledge.

Carter, David. Big Money in Books. 2007. 244p. pap. 25.50 *(978-1-84799-990-0(5))* Lulu Enterprises Inc.

Ceballos Viro, Alvaro. Ediciones Alemanas en Español (1850-1900) 2009. (SPA., Illus.). 416p. pap. *(978-84-8489-482-7(7))* Iberoamericana Vervuert Publishing Corp.

Connelly, Valerie. Calling All Authors: How to Publish with Your Eyes Wide Open. 2007. (ENG.). 316p. per. 19.95 *(978-1-933449-43-2(8))* Nightengale Pr.

Cram101 Textbook Reviews & Cram101 Textbook Reviews. Outlines & Highlights for Book Production & Publishing in Britain 1375-1475 by Derek Pearsall, Isbn: 9780521037211. 2011. 88p. pap. 27.95 ***(978-1-4288-4403-2(1))*** Cram101 Inc.

Croenen, Godfried, et al, eds. Patrons, Authors & Workshops: Books & Book Production in Paris Around 1400. 2006. (Synthema Ser.: Vol. 4). (FRE & ENG., Illus.). 530p. (C). pap. 101.00 *(978-90-429-1707-1(5))* Peeters Pubs. & Booksellers BEL. Dist: Brown, David Bk. Co., The.

Daniels, Rhiannon. Boccaccio & the Book: Production & Reading in Italy 1340-1520. 2009. (Legenda Italian Perspectives Ser.). (ENG., Illus.). 240p. (C). 89.50 *(978-1-906540-49-4(7))* European Humanities Research Ctr. GBR. Dist: Brown, David Bk. Co., The.

Davies, Gill & Balkwill, Richard. The Professionals' Guide to Publishing: A Practical Introduction to Working in the Publishing Industry. 2011. (ENG.). 352p. pap. 49.95 *(978-0-7494-5541-5(1))* Kogan Page, Ltd. GBR. Dist: Ingram Pub. Services.

Duff, E. Gordon. A Century of the English Book Trade: Short Notices of All Printers, Stationers, Book-Binders, & Others Connected with It from the Issue of the First Dated Book in 1457 to the Incorporation of the Company of Stationers In 1557. 2011. (Cambridge Library Collection - Printing & Publishing History Ser.). 242p. pap. 22.99 *(978-1-108-02676-5(1))* Cambridge Univ. Pr.

Eberspächer, Jörg, ed. Die Zukunft der Printmedien: Tagungsband. 2007. (GER.). 260p. per. 64.95 *(978-3-540-43356-9(2))* Springer.

Elicksen, Debbie. Book Publishing 101: Workbook. 2nd ed. 2010. 20.00 *(978-0-9865956-1-5(6))* Booklocker.com, Inc.

Escalante Gonzalbo, Fernando. A la Sombra de Los Libros: Lectura, Mercado y Vida Pública. 2007. (Jornadas Ser.). (SPA.). 361p. pap. 32.99 *(978-968-12-1323-7(8))* El Colegio de México, A.C., Biblioteca Miguel Cosio Villegas MEX. Dist: Fondo de Cultura Economica USA.

Fraser, Jay. The American Publisher: Paying the Cost of Corporatism & Censorship for Writing the Truth about Cuba, Russia, & the War on Terror. 2010. (Illus.). 256p. 28.00 *(978-1-879915-22-0(7))* Signal Peak Pr. LLC.

Frishman, Rick. Interviews from the Million Dollar Rolodex. 2007. (ENG.). 133p. per. 9.95 *(978-1-60037-251-3(1))* Morgan James Publishing.

Garvey, Nathan. The Celebrated George Barrington: A Spurious Author; the Book Trade, & Botany Bay. 2008. 327p. 49.95 *(978-1-875567-54-6(2))* Hordern Hse. AUS. Dist: Oak Knoll Pr.

Gillespie, Alexandra & Wakelin, Daniel, eds. The Production of Books in England 1350-1500. 2011. (Cambridge Studies in Palaeography & Codicology Ser.). (ENG., Illus.). 396p. 95.00 *(978-0-521-88979-7(0))* Cambridge Univ. Pr.

Gomez, Jeff. Print Is Dead: Books in Our Digital Age. 2009. (ENG.). 304p. pap. 16.95 *(978-0-230-61446-8(9))* Palgrave Macmillan.

Hagen, Oliver A., ed. Digital Books: Competition & Commerce. 2010. (Media & Communications - Technologies, Policies & Challenges Ser.). (Illus.). 140p. 130.00 *(978-1-61728-299-7(5))* Nova Science Pubs., Inc.

Hamilton, April. The Indie Author Guide: Self-Publishing Strategies Anyone Can Use. 2nd ed. 2010. (ENG., Illus.). 304p. pap. 19.99 *(978-1-58297-994-6(4),* Writer's Digest Bks.) F&W Media, Inc.

Haynes, Christine. Lost Illusions: The Politics of Publishing in Nineteenth-Century France. 2010. (Harvard Historical Studies: 167). (Illus.). 346p. 47.50 *(978-0-674-03576-8(3))* Harvard Univ. Pr.

Hinks, John & Armstrong, Catherine, eds. Book Trade Connections from the Seventeenth to the Twentieth Centuries. 2008. (Illus.). 281p. 49.95 *(978-1-58456-229-0(3))* Oak Knoll Pr.

Horowitz, Shel. Grassroots Marketing for Authors & Publishers. 2007. 290p. pap. 24.95 *(978-0-7414-3469-2(5))* Infinity Publishing.

Institute for Publishing Research Staff & Open Book Publishing Staff. Book Industry TRENDS 2007. annuals 30th ed. 2007. 256p. 875.00 net. *(978-0-940016-89-7(3))* Bk. Industry Study Group, Inc.

Jager, Georg, ed. Geschichte des Deutschen Buchhandels im 19 und 20 Jh, Vol. 3. 2010.Tr. of History of the German Book Trade in the 19th & 20th Century. (GER.). 579p. *(978-3-598-24804-7(0))* Saur, K. G. Verlag GmbH & Co.

Kanouse, Patrick. The Nook Book: An Unofficial Guide. 2nd rev. ed. 2011. (Illus.). 336p. pap. 14.99 ***(978-0-7897-4908-6(4))*** Que.

Lee, Marshall, et al. Bookmaking: Editing, Design, Production. 3rd ed. 2009. (ENG., Illus.). 494p. pap. 31.50 net. *(978-0-393-73296-2(7),* 73296) Norton, W. W. & Co., Inc.

Lupton, Ellen. Indie Publishing: How to Design & Produce Your Own Book. Lupton, Ellen, ed. 2008. (ENG., Illus.). 112p. pap. 24.95 *(978-1-56898-760-6(9))* Princeton Architectural Pr.

Maclean, Ian. Scholarship, Commerce, Religion: The Learned Book in the Age of Confessions, 1560-1630. 2012. (ENG., Illus.). 392p. 49.95 ***(978-0-674-06208-5(5))*** Harvard Univ. Pr.

Marantz, Kenneth A. & Marantz, Sylvia S. Creating Picturebooks: Interviews with Editors, Art Directors, Reviewers, Booksellers, Professors, Librarians & Showcasers. alt. ed. 2006. (ENG.). 247p. per. 49.95 *(978-0-7864-2734-5(5))* McFarland & Co., Inc. Pubs.

Martin, Gail. Launching Your Books Without Losing Your Mind. 2010. 124p. pap. 13.99 *(978-1-935361-06-0(6))* Comfort Publishing Services, LLC.

Milliot, Jim, ed. 2009 Book Consumer Annual Review: U.S. Demographics & Buying Behaviors. 2010. 112p. pap. 999.00 *(978-0-8352-5081-8(4))* Bowker LLC, R. R.

Milliot, Jim, ed. 2010-2011 U.S. Book Consumer Demographics & Buying Behaviors Annual Review. 2011. 122p. pap. 999.00 ***(978-0-8352-5084-9(9))*** Bowker LLC, R. R.

Moses, James. Children's Publishing, Media & Entertainment. 252p. 265.00 *(978-0-9626749-7-6(4))* Primary Research Group.

Ooligan Press. Rethinking Paper & Ink: The Sustainable Publishing Revolution. 2011. (OpenBook Ser.). (ENG.). 168p. pap. 21.95 *(978-1-932010-39-8(4))* Ooligan Pr.

Price, Lynn. The Writer's Essential Tackle Box: Getting a Hook on the Publishing Industry. 2009. (Get It Write Ser.). (ENG.). 380p. pap. 19.95 *(978-1-933016-34-4(5))* Behler Pubns., LLC.

Rautenberg, Ursula. Buchwissenschaft in Deutschland: Ein Handbuch: Theorie und Forschung / Fachkommunikation, Lehre, Institutionen und Gesellschaften. Rautenberg, Ursula, ed. 2010.Tr. of Book Studies in Germany: A Handbook. (GER., Illus.). XXX, 1109p. 210.00 *(978-3-11-020036-2(8))* De Gruyter, Walter Inc.

Rautenberg, Ursula, ed. Buchwissenschaft in Deutschland: Ein Handbuch: Theorie und Forschung / Fachkommunikation, Lehre, Institutionen und Gesellschaften. 2010.Tr. of Book Studies in Germany: A Handbook. (GER.). XXX, 1109p. 321.00 ***(978-3-11-173658-7(X))*** De Gruyter, Walter Inc.

Reid, Hugh. The Nature & Uses of Eighteenth-Century Book Subscription Lists. 2010. iv, 67p. *(978-0-7734-3757-9(6))* Mellen, Edwin Pr., The.

Rivers. Books & Their Readers: New Essays. 294p. *(978-0-8264-7194-9(3))* Continuum International Publishing Group, Ltd.

Schiffrin, Andre. Words & Money. 2010. (ENG.). 176p. 23.95 *(978-1-84467-680-4(3),* 844680) Verso Bks. GBR. Dist: Norton, W. W. & Co., Inc.

Schmidt, Günter. Bibliographie Zur Geschichte des Buch- und Zeitungswesens in ThüRingen. (GER.). 105p. *(978-3-932087-01-1(1))* Bow Historical Bks.

Schwartz, Lowell H. & Helmus, Todd C. Barriers to the Broad Dissemination of Creative Works in the Arab World. 2009. 58p. pap. 23.00 *(978-0-8330-4730-4(2),* MG-879) RAND Corp., The.

Seita, Masahiro. Watakushi No Shuppan Nenkan. (JPN., Illus.). 190 p. *(978-4-947602-43-5(0))* Bow Historical Bks.

Sharpe, Kevin & Zwicker, Steven N. Reading, Society, & Politics in Early Modern England. 2010. (ENG.). 374p. pap. 42.00 *(978-0-521-16851-9(1))* Cambridge Univ. Pr.

Siia & Perkins, Emily. The Experts' Guide to the K-12 School Market. 2nd ed. 2008. (Illus.). xii, 262p. pap. *(978-0-615-20522-9(4))* Software & Information Industry Assn.

Smith, Helen. 'Grossly Material Things' Women & Book Production in Early Modern England. 2012. (ENG., Illus.). 272p. 110.00 ***(978-0-19-965158-0(2))*** Oxford Univ. Pr., Inc.

Striphas, Ted. The Late Age of Print: Everday Book Culture from Consumerism to Control. 2011. (ENG.). 272p. (gr. 17). pap. 18.50 *(978-0-231-14815-3(1))* Columbia Univ. Pr.

—The Late Age of Print: Everyday Book Culture from Consumerism to Control. 2009. (ENG., Illus.). 272p. (gr. 17). 27.50 *(978-0-231-14814-6(3))* Columbia Univ. Pr.

Walker, Gregory. Soviet Book Publishing Policy. 2008. (Cambridge Russian, Soviet & Post-Soviet Studies). (ENG.). 184p. pap. 42.00 *(978-0-521-06719-5(7))* Cambridge Univ. Pr.

Walsby, Malcolm & Kemp, Graeme. The Book Triumphant: Print in Transition in the Sixteenth & Seventeenth Centuries. 2011. (Illus.). XVI, 380p. ***(978-90-04-20723-3(6))*** BRILL.

Walton, Charles, ed. Into Print: Limits & Legacies of the Enlightenment, Essays in Honor of Robert Darnton. 2011. (Penn State Studies in the History of the Book Ser.). (ENG.). 248p. 49.95 ***(978-0-271-05012-6(8))*** Pennsylvania State Univ. Pr.

Webb, Celia & Webb, Mack H. Publish Today! a Helpful Guide to Book Publishing for Authors & Self Publishers. 2010. 120p. pap. 14.95 *(978-0-9779576-7-5(5))* Pilinut Pr., Inc.

Weedon, Alexis. Victorian Publishing. Date not set. (Illus.). 192p. *(978-0-8264-5196-5(9))* Continuum International Publishing Group, Ltd.

Who's Buying Information. 3rd ed. 2006. (Who's Buying Ser.). 83p. pap. 59.95 *(978-1-933588-16-2(0))* New Strategist Pubns., Inc.

Yager, Fred & Yager, Jan. Career Opportunities in the Publishing Industry, Second Edition. 2nd rev. ed. 2009. (Career Opportunities Ser.). 336p. (C). (gr. 9-18). 49.50 *(978-0-8160-7542-3(5),* Ferguson Publishing Co.) Facts On File, Inc.

Yager, Fred, et al. Career Opportunities in the Publishing Industry, Second Edition. 2nd rev. ed. 2009. (Career Opportunities Ser.). 336p. (C). (gr. 9-18). pap. 18.95 *(978-0-8160-7543-0(3),* Checkmark Bks.) Facts On File, Inc.

BOOK INDUSTRIES AND TRADE—DATA PROCESSING

see also Computerized Typesetting

Brandt, Richard L. One Click: Jeff Bezos & the Rise of Amazon.Com. 2011. (ENG.). 224p. (gr. 12). 25.95 *(978-1-59184-375-7(8),* Portfolio (Hardcover)) Penguin Group (USA) Inc.

BOOK INDUSTRIES AND TRADE—DICTIONARIES

Stokes, Roy. Bibliographical Companion. 2011. (ENG.). 308p. pap. 40.00 *(978-0-8108-6047-6(3))* Scarecrow Pr., Inc.

BOOK INDUSTRIES AND TRADE—DIRECTORIES

Bowker Staff, ed. Publishers, Distributors & Wholesalers in the US, 2 vols. 32nd rev. ed. 2010. 525.00 *(978-1-59237-653-7(3))* 32nd rev. ed. 2010. 525.00 *(978-1-59237-652-0(5))* 33rd rev. ed. 2011. 550.00 *(978-1-59237-731-2(9))* 33rd rev. ed. 2011. 550.00 *(978-1-59237-730-5(0))* Grey Hse. Publishing.

—Publishers, Distributors & Wholesalers of the United States, 2010, 2 vols. 2009. 500.00 *(978-0-8352-5022-1(9))* Bowker LLC, R. R.

—Publishers, Distributors & Wholesalers of the United States, 2011, 2 vols. 32nd rev. ed. 2010. 525.00 *(978-1-59237-651-3(7))* Grey Hse. Publishing.

—Publishers, Distributors & Wholesalers of the United States, 2012, 2 vols. 33rd rev. ed. 2011. 550.00 *(978-1-59237-729-9(7))* Grey Hse. Publishing.

Information Today Inc, creator. American Book Trade Directory. 55th ed. 2009. (American Book Trade Directory Ser.). (Illus.). 1632p. 375.00 *(978-1-57387-345-1(4))* Information Today, Inc.

Publishers Association Staff, told to. Directory of Publishing 2011: United Kingdom & the Republic of Ireland. 2010. (ENG.). 192p. pap. 200.00 incl. lp *(978-1-4411-8442-9(2))* Continuum International Publishing Group, Ltd. GBR. Dist: National Bk. Network.

Publishers Directory, 3.0. 36th ed. 2011. pap. 720.00 *(978-1-4144-5988-2(2))* Cengage Gale.

BOOK INDUSTRIES AND TRADE—EXHIBITIONS

see also Books—History—Exhibitions

Gordon, Elizabeth. Woolf's-Head Publishing: The Highlights & New Lights of the Hogarth Press. 2009. (ENG.). 142p. pap. *(978-1-55195-240-6(8))* Univ. of Alberta Pr. CAN. Dist: Michigan State Univ. Pr.

Keller, Christoph, ed. Kiosk: Modes of Multiplication. 2010. (ENG., Illus.). 344p. pap. 55.00 *(978-3-03764-075-3(8))* JRP Ringier Kunstverlag AG CHE. Dist: D.A.P./Distributed Art Pubs.

Maffei, Giorgio & Picciau, Maura, eds. The Book As A Work of Art, 1 vol. 2007. (ENG., Illus.). 160p. pap. 55.00 *(978-88-7570-037-9(0))* Corraini ITA. Dist: D.A.P./Distributed Art Pubs.

Myers, Robin, et al, eds. Fairs, markets & the itinerant book Trade. 2007. (Publishing Pathways Ser.). (Illus.). 240p. 47.50 *(978-1-58456-200-9(5))* Oak Knoll Pr.

Nahson, Claudia J., ed. The Art of William Steig. 2007. (ENG., Illus.). 208p. 40.00 *(978-0-300-12478-1(3))* Yale Univ. Pr.

Overholt, John. A Monument More Durable Than Brass: Donald & Mary Hyde Collection of Dr. Samuel Johnson. Horrocks, Thomas A., ed. 2010. (Houghton Library Publications). (Illus.). 130p. 35.00 *(978-0-9818858-2-7(9))* Harvard Univ. Pr.

Panayotova, Stella, ed. The Cambridge Illuminations: The Conference Papers. 2007. (Studies in Medieval & Early Renaissance Art History Ser.). (Illus.). 334p. 174.00 *(978-1-905375-17-2(4))* Miller, Harvey Pubs. GBR. Dist: Brown, David Bk. Co., The.

Prince, Richard. Richard Prince: American Prayer. 2011. (ENG., Illus.). 600p. pap. 65.00 *(978-0-8478-3649-9(5))* Rizzoli International Pubns., Inc.

BOOK INDUSTRIES AND TRADE—HISTORY

Álvarez Márquez, María del Carmen. Impresores, Libreros y Mercaderes de Libros en la Sevilla Del Quinientos, 2 vols. 2009. (SPA.). (978-84-7956-060-7(6)) Libros Pórtico.

Amory, Hugh & Hall, David D., eds. A History of the Book in America: Volume I: the Colonial Book in the Atlantic World. 2010. (ENG., Illus.). 664p. 60.00 (978-0-8078-3404-6(1)) Univ. of North Carolina Pr.

—A History of the Book in America Vol. 1: The Colonial Book in the Atlantic World. 2007. (ENG., Illus.). 664p. pap. 36.95 (978-0-8078-5826-4(9)) Univ. of North Carolina Pr.

Arber, Edward. A Transcript of the Registers of the Company of Stationers of London, 1554-1640 A.D. 2006. (978-1-57898-617-0(6)) Martino Publishing.

Barnhisel, Greg & Turner, Catherine, eds. Pressing the Fight: Print, Propaganda, & the Cold War. 2010. (Illus.). 312p. 39.95 net. (978-1-55849-736-8(6)) Univ. of Massachusetts Pr.

Baron, Sabrina Alcorn, et al. Agent of Change: Print Culture Studies after Elizabeth L. Eisenstein. 2007. (Studies in Print Culture & the History of the Book). (Illus.). (C). (978-1-55849-592-0(4)) Univ. of Massachusetts Pr.

Booton, Diane E. Manuscripts, Market & the Transition to Print in Late Medieval Brittany. 2010. (Illus.). 490p. 144.95 (978-0-7546-6623-3(9)) Ashgate Publishing Co.

Bradley, Sue, ed. The British Book Trade: An Oral History. 2009. (ENG.). 304p. 49.00 (978-0-7123-4957-4(X)) British Library, The GBR. Dist: Chicago Distribution Ctr.

Briggs, Asa. A History of Longmans & Their Books, 1724-1990: Longevity in Publishing. 2008. 110.00 (978-1-58456-234-4(X)) Oak Knoll Pr.

Brouillette, Sarah. Postcolonial Writers in the Global Literary Marketplace. (ENG., 2011. Illus.). 216p. pap. 28.00 (978-0-230-34643-7(X)) 2007. 240p. 95.00 (978-0-230-50784-5(0)) Palgrave Macmillan.

Brown, Ellen Firsching & Wiley, John. Margaret Mitchell's Gone with the Wind: A Bestseller's Odyssey from Atlanta to Hollywood. 2011. (ENG., Illus.). 438p. 26.95 (978-1-58979-567-9(9)) Taylor Trade Publishing.

Brown, Kate. Enlightenment & Expansion, 1707-1800, 2. McDougall, Warren & Brown, Stephen, eds. 2011. (Edinburgh History of the Book in Scotland Ser.: Vol. 2). (ENG., Illus.). 400p. (gr. 17). 240.00 (978-0-7486-1912-2(7)) Edinburgh Univ. Pr. GBR. Dist: Columbia Univ. Pr.

Casper, Scott E., et al. A History of the Book in America Vol. 3: The Industrial Book, 1840-1880. 2007. (ENG., Illus.). 560p. 65.00 (978-0-8078-3085-7(2)) Univ. of North Carolina Pr.

Castellano, Philippe, ed. Dos Editores de Barcelona Por América Latina: Fernando y Santiago Salvat Espasa. 2010. (CAT & SPA.). 414p. pap. 29.80 (978-84-8489-522-0(X)) Iberoamericana Vervuert Publishing Corp.

Cruz, Laura. The Paradox of Prosperity: The Leiden Booksellers' Guild & the Distribution of Books in Early Modern Europe. 2009. 256p. 55.00 (978-1-58456-235-1(8)) Oak Knoll Pr.

Curwen, Henry. A History of Booksellers: The Old & the New. 2010. (Cambridge Library Collection - Printing & Publishing History Ser.). (Illus.). 526p. pap. 37.99 (978-1-108-02143-2(3)) Cambridge Univ. Pr.

Dahl, Gina. Books in Early Modern Norway. 2011. (Library of the Written Word Ser.). (Illus.). XII, 252p. (978-90-04-20720-2(1)) BRILL.

Duff, E. Gordon. A Century of the English Book Trade: Short Notices of All Printers, Stationers, Book-Binders, & Others Connected with It from the Issue of the First Dated Book in 1457 to the Incorporation of the Company of Stationers In 1557. 2011. (Cambridge Library Collection - Printing & Publishing History Ser.). 242p. pap. 22.99 (978-1-108-02676-5(1)) Cambridge Univ. Pr.

—The Printers, Stationers, & Book-Binders of Westminster & London from 1476 to 1535. (Illus.). reprint ed. (978-0-405-08467-6(6)) Ayer Co. Pubs., Inc.

—Printers, Stationers & Bookbinders of London & Westminster in the Fifteenth Century. 2011. (Cambridge Library Collection - Printing & Publishing History Ser.). 140p. pap. 19.99 (978-1-108-02675-8(3)) Cambridge Univ. Pr.

Everton, Michael J. The Grand Chorus of Complaint: Authors & the Business Ethics of American Publishing, 1 vol. 2011. (ENG., Illus.). 256p. 65.00 (978-0-19-975178-5(1)) Oxford Univ. Pr., Inc.

Feather. Book Publishing 4-Vol. Set, 4 vols. 2011. (Critical Concepts in Media & Cultural Studies). 1816p. (C). 1140.00 (978-0-415-49009-2(X)) Routledge.

Feather, John. The Provincial Book Trade in Eighteenth-Century England. 2008. (Cambridge Studies in Publishing & Printing History Ser.). (ENG.). 196p. (C). pap. 42.00 (978-0-521-05552-9(0)) Cambridge Univ. Pr.

Finkelstein, David & McCleery, Alistair. An Introduction to Book History. 2nd rev. ed. 2012. (ENG.). 168p. (C). 130.00 (978-0-415-68805-5(1)); pap. 44.95 (978-0-415-68806-2(X)) Routledge.

Fraser, Robert. Book History Through Postcolonial Eyes: Rewriting the Script. 2008. (Illus.). XIV, 210p. 37.95 (978-0-415-40294-1(8)); 120.00 (978-0-415-40293-4(X)) Routledge.

Fraser, Robert & Hammond, Mary, eds. Books Without Borders, Volume 1: The Cross-National Dimension in Print Culture, 2 vols. 2008. (ENG., Illus.). 224p. 89.00 (978-0-230-21029-5(5)) Palgrave Macmillan.

Freedman, Jeffrey. Books Without Borders in Enlightenment Europe: French Cosmopolitanism & German Literary Markets. 2012. (Material Texts). (Illus.). 384p. (C). 79.95 (978-0-8122-4389-5(7)) Univ. of Pennsylvania Pr.

Fudge, John D. Commerce & Print in the Early Reformation. 2007. (Northern World Ser.). (Illus.). 289p. (978-90-04-15662-3(3)) BRILL.

Gaskell, Philip. New Introduction to Bibliography: The Classic Manual of Bibliography. rev. ed. 2007. (Illus.). 438p. pap. (978-1-873040-30-0(X)) Bow Historical Bks.

Gerson, Carole & Michon, Jacques, eds. History of the Book in Canada, 1918-1980 Vol. 3, 3 vols. 2007. (ENG., Illus.). 696p. (978-0-8020-9047-8(8)) Univ. of Toronto Pr.

González, Carlos Alberto. New World Literacy: Writing & Culture Across the Atlantic, 1500-1700. 2011. (ENG.). 296p. 75.00 (978-1-61148-026-9(4)) Bucknell Univ. Pr.

Gross, Robert A. & Kelley, Mary, eds. A History of the Book in America: Volume 2: an Extensive Republic: Print, Culture, & Society in the New Nation, 1790-1840. 2010. (ENG., Illus.). 672p. 60.00 (978-0-8078-3339-1(8)) Univ. of North Carolina Pr.

Hall, David D. Ways of Writing: The Practice & Politics of Text-Making in Seventeenth-Century New England. (Material Texts). 248p. (C). 2012. pap. 22.50 (978-0-8122-2208-1(3)) 2008. (Illus.). 49.95 (978-0-8122-4102-0(9)) Univ. of Pennsylvania Pr.

Hall, David D., ed. A History of the Book in America (five-volume Set), 5 vols. 2010. (ENG., Illus.). 300.00 (978-0-8078-3415-2(7)) Univ. of North Carolina Pr.

Heller, Marvin J. Studies in the Making of the Early Hebrew Book. 2007. (Studies in Jewish History & Culture (Formerly Studies in E Ser.). (Illus.). 419p. (978-90-04-15759-0(X)) BRILL.

Hench, John B. Books as Weapons: Propaganda, Publishing, & the Battle for World Markets in the Era of World War II. 2010. (Illus.). 320p. 35.00 (978-0-8014-4891-1(3)) Cornell Univ. Pr.

Hinks, John & Day, Matthew, eds. From Compositors to Collectors: Essays on Book-Trade History. 2012. 75.00 (978-1-58456-301-3(X)) Oak Knoll Pr.

Holman, Valerie. Print for Victory: Book Publishing in England, 1939-1945. 2008. (ENG., Illus.). 304p. 39.95 (978-0-7123-5001-3(2)) British Library, The GBR. Dist: Chicago Distribution Ctr.

Howard-Hill, T. H. The British Book Trade, 1475-1890: A Bibliography, 2 vols. 2009. 175.00 (978-1-58456-255-9(2)) Oak Knoll Pr.

Howsam, Leslie & Raven, James, eds. Books between Europe & the Americas: Connections & Communities, 1620-1860. 2011. (ENG., Illus.). 352p. 85.00 (978-0-230-28567-5(8)) Palgrave Macmillan.

Hruschka, John. How Books Came to America: The Rise of the American Book Trade. 2012. (Penn State Studies in the History of the Book Ser.). (ENG.). 256p. 74.95 (978-0-271-05081-2(0)) Pennsylvania State Univ. Pr.

Hudi, József. Könyv és Társadalom: Könyvkultúra és Muvelodés a XVIII-XIX. Századi Veszprém Megyében. 2009. (HUN., Illus.). 276p. (978-963-200-566-9(X)); (978-963-693-204-6(2)) Gondolat Konyvkiado.

Hutton, Clare & Walsh, Patrick. The Oxford History of the Irish Book, Volume V: The Irish Book in English, 1891-2000. 2011. (History of the Irish Book Ser.). (ENG., Illus.). 776p. 175.00 (978-0-19-924911-4(3)) Oxford Univ. Pr., Inc.

Jacobsson, Roger. Typographic Man: Medielandskap I Förändring: Studier I Provinsens Tryckkultur. 2009. (SWE., Illus.). 353p. (978-91-7331-286-8(X)) Carlsson bokforlag AB.

Jäger, Georg, et al. Geschichte des Deutschen Buchhandels Im 19. und 20. Jahrhundert. 2007. (GER., Illus.). 530p. (978-3-598-24808-5(3)) Saur, K. G. Verlag GmbH & Co.

Kü, et al. Die Reichsschrifttumskammer: Geschichte einer berufsständischen Zwangsorganisation unter besonderer Berücksichtigung des Buchhandels. 2010. 108p. pap. (978-3-8364-3263-4(3)) VDM Verlag Dr. Mueller e.K.

Kaestle, Carl F. & Radway, Janice A. A History of the Book in America: Volume 4: Print in Motion: the Expansion of Publishing & Reading in the United States, 1880-1940. 2009. (ENG., Illus.). 688p. 60.00 (978-0-8078-3186-1(7)) Univ. of North Carolina Pr.

Keymer, Thomas & Sabor, Peter. 'Pamela' in the Marketplace: Literary Controversy & Print Culture in Eighteenth-Century Britain & Ireland. 2009. (ENG., Illus.). 308p. pap. 42.00 (978-0-521-11018-1(1)) Cambridge Univ. Pr.

Khoury, George. Image Comics: The Road to Independence. 2007. (Illus.). 280p. pap. 34.95 (978-1-893905-71-9(3)) TwoMorrows Publishing.

Lindquist, Eric N., et al. Agent of Change: Print Culture Studies after Elizabeth L. Eisenstein. Baron, Sabrina Alcorn & Lindquist, Eric N., eds. Shevlin, Eleanor F., ed. 2007. (Studies in Print Culture & the History of the Book). (Illus.). 442p. per. 29.95 (978-1-55849-593-7(2)) Univ. of Massachusetts Pr.

Loughran, Trish. The Republic in Print: Print Culture in the Age of U. S. Nation Building, 1770-1870. (ENG., Illus.). 568p. (gr. 17). 2009. pap. 26.50 (978-0-231-13909-0(8)) 2007. 75.00 (978-0-231-13908-3(X)) Columbia Univ. Pr.

Lyons, Martyn. Reading Culture & Writing Practices in Nineteenth-Century France. 2008. (Studies in Book & Print Culture Ser.). (FRE & ENG., Illus.). 272p. (978-0-8020-9357-8(4)) Univ. of Toronto Pr.

MacIntyre, Iona. Women & Print Culture in Post-Independence Buenos Aires. 2010. (Monografías A Ser.: Volume 284). 224p. 90.00 (978-1-85566-196-7(9), Tamesis Bks.) Boydell & Brewer, Ltd. GBR. Dist: Boydell & Brewer, Inc.

Maclaren, Eli. Dominion & Agency: Copyright & the Structuring of the Canadian Book Trade, 1867-1918. 2011. (Studies in Book & Print Culture Ser.). (Illus.). 224p. (978-1-4426-4321-5(8)) Univ. of Toronto Pr.

Maclean, . W. F. & Maclean, Ian. Learning & the Market Place: Essays in the History of the Early Modern Book. 2009. (Library of the Written Word Ser.). (Illus.). 445p. (978-90-04-17550-1(4)) BRILL.

MacSkimming, Roy. The Perilous Trade: Book Publishing in Canada, 1946-2006. 2007. (Illus.). 512p. per. 21.95 (978-0-7710-5494-5(7), McClelland & Stewart) McClelland & Stewart CAN. Dist: Random Hse., Inc.

Maruca, Lisa. The Work of Print: Authorship & the English Text Trades, 1660-1760. 2007. (Literary Conjugations Ser.). (ENG., Illus.). 240p. 80.00 (978-0-295-98744-6(8)) Univ. of Washington Pr.

Maruca, Lisa M. The Work of Print: Authorship & the English Text Trades, 1660-1760. 2007. (Literary Conjugations, a Robert B. Heilman Book Ser.). (ENG., Illus.). 240p. per. 24.95 (978-0-295-98757-6(X)) Univ. of Washington Pr.

McKitterick, David, ed. The Cambridge History of the Book in Britain Vol. 6: 1830-1914, 7 vols. 2009. (Cambridge History of the Book in Britain Ser.). (Illus.). 826p. 180.00 (978-0-521-86624-8(3)) Cambridge Univ. Pr.

McLeod, Jane. Licensing Loyalty: Printers, Patrons, & the State in Early Modern France. 2011. (Penn State Studies in the History of the Bk Ser.). (ENG.). 280p. 74.95 (978-0-271-03768-4(7)) Pennsylvania State Univ. Pr.

McMurran, M. H. The Spread of Novels: Translation & Prose Fiction in the Eighteenth Century. 2009. (Translation/Transnation Ser.). (ENG., Illus.). 272p. (C). pap. 27.95 (978-0-691-14153-4(3)) Princeton Univ. Pr.

McMurran, Mary Helen. The Spread of Novels: Translation & Prose Fiction in the Eighteenth Century. 2009. (Translation/Transnation Ser.). (ENG., Illus.). 272p. (C). 65.00 (978-0-691-14152-7(5)) Princeton Univ. Pr.

Moore, Sean D. Swift, the Book, & the Irish Financial Revolution: Satire & Sovereignty in Colonial Ireland. 2010. (ENG.). 288p. (gr. 17). 65.00 (978-0-8018-9507-4(3)) Johns Hopkins Univ. Pr.

Morison, Stanley. John Bell, 1745-1831: A Memoir. 2009. (ENG.). 236p. pap. 36.99 (978-0-521-14314-1(4)) Cambridge Univ. Pr.

Munro, Craig. Paper Empires, 1946-2005 Vol. 3. Sheahan-Bright, Robyn, ed. 2006. (Illus.). 432p. (History of the Book in Australia Ser.). pap. 75.95 (978-0-7022-3559-7(8)); (History of the Book in Australia Ser.: Bk. 3). pap. 56.95 (978-0-7022-3573-3(3)) Univ. of Queensland Pr. AUS. Dist: Independent Pubs. Group.

Murphy, James H., ed. The Irish Book in English, 1800-1890, Vol. IV. 2011. (History of the Irish Book Ser.). (ENG., Illus.). 752p. 175.00 (978-0-19-818731-8(9)) Oxford Univ. Pr., Inc.

Myers, Robin, et al, eds. Books for Sale: The Advertising & Promotion of Print since the Fifteenth Century. 2009. (Illus.). xvi, 191p. 49.95 (978-1-58456-265-8(X)) Oak Knoll Pr.

—Books on the Move: Tracking Copies Through Collections & the Book Trade. 2007. (Publishing Pathways Ser.). (Illus.). 180p. 49.95 (978-1-58456-219-1(6)) Oak Knoll Pr.

—Music & the Book Trade: From the Sixteenth to the Twentieth Century. 2008. 240p. 49.95 (978-1-58456-245-0(5)) Oak Knoll Pr.

Myers, Robin, et al. Owners, Annotators & the Signs of Reading. (Publishing Pathways Ser.). (Illus.). xv, 231p. (C). (978-1-58456-171-2(8)) Oak Knoll Pr.

Newfeld, Frank. Drawing on Type. 2008. (ENG., Illus.). 336p. pap. 27.95 (978-0-88984-304-2(X)) Porcupine's Quill, Inc. CAN. Dist: Univ. of Toronto Pr.

Nord, David Paul, et al, eds. A History of the Book in America: Volume 5: the Enduring Book: Print Culture in Postwar America. 2009. (ENG., Illus.). 632p. 60.00 (978-0-8078-3285-1(5)) Univ. of North Carolina Pr.

North, Marcy L. The Anonymous Renaissance: Cultures of Discretion in Tudor-Stuart England. Date not set. pap. 22.00 (978-0-226-59438-5(6)) Univ. of Chicago Pr.

Pettegree, Andrew. The Book in the Renaissance. 2011. (ENG., Illus.). 440p. pap. 25.00 (978-0-300-17821-0(2)) Yale Univ. Pr.

Pon, Lisa & Kallendorf, Craig. The Books of Venice. 2009.Tr. of Libro Veneziano. (ITA & ENG.). 632p. pap. 85.00 (978-1-58456-257-3(9)) Oak Knoll Pr.

Prough, Jennifer Sally. Straight from the Heart: Gender, Intimacy, & the Cultural Production of Shojo Manga. 2011. 58.00 (978-0-8248-3457-9(7)); pap. 24.00 (978-0-8248-3528-6(X)) Univ. of Hawaii Pr.

Raven, James. The Business of Books: Booksellers & the English Book Trade, 1450-1850. 2007. (ENG., Illus.). 512p. 65.00 (978-0-300-12261-9(6)) Yale Univ. Pr.

Rees, Thomas. Reminiscences of Literary London from 1779 To 1853: With Interesting Anecdotes of Publishers, Authors & Book Auctioneers of that Period. Britton, John, ed. 2010. (Cambridge Library Collection - Printing & Publishing History Ser.). (ENG., Illus.). 180p. pap. 19.99 (978-1-108-00917-1(4)) Cambridge Univ. Pr.

Renouard, Philippe. Imprimeurs parisiens, libraires, fondeurs de caractères et correcteurs d'imprimerie, depuis l'introduction de l'imprimerie a Paris (1470) jusqu'a la fin du XVIe Siècle: Leurs adresses, marques, enseignes, dates d'exercice. Notes sur leurs familles, leurs alliances et leur descendance, d'après les renseignements bibliographiques et des documents Inédits. 2011. (Cambridge Library Collection - Printing & Publishing History Ser.). (FRE., Illus.). 508p. pap. 37.99 (978-1-108-03534-7(5)) Cambridge Univ. Pr.

Rogal, Samuel J. John Wesley's Book Stock & the Arminian Magazine Catalogue of 1789. 2006. 186p. (C). 99.95 (978-0-7734-5541-2(8)) Mellen, Edwin Pr., The.

Rukavina, Alison. The Development of the International Book Trade, 1870-1895: Tangled Networks. 2010. (ENG., Illus.). 200p. 84.00 (978-0-230-27563-8(X)) Palgrave Macmillan.

Runge, Laura L. Producing the Eighteenth-Century Book: Writers & Publishers in England, 1650-1800. 2009. (ENG.). 65.00 (978-1-61149-126-5(6)) Univ. of Delaware Pr.

Runge, Laura L. & Rogers, Pat. Producing the Eighteenth-Century Book: Writers & Publishers in England, 1650-1800. 2009. (Illus.). 298p. 65.00 (978-0-87413-069-0(7)) Univ. of Delaware Pr.

Sadana, Rashmi. English Heart, Hindi Heartland: The Political Life of Literature in India. 2012. (FlashPoints Ser.). (ENG., Illus.). 242p. pap. 49.95 (978-0-520-26957-6(8)) Univ. of California Pr.

Salvat Espasa, Fernando, et al. DOS Editores de Barcelona Por América Latina: Fernando y Santiago Salvat Espasa: Epistolario Bilingüe 1912-1914, 1918 y 1923. 2010. (CAT & SPA.). 414p. (978-3-86527-552-3(4)) Iberoamericana Editorial Vervuert.

St Clair, William. The Reading Nation in the Romantic Period. 2007. (ENG., Illus.). 796p. per. 50.00 (978-0-521-69944-0(4)) Cambridge Univ. Pr.

Tatlock, Lynne, ed. Publishing Culture & the Reading Nation: German Book History in the Long Nineteenth Century. 2010. (Studies in German Literature Linguistics & Culture Ser.: Volume 76). (GER & ENG., Illus.). 356p. 75.00 (978-1-57113-402-8(6)) Camden Hse.

Ten Harmsel, Larry & Van Til, Reinder. An Eerdmans Century: 1911-2011. 2011. 192p. 20.00 (978-0-8028-6658-5(1)) Eerdmans, William B. Publishing Co.

Turnovsky, Geoffrey. The Literary Market: Authorship & Modernity in the Old Regime. 2009. (Material Texts). (Illus.). 280p. (C). 59.95 (978-0-8122-4195-2(9)) Univ. of Pennsylvania Pr.

Weddle, Jeff. Bohemian New Orleans: The Story of the Outsider & Loujon Press. 2007. (ENG., Illus.). 220p. 30.00 (978-1-57806-974-3(2)) Univ. Pr. of Mississippi.

Wittmann, Reinhard. Buchmarkt und Lektüre Im 18. und 19. Jahrhundert: Beiträge Zum Literarischen Leben, 1750-1880. (Studien und Texte zur Sozialgeschichte der Literatur Ser.). (GER., Illus.). XII, 252p. 105.00 (978-3-11-183418-4(2)) De Gruyter, Walter Inc.

Yang, Hu & Xiao, Yang. Chinese Publishing. 3rd ed. 2012. (Introductions to Chinese Culture Ser.). (ENG., Illus.). 212p. pap. 19.99 (978-0-521-18675-9(7)) Cambridge Univ. Pr.

Yeo, Matthew. The Acquisition of Books by Chetham's Library, 1655-1700. 2011. (Illus.). XX, 264p. (978-90-04-20655-6(5)) BRILL.

2010. 2010.Tr. of Yearbook for Central & East German History. Journal of Comparative & Prussian Regional History. 240p. (978-3-11-023352-0(5)) Saur, K. G. Verlag GmbH & Co.

BOOK JACKETS

Cook, Brian. Brian Cook's Landscapes of Britain. (ENG., Illus.). 2012. 128p. 14.95 (978-1-84994-036-8(3)) 2011. 144p. 29.95 (978-1-906388-78-2(4)) Anova Bks. GBR. (Batsford, B. T. Ltd.). Dist: Sterling Publishing Co., Inc.

Tanselle, G. Thomas. Book-Jackets: Their History, Forms, & Use. 2011. (978-1-883631-13-0(0)) Bibliographical Society of the Univ. of Virginia.

BOOK LISTS

see Best Books

BOOK-MAKING (BETTING)

Conklin, Les. Betting Horses to Win. 2011. 186p. 42.95 (978-1-258-06882-0(6)) Literary Licensing, LLC

BOOK-MARKS (OWNERS' MARKS)

see Books—Owners' Marks

BOOK NUMBERS

see Shelflisting

BOOK NUMBERS, PUBLISHERS' STANDARD

see Publishers' Standard Book Numbers

BOOK OF CHANGES

see Yi Jing

BOOK OF COMMON PRAYER

see Church of England—Book of Common Prayer; Episcopal Church—Book of Common Prayer

BOOK OF JUBILEES

Boccaccini, Gabriele, et al. Enoch & the Mosaic Torah: The Evidence of Jubilees. 2009. 496p. pap. 55.00 (978-0-8028-6409-3(0)) Eerdmans, William B. Publishing Co.

The Book of Jubilees: The Little Genesis. 224p. reprint ed. 68.00 (978-0-7222-9904-3(4)) Library Reprints, Inc.

Charles, R. H. The Book of Jubilees. 2007. 232p. per. 18.75 (978-1-60206-658-8(2)) Cosimo, Inc.

—The Book of Jubilees. 2007. 264p. pap. 14.99 (978-1-59986-810-3(5), FQ Classics) Filiquarian Publishing, LLC.

—The Book of Jubilees. 2011. 110p. pap. 8.99 (978-1-61720-184-4(7)) Wilder Pubns., Ltd.

Hanneken, Todd Russell. The Subversion of the Apocalypses in the Book of Jubilees. 2012. pap. (978-1-58983-642-6(1)) Society of Biblical Literature.

Kugel, James L. A Walk Through Jubilees: Studies in the Book of Jubilees & the World of Its Creation. 2012. (Supplements to the Journal for the Study of Judaism Ser.: Vol. 156). (ENG., Illus.). xiii, 434p. (978-90-04-21768-3(1)) BRILL.

Loader, William. Enoch, Levi, & Jubilees on Sexuality: Attitudes Toward Sexuality in the Early Enoch Literature, the Aramaic Levi Document, & the Book of Jubilees. 2007. 350p. per. 38.00 (978-0-8028-2583-4(4)) Eerdmans, William B. Publishing Co.

Mason, Eric F., ed. A Teacher for All Generations (2 vol. Set) Essays in Honor of James C. VanderKam, 2 vols. 2011. (Supplements to the Journal for the Study of Judaism Ser.). (Illus.). lxx, 1004p. (978-90-04-21520-7(4)) BRILL.

Park, Sejin. Pentecost & Sinai: The Festival of Weeks as a Celebration of the Sinai Event. 2008. (Library of Hebrew Bible/Old Testament Studies, the Ser.). (ENG.). 304p. 130.00 (978-0-567-02727-6(9), T&T Clark Int'l) Continuum International Publishing Group, Ltd. GBR. Dist: National Bk. Network.

Segal, Michael. The Book of Jubilees: Rewritten Bible, Redaction, Ideology, & Theology. 2007. (Supplements to the Journal for the Study of Judaism Ser.: Vol. 117). 380p. *(978-90-04-15057-7(9))* BRILL.

BOOK OF MORMON

Anderson, Ross J. Understanding the Book of Mormon: A Quick Christian Guide to the Mormon Holy Book, 1 vol. 2009. (ENG.). 128p. pap. 14.99 *(978-0-310-28321-8(3))* Zondervan.

Arnold, Marilyn. From the Heart: Charity in the Book of Mormon. 2011. pap. 13.99 *(978-1-59955-485-3(2))* Cedar Fort, Inc./CFI Distribution.

Bassett, Doug, compiled by. Doctrinal Insights to the Book of Mormon. 2007. 326p. pap. 24.99 *(978-1-59955-051-0(2))* Cedar Fort, Inc./CFI Distribution.

Bassett, K. Douglas, compiled by. Doctrinal Insights to the Book of Mormon: Volume 3: Helaman Through Moroni. 2008. 231p. pap. 24.99 *(978-1-59955-056-5(3))* Cedar Fort, Inc./CFI Distribution.

—Doctrinal Insights to the Book of Mormon Volume Two: Jacob Through Alma. 2007. 273p. per. 24.99 *(978-1-59955-055-8(5))* Cedar Fort, Inc./CFI Distribution.

Belliston, Angus H. Mormon: Mighty Man of God. 2008. 86p. pap. 9.99 *(978-1-59955-132-6(2))* Cedar Fort, Inc./CFI Distribution.

Bennett, Bob. Leap of Faith. 2009. 336p. 29.95 *(978-1-60641-053-0(9))* Deseret Bk. Co.

Berrett, William E. Teachings of the Book of Mormon. 2011. 134p. 40.95 ***(978-1-258-04184-7(7))*** Literary Licensing, LLC.

Bigelow, Christopher Kimball. The Timechart History of Mormonism: From Premortality to the Present. 2007. (Illus.). 31p. 17.99 *(978-1-903025-40-6(0))* Worth Pr. Ltd. GBR. Dist: Book Sales, Inc.

Bowman, David. Dude! Don't Be a Lemuel! 2011. (YA). pap. 11.99 ***(978-1-59955-943-8(9))*** Cedar Fort, Inc./CFI Distribution.

Brewster, Hoyt. Who's Who: A BK of Mormon Ready Reference. 2007. 288p. pap. 14.95 *(978-1-59038-755-9(4))* Deseret Bk. Co.

Brinkerhoff, Val & Allen, Joseph L. Visualizing the Lands of the Book of Mormon. 2007. (Illus.). iv, 102p. *(978-1-59811-403-4(4))* Covenant Communications.

Brown, S. Kent & Johnson, Peter, eds. Journey of Faith: From Jerusalem to the Promised Land. 2006. (Illus.). ix, 172p. (C). *(978-0-8425-2644-9(7),* F. A. R. M. S.) Brigham Young Univ.

Bryant, Verda E. Between the Covers of the Book of Mormon. 2007. (ENG.). 176p. 37.95 *(978-0-548-04865-8(7))* Kessinger Publishing, LLC.

Burningham, Janet. Family Home Evening with the Book of Mormon: Lessons to Help Your Family Learn & Apply Important Truths from the Book of Mormon. 2007. pap. 14.99 *(978-1-59955-127-2(6))* Cedar Fort, Inc./CFI Distribution.

Bushman, Richard Lyman. Believing History: Latter-Day Saint Essays. Neilson, Reid L. & Woodworth, Jed, eds. 2007. (ENG., Illus.). 312p. (gr. 17). pap. 27.00 *(978-0-231-13007-3(4))* Columbia Univ. Pr.

Bytheway, John. When Times Are Tough: 5 Scriptures That Will Help You Get Through Almost Anything. 2010. 176p. pap. 10.99 *(978-1-60641-848-2(3))* Deseret Bk. Co.

Chase, Randal. Making Precious Things Plain: A Book of Mormon Study Guide: Volume 2: Alma 17-3 Nephi 7. 2008. (Illus.). 209p. pap. 24.99 *(978-1-59955-130-2(6))* Cedar Fort, Inc./CFI Distribution.

Chase, Randal S. Making Precious Things Plain: Volume 1: 1 Nephi-Alma 16. 2007. 299p. per. 26.99 *(978-1-59955-078-7(4))* Cedar Fort, Inc./CFI Distribution.

Christianson, Jack R. & Bassett, K. Douglas. Life Lessons from the Book of Mormon. 2007. 245p. per. 16.99 *(978-1-59955-079-4(2))* Cedar Fort, Inc./CFI Distribution.

Chronology of the book of Mormon records an in-depth Look. 2007. per. *(978-1-893181-92-2(8))* Martell Publishing Co.

Church of Jesus Christ of Latter-Day Saints Staff, contrib. by. Ang Libro ni Mormon: Isa Pa Ka Katipan Nahanungod Kay Jesucristo. (Illus.). xv, 727p. *(978-1-59297-577-8(1))* Church of Jesus Christ of Latter Day Saints, Church History Dept.

Cook, Grant Osmond, III. The Life of Christ: From the Joseph Smith Translation of the Four Gospels with Modern Scripture. 2006. 240p. 24.95 *(978-0-9787997-0-0(4))* Rockshire Publishing, LLC.

Decker, Tony. Why I Believe the Book of Mormon: And Why Anybody Can. 2007. 280p. per. 17.95 *(978-0-929753-26-3(7),* Stratford Bks.) Paramount Bks.

DiGirolamo, Vincent. Principles with Promise: Study Companion for the Book of Mormon: Another Testament of Jesus Christ. 2008. 296p. pap. 32.99 *(978-0-9786815-2-4(5))* Celestine Publishing, LLC.

Eaton, Robert I. Digging Deeper: Understanding & Applying Life-Changing Doctrines from the Book of Mormon. 2006. (Illus.). xi, 192p. 25.95 *(978-1-59038-618-7(3))* Deseret Bk. Co.

Ferguson, Thomas Stuart & Hunter, Milton R. Ancient America & the Book of Mormon. 2011. 466p. 57.95 ***(978-1-258-01237-3(5))*** Literary Licensing, LLC.

Funk, Camille. Learning to Read Using the Book of Mormon Volume One: 1 Nephi Through 2 Nephi 26. 2007. (Learning to Read Using the Book of Mormon Ser.). (Illus.). 220p. pap. 19.99 *(978-1-59955-002-2(4))* Cedar Fort, Inc./CFI Distribution.

Gardner, Brant. The Gift & Power: Translating the Book of Mormon. 2011. ***(978-1-58958-131-9(8))*** Kofford, Greg Books, Inc.

—Second Witness: Analytical & Contextual Commentary on the Book of Mormon: 1 Nephi. 2007. 39.95 *(978-1-58958-041-1(9))* Kofford, Greg Books, Inc.

—Second Witness: Analytical & Contextual Commentary on the Book of Mormon: 2 Nephi through Jacob. 2007. 39.95 *(978-1-58958-042-8(7))* Kofford, Greg Books, Inc.

—Second Witness: Analytical & Contextual Commentary on the Book of Mormon: 4 Nephi through Moroni. 2007. 39.95 *(978-1-58958-046-6(X))* Kofford, Greg Books, Inc.

—Second Witness: Analytical & Contextual Commentary on the Book of Mormon: Alma. 2007. 49.95 *(978-1-58958-044-2(3))* Kofford, Greg Books, Inc.

—Second Witness: Analytical & Contextual Commentary on the Book of Mormon: Enos through Mosiah. 2007. 39.95 *(978-1-58958-043-5(5))* Kofford, Greg Books, Inc.

—Second Witness: Analytical & Contextual Commentary on the Book of Mormon: Helaman through 3 Nephi. 2007. 39.95 *(978-1-58958-045-9(1))* Kofford, Greg Books, Inc.

—Second Witness: Analytical & Contextual Commentary on the Book of Mormon, Six-Volume Set. 2008. 225.00 *(978-1-58958-047-3(8))* Kofford, Greg Books, Inc.

Gaunt, Dennis. Bad Guys of the Book of Mormon. 2011. (YA). pap. 15.99 *(978-1-60908-058-7(0))* Deseret Bk. Co.

George, Carl. Thank You for the Book of Mormon. 2007. 132p. per. 13.99 *(978-1-60266-230-8(4))* Xulon Pr., Inc.

Givens, Terryl L. The Book of Mormon. 2009. (Very Short Introductions Ser.). (ENG., Illus.). 152p. pap. 11.95 *(978-0-19-536931-1(9))* Oxford Univ. Pr., Inc.

God's Holy Words. 2009. 128p. pap. 10.99 *(978-1-4389-9660-8(8))* AuthorHouse.

Gutjahr, Paul C. Book of Mormon: A Biography. 2012. (Lives of Great Religious Bks.). (ENG., Illus.). 280p. 24.95 ***(978-0-691-14480-1(X))*** Princeton Univ. Pr.

Hansen, Vaughn E. Cumorah: A Land Choice above All Other Lands. 2011. 96p. pap. 8.99 ***(978-1-59955-950-6(1))*** Cedar Fort, Inc./CFI Distribution.

Hardy, Grant. Understanding the Book of Mormon: A Reader's Guide, 1 vol. 2010. (ENG.). 336p. 29.95 *(978-0-19-973170-1(5))* Oxford Univ. Pr., Inc.

Heater, Claude. A Review of the Most Correct Book on Earth. 2007. 404p. per. 24.99 *(978-1-60266-494-4(3))* Xulon Pr., Inc.

Heroes from the BK Mormon. 2007. 224p. pap. 14.95 *(978-1-59038-761-0(9))* Deseret Bk. Co.

Hill, Theresa Snow. Stories from the Book of Mormon. 2011. 266p. 47.95 ***(978-1-258-04263-9(0))*** Literary Licensing, LLC.

Hilton, John. The Little BK of Book of Mormon Evidence. 2007. 96p. pap. 6.95 *(978-1-59038-850-1(X))* Deseret Bk. Co.

Holland, Jeffrey R. Christ & the New Covenant: The Messianic Message of the Book of Mormon. 2006. 39.95 *(978-1-59038-613-2(2))* Deseret Bk. Co.

Hunt, James H. Mormonism: Embracing the Origin, Rise & Progress of the Sect with an Examination of the Book of Mormon. 2007. (ENG.). 344p. 46.95 *(978-0-548-13699-7(8))* 2006. pap. 31.95 *(978-1-4286-4859-3(3))* Kessinger Publishing, LLC.

Hunter, Milton R. Christ in Ancient Americ: Archaeology & the Book of Mormon V2. 2011. 288p. 48.95 ***(978-1-258-00185-8(3))*** Literary Licensing, LLC.

Johnson, Daniel, et al. An LDS Guide to Mesoamerica. 2008. 176p. 29.99 *(978-1-59955-120-3(9))* Cedar Fort, Inc./CFI Distribution.

Kendall, Michelle. A Book of Mormon Christmas. 2011. (J). 15.99 *(978-1-59955-508-9(5))* Cedar Fort, Inc./CFI Distribution.

Kirkham, Francis W. Source Material Concerning the Origin of. 2006. pap. 22.95 *(978-1-4286-3650-7(1))* Kessinger Publishing, LLC.

Larsen, David R. How to Remember Everything in the Book of Mormon. 2007. pap. 14.99 *(978-1-59955-099-2(7))* Cedar Fort, Inc./CFI Distribution.

Ludlow, Daniel H. Unlocking the Book of Mormon: An Easy-To-Use Side-By-Side Commentary. 2007. (Illus.). vi, 531p. pap. *(978-1-59811-463-8(8))* Covenant Communications.

McConkie, Clay. 600 BC: the Departure of Lehi: A Landmark of Time. 2007. 165p. per. 12.99 *(978-1-55517-917-5(7))* Cedar Fort, Inc./CFI Distribution.

McConkie, Joseph. Doctrinal Commentary on the BK of Mormon Set. 2007. 1740p. pap. 49.95 *(978-1-59038-776-4(7))* Deseret Bk. Co.

McConkie, Joseph & Millet, Robert. Doctrinal Commentary on the BK of Mormon. 2007. 384p. pap. 16.95 *(978-1-59038-524-1(1));* 448p. pap. 16.95 *(978-1-59038-526-5(8));* 432p. pap. 21.99 *(978-1-59038-523-4(3));* 476p. pap. 16.95 *(978-1-59038-525-8(X))* Deseret Bk. Co.

McGavin, E. Cecil. How We Got the Book of Mormon. 2011. 138p. 40.95 ***(978-1-258-07230-8(0))*** Literary Licensing, LLC.

Meldrum, D. Jeffrey & Stephens, Trent D. Who Are the Children of Lehi? DNA & the Book of Mormon. 2007. 29.95 *(978-1-58958-048-0(6))* Kofford, Greg Books, Inc.

Melekin, Embaye. The African Bible: The Records of the Abyssinian Prophets. 2011. 730p. pap. 23.99 ***(978-1-4628-6191-0(1))*** Xlibris Corp.

Merrick, Christine C. And It Came to Pass: The Book of Mormon Chronicles. 2008. 294p. pap. 15.99 *(978-1-59955-152-4(7))* Cedar Fort, Inc./CFI Distribution.

Moore, H. B. Women of the Book of Mormon: Insights & Inspirations. 2010. (Illus.). 102p. *(978-1-60861-007-5(1))* Covenant Communications.

Nehring, Karl W. Reading & Responding to the Book of Mormon. 2009. pap. 15.99 *(978-1-59955-246-0(9))* Cedar Fort, Inc./CFI Distribution.

Newell, Lloyd D. He Shall Fulfill All of His Promises: Daily Hope & Encouragement from the Scriptures. 2010. 18.99 *(978-1-60641-837-6(8))* Deseret Bk. Co.

Nibley, Hugh. An Approach to the Book of Mormon: Course of Study for the Melchizedek Priesthood Quorums of the Church of Jesus Christ of Latter-Day Saints. 2011. 432p. 56.95 ***(978-1-258-01322-6(3))*** Literary Licensing, LLC.

Nyman, Monte S. 28 Truths Taught by the Book of Mormon. 2011. (ENG.). 410p. pap. 19.99 ***(978-1-937458-01-0(6))*** Sourced Media Bks.

Ogden, D. Kelly. Verse By Verse: The Book of Mormon. 2011. 512p. 35.99 ***(978-1-60641-477-4(1))*** Deseret Bk. Co.

Ogden, D. Kelly & Skinner, Andrew C. Verse by Verse, the Book of Mormon. 2011. 35.99 *(978-1-60908-740-1(2))* Deseret Bk. Co.

Otten, L. G. & Caldwell, C. M. Sacred Truths of the Book of Mormon, 2 vols. 2007. (Illus.). *(978-1-59811-082-1(9)); (978-1-59811-083-8(7))* Covenant Communications.

Peacock, George M. Unlocking the Idioms: An LDS Perspective on Understanding Scriptural Idioms. 2009. pap. 15.99 *(978-1-59955-241-5(8))* Cedar Fort, Inc./CFI Distribution.

Peterson, Daniel C., ed. The Book of Mormon & DNA Research. 2008. pap. 14.95 *(978-0-8425-2706-4(0),* F. A. R. M. S.) Brigham Young Univ.

Peterson, H. Donl. Moroni: Ancient Prophet, Modern Messenger. 2008. 211p. pap. 14.99 *(978-1-59955-141-8(1))* Cedar Fort, Inc./CFI Distribution.

Pierce, Florence. The Story of the Book of Mormon. 2011. 472p. 57.95 ***(978-1-258-04177-9(4))*** Literary Licensing, LLC.

Pinegar, Ed J. & Allen, Richard J. Book of Mormon Who's Who: A Comprehensive Guide to the People in the Book of Mormon. 2007. (Illus.). vii, 208p. *(978-1-59811-420-1(4))* Covenant Communications.

—Commentaries & Insights on the Book of Mormon: 1 Nephi-Alma 29. 2007. ix, 630p. *(978-1-59811-461-4(1))* Covenant Communications.

—Rejoice in Christ: Daily Inspiration from the Book of Mormon. 2007. vi, 393p. pap. *(978-1-59811-454-6(9))* Covenant Communications.

Potter, George. Nephi in the Promised Land. 2009. 29.99 *(978-1-59955-129-6(2))* Cedar Fort, Inc./CFI Distribution.

Potter, George, et al. The Voyages of the Book of Mormon. 2011. 39.99 ***(978-1-59955-946-9(3))*** Cedar Fort, Inc./CFI Distribution.

Price, Lynn F. One in Thine Hand: The Stick of Judah & the Stick of Joseph. 2007. 365p. per. 21.99 *(978-0-88290-816-8(2))* Cedar Fort, Inc./CFI Distribution.

Rasmussen, Vicki Lynn. Head Start with the Book of Mormon: Using the Scriptures to Teach Children Reading & Writing Skills. 2007. 129p. per. 12.99 *(978-1-59955-067-1(9))* Cedar Fort, Inc./CFI Distribution.

Rees, Robert A. & England, Eugene, eds. The Reader's Book of Mormon 7 Volume Boxed Set. 2007. pap. 40.00 *(978-1-56085-175-2(9))* Signature Bks., LLC.

Reynolds, George & Sjodahl, Janne M. Commentary on the Book of Mormon, 7 vols, Vol. 4. 451p. 9.95 *(978-0-87747-042-7(1))* Deseret Bk. Co.

Ridges, David J. Book of Mormon Made Easier. 2011. ***(978-1-59955-949-0(8))***; (Illus.). ***(978-1-59955-962-9(5))***; (Illus.). ***(978-1-59955-961-2(7))*** Cedar Fort, Inc./CFI Distribution.

—The Book of Mormon Made Easier Part 1: 1 Nephi Through Words of Mormon. 2007. (Gospel Studies: 4). (Illus.). 450p. pap. 24.95 *(978-1-55517-725-6(5),* 77255) Cedar Fort, Inc./CFI Distribution.

—65 Signs of the Times: Leading up to the Second Coming. 2009. pap. 14.99 *(978-1-59955-366-5(X))* Cedar Fort, Inc./CFI Distribution.

Ridges, David J., comment. Your Study of the Book of Mormon Made Easier: Gospel Study Series Part 2 - Mosiah through Alma. 2007. (Gospel Studies: Vols. 4-5). (Illus.). pap. 24.95 *(978-1-55517-761-4(1))* Cedar Fort, Inc./CFI Distribution.

—Your Study of the Book of Mormon Made Easier - Helaman through Moroni: Gospel Study Series Part 3. 2007. pap. 24.95 *(978-1-55517-787-4(5))* Cedar Fort, Inc./CFI Distribution.

Rose, Tom G. Proof: How to Know the Book of Mormon Is True. 2011. 144p. pap. 9.99 ***(978-1-59955-889-9(0))*** Cedar Fort, Inc./CFI Distribution.

Shook, Charles A. True Origin of the Book of Mormon. 2006. pap. 24.95 *(978-1-4286-4693-3(0))* Kessinger Publishing, LLC.

Skinner, Andrew C. & Strathearn, Gaye, eds. Third Nephi: An Incomparable Scripture. 2011. (C). 34.99 ***(978-1-60908-907-8(3))*** Deseret Bk. Co.

Skousen, Royal, ed. The Book of Mormon: The Earliest Text. Smith, Joseph, Jr., tr. 2009. (Illus.). 848p. 35.00 *(978-0-300-14218-1(8))* Yale Univ. Pr.

Smith, Elder I. M. The Book of Mormon Vindicated: Scriptural Evidences of the Divine Authenticity of the Book of Mormon. 2007. (ENG.). 122p. 35.95 *(978-0-548-04889-4(4))* Kessinger Publishing, LLC.

Smith, Joseph. The Book of Mormon. 2009. (Amer Philosophy, Religion Ser.). (ENG.). 580p. pap. 33.95 *(978-1-4290-1800-5(3))* Applewood Bks.

—The Book of Mormon. 2009. 502p. pap. *(978-1-4588-6410-9(3))* Books LLC.

—The Book of Mormon. 2009. 572p. 44.99 *(978-1-59547-496-4(X))* NuVision Pubns., LLC.

Smith, Joseph, Jr., tr. Book of Mormon: Another Testament of Jesus Christ. 2008.Tr. of Mormons Bok Annu Ett Jesu Kristi Testamente. (SWE., Illus.). 814p. 3.00 *(978-1-59297-626-3(3))* Church of Jesus Christ of Latter Day Saints, Church History Dept.

Smith, Joseph, tr. Mormon's Book. 2008. 720p. 29.95 *(978-0-9661731-2-3(0))* Cleverly Group, The.

Snuffer, Denver C., Jr. Nephi' Isaiah: A Prophetic Look at the Latter Days. 2006. 310p. per. 20.99 *(978-0-9740158-3-5(0))* Mill Creek Pr., LLC.

Sperry Symposium, compiled by. Things Which My Father Saw: Approaches to Lehi's Dream & Nephi's Vision. 2011. 31.99 *(978-1-60908-738-8(0))* Deseret Bk. Co.

Spiritual Matters: Wisdom & Inspiration from the BK of Mormon. 2008. 168p. pap. 11.95 *(978-1-59992-080-1(8))* Leatherwood Pr.

Stawski, Willard. That Ye May Prosper: Meaningful Lessons from the Book of Mormon. 2007. 167p. per. 12.99 *(978-1-59955-030-5(X))* Cedar Fort, Inc./CFI Distribution.

Swift, Charles & Strathearn, Gaye. Living the Book of Mormon: The 36th Annual Sidney B. Sperry Symposium. 2007. 25.95 *(978-1-59038-799-3(6))* Deseret Bk. Co.

Swint, Mark. Compare Isaiah: A Look at Biblical Scriptures in the Book of Mormon. 2009. pap. 12.99 *(978-0-88290-960-8(6))* Cedar Fort, Inc./CFI Distribution.

Turley, Rick & Slaughter, William. How We Got the Book of Mormon. 2011. (Illus.). xv, 154p. (C). 17.99 net. *(978-1-60908-062-4(9))* Deseret Bk. Co.

Washburn, J. A. & Washburn, J. N. An Approach to the Study of the Book of Mormon Geography. 2007. (ENG.). 226p. 41.95 *(978-0-548-04876-4(2))* Kessinger Publishing, LLC.

Wayment, Thomas A. The Greatest Teacher. 2008. *(978-1-59038-956-0(5))* Deseret Bk. Co.

Welch, John W. The Legal Cases in the Book of Mormon. 2008. (Illus.). 29.95 *(978-0-8425-2712-5(5),* Brigham Young Univ. Pr.) Brigham Young Univ.

Welch, John W. & Dant, Doris R. The Book of Mormon Paintings of Minerva Teichert. 2007. (Illus.). pap. 24.95 *(978-0-8425-2677-7(3),* Brigham Young Univ. Studies) Brigham Young Univ.

Welch, John W. & Welch, J. Gregory. Charting the Book of Mormon: Visual Aids for Personal Study & Teaching, CD-ROM. 2008. cd-rom *(978-0-8425-2709-5(5),* Brigham Young Univ. Studies) Brigham Young Univ.

West, Roy A. An Introduction to the Book of Mormon a Religious Literary Study. 2007. (ENG.). 114p. 34.95 *(978-0-548-04868-9(1))* Kessinger Publishing, LLC.

Wilson, Timothy B. A Plain English Reference to the Book of Mormon. 2011. pap. 19.99 *(978-1-55517-401-9(9))* Cedar Fort, Inc./CFI Distribution.

Wirth, Diane E. Decoding Ancient America: A Guide to the Archaeology of the Book of Mormon. 2007. (Illus.). 119p. per. 12.99 *(978-0-88290-820-5(0))* Cedar Fort, Inc./CFI Distribution.

Woods, Debra Sansing. Mothering with Spiritual Power: Book of Mormon Inspirations for Raising a Righteous Family. 2007. 131p. per. 12.99 *(978-1-59955-059-6(8))* Cedar Fort, Inc./CFI Distribution.

Ziegler, Wesley. An Analysis of the Book of Mormon. 2007. (ENG.). 176p. 37.95 *(978-0-548-04883-2(5))* Kessinger Publishing, LLC.

BOOK OF THE DEAD

Boker, George H. The Book of the Dead by George H Boker. 2006. 216p. per. 20.99 *(978-1-4255-1761-8(7))* MPublishing.

Borghouts, Joris F. Book of the Dead [39]: From Shouting to Structure. 2007. (Studien zum altaegyptischen Totenbuch Ser.). (ENG.). 110p. (C). pap. 60.00 *(978-3-447-05228-3(7))* Harrassowitz, Otto Verlag DEU. Dist: ISD.

Budge, E. A. Wallis. The Book of the Dead. 2008. 48p. pap. 6.45 *(978-1-60597-489-7(7),* Book Jungle) Standard Pubns., Inc.

Budge, E. A. Wallis, tr. The Egyptian Book of the Dead. 2011. (ENG.). 128p. pap. 9.99 *(978-0-7858-2807-5(9),* 0785828079, Chartwell) Book Sales, Inc.

Nyord, Rune. Breathing Flesh: Conceptions of the Body in the Ancient Egyptian Coffin Texts. 2009. (Illus.). 645p. pap. 138.00 *(978-87-635-2605-0(0))* Museum Tusculanum Pr. DNK. Dist: Chicago Distribution Ctr.

Rhodes, Michael. Books of the Dead Belonging to Tshemmin & Neferirnub. 2011. (Brigham Young University - Studies in the Book of Abraham Ser.). (EGY., Illus.). 168p. 89.95 *(978-0-8425-2772-9(9),* Maxwell, Neal A. Institute for Religious Scholarship) Brigham Young Univ.

Rush, John A. The Twelve Gates: A Spiritual Passage Through the Egyptian Books of the Dead. 2007. (ENG., Illus.). 328p. pap. 26.95 *(978-1-58394-175-1(4),* Frog Ltd.) North Atlantic Bks.

Stöhr, Simone. Totenbuch-Forschungen: Gesammelte Beiträge des 2. Internationalen Totenbuch-Symposiums, Bonn, 25. Bis 29. September 2005. Backes, Burkhard & Munro, Irmtraut, eds. 2007. (Studien Zum Altägyptischen Totenbuch Ser.: Vol. 11). (FRE, GER & ENG., Illus.). 380p. (C). pap. 102.00 *(978-3-447-05470-6(0))* Harrassowitz, Otto Verlag DEU. Dist: ISD.

Taylor, John H. Spells for Eternity: The Ancient Egyptian Book of the Dead. 2010. (ENG., Illus.). 128p. (C). pap. 19.95 *(978-0-7141-1990-8(3))* British Museum Pr. GBR. Dist: Brown, David Bk. Co., The.

Töpfer, Susanne & Müller-Roth, Marcus. Das Ende der Totenbuchtradition und der Übergang Zum Buch Vom Atmen: Die Totenbücher des Monthemhat (PTübingen2012) und der Tanedjmet (PLouvre N 3085) 2011. (Handschriften des altägyptischen Totenbuches Ser.). (GER., Illus.). 138p. (C). 134.00 ***(978-3-447-06460-6(9))*** Harrassowitz, Otto Verlag DEU. Dist: ISD.

Wasserman, James, ed. The Egyptian Book of the Dead: The Book of Going Forth by Day. Faulkner, Raymond, tr. from EGY. 2nd ed. 2009. (ENG., Illus.). 176p. 125.00 *(978-0-9817736-0-5(5))* KWS Pubs.

Wuthrich, Annik. Elements de theologie Thebaine: Les chapitres supplementaires du Livre des Morts. 2010. (Studien Zum Altägyptischen Totenbuch Ser.). (FRE.). 272p. (C). pap. 96.00 *(978-3-447-06235-0(5))* Harrassowitz, Otto Verlag DEU. Dist: ISD.

BOOK ORNAMENTATION

Loring, Rosamond B. Decorated Book Papers: Being an Account of Their Designs & Fashions. Mayo, Hope, ed. 4th ed. 2008. (Houghton Library Publications). (Illus.). 215p. 50.00 *(978-0-9765472-6-6(0))* Harvard Univ. Pr.

—Marbled & Paste Papers: Rosamond Loring's Recipe Book: A Facsimile of Her Manuscript Notebook. 2007. (Houghton Library Publications Ser.). (Illus.). 32p. pap. 25.00 *(978-0-9765472-5-9(2))* Harvard Univ. Pr.

Shirley, Rodney. Courtiers & Cannibals, Angels & Amazons: The art of the decorative cartographic Titlepage. 2009. (Illus.). 272p. 89.00 *(978-90-6194-060-9(5))* HES & DE GRAAF Pubs. BV NLD. Dist: Oak Knoll Pr.

BOOK-PLATES

see Bookplates

BOOK PRICES

see Books—Prices

BOOK PRIZES
see Literary Prizes

BOOK RARITIES
see Rare Books

BOOK REGISTRATION, NATIONAL
see also Bibliography, National; Copyright

Partridge, R. C. Barrington. History of the Legal Deposit of Books. 2006. 384p. per. *(978-1-4067-3532-1(9)*, Hesperides Pr.) Read Bks.

BOOK REPAIRING
see Books—Conservation and Restoration

BOOK REVIEWING
Here are entered works on the technique of writing reviews. Collections of reviews are entered under the heading Books—Reviews.
see also Book Talks

Burger, Nash K. The Road to West 43rd Street. 2009. (ENG.). 192p. pap. 25.00 *(978-1-60473-260-3(1))* Univ. Pr. of Mississippi.

Calvani, Mayra & Edwards, Anne K. The Slippery Art of Book Reviewing. 2008. 180p. pap. 16.95 *(978-1-933353-22-7(8))* Twilight Times Bks.

Dawidowicz, Paula. Literature Reviews Made Easy: A Quick Guide to Success. 2010. *(978-1-61735-192-1(X))*; pap. *(978-1-61735-191-4(1))*; E-Book *(978-1-61735-193-8(8))* Information Age Publishing, Inc.

GALE, Kate, ed. The Los Angeles Review No. 5. 5th ed. 2008. 192p. pap. 20.00 *(978-1-59709-148-0(0))* Red Hen Pr.

Green, Jack & Moore, Steven. Fire the Bastards! 2nd ed. 2012. (ENG.). 88p. pap. 12.95 *(978-1-56478-609-8(9)*, 478609) Dalkey Archive Pr.

Hooper, Brad. Writing Reviews for Readers' Advisory. 2010. 128p. *(978-0-8389-1017-7(3))* American Library Assn.

Horning, Kathleen T. From Cover to Cover: Evaluating & Reviewing Children's Books. rev. ed. 2010. (ENG.). 240p. pap. 14.99 *(978-0-06-077757-9(5)*, Collins) HarperCollins Pubs.

Hyland, Ken & Diani, Giuliana, eds. Academic Evaluation: Review Genres in University Settings. 2009. (ENG., Illus.). 256p. 95.00 *(978-0-230-22433-9(4))* Palgrave Macmillan.

McKenzie, Janet. The Windeatt Dictionary: Pre-Vatican II Terms & Catholic Words from Mary Fabyan Windeatt's Saint Biographies. 2007. 112p. (J). per. 11.95 *(978-1-934185-16-2(7))* Biblio Resource Pubns., Inc.

Muller, Jake. Writing in the Social Sciences: A Guide for Term Papers & Book Reviews. 2010. (ENG., Illus.). 168p. (C). 29.95 *(978-0-19-543026-4(3))* Oxford Univ. Pr., Inc.

Pool, Gail. Faint Praise: The Plight of Book Reviewing in America. 2007. (ENG., 184p. (C). Illus.). 34.95 *(978-0-8262-1727-1(3))*; per. 19.95 *(978-0-8262-1728-8(1))* Univ. of Missouri Pr.

BOOK REVIEWS
see Books—Reviews

BOOK SALES
see Books—Prices; Booksellers and Bookselling

BOOK SELECTION
see also Best Books; Bibliography of Bibliographies; Book Collecting; Book Collectors; Books and Reading

Bergart, Robin & Lewis, Vivian. Sudden Selector's Guide to Business Resources. 2007. xv, 70p. 28.50 *(978-0-8389-8414-7(2))* American Library Assn.

The Best Reading Hints on the Selection of Books; 2006. 264p. per. 23.99 *(978-1-4255-2335-0(8))* MPublishing.

Bradbury, Judy, ed. Children's Book Corner Set, Bk. 4: A Read-Aloud Resource with Tips, Techniques & Plans for Teachers, Their Students & Their Parents, 4 vols. 2006. pap. 99.95 *(978-1-59158-459-9(0)*, LU4590) Libraries Unlimited, Inc.

Lehman, Barbara A., et al, eds. Reading Globally, K-8: Connecting Students to the World Through Literature. 2010. (Illus.). 248p. pap. *(978-1-4129-7392-2(9))* Corwin Pr.

Mallett, Margaret. Choosing & Using Fiction & Non-Fiction 3-11. 2010. (ENG., Illus.). 416p. 155.00 *(978-0-415-48458-9(8))* Routledge.

Mesmer, Heidi Anne E. Tools for Matching Readers to Texts: Research-Based Practices. 2007. (Solving Problems in Teaching of Literacy Ser.). (ENG.). 180p. (gr. k-6). 50.00 *(978-1-59385-598-7(2))* Guilford Pubns., Inc.

BOOK-SHELVES
see Shelving for Books

BOOK SHOPS
see Bookstores

BOOK STORES
see Bookstores

BOOK STUDY GROUPS
see Book Clubs (Discussion Groups)

BOOK TALKS

Baxter, Kathleen A. & Kochel, Marcia Agness. Gotcha Again for Guys! More Nonfiction Books to Get Boys Excited about Reading. 2010. (Illus.). xiii, 248p. E-Book *(978-1-59884-377-4(X))*; 248p. pap. 35.00 *(978-1-59884-376-7(1)*, A2702P) Libraries Unlimited, Inc.

—Gotcha Good! Nonfiction Books to Get Kids Excited about Reading, 1 vol. 2008. (Illus.). 268p. pap. 35.00 *(978-1-59158-654-8(2)*, LU8654) Libraries Unlimited, Inc.

Clark, Ruth E. Cox. Tantalizing Tidbits for Teens 2: More Quick Booktalks for the Busy High School Library Media Specialist, 1 vol. 2007. 152p. pap. 36.95 *(978-1-58683-235-3(2)*, A2459P) Linworth Publishing, Inc.

Cyr, Ann-Marie & Gillespie, Kellie M. Something to Talk About: Creative Booktalking for Adults. 2006. (ENG.). 134p. per. 45.00 *(978-0-8108-5436-9(8))* Scarecrow Pr., Inc.

Diamant-Cohen, Betsy & Levi, Selma K. Booktalking Bonanza: Ten Ready-To-Use Multimedia Sessions for the Busy Librarian. 2008. (Illus.). 240p. 40.00 *(978-0-8389-0965-2(5))* American Library Assn.

Gillespie, John T. & Naden, Corinne J. Classic Teenplots: A Booktalk Guide to Use with Readers Ages 12-18, 1 vol. 2006. (Children's & Young Adult Literature Reference Ser.). 368p. 55.00 *(978-1-59158-312-7(8)*, LU3128) Libraries Unlimited, Inc.

Jarrell, Jill S. & Cannon, Tara C. Cooler Than Fiction: A Planning Guide for Teen Nonfiction Booktalks. 2010. (ENG., Illus.). 199p. pap. 45.00 *(978-0-7864-4886-9(5))* McFarland & Co., Inc. Pubs.

Keane, Nancy J. & Cavanaugh, Terence W. The Tech-Savvy Booktalker: A Guide for 21st-Century Educators, 1 vol. 2008. (Illus.). 176p. pap. 35.00 *(978-1-59158-637-1(2)*, LU8637) Libraries Unlimited, Inc.

Mahood, Kristine. Booktalking with Teens, 1 vol. 2010. (Libraries Unlimited Professional Guides for Young Adult Librarians Ser.). 289p. pap. 45.00 *(978-1-59158-714-9(X)*, LU8714) Libraries Unlimited, Inc.

Schall, Lucy. Booktalks & Beyond: Promoting Great Genre Reads to Teens, 1 vol. 2007. 296p. per. 40.00 *(978-1-59158-466-7(3)*, LU4663) Libraries Unlimited, Inc.

—Genre Talks for Teens: Booktalks & More for Every Teen Reading Interest, 1 vol. 2009. 309p. pap. 40.00 *(978-1-59158-743-9(3)*, LU8743) Libraries Unlimited, Inc.

—Value-Packed Booktalks: Genre Talks & More for Teen Readers. 2011. E-Book *(978-1-59884-736-9(8))* Libraries Unlimited, Inc.

—Value-Packed Booktalks: Genre Talks & More for Teen Readers, 1 vol. 2011. 261p. pap. 45.00 *(978-1-59884-735-2(X)*, A3329P) Pearson Education GBR. Dist: ABC-CLIO, LLC.

York, Sherry. Booktalking Authentic Multicultural Literature: Fiction & History for Young Readers, 1 vol. 2009. 160p. pap. 39.95 *(978-1-58683-300-8(6)*, A2458P) Linworth Publishing, Inc.

—Booktalking Authentic Multicultural Literature: Fiction, History, & Memoirs for Teens, 1 vol. 2008. 160p. pap. 39.95 *(978-1-58683-299-5(9)*, A2446P) Linworth Publishing, Inc.

BOOK THEFTS
see also Libraries—Security Measures

Bartlett, Allison Hoover. The Man Who Loved Books Too Much: The True Story of a Thief, a Detective, & a World of Literary Obsession. 2010. (ENG.). 288p. (gr. 12). 15.00 *(978-1-59448-481-0(3)*, Riverhead Trade (Paperbacks)) Penguin Group (USA) Inc.

Kahn, Miriam. The Library Security & Safety Guide to Prevention, Planning, & Response. 2008. 50.00 *(978-0-8389-0949-2(3))* American Library Assn.

McDade, Travis. The Book Thief: The True Crimes of Daniel Spiegelman, 1 vol. annot. ed. 2006. 200p. 49.95 *(978-0-275-99331-3(0)*, C9331, Praeger Pubs.) Greenwood Publishing Group, Inc.

Wilkie, Everett C. Guide to Security Considerations & Practices for Rare Book, Manuscript, & Special Collection Libraries. 2011. *(978-0-8389-9338-5(9))*; pap. *(978-0-8389-8592-2(0))*; E-Book *(978-0-8389-9337-8(0))* Assn. of College & Research Libraries.

BOOK TRADE
see Book Industries and Trade; Booksellers and Bookselling; Publishers and Publishing

BOOK WORKS (ART)
see Artists' Books

BOOKBINDING
see also Book Ornamentation; Marbling (Bookbinding)

Abbott, Kathy. Bookbinding. 2010. (ENG., Illus.). 160p. instr.'s gde. ed. 29.95 *(978-1-84797-153-1(9))* Crowood Pr., Ltd. GBR. Dist: Independent Pubs. Group.

Bolofo, Koto. Große Komplikation / Grande Complication, 1 vol. 2010. (ENG & GER., Illus.). 104p. 118.00 *(978-3-86930-055-9(8))* Steidl, Gerhard Druckerei und Verlag DEU. Dist: Innovative Logistics.

Bond, W. H. Thomas Hollis of Lincoln's Inn: A Whig & His Books. 2009. (Sandars Lectures in Bibliography Ser.). (ENG.). 152p. pap. 28.99 *(978-0-521-11480-6(2))* Cambridge Univ. Pr.

Cambras, Josep. Bookbinding: Techniques & Projects. 2008. (Decorative Techniques Ser.). (ENG., Illus.). 144p. pap. 26.99 *(978-0-7641-6084-4(2))* Barron's Educational Series, Inc.

Cobden-Sanderson, T. J. Ecce Mundus: Industrial Ideals & the Book Beautiful. 2011. 40p. 35.95 *(978-1-258-05742-8(5))* Literary Licensing, LLC.

Cockerell, Douglas. Bookbinding & the Care of Books: A Handbook for Amateurs, Bookbinders & Librarians. 2008. 176p. pap. 13.94 *(978-1-4357-4339-7(3))* Lulu Enterprises Inc.

Cockerell, Douglas. Bookbinding, & the Care of Books; a Handbook for Amateurs, Bookbinders & Librarians. 2011. 354p. pap. 32.75 *(978-1-174-66795-4(8))* BiblioBazaar.

Davenport, Cyril. English Embroidered Bookbindings. 2011. 120p. *(978-1-84902-509-6(6))* Benediction Classics.

Davenport, Cyril James Humphries. English Embroidered Bookbindings. 2007. (Illus.). 92p. pap. *(978-1-84830-023-1(9)*, Wildhern Pr.); 88p. per. *(978-1-4068-1846-8(1))* Echo Library.

Diehn, Gwen. The Decorated Journal: Creating Beautifully Expressive Journal Pages. 2006. (Illus.). 128p. pap. 14.95 *(978-1-57990-956-7(6))* Lark Bks.

—Live & Learn: Real Life Journals - Designing & Using Handmade Books. 2010. (AARP Ser.). (ENG.). 180p. 24.95 *(978-1-60059-492-2(1))* Lark Bks.

Douglas Cockerell. Bookbinding, & the Care of Books - a Text-Book for Bookbinders & Librarians. 2008. (Illus.). 344p. 42.45 *(978-1-4437-3809-5(3))* Barclay Pr., Inc.

—Bookbinding, & the Care of Books - a Text-Book for Bookbinders & Librarians. 2007. (ENG.). 340p. per. *(978-1-4086-2958-1(5))* Read Bks.

Duff, E. Gordon. The English Provincial Printers, Stationers & Bookbinders To 1557. 2011. (ENG.). 172p. pap. 19.99 *(978-0-521-14744-6(1))* Cambridge Univ. Pr.

Foot, Mirjam & Davis, Henry. A Collection of Book Bindings, 3 vols. 2010. (Illus.). 527p. 125.00 *(978-1-58456-272-6(2))* Oak Knoll Pr.

French, Hannah D. Bookbinding in Early America: Seven Essays on Masters & Methods. 2010. (ENG.). 230p. 50.00 *(978-1-4379-7119-4(9))* DIANE Publishing Co.

Golden, Alisa. Painted Paper: Techniques & Projects for Handmade Books & Cards. 2009. (ENG., Illus.). 176p. pap. 17.95 *(978-1-60059-547-9(2))* Lark Bks.

Golden, Alisa J. Making Handmade Books: 100+ Bindings, Structures & Forms. 2011. (ENG., Illus.). 256p. pap. 19.95 *(978-1-60059-587-5(1))* Lark Bks.

Gravois, Michael. The Big Book of Reading Response Activities: Dozens of Engaging Activities, Graphic Organizers, & Other Reproducibles to Use Before, During, & after Reading. 2007. (Teaching Resources Ser.). (ENG., Illus.). 160p. (gr. 2-3). pap. 18.99 *(978-0-439-79683-5(0)*, Teaching Resources) Scholastic, Inc.

—Reading Response Activities: Dozens of Engaging Activities, Graphic Organizers, & Other Reproducibles to Use Before, During, & after Reading. 2007. (Big Book of Reading Response Activities Ser.). (ENG., Illus.). 160p. (gr. 4-6). pap. 18.99 *(978-0-439-76062-1(3)*, Teaching Resources) Scholastic, Inc.

Hannett, John. Bibliopegia: Or the Art of Bookbinding, in All its Branches. 2010. (Cambridge Library Collection - Printing & Publishing History Ser.). (Illus.). 220p. pap. 24.00 *(978-1-108-02144-9(1))* Cambridge Univ. Pr.

—An Inquiry into the Nature & Form of the Books of the Ancients: With a History of the Art of Bookbinding, from the Times of the Greeks & Romans to the Present Day. 2010. (Cambridge Library Collection - History of Printing, Publishing & Libraries Ser.). (ENG., Illus.). 248p. pap. 22.99 *(978-1-108-02482-2(3))* Cambridge Univ. Pr.

Hemachandra, Ray. Lark Studio Series: Handmade Books. 2010. (ENG., Illus.). 204p. 12.95 *(978-1-60059-682-7(7))* Lark Bks.

Hobson, G. D. English Binding Before 1500. 2010. (ENG.). 188p. pap. 19.99 *(978-0-521-13728-7(4))* Cambridge Univ. Pr.

Krause, Dorothy Simpson. Book + Art: Handcrafting Artists' Books. 2009. (ENG., Illus.). 144p. pap. 24.99 *(978-1-60061-154-4(0)*, North Light Bks.) F&W Media, Inc.

Krupp, Andrea. Bookcloth in England & America, 1823-50. 2008. (Illus.). 102p. pap. 35.00 *(978-1-58456-213-9(7))* Oak Knoll Pr.

Lark. 500 Handmade Books: Inspiring Interpretations of a Timeless Form. 2008. (500 Ser.). (ENG., Illus.). 420p. pap. 24.95 *(978-1-57990-877-5(2))* Lark Bks.

Lark Books Staff. The Penland Book of Handmade Books: Master Classes in Bookmaking Techniques. LaFerla, Jane & Gunter, Alice, eds. 2008. (Penland Ser.). (ENG., Illus.). 232p. pap. 19.95 *(978-1-60059-300-0(3))* Lark Bks.

Lindsay, Jen. Fine Bookbinding: A Technical Guide. 2009. (Illus.). 215p. pap. 59.95 *(978-1-58456-268-9(4))* Oak Knoll Pr.

Loring, Rosamond B. Decorated Book Papers: Being an Account of Their Designs & Fashions. Mayo, Hope, ed. 4th ed. 2008. (Houghton Library Publications). (Illus.). 215p. 50.00 *(978-0-9765472-5-6(0))* Harvard Univ. Pr.

Matthews, William. Modern Bookbinding Practically Considered. 2009. 48p. pap. *(978-0-217-02425-9(4))* Books LLC.

McCafferty, Kathleen. Making Mini Books: Big Ideas for 30+ Little Projects. 2012. (ENG., Illus.). 144p. pap. 19.95 *(978-1-4547-0200-9(1))* Lark Bks.

Miller, Julia. Books Will Speak Plain: A Handbook for Identifying & Describing Historical Bindings. 2010. (ENG., Illus.). 592p. (C). 80.00 *(978-0-9797974-3-9(8))* Legacy Pr., The.

Nicola, Irma Harve. Serials Binding: A Simple & Complete Guidebook to Processes. (Illus.). 2009. (ENG.). 102p. 125.00 *(978-0-7890-2504-3(3))* 2008. 248p. pap. 35.95 *(978-0-7890-2505-0(1))* Routledge.

Oldham. English Blind Stamped Bindings. 2010. (ENG.). 212p. pap. 27.99 *(978-0-521-13664-8(4))* Cambridge Univ. Pr.

Oldham, J. Basil. Blind Panels of English Binders. 2010. (ENG.). 140p. pap. 27.99 *(978-0-521-13662-4(8))* Cambridge Univ. Pr.

Prideaux, S. T. Catalogue of Books Bound by S. T. Prideaux. (Illus.). 46p. 40.00 *(978-0-935164-02-2(2))* Oak Knoll Pr.

Publish Yourself: How to Print & Bind Your Own Books at Home. 2007. (YA). per. 10.95 *(978-0-9791014-2-7(5))* Gold Seal Pub.

Quentin-Bauchart, Ernest. Les Femmes Bibliophiles de France, 2 Vols. reprint ed. 250.00 *(978-0-7222-1916-4(4))* Library Reprints, Inc.

Quick Printers' Ratios, Vol. XIII. 155.00 Printing Industries of America, Inc.

Raby, Julian & Tanindi, Zeren. Turkish Bookbinding in the 15th Century: The Foundation of an Ottoman Court Style. Stanley, Tim, ed. 2006. (ENG., Illus.). 256p. *(978-1-898592-01-3(2))* Azimuth Editions.

Richards, Constance E. Making Books & Journals: 20 Great Weekend Projects. 2011. (ENG., Illus.). 80p. pap. 9.95 *(978-1-60059-994-1(X)*, RSP) Lark Bks.

Roddis, Sue. Handmade Decorative Books. 2010. (Passion for Paper Ser.). (ENG., Illus.). 80p. pap. 19.95 *(978-1-84448-314-3(2))* Search Pr., Ltd. GBR. Dist: Independent Pubs. Group.

Samford, C. Clement. The Bookbinder in Eighteenth Century Williamsburg: An Account of His Life & Times, & of His Craft. 2011. 36p. 35.95 *(978-1-258-04304-9(1))* Literary Licensing, LLC.

Smith, Esther K. How to Make Books: Fold, Cut & Stitch Your Way to a One-of-a-Kind Book. 2007. (ENG., Illus.). 128p. 25.00 *(978-0-307-35336-8(2)*, Potter Craft) Crown Publishing Group.

Stein, Jeannine. Adventures in Bookbinding: Hand Crafting Mixed-Media Books. 2011. (ENG., Illus.). 144p. pap. 24.99 *(978-1-59253-687-0(5)*, 1592536875) Quayside.

—Adventures in Bookbinding: Handcrafting Mixed-Media Books. 2011. (Illus.). 144p. E-Book *(978-1-61058-021-2(4)*, Quarry Books) Quayside.

—Re-Bound: Creating Handmade Books from Recycled & Repurposed Materials. 2009. (ENG., Illus.). 144p. pap. 24.99 *(978-1-59253-524-8(0)*, 1592535240, Quarry Books) Quayside.

Taylor, Terry. Eco Books: Inventive Projects from the Recycling Bin. 2009. (ENG., Illus.). 144p. pap. 22.95 *(978-1-60059-394-9(1))* Lark Bks.

Thomas, Peter & Thomas, Donna. More Making Books by Hand: Exploring Miniature Books, Alternative Structures, & Found Objects. 2007. (Illus.). 142p. pap. 19.00 *(978-1-4223-6592-2(1))* DIANE Publishing Co.

Thompson, Jason. Playing with Books: The Art of Upcycling, Deconstructing, & Reimagining the Book. 2010. (Playing Ser.). (ENG., Illus.). 152p. pap. 24.99 *(978-1-59253-600-9(X)*, 159253600X) Quayside.

Van Tassell, Michelle. Quiet-Time Busy Books: Fun Fabric Pages Personalized for Your Little One. 2008. (ENG., Illus.). 64p. pap. 19.95 *(978-1-57120-401-1(6))* C & T Publishing.

W. J. E. Crane. Bookbinding for Amateurs - 1903. 2007. 196p. per. 14.95 *(978-1-60386-031-4(2)*, Merchant Bks.) Rough Draft Printing.

Weinstein, Michael. Paperback Covers. 2008. (Illus.). 440p. pap. 32.75 *(978-0-936428-19-2(8))* Polygona Publishing Hse.

Weston, Heather. Bookcraft: Techniques for Binding, Folding, & Decorating to Create Books & More. 2008. (ENG., Illus.). 128p. pap. 22.99 *(978-1-59253-455-5(4)*, 1592534554, Quarry Books) Quayside.

Wheatley, Henry Benjamin. Remarkable Bindings in the British Museum: Selected for their Beauty or Historic Interest. 2010. (Cambridge Library Collection - Printing & Publishing History Ser.). (Illus.). 340p. pap. 28.99 *(978-1-108-02151-7(4))* Cambridge Univ. Pr.

Zaehnsdorf, Joseph W. The Art of Bookbinding: The Classic Victorian Handbook. 2nd ed. 2007. (Dover Craft Bks.). (ENG., Illus.). 224p. per. 10.95 *(978-0-486-45733-8(8))* Dover Pubns., Inc.

Zamrzla, Erin. At Home with Handmade Books: 28 Extraordinary Bookbinding Projects Made from Ordinary & Repurposed Materials. 2011. (Make Good: Crafts + Life Ser.). (ENG., Illus.). 160p. pap. 21.95 *(978-1-59030-822-6(0)*, Trumpeter) Shambhala Pubns., Inc.

Zerdoun Bat-Yehouda, Monique, et al. Matériaux du Livre Médiéval: Actes du Colloque du Groupement de Recherche (GDR) 2836 "Matériaux du Livre Médiéval", Paris, CNRS, 7-8 Novembre 2007. 2010. (FRE., Illus.). xxiii, 324p. *(978-2-503-53386-5(8))* Brepols Pubs.

BOOKBINDING—EXHIBITIONS

Bodleian Library Staff. An Artful Craft: Fine & Historic Bookbindings from the Broxbourne Library & Other Collections. 2009. (Illus.). 288p. 65.00 *(978-1-85124-347-1(X))* Bodleian Library GBR. Dist: Chicago Distribution Ctr.

Cook, Christopher D. Love Thy Neighbor: An Exhibition Commemorating the Completion of the Episcopal Chapel of St. John the Divine. 2007. (ENG., Illus.). 28p. 3.00 *(978-0-9788134-1-3(3))* Rare Book & Manuscript Library.

Koch, Jeanette, ed. Bound for Success: Catalogue for Designer Bookbinders International Competition 2009. 2009. (ENG., Illus.). 112p. 65.00 *(978-1-85124-352-5(6))* Bodleian Library GBR. Dist: Chicago Distribution Ctr.

Spawn, Willman & Kinsella, Thomas E. American Signed Bindings Through 1876. 2007. (Illus.). 299p. 85.00 *(978-1-58456-208-5(0))* Oak Knoll Pr.

BOOKBINDING—REPAIRING

Driscoll, Matthew & Mósesdóttir, Ragnheiður, eds. Care & Conservation of Manuscripts 11: Proceedings of the Eleventh International Seminar Held at the University of Copenhagen 24th-25th April 2008. 2009. 313p. pap. 43.00 *(978-87-635-3099-6(6))* Museum Tusculanum Pr. DNK. Dist: Chicago Distribution Ctr.

Lavender, Kenneth & BonaDea, Artemis. Book Repair: A How-To-Do-It Manual. 2nd ed. 2011. *(978-1-55570-747-7(5))* Neal-Schuman Pubs., Inc.

Thiel, Sarah Goodwin. Build It Once: A Basic Primer for the Creation of Online Exhibitions. 2007. (Build It Once Ser.). (ENG., Illus.). 112p. per. 45.00 *(978-0-8108-5225-9(X))* Scarecrow Pr., Inc.

BOOKCASES
see Shelving for Books

BOOKER, JOHN MANNING

Shine, Hill, ed. Booker Memorial Studies: Eight Essays on Victorian Literature in Memory of John Manning Booker, 1881-1948. 2011. (ENG.). 198p. pap. 30.00 *(978-0-8078-6828-7(0))* Univ. of North Carolina Pr.

BOOKKEEPERS
see Accountants

BOOKKEEPING
see also Accounting; Card System in Business; Depreciation; Financial Statements

also subdivision Accounting under topical headings
Barich, Thomas & Barich, Thomas A. QuickBooks 2010 QuickSteps. 2009. (QuickSteps Ser.). (Illus.). 224p. pap. 21.99 *(978-0-07-163332-1(4),* 0071633324) McGraw-Hill Osborne.
Bragg, Steven M. Bookkeeping Essentials: How to Succeed as a Bookkeeper. 2011. (ENG., Illus.). 335p. pap. 29.95 *(978-0-470-88255-9(7),* Wiley) Wiley, John & Sons, Inc.
Bryant, Henry Beadman. Bryant & Stratton's Common School Book-Keeping by H B Bryant, & H D Stratton & S S Packard. 2006. 196p. per. 18.99 *(978-1-4255-1631-4(9))* MPublishing.
Clark, Lydia. How to Open & Operate a Financially Successful Bookkeeping Business: With Companion CD-ROM. 2011. (ENG.). 288p. pap. 39.95 *(978-1-60138-277-1(4))* Atlantic Publishing Co.
Consumer Dummies Staff & Epstein, Lita. Bookkeeping Kit for Dummies. 2012. (ENG.). 432p. pap. 34.99 ***(978-1-118-11645-6(3),*** For Dummies) Wiley, John & Sons, Inc.
Cram101 Textbook Reviews Staff. Outlines & Highlights for Century 21 Accounting: General Journal by Gilbertson & Lehman, ISBN. 2009. 226p. pap. 30.95 *(978-1-4288-2915-2(6));* 228p. pap. 31.95 *(978-1-4288-7809-9(2))* Cram101 Inc.
Drew, William A. Practical Book-Keeping, Containing Thorough Instruction in Journalizing, Posting, & Closing. 2006. 160p. per. 18.99 *(978-1-4255-1205-7(4))* MPublishing.
Epstein, Lita. Bookkeeping Workbook for Dummies. 2007. (ENG., Illus.). 288p. per. 19.99 *(978-0-470-16983-4(4),* For Dummies) Wiley, John & Sons, Inc.
Ferraino, Cindy. The Complete Dictionary of Accounting & Bookkeeping Terms Explained Simply. 2010. (ENG.). 288p. pap. 24.95 *(978-1-60138-325-9(8))* Atlantic Publishing Co.
Foster, Benjamin Franklin. A Concise Treatise on Commercial Book-Keeping, Elucidating the Principles & Practice of Double Entry by B F Foster. 2006. 192p. per. 18.99 *(978-1-4255-1530-0(4))* MPublishing.
Fulton, Levi S. A Practical System of Book-Keeping by Single & Double Entry: Containing Forms of Books & Practical Exercises, Adapted to the Use of the Farmer, M. 2006. 268p. per. 23.99 *(978-1-4255-2469-2(9));* 300p. per. 23.99 *(978-1-4255-2938-3(0))* MPublishing.
—A Practical System of Book-Keeping by Single & Double Entry: Containing Forms of Books & Practical Exercises, Adapted to the Use of the Farmer, Me. 2006. 300p. per. 23.99 *(978-1-4255-2908-6(9))* MPublishing.
Gomes, Delfina. Accounting Change in Central Government. 2009. 308p. pap. *(978-3-639-20070-6(5))* VDM Verlag Dr. Mueller e.K.
Gordon, D. P. & Hussey, A. E. First Steps in Bookkeeping. rev. ed. (Illus.). 48p. pap. *(978-0-909465-42-1(8),* UNSW Press) NewSouth Publishing.
Ivens, Kathy. Running QuickBooks in Nonprofits: 2nd Edition: The Only Comprehensive Guide for Nonprofits Using QuickBooks. 2nd ed. 2011. (ENG.). 512p. pap. 36.95 *(978-1-932925-30-2(9))* CPA911 Publishing.
Joyce, Tim. Cambridge Checkpoints VCE Accounting Unit 3 2008. 2007. (Cambridge Checkpoints Ser.). pap. *(978-0-521-71577-5(6))* Cambridge Univ. Pr.
Kelly, Jane. Bookkeeping. 2009. (Illus.). 296p. pap., wbk. ed. 26.50 *(978-0-470-74420-8(0),* For Dummies) Wiley, John & Sons, Inc.
Kravitz, Wallace W. & Fitzpatrick, Kathleen. E-Z Bookkeeping. 4th rev. ed. 2010. (Barron's E-Z Ser.). (ENG.). 336p. pap. 14.99 *(978-0-7641-4133-1(3))* Barron's Educational Series, Inc.
Lerner, Joel, et al. Schaum's Outline of Bookkeeping & Accounting, Fourth Edition. 4th ed. 2009. (Schaum's Outline Ser.). (ENG.). 480p. (C). pap. 20.00 *(978-0-07-163536-3(X),* 007163536X) McGraw-Hill Cos., The.
Long, Michelle. How to Start a Home-Based Bookkeeping Business. 2011. (Home-Based Business Ser.). (ENG.). 208p. pap. 18.95 *(978-0-7627-6126-5(1))* Globe Pequot Pr., The.
Lymer, Andy, et al. Get to Grips with Book Keeping. 2010. (Teach Yourself Ser.). (ENG., Illus.). 484p. pap. 23.95 *(978-1-4441-0298-7(2),* Hodder & Stoughton) Hodder General Publishing Div. GBR. Dist: Independent Pubs. Group.
Marshall, Peter. Computerised Book-Keeping: An Accredited Textbook of the Institute of Certified Bookkeepers. 2010. (ENG., Illus.). 375p. pap. 34.00 *(978-1-84528-397-1(X))* How To Books GBR. Dist: Parkwest Pubns., Inc.
—Mastering Book-Keeping. 8th ed. 2009. (Illus.). 192p. pap. 26.00 *(978-1-84528-324-7(4))* How To Books GBR. Dist: Parkwest Pubns., Inc.
—Mastering Book-Keeping: A Complete Guide to the Principles & Practice of Business Accounting. 9th ed. 2010. (ENG., Illus.). 541p. pap. 34.00 *(978-1-84528-446-6(1))* How To Books GBR. Dist: Parkwest Pubns., Inc.
Mason, Roger. Bookkeeping & Accounting. 2008. (Instant Manager Ser.). (ENG.). 224p. pap. 19.95 *(978-0-340-97286-1(6),* Hodder & Stoughton) Hodder General Publishing Div. GBR. Dist: Independent Pubs. Group.
Mayhew, Ira. Mayhew's Practical Book-Keeping Embracing Single & Double Entry, Commercial Calculations, & the Philosophy & Morals of Business by Ira Mayhe. 2006. 232p. per. 20.99 *(978-1-4255-1922-3(9))* MPublishing.
—Mayhew's Practical Book Keeping Embracing Single & Double Entry, Commercial Calculations, & the Philosophy & Morals of Business by Ira Mayhe. 2006. 228p. per. 20.99 *(978-1-4255-1943-8(1))* MPublishing.
—Mayhew's Practical Book-Keeping Key by Ira Mayhew. 2006. 128p. per. 16.99 *(978-1-4255-0854-8(5))* MPublishing.
—A Practical System of Book-Keeping by Single & Double Entry by Ira Mayhew. 2006. 148p. per. 16.99 *(978-1-4255-1103-6(1));* per. 16.99 *(978-1-4255-1056-5(6))* MPublishing.
Meise, Eric. Momentum Accounting for Trends. 2010. 316p. pap. *(978-3-639-16051-2(7))* VDM Verlag Dr. Mueller e.K.
Mohr, Angie. Bookkeepers' Boot Camp: Get a Grip on Accounting Basics. 2nd ed. 2010. (ENG.). 204p. pap. 18.95 *(978-1-77040-044-3(3))* Self-Counsel Pr., Inc. CAN. Dist: National Bk. Network.
—Start & Run a Bookkeeping Business. 2010. (Start & Run ... Ser.). (ENG., Illus.). 192p. pap. 17.95 *(978-1-55180-641-9(X))* Self-Counsel Pr., Inc. CAN. Dist: Midpoint Trade Bks., Inc.
Mucha-Aydlott, Julie. How to open your own in-home bookkeeping service 2nd Edition. 2007. per. 69.95 *(978-0-9746093-9-3(0))* San Diego Business Accounting Solutions a Non CPA Firm.
—I have QuickBooks, Now What? For the Self-Employed. 2007. 342p. per. 29.95 *(978-0-9794124-0-0(4))* San Diego Business Accounting Solutions a Non CPA Firm.
Murcia, Eligia. Record Keeping for Small Rural Businesses. (Technical Notes Ser.: No. 26). (Illus.). 25p. (Orig.). pap. 2.00 *(978-0-932288-75-2(8))* Univ. of Massachusetts, Ctr. for International Education.
Quinn, Martin. Book-keeping & Accounts for Entrepreneurs. 2009. (ENG., Illus.). 208p. (C). pap. 24.99 *(978-0-273-72395-0(2))* FT Press.
—Brilliant Book-Keeping: How to Keep Your Business Efficient & Cost-Effective. 2010. (ENG., Illus.). 232p. (C). pap. 19.99 *(978-0-273-73178-8(5))* FT Press.
Sangster, Alan & Wood, Frank. Frank Wood's Business Accounting, Vol. 1. 12th rev. ed. 2011. (ENG., Illus.). 779p. pap. 107.50 ***(978-0-273-75928-7(0))*** Pearson Education, Ltd. GBR. Dist: Trans-Atlantic Pubns., Inc.
Wood, Frank & Robinson, Sheila. Book-keeping & Accounts. 7th ed. 2009. (ENG., Illus.). 640p. pap. 87.50 *(978-0-273-71805-5(3))* Financial Times/Prentice Hall.

BOOKKEEPING—STUDY AND TEACHING
see Accounting—Study and Teaching

BOOKMAKING (BETTING)
see Book-Making (Betting)

BOOKMARKS (OWNERS' MARKS)
see Books—Owners' Marks

BOOKMOBILES
MacCreaigh, Erica & Dilger-Hill, Jeannie, eds. On the Road with Outreach: Mobile Library Services, 1 vol. 2009. 348p. pap. 50.00 *(978-1-59158-678-4(X),* LU678X) Libraries Unlimited, Inc.

BOOKPLATES
Gade, Gerhard. Norwegian Ex Libris. 2011. 50p. pap. 26.45 ***(978-1-4460-8010-8(2))*** Research Pr.
Grafton, Carol Belanger, ed. Bookplate Designs CD-ROM & Book. 2008. (Dover Electronic Clip Art Ser.). (ENG., Illus.). 48p. pap. 16.95 *(978-0-486-99878-7(9))* Dover Pubns., Inc.
Hopkinson, Martin. Ex Libris: The Art of Bookplates. 2011. (Illus.). 112p. pap. 15.00 *(978-0-300-17163-1(3))* Yale Univ. Pr.
Junge, Carl S. Ex Libris. 2011. 100p. 39.95 ***(978-1-258-00349-4(X))*** Literary Licensing, LLC.
Livingstone, Karen. Voysey Bookplates. 2011. (ENG., Illus.). 248p. 49.50 *(978-1-85149-640-2(8))* Antique Collectors' Club.
Prescott, Winward. Masonic Bookplates. 2009. 36p. pap. 15.95 *(978-1-104-23626-7(5))* Kessinger Publishing, LLC.
Slow Food Editore Staff, ed. Terra Madre People. 2010. (ENG.). 10.00 *(978-1-60358-278-0(9))* Chelsea Green Publishing.

BOOKS
see also Artists' Books; Best Books; Bibliography; Block Books; Book Design; Cataloging; Chapbooks; Classification—Books; Colophons; Copyright; Dedications; Electronic Books; Illumination of Books and Manuscripts; Illustration of Books; Libraries; Literature; Manuscripts; Paperbacks; Printing; Publishers and Publishing; Rare Books; Shelving for Books; Title Pages
also headings beginning with the word Book
Aldis, Harry Gidney, et al. The Printed Book. 2nd rev. ed. 2011. (ENG.). 166p. pap. 19.99 ***(978-0-521-23872-4(2))*** Cambridge Univ. Pr.
Beach, Alison I. Women as Scribes: Book Production & Monastic Reform in Twelfth-Century Bavaria. 2009. (Cambridge Studies in Palaeography & Codicology Ser.). (ENG.). 216p. pap. 34.99 *(978-0-521-12694-6(0))* Cambridge Univ. Pr.
Bennett, Arnold. Books & Persons. 2008. 240p. pap. 24.99 *(978-0-554-34708-0(3));* 27.99 *(978-0-554-25405-0(0))* BiblioBazaar.
—Books & Persons. 2007. (ENG.). 184p. per. *(978-1-4065-4779-5(4))* Dodo Pr.
—Books & Persons. 2010. (Illus.). 104p. pap. 13.38 *(978-1-4432-0626-6(1))* General Bks. LLC.
—Books & Persons. 2010. 164p. pap. *(978-1-4076-1494-6(0))* 2009. 168p. pap. *(978-1-4076-0548-7(8))* HardPr.
Chamblee, Angela. An Ancient African Wisdom Book: Commentary on the Instruction of Ptahhotep. 2010. 224p. pap. 28.95 *(978-0-595-62411-9(1))* iUniverse, Inc.
Cheng, Victor. Bookmercial Marketing: Why Books Replace Brochures in the Credibility Age. 2008. 180p. pap. 16.95 *(978-0-9746624-7-7(8))* Innovation Pr.
Cobden-Sanderson, T. J. Ecce Mundus: Industrial Ideals & the Book Beautiful. 2011. 40p. 35.95 ***(978-1-258-05742-8(5))*** Literary Licensing, LLC.
Cram101 Textbook Reviews & Cram101 Textbook Reviews. Outlines & Highlights for Book Production & Publishing in Britain 1375-1475 by Derek Pearsall, Isbn: 9780521037211. 2011. 88p. pap. 27.95 ***(978-1-4288-4403-2(1))*** Cram101 Inc.
Ditchfield, Peter Hampson. Books Fatal to Their Authors. 2007. (ENG.). 144p. pap. 18.99 *(978-1-4264-3029-9(9))* BiblioBazaar.
—Books Fatal to Their Authors. 2009. 112p. pap. *(978-0-217-44909-0(3))* Books LLC.
Elliott, Janet L. Page by Page: A Practical Guide to Using the Writer's Notebook in Grades 3-8. 2008. pap. *(978-0-8141-3500-6(5))* National Council of Teachers of English.
Espana, Gonzalo. Letras en el Fuego: El libro en Bogotá. 2007. (SPA.). pap. *(978-958-30-2567-9(4))* Panamericana Editorial.
Fletcher, Jain. Collection-level Cataloging: Bound-with Books, 1 vol. 2010. (Third Millennium Cataloging Ser.). (Illus.). 95p. pap. 45.00 *(978-1-59158-543-5(0),* LU8543) Libraries Unlimited, Inc.
Flint, Christopher. Print & the Page in Eighteenth-Century Fiction. 2011. (ENG., Illus.). 294p. 95.00 *(978-1-107-00839-7(5))* Cambridge Univ. Pr.
Fondo de Cultura Económica Staff, creator. Congreso Internacional del Mundo del Libro: 7-10 Septiembre, 2009, Ciudad de Mexico: Memoria. 2009. (Tezontle Ser.). (SPA.). 348p. pap. *(978-607-16-0148-3(7))* Fondo de Cultura Economica.
Horster, Marietta & Reitz, Christiane, eds. Condensing texts - condensed Texts. 2010. (Palingenesia. Schriftenreihe fur Klassische Altertumswissenschaft Ser.). (GER & ENG., Illus.). 764p. (C). 149.00 *(978-3-515-09395-8(8))* Steiner, Franz Verlag Wiesbaden GmbH DEU. Dist: Brown, David Bk. Co., The.
Kielhofner, Gary. Cram101 Textbook Outlines to Accompany Model of Human Occupation, Gary Kielhofner, 4th Edition. 2011. 96p. pap. 27.95 ***(978-1-61654-055-5(5))*** Cram101 Inc.
Klentschy, Michael P. Using Science Notebooks in Middle School. 2010. *(978-1-936137-04-6(6))* National Science Teachers Assn.
Lang, Andrew. Books & Bookmen. 2009. 166p. 22.99 *(978-1-110-00813-1(9));* pap. 16.99 *(978-1-110-00811-7(2))* BiblioBazaar.
—Books & Bookmen. 2009. 66p. pap. *(978-0-217-44913-7(1))* Books LLC.
—Books & Bookmen. 2007. 92p. per. *(978-1-4065-2607-3(X))* Dodo Pr.
—Books & Bookmen. 2008. 160p. 36.95 *(978-1-4369-0470-4(6));* pap. 21.95 *(978-1-4367-9121-2(9))* Kessinger Publishing, LLC.
—The Library. reprint ed. 40.00 *(978-0-404-03816-8(6))* AMS Pr., Inc.
—The Library. 2007. 92p. per. *(978-1-4065-2627-1(4))* Dodo Pr.
—The Library. 2007. (ENG.). 218p. 39.95 *(978-0-548-04543-5(7))* Kessinger Publishing, LLC.
Lang, Andrew & Dobson, Austin. The Library. 2nd enl. ed. reprint ed. 40.00 *(978-0-404-03844-1(1))* AMS Pr., Inc.
Lark Books Staff. The Penland Book of Handmade Books: Master Classes in Bookmaking Techniques. LaFerla, Jane & Gunter, Alice, eds. 2008. (Penland Ser.). (ENG., Illus.). 232p. pap. 19.95 *(978-1-60059-300-0(3))* Lark Bks.
Lee, Marshall, et al. Bookmaking: Editing, Design, Production. 3rd ed. 2009. (ENG., Illus.). 494p. pap. 31.50 net. *(978-0-393-73296-2(7),* 73296) Norton, W. W. & Co., Inc.
Mandelbrote, Giles, ed. The Arcadian Library: Bindings & Provenance. 2012. (Studies in the Arcadian Library). (ENG., Illus.). 416p. 250.00 ***(978-0-19-965481-9(6))*** Oxford Univ. Pr., Inc.
Monkhouse, Allan. Books & Plays. 2009. 238p. 28.99 *(978-1-110-64756-9(5));* 238p. pap. 25.75 *(978-1-110-64754-5(9));* (ENG.). 237p. pap. 20.99 *(978-1-110-64751-4(4),* BiblioLife); (ENG.). 237p. pap. 22.99 *(978-1-110-64753-8(0),* BiblioLife) BiblioBazaar.
—Books & Plays. 2007. (ENG.). 224p. 39.95 *(978-0-548-33004-3(2));* per. 24.95 *(978-1-4326-8876-9(6))* Kessinger Publishing, LLC.
Murphy, Lynda & Rugg, Julie. A Book Addict's Treasury. 2006. (ENG.). 240p. 16.95 *(978-0-7112-2685-2(7))* Lincoln, Frances Ltd. GBR. Dist: Perseus-PGW.
Nelson, Bradley J. The Persistance of Presence: Emblem & Ritual in Baroque Spain. 2010. (University of Toronto Romance Ser.). (ENG & ABK., Illus.). 272p. *(978-0-8020-9977-8(7))* Univ. of Toronto Pr.
Occhipinti, Lisa. The Repurposed Library: 33 Craft Projects That Give Old Books New Life. 2011. (ENG., Illus.). 144p. pap. 24.95 *(978-1-58479-909-2(9))* Stewart, Tabori & Chang.
Powers, Alan. Living with Books. 2006. (ENG., Illus.). 144p. pap. 19.95 *(978-1-4027-4212-5(6))* Sterling Publishing Co., Inc.
Ruan, Felipe. Pícaro & Cortesano: Identity & the Forms of Capital in Early Modern Spanish Picaresque Narrative & Courtesy Literature. 2011. (ENG.). 180p. 65.00 *(978-1-61148-050-4(7))* Bucknell Univ. Pr.
Saunders, Frederick. The Story of Some Famous Books. 2010. 226p. pap. 25.75 *(978-1-146-42435-6(3))* 2010. 230p. pap. 25.75 *(978-1-144-25062-9(5))* 2009. 232p. 23.99 *(978-1-103-10109-2(9))* 2009. 232p. pap. 17.99 *(978-1-103-10107-8(2))* BiblioBazaar.
—The Story of Some Famous Books. 2010. 78p. pap. *(978-1-153-16762-8(X))* Books LLC.
—The Story of Some Famous Books. 2009. 86p. pap. 14.14 *(978-1-151-55778-0(1))* General Bks. LLC.
—The Story of Some Famous Books. 2010. 220p. 31.96 *(978-1-163-34321-0(8))* 2010. 220p. pap. 19.96 *(978-1-162-72270-2(3))* 2007. (ENG.). 218p. 39.95 *(978-0-548-03180-3(0))* Kessinger Publishing, LLC.
Stein, Susan. The Complete Fabric Artist's Workshop: Exploring Techniques & Materials for Creating Fashion & Decor Items from Artfully Altered Fabric. 2011. (ENG., Illus.). 256p. pap. 24.99 *(978-1-58923-663-9(7),* 1589236637) Quayside.
Thompson, Jason. Playing with Books: The Art of Upcycling, Deconstructing, & Reimagining the Book. 2010. (Playing Ser.). (ENG., Illus.). 152p. pap. 24.99 *(978-1-59253-600-9(X),* 159253600X) Quayside.
Walsby, Malcolm & Kemp, Graeme. The Book Triumphant: Print in Transition in the Sixteenth & Seventeenth Centuries. 2011. (Illus.). XVI, 380p. ***(978-90-04-20723-3(6))*** BRILL.
Watt, Sofia. Libro de los Libros (Book about Books) (SPA.). 14.95 *(978-84-283-1775-7(5))* Paraninfo, Editorial S. A. ESP. Dist: AIMS International Bks., Inc.
Watts, James W., ed. Iconic Books & Texts. 2012. (ENG.). 352p. (C). 99.95 ***(978-1-84553-985-6(0))*** Equinox Publishing Ltd. GBR. Dist: ISD.
Webb, Celia & Webb, Mack H. Publish Today! a Helpful Guide to Book Publishing for Authors & Self Publishers. 2010. 120p. pap. 14.95 *(978-0-9779576-7-5(5))* Pilinut Pr., Inc.
Weston, Heather. Bookcraft: Techniques for Binding, Folding, & Decorating to Create Books & More. 2008. (ENG., Illus.). 128p. pap. 22.99 *(978-1-59253-455-5(4),* 1592534554, Quarry Books) Quayside.
Whiting, Lilian. The World Beautiful in Books. 2008. 420p. 30.99 *(978-0-559-72003-1(3));* pap. 33.75 *(978-0-559-72001-7(7))* BiblioBazaar.
—The World Beautiful in Books. 2008. 424p. 49.95 *(978-1-4374-4297-7(8));* pap. 34.95 *(978-1-4373-4834-7(3))* Kessinger Publishing, LLC.
Ziegler, Scott. The Book & Philosophy - the Role of the Book As a Medium for Philosophy in Deleuze, Derrida & Smith. 2008. 68p. pap. *(978-3-639-04903-9(9))* VDM Verlag Dr. Mueller e.K.

BOOKS—APPRAISAL
see Books and Reading; Criticism; Literature—History and Criticism

BOOKS—BEST SELLERS
see Best Sellers

BOOKS—CENSORSHIP
see Censorship

BOOKS—COLLECTORS AND COLLECTING
see Book Collecting; Book Collectors

BOOKS—CONSERVATION AND RESTORATION
see also Manuscripts—Conservation and Restoration
Anon. General. 2009. 700p. pap. 36.45 *(978-1-4446-2707-7(4))* Harrison House Pubs.
Balloffet, Nelly. Preservation & Conservation for Libraries & Archives. *(978-0-8389-1005-4(X))* American Library Assn.
Burns, Islay. The Sanctity of Home - Being Words of Counsel & Incitement to Christian Fathers & Mothers. 2009. 104p. pap. 26.45 *(978-1-4446-6511-6(1))* Thorndike Pr.
The Changing Book: Transitions in Design, Production, & Preser. 2008. (ENG.). 270p. 75.00 *(978-0-7890-3460-1(3))* Routledge.
Davisson, Melville. The Mountain School-Teacher. 2009. 200p. pap. 27.95 *(978-1-4446-1940-9(3))* Audubon Pr. & Christian Bk. Service.
Douglas Cockerell. Bookbinding, & the Care of Books - a Text-Book for Bookbinders & Librarians. 2008. (Illus.). 344p. 42.45 *(978-1-4437-3809-5(3))* Barclay Pr., Inc.
—Bookbinding, & the Care of Books - a Text-Book for Bookbinders & Librarians. 2007. (ENG.). 340p. per. *(978-1-4086-2958-1(5))* Read Bks.
Etherington, Don. Bookbinding & Conservation: A Sixty-Year Odyssey of Art & Craft. 2010. (Illus.). xi, 156p. 49.95 *(978-1-58456-277-1(3))* Oak Knoll Pr.
Greenfield, Jane. The Care of Fine Books. 2007. (ENG., Illus.). 160p. per. 12.95 *(978-1-60239-078-2(9),* 239078) Skyhorse Publishing Co., Inc.
Lavender, Kenneth & BonaDea, Artemis. Book Repair: A How-To-Do-It Manual. 2nd ed. 2011. ***(978-1-55570-747-7(5))*** Neal-Schuman Pubs., Inc.
Miller, James. Mounting Objects with Clear Film. 2008. 32p. 15.00 *(978-0-938655-23-7(X))* Columba Publishing Co., Inc.
Patkus, Beth. Assessing Preservation Needs: A Self-Survey Guide. 2008. 83p. pap. 20.00 *(978-0-9634685-5-0(3))* Northeast Document Conservation Ctr.
Scianna, Nicolangelo. Solving Cases — Book & Paper Artefact Restoration. 2010. (ENG., Illus.). 272p. (C). pap. 94.00 ***(978-2-503-53343-8(4))*** Brepols Pubs. BEL. Dist: ISD.
Thiel, Sarah Goodwin. Build It Once: A Basic Primer for the Creation of Online Exhibitions. 2007. (Build It Once Ser.). (ENG., Illus.). 112p. per. 45.00 *(978-0-8108-5225-9(X))* Scarecrow Pr., Inc.
Wiker, Benjamin. 10 Books Every Conservative Must Read: Plus Four Not to Miss & One Impostor. 2010. (ENG.). 369p. 27.95 *(978-1-59698-604-6(2))* Regnery Publishing, Inc., An Eagle Publishing Co.

BOOKS—DEDICATIONS
see Dedications

BOOKS—EXHIBITIONS
see Book Industries and Trade—Exhibitions; Books—History—Exhibitions

BOOKS—FIRST EDITIONS
see First Editions

BOOKS—FORMAT
see also Miniature Books
Allen, Graham, et al, eds. Readings on Audience & Textual Materiality, 1 vol. 2011. (History of the Book Ser.). (ENG., Illus.). 240p. 99.00 *(978-1-84893-159-6(X))* Pickering & Chatto Pubs., Ltd. GBR. Dist: Ashgate Publishing Co.
Stein, Jeannine. Re-Bound: Creating Handmade Books from Recycled & Repurposed Materials. 2009. (ENG., Illus.). 144p. pap. 24.99 *(978-1-59253-524-8(0),* 1592535240, Quarry Books) Quayside.
Taylor, Terry. Eco Books: Inventive Projects from the Recycling Bin. 2009. (ENG., Illus.). 144p. pap. 22.95 *(978-1-60059-394-9(1))* Lark Bks.

BOOKS—HISTORY

see also Bibliography, Critical; Block Books; Incunabula; Printing—History

Amory, Hugh & Hall, David D., eds. A History of the Book in America Vol. 1: The Colonial Book in the Atlantic World. 2007. (ENG., Illus.). 664p. pap. 36.95 *(978-0-8078-5826-4(9))* Univ. of North Carolina Pr.

Baez, Fernando. A Universal History of the Destruction of Books: From Ancient Sumer to Modern-Day Iraq. MacAdam, Alfred, tr. from SPA. 2008. (ENG., Illus.). 1p. 25.00 *(978-1-934633-01-4(1))* Atlas & Co.

Bagnall, Roger S. Livres chretiens antiques D'Egypte. 2009. (HAUTES ETUDES du MONDE GReCO-ROMAIN Ser.). (FRE., Illus.). 128p. (C). pap. 66.00 *(978-2-600-01350-5(4))* Droz, Librairie CHE. Dist: Brown, David Bk. Co., The.

Baron, Sabrina Alcorn, et al. Agent of Change: Print Culture Studies after Elizabeth L. Eisenstein. 2007. (Studies in Print Culture & the History of the Book). (Illus.). (C). *(978-1-55849-592-0(4))* Univ. of Massachusetts Pr.

Bibliographic Volume: International Organization Bibliography & Resources. 2010. (Yearbook of International Organizations 2010/2011 Ser.). XIV, 680p. *(978-3-11-023034-5(8))* Saur, K. G. Verlag GmbH & Co.

Bischoff, Bernhard. Manuscripts & Libraries in the Age of Charlemagne. 2007. (Cambridge Studies in Palaeography & Codicology Ser.). (ENG.). 212p. pap. 32.00 *(978-0-521-03711-2(5))* Cambridge Univ. Pr.

Booton, Diane E. Manuscripts, Market & the Transition to Print in Late Medieval Brittany. 2010. (Illus.). 490p. 144.95 *(978-0-7546-6623-3(9))* Ashgate Publishing Co.

Bringhurst, Robert. The Surface of Meaning: Books & Book Design in Canada. 2009. (ENG.). 240p. 59.95 *(978-0-9738727-2-9(1),* Canadian Centre for Studies in Publishing) CCSP Pr. CAN. Dist: Perseus-PGW.

Collins, Paul. The Book of William: How Shakespeare's First Folio Conquered the World. (ENG., Illus.). 256p. 2010. pap. 15.00 *(978-1-59691-196-3(4))* 2009. 25.00 *(978-1-59691-195-6(6))* Bloomsbury Publishing.

Coron, Sabine. Livres en Bouche: Cinq Siècles D'art Culinaire Français, du Quatorzième Au Dix-Huitième Siècle. (FRE., Illus.). 251p. *(978-2-7056-6438-1(6))* Hermann, Editeurs des Sciences & des Arts.

Cowley, Des & Williamson, Clare. The World of the Book. (ENG.). 2010. 264p. pap. 32.95 *(978-0-522-85719-1(1))* 2008. (Illus.). 240p. 47.00 *(978-0-522-85378-0(1),* Miegunyah Pr., The) Melbourne Univ. Publishing AUS. Dist: Independent Pubs. Group.

Croenen, Godfried, et al, eds. Patrons, Authors & Workshops: Books & Book Production in Paris Around 1400. 2006. (Synthema Ser.: Vol. 4). (FRE & ENG., Illus.). 530p. (C). pap. 101.00 *(978-90-429-1707-1(5))* Peeters Pubs. & Booksellers BEL. Dist: Brown, David Bk. Co., The.

Da Rold, Orietta & Treharne, Elaine, eds. Textual Cultures: Cultural Texts. 2010. (Essays & Studies: Volume 63). (Illus.). 236p. 50.00 *(978-1-84384-239-2(4),* D. S. Brewer) Boydell & Brewer, Ltd. GBR. Dist: Boydell & Brewer, Inc.

Darnton, Robert. The Case for Books: Past, Present, & Future. (ENG., Illus.). 2010. 256p. pap. 13.95 *(978-1-58648-902-1(X))* 2009. 23.95 *(978-1-58648-847-5(3))* PublicAffairs.

Daybell, James & Hinds, Peter, eds. Material Readings of Early Modern Culture: Texts & Social Practices, 1580-1730. 2011. (Early Modern Literature in History Ser.). (ENG., Illus.). 288p. 95.00 *(978-0-230-22352-3(4))* Palgrave Macmillan.

Dédame, Roger. Les Artsans de L'écrit: Des Origines à L'ère Numérique. 2009. (FRE., Illus.). 367p. *(978-2-84654-215-9(5))* Les Indes Savantes.

Department of Information & Collections, ed. Annual Bibliography of the History of the Printed Book & Libraries: Volume 31. 2010. (Annual Bibliography of the History of the Printed Book & Libraries Ser.). lvi, 696p. pap. 459.00 *(978-90-481-6972-6(0),* 9048169720) Springer.

Dept. of Special Collections of the Koninklijke Bibliotheek, ed. Annual Bibliography of the History of the Printed Book & Libraries: Volume 29. 2010. (Annual Bibliography of the History of the Printed Book & Libraries Ser.). 698p. pap. 419.00 *(978-90-481-5929-1(6),* 9048159296) Springer.

—Annual Bibliography of the History of the Printed Book & Libraries: Volume 30. 2010. (Annual Bibliography of the History of the Printed Book & Libraries Ser.). 656p. pap. 429.00 *(978-90-481-6454-7(0),* 9048164540) Springer.

Driver, Martha, ed. Journal of the Early Book Society VOL. 10. 2007. 308p. pap. 40.00 *(978-0-944473-84-9(9))* Pace Univ. Pr.

Driver, Martha W., ed. Journal of the Early Book Society VOL 11. 2008. 308p. pap. 40.00 *(978-0-944473-88-7(1))* Pace Univ. Pr.

Eisenstein, Elizabeth L. Divine Art, Infernal Machine: The Reception of Printing in the West from First Impressions to the Sense of an Ending. 2011. (Material Texts). (Illus.). 384p. (C). 45.00 *(978-0-8122-4280-5(7))* Univ. of Pennsylvania Pr.

Eliot, Simon, et al, eds. Literary Cultures & the Material Book. 2007. (British Library - British Library Studies in the History of the Book Ser.). (ENG., Illus.). 448p. 80.00 *(978-0-7123-0684-3(6))* British Library, The GBR. Dist: Chicago Distribution Ctr.

Ferris, Ina & Keen, Paul, eds. Bookish Histories: Books, Literature & Commercial Modernity, 1700-1900. 2009. (Palgrave Studies in the Enlightenment, Romanticism & the Cultures of Print Ser.). (ENG., Illus.). 256p. 89.00 *(978-0-230-22231-1(5))* Palgrave Macmillan.

Finkelstein, David & McCleery, Alistair. The Edinburgh History of the Book in Scotland Vol. 4: Professionalism & Diversity, 1880-2000, 4. 2008. (Edinburgh History of the Book in Scotland Ser.). (ENG., Illus.). 544p. (gr. 17). 190.00 *(978-0-7486-1829-3(5))* Edinburgh Univ. Pr. GBR. Dist: Columbia Univ. Pr.

Finkelstein, David & McCleery, Alistair. An Introduction to Book History. 2nd rev. ed. 2012. (ENG.). 168p. (C). 130.00 ***(978-0-415-68805-5(1))***; pap. 44.95 ***(978-0-415-68806-2(X))*** Routledge.

Fraser, Robert. Book History Through Postcolonial Eyes: Rewriting the Script. 2008. (Illus.). XIV, 210p. 37.95 *(978-0-415-40294-1(8))*; 120.00 *(978-0-415-40293-4(X))* Routledge.

Fraser, Robert & Hammond, Dr, Mary, eds. Books Without Borders, Volume 2: Perspectives from South Asia, 2 vols. 2008. (ENG., Illus.). 232p. 89.00 *(978-0-230-21033-2(3))* Palgrave Macmillan.

Fraser, Robert & Hammond, Mary, eds. Books Without Borders, Volume 1: The Cross-National Dimension in Print Culture, 2 vols. 2008. (ENG., Illus.). 224p. 89.00 *(978-0-230-21029-5(5))* Palgrave Macmillan.

Frost, Simon & Rix, Robert, eds. Moveable Type, Mobile Nations: Interactions in Transnational Book History: Angles on the English-Speaking World, Vol. 10. 2010. 172p. pap. 23.00 *(978-87-635-3510-6(6))* Museum Tusculanum Pr. DNK. Dist: Chicago Distribution Ctr.

Gardt, Andreas, et al, eds. Buchkultur und Wissensvermittlung in Mittelalter und Früher Neuzeit. 2011.Tr. of Book Culture & Knowledge Transfer in the Middle Ages & the Early Modern Age. (GER., Illus.). XIV, 310p. E-Book 210.00 ***(978-3-11-026880-5(9))***; 140.00 ***(978-3-11-026870-6(1))*** De Gruyter, Walter Inc.

Gerson, Carole & Michon, Jacques, eds. History of the Book in Canada, 1918-1980 Vol. 3, 3 vols. 2007. (ENG., Illus.). 696p. *(978-0-8020-9047-8(8))* Univ. of Toronto Pr.

Green, Jonathan. Printing & Prophecy: Prognostication & Media Change, 1450-1550. 2011. (Cultures of Knowledge in the Early Modern World Ser.). (ENG.). 280p. (C). 70.00 ***(978-0-472-11783-3(1))***; E-Book ***(978-0-472-02758-3(1))*** Univ. of Michigan Pr.

Greenspan, Ezra & Rose, Jonathan, eds. Book History Volume 10. 2007. (Book History Ser.). (Illus.). 319p. 57.00 *(978-0-271-02766-1(5))* Pennsylvania State Univ. Pr.

Gries, Zeev. The Book in the Jewish World, 1700-1900. 2010. 251p. pap. 24.95 *(978-1-906764-05-0(0))* Littman Library of Jewish Civilization, The GBR. Dist: International Specialized Bk. Services.

Hannett, John. An Inquiry into the Nature & Form of the Books of the Ancients: With a History of the Art of Bookbinding, from the Times of the Greeks & Romans to the Present Day. 2010. (Cambridge Library Collection - History of Printing, Publishing & Libraries Ser.). (ENG., Illus.). 248p. pap. 22.99 *(978-1-108-02482-2(3))* Cambridge Univ. Pr.

Hogg, James. Books in Numbers. Francis, David et al, eds. 2008. (ENG.). 488p. (gr. 17). 60.00 *(978-962-996-331-6(0))* Chinese Univ. of Hong Kong, The HKG. Dist: Columbia Univ. Pr.

Howsam, Leslie. Old Books & New Histories: An Orientation to Studies in Book & Print Culture. 2006. (Studies in Book & Print Culture). (ENG., Illus.). 128p. *(978-0-8020-9196-3(2))*; pap. *(978-0-8020-9438-4(4))* Univ. of Toronto Pr.

Inmann, Christiane. Forbidden Fruit: The History of Women & Books in Art. 2009. (Illus.). 208p. *(978-3-7913-4077-7(8))* Prestel Verlag GmbH & Co KG.

Jurilla, Patricia May B. Tagalog Bestsellers of the Twentieth Century: A History of the Book in the Philippines. (Illus.). xi, 264p. 50.00 *(978-971-550-563-5(5))* Ateneo de Manila Univ. Pr. PHL. Dist: Univ. of Hawaii Pr.

Kenyon, Frederic G. Books & Readers in Ancient Greece & Rome. 2007. pap. ***(978-1-4067-5559-6(1))*** Read Bks.

Kirk, Rudolph, et al, eds. The Journal of the Rutgers University Library, V5, No 2, June 1942. 2011. 44p. 35.95 ***(978-1-258-09374-7(X))*** Literary Licensing, LLC.

Kovac, Miha. Here Comes the Book: Never Mind the Web. 2008. 204p. pap. *(978-1-84334-405-6(X),* Chandos Publishing) Woodhead Publishing Ltd.

—Never Mind the Web: Here Comes the Book. 2008. 204p. *(978-1-84334-406-3(8),* Chandos Publishing) Woodhead Publishing Ltd.

Lapidge, Michael & Gneuss, Helmut, eds. Learning & Literature in Anglo-Saxon England: Studies Presented to Peter Clemoes on the Occasion of his Sixty-Fifth Birthday. 2010. (ENG.). 492p. pap. 50.00 *(978-0-521-12871-1(4))* Cambridge Univ. Pr.

Levarie, Norma. The Art & History of Books. (Illus.). xx, 315p. *(978-0-7123-0394-1(4))* Bow Historical Bks.

Levey, Martin. Mediaeval Arabic Bookmaking & Its Relation to Early Chemistry & Pharmacology. 2011. 80p. 37.95 ***(978-1-258-03182-4(5))*** Literary Licensing, LLC.

Lindquist, Eric N., et al. Agent of Change: Print Culture Studies after Elizabeth L. Eisenstein. Baron, Sabrina Alcorn & Lindquist, Eric N., eds. Shevlin, Eleanor F., ed. 2007. (Studies in Print Culture & the History of the Book). (Illus.). 442p. per. 29.95 *(978-1-55849-593-7(2))* Univ. of Massachusetts Pr.

Littau, Karin. Theories of Reading: Books, Bodies, & Bibliomania. (ENG., Illus.). 208p. 2007. 69.95 *(978-0-7456-1658-2(5))* 2006. pap. 26.95 *(978-0-7456-1659-9(3))* Polity Pr. GBR. Dist: Wiley, John & Sons, Inc.

Lommen, Michael & Lommen, Mathieu, eds. The Book of Books: 500 Years of Graphic Innovation. 2012. (ENG., Illus.). 464p. 65.00 *(978-0-500-51591-4(3),* 551591) Thames & Hudson.

Lyons, Martyn. Books: A Living History. 2011. (ENG., Illus.). 224p. 34.95 *(978-1-60606-083-4(X),* J. Paul Getty Museum) Getty Pubns.

Magennis, Hugh & Wilcox, Jonathan, eds. The Power of Words: Anglo-Saxon Studies Presented to Donald G. Scragg on His Seventieth Birthday. 2006. (Medieval European Studies: VIII). (ENG., Illus.). 434p. per. 44.95 *(978-1-933202-15-0(7))* West Virginia Univ. Pr.

Margoliouth, D. S. The Homer of Aristotle. 2009. 258p. 30.99 *(978-1-110-47513-1(6))*; pap. 25.75 *(978-1-110-47509-4(8))* BiblioBazaar.

—The Homer of Aristotle. 2006. *(978-1-57898-590-6(0))* Martino Publishing.

McKitterick, David, ed. The Cambridge History of the Book in Britain Vol. 6: 1830-1914, 7 vols. 2009. (Cambridge History of the Book in Britain Ser.). (Illus.). 826p. 180.00 *(978-0-521-86624-8(3))* Cambridge Univ. Pr.

Morgan, Nigel & Thomson, Rodney M., eds. The Cambridge History of the Book in Britain; Volume II: 1100-1400, 7 vols. 2008. (Cambridge History of the Book in Britain Ser.). (ENG., Illus.). 722p. 166.00 *(978-0-521-78218-0(X))* Cambridge Univ. Pr.

Pantaleo, Sylvia & Sipe, Lawrence R. Postmodern Picturebooks: Play, Parody, & Self-Referentiality. 2008. (Routledge Research in Education Ser.). (ENG., Illus.). 280p. 140.00 *(978-0-415-96210-0(2))* Routledge.

Parkes, M. B. Their Hands Before Our Eyes: A Closer Look at Scribes: The Lyell Lectures Delivered in the University of Oxford, 1999. 2008. (Lyell Lectures delivered in the University of Oxford 1999 Ser.). (Illus.). 278p. 124.95 *(978-0-7546-6337-9(X))* Ashgate Publishing Co.

Pearson, David. Books As History: The Importance of Books Beyond Their Texts. 2008. (Illus.). 208p. 49.95 *(978-1-58456-233-7(1))* Oak Knoll Pr.

Pettegree, Andrew. The Book in the Renaissance. 2011. (ENG., Illus.). 440p. pap. 25.00 *(978-0-300-17821-0(2))* Yale Univ. Pr.

Pon, Lisa & Kallendorf, Craig. The Books of Venice. 2009.Tr. of Libro Veneziano. (ITA & ENG.). 632p. pap. 85.00 *(978-1-58456-257-3(9))* Oak Knoll Pr.

Riffaud, Alain. La Ponctuation du theatre imprime au XVIIe Siecle. 2007. (TRAVAUX du GRAND SIeCLE Ser.). (FRE., Illus.). 232p. (C). pap. 104.00 *(978-2-600-01157-0(9))* Droz, Librairie CHE. Dist: Brown, David Bk. Co., The.

Rose, Jonathan & Eliot, Simon, eds. A Companion to the History of the Book. (Blackwell Companions to Literature & Culture Ser.: 98). (ENG., Illus.). 616p. 2009. pap. 54.95 *(978-1-4051-9278-1(X))* 2007. 195.00 *(978-1-4051-2765-3(1))* Wiley, John & Sons, Inc. (Wiley-Blackwell).

Runge, Laura L. Producing the Eighteenth-Century Book: Writers & Publishers in England, 1650-1800. 2009. (ENG.). 65.00 *(978-1-61149-126-5(6))* Univ. of Delaware Pr.

Runge, Laura L. & Rogers, Pat. Producing the Eighteenth-Century Book: Writers & Publishers in England, 1650-1800. 2009. (Illus.). 298p. 65.00 *(978-0-87413-069-0(7))* Univ. of Delaware Pr.

Shevchenko, Nadezda. Eine Historische Anthropologie des Buches: Bücher in der Preussischen Herzogsfamilie Zur Zeit der Reformation. 2007. (Veröffentlichungen des Max-Planck-Instituts Für Geschichte Ser.). (GER., Illus.). 392p. (C). 83.00 *(978-3-525-35883-2(0))* Vandenhoeck & Ruprecht GmbH & Co. KG DEU. Dist: ISD.

Sloos, Louis, ed. Warfare & the Age of Printing: Catalogue of Early Printed Books from before 1801 in Dutch Military Collections. 2009. 656p. *(978-90-04-17241-8(6))* BRILL.

Suarez, Michael F., ed. The Oxford Companion to the Book, 2 vols. 2010. (ENG., Illus.). 1408p. 345.00 *(978-0-19-860653-6(2))* Oxford Univ. Pr., Inc.

Subject Volume: Global Action Networks: classified directory & Index. 2010. (Yearbook of International Organizations 2010/2011 Ser.). 1552p. *(978-3-11-023033-8(X))* Saur, K. G. Verlag GmbH & Co.

Taylor, Isaac. History of the Transmission of Ancient Books to Modern Times. 2008. 428p. 30.99 *(978-0-559-33503-7(2))*; pap. 34.75 *(978-0-559-33502-0(4))* BiblioBazaar.

—History of the Transmission of Ancient Books to Modern Times. 2009. 202p. pap. *(978-0-217-48764-1(5))*; 214p. pap. *(978-0-217-48761-0(0))* Books LLC.

—History of the Transmission of Ancient Books to Modern Times. 2009. 214p. pap. 19.99 *(978-0-217-92962-2(1))* General Bks. LLC.

—History of the Transmission of Ancient Books to Modern Times. 2007. (ENG.). 272p. 42.95 *(978-0-548-36814-5(7))*; per. 27.95 *(978-0-548-31118-9(8))* Kessinger Publishing, LLC.

Wagner, Bettina & Reed, Marcia. Early Printed Books As Material Objects: Proceedings of the Conference Organized by the IFLA Rare Books & Manuscripts Section, Munich, 19-21 August 2009. 2010. (IFLA Publications). (ENG., Illus.). XII, 367p. ***(978-3-11-025324-5(0))*** Saur, K. G. Verlag GmbH & Co.

Walsby, Malcolm. The Printed Book in Brittany, 1486-1600. 2011. (Illus.). XIV, 392p. ***(978-90-04-20451-5(2))*** BRILL.

Who's Who in International Organizations. 2010. (Yearbook of International Organizations 2010/2011 Ser.). 1040p. *(978-3-11-023036-9(4))* Saur, K. G. Verlag GmbH & Co.

Zerdoun Bat-Yehouda, Monique, et al. Matériaux du Livre Médiéval: Actes du Colloque du Groupement de Recherche (GDR) 2836 "Matériaux du Livre Médiéval", Paris, CNRS, 7-8 Novembre 2007. 2010. (FRE., Illus.). xxiii, 324p. *(978-2-503-53386-5(8))* Brepols Pubs.

2010. 2010.Tr. of Yearbook for Central & East German History. Journal of Comparative & Prussian Regional History. 240p. *(978-3-11-023352-0(5))* Saur, K. G. Verlag GmbH & Co.

2011. 2010.Tr. of Bavarian Yearbook. Directory of Local, State & Federal Administration, Associations & Public Institutions. 90th Year 2011. (GER.). 631p. pap. *(978-3-11-023077-2(1))* Saur, K. G. Verlag GmbH & Co.

BOOKS—HISTORY—EXHIBITIONS

Here are entered works on exhibitions illustrating the history of the book and book arts in general, including writing, printing, binding, illustration, collection and preservation of books in libraries, etc.

see also Book Industries and Trade—Exhibitions; Library Exhibits

Ashworth, William B., Jr. Further Out: An Exhibition from the Collections of the Linda Hall Library. 2007. 10.00 *(978-0-9763590-3-6(0))* Linda Hall Library.

—Ice: An Exhibition of Rare Books from the Collection of the Linda Hall Library. 2008. (Illus.). 96p. per. 20.00 *(978-0-9763590-4-3(9))* Linda Hall Library.

Avdoyan, Levon. To Know Wisdom & Instruction: A Visual Survey of the Armenian Literary Tradition: An Exhibition of Items from the Library of Congress in Commemoration of 500 Years of Armenian Printing. 2012. ***(978-0-8444-9535-4(2))*** Library of Congress.

Bradley, Bruce & Ashworth, William B., Jr. Napoleon & the Scientific Expedition to Egypt: An Exhibition of the Description de L'Égypte (1809-1828) 2006. 10.00 *(978-0-9763590-2-9(2))* Linda Hall Library.

Brown, Sylvia & Considine, John. Marginated: Seventeenth-Century Books & Traces of their Readers. 2010. (ENG.). 161p. pap. *(978-1-55195-256-7(4))* Univ. of Alberta Pr. CAN. Dist: Michigan State Univ. Pr.

Chew, Samuel C., intro. The British Tradition: Illustrated in Historical Documents, Autograph & Illuminated Manuscripts, Drawings & Printed Books. 2011. 66p. 36.95 ***(978-1-258-04830-3(2))*** Literary Licensing, LLC.

Giordano, Antonella & Zabagli, Franco, eds. Pasolini: Dal Laboratorio. 2010. (ITA., Illus.). 136p. (C). pap. 48.00 *(978-88-596-0848-6(1))* Polistampa ITA. Dist: Brown, David Bk. Co., The.

Louisiana Purchase Exposition, St. Louis in 1904: A Collection of Official Guidebooks & Miscellaneous Publications Set: A Collection of Official Guidebooks & Miscellaneous Publications, 4 vols. 2009. 2700p. 1090.00 *(978-4-902454-51-2(3))* Routledge.

Maffei, Giorgio & Picciau, Maura, eds. The Book As A Work of Art, 1 vol. 2007. (ENG., Illus.). 160p. pap. 55.00 *(978-88-7570-037-9(0))* Corraini ITA. Dist: D.A.P./Distributed Art Pubs.

Manghetti, Gloria & Porto, Silvia, eds. Bruciamo le biblioteche... il libro futurista nelle collezioni pubbliche Fiorentine - Album, 1909-1994. 2009. (ITA., Illus.). 92p. (C). pap. 27.00 *(978-88-596-0591-1(1))* Polistampa ITA. Dist: Brown, David Bk. Co., The.

Ong, George & Holzenberg, Eric. For Jean Grolier & His Friends: 125 Years of Grolier Club Exhibitions & Publications, 1884-2008. 2009. (Illus.). 500p. 300.00 *(978-1-60583-019-3(4))* Grolier Club of New York, The.

Pule, John. Hauaga: The Art of John Pule. Thomas, Nicholas, ed. 2010. (Illus.). 184p. 120.00 *(978-1-877372-80-3(3))* Otago University Pr. NZL. Dist: International Specialized Bk. Services.

Pyne, Charlynn Spencer. The Pavilion of the States at the National Book Festival, 2002-2006. 2007. (Illus.). 12p. *(978-0-8444-1173-6(6))* Library of Congress.

BOOKS—MARKETING

Alexander, Kwame. Do the Write Thing: Seven Steps to Publishing Success. 2nd ed. 2011. (ENG.). 208p. pap. 16.95 *(978-0-9748142-5-4(3))* Nunes Productions,Ny Words Pr.

Baverstock, Alison. How to Market Books: The Essential Guide to Maximizing Profit & Exploiting All Channels to Market. 4th rev. ed. 2008. (ENG.). 336p. per. 50.00 *(978-0-7494-5020-5(7))* Kogan Page, Ltd. GBR. Dist: Ingram Pub. Services.

—Marketing Your Book: an Author's Guide: How to Target Agents, Publishers & Readers. 2nd ed. 2007. (ENG., Illus.). 256p. per. 18.95 *(978-0-7136-7383-8(4),* Methuen Drama) A & C Black GBR. Dist: Macmillan.

Bolme, Sarah. Your Guide to Marketing Books in the Christian Marketplace. 2006. 192p. per. 17.99 *(978-0-9725546-5-7(3),* 704-277-7194) 2nd rev. ed. 2009. (ENG.). 240p. pap. 23.99 *(978-0-9725546-8-8(8))* CREST Pubns.

Burgett, Douglas. Niche Publishing: Publish Profitably Every Time. 2008. (Illus.). 204p. pap. 15.00 *(978-0-9796295-2-5(7))* Communication Unlimited.

Camacho, Austin S. Successfully Marketing Your Novel: In the 21st Century. 2008. (Illus.). 220p. pap. 14.99 *(978-0-9762181-8-0(6))* Intrigue Publishing.

Chandler, eng & Chandler, Stephanie. The Author's Guide to Building an Online Platform: Leveraging the Internet to Sell More Books. 2008. (ENG.). 160p. pap. 14.95 *(978-1-884956-82-9(3))* Quill Driver Bks.

CHARLES, R. O. D. N. E. Y. Book Marketing Basics - the New Model for Promoting Your Book. 2007. 108p. per. 14.95 *(978-1-4218-9996-1(5))* 1st World Publishing, Inc.

Charles, Rodney & 1st World Publishing. Book Marketing Basics; the New Model for Promoting Your Book. 2007. (Illus.). 108p. 21.95 *(978-1-4218-9997-8(3))* 1st World Publishing, Inc.

Cooke, Daniel. Sell & Market Your Book: A Step-by-Step Guide. 2010. 172p. pap. 11.99 *(978-1-4490-7499-9(5))* AuthorHouse.

Deval, Jacqueline. Publicize Your Book: An Insider's Guide to Getting Your Book the Attention It Deserves. rev. ed. 2008. (ENG.). 320p. (gr. 12-18). 18.00 *(978-0-399-53431-7(8),* Perigee Trade) Penguin Group (USA) Inc.

Eager, Rob. Sell Your Book Like Wildfire: The Writer's Guide to Marketing & Publicity. 2012. (ENG.) 288p. pap. 16.99 ***(978-1-59963-421-0(X),*** Writer's Digest Bks.) F&W Media, Inc.

Fry, Patricia. Promote Your Book: Over 250 Proven, Low-Cost Tips & Techniques for the Enterprising Author. 2011. (ENG.). 224p. pap. 19.95 *(978-1-58115-857-1(2),* 115857, Allworth Pr.) Skyhorse Publishing Co., Inc.

Fullerlove, Vivian L. How to Book, Promote & Publicize your Own Book Tour. 2009. pap. 16.95 *(978-1-61584-535-4(6))* Independent Pub.

Hoenig, Carol. The Author's Guide to Planning Book Events: Tips & Tools for Bookselling Success. 2007. 152p. per. 13.95 *(978-1-58348-476-0(0))* iUniverse, Inc.

Horowitz, Shel. Grassroots Marketing for Authors & Publishers. 2007. 290p. pap. 24.95 *(978-0-7414-3469-2(5))* Infinity Publishing.

Howick, E. Keith, Jr. Blow Us Away! Publishers' Secrets for Successful Manuscripts. 2010. (ENG.). 173p. pap. 16.95 *(978-1-886249-39-4(3))* WindRiver Publishing, Inc.

Kremer, John. Here's What You Sould Know about Book Promotion. 2007. 96p. per. 10.00 *(978-0-9787490-5-7(7))* Bertillion Bks.

Martin, Gail. Launching Your Books Without Losing Your Mind. 2010. 124p. pap. 13.99 *(978-1-935361-06-0(6))* Comfort Publishing Services, LLC.

Matthews, Nicole & Moody, Nickianne, eds. Judging a Book by Its Cover: Fans, Publishers, Designers, & the Marketing of Fiction. 2007. (Illus.). 214p. 99.95 *(978-0-7546-5731-6(0))* Ashgate Publishing Co.

Mentzer, Leon. Amen! A Simple Guide to Self-Marketing Your Christian Book. 2007. 151p. per. 12.99 *(978-1-60247-467-3(2))* Tate Publishing & Enterprises, LLC.

Miller, J. Steve & Miller, Cherie K. Sell More Books! Book Marketing & Publishing for Low Profile & Debut Authors Rethinking Book Publicity after the Digital Revolutions. 2011. 320p. pap. ***(978-0-9818756-3-7(7))*** Wisdom Creek Pr.

Myers, Robin, et al, eds. Books for Sale: The Advertising & Promotion of Print since the Fifteenth Century. 2009. (Illus.). xvi, 191p. 49.95 *(978-1-58456-265-8(X))* Oak Knoll Pr.

Obey, Anthony & Obey, Crystal. Start Small Finish Big in Self Publishing. 2007. 120p. per. 25.00 *(978-1-59268-077-1(1))* G M A Publishing & Inspiration Pr.

Price, Lynn. The Writer's Essential Tackle Box: Getting a Hook on the Publishing Industry. 2009. (Get It Write Ser.). (ENG.). 380p. pap. 19.95 *(978-1-933016-34-4(5))* Behler Pubns., LLC.

Reid, Ellen. Putting Your Best Book Forward: A Book Shepherd's Secrets to Producing Award-Winning Books That Sell. 2010. (Illus.). 115p. pap. 19.95 *(978-0-9841441-3-6(7))* Little Moose Pr.

Rutledge, Patrice-Anne. The Web-Savvy Writer: Book Promotion with a High-Tech Twist. 2006. 248p. per. 19.95 *(978-0-9778304-0-4(3))* Pacific Ridge.

Sansevieri, Penny. From Book to Bestseller: An Insider's Guide to Publicizing & Marketing Your Book! 2006. (ENG.). 339p. per. 17.95 *(978-1-60037-085-4(3))* Morgan James Publishing.

Terrell, P. M. Take the Mystery Out of Promoting Your Book. 2006. 213p. per. 15.00 *(978-1-928662-43-3(9))* Palari Publishing LLP.

BOOKS—MICROSCOPIC EDITIONS
see Miniature Books

BOOKS—MINIATURE EDITIONS
see Miniature Books

BOOKS—OWNERS' MARKS
see also Book Collecting; Bookplates; Marginalia

Brown, Sylvia & Considine, John. Marginated: Seventeenth-Century Books & Traces of their Readers. 2010. (ENG.). 161p. pap. *(978-1-55195-256-7(4))* Univ. of Alberta Pr. CAN. Dist: Michigan State Univ. Pr.

Crow, Judy, ed. Bookmarks for All Occasions. 2008. (ENG.). 22p. pap. 6.95 *(978-1-57367-327-3(7))* Annie's Publishing, LLC.

De Ricci, Seymour. English Collectors of Books & Manuscripts, 1530-1930: And Their Marks of Ownership. 2011. (ENG.). 228p. pap. 22.99 *(978-0-521-15646-2(7))* Cambridge Univ. Pr.

Rubiano, Margaret, illus. & des. Emoticons i-Clips Magnetic Bookmarks. 2010. 8p. 3.95 *(978-1-4413-0378-3(2))* Peter Pauper Pr. Inc.

Ruiz, Don Miguel. The Four Agreements Beaded Bookmark. 2010. 1p. 2.95 *(978-1-4413-0376-9(6))* Peter Pauper Pr. Inc.

Shutterstock, illus. Butterflies i-Clips Magnetic Bookmarks. 2010. 8p. 3.95 *(978-1-4413-0377-6(4))* Peter Pauper Pr. Inc.

BOOKS—PIRATED EDITIONS
see Copyright—Unauthorized Reprints

BOOKS—PRESERVATION
see Books—Conservation and Restoration

BOOKS—PRICES

Bookman's Price Index. (ENG.). 2007. (Bookman's Price Ser.: Vol. 87). 1440p. 625.00 *(978-0-7876-9507-1(6))* Vol. 89. 2008. (Bookman's Price Index Ser.: Vol. 89). 1552p. 625.00 *(978-0-7876-9509-5(2))* Vol. 92. 2010. (Bookman's Price Index Ser.). 625.00 *(978-1-4144-0658-9(4))* Cengage Gale.

Bookman's Price Index: A Guide to the Values of Rare & Other Out-of-Print Books. 2011. 625.00 *(978-1-4144-0660-2(6))* Cengage Gale.

Bradford, Thomas Lindsley. The Bibliographer's Manual of American History. 2009. 372p. pap. *(978-1-151-73799-1(2))*; 386p. pap. *(978-0-217-29121-7(X))* Books LLC.

—The Bibliographer's Manual of American History. 2009. 420p. pap. 21.51 *(978-0-217-37914-4(1))* General Bks. LLC.

—The Bibliographer's Manual of American History, 5 vol., set. reprint ed. 625.00 *(978-0-7222-6993-0(5))* Library Reprints, Inc.

Brinley, George. Catalogue of the American Library of George Brinley, 5 pts. in 2 vols. Trumbull, J. Hammond, ed. reprint ed. lib. bdg. 125.00 *(978-0-404-01081-2(4))* AMS Pr., Inc.

Edwards, Patricia "Eddie" & Peckham, Peter. Antique Trader Collectible Cookbooks Price Guide. 2008. (ENG.). 304p. pap. 21.99 *(978-0-89689-669-7(2))* Krause Pubns.

Gale Editor, ed. Bookman's Price Index: A Guide to the Values of Rare & Other Out-of-Print Books. 2011. 1291p. lib. bdg. 625.00 *(978-1-4144-0661-9(4))* Cengage Gale.

Gale Editors, ed. Bookman's Price Index, Vol. 85. 2006. (Bookman's Price Index Ser.). (ENG.). 1312p. 625.00 *(978-0-7876-9505-7(X))* Cengage Gale.

A Guide to the Values of Rare & Other Out-of-Print Books, 90. 2009. (Bookman's Price Index Ser.). (ENG.). 1504p. 625.00 *(978-0-7876-9510-1(6))* Cengage Gale.

McGrath, Anne. Bookman's Price Index, Vol. 88. 2008. (Bookman's Price Index Ser.). (ENG.). 1376p. 625.00 *(978-0-7876-9508-8(4))* Cengage Gale.

McGrath, Anne F. Bookman's Price Cumulative Index to Vol 80-85. 2007. (Bookman's Price Ser.). (ENG.). 800p. 663.00 *(978-1-4144-0999-3(0))* Cengage Gale.

McGrath, Anne F., ed. Bookman's Price Index: A Guide to the Values of Rare & Other Out of Print Books, Vol. 86. 2007. (Bookman's Price Ser.). 1312p. 625.00 *(978-0-7876-9506-4(8))* Cengage Gale.

Sterne, Laurence. A Facsimile Reproduction of a Unique Catalogue of Laurence Sterne's Library. Whibley, Charles, ed. reprint ed. 29.50 *(978-0-404-52356-5(0))* AMS Pr., Inc.

BOOKS—PSYCHOLOGY
see also Authors and Readers; Books and Reading

Time Out Guides Staff. Time Out 1000 Books to Change Your Life. Derbyshire, Jonathan, ed. 2007. (Time Out Guides). (ENG., Illus.). 280p. per. 16.95 *(978-1-84670-052-1(3))* Time Out Guides Ltd. GBR. Dist: Perseus-PGW.

BOOKS—REPAIRING
see Books—Conservation and Restoration

BOOKS—REPRINTS, UNAUTHORIZED
see Copyright—Unauthorized Reprints

BOOKS—RESTORATION
see Books—Conservation and Restoration

BOOKS—REVIEWS
Here are entered collections of reviews. Works on the technique of writing reviews are entered under the heading Book Reviewing.
see also Book Reviewing

A-and-c, Black. Bloomsbury Good Reading Guide. 7th ed. 2006. (ENG.). 496p. per. 14.95 *(978-0-7136-7587-0(X))* A & C Black GBR. Dist: Macmillan.

Borges, Jorge Luis. Textos Cautivos: Ensayos Reseñas en "El Hogar" [de Buenos Ayres]. Sacerio-Garí, Enrique & Rodríguez Monegal, Emir, eds. (SPA., Illus.). 248p. *(978-84-7223-092-7(9)*, 6030) Tusquets Editores.

Connolly, Cyril. Condemned Playground. 2006. 296p. per. *(978-1-4067-2652-7(4)*, Hesperides Pr.) Read Bks.

Downs, Robert B. Books That Changed the South. 2011. (ENG.). 310p. pap. 40.00 ***(978-0-8078-9653-2(5))*** Univ. of North Carolina Pr.

Farrel, James T. League of Frightened Philistines & Oth. 2006. 212p. per. *(978-1-4067-3034-0(3)*, Hesperides Pr.) Read Bks.

Feldman, Jessica R. & Stilling, Robert, eds. What Should I Read Next? 70 University of Virginia Professors Recommend Readings in History, Politics, Literature, Math, Science, Technology, the Arts, & More. 2008. (ENG., Illus.). 296p. pap. 19.50 *(978-0-8139-2736-7(6))* Univ. Pr. of Virginia.

Ferguson, Dana. Book Review Index 2007 Cumulation. 2007th rev. ed. 2007. (Book Review Index Ser.). (ENG.). 1408p. 513.00 *(978-0-7876-7843-2(0))* Cengage Gale.

—Children's Book Review 2008: Annual Cumalation. 2008th rev. ed. 2008. (Children's Book Review Index Ser.). (ENG.). 624p. 267.00 *(978-0-7876-9545-3(9))* Cengage Gale.

Ferguson, Dana, ed. Children's Book Review Index. 2007th ed. 2007. (Children's Book Review Index Ser.). (ENG.). 640p. 267.00 *(978-0-7876-7938-5(0))* Cengage Gale.

Gale Editor, ed. Book Review Index, 3 vols. 2012th ed. 2011. 1290p. pap. 513.00 *(978-1-4144-5810-6(X))* Cengage Gale.

—Book Review Index: Cumulative Index. 2011th ed. 2011. lib. bdg. 513.00 *(978-1-4144-5814-4(2))* Cengage Gale.

—Children's Book Review Index. 2011th ed. 2011. 909p. lib. bdg. 267.00 *(978-1-4144-6185-4(2))* Cengage Gale.

Gale Editors, ed. Book Review Index Cumulation. 2006th ed. 2006. (Book Review Index Ser.). (ENG.). 1416p. 513.00 *(978-0-7876-7842-5(2))* Cengage Gale.

Gardner, John E. On Writers & Writing. 2009. (ENG.). 320p. pap. 15.95 *(978-1-58243-494-0(8)*, Counterpoint Pr.) Basic Bks. GBR. Dist: Perseus-PGW.

Gass, William H. Life Sentences: Literary Judgments & Accounts. 2012. (ENG.). 368p. 28.95 ***(978-0-307-59584-3(6)***, Knopf) Knopf Doubleday Publishing Group.

Hubbell, Jay B. American Literature, V10, No 2, May 1938: A Journal of Literary History, Criticism, & Bibliography. Hubbell, Jay B. et al, eds. 2011. 160p. 41.95 ***(978-1-258-03674-4(6))*** Literary Licensing, LLC.

Johnson, R. Brimley. Famous Reviews. 2009. 564p. 33.99 *(978-0-559-13399-2(5))*; 36.99 *(978-0-559-13387-9(1))*; pap. 41.75 *(978-0-559-13394-7(4))*; pap. 42.75 *(978-0-559-13390-9(1))* BiblioBazaar.

Johnson, R. Brimley, ed. Famous Reviews. 2008. 484p. pap. *(978-1-4065-9929-9(8))* Dodo Pr.

Keenoy, Ray & Brown, Saskia, eds. Babel Guide to Italian Fiction in Translation. (Babel Guides). (ENG & ITA., Illus.). 183p. pap. *(978-1-899460-00-7(4))* Boulevard/Babel, Ltd.

Kerby, Carl. Remote Control: The Power of Hollywood on Today's Culture. 2006. (Illus.). 116p. per. 9.99 *(978-0-89051-491-7(7))* Master Bks.

Lago, Mary. The BBC Talks of E. M. Forster, 1929-1960. Hughes, Linda, ed. 2008. (ENG.). 494p. (C). 59.95 *(978-0-8262-1800-1(8))* Univ. of Missouri Pr.

Leonard, John. Reading for My Life: Writings, 1958-2008. 2012. (ENG.). 400p. (gr. 12). 35.00 ***(978-0-670-02308-0(6)***, Viking Adult) Penguin Group (USA) Inc.

Lessing, Doris. Time Bites: Views & Reviews. 2006. (ENG.). 384p. per. 14.95 *(978-0-06-083141-7(3)*, HarperPerennial) HarperCollins Pubs.

Li, Shouyi. Minguo Shu Ying: 1940-1949.9: Minguo Shuying. 2010. (CHI., Illus.). 197p. *(978-7-80663-754-8(0))* China Bk. Shop.

Mendelsohn, Daniel. How Beautiful It Is & How Easily It Can Be Broken. (ENG.). 480p. 2009. pap. 16.99 *(978-0-06-145644-2(6)*, HarperPerennial) 2008. 26.95 *(978-0-06-145643-5(8))* HarperCollins Pubs.

Myerson, Joel, ed. Emerson & Thoreau: The Contemporary Reviews. 2009. (American Critical Archives Ser.). (ENG.). 484p. pap. 51.00 *(978-0-521-11410-3(1))* Cambridge Univ. Pr.

Nussbaum, Martha C. Philosophical Interventions: Reviews 1986-2011, 1 vol. 2012. (ENG.). 352p. 29.95 ***(978-0-19-977785-3(3))*** Oxford Univ. Pr., Inc.

O'Connor, Flannery. The Presence of Grace & Other Book Reviews. Martin, Carter W., ed. 2008. (ENG.). 192p. per. 22.95 *(978-0-8203-3139-3(2))* Univ. of Georgia Pr.

Ott, Bill. The Back Page. 2009. 27.00 *(978-0-8389-0997-3(3))* American Library Assn.

Parini, Jay. Promised Land: Thirteen Books That Changed America. 2010. (ENG & ABK., Illus.). 400p. pap. 16.95 *(978-0-307-38618-2(X)*, Anchor) Knopf Doubleday Publishing Group.

Pater, Walter. Sketches & Reviews. reprint ed. lib. bdg. 98.00 *(978-0-7426-2429-0(3))* Classic Bks.

Persky, Stan. Reading the 21st Century: Books of the Decade, 2000-2009. 2011. (ENG.). 264p. (C). ***(978-0-7735-3909-9(3))*** McGill-Queen's Univ. Pr.

Porter, Katherine Anne. This Strange, Old World & Other Book Reviews by Katherine Anne Porter. Unrue, Darlene Harbour, ed. 2008. (ENG.). 192p. pap. 24.95 *(978-0-8203-3353-3(0))* Univ. of Georgia Pr.

Quinn, Mary Ellen, ed. Reference Books Bulletin. (Reference Books Bulletin Ser.). 96p. 2007. per. 29.50 *(978-0-8389-8412-3(6))* 2006. (Illus.). per. 29.50 *(978-0-8389-8333-1(2))* American Library Assn.

Radulovic, Jovan, et al. Novine Citalista Beogradskog: 1/3. Januar 1847.-2/14. Januar 1849. 2008. 488p. *(978-86-7191-134-4(9))* Biblioteka grada Beograda.

Rennison, Nick. Bloomsbury Good Reading Guide. 8th ed. 2009. (ENG., Illus.). 544p. pap. 14.95 *(978-1-4081-1395-0(3))* A & C Black GBR. Dist: Macmillan.

—100 Must-Read Historical Novels. Rennison, Nick, ed. 2009. (ENG., Illus.). 192p. pap. 9.99 *(978-1-4081-1396-7(1))* A & C Black GBR. Dist: Macmillan.

Rigelhof, T. F. Hooked on Canadian Books: The Good, the Better, & the Best Canadian Novels since 1984. 2010. (ENG.). 336p. 32.00 *(978-1-897151-75-4(6))* Cormorant Bks. Inc. CAN. Dist: Univ. of Toronto Pr.

Smith, S. Stephenson. The Craft of the Critic. 2007. (ENG.). 414p. 49.95 *(978-0-548-06845-8(3))* Kessinger Publishing, LLC.

Squire, John C. Books Reviewed. 2010. (Illus.). 178p. pap. 23.89 *(978-1-150-87228-0(4))* General Bks. LLC.

—Books Reviewed. 2010. 304p. pap. 23.16 *(978-1-163-90475-6(9))* 2008. 302p. 43.95 *(978-0-548-92780-9(4))* 2007. 320p. per. 28.95 *(978-0-548-60887-6(3))* Kessinger Publishing, LLC.

Taylor, Alan. Writing Early American History. 2006. 280p. (C). per. 24.95 *(978-0-8122-1910-4(4))* Univ. of Pennsylvania Pr.

Thomson Gale Staff. Book Review Index Subscription. 2006. 427.00 *(978-0-7876-7852-4(X))* Cengage Gale.

Tyson, Brian. Bernard Shaw's Book Reviews, Vol. 1. 2008. pap. 33.95 *(978-0-271-02781-4(9))* Pennsylvania State Univ. Pr.

Updike, John. Higher Gossip: Essays & Criticism. Carduff, Christopher, ed. 2011. (ENG., Illus.). 528p. 40.00 *(978-0-307-95715-3(2)*, Knopf) Knopf Doubleday Publishing Group.

Wagner, Laura. Let Me Tell You How I Really Feel: The Uncensored Book Reviews of Classic Images' Laura Wagner, 2001-2010. 2009. 252p. pap. 19.95 *(978-1-59393-503-0(X))* BearManor Media.

Welty, Eudora. A Writer's Eye: Collected Book Reviews. McHaney, Pearl Amelia, ed. 2009. (ENG.). 280p. pap. 25.00 *(978-1-60473-261-0(X))* Univ. Pr. of Mississippi.

Williamson, Eric. Say It Hot: Essays on American Writers Living, Dying, & Dead. 2011. (Illus.). 224p. pap. 24.95 *(978-1-933896-38-0(8))* Texas Review Pr.

Wilson, John. Magill's Literary Annual, 2010, 2 vols., Set. 2010. 1000p. 150.00 *(978-1-58765-655-2(8))* Salem Pr., Inc.

Wilson, John D. & Kellman, Steven G., eds. Magill's Literary Annual, 2 vols., Set. 2011. 1000p. 150.00 *(978-1-58765-815-0(1))* Salem Pr., Inc.

BOOKS—SELECTION
see Book Selection

BOOKS, ARTISTS'
see Artists' Books

BOOKS, BIRTHDAY
see Birthday Books

BOOKS, CASSETTE
see Audiobooks

BOOKS, CHAINED
see Chained Books

BOOKS, EXPURGATED
see Expurgated Books

BOOKS, FILMED
see Film Adaptations

BOOKS, FRAGMENTARY
see Unfinished Books

BOOKS, ILLUSTRATED
see Illustrated Books; Illustration of Books

BOOKS, MICROSCOPIC
see Miniature Books

BOOKS, MINIATURE
see Miniature Books

BOOKS, OUT-OF-PRINT
see Out-of-Print Books

BOOKS, PRIVATELY PRINTED
see Privately Printed Books

BOOKS, PROHIBITED
see Prohibited Books

BOOKS, RECORDED
see Audiobooks

BOOKS, REFERENCE
see Reference Books

BOOKS, SACRED
see Sacred Books

BOOKS, UNFINISHED
see Unfinished Books

BOOKS AND READING
Here are entered works on the significance of books in people's lives, including their attitude toward and interest in reading. Works on the art of reading are entered under Reading.
see also Authors and Readers; Best Sellers; Book Selection; Books—Reviews; Classification—Books; Expurgated Books; Fiction in Libraries; Group Reading; Libraries; Literature; Popular Literature; Prohibited Books; Readability (Literary Style); Reading Interests; Reference Books
also subdivision Books and Reading under classes of persons or ethnic groups for works which discuss their reading interests, and-or lists of recommended reading for the group; e.g. Children—Books and Reading

Ablow, Rachel. The Marriage of Minds: Reading Sympathy in the Victorian Marriage Plot. 2007. (ENG.). 248p. 55.00 *(978-0-8047-5466-8(7))* Stanford Univ. Pr.

Ablow, Rachel, ed. The Feeling of Reading: Affective Experience & Victorian Literature. 2010. (ENG., Illus.). 224p. pap. 32.50 *(978-0-472-05107-6(5))*; (C). 80.00 *(978-0-472-07107-4(6))* Univ. of Michigan Pr.

Acree Jr., William Garrett. Everyday Reading: Print Culture & Collective Identity in the Rio de la Plata, 1780-1910. 2011. (ENG., Illus.). 304p. 55.00 *(978-0-8265-1789-0(7))* Vanderbilt Univ. Pr.

Ainsworth, David. Milton & the Spiritual Reader. 2010. 244p. pap. 39.95 *(978-0-415-88390-0(3))* Routledge.

Al, Montgomery ET, et al. Ways of Reading. 3rd rev. ed. 2006. (ENG., Illus.). 384p. (C). 141.00 *(978-0-415-34633-7(9))* Routledge.

—Ways of Reading: Advanced Reading Skills for Students of English Literature. 3rd rev. ed. 2006. (ENG., Illus.). 384p. (C). 37.95 *(978-0-415-34634-4(7))* Routledge.

Ash, Russell & Lake, Brian. Bizarre Books: A Compendium of Classic Oddities. 2007. (Illus.). 224p. per. 14.95 *(978-0-06-134665-1(9)*, HarperPerennial) HarperCollins Pubs.

Atwell, Nancie. Reading Zone: How to Help Kids Become Skilled, Passionate, Habitual, Critical Readers. 2007. (ENG., Illus.). 144p. (gr. k-12). pap. 16.99 *(978-0-439-92644-7(0)*, Teaching Resources) Scholastic, Inc.

Aubry, Timothy Richard. Reading as Therapy: What Contemporary Fiction Does for Middle-Class Americans. 2011. 268p. pap. 39.95 *(978-1-58729-955-1(0))* Univ. of Iowa Pr.

Baron, Robert C. & Wright, Conrad Edick. The Libraries, Leadership, & Legacy of John Adams & Thomas Jefferson. 2010. (ENG.). 304p. 35.00 *(978-1-936218-08-0(9))* Fulcrum Publishing.

Barr, Catherine & Gillespie, John T. Best Books for Middle School & Junior High Readers, Grades 6-9, 1 vol. 2nd ed. 2009. (Children's & Young Adult Literature Reference Ser.). 1242p. 85.00 *(978-1-59158-573-2(2)*, LU8573) Libraries Unlimited, Inc.

Basbanes, Nicholas A. Every Book Its Reader: The Power of the Printed Word to Stir the World. 2006. (ENG., Illus.). 400p. pap. 15.95 *(978-0-06-059324-7(5)*, HarperPerennial) HarperCollins Pubs.

Bayard, Pierre. How to Talk about Books You Haven't Read. 2009. (ENG.). 208p. pap. 14.00 *(978-1-59691-543-5(9))* Bloomsbury Publishing.

—How to Talk about Books You Haven't Read. Mehlman, Jeffrey, tr. from FRE. 2007. (ENG., Illus.). 208p. 19.95 *(978-1-59691-469-8(6))* Bloomsbury Publishing.

Beam, Alex. A Great Idea at the Time: The Rise, Fall, & Curious Afterlife of the Great Books. 2008. (ENG., Illus.). 256p. 24.95 *(978-1-58648-487-3(7))* Perseus Bks. Group.

Beha, Christopher. The Whole Five Feet: What the Great Books Taught Me about Life, Death, & Pretty Much Everthing Else. 2010. (ENG.). 272p. pap. 14.00 *(978-0-8021-4485-0(3)*, Grove Pr.) Grove/Atlantic, Inc.

Beloe, William. Anecdotes of Literature & Scarce Books. 2009. 210p. pap. *(978-0-217-68448-4(3))*; 226p. pap. *(978-0-217-68464-4(5))*; 166p. pap. *(978-0-217-16997-4(X))*; 274p. pap. *(978-0-217-17005-5(6))*; 210p. pap. *(978-0-217-17009-3(9))*; 186p. pap. *(978-0-217-17011-6(0))*; 288p. pap. *(978-1-4590-3230-9(6))*; 154p. pap. *(978-0-217-77806-0(2))*; 200p. pap. *(978-0-217-77803-9(8))* Books LLC.

—Anecdotes of Literature & Scarce Books. 2009. 236p. pap. 19.99 *(978-0-217-68444-6(0))* General Bks. LLC.

—Anecdotes of Literature & Scarce Books. 2006. (ENG.). pap. 37.95 *(978-1-4286-4289-8(7))*; (ENG.). pap. 40.95 *(978-1-4286-4288-1(9))*; (ENG.). pap. 37.95 *(978-1-4286-4287-4(0))*; (ENG.). pap. 36.95 *(978-1-4286-4286-7(2))*; (ENG.). pap. 37.95 *(978-1-4286-4285-0(4))*; pap. 37.95 *(978-1-4286-4284-3(6))* Kessinger Publishing, LLC.

Bennett, Arnold. Literary Taste: How to Form It. 2007. 84p. per. *(978-1-4065-4794-8(8))* Dodo Pr.

—Literary Taste — How to Form It: With detailed instructions for collecting a complete library of English Literature. 2010. (ENG.). 132p. pap. 20.75 (978-1-178-03641-1(3)) BiblioBazaar.

—Literary Taste; How to Form It with Detailed Instructions for Collecting a Complete Library of English Literature. 2010. (Illus.). 50p. pap. 20.00 (978-1-153-74417-1(1)) General Bks. LLC.

Bennett, Arnold & Swinnerton, Frank. Literary Taste; How to Form It, with Detailed Instructions for Collecting a Complete Library of English Literature. 2010. 138p. pap. 20.75 (978-1-177-85195-4(4)) BiblioBazaar.

Bennett, Benjamin. The Dark Side of Literacy: Literature & Learning Not to Read. 2008. (ENG.). 300p. 65.00 (978-0-8232-2916-1(5)) Fordham Univ. Pr.

The Best Reading Hints on the Selection of Books; 2006. 264p. per. 23.99 (978-1-4255-2335-0(8)) MPublishing.

Birkerts, Sven. The Gutenberg Elegies: The Fate of Reading in an Electronic Age. 2006. (ENG., Illus.). 272p. per. 16.00 (978-0-86547-957-9(7)) Faber & Faber, Inc.

Birrell, Augustine. In the Name of the Bodleian & Other Essays. 2008. 188p. 22.99 (978-0-554-33488-2(7)) 2008. 188p. 25.99 (978-0-554-24185-2(4)) 2007. (ENG.). 170p. pap. 19.99 (978-1-4264-5911-5(4)) 2007. (ENG.). 186p. pap. 21.99 (978-1-4264-5979-5(3)) BiblioBazaar.

—In the Name of the Bodleian & Other Essays. 2008. 168p. pap. (978-1-4099-5152-0(3)) Dodo Pr.

—In the Name of the Bodleian & Other Essays. 2007. (ENG.). 320p. 45.95 (978-0-548-18620-6(3)); 324p. per. 30.95 (978-1-4304-8949-8(9)) Kessinger Publishing, LLC.

Bostwick, Arthur E. A Librarian's Open Shelf. 2008. 292p. 28.99 (978-0-554-24649-9(X)) 2008. 292p. 25.99 (978-0-554-33952-8(8)) 2006. (ENG.). 262p. pap. 21.99 (978-1-4264-7042-4(8)) 2007. 288p. pap. 23.99 (978-1-4264-7118-6(1)) BiblioBazaar.

Bowis, Duncan & Andrews, Stephen. 100 Must-Read Books for Men. 2008. (ENG., Illus.). 208p. 9.95 (978-0-7136-8873-3(4)) A & C Black GBR. Dist: Macmillan.

Brottman, Mikita. The Solitary Vice: Against Reading. 2008. (ENG., Illus.). 224p. per. 14.95 (978-1-59376-187-5(2)) Basic Bks.

Brown, Kate. Enlightenment & Expansion, 1707-1800, 2. McDougall, Warren & Brown, Stephen, eds. 2011. (Edinburgh History of the Book in Scotland Ser.: Vol. 2). (ENG., Illus.). 400p. (gr. 17). 240.00 **(978-0-7486-1912-2(7))** Edinburgh Univ. Pr. GBR. Dist: Columbia Univ. Pr.

Brown, Sylvia & Considine, John. Marginated: Seventeenth-Century Books & Traces of their Readers. 2010. (ENG.). 161p. pap. (978-1-55195-256-7(4)) Univ. of Alberta Pr. CAN. Dist: Michigan State Univ. Pr.

Browne, Murray. The Book Shopper: A Life in Review. 2009. (ENG.). 250p. pap. 14.95 (978-1-58988-056-6(0)) Dry, Paul Bks., Inc.

Bruns, Cristina Vischer. Why Literature? The Value of Literary Reading & What It Means for Teaching. 2011. (ENG.). 176p. 80.00 (978-1-4411-2520-0(5)); pap. 24.95 (978-1-4411-2465-4(9)) Continuum International Publishing Group, Ltd. GBR. Dist: National Bk. Network.

Burke, Michael. Literary Reading, Cognition, & Emotion: An Exploration of the Oceanic Mind. 2010. (Routledge Studies in Rhetoric & Stylistics Ser.). (ENG., Illus.). 298p. (C). 125.00 (978-0-415-87232-4(4)) Routledge.

Burns, Liz. Literature & Therapy: A Systemic View. 2009. 200p. pap. 36.95 (978-1-85575-594-9(7)) Karnac Bks. GBR. Dist: Stylus Publishing, LLC.

Callil, Carmen, et al. Stop What You're Doing & Read This! 2012. (ENG.). 192p. pap. 9.95 **(978-0-09-956594-9(3))** Random Hse. GBR. Dist: Independent Pubs. Group.

Canfield, Jack L. You've Got to Read This Book! 55 People Tell the Story of the Book That Changed Their Life. 2009. 286p. pap. 15.00 (978-1-4379-6765-4(5)) DIANE Publishing Co.

Carlile, Susan, ed. Masters of the Marketplace: British Women Novelists of The 1750s. 2011. (978-0-9823720-0-5(0)) Lehigh Univ. Pr.

Carlyle, Thomas. On the Choice of Books. 2009. 202p. 28.99 (978-1-110-56770-6(7)); pap. 23.75 (978-1-110-56768-3(5)) BiblioBazaar.

—On the Choice of Books. 2009. 48p. pap. (978-0-217-96829-4(5)) Books LLC.

—On the Choice of Books. 2007. (ENG.). pap. (978-1-4065-1278-6(8)) Dodo Pr.

—On the Choice of Books. 2007. 100p. per. (978-1-4068-4385-9(7)) Echo Library.

—Thomas Carlyles Inaugural Address at Edi. 2006. pap. 16.95 (978-1-4286-3736-3(2)) Kessinger Publishing, LLC.

Cézanne, Jeannette. Open Your Heart with Reading: Mastering Life Through Love of Stories. 2007. (Illus.). 187p. per. 14.95 (978-1-60166-011-4(1), Open Your Heart) Transformation Publishing.

Chancellor, John. The Library in the TVA Adult Education Program. 75p. reprint ed. lib. bdg. 88.00 (978-0-7222-0389-7(6)) Library Reprints, Inc.

Chartier, Roger. Inscription & Erasure: Literature & Written Culture from the Eleventh to the Eighteenth Century. Goldhammer, Arthur, tr. (Material Texts). 224p. (C). 2008. pap. 24.95 (978-0-8122-2046-9(3)) 2007. 55.00 (978-0-8122-3995-9(4)) Univ. of Pennsylvania Pr.

Collinson, Ian. Everday Readers: Reading & Popular Culture. 2009. (ENG.). 163p. (C). pap. 35.00 (978-1-84553-356-4(9)) Equinox Publishing Ltd. GBR. Dist: ISD.

Conroy, Pat. My Reading Life. 2010. (ENG., Illus.). 352p. 25.00 (978-0-385-53357-7(8), Talese, Nan A.) Knopf Doubleday Publishing Group.

—My Reading Life. Lt. ed. 2010. (ENG.). 352p. pap. 25.00 (978-0-7393-7784-0(1)) Random Hse. Large Print.

Cook, Edward. More Literary Recreations. 2008. 420p. pap. (978-1-4086-8846-5(8)) Read Bks.

Cook, Edward Tyas. More Literary Recreations. 2009. (ENG.). 420p. 41.99 (978-1-116-99040-9(7)); pap. 33.75 (978-1-116-99041-6(5)) BiblioBazaar.

Cooke, Simon & Goldman, Paul. Reading Victorian Illustration: 1855-1875: Spoils of the Lumber Room. 2012. (Illus.). 225p. 99.95 **(978-1-4094-1165-9(6))** Ashgate Publishing Co.

Corrigan, Maureen. Leave Me Alone, I'm Reading: Finding & Losing Myself in Books. 2007. (Vintage Ser.). (ENG.). 240p. pap. 14.95 (978-0-375-70903-6(7), Vintage) Knopf Doubleday Publishing Group.

Croft-Cooke, Rupert. The Wintry Sea. 2012. 200p. pap. **(978-1-4482-0514-1(X)**, 146522, Bloomsbury Reader) Bloomsbury Publishing Plc.

Cyr, Ann-Marie & Gillespie, Kellie M. Something to Talk About: Creative Booktalking for Adults. 2006. (ENG.). 134p. pap. 45.00 (978-0-8108-5436-9(8)) Scarecrow Pr., Inc.

Daniell, Beth & Mortensen, Peter, eds. Women & Literacy: Local & Global Inquiries for a New Century. 2007. (NCTE-Routledge Research Ser.). (Illus.). 360p. 45.95 (978-0-8058-6007-8(X)); 120.00 (978-0-8058-6006-1(1)) Erlbaum, Lawrence Assocs., Inc.

Darnton, Robert. The Case for Books; Past, Present, & Future. (ENG., Illus.). 2010. 256p. pap. 13.95 (978-1-58648-902-1(X)) 2009. 23.95 (978-1-58648-847-5(3)) PublicAffairs.

Davis, Peter & Koontz, Tom. Poet's Bookshelf 2: Contemporary Poets on Books That Shaped Their Art. 2008. (978-0-935306-53-8(6)) Barnwood Pr. Cooperative.

Diamant-Cohen, Betsy. Children's Services: Partnerships for Success. 2010. (Illus.). 128p. 50.00 (978-0-8389-1044-3(0)) American Library Assn.

Díez Borque, José María. Literatura (Novela, Poesía, Teatro) en Bibliotecas Particulares del Siglo de Oro Español (1600-1650) 2010. (Biblioteca Aurea Hispánica Ser.). pap. 29.80 **(978-84-8489-532-9(7))** Iberoamericana Vervuert Publishing Corp.

Dirda, Michael. Book by Book: Notes on Reading & Life. 2007. (ENG.). 192p. pap. 14.99 (978-0-8050-8338-5(3), Owl Bks.) Holt, Henry & Co.

Dorfman, Ariel. The Empire's Old Clothes: What the Lone Ranger, Babar, & Other Innocent Heroes Do to Our Minds. 2010. (ENG.). 224p. 79.95 (978-0-8223-4659-3(1)); pap. 22.95 (978-0-8223-4671-5(0)) Duke Univ. Pr.

Duffus, R. L. Books: Their Place in Democracy. 2007. (ENG.). 238p. 41.95 (978-0-548-05867-1(9)) Kessinger Publishing, LLC.

Dupuich, Dominique. Living with Books. 2010. (ENG., Illus.). 192p. 45.00 (978-0-500-51543-3(3), 551543) Thames & Hudson.

Dupuich, Dominique & Beaufre, Roland. Living with Books. 2012. (ENG., Illus.). 192p. pap. 26.95 **(978-0-500-29030-9(X)**, 529030) Thames & Hudson.

Durant, Alan, et al. Ways of Reading: Advanced Reading Skills for Students of English Literature. 4th rev. ed. 2012. (ENG., Illus.). 304p. (C). pap. 39.95 (978-0-415-67747-9(5)); 140.00 (978-0-415-67748-6(3)) Routledge.

Edmondson, Belinda. Caribbean Middlebrow: Leisure Culture & the Middle Class. 2009. (Illus.). 232p. 45.00 (978-0-8014-4814-0(X)) Cornell Univ. Pr.

Edwards, Lee. Reading the Right Books: A Guide for the Intelligent Conservative 2nd ed. 2009. xv, 163p. pap. (978-0-89195-133-9(4)) Heritage Foundation.

Ermakova, M. E. M.V. Lomonosov V Knizhnoi Kulture Rossii: Universalnost Genia: M. V. Lomonosov I Knizhnaia Kultura Rossii: "Kolumb Rossiiskol Nauki", "IA Znak Bessmertiia Sebe Vozdvignul" Izdaniia Trudov Uchenogo-Entsiklopedista: Katalog Materialov o M.V. Lomonosove I Izdanii Ego Trudov. 2010. (Illus.). 143p. (978-5-7510-0490-3(6)) Rossijskaja Gosucarstvennaja Biblioteka.

Eubanks, Charlotte. Miracles of Book & Body: Buddhist Textual Culture & Medieval Japan. 2010. (Buddhisms Ser.). (Illus.). 275p. 49.95 (978-0-520-26561-5(0)) Univ. of California Pr.

Farr, Cecilia Konchar & Harker, Jaime, eds. The Oprah Affect: Critical Essays on Oprah's Book Club. 2008. 336p. (C). 74.50 (978-0-7914-7615-4(4)); pap. 29.95 (978-0-7914-7616-1(2)) State Univ. of New York Pr.

Faulkner, Marilyn Green. Back to the Best Books. 2010. 260p. 29.99 (978-1-4535-0811-4(2)); pap. 19.99 (978-1-4535-0810-7(4)) Xlibris Corp.

Felski, Rita. Uses of Literature. 2008. (Blackwell Manifestos Ser.). (ENG.). 160p. pap. 33.95 (978-1-4051-4724-8(5)); 99.95 (978-1-4051-4723-1(7)) Wiley, John & Sons, Inc. (Wiley-Blackwell).

Finkelstein, David & McCleery, Alistair. The Book History Reader. Finkelstein, David & McCleery, Alistair, eds. 2nd rev. ed. 2006. (ENG., Illus.). 576p. 157.00 (978-0-415-35947-4(3)) Routledge.

—The Book History Reader. 2nd rev. ed. 2006. (ENG., Illus.). 576p. per. 49.95 (978-0-415-35948-1(1)) Routledge.

Fitch, George Hamlin. Comfort Found in Good Old Books. 2007. (ENG.). 256p. 42.95 (978-0-548-01549-0(X)) Kessinger Publishing, LLC.

Fitzgerald, William. Martial: The World of the Epigram. 2007. 248p. 37.50 (978-0-226-25253-7(1)) Univ. of Chicago Pr.

Fondo de Cultura Económica Staff, creator. Congreso Internacional del Mundo del Libro: 7-10 Septiembre, 2009, Ciudad de Mexico: Memoria. 2009. (Tezontle Ser.). (SPA.). 348p. pap. (978-607-16-0148-3(7)) Fondo de Cultura Economica.

Ford, Deborah B. Scary, Gross, & Enlightening, 1 vol. 2009. 158p. pap. 36.00 (978-1-58683-344-2(8), A2654P) Libraries Unlimited, Inc.

Foster, Thomas C. How to Read Novels Like a Professor: A Jaunty Exploration of the World's Favorite Literary Form. 2008. (ENG.). 304p. pap. 13.99 (978-0-06-134040-6(5), HarperPerennial) HarperCollins Pubs.

Garvey, Nathan. The Celebrated George Barrington: A Spurious Author, the Book Trade, & Botany Bay. 2008. 327p. 49.95 (978-1-875567-54-6(2)) Hordern Hse. AUS. Dist: Oak Knoll Pr.

Gaskell, Philip. New Introduction to Bibliography: The Classic Manual of Bibliography. rev. ed. 2007. (Illus.). 438p. pap. (978-1-873040-30-0(X)) Bow Historical Bks.

Gass, William H. Life Sentences: Literary Judgments & Accounts. 2012. (ENG.). 368p. 28.95 **(978-0-307-59584-3(6)**, Knopf) Knopf Doubleday Publishing Group.

Gass, William H. A Temple of Texts. 2007. (Dalkey Archive Scholarly Ser.). (ENG.). 418p. per. 14.95 (978-1-56478-468-1(1), 478468) Dalkey Archive Pr.

Goldberg, Gravity & Serravallo, Jennifer. Conferring with Readers: Supporting Each Student's Growth & Independence. 2007. (Illus.). 224p. pap. 30.00 (978-0-325-01101-1(X), E01101) Heinemann.

Goldberg, Sander M. Constructing Literature in the Roman Republic. 2010. (ENG.). 262p. (C). pap. 35.99 (978-0-521-17419-0(8)) Cambridge Univ. Pr.

Goldstein, Philip & Machor, James L. New Directions in American Reception Study. 2008. (ENG., Illus.). 544p. per. 45.00 (978-0-19-532088-6(3)) Oxford Univ. Pr., Inc.

Gomez, Jeff. Print Is Dead: Books in Our Digital Age. 2009. (ENG.). 304p. pap. 16.95 (978-0-230-61446-8(9)) Palgrave Macmillan.

Gruber, Ira D. Books & the British Army in the Age of the American Revolution. 2010. (ENG., Illus.). 360p. 55.00 (978-0-8078-3378-0(9)) Univ. of North Carolina Pr.

Gutch, Arthur Q. For People Who Love Books. 2010. pap. 18.95 (978-0-7414-5800-1(4)) Infinity Publishing.

Hadas, Rachel. Strange Relation. 2011. (ENG.). 204p. pap. 16.95 (978-1-58988-061-0(7)) Dry, Paul Bks., Inc.

Hallman, J. C., ed. The Story about the Story: Great Writers Explore Great Literature. 2009. (ENG.). 420p. pap. 18.95 (978-0-9802436-9-7(6)) Tin Hse. Bks., LLC.

Hammond, Mary. Reading, Publishing & the Formation of Literary Taste in England, 1880-1914. 2006. (Nineteenth Century Ser.). (Illus.). 222p. 110.00 (978-0-7546-5668-5(3)) Ashgate Publishing Co.

Haywood, Ian. The Revolution in Popular Literature: Print, Politics & the People, 1790-1860. 2008. (Cambridge Studies in Nineteenth-Century Literature & Culture Ser.). (ENG., Illus.). 352p. pap. 46.00 (978-0-521-10349-7(5)) Cambridge Univ. Pr.

Hendricks, Gay & Canfield, Jack L. You've Got to Read This Book! 55 People Tell the Story of the Book That Changed Their Life. 2007. (ENG.). 304p. pap. 14.99 (978-0-06-089175-6(0), William Morrow Paperbacks) HarperCollins Pubs.

Hiebert, Elfrieda H. Reading More, Reading Better. Hiebert, Elfrieda H., ed. 2009. (Solving Problems in the Teaching of Literacy Ser.). (ENG., Illus.). 273p. (gr. k-12). 35.00 (978-1-60623-285-9(1)); 60.00 (978-1-60623-286-6(X)) Guilford Pubns., Inc.

Hirschler, Konrad. The Written Word in the Medieval Arabic Lands: A Social & Cultural History of Reading Practices. 2012. (ENG., Illus.). 224p. (gr. 17). 105.00 **(978-0-7486-4256-4(0))** Edinburgh Univ. Pr. GBR. Dist: Columbia Univ. Pr.

Hoffman, James V., et al. National Reading Conference Yearbook, Vol. 50. Date not set. 60.00 (978-1-893591-03-5(4)) National Reading Conference.

Hogges, Ralph. The Love of Books & Academic Excellence: A Memoir, 1 vol. 2010. 74p. pap. 19.95 (978-1-4512-0082-9(X)) PublishAmerica, Inc.

Holmes, Diana. Romance & Readership in Twentieth-Century France: Love Stories. 2007. (Oxford Studies in Modern European Culture Ser.). (ENG.). 176p. 99.00 (978-0-19-924984-8(9)) Oxford Univ. Pr., Inc.

Huot, Sylvia. The Romance of the Rose & Its Medieval Readers: Interpretation, Reception, Manuscript Transmission. 2007. (Cambridge Studies in Medieval Literature Ser.). (ENG., Illus.). 424p. per. 79.00 (978-0-521-03931-4(2)) Cambridge Univ. Pr.

Ivanov, Rainer D. Reading at Risk: A Survey of Literary Reading in America. 2009. (Series: Education in a Competitive & Globalizing World Ser.). pap. 37.00 (978-1-60692-582-9(2)) Nova Science Pubs., Inc.

Jacobsson, Roger. Typographic Man: Medielandskap I Förändring: Studier I Provinsens Tryckkultur. 2009. (SWE., Illus.). 353p. (978-91-7331-286-8(X)) Carlsson bokforlag AB.

Johnson, William A. Readers & Reading Culture in the High Roman Empire: A Study of Elite Communities, 1 vol. 2012. (Classical Culture & Society Ser.). (ENG., Illus.). 240p. pap. 35.00 **(978-0-19-992671-8(9))** Oxford Univ. Pr., Inc.

Johnson, William A. & Parker, Holt N., eds. Ancient Literacies: The Culture of Reading in Greece & Rome, 1 vol. 2011. (ENG., Illus.). 448p. pap. 35.00 (978-0-19-979398-3(0)) Oxford Univ. Pr., Inc.

Kaestle, Carl F. & Radway, Janice A. A History of the Book in America: Volume 4: Print in Motion: the Expansion of Publishing & Reading in the United States, 1880-1940. 2009. (ENG., Illus.). 683p. 60.00 (978-0-8078-3186-1(7)) Univ. of North Carolina Pr.

Kenny, Des. Kenny's Choice: 101 Irish Books You Must Read. 2009. (ENG., Illus.). 332p. pap. 35.95 (978-1-85607-967-9(8)) Currach Pr. IRL. Dist: Dufour Editions, Inc.

Kenyon, Frederic G. Books & Readers in Ancient Greece & Rome. 2007. pap. **(978-1-4067-5559-6(1))** Read Bks.

Khair, Tabish & Doubinsky, Sébastien. Reading Literature Today: Two Complementary Essays & a Conversation. 2011. 190p. (C). pap. 23.00 **(978-81-321-0688-3(1)**, E06683P) SAGE Pubns., Inc.

Kniffel, Leonard, ed. Reading with the Stars: A Celebration of Books & Libraries. 2011. (ENG., Illus.). 160p. 17.95 (978-1-61608-277-2(1), 608277) Skyhorse Publishing Co., Inc.

Knight, Rachelle Rogers. Read, Remember, Recommend. 2010. (ENG.). 320p. pap. 15.99 (978-1-4022-3718-8(9)) Sourcebooks, Inc.

Kornicki, P F, et al, eds. The Female As Subject: Reading & Writing in Early Modern Japan. 2010. (Illus.). 279p. 70.00 (978-1-929280-64-3(5)); pap. 26.00 (978-1-929280-65-0(3)) Univ. of Michigan, Ctr. for Japanese Studies.

Kuhns, Oscar. The Love of Books & Reading. 2007. (ENG.). 168p. 36.95 (978-0-548-09061-9(0)) Kessinger Publishing, LLC.

Landy, Joshua. How to Do Things with Fictions, 1 vol. 2012. (ENG., Illus.). 288p. 55.00 **(978-0-19-518856-1(X))** Oxford Univ. Pr., Inc.

Lang, Andrew. Adventures among Books. 2008. 328p. pap. 21.95 (978-1-4357-4933-7(2)) Lulu Enterprises Inc.

Lantos, James, ed. & comment. Books. 2009. (Applewood's Pictorial America Ser.). (ENG.). 56p. pap. 9.95 (978-1-60889-023-1(6)) Applewood Bks.

Lawrence, David R. The Complete Soldier: Military Books & Military Culture in Early Stuart England, 1603-1645. 2008. (History of Warfare Ser.). (Illus.). 464p. (978-90-04-17079-7(0)) BRILL.

Levine, George. How to Read the Victorian Novel. 2007. (How to Study Literature Ser.). (ENG.). 200p. 110.95 (978-1-4051-3055-4(5)); per. 32.95 (978-1-4051-3056-1(3)) Wiley, John & Sons, Inc. (Wiley-Blackwell).

Li, Feng & Branner, David Prager, eds. Writing & Literacy in Early China: Studies from the Columbia Early China Seminar. 2011. (ENG., Illus.). 480p. (C). 50.00 (978-0-295-99152-8(6)) Univ. of Washington Pr.

Library in a Book Set, 33-Volumes, 32 vols., Set. 2009. (Library in a Book Ser.). (C). (gr. 9-18). 1170.00 (978-0-8160-8207-0(3)) Facts On File, Inc.

Longhurst, Derek, ed. Gender Genre & Narrative Pleasure Rle, Volume 9. 2012. (RLE: Women, Feminism & Literature Ser.). (ENG.). 240p. (C). 115.00 **(978-0-415-52326-4(5))** Routledge.

Loveman, Kate. Reading Fictions, 1660-1740: Deception in English Literary & Political Culture. 2008. (Illus.). 232p. 99.95 (978-0-7546-6237-2(3)) Ashgate Publishing Co.

Luey, Beth. Expanding the American Mind: Books & the Popularization of Knowledge. 2010. 224p. pap. 24.95 (978-1-55849-817-4(6)); lib. bdg. 80.00 (978-1-55849-816-7(8)) Univ. of Massachusetts Pr.

Lyons, Martyn. Reading Culture & Writing Practices in Nineteenth-Century France. 2008. (Studies in Book & Print Culture Ser.). (FRE & ENG., Illus.). 272p. (978-0-8020-9357-8(4)) Univ. of Toronto Pr.

Mabie, Hamilton Wright. Books & Culture. 2008. 120p. 21.99 (978-0-554-38118-3(4)) 2008. 120p. 24.99 (978-0-554-28815-4(X)) 2007. (ENG.). 112p. pap. 18.99 (978-1-4346-6334-4(5)) 2007. (ENG.). 118p. pap. 19.99 (978-1-4346-6335-1(3)) BiblioBazaar.

—Books & Culture. 2009. 102p. pap. (978-1-4588-2524-7(8)) Books LLC.

—Books & Culture. 2007. (ENG.). 100p. per. (978-1-4065-2952-4(4)) Dodo Pr.

—Books & Culture. 2007. (ENG.). 280p. 42.95 (978-0-548-05084-2(8)) Kessinger Publishing, LLC.

MacLean, Malcolm S. & Holmes, Elisabeth K., eds. Men & Books. 2009. 438p. 51.95 (978-1-104-83558-3(4)) 2007. (ENG.). 436p. per. 36.95 (978-0-548-38519-7(X)) Kessinger Publishing, LLC.

Madden, Frank. Exploring Literature: Writing & Arguing about Fiction, Poetry, Drama, & the Essay. 3rd rev. ed. 2006. (Illus.). 1372p. per. 88.00 (978-0-321-36630-6(1)) Longman Publishing.

—Exploring Literature Writing & Arguing about Fiction, Poetry, Drama, & the Essay. 5th rev. ed. 2011. (ENG., Illus.). 1360p. (C). pap. 100.00 (978-0-205-18479-8(0), Prentice Hall) Prentice Hall PTR.

Manguel. City of Words (h) 2008. 166p. (978-1-84706-270-3(9)) Continuum International Publishing Group, Ltd.

Manguel, Alberto. A Reader on Reading. (Illus.). 320p. 2011. (ENG.). pap. 18.00 (978-0-300-17208-9(7)) 2010. 27.50 (978-0-300-15982-0(X)) Yale Univ. Pr.

Martin, Jeff & Magee, C. Max, eds. The Late American Novel: Writers on the Future of Books. 2011. (ENG.). 192p. pap. 14.95 (978-1-59376-404-3(9), Soft Skull Pr.) Counterpoint LLC.

Maurice, Frederick Denison. The Friendship of Books: And Other Lectures. Hughes, Thomas, ed. 2011. (Cambridge Library Collection - Literary Studies). (ENG.). 426p. pap. 31.99 **(978-1-108-03186-8(2))** Cambridge Univ. Pr.

McCuen, Jo Ray. Reading for Writers. pap. 78.95 (978-0-8384-8768-6(8)) Cengage Heinle.

McGuire, Hugh & O'Leary, Brian. Book: A Futurist's Manifesto. 2012. (ENG.). 189p. pap. 24.99 **(978-1-4493-0560-4(1))** O'Reilly Media, Inc.

McHaney, Pearl Amelia, ed. Eudora Welty: Writers' Reflections upon First Reading Welty. 2010. pap. 21.95 (978-1-57003-936-2(4)) Univ. of South Carolina Pr.

Mead, Barbara, ed. Reading Group Choices 2009: Selections for Lively Book Discussions. 2008. 175p. pap. 6.95 net. (978-0-9759742-4-7(6)) Reading Group Choices.

Mead, Barbara Drummond Mead, ed. Reading Group Choices 2008: Selections for Lively Book Discussion, Volume 14. 2007. 160p. pap. 6.95 (978-0-9759742-3-0(8)) Reading Group Choices.

Miall, David S. Literary Reading: Empirical & Theoretical Studies. 2006. (Illus.). 242p. (C). pap. 34.95 (978-0-8204-8647-5(7)) Lang, Peter Publishing, Inc.

Miedema, John. Slow Reading. 2009. pap. 12.00 (978-0-9802004-4-7(X)) Litwin Bks., LLC.

Mikulecky, Beatrice S. A Short Course in Teaching Reading Skills. 2nd ed. 2011. (ENG., Illus.). 208p. (C). pap. 53.00 (978-0-13-136385-4(9)) Prentice Hall, ESL Dept.

Miles, Robert. Romantic Misfits. 2008. (Palgrave Studies in the Enlightenment, Romanticism & the Cultures of Print Ser.). (ENG.). 256p. 84.00 (978-1-4039-8993-2(1)) Palgrave Macmillan.

Miller, Andrew H. The Burdens of Perfection: On Ethics & Reading in Nineteenth-Century British Literature. 2011. 278p. pap. 24.95

(978-0-8014-7718-8(2)) 2008. (Illus.). 264p. 41.95 *(978-0-8014-4661-0(9))* Cornell Univ. Pr.

Miller, Laura. The Magician's Book: A Skeptic's Adventures in Narnia. 2009. (ENG.). 336p. pap. 14.99 *(978-0-316-01765-7(5)*, Back Bay Bks.) Little Brown & Co.

Miller, Laura J. Reluctant Capitalists: Bookselling & the Culture of Consumption. 2007. 328p. per. 22.50 *(978-0-226-52591-4(0))* Univ. of Chicago Pr.

Mittelmark, Howard & Newman, Sandra. Read This Next: 500 of the Best Books You'll Ever Read. 2010. (ENG.). 464p. pap. 14.99 *(978-0-06-185603-7(7)*, HarperPerennial) HarperCollins Pubs.

Moore, Charles H. What to Read, & How to Read, Being Classified Lists of Choice Reading, with Appropriate Hints & Emarks, Adapted to the Eneral Reader, to Subscribe. 2006. 160p. per. 18.99 *(978-1-4255-1207-1(0))* MPublishing.

Morrissey, Lee. The Constitution of Literature: Literacy, Democracy, & Early English Literary Criticism. 2007. (ENG.). 256p. 60.00 *(978-0-8047-5786-7(0))* Stanford Univ. Pr.

Munro, Craig. Paper Empires, 1946-2005 Vol. 3. Sheahan-Bright, Robyn, ed. 2006. (Illus.). 432p. (History of the Book in Australia Ser.). pap. 75.95 *(978-0-7022-3559-7(8))*; (History of the Book in Australia Ser.: Bk. 3). pap. 56.95 *(978-0-7022-3573-3(3))* Univ. of Queensland Pr. AUS. Dist: Independent Pubs. Group.

Murphy, Andrew. Shakespeare for the People: Working Class Readers, 1800-1900. 2010. (ENG.). 256p. pap. 35.99 *(978-0-521-17655-2(7))* Cambridge Univ. Pr.

Myers, Robin, et al. Owners, Annotators & the Signs of Reading. (Publishing Pathways Ser.). (Illus.). xv, 231p. (C). *(978-1-58456-171-2(8))* Oak Knoll Pr.

Nafisi, Azar. Reading Lolita in Tehran: A Memoir in Books. 2008. (ENG.). 400p. pap. 18.00 *(978-0-8129-7930-5(3)*, Random Hse. Trade Paperbacks) Random House Publishing Group.

Nash, John. James Joyce & the Act of Reception: Reading, Ireland, Modernism. 2010. (ENG., Illus.). 232p. pap. 36.99 *(978-0-521-12886-5(2))* Cambridge Univ. Pr.

Nylan, Michael. Yang Xiong & the Pleasures of Reading & Classical Learning in China. 2011. ***(978-0-940490-32-1(3))*** American Oriental Society.

Oakley, Henry Augustus. Outline of a Course of English Reading, Based on That Prepared for the Mercantile Library Association of the City of New-York, by the Late Chancellor. 2006. 132p. per. 16.99 *(978-1-4255-0938-5(X))* MPublishing.

O'Hear, Anthony, ed. The Great Books: A Journey Through 2,500 Years of the West's Classic Literature. 2009. (ENG., Illus.). 400p. (C). 28.00 *(978-1-933859-78-1(4))* ISI Bks.

Osborne, Susan. Bloomsbury Essential Guide for Reading Groups. Osborne, Susan, ed. 6th ed. 2008. (ENG.). 272p. pap. 16.95 *(978-0-7136-7598-6(5))* A & C Black GBR. Dist: Macmillan.

Ott, Bill. The Back Page. 2009. 27.00 *(978-0-8389-0997-3(3))* American Library Assn.

Ozma, Alice. The Reading Promise: My Father & the Books We Shared. 2011. 44.99 ***(978-1-61113-707-1(1)**, Sound Library)* AudioGO.

—The Reading Promise: My Father & the Books We Shared. (ENG.). 2012. 320p. pap. 14.99 ***(978-0-446-58378-7(2))*** 2011. 304p. 24.99 *(978-0-446-58377-0(4))* Grand Central Publishing.

—The Reading Promise: My Father & the Books We Shared. l.t. ed. 2011. 352p. 32.99 ***(978-1-4104-3957-4(7))*** Thorndike Pr.

Palmer, Beth & Buckland, Adelene. A Return to the Common Reader: Print Culture & the Novel 1850-1900. 2011. (Illus.). 204p. 99.95 *(978-1-4094-0027-1(1))* Ashgate Publishing Co.

Pappa, Joseph. Carnal Reading. 2011. (ENG.). 160p. 60.00 *(978-1-61149-004-6(9))* Univ. of Delaware Pr.

—Carnal Reading: Early Modern Language & Bodies. 2011. *(978-0-87413-774-3(8))* Univ. of Delaware Pr.

Parini, Jay. Promised Land: Thirteen Books That Changed America. 2010. (ENG & ABK., Illus.). 400p. pap. 16.95 *(978-0-307-38618-2(X)*, Anchor) Knopf Doubleday Publishing Group.

Parisian, Catherine M. The First White House Library: A History & Annotated Catalogue. 2010. 336p. 55.00 *(978-0-271-03713-4(X))* Pennsylvania State Univ. Pr.

Patrick, Kathy L. The Pulpwood Queens' Tiara-Wearing, Book-Sharing Guide to Life. l.t. ed. 2008. 485p. (YA). 29.95 *(978-1-4104-0782-5(9))* Thorndike Pr.

Pawley, Christine. Reading Places: Literacy, Democracy, & the Public Library in Cold War America. 2010. 272p. (C). pap. 28.95 *(978-1-55849-822-8(2))*; lib. bdg. 80.00 *(978-1-55849-821-1(4))* Univ. of Massachusetts Pr.

Pearl, Nancy. Girl Discovers Reading Then Discovers Life. 2011. (ENG.). 176p. pap. 10.95 *(978-1-57061-767-6(8))* Sasquatch Bks.

Pearson Staff & Bonilla, Paula. What Every Student Should Know about Reading a Novel. 2012. (What Every Student Should Know about... (WESSKA Series) Ser.). (ENG.). (C). pap. 9.40 ***(978-0-205-87052-3(X)**,* Prentice Hall) Prentice Hall PTR.

Phillips, Tom. Readers: Vintage People on Photo Postcards. 2011. (Bodleian Library - Photo Postcards from the Tom Phillips Archive Ser.). (Illus.). 112p. 25.00 *(978-1-85124-359-4(3))* Bodleian Library GBR. Dist: Chicago Distribution Ctr.

Piper, Andrew. Book Was There: Reading in Electronic Times. 2012. (Illus.). 200p. 22.50 ***(978-0-226-66978-6(5))*** Univ. of Chicago Pr.

Polastron, Lucien X. The Great Digitization: And the Quest to Know Everything. 2009. (ENG.). 1p. pap. 16.95 *(978-1-59477-243-6(6)*, Inner Traditions) Inner Traditions International, Ltd.

Polette, Nancy. Get up & Move with Nonfiction Grades 4-8, 1 vol. 2007. (Illus.). 176p. per. 30.00 *(978-1-59158-661-6(5)*, TIP8661, Teacher Ideas Pr.) Libraries Unlimited, Inc.

Popek, Michael. Forgotten Bookmarks: A Bookseller's Collection of Odd Things Lost Between the Pages. 2011. (ENG., Illus.). 192p. (gr. 12). 18.95 *(978-0-399-53701-1(5)*, Perigee Trade) Penguin Group (USA) Inc.

Porter, Noah. Books & Reading; or, What Books Shall I Read & How Shall I Read Them? by Noah Porter. 2006. 412p. per. 26.99 *(978-1-4255-4379-2(0))* MPublishing.

Potter, Alonzo. Handbook for Readers & Students, Intended As a Help to Individuals, Associations, School Districts & Seminaries of Learning, in the Selection of W. 2006. 332p. per. 23.99 *(978-1-4255-3340-3(X))* MPublishing.

Poyatos, Fernando. Textual Translation & Live Translation: The Total Experience of Nonverbal Communication in Literature, Theater & Cinema. 2008. (Illus.). 354p. (C). 158.00 *(978-90-272-3249-6(0))* Benjamins, John Publishing Co.

Preddy, Leslie B. Social Readers: Promoting Reading in the 21st Century, 1 vol. 2010. (Illus.). 223p. pap. 35.00 *(978-1-59158-869-6(3)*, LU8869) Libraries Unlimited, Inc.

Prose, Francine. Reading Like a Writer: A Guide for People Who Love Books & for Those Who Want to Write Them. (P. S. Ser.). (ENG.). 2007. 320p. pap. 13.99 *(978-0-06-077705-0(2)*, HarperPerennial) 2006. 288p. 23.99 *(978-0-06-077704-3(4))* HarperCollins Pubs.

Proust, Marcel. Days of Reading. 2009. (Penguin Great Ideas Ser.). (ENG.). 128p. (gr. 12-18). 10.00 *(978-0-14-104253-4(2)*, Penguin (Non-Classics)) Penguin Group (USA) Inc.

Proust, Marcel & Ruskin, John. On Reading. Searls, Damion, tr. from FRE. 2011. (On Ser.). (ENG.). 112p. pap. 12.95 *(978-1-84391-616-1(9))* Hesperus Pr. GBR. Dist: Independent Pubs. Group.

Pycroft, James. A Course of English Reading, Adapted to Every Taste & Capacity: With Literary Anecdotes. by the Rev. James Pycroft ... 2006. 356p. per. 26.99 *(978-1-4255-3600-8(X))* MPublishing.

Pyne, Charlynn Spencer. The Pavilion of the States at the National Book Festival, 2002-2006. 2007. (Illus.). 12p. *(978-0-8444-1173-6(6))* Library of Congress.

Queenan, Joe. One for the Books. 2012. (ENG.). 256p. 24.95 ***(978-0-670-02582-4(8)**,* Viking Adult) Penguin Group (USA) Inc.

Quiller-Couch, Arthur Thomas. On the Art of Reading. 2008. (ENG.). 236p. (C). pap. 34.99 *(978-0-521-73683-1(8))* Cambridge Univ. Pr.

—On the Art of Reading. 2007. 184p. per. *(978-1-4065-3975-2(9))* Dodo Pr.

—On the Art of Reading. 2007. (ENG.). 236p. per. *(978-1-4086-3309-0(4))* Read Bks.

—On the Art of Reading. 2008. (ENG.). 244p. pap. 13.95 *(978-1-4385-1081-1(0)*, Book Jungle) Standard Pubns., Inc.

Ramone, Jenni & Cousins, Helen. The Richard & Judy Book Club Reader: Popular Texts & the Practices of Reading. 2011. 224p. 99.95 ***(978-1-4094-0133-9(2))*** Ashgate Publishing Co.

Ratcliffe, Sophie. On Sympathy. 2009. (Oxford English Monographs). (ENG., Illus.). 240p. 125.00 *(978-0-19-923987-0(8))* Oxford Univ. Pr., Inc.

Reed, Adam. Literature & Agency. 2011. (Studies in Book & Print Culture Ser.). 272p. ***(978-1-4426-4248-5(3))*** Univ. of Toronto Pr.

Reid, Hugh. The Nature & Uses of Eighteenth-Century Book Subscription Lists. 2010. iv, 67p. *(978-0-7734-3757-9(6))* Mellen, Edwin Pr., The.

Reinburg, Virginia. French Books of Hours: Making an Archive of Prayer, C. 1400-1600. 2012. (ENG., Illus.). 312p. 99.00 ***(978-1-107-00721-5(6))*** Cambridge Univ. Pr.

Rendeiro, Margarida. The Literary Institution in Portugal since the Thirties: An Analysis under Special Consideration of the Publishing Market. 2010. (Illus.). 394p. pap. *(978-3-0343-0050-6(6))* Lang, Peter.

Repplier, Agnes. Books & Men. 2009. 234p. 32.99 *(978-1-115-42268-0(5))*; 234p. 28.99 *(978-1-115-42266-6(9))*; 234p. pap. 24.75 *(978-1-115-42262-8(6))*; 234p. pap. 25.75 *(978-1-115-42264-2(2))*; 232p. 28.99 *(978-1-113-63034-6(5))*; 232p. pap. 25.75 *(978-1-113-63033-9(7))*; 232p. pap. 24.75 *(978-1-113-63032-2(9))*; 232p. 23.99 *(978-1-103-47684-8(X))*; 232p. 23.99 *(978-1-103-46886-7(3))*; 232p. pap. 17.99 *(978-1-103-47679-4(3))*; 232p. pap. 17.99 *(978-1-103-46882-9(0))*; 232p. 23.99 *(978-1-103-31179-8(4))*; 232p. pap. 17.99 *(978-1-103-31176-7(X))* BiblioBazaar.

—Books & Men. 2009. 86p. pap. *(978-1-4588-2522-3(1))* Books LLC.

—Books & Men. 2009. 86p. pap. 14.14 *(978-1-151-62439-0(X))* General Bks. LLC.

—Books & Men. 2007. (ENG.). 228p. 41.95 *(978-0-548-16835-6(0))*; 232p. per. 26.95 *(978-1-4304-6561-4(1))* Kessinger Publishing, LLC.

—Books & Men. 2007. (ENG.). 232p. per. *(978-1-4067-2458-5(0))* Read Bks.

Richardson, Robert D. First We Read, Then We Write: Emerson on the Creative Process. 2009. (ENG.). 112p. 19.95 *(978-1-58729-793-9(0))* Univ. of Iowa Pr.

Rivers. Books & Their Readers: New Essays. 294p. *(978-0-8264-7194-9(3))* Continuum International Publishing Group, Ltd.

Roberts, Robert C., et al. Finding a Common Thread: Reading Great Texts from Homer to O'Connor. 2012. (ENG.). 456p. (C). pap. 35.00 ***(978-1-58731-254-0(9))*** St. Augustine's Pr., Inc.

Robertson, Duncan. Lectio Divina. 2011. 224p. pap. 34.95 ***(978-0-87907-238-4(5))*** Cistercian Pubns., Inc.

—Lectio Divina: The Medieval Experience of Reading. 2011. E-Book ***(978-0-87907-204-9(0))*** Cistercian Pubns., Inc.

Rooney, Kathleen. Reading with Oprah: The Book Club That Changed America. 2nd ed. 2008. 284p. per. 17.95 *(978-1-55728-873-8(9))* Univ. of Arkansas Pr.

Roosevelt, Theodore. A Book Lover's Holidays in the Open. 2007. (ENG.). 390p. 48.95 *(978-0-548-02284-9(4))* Kessinger Publishing, LLC.

—A Book Lover's Holidays in the Open. 373p. reprint ed. 98.00 *(978-0-7222-9563-2(4))* Library Reprints, Inc.

Round, Phillip. Removable Type: Histories of the Book in Indian Country, 1663-1880. 2010. (ENG., Illus.). 272p. 59.95 *(978-0-8078-3390-2(8))*; pap. 24.95 *(978-0-8078-7120-1(6))* Univ. of North Carolina Pr.

Ruskin, J. Selections. 2009. (ENG.). 248p. pap. 34.99 *(978-0-521-10926-0(4))* Cambridge Univ. Pr.

Ruskin, John. Sesame & Lilies. 2009. 212p. 28.99 *(978-1-116-17981-1(4))* 2009. 212p. 32.99 *(978-1-116-17980-4(6))* 2009. 212p. pap. 23.75 *(978-1-116-17983-5(0))* 2009. 204p. 23.99 *(978-1-103-31586-4(2))* 2009. 204p. pap. 17.99 *(978-1-103-31583-3(8))* 2008. 120p. 24.99 *(978-0-554-21845-8(3))* 2008. 120p. 21.99 *(978-0-554-31148-7(8))* 2006. (ENG.). 124p. pap. 18.99 *(978-1-4264-1067-3(0))* BiblioBazaar.

—Sesame & Lilies. 2009. 84p. pap. *(978-0-217-98937-4(3))*; 74p. pap. *(978-0-217-05182-8(0))*; 96p. pap. *(978-0-217-05185-9(5))*; 70p. pap. *(978-0-217-05188-0(X))*; 192p. pap. *(978-1-4588-4848-2(5))*; 174p. pap. *(978-1-4588-4849-9(3))* Books LLC.

—Sesame & Lilies. 2007. (ENG.). 116p. per. *(978-1-4065-6375-7(7))* Dodo Pr.

—Sesame & Lilies. 2007. (ENG.). 88p. per. *(978-1-4068-4089-6(0))* Echo Library.

—Sesame & Lilies. 2012. 220p. pap. 24.75 ***(978-1-276-65663-4(7))*** 2012. 98p. pap. 18.75 ***(978-1-277-10959-7(1))*** 2010. (ENG.). 262p. pap. 27.75 *(978-1-176-97589-7(7))* 2010. (ENG.). 272p. pap. 27.75 *(978-1-177-51252-7(1))* 2010. 290p. pap. 28.75 *(978-1-175-80052-7(X))* 2010. 240p. pap. 26.75 *(978-1-149-54405-1(8))* 2010. 346p. 36.99 *(978-1-140-02419-4(1))* 2010. 122p. 28.99 *(978-1-140-63842-1(4))* 2010. 346p. pap. 32.75 *(978-1-140-02420-0(5))* 2010. 118p. pap. 19.75 *(978-1-145-40502-8(9))* 2009. (ENG.). 211p. pap. 22.99 *(978-1-116-17984-2(9)*, BiblioLife) 2009. (ENG.). 211p. pap. 20.99 *(978-1-116-17985-9(7)*, BiblioLife) BiblioBazaar.

—Sesame & Lilies. 2011. 80p. pap. 5.99 ***(978-1-4209-4116-6(X))*** Digireads.com.

—Sesame & Lilies. 2010. (Illus.). 82p. pap. 20.00 *(978-1-153-74617-5(4))* General Bks. LLC.

—Sesame & Lilies. 220p. 2011. 39.95 ***(978-1-169-84656-2(4))*** 2010. 31.96 *(978-1-163-22477-9(4))* 2010. pap. 19.96 *(978-1-162-72379-2(3))* Kessinger Publishing, LLC.

—Sesame & Lilies; 2010. 252p. pap. 26.75 *(978-1-176-10122-7(6))* BiblioBazaar.

—Sesame & Lilies. l.t. ed. 2006. (ENG.). 118p. pap. 19.99 *(978-1-4264-1073-4(5))* BiblioBazaar.

—Sesame & Lilies Two Lectures Delivered at Manchester In 1864. 2006. 152p. per. 18.99 *(978-1-4255-1165-4(1))* MPublishing.

—Sesame & Lilies Three Lectures. 2006. pap. 15.95 *(978-1-60206-001-2(0)*, Cosimo Classics) Cosimo, Inc.

—Sesame Library Sesame & Lilies. 2006. 256p. per. *(978-1-4067-3317-4(2)*, Hesperides Pr.) Read Bks.

Ruskin, John & Hufford, Lois Grosvenor. Sesame & Lilies. 2010. 144p. pap. 21.75 *(978-1-141-70634-1(2))* BiblioBazaar.

Ruskin, John & Linn, James Weber. Sesame & Lilies. 2010. 166p. pap. 21.75 *(978-1-148-24004-6(7))*; pap. 21.75 *(978-1-147-92748-1(0))*; pap. 21.75 *(978-1-141-27823-7(5))* BiblioBazaar.

Sankovitch, Nina. Tolstoy & the Purple Chair: My Year of Magical Reading. (ENG.). 2012. 256p. pap. 14.99 *(978-0-06-199985-7(7)*, HarperPerennial) 2011. 320p. 23.99 *(978-0-06-199984-0(9))* HarperCollins Pubs.

Savanur, S. Development & Sustenance of Reading Habit. 2011. 150p. 24.00 *(978-81-7000-632-9(5))* Ess Ess Pubns. IND. Dist: International Specialized Bk. Services.

Schwartz, Lowell H. & Helmus, Todd C. Barriers to the Broad Dissemination of Creative Works in the Arab World. 2009. 58p. pap. 23.00 *(978-0-8330-4730-4(2)*, MG-879) RAND Corp., The.

Schwarz, Daniel R. In Defense of Reading: Teaching Literature in the Twenty-First Century. 2008. (Blackwell Manifestos Ser.). (ENG.). 216p. pap. 35.95 *(978-1-4051-3099-8(7))*; 104.95 *(978-1-4051-3098-1(9))* Wiley, John & Sons, Inc. (Wiley-Blackwell).

Sedo, DeNel Rehberg, ed. Reading Communities from Salons to Cyberspace. 2011. (ENG., Illus.). 240p. 85.00 *(978-0-230-29988-7(1))* Palgrave Macmillan.

Shannon, Patrick. Reading Wide Awake: Politics, Pedagogies, & Possibilities. 2011. 144p. pap. 25.95 ***(978-0-8077-5242-5(8))*** Teachers College Pr., Teachers College, Columbia Univ.

Sharpe, Kevin & Zwicker, Steven N. Reading, Society, & Politics in Early Modern England. 2010. (ENG.). 374p. pap. 42.00 *(978-0-521-16851-9(1))* Cambridge Univ. Pr.

Shriver, Lionel, frwd. The Book Club Bible: The Definitive Guide That Every Book Club Member Needs. 2008. (ENG.). 224p. pap. 15.95 *(978-1-84317-269-7(0))* O'Mara, Michael Bks., Ltd. GBR. Dist: Independent Pubs. Group.

Smiley, Jane. 13 Ways of Looking at the Novel. 2006. (ENG.). 608p. pap. 16.95 *(978-1-4000-3318-8(7)*, Anchor) Knopf Doubleday Publishing Group.

Smith, Amy Elizabeth. All Roads Lead to Austen. 2012. (ENG.). 384p. pap. 14.99 ***(978-1-4022-6585-3(9))*** Sourcebooks, Inc.

Spacks, Patricia Meyer. On Rereading. 2011. (ENG.). 304p. 26.95 *(978-0-674-06222-1(1)*, Belknap Pr.) Harvard Univ. Pr.

St Clair, William. The Reading Nation in the Romantic Period. 2007. (ENG., Illus.). 796p. per. 50.00 *(978-0-521-69944-0(4))* Cambridge Univ. Pr.

Steiner, George. My Unwritten Books. 2008. (ENG.). 192p. 23.95 *(978-0-8112-1703-3(5))* New Directions Publishing Corp.

Stidger, William Le Roy. The Place of Books in the Life We Live. 2007. (ENG.). 194p. 37.95 *(978-0-548-07072-7(5))* Kessinger Publishing, LLC.

Striphas, Ted. The Late Age of Print: Everday Book Culture from Consumerism to Control. 2011. (ENG.). 272p. (gr. 17). pap. 18.50 *(978-0-231-14815-3(1))* Columbia Univ. Pr.

—The Late Age of Print: Everyday Book Culture from Consumerism to Control. 2009. (ENG., Illus.). 272p. (gr. 17). 27.50 *(978-0-231-14814-6(3))* Columbia Univ. Pr.

Sutherland, John. Bestsellers (Routledge Revivals) 2010. (Routledge Revivals Ser.). (ENG.). 282p. 115.00 *(978-0-415-61124-4(5))* Routledge.

—Curiosities of Literature: A Feast for Book Lovers. 2009. (ENG., Illus.). 288p. 22.95 *(978-1-60239-371-4(0)*, 239371) Skyhorse Publishing Co., Inc.

Sweeney, Megan. Reading Is My Window: Books & the Art of Reading in Women's Prisons. 2010. (ENG., Illus.). 360p. 65.00 *(978-0-8078-3352-0(5))*; pap. 22.95 *(978-0-8078-7100-3(1))* Univ. of North Carolina Pr.

Tatlock, Lynne, ed. Publishing Culture & the Reading Nation: German Book History in the Long Nineteenth Century. 2010. (Studies in German Literature Linguistics & Culture Ser.: Volume 76). (GER & ENG., Illus.). 356p. 75.00 *(978-1-57113-402-8(6))* Camden Hse.

Teres, Harvey Michael. The Word on the Street: Linking the Academy & the Common Reader. 2010. (New Public Scholarship Ser.). (ENG.). 220p. (C). 75.00 *(978-0-472-07136-4(X))*; (Illus.). pap. 32.50 *(978-0-472-05136-6(9))* Univ. of Michigan Pr.

Tharoor, Shashi. Bookless in Baghdad: Reflections on Writing & Writers. 2012. (ENG.). 288p. pap. 14.95 ***(978-1-61145-408-6(5)**,* 611408, Arcade Publishing) Skyhorse Publishing Co., Inc.

Therman, Cecilia. Readers' Responses versus Reader-response Theories: An Empirical Study. 2008. 140p. pap. *(978-3-639-09037-6(3))* VDM Verlag Dr. Mueller e.K.

Ulin, David L. The Lost Art of Reading: Why Books Matter in a Distracted Time. 2010. (ENG.). 160p. 12.95 *(978-1-57061-670-9(1))* Sasquatch Bks.

van der Werf, Huib Haye, ed. The Architecture of Knowledge. 2010. (ENG & MUL., Illus.). 124p. pap. 40.00 *(978-90-5662-747-8(3))* NAi Uitgevers / Publishers Stichting NLD. Dist: D.A.P./Distributed Art Pubs.

Van Doren, Charles. The Joy of Reading: A Passionate Guide to 189 of the World's Best Authors & Their Works. 2008. (ENG.). 544p. 24.95 *(978-1-4022-1160-7(0))* Sourcebooks, Inc.

Vargas, Llosa M. In Praise of Reading & Fiction: The Nobel Lecture, 1 vol. Grossman, Edith, tr. from SPA. 2011. (ENG.). 48p. 16.00 *(978-0-374-17575-7(6))* Farrar, Straus & Giroux.

Vaughn, Leigh Ann, ed. Regulatory Fit & Persuasion Through Advocacy Messages & Narratives. 2010. (Psychology Research Progress Ser.). 58p. pap. 43.00 *(978-1-60876-887-5(2))* Nova Science Pubs., Inc.

Wadsworth, Sarah. In the Company of Books: Literature & Its Classes in Nineteenth-Century America. 2006. (Studies in Print Culture & the History of the Book). (Illus.). 278p. 80.00 *(978-1-55849-540-1(1))*; per. 24.95 *(978-1-55849-541-8(X))* Univ. of Massachusetts Pr.

Walsh, George. Great Books You Should Have Read (and Probably Didn't) 2006. (50 Plus One Ser.). (ENG.). 208p. pap. *(978-1-933766-08-9(5))* Encouragement Pr., 2nd Edition, LLC.

Walton, Charles, ed. Into Print: Limits & Legacies of the Enlightenment, Essays in Honor of Robert Darnton. 2011. (Penn State Studies in the History of the Book Ser.). (ENG.). 248p. 49.95 ***(978-0-271-05012-6(8))*** Pennsylvania State Univ. Pr.

Watt, Adam. Reading in Proust's a la Recherche: 'Le Délire de la Lecture' 2009. (Oxford Modern Languages & Literature Monographs). (ENG.). 234p. 120.00 *(978-0-19-956617-4(8))* Oxford Univ. Pr., Inc.

Welch, Myrtle I. Reading As a Struggle. 2009. 168p. pap. *(978-3-639-12984-7(9))* VDM Verlag Dr. Mueller e.K.

Werris, Wendy. An Alphabetical Life: Living It up in the World of Books. 2006. (ENG., Illus.). 336p. per. 15.95 *(978-0-7867-1817-7(X))* Da Capo Pr., Inc.

Who's Buying Information Products & Services. 4th ed. 2007. (Who's Buying Ser.). 81p. pap. 59.95 *(978-1-933588-60-5(8))* New Strategist Pubns., Inc.

Wiker, Benjamin. 10 Books Every Conservative Must Read: Plus Four Not to Miss & One Impostor. 2010. (ENG.). 369p. 27.95 *(978-1-59698-604-6(2))* Regnery Publishing, Inc., An Eagle Publishing Co.

Williams, Pat & Matthews Rose, Peggy. Read for Your Life: 11 Ways to Better Yourself Through Books. 2007. (ENG.). 284p. pap. 14.95 *(978-0-7573-0545-0(8))* Health Communications, Inc.

Wilson, Christopher P. The Labor of Words: Literary Professionalism in the Progressive Era. 2010. (ENG.). 268p. pap. 24.95 *(978-0-8203-3698-5(X))* Univ. of Georgia Pr.

Wittmann, Reinhard. Buchmarkt und Lektüre Im 18. und 19. Jahrhundert: Beiträge Zum Literarischen Leben, 1750-1880. (Studien und Texte zur Sozialgeschichte der Literatur Ser.). (GER., Illus.). XII, 252p. 105.00 ***(978-3-11-183418-4(2))*** De Gruyter, Walter Inc.

Womack, Kenneth, ed. Books & Beyond: The Greenwood Encyclopedia of New American Reading, 4 vols. 2008. 1352p. 399.95 *(978-0-313-33738-3(1)*, GR3738) Greenwood Publishing Group, Inc.

Wright, Thomas. Built of Books: How Reading Defined the Life of Oscar Wilde. 2010. (ENG.). 384p. pap. 18.00 *(978-0-8050-9246-2(3)*, Holt Paperback) St. Martin's Pr.

Wyatt, Neal. The Readers' Advisory Guide to Nonfiction. 2007. (ALA Readers' Advisory Ser.). 318p. per. 48.00 *(978-0-8389-0936-2(1))* American Library Assn.

BOOKS AND READING—HISTORY

Allan, David. Commonplace Books & Reading in Georgian England. 2010. (ENG.). 320p. 95.00 *(978-0-521-11534-6(5))* Cambridge Univ. Pr.

—A Nation of Readers: The Lending Library in Georgian England. 2009. (ENG., Illus.). 288p. 85.00 *(978-0-7123-4967-3(7))* British Library, The GBR. Dist: Chicago Distribution Ctr.

Allen, Graham, et al, eds. Readings on Audience & Textual Materiality, 1 vol. 2011. (History of the Book Ser.). (ENG., Illus.). 240p. 99.00 *(978-1-84893-159-6(X))* Pickering & Chatto Pubs., Ltd. GBR. Dist: Ashgate Publishing Co.

Anderson, Thomas Page & Netzley, Ryan. Acts of Reading: Interpretation, Reading Practices, & the Idea of the Book in John Foxe's Actes & Monuments. 2009. (Illus.). 306p. 65.00 *(978-0-87413-081-2(6))* Univ. of Delaware Pr.

Augst, Thomas & Carpenter, Kenneth, eds. Institutions of Reading: The Social Life of Libraries in the United States. 2007. (Studies in Print Culture & the History of the Book). (Illus.). 368p. 80.00 *(978-1-55849-590-6(8))*; per. 28.95 *(978-1-55849-591-3(6))* Univ. of Massachusetts Pr.

Bannet, Eve Tavor. Transatlantic Stories & the History of Reading, 1720-1810: Migrant Fictions. 2011. (ENG., Illus.). 306p. 90.00 *(978-1-107-00746-8(1))* Cambridge Univ. Pr.

Barton, Anna Jane & Barton, Anna. Tennyson's Name: Identity & Responsibility in the Poetry of Alfred Lord Tennyson. 2008. (Nineteenth Century Ser.). 174p. 99.95 *(978-0-7546-6408-6(2))* Ashgate Publishing Co.

Beam, Alex. A Great Idea at the Time: The Rise, Fall, & Curious Afterlife of the Great Books. 2009. (ENG., Illus.). 256p. pap. 13.95 *(978-1-58648-776-8(0))* PublicAffairs.

Beckett, Sandra. Crossover Fiction. 2009. 346p. pap. 39.95 *(978-0-415-87936-1(1))* Routledge.

Beckett, Sandra L. Crossover Fiction: Global & Historical Perspectives. 2008. (Children's Literature & Culture Ser.). XIV, 346p. 136.00 *(978-0-415-98033-3(X))* Routledge.

Blaak, J. Literacy in Everyday Life: Reading & Writing in Early Modern Dutch Diaries. 2009. (Illus.) 448p. *(978-90-04-17740-6(X))* BRILL.

Blair, Amy. Reading Up: Middle-Class Readers & the Culture of Success in the Early Twentieth-Century United States. 2011. (ENG.). 256p. 76.50 *(978-1-4399-0667-5(X))*; pap. 28.95 ***(978-1-4399-0668-2(8))*** Temple Univ. Pr.

Bloom, Clive. Bestsellers: Popular Fiction since 1900. 2nd ed. 2008. (ENG., Illus.). 352p. pap. 74.95 *(978-0-230-53689-0(1))* Palgrave Macmillan.

—Bestsellers: Popular Fiction Since 1900. 2nd ed. 2008. (ENG.). 352p. 110.00 *(978-0-230-53688-3(3))* Palgrave Macmillan.

Brannon, Julie Sloan. Who Reads Ulysses? The Common Reader & the Rhetoric of the Joyce Wars. 2009. 206p. 39.95 *(978-0-415-80347-2(0))* Routledge.

Brayman Hackel, Heidi. Reading Material in Early Modern England: Print, Gender, & Literacy. 2009. (ENG., Illus.). 336p. pap. 36.99 *(978-0-521-10415-9(7))* Cambridge Univ. Pr.

Brayman Hackel, Heidi & Kelly, Catherine E., eds. Reading Women: Literacy, Authorship, & Culture in the Atlantic World, 1500-1800. 2009. (Material Texts). (Illus.). 280p. (C). pap. 22.50 *(978-0-8122-2080-3(3))* Univ. of Pennsylvania Pr.

Brown, Cynthia Jane. The Queen's Library: Image-Making at the Court of Anne of Brittany, 1477-1514. 2010. (Material Texts). (Illus.). 416p. (C). 79.95 *(978-0-8122-4282-9(3))* Univ. of Pennsylvania Pr.

Cambers, Andrew. Godly Reading: Print, Manuscript & Puritanism in England, 1580-1720. 2011. (Cambridge Studies in Early Modern British History Ser.). (ENG., Illus.). 318p. 99.00 *(978-0-521-76489-6(0))* Cambridge Univ. Pr.

Cameron, Kenneth Walter. Emerson & Thoreau As Readers: Selected Chapters from the Transcendentalists & Minerva. 2011. 122p. 40.95 ***(978-1-258-02339-3(3))*** Literary Licensing, LLC.

Carlile, Susan. Masters of the Marketplace: British Women Novelists of the 1750s. 2010. (ENG.). 268p. 60.00 *(978-1-61146-012-4(3))* Lehigh Univ. Pr.

Casper, Scott E., et al. A History of the Book in America Vol. 3: The Industrial Book, 1840-1880. 2007. (ENG., Illus.). 560p. 65.00 *(978-0-8078-3085-7(2))* Univ. of North Carolina Pr.

Cataldo, Laura J. What Do I Read Next? Nonfiction, 2005-2010: A Reader's Guide to Current NonFiction. 2011. 242.00 *(978-1-4144-4847-3(3))* Cengage Gale.

Cohen, Matt. The Networked Wilderness: Communicating in Early New England. 2009. (ENG., Illus.). 296p. 67.50 *(978-0-8166-6097-1(2))*; pap. 22.50 *(978-0-8166-6098-8(0))* Univ. of Minnesota Pr.

Colclough, Stephen. Consuming Texts: Readers & Reading Communities, 1695-1870. 2007. (ENG., Illus.). 256p. 95.00 *(978-0-230-52538-2(5))* Palgrave Macmillan.

Cressy, David. Literacy & the Social Order: Reading & Writing in Tudor & Stuart England. 2006. (ENG., Illus.). 260p. pap. 53.00 *(978-0-521-03246-9(6))* Cambridge Univ. Pr.

Crone, Rosalind & Towheed, Shafquat, eds. The History of Reading Vol. 3: Methods, Strategies, Tactics, 3 vols. 2011. (ENG., Illus.). 224p. 85.00 *(978-0-230-24756-7(3))* Palgrave Macmillan.

Cuddy-Keane, Melba. Virginia Woolf, the Intellectual, & the Public Sphere. 2007. (ENG.). 248p. pap. 50.00 *(978-0-521-03538-5(4))* Cambridge Univ. Pr.

Dahl, Gina. Book Collections of Clerics in Norway, 1650-1750. 2010. (Studies in the History of Christian Traditions). (Illus.). ix, 365p. *(978-90-04-18899-0(1))* BRILL.

Dahl, Gina. Books in Early Modern Norway. 2011. (Library of the Written Word Ser.). (Illus.). XII, 252p. ***(978-90-04-20720-2(1))*** BRILL.

Dames, Nicholas. The Physiology of the Novel: Reading, Neural Science, & the Form of Victorian Fiction. 2007. (ENG., Illus.). 288p. 125.00 *(978-0-19-920896-8(4))* Oxford Univ. Pr., Inc.

Das, Nandini. Renaissance Romance: The Transformation of English Prose Fiction 1570-1620. 2011. (Illus.). 254p. 99.95 *(978-1-4094-1013-3(7))* Ashgate Publishing Co.

Davis, Philip. Why Victorian Literature Still Matters. 2008. (Blackwell Manifestos Ser.). (ENG.). 184p. pap. 29.95 *(978-1-4051-3579-5(4)*, Wiley-Blackwell) Wiley, John & Sons, Inc.

Daybell, James & Hinds, Peter, eds. Material Readings of Early Modern Culture: Texts & Social Practices, 1580-1730. 2011. (Early Modern Literature in History Ser.). (ENG., Illus.). 288p. 95.00 *(978-0-230-22352-3(4))* Palgrave Macmillan.

DeMaria, Robert, Jr. Samuel Johnson & the Life of Reading. 2009. (ENG.). 288p. (gr. 17). pap. 30.00 *(978-0-8018-9242-4(2))* Johns Hopkins Univ. Pr.

Falconer, Rachel. The Crossover Novel. 2009. 264p. pap. 39.95 *(978-0-415-87937-8(X))* Routledge.

Feather, John. The Provincial Book Trade in Eighteenth-Century England. 2008. (Cambridge Studies in Publishing & Printing History Ser.). (ENG.). 196p. (C). pap. 42.00 *(978-0-521-05552-9(0))* Cambridge Univ. Pr.

Fergus, Jan. Provincial Readers in Eighteenth-Century England. 2007. (ENG., Illus.). 336p. 135.00 *(978-0-19-929782-5(7))* Oxford Univ. Pr., Inc.

Finkelstein, David & McCleery, Alistair. An Introduction to Book History. 2nd rev. ed. 2012. (ENG.). 168p. (C). 130.00 ***(978-0-415-68805-5(1))***; pap. 44.95 ***(978-0-415-68806-2(X))*** Routledge.

Franta, Andrew. Romanticism & the Rise of the Mass Public. 2009. (Cambridge Studies in Romanticism Ser.). (ENG.). 260p. pap. 38.99 *(978-0-521-11710-4(0))* Cambridge Univ. Pr.

Fraser, Robert & Hammond, Mary, eds. Books Without Borders, Volume 1: The Cross-National Dimension in Print Culture, 2 vols. 2008. (ENG., Illus.). 224p. 89.00 *(978-0-230-21029-5(5))* Palgrave Macmillan.

Fulton, Thomas. Historical Milton. 2010. 320p. pap. 28.95 *(978-1-55849-845-7(1))* Univ. of Massachusetts Pr.

—Historical Milton: Manuscript, Print, & Political Culture in Revolutionary England. 2010. (Illus.). xv, 304p. *(978-1-55849-844-0(3))* Univ. of Massachusetts Pr.

Gerson, Carole & Michon, Jacques, eds. History of the Book in Canada, 1918-1980 Vol. 3, 3 vols. 2007. (ENG., Illus.). 696p. *(978-0-8020-9047-8(8))* Univ. of Toronto Pr.

Giné, Marta & Hibbs, Solange, eds. Traducción y Cultura: La Literatura Traducida en la Prensa Hispánica (1868-98) 2010. (Relaciones literarias en el Ambito Hispanico. Traduccion, Literatura y Cultura Ser.). (SPA., Illus.). 505p. pap. *(978-3-0343-0366-8(1))* Lang, Peter.

Goldstein, Philip & Goldstein, Philip. Modern American Reading Practices: Between Aesthetics & History. 2008. (ENG.). 192p. 89.00 *(978-0-230-61225-9(3))* Palgrave Macmillan.

González, Carlos Alberto. New World Literacy: Writing & Culture Across the Atlantic, 1500-1700. 2011. (ENG.). 296p. 75.00 *(978-1-61148-026-9(4))* Bucknell Univ. Pr.

Green, D. H. Women Readers in the Middle Ages. 2011. (Cambridge Studies in Medieval Literature Ser.). (ENG., Illus.). 312p. pap. 39.99 *(978-0-521-17437-4(6))* Cambridge Univ. Pr.

Greenspan, Ezra & Rose, Jonathan, eds. Book History Volume 10. 2007. (Book History Ser.). (Illus.). 319p. 57.00 *(978-0-271-02766-1(2))* Pennsylvania State Univ. Pr.

Gross, Robert A. & Kelley, Mary, eds. A History of the Book in America: Volume 2: an Extensive Republic: Print, Culture, & Society in the New Nation, 1790-1840. 2010. (ENG., Illus.). 672p. 60.00 *(978-0-8078-3339-1(8))* Univ. of North Carolina Pr.

Grossman, Marshall. Reading Renaissance Ethics. 2007. (ENG.). 304p. 110.00 *(978-0-415-40634-5(X))*; (Illus.). 291p. per. 35.95 *(978-0-415-40635-2(8))* Routledge.

Gunzenhauser, Bonnie, ed. Reading in History: New Methodologies from the Anglo-American Tradition, 1 vol. 2010. (History of the Book Ser.). (ENG.). 200p. 99.00 *(978-1-85196-628-8(5))* Pickering & Chatto Pubs., Ltd. GBR. Dist: Ashgate Publishing Co.

Hall, James W. Hit Lit: Cracking the Code of the Twentieth Century's Biggest Bestsellers. 2012. (ENG.). 336p. E-Book ***(978-0-679-60496-9(0))***; pap. 16.00 ***(978-0-8129-7095-1(0))*** Random House Publishing Group. (Random Hse. Trade Paperbacks).

Hall, Thomas N. & Scragg, D. G. Anglo-Saxon Books & Their Readers: Essays in Celebration of Helmut Gneuss's Handlist of Anglo-Saxon Manuscripts. 2008. 45.00 *(978-1-58044-137-7(8))*; pap. 25.00 *(978-1-58044-138-4(6))* Medieval Institute Pubns.

Halsey, Katie & Owens, W. R., eds. The History of Reading Vol. 2: Evidence from the British Isles, C. 1750-1950, 3 vols. 2011. (ENG., Illus.). 232p. 85.00 *(978-0-230-24755-0(5))* Palgrave Macmillan.

Hawkins, Ann R., ed. Teaching Bibliography, Textual Criticism, & Book History, 1 vol. 2006. (ENG.). 199p. 99.00 *(978-1-85196-834-3(2))* Pickering & Chatto Pubs., Ltd. GBR. Dist: Ashgate Publishing Co.

Heinzelmann, Tobias & Sievert, Henning, eds. Buchkultur im Nahen Osten des 17. und 18. Jahrhunderts. 2010. (Welten des Islams/Worlds of Islam/Mondes de l'Islam Ser.). (GER.). 266p. pap. *(978-3-0343-0451-1(X))* Lang, Peter.

Hemminghaus, Edgar H. Mark Twain in Germany: Columbia University Germanic Studies V9. Fife, Robert Herndon, ed. 2011. 180p. 42.95 ***(978-1-258-03278-4(3))*** Literary Licensing, LLC.

Hobbins, Daniel. Authorship & Publicity Before Print: Jean Gerson & the Transformation of Late Medieval Learning. 2009. (Middle Ages Ser.). (Illus.). 352p. (C). 55.00 *(978-0-8122-4155-6(X))* Univ. of Pennsylvania Pr.

Hochman, Barbara. Uncle Tom's Cabin & the Reading Revolution: Race, Literacy, Childhood & Fiction, 1851¿1911. 2011. (Illus.). 352p. (ENG.). pap. 28.95 *(978-1-55849-894-5(X))*; lib. bdg. 80.00 *(978-1-55849-893-8(1))* Univ. of Massachusetts Pr.

Holman, Valerie. Print for Victory: Book Publishing in England, 1939-1945. 2008. (ENG., Illus.). 304p. 39.95 *(978-0-7123-5001-3(2))* British Library, The GBR. Dist: Chicago Distribution Ctr.

Hudi, József. Könyv és Társadalom: Könyvkultúra és Muvelodés a XVIII-XIX. Századi Veszprém Megyében. 2009. (HUN., Illus.). 276p. *(978-963-200-566-9(X))*; *(978-963-693-204-6(2))* Gondolat Konyvkiado.

Ife, B. W. Reading & Fiction in Golden-Age Spain: A Platonist Critique & Some Picaresque Replies. 2009. (Cambridge Iberian & Latin American Studies). 224p. pap. 33.99 *(978-0-521-12120-0(5))* Cambridge Univ. Pr.

Ishihara, Tsuyoshi. Mark Twain in Japan: The Cultural Reception of an American Icon. 2011. (MARK TWAIN & HIS CIRCLE Ser.). (ENG., Illus.). 200p. (C). (gr. 13). pap. 25.00 *(978-0-8262-1961-9(6))* Univ. of Missouri Pr.

Jack, Belinda. The Woman Reader. 2012. (ENG., Illus.). 336p. 30.00 ***(978-0-300-12045-5(1))*** Yale Univ. Pr.

Jajdelska, Elspeth. Silent Reading & the Birth of the Narrator. 2007. (Studies in Book & Print Culture Ser.). (ENG., Illus.). 256p. *(978-0-8020-9364-6(7))* Univ. of Toronto Pr.

Jensen, Kristian. Revolution & the Antiquarian Book: Reshaping the Past, 1780-1815. 2011. (ENG., Illus.). 328p. 90.00 *(978-1-107-00051-3(3))* Cambridge Univ. Pr.

Jones, E. A. & Walsham, Alexandra, eds. Syon Abbey & Its Books: Reading, Writing & Religion in England, C. 1400-1700. 2010. (Studies in Modern British Religious History Ser.: Volume 24). (Illus.). 288p. 90.00 *(978-1-84383-547-9(9)*, Boydell Press) Boydell & Brewer, Ltd. GBR. Dist: Boydell & Brewer, Inc.

Kallendorf, Craig. The Virgilian Tradition: Book history & the history of Reading. 2007. (Variorum Collected Studies). (Illus.). 320p. 154.95 *(978-0-7546-5923-5(2))* Ashgate Publishing Co.

Kent, Charles. Charles Dickens As a Reader by Charles Kent. 2006. 288p. per. 23.99 *(978-1-4255-2655-9(1))* MPublishing.

King, John N., ed. Tudor Books & Readers: Materiality & the Construction of Meaning. 2010. (ENG., Illus.). 288p. 95.00 *(978-0-521-51494-1(0))* Cambridge Univ. Pr.

Knight, Charles. The Old Printer & the Modern Press. 2010. (Cambridge Library Collection - Printing & Publishing History Ser.). (Illus.). 332p. pap. 28.99 *(978-1-108-00922-5(0))* Cambridge Univ. Pr.

Liebler, Naomi Conn. Early Modern Prose Fiction: The Cultural Politics of Reading. 2006. 185p. (Routledge Research in Postcolonial Literatures Ser.: Vol. 14). 120.00 *(978-0-415-35840-8(X))*; per. 34.95 *(978-0-415-35841-5(8))* Routledge.

Littau, Karin. Theories of Reading: Books, Bodies, & Bibliomania. (ENG., Illus.). 208p. 2007. 69.95 *(978-0-7456-1658-2(5))* 2006. pap. 26.95 *(978-0-7456-1659-9(3))* Polity Pr. GBR. Dist: Wiley, John & Sons, Inc.

Lupton, Christina. Knowing Books: The Consciousness of Mediation in Eighteenth-Century Britain. 2011. (Material Texts). 200p. (C). 55.00 ***(978-0-8122-4372-7(2))*** Univ. of Pennsylvania Pr.

Lyons, Martyn. Books: A Living History. 2011. (ENG., Illus.). 224p. 34.95 *(978-1-60606-083-4(X)*, J. Paul Getty Museum) Getty Pubns.

Maatta, Stephanie L. A Few Good Books: Using Contemporary Readers' Advisory Strategies to Connect Readers with Books. 2010. (Illus.). 400p. 74.95 *(978-1-55570-669-2(X))* Neal-Schuman Pubs., Inc.

Machor, James L. Reading Fiction in Antebellum America: Informed Response & Reception Histories, 1820-1865. 2011. (ENG.). 424p. (gr. 17). 75.00 *(978-0-8018-9874-7(9))* Johns Hopkins Univ. Pr.

Mcparland, Robert P. Charles Dickens's American Audience. 2010. (ENG.). 252p. 78.99 *(978-0-7391-1857-3(9))* Lexington Bks.

Monaghan, E. Jennifer. Learning to Read & Write in Colonial America. 2007. (Studies in Print Culture & the History of the Book). (Illus.). 491p. per. 28.95 *(978-1-55849-581-4(9))* Univ. of Massachusetts Pr.

Moore, Tara & Commonwealth Universities Association London Staff. Victorian Christmas in Print. 2009. (Nineteenth-Century Major Lives & Letters Ser.). (ENG., Illus.). 208p. 89.00 *(978-0-230-61654-7(2))* Palgrave Macmillan.

Nash, George H. Books & Founding Fathers. 2007. 64p. pap. 8.00 *(978-1-884532-91-7(8))* ISI Bks.

Nelson, Claudia. Precocious Children & Childish Adults: Age Inversion in Victorian Literature. 2012. (ENG.). 224p. (gr. 17). 50.00 ***(978-1-4214-0534-6(2))*** Johns Hopkins Univ. Pr.

Parisian, Catherine M. Frances Burney's Cecilia: A Publishing History. 2012. (Ashgate Studies in Publishing History Ser.). (Illus.). 275p. 104.95 ***(978-1-4094-1820-7(0))*** Ashgate Publishing Co.

Potter, Franz J., ed. Literary Mushrooms: Tales from the Gothic Chapbooks, 1800-1830. 2007. 240p. *(978-0-9795871-2-2(3))*; Vol.2. *(978-0-9795871-4-6(X))* Zittaw Pr.

Prendergast, Ryan. Reading, Writing, & Errant Subjects in Inquisitorial Spain. 2011. 146p. 89.95 *(978-1-4094-1865-8(0))* Ashgate Publishing Co.

Quay, Sara E. & Watling, Gabrielle, eds. Cultural History of Reading, 2 vols. 2008. (Illus.). 1088p. 199.95 *(978-0-313-33744-4(6)*, GR3744, Greenwood Pr.) Greenwood Publishing Group, Inc.

Ratner, Lorman, et al. Paradoxes of Prosperity: Wealth Seeking in Pre-Civil War America. 2009. (ENG.). 168p. 40.00 *(978-0-252-03453-4(8))* Univ. of Illinois Pr.

Raven, James, et al, eds. The Practice & Representation of Reading in England. 2007. (ENG.). 332p. pap. 56.00 *(978-0-521-02323-8(8))* Cambridge Univ. Pr.

Reed, Christopher A. From Woodblocks to the Internet: Chinese Publishing & Print Culture in Transition, circa 1800 To 2008. Brokaw, Cynthia, ed. (Sinica Leidensia Ser.). (CHI & ENG., Illus.). 416p. *(978-90-04-18527-2(5))* BRILL.

Robbins, Jill. Crossing Through Chueca: Lesbian Literary Culture in Queer Madrid. 2011. 232p. 67.50 *(978-0-8166-6989-9(9))*; pap. 22.50 *(978-0-8166-6990-5(2))* Univ. of Minnesota Pr.

Romaine, Susan Steffensen. Readers & Leaders, 1 vol. 2007. (Illus.). 160p. per. 35.00 *(978-1-59158-516-9(3)*, LU5163) Libraries Unlimited, Inc.

Rose, Jonathan. The Intellectual Life of the British Working Classes. 2nd ed. 2010. (Illus.). 544p. pap. 33.00 *(978-0-300-15365-1(1))* Yale Univ. Pr.

Salter, Elisabeth. Vernacularity in England & Wales, C. 1300-1550. Wicker, Helen, ed. 2011. (Utrecht Studies in Medieval Literacy Ser.). (ENG., Illus.). 335p. (C). 102.00 *(978-2-503-52883-0(X))* Brepols Pubs. BEL. Dist: ISD.

Sauer, Elizabeth. Reading the Nation. 2009. (ENG.). 260p. 34.95 *(978-0-415-44524-5(8))* Routledge.

Sauer, Elizabeth & Wright, Julia M. Reading the Nation. 2009. (ENG.). 260p. 110.00 *(978-0-415-44523-8(X))* Routledge.

Sherman, William H. Used Books: Marking Readers in Renaissance England. 2009. (Material Texts). (Illus.). 288p. (C). pap. 19.95 *(978-0-8122-2084-1(6))* Univ. of Pennsylvania Pr.

Shields, David S. & Meléndez, Mariselle. Liberty! Egalité! Independencia! Print Culture, Enlightenment, & Revolution in the Americas, 1776-1838: Papers from a Conference at the American Antiquarian Society in June 2006 [and] the James Russell Wiggins Lecture, "We Declare You Independent Whether You Wish It or Not": The Print Culture of Early Filibusterism. 2007. 25.00 *(978-1-929545-46-9(0))* American Antiquarian Society.

Silverman, Gillian. Bodies & Books: Reading & the Fantasy of Communion in Nineteenth-Century America. 2012. (Illus.). 256p. (C). 55.00 ***(978-0-8122-4415-1(X))*** Univ. of Pennsylvania Pr.

Spiller, Elizabeth. Reading & the History of Race in the Renaissance. 2011. (ENG.). 264p. 90.00 *(978-1-107-00735-2(6))* Cambridge Univ. Pr.

Steinberg, Justin. Accounting for Dante: Urban Readers & Writers in Late Medieval Italy. 2007. (Devers series in Dan Ser.). 232p. pap. 30.00 *(978-0-268-04122-9(9))* Univ. of Notre Dame Pr.

Stokic, Gordana. Knjiga I Biblioteke Kod Srba U Srednjem Veku. 2008. (SER., Illus.). 106p. *(978-86-85131-04-2(9))* Gradska biblioteka u Novom Sadu.

Summit, Jennifer. Memory's Library: Medieval Books in Early Modern England. 2011. (Illus.). 354p. pap. 27.50 *(978-0-226-78170-9(4))* Univ. of Chicago Pr.

Sutherland, John. Bestsellers: A Very Short Introduction. 2007. (Very Short Introductions Ser.). (ENG., Illus.). 144p. per. 11.95 *(978-0-19-921489-1(1))* Oxford Univ. Pr., Inc.

—The Longman Companion to Victorian Fiction. 2nd ed. 2009. (ENG., Illus.). 736p. pap. 45.00 *(978-1-4082-0390-3(1))* Longman Publishing Group.

Szabari, Antónia. Less Rightly Said: Scandals & Readers in Sixteenth-Century France. 2009. (ENG., Illus.). 304p. 60.00 *(978-0-8047-6292-2(9))* Stanford Univ. Pr.

Takseva, Tatjana. Seventeenth-Century Poetic Genres As Social Categories: A New Reading of the Poetry of John Donne. 2010. (Illus.). vi, 321p. 119.95 *(978-0-7734-3606-0(5)*, Mellen, Edwin Pr., The.

Towheed, Shafquat, et al, eds. History of Reading. 2010. (ENG., Illus.). 480p. 135.00 *(978-0-415-48420-6(0))* Routledge.

Towheed, Shafquat & Owens, W. R., eds. The History of Reading Vol. 1: International Perspectives, C. 1500-1990, 3 vols. 2011. (ENG., Illus.). 232p. 85.00 *(978-0-230-24751-2(2))* Palgrave Macmillan.

Tucker, Amy. The Illustration of the Master: Henry James & the Magazine Revolution. 2010. (ENG., Illus.). 280p. 60.00 *(978-0-8047-6874-0(9))* Stanford Univ. Pr.

Van linthout, Ine. Das Buch in der nationalsozialistischen Propagandapolitik. 2011. (Studien und Texte zur Sozialgeschichte der Literatur Ser.). (GER., Illus.). XI, 437p. 140.00 ***(978-3-11-025271-2(6))*** De Gruyter, Walter Inc.

Visser, Arnoud. Reading Augustine in the Reformation: The Flexibility of Intellectual Authority in Europe, 1500-1620, 1 vol. 2011. (Oxford Studies in Historical Theology Ser.). (ENG.). 256p. 74.00 *(978-0-19-976593-5(6))* Oxford Univ. Pr., Inc.

Vlock, Deborah. Dickens, Novel Reading, & the Victorian Popular Theatre. 2006. (Cambridge Studies in Nineteenth-Century Literature & Culture Ser.). (ENG., Illus.). 244p. pap. 45.00 *(978-0-521-02688-8(1))* Cambridge Univ. Pr.

Wakelin, Daniel. Humanism, Reading, & English Literature 1430-1530. 2007. (ENG.). 272p. 125.00 *(978-0-19-921588-1(X))* Oxford Univ. Pr., Inc.

Waller, Philip. Writers, Readers, & Reputations: Literary Life in Britain 1870-1918. 2008. (ENG., Illus.). 1200p. pap. 74.00 *(978-0-19-954120-1(5))* Oxford Univ. Pr., Inc.

Walsby, Malcolm. The Printed Book in Brittany, 1486-1600. 2011. (Illus.). XIV, 392p. ***(978-90-04-20451-5(2))*** BRILL.

Wang, Yugen. Ten Thousand Scrolls: Reading & Writing in the Poetics of Huang Tingjian & the Late Northern Song. 2011. (Harvard-Yenching Institute Monograph Ser.: 76). (ENG.). 300p. 39.95 *(978-0-674-06255-9(8))* Harvard Univ., Asia Ctr.

Windscheffel, Ruth Clayton & Windscheffel, Ruth Clayto. Reading Gladstone. 2008. (ENG., Illus.). 256p. 84.00 *(978-0-230-00765-9(1))* Palgrave Macmillan.

Winsbury, Rex. The Roman Book. 2009. (Illus.). 240p. pap. 34.95 *(978-0-7156-3829-3(7))* Duckworth Publishers GBR. Dist: International Publishers Marketing.

Winter, Sarah. The Pleasures of Memory: Learning to Read with Charles Dickens. 2nd ed. 2011. (ENG., Illus.). 448p. 65.00 *(978-0-8232-3352-6(9))* Fordham Univ. Pr.

B

Wright, T. G. Literary Culture in Early New England, 1620-1730. (Illus.). reprint ed. lib. bdg. 98.00 *(978-0-7222-0665-2(8))* Library Reprints, Inc.

Yeo, Matthew. The Acquisition of Books by Chetham's Library, 1655-1700. 2011. (Illus.). XX, 264p. ***(978-90-04-20665-6(5))*** BRILL.

BOOKS AND READING FOR CHILDREN

see Children—Books and Reading

BOOKS AND READING FOR YOUTH

see Youth—Books and Reading

BOOKS FOR CHILDREN

see Children—Books and Reading; Children's Literature

BOOKS FOR THE BLIND

see Blind—Books and Reading

BOOKS IN MACHINE-READABLE FORM

see Electronic Books

BOOKS ISSUED IN SERIES

see Series (Publications)

BOOKS OF HOURS

Annual Guide for Liturgy of the Hours. 1.75 *(978-0-89942-443-9(0))* Catholic Bk. Publishing Corp.

Bagnoli, Martina. Prayers in Code: Books of Hours from Renaissance France. 2009. pap. *(978-0-911886-72-6(9))* Walters Art Museum, US.

Duffy, Eamon. Marking the Hours: English People & Their Prayers, 1240-1570. 2011. (ENG., Illus.). 208p. pap. 25.00 *(978-0-300-17058-0(0))* Yale Univ. Pr.

Husband, Timothy. The Art of Illumination: The Limbourg Brothers & the Belles Heures of Jean de France, Duc de Berry. 2008. 65.00 *(978-1-58839-294-7(5))* Metropolitan Museum of Art, The.

Longon, Jean, et al. The Très Riches Heures of Jean, Duke of Berry. 2008. (Illus.). 224p. 125.00 *(978-0-8076-1596-6(X))* Braziller, George Inc.

Reinburg, Virginia. French Books of Hours: Making an Archive of Prayer, C. 1400-1600. 2012. (ENG., Illus.). 312p. 99.00 ***(978-1-107-00721-5(6))*** Cambridge Univ. Pr.

Stirnemann, Patr & Gousset, Marie. Hours of Etienne Chebalier by Jean Fouquet. 2006. 88p. pap. *(978-2-85056-633-2(0))* Somogy Editions d'Art.

Wieck, Roger. Picturing Piety: The Book of Hours. 2007. (Enluminures, Paris & Chicago Ser.). (FRE & ENG., Illus.). 276p. pap. 25.00 *(978-1-903470-65-7(X))* Holberton, Paul Publishing GBR. Dist: Casemate Pubs. & Bk. Distributors, LLC.

BOOKS OF KNOWLEDGE

see Encyclopedias and Dictionaries

BOOKSELLERS AND BOOKSELLING

see also Antiquarian Booksellers; Book Clubs (Bookselling); Books—Prices; Booksellers' Catalogs; Bookstores; Copyright; Publishers and Publishing

Ashuntantang, Joyce B. Landscaping Postcoloniality: The Dissemination of Cameroon Anglophone Literature. 2009. 188p. pap. *(978-9956-558-29-2(X))* Langaa Research & Publishing Common Initiative Group CMR. Dist: Michigan State Univ. Pr.

Barbierato, Federico. The Inquisitor in the Hat Shop: Inquisition, Forbidden Books & Unbelief in Early Modern Venice. 2012. 430p. 124.95 ***(978-1-4094-3547-1(4))*** Ashgate Publishing Co.

Beach, Sylvia. The Letters of Sylvia Beach. Walsh, Keri, ed. 2011. (ENG., Illus.). 376p. (gr. 17). pap. 19.95 ***(978-0-231-14537-4(3))*** Columbia Univ. Pr.

Burton, John Hill. The Book-Hunter. 2008. 400p. 29.99 *(978-0-554-39245-5(3))*; 31.99 *(978-0-554-29942-6(9))* BiblioBazaar.

—The Book-Hunter. 2009. 294p. pap. *(978-1-4588-6390-4(5))* Books LLC.

—The Book-Hunter. 2006. (ENG.). 428p. per. 26.99 *(978-1-4255-4653-3(6))* MPublishing.

Carter, David. Big Money in Books. 2007. 244p. pap. 25.50 *(978-1-84799-990-0(5))* Lulu Enterprises Inc.

Cornier, Nadia & Barnholdt, Laure. Writing & Selling the Young Adult Novel. 2006. (Illus.). 240p. pap. 14.99 *(978-1-58297-426-2(8)*, Writer's Digest Bks.) F&W Media, Inc.

Ditzler, Pat & Dumas, JoAnn. A Book Sale How-to Guide: More Money, Less Stress. 2010. pap. *(978-0-8389-1074-0(2))* American Library Assn.

Duffus, R. L. Books: Their Place in Democracy. 2007. (ENG.). 238p. 41.95 *(978-0-548-05867-1(9))* Kessinger Publishing, LLC.

Escalante Gonzalbo, Fernando. A la Sombra de Los Libros: Lectura, Mercado y Vida Pública. 2007. (Jornadas Ser.). (SPA.). 361p. pap. 32.99 *(978-968-12-1323-7(8))* El Colegio de México, A.C., Biblioteca Miguel Cosio Villegas MEX. Dist: Fondo de Cultura Economica USA.

Galsworthy, John. Saint's Progress. 2008. 308p. 28.99 *(978-0-554-38343-9(8))* 2008. 308p. 29.99 *(978-0-554-29040-9(5))* 2007. (ENG.). 278p. per. 21.99 *(978-1-4346-6796-0(0))* BiblioBazaar.

—Saint's Progress. 2007. (ENG.). 284p. per. *(978-1-4065-1737-8(2))* Dodo Pr.

—Saint's Progress. 2008. 474p. 52.95 *(978-1-4365-4359-0(2))* 2007. (ENG.). 476p. per. 37.95 *(978-0-548-72930-4(1))* Kessinger Publishing, LLC.

—Saint's Progress. 2007. (ENG.). 412p. 39.95 *(978-1-4344-8525-0(0))*; per. 22.95 *(978-1-4344-8524-3(2))* Wildside Pr., LLC.

—Saint's Progress. 2010. 478p. pap. 37.75 *(978-1-177-19035-0(4))*; 422p. pap. 34.75 *(978-1-148-18809-6(6))*; 420p. pap. 34.75 *(978-1-143-78672-3(6))*; 424p. pap. 34.75 *(978-1-142-39482-0(4))*; 416p. pap. 34.75 *(978-1-141-99914-9(5))* BiblioBazaar.

—Saint's Progress. 2010. (Illus.). 168p. pap. 25.41 *(978-1-4432-1224-3(5))* 2009. 186p. pap. 25.41 *(978-1-150-15948-0(0))* General Bks. LLC.

—Saint's Progress. 2010. 476p. 42.36 ***(978-1-164-43318-7(0))***; pap. 30.36 ***(978-1-164-04649-3(7))*** Kessinger Publishing, LLC.

Galsworthy, John. Saint's Progress. l.t. ed. 2007. (ENG.). 304p. per. 24.99 *(978-1-4346-6797-7(9))* BiblioBazaar.

—Saint's Progress. reprint ed. lib. bdg. 98.00 *(978-0-7426-2773-4(X))* Classic Bks.

Hill, Heywood & Smith, John Saumarez. A Spy in the Bookshop: Letters Between Heywood Hill & John Saumarez Smith, 1966-74. 2006. (ENG., Illus.). 160p. 21.95 *(978-0-7112-2698-2(9))* Lincoln, Frances Ltd. GBR. Dist: Perseus-PGW.

Hoenig, Carol. The Author's Guide to Planning Book Events: Tips & Tools for Bookselling Success. 2007. 152p. per. 13.95 *(978-1-58348-476-0(0))* iUniverse, Inc.

Horner, Craig & Harrold, Edmund. The Diary of Edmund Harrold, Wigmaker of Manchester 1712-15. 2008. (Illus.). 216p. 124.95 *(978-0-7546-6172-6(5))* Ashgate Publishing Co.

Ilsoe, Harald. Biblioteker til Salg: Om danske bogauktioner og Kataloger 1661-1811. 280p. 54.00 *(978-87-635-0447-8(2))* Museum Tusculanum Pr. DNK. Dist: Chicago Distribution Ctr.

Jager, Georg, ed. Geschichte des Deutschen Buchhandels im 19 und 20 Jh, Vol. 3. 2010.Tr. of History of the German Book Trade in the 19th & 20th Century. (GER.). 579p. *(978-3-598-24804-7(0))* Saur, K. G. Verlag GmbH & Co.

Jerrold, Walter. The Autolycus of the Bookstalls. 2009. 206p. 28.99 *(978-1-110-64374-5(8))* 2009. 206p. pap. 23.75 *(978-1-110-64373-8(X))* 2008. 208p. 24.99 *(978-0-554-42370-8(7))* 2008. 208p. 27.99 *(978-0-554-42358-6(8))* 2008. 208p. pap. 23.75 *(978-0-554-42367-8(7))* 2008. 208p. pap. 24.75 *(978-0-554-42362-3(6))* BiblioBazaar.

—The Autolycus of the Bookstalls. 2008. 204p. 39.95 *(978-1-4372-0589-3(5))*; pap. 24.95 *(978-1-4370-7615-8(7))* Kessinger Publishing, LLC.

Jud, Brian. How to Make Real Money Selling Books: A Complete Guide to the Book Publishers' World of Special Sales. 2008. (ENG.). 248p. pap. 24.95 *(978-0-7570-0213-7(7))* Square One Pubs.

Knight, Charles. Shadows of the Old Booksellers. 2009. 210p. pap. *(978-0-217-25349-9(0))* Books LLC.

—Shadows of the Old Booksellers. 2009. 168p. pap. 19.99 *(978-0-217-98985-5(3))* General Bks. LLC.

Kogos, Emily. Access to & Use of Information by Booktrade Entrepreneurs. 2010. 264p. pap. *(978-3-639-25120-3(2))* VDM Verlag Dr. Mueller e.K.

Labriola, John. Christ-Centered Selling: A Scripturally Based Guide to Principled, Profitable Persuasion. 2007. 203p. per. 13.99 *(978-1-59886-744-2(X))* Tate Publishing & Enterprises, LLC.

Laties, Andrew. Rebel Bookseller: Why Indie Bookstores Represent Everything You Want to Fight for from Free Speech to Buying Local to Building Communities. 2nd ed. 2011. (ENG., Illus.). 336p. pap. 16.95 *(978-1-60980-139-7(3))* Seven Stories Pr.

Markham, Sheila. A Book of Booksellers: Conversations with the Antiquarian Book Trade, 1991-2003. 2007. pap. 29.95 *(978-1-58456-207-8(2))* Oak Knoll Pr.

Martin, Gail. Launching Your Books Without Losing Your Mind. 2010. 124p. pap. 13.99 *(978-1-935361-06-0(6))* Comfort Publishing Services, LLC.

Miller, Laura J. Reluctant Capitalists: Bookselling & the Culture of Consumption. 2007. 328p. per. 22.50 *(978-0-226-52591-4(0))* Univ. of Chicago Pr.

Myers, Robin, et al, eds. Fairs, markets & the itinerant book Trade. 2007. (Publishing Pathways Ser.). (Illus.). 240p. 47.50 *(978-1-58456-200-9(5))* Oak Knoll Pr.

Plomer, Henry Robert, et al. A Dictionary of the Printers & Booksellers Who Were at Work in England, Scotland & Ireland from 1726 To 1775. 2008. 75.00 *(978-1-57898-696-5(6))* Martino Publishing.

Ramone, Jenni & Cousins, Helen. The Richard & Judy Book Club Reader: Popular Texts & the Practices of Reading. 2011. 224p. 99.95 ***(978-1-4094-0133-9(2))*** Ashgate Publishing Co.

Reader, Lesley & Gilmour, Lesley. Book Lovers' London. 4th rev. ed. 2010. (ENG., Illus.). 384p. pap. 13.95 *(978-1-902910-34-5(6))* Metro Pubns. GBR. Dist: Independent Pubs. Group.

Roberts, William. The Earlier History of English Bookselling. 2008. 357p. 31.99 *(978-0-559-03817-4(8))*; 29.99 *(978-0-559-03828-0(3))*; pap. 32.75 *(978-0-559-03822-8(4))*; pap. 31.75 *(978-0-559-03825-9(9))* BiblioBazaar.

—The Earlier History of English Bookselling. 2009. 192p. pap. 19.99 *(978-1-150-62206-9(7))* General Bks. LLC.

—The Earlier History of English Bookselling. 2007. (ENG.). 356p. 46.95 *(978-0-548-36362-1(5))*; per. 31.95 *(978-0-548-30653-6(2))* Kessinger Publishing, LLC.

Seck, Bryan J. The Mark: A Real Sales Guy Approach to Selling Corporate Accounts. 2011. 116p. 24.99 ***(978-1-4634-0427-7(1))***; pap. 19.99 ***(978-1-4634-0428-4(X))*** AuthorHouse.

Silver, Joel. Dr. Rosenbach & Mr. Lilly: Book Collecting in a Golden Age. 2011. ***(978-1-58456-295-5(1))*** Oak Knoll Pr.

Striphas, Ted. The Late Age of Print: Everday Book Culture from Consumerism to Control. 2011. (ENG.). 272p. (gr. 17). pap. 18.50 *(978-0-231-14815-3(1))* Columbia Univ. Pr.

—The Late Age of Print: Everyday Book Culture from Consumerism to Control. 2009. (ENG., Illus.). 272p. (gr. 17). 27.50 *(978-0-231-14814-6(3))* Columbia Univ. Pr.

Thompson, John B. Merchants of Culture: The Publishing Business in the Twenty-First Century. 2012. (ENG.). 464p. (gr. 12). 17.00 ***(978-0-452-29772-2(9)***, Plume) Penguin Group (USA) Inc.

Tinsley, William. Random Recollections of an Old Publisher. 2010. (Cambridge Library Collection - Printing & Publishing History Ser.). (ENG.). 364p. pap. 29.99 *(978-1-108-00926-3(3))*; (Illus.). 392p. pap. 31.99 *(978-1-108-00924-9(7))* Cambridge Univ. Pr.

Wadsworth, Sarah. In the Company of Books: Literature & Its Classes in Nineteenth-Century America. 2006. (Studies in Print Culture & the History of the Book). (Illus.). 278p. 80.00 *(978-1-55849-540-1(1))*; per. 24.95 *(978-1-55849-541-8(X))* Univ. of Massachusetts Pr.

BOOKSELLERS AND BOOKSELLING—BIBLIOGRAPHY

Caso, Adolph & Faulkner, William. Centennial Special, 1909 to 2009, Branden Books: Featuring William Faulkner's 1924 First Book, The Marble Faun. 2009. pap. *(978-0-8283-2192-1(2))* Branden Bks.

Morison, Stanley. John Bell, 1745-1831: A Memoir. 2009. (ENG.). 236p. pap. 36.99 *(978-0-521-14314-1(4))* Cambridge Univ. Pr.

BOOKSELLERS AND BOOKSELLING—BIOGRAPHY

Baines, Paul & Rogers, Pat. Edmund Curll, Bookseller. 2007. (ENG., Illus.). 400p. 65.00 *(978-0-19-927898-5(9))* Oxford Univ. Pr., Inc.

Brandt, Richard L. One Click: Jeff Bezos & the Rise of Amazon.Com. 2011. (ENG.). 224p. (gr. 12). 25.95 *(978-1-59184-375-7(8)*, Portfolio (Hardcover)) Penguin Group (USA) Inc.

Buzbee, Lewis. Yellow-Lighted Bookshop: A Memoir, a History. 2008. (ENG.). 224p. pap. 14.00 *(978-1-55597-510-4(0))* Graywolf Pr.

Marston, Edward. After Work: Fragments from the Workshop of an Old Publisher. 2010. 412p. pap. 34.75 *(978-1-142-74803-6(0))*; 416p. pap. 34.75 *(978-1-143-03142-7(3))* BiblioBazaar.

—After Work: Fragments from the Workshop of an Old Publisher. 2009. 210p. pap. *(978-1-4590-2912-5(7))* Books LLC.

—After Work: Fragments from the Workshop of an Old Publisher. 2010. 414p. 39.96 ***(978-1-164-79445-5(0))*** 2010. 414p. pap. 27.96 ***(978-1-164-56119-4(7))*** 2008. 416p. 49.95 *(978-1-4369-9558-0(2))* 2008. 416p. pap. 34.95 *(978-1-4367-6231-1(6))* Kessinger Publishing, LLC.

McMurtry, Larry. Books: A Memoir. 2009. (ENG.). 272p. pap. 14.00 *(978-1-4165-8335-6(1))* Simon & Schuster.

Mercer, Jeremy. Time Was Soft There: A Paris Sojourn at Shakespeare & Co. 2006. (ENG.). 272p. pap. 15.00 *(978-0-312-34740-6(5))* Picador.

Morison, Stanley. Ichabod Dawks & his Newsletter: With an Account of the Dawks Family. 2009. (ENG.). 60p. pap. 27.99 *(978-0-521-16301-9(3))* Cambridge Univ. Pr.

Oliphant, Dave. Harbingers of Books to Come: A Texan's Literary Life. 2009. (ENG.). 548p. 24.95 *(978-0-916727-60-4(2))* Wings Pr.

West, William. Fifty Years' Recollections of an Old Bookseller. 2009. 164p. pap. 19.99 *(978-0-217-93705-4(5))* General Bks. LLC.

BOOKSELLERS AND BOOKSELLING—COLPORTAGE, SUBSCRIPTION TRADE, ETC.

see also Bible—Publication and Distribution

Hoeflich, Michael H. & Jamail Center for Legal Research Staff, contrib. by. Subscription Publishing & the Sale of Law Books in Antebellum America. 2007. (Illus.). 23p. pap. *(978-0-935630-71-8(6))* Univ. of Texas, Tarlton Law Library.

Reid, Hugh. The Nature & Uses of Eighteenth-Century Book Subscription Lists. 2010. iv, 67p. *(978-0-7734-3757-9(6))* Mellen, Edwin Pr., The.

Spicer, William Ambrose. Our Day: In the Light of Prophecy. 2008. 396p. pap. 14.95 *(978-1-59594-814-4(7)*, Wingspan Pr.) WingSpan Publishing.

BOOKSELLERS AND BOOKSELLING—DIRECTORIES

Bowker Staff, ed. Publishers, Distributors & Wholesalers of the United States, 2010, 2 vols. 2009. 500.00 *(978-0-8352-5022-1(9))* Bowker LLC, R. R.

International ISBN Agency, ed. Publishers International ISBN Directory 2010. 37th ed. 2010. *(978-3-11-023076-5(3))* Saur, K. G. Verlag GmbH & Co.

—Publishers International ISBN Directory 2011. 37th ed. 2010. (Illus.). *(978-3-11-023074-1(7))* Saur, K. G. Verlag GmbH & Co.

International ISBN Agency, ed. Publishers' International ISBN Directory 2011. 37th ed. 2010. (ENG.). LXXX, 7122p. ***(978-3-11-916311-8(2))*** Saur, K. G. Verlag GmbH & Co.

International ISBN Agency Staff, ed. Publishers' International ISBN Directory: EBookPlus. 36th ed. 2009. (Illus.). LX, 6258p. *(978-3-598-21595-7(9))* Saur, K. G. Verlag GmbH & Co.

BOOKSELLERS AND BOOKSELLING—HISTORY

Baines, Paul & Rogers, Pat. Edmund Curll, Bookseller. 2007. (ENG., Illus.). 400p. 65.00 *(978-0-19-927898-5(9))* Oxford Univ. Pr., Inc.

Bradley, Sue, ed. The British Book Trade: An Oral History. 2009. (ENG.). 304p. 49.00 *(978-0-7123-4957-4(X))* British Library, The GBR. Dist: Chicago Distribution Ctr.

Broomans, Petra & Ronne, Marta, eds. In the Vanguard of Cultural Transfer: Cultural Transmitters & Authors in Peripheral Literary Fields. 2010. (Studies on Cultural Transfer & Transmission Ser.). (ENG.). 183p. (C). pap. 28.00 ***(978-90-77922-81-1(4))*** Barkhuis Publishing NLD. Dist: Brown, David Bk. Co., The.

Cortenraad, Hans Willem, ed. Centraal Boekhuis: Logistiek van boeken in veranderend Perspectief. 2009. (Tiele-Lezing Ser.). (DUT.). 32p. pap. *(978-90-8964-096-3(7))* Amsterdam Univ. Pr.

Cruz, Laura. The Paradox of Prosperity: The Leiden Booksellers' Guild & the Distribution of Books in Early Modern Europe. 2009. 256p. 55.00 *(978-1-58456-235-1(8))* Oak Knoll Pr.

Curwen, Henry. A History of Booksellers: The Old & the New. 2010. (Cambridge Library Collection - Printing & Publishing History Ser.). (Illus.). 526p. pap. 37.99 *(978-1-108-02143-2(3))* Cambridge Univ. Pr.

Dean, Irvine & Irvine, Dean. Editing Modernity: Women & Little Magazine Cultures in Canada, 1916-1956. 2008. (Studies in Book & Print Culture Ser.). (ENG.). 304p. *(978-0-8020-9271-7(3))* Univ. of Toronto Pr.

Feather, John. The Provincial Book Trade in Eighteenth-Century England. 2008. (Cambridge Studies in Publishing & Printing History Ser.). (ENG.). 196p. (C). pap. 42.00 *(978-0-521-05552-9(0))* Cambridge Univ. Pr.

Fyfe, Aileen. Steam-Powered Knowledge: William Chambers & the Business of Publishing, 1820-1860. 2012. (ENG., Illus.). 336p. 50.00 ***(978-0-226-27651-9(1))*** Univ. of Chicago Pr.

Gillies, Mary Ann. The Professional Literary Agent in Britain, 1880-1920: Women & Little Magazine Cultures in Canada, 1916-1956. 2007. (Studies in Book & Print Culture Ser.). (ENG.). 304p. *(978-0-8020-9147-5(4))* Univ. of Toronto Pr.

Hruschka, John. How Books Came to America: The Rise of the American Book Trade. 2012. (Penn State Studies in the History of the Book Ser.). (ENG.). 256p. 74.95 ***(978-0-271-05081-2(0))*** Pennsylvania State Univ. Pr.

Jäger, Georg, et al. Geschichte des Deutschen Buchhandels im 19. und 20. Jahrhundert. 2007. (GER., Illus.). 530p. *(978-3-598-24808-5(3))* Saur, K. G. Verlag GmbH & Co.

Kovac, Miha. Here Comes the Book: Never Mind the Web. 2008. 204p. pap. *(978-1-84334-405-6(X)*, Chandos Publishing) Woodhead Publishing Ltd.

—Never Mind the Web: Here Comes the Book. 2008. 204p. *(978-1-84334-406-3(8)*, Chandos Publishing) Woodhead Publishing Ltd.

McCleery, Alistair, et al, eds. Honest Trade: Booksellers & Bookselling in Scotland. 2009. (ENG., Illus.). 192p. pap. 23.00 *(978-0-85976-673-9(X)*, Tuckwell Pr.) Birlinn, Ltd. GBR. Dist: Independent Pubs. Group.

Myers, Robin, et al, eds. Books for Sale: The Advertising & Promotion of Print since the Fifteenth Century. 2009. (Illus.). xvi, 191p. 49.95 *(978-1-58456-265-8(X))* Oak Knoll Pr.

Myers, Robin & Harris, Michael, eds. Genius for Letters. (Illus.). 176p. *(978-1-873040-24-9(5))* Bow Historical Bks.

Onosaka, Junko R. Feminist Revolution in Literacy. 2010. 224p. pap. 39.95 *(978-0-415-88260-6(5))* Routledge.

Ten Harmsel, Larry & Van Til, Reinder. An Eerdmans Century: 1911-2011. 2011. 192p. 20.00 ***(978-0-8028-6658-5(1))*** Eerdmans, William B. Publishing Co.

Vogeley, Nancy J. The Bookrunner: A History of Inter-American Relations: Print, Politics, & Commerce in the United States & Mexico, 1800-1830. 2011. ***(978-1-60618-011-2(8))*** American Philosophical Society.

Yeo, Matthew. The Acquisition of Books by Chetham's Library, 1655-1700. 2011. (Illus.). XX, 264p. ***(978-90-04-20665-6(5))*** BRILL.

BOOKSELLERS AND BOOKSELLING—SUBSCRIPTION TRADE

see Booksellers and Bookselling—Colportage, Subscription Trade, etc.

BOOKSELLERS' CATALOGS

Henry Holt and Company Staff. Catalog Fall 2003. *(978-0-8050-7474-1(0))* Holt, Henry & Co.

Ong, George. From Almeloveen to Whittington: Book & Manuscript Catalogues, 1545-1995 from the Collection of George Ong. 2007. (ENG., Illus.). 72p. pap. 20.00 *(978-0-910672-70-2(9))* Grolier Club of New York, The.

Quaritch, Bernard, compiled by. 10,000 Rare Books Published Before 1860 - a Catalog. 2008. 568p. pap. 32.95 *(978-1-934939-26-0(9))* Wexford College Pr.

UK Catalogue, Vol. 2. 2007. *(978-1-4278-0487-7(7))* TOKYOPOP, Inc.

UK Sneaks, Vol. 2. 2007. *(978-1-4278-0507-2(5))* TOKYOPOP, Inc.

U.S. Seasonal Catalogue, Vol. 3. 2007. *(978-1-4278-0488-4(5))* TOKYOPOP, Inc.

BOOKSELLERS' CATALOGS—GREAT BRITAIN

Binski, Paul & Zutshi, Patrick. Western Illuminated Manuscripts: A Catalogue of the Collection in Cambridge University Library. 2011. (Illus.). 532p. 275.00 *(978-0-521-84892-3(X))* Cambridge Univ. Pr.

Edwards, Edward. Lives of the Founders of the British Museum: With Notices of its Chief Augmentors & Other Benefactors, 1570-1870. 2010. (Cambridge Library Collection - Printing & Publishing History Ser.). (ENG., Illus.). 396p. pap. 31.99 *(978-1-108-01496-0(8))*; 436p. pap. 32.99 *(978-1-108-01495-3(X))* Cambridge Univ. Pr.

Elton, Oliver. Frederick York Powell V1 Memoir & Lett. 2006. pap. 38.95 *(978-1-4286-3629-3(3))* Kessinger Publishing, LLC.

—Frederick York Powell V2 Occasional Writ. 2006. pap. 38.95 *(978-1-4286-3628-6(5))* Kessinger Publishing, LLC.

Jeans, E. Catalogue of Books in All Branches of Li. 2006. pap. 26.99 *(978-1-4255-4062-3(7))* MPublishing.

Nineteenth Century Short Title Catalogue, Series 2. 800p. pap. *(978-0-907977-76-6(6))* Bow Historical Bks.

Wheatley, Henry Benjamin. How to Make an Index. 2010. (Cambridge Library Collection - Printing & Publishing History Ser.). 252p. pap. 17.99 *(978-1-108-02150-0(6))* Cambridge Univ. Pr.

Wing, Donald, compiled by. Short-Title Catalogue of Books Printed in England, Scotland, Ireland, 1641-1700, 3 vols. 2007. 1600p. reprint ed. 225.00 *(978-1-57898-170-0(0))* Martino Publishing.

BOOKSHOPS

see Bookstores

BOOKSTORES

see also Antiquarian Booksellers

Bruno, Guido. Adventures in American Bookshops, Antique Stores & Auction Rooms. 2009. 130p. 24.99 *(978-1-116-77686-7(3))* 2009. 130p. 28.99 *(978-1-116-77685-0(5))* 2009. 130p. pap. 19.75 *(978-1-116-77688-1(X))* 2009. 130p. pap. 20.75 *(978-1-116-77687-4(1))* 2008. 132p. 21.99 *(978-0-559-42179-2(6))* 2008. 132p. pap. 19.75 *(978-0-559-42178-5(8))* BiblioBazaar.

—Adventures in American Bookshops, Antique Stores & Auction Rooms. 2009. 92p. pap. (978-0-217-67621-2(9)) Books LLC.
—Adventures in American Bookshops, Antique Stores & Auction Rooms. 2008. 132p. 35.95 (978-1-4368-9403-6(4)); pap. 20.95 (978-1-4367-6143-7(3)) Kessinger Publishing, LLC.
How to Open & Operate a Financially Successful Bookstore on Amazon & Other Web Sites: With Companion CD-ROM. 2012. (ENG.). 288p. pap. 39.95 (978-1-60138-333-4(9)) Atlantic Publishing Co.
Joseph, Marc. New & Used, 1 vol. 2009. (ENG., Illus.). 150p. 45.00 (978-3-86521-273-3(5)) Steidl, Gerhard Druckerei und Verlag DEU. Dist: Innovative Logistics.
Laties, Andrew. Rebel Bookseller: Why Indie Bookstores Represent Everything You Want to Fight for from Free Speech to Buying Local to Building Communities. 2nd ed. 2011. (ENG., Illus.). 336p. pap. 16.95 (978-1-60980-139-7(3)) Seven Stories Pr.
Reader, Lesley & Gilmour, Lesley. Book Lovers' London. 4th rev. ed. 2010. (ENG., Illus.). 384p. pap. 13.95 (978-1-902910-34-5(6)) Metro Pubns. GBR. Dist: Independent Pubs. Group.
Smith, Gibbs & Smith, Gibbs M. The Art of the Bookstore: The Bookstore Paintings of Gibbs M. Smith. 2009. (ENG., Illus.). 96p. 35.00 (978-1-4236-0643-7(4)) Gibbs Smith, Publisher.

BOOKSTORES—HISTORY

Mercer, Jeremy. Time Was Soft There: A Paris Sojourn at Shakespeare & Co. 2006. (ENG.). 272p. pap. 15.00 (978-0-312-34740-6(5)) Picador.

BOOKSTORES—MANAGEMENT

Miller, Laura J. Reluctant Capitalists: Bookselling & the Culture of Consumption. 2007. 328p. per. 22.50 (978-0-226-52591-4(0)) Univ. of Chicago Pr.

BOOKWORKS (ART)

see Artists' Books

BOOLEAN ALGEBRA

see Algebra, Boolean

BOOMERANGS

Lorenz, Ralph D. Spinning Flight: Dynamics of Frisbees, Boomerangs, Samaras, & Skipping Stones. (ENG., Illus.). xxi, 346p. 2010. pap. 69.95 (978-1-4419-2153-6(2), 1441921532) 2006. 69.95 (978-0-387-30779-4(6), 0387307796) Springer.

BOONE, DANIEL, 1734-1820

Abbott, John S. C. Daniel Boone: Pioneer of Kentucky. (American Pioneers & Patriots Ser.). 331p. reprint ed. 98.00 (978-0-7222-8368-4(7)) Library Reprints, Inc.
—Daniel Boone: The Pioneer of Kentucky. 2008. (Illus.). 216p. pap. (978-1-4099-0793-0(7)) Dodo Pr.
—Daniel Boone: The Pioneer of Kentucky. 331p. reprint ed. 98.00 (978-0-7222-8463-6(2)) Library Reprints, Inc.
—Daniel Boone the Pioneer of Kentucky. 2007. (ENG.). 346p. 46.95 (978-0-548-03538-2(5)) Kessinger Publishing, LLC.
Bogart, William Henry. Daniel Boone & the Hunters of Kentucky. 2007. (ENG.). 472p. 52.95 (978-0-548-13308-8(5)) 2006. pap. 37.95 (978-1-4286-4399-4(0)) Kessinger Publishing, LLC.
Boone, Daniel & Hawkes, Francis Lister. Daniel Boone's Own Story & the Adventures of Daniel Boone. 2010. (ENG.). 128p. pap. 5.95 (978-0-486-47690-2(1)) Dover Pubns., Inc.
Brown, Meredith Mason. Frontiersman: Daniel Boone & the Making of America. 2009. (Illus.). 416p. 34.95 (978-0-8071-3356-9(6)) Louisiana State Univ. Pr.
Bruce, H. Addington. Daniel Boone & the Wilderness Road. 2007. 388p. 48.95 (978-0-548-11113-0(8)) Kessinger Publishing, LLC.
—Daniel Boone & the Wilderness Road. 349p. reprint ed. lib. bdg. 98.00 (978-0-7222-4855-3(5)) Library Reprints, Inc.
Ellis, Nancy. Life & Times of Col. Daniel Boone. 2011. 196p. pap. 16.95 (978-1-4520-3849-0(X)) AuthorHouse.
Flint, Timothy. First White Man of the West or the Life. 2006. pap. 27.95 (978-1-4286-4466-3(0)) Kessinger Publishing, LLC.
—The First White Man of the West; or, the Life & Exploits of Col Dan'L Boone, the First Settler of Kentucky; Interspersed with Incidents in the Earl. 2006. 256p. per. 23.99 (978-1-4255-2191-2(6)) MPublishing.
—The Life & Adventures of Daniel Boone, the First Settler of Kentucky, Interspersed with Incidents in the Early Annals of the Country. 2006. 260p. per. 23.99 (978-1-4255-2302-2(1)) MPublishing.
Hammon, Neal O., ed. My Father, Daniel Boone: The Draper Interviews with Nathan Boone. 2012. (ENG., Illus.). 200p. pap. 17.95 (978-0-8131-3465-9(X)) Univ. Pr. of Kentucky.
Harley, Cecil B. Life & Times of Col. Daniel Boone. 2006. (ENG.). 212p. pap. 20.99 (978-1-4264-7484-2(9)); 234p. pap. 22.99 (978-1-4264-7561-0(6)) BiblioBazaar.
Hartley, Cecil B. Life of Daniel Boone the Great Western H. 2006. pap. 26.99 (978-1-4255-3761-6(8)) MPublishing.
—The Life of Daniel Boone the Great Western Hunter & Pioneer. 2007. (ENG.). 360p. 46.95 (978-0-548-02771-4(4)) Kessinger Publishing, LLC.
Hartley, Cecil B. & Boone, Daniel. Life & Times of Colonel Daniel Boone. 2007. (Illus.). 216p. per. (978-1-4065-3257-9(6)) Dodo Pr.
Hill, George Canning. Life & Adventures of Daniel Boone, the Pioneer of Kentucky: A Biography. 2011. 262p. 47.95 **(978-1-258-00608-2(1))** Literary Licensing, LLC.
Lofaro, Michael A. Daniel Boone: An American Life. 2012. (ENG., Illus.). 248p. pap. 19.95 (978-0-8131-3462-8(5)) Univ. Pr. of Kentucky.
Morgan, Robert. Boone: A Biography. (ENG., Illus.). 538p. 2008. pap. 18.95 (978-1-56512-615-2(7), 1565126157) 2007. 29.95 (978-1-56512-455-4(3), 1565124553, Shannon Ravenel Bks.) Algonquin Bks. of Chapel Hill.
Reid, Darren R., ed. Daniel Boone & Others on the Kentucky Frontier: Autobiographies & Narratives, 1769-1795. 2009. (ENG., Illus.). 228p. pap. 45.00 (978-0-7864-4377-2(4)) McFarland & Co., Inc. Pubs.
Skinner, Constance Lindsay. Pioneers of the Old Southwest: A Chronicle of the Dark & Bloody Ground. 2010. 324p. pap. 30.75 (978-1-145-52603-7(9)) 2010. 332p. pap. 31.75 (978-1-142-37151-7(4)) 2010. 330p. pap. 31.75 (978-1-142-19781-0(6)) 2009. 332p. 25.99 (978-1-103-63541-2(7)) 2009. 332p. pap. 19.99 (978-1-103-63539-9(5)) BiblioBazaar.
—Pioneers of the Old Southwest: A Chronicle of the Dark & Bloody Ground. 2008. 156p. pap. (978-1-4099-4579-6(0)) Dodo Pr.
—Pioneers of the Old Southwest: A Chronicle of the Dark & Bloody Ground. 304p. reprint ed. 98.00 (978-0-7222-7133-9(6)) Library Reprints, Inc.
Thwaites, Reuben Gold. Daniel Boone. 2009. 296p. 34.99 (978-1-115-89769-3(1)); 30.99 (978-1-115-89770-9(5)); pap. 28.75 (978-1-115-89771-6(3)); pap. 27.75 (978-1-115-89772-3(1)) BiblioBazaar.
—Daniel Boone. 2007. (ENG.). 316p. 45.95 (978-0-548-11347-9(5)) Kessinger Publishing, LLC.
Wallace, Paul A. W. Daniel Boone in Pennsylvania. 2007. (Illus.). 20p. pap. (978-1-4223-1497-5(9)) DIANE Publishing Co.
White, Stewart Edward. Daniel Boone: Wilderness Scout. 15.95 (978-0-8486-1509-7(2)) Amereon LTD.
—Daniel Boone: Wilderness Scout. 2009. 320p. 25.99 (978-1-103-27059-0(1)); pap. 19.99 (978-1-103-27057-6(5)) BiblioBazaar.

BOONE, REBECCA BRYAN, FL. 1775

Fuller, T. A. The Spear & the Spindle: Ancestors of Sir Francis Bryan 1550. 2008. 146p. (Orig.). pap. 25.50 (978-1-55613-842-3(3)) Heritage Bks.

BOONE FAMILY

Fuller, T. A. The Spear & the Spindle: Ancestors of Sir Francis Bryan 1550. 2008. 146p. (Orig.). pap. 25.50 (978-1-55613-842-3(3)) Heritage Bks.

BOOT AND SHOE WORKERS

see Shoemakers

BOOTH, EDWIN, 1833-1893

Booth, Edwin. The Miscellaneous Plays of Edwin Booth V3. Winter, William, ed. 2007. (ENG.). 328p. 45.95 (978-0-548-18947-4(1)); pap. 30.95 (978-1-4304-9380-8(1)) Kessinger Publishing, LLC.
Copeland, Charles Townsend. Edwin Booth. 2008. 183p. 22.99 (978-0-559-01951-7(3)); 25.99 (978-0-559-01942-5(4)); pap. 21.75 (978-0-559-01949-4(1)); pap. 22.75 (978-0-559-01946-3(7)) BiblioBazaar.
—Edwin Booth. 2007. (ENG.). 188p. 37.95 (978-0-548-10753-9(X)) Kessinger Publishing, LLC.
—Edwin Booth. (Beacon Biographies Ser.). 159p. reprint ed. 88.00 (978-0-7222-8525-1(6)) Library Reprints, Inc.
Goodale, Katherine. Behind the Scenes with Edwin Booth. 2007. (ENG.). 364p. per. (978-1-4067-5433-9(1)) Read Bks.
Hutton, Laurence. Edwin Booth. 2008. 80p. pap. 17.75 (978-0-559-78876-5(2)) BiblioBazaar.
Ruggles, Eleanor. Prince of Players: Edwin Booth. 27.95 (978-0-89190-565-3(0)) Amereon LTD.
Schoch, Richard. Macready, Booth, Terry, Irving: Great Shakespeareans. Schoch, Richard, ed. 2011. (Great Shakespeareans Ser.). (ENG., Illus.). 224p. 140.00 (978-0-8264-4225-3(0)) Continuum International Publishing Group, Ltd. GBR. Dist: National Bk. Network.
Winter, William. Life & Art of Edwin Booth. 2009. (ENG.). 355p. 38.99 (978-1-117-32957-4(7)) 2009. (ENG.). 355p. pap. 31.75 (978-1-117-32958-1(5)) 2009. 360p. 26.99 (978-1-103-07927-8(1)) 2009. 360p. pap. 20.99 (978-1-103-07924-7(7)) 2008. 360p. 29.99 (978-0-559-66929-3(1)) 2008. 360p. pap. 31.75 (978-0-559-66926-2(7)) BiblioBazaar.
—Life & Art of Edwin Booth. 2007. (ENG.). 364p. per. (978-1-4067-3017-3(3)) Read Bks.

BOOTH, JOHN WILKES, 1838-1865

Bates, Finis L. Escape & Suicide of John Wilkes Booth. 2009. (Civil War Ser.). (ENG.). 351p. pap. 19.95 (978-1-4290-1101-3(7)) Applewood Bks.
—The First True Account of Lincoln's Assassination. 2007. 352p. (ENG.). 32.95 (978-1-4344-8385-0(1)); per. 19.95 (978-1-4344-8384-3(3)) Wildside Pr., LLC.
Goodrich, Thomas. The Darkest Dawn: Lincoln, Booth, & the Great American Tragedy. 2006. (ENG., Illus.). 376p. pap. 21.95 (978-0-253-21889-6(6), 0253218896) Indiana Univ. Pr.
Jones, Thomas A. J Wilkes Booth. 2009. 48p. pap. (978-0-217-22760-5(0)) Books LLC.
—J Wilkes Booth. 2007. 128p. per. 20.95 (978-1-4209-2990-4(9)) Digireads.com.
Stewart, John. Confederate Spies at Large: The Lives of Lincoln Assassination Conspirator Tom Harbin & Charlie Russell. 2006. (ENG., Illus.). 219p. per. 35.00 (978-0-7864-2868-7(6)) McFarland & Co., Inc. Pubs.
Swanson, James L. Manhunt. 2011. 15.12 (978-0-7848-3544-9(6), Everbind) Marco Bk. Co.
—Manhunt: The 12-Day Chase for Lincoln's Killer. 2007. (P. S. Ser.). (ENG., Illus.). 496p. pap. 15.99 (978-0-06-051850-9(2), William Morrow Paperbacks) HarperCollins Pubs.
Swanson, James L. & Weinberg, Daniel R. Lincoln's Assassins: Their Trial & Execution. (Illus.). 160p. 2008. (ENG.). pap. 19.95 (978-0-06-123762-1(0), HarperPerennial) 2006. 39.95 (978-0-06-123761-4(2), Morrow, William & Co.) HarperCollins Pubs.
Taylor, Phil. Montreal & the Assassination of Abraham Lincoln: John Wilkes Booth's Unexplained Visit to Montreal in October 1864. 2013. (ENG., Illus.). 185p. pap. 19.95 **(978-1-926824-08-6(3))** Baraka Bks. CAN. Dist: Independent Pubs. Group.
Townsend, George Alfred. Life Crime & Capture of John Wilkes Bo. 2006. pap. (978-1-4068-0987-9(X)) Echo Library.
—The Life, Crime & Capture of John Wilkes Booth. 2009. 140p. 21.99 (978-0-559-09801-7(4)); 24.99 (978-0-559-09787-4(5)); pap. 15.99 (978-0-559-09796-6(4)); pap. 20.99 (978-0-559-09792-8(1)) BiblioBazaar.
Townsend, George Alfred. The Life, Crime, & Capture of John Wilkes Booth, with a Full Sketch of the Conspiracy of Which He Was the Leader, & the Pursuit, Trial & Executi. 2011. 84p. pap. 14.99 **(978-1-4255-0344-4(6))** MPublishing.
William L. Richter. Sic Semper Tyrannis: Why John Wilkes Booth Shot Abraham Lincoln. 2009. 200p. pap. 16.95 (978-1-4401-7026-3(6)) iUniverse, Inc.
Zanca, Kenneth J. Catholics & Mrs. Mary Surratt: How They Responded to the Trial & Execution of the Lincoln Conspirator. 2008. (ENG.). pap. 35.99 (978-0-7618-4023-7(0)) Univ. Pr. of America, Inc.

BOOTH, JUNIUS BRUTUS, 1796-1852

Archer, Stephen M. Junius Brutus Booth: Theatrical Prometheus. 2010. (Illus.). 364p. pap. 35.00 (978-0-8093-3000-3(8)); 346p. E-Book (978-0-8093-8592-3(9)) Southern Illinois Univ. Pr.
Gould, Thomas Ridgeway. The Tragedian; an Essay on the Histrionic Genius of Junius Brutus Booth by Thomas R Gould. 2006. 208p. per. 20.99 (978-1-4255-1692-5(0)) MPublishing.

BOOTH, WILLIAM, 1829-1912

Begbie, Harold. The Life of General William Booth: the Founder of the Salvation Army. 2007. (ENG.). 480p. per. 38.95 (978-1-4304-4438-1(X)) Kessinger Publishing, LLC.
Moyles, R. G. I Knew William Booth: An Album of Remembrances. 2007. (Illus.). 151p. pap. 5.00 (978-0-9740940-9-0(9)) Salvation Army National Pubns., The.
Moyles, R. G. William Booth in America: Six Visits 1886-1907. 2010. (Illus.). xi, 227p. pap. **(978-0-9792266-9-4(4)**, Crest Bks.) Salvation Army National Pubns., The.
Nygaard, Norman E. Trumpet of Salvation: A Biographical Novel on the Lives of William & Catherine Booth. 2011. 180p. 42.95 **(978-1-258-08251-2(9))** Literary Licensing, LLC.
Railton, George Scott. The Authoritative Life of General William Booth. 2008. 412p. 30.99 (978-0-554-34126-2(3)) 2008. 412p. 32.99 (978-0-554-24823-3(9)) 2006. (ENG.). 368p. pap. 25.99 (978-1-4264-7464-4(4)) 2007. 410p. pap. 28.99 (978-1-4264-7541-2(1)) BiblioBazaar.
—The Authoritative Life of General William Booth. 2007. (ENG.). 288p. per. (978-1-4068-3684-4(2)) Echo Library.
—The Authoritative Life of General William Booth. 2008. 352p. pap. 21.95 (978-1-60597-415-6(3), Book Jungle) Standard Pubns., Inc.
Steele, Harold C. I Was a Stranger: The Faith of William Booth, Founder of the Salvation Army. 2011. 200p. 44.95 **(978-1-258-02597-7(3))** Literary Licensing, LLC.

BOOTHE, CLARE, 1903-1987

see Luce, Clare Boothe, 1903-1987

BOOTS AND SHOES

see also Leather; Moccasins

Abellan, Miquel. Shoes: Fashion & Desire. Abellon, Miquel, ed. 2011. (ENG & SPA., Illus.). 192p. pap. 77.50 **(978-84-15223-33-7(1))** Instituto Monsa de Ediciones, S.A. ESP. Dist: Trans-Atlantic Pubns., Inc.
Antin, Eleanor. 100 Boots: A Book of Postcards. 2010. (Green Integer Ser.). (ENG.). 130p. pap. 12.95 (978-1-933382-59-3(7)) Green Integer.
Armani, Cendrine. Felted Bags, Boots & Other Things: 56 Projects. 2008. (ENG., Illus.). 64p. pap. 17.95 (978-1-84448-282-5(0)) Search Pr., Ltd. GBR. Dist: Independent Pubs. Group.
Ashleigh, Caroline. Warman's Shoes Field Guide. 2010. (ENG., Illus.). 512p. pap. 14.99 (978-1-4402-0898-0(0)) Krause Pubns.
Atkinson, Jeremy. Clogs & Clogmaking. 2009. (Shire Library). (ENG., Illus.). 32p. pap. 11.95 (978-0-85263-565-7(2)) Shire Pubns., Ltd. GBR. Dist: Random Hse., Inc.
Beard, Tyler. The Cowboy Boot Book. (Illus.). 159.60 (978-0-87905-493-9(X)) Gibbs Smith, Publisher.
Bergstein, Rachelle. Women from the Ankle Down: The Story of Shoes & How They Define Us. 2012. (ENG.). 304p. 24.99 **(978-0-06-196961-4(3))** HarperCollins Pubs.
BIA. Leading Clothing, Footwear, & Textile Manufacturers of the USA. 6th rev. ed. 2006. 380p. (J). pap. 249.00 (978-1-4187-4429-8(8)) Business Information Agency.
Blahnik, Manolo. Manolo's New Shoes. 2010. (ENG., Illus.). 200p. pap. 50.00 (978-1-58093-282-0(7)) Monacelli Pr., Inc.
Bossan, Marie-Josèphe. The Art of the Shoe. 2007. (ENG., Illus.). 255p. 39.95 (978-1-85995-694-6(7)) Parkstone International GBR. Dist: Ingram Pub. Services.
Campbell, Kimberly C., et al. Clothing Through American History: The Civil War Through the Gilded Age, 1861-1899. 2010. (Illus.). 409p. 85.00 (978-0-313-33551-8(6), GR3551) Greenwood Publishing Group, Inc.
Chantelau, Ernst, ed. Diabetische Füße und Ihre Schuhversorgung. 2nd ed. 2010.Tr. of Diabetic Foot & its Correct Shoe. (GER., Illus.). XII, 153p. pap. 70.00 (978-3-11-021943-2(3)) De Gruyter, Walter Inc.
Choklat, Aki. Footwear Design. 2012. (ENG., Illus.). 192p. pap. 40.00 **(978-1-85669-745-3(2))** King, Laurence Publishing GBR. Dist: Hachette Bk. Group.
Clais, Ann-Marie. Sergio Rossi. 2007. (ENG., Illus.). 79p. 25.00 (978-2-7594-0170-3(7)) Assouline FRA. Dist: Perseus Distribution.
Cox, Caroline. Vintage Shoes. 2011. (ENG.). 224p. pap. 29.99 (978-0-06-200737-7(8), Collins Design) HarperCollins Pubs.
—Vintage Shoes: Collecting & Wearing Twentieth-Century Designer Footwear. 2008. 224p. 39.95 (978-0-06-166576-9(2), Collins Design) HarperCollins Pubs.
Cresson, L. D., ed. & illus. The American Footwear Designer. 2008. 134p. lib. bdg. (978-0-9796651-2-7(4), Books on Footwear) LDCresson.
—Designing, Cutting & Grading Boot & Shoe Patterns: A Complete Manual for the Stitching Room, by an Expert of Thirty Years Charles B Hatfield. 2008. (ENG.). 135p. 124.95 (978-0-9796651-0-3(8), Books on Footwear) LDCresson.
—Modern Course in Shoe Design & Model Cutting: Reprint of 1925 title by Elmer Travers & Dr. Louis H Werner with redrawn fold-out Patterns. 2008. (ENG.). 161p. (978-0-9796651-1-0(6)) LDCresson.
Crowe, Lauren Goldstein & de Rosen, Sagra Maceira. The Towering World of Jimmy Choo: A Glamorous Story of Power, Profits, & the Pursuit of the Perfect Shoe. 2010. (ENG.). 240p. pap. 15.00 (978-1-60819-040-9(4)) Bloomsbury Publishing.
de Hugo, Caroline. Baby Booties: Eighteen Pretty Pairs to Knit. 2012. (Made in France Ser.). (ENG., Illus.). 64p. pap. 24.95 **(978-1-74196-971-9(9))** Murdoch Bks. Pty Ltd. AUS. Dist: Independent Pubs. Group.
Deeble, Sandra. A Passion for Stilettos. 2006. (ENG., Illus.). 64p. (978-1-84597-262-2(7)) Ryland Peters & Small.
DeMello, Margo. Feet & Footwear: A Cultural Encyclopedia. 2009. 352p. 95.00 (978-0-313-35714-5(5), GR5714) Greenwood Publishing Group, Inc.
Design Museum Staff. Fifty Shoes That Changed the World. 2009. (ENG., Illus.). 112p. 20.00 (978-1-84091-539-6(0), Conran Octopus) Octopus Publishing Group GBR. Dist: Hachette Bk. Group.
Eldershaw, Jane. Heart & Sole: The Shoes of My Life. Date not set. pap. (978-0-312-32306-6(9)); mass mkt. (978-0-312-99412-9(5)) St. Martin's Pr. (St. Martin's Paperbacks).
Evans, Dave. Cool Hunting: A Guide to High Design & Innovation. 2007. (ENG., Illus.). 256p. pap. 24.95 (978-1-904915-22-5(1)) Southbank Publishing GBR. Dist: Independent Pubs. Group.
Farrelly, Liz. Sneakers: Size Isn't Everything. (Illus.). 240p. 49.50 (978-1-86154-007-2(8), Booth-Clibborn Editions GBR. Dist: Hachette Bk. Group.
Farson, Laura. Knitting Scandinavian Slippers & Socks. 2012. (ENG., Illus.). 80p. pap. **(978-1-60468-049-2(0))** Martingale & Co.
Garcia, Bobbito. Where'd You Get Those? New York City's Sneaker Culture, 1960-1987, 1 vol. 2006. (ENG., Illus.). 280p. pap. 29.95 (978-0-9725920-3-1(2)) Testify Bks., Inc.
Garsault, François A. de. M. de Garsault's 1767 Art of the Shoemaker: An Annotated Translation. Saguto, D. A., tr. from FRE. 2009. (Costume Society of America Ser.). (ENG.). 304p. 65.00 (978-0-89672-650-5(9)) Texas Tech Univ. Pr.
Garsault, François A. de & Saguto, D. A. M. de Garsault's 1767 Art of the Shoemaker: An Annotated Translation. 2009. (FRE & ENG.). (978-0-87935-239-4(6)) Colonial Williamsburg Foundation.
Grew, Francis, et al. Shoes & Pattens. 2nd ed. 2011. (Medieval Finds from Excavations in London Ser.: Volume 2). (Illus.). 152p. pap. 34.95 (978-1-84383-238-6(0)) Boydell & Brewer, Inc.
Guarnaccia, Matteo & Beatrice, Luca, eds. Vivienne Westwood Shoes, 1 vol. 2007. (ENG., Illus.). 192p. 65.00 (978-88-89431-84-9(9)) Damiani ITA. Dist: D.A.P./Distributed Art Pubs.
Gute, Charles & Gentili, Moreno, eds. Bally: Since 1851. 2007. (ENG., Illus.). 128p. 45.00 (978-88-7624-873-3(0)) Skira Editore ITA. Dist: Random Hse., Inc.
Harris, Georgina. Why Girls Love Shoes. 2006. (Illus.). 64p. 9.95 (978-1-907030-74-1(3)) CICO Bks. GBR. Dist: Ryland Peters & Small.
Heard, Neal. Sneakers. 2009. (ENG., Illus.). 464p. 27.95 (978-1-84732-107-7(0)); 3rd ed. 40.00 (978-1-84732-108-4(9)) Carlton Bks., Ltd. GBR. Dist: Sterling Publishing Co., Inc.
Hilderbrand, Dwane S. Footwear, the Missed Evidence: A Guide to the Collection & Preservation of Forensic Footwear Impression Evidence. 2007. (Illus.). 224p. spiral bd. 49.95 (978-1-933373-04-1(0)) Staggs Publishing.
Hoffman, Phyllis. Honey, It's All in the Shoes: Celebrating the Footsteps of the Contemporary Woman. 2009. (ENG.). 184p. pap. 15.95 (978-0-7573-0757-7(4)) Health Communications, Inc.
Howell, L. Daniel. The Barefoot Book: 50 Great Reasons to Kick off Your Shoes. 2010. (ENG.). 168p. pap. 12.95 (978-0-89793-554-8(3)) Hunter Hse., Inc.
Huey, Sue & Proctor, Rebecca. New Shoes: Contemporary Footwear Design. (ENG., Illus.). 208p. 2007. 40.00 (978-1-85669-507-7(7)) 2011. pap. 17.95 (978-1-85669-767-5(3)) King, Laurence Publishing GBR. Dist: Hachette Bk. Group.
Intercity. Art & Sole: Contemporary Sneaker Art & Design. 2012. (ENG., Illus.). 240p. pap. 16.95 **(978-1-85669-881-8(5))** King, Laurence Publishing GBR. Dist: Hachette Bk. Group.

B

Jacobbi, Paola. I Want Those Shoes! 2007. (ENG., Illus.). 160p. 18.00 *(978-0-7432-7774-7(0)*, Scribner) Scribner.
Jones, Jessica. Shoe Love: In Pop-Up. 2010. (ENG., Illus.). 36p. 19.95 *(978-1-60710-086-7(X)*, Thunder Bay Pr.) Advantage Pubs. Group.
June, Jennifer. Cowboy Boots: Art & Sole. 2010. (ENG., Illus.). 336p. 9.98 *(978-0-7893-2049-0(5)*, Rizzoli Universe Promotional Bks.) Rizzoli International Pubns., Inc.
—Cowboy Boots: The Art & Sole. 2007. (ENG., Illus.). 336p. 22.50 *(978-0-7893-1537-3(8))* Universe Publishing.
Katovsky, Bill & Larson, Peter. Tread Lightly: Form, Footwear, & the Quest for Injury-Free Running. 2012. (ENG., Illus.). 256p. pap. 16.95 ***(978-1-61608-374-8(3)***, 608374) Skyhorse Publishing Co., Inc.
Koole, Avenishe. Heavenly Soles. 2011. 116p. pap. ***(978-3-8443-1321-5(4))*** Lambert Academic Publishing.
Louboutin, Christian. Christian Louboutin. 2011. (ENG., Illus.). 304p. 150.00 *(978-0-8478-3651-2(7))* Rizzoli International Pubns., Inc.
Lynx, David & Vlcek, Debbie, eds. Head over Heels over Heels: One Collector's Love Affair with Shoes. 2011. (Illus.). 64p. mass mkt. 9.95 ***(978-1-928707-10-3(6))*** Yakima Valley Museum.
Maat, Matthijs & Smits, Kim. Custom Kicks. 2008. (ENG., Illus.). 224p. pap. 19.95 *(978-1-85669-542-8(5))* King, Laurence Publishing GBR. Dist: Hachette Bk. Group.
Mason, Lorine. Boutique Slippers: 9 Slippers from Fat Quarters. 2011. (ENG., Illus.). 48p. pap. 11.95 *(978-1-59217-340-2(3))* Annie's Publishing, LLC.
McDiarmid, Andrew. Bootblacking 101: A Handbook. 2007. (Boner Bks.). (Illus.). 93p. per. 17.95 *(978-1-887895-69-9(8))* Nazca Plains Corp., The.
Mellon, Tamara, pref. Jimmy Choo. 2012. (ENG., Illus.). 192p. 75.00 ***(978-0-8478-3748-9(3))*** Rizzoli International Pubns., Inc.
Mitchell, Louise, et al. Stepping Out: Three Centuries of Shoes. rev. ed. 2008. (Illus.). 96p. pap. 35.00 *(978-1-86317-124-3(X)*, Lund Humphries Pubs.) Ashgate Publishing, Ltd. GBR. Dist: Ashgate Publishing Co.
Mosca, Vincent & Staheli, Lynn. What Parents Should Know about Flatfeet, Intoeing, Bent Legs, & Shoes for Children. Staheli, Lana, ed. Lebel, Udi, tr. 2009. (HEB.). 8p. 0.70 *(978-1-60189-052-8(4))* Global HELP Organization.
Nahshon, Edna, ed. Jews & Shoes. 2008. (ENG., Illus.). 288p. 109.95 *(978-1-84788-049-9(5))*; pap. 34.95 *(978-1-84788-050-5(9))* Berg Pubs. GBR. Dist: Macmillan.
Oakes, Jill & Riewe, Rick. Alaska Eskimo Footwear. 2007. (Illus.). 176p. pap. 29.95 *(978-1-60223-006-4(4))* Univ. of Alaska Pr.
Palladini, Doug. Vans: Off the Wall - Stories of Sole from Vans Originals. 2009. (ENG., Illus.). 208p. 27.50 *(978-0-8109-8375-5(3))* Abrams.
Peters, Rolf-Herbert. Puma Story: The Remarkable Turnaround of an Endangered Species into One of the World's Hottest Sportlifestyle Brands, 1 vol. 2009. (ENG.). 240p. 24.99 *(978-1-905736-40-9(1))* Marshall Cavendish Corp.
Polcyn, Amy. Knit a Dozen Plus Slippers. 2010. (ENG.). 32p. pap. 8.95 *(978-1-59217-302-0(0)*, House of White Birches, Inc.) Annie's Publishing, LLC.
Pratt, Lucy & Woolley, Linda. Shoes. 2008. (ENG., Illus.). 128p. pap. 16.95 *(978-1-85177-537-8(4))* V & A Pubns. GBR. Dist: Hachette Bk. Group.
Quinn, Bradley. The Boot. 2010. (ENG., Illus.). 192p. 40.00 *(978-1-85669-663-0(4))* King, Laurence Publishing GBR. Dist: Hachette Bk. Group.
Riello, Giorgio & McNeil, Peter, eds. Shoes: A History from Sandals to Sneakers. 2011. (ENG., Illus.). 448p. pap. 29.95 *(978-0-85785-038-6(5))* Berg Pubs. GBR. Dist: Macmillan.
Semmelhack, Elizabeth. Heights of Fashion: A History of the Elevated Shoe. 2008. (Illus.). 116p. pap. 30.00 *(978-1-934772-94-2(1))* Periscope Publishing.
Stevens-Heebner, Marty. Altered Shoes: A Step-by-Step Guide to Creating Fabulous Footwear. 2009. (ENG., Illus.). 128p. pap. 22.99 *(978-1-60061-126-1(5))* Krause Pubns.
Storelli, Patricia. The Magic Pointe Shoes. 2011. 372p. pap. 25.95 ***(978-1-60594-691-7(5)***, Llumina Pr.) Aeon Publishing Inc.
Tanenbaum, Leora. Bad Shoes & the Women Who Love Them. 2010. (ENG., Illus.). 192p. pap. 13.95 *(978-1-58322-904-0(3))* Seven Stories Pr.
Tyrrell, Wendy & Carter, Gwenda. Therapeutic Footwear: A Comprehensive Guide. 2008. (ENG., Illus.). 352p. (C). 83.95 *(978-0-443-06883-6(6)*, Churchill Livingstone) Elsevier - Health Sciences Div.
Vartanian, Ivan, ed. High Heels: Fashion, Femininity & Seduction. 2012. (ENG., Illus.). 192p. 49.95 ***(978-1-935202-69-1(3))*** D.A.P./Distributed Art Pubs.
Vass, Laszlo & Molnar, Magda. Handmade Shoes for Men. 2008. (Fashion Ser.). (Illus.). 215p. 24.95 *(978-0-8416-0161-1(5))* American Map Corp.
Veldmeijer, Andre J. Sandals, shoes & other leatherwork from the Coptic Monastery Deir El-Bachit: Analysis & Catalogue. 2012. (ENG., Illus.). 276p. (C). pap. 144.00 ***(978-90-8890-074-7(4))*** Sidestone Pr. NLD. Dist: Brown, David Bk. Co., The.
Veldmeijer, Andre J. Tutankhamun's Footwear: Studies of Ancient Egyptian Footwear. 2010. (ENG., Illus.). 310p. (C). 180.00 *(978-90-78707-10-3(0))* DrukWare NLD. Dist: Brown, David Bk. Co., The.
—Tutankhamun's Footwear: Studies of Ancient Egyptian Footwear. 2012. (ENG., Illus.). 312p. (C). pap. 140.00 ***(978-90-8890-076-1(0))*** Sidestone Pr. NLD. Dist: Brown, David Bk. Co., The.
Verin, Helene. Beth Levine Shoes. 2009. (ENG., Illus.). 176p. 37.50 *(978-1-58479-759-3(2))* Stewart, Tabori & Chang.
Walford, Jonathan. The Seductive Shoes: Four Centuries of Fashion Footwear. 2007. (ENG., Illus.). 288p. 42.00 *(978-1-58479-622-0(7))* Stewart, Tabori & Chang.
Werd, Matthew B. & Knight, E. Leslie, eds. Athletic Footwear & Orthotics in Sports Medicine. 2010. (ENG., Illus.). xvi, 400p. pap. 29.95 *(978-0-387-76415-3(1)*, 0387764151) Springer.
Wilcox, R. Turner. The Mode in Footwear: A Historical Survey with 53 Plates. 2008. (Dover Fashion & Costumes Ser.). (ENG., Illus.). 208p. pap. 12.95 *(978-0-486-46761-0(9))* Dover Pubns., Inc.
Williams, Anita Ellen & Nester, Chris. Footwear & Foot Orthoses. 2010. (Pocket Podiatry Ser.). (ENG., Illus.). 176p. (C). pap. 52.95 *(978-0-7020-3042-0(2)*, Churchill Livingstone) Elsevier - Health Sciences Div.
Williams, Yvonne L. It's All about the Shoes: Hope, Heartbreak & the Search for the Perfect Pair. 2007. (ENG., Illus.). 96p. 12.95 *(978-1-4022-0712-9(3))* Sourcebooks, Inc.
Wintour, Anna, et al. Manolo Blahník Drawings. 2nd ed. 2009. (ENG., Illus.). 200p. (Orig.). pap. 15.95 *(978-0-500-28809-2(7)*, 528809) Thames & Hudson.

BOOTS AND SHOES—REPAIRING
Reinhardt, Angela Dawn. Pointe Shoes: Tips & Tricks. 2008. (Illus.). 110p. pap. 29.50 *(978-1-85273-115-1(X))* Dance Bks., Ltd. GBR. Dist: Trans-Atlantic Pubns., Inc.

BOOTS AND SHOES—TRADE AND MANUFACTURE
see also Shoemakers
BIA. Key Clothing, Footwear, & Textile Manufacturers of Russia & the Former Soviet Republics. 6th rev. ed. 2006. 350p. (J). pap. 249.00 *(978-1-4187-4481-6(6))* Business Information Agency.
—Key Russian Manufacturers & Suppliers of Footwear. 6th rev. ed. 2006. 444p. (J). pap. 249.00 *(978-1-4187-4510-3(3))* Business Information Agency.
—Major Footwear Wholesalers of the World. 6th rev. ed. 2006. 300p. (J). pap. 249.00 *(978-1-4187-4326-0(7))* Business Information Agency.
—Major Men's & Women's Footwear Manufacturers of the World. 6th rev. ed. 2006. 300p. (J). pap. 249.00 *(978-1-4187-4251-5(1))* Business Information Agency.
Cheng, Chih-Peng. Deciphering a Global Industry. 2007. 256p. per. *(978-3-8364-1772-3(3))* VDM Verlag Dr. Mueller e.K.
Dulio, Sergio & Boér, Claudio Roberto. Mass Customization & Footwear - Myth, Salvation or Reality? A Comprehensive Analysis of the Adoption of the Mass Customization Paradigm in Footwear, from the Perspective of the Euroshoe (Extended User Oriented Shoe Enterprise) Research Project. 2007. (ENG., Illus.). x, 177p. 159.00 *(978-1-84628-864-7(9)*, 1846288649) Springer.
Gallegos, Alvaro Z. What's This Shoe All About? 2011. 56p. pap. ***(978-1-4269-7934-7(7))*** Trafford Publishing (UK) Ltd.
Jansen, Jan, et al. Jan Jansen. 2007. (ENG., Illus.). 200p. 50.00 *(978-90-5897-725-0(0))* Lannoo Pubs./Racine.
Kayser, Pedro. The Brazilian Shoe Industry - Competing in International Markets. 2009. 152p. pap. *(978-3-639-16644-6(2))* VDM Verlag Dr. Mueller e.K.
Lowell, Levi, illus. The Original Guide to Shoe Customization. 2008. 26p. pap. 15.95 *(978-0-9786400-1-9(2))* St. Croix Antiquarian Booksellers.
Maceira de Rosen, Sagra & Goldstein Crowe, Lauren. The Towering World of Jimmy Choo: A Glamorous Story of Power, Profits, & the Pursuit of the Perfect Shoe. 2009. (ENG.). 240p. 26.00 *(978-1-59691-391-2(6))* Bloomsbury Publishing.
Mulligan, William H., Jr. The Shoemakers of Lynn, Massachusetts, 1850-1880: The Family During the Transition from Hand to Machine Labor. 2006. 180p. *(978-0-7734-5586-3(8))* Mellen, Edwin Pr., The.
Norton, Thomas L. Trade Union Policies in the Massachusetts Shoe Industry. (Columbia University, Studies in the Social Sciences: No. 372). reprint ed. 27.50 *(978-0-404-51372-6(7))* AMS Pr., Inc.
Shephard, Norma. In Step with Fashion: 200 Years of Shoe Styles. 2008. (Illus.). 160p. pap. 29.99 *(978-0-7643-2817-6(4))* Schiffer Publishing, Ltd.
Walford, Jonathan. Shoes A-Z: Designers, Brands, Manufacturers & Retailers. 2010. (ENG., Illus.). 256p. 29.95 *(978-0-500-51526-6(3)*, 551526) Thames & Hudson.

BOOTSTRAP (STATISTICS)
Aga, Mosisa. Parametric Bootstrap for Linear Regression with Long-Memory Errors. 2010. 64p. pap. *(978-3-8383-4061-6(2))* Lambert Academic Publishing.
Chernick, Michael R. Bootstrap Methods: A Guide for Practitioners & Researchers. 2nd ed. 2007. (Wiley Series in Probability & Statistics Ser.: 619). (ENG., Illus.). 400p. 146.00 *(978-0-471-75621-7(0)*, Wiley-Interscience) Wiley, John & Sons, Inc.
Chernick, Michael R. & LaBudde, Robert A. An Introduction to Bootstrap Methods with Applications to R. 2011. (ENG., Illus.). 240p. 99.95 *(978-0-470-46704-6(5)*, Wiley) Wiley, John & Sons, Inc.
El Halimi, Rachid. Nonlinear ed-Effects Models & Bootstrap Resampling. 2009. 320p. pap. *(978-3-639-15317-0(0))* VDM Verlag Dr. Mueller e.K.
Godfrey, Leslie. Bootstrap Tests for Regression Models. 2009. (Palgrave Texts in Econometrics Ser.). (ENG., Illus.). 224p. 110.00 *(978-0-230-20230-6(6))*; 344p. pap. 36.00 *(978-0-230-20231-3(4))* Palgrave Macmillan.
Long, Jeffrey D., et al. Comparing Groups: Randomization & Bootstrap Methods Using R. 2011. (ENG., Illus.). 332p. 110.00 *(978-0-470-62169-1(9)*, Wiley) Wiley, John & Sons, Inc.
Mendenhall, William & Sincich, Terry. Statistics for Engineering & the Sciences. 5th rev. ed. 2006. (ENG., Illus.). 1072p. (C). pap. 88.00 *(978-0-13-187706-1(2)*, Prentice Hall) Prentice Hall PTR.
Mudelsee, Manfred. Climate Time Series Analysis: Classical Statistical & Bootstrap Methods. 2010. (Atmospheric & Oceanographic Sciences Library). (Illus.). xxxiv, 474p. 199.00 *(978-90-481-9481-0(4)*, 9048194814) Springer.
Navidi, William. Statistics for Engineers & Scientists. 3rd ed. 2010. (ENG., Illus.). 928p. (C). 200.67 *(978-0-07-337633-2(7)*, 0073376337, McGraw-Hill Science, Engineering & Mathematics) McGraw-Hill Higher Education.
Navidi, William C. Statistics for Engineers & Scientists. 2nd rev. ed. 2007. (ENG., Illus.). 675p. (C). 173.75 *(978-0-07-330949-1(4)*, 0073309494, McGraw-Hill Science, Engineering & Mathematics) McGraw-Hill Higher Education.
Navidi, William Cyrus. Statistics for Engineers & Scientists. 2nd ed. 2007. (Illus.). xviii, 901p. *(978-0-07-312779-8(5))* McGraw-Hill Cos., The.
Socher, Richard. Automatic Extension of Semantic Lexicons with a Bootstrapping Algorithm - Using Corpora to Learn Semantic Features. 2008. 104p. pap. *(978-3-639-03137-9(7))* VDM Verlag Dr. Mueller e.K.
Zoubir, Abdelhak M. & Iskander, D. Robert. Bootstrap Techniques for Signal Processing. 2007. (ENG., Illus.). 232p. per. 53.00 *(978-0-521-03405-0(1))* Cambridge Univ. Pr.

BORAX
Spears, John R. Illustrated Sketches of Death Valley & Other Borax Deserts of the Pacific Coast. 2007. (ENG., Illus.). 228p. 39.95 *(978-0-548-34723-2(9))*; per. 24.95 *(978-0-548-28940-2(9))* Kessinger Publishing, LLC.

BORDEAUX (FRANCE)
Bonin, Hubert. Banque et Bourgeoisies: La Société bordelaise de CIC (1880-2005) 2010. (FRE., Illus.). 434p. pap. 70.95 *(978-90-5201-603-0(8))* PIE - Peter Lang BEL. Dist: Lang, Peter.
Brault, Richard. Best Chateaux in Bordeaux. (Illus.). 192p. pap. 9.95 *(978-0-9656956-8-8(9))* Les Editions Richard Brault, Inc.
Dodd, Jan & Rough Guides Staff. Dordogne & the Lot. 4th ed. 2010. (ENG., Illus.). 456p. 21.99 *(978-1-84836-462-2(8))* Rough Guides, Ltd. GBR. Dist: Dorling Kindersley Publishing, Inc.
Dorling Kindersley Publishing Staff. DK Eyewitness Travel Guide: Dordogne, Bordeaux & the Southwe st Coast: Dordogne, Bordeaux & the Southwe st Coast. 2012. (Eyewitness Travel Guide Ser.). (ENG.). 320p. pap. 25.00 *(978-0-7566-8425-9(0))* Dorling Kindersley Publishing, Inc.
Joseph, Robert. Bordeaux & Its Wines. 2008. (ENG., Illus.). 144p. pap. *(978-1-84483-605-5(3))* Duncan Baird Pubs. GBR. Dist: Sterling Publishing Co., Inc.
Locken, E. Travel Journal Bordeaux. 2010. 192p. pap. 19.99 *(978-0-557-34175-7(2))* Lulu Enterprises Inc.
Pierre, Roger St. Bordeaux & the Wine Region. 2010. (Frommer's Day by Day - Pocket Ser.). (ENG.). 192p. pap. 12.99 *(978-0-470-72173-5(1)*, Wiley) Wiley, John & Sons, Inc.
Vernière, Laure. Bordeaux. 2008. *(978-2-7594-0284-7(3))* Assouline.

BORDEN, GAIL, 1801-1874
Frantz, Joe B. Gail Borden: Dairyman to A Nation. 2011. 354p. 51.95 ***(978-1-258-01976-1(0))*** Literary Licensing, LLC.

BORDEN, LIZZIE, 1860-1927
Holba, Annette M. Lizzie Borden Took an Axe, or Did She? a Rhetorical Inquiry. 2008. 192p. pap. 25.00 *(978-1-934844-01-4(2))* Teneo Pr.
Samuels, Charles & Samuels, Louise. The Girl in the House of Hate: Being an Exact & Faithful Account of the Trial of Lizzie Borden. 18.95 *(978-0-89190-108-2(6))* Amereon LTD.
Watson, Elizabeth Elaine. Lizzie Didn't Do It: Emma Did! 2011. pap. *(978-0-8283-2206-5(6))* Branden Bks.

BORDEN, ROBERT, SIR, 1854-1937
Macquarrie, Heath, ed. Robert Laird Borden Vol. 2: His Memoirs, 2 vols. 261p. pap. 19.95 *(978-0-7710-9747-8(6))* McClelland & Stewart CAN. Dist: Random Hse. of Canada, Ltd.
Thornton, Martin. Sir Robert Borden? Canada. 2011. (Makers of the Modern World Ser.). (ENG., Illus.). 220p. 19.95 *(978-1-905791-84-2(4))* Haus Publishing GBR. Dist: Consortium Bk. Sales & Distribution.

BORDER COLLIE
Bedwell Wilson, Wendy. Border Collie. 2012. (Smart Owner's Guide Ser.). (ENG.). 176p. 17.95 ***(978-1-59378-782-0(0))*** Kennel Club Bks.
Devine, Michael. Border Collies: Everything about Purchase, Care, Nutrition, Behavior, & Training. 2nd rev. ed. 2007. (Complete Pet Owner's Manual Ser.). (ENG., Illus.). 96p. pap. 8.99 *(978-0-7641-3644-3(5))* Barron's Educational Series, Inc.
Libby, Tracy. The Border Collie. 2006. (Terra-Nova Ser.). (Illus.). 207p. 19.95 *(978-0-7938-3676-5(X))* TFH Pubns., Inc.
McCaig, Donald. The Dog Wars: How the Border Collie Battled the American Kennel Club. 2007. (ENG.). 192p. per. 15.00 *(978-0-9794690-0-8(7)*, 900) Outrun Pr.
—Eminent Dogs, Dangerous Men: Searching Through Scotland for a Border Collie. 2007. (ENG., Illus.). 240p. per. 15.95 *(978-1-59921-059-9(2)*, Lyons Pr.) Globe Pequot Pr., The.
Price, Carol. Collins Dog Owner's Guide - Border Collie. 2012. (Pet Owner's Guide Ser.). (ENG., Illus.). 144p. pap. 14.95 ***(978-0-00-743668-2(8))*** HarperCollins Pubs. Ltd. GBR. Dist: Independent Pubs. Group.
Sheepdog Glory: The story of a working border Collie. 2008. (Illus.). 200p. pap. 15.00 *(978-0-9794690-2-2(3))* Outrun Pr.
Sherlock, Patti. A Dog for All Seasons: A Memoir. 2010. (ENG.). 256p. 24.99 *(978-0-312-57792-6(3)*, Dunne, Thomas Bks.) St. Martin's Pr.

BORDER LIFE
see Frontier and Pioneer Life

BORDER TAXES
see Tariff

BORDER TERRIER
Alderton, David. You & Your Border Terrier: The Essential Guide. 2010. (ENG., Illus.). 96p. pap. 19.95 *(978-1-84584-319-9(3)*, 1845843193, Hubble & Hattie) Veloce Publishing Ltd. GBR. Dist: MBI Distribution Services/Quayside Distribution.
Jennings, Kate. Stanley & Sophie. 2009. (ENG.). 208p. pap. 15.00 *(978-1-4165-6030-2(0)*, Scribner) Scribner.
—Stanley & Sophie: A Memoir. l.t. ed. 2009. 246p. 31.50 *(978-1-4104-1200-3(8))* Thorndike Pr.
Linzy, Jan, et al. Border Terrier Champions, 2010-2011. 2011. (Illus.). 126p. spiral bd. 40.95 ***(978-1-55893-327-9(1))*** Camino E.E. & Bk. Co.
Long, Lorie. Border Terrier: Breed Lover's Guide, 1 vol. 2011. (ENG., Illus.). 144p. 14.95 *(978-0-7938-4181-3(X))* TFH Pubns., Inc.

BORDER TERRIERS
see Border Terrier

BORDERLANDS, UNITED STATES-MEXICO
see Mexican-American Border Region

BORDERLINE PERSONALITY DISORDER
Aguirre, Blaise A. Borderline Personality Disorder in Adolescents: A Complete Guide to Understanding & Coping When Your Adolescent Has BPD. 2007. (ENG., Illus.). 288p. per. 16.95 *(978-1-59233-287-8(0)*, 1592332870) Quayside.
Akhtar, Salman, et al, eds. Severe Personality Disorders. 2007. (ENG., Illus.). 264p. 115.00 *(978-0-521-85651-5(5))* Cambridge Univ. Pr.
Arntz, Arnoud & van Genderen, Hannie. Schema Therapy for Borderline Personality Disorder. Drost, Jolijn, tr. from DUT. 2009. (ENG., Illus.). 206p. 118.95 *(978-0-470-51080-3(3))*; 216p. pap. 52.95 *(978-0-470-51081-0(1))* Wiley, John & Sons, Inc. (Wiley-Blackwell).
Bach, Alexander. Bye Bye Bonsai Baby. 2010. 418p. pap. 29.95 *(978-0-557-44363-5(6))* Lulu Enterprises Inc.
Baker, Bobby. Diary Drawings. 2010. (ENG., Illus.). 224p. pap. 22.95 ***(978-1-84668-374-9(2))*** Profile Bks. Ltd. GBR. Dist: Consortium Bk. Sales & Distribution.
Bateman, Anthony & Fonagy, Peter. Mentalization-Based Treatment for Borderline Personality Disorder. 2006. (ENG., Illus.). 208p. per., instr.'s gde. ed. 49.99 *(978-0-19-857090-5(2))* Oxford Univ. Pr., Inc.
Blizard, Ruth A. & Howell, Elizabeth F. Empathic Treatment of Borderline Personality: A Disorder of Trauma, Attachment, & Dissociation. 2008. 248p. *(978-0-7890-2633-0(3))*; pap. *(978-0-7890-2634-7(1))* Haworth Pr., Inc., The.
Camh. Borderline Personality Disorder: An Information Guide for Families. 2009. 70p. pap. ***(978-0-88868-819-4(9))*** Centre for Addiction & Mental Health.
Dobbs, Bon. When Hope Is Not Enough. 2008. 181p. pap. 19.95 *(978-1-4357-1919-4(0))* Lulu Enterprises Inc.
Drob, Liliana Rusansky. Borderline Personality Disorder. 2008. 224p. pap. *(978-3-639-04282-5(4))* VDM Verlag Dr. Mueller e.K.
Elliott, Charles H., et al. Borderline Personality Disorder for Dummies. 2009. (ENG., Illus.). 384p. pap. 19.99 *(978-0-470-46653-7(7)*, For Dummies) Wiley, John & Sons, Inc.
Farrell, Joan M. & Shaw, Ida A. Group Schema Therapy for Borderline Personality Disorder: A Step-by-Step Treatment Manual with Patient Workbook. 2nd ed. 2012. (ENG.). 328p. 107.50 ***(978-1-119-95828-4(8))***; pap. 49.50 ***(978-1-119-95829-1(6))*** Wiley, John & Sons, Inc. (Wiley-Blackwell).
Fruzzetti, Alan E. The Family Guide to Borderline Personality Disorder: Finding Peace in Your Family Using Dialectical Behavior Therapy. 2013. (ENG.). 224p. pap. 17.95 *(978-1-60882-040-5(8))* New Harbinger Pubns.
Gammelgaard, Judy. Betweenity: A Discussion of the Concept of Borderline. 2010. (New Library of Psychoanalysis Ser.). (ENG.). 280p. (C). pap. 37.95 *(978-0-415-54390-3(8))*; 105.00 *(978-0-415-54389-7(4))* Routledge.
Green. Resonance of Suffering: Countertransference in Non-Neurotic Structures. 2nd rev. ed. 2010. (IPA: the International Psychoanalysis Library). 256p. pap. 49.95 *(978-1-85575-749-3(4))* Karnac Bks. GBR. Dist: Stylus Publishing, LLC.
Green, Andre, ed. Resonance of Suffering: Countertransference in Non-Neurotic Structures. 2007. (IPA: the International Psychoanalysis Library). (Illus.). 256p. (C). pap. 49.95 *(978-1-905888-01-6(5))* Karnac Bks. GBR. Dist: Stylus Publishing, LLC.
Healy, Chris. Understanding Your Borderline Personality Disorder. 2008. (Wiley Series in Psychoeducation? Ser.: 2). (ENG., Illus.). 206p. pap., wbk. ed. 57.95 *(978-0-470-98655-4(7)*, Wiley) Wiley, John & Sons, Inc.
Hoffman, Perry D., et al, eds. Borderline Personality Disorder: Meeting the Challenges to Successful Treatment. 2008. (ENG., Illus.). 275p. 125.00 *(978-0-7890-3233-1(3))*; pap. 44.95 *(978-0-7890-3234-8(1))* Routledge.
Jackson, Marian H. & Westbrook, Linda F., eds. Borderline Personality Disorder: New Research. 2009. 137.00 *(978-1-60692-460-0(5))* Nova Science Pubs., Inc.
Johnson, Merri Lisa. Girl in Need of a Tourniquet: Memoir of a Borderline Personality. 2010. (ENG.). 256p. pap. 16.95 *(978-1-58005-305-1(X))* Seal Pr.
Karpus, Michelle. On Knife's Edge: A Young Girl's Journey Through Borderline Personality Disorder. 2010. 84p. pap. *(978-1-84991-249-5(1))* Chipmunkapublishing.
Krawitz, Roy & Jackson, Wendy. Borderline Personality Disorder. 2nd ed. 2008. (Facts Ser.). (ENG., Illus.). 152p. pap. 27.50 *(978-0-19-920296-6(6))* Oxford Univ. Pr., Inc.

Kreger, Randi. The Essential Family Guide to Borderline Personality Disorder: New Tools & Techniques to Stop Walking on Eggshells. 2008. (ENG.). 304p. pap. 14.95 *(978-1-59285-363-2(3))* Hazelden Publishing & Educational Services.

Kreisman, Jerold Jay & Straus, Hal. I Hate You — Don't Leave Me: Understanding the Borderline Personality. 2010. (ENG.). 288p. (gr. 12). 15.00 *(978-0-399-53621-2(3)*, Perigee Trade) Penguin Group (USA) Inc.

Lachkar, Joan. How to Talk to a Borderline. 2010. (ENG., Illus.). 196p. (C). 44.95 *(978-0-415-87649-0(4))* Routledge.

Macard, L. To Live with Myself. 2007. pap. *(978-1-84747-084-3(X))* Chipmunkapublishing.

Manning, Shari Y. Loving Someone with Borderline Personality Disorder: How to Keep Out-of-Control Emotions from Destroying Your Relationship. 2011. (ENG.). 253p. 40.00 *(978-1-60918-195-6(6))*; pap. 16.95 *(978-1-59385-607-6(5))* Guilford Pubns., Inc.

Mason, Paul & Kreger, Randi. Stop Walking on Eggshells: Taking Your Life Back When Someone You Care about Has Borderline Personality Disorder. 2nd rev. ed. 2010. (ENG.). 288p. pap. 18.95 *(978-1-57224-690-4(1))* New Harbinger Pubns.

Meares, Russell. A Dissociation Model of Borderline Personality Disorder. 2012. (Norton Series on Interpersonal Neurobiology Ser.). (ENG.). 304p. 39.95 ***(978-0-393-70585-0(4)***, 70585) Norton, W. W. & Co., Inc.

Mondimore, Francis Mark & Kelly, Patrick. Borderline Personality Disorder: New Reasons for Hope. 2011. (Johns Hopkins Press Health Book Ser.). (ENG., Illus.). 312p. pap. 19.95 ***(978-1-4214-0314-4(5))***; (gr. 17). 45.00 ***(978-1-4214-0313-7(7))*** Johns Hopkins Univ. Pr.

Monks, Millicent. Songs of Three Islands: A Story of Mental Illness in an Iconic American Family. 2010. (ENG.). 250p. 24.00 *(978-1-934633-34-2(8)*, 934634) Atlas & Co.

Moonshine, Cathy. Acquiring Competency & Achieving Proficiency with Dialectical Behavior Therapy, Volume 1: The Clinician's Guidebook. 2008. (Illus.). 241p. pap. 29.99 *(978-0-9790218-4-8(7))* PESI Healthcare - PHC Publishing Group.

—Acquiring Competency & Achieving Proficiency with Dialectical Behavior Therapy, Volumes I & II: The Clinician's Guidebook/the Worksheets. 2008. pap. 49.99 *(978-0-01-533904-3(1))* PESI Healthcare - PHC Publishing Group.

Paris, Joel. Treatment of Borderline Personality Disorder: A Guide to Evidence-Based Practice. (ENG.). 260p. 2010. pap. 28.00 *(978-1-60623-864-6(7))* 2008. 50.00 *(978-1-59385-834-6(5))* Guilford Pubns., Inc.

Porr, Valerie. Overcoming Borderline Personality Disorder: A Family Guide for Healing & Change. 2010. (ENG.). 320p. pap. 24.95 *(978-0-19-537958-7(6))* Oxford Univ. Pr., Inc.

Potter, Nancy. Mapping the Edges & the In-between: A critical analysis of Borderline Personality Disorder. 2009. (International Perspectives in Philosophy & Psychiatry Ser.). (ENG.). 196p. pap. 59.95 *(978-0-19-853021-3(8))* Oxford Univ. Pr., Inc.

Roberson, Arlene. Borderline Traits. 2010. 190p. 29.99 *(978-1-4535-1244-9(6))*; pap. 19.99 *(978-1-4535-1243-2(8))* Xlibris Corp.

Roberts, Donald D. & Roberts, Deanda S. Another Chance to Be Real: Attachment & Object Relations Treatment of Borderline Personality Disorder. 2007. (ENG.). 186p. 89.50 *(978-0-7657-0553-2(2))*; per. 41.99 *(978-0-7657-0554-9(0))* Rowman & Littlefield Publishers, Inc. (Aronson, Jason).

Rossiter, Rachel. Dialectical Behaviour Therapists. 2009. 184p. pap. *(978-3-639-17358-1(9))* VDM Verlag Dr. Mueller e.K.

Sansone, Randy A. & Sansone, Lori A. Borderline Personality in the Medical Setting: Unmasking & Managing the Difficult Patient. 2007. 79.00 *(978-1-60021-451-5(7))* Nova Science Pubs., Inc.

Schiltz, Lony, ed. Investigating the Traumatogenic Hypothesis of Borderline Functioning: A Research Report. 2011. (Psychology Research Progress Ser.). 230p. 75.00 ***(978-1-61470-810-0(X))*** Nova Science Pubs., Inc.

Stringer, Kathi. Psych 101 - What you didn't learn in nursing School. 2008. 316p. pap. 21.95 *(978-0-615-19313-7(7))* Stringer, Kathi.

Swales, Michaela & Heard, Heidi. Dialectical Behaviour Therapy: Distinctive Features. 2009. (CBT Distinctive Features Ser.). (ENG., Illus.). 184p. (C). 95.00 *(978-0-415-44457-6(8))*; pap. 17.95 *(978-0-415-44458-3(6))* Routledge.

Van Gelder, Kiera. The Buddha & the Borderline: My Recovery from Borderline Personality Disorder through Dialectical Behavior Therapy, Buddhism, & Online Dating. 2010. (ENG.). 280p. pap. 17.95 *(978-1-57224-710-9(X))* New Harbinger Pubns.

Wang, Charles R. Profound States of Despair: Treating Emptiness. 2008. pap. *(978-1-59942-943-4(8))* Universal Pubs.

Zanarini, Mary C. McLean Screening Instrument for Borderline Personality Disorder (MSI-BPD) 2008. 50p. pap. 37.95 *(978-0-7637-6310-7(1))* Jones & Bartlett Learning, LLC.

—Zanarini Rating Scale for Borderline Personality Disorder (ZAN-BPD) 2007. 80p. pap. 30.95 *(978-0-7637-6311-4(X))* Jones & Bartlett Learning, LLC.

BORDERS OF ENGLAND (ENGLAND)—DESCRIPTION AND TRAVEL

Turnbull, Ronald. Battle Valleys: A Portrait of the Border. 2012. (ENG., Illus.). 112p. 24.95 ***(978-0-7112-3229-7(6))*** Lincoln, Frances Ltd. GBR. Dist: Perseus-PGW.

BORDERS REGION (SCOTLAND)

Adams, John A., Jr. Conflict & Commerce on the Rio Grande: Laredo, 1755-1955. 2008. (Canseco-Keck History Ser.: No. 12). (ENG., Illus.). 304p. 29.95 *(978-1-60344-042-4(9))* Texas A&M Univ. Pr.

BOREDOM

Brown, Erica. Spiritual Boredom: Rediscovering the wonder of Judaism. 2009. 224p. 21.99 *(978-1-58023-405-4(4))* Jewish Lights Publishing.

Corvinelli, Antonietta. Boredom in Recovery from Substance Use Disorder. 2009. 144p. pap. *(978-3-639-16364-3(8))* VDM Verlag Dr. Mueller e.K.

Gibbs, Ryan M. Idle Time. 2011. 72p. pap. 10.00 ***(978-1-4567-6295-7(8))*** AuthorHouse.

Haugen, Gary A. Just Courage: God's Great Expedition for the Restless Christian. 2008. (ENG.). 150p. 18.00 *(978-0-8308-3494-5(X)*, IVP Bks.) InterVarsity Pr.

Kerstjens, Theo. Exciting Moments Versus Boring Routine: Exciting Ideas for Turning Routine & Boredom into More Joy of Living. 2010. 136p. pap. 10.99 *(978-1-4490-8837-8(6))* AuthorHouse.

Kolve, Carolee Nance. Golden Reflections: A Dog's Tale. 2010. 32p. pap. 14.99 *(978-1-4490-4641-5(X))* AuthorHouse.

Maeland, Bard & Brunstad, Paul Otto. Enduring Military Boredom: From 1750 to the Present. 2009. (ENG.). 256p. 89.00 *(978-0-230-57783-1(0))* Palgrave Macmillan.

Toohey, Peter. Boredom: A Lively History. 2012. (ENG., Illus.). 224p. pap. 16.00 ***(978-0-300-18184-5(1))*** 2011. *(978-83-00-14110-4(3))* Yale Univ. Pr.

BORES (TIDAL PHENOMENA)

Chanson, Hubert. Tidal Bores, Aegir, Eagre, Mascaret, Pororoca: Theory & Observations. 2011. 300p. 96.00 *(978-981-4335-41-6(X))* World Scientific Publishing Co., Inc.

Witts, Chris. The Severn Bore an Illustrated Guide. 2012. (Illus.). 96p. pap. 22.95 ***(978-1-84868-973-2(X))*** Amberley Publishing GBR. Dist: Casemate Pubs. & Bk. Distributors, LLC.

BORG, BJORN, 1956-

Cronin, Matthew. Epic: John McEnroe, Björn Borg, & the Greatest Tennis Season Ever. 2011. (ENG., Illus.). 312p. 25.95 *(978-0-470-19062-3(0)*, Wiley) Wiley, John & Sons, Inc.

Tignor, Stephen. High Strung: Bjorn Borg, John McEnroe, & the Untold Story of Tennis's Fiercest Rivalry. 2011. (ENG., Illus.). 256p. 25.99 *(978-0-06-200984-5(2))* HarperCollins Pubs.

BORGES, JORGE LUIS, 1899-1986

Aizenberg, Edna. The Aleph Weaver: Biblical, Kabbalistic & Judaic Elements in Borges. 25.00 *(978-0-916379-12-4(4))* Scripta Humanistica.

—Borges, el Tejedor Del Aleph y Otros Ensayos: Del Hebraísmo Al Poscolonialismo. 2006. (SPA., Illus.). 169p. pap. 18.95 *(978-84-88906-59-5(5))* Iberoamericana Editorial Vervuert ESP. Dist: Fondo de Cultura Economica USA.

Bloch, W. L. & Bloch, William Goldbloom. The Unimaginable Mathematics of Borges' Library of Babel. 2008. (ENG., Illus.). 160p. (C). 19.95 *(978-0-19-533457-9(4))* Oxford Univ. Pr., Inc.

Borges, Jorge Luis. Biblioteca Personal: Prólogos. (SPA., Illus.). 173p. 14.95 *(978-84-206-3317-6(8)*, AZ3178) Alianza Editorial, S. A. ESP. Dist: Continental Bk. Co., Inc.

—Everything & Nothing. Yates, Donald A. et al, trs. 2010. (Pearls Ser.). (ENG., Illus.). 96p. pap. 9.95 *(978-0-8112-1883-2(X)*, 21883) New Directions Publishing Corp.

—On Argentina. Levine, Suzanne Jill & Mac Adam, Alfred, eds. 2010. (ENG.). 192p. (gr. 12). 15.00 *(978-0-14-310573-2(6)*, Penguin Classics) Penguin Group (USA) Inc.

—On Mysticism. Levine, Suzanne Jill & Kodama, Maria, eds. 2010. (ENG.). 128p. (gr. 12). 14.00 *(978-0-14-310569-5(8)*, Penguin Classics) Penguin Group (USA) Inc.

Butler, Rex. Borges' Short Stories: A Reader's Guide. 2010. (Reader's Guides). (ENG.). 160p. 24.95 *(978-0-8264-5213-9(2))* Continuum International Publishing Group, Ltd. GBR. Dist: National Bk. Network.

Butler, Rex & Butler. Borges' Short Stories: A Reader's Guide. 2010. (Reader's Guides). (ENG.). 160p. 90.00 *(978-0-8264-4298-7(6))* Continuum International Publishing Group, Ltd. GBR. Dist: National Bk. Network.

Casares, Adolfo Bioy. Borges. 2007. (SPA., Illus.). 1663p. *(978-950-732-085-9(7))* Ediciones Destino.

Casares, Adolfo Bioy & Bioy Casares, Adolfo. Borges. 2006. 1664p. 58.95 *(978-84-233-3873-3(8))* Ediciones Destino ESP. Dist: Planeta Publishing Corp.

Crossan, John Dominic. Raid on the Articulate: Comic Eschatology in Jesus & Borges. 2008. 224p. pap. 25.00 *(978-1-55635-822-7(9))* Wipf & Stock Pubs.

Dabove, Juan Pablo. Jorge Luis Borges: Políticas de la Literatura. 2008. (SPA.). 371p. pap. *(978-1-930744-34-9(X))* Instituto Internacional de Literatura Iberoamericana (IILI).

Egginton, William & Johnson, David E., eds. Thinking with Borges. 2009. (ENG.). 234p. pap. 24.00 *(978-1-934542-11-8(3))* Davies Group Pubs., The.

Ferretti, Victor Andres. Boreale Geltung: Zu Nordlichkeit, Raum und Imaginarem im Werkvon Jorge Luis Borges. (GER.). 344p. pap. 68.95 *(978-3-631-56638-1(7))* Lang, Peter GmbH, Europaischer Verlag der Wissenschaften DEU. Dist: Lang, Peter Publishing, Inc.

Flynn, Annette U. Quest for God in the Work of Borges. 2009. (Continuum Literary Studies). (ENG.). 240p. 120.00 *(978-1-84706-053-2(6))* Continuum International Publishing Group, Ltd. GBR. Dist: National Bk. Network.

Flynn, Annette U. The Quest for God in the Work of Borges. 2012. (ENG.). 240p. pap. 44.95 ***(978-1-4411-8510-5(0))*** Continuum International Publishing Group, Ltd. GBR. Dist: National Bk. Network.

Gil Guerrero, Herminia. Poética Narrativa de Jorge Luis Borges. 2008. 191p. pap. 24.80 *(978-84-8489-398-1(7))* Iberoamericana Vervuert Publishing Corp.

Gracia, Jorge J. E. Painting Borges: Philosophy Interpreting Art Interpreting Literature. 2012. (SUNY series in Latin American & Iberian Thought & Culture Ser.). (ENG.). 288p. 90.00 ***(978-1-4384-4177-1(0))***; pap. 25.95 ***(978-1-4384-4178-8(9))*** State Univ. of New York Pr.

Herbrechter, Stefan & Callus, Ivan. Cy-Borges: Memories of the Posthuman in the Work Ofjorge Luis Borges. 2009. 224p. 49.50 *(978-0-8387-5715-4(4))* Bucknell Univ. Pr.

Humberto, Nunez-Faraco. Borges & Dante: Echoes of a Literary Friendship, Vol. 20. 2006. (European Connections Ser.). 230p. pap. 49.95 *(978-0-8204-7517-2(3))* Lang, Peter Publishing, Inc.

Jenckes, Kate. Reading Borges after Benjamin: Allegory, Afterlife, & the Writing of History. 2008. (SUNY Series in Latin American & Iberian Thought & Culture). 165p. per. 24.95 *(978-0-7914-6990-3(5))* State Univ. of New York Pr.

Johnson, David E. Kant's Dog: On Borges, Philosophy, & the Time of Translation. 2012. (SUNY series in Latin American & Iberian Thought & Culture Ser.). (ENG.). 272p. 75.00 ***(978-1-4384-4265-5(3))*** State Univ. of New York Pr.

Kefala, Eleni. Peripheral (Post) Modernity: The Syncretist Aesthetics of Borges, Piglia, Kalokyris & Kyriakidis. 2007. 316p. (C). 77.95 *(978-0-8204-8639-0(6))* Lang, Peter Publishing, Inc.

Manguel, Alberto. With Borges. 2006. (ENG.). 77p. per. 11.95 *(978-1-84659-005-4(1)*, Telegram Bks.) Saqi Bks. GBR. Dist: Consortium Bk. Sales & Distribution.

McNeese, Tim. Jorge Luis Borges. 2008. (Great Hispanic Heritage Ser.). (Illus.). 120p. (gr. 6-12). lib. bdg. 35.00 *(978-0-7910-9665-9(3)*, Chelsea Hse.) Facts On File, Inc.

Nahson, Daniel. La Critica Del Mito: Borges y la Literatura Como Sueño de Vida. 2009. (SPA.). 362p. pap. 36.00 *(978-84-8489-383-7(9))* Iberoamericana Vervuert Publishing Corp.

Novillo-Corvalan, Patricia. Borges & Joyce: An Infinite Conversation. 2011. (Legenda Main Ser.). (ENG.). 204p. (C). 89.50 *(978-1-907625-05-3(4))* European Humanities Research Ctr. GBR. Dist: Brown, David Bk. Co., The.

Olea Franco, Rafael. In Memoriam: Jorge Luis Borges. 2008. (Estudios Lingüísticos y Literarios Ser.). (SPA.). 420p. pap. 38.99 *(978-968-12-1361-9(0))* El Colegio de México, A.C., Biblioteca Miguel Cosio Villegas MEX. Dist: Fondo de Cultura Economica USA.

Pastormerlo, Sergio. Borges Critico. 2007. (Tierra Firme Ser.). (SPA.). 197p. pap. 13.95 *(978-950-557-711-8(7))* Fondo de Cultura Economica USA.

Paul, Kong Kim Por. The Raiders & Writers of Cervantes'Archive: Borges, Puig, & Marquez. 2009. 154p. 99.95 *(978-0-7546-6533-5(X))* Ashgate Publishing Co.

Richardson, Bill. Borges & Space. 2012. (Hispanic Studies: Culture & Ideas Ser.: 41). (ENG.). 256p. pap. 54.95 ***(978-3-0343-0246-3(0))*** Lang, Peter AG GBR. Dist: Lang, Peter.

Sarlo, Beatriz. Jorge Luis Borges: A Writer on the Edge. King, John, ed. 2007. (Critical Studies in Latin American Culture). (ENG.). 176p. (gr. 13). per. 19.95 *(978-1-84467-588-3(2)*, 844588) Verso Bks. GBR. Dist: Norton, W. W. & Co., Inc.

Sasson-Henry, Perla & Sassón-Henry, Perla. Borges 2.0: From Text to Virtual Worlds. 2007. (Latin America: Interdisciplinary Studies). 136p. (C). 58.95 *(978-0-8204-9714-3(2))* Lang, Peter Publishing, Inc.

Sorrentino, Fernando. Seven Conversations with Jorge Luis Borges. Zlotchew, Clark M., tr. from SPA. 2010. (ENG.). 220p. pap. 16.95 *(978-1-58988-060-3(9))* Dry, Paul Bks., Inc.

Strathern, Paul. Borges in 90 Minutes. 2006. (Great Writers in 90 Minutes Ser.). (ENG.). 128p. 16.95 *(978-1-56663-695-7(7))*; per. 8.95 *(978-1-56663-694-0(9))* Dee, Ivan R. Pub.

Tcherepashenets, Nataly. Place & Displacement in the Narrative Worlds of Jorge Luis Borges & Julio Cortázar. 2007. (Currents in Comparative Romance Languages & Literatures Ser.: Vol. 151). 222p. (C). 68.95 *(978-0-8204-6395-7(7))* Lang, Peter Publishing, Inc.

Thon, Sonia R. Contexto, Estilo y Forma en la Obra de Jorge Luis Borges y Manuel Puig. 2011. 141p. 99.95 *(978-0-7734-1392-4(8))* Mellen, Edwin Pr., The.

Toro, Alfonso de & Toro, Fernando de, eds. Jorge Luis Borges: Pensamiento y Saber en el Siglo XX. 2006. (SPA., Illus.). 376p. pap. 38.00 *(978-84-95107-39-8(2))* Iberoamericana Editorial Vervuert ESP. Dist: Fondo de Cultura Economica USA.

Wilson, Jason. Jorge Luis Borges. 2006. (Critical Lives (Reaktion Books) Ser.). (ENG., Illus.). 176p. per. 16.95 *(978-1-86189-286-7(1))* Reaktion Bks., Ltd. GBR. Dist: Chicago Distribution Ctr.

Zlotchew, Clark M. Varieties of Magic Realism. 2007. 186p. *(978-1-930879-47-8(4))* Ediciones Nuevo Espacio-AcademicPressENE.

BORGHESE, MARIA PAOLINA BONAPARTE, PRINCIPESSA, 1780-1825

see Bonaparte, Paolina, 1780-1825

BORGIA, CESARE, 1476-1507

Sabatini, Rafael. The Life of Cesare Borgia. 2007. (ENG.). 344p. pap. 23.99 *(978-1-4346-7544-6(0))*; 382p. pap. 26.99 *(978-1-4346-7545-3(9))* BiblioBazaar.

—The Life of Cesare Borgia. 2007. (ENG.). 328p. per. *(978-1-4065-4264-6(4))* Dodo Pr.

—The Life of Cesare Borgia. 2006. (ENG.). pap. *(978-1-4068-0471-3(1))* Echo Library.

—The Life of Cesare Borgia. 2010. pap. 75.76 *(978-1-61719-412-2(3))* Gorgias Pr., LLC.

Strathern, Paul. The Artist, the Philosopher, & the Warrior: Da Vinci, Machiavelli, & Borgia & the World They Shaped. 2011. (ENG., Illus.). 480p. pap. 18.00 *(978-0-553-38614-1(X))* Random House Publishing Group.

—The Artist, the Philosopher, & the Warrior: The Intersecting Lives of Da Vinci, Machiavelli, & Borgia & the World They Shaped. 2009. (ENG., Illus.). 480p. 30.00 *(978-0-553-80752-3(8))* Random House Publishing Group.

BORGIA, LUCREZIA, 1480-1519

Copelin, David. Bella Donna. 2007. (ENG., Illus.). 96p. pap. 16.95 *(978-0-88754-840-6(7))* Theatre Communications Group, Inc.

d'Este, Antonino. The Real Lucrezia Borgia. 2009. 177p. pap. 22.56 *(978-1-4303-2500-0(3))* Lulu Enterprises Inc.

Gregorovius, Ferdinand. Lucretia Borgia. Garner, John Leslie, tr. 2008. (Illus.). 344p. pap. *(978-1-4099-1521-8(2))* Dodo Pr.

Ryley, M. Beresford. Queens of the Renaissance. 2009. 372p. 33.99 *(978-1-116-80851-3(X))* 38.99 *(978-1-116-80850-6(1))*; pap. 32.75 *(978-1-116-80852-0(8))*; pap. 31.75 *(978-1-116-80853-7(6))* BiblioBazaar.

—Queens of the Renaissance. 2007. (ENG.). 412p. per. 34.95 *(978-0-548-78699-4(2))* Kessinger Publishing, LLC.

BORGIA FAMILY

Anonymous. Pope Alexander VI & His Court: Extracts from the Latin diary of Johannes Burchardus. 2009. 228p. 28.99 *(978-1-116-56221-7(9))*; pap. 24.75 *(978-1-116-56223-1(5))* pap. 25.75 *(978-1-116-56222-4(7))* BiblioBazaar.

Dumas, Alexandre. The Borgias (Fom Celebrated Crime) 2008. 192p. per. 7.99 *(978-1-60450-138-4(3))* Arc Manor.

Hibbert, Christopher. The Borgias & Their Enemies: 1431-1519. 2009. (ENG.). 336p. pap. 15.95 *(978-0-547-24781-6(8)*, Mariner Bks.) Houghton Mifflin Harcourt Trade & Reference Pubs.

BORGLUM, JOHN GUTZON DE LA MOTHE, 1867-1941

Borglum, Gutsom. Six Wars at a Time. 2007. 400p. per. 13.95 *(978-0-913062-37-1(5)*, Fenwyn Pr.

Carter, Robin Borglum. Gutzon Borglum: His Life & Work. 2007. (ENG.). 95p. per. 19.95 *(978-0-9752617-9-8(7))* Mount Rushmore Bookstores.

Casey, Robert J., et al. Give the Man Room: The Story of Gutzon Borglum. 2011. 348p. 51.95 ***(978-1-258-00413-2(5))*** Literary Licensing, LLC.

Dean, Robert J. Living Granite: The Story of Borglum & the Mount Rushmore Memorial. 2011. 128p. 40.95 ***(978-1-258-00654-9(5))*** Literary Licensing, LLC.

BORIDES

Suzuki, Souta & Fukuda, Kouki. Magnesium Diboride (MGB2) Superconductor Research. Suzuki, Souta & Fukuda, Kouki, eds. 2008. (Illus.). xii, 303p. 150.00 *(978-1-60456-566-9(7))* Nova Science Pubs., Inc.

BORING

Here are entered works relating to the operation of cutting holes in earth or rocks, in order to determine the nature of the strata penetrated, or to furnish an outlet for water, oil, or gas. Works on the drilling and boring of holes in metal, wood, and other materials, as carried on in workshops, etc., for construction or manufacturing purposes are entered under Drilling and Boring.

see also Core Drilling; Drilling Muds; Gas Well Drilling; Oil Well Drilling; Underwater Drilling

Australian Drilling, The, ed. Drilling: The Manual of Methods, Applications, & Management. 2nd rev. ed. 2012. (ENG., Illus.). 640p. 149.95 *(978-1-4398-1420-8(1)*, CRC Press) Taylor & Francis Group GBR. Dist: Taylor & Francis Group.

Bar-Cohen, Yoseph & Zacny, Kris, eds. Drilling in Extreme Environments: Penetration & Sampling on Earth & Other Planets. 2009. (ENG., Illus.). 827p. 220.00 *(978-3-527-40852-8(5)*, Wiley-VCH) Wiley, John & Sons, Inc.

Bloetscher, Frederick, et al. Siting, Drilling, & Construction of Water Supply Wells. 2008. (Illus.). 206p. 189.00 *(978-1-58321-516-6(6))* American Water Works Assn.

Cram101 Textbook Reviews & Cram101 Textbook Reviews. Outlines & Highlights for Formulas & Calculations for Drilling Operations by Robello Samuel. 2011. 122p. pap. 28.95 ***(978-1-61830-845-0(9))*** Cram101 Inc.

Harms, Ulrich, et al, eds. Continental Scientific Drilling: A Decade of Progress, & Challenges for the Future. 2007. (ENG., Illus.). x, 366p. 149.00 *(978-3-540-68777-1(7)*, 3540687777) Springer.

—Continental Scientific Drilling: A Decade of Progress, & Challenges for the Future. 2010. (ENG., Illus.). x, 366p. pap. 149.00 *(978-3-642-08830-8(9)*, 3642088309) Springer.

Inglis, T. A. Directional Drilling. 2010. (Petroleum Engineering & Development Studies). 280p. pap. 167.00 *(978-90-481-5804-1(4)*, 9048158044) Springer.

New Developments in Upstream Oil & Gas Technologies: Hearing Before the Committee on Energy & Natural Resources, United States Senate, One Hundred Twelfth Congress, First Session, to Receive Testimony on New Developments in Upstream Oil & Gas Technologies, May 20, 2011. 2011. iii, 60p. ***(978-0-16-089125-0(6)***, 552-070-43137-3) United States Government Printing Office.

Rustan, Agne, et al, eds. Mining & Rock Construction Technology: Rock Mechanics, Drilling & Blasting. 2010. (ENG., Illus.). 466p. (C). 119.95 *(978-0-415-60043-9(X)*, CRC Press) Taylor & Francis Group GBR. Dist: Taylor & Francis Group.

Samuel, G. Robello. Downhole Drilling Tools: Theory & Practice for Engineers & Students. 2007. (Illus.). 648p. 195.00 *(978-1-933762-13-5(6))* Gulf Publishing Co.

Vieira, Joao Luiz. Controlled Directional Drilling. 4th ed. 2009. *(978-0-88698-254-6(5))* Petroleum Extension Service (PETEX).

BORINGS

Here are entered the results of boring operations conducted in various parts of the earth to determine the nature of the strata penetrated.

see also *Oil Well Logging*

Arihood, Leslie D. Processing, Analysis, & General Evaluation of Well-Driller Logs for Estimating Hydrogeologic Parameters of the Glacial Sediments in a Ground-Water Flow Model of the Lake Michigan Basin. 2009. (Illus.). vi, 26p. pap. *(978-1-4113-2302-5(5))* United States Geological Survey.

BORMANN, MARTIN, 1900-1945

Whiting, Charles. The Hunt for Martin Bormann. 2011. (Illus.). 240p. pap. 24.95 *(978-1-84884-289-2(9))* Pen & Sword Bks. Ltd. GBR. Dist: Casemate Pubs. & Bk. Distributors, LLC.

BORN AGAIN CHRISTIANITY

see *Conversion; Regeneration (Theology); Salvation*

BORNEO

Bock, Carl A. The Head-Hunters of Borneo: A Narrative of Travel up the Mahakkam & Down the Barito. 2nd ed. reprint ed. 125.00 *(978-0-404-16698-4(9))* AMS Pr., Inc.

Couderc, Pascal & Sillander, Kenneth. Ancestors in Borneo Societies: Death, Transformation, & Social Immortality. 2012. (Illus.). 432p. ***(978-87-7694-091-1(8))*** Nordic Institute of Asian Studies.

Garbutt, Nick & Prudente, J. Cede. Wild Borneo: The Wildlife & Scenery of Sabah, Sarawak, Brunei, & Kalimantan. 2006. (ENG., Illus.). 176p. (gr. 17). 36.95 *(978-0-262-07274-8(2))* MIT Pr.

Harrop, Thomas. Borneo. 2010. 192p. pap. 65.00 *(978-0-557-42639-3(1))* Lulu Enterprises Inc.

Lumholtz, Carl. Through Central Borneo: An Account of Two Years' Travel in the Land of Head-Hunters Between the Years 1913 And 1917. 2007. (ENG.). 400p. pap. 25.99 *(978-1-4264-2514-1(7))* BiblioBazaar.

—Through Central Borneo: An Account of Two Years' Travel in the Land of Head-Hunters Between the Years 1913 And 1918. l.t. ed. 2006. 430p. pap. 28.99 *(978-1-4264-2537-0(6))* BiblioBazaar.

Lumholtz, Karl S. Through Central Borneo: An Account of Two Years' Travel in the Land of the Head-Hunters Between the Years 1913 & 1917, 2 vols., Set. (Illus.). reprint ed. 53.00 *(978-0-404-16760-8(8))* AMS Pr., Inc.

Martin, Peter W. & Sercombe, Peter G. Languages in Borneo: Diachronic & Synchronic Perspectives. 2009. (Illus.). x, 328p. *(978-1-929900-11-4(2))* Borneo Research Council, Inc.

Mershon, Elizabeth. With the Wild Men of Borneo. 2007. (ENG.). 128p. 35.95 *(978-0-548-10661-7(4))* Kessinger Publishing, LLC.

Munan, Heidi. Borneo: A Survival Guide to Customs & Etiquette. 2009. 264p. pap. 15.95 *(978-0-7614-5659-9(7))* Marshall Cavendish Corp.

Munan, Heidi & Cavendish, Marshall. Cultureshock! Borneo, 1 vol. 2007. (Cultureshock Borneo: A Survival Guide to Customs & Etiquette Ser.). (ENG., Illus.). 32p. pap. 15.95 *(978-0-7614-2489-5(X))* Marshall Cavendish Corp.

Pryer, Ada. A Decade in Borneo. 2009. 138p. pap. *(978-1-151-29038-0(6))* Books LLC.

Puri, Rajindra K. Deadly Dances in the Bornean Rainforest: Hunting Knowledge of the Penan Benalui. 2010. (Verhandelingen Van Het Koninklijk Instituut Voor Taal-, Land Ser.). (ENG., Illus.). 417p. pap. 44.00 *(978-90-6718-239-3(7))* KITLV Pr. NLD. Dist: Univ. of Hawaii Pr.

Robinson, Daniel. Borneo. 2nd rev. ed. 2011. (Regional Guide Ser.). (ENG., Illus.). 332p. (Orig.). pap. 24.99 *(978-1-74179-215-7(0))* Lonely Planet Pubns.

Rutter, Owen. British North Borneo: An Account of Its History, Resources & Native Tribes. reprint ed. 37.50 *(978-0-404-16775-2(6))* AMS Pr., Inc.

Thiessen, Tamara. Borneo. 2nd ed. 2009. (Bradt Travel Guide Ser.). (ENG., Illus.). 208p. pap. 27.99 *(978-1-84162-252-1(4))* Bradt Travel Guides GBR. Dist: Globe Pequot Pr., The.

Walker, H. Wilfrid. Wanderings among South Sea Savages & in Borneo & the Philippines. 2010. 362p. pap. 32.75 *(978-1-177-77272-3(8))*; (ENG.). 374p. pap. 33.75 *(978-1-176-50368-7(5))* BiblioBazaar.

—Wanderings among South Sea Savages & in Borneo & the Philippines. 2010. 110p. pap. *(978-1-152-10943-8(X))* Books LLC.

—Wanderings among South Sea Savages & in Borneo & the Philippines. 2008. (ENG.). 140p. per. *(978-1-4065-5069-6(8))* Dodo Pr.

—Wanderings among South Sea Savages & in Borneo & the Philippines. 2010. 98p. pap. 20.00 *(978-1-153-73223-9(8))* General Bks. LLC.

—Wanderings among South Sea Savages & in Borneo & the Philippines. 2010. 124p. 28.76 ***(978-1-169-25237-0(0))***; pap. 16.76 ***(978-1-162-71624-4(X))***; 35.95 *(978-1-161-48488-5(4))* Kessinger Publishing, LLC.

BORNEO—HISTORY

Annett, Roger. Drop Zone Borneo - the RAF Campaign 1963-65: 'the Most Successful Use of Armed Forces in the Twentieth Century' 2011. (Illus.). 160p. pap. 24.95 *(978-1-84884-405-6(0))* Pen & Sword Bks. Ltd. GBR. Dist: Casemate Pubs. & Bk. Distributors, LLC.

Couderc, Pascal & Sillander, Kenneth. Ancestors in Borneo Societies: Death, Transformation, & Social Immortality. 2012. (Illus.). 432p. pap. ***(978-87-7694-092-8(6))*** Nordic Institute of Asian Studies.

Dixon, Paul. Borneo: Travel Guide to Borneo. 3rd ed. 2010. (Footprint - Handbooks Ser.). (ENG., Illus.). 352p. (Orig.). 25.95 *(978-1-907263-06-4(3))* Footprint Handbooks GBR. Dist: Globe Pequot Pr., The.

Dove, Michael R. The Banana Tree at the Gate: A History of Marginal Peoples & Global Markets in Borneo. 2011. (Yale Agrarian Studies Ser.). (ENG., Illus.). 352p. 55.00 *(978-0-300-15321-7(X))* Yale Univ. Pr.

Gin, Keat. The Japanese Occupation of Borneo, 1941-45. 2011. (Routledge Studies in the Modern History of Asia Ser.). (ENG., Illus.). 224p. (C). 140.00 *(978-0-415-45663-0(0))* Routledge.

Jackson, Robert. The Malayan Emergency. 2008. (Illus.). 156p. 39.95 *(978-1-84415-775-4(X))* Pen & Sword Bks. Ltd. GBR. Dist: Casemate Pubs. & Bk. Distributors, LLC.

Keat Gin, Ooi. Postwar Borneo 1945-50. 2012. (ENG., Illus.). 240p. (C). 140.00 ***(978-0-415-55959-1(6))*** Routledge.

Koninck, Rodolphe de, et al. Borneo Transformed: Agricultural Expansion on the Southeast Asian Frontier. 2011. (Illus.). ix, 216p. 32.00 ***(978-9971-69-544-6(8))*** National Univ. of Singapore Pr. SGP. Dist: Univ. of Hawaii Pr.

Lauren, Jillian. Some Girls: My Life in a Harem. 2010. (ENG.). 352p. (gr. 12). 15.00 *(978-0-452-29631-2(5)*, Plume) Penguin Group (USA) Inc.

Lumholtz, Carl. Through Central Borneo. 2009. 264p. 24.99 *(978-1-103-77391-6(7))* 2009. 264p. pap. 18.99 *(978-1-103-77385-5(2))* 2008. 432p. 32.99 *(978-0-554-22511-1(5))* 2008. 432p. 30.99 *(978-0-554-31814-1(8))* BiblioBazaar.

—Through Central Borneo. 2009. 206p. pap. *(978-1-4590-0929-5(0))*; 180p. pap. *(978-1-4590-0932-5(0))* Books LLC.

—Through Central Borneo. 2008. 316p. pap. *(978-1-4099-0704-6(X))* Dodo Pr.

Macdonald, David. Expedition to Borneo. 2007. 212p. per. 25.00 *(978-1-59048-243-8(3))* Long Riders' Guild Pr., The.

Metcalf, Peter. The Life of the Longhouse: An Archaeology of Ethnicity. 2009. (ENG., Illus.). 358p. 88.00 *(978-0-521-11098-3(X))* Cambridge Univ. Pr.

Thiessen, Tamara. Borneo: Sabah - Brunei - Sarawak. 2nd rev. ed. 2012. (Bradt Travel Guide Ser.). (ENG., Illus.). 320p. pap. 27.99 ***(978-1-84162-390-0(3))*** Bradt Travel Guides GBR. Dist: Globe Pequot Pr., The.

Van der Bijl, Nick & Van der Bijl, Nicholas. Confrontation: The War with Indonesia, 1962-1966. 2007. (Illus.). 240p. 39.95 *(978-1-84415-595-8(1))* Pen & Sword Bks. Ltd. GBR. Dist: Casemate Pubs. & Bk. Distributors, LLC.

BORON

Adair, Rick. Boron. 2009. (Understanding the Elements of the Periodic Table Ser.). 48p. (gr. 6-6). 53.00 *(978-1-60854-637-4(3)*, Rosen Central) Rosen Publishing Group, Inc., The.

Ahmed, Iftikhar & FUJIWARA, Toru. Boron-Tolerance in Bacteri. 2010. 84p. pap. *(978-3-639-25890-5(8))* VDM Verlag Dr. Mueller e.K.

Damiri, Basma. Risk Characterization for Boron & Aquatic Plants & Animals. 2010. 108p. pap. *(978-3-639-22207-4(5))* VDM Verlag Dr. Mueller e.K.

Demirci, Umit B. & Miele, Philippe, eds. Boron Hydrides, High Potential Hydrogen Storage Materials. 2010. (Chemistry Research & Applications Ser.). 155.00 *(978-1-61668-361-0(9))* Nova Science Pubs., Inc.

Gulyás, Henrik & Fernández, Elena. Influence of the Borane Reagent Structure on Catalytic Synthesis of Organoboranes. 2011. pap. *(978-1-61209-340-6(X))* Nova Science Pubs., Inc.

Hasan, Heather. The Boron Elements: Boron, Aluminum, Gallium, Indium, Thallium. 2009. (Understanding the Elements of the Periodic Table Ser.). (ENG., Illus.). 48p. (YA). (gr. 5-9). lib. bdg. 26.50 *(978-1-4358-5333-1(4))* Rosen Publishing Group, Inc., The.

Luches, Armando & Caricato, Anna Paola. Laser-Assisted Deposition of Boron Nitride Thin Films & Nanotubes. 2011. (Series: Lasers & Electro-Optics Research & Technology Ser.). pap. 43.00 *(978-1-61122-420-7(9))* Nova Science Pubs., Inc.

Mohib Muazzam Naz, Raja, et al. Effect of Boron on the Growth & Yield of Tomato. 2011. 68p. pap. ***(978-3-8443-0700-9(1))*** Lambert Academic Publishing.

Naeem, Muhammad Asif & Aamer Maqsood, Muhammad. Boron Requirement of Mungbean. 2011. 96p. pap. ***(978-3-8443-0423-7(1))*** Lambert Academic Publishing.

Nievaart, Victor Alexander. Spectral Tailoring for Boron Neutron Capture Therapy. 2007. (Illus.). xvii, 118p. pap. 59.00 *(978-1-58603-762-8(5)*, Delft University Pr) IOS Pr., Inc.

Orlovskaya, Nina & Lugovy, Mykola, eds. Boron Rich Solids: Sensors, Ultra High Temperature Ceramics, Thermoelectrics, Armor. 2010. (NATO Science for Peace & Security Series B: Physics & Biophysics Ser.). x, 375p. 229.00 *(978-90-481-9817-7(8)*, 9048198178); (ENG.). pap. 119.00 *(978-90-481-9823-8(2)*, 9048198232) Springer.

Pardasani, R. T. & Pardasani, Pushpa. Chemical Shifts & Coupling Constants for Boron-11. 2009. (Landolt-Börnstein: Numerical Data & Functional Relationships in Science & Technology Ser.). viii, 579p. 4039.00 *(978-3-642-01993-7(5)*, 3642019935) Springer.

Perkins, Gary L. Boron: Compounds, Production & Application. 2011. (Series: Materials Science & Technologies Ser.). (Illus.). 631p. 325.00 *(978-1-61761-760-7(1))* Nova Science Pubs., Inc.

Pla, Patricia, et al. Boron Dilution in Pressurizer Water Reactors. 2010. 276p. pap. *(978-3-8383-8373-6(7))* Lambert Academic Publishing.

Xu, Fangsen, et al, eds. Advances in Plant & Animal Boron Nutrition: Proceedings of the 3rd International Symposium on all Aspects of Plant & Animal Boron Nutrition. 2010. xvi, 402p. pap. 259.00 *(978-90-481-7356-3(6)*, 9048173566) Springer.

Zheng, Xuejia. Xin Xing Han Peng Cai Liao: Xinxing Han Peng Cailiao. 2010. (CHI., Illus.). 212p. *(978-7-122-07242-9(8))* Chemical Industry Pr.

BORON ORGANIC COMPOUNDS

see *Organoboron Compounds*

BOROUGHS

Adolphus, Ballard, ed. British Borough Charters 1042-1216. 2010. (Cambridge Library Collection - History Ser.). 420p. pap. 31.99 *(978-1-108-01033-7(4))* Cambridge Univ. Pr.

Ballard, Adolphus. The English Borough in the Twelfth Century: Being Two Lectures Delivered in the Examination Schools, Oxford, on 22 & 29 October 1913. 2011. (ENG.). 96p. pap. 19.99 ***(978-0-521-23788-8(2))*** Cambridge Univ. Pr.

Ballard, Adolphus & Tait, James, eds. British Borough Charters, 1216-1307. 2010. (Cambridge Library Collection - History Ser.). (ENG.). 508p. pap. 37.99 *(978-1-108-01034-4(2))* Cambridge Univ. Pr.

Bateson, Mary. Borough Customs. 2009. 414p. pap. *(978-1-4590-5754-8(6))*; 430p. pap. *(978-0-217-68835-2(7))* Books LLC.

Bateson, Mary, ed. Borough Customs. (Selden Society Annual Ser.: Vol. 18, 1904). Vol. I. 95.00 *(978-0-85423-006-8(8))* Vol. II. 95.00 *(978-0-85423-095-2(5))* Selden Society GBR. Dist: Hein, William S. & Co., Inc.

Macdonald, Alan R. The Burghs & Parliament in Scotland: The Early Modern Burghs & Parliament. 2007. (Illus.). 254p. 124.95 *(978-0-7546-5328-8(5))* Ashgate Publishing Co.

Weinbaum, Martin, ed. British Borough Charters, 1307-1660. 2010. (Cambridge Library Collection - History Ser.). (ENG.). 314p. pap. 24.99 *(978-1-108-01035-1(0))* Cambridge Univ. Pr.

BORROMEO, CHARLES, SAINT, 1538-1584

see *Charles Borromeo, Saint, 1538-1584*

BORROW, GEORGE HENRY, 1803-1881

Borrow, George. Isopel Berners. Seccombe, Thomas, ed. 2009. 304p. pap. *(978-1-4099-3269-7(9))* Dodo Pr.

—Letters of George Borrow to the British & Foreign Bible Society. Darlow, T. H., ed. 2008. 376p. pap. *(978-1-4099-3270-3(2))* Dodo Pr.

Borrow, George Henry. Isopel Berners. 2008. 304p. 29.99 *(978-0-554-23958-3(2))*; 28.99 *(978-0-554-33261-1(2))* BiblioBazaar.

—Isopel Berners: The History of certain doings in a Staffordshire Dingle, July 1825. 2007. (ENG.). 274p. pap. 21.99 *(978-1-4264-5194-2(6))*; 302p. pap. 24.99 *(978-1-4264-5495-0(3))* BiblioBazaar.

—Letters of George Borrow to the British & Foreign Bible Society. 2008. 428p. 30.99 *(978-0-554-38874-8(X))* 2008. 428p. 32.99 *(978-0-554-29571-8(7))* 2007. (ENG.). 384p. pap. 25.99 *(978-1-4346-7924-6(1))* 2007. (ENG.). 426p. pap. 28.99 *(978-1-4346-7925-3(X))* BiblioBazaar.

—Letters of George Borrow to the British & Foreign Bible Society. 2009. 278p. pap. *(978-1-150-67704-5(X))* Books LLC.

—Letters of George Borrow to the British & Foreign Bible Society, Published by Direction of the Committee. 2010. 268p. pap. 30.44 *(978-1-152-17287-6(5))* General Bks. LLC.

—Letters of George Borrow to the British & Foreign Bible Society, Published by the Direction of the Committee. 2009. 260p. pap. 29.71 *(978-1-151-50451-7(3))* General Bks. LLC.

—Works, 16 vols., Set. Shorter, Clement King, ed. reprint ed. 1224.00 *(978-0-404-00970-0(0))* AMS Pr., Inc.

Jenkins, Herbert. The Life of George Borrow. 2007. (ENG.). 428p. per. *(978-1-4065-2728-5(9))* Dodo Pr.

—The Life of George Borrow. 2010. 396p. pap. 27.96 *(978-1-162-69987-5(6))*; 39.96 ***(978-1-169-33557-8(8))***; 49.95 *(978-1-161-46852-6(8))* Kessinger Publishing, LLC.

Jenkins, Herbert George. The Life of George Borrow. 2010. (Illus.). 280p. pap. 35.91 *(978-1-153-70919-4(8))* General Bks. LLC.

Jenkins, Herbert George & Borrow, George Henry. The Life of George Borrow. 2010. (ENG.). 554p. pap. 42.75 *(978-1-177-53493-2(2))* BiblioBazaar.

Shorter, Clement King. George Borrow & His Circle. 2009. 492p. 33.99 *(978-0-559-11023-8(5))*; 31.99 *(978-0-559-11036-8(7))*; pap. 38.75 *(978-0-559-11026-9(X))*; pap. 37.75 *(978-0-559-11032-0(4))* BiblioBazaar.

—George Borrow & His Circle. 2008. (Illus.). 440p. pap. *(978-1-4065-6997-1(6))* Dodo Pr.

—George Borrow & His Circle. 2010. (Illus.). 266p. pap. 34.51 *(978-1-4432-0665-5(2))* General Bks. LLC.

—Immortal Memories. 2008. 180p. 22.99 *(978-0-554-37307-2(6))* 2008. 180p. 25.99 *(978-0-554-28004-2(3))* 2007. 160p. pap. 19.99 *(978-1-4346-4493-0(6))* 2007. 178p. pap. 21.99 *(978-1-4346-4494-7(4))* BiblioBazaar.

—Immortal Memories. 2009. 118p. pap. *(978-0-217-49313-0(0))*; pap. *(978-0-217-22994-4(8))* Books LLC.

—Immortal Memories. 2009. 148p. pap. *(978-1-4065-6998-8(4))* Dodo Pr.

Thomas, Edward. George Borrow. 2008. 336p. 28.99 *(978-0-554-34938-1(8))*; 29.99 *(978-0-554-25635-1(5))* BiblioBazaar.

—George Borrow. 2006. pap. *(978-1-4068-0957-2(8))* Echo Library.

—George Borrow: The Man & His Books. 2007. (ENG.). 296p. pap. 21.99 *(978-1-4264-9366-9(5))*; 332p. pap. 24.99 *(978-1-4264-9747-6(4))* BiblioBazaar.

—George Borrow: The Man & His Books. 2009. (Illus.). 316p. pap. *(978-1-4099-0645-2(0))* Dodo Pr.

—George Borrow: The Man & His Books. 2007. 404p. 49.95 *(978-0-548-55346-6(7))*; (ENG.). per. 34.95 *(978-0-548-51076-6(8))* Kessinger Publishing, LLC.

BORSTAL SYSTEM

see *Juvenile Detention Homes*

BORZOI

Borzoi: The Russian Wolfhound - A Dog Anthology (A Vintage Dog Books Breed Classic) 2007. 80p. per. *(978-1-4067-9115-0(6))* Read Bks.

Scott, Desiree. Borzoi. 2006. (Comprehensive Owners Guide Ser.). (ENG., Illus.). 155p. 19.95 *(978-1-59378-304-4(3))* Kennel Club Bks.

BOSCH, HIERONYMUS, D. 1516

Blum, Angela, tr. from ENG. El Bosco. 2008. (SPA.). *(978-958-30-2808-3(8))* Panamericana Editorial.

Bosing, Walter. Bosch. 2010. (25 Ser.). (ENG.). 96p. 14.99 *(978-3-8365-1340-1(4))* TASCHEN DEU. Dist: Ingram Pub. Services.

Cuttler, Charles D. Hieronymus Bosch: Late Work. 2012. (ENG., Illus.). 436p. (C). 300.00 *(978-1-904597-44-5(0))* Pindar Pr. GBR. Dist: Brown, David Bk. Co., The.

Falk, Kurt. The Unknown Hieronymus Bosch. 2008. (ENG., Illus.). 116p. pap. 29.95 *(978-1-55643-759-5(5))* North Atlantic Bks.

Falkenburg, Reindert. Hieronymus Bosch: The Land of Unlikeness. 2012. (ENG., Illus.). 320p. 95.00 ***(978-90-400-7767-8(3))*** Waanders B.V., Uitgeverij NLD. Dist: National Bk. Network.

Lewis-Anthony, Justin. Circles of Thorns: Hieronymus Bosch & Being Human. 2009. (ENG., Illus.). 192p. *(978-1-84706-509-4(0))* Continuum International Publishing Group, Ltd.

—Circles of Thorns: Hieronymus Bosch & Being Human. 2009. (ENG., Illus.). 200p. 27.95 *(978-1-906286-21-7(3))* Mowbray, A. R. & Co., Ltd. GBR. Dist: National Bk. Network.

Rembert, Virginia Pitts. Hieronymus Bosch. 2012. (Best Of Ser.). (ENG., Illus.). 200p. 19.95 ***(978-1-906981-41-9(8))*** Parkstone Pr. USA, Ltd.

Silver, Larry. Hieronymus Bosch. 2006. (ENG., Illus.). 424p. 150.00 *(978-0-7892-0901-6(2))* Abbeville Pr., Inc.

BOSCO, GIOVANNI, SAINT, 1815-1888

Bosco, John. Memoirs of the Oratory of Saint Francis de Sales: The Autobiography of Saint John Bosco. Lyons, Daniel, tr. abr. ed. 2007. 198p. pap. 12.00 *(978-0-89944-184-9(X))* Salesiana Pubs.

BOSCO, HENRI, 1888-1976

Baudry, R. Henri Bosco et la Tradition du Merveilleux. 2010. (FRE.). 248p. *(978-2-7078-1308-4(7))* Librairie-Editions Nizet.

BOSE, SUBHAS CHANDRA, 1897-1945

Basu, Kanailal. Netaji: Rediscovered. 2010. 500p. 30.99 *(978-1-4490-5568-4(0))* 2010. 500p. pap. 20.49 *(978-1-4490-5567-7(2))* 2009. 504p. pap. 21.95 *(978-1-4343-6632-0(4))* AuthorHouse.

Bose, Sugata. His Majesty's Opponent: Subhas Chandra Bose & India's Struggle Against Empire. 2011. (Illus.). 448p. 35.00 *(978-0-674-04754-9(0)*, Belknap Pr.) Harvard Univ. Pr.

Hayes, Romain. Subhas Chandra Bose in Nazi Germany: Politics, Intelligence, & Propaganda 1941-43. 2011. (Columbia/Hurst Ser.). (ENG.). 224p. (gr. 17). 30.00 *(978-0-231-70234-8(5))* Columbia Univ. Pr.

Lebra, Joyce C. Women Against the Raj: The Rani of Jhansi Regiment. 2008. 168p. *(978-981-230-809-2(1))* Institute of Southeast Asian Studies.

O'Malley, Kate. Ireland, India & Empire: Indo-Irish Radical Connections, 1919-64. 2010. (Studies in Imperialism Ser.). (ENG., Illus.). 224p. pap. 30.95 *(978-0-7190-8171-2(8))* Manchester Univ. Pr. GBR. Dist: Macmillan.

Vas, Eric A. Subhas Chandra Bose: The Man & His Times. 2008. (Illus.). 269p. *(978-81-7062-243-7(3))* Lancer International, Lancer Pr.

BOSE-EINSTEIN PARTICLES

see *Bosons*

BOSNIA AND HERCEGOVINA

Bennett, Clinton. In Search of Solutions: The Problem of Religion & Conflict. 2009. (Religion & Violence Ser.). (ENG., Illus.). 284p. (C). 99.50 *(978-1-84553-239-0(2))*; 34.95 *(978-1-84553-240-6(6))* Equinox Publishing Ltd. GBR. Dist: ISD.

BOSNIA AND HERCEGOVINA—BIOGRAPHY

Demick, Barbara. Logavina Street: Life & Death in a Sarajevo Neighborhood. 2012. (ENG., Illus.). 272p. pap. 16.00 ***(978-0-8129-8276-3(2))*** Spiegel & Grau.

Facing Memory: Student Memoirs from Bosnia. 2007. per. *(978-1-932948-25-7(2))* Student Pr. Initiative.

Feto, Berina, et al. Bijase to Generacija- 2009. 202p. *(978-9958-590-82-5(4))* Connectum.

Koblar, Stanislav. Cetrta Stran Trikotnika: Znameniti Slovenci in Slovenska Druztva V Bosni in Hercegovini, 1878-2000. 2008. (SLV., Illus.). 465p. *(978-961-01-0377-6(4))* Mladinska Knjiga Zalozba, d.d.

Reid, Atka & Schofield, Hana. Goodbye Sarajevo: A True Story of Courage, Love & Survival. 2012. (ENG., Illus.). 352p. pap. 28.00 ***(978-1-4088-1456-7(0))*** Bloomsbury Publishing.

BOSNIA AND HERCEGOVINA—DESCRIPTION AND TRAVEL

Anon. In the Land of the Bora or Camp Life & Sport in Dalmatia & the Herzegovina. 2009. 414p. pap. 31.45 *(978-1-4446-4093-9(3))* Thorndike Pr.

Clancy, Tim. Bosnia & Herzegovina. 3rd ed. 2010. (ENG., Illus.). 288p. pap. 25.99 *(978-1-84162-317-7(2))* Bradt Travel Guides GBR. Dist: Globe Pequot Pr., The.

Cresswell, Peter Jon. Bosnia, Serbia & Montenegro. 2nd ed. 2009. (Travellers - Thomas Cook Ser.). (ENG., Illus.). 176p. pap. 16.95 *(978-1-84848-150-3(0))* Cook, Thomas Publishing GBR. Dist: Globe Pequot Pr., The.

Evans, Arthur. Through Bosnia & the Herzegovina of Foot During the Insurrection. 435p. reprint ed. 98.00 *(978-0-7222-1950-8(4))* Library Reprints, Inc.
—Through Bosnia & the Herzegovina on Foot During the Insurrection, August & September 1875 (with an Historical Review of Bosnia & a Glimpse at Th. 2007. 508p. per. 29.95 *(978-1-60206-270-2(6))* Cosimo, Inc.
Hammond, Elizabeth. Bosnia & Herzegovina. 2009. (Culture Smart! Ser.). (ENG., Illus.). 168p. pap. 9.95 *(978-1-85733-484-5(1))* Kuperard Pubs. GBR. Dist: Random Hse., Inc.
Locken, E. Travel Journal Bosnia & Herzegovina. 2010. 192p. pap. 19.99 *(978-0-557-43274-5(X))* Lulu Enterprises Inc.

BOSNIA AND HERCEGOVINA—ECONOMIC CONDITIONS

Efendic, Adnan. Institutions & Economic Performance in Transition Countries. 2010. 348p. pap. *(978-3-8383-8209-8(9))* Lambert Academic Publishing.
Hlivnjak, Sandra. Current Account Sustainability. 2011. 492p. pap. ***(978-3-8443-8431-4(6))*** Lambert Academic Publishing.
Icon Group International, Inc. Staff, compiled by. The 2006 Economic & Product Market Databook for Banja Luca, Bosnia & Herzegovina. 2006. 618p. ring bd. 95.00 *(978-0-497-80137-3(X))* Icon Group International, Inc.
—The 2006 Economic & Product Market Databook for Mostar, Bosnia & Herzegovina. 2006. 618p. ring bd. 95.00 *(978-0-497-81061-0(1))* Icon Group International, Inc.
—The 2006 Economic & Product Market Databook for Prijedor, Bosnia & Herzegovina. 2006. 618p. ring bd. 95.00 *(978-0-497-81292-8(4))* Icon Group International, Inc.
—The 2006 Economic & Product Market Databook for Sarajevo, Bosnia & Herzegovina. 2006. 618p. ring bd. 95.00 *(978-0-497-81474-8(9))* Icon Group International, Inc.
—The 2006 Economic & Product Market Databook for Tuzla, Bosnia & Herzegovina. 2006. 618p. ring bd. 95.00 *(978-0-497-81740-4(3))* Icon Group International, Inc.
—The 2006 Economic & Product Market Databook for Zenica, Bosnia & Herzegovina. 2006. 618p. ring bd. 95.00 *(978-0-497-81856-2(6))* Icon Group International, Inc.
Ohanyan, Anna. NGOs, IGOs, & the Network Mechanisms of Post-Conflict Global Governance in Microfinance. 2008. (ENG.). 256p. 89.00 *(978-0-230-60759-9(1))* Palgrave Macmillan.
Solioz, Christophe. Turning Points in Post-War Bosnia: Ownership Process & European Integration (Second. 2nd rev. ed. 2007. (Illus.). 171p. (C). pap. 38.00 *(978-3-8329-2513-0(9))* Nomos Verlagsgesellschaft DEU. Dist: International Specialized Bk. Services.
Suljkanovic, Midran. Corporate Governance in Post-Privatized Bosnia & Herzegovin. 2010. 88p. pap. *(978-3-639-25364-1(7))* VDM Verlag Dr. Mueller e.K.
Terterov, Marat & Hensor, Alica. Bosnia & Herzegovina's Business Environment. 2008. (ENG.). 215p. pap. 75.00 *(978-1-84673-062-7(7)*, GMB Publishing Ltd.) Blue Ibex Ltd. GBR. Dist: Ingram Pub. Services.

BOSNIA AND HERCEGOVINA—ETHNIC RELATIONS

Baljak, Aladin. Bosni: The Security Dilemma that Did Not Exist - an Investigation into the Causes of Ethnic Violence. 2008. 80p. pap. *(978-3-639-03019-8(2))* VDM Verlag Dr. Mueller e.K.
Batic, Goran. The Question of National Identity of Bosnia & Herzegovin. 2009. 80p. pap. *(978-3-639-07943-2(4))* VDM Verlag Dr. Mueller e.K.
Mahmutcehajic, Rusmir. Maintaining the Sacred Center: The Bosnian City of Stolac. 2011. (ENG., Illus.). 312p. pap. 24.95 *(978-1-935493-91-4(4))* World Wisdom, Inc.
Pickering, Paula M. Peacebuilding in the Balkans: The View from the Ground Floor. 2007. (Illus.). 242p. 41.95 *(978-0-8014-4576-7(0))* Cornell Univ. Pr.
Ramet, Sabrina P. & Valenta, Marko. The Bosnian Diaspora: Integration in Transnational Communities. 2011. (Research in Migration & Ethnic Relations Ser.). (Illus.). 356p. 124.95 ***(978-1-4094-1252-6(0))*** Ashgate Publishing Co.
Toal, Gerard & Dahlman, Carl T. Bosnia Remade: Ethnic Cleansing & Its Reversal, 1 vol. 2011. (ENG., Illus.). 496p. 39.95 *(978-0-19-973036-0(9))* Oxford Univ. Pr., Inc.

BOSNIA AND HERCEGOVINA—FOREIGN RELATIONS

Belloni, Roberto. State Building & International Intervention in Bosnia. 2008. (Illus.). XII, 228p. 150.00 *(978-0-415-44925-0(1))* Routledge.
Dauphinee, Elizabeth. The Ethics of Researching War: Looking for Bosnia. 2007. (New Approaches to Conflict Analysis Ser.). (ENG.). 168p. pap. 26.00 *(978-0-7190-7615-2(3))* Manchester Univ. Pr. GBR. Dist: Macmillan.
Innes, Michael A., ed. Bosnian Security after Dayton: New Perspectives. 2006. (Contemporary Security Studies). (Illus.). 227p. 160.00 *(978-0-415-39958-6(0))* Routledge.
Ramet, Sabrina P. & Valenta, Marko. The Bosnian Diaspora: Integration in Transnational Communities. 2011. (Research in Migration & Ethnic Relations Ser.). (Illus.). 356p. 124.95 ***(978-1-4094-1252-6(0))*** Ashgate Publishing Co.
Sejfija, Ismet. NVO Sektor U BiH Tranzicijski Izazovi. 2009. 352p. *(978-9958-12-122-7(0))* Esic, Simo, Bosanska rijec - Bosnisches Wort.
Solioz, Christophe. Turning Points in Post-War Bosnia: Ownership Process & European Integration (Second. 2nd rev. ed. 2007. (Illus.). 171p. (C). pap. 38.00 *(978-3-8329-2513-0(9))* Nomos Verlagsgesellschaft DEU. Dist: International Specialized Bk. Services.
Terterov, Marat & Henson, Alica. Bosnia & Herzegovina's Business Environment. 2008. (ENG.). 215p. pap. 75.00 *(978-1-84673-062-7(7)*, GMB Publishing Ltd.) Blue Ibex Ltd. GBR. Dist: Ingram Pub. Services.

BOSNIA AND HERCEGOVINA—HISTORY

Alves, Bruno. Holocaustizing Bosni. 2008. 104p. pap. *(978-3-639-05978-6(6))* VDM Verlag Dr. Mueller e.K.
Andreas, Peter. Blue Helmets & Black Markets: The Business of Survival in the Siege of Sarajevo. 2008. (Illus.). 240p. 25.00 *(978-0-8014-4355-8(5))* Cornell Univ. Pr.
Baljak, Aladin. Bosni: The Security Dilemma that Did Not Exist - an Investigation into the Causes of Ethnic Violence. 2008. 80p. pap. *(978-3-639-03019-8(2))* VDM Verlag Dr. Mueller e.K.
Barry, Ben. Cold War: Front Line Operations in Bosnia. 2008. (ENG., Illus.). 320p. 42.95 *(978-1-86227-449-5(5))* History Pr. Ltd.,The GBR. Dist: Independent Pubs. Group.
Bezrob, Anne Marie Du Preez. Sarajevo Roses: War Memoir of a Peacekeeper. 2006. (Illus.). 390p. per. 12.95 *(978-1-77007-031-8(1))* Struik Pubs. ZAF. Dist: International Publishers Marketing.
Bolkovac, Kathryn & Lynn, Cari. The Whistleblower: Sex Trafficking, Military Contractors, & One Woman's Fight for Justice. movie tie-in ed. 2011. (ENG., Illus.). 256p. 25.00 *(978-0-230-10802-8(4))* Palgrave Macmillan.
Bougarel, Xavier, et al, eds. The New Bosnian Mosaic: Identities, Memories & Moral Claims in a Post-War Society. 2007. (Illus.). 352p. 124.95 *(978-0-7546-4563-4(0))* Ashgate Publishing Co.
Cekic, Smail. Zlocini Nad Djecom Sarajeva U Opsadi. 2010. (Illus.). 867p. *(978-9958-740-63-3(X))* Institut Za Istrazivanje Zlocina Protiv Covjecnosti I Medunarodnog Prava.
Cuvalo, Ante. The A to Z of Bosnia & Herzegovina. 2010. (A to Z Guide Ser.). (ENG.). 506p. pap. 34.45 *(978-0-8108-7647-7(7))* Scarecrow Pr., Inc.
—Historical Dictionary of Bosnia & Herzegovina. 2nd ed. 2007. (Historical Dictionaries of Europe Ser.). (ENG.). 504p. 115.00 *(978-0-8108-5084-2(2))* Scarecrow Pr., Inc.
Danto, Arthur C., et al. Bosnia & Herzegovina: Identity, Nationalist Landscapes & the Future of the State, EEM #711. 2008. (ENG., Illus.). 200p. (gr. 17). 40.00 *(978-0-88033-609-3(9))* Eastern European Monographs.
Delpla, Isabelle, et al. Investigating Srebrenica: Institutions, Facts, Responsibilities. 2012. (ENG.). 224p. 70.00 ***(978-0-85745-472-0(2))***; E-Book ***(978-0-85745-473-7(0))*** Berghahn Bks., Inc.
Demick, Barbara. Logavina Street: Life & Death in a Sarajevo Neighborhood. 2012. (ENG., Illus.). 272p. pap. 16.00 ***(978-0-8129-8276-3(2))*** Spiegel & Grau.
Demirci, Sevtap. British Public Opinion Towards the Ottoman Empire During the Two Crises. 2010. 87.68 *(978-1-61719-136-7(1))* Gorgias Pr., LLC.
Doubt, Keith. Understanding Evil: Lessons from Bosnia. 2nd ed. 2007. (ENG.). 184p. 65.00 *(978-0-8232-2700-6(6))* Fordham Univ. Pr.
Evans, Arthur. Through Bosnia & the Herzegovina of Foot During the Insurrection. 435p. reprint ed. 98.00 *(978-0-7222-1950-8(4))* Library Reprints, Inc.
—Through Bosnia & the Herzegovina on Foot During the Insurrection, August & September 1875 (with an Historical Review of Bosnia & a Glimpse at Th. 2007. 508p. per. 29.95 *(978-1-60206-270-2(6))* Cosimo, Inc.
Evetovics, Ivan. Bosnia. 2008. 60p. pap. *(978-3-639-01623-9(8))* VDM Verlag Dr. Mueller e.K.
Fabijancic, Tony. Bosnia: In the Footsteps of Gavrilo Princip. 2010. (Wayfarer Ser.). (ENG., Illus.). 264p. pap. 29.95 *(978-0-88864-519-7(8))* Univ. of Alberta Pr. CAN. Dist: Michigan State Univ. Pr.
Farrand, Robert. Reconstruction & Peace Building in the Balkans: The Brcko Experience. 2011. (ENG.). 310p. 44.95 *(978-1-4422-1235-0(7))* Rowman & Littlefield Publishers, Inc.
Greble, Emily. Sarajevo, 1941-1945: Muslims, Christians, & Jews in Hitler's Europe. 2011. (Illus.). 304p. 35.00 *(978-0-8014-4921-5(9))* Cornell Univ. Pr.
Hoare, Marko Attila. Genocide & Resistance in Hitler's Bosnia: The Partisans & the Chetniks, 1941-1943. 2007. (British Academy Postdoctoral Fellowship Monographs). (ENG., Illus.). 400p. 135.00 *(978-0-19-726380-8(1))* Oxford Univ. Pr., Inc.
—The History of Bosnia: From the Middle Ages to the Present Day. 2007. (ENG., Illus.). 520p. 45.00 *(978-0-86356-953-1(6))* Saqi Bks. GBR. Dist: Consortium Bk. Sales & Distribution.
Koblar, Stanislav. Cetrta Stran Trikotnika: Znamenití Slovenci in Slovenska Druztva V Bosni in Hercegovini, 1878-2000. 2008. (SLV., Illus.). 465p. *(978-961-01-0377-6(4))* Mladinska Knjiga Zalozba, d.d.
Ljubovic, Amir. The Works in Logic by Bosniac Authors in Arabic. 2008. 250p. (C). *(978-90-04-16856-5(7))* BRILL.
Macek, Ivana. Sarajevo under Siege: Anthropology in Wartime. 2011. (Ethnography of Political Violence Ser.). (Illus.). 272p. (C). pap. 24.95 ***(978-0-8122-2189-3(3))*** Univ. of Pennsylvania Pr.
Mahmutcehajic, Rusmir. Maintaining the Sacred Center: The Bosnian City of Stolac. 2011. (ENG., Illus.). 312p. pap. 24.95 *(978-1-935493-91-4(4))* World Wisdom, Inc.
O'Shea, Brendan. Bosnia's Bloody Battlefield: Bihac. 2012. (ENG., Illus.). 288p. pap. 24.95 ***(978-0-7524-6595-1(3))*** History Pr. Ltd.,The GBR. Dist: Independent Pubs. Group.
Raugh, Harold E. & Dolan, Nels. V Corps in Bosnia-Herzegovina, 1995-1996: An Oral History. 2010. *(978-0-9841901-2-6(0))* United States Government Printing Office.
Reid, Atka & Schofield, Hana. Goodbye Sarajevo: A True Story of Courage, Love & Survival. 2012. (ENG., Illus.). 352p. pap. 28.00 ***(978-1-4088-1456-7(0))*** Bloomsbury Publishing.
Rohde, David. Endgame: The Betrayal & Fall of Srebrenica, Europe's Worst Massacre since World War II. 2012. (ENG., Illus.). 480p. (gr. 12). 20.00 ***(978-0-14-312031-5(X)***, Penguin (Non-Classics)) Penguin Group (USA) Inc.
Sadic, Adin. Communication Regulatory Agency in Bosnia & Herzegovina 1998-2005 - History & Development. 2008. 256p. per. *(978-3-8364-6359-1(8))* VDM Verlag Dr. Mueller e.K.
Sijivo, Galib. Bosna I Hercegovina U XIX Stoljecu U Spisima Stranih Izvjestaca. 2008. 761p. *(978-9958-34-042-0(9))* Planjax.
Smith, David James. One Morning in Sarajevo 28 June 1914. 2009. (ENG., Illus.). 352p. 14.95 *(978-0-7538-2584-6(8)*, Phoenix) Orion Publishing Group, Ltd. GBR. Dist: Sterling Publishing Co., Inc.
Sweeney, Leo, et al. Authentic Metaphysics in an Age of Unreality. 2nd ed. 2007. 448p. pap. 49.00 *(978-1-59752-215-1(5)*, Wipf and Stock) Wipf & Stock Pubs.
Toal, Gerard & Dahlman, Carl T. Bosnia Remade: Ethnic Cleansing & Its Reversal, 1 vol. 2011. (ENG., Illus.). 496p. 39.95 *(978-0-19-973036-0(9))* Oxford Univ. Pr., Inc.
Tochman, Wojciech. Like Eating a Stone: Surviving the Past in Bosnia. Lloyd-Jones, Antonia, tr. 2008. (ENG.). 176p. 20.00 *(978-1-934633-14-4(3)*, 934614) Atlas & Co.
Tompuri, Elina. Rape Warfare in the Bosnian War. 2010. 116p. pap. *(978-3-8383-6492-6(9))* Lambert Academic Publishing.
Unal, Hasan. Ottoman Foreign Policy During the Bosnian Annexation Crisis, 1908-1909. 2009. (Routledge Studies in Middle Eastern History Ser.). 240p. 105.00 *(978-0-7146-5452-2(3)*, RU33410) Routledge.

BOSNIA AND HERCEGOVINA—POLITICS AND GOVERNMENT

Aitchison, Andy. Making the Transition: International Intervention, State-Building & Criminal Justice Reform in Bosnia & Herzegovina. 2011. (Transitional Justice Ser.: Vol. 3). 270p. 90.00 *(978-94-000-0140-4(1))* Intersentia Uitgevers N.V. BEL. Dist: International Specialized Bk. Services.
Baljak, Aladin. Bosni: The Security Dilemma that Did Not Exist - an Investigation into the Causes of Ethnic Violence. 2008. 80p. pap. *(978-3-639-03019-8(2))* VDM Verlag Dr. Mueller e.K.
Bennett, Christopher. Bosnia's Paralysed Peace. 2012. (Columbia/Hurst Ser.). (ENG.). 288p. (gr. 17). 29.50 *(978-0-231-70160-0(8))* Columbia Univ. Pr.
Bliesemann de Guevara, Berit. Staatlichkeit in Zeiten des Statebuilding: Intervention und Herrschaft in Bosnien und Herzegowina. 2009. (Strategische Kultur Europas Ser.). (GER.). 368p. 75.95 *(978-3-631-58966-3(2))* Lang, Peter GmbH, Europaischer Verlag der Wissenschaften DEU. Dist: Lang, Peter.
Bolkovac, Kathryn & Lynn, Cari. The Whistleblower: Sex Trafficking, Military Contractors, & One Woman's Fight for Justice. 2011. (ENG., Illus.). 256p. pap. 16.00 *(978-0-230-11522-4(5))* Palgrave Macmillan.
Chandler, David. Peace Without Politics? Ten Years of State-Building in Bosnia. 2007. CLXXXVIIIp. 39.95 *(978-0-415-46382-9(3))* Routledge.
Coles, Kimberley. Democratic Designs: International Intervention & Electoral Practices in Postwar Bosnia-Herzegovina. 2007. (ENG., Illus.). 320p. (C). pap. 29.95 *(978-0-472-06985-9(3))* Univ. of Michigan Pr.
Coles, Kimberley Anne & Coles, Kimberley. Democratic Designs: International Intervention & Electoral Practices in Postwar Bosnia-Herzegovina. 2007. (ENG., Illus.). 320p. (C). 90.00 *(978-0-472-09985-6(X))* Univ. of Michigan Pr.
Dauphinee, Elizabeth. The Ethics of Researching War: Looking for Bosnia. 2007. (New Approaches to Conflict Analysis Ser.). (ENG.). 168p. 79.00 *(978-0-7190-7609-1(9))*; pap. 26.00 *(978-0-7190-7615-2(3))* Manchester Univ. Pr. GBR. Dist: Macmillan.
Eralp, Doga Ulas. Politics of the European Union in Bosnia-Herzegovina: Between Conflict & Democracy. 2012. (ENG.). 148p. (gr. 17). 55.00 ***(978-0-7391-4945-4(8))*** Lexington Bks.
Farrand, Robert William & Frendak-Blume, Allison. Reconstruction & Peace Building in the Balkans: The Brcko Experience. 2011. ***(978-1-4422-1237-4(3))*** Rowman & Littlefield Publishers, Inc.
Friedman, Francine. Bosnia & Herzegovina: A Polity on the Brink. 2006. 41.95 *(978-0-415-36849-0(9))* Routledge.
Fulfilling the Promise of Peace: Human Rights, Peace, & Reconciliation in Northern Ireland & Bosnia: Hearing Before the Subcommittee on International Organizations, Human Rights, & Oversight of the Committee on Foreign Affairs, House of Representatives, One Hundred Eleventh Congress, Second Session, September 16, 2010. 2010. iii, 89p. ***(978-0-16-087579-3(X)***, 552-070-42210-2) United States Government Printing Office.
Gross, Eva, et al, eds. Evaluating the EU's Crisis Missions in the Balkans. 2007. (ENG., Illus.). 250p. pap. 25.00 *(978-92-9079-709-8(6))* Ctr. for European Policy Studies BEL. Dist: Brookings Institution Pr.
Kolind, Torsten. Post-War Identification: Everyday Muslim Counterdiscourse in Bosnia Herzegovina. 2008. (ENG., Illus.). 315p. (C). pap. 53.00 *(978-87-7934-313-9(9))* Aarhus Universitetsforlag DNK. Dist: ISD.
Lepara, Aida. Political Situation in Bosnia & Herzegovina after Dayton Agreement - 2010. 64p. pap. *(978-3-8383-5715-7(9))* Lambert Academic Publishing.
Manning, Carrie. The Making of Democrats: Elections & Party Development in Postwar Bosnia, el Salvador, & Mozambique. 2008. (ENG., Illus.). 208p. 89.00 *(978-0-230-60030-0(1))* Palgrave Macmillan.
Nettelfield, Lara J. Courting Democracy in Bosnia & Herzegovina: The Hague Tribunal's Impact in a Postwar State. 2010. (Cambridge Studies in Law & Society Ser.). (ENG., Illus.). 352p. 98.00 *(978-0-521-76380-6(0))* Cambridge Univ. Pr.
Ohanyan, Anna. NGOs, IGOs, & the Network Mechanisms of Post-Conflict Global Governance in Microfinance. 2008. (ENG.). 256p. 89.00 *(978-0-230-60769-9(1))* Palgrave Macmillan.
Parish, Matthew. A Free City in the Balkans: Reconstructing a Divided Society in Bosnia. 2009. (International Library of War Studies). (ENG., Illus.). 256p. 93.00 *(978-1-84885-002-6(6))* I. B. Tauris & Co., Ltd. GBR. Dist: Macmillan.
Pickering, Paula M. Peacebuilding in the Balkans: The View from the Ground Floor. 2007. (Illus.). 242p. 41.95 *(978-0-8014-4576-7(0))* Cornell Univ. Pr.
Solioz, Christophe. Turning Points in Post-War Bosnia: Ownership Process & European Integration (Second. 2nd rev. ed. 2007. (Illus.). 171p. (C). pap. 38.00 *(978-3-8329-2513-0(9))* Nomos Verlagsgesellschaft DEU. Dist: International Specialized Bk. Services.
Starcevic-Srkalovic, Lejla. The Democratization Process in Post-Dayton Bosnia & Herzegovina & the Role of the European Union. 2010. 272p. pap. 74.00 *(978-3-8329-5595-3(X))* Nomos Verlagsgesellschaft DEU. Dist: International Specialized Bk. Services.
Vesovic, Marko. Tunjo Veliki I U Tunje Mali. 2009. 289p. *(978-9958-33-014-8(8))* Rabic.
Weller. Internationalized State-Building after Violent Conflict. Wolff, Stefan, ed. 2007. (Association for the Study of Nationalities Ser.). (ENG.). 112p. 150.00 *(978-0-415-42080-8(6))* Routledge.

BOSNIA AND HERCEGOVINA—SOCIAL CONDITIONS

Alves, Bruno. Holocaustizing Bosni. 2008. 104p. pap. *(978-3-639-05978-6(6))* VDM Verlag Dr. Mueller e.K.
Andreas, Peter. Blue Helmets & Black Markets: The Business of Survival in the Siege of Sarajevo. 2008. (Illus.). 240p. 25.00 *(978-0-8014-4355-8(5))* Cornell Univ. Pr.
Bergoffen, Debra. Contesting the Politics of Genocidal Rape: Affirming the Dignity of the Vulnerable Body. 2011. (Routledge Research in Gender & Society Ser.). (ENG.). 144p. (C). 125.00 *(978-0-415-89127-1(2))* Routledge.
Berman, David M. The War Schools of Dobrinja: Reading, Writing, & Resistance During the Siege of Sarajevo. 2007. *(978-1-880192-55-9(1))* Caddo Gap Pr.
Chary, Meena. Systematic Sexual Violence. 2009. 124p. pap. *(978-3-639-17320-8(1))* VDM Verlag Dr. Mueller e.K.
Dauphinee, Elizabeth. The Ethics of Researching War: Looking for Bosnia. 2007. (New Approaches to Conflict Analysis Ser.). (ENG.). 168p. 79.00 *(978-0-7190-7609-1(9))* Manchester Univ. Pr. GBR. Dist: Macmillan.
Evetovics, Ivan. Bosnia. 2008. 60p. pap. *(978-3-639-01623-9(8))* VDM Verlag Dr. Mueller e.K.
Friesendorf, Cornelius. The Military & Law Enforcement in Peace Operations: Lessons from Bosnia-Herzegovina & Kosovo. 2010. (ENG.). 208p. pap. 44.95 *(978-3-643-80043-5(6))* Lit Verlag DEU. Dist: Transaction Pubs.
Haveric, Dzavid. Islamisation of Bosni. 2008. 136p. pap. *(978-3-639-05395-1(8))* VDM Verlag Dr. Mueller e.K.
Kolind, Torsten. Post-War Identification: Everyday Muslim Counterdiscourse in Bosnia Herzegovina. 2008. (ENG., Illus.). 315p. (C). pap. 53.00 *(978-87-7934-313-9(9))* Aarhus Universitetsforlag DNK. Dist: ISD.
Kusljic, Dorde. Transition in Bosni. 2009. 54p. pap. *(978-3-639-16343-8(5))* VDM Verlag Dr. Mueller e.K.
Markowitz, Fran. Sarajevo: A Bosnian Kaleidoscope. 2010. (Interp Culture New Millennium Ser.). (ENG., Illus.). 240p. 70.00 *(978-0-252-03526-5(7))*; pap. 25.00 *(978-0-252-07713-5(X))* Univ. of Illinois Pr.
Ramet, Sabrina P. & Valenta, Marko. The Bosnian Diaspora: Integration in Transnational Communities. 2011. (Research in Migration & Ethnic Relations Ser.). (Illus.). 356p. 124.95 ***(978-1-4094-1252-6(0))*** Ashgate Publishing Co.
Skjelsbæk, Inger. The Political Psychology of War Rape. 2011. (War, Politics & Experience Ser.). (ENG., Illus.). 192p. (C). 135.00 *(978-0-415-67117-0(5))* Routledge.
Solioz, Christophe. Turning Points in Post-War Bosnia: Ownership Process & European Integration (Second. 2nd rev. ed. 2007. (Illus.). 171p. (C). pap. 38.00 *(978-3-8329-2513-0(9))* Nomos Verlagsgesellschaft DEU. Dist: International Specialized Bk. Services.
Wagner, Sarah. To Know Where He Lies: DNA Technology & the Search for Srebrenica's Missing. 2008. (Illus.). 352p. 55.00 *(978-0-520-25574-6(7))*; pap. 26.95 *(978-0-520-25575-3(5))* Univ. of California Pr.

BOSNIA AND HERCEGOVINA—SOCIAL LIFE AND CUSTOMS

Fine, John. The Bosnian Church: Its Place in State & Society from the Thirteenth to the Fifteenth Century. 2007. (ENG.). 448p. 49.95 *(978-0-86356-503-8(4))* Saqi Bks. GBR. Dist: Consortium Bk. Sales & Distribution.
Hammond, Elizabeth. Bosnia & Herzegovina. 2009. (Culture Smart! Ser.). (ENG., Illus.). 168p. pap. 9.95 *(978-1-85733-484-5(1))* Kuperard Pubs. GBR. Dist: Random Hse., Inc.
Mahmutcehajic, Rusmir. Maintaining the Sacred Center: The Bosnian City of Stolac. 2011. (ENG., Illus.). 312p. pap. 24.95 *(978-1-935493-91-4(4))* World Wisdom, Inc.
Malic, Nebojsa. Culture & Customs of Bosnia & Herzegovina, 1 vol. (Culture & Customs of Europe Ser.). (Illus.). 192p. 49.95 *(978-0-313-36246-0(7)*, GR6246) Greenwood Publishing Group, Inc.
Vucinich, Wayne S. Memoirs of My Childhood in Yugoslavia. 2007. (Illus.). 226p. 35.00 *(978-0-930664-27-5(2))* Society for the Promotion of Science & Scholarship, Inc.
Weible, Wayne. Medjugorje the Message. 2009. cd-rom 24.99 *(978-0-9820407-2-0(5)*,) New Hope Pr.

BOSONS

Almanea, Arafat, et al. Bose-Einstein Condensation Dynamics. 2011. 204p. pap. ***(978-3-8443-9105-3(3))*** Lambert Academic Publishing.
Alverson, George, et al, eds. Susy09: 7th International Conference on Supersymmetry & the Unification of Fundamental Interactions. 2010. (AIP

B

Conference Proceedings / High Energy Physics Ser.). 1184p. 399.00 *(978-0-7354-0737-4(1)*, 0735407371, AIP Pr.) Springer.

Arslan, Hasan. Extra Gauge Bosons in E6 Models. 2011. 96p. pap. ***(978-3-8443-8014-9(0))*** Lambert Academic Publishing.

Bakhtiari, Mohammad Reza. Quantum Gases in Quasi-One-Dimensional Arrays. 2008. (Publications of the Scuola Normale Superiore / Theses (Scuola Normale Superiore) Ser.). spiral bd. 29.95 *(978-88-7642-319-2(2))* Scuola Normale Superiore ITA. Dist: Springer.

Bijker, Roelof, et al, eds. Latin-American School of Physics - XL ELAF: Symmetries in Physics: Symmetries in Physics. 2011. (AIP Conference Proceedings / Mathematical & Statistical Physics Ser.). 402p. pap. 150.00 ***(978-0-7354-0890-6(4)***, 0735408904, AIP Pr.) Springer.

Feng, Jonathan L., ed. Susy06: The 14th International Conference on Supersymmetry & the Unification of Fundamental Interactions. 2007. (AIP Conference Proceedings Ser.). 742p. 294.00 *(978-0-7354-0410-6(0))* American Institute of Physics.

Griffin, Allan, et al. Bose-Condensed Gases at Finite Temperatures. 2009. (ENG., Illus.). 474p. 127.00 *(978-0-521-83702-6(2))* Cambridge Univ. Pr.

Haussmann, Rudolf. Self-consistent Quantum-Field Theory & Bosonization for Strongly Correlated Electron Systems. 2011. (Lecture Notes in Physics Monographs). (ENG.). viii, 175p. pap. 99.00 *(978-3-642-08509-3(1)*, 3642085091) Springer.

Hong, Christopher J. The Large Hadron Collider & Higgs Boson Research. 2011. (Series: Physics Research & Technology Ser.). (Illus.). 317p. 89.00 *(978-1-61761-933-5(7))* Nova Science Pubs., Inc.

Iachello, F. & Arima, A. The Interacting Boson Model. 2006. (Cambridge Monographs on Mathematical Physics). (ENG., Illus.). 264p. pap. 56.00 *(978-0-521-02879-0(5))* Cambridge Univ. Pr.

Kevrekidis, Panayotis G., et al, eds. Emergent Nonlinear Phenomena in Bose-Einstein Condensates: Theory & Experiment. (Springer Series on Atomic, Optical, & Plasma Physics Ser.). (Illus.). 2010. xxii, 406p. pap. 209.00 *(978-3-642-09272-5(1)*, 3642092721) 2007. 402p. 209.00 *(978-3-540-73590-8(9))* Springer.

Ko, Pyungwon. Supersymmetry & the Unification of Fundamental Interactions. 2009. (AIP Conference Proceedings / High Energy Physics Ser.). 660p. 279.00 *(978-0-7354-0609-4(X))* American Institute of Physics.

Kucharczyk, Marcin. Determination of Hadron Emitter Radii in Z^0 Decays to Hadrons at Lep. 2011. 100p. pap. ***(978-3-8454-0226-0(1))*** Lambert Academic Publishing.

Kuster, Markus, et al, eds. Axions: Theory, Cosmology, & Experimental Searches. 2010. (Lecture Notes in Physics Ser.). (Illus.). xii, 246p. pap. 109.00 *(978-3-642-09263-3(2)*, 3642092632) Springer.

Kuster, Markus & Beltrán, Berta, eds. Axions: Theory, Cosmology, & Experimental Searches. 2007. (Lecture Notes in Physics Ser.). (Illus.). 245p. 109.00 *(978-3-540-73517-5(8))* Springer.

Lincoln, Don. The Quantum Frontier: The Large Hadron Collider. 2009. (ENG., Illus.). 192p. 26.00 *(978-0-8018-9144-1(2))* Johns Hopkins Univ. Pr.

Matthews, Paige E., ed. Bose-Einstein Condensates: Theory, Characteristics, & Current Research. 2010. (Physics Research & Technology Ser.). (Illus.). x, 265p. 190.00 *(978-1-61728-114-3(X))* Nova Science Pubs., Inc.

McKinney, Brett. Many-Body Dimensional Perturbation Theory for Quantum Confined Systems. 2008. 176p. pap. *(978-3-639-07518-2(8))* VDM Verlag Dr. Mueller e.K.

Mee, Nicholas. Higgs Force: The Symmetry-Breaking Force that Makes the World an Interesting Place. 2012. (ENG., Illus.). 330p. 50.00 ***(978-0-7188-9278-4(X))*** Lutherworth Pr., The. GBR. Dist: Brown, David Bk. Co., The.

Naik, Devang. Quantum Degenerate Bose Gases: Building the Testbed to Study Many Body Physics. 2008. 216p. per. *(978-3-8364-6141-2(2))* VDM Verlag Dr. Mueller e.K.

Pethick, C. J. & Smith, H. Bose-Einstein Condensation in Dilute Gases. 2nd rev. ed. 2008. (ENG., Illus.). 584p. (C). 84.00 *(978-0-521-84651-6(X))* Cambridge Univ. Pr.

Sakmann, Kaspar. Many-Body Schrödinger Dynamics of Bose-Einstein Condensates. 2011. (Springer Theses Ser.). (ENG., Illus.). xii, 130p. 129.00 ***(978-3-642-22865-0(8)***, 3642228658) Springer.

Sample, Ian. Massive: The Missing Particle That Sparked the Greatest Hunt in Science. 2012. (ENG.). 288p. (gr. 9). pap. 16.99 ***(978-0-465-02852-8(7))*** Basic Bks.

Sasaki, Shosuke. Bose-Einstein Condensation in Nonlinear System. 2010. (Physics Research & Technology Ser.). pap. 47.00 *(978-1-61668-754-0(1)*, Nova Novinka) Nova Science Pubs., Inc.

Saut, Jean-Claude. Stationary & Time Dependent Gross-Pitaevskii Equations. Farina, Alberto, ed. 2008. (Contemporary Mathematics Ser.). (Illus.). 180p. pap. 61.00 *(978-0-8218-4357-4(5))* American Mathematical Society.

Seifer, Emerson D. Bosons, Ferromagnetism & Crystal Growth Research. 2006. (Horizons in World Physics Ser.: Vol. 257). (Illus.). 256p. 225.00 *(978-1-60021-367-0(7))* Nova Science Pubs., Inc.

Tanner, David B. & Bibber, Karl van, eds. Axions 2010: Proceedings of the International Conference. 2010. (AIP Conference Proceedings / High Energy Physics Ser.). 190p. 147.00 *(978-0-7354-0824-1(6)*, 0735408246, AIP Pr.) Springer.

Tenchini, Roberto & Verzegnassi, Claudio. The Physics of the Z & W Bosons. 2008. (Illus.). 419p. 135.00 *(978-981-270-702-4(6))* World Scientific Publishing Co., Inc.

Ueda, Masahito. Fundamentals & New Frontiers of Bose-Einstein Condensation. 2010. 368p. 85.00 *(978-981-283-959-6(3))* World Scientific Publishing Co., Inc.

Verbeure, André F. Many-Body Boson Systems: Half a Century Later. 2010. (Theoretical & Mathematical Physics Ser.). x, 189p. 89.95 *(978-0-85729-108-0(4)*, 0857291084) Springer.

Zöllner, Sascha. Ultracold Bosons in One Dimension. 2010. 124p. pap. *(978-3-8383-5745-4(0))* Lambert Academic Publishing.

BOSS RULE

see Political Corruption

BOSSUET, JACQUES BENIGNE, 1627-1704

Preyat, Fabrice. Le Petit Concile de Bossuet et la Christianisation des Murs et des Pratiques Littéraires Sous Louis XIV. (FRE.). 570p. *(978-3-8258-8716-2(2)*, Adlard Coles) Lit Verlag.

BOSTON (MASS.)

American Map, creator. Metro Boston Eastern Massachusetts Street Atlas. 8th ed. 2008. (American Map Ser.). (Illus.). 264p. 24.95 *(978-1-55751-393-9(7))* American Map Corp.

Boston City Map. 2009. pap. 4.95 *(978-0-915983-14-8(1))* Global Graphics.

Cooley, Laverne C. & Cotton, John. A Short Biography of John Cotton of Boston & a Cotton Genealogy of His Descendants. 2011. 146p. 40.95 ***(978-1-258-06107-4(4))*** Literary Licensing, LLC.

Emerson, Ralph Waldo. Natural History of the Intellect: The Last Lectures of Ralph Waldo Emerson. York, Maurice & Spaulding, Rick, eds. 2008. (Illus.). 160p. pap. 22.95 *(978-0-9801190-1-5(4))* Wrightwood Pr.

Icon Group International, Inc. Staff, compiled by. The 2006 Economic & Product Market Databook for Boston , United States. 2006. 618p. ring bd. 95.00 *(978-0-497-80228-8(7))* Icon Group International, Inc.

Morgan, Jessica. ICA/Vita Brevis 1998-2003 History, 1 vol. Meehan, Carole A., ed. 2008. (ENG., Illus.). 160p. 40.00 *(978-3-88243-816-1(9))* Steidl, Gerhard Druckerei und Verlag DEU. Dist: Innovative Logistics.

Rosell, Garth M. Boston's Historic Park Street Church: The Story of an Evangelical Landmark, 1 vol. 2009. 192p. pap. 14.99 *(978-0-8254-3595-9(1))* Kregel Pubns.

Shackleton, Robert. The Book of Boston. 2009. 202p. pap. *(978-1-4588-6395-9(6))*; pap. *(978-0-217-06607-5(0))* Books LLC.

—The Book of Boston. 2008. 376p. 48.95 *(978-1-4366-5685-6(0))*; pap. 33.95 *(978-0-548-87637-4(1))* Kessinger Publishing, LLC.

Sherman, Paul. Big Screen Boston: From Mystery Street to the Departed & Beyond. 2008. pap. *(978-0-9776397-4-8(6))* Black Bars Publishing.

BOSTON (MASS.)—BIOGRAPHY

Adams, Jim. The Immortal Tavern. 2008. 216p. pap. 12.95 *(978-1-4327-1943-2(2))* Outskirts Pr., Inc.

Albee, John. Confessions of Boyhood. 2006. (ENG.). 26.95 *(978-1-4218-2967-8(3))*; pap. 11.95 *(978-1-4218-3067-4(1))* 1st World Publishing, Inc.

—Confessions of Boyhood. 2008. 272p. 25.99 *(978-0-559-26057-5(1))* 2008. 272p. pap. 26.75 *(978-0-559-26055-1(5))* 2008. 164p. 22.99 *(978-0-554-36716-3(5))* 2008. 164p. 25.99 *(978-0-554-27413-3(2))* 2008. 210p. 25.99 *(978-0-554-64482-0(7))* 2008. 272p. 28.99 *(978-0-554-64472-1(X))* 2008. 98p. pap. 26.75 *(978-0-554-64481-3(9))* 2008. 281p. pap. 27.75 *(978-0-554-64477-6(0))* 2007. (ENG.). 148p. pap. 18.99 *(978-1-4346-3174-9(5))* 2007. 160p. pap. 21.99 *(978-1-4346-3175-6(3))* BiblioBazaar.

—Confessions of Boyhood. 2009. 148p. pap. *(978-1-4099-3972-6(3))* Dodo Pr.

Aloisi, James A., Jr. Magic in the Air: The Times & Life of Boston's Honey Fitz. 2007. pap. 12.95 *(978-0-9788259-0-4(X))* Chilmark Pr., The.

Bailey, Solon I. Biographical Memoir of Edward Charles Pickering, 1846-1919: National Academy of Sciences, Biographical Memoirs, V15, Fifth Memoir. 2011. 26p. 35.95 ***(978-1-258-07172-1(X))*** Literary Licensing, LLC.

Becnel, George. Big Boy: The Life & (Often Hilarious) Times of Norman Swanner. 2008. 188p. pap. 21.49 *(978-1-4389-2539-4(5))* AuthorHouse.

Bennett, Brennan. College Basketball & Life's Greatest Lesson. 2010. 243p. 29.72 *(978-0-557-42616-4(2))*; (ENG.). pap. 14.99 *(978-0-557-44687-2(2))* Lulu Enterprises Inc.

Brett, Bill, photos by. Boston: An Extended Family. 2007. (ENG., Illus.). 136p. 27.95 *(978-1-933212-38-8(1))* Commonwealth Editions.

Browne, L. C. Review of the Life & Writings of M Hal. 2006. pap. 31.95 *(978-1-4286-5959-9(5))* Kessinger Publishing, LLC.

Burke, Timothy M. The Paradiso Files: On the Trail of Boston's Unknown Serial Killer. 2008. (ENG., Illus.). 368p. 16.95 *(978-1-58642-149-6(2))* Steerforth Pr.

Carr, Howie. Hitman: The Untold Story of Johnny Martorano: Whitey Bulger's Enforcer & the Most Feared Gangster in the Underworld. l.t. ed. 2011. 700p. 31.99 *(978-1-4104-3698-6(5))* Thorndike Pr.

Clarke, Theodore G. Boston Curiosities: A History of Extraordinary Personalities, Portentous Places, & Singular Events. 2008. pap. 17.99 *(978-1-59629-580-3(5))* History Pr., The.

Clarke, Theodore G. & Armstrong, Annabelle M. Beacon Hill, Back Bay, & the Building of Boston's Golden Age. 2010. (ENG., Illus.). 128p. pap. 19.99 *(978-1-59629-161-4(3))* History Pr., The.

Cohen, Morris A. & Cohen, Richard Shain. Healing after Dark: Pioneering Compassionate Medicine at the Boston Evening Clinic. 2011. (Illus.). 184p. pap. 14.95 ***(978-1-926918-44-0(4)***, CCB Publishing) CCB Publishing CAN. Dist: Gardners Bks. Ltd.

Dall, William H. Biographical Memoir of Charles Abiathar White, 1826-1910: National Academy of Sciences, Biographical Memoirs, V7, No. 9, July 1911. 2011. 24p. 35.95 ***(978-1-258-07184-4(3))*** Literary Licensing, LLC.

Dixon, Robert. Fore & Aft. 2008. 208p. pap. 14.95 *(978-0-9795949-6-0(0))* Flat Hammock Pr.

Downing, Michael. Life with Sudden Death: A Tale of Moral Hazard & Medical Misadventure. 2009. (ENG.). 256p. 25.00 *(978-1-58243-522-0(7)*, Counterpoint Pr.) Basic Bks. GBR. Dist: Perseus-PGW.

Farmer Sr., Karl V. I Know Life's Not Supposed to Be Fair. 2011. 66p. pap. 15.99 ***(978-1-4568-7162-8(5))*** Xlibris Corp.

Franck, Peggy & Franck, Peggy Miller. Prides Crossing: The Unbridled Life & Impatient Times of Eleonora Randolph Sears. 2009. (ENG.). 336p. 27.95 *(978-1-933212-99-9(3))* Commonwealth Editions.

Fulton, Justin D. (Justin Dewey). Memoir of Timothy Gilbert, by Justin D Fulton. 2006. 260p. per. 23.99 *(978-1-4255-2299-5(8))* MPublishing.

Graboys, Thomas & Zheutlin, Peter. Life in the Balance: A Physician's Memoir of Life, Love, & Loss with Parkinson's Disease & Dementia. 2009. (ENG.). 232p. pap. 14.95 *(978-1-4027-6873-6(7))* Union Square Pr.

Griffin, Edward M. Old Brick: Charles Chauncy of Boston, 1705-1787. 2009. (ENG.). 264p. pap. 50.00 *(978-0-8166-5777-3(7))* Univ. of Minnesota Pr.

Guarino, Robert E. Beacon Street: A Highway of History. 2011. 128p. pap. 19.99 *(978-1-60949-124-6(6))* History Pr., The.

Herron, Edward A. & Herron, Edward A. First Scientist of Alask: William Healey Dall. 2011. 192p. 42.95 ***(978-1-258-07398-5(6))*** Literary Licensing, LLC.

Howard, Simeon. A Sermon Preached in Boston. 2008. 46p. pap. 12.95 *(978-0-557-00814-8(X))* Lulu Enterprises Inc.

Hubbard, Donald. The Heavenly Twins of Boston Baseball: A Dual Biography of Hugh Duffy & Tommy McCarthy. 2008. (ENG., Illus.). 252p. pap. 29.95 *(978-0-7864-3455-8(4))* McFarland & Co., Inc. Pubs.

Isenberg, Michael. The Longest Year: One Family's Journey of Life, Death & Love. 2009. 268p. pap. 15.95 *(978-1-60860-046-5(7)*, Eloquent Bks.) AEG Literary Publishing Services, Inc.

Kellen, William V. James Robert Dunbar A Memorial. 2006. pap. 16.95 *(978-1-4286-5402-0(X))* Kessinger Publishing, LLC.

Kenney, Charles. Rescue Men. 2007. (ENG.). 352p. 26.00 *(978-1-58648-310-4(2))* PublicAffairs.

Kingsley, Florence Morse. The Life of Henry Fowle Durant Founder of Wellesley College. 2007. (ENG.). 376p. 48.95 *(978-0-548-01031-0(5))* Kessinger Publishing, LLC.

Lawrence, Amos. Extracts from the Diary & Correspondence of the Late Amos Lawrence; with a Brief Account of Some Incidents in His Life Ed by His Son, William R L. 2006. 384p. per. 26.99 *(978-1-4255-4065-4(1))*; 392p. per. 26.99 *(978-1-4255-4166-8(6))* MPublishing.

MacDonald, Michael Patrick. All Souls: A Family Story from Southie. 2007. (ENG., Illus.). 296p. per. 14.95 *(978-0-8070-7213-4(3))* Beacon Pr.

—Easter Rising: A Memoir of Roots & Rebellion. 11th ed. 2008. (ENG., Illus.). 256p. pap. 13.95 *(978-0-618-91863-8(9)*, Mariner Bks.) Houghton Mifflin Harcourt Trade & Reference Pubs.

MacQuarrie, Brian. The Ride: A Shocking Murder & a Bereaved Father's Journey from Rage to Redemption. 2009. (ENG., Illus.). 304p. 26.00 *(978-0-306-81626-0(1))* Da Capo Pr., Inc.

—The Ride: The Jeffrey Curley Murder & Its Aftermath. 2010. (ENG., Illus.). 304p. pap. 16.00 *(978-0-306-81872-1(8))* Da Capo Pr., Inc.

Malloy, Mary. Devil on the Deep Blue Sea: The Notorious Career of Captain Samuel Hill of Boston. 2006. (Illus.). 314p. per. 24.00 *(978-0-9722854-1-4(5))* Bullbrier Pr.

Marchione, William P. Allston-Brighton in Transition: From Cattle Town to Streetcar Suburb. 2007. (Illus.). 159p. pap., per. 21.99 *(978-1-59629-252-9(0))* History Pr., The.

—Boston Miscellany: An Episodic History of the Hub. 2008. 128p. pap. 18.99 *(978-1-59629-587-2(2))* History Pr., The.

Meston, Daja Wangchuk. Comes the Peace: My Journey to Forgiveness. 2011. (ENG.). 272p. pap. 18.99 *(978-0-7432-8761-6(4)*, Free Pr.) Free Pr.

Mitchell, John Hanson. Looking for Mr. Gilbert: The Reimagined Life of an African American. 2006. (ENG., Illus.). 288p. per. 16.00 *(978-1-59376-142-4(2))* Counterpoint LLC.

[Mumford, Thomas James]. Memoir of Samuel Joseph May. 2006. 320p. per. 23.99 *(978-1-4255-3096-9(6))* MPublishing.

O'Neill, Gerard. Rogues & Redeemers: When Politics Was King in Irish Boston. 2012. (ENG., Illus.). 416p. 26.00 *(978-0-307-40536-4(2))* Crown Publishing Group.

Perkins, Steven G. William Dady: 1630 Immigrant to Boston His Descendants & Their Branch & Allied Families. 2008. (ENG., Illus.). 470p. lib. bdg. 55.00 *(978-0-944619-88-9(6)*, AD2189) Gregath Publishing Co.

Puleo, Stephen. The Boston Italians: A Story of Pride, Perseverance, & Paesani, from the Years of the Great Immigration to the Present Day. 2008. (ENG.). 344p. pap. 17.00 *(978-0-8070-5037-8(7))* Beacon Pr.

Quincy, Edmund. Life of Josiah Quincy of Massachusetts. 2009. (ENG.). 577p. 44.99 *(978-1-117-39375-9(5))*; 578p. pap. 42.75 *(978-1-117-39376-6(3))* BiblioBazaar.

—Life of Josiah Quincy of Massachusetts. 2009. 446p. pap. 30.15 *(978-0-217-50379-2(9))* General Bks. LLC.

—Life of Josiah Quincy of Massachusetts. 2007. (ENG.). 580p. 58.95 *(978-0-548-11664-7(4))* Kessinger Publishing, LLC.

—Life of Josiah Quincy of Massachusetts by His Son Edmund Quincy. 2006. 580p. per. 32.99 *(978-1-4255-6291-5(4))* MPublishing.

Sacco, Anthony J. Echoes in the Wind: A Biography of Guy Vitale, East Boston High School Sports Great. 2007. 560p. per. 32.95 *(978-0-595-45522-5(0))* iUniverse, Inc.

Sammarco, Anthony. Dorchester a Compendium. 2011. 128p. pap. 19.99 ***(978-1-60949-174-1(2))*** History Pr., The.

Sammarco, Anthony Mitchell. Dorchester: A Compendium. 2011. ***(978-1-60949-217-5(X))*** History Pr., The.

Scott, Jacob Richardson, et al. To Thee This Temple: The Life, Diary & Friends of Jacob Richardson Scott, 1815-1861. 2011. 418p. 54.95 ***(978-1-258-10363-7(X))*** Literary Licensing, LLC.

Shea, John R. Rat Bastards: The South Boston Irish Mobster Who Took the Rap When Everyone Else Ran. 2007. (ENG., Illus.). 304p. pap. 14.99 *(978-0-06-123289-3(0)*, William Morrow Paperbacks) HarperCollins Pubs.

Shea, John "Red". Rat Bastards: The Life & Times of South Boston's Most Honorable Top Irish Mobster. 2007. 320p. pap. 7.99 *(978-0-06-083717-4(9))* HarperCollins Pubs.

Stearns, Samuel H. Life of Samuel H Stearns. 2007. (ENG.). 256p. 42.95 *(978-0-548-14509-8(1))* 2006. pap. 27.95 *(978-1-4286-5812-7(2))* Kessinger Publishing, LLC.

Steinberg, Avi. Running the Books: The Adventures of an Accidental Prison Librarian. (ENG.). 416p. 2011. pap. 16.00 *(978-0-7679-3131-1(9)*, Anchor) 2010. 26.00 *(978-0-385-52909-9(0)*, Talese, Nan A.) Knopf Doubleday Publishing Group.

Stevens, Peter F. Hidden History of the Boston Irish: Little-Known Stories from Ireland's Next Parish Over. 2008. (Illus.). 160p. pap. 19.99 *(978-1-59629-450-9(7))* History Pr., The.

Trask, William B. Memoir of David Clapp. 2006. pap. 15.95 *(978-1-4286-5506-5(9))* Kessinger Publishing, LLC.

Trask, William Blake. Memoir of Elias Nason. 2006. pap. 15.95 *(978-1-4286-5389-4(9))* Kessinger Publishing, LLC.

Upper, Dennis. Long Story Short: A Memoir. 2007. 220p. 27.95 *(978-0-595-69455-6(1))* iUniverse, Inc.

Vonnegut, Mark. Just Like Someone Without Mental Illness Only More So: A Memoir. (Illus.). 224p. 2011. (ENG.). pap. 15.00 *(978-0-385-34380-0(9))* 2010. 24.00 *(978-0-385-34379-4(5)*, Delacorte Pr) Random House Publishing Group.

Ware, John. Memoir of the Life of Henry Ware, Jr , by His Brother, John Ware. 2006. 568p. per. 32.99 *(978-1-4255-6195-6(0))* MPublishing.

Washington, Phyllis. Ghetto Love Yourself. 2009. 68p. pap. 14.99 *(978-1-4490-1419-3(4))* AuthorHouse.

Weir, Meghan. Between Expectations: Lessons from a Pediatric Residency. 2011. (ENG.). 288p. 25.00 *(978-1-4391-8907-8(2)*, Free Pr.) Free Pr.

Zevitas, Steven J. Petee - the Islander: Petee. 2011. 184p. 26.95 *(978-1-4502-7323-7(8))*; pap. 16.95 *(978-1-4502-7322-0(X))* iUniverse, Inc.

BOSTON (MASS.)—DESCRIPTION AND TRAVEL

American Map Corp, creator. Metro Boston Massachusetts Pocket Atlas. 2007. (American Map Ser.). (Illus.). 200p. 12.95 *(978-1-55751-339-7(2))* American Map Corp.

Arrison, Julie. Franklin Park. 2009. (Images of America Ser.). (ENG., Illus.). 128p. pap. 21.99 *(978-0-7385-6531-6(8))* Arcadia Publishing.

Boston Globe Staff. Boston's Secret Spaces: 50 Hidden Corners in & Around the Hub. 2009. (ENG., Illus.). 112p. 16.95 *(978-0-7627-5062-7(6))* Globe Pequot Pr., The.

Brett, Bill, photos by. Boston, a Year in the Life. 2008. (Illus.). 192p. 29.95 *(978-1-933212-74-6(8))* Commonwealth Editions.

Brox, Andrea. The Student Guide to Boston. pap. 9.95 *(978-0-924771-21-7(6))* Brick Hse. Publishing Co.

Chartwell Books Staff & Holmes, Alexander. Boston: The Growth of the City. 2007. (Growth of the City/State Ser.). (ENG., Illus.). 160p. 9.99 *(978-0-7858-2216-5(X)*, 078582216X, Chartwell) Book Sales, Inc.

Clarke, Theodore G. Boston Curiosities: A History of Extraordinary Personalities, Portentous Places, & Singular Events. 2008. pap. 17.99 *(978-1-59629-580-3(5))* History Pr., The.

Dane, Jan Faust. Rather Boston: A Compendium of Desirable Independent Eating + Shopping Establishments. 2012. (Rather Ser.). (ENG.). 192p. pap. 14.95 *(978-0-9833145-4-7(3))* Cabazon Bks.

Downey, JoAnna & Lau, Christian J. The Dog Lover's Companion to Boston: The Inside Scoop on Where to Take Your Dog. 4th ed. 2007. (Dog Lover's Companion Guides). (ENG., Illus.). 330p. per. 17.95 *(978-1-56691-972-2(X))* Avalon Travel Publishing.

Drake, Samuel Adams. Old Landmarks & Historic Personages of Boston. 2009. 454p. pap. *(978-0-217-52486-5(9))* Books LLC.

—Old Landmarks & Historic Personages of Boston. (Illus.). reprint ed. lib. bdg. 98.00 *(978-0-7222-0653-9(4))* Library Reprints, Inc.

—Old Landmarks & Historic Personages of Boston. 2006. (ENG.). 504p. per. 29.99 *(978-1-4255-5601-3(9))* MPublishing.

Earls, Alan R. Greater Boston's Blizzard Of 1978. 2008. (Images of America Ser.). (ENG., Illus.). 128p. per. 21.99 *(978-0-7385-5519-5(3))* Arcadia Publishing.

Forest, Christopher. Boston's Haunted History: Exploring the Ghosts & Graves of Beantown. 2008. (Illus.). 128p. pap. 12.95 *(978-0-7643-2874-9(3))* Schiffer Publishing, Ltd.

Goodwin, Nicholas. Spooky Creepy Boston. 2010. (Illus.). 160p. pap. 14.99 *(978-0-7643-3612-6(6))* Schiffer Publishing, Ltd.

Grossman, Jane, et al. Boston Foot Notes. 2nd rev. ed. 2009. (ENG., Illus.). 256p. pap. 14.95 *(978-0-88150-888-8(8)*, 150888) Countryman Pr.
Halper, Donna L. Boston Radio: 1920-2010. 2011. (Images of America Ser.). (Illus.). 128p. pap. 21.99 *(978-0-7385-7410-3(4))* Arcadia Publishing.
Hantover, Jeffrey. City in Time - Boston. 2008. (City in Time Ser.). (ENG., Illus.). 144p. 14.95 *(978-1-4027-3300-0(3))* Sterling Publishing Co., Inc.
Hobson, Barbara Meil & Wright, Paul M. Boston, a State of Mind: An Exhibition Record. pap. 5.00 *(978-0-89073-097-3(0)*, 183) Boston Public Library.
Hughes, Judith E. Tammy Does Boston. 2010. (ENG.). 84p. 14.95 *(978-0-615-31806-6(1))* Malyszko Photography.
Kennedy, Patrick L. Boston Then & Now (Compact) 2010. (Then & Now Thunder Bay Ser.). (ENG., Illus.). 144p. pap. 12.95 *(978-1-59223-878-1(5)*, Thunder Bay Pr.) Advantage Pubs. Group.
Lisicky, Michael J. Filene's: Boston's Great Specialty Store. 2012. (Images of America Ser.). (ENG., Illus.). 128p. pap. 21.99 ***(978-0-7385-9158-2(0))*** Arcadia Publishing.
Marchione, William P. Allston-Brighton in Transition: From Cattle Town to Streetcar Suburb. 2007. (Illus.). 159p. pap., per. 21.99 *(978-1-59629-252-9(0))* History Pr., The.
Martin, Mary L. & Rooney, E. Ashley. Boston: Past & Present. 2008. (Illus.). 128p. pap. 24.99 *(978-0-7643-3058-2(6))* Schiffer Publishing, Ltd.
McLaughlin, Robert. Pleasure Island. 2009. (Images of America Ser.). (ENG., Illus.). 128p. pap. 21.99 *(978-0-7385-6460-9(5))* Arcadia Publishing.
Moore, Barbara W. & Weesner, Gail. Beacon Hill: A Living Portrait. 2008. (ENG., Illus.). 144p. 38.00 *(978-0-9632077-4-6(1))*; pap. 28.00 *(978-0-9632077-5-3(X))* Centry Hill Pr.
Morris, Marie. Boston Day by Day. 2nd ed. 2009. (Frommer's Day by Day - Pocket Ser.: 58). (ENG., Illus.). 192p. pap. 12.99 *(978-0-470-49766-1(1)*, Frommers) Wiley, John & Sons, Inc.
Nowitz, Richard, photos by. Boston Impressions. 2008. (Illus.). 80p. pap. 12.95 *(978-1-56037-437-4(3))* Farcountry Pr.
Olia, Maria T. The Little Black Book of Boston: The Essential Guide to the Heart of New England. 2008. (Little Black Book Ser.). (Illus.). 214p. spiral bd. 12.95 *(978-1-59359-897-6(1))* Peter Pauper Pr. Inc.
Orwig, Timothy, text. Historic Photos of Boston. 2006. (Historic Photos Ser.). (ENG., Illus.). 206p. 39.95 *(978-1-59652-305-0(0))* Turner Publishing Co.
Richmond, Arthur P. Boston Wide. 2009. (Illus.). 160p. 39.99 *(978-0-7643-3273-9(2))* Schiffer Publishing, Ltd.
Sammarco, Anthony Mitchell. Hyde Park. 2011. (Then & Now Ser.). (ENG., Illus.). 96p. pap. 21.99 ***(978-0-7385-7396-0(5))*** Arcadia Publishing.
Sammarco, Anthony Mitchell. South Boston. 2006. (Then & Now Ser.). (ENG., Illus.). 96p. per. 21.99 *(978-0-7385-3948-5(1))* Arcadia Publishing.
Schweikart, Lynn. Peaceful Places: Boston - 121 Tranquil Sites in the City & Beyond. 2011. (Peaceful Places Ser.). (ENG., Illus.). 240p. pap. 14.95 *(978-0-89732-542-4(7))* Menasha Ridge Pr., Inc.
Silverleaf Press. 100 Miles from Home: Boston: 25 Great Day Trips. 2011. 128p. pap. 12.95 *(978-1-934393-44-4(4))* Silverleaf Pr.
Sullivan, Jim. South Boston. 2007. (Postcard History Ser.). (Illus.). 128p. per. 19.99 *(978-0-7385-5528-7(2))* Arcadia Publishing.
Sweeney, Emily. Boston Organized Crime. 2012. (Images of America Ser.). (ENG., Illus.). 128p. pap. 21.99 ***(978-0-7385-7673-2(5))*** Arcadia Publishing.
Tougias, Michael. Exploring the Hidden Charles: A Guide to Outdoor Activities on Boston's Celebrated River. 2008. Orig. Title: The Hidden Charles. (ENG., Illus.). 208p. pap. 15.95 *(978-0-9785766-5-3(9))* On Cape Pubns.
Welsch, Ulrike, photos by. Boston at Its Best. 2007. (At Its Best Ser.). (ENG., Illus.). 64p. pap. 12.95 *(978-1-933212-48-7(9))* Commonwealth Editions.
Willis, Catherine J. Boston Public Library. 2011. (Images of America Ser.). (Illus.). 128p. pap. 21.99 *(978-0-7385-7506-3(2))* Arcadia Publishing.
Worek, Jordan. Boston. 2010. (America the Beautiful Ser.). (ENG., Illus.). 96p. 18.95 *(978-1-55407-591-1(2))* Firefly Bks., Ltd.

BOSTON (MASS.)—DIRECTORIES

Boston Parents' Paper Staff, compiled by. Children's Yellow Pages: A Resource Book for Parents & Children, 1987 Boston Edition. pap. 7.95 *(978-0-201-11165-1(9))* Addison-Wesley Longman, Inc.
Gilbert, Jennifer. Free Art Spaces: Artist's Directory of Alternative Exhibit Spaces. Long, Christpher, ed. (Illus.). 72p. (Orig.). pap. *(978-1-887724-00-5(1))* Fremantle Pr./DeHavilland.
Not for Tourists Staff. Boston 2009. 5th rev. ed. 2008. (Illus.). 384p. 16.95 *(978-0-9814887-3-8(0))* Not for Tourists, Inc.
Not For Tourists Staff. Not for Tourists Guide to Boston: 2012. 2011. (ENG., Illus.). 368p. pap. 16.95 ***(978-1-61608-530-8(4)***, 608530, Not For Tourist) Skyhorse Publishing Co., Inc.
Not for Tourists Staff. Not for Tourists Guide to Boston 2008. 2007. 337p. 15.95 *(978-0-9793945-3-9(8))* Not for Tourists, Inc.

BOSTON (MASS.)—FIRST CHURCH OF CHRIST, SCIENTIST

Armstrong, Joseph. Mother Church A History of the Building. 2006. pap. 20.95 *(978-1-4286-4983-5(2))* Kessinger Publishing, LLC.
Eddy, Mary Baker. Church Manual: Of the First Church of Christ, Scientist, in Boston, Massachusetts. 138p. reprint ed. 18.00 *(978-0-87952-084-7(1))* Eddy, The Writings of Mary Baker.
—The First Church of Christ, Scientist, & Miscellany. 366p. reprint ed. pap. 16.00 *(978-0-87952-041-0(8))* Eddy, The Writings of Mary Baker.

BOSTON (MASS.)—GUIDEBOOKS

Avalon Travel Publishing Staff, compiled by. Moon Metro Boston. 2nd ed. 2007. (Moon Metro Ser.). (ENG., Illus.). 96p. pap. 14.95 *(978-1-56691-974-6(6))* Avalon Travel Publishing.
Bahne, Charles. Chronicles of Old Boston: Exploring New England's Historic Capital. 2012. (ENG., Illus.). 288p. pap. 19.95 ***(978-0-9846334-0-1(5))*** Museyon Inc.
Barrett, Pam. Boston. 2009. (Step by Step Ser.). (ENG., Illus.). 128p. pap. 16.99 *(978-981-258-964-4(3))* APA Publications Services SGP. Dist: Ingram Pub. Services.
Berard, Nicole. Museums of Boston: A Guide for Residents & Visitors. 2007. 152p. per. 14.95 *(978-1-59416-047-9(3))* Westholme Publishing.
Blessing, Anna H. Eat. shop Boston: The Indispensable Guide to Inspired, Locally Owned Eating & Shopping Establishments. 2nd rev. ed. 2009. (ENG.). 192p. pap. 14.95 *(978-0-9799557-9-2(3))* Cabazon Bks.
Boston. 2nd ed. 2012. (Step by Step Ser.). (Illus.). 128p. pap. 16.99 ***(978-1-78005-073-7(9))*** APA Publications Services SGP. Dist: Ingram Pub. Services.
Brein, Michael. Boston - Michael Brein's Guides to Sightseeing. 2007. 2p. pap. 10.00 *(978-1-886590-24-3(9))* Brein, Michael Inc.
Downey, JoAnna & Lau, Christian J. The Dog Lover's Companion to Boston: The Inside Scoop on Where to Take Your Dog. 4th ed. 2007. (Dog Lover's Companion Guides). (ENG., Illus.). 330p. per. 17.95 *(978-1-56691-972-2(X))* Avalon Travel Publishing.
Elkins, Elizabeth A. Jean Lafitte International: Boston. Elkins, Elizabeth A., ed. Date not set. (Jean Lafitte International Ser.). 212p. (Orig.). pap. 20.00 *(978-0-9701864-7-8(9))* E E Productions.
Felton, Robert Todd. Walking Boston: 36 Tours Through Beantown's Cobblestone Streets, Historic Districts, Ivory Towers, & New Waterfront. 2008. (Walking Ser.). (ENG., Illus.). 238p. pap. 17.95 *(978-0-89997-448-4(1))* Wilderness Pr.
Ferguson, John W. Why Fenway: Exploring the Red Sox Mystique. 2011. (ENG.). 144p. pap. 19.95 *(978-1-60078-533-7(6))* Triumph Bks.
Fodor's Travel Publications, Inc. Staff. Fodor's Boston 2012. 2011. (Full-Color Gold Guides). (ENG.). 400p. pap. 18.99 *(978-0-679-00925-2(6)*, Fodor's) Fodor's Travel Pubns.
—Fodor's Boston, 27th Edition. 2012. (Full-color Travel Guide Ser.). (ENG.). 400p. pap. 19.99 ***(978-0-307-92923-5(X)***, Fodor's) Fodor's Travel Pubns.
Fodor's Travel Publications, Inc. Staff. Fodor's Boston's 25 Best, 7th Edition. 2010. (25 Best Ser.). (ENG.). 128p. pap. 11.99 *(978-1-4000-0540-6(X)*, Fodor's) Fodor's Travel Pubns.
Frieswick, Kris. Boston: Secrets of Living the Good Life — For Free! 2nd ed. 2009. (Cheap Bastard Ser.). (ENG., Illus.). 336p. pap., instr.'s gde. ed. 14.95 *(978-0-7627-5022-1(7))* Globe Pequot Pr., The.
Glassman-Jaffe, Marcia. Boston: Where to Go & What to Do with the Kids. 2009. (Are We Almost There? Ser.). (ENG., Illus.). 64p. 7.95 *(978-0-7627-5282-9(3))* Globe Pequot Pr., The.
Gorey, Jon & Favata, Gina. Newcomer's Handbook for Moving to & Living in Boston: Including Cambridge, Brookline, & Somerville. 4th ed. 2008. 480p. pap. 26.95 *(978-0-912301-85-3(6))* First Bks.
Harris, Patricia & Lyon, David. Eyewitness Travel Guide - Boston. 2011. (Eyewitness Travel Guides). (ENG., Illus.). 208p. 20.00 *(978-0-7566-6973-7(1))* Dorling Kindersley Publishing, Inc.
Harris, Patricia, et al. Eyewitness Travel Guides Top Ten Boston. 2011. (Eyewitness top 10 travel Guide Ser.). (ENG.). 160p. 14.00 *(978-0-7566-6962-1(6))* Dorling Kindersley Publishing, Inc.
Harvard Student Agencies, Inc. & Avalon Travel Publishing Staff. Let's Go Boston: The Student Travel Guide. 2011. (Let's Go Ser.). (ENG., Illus.). 444p. pap. 17.95 *(978-1-59880-710-3(2)*, Let's Go) Avalon Travel Publishing.
Hesperides. Rand Mcnally & Co's Handy Guide to Boston & Environs. 2007. 204p. per. *(978-1-4067-6658-5(5)*, Hesperides Pr.) Read Bks.
Hopkins, Hilary. Boston's Historic Places — So What? An Interactive Guide for the Thoughtful Walker. 2009. (Illus.). 96p. pap. 8.00 *(978-0-692-00307-7(X))* Jewelweed Bks.
Howell, Steven. Photographing Boston: Where to Find Perfect Shots & How to Take Them. 2011. (Photographer's Guide Ser.). (ENG., Illus.). 96p. pap. 15.95 *(978-0-88150-916-8(7)*, 150916) Countryman Pr.
Hull, Sarah & Rough Guides Staff. Boston - The Rough Guide. 6th ed. 2011. (ENG., Illus.). 340p. 18.99 *(978-1-84836-588-9(8))* Rough Guides, Ltd. GBR. Dist: Dorling Kindersley Publishing, Inc.
Klein, Christopher. The Die-Hard Sports Fan's Guide to Boston: A Spectator's Handbook. 2009. (ENG., Illus.). 269p. pap. 17.95 *(978-1-934598-04-7(6))* Union Park Pr.
Knopf Guides Staff. Boston. 2011. (Knopf Mapguides Ser.). (ENG., Illus.). 48p. pap. 10.95 *(978-0-307-26589-0(7)*, Knopf) Knopf Doubleday Publishing Group.
Kooker, Naomi, et al, eds. Boston Restaurants 2008-2009: Including Cape Cod, Martha's Vineyard & Nantucket. 2008. (ENG., Illus.). 288p. pap. 14.95 *(978-1-57006-963-5(8))* Zagat Survey.
Lantos, James, ed. Boston. 2009. (ENG.). 56p. pap. 9.95 *(978-1-4290-9701-7(9))* Applewood Bks.
Lawrence, Rachel, ed. Boston Insight City Guide. 4th ed. 2010. (City Guide Ser.). (ENG., Illus.). 256p. pap. 19.99 *(978-981-282-232-1(1))* APA Publications Services SGP. Dist: Ingram Pub. Services.
Lonely Planet Staff & Vorhees, Mara. Boston. 2009. (Best Of Ser.). (ENG., Illus.). 176p. pap. 14.99 *(978-1-74179-603-2(2))* Lonely Planet Pubns.
Lowenstein, Mark. Great Runs in Boston. 2009. (ENG., Illus.). 128p. pap. 17.95 *(978-0-9822485-2-2(0))* Fresh Tracks Pr.
Luong, Minh T., ed. Hungry? Boston: The Lowdown on Where the Real People Eat! rev. ed. 2008. (Hungry? City Guides). (Illus.). 307p. pap. 14.95 *(978-1-893329-41-6(0))* Hungry City Guides.
MacKinnon, Kim Foley. Outdoors with Kids Boston: 100 Fun Places to Explore in & Around the City. 2012. (AMC Outdoors with Kids Ser.). (ENG., Illus.). 288p. pap. 18.95 ***(978-1-934028-60-5(6))*** Appalachian Mountain Club Bks.
Mantzaris, Anna. Freedom Trail: A Guided Tour Through History. 2010. (Timeline Ser.). (ENG., Illus.). 96p. pap. 15.95 *(978-0-7627-5741-1(8))* Globe Pequot Pr., The.
Meras, Phyllis. The Historic Shops & Restaurants of Boston: A Guide to Century-Old Establishments in the City & Surrounding Towns. 2007. (ENG.). 224p. 16.95 *(978-1-892145-44-4(8))* Little Bookroom.
Mirsky, Steve. Best Hikes near Boston. 2011. (Best Hikes near Ser.). (ENG., Illus.). 224p. pap. 18.95 *(978-0-7627-6091-6(5)*, Falcon Guides) Globe Pequot Pr., The.
Mobil US City Gd. Boston. 2009. (CITY GUIDE-DOMESTIC Ser.). 192p. 16.95 *(978-0-8416-0737-8(0))* Langenscheidt Publishing Group.
Morgan, Keith N., et al. Buildings of Massachusetts: Metropolitan Boston. 2009. (Buildings of the United States Ser.). (ENG., Illus.). 688p. (gr. 17). 75.00 *(978-0-8139-2709-1(9))* Univ. Pr. of Virginia.
Morris, Marie. Boston Day by Day. 2nd ed. 2009. (Frommer's Day by Day - Pocket Ser.: 58). (ENG., Illus.). 192p. pap. 12.99 *(978-0-470-49766-1(1)*, Frommers) Wiley, John & Sons, Inc.
—Frommer's Boston 2012. 7th ed. 2011. (Frommer's Complete Ser.). (ENG., Illus.). 384p. pap. 19.99 *(978-1-118-01721-0(8)*, Frommers) Wiley, John & Sons, Inc.
Not For Tourists. Not for Tourists Guide to Boston, 7th Edition. 7th ed. 2011. (Not for Tourists Ser.). (ENG., Illus.). 376p. pap. 18.99 *(978-0-9825951-5-2(6))* Not For Tourists, Inc.
Not for Tourists Staff. Boston 2009. 5th rev. ed. 2008. (Illus.). 384p. 16.95 *(978-0-9814887-3-8(0))* Not for Tourists, Inc.
Not For Tourists Staff. Boston 2010. 2009. (Not for Tourists Guidebooks Ser.). (ENG., Illus.). 376p. pap. 16.99 *(978-0-9795339-1-4(0))* Not For Tourists, Inc.
Not For Tourists Staff. Not for Tourists Guide to Boston: 2012. 2011. (ENG., Illus.). 368p. pap. 16.95 ***(978-1-61608-530-8(4)***, 608530, Not For Tourist) Skyhorse Publishing Co., Inc.
Not for Tourists Staff. Not for Tourists Guide to Boston 2007. 3rd ed. 2006. 337p. 14.95 *(978-0-9778031-2-5(0)*, Not For Tourists) Not for Tourists, Inc.
—Not for Tourists Guide to Boston 2008. 2007. 337p. 15.95 *(978-0-9793945-3-9(8))* Not for Tourists, Inc.
Ochterbeck, Cynthia Clayton & Schnuer, Jenna. Must Sees Boston Michelin. 2nd ed. 2009. (Must Sees Ser.). (ENG., Illus.). 160p. pap. 11.99 *(978-1-906261-64-1(4))* Michelin Travel & Lifestyle.
O'Neil, Luke. Boston's Best Dive Bars: Drinking & Diving in Beantown. 2011. (Best Dive Bars Ser.). (ENG., Illus.). 176p. pap. 12.95 ***(978-1-935439-25-7(1)***, Gamble Guides) Ig Publishing, Inc.
OPUS Staff & Other Publisher Map Staff. Map Bostonian Boston Map Ma. 2011. 5.95 *(978-1-933535-11-1(3))* Opus Publishing.
—Map Bostonian Boston Mapguide Ma. 2011. 6.95 *(978-1-933535-13-5(X))* Opus Publishing.
Page, Janice & Arnett, Alison, eds. Dining Out: 52 Reviews of Boston's Top Restaurants. 2007. 109p. per. 9.95 *(978-0-9790137-5-1(5))* Boston Globe, The.
Page, Janice & Cortissoz, Ann, eds. Cheap Eats: 52 Real Deal Meals in Greater Boston. 2007. (Cheap Eats: Dining Deals in Greater Boston for 52 Weeks Ser.). 109p. per. 9.95 *(978-0-9790137-3-7(9))* Boston Globe, The.
Pietrzyk, Cindi D. Boston's Freedom Trail, 9th: Trace the Path of American History. 2011. (ENG., Illus.). 128p. pap. 9.95 *(978-0-7627-7298-8(0))* Globe Pequot Pr., The.
PopOut Products. Boston Inside Out. 2010. 64p. 10.95 *(978-1-84587-803-0(5))* Globe Pequot Pr., The.
Rackow, Paula, ed. Where Boston PopOut Cityguide. 2008. (ENG., Illus.). 64p. 9.95 *(978-0-7627-4699-6(8))* Globe Pequot Pr., The.
Scheff, Jonathan. Boston Icons: 50 Symbols of Beantown. 2011. (Icons Ser.). (ENG., Illus.). 112p. 16.95 *(978-0-7627-4817-4(6))* Globe Pequot Pr., The.
Seasholes, Nancy S. Walking Tours of Boston's Made Land. 2006. (ENG., Illus.). 224p. (gr. 17). per. 18.95 *(978-0-262-69339-4(9))* MIT Pr.
Smith, Barbara Brown & Smith, Barbara B. Rise & Dine: Breakfast in Boston. 2007. (ENG., Illus.). 192p. pap. 12.95 *(978-1-55591-607-7(4))* Fulcrum Publishing.
Southworth, Michael & Southworth, Susan. Boston: Contemporary Landmarks, Urban Design, Parks, Historic Buildings & Neighborhoods. 3rd ed. 2008. (ENG., Illus.). 384p. pap. 29.95 *(978-0-7627-4337-7(9))* Globe Pequot Pr., The.
Stanwood, Edward. Boston Illustrated. 2006. (Illus.). 176p. per. 18.99 *(978-1-4255-1371-9(9))* MPublishing.
Thomas Cook Publishing. Traveller Guides Boston & New England, 4th: Popular, compact guides for discovering the very best of country, regional & city Destinations. 4th ed. 2011. (Travellers - Thomas Cook Ser.). (ENG., Illus.). 192p. pap. 16.95 *(978-1-84848-443-6(7))* Cook, Thomas Publishing GBR. Dist: Globe Pequot Pr., The.
Time Out Guides Staff. Time Out Boston. 5th ed. 2011. (Time Out Guides). (ENG., Illus.). 280p. pap. 19.95 *(978-1-84670-188-7(0))* Time Out Guides Ltd. GBR. Dist: Perseus-PGW.
Tourville, Jacqueline. Moon Take a Hike Boston: 86 Hikes within 2 Hours of the City. 2011. (Moon Outdoors Ser.). (ENG., Illus.). 328p. pap. 17.99 *(978-1-59880-760-8(9))* Avalon Travel Publishing.
Turner, Roger L. & Turner, Roger. Bicycling on Boston's North Shore. 2007. (ENG., Illus.). 192p. pap. 15.95 *(978-1-58465-528-2(3))* Univ. Pr. of New England.
Wallace, David. 48 Hours Boston: Timed Tours for Short Stays. 2009. (ENG., Illus.). 32p. 7.95 *(978-0-7627-4924-9(5))* Globe Pequot Pr., The.
Wallpaper Magazine Editors, ed. Boston - Wallpaper City Guide. 2009. (ENG., Illus.). 128p. pap. 9.95 *(978-0-7148-4895-2(6))* Phaidon Pr., Inc.
Wallpaper Magazine Editors, ed. Wallpaper* City Guide Boston 2013. 2012. (ENG.). 128p. pap. 9.95 ***(978-0-7148-6430-3(7))*** Phaidon Pr., Inc.
Weatherall, Helen. Boston: Including Coastal & Interior Regions, & New Hampshire. 2008. (60 Hikes within 60 Miles Ser.). (ENG., Illus.). 376p. pap. 18.95 *(978-0-89732-636-0(9))* Menasha Ridge Pr., Inc.
Wurman, Richard Saul & Wurman, Richard S. Access Boston. 8th ed. 2007. (Access Boston Ser.). (Illus.). 256p. pap. 21.95 *(978-0-06-114791-3(5))* HarperCollins Pubs.
Zagat Survey Staff. 2011/12 Boston Restaurants. 2011. (ZAGAT Restaurant Guides). (ENG.). 304p. pap. 15.95 *(978-1-60478-350-6(8))* Zagat Survey.
—2011/12 Boston ZAGAT. com & Book Pack. 2011. 29.95 *(978-1-60478-361-2(3))* Zagat Survey.
Zagat Survey Staff, creator. Zagat Boston Restaurants. rev. ed. 2007. (ENG.). 256p. pap. 14.95 *(978-1-57006-863-8(1))* Zagat Survey.
—Zagat. com & Book Pack. 2008. (ENG., Illus.). 268p. 29.95 *(978-1-57006-985-7(9))* Zagat Survey.
—Zagat. com Boston Restaurants. 2007. (ENG.). 29.95 *(978-1-57006-933-8(6))* Zagat Survey.
Zagat Survey Staff, ed. Zagat. com W.Boston 2009/10. 2008. (ENG.). 29.95 *(978-1-60478-201-1(3))* Zagat Survey.

BOSTON (MASS.)—HISTORY

Archer, Richard. As If an Enemy's Country: The British Occupation of Boston & the Origins of Revolution. (Pivotal Moments in American History Ser.). (ENG., Illus.). 304p. 2012. pap. 16.95 ***(978-0-19-989577-9(5))*** 2010. 24.95 *(978-0-19-538247-1(1))* Oxford Univ. Pr., Inc.
Arrison, Julie. Franklin Park. 2009. (Images of America Ser.). (ENG., Illus.). 128p. pap. 21.99 *(978-0-7385-6531-6(8))* Arcadia Publishing.
Bahne, Charles. Chronicles of Old Boston: Exploring New England's Historic Capital. 2012. (ENG., Illus.). 288p. pap. 19.95 ***(978-0-9846334-0-1(5))*** Museyon Inc.
Boston Fire Historical Society. Boston's Fire Trail: A Walk Through the City's Fire & Firefighting History. 2007. (Illus.). 126p. per. 19.99 *(978-1-59629-361-8(6))* History Pr., The.
Boston Registry Department Staff. Records Relating to the Early History of Boston, 39 vols. reprint ed. *(978-0-404-12343-7(0))* AMS Pr., Inc.
Brown-West, Orikaye G. In DEFENSE of the BIG DIG: How Politics Affected the Planning, Design & Construction of the Boston Central Artery/Tunnel Project. 2008. 281p. 39.74 *(978-1-4303-1265-9(3))* Lulu Enterprises Inc.
Buckley, Steve. Wicked Good Year: How the Red Sox, Patriots, & Celtics Turned the Hub of the Universe into the Capital of Sports. 2010. (ENG.). 352p. pap. 14.99 *(978-0-06-178739-3(6))* HarperCollins Pubs.
Bureau of Statistics of Labor Staff. The Working Girls of Boston. 133p. reprint ed. 88.00 *(978-0-7222-1872-3(9))* Library Reprints, Inc.
Carp, Benjamin L. Defiance of the Patriots: The Boston Tea Party & the Making of America. 2010. (ENG., Illus.). 328p. 30.00 *(978-0-300-11705-9(1))* Yale Univ. Pr.
Clapp, William Warland. A Record of the Boston Stage. 2009. 284p. pap. 21.98 *(978-0-217-67225-2(6))* General Bks. LLC.
Clarke, Theodore G. Boston Curiosities: A History of Extraordinary Personalities, Portentous Places, & Singular Events. 2008. pap. 17.99 *(978-1-59629-580-3(5))* History Pr., The.
Clarke, Theodore G. & Armstrong, Annabelle M. Beacon Hill, Back Bay, & the Building of Boston's Golden Age. 2010. (ENG., Illus.). 128p. pap. 19.99 *(978-1-59629-161-4(3))* History Pr., The.
Clinger, Julia. It Happened in Boston. 2007. (It Happened in Ser.). (ENG., Illus.). 160p. pap. 12.95 *(978-0-7627-4134-2(1)*, Falcon Guides) Globe Pequot Pr., The.
Cohen, Morris A. & Cohen, Richard Shain. Healing after Dark: Pioneering Compassionate Medicine at the Boston Evening Clinic. 2011. (Illus.). 184p. ***(978-1-926918-43-3(6)***, CCB Publishing) CCB Publishing.
Connelly, Richard. Returning to Quarters: A History of Boston Firehouses. 2010. 272p. pap. 23.95 *(978-1-4251-8068-3(X))* Trafford Publishing.
Crawford, Mary C. Old Boston Days & Ways. (Illus.). reprint ed. lib. bdg. 98.00 *(978-0-7222-0655-3(0))* Library Reprints, Inc.
Crawford, Mary Caroline. Old Boston in Colonial Days or St Botolph's Town: from the Time Of. 2006. (ENG.). 480p. per. 38.95 *(978-1-4286-6333-6(9))* Kessinger Publishing, LLC.
Dawson, David & Sabin, Thomas, eds. The Cradle of American Neurology: The Harvard Neurological Unit at the Boston City Hospital. 2011. (Illus.). 222p. pap. 28.95 ***(978-1-884186-48-6(3))*** Hollis Publishing Co.
Dayton, Cornelia H. & Salinger, Sharon V. Warning Out: Robert Love's Search for Strangers in Pre-Revolutionary Boston. 2010. (ENG.). 240p. *(978-0-8070-7150-2(1))* Beacon Pr.
Dorchester antiquarian and historical so. The History of the Town of Dorchester, Massachusetts, by a Committee of the Dorchester Antiquarian & Historical Society. 2006. 688p. per. 36.99 *(978-1-4255-6841-2(6))* MPublishing.
Drake, Samuel Adams. Old Boston: Taverns & Tavern Clubs. 2009. 176p. 22.99 *(978-1-103-85644-2(8))*; pap. 16.99 *(978-1-103-85635-0(9))* BiblioBazaar.

B

—Old Landmarks & Historic Personages of Boston. 2009. 454p. pap. *(978-0-217-52486-5(9))* Books LLC.
—Old Landmarks & Historic Personages of Boston. 2006. (ENG.). 504p. per. 29.99 *(978-1-4255-5601-3(9))* MPublishing.
Earls, Alan R. Greater Boston's Blizzard Of 1978. 2008. (Images of America Ser.). (ENG., Illus.). 128p. per. 21.99 *(978-0-7385-5519-5(3))* Arcadia Publishing.
Esposito, John C. Fire in the Grove: The Cocoanut Grove Tragedy & Its Aftermath. 2006. (ENG., Illus.). 288p. per. 16.95 *(978-0-306-81501-0(X))* Da Capo Pr., Inc.
Everett, Edward. Dorchester in 1630, 1776, & 1855 an Oration Delivered on the Fourth of July, 1855, by Edward Everett Also an Account of the Proceedings in Dorches. 2006. 168p. per. 18.99 *(978-1-4255-1316-0(6))* MPublishing.
French, Allen. The Siege of Boston. 2010. (ENG.). 488p. pap. 38.75 *(978-1-177-45810-8(1))* 2010. 490p. pap. 38.75 *(978-1-142-18224-3(X))* 2009. 478p. 42.99 *(978-1-113-89492-2(X))* 2009. 478p. pap. 37.75 *(978-1-113-89490-8(3))* 2009. (ENG.). 477p. pap. 28.99 *(978-1-113-89487-8(3),* BiblioLife) 2009. (ENG.). 477p. pap. 30.99 *(978-1-113-89488-5(1),* BiblioLife) BiblioBazaar.
—The Siege of Boston. 2009. 168p. pap. *(978-1-151-27310-9(4))* Books LLC.
—The Siege of Boston. 2009. (Illus.). 226p. pap. *(978-1-4099-8851-9(1))* Dodo Pr.
—The Siege of Boston. 2010. (Illus.). 134p. pap. 22.35 *(978-1-153-81750-9(0))* General Bks. LLC.
—The Siege of Boston. 2010. 478p. pap. 30.36 *(978-1-163-79934-5(3))* 2007. 480p. 52.95 *(978-0-548-55834-8(5))* 2007. (ENG.). 480p. per. 37.95 *(978-0-548-50174-0(2))* Kessinger Publishing, LLC.
Frommer, Harvey. Remembering Fenway Park: An Oral & Narrative History of the Home of the Boston Red Sox. 2011. (ENG., Illus.). 240p. 45.00 *(978-1-58479-852-1(1))* Stewart, Tabori & Chang.
Frothingham, Richard. History of the Siege of Boston, & of the Battles of Lexington, Concord, & Bunker Hill. 2009. 312p. pap. *(978-1-150-74766-3(8))* Books LLC.
—History of the Siege of Boston, & of the Battles of Lexington, Concord, & Bunker Hill. 422p. reprint ed. 98.00 *(978-0-7222-7694-5(X))* Library Reprints, Inc.
Goldfeld, Alex R. The North End: A Brief History of Boston's Oldest Neighborhood. 2009. (Brief History Ser.). (ENG., Illus.). 192p. pap. 19.99 *(978-1-59629-518-6(X))* History Pr., The.
Guarino, Robert E. Beacon Street: A Highway of History. 2011. 128p. pap. 19.99 *(978-1-60949-124-6(6))* History Pr., The.
Hantover, Jeffrey. City in Time - Boston. 2008. (City in Time Ser.). (ENG., Illus.). 144p. 14.95 *(978-1-4027-3300-0(3))* Sterling Publishing Co., Inc.
Henshaw, William. The Orderly Books of Colonel William Henshaw, October 1, 1775 Through October 3 1776. 2011. 232p. 46.95 ***(978-1-258-09505-5(X))*** Literary Licensing, LLC.
Hesperides. And This Is Boston. 2007. 284p. per. *(978-1-4067-5195-6(2),* Hesperides Pr.) Read Bks.
Kennedy, Patrick L. Boston Then & Now (Compact) 2010. (Then & Now Thunder Bay Ser.). (ENG., Illus.). 144p. pap. 12.95 *(978-1-59223-878-1(5),* Thunder Bay Pr.) Advantage Pubs. Group.
Lisicky, Michael J. Filene's: Boston's Great Specialty Store. 2012. (Images of America Ser.). (ENG., Illus.). 128p. pap. 21.99 ***(978-0-7385-9158-2(0))*** Arcadia Publishing.
Louis, David N. & Young, Robert H. Keen Minds to Explore the Dark Continents of Disease: A History of the Pathology Services at Massachusetts General Hospital. 2011. 0.00 ***(978-0-615-48638-3(X))*** U. S. ISBN Agency.
Marchione, William P. Allston-Brighton in Transition: From Cattle Town to Streetcar Suburb. 2007. (Illus.). 159p. pap., per. 21.99 *(978-1-59629-252-9(0))* History Pr., The.
—Boston Miscellany: An Episodic History of the Hub. 2008. 128p. pap. 18.99 *(978-1-59629-587-2(2))* History Pr., The.
Martin, Mary L. & Rooney, E. Ashley. Boston: Past & Present. 2008. (Illus.). 128p. pap. 24.99 *(978-0-7643-3058-2(6))* Schiffer Publishing, Ltd.
McLain, Susan R. Butler County: The Boston Studio Collection. 2009. (Images of America Ser.). (ENG., Illus.). 128p. pap. 21.99 *(978-0-7385-6051-9(0))* Arcadia Publishing.
McLaughlin, Robert. Pleasure Island. 2009. (Images of America Ser.). (ENG., Illus.). 128p. pap. 21.99 *(978-0-7385-6460-9(5))* Arcadia Publishing.
McNulty, Elizabeth, et al. Boston Then & Now. 2nd ed. 2009. (Then & Now Thunder Bay Ser.). (ENG.). 144p. 19.95 *(978-1-59223-963-4(3),* Thunder Bay Pr.) Advantage Pubs. Group.
Mitchell, John Hanson. The Paradise of All These Parts: A Natural History of Boston, 1 vol. 2009. (ENG.). 272p. pap. 16.00 *(978-0-8070-7149-6(8))* Beacon Pr.
Mulder, Arnold. The Sand Doctor. reprint ed. lib. bdg. 125.00 *(978-0-7222-0150-3(8))* Library Reprints, Inc.
Nason, Elias. Sir Charles Henry Frankland, Baronet; or Boston in the Colonial Times by Elias Nason. 2006. 136p. per. 16.99 *(978-1-4255-0976-7(2))* MPublishing.
Nelson, James L. With Fire & Sword: The Battle of Bunker Hill & the Beginning of the American Revolution. 2011. (ENG., Illus.). 384p. 27.99 *(978-0-312-57644-8(7),* Dunne, Thomas Bks.) St. Martin's Pr.
—With Fire & Sword: The Battle of Bunker Hill & the Beginning of the American Revolution. l.t. ed. 2011. (Illus.). 595p. 31.99 *(978-1-4104-3824-9(4))* Thorndike Pr.
Newman, William A., et al. Boston's Back Bay: The Story of America's Greatest Nineteenth-Century Landfill Project. 2007. (ENG., Illus.). 252p. pap. 22.95 *(978-1-55553-680-0(8),* Northeastern University Pr.) Univ. Pr. of New England.
Nowlin, Bill & Prime, Jim. Fenway Park at 100: Baseball's Hometown. 2012. (ENG., Illus.). 176p. 29.95 ***(978-1-61321-001-7(9),*** 613001) Skyhorse Publishing Co., Inc.
O'Connor, Thomas H. The Boston Irish: A Political History. 2007. 363p. 30.00 *(978-1-4223-9157-0(4))* DIANE Publishing Co.
O'Connor, Thomas H., ed. Two Centuries of Faith: The Influence of Catholicism on Boston: 1808-2008. 2009. (Church in the 21st Century Ser.). (ENG.). 344p. pap. 39.95 *(978-0-8245-2531-6(0))* Crossroad Publishing Co., The.
Orwig, Timothy, text. Historic Photos of Boston. 2006. (Historic Photos Ser.). (ENG., Illus.). 206p. 39.95 *(978-1-59652-305-0(0))* Turner Publishing Co.
Parker, Theodore. The Trial of Theodore Parker. 2008. 248p. 27.99 *(978-0-554-60962-1(2));* 245p. pap. 26.75 *(978-0-554-60964-5(9))* BiblioBazaar.
Pencak, William. Contested Commonwealths: Essays in American History. 2011. (ENG.). 382p. 85.00 ***(978-1-61146-083-4(2))*** Lehigh Univ. Pr.
Pepe, William J. & Pepe, Elaine A. Boston. 2009. (Postcard History Ser.). (ENG., Illus.). 128p. pap. 21.99 *(978-0-7385-6541-5(5))* Arcadia Publishing.
Pietrzyk, Cindi D. Boston's Freedom Trail, 9th: Trace the Path of American History. 2011. (ENG., Illus.). 128p. pap. 9.95 *(978-0-7627-7298-8(0))* Globe Pequot Pr., The.
Puleo, Stephen. A City So Grand: The Rise of an American Metropolis, Boston, 1850-1900. 2010. (ENG.). 320p. 26.95 *(978-0-8070-5043-9(1))* Beacon Pr.
—A City So Grand: The Rise of an American Metropolis, Boston 1850-1900. 2011. 312p. pap. 16.00 *(978-0-8070-0149-3(X))* Beacon Pr.
Quigley, David. The Boston Busing Crisis: A Brief History with Documents. 2013. (Bedford Series in History & Culture Ser.). (ENG.). 208p. (C). pap. 15.95 *(978-0-312-45884-3(3))* Bedford/Saint Martin's.
Quincy, Josiah. A Municipal History of Boston During Two Centuries. 2009. (City Ser.). (ENG.). 468p. pap. 28.95 *(978-1-4290-2216-3(7))* Applewood Bks.
—A Municipal History of the Town & City of Boston, During Two Centuries from September 17, 1630, to September 17, 1830 by Josiah Quincy. 2006. 468p. per. 29.99 *(978-1-4255-5201-5(3))* MPublishing.
Rawson, Michael. Eden on the Charles: The Making of Boston. 2010. (ENG., Illus.). 384p. 29.95 *(978-0-674-04841-6(5))* Harvard Univ. Pr.
Remy, Jerry & Sandler, Corey. Red Sox Heroes: The Remdawg's All-Time Favorite Red Sox, Great Moments, & Top Teams. 2009. (ENG., Illus.). 288p. 24.95 *(978-1-59921-406-1(7),* Lyons Pr.) Globe Pequot Pr., The.
Rennella, Mark. The Boston Cosmopolitans: International Travel & American Arts & Letters. 2008. (ENG., Illus.). 288p. 89.00 *(978-0-230-60382-0(3))* Palgrave Macmillan.
Reynolds, Bill. Rise of a Dynasty: The '57 Celtics, the First Banner, & the Dawning of a New America. 2011. (ENG.). 304p. (gr. 12). 15.00 *(978-0-451-23480-3(4),* N A L Trade) Penguin Group (USA) Inc.
Robbins, Chandler, abr. A History of the Second Church. 2009. (Amer Philosophy, Religion Ser.). (ENG.). 344p. pap. 21.95 *(978-1-4290-1980-4(8))* Applewood Bks.
Robinson, Guy. Do You Know Boston? A Challenging Little Quiz about the People, Places, & Amazing History of America's Oldest Major City. 2008. (ENG.). 48p. pap. 5.95 *(978-1-4022-1301-4(8))* Sourcebooks, Inc.
Rowe, John. Letters & Diary of John Rowe. 453p. reprint ed. 98.00 *(978-0-7222-7625-9(7))* Library Reprints, Inc.
Sammarco, Anthony. Dorchester a Compendium. 2011. 128p. pap. 19.99 ***(978-1-60949-174-1(2))*** History Pr., The.
Sammarco, Anthony M. Boston's North End. 2007. (Then & Now Ser.). (ENG., Illus.). 96p. per. 21.99 *(978-0-7385-5503-4(7))* Arcadia Publishing.
Sammarco, Anthony Mitchell. Dorchester: A Compendium. 2011. ***(978-1-60949-217-5(X))*** History Pr., The.
—Hyde Park. 2011. (Then & Now Ser.). (ENG., Illus.). 96p. pap. 21.99 ***(978-0-7385-7396-0(5))*** Arcadia Publishing.
Sammarco, Anthony Mitchell. South Boston. 2006. (Then & Now Ser.). (ENG., Illus.). 96p. per. 21.99 *(978-0-7385-3948-5(1))* Arcadia Publishing.
Snow, Caleb. A History of Boston. 2009. (City Ser.). (ENG.). 436p. pap. 26.95 *(978-1-4290-2191-3(8))* Applewood Bks.
Stevens, Peter F. Hidden History of the Boston Irish: Little-Known Stories from Ireland's Next Parish Over. 2008. (Illus.). 160p. pap. 19.99 *(978-1-59629-450-9(7))* History Pr., The.
Stout, Glenn. Fenway 1912: The Birth of a Ballpark, a Championship Season, & Fenway's Remarkable First Year. (ENG.). 416p. 2012. pap. 14.95 ***(978-0-547-84457-2(3),*** Mariner Bks.) 2011. (Illus.). 26.00 *(978-0-547-19562-9(1))* Houghton Mifflin Harcourt Trade & Reference Pubs.
Sullivan, Jim. South Boston. 2007. (Postcard History Ser.). (Illus.). 128p. per. 19.99 *(978-0-7385-5528-7(2))* Arcadia Publishing.
Sweeney, Emily. Boston Organized Crime. 2012. (Images of America Ser.). (ENG., Illus.). 128p. pap. 21.99 ***(978-0-7385-7673-2(5))*** Arcadia Publishing.
To, Wing-Kai & Chinese Historical Society of New England. Chinese in Boston: 1870-1965. 2008. (Images of America Ser.). (ENG., Illus.). 128p. per. 21.99 *(978-0-7385-5529-4(0))* Arcadia Publishing.
Venable, David. Boston Bound. 2011. 214p. pap. 14.95 ***(978-1-4575-0139-5(2))*** Dog Ear Publishing, LLC.
Whitcomb, Harriet Manning. Annals & Reminiscences of Jamaica Plain. 2009. 72p. pap. 16.75 *(978-1-110-40431-5(X))* BiblioBazaar.
Winslow, Anna G. Diary of Anna Green Winslow: A Boston School Girl Of 1771. Earle, Alice M., ed. 2007. (ENG.). 158p. 36.95 *(978-0-548-24581-1(9));* 160p. per. 21.95 *(978-1-4326-4787-2(3))* Kessinger Publishing, LLC.
Winslow, Anna Green. Diary of Anna Green Winslow: A Boston School Girl of 1771. 2009. 164p. 26.99 *(978-1-110-11518-1(0))* 2009. 164p. pap. 20.75 *(978-1-110-11516-7(4))* 2007. (ENG.). 92p. pap. 16.99 *(978-1-4346-9968-8(4))* 2007. (ENG.). 104p. pap. 19.99 *(978-1-4346-9969-5(2))* BiblioBazaar.
Winsor, Justin, ed. Memorial History of Boston, 1630-1880 Set, 4 vols. (Illus.). reprint ed. lib. bdg. 500.00 *(978-0-7222-0644-7(5))* Library Reprints, Inc.
Wisnia, Saul. Fenway Park:the Centennial: 100 Years of Red Sox Baseball. 2011. (ENG., Illus.). 176p. 29.99 *(978-0-312-64274-7(1))* St. Martin's Pr.
Zonderman, David A. Uneasy Allies: Working for Labor Reform in Nineteenth-Century Boston. 2011. (Illus.). 336p. pap. 28.95 *(978-1-55849-866-2(4));* lib. bdg. 80.00 *(978-1-55849-865-5(6))* Univ. of Massachusetts Pr.

BOSTON (MASS.)—INTELLECTUAL LIFE

Crawford, Mary Caroline. Romantic Days in Old Boston: The Story of the City & of Its People During the Nineteenth Century. 2007. (ENG.). 494p. 53.95 *(978-0-548-01845-3(6))* Kessinger Publishing, LLC.
Foster, Russell J. Daughter of Boston: The Extraordinary Diary of a Nineteenth-century Woman, Caroline Healey Dall. Deese, Helen R., ed. 2006. (ENG.). 488p. pap. 20.00 *(978-0-8070-5035-4(0))* Beacon Pr.
Holmes, Oliver Wendell. The Autocrat of the Breakfast Table. 2009. 336p. 25.99 *(978-1-103-76553-9(1));* pap. 19.99 *(978-1-103-76548-5(5))* BiblioBazaar.
—The Autocrat of the Breakfast Table. 2010. 96p. pap. *(978-1-151-90717-2(0))* 2010. 90p. pap. *(978-1-151-90714-1(6))* 2009. 156p. pap. *(978-0-217-88605-5(1))* Books LLC.
—The Autocrat of the Breakfast Table. 2008. 232p. pap. *(978-1-4065-6122-7(3))* Dodo Pr.
—The Autocrat of the Breakfast Table. 2008. 308p. pap. *(978-1-4097-6304-8(8))* Read Bks.
—The Autocrat of the Breakfast Table. 2008. 396p. 29.95 *(978-1-4344-6901-4(8));* pap. 14.95 *(978-1-4344-6900-7(X))* Wildside Pr., LLC.
—The Autocrat of the Breakfast-Table. 2009. 340p. 25.99 *(978-1-103-03878-7(8))* 2009. 340p. pap. 19.99 *(978-1-103-03875-6(3))* 2008. (ENG.). 344p. 36.99 *(978-1-4264-7878-9(X))* 2008. (ENG.). 344p. 32.99 *(978-1-4264-7894-9(1))* 2008. (ENG.). 344p. pap. 31.75 *(978-1-4264-7889-5(5))* 2008. (ENG.). 344p. pap. 32.75 *(978-1-4264-7883-3(6))* BiblioBazaar.
—The Autocrat of the Breakfast-Table. 2009. 228p. pap. *(978-1-4588-5984-6(3));* 216p. pap. *(978-0-217-62124-3(4))* Books LLC.
—The Autocrat of the Breakfast-Table. 2009. 214p. pap. *(978-1-4446-6193-4(0),* Pomona Pr.) Read Bks.
Rennella, Mark. The Boston Cosmopolitans: International Travel & American Arts & Letters. 2008. (ENG., Illus.). 288p. 89.00 *(978-0-230-60382-0(3))* Palgrave Macmillan.
Wolff, Katherine. Culture Club: The Curious History of the Boston Athenaeum. 2009. (Illus.). 256p. 80.00 net. *(978-1-55849-713-9(7));* (ENG., pap. 26.95 net. *(978-1-55849-714-6(5))* Univ. of Massachusetts Pr.

BOSTON (MASS.)—ISABELLA STEWART GARDNER MUSEUM

see Isabella Stewart Gardner Museum

BOSTON (MASS.)—POLICE

see Police—Massachusetts—Boston

BOSTON (MASS.)—POLITICS AND GOVERNMENT

Barr, Cynthia M. Boston Zoning: A Lawyer's Handbook. 2007. (ENG.). pap. *(978-1-57589-483-6(1))* Massachusetts Continuing Legal Education, Inc.
Boston (Mass.). Proceedings at the Dedication of the City Hall, September 18 1865. 2011. 38p. pap. 11.99 ***(978-1-4181-9544-1(8))*** MPublishing.
Clarke, Theodore G. Brookline, Alston-Brighton, & the Renewal of Boston. 2010. *(978-1-60949-185-7(8))* History Pr., The.
Clavel, Pierre. Activists in City Hall: The Progressive Response to the Reagan Era in Boston & Chicago. 2010. (Illus.). 224p. 65.00 *(978-0-8014-4929-1(4));* pap. 19.95 *(978-0-8014-7655-6(0))* Cornell Univ. Pr.
Greenidge, Kerri & Allison, Robert. Boston's Abolitionists. 2006. (NE Remembers Ser.). (ENG., Illus.). 96p. per. 12.95 *(978-1-933212-19-7(5))* Commonwealth Editions.
Massachusetts. Supreme Judicial Court. A Digest of Decisions of Municipal Interest of the Supreme Judicial Court of Massachusetts. 2006. 168p. per. 18.99 *(978-1-4255-1369-6(7))* MPublishing.
O'Connor, Thomas H. The Boston Irish: A Political History. 2007. 363p. 30.00 *(978-1-4223-9157-0(4))* DIANE Publishing Co.
O'Neill, Gerard. Rogues & Redeemers: When Politics Was King in Irish Boston. 2012. (ENG., Illus.). 416p. 26.00 *(978-0-307-40536-4(2))* Crown Publishing Group.
Quincy, Josiah. A Municipal History of Boston During Two Centuries. 2009. (City Ser.). (ENG.). 468p. pap. 28.95 *(978-1-4290-2216-3(7))* Applewood Bks.
—A Municipal History of the Town & City of Boston, During Two Centuries from September 17, 1630, to September 17, 1830 by Josiah Quincy. 2006. 468p. per. 29.99 *(978-1-4255-5201-5(3))* MPublishing.

BOSTON (MASS.)—SOCIAL CONDITIONS

Aguilar-San Juan, Karin. Little Saigons: Staying Vietnamese in America. 2009. (Illus.). 248p. (ENG.). 67.50 *(978-0-8166-5485-7(9));* pap. 22.50 *(978-0-8166-5486-4(7))* Univ. of Minnesota Pr.
Connelly, Michael P. Rebound! Basketball, Busing, Larry Bird, & the Rebirth of Boston. 2008. (ENG., Illus.). 304p. 25.00 *(978-0-7603-3501-7(X),* 076033501X, MVP Bks.) MBI Publishing Co. LLC.
Feinstein-Whittaker, Marjorie & Wilner, Lynda Katz, creators. Boston RULES: Regional Dialect Modification. 2011. 90p. 40.00 *(978-0-9830258-1-8(9))* Successfully Speaking.
Hartley, Benjamin L. Evangelicals at a Crossroads: Revivalism & Social Reform in Boston, 1860-1910. 2011. (Revisiting New England Ser.). (Illus.). 304p. (C). 85.00 *(978-1-58465-928-0(9));* (ENG., pap. 39.95 *(978-1-58465-929-7(7))* Univ. Pr. of New England. (University of New Hampshire Press).
Kalafatas, Michael N. Bird Strike: The Crash of the Boston Electra. 2010. (ENG., Illus.). 200p. 24.95 *(978-1-58465-897-9(5),* Brandeis University Press) Univ. Pr. of New England.
Kamensky, Jane. The Exchange Artist: A Tale of High-Flying Speculation & America's First Banking Collapse. 2008. (ENG.). 464p. (gr. 12-18). 17.00 *(978-0-14-311490-1(5),* Penguin (Non-Classics)) Penguin Group (USA) Inc.
MacDonald, Michael Patrick. All Souls: A Family Story from Southie. 2007. (ENG., Illus.). 296p. per. 14.95 *(978-0-8070-7213-4(3))* Beacon Pr.
—Easter Rising: A Memoir of Roots & Rebellion. 11th ed. 2008. (ENG., Illus.). 256p. pap. 13.95 *(978-0-618-91863-8(9),* Mariner Bks.) Houghton Mifflin Harcourt Trade & Reference Pubs.
McDermott, Monica. Working-Class White: The Making & Unmaking of Race Relations. 2006. (Illus.). 196p. pap., per. 26.95 *(978-0-520-24809-0(0))* Univ. of California Pr.
Miller, Neil. Banned in Boston: The Watch & Ward Society's Crusade Against Books, Burlesque, & the Social Evil. 2010. (ENG.). 240p. 26.95 *(978-0-8070-5112-2(8))* Beacon Pr.
Puleo, Stephen. A City So Grand: The Rise of an American Metropolis, Boston, 1850-1900. 2010. (ENG.). 320p. 26.95 *(978-0-8070-5043-9(1))* Beacon Pr.
—A City So Grand: The Rise of an American Metropolis, Boston 1850-1900. 2011. 312p. pap. 16.00 *(978-0-8070-0149-3(X))* Beacon Pr.
Rawson, Michael. Eden on the Charles: The Making of Boston. 2010. (ENG., Illus.). 384p. 29.95 *(978-0-674-04841-6(5))* Harvard Univ. Pr.
Reynolds, Bill. '78: The Boston Red Sox, a Historic Game, & a Divided City. 2010. (ENG.). 320p. (gr. 12-18). 15.00 *(978-0-451-22922-9(3),* N A L Trade) Penguin Group (USA) Inc.
Shea, John R. Rat Bastards: The South Boston Irish Mobster Who Took the Rap When Everyone Else Ran. 2007. (ENG., Illus.). 304p. pap. 14.99 *(978-0-06-123289-3(0),* William Morrow Paperbacks) HarperCollins Pubs.
Shea, John "Red". Rat Bastards: The Life & Times of South Boston's Most Honorable Top Irish Mobster. 2007. 320p. pap. 7.99 *(978-0-06-083717-4(9))* HarperCollins Pubs.
Smith, Kirk P. Effectiveness of Catch Basins Equipped with Hoods in Retaining Gross Solids & Hydrocarbons in Highway Runoff, Southeast Expressway, Boston, Massachusetts, 2008-09. 2010. (Illus.). vii, 24p. ***(978-1-4113-3032-0(3))*** United States Geological Survey.
Torre, Jose R. The Political Economy of Sentiment: Paper Credit & the Scottish Enlightenment in Early Republic Boston, 1780-1820, 1 vol. 2006. (Financial History Ser.). (ENG., Illus.). 262p. 99.00 *(978-1-85196-885-5(7))* Pickering & Chatto Pubs., Ltd. GBR. Dist: Ashgate Publishing Co.
Vale, Lawrence J. From the Puritans to the Projects: Public Housing & Public Neighbors. 2007. (Illus.). 482p. per. 26.50 *(978-0-674-02575-2(X))* Harvard Univ. Pr.
Weber, Jody Marie. The Evolution of Aesthetic & Expressive Dance in Boston. 2009. 288p. 109.99 *(978-1-60497-621-2(7))* Cambria Pr.
Williams, Tony. The Pox & the Covenant: Mather, Franklin, & the Epidemic That Changed America's Destiny. (ENG.). 304p. 2011. pap. 15.99 *(978-1-4022-6093-3(8))* 2010. (Illus.). 24.99 *(978-1-4022-3605-1(0))* Sourcebooks, Inc.

BOSTON (MASS.)—SOCIAL LIFE AND CUSTOMS

Brett, Bill, photos by. Boston, a Year in the Life. 2008. (Illus.). 192p. 29.95 *(978-1-933212-74-6(8))* Commonwealth Editions.
Crawford, Mary C. Old Boston Days & Ways. (Illus.). reprint ed. lib. bdg. 98.00 *(978-0-7222-0655-3(0))* Library Reprints, Inc.
Crawford, Mary Caroline. Romantic Days in Old Boston: The Story of the City & of Its People During the Nineteenth Century. 2007. (ENG.). 494p. 53.95 *(978-0-548-01845-3(6))* Kessinger Publishing, LLC.
Ferraiuolo, Augusto. Religious Festive Practices in Boston's North End: Ephemeral Identities in an Italian American Community. 2009. (SUNY Series in Italian/American Culture Ser.). 252p. 75.00 *(978-1-4384-2809-3(X));* (Illus.). pap. 24.95 *(978-1-4384-2810-9(3))* State Univ. of New York Pr. (Suny Pr.).
MacDonald, Michael Patrick. All Souls: A Family Story from Southie. 2007. (ENG., Illus.). 296p. per. 14.95 *(978-0-8070-7213-4(3))* Beacon Pr.
—Easter Rising: A Memoir of Roots & Rebellion. 11th ed. 2008. (ENG., Illus.). 256p. pap. 13.95 *(978-0-618-91863-8(9),* Mariner Bks.) Houghton Mifflin Harcourt Trade & Reference Pubs.
Martin, Mary L. & Rooney, E. Ashley. Boston: Past & Present. 2008. (Illus.). 128p. pap. 24.99 *(978-0-7643-3058-2(6))* Schiffer Publishing, Ltd.
Orwig, Timothy, text. Historic Photos of Boston. 2006. (Historic Photos Ser.). (ENG., Illus.). 206p. 39.95 *(978-1-59652-305-0(0))* Turner Publishing Co.
Rennella, Mark. The Boston Cosmopolitans: International Travel & American Arts & Letters. 2008. (ENG., Illus.). 288p. 89.00 *(978-0-230-60382-0(3))* Palgrave Macmillan.
Sammarco, Anthony. Dorchester a Compendium. 2011. 128p. pap. 19.99 ***(978-1-60949-174-1(2))*** History Pr., The.
Willis, Catherine J. Boston Public Library. 2011. (Images of America Ser.). (Illus.). 128p. pap. 21.99 *(978-0-7385-7506-3(2))* Arcadia Publishing.
Winslow, Anna G. Diary of Anna Green Winslow: A Boston School Girl Of 1771. Earle, Alice M., ed. 2007. (ENG.). 158p. 36.95 *(978-0-548-24581-1(9));* 160p. per. 21.95 *(978-1-4326-4787-2(3))* Kessinger Publishing, LLC.

Winslow, Anna Green. Diary of Anna Green Winslow: A Boston School Girl of 1771. 2009. 164p. 26.99 *(978-1-110-11518-1(0))* 2009. 164p. pap. 20.75 *(978-1-110-11516-7(4))* 2007. (ENG.). 92p. pap. 16.99 *(978-1-4346-9968-8(4))* 2007. (ENG.). 104p. pap. 19.99 *(978-1-4346-9969-5(2))* BiblioBazaar.

BOSTON ATHENAEUM

Boston Athenaeum Staff. A Catalogue of the Washington Collection in the Boston Athenaum. 566p. reprint ed. 98.00 *(978-0-7222-8913-6(8))* Library Reprints, Inc.

Cushing, Stanley Ellis & Dearinger, David B. Acquired Tastes: 200 Years of Collecting for the Boston Athenaeum. 2007. (Illus.). 388p. 65.00 *(978-0-934552-73-8(8))* Boston Athenaeum Library.

Wendorf, Richard. The Boston Athenaeum: Bicentennial Essays. 2010. (Illus.). 406p. lib. bdg. 40.00 *(978-0-934552-76-9(2))* Boston Athenaeum Library.

Wolff, Katherine. Culture Club: The Curious History of the Boston Athenaeum. 2009. (Illus.). 256p. 80.00 net. *(978-1-55849-713-9(7))*; (ENG., pap. 26.95 net. *(978-1-55849-714-6(5))* Univ. of Massachusetts Pr.

BOSTON BRAVES (BASEBALL TEAM)

see also Atlanta Braves (Baseball Team); Milwaukee Braves (Baseball Team)

Nowlin, Bill. Spahn, Sain, & Teddy Ballgame: Boston's (almost) Perfect Baseball Summer Of 1948. 2008. (ENG.). 24p. pap. 19.95 *(978-1-57940-160-3(0))* Rounder Bks.

BOSTON BRUINS (HOCKEY TEAM)

Babineau, Steve & Simpson, Rob. Black & Gold: Four Decades of the Boston Bruins in Photographs. 2nd ed. 2011. (ENG., Illus.). 304p. 34.95 ***(978-1-118-17278-0(7)**,* Wiley) Wiley, John & Sons, Inc.

Hiam, C. Michael. Eddie Shore & that Old-Time Hockey. 2011. (ENG., Illus.). 344p. pap. 19.95 *(978-0-7710-4129-7(2)*, McClelland & Stewart) McClelland & Stewart CAN. Dist: Random Hse., Inc.

—Eddie Shore & That Old-Time Hockey. 2010. (ENG., Illus.). 336p. 27.95 *(978-0-7710-4127-3(6)*, McClelland & Stewart) McClelland & Stewart CAN. Dist: Random Hse., Inc.

Kalman, Matt. 100 Things Bruins Fans Should Know & Do Before They Die. (100 Things... Fans Should Know Ser.). (ENG.). 320p. 2010. pap. 14.95 *(978-1-60078-383-8(X))* 2nd ed. 2011. (Illus.). pap. 14.95 ***(978-1-60078-699-0(5))*** Triumph Bks.

Keene, Kerry. Tales from the Boston Bruins Locker Room: A Collection of the Greatest Bruins Stories Ever Told. 2011. (ENG., Illus.). 192p. 19.95 ***(978-1-61321-058-1(2)**,* 613058) Skyhorse Publishing Co., Inc.

NHL. The Year of the Bruins: Celebrating Boston's 2010-11 Stanley Cup Championship Season. 2011. (ENG., Illus.). 160p. pap. 19.99 ***(978-0-7710-5101-2(8)**,* McClelland & Stewart) McClelland & Stewart CAN. Dist: Random Hse., Inc.

Nichols, John. The NHL - History & Heroes: The Story of the Boston Bruins. 2008. (NHL: History & Heroes Ser.). (Illus.). 44p. (YA). (gr. 5-9). 22.95 *(978-1-58341-614-3(5))* Creative Co., The.

Simpson, Rob & Babineau, Steve. Black & Gold: Four Decades of the Boston Bruins in Photographs. 2nd ed. 2008. (ENG.). 272p. 34.95 *(978-0-470-15473-1(X)*, Wiley) Wiley, John & Sons, Inc.

The Boston Globe Staff. Killer B's: The Boston Bruins Capture Their First Stanley Cup in 39 Years. 2011. (ENG.). 128p. pap. 14.95 ***(978-1-60078-683-9(9))*** Triumph Bks.

Wee, K. P. Bad Managers' Decisions: Why the Longest Drought in Boston's History Happened (1986-2003) 2009. 66p. pap. 15.95 *(978-1-4357-3149-3(2))* Lulu Enterprises Inc.

BOSTON CELTICS (BASKETBALL TEAM)

Boston Celtics. 2008. 240p. pap. 16.95 *(978-1-932714-55-5(3))* Savas Beatie.

Boston Globe Staff. Banner 18: The Surprising Road to Another Boston Celtics Championship. 2010. 128p. pap. 14.95 *(978-1-60078-531-3(X))* Triumph Bks.

Buckley, Steve. Wicked Good Year: How the Red Sox, Patriots, & Celtics Turned the Hub of the Universe into the Capital of Sports. 2010. (ENG.). 352p. pap. 14.99 *(978-0-06-178739-3(6))* HarperCollins Pubs.

Connelly, Michael P. Rebound! Basketball, Busing, Larry Bird, & the Rebirth of Boston. 2008. (ENG., Illus.). 304p. 25.00 *(978-0-7603-3501-7(X)*, 076033501X, MVP Bks.) MBI Publishing Co. LLC.

Freedman, Lew. Dynasty: Auerbach, Cousy, Havlicek, Russell, & the Rise of the Boston Celtics. 2011. (ENG., Illus.). 240p. pap. 14.95 *(978-0-7627-7356-5(1)*, Lyons Pr.) Globe Pequot Pr., The.

Frisch, Aaron. Boston Celtics. 2008. (NBA Champions Ser.). (Illus.). 24p. (J). (gr. 4-7). lib. bdg. 24.25 *(978-1-58341-504-7(1)*, Creative Education) Creative Co., The.

Hubbard, Donald. 100 Things Celtics Fans Should Know & Do Before They Die. 2010. (100 Things... Fans Should Know Ser.). (ENG.). 256p. pap. 14.95 *(978-1-60078-411-8(9))* Triumph Bks.

Johnson, Richard A. & Johnson, Robert Hamilton. The Celtics in Black & White. 2006. (ENG., Illus.). 144p. per. 26.99 *(978-0-7385-4530-1(9))* Arcadia Publishing.

Lazenby, Roland. Boston Celtics Basketball Vault: The History of a Proud Franchise. 2011. (ENG., Illus.). 144p. 49.95 ***(978-0-7948-3296-4(2))*** Whitman Publishing LLC.

May, Peter. The Big Three. 2007. (ENG., Illus.). 288p. pap. 19.95 *(978-1-4165-5207-9(3))* Simon & Schuster.

—The Last Banner: The Story of the 1985-86 Celtics & the NBA's Greatest Team of All Time. 2007. (ENG., Illus.). 304p. pap. 20.95 *(978-1-4165-5212-3(X))* Simon & Schuster.

—Top of the World: The Inside Story of the Boston Celtics' Amazing One-Year Turnaround to Become NBA Champions. 2009. (ENG., Illus.). 264p. pap. 14.95 *(978-0-306-81858-5(2))* Da Capo Pr., Inc.

Reynolds, Bill. Rise of a Dynasty: The '57 Celtics, the First Banner, & the Dawning of a New America. 2011. (ENG.). 304p. (gr. 12). 15.00 *(978-0-451-23480-3(4)*, N A L Trade) Penguin Group (USA) Inc.

Ross, Alan. Lakers Glory: For the Love of Kobe, Magic, & Mikan. 2006. (ENG., Illus.). 256p. pap. 12.95 *(978-1-58182-554-1(4))* Turner Publishing Co.

BOSTON COLLEGE

Durant, Samantha & Gossett, Kelley. Boston College 2012: Off the Record. 2011. 188p. pap. 16.95 ***(978-1-4274-0350-6(3))*** College Prowler, Inc.

BOSTON EVENING TRANSCRIPT

Cohen, Morris A. & Cohen, Richard Shain. Healing after Dark: Pioneering Compassionate Medicine at the Boston Evening Clinic. 2011. (Illus.). 184p. pap. 14.95 ***(978-1-926918-44-0(4)**,* CCB Publishing) CCB Publishing CAN. Dist: Gardners Bks. Ltd.

BOSTON HARBOR ISLANDS (MASS.)

Jones, Laura Thibodeau. Generations: 1891 -1940 Living on the Islands of Boston Harbor. 2011. 248p. pap. 56.26 ***(978-1-4634-3877-7(X))*** AuthorHouse.

Kales, David. The Boston Harbor Islands: A History of an Urban Wilderness. 2007. (Illus.). 158p. pap., per. 19.99 *(978-1-59629-290-1(2))* History Pr., The.

Schorow, Stephanie. East of Boston: Notes from the Harbor Islands. 2008. pap. 19.99 *(978-1-59629-379-3(9))* History Pr., The.

Snow, Edward Rowe. The Islands of Boston Harbor. 2008. (Snow Centennial Editions Ser.). (ENG., Illus.). 244p. pap. 14.95 *(978-1-933212-85-2(3))* Commonwealth Editions.

BOSTON MASSACRE, 1770

Allison, Robert J. The Boston Massacre. 2006. (NE Remembers Ser.). (ENG., Illus.). 86p. per. 12.95 *(978-1-933212-10-4(1))* Commonwealth Editions.

York, Neil Longley. The Boston Massacre: A History with Documents. 2010. (ENG., Illus.). 280p. (C). 135.00 *(978-0-415-87348-2(7))*; pap. 26.95 *(978-0-415-87349-9(5))* Taylor & Francis Group GBR. (Routledge). Dist: Taylor & Francis Group.

BOSTON METROPOLITAN AREA (MASS.)

Arrow Maps, creator. Metro Boston/Eastern Massachusetts Laminated Street Atlas. 8th ed. 2007. (American Map Ser.). (Illus.). 264p. 69.95 *(978-1-55751-332-8(5))* Arrow Map, Inc.

—Metro Boston/Eastern Massachusetts Street Atlas. 8th ed. 2007. (Metro Boston Eastern Massachusetts Street Atlas Ser.). (Illus.). 264p. 24.95 *(978-1-55751-318-2(X))* Arrow Map, Inc.

BOSTON MUSEUM (1847-1903)

Ryan, Kate. Old Boston Museum Days. 2009. 92p. pap. 20.00 *(978-1-151-53588-7(5))* General Bks. LLC.

—Old Boston Museum Days. 2008. 308p. 43.95 *(978-1-4365-6106-8(X))* 2007. (ENG.) 312p. per. 28.95 *(978-0-548-76111-3(6))* Kessinger Publishing, LLC.

—Old Boston Museum Days. 2007. (ENG.). 312p. per. *(978-1-4067-4168-1(X))* Read Bks.

BOSTON MUSEUM OF FINE ARTS

see Museum of Fine Arts, Boston

BOSTON POST ROADS

Jaffe, Eric. The King's Best Highway: The Lost History of the Boston Post Road, the Route That Made America. 2010. (ENG., Illus.). 336p. 27.50 *(978-1-4165-8614-2(8)*, Scribner) Scribner.

BOSTON PUBLIC LIBRARY

McCord, David. As Built with Second Thoughts, Reforming What Was Old. pap. 2.00 *(978-0-89073-099-7(7)*, 221) Boston Public Library.

Sargent, John Singer. John Singer Sargent's Triumph of Religion at the Boston Public Library: Creation & Restoration. Khandekar, Narayan et al, eds. 2010. (ENG., Illus.). 296p. 65.00 *(978-0-300-12290-9(X))* Yale Univ. Pr.

Sargent, John Singer, et al. John Singer Sargent's Triumph of Religion at the Boston Public Library: Creation & Restoration. 2010. (Illus.). 295p. *(978-1-891771-51-4(5))* Harvard Univ. Art Museums.

Willis, Catherine J. Boston Public Library. 2011. (Images of America Ser.). (Illus.). 128p. pap. 21.99 *(978-0-7385-7506-3(2))* Arcadia Publishing.

BOSTON RED SOX (BASEBALL TEAM)

Anderson, Ron. Long Taters: A Baseball Biography of George Boomer Scott. 2011. (ENG.). 308p. pap. 29.95 *(978-0-7864-4976-7(4))* McFarland & Co., Inc. Pubs.

Borer, Michael Ian. Faithful to Fenway: Believing in Boston, Baseball, & America's Most Beloved Ballpark. 2008. (ENG., Illus.). 288p. pap. 19.95 *(978-0-8147-9977-2(9))* New York Univ. Pr.

Bradley, Richard. The Greatest Game: The Day That Bucky, Yaz, Reggie, Pudge, & Company Played the Most Memorable Game in Baseball's Most Intense Rivalry. 2009. (ENG.). 304p. pap. 19.99 *(978-1-4165-3439-6(3)*, Free Pr.) Free Pr.

Browne, Ian. Dice-K: The First Season of the Red Sox $100 Million Man. 2008. (ENG., Illus.). 240p. per. 16.95 *(978-1-59921-347-7(8)*, Lyons Pr.) Globe Pequot Pr., The.

Brush, Daniel. Boston Red Sox: An Interactive Guide to the World of Sports. 2009. (Sports by the Numbers Ser.). (Illus.). 240p. pap. 16.95 *(978-1-932714-66-1(9))* Savas Beatie.

Buckley, Steve. Wicked Good Year: How the Red Sox, Patriots, & Celtics Turned the Hub of the Universe into the Capital of Sports. 2010. (ENG.). 352p. pap. 14.99 *(978-0-06-178739-3(6))* HarperCollins Pubs.

Burgess, Chuck & Nowlin, Bill. Love That Dirty Water: The Standells & the Improbable Red Sox Victory Anthem. 2007. (ENG., Illus.). 176p. per. 14.95 *(978-1-57940-146-7(5))* Rounder Bks.

Cafardo, Nick. 100 Things Red Sox Fans Should Know & Do Before They Die. (100 Things... Fans Should Know Ser.). (ENG.). 2011. 240p. pap. 14.95 *(978-1-60078-632-7(4))* 2008. (Illus.). 192p. 19.95 *(978-1-60078-053-0(9))* Triumph Bks.

Caple, Jim & Buckley, Steve. The Best Boston Sports Arguments: The 100 Most Controversial, Debatable Questions for Die-Hard Boston Fans. 2006. (Best Sports Arguments Ser.). (ENG., Illus.). 272p. per. 19.99 *(978-1-4022-0822-5(7))* Sourcebooks, Inc.

Carey, Pamela. Minor League Mom: A Mother's Journey Through the Red Sox Farm Teams. 2009. 336p. pap. 16.95 *(978-1-891724-17-6(7)*, Barking Cat Bks.) New River Pr.

Castiglione, Joe & Lyons, Douglas B. Can You Believe It? 30 Years of Insider Stories with the Boston Red Sox. 2012. (ENG.). 272p. 24.95 ***(978-1-60078-667-9(7))*** Triumph Bks.

Cofman, Mark. 162 - 0: The Greatest Wins in Red Sox History. 2010. (162-0: Imagine... Ser.). (ENG.). 304p. pap. 16.95 *(978-1-60078-345-6(7))* Triumph Bks.

Cole, Milton & Kaplan, Jim. The Boston Red Sox: An Illustrated History. (Illus.). 20'C. 115p. *(978-1-57215-612-8(0))* 2009. 111p. *(978-1-57215-523-7(X))* World Pubns. Group, Inc. (JG Pr.).

Desrochers, Dan, ed. The 1967 Impossible Dream Red Sox: Pandemonium on the Field. 2007. (ENG., Illus.). 340p. per. 19.95 *(978-1-57940-141-2(4))* Rounder Bks.

Felber, Bill. A Game of Brawl: The Orioles, the Beaneaters, & the Battle for the 1897 Pennant. 2007. (ENG., Illus.). 320p. 24.95 *(978-0-8032-1136-0(8))* Univ. of Nebraska Pr.

Ferguson, John W. Why Fenway: Exploring the Red Sox Mystique. 2011. (ENG.). 144p. pap. 19.95 *(978-1-60078-533-7(6))* Triumph Bks.

Frascella, John. Theology: How a Boy Wonder Led the Red Sox to the Promised Land. 2009. (ENG.). 208p. pap. 14.95 *(978-0-9814536-9-9(4)*, Cambridge House Pr.) Sterling & Ross Pubs.

Frost, Mark. Game Six: The Triumph of America's Pastime. 416p. 2010. (ENG.). pap. 15.99 *(978-1-4013-1026-4(5))* 2009. 26.99 *(978-1-4013-2310-3(3))* Hyperion Pr.

Gillette, Gary & Palmer, Pete, eds. The Ultimate Red Sox Companion: A Complete Statistical & Reference Guide. 2007. 400p. per. 24.95 *(978-1-934186-02-2(3))* Maple Street Press LLC.

Goode, Jon & Goode, Laurie. Pitching with the Papelbons. 2007. pap. 19.95 *(978-1-60461-804-4(3))* Independent Pub.

Green, David. 101 Reasons to Love the Red Sox: And 10 Reasons to Hate the Yankees. rev. ed. 2008. (ENG., Illus.). 120p. 15.95 *(978-1-58479-714-2(2))* Stewart, Tabori & Chang.

Gutlon, Jerry M. It Was Never about the Babe: The Red Sox, Racism, Mismanagement, & the Curse of the Bambino. 2009. (ENG., Illus.). 336p. 24.95 *(978-1-60239-349-3(4)*, 239349) Skyhorse Publishing Co., Inc.

Gutman, Bill. What If the Babe Had Kept His Red Sox? And Other Fascinating Alternate Histories from the World of Sports. 2008. 290p. pap. 14.95 *(978-1-60239-629-6(9))* Skyhorse Publishing Co., Inc.

Holley, Michael. Red Sox Rule: Terry Francona & Boston's Rise to Dominance. 2009. (ENG.). 256p. pap. 15.99 *(978-0-06-145855-2(4))* 2008. (Illus.). 224p. 25.95 *(978-0-06-145854-5(6))* HarperCollins Pubs.

Hubbard, Donald. The Red Sox Before the Babe: Boston's Early Days in the American League, 1901-1914. 2009. (ENG., Illus.). 236p. pap. 35.00 *(978-0-7864-3911-9(4))* McFarland & Co., Inc. Pubs.

Johnson, Richard. Field of Our Fathers: An Illustrated History of Fenway Park, 1912-2012. 2011. (ENG.). 320p. 35.00 ***(978-1-60078-423-1(2))*** Triumph Bks.

Lantos, James. Boston Baseball. Lantos, Jim & Lantos, Jim, eds. 2009. (Applewood's Pictorial America Ser.). (ENG.). 56p. pap. 9.95 *(978-1-60889-009-5(0))* Applewood Bks.

Latchford, Jennifer & Oreste, Rod. Red Sox Legends. 2007. (Images of Baseball Ser.). (ENG., Illus.). 128p. per. 9.99 *(978-0-7385-4979-8(7))* Arcadia Publishing.

Laurila, David. Interviews from Red Sox Nation. rev. ed. 2008. 416p. pap. 17.95 *(978-1-934186-14-5(7))* Maple Street Press LLC.

Lieb, Frederick G. The Boston Red Sox. Date not set. 276p. 23.95 *(978-0-8488-2357-3(5))* Amereon LTD.

Macomber, Michael, ed. The Red Sox & Philosophy: Green Monster Meditations. 2010. (Popular Culture & Philosophy Ser.). (ENG.). 320p. pap. 19.95 *(978-0-8126-9677-6(8))* Open Court Publishing Co.

Massarotti, Tony. Dynasty: The Inside Story of How the Red Sox Became a Baseball Powerhouse. 2009. (ENG., Illus.). 336p. pap. 17.95 *(978-0-312-56395-0(7)*, St. Martin's Griffin) St. Martin's Pr.

McNeil, William F. Red Sox Nation Guide to the Players. 2008. (ENG.). 240p. pap. 9.95 *(978-1-55553-699-2(9)*, Northeastern University Pr.) Univ. Pr. of New England.

—Red Sox Roll Call: 200 Memorable Players, 1901-2010. 2012. (ENG., Illus.). 240p. pap. 45.00 *(978-0-7864-647?-5(2))* McFarland & Co., Inc. Pubs.

Mnookin, Seth. Feeding the Monster: How Money, Smarts, & Nerve Took a Team to the Top. 2007. (ENG., Illus.). 464p. pap. 15.00 *(978-0-7432-8682-4(0))* Simon & Schuster.

Nemec, David & Flatow, Scott. The Ultimate Boston Red Sox Baseball Challenge. 2008. (ENG., Illus.). 208p. pap. 10.95 *(978-1-58979-375-0(7))* Taylor Trade Publishing.

New York Times Staff, as told by. The New York Times - Greatest Moments in Red Sox History. 2007. *(978-1-934653-03-6(9))* RetroGraphics Publishing Inc.

Nichole, Schrafft & Nichole, Schrafft. A Field Guide to Washington, D. C. 2009. (Illus.). 64p. (J). pap. 16.95 *(978-1-885435-97-2(5))* Twin Lights Pubs., Inc.

Nichols, John. The Story of the Boston Red Sox. 2007. (Baseball, the Great American Game Ser.). (Illus.). 48p. (YA). (gr. 4-7). lib. bdg. 32.80 *(978-1-58341-481-1(9))* Creative Co., The.

Nowlin, Bill. The Great Red Sox Spring Training Tour Of 1911: Sixty-Three Games, Coast to Coast. 2010. (ENG., Illus.). 204p. pap. 29.95 *(978-0-7864-6124-0(1))* McFarland & Co., Inc. Pubs.

—Lefty, Double-X, & the Kid: The 1939 Red Sox, a Team in Transition. 2009. (ENG.). 210p. pap. 18.95 *(978-1-57940-162-7(7))* Rounder Bks.

—Red Sox Threads: Odds & Ends from Red Sox History. 2008. (ENG.). 600p. pap. 18.95 *(978-1-57940-157-3(0)*, Rounder Bks.

—Spahn, Sain, & Teddy Ballgame: Boston's (almost) Perfect Baseball Summer Of 1948. 2008. (ENG.). 24p. pap. 19.95 *(978-1-57940-160-3(0))* Rounder Bks.

—The Ultimate Red Sox Home Run Guide. 2009. (ENG.). 210p. pap. 18.95 *(978-1-57940-163-4(5))* Rounder Bks.

Nowlin, Bill, et al, eds. When Boston Still Had the Babe: The 1918 World Series Champion Red Sox. 2008. (ENG., Illus.). 288p. pap. 18.95 *(978-1-57940-159-7(7))* Rounder Bks.

Nowlin, Bill & Prime, Jim. Amazing Tales from the Boston Red Sox Dugout: A Collection of the Greatest Red Sox Stories Ever Told. 2012. (Tales from the Team Ser.). (ENG., Illus.). 320p. 24.95 ***(978-1-61321-023-9(X)**,* 613023) Skyhorse Publishing Co., Inc.

—Fenway Park at 100: Baseball's Hometown. 2012. (ENG., Illus.). 176p. 29.95 ***(978-1-61321-001-7(9)**,* 613001) Skyhorse Publishing Co., Inc.

Nowlin, Bill & Prime, Jim. The Red Sox World Series Encyclopedia. 2008. (ENG.). 272p. pap. 18.95 *(978-1-57940-161-0(9))* Rounder Bks.

Nowlin, Bill & Silverman, Matthew. Red Sox by the Numbers: A Complete Team History of the Boston Red Sox by Uniform Number. 2010. (ENG., Illus.). 352p. pap. 14.95 *(978-1-60239-995-2(6)*, 239995) Skyhorse Publishing Co., Inc.

O'Connell, Brian. Johnny Damon. 2008. (Baseball Superstars Ser.). 128p. (YA). (gr. 7-12). 30.00 *(978-0-7910-9645-8(7))*; (Illus.). (gr. 6-12). pap. 11.95 *(978-0-7910-9845-5(1)*, Checkmark Bks.) Facts On File, Inc.

Ortiz, David & Massarotti, Tony. Big Papi: My Story of Big Dreams & Big Hits. 2008. (ENG., Illus.). 288p. pap. 14.95 *(978-0-312-38344-2(4)*, St. Martin's Griffin) St. Martin's Pr.

Pahigian, Joshua R. The Red Sox in the Playoffs: A Postseason History, 1903-2005. 2006. (ENG., Illus.). 285p. per. 39.95 *(978-0-7864-2778-9(7))* McFarland & Co., Inc. Pubs.

Pennington, Richard. Boston Red Sox Trivia Teasers. 2007. (Illus.). 144p. per. 16.95 *(978-1-931599-82-5(3))* Big Earth Publishing.

Pesky, Johnny & Mullen, Maureen. Diary of a Red Sox Season, 2007. 2008. (ENG., Illus.). 192p. 19.95 *(978-1-60078-068-4(7))* Triumph Bks.

Petrocelli, Rico & Scoggins, Charles. Rico Petrocelli's Tales from the Impossible Dream. 2008. (Tales Ser.). (Illus.). 192p. per. 15.95 *(978-1-59670-292-9(3))* Sports Publishing, LLC.

Petrocelli, Rico & Scoggins, Chaz. Rico Petrocelli's Tales from the Impossible Dream Red Sox. 2007. (Illus.). 215p. 19.95 *(978-1-59670-191-5(9))* Sports Publishing, LLC.

Quigley, Brendan. Red Sox Rule! Word Search Puzzle Book. 2010. (ENG.). 64p. pap. 7.95 *(978-1-60433-144-8(5))* Cider Mill Pr. Bk. Pubs., LLC.

Reis, Ronald A. Ted Williams. 2008. (Baseball Superstars Ser.). (Illus.). 136p. (gr. 6-12). lib. bdg. 30.00 *(978-0-7910-9545-4(2)*, Chelsea Hse.) Facts On File, Inc.

Remy, Jerry & Sandler, Corey. Jerry Remy's Red Sox Heroes. 2010. (Illus.). 288p. pap. 12.95 *(978-1-59921-970-7(0))* Globe Pequot Pr., The.

—Red Sox Heroes: The Remdawg's All-Time Favorite Red Sox, Great Moments, & Top Teams. 2009. (ENG., Illus.). 288p. 24.95 *(978-1-59921-406-1(7)*, Lyons Pr.) Globe Pequot Pr., The.

Reynolds, Bill. '78: The Boston Red Sox, a Historic Game, & a Divided City. 2010. (ENG.). 320p. (gr. 12-18). 15.00 *(978-0-451-22922-9(3)*, N A L Trade) Penguin Group (USA) Inc.

Robinson, Guy. Do You Know the Boston Red Sox? Test Your Expertise with These Fastball Questions (and a Few Curves) about Your Favorite Team's Hurlers, Sluggers, Stats & Most Memorable Moments. 2008. (ENG.). 48p. pap. 5.95 *(978-1-4022-1419-6(7))* Sourcebooks, Inc.

Rucker, Mark. Boston Red Sox & the Meaning of Life. 2009. (ENG., Illus.). 400p. 19.99 *(978-0-7603-3506-2(0)*, 0760335060, MVP Bks.) MBI Publishing Co. LLC.

Russell, Scott. Too Much Time on His Hands: The Unauthorized Ultimate Statistical Guide of the World Champion Boston Red Sox. 2008. 146p. pap. 14.95 *(978-0-9796722-3-1(6))* Dirty Water Publishing.

Scoggins, Chaz. Game of My Life Boston Red Sox: Memorable Stories of Red Sox Baseball. 2008. (Game of My Life Ser.). (Illus.). 236p. per. 16.95 *(978-1-59670-295-0(8))* Sports Publishing, LLC.

Shalin, Neil. Red Sox Triviology: Fascinating Facts from the Bleacher Seats. 2011. (Triviology: Fascinating Facts Ser.). (ENG.). 128p. pap. 9.95 ***(978-1-60078-623-5(5))*** Triumph Bks.

Shaughnessy, Dan. Fenway, Expanded & Updated: A Biography in Words & Pictures. 2007. (ENG., Illus.). 192p. 29.95 *(978-0-618-73736-9(7))* Houghton Mifflin Harcourt Trade & Reference Pubs.

—Reversing the Curse: Inside the 2004 Boston Red Sox. 2008. (ENG.). 260p. 23.00 (978-1-4379-5137-0(6)) DIANE Publishing Co.

Simmons, Bill. Now I Can Die in Peace: How the Sports Guy Found Salvation Thanks to the World Champion (Twice!) Red Sox. 2009. (ENG.). 464p. pap. 16.00 (978-1-933060-72-9(7), Ballantine Bks.) Random House Publishing Group.

Snyder, John. 365 Oddball Days in Boston Red Sox History. 2009. (ENG.). 384p. pap. 12.95 (978-1-57860-344-2(7)) Clerisy Pr.

Stout, Glenn. Fenway 1912: The Birth of a Ballpark, a Championship Season, & Fenway's Remarkable First Year. (ENG.). 416p. 2012. pap. 14.95 **(978-0-547-84457-2(3)**, Mariner Bks.) 2011. (Illus.). 26.00 (978-0-547-19562-9(1)) Houghton Mifflin Harcourt Trade & Reference Pubs.

Updike, John. Hub Fans Bid Kid Adieu: John Updike on Ted Williams. Books on Tape, Inc.

—Hub Fans Bid Kid Adieu: John Updike on Ted Williams. 2010. (ENG.). 64p. (gr. 12). 15.00 (978-1-59853-071-1(2)) Library of America, The.

Vaccaro, Mike. The First Fall Classic: The Red Sox, the Giants, & the Cast of Players, Pugs, & Politicos Who Reinvented the World Series In 1912. 2010. (ENG., Illus.). 320p. pap. 15.95 (978-0-7679-2968-4(3), Anchor) Knopf Doubleday Publishing Group.

Wadsworth Schrafft, Nichole. A Field Guide to Fenway Park. 2nd ed. 2009. (Illus.). 64p. (J). pap. 16.95 (978-1-885435-99-6(1)) Twin Lights Pubs., Inc.

Walsh, James & Mastroyin, Steve, eds. Maple Street Press Red Sox 2007. 2007. (Maple Street Press Red Sox Annual Ser.). (Illus.). 112p. per. 14.95 (978-0-9777436-6-7(7)) Maple Street Press LLC.

Wasif, Andy. Red Sox University: Baseball's Foremost Institution of Higher Learning. 2009. (ENG.). 192p. pap. 14.95 (978-1-60078-218-3(3)) Triumph Bks.

Wee, K. P. Bad Managers' Decisions: Why the Longest Drought in Boston's History Happened (1986-2003) 2009. 66p. pap. 15.95 (978-1-4357-3149-3(2)) Lulu Enterprises Inc.

—1991: the Red Sox, Baseball, & Hockey Memories. 2009. 121p. 27.95 (978-1-4357-2703-8(7)) 2008. 139p. pap. 18.95 (978-1-4357-1375-8(3)) Lulu Enterprises Inc.

Whalen, Thomas. When the Red Sox Ruled: Baseball's First Dynasty, 1912-1918. 2011. (ENG.). 240p. 24.95 (978-1-56663-745-9(7)) Dee, Ivan R. Pub.

Wisnia, Saul. Fenway Park:the Centennial: 100 Years of Red Sox Baseball. 2011. (ENG., Illus.). 176p. 29.99 (978-0-312-64274-7(1)) St. Martin's Pr.

Yastrzemski, Carl. Yastrzemski. 2007. (Icons of Major League Baseball: Ser.). (ENG., Illus.). 246p. 34.95 (978-1-59071-089-0(4)) Rugged Land.

BOSTON STRANGLER, 1931-1973

see De Salvo, Albert Henry, 1931-1973

BOSTON SYMPHONY ORCHESTRA

Keches, Krysten A. Boston Youth Symphony Orchestras. 2007. (Images of America Ser.). (ENG., Illus.). 128p. per. 19.99 (978-0-7385-5525-6(8)) Arcadia Publishing.

Leichtentritt, Hugo. Serge Koussevitzky: The Boston Symphony Orchestra & the New American Music. 2011. 208p. 44.95 **(978-1-258-03867-0(6))** Literary Licensing, LLC.

North, James H. Boston Symphony Orchestra: An Augmented Discography. 2008. (ENG.). 340p. 70.00 (978-0-8108-6209-8(3)) Scarecrow Pr., Inc.

BOSTON TEA PARTY, 1773

Allison, Robert J. The Boston Tea Party. 2007. (NE Remembers Ser.). (ENG., Illus.). 88p. per. 12.95 (978-1-933212-11-1(X)) Commonwealth Editions.

Carp, Benjamin L. Defiance of the Patriots: The Boston Tea Party & the Making of America. (ENG., Illus.). 328p. 2011. pap. 20.00 (978-0-300-17812-8(3)) 2010. 30.00 (978-0-300-11705-9(1)) Yale Univ. Pr.

Doe, John. Boston Tea Party: Phase II. 2010. 120p. pap. 12.95 (978-1-4502-2189-4(0)) iUniverse, Inc.

Forman, Sam. Dr. Joseph Warren: The Boston Tea Party, Bunker Hill, & the Birth of American Liberty. 1 vol. 2011. (ENG., Illus.). 400p. 29.95 (978-1-4556-1474-5(2)) Pelican Publishing Co., Inc.

Knollenberg, Bernhard. Did Samuel Adams Provoke the Boston Tea Party & the Clash at Lexington: American Antiquarian Society, V70, No. 2. 2011. 16p. pap. 35.95 **(978-1-258-06979-7(2))** Literary Licensing, LLC.

Ramsburg, Karen. Smith Rebellion 1765 Gives Rise to Modern Politics. 2011. 164p. 25.95 **(978-1-4620-5780-1(2))**; pap. 15.95 **(978-1-4620-5781-8(0))** iUniverse, Inc.

Unger, Harlow Giles. American Tempest: How the Boston Tea Party Sparked a Revolution. (ENG.). 304p. 2012. pap. 16.00 **(978-0-306-82079-3(X))** 2011. (Illus.). 26.00 (978-0-306-81962-9(7)) Da Capo Pr., Inc.

BOSTON TEA PARTY, 1773—JUVENILE LITERATURE

Doeden, Matt. The Boston Tea Party. 2007. (Graphic History Ser.). (ENG.). 32p. (gr. 3-4). lib. bdg. 299.90 (978-1-4296-0869-5(2), Graphic Library) Capstone Pr., Inc.

BOSTON TERRIER

Bedwell-Wilson, Wendy. Boston Terriers for Dummies. 2007. (ENG., Illus.). 296p. per. 16.99 (978-0-470-12768-1(6), For Dummies) Wiley, John & Sons, Inc.

Bulanda, Susan. Boston Terriers. 3rd ed. 2012. (Complete Pet Owner's Manual Ser.). (ENG., Illus.). 96p. pap. 8.99 **(978-0-7641-4747-0(1))** Barron's Educational Series, Inc.

Gewirtz, Elaine Waldorf. Boston Terrier. 1 vol. 2010. (ENG., Illus.). 224p. 19.95 (978-0-7938-3601-7(8), 1320894) TFH Pubns., Inc.

Grayson, Robert. The Boston Terrier. 2011. (978-1-932904-80-2(8)); (978-1-932904-74-1(3)) Eldorado Ink.

Linzy, Jan & Pata, Sharae. Boston Terrier Champions, 2003-2006. 2007. (Illus.). 141p. spiral bd. 46.95 (978-1-55893-230-2(5)) Camino E.E. & Bk. Co.

Marginean, Jeff. My Buddy Butch: Confessions of a New Dog Dad. 2008. 300p. pap. 14.95 (978-0-9814621-0-3(3)) JEMAR Entertainment, Inc.

Swager, Peggy. Boston Terrier. 2011. (Smart Owner's Guide Ser.). (ENG.). 176p. pap. 15.95 (978-1-59378-791-2(X)) Kennel Club Bks.

Swager, Peggy O. Boston Terrier. 2011. (Smart Owner's Guide Ser.). (ENG.). 176p. 17.95 (978-1-59378-787-5(1)) Kennel Club Bks.

Waldorf Gewirtz, Elaine & Gewirtz, Elaine Waldorf. Boston Terrier: Your Happy Healthy Pet. 2nd rev. ed. 2006. (Happy Healthy Pet Ser.: 39). (ENG., Illus.). 144p. 12.99 (978-0-471-74818-2(8), Howell Bk. Hse.) Wiley, John & Sons, Inc.

BOSTON TERRIERS

see Boston Terrier

BOSTON UNIVERSITY

Boston University. General Catalogue of Boston University 187273. 2011. 22p. pap. 11.99 **(978-1-4181-9125-2(6))** MPublishing.

Candal, Cara Stillings. Partnering for Progress: Boston University, the Chelsea Public Schools, & Urban Education Reform. 2009. 152p. (978-1-60752-123-5(7)); pap. (978-1-60752-122-8(9)) Information Age Publishing, Inc.

Cguide Staff, ed. Boston University: The Need to Know & Where to Go Guide to College Life. 2008. (Cguides Ser.). (ENG., Illus.). 110p. pap. 12.95 (978-1-59186-816-3(5)) Cool Springs Pr.

Foxman, Janet. Disposable Camera. 2012. (Phoenix Poets Ser.). 88p. pap. 18.00 **(978-0-226-92411-3(4))** Univ. of Chicago Pr.

Santana, Stephanie, et al. Boston University 2012: Off the Record. 2011. 192p. pap. 16.95 **(978-1-4274-0351-3(1))** College Prowler, Inc.

Walker, Caren. Boston University off the Record. Burns, Adam et al, eds. 2006. (College Prowler: Boston University off the Record Ser.). (ENG.). 159p. per. 16.95 (978-1-4274-0024-6(5)) College Prowler, Inc.

BOSWELL, JAMES, 1740-1795

Boswell, James. The General Correspondence of James Boswell, 1757-1763. Hankins, David & Caudle, James, eds. 2006. (Private Papers of James Boswell). (ENG.). 568p. 85.00 (978-0-300-08306-4(8)) Yale Univ. Pr.

—James Boswell: As His Contemporaries Saw Him. Larson, Lyle, ed. 2008. (Illus.). 256p. (C). 52.50 (978-0-8386-4171-2(7)) Fairleigh Dickinson Univ. Pr.

—James Boswell: The Journal of His German & Swiss Travels 1764. Danziger, Marlies K., ed. 2008. (Yale Editions of the Private Papers Jame Ser.). (ENG & FRE., Illus.). 490p. 110.00 (978-0-300-12360-9(4)) Yale Univ. Pr.

—Letters, 2 vols. reprint ed. 59.00 (978-0-403-04137-4(6)) Somerset Pubs., Inc.

—London Journal 1762-1763. 2010. (ENG.). 656p. (gr. 12). pap. 17.00 (978-0-14-043650-1(2), Penguin Classics) Penguin Group (USA) Inc.

Boswell, James, et al, contrib. by. The Correspondence of James Boswell & William Johnson Temple, 1756-1795. 528p. 95.00 (978-0-7486-0758-7(7)) Edinburgh Univ. Pr. GBR. Dist: Columbia Univ. Pr.

Bronson, Bertrand H. Johnson Agonistes & Other Essays. 2012. (ENG.). 164p. pap. 34.99 **(978-1-107-69542-9(2))** Cambridge Univ. Pr.

—Johnson & Boswell: Three Essays. 2011. 118p. 39.95 **(978-1-258-02667-7(8))** Literary Licensing, LLC.

Dowling, William C. The Boswellian Hero. 2008. (ENG.). 224p. pap. 22.95 (978-0-8203-3310-6(7)) Univ. of Georgia Pr.

Fitzgerald, Percy Hetherington. Boswell's Autobiography. 2010. 116p. pap. (978-1-151-92905-1(0)) Books LLC.

Johnson, Samuel. Journey to the Western Islands of Scotland. 2010. 100p. pap. 7.46 (978-1-4432-0354-8(8)) General Bks. LLC.

—Journey to the Western Islands of Scotland. 2008. 164p. pap. 11.95 (978-1-60597-452-1(8), Book Jungle) Standard Pubns., Inc.

—A Journey to the Western Islands of Scotland. 2011. 398p. pap. 33.75 **(978-1-173-65407-8(0))** 2010. (ENG.). 392p. pap. 33.75 (978-1-178-00558-5(5)) 2010. 402p. pap. 34.75 (978-1-176-75192-7(1)) 2010. 278p. pap. 27.75 (978-1-170-04761-3(0), Gale ECCO, Print Editions) 2010. 396p. pap. 33.75 (978-1-140-86708-1(3), Gale ECCO, Print Editions) 2010. 394p. pap. 33.75 (978-1-140-72184-0(4), Gale ECCO, Print Editions) 2010. 404p. pap. 34.75 (978-1-148-97494-1(6)) 2010. 274p. pap. 27.75 (978-1-141-77124-0(1)) 2010. 398p. pap. 33.75 (978-1-142-78560-4(2)) 2008. 216p. 24.99 (978-0-559-14937-5(9)) 2008. 216p. pap. 17.99 (978-0-559-14934-4(4)) 2008. 184p. 22.99 (978-0-554-36059-1(4)) 2008. 184p. 25.99 (978-0-554-26756-2(X)) 2007. (ENG.). 168p. pap. 19.99 (978-1-4346-1703-3(3)) 2007. (ENG.). 180p. pap. 21.99 (978-1-4346-1872-6(2)) BiblioBazaar.

—A Journey to the Western Islands of Scotland. 2009. 174p. pap. (978-1-4432-8777-7(6)) Books LLC.

—A Journey to the Western Islands of Scotland. 2007. 156p. per. (978-1-4065-3504-4(4)) Dodo Pr.

—A Journey to the Western Isles of Scotland. 2009. 146p. pap. 5.99 (978-1-60450-370-8(X)) Arc Manor.

Johnson, Samuel & Boswell, James. A Journey to the Western Islands of Scotland: And, the Journal of a Tour to the Hebrides. 2007. (Illus.). xv, 425p. pap. (978-0-7607-8336-8(5)) Barnes & Noble, Inc.

—A Journey to the Western Islands of Scotland: And, the Journal of a Tour to the Hebrides. 2008. (ENG., Illus.). 416p. pap. 11.95 (978-0-486-45554-9(8)) Dover Pubns., Inc.

Johnson, Samuel & Johnson, Samuel. A Journey to the Western Islands of Scotland. 2010. 522p. pap. 39.75 (978-1-147-02078-6(7)) BiblioBazaar.

Leask, William Keith. James Boswell. 2009. 164p. pap. 21.95 (978-1-120-30307-3(9)) Kessinger Publishing, LLC.

—James Boswell. 2007. (ENG.). 164p. per. (978-1-4086-2699-3(3)) Read Bks.

Lustig, Irma S., ed. Boswell: Citizen of the World, Man of Letters. 2009. (ENG.). 296p. pap. 30.00 (978-0-8131-9276-5(5)) Univ. Pr. of Kentucky.

Mallory, George. Boswell the Biographer. 2009. 350p. 32.99 (978-1-113-63076-6(0)); 350p. pap. 32.75 (978-1-113-63075-9(2)); 350p. pap. 31.75 (978-1-113-63074-2(4)); (ENG.). 348p. pap. 23.99 (978-0-559-13624-5(2)) 2008. (ENG.). 348p. pap. 23.99 (978-1-113-63072-8(8), BiblioLife) BiblioBazaar.

O'Connell, Jeffrey & O'Connell, Thomas E. Friendships Across Ages: Johnson & Boswell; Holmes & Laski. 2007. (ENG.). 202p. 62.99 (978-0-7391-2034-7(4)) Lexington Bks.

Starr, William W. Whisky, Kilts, & the Loch Ness Monster: Traveling Through Scotland with Boswell & Johnson. 2010. 240p. 29.95 (978-1-57003-948-5(8)) Univ. of South Carolina Pr.

Vance, John A., ed. Boswell's Life of Johnson: New Questions, New Answers. 2009. (ENG.). 288p. pap. 24.95 (978-0-8203-3376-2(X)) Univ. of Georgia Pr.

BOTANIC MEDICINE

see Medicine, Botanic

BOTANICAL ARCHAEOLOGY

see Plant Remains (Archaeology)

BOTANICAL CHEMISTRY

see also Plant Hormones; Plants—Chemical Analysis; Wood—Chemistry

Alam, Nazmul. Antimicrobial Activity of Brownlowia Ters. 2011. 56p. pap. **(978-3-8443-0294-3(8))** Lambert Academic Publishing.

Aqil, Farrukh & Ahmad, Iqbal. Biological Activities of Certain Indian Medicinal Plants. 2010. 256p. pap. (978-3-8383-4069-2(8)) Lambert Academic Publishing.

Arumugam, Deepa. In Vitro Studies in Salacia Beddomei Gamble-an Endemic Woody Climber. 2010. 168p. pap. (978-3-8383-8793-2(7)) Lambert Academic Publishing.

Bidlack, Wayne R. & Meskin, Mark S., eds. Phytochemicals: Aging & Health. 2008. (ENG., Illus.). 232p. 139.95 (978-1-4200-6137-6(2), CRC Press) Taylor & Francis Group GBR. Dist: Taylor & Francis Group.

Bohm, Bruce A. The Geography of Phytochemical Races. 2008. (ENG., Illus.). xviii, 350p. 199.00 (978-1-4020-9051-6(X), 140209051X) Springer.

Brett, C. T. & Hillman, John R., eds. SEBS 28 Biochemistry of Plant Cell Walls. 2008. (Society for Experimental Biology Seminar Ser.). (ENG.). 328p. pap. 61.00 (978-0-521-10363-3(0)) Cambridge Univ. Pr.

Das, Dipak K. & Vangen, Ole Sigbjorn, eds. Resveratrol & Health. 2011. (Annals of the New York Academy of Sciences Ser.: 71). (ENG., Illus.). 252p. pap. 130.00 (978-1-57331-814-3(0), Wiley-Blackwell) Wiley, John & Sons, Inc.

Dashek, William V., ed. Methods in Plant Electron Microscopy & Cytochemistry. 2010. (Illus.). 312p. pap. 124.00 (978-1-61737-199-8(8), 1617371998) Humana Pr.

Fraga, Cesar G., et al. Plant Phenolics & Human Health: Biochemistry, Nutrition, & Pharmacology. Fraga, Cesar G., ed. 2009. (Wiley-IUBMB Series on Biochemistry & Molecular Biology Ser.: 1). (ENG., Illus.). 593p. 150.00 (978-0-470-28721-7(7), Wiley) Wiley, John & Sons, Inc.

Gleason. Plant Biochemistry. rev. ed. 2011. 248p. pap. 125.95 (978-0-7637-6401-2(9)) Jones & Bartlett Learning, LLC.

Grill, D., et al, eds. Significance of Glutathione to Plant Adaptation to the Environment. 2010. (Plant Ecophysiology Ser.). 280p. pap. 169.00 (978-90-481-5894-2(X), 904815894X) Springer.

Hanchinamane Ramegowda, Dr Nataraj & Hanchinamane Ramegowda, Nataraj. Market Samples Analysis of Saraca Indica Linn. 2011. 60p. pap. **(978-3-8443-9077-3(4))** Lambert Academic Publishing.

Hanson, James Ralph. Chemistry in the Garden. alt. ed. 2009. (ENG., Illus.). 158p. pap. 24.00 (978-1-84755-957-9(3)) Royal Society of Chemistry, The GBR. Dist: Ingram Pub. Services.

Hegnauer, R. Chemotaxonomie der Pflanzen: Band 11a: Leguminosae: A. Allgemeiner Teil - B. Chemische Charakterzüge der Leguminosae. 2007. (Lehrbücher und Monographien aus dem Gebiete der exakten Wissenschaften / Chemische Reihe Ser.). (GER., Band 11a. Illus.). 556p. 500.50 (978-3-7643-2979-2(3)) Vol. 9. 609.00 (978-3-7643-2299-1(3)) Springer.

Heldt, Hans-Walter & Piechulla, Birgit. Plant Biochemistry. 4th ed. 2010. (ENG., Illus.). 656p. 99.95 (978-0-12-384986-1(1), Academic Pr.) Elsevier Science & Technology Bks.

Jackson, John F. & Linskens, H. F., eds. Analysis of Taste & Aroma. 2010. (Molecular Methods of Plant Analysis Ser.). (Illus.). xiii, 269p. pap. 279.00 (978-3-642-07513-1(4), 3642075134) Springer.

Johll, Matthew. Investigating Chemistry (Loose Leaf) 3rd ed. 2011. (ENG.). 495p. (C). 87.95 **(978-1-4641-0276-9(7))** Freeman, W. H. & Co.

Kathurima, Morris. Antimicrobial Activity & Phytochemical Evaluation. 2010. 52p. pap. (978-3-639-24686-5(1)) VDM Verlag Dr. Mueller e.K.

Kaushik, Vichitra, et al. Evaluation of New Bicyclic Lactone 'Michelianone' 2011. 84p. pap. **(978-3-8443-5309-0(3))** Lambert Academic Publishing.

—Evaluation of New Lupane-Type Triterpene 'Diospyrosonate' 2011. 84p. pap. **(978-3-8443-0104-5(6))** Lambert Academic Publishing.

—Preliminary Phytochemical Investigation & Evaluation. 2011. 64p. pap. **(978-3-8443-1536-3(5))** Lambert Academic Publishing.

Kobayashi, Takeshi. Recent Progress of Biochemical & Biomedical Engineering in Japan I. 2010. (Advances in Biochemical Engineering Biotechnology Ser.). (Illus.). xii, 218p. pap. 249.00 (978-3-642-05800-4(0), 3642058000) Springer.

Ley, Beth M. PhytoNutrients: Medicinal Nutrients Found in Foods - Revised & Updated. 2007. 64p. 5.95 (978-1-890766-39-9(9)) BL Pubns.

Matsumoto, Takumi, ed. Phytochemistry Research Progress. 2008. (Illus.). 223p. (C). 89.00 (978-1-60456-232-3(3)) Nova Science Pubs., Inc.

Nguyen, Henry T. & Bohnert, Hans J. Bioengineering & Molecular Biology of Plant Pathways. 2008. (Advances in Plant Biochemistry & Molecular Biology Ser.: 1). (ENG., Illus.). 504p. 169.95 (978-0-08-044972-2(7), Pergamon) Elsevier Science & Technology Bks.

Niklas, Karl J. & Spatz, Hanns-Christof. Plant Physics. 2012. (ENG., Illus.). 448p. 55.00 **(978-0-226-58632-8(4))** Univ. of Chicago Pr.

Nobel, Park S. Physicochemical & Environmental Plant Physiology. 4th ed. 2009. (ENG., Illus.). 600p. 92.95 (978-0-12-374143-1(2), Academic Pr.) Elsevier Science & Technology Bks.

Pérez Gutiérrez, Rosa Martha. Handbook of Compounds with Antiprotozoal Activity Isolated from Plants. 2007. 89.00 (978-1-60021-561-2(0)) Nova Science Pubs., Inc.

Pusztai, A. Plant Lectins. 2008. (Chemistry & Pharmacology of Natural Products Ser.). (ENG.). 272p. pap. 53.00 (978-0-521-06320-3(5)) Cambridge Univ. Pr.

Quideau. Chemistry & Biology of Ellagitannins. 2009. (Illus.). 300p. 150.00 (978-981-279-740-7(8)) World Scientific Publishing Co., Inc.

Romeo, John T., ed. Integrative Plant Biochemistry. 2006. (Recent Advances in Phytochemistry Ser.: Vol. 40). (ENG., Illus.). 346p. 290.00 (978-0-08-045125-1(X), Elsevier Science) Elsevier Science & Technology Bks.

Séquin, Margareta. The Chemistry of Plants: Perfumes, Pigments, & Poisons. 2012. (ENG., Illus.). 226p. 40.00 **(978-1-84973-334-2(1))** Royal Society of Chemistry, The GBR. Dist: Ingram Pub. Services.

Semmar, Nabil, ed. Chemotaxonomical Analyses of Herbaceous Plants Based on Phenolic & Terpenic Patterns: Flexible Tools to Survey Biodiversity in Grasslands. 2010. 69.00 (978-1-61668-789-2(4)) Nova Science Pubs., Inc.

Singh, A., ed. Herbalism, Phytochemistry & Ethnopharmacology. 2011. (ENG., Illus.). 280p. 119.95 (978-1-57808-697-9(3)) BIOS Scientific Publishers Ltd. GBR. Dist: Taylor & Francis Group.

Sinha, Nirmal K., et al. Handbook of Vegetables & Vegetable Processing. 2011. 776p. 279.95 (978-0-470-95834-6(0)) 2010. (ENG., Illus.). 788p. 315.00 (978-0-8138-1541-1(X)) Wiley, John & Sons, Inc. (Wiley-Blackwell).

Skenderi, Gazmend. Medicinal Phytochemistry: Chemical, Pharmacological, & Taxonomical Checklist of Bioactive Compounds from Plants. 2008. (978-0-9713209-1-8(8)) Herbacy Pr.

Srivastava, M. M., et al, eds. Chemistry of Phytopotentials: Health, Energy & Environmental Perspectives: Health, Energy & Environmental Perspectives. 2011. (ENG., Illus.). 400p. 179.00 **(978-3-642-23393-7(7)**, 3642233937) Springer.

Steer, Martin, et al. Plant Biochemistry. 2008. (ENG., Illus.). 500p. (C). pap. 120.00 (978-0-8153-4121-5(0), Garland Science) Taylor & Francis Group.

Upton, Roy, et al, eds. American Herbal Pharmacopoeia: Botanical Pharmacognosy - Microscopic Characterization of Botanical Medicines. 2011. (ENG., Illus.). 800p. 169.95 (978-1-4200-7326-3(5), CRC Press) Taylor & Francis Group GBR. Dist: Taylor & Francis Group.

Voragen, Fons, et al, eds. Advances in Pectin & Pectinase Research. 2012. (ENG.). 514p. pap. 309.00 (978-90-481-6229-1(7), 9048162297) Springer.

Waksmundzka-Hajnos, Monika, et al. Thin Layer Chromatography in Phytochemistry. 2008. (Chromatographic Science Ser.). (ENG., Illus.). 896p. 205.95 (978-1-4200-4677-9(2), CRC Press) Taylor & Francis Group GBR. Dist: Taylor & Francis Group.

Wallsgrove, R. M., ed. Amino Acids & their Derivatives in Higher Plants. 2008. (Society for Experimental Biology Seminar Ser.). (ENG., Illus.). 296p. pap. 58.00 (978-0-521-05051-7(0)) Cambridge Univ. Pr.

Wink, Michael. Biochemistry of Plant Secondary Metabolism, Volume 40, 2nd Edition. 2nd ed. 2010. (Annual Plant Reviews Ser.: 47). (ENG., Illus.). 464p. 219.95 (978-1-4051-8397-0(7), Wiley-Blackwell) Wiley, John & Sons, Inc.

Wink, Michael & Van Wyk, Ben-Erik. Mind-Altering & Poisonous Plants of the World. 2008. (ENG., Illus.). 464p. 49.95 (978-0-88192-952-2(2), 0881929522) Timber Pr., Inc.

BOTANICAL CLASSIFICATION

see Plants—Classification

BOTANICAL GARDENS

see also Arboretums

Angel, Heather. Heather Angel's Wild Kew. 2010. (Illus.). 128p. pap. 18.00 (978-1-84246-402-1(7)) Kew Publishing GBR. Dist: Chicago Distribution Ctr.

Ashburner, Kenneth & McAllister, Hugh. The Genus Betula. 2012. (Royal Botanic Gardens, Kew - Botanical Magazine Monograph Ser.). (Illus.). 300p. 79.00 **(978-1-84246-141-9(9))** Kew Publishing GBR. Dist: Chicago Distribution Ctr.

Atasoy, Nurhan & Scott, Philippa. The Bakewell Ottoman Garden at the Missouri Botanical Garden. McNulty, Elizabeth, ed. 2010. 14.95 (978-0-615-39205-9(9)) Missouri Botanical Garden.

Bauer, Gene. Botanical Serigraphs: The Gene Bauer Collection. 2010. (ENG.). 264p. 40.00 (978-1-58948-253-1(0), ESRI Pr.) ESRI, Inc.

Beentje, H. J. & Ghazanfar, S. A., eds. Flora of Tropical East Africa: Solanaceae. 2012. (Royal Botanic Gardens, Kew-Flora of Tropical East Africa Ser.). (Illus.). 120p. pap. 52.00 (978-1-84246-395-6(0)) Kew Publishing GBR. Dist: Chicago Distribution Ctr.

Beentje, Henk. Flora of Tropical East Africa: Commelinaceae. 2012. (Royal Botanic Gardens, Kew - Flora of Tropical East Africa Ser.). (Illus.). 450p. pap. 75.00 (978-1-84246-436-6(1)) Kew Publishing GBR. Dist: Chicago Distribution Ctr.

Bowden, Robert, et al. Florida Oasis a Photographic Tour of Harry P. Leu Gardens. 2010. (ENG., Illus.). 176p. 34.95 *(978-1-59186-482-0(8),* 1591864828) Cool Springs Pr.

Brooks, Ann. 'A Veritable Eden.' The Manchester Botanic Garden - A History. 2011. (ENG., Illus.). 160p. pap. 49.95 *(978-1-905119-37-0(2))* Windgather Pr. GBR. Dist: Brown, David Bk. Co., The.

Camenson, Blythe. Opportunities in Landscape Architecture, Botanical Gardens & Arboreta Careers. 2007. (Opportunities in... Ser.). (ENG.). 160p. per. 13.95 *(978-0-07-147608-9(3),* 0071476083) McGraw-Hill Cos., The.

Chicago Botanic Garden, creator. A Journey to Nine Islands. 2008. (Illus.). 96p. per. 21.95 *(978-0-939914-09-8(3))* Chicago Horticultural Society/Chicago Botanic Garden.

Cool Springs Press Publications Staff. Desert Gardens: A Photographic Tour of the Arizona-Sonora Desert Museum. Brusca, Richard C., ed. 2010. (ENG.). 176p. 34.95 *(978-1-59186-458-5(5),* 1591864585) Cool Springs Pr.

Drewitt, Frederic Dawtrey. The Romance of the Apothecaries' Garden at Chelsea. 2010. (Cambridge Library Collection - Life Sciences Ser.). (Illus.). 230p. pap. 22.99 *(978-1-108-01587-5(5))* Cambridge Univ. Pr.

Dunne, Niall, ed. Great Natives for Tough Places. 2009. (Brooklyn Botanic Garden All-Region Guide Ser.). (ENG., Illus.). 120p. pap. 12.95 *(978-1-889538-48-8(5))* Brooklyn Botanic Garden.

Fallen, Anne-Catherine & Shimizu, Holly H. A Botanic Garden for the Nation: The United States Botanic Garden. 2007. (ENG., Illus.). 180p. 69.00 *(978-0-16-076772-2(5))* United States Government Printing Office.

Field, Henry. Memoirs of the Botanic Garden at Chelsea: Belonging to the Society of Apothecaries of London. Semple, R. H., ed. 2011. (Cambridge Library Collection - Life Sciences Ser.). (ENG., Illus.). 290p. pap. 23.99 ***(978-1-108-03748-8(8))*** Cambridge Univ. Pr.

Fisher, Celia. The Golden Age of Flowers: Botanical Illustration in the Age of Discovery, 1600-1800. 2011. (Illus.). 144p. 29.95 *(978-0-7123-5820-0(X))* British Library, The GBR. Dist: Chicago Distribution Ctr.

Geon, Bryan. Splendid Pathways: A Tour Through the World's Finest Botanical Gardens. 2007. (Illus.). 280p. pap. 29.95 *(978-1-894622-71-4(5))* Warwick Publishing CAN. Dist: Perseus Distribution.

Heffernan, Maureen, ed. The Coastal Maine Botanical Gardens. 2012. (ENG.). 144p. 34.95 *(978-0-89272-941-8(4))* Down East Bks.

Hohn, Timothy C. Curatorial Practices for Botanical Gardens. 2007. (ENG., Illus.). 236p. 42.95 *(978-0-7591-1063-2(8))* AltaMira Pr.

Johnson, Nuala C. Nature Displaced, Nature Displayed: Order & Beauty in Botanical Gardens. 2011. (Tauris Historical Geography Ser.). (ENG., Illus.). 272p. 90.00 *(978-1-84885-712-4(8))* I. B. Tauris & Co., Ltd. GBR. Dist: Macmillan.

Kelaidis, Panayoti, ed. Flourish: A Visionary Garden in the American West. 2009. (ENG.). 26.95 *(978-1-55566-429-9(6))* Johnson Bks.

Kirk, Lynn J. & Robinson, Frank L. Lewis Ginter Botanical Garden: 25 Years & Growing. 2009. *(978-1-57864-553-4(0)); (978-1-57864-552-7(2))* Donning Co. Pubs.

Kraft, Joy W. The Cincinnati Zoo & Botanical Garden. 2010. (Images of America Ser.). (ENG., Illus.). 128p. pap. 21.99 *(978-0-7385-7782-1(0))* Arcadia Publishing.

Lamb, Christian. This Infant Adventure: Offspring of the Royal Gardens at Kew. 2010. (ENG., Illus.). 224p. 29.95 *(978-1-903071-29-8(1))* Bene Factum Publishing, Ltd. GBR. Dist: Independent Pubs. Group.

LeHoven, Susan Jane. Na' Aina Kai Botanical Gardens & Sculpture Park: A Collection of Beauty. 2011. 144p. 29.95 *(978-1-893871-02-1(9))* TV Juice Productions.

Löhne, Cornelia, et al. Natur und Nachhaltigkeit: Innovative Bildungsangebote in Botanischen Gärten, Zoos und Freilichtmuseen: Ergebnisse des F+E-Vorhabens "Innovative Bildungsangebote Durch Botanische Gärten, Zoologische Gärten und Freilichtmuseen" 2009. (GER., Illus.). 171p. *(978-3-7843-3978-8(6))* Landwirtschaftsverlag GmbH.

Lyden, Anne M. Descanso: Los Angeles Hidden Oasis. 2007. (ENG., Illus.). 96p. pap. 24.95 *(978-1-890449-40-7(7))* Balcony Pr.

Lyons, Gary. Desert Plants: A Curator's Introduction to the Huntington Desert Garden. 2007. (Huntington Library Garden Ser.). (Illus.). 127p. pap. 24.95 *(978-0-87328-231-4(0)); (978-0-87328-218-5(3))* Huntington Library Pr.

Marr, Warren & Marr, Warren, photos by. Descanso. 2007. (ENG., Illus.). 96p. 42.95 *(978-1-890449-37-7(7))* Balcony Pr.

McPherson, Alan. Botanic Gems Indiana Public Gardens: Including Greater Chicago, Dayton, Cincinnati & Louisville. 2009. 136p. pap. 36.49 *(978-1-4343-7772-2(5))* AuthorHouse.

Mickulas, Peter Philip. Britton's Botanical Empire: The New York Botanical Garden & American Botany, 1888-1929. 2007. (Memoirs of the New York Botanical Garden Ser.: Vol. 94). (Illus.). 316p. *(978-0-89327-479-5(8))* New York Botanical Garden, The.

Monem, Nadine Kathe. Botanic Gardens: A Living History. Craig, Blanche, ed. 2007. (ENG., Illus.). 295p. 59.95 *(978-1-904772-72-9(2))* Black Dog Publishing Ltd. GBR. Dist: Perseus Distribution.

Morris, Deborah. Royal Botanic Gardens Melbourne: A Life & Times. (Illus.). 160p. 50.00 *(978-1-86508-551-7(0))* Allen & Unwin AUS. Dist: Independent Pubs. Group.

Nelson, Gil. Botanical Keys to Florida's Trees, Shrubs, & Woody Vines. 2011. (ENG.). 200p. pap. 19.95 *(978-1-56164-499-5(4))* Pineapple Pr., Inc.

Nesbitt, Don. Krohn Conservatory: Jewel of Cincinnati Parks. 2011. (ENG.). pap. 24.95 *(978-0-615-46462-6(9))* Bramkamp Printing Co., Inc.

Normark, D. Botanical Gardens at the Huntington. Huntington Library Staff, ed. 3rd ed. 2008. (Huntington Library Garden Ser.). (Illus.). 200p. pap. 29.95 *(978-0-87328-238-3(8))* Huntington Library Pr.

Oehler, David A. Cincinnati Zoo & Botanical Gardens. 2009. (Great Zoos of the United States Ser.). 24p. (gr. 3-4). 42.50 *(978-1-61513-221-8(X),* PowerKids Pr.) Rosen Publishing Group, Inc., The.

Oldfield, Sara. Botanic Gardens: Modern-Day Arks. 2010. (ENG., Illus.). 240p. (gr. 17). 29.95 *(978-0-262-01516-5(1))* MIT Pr.

—Great Botanic Gardens of the World. 2008. (ENG., Illus.). 160p. 39.95 *(978-1-84537-593-5(9))* New Holland Pubs., Ltd. GBR. Dist: National Bk. Network.

Rabehevitra, David, et al. Guide de terrain des arbres de la foret littorale du Sud Est de Madagascar. 2012. (Illus.). 400p. pap. 82.00 *(978-1-84246-446-5(9))* Kew Publishing GBR. Dist: Chicago Distribution Ctr.

Rutenberg, Linda, photos by. English Garden at Night, 1 vol. 2010. (ENG.). 176p. 40.00 *(978-0-9769127-8-1(3))* Verve Editions.

Stanic, Borislav. Museum Companion to Los Angeles: A Guide to Museums, Historic Houses, Libraries, Special Collections, Botanical Gardens & Zoos in Los Angeles County. 3rd rev. ed. 2010. (Illus.). 287p. pap. 24.95 *(978-1-889224-03-9(0))* Museon Publishing.

Tripp, Kim E. & Forrest, Todd, contrib. by. The New York Botanical Garden. 2006. (ENG., Illus.). 248p. 50.00 *(978-0-8109-5744-2(2))* Abrams.

Valentin, Valentin. Neuer Botanischer Garten Shanghai: Shanghai New Botanic Garden. 2008. (GER & ENG., Illus.). 96p. pap. 40.00 *(978-3-939633-58-7(5))* Jovis Verlag GmbH DEU. Dist: D.A.P./Distributed Art Pubs.

VV., AA., et al. Memoria y Naturaleza: El Archivo Del Real Jardín Botánico de Madrid. San Pío Aledrén, Pilar, ed. 2009. (ENG & SPA., Illus.). 269p. *(978-84-9785-618-8(X))* Consejo Superior de Investigaciones Científicas.

Wedge, Russel. Christchurch Botanic Gardens: A sense of Place. 2010. 116p. pap. *(978-3-8383-7539-4(0))* Lambert Academic Publishing.

Whitton, Kevin J. & Whitton, Michelle, photos by. A Pocket Guide to Hawai'i's Botanical Gardens. 2009. pap. 8.95 *(978-1-56647-903-5(7))* Mutual Publishing LLC.

Wingate, Marty. The Bellevue Botanical Garden: Celebrating the First 15 Years. 2007. (Illus.). 111p. pap. *(978-0-9793221-0-5(3))* Bellevue Botanical Garden Society.

BOTANICAL GEOGRAPHY

see Phytogeography

BOTANICAL ILLUSTRATION

The American Society of Botanical Artists & the Horticultural Society of New York Present: The Ninth Annual International Juried Botanical Art Exhibition 2006. 2006. per. 20.00 *(978-0-9744153-4-5(0))* American Society of Botanical Artists.

Baldwin, Mariella. Botanical Painting. 2012. (ENG., Illus.). 144p. 29.95 ***(978-1-84797-277-4(2))*** Crowood Pr., Ltd. GBR. Dist: Independent Pubs. Group.

Beckett, Elspeth. Illustrated Flora of Mallorca. (SPA., Illus.). 226p. *(978-84-273-0714-8(4))* Moll, Editorial ESP. Dist: Vine Hse. Distribution.

Besler, Basilius. Besler's Book of Flowers & Plants: 73 Full-Color Plates from Hortus Eystettensis 1613. 2007. (Dover Pictorial Archive Ser.). (ENG., Illus.). 80p. per. 14.95 *(978-0-486-46005-5(3))* Dover Pubns., Inc.

Besler, Basilius & Dressendörfer, Werner. The Book of Plants: The Complete Plates. annot. ed. 2007. (ENG., Illus.). 443p. 29.99 *(978-3-8228-3809-9(8))* TASCHEN DEU. Dist: Ingram Pub. Services.

Bleichmar, Daniela. Visible Empire: Botanical Expeditions & Visual Culture in the Hispanic Enlightenment. 2012. (ENG., Illus.). 288p. 55.00 *(978-0-226-05853-5(0))* Univ. of Chicago Pr.

Brodie, Christina. Drawing & Painting Plants. 2007. (ENG., Illus.). 144p. pap. 29.95 *(978-0-88192-841-9(0),* 0881928410) Timber Pr., Inc.

Bruno, Lugene. 13th International Exhibition of Botanical Art & Illustration. 2010. (ENG., Illus.). 197p. pap. 25.00 *(978-0-913196-84-7(3))* Hunt Institute for Botanical Documentation.

Cardaci, Diane. Flowers & Botanicals. 2010. (Drawing Made Easy Ser.). 64p. 34.25 *(978-1-936309-10-8(6))* Foster, Walter Publishing, Inc.

Carr, Emily & Woods, Emily Henrietta. Wild Flowers, 1 vol. 2010. (ENG., Illus.). 96p. per. *(978-0-7726-5453-3(0))* Royal British Columbia Museum.

Cribb, Phillip & Tibbs, Mike. A Very Victorian Passion: The Orchid Paintings of John Day, 1863-1888. 2006. (ENG., Illus.). 464p. 95.00 *(978-1-897739-21-1(4))* Blacker Design Publishing.

Dion, Mark & Courtney, Julie. Travels of William Bartram Reconsidered. 2010. (Illus.). 111p. 35.00 *(978-0-615-25748-8(8))* Bartram, John Assn.

Dressendorfer, Werner. Vilmorin, The vegetable garden. Der Gemüsegarten. 2010. (ENG.). 108p. pap. 99.99 *(978-3-8365-1777-5(9))* TASCHEN DEU. Dist: Ingram Pub. Services.

Evans, Henry. Botanical Prints. 2011. (ENG., Illus.). 96p. pap. 24.95 *(978-1-58243-637-1(1),* Counterpoint) Counterpoint LLC.

Fletcher, Adelene. The Watercolour Flower Painter's A to Z: An Illustrated Directory of Techniques for Painting 50 Popular Flowers. 2010. (ENG., Illus.). 128p. pap. 19.95 *(978-1-84448-125-5(5))* Search Pr., Ltd. GBR. Dist: Independent Pubs. Group.

Foster, Clare. Painterly Plants. 2012. (ENG., Illus.). 160p. 39.95 ***(978-1-85894-555-2(0))*** Merrell Pubs. Ltd. GBR. Dist: Perseus Distribution.

Garbari, Fabio & Tongiorgi Tomasi, Lucia. Flora: The Erbario Miniato & other Drawings, 2 vols. 2007. (Paper Museum of Cassiano Dal Pozzo. Ser. B: Natural History Ser.). (Illus.). 750p. (C). 313.00 *(978-1-905375-18-9(2))* Brepols Pubs. BEL. Dist: Brown, David Bk. Co., The.

Hollender, Wendy. Botanical Drawing in Color: A Basic Guide to Mastering Realistic Form & Naturalistic Color. 2010. (ENG., Illus.). 144p. pap. 24.99 *(978-0-8230-0706-6(5))* Watson-Guptill Pubns., Inc.

Hopper, Stephen D. Life on the Rocks: The Art of Survival. 2nd ed. 2008. (ENG.). 192p. 25.00 *(978-1-921361-28-9(X))* Fremantle Pr. AUS. Dist: Independent Pubs. Group.

Ivey, Robert DeWitt. Flowering Plants of New Mexico: Fifth Edition. 2008. (Illus.). 572p. spiral bd. 55.00 *(978-0-9612170-4-4(9))* Ivey, R.D.

Keeler, Nancy, text. Gardens in Perpetual Bloom. 2010. (ENG., Illus.). 136p. pap. 24.95 *(978-0-87846-749-5(1))* Museum of Fine Arts, Boston.

Kress, W. John & Sherwood, Shirley. The Art of Plant Evolution. 2010. (Illus.). 320p. (ENG.). 53.00 *(978-1-84246-421-2(3));* pap. 41.00 *(978-1-84246-417-5(5))* Kew Publishing GBR. Dist: Chicago Distribution Ctr.

Kurz, Don. Shrubs & Woody Vines of Missouri Field Guide. 2009. 156p. pap. 9.99 *(978-1-887247-69-5(6))* Missouri Dept. of Conservation.

Kusukawa, Sachiko. Picturing the Book of Nature: Image, Text, & Argument in Sixteenth-Century Human Anatomy & Medical Botany. 2012. (ENG., Illus.). 304p. 45.00 *(978-0-226-46529-6(2))* Univ. of Chicago Pr.

Lack, H. Walter. Alexander Von Humboldt: The Botanicals of America. 2009. (Illus.). 288p. 185.00 *(978-3-7913-4142-2(1))* Prestel Publishing.

Leech, Lizabeth. Botany for Artists. 2012. (ENG., Illus.). 224p. 34.95 ***(978-1-84797-278-1(0))*** Crowood Pr., Ltd. GBR. Dist: Independent Pubs. Group.

Leith-Ross, Prudence. The Florilegium of Alexander Marshal: In the Collection of Her Majesty the Queen at Windsor Castle. 2006. (ENG., Illus.). 384p. 200.00 *(978-1-902163-05-5(2))* Royal Collection Enterprises Ltd. GBR. Dist: Chicago Distribution Ctr.

Marcus, Cora & Kyer, Libby. Today's Botanical Artists. 2008. (Illus.). 160p. 29.95 *(978-0-7643-2905-0(7))* Schiffer Publishing, Ltd.

Martin, Clair G. The Huntington Rose Garden: A Centennial Celebration. 2009. (Huntington Library Garden Ser.). (Illus.). 130p. 29.95 *(978-0-87328-241-3(8))* Huntington Library Pr.

Martin, Rosie & Thurstan, Meriel. Botanical Illustration with Eden. 2008. (ENG., Illus.). 144p. pap. 19.95 *(978-0-7134-9074-9(8),* Batsford, B. T. Ltd.) Anova Bks. GBR. Dist: Sterling Publishing Co., Inc.

—Contemporary Botanical Illustration: Challenging Colour & Texture. 2008. (ENG., Illus.). 144p. 27.95 *(978-0-7134-9078-7(0),* Batsford, B. T. Ltd.) Anova Bks. GBR. Dist: Sterling Publishing Co., Inc.

Mathieson, Arthur C. & Dawes, Clinton J. The Seaweeds of Florida. 2008. (ENG., Illus.) 656p. 100.00 *(978-0-8130-3148-4(6))* Univ. Pr. of Florida.

Mortimer, Ann. Flowers in the Landscape. 2010. (Watercolour Tips & Techniques Ser.). (ENG., Illus.). 96p. pap. 19.95 *(978-1-84448-331-0(2))* Search Pr., Ltd. GBR. Dist: Independent Pubs. Group.

Nickelsen, Kärin. Draughtsmen, Botanists & Nature: The Construction of Eighteenth-Century Botanical Illustrations. 2006. (Archimedes Ser.). (ENG., Illus.). ix, 295p. 139.00 *(978-1-4020-4819-7(X),* 140204819X) Springer.

Nickelsen, Kärin. Draughtsmen, Botanists & Nature: The Construction of Eighteenth-Century Botanical Illustrations. 2010. (Archimedes Ser.). (Illus.). ix, 295p. pap. 139.00 *(978-90-481-7199-6(7),* 9048171997) Springer.

Ochoa, Carlos M. The Potatoes of South America: Bolivia. Ugent, Donald, tr. 2011. (ENG., Illus.). 570p. pap. 70.00 *(978-0-521-18990-3(X))* Cambridge Univ. Pr.

Oxley, Valerie. Botanical Illustration. 2009. (ENG., Illus.). 192p. pap. 45.00 *(978-1-84797-051-0(6))* Crowood Pr., Ltd. GBR. Dist: Independent Pubs. Group.

Payne, Michelle. Marianne North: A Very Intrepid Painter. 2011. (Illus.). 96p. pap. 20.00 *(978-1-84246-430-4(2))* Kew Publishing GBR. Dist: Chicago Distribution Ctr.

Ravet-Haevermans, Agathe. The Art of Botanical Drawing: An Introductory Guide. 2009. (ENG., Illus.). 96p. pap. 19.95 *(978-0-88192-990-4(5),* 0881929905) Timber Pr., Inc.

Redoute, Pierre Joseph. The Roses: The Complete Plates. 25th rev. ed. 2007. (ENG., Illus.). 203p. 19.99 *(978-3-8228-3810-5(1))* TASCHEN DEU. Dist: Ingram Pub. Services.

Redoute, Pierre Joseph & Sowerby, James. Roses. 2011. (ENG., Illus.). 288p. pap. 22.99 *(978-0-06-203955-2(5),* Collins Design) HarperCollins Pubs.

Renaux, Alain. Louis XIV's Botanical Engravings. 2008. (Illus.). 144p. 80.00 *(978-1-84822-000-3(6),* Lund Humphries Pubs.) Ashgate Publishing, Ltd. GBR. Dist: Ashgate Publishing Co.

Richman, Irwin. Seed Art: The package made me buy it. 2008. (Illus.). 176p. pap. 29.95 *(978-0-7643-2819-0(0))* Schiffer Publishing, Ltd.

Ross, Prudence Leith, et al. Mr. Marshal's Flower Book: Being a Compendium of the Flower Portraits of Alexander Marshal Esq. As Created for His Magnificent Florilegium. 2010. (Illus.). 192p. 19.95 *(978-1-905686-03-2(X))* Royal Collection Enterprises Ltd. GBR. Dist: Antique Collectors' Club.

Rossi-Wilcox, Susan M., et al. Drawing upon Nature: Studies for the Blaschkas' Glass Models. 2007. (Illus.). 167p. pap. 24.95 *(978-0-87290-166-7(1))* Corning Museum of Glass.

Roth, Dietrich, ed. Das Moller-Florilegium: Hans Simon Holtzbeckers Blumenalbum für den Bürgermeister Barthold Moller. 2007. (GER., Illus.). 336p. (C). 150.00 *(978-3-7774-3425-4(6))* Hirmer Verlag GmbH DEU. Dist: Brown, David Bk. Co., The.

Royal Botanic Gardens, Kew. Official Guide to the Marianne North Gallery. 2010. (Illus.). 208p. 22.00 *(978-1-84246-424-3(8))* Kew Publishing GBR. Dist: Chicago Distribution Ctr.

Saunders, Gill. Picturing Plants: An Analytical History of Botanical Illustration. 2nd ed. 2009. (ENG., Illus.). 153p. 50.00 *(978-0-9817736-4-3(8))* KWS Pubs.

Scott, Mary Ann & Stevens, Margaret. Botanical Sketchbook. 2010. (ENG., Illus.). 128p. 24.95 *(978-1-59668-232-0(9))* Interweave Pr., LLC.

Sheehan, Tom & Sheehan, Marion. An Illustrated Survey of Orchid Genera. 2009. (ENG.). 424p. pap. 99.00 *(978-1-60469-064-4(X),* 160469064X) Timber Pr., Inc.

Sherwood, Shirley. A New Flowering: 1000 Years of Botanical Art. 2006. (ENG., Illus.). 200p. pap. 39.95 *(978-1-85444-206-2(6))* Ashmolean Museum GBR. Dist: Antique Collectors' Club.

Sherwood, Shirley, frwd. The American Society of Botanical Artists & the Horticultural Society of New York Present: The Tenth Annual International Juried Botanical Art Exhibition 2007. 2007. per. 20.00 *(978-0-9744153-5-2(9))* American Society of Botanical Artists.

Sherwood, Shirley & Rix, Martyn. Treasures of Botanical Art: Icons from the Shirley Sherwood & Kew Collections. (ENG., Illus.). 272p. 2009. pap. *(978-1-84246-221-8(0))* 2008. *(978-1-84246-368-0(3))* Antique Collectors' Club. (Royal Botanic Gardens Edinburg).

Smith, Gideon & Crouch, Neil. Guide to Succulents of Southern Africa. 2009. (Illus.). 136p. pap. 19.95 *(978-1-77007-662-4(X))* Struik Pubs. ZAF. Dist: International Publishers Marketing.

Stevens, Margaret & Society of Botanical Artists Staff. The Botanical Palette: Color for the Botanical Painter. 2008. 144p. 29.95 *(978-0-06-162667-8(8))* Smithsonian Institution Pr.

Strid, Arne & Strid, Barbro, eds. Flora Graeca Sibthorpian: Sive plantarum rariorum historia, quas in provinciis aut insulis Graeciae legit, investigavit et depingi curavit Johannes Sibthorp, 3, 2. 2010. (ENG & LAT., Illus.). 412p. reprint ed. lib. bdg. 350.00 *(978-3-906166-80-3(5),* Gantner Publishing) Koeltz Scientific Bks. DEU. Dist: Lubrecht & Cramer, Ltd.

Tait, Wendy. Flowers in Watercolour. 2011. (What to Paint Ser.). (ENG., Illus.). 112p. pap. 21.95 *(978-1-84448-658-8(3))* Search Pr., Ltd. GBR. Dist: Independent Pubs. Group.

Tancin, Charlotte, et al. Botany & History Entwined: Rachel Hunt's Legacy. 2011. (Illus.). 98p. pap. 22.00 ***(978-0-913196-85-4(1))*** Hunt Institute for Botanical Documentation.

Terry, Henry. A Victorian Flower Album: God's Floral Gems, Glistening on the Verdant Face of Nature: Collected & Painted in the Summer Evenings of 1873, As a Pleasing Recreation. (Illus.). ix, 119p. *(978-1-84067-306-7(0))* Caxton Editions.

Thomson, George Malcolm. The Ferns & Fern Allies of New Zealand. 2010. 154p. pap. 27.45 *(978-1-4455-6643-6(5))* Research Pr.

White, James J. & Bruno, Lugene B. 12th International Exhibition of Botanical Art & Illustration. 2007. (ENG., Illus.). 190p. pap. 25.00 *(978-0-913196-82-3(7))* Hunt Institute for Botanical Documentation.

White, James J., et al. Botanicals: Enfironmental Expressions in Art. the Alisa & Isaac M. Sutton Collection. 2009. (ENG., Illus.). 133p. pap. 35.00 *(978-0-913196-83-0(5))* Hunt Institute for Botanical Documentation.

BOTANICAL MUSEUMS

see also Herbaria

Royal Botanic Gardens, Kew. Official Guide to the Marianne North Gallery. 2010. (Illus.). 208p. 22.00 *(978-1-84246-424-3(8))* Kew Publishing GBR. Dist: Chicago Distribution Ctr.

BOTANICAL NAMES

see Plants—Nomenclature

BOTANICAL NOMENCLATURE

see Plants—Nomenclature

BOTANICAL RESEARCH

see Botany—Research

BOTANICAL SPECIMENS—COLLECTION AND PRESERVATION

see Plants—Collection and Preservation

BOTANICAL SYSTEMATICS

see Plants—Classification

BOTANICAL TAXONOMY

see Plants—Classification

BOTANISTS

see also Horticulturists

Fry, Carolyn & Knowlden, Martin. The World of Kew. 2007. (ENG., Illus.). 224p. 29.95 *(978-0-563-49378-5(X),* BBC Bks.) Ebury Publishing GBR. Dist: Independent Pubs. Group.

George, Sam & George, Samantha. Botany, Sexuality & Women's Writing 1760-1830: From Modest Shoot to Forward Plant. 2008. (ENG., Illus.). 288p. 89.00 *(978-0-7190-7697-8(8))* Manchester Univ. Pr. GBR. Dist: Macmillan.

Gianquitto, Tina. "Good Observers of Nature" American Women & the Scientific Study of the Natural World, 1820-1885. 2007. (ENG., Illus.). 232p. 59.95 *(978-0-8203-2918-5(5));* per. 24.95 *(978-0-8203-2919-2(3))* Univ. of Georgia Pr.

Goss, Andrew. The Floracrats: State-Sponsored Science & the Failure of the Enlightenment in Indonesia. 2011. (New Perspectives in Se Asian Studies). (ENG., Illus.). 264p. pap. 26.95 *(978-0-299-24864-2(X))* Univ. of Wisconsin Pr.

Reeder, Melanie. A Sangoma's Story: The Calling of Elliot Ndlovu. 2012. (ENG., Illus.). 232p. (gr. 12). pap. 26.95 ***(978-0-14-302616-7(X),*** Penguin Global) Penguin Group (USA) Inc.

Ristaino, Jean, ed. Pioneering Women & Plant Pathology. 2008. (Illus.). 352p. 89.00 *(978-0-89054-359-7(3))* American Phytopathological Society, The.

Williams, R. L. French Botany in the Enlightenment: The Ill-fated Voyages of la Parouse & his Rescuers. 2010. (International Archives of the History of Ideas /

archives internationales d'histoire des Idées Ser.). 248p. pap. 110.00 *(978-90-481-6213-0(0),* 9048162130) Springer.

BOTANISTS—BIOGRAPHY

Ayres, Peter A. The Aliveness of Plants: The Darwins at the Dawn of Plant Science, 1 vol. 2008. (ENG., Illus.). 256p. 99.00 *(978-1-85196-970-8(5))* Pickering & Chatto Pubs., Ltd. GBR. Dist: Ashgate Publishing Co.

Ayres, Peter G. Shaping Ecology: The Life of Arthur Tansley. 2nd ed. 2012. (ENG.). 226p. 99.95 ***(978-0-470-67156-6(4),*** Wiley-Blackwell) Wiley, John & Sons, Inc.

—Shaping Ecology: The Life of Arthur Tansley. 2nd ed. 2012. (ENG.). 226p. pap. 29.95 ***(978-0-470-67154-2(8),*** Wiley-Blackwell) Wiley, John & Sons, Inc.

Banks, Joseph. Journal of the Right Hon. Sir Joseph Banks Bart. , K. B. , P. R. S. During Captain Cook's First Voyage in H. M. S. Endeavour in 1768-71 to Terra del Fuego, Otahite, New Zealand, Australia, the Dutch East Indies, Etc. Hooker, Joseph Dalton, ed. 2011. (Cambridge Library Collection - Travel & Exploration Ser.). (ENG., Illus.). 532p. pap. 39.99 *(978-1-108-02916-2(7))* Cambridge Univ. Pr.

Bell, Stephen. A Life in Shadow: Aimé Bonpland in Southern South America, 1817-1858. 2010. (ENG., Illus.). 336p. 65.00 *(978-0-8047-5260-2(5))* Stanford Univ. Pr.

Bennett, Rick & Calla, Susan. A Rare Botanical Legacy: The Contributions of Ruby & Arthur Van Deventer in Northwestern California. 2009. *(978-1-59714-116-1(X))* Heyday.

Beretta, Marco & Tosi, Alessandro. Linnaeus in Italy: The Spread of a Revolution in Science. 2007. (Uppsala Studies in History of Science). *(978-0-88135-393-8(0))* Watson Publishing International, LLC.

Berkeley, Edmund. Dr. John Mitchell: The Man Who Made the Map of North America. 2011. (ENG.). 302p. pap. 40.00 ***(978-0-8078-9618-1(7))*** Univ. of North Carolina Pr.

Boewe, Charles E. The Life of C.S. Rafinesque: A Man of Uncommon Zeal. 2011. ***(978-1-60618-922-1(0))*** American Philosophical Society.

Call, R. W. Life & Writings of Rafinesque. 227p. reprint ed. lib. bdg. 98.00 *(978-0-7222-4931-4(4))* Library Reprints, Inc.

Deleuze, J. P. F. The Annotated Memoirs of the Life & Botanical Travels of André Michaux: Notice Historique sur André Michaux. Koenig, Carl D. E. & Sims, John, trs. 2011.Tr. of Nistorical Note on André Michaux. (Illus.). 70p. pap. 11.95 ***(978-0-9718763-3-0(9))*** Fevertree Pr.

Dobkin de Rios, Marlene. The Psychedelic Journey of Marlene Dobkin de Rios. 2009. (ENG.). 1p. pap. 16.95 *(978-1-59477-313-6(0),* Park Street Pr.) Inner Traditions International, Ltd.

Endersby, Jim. Imperial Nature: Joseph Hooker & the Practices of Victorian Science. (Illus.). 448p. 2010. pap. 25.00 *(978-0-226-20792-6(7))* 2008. 35.00 *(978-0-226-20791-9(9))* Univ. of Chicago Pr.

Fry, Carolyn. The Plant Hunters. 2010. (ENG., Illus.). 64p. 39.95 *(978-0-233-00244-6(8))* Andre Deutsch GBR. Dist: Sterling Publishing Co., Inc.

Gee, Wilson P. South Carolina Botanists. (Illus.). 52p. reprint ed. lib. bdg. 88.00 *(978-0-7222-4575-0(0))* Library Reprints, Inc.

Griggs, Pat. Joseph Hooker: Botanical Trailblazer. 2012. (Illus.). 64p. pap. 17.00 ***(978-1-84246-469-4(8))*** Kew Publishing GBR. Dist: Chicago Distribution Ctr.

Haygood, Tamara Miner. Henry William Ravenel, 1814-1887: South Carolina Scientist in the Civil War Era. 2006. (History Amer Science & Technol Ser.). (Illus.). 224p. per. 29.95 *(978-0-8173-5372-8(0))* Univ. of Alabama Pr.

Hooker, Joseph Dalton. Life & Letters of Sir Joseph Dalton Hooker O. M. , G. C. S. I. Huxley, Leonard, ed. 2011. (Cambridge Library Collection - Life Sciences Ser.). (ENG.). 592p. pap. 43.00 *(978-1-108-03101-1(3));* (Illus.). 574p. pap. 39.99 *(978-1-108-03100-4(5))* Cambridge Univ. Pr.

Katz, Shmuel. Aaronsohn Saga. 2007. 370p. 29.95 *(978-965-229-416-6(0))* Gefen Publishing Hse., Ltd ISR. Dist: Gefen Bks.

Kelly, Howard A. Some American Medical Botanists Commemorated in Our Botanical Nomenclature. 2008. 304p. 43.95 *(978-0-548-98398-0(4))* 2007. 308p. per. 28.95 *(978-0-548-66346-2(7))* Kessinger Publishing, LLC.

—Some American Medical Botanists Commemorated in Our Botanical Nomenclature. 2008. 304p. pap. *(978-1-4097-0848-3(9))* Read Bks.

Moore, Wendy. Wedlock: The True Story of the Disastrous Marriage & Remarkable Divorce of Mary Eleanor Bowes, Countess of Strathmore. 2010. 400p. pap. 15.00 *(978-0-307-38337-2(7),* Three Rivers Pr.) Crown Publishing Group.

Mueggler, Erik. The Paper Road: Archive & Experience in the Botanical Exploration of West China & Tibet. 2011. (ENG., Illus.). 346p. 70.00 *(978-0-520-26902-6(0));* pap. 29.95 *(978-0-520-26903-3(9))* Univ. of California Pr.

Nabhan, Gary Paul. Where Our Food Comes From: Retracing Nikolay Vavilov's Quest to End Famine. 2011. (ENG., Illus.). 264p. pap. 24.00 *(978-1-61091-003-3(6))* Island Pr.

Nathan, Simon & Varnham, Mary, eds. The Amazing World of James Hector: Explorer, Doctor, Geologist, Botanist, Natural Historian, & One of New Zealand's Most Remarkable Figures. 2009. (Awa Science Ser.). (ENG., Illus.). 186p. pap. 17.95 *(978-0-9582750-7-1(6))* Awa Pr. NZL. Dist: Independent Pubs. Group.

Nisbet, Jack. The Collector: David Douglas & the Natural History of the Northwest. (ENG., Illus.). 304p. 2010. pap. 16.95 *(978-1-57061-667-9(1))* 2009. 23.95 *(978-1-57061-613-6(2))* Sasquatch Bks.

O'Brien, Seamus. In the Footsteps of Augustine Henry. 2011. (ENG., Illus.). 376p. 85.00 *(978-1-870673-73-0(5))* Antique Collectors' Club.

Oliver, F. W., ed. Makers of British Botany: A Collection of Biographies by Living Botanists. 2010. (Cambridge Library Collection - Life Sciences Ser.). (Illus.). 400p. pap. 31.99 *(978-1-108-01602-5(2))* Cambridge Univ. Pr.

Pulteney, Richard. Historical & Biographical Sketches of the Progress of Botany in England: From its Origin to the Introduction of the Linnaean System. 2011. (Cambridge Library Collection - Life Sciences Ser.). (ENG.). 400p. pap. 31.99 ***(978-1-108-03733-4(X));*** 386p. pap. 31.99 ***(978-1-108-03732-7(1))*** Cambridge Univ. Pr.

Reinikka, Merle A. A History of the Orchid. 2008. (ENG.). 348p. pap. 40.00 *(978-1-60469-047-7(X),* 160469047X) Timber Pr., Inc.

Ridley, Glynis. The Discovery of Jeanne Baret: A Story of Science, the High Seas, & the First Woman to Circumnavigate the Globe. 2011. (ENG., Illus.). 304p. pap. 15.00 *(978-0-307-46353-1(2))* Broadway Bks.

—The Discovery of Jeanne Baret: A Story of Science, the High Seas, & the First Woman to Circumnavigate the Globe. 2010. (ENG., Illus.). 304p. 25.00 *(978-0-307-46352-4(4),* Crown) Crown Publishing Group.

Rousseau, George S. Notorious Sir John Hill: The Man Destroyed by Ambition in the Era of Celebrity. 2012. (ENG.). 424p. (gr. 17). 90.00 ***(978-1-61146-120-6(0))*** Lehigh Univ. Pr.

Shores, Elizabeth Findley. On Harper's Trail: Roland Mcmillan Harper, Pioneering Botanist of the Southern Coastal Plain. (ENG., Illus.). 296p. 2010. pap. 24.95 *(978-0-8203-3522-3(3))* 2008. 42.95 *(978-0-8203-3100-3(7))* Univ. of Georgia Pr.

Taylor, Judith M. The Global Migrations of Ornamental Plants: How the World Got into Your Garden. 2009. (Illus.). 312p. 40.00 *(978-1-930723-69-6(5))* Missouri Botanical Garden Pr.

Troyer, James R. Nature's Champion: B. W. Wells, Tar Heel Ecologist. 2007. (ENG.). 268p. pap. 25.95 *(978-0-8078-5870-7(6))* Univ. of North Carolina Pr.

Walravens, Hartmut. Joseph Franz Rock (1884-1962). Tagebuch der Reise von Chieng Mai nach Yunnan, 1921-1922. Briefwechsel mit C. S. Sargent, University of Washington, Johannes Schubert und Robert Koc. 2007. (Beitrage zur Kultur- und Geistesgeschichte Asiens Ser.). (GER.). 580p. (C). pap. 105.00 *(978-3-7001-3830-3(X))* Austrian Academy of Sciences Press AUT. Dist: Brown, David Bk. Co., The.

Walters, S. M. & Stow, E. A. Darwin's Mentor: John Stevens Henslow, 1796-1861. 2009. (Illus.). 368p. pap. 38.99 *(978-0-521-11799-9(2))* Cambridge Univ. Pr.

Wilson, Edward O. & Durán, José María Gómez. Kingdom of Ants: José Celestino Mutis & the Dawn of Natural History in the New World. 2010. (ENG., Illus.). 120p. 24.95 *(978-0-8018-9785-6(8))* Johns Hopkins Univ. Pr.

BOTANY

see also Algology; Aquatic Plants; Botany, Medical; Climbing Plants; Ferns; Fertilization of Plants; Fruit; Herbaria; Leaves; Mycology; Paleobotany; Palynology; Plant Anatomy; Plant Ecology; Plant Morphology; Plants; Seeds; Shrubs; Trees; Weeds

also divisions, classes, etc. of the vegetable kingdom, e.g. Cryptogams; Fungi; also headings beginning with the word Plant; and names of plants

Ahmad, Irfan, et al. Morus Alba Cuttings As Influenced by Covering with Plastic Sheet. 2011. 88p. pap. ***(978-3-8443-3422-7(X))*** Lambert Academic Publishing.

Allen, Grant. The Story of the Plants. 2009. 234p. pap. 25.75 *(978-1-117-66449-1(X))* BiblioBazaar.

—The Story of the Plants. 2008. 232p. 41.95 *(978-1-4365-5654-5(6))* 2007. (ENG.). 236p. per. 26.95 *(978-0-548-76546-3(4))* Kessinger Publishing, LLC.

—The Story of the Plants. 2007. (ENG.). 232p. per. *(978-1-4067-7192-3(9))* Read Bks.

Amna, Javaid & Taskeen, Badar. Biosorption in Single & Multi-Metal Systems: Simultaneous Removal of Heavy Metals Through Myco & Phyto Adsorbents. 2011. 52p. pap. ***(978-3-639-33835-5(9))*** VDM Verlag Dr. Mueller e.K.

Baertels, Andreas. Farbatlas Tropenpflanzen: Zier- und Nutzpflanzen 4. 4th rev. ed. (Illus.). 384p. 30.00 *(978-3-8001-3480-9(2))* Ulmer, Eugen Gmbh DEU. Dist: Balogh International, Inc.

Baginsky, Sacha & Fernie, Alisdair R., eds. Plant Systems Biology. 2007. (Experientia Supplementum Ser.). (Illus.). xiii, 357p. (C). 219.00 *(978-3-7643-7261-3(3),* 3764372613) Birkhauser Boston.

Beerling, David. The Emerald Planet: How Plants Changed Earth's History. 2007. (Illus.). 304p. 32.95 *(978-0-19-280602-4(5))* Oxford Univ. Pr., Inc.

Berg, Linda R. Introductory Botany: Plants, People, & the Environment. 2nd ed. 2007. (ENG.). 648p. (C). 217.95 *(978-0-534-46669-5(9))* Brooks/Cole.

—Introductory Botany: Plants, People & the Environment. 2nd ed. 2007. (ENG., Illus.). 1p. (C). 217.95 *(978-0-495-38478-6(X))* Brooks/Cole.

Bhatt, Arvind. Viability & Variability in Genus Swertia. 2010. 124p. pap. *(978-3-8383-9327-8(9))* Lambert Academic Publishing.

Bidlack, James & Jansky, Shelley. Loose Leaf Version of Stern's Introductory Plant Biology. 12th ed. 2010. (ENG.). (C). ring bd. 121.33 *(978-0-07-745219-3(4),* 0077452194, McGraw-Hill Science, Engineering & Mathematics) McGraw-Hill Higher Education.

Bidlack, James E., et al. Stern's Introductory Plant Biology. 12th ed. 2010. (ENG., Illus.). 640p. (C). 173.33 *(978-0-07-304052-3(5),* 0073040525, McGraw-Hill Science, Engineering & Mathematics) McGraw-Hill Higher Education.

Bojnansky, Vit & Fargasova, Agata. Atlas of Seeds & Fruits of Central & East-European Flora: The Carpathian Mountains Region. 2007. (Illus.). 1046p. 629.00 *(978-1-4020-5361-0(4),* 1402053614) Springer.

Bresinsky, Andreas, et al. Strasburger's Plant Sciences: Including Prokaryotes & Fungi. 2012. (ENG.). 1100p. 679.00 *(978-3-642-15517-8(0),* 3642155170) Springer.

Brown, Laurie. Applied Principles of Horticultural Science. 3rd rev. ed. 2008. (ENG., Illus.). 344p. pap. 41.95 *(978-0-7506-8702-7(9))* Routledge.

Bryant, John A. & Hodson, Martin J. Functional Biology of Plants. 2012. (ENG.). 334p. 149.95 ***(978-0-470-69940-9(X),*** Wiley-Blackwell) Wiley, John & Sons, Inc.

Candolle, Augustin Pyramus de & Sprengel, Kurt. Elements of the Philosophy of Plants: Containing the Principles of Scientific Botany; Nomenclature, Theory of Classification, Phythography; Anatomy, Chemistry, Physiology, Geography, & Diseases of Plants. 2011. (Cambridge Library Collection - Life Sciences Ser.). (ENG., Illus.). 532p. pap. 37.99 ***(978-1-108-03746-4(1))*** Cambridge Univ. Pr.

Caneva, Giulia, et al. Plant Biology for Cultural Heritage: Biodeterioration & Conservation. 2009. (Illus.). 400p. pap. 70.00 *(978-0-89236-939-3(6))* Oxford Univ. Pr., Inc.

Capon, Brian. Botany for Gardeners: Third Edition. 3rd ed. 2010. (ENG., Illus.). 268p. pap. 19.95 *(978-1-60469-095-8(X),* 160469095X) Timber Pr., Inc.

Carolina Biological Staff, compiled by. Affecting Plant Responses. 2009. (Inquiries in Science Biology Ser.). *(978-1-4350-0374-3(8));* tchr. ed., spiral bd. *(978-1-4350-0373-6(X))* Carolina Biological Supply Co.

Casper, Julie Kerr. Plants: Life from the Earth. 2007. (Natural Resources Ser.). (Illus.). 208p. (YA). (gr. 7-12). lib. bdg. 39.50 *(978-0-8160-6358-1(3))* Facts On File, Inc.

Cochrane, Theodore S. Prairie Plants of the University of Wisconsin-Madison Arboretum. 2006. (Illus.). 364p. pap. 35.00 *(978-0-9789590-0-5(0))* Univ. of Wisconsin Pr.

Cooke, Mordecai Cubitt. The Woodlands. 2010. 290p. pap. 30.45 *(978-1-4460-0817-1(7))* Thorndike Pr.

Coruzzi, Gloria & Gutiérrez, Rodrigo, eds. Plant Systems Biology, Volume 35. annot. ed. 2009. (Annual Plant Reviews Ser.: 52). (ENG., Illus.). 376p. 239.95 *(978-1-4051-6283-8(X),* Wiley-Blackwell) Wiley, John & Sons, Inc.

Coupland, Justine & Dolan. Plant Biology. 2009. (ENG., Illus.). 679p. (C). pap. 135.00 *(978-0-8153-4025-6(7),* Garland Science) Taylor & Francis Group.

Cram101 Textbook Reviews Staff. Outlines & Highlights for Plant Biology by Graham, Isbn: 0131469061. 2008. 328p. pap. 16.95 *(978-1-4288-6079-7(7))* Cram101 Inc.

—Outlines & Highlights for Plant Biology by Rost Isbn. 2008. 176p. pap. 12.95 *(978-1-4288-5885-5(7))* Cram101 Inc.

—Outlines & Highlights for Plants & Society by Levetin, Isbn: 0072528427. 2008. 260p. pap. 14.95 *(978-1-4288-5913-5(6))* Cram101 Inc.

—Outlines & Highlights for Plants & Society by Levetin, Isbn: 9780077221256. 2008. 360p. pap. 17.95 *(978-1-4288-5941-8(1))* Cram101 Inc.

Darwin, Charles. The Power of Movement in Plants. 2009. (Cambridge Library Collection - Life Sciences Ser.). (ENG.). 608p. pap. 35.99 *(978-1-108-00360-5(5))* Cambridge Univ. Pr.

—The Power of Movement in Plants. 2010. (Illus.). 310p. pap. 38.69 *(978-1-153-71738-0(7))* General Bks. LLC.

—The Power of Movement in Plants. 2010. 352p. pap. *(978-1-4076-3307-7(4))* HardPr.

—The Power of Movement in Plants. 2010. 494p. 43.16 *(978-1-169-35106-6(9));* pap. 31.16 ***(978-1-162-70543-9(4));*** 53.95 *(978-1-161-47407-7(2))* Kessinger Publishing, LLC.

Darwin, Charles & Darwin, Francis. The Power of Movement in Plants. 2010. (ENG.). 612p. pap. 45.75 *(978-1-171-76564-6(9));* (ENG.). 612p. pap. 45.75 *(978-1-171-74357-6(2));* (ENG.). 620p. pap. 45.75 *(978-1-177-61140-4(6));* (ENG.). 620p. pap. 45.75 *(978-1-176-50592-6(0));* 612p. pap. 45.75 *(978-1-148-94699-3(1));* 612p. pap. 45.75 *(978-1-148-34598-7(1));* 626p. pap. 45.75 *(978-1-147-05651-8(X));* 618p. pap. 45.75 *(978-1-146-50148-4(X));* 620p. pap. 45.75 *(978-1-143-96009-3(2));* 598p. pap. 44.75 *(978-1-144-12975-8(3));* 614p. pap. 45.75 *(978-1-145-89392-4(9));* 638p. pap. 45.75 *(978-1-142-97868-6(0))* BiblioBazaar.

Elpel, Thomas J. Shanleya's Quest: Patterns in Plants Card Game. (Illus.). (YA). 12.50 *(978-1-892784-23-0(8),* 1513) HOPS Pr., LLC.

Esser, Karl, et al. Progress in Botany 68. 2010. (Progress in Botany Ser.). (Illus.). xviii, 405p. pap. 295.00 *(978-3-642-07193-5(7),* 3642071937) Springer.

Figuier, Louis. The Vegetable World: Being A History of Plants, with their Structure & Peculiar Properties. Adapted from the Work of Louis Figuier. with A Glossary. 2006. 600p. per. 32.99 *(978-1-4255-6407-0(0))* MPublishing.

Flower, Charles. Where Have All the Flowers Gone? Restoring Wildflowers to the Countryside. 2009. (ENG., Illus.). 216p. pap. 35.00 *(978-1-901092-82-0(8))* Papadakis Dist A/C.

France, R. H. Germs of Mind in Plants. Simons, A. M., tr. from GER. (Science for the Workers Ser.). (Illus.). 151p. 10.00 *(978-0-88286-083-1(6))* Kerr, Charles H. Publishing Co.

Gan, Susheng, ed. Annual Plant Reviews, Senescence Processes in Plants, Volume 26. 2007. (Annual Plant Reviews Ser.: 30). (ENG., Illus.). 352p. 247.00 *(978-1-4051-3984-7(6),* Wiley-Blackwell) Wiley, John & Sons, Inc.

Garner, Jerry. Careers in Horticulture & Botany. 2nd rev. ed. 2006. (Professional Careers Ser.). (ENG.). 192p. per. 16.95 *(978-0-07-146773-5(4),* 0071467734) McGraw-Hill Cos., The.

Gibson, J. Phil & Gibson, Terri R. Plant Diversity. 2007. (Green World Ser.). (Illus.). 144p. (gr. 6-12). lib. bdg. 37.50 *(978-0-7910-8960-6(6),* Chelsea Hse.) Facts On File, Inc.

Glass, Marihelen & Parker, Rick. Fundamentals of Plant Science. 2008. (Texas Science Ser.). (ENG., Illus.). 704p. (C). 124.95 *(978-1-4180-0081-3(7))* Delmar Cengage Learning.

Gould, Donna. Our Trail. 2007. *(978-1-929830-20-6(3))* Innovations Pr.

Gray, Asa. The Botanical Text-Book, an Introduction to Scientific Botany, Both Structural & Systematic. 2006. 536p. per. 29.99 *(978-1-4255-5991-5(3))* MPublishing.

—Field, Forest, & Garden Botany. 2009. 376p. 26.99 *(978-1-103-34336-2(X));* pap. 20.99 *(978-1-103-34335-5(1))* BiblioBazaar.

—First Lessons in Botany & Vegetable Physiology. 2010. 252p. pap. 26.75 *(978-1-145-86179-4(2))* BiblioBazaar.

—First Lessons in Botany & Vegetable Physiology. 2008. 252p. 41.95 *(978-1-4369-3953-9(4));* pap. 26.95 *(978-1-4368-4757-5(5))* Kessinger Publishing, LLC.

Gupta, S. K. Biology & Breeding of Crucifers. Gupta, Surinder Kumar, ed. 2009. (ENG., Illus.). 405p. 154.95 *(978-1-4200-8608-9(1),* CRC Press) Taylor & Francis Group GBR. Dist: Taylor & Francis Group.

Hakeem, Khalid. Nitrogen Use Efficiency in Plants. 2011. 60p. pap. ***(978-3-8454-1958-9(X))*** Lambert Academic Publishing.

Hall, D. W. & Byrd, Jason. Forensic Botany: A Practical Guide. 2012. (Essential Forensic Science Ser.). (ENG.). 216p. 149.95 ***(978-0-470-66409-4(6),*** Wiley-Blackwell) Wiley, John & Sons, Inc.

Hall, David & Byrd, Jason. Forensic Botany: A Practical Guide. 2012. (Essential Forensic Science Ser.). (ENG.). 216p. pap. 79.95 ***(978-0-470-66123-9(2),*** Wiley-Blackwell) Wiley, John & Sons, Inc.

Hall, Matthew. Plants As Persons: A Philosophical Botany. Hall, Matthew, ed. 2011. (SUNY series on Religion & the Environment Ser.). (ENG.). 224p. pap. 24.95 *(978-1-4384-3428-5(6))* State Univ. of New York Pr.

—Plants as Persons: A Philosophical Botany. 2011. (SUNY series on Religion & the Environment Ser.). 224p. 75.00 *(978-1-4384-3429-2(4))* State Univ. of New York Pr.

Halle, Francis. In Praise of Plants. Lee, David, tr. 2011. 336p. pap. 24.95 ***(978-1-60469-262-4(6))*** Timber Pr., Inc.

Hemming, David, ed. Animal Sciences / Plant Sciences Reviews Set. 2011. 510p. 370.00 ***(978-1-84593-888-8(7))*** CABI GBR. Dist: Stylus Publishing, LLC.

—Plant Sciences Reviews 2010. 2011. (CAB Reviews Ser.). 304p. 265.00 ***(978-1-84593-878-9(X))*** CABI GBR. Dist: Stylus Publishing, LLC.

Henfrey, Arthur. Botanical & Physiological Memoirs. 2009. 310p. pap. 27.64 *(978-1-150-65380-3(9))* General Bks. LLC.

—Reports & Papers on Botany. Henfrey, Arthur, ed. 2010. 550p. 57.95 *(978-1-160-98394-5(1))* Kessinger Publishing, LLC.

Henfrey, Arthur, ed. Botanical & Physiological Memoirs. 2010. 610p. pap. 35.96 *(978-1-163-99250-0(X))* 2008. 608p. 59.95 *(978-0-548-99937-0(6))* 2007. (ENG.). 612p. per. 44.95 *(978-0-548-64714-1(3))* Kessinger Publishing, LLC.

—Reports & Papers on Botany. 2010. 550p. pap. 42.95 ***(978-1-160-71167-8(4))*** Kessinger Publishing, LLC.

Hodson, Martin J. & Bryant, John A. Functional Biology of Plants. 2012. (ENG.). 334p. pap. 99.95 ***(978-0-470-69939-3(6),*** Wiley-Blackwell) Wiley, John & Sons, Inc.

Holmes, Caroline. Why Do Violets Shrink? Answers to 280 Thorny Questions on the World of Plants. 2009. (ENG., Illus.). 288p. 24.95 *(978-0-7509-4628-5(8))* History Pr. Ltd., The GBR. Dist: Independent Pubs. Group.

Hooker, J. D. Botany. 2010. 118p. pap. 26.95 *(978-1-4455-4306-2(0))* Harrison House Pubs.

Ingrouille, Martin J., et al. Plants: Diversity & Evolution. 2006. (ENG., Illus.). 456p. per. 75.00 *(978-0-521-79433-6(1))* Cambridge Univ. Pr.

Jackson, Benjamin Daydon, ed. Catalogue of Plants Cultivated in the Garden of John Gerard, in the Years 1596-1599. 2011. (Cambridge Library Collection - Life Sciences Ser.). (ENG.). 92p. pap. 19.99 ***(978-1-108-03715-0(1))*** Cambridge Univ. Pr.

Jenks, Matthew A. & Wood, Andrew J., eds. Plant Desiccation Tolerance. 2007. (ENG., Illus.). 340p. 230.95 *(978-0-8138-1263-2(1),* Wiley-Blackwell) Wiley, John & Sons, Inc.

Jussieu, Adrien de. The Elements of Botany. Wilson, James Hewetson, tr. 2011. (Cambridge Library Collection - Life Sciences Ser.). (ENG., Illus.). 790p. pap. 50.00 ***(978-1-108-03731-0(3))*** Cambridge Univ. Pr.

Kader, Jean-Claude & Delseny, Michel, contrib. by. Advances in Botanical Research. (ENG.). 2011. 506p. 193.00 ***(978-0-12-385851-1(8))*** 2010. 275p. 193.00 *(978-0-12-380868-4(5))* 2010. 224p. 193.00 *(978-0-12-380870-7(7))* 2010. 296p. 193.00 *(978-0-12-380872-1(3))* 2009. 228p. 193.00 *(978-0-12-374835-5(6))* 2008. 280p. 193.00 *(978-0-12-374600-9(0))* 2008. 288p. 193.00 *(978-0-12-374327-5(3))* Elsevier Science & Technology Bks. (Academic Pr.).

—Advances in Botanical Research: Incorporating Advances in Plant Pathology. 2007. (Advances in Botanical Research Ser.). (ENG., Illus.). 312p. 193.00 *(978-0-12-373705-2(2),* Academic Pr.) Elsevier Science & Technology Bks.

Kader, Jean-Claude & Delseny, Michel, contrib. by. Advances in Botanical Research Pt. B: Biosynthesis of Vitamins in Plants - Vitamins B6, B8, B9, C, E, K. 2011. (ENG.). 337p. 193.00 ***(978-0-12-385853-5(4),*** Academic Pr.) Elsevier Science & Technology Bks.

Kader, Jean-Claude & Delseny, Michel, eds. Advances in Botanical Research. 2008. (ENG.). 300p. 193.00 *(978-0-12-374735-8(X),* Academic Pr.) Elsevier Science & Technology Bks.

Kadereit, Joachim W. & Jeffrey, Charles. Flowering Plants. Eudicots: Asterales. 2010. (Families & Genera of Vascular Plants Ser.). (Illus.). xii, 635p. pap. 449.00 *(978-3-642-06822-5(7),* 3642068227) Springer.

Kole, Chittaranjan. Wild Crop Relatives: Genomic & Breeding Resources - Millets & Grasses. Kole, Chittaranjan, ed. 2010. (ENG., Illus.). xxiv, 318p. 209.00 *(978-3-642-14254-3(0),* 3642142540) Springer.

Kragler, Fredrich & Hülskamp, Martin, eds. Short & Long Distance Signaling. 2011. (Advances in Plant Biology Ser.). 450p. 189.00 *(978-1-4419-1531-3(1),* 1441915311) Springer.

Kratz, Rene Fester. Botany for Dummies. 2011. (ENG., Illus.). 384p. pap. 19.99 *(978-1-118-00672-6(0),* For Dummies) Wiley, John & Sons, Inc.

Kress, W. John, ed. Botanical Progress, Horticultural Innovations & Cultural Change, Vol. 28. 2007. (Dumbarton Oaks Colloquium Series in the History of Landscape Architecture Ser.: 28). (Illus.). 288p. pap. 40.00 *(978-0-88402-327-2(3))* Dumbarton Oaks.

Kumar, Satesh & S. K. Sharma. Biofertilizer Application Technology in Tomato. 2010. 140p. pap. *(978-3-8383-1457-0(3))* Lambert Academic Publishing.

Lü & ttge, Ulrich E. Progress in Botany 72. Lüttge, Ulrich et al, eds. 2010. (Progress in Botany Ser.). xi, 393p. 239.00 *(978-3-642-13144-8(1),* 3642131441) Springer.

Leech, Lizabeth. Botany for Artists. 2012. (ENG., Illus.). 224p. 34.95 ***(978-1-84797-278-1(0))*** Crowood Pr., Ltd. GBR. Dist: Independent Pubs. Group.

Lodari, Carola. Villa Taranto: Captain McEacham's Garden. (ITA., Illus.). 96p. *(978-88-422-0290-5(6))* Allemandi.

Lubbock, John. On Buds & Stipules. 2011. 266p. pap. 29.95 ***(978-1-4460-7756-6(X))*** Palmer Pr., The.

Luttge, U. & Murata, J., eds. Progress in Botany: Volume 68. 2007. (Progress in Botany Ser.) (Illus.). 405p. 295.00 *(978-3-540-36830-4(2),* 3540368302) Springer.

Lüttge, Ulrich. Clusia: A Woody Neotropical Genus of Remarkable Plasticity & Diversity. 2010. (Ecological Studies). (Illus.). xiv, 273p. pap. 169.00 *(978-3-642-07209-3(7),* 3642072097) Springer.

Lüttge, Ulrich, et al. Progress in Botany 69. 2010. (Progress in Botany Ser.). (Illus.). xii, 480p. pap. 329.00 *(978-3-642-09204-6(7),* 3642092047) Springer.

Lüttge, Ulrich, et al, eds. Progress in Botany Vol. 73. 2011. (Progress in Botany Ser.). (ENG., Illus.). ix, 310p. 189.00 ***(978-3-642-22745-5(7),*** 3642227457) Springer.

Lüttge, Ulrich E. Progress in Botany. 2008. (Progress in Botany Ser.). (Illus.). 290p. 219.00 *(978-3-540-68420-6(4))* Springer.

Lüttge, Ulrich E., et al. Progress in Botany / Volume 69. 2007. (Progress in Botany Ser.). (Illus.). 471p. 329.00 *(978-3-540-72953-2(4))* Springer.

Lüttge, Ulrich E., et al, eds. Progress in Botany, Vol. 71. 2009. (Progress in Botany Ser.). (ENG., Illus.). x, 422p. 239.00 *(978-3-642-02166-4(2),* 3642021662) Springer.

Maeterlinck, Maurice. The Intelligence of Flowers. 2007. 77p. 38.50 *(978-0-7914-7273-6(6));* per. 19.95 *(978-0-7914-7274-3(4))* State Univ. of New York Pr.

Mahesh, S. Plant Molecular Biotechnology. 2008. (Illus.). 432p. (C). *(978-1-906574-14-7(6))* New Age Science, Ltd.

Manning. What Kinda Cactus Izzat? pap. 6.95 *(978-0-918080-95-0(9))* Rio Nuevo Pubs.

Mauseth, James D. Botany: An Introduction to Plant Biology. 4th rev. ed. 2008. 672p. 173.95 *(978-0-7637-5345-0(9))* Jones & Bartlett Learning, LLC.

Meier, Iris. Functional Organization of the Plant Nucleus. 2008. (Plant Cell Monographs). (Illus.). 205p. 159.00 *(978-3-540-71057-8(4))* Springer.

Merchant, Sabeeha S., ed. Annual Review of Plant Biology 2011. 2011. 611p. 240.00 ***(978-0-8243-0662-5(7))*** Annual Reviews, Inc.

Mohlenbrock, Robert H. Sedges: Carex. 2nd ed. 2011. (Illus.). 193p. E-Book *(978-0-8093-8627-7(5));* 456p. 65.00 *(978-0-8093-3024-9(5))* Southern Illinois Univ. Pr.

Muhammad, Sanusi & A. AMUSA, N. Introductory Botany. 2011. 260p. pap. ***(978-3-8383-2556-9(7))*** Lambert Academic Publishing.

Muir, John. A Thousand Mile Walk to the Gulf. 2007. (Twelve-Point Ser.). lib. bdg. 25.00 *(978-1-58287-454-8(9));* lib. bdg. 26.00 *(978-1-58287-939-0(7))* North Bks.

Nagata, Toshiyuki & Tabata, Satoshi, eds. Brassicas & Legumes: From Genome Structure to Breeding. 2010. (Biotechnology in Agriculture & Forestry Ser.). (Illus.). xx, 268p. pap. 289.00 *(978-3-642-07662-6(9),* 3642076629) Springer.

New Jersey Geological Survey Staff. Mineralogy, Botany, Zoology Set, 2 pts. (Illus.). reprint ed. lib. bdg. 125.00 *(978-0-7222-0229-6(6))* Library Reprints, Inc.

Novotny, Vojtech. Notebooks from New Guinea: Reflections on Life, Nature, & Science from the Depths of the Rainforest. 2011. (ENG., Illus.). 272p. pap. 17.95 *(978-0-19-960964-2(0))* Oxford Univ. Pr., Inc.

Oliver, Francis Wall. The Natural History of Plants - Their Forms, Growth, Reproduction, & Distribution - Half. 2010. 398p. pap. 32.45 *(978-1-4446-9470-3(7))* Barclay Pr., Inc.

Our Secrets to Success with Proteas. 3rd rev. ed. 2006. *(978-0-9595405-7-4(1))* Protea Flora Nursery.

Rafinesque, C. S. Flora Telluriana. 2009. (ENG.). 471p. pap. 28.99 *(978-1-117-01310-7(3),* BiblioLife) BiblioBazaar.

Raven, Peter, et al. Laboratory Manual to accompany Stern's Introductory Plant Biology. 12th ed. 2010. (ENG., Illus.). 256p. (C). spiral bd. 82.33 *(978-0-07-304053-0(3),* 0073040533, McGraw-Hill Science, Engineering & Mathematics) McGraw-Hill Higher Education.

Ray, Charles & Feser, Cathy. The Conifer & Broadleaf Trees of the South. 2011. 148p. pap. 36.95 ***(978-1-936343-65-2(7))*** Peppertree Pr., The.

Roberts, Keith, ed. Handbook of Plant Science, 2 vols. 2008. (ENG., Illus.). 1648p. 640.00 *(978-0-470-05723-0(8),* Wiley-Interscience) Wiley, John & Sons, Inc.

Ruskin, John. Proserpina, Volume I & Volume II. Studies of Wayside Flowers. 2010. 300p. pap. 48.95 *(978-1-4092-0933-1(4))* Lulu Enterprises Inc.

—Proserpina, Volume II. 2010. 128p. pap. 41.50 *(978-1-4092-0696-5(3))* Lulu Enterprises Inc.

Sachs, Julius. A Text-Book of Botany: Morphological & Physiological. 2011. (Cambridge Library Collection - Life Sciences Ser.). (ENG., Illus.). 876p. pap. 53.00 ***(978-1-108-03832-4(8))*** Cambridge Univ. Pr.

Scheckler, Steven, et al. Plant Tutor. Date not set. (Life Science Ser.). pap., wbk. ed. 25.00 *(978-0-7637-0442-1(3))* Jones & Bartlett Learning, LLC.

Schultes, Richard Evans & von Reis, Siri. Ethnobotany: Evolution of a Discipline. 2008. (ENG.). 416p. pap. 49.95 *(978-0-88192-972-0(7),* 0881929727) Timber Pr., Inc.

Science Press Staff, ed. Pharmaceutical Botany. 2012. (ENG., Illus.). 344p. 119.95 *(978-1-4398-1745-2(6),* Taylor & Francis) Taylor & Francis Group GBR. Dist: Taylor & Francis Group.

Sewall, Joseph Addison. A Condensed Botany; Designed As a Text-Book for Common Schools, & an Elementary Work in High Schools & Academies by Joseph a Sewall. 2011. 108p. pap. 16.99 ***(978-1-4255-9070-3(5))*** MPublishing.

Sharma, Himanshu & Kumar, Ashwani. Pharmacognostical Studies on Some Selected Medicinal Plants. 2011. 236p. pap. ***(978-3-8454-0785-2(9))*** Lambert Academic Publishing.

Short, Barb. Botany for Bloomin' Idiots: Book 1 - Talkin' the Talk. 2007. (Illus.). 192p. per. 29.95 *(978-0-9762714-3-7(5))* Fence Row Publishing.

Silvertown, Jonathan. An Orchard Invisible: A Natural History of Seeds. (ENG., Illus.). 224p. 2010. pap. 17.00 *(978-0-226-75774-2(9))* 2009. 25.00 *(978-0-226-75773-5(0))* Univ. of Chicago Pr.

Simblet, Sarah & Dorling Kindersley Publishing Staff. Botany for the Artist: An Inspirational Guide to Drawing Plants. 2010. (ENG., Illus.). 256p. (gr. 12-18). 40.00 *(978-0-7566-5250-0(2))* Dorling Kindersley Publishing, Inc.

Smith, James Edward. Memoir & Correspondence of the Late Sir James Edward Smith, M. D. Smith, Pleasance, ed. 2011. (Cambridge Library Collection - Life Sciences Ser.). (ENG.). 622p. pap. 43.00 ***(978-1-108-03708-2(9));*** (Illus.). 636p. pap. 43.00 ***(978-1-108-03707-5(0))*** Cambridge Univ. Pr.

Souza, Ricardo M., ed. Plant-Parasitic Nematodes of Coffee. 2010. xvi, 340p. pap. 239.00 *(978-90-481-7967-1(X),* 904817967X) Springer.

Stern, Kingsley R., et al. Introductory Plant Biology. 11th rev. ed. 2007. 640p. *(978-0-07-283067-5(0))* McGraw-Hill Cos., The.

Terrien, Jean, et al. Light, Vegetation & Chlorophyl. 7.95 *(978-0-8022-1705-9(2))* Philosophical Library, Inc.

Thangadurai, D., et al. Mycorrhizal Biotechnology. 2010. (ENG., Illus.). 226p. 89.95 *(978-1-57808-691-7(4))* BIOS Scientific Publishers Ltd. GBR. Dist: Taylor & Francis Group.

Trelease, William. Winter Botany. 2010. 196p. pap. 28.01 *(978-1-153-21253-3(6))* General Bks. LLC.

Uno, Gordon E. Introductory Botany Workbook. rev. ed. 2010. (ENG.). 158p. spiral bd. 54.00 *(978-0-7872-7733-8(9))* Kendall Hunt Publishing Co.

van Ewyk, Anthony Leopold. Plants: A Marvellous Green Creation. 2007. 168p. per. *(978-1-84401-847-5(4))* Athena Pr.

Varshney, Rajeev K. & Tuberosa, Roberto, eds. Genomics-Assisted Crop Improvement: Vol 2: Genomics Applications in Crops. 2010. xx, 509p. pap. 259.00 *(978-90-481-7600-7(X),* 904817600X) Springer.

Wajad, Nazeer. Inheritance Pattern of Some Yield Contributing Traits in Spring Wheat: Differential Gene Expression Patterns for Some Polygenically Controlled Yield Contributing Traits in Wheat (Triticum Aestivum L.) 2011. 84p. pap. ***(978-3-639-33106-6(0))*** VDM Verlag Dr. Mueller e.K.

Walker, Timothy. Plants: A Very Short Introduction. 2012. (Very Short Introductions Ser.). (ENG., Illus.). 144p. pap. 11.95 ***(978-0-19-958406-2(0))*** Oxford Univ. Pr., Inc.

Walters, Martin & Lavelle, Michael. The Illustrated Encyclopedia of Wild Flowers & Flora of the World: An Expert Reference & Identification Guide to over 1730 Wild Flowers & Plants from Every Continent. Walters, Martin, ed. 2012. (ENG., Illus.). 512p. 35.00 *(978-0-7548-1972-1(8))* Anness Publishing GBR. Dist: National Bk. Network.

Wharton, David A. Life at the Limits: Organisms in Extreme Environments. 2007. (ENG., Illus.). 320p. pap. 36.99 *(978-0-521-03990-1(8))* Cambridge Univ. Pr.

Williams, Claire G. Conifer Reproductive Biology. 2009. (ENG., Illus.). xvi, 172p. 69.95 *(978-1-4020-9601-3(1),* 1402096011) Springer.

Wisconsin Fast Plants Program-Plant Patholog. Teaching with Fast Plants: Learning Science Concepts Through the Engaging Fast Plant Life Cycle. 2nd rev. ed. 2011. (ENG.). 156p. spiral bd. 42.95 ***(978-0-7575-9146-4(9))*** Kendall Hunt Publishing Co.

Yadav, Shyam S., et al, eds. Lentil: An Ancient Crop for Modern Times. 2010. xxiv, 462p. pap. 259.00 *(978-90-481-7605-2(0),* 9048176050) Springer.

Yanes, Carlos Vasquez. Como Viven las Plantas. (Ciencia para Todos Ser.). (SPA.). pap. 6.99 *(978-968-16-2711-9(3))* Fondo de Cultura Economica USA.

BOTANY—ANATOMY

see Plant Anatomy

BOTANY—BIBLIOGRAPHY

Frodin, David G. Guide to Standard Floras of the World: An Annotated, Geographically Arranged Systematic bibliography of the Principal Floras, Enumerations, Checklists & Chorological Atlases of Different Areas. 2nd rev. ed. 2001. (ENG.). 1126p. pap. 150.00 *(978-0-521-18977-4(2))* Cambridge Univ. Pr.

Kew Bulletin. 2009. 174p. pap. *(978-0-217-96517-0(2))* Books LLC.

Tancin, Charlotte, et al. Botany & History Entwined: Rachel Hunt's Legacy. 2011. (Illus.). 98p. pap. 22.00 ***(978-0-913196-85-4(1))*** Hunt Institute for Botanical Documentation.

BOTANY—CLASSIFICATION

see Plants—Classification

BOTANY—DATA PROCESSING

Fourcaud, Thierry & Zhang, Xiao-Peng. PMA 2006: Second International Symposium on Plant Growth Modeling, Simulation, Visualization & Their Applications: Proceedings, 13-17 October 2006, Beijing, P.R. China. 2007. (Illus.). xiv, 336p. *(978-0-7695-2851-9(1))* IEEE Computer Society Pr.

Stuessy, Tod F. Plant Taxonomy: The Systematic Evaluation of Comparative Data. 2nd ed. 2008. (ENG., Illus.). 568p. (gr. 17). 99.50 *(978-0-231-14712-5(0))* Columbia Univ. Pr.

Vagelas, Ioannis, et al. Modelling Plant Science Dat. 2010. 104p. pap. *(978-3-8383-7753-7(2))* Lambert Academic Publishing.

BOTANY—DICTIONARIES

Alcock, Randal H. Botanical Names for English Readers. 2010. 128p. pap. 21.79 *(978-1-153-30396-5(5))* General Bks. LLC.

Allaby, Michael. A Dictionary of Plant Sciences. 3rd ed. 2012. (Oxford Paperback Reference Ser.). (ENG., Illus.). 544p. (Orig.). pap. 21.95 ***(978-0-19-960057-1(0))*** Oxford Univ. Pr., Inc.

Applewood Books, creator. History of Vegetable Substances. 2008. (Cooking in America Ser.). (ENG.). 436p. pap. 26.95 *(978-1-4290-1219-5(6))* Applewood Bks.

Gilbert-Carter, H. Glossary of the British Flora. 2009. (LAT & ENG.). 124p. pap. 28.99 *(978-0-521-11488-2(8))* Cambridge Univ. Pr.

Gledhill, David. The Names of Plants. 4th rev. ed. 2008. (ENG., Illus.). 434p. pap. 53.00 *(978-0-521-68553-5(2))* Cambridge Univ. Pr.

Hart, G. T. Plants in Literature & Life. 2011. 488p. pap. ***(978-1-77067-441-7(1))*** FriesenPress.

Henslow, John Stevens. A Dictionary of Botanical Terms. 2009. (Cambridge Library Collection - Life Sciences Ser.). (ENG.). 228p. pap. 16.99 *(978-1-108-00131-1(9))* Cambridge Univ. Pr.

Moffett, Rodney. Sesotho Plant & Animal Names & Plants Used by the Basotho. 2010. (AFR & ENG.). xi, 306p. *(978-1-920383-08-4(5))* Sun Media.

Stewart, Amy. Wicked Plants: The Weed That Killed Lincoln's Mother & Other Botanical Atrocities. 2009. (ENG., Illus.). 223p. 18.95 *(978-1-56512-683-1(1),* 1565126831) Algonquin Bks. of Chapel Hill.

Young, James A. & Young, Cheryl G. Seeds of Woody Plants in North America. rev. enl. ed. 2009. (ENG.). 416p. pap. 49.95 *(978-1-60469-112-2(3),* 1604691123) Timber Pr., Inc.

BOTANY—EARLY WORKS

see Botany—Pre-Linnean Works

BOTANY—ECOLOGY

see Plant Ecology

BOTANY—EMBRYOLOGY

see also Germination; Seeds

Batygina. Embryology Flowering Plants: Vol 3: Terminology & Concepts Vol 3. 2009. (Embryology of Flowering Plants Ser.). (ENG.). 598p. 139.95 *(978-1-57808-265-0(X))* BIOS Scientific Publishers Ltd. GBR. Dist: Taylor & Francis Group.

Bhojwani, S. S. & Woong-Young Soh, eds. Current Trends in the Embryology of Angiosperms. 2010. 544p. pap. 329.00 *(978-90-481-5679-5(3),* 9048156793) Springer.

Jean, Roger V. Phyllotaxis: A Systemic Study in Plant Morphogenesis. 2009. (ENG., Illus.). 404p. pap. 69.00 *(978-0-521-10469-2(6))* Cambridge Univ. Pr.

Juarez, Michelle T. Dorsoventral Patterning of Maize Lateral Organs. 2010. 128p. pap *(978-3-8383-8482-5(2))* Lambert Academic Publishing.

Suarez, Maria F. & Bozhkov, Peter V., eds. Plant Embryogenesis. 2007. (Methods in Molecular Biology Ser.). (Illus.). 164p. 129.00 *(978-1-58829-931-4(7),* 1588299317) Humana Pr.

Suarez, Maria Fernanda & Bozhkov, Peter V., eds. Plant Embryogenesis. 2010. (Methods in Molecular Biology Ser.). (Illus.). x, 184p. pap. 129.00 *(978-1-61737-848-5(8),* 1617378488) Humana Pr.

Thorpe, Trevor A. & Yeung, Edward C. Plant Embryo Culture: Methods & Protocols. 2011. (Illus.). xi, 377p. ***(978-1-61737-988-8(3))*** Humana Pr.

Thorpe, Trevor A. & Yeung, Edward C., eds. Plant Embryo Culture: Methods & Protocols. 2011. (Methods in Molecular Biology Ser.). (Illus.). xii, 380p. 139.00 *(978-1-61737-987-1(5),* 1617379875) Humana Pr.

BOTANY—FIELDWORK

Tom, Cooperrider. Botanical Essays from Kent. 2011. 80p. 16.95 *(978-1-60635-043-0(9))* Kent State Univ. Pr.

BOTANY—GEOGRAPHICAL DISTRIBUTION

see Phytogeography

BOTANY—HISTORY

Aitken, Richard. Botanical Riches: Stories of Botanical Exploration. 2008. (Illus.). 256p. pap. 50.00 *(978-1-84822-010-2(3),* Lund Humphries Pubs.) Ashgate Publishing, Ltd. GBR. Dist: Ashgate Publishing Co.

—Botanical Riches: Stories of Botanical Exploration. 2006. (Illus.). 256p. 44.95 *(978-0-522-85201-1(7))* Melbourne Univ. Publishing AUS. Dist: Independent Pubs. Group.

Alcock, Randal H. Botanical Names for English Readers. 2010. 128p. pap. 21.79 *(978-1-153-30396-5(5))* General Bks. LLC.

Arber, Agnes. Herbals - Their Origin & Evolution: A Chapter in the History of Botany, 1470-1670. 2010. (Cambridge Library Collection - Life Sciences Ser.). (Illus.). 408p. pap. 31.99 *(978-1-108-01671-1(5))* Cambridge Univ. Pr.

Bonavia, E. The Flora of the Assyrian Monuments. 2009. (ENG.). 250p. 32.99 *(978-1-117-15634-7(6));* 252p. pap. 25.75 *(978-1-117-15635-4(4))* BiblioBazaar.

Dressendörfer, Werner. Thornton: Temple of Flora. Lamers-Schuetze, Petra, ed. Lt. ed. 2008. (Illus.). 110p. 150.00 *(978-3-8228-5273-6(2))* TASCHEN DEU. Dist: Ingram Pub. Services.

Earle, A. Scott & Reveal, James L. Lewis & Clark's Green World: The Expedition & Its Plants. 2006. (Illus.). 256p. reprint ed. 35.00 *(978-1-4223-5804-7(6))* DIANE Publishing Co.

Gribbin, Mary & Gribbin, John. Flower Hunters. 2009. (ENG., Illus.). 320p. (YA). pap. 19.95 *(978-0-19-956182-7(6))* Oxford Univ. Pr., Inc.

Hageneder, Fred. Yew: A History. 2011. (ENG., Illus.). 320p. pap. 39.95 *(978-0-7524-5945-5(7))* History Pr. Ltd., The GBR. Dist: Independent Pubs. Group.

Hardy. Ancient Botany. 2007. (Sciences of Antiquity Ser.). CCXXIVp. 34.95 *(978-0-415-31120-5(9))* Routledge.

Hardy, Gavin. Ancient Botany. 2007. (Sciences of Antiquity Ser.). CCXXIVp. 110.00 *(978-0-415-31119-9(5))* Routledge.

Harré, Rom. Pavlov's Dogs & Schrödinger's Cat: Scenes from the Living Laboratory. 2010. (ENG., Illus.). 288p. pap. 18.95 *(978-0-19-923857-6(X))* Oxford Univ. Pr., Inc.

Jenyns, Leonard. Memoir of the Rev. John Stevens Henslow, M. A., F. L. S., F. G. S., F. C. P. S. Late Rector of Hitcham, & Professor of Botany in the University of Cambridge. 2011. (Cambridge Library Collection - Life Sciences Ser.). (ENG., Illus.). 300p. pap. 23.99 ***(978-1-108-03520-0(5))*** Cambridge Univ. Pr.

Laws, Bill. Fifty Plants That Changed the Course of History. 2011. (ENG., Illus.). 224p. 29.95 *(978-1-55407-798-4(2))* Firefly Bks., Ltd.

Mwakikagile, Godfrey. Botswana: Profile of A Nation. 2010. 158p. pap. 14.95 *(978-9987-9322-9-0(0))* Continental Pr.

Nisbet, Jack. The Collector: David Douglas & the Natural History of the Northwest. (ENG., Illus.). 304p. 2010. pap. 16.95 *(978-1-57061-667-9(1))* 2009. 23.95 *(978-1-57061-613-6(2))* Sasquatch Bks.

Price, T. Douglas & Gebauer, Anne B., eds. Last Hunters - First Farmers: New Perspectives on the Prehistory Transition to Agriculture. (Advanced Seminar Ser.). (Illus.). 354p. pap. 29.95 *(978-0-933452-91-6(8))* School for Advanced Research Pr./SAR Pr.

Sachs, Julius Von & Balfour, Isaac B. History of Botany, 1530-1860. 568p. reprint ed. lib. bdg. 98.00 *(978-0-7222-3076-3(1))* Library Reprints, Inc.

Segura Munguía, Santiago & Torres Ripa, Javier. Historia de Las Plantas en el Mundo Antiguo. 2009. (SPA., Illus.). 480p. *(978-84-00-08860-6(3))* Consejo Superior de Investigaciones Científicas.

Segura Munguía, Santiago, et al. Historia de Las Plantas en el Mundo Antiguo. 2009. (SPA., Illus.). 480p. *(978-84-9830-202-8(1))* Consejo Superior de Investigaciones Científicas.

Tancin, Charlotte, et al. Botany & History Entwined: Rachel Hunt's Legacy. 2011. (Illus.). 98p. pap. 22.00 ***(978-0-913196-85-4(1))*** Hunt Institute for Botanical Documentation.

Wulf, Andrea. The Brother Gardeners: Botany, Empire & the Birth of an Obsession. 2009. (ENG., Illus.). 368p. 35.00 *(978-0-307-27023-8(8),* Knopf) Knopf Doubleday Publishing Group.

BOTANY—LABORATORY MANUALS

Berg, Linda R., et al. Introductory Botany: Plants, People & the Environment. 2nd ed. 2007. (ENG.). 160p. (C). per. 69.95 *(978-0-495-10509-1(0))* Brooks/Cole.

Chau. Exploring the World of Plants: General Botany Laboratory Manual. 2nd rev. ed. 2011. (ENG.). 288p. pap. 50.00 ***(978-0-7575-9625-4(8))*** Kendall Hunt Publishing Co.

Glass. Fundamentals of Plant Science, Lab Manual. 2007. (C). pap. 34.95 *(978-1-4180-0084-4(1))* Delmar Cengage Learning.

Hacisalihoglu, Gokhan. Plant Biology Concepts & Laboratory Manual. rev. ed. 2012. (ENG.). 114p. spiral bd. 57.95 ***(978-0-7575-8913-3(8))*** Kendall Hunt Publishing Co.

Keeley, Sterling C. Botany 101 Laboratory Manual. rev. ed. 2010. (ENG.). 174p. spiral bd. 53.45 *(978-0-7872-7858-8(0))* Kendall Hunt Publishing Co.

Rushforth, Samuel R., et al. A Photographic Atlas for the Botany Laboratory, Fifth Edition. 5th ed. 2008. (Illus.). 208p. (C). ring bd. 37.95 net. *(978-0-89582-770-8(0))* Morton Publishing Co.

Thompson, Rahmona. General Botany Laboratory Manual. rev. ed. 2010. (ENG.). 100p. spiral bd. 49.00 *(978-0-7575-4880-2(6))* Kendall Hunt Publishing Co.

Thorpe, Trevor A. & Yeung, Edward C. Plant Embryo Culture: Methods & Protocols. 2011. (Illus.). xi, 377p. ***(978-1-61737-988-8(3))*** Humana Pr.

BOTANY—MAPPING

see Vegetation Mapping

BOTANY—METHODOLOGY

Metzler, Kenneth J. & Barrett, Juliana P. The Vegetation of Connecticut: A Preliminary Classification. 2006. per. 14.95 *(978-0-942081-15-2(3))* Connecticut Dept. of Environmental Protection, Connecticut Geological & Natural History Survey.

Stohlgren, Thomas J. Measuring Plant Diversity: Lessons from the Field. 2006. (ENG., Illus.). 408p. 60.00 *(978-0-19-517233-1(7))* Oxford Univ. Pr., Inc.

Vercoe, Philip E., et al, eds. In vitro screening of plant resources for extra-nutritional attributes in ruminants: nuclear & related Methodologies: Nuclear & related Methodologies. 2009. (ENG., Illus.). xii, 247p. 179.00 *(978-90-481-3296-6(7),* 9048132967) Springer.

BOTANY—MORPHOLOGY
see Plant Morphology

BOTANY—NOMENCLATORS
see Plants—Nomenclature

BOTANY—NOMENCLATURE
see Plants—Nomenclature

BOTANY—NOMENCLATURE (POPULAR)
see Plant Names, Popular

BOTANY—ORGANOGRAPHY

Cronk, Quentin. The Molecular Organography of Plants. 2009. (ENG., Illus.). 384p. 165.00 *(978-0-19-955035-7(2))*; pap. 75.00 *(978-0-19-955036-4(0))* Oxford Univ. Pr., Inc.

Henslow, John Stevens. The Principles of Descriptive & Physiological Botany. 2009. (Cambridge Library Collection - Life Sciences Ser.). (ENG.). 340p. pap. 28.99 *(978-1-108-00186-1(6))* Cambridge Univ. Pr.

BOTANY—OUTLINES, SYLLABI, ETC.

Cram101 Textbook Reviews. Outlines & Highlights for Botany: An Introduction to Plant Biology by James D. Mauseth, ISBN. 2010. 282p. pap. 32.95 *(978-1-61698-439-7(2))* Cram101 Inc.

Cram101 Textbook Reviews. Outlines & Highlights for Fundamentals of Plant Science by Marihelen Glass. 2011. 248p. pap. 31.95 ***(978-1-61490-899-9(0))*** Cram101 Inc.

Cram101 Textbook Reviews & Cram101 Textbook Reviews. Outlines & Highlights for Introductory Botany by Linda R Berg, Isbn: 9780495384786 049538478x. 2011. 494p. pap. 36.95 ***(978-1-61490-041-2(8))*** Cram101 Inc.

Cram101 Textbook Reviews Staff. Outlines & Highlights for Introductory Plant Biology by Stern Isbn: 9780073314211. 2008. 276p. pap. 15.95 *(978-1-4288-6026-1(6))* Cram101 Inc.

BOTANY—PATHOLOGY
see Plant Diseases

BOTANY—PERIODICALS

Kader, Jean-Claude & Delseny, Michel, contrib. by. Advances in Botantical Research. 2011. (ENG.). 180p. 193.00 *(978-0-12-381518-7(5)*, Academic Pr.) Elsevier Science & Technology Bks.

BOTANY—PHYSIOLOGY
see Plant Physiology

BOTANY—PHYTOGRAPHY
see Botany

BOTANY—PICTORIAL WORKS

Anonymous. Icones Plantarum: Or Figures with Brief Descriptive Characters & Remarks of New or Rare Plants Selected from the Author's Herbarium. 2010. 294p. pap. 28.75 *(978-1-144-84529-0(7))* BiblioBazaar.

—Icones Plantarum: Or Figures, with Brief Descriptive Characters & Remarks, of New or Rare Plants, Selected from the Author's Herbarium, Volume 2. 2010. 300p. pap. 29.75 *(978-1-144-80359-7(4))* BiblioBazaar.

Applewood Books, creator. History of Vegetable Substances. 2008. (Cooking in America Ser.). (ENG.). 436p. pap. 26.95 *(978-1-4290-1219-5(6))* Applewood Bks.

Armengol, Manel, photos by. Herbarium. 2008. (ENG., Illus.). 156p. 54.00 *(978-84-7506-784-1(0))* Turner, Ediciones S.A. ESP. Dist: D.A.P./Distributed Art Pubs.

Bates, Joe & Nichols, Sarah. Celebrating Vallejo's Urban Forest. 2009. *(978-1-61623-808-7(9))* Independent Pub.

Blackwell, Lewis. The Life & Love of Trees. 2009. (ENG., Illus.). 200p. 50.00 *(978-0-473-15095-2(6))* Chronicle Bks. LLC.

Dodson, Carolyn. A Guide to Plants of the Northern Chihuahuan Desert. 2012. *(978-0-8263-5022-0(4))*; (ENG., Illus.). 208p. pap. 24.95 *(978-0-8263-5021-3(6))* Univ. of New Mexico Pr.

Dressendörfer, Werner. Thornton: Temple of Flora. Lamers-Schuetze, Petra, ed. l.t. ed. 2008. (Illus.). 110p. 150.00 *(978-3-8228-5273-6(2))* TASCHEN DEU. Dist: Ingram Pub. Services.

Hong, Deyuan, ed. Flora of China Illustrations, Vol. 13: Clusiaceae through Araliaceae. 2008. (Illus.). 491p. 125.00 *(978-1-930723-80-1(6))* Missouri Botanical Garden Pr.

—Flora of China Illustrations, Volume 10: Fabaceae. 2011. (Illus.). 680p. 175.00 *(978-1-930723-98-6(9))* Missouri Botanical Garden Pr.

—Flora of China Illustrations, Volume 12: Hippocastanaceae through Theaceae. 2008. (Illus.). 475p. 125.00 *(978-1-930723-79-5(2))* Missouri Botanical Garden Pr.

Hooker, Joseph Dalton. Icones Plantarum: Or Figures, with Brief Descriptive Characters & Remarks, of New or Rare Plants, Selected from the Author's Herbarium, Volume 8,andnb. 2010. 372p. pap. 32.75 *(978-1-142-69349-7(X))* BiblioBazaar.

Hooker, William Jackson. Icones Plantarum: Or, Figures, with Brief Descriptive Characters & Remarks of New or Rare Plants, Selected from the Author's Herbarium. 2011. (Cambridge Library Collection - Life Sciences Ser.). (ENG.). 210p. pap. 22.99 ***(978-1-108-03926-0(X))***; 214p. pap. 22.99 ***(978-1-108-03923-9(5))***; 212p. pap. 22.99 ***(978-1-108-03925-3(1))***; 214p. pap. 22.99 ***(978-1-108-03928-4(6))***; 214p. pap. 22.99 ***(978-1-108-03929-1(4))***; 212p. pap. 22.99 ***(978-1-108-03922-2(7))***; 224p. pap. 22.99 ***(978-1-108-03930-7(8))***; 212p. pap. 22.99 ***(978-1-108-03927-7(8))***; 214p. pap. 22.99 ***(978-1-108-03921-5(9))***; (Illus.). 214p. pap. 22.99 ***(978-1-108-03924-6(3))*** Cambridge Univ. Pr.

Hooker, William Jackson & Hooker, Joseph Dalton. Icones Plantarum: Or Figures with Brief Descriptive Characters & Remarks of New or Rare Plants Selected from the Author's Herbarium. 2010. 368p. pap. 32.75 *(978-1-144-92747-7(1))* BiblioBazaar.

—Icones Plantarum: Or Figures, with Brief Descriptive Characters & Remarks, of New or Rare Plants, Selected from the Author's Herbarium, Volume 3. 2010. 290p. pap. 28.75 *(978-1-144-81464-7(2))*; 384p. pap. 33.75 *(978-1-144-22829-1(8))* BiblioBazaar.

—Icones Plantarum: Or Figures, with Brief Descriptive Characters & Remarks, of New or Rare Plants, Selected from the Author's Herbarium, Volume 39,andn. 2010. 418p. pap. 34.75 *(978-1-144-05964-2(X))* BiblioBazaar.

—Icones Plantarum: Or Figures, with Brief Descriptive Characters & Remarks, of New or Rare Plants, Selected from the Author's Herbarium, Volume 4. 2010. 404p. pap. 34.75 *(978-1-144-93171-9(1))* BiblioBazaar.

—Icones Plantarum: Or Figures, with Brief Descriptive Characters & Remarks, of New or Rare Plants, Selected from the Author's Herbarium, Volume 5. 2010. 376p. pap. 33.75 *(978-1-144-92973-0(3))* BiblioBazaar.

—Icones Plantarum: Or Figures, with Brief Descriptive Characters & Remarks, of New or Rare Plants, Selected from the Author's Herbarium, Volume 6,andnb. 2010. 420p. pap. 34.75 *(978-1-144-77936-6(7))* BiblioBazaar.

—Icones Plantarum: Or Figures, with Brief Descriptive Characters & Remarks, of New or Rare Plants, Selected from the Author's Herbarium, Volume 7,andnb. 2010. 372p. pap. 32.75 *(978-1-142-68283-5(8))* BiblioBazaar.

—Icones Plantarum: Or Figures, with Brief Descriptive Characters & Remarks, of New or Rare Plants, Selected from the Author's Herbarium, Volume 8,andnb. 2010. 404p. pap. 34.75 *(978-1-144-78752-1(1))* BiblioBazaar.

Rushforth, Samuel R., et al. A Photographic Atlas for the Botany Laboratory, Fifth Edition. 5th ed. 2008. (Illus.). 208p. (C). ring bd. 37.95 net. *(978-0-89582-770-8(0))* Morton Publishing Co.

BOTANY—PRE-LINNEAN WORKS
see also Herbs; Medicine, Medieval

Becher, Karl & Klebs, Arnold C. A Catalogue of Early Herbals: Mostly from the Well-Known Library of Dr. Karl Becher, Karlsbad: with an Introduction by Arnold C. Klebs. 2008. (Illus.). 55.00 *(978-1-57898-646-0(X))* Martino Publishing.

Besler, Basilius. Besler's Book of Flowers & Plants: 73 Full-Color Plates from Hortus Eystettensis 1613. 2007. (Dover Pictorial Archive Ser.). (ENG., Illus.). 80p. per. 14.95 *(978-0-486-46005-5(3))* Dover Pubns., Inc.

Besler, Basilius & Dressendörfer, Werner. The Book of Plants: The Complete Plates. annot. ed. 2007. (ENG., Illus.). 443p. 29.99 *(978-3-8228-3809-9(8))* TASCHEN DEU. Dist: Ingram Pub. Services.

Parkinson, John. A Garden of Pleasant Flowers. 2009. 100p. pap. *(978-1-4432-9615-1(5))* Books LLC.

Roth, Dietrich, ed. Das Moller-Florilegium: Hans Simon Holtzbeckers Blumenalbum für den Bürgermeister Barthold Moller. 2007. (GER., Illus.). 336p. (C). 150.00 *(978-3-7774-3425-4(6))* Hirmer Verlag GmbH DEU. Dist: Brown, David Bk. Co., The.

Rumphius, Georgius Everhardus. The Ambonese Herbal Vol. 1, Bk. I: Containing All Sorts of Trees, That Bear Edible Fruits, & Are Husbanded by People, 6 vols. Beekman, E. M., tr. from DUT. 2011. (Illus.). 548p. 85.00 *(978-0-300-15370-5(8))* Yale Univ. Pr.

Woodward, Marcus. Leaves from Gerard's Herball. 2008. (Illus.). 324p. *(978-1-4437-3340-3(7))*, Pomona Pr.) Read Bks.

BOTANY—RESEARCH

De Rueda, Marta F. The Royal Botanical Expedition to the Nuevo Reyno de Granada: Mutis & His Contemporaries. Boyington, Benjamin & Sanders, Gabrielle, eds. (Illus.). 20p. (Orig.). pap. *(978-1-883592-09-7(7))* Permanent Mission of Colombia to the United Nations.

Evert, Ray F. Esau's Plant Anatomy: Meristems, Cells, & Tissues of the Plant Body: Their Structure, Function, & Development. 3rd rev. ed. 2006. (ENG., Illus.). 624p. 209.95 *(978-0-471-73843-5(3)*, Wiley-Liss) Wiley, John & Sons, Inc.

Gogi, M. Dildar, et al. Integrated Management of Melon Fruit Fly in Bitter Gourd. 2011. 220p. pap. ***(978-3-639-32724-3(1))*** VDM Verlag Dr. Mueller e.K.

Gomathi, R. & Subashini, S. R. Protective Chemicals on Salt Stressed Banana Plants. 2011. 100p. pap. ***(978-3-8454-0856-9(1))*** Lambert Academic Publishing.

Gupta, Surinder Kumar, ed. Advances in Botanical Research: Rapeseed Breeding. 2007. (Advances in Botanical Research Ser.). (ENG., Illus.). 584p. 193.00 *(978-0-12-374098-4(3)*, Academic Pr.) Elsevier Science & Technology Bks.

Hennig, Lars & Köhler, Claudia. Plant Developmental Biology: Methods & Protocols. 2010. (Illus.). xi, 448p. E-Book ***(978-1-60761-765-5(X))*** Humana Pr.

Hussain, Khalid, et al. Abiotic Stresses in Crops. 2010. 88p. pap. *(978-3-639-28224-5(8))* VDM Verlag Dr. Mueller e.K.

Jacquot, Jean-Pierre. Oxidative Stress & Redox Regulation in Plants. 2009. (ENG.). 350p. 193.00 *(978-0-12-378622-7(3)*, Academic Pr.) Elsevier Science & Technology Bks.

Kader, Jean-Claude & Delseny, Michel, contrib. by. Advances in Botanical Research. (ENG.). 2011. 506p. 193.00 ***(978-0-12-385851-1(8))*** 2010. 275p. 193.00 *(978-0-12-380868-4(5))* 2010. 224p. 193.00 *(978-0-12-380870-7(7))* 2010. 296p. 193.00 *(978-0-12-380872-1(3))* 2009. 228p. 193.00 *(978-0-12-374835-5(6))* 2008. 280p. 193.00 *(978-0-12-374600-9(0))* 2008. 288p. 193.00 *(978-0-12-374327-5(3))* Elsevier Science & Technology Bks. (Academic Pr.).

—Advances in Botanical Research: Incorporating Advances in Plant Pathology. 2007. (Advances in Botanical Research Ser.). (ENG., Illus.). 312p. 193.00 *(978-0-12-373705-2(2)*, Academic Pr.) Elsevier Science & Technology Bks.

—Advances in Botanical Research Pt. B: Biosynthesis of Vitamins in Plants - Vitamins B6, B8, B9, C, E, K. 2011. (ENG.). 337p. 193.00 ***(978-0-12-385853-5(4)***, Academic Pr.) Elsevier Science & Technology Bks.

Kader, Jean-Claude & Delseny, Michel, contrib. by. Advances in Botantical Research. 2011. (ENG.). 180p. 193.00 *(978-0-12-381518-7(5)*, Academic Pr.) Elsevier Science & Technology Bks.

Kader, Jean-Claude & Delseny, Michel, eds. Advances in Botanical Research. 2008. (ENG.). 300p. 193.00 *(978-0-12-374735-8(X)*, Academic Pr.) Elsevier Science & Technology Bks.

Kaushik, Vichitra, et al. Preliminary Phytochemical Investigation & Evaluation. 2011. 60p. pap. ***(978-3-8454-1233-7(X))*** Lambert Academic Publishing.

Lanza, Robert, ed. Stem Cell Anthology: From Stem Cell Biology, Tissue Engineering, Cloning, Regenerative Medicine & Biology. 2009. (ENG., Illus.). 422p. 155.00 *(978-0-12-375682-4(0)*, Academic Pr.) Elsevier Science & Technology Bks.

Leebens-Mack, J. H., ed. Developmental Genetics of the Flower. 2006. (Advances in Botanical Research Ser.). (ENG., Illus.). 616p. 193.00 *(978-0-12-005944-7(4)*, Academic Pr.) Elsevier Science & Technology Bks.

Munier-Jolain, Nathalie. Physiology of the Pea Crop. 2010. (ENG., Illus.). 298p. 99.95 *(978-1-57808-570-5(5)*, CRC Press) Taylor & Francis Group GBR. Dist: Taylor & Francis Group.

Rebeille, Fabrice & Douce, Roland. Biosynthesis of Vitamins in Plants Pt. A: Vitamins A, B1, B2, B3, B5. 2011. (ENG.). 322p. 193.00 ***(978-0-12-386479-6(8)***, Academic Pr.) Elsevier Science & Technology Bks.

Sadeghi, Tahereh & Sedaghat, Reza. Investigation of Advertisement Strategies Regarded to Iran's Pistachio. 2011. 148p. pap. ***(978-3-8443-1281-2(1))*** Lambert Academic Publishing.

BOTANY—STUDY AND TEACHING

Barrett, Katharine D., et al. Botany on Your Plate: Investigating the Plants We Eat. 2008. (Illus.). 88p. *(978-0-915873-49-4(4))* National Gardening Assn., Inc., The.

Johnson, Palmer O. Curricular Problems in Science at the College Level. 2009. (ENG.). 206p. pap. 50.00 *(978-0-8166-6066-7(2))* Univ. of Minnesota Pr.

Lawrence, Debbie & Lawrence, Richard. World of Plants. 2006. (God's Design for Life Ser.). (Illus.). 118p. per. 22.99 *(978-1-893345-88-1(2))* Answers in Genesis Ministries.

—The World of Plants. 3rd ed. 2009. (God's Design for Life Ser.). (Illus.). 144p. (J). pap. 24.99 *(978-1-60092-159-9(0))* Answers in Genesis Ministries.

Pranis, Eve & Cohen, Joy. Growlab: Activities for Growing Minds. 2nd ed. 2009. (Illus.). xi, 307p. *(978-0-915873-53-1(2))* National Gardening Assn., Inc., The.

Rushforth, Samuel R., et al. A Photographic Atlas for the Botany Laboratory, Fifth Edition. 5th ed. 2008. (Illus.). 208p. (C). ring bd. 37.95 net. *(978-0-89582-770-8(0))* Morton Publishing Co.

BOTANY—TERMINOLOGY

Gilbert-Carter, H. Glossary of the British Flora. 2009. (LAT & ENG.). 124p. pap. 28.99 *(978-0-521-11488-2(8))* Cambridge Univ. Pr.

Hart, G. T. Plants in Literature & Life. 2011. 488p. pap. ***(978-1-77067-441-7(1))*** FriesenPress.

Mandrin, Isabelle. Griechische und griechisch vermittelte Elemente in der Synonymenliste Alphita: Ein Beitrag zur Geschichte der medizinischen Fachterminologie im lateinischen Mittelalter. 2008. (Lateinische Sprache und Literatur des Mittelalters Ser.). (LAT, GRE & GER., Illus.). 269p. pap. *(978-3-03911-463-4(8))* Lang, Peter.

BOTANY—VARIATION

Halewood Michael, ed. Farmers' Crop Varieties & Farmers' Rights: Challenges in Taxonomy & Law. 2012. (Issues in Agricultural Biodiversity Ser.). (ENG., Illus.). 288p. 150.00 *(978-1-84407-890-5(6))* Earthscan GBR. Dist: Taylor & Francis Group.

—Farmers' Crop Varieties & Farmers' Rights: Challenges in Taxonomy & Law. 2012. (Issues in Agricultural Biodiversity Ser.). (ENG., Illus.). 288p. pap. 59.95 *(978-1-84407-891-2(4))* Earthscan LLC.

Semal, J., ed. Somaclonal Variations & Crop Improvement. 2010. (Advances in Agricultural Biotechnology Ser.). (ENG.). 292p. pap. 279.00 *(978-90-481-8295-4(6))*, 9048182956) Springer.

BOTANY—AFRICA

Abbadie, Luc, et al, eds. Lamto: Structure, Functioning, & Dynamics of a Savanna Ecosystem. 2010. (Ecological Studies). (Illus.). xx, 415p. pap. 179.00 *(978-1-4419-2854-2(5)*, 1441928545) Springer.

Abebrese, Samuel. Crossability of Nericas. 2011. 52p. pap. ***(978-3-8443-1984-2(0))*** Lambert Academic Publishing.

Anderson, David, et al. The Khat Controversy: Stimulating the Debate on Drugs. 2007. (Cultures of Consumption Ser.). (ENG., Illus.). 256p. pap. 31.95 *(978-1-84520-251-4(1))* Berg Pubs. GBR. Dist: Macmillan.

Annan, Kofi. Wound Healing Properties of Some Indigenous Ghanaian Plants. 2011. 224p. pap. ***(978-3-8433-7169-8(5))*** Lambert Academic Publishing.

Ball, John. Terrestrial African Orchids. 2009. 270p. pap. 95.00 *(978-0-557-18333-3(2))* Lulu Enterprises Inc.

Beentje, H. J. & Ghazanfar, S. A., eds. Flora of Tropical East Africa: Apocynaceae II. 2012. (Royal Botanic Gardens, Kew-Flora of Tropical East Africa Ser.). (Illus.). 350p. pap. 124.00 *(978-1-84246-396-3(9))* Kew Publishing GBR. Dist: Chicago Distribution Ctr.

—Flora of Tropical East Africa: Cyperaceae. 2010. (Royal Botanic Gardens, Kew-Flora of Tropical East Africa Ser.). (Illus.). 470p. pap. 154.00 *(978-1-84246-397-0(7))* Kew Publishing GBR. Dist: Chicago Distribution Ctr.

—Flora of Tropical East Africa: Malvaceae. 2010. (Royal Botanic Gardens, Kew-Flora of Tropical East Africa Ser.). (Illus.). 174p. pap. 91.00 *(978-1-84246-189-1(3))* Kew Publishing GBR. Dist: Chicago Distribution Ctr.

—Flora of Tropical East Africa: Solanaceae. 2012. (Royal Botanic Gardens, Kew-Flora of Tropical East Africa Ser.). (Illus.). 120p. pap. 52.00 *(978-1-84246-395-6(0))* Kew Publishing GBR. Dist: Chicago Distribution Ctr.

Beentje, Henk. Aspleniaceae. 2008. (Illus.). 75p. pap. 50.00 ***(978-1-84246-202-7(4))*** Kew Publishing GBR. Dist: Chicago Distribution Ctr.

Beentje, Henk. Flora of Tropical East Africa: Commelinaceae. 2012. (Royal Botanic Gardens, Kew - Flora of Tropical East Africa Ser.). (Illus.). 450p. pap. 75.00 *(978-1-84246-436-6(1))* Kew Publishing GBR. Dist: Chicago Distribution Ctr.

Beentje, Henk J. & Ghazanfar, S. A., eds. Flora of Tropical East Africa: Acanthaceae II, 2 vols. 2010. (Royal Botanic Gardens, Kew-Flora of Tropical East Africa Ser.). (Illus.). 350p. pap. 136.00 *(978-1-84246-386-4(1))* Kew Publishing GBR. Dist: Chicago Distribution Ctr.

Bobe, René, et al, eds. Hominin Environments in the East African Pliocene: An Assessment of the Faunal Evidence. 2010. (Vertebrate Paleobiology & Paleoanthropology Ser.). xx, 356p. pap. 129.00 *(978-90-481-6791-3(4)*, 9048167914) Springer.

Borokini, Temitope. Conservation & Utilization of Medicinal Plants in Nigeri. 2011. 76p. pap. ***(978-3-8433-9184-9(X))*** Lambert Academic Publishing.

Carney, Judith & Rosomoff, Richard Nicholas. In the Shadow of Slavery: Africa's Botanical Legacy in the Atlantic World. 2011. (ENG., Illus.). 296p. pap. 18.95 *(978-0-520-26996-5(9))* Univ. of California Pr.

Chakanda, Robert. Rice Genetic Diversity in Post-War Sierra Leone. 2010. 128p. pap. *(978-3-8383-6126-0(1))* Lambert Academic Publishing.

Cheek, Martin, et al. The Plants of Dom, Bamenda Highlands, Cameroon: A Conservation Checklist. 2010. (Illus.). 162p. pap. 64.00 *(978-1-84246-398-7(5))* Kew Publishing GBR. Dist: Chicago Distribution Ctr.

Court, Doreen. Succulent Flora of Southern Africa. 2011. 336p. 37.95 *(978-1-77007-587-0(9))* Random Hse. Struik (Pty.), Ltd. ZAF. Dist: International Publishers Marketing.

Crouch, Neil, et al. Ferns of Southern Africa: A Comprehensive Guide. 2011. (Illus.). 760p. pap. 50.00 *(978-1-77007-910-6(6))* Random Hse. Struik (Pty.), Ltd. ZAF. Dist: International Publishers Marketing.

Dlamini, Cliff. Establishing University Botanical Gardens. 2011. 60p. pap. ***(978-3-8454-1422-5(7))*** Lambert Academic Publishing.

—Invasive Alien Plants Management Framework. 2011. 104p. pap. ***(978-3-8454-0681-7(X))*** Lambert Academic Publishing.

Dzobo, Kevin. Characterization of Polyphenols in Desiccation Tolerant Plants. 2011. 164p. pap. ***(978-3-8443-1708-4(2))*** Lambert Academic Publishing.

Eni, Angela. Viruses Infecting Yam in Ghana, Togo & Benin in West Afric. 2011. 164p. pap. ***(978-3-8443-8249-5(6))*** Lambert Academic Publishing.

Enock, Amboga, et al. The Antimycobacterial Efficacy of Herbs: Antimycobacterial Efficacy of Selected Herbs Used by Herbalists to Treat Tuberculosis in Kisii County in Kenya. 2011. 52p. pap. ***(978-3-639-34151-5(1))*** VDM Verlag Dr. Mueller e.K.

Exell, A. W. Flora Zambesiaca: Dioscoreaceae, Taccaceae, Burmanniaceae, Pandanaceae, Velloziaceae, Colchicaceae, Liliaceae, Smilacaceae. 2010. (Illus.). 208p. pap. 118.00 *(978-1-84246-193-8(1))* Kew Publishing GBR. Dist: Chicago Distribution Ctr.

Fajinmi, Ayodele. Epidemiology & Control of Pepper Veinal Mottle Virus Disease of Pepper. 2010. 136p. pap. *(978-3-8383-8484-9(9))* Lambert Academic Publishing.

Fowler, Dennis G. Zambian Plants Used as Traditional Fever Cures. 2011. 294p. pap. 100.00 *(978-1-84246-460-1(4))* Kew Publishing GBR. Dist: Chicago Distribution Ctr.

Gemessa, Sinafikeh. Economic Analysis of Farmers' Preferences for Crop Variety Traits. 2010. 132p. pap. *(978-3-8383-4554-3(1))* Lambert Academic Publishing.

Ghazanfar, Shahina A., et al. Scrophulariaceae. 2008. (Illus.). 211p. pap. 113.00 ***(978-1-84246-192-1(3))*** Kew Publishing GBR. Dist: Chicago Distribution Ctr.

Harvey, Yvette & Tchiengue, Barthelemy. The Plants of Lebialem Highlands, Cameroon: A Conservation Checklist. 2010. (Illus.). 170p. pap. 64.00 *(978-1-84246-399-4(3))* Kew Publishing GBR. Dist: Chicago Distribution Ctr.

Heath, Alison & Heath, Roger. Plants of Northern Botswana: Including the Okavango Delta. 2010. (Illus.). 593p. 125.00 *(978-1-84246-183-9(4))* Kew Publishing GBR. Dist: Chicago Distribution Ctr.

Hooker, William Jackson, ed. Niger Flora: Or, an Enumeration of the Plants of Western Tropical Africa. 2011. (Cambridge Library Collection - Life Sciences Ser.). (ENG., Illus.). 668p. pap. 48.00 *(978-1-108-03038-0(6))* Cambridge Univ. Pr.

Kolech, Semagn Asredie. Associations among Yield & Yield Related Characters in Potato. 2011. 112p. pap. ***(978-3-8433-9319-5(2))*** Lambert Academic Publishing.

La Croix, Isobyl. African Orchids in the Wild & in Cultivation. 2009. (ENG.). 423p. pap. 39.95 *(978-1-60469-121-4(2)*, 1604691212) Timber Pr., Inc.

Makumbe, Milton. Woody Plant Species Diversity & Structure on Termitaria in Zimbabwe. 2010. 104p. pap. *(978-3-8383-7845-9(8))* Lambert Academic Publishing.

Minzangi, Kazadi. Study of Oil from Wild Plants of Kivu, Dr Congo. 2011. 116p. pap. ***(978-3-8443-2388-7(0))*** Lambert Academic Publishing.

Mohammed, Maarouf. Forage Sorghum Hybrids. 2010. 104p. pap. *(978-3-8383-7932-6(2))* Lambert Academic Publishing.

Mukankusi, Clare. Common Bean Improvement. 2011. 204p. pap. *(978-3-8383-8925-7(5))* Lambert Academic Publishing.

Ndenecho, Emmanuel Neba. Ethnobotanic Resources of Tropical Montane Forests Indigenous Uses of Plants in the Cameroon Highland Ecoregion. 2011. 242p. pap. *(978-9956-717-30-9(4))* Langaa Research & Publishing Common Initiative Group.

Nyananyo, B. L. Plants from the Niger Delta. 2007. (Illus.). 403p. pap. *(978-978-37314-6-2(7))* Onyoma Research Publications NGA. Dist: Michigan State Univ. Pr.

Obakeng, Obolokile Thothi. Soil Moisture Dynamics & Evapotranspiration at the Fringe of the Botswana Kalahari, with Emphasis on Deep Rooting Vegetation. 2007. (Illus.). xiv, 225p. pap. *(978-90-6164-254-1(X))* International Trade Ctr.

Olufokunbi, Olumide. Mushroom & Sclerotium of Pleurotus Tuberregium in Nigeri. 2011. 80p. pap. *(978-3-8443-1200-9(3))* Lambert Academic Publishing.

Onana, Jean-Michel & Cheek, Martin. Red Data Book of the Flowering Plants of Cameroon: IUCN Global Assessments. 2012. (Illus.). 500p. pap. 140.00 *(978-1-84246-429-8(9))* Kew Publishing GBR. Dist: Chicago Distribution Ctr.

Onana, Jean-Michel, et al. The Plants of Mefou proposed National Park, Central Province, Cameroon: A Conservation Checklist. 2012. (Illus.). 225p. pap. 73.00 *(978-1-84246-400-7(0))* Kew Publishing GBR. Dist: Chicago Distribution Ctr.

Pakia, Mohammed & Pakia, Mohamed. African Traditional Plant Knowledge Today: An Ethnobotanical Study of the Digo at the Kenya Coast. 2007. (Beitrage Zur Afrika-Forschung Ser.). (ENG., Illus.). 224p. (gr. 11). pap. 49.95 *(978-3-8258-9055-8(2))* Lit Verlag DEU. Dist: Transaction Pubs.

Paton, A. J. Lamiaceae. Beentje, H. J. & Ghazanfar, S. A., eds. 2010. (Royal Botanic Gardens, Kew-Flora of Tropical East Africa Ser.). (Illus.). 432p. pap. 167.00 *(978-1-84246-372-7(1))* Kew Publishing GBR. Dist: Chicago Distribution Ctr.

Robey, Melvin J. African Violets - Gifts from Nature: The Series. 2010. (Illus.). 156p. pap. 43.49 *(978-1-4490-5100-6(6))* AuthorHouse.

Shittu, Lukeman A. Joseph. Reproductive Impacts of Sesame Leaves Lignans in Adult Males Sd Rats. 2010. 224p. pap. *(978-3-8383-8206-7(4))* Lambert Academic Publishing.

Steentoft, Margaret. Flowering Plants in West Africa. 2008. (ENG.). 356p. (C). pap. 74.00 *(978-0-521-06312-8(4))* Cambridge Univ. Pr.

Stewart, Joyce, et al. Angraecoid Orchids: Species from the African Region. 2006. (ENG., Illus.). 432p. 69.95 *(978-0-88192-788-7(0)*, 0881927880) Timber Pr., Inc.

Swanevelder, Dirk & Fisher, Roger C. Clivia: Nature & Nurture. 2012. (Illus.). 224p. 44.95 *(978-1-875093-61-8(3))* International Publishers Marketing.

Timberlake, Jonathan. Flora Zambesiaca. 2011. (Royal Botanic Gardens, Kew - Flora Zambesiaca Ser.). (Illus.). 92p. pap. 44.00 *(978-1-84246-209-6(1))* Kew Publishing GBR. Dist: Chicago Distribution Ctr.

Timberlake, Jonathan, ed. Flora Zambesiaca Volume 13 Part 4: Xyridaceae, Eriocaulaceae, Typhaceae, Restionaceae, Flagellariaceae, Juncaceae, Musaceae, Strelitziaceae, Costaceae, Zingiberaceae, Cannaceae, Marantaceae. 2010. (Royal Botanic Gardens, Kew - Flora Zambesiaca Ser.). (Illus.). 166p. pap. 66.00 *(978-1-84246-194-5(X))* Kew Publishing GBR. Dist: Chicago Distribution Ctr.

van der Burgt, Xander, ed. Systematics & Conservation of African Plants: Proceedings of the 18th AETFAT Congress, Yaounde, Cameroon. 2010. (Illus.). 882p. pap. 182.00 *(978-1-84246-388-8(8))* Kew Publishing GBR. Dist: Chicago Distribution Ctr.

Woldemariam, Ephrem Tilahun. Trace Metals in Ethiopian Khat. 2010. 68p. pap. *(978-3-639-26822-5(9))* VDM Verlag Dr. Mueller e.K.

BOTANY—ALASKA

Kelso, Fran. Plant Lore of an Alaskan Island: Foraging in the Kodiak Archepelago. 2011. 348p. pap. 82.00 *(978-1-4634-2395-7(0))* AuthorHouse.

Laursen, Gary A. & Seppelt, Rodney David. Common Interior Alaska Cryptogams: Fungi, Lichenicolous Fungi, Lichenized Fungi, Slime Molds, Mosses & Liverworts. 2nd ed. 2009. (ENG., Illus.). 256p. pap. 28.95 *(978-1-60223-058-3(7))* Univ. of Alaska Pr.

Smith, Ronald L. Interior & Northern Alaska: A Natural History. 2008. (ENG., Illus.). 406p. pap. 28.95 *(978-1-887542-74-6(4))* Book Pubs. Network.

BOTANY—AMERICA

Allen, Bruce. Moss Flora of Central America: Part 3. Anomodontaceae — Symphyodontaceae. 2010. (Monographs in Systematic Botany from the Missouri Botanical Garden). (Illus.). 731p. 110.00 *(978-1-930723-95-5(4))* Missouri Botanical Garden Pr.

Griffith, Lawrence. Flowers & Herbs of Early America. 2010. (ENG., Illus.). 304p. 24.00 *(978-0-300-16454-1(8))* Yale Univ. Pr.

Hammel, B. E., et al, eds. Manual de Plantas de Costa Rica Vol. VI: Dicotiledóneas: Haloragaceae-Phytolaccaceae (MSB 111) 2007. (Monographs in Systematic Botany from the Missouri Botanical Garden). (SPA.). 125.00 *(978-1-930723-60-3(1))* Missouri Botanical Garden Pr.

McPherson, Stewart. Pitcher Plants of the Americas. 2006. (Illus.). 320p. 44.95 *(978-0-939923-75-5(0))*; pap. 34.95 *(978-0-939923-74-8(2))* McDonald & Woodward Publishing Co., The.

Perry, Jesse P. The Pines of Mexico & Central America. 2009. (ENG.). 234p. pap. 39.95 *(978-1-60469-110-8(7)*, 1604691107) Timber Pr., Inc.

Staller, John Edward. Maize Cobs & Cultures: History of Zea mays L. History of Zea mays L. 2009. (ENG., Illus.). x, 262p. 179.00 *(978-3-642-04505-9(7)*, 3642045057) Springer.

Wainwright, Mark. Tropical Plants of Costa Rica: A Guide to Native & Exotic Flora. 2007. (Illus.). 529p. 76.95 *(978-0-8014-4588-0(4)*, Comstock Publishing Assocs.) Cornell Univ. Pr.

BOTANY—ANTARCTICA

Aleksandrova, Vera D. & Aleksandrova, V. D. The Arctic & Antarctic: Their Division into Geobotanical Areas. Lvve, Doris, tr. from RUS. 2009. (ENG., Illus.). 264p. pap. 38.99 *(978-0-521-11426-4(8))* Cambridge Univ. Pr.

BOTANY—ARCTIC REGIONS

Aleksandrova, Vera D. & Aleksandrova, V. D. The Arctic & Antarctic: Their Division into Geobotanical Areas. Lvve, Doris, tr. from RUS. 2009. (ENG., Illus.). 264p. pap. 38.99 *(978-0-521-11426-4(8))* Cambridge Univ. Pr.

Ghazanfar, S. A. & Fisher, M., eds. Vegetation of the Arabian Peninsula. 2010. (Geobotany Ser.). 372p. pap. 349.00 *(978-90-481-5020-5(5)*, 9048150205) Springer.

Golovatch, S. I., ed. Species & Communities in Extreme Environments. 2009. 530p. 187.50 *(978-954-642-452-5(8))* Pensoft Pubs. BGR. Dist: Coronet Bks.

BOTANY—ASIA

Abbasi, Arshad Mehmood, et al. Medicinal Plant Biodiversity of Lesser Himalayas-Pakistan. 2011. (ENG., Illus.). xii, 220p. 189.00 *(978-1-4614-1574-9(8)*, 1461415748) Springer.

Acharya, Ram Prasad, et al. Value Chain Analysis of Maps of Mid & Far Western Region of Nepal. 2011. 116p. pap. *(978-3-8454-0734-0(4))* Lambert Academic Publishing.

Aftab, Javed & Shameel, Mustafa. Phycochemistry & Bioactivity of Some Algae from Miani Hor. Balochistan. 2010. 236p. pap. *(978-3-639-26821-8(0))* VDM Verlag Dr. Mueller e.K.

Ahmed, Ashfaque & Hoque, Sirajul. Ecology of the Coastal Zone of Bangladesh. 2011. 68p. pap. *(978-3-8443-0289-9(1))* Lambert Academic Publishing.

Aly, Khan. Nematodes Associated with Chilli & Their Control: Control Using Organic Amendments & Chemical Nematicides. 2011. 64p. pap. *(978-3-639-34282-6(8))* VDM Verlag Dr. Mueller e.K.

Aly, Khan & Samad, M. Afzal. Association of Nematodes with Date-Palm in Balochistan: Association of Nematode with Date-Palm in Lasbela District, Balochistan. 2011. 60p. pap. *(978-3-639-33406-7(X))* VDM Verlag Dr. Mueller e.K.

Askari, S. H. Abid. Poisonous Plants of Pakistan. 2011. (ENG., Illus.). 400p. 49.99 *(978-0-19-597789-9(0))* Oxford Univ. Pr., Inc.

Boroding-Grabovskay. Plants of Central Asia Vol 12. 2007. (Plants of Central Asia Ser.). (ENG.). 206p. 119.95 *(978-1-57808-441-8(5))* BIOS Scientific Publishers Ltd. GBR. Dist: Taylor & Francis Group.

Chalooddong, Kulthida & P. Shivakoti, Ganesh. An Economic Analysis of Oil Palm Plantation in Northeastern Thailand. 2011. 128p. pap. *(978-3-8443-0354-4(5))* Lambert Academic Publishing.

Chandra, S. & Srivastava, M., eds. Pteridology in the New Millennium: NBRI Golden Jubilee Volume in Honour of Professor B. K. Nayar. 2010. 544p. pap. 235.00 *(978-90-481-6222-2(X)*, 904816222X) Springer.

Cheema, Uzman Bashir & Iqbal Sultan, Javed. Fodder Tree Leaves. 2010. 76p. pap. *(978-3-8383-9751-1(7))* Lambert Academic Publishing.

, Collective, Collective. Singapore Biodiversity: An Encyclopedia of the Natural Environment. 2011. (ENG., Illus.). 496p. 50.00 *(978-981-4260-08-4(8)*, Didier Millet,Csi) Continental Sales, Inc.

Cope, T. A. Flora of the Arabian Peninsula & Socotra Pt. 1, 5, part 1. 2009. (ENG., Illus.). 408p. (gr. 17). 375.00 *(978-0-7486-3457-6(6))* Edinburgh Univ. Pr. GBR. Dist: Columbia Univ. Pr.

Cox, Peter, et al. Seeds of Adventure: In Search of Plants. 2008. (ENG., Illus.). 416p. *(978-1-870673-58-7(1)*, Antique Collectors Club Dist) Antique Collectors' Club.

de Kok, Rogier & Utteridge, Tim. Plants of East Sabah. 2010. (Illus.). 176p. pap. 45.00 *(978-1-84246-378-9(0))* Kew Publishing GBR. Dist: Chicago Distribution Ctr.

Fm, Prof Dr Bilqees, et al. Nematodes Associated with Apple. 2010. 108p. pap. *(978-3-639-25991-9(2))* VDM Verlag Dr. Mueller e.K.

Fm, Prof Dr Bilqees, et al. Nematodes Associated with Banana in Karachi, Sindh, Pakistan: Nematodes in Banana Root. 2011. 148p. pap. *(978-3-639-32498-3(6))* VDM Verlag Dr. Mueller e.K.

Gardezi, Syed Dilnawaz & Gohor, Maria. Genetic Diversity of Olea Caspidat. 2010. 60p. pap. *(978-3-8383-8141-1(6))* Lambert Academic Publishing.

Gardezi, Syed Dilnawaz & M Ishtiaq Khaliq. Genetic Diversity in Baburi. 2010. 68p. pap. *(978-3-8383-8095-7(9))* Lambert Academic Publishing.

Ghafoor, Sajid Ul, et al. Molecular Analysis of Ephedra Species Found in Pakistan. 2010. 56p. pap. *(978-3-639-23293-6(3))* VDM Verlag Dr. Mueller e.K.

Ghimire, Surya Kant. Molecular & Genetic Analysis of Asian Wheat. 2011. 176p. pap. *(978-3-8443-0986-7(1))* Lambert Academic Publishing.

Grubov, V. I. Plants of Central Asia. 2007. (Plants of Central Asia Ser.). (ENG.). 148p. 79.95 *(978-1-57808-123-3(8))* BIOS Scientific Publishers Ltd. GBR. Dist: Taylor & Francis Group.

Hooker, Joseph Dalton. Himalayan Journals: Or, Notes of a Naturalist in Bengal, the Sikkim & Nepal Himalayas, the Khasia Mountains, Etc. 2011. (Cambridge Library Collection - Life Sciences Ser.). (ENG., Illus.). 522p. pap. 37.99 *(978-1-108-02936-0(1))*; 462p. pap. 34.99 *(978-1-108-02935-3(3))* Cambridge Univ. Pr.

Iqbal, Muhammad, et al. Bakanae Disease of Rice in Pakistan. 2011. 96p. pap. *(978-3-639-32593-5(1))* VDM Verlag Dr. Mueller e.K.

Khan, Dr Aly, et al. Nematodes Associated with Mango (Mangifera Indica L.) & Their Control: Using Plant Extracts & Histopathology. 2011. 56p. pap. *(978-3-639-32382-5(3))* VDM Verlag Dr. Mueller e.K.

Khan, Hafiz Azhar Ali, et al. Gall Formation in Mango, Mangifera Indica L. Varietal Preference, Intra-Tree Distribution & the Factors Mediating Gall Abundance. 2011. 100p. pap. *(978-3-639-33584-2(8))* VDM Verlag Dr. Mueller e.K.

Kingdon-Ward, Frank. Burma's Icy Mountains. 2nd ed. 2006. (ENG., Illus.). 296p. pap. 26.95 *(978-974-524-084-1(2))* Orchid Pr. THA. Dist: National Bk. Network.

—Return to the Irrawaddy. 2007. (ENG., Illus.). 224p. pap. 26.00 *(978-974-524-086-5(9))* Orchid Pr. THA. Dist: National Bk. Network.

Landsberger, Benno. Die Fauna des alten Mesopotamien nach der 14. (Ancient Mesopotamian Texts & Studies). reprint ed. 34.50 *(978-0-404-18190-1(2))* AMS Pr., Inc.

MacLeod, Bill. Doctors Tell All about Noni Juice. 2009. 44p. pap. 16.99 *(978-1-4490-0871-0(2))* AuthorHouse.

Malyschev, L. I., ed. Flora of Siberia: Asteraceae, 12. 2007. (Flora of Siberia Ser.). (ENG.). 222p. 119.95 *(978-1-57808-111-0(4))* BIOS Scientific Publishers Ltd. GBR. Dist: Taylor & Francis Group.

Pandey, Hp & SK Chauhan. Turmeric: The Living Gold of Nature. 2011. 168p. pap. *(978-3-8433-8349-3(9))* Lambert Academic Publishing.

Parvin, Most. Nazma, et al. Chemical & Biological Investigations of Dillenia Indic. 2011. 124p. pap. *(978-3-8383-0255-3(9))* Lambert Academic Publishing.

Pokharel, Swechha. Biological Hazards Associated with Street Foods of Nepal. 2011. 116p. pap. *(978-3-8443-0969-0(1))* Lambert Academic Publishing.

Razzaq, Abdul, et al. Ethnomedicinal Potential of Vascular Plants of Changa Valley. 2010. 68p. pap. *(978-3-639-27304-5(4))* VDM Verlag Dr. Mueller e.K.

Razzaq, Kashif. Foliar Zinc Affects Growth, Yield & Quality of Kinnow Mandarin. 2011. 108p. pap. *(978-3-8443-0123-6(2))* Lambert Academic Publishing.

Shittu, Lukeman A. Joseph. Reproductive Impacts of Sesame Leaves Lignans in Adult Males Sd Rats. 2010. 224p. pap. *(978-3-8383-8206-7(4))* Lambert Academic Publishing.

Siebert, Stephen F. The Nature & Culture of Rattan: Reflections on Vanishing Life in the Forests of Southeast Asia. 2012. (Illus.). xii, 145p. 44.00 *(978-0-8248-3536-1(0))* Univ. of Hawaii Pr.

Tanaka, Yoshitaka & Van Ke, Nguyen. Edible Wild Plants of Vietnam: The Bountiful Garden. 2007. (ENG., Illus.). 176p. pap. 26.00 *(978-974-524-089-6(3))* Orchid Pr. THA. Dist: National Bk. Network.

Thompson, Reginald C. A Dictionary of Assyrian Botany. (Ancient Mesopotamian Texts & Studies). reprint ed. 45.00 *(978-0-404-18221-2(6))* AMS Pr., Inc.

Thorogood, Chris. Alkaloids: Properties, Applications & Pharmacological Effects. Cassiano, Nicole M., ed. 2010. (Biochemistry Research Trends Ser.). 98.00 *(978-1-61668-974-2(9))* Nova Science Pubs., Inc.

Thorogood, Chris, ed. The Malaysian Nepenthes: Evolutionary & Taxonomic Perspectives. 2010. (Botanical Research & Practices Ser.). 89.00 *(978-1-61668-306-1(6))* Nova Science Pubs., Inc.

Uprety, Yadav & C. Poudel, Ram. Medicinal Plants of Nepal. 2010. 124p. pap. *(978-3-8383-7738-4(9))* Lambert Academic Publishing.

Walravens, Hartmut. Joseph Franz Rock (1884-1962). Tagebuch der Reise von Chieng Mai nach Yunnan, 1921-1922. Briefwechsel mit C. S. Sargent, University of Washington, Johannes Schubert und Robert Koc. 2007. (Beitrage zur Kultur- und Geistesgeschichte Asiens Ser.). (GER.). 580p. (C). pap. 105.00 *(978-3-7001-3830-3(X))* Austrian Academy of Sciences Press AUT. Dist: Brown, David Bk. Co., The.

Wiart, Christophe. Medicinal Plants from the East. 2010. (ENG., Illus.). 712p. 155.95 *(978-1-904761-85-3(2))* Nottingham Univ. Pr. GBR. Dist: Independent Pubs. Group.

Zashim Uddin, Dr. Mohammad, et al. Plant Genetic Resources of Rema-Kalenga Wildlife Sanctuary. 2011. 128p. pap. *(978-3-8443-0343-8(X))* Lambert Academic Publishing.

BOTANY—AUSTRALIA

Australian Biological Resources Study. Flora of Australia Volume 57: Lichens 5. 2009. (Flora of Australia Ser.). 708p. 122.00 *(978-0-643-09688-2(4))* CSIRO Publishing AUS. Dist: Stylus Publishing, LLC.

Australian Biological Resources Study Staff. Flora of Australia: Poaceae 2. 2009. (Flora of Australia Ser.). (Illus.). 420p. 115.00 *(978-0-643-09629-5(9))* CSIRO Publishing AUS. Dist: Stylus Publishing, LLC.

—Flora of Australia Vol. 57: Lichens 5. 2009. (Flora of Australia Ser.). 708p. pap. 95.00 *(978-0-643-09689-9(2))* CSIRO Publishing AUS. Dist: Stylus Publishing, LLC.

Australian Biological Resources Study Staff, ed. & told to. Flora of Australia: Poaceae 2. 2009. (Flora of Australia Ser.). (Illus.). 420p. pap. 97.00 *(978-0-643-09630-1(2))* CSIRO Publishing AUS. Dist: Stylus Publishing, LLC.

Chapman, Lynne, et al. Tea Roses: Old Roses for Warm Gardens. 2008. (Illus.). 240p. 59.95 *(978-1-877058-67-7(X))* Rosenberg Publishing Pty, Ltd. AUS. Dist: International Specialized Bk. Services.

Clarke, Philip. Aboriginal People & Their Plants. 2007. (Illus.). 192p. 39.95 *(978-1-877058-51-6(3))* Rosenberg Publishing Pty, Ltd. AUS. Dist: International Specialized Bk. Services.

Clarke, Philip A. Aboriginal Plant Collectors: Botanists & Australian Aboriginal People in the Nineteenth Century. 2008. (Illus.). 191p. (C). 39.95 *(978-1-877058-68-4(8))* Rosenberg Publishing Pty, Ltd. AUS. Dist: International Specialized Bk. Services.

CSIRO Pub. Staff. Winteraceae to Platanaceae, Vol. 2. 2007. (Flora of Australia Ser.). (Illus.). 504p. 125.00 *(978-0-643-05967-2(9))*; pap. 106.00 *(978-0-643-05968-9(7))* CSIRO Publishing AUS. Dist: Stylus Publishing, LLC.

Gregory, J. W. Australia. 2012. (ENG.). 136p. pap. 19.99 *(978-1-107-63940-9(9))* Cambridge Univ. Pr.

Head, Lesley, et al. Ingrained: A Human Bio-Geography of Wheat. 2012. (Illus.). 236p. 99.95 *(978-1-4094-3787-1(6))* Ashgate Publishing Co.

Hopper, Stephen D. Life on the Rocks: The Art of Survival. 2nd ed. 2008. (ENG.). 192p. 25.00 *(978-1-921361-28-9(X))* Fremantle Pr. AUS. Dist: Independent Pubs. Group.

Huisman, John M. Algae of Australia: Nemaliales. 2006. (Illus.). 164p. 79.95 *(978-0-643-09378-2(8))* CSIRO Publishing AUS. Dist: Stylus Publishing, LLC.

Jones, David L. & Jones, David. A Complete Guide to Native Orchids in Australia: Including the Island Territories. 2007. (ENG., Illus.). 496p. 59.95 *(978-1-877069-12-3(4))* New Holland Pubs. Pty, Ltd. AUS. Dist: Tuttle Publishing.

Kraft, Gerald T. Algae of Australia: The Marine Benthic Algae of Lord Howe Island & the Southern Great Barrier Reef. 2007. 356p. 110.00 *(978-0-643-09432-1(6))* CSIRO Publishing AUS. Dist: Stylus Publishing, LLC.

Lofts, Graeme & Gill, Peg. Australia's Dangerous Creatures for Dummies. 2008. (ENG.). 346p. pap. 19.99 *(978-0-7314-0722-4(9)*, For Dummies) Wiley, John & Sons, Inc.

Persely, Denis. Diseases of Fruit Crops in Australia. House, Susan & Cooke, Tony, eds. 2010. (Illus.). 288p. 85.00 *(978-0-643-06971-8(2))* CSIRO Publishing AUS. Dist: Stylus Publishing, LLC.

Scherrer, Pascal. Monitoring Alpine Vegetation Change. 2011. 332p. pap. *(978-3-8443-9846-5(5))* Lambert Academic Publishing.

Stock, Daniel. The Dynamics of Lantana Invasion of Subtropical Rainforest. 2008. 356p. pap. *(978-3-639-05362-8(3))* VDM Verlag Dr. Mueller e.K.

Sweedman, Luke & Merritt, David, eds. Australian Seeds: A Guide to their collection, Identification & Biology. 2006. (Illus.). 272p. pap. 61.95 *(978-0-643-09298-3(6))* CSIRO Publishing AUS. Dist: Stylus Publishing, LLC.

BOTANY—BARBADOS

Carrington, Sean. Wild Plants of Barbados. 2nd ed. 2007. (MacMillan Caribbean Natural History Ser.). (ENG., Illus.). 248p. pap. 15.00 *(978-1-4050-9407-8(9))* Macmillan Caribbean GBR. Dist: Interlink Publishing Group, Inc.

BOTANY—BRAZIL

Baptista, Dalton Holland & Harding, Patricia A. Orchids of Brazil: Oncidiinae - Part 1, vol. 1. 2011.Tr. of Orquídeas do Brasil. (ENG., Illus.). 224p. 46.00 *(978-0-9836747-0-2(1))* Harding, Patricia Ann.

Hind, D J N & Miranda, E. B. Preliminary List of the Compositeae in Northeastern Brazil. 2007. 104p. pap. 64.00 *(978-1-84246-219-5(9))* Kew Publishing GBR. Dist: Chicago Distribution Ctr.

Lack, H. Walter. Martius - Book of Palm. Lamers-Schutze, Petra, ed. 2009. (GER, FRE & ENG., Illus.). 450p. 150.00 *(978-3-8365-1779-9(5))* TASCHEN DEU. Dist: Ingram Pub. Services.

Lucas, E., et al. Preliminary List of the Myrtaceae in Northeastern Brazil: Repatriation of Kew Herbarium Data for the Flora of Northeastern Brazil Series, Volume 5. 2012. (Royal Botanic Gardens, Kew - Repatriation of Kew Herbarium Data for the Flora Of Ser.). (POR., Illus.). 120p. pap. 58.00 *(978-1-84246-428-1(0))* Kew Publishing GBR. Dist: Chicago Distribution Ctr.

Pansarin, Emerson Ricardo & Pansarin, Ludmila Mickeliunas. The Family Orchidaceae in the Serra do Japi, Sao Paulo state, Brazil. 2010. (Illus.). 289p. 409.00 *(978-3-211-99754-3(7)*, 3211997547) Springer.

Roosevelt, Theodore. Through the Brazilian Wilderness: Or My Voyage along the River of Doubt. 2009. 200p. pap. 12.95 *(978-1-60459-618-2(X))* Wilder Pubns., Ltd.

Santos, Eduardo Fernando Dos & Carlos, Roberto Ferreira Brandão. Structure of Wasp Assemblage (Insecta: Hymenoptera, Vespoidea) Taxonomic & Functional Diversity, & Spatial Organization along an Elevational Gradient in the Atlantic Rain Forest, Brazil. 2011. 60p. pap. *(978-3-639-27676-3(0))* VDM Verlag Dr. Mueller e.K.

BOTANY—CANADA

Armitage, Allan M. Armitage's Vines & Climbers: A Gardener's Guide to the Best Vertical Plants. 2010. (ENG., Illus.). 212p. 29.95 *(978-1-60469-039-2(9)*, 1604690399) Timber Pr., Inc.

Barkworth, Mary E., et al, eds. Manual of Grasses for North America. 2007. (ENG., Illus.). 640p. (C). (gr. 13). per. 89.95 *(978-0-87421-686-8(9)*, Utah State Univ. Pr.) Univ. Pr. of Colorado.

Basu, Saikat. Production of High Quality Fenugreek. 2009. 176p. pap. *(978-3-639-12378-4(6))* VDM Verlag Dr. Mueller e.K.

Beresford-Kroeger, Diana. Arboretum Borealis: A Lifeline of the Planet. 2010. (ENG.). 168p. 80.00 *(978-0-472-07114-2(9))*; (Illus.). pap. 32.50 *(978-0-472-05114-4(8))* Univ. of Michigan Pr.

Brayshaw, T. Christopher. Buttercups, Waterlilies & Their Relatives in British Columbia. (ENG., Illus.). 253p. pap. 24.95 *(978-0-7718-8739-0(6))* Royal British Columbia Museum CAN. Dist: Univ. of British Columbia Pr.

—Catkin-Bearing Plants of British Columbia, 1 vol. 2010. (ENG., Illus.). 220p. pap. *(978-0-7718-9458-9(9))* Royal British Columbia Museum.

Bryson, Charles T. & DeFelice, Michael S., eds. Weeds of the Midwestern United States & Central Canada. 2010. (ENG., Illus.). 440p. pap. 44.95 *(978-0-8203-3506-3(1))* Univ. of Georgia Pr.

Cuthbert, Andrew J. Prevalence & Distribution of Invasive Species. 2010. 72p. pap. *(978-3-639-24003-0(0))* VDM Verlag Dr. Mueller e.K.

Deichmann, Hank. Out & about in New Brunswick. 2008. (ENG., Illus.). 165p. pap. 15.00 *(978-1-894372-35-6(6))* DreamCatcher Publishing CAN. Dist: Univ. of Toronto Pr.

B

Elias, Thomas & Dykeman, Peter. Edible Wild Plants: A North American Field Guide to over 200 Natural Foods. 2009. (ENG., Illus.). 288p. pap. 19.95 *(978-1-4027-6715-9(3))* Sterling Publishing Co., Inc.

Hass, Richard, et al. Growing Roses in Cold Climates. rev. ed. 2012. (Illus.). 272p. pap. 34.95 ***(978-0-8166-7593-7(7))*** Univ. of Minnesota Pr.

Karst, Amanda, et al. Edible & Medicinal Plants of Canada. 2009. (ENG., Illus.). 448p. pap. *(978-1-55105-572-5(4))* Lone Pine Publishing.

Klimaszewski, Jan. Biodiversity, Biosystematics & Ecology of Canadian Coleoptera. Majka, Christopher G., ed. 2008. (ZooKeys Ser.). (Illus.). 402p. pap. 187.50 *(978-954-642-451-8(X))* Pensoft Pubs. BGR. Dist: Coronet Bks.

Mulligan, Gerald A. & Munro, Derek B. Poisonous Plants of Canada. (Illus.). 96p. pap. *(978-0-660-13467-3(5))* Canadian Government Publishing.

North American Rock Garden Society. Bulbs of North Americ. McGary, Jane, ed. 2009. (ENG.). 308p. pap. 29.95 *(978-1-60469-079-8(8)*, 1604690798) Timber Pr., Inc.

Schnell, Donald E. Carnivorous Plants of the United States & Canad. 2009. (ENG.). 468p. pap. 39.95 *(978-1-60469-108-5(5)*, 1604691085) Timber Pr., Inc.

Skinner, Hugh & Williams, Sara. Best Groundcovers & Vines for the Prairies, 1 vol. 2007. (ENG., Illus.). 240p. pap. 18.99 *(978-1-894856-80-5(5))* Fitzhenry & Whiteside, Ltd. CAN. Dist: Ingram Pub. Services.

Sutton, George Miksch, et al. The Exploration of Southampton Island, Hudson Bay: Memoirs of the Carnegie Museum, V12, Part 2, Section 5. 2011. 48p. 35.95 ***(978-1-258-09501-7(7))*** Literary Licensing, LLC.

Tiner, Ralph W. Field Guide to Tidal Wetland Plants of the Northeastern United States & Neighboring Canada: Vegetation of Beaches, Tidal Flats, Rocky Shores, Marshes, Swamps, & Coastal Ponds. 2008. (Illus.). 416p. pap. 29.95 *(978-1-55849-667-5(X))*; lib. bdg. 98.00 *(978-1-55849-666-8(1))* Univ. of Massachusetts Pr.

Tozer, Frank. The Uses of Wild Plants: Using & Growing the Wild Plants of the United States & Canada. 2007. (ENG., Illus.). 264p. per. 24.95 *(978-0-9773489-0-9(3))* Green Man Publishing.

Traill, Catherine Parr (Strickland). Studies of Plant Life in Canada: Or, Gleanings from Forest, Lake & Plain. 2011. (Cambridge Library Collection - Life Sciences Ser.). (ENG., Illus.). 350p. pap. 28.99 ***(978-1-108-03375-6(X))*** Cambridge Univ. Pr.

Walsh, N. G. Flora of Victoria, Vol. 2. pap. *(978-0-409-30849-5(8)*, Butterworth-Heinemann) Elsevier Science & Technology Bks.

Wetzel, Suzanne, et al. Bioproducts from Canada's Forests: New Partnerships in the Bioeconomy. 2010. (ENG.). xv, 257p. pap. 209.00 *(978-90-481-7248-1(9)*, 9048172489) Springer.

Wood, Alphonso. A Class-Book of Botany. 2006. 648p. per. 34.99 *(978-1-4255-6673-9(1))* MPublishing.

BOTANY—CANARY ISLANDS

Flowers of the Canary Islands. *(978-88-8029-638-6(8))* Casa Editrice Bonechi.

BOTANY—CARIBBEAN AREA

Axelrod, Franklin. A Systematic Vademecum to the Vascular Plants of Puerto Rico. 2011. 420p. (YA). pap. 45.00 *(978-1-889878-33-1(2))* Botanical Research Institute of Texas.

Been, Diana B. The Jamaican Herbalist: Use of Herbs in Jamaica. Date not set. 200p. (Orig.). pap. 15.00 *(978-0-9649550-2-8(4))* Been Bks.

Jansen-Jacobs, M. J., ed. Flora of the Guianas Series C: Bryophytes Fascicle 2. 2011. (Royal Botanic Gardens, Kew - Flora of the Guianas Ser.). (Illus.). 200p. pap. 115.00 *(978-1-84246-459-5(0))* Kew Publishing GBR. Dist: Chicago Distribution Ctr.

Ligon, Richard. True & Exact History of the Island of Barbados. Kupperman, Karen Ordahl, ed. & intro. by. 2011. 201p. (C). pap. 15.95 *(978-1-60384-620-2(4))*; lib. bdg. 48.00 *(978-1-60384-621-9(2))* Hackett Publishing Co., Inc.

Luer, Carlyle A. Icones Pleurothallidinarum XXX (30) Lepanthes of Jamaica; Systematics of Stelis, Stelis of Ecuador, Part Four. 2009. (Illus.). 265p. 80.00 *(978-1-930723-82-5(2))* Missouri Botanical Garden Pr.

Proctor, George R. Flora of the Cayman Islands: Revised Edition. rev. ed. 2012. (Illus.). 768p. 136.00 *(978-1-84246-403-8(5))* Kew Publishing GBR. Dist: Chicago Distribution Ctr.

Warner, Monica. Herbal Plants of Jamaica: Bush Teas, Bush Baths, Flavourings & Spices. rev. ed. 2007. (MacMillan Caribbean Natural History Ser.). (ENG., Illus.). 184p. pap. 15.00 *(978-1-4050-6566-5(4))* Macmillan Caribbean GBR. Dist: Interlink Publishing Group, Inc.

BOTANY—CHILE

Moreira Muñoz, Andrés. Plant Geography of Chile. 2010. (Plant & Vegetation Ser.). (Illus.). 250p. 209.00 *(978-90-481-8747-8(8)*, 9048187478) Springer.

Schultes, Richard Evans & Ruiz, Hipólito. The Journals of Hipolito Ruiz. 2009. (ENG.). 368p. pap. 44.95 *(978-1-60469-082-8(8)*, 1604690828) Timber Pr., Inc.

BOTANY—CHINA

Ahn, Jaebok. Traditional Chinese Medicinal Herbs. 2009. pap. 49.50 *(978-1-61623-252-8(8))* Independent Pub.

Cao, Kun-Fang & Enright, Neal J., eds. Plant Ecology in China. 2010. (Illus.). vi, 202p. 189.00 *(978-90-481-9992-1(1)*, 9048199921) Springer.

Chapman, Geoffrey P. & Wang, Yin-Zheng. The Plant Life of China: Diversity & Distribution. 2010. (ENG., Illus.). xiii, 256p. pap. 139.00 *(978-3-642-07599-5(1)*, 3642075991) Springer.

Chen, Anni & Yang, Wei. Hua Shuo Fujian Hong Cha. 2009. (CHI., Illus.). *(978-7-5335-3448-6(4))* Fujian Science & Technology Publishing Hse.

Flanagan, Mark & Kirkham, Tony. Wilson's China: A Century On. 2010. (Illus.). 256p. 46.00 *(978-1-84246-394-9(2))* Kew Publishing GBR. Dist: Chicago Distribution Ctr.

Grey-Wilson, Christopher & Cribb, Phillip. Guide to the Flowers of Western China. 2011. (Illus.). 642p. 115.00 *(978-1-84246-169-3(9))* Kew Publishing GBR. Dist: Chicago Distribution Ctr.

Hong, Deyuan, ed. Flora of China Illustrations, Vol. 11: Oxalidaceae through Aceraceae. 2009. (Illus.). 634p. 140.00 *(978-1-930723-78-8(4))* Missouri Botanical Garden Pr.

—Flora of China Illustrations, Vol. 13: Clusiaceae through Araliaceae. 2008. (Illus.). 491p. 125.00 *(978-1-930723-80-1(6))* Missouri Botanical Garden Pr.

—Flora of China Illustrations, Volume 10: Fabaceae. 2011. (Illus.). 680p. 175.00 *(978-1-930723-98-6(9))* Missouri Botanical Garden Pr.

—Flora of China Illustrations, Volume 12: Hippocastanaceae through Theaceae. 2008. (Illus.). 475p. 125.00 *(978-1-930723-79-5(2))* Missouri Botanical Garden Pr.

—Flora of China, Volume 10, Fabaceae. 2010. 642p. 140.00 *(978-1-930723-91-7(1))* Missouri Botanical Garden Pr.

—Flora of China, Volume 19: Cucurbitaceae through Valerianaceae with Annonaceae & Berberidaceae. 2011. 884p. 160.00 *(978-1-935641-04-9(2))* Missouri Botanical Garden Pr.

—Flora of China, Volume 23: Acoraceae through Cyperaceae. 2010. 515p. 125.00 *(978-1-930723-99-3(7))* Missouri Botanical Garden Pr.

—Flora of China, Volume 25: Orchidaceae. 2009. 570p. 125.00 *(978-1-930723-90-0(3))* Missouri Botanical Garden Pr.

Hu, Shiu-ying. Food Plants of China. Haggith, Toby & Newman, Joanna, eds. 2006. (ENG., Illus.). 928p. (gr. 17). pap. 45.00 *(978-962-996-229-6(2))* Chinese Univ. of Hong Kong, The HKG. Dist: Columbia Univ. Pr.

Kilpatrick, Jane. Gifts from the Gardens of China. 2007. (ENG., Illus.). 288p. 70.00 *(978-0-7112-2630-2(X))* Lincoln, Frances Ltd. GBR. Dist: Perseus-PGW.

Luo, Yiqi. Ecology in the Yangtze River Estuary. Yang, Shi-Lun, ed. 2010. (Ecological Studies). (ENG., Illus.). 496p. 149.00 *(978-0-387-76769-7(X))* Springer.

Mueggler, Erik. The Paper Road: Archive & Experience in the Botanical Exploration of West China & Tibet. 2011. (ENG., Illus.). 346p. 70.00 *(978-0-520-26902-6(0))*; pap. 29.95 *(978-0-520-26903-3(9))* Univ. of California Pr.

Qin, Boqiang. Lake Taihu, China: Dynamics & Environmental Change. 2008. (Monographiae Biologicae Ser.). (Illus.). 350p. 259.00 *(978-1-4020-8554-3(0))* Springer.

Robert Wahiti, Gituru. Reproductive Ecology of the Endangered Aquatic Plant Caldesia Grandis. 2010. 124p. pap. *(978-3-639-27003-7(7))* VDM Verlag Dr. Mueller e.K.

Tatt, Ong Hean. Chinese Plant Sumbolisms. pap. 12.95 *(978-967-978-672-9(2)*, Weatherhill, Inc.) Shambhala Pubns., Inc.

Walravens, Hartmut, ed. Joseph Franz Rock: Phytogeography of Northwest & Southwest China. 2011. (Veroffentlichungen zur Kulturund Geistesgeschichte Asiens Ser.). (GER., Illus.). 356p. (C). pap. 89.00 *(978-3-7001-6726-6(1))* Austrian Academy of Sciences Press AUT. Dist: Brown, David Bk. Co., The.

Wang, Chi Wu. The Forests of Chin: With A Survey of Grassland & Desert Vegetation. 2011. 326p. 50.95 ***(978-1-258-10361-3(3))*** Literary Licensing, LLC.

Wilson, Ernest Henry. A Naturalist in Western China with Vasculum, Camera & Gun: Being Some Account of Eleven Years' Travel. 2011. (Cambridge Library Collection - Life Sciences Ser.). (ENG.). 344p. pap. 28.99 *(978-1-108-03046-5(7))*; (Illus.). 408p. pap. 31.99 *(978-1-108-03045-8(9))* Cambridge Univ. Pr.

Wu, Zhengyi & Raven, Peter H. Flora of China Illustrations, Volume 25: Orchidaceae. 2010. (Illus.). 666p. 175.00 *(978-1-930723-89-4(X))* Missouri Botanical Garden Pr.

Xingjian, Qian & Xiaoyan, He. Famous Flowers in China. 2010. (Discovering China Ser.). (ENG., Illus.). 112p. 14.95 *(978-1-60652-156-4(X))* Reader's Digest Assn., Inc., The.

BOTANY—CHINA—TIBET

Kingdom-Ward, Frank. A Plant Hunter in Tibet. 2006. (ENG., Illus.). 317p. pap. 26.00 *(978-974-524-087-2(7))* Orchid Pr. THA. Dist: National Bk. Network.

Ward, Frank Kingdon & Prifti, Peter. A Plant Hunter in Tibet. 2006. (ENG., Illus.). 256p. 395.00 *(978-0-7103-1197-9(4))* Routledge.

BOTANY—EGYPT

A. Shoeib, Alla. Studies on the Fire Blight Disease of Pears. 2011. 68p. pap. ***(978-3-8443-3174-5(3))*** Lambert Academic Publishing.

Germer, Renate. Handbuch der altagyptischen Heilpflanzen. 2008. (Philippika Ser.). (GER.). 388p. (C). 48.00 *(978-3-447-05632-8(0))* Harrassowitz, Otto Verlag DEU. Dist: ISD.

Pande, Punya Prasad. Sclerotinia Crown & Stem Rot of Egyptian Clover. 2011. 88p. pap. ***(978-3-8443-0746-7(X))*** Lambert Academic Publishing.

Rabei, Sami. A Morphological, Anatomical & Taxonomic Study of Umbelliferae in Egypt. 2011. 364p. pap. ***(978-3-8443-1121-1(1))*** Lambert Academic Publishing.

Saad, Ahmed, et al. Forage Potentiality Assessment of Egyptian Indigenous-Native Legumes. 2011. 192p. pap. ***(978-3-8433-9425-3(3))*** Lambert Academic Publishing.

Zahran, M. A. & Willis, A. J. The Vegetation of Egypt. 2nd ed. 2008. (Plant & Vegetation Ser.). (Illus.). xx, 440p. 329.00 *(978-1-4020-8755-4(1))* Springer.

BOTANY—ETHIOPIA

Ayalew, Yenenesh, et al. Edible Plants: Species diversity & significance to food Security. 2010. 88p. pap. *(978-3-639-24772-5(8))* VDM Verlag Dr. Mueller e.K.

Beemnet, Mengesha. Characterstics of Ethiopian Coriander. 2010. 116p. pap. *(978-3-639-24842-5(2))* VDM Verlag Dr. Mueller e.K.

Gatew, Shetie & Argaw, Mekuria. The Ecological & Socio-Economic Impacts of Invasive Plant Species. 2010. (Illus.). 88p. pap. *(978-3-639-10432-5(3))* VDM Verlag Dr. Mueller e.K.

Takele, Serekebirhan. Ecological Study of Rodents in Sugarcane Plantations, Ethiopi. 2011. 84p. pap. ***(978-3-8433-9190-0(4))*** Lambert Academic Publishing.

Tesfaye, Binyam. Effect of Processing on Some Quality Attributes of Mango Fruit Leather. 2011. 152p. pap. ***(978-3-8443-0629-3(3))*** Lambert Academic Publishing.

BOTANY—EUROPE

Bentham, George. Catalogue des plantes indigènes des Pyrénées et du Bas Languedoc: Avec des notes et observations sur les espèces nouvelles ou peu Connues. 2011. (Cambridge Library Collection - Life Sciences Ser.). (FRE.). 134p. pap. 19.99 ***(978-1-108-03737-2(2))*** Cambridge Univ. Pr.

Bevan-Jones, Robert. Poisonous Plants: A Cultural & Social History. 2009. (ENG., Illus.). 215p. pap. 50.00 *(978-1-905119-21-9(6))* Windgather Pr. GBR. Dist: Brown, David Bk. Co., The.

Bowles, E. A. My Garden in Spring. 2008. (ENG.). 404p. pap. 24.95 *(978-1-60469-041-5(0)*, 1604690410) Timber Pr., Inc.

—My Garden in Summer. 2008. (ENG.). 396p. pap. 24.95 *(978-1-60469-042-2(9)*, 1604690429) Timber Pr., Inc.

Carlile, Bill & Coules, Anne. Control of Crop Diseases. 3rd rev. ed. 2012. (ENG., Illus.). 200p. (C). pap. 48.00 ***(978-0-521-13331-9(9))*** Cambridge Univ. Pr.

Clapham, A. R., et al. Flora of the British Isles: Illustrations, 4 vols. 2010. (ENG., Illus.). 521p. pap. 70.00 *(978-0-521-14929-7(0))* Cambridge Univ. Pr.

Cullen, James, et al, eds. The European Garden Flora: Volume 1, Monocotyledons: Alismataceae to Orchidaceae: A Manual for the Identification of Plants Cultivated in Europe, Both Out-of-Doors & under Glass, 5 vols. 2nd ed. 2011. (European Garden Flora Ser.). (ENG., Illus.). 688p. 250.00 *(978-0-521-76147-5(6))* Cambridge Univ. Pr.

Denk, Thomas, et al. Late Cainozoic Floras of Iceland: 15 Million Years of Vegetation & Climate History in the Northern Atlantic. 2011. (Topics in Geobiology Ser.). (ENG., Illus.). x, 870p. 209.00 *(978-94-007-0371-1(6)*, 9400703716) Springer.

Egmond, Florike. The World of Carolus Clusius: Natural History in the Making, 1550-1610, 1 vol. 2010. (Perspectives in Economic & Social History Ser.). (ENG., Illus.). 312p. 99.00 *(978-1-84893-008-7(9))* Pickering & Chatto Pubs., Ltd. GBR. Dist: Ashgate Publishing Co.

Ellenberg, Heinz H. & Ellenberg, Heinz. Vegetation Ecology of Central Europe. Strutt, Gordon K., tr. from GER. 4th rev. ed. 2009. (ENG., Illus.). 756p. pap. 95.00 *(978-0-521-11512-4(4))* Cambridge Univ. Pr.

Fedorov, A. A., ed. Flora of Russia Vol. 4: The European Part & Bordering Regions. 2006. (ENG., Illus.). 722p. 247.95 *(978-90-5410-759-0(6)*, CRC Press) Taylor & Francis Group GBR. Dist: Taylor & Francis Group.

Hegi, Gustav. Illustrierte Flora von Mitteleuropa. Pteridophyta - Spermatophyta (Illustrated Flora of Central Europe) Band II: Spermatophyta - Angiospermae - Monocotyledones 2. Von Conert, Hans et al, eds. 3rd rev. ed. Date not set. (Illus.). Tl. 2. *(978-3-8263-3026-1(9))*Tl. 3. *(978-3-8263-3027-8(7))* Wiley, John & Sons, Ltd. (Wiley-Blackwell).

—Illustrierte Flora von Mitteleuropa. Pteridophyta - Spermatophyta (Illustrated Flora of Central Europe) Band IV: Spermatophyta - Angiospermae - Dicotyledones 2, Tl. 2C. Von Conert, Hans et al, eds. 2nd rev. ed. Date not set. *(978-3-8263-3065-0(X)*, Wiley-Blackwell) Wiley, John & Sons, Ltd.

—Illustrierte Flora von Mitteleuropa. Pteridophyta - Spermatophyta (Illustrated Flora of Central Europe) Band VI: Spermatophyta - Angiospermae - Dicotyledones 4. Von Conert, Hans et al, eds. Date not set. (Illus.). Tl. 2, Lfg. 3. 2nd rev. ed. pap. *(978-3-8263-3028-5(5))*Tl. 2, Lfg. 4. rev. ed. pap. *(978-3-8263-3081-0(1))* Wiley, John & Sons, Ltd. (Wiley-Blackwell).

Knees, Sabina. The European Garden Flora Vol. 2: Dicotyledons - Casuarinaceae to Cruciferae - A Manual for the Identification of Plants Cultivated in Europe, Both Out-of-Doors & under Glas, 5 vols. Cullen, James & Cubey, H. Suzanne, eds. 2nd ed. 2011. (European Garden Flora Ser.). (Illus.). 660p. 250.00 ***(978-0-521-76151-2(4))*** Cambridge Univ. Pr.

—The European Garden Flora Vol. 3: A Manual for the Identification of Plants Cultivated in Europe, Both Out-of-Doors & under Glass, 5 vols. Cullen, James & Cubey, H. Suzanne, eds. 2nd ed. 2011. (European Garden Flora Ser.). (ENG., Illus.). 640p. 250.00 ***(978-0-521-76155-0(7))*** Cambridge Univ. Pr.

—The European Garden Flora Vol. 4: A Manual for the Identification of Plants Cultivated in Europe, Both Out-of-Doors & under Glass, 5 vols. Cubey, H. Suzanne & Cullen, James, eds. 2nd ed. 2011. (European Garden Flora Ser.). (ENG., Illus.). 630p. 250.00 ***(978-0-521-76160-4(3))*** Cambridge Univ. Pr.

—The European Garden Flora Vol. 5: Boraginaceae to Compositae, 5 vols. Cullen, James & Cubey, H. Suzanne, eds. 2nd ed. 2011. (European Garden Flora Ser.). (ENG., Illus.). 660p. 250.00 ***(978-0-521-76164-2(6))*** Cambridge Univ. Pr.

Mingazova, N. M. Bioraznoobrazie I Tipologiia Karstovykh Ozer Povolzhia. 2009. (RUS., Illus.). 220p. *(978-5-98180-737-4(7))* Izdatel'stvo Kazanskogo universiteta.

Moore, D. M., ed. Flora Europaea Check-List & Chromosome Index. 2009. (Flora Europaea Ser.). (ENG.). 436p. pap. 55.00 *(978-0-521-10573-6(0))* Cambridge Univ. Pr.

Schiebinger, Londa & Swan, Claudia, eds. Colonial Botany: Science, Commerce, & Politics in the Early Modern World. 2007. (Illus.). 352p. (C). per. 24.95 *(978-0-8122-2009-4(9))* Univ. of Pennsylvania Pr.

Sekulová, et al. Alpine und subalpine Silikatvegetation des Nationalparks Niedere Tatra: Slowakei. 2009. 112p. pap. *(978-3-639-21716-2(0))* VDM Verlag Dr. Mueller e.K.

Taylor, Marianne. A Naturalist's Guide to Garden Wildlife. 2010. (Naturalists' Guides). (Illus.). 160p. pap. 14.95 *(978-1-906780-14-2(5))* Beaufoy, John Publishing GBR. Dist: Midpoint Trade Bks., Inc.

Tutin, T. G., et al, eds. Flora Europaea. 2010. (Flora Europaea Ser.). (ENG.). 500p. pap. 35.99 *(978-0-521-15367-6(0))*; (ENG.). 416p. pap. 35.99 *(978-0-521-15368-3(9))*; 2nd rev. ed. 630p. pap. 35.99 *(978-0-521-15366-9(2))*; 7th ed. (ENG.). 552p. pap. 35.99 *(978-0-521-15369-0(7))* Cambridge Univ. Pr.

Vellve, Renee. Saving the Seed: Genetic diversity & European Agriculture. 2009. (Natural Resource Management Set Ser.). (ENG.). 210p. 110.00 *(978-1-84971-020-6(1))* Routledge.

Walker, D. & West, R. G., eds. Studies in the Vegetational History of the British Isles: Essays in Honour of Harry Godwin. 2009. (ENG.). 284p. pap. 42.00 *(978-0-521-11201-7(X))* Cambridge Univ. Pr.

Webb, D. A. Flora Europaea. Tutin, T. G. et al, eds. 2010. (Flora Europaea Ser.). 506p. pap. 35.99 *(978-0-521-15370-6(0))* Cambridge Univ. Pr.

Whitton, B. A., et al, eds. The Freshwater Algal Flora of the British Isles: An Identification Guide to Freshwater & Terrestrial Algae. 2nd rev. ed. 2011. (ENG., Illus.). 896p. 199.00 *(978-0-521-19375-7(3))* Cambridge Univ. Pr.

Widstrand, Staffan, et al. Wild Wonders of Europe. 2010. (ENG., Illus.). 288p. 50.00 *(978-0-8109-9614-4(6))* Abrams.

Zolyomi, Agnes. Alteration of the Alpine Vegetation Due to Climate Change. 2009. 96p. pap. *(978-3-639-21423-9(4))* VDM Verlag Dr. Mueller e.K.

BOTANY—FRANCE

Lorence, David H. & Wagner, Warren L. Introduction to Botany of the Marquesas Islands: New Taxa, Combinations & Revisions. 2011. (PhytoKeys Ser.). (Illus.). 156p. pap. 115.00 ***(978-954-642-598-0(2))*** Pensoft Pubs. BGR. Dist: Coronet Bks.

Munier-Jolain, Nathalie. Physiology of the Pea Crop. 2010. (ENG., Illus.). 298p. 99.95 *(978-1-57808-570-5(5)*, CRC Press) Taylor & Francis Group GBR. Dist: Taylor & Francis Group.

Renaux, Alain. Louis XIV's Botanical Engravings. 2008. (Illus.). 144p. 80.00 *(978-1-84822-000-3(6)*, Lund Humphries Pubs.) Ashgate Publishing, Ltd. GBR. Dist: Ashgate Publishing Co.

Williams, R. L. Botanophilia in Eighteenth-Century France: The Spirit of the Enlightenment. 2010. (International Archives of the History of Ideas / archives internationales d'histoire des Idées Ser.). (Illus.). 204p. pap. 139.00 *(978-90-481-5678-8(5)*, 9048156785) Springer.

—French Botany in the Enlightenment: The Ill-fated Voyages of la Parouse & his Rescuers. 2010. (International Archives of the History of Ideas / archives internationales d'histoire des Idées Ser.). 248p. pap. 110.00 *(978-90-481-6213-0(0)*, 9048162130) Springer.

BOTANY—GERMANY

Delling, Heike. Erarbeitung Von Verfahrensbeschreibungen, Zeitbedarf und Anwendungskosten Für Spezielle Pflanzenschutzmassnahmen Im ökologischen Landbau: Produktionsverfahren Mais, Kartoffeln, Getreide. 2008. (GER., Illus.). 48p. *(978-3-930037-47-6(5))* Biologische Bundesanstalt fur Land- und Forstwirtschaft.

BOTANY—GREAT BRITAIN

Allison, Keith. A Guide to Plants Poisonous to Horses. 2011. (ENG., Illus.). 96p. pap. 22.95 ***(978-0-85131-958-2(0))***, Allen, J. A. & Company, Limited) Hale, Robert Ltd. GBR. Dist: Independent Pubs. Group.

Ayres, Peter A. The Aliveness of Plants: The Darwins at the Dawn of Plant Science, 1 vol. 2008. (ENG., Illus.). 256p. 99.00 *(978-1-85196-970-8(5))* Pickering & Chatto Pubs., Ltd. GBR. Dist: Ashgate Publishing Co.

Chinery, Michael, compiled by. Britain's Plant Galls: A Photographic Guide to 100 of the Commoner Plant Galls of Britain. 2011. (Britain's Wildlife Ser.). (ENG., Illus.). 96p. (C). pap. 21.95 ***(978-1-903657-43-0(1))*** Princeton Univ. Pr.

Coombes, Allen J. The A to Z of Plant Names: A Quick Reference Guide to 4000 Garden Plants. 2012. (ENG.). 312p. 19.95 ***(978-1-60469-196-2(4))*** Timber Pr., Inc.

Cordle, Celia. Out of the Hay & into the Hops: Hop Cultivation in Wealden Kent & Hop Marketing in Southwark, 1744-2000. 2011. (Studies in Regional & Local History Ser.). (Illus.). 192p. pap. 37.95 ***(978-1-907396-04-5(7))*** Univ. of Hertfordshire Pr. GBR. Dist: Independent Pubs. Group.

Crowther, S. M., et al, eds. The Medicalization of Cannabis. 2010. (Illus.). 130p. pap. *(978-0-85484-129-5(6))* Wellcome Institute for the History of Medicine.

Curtis, William. Flora Londinensis: Or plates & descriptions of such plants as grow wild in the environs of London. 2010. (Illus.). 452p. pap. 36.75 *(978-1-140-96631-9(6)*, Gale ECCO, Print Editions) BiblioBazaar.

Eastoe, Jane. Wild Food: Foraging for Food in the Wild. 2008. (ENG., Illus.). 96p. 14.95 *(978-1-905400-59-1(4))* Anova Bks. GBR. Dist: Independent Pubs. Group.

Fraser, Mike & Fraser, Liz. The Smallest Kingdom: Plants & Plant Collectors at the Cape of Good Hope. 2011. (Illus.). 220p. 46.00 *(978-1-84246-389-5(6))* Kew Publishing GBR. Dist: Chicago Distribution Ctr.

Greenwood, Eric. Flora of North Lancashire. 2012. (Illus.). 656p. 79.95 ***(978-1-874181-89-7(6))*** International Publishers Marketing.

Groves, James. The British Charophyta. 2010. 96p. pap. 20.00 *(978-1-153-30750-5(2))* General Bks. LLC.
Hatfield, Gabrielle. Herbal: The Curious Stories of Britain's Wild Plants. 2009. (ENG., Illus.). 450p. (gr. 12-18). 18.00 *(978-0-14-102514-8(X)*, Penguin Global) Penguin Group (USA) Inc.
Hooker, Joseph Dalton. The Student's Flora of the British Islands. 2010. 524p. pap. 34.95 *(978-1-4460-3183-4(7))* Thorndike Pr.
Moore, Thomas. British Ferns & Their Allies: An Abridgement of the Popular History of British Ferns. 2007. (ENG.). 136p. 35.95 *(978-0-548-05276-1(X))* Kessinger Publishing, LLC.
Oliver, F. W., ed. Makers of British Botany: A Collection of Biographies by Living Botanists. 2010. (Cambridge Library Collection - Life Sciences Ser.). (Illus.). 400p. pap. 31.99 *(978-1-108-01602-5(2))* Cambridge Univ. Pr.
Perring, Franklyn Hugh, et al. A Flora of Cambridgeshire. 2009. (Cambridge Library Collection - Cambridge Ser.). (Illus.). 400p. pap. 31.99 *(978-1-108-00240-0(4))* Cambridge Univ. Pr.
Pickworth Farrow, E. Plant Life on East Anglian Heaths: Being Observational & Experimental Studies of the Vegetation of Breckland. 2012. (ENG.). 166p. pap. 42.99 ***(978-1-107-60510-7(5))*** Cambridge Univ. Pr.
Pollington, Stephen, ed. Leechcraft: Early English Charms, Plant Lore, & Healing. 2nd ed. 2008. (ENG., Illus.). 539p. (C). pap. 39.95 *(978-1-898281-47-4(5))* Anglo-Saxon Bks. GBR. Dist: Brown, David Bk. Co., The.
Pulteney, Richard. Historical & Biographical Sketches of the Progress of Botany in England: From Its Origin to the Introduction of the Linnaean System. 2011. (Cambridge Library Collection - Life Sciences Ser.). (ENG.). 400p. pap. 31.99 ***(978-1-108-03733-4(X))***; 386p. pap. 31.99 ***(978-1-108-03732-7(1))*** Cambridge Univ. Pr.
Richens, R. H. Elm. 2012. (ENG.). 360p. pap. 45.00 *(978-0-521-29462-1(2))* Cambridge Univ. Pr.
Rotherham, Ian. Peat & Peat Cutting. 2009. (Shire Library). (ENG., Illus.). 64p. pap. 12.95 *(978-0-7478-0705-6(1))* Shire Pubns., Ltd. GBR. Dist: Random Hse., Inc.
Salisbury, William. The Botanist's Companion, Volume II. 2007. (ENG.). 256p. pap. 21.99 *(978-1-4264-6031-9(7))*; 294p. pap. 23.99 *(978-1-4264-6102-6(X))* BiblioBazaar.
Sterry, Paul. British Wildlife: A Photographic Guide to Every Common Species. 2008. (Collins Complete Photo Guides). (ENG., Illus.). 320p. pap. 31.95 *(978-0-00-723683-1(2))* HarperCollins Pubs. Ltd. GBR. Dist: Independent Pubs. Group.
—Collins Complete British Animals: A Photographic Guide to Every Common Species. 2010. (Collins Complete Guide Ser.). (ENG., Illus.). 224p. pap. 24.95 *(978-0-00-734950-0(5))* HarperCollins Pubs. Ltd. GBR. Dist: Independent Pubs. Group.
Sterry, Paul & Hughes, Barry. Complete British Mushrooms & Toadstools: The Essential Photograph Guide to Britain's Fungi. 2009. (ENG., Illus.). 384p. pap. 27.95 *(978-0-00-723224-6(1))* HarperCollins Pubs. Ltd. GBR. Dist: Independent Pubs. Group.
Sutton, Brian, ed. A Century of Mycology. 2008. (ENG., Illus.). 416p. pap. 83.00 *(978-0-521-05019-7(7))* Cambridge Univ. Pr.
Tansley, A. G. The British Islands & their Vegetation Set, 2 vols. 2009. (ENG.). 1180p. pap. 137.00 *(978-0-521-75772-0(X))* Cambridge Univ. Pr.
Taylor, Marianne. A Naturalist's Guide to Garden Wildlife. 2010. (Naturalists' Guides). (Illus.). 160p. pap. 14.95 *(978-1-906780-14-2(5))* Beaufoy, John Publishing GBR. Dist: Midpoint Trade Bks., Inc.
Titchmarsh, Alan. How to Garden: Perennial Garden Plants. 2011. (How to Garden Ser.). (ENG., Illus.). 144p. pap. 12.95 *(978-1-84607-911-5(X))* BBC Worldwide GBR. Dist: Independent Pubs. Group.
—Nature of Britain: A Celebration of Our Landscape & Wildlife. 2008. (ENG., Illus.). 336p. 35.00 *(978-0-563-49398-3(4))* Random Hse. GBR. Dist: Independent Pubs. Group.
Vickery, Roy. Garlands, Conkers & Mother-Die: British & Irish Plant-Lore. 2010. (ENG., Illus.). 240p. 29.95 *(978-1-4411-0195-2(0))* Continuum International Publishing Group, Ltd. GBR. Dist: National Bk. Network.
Walters, S. M. The Shaping of Cambridge Botany: A Short History of Whole-Plant Botany in Cambridge from the Time of Ray into the Present Century. 2009. (Cambridge Library Collection - Cambridge Ser.). (ENG., Illus.). 144p. pap. 19.99 *(978-1-108-00230-1(7))* Cambridge Univ. Pr.
West, R. G. Plant Life of the Quaternary Cold Stages: Evidence from the British Isles. 2011. (ENG., Illus.). 342p. pap. 65.00 *(978-0-521-18892-0(X))* Cambridge Univ. Pr.

BOTANY—GREECE

Strid, Arne, ed. Mountain Flora of Greece, 2 vols., Vol. 1, Set. 2010. (ENG.). 852p. (C). pap. 78.00 *(978-0-521-12724-0(6))* Cambridge Univ. Pr.

BOTANY—GUINEA

Jansen-Jacobs, M. J. Flora of the Guianas Series A: Phanerogams Fascicle 27: 71. Cyrillaceae, 79. Theophrastaceae, 86. Habdodendraceae, 90. Proteaceae, 100. Combretaceae, 113. Dichapetalaceae, 167. Limnocharitaceae, 168. Alismataceae. 2012. (Royal Botanic Gardens, Kew-Flora of the Guianas Ser.). (Illus.). 214p. pap. 87.00 *(978-1-84246-418-2(3))* Kew Publishing GBR. Dist: Chicago Distribution Ctr.
Wright, Heather E., et al, eds. Une Evaluation Biologique Rapide de Trois Foret Classees du Sud-Est de la Guinee. 2006. (Conservation International Rapid Assessment Program Ser.). (FRE & ENG., Illus.). 248p. per. 19.95 *(978-1-881173-48-9(8))* Conservation International.

BOTANY—HAWAII

Bohm, Bruce. Hawaii's Native Plants. 2009. 220p. pap. 14.95 *(978-1-56647-905-9(3))* Mutual Publishing LLC.
Greenwell, Amy Beatrice Holdsworth. Amy Greenwell's Ethnobotanical Guide to Native Hawaiian Plants. 2009. (Illus.). 135p. pap. 12.95 *(978-1-58178-092-5(3))* Bishop Museum Pr.
Hall, John B. A Hiker's Guide to Trailside Plants in Hawaii. 2008. pap. *(978-1-56647-872-4(3))* Mutual Publishing LLC.
Magnacca, Karl N. & O'Grady, Patrick M. Revision of the Modified Mouthparts Species Group of Hawaiian Drosophila (Diptera: Drosophilidae) The Ceratostoma, Freycinetiae, Semifuscata, & Setiger Subgroups, & Unplaced Species. 2009. (UC Publications in Entomology Ser.). (Illus.). viii, 94p. pap. 65.00 *(978-0-520-09873-2(0))* Univ. of California Pr.
Palmer, Daniel D. Hawaii's Ferns & Fern Allies. 2008. (Illus.). 324p. pap. 25.00 *(978-0-8248-3347-3(3))* Univ. of Hawaii Pr.
Smathers, Garrett A. & Mueller-Dombois, Dieter. Hawaii: The Fires of Life: Rebirth in Volcano Land, Five Decades of Vegetation Development in the Devastation Area, Site of the 1959 Kilauea Iki Eruption, Hawaii Volcanoes National Park. 2007. 142p. pap. 14.95 *(978-1-56647-818-2(9))* Mutual Publishing LLC.

BOTANY—INDIA

Aluri, Jacob Solomon Raju. Reproductive Ecology of Dry Season Ornithophilous Tree Species. 2009. 122p. pap. *(978-3-639-18413-6(0))* VDM Verlag Dr. Mueller e.K.
Baruah, Akhil. Tejpat - the Indian Bay Leaves. 2011. 116p. pap. ***(978-3-8443-0579-1(3))*** Lambert Academic Publishing.
Bhattacharya, Debojyoti. Antimicrobial Studies of Indian Medicinal Plants. 2011. 72p. pap. ***(978-3-8443-2053-4(9))*** Lambert Academic Publishing.
Blatter, E. & D'Almeida, J. F. The Ferns of Bombay. 2008. 272p. 42.95 *(978-0-548-98148-1(5))* 2007. (ENG.). 276p. per. 27.95 *(978-0-548-66617-3(2))* Kessinger Publishing, LLC.
Borah, Debajit & Mishra, Vimalendra. Phytochemical Values of Some Traditionally Used Plant Parts in Ind. 2011. 88p. pap. ***(978-3-8443-0387-2(1))*** Lambert Academic Publishing.
Dave, Deeksha. A Study of the Grasses of South-East Rajasthan,Indi. 2011. 240p. pap. ***(978-3-8443-1146-4(7))*** Lambert Academic Publishing.
De, Biman & Ashim Chandra Sinha, Prof. Integrated Nutrient Management on Rapeseed. 2011. 124p. pap. ***(978-3-8443-8864-0(8))*** Lambert Academic Publishing.
Dogra, Kuldip Singh, et al. Impact of Invasive Plant Species. 2010. 388p. pap. *(978-3-8383-6686-9(7))* Lambert Academic Publishing.
Drury, Heber. The Useful Plants of Indi. 2010. 528p. pap. 35.45 *(978-1-4460-2372-3(9))* Research Pr.
Dutt, Harish C. Ecology of Medicinal Plants of Neeru Watershed in North West Himalayas. 2010. 164p. pap. *(978-3-8383-8591-4(8))* Lambert Academic Publishing.
Dwivedi, Anil K., et al. Biotic Potential & the Abiotic Stress. 2011. 416p. pap. ***(978-3-8454-1211-5(9))*** Lambert Academic Publishing.
Gardezi, Syed Dilnawaz & Zubair Khan, Muhammad. Autumn Olive a Medicinal Plant from Azad Jammu & Kashmir. 2010. 128p. pap. *(978-3-8383-5979-3(8))* Lambert Academic Publishing.
Gulati, Kavita. Recent Advances in Herbal Drug Research & Therapy. Ray, Arunabha, ed. 2010. 480p. (C). *(978-93-80026-97-8(8))* I.K. International Publishing House Pvt. Ltd.
Hooker, Joseph Dalton & Thomson, Thomas. Flora Indica: Being a Systematic Account of the Plants of British India, Together with Observations on the Structure & Affinities of their Natural Order & Genera. 2011. (Cambridge Library Collection - Life Sciences Ser.). (ENG., Illus.). 592p. pap. 43.00 ***(978-1-108-03749-5(6))*** Cambridge Univ. Pr.
Jacob Solomon Raju, Aluri. Reproductive Ecology of Cycas Beddomei & C Sphaerca. 2010. 64p. pap. *(978-3-8383-4544-4(4))* Lambert Academic Publishing.
Jadhav, Shailesh & Madhurima Lall, B. Fungal Biodiversity of Hospital Are. 2011. 316p. pap. ***(978-3-8443-1733-6(3))*** Lambert Academic Publishing.
Jha, Bhavanath, et al. Seaweeds of India: The Diversity & Distribution of Seaweeds of Gujarat Coast. 2009. (Developments in Applied Phycology Ser.). (ENG., Illus.). xii, 216p. 159.00 *(978-90-481-2487-9(5)*, 9048124875) Springer.
Kabeer, K. Althaf Ahamed & Nair, V. J. Flora of Tamil Nadu — Grasses. 2009. (Illus.). xxxii, 524p. *(978-81-8177-031-8(5))* Botanical Survey of India.
Kabnoorkar, Panchshila & Deokule, Subhash. Biodeterioration of Chemical Constituents. 2011. 312p. pap. ***(978-3-8433-9160-3(2))*** Lambert Academic Publishing.
Kolady, Deepthi. Public-Private Partnership & Genetically Engineered Eggplant. 2010. 128p. pap. *(978-3-8383-2025-0(5))* Lambert Academic Publishing.
Lakhanpal, T. N., et al. Biology of Indian Morels. 2010. 266p. (C). *(978-93-80578-24-8(5))* I.K. International Publishing House Pvt. Ltd.
Laxminarayan, Ramanan. Closing India's Nutrition Gap: The Role of Golden Mustard in Fighting Vitamin a Deficiency. 2007. pap. *(978-1-933115-66-5(1))* Earthscan LLC.
Panduranga Raju, Mudunuri & Seetharami Reddi, T. V. V. Ethnobotany of the Konda Reddis. 2011. 324p. pap. ***(978-3-8433-9261-7(7))*** Lambert Academic Publishing.
Ramachandran, Veerambakkam. Proceedings of the National Seminar. 2010. 212p. pap. *(978-3-8383-8415-3(6))* Lambert Academic Publishing.
Raut, Ninad, et al. Monograph of Family Acanthaceae from Mumbai, Western Indi. 2011. 156p. pap. ***(978-3-8443-9361-3(7))*** Lambert Academic Publishing.
Royal Botanic Garden, Calcutta Staff. The Aconites of India: A Monograph by Otto Stapf, with A Sketch of the Life of Francis Hamilton (Once Buchanan), Vol. X, Pt. 2. (Illus.). lxxv, 197p. 69.00 *(978-0-88065-014-4(1))* Scholarly Pubns.
Singh, K. K. Neem. 2009. (Illus.). xix, 546p. (C). *(978-81-89866-00-6(1))* I.K. International Publishing House Pvt. Ltd.
Singh, Minu, et al. Mineral Nutrition of Turmeric. 2011. 88p. pap. ***(978-3-8454-0021-1(8))*** Lambert Academic Publishing.
Sood, Sarvesh, et al. Indian Bio-Fences. 2011. 300p. pap. ***(978-3-8433-8027-0(9))*** Lambert Academic Publishing.
Sultana, Tayyaba, et al. Geographical Distribution of Lentils in Pakistan. 2010. 188p. pap. *(978-3-639-21296-9(7))* VDM Verlag Dr. Mueller e.K.
Suneetha, J. & Seetharami Reddi, T. V. V. Ethnobotany of East Godavari District, Andhra Pradesh. 2011. 608p. pap. ***(978-3-8443-0587-6(4))*** Lambert Academic Publishing.
Swamy, N. Suryanarayana & Reddi, T. V. V. Seetharami. Ethnobotanical Knowledge of Adilabad District, Andhra Pradesh. 2011. 428p. pap. ***(978-3-8443-1175-4(0))*** Lambert Academic Publishing.
Vimala, Yapadinna. Antimicrobial Activity of Decalepsis Hamiltoni. 2011. 84p. pap. ***(978-3-8443-0701-6(X))*** Lambert Academic Publishing.

BOTANY—INDONESIA

Alfred, Ernst. The New Flora of the Volcanic Island of Krakatau. Seward, A. C., tr. from GER. 2009. (Cambridge Library Collection - Life Sciences Ser.). (ENG., Illus.). 104p. pap. 19.99 *(978-1-108-00433-6(4))* Cambridge Univ. Pr.
Listiawati, Agustina & Siregar, Chairani. Entuyut (Nepenthes) Asal Kalimantan Barat. 2008. (IND., Illus.). v, 88p. *(978-979-17723-2-7(0))* Universitas Tanjungpura Pr.
Rumphius, Georgius Everhardus. The Ambonese Herbal, 6 vols. Beekman, E. M., tr. from DUT. 2011. (Illus.). Vol. 3,Bk. 4. 720p. 85.00 *(978-0-300-15372-9(4))* Vol. 5, Bk. XII. (ENG., 640p. 85.00 *(978-0-300-15374-3(0))* Vol. 6. 144p. 85.00 *(978-0-300-15375-0(9))* Yale Univ. Pr.
—The Ambonese Herbal Vol. 1, Bk. I: Containing All Sorts of Trees, That Bear Edible Fruits, & Are Husbanded by People, 6 vols. Beekman, E. M., tr. from DUT 2011. (Illus.). 548p. 85.00 *(978-0-300-15370-5(8))* Yale Univ. Pr.
—The Ambonese Herbal Vol. 2, Bk. 2: Containing the Aromatic Trees, 6 vols. Beekman, E. M., tr. from DUT. 2011. (ENG., Illus.). 688p. 85.00 *(978-0-300-15371-2(6))* Yale Univ. Pr.
—The Ambonese Herbal Vol. 4, Bk. VIII: Containing Potherbs Used for Good, Medicine, & Sport - Concerning Bindweeds, As Well As Twining & Creeping Plants, 6 vols. Beekman, E. M., tr. from DUT. 2011. (ENG., Illus.). 624p. 85.00 *(978-0-300-15373-6(2))* Yale Univ. Pr.
Steenis, C. G. G. J. Van. The Mountain Flora of Java. 2nd ed. 2006. (Illus.). 90p. *(978-90-04-15347-9(0))* BRILL.

BOTANY—IRAQ

Giovino, Mariana. The Assyrian Sacred Tree: A History of Interpretations. 2007. (Orbis Biblicus et Orientalis Ser.). (GER & ENG., Illus.). 306p. (C). 102.00 *(978-3-525-53028-3(5))* Vandenhoeck & Ruprecht GmbH & Co. KG DEU. Dist: ISD.

BOTANY—IRELAND

Nelson, Charles E. & Walsh, Wendy. The Wild & Garden Plants of Ireland. 2009. (ENG., Illus.). 280p. 45.00 *(978-0-500-51456-6(9)*, 551456) Thames & Hudson.
Nelson, E. Charles. An Irishman's Cuttings: Tales of Irish Gardens & Gardeners, Plants & Plant-Hunters. 2010. (ENG., Illus.). 224p. 54.95 *(978-1-84889-005-3(2))* Collins Pr., The IRL. Dist: Dufour Editions, Inc.
O'Mahony, Tony. The Flora of Cork City & County. 2010. (ENG., Illus.). 456p. 59.95 *(978-1-84889-020-6(6))* Collins Pr., The IRL. Dist: Dufour Editions, Inc.
Parnell, John & Curtis, Tom, eds. Webb's an Irish Flora. 8th ed. 2012. (Illus.). 384p. 49.95 ***(978-1-85918-478-3(2))*** Cork Univ. Pr. IRL. Dist: Stylus Publishing, LLC.
Sterry, Paul. Collins Complete Irish Wildlife. 2010. (Collins Complete Guide Ser.). (ENG., Illus.). 320p. pap. 24.95 *(978-0-00-734951-7(3))* HarperCollins Pubs. Ltd. GBR. Dist: Independent Pubs. Group.
Sterry, Paul & Hughes, Barry. Complete British Mushrooms & Toadstools: The Essential Photograph Guide to Britain's Fungi. 2009. (ENG., Illus.). 384p. pap. 27.95 *(978-0-00-723224-6(1))* HarperCollins Pubs. Ltd. GBR. Dist: Independent Pubs. Group.
Tansley, A. G. The British Islands & their Vegetation Set, 2 vols. 2009. (ENG.). 1180p. pap. 137.00 *(978-0-521-75772-0(X))* Cambridge Univ. Pr.
Vickery, Roy. Garlands, Conkers & Mother-Die: British & Irish Plant-Lore. 2010. (ENG., Illus.). 240p. 29.95 *(978-1-4411-0195-2(0))* Continuum International Publishing Group, Ltd. GBR. Dist: National Bk. Network.
West, R. G. Plant Life of the Quaternary Cold Stages: Evidence from the British Isles. 2011. (ENG., Illus.). 342p. pap. 65.00 *(978-0-521-18892-0(X))* Cambridge Univ. Pr.
Whelan, Paul. Lichens of Ireland: An Illustrated Introduction to over 250 Species. 2012. (ENG., Illus.). 160p. pap. 33.95 ***(978-1-84889-137-1(7))*** Collins Pr., The IRL. Dist: Dufour Editions, Inc.

BOTANY—ISLANDS OF THE PACIFIC

Gillespie, John W. New Plants from Fiji-I. (Illus.). pap. 30.00 *(978-0-527-02180-1(6)*, BO74K) Periodicals Service Co.
—New Plants from Fiji-II, 1931. (Illus.). pap. 18.00 *(978-0-527-02189-4(X)*, BO83K) Periodicals Service Co.
—New Plants from Fiji-III, 1932. (Illus.). pap. 18.00 *(978-0-527-02197-9(0)*, BO91K) Periodicals Service Co.
Miller, David Philip & Reill, Peter Hanns, eds. Visions of Empire: Voyages, Botany, & Representations of Nature. 2010. (ENG., Illus.). 394p. pap. 36.99 *(978-0-521-17261-5(6))* Cambridge Univ. Pr.
Parham, H. B. Fiji Native Plants, with Their Medicinal & Other Uses. reprint ed. 32.50 *(978-0-404-14162-2(5))* AMS Pr., Inc.
Robson, Kathleen A., et al. Encyclopedia of Northwest Native Plants for Gardens & Landscapes. 2008. (ENG., Illus.). 532p. 59.95 *(978-0-88192-863-1(1)*, 0881928631) Timber Pr., Inc.

BOTANY—ITALY

Beretta, Marco & Tosi, Alessandro. Linnaeus in Italy: The Spread of a Revolution in Science. 2007. (Uppsala Studies in History of Science). *(978-0-88135-393-8(0))* Watson Publishing International, LLC.

BOTANY—JAPAN

Petersen, David & Conti, Mancy. Survivors: the A-bombed Trees of Hiroshima. 2008. 333p. pap. 36.95 *(978-1-4092-0501-2(0))* Lulu Enterprises Inc.
Schmid, Wolfram George. The Genus Host. 2009. (ENG.). 472p. pap. 59.95 *(978-1-60469-048-4(8)*, 1604690488) Timber Pr., Inc.

BOTANY—LATIN AMERICA

Bernhardt, Ed. Medicinal Plants of Costa Rica. 2008. pap. 12.00 *(978-0-9705678-9-5(8))* Zona Tropical Pubns.
Duke, James A. Duke's Handbook of Medicinal Plants of Latin America. 2008. (ENG., Illus.). 832p. 129.95 *(978-1-4200-4316-7(1)*, CRC Press) Taylor & Francis Group GBR. Dist: Taylor & Francis Group.
Jansen-Jacobs, M. J. Flora of the Guianas Series A: Phanerogams Fascicle 28: Leguminosae Subfamily 87. Mimosoideae. 2011. (Royal Botanic Gardens, Kew-Flora of the Guianas Ser.). (Illus.). 360p. pap. 127.00 *(978-1-84246-437-3(X))* Kew Publishing GBR. Dist: Chicago Distribution Ctr.
Lundell, Cyrus L. The Vegetation of Peten. (Carnegie Institution of Washington Publications: No. 478). reprint ed. 35.00 *(978-0-404-16270-2(3))* AMS Pr., Inc.
Pursell, Ronald A. Fissidentaceae. 2007. (Illus.). 278p. *(978-0-89327-483-2(6))* New York Botanical Garden, The.
Sipman, H. J. M., et al. Hypotrachyna (Parmeliaceae, Lichenized Fungi) 2009. (Illus.). 176p. ***(978-0-89327-502-0(6))*** New York Botanical Garden, The.
Ståhl, Bertil. Theophrastaceae. 2010. (Illus.). 160p. ***(978-0-89327-507-5(7))*** New York Botanical Garden, The.
Zuchowski, Willow. Tropical Blossoms of Costa Rica. 2008. pap. 12.00 *(978-0-9705678-8-8(X))* Zona Tropical Pubns.
—Tropical Trees of Costa Rica. 2008. pap. 12.00 *(978-0-9705678-7-1(1))* Zona Tropical Pubns.

BOTANY—MADAGASCAR

Cribb, Phillip & Hermans, Johan. Field Guide to the Orchids of Madagascar. 2010. (Illus.). 456p. 109.00 *(978-1-84246-158-7(3))* Kew Publishing GBR. Dist: Chicago Distribution Ctr.

BOTANY—MEDITERRANEAN REGION

Harris, Stephen. The Magnificent Flora Graeca: How the Mediterranean Came to the English Garden. 2007. (Illus.). 192p. 60.00 *(978-1-85124-306-8(2))* Bodleian Library GBR. Dist: Chicago Distribution Ctr.
Heinrich, Michael, et al. Local Mediterranean Food Plants & Nutraceuticals, Vol. 59. (Forum of Nutrition Ser.: Vol. 59). (Illus.). *(978-3-8055-8124-0(6))* Karger, S. AG.
Maxted, N. & Bennett, Sarita Jane, eds. Plant Genetic Resources of Legumes in the Mediterranean. 2010. (Current Plant Science & Biotechnology in Agriculture Ser.). (Illus.). 408p. pap. 289.00 *(978-90-481-5613-9(0)*, 9048156130) Springer.
Ruigómez, Juan Manuel, ed. Mediterranean Seagrasses. 2011. (Marine & Freshwater Botany Ser.). (Illus.). 190p. pap. 140.00 *(978-3-11-022966-0(8))* De Gruyter, Walter Inc.
Strid, Arne & Strid, Barbro, eds. Flora Graeca Sibthorpian: Sive plantarum rariorum historia, quas in provinciis aut insulis Graeciae legit, investigavit et depingi curavit Johannes Sibthorp, 3, 2. 2010. (ENG & LAT., Illus.). 412p. reprint ed. lib. bdg. 350.00 *(978-3-906166-80-3(5)*, Gantner Publishing) Koeltz Scientific Bks. DEU. Dist: Lubrecht & Cramer, Ltd.

BOTANY—MEXICO

Akers, Brian, ed. The Sacred Mushrooms of Mexico: Assorted Texts. 2006. (ENG.). 192p. per. 34.99 *(978-0-7618-3582-0(2))* Univ. Pr. of America, Inc.
Arrieta, Yolanda Herrera & Peterson, Paul M. Muhlenbergia (Poaceae) de Chihuahua, Mexico. 2006. (SIDA, Botanical Miscellany Ser.: 29). (SPA.). pap. *(978-1-889878-16-4(2))* Botanical Research Institute of Texas.
Bateman, James. Orchids of Mexico & Guatemala. 2010. 175p. pap. 64.95 *(978-0-557-65983-8(3))* Lulu Enterprises Inc.
Borhidi, Attila. Rubiaces de Mexico. (SPA., Illus.). 512p. (C). *(978-963-05-8265-0(1))* Akademia Kiado.
Dicht, Reto & Lüthy, Adrian D. Coryphantha: Cacti of Mexico & Southern USA. 2010. Orig. Title: Coryphantha. (Illus.). viii, 200p. pap. 159.00 *(978-3-642-06096-0(X)*, 364206096X) Springer.
Friese, Kurt Michael, et al. Chasing Chiles: Hot Spots along the Pepper Trail. 2011. (ENG.). 224p. pap. 17.95 *(978-1-60358-250-6(9))* Chelsea Green Publishing.
Lieth, Helmut, et al, eds. Mangroves & Halophytes: Restoration & Utilisation. (Tasks for Vegetation Science Ser.). (Illus.). 2010. lviii, 162p. pap. 179.00 *(978-90-481-7704-2(9)*, 9048177049) 2008. 214p. 179.00 *(978-1-4020-6719-8(4)*, 1402067194) Springer.
Perry, Jesse P. The Pines of Mexico & Central America. 2009. (ENG.). 234p. pap. 39.95 *(978-1-60469-110-8(7)*, 1604691107) Timber Pr., Inc.

B

Ramirez-Lozano, Roque G. Browse Foliage As Protein Supplement for Sheep Fed Low Quality Diets. 2011. 120p. pap. (978-3-8443-3156-1(5)) Lambert Academic Publishing.

Rebman, Jon Paul, et al. Baja California Plant Field Guide. 3rd ed. 2012. (978-0-916251-18-5(7)) Sunbelt Pubns., Inc.

Turner, Billie. The Comps of Mexico: Chapter 8: Liabeae & Vernonieae. 2007. per. (978-0-9792529-0-7(3)) Texensis Publishing.

BOTANY—MIDDLE EAST

Batanouny, Kamal H. Plants in the Deserts of the Middle East. 2010. (Adaptations of Desert Organisms Ser.). (Illus.). xii, 193p. pap. 319.00 (978-3-642-08092-0(8), 3642080928) Springer.

Dowling, Alfred E. P. Raymund. The Flora of the Sacred Nativity. 2009. 104p. pap. 19.99 (978-1-151-57908-9(4)) General Bks. LLC.

Gichua, Moses. Survival Challenges of a Resilient Desert Tree. 2009. 52p. pap. (978-3-639-20245-8(7)) VDM Verlag Dr. Mueller e.K.

Pickering, Helen & Patzelt, Annette. Field Guide to the Wild Plants of Oman. 2010. (ENG., Illus.). 281p. 64.00 (978-1-84246-177-8(X)) Kew Publishing GBR. Dist: Chicago Distribution Ctr.

Sadeghi, Tahereh & Sedaghat, Reza. Investigation of Advertisement Strategies Regarded to Iran's Pistachio. 2011. 148p. pap. (978-3-8443-1281-2(1)) Lambert Academic Publishing.

BOTANY—NETHERLANDS

A-Tjak, Dennis. Royal Flowers of the Netherlands. 2009. (ENG., Illus.). 192p. (978-90-5897-977-3(6), Lannoo Pubs. (Acc)) Antique Collectors' Club.

Faasse, Patricia E. In Splendid Isolation: A History of the Willie Commelin Scholten Phytopathology Laboratory, 1894-1992. 2010. (Edita - History of Science & Scholarship in the Netherlands Ser.). (ENG., Illus.). 304p. 60.00 (978-90-6984-541-8(5)) Koninklijke Nederlandse Academie van Wetenschappen NLD. Dist: Chicago Distribution Ctr.

Schipper, C. A., ed. Assessment of Effects of Chemical Contaminants in Dredged Material on Marine: Ecosystems & Human Health. 2009. (Deltares Select Ser.). 164p. pap. 85.00 (978-1-60750-085-8(X)) IOS Pr., Inc.

BOTANY—NEW GUINEA

Novotny, Vojtech & Short, David. Notebooks from New Guinea: Reflections on Life, Nature, & Science from the Depths of the Rainforest. 2009. (ENG., Illus.). 256p. 39.95 (978-0-19-956165-0(6)) Oxford Univ. Pr., Inc.

Van Royen, P. Alpine Flora of New Guinea, 4 vols., Set. Incl. Vol. 1. General. 1980. lib. bdg. 66.00 (978-3-7682-1243-4(2)); Vol. 2. Taxonomic Pt. 1: Cupressaceae to Poaceae. 1980. lib. bdg. 198.00 (978-3-7682-1244-1(0)); Vol. 3. Taxonomic Pt. 2: Winteraceae to Polygonaceae. 1982. lib. bdg. 198.00 (978-3-7682-1245-8(9)); Vol. 4. Taxonomic Pt. 3: Fagaceae to Asteraceae. 1983. lib. bdg. 660.00 (978-3-7682-1246-5(7)); 660.00 (978-3-7682-1247-2(5)) Lubrecht & Cramer, Ltd.

World Health Organization. Medicinal Plants in Papua New Guinea. 2009. (Western Pacific Ser.). 321p. pap. 42.00 (978-92-9061-249-0(5)) World Health Organization.

BOTANY—NEW ZEALAND

Cockayne, Leonard. The Vegetation of New Zealand. 2011. (Cambridge Library Collection - Life Sciences Ser.). (ENG., Illus.). 582p. pap. 43.00 (978-1-108-03238-4(9)) Cambridge Univ. Pr.

Engel, John J. & Glenny, David. A Flora of the Liverworts & Hornworts of New Zealand. 2008. (Monographs in Systematic Botany from the Missouri Botanical Garden: Vol. 110). (Illus.). (978-1-930723-66-5(0)) Missouri Botanical Garden Pr.

—A Flora of the Liverworts & Hornworts of New Zealand, Vol. 1. 2008. (Monographs in Systematic Botany from the Missouri Botanical Garden). (Illus.). 898p. 105.00 (978-1-930723-67-2(9)) Missouri Botanical Garden Pr.

Hooker, Joseph Dalton. Handbook of the New Zealand Flora: A Systematic Description of the Native Plants of New Zealand & the Chatham, Kermadec's, Lord Auckland's, Campbell's, & Macquarrie's Islands, 2 vols. 2011. (Cambridge Library Collection - Life Sciences Ser.). Vol. 1. 484p. pap. 35.99 (978-1-108-03039-7(4)) Vol. 2. 416p. pap. 31.99 (978-1-108-03040-3(8)) Cambridge Univ. Pr.

—Handbook of the New Zealand Flora 2 Volume Set: A Systematic Description of the Native Plants of New Zealand & the Chatham, Kermadec's, Lord Auckland's, Campbell's, & Macquarrie's Islands. 2011. (Cambridge Library Collection - Life Sciences Ser.). 894p. pap., pap. 66.00 (978-1-108-03041-0(6)) Cambridge Univ. Pr.

BOTANY—NORTH AMERICA

see also Wild Flowers—United States

Allen, Sarah G., et al. Marine Mammals of the Pacific Coast: Baja, California, Oregon, Washington, British Columbia. 2011. (California Natural History Guides). (Illus.). 584p. 60.00 (978-0-520-26544-8(0)); pap. 24.95 (978-0-520-26545-5(9)) Univ. of California Pr.

Anderton, Laurel K. & Barkworth, Mary E., eds. Grasses of the Intermountain Region. 2009. (ENG.). 576p. (C). (gr. 13). pap. 74.95 (978-0-87421-765-0(2), Utah State Univ. Pr.) Univ. Pr. of Colorado.

Antoniades, Dermot, et al. Diatoms of North America: The Freshwater Floras of Prince Patrick, Ellef Ringnes & Northern Ellesmere Islands from the Canadian Arctic Archipelago. Lange-Bertalot, Horst, ed. 2007. (Iconographia Diatomologica Ser.: Vol. 17). (Illus.). 530p. 225.00 (978-3-906166-50-6(3), Gantner Publishing) Koeltz Scientific Bks. DEU. Dist: Lubrecht & Cramer, Ltd.

Barkworth, Mary E., et al, eds. Manual of Grasses for North America. 2007. (ENG., Illus.). 640p. (C). (gr. 13). per. 89.95 (978-0-87421-686-8(9), Utah State Univ. Pr.) Univ. Pr. of Colorado.

Barton, William Paul Crillon. A Flora of North America - 2009. 178p. pap. 27.45 (978-1-4446-5335-9(0)) Harrison House Pubs.

Benoliel, Doug. Northwest Foraging: The Classic Guide to Edible Plants of the Pacific Northwest. 2011. (Illus.). 220p. E-Book (978-1-59485-367-8(3)) Mountaineers Bks., The.

Bessette, Alan. North American Mushrooms: A Guide to the Genus Tricholoma. 2012. E-Book (978-0-292-74234-5(7)) Univ. of Texas Pr.

Bessette, Alan, et al. Milk Mushrooms of North America: A Field Identification Guide to the Genus Lactarius. 2009. (978-0-8156-3229-0(0)) Syracuse Univ. Pr.

Bessette, Alan E., et al. North American Boletes: A Color Guide to the Fleshy Pored Mushrooms. 2010. (Illus.). 396p. pap. (978-0-8156-3244-3(4)) Syracuse Univ. Pr.

Brown, Paul Martin. Wild Orchids of the Prairies & Great Plains Region of North America. 2006. (ENG., Illus.). 352p. pap. 29.95 (978-0-8130-2975-7(9)) Univ. Pr. of Florida.

Chmielewski, Jerry G. A Pictorial & Ethnobotanical Guide to Plants of Eastern North America. 2011. 364p. pap. 85.88 (978-1-4567-4845-6(9)) AuthorHouse.

Coombes, Allen J. The A to Z of Plant Names: A Quick Reference Guide to 4000 Garden Plants. 2012. (ENG.). 312p. 19.95 (978-1-60469-196-2(4)) Timber Pr., Inc.

Dodson, Carolyn. A Guide to Plants of the Northern Chihuahuan Desert. 2012. (978-0-8263-5022-0(4)); (ENG., Illus.). 208p. pap. 24.95 (978-0-8263-5021-3(6)) Univ. of New Mexico Pr.

Douglas, David. Journal Kept by David Douglas during his Travels in North America 1823-1827: Together with a Particular Description of Thirty-Three Species of American Oaks & Eighteen Species of Pinus. 2011. (Cambridge Library Collection - Life Sciences Ser.). (ENG., Illus.). 380p. pap. 31.99 (978-1-108-03377-0(6)) Cambridge Univ. Pr.

Edwards, Barbara & Olivella, Mary. From Tree to Table: Growing Backyard Fruit Trees in the Pacific Maritime Climate. 2011. (ENG.). 192p. pap. (978-1-59485-518-4(8)); E-Book (978-1-59485-519-1(6)) Mountaineers Bks., The.

Flora of North America Editorial Committ, creator. Bryophytes Vol. 27, Pt. 1: Mosses. 2007. (Flora of North America Ser.). (ENG., Illus.). 734p. 95.00 (978-0-19-531823-4(4)) Oxford Univ. Pr., Inc.

Flora of North America Editorial Committee, ed. Flora of North American, Vol. 8. 2009. (Flora n America Ser.). (ENG., Illus.). 624p. 95.00 (978-0-19-534026-6(4)) Oxford Univ. Pr., Inc.

—Magnoliophyta Vol. 7: Salicaceae to Brassicaceae. 2010. (Flora of North America Ser.). (ENG., Illus.). 500p. 95.00 (978-0-19-531822-7(6)) Oxford Univ. Pr., Inc.

Gray, Asa. Manual of the Botany of the Northern United States. 2009. 128p. pap. (978-0-217-01562-2(X)); 176p. pap. (978-0-217-01578-3(6)) Books LLC.

Harshberger, John W. Phytogeographic Survey of North America: A Consideration of the Phytogeography of the North American Continent, Including Mexico, Central America & the West Indies. (Illus.). 790p. reprint ed. lib. bdg. 148.00 (978-0-7222-3077-0(X)) Library Reprints, Inc.

Jaynes, Richard A. Kalmia: Mountain Laurel & Related Species. 3rd ed. 2009. (ENG.). 362p. pap. 34.95 (978-1-60469-122-1(0), 1604691220) Timber Pr., Inc.

John M. Coulter. A Preliminary Revision of the North American Species of Cactus, Anhalonium, & Lophophora. 2006. (ENG.). 72p. pap. 16.99 (978-1-4264-0040-7(3)); 70p. pap. 12.99 (978-1-4264-0169-5(8)) BiblioBazaar.

Kratsch, Heidi, ed. Water-Efficient Landscaping in the Intermountain West: A Step by Step Guide for Professionals & Do it Yourselfers. 2010. (ENG.). 232p. pap. 29.95 (978-0-87421-789-6(X), Utah State Univ. Pr.) Univ. Pr. of Colorado.

Losing Ground: The War on Buffelgrass in the Sonoran Desert: Oversight Field Hearing Before the Subcommittee on National Parks, Forests, & Public Lands of the Committee on Natural Resources, U.S. House of Representatives, One Hundred Eleventh Congress, Second Session, Saturday, April 10, 2010, in Tucson, Arizona. 2010. iii, 48p. (978-0-16-086591-6(3), 552-070-41579-3) United States Government Printing Office.

Lyle, Katie. Complete Guide to Edible Wild Plants Mushrooms Fruits & Nuts E02. 2nd ed. 2010. (Guide to Ser.). (ENG., Illus.). 224p. pap. 14.95 (978-1-59921-887-8(9), Falcon Guides) Globe Pequot Pr., The.

McLaughlin, Steven P. Tundra to Tropics: The Floristic Plant Geography of North America. 2007. (Illus.). 58p. pap. 20.00 (978-1-889878-17-1(0)) Botanical Research Institute of Texas.

Moerman, Daniel E. & Eierman, Colby. Native American Food Plants: An Ethnobotanical Dictionary. 2010. (ENG & ACE., Illus.). 458p. 34.95 (978-1-60469-189-4(1), 1604691891) Timber Pr., Inc.

—Native American Medicinal Plants: An Ethnobotanical Dictionary. 2009. (ENG., Illus.). 800p. pap. 29.95 (978-0-88192-987-4(5), 0881929875) Timber Pr., Inc.

National Research Council Staff. Status of Pollinators in North America. 2007. (ENG.). 322p. pap. 56.00 (978-0-309-10289-6(8)) National Academies Pr.

Nold, Robert. High & Dry: Gardening with Cold-Hardy Dryland Plants. 2008. (ENG., Illus.). 420p. 34.95 (978-0-88192-872-3(0), 0881928720) Timber Pr., Inc.

Reaume, Tom. 620 Wild Plants of North America. 2008. (Canadian Plains Studies(CPS) Ser.). (ENG., Illus.). 784p. 65.00 (978-0-88977-214-4(2)) Canadian Plains Research Ctr. CAN. Dist: Univ. of Toronto Pr.

Rogers, Robert. The Fungal Pharmacy: The Complete Guide to Medicinal Mushrooms & Lichens of North America. 2011. (ENG., Illus.). 608p. pap. 29.95 (978-1-55643-953-7(9)) North Atlantic Bks.

Stubbendieck, James L., et al. North American Wildland Plants: A Field Guide. 2nd ed. 2011. (ENG., Illus.). 520p. pap. 35.00 (978-0-8032-3485-7(6)) Univ. of Nebraska Pr.

Telander, Todd. Mushrooms: A Falcon Field Guide [tm]. 2012. (Falcon Field Guide Ser.). (ENG., Illus.). 104p. pap. 9.95 (978-0-7627-7423-4(1), Falcon Guides) Globe Pequot Pr., The.

Trudell, Steven A., et al. North American Mushrooms: A Guide to the Genus Tricholoma. 2013. (ENG.). 224p. pap. 29.95 (978-0-292-74233-8(9)) Univ. of Texas Pr.

Turner, Nancy J. & von Aderkas, Patrick. Common Poisonous Plants & Mushrooms: How to Identify More Than 200 Toxic Plants Found in Homes, Gardens, & Open Spaces. 2009. (ENG., Illus.). 376p. 29.95 (978-0-88192-929-4(8), 0881929298) Timber Pr., Inc.

Welsh, Stanley L. North American Species of Astragalus. 2006. (Illus.). (C). (978-0-8425-2662-3(5), Brigham Young Univ. Pr.) Brigham Young Univ.

Whitney, Stephen R. & Hart, Elizabeth Briars. Southwest Cacti, Trees & Shrubs. 2006. (Mac's Guides). (ENG., Illus.). 1p. 6.95 (978-1-59485-016-5(X)) Mountaineers Bks., The.

Young, James A. & Clements, Charlie D. Cheatgrass: Fire & Forage on the Range. 2009. (ENG., Illus.). 368p. 44.95 (978-0-87417-765-7(0)) Univ. of Nevada Pr.

Young, James A. & Young, Cheryl G. Seeds of Woody Plants in North America. rev. enl. ed. 2009. (ENG.). 416p. pap. 49.95 (978-1-60469-112-2(3), 1604691123) Timber Pr., Inc.

BOTANY—PANAMA

Garwood, Nancy C. Seedlings of Barro Colorado Island. 2009. (Illus.). 520p. 99.95 (978-0-8014-4753-2(4), Comstock Publishing Assocs.) Cornell Univ. Pr.

BOTANY—PERU

Lack, H. Walter. Martius - Book of Palm. Lamers-Schutze, Petra, ed. 2009. (GER, FRE & ENG., Illus.). 450p. 150.00 (978-3-8365-1779-9(5)) TASCHEN DEU. Dist: Ingram Pub. Services.

Schultes, Richard Evans & Ruiz, Hipólito. The Journals of Hipolito Ruiz. 2009. (ENG.). 368p. pap. 44.95 (978-1-60469-082-8(8), 1604690828) Timber Pr., Inc.

Towle, Margaret A. The Ethnobotany of Pre-Columbian Peru. 2007. (ENG., Illus.). 183p. pap. 19.95 (978-0-202-30930-9(4)) Aldine Transaction.

BOTANY—PHILIPPINES

Merrill, Elmer D. An Enumeration of Philippine Flowering Plants. 2009. (ENG.). 474p. 33.99 (978-1-117-71999-3(5), BiblioLife); pap. 36.75 (978-1-117-72000-5(4)); pap. 28.99 (978-1-117-72001-2(2), BiblioLife) BiblioBazaar.

BOTANY—SINGAPORE

Koh, Hwee Ling. A Guide to Medicinal Plants: An Illustrated Scientific & Medicinal Approach. 2009. 312p. 99.00 (978-981-283-709-7(4)) World Scientific Publishing Co., Inc.

BOTANY—SOUTH AFRICA

Butchart, Duncan. Wild about Johannesburg. (Illus.). 128p. pap. 14.95 (978-1-86812-595-1(5)) Southern Bk. Pubs. ZAF. Dist: Continental Enterprises Group, Inc. (CEG).

Carruthers, Vincent. The Wildlife of Southern Africa: A Field Guide to the Animals & Plants of the Region. 2008. (Illus.). 320p. pap. 28.00 (978-1-77007-704-1(9)) Struik Pubs. ZAF. Dist: International Publishers Marketing.

Emmett, et al. Game Ranger in Your Backpack: All-in-one interpretive Guide to the Lowveld. 2012. (Illus.). 352p. pap. 37.95 (978-1-920217-06-8(1)) International Publishers Marketing.

Gutteridge, Lee. The Bushveld: A South African Field Guide. 2011. 704p. pap. 49.95 (978-1-920143-53-4(X)) 30° South Pubs. ZAF. Dist: International Publishers Marketing.

Henderson, Andrew, et al. Palms of Southern Asia. 2009. (Princeton Field Guides). (ENG., Illus.). 264p. (C). 90.00 (978-0-691-13449-9(9)) Princeton Univ. Pr.

Hoberman, Gerald. The World's Richest Floral Kingdom: South Africa's Botanical Wonderland. 2009. (Meridian Ser. - an imprint of the Hoberman Collection: the World's Richest Floral Kingdom (South Africa's Botanical Wonderland) Ser.). (Illus.). 64p. 9.95 (978-1-919939-50-6(4)) Hoberman, Gerald Pubns. ZAF. Dist: Perseus Bks. Group.

Joubert, Leonie. Invaded: The Biological Invasion of South Africa. 2009. (ENG.). 368p. pap. 39.95 (978-1-86814-478-5(X)) Witwatersrand Univ. Pr. Pubns. ZAF. Dist: Transaction Pubs.

Pepler, Dave. Forever Green. 2010. 160p. pap. 39.95 (978-0-7981-5094-1(7)) NB Pubs. Ltd. ZAF. Dist: International Publishers Marketing.

Smith, Gideon & Crouch, Neil. Guide to Succulents of Southern Africa. 2009. (Illus.). 136p. pap. 19.95 (978-1-77007-662-4(X)) Struik Pubs. ZAF. Dist: International Publishers Marketing.

BOTANY—SOUTH AMERICA

Alvarez Mejía, Luis Miguel. Plantas de la Región Centro-Sur de Caldas. 2007. (SPA., Illus.). 526p. (978-958-8319-24-7(2)) Univ. de Caldas.

Carvajal Rojas, Lyndon & Murillo-A, José. Análisis Florístico y Fitogeográfico Del Sector Nororiental de la Sierra de la Macarena, Colombia. 2007. (SPA., Illus.). 214p. (978-958-8337-19-7(4)) Universidad Distrital Francisco Jose de Caldas.

Cornejo, Fernando & Janovec, John. Seeds of Amazonian Plants. 2010. (Princeton Field Guides). (ENG., Illus.). 186p. pap. 35.00 (978-0-691-14647-8(0)) Princeton Univ. Pr.

Isaza, Carolina. Palm Fibre in South Americ. 2011. 92p. pap. (978-3-8433-8704-0(4)) Lambert Academic Publishing.

Kronik, Jakob. Living Knowledge. 2010. 220p. pap. (978-3-8383-4490-4(1)) Lambert Academic Publishing.

Luer, Carlyle A. Icones Pleurothallidinarum XXX (30) Lepanthes of Jamaica; Systematics of Stelis, Stelis of Ecuador, Part Four. 2009. (Illus.). 265p. 80.00 (978-1-930723-82-5(2)) Missouri Botanical Garden Pr.

—Icones Pleurothallidinarum XXXI (31) Lepanthes of Boliva; Systematics of Octomeria Species North & West of Brazil. 2010. (Illus.). 154p. pap. 65.00 (978-1-935641-00-1(X)) Missouri Botanical Garden Pr.

Maguire, Bassett, et al. The Botany of the Guayana Highland, Part: Memoirs of the New York Botanical Garden, V8, No. 2, April 1953. 2011. 78p. 37.95 (978-1-258-09113-2(5)) Literary Licensing, LLC.

Roth, I. & Lindorf, H. South American Medicinal Plants: Botany, Remedial Properties & General Use. 2010. (Illus.). xi, 492p. pap. 329.00 (978-3-642-07544-5(4), 3642075444) Springer.

Zuloaga, Fernando O., et al, eds. Catalogo de las Plantas Vasculares del Cono Sur, 3 vols. 2008. (SPA.). 3348p. 375.00 (978-1-930723-70-2(9)) Missouri Botanical Garden Pr.

Zuloaga, Fernando O., et al. Catálogo de Las Plantas Vasculares Del Cono Sur: (Argentina, Sur de Brasil, Chile, Paraguay y Uruguay), 3 vols. 2008. (SPA., Illus.). vi, 3348p. (978-1-930723-75-7(X)); (978-1-930723-74-0(1)); (978-1-930723-76-4(8)) Missouri Botanical Garden Pr.

BOTANY—SOVIET UNION

Cambridge University Press Staff, ed. Index to Flora of the USSR. 2006. (Flora of the USSR Ser.: 31). (Illus.). 684p. lib. bdg. 225.00 (978-3-906166-51-3(1), Gantner Publishing) Koeltz Scientific Bks. DEU. Dist: Lubrecht & Cramer, Ltd.

Czerepanov, S. K. Vascular Plants of Russia & Adjacent States (the Former USSR) 2007. (ENG., Illus.). 532p. pap. 105.00 (978-0-521-04483-7(9)) Cambridge Univ. Pr.

Fedorov, A. A., ed. Flora of Russia Vol. 4: The European Part & Bordering Regions. 2006. (ENG., Illus.). 722p. 247.95 (978-90-5410-759-0(6), CRC Press) Taylor & Francis Group GBR. Dist: Taylor & Francis Group.

Kashina, L. I., et al. Flora of Siberia: Keys to Families (Dichotomous & Polytomous), Supplements on Taxonomy & Chorology of Genera & Species & Alphabetical Indices to Genera & Species of Plants. Malyschev, L. I., ed. 2008. (Flora of Siberia Ser.). (ENG., Illus.). 210p. 99.95 (978-1-57808-113-4(0)) BIOS Scientific Publishers Ltd. GBR. Dist: Taylor & Francis Group.

Levin, Gregory M. Pomegranate Roads: A Soviet Botanist's Exile from Eden. Baer, Barbara L., ed. 2006. (Illus.). 216p. pap. 18.00 (978-0-9649497-6-8(8)) Floreant Pr.

Seledets, Vitaly P. & Probatova, Nina S. Ecological Ranges & Ecological Niches of Plant Species in the Monsoon Zone of Pacific Russia. 2012. pap. (978-1-62100-434-9(1)) Nova Science Pubs., Inc.

Sukhorukikh, IU I. Lesnye Plodovye Vidy Severo-Zapadnogo Kavkaza: V Trekh Knigakh. 2010. (RUS., Illus.). (978-5-9703-0267-5(8)) Kacestvo.

Tzvelev. Flora of Russia, Vol. 10B. 2007. (ENG.). 480p. 304.45 (978-90-5410-761-3(8), Taylor & Francis) Taylor & Francis Group GBR. Dist: Taylor & Francis Group.

BOTANY—SPAIN

Amat Llombart, Pablo & Llombart, Pablo Amat. La Propiedad Industrial Sobre Obtenciones Vegetales y Organismos Transgénicos. 2007. (SPA.). 414p. (978-84-8456-767-7(2)) Tirant lo Blanch.

Beckett, Elspeth. Illustrated Flora of Mallorca. (SPA., Illus.). 226p. (978-84-273-0714-8(4)) Moll, Editorial ESP. Dist: Vine Hse. Distribution.

Bleichmar, Daniela. Visible Empire: Botanical Expeditions & Visual Culture in the Hispanic Enlightenment. 2012. (ENG., Illus.). 288p. 55.00 (978-0-226-05853-5(0)) Univ. of Chicago Pr.

BOTANY—TROPICS

Benzing, David H. Vascular Epiphytes: General Biology & Related Biota. 2008. (Cambridge Tropical Biology Ser.). (ENG.). 376p. pap. 74.00 (978-0-521-04895-8(8)) Cambridge Univ. Pr.

Litz, Richard E. The Mango: Botany, Production & Uses. 2nd ed. 2009. (Illus.). 696p. 255.00 (978-1-84593-489-7(X)) CABI GBR. Dist: Stylus Publishing, LLC.

Rundel, Philip W., et al, eds. Tropical Alpine Environments: Plant Form & Function. 2008. (ENG., Illus.). 392p. pap. 79.00 (978-0-521-05411-9(7)) Cambridge Univ. Pr.

BOTANY—TURKEY

Davis, Peter. Flora of Turkey, 11 vols., Set. 2009. (Flora of Turkey Ser.). (ENG., Illus.). 7724p. (gr. 17). 3600.00 (978-0-7486-3777-5(X)) Edinburgh Univ. Pr. GBR. Dist: Columbia Univ. Pr.

BOTANY—UNITED STATES

see also Botany—Alaska; Botany—Hawaii

Albright, Carla. Coastal Gardening in the Pacific Northwest: From Northern California to British Columbia. 2007. (ENG., Illus.). 256p. per. 19.95 (978-1-58979-317-0(X)) Taylor Trade Publishing.

Allred, Kelly W. Flora Neomexicana II: Glossarium Nominum. 2009. 142p. 29.95 (978-0-557-05313-1(7)); pap. 19.95 (978-0-557-05157-1(6)) Lulu Enterprises Inc.

Armitage, Allan M. Armitage's Vines & Climbers: A Gardener's Guide to the Best Vertical Plants. 2010. (ENG., Illus.). 212p. 29.95 *(978-1-60469-039-2(9),* 1604690399) Timber Pr., Inc.

Arnett, Joseph. Field Guide to the Rare Plants of Washington. Camp, Pamela & Gamon, John G., eds. 2011. (ENG., Illus.). 404p. pap. 39.95 *(978-0-295-99092-7(9))* Univ. of Washington Pr.

Arnfield, Edwin A. Roadside Guide to Michigan Plants, Trees, & Flowers: An Ecological Approach. 2009. (ENG., Illus.). 124p. pap. 18.95 *(978-1-933926-12-4(0))* Arbutus Pr.

Baker, Christine. Cherry Blossom Land at Branch Brook Park: A Bamberger Fuld Legacy. 2010. 32p. pap. 17.95 *(978-1-4520-0014-5(X))* AuthorHouse.

Barkworth, Mary E., et al, eds. Manual of Grasses for North America. 2007. (ENG., Illus.). 640p. (C). (gr. 13). per. 89.95 *(978-0-87421-686-8(9),* Utah State Univ. Pr.) Univ. Pr. of Colorado.

Beal, W. J. Michigan Flora: A List of the Fern & Seed Plants Growing Without Cultivation. 3rd ed. (Illus.). reprint ed. lib. bdg. 125.00 *(978-0-7222-0080-3(3))* Library Reprints, Inc.

Beardslee, Henry C. Catalogue of the Plants of Ohio, Including Flowering Plants, Ferns, Mosses & Liverworts by H C Beardslee. 2011. 26p. pap. 11.99 ***(978-1-4181-9289-1(9))*** MPublishing.

Beers, Terry & Elrod, Emily. Califauna: A Literary Field Guide. 2007. (California Legacy Ser.). (Illus.). 293p. per. *(978-1-59714-049-2(X))* Santa Clara Univ., de Saisset Museum.

Berkeley, Edmund. Dr. John Mitchell: The Man Who Made the Map of North America. 2011. (ENG.). 302p. pap. 40.00 ***(978-0-8078-9618-1(7))*** Univ. of North Carolina Pr.

Bessette, Alan E., et al. Mushrooms of the Southeastern United States. 2007. (Illus.). 373p. 95.00 *(978-0-8156-3112-5(X))* Syracuse Univ. Pr.

Binetti, Marianne & Peters, Laura. Herb Gardening for Washington & Oregon. 2008. (ENG., Illus.). 256p. per. *(978-976-8200-39-6(1))* Lone Pine Publishing International Inc.

Blackwell, Laird R. Tahoe Wildflowers: A Month-by-Month Guide to Wildflowers in the Tahoe Basin & Surrounding Areas. 2007. (Falcon Guide Ser.). (ENG., Illus.). 128p. pap. 14.95 *(978-0-7627-4369-8(7),* Falcon Guides) Globe Pequot Pr., The.

Blanchan, Neltje. Nature's Garden. 2009. 336p. pap. *(978-0-217-73053-2(1));* 526p. pap. *(978-0-217-73057-0(4));* 354p. pap. *(978-0-217-02500-3(5))* Books LLC.

—Nature's Garden. 2007. (ENG.). 434p. 51.95 *(978-0-548-02082-1(5))* Kessinger Publishing, LLC.

Block, Timothy A. & Rhoads, Ann Fowler. Aquatic Plants of Pennsylvania: A Complete Reference Guide. 2011. (Illus.). 320p. (C). 59.95 *(978-0-8122-4306-2(4))* Univ. of Pennsylvania Pr.

Bone, Eugenia. Mycophilia: Revelations from the Weird World of Mushrooms. 2011. (ENG., Illus.). 368p. 25.99 *(978-1-60529-407-0(1))* Rodale Pr., Inc.

Brown, C. A. Ferns & Flowering Plants of Isle Royale, Michigan. (Illus.). reprint ed. lib. bdg. 125.00 *(978-0-7222-0083-4(8))* Library Reprints, Inc.

Bryson, Charles T. & DeFelice, Michael S., eds. Weeds of the Midwestern United States & Central Canada. 2010. (ENG., Illus.). 440p. pap. 44.95 *(978-0-8203-3506-3(1))* Univ. of Georgia Pr.

Cartron, Jean-Luc E., et al. A Field Guide to the Plants & Animals of the Middle Rio Grande Bosque. 2008. (ENG., Illus.). 391p. pap. 21.95 *(978-0-8263-4269-0(8))* Univ. of New Mexico Pr.

Chafin, Linda G. Field Guide to the Rare Plants of Georgia. 2007. ring bd. 34.95 *(978-0-9779621-1-2(3))* State Botanical Garden of Georgia.

—Field Guide to the Rare Plants of Georgia. 2007. (ENG., Illus.). 540p. pap. 34.95 *(978-0-9779621-0-5(5))* State Botanical Garden of Georgia.

Clarke, Oscar F., et al. Flora of the Santa Ana River & Environs: With References to World Botany. 2007. (Illus.). 495p. pap. *(978-1-59714-050-8(3))* Heyday.

Cole, Emma J. Grand Rapids Flora. (Illus.). reprint ed. lib. bdg. 125.00 *(978-0-7222-0084-1(6))* Library Reprints, Inc.

Common Western Range Plants. Date not set. *(978-1-56918-211-6(6))* Visual Education Productions.

Davidson, Alice Merritt. California Plants in Their Homes - a Botanical Reader for Children. 2010. 364p. pap. 31.95 ***(978-1-4455-4322-2(2))*** Barclay Pr., Inc.

Deam, Charles C. Flora of Indiana Set, 2 vols. 1236p. reprint ed. lib. bdg. 250.00 *(978-0-7222-0409-2(4))* Library Reprints, Inc.

Del Tredici, Peter. Wild Urban Plants of the Northeast: A Field Guide. 2010. (Illus.). 392p. pap. 29.95 *(978-0-8014-7458-3(2))* Cornell Univ. Pr.

Dicht, Reto & Lüthy, Adrian D. Coryphantha: Cacti of Mexico & Southern USA. 2010. Orig. Title: Coryphantha. (Illus.). viii, 200p. pap. 159.00 *(978-3-642-06096-0(X),* 364206096X) Springer.

Distribution of Texas' Grasses. 2011. (Illus.). 200p. (YA). pap. *(978-1-889878-32-4(4))* Botanical Research Institute of Texas.

Dodge, Charles K. Contributions to the Botany of Michigan. (Illus.). reprint ed. lib. bdg. 125.00 *(978-0-7222-0086-5(2))* Library Reprints, Inc.

Donaldson, Charles Snyder, et al. The Plant Life of Highlands Hammock, Florid. 2011. 68p. 36.95 ***(978-1-258-05317-8(9))*** Literary Licensing, LLC.

Earle, A. Scott & Reveal, James L. Lewis & Clark's Green World: The Expedition & its Plants. 2006. (Illus.). 256p. reprint ed. 35.00 *(978-1-4223-5804-7(6))* DIANE Publishing Co.

Edwards, Barbara & Olivella, Mary. From Tree to Table: Growing Backyard Fruit Trees in the Pacific Maritime Climate. 2011. (ENG.). 192p. pap. ***(978-1-59485-518-4(8))***; E-Book ***(978-1-59485-519-1(6))*** Mountaineers Bks., The.

Elias, Thomas & Dykeman, Peter. Edible Wild Plants: A North American Field Guide to over 200 Natural Foods. 2009. (ENG., Illus.). 288p. pap. 19.95 *(978-1-4027-6715-9(3))* Sterling Publishing Co., Inc.

Evenhuis, N. L. & Fitzsimmons, J. Michael. Biology of Hawaiian Streams & Estuaries: Proceedings of the Symposium on the Biology of Hawaiian Streams & Estuaries: Hilo, Hawaii, 26-27 April 2005. 2007. (Illus.). viii, 334p. pap. *(978-1-58178-053-6(2))* Bishop Museum Pr.

The Everglades Handbook. 2011. (C). 59.95 ***(978-1-4398-0264-9(5),*** **CRC Press)** Taylor & Francis Group GBR. Dist: Taylor & Francis Group.

Everitt, James H., et al. Grasses of South Texas: A Guide to Identification & Value. 2011. (Grover E. Murray Studies in the American Southwest Ser.). (ENG., Illus.). 336p. (C). pap. 49.95 *(978-0-89672-668-0(1))* Texas Tech Univ. Pr.

Evert, Ray F. Esau's Plant Anatomy: Meristems, Cells, & Tissues of the Plant Body: Their Structure, Function, & Development. 3rd rev. ed. 2006. (ENG., Illus.). 624p. 209.95 *(978-0-471-73843-5(3),* Wiley-Liss) Wiley, John & Sons, Inc.

Fairchild, Barbara. Tried & True Missouri Native Plants for Your Yard. 2007. 58p. pap. 7.95 *(978-1-887247-58-0(0))* Missouri Dept. of Conservation.

Fillius, Margaret L. Native Plants: Torrey Pines State Reserve & nearby San Diego County Locations. 2nd rev. ed. 2007. spiral bd. *(978-0-9769047-1-7(3))* Fillius Interests.

Flowers, Seville, et al. Ecological Studies of the Flora & Fauna of Flaming Gorge Reservoir Basin, Utah & Wyoming. (Upper Colorado Ser.: No. 3). reprint ed. 42.00 *(978-0-404-60648-0(2))* AMS Pr., Inc.

Friend, Sandra. Exploring Florida's Botanical Wonders: A Guide to Ancient Trees, Unique Flora, & Wildflower Walks. 2009. (Wild Florida Ser.). (ENG., Illus.). 160p. pap. 24.95 *(978-0-8130-3411-9(6))* Univ. Pr. of Florida.

Gadd, Alix Marie Craig. Northern Colorado Plants: A Field Guide to the Flora of the Northern Front Range Urban Corridor. 2007. (Illus.). 136p. pap. 19.95 *(978-0-9639642-1-0(7),* NCP1) Travertine Pr.

Gargiullo, Margaret B. A Guide to Native Plants of the New York City Region. 2007. (ENG., Illus.). 306p. 49.95 *(978-0-8135-4042-9(9))* Rutgers Univ. Pr.

Garwood, Nancy C. Seedlings of Barro Colorado Island. 2009. (Illus.). 520p. 99.95 *(978-0-8014-4753-2(4),* Comstock Publishing Assocs.) Cornell Univ. Pr.

Gattinger, Augustin. The Flora of Tennessee & a Philosophy of Botany. (Illus.). 296p. reprint ed. lib. bdg. 98.00 *(978-0-7222-4849-2(0))* Library Reprints, Inc.

Gilmore, Melvin R. Uses of Plants by the Indians of the Missouri River Region. (Illus.). reprint ed. lib. bdg. 98.00 *(978-0-7222-0752-9(2))* Library Reprints, Inc.

Gisel, Bonnie Johanna & Joseph, Stephen J. Nature's Beloved Son: Rediscovering John Muir's Botanical Legacy. 2008. (Illus.). 256p. *(978-1-59714-106-2(2))* Heyday.

Gleason, H. A. The Plants of Michigan. (Illus.). reprint ed. lib. bdg. 125.00 *(978-0-7222-0088-9(9))* Library Reprints, Inc.

Haines, Arthur. New England Wildflower Society's Flora Novae Angliae: A Manual for the Identification of Native & Naturalized Vascular Plants of New England. 2011. (ENG., Illus.). 1008p. 85.00 *(978-0-300-17154-9(4))* Yale Univ. Pr.

Harp, Mark & Beck, Alison. Water Garden Plants for Washington & Oregon. 2008. (ENG., Illus.). 288p. per. *(978-976-8200-40-2(5))* Lone Pine Publishing International Inc.

Hass, Richard, et al. Growing Roses in Cold Climates. rev. ed. 2012. (Illus.). 272p. pap. 34.95 ***(978-0-8166-7593-7(7))*** Univ. of Minnesota Pr.

Haygood, Tamara Miner. Henry William Ravenel, 1814-1887: South Carolina Scientist in the Civil War Era. 2006. (History Amer Science & Technol Ser.). (Illus.). 224p. per. 29.95 *(978-0-8173-5372-8(0))* Univ. of Alabama Pr.

Heizer, Roy. Atlanta's Garden Plants. 2011. (Illus.). 144p. *(978-0-7643-3610-6(2),* Schiffer Publishing Ltd) Schiffer Publishing, Ltd.

Hipp, Andrew L. Field Guide to Wisconsin Sedges: An Introduction to the Genus Carex (Cyperaceae) 2008. (ENG., Illus.). 280p. pap. 27.95 *(978-0-299-22594-0(1))* Univ. of Wisconsin Pr.

Horn, Evelyn. Still Following the Feathered & Flowered: Quiet Adventures in the Realm of Birds & Flowers. 2007. pap. 17.95 *(978-0-9779965-9-9(X))* Lifetime Chronicle Pr.

Huegel, Craig N. Native Plant Landscaping for Florida Wildlife. 2010. (ENG., Illus.). 320p. pap. 24.95 *(978-0-8130-3494-2(9))* Univ. Pr. of Florida.

Huegel, Craig N. Native Wildflowers & Other Ground Covers for Florida Landscapes. 2012. (ENG., Illus.). 336p. pap. 29.95 ***(978-0-8130-3980-0(0))*** Univ. Pr. of Florida.

Ingram, Stephen. Cacti, Agaves, & Yuccas of California & Nevada. 2008. (Illus.). 256p. (ENG.). 35.95 *(978-0-9789971-1-3(5));* pap. 25.95 *(978-0-9789971-0-6(7))* Cachuma Pr.

Irish, Mary. Trees & Shrubs for the Southwest: Woody Plants for Arid Gardens. 2008. (ENG., Illus.). 332p. 34.95 *(978-0-88192-905-8(0),* 0881929050) Timber Pr., Inc.

Ivey, Robert DeWitt. Flowering Plants of New Mexico: Fifth Edition. 2008. (Illus.). 572p. spiral bd. 55.00 *(978-0-9612170-4-4(9))* Ivey, R.D.

Jacobson, Arthur Lee. Wild Plants of Greater Seattle: 2nd Edition. 2008. (Illus.). 496p. pap. 24.95 *(978-0-9622918-5-2(4))* Jacobson, Arthur Lee.

Junak, Steve. A Flora of San Nicolas Island, California. 2008. (Illus.). 235p. pap. *(978-0-916436-06-3(3))* Santa Barbara Botanic Garden.

Kamas, Jim & Stein, Larry. Texas Peach Handbook. 2011. (AgriLife Research & Extension Service Ser.). (Illus.). 172p. pap. 24.95 *(978-1-60344-266-4(9))* Texas A&M Univ. Pr.

Kaul, Robert B., et al. Flora of Nebraska. 2nd ed. 2011. (Illus.). 1000p. pap. ***(978-1-56161-018-1(5))*** Univ. of Nebraska-Lincoln, Institute of Agriculture & Natural Resources, Conservation & Survey Div.

Keator, Glenn & Keator, G. California Plant Families: West of the Sierran Crest & Deserts. 2009. (ENG., Illus.). 272p. 65.00 *(978-0-520-23709-4(9));* pap. 29.95 *(978-0-520-25924-9(5))* Univ. of California Pr.

Keator, Glenn & Middlebrook, Alrie. Designing California Native Gardens: The Plant Community Approach to Artful, Ecological Gardens. 2007. (Illus.). 342p. 70.00 *(978-0-520-23978-4(4));* pap. 34.95 *(978-0-520-25110-6(5))* Univ. of California Pr.

Kingsland, Sharon E. The Evolution of American Ecology, 1890-2000. 2008. (ENG., Illus.). 328p. (gr. 17). pap. 25.00 *(978-0-8018-9087-1(X))* Johns Hopkins Univ. Pr.

Knapp, Denise A., ed. Flora & Ecology of the Santa Monica Mountains. 2007. (Illus.). 198p. pap. 40.00 *(978-0-9796277-0-5(2))* Southern California Botanists.

Knepper, David A. & Musselman, Lytton John. Plants of the Chesapeake Bay: A Guide to Wildflowers, Grasses, Aquatic Vegetation, Trees, Shrubs, & Other Flora. 2012. (ENG., Illus.). 232p. (gr. 17). 65.00 ***(978-1-4214-0497-4(4))*** Johns Hopkins Univ. Pr.

—Plants of the Chesapeake Bay: A Guide to Wildflowers, Grasses, Aquatic Vegetation, Trees, Shrubs, & Other Flora. 2012. (ENG., Illus.). 232p. pap. 24.95 ***(978-1-4214-0498-1(2))*** Johns Hopkins Univ. Pr.

Kramer, Jack. Bromeliads for Home & Garden. 2011. (ENG., Illus.). 176p. pap. 26.95 *(978-0-8130-3544-4(9))* Univ. Pr. of Florida.

Krings, Alexander. Manual of the Vascular Flora of Nags Head Woods, Outer Banks, North Carolina. 2010. (Illus.). 308p. ***(978-0-89327-500-6(X),*** New York Botanical Garden Pr., The) New York Botanical Garden, The.

Lakela, Olga. A Flora of Northeastern Minnesota. 2009. (ENG.). 558p. pap. 60.00 *(978-0-8166-5808-4(0))* Univ. of Minnesota Pr.

Lamb, Susan. 100 Common Wildflowers Tallgrass Prairie. 2007. (Illus.). 72p. pap. 9.95 *(978-1-58369-102-1(2))* Western National Parks Assn.

Lapham, Increase A. Fauna & Flora of Wisconsin by I a Lapham. 2006. 116p. per. 16.99 *(978-1-4255-0733-6(6))* MPublishing.

Lightner, James. San Diego County Native Plants. 3rd ed. 2011. (Illus.). 428p. ***(978-0-9749981-3-8(3))*** San Diego Flora.

Lodge, Thomas E. The Everglades: Understanding the Ecosystem. 3rd ed. 2010. (ENG., Illus.). 422p. (C). instr.'s hndbk. ed. 59.95 *(978-1-4398-0262-5(9),* CRC Press) Taylor & Francis Group GBR. Dist: Taylor & Francis Group.

Loflin, Brian & Loflin, Shirley. Texas Cacti. 2009. (TAM Nature Guides Ser.: No. 42). (ENG.). 312p. pap. 24.00 *(978-1-60344-108-7(5))* Texas A&M Univ. Pr.

Lonard, Robert I., et al. Weeds in South Texas & Northern Mexico: A Guide to Identification. 2007. (Illus.). 240p. pap. 19.95 *(978-0-89672-614-7(2))* Texas Tech Univ. Pr.

Louisiana. Botanical Survey. Report of Botanical Survey of Southern & Central Louisiana, Made During the Year 1870, by a Featherman. 2006. 136p. per. 13.99 *(978-1-4255-0944-6(4))* MPublishing.

Luther, Harry & Benzing, David H. Native Bromeliads of Florida. 2009. (ENG.). 126p. 16.95 *(978-1-56164-448-3(X))* Pineapple Pr., Inc.

Magee, Dennis W. & Ahles, Harry E. Flora of the Northeast: A Manual of the Vascular Flora of New York & Adjacent New York. 2007. (Illus.). 1264p. 95.00 *(978-1-55849-577-7(0))* Univ. of Massachusetts Pr.

Malrose, Mary Alice, ed. Our First Family's Home: The Ohio Governor's Residence & Heritage Garden. 2008. (ENG., Illus.). 144p. pap. 20.00 *(978-0-8214-1791-1(6))* Ohio Univ. Pr.

Marlowe, Jean. Smoky Mountain Secrets: Folk Remedies for the Nature Lover. 2011. 80p. pap. 29.95 ***(978-1-4327-7275-8(9))*** Outskirts Pr., Inc.

Marlowe, Scott. The Cryptid Creatures of Florid. 2011. 116p. pap. ***(978-1-905723-77-5(6))*** CFZ Pr.

McMillan, Patrick D. Rhynchospora (Cyperaceae) of South Carolina & the Eastern United States. 2007. (Biota of South Carolina Ser.: Vol. 5). (Illus.). 269p. *(978-0-9753471-9-5(5))* Clemson Univ. Public Service Publishing.

Metzler, Kenneth J. & Barrett, Juliana P. The Vegetation of Connecticut: A Preliminary Classification. 2006. per. 14.95 *(978-0-942081-15-2(3))* Connecticut Dept. of Environmental Protection, Connecticut Geological & Natural History Survey.

Michigan. Geological Survey. First Biennial Report of the Progress of the Geological Survey of Michigan. 2006. 348p. per. 23.99 *(978-1-4255-3510-0(0))* MPublishing.

Mickulas, Peter Philip. Britton's Botanical Empire: The New York Botanical Garden & American Botany, 1888-1929. 2007. (Memoirs of the New York Botanical Garden Ser.: Vol. 94). (Illus.). 316p. *(978-0-89327-479-5(8))* New York Botanical Garden, The.

Miller, James H., et al. Field Guide for the Identification of Invasive Plants in Southern Forests. 2011. 126p. (C). pap. 35.00 ***(978-1-4379-8745-4(1))*** DIANE Publishing Co.

Mohlenbrock, Robert H. Acanthaceae to Myricaceae: Water Willows to Wax Myrtles. 2008. (Aquatic & Standing Water Plants of the Central Midwest Ser.). (ENG., Illus.). 416p. 67.00 *(978-0-8093-2790-4(2))* Southern Illinois Univ. Pr.

—Nelumbonaceae to Vitaceae: Water Lotuses to Grapes. 2010. (Aquatic & Standing Water Plants of the Central Midwest Ser.). (ENG., Illus.). 488p. 67.00 *(978-0-8093-2894-9(1))* Southern Illinois Univ. Pr.

Mohlenbrock, Robert H. & Thomson, Paul M. Flowering Plants: Smartweeds to Hazelnuts. 2nd ed. 2009. (Illustrated Flora of Illinois Ser.). (ENG., Illus.). 304p. 65.00 *(978-0-8093-2926-7(3))* Southern Illinois Univ. Pr.

Moore, Michael. Medicinal Plants of the Pacific West. 2011. (ENG., Illus.). 360p. pap. 24.95 ***(978-0-89013-539-6(8))*** Museum of New Mexico Pr.

Morley, Thomas. Spring Flora of Minnesota: Including Common Cultivated Plants. 2009. (ENG.). 288p. pap. 50.00 *(978-0-8166-5831-2(5))* Univ. of Minnesota Pr.

Muir, John. A Thousand-Mile Walk to the Gulf. 2009. 270p. 30.99 *(978-1-110-62183-5(3));* 270p. pap. 26.75 *(978-1-110-62180-4(9));* (ENG.). 269p. pap. 21.99 *(978-1-110-62177-4(9),* BiblioLife); (ENG.). 269p. pap. 23.99 *(978-1-110-62178-1(7),* BiblioLife) BiblioBazaar.

—A Thousand-Mile Walk to the Gulf. 2009. 104p. pap. *(978-0-217-31253-0(5))* Books LLC.

—A Thousand-Mile Walk to the Gulf. Bade, William Frederic, ed. 2008. (Illus.). 124p. pap. *(978-1-4099-4179-8(5))* Dodo Pr.

—A Thousand-Mile Walk to the Gulf. Bade, William Frederic, ed. 2008. 274p. 42.95 *(978-0-548-98154-2(X))* 2007. (ENG.). 276p. per. 27.95 *(978-0-548-66593-0(1))* Kessinger Publishing, LLC.

—A Thousand-Mile Walk to the Gulf. 219p. reprint ed. lib. bdg. 98.00 *(978-0-7222-0164-0(8))* Library Reprints, Inc.

Neyland, Ray. A Field Guide to the Ferns & Lycophytes of Louisiana, Including East Texas, Southern Arkansas, & Mississippi. 2011. (Illus.). 104p. pap. 24.95 *(978-0-8071-3785-7(5))* Louisiana State Univ. Pr.

Nicollet, Joseph Nicolas. Report Intended to Illustrate a Map of the Hydrographical Basin of the Upper Mississippi River. (Illus.). 170p. reprint ed. lib. bdg. 88.00 *(978-0-7222-4741-9(9))* Library Reprints, Inc.

Nikitin, Viktor. Plant Guide for U. S. Coastal Restoration & Protection. Esposito, Carmen, ed. 2011. (Botanical Research & Practices Ser.). (Illus.). vii, 131p. pap. 47.00 ***(978-1-61324-863-8(6),*** Nova Science Pubs., Inc.

Nolan, Justin M. Wild Harvest in the Heartland: Ethnobotany in Missouri's Little Dixie. 2007. (ENG., 100p. Illus.). 52.50 *(978-0-7618-3652-0(7));* pap. 26.50 *(978-0-7618-3653-7(5))* Univ. Pr. of America, Inc.

North American Rock Garden Society. Bulbs of North Americ. McGary, Jane, ed. 2009. (ENG.). 308p. pap. 29.95 *(978-1-60469-079-8(8),* 1604690798) Timber Pr., Inc.

Paetzel, Mary. Solitary Wasps & Bees: Their Hidden World in the Siskiyou Mountains. 2010. 174p. pap. 56.20 *(978-0-557-36970-6(3))* Lulu Enterprises Inc.

Palmer, Ernest J. The Flowering Plants of Missouri. annot. ed. (Illus.). 483p. reprint ed. lib. bdg. 98.00 *(978-0-7222-0436-3(8))* Library Reprints, Inc.

Peskin, Perry K. The Search for Lost Habitats: 30 Years of Exploring for Rare & Endangered Plants - Book I. 2006. (Illus.). 272p. pap. 34.95 *(978-1-933197-16-6(1))* Orange Frazer Pr.

Peterson, Maude. How to Know Wild Fruits. 2009. (Gardening in America Ser.). (ENG., Illus.). 392p. pap. 24.95 *(978-1-4290-1423-6(7))* Applewood Bks.

Pike, Carolyn. Black Oak Decline on New York's Long Island. 2011. 132p. pap. ***(978-3-8443-1881-4(X))*** Lambert Academic Publishing.

Porter, Read. Strategies for Effective State Early Detection/Rapid Response Programs for Plant Pests & Pathogens. 2007. iii, 97p. *(978-1-58576-118-0(4))* Environmental Law Institute.

Powell, A. Michael, et al. Cacti of Texas: A Field Guide. 2008. (Grover E. Murray Studies in the American Southwest). 400p. pap. 24.95 *(978-0-89672-611-6(8))* Texas Tech Univ. Pr.

Rabeler, Richard K. Gleason's Plants of Michigan: A Field Guide. Armentrout, Vivienne N., ed. 2007. (ENG., Illus.). 400p. per. 26.95 *(978-0-472-03246-4(1))* Univ. of Michigan Pr.

Ratzlaff, Neal S. & Barth, Roland E. Field Guide to Trees, Shrubs, Woody Vines, Grasses, Sedges & Rushes: Fontenelle Forest & Neale Woods Nature Centers. 2007. 25.00 *(978-0-9748014-1-4(0))* Fontenelle Nature Assn.

Reznicek, Anton A., et al. Field Manual of Michigan Flora. 2012. (ENG., Illus.). 1008p. 25.00 ***(978-0-472-11811-3(0))*** Univ. of Michigan Pr.

Rhoads, Ann Fowler & Block, Timothy A. The Plants of Pennsylvania: An Illustrated Manual. 2nd ed. 2007. (Illus.). 1056p. (C). 79.95 *(978-0-8122-4003-0(0))* Univ. of Pennsylvania Pr.

Richardson, Alfred & King, Ken. Plants of Deep South Texas: A Field Guide to the Woody & Flowering Species. 2011. (Perspectives on South Texas, sponsored by Texas A&M University-Kingsville Ser.). (ENG., Illus.). 448p. pap. 30.00 *(978-1-60344-144-5(1))* Texas A&M Univ. Pr.

Ritter, Matt. Plants of San Luis Obispo: Their Lives & Stories. rev. ed. 2011. (ENG., Illus.). 168p. pap. 23.27 *(978-0-7575-2678-7(0))* Kendall Hunt Publishing Co.

Roberts, Fred M., Jr. The Vascular Plants of Orange County, California: An Annotated Checklist. 2008. (ENG., Illus.). 256p. (C). pap. 17.95 *(978-0-9643847-3-6(6))* Roberts, F.M. Publishing.

Rocky Mountain Research Station, Forest Service (U.S.) & Forest Service (U.S.) Staff, compiled by. Wildland Fire Ecosystems: Fire & Nonnative Invasive Plants. 2008. (ENG., Illus.). 363p. pap. 59.00 *(978-0-16-081465-5(0),* Forest Service) United States Government Printing Office.

Rosendahl, Carl O. & Butters, Frederick K. Guide to the Autumn Flowers of Minnesota: Field & Garden. (Illus.). 77p. reprint ed. lib. bdg. 88.00 *(978-0-7222-4760-0(5))* Library Reprints, Inc.

—Guide to the Ferns & Fern Allies of Minnesota. (Illus.). 22p. reprint ed. lib. bdg. 88.00 *(978-0-7222-4754-9(0))* Library Reprints, Inc.

Rothrock, Paul Ernest. Sedges of Indiana & the Adjacent States: The Non-Carex Species. 2009. *(978-1-883362-14-0(8))* Indiana Academy of Science.

Sawyer, John O., et al. A Manual of California Vegetation/John O. Sawyer, Todd Keeler-Wolf, Julie Evens. 2nd ed. 2009. *(978-0-943460-49-9(2))* Univ. of California Pr.

Schnell, Donald E. Carnivorous Plants of the United States & Canad. 2009. (ENG.). 468p. pap. 39.95 *(978-1-60469-108-5(5),* 1604691085) Timber Pr., Inc.

Schummer, Michael L., et al. A Guide to Moist-Soil Wetland Plants of the Mississippi Alluvial Valley. 2011. (ENG.). 256p. pap. 40.00 *(978-1-61703-146-5(1))* Univ. Pr. of Mississippi.

B

Shaw, Robert B. Field Guide to Texas Grasses: Institute of Renewable Natural Resources. 2012. (AgriLife Research & Extension Service Ser.). (Illus.). 1088p. pap. 45.00 (978-1-60344-186-5(7), TAMU Pr.) Texas A&M Univ. Pr.
Shores, Elizabeth Findley. On Harper's Trail: Roland Mcmillan Harper, Pioneering Botanist of the Southern Coastal Plain. (ENG., Illus.). 296p. 2010. pap. 24.95 (978-0-8203-3522-3(3)) 2008. 42.95 (978-0-8203-3100-3(7)) Univ. of Georgia Pr.
Shreve, Forrest, et al. The Plant Life of Maryland. 2010. 623p. pap. 34.95 (978-0-557-64628-9(6)) Lulu Enterprises Inc.
Sivinski, R. C. Checklist of Vascular Plants in the Sandia & Manzano Mountains of Central New Mexico. 2007. 67p. pap. 10.00 (978-0-9794517-0-6(1)) Museum of Southwest Biology Pubn. Series.
Smith, Welby R. Native Orchids of Minnesota. 2012. (Illus.). 400p. pap. 34.95 (978-0-8166-7823-5(5)) Univ. of Minnesota Pr.
Smyth, Bernard B. Plants & Flowers of Kansas. (Illus.). 118p. reprint ed. lib. bdg. 88.00 (978-0-7222-4892-8(X)) Library Reprints, Inc.
Spaulding, Daniel D. Ferns of Alabama. 2012. (978-0-8173-5647-7(9)) Univ. of Alabama Pr.
Springer, Judith D., et al. Field Guide to Forest & Mountain Plants of Northern Arizona: From the Mogollon Rim & White Mountains North. 2009. pap. (978-0-578-02191-1(9)) Ecological Restoration Institution Northern Arizona Univ.
Steiner, Lynn M. Landscaping with Native Plants of Wisconsin. rev. ed. 2007. (ENG., Illus.). 192p. pap. 24.95 (978-0-7603-2969-6(9), 0760329699, Voyageur Pr) MBI Publishing Co. LLC.
Steyermark, Julian A. Spring Flora of Missouri. 585p. reprint ed. lib. bdg. 98.00 (978-0-7222-0518-1(X)) Library Reprints, Inc.
Studebaker, Stacy. Wildflowers & Other Plant Life of the Kodiak Archipelago. 2010. pap. 25.00 (978-1-57833-479-7(9)) Todd Communications.
Stutzenbaker, Charles D. Aquatic & Wetland Plants of the Western Gulf Coast. 2010. (Illus.). 468p. pap. 40.00 (978-1-60344-222-0(7)) Texas A&M Univ. Pr.
Taylor, Walter Kingsley. A Guide to Florida Grasses. 2009. (ACE & ENG., Illus.). 384p. pap. 49.95 (978-0-8130-3319-8(5)) Univ. Pr. of Florida.
Tozer, Frank. The Uses of Wild Plants: Using & Growing the Wild Plants of the United States & Canada. 2007. (ENG., Illus.). 264p. per. 24.95 (978-0-9773489-0-9(3)) Green Man Publishing.
Turner, Jan Loechell & Turner, Charles Allen. Wildflowers of Canyon de Chelly. 3rd rev. ed. 2008. (ENG., Illus.). 54p. spiral bd. 15.95 (978-0-9772171-5-1(9)) Rabbitbrush Publishing.
Turner, Matt Warnock. Remarkable Plants of Texas: Uncommon Accounts of Our Common Natives. 2009. (Corrie Herring Hooks Ser.: No. 62). (ENG., Illus.). 320p. 29.95 (978-0-292-71851-7(9)) Univ. of Texas Pr.
Univ. Florida/Ifas/center For Aquatic And Invasive Plants & Ramey, Vic, prods. Grasses, Sedges & Rushes of Wetlands ID Deck: Identification Deck with notes about wildlife Use. 2007. (Illus.). 92p. ring bd. 20.00 (978-0-9700046-4-2(8), CAIP Information Office) Univ. of Florida, Ctr. for Aquatic & Invasive Plants.
Van Buren, Renee, photos by. Woody Plants of Utah: An Identification Key & Field Guide to Native & Naturalized Trees, Shrubs, Vines, & Cacti. 2011. E-Book (978-0-87421-825-1(X), Utah State Univ. Pr.) Univ. Pr. of Colorado.
Van Buren, Renee, et al. Woody Plants of Utah: Identification Key & Field Guide to Native & Naturalized Trees, Shrubs, Vines & Cacti. 2011. (ENG.). 504p. (gr. 13). pap. 39.95 (978-0-87421-824-4(1), Utah State Univ. Pr.) Univ. Pr. of Colorado.
Vizgirdas, Ray S. & Rey-Vizgirdas, Edna M. Wild Plants of the Sierra Nevada. 2009. (ENG.). 384p. pap. 29.95 (978-0-87417-789-3(8)) Univ. of Nevada Pr.
Webb, Robert H., et al. The Ribbon of Green: Change in Riparian Vegetation in the Southwestern United States. 2007. (ENG., Illus.). 480p. 75.00 (978-0-8165-2588-1(9)) Univ. of Arizona Pr.
Weber, Larry. Fascinating Fungi of the North Woods. 2nd ed. 2011. 136p. pap. (978-1-936571-03-1(X)) Kollath-Stensaas Pubs.
Weber, William A. & Wittmann, Ronald C. Bryophytes of Colorado: Mosses, Liverworts, & Hornworts. 2007. per. 29.95 (978-0-9790909-1-2(1)) Pilgrims Process, Inc.
—Colorado Flora. 4th ed. 2011. E-Book (978-1-60732-143-9(2)) Univ. Pr. of Colorado.
—Colorado Flora: Eastern Slope. 4th ed. 2011. E-Book (978-1-60732-141-5(6)) Univ. Pr. of Colorado.
—Colorado Flora: Eastern Slope. 4th ed. 2012. (ENG., Illus.). 608p. pap. 27.95 (978-1-60732-140-8(8)) Univ. Pr. of Colorado.
—Colorado Flora: Western Slope. 4th ed. 2012. (Illus.). 608p. pap. 27.95 (978-1-60732-142-2(4)) Univ. Pr. of Colorado.
Weeks, Sally S., et al. Shrubs & Woody Vines of Indiana & the Midwest: Identification, Wildlife Values, & Landscaping Use. 2012. 475p. pap. 45.00 (978-1-55753-610-5(4)) Purdue Univ. Pr.
Wilken, Dieter. The Jepson Manual: Vascular Plants of California. Baldwin, Bruce G. et al, eds. 2nd rev. ed. 2012. (ENG., Illus.). 1600p. 125.00 (978-0-520-25312-4(4)) Univ. of California Pr.
Williams, Dave. The Tallgrass Prairie Center Guide to Seed & Seedling Identification in the Upper Midwest. 2010. (Bur Oak Guide Ser.). (Illus.). 138p. pap. 14.00 (978-1-58729-902-5(X)) Univ. of Iowa Pr.
Willoughby, John W. & Ashworth, Vanessa. Strategies & Solutions: California Native Plant Society 2009 Conservation Conference Proceedings. 2011. pap. (978-0-943460-50-5(5)) California Native Plant Society.
Wilson, Barbara L., et al. Field Guide to the Sedges of the Pacific Northwest 2008. (ENG., Illus.). 432p. pap. 35.00 (978-0-87071-197-8(0)) Oregon State Univ. Pr.
Winchell, Alexander. Report, Historical & Statistical, on the Collections in Geology, Zo?Ology & Botany in the Museum of the University of Michigan, Made to the Board. 2011. 28p. pap. 11.99 (978-1-4181-9290-7(2)) MPublishing.
Wood, Alphonso. A Class-Book of Botany. 2006. 648p. per. 34.99 (978-1-4255-6673-9(1)) MPublishing.
Woodbury, Angus M., et al. Ecological Studies of Flora & Fauna in Glen Canyon. (Glen Canyon Ser.: No. 7). reprint ed. 42.00 (978-0-404-60640-4(7)) AMS Pr., Inc.
—Ecological Studies of the Flora & Fauna of Navajo Reservoir Basin, Colorado & New Mexico. (Upper Colorado Ser.: No. 5). reprint ed. 34.50 (978-0-404-60655-8(5)) AMS Pr., Inc.
—Ecological Studies of the Flora & Fauna of the Curecanti Reservoir Basins, Western Colorado. (Upper Colorado Ser.: No. 8). reprint ed. 42.50 (978-0-404-60659-6(8)) AMS Pr., Inc.
—A Survey of Vegetation in the Curecanti Reservoir Basins. (Upper Colorado Ser.: No. 6). reprint ed. 17.50 (978-0-404-60656-5(3)) AMS Pr., Inc.
—A Survey of Vegetation in the Flaming Gorge Basin. (Upper Colorado Ser.: No. 2). reprint ed. 30.00 (978-0-404-60645-9(8)) AMS Pr., Inc.
—Survey of Vegetation in the Navajo Reservoir Basin. (Upper Colorado Ser.: No. 4). reprint ed. 25.00 (978-0-404-60651-0(2)) AMS Pr., Inc.
Wooton, E. O. & Standley, Paul C. Flora of New Mexico. 2009. (ENG.). 795p. 48.99 (978-1-117-34578-9(5)); pap. 33.99 (978-1-117-34580-2(7), BiblioLife); pap. 53.75 (978-1-117-34579-6(3)) BiblioBazaar.
Wunderlin, Richard P. & Hansen, Bruce F. Guide to the Vascular Plants of Florida. 3rd ed. 2011. (ENG., Illus.). 812p. 44.95 (978-0-8130-3543-7(0)) Univ. Pr. of Florida.
Yetman, David. The Great Cacti: Ethnobotany & Biogeography. 2008. (Southwest Center Ser.). (ENG., Illus.). 320p. 59.95 (978-0-8165-2431-0(9)) Univ. of Arizona Pr.
Zuchowski, Willow. Tropical Plants of Costa Rica: A Guide to Native & Exotic Flora. 2007. (Illus.). 529p. pap. 35.00 (978-0-8014-7374-6(8), Comstock Publishing Assocs.) Cornell Univ. Pr.
Zwinger, Ann, frwd. River & Desert Plants of the Grand Canyon. 2006. (Illus.). 261p. pap. 22.00 (978-0-87842-523-5(3)) Mountain Pr. Publishing Co., Inc.

BOTANY—VENEZUELA

Lieth, Helmut, et al, eds. Mangroves & Halophytes: Restoration & Utilisation. (Tasks for Vegetation Science Ser.). (Illus.). 2010. lviii, 162p. pap. 179.00 (978-90-481-7704-2(9), 9048177049) 2008. 214p. 179.00 (978-1-4020-6719-8(4), 1402067194) Springer.

BOTANY—VIETNAM

Vo, Thai Dan. Genetic Diversity of Vietnam Te. 2010. 156p. pap. (978-3-639-20138-3(8)) VDM Verlag Dr. Mueller e.K.

BOTANY, AGRICULTURAL

see Botany, Economic

BOTANY, ECONOMIC

see also Dye Plants; Forest Products; Grain; Grasses; Plant Introduction; Plants, Edible; Plants, Useful; Poisonous Plants; Textile Fibers; Weeds

Ambrosoli, Mauro. The Wild & the Sown: Botany & Agriculture in Western Europe, 1350-1850. 2009. (Past & Present Publications). (ENG., Illus.). 504p. pap. 58.00 (978-0-521-10881-2(0)) Cambridge Univ. Pr.
Candolle, Alphonse de. The Origin of Cultivated Plants. 2011. (Cambridge Library Collection - Life Sciences Ser.). (ENG.). 482p. pap. 35.99 (978-1-108-03890-4(5)) Cambridge Univ. Pr.
Coville, Frederick V., pref. The Useful Plants of the Island of Guam. 2009. (ENG., Illus.). 416p. 75.00 (978-0-9823576-0-6(5)) Guerrero, Jllette Leon.
Cram101 Textbook Reviews Staff. Outlines & Highlights for Plants & Society by Levetin, Isbn: 0072528427. 2008. 260p. pap. 14.95 (978-1-4288-5913-5(6)) Cram101 Inc.
—Outlines & Highlights for Plants & Society by Levetin, Isbn: 9780077221256. 2008. 360p. pap. 17.95 (978-1-4288-5941-8(1)) Cram101 Inc.
Drury, Heber. The Useful Plants of Indi. 2010. 528p. pap. 35.45 (978-1-4460-2372-3(9)) Research Pr.
Elzebroek, A. T. G. & Wind, K., eds. Guide to Cultivated Plants. 2008. (Illus.). 496p. 180.00 (978-1-84593-356-2(7)) CABI GBR. Dist: Stylus Publishing, LLC.
Goss, Andrew. The Floracrats: State-Sponsored Science & the Failure of the Enlightenment in Indonesia. 2011. (New Perspectives in Se Asian Studies). (ENG., Illus.). 264p. pap. 26.95 (978-0-299-24864-2(X)) Univ. of Wisconsin Pr.
Henry, Robert. Plant Resources for Food, Fuel & Conservation. 2009. (ENG., Illus.). 200p. 79.95 (978-1-84407-721-2(7)) Routledge.
Lehner, Ernst & Lehner, Johanna. Folklore & Odysseys of Food & Medicinal Plants. 2011. 130p. 40.95 (978-1-258-02254-9(0)) Literary Licensing, LLC.
Martinez, Miguel Angel. Las Contribuciones Iberoamericanas al Mundo: Botanica, Medicina, Agricultura. (Biblioteca Iberoamericana Ser.). (SPA.). 127p. 18.95 (978-84-207-3090-5(4), GS024) Grupo Anaya, S.A. ESP. Dist: Continental Bk. Co., Inc.
McMahon, Margaret E., et al. Plant Science: Growth, Development, & Utilization of Cultivated Plants. 5th rev. ed. 2010. (ENG., Illus.). 688p. (C). pap. 120.60 (978-0-13-501407-3(7), Prentice Hall) Prentice Hall PTR.
Murphy, Denis. Plants, Biotechnology & Agriculture. 2011. (Modular Texts). 312p. 145.00 (978-1-84593-913-7(1)) CABI GBR. Dist: Stylus Publishing, LLC.
Murphy, Denis J. Plants, Biotechnology & Agriculture. 2011. (978-1-84593-871-0(2)) CABI.
—Plants, Biotechnology & Agriculture. 2011. (Modular Texts). 312p. pap. 75.00 (978-1-84593-688-4(4)) CABI GBR. Dist: Stylus Publishing, LLC.
Schiebinger, Londa & Swan, Claudia, eds. Colonial Botany: Science, Commerce, & Politics in the Early Modern World. 2007. (Illus.). 352p. (C). per. 24.95 (978-0-8122-2009-4(9)) Univ. of Pennsylvania Pr.
Seadh, Saleh. Agricultural Studies on Sugar Beet Crop. 2010. 136p. pap. (978-3-8383-5704-1(3)) Lambert Academic Publishing.
Simmonds, P.L. Commercial Products of the Vegetable Kin. 2006. pap. (978-1-4068-2200-7(0)) Echo Library.
Smale, Melinda. Measuring the Economic Impacts of Transgenic Crops in Developing Agriculture during the First Decade: Approaches, Findings, & Future Directions. 2009. (978-0-89629-511-7(7)) International Food Policy Research Institute.
Tozer, Frank. The Uses of Wild Plants: Using & Growing the Wild Plants of the United States & Canada. 2007. (ENG., Illus.). 264p. per. 24.95 (978-0-9773489-0-9(3)) Green Man Publishing.
Turner, Nancy J. Plant Technology of First Peoples in British Columbia, 1 vol. 2010. (ENG., Illus.). 260p. pap. (978-0-7726-5847-0(1)) Royal British Columbia Museum.

BOTANY, FOSSIL

see Paleobotany

BOTANY, MEDICAL

Here are entered works on the discipline of medical botany. Works on the description and-or the cultivation of medicinal plants are entered under Medicinal Plants.

see also Botany—Pre-Linnean Works; Herbs—Therapeutic Use; Materia Medica, Vegetable; Medicinal Plants; Plants—Assimilation

The creative herbal Home. 2007. per. 17.95 (978-0-9766771-1-6(3), Living with Herbs) herbspirit.
Culpeper, Nicholas. The English Physician. Flannery, Michael A., ed. & footn. by. annot. ed. 2007. (Illus.). 104p. 35.00 (978-0-8173-1558-0(6)) Univ. of Alabama Pr.
Cupp, Melanie Johns. Toxicology & Clinical Pharmacology of Herbal Products. 2010. (Forensic Science & Medicine Ser.). (Illus.). 344p. pap. 129.00 (978-1-61737-190-5(4), 1617371904) Humana Pr.
Fernie, W. T. Herbal Simples Approved for Modern Uses of Cure. 2007. 556p. per. (978-1-4065-2368-3(2)) Dodo Pr.
Fusetani, N., ed. Drugs from the Sea. (Illus.). (978-3-8055-7098-5(8)) Karger, S. AG.
Germer, Renate. Handbuch der altagyptischen Heilpflanzen. 2008. (Philippika Ser.). (GER.). 388p. (C). 48.00 (978-3-447-05632-8(0)) Harrassowitz, Otto Verlag DEU. Dist: ISD.
Godfrey, Anthony, et al. Principles & Practices of Naturopathic Botanical Medicine, Vol 1: Volume 1: Botanical Medicine Monographs. 2010. 2500p. 124.95 (978-1-897025-26-0(2)) Canadian College of Naturopathic Medicine Pr. CAN. Dist: SCB Distributors.
Goodman, Jordan & Walsh, Vivien. The Story of Taxol: Nature & Politics in the Pursuit of an Anti-Cancer Drug. 2006. (ENG., Illus.). 300p. pap. 38.99 (978-0-521-03250-6(4)) Cambridge Univ. Pr.
Hildegard von Bingen. Physica: Liber subtilitatum diversarum naturarum Creaturarum. Hildebrandt, Reiner & Gloning, Thomas, eds. 2010. (LAT & GER., Illus.). IX, 1023p. 349.00 (978-3-11-021589-2(6)) De Gruyter, Walter Inc.
Hsu, Elisabeth & Harris, Stephen, eds. Plants, Health & Healing: On the Interface of Ethnobotany & Medical Anthropology. 2010. (EH Ser.). (Illus.). 328p. 95.00 (978-1-84545-060-1(4)) Berghahn Bks., Inc.
Joshi, Dipti, et al. Anticancer Activity of Casearia Esculenta in Experimental Models. 2011. 68p. pap. (978-3-8443-2819-6(X)) Lambert Academic Publishing.
Katerere, R. David & Luseba, Dibungi, eds. Ethnoveterinary Botanical Medicine: Herbal Medicines for Animal Health. 2010. (ENG., Illus.). 450p. 139.95 (978-1-4200-4560-4(1), CRC Press) Taylor & Francis Group GBR. Dist: Taylor & Francis Group.
Krauss, Beatrice H. Native Plants Used As Medicine in Hawaii. pap. 4.50 (978-0-681-02810-4(6)) Booklines Hawaii, Ltd.
Laroche, Rebecca. Medical Authority & Englishwomen's Herbal Texts 1550-1650. 2009. (Literary & Scientific Cultures of Early Modernity Ser.). (Illus.). 208p. 99.95 (978-0-7546-6678-3(6)) Ashgate Publishing Co.
Leyel, C. F. Hearts Ease Herbs for the Heart. 2008. 15.95 (978-0-7873-1422-4(6)) Health Research.
Lindley, John. Flora Medica: A Botanical Account of All the More Important Plants Used in Medicine, in Different Parts of the World. 2011. (Cambridge Library Collection - Life Sciences Ser.). (ENG.). 676p. pap. 45.00 (978-1-108-03845-4(X)) Cambridge Univ. Pr.
Medicinal & Aromatic Plants IX. 2011. (Biotechnology in Agriculture & Forestry Ser.). (ENG., Illus.). xix, 414p. pap. 589.00 (978-3-642-08229-0(7), 3642082297) Springer.
Meyer, Clarence. Vegetarian Medicines. 2007. (Illus.). 104p. (Orig.). pap. 9.00 (978-0-914875-49-9(3), Historical Images) Bright Mountain Bks., Inc.
Mittal, Rakhi. Memory-Boosting Effect of Bacopa Monnieri. 2010. 132p. pap. (978-3-8383-5063-9(4)) Lambert Academic Publishing.
Morrow, John Andrew. Encyclopedia of Islamic Herbal Medicine. 2011. (ENG., Illus.). 235p. pap. 55.00 (978-0-7864-4707-7(9)) McFarland & Co., Inc. Pubs.
Patel, Ansar, et al. Hepatoprotective Activity of New Polyherbal Formulation. 2011. 112p. pap. (978-3-8443-1172-3(6)) Lambert Academic Publishing.
Pendell, Dale. Gnosis: Plant Teachers & the Poison Path. rev. ed. 2010. (Pharmako Ser.). (ENG., Illus.). 308p. pap. 19.95 (978-1-55643-804-2(4)) North Atlantic Bks.
Preedy, Victor & Watson, R., eds. Botanical Medicine in Clinical Practice. 2008. (Illus.). 944p. (C). 370.00 (978-1-84593-413-2(X)) CABI GBR. Dist: Stylus Publishing, LLC.
Rafinesque, C. S. Medical Flora: Or Manual of the Medical Botany of the United States of North America, 2 vols., Set. (Illus.). reprint ed. 60.00 (978-0-404-13191-3(3)) AMS Pr., Inc.
Robinson, James & Nielson, Nancy. Natural Healing & Prevention Secrets. pap. 19.95 (978-0-9638596-1-7(7)) American Publishing Corp.
Scheid, Volker, et al. Chinese Herbal Medicine: Formulas & Strategies. 2nd ed. 2009. 1019p. 120.00 (978-0-939616-67-1(X)) Eastland Pr.
Scott, Robert. Decoding Myth-Information. 2010. 133p. pap. 17.95 (978-1-4452-7927-5(4)) Lulu Enterprises Inc.
Skenderi, Gazmend. Concise Herbal Handbook: A Quick Reference to Constituents, Properties, Uses, Dosages, & Cautions of over 800 Herbs, Spices, Essential Oils, Lipids, Etc. 2nd rev. enl. ed. 2007. Orig. Title: Herbal Vade Mecum. (978-0-9713209-4-9(2)); pap. (978-0-9713209-3-2(4)) Herbacy Pr.
—Handbook of Medicinal Plants & Botanicals: Plants (A to Z by Genera & Species) & Medicinal, Flavoring & Fragrant Botanicals (Constituents, Properties, Uses, Cautions, Etc.) 2009. (978-0-9713209-5-6(0)) Herbacy Pr.
Smith, John. Foods, Herbs, Health & Healing. 2009. (Illus.). 138p. 22.50 (978-1-60860-653-5(8), Strategic Bk. Publishing) AEG Literary Publishing Services, Inc.
Sumner, Judith. Natural History of Medicinal Plants. 2008. (ENG.). 252p. pap. 24.95 (978-0-88192-957-7(3), 0881929573) Timber Pr., Inc.
Tallmadge, Guy Kasten. The Prescription, from Antiquity to the Renaissance: Ciba Symposia, V9, No. 8, November 1947. Caspari-Rosen, Beate, ed. 2011. 34p. 35.95 (978-1-258-04990-4(2)) Literary Licensing, LLC.
Teetgen, Ada. Profitable Herb Growing & Collecting. 2008. 212p. (978-1-4437-3737-1(2), Home Farm Bks.) Read Bks.
Yin-fang, Dai & Cheng-jun, Liu. Fruits as Medicine. 132p. pap. 9.95 (978-967-978-629-3(3), Weatherhill, Inc.) Shambhala Pubns., Inc.

BOTANY BAY (N.S.W.)

Barrington, George. A Voyage to Botany Bay with- a Sequel to a Voyage to Botany Bay. 2007. 148p. per. (978-1-4068-8000-7(0)) Echo Library.
Tench, Watkin. A Complete Account of the Settlement at Port Jackson. 2009. 196p. pap. (978-1-4099-0447-2(4)) Dodo Pr.
—A Narrative of the Expedition to Botany. 2006. pap. (978-1-4068-0834-6(2)) Echo Library.
—A Narrative of the Expedition to Botany Bay. 2009. 72p. pap. (978-1-4099-0448-9(2)) Dodo Pr.
—A Narrative of the Expedition to Botany Bay. 2010. 58p. pap. 13.56 (978-1-162-64953-5(4)); 25.56 (978-1-169-21217-6(4)); 31.95 (978-1-161-41818-7(0)) Kessinger Publishing, LLC.
—A Narrative of the Expedition to Botany-Bay. 2010. 46p. pap. 8.09 (978-1-153-58556-9(1)) General Bks. LLC.

BOTANY IN ARCHAEOLOGY

see Plant Remains (Archaeology)

BOTANY OF THE BIBLE

see Nature in the Bible

BOTERO, FERNANDO, 1932-

Cau, Jean. Botero: Bullfight. (FRE., Illus.). 164p. 95.00 (978-2-85047-159-9(3)) La Bibliotheque des Arts FRA. Dist: D.A.P./Distributed Art Pubs.
Chiappini, Rudy. Botero: Works 1994-2007. 2008. (ENG., Illus.). 196p. 29.95 (978-88-6130-295-2(5)) Rizzoli International Pubns., Inc.
Peter Selz. Botero in La: Drawings Paintings Sculpture. 2010. (Illus.). 58p. 20.00 (978-0-9794823-0-4(5)) Tasende Gallery.
Sillevis, John. The Baroque World of Fernando Botero. 2007. (ENG., Illus.). 283p. 65.00 (978-0-300-12359-3(0)) Yale Univ. Pr.
Sillevis, John & Botero, Fernando. The Baroque World of Fernando Botero. 2007. (978-0-88397-148-2(8)); (Illus.). 283p. (978-0-88397-147-5(X)) Art Services International.
Spies, Werner, ed. Botero: Paintings & Drawings. 2007. (Illus.). 179p. pap. 19.95 (978-3-7913-3806-4(4)) Prestel Publishing.

BOTOX (TRADEMARK)

see Botulinum Toxin

BOTSWANA

Dow, Unity & Essex, Max. Saturday Is for Funerals. 2011. (ENG.). 240p. pap. 14.95 (978-0-674-06183-5(7)) Harvard Univ. Pr.
Icon Group International, Inc. Staff, compiled by. The 2006 Economic & Product Market Databook for Francistown, Botswana. 2006. 618p. ring bd. 95.00 (978-0-497-80552-4(9)) Icon Group International, Inc.
—The 2006 Economic & Product Market Databook for Kanye, Botswana. 2006. 618p. ring bd. 95.00 (978-0-497-81970-5(8)) Icon Group International, Inc.
Lewanika, Lucas. Strategically Positioning Botswana Development Corporation in the Mkt. 2010. 108p. pap. (978-3-8383-5844-4(9)) Lambert Academic Publishing.
Livingston, Julie. Improvised Medicine: An African Oncology Ward in an Emerging Cancer Epidemic. 2012. (ENG., Illus.). 256p. pap. 23.95 (978-0-8223-5342-3(3)) Duke Univ. Pr.

—Improvising Medicine: An African Oncology Ward in an Emerging Cancer Epidemic. 2012. (ENG., Illus.). 256p. 84.95 **(978-0-8223-5327-0(X))** Duke Univ. Pr.

Main, Michael. Botswana: A Quick Guide to Customs & Etiquette. 2007. (Culture Smart Ser.). (ENG., Illus.). 168p. pap. 9.95 *(978-1-85733-340-4(3))* Kuperard Pubs. GBR. Dist: Random Hse., Inc.

Molosiwa, Kgomotso. Payment for Ecosystem Services. 2011. 124p. pap. **(978-3-8433-8046-1(5))** Lambert Academic Publishing.

Pons, Alain & Balliet, Christine. Botswana. 2006. (Safari Companion Ser.). (ENG., Illus.). 72p. (Orig.). pap. 14.95 *(978-1-901268-22-5(5)*, 1901268225) Evans Mitchell Bks. GBR. Dist: MBI Distribution Services/Quayside Distribution.

Raditloaneng, Wapula Nelly. Women, Poverty & Literacy. 2010. 184p. pap. *(978-3-8383-6726-2(X))* Lambert Academic Publishing.

Ramsay, Jeff, et al. Historical Dictionary of Botswana. 4th ed. 2008. (Historical Dictionaries of Africa Ser.). (ENG., Illus.). 512p. 128.00 *(978-0-8108-5467-3(8))* Scarecrow Pr., Inc.

Tatnall, Arthur, et al, eds. Information Technology & Managing Quality Education: 9th IFIP WG 3. 7 Conference on Information Technology in Educational Management, ITEM 2010, Kasane, Botswana, July 26-30, 2010, Revised Selected Papers. 2011. (IFIP Advances in Information & Communication Technology Ser.). (Illus.). viii, 205p. 109.00 *(978-3-642-19714-7(0)*, 3642197140) Springer.

Werbner, Richard. Holy Hustlers, Schism, & Prophecy: Apostolic Reformation in Botswana. 2011. (Anthropology of Christianity Ser.). (ENG., Illus.). 268p. 60.00 *(978-0-520-26853-1(9))*; 228p. pap. 24.95 *(978-0-520-26854-8(7))* Univ. of California Pr.

BOTSWANA—DESCRIPTION AND TRAVEL

Brough, Alan. Botswana Travel Pack, 6th. 6th ed. 2010. (Globetrotter Travel Packs Ser.). (ENG., Illus.). 128p. 14.95 *(978-1-84773-676-5(9)*, Globetrotter) New Holland Pubs., Ltd. GBR. Dist: Globe Pequot Pr., The.

Campbell, Alec C. Tsodilo Hills: Copper Bracelet of the Kalahari. 2010. (ENG.). 179p. pap. 39.95 *(978-0-87013-858-4(8))* Michigan State Univ. Pr.

Copeland, Mike. Getaway Guide to Botswana. 2011. 192p. pap. 23.00 **(978-1-920289-31-7(3))** Ball, Jonathan Pubs. ZAF. Dist: International Publishers Marketing.

Copeland, Mike. Getaway Guide to Botswana: Where Time Stands Still. 2009. (Illus.). 192p. pap. 18.00 *(978-1-919938-80-6(X))* Sunbird Publishing ZAF. Dist: International Publishers Marketing.

Darkoh, Michael Bernard Kwesi & Elizeri Mbaiwa, Joseph. Natural Resource Use & Land Use Conflicts. 2010. 124p. pap. *(978-3-8383-7018-7(X))* Lambert Academic Publishing.

Hamandawana, Hamisai. Environmental Changes in Botswana's Okavango Delta Region: 1849-2001. 2010. 652p. pap. *(978-3-8383-0160-0(9))* Lambert Academic Publishing.

Locken, E. Travel Journal Botswana. 2010. 192p. pap. 19.99 *(978-0-557-43275-2(8))* Lulu Enterprises Inc.

Lonely Planet Staff & Firestone, Matthew. Botswana & Namibia. 2nd rev. ed. 2010. (Multi Country Guide Ser.). (ENG., Illus.). 424p. pap. 27.99 *(978-1-74104-922-0(9))* Lonely Planet Pubns.

Main, Mike. Visitors' Guide to Botswana. 3rd ed. (Illus.). 220p. pap. 17.95 *(978-1-86812-657-6(9))* Southern Bk. Pubs. ZAF. Dist: Continental Enterprises Group, Inc. (CEG).

McIntyre, Chris. Botswana: Okavango Delta - Chobe - Northern Kalahari. 3rd ed. 2010. (ENG., Illus.). 512p. pap. 26.99 *(978-1-84162-308-5(3))* Bradt Travel Guides GBR. Dist: Globe Pequot Pr., The.

Michler, Ian. Botswana: The Insider's Guide. 2nd ed. 2009. (Illus.). 192p. pap. 28.00 *(978-1-77007-461-3(9))* Struik Pubs. ZAF. Dist: International Publishers Marketing.

BOTTICELLI, SANDRO, 1447?-1510

Ewing, Lucy Elizabeth Lee. George Frederick Watts, Sandro Botticelli, Matthew Arnold. 2009. 84p. pap. 17.95 *(978-1-104-05814-2(6))* Kessinger Publishing, LLC.

Gebhart, Mile, et al. Botticelli. 2010. (Temporis Ser.). (ENG., Illus.). 256p. 39.95 *(978-1-84484-643-6(1))* Parkstone International GBR. Dist: Ingram Pub. Services.

Gillies, Jean. Botticelli's Primavera: The Young Lorenzo's Transformation. 2010. 248p. pap. 19.95 *(978-1-4502-2161-0(0))* iUniverse, Inc.

H. F. Ullmann Staff, ed. Botticelli. 2008. (Masters Ser.). 120p. ring bd. 9.95 *(978-0-8416-0075-1(9))* American Map Corp.

Hatfield, Rab, ed. Sandro Botticelli Herbert Horn. 2009. 160p. pap. 24.95 *(978-88-95250-04-5(4))* Syracuse Univ. Pr.

Hubbard, Elbert. Little Journeys to the Homes of Eminent Artists. 2009. 40p. pap. 12.99 *(978-1-110-79401-0(0))* BiblioBazaar.

—Little Journeys to the Homes of Eminent Artists. 2009. 48p. pap. *(978-0-217-50806-3(5))* Books LLC.

Kermode, Frank. Forms of Attention: Botticelli & Hamlet. 2011. (ENG.). 112p. pap. 16.00 *(978-0-226-43175-8(4))* Univ. of Chicago Pr.

Poletti, Federico & Botticelli, Sandro. Botticelli. 2011. (ENG., Illus.). 160p. pap. 12.95 **(978-3-7913-4618-2(0))** Prestel Publishing.

Roberto, Brother. I Walk with Giants: A Story of Sandro Botticelli. 2011. 94p. 38.95 **(978-1-258-07959-8(3))** Literary Licensing, LLC.

Santi, Bruno. Botticelli. (Grandes Maestros del Arte Ser.). (SPA., Illus.). 80p. (Orig.). pap. 12.99 *(978-1-878351-34-0(6))* Riverside Bk. Co., Inc.

Simonetta, Marcello. The Montefeltro Conspiracy: A Renaissance Mystery Decoded. 2008. (ENG., Illus.). 272p. 26.00 *(978-0-385-52468-1(4))* Knopf Doubleday Publishing Group.

Zoellner, Frank. Botticelli. 2009. (Illus.). 320p. 65.00 *(978-3-7913-4358-7(0))* Prestel Publishing.

Zuffi, Stefano. Botticelli's Birth of Venus: Art Mysteries. 2012. (ENG., Illus.). 80p. pap. 24.95 **(978-88-6648-050-1(9))** Antique Collectors' Club.

BOTTLED GAS

see Liquefied Petroleum Gas

BOTTLES

Erbulut, Deniz Ufuk. An Intelligent Process Design for Stretch Blow Moulding. 2010. 216p. pap. *(978-3-639-22465-8(5))* VDM Verlag Dr. Mueller e.K.

Flanagan, Jane. The Wonderful World of Collecting Perfume Bottles. 2nd ed. 2008. (ENG., Illus.). 288p. 29.95 *(978-1-57432-612-3(0)*, 1574326120) Collector Bks.

Gerth, Ellen C. Bottles from the Deep: Patent Medicines, Bitters, & Other Bottles from the Wreck of the Steamship Republic. 2006. (Illus.). 112p. pap. 12.00 *(978-1-933034-07-2(5))* Shipwreck Heritage Pr., LLC.

Hastin, Bud. Bud Hastin's Avon Collector's Encyclopedia. 18th rev. ed. 2007. (Bud Hastin's Avon Collector's Encyclopedia Ser.). (ENG., Illus.). 672p. per. 29.95 *(978-1-57432-565-2(5)*, 1574325655) Collector Bks.

Husfloen, Kyle & Dolnick, Penny. Antique Trader Perfume Bottles Price Guide. 2009. (ENG.). 288p. pap. 19.99 *(978-0-89689-671-0(4))* Krause Pubns.

Monsen, Randall B. & Defina, Michael. The World of Perfume: Perfume Bottle Auction XV. 2006. (Illus.). 131p. 45.00 *(978-1-928655-05-3(X))* Monsen & Baer.

Nolt, Sam, et al. The Lancaster Bottle Book: A Definitive Guide to Lancaster Bottle Collecting. 2007. spiral bd. 39.95 *(978-1-4276-2616-5(2))* Aardvark Global Publishing.

Olins, Gwen & Olins, Evan. Lei in a Bottle. 2008. (ENG.). 84p. pap. 24.95 *(978-0-9794649-3-5(5))* Hula Moon Pr.

Polak, Michael. Bottles. 6th ed. 2009. (ENG.). 552p. pap. 21.99 *(978-0-89689-733-5(8))* Krause Pubns.

—Warman's Bottles Field Guide. 3rd ed. 2010. (ENG.). 512p. pap. 14.99 *(978-1-4402-1240-6(6))* Krause Pubns.

Rock, Jim. Basic Bottle Identification. fac. ed. 32p. reprint ed. pap. 3.75 *(978-1-55567-910-1(2))* Coyote Pr.

Rosen, Marc. Glamour Icons: Perfume Bottle Design. 2011. (ENG., Illus.). 204p. 85.00 *(978-1-85149-660-0(2))* Antique Collectors' Club.

Schunk, Martin. American Antique Bottles Identification Pocket Guide. 2007. 74p. per. 8.99 *(978-0-9789784-0-2(4))* Historic Publishing.

Tachwali, Yahia. Sensor Fusion Based Plastic Bottles Classification System. 2009. 168p. pap. *(978-3-639-14924-1(6))* VDM Verlag Dr. Mueller e.K.

The Ohio Bottle Club, compiled by. Ohio Bottle Book. 2007. 183p. spiral bd. 27.00 *(978-0-9672032-2-5(8))* Ohio Bottle Club, Inc., The.

Triviño, Santi. Water Pack! H2O Deluxe. Trivino, Santi & Minguet, Josep Maria, eds. 2010. (ENG., Illus.). 160p. pap. 57.50 *(978-84-96823-56-3(3))* Instituto Monsa de Ediciones, S.A. ESP. Dist: Trans-Atlantic Pubns., Inc.

BOTTLING

see also Beverage Industry

Dege, Nicholas, ed. Technology of Bottled Water. 3rd ed. 2011. (ENG., Illus.). 464p. 209.99 *(978-1-4051-9932-2(6)*, Wiley-Blackwell) Wiley, John & Sons, Inc.

BOTTOM DEPOSITS (OCEANOGRAPHY)

see Marine Sediments

BOTULINUM TOXIN

Arora, Vipal. Winning Back Your Independence with Cosmetic Dermatology - Basics of Medical Aesthetics & Cosmetic Dermatology: Botox - A Cosmetic. 2008. 200p. 99.95 *(978-1-4357-1397-0(4))* Lulu Enterprises Inc.

BOTULINUM TOXIN—POPULAR WORKS

Kane, Michael. The Botox Book: Everything You Need to Know about the Breakthrough Technique That Reverses Wrinkles & Lifts Years from Brows, Necks & Chins, by the Foremost Medical Expert on the Technique. mass mkt. *(978-0-312-98781-7(1)*, St. Martin's Paperbacks) St. Martin's Pr.

BOTULINUM TOXIN—THERAPEUTIC USE

Benedetto, Anthony, ed. Botulinum Toxin in Clinical Dermatology. 2nd rev ed. 2010. (ENG., Illus.). 296p. *(978-0-415-47636-2(4))* Informa Healthcare.

Chancellor, Michael B. & Smith, Christopher P. Botulinum Toxin in Urology. 2011. (ENG., Illus.). xviii, 204p. 139.00 *(978-3-642-03579-1(5)*, 3642035795) Springer.

Cooper, Grant, ed. Therapeutic Uses of Botulinum Toxin. 2010. (Musculoskeletal Medicine Ser.). (Illus.). xiv, 242p. pap. 149.00 *(978-1-61737-842-3(9)*, 1617378429) Humana Pr.

Hill, Pamela. Botox, Dysport, Dermal Fillers & Sclerotherapy. 2nd ed. 2010. (ENG.). 304p. (C). pap. 56.95 *(978-1-4354-3864-4(7)*, Milady Publishing Co.) Delmar Cengage Learning.

Jankovic, Joseph, et al. Botulinum Toxin: Therapeutic Clinical Practice & Science. 2009. (ENG., Illus.). 512p. 113.00 *(978-1-4160-4928-9(2)*, Saunders) Elsevier - Health Sciences Div.

Kane, Michael. The Botox Book: Everything You Need to Know about the Breakthrough Technique That Reverses Wrinkles & Lifts Years from Brows, Necks & Chins, by the Foremost Medical Expert on the Technique. mass mkt. *(978-0-312-98781-7(1)*, St. Martin's Paperbacks) St. Martin's Pr.

Sherrill, Jamie. Nurse Jamie's Botox Diaries: Real Stories from A Fake World. 2007. 188p. per. 17.95 *(978-0-9797286-0-0(6))* Red Carpet Pr., The.

Small, Rebecca & Hoang, Dalano, eds. A Practical Guide to Botulinum Toxin Procedures. 2011. (ENG., Illus.). 144p. 99.95 **(978-1-60913-147-0(9))** Lippincott Williams & Wilkins.

Truong, Daniel D., et al, eds. Manual of Botulinum Toxin Therapy. 2009. (Illus.). 234p. 94.00 *(978-0-521-69442-1(6))* Cambridge Univ. Pr.

BOTULISM

Emmeluth, Donald. Botulism. 2nd rev. ed. 2010. (Deadly Diseases & Epidemics Ser.). (Illus.). 144p. (C). (gr. 9-18). 34.95 *(978-1-60413-235-9(3)*, Chelsea Hse.) Facts On File, Inc.

Rasetti-Escargueil, Christine & Surman-Lee, Susanne, eds. Clostridium Botulinum: A Spore Forming Organism & a Challenge to Food Safety. 2011. (Advances in Food Safety & Food Microbiology (Series Editor: Dr. Anderson de Souza Sant'ana) Ser.). 75.00 **(978-1-61470-575-8(5))** Nova Science Pubs., Inc.

BOTVINNIK, MIKHAIL MOISEEVICH, 1911-1995

Botvinnik, Mikhail. Botvinnik - Petrosian: 1963 World Chess Championship Match. 2010. (ENG.). 144p. pap. 22.95 *(978-90-5691-314-4(X)*, New In Chess,Csi) Continental Sales, Inc.

Craig, Pritchett. Chess Secrets: Giants of Innovation. 2011. (ENG.). 288p. pap. 27.95 **(978-1-85744-671-5(2))** Everyman Chess GBR. Dist: Globe Pequot Pr., The.

BOUCHER, FRANCOIS, 1703-1770

Dulau, Anne. Boucher & Chardin: Masters of Modern Manners. 2008. (Illus.). 128p. pap. 50.00 *(978-1-903470-75-6(7))* Holberton, Paul Publishing GBR. Dist: Casemate Pubs. & Bk. Distributors, LLC.

Hyde, Melissa & Ledbury, Mark, eds. Rethinking Boucher. 2006. (Issues & Debates Ser.: Vol. 15). (Illus.). 304p. pap. 55.00 *(978-0-89236-825-9(X))* Oxford Univ. Pr., Inc.

BOUCICAULT, DION, 1820-1890

McFeely, Deirdre. Dion Boucicault: Irish Identity on Stage. 2012. (ENG., Illus.). 228p. 99.00 **(978-1-107-00793-2(3))** Cambridge Univ. Pr.

Walsh, Townsend. Career of Dion Boucicault. 2009. 110p. pap. 14.14 *(978-1-150-65378-0(7))* General Bks. LLC.

—The Career of Dion Boucicault. 2009. 260p. 24.99 *(978-1-103-75835-7(7))*; pap. 18.99 *(978-1-103-75828-9(4))* BiblioBazaar.

—The Career of Dion Boucicault. 2009. 112p. pap. 19.99 *(978-1-151-11299-6(2))* General Bks. LLC.

—The Career of Dion Boucicault. 2007. (ENG.). 246p. 41.95 *(978-0-548-22811-1(6))*; 248p. per. 26.95 *(978-1-4325-5070-7(5))* Kessinger Publishing, LLC.

BOUDICA, QUEEN, D. 62

see Boadicea, Queen, D. 62

BOUDICCA, QUEEN, D. 62

see Boadicea, Queen, D. 62

BOUDINOT, ELIAS, D. 1839

Parins, James W. Elias Cornelius Boudinot: A Life on the Cherokee Border. 2006. (American Indian Lives Ser.). (ENG.). 262p. pap. 24.95 *(978-0-8032-2074-4(X))* Univ. of Nebraska Pr.

BOUGAINVILLE, LOUIS ANTOINE DE, COMTE, 1729-1811

Diderot, Denis. Le Neveu de Rameau et la Reve de d'Alembert, Supplement au Voyage de Bougainville, et Autres Dialogues. (Folio Ser.: No. 761). (FRE.). (Orig.). pap. 16.95 *(978-2-07-036761-0(4))* Schoenhofs Foreign Bks., Inc.

Dunmore, John. Storms & Dreams: The Life of Louis de Bougainville. (University of Alaska Press - Lives of Great Explorers Ser.). (Illus.). 304p. 2008. per. 24.95 *(978-1-60223-001-9(3))* 2007. 45.00 *(978-1-60223-000-2(5))* Univ. of Alaska Pr.

Ridley, Glynis. The Discovery of Jeanne Baret: A Story of Science, the High Seas, & the First Woman to Circumnavigate the Globe. 2011. (ENG., Illus.). 304p. pap. 15.00 *(978-0-307-46353-1(2))* Broadway Bks.

—The Discovery of Jeanne Baret: A Story of Science, the High Seas, & the First Woman to Circumnavigate the Globe. 2010. (ENG., Illus.). 304p. 25.00 *(978-0-307-46352-4(4)*, Crown) Crown Publishing Group.

BOULANGER, NADIA, 1887-1979

Potter, Caroline. Nadia & Lili Boulanger. 2006. (Illus.). 208p. 110.00 *(978-0-7546-0472-3(1))* Ashgate Publishing Co.

BOULDER (COLO.)

Barton, Mike. Boulder Impressions. 2006. 96p. 19.95 *(978-0-9801024-0-6(5))* Boulder Pr.

Boulder Group, Boulder Group. Best Boulder Hikes: A Colorado Mountain Club Pack Guide. 2009. 96p. pap. *(978-0-9799663-4-7(5))* Colorado Mountain Club Pr., The.

Boulder's Favorite Places. 2006. (Colorado Littlebooks). (Illus.). 64p. 14.95 *(978-1-56579-534-1(2))* Westcliffe Pubs.

D'Antonio, Bob. Boulder Canyon Rock Climbs. 2009. (Illus.). 284p. pap. 35.00 *(978-0-9792644-8-1(0))* Wolverine Publishing, LLC.

Lambrecht, Mona & Boulder History Museum. Boulder: 1859-1919. 2008. (Images of America Ser.). (ENG., Illus.). 128p. pap. 21.99 *(978-0-7385-5890-5(7))* Arcadia Publishing.

Leggett, Ann Alexander & Brown, Roz. Boulder & Rocky Mountain National Park. 9th ed. 2009. (Insiders' Guide Ser.). (ENG., Illus.). 352p. pap. 18.95 *(978-0-7627-5027-6(8)*, Insiders' Guide) Globe Pequot Pr., The.

Pettem, Silvia. Boulder: A Sense of Time & Place Revisited. 2010. (American Chronicles Ser.). (ENG., Illus.). 144p. pap. 19.99 *(978-1-59629-974-0(6))* History Pr., The.

—Only in Boulder: The County's Colorful Characters. 2010. (American Chronicles Ser.). (ENG., Illus.). 160p. pap. 19.99 *(978-1-59629-975-7(4))* History Pr., The.

Rand McNally, creator. Boulder/Longmont Street Guide. 2008. spiral bd. 17.95 *(978-0-528-86825-2(X))* Rand McNally.

Salcedo-Chourre, Tracy. Best Easy Day Hikes Boulder. 2nd ed. 2011. (Best Easy Day Hikes Ser.). (ENG., Illus.). 104p. pap. 9.95 *(978-0-7627-6103-6(2)*, Falcon Guides) Globe Pequot Pr., The.

BOULDER COUNTY (COLO.)

Pettem, Silvia. Only in Boulder: The County's Colorful Characters. 2010. (American Chronicles Ser.). (ENG., Illus.). 160p. pap. 19.99 *(978-1-59629-975-7(4))* History Pr., The.

BOULDER DAM (ARIZ. AND NEV.)

see Hoover Dam (Ariz. and Nev.)

BOULDING, KENNETH, 1910-

Dolfsma, Wilfred & Kesting, Stefan. Interdisciplinary Economics. 2012. (Routledge Studies in the History of Economics Ser.). (ENG.). 288p. (C). 150.00 **(978-0-415-48347-6(6))** Routledge.

BOULEZ, PIERRE, 1925-

Ahearne, Jeremy. Pierre Bourdieu & the Literary Field, Vol. 35, No. 1. Speller, John, ed. 2012. (ENG.). 128p. (gr. 17). pap. 32.50 **(978-0-7486-4713-2(9))** Edinburgh Univ. Pr. GBR. Dist: Columbia Univ. Pr.

Gärtner, Susanne. Werkstatt-Spuren: Die Sonatine von Pierre Boulez: Eine Studie zu Lehrzeit und Frühwerk. 2008. (Publikationen der Schweizerischen Musikforschenden Gesellschaft Serie II Publicatons de la Société Suisse de Musicologie Série II Ser.). 408p. pap. *(978-3-03911-202-9(3))* Lang, Peter.

Goldman, Jonathan. The Musical Language of Pierre Boulez: Writings & Compositions. 2011. (Music Since 1900 Ser.). (ENG., Illus.). 268p. 90.00 *(978-0-521-51490-3(8))* Cambridge Univ. Pr.

Peyser, Joan. To Boulez & Beyond. 2007. (ENG., Illus.). 388p. per. 55.00 *(978-0-8108-5877-0(0))* Scarecrow Pr., Inc.

—To Boulez & Beyond: Music in Europe since the Rite of Spring. 2008. (ENG.). 382p. 25.00 *(978-1-4379-5410-3(9))* DIANE Publishing Co.

Thomson, Pat. Understanding the Field of Educational Leadership: Pierre Bourdieu. 2012. (Critical Studies in Educational Leadership, Management & Administration Ser.). (ENG.). 224p. (C). 135.00 *(978-0-415-60355-3(2))* Routledge.

BOULTON, MATTHEW, 1728-1809

Dickinson, H. W. Matthew Boulton. 2010. (Cambridge Library Collection - Technology Ser.). (Illus.). 266p. pap. 23.99 *(978-1-108-01224-9(8))* Cambridge Univ. Pr.

Goodison, Nicholas. Matthew Boulton: Ormolu. 2006. (ENG., Illus.). 432p. 140.00 *(978-0-903432-70-2(6))* Christie, Manson & Woods, Ltd. GBR. Dist: Antique Collectors' Club.

Mason, Shena. Matthew Boulton: Selling What All the World Desires. 2009. (ENG., Illus.). 304p. 75.00 *(978-0-300-14358-4(3))* Yale Univ. Pr.

Mason, Shena, ed. A Lost Landscape: Matthew Boulton's Gardens at Soho. 2010. (ENG., Illus.). 128p. 32.95 *(978-1-86077-563-5(2))* History Pr. Ltd.,The GBR. Dist: Independent Pubs. Group.

BOULTON AND WATT (BIRMINGHAM, ENGLAND)

see James Watt and Company (Birmingham, England)

BOUMPE (AFRICAN PEOPLE)

see Mende (African People)

BOUNDARIES

see also Continental Shelf; Geopolitics

also names of countries, states, etc. with or without subdivision Boundaries; also subdivision Territorial Question under names of wars

Aaron, Jane, et al, eds. Gendering Border Studies. 2010. (Illus.). 281p. pap. 35.00 *(978-0-7083-2170-6(4))* Univ. of Wales Pr. GBR. Dist: Chicago Distribution Ctr.

Andreas, Peter. Border Games. 2nd rev. ed. 2009. (Cornell Studies in Political Economy Ser.). (Illus.). 176p. 62.95 *(978-0-8014-4810-2(7))*; pap. 21.00 *(978-0-8014-7540-5(6))* Cornell Univ. Pr.

Bartolini, Stefano. Restructuring Europe: Centre Formation, System Building & Political Structuring Between the Nation-State & the European Union. 2007. (ENG., Illus.). 448p. per. 55.00 *(978-0-19-923187-4(7))* Oxford Univ. Pr., Inc.

Betteridge, Thomas. Borders & Travellers in Early Modern Europe. 2007. (Illus.). 204p. 124.95 *(978-0-7546-5351-6(X))* Ashgate Publishing Co.

Brett, Annabel. Changes of State - Nature & the Limits of the City in Early Modern Natural Law. 2011. (ENG., Illus.). 234p. (C). 35.00 *(978-0-691-14193-0(2))* Princeton Univ. Pr.

Brettell, Caroline B. Constructing Borders/Crossing Boundaries: Race, Ethnicity, & Immigration. 2008. (ENG.). 342p. pap. 36.99 *(978-0-7391-1570-1(7))* Lexington Bks.

Breugnot, Jacqueline, ed. Les Escapes Frontaliers: Laboratoires de la Citoyennete Europeenne. (FRE.). 215p. pap. 46.95 *(978-3-03911-305-7(4))* Lang, Peter Publishing, Inc.

Brown, Charles S. & Toadvine, Ted, eds. Nature's Edge: Boundary Explorations in Ecological Theory & Practice. 2007. (SUNY Series in Environmental Philosophy & Ethics). (Illus.). 240p. (C). 74.50 *(978-0-7914-7121-0(7))*; 231p. per. 29.95 *(978-0-7914-7122-7(5))* State Univ. of New York Pr.

Brown, Wendy. Walled States, Waning Sovereignty. 2010. (ENG., Illus.). 167p. (gr. 17). 25.95 *(978-1-935408-08-6(9))* Zone Bks.

Brunet-Jailly, Emmanuel, ed. Borderlands: Comparing Border Security in North America & Europe. 2007. (Governance Ser.). (ENG., Illus.). 406p. (gr. 13). pap. *(978-0-7766-0651-4(4))* Univ. of Ottawa Pr./Presses de l'Universite d'Ottawa.

Cram101 Textbook Reviews & Cram101 Textbook Reviews. Outlines & Highlights for Borderlines & Borderlands: Political Oddities at the Edge of the Nation-State by Alexander Diener, ISBN. 2011. 370p. pap. 34.95 ***(978-1-61461-312-1(5))*** Cram101 Inc.

Crocker, John. Moving Beyond Boundaries. 2008. 148p. per. *(978-3-8364-5768-2(7))* VDM Verlag Dr. Mueller e.K.

Cruz, Laura. Boundaries & Their Meanings in the History of the Netherlands. Kaplan, Benjamin & Carlson, Mary Beth, eds. 2009. (Studies in Central European Histories Ser.). 262p. *(978-90-04-17637-9(3))* BRILL.

Curzon, George. Frontiers. 2009. 48p. pap. *(978-1-4099-3145-4(5))* Dodo Pr.

Diamandouros, Nikiforos, et al, eds. Spatial Conceptions of the Nation: Modernizing Geographies in Greece & Turkey. 2010. (International Library of Historical Studies). (ENG., Illus.). 320p. 92.50 *(978-1-84885-131-3(6)*, Tauris Academic Studies) I. B. Tauris & Co., Ltd. GBR. Dist: Macmillan.

Diener, Alexander & Hagen, Joshua. Borderlines & Borderlands. 2010. (ENG., Illus.). 292p. pap. 35.00 *(978-0-7425-5636-2(0))* Rowman & Littlefield Publishers, Inc.

Diener/Hagen. Borderlines & Borderlands. 2010. (ENG., Illus.). 292p. 79.99 *(978-0-7425-5635-5(2))* Rowman & Littlefield Education.

Donnan, Hastings. Borderlands: Ethnographic Approaches to Security, Power, & Identity. 2010. (ENG.). 158p. pap. 26.50 *(978-0-7618-5123-3(2))* Univ. Pr. of America, Inc.

El Ouali, Abdelhamid. Territorial Integrity in a Globalizing World: International Law & States' Quest for Survival. 2012. (ENG.). xix, 349p. 139.00 ***(978-3-642-22868-1(2)***, 3642228682) Springer.

Gainsborough, Martin, ed. On the Borders of State Power: Frontiers in the Greater Mekong Sub-Region. 2008. (Routledge Studies in the Modern History of Asia Ser.). (ENG., Illus.). 128p. (C). 150.00 *(978-0-415-41465-4(2))* Routledge.

Gavrilis, George. The Dynamics of Interstate Boundaries. (ENG., Illus.). 2010. 208p. pap. 26.99 *(978-0-521-15624-0(6))* 2008. 216p. 84.00 *(978-0-521-89899-7(4))* Cambridge Univ. Pr.

Ghebrewebet, Helen. Identifying Units of Statehood & Determining International Boundaries: A Revised Look at the Doctrine of Uti Possidetis & the Principle of Self-Determination, Vol. 66. 2006. (Schriften Zum Internationalen und Zum Offentlichen Recht Ser.). xiv,193p. pap. *(978-0-8204-9881-2(5))* Lang, Peter AG.

Gierstberg, Frits, ed. Vesselina Nikolaeva: Simply a Line. 2010. (ENG., Illus.). 144p. 60.00 *(978-90-5662-699-0(X))* NAi Uitgevers / Publishers Stichting NLD. Dist: D.A.P./Distributed Art Pubs.

Gutheil, Thomas G. & Brodsky, Archie. Preventing Boundary Violations in Clinical Practice. (ENG.). 340p. 2011. pap. 25.00 ***(978-1-4625-0443-5(4))*** 2008. 45.00 *(978-1-59385-691-5(1))* Guilford Pubns., Inc.

Halley, Jean & Halley, Jean O'Malley. Boundaries of Touch: Parenting & Adult-Child Intimacy. 2008. (ENG.). 224p. pap. 26.00 *(978-0-252-07581-0(1))* Univ. of Illinois Pr.

Hansen, Jerry. State Boundaries of America: How, Why, & When American State Lines were Formed. 2007. pap. 24.00 *(978-0-7884-4456-2(5))* Heritage Bks.

Iseminger, Gordon L. The Quartzite Border: Surveying & Marking the North Dakota-South Dakota Boundary, 1891-1892. 2007. (ENG., Illus.). 150p. pap. 17.95 *(978-0-931170-40-9(0))* Ctr. for Western Studies.

Karolewski, Ireneusz & Suszycki, Andrzej. The Nation & Nationalism in Europe: An Introduction. 2011. (ENG.). 272p. (gr. 17). 100.00 *(978-0-7486-3806-2(7))* Edinburgh Univ. Pr. GBR. Dist: Columbia Univ. Pr.

Karolewski, Ireneusz & Suszycki, Andrzej Marcin. The Nation & Nationalism in Europe: An Introduction. 2011. (ENG.). 272p. (gr. 17). pap. 32.00 *(978-0-7486-3807-9(5))* Edinburgh Univ. Pr. GBR. Dist: Columbia Univ. Pr.

Karolewski, Ireneusz Pawel & Suszycki, Andrzej Marcin. Multiplicity of Nationalism in Contemporary Europe. 2009. (ENG.). 292p. 83.99 *(978-0-7391-2307-2(6))* Lexington Bks.

Khosravi, Shahram. 'Illegal' Traveller: An Auto-Ethnography of Borders. 2010. (Global Ethics Ser.). (ENG.). 176p. 84.00 *(978-0-230-23079-8(2))* Palgrave Macmillan.

Major, Patrick. Behind the Berlin Wall: East Germany & the Frontiers of Power. 2010. (ENG., Illus.). 352p. 99.00 *(978-0-19-924328-0(X))* Oxford Univ. Pr., Inc.

Maleuvre, Didier. The Horizon: A History of Our Infinite Longing. 2011. (ENG., Illus.). 392p. 29.95 *(978-0-520-26743-5(5))* Univ. of California Pr.

Mares, David R. & Palmer, David Scott. Power, Institutions, & Leadership in War & Peace: Lessons from Peru & Ecuador, 1995-1998. 2012. (ENG., Illus.). 202p. 55.00 ***(978-0-292-73569-9(3))*** Univ. of Texas Pr.

—Power, Institutions, & Leadership in War & Peace: Lessons from Peru & Ecuador, 1995/1998. 2012. E-Book ***(978-0-292-73570-5(7))*** Univ. of Texas Pr.

Mau, Steffen, et al. Liberal States & the Freedom of Movement: Selective Borders, Unequal Mobility. 2012. (Transformations of the State Ser.). (ENG., Illus.). 280p. 85.00 ***(978-0-230-27784-7(5))*** Palgrave Macmillan.

McGee, Brenda. Frontiers, Bk. 1. 2007. (ENG.). 288p. (gr. 6-6). pap. 79.95 *(978-1-59363-300-4(9))* Prufrock Pr.

McKeown, Adam M. Melancholy Order: Asian Migration & the Globalization of Borders. 2011. (Columbia Studies in International & Global History Ser.). (ENG., Illus.). 472p. (gr. 17). pap. 26.50 *(978-0-231-14077-5(0))* Columbia Univ. Pr.

McLinden, Gerard. Border Management Modernization. 2011. (Illus.). xii, 381p. E-Book *(978-0-8213-8597-5(6))* World Bank Pubns.

McLinden, Gerard, et al, eds. Border Management Modernization. 2010. (ENG., Illus.). 400p. pap. 39.95 *(978-0-8213-8596-8(8)*, 9780821385968) World Bank Pubns.

Mic & Cristoloveanu, Sorin. Frontiers in Electronics, Vol. 50. 2009. (Illus.). 336p. 88.00 *(978-981-4273-01-5(5))* World Scientific Publishing Co., Inc.

Mojtahed-Zadeh, Pirouz. Boundary Politics & International Boundaries of Iran: A Study of the Origin, Evolution, & Implications of the Boundaries of Modern Iran with Its 1. 2007. 372p. per. 25.95 *(978-1-58112-933-5(5))* Universal Pubs.

Mullin, David, ed. Places in Between: The Archaeology of Social, Cultural & Geographical Borders & Borderlands. 2011. (ENG., Illus.). 104p. (C). pap. 60.00 *(978-1-84217-983-3(7))* Oxbow Bks., Ltd. GBR. Dist: Brown, David Bk. Co., The.

Nuñez-Neto, Blas & Garcia, Michael John. Border Security: Barriers along the U. S. International Border. 2009. pap. 49.00 *(978-1-60692-171-5(1))* Nova Science Pubs., Inc.

Nunn, Astrid. Mauern als Grenzen. Nunn, Astrid, ed. 2009. (GER., Illus.). 216p. (C). 45.00 *(978-3-8053-3934-6(8))* Zabern, Philipp von Verlag, GmbH DEU. Dist: Brown, David Bk. Co., The.

Olesnavage. Our Boundary. 2009. 132p. pap. 12.95 *(978-1-59858-991-7(1))* Dog Ear Publishing, LLC.

Oosthuizen, Susan. Landscapes Decoded: The Origins & Development of Cambridgeshire's Medieval Fields. Fox, Harold & Goose, Nigel, eds. 2007. (ENG., Illus.). 160p. per. 29.95 *(978-1-902806-58-7(1))* Univ. of Hertfordshire Pr. GBR. Dist: Independent Pubs. Group.

Pickering, Sharon & Weber, Leanne, eds. Borders, Mobility & Technologies of Control. 2010. (ENG.). xi, 222p. pap. 159.00 *(978-90-481-7221-4(7)*, 9048172217) Springer.

Popescu, Gabriel. Bordering & Ordering the Twenty-First Century: Understanding Borders. 2011. (Human Geography in the New Millennium: Issues & Applications Ser.). (ENG., Illus.). 192p. 80.00 *(978-0-7425-5621-8(2))* Rowman & Littlefield Publishers, Inc.

Popescu, Gabriel. Understanding Borders: Bordering & Ordering the Twenty-First Century. 2011. ***(978-1-4422-1325-8(6))***; (ENG., Illus.). 192p. pap. 32.95 ***(978-0-7425-5622-5(0))*** Rowman & Littlefield Publishers, Inc.

Preshlenova, Roumiana. Frontiers Revisited. 2011. 52p. pap. ***(978-3-8443-1837-1(2))*** Lambert Academic Publishing.

Preyer, G. & Bös, Mathias, eds. Borderlines in a Globalized World: New Perspectives in a Sociology of the World-System. 2010. (Social Indicators Research Ser.). 240p. pap. 229.00 *(978-90-481-5979-6(2)*, 9048159792) Springer.

Rajaram, Prem Kumar & Grundy-Warr, Carl, eds. Borderscapes: Hidden Geographies & Politics at Territory's Edge. (Borderlines Ser.). (Illus.). 344p. 2008. 75.00 *(978-0-8166-4925-9(1))* 2007. pap. 25.00 *(978-0-8166-4926-6(X))* Univ. of Minnesota Pr.

Schmitz, Eileen. Staying in Bounds: Straight Talk on Boundaries for Effective Ministry. 2010. 208p. pap. 25.99 *(978-0-8272-3481-9(3))* Chalice Pr.

Sheffer, Edith. Burned Bridge: How East & West Germans Made the Iron Curtain, 1 vol. 2011. (ENG., Illus.). 384p. 29.95 *(978-0-19-973704-8(5))* Oxford Univ. Pr., Inc.

Sufian, Sandy & Levine, Mark, eds. Reapproaching Borders: New Perspectives on the Study of Israel-Palestine. 2007. (ENG., Illus.). 336p. 85.00 *(978-0-7425-4638-7(1))*; per. 32.95 *(978-0-7425-4639-4(X))* Rowman & Littlefield Publishers, Inc.

Tolman, Deborah A. Darlingtonia Fens of Southwestern Oregon. 2008. 104p. pap. *(978-3-639-03695-4(6))* VDM Verlag Dr. Mueller e.K.

Vaughan-Williams, Nick. Border Politics: The Limits of Sovereign Power. 2012. (ENG., Illus.). 272p. (gr. 17). pap. 32.50 ***(978-0-7486-4485-8(7))*** Edinburgh Univ. Pr. GBR. Dist: Columbia Univ. Pr.

Victor Prescott and Gillian D. Staff. Terrestrial International Frontiers & Boundaries. 2008. 482p. *(978-90-04-16785-8(4))* BRILL.

Vizcaya, Benita Samperdro & Doubleday, Simon R. Border Interrogations: Questioning Spanish Frontiers. 2008. (Remapping Cultural History Ser.: Vol. 8). 278p. (C). 85.00 *(978-1-84545-434-0(0))* Berghahn Bks., Inc.

Voller, Vaughan. Numerical Methods for Moving Boundaries & Phase Change Problems. 2006. 384p. 150.00 *(978-0-470-84824-1(3))* Wiley, John & Sons, Inc.

Wastl-Walter, Doris, ed. Ashgate Research Companion to Border Studies. 2011. (Illus.). 728p. 175.00 *(978-0-7546-7406-1(1))* Ashgate Publishing Co.

Williams, John. The Ethics of Territorial Borders: Drawing Lines in the Shifting Sand. annot. ed. 2006. (ENG.). 192p. 95.00 *(978-0-230-00252-4(8))* Palgrave Macmillan.

Wilson, Thomas M. & Donnan, Hastings, eds. A Companion to Border Studies. 2012. (Wiley-Blackwell Companions to Anthropology Ser.: 26). (ENG.). 640p. 195.00 ***(978-1-4051-9893-6(1)***, Wiley-Blackwell) Wiley, John & Sons, Inc.

Zartman, I. William, ed. Understanding Life in the Borderlands: Boundaries in Depth & in Motion. 2010. (Studies in Security & International Affairs Ser.). (ENG., Illus.). 256p. pap. 24.95 *(978-0-8203-3407-3(3))*; lib. bdg. 69.95 *(978-0-8203-3385-4(9))* Univ. of Georgia Pr.

BOUNDARIES (ESTATES)

see also Adjoining Landowners

Doskow, Emily & Jordan, Cora. Neighbor Law: Fences, Trees, Boundaries & Noise. 7th ed. 2011. 403p. E-Book *(978-1-4133-1346-8(9))*; (ENG.). 424p. pap. 29.99 *(978-1-4133-1320-8(5))* NOLO.

Estopinal, Stephen V. & Lathrop, Wendy. Professional Surveyors & Real Property Descriptions: Composition, Construction, & Comprehension. 2011. (ENG., Illus.). 288p. 110.00 *(978-0-470-54259-0(4)*, Wiley) Wiley, John & Sons, Inc.

Neunzert, Gaby M. Subdividing the Land Metes & Bounds & Rectangular. 2010. (ENG., Illus.). 172p. 79.95 *(978-1-4398-2747-5(8)*, CRC Press) Taylor & Francis Group GBR. Dist: Taylor & Francis Group.

Robillard, Walter G. & Wilson, Donald A. Evidence & Procedures for Boundary Location. 6th ed. 2011. (ENG., Illus.). 672p. 140.00 *(978-0-470-40478-2(7)*, Wiley) Wiley, John & Sons, Inc.

Robillard, Walter G., et al. Brown's Boundary Control & Legal Principles. 6th ed. 2009. (ENG., Illus.). 496p. 140.00 *(978-0-470-18354-0(3)*, Wiley) Wiley, John & Sons, Inc.

Wilson, Donald A. Forensic Procedures for Boundary & Title Investigation. 2008. (ENG., Illus.). 464p. 110.00 *(978-0-470-11369-1(3)*, Wiley) Wiley, John & Sons, Inc.

BOUNDARY CONDITIONS (DIFFERENTIAL EQUATIONS)

see Boundary Value Problems

BOUNDARY ELEMENT METHODS

Aliabadi, M. H. Boundary Element Methods in Engineering & Sciences. 2010. (Illus.). 412p. 124.00 *(978-1-84816-579-3(X))* Imperial College Pr. GBR. Dist: World Scientific Publishing Co., Inc.

Ammari, Habib, et al. Layer Potential Techniques in Spectral Analysis. 2009. (Mathematical Surveys & Monographs). (Illus.). 202p. 69.00 *(978-0-8218-4784-8(8))* American Mathematical Society.

Ang, Whye-Teong. A Beginner's Course in Boundary Element Methods. 2007. 256p. per. 25.95 *(978-1-58112-974-8(2))* Universal Pubs.

Beer, Gernot, et al. The boundary element method with Programming. 2008. 159.00 *(978-3-211-71574-1(6))* Springer.

—The Boundary Element Method with Programming: For Engineers & Scientists. 2010. (Illus.). xiv, 494p. pap. 159.00 *(978-3-211-99900-4(0)*, 3211999000) Springer.

Brebbia, C. A., ed. Boundary Elements & Other Mesh Reduction Methods XXXII. 2010. (WIT Transactions on Modelling & Simulation Ser.: 50). (Illus.). 336p. 256.00 *(978-1-84564-470-3(0))* WIT Pr GBR. Dist: WIT Pr.

—Mesh Reduction Methods: Bem/mrm Xxxi. 2009. (WIT Transactions on Modelling & Simulation Ser.: 49). (Illus.). 432p. 295.00 *(978-1-84564-197-9(3))* WIT Pr GBR. Dist: WIT Pr.

Brebbia, C. A., et al, eds. Boundary Elements & Other Mesh Reduction Methods XXIX. 2007. (WIT Transactions on Modelling & Simulation Ser.: Vol. 44). (Illus.). 352p. 225.00 *(978-1-84564-076-7(4))* WIT Pr GBR. Dist: WIT Pr.

Brebbia, C. A. & Poljak, D., eds. Boundary Elements & Other Mesh Reduction Methods, 34. 2012. (Illus.). 300p. lib. bdg. 258.00 ***(978-1-84564-622-6(3))*** WIT Pr GBR. Dist: WIT Pr.

Brebbia, C. A. & Popov, V., eds. Boundary Elements & Other Mesh Reduction Methods XXXIII. 2011. (WIT Transactions on Modelling & Simulation Ser.: 52). (ENG., Illus.). 368p. lib. bdg. 316.00 *(978-1-84564-542-7(1))* WIT Pr GBR. Dist: WIT Pr.

Burczynski, Tadeusz, ed. IUTAM/IACM/IABEM Symposium on Advanced Mathematical & Computational Mechanics Aspects of the Boundary Element Method. 2012. (ENG., Illus.). 440p. pap. 244.00 *(978-90-481-5737-2(4)*, 9048157374) Springer.

Cai, Meifeng, ed. Rock Mechanics: Achievements & Ambitions. 2011. (ENG.). 1058p. (C). 259.00 ***(978-0-415-62080-2(5)***, CRC Press) Taylor & Francis Group GBR. Dist: Taylor & Francis Group.

Chudinovich, Igor. Variational & Potential Methods for a Class of Linear Hyperbolic Evolutionary Processes. 2010. (Springer Monographs in Mathematics Ser.). xii, 148p. pap. 169.00 *(978-1-84996-946-8(9)*, 1849969469) Springer.

De-hao Yu. Natural Boundary Integral Method & Its Applications. 2010. (Mathematics & Its Applications Ser.). (Illus.). 552p. pap. 279.00 *(978-90-481-5948-2(2)*, 9048159482) Springer.

Duddeck, Fabian M. E. Fourier BEM: Generalization of Boundary Element Methods by Fourier Transform. 2011. (Lecture Notes in Applied & Computational Mechanics Ser.). (ENG., Illus.). iv, 181p. pap. 139.00 *(978-3-642-07727-2(7)*, 3642077277) Springer.

Farcas, Adrian. Dual Reciprocity Boundary Element Methods for Solving Inverse Problems. 2010. 228p. pap. *(978-3-8383-6140-6(7))* Lambert Academic Publishing.

Gao, Xiao-Wei & Davies, Trevor G. Boundary Element Programming in Mechanics. 2011. (ENG., Illus.). 272p. pap. 50.00 *(978-1-107-40025-2(2))* Cambridge Univ. Pr.

Gaul, Lothar, et al. Boundary Element Methods for Engineers & Scientists. 2012. (ENG., Illus.). xvi, 488p. pap. 159.00 *(978-3-642-05589-8(3)*, 3642055893) Springer.

Hall, W. S. & Oliveto, G., eds. Boundary Element Methods for Soil-Structure Interaction. 2010. 440p. pap. 249.00 *(978-90-481-6295-6(5)*, 9048162955) Springer.

Holmes, John J. Modeling of A Ships Ferromagnetism. 2007. (Synthesis Lectures on Computational Electromagnetics Ser.). 100p. pap. 40.00 *(978-1-59829-250-3(1))* Morgan & Claypool Pubs.

Hromadka, Theodore V. & Whitley, Robert J. Advances in the Complex Variable Boundary Element Method. 2010. (ENG., Illus.). xiv, 408p. pap. 159.00 *(978-1-84996-997-0(3)*, 1849969973) Springer.

Hsiao, George C. & Wendland, Wolfgang L. Boundary Integral Equations. 2010. (Applied Mathematical Sciences Ser.). xx, 620p. pap. 129.00 *(978-3-642-05733-5(0)*, 3642057330) Springer.

Langer, Ulrich, et al, eds. Fast Boundary Element Methods in Engineering & Industrial Applications. 2012. (Lecture Notes in Applied & Computational Mechanics Ser.). (ENG., Illus.). xii, 272p. 139.00 ***(978-3-642-25669-1(4)***, 3642256694) Springer.

Linkov, A. M. Boundary Integral Equations in Elasticity Theory. 2010. (Solid Mechanics & Its Applications Ser.). xiii, 274p. pap. 169.00 *(978-90-481-6000-6(6)*, 9048160006) Springer.

Liu, Yijun. Fast Multipole Boundary Element Method: Theory & Applications in Engineering. 2009. (ENG., Illus.). 254p. 88.00 *(978-0-521-11659-6(7))* Cambridge Univ. Pr.

Manolis, G. D. & Polyzos, D., eds. Recent Advances in Boundary Element Methods: A Volume to Honor Professor Dimitri Beskos. 2009. (ENG., Illus.). xxxviii, 470p. 189.00 *(978-1-4020-9709-6(3)*, 1402097093) Springer.

Marburg, Steffen. Computational Acoustics of Noise Propagation in Fluids: Finite & Boundary Element Methods. 2008. (ENG., Illus.). xiv, 578p. 189.00 *(978-3-540-77447-1(5)*, 3540774475) Springer.

Marburg, Steffen & Nolte, Bodo, eds. Computational Acoustics of Noise Propagation in Fluids - Finite & Boundary Element Methods. 2010. (ENG., Illus.). xiv, 578p. pap. 189.00 *(978-3-642-09608-2(5)*, 3642096085) Springer.

Maz'ya, Vladimir & Soloviev, Alexander. Boundary Integral Equations on Contours with Peaks. 2009. (Operator Theory: Advances & Applications Ser.). (ENG.). 356p. 209.00 *(978-3-0346-0170-2(0)*, 3034601700) Birkhauser Verlag AG CHE. Dist: Springer.

Michielssen, Eric & Shanker, Balasubramaniam. Fast Time Domain Integral Equation Solvers. 2013. (IEEE Press Series on Electromagnetic Wave Theory Ser.). (ENG., Illus.). 400p. 130.00 *(978-0-470-47877-6(2)*, Wiley-IEEE Pr.) Wiley, John & Sons, Inc.

Nichita, Constantin. Numerical Simulation of Magneto-Rheological Fluids. 2009. 92p. pap. *(978-3-639-17390-1(2))* VDM Verlag Dr. Mueller e.K.

Pechstein, Clemens. Finite & Boundary Element Tearing & Interconnecting Solvers for Multiscale Problems. 2012. (Lecture Notes in Computational Science & Engineering Ser.). (ENG.). 300p. 109.00 ***(978-3-642-23587-0(5)***, 3642235875) Springer.

Peratta, C. & Peratta, A. Modelling the Human Body Exposure to ELF Electric Fields. 2010. (Topics in Engineering Ser.: 47). (Illus.). 160p. 118.00 *(978-1-84564-418-5(2))* WIT Pr GBR. Dist: WIT Pr.

Rap, Alexandru. Boundary Element Methods for Solving Inverse Problems. 2010. 212p. pap. *(978-3-8383-5190-2(8))* Lambert Academic Publishing.

Rjasanow, Sergej & Steinbach, Olaf. The Fast Solution of Boundary Integral Equations. (Mathematical & Analytical Techniques with Applications to Engineering Ser.). (Illus.). 2010. xii, 284p. pap. 179.00 *(978-1-4419-4160-2(6)*, 1441941606) 2007. 279p. 179.00 *(978-0-387-34041-8(6)*, 0387340416) Springer.

Sapountzakis, Evangelos, ed. Recent Developments in Boundary Element Methods: A Volume to Honour Professor John T. Katsikadelis. 2010. (Illus.). 416p. lib. bdg. *(978-1-84564-492-5(1))* WIT Pr.

Sauter, Stefan & Schwab, Christoph. Boundary Element Methods. 2009. (Springer Series in Computational Mathematics Ser.). (Illus.). 500p. 124.00 *(978-3-540-68092-5(6))* Springer.

Schanz, Martin. Wave Propagation in Viscoelastic & Poroelastic Continua: A Boundary Element Approach. 2010. (Lecture Notes in Applied & Computational Mechanics Ser.). (Illus.). x, 170p. pap. 219.00 *(978-3-642-07490-5(1)*, 3642074901) Springer.

Schanz, Martin & Steinbach, Olaf. Boundary Element Analysis: Mathematical Aspects & Applications. 2007. (Lecture Notes in Applied & Computational Mechanics Ser.: Vol. 29). (Illus.). x, 354p. 219.00 *(978-3-540-47465-4(X))* Springer.

Schanz, Martin & Steinbach, Olaf, eds. Boundary Element Analysis: Mathematical Aspects & Applications. 2010. (Lecture Notes in Applied & Computational Mechanics Ser.). (Illus.). x, 354p. pap. 219.00 *(978-3-642-07999-3(7)*, 3642079997) Springer.

Schetz, et al. Boundary Layer Analysis. 2nd ed. 2011. (Illus.). xxiii, 652p. ***(978-1-60086-823-8(1)***, Branch Line Video) American Institute of Aeronautics & Astronautics.

Skerget, L., ed. Boundary Elements & Other Mesh Reduction Methods XXX. 2008. (WIT Transactions on Modelling & Simulation Ser.: 47). (Illus.). 288p. 190.00 *(978-1-84564-121-4(3))* WIT Pr GBR. Dist: WIT Pr.

Skerget, L., et al, eds. Domain Decomposition Techniques for Boundary Elements: Application to Fluid Flow. 2007. (Advances in Boundary Elements Ser.: 21). (Illus.). 320p. 195.00 *(978-1-84564-100-9(0))* WIT Pr GBR. Dist: WIT Pr.

Steinbach, Olaf. Numerical Approximation Methods for Elliptic Boundary Value Problems: Finite & Boundary Elements. 2010. (ENG.). xii, 388p. pap. 59.95 *(978-1-4419-2173-4(7)*, 1441921737) Springer.

Stroud, Ian. Boundary Representation Modelling Techniques. 2006. (ENG., Illus.). xx, 788p. 175.00 *(978-1-84628-312-3(4)*, 1846283124) Springer.

Stroud, Ian Anthony. Boundary Representation Modelling Techniques. 2010. (ENG., Illus.). xx, 788p. pap. 175.00 *(978-1-84996-578-1(1)*, 1849965781) Springer.

Sutradhar, Alok, et al. Symmetric Galerkin Boundary Element Method. (ENG., Illus.). xviii, 276p. 2010. pap. 129.00 *(978-3-642-08829-2(5)*, 3642088295) 2008. 129.00 *(978-3-540-68770-2(X)*, 354068770X) Springer.

Taigbenu, Akpofure E. The Green Element Method. 2010. (ENG.). 376p. pap. 199.00 *(978-1-4419-5087-1(7)*, 1441950877) Springer.

Wendland, Wolfgang & Hsiao, George C. Boundary Integral Equations. 2008. (Applied Mathematical Sciences Ser.). (Illus.). 300p. 129.00 *(978-3-540-15284-2(9))* Springer.

Wu, Jiangwei. Advanced Application of the Boundary Element Method. 2009. 148p. pap. *(978-3-639-17442-7(9))* VDM Verlag Dr. Mueller e.K.

Zhou, Jianxin & Chen, Goong. Boundary Element Methods, Vol. 4. 2nd ed. 2010. (Atlantis studies in mathematics for engineering & science Ser.: Vol. 6). 700p. 165.00 *(978-90-78677-31-4(7))* World Scientific Publishing Co., Inc.

BOUNDARY LAYER

see also Laminar Flow

Babinsky, Holger & Harvey, John, eds. Shock Wave-Boundary-Layer Interactions. 2011. (Cambridge Aerospace Ser.). (ENG., Illus.). 480p. 125.00 ***(978-0-521-84852-7(0))*** Cambridge Univ. Pr.

Baklanov, A. & Grisogono, B., eds. Atmospheric Boundary Layers: Nature, Theory & Applications to Environmental Modelling & Security. 2007. (ENG., Illus.). vi, 246p. 149.00 *(978-0-387-74318-9(9))*, 0387743189) Springer.

Baklanov, Alexander & Grisogono, Branko, eds. Atmospheric Boundary Layers: Nature, Theory, & Application to Environmental Modelling & Security. 2010. (ENG., Illus.). vi, 246p. pap. 149.00 *(978-1-4419-2555-8(4)*, 1441925554) Springer.

Broecker, Wally. The Great Ocean Conveyor: Discovering the Trigger for Abrupt Climate Change. 2010. (ENG., Illus.). 172p. (C). 27.95 *(978-0-691-14354-5(4))* Princeton Univ. Pr.

Clavero, Carmelo, et al, eds. BAIL 2010 - Boundary & Interior Layers, Computational & Asymptotic Methods. 2011. (Lecture Notes in Computational Science & Engineering Ser.). (ENG., Illus.). vii, 300p. 124.00 *(978-3-642-19664-5(0)*, 3642196640) Springer.

Cousteix, Jean & Mauss, Jacques. Asymptotic Analysis & Boundary Layers. (Scientific Computation Ser.). (Illus.). xviii, 432p. 2010. pap. 149.00 *(978-3-642-07983-2(0)*, 3642079830) 2007. 149.00 *(978-3-540-46488-4(3)*, 3540464883) Springer.

Encyclopaedia Britannica, Inc., compiled by. Boundary Layer Control. 2009. 49.00 *(978-1-60835-044-5(4))* Encyclopaedia Britannica, Inc.

—Fundamentals of Boundary Layers. 2009. 49.00 *(978-1-60835-053-7(3))* Encyclopaedia Britannica, Inc.

G, Mrudula & Mohankumar, K. Tropical Cyclone Induced Changes in Tropoposphere. 2010. 212p. pap. *(978-3-639-22639-3(9))* VDM Verlag Dr. Mueller e.K.

Garratt, John R. & Taylor, P. A., eds. Boundary-Layer Meteorology - 25th Anniversary Volume, 1970-1995: Invited Reviews & Selected Contributions to Recognise Ted Munn's Contribution as Editor over the Past 25 Years. 2010. (ENG.). 436p. pap. 99.95 *(978-90-481-4740-3(9)*, 9048147409) Springer.

Gultepe, Ismail, ed. Fog & Boundary Layer Clouds: Fog Visibility & Forecasting. 2007. (Pageoph Topical Volumes Ser.). 316p. pap. 109.00 *(978-3-7643-8418-0(2))* Birkhauser Verlag AG CHE. Dist: Springer.

Hegarty, Alan F. BAIL 2008 - Boundary & Interior Layers: Proceedings of the International Conference on Boundary & Interior Layers - Computational & Asymptotic Methods, Limerick, July 2008. Hegarty, Alan et al, eds. 2009. (Lecture Notes in Computational Science & Engineering Ser.). (ENG., Illus.). xvi, 312p. pap. 129.00 *(978-3-642-00604-3(3)*, 3642006043) Springer.

Heinemann, Hans-Joachim. Iutam Symposium on One Hundred Years of Boundary Layer Research: Proceedings of the Iutam Symposium Held at DLR-Gottingen, Germany, August 12-14, 2004. Meier, G. E. A & Sreenivasan, K. R., eds. 2006. (Solid Mechanics & Its Applications Ser.). (Illus.). xi, 494p. 239.00 *(978-1-4020-4149-5(7)*, 1402041497) Springer.

Mohanakumar, K. Stratosphere Troposphere Interactions: An Introduction. 2010. (ENG., Illus.). xvii, 416p. pap. 99.00 *(978-90-481-7809-4(6)*, 9048178096) Springer.

O'Kane, Terence. The Statistical Dynamics of Geophysical Flows. 2010. 216p. pap. *(978-3-8383-7116-0(X))* Lambert Academic Publishing.

Reuten, Christian. Upslope Flow Systems - Scaling, Structure, & Kinematics in Tank & Atmosphere. 2008. 200p. pap. *(978-3-639-00757-2(3))* VDM Verlag Dr. Mueller e.K.

Rosser, Kevin. Study of the Planetary Boundary Layer. 2010. 128p. pap. *(978-3-8383-1879-0(X))* Lambert Academic Publishing.

Saric, Sanjin. Turbulent Flow Separation Control by Boundary-Layer Forcing - a Computational Study. 2008. 144p. pap. *(978-3-8364-9984-2(3))* VDM Verlag Dr. Mueller e.K.

Schetz, et al. Boundary Layer Analysis. 2nd ed. 2011. (Illus.). xxiii, 652p. ***(978-1-60086-823-8(1)***, Branch Line Video) American Institute of Aeronautics & Astronautics.

Sharan, Maithili & Raman, Sethu, eds. Atmospheric & Oceanic Mesoscale Processes. 2007. (Pageoph Topical Volumes Ser.). 430p. pap. 109.00 *(978-3-7643-8492-0(1)*, 3764384921) Birkhauser Verlag AG CHE. Dist: Springer.

Surah, Dr. D. & Surah, D. Investigation of Attachment Line Boundary Layers in Hypersonic Flows. 2010. 404p. pap. *(978-3-8383-6268-7(3))* Lambert Academic Publishing.

Vazquez, Rafael & Krstic, Miroslav. Control of Turbulent & Magnetohydrodynamic Channel Flows: Boundary Stabilization & State Estimation. 2007. (Systems & Control: Foundations & Applications Ser.). (Illus.). 211p. 79.95 *(978-0-8176-4698-1(1))* Birkhauser Verlag AG CHE. Dist: Springer.

Wagner, Siegfried, et al, eds. Recent Results in Laminar-Turbulent Transition: Selected numerical & experimental contributions from the DFG priority programme Transition in Germany. 2010. (Notes on Numerical Fluid Mechanics & Multidisciplinary Design Ser.). (ENG.). xiv, 324p. pap. 289.00 *(978-3-642-07345-8(X)*, 364207345X) Springer.

Wan, Qun. Boundary Layer Receptivity on a Compliant Surface. 2010. 144p. pap. *(978-3-639-23248-6(8))* VDM Verlag Dr. Mueller e.K.

BOUNDARY VALUE PROBLEMS

see also Scattering (Mathematics)

Abell, Martha L. & Braselton, James P. Introductory Differential Equations: With Boundary Value Problems. 3rd ed. 2009. (ENG.). 744p. (C). 155.00 *(978-0-12-374935-2(2)*, Academic Pr.) Elsevier Science & Technology Bks.

Agarwal, R. P. Focal Boundary Value Problems for Differential & Difference Equations. 2010. (Mathematics & Its Applications Ser.). 304p. pap. 249.00 *(978-90-481-5005-2(1)*, 9048150051) Springer.

Agarwal, Ravi P. & O'Regan, Donal. Ordinary & Partial Differential Equations: With Special Functions, Fourier Series, & Boundary Value Problems. 2009. (Universitext Ser.). (Illus.). 400p. pap. 59.95 *(978-0-387-79145-6(0))*; xiv, 410p. *(978-0-387-79146-3(9))* Springer.

Agmon, Shmuel. Lectures on Elliptic Boundary Value Problems. 2010. (AMS Chelsea Publishing Ser.). (Illus.). 210p. 40.00 *(978-0-8218-4910-1(7)*, Chelsea Publishing Co., Inc.) American Mathematical Society.

Al-Gwaiz, Mohammed Abdelrahman & Al-Gwaiz, M. A. Sturm-Liouville Theory & Its Applications. 2007. (Springer Undergraduate Mathematics Ser.). (Illus.). 264p. per. 49.95 *(978-1-84628-971-2(8))* Springer.

Andres, J. & Górniewicz, Lech. Topological Fixed Point Principles for Boundary Value Problems. 2011. (Topological Fixed Point Theory & Its Applications Ser.). (ENG.). 761p. pap. 129.00 *(978-90-481-6318-2(8)*, 9048163188) Springer.

Articolo, George A. & A. Articolo, George. Partial Differential Equations & Boundary Value Problems with Maple. 2nd ed. 2009. (ENG., Illus.). 744p. pap. 72.95 *(978-0-12-374732-7(5)*, Academic Pr.) Elsevier Science & Technology Bks.

Atakhodzhaev, Mukarram A. Ill-Posed Internal Boundary Value Problems for the Biharmonic Equation. (Inverse & Ill-Posed Problems Ser.). (ENG.). VIII, 158p. 270.00 ***(978-3-11-184984-3(8))*** De Gruyter, Walter Inc.

Aubin, Jean-Pierre. Approximation of Elliptic Boundary-Value Problems. 2007. (Dover Books on Mathematics Ser.). (ENG.). 384p. per. 19.95 *(978-0-486-45791-8(5))* Dover Pubns., Inc.

Barbu, Luminita & Morosanu, Gheorghe. Singularly Perturbed Boundary-Value Problems. 2007. (International Series of Numerical Mathematics Ser.). xiii, 230p. 149.00 *(978-3-7643-8330-5(5)*, 3764383305) Birkhauser Verlag AG CHE. Dist: Springer.

Barbu, Viorel. Partial Differential Equations & Boundary Value Problems. 2010. (Mathematics & Its Applications Ser.). 292p. pap. 239.00 *(978-90-481-5028-1(0)*, 9048150280) Springer.

Bebendorf, Mario. Hierarchical Matrices: A Means to Efficiently Solve Elliptic Boundary Value Problems. 2008. (Lecture Notes in Computational Science & Engineering Ser.). (Illus.). 270p. pap. 139.00 *(978-3-540-77146-3(8))* Springer.

Ben-Artzi, Matania & Falcovitz, Joseph. Generalized Riemann Problems in Computational Fluid Dynamics. 2010. (Cambridge Monographs on Applied & Computational Mathematics Ser.). (ENG.). 366p. pap. 45.00 *(978-0-521-17327-8(2))* Cambridge Univ. Pr.

Bidégaray-Fesquet, Brigitte. Hiérarchie de modèles en optique quantique: De Maxwel-Bloch à Schrödinger non-linéaire. 2006. (Mathématiques et Applications Ser.). (FRE., Illus.). XIII, 175p. pap. 49.95 *(978-3-540-27238-0(0)*, 3540272380) Springer.

Birman, M. S. & Uraltseva, N. N., eds. Nonlinear Equations & Spectral Theory. 2007. (Advances in the Mathematical Sciences Ser.: Vol. 2). (Illus.). 246p. 112.00 *(978-0-8218-4209-6(9))* American Mathematical Society.

Borsuk, Mikhail. Transmission Problems for Elliptic Second-Order Equations in Non-Smooth Domains. 2010. (Frontiers in Mathematics Ser.). (Illus.). 200p. pap. 49.95 *(978-3-0346-0476-5(9)*, 3034604769) Birkhauser Verlag AG CHE. Dist: Springer.

Borthakur, Prakash Jyoti & C. HAZARIKA, G. Variable Viscosity & Thermal Conductivity on Micropolar Fluid. 2010. 224p. pap. *(978-3-639-21581-6(8))* VDM Verlag Dr. Mueller e.K.

Boyce, William E. Elementary Differential Equations & Boundary Value Problems 8th Edition ODE Architect CD with MATLAB Tutorial CD & Wiley Plus Set. 8th rev. ed. 2006. (Wiley Plus Products Ser.). 161.95 *(978-0-470-14075-8(5))* Wiley, John & Sons, Inc.

—Elementary Differential Equations & Boundary Value Problems 8th Edition with ODE Architect CD & Elementary Linear Algebra with Applications 9th Edition Set. 2006. 1664p. 253.95 *(978-0-470-13636-2(7))* Wiley, John & Sons, Inc.

—Elementary Differential Equations & Boundary Valueproblems. 8th ed. 2006. pap. 68.95 *(978-0-470-07543-2(0))* Wiley, John & Sons, Inc.

—Elementary Differential Equations & Boundary Valuue Problems 8th Edition with ODE Architect CD with Wiley Plus Set. 8th rev. ed. 2006. (Wiley Plus Products Ser.). 134.95 *(978-0-470-10310-4(8)*, Sybex) Wiley, John & Sons, Inc.

Boyce, William E. & DiPrima, Richard C. Elementary Differential Equations. 10th ed. 2010. (C). 100.00 *(978-0-470-45832-7(1)*, Wiley) Wiley, John & Sons, Inc.

—Elementary Differential Equations & Boundary Value Problems. (ENG., (C). 9th ed. 2008. Illus.). 320p. pap. 71.95 *(978-0-470-38335-3(6))* 10th ed. 2010. 135.00 *(978-0-470-45831-0(3))* Wiley, John & Sons, Inc. (Wiley).

—Student Solutions Manual to accompany Boyce Elementary Differential Equations 10th Edition & Elementary Differential Equations w/ Boundary Value Problems 8th Edition. 10th ed. 2012. (ENG.). 600p. (C). pap. 49.95 *(978-0-470-45833-4(X)*, Wiley) Wiley, John & Sons, Inc.

Brannan, James R. Differential Equations with Boundary Value Problems. 2009. (ENG.). 528p. (C). pap. 43.95 *(978-0-470-41851-2(6)*, Wiley) Wiley, John & Sons, Inc.

Brannan, James R., et al. Differential Equations with Boundary Value Problems: An Introduction to Modern Methods & Applications. 2009. (ENG., Illus.). 976p. (C). 223.95 *(978-0-470-41850-5(8)*, Wiley) Wiley, John & Sons, Inc.

Brelot, Marcel. On Topologies & Boundaries in Potential Theory. 2008. (Lecture Notes in Mathematics Ser.). 184p. pap. 39.95 *(978-3-540-05327-9(1)*, 3540053271) Springer.

Brown, James Ward & Churchill, Ruel V. Fourier Series & Boundary Value Problems. (ENG., Illus.). (C). 7th rev. ed. 2006. 384p. 173.44 *(978-0-07-305193-2(4)*, 0073051934) 8th ed. 2011. 416p. 200.33 *(978-0-07-803597-5(X)*, 007803597X) McGraw-Hill Higher Education. (McGraw-Hill Science, Engineering & Mathematics).

Cabada, Alberto, et al, eds. Mathematical Models in Engineering, Biology & Medicine: International Conference on Boundary Value Problems: Mathematical Models in Engineering, Biology & Medicine. 2009. (AIP Conference Proceedings Ser.). (Illus.). 370p. 166.00 *(978-0-7354-0660-5(X))* American Institute of Physics.

Carmichael, Richard D., et al. Boundary Values & Convolution in Ultradistribution Spaces. 2007. (Ser. on ANALYSIS, APPLICATIONS & COMPUTATION Ser.). 250p. (C). 85.00 *(978-981-270-769-7(7))* World Scientific Publishing Co., Inc.

Choudhury, Jayanta & Christov, Christo I. Stationary-Propagating Solutions of the Boussinesq Equation in 2d Numerical & Asymptotic Investigation of Localized Solutions Using Finite-Differen. 2009. 84p. pap. *(978-3-639-10818-7(3))* VDM Verlag Dr. Mueller e.K.

Chung, Hyuck. Mathematical Studies of Wave Propagation in Sea-Ice Sea-Ice Dynamics. 2008. 152p. pap. *(978-3-639-10852-1(3))* VDM Verlag Dr. Mueller e.K.

Clavero, Carmelo, et al, eds. BAIL 2010 - Boundary & Interior Layers, Computational & Asymptotic Methods. 2011. (Lecture Notes in Computational Science & Engineering Ser.). (ENG., Illus.). vii, 300p. 124.00 *(978-3-642-19664-5(0)*, 3642196640) Springer.

Coddington, E. A. Regular Boundary Value Problems Associated Pairs of Ordinary Diff Expressions. 2008. (Lecture Notes in Mathematics Ser.). pap. 46.00 *(978-3-540-10706-4(1))* Springer.

Cousteix, Jean & Mauss, Jacques. Asymptotic Analysis & Boundary Layers. (Scientific Computation Ser.). (Illus.). xviii, 432p. 2010. pap. 149.00 *(978-3-642-07983-2(0)*, 3642079830) 2007. 149.00 *(978-3-540-46488-4(3)*, 3540464883) Springer.

Cram101 Textbook Reviews Staff. Outlines & Highlights for Differential Equations by John Polking, Isbn: 9780131437388. 2009. 248p. pap. 31.95 *(978-1-4288-3747-8(7))*; 96p. pap. 27.95 *(978-1-4288-7663-7(4))* Cram101 Inc.

—Outlines & Highlights for Differential Equations with Boundary-Value Problems by Zill & Cullen, Isbn: 9780495108368. 2009. 240p. pap. 31.95 *(978-1-4288-2683-4(4))*; 200p. pap. 30.95 *(978-1-4288-7825-9(4))* Cram101 Inc.

—Outlines & Highlights for Elementary Differential Equations & Boundary Value Problems, 9th Edition by William E Boyce, Isbn: 9780470383346. 2009. 200p. pap. 30.95 *(978-1-4288-9744-1(5))* Cram101 Inc.

—Outlines & Highlights for Elementary Differential Equations with Boundary Value Problems by C Henry Edwards, Isbn: 9780136006138. 2009. 186p. pap. 30.95 *(978-1-4288-2275-7(5))*; 58p. pap. 26.95 *(978-1-4288-9963-6(4))* Cram101 Inc.

De Castro, Manuela. Theoretical Aspects of Absorbing Boundary Conditions. 2010. 68p. pap. *(978-3-639-23772-6(2))* VDM Verlag Dr. Mueller e.K.

De-hao Yu. Natural Boundary Integral Method & Its Applications. 2010. (Mathematics & Its Applications Ser.). (Illus.). 552p. pap. 279.00 *(978-90-481-5948-2(2)*, 9048159482) Springer.

Dierkes, Ulrich, et al. Global Analysis of Minimal Surfaces. 2nd ed. 2010. (Grundlehren der mathematischen Wissenschaften Ser.). (Illus.). 550p. 129.00 *(978-3-642-11705-3(8)*, 3642117058) Springer.

—Minimal Surfaces: Part I. 2nd ed. 2010. (Grundlehren der mathematischen Wissenschaften Ser.). (ENG., Illus.). xvi, 708p. 129.00 *(978-3-642-11697-1(3)*, 3642116973) Springer.

—Regularity of Minimal Surfaces. 2nd ed. 2010. (Grundlehren der mathematischen Wissenschaften Ser.). (ENG., Illus.). xviii, 668p. 129.00 *(978-3-642-11699-5(X)*, 364211699X) Springer.

Duffy, Dean G. Mixed Boundary Value Problems. 2008. (Chapman & Hall/CRC Applied Mathematics & Nonlinear Science Ser.). (ENG., Illus.). 488p. 109.95 *(978-1-58488-579-5(3)*, Chapman & Hall/CRC) CRC Pr. LLC.

Duits, Maurice, et al. The Hermitian Two Matrix Model with an Even Quartic Potential. 2012. (Memoirs of the American Mathematical Society Ser.). 105p. pap. 70.00 ***(978-0-8218-6928-4(0))*** American Mathematical Society.

Dumett, Miguel. A Numerical Method for Anisotropic Elliptic Boundary Value Problems. 2010. 148p. pap. *(978-3-8383-2233-9(9))* Lambert Academic Publishing.

Edwards & Penney & Cram101 Textbook Reviews Staff. Differential Equations & Boundary Value Problems. 2007. 160p. per. 12.95 *(978-1-4288-3474-3(5))* Cram101 Inc.

Edwards, C. Henry, et al. Differential Equations & Boundary Value Problems: Computing & Modeling. 4th ed. 2007. (ENG., Illus.). 816p. (C). 154.67 *(978-0-13-156107-6(3)*, Prentice Hall) Prentice Hall PTR.

Edwards, Henry & Penney, David. Applications Manual for Differential Equations & Boundary Value Problems: Computing & Modeling. 4th ed. 2007. (ENG.). 352p. (C). pap. 36.67 *(978-0-13-600679-4(5)*, Prentice Hall) Prentice Hall PTR.

Elementary Differential Equations & Boundary Value Problems, Eighth Edition with ODE Architect CD Desktop Edition. 2007. (Wiley Desktop Editions Ser.). 141.95 *(978-0-470-24078-6(4))* Wiley, John & Sons, Inc.

Elliptic Boundary Value Problems on Corner Domains: Smoothness & Asymptotics of Solutions. 2008. (Lecture Notes in Mathematics Ser.). pap. 59.95 *(978-3-540-50169-5(X))* Springer.

Eom, Hyo J. Electromagnetic Wave Theory for Boundary-Value Problems: An Advanced Course on Analytical Methods. 2010. (ENG., Illus.). xvi, 314p. pap. 169.00 *(978-3-642-05955-1(4)*, 3642059554) Springer.

Fichera, Gaetano. Linear Elliptic Differential Systems & Eigenvalue Problems. 2007. (Lecture Notes in Mathematics Ser.). 180p. per. 39.95 *(978-3-540-03351-6(3))* Springer.

Friedman, Avner. Variational Principles & Free-Boundary Problems. 2010. (Dover Books on Mathematics Ser.). (ENG.). 720p. pap. 29.95 *(978-0-486-47853-1(X))* Dover Pubns., Inc.

Gaines, R. E. & Mawhin, J. L. Coincidence Degree & Nonlinear Differential Equations. 2008. (Lecture Notes in Mathematics Ser.). 276p. pap. 59.95 *(978-3-540-08067-1(8))* Springer.

Galdi, Giovanni P. An Introduction to the Mathematical Theory of the Navier-Stokes Equations: Volume 1: Linearized Steady Problems. 2nd ed. 2010. (Applied Mathematical Sciences Ser.). (Illus.). xiii, 583p. 149.00 *(978-0-387-09619-3(1))* Springer.

Galin, L. A. Contact Problems: The legacy of L. A. Galin. Gladwell, G. M., ed. 2010. (Solid Mechanics & Its Applications Ser.). Orig. Title: Contact Problems of Elasticity & Viscoelasticity. xiv, 318p. pap. 199.00 *(978-90-481-8056-1(2)*, 9048180562) Springer.

Galin, L. a. & Galin, L. A. Contact Problems: The legacy of L. A. Galin. Gladwell, G. M. L., ed. 2008. (Solid Mechanics & Its Applications Ser.). Orig. Title: Contact Problems of Elasticity & Viscoelasticity. xiv, 318p. 199.00 *(978-1-4020-9042-4(0))* Springer.

Gazzola, Filippo, et al. Polyharmonic Boundary Value Problems: Positivity Preserving & Nonlinear Higher Order Elliptic Equations in Bounded Domains. 2010. (Lecture Notes in Mathematics Ser.). (ENG., Illus.). xviii, 423p. pap. 89.95 *(978-3-642-12244-6(2)*, 3642122442) Springer.

Gorgidze, Ivane. Mechanics of the Continuous Environment Issues: Dedicated to the 120th Birth Anniversary of Academician Nikoloz Muskhelishvili. 2012. ***(978-1-62100-496-7(1))*** Nova Science Pubs., Inc.

Goswami, Jaideva C. & Chan, Andrew K. Fundamentals of Wavelets: Theory, Algorithms, & Applications. 2nd ed. 2011. (Wiley Series in Microwave & Optical Engineering Ser.: 219). (ENG., Illus.). 359p. 121.00 *(978-0-470-48413-5(6)* Wiley) Wiley, John & Sons, Inc.

Hakobyan, Vahram. Stress Concentration near Defects in Homogeneous & Compound Bodies. 2011. 148p. pap. ***(978-3-8454-1071-5(X))*** Lambert Academic Publishing.

Hamilton, R. S. Harmonic Maps of Manifolds with Boundary. 2008. (Lecture Notes in Mathematics Ser.). (ENG.). pap. 39.95 *(978-3-540-07185-3(7)*, 3540071857) Springer.

Hanna, J. Ray & Rowland, John H. Fourier Series, Transforms, & Boundary Value Problems. 2nd ed. 2008. (Dover Books on Mathematics Ser.). (ENG.). 368p. pap. 21.95 *(978-0-486-46673-6(6))* Dover Pubns., Inc.

Hastings, Stuart P. & McLeod, J. Bryce. Classical Methods in Ordinary Differential Equations: With Applications to Boundary Value Problems. 2011. (Graduate Studies in Mathematics Ser.). (Illus.). 373p. 63.00 ***(978-0-8218-4694-0(9))*** American Mathematical Society.

Hegarty, Alan F. BAIL 2008 - Boundary & Interior Layers: Proceedings of the International Conference on Boundary & Interior Layers - Computational & Asymptotic Methods, Limerick, July 2008. Hegarty, Alan et al, eds. 2009. (Lecture Notes in Computational Science & Engineering Ser.). (ENG., Illus.). xvi, 312p. pap. 129.00 *(978-3-642-00604-3(3)*, 3642006043) Springer.

Iooss, Gerard & Plotnikov, Pavel I. Small Divisor Problem in the Theory of Three-Dimensional Water Gravty Waves. 2009. (Memoirs of the American Mathematical Society Ser.). (Illus.). 128p. pap. 67.00 *(978-0-8218-4382-6(6))* American Mathematical Society.

Ivchenko, I. N. Analytical Methods for Problems of Molecular Transport. 2007. (Fluid Mechanics & Its Applications Ser.). xxiv, 409p. 139.00 *(978-1-4020-5864-6(0))* Springer.

Ivrii, V. Precise Spectral Asymptotics for Elliptic Operators Acting in Fiberings over Manifolds with Boundary. 2008. (Lecture Notes in Mathematics Ser.). pap. 46.00 *(978-3-540-13361-2(5))* Springer.

Kabanikhin, Sergey I. Inverse & Ill-Posed Problems: Theory & Applications. 2011. (Inverse & Ill-Posed Problems Ser.). (ENG., Illus.). XVI, 459p. 140.00 ***(978-3-11-022400-9(3))***; 210.00 ***(978-3-11-174043-0(9))*** De Gruyter, Walter Inc.

Kamenskii, G. A. Extrema of Nonlocal Functionals & Boundary Value Problems for Functional Differential Equations. 2007. 225p. (C). 89.00 *(978-1-60021-564-3(5))* Nova Science Pubs., Inc.

Kapanadze, D. V. & Schulze, Bert-Wolfgang. Crack Theory & Edge Singularities. 2010. (Mathematics & Its Applications Ser.). 516p. pap. 239.00 *(978-90-481-6384-7(6)*, 9048163846) Springer.

Kappeler, Thomas & Pöschel, Jürgen. KdV & KAM. 2010. (Ergebnisse der Mathematik und Ihrer Grenzgebiete. 3. Folge a Series of Modern Surveys in Mathematics Ser.). xii, 279p. pap. 149.00 *(978-3-642-05694-9(6)*, 3642056946) Springer.

Kauffman, Robert M., et al. The Deficiency Index Problem for Powers of Ordinary Differential Expressions. 2008. (Lecture Notes in Mathematics Ser.). 120p. pap. 26.00 *(978-3-540-08523-2(8))* Springer.

Kokilashvili, Vakhtang & Paatashvili, Vakhtang, eds. Boundary Value Problems for Analytic & Harmonic Functions in Nonstandard Banach Function Spaces. 2012. 260p. ***(978-1-61942-301-5(4))*** Nova Science Pubs., Inc.

Kolodziej & Zielinski. Boundary Collocation Techniques & their Application in Engineering. 2009. (Illus.). 336p. 230.00 *(978-1-84564-394-2(1))* WIT Pr GBR. Dist: WIT Pr.

Korman, Philip. Global Solution Curves for Semilinear Elliptic Equations. 2012. 245p. 90.00 ***(978-981-4374-34-7(2))*** World Scientific Publishing Co., Inc.

Kozlov, Vladimir & Maz'ya, Vladimir. Differential Equations with Operator Coefficients: With Applications to Boundary Value Problems for Partial Differential Equations. 2010. (Springer Monographs in Mathematics Ser.). xx, 442p. pap. 169.00 *(978-3-642-08453-9(2),* 3642084532) Springer.

Krauskopf, Bernd, et al, eds. Numerical Continuation Methods for Dynamical Systems: Path following & boundary value Problems. 2007. (Understanding Complex Systems Ser.). (Illus.). iv, 412p. 239.00 *(978-1-4020-6355-8(5))* Springer.

Ladyzhenskaya, O. A. The Boundary Value Problems of Mathematical Physics. Lohwater, J., tr. 2010. (Applied Mathematical Sciences Ser.). xxxiv, 322p. pap. 100.00 *(978-1-4419-2824-5(3),* 1441928243) Springer.

Makai, Mihály. Group Theory Applied to Boundary Value Problems with Applications to Reactor Physics. 2011. (Mathematics Research Developments Physics Research & Technology Ser.). 520p. 195.00 *(978-1-61761-477-4(7))* Nova Science Pubs., Inc.

Marinoschi, G. Functional Approach to Nonlinear Models of Water Flow in Soils. 2010. (Mathematical Modelling: Theory & Applications Ser.). (Illus.). xv, 316p. pap. 119.00 *(978-90-481-7216-0(0),* 9048172160) Springer.

Mazya, Vladimir & Rossmann, Jurgen. Elliptic Equations in Polyhedral Domains. 2010. (Mathematical Surveys & Monographs). (Illus.). 608p. 123.00 *(978-0-8218-4983-5(2))* American Mathematical Society.

McFall, Kevin. An Artificial Neural Network Method for Solving Boundary Value Problems - with Arbitrary Irregular Boundary Conditions. 2008. 172p. per. *(978-3-8364-5955-6(8))* VDM Verlag Dr. Mueller e.K.

Mikhailov, G. A. Parametric Estimates by the Monte Carlo Method. (ENG.). VIII, 188p. 328.00 ***(978-3-11-187324-4(2))*** De Gruyter, Walter Inc.

Mohyud-Din, Syed. Variational Iteration Techniques for Boundary Value Problems. 2010. 196p. pap. *(978-3-639-27664-0(7))* VDM Verlag Dr. Mueller e.K.

Moore, Eliakim Hastin. New Haven Mathematical Colloquium. 2006. 236p. per. *(978-1-4067-1221-6(3),* Hesperides Pr.) Read Bks.

Motreanu, Dumitru & Radulescu, Vicentiu D. Variational & Non-Variational Methods in Nonlinear Analysis & Boundary Value Problems. 2010. (Nonconvex Optimization & Its Applications Ser.). 388p. pap. 219.00 *(978-1-4419-5248-6(9),* 1441952489) Springer.

Muskhelishvili, N. I. Singular Integral Equations: Boundary Problems of Function Theory & Their Application to Mathematical Physics. Radok, J. R. M. & Radok, J.R.M., trs. from RUS. 2nd ed. 2008. (Dover Books on Physics Ser.). (ENG., Illus.). 464p. pap. 24.95 *(978-0-486-46242-4(0))* Dover Pubns., Inc.

Nagle, R. Kent, et al. Fundamentals of Differential Equations & Boundary Value Problems. 6th rev. ed. 2011. (ENG., Illus.). 888p. (C). 154.67 *(978-0-321-74774-7(7))* Addison Wesley.

—Fundamentals of Differential Equations & Boundary Value Problems, Books a la Carte Edition. 6th ed. 2012. (ENG.). (C). ring bd. 102.67 ***(978-0-321-78514-5(2))*** Addison Wesley.

—Student's Solutions Manual for Fundamentals of Differential Equations 8e & Fundamentals of Differential Equations & Boundary Value Problems 6e. 6th rev. ed. 2011. (ENG.). 720p. (C). pap. 36.67 ***(978-0-321-74834-8(4))*** Addison Wesley.

Ogbu Mbadiwe, Hilary. Periodic Solutions of Some Nonlinear Boundary Value Problems of Ode's. 2011. 144p. pap. ***(978-3-8443-1760-2(0))*** Lambert Academic Publishing.

Pak, Hee Chul. Mathematical analysis for thin film capacitance via homogenization. 2008. 68p. pap. *(978-3-639-10423-3(4))* VDM Verlag Dr. Mueller e.K.

Pati, Arati. Incompressible Viscous Flow with Moving Boundaries. 2009. 204p. pap. *(978-3-639-18832-5(2))* VDM Verlag Dr. Mueller e.K.

Pinsky, Mark A. Partial Differential Equations & Boundary-Value Problems with Applications. 3rd rev. ed. 2011. (Pure & Applied Undergraduate Texts). 526p. 79.00 ***(978-0-8218-6889-8(6))*** American Mathematical Society.

Pommerenke, Christian. Boundary Behaviour of Conformal Maps. 2010. (Grundlehren der mathematischen Wissenschaften Ser.). (Illus.). x, 300p. pap. 129.00 *(978-3-642-08129-3(0),* 3642081290) Springer.

Powers, David L. Boundary Value Problems: And Partial Differential Equations. 6th ed. 2009. (ENG.). 520p. (C). 89.95 *(978-0-12-374719-8(8),* Academic Pr.) Elsevier Science & Technology Bks.

Roitberg, Y. Boundary Value Problems in the Spaces of Distributions. 2010. (Mathematics & Its Applications Ser.). 288p. pap. 160.00 *(978-90-481-5343-5(3),* 9048153433) Springer.

Saanouni, K. Numerical Simulation in Shaping Materials & Structures. 2012. (Iste Ser.: 614). (ENG.). 245.00 ***(978-1-84821-348-7(4),*** Wiley-ISTE) Wiley, John & Sons, Inc.

Sakamoto, Reiko. Hyperbolic Boundary Value Problems. 2009. (ENG.). 224p. pap. 46.00 *(978-0-521-10759-4(8))* Cambridge Univ. Pr.

Santos, Lisa, et al, eds. Free Boundary Problems: Theory & Applications. 2006. (International Series of Numerical Mathematics: Vol. 154). (Illus.). 460p. 189.00 *(978-3-7643-7718-2(6),* 3764377186) Birkhauser Boston.

Saranen, Jukka & Vainikko, Gennadi. Periodic Integral & Pseudodifferential Equations with Numerical Approximation. 2010. (Springer Monographs in Mathematics Ser.). xi, 452p. pap. 129.00 *(978-3-642-07538-4(X),* 364207538X) Springer.

Schaaf, R. Global Solution Branches of Two Point Boundary Value Problems. 2008. (Lecture Notes in Mathematics Ser.). pap. 39.95 *(978-3-540-53514-0(4))* Springer.

Shiryaev, Albert & Peskir, Goran. Optimal Stopping & Free-Boundary Problems. 2006. (Lectures in Mathematics ETH Zürich). (Illus.). 500p. 69.95 *(978-3-7643-2419-3(8),* 3764324198) Birkhauser Boston.

Simader, Christian G. On Dirichlet's Boundary Value Problem. 2008. (Lecture Notes in Mathematics Ser.). 252p. pap. 46.00 *(978-3-540-05903-5(2),* 3540059032) Springer.

Snider, Arthur, et al. Fundamentals of Differential Equations with Boundary Value Problems. 5th rev. ed. 2010. (ENG.). 944p. (C). 154.67 *(978-0-321-38843-8(7))* Addison Wesley.

Sobolev, S. L. Some Applications of Functional Analysis in Mathematical Physics. 3rd rev. ed. 2008. (Translations of Mathematical Monographs Ser.). 286p. pap. 99.00 *(978-0-8218-1937-1(2))* American Mathematical Society.

Stakgold, Ivar & Holst, Michael J. Green's Functions & Boundary Value Problems. 3rd ed. 2011. (Pure & Applied Mathematics: a Wiley Series of Texts, Monographs & Tracts Ser.: 99). (ENG., Illus.). 888p. 137.00 *(978-0-470-60970-5(2),* Wiley) Wiley, John & Sons, Inc.

Steinbach, Olaf. Numerical Approximation Methods for Elliptic Boundary Value Problems: Finite & Boundary Elements. (ENG.). xii, 388p. 2010. pap. 59.95 *(978-1-4419-2173-4(7),* 1441921737) 2007. (Illus.). 59.95 *(978-0-387-31312-2(5),* 0387313125) Springer.

Sychev, Vladimir V., et al. Asymptotic Theory of Separated Flows. 2008. (ENG., Illus.). 348p. pap. 48.00 *(978-0-521-06587-0(9))* Cambridge Univ. Pr.

Taira, K. Elliptic Boundary Value Problems. 2008. (Lecture Notes in Mathematics Ser.). pap. 26.00 *(978-3-540-54996-3(X))* Springer.

Taira, Kazuaki. Boundary Value Problems & Markov Processes. 2nd ed. 2009. (Lecture Notes in Mathematics Ser.). (ENG., Illus.). xii, 186p. pap. 59.95 *(978-3-642-01676-9(6),* 3642016766) Springer.

—Semigroups, Boundary Value Problems & Markov Processes. 2010. (Springer Monographs in Mathematics Ser.). (ENG., Illus.). xi, 337p. pap. 129.00 *(978-3-642-07371-7(9),* 3642073719) Springer.

Tardu, Sedat. Statistical Approach in Wall Turbulence. 11th ed. 2011. (Iste Ser.: 534). (ENG., Illus.). 336p. 145.00 ***(978-1-84821-262-6(3),*** Wiley-ISTE) Wiley, John & Sons, Inc.

Temirbolat, Serikkali E. Ill-Posed Boundary-Value Problems. (Inverse & Ill-Posed Problems Ser.). (ENG.). VIII, 144p. 300.00 ***(978-3-11-182608-0(2))*** De Gruyter, Walter Inc.

Vasil'ev, V. Wave Factorization of Elliptic Symbols: Theory & Applications: Introduction to the Theory of Boundary Value Problems in Non-Smooth Domains. 2010. 192p. pap. 107.00 *(978-90-481-5545-3(2),* 9048155452) Springer.

Vassilicos, J. C., ed. Intermittency in Turbulent Flows. 2010. (ENG., Illus.). 290p. pap. 55.00 *(978-0-521-15942-5(3))* Cambridge Univ. Pr.

Vazquez, Juan Luis. The Porous Medium Equation: Mathematical Theory. 2006. (Oxford Mathematical Monographs). (ENG., Illus.). 648p. 150.00 *(978-0-19-856903-9(3))* Oxford Univ. Pr., Inc.

Visintin, Augusto. Differential Models of Hysteresis. 2010. (Applied Mathematical Sciences Ser.). (Illus.). xi, 407p. pap. 135.00 *(978-3-642-08132-3(0),* 3642081320) Springer.

Vol'pert, A. I. & Hudjaev, S. I. Analysis in Classes of Discontinuous Functions & Equations of Mathematical Physics. 2010. (Mechanics: Analysis Ser.). 704p. pap. 719.00 *(978-90-481-8286-2(7),* 9048182867) Springer.

Wentworth, Stuart M. Introduction to Electromagnetics, WileyPlus Set: Early Transmission. 2006. 15.00 *(978-0-470-10023-3(0),* Jossey-Bass) Wiley, John & Sons, Inc.

Willatzen, Morten & Lew Yan Voon, Lok C. Separable Boundary-Value Problems in Physics. 2011. (ENG., Illus.). 398p. 135.00 *(978-3-527-41020-0(1),* Wiley-VCH) Wiley, John & Sons, Inc.

Wloka, J. T., et al. Boundary Value Problems for Elliptic Systems. 2008. (ENG., Illus.). 656p. pap. 116.00 *(978-0-521-06143-8(1))* Cambridge Univ. Pr.

Yosibash, Zohar. Singularities in Elliptic Boundary Value Problems & Elasticity & Their Connection with Failure Initiation. 2011. (Interdisciplinary Applied Mathematics Ser.). (ENG., Illus.). xxi, 459p. 124.00 ***(978-1-4614-1507-7(1),*** 1461415071) Springer.

Yuferev, Sergey V. & Ida, Nathan. Surface Impedance Boundary Conditions: A Comprehensive Approach. 2009. (ENG., Illus.). 410p. 139.95 *(978-1-4200-4489-8(3),* CRC Press) Taylor & Francis Group GBR. Dist: Taylor & Francis Group.

Zill & Cullen & Cram101 Textbook Reviews Staff. Differential Equations with Boundary-Value Problems. 2007. 132p. per. 11.95 *(978-1-4288-3490-3(7))* Cram101 Inc.

Zill, Dennis G. & Cullen, Michael R. Differential Equations with Boundary-Value Problems. 7th ed. 2008. (ENG.). 336p. (C). pap. 82.95 *(978-0-495-38316-1(3))* Brooks/Cole.

BOUNDARY VALUE PROBLEMS—NUMERICAL SOLUTIONS

see also Eigenfunctions

Alshin, A. B., et al. Blow up in Nonlinear Sobolev Type Equations. 2011. (De Gruyter Series in Nonlinear Analysis & Applications Ser.). (ENG.). XII, 648p. 182.00 ***(978-3-11-025527-0(8))*** De Gruyter, Walter Inc.

Al'shin, Alexander B., et al. Blow-up in Nonlinear Sobolev Type Equations. 2011. (De Gruyter Series in Nonlinear Analysis & Applications Ser.). (ENG., Illus.). XII, 648p. 280.00 ***(978-3-11-218918-4(3))*** De Gruyter, Walter Inc.

Bensoussan, Alain, et al. Asymptotic Analysis for Periodic Structures. 2011. (AMS Chelsea Publishing Ser.). 392p. 61.00 ***(978-0-8218-5324-5(4),*** Chelsea Publishing Co., Inc.) American Mathematical Society.

Brebbia, C. A., ed. Mesh Reduction Methods: Bem/mrm Xxxi. 2009. (WIT Transactions on Modelling & Simulation Ser.: 49). (Illus.). 432p. 295.00 *(978-1-84564-197-9(3))* WIT Pr GBR. Dist: WIT Pr.

Brenner, Susanne C. & Scott, L. Ridgway. The Mathematical Theory of Finite Element Methods. 3rd ed. 2007. (Texts in Applied Mathematics Ser.). (Illus.). 397p. 79.95 *(978-0-387-75933-3(6))* Springer.

Brenner, Susanne C. & Scott, Ridgway. The Mathematical Theory of Finite Element Methods. 3rd ed. 2010. (Texts in Applied Mathematics Ser.). (Illus.). xviii, 402p. pap. 79.95 *(978-1-4419-2611-1(9),* 1441926119) Springer.

Bulirsch, R., et al, eds. Numerical Treatment of Differential Equations: Proceedings of a Conference, Held at Oberwolfach, July 4-10, 1976. 2008. (Lecture Notes in Mathematics Ser.). 236p. pap. 46.00 *(978-3-540-08539-3(4))* Springer.

Fitzpatrick, P. Topological Methods for Ordinary Differential Equations: Lectures given at the 1st Session of the Centro Internazionale Matematico Estivo (C.I.M.E.) held in Montecatini Terme, Italy, June 24-July 2, 1991. 2008. (Lecture Notes in Mathematics Ser.). 218p. pap. 59.95 *(978-3-540-56461-4(6))* Springer.

Grisvard, P. Elliptic Problems in Nonsmooth Domains. 2011. (ENG., Illus.). 425p. pap. ***(978-1-61197-202-3(7))*** Society for Industrial and Applied Mathematics.

Leipholz, U. Direct Variational Methods & Eigenvalue Problems in Engineering. 2010. (Mechanics of Elastic Stability Ser.). 260p. pap. 359.00 *(978-90-481-8466-8(5),* 9048184665) Springer.

Nhawu, Gerald. Low-Frequency Asymmetric Vibrations a Thin Shell with a Turning Point. 2011. 68p. pap. ***(978-3-8443-0316-2(2))*** Lambert Academic Publishing.

Oden, J. T. & Reddy, J. N. An Introduction to the Mathematical Theory of Finite Elements. 2011. (Dover Books on Engineering Ser.). (ENG.). 448p. pap. 24.95 *(978-0-486-46299-8(4))* Dover Pubns., Inc.

Sumarti, Novriana. Numerical Methods for Solving Two-Point Boundary Value Problems. 2009. 212p. pap. *(978-3-639-13787-3(6))* VDM Verlag Dr. Mueller e.K.

Verhulst, Ferdinand. Methods & Applications of Singular Perturbations: Boundary Layers & Multiple Timescale Dynamics. 2010. (Texts in Applied Mathematics Ser.). xvi, 328p. pap. 69.95 *(978-1-4419-1992-2(9),* 1441919929) Springer.

BOUNDARY WAVES (OCEANOGRAPHY)

see Internal Waves

BOUNTIES, MILITARY

see also Recruiting and Enlistment

Raff, George W. (George Wertz). A Manual of Pensions, Bounty, & Pay: Containing the Laws, Forms & Regulations Relating to Pensions, Bounty Land, Bounty Money, Pay, Claims for Hor. 2006. 496p. per. 29.99 *(978-1-4255-5585-6(3))* MPublishing.

BOUNTIES, MILITARY—UNITED STATES

Asch, Beth J., et al. Cash Incentives & Military Enlistment, Attrition, & Reenlistment. 2010. 195p. pap. 39.00 *(978-0-8330-4966-7(6))* RAND Corp., The.

Belknap, William W. Bounties to Black Soldiers. 2009. 255p. ***(978-0-7884-7625-9(4))*** Heritage Bks.

Belknap, Wm. W. Bounties to Black Soldiers. 2009. pap. 25.50 *(978-0-7884-4822-5(6))* Heritage Bks.

Bockstruck, Lloyd DeWitt. Bounty & Donation Land Grants in British Colonial America. 2007. xvi, 464p. 50.00 *(978-0-8063-1780-9(9))* Genealogical Publishing Co., Inc.

Hunt, William. A Familiar Digest of All the Pension & Bounty Land Laws of the United States Now in Force, Systematically Arranged by William Hunt, Cousellor At. 2006. 112p. per. 16.99 *(978-1-4255-0782-4(4))* MPublishing.

Rose, Christine. Military Bounty Land, 1776-1855. 2011. (Illus.). xx, 156p. ***(978-0-929626-20-8(6))*** Rose Family Assn.

Wardell, Patrick G. Virginia & West Virginia Genealogical Data from Revolutionary War Pension & Bounty Land Warrant Records, Volume 2 Dabbs-Hyslop. 2008. pap. 35.00 *(978-0-7884-0302-6(8))* Heritage Bks.

BOUNTY (SHIP)

Barrow, John. Eventful History of the Mutiny & Pirat. 2006. pap. *(978-1-4065-1084-3(X))* Dodo Pr.

Barrow, John. The Mutiny & Piratical Seizure of H. M. S. Bounty. 2011. (Cambridge Library Collection - History Ser.). (ENG., Illus.). 416p. pap. 31.99 ***(978-1-108-03141-7(2))*** Cambridge Univ. Pr.

Bligh, William. The Bounty Mutiny: Captain William Bligh's Firsthand Account of the Last Voyage of HMS Bounty. 2008. *(978-1-934941-06-5(9))* Red & Black Pubs.

—The Mutiny on Board H. M. S. Bounty. Laurel Associates Inc Staff, ed. 2008. (Graphic Novels Ser.). (ENG., Illus.). 16p. (YA). (gr. 9-12). tchr. ed., pupil's gde. ed. 7.95 incl. cd-rom *(978-1-59905-306-6(3))* Saddleback Educational Publishing.

—The Mutiny on Board H. M. S. Bounty. 2010. (Saddleback's Illustrated Classics Ser.). (ENG., Illus.). 64p. (YA). (gr. 9-12). lib. bdg. 19.95 *(978-1-59905-911-2(8))* Saddleback Educational Publishing.

—Mutiny on the Bounty. 2010. (ENG.). 224p. pap. 8.95 *(978-0-486-47257-7(4))* Dover Pubns., Inc.

—Mutiny on the Bounty. 2006. (Adventure Classics Ser.). (ENG., Illus.). 432p. (gr. 3-6). 12.95 *(978-88-544-0123-5(4),* White Star) Rizzoli International Pubns., Inc.

—Mutiny on the H. M. S. Bounty. 24.95 *(978-0-8488-1278-2(6))* Amereon LTD.

—The Voyage of H M S Bounty: The True Story of an 18th Century Voyage of Exploration & Mutiny. 2008. 228p. *(978-1-84677-492-8(6));* pap. *(978-1-84677-491-1(8))* Leonaur Ltd.

—A Voyage to the South Sea. 2008. 268p. 28.99 *(978-0-554-25295-7(3))* BiblioBazaar.

—A Voyage to the South Sea. 2008. (Illus.). 248p. pap. *(978-1-4099-5181-0(2))* Dodo Pr.

—A Voyage to the South Sea: For the Purpose of Conveying the Bread-Fruit Tree. 2007. (ENG.). 232p. pap. 20.99 *(978-1-4264-8593-0(X));* 264p. pap. 23.99 *(978-1-4264-8650-0(2))* BiblioBazaar.

Edwards, Edward & George, Hamilton. The Voyage of H M S Pandor: In Pursuit of the Mutineers of the Bounty in the South Seas-1790-1791. Basil, Thomson, ed. 2008. 160p. *(978-1-84677-602-1(3))* Leonaur Ltd.

Edwards, Edward & Hamilton, George. The Voyage of H M S Pandor: In Pursuit of the Mutineers of the Bounty in the South Seas-1790-1791. Thomson, Basil, ed. 2008. 160p. pap. *(978-1-84677-601-4(5))* Leonaur Ltd.

Maxton, Donald A. The Mutiny on H. M. S. Bounty: A Guide to Nonfiction, Fiction, Poetry, Films, Articles, & Music. 2008. (ENG., Illus.). 264p. pap. 35.00 *(978-0-7864-3064-2(8))* McFarland & Co., Inc. Pubs.

McFarland, Alfred. Mutiny in the Bounty! & the Story of the Pitcairn Islanders. 2007. 264p. per. *(978-1-905748-36-5(1))* Rediscovery Bks.

Morrison, James. After the Bounty: A Sailor's Account of the Mutiny & Life in the South Seas. Maxton, Donald, ed. & anno. by. 2009. (Illus.). 270p. 29.95 *(978-1-59797-371-7(8))* Potomac Bks., Inc.

Sir John Barrow. The Eventful History of the Mutiny & Piratical Seizure of H. M. S. Bounty: Its Cause & Consequences. I.t. ed. 2007. (ENG.). 296p. pap. 23.99 *(978-1-4264-8057-7(1))* BiblioBazaar.

BOUNTY HUNTERS

Chapman, Duane "Dog". Where Mercy Is Shown, Mercy Is Given. (ENG.). 2011. 304p. mass mkt. 7.99 *(978-0-7868-9135-1(1))* 2010. 336p. 26.99 *(978-1-4013-2371-4(5))* Hyperion Pr.

Christian, Glynn. Mrs Christian, Bounty Mutineer - Fletcher Stole the Ship: She gave women the Vote. 2011. 436p. pap. 24.00 ***(978-1-59048-050-2(3))*** Long Riders' Guild Pr., The.

James, Richard, Sr. Secrets of a Bounty Hunter. 2008. (Illus.). 164p. pap. 24.95 *(978-0-9815294-0-0(2),* Secrets Series) Our Gang Publishing.

James, Richard. Secrets of a Modern Day Bounty Hunter. 2008. (Illus.). 164p. cd-rom 24.95 *(978-0-9815294-2-4(9))* Our Gang Publishing.

BOUQUET, HENRY, 1719-1765

Cort, Cyrus & Smith, William. Bouquet & the Ohio Indian War: Two Accounts of the Campaigns Of 1763-1764. 2008. 264p. *(978-1-84677-584-0(1));* pap. *(978-1-84677-583-3(3))* Leonaur Ltd.

BOUQUET'S EXPEDITION, 1763

see also Pontiac's Conspiracy, 1763-1765

Bouquet, Henry. Historical Account of Bouquets Expeditio. 2006. pap. 21.95 *(978-1-4286-4788-6(0))* Kessinger Publishing, LLC.

—Historical Account of Bouquet's Expedition Against the Ohio Indians in 1764. 2007. 168p. 36.95 *(978-0-548-13642-3(4))* Kessinger Publishing, LLC.

Cort, Cyrus & Smith, William. Bouquet & the Ohio Indian War: Two Accounts of the Campaigns Of 1763-1764. 2008. 264p. *(978-1-84677-584-0(1));* pap. *(978-1-84677-583-3(3))* Leonaur Ltd.

Parkman, Francis. Historical Account of Bouquet's Expedition Against the Ohio Indians in 1764. 2008. 154p. 36.95 *(978-0-548-91391-8(9))* 2007. 156p. per. 21.95 *(978-0-548-59697-5(2))* Kessinger Publishing, LLC.

Smith, William. Historical Account of Bouquet's Expedition Against the Ohio Indians in 1764. 2010. 156p. pap. 11.95 *(978-1-4290-4542-1(6))* Applewood Bks.

BOURBON, HOUSE OF

Bingham, Denis A. Marriages of the Bourbons, 2 vols. (Illus.). reprint ed. 95.00 *(978-0-404-00890-1(9))* AMS Pr., Inc.

Duindam, Jeroen. Vienna & Versailles: The Courts of Europe's Dynastic Rivals, 1550-1780. 2007. (New Studies in European History Ser.). (ENG.). 392p. pap. 79.00 *(978-0-521-71476-1(1))* Cambridge Univ. Pr.

Shennan, J. H. The Bourbons: The History of a Dynasty. (ENG., Illus.). 232p. 2008. pap. 29.95 *(978-1-84725-200-5(1))* 2007. 44.95 *(978-1-85285-523-9(1))* Continuum International Publishing Group, Ltd. GBR. (Hambledon Continuum). Dist: National Bk. Network.

Thomson, Oliver. Impossible Bourbons. 2009. (Illus.). 224p. 29.95 *(978-1-84868-356-3(1))* Amberley Publishing GBR. Dist: Casemate Pubs. & Bk. Distributors, LLC.

BOURBON WHISKEY

see Whiskey

BOURGEOIS, LOUISE, 1911-2010

Bernadac, Marie-Laure. Louise Bourgeois. 2007. (ENG., Illus.). 216p. 45.00 *(978-2-08-030553-4(0))* Flammarion et Cie FRA. Dist: Random Hse., Inc.

Bourgeois, Louise. The Blind Leading the Blind. 2008. (ENG & FRE., Illus.). 112p. 49.95 *(978-2-7427-7919-2(1))* Actes Sud FRA. Dist: D.A.P./Distributed Art Pubs.

—Designing. (Illus.). 264p. *(978-3-250-10131-4(1))* Ammann Verlag.

—Louise Bourgeois: Blue Days & Pink Days. pap. 55.00 *(978-88-87029-04-8(0))* Fondazione Prada ITA. Dist: D.A.P./Distributed Art Pubs.

Bourgeois, Louise, et al. Moi Eugénie Grandet. 2010. (FRE., Illus.). 135p. *(978-2-07-013101-3(7))* Gallimard, Editions.

Celant, Germano. Louise Bourgeois: The Fabric Works. 2011. (ENG., Illus.). 336p. 90.00 *(978-88-572-0654-7(8))* Skira Editore ITA. Dist: Random Hse., Inc.

Cohen, Silvio, tr. Louise Bourgeois, Scultura e Opere Grafiche. 2006.Tr. of Louise Bougeois, Sculpture & Graphic Works. (ITA & ENG., Illus.). 63p. 20.00 *(978-0-9791751-1-4(9))* Bader, Christine Edition.

Coxon, Ann. Louise Bourgeois. 2010. (ENG., Illus.). 540p. pap. 27.50 *(978-1-85437-882-8(1))* Tate Publishing, Ltd. GBR. Dist: Hachette Bk. Group.

Crone, Rainer F., et al. Louise Bourgeois: The Secret of the Cells. 2011. (ENG., Illus.). 192p. pap. 19.95 ***(978-3-7913-4562-8(1))*** Prestel Publishing.

Curiger, Bice, ed. Parkett 82 Summer 2008: Rachel Harrison, Pawel Althamer & Louise Bourgeois. 2008. (ENG., Illus.). 300p. pap. 32.00 *(978-3-907582-42-8(X))* Parkett Verlag AG CHE. Dist: D.A.P./Distributed Art Pubs.

Jahn, Andrea. Louise Bourgeois - Subversionen des Koerpers: Die Kunst der 40er bis 70er Jahre. (GER., Illus.). 270p. *(978-3-496-01185-9(8))* Reimer, Dietrich.

Kellein, Thomas. Louise Bourgeois: La Famille, 1 vol. 2006. (ENG., Illus.). 242p. 45.00 *(978-1-933045-42-9(6))* D.A.P./Distributed Art Pubs.

Larratt-Smith, Philip, ed. Louise Bourgeois: the Return of the Repressed: Psychoanalytic Writings. 2012. (ENG., Illus.). 500p. 75.00 ***(978-1-900828-37-6(5))*** Violette Editions GBR. Dist: D.A.P./Distributed Art Pubs.

Morris, Frances & Bernadac, Marie-Laure, eds. Louise Bourgeois. 2008. (ENG., Illus.). 320p. 65.00 *(978-0-8478-3131-9(0))* Rizzoli International Pubns., Inc.

Nixon, Mignon. Fantastic Reality: Louise Bourgeois & a Story of Modern Art. 2008. (October Bks.). (ENG., Illus.). 352p. (gr. 17). pap. 24.95 *(978-0-262-64070-1(8))* MIT Pr.

Stern, H. Peter. Louise Bourgeois. 2008. (Illus.). 71p. 39.95 *(978-0-9606270-8-0(1))* Storm King Art Ctr.

Stoops, Susan L. Louise Bourgeois: The Woven Child (in Context) 2006. *(978-0-936042-15-2(X))* Worcester Art Museum.

Udo, Kittelmann & Silke, Krohn, eds. Hans Bellmer / Louise Bourgeois: Double Sexus. 2010. 160p. 60.00 *(978-3-89955-403-8(5))* Die Gestalten Verlag DEU. Dist: Prestel Publishing.

van Gelder, Alex, photos by. Alex van Gelder: Louise Bourgeois, Armed Forces. 2011. (ENG., Illus.). 48p. 45.00 *(978-84-343-1253-1(0))* Poligrafa, Ediciones, S. A. ESP. Dist: D.A.P./Distributed Art Pubs.

Weiermair, Peter, ed. Louise Bourgeois: Aller-Retour, 1 vol. 2006. (ENG & GER., Illus.). 216p. 50.00 *(978-3-938821-19-0(1))* Verlag fur Moderne Kunst DEU. Dist: D.A.P./Distributed Art Pubs.

BOURGEOISIE
see Middle Class

BOURGEOYS, MARGUERITE, SAINT, 1620-1700

Anonymous. The Life of Venerable Sister Margaret Bourgeois. 2007. (ENG.). 142p. pap. 18.99 *(978-1-4346-5029-0(4))*; 154p. pap. 21.99 *(978-1-4346-5030-6(8))* BiblioBazaar.

Simpson, Patricia. Marguerite Bourgeoys et la Congregation de Notre Dame, 1665-1700. Beaudry, Albert, tr. from ENG. 2007. (FRE & ENG., Illus.). 328p. (C). per. *(978-0-7735-3274-8(9))* McGill-Queen's Univ. Pr.

BOURGET, PAUL CHARLES JOSEPH, 1852-1935

Secor, Walter Todd. Paul Bourget & the Nouvelle. 2007. (ENG.). 276p. 42.95 *(978-0-548-14723-8(X))* 2006. pap. 27.95 *(978-1-4286-6123-3(9))* Kessinger Publishing, LLC.

BOURGOGNE (FRANCE)
see Burgundy (France)

BOURKE-WHITE, MARGARET, 1906-1971

Weissman, Terri, et al. American Modern: Documentary Photography. 2010. (Illus.). 213p. 39.95 *(978-0-520-26562-2(9))* Univ. of California Pr.

BOURNEMOUTH (ENGLAND)

Crawford, Alison. Bournemouth. 2009. (Britain in Old Photographs Ser.). (ENG., Illus.). 128p. pap. 24.95 *(978-0-7524-4943-2(5))* History Pr. Ltd.,The GBR. Dist: Independent Pubs. Group.

Needham, John. Bournemouth Past & Present. 2010. (ENG., Illus.). 96p. pap. 23.95 *(978-0-7524-5569-3(9))* History Pr. Ltd.,The GBR. Dist: Independent Pubs. Group.

BOUTAN LANGUAGE
see Tibetan Language

BOUTIQUE BREWERIES
see Microbreweries

BOUTIQUES
see Stores, Retail

BOUVIER DES FLANDRES

Linzy, Jan, et al. Bouvier des Flandres Champions, 1985-2006. 2007. (Illus.). 201p. spiral bd. 46.95 *(978-1-55893-232-6(1))* Camino E.E. & Bk. Co.

BOVARY, EMMA (FICTITIOUS CHARACTER)

Amann, Elizabeth. Importing Madame Bovary: The Politics of Adultery. 2006. (ENG.). 284p. 89.00 *(978-1-4039-7606-2(6))* Palgrave Macmillan.

BOVINE BRUCELLOSIS
see Brucellosis in Cattle

BOVINE SPONGIFORM ENCEPHALOPATHY
see also Creutzfeldt-Jakob Disease

Becker, Geoffrey S., et al. Mad Cow Disease (Bovine Spongiform Encephalopathy) 2008. 39.00 *(978-1-60456-324-5(9))* Nova Science Pubs., Inc.

Cummings, Louise. Rethinking the BSE Crisis: A Study of Scientific Reasoning under Uncertainty. 2010. (ENG.). xv, 242p. 209.00 *(978-90-481-9503-9(9))*, 9048195039) Springer.

Faillace, Linda. Mad Sheep: The True Story Behind the USDA's War on a Family Farm. 2007. (ENG.). 336p. pap. 17.95 *(978-1-933392-76-9(2))* Chelsea Green Publishing.

Ferrari, Matteo. Risk Perception Culture & Legal Change: A Comparative Study on Food Safety in the Wake of the Mad Cow Crisis. 2009. 216p. 124.95 *(978-0-7546-7811-3(3))* Ashgate Publishing Co.

Harris, David A. Mad Cow Disease & Related Spongiform Encephalopathies. 2010. (Current Topics in Microbiology & Immunology Ser.). (Illus.). ix, 219p. pap. 239.00 *(978-3-642-05756-4(X))*, 364205756X) Springer.

The Importation of Canadian Beef That Comes from Animals Older Than 30 Months of Age: Field Hearing Before the Subcommittee on Interstate Commerce, Trade, & Tourism of the Committee on Commerce, Science, & Transportation, United States Senate, One Hundred Tenth Congress, First Session, February 21, 2007. 2007. (Illus.). iii, 48p. *(978-0-16-079375-2(0))*, 552-070-36405-6) United States Government Printing Office.

Kukucha, Christopher John & Luu, Joanne. Sacred Cow? Canada's Response to the BSE Crisis: Evaluating North American Integration, Science, & Questions of Intrusiveness & Autonomy. 2007. 48p. pap. *(978-1-882582-59-4(4))* Canadian-American Ctr.

Lister, Sarah A. & Becker, Geoffrey S. Bovine Spongiform Encephalopathy (BSE, or Mad Cow Disease) Current & Proposed Safeguards. 2008. pap. 29.00 *(978-1-60692-635-2(7))* Nova Science Pubs., Inc.

Morina, Rifat. Dna Analysis of Candidate Genes for Bse Susceptibility or Resistance. 2010. 88p. pap. *(978-3-639-24644-5(6))* VDM Verlag Dr. Mueller e.K.

Packer, Richard. The Politics of BSE. annot. ed. 2006. (ENG., Illus.). 320p. 110.00 *(978-1-4039-8529-3(4))* Palgrave Macmillan.

Singh, Patrick. Lethal Souvenir. 2008. 152p. per. 11.95 *(978-1-4327-1594-6(1))* Outskirts Pr., Inc.

BOW AND ARROW
see also Archery; Crossbow; Hunting with Bow and Arrow

Alrune, Flemming & Wulf Hein. The Bowbuilder's Book: European Bow Building from the Stone Age to Today. 2007. (Illus.). 232p. pap. 34.95 *(978-0-7643-2789-6(5))* Schiffer Publishing, Ltd.

Bertalan, Dan. Traditional Bowyer's Encyclopedia: The Complete Guide to Bow Making. 2011. (ENG., Illus.). 568p. pap. 19.95 *(978-1-61608-114-0(7))*, 608114) Skyhorse Publishing Co., Inc.

Burch, Monte. Making Native American Hunting, Fighting, & Survival Tools: The Complete Guide to Making & Using Traditional Tools. 2007. (ENG., Illus.). 272p. pap. 16.95 *(978-1-59921-093-3(2))*, Lyons Pr.) Globe Pequot Pr., The.

Camera, Anthony. Shooting the Stickbow. 2008. 396p. pap. 19.95 *(978-1-60264-244-7(3))* Virtualbookworm.com Publishing, Inc.

Hamm, Jim. Bows & Arrows of the Native Americans: A Step-by-Step Guide to Wooden Bows, Sinew-Backed Bows, Composite Bows, Strings, Arrows & Quivers. 2007. (ENG., Illus.). 160p. per. 14.95 *(978-1-59921-083-4(5))*, Lyons Pr.) Globe Pequot Pr., The.

Hamm, Jim, et al. The Traditional Bowyer's Bible, Volume 4. 2008. (Traditional Bowyer's Bible Ser.). (ENG., Illus.). 320p. pap. 22.95 *(978-1-59921-453-5(9))*, Lyons Pr.) Globe Pequot Pr., The.

Hanna, Jason. Antique Trader Indian Arrowheads Price Guide. 2007. (ENG., Illus.). 272p. pap. 19.99 *(978-0-89689-540-9(8))* Krause Pubns.

Hübschmann, Volkmar, ed. Bow Accessories. 2008. (Illus.). 208p. bds. 34.99 *(978-0-7643-3035-3(7))* Schiffer Publishing, Ltd.

Jones, David E. Poison Arrows: North American Indian Hunting & Warfare. 2009. (ENG.). 136p. pap. 19.95 *(978-0-292-72229-3(X))* Univ. of Texas Pr.

Landrus, Matthew Hayden. Leonardo Da Vinci's Giant Crossbow. 2009. (ENG., Illus.). 200p. 59.95 *(978-3-540-68915-7(X))* Springer.

Mason, Otis Tufton. North American Bows, Arrows, & Quivers. 2007. (ENG., Illus.). 184p. pap. 14.95 *(978-1-60239-115-4(7))*, 239115) Skyhorse Publishing Co., Inc.

Middleton, Richard. The Practical Guide to Man-Powered Weapons & Ammunition: Experiments with Catapults, Musketballs, Stonebows, Blowpipes, Big Airguns, & Bullet Bows. 2007. (ENG., Illus.). 224p. per. 14.95 *(978-1-60239-147-5(5))*, 239147) Skyhorse Publishing Co., Inc.

Pope, Saxton. Hunting with the Bow & Arrow. 2011. 286p. pap. 12.95 ***(978-1-61427-117-8(8))*** Martino Publishing.

Pope, Saxton T. A Study of Bows & Arrows. 2011. 110p. pap. 14.95 ***(978-1-61427-137-6(2))*** Martino Publishing.

Pope, Saxton Temple. A Study of Bows & Arrows. 2011. 108p. 39.95 ***(978-1-258-09776-9(1))*** Literary Licensing, LLC.

Soar, Hugh & Stretton, Mark. Secrets of English War Bow. 2006. (Illus.). 240p. pap. 19.95 *(978-1-59416-126-1(7))* Westholme Publishing.

Soar, Hugh D. H. The Crooked Stick. 2009. (ENG., Illus.). 240p. pap. 14.95 *(978-1-59416-090-5(2))* Westholme Publishing.

—The Romance of Archery: A Social History of the Longbow. 2008. (ENG., Illus.). 224p. 24.95 *(978-1-59416-067-7(8))* Westholme Publishing.

—Secrets of the English War Bow. 2006. (Illus.). 240p. 35.00 *(978-1-59416-025-7(2))* Westholme Publishing.

Soar, Hugh D. H. Straight & True: A Select History of the Arrow. 2012. (ENG., Illus.). 264p. 22.00 ***(978-1-59416-147-6(X))*** Westholme Publishing.

Strickland, Matthew & Hardy, Robert. The Great Warbow: From Hastings to the Mary Rose. 2011. (ENG., Illus.). 560p. 57.95 *(978-0-85733-090-1(X))*, 085733090X) Haynes Publishing PLC GBR. Dist: MBI Distribution Services/Quayside Distribution.

Wilcox, Slim. The Art of Making Selfbows. 2009. (Illus.). 192p. pap. 59.95 *(978-1-4389-9199-3(1))* AuthorHouse.

Wilson, Thomas. Arrowpoints, Spearheads, & Knives of Prehistoric Times. 2009. 376p. 48.95 *(978-1-104-70354-7(8))*; pap. 33.95 *(978-1-104-61893-3(1))* Kessinger Publishing, LLC.

BOW HUNTING
see Hunting with Bow and Arrow

BOWDITCH, NATHANIEL, 1773-1838

Bowditch, Nathaniel, abr. Memoir of Nathaniel Bowditch. 2011. 180p. pap. 13.95 ***(978-1-4290-9745-1(0))*** Applewood Bks.

Loring, Augustus P. Nathaniel Bowditch of Salem & Boston N. 2006. pap. 15.95 *(978-1-4286-6061-8(5))* Kessinger Publishing, LLC.

BOWDOIN COLLEGE

Loucks, Danica, et al. Bowdoin College 2012: Off the Record. 2011. 196p. pap. 16.95 ***(978-1-4274-0352-0(X))*** College Prowler, Inc.

Lund, Erik & Lund, Diane. Song for an Unsung Hero. 2009. (Illus.). xv, 277p. *(978-0-615-27447-8(1))* Lund, Erik.

BOWEL—DISEASES
see Inflammatory Bowel Diseases; Intestines—Diseases

BOWEN, ELIZABETH, 1899-1973

Corcoran, Neil. Elizabeth Bowen: The Enforced Return. 2008. (ENG.). 220p. (C). pap. 39.95 *(978-0-19-953213-1(3))* Oxford Univ. Pr., Inc.

Glendinning, Victoria. Elizabeth Bowen. 2006. (ENG., Illus.). 368p. pap. 15.95 *(978-0-307-27740-4(2))*, Anchor) Knopf Doubleday Publishing Group.

Glendinning, Victoria, ed. Love's Civil War: Elizabeth Bowen & Charles Ritchie. 2009. (ENG., Illus.). 496p. pap. 19.95 *(978-0-7710-3568-5(3))*, Emblem Edns) McClelland & Stewart CAN. Dist: Random Hse., Inc.

Hepburn, Allan, ed. Listening In: Broadcasts, Speeches, & Interviews by Elizabeth Bowen. 2010. (ENG.). 352p. (gr. 17). 135.00 *(978-0-7486-4041-6(X))*; pap. 45.00 *(978-0-7486-4042-3(8))* Edinburgh Univ. Pr. GBR. Dist: Columbia Univ. Pr.

Mccormack. Dissolute Characters: Irish literary history through Balzac, Sheridan le Fanu, Yeats & Bowen. 2011. (ENG.). 265p. pap. 29.95 *(978-0-7190-8563-5(2))* Manchester Univ. Pr. GBR. Dist: Macmillan.

Walshe, Eibhear, ed. Elizabeth Bowen. 2009. 216p. 74.95 *(978-0-7165-2916-3(5))*; pap. 34.95 *(978-0-7165-2917-0(3))* Irish Academic Pr. IRL. Dist: International Specialized Bk. Services.

BOWEN FAMILY

Cruise, M. T. W. The Truth Is the Light If It's Told in the Dark, 1. 2007. (Illus.). 171p. per. 24.95 *(978-0-9790433-0-7(1))*, 200) Cruise, M. T. W.

BOWER FAMILY

Weiss, Lister O. & Weiss, Edna M. Fetzer. A History & Genealogy of Hans Bauer & His Descendants. 2011. 124p. 40.95 ***(978-1-258-06583-6(5))*** Literary Licensing, LLC.

BOWIE, DAVID, 1947-

Cann, Kevin, text. Any Day Now: David Bowie - The London Years, 1947-1974. 2011. (ENG., Illus.). 336p. pap. 45.00 *(978-0-9552017-7-6(2))* Adelita Ltd. GBR. Dist: D.A.P./Distributed Art Pubs.

Doggett, Peter. The Man Who Sold the World: David Bowie & The 1970s. 2012. (ENG.). 400p. 26.99 ***(978-0-06-202465-7(5))*** HarperCollins Pubs.

Pegg, Nicholas. The Complete David Bowie. 6th ed. 2011. (ENG.). 704p. pap. 24.95 *(978-0-85768-290-1(3))*, Titan Bks.) Titan Bks. Ltd. GBR. Dist: Random Hse., Inc.

Perone, James E. The Words & Music of David Bowie, 1 vol. 2007. (Praeger Singer-Songwriter Collection Ser.). (Illus.). 224p. 44.95 *(978-0-275-99245-3(4))*, C9245, Praeger Pubs.) Greenwood Publishing Group, Inc.

Seabrook, Thomas Jerome. Bowie in Berlin: A New Career in a New Town. 2008. (ENG., Illus.). 272p. pap. 19.95 *(978-1-906002-08-4(8))*, 1906002088, Jawbone) Outline Pr., Ltd. GBR. Dist: Leonard, Hal Corp.

Spitz, Marc. Bowie: A Biography. 2010. (ENG.). 448p. pap. 17.00 *(978-0-307-71699-6(6))*, Three Rivers Pr.) Crown Publishing Group.

Stevenson, Nick. David Bowie: Fame, Sound & Vision. rev. ed. 2006. (Polity Celebrities Ser.). (ENG.). 232p. 69.95 *(978-0-7456-2939-1(3))*; pap. 22.95 *(978-0-7456-2940-7(7))* Polity Pr. GBR. Dist: Wiley, John & Sons, Inc.

Thomas, Gareth, ed. David Bowie: The Illustrated Biographies. 2011. (ENG., Illus.). 224p. pap. 18.95 ***(978-1-56649-093-1(6))*** Welcome Rain Pubs.

Thompson, Dave. Your Pretty Face Is Going to Hell: The Dangerous Glitter of David Bowie, Iggy Pop, & Lou Reed. 2009. (ENG.). 320p. pap. 19.99 *(978-0-87930-985-5(7))*, 0879309857, Backbeat Books) Leonard, Hal Corp.

Trynka, Paul. David Bowie - Starman. 2011. (ENG., Illus.). 544p. 25.99 *(978-0-316-03225-4(5))* Little Brown & Co.

Welch, Chris. David Bowie: The Story Behind Every Song. 2011. (Stories Behind the Songs Ser.). (ENG., Illus.). 192p. 14.95 *(978-1-84732-663-8(3))* Carlton Bks., Ltd. GBR. Dist: Sterling Publishing Co., Inc.

BOWITCH, HENRY INGERSOLL, 1808-1892

Bowditch, Vincent Y. Life & Correspondence of Henry Ingersoll Bowditch. 2009. (ENG.). 367p. 38.99 *(978-1-117-17943-8(5))*; (ENG.). 367p. pap. 31.75 *(978-1-117-17944-5(3))*; 422p. 41.99 *(978-1-115-28903-0(9))*; 422p. 34.99 *(978-1-115-28902-3(0))*; 422p. pap. 33.75 *(978-1-115-28900-9(4))*; 422p. pap. 34.75 *(978-1-115-28901-6(2))* BiblioBazaar.

BOWLES, JANE AUER, 1917-1973

Adams, Don. Alternative Paradigms of Literary Realism. 2009. (ENG.). 212p. 89.00 *(978-0-230-62186-2(4))* Palgrave Macmillan.

Tippins, Sherill. February House: The Story of W. H. Auden, Carson McCullers, Jane & Paul Bowles, Benjamin Britten, & Gypsy Rose Lee under One Roof in Brooklyn. 2006. (ENG., Illus.). 336p. pap. 18.95 *(978-0-618-71197-0(X))* Houghton Mifflin Harcourt Publishing Co.

BOWLES, PAUL, 1910-1999

Bowles, Paul. Travels: Collected Writings, 1950-1993. 2011. (ENG.). 504p. pap. 16.99 *(978-0-06-206763-0(X))*, Ecco) HarperCollins Pubs.

—Without Stopping: An Autobiography. 2006. (Ecco Ser.). (Illus.). 400p. per. 15.95 *(978-0-06-113741-9(3))*, HarperPerennial) HarperCollins Pubs.

Carr, Virginia Spencer. Paul Bowles: A Life. 2009. (ENG.). 428p. pap. 21.95 *(978-0-8101-2525-4(0))* Northwestern Univ. Pr.

Fortuny, Kim. AMER Writer in Istanbul. 2009. 224p. 34.95 *(978-0-8156-3236-8(3))* Syracuse Univ. Pr.

Tippins, Sherill. February House: The Story of W. H. Auden, Carson McCullers, Jane & Paul Bowles, Benjamin Britten, & Gypsy Rose Lee under One Roof in Brooklyn. 2006. (ENG., Illus.). 336p. pap. 18.95 *(978-0-618-71197-0(X))* Houghton Mifflin Harcourt Publishing Co.

BOWLES, SAMUEL, 1826-1878

Merriam, George S. The Life & Times of Samuel Bowles V1. 2007. (ENG.). 432p. 51.95 *(978-0-548-10285-5(6))* Kessinger Publishing, LLC.

—The Life & Times of Samuel Bowles V2. 2007. (ENG.). 528p. 55.95 *(978-0-548-10286-2(4))* Kessinger Publishing, LLC.

Merriam, George Spring. The Life & Times of Samuel Bowles. 2010. 228p. pap. *(978-1-153-00948-5(X))* 2009. 402p. pap. *(978-1-150-40624-9(0))* 2009. 272p. pap. *(978-0-217-59368-7(2))* Books LLC.

BOWLES, WILLIAM AUGUSTUS, 1764-1805

Din, Gilbert C. War on the Gulf Coast: The Spanish Fight against William Augustus Bowles. 2012. (ENG., Illus.). 360p. 69.95 *(978-0-8130-3752-3(2))* Univ. Pr. of Florida.

BOWLING

Fazio, Buzz. Bowling to Win: Bowling Fundamentals Plus Expert Tips for Individual & Team Play. Cruchon, Steve, ed. 2011. 78p. 37.95 ***(978-1-258-07241-4(6))*** Literary Licensing, LLC.

Forrest, A. J. & Iannucci, Lisa. Bowling for Dummies. 2010. (ENG., Illus.). 336p. pap. 19.99 *(978-0-470-60159-4(0))*, For Dummies) Wiley, John & Sons, Inc.

Friedman, Robert J. Shoe Up! 2009. pap. 10.00 *(978-1-61623-023-4(1))* Independent Pub.

Fulgaro, John M. National Bowling League: One Year Wonder, 1961-1962. 2008. (Illus.). 243p. *(978-1-885497-04-8(0))*, Jossey-Bass) Wiley, John & Sons, Inc.

Grinfelds, Vesma & Hultstrand, Bonnie. Right down Your Alley: The Complete Book of Bowling. 7th ed. 2011. (ENG.). 192p. (C). pap. 48.95 *(978-0-8400-4807-3(6))*, Brooks/Cole.

Jowdy, John. Bowling Execution. 2nd ed. 2009. (ENG., Illus.). 224p. pap. 19.95 *(978-0-7360-7538-1(0))* Human Kinetics Pubs.

Kaczkowski, Manya. Milwaukee's Historic Bowling Alleys. 2010. (Images of America Ser.). (Illus.). 128p. pap. 21.99 *(978-0-7385-8378-5(2))* Arcadia Publishing.

Oatis, Gary L. True Bowler Adjustments. 2009. 90p. pap. 25.00 *(978-0-615-26280-2(5))* Oatis, Gary L.

Pagnoni, Mario. The Joy of Bocce. 3rd rev. ed. 2010. 220p. pap. 18.45 *(978-1-4520-4709-6(X))* AuthorHouse.

Price, Robert G. The Ultimate Guide to Weight Training for Bowling. 2nd rev. ed. 2008. (Ultimate Guide to Weight Training for Sports Ser.). (Illus.). 168p. pap. 16.95 *(978-1-932549-58-4(7))* Price World Publishing.

Schmidt, Doug. They Came to Bowl: How Milwaukee Became America's Tenpin Capital. 2007. (ENG., Illus.). 286p. pap. 24.95 *(978-0-87020-387-9(8))* Wisconsin Historical Society.

Timbs, John. Historic Ninepins. 2008. 364p. 29.99 *(978-0-559-40329-3(1))*; pap. 31.75 *(978-0-559-40327-9(5))* BiblioBazaar.

—Historic Ninepins. 2008. 364p. 46.95 *(978-1-4369-8265-8(0))*; pap. 31.95 *(978-1-4368-7162-4(X))* Kessinger Publishing, LLC.

Wiggins, Roy. Short Mat Bowling - an Illustrated Guide to This Challenging Sport. 2nd ed. 2008. (Illus.). 52p. pap. *(978-0-7552-0448-9(4))* Authors OnLine, Ltd.

BOWLING ON THE GREEN
see Bowls (Game)

BOWLS (GAME)

Allan, Gordon. Bowling Enchanted Woods. (Illus.). 102p. pap. *(978-1-898595-00-7(3))* Sussex Academic Pr. GBR. Dist: International Specialized Bk. Services.

Bell, John. Bowls: Skills, Techniques, Tactics. 2007. (Crowood Sports Guides). (ENG., Illus.). 128p. pap. 24.95 *(978-1-86126-968-3(4))* Crowood Pr., Ltd. GBR. Dist: Independent Pubs. Group.

Marsh, Alex. Sex & Bowls & Rock & Roll: How I Swapped My Rock Dreams for Village Greens. 2010. (ENG.). 288p. 14.95 *(978-0-00-735547-1(5))* HarperCollins Pubs. Ltd. GBR. Dist: Independent Pubs. Group.

BOXER (DOG BREED)

Abraham, Stephanie. Boxer. 2nd ed. 2008. (Happy Healthy Pet Ser.: 100). (ENG., Illus.). 144p. 16.99 *(978-0-470-22182-2(8))*, Howell Bk. Hse.) Wiley, John & Sons, Inc.

Albert, Terry. Boxer. 2011. *(978-0-7938-3723-6(5))* TFH Pubns., Inc.

Dog Fancy Magazine, compiled by. Boxer. 2010. (Smart Owner's Guide Ser.). (ENG.). 176p. (gr. 6). 17.95 *(978-1-59378-765-3(0))* Kennel Club Bks.

Dog Fancy Staff, compiled by. Boxer. 2010. (Smart Owner's Guide Ser.). (ENG.). 176p. (gr. 6). pap. 15.95 *(978-1-59378-744-8(8))* Kennel Club Bks.

Gallagher, Cynthia P. Boxer, 1 vol. 2010. (DogLife Ser.). (ENG., Illus.). 224p. 19.95 *(978-0-7938-3602-4(6))*, 1320895) TFH Pubns., Inc.

—Boxers. 2006. (Animal Planet Pet Care Library). (Illus.). 111p. 11.95 *(978-0-7938-3759-5(6))* TFH Pubns., Inc.

Hautmann, Chad. The Boxer. (Illus.). 112p. 2009. (ENG.). 14.95 *(978-1-932904-43-7(3))* 2008. lib. bdg. 32.95 *(978-1-932904-19-2(0))* Eldorado Ink.

Hustace Walker, Joan. Training Your Boxer. 2nd rev. ed. 2011. (Training Your Dog Ser.). (ENG.). 160p. pap. 12.99 *(978-0-7641-4600-8(9))* Barron's Educational Series, Inc.

Sakson, Sharon. Boxers. 2011. (Barron's Dog Bibles Ser.). (ENG., Illus.). 160p. 18.99 *(978-0-7641-9770-3(3))* Barron's Educational Series, Inc.

Sakson, Sharon R. Boxers. 2010. *(978-0-7641-4490-5(1))* Barron's Educational Series, Inc.

Walker, Joan Hustace. The Boxer Handbook. 2nd rev. ed. 2010. (Barron's Pet Handbooks Ser.). (ENG., Illus.). 208p. pap. 12.99 *(978-0-7641-4342-7(5))* Barron's Educational Series, Inc.

—Boxers. 2010. (Complete Pet Owner's Manuals Ser.). (ENG., Illus.). 96p. pap. 8.99 *(978-0-7641-4326-7(3))* Barron's Educational Series, Inc.

BOXER REBELLION, CHINA, 1899-1901

see China—History—Boxer Rebellion, 1899-1901

BOXERS

see China—History—Boxer Rebellion, 1899-1901

BOXERS (DOGS)

see Boxer (Dog Breed)

BOXERS (SPORTS)

Aycock, Colleen & Scott, Mark. Joe Gans: A Biography of the First African American World Boxing Champion. 2008. (ENG., Illus.). 294p. pap. 35.00 *(978-0-7864-3994-2(7))* McFarland & Co., Inc. Pubs.

Aycock, Colleen & Scott, Mark, eds. The First Black Boxing Champions: Essays on Fighters of the 1800s to The 1920s. 2011. (ENG., Illus.). 302p. 45.00 *(978-0-7864-4991-0(8))* McFarland & Co., Inc. Pubs.

Banks, Nicholas W., Jr. True Adventures of Nick: Man of War. 2007. pap. 12.00 *(978-0-8059-9148-2(4))* Dorrance Publishing Co., Inc.

Battling Siki: A Tale of Ring Fixes, Race, & Murder in The 1920s. 2008. 360p. pap. 19.95 *(978-1-55728-888-2(7))* Univ. of Arkansas Pr.

Bodner, Allen. When Boxing Was a Jewish Sport. 2011. (Excelsior Editions Ser.). (Illus.). 246p. pap. 24.95 *(978-1-4384-3608-1(4))* State Univ. of New York Pr.

Brogan, Wrigley. The Last Round: Roberto Duran's Last Win. 2006. per. 15.00 *(978-0-9705148-2-0(4))* Ink & Lens, Ltd.

Brooke-Ball, Peter, et al. The Boxing Album: an Illustrated History: The complete story of boxing from the pugilists of the classical amphitheatre to the heroes of Today. 2012. (ENG., Illus.). 264p. pap. 16.99 ***(978-1-78019-058-7(1))*** Anness Publishing GBR. Dist: National Bk. Network.

Bruno, Peter A. & Bruno, Angela R. Dying to Fight: The Tony Bruno Story. 2008. 218p. 24.95 *(978-1-4327-2572-3(6))*; pap. 18.95 *(978-1-4327-2501-3(7))* Outskirts Pr., Inc.

Caduto, Tommy Jon. Fight or Die: The Vinny Paz Story. 2010. (ENG., Illus.). 240p. pap. 12.95 *(978-1-59921-967-7(0)*, Lyons Pr.) Globe Pequot Pr., The.

Carney, James M., Jr. Ultimate Tough Guy. 2009. (Illus.). 308p. pap. 22.00 *(978-0-578-01055-7(0))* Achill Publishing.

Carter, Rubin. The Sixteenth Round: From Number 1 Contender to Number 45472. 2011. (ENG.). 368p. pap. 16.95 *(978-1-56976-567-8(7)*, Hill, Lawrence Bks.) Chicago Review Pr., Inc.

Cavanaugh, Jack. Tunney: Boxing's Brainiest Champ & His Upset of the Great Jack Dempsey. 2007. (ENG.). 496p. pap. 15.95 *(978-0-8129-6783-8(6)*, Ballantine Bks.) Random House Publishing Group.

Century, Douglas. Barney Ross: The Life of a Jewish Fighter. 2009. (ENG., Illus.). 240p. pap. 12.95 *(978-0-8052-1173-3(X)*, Schocken) Knopf Doubleday Publishing Group.

Chapman, Mike. Oklahoma Shooter: The Dan Hodge Story. 2009. (Illus.). 198p. pap. 22.95 *(978-0-9819484-0-9(5))* Culture Hse.

Clement, Ben. Giants on My Shoulders/As Told by Ali Muhammad; Aka Frank Steele, the Man of Steel. 2009. 296p. 27.75 *(978-1-60693-960-4(2)*, Strategic Bk. Publishing) AEG Literary Publishing Services, Inc.

Clifton, Guy. Dempsey in Nevada. 2007. (Illus.). 216p. 24.95 *(978-0-930083-33-5(4))* Bacon, Jack & Co.

Coomber, Richard & Nelson, Johnny. Hard Road to Glory: How I Became Champion of the World. 2007. (ENG., Illus.). 290p. 33.95 *(978-1-84454-430-1(3))* Blake, John Publishing, Ltd. GBR. Dist: Independent Pubs. Group.

Corpas, Jose. New York City's Greatest Boxers. 2006. (Images of Sports Ser.). (ENG., Illus.). 128p. per. 19.99 *(978-0-7385-4901-9(0))* Arcadia Publishing.

Cushman, Tom. Muhammad Ali & the Greatest Heavyweight Generation. 2009. 208p. 35.00 *(978-0-9822489-3-5(8))*; pap. 19.00 *(978-0-9822489-2-8(X))* Southeast Missouri State Univ. Pr.

Davison, John. John Davison: Little Man, Big Heart. 2007. (ENG., Illus.). 288p. pap. 34.95 *(978-1-84454-442-4(7))* Blake, John Publishing, Ltd. GBR. Dist: Independent Pubs. Group.

De La Hoya, Oscar & Springer, Steve. Un Sueno Americano: Mi Historia. 2009. (SPA.). 304p. pap. 12.99 *(978-0-06-172542-5(0)*, Rayo) HarperCollins Pubs.

De La Hoya, Oscar, et al. American Son: My Story. 2009. (ENG.). 288p. pap. 14.99 *(978-0-06-157312-5(4))* HarperCollins Pubs.

DeMarco, Tony & Zappala, Ellen. Nardo: Memoirs of a Boxing Champion. 2011. pap. ***(978-1-881901-81-5(5))***; pap. ***(978-1-881901-82-2(3))*** LEGAS.

Duthel, Heinz. Muhammad Ali the greatest Champ by Heinz Duthel. 2010. 89p. pap. 19.90 *(978-1-4452-9849-8(X))* Lulu Enterprises Inc.

Ezra, Michael. Muhammad Ali: The Making of an Icon. 2009. (Sporting Ser.). (ENG.). 248p. pap. 26.95 *(978-1-59213-662-9(1))*; (Illus.). 71.50 *(978-1-59213-661-2(3))* Temple Univ. Pr.

Fenske, Doug Dane. Holding on- I Sued the Mafia & Lived to Tell about It the Story of Sundance Dane & Kerri James. 2011. 290p. pap. 17.50 ***(978-1-60911-328-5(4)**, Strategic Bk. Publishing)* AEG Literary Publishing Services, Inc.

Finger, David E. Rocky Lives! Heavyweight Boxing Upsets of The 1990s. 2006. (Illus.). 352p. per. 17.95 *(978-1-57488-906-2(0))* Potomac Bks., Inc.

Foreman, George. God in My Corner, 0 vols. 2007. (Illus.). 320p. 22.99 *(978-0-8499-0314-4(9))* Nelson, Thomas Inc.

Froch, Carl. The Cobra: My Story. 2011. (ENG., Illus.). 336p. 32.95 ***(978-0-09-193829-1(5))*** Ebury Publishing GBR. Dist: Independent Pubs. Group.

Gallimore, Andrew. Babyface Goes to Hollywood: The Jimmy McLarnin Story. 2009. (ENG., Illus.). 320p. pap. 18.95 ***(978-1-84717-116-0(8))*** O'Brien Pr., Ltd., The IRL. Dist: Dufour Editions, Inc.

—A Bloody Canvas: The Mike McTigue Story. 2008. (ENG., Illus.). 352p. pap. 26.95 *(978-1-85635-536-0(5))* Mercier Pr., Ltd., The IRL. Dist: Dufour Editions, Inc.

—Occupation - Prizefighter: Freddie Welsh's Quest for the World Championship. 2006. (ENG., Illus.). 380p. pap. 24.95 *(978-1-85411-395-5(X))* Seren Bks. GBR. Dist: Independent Pubs. Group.

Gildea, William. The Longest Fight: In the Ring with Joe Gans, Boxing's First African-American Champion. 2012. (ENG., Illus.). 256p. 26.00 ***(978-0-374-28097-0(5))*** Farrar, Straus & Giroux.

Giudice, Christian. Beloved Warrior: The Rise & Fall of Alexis Argüello. 2012. (Illus.). 224p. 26.95 ***(978-1-59797-709-8(8))*** Potomac Bks., Inc.

Giudice, Christian. Hands of Stone: The Life & Legend of Roberto Duran. (ENG., Illus.). 2009. 384p. pap. 14.95 *(978-1-903854-75-4(X))* 2006. 320p. 24.95 *(978-1-903854-55-6(5))* Milo Bks. GBR. Dist: Consortium Bk. Sales & Distribution.

Gorman, Bartley. Bareknuckle: Memoirs of the Undefeated Champion. 2011. (ENG.). 320p. (gr. 12). 16.00 *(978-1-59020-390-3(9))* Overlook Pr., The.

Gray, William B. Boxing's Top 100: The Greatest Champions of All Time. 2006. pap. 24.95 *(978-1-880876-12-1(4))* Diamond Library.

Halloran, Bob. Irish Thunder: The Hard Life & Times of Micky Ward. 2010. (Illus.). 347p. pap. 14.95 *(978-0-7627-6986-5(6)*, Lyons Pr.) Globe Pequot Pr., The.

Hauser, Thomas. Boxing Is ... Reflections on the Sweet Science. 2010. (ENG.). 335p. pap. 22.50 *(978-1-55728-942-1(5))* Univ. of Arkansas Pr.

—An Unforgiving Sport: An Inside Look at Another Year in Boxing. 2009. (ENG.). 328p. pap. 22.50 *(978-1-55728-910-0(7))* Univ. of Arkansas Pr.

Hauser, Thomas & LaMotta, Vikki. Knockout! The Sexy, Violent, Extraordinary Life of Vikki Lamotta. 2006. (ENG., Illus.). 200p. *(978-1-894963-51-0(2))* Sport Media Publishing.

Haygood, Wil. Sweet Thunder: The Life & Times of Sugar Ray Robinson. 2009. (ENG., Illus.). 480p. 27.95 *(978-1-4000-4497-9(9))* Knopf, Alfred A. Inc.

Hide, Herbie. Nothing but Trouble? My Story. 2009. (ENG., Illus.). 260p. 28.95 *(978-1-84454-706-7(X))* Blake, John Publishing, Ltd. GBR. Dist: Independent Pubs. Group.

Holyfield, Evander. Becoming Holyfield: A Fighter's Journey. 2008. (ENG., Illus.). 288p. pap. 19.95 *(978-1-4165-3487-7(3)*, Beyond Words/Atria Bks.) Atria Bks.

Holyfield, Evander & Gruenfeld, Lee. Becoming Holyfield: A Fighter's Journey. 2008. (ENG., Illus.). 288p. 25.00 *(978-1-4165-3486-0(5)*, Beyond Words/Atria Bks.) Atria Bks.

Horsley, Richy & Richards. Born to Fight: The True Story of Richy 'Crazy Horse' Horsley. 2008. (ENG., Illus.). 266p. pap. 15.95 *(978-1-84454-556-8(3))* Blake, John Publishing, Ltd. GBR. Dist: Independent Pubs. Group.

Hughes, Brian & Hughes, Damian. Hit Man: The Thomas Hearns Story. 2010. (ENG., Illus.). 272p. pap. 17.95 *(978-1-903854-90-7(3))* Milo Bks. GBR. Dist: Consortium Bk. Sales & Distribution.

Hugman, Barry J. The British Boxing Board of Control Boxing Yearbook 2010. 2010. (ENG., Illus.). 320p. 36.95 *(978-1-84596-486-3(1))* Mainstream Publishing Co., Ltd. GBR. Dist: Independent Pubs. Group.

Hugman, Barry J., ed. The British Boxing Board of Control Boxing Yearbook 2009. anniv. ed. 2008. (ENG., Illus.). 320p. pap. 37.95 *(978-1-84596-325-5(3))* Mainstream Publishing Co., Ltd. GBR. Dist: Independent Pubs. Group.

Hurley, Jon. Tom Cribb: The Life of the Black Diamond. 2009. (ENG., Illus.). 288p. 36.95 *(978-0-7524-4751-3(3))* History Pr. Ltd.,The GBR. Dist: Independent Pubs. Group.

—Tom Spring: All England Bareknuckle Champion. (Illus.). 192p. 32.50 *(978-0-7524-2404-0(1))* History Pr. Ltd.,The GBR. Dist: Trafalgar Square Publishing.

Jarrett, John. Champ in the Corner: The Ray Arcel Story. 2008. (ENG., Illus.). 224p. 35.00 *(978-0-7524-4446-8(8))* History Pr. Ltd.,The GBR. Dist: Independent Pubs. Group.

Johnson, Jack. My Life & Battles. Rivers, Christopher, ed. 2007. (Illus.). 152p. 39.95 *(978-0-275-99964-3(5)*, C9964, Praeger Pubs.) Greenwood Publishing Group, Inc.

—My Life & Battles. Rivers, Christopher, tr. from FRE. 2009. (Illus.). 152p. pap. 19.95 *(978-1-59797-267-3(3))* Potomac Bks., Inc.

Kent, Graeme. Boxing. 2010. (ENG.). 144p. 17.95 *(978-0-7524-5253-1(3))* History Pr. Ltd.,The GBR. Dist: Independent Pubs. Group.

—The Great White Hopes: The Quest to Defeat Jack Johnson. 2007. (Illus.). 253p. per. 14.95 *(978-0-7509-4613-1(X))* History Pr. Ltd.,The GBR. Dist: Independent Pubs. Group.

Kershner, Jim. Carl Maxey: A Fighting Life. 2012. (ENG., Illus.). 288p. pap. 19.95 ***(978-0-295-99231-0(X))*** Univ. of Washington Pr.

Khan, Amir. Amir Khan: A Boy from Bolton: My Story. 2007. (ENG., Illus.). 208p. pap. 15.95 *(978-0-7475-8805-4(8))* Bloomsbury Publishing Plc GBR. Dist: Independent Pubs. Group.

—Amir Khan - A Boy from Bolton: My Story. 2006. (ENG., Illus.). 224p. 32.95 *(978-0-7475-8760-6(4))* Bloomsbury Publishing Plc GBR. Dist: Independent Pubs. Group.

Kidney, Christine. Muhammad Ali: An Illustrated Biography. 2009. (ENG.). 224p. pap. 16.95 *(978-1-56649-997-2(6))* Welcome Rain Pubs.

Kimball, George. Four Kings: Leonard, Hagler, Hearns, Duran & the Last Great Era of Boxing. (ENG.). 2009. 352p. pap. 16.95 *(978-1-59013-238-6(6))* 2008. 340p. 22.95 *(978-1-59013-162-6(2))* McBooks Pr., Inc.

—Manly Art: They Can Run - But They Can't Hide. 2011. (ENG.). 384p. 24.95 *(978-1-59013-571-6(7))* McBooks Pr., Inc.

Klein, Binnie. Blows to the Head: How Boxing Changed My Mind. 2010. (Excelsior Editions Ser.). (ENG., Illus.). 144p. 19.95 *(978-1-4384-3001-0(9))* State Univ. of New York Pr.

Kriegel, Mark. Good Son: The Life of Ray Boom Boom Mancini. 2012. (ENG., Illus.). 320p. 27.00 ***(978-0-7432-8635-0(9)**, Free Pr.)* Free Pr.

Lawton, James. Mission Impossible: How Lennox Lewis Unified the World Heavyweight Title. (Illus.). 256p. 35.00 *(978-1-84018-272-9(5))* Mainstream Publishing Co., Ltd. GBR. Dist: Trafalgar Square Publishing.

Leonard, Sugar Ray & Arkush, Michael. The Big Fight: My Life in & Out of the Ring. 2011. (ENG., Illus.). 320p. (gr. 12). 26.95 *(978-0-670-02272-4(1)*, Viking Adult) Penguin Group (USA) Inc.

Levy, Alan Howard. Floyd Patterson: A Boxer & a Gentleman. 2008. (ENG., Illus.). 297p. pap. 35.00 *(978-0-7864-3950-8(5))* McFarland & Co., Inc. Pubs.

Lowry, Tiger. Gods in My Corner A Portrait of an Ameri. 2007. (Illus.). 202p. pap. 24.95 *(978-1-4241-5105-9(8))* PublishAmerica, Inc.

Lynch, Kevin. Octagon. deluxe ed. 2007. 392p. *(978-1-57687-416-5(8)*, powerHouse Bks.) powerHouse Cultural Entertainment, Inc.

MacDougall, Paul. Distinction Earned: Cape Breton's Boxing Legends, 1946-1970, 1 vol. 2010. 178p. pap. ***(978-1-897009-48-2(8))*** Cape Breton Univ. Pr.

Malinowski, Scoop. Heavyweight Armageddon! The Tyson-Lewis Championship Battle. 2008. pap. *(978-1-934841-16-7(1))* Zumaya Pubns. LLC.

Mason, Rocky. Gumshield to Greasepaint. 2010. (Illus.). 348p. pap. 17.99 *(978-1-4490-7507-1(X))* AuthorHouse.

McGuigan, Barry. Cyclone: My Story. (ENG., Illus.). 2012. 280p. 22.95 ***(978-0-7535-3995-8(0))*** 2011. 288p. 34.95 ***(978-0-7535-3994-1(2))*** Virgin Bks. Ltd. GBR. Dist: Independent Pubs. Group.

McLean, Lenny & Gerrard, Peter. The Guv'nor Tapes: Lenny Mclean's Unpublished Stories, as Told by the Man Himself. 2007. (ENG., Illus.). 256p. per. 13.95 *(978-1-84454-358-8(7))* Blake, John Publishing, Ltd. GBR. Dist: Independent Pubs. Group.

Mead, Chris. Joe Louis: Black Champion in White America. 2010. (ENG., Illus.). 352p. pap. 12.95 *(978-0-486-47182-2(9))* Dover Pubns., Inc.

Mee, Bob. Liston & Ali: The Ugly Bear & the Boy Who Would Be King. 2011. (ENG., Illus.). 336p. 24.95 *(978-1-61608-369-4(7)*, 608369) Skyhorse Publishing Co., Inc.

Mendiola, Victor, et al. Los últimos Héroes de la Península. 2009. (SPA., Illus.). 95p. *(978-84-92480-69-2(6))*; *(978-607-7515-39-5(6))* R.M. Editorial, S.A. de C.V.

Mercante, Arthur & Guarnieri, Phil. Inside the Ropes. 2007. (ENG.). 248p. pap. 15.95 *(978-1-59013-140-4(1))* McBooks Pr., Inc.

Merritt, Carl. Fighting to the Death: My Life in the World's Deadliest Fight Game. 2009. (ENG., Illus.). 264p. pap. 14.95 *(978-1-84454-690-9(X))* Blake, John Publishing, Ltd. GBR. Dist: Independent Pubs. Group.

Monaghan, Paddy. Street Fighting Man. 2008. (ENG.). 288p. 34.95 *(978-1-84454-553-7(9))* Blake, John Publishing, Ltd. GBR. Dist: Independent Pubs. Group.

Monninger, Joseph. Two Ton: One Night, One Fight - Tony Galento V. Joe Louis. 2007. (ENG., Illus.). 208p. per. 13.95 *(978-1-58642-138-0(7))* Steerforth Pr.

Montoya, Delilah, photos by. Women Boxers: The New Warriors. 2006. (Illus.). 96p. per. 24.95 *(978-1-55885-475-8(4))* Arte Publico Pr.

Myler, Patrick. Dan Donnelly 1788-1820: Pugilist, Publican, Playboy. 2011. (ENG., Illus.). 214p. pap. 24.95 *(978-1-84351-158-8(4))* Lilliput Pr., Ltd., The IRL. Dist: Dufour Editions, Inc.

Nelson, Johnny. Hard Road to Glory: How I Became Champion of the World. 2010. (ENG., Illus.). 292p. pap. 13.95 *(978-1-84454-895-8(3))* Blake, John Publishing, Ltd. GBR. Dist: Independent Pubs. Group.

Newsham, Gavin. The Official Treasures of Muhammad Ali. 2010. (ENG., Illus.). 64p. 34.95 *(978-1-84732-671-3(4))* Carlton Bks., Ltd. GBR. Dist: Sterling Publishing Co., Inc.

Nicholson, Kelly Richard. Hitters, Dancers & Ring Magicians: Seven Boxers of the Golden Age. 2010. (ENG., Illus.). 226p. pap. 29.95 *(978-0-7864-4990-3(X))* McFarland & Co., Inc. Pubs.

Nwamu, Punchin' Pat. They're Just My Friends. 2008. pap. 17.00 *(978-0-8059-8709-6(6))* Dorrance Publishing Co., Inc.

O'Toole, Andrew. Sweet William: The Life of Billy Conn. 2010. (Sport & Society Ser.). (ENG., Illus.). 376p. pap. 19.95 *(978-0-252-07745-6(8))* Univ. of Illinois Pr.

Page, Joseph S. Primo Carnera: The Life & Career of the Heavyweight Boxing Champion. 2010. (ENG., Illus.). 257p. pap. 35.00 *(978-0-7864-4810-4(5))* McFarland & Co., Inc. Pubs.

Paloolian, Mark. Brutality: The Tragic Story of Stanley Ketchel, the Michigan Assassin. 2009. 264p. pap. 19.95 *(978-1-60494-210-1(X))* Wheatmark.

Paxton, Bill. The Fearless Harry Greb: Biography of a Tragic Hero of Boxing. 2009. (ENG., Illus.). 260p. pap. 39.95 *(978-0-7864-4016-0(3))* McFarland & Co., Inc. Pubs.

Petersen, Bob. Peter Jackson: A Biography of the Australian Heavyweight Champion, 1860-1901. 2011. (ENG., Illus.). 260p. pap. 39.95 *(978-0-7864-5881-3(X))* McFarland & Co., Inc. Pubs.

Pitluk, Adam. Standing Eight: The Inspiring Story of Jesus el Matador Chavez, Who Became Lightweight Champion of the World. 2007. (ENG., Illus.). 272p. per. 14.95 *(978-0-306-81535-5(4))* Da Capo Pr., Inc.

Plimpton, George. Shadow Box: An Amateur in the Ring. 2010. (ENG.). 336p. pap. 16.95 *(978-1-59921-810-6(0)*, Lyons Pr.) Globe Pequot Pr., The.

Pollack, Adam J. In the Ring with Bob Fitzsimmons. 2007. ***(978-0-9799822-0-0(0))*** Pollack, Adam J.

Pollack, Adam J. John L. Sullivan: The Career of the First Gloved Heavyweight Champion. 2006. (ENG., Illus.). 254p. per. 35.00 *(978-0-7864-2558-7(X))* McFarland & Co., Inc. Pubs.

Ponce, Francisco. Julio Cesar Chavez.Tr. of Julio Cesar Chavez - So Long to the Glory. (SPA.). 14.95 *(978-970-05-1277-8(0))* Baker & Taylor Bks.

Poole, Gary Andrew. PacMan: Behind the Scenes with Manny Pacquiao — The Greatest Pound-for-Pound Fighter in the World. 2010. (ENG., Illus.). 280p. 25.00 *(978-0-306-81949-0(X))* Da Capo Pr., Inc.

—PacMan: Behind the Scenes with Manny Pacquiao — the Greatest Pound-for-Pound Fighter in the World. 2011. (ENG., Illus.). 304p. pap. 15.00 *(978-0-306-82045-8(5))* Da Capo Pr., Inc.

Poolman, Jeremy. Gypsy Jem Mace: Being One Man's Search for His Forgotten Famous Ancestor. 2008. (ENG., Illus.). 232p. 29.95 *(978-0-233-00225-5(1))* Andre Deutsch GBR. Dist: Independent Pubs. Group.

Potgieter, Deon. Rose of Soweto: The Dingaan Thobela Story. 2010. (ENG.). 316p. 19.00 *(978-0-14-302615-0(1)*, Penguin Global) Penguin Group (USA) Inc.

Press, Ammonite, ed. 100 Years of Boxing. 2010. (ENG., Illus.). 300p. pap. 19.95 *(978-1-906672-55-3(5)*, Ammonite Pr.) AE Pubns. GBR. Dist: BookMasters Distribution Services (BDS).

Price, Malcolm & Richards, Steve. Street Warrior. (Illus.). 288p. 32.50 *(978-1-904034-63-6(2))* Blake, John Publishing, Ltd. GBR. Dist: Trafalgar Square Publishing.

Rafiq, Fiaz. Muhammad Ali: Conversations. 2011. 352p. 24.95 *(978-0-9562586-4-9(6))* Health 'n' Life Publishing GBR. Dist: Midpoint Trade Bks., Inc.

Ribalow, Harold U. Fighter from Whitechapel: The Story of Daniel Mendoza. 2011. 160p. 41.95 ***(978-1-258-07324-4(2))*** Literary Licensing, LLC.

Robert, Edwards. Henry Cooper - Authorised. 2012. (ENG., Illus.). 288p. 14.95 ***(978-1-84358-946-4(X))*** Blake, John Publishing, Ltd. GBR. Dist: Independent Pubs. Group.

Roberts, James B. & Skutt, Alexander G. The Boxing Register: International Boxing Hall of Fame Official Record Book. 5th ed. 2011. (ENG., Illus.). 944p. (Orig.). pap. 29.95 *(978-1-59013-499-3(0))* McBooks Pr., Inc.

Roberts, Randy. Joe Louis: Hard Times Man. 2012. (ENG., Illus.). 328p. pap. 17.50 *(978-0-300-17763-3(1))* Yale Univ. Pr.

Robinson, Sugar Ray. Sugar Ray. 31.95 *(978-0-8488-1537-0(8))* Amereon LTD.

Rodriguez, Robert G. The Regulation of Boxing: A History & Comparative Analysis of Policies among American States. 2009. (ENG., Illus.). 233p. pap. 35.00 *(978-0-7864-3862-4(2))* McFarland & Co., Inc. Pubs.

Ross, Ron. Untitled on Boxer Al Davis & the Rise & Fall of Murder Inc. Date not set. pap. *(978-0-312-30639-7(3)*, St. Martin's Paperbacks) St. Martin's Pr.

—Untitled On Boxer Al Davis & The Rise & Fall Of Murder Inc. Date not set. mass mkt. *(978-0-312-98538-7(X)*, St. Martin's Paperbacks) St. Martin's Pr.

Runstedtler, Theresa. Jack Johnson, Rebel Sojourner: Boxing in the Shadow of the Global Color Line. 2012. (American Crossroads Ser.). (ENG., Illus.). 376p. 34.95 ***(978-0-520-27160-9(2))*** Univ. of California Pr.

Ruth, Babe. Home Run King - How Pep Pindar Won Title. 20.95 *(978-0-8488-1586-8(6))* Amereon LTD.

Samuels, Charles. The Magnificent Rube: The Life & Gaudy Times of Tex Rickard. 2011. 320p. 50.95 ***(978-1-258-04957-7(0))*** Literary Licensing, LLC.

Schulberg, Budd. Ringside: A Treasury of Boxing Reportage. (ENG., Illus.). 2007. 384p. per. 16.95 *(978-1-56663-749-7(X))* 2006. 368p. 27.50 *(978-1-56663-707-7(4))* Dee, Ivan R. Pub.

The check digit for ISBN-10 appears in parentheses after the full ISBN-13

Shaw, Roy. Pretty Boy. 2006. (ENG., Illus.). 224p. per. 14.99 *(978-1-85782-551-0(9))* Blake, John Publishing, Ltd. GBR. Dist: Independent Pubs. Group.

Shaw, Roy & Kray, Kate. Pretty Boy. 2007. (Illus.). 218p. 24.95 *(978-1-84454-289-5(0))* Blake, John Publishing, Ltd. GBR. Dist: Independent Pubs. Group.

—Roy Shaw Unleashed. (Illus.). 288p. 32.50 *(978-1-904034-35-3(7))* Blake, John Publishing, Ltd. GBR. Dist: Trafalgar Square Publishing.

Shropshire, Kenneth. Being Sugar Ray: The Life of Sugar Ray Robinson, America's Greatest Boxer & the First Celebrity Athlete. 2008. (ENG., Illus.). 272p. per. 16.95 *(978-0-465-07804-2(4),* Basic Civitas Bks.) Basic Bks.

Springer, Steve & Chavez, Blake. Hard Luck: The Triumph & Tragedy of Irish Jerry Quarry. 2011. (ENG., Illus.). 304p. 24.95 *(978-1-59921-996-7(4),* Lyons Pr.) Globe Pequot Pr., The.

Stead, Peter & Williams, Gareth, eds. Wales & Its Boxers: The Fighting Tradition. 2009. (Illus.). 192p. 25.00 *(978-0-7083-1915-4(7))* Univ. of Wales Pr. GBR. Dist: Chicago Distribution Ctr.

Stratton, W. K. Boxing Shadows. 2009. (ENG., Illus.). 195p. 24.95 *(978-0-292-72129-6(3))* Univ. of Texas Pr.

—Floyd Patterson: The Fighting Life of Boxing's Invisible Champion. 2012. (ENG., Illus.). 288p. 25.00 *(978-0-15-101430-9(2))* Houghton Mifflin Harcourt Trade & Reference Pubs.

Thomas, Anthony & McLean, Lenny. The Guv'nor: Through the Eyes of Others. 2007. (ENG., Illus.). 288p. per. 15.95 *(978-1-84454-475-2(3))* Blake, John Publishing, Ltd. GBR. Dist: Independent Pubs. Group.

Tinti, Gabriele, ed. New York Shots: A Boxing Tale. 2012. (ENG., Illus.). 52p. 30.00 ***(978-88-422-1982-8(7))*** Allemandi, Umberto & Co. GBR. Dist: National Bk. Network.

Torres, Jose & Sugar, Bert Randolph. Sting Like a Bee: The Muhammad Ali Story. 2009. (ENG., Illus.). 224p. pap. 17.95 *(978-0-8032-2056-0(1),* Bison Bks.) Univ. of Nebraska Pr.

Torrey, Joey. Bamboozled: The Joey Torrey Story. Biel, Joe, ed. 2008. (Illus.). 64p. 5.00 *(978-1-934620-31-1(9))* Microcosm Publishing.

Tunney, Jay R. The Prizefighter & the Playwright: Gene Tunney & George Bernard Shaw. 2010. (ENG., Illus.). 288p. 35.00 *(978-1-55407-641-3(2))* Firefly Bks., Ltd.

Venezia, Carol Huebner. Boxers, 1 vol. 2008. (ENG & GER., Illus.). 72p. pap. 30.00 *(978-3-86521-219-1(0))* Steidl, Gerhard Druckerei und Verlag DEU. Dist: Innovative Logistics.

Wacquant, Loic. Body & Soul: Notebooks of an Apprentice Boxer. 2006. (ENG., Illus.). 288p. per. 20.00 *(978-0-19-530562-3(0))* Oxford Univ. Pr., Inc.

Waltzer, Jim. The Battle of the Century: Dempsey, Carpentier, & the Birth of Modern Promotion, 1 vol. 2011. (Illus.). 238p. 44.95 *(978-0-313-38244-4(1),* A2664C) Greenwood Publishing Group, Inc.

—The Battle of the Century: Dempsey, Carpentier, & the Birth of Modern Promotion. 2011. x, 238p. E-Book *(978-0-313-38245-1(X),* Praeger Pubs.) Greenwood Publishing Group, Inc.

Ward, Micky & Layden, Joe. A Warrior's Heart: The True Story of Life Before & Beyond the Fighter. 2012. (ENG., Illus.). 304p. (gr. 12). 25.95 ***(978-0-425-24755-6(4),*** Berkley Hardcover) Penguin Group (USA) Inc.

Welch, Ian. Greatest Moments of Boxing. 2008. (Greatest Moments Ser.). (ENG., Illus.). 96p. *(978-1-905229-43-6(0),* 1906229430) G2 Entertainment Ltd.

Welch, Ian & Prisk, Clyde. The A-Z of Boxing: A Boxing A to Z. 2009. (Little Book Ser.). (ENG., Illus.). 128p. *(978-1-906635-30-5(7),* 1906635307) G2 Entertainment Ltd.

White, Jaclyn Weldon. The Greatest Champion That Never Was: The Life of W. L. "Young" Stribling. 2011. 320p. 30.00 *(978-0-88146-252-4(7))* Mercer Univ. Pr.

White, Richard. Wrestlers in History: Real People & Legends. 2010. 256p. pap. 16.00 *(978-1-935271-45-1(8))* Published by Westview, Inc.

Winters, Mark. Axis of Greatness: Muhammad Ali, Sugar Ray Leonard & Angelo Dundee. 2008. (ENG., Illus.). 240p. 27.95 *(978-1-906217-60-0(2))* Aurum Pr., Ltd. GBR. Dist: Independent Pubs. Group.

Wood, Peter Weston. Confessions of a Fighter: Battling Through the New York Golden Gloves. 2007. (Golden Gloves Classic Bks.). 213p. per. 19.95 *(978-0-9789683-1-1(X))* Ringside Bks.

Wright, John D. The Terror of Terre Haute: Bud Taylor & The 1920s. 2008. 332p. pap. 20.00 *(978-1-59858-761-6(7))* Dog Ear Publishing, LLC.

Yates, Lew & O'Mahoney, Bernard. Wild Thing: The True Story of Britain's One & Only Guvnor. 2007. (ENG., Illus.). 272p. pap. 22.00 *(978-1-84596-269-2(9))* Mainstream Publishing Co., Ltd. GBR. Dist: Independent Pubs. Group.

—Wild Thing: The True Story of Britain's Rightful Guv'nor. 2009. (ENG., Illus.). 272p. pap. 15.95 *(978-1-84596-352-1(0))* Mainstream Publishing Co., Ltd. GBR. Dist: Independent Pubs. Group.

Youmans, Gary. The Onion Picker: Carmen Basilio & Boxing in The 1950s. 2007. (Illus.). 214p. 24.95 *(978-0-8156-8175-5(5))* Syracuse Univ. Pr.

Zirin, Dave. Muhammad Ali Handbook. 2007. (Handbook Ser.). 432p. *(978-1-84072-684-8(9))* M Q Pubns.

—Muhammad Ali Handbook. 2007. (Illus.). 431p. 25.00 *(978-1-84601-155-9(8))* M Q Pubns. GBR. Dist: Ingram Pub. Services.

BOXES

see also Bandboxes; Matchboxes

Birkey, Steve. Making Puzzleboxes Using a Bandsaw. 2009. (Illus.). 95p. 61.99 *(978-1-4415-4267-0(1))* Xlibris Corp.

Bowers, Bill. Turning Boxes with Friction-Fitted Lids. 2008. (Illus.). 64p. pap. 14.99 *(978-0-7643-3027-8(6))* Schiffer Publishing, Ltd.

Cholmeley-Jones, Edwina. Bandboxes: Tips, Tools, & Techniques for Learning the Craft. 2009. (Heritage Crafts Ser.). (ENG., Illus.). 132p. 24.95 *(978-0-8117-0503-5(X))* Stackpole Bks.

Garrofe, Josep M. Antique Packaging. 2008. (Illus.). 391p. 29.95 *(978-1-58423-318-3(4))* Gingko Pr., Inc.

Hollander, Tom & Hollander, Cindy. Constructing & Covering Boxes. 2009. (Illus.). 64p. pap. 14.99 *(978-0-7643-3158-9(2))* Schiffer Publishing, Ltd.

Johnston, Michael. Making Stained Glass Boxes. 2009. (ENG., Illus.). 144p. pap. 21.95 *(978-0-8117-3594-0(X))* Stackpole Bks.

Léonforte, Pierre, et al. Louis Vuitton: 100 Legendary Trunks. 2010. (ENG., Illus.). 496p. 125.00 *(978-0-8109-8247-5(1))* Abrams.

MacKay, Gary. Box-Making Projects for the Scroll Saw: 30 Woodworking Projects That Are Surprisingly Easy to Make. 2006. (ENG., Illus.). 144p. pap. 17.95 *(978-1-56523-294-5(1))* Fox Chapel Publishing Co., Inc.

McCreight, Tim. Boxes & Lockets: Metalsmithing Techniques. (Illus.). 144p. *(978-90-5703-682-8(7))* Craftsman House, B V I VGB. Dist: Gordon & Breach Publishing Group.

Obrien, Karen & Soucy, Joe, Joe. Lunch Boxes Field Guide. 2008. (ENG.). 512p. pap. 12.99 *(978-0-89689-726-7(5))* Krause Pubns.

Pretl, Julia S. Julia Pretl's Big Book of Beadwork: 32 Projects for Adventurous Beaders. 2010. (ENG., Illus.). 320p. pap. 24.99 *(978-1-58923-527-4(4),* 1589235274) Quayside.

—Little Bead Boxes: 12 Miniature Boxes Built with Beads. 2006. (ENG., Illus.). 112p. pap. 21.95 *(978-1-58923-291-4(7),* 1589232917) Quayside.

Purdy, Strother. Traditional Box Projects. 2010. (ENG., Illus.). 160p. pap. 24.95 *(978-1-60085-110-0(X))* Taunton Pr., Inc.

Webster, Leslie. The Franks Casket. 2012. (Objects in Focus Ser.). (ENG., Illus.). 64p. (C). pap. 10.00 *(978-0-7141-2818-4(X))* British Museum Pr. GBR. Dist: Brown, David Bk. Co., The.

BOXING

Abbas, Ali. 2008. (FRE.). 128p. *(978-2-916355-23-6(5))* Editions Intervalles.

Anderson, Jack. The Legality of Boxing. 2010. 240p. pap. 39.95 *(978-0-415-57436-5(5))* Routledge.

—The Legality of Boxing: A Punch Drunk Love? 2007. 216p. 150.00 *(978-0-415-42932-0(3),* Routledge) Taylor & Francis Group GBR. Dist: Taylor & Francis Group.

Battling Siki: A Tale of Ring Fixes, Race, & Murder in The 1920s. 2008. 360p. pap. 19.95 *(978-1-55728-868-2(7))* Univ. of Arkansas Pr.

Blower, Gary. Boxing: Training, Skills & Techniques. 2006. (ENG., Illus.). 192p. pap. 24.95 *(978-1-86126-902-7(1))* Crowood Pr., Ltd. GBR. Dist: Independent Pubs. Group.

Bryant, Vickie & Hess, Camille. Top O' Hill Terrace. 2012. (Images of America Ser.). (ENG., Illus.). 128p. pap. 21.99 ***(978-0-7385-8527-7(0))*** Arcadia Publishing.

Bybee, Frank. The Worley Warrior. 2011. 132p. 23.99 ***(978-1-4634-2080-2(3))*** AuthorHouse.

Callis, Tracy G. & Johnston, Chuck. Boxing in the Los Angeles Area 1880-2005. 2008. (Illus.). 162p. pap. 29.95 *(978-0-615-19933-7(X))* Pastime Memorabilia.

Carter, Rubin. The Sixteenth Round: From Number 1 Contender to Number 45472. 2011. (ENG.). 368p. pap. 16.95 *(978-1-56976-567-8(7),* Hill, Lawrence Bks.) Chicago Review Pr., Inc.

Chaves, Ramiro, et al, photos by. Victor Mendiola & Ramiro Chaves: Last Heroes of the Peninsula. 2010. (ENG., Illus.). 96p. 29.95 *(978-84-92480-71-5(8))* RM Verlag, S.L. ESP. Dist: D.A.P./Distributed Art Pubs.

Clifton, Guy. Dempsey in Nevada. 2007. (Illus.). 216p. 24.95 *(978-0-930083-33-5(4))* Bacon, Jack & Co.

Corbett, James J. Scientific Boxing: The Deluxe Edition. 2008. 132p. pap. 19.95 *(978-0-9737698-9-0(0))* Promethean Pr.

Curtis, Ronald J. Boxing Champions of the Heavyweight Division 1882-2010. 2010. 302p. 29.99 *(978-1-4535-1467-2(8));* pap. 19.99 *(978-1-4535-1466-5(X))* Xlibris Corp.

Cushman, Tom. Muhammad Ali & the Greatest Heavyweight Generation. 2009. 208p. 35.00 *(978-0-9822489-3-5(8));* pap. 19.00 *(978-0-9822489-2-8(X))* Southeast Missouri State Univ. Pr.

Davies, John. Slings & Arrows. 2011. 368p. pap. ***(978-1-907611-56-8(8))*** Paragon Publishing, Rothersthorpe.

Dempsey, Jack & Stearns, Myron M. Round by Round: An Autobiography. 2011. 344p. 51.95 ***(978-1-258-00810-9(6))*** Literary Licensing, LLC.

Driscoll, Jim. Out-Fighting or Long-Range Boxing: The Deluxe Edition. 2008. 96p. pap. 18.95 *(978-0-9737698-4-5(X))* Promethean Pr.

—Ringcraft: The Deluxe Edition. 2008. 116p. pap. 19.95 *(978-0-9810202-1-1(6))* Promethean Pr.

—The Straight Left & How to Cultivate It: The Deluxe Edition. 2008. 112p. pap. 19.95 *(978-0-9810202-0-4(8))* Promethean Pr.

—The Text Book of Boxing. 2008. 104p. pap. 19.95 *(978-0-9737698-2-1(3))* Promethean Pr.

Dumas, Andy & Dumas, Jamie. Knockout Fitness: Boxing Workouts to Get You in the Best Shape of Your Life. 2009. (ENG., Illus.). 192p. pap. 14.95 *(978-1-60239-299-1(4),* 239299) Skyhorse Publishing Co., Inc.

Dundee, Angelo, et al. My View from the Corner: A Life in Boxing. 2009. (ENG., Illus.). 336p. pap. 21.00 *(978-0-07-162847-1(9),* 0071628479) McGraw-Hill Cos., The.

Dunn, Katherine. One Ring Circus: Dispatches from the World of Boxing. 2009. (ENG.). 248p. pap. 16.95 *(978-0-9801394-2-6(2))* Schaffner Pr., Inc.

Edwards, William. Art of Boxing & Science of Self-Defense: Together with A Manual of Training. 2011. 112p. 39.95 ***(978-1-258-01894-8(2))*** Literary Licensing, LLC.

Erenberg, Lewis A. The Greatest Fight of Our Generation: Louis vs. Schmeling. 2007. (ENG., Illus.). 288p. per. 17.95 *(978-0-19-531999-6(0))* Oxford Univ. Pr., Inc.

Farrell, Bill. Cradle of Champions: 80 Years of New York Daily News Golden Gloves. 2007. (Illus.). 183p. 24.95 *(978-1-59670-205-9(2))* Sports Publishing, LLC.

Finegan, Billy. Boxing for Beginners: A Guide to Competition & Fitness. 2008. (ENG., Illus.). 192p. pap. 14.99 *(978-1-55870-850-1(2),* Betterway Bks.) F&W Media, Inc.

Fleischer, Nat. Gentleman Jim: The Story of James J. Corbett. 2011. 132p. 40.95 ***(978-1-258-02564-9(7))*** Literary Licensing, LLC.

—Jack Dempsey: The Idol of Fistiana. 2011. 234p. 46.95 ***(978-1-258-00366-1(X))*** Literary Licensing, LLC.

Forward by Donovan Craig, Scott Shetler. Kettlebell Conditioning for MMA & Other Fight Sports. 2010. 48p. pap. 34.95 *(978-0-557-53662-7(6))* Lulu Enterprises Inc.

Goldman, Herbert G. Boxing: A Worldwide Record of Bouts & Boxers, 4 vols. 2012. (ENG., Illus.). 1752p. pap. 195.00 *(978-0-7864-6054-0(7))* McFarland & Co., Inc. Pubs.

Gotay Ma Mps, Al. Boxing Basics: The Techniques & Knowledge Needed to Excel in the Sport of Boxing. 2008. (Illus.). 181p. pap. 24.95 *(978-1-4327-2506-8(6))* Outskirts Pr., Inc.

Grant, J. E. Power Punches. 2009. 242p. pap. 15.18 *(978-0-557-00235-1(4))* Lulu Enterprises Inc.

Halloran, Bob. Irish Thunder: The Hard Life & Times of Micky Ward. (ENG.). 296p. 2010. pap. 14.95 *(978-1-59921-907-3(7))* 2007. (Illus.). 24.95 *(978-1-59921-220-3(X))* Globe Pequot Pr., The. (Lyons Pr.).

Hatmaker, Mark. Boxer's Book of Conditioning & Drilling. 2011. (ENG., Illus.). 192p. pap. 12.95 *(978-1-935937-28-9(6))* Tracks Publishing.

—No Holds Barred Fighting: The Ultimate Guide to Conditioning - Elite Exercises & Training for NHB Competition & Total Fitness. 2007. (No Holds Barred Fighting Ser.). (ENG.). 192p. pap. 12.95 *(978-1-884654-29-9(0))* Tracks Publishing.

Hauser, Thomas. Boxing Is ... Reflections on the Sweet Science. 2010. (ENG.). 335p. pap. 22.50 *(978-1-55728-942-1(5))* Univ. of Arkansas Pr.

—The Boxing Scene. 2008. (Sporting Ser.). (ENG.). 256p. 78.50 *(978-1-59213-976-7(0));* pap. 25.95 *(978-1-59213-977-4(9))* Temple Univ. Pr.

—The Greatest Sport of All: An Inside Look at Another Year in Boxing. 2007. 303p. per. 22.50 *(978-1-55728-859-2(3))* Univ. of Arkansas Pr.

—An Unforgiving Sport: An Inside Look at Another Year in Boxing. 2009. (ENG.). 328p. pap. 22.50 *(978-1-55728-910-0(7))* Univ. of Arkansas Pr.

Hauser, Thomas. Winks & Daggers: An Inside Look at Another Year in Boxing. 2011. 292p. pap. 24.95 ***(978-1-55728-970-4(0))*** Univ. of Arkansas Pr.

Hawkes, Dave. A Builder's Life. 2009. 68p. pap. 10.49 *(978-1-4389-5005-1(5))* AuthorHouse.

Heiskanen, Benita. The Urban Geography of Boxing: Race, Class, & Gender in the Ring. 2012. (Routledge Research in Sport, Culture & Society Ser.). (ENG.). 210p. (C). 125.00 ***(978-0-415-50226-9(8))*** Routledge.

Hugman, Barry J. The British Boxing Board of Control Boxing Yearbook 2010. 2010. (ENG., Illus.). 320p. 36.95 *(978-1-84596-486-3(1))* Mainstream Publishing Co., Ltd. GBR. Dist: Independent Pubs. Group.

Hugman, Barry J., ed. The British Boxing Board of Control Boxing Yearbook 2009. anniv. ed. 2008. (ENG., Illus.). 320p. pap. 37.95 *(978-1-84596-325-5(3))* Mainstream Publishing Co., Ltd. GBR. Dist: Independent Pubs. Group.

J.J. Johnston And Nick Beck. Baby Face & Pop. 2011. 184p. 29.99 ***(978-1-4568-4337-3(0));*** pap. 19.99 ***(978-1-4568-4336-6(2))*** Xlibris Corp.

Job, Bertram. Boxing. 2006. (Illus.). 420p. 39.95 *(978-3-89985-033-8(5))* Feierabend Verlag OHG DEU. Dist: Perseus-PGW.

Jordan, Barry D. & Herrera, Joseph E., eds. Medical Aspects of Boxing. 2nd ed. 2010. (Musculoskeletal Medicine Ser.). 450p. 165.00 *(978-1-60327-230-8(5))* Humana Pr.

Kimball, George. Manly Art: They Can Run - But They Can't Hide. 2011. (ENG.). 384p. 24.95 *(978-1-59013-571-6(7))* McBooks Pr., Inc.

Kimball, George & Schulian, John, eds. At the Fights: American Writers on Boxing. 2011. (ENG.). 560p. (gr. 12). 35.00 *(978-1-59853-092-6(5))* Library of America, The.

Kluck, Ted A. Facing Tyson: Fifteen Fighters, Fifteen Stories. 2006. (ENG., Illus.). 272p. 22.95 *(978-1-59228-919-6(3),* Lyons Pr.) Globe Pequot Pr., The.

Lachica, Alan & Werner, Doug. Boxing's Ten Commandments: Essential Training for the Sweet Science. 2007. (ENG., Illus.). 192p. per. 12.95 *(978-1-884654-28-2(2))* Tracks Publishing.

Lawton, James. Mission Impossible: How Lennox Lewis Unified the World Heavyweight Title. (Illus.). 256p. 35.00 *(978-1-84018-272-9(5))* Mainstream Publishing Co., Ltd. GBR. Dist: Trafalgar Square Publishing.

Layden, Joe. The Last Great Fight: The Extraordinary Tale of Two Men & How One Fight Changed Their Lives Forever. 2008. (ENG.). 320p. pap. 16.99 *(978-0-312-35331-5(6),* St. Martin's Griffin) St. Martin's Pr.

Leonard, Sugar Ray & Arkush, Michael. The Big Fight: My Life in & Out of the Ring. (ENG., Illus.). 320p. (gr. 12). 2012. pap. 16.00 ***(978-0-452-29804-0(0),*** Plume) 2011. 26.95 *(978-0-670-02272-4(1),* Viking Adult) Penguin Group (USA) Inc.

Liebling, A. J. A. J. Liebling: The Sweet Science & Other Writings. Hamill, Pete, ed. 2008. (ENG.). 1050p. (gr. 12). 40.00 *(978-1-59853-040-7(2))* Library of America, The.

Lindholm, David & Karlsson, Ulf. Bare-Knuckle Boxer's Companion: Learning How to Hit Hard & Train Tough from the Early Boxing Masters. 2009. (Illus.). 136p. pap. 20.00 *(978-1-58160-700-0(8))* Paladin Pr.

Lynch, Bohun. Knuckles & Gloves. 2006. 280p. pap. 27.95 *(978-1-104-09641-0(2))* Kessinger Publishing, LLC.

—Knuckles & Gloves. 2007. (Illus.). 217p. per. 35.00 *(978-1-58160-590-7(0))* Paladin Pr.

Lynch, Kevin. Octagon. deluxe ed. 2007. 392p. *(978-1-57687-416-5(8),* powerHouse Bks.) powerHouse Cultural Entertainment, Inc.

MacDougall, Paul. Distinction Earned: Cape Breton's Boxing Legends, 1946-1970, 1 vol. 2010. 178p. pap. ***(978-1-897009-48-2(8))*** Cape Breton Univ. Pr.

McKenzie, Clinton & Lissenden, Hilary. Boxing Fitness. 2011. (ENG., Illus.). 192p. pap. 25.95 *(978-1-4081-3315-6(6))* A & C Black GBR. Dist: Macmillan.

—Boxing for Fitness: Safe & Fun Workouts to Get You Fighting Fit. 2011. (ENG.). 180p. pap. 24.95 *(978-1-55407-906-3(3))* Firefly Bks., Ltd.

McLennan, Wayne. Tent Boxing: An Australian Journey. 2008. (ENG.). 256p. pap. 24.95 *(978-1-86207-854-3(8))* Granta Bks. GBR. Dist: Independent Pubs. Group.

Mendiola, Victor, et al. Los últimos Héroes de la Península. 2009. (SPA., Illus.). 95p. *(978-607-7515-39-5(6));* *(978-84-92480-69-2(6))* R.M. Editorial, S.A. de C.V.

Merz, Mischa. The Sweetest Thing: A Boxer's Memoir. 2011. (ENG., Illus.). 304p. pap. 18.95 *(978-1-58322-928-6(0))* Seven Stories Pr.

Mora, Manuel A. Stanley Ketchel: A Life of Triumph & Prophecy. 2010. 232p. pap. 15.99 *(978-1-4343-2370-5(6))* AuthorHouse.

Myler, Thomas. The Sweet Science Goes Sour: How Scandal Brought Boxing to Its Knees. 2006. (ENG., Illus.). 272p. pap. 16.00 *(978-1-55365-233-5(9),* Greystone Bks.) D&M Pubs. Inc. CAN. Dist: Perseus-PGW.

Nelson, Battling. Life, Battles & Career of Battling Nelson. Villadsen, Rene, ed. 2011. 226p. pap. 26.90 ***(978-87-7114-265-5(7))*** Bks. on Demand.

North, Michael. At the Apron: A Night at the Fights. 2011. 124p. 23.95 ***(978-1-4620-3669-1(4));*** pap. 13.95 ***(978-1-4620-3670-7(8))*** iUniverse, Inc.

Oates, Joyce Carol. On Boxing. 2006. (P. S. Ser.). (ENG., Illus.). 304p. per. 14.99 *(978-0-06-087450-6(3),* HarperPerennial) HarperCollins Pubs.

Oates, Ralph. The Ultimate Boxing Quiz Book: 1,200 Questions on Great Boxing HIST. 2009. 150p. 19.95 *(978-1-905358-64-8(8))* Apex Publishing Ltd., Essex GBR. Dist: APG Sales & Distribution Services.

Oliver, Ian. Boxing Fitness. 2nd rev. ed. 2007. (Illus.). 160p. pap. *(978-0-9545759-8-4(9))* Snowbooks Ltd.

—Punch Your Way to Fitness: How to use focus pads & punchbags to achieve your best ever fitness Level. (Illus.). 128p. *(978-1-905005-31-4(8))* Snowbooks Ltd.

Onello, R. Michael. Boxing: Advanced Tactics & Strategies. 2007. (Illus.). 140p. per. 14.95 *(978-1-880336-95-3(2))* Turtle Pr. Corp.

Ortiz, Johnny. My Life among the Icons: A Fascinating Memoir of a Raconteur Whose Life Intersected with the Giants of Sports & the Glamour of Hollywood. 2011. 480p. pap. 22.76 ***(978-1-4634-1904-2(X));*** 30.79 ***(978-1-4634-1903-5(1))*** AuthorHouse.

Patterson, Floyd. The International Boxing Hall of Fame's Basic Boxing Skills: A Step-by-Step Illustrated Introduction to the Sweet Science. 2007. (Illus.). 104p. per. 14.95 *(978-1-60239-020-1(7))* Skyhorse Publishing Co., Inc.

Reyna, Pedro. The Last Boxing Fan. 2010. 160p. pap. 14.95 *(978-0-557-42329-3(5))* Lulu Enterprises Inc.

Riem, Andreas & Kleymann, Michael. Fitness Boxing. 2008. (Illus.). 120p. pap. 17.95 *(978-1-84126-251-2(X))* Meyer & Meyer Sport, Ltd. GBR. Dist: Cardinal Pubs. Group.

Roach, Freddie. It May End up Killing You: Hard Fought Lessons from a Life in the Ring. 2012. (ENG., Illus.). 320p. 24.95 *(978-1-61608-030-3(2),* 608030) Skyhorse Publishing Co., Inc.

Roca, Hector & Silverglade, Bruce. The Gleason's Gym Total Body Boxing Workout for Women: A 4-Week Head-to-Toe Makeover. 2007. (ENG., Illus.). 256p. pap. 16.99 *(978-0-7432-8658-6(X),* Touchstone) Touchstone.

Rodriguez, Robert G. The Regulation of Boxing: A History & Comparative Analysis of Policies among American States. 2009. (ENG., Illus.). 233p. pap. 35.00 *(978-0-7864-3862-4(2))* McFarland & Co., Inc. Pubs.

Rotella, Carlo. Playing in Time: Essays, Profiles, & Other True Stories. 2012. (Illus.). 288p. 27.50 ***(978-0-226-72309-1(5))*** Univ. of Chicago Pr.

Santolquito, Joe & Gordon, Robert. Izzy: A Tale of Family, Philly, & the Fight Against All Odds. 2006. 200p. 19.95 *(978-1-60008-007-4(3),* Rooftop Publishing) AuthorHouse.

Schinke, Robert J. The Mental Edge in Boxing. 2011. (Series: Sports & Athletics Preparation, Performance, & Psychology Ser.). 166p. 140.00 *(978-1-61324-296-4(4))* Nova Science Pubs., Inc.

Scott, David. The Art & Aesthetics of Boxing. 2009. (ENG., Illus.). 224p. 40.00 *(978-0-8032-1386-9(7))* Univ. of Nebraska Pr.

Scurti, Richard. Boxing's, Greatest Interviews!! Boxing Biggest Star's Speak! Ray Leonard to Oscar de la Hoya to Sylvester Stallone! 2008. 152p. pap. 14.95 *(978-0-595-47947-4(2))* iUniverse, Inc.

Singh, M. Ed. The Art of Western Tai Chi Ch'Uan: The Supreme Ultimate & Sweet Science of Boxing with 13 Limbs. 2010. 268p. 26.95 *(978-1-60860-920-8(0),* Eloquent Bks.) AEG Literary Publishing Services, Inc.

Sondhi, Rakesh. Advanced Boxing: Training, Skills & Techniques. 2012. (ENG., Illus.). 192p. pap. 24.95 ***(978-1-84797-297-2(7))*** Crowood Pr., Ltd. GBR. Dist: Independent Pubs. Group.

Sterritt, Mike. The Great Underrated Boxers. 2011. 52p. pap. 9.95 *(978-1-4502-8912-2(6))* Universe Inc.

B

Sugar, Bert Randolph & Atlas, Teddy. The Ultimate Book of Boxing Lists. 2011. (ENG., Illus.). 240p. pap. 14.95 *(978-0-7624-4013-9(9))* Running Pr. Bk. Pubs.

Taschen, Benedikt. Greatest of All Time: A Tribute to Muhammad Ali. 2010. (Go Ser.). (ENG., Illus.). 652p. 150.00 *(978-3-8365-2067-6(2))* TASCHEN DEU. Dist: Ingram Pub. Services.

Tinti, Gabriele, ed. New York Shots: A Boxing Tale. 2012. (ENG., Illus.). 52p. 30.00 ***(978-88-422-1982-8(7))*** Allemandi, Umberto & Co. GBR. Dist: National Bk. Network.

Varlotta, Gerard P. & Jordan, Barry D. Medical Issues in Boxing, an Issue of Clinics in Sports Medicine. 2009. (Clinics: Orthopedics Ser.: 28-4). (ENG.). 99.00 *(978-1-4377-1276-6(2),* Saunders) Elsevier - Health Sciences Div.

Vidal, Guillermo. Boxing for Cuba: An Immigrant's Story of Despair, Endurance & Redemption. 2007. (ENG.). 240p. pap. 19.95 *(978-0-9789456-0-2(3),* Ghost Road Pr.) Ghost Road Publishing Group, Inc.

Waring, Rob. Making a Thai Boxing Champion (US) 2008. (ENG.). 24p. (C). pap. 10.95 *(978-1-4240-4442-9(1))* Cengage Heinle.

Warnick, Jason E. & Martin, W. Daniel, eds. Advancements in the Scientific Study of Combative Sports. 2010. (Sports & Athletics Preparation, Performance, & Psychology Ser.). (Illus.). 226p. 89.00 *(978-1-60876-733-5(7))* Nova Science Pubs., Inc.

Welch, Ian & Prisk, Clyde. The A-Z of Boxing: A Boxing A to Z. 2009. (Little Book Ser.). (ENG., Illus.). 128p. *(978-1-906635-30-5(7),* 1906635307) G2 Entertainment Ltd.

Wellings, Steve. Irish Boxing Review: 2011 Edition. 2011. 290p. pap. 18.95 ***(978-1-4467-8990-2(X))*** Lulu Enterprises Inc.

Whatley, Anthony. Ghosts of the Fisher. 2007. (Illus.). 132p. per. 13.50 *(978-1-84426-443-8(2))* Upfront Publishing Ltd. GBR. Dist: Printondemand-worldwide.com.

White, John, Jr. Boxing Miscellany. 2010. (ENG.). 160p. 18.95 *(978-1-84732-378-1(2))* Carlton Bks., Ltd. GBR. Dist: Independent Pubs. Group.

Winters, Mark. Axis of Greatness: Muhammad Ali, Sugar Ray Leonard & Angelo Dundee. 2008. (ENG., Illus.). 240p. 27.95 *(978-1-906217-60-0(2))* Aurum Pr., Ltd. GBR. Dist: Independent Pubs. Group.

Wood, Peter Weston. A Clenched Fist: The Making of a Golden Gloves Champion. 2007. 232p. per. 19.95 *(978-0-9789683-0-4(1))* Ringside Bks.

BOXING—HISTORY

Arkush, Michael. The Fight of the Century: Ali vs. Frazier March 8 1971. 2007. (ENG., Illus.). 272p. 25.95 *(978-0-470-05642-4(8),* Wiley) Wiley, John & Sons, Inc.

Atlas, Teddy & Alson, Peter. Atlas: From the Streets to the Ring - A Son's Struggle to Become a Man. 2007. (ENG., Illus.). 304p. pap. 13.99 *(978-0-06-054241-2(1),* Harper Paperbacks) HarperCollins Pubs.

Aycock, Colleen & Scott, Mark, eds. The First Black Boxing Champions: Essays on Fighters of the 1800s to The 1920s. 2011. (ENG., Illus.). 302p. 45.00 *(978-0-7864-4991-0(8))* McFarland & Co., Inc. Pubs.

Baker, Mark Allen. Title Town, USA: Boxing in Canastota, New York. 2010. (ENG., Illus.). 160p. pap. 19.99 *(978-1-59629-769-2(7))* History Pr., The.

Boddy, Kasia. Boxing: A Cultural History. (ENG., Illus.). 480p. 2009. pap. 29.95 *(978-1-86189-411-3(2))* 2008. 35.00 *(978-1-86189-369-7(8))* Reaktion Bks., Ltd. GBR. Dist: Chicago Distribution Ctr.

Bodner, Allen. When Boxing Was a Jewish Sport. 2011. (Excelsior Editions Ser.). (Illus.). 246p. pap. 24.95 *(978-1-4384-3608-1(4))* State Univ. of New York Pr.

Brooke-Ball, Peter, et al. The Boxing Album: an Illustrated History: The complete story of boxing from the pugilists of the classical amphitheatre to the heroes of Today. 2012. (ENG., Illus.). 264p. pap. 16.99 ***(978-1-78019-058-7(1))*** Anness Publishing GBR. Dist: National Bk. Network.

Bryar, Thomas A. The Greatest Muhammad Ali Quiz Book: Hundreds of Questions about Muhammad Ali, His Life, His Times & His Opponents. 2011. 224p. pap. 17.09 ***(978-1-4389-7591-7(0))*** AuthorHouse.

Clement, Ben. Giants on My Shoulders/As Told by Ali Muhammad; Aka Frank Steele, the Man of Steel. 2009. 296p. 27.75 *(978-1-60693-960-4(2),* Strategic Bk. Publishing) AEG Literary Publishing Services, Inc.

Curtin, Sean. Chicago Amateur Boxing. 2006. (Images of Sports Ser.). (ENG., Illus.). 128p. per. 19.99 *(978-0-7385-4138-9(9))* Arcadia Publishing.

Dahlberg, Tim. Fight Town: Las Vegas — the Boxing Capital of the World. 2007. (Illus.). 228p. pap. 24.95 *(978-1-932173-66-6(8))* Stephens Pr. LLC.

Evans, Gavin. Kings of the Ring: The History of Heavyweight Boxing. 2008. (Illus.). 227p. pap. 17.95 *(978-0-297-85345-9(7),* Weidenfeld & Nicolson) Orion Publishing Group, Ltd. GBR. Dist: Sterling Publishing Co., Inc.

Finger, David E. Rocky Lives! Heavyweight Boxing Upsets of The 1990s. 2006. (Illus.). 352p. per. 17.95 *(978-1-57488-906-2(0))* Potomac Bks., Inc.

Gallimore, Andrew. A Bloody Canvas: The Mike McTigue Story. 2008. (ENG., Illus.). 352p. pap. 26.95 *(978-1-85635-536-0(5))* Mercier Pr., Ltd., The. IRL. Dist: Dufour Editions, Inc.

Gorman, Bartley. Bareknuckle: Memoirs of the Undefeated Champion. 2011. (ENG.). 320p. (gr. 12). 16.00 *(978-1-59020-390-3(9))* Overlook Pr., The.

Gorn, Elliott J. The Manly Art: Bare-Knuckle Prize Fighting in America. 2010. (Illus.). 336p. pap. 19.95 *(978-0-8014-7608-2(9))* Cornell Univ. Pr.

Grace, Kevin. Cincinnati Boxing. 2006. (Images of Sports Ser.). (ENG., Illus.). 128p. per. 19.99 *(978-0-7385-4112-9(5))* Arcadia Publishing.

Gray, William B. Boxing's Top 100: The Greatest Champions of All Time. 2006. pap. 24.95 *(978-1-880876-72-1(4))* Diamond Library.

Henry, Tom & Brown, Dave. Inside Fighter: Dave Brown's Remarkable Stories of Canadian Boxing. unabr. ed. (ENG., Illus.). 256p. *(978-1-55017-266-9(2))* Harbour Publishing Co., Ltd.

Johnson, John & Long, Bill. Tyson-Douglas: The Inside Story of the Upset of the Century. 2007. (Illus.). 272p. 25.95 *(978-1-59797-068-6(9))* Potomac Bks., Inc.

Kaye, Andrew M. The Pussycat of Prizefighting: Tiger Flowers & the Politics of Black Celebrity. 2007. (ENG., Illus.). 232p. per. 22.95 *(978-0-8203-2910-9(X))* Univ. of Georgia Pr.

Kelly, Jason. Shelby's Folly: Jack Dempsey, Doc Kearns, & the Shakedown of a Montana Boomtown. (ENG., Illus.). 2012. 240p. pap. 16.95 ***(978-0-8032-4004-9(X),*** Bison Bks.) 2010. 238p. 26.95 *(978-0-8032-2655-5(1))* Univ. of Nebraska Pr.

Kent, Graeme. Boxing. 2010. (ENG.). 144p. 17.95 *(978-0-7524-5253-1(3))* History Pr. Ltd.,The GBR. Dist: Independent Pubs. Group.

Kimball, George. Four Kings: Leonard, Hagler, Hearns, Duran & the Last Great Era of Boxing. 2008. (ENG.). 340p. 22.95 *(978-1-59013-162-6(2))* McBooks Pr., Inc.

Lang, Arne K. Prizefighting: An American History. 2008. (ENG., Illus.). 274p. 55.00 *(978-0-7864-3654-5(9))* McFarland & Co., Inc. Pubs.

Margolick, David. Beyond Glory: Joe Louis vs. Max Schmeling, & a World on the Brink. 2006. (Vintage Ser.). (ENG., Illus.). 464p. per. 18.95 *(978-0-375-72619-4(5),* Vintage) Knopf Doubleday Publishing Group.

McMillan, Jim. The Alternative View of a Boxers Record: A Story of Professional Boxing in the 1980's And 90's. 2011. 304p. pap. 18.68 ***(978-1-4567-7919-1(2))*** AuthorHouse.

Mitchell, Kevin. Jacobs Beach: The Mob, the Fights, the Fifties. 2010. (ENG., Illus.). 320p. 26.95 *(978-1-60598-123-9(0),* 605123) Pegasus Bks.

Monninger, Joseph. Two Ton: One Night, One Fight - Tony Galento V. Joe Louis. 2007. (ENG., Illus.). 208p. per. 13.95 *(978-1-58642-138-0(7))* Steerforth Pr.

Myler, Patrick. Ring of Hate: Joe Louis vs. Max Schmeling: The Fight of the Century. 2010. (ENG.). 246p. 25.00 *(978-1-4379-7394-5(9))* DIANE Publishing Co.

Nicholson, Kelly Richard. Hitters, Dancers & Ring Magicians: Seven Boxers of the Golden Age. 2010. (ENG., Illus.). 226p. pap. 29.95 *(978-0-7864-4990-3(X))* McFarland & Co., Inc. Pubs.

O'Dell, Derek & Brooke-Ball, Peter. The Greatest Ever Boxing Matches: 80 epic encounters from the history of Boxing. Snelling, O. F., ed. 2010. (ENG., Illus.). 128p. pap. 17.99 *(978-1-84476-771-7(X))* Anness Publishing GBR. Dist: National Bk. Network.

Oden, John. Life in the Ring: Lessons & Inspiration from the Sport of Boxing Including Muhammad Ali, Oscar de la Hoya, Jake Lamotta, George Foreman, Floyd Patterson, & Rocky Marciano. 2009. (ENG., Illus.). 224p. pap. 15.00 *(978-1-57826-311-0(5))* Hatherleigh Co., Ltd., The.

Pacheco, Ferdie. Tales from the 5th Street Gym: Ali, the Dundees, & Miami's Golden Age of Boxing. 2010. (ENG., Illus.). 208p. 27.50 *(978-0-8130-3436-2(1))* Univ. Pr. of Florida.

Ponce, Francisco. Julio Cesar Chavez.Tr. of Julio Cesar Chavez - So Long to the Glory. (SPA.). 14.95 *(978-970-05-1277-8(0))* Baker & Taylor Bks.

Powley, Adam. When Boxing Was Boxing: A Nostalgic Look at a Century of Boxing. 2011. (ENG., Illus.). 208p. 29.95 *(978-0-85733-166-3(3),* 0857331663) Haynes Publishing PLC GBR. Dist: MBI Distribution Services/Quayside Distribution.

Press, Ammonite, ed. 100 Years of Boxing. 2010. (ENG., Illus.). 300p. pap. 19.95 *(978-1-906672-55-3(5),* Ammonite Pr.) AE Pubns. GBR. Dist: BookMasters Distribution Services (BDS).

Roberts, James B. & Skutt, Alexander G. The Boxing Register: International Boxing Hall of Fame Official Record Book. 5th ed. 2011. (ENG., Illus.). 944p. (Orig.). pap. 29.95 *(978-1-59013-499-3(0))* McBooks Pr., Inc.

Runstedtler, Theresa. Jack Johnson, Rebel Sojourner: Boxing in the Shadow of the Global Color Line. 2012. (American Crossroads Ser.). (ENG., Illus.). 376p. 34.95 ***(978-0-520-27160-9(2))*** Univ. of California Pr.

Sares, Theodore Roland. Boxing Is My Sanctuary: A Collection of Essays. 2007. 400p. (ENG.). 35.95 *(978-0-595-68992-7(2));* per. 25.95 *(978-0-595-44594-3(2))* iUniverse, Inc.

Schwartz, Henry. From the Corners of the Ring to the Corners of the Earth: The Adventures Behind the Champions. 2009. pap. 29.95 *(978-1-61623-359-4(1))* Independent Pub.

Shapiro, Anton. Chasing the Crown: An Unauthorized History of Boxing's Richest Prize. 2010. (Illus.). 140p. pap. 19.58 *(978-1-4520-2957-3(1))* AuthorHouse.

Silver, Mike. The Arc of Boxing: The Rise & Decline of the Sweet Science. 2008. (ENG., Illus.). 240p. 55.00 *(978-0-7864-3849-5(5))* McFarland & Co., Inc. Pubs.

Stead, Peter & Williams, Gareth, eds. Wales & Its Boxers: The Fighting Tradition. 2009. (Illus.). 192p. 25.00 *(978-0-7083-1915-4(7))* Univ. of Wales Pr. GBR. Dist: Chicago Distribution Ctr.

Tracy Callis And Chuck Johnston. Boxing in the Los Angeles Are: 1880-2005. 2009. 168p. pap. 24.95 *(978-1-4269-1688-5(4))* Trafford Publishing.

Vaccaro, Mike. 194 - The Greatest Year in Sports: Two Baseball Legends, Two Boxing Champs, & the Unstoppable Thoroughbred Who Made History in the Shadow of War. 2008. (ENG.). 320p. pap. 17.00 *(978-0-7679-2416-0(9))* Broadway Bks.

Waltzer, Jim. The Battle of the Century: Dempsey, Carpentier, & the Birth of Modern Promotion, 1 vol. 2011. (Illus.). 238p. 44.95 *(978-0-313-38244-4(1),* A2664C) Greenwood Publishing Group, Inc.

—The Battle of the Century: Dempsey, Carpentier, & the Birth of Modern Promotion. 2011. x, 238p. E-Book *(978-0-313-38245-1(X),* Praeger Pubs.) Greenwood Publishing Group, Inc.

Warren, Ian. Outlaw Governance. 2009. 340p. pap. *(978-3-639-16376-6(1))* VDM Verlag Dr. Mueller e.K.

Welch, Ian. Greatest Moments of Boxing. 2008. (Greatest Moments Ser.). (ENG., Illus.). 96p. *(978-1-906229-43-6(0),* 1906229430) G2 Entertainment Ltd.

Youmans, Gary. The Onion Picker: Carmen Basilio & Boxing in The 1950s. 2007. (Illus.). 214p. 24.95 *(978-0-8156-8175-5(5))* Syracuse Univ. Pr.

BOY GEORGE, 1961-

Boy George & Bright, Spencer. Take It Like a Man: The Autobiography of Boy George. 2012. 512p. pap. 15.99 ***(978-0-06-211778-6(5))*** HarperCollins Pubs.

George, Boy & Gorman, Paul. Straight. 2007. (Illus.). 283p. reprint ed. 35.00 *(978-1-4223-9019-1(5))* DIANE Publishing Co.

BOY SCOUTS

Arango, Omar Adolfo. Piernas de Acero: Israel Valderrama y Su Cronica Sobre 25,000 Kilometros de un Increible Viaje en Bicicleta. 2010. (SPA & ENG., Illus.). 256p. per. 15.00 *(978-0-88962-865-6(3))* Mosaic Pr.

Baden-Powell, Heather. Baden-Powell: A Family Album. 2008. (ENG., Illus.). 224p. pap. 34.95 *(978-0-7509-4441-0(2))* History Pr. Ltd.,The GBR. Dist: Independent Pubs. Group.

Baden-Powell, Robert. Playing the Game: A Baden-Powell Compendium. Sica, Mario, ed. (ENG., Illus.). 2008. 448p. pap. 17.95 *(978-0-330-44235-0(X))* 2007. 368p. 29.95 *(978-1-4050-8827-5(3))* Macmillan Pubs., Ltd. GBR. Dist: Independent Pubs. Group.

—Scouting for Boys: The Original 1908 Edition. 2007. (Dover Value Editions Ser.). (ENG., Illus.). 432p. per. 12.95 *(978-0-486-45719-2(2))* Dover Pubns., Inc.

—Scouts' Book of Heroes: A Record of Scouts' Work in the Great War. 2009. 338p. pap. *(978-1-84734-950-7(1))* Naval & Military Pr., The.

—Young Knights of the Empire. 2008. (Illus.). 240p. 27.99 *(978-0-554-23737-4(7));* 24.99 *(978-0-554-33040-2(7))* BiblioBazaar.

—Young Knights of the Empire: Their Code, & Further Scout Yarns. 2007. (ENG.). 208p. pap. 20.99 *(978-1-4264-4970-3(4));* 238p. pap. 22.99 *(978-1-4264-5271-0(3))* BiblioBazaar.

Barcelo, Louis P. Scouting for Catholics Adding the Supern. 2006. pap. 21.95 *(978-1-4286-6148-6(4))* Kessinger Publishing, LLC.

Barker, Shane. I Thought Scout Uniforms Were Fireproof! Putting the Fun in Scouting. 2011. 112p. pap. 8.99 *(978-1-59955-524-9(7))* Cedar Fort, Inc./CFI Distribution.

Beard, Dan, contrib. by. Scouting Magazine: Equipment Number 1921. 2006. (ENG.). 36p. 24.99 *(978-1-58057-487-7(4),* SCOUTING21K-M) Digital Antiquaria, Inc.

Beard, Daniel Carter. Hardly a Man Is Now Alive: The Autobiography of Dan Beard. 2011. 392p. 53.95 ***(978-1-258-00459-0(3))*** Literary Licensing, LLC.

Bell, Randall. QuickMarks: Boy Scouts. 2006. (Illus.). 6p. vinyl bd. 4.99 *(978-0-9765486-9-0(0))* Owners Manual Pr.

Birkby, Robert. Boy Scouts of America Scout Stuff: A Centennial History of Scouting Memorabilia. 2011. (ENG.). 240p. 35.00 *(978-0-7566-8873-8(6))* Dorling Kindersley Publishing, Inc.

Birkby, Robert. DK Eyewitness Books: Boy Scouts of America: Boy Scouts of America. 2012. (ENG.). 64p. (J). (gr. 2-4). 16.99 ***(978-0-7566-9770-9(0))*** Dorling Kindersley Publishing, Inc.

Boice, Trina. Primarily for Cub Scouts. 2009. 170p. pap. 12.99 *(978-1-59955-352-8(X))* Cedar Fort, Inc./CFI Distribution.

Boy Scouts of America. The Boys' Life Book of Outdoor Skills. 2012. (ENG., Illus.). 192p. 21.95 ***(978-0-7627-8014-3(2),*** Lyons Pr.) Globe Pequot Pr., The.

Boy Scouts Of America. Cub Scout Song Book. 2011. 34p. 35.95 ***(978-1-258-07070-0(7))*** Literary Licensing, LLC.

—How Book of Cub Scouting. 2011. 450p. 57.95 ***(978-1-258-07744-0(2))*** Literary Licensing, LLC.

—Scouting with Handicapped Boys. 2011. 68p. 36.95 ***(978-1-258-03596-9(0))*** Literary Licensing, LLC.

—The Scoutmaster & His Troop: What Every Scoutmaster Wants to Know. 2011. 66p. 36.95 ***(978-1-258-05040-5(4))*** Literary Licensing, LLC.

Boy Scouts Of America, ed. Explorer Manual. 2011. 402p. 54.95 ***(978-1-258-07260-5(2))*** Literary Licensing, LLC.

Boy Scouts of America & Boy Scouts Of America. Boy Scouts Handbook, 1st Edition 1911. 2011. 570p. ***(978-1-84902-369-6(7))*** Benediction Classics.

Boy Scouts of America Staff. Boy Scouts Handbook. 2007. pap. *(978-956-291-498-7(4))* Editorial Benei Noaj.

Boy Scouts of America Staff. Boy Scouts Handbook: Original 1911 Edition. 2012. (ENG., Illus.). 448p. (gr. 3-9). pap. 14.95 ***(978-1-61608-198-0(8),*** 608198) Skyhorse Publishing Co., Inc.

Chief: A Biography of Zack Cross. 2009. pap. 19.00 *(978-0-615-30320-8(X))* Greater Alabama Council, Boy Scouts of America.

Csatari, Joseph. Norman Rockwell Boy Scout Amer. Dorling Kindersley Publishing Staff, ed. 2009. (ENG.). 160p. (gr. 12). 24.95 *(978-0-7566-3520-6(9))* Dorling Kindersley Publishing, Inc.

Division of, Personnel. Scouting Personnel A Manual of Human Rel. 2006. pap. 24.95 *(978-1-4286-6120-2(4))* Kessinger Publishing, LLC.

Dorling Kindersley Publishing Staff. Boy Scouts of America's Be Prepared Navigation. 2008. 160p. (J). (gr. 6-12). pap. 12.99 *(978-0-7566-3719-4(8))* Dorling Kindersley Publishing, Inc.

Eastman, Charles A. Indian Scout Talks A Guide for Boy Scout. 2006. pap. 24.95 *(978-1-4286-4388-8(5))* Kessinger Publishing, LLC.

Eggleston, George Cary. Captain Sam, or, the Boy Scouts of 1814. 2007. (Illus.). 136p. per. *(978-1-4065-1785-9(2))* Dodo Pr.

Eskow, Philip G. Camping for Beginners. 2008. 104p. pap. 15.99 *(978-1-4257-8984-8(6))* Xlibris Corp.

Grove, Terry. A Comprehensive Guide to the Eagle Scout Award: Twentieth Century Edition. 2008. (Illus.). 182p. per. 25.00 *(978-0-9776534-8-5(X));* (ENG., per. 40.00 *(978-0-9776534-9-2(8))* Reliance Media, Inc.

—The Kekeenowin of the Wimachtendienk: 1915 To 1948. 2007. (Illus.). 441p. per. 35.00 *(978-0-9776534-6-1(3));* (ENG., per. 50.00 *(978-0-9776534-7-8(1))* Reliance Media, Inc.

Guidelines for Leading Your Congregation 2009-2012 - Scouting & Civic Youth-Serving Ministry: Building Effective Scouting Ministry in Your Church. 2008. 2.95 *(978-0-687-64742-2(8))* Abingdon Pr.

Hammaker, Ben "Stretch". Northbound: The Daily Account of an Appalachian Trail Thru-Hike, 1 vol. 2009. 150p. pap. 24.95 *(978-1-4489-2914-6(8))* PublishAmerica, Inc.

Jeal, Tim. Baden-Powell: Founder of the Boy Scouts. 2007. (ENG., Illus.). 720p. pap. 19.00 *(978-0-300-12513-9(5))* Yale Univ. Pr.

Koppelman, Andrew & Wolff, Tobias Barrington. A Right to Discriminate? How the Case of Boy Scouts of America V. James Dale Warped the Law of Free Association. 2009. (ENG.). 192p. 38.00 *(978-0-300-12127-8(X))* Yale Univ. Pr.

McCord, Thomas O., et al. Patrol Stunts: 259 Projects for Scout Patrols. 2011. 36p. 35.95 ***(978-1-258-03246-3(5))*** Literary Licensing, LLC.

Perry, Rick. On My Honor: Why the American Values of the Boy Scouts Are Worth Fighting For. 2008. (Illus.). 226p. 25.95 *(978-0-9796462-2-5(7))* Stroud & Hall Publishing.

Price, Luther Edmunds & Gray, Frank F. Thirty Years of Scout Camping: History of Glen Gray & Other Camps in Northern New Jersey. 2011. 128p. 40.95 ***(978-1-258-06250-7(X))*** Literary Licensing, LLC.

Ripley, G. Sherman & Boy Scouts Of America. Fun Around the Campfire. 2011. 116p. 39.95 ***(978-1-258-06051-0(5))*** Literary Licensing, LLC.

Robert Baden-Powell. Scouting for Boys: The Original Edition. 2007. 424p. (SPA.). *(978-956-291-508-3(5));* per. *(978-956-291-507-6(7))* Editorial Benei Noaj.

Rogers, Jay L. Levy's Boy & Girl Scout Cachet Covers of the United States: Volume I & II 1910-1960 2nd Edition, Vol. 12. 2nd ed. 2007. (Illus.). 253p. per. 29.95 *(978-0-9796338-0-5(X),* SOSSI) Scouts on Stamps Society International, Inc.

Russell, Thomas H. Stories of Boy Scouts & Girls' Open Air Clubs. 2007. (ENG.). 352p. 46.95 *(978-0-548-03244-2(0))* Kessinger Publishing, LLC.

Seton, Ernest Thompson. The Preacher of Cedar Mountain: A Tale of the Open Country. 2008. 440p. 30.99 *(978-0-559-59437-3(2));* pap. 34.75 *(978-0-559-59434-2(8))* BiblioBazaar.

Smith, Charles Frederick. Boy Scout Games. 2011. 258p. 47.95 ***(978-1-258-07139-4(8))*** Literary Licensing, LLC.

Stattler, Gary L. A short history of the winnebago council, boy scouts of america, & it's Camps. 2007. per. 20.00 *(978-1-888461-12-1(8))* Islewest Publishing.

Thorne, Troy. Pinewood Derby Designs & Patterns: The Ultimate Guide to Creating the Coolest Car. 2010. (ENG.). 118p. pap. 12.95 *(978-1-56523-341-6(7))* Fox Chapel Publishing Co., Inc.

Townley, Alvin. Spirit of Adventure: Eagle Scouts & the Making of America's Future. 2009. (ENG., Illus.). 320p. 24.95 *(978-0-312-37898-1(X),* Dunne, Thomas Bks.) St. Martin's Pr.

Wills, Chuck. Boy Scouts of America: A Centennial History. 2009. (ENG.). 288p. (gr. 12). 35.00 *(978-0-7566-5634-8(6))* Dorling Kindersley Publishing, Inc.

Witt, David. The Scouter's Companion: Tips & Stories Celebrating 100 Years, 1 vol. Smith, Jared, ed. 2010. (ENG., Illus.). 144p. pap. 9.99 *(978-1-4236-0604-8(3))* Gibbs Smith, Publisher.

BOYCOTTS

Bongiorni, Sara. A Year Without "Made in China" One Family's True Life Adventure in the Global Economy. 2007. (ENG.). 256p. 24.95 *(978-0-470-11613-5(7),* Wiley) Wiley, John & Sons, Inc.

—Year Without "Made in China" One Family's True Life Adventure in the Global Economy. 2008. (ENG.). 256p. pap. 14.95 *(978-0-470-37920-2(0),* Wiley) Wiley, John & Sons, Inc.

Carson, Tracy M. Tomorrow It Could Be You: Strikes & Boycotts in South Africa, 1978-1982. 2011. (ENG., Illus.). 325p. pap. 72.95 *(978-3-0343-0119-0(7))* Lang, Peter AG GBR. Dist: Lang, Peter.

Fanning, Tim. The Fethard-on-Sea Boycott. 2010. (ENG., Illus.). 240p. pap. 26.95 *(978-1-84889-032-9(X))* Collins Pr., The. IRL. Dist: Dufour Editions, Inc.

Glickman, Lawrence B. Buying Power: A History of Consumer Activism in America. (Illus.). 424p. 2012. (ENG.). pap. 27.50 ***(978-0-226-29867-2(1))*** 2009. 45.00 *(978-0-226-29865-8(5))* Univ. of Chicago Pr.

Kelley, Blair L. M. Right to Ride: Streetcar Boycotts & African American Citizenship in the Era of Plessy V. Ferguson. 2010. (John Hope Franklin Series in African American History & Culture Ser.). (ENG., Illus.). 304p. 59.95 *(978-0-8078-3354-4(1));* pap. 21.95 *(978-0-8078-7101-0(X))* Univ. of North Carolina Pr.

Li, Qianpin. Consumer Boycotts in Contemporary Chin. 2010. 280p. pap. *(978-3-8383-8082-7(7))* Lambert Academic Publishing.

Oosterhoff, Siny. On Olympic Boycotts. 2011. 168p. pap. ***(978-3-8433-8678-4(1))*** Lambert Academic Publishing.

Robertson, Sheila Hurtig. Shattered Hopes: Canada's Boycott of the 1980 Olympics Games. 2012. (ENG.). pap. ***(978-1-927403-08-2(1))*** Iguana Bks.

Sarantakes, Nicholas Evan. Dropping the Torch: Jimmy Carter, the Olympic Boycott, & the Cold War. 2010. (ENG., Illus.). 352p. 90.00 *(978-0-521-19477-8(6));* pap. 28.99 *(978-0-521-17666-8(2))* Cambridge Univ. Pr.

Spagna, Ana Maria. Test Ride on the Sunnyland Bus: A Daughter's Civil Rights Journey. 2010. (River Teeth Literary Nonfiction Prize Ser.). (ENG., Illus.). 286p. pap. 19.95 *(978-0-8032-1712-6(9),* Bison Bks.) Univ. of Nebraska Pr.
Stanton, Mary. The Hand of Esau: Montgomery's Jewish Community & the Bus Boycott. 2007. (Illus.). 194p. per. 15.95 *(978-1-57966-041-3(X))* River City Publishing.
—Journey Toward Justice: Juliette Hampton Morgan & the Montgomery Bus Boycott. 2006. (ENG., Illus.). 296p. 29.95 *(978-0-8203-2857-7(X))* Univ. of Georgia Pr.
Williams, Donnie & Greenhaw, Wayne. The Thunder of Angels: The Montgomery Bus Boycott & the People Who Broke the Back of Jim Crow. 2007. (ENG., Illus.). 320p. per. 14.95 *(978-1-55652-676-3(8),* Hill, Lawrence Bks.) Chicago Review Pr., Inc.

BOYD, BELLE, 1844-1900

Boyd, Belle. Belle Boyd in Camp & Prison. 2010. 320p. pap. 30.75 *(978-1-144-03776-3(X))* BiblioBazaar.
—Belle Boyd in Camp & Prison. 2009. 90p. pap. *(978-0-217-39780-3(8))* Books LLC.
—Belle Boyd in Camp & Prison. 2010. (Illus.). 72p. pap. 6.39 *(978-1-154-30582-1(1))* General Bks. LLC.
—Belle Boyd in Camp & Prison. 2007. 468p. 52.95 *(978-0-548-33186-6(3));* per. 37.95 *(978-1-4326-9067-0(1))* Kessinger Publishing, LLC.
—Belle Boyd, in Camp & Prison. 2009. 308p. 32.99 *(978-1-110-08137-0(5));* pap. 28.75 *(978-1-110-08136-3(7))* BiblioBazaar.
Boyd, Belle & Hardinge, Sam Wilde. Belle Boyd in Camp & Prison. 2010. 470p. pap. 37.75 *(978-1-144-65285-0(5))* BiblioBazaar.
Sigaud, Louis A. Belle Boyd - Confederate Spy. 2007. 272p. per. *(978-1-4067-5439-1(0))* Read Bks.

BOYD, ROBERT, 1578-1627

Wodrow, Robert. Collections upon the Lives of the Reformers & Most Eminent Ministers of the Church of Scotland, 2 vols. in 3 pts. (Maitland Club, Glasgow Publications: No. 32). reprint ed. 105.00 *(978-0-404-52993-2(3))* AMS Pr., Inc.
—Collections upon the Lives of the Reformers & Most Eminent Ministers of the Church of Scotland. 2010. 390p. pap. 33.75 *(978-1-148-54786-2(X))* BiblioBazaar.
—Collections upon the Lives of the Reformers & Most Eminent Ministers of the Church of Scotland. 2009. 308p. pap. *(978-1-150-33967-7(5))* Books LLC.
—Collections upon the Lives of the Reformers & Most Eminent Ministers of the Church of Scotland. 2010. 248p. pap. 23.37 *(978-1-154-40340-4(8))* General Bks. LLC.

BOYD, WILLIAM, 1895-1972

Boyd, Grace Bradley & Cochran, Michael. Hopalong Cassidy - an American Legend. 2008. 368p. 75.00 *(978-1-60360-066-8(3))* Gemstone Publishing, Inc.

BOYD, WILLIAM KENNETH, 1879-1938

Jackson, David Kelly, ed. American Studies in Honor of William Kenneth Boyd. 2011. 388p. 53.95 ***(978-1-258-09066-1(X))*** Literary Licensing, LLC.

BOYDEN, FRANK L. (FRANK LEAROYD), 1879-1972

Boyden, Frank, et al. Frank Boyden: The Empathies. 2007. (ENG., Illus.). 80p. pap. 19.95 *(978-1-930957-57-2(2))* Ford, Hallie Museum of Art.

BOYLE, ROBERT, 1627-1691

Alexander, Peter. Ideas, Qualities & Corpuscles: Locke & Boyle on the External World. 2009. (ENG.). 348p. pap. 46.00 *(978-0-521-10734-1(2))* Cambridge Univ. Pr.
Budgell, Eustace. Memoirs of the Lives & Characters of the Illustrious Family of the Boyles. 2009. 98p. pap. 14.14 *(978-1-151-64325-4(4))* General Bks. LLC.
—Memoirs of the Lives & Characters of the Illustrious Family of the Boyles: Particularly of the Late Eminently Learned Charles Earl of Orrery. in Whi. 2010. 340p. pap. 31.75 *(978-1-142-72254-8(6))* BiblioBazaar.
Comeanu, Sorana. Regimens of the Mind: Boyle, Locke, & the Early Modern Cultura Animi Tradition. 2012. (ENG.). 320p. 50.00 *(978-0-226-11639-6(5))* Univ. of Chicago Pr.
Hunt, Richard McMasters. The Place of Religion in the Science of Robert Boyle. 2011. 88p. 38.95 ***(978-1-258-01107-9(7))*** Literary Licensing, LLC.
Hunter, Michael. Boyle: Between God & Science. 2010. (Illus.). 384p. pap. 28.00 *(978-0-300-16931-7(0))* Yale Univ. Pr.
Hunter, Michael, et al. The Boyle Papers: Understanding the Manuscripts of Robert Boyle. 2007. (Illus.). 688p. 154.95 *(978-0-7546-5568-8(7))* Ashgate Publishing Co.
Knight, Harriet. Organising Natural Knowledge in the Seventeenth Century. 2011. 400p. pap. ***(978-3-8443-9452-8(4))*** Lambert Academic Publishing.
Schaffer, Steven & Schaffer, Simon. Leviathan & the Air-Pump - Hobbes, Boyle, & the Experimental Life. 2011. (ENG., Illus.). 440p. (C). pap. 29.95 *(978-0-691-15020-8(6))* Princeton Univ. Pr.

BOYS

see also Adolescent Boys; Boy Scouts; Children; Church Work with Children; Fathers and Sons; Mothers and Sons; Young Men; Youth

Baggerman, R.M., JA; Dekker. Child of the Enlightenment: Revolutionary Europe Reflected in a Boyhood Diary. 2009. (Egodocuments & History Ser.). 512p. *(978-90-04-17269-2(6))* BRILL.
Baxter, Kathleen A. & Kochel, Marcia Agness. Gotcha Again for Guys! More Nonfiction Books to Get Boys Excited about Reading. 2010. (Illus.). xiii, 248p. E-Book *(978-1-59884-377-4(X));* 248p. pap. 35.00 *(978-1-59884-376-7(1),* A2702P) Libraries Unlimited, Inc.
Biddulph, Steve. Raising Boys: Why Boys Are Different - & How to Help Them Become Happy & Well-Balanced Men. 2nd rev. ed. 2008. (ENG., Illus.). 224p. pap. 14.99 *(978-1-58761-328-9(X),* Celestial Arts) Ten Speed Pr.
Brozo, William G. To Be a Boy, to Be a Reader: Engaging Teen & Preteen Boys in Active Literacy, Second Edition. 2nd ed. 2010. (ENG.). pap. 28.95 *(978-0-87207-508-5(7))* International Reading Assn.
Cleveland, Kathleen Palme. Teaching Boys Who Struggle in School: Strategies That Turn Underachievers into Successful Learners. 2011. 233p. pap. 27.95 *(978-1-4166-1150-9(9))* Assn. for Supervision & Curriculum Development.
Corbett, Ken. Boyhoods: Rethinking Masculinities. (ENG.). 288p. 2011. pap. 17.00 *(978-0-300-17121-1(8))* 2009. 26.00 *(978-0-300-14984-5(0))* Yale Univ. Pr.
Curran, Joseph S. One More Clean Shirt. 2008. 64p. pap. 16.95 *(978-1-60474-405-7(7))* PublishAmerica, Inc.
Davison, Kevin G. Negotiating Masculinities & Bodies in Schools: The Implications of Gender Theory for the Education of Boys. 2007. 212p. 109.95 *(978-0-7734-5354-8(7))* Mellen, Edwin Pr., The.
Drexler, Peggy & Gross, Linden. Raising Boys Without Men: How Maverick Moms are Creating the Next Generation of Exceptional Men. 2006. (ENG.). 240p. pap. 14.95 *(978-1-59486-538-1(8))* Rodale Pr., Inc.
Erwin, Cheryl L. The Everything Parent's Guide to Raising Boys: A Complete Handbook to Develop Confidence, Promote Self-Esteem, & Improve Communication. 2nd ed. 2010. (ENG.). 304p. pap. 14.95 *(978-1-4405-0689-5(2))* Adams Media Corp.
Figueroa, Shelly & LePage, Karen. Sewing for Boys: 24 Projects to Create a Handmade Wardrobe. 2011. (ENG., Illus.). 144p. 24.99 *(978-0-470-94955-9(4),* Wiley) Wiley, John & Sons, Inc.
Geda, Fabio. In the Sea There Are Crocodiles: Based on the True Story of Enaiatollah Akbari. 2011. (ENG., Illus.). 224p. 22.95 *(978-0-385-53473-4(6),* Doubleday) Knopf Doubleday Publishing Group.
Glover, Lorri. Southern Sons: Becoming Men in the New Nation. (ENG.). 264p. (gr. 17). 2010. pap. 25.00 *(978-0-8018-9821-1(8))* 2007. 50.00 *(978-0-8018-8498-6(5))* Johns Hopkins Univ. Pr.
Grant, Stephen, et al. BAM! Boys Advocacy & Mentoring: A Leader's Guide to Facilitating Strengths-Based Groups for Boys, Helping Boys Make Better Contact by Making Better Contact with Them. 2007. (Routledge Series on Counseling & Psychotherapy with Boys & Men). (ENG.). 192p. 39.95 *(978-0-415-96318-3(4))* Routledge.
Gurian Institute Staff, et al. It's a Baby Boy! The Unique Wonders & Special Nature of Your Son from Pregnancy to Two Years. 2009. (ENG., Illus.). 160p. pap. 15.95 *(978-0-470-24338-1(4),* Jossey-Bass) Wiley, John & Sons, Inc.
Gurian, Michael. The Purpose of Boys: Helping Our Sons Find Meaning, Significance, & Direction in Their Lives. (ENG.). 272p. 2010. pap. 16.95 *(978-0-470-40182-8(5))* 2009. 26.95 *(978-0-470-24337-4(6))* Wiley, John & Sons, Inc. (Jossey-Bass).
—The Wonder of Boys: What Parents, Mentors & Educators Can Do to Shape Boys into Exceptional Men. 20th anniv. ed. 2006. (ENG.). 320p. (gr. 12-18). 15.95 *(978-1-58542-528-0(1),* Tarcher) Penguin Group (USA) Inc.
Haen, Craig ed. Engaging Boys in Treatment. 2011. (Routledge Series on Counseling & Psychotherapy with Boys & Men Ser.). (ENG., Illus.). 346p. 125.00 *(978-0-415-87405-2(X));* pap. 39.95 *(978-0-415-87406-9(8))* Routledge.
Hansen, Sally. Gender Differences & Writing. 2010. 100p. pap. *(978-3-8383-1858-5(7))* Lambert Academic Publishing.
Harding, David J. Living the Drama: Community, Conflict, & Culture among Inner-City Boys. 2010. (ENG., Illus.). 336p. pap. 25.00 *(978-0-226-31665-9(3));* 75.00 *(978-0-226-31664-2(5))* Univ. of Chicago Pr.
Harmon, Judson A. Be Home by Dark: Humorous Stories of Youthful Misadventure. 2008. (Illus.). 78p. pap. 15.00 *(978-0-9799963-8-2(4))* IGI Pr.
Harrington, Ingrid. Boys in Schools: Early School Leaving & Masculinity. 2010. 216p. pap. *(978-3-639-23938-6(5))* VDM Verlag Dr. Mueller e.K.
Helgoe, Laurie A. & Helgoe, Barron M. Raising Boys - The Complete Idiot's Guide. 2008. (Complete Idiot's Guide Ser.). (ENG., Illus.). 320p. (gr. 12-18). 14.95 *(978-1-59257-730-9(X),* Alpha Bks.) Penguin Group (USA) Inc.
Henrich, Karen. The Wonder of Boys: The World Through a Boy's Eyes. 2007. (ENG., Illus.). 128p. 14.95 *(978-1-58182-612-8(5))* Turner Publishing Co.
Heos, Bridget. Guys: Being Best Friends. 2012. (Relationships 101 Ser.). (ENG.). 48p. (YA). (gr. 5-8). pap. 11.75 ***(978-1-4488-6835-3(1));*** lib. bdg. 27.95 ***(978-1-4488-6832-2(7))*** Rosen Publishing Group, Inc., The.
Hoben, Allan. The Minister & the Boy. 2008. 128p. 21.99 *(978-0-554-36129-1(9));* 24.99 *(978-0-554-26826-2(4))* BiblioBazaar.
—The Minister & the Boy: A Handbook for Churchmen Engaged in Boys' Work. 2009. 208p. 23.99 *(978-0-559-90886-6(5))* 2009. 208p. pap. 17.99 *(978-0-559-90885-9(7))* 2007. (ENG.). 114p. pap. 18.99 *(978-1-4346-1950-1(8))* 2007. (ENG.). 126p. pap. 19.99 *(978-1-4346-1953-2(2))* BiblioBazaar.
Hobry, Jack. Lost Boys. 2010. 255p. pap. 17.95 *(978-1-58241-373-0(8))* Harbor Directories, Inc.
Hornayoun, Ana. That Crumpled Paper Was Due Last Week: Helping Disorganized & Distracted Boys Succeed in School & Life. 2010. (ENG.). 304p. (gr. 12-18). 15.95 *(978-0-399-53559-8(4),* Perigee Trade) Penguin Group (USA) Inc.
Iggulden, Conn & Iggulden, Hal. The Dangerous Book for Boys. 2012. 288p. 12.99 ***(978-0-06-220897-2(7),*** Morrow, William & Co.) HarperCollins Pubs.
—The Dangerous Book for Boys: Australian Edition. 2007. (Illus.). 304p. *(978-0-7322-8635-4(2))* HarperCollins Pubs. Australia.
—Dangerous Book for Boys: Das einzig wahre Handbuch für Väter und ihre Söhne. 2007. (ENG., Illus.). 288p. (gr. 4-7). 26.95 *(978-0-06-124358-5(2),* Morrow, William & Co.) HarperCollins Pubs.
—The Dangerous Book for Boys: New Zealand Edition. 2008. (Illus.). 304p. *(978-1-86950-709-1(6))* HarperCollins Pubs. Australia.
James, Abigail Norfleet, ed. Teaching the Male Brain: How Boys Think, Feel, & Learn in School. 2007. (Illus.). 304p. 90.95 *(978-1-4129-3662-0(4),* B36624C); per. 39.95 *(978-1-4129-3663-7(2),* B36624P) Corwin Pr.
James, Stephen & Thomas, David S. Wild Things: The Art of Nurturing Boys. 2009. (ENG.). 368p. pap. 14.99 *(978-1-4143-2227-8(5))* Tyndale Hse. Pubs.
Jha, Jyotsna & Kelleher, Fatimah. Boys' Underachievement in Education. 2007. (ENG., Illus.). 147p. (C). pap. 38.00 *(978-0-85092-845-7(1))* Iwokrama International Rain Forest Programme GUY. Dist: Stylus Publishing, LLC.
Kehler, Michael. Boys' Bodies: Speaking the Unspoken. 2010. (Adolescent Cultures, School & Society Ser.). 256p. (C). 129.95 *(978-1-4331-0625-2(4));* pap. 33.95 *(978-1-4331-0625-5(6))* Lang, Peter Publishing, Inc.
Kiselica, Mark, et al, eds. Counseling Troubled Boys: A Guidebook for Professionals. 2007. (Routledge Series on Counseling & Psychotherapy with Boys & Men: Vol. 1). (ENG., Illus.). 336p. 39.95 *(978-0-415-95547-8(5))* Routledge.
Krei, Adalbert. Ten Guardian Angels & a Tin Tub: A Memoir. 2011. pap. 14.99 *(978-1-61739-922-0(1))* Tate Publishing & Enterprises, LLC.
Leone, James E. Concepts in Male Health: Perspectives Across the Lifespan. 2012. (Public Health/AAHE Ser.: 21). (ENG., Illus.). 480p. pap. 75.00 ***(978-0-470-48638-2(4),*** Jossey-Bass) Wiley, John & Sons, Inc.
Loeber, Rolf & Farrington, David P. Young Homicide Offenders & Victims: Risk Factors, Prediction, & Prevention from Childhood. 2011. (Longitudinal Research in the Social & Behavioral Sciences: an Interdisciplinary Ser.). (Illus.). xxi, 200p. 129.00 *(978-1-4419-9948-1(5),* 1441999485) Springer.
Martino, Wayne, et al. The Problem with Boys' Education: Beyond the Backlash. 2009. (ENG., Illus.). 312p. pap. 43.95 *(978-1-56023-683-2(3));* 125.00 *(978-1-56023-682-5(5))* Routledge.
Martino, Wayne J. & Rezai-Rashti, Goli. Gender, Race, & the Politics of Role Modeling: The Influence of Male Teachers. 2011. (Routledge Research in Education Ser.). (ENG.). 286p. (C). 125.00 *(978-0-415-87866-1(7))* Routledge.
Mason, Christopher P. Crossing into Manhood: A Men's Studies Curriculum. 2006. (Illus.). 69.95 *(978-1-934043-30-1(3))* Cambria Pr.
Mavor, Carol. Reading Boyishly: Roland Barthes, J. M. Barrie, Jacques Henri Lartigue, Marcel Proust, & D. W. Winnicott. 2008. (ENG., Illus.). 536p. 99.95 *(978-0-8223-3886-4(6));* pap. 29.95 *(978-0-8223-3962-5(5))* Duke Univ. Pr.
McLean, William A. Women Helping Boys to Become Men. 2009. 60p. pap. 11.00 *(978-1-4389-9664-6(0))* AuthorHouse.
Meeker, Meg. Boys Should Be Boys: 7 Secrets to Raising Healthy Sons. 2009. (ENG.). 304p. pap. 15.00 *(978-0-345-51369-4(X),* Ballantine Bks.) Random House Publishing Group.
—Boys Should Be Boys: 7 Secrets to Raising Healthy Sons. 2008. (ENG.). 287p. 24.95 *(978-1-59698-057-0(5))* Regnery Publishing, Inc., An Eagle Publishing Co.
Mills, Martin, et al. Boys & Schooling. 2008. (ENG.). 256p. 89.00 *(978-0-230-51701-1(3))* Palgrave Macmillan.
O'Donnel, Sharon. House of Testosterone: One Mom's Survival in a Household of Males. 2008. (ENG.). 208p. pap. 12.95 *(978-0-547-00592-8(X))* Houghton Mifflin Harcourt Trade & Reference Pubs.
Pollack, William. Real Boys: Rescuing Our Sons from the Myths of Boyhood. 480p. pap. 35.00 *(978-0-908011-42-1(3))* Scribe Pubns. AUS. Dist: Independent Pubs. Group.
Rao, Anthony & Seaton, Michelle. The Way of Boys: Promoting the Social & Emotional Development of Young Boys. 2010. (ENG.). 304p. pap. 14.99 *(978-0-06-170783-4(X),* Harper Paperbacks) HarperCollins Pubs.
Reichert, Michael. Reaching Boys, Teaching Boys: Strategies That Work — And Why. 2010. (ENG.). 288p. pap. 29.95 *(978-0-470-53278-2(5),* Jossey-Bass) Wiley, John & Sons, Inc.
Rosser, Derek. Call Me Valentine. 2011. 88p. pap. 9.99 ***(978-1-907728-19-8(8))*** Pneuma Springs Publishing GBR. Dist: Lightning Source, Inc.
Smith, Wade C. Say Fellows- Fifty Practical Talks with Boys on Life's Big Issues. 2007. (ENG.). 134p. pap. 18.99 *(978-1-4346-0856-7(5));* 152p. pap. 21.99 *(978-1-4346-0883-3(2))* BiblioBazaar.
—Say Fellows- Fifty Practical Talks with Boys on Life's Big Issues. 2008. 132p. pap. *(978-1-4099-3825-5(5))* Dodo Pr.
Sprung, Barbara, et al. Supporting Boys' Learning: Strategies for Teacher Practice. 2010. (ENG.). 120p. pap. 23.95 *(978-0-8077-5104-6(9));* 56.00 *(978-0-8077-5105-3(7))* Teachers College Pr., Teachers College, Columbia Univ.
Stott, Roscoe Gilmore. How to Win Boys: A Book of Information & Inspiration for the Sunday School Worker. 2007. (ENG.). 180p. 37.95 *(978-0-548-06210-4(2))* Kessinger Publishing, LLC.
Stratton, M. L. The Little Book of Boys. 2011. (ENG.). 128p. 10.95 ***(978-1-4405-2895-8(0))*** Adams Media Corp.
Sullivan, Michael. Serving Boys Through Readers' Advisory. 2009. 160p. 48.00 *(978-0-8389-1022-1(X))* American Library Assn.
Taylor, Bayard. Boys of Other Countries. 2009. 284p. 34.99 *(978-1-117-16314-7(8));* pap. 27.75 *(978-1-117-16315-4(6))* BiblioBazaar.
—Boys of Other Countries. 2009. 64p. (gr. 4-7). pap. 14.14 *(978-0-217-68986-1(8))* General Bks. LLC.
Thompson, Michael & Barker, Teresa. It's a Boy! Understanding Your Son's Development from Birth to Age 18. 2008. (ENG., Illus.). 480p. 27.00 *(978-0-345-49395-8(8),* Ballantine Bks.) Random House Publishing Group.
—It's a Boy! Your Son's Development from Birth to Age 18. 2009. (ENG., Illus.). 480p. pap. 17.00 *(978-0-345-49396-5(6),* Ballantine Bks.) Random House Publishing Group.
van de Griendt, Martijn, photos by. Smokin' Boys Smokin' Girls. 2010. (DUT & ENG., Illus.). 144p. pap. 24.95 *(978-90-5330-633-8(1))* Mets en Schilt Uitgevers NLD. Dist: Ingram Pub. Services.
Walsh, Brian R. Boys Should Be Boys: A Headmaster's Reflections. 2008. 216p. 29.95 *(978-0-9720307-6-2(X))* TMC Bks. L.L.C.
Wannamaker, Annette. Mediated Boyhoods: Boys, Teens, & Young Men in Popular Media & Culture. 2011. (Illus.). ix, 267p. 129.95 *(978-1-4331-0541-8(1));* pap. 129.95 *(978-1-4331-0540-1(3))* Lang, Peter Publishing, Inc.
Whelen, John. Boys & Their Schooling: The Experience of Becoming Someone Else. 2011. (Routledge Research in Education Ser.). (ENG., Illus.). 296p. (C). 125.00 *(978-0-415-87917-0(5))* Routledge.
Zambo, Debby & Brozo, William G. Bright Beginnings for Boys: Engaging Young Boys in Active Literacy. 2009. (ENG.). 683p. pap. 24.95 *(978-0-87207-683-9(0))* International Reading Assn.

BOYS—BIOGRAPHY

see also Biography—Juvenile Literature, Children in the Bible

Bartulski, Barrie C. The Red Schwinn Bicycle: A Sentimental Journey. 2007. 128p. per. 13.95 *(978-0-595-41094-1(4))* iUniverse, Inc.
Benyo, Richard. Jim Thorpe Never Slept Here: And Other Stories from a Mauch Chunk, Pennsylvania Boyhood. 2008. (Illus.). 275p. pap. 20.00 *(978-1-58966-166-0(4))* Univ. of Scranton Pr.
Bob, Hippie. Hippie Bob & the Chocolate Factory: A true Fairytale. 2009. 192p. pap. 16.49 *(978-1-4389-7009-7(9))* AuthorHouse.
Brooks, Cyrus. Rayoe's Crew. 2009. 128p. pap. 13.95 *(978-1-4401-1439-7(0))* iUniverse, Inc.
Brown, Maxine. Inspired: The True Story of Two Amazing Boys. 2007. 192p. pap. 17.95 *(978-1-58501-102-5(9),* SterlingHouse Books) SterlingHouse Pubs., Inc.
Buck, James. Growing up on the Streets of Philadelphia. 2007. pap. *(978-0-9800195-0-6(8))* El Sobrante Pr.
Corson, Justin R. Gutbuster: An Ulcerative Colitis Survivor's Story. 2007. per. *(978-0-9801439-0-4(X))* Town & Country Reprographics.
Crisp, David. My Life as an Orphan. 2008. (Illus.). 472p. pap. *(978-1-84748-214-3(7))* Athena Pr.
Crofts, Andrew. The Little Hero: One Boy's Fight for Freedom - Iqbal Masih's Story. 2006. (ENG.). 265p. per. 17.95 *(978-1-904132-84-4(7))* Vision Paperbacks GBR. Dist: Independent Pubs. Group.
de Yonge, Jack. Boom Town Boy: Coming of Age in Alaska's Lost Frontier. 2010. (ENG., Illus.). 224p. (gr. 9). pap. 14.95 *(978-1-935347-06-4(3))* Epicenter Pr., Inc.
Deane, George. Homespun. 2007. (ENG.). 304p. per. 29.95 *(978-1-4241-1030-8(0))* PublishAmerica, Inc.
Flinchbaugh, C. Hope & Austen, Jessica. Out of North Korea: A Korean Boy Tells His Rescue Story in Pictures. 2011. (Illus.). 80p. 16.99 ***(978-1-60066-274-4(9))*** WingSpread Publishers.
Hardwell, Bart. Escaping Obstacles. 2008. 212p. 24.99 *(978-1-60477-976-9(4));* pap. 14.99 *(978-1-60477-975-2(6))* Xulon Pr., Inc.
Hoffmeister, Peter Brown. The End of Boys. 2011. (ENG.). 224p. pap. 14.95 *(978-1-59376-420-3(0),* Soft Skull Pr.) Counterpoint LLC.
Jefferys, Macon. Memoirs of a Mule Rider: A Poor Southern Farm Boy's Journey Through the Twentieth Century. 2009. 588p. pap. 33.95 *(978-1-4401-2999-5(1))* iUniverse, Inc.
Jones, Rodster. Boyhood Memories: Sometimes My Pants Felt Funny, 1 vol. 2009. 73p. pap. 16.95 *(978-1-4489-8582-1(X))* PublishAmerica, Inc.
Lloyd, Jack. Endless Summer: My life with the beach Boys. 2010. 238p. pap. 19.95 *(978-1-59393-113-1(1))* BearManor Media.
McReynolds, Charles B. Memories of an Old Geezer. 2008. 220p. pap. 15.95 *(978-1-934248-90-4(8))* Mill City Pr., Inc.
Messner, Michael A. King of the Wild Suburb: A memoir of fathers, sons & Guns. 2011. 154p. pap. 14.95 ***(978-1-935514-90-9(3))*** Plain View Pr.
Park, Dave. Angling Vagabond: A Glorious Boyhood. 2008. 144p. 21.00 *(978-1-4251-6414-0(5))* Trafford Publishing.
Pfeiffer, Werner. Questions: A Childhood Ambushed by War. A Memoir. 2008. 440p. pap. 27.95 *(978-1-4401-0667-5(3))* iUniverse, Inc.
Schroff, Laura & Tresniowski, Alex. An Invisible Thread: The True Story of an 11-Year-Old Panhandler, a Busy Sales Executive, & an Unlikely Meeting with Destiny. l.t. ed. 2012. (ENG.). 335p. 31.99 ***(978-1-4104-4786-9(3),*** Wheeler Publishing, Inc.) Cengage Gale.
Silvin, Richard Rene. I Survived Swiss Boarding Schools. 2006. pap. 14.95 *(978-0-9764052-9-0(6))* Thomas Max Publishing.
Stutterheim, John K. The Diary of Prisoner 17326: A Boy's Life in a Japanese Labor Camp. 2009. (World War II: the Global, Human, & Ethical Dimension Ser.). (ENG., Illus.). 228p. 37.00 *(978-0-8232-3150-8(X))* Fordham Univ. Pr.
Wedlake, Nick. Eat the Pretty Ones: A Testament. 2009. 236p. 24.99 *(978-1-4490-1714-9(2));* pap. 14.49 *(978-1-4389-8106-2(6))* AuthorHouse.
Williams, Randy. R Dee of South Ward Street, 1 vol. 2010. 92p. pap. 19.95 *(978-1-60703-624-1(X))* PublishAmerica, Inc.

BOYS—CONDUCT OF LIFE

Besley, Adrian. The Outdoor Book for Adventurous Boys: Essential Skills & Activities for Boys of All Ages. 2008. (Illus.). 224p. pap. 16.95 (978-1-59921-341-5(9), Lyons Pr.) Globe Pequot Pr., The.

Bond, Douglas. Fathers & Sons, Volume 1: Stand Fast in the Way of Truth. 2008. 331p. per. (978-1-59638-076-9(4)) P & R Publishing.

—Fathers & Sons, Volume 2: Hold Fast in a Broken World. 2008. (Fathers & Sons Ser.). 285p. pap. 14.99 (978-1-59638-077-6(2)) P & R Publishing.

Bridges, John & Curtis, Bryan. 50 Things Every Young Gentleman Should Know: What to Do, When to Do It, & Why. 2012. 208p. (J). 16.99 **(978-1-4016-0465-3(X))** Nelson, Thomas Inc.

Carmichiel, Joe. Permanent Adolescence: Why Boys Don't Grow Up. 2008. (ENG.). 235p. pap. 14.95 (978-0-88282-335-5(3)) New Horizon Pr. Pubs., Inc.

Chisholm, Dana S. Single Moms Raising Sons: Preparing Boys to Be Men When There's No Man Around. 2006. (ENG.). 192p. pap. 14.99 (978-0-8341-2308-3(8), 083-412-3088) Beacon Hill Pr. of Kansas City.

Cutler, Tom. 211 Things a Bright Boy Can Do. 2007. (ENG., Illus.). 336p. (gr. 12-18). 15.95 (978-0-399-53415-7(6), Perigee Trade) Penguin Group (USA) Inc.

Daly, Jim, illus. Training up a Little Guy: Inspiration & Wisdom for Raising Boys. 2006. 32p. 14.99 (978-0-7369-1801-5(9)) Harvest Hse. Pubs.

Dean, Jeffrey. One-Liner Wisdom for Today's Guys. 2006. (Between the Lines Ser.). (ENG., Illus.). 128p. pap. 9.00 (978-1-59052-971-3(5), Multnomah) Doubleday Religious Publishing Group, The.

Garande, Jaimie Oliver. From Father to Son: 17 Lessons for Successful Living. 2009. 104p. pap. 12.49 (978-1-4389-8838-2(9)) AuthorHouse.

Holliday, H. Reconnecting, Redirecting, & Redefining 21st Century Males. 2011. (ENG., Illus.). 168p. 50.00 (978-1-61048-475-6(4)); pap. 24.95 (978-1-61048-476-3(2)) Rowman & Littlefield Education.

Holliday, H. E. Reconnecting, Redirecting, & Redefining 21st Century Males. 2011. **(978-1-61048-477-0(0))** Rowman & Littlefield Education.

Jack, Zachary Michael. Uncle Henry Wallace: Letters to Farm Families. 2008. (ENG.). 215p. pap. 19.95 (978-1-55753-493-4(4)) Purdue Univ. Pr.

Johnson, Kelly H., et al. A Better Man: True American Heroes Speak to Young Men on Love, Power, Pride & What It Really Means to Be a Man. 2009. (Illus.). 286p. pap. 25.95 (978-1-883911-84-3(2)) Brandylane Pubs., Inc.

Just for Boys. 2006. pap. 8.99 (978-1-60034-298-1(1)) Xulon Pr., Inc.

Kunjufu, Jawanza. Raising Black Boys. 2007. (ENG., Illus.). 200p. pap. 19.95 (978-1-934155-07-3(1)) African American Images.

Lashlie, Celia. He'll Be OK: Growing Gorgeous Boys into Good Men. 2007. 224p. (978-0-7322-8450-3(3)) HarperCollins Pubs. Australia.

Mastrich, Jim. Really Winning. Date not set. pap. (978-0-312-32014-0(0), St. Martin's Paperbacks) St. Martin's Pr.

Mcclure, Ali. Making It Better for Boys in Schools, Families & Communities. 2008. (ENG., Illus.). 176p. 34.95 (978-1-85539-435-3(9), Network Continuum Education) Continuum International Publishing Group, Ltd. GBR. Dist: National Bk. Network.

Men of Integrity, compiled by. Boys to Men: 31 Day Devotional. 2006. 70p. (YA). per. 12.95 (978-0-9773973-2-7(7)) Cole Publishing.

Neall, Lucinda. About Our Boys: A Practical Guide to Bringing out the Best in Boys. 2007. 224p. pap. 27.50 (978-1-84753-576-4(3)) Lulu Enterprises Inc.

Olshine, David. I Want to Talk with My Teen about Guy Stuff. 2006. (I Want to Talk with My Teen Ser.). 96p. pap. 9.99 (978-0-7847-1894-0(6)) Standard Publishing.

Powell, Michael. The Guide for Guys: An Extremely Useful Manual for Old Boys & Young Men. 2008. (ENG., Illus.). 208p. 9.95 (978-1-4027-6315-1(8)) Sterling Publishing Co., Inc.

Rao, Anthony & Seaton, Michelle. The Way of Boys: Raising Healthy Boys in a Challenging & Complex World. 2009. 304p. 25.99 (978-0-06-170782-7(1), Morrow, William & Co.) HarperCollins Pubs.

Smith, Crystal. The Achilles Effect: What Pop Culture Is Teaching Young Boys about Masculinity. 2011. 240p. 28.95 (978-1-4502-8501-8(5)); pap. 18.95 (978-1-4502-8499-8(X)) iUniverse, Inc.

Sorenson, Jack, illus. Growing up Cowboy. 2008. 32p. 15.99 (978-0-7369-2228-9(8)) Harvest Hse. Pubs.

Stephenson, Bret. From Boys to Men: Spiritual Rites of Passage in an Indulgent Age. 2006. (ENG., Illus.). 1p. per. 18.95 (978-1-59477-140-8(5)) Inner Traditions International, Ltd.

Weinfeld, Rich & Neu, Terry W. Helping Boys Succeed in School: A Practical Guide for Parents & Teachers. 2006. (ENG.). 256p. pap. 16.95 (978-1-59363-198-7(7)) Prufrock Pr.

West, Kay. How to Raise a Gentleman: A Civilized Guide to Helping Your Son Through His Uncivilized Childhood. 2012. 208p. 16.99 **(978-1-4016-0461-5(7))** Nelson, Thomas Inc.

BOYS—JUVENILE LITERATURE

Wiggin, Kate Douglas. The Story of Patsy. 2010. (ENG.). 84p. pap. 18.75 (978-1-177-55174-8(8)); (ENG.). 96p. pap. 18.75 (978-1-177-00804-4(1)); (ENG.). 98p. pap. 18.75 (978-1-177-00815-0(7)); 96p. pap. 18.75 (978-1-178-06086-7(1)); 94p. pap. 18.75 (978-1-143-59571-4(8)); 102p. pap. 18.75 (978-1-141-46685-4(7)); 100p. pap. 18.75 (978-1-141-23319-9(3)); 100p. pap. 18.75 (978-1-141-19364-6(7)); 94p. pap. 18.75 (978-1-141-77683-2(9)) BiblioBazaar.

—The Story of Patsy. 2007. (ENG.). 52p. per. (978-1-4065-7777-8(4)) Dodo Pr.

—The Story of Patsy. 2010. 28p. pap. 14.14 (978-1-4432-5124-2(0)) General Bks. LLC.

—The Story of Patsy. 88p. 2011. 33.95 **(978-1-169-84300-4(X))** 2010. pap. 15.16 (978-1-162-71855-2(2)) 2010. 27.16 **(978-1-168-97467-9(4))** 2010. 33.95 (978-1-161-48701-5(8)) Kessinger Publishing, LLC.

BOYS—PRAYERS AND DEVOTIONS

O'Neal, Jayce. No Girls Allowed: Devotions for Boys. 2010. (ENG.). 256p. (J). pap. 9.99 (978-1-4143-3589-6(X), Tyndale Kids) Tyndale Hse. Pubs.

Strauss, Ed. The Ultimate Devo for Boys: 365 Daily Devotions. 2009. (2:52 Ser.). (ENG.). 416p. (J). pap. 12.99 (978-0-310-71314-2(5)) Zonderkidz.

BOYS—RELIGIOUS LIFE

Balducci, Rachel. How Do You Tuck in a Superhero? And Other Delightful Mysteries of Raising Boys. 2010. 208p. pap. 12.99 (978-0-8007-3372-8(X)) Revell.

Baldwin, Stan. Preguntas Dificiles Que Hacen Chicos: Tough Questions Boys Ask. (SPA.). 64p. (978-84-7228-226-1(0), 220710) Clie, Editorial.

Bond, Douglas. Fathers & Sons, Volume 1: Stand Fast in the Way of Truth. 2008. 331p. per. (978-1-59638-076-9(4)) P & R Publishing.

—Fathers & Sons, Volume 2: Hold Fast in a Broken World. 2008. (Fathers & Sons Ser.). 285p. pap. 14.99 (978-1-59638-077-6(2)) P & R Publishing.

Celebrating My First Communion: Padded Boys Set. 12.95 (978-0-89942-749-2(9), C806/42B, Resurrection Pr.) Catholic Bk. Publishing Corp.

Dean, Jeffrey. One-Liner Wisdom for Today's Guys. 2006. (Between the Lines Ser.). (ENG., Illus.). 128p. pap. 9.00 (978-1-59052-971-3(5), Multnomah) Doubleday Religious Publishing Group, The.

Dykstra, Robert C., et al. Losers, Loners, & Rebels: The Spiritual Struggles of Boys. 2007. (ENG.). 204p. per. 20.00 (978-0-664-22961-0(1)) Westminster John Knox Pr.

Fincher, Kathy, illus. Remembrance of My First Holy Communion-Boy. 2008. 28p. 14.95 (978-0-88271-780-7(4)) Regina Pr., Malhame & Co.

George, Jim & George, Elizabeth. A Little Boy after God's Own Heart. 2007. (Illus.). 32p. (J). 15.99 (978-0-7369-1782-7(9)) Harvest Hse. Pubs.

Wilson, Douglas. Future Men. 2011. **(978-1-59128-110-8(5))** Canon Pr.

Young, Hal & Young, Melanie. Raising Real Men: Surviving, Teaching & Appreciating Boys. 2010. 256p. pap. 15.00 (978-0-9841443-0-3(7)) Great Waters Pr.

BOYS IN THE BIBLE

see Children in the Bible

BOYS' TOWNS

see Children—Institutional Care

BRABANT (BELGIUM)

Caen, Joost. The Creation of Stained Glass in the Low Countries During the Renaissance & Baroque Eras: Materials & Techniques. 2009. (Corpus Vitrearum, Belgium, Studies). (ENG., Illus.). 456p. (C). 123.00 (978-1-905375-64-6(6)) Brepols Pubs. BEL. Dist: Brown, David Bk. Co., The.

BRACCIOLINI, POGGIO, 1380-1459

Ross, John Wilson. Tacitus & Bracciolini: The Annals Forged in the XVth Century. 2007. (ENG.). 304p. pap. 23.99 (978-1-4264-3391-7(3)); 332p. pap. 24.99 (978-1-4264-3441-9(3)) BiblioBazaar.

—Tacitus & Bracciolini: The Annals Forged in the XVth Century. 2007. 224p. per. (978-1-4068-4051-3(3)) Echo Library.

BRACERO FAMILY

Cohen, Deborah. Braceros: Migrant Citizens & Transnational Subjects in the Postwar United States & Mexico. 2011. (ENG., Illus.). 392p. 39.95 (978-0-8078-3359-9(2)) Univ. of North Carolina Pr.

BRACES, ORTHODONTIC

see Orthodontic Appliances

BRACHIAL PLEXUS

Ahmad, Muhammad Reda. Management of Late Obstetric Brachial Plexus Palsy. 2011. 156p. pap. **(978-3-8383-9534-0(4))** Lambert Academic Publishing.

Kumar, Amit, et al. Effect of Adding Fentanyl & Buprenorphine to L a in Brachial Block. 2011. 92p. pap. **(978-3-8443-1749-7(X))** Lambert Academic Publishing.

Nath, Rahul. Obstetric Brachial Plexus Injuries. 2006. (ENG., Illus.). 116p. per. 24.95 (978-1-58939-970-9(6)) Virtualbookworm.com Publishing, Inc.

Yang, Lynda J-S, et al. Practical Management of Pediatric & Adult Brachial Plexus Palsies. 2011. (ENG., Illus.). 408p. 249.00 (978-1-4377-0575-1(8), Saunders) Elsevier - Health Sciences Div.

BRACHIOPODA

Copper, Paul & Li, Rongyu. Early Silurian (Llandovery) Orthide Brachiopods from Anticosti Island, Eastern Canada The O/S Extinction Recovery Fauna, No. 76. 2006. (Special Papers in Palaeontology Ser.: 2). (ENG., Illus.). 80p. per. 145.95 (978-1-4051-6012-4(8), Wiley-Blackwell) Wiley, John & Sons, Inc.

BRACHIOPODA, FOSSIL

Alvarez, Fernando & Curry, Gordon, eds. Special Papers in Palaeontology No. 84: Evolution & Development of the Brachiopod Shell, Number 84. 2011. (Special Papers in Palaeontology Ser.). (ENG., Illus.). 334p. pap. 127.95 (978-1-4443-3937-6(0), Wiley-Blackwell) Wiley, John & Sons, Inc.

Baarli, B. G. Orthacean & Strophomenid Brachiopods from the Lower Silurian of the Central Oslo Region, Number 39. 2006. (Fossils & Strata Monograph Ser.: 39). (ENG.). 92p. pap. 44.95 (978-82-00-37659-0(1), Wiley-Blackwell) Wiley, John & Sons, Inc.

Davidson, Thomas. British Fossil Brachiopoda. (Cambridge Library Collection - Life Sciences Ser.). (ENG.). 2012. 528p. pap. 55.00 **(978-1-108-03821-8(2))** 2011. 532p. pap. 55.00 **(978-1-108-03817-1(4))** 2011. 172p. pap. 28.99 **(978-1-108-03822-5(0))** 2011. 504p. pap. 52.00 **(978-1-108-03818-8(2))** 2011. 476p. pap. 50.00 **(978-1-108-03820-1(4))** 2011. (Illus.). 682p. pap. 60.00 **(978-1-108-03819-5(0))** Cambridge Univ. Pr.

Holmer, L. E. & Popov, L. Cambrian-Ordovician Lingulate Brachiopods from Scandinavia, Kazakhstan & South Ural Mountains, Number 35. 2006. (Fossils & Strata Monograph Ser.: 35). (ENG.). 156p. pap. 59.95 (978-82-00-37651-4(6), Wiley-Blackwell) Wiley, John & Sons, Inc.

Nielsen, Claus, et al. Brachiopoda - Fossil & Recent, Volume 54. Harper, David A. T. et al, eds. 2009. (Fossils & Strata Monograph Ser.: 54). (ENG., Illus.). 336p. pap. 84.95 (978-1-4051-8664-3(X), Wiley-Blackwell) Wiley, John & Sons, Inc.

Perry, David G. Brachiopoda & Biostratigraphy of the Silurian-Devonian Delorme Formation in the District of Mackenzie, No. 138. (Illus.). 851p. pap. (978-0-88854-304-2(2)) BRILL.

BRACHYGRAPHY

see Abbreviations; Shorthand

BRACHYURA

see Crabs

BRACKENRIDGE, H. H. (HUGH HENRY), 1748-1816

Vincent, William Ellsworth. Hugh Henry Brackenridge & the Rising Glory of America. 2008. 236p. pap. 24.95 (978-1-60672-906-9(3)) PublishAmerica, Inc.

BRACKISH WATER BIOLOGY

Melzian, Brian D., et al, eds. Coastal Monitoring Through Partnerships. 2011. (ENG.). 420p. pap. 109.00 (978-90-481-6203-1(3), 9048162033) Springer.

BRADBURY, RAY, 1920-

Bloom, Harold. Ray Bradbury. 2nd rev. ed. 2010. (Bloom's Modern Critical Views Ser.). 246p. (C). (gr. 9-18). 45.00 (978-1-60413-805-4(X), Chelsea Hse.) Facts On File, Inc.

Bloom, Harold, ed. Ray Bradbury's Fahrenheit 451, New Edition. 2nd rev. ed. 2008. (Bloom's Modern Critical Interpretations Ser.). 144p. (C). (gr. 9). 45.00 (978-1-60413-144-4(6), Chelsea Hse.) Facts On File, Inc.

Bradbury, Ray. Fahrenheit 451. Bloom, Harold, ed. 2007. (Bloom's Guides). 96p. (C). (gr. 9-13). lib. bdg. 30.00 (978-0-7910-9294-1(1), Chelsea Hse.) Facts On File, Inc.

Eller, Jonathan R. Becoming Ray Bradbury. 2011. (ENG., Illus.). 360p. 34.95 **(978-0-252-03629-3(8))** Univ. of Illinois Pr.

Kahveci, Sirin. Metaphorical Death of the Character & the Text's Consuming Power. 2011. 76p. pap. **(978-3-8433-8836-8(9))** Lambert Academic Publishing.

Mancini, Candice. Censorship in Ray Bradbury's Fahrenheit 451. 2011. (Social Issues in Literature Ser.). 224p. lib. bdg. 38.45 (978-0-7377-5288-5(2)); (ENG., Illus.). pap. 26.50 (978-0-7377-5289-2(0)) Cengage Gale. (Greenhaven Pr., Inc.).

Stephens, Piers G. H. Nature, Liberty & Dystopia: On the Moral Significance of Nature for Human Freedom. 2013. (Routledge Research in Environmental Politics Ser.). (ENG.). 224p. (C). 130.00 (978-0-415-38506-0(7)) Routledge.

Touponce, William F., ed. The New Ray Bradbury Review, No. 1. 2008. pap. 25.00 (978-0-87338-990-7(5)) Kent State Univ. Pr.

Weller, Sam & Bradbury, Ray. Listen to the Echoes: The Ray Bradbury Interviews. 2010. (ENG., Illus.). 336p. pap. 18.95 (978-1-935554-03-5(4)) Melville Hse. Publishing.

Willia, Touponce, ed. New Ray Bradbury Review. 2011. 92p. pap. 25.00 (978-1-60635-037-9(4)) Kent State Univ. Pr.

BRADDOCK, EDWARD, 1695-1755

Bricker, Calvin, Jr. & Powell, Walter L. Conflict on the Conococheague, 1755-1758: Terror in the backcountry of Pennsylvania & Maryland. Werner, Leda M., ed. 2008. (Illus.). 81p. pap. 10.00 (978-0-615-25164-6(1)) Conococheague Institute.

Crocker, Thomas E. Braddock's March: How the Man Sent to Seize a Continent Changed American History. (ENG., Illus.). 2011. 352p. pap. 15.95 **(978-1-59416-152-0(6))** 2009. 384p. 28.00 (978-1-59416-096-7(1)) Westholme Publishing.

McCardell, Lee. Ill-Starred General: Braddock of the Coldstream Guards. Starrett, Agnes L., ed. 2011. 356p. 51.95 **(978-1-258-02749-0(6))** Literary Licensing, LLC.

BRADDOCK'S CAMPAIGN, 1755

Clary, David A. George Washington's First War: His Early Military Adventures. 2011. (ENG., Illus.). 384p. pap. 16.00 (978-1-4391-8111-9(X)); 27.00 (978-1-4391-8110-2(1)) Simon & Schuster.

Crocker, Thomas E. Braddock's March: How the Man Sent to Seize a Continent Changed American History. 2011. (ENG., Illus.). 352p. pap. 15.95 **(978-1-59416-152-0(6))** Westholme Publishing.

Hadden, James. Washington's Early Campaigns: The French Post Expedition, Great Meadows & Braddock's Defeat-including Braddock's Orderly Books. 2009. 184p. (978-1-84677-628-1(7)); pap. (978-1-84677-627-4(9)) Leonaur Ltd.

Sargent, Winthrop, abr. The History of an Expedition. 2009. (Military History Ser.). (ENG.). 443p. pap. 27.95 (978-1-4290-2120-3(9)) Applewood Bks.

BRADFORD, WILLIAM, 1588-1657

Bradford, William. History of Plimoth Plantation. 2010. (Historiography Ser.). 643p. pap. 37.95 (978-1-4290-2285-9(X)) Applewood Bks.

Dexter, Henry Martyn. Mourt's Relation or Journal of the Plantation at Plymouth. 2007. 232p. per. 15.45 (978-1-59462-666-1(9), Book Jungle) Standard Pubns., Inc.

Donohue, Betty Booth. Bradford's Indian Book: Being the True Roote & Rise of American Letters as Revealed by the Native Text Embedded in of Plimoth Plantation. 2011. (ENG., Illus.). 176p. 69.95 (978-0-8130-3737-0(9)) Univ. Pr. of Florida.

Nathaniel Philbrick. Mayflower: A Story of Courage, Communtiy, & War. l.t. ed. 2007. (ENG.). 752p. (J). pap. 15.95 (978-1-59413-186-8(4), Large Print Pr.) Thorndike Pr.

Pafford, John M. How Firm a Foundation: William Bradford & Plymouth. 2008. 140p. pap. 19.00 (978-0-7884-2140-2(9)) Heritage Bks.

Philbrick, Nathaniel. Mayflower: A Story of Courage, Community, & War. 2007. (ENG., Illus.). 480p. (gr. 12-18). 16.00 (978-0-14-311197-9(3), Penguin (Non-Classics)) Penguin Group (USA) Inc.

Pope, Charles Henry. The Plymouth Scrap Book: The Oldest Original Documents Extant in Plymouth Archives. 149p. reprint ed. 88.00 (978-0-7222-6649-6(9)) Library Reprints, Inc.

Thompson, Jon. After Paradise - Essays on the Fate of American Writing. 2009. 136p. pap. (978-1-84861-041-5(6)) Shearsman Bks.

BRADFORD, WILLIAM, 1663-1752

Wallace, John. An Address Delivered at the Celebration by the New York Historical Society, May 20 1863. 2009. (Amer Philosophy, Religion Ser.). (ENG.). 124p. pap. 11.95 (978-1-4290-1924-8(7)) Applewood Bks.

BRADLAUGH, CHARLES, 1833-1891

Courtney, Janet Elizabeth Hogarth. Freethinkers of the Nineteenth Century. 2009. 142p. pap. 19.99 (978-0-217-93713-9(6)) General Bks. LLC.

—Freethinkers of the Nineteenth Century. 2008. 284p. pap. (978-1-4097-6403-8(6)); pap. (978-1-4097-1919-9(7)) Read Bks.

Headingley, Adolphe. The Biography of Charles Bradlaugh. 2009. 72p. pap. (978-0-217-57329-0(0)) Books LLC.

Robertson, John M. Charles Bradlaugh. 2007. (ENG.). 140p. 35.95 (978-0-548-14850-1(3)) 2006. pap. 20.95 (978-1-4286-6357-2(6)) Kessinger Publishing, LLC.

BRADLEE, BENJAMIN C., 1921-

Bradlee, Ben. Conversations with Kennedy. 640p. 7.98 (978-1-56852-292-0(4), Konecky & Konecky) Konecky, William S. Assocs., Inc.

BRADLEY, ANDREW CECIL, 1851-1935

DiPietro, Cary, ed. Bradley, Greg, Folger: Great Shakespeareans. 2011. (Great Shakespeareans Ser.). (ENG.). 224p. 140.00 (978-0-8264-4611-4(6)) Continuum International Publishing Group, Ltd. GBR. Dist: National Bk. Network.

BRADLEY, BILL, 1943-

Bradley, Bill. Life on the Run. 2009. (ENG.). 288p. pap. 29.95 (978-1-4128-1274-0(7)) Transaction Pubs.

BRADLEY, F. H. (FRANCIS HERBERT), 1846-1924

Allard, James. The Logical Foundations of Bradley's Metaphysics: Judgment, Inference, & Truth. 2011. (ENG.). 262p. pap. 35.99 (978-0-521-17421-3(X)) Cambridge Univ. Pr.

Bosanquet, Bernard. Knowledge & Reality. 2009. 192p. pap. (978-0-217-22969-2(7)) Books LLC.

Bosanquet, Bernard. Knowledge & Reality: A Criticism of Mr F. H. Bradley's 'Principles of Logic' 2011. (Cambridge Library Collection - Philosophy Ser.). (ENG.). 350p. pap. 28.99 **(978-1-108-04018-1(7))** Cambridge Univ. Pr.

Candlish, Stewart. The Russell/Bradley Dispute & its Significance for Twentieth Century Philosophy. 2009. (ENG.). 240p. pap. 36.00 (978-0-230-23051-4(2)) Palgrave Macmillan.

—The Russell/Bradley Dispute & Its Significance for Twentieth-Century Philosophy. annot. ed. 2007. (ENG.). 256p. 100.00 (978-0-230-50685-5(2)) Palgrave Macmillan.

Mallinson, J. E. T. S. Eliot's Interpretation of F. H. Bradley: Seven Essays. 2010. 106p. pap. 89.95 (978-90-481-6162-1(2), 9048161622) Springer.

BRADLEY, OMAR NELSON, 1893-1981

Axelrod, Alan. Bradley. (Great Generals Ser.). (ENG., Illus.). 224p. 2009. pap. 12.95 (978-0-230-61444-4(2)) 2007. 21.95 (978-0-230-60018-8(2)) Palgrave Macmillan.

DeFelice, Jim. Omar Bradley: General at War. 2011. (ENG., Illus.). 400p. 29.95 (978-1-59698-139-3(3)) Regnery Publishing, Inc., An Eagle Publishing Co.

Jordan, Jonathan W. Brothers, Rivals, Victors: Eisenhower, Patton, Bradley & the Partnership That Drove the Allied Conquest in Europe. 2011. (ENG.). 672p. (gr. 12). 28.95 (978-0-451-23212-0(7), N A L Hardcover) Penguin Group (USA) Inc.

Jordan, Jonathan W. Brothers, Rivals, Victors: Eisenhower, Patton, Bradley & the Partnership that Drove the Allied Conquest in Europe. 2012. (ENG.). 672p. (gr. 12). 17.00 **(978-0-451-23583-1(5))**, N A L Trade) Penguin Group (USA) Inc.

Latawski, Paul. D-Day Landings: The Falaise Pocket. 2012. (D-Day Landings Ser.). (ENG., Illus.). 192p. pap. 17.95 **(978-0-7524-7663-6(7))** History Pr. Ltd.,The GBR. Dist: Independent Pubs. Group.

Zaloga, Steven. Omar Bradley. 2012. (Command Ser.). (ENG., Illus.). 64p. pap. 17.95 **(978-1-84908-660-8(5))** Osprey Publishing, Ltd. GBR. Dist: Random Hse., Inc.

BRADSHAW, TERRY, 1948-

Bradshaw, Terry. It's Only a Game. 2011. (ENG.). 384p. pap. 23.99 **(978-1-4516-6897-1(X))** Pocket Books.

BRADSTREET, ANNE, 1612?-1672

Boschman, Robert. In the Way of Nature: Ecology & Westward Expansion in the Poetry of Anne Bradstreet, Elizabeth Bishop & Amy Clampitt. 2009. (ENG.). 236p. pap. 39.95 (978-0-7864-3356-8(6)) McFarland & Co., Inc. Pubs.
Campbell, Helen. Anne Bradstreet & Her Time. 2008. 344p. 28.99 (978-0-554-33096-9(2)) 2008. 344p. 29.99 (978-0-554-23793-0(8)) 2007. (ENG.). 300p. pap. 21.99 (978-1-4264-5026-6(5)) 2006. 342p. pap. 24.99 (978-1-4264-5327-4(2)) BiblioBazaar.
—Anne Bradstreet & Her Time. 2007. (ENG.). 228p. per. (978-1-4068-4173-2(0)) Echo Library.
Campbell, Helen S. Anne Bradstreet & Her Time. 2007. pap. (978-1-4065-1247-2(8)) Dodo Pr.
Dykeman, Therese Boos. Contributions by Women to Early American Philosophy: Anne Bradstreet, Mercy Otis Warren, & Judith Sargent Murray. 2009. (Illus.). 348p. 119.95 (978-0-7734-4685-4(0)) Mellen, Edwin Pr., The.

BRADWARDINE, THOMAS, 1290?-1349

Leff, Gordon. Bradwardine & the Pelagians: A Study of his 'de Causa Dei' & it's Opponents. 2008. (Cambridge Studies in Medieval Life & Thought: New Ser.). (ENG.). 300p. pap. 38.99 (978-0-521-08162-7(9)) Cambridge Univ. Pr.
Read, S. Thomas Bradwardine, Insolubilia. 2010. (Dallas Medieval Texts & Translations Ser.). (ENG.). 227p. (C). pap. 57.00 (978-90-429-2317-1(2)) Peeters Pubs. & Booksellers BEL. Dist: Brown, David Bk. Co., The.

BRADY, IAN, 1938-

Cowley, Chris. Face to Face with Evil: Conversations with Ian Brady. 2011. (ENG., Illus.). 290p. pap. 13.95 (978-1-84454-981-8(X)) Blake, John Publishing, Ltd. GBR. Dist: Independent Pubs. Group.

BRADY, JAMES BUCHANAN, 1856-1917

Morell, Parker. Diamond Jim: The Life & Times of James Buchanan Brady. 2007. (ENG.). 340p. 46.95 (978-0-548-05990-6(X)) Kessinger Publishing, LLC.

BRADY, MATHEW B., 1823-1896

Milhollen, Hirst D. Civil War Photographs, 1861-1865. Milhollen, Hirst D. & Mugridge, Donald H., eds. 2011. 88p. 38.95 (978-1-258-01786-6(5)) Literary Licensing, LLC.
Phillips, John Ransom & Trachtenberg, Alan. Ransoming Mathew Brady. 2010. (ENG., Illus.). 300p. 60.00 (978-1-55595-326-3(3)) Hudson Hills Pr. LLC.
Savas, Theodore P. Brady's Civil War Journal: Day-by-Day Events 1861-1865. 2008. 256p. 24.95 (978-1-60239-292-2(7)) Skyhorse Publishing Co., Inc.
Savas, Theodore P. Brady's Civil War Journal: Photographing the War, 1861-65. 2012. (ENG., Illus.). 256p. 29.95 (978-1-62087-052-5(5), 620052) Skyhorse Publishing Co., Inc.

BRADYKININ

see Kinins

BRAGG, BRAXTON, 1817-1876

Hallock, Judith Lee. Braxton Bragg & Confederate Defeat, V. II. 2009. (ENG., Illus.). 312p. pap. 29.95 (978-0-8173-5594-4(4)) Univ. of Alabama Pr.
Martin, Samuel J. General Braxton Bragg, C. S. A. 2011. (ENG., Illus.). 536p. 55.00 (978-0-7864-5934-6(4)) McFarland & Co., Inc. Pubs.

BRAGG, WILLIAM LAWRENCE, SIR, 1890-1971

Jenkin, John. William & Lawrence Bragg, Father & Son: The Most Extraordinary Collaboration in Science. (ENG., Illus.). 500p. 2011. pap. 45.00 (978-0-19-960670-2(6)) 2008. 85.00 (978-0-19-923520-9(1)) Oxford Univ. Pr., Inc.

BRAHE, TYCHO, 1546-1601

Brewster, David. Martyrs of Science or the Lives of Galil. 2006. pap. 28.95 (978-1-4286-4147-1(5)) Kessinger Publishing, LLC.
Christianson, John Robert. On Tycho's Island: Tycho Brahe & His Assistants, 1570-1601. 2009. (ENG., Illus.). 464p. pap. 58.00 (978-0-521-10106-6(9)) Cambridge Univ. Pr.
Jardine, Nicholas, et al. La Guerre des Astronomes: La Querelle Au Sujet de L'origine du Système Géo-Héliocentrique à la Fin du XVIe Siècle. 2008. (LAT & FRE., Illus.). (C). 286p. pap. 60.00 (978-2-251-34513-0(2)); 852p. pap. 128.00 (978-2-251-34512-3(4)) Societe d'edition Les Belles lettres FRA. Dist: ISD.
Mosley, Adam. Bearing the Heavens: Tycho Brahe & the Astronomical Community of the Late Sixteenth Century. (ENG.). 2011. 370p. pap. 45.00 (978-1-107-40365-9(0)) 2007. (Illus.). 368p. 126.00 (978-0-521-83866-5(5)) Cambridge Univ. Pr.
Thoren, Victor E. The Lord of Uraniborg: A Biography of Tycho Brahe. 2007. (ENG., Illus.). 536p. pap. 100.00 (978-0-521-03307-7(1)) Cambridge Univ. Pr.

BRAHMAN MYTHOLOGY

see Hindu Mythology; Vedas

BRAHMANANDA, SWAMI, 1863-1922

Atmashraddhananda. Swami Brahmananda As We Saw Him: Reminiscences of Monastic & Lay Devotees. 2010. (Illus.). xii, 588p. (978-81-7823-549-3(8)) Sri Ramakrishna Math.
Vedanta Press. Memories of Maharaj: New Reminiscences by Disciples & Devotees. 2011. 80p. 37.95 (978-1-258-03430-6(1)) Literary Licensing, LLC.

BRAHMANAS

Cavallin, Clemens. The Efficacy of Sacrifice. 2011. 236p. pap. (978-3-8433-8956-3(X)) Lambert Academic Publishing.
Girard, René. Sacrifice. 2011. (Breakthroughs in Mimetic Theory Ser.). (ENG.). 104p. pap. 14.95 (978-0-87013-992-5(4)) Michigan State Univ. Pr.
Jamison, Stephanie. The Ravenous Hyenas & the Wounded Sun: Myth & Ritual in Ancient India. 2011. (Myth & Poetics Ser.). (Illus.). 360p. pap. 35.00 (978-0-8014-7732-4(8)) Cornell Univ. Pr.
The Satapatha-Brahmana, 5 Vols. reprint ed. 340.00 (978-0-7222-9947-0(8)) Library Reprints, Inc.

BRAHMANISM

see also Caste—India; Hindu Sects; Hinduism

Bandyopadhyaya, Jayantanuja. Class & Religion in Ancient India. 2008. (Anthem Press India Ser.). (ENG.). 264p. 80.00 (978-1-84331-727-2(3)) Anthem Pr. GBR. Dist: Books International, Inc.
Bronkhorst, Johannes. Buddhism in the Shadow of Brahmanism. 2011. 320p. (978-90-04-20140-8(8)) BRILL.
Champakalakshmi, R. Religion, Tradition, & Ideology: Pre-colonial South India. 2011. (ENG., Illus.). 600p. 110.00 (978-0-19-807059-7(4)) Oxford Univ. Pr., Inc.
Desamukha, Panjabarava. The Origin & Development of Religion in Vedic Literature. 2007. 385p. 75.00 (978-1-57898-583-8(8)) Martino Publishing.
Jolly, Julius. The Minor Law-Books. 396p. reprint ed. 68.00 (978-0-7222-9955-5(9)) Library Reprints, Inc.
Jolly, Julius, et al. The Minor Law-Books. 2009. 422p. 41.99 (978-1-117-00438-9(4)); (ENG.). 421p. pap. 34.75 (978-1-117-00439-6(2)) BiblioBazaar.
Ray, Nihar-Ranjan. Brahmanical Gods in Burma: A Chapter of Indian Art & Iconography. reprint ed. 32.50 (978-0-404-16852-0(3)) AMS Pr., Inc.
Sankara. The Vedanta Sutras of Badarayana, Part 1-2. Thibaut, George, tr. 2011. 1086p. 84.95 (978-1-258-05692-6(5)) Literary Licensing, LLC.
Smith, Harold F. Outline of Hinduism. 2007. 140p. per. (978-1-4067-8944-7(5), Pierides Pr.) Read Bks.
Wynne, Alexander. The Origin of Buddhist Meditation. 2009. 174p. pap. 39.95 (978-0-415-54467-2(X)) 2007. 169p. 160.00 (978-0-415-42387-8(2)) Routledge.
Zacharias, Hans Conrad Ernst. Studies on Hinduism V1: Vedism. 2011. 218p. 44.95 (978-1-258-00773-7(8)) Literary Licensing, LLC.
—Studies on Hinduism V2: Brahmanism. 2011. 224p. 44.95 (978-1-258-00780-5(0)) Literary Licensing, LLC.
—Studies on Hinduism V3: Philosophical Brahmanism. 2011. 216p. 44.95 (978-1-258-00781-2(9)) Literary Licensing, LLC.
—Studies on Hinduism V4: Sectarian Religions & Philosophical Systems. 2011. 272p. 47.95 (978-1-258-00782-9(7)) Literary Licensing, LLC.

BRAHMANS

Anslow, Maurice. I Am Brahman: A Personal Quest into the Advaita Reality. 2010. (ENG.) 126p. pap. 16.95 (978-1-84694-366-9(3)) O Bks., John Hunt.
Jacobi, Hermann. The Dates of the Philosophical Sutras of the Brahmans. 2010. pap., pap. 19.48 (978-1-61143-150-6(6)) Gorgias Pr., LLC.
Olivelle, Patrick. Ascetics & Brahmins: Studies in Ideologies & Institutions. 2011. (Cultural, Historical & Textual Studies of Religions Ser.). (Illus.). 328p. 99.00 (978-0-85728-432-7(0)) Anthem Pr. GBR. Dist: Books International, Inc.

BRAHMS, JOHANNES, 1833-1897

Bozarth, George S., et al. Johannes Brahms & George Henschel: An Enduring Friendship. 2008. (ENG., Illus.). 355p. pap. 44.00 (978-0-89990-140-4(9)) Harmonie Park Pr.
Brahms. Brahms - Symphony No. 3. 2008. (ENG.). 106p. pap. 16.99 incl. audio compact disk (978-3-7957-6519-4(6), 3795765196) Schott Musik International GmbH & Co. KG DEU. Dist: Leonard, Hal Corp.
—Brahms - Violin Concerto. 2008. (ENG.). 116p. pap. 16.99 incl. audio compact disk (978-3-7957-6526-2(9), 3795765269) Schott Musik International GmbH & Co. KG DEU. Dist: Leonard, Hal Corp.
Brahms, Johannes. Hungarian Dances & Other Works for Solo Piano. 2007. (Dover Music for Piano Ser.). (ENG.). 64p. pap. 6.95 (978-0-486-45722-2(2)) Dover Pubns., Inc.
Bruch. Brahms - Violin Concerto No. 1. 2008. (ENG.). 106p. pap. 14.99 incl. audio compact disk (978-3-7957-6518-7(8), 3795765188) Schott Musik International GmbH & Co. KG DEU. Dist: Leonard, Hal Corp.
Bülow, Hans von & Hinrichsen, Hans-Joachim. Hans Von Bülow's Letters to Johannes Brahms: A Research Edition. 2012. E-Book (978-0-8108-8216-4(7)) Scarecrow Pr., Inc.
Clive, Peter & Clive, H. P. Brahms & His World: A Biographical Dictionary. 2006. (ENG.). 640p. 116.00 (978-0-8108-5721-6(9)) Scarecrow Pr., Inc.
Deiters, Hermann. Johannes Brahms: A Biographical Sketch. Newmarch, Rosa, tr. 2009. (Cambridge Library Collection - Music Ser.). (ENG., Illus.). 176p. pap. 21.00 (978-1-108-00479-4(2)) Cambridge Univ. Pr.
Floros, Constantin & Bernhardt-Kabisch, Ernest. Johannes Brahms, Free but Alone: A Life for a Poetic Music. 2010. (Illus.). x, 291p. 72.95 (978-3-631-61260-6(5)) Lang, Peter Publishing, Inc.
Frisch, Walter & Karnes, Kevin C., eds. Brahms & His World. rev. ed. 2009. (Bard Music Festival Ser.). (ENG., Illus.). 480p. (C). 70.00 (978-0-691-14343-9(9)); pap. 27.95 (978-0-691-14344-6(7)) Princeton Univ. Pr.
Geiringer, Karl. Brahms His Life & Work. 2011. 394p. pap. 33.75 (978-1-174-62833-7(2)) BiblioBazaar.
Geiringer, Karl. On Brahms & His Circle: Essays & Documentary Studies. 2006. (Detroit Monographs in Musicology/Studies in Music: No. 49). (ENG., Illus.). 448p. 56.00 (978-0-89990-136-7(0)) Harmonie Park Pr.
Hal Leonard Corporation Staff. Unlocking the Masters Set: Bach's Keyboard Music, Beethoven's Symphonies, & Brahms - A Listener's Guide. deluxe ed. 2010. (ENG.). 500p. pap. 55.00 incl. audio compact disk (978-1-57467-192-6(8), 1574671928, Amadeus Press) Leonard, Hal Corp.
Hinrichsen, Hans-Joa. Hans Von Bulow's Letters to Johannes Brahms. 2011. (ENG., Illus.). 170p. (gr. 17). 75.00 (978-0-8108-8215-7(9)) Scarecrow Pr., Inc.
Hull, Kenneth. Brahms Symphony No. 4. Date not set. (978-0-393-03600-2(9)) Norton, W. W. & Co., Inc.
Hurwitz, David & Hurwitz. Brahms's Symphonies: A Closer Look. 2009. (Magnum Opus Ser.). (ENG., Illus.). 144p. pap. 19.95 (978-0-8264-3164-6(X)) Continuum International Publishing Group, Ltd. GBR. Dist: National Bk. Network.
May, Florence. The Life of Johannes Brahms. 2008. 328p. 28.99 (978-0-559-50979-7(0)); pap. 30.75 (978-0-559-50975-9(8)) BiblioBazaar.
—The Life of Johannes Brahms. 2009. 266p. pap. 20.31 (978-1-4589-2569-5(2)); 230p. pap. 20.21 (978-1-4589-2567-1(6)) General Bks. LLC.
—The Life of Johannes Brahms Second Edition, Revised. 2nd ed. 2009. (Illus.). 768p. pap. (978-1-84955-035-2(2)) Travis & Emery Music Bookshop.
McClelland, Ryan. Brahms & the Scherzo: Studies in Musical Narrative. 2010. (Illus.). 336p. 124.95 (978-0-7546-6810-7(X)) Ashgate Publishing Co.
Owen, Barbara. The Organ Music of Johannes Brahms. 2007. (ENG., Illus.). 208p. 40.00 (978-0-19-531107-5(8)) Oxford Univ. Pr., Inc.
Pascall, Robert. Brahms: Biographical, Documentary & Analytical Studies. 2008. (ENG., Illus.). 224p. pap. 32.99 (978-0-521-08836-7(4)) Cambridge Univ. Pr.
Platt, Heather, ed. Johannes Brahms. 2nd rev. ed. 2011. (Routledge Music Bibliographies Ser.). (ENG.). 576p. 150.00 (978-0-415-99456-9(X)) Routledge.
Quigley. Johannes Brahms, 2 vols. pap. 165.00 (978-0-8108-3501-6(0)) Scarecrow Pr., Inc.
Russell, Peter. Johannes Brahms & Klaus Groth: The Biography of a Friendship. 2006. (Illus.). 206p. 110.00 (978-0-7546-5544-2(X)) Ashgate Publishing Co.
Schmitz, Peter. Johannes Brahms und der Leipziger Musikverlag Breitkopf & Härtel. 2009. (Abhandlungen zur Musikgeschichte Ser.). (GER., Illus.). 393p. (C). 84.00 (978-3-89971-728-0(7)) Vandenhoeck & Ruprecht GmbH & Co. KG DEU. Dist: ISD.
Smith, Peter H. & Platt, Heather A., eds. Expressive Intersections in Brahms: Essays in Analysis & Meaning. 2012. (Musical Meaning & Interpretation Ser.). (ENG., Illus.). 336p. 44.95 (978-0-253-35705-2(5), 0253357055) Indiana Univ. Pr.
Van Rij, Inge. Brahms's Song Collections. 2006. (ENG., Illus.). 280p. 108.99 (978-0-521-83558-9(5)) Cambridge Univ. Pr.
van Rij, Inge. Brahms's Song Collections. 2009. (ENG., Illus.). 284p. pap. 42.00 (978-0-521-12182-8(5)) Cambridge Univ. Pr.
Young, John Bell. Brahms. 2008. (Unlocking the Masters Ser.). (ENG.). 224p. pap. 22.99 incl. audio compact disk (978-1-57467-171-1(5), 1574671715, Amadeus Press) Leonard, Hal Corp.

BRAID

Carey, Jacqui. Japanese Braiding: The Art of Kumihimo. 2009. (ENG., Illus.). 96p. spiral bd. 21.95 (978-1-84448-426-3(2)) Search Pr., Ltd. GBR. Dist: Independent Pubs. Group.
—200 Braids to Twist, Knot, Loop, or Weave. 2007. (ENG., Illus.). 256p. 27.95 (978-1-59668-018-0(0)) Interweave Pr., LLC.
Imperia, Giovanna. Kumihimo Wire Jewelry: Essential Techniques & 20 Jewelry Projects for the Japanese Art of Braiding. 2011. (ENG., Illus.). 144p. pap. 21.99 (978-0-8230-8551-4(1)) Watson-Guptill Pubns., Inc.
Kim, Hee-Jin. Maedeup: The Art of Traditional Korean Knots. 2007. (Illus.). 160p. pap. (978-1-56591-233-5(0)) Hollym International Corp.
Miller, Jane Hardy. French Braid Transformation. 2011. (ENG., Illus.). 80p. pap. 24.95 (978-1-60705-228-9(8)) C & T Publishing.
Stormes, Chuck & Reeves, Don. Luis Ortega's Rawhide Artistry: Braiding in the California Tradition. 2010. (Western Legacies Ser.). (ENG., Illus.). 160p. (C). pap. 29.95 (978-0-8061-4091-9(7)) Univ. of Oklahoma Pr.

BRAID THEORY

Berger, Mitchell A., et al. Lectures on Topological Fluid Mechanics. Ricca, Renzo L., ed. 2009. (Lecture Notes in Mathematics / Fondazione C. I. M. E., Firenze Ser.). (ENG., Illus.). xii, 221p. pap. 69.95 (978-3-642-00836-8(4), 3642008364) Springer.
Berrick, A. Jon. Braids: Introductory Lectures on Braids, Configurations & Their Applications. 2009. (Illus.). 416p. 111.00 (978-981-4291-40-8(4)) World Scientific Publishing Co., Inc.
Broué, Michel. Introduction to Complex Reflection Groups & Their Braid Groups. 2010. (Lecture Notes in Mathematics Ser.). (Illus.). xi, 138p. pap. 49.95 (978-3-642-11174-7(2), 3642111742) Springer.
Dehornoy, Patrick, et al. Ordering Braids. 2008. (Mathematical Surveys & Monographs Ser.). (Illus.). 323p. 92.00 (978-0-8218-4431-1(8)) American Mathematical Society.
Feder, Elie. Algorithmic Problems in the Braid Group. 2009. 84p. pap. (978-3-639-13898-6(8)) VDM Verlag Dr. Mueller e.K.
Iqbal, Zaffar. The Braid Groups. 2011. 64p. pap. (978-3-8443-2156-2(X)) Lambert Academic Publishing.
Kassel, Christia & Turaev, Vladimir. Braid Groups. 2007. (Graduate Texts in Mathematics Ser.). (Illus.) 320p. (C). 64.95 (978-0-387-33841-5(1)) Springer.
Kassel, Christian & Turaev, Vladimir. Braid Groups. 2010. (Graduate Texts in Mathematics Ser.). (Illus.). xi, 340p. pap. 64.95 (978-1-4419-2220-5(2), 1441922202) Springer.
Murasugi, Kunio & Kurpita, B. A Study of Braids. 2010. (Mathematics & Its Applications Ser.). (Illus.). 288p. pap. 139.00 (978-90-481-5245-2(3), 9048152453) Springer.

BRAIDED RUGS

see Rugs, Braided

BRAIDISM

see Hypnotism

BRAILLE BOOKS

see Blind—Books and Reading

BRAILLE MUSIC NOTATION

see also Blind—Printing and Writing Systems

Díaz Villarías, Mercedes. Canciones en Braille. 2008. (SPA.). 108p. pap. 40.50 (978-1-4092-1350-5(1)) Lulu Enterprises Inc.
Ockelford, Adam & Matawa, Christina. Focus on Music Vol. 2: Exploring the Musicality of Children & Young People with Retinopathy of Prematurity. 2010. (ENG., Illus.). 140p. pap. 20.95 (978-0-85473-861-8(4)) Institute of Education GBR. Dist: Stylus Publishing, LLC.

BRAILLE SYSTEM

see Blind—Printing and Writing Systems

BRAIN

see also Alpha Rhythm; Basal Ganglia; Brain Stem; Cerebellum; Cerebral Cortex; Cerebral Hemispheres; Cerebrospinal Fluid; Dreams; Head; Hypothalamus; Limbic System; Memory; Mind and Body; Nervous System; Pituitary Gland; Psychology; Sleep; Thalamus

Ackerman, Sandra. Discovering the Brain. 2009. 140p. pap. 7.30 (978-1-151-08294-7(5)) General Bks. LLC.
Al-Chalabi, Ammar, et al. Brain. 2008. (Beginners Guide (Oneworld) Ser.). (ENG., Illus.). 192p. pap. 14.95 (978-1-85168-594-3(4)) Oneworld Pubns. GBR. Dist: National Bk. Network.
Alper, Matthew. The 'God' Part of the Brain: A Scientific Interpretation of Human Spirituality & God. 2008. (ENG.). 288p. pap. 16.99 (978-1-4022-1452-3(9)) Sourcebooks, Inc.
Alves, Angelo M. A Quest for Control of the Visceral Brain-the Emotional Brain: A New Paradigm for the Twenty-first Century, Transcranial Brain Stimulation-Modulation. 2008. (Illus.). 304p. pap. 100.00 (978-0-8059-7527-7(6)) Dorrance Publishing Co., Inc.
Amen, Daniel G. The Amen Solution: The Brain Healthy Way to Get Thinner, Smarter, Happier. 2011. (ENG., Illus.). 368p. pap. 16.00 (978-0-307-46361-6(3) Three Rivers Pr.) Crown Publishing Group.
—The Amen Solution: The Brain Healthy Way to Lose Weight & Keep It Off. 2011. (Illus.). 368p. 25.99 (978-0-307-46360-9(5), Harmony) Crown Publishing Group.
—The Brain in Love: 12 Lessons to Enhance Your Love Life. 2009. (ENG., Illus.). 288p. pap. 14.00 (978-0-307-58789-3(4), Three Rivers Pr.) Crown Publishing Group.
—Change Your Brain, Change Your Body: Use Your Brain to Get & Keep the Body You Have Always Wanted. 2010. (ENG., Illus.). 384p. pap. 16.00 (978-0-307-46358-6(3), Three Rivers Pr.); 25.99 (978-0-307-46357-9(5), Harmony) Crown Publishing Group.
—Change Your Brain, Change Your Body Cookbook: Cook Right to Live Longer, Look Younger, Be Thinner & Decrease Your Risk of Obesity, Depression, Alzheimer's Disease, Heart Disease, Cancer & Diabetes. 2010. 167p. 29.95 (978-1-886554-27-6(7)) MindWorks Pr.
—Change Your Brain, Change Your Body Daily Journal. 2010. 233p. spiral bd. 19.95 (978-1-886554-30-6(7)) MindWorks Pr.
—Change Your Brain, Change Your Body Questionnaires: With Scoring Keys. 2010. 34p. pap. 49.95 (978-1-886554-31-3(5)) MindWorks Pr.
—Healing the Hardware of the Soul: Enhance Your Brain to Improve Your Work, Love, & Spiritual Life. 2008. (ENG., Illus.). 304p. pap. 15.00 (978-1-4391-0039-4(X), Free Pr.) Free Pr.
—Magnificent Mind at Any Age: Natural Ways to Unleash Your Brain's Maximum Potential. 2009. (ENG., Illus.). 352p. pap. 16.00 (978-0-307-33910-2(6), Three Rivers Pr.) Crown Publishing Group.
—Making a Good Brain Great: The Amen Clinic Program for Achieving & Sustaining Optimal Mental Performance. 2006. (ENG., Illus.). 336p. per. 15.00 (978-1-4000-8209-4(9), Three Rivers Pr.) Crown Publishing Group.
Amen, Daniel G. Use Your Brain to Change Your Age: Secrets to Look, Feel, & Think Younger Every Day. 2012. (ENG., Illus.). 384p. 26.00 (978-0-307-88854-9(1), Crown Archetype) Crown Publishing Group.
Amthor, Frank. Neuroscience for Dummies. 2011. (ENG.). 384p. pap. 21.99 (978-1-118-08686-5(4), For Dummies) Wiley, John & Sons, Inc.
Anderson, Nina & Meiser, Frances. The Smart Brain Train: How to Keep Your Brain Healthy & Wise. 2007. (Illus.). 52p. per. 7.95 (978-1-884820-87-8(5)) SAFE GOODS/ATN Publishing.
Apps, Jennifer Niskala & Walter, Kevin D., eds. Pediatric & Adolescent Concussion: Diagnosis, Management, & Outcomes. 2011. (ENG., Illus.). xv, 212p. 79.95 (978-0-387-89544-4(2), 0387895442) Springer.
Arden, John B. Rewire Your Brain: Think Your Way to a Better Life. 2010. (ENG.). 256p. pap. 15.95 (978-0-470-48729-7(1), Wiley) Wiley, John & Sons, Inc.
Armstrong, Thomas. The Power of Neurodiversity: Unleashing the Advantages of Your Differently Wired Brain. 2011. (ENG.). 288p. pap. 16.00 (978-0-7382-1524-2(4)) Da Capo Pr., Inc.
Ashwell, Ken, ed. The Brain Book: Development, Function, Disorder, Health. 2012. (ENG., Illus.). 352p. 45.00 (978-1-77085-126-9(7)) Firefly Bks., Ltd.
Asp, Elissa D. & de de Villiers, Jessica. When Language Breaks Down: Analysing Discourse in Clinical Contexts. 2010. (ENG., Illus.). 270p. pap. 38.99 (978-0-521-71824-0(4)) Cambridge Univ. Pr.

B

Athans,, Catherine, Catherine & Louvel, Marie-France. The Heart Brain: Did You Know You Have 3 Brains? 2011. 101p. pap. 28.95 (978-0-9794380-2-8(0)) Angels Island Pr.

Aubele, Teresa, et al. Train Your Brain to Get Happy. 2011. E-Book (978-1-4405-2668-8(0)) Adams Media Corp.

Aubele, Teresa, et al. Train Your Brain to Get Happy: The Simple Program That Primes Your Grey Cells for Joy, Optimism, & Serenity. 2011. (ENG.). 256p. pap. 16.95 (978-1-4405-1181-3(0)) Adams Media Corp.

Backman, Lars, et al. Memory, Aging & the Brain: A Festschrift in Honour of Lars-Goran Nilsson. Nyberg, Larseric, ed. 2009. (Psychology Press Festschrift Ser.). (ENG., Illus.). 368p. 90.00 (978-1-84169-692-8(7), Psychology Press) Taylor & Francis Group GBR. Dist: Taylor & Francis Group.

Banerjee, Rahul & Chakrabarti, Bikas K., eds. Models of Brain & Mind: Physical, Computational & Psychological Approaches. 2008. (Progress in Brain Research Ser.). (ENG., Illus.). 350p. 268.00 (978-0-444-53050-9(9), Elsevier Science) Elsevier Science & Technology Bks.

Beauregard, Mario. Brain Wars: The Scientific Battle over the Existence of the Mind & the Proof That Will Change the Way We Live Our Lives. 2012. (ENG.). 256p. 26.99 (978-0-06-207156-9(4), HarperOne) HarperCollins Pubs.

Beauregard, Mario & O'Leary, Denyse. The Spiritual Brain: A Neuroscientist's Case for the Existence of the Soul. (ENG.). 384p. 2008. pap. 14.99 (978-0-06-162598-5(1)) 2007. (Illus.). 25.95 (978-0-06-085883-4(4)) HarperCollins Pubs. (HarperOne).

Becker, Patrick. In der Bewusstseinsfalle? Geist und Gehirn in der Diskussion von Theologie, Philosophie und Naturwissenschaften. 2009. (Religion, Theologie und Naturwissenschaft / Religion, Theology & Natural Science Ser.). (GER., Illus.). 277p. (C). 68.00 (978-3-525-56982-5(3)) Vandenhoeck & Ruprecht GmbH & Co. KG DEU. Dist: ISD.

Benedetti, Fabrizio. The Patient's Brain: The Neuroscience Behind the Doctor-Patient Relationship. 2011. (ENG., Illus.). 328p. pap. 65.00 (978-0-19-957951-8(2)) Oxford Univ. Pr., Inc.

Berczi, Istvan, contrib. by. The Brain & Host Defense. 2010. (NeuroImmune Biology Ser.: 9). (ENG., Illus.). 358p. 195.00 (978-0-444-53544-3(6)) Elsevier Science & Technology Bks.

Blanton & Zadina. Brain Power! 2008. 24.95 (978-0-8058-6182-2(3)) Erlbaum, Lawrence Assocs., Inc.

Bloom, Floyd E. Best of the Brain from Scientific American. 2007. (Illus.). 270p. 25.00 (978-1-932594-22-5(1)) Dana Pr., The.

Boleyn-Fitzgerald, Miriam. Pictures of Mind: What the New Neuroscience Tells Us About Who We Are. 2010. (FT Press Science Ser.). (ENG., Illus.). 208p. 25.99 (978-0-13-715516-3(6)) FT Press.

Bolzan, Scott, et al. My Life, Deleted: A Memoir. 2011. (ENG.). 256p. 25.99 (978-0-06-202547-0(3), HarperOne) HarperCollins Pubs.

Borsook, David, et al, eds. The Migraine Brain: Imaging, Structure, & Function. 2012. (ENG.). 400p. 145.00 (978-0-19-975456-4(X)) Oxford Univ. Pr., Inc.

Braddick, Oliver, et al. Gene Expression to Neurobiology & Behaviour: Human Brain Development & Developmental Disorders. 2011. (ENG., Illus.). 376p. 268.00 (978-0-444-53884-0(4), Elsevier Science) Elsevier Science & Technology Bks.

Brandson, Curtis M. Brain Research Developments. 2011. (978-1-61122-066-7(1)) Nova Science Pubs., Inc.

Braverman, Eric R. Younger Brain, Sharper Mind: A 6-Step Plan for Preserving & Improving Memory & Attention at Any Age from America's Brain Doctor. 2012. (ENG.). 304p. 25.99 (978-1-60529-422-3(5)) Rodale Pr., Inc.

Brewer, Warrick, et al, eds. Olfaction & the Brain. 2006. (ENG., Illus.). 382p. 171.00 (978-0-521-84922-7(5)) Cambridge Univ. Pr.

Brian, Kate, pseud. The Complete Guide to IVF: An Inside View of Fertility Clinics & Treatment. 2010. (ENG.). 304p. pap. 15.95 (978-0-7499-5249-5(0)) Piatkus Bks. GBR. Dist: Independent Pubs. Group.

Brizendine, Louann. The Male Brain: A Breakthrough Understanding of How Men & Boys Think. 2010. (ENG.). 304p. 24.99 (978-0-7679-2753-6(2)) Broadway Bks.

Brockman, John. The Mind: Leading Scientists Explore the Brain, Memory, Personality, & Happiness. 2011. (ENG.). 288p. pap. 14.99 (978-0-06-202584-5(8), HarperPerennial) HarperCollins Pubs.

Buzan, Tony & Griffiths, Chris. Mind Maps for Business: Revolutionise Your Business Thinking & Practise. 2010. (Illus.). 255p. pap. (978-1-4066-4290-2(8)) Pearson Education, Ltd.

Calderwood, Henry. The Relations of Mind & Brain. 2009. 358p. pap. (978-0-217-76549-7(1)) Books LLC.

—The Relations of Mind & Brain. 2007. (ENG.). 546p. 57.95 (978-0-548-02142-2(2)) Kessinger Publishing, LLC.

Call, Nicola. The Thinking Child: Brain-Based Learning for the Early Years Foundation Stage. 2nd rev. ed. 2010. (ENG., Illus.). 160p. 39.95 (978-1-85539-472-8(3)) Continuum International Publishing Group, Ltd. GBR. Dist: National Bk. Network.

Canavero, Sergio. Textbook of Therapeutic Cortical Stimulation. 2009. (Illus.). xiv, 450p. 79.00 (978-1-60692-537-9(7)) Nova Science Pubs., Inc.

Carey, Leeanne M., ed. Stroke Rehabilitation: Insights from Neuroscience & Imaging. 2012. (ENG.). 280p. 135.00 (978-0-19-979788-2(9)) Oxford Univ. Pr., Inc.

Carson, Shelley. Your Creative Brain: Seven Steps to Maximize Imagination, Productivity, & Innovation in Your Life. 2010. (Harvard Health Publications). (ENG.). 384p. 24.95 (978-0-470-54763-2(4), Jossey-Bass) Wiley, John & Sons, Inc.

Carter, Philip. The Brain Fitness Workout: Brain Boosting Puzzles to Improve Your Memory, Concentration, Decision Making Skills & Mental Flexibility. 2010. (ENG., Illus.). 208p. pap. 14.95 (978-0-7494-5982-6(4)) Kogan Page, Ltd. GBR. Dist: Ingram Pub. Services.

Carter, Rita. Mapping the Mind: Revised & Updated Edition. 2nd ed. 2010. (ENG.). 224p. pap. 29.95 (978-0-520-26628-5(5)) Univ. of California Pr.

Cartwright, Rosalind. The Twenty-four Hour Mind: The Role of Sleep & Dreaming in Our Emotional Lives. 1 vol. 2010. (ENG., Illus.). 224p. 27.95 (978-0-19-538683-7(3)) Oxford Univ. Pr., Inc.

Cartwright, Rosalind D. The Twenty-four Hour Mind: The Role of Sleep & Dreaming in Our Emotional Lives. 2012. (ENG.). 224p. pap. 17.95 (978-0-19-989628-8(3)) Oxford Univ. Pr., Inc.

Cass, Dennis. Head Case: How I Almost Lost My Mind Trying to Understand My Brain. 2008. (P. S. Ser.). (ENG.). 240p. pap. 13.95 (978-0-06-059473-2(X), HarperPerennial) HarperCollins Pubs.

Changizi, Mark A. The Brain from 25,000 Feet: High Level Explorations of Brain Complexity, Perception, Induction & Vagueness. 2010. (Synthese Library). 341p. pap. 159.00 (978-90-481-6244-4(0), 9048162440) Springer.

Code, Chris, ed. The Representation of Language in the Brain: A Special Issue of Aphasiology. 2006. (Special Issues of Aphasiology Ser.). (ENG., Illus.). 368p. 125.00 (978-1-84169-817-5(2), Psychology Press) Taylor & Francis Group GBR. Dist: Taylor & Francis Group.

Cohen, David & Breggin, Peter R. Your Drug May Be Your Problem: How & Why to Stop Taking Psychiatric Medications. rev. ed. 2007. (ENG.). 336p. per. 17.99 (978-0-7382-1098-8(6)) Da Capo Pr., Inc.

Conrad, Cheryl D., ed. Handbook of Stress: Neuropsychological Effects on the Brain. 2011. (Blackwell Handbooks of Behavioral Neuroscience Ser.: 3). (ENG., Illus.). 720p. 199.95 (978-1-4443-3023-6(3), Wiley-Blackwell) Wiley, John & Sons, Inc.

Cozolino, Louis. The Social Neuroscience of Education: Optimizing Attachment & Learning in the Classroom. 2012. (ENG.). 304p. 37.50 (978-0-393-70609-3(5), 70609) Norton, W. W. & Co., Inc.

Cram101 Textbook Reviews. Outlines & Highlights for 12 Brain/Mind Learning Principles in Action: Developing Executive Functions of the Human Brain by Renate Caine, ISBN. 2011. 66p. pap. 27.95 (978-1-4288-5982-1(9)) Cram101 Inc.

—Outlines & Highlights for Introduction to Brain & Behavior by Bryan Kolb, Ian Q Whishaw, Isbn: 9780716711872. 2010. 166p. pap. 29.95 (978-1-61698-720-6(0)) Cram101 Inc.

—Outlines & Highlights for Introduction to Brain & Behavior by Bryan Kolb, Isbn: 9780716770695. 2010. 176p. pap. 29.95 (978-1-61698-043-6(5)) Cram101 Inc.

Cram101 Textbook Reviews. Outlines & Highlights for the Neuropsychology of Women by Elaine Fletcher-Janzen. 2011. 84p. pap. 27.95 (978-1-61905-228-4(8)) Cram101 Inc.

Cram101 Textbook Reviews & Cram101 Textbook Reviews. Outlines & Highlights for an Introduction to Brain & Behavior by Bryan Kolb, Isbn: 9780716776918. 2011. 438p. pap. 36.95 (978-1-61461-147-9(5)) Cram101 Inc.

—Outlines & Highlights for Brain & Behavior: An Introduction to Biological Psychology by Bob Garrett, ISBN. 2011. 134p. pap. 28.95 (978-1-4288-5924-1(1)) Cram101 Inc.

—Outlines & Highlights for Brain Atlas: A Visual Guide to the Human Central Nervous System by Thomas Woolsey, ISBN. 2011. 520p. pap. 38.95 (978-1-61461-087-8(8)) Cram101 Inc.

—Outlines & Highlights for Introduction to Biopsychology by Andrew Wickens. 2011. 170p. pap. 29.95 (978-1-61830-599-2(9)) Cram101 Inc.

Cram101 Textbook Reviews Staff. Outlines & Highlights for Introduction to Brain & Behavior by Bryan Kolb, Ian Q Whishaw, Isbn: 9780716711872. 2009. 144p. pap. 28.95 (978-1-4288-8042-9(9)) Cram101 Inc.

Craver, Carl F. Explaining the Brain. (ENG., 328p. 2009. Illus.). pap. 39.95 (978-0-19-956822-2(7)) 2007. 55.00 (978-0-19-929931-7(5)) Oxford Univ. Pr., Inc.

Culverhouse, Gay. Throwaway Players: Concussion Crisis from Pee Wee Football to the NFL. 2011. (ENG.). 250p. pap. 15.95 (978-1-933016-70-2(1)) Behler Pubns., LLC.

Cummings, Ingrid E. Vigorous Mind: Cross-Train Your Brain to Break Through Mental, Emotional, & Professional Boundaries. 2008. (ENG.). 288p. pap. 14.95 (978-0-7573-0698-3(5)) Health Communications, Inc.

Dana Press Staff. Cerebrum 2008: Emerging Ideas in Brain Science. Read, Cynthia A., ed. 2008. (Illus.). 225p. pap. 14.95 (978-1-932594-33-1(7)) Dana Pr., The.

—Cerebrum 2009: Emerging Ideas in Brain Science. 2009. (Illus.). 188p. pap. 14.95 (978-1-932594-44-7(2)) Dana Pr., The.

Darling-Kuria, Nikki. Brain-Based Early Learning Activities: Connecting Theory & Practice. 2010. (ENG.). 264p. pap. 29.95 (978-1-933653-86-0(8)) Redleaf Pr.

Davidson, Richard J. & Begley, Sharon. The Emotional Life of Your Brain: How Its Unique Patterns Affect the Way You Think, Feel, & Live - & How You Can Change Them. 2012. (ENG.). 304p. (gr. 12). 25.95 (978-1-59463-089-7(5), Hudson Street Pr.) Penguin Group (USA) Inc.

Davis, Karen D. New Techniques for Examining the Brain. 2007. (Gray Matter Ser.). (Illus.). 120p. (YA). (gr. 9-12). lib. bdg. 35.00 (978-0-7910-8959-0(2)) Facts On File, Inc.

Dawkins, Bonnie U., et al, eds. Intentional Teaching: The Let Me Learn Classroom in Action. 2010. (Illus.). 184p. pap. 34.95 (978-1-4129-5186-9(0), B51852P) Corwin Pr.

De Deyn, Peter Paul & Van Dam, Debby, eds. Animal Models of Dementia. 2010. (Neuromethods Ser.). (ENG., Illus.). xv, 710p. 179.00 (978-1-60761-897-3(4), 1607618974) Humana Pr.

Dean, Carolyn, et al. 365 Ways to Boost Your Brain Power: Tips, Exercise, Advice. 2009. (ENG.). 224p. pap. 7.95 (978-1-60550-060-7(7)) Adams Media Corp.

Della Sala, Sergio, ed. Tall Tales about the Mind & Brain: Separating Fact from Fiction. 2007. (ENG., Illus.). 552p. (C). per. 75.00 (978-0-19-856877-3(0)) Oxford Univ. Pr., Inc.

Dietrich, Dietmar, et al, eds. Simulating the Mind: A Technical Neuropsychoanalytical Approach. 2010. (ENG., Illus.). xvii, 436p. pap. 179.00 (978-3-211-99869-4(1), 3211998691) Springer.

Dommett, Eleanor, et al. Learning & the Brain Pocketbook. 2011. (Illus.). 128p. pap. (978-1-906610-25-8(8), Teachers' Pocketbooks) Management Pocketbooks GBR. Dist: Ware-Pak, Inc.

Doya, Kenji, et al, eds. Bayesian Brain: Probabilistic Approaches to Neural Coding. 2011. (Computational Neuroscience Ser.). (ENG., Illus.). 344p. (gr. 17). pap. 26.00 (978-0-262-51601-3(2)) MIT Pr.

Driscoll, Patricia & Straus, Celia. Hidden Battles on Unseen Fronts: Stories of American Soldiers with Traumatic Brain Injury & PTSD. 2010. (Illus.). 320p. pap. 18.95 (978-1-935149-40-8(7)) Casemate Pubs. & Bk. Distributors, LLC.

Drubach, Daniel. Grey Matter: A User's Manual for Your Brain. 2009. 265p. 24.99 (978-0-13-701670-9(0)) FT Press.

Duncan, John. How Intelligence Happens. 2012. (ENG., Illus.). 256p. pap. 18.00 (978-0-300-17772-5(0)) Yale Univ. Pr.

Dwyer, Helen, ed. The Brain. 2011. (Curriculum Connections: Psychology Ser.). (Illus.). 112p. lib. bdg. 39.95 (978-1-936333-16-5(3)) Brown Bear Bks.

Eagleman, David. Incognito: The Secret Lives of the Brain. (Vintage Ser.). (ENG.). 304p. 2012. pap. 15.95 (978-0-307-38992-3(8), Vintage) 2011. (Illus.). 26.95 (978-0-307-37733-3(4), Pantheon) Knopf Doubleday Publishing Group.

Edelman, Gerald M. Second Nature: Brain Science & Human Knowledge. (ENG., Illus.). 224p. 2007. per. 15.00 (978-0-300-12594-8(1)) 2006. 24.00 (978-0-300-12039-4(7)) Yale Univ. Pr.

Eide, Brock L. & Eide, Fernette F. The Dyslexic Advantage: Unlocking the Hidden Potential of the Dyslexic Brain. 2011. (ENG.). 304p. (gr. 12). 25.95 (978-1-59463-079-8(8), Hudson Street Pr.) Penguin Group (USA) Inc.

Elsersawi, A. & Elsersawi, D. The Book of Intelligence & Brain Disorder: Your Brain Must Have All Forms of Intelligence: Iq, Eq, & Cq. 2010. 240p. pap. 18.33 (978-1-4269-4466-6(7)) Trafford Publishing.

Feinstein, Sheryl. Learning & the Brain: A Comprehensive Guide for Educators, Parents, & Teachers. 2007. (ENG., Illus.). 562p. per. 37.95 (978-1-57886-615-1(4)) Rowman & Littlefield Education.

—Teaching the at-Risk Teenage Brain. 2007. (ENG., Illus.). 162p. 55.00 (978-1-57886-646-5(4)); per. 23.95 (978-1-57886-647-2(2)) Rowman & Littlefield Education.

Fernandez, Alvaro & Goldberg, Elkhonon. The Sharp Brains Guide to Brain Fitness. 2009. 184p. pap. 14.95 (978-0-9823629-0-7(0)) SharpBrians, Inc.

Ferrier, David. The Functions of the Brain. 2009. 260p. pap. (978-1-4588-7460-3(5)) Books LLC.

—The Functions of the Brain. Wozniak, Robert H., ed. (Classics in Psychology Ser.). (Illus.). 343p. (978-1-85506-665-6(3), Burns & Oates) Continuum International Publishing Group, Ltd.

Feuerstein, Reuven, et al. Beyond Smarter: Mediated Learning & the Brain's Capacity for Change. 2010. (ENG., Illus.). 192p. pap. 29.95 (978-0-8077-5118-3(9)); 60.00 (978-0-8077-5119-0(7)) Teachers College Pr., Teachers College, Columbia Univ.

Fine, Cordelia. Delusions of Gender: How Our Minds, Society, & Neurosexism Create Difference. 2011. (ENG & ACH.). 338p. pap. 16.95 (978-0-393-34024-2(4), 34024) Norton, W. W. & Co., Inc.

—A Mind of Its Own: How Your Brain Distorts & Deceives. 2008. (ENG.). 256p. pap. 15.95 (978-0-393-33163-9(6), 33163) Norton, W. W. & Co., Inc.

Flynn, Cian E. & Callaghan, Brandon R., eds. Neuroanatomy Research Advances. 2009. (Neuroanatomy Research at the Leading Edge Ser.). 129.00 (978-1-60741-610-4(7), Nova Biomedical Bks.) Nova Science Pubs., Inc.

Frank, Lone. The Neurotourist: Postcards from the Edge of Brain Science. 2011. (ENG., Illus.). 244p. 14.95 (978-1-85168-796-1(3)) Oneworld Pubns. GBR. Dist: National Bk. Network.

Franklin, Keith B. J. & Paxinos, George. The Mouse Brain in Stereotaxic Coordinates. 3rd ed. 2007. (ENG., Illus.). 360p. 210.00 (978-0-12-369460-7(4), Academic Pr.) Elsevier Science & Technology Bks.

Freedman, Jeri. Your Beautiful Brain: Keeping Your Brain Healthy. 2012. (Healthy Habits Ser.). (ENG., Illus.). 64p. (YA). (gr. 5-8). lib. bdg. 31.95 (978-1-4488-6952-7(8), Rosen Central) Rosen Publishing Group, Inc., The.

Fuchs, Susanne & Hoole, Philip, eds. Between the Regular & the Particular in Speech & Language. 2010. 272p. 72.95 (978-3-631-58686-0(8)) Lang, Peter GmbH, Europaischer Verlag der Wissenschaften DEU. Dist: Lang, Peter.

Funahashi, Shintaro, ed. Representation & Brain. 2011. (ENG., Illus.). xii, 366p. pap. 179.00 (978-4-431-99825-9(X), 443199825X) Springer.

Gage, Fred H. Retrotransposition, Diversity & the Brain. 2010. (Research & Perspectives in Neurosciences Ser.). (Illus.). xii, 123p. pap. 129.00 (978-3-642-09437-8(6), 3642094376) Springer.

Gallagher, Shaun. Brainstorming: Views & Interviews on the Mind. 2008. (ENG., Illus.). 276p. 80.00 (978-1-84540-147-4(6)) Imprint Academic GBR. Dist: Ingram Pub. Services.

Gallucci, Massimo, et al. Radiographic Atlas of Skull & Brain Anatomy. 2010. (Illus.). x, 362p. pap. 259.00 (978-3-642-07059-4(0), 3642070590) Springer.

Garlick, Dennis. Intelligence & the Brain: Solving the Mystery of Why People Differ in IQ & How a Child can be a Genius. 2010. (Illus.). 246p. 27.99 (978-0-615-31921-6(1)) Aesop Pr.

Garnett, Steve. Using Brainpower in the Classroom: 5 Steps to Accelerate Learning. 2006. (Illus.). 176p. 160.00 (978-0-415-34382-4(8)) Routledge.

Gazzaniga, Michael S. Who's in Charge? Free Will & the Science of the Brain. 2011. (ENG., Illus.). 272p. 27.99 (978-0-06-190610-7(7), Ecco) HarperCollins Pubs.

Gazzaniga, Michael S., ed. The Cognitive Neurosciences. 4th ed. 2009. (ENG., Illus.). 1312p. (gr. 17). 184.00 (978-0-262-01341-3(X)) MIT Pr.

Gerdes, Lee. Limitless You: The Infinite Possibilities of a Balanced Brain. 2011. (ENG.). 328p. pap. 18.95 (978-1-897238-58-5(4)) Namaste Publishing, Inc. CAN. Dist: Perseus-PGW.

Gil-Perotín, Sara, et al. Identification & Characterization of Neural Progenitor Cells in the Adult Mammalian Brain. 2009. (Advances in Anatomy, Embryology & Cell Biology Ser.). (ENG., Illus.). xii, 104p. pap. 159.00 (978-3-540-88718-8(0)) Springer.

Gillett, Grant. The Mind & its Discontents. 2nd ed. 2009. (International Perspectives in Philosophy & Psychiatry Ser.). (ENG.). 420p. pap. 75.00 (978-0-19-923754-8(9)) Oxford Univ. Pr., Inc.

Goldstein, Gerald & Beers, Sue R., eds. Rehabilitation. 2010. (Human Brain Function: Assessment & Rehabilitation Ser.). 308p. pap. 119.00 (978-1-4419-3279-2(8), 1441932798) Springer.

Gonzalez-Wallace, Michael. Super Body, Super Brain: The Workout That Does It All. 2011. (ENG.). 256p. pap. 19.99 (978-0-06-194528-1(5), HarperOne) HarperCollins Pubs.

Gossard, Jean-Pierre. Breathe, Walk & Chew Pt. 2: The Neural Challenge. 2011. (ENG.). 266p. 268.00 (978-0-444-53825-3(9)) Elsevier Science & Technology Bks.

Grigorev, A. I. Mozg: Fundamentalnye I Prikladnye Problemy, Po Materialam Nauchnoi Sessii Obshchego Sobraniia Rossiiskoi Akademii Nauk, 15-16 Dekabria 2009 G. 2010. (RUS., Illus.). 284p. (978-5-02-037485-0(7)) Nauka.

Grillner, Sten & Graybiel, Ann M., eds. Microcircuits: The Interface Between Neurons & Global Brain Function. 2006. (Dahlem Workshop Reports: Vol. 93). (ENG., Illus.). 472p. (gr. 17). 58.00 (978-0-262-07278-6(5)) MIT Pr.

Grossblatt, Ben. The Amazing Squishy Brain. 2010. 32p. mass mkt. 27.99 (978-1-60380-084-6(0)) becker&mayer! books.

Haken, Hermann. Brain Dynamics: An Introduction to Models & Simulations. 2nd ed. (Springer Series in Synergetics Ser.). (Illus.). 2010. xiv, 333p. pap. 109.00 (978-3-642-09450-7(3), 3642094503) 2008. 287p. 109.00 (978-3-540-75236-3(6)) Springer.

Hakim, Arif. Brain & Reading Process. 2010. 88p. pap. (978-3-8383-6767-5(7)) Lambert Academic Publishing.

Hardiman, Mariale. The Brain-Targeted Teaching Model for 21st-Century Schools. 2012. 256p. pap. 36.95 (978-1-4129-9198-8(6), B91988P) Corwin Pr.

Harrison, Connie & Cathcart, Susan. Brain-Based Study Strategies: A Guide for Adult Learners. 2009. (978-1-935356-02-8(X)) Baker College Publishing Co.

Hays, Sean, et al, eds. Nanotechnology, the Brain, & the Future. 2012. (Yearbook of Nanotechnology in Society Ser.). (ENG., Illus.). x, 290p. 129.00 (978-94-007-1786-2(5), 9400717865) Springer.

He, Bin, ed. Modeling & Imaging of Bioelectrical Activity: Principles & Applications. 2010. (Bioelectric Engineering Ser.). (Illus.). xvi, 334p. pap. 249.00 (978-1-4419-3429-1(4), 1441934294) Springer.

Healan, Tammy. I Live Inside Your Head. 2011. 28p. pap. 12.49 (978-1-4343-6832-4(7)) AuthorHouse.

Heida, Tjitske. The Subthalamic Nucleus. 2008. (Advances in Anatomy, Embryology & Cell Biology Ser.). spiral bd. 189.00 (978-3-540-79461-5(1), 3540794611) Springer.

Heller, Samantha. Get Smart: Samantha Heller's Nutrition Prescription for Boosting Brain Power & Optimizing Total Body Health. 2010. (ENG., Illus.). 264p. 43.00 (978-0-8018-9375-9(5)); pap. 19.95 (978-0-8018-9376-6(3)) Johns Hopkins Univ. Pr.

Henslin, Earl. This Is Your Brain in Love: New Scientific Breakthroughs for a More Passionate & Emotionally Healthy Marriage, 0 vols. 2010. 224p. pap. 14.99 (978-0-7852-2875-2(6)) Nelson, Thomas Inc.

Hielscher, Andreas & Taroni, Paola. Diffuse Optical Imaging III. 2011. (Proceedings of SPIE Ser.). 340p. pap. 120.00 (978-0-8194-8685-1(X)) SPIE.

Higgins, Edmund & George, Mark S. Brain Stimulation Therapies for the Practicing Clinician. 2009. 224p. 80.00 (978-1-58562-280-1(4)) American Psychiatric Publishing, Inc.

Hillenbrand, Claudia M. & Huisman, Thierry A. G. M. MRI of the Newborn, Part 2, an Issue of Magnetic Resonance Imaging Clinics. 2011. (Clinics: Radiology Ser.: 20-1). (ENG.). 115.00 (978-1-4557-3887-8(5), Saunders) Elsevier - Health Sciences Div.

Hinrichs, Bruce H. Mind as Mosaic: The Robot in the Machine. 2007. (ENG.). per. 30.00 (978-0-9790129-0-7(2)) Ellipse Publishing Co.

Hogue, David A. Remembering the Future, Imagining the Past: Story, Ritual, & the Human Brain. 2009. 224p. pap. 25.00 (978-1-60608-860-9(2), Wipf and Stock) Wipf & Stock Pubs.

Holbrook, Martin L. Hygiene of the Brain & Nerves & the Cure of Nervousness. reprint ed. 27.50 (978-0-404-60862-0(0)) AMS Pr., Inc.

Holford, Patrick. New Optimum Nutrition for the Mind. 1 vol. exp. ed. 2009. 506p. pap. 22.95 (978-1-59120-259-2(0)) Basic Health Pubns., Inc.

Hood, Bruce. The Self Illusion: How the Social Brain Creates Identity. 2012. 368p. 29.95 (978-0-19-989759-9(X)) Oxford Univ. Pr., Inc.

Hooper, Nigel M. & Lendeckel, Uwe, eds. The ADAM Family of Proteases. 2010. (Proteases in Biology & Disease Ser.). xiv, 344p. pap. 179.00 (978-1-4419-3775-9(7), 1441937757) Springer.

How Can Research on the Brain Inform & Expand Our Thinking about Human Development? (Illus.). 64p. pap. (978-3-8055-8211-7(0)) Karger, S. AG.

Hubert, Bill. Resonance: Elise & other Bal-A-Vis-X Stories. 2007. 402p. pap. 30.00 (978-0-9708085-5-4(0)) Bal-A-Vis-X, Inc.

Huisman, Thierry A. G. M. & Hillenbrand, Claudia M. MRI of the Newborn Pt. 1: Magnetic Resonance Imaging Clinics of North America. 2011. (Clinics: Radiology Ser.: 19-4). (ENG., Illus.). 110.00 (978-1-4377-2692-3(5), Saunders) Elsevier - Health Sciences Div.

Hussain, A. Brain Inspired Cognitive Systems 2008. 2010. (Illus.). xiv, 384p. E-Book **(978-0-387-79100-5(0))** Springer.

Hygino, Celso. Clinical Applications of Diffusion Imaging of the Brain, an Issue of Neuroimaging Clinics. 2011. (Clinics: Radiology Ser.: 21-1). (ENG., Illus.). 208p. 110.00 (978-1-4557-0468-2(7), Saunders) Elsevier - Health Sciences Div.

The Impact of Concussions on High School Athletes: Hearing Before the Committee on Education & Labor, U.S. House of Representatives, One Hundred Eleventh Congress, Second Session, Hearing Held in Washington, DC, May 20, 2010. 2010. (Illus.). iii, 65p. **(978-0-16-087390-4(8),** 552-070-42083-5) United States Government Printing Office.

The Impact of Concussions on High School Athletes: The Local Perspective: Field Hearing Before the Subcommittee on Healthy Families & Communities, Committee on Education & Labor, U.S. House of Representatives, One Hundred Eleventh Congress, Second Session, Hearing Held in Selden, NY, September 13, 2010. 2010. iii, 41p. **(978-0-16-087794-0(6),** 552-070-42298-6) United States Government Printing Office.

Ishii, Shin, et al, eds. Bayesian Brain: Probabilistic Approaches to Neural Coding. 2006. (Computational Neuroscience Ser.). (ENG., Illus.). 344p. (gr. 17). 58.00 (978-0-262-04238-3(X)) MIT Pr.

Ivancevic, Vladimir G. & Ivancevic, Tijana T. Neuro-Fuzzy Associative Machinery for Comprehensive Brain & Cognition Modelling. 2010. (Studies in Computational Intelligence Ser.). (Illus.). xii, 730p. pap. 239.00 (978-3-642-07998-6(9), 3642079989) Springer.

Jandial, Rahul, ed. Frontiers in Brain Repair. 2010. (Advances in Experimental Medicine & Biology Ser.). (ENG., Illus.). xviii, 130p. 149.00 (978-1-4419-5818-1(5), 1441958185) Springer.

Jensen, Eric. Enriching the Brain: How to Maximize Every Learner's Potential. 2008. (ENG., Illus.). 352p. per. 18.95 (978-0-470-22389-5(8), Jossey-Bass) Wiley, John & Sons, Inc.

—Introduction to Brain-Compatible Learning. 2nd ed. 2007. (Illus.). 136p. 66.95 (978-1-4129-5407-5(X), B5407XC); per. 27.95 (978-1-4129-5418-1(5), B5407XP) Corwin Pr.

Jensen, Eric P. Brain-Based Learning: The New Paradigm of Teaching. 2nd ed. 2008. (Illus.). 288p. pap. 39.95 (978-1-4129-6256-8(0), B62551P) Corwin Pr.

Jensen, Eric P. & Palmer, Lyelle L., eds. Bright Brain: Learning Readiness Stimulators. 2007. 97.95 (978-0-9637832-6-4(2), B83262K) Corwin Pr.

Jirsa, Viktor K. & McIntosh, A R, eds. Handbook of Brain Connectivity. 2007. (Understanding Complex Systems Ser.). (Illus.). 528p. 199.00 (978-3-540-71462-0(6), 3540714626) Springer.

Johnson, Joseph, et al. Breathe, Walk & Chew: The Neural Challenge, 2 vols. 2010. (Progress in Brain Research Ser.). (ENG., Illus.). 248p. 268.00 (978-0-444-53613-6(2), Elsevier Science) Elsevier Science & Technology Bks.

Jones, Frederic Wood & Porteus, Stanley David. The Matrix of the Mind. 2011. 432p. 56.95 **(978-1-258-05889-0(8))** Literary Licensing, LLC.

Jordan-Young, Rebecca M. Brain Storm: The Flaws in the Science of Sex Differences. (Illus.). 408p. 2011. (ENG.). pap. 19.95 (978-0-674-06351-8(1)) 2010. 35.00 (978-0-674-05730-2(9)) Harvard Univ. Pr.

Juan, Stephen. The Odd Brain: Mysteries of Our Weird & Wonderful Brains Explained. 2006. (ENG.). 336p. pap. 10.95 (978-0-7407-6159-1(5)) Andrews McMeel Publishing.

Kaufeldt, Martha M. Begin with the Brain: Orchestrating the Learner-Centered Classroom. Kaufeldt, Martha M., ed. 2nd ed. 2009. (Illus.). 256p. 86.95 (978-1-4129-7157-7(8), B71577C); pap. 39.95 (978-1-4129-7158-4(6), B71577P) Corwin Pr.

Kelso, J. A. Scott, et al. The Complementary Nature. 2008. (ENG., Illus.). 344p. (gr. 17). per. 20.00 (978-0-262-61222-7(4)) MIT Pr.

Kiner, Robert W. & Feinstein, Sheryl G. The Brain & Strengths Based School Leadership. 2011. (Illus.). 224p. pap. 36.95 (978-1-4129-8845-2(4), B88452P) Corwin Pr.

Klemm, W. R. Atoms of Mind: The Ghost in the Machine Materializes. 2011. (ENG., Illus.). xix, 300p. 209.00 (978-94-007-1096-2(8), 9400710968) Springer.

Kolb & Kolb, Bryan. Introduction to Brain & Behavior Study Guide. 3rd ed. 2010. (ENG.). 344p. (C). pap. 33.95 (978-1-4292-3416-0(4)) Worth Pubs., Inc.

Kolb, Bryan & Whishaw, Ian Q. An Introduction to Brain & Behavior. 3rd ed. 2009. (ENG., Illus.). 608p. (C). 157.95 (978-0-7167-7691-8(X)) Worth Pubs., Inc.

Kornblatt, Sondra. A Better Brain at Any Age: The Holistic Way to Improve Your Memory, Reduce Stress, & Sharpen Your Wits. 2008. (ENG., Illus.). 248p. pap. 14.95 (978-1-57324-320-9(5), Conari Pr.) Red Wheel/Weiser.

—Brain Fitness for Women: Keeping Your Head Clear & Your Mind Sharp at Any Age. 2012. (ENG.). 224p. pap. 14.95 (978-1-57324-490-9(2), Conari Pr.) Red Wheel/Weiser.

Krichmar, Jeffrey & Wagatsuma, Hiroaki. Neuromorphic & Brain-Based Robots. 2011. (ENG., Illus.). 376p. 110.00 (978-0-521-76878-8(0)) Cambridge Univ. Pr.

Kuhar, Michael & Wrobel, Sylvia. The Addicted Brain: Why We Abuse Drugs, Alcohol, & Nicotine. 2011. (FT Press Science Ser.). (ENG., Illus.). 240p. 29.99 **(978-0-13-254250-0(1))** FT Press.

Kuhlenbeck, Hartwig. Brain & Consciousness: Some Prolegomena to an Approach of the Problem. 2011. 350p. 51.95 **(978-1-258-01800-9(4))** Literary Licensing, LLC.

Kuhn, Cynthia M. & Koob, George F., eds. Advances in the Neuroscience of Addiction. 2010. (Frontiers in Neuroscience Ser.). (ENG., Illus.). 238p. 139.95 (978-0-8493-7391-6(3), CRC Press) Taylor & Francis Group GBR. Dist: Taylor & Francis Group.

Kurzweil, Ray. How to Create a Mind: The Secret of Human Thought Revealed. 2012. (ENG., Illus.). 384p. 27.95 **(978-0-670-02529-9(1),** Viking Adult) Penguin Group (USA) Inc.

Larimore, Walt & Larimore, Barb. His Brain, Her Brain: How Divinely Designed Differences Can Strengthen Your Marriage, 1 vol. 2008. (ENG., Illus.). 224p. (gr. 13). pap. 14.99 (978-0-310-24028-0(X)) Zondervan.

Lask, Bryan & Frampton, Ian. Eating Disorders & the Brain. 2011. 98.95 (978-1-119-97365-2(1)) Wiley, John & Sons, Inc.

Laster, Madlon T. Brain-Based Teaching for All Subjects: Patterns to Promote Learning. 2007. (ENG., Illus.). 136p. 65.00 (978-1-57886-721-9(5)) Rowman & Littlefield Education.

—Brain-Based Teaching for All Subjects: Patterns to Promote Learning. 2007. (ENG., Illus.). 180p. per. 29.95 (978-1-57886-722-6(3)) Rowman & Littlefield Publishers, Inc.

—Teach the Way the Brain Learns: Curriculum Themes Build Neuron Networks. 2009. (ENG., Illus.). 220p. 74.95 (978-1-60709-136-3(4)); pap. 35.95 (978-1-60709-137-0(2)) Rowman & Littlefield Education.

Lawlis, Frank. The IQ Answer: Maximizing Your Child's Potential. 2007. (ENG.). 272p. (gr. 12-18). 15.00 (978-0-452-28868-3(1), Plume) Penguin Group (USA) Inc.

Le Fanu, James. Why Us? How Science Rediscoveerd the Mystery of Ourselves. 2010. (Vintage Ser.). (ENG., Illus.). 336p. pap. 16.00 (978-1-4000-3054-5(4), Vintage) Knopf Doubleday Publishing Group.

Leaf, Caroline. Brain Time: Learn how to Learn. 2007. (Illus.). 74p. per. 24.99 (978-0-9801223-1-2(7)) Switch on your brain USA.

—Switch on your Brain. 2007. (Illus.). 212p. 40.00 (978-0-9801223-0-5(9)) Switch on your brain USA.

—Who Switched off My Brain? Controlling toxic thoughts & Emotions. 2008. (Illus.). 144p. 21.99 (978-0-9801223-2-9(5)) Switch on your brain USA.

Lee, Ilchi. Brain Wave Vibration: Getting Back into the Rhythm of A Happy, Healthy Life. 2010. 224p. pap. 14.95 (978-1-935127-36-9(5)) BEST Life Media.

—Principles of Brain Management: A practical approach to making the most of your Brain. 2007. 117p. pap. 13.95 (978-0-9799388-0-1(5)) BEST Life Media.

Lee, Ilchi & Jones, Jessie. In Full Bloom: A Brain Education Guide for Successful Aging. 2008. (Illus.). 231p. pap. 18.95 (978-0-9799388-4-9(8)) BEST Life Media.

Lewellen, Gale R. & Torgerud, Steven Ray. Human Cns Structure. 7th rev. ed. 2011. (ENG.). 282p. spiral bd. 73.01 (978-0-7575-8470-1(5)) Kendall Hunt Publishing Co.

Lewis, Fran. Sharp As a Tack or Scrambled Eggs. 2010. 106p. 24.99 (978-1-4500-8763-6(9)) Xlibris Corp.

Lind-Kyle, Patt. Heal Your Mind, Rewire Your Brain: Applying the Exciting New Science of Brain Synchrony for Creativity, Peace & Presence. 2010. 256p. pap. 17.95 (978-1-60415-058-2(0)) Energy Psychology Pr.

Loeb, Jacques. Comparative Physiology of the Brain & Comparative Psychology. 2010. (ENG.). 336p. pap. 31.75 (978-1-171-60508-9(0)) 2010. (ENG.). 342p. pap. 32.75 (978-1-176-26468-7(0)) 2010. 330p. pap. 31.75 (978-1-148-22685-9(0)) 2010. 322p. pap. 30.75 (978-1-149-14924-9(8)) 2010. 332p. pap. 31.75 (978-1-146-36950-3(6)) 2010. 316p. pap. 30.75 (978-1-147-55057-3(3)) 2010. 330p. pap. 31.75 (978-1-145-94150-2(8)) 2009. 326p. 32.99 (978-1-113-66265-1(4)) 2009. 326p. 29.99 (978-1-113-66266-8(2)) 2009. (ENG.). 324p. pap. 23.99 (978-1-113-66257-6(3), BiblioLife) 2009. 326p. pap. 29.75 (978-1-113-66261-3(1)) 2009. 326p. pap. 30.75 (978-1-113-66263-7(8)) 2009. 328p. 25.99 (978-1-103-90718-2(2)) 2009. 328p. pap. 19.99 (978-1-103-90712-0(3)) BiblioBazaar.

—Comparative Physiology of the Brain & Comparative Psychology. 2009. 172p. pap. (978-0-217-19318-4(8)); 184p. pap. (978-1-4590-4386-2(3)) Books LLC.

—Comparative Physiology of the Brain & Comparative Psychology. 2008. 332p. 45.95 (978-1-4369-7135-5(7)); pap. 30.95 (978-1-4368-1114-9(7)) Kessinger Publishing, LLC.

Maccaro, Janet. Brain Boosting Foods: 50 Ways to Improve Your Memory, Unclutter Your Mind, & Get Your Brain Working at Its Highest Capacity by Eating Right. 2008. (ENG.). 160p. pap. 9.99 (978-1-59979-225-5(7), Siloam Pr.) Charisma Media.

MacDonald, Matthew. Your Brain. rev. ed. 2008. (Missing Manual Ser.). (ENG., Illus.). 280p. pap. 24.99 (978-0-596-51778-6(5), Pogue Pr.) O'Reilly Media, Inc.

MacDonald, Stephen James. Crime & Dyslexi. 2010. 120p. pap. (978-3-639-17752-7(5)) VDM Verlag Dr. Mueller e.K.

Manchev. Epidemiology of the Risk Factors for Cerebrovascular Disease. 2010. (Illus.). 120p. pap. 13.99 (978-1-4490-5507-3(9)) AuthorHouse.

Maney, Kevin & Ranadive, Vivek. The Two-Second Advantage: How We Succeed by Anticipating the Future — Just Enough. 2011. (ENG.). 256p. 25.00 (978-0-307-88765-8(0), Crown Business) Crown Publishing Group.

Mangan, Margaret Angermeyer. Brain-Compatible Science. 2nd rev. ed. 2006. (Illus.). 248p. 85.95 (978-1-4129-3995-9(X), B3995XC); per. 38.95 (978-1-4129-3996-6(8), B3995XP) Corwin Pr.

Marani, Enrico. The Subthalamic Nucleus. 2008. (Advances in Anatomy, Embryology & Cell Biology Ser.). spiral bd. 169.00 (978-3-540-79459-2(X), 354079459X) Springer.

Marín-Padilla, Miguel. The Human Brain: Prenatal Development & Structure. 2010. (ENG., Illus.). xii, 145p. 139.00 (978-3-642-14723-4(2), 3642147232) Springer.

Marshall, Louise H. & Magoun, Horace W. Discoveries in the Human Brain: Neuroscience Prehistory, Brain Structure, & Function. 2010. 336p. pap. 109.00 (978-1-61737-034-2(7), 1617370347) Humana Pr.

Martin, Justin McCory. Brain. 2010. (Illus.). 16p. **(978-0-545-24800-6(0))** Scholastic, Inc.

Materna, Laurie. Jump-Start the Adult Learner: How to Engage & Motivate Adults Using Brain-Compatible Strategies. 2007. (Illus.). 232p. 85.95 (978-1-4129-5293-4(X), B5293XC); per. 38.95 (978-1-4129-5294-1(8), B5293XP) Corwin Pr.

McCleary, Larry. The Brain Trust Program: A Scientifically Based Three-Part Plan to Improve Memory, Elevate Mood, Enhance Attention, Alleviate Migraine & Menopausal Symptoms, & Boost Mental Energy. 2008. (ENG.). 288p. (gr. 12-18). 14.95 (978-0-399-53454-6(7), Perigee Trade) Penguin Group (USA) Inc.

McClintic, Carol, et al. 12 Brain/Mind Learning Principles in Action: Developing Executive Functions of the Human Brain. Caine, Renate Nummela et al, eds. 2nd ed. 2008. (Illus.). 304p. pap. 44.95 (978-1-4129-6107-3(6), B61066P) Corwin Pr.

Medina, John. Brain Rules: 12 Principles for Surviving & Thriving at Work, Home, & School. 2009. (ENG., Illus.). 301p. pap. 15.00 (978-0-9797777-4-5(7)) Pear Pr.

Meehan, M.D., William P. Kids, Sports, & Concussion: A Guide for Coaches & Parents, 1 vol. 2011. (Praeger Series on Contemporary Health & Living Ser.). (Illus.). 192p. 34.95 (978-0-313-38730-2(3), A3160C) Greenwood Publishing Group, Inc.

Meehan, William P. Kids, Sports, & Concussion: A Guide for Coaches & Parents. 2011. E-Book **(978-0-313-38731-9(1),** Praeger Pubs.) Greenwood Publishing Group, Inc.

Meehan, William P. & Micheli, Lyle J. Concussion in Sports, an Issue of Clinics in Sports Medicine. 2010. (Clinics: Orthopedics Ser.: 30-1). (ENG., Illus.). 240p. 110.00 (978-1-4557-0506-1(3), Saunders) Elsevier - Health Sciences Div.

Millers, Donald. How Our Brain Works: The Construction & Functionality of Your Brain Presented & Explained. 2010. 300p. 31.95 (978-1-4502-2037-8(1)); pap. 21.95 (978-1-4502-0877-2(0)) iUniverse, Inc.

Minirth, Frank B. Boost Your Brainpower: Proven Ways to Keep Your Mind Young, 1 vol. 2010. (ENG.). 192p. reprint ed. pap. 12.99 (978-0-8007-3357-5(6)) Revell.

Minirth, Frank B. & Minirth, Frank. A Brilliant Mind: Proven Ways to Increase Your Brainpower. 2007. 192p. pap. 12.99 (978-0-8007-3187-8(5)) Revell.

Mira, José, et al. Methods & Models in Artificial & Natural Computation: A Homage to Professor Mira's Scientific Legacy: Third International Work-Conference on the Interplay Between Natural & Artificial Computation, IWINAC 2009, Santiago de Compostela, Spain, June 22-26, 2009, Proceedings, Part I. 2009. (Lecture Notes in Computer Science / Theoretical Computer Science & General Issues Ser.). (ENG.). xxi, 530p. pap. 109.00 (978-3-642-02263-0(4), 3642022634) Springer.

Mitagvaria, Nodar P. & (James) Bicher, Haim I. Cerebral Blood Flow Regulation. 2009. 79.00 (978-1-60692-163-0(0)) Nova Science Pubs., Inc.

Morales-Dorta, José. Tu Cerebro, una Maravilla Del Universo: Conocelo. 2007. (SPA.). (978-1-59835-063-0(3)) Cambridge BrickHouse, Inc.

Mourtzikos, Karen, et al, eds. Positron Emmission Tomography Computed Tomography: A Disease-Oriented Approach. 2008. (ENG., Illus.). 480p. 500.00 incl. cd-rom (978-0-8493-8087-7(1), Informa Healthcare) Taylor & Francis Group GBR. Dist: Taylor & Francis Group.

Neirynck, Jacques & Garey, Laurence. Your Brain & Your Self - What You Need to Know. 2008. (Illus.). 130p. pap. 69.95 (978-3-540-87522-2(0)) Springer.

Nelson, Kevin. The Spiritual Doorway in the Brain: A Neurologist's Search for the God Experience. 2012. (ENG., Illus.). 336p. (gr. 12). 16.00 **(978-0-452-29758-6(3),** Plume) Penguin Group (USA) Inc.

Neuper, Christa & Klimesch, Wolfgang, eds. Event-Related Dynamics of Brain Oscillations. 2006. (Progress in Brain Research Ser.: Vol. 159). (ENG., Illus.). 464p. 268.00 (978-0-444-52183-5(6), Elsevier Science) Elsevier Science & Technology Bks.

Newberg, Andrew B. Principles of Neurotheology. 2010. (Ashgate Science & Religion Ser.). (Illus.). 286p. 99.95 (978-1-4094-0810-9(8)); pap. 29.95 (978-0-7546-6994-4(7)) Ashgate Publishing Co.

Ng. Brain-Mind Machinery. 2009. (Illus.). xii, 371p. 81.00 (978-981-279-025-5(X)) World Scientific Publishing Co., Inc.

Nicholls, John G., et al. From Neuron to Brain. 5th rev. ed. 2011. 580p. **(978-0-87893-609-0(2))** Sinauer Assocs., Inc.

Nolte, John & Angevine, Jay B., Jr. The Human Brain in Photographs & Diagrams. 3rd rev. ed. 2007. (ENG., Illus.). 272p. pap. 64.95 (978-0-323-04573-5(1), Mosby) Elsevier - Health Sciences Div.

Nowinski, Wieslaw. The Human Brain in 1492 Pieces: Structure, Vasculature, & Tracts. 2010. (ENG.). 16p. cd-rom 349.99 (978-1-60406-551-0(6)) Thieme Medical Pubs., Inc.

Nunn, Kenneth, et al. Who's Who of the Brain: A Guide to Its Inhabitants, Where They Live & What They Do. 2008. (ENG., Illus.). 240p. pap. (978-1-84310-470-4(9)) Kingsley, Jessica Ltd.

Nussbaum, Paul. Save Your Brain: The 5 Things You Must Do to Keep Your Mind Young & Sharp. 2010. (ENG., Illus.). 224p. pap. 16.95 (978-0-07-171376-4(X), 007171376X) McGraw-Hill Cos., The.

Olken, Hyman. Opening the Door to the Brain: Granular Cell Neuron Masses. (Illus.). 30p. (Orig.). pap. 12.00 (978-0-934818-05-6(3)) Olken Pubns.

Omalu, Bennet. Play Hard, Die Young: Football Dementia, Depression, & Death. 2008. 163p. per. 15.95 (978-0-9800395-0-4(9)) Neo-Forenxis Bks.

Orsucci, Franco & Sala, Nicoletta. Neuroscience in the Age of Complexity. 2011. (Neuroscience Research Progress Ser.). (Illus.). 169p. 195.00 (978-1-61122-046-9(7)) Nova Science Pubs., Inc.

Page, Martyn & Carter, Rita. The Human Brain Book. 2009. (ENG.). 256p. 40.00 (978-0-7566-5441-2(6)) Dorling Kindersley Publishing, Inc.

Paxinos, George & Franklin, Keith B. J. The Mouse Brain in Stereotaxic Coordinates, Compact: The Coronal Plates & Diagrams. 3rd rev. ed. 2008. (ENG., Illus.). 256p. spiral bd. 103.00 (978-0-12-374244-5(7), Academic Pr.) Elsevier Science & Technology Bks.

Paxinos, George & Watson, Charles. The Rat Brain: In Stereotaxic Coordinates. 6th ed. 2006. (ENG., Illus.). 456p. spiral bd. 210.00 (978-0-12-547612-6(4), Academic Pr.) Elsevier Science & Technology Bks.

Peng, Fred C. C. Language in the Brain: Critical Assessments. 2008. (ENG.). 352p. 60.00 (978-0-8264-3884-3(9)) Continuum International Publishing Group, Ltd. GBR. Dist: National Bk. Network.

Pete, Brain M. Twelve Brain Principles That Make the Difference. 2007. (978-1-4129-5177-7(1)) Corwin Pr.

Philp, Raleigh. Engaging 'Tweens & Teens: A Brain-Compatible Approach to Reaching Middle & High School Students. 2006. (Illus.). 232p. per. 36.95 (978-1-890460-49-5(4), B60494P) Corwin Pr.

Pickering, Andrew. The Cybernetic Brain: Sketches of Another Future. 2011. (Illus.). 536p. pap. 30.00 (978-0-226-66790-4(1)); (ENG., 55.00 (978-0-226-66789-8(8)) Univ. of Chicago Pr.

Pizzato, Mark. Inner Theatres of Good & Evil: The Mind's Staging of Gods, Angels & Devils. 2010. (ENG., Illus.). 368p. pap. 65.00 (978-0-7864-4260-7(3)) McFarland & Co., Inc. Pubs.

Platchias, Dimitris. Phenomenal Consciousness: Understanding the Relation Between Experience & Neural Processes in the Brain. 2011. 224p. (978-0-7735-3834-4(8)); (ENG.). (C). pap. (978-0-7735-3835-1(6)) McGill-Queen's Univ. Pr.

Pohlman, Craig. Revealing Minds: Assessing to Understand & Support Struggling Learners. 2007. (ENG., Illus.). 352p. per. 29.95 (978-0-7879-8790-9(5), Jossey-Bass) Wiley, John & Sons, Inc.

Polakof, Sergio. Brain Glucosensing: Physiological Implications. 2011. (Neurology - Laboratory & Clinical Research Developments Ser.). 43.00 (978-1-61761-334-0(7)) Nova Science Pubs., Inc.

Posner, Michael, et al. Cerebrum 2010: Emerging Ideas in Brain Science. 2010. (ENG.). 252p. pap. 14.95 (978-1-932594-49-2(3)) Dana Pr., The.

Purves, Dale. Brains: How They Seem to Work. 2010. (FT Press Science Ser.). (ENG., Illus.). 320p. 39.99 (978-0-13-705509-8(9)) FT Press.

Rabinovich, M. I., et al. Principles of Brain Dynamics: Global State Interactions. 2012. **(978-0-262-01764-0(4))** MIT Pr.

Ragusa, Moreah. The New Marriage Paradigm: Inspiring the Transformation & Evolution of Committed Relationships. 2007. 232p. per. (978-0-9781145-0-3(7)) CreateBooks.

Ramachandran, V. S. The Tell-Tale Brain: A Neuroscientist's Quest for What Makes Us Human. 2011. (ENG., Illus.). 357p. 26.95 (978-0-393-07782-7(9), 7782) Norton, W. W. & Co., Inc.

—Untitled Work On The Human Brain. Date not set. 26.00 (978-0-8050-6676-0(4)) Holt, Henry & Co.

Ratey, John J. Spark: The Revolutionary New Science of Exercise & the Brain. 2011. (ENG.). 304p. pap. 15.99 (978-0-316-11351-9(4), Back Bay Bks.) Little Brown & Co.

Rathbun, Ron W. The Mind & Self-Reflection: A New Way to Read with Your Mind. 2010. 278p. pap. 21.99 (978-0-9643519-5-0(1)) Quiescence Publishing.

Read, Cynthia A., ed. Cerebrum 2007: Emerging Ideas in Brain Science. 2007. (Illus.). 225p. per. 14.95 (978-1-932594-24-9(8)) Dana Pr., The.

Resch, Casey J. Focus on Brain Research. 2006. 225.00 (978-1-60021-395-3(2)) Nova Science Pubs., Inc.

Restak, Richard. The Naked Brain: How the Emerging Neurosociety Is Changing How We Live, Work, & Love. 2007. (ENG., Illus.). 272p. pap. 13.95 (978-1-4000-9809-5(2), Three Rivers Pr.) Crown Publishing Group.

Robbins, Trevor, et al. The Neurobiology of Addiction. 2010. (ENG., Illus.). 308p. 89.50 (978-0-19-956215-2(6)) Oxford Univ. Pr., Inc.

Rogers, Kara, ed. The Brain & the Nervous System. 2010. (Human Body Ser.). 280p. (YA). (ENG.). lib. bdg. 45.00 (978-1-61530-136-2(4)); (Illus.). 90.00 (978-1-61530-262-8(X)) Rosen Publishing Group, Inc., The.

Rolls, Edmund T. Neuroculture: On the implications of brain Science. 2012. (ENG., Illus.). 400p. 57.99 **(978-0-19-969547-8(4))** Oxford Univ. Pr., Inc.

Rose, Steven. The Future of the Brain: The Promise & Perils of Tomorrow's Neuroscience. 2006. (ENG., Illus.). 352p. per. 19.95 (978-0-19-530893-8(X)) Oxford Univ. Pr., Inc.

Rough Guides Staff & Gibb, Barry J. The Rough Guide to the Brain. 2nd ed. 2012. (Rough Guide To... Ser.). (ENG., Illus.). 312p. 18.99 **(978-1-4053-9006-4(9))** Rough Guides, Ltd. GBR. Dist: Dorling Kindersley Publishing, Inc.

Running Press Staff & Encyclopedia Britannica Staff. The Britannica Guide to the Brain: A Guided Tour of the Brain - Mind, Memory & Intelligence. 2008. (ENG.). 256p. pap. 13.95 *(978-0-7624-3369-8(8))* Running Pr. Bk. Pubs.

Savic-Berglund, Ivanka. Sex Difference in the Human Brain, Their Underpinnings & Implications. 2011. (ENG., Illus.). 216p. 268.00 *(978-0-444-53630-3(2))* Elsevier Science & Technology Bks.

Savino, Wilson, et al, eds. Neuroimmunomodulation: From Fundamental Biology to Therapy. 2009. (Annals of the New York Academy of Sciences Ser.: 8). (ENG., Illus.). 300p. pap. 134.95 *(978-1-57331-746-7(2)*, Wiley-Blackwell) Wiley, John & Sons, Inc.

Scaddan, Michael A. 40 Engaging Brain-Based Tools for the Classroom. 2008. (Illus.). 144p. 76.95 *(978-1-4129-4913-2(0)*, B49132C); pap. 33.95 *(978-1-4129-4914-9(9)*, B49132P) Corwin Pr.

Scarabino, T. & Salvolini, U., eds. Atlas of Morphology & Functional Anatomy of the Brain. 2010. Orig. Title: Atlante Morfo-Funzionale del Cervello. (Illus.). x, 127p. pap. 115.00 *(978-3-642-06742-6(5)*, 3642067425) Springer.

Scharfman, Helen E., ed. The Dentate Gyrus: A Comprehensive Guide to Structure, Function, & Clinical Implications. 2007. (Progress in Brain Research Ser.). (ENG., Illus.). 840p. 268.00 *(978-0-444-53015-8(0)*, Elsevier Science) Elsevier Science & Technology Bks.

Schenck, Jeb. Teaching & the Adolescent Brain: An Educator's Guide. 2011. (ENG., Illus.). 400p. pap. 37.00 *(978-0-393-70621-5(4)*, 70621) Norton, W. W. & Co., Inc.

Schulkin, Jay. Effort: A Behavioral Neuroscience Perspective on the Will. 2006. (ENG., Illus.). 200p. per. 41.95 *(978-0-8058-6010-8(X)*, Psychology Press) Taylor & Francis Group GBR. Dist: Taylor & Francis Group.

Schwartz, Jeffrey & Gladding, Rebecca. You Are Not Your Brain: The 4-Step Solution for Changing Bad Habits, Ending Unhealthy Thinking, & Taking Control of Your Life. 2011. (ENG.). 368p. (gr. 12). 26.00 *(978-1-58333-426-3(2)*, Avery) Penguin Group (USA) Inc.

Schwed, Amy & Melichar-Utter, Janice. Brain-Friendly Study Strategies, Grades 2-8: How Teachers Can Help Students Learn. 2007. (Illus.). 208p. 85.95 *(978-1-4129-6105-9(X)*, B42519C) Corwin Pr.

Scientific American Staff & Horstman, Judith. The Scientific American Brave New Brain: How Neuroscience, Brain-Machine Interfaces, Neuroimaging, Psychopharmacology, Epigenetics, the Internet, & Our Own Minds Are Stimulating & Enhancing the Future of Mental Power. 2010. (Scientific American Ser.: 1). (ENG., Illus.). 208p. 25.95 *(978-0-470-37624-9(4)*, Jossey-Bass) Wiley, John & Sons, Inc.

—The Scientific American Day in the Life of Your Brain: A 24 Hour Journal of What's Happening in Your Brain As You Sleep, Dream, Wake Up, Eat, Work, Play, Fight, Love, Worry, Compete, Hope, Make Important Decisions, Age & Change. 2009. (Scientific American Ser.: 2). (ENG., Illus.). 264p. 25.95 *(978-0-470-37623-2(6)*, Jossey-Bass) Wiley, John & Sons, Inc.

Sebastien, Paul & Balabuszko-Reay, Jim. BrainReady - BrainFlex Worksheets, Volume 1. 2007. (ENG.). 64p. per. 12.99 *(978-1-4303-0686-3(6))* Lulu Enterprises Inc.

Sekihara, Kensuke & Nagarajan, Srikatan S. Adaptive Spatial Filters for Electromagnetic Brain Imaging. 2010. (Series in Biomedical Engineering Ser.). (Illus.). xi, 245p. pap. 179.00 *(978-3-642-09827-7(4)*, 3642098274) Springer.

Shallice, Tim & Cooper, Richard P. The Organisation of Mind. 2011. (ENG., Illus.). 584p. pap. 65.00 *(978-0-19-957924-2(5))* Oxford Univ. Pr., Inc.

Siegel, Daniel J. The Developing Mind, Second Edition: How Relationships & the Brain Interact to Shape Who We Are. 2nd rev. ed. 2012. (ENG.). 506p. 55.00 ***(978-1-4625-0390-2(X))*** Guilford Pubns., Inc.

Slobounov, Semyon M. & Sebastianelli, Wayne J., eds. Foundations of Sport-Related Brain Injuries. 2010. (ENG., Illus.). xx, 484p. pap. 135.00 *(978-1-4419-4091-9(X)*, 144194091X) Springer.

Smilkstein, Rita, et al. Igniting Student Potential: Teaching with the Brain's Natural Learning Process. 2006. (Illus.). 232p. 82.95 *(978-1-4129-1705-6(0)*, B17050C); pap. 36.95 *(978-1-4129-1706-3(9)*, B17050P) Corwin Pr.

Smith, Alistair. Unleashing Learning Potential: How the Brain Works. 2007. 312p. pap. *(978-1-85539-359-2(X)*, Network Educational Pr. Ltd.) Continuum International Publishing Group, Ltd.

Smith, Kenneth J. Challenging Units for Gifted Learners: Teaching the Way Gifted Students Think - Math. 2010. (ENG.). 200p. pap. 19.95 *(978-1-59363-497-1(8))* Prufrock Pr.

Smith, Shawn. The User's Guide to the Human Mind: Why Our Brains Make Us Unhappy, Anxious, & Neurotic & What We Can Do about It. 2011. (ENG., Illus.). 216p. pap. 16.95 *(978-1-60882-052-8(1))* New Harbinger Pubns.

Sousa, David A. How the Brain Influences Behavior: Management Strategies for Every Classroom. 2008. (Illus.). 264p. 90.95 *(978-1-4129-5869-1(5)*, B58691C); pap. 41.95 *(978-1-4129-5870-7(9)*, B58691P) Corwin Pr.

—How the Brain Learns. 4th ed. 2011. (Illus.). 336p. pap. 44.95 ***(978-1-4129-9797-3(6)***, B97973P) Corwin Pr.

Sousa, David A. How the Brain Learns: A Multimedia Kit for Professional Development. 3rd ed. 2008. 64p. 360.00 *(978-1-4129-6758-7(9)*, B67587K) Corwin Pr.

Sousa, David A., ed. Mind, Brain, & Education: Neuroscience Implications for the Classroom. 2010. 312p. lib. bdg. 34.95 *(978-1-935249-63-4(0))* Solution Tree Pr.

Sousa, David A. & Tomlinson, Carol Ann. Differentiation & the Brain: How Neuroscience Supports the Learner-Friendly Classroom. 2010. (ENG.). 216p. pap. 29.95 *(978-1-935249-59-7(2))*; lib. bdg. 64.95 *(978-1-935249-60-3(6))* Solution Tree Pr.

Sprenger, Marilee. Becoming a Wiz at Brain-Based Teaching: How to Make Every Year Your Best Year. 2nd rev. ed. 2006. (Illus.). 224p. 82.95 *(978-1-4129-2795-6(1)*, B27951C); per. 36.95 *(978-1-4129-2796-3(X)*, B27951P) Corwin Pr.

—Differentiation Through Learning Styles & Memory. 2nd ed. 2008. (Illus.). 184p. pap. 34.95 *(978-1-4129-5545-4(9)*, B55440P) Corwin Pr.

Sprenger, Marilee B. Differentiation Through Learning Styles & Memory. 2nd ed. 2008. (Illus.). 184p. 78.95 *(978-1-4129-5544-7(0)*, B55440C) Corwin Pr.

Steen, R. Grant. The Evolving Brain: The Known & the Unknown. 2007. (ENG., Illus.). 1p. 28.98 *(978-1-59102-480-4(3))* Prometheus Bks., Pubs.

Steriade, Mircea M. & McCarley, Robert W. Brain Control of Wakefulness & Sleep. 2nd ed. 2010. (ENG., Illus.). xviii, 728p. pap. 199.00 *(978-1-4419-3470-3(7)*, 1441934707) Springer.

Strauch, Barbara. The Secret Life of the Grown-Up Brain: The Surprising Talents of the Middle-Aged Mind. 2011. (ENG.). 256p. (gr. 12). 16.00 *(978-0-14-311887-9(0)*, Penguin (Non-Classics)) Penguin Group (USA) Inc.

—The Secret Life of the Grown-up Brain: The Surprising Talents of the Middle-aged Mind. l.t. ed. 2010. (ENG.). 347p. 31.99 *(978-1-4104-2995-7(4))* Thorndike Pr.

Sweeney, Michael. Brain: The Complete Mind. 2009. (ENG., Illus.). 352p. 40.00 *(978-1-4262-0547-7(3)*, National Geographic) National Geographic Society.

Sweeney, Michael S. Brain: The Complete Mind. 2009. (Illus.). ix, 342p. *(978-1-4262-0548-4(1))* National Geographic Society.

Sweeney, Michael S. & National Geographic Editors. Brainworks: The Mind-Bending Science of How You See, What You Think, & Who You Are. 2011. (ENG., Illus.). 224p. 27.00 *(978-1-4262-0757-0(3)*, National Geographic) National Geographic Society.

Sylwester, Robert. A Child's Brain: The Need for Nurture. 2010. (Illus.). 200p. pap. 31.95 *(978-1-4129-6271-1(4)*, B62704P) Corwin Pr.

Tammet, Daniel. Embracing the Wide Sky: A Tour Across the Horizons of the Mind. 2009. (ENG.). 320p. pap. 15.00 *(978-1-4165-7618-1(5)*, Free Pr.) Free Pr.

Taylor, John G. The Mind: A User's Manual. 2006. (ENG., Illus.). 302p. per. 21.95 *(978-0-470-02222-1(1)*, Wiley) Wiley, John & Sons, Inc.

Tiger, Lionel & McGuire, Michael. God's Brain. 2010. (ENG., Illus.). 265p. 25.00 *(978-1-61614-164-6(6))* Prometheus Bks., Pubs.

Time Magazine Editors & Kluger, Jeffrey. Your Brain: A User's Guide. 2010. (ENG., Illus.). 144p. 29.95 *(978-1-60320-094-3(0)*, Time Bks.) Time Home Entertainment, Inc.

Tokoro, Mario & Mogi, Ken, eds. Creativity & the Brain. 2007. (Illus.). 143p. pap. 58.00 *(978-981-270-019-3(6))* World Scientific Publishing Co., Inc.

Tokuhama-Espinosa, Tracey. Mind, Brain, & Education Science: A Comprehensive Guide to the New Brain-Based Teaching. 2010. (ENG., Illus.). 464p. pap. 34.95 *(978-0-393-70607-9(9)*, 70607) Norton, W. W. & Co., Inc.

Traver, Kelly & Sargent, Betty Kelly. The Program: The Brain-Smart Approach to the Healthiest You - The Life-Changing 12-Week Method. 2009. (ENG., Illus.). 400p. 27.99 *(978-1-4391-0998-4(2)*, Beyond Words/Atria Bks.) Atria Bks.

Vaas, Rudy & Vaas, Rüdiger. Brave New Neuro-World: The Future of the Human Brain - Intervention, Explanation, Ethics. 2014. Orig. Title: Schöne neue Neuro-Welt. (ENG., Illus.). 170p. 25.00 *(978-3-540-88858-1(6)*, 3540888586) Springer.

Vanderwolf, C. H. The Evolving Brain: The Mind & the Neural Control of Behavior. (ENG., Illus.). x, 104p. 2010. pap. 64.95 *(978-1-4419-4170-1(3)*, 1441941703) 2006. 64.95 *(978-0-387-34229-0(X)*, 038734229X) Springer.

Vanderwolf, Case H. An Odyssey Through the Brain, Behavior & the Mind. 2010. (ENG.). 192p. pap. 129.00 *(978-1-4419-5335-3(3)*, 1441953353) Springer.

Vasquez-Cropper, Marie. Engaging Cognitive Neurosciences in the Classroom. 2008. 56p. pap. *(978-3-639-03834-7(7))* VDM Verlag Dr. Mueller e.K.

Vesalius, Andreas, et al. On the Fabric of the Human Body: A Translation of de Humani Corporis Fabrica Libri Septem. 2009. *(978-0-930405-90-8(0))* Norman Publishing.

Von Hofsten, Claes & Rosander, Kerstin, eds. From Action to Cognition. 2007. (Progress in Brain Research Ser.). (ENG., Illus.). 466p. 268.00 *(978-0-444-53016-5(9)*, Elsevier Science) Elsevier Science & Technology Bks.

von Neumann, John & Kurzweil, Ray. The Computer & the Brain. 3rd ed. 2012. (Silliman Memorial Lectures Ser.). (ENG.). 136p. pap. 15.00 ***(978-0-300-18111-1(6))*** Yale Univ. Pr.

Walsh, Gregory & Lavery, Michael. Whole Brain Power: The Fountain of Youth for the Mind & Body (HardCover Edition) 2008. 308p. 47.32 *(978-0-557-02621-0(0))* Lulu Enterprises Inc.

Wang, Sam & Aamodt, Sandra. Welcome to Your Brain: Why You Lose Your Car Keys but Never Forget How to Drive & Other Puzzles of Everyday Behavior. 2008. (ENG., Illus.). 256p. pap. 15.00 *(978-1-59691-523-7(4))* Bloomsbury Publishing.

Watson, Charles, et al. The Brain: An Introduction to Functional Neuroanatomy. 2010. (ENG.). 216p. 59.95 *(978-0-12-373889-9(X)*, Academic Pr.) Elsevier Science & Technology Bks.

Wehrenberg, Margaret. The 10 Best-Ever Anxiety Management Techniques: Understanding How Your Brain Makes You Anxious & What You Can Do to Change It. 2008. (ENG., Illus.). 256p. pap. 19.95 *(978-0-393-70556-0(0)*, 70556) Norton, W. W. & Co., Inc.

Weil, Andrew & Small, Gary. The Healthy Brain Kit: Clinically Proven Tools to Boost Your Memory, Sharpen Your Mind, & Keep Your Brain Young. 2007. (Illus.). 52p. audio compact disk 26.95 *(978-1-59179-530-8(3)*, KT01086D) Sounds True, Inc.

Westen, Drew & Kowalski, Robin M. Psychology. 5th ed. 2008. (ENG., Illus.). 824p. (C). 179.95 *(978-0-470-08762-6(5)*, Wiley) Wiley, John & Sons, Inc.

Wigan, A. L. New View of Insanity the Duality of the. 2006. pap. 31.95 *(978-1-4286-4534-9(9))* Kessinger Publishing, LLC.

Willis, Judy. Brain-Friendly Strategies for the Inclusion Classroom: Insights from a Neurologist & Classroom Teacher. 2007. (Illus.). 227p. per. 25.95 *(978-1-4166-0539-3(8))* Assn. for Supervision & Curriculum Development.

—How Your Child Learns Best: Brain-Friendly Strategies You Can Use to Ignite Your Child's Learning & Increase School Success. 2008. (ENG., Illus.). 336p. pap. 18.99 *(978-1-4022-1346-5(8))* Sourcebooks, Inc.

—Inspiring Middle School Minds: Gifted, Creative, & Challenging. 2009. 326p. pap. 24.95 *(978-0-910707-93-0(6))* Great Potential Pr., Inc.

—Research-Based Strategies to Ignite Student Learning: Insights from a Neurologist & Classroom Teacher. 2006. 125p. per. 21.95 *(978-1-4166-0370-2(0))* Assn. for Supervision & Curriculum Development.

—Teaching the Brain to Read: Strategies for Improving Fluency, Vocabulary, & Comprehension. 2008. xiv, 176p. pap. 23.95 *(978-1-4166-0688-8(2))* Assn. for Supervision & Curriculum Development.

Winner, Paul. 7 Steps to a Healthy Brain. 2008. 228p. pap. 21.95 *(978-1-4357-1068-9(1))* Lulu Enterprises Inc.

Wolfe, Pat. Brain Matters: Translating Research into Classroom Practice, 2nd Edition. 2nd ed. 2010. 247p. pap. 27.95 *(978-1-4166-1067-0(7))* Assn. for Supervision & Curriculum Development.

Zeman, Adam. A Portrait of the Brain. 2009. (ENG., Illus.). 256p. pap. 18.00 *(978-0-300-15831-1(9))* Yale Univ. Pr.

BRAIN—ABNORMALITIES

see also Cerebral Palsy

Connors, Susan & Zimmerman, Andrew, eds. Maternal Influences on Fetal Neurodevelopment: Clinical & Research Aspects. 2010. (ENG., Illus.). xii, 166p. 139.00 *(978-1-60327-920-8(2)*, 1603279202) Humana Pr.

Lanzino, Giuseppe & Spetzler, Robert F. Cavernous Malformations of the Brain & Spinal Cord. 2007. 139.95 *(978-3-13-141891-3(5))* Thieme Medical Pubs., Inc.

Lanzino, Giuseppe & Spetzler, Robert F., eds. Cavernous Malformations of the Brain & Spinal Cord. 2007. (ENG.). 139p. pap. 149.99 *(978-1-58890-343-3(5))* Thieme Medical Pubs., Inc.

Murmu, Meena Sriti. Stress During Pregnancy Can Alter Offspring's Brain Development. 2008. 108p. pap. *(978-3-639-00649-0(6))* VDM Verlag Dr. Mueller e.K.

Rummel-Hudson, Robert. Schuyler's Monster: A Father's Journey with His Wordless Daughter. 2009. (ENG.). 288p. pap. 15.95 *(978-0-312-53880-4(4)*, St. Martin's Griffin) St. Martin's Pr.

BRAIN—ABNORMITIES AND DEFORMITIES

see Brain—Abnormalities

BRAIN—AGING

Aizenstein, Howard J., et al. Neuroimaging Research in Geriatric Mental Health. 2010. (Illus.). xiii, 263p. E-Book ***(978-0-8261-1116-6(5))*** Springer Publishing Co., Inc.

Ballesteros, Soledad. Ageing, Cognition, & Neuroscience: A Special Issue of the European Journal of Cognitive Psychology. 2009. (Special Issues of the European Journal of Cognitive Psychology Ser.). (ENG., Illus.). 296p. 79.95 *(978-1-84872-707-6(0)*, Psychology Press) Taylor & Francis Group GBR. Dist: Taylor & Francis Group.

Cabeza, Roberto, et al, eds. Cognitive Neuroscience of Aging: Linking Cognitive & Cerebral Aging. 2009. (ENG., Illus.). 408p. pap. 45.00 *(978-0-19-538822-0(4))* Oxford Univ. Pr., Inc.

Cohen, Gene D. The Mature Mind: The Positive Power of the Aging Brain. 2006. (ENG.). 256p. per. 16.99 *(978-0-465-01204-6(3))* Basic Bks.

—The Mature Mind: The Positive Power of the Aging Brain. rev. ed. 2007. (Thorndike Health, Home & Learning Ser.). (Illus.). 359p. 30.95 *(978-0-7862-9279-0(2))* Thorndike Pr.

Cozolino, Louis & Cozolino, Louis J. The Healthy Aging Brain: Sustaining Attachment, Attaining Wisdom. 2008. (Norton Series on Interpersonal Neurobiology Ser.). (ENG.). 380p. 29.95 *(978-0-393-70513-3(7)*, 70513) Norton, W. W. & Co., Inc.

De Leon, Mony J., et al, eds. Imaging & the Aging Brain. 2007. (Annals of the New York Academy of Sciences Ser.: Vol. 1095). (ENG., Illus.). 252p. pap. 149.95 *(978-1-57331-659-0(8)*, Wiley-Blackwell) Wiley, John & Sons, Inc.

de Vellis, Jean, ed. Neuroglia in the Aging Brain. 2010. (Contemporary Neuroscience Ser.). (Illus.). 536p. pap. 199.00 *(978-1-61737-088-5(6)*, 1617370886) Humana Pr.

Desai, Abhilash K. Healthy Brain Aging: Evidence Based Methods to Preserve Brain Function & Prevent Dementia - Clinics in Geriatric Medicine. 2010. (Clinics: Internal Medicine Ser.: 26-1). (ENG., Illus.). xii, 170p. 105.00 *(978-1-4377-1822-5(1)*, Saunders) Elsevier - Health Sciences Div.

Erwin, Joseph M. & Hof, Patrick R., eds. Aging in Non-Human Primates, Vol. 31. (Interdisciplinary Topics in Gerontology Ser.: Vol. 31). (Illus.). *(978-3-8055-7312-2(X))* Karger, S. AG.

Evans, Simon J. & Burghardt, Paul R. Brain Fit for Life: A User's Guide to Life-Long Brain Health & Fitness. 2008. (Illus.). 240p. 24.95 *(978-0-9817258-0-2(5))* River Pointe Pubns.

Gelb, Michael J. & Howell, Kelly. Brain Power: Improve Your Mind as You Age. 2011. (ENG.). 248p. pap. 14.95 ***(978-1-60868-073-3(8))*** New World Library.

Gupta, Ekta, et al. Morphometric Analysis of Corpus Callosum in Both Sexes- a Mri Study. 2011. 104p. pap. ***(978-3-8443-0704-7(4))*** Lambert Academic Publishing.

Hof, Patrick R. & Mobbs, Charles V., eds. Handbook of the Neuroscience of Aging. 2009. (ENG., Illus.). 740p. 185.00 *(978-0-12-374898-0(4)*, Academic Pr.) Elsevier Science & Technology Bks.

Jagust, William & D'Esposito, Mark, eds. Imaging the Aging Brain. 2009. (ENG., Illus.). 384p. 125.00 *(978-0-19-532887-5(6))* Oxford Univ. Pr., Inc.

Mendelson, Scott D. Beyond Alzheimer's: How to Avoid the Modern Epidemic of Dementia. 2009. (ENG.). 272p. 24.95 *(978-1-59077-157-0(5))* Evans, M. & Co., Inc.

Newberg, Andrew B. & Alavi, Abass. Aging Brain: An Issue of PET Clinics. 2010. (Clinics: Radiology Ser.: 5-1). (ENG., Illus.). xii, 130p. 79.00 *(978-1-4377-1941-3(4)*, Saunders) Elsevier - Health Sciences Div.

Nussbaum, Paul. Your Brain Health Lifestyle: A Proactive Program to Preserve Your Life Story. 2007. pap. 15.00 *(978-1-59571-184-7(8))* Word Association Pubs.

Restak, Richard. Think Smart: A Neuroscientist's Prescription for Improving Your Brain's Performance. 2010. (ENG., Illus.). 288p. (gr. 12-18). 16.00 *(978-1-59448-443-8(0)*, Riverhead Trade (Paperbacks)) Penguin Group (USA) Inc.

Riddle, David R. Brain Aging: Models, Methods, & Mechanisms. 2007. (Frontiers in Neuroscience Ser.). (ENG., Illus.). 408p. 162.95 *(978-0-8493-3818-2(2)*, CRC Press) Taylor & Francis Group GBR. Dist: Taylor & Francis Group.

Scientific American & Horstman, Judith. The Scientific American Healthy Aging Brain: The Neuroscience of Making the Most of Your Mature Mind. 2012. (Scientific American Ser.: 4). (ENG.). 272p. 25.95 ***(978-0-470-64773-8(6)***, Jossey-Bass) Wiley, John & Sons, Inc.

Small, Gary. The Memory Bible: An Innovative Strategy for Keeping Your Brain Young. 2007. (ENG.). 320p. pap. 16.95 *(978-1-4013-0922-0(4))* Hyperion Pr.

BRAIN—ANALYSIS AND CHEMISTRY

see Brain Chemistry

BRAIN—ATLASES

Adesina, A. M. Atlas of Pediatric Brain Tumors. 2009. 250p. 175.00 *(978-1-60327-182-0(1))* Humana Pr.

Bayer, Shirley A. & Altman, Joseph. Atlas of Human Central Nervous System Development -5 Volume Set, 5 vols. 2007. (ENG.). 850.00 *(978-1-4200-6800-9(8)*, CRC Press) Taylor & Francis Group GBR. Dist: Taylor & Francis Group.

Catani, Marco & Thiebaut de Schotten, Michel. Atlas of Human Brain Connections. 2012. (ENG.). 456p. 159.95 *(978-0-19-954116-4(7))* Oxford Univ. Pr., Inc.

Danaila, L., et al. Atlas of Surgical Pathology of the Brain. Cinca, Silvia, ed. pap. 39.99 *(978-1-930387-04-1(0))* Moonfall Pr.

Dong. The Allen Reference Atlas: A Digital Color Brain Atlas of the C57BL/6J Male Mouse. 2008. (ENG., Illus.). 376p. pap. 245.00 *(978-0-470-05408-6(5)*, Wiley) Wiley, John & Sons, Inc.

Dong, Hong wei & Allen Institute for Brain Science Staff. Allen Reference Atlas: A Digital Brain Atlas of C57BL/6J Male Mouse. 2007. 1p. pap. 195.00 *(978-0-470-05356-0(9)*, Wiley) Wiley, John & Sons, Inc.

Dong, Hongwei. Allen Reference Atlas SET. 2007. 100p. pap. 335.00 incl. cd-rom *(978-0-470-14757-3(1)*, Wiley) Wiley, John & Sons, Inc.

Fix, James D. Atlas of the Human Brain & Spinal Cord. 2nd rev. ed. 2008. (Illus.). 223p. spiral bd. 76.95 *(978-0-7637-5318-4(1))* Jones & Bartlett Learning, LLC.

Frahm, Jens, et al. Magnetic Resonance Imaging of the Rhesus Monkey Brain. 2009. (ENG., Illus.). 263p. (C). 369.00 *(978-3-525-40424-9(7))* Vandenhoeck & Ruprecht GmbH & Co. KG DEU. Dist: ISD.

Hardman, Craig D. & Ashwell, Ken W. S. Stereotaxic & Chemoarchitectural Atlas of the Brain of the Common Marmoset (Callithrix Jacchus) 2012. (ENG., Illus.). 515p. 179.95 ***(978-1-4398-3778-8(3)***, CRC Press) Taylor & Francis Group GBR. Dist: Taylor & Francis Group.

Höhne, Karl-Heinz. VOXEL-MAN 3D-Navigator: Brain & Skull: Regional, Functional, & Radiological Anatomy. 2nd ed. 2009. (GER & ENG., Illus.). 99.00 *(978-3-642-01211-2(6))* Springer.

Jansen, Heiko T., et al. An Atlas of the Sheep Brain. 2012. (ENG., Illus.). 128p. pap. 125.00 *(978-0-470-08477-9(4)*, Wiley) Wiley, John & Sons, Inc.

Kingsley, Robert E. & Kingsley, Robert D. Interactive Atlas of the Human Brain. 2007. cd-rom 350.00 *(978-1-58829-960-4(0)*, 1588299600) 2007. cd-rom 99.50 *(978-1-58829-798-3(5)*, 1588297985) 2nd ed. 2008. cd-rom 129.00 *(978-1-60327-493-7(6))* Humana Pr.

Mai, Juergen K., et al. Atlas of the Human Brain. 3rd ed. 2007. (ENG., Illus.). 280p. spiral bd. 210.00 *(978-0-12-373603-1(X)*, Academic Pr.) Elsevier Science & Technology Bks.

Nolte, John & Angevine, Jay B., Jr. The Human Brain in Photographs & Diagrams. 3rd rev. ed. 2007. (ENG., Illus.). 272p. pap. 64.95 *(978-0-323-04573-5(1)*, Mosby) Elsevier - Health Sciences Div.

Nowinski, Wieslaw L., et al. The Cerefy Atlas of Cerebral Vasculature. 2009. (ENG.). cd-rom 209.99 *(978-1-60406-090-4(5))* Thieme Medical Pubs., Inc.

Oishi, Kenichi, et al. MRI Atlas of Human White Matter. 2nd ed. 2010. (ENG.). 266p. 199.95 *(978-0-12-382081-5(2)*, Academic Pr.) Elsevier Science & Technology Bks.

Orrison, William W. Atlas of Brain Function. 2nd ed. 2008. (ENG., Illus.). 316p. pap. 89.99 *(978-1-58890-525-3(X))* Thieme Medical Pubs., Inc.

Osborn, Anne G., et al. Brain & Spine. 2008. (EXPERTddx™ Ser.). (ENG., Illus.). 1000p. 329.00 *(978-1-931884-02-0(1))* Lippincott Williams & Wilkins.

Palazzi, Xavier. The Beagle Brain in Stereotaxic Coordinates. 2011. (ENG., Illus.). xvii, 119p. 189.00 *(978-1-4419-8371-8(6)*, 1441983716) Springer.

Palazzi, Xavier & Bordier, Nicole. The Marmoset Brain in Stereotaxic Coordinates. 2008. 129.00 ***(978-0-387-78384-0(9)***, 0387783849) Springer.

Paxinos, George & Watson, Charles. Chemoarchitectonic Atlas of the Mouse Brain. 2009. (ENG., Illus.). 285.00 *(978-0-12-374238-4(2)*, Academic Pr.) Elsevier Science & Technology Bks.

—The Rat Brain in Stereotaxic Coordinates: Hard Cover Edition. 6th ed. 2007. (ENG.). 456p. 210.00 *(978-0-12-374121-9(1)*, Academic Pr.) Elsevier Science & Technology Bks.

Paxinos, George & Watson, Charles, eds. BrainNavigator. 2009. 0.02 *(978-0-12-374958-1(1)*, Academic Pr.) Elsevier Science & Technology Bks.

Paxinos, George, et al. The Marmoset Brain in Stereotaxic Coordinates. 2011. (ENG.). 324p. pap. 179.95 ***(978-0-12-415818-4(8)***, Academic Pr.) Elsevier Science & Technology Bks.

Paxinos, George, et al. The Rhesus Monkey Brain: In Stereotaxic Coordinates. 2nd ed. 2008. (ENG., Illus.). 416p. 260.00 *(978-0-12-373619-2(6)*, Academic Pr.) Elsevier Science & Technology Bks.

Pinel, John P. J. & Edwards, Maggie. A Colorful Introduction to the Anatomy of the Human Brain: A Brain & Psychology Coloring Book. 2nd ed. 2007. (ENG., Illus.). 264p. (C). per. 24.00 *(978-0-205-54874-3(1))* Allyn & Bacon, Inc.

Ramachandra, Renuka & Subramanian, Thyagarajan. Atlas of the Neonatal Rat Brain. 2011. (ENG., Illus.). 188p. 159.95 *(978-1-4398-4012-2(1)*, CRC Press) Taylor & Francis Group GBR. Dist: Taylor & Francis Group.

Saleem, Kadharbatcha S. & Logothetis, Nikos K. A Combined MRI & Histology Atlas of the Rhesus Monkey Brain in Stereotaxic Coordinates. 2nd ed. 2012. (ENG., Illus.). 402p. 249.95 ***(978-0-12-385087-4(8)***, Academic Pr.) Elsevier Science & Technology Bks.

Schoonover, Carl Edward. Portraits of the Mind: Visualizing the Brain from Antiquity to the 21st Century. 2010. (ENG., Illus.). 240p. 35.00 *(978-0-8109-9033-3(4))* Abrams.

BRAIN—BLOOD-VESSELS

see also Blood-Brain Barrier; Intracranial Aneurysms

Auer, Ludwig M. & Kassell, N., eds. Timing of Aneurysm Surgery. (ENG.). XIV, 685p. 314.00 ***(978-3-11-188494-3(5))*** De Gruyter, Walter Inc.

Bradac, Gianni Boris & Boccardi, Edoardo. Cerebral Angiography: Normal Anatomy & Vascular Pathology. 2011. (ENG., Illus.). xiii, 314p. 189.00 *(978-3-642-15677-9(0)*, 3642156770) Springer.

Helio, Tomas R., ed. The Blood Brain Barrier. 2008. 129.00 *(978-1-60456-894-3(1))* Nova Science Pubs., Inc.

Mitagvaria, Nodar P. & (James) Bicher, Haim I. Cerebral Blood Flow Regulation. 2009. 79.00 *(978-1-60692-163-0(0))* Nova Science Pubs., Inc.

Morris, P. Pearse. Practical Neuroangiography. 2nd rev. ed. 2006. (Illus.). 560p. 225.99 *(978-0-7817-6515-2(3))* Lippincott Williams & Wilkins.

Nowinski, Wieslaw L., et al. The Cerefy Atlas of Cerebral Vasculature. 2009. (ENG.). cd-rom 209.99 *(978-1-60406-090-4(5))* Thieme Medical Pubs., Inc.

Qureshi, Adnan I., ed. Textbook of Interventional Neurology. 2011. (ENG., Illus.). 506p. 140.00 *(978-0-521-87639-1(7))* Cambridge Univ. Pr.

Rhodes, Marie A. CCSVI as the Cause of Multiple Sclerosis: The Science Behind the Controversial Theory. Moore, Elaine A., ed. 2011. (McFarland Health Topics Ser.). (ENG. Illus.). 257p. pap. 35.00 *(978-0-7864-6038-0(5))* McFarland & Co., Inc. Pubs.

Rigamonti, Daniele, ed. Cavernous Malformations of the Nervous System. 2011. (ENG., Illus.). 208p 135.00 *(978-0-521-76427-8(0))* Cambridge Univ. Pr.

Rosenwasser, Robert H. & Jabbour, Pascal M. Neuroendovascular Management: Cranial & Spinal Disorders - An Issue of Neurosurgery Clinics. 2009. (Clinics: Surgery Ser.: 20-4). (ENG.). 99.00 *(978-1-4377-1574-3(5)*, Saunders) Elsevier - Health Sciences Div.

Sheikh, Professor Bassem. Intracranial Arteriovenous Malformations. 2011. 128p. pap. ***(978-3-8454-0660-2(7))*** Lambert Academic Publishing.

BRAIN—CANCER

Badgett, Sandy. Remembering Laura: Letting Go of Life with Beauty & Grace. 2009. pap. 14.99 *(978-1-60799-078-9(4))* Tate Publishing & Enterprises, LLC.

Beaucher, Christopher Scott. Loved by an ANGEL: The Story of a 9 Year Olds Lifelong Battle with Cancer, but Never Her Faith! 2010. 280p. 25.99 *(978-1-4520-4598-6(4))*; pap. 17.95 *(978-1-4520-4597-9(6))* AuthorHouse.

Czlonka, Rod. Decide to Live - Second Edition. 2010. 263p. pap. 20.00 *(978-0-557-71775-0(2))* Lulu Enterprises Inc.

Dann, Patty. The Goldfish Went on Vacation: A Memoir of Loss (and Learning to Tell the Truth about It) 2007. (ENG.). 176p. per. 11.95 *(978-1-59030-564-5(7)*, Trumpeter) Shambhala Pubns., Inc.

Desserich, Brooke & Desserich, Keith. Notes Left Behind. 2010. (ENG.). 288p. pap. 14.99 *(978-0-06-188640-9(8)*, Harper Paperbacks) HarperCollins Pubs.

Eggspuehler, Don. Star Benchwarmers: A Family Memoir. 2011. 336p. 28.49 *(978-1-4520-8308-7(8))* AuthorHouse.

Eilers, Shannon. Losing Lol: A Memoir of Reckless Behavior in a Time of Tragedy. 2010. 140p. pap. 15.99 *(978-1-4490-7933-8(4))* AuthorHouse.

—Losing Lola: A Memoir of Reckless Behavior in a Time of Tragedy. 2010. 140p. 24.99 *(978-1-4490-7934-5(2))* AuthorHouse.

Freedman, Jeri. Brain Cancer: Current & Emerging Trends in Detection & Treatment. 2009. (Cancer & Modern Science Ser.). 64p. (gr. 5-5). 58.50 *(978-1-61511-770-3(9))* Rosen Publishing Group, Inc., The.

Fritz, Robert. What's the Next Step? My Journey with Cancer as a Caregiver & then as a Caretaker. 2011. 168p. 25.95 *(978-1-4502-9630-4(0))*; pap. 15.95 *(978-1-4502-9631-1(9))* iUniverse, Inc.

Hassey, Patrick. Eyes Through You. 2011. 228p. pap. 15.79 ***(978-1-4567-3915-7(8))*** AuthorHouse.

Hoeger, Martin A. One Left Handed Hug. 2009. 160p. pap. 16.50 *(978-1-4389-4821-8(2))* AuthorHouse.

Iris Sechriest. Sybil's Choice. 2009. 180p. pap. 16.95 *(978-1-4401-6858-1(X))* iUniverse, Inc.

Jambeck, Nick. Dying to Love Again. 2009. 112p. pap. 14.98 *(978-0-557-09767-8(3))* Lulu Enterprises Inc.

Kleinberg. Johns Hopkins Patient Guide to Brain Cancer. rev. ed. 2011. 192p. pap. 22.95 *(978-0-7637-7425-7(1))* Jones & Bartlett Learning, LLC.

Kleinberg, Lawrence, ed. Brainn Metastasis: A Multidisciplinary Approach. 2008. (Illus.). 256p. 125.00 *(978-1-933864-43-3(5))* Demos Medical Publishing, LLC.

Kozar, Richard. The Book of Chad. 2010. *(978-1-59556-038-4(6))* OTTN Publishing.

Lefevers, Jay. Cancer on the Brain: One Man's Journey of Baseball, Business, & Beating the Odds. 2012. (ENG.). 18.95 ***(978-1-937110-24-6(9))*** Emerald Bk. Co.

MacDougall, Judy F. Ruby, a Child of the King. 2011. (Illus.). ***(978-1-77069-174-2(X))*** Word Alive Pr.

Mehta, Minnesh & Mehta, Minesh P. Principles & Practice of Neuro-Oncology: A Multidisciplinary Approach. 2010. 769.00 *(978-1-933864-78-5(8))* Demos Medical Publishing, LLC.

Minnick, Christy. Hug Life. 2010. 396p. pap. 20.99 *(978-1-60957-062-0(6))* Xulon Pr., Inc.

O'Kelly, Eugene. Chasing Daylight: How My Forthcoming Death Transformed My Life. 2007. (ENG., Illus.). 160p. per. 14.95 *(978-0-07-149993-4(8)*, 0071499938) McGraw-Hill Cos., The.

Raizer, Jeffrey J. & Abrey, Lauren E., eds. Brain Metastases. 2007. (Cancer Treatment & Research Ser.). (Illus.). 239p. 169.00 *(978-0-387-69221-0(5))* Springer.

Rao, Ganesh & D'Ambrosio, Anthony. Management of Brain Metastses: Neurosurgery Clinics of North America. 2010. (Clinics: Surgery Ser.: 22-1). (ENG., Illus.). 128p. 110.00 *(978-1-4557-0471-2(7)*, Saunders) Elsevier - Health Sciences Div.

Rosen, Ruthe. Never Give Up: How to Find Hope & Purpose in Adversity. 2011. 200p. pap. 16.95 ***(978-1-879384-86-6(8))*** Cypress Hse.

Sahgal, Arjun, et al, eds. Bone & Brain Metastases: Advances in Research & Treatment. 2010. (Health & Human Development (Joav Merrick); Ser.). 235.00 *(978-1-61668-365-8(1))* Nova Science Pubs., Inc.

Salvatti, Elena K. Brain Cancer, Tumor Targeting, & Cervical Cancer. 2011. (Cancer Etiology, Diagnosis & Treatments Ser.). 304p. 89.00 *(978-1-61122-738-3(0))* Nova Science Pubs., Inc.

Servan-Schreiber, David. Not the Last Goodbye: On Life, Death, Healing, & Cancer. 2011. (ENG.). 176p. (gr. 12). 22.00 ***(978-0-670-02591-6(7)***, Viking Adult) Penguin Group (USA) Inc.

Shiller, Romy. Who Knew? A Continuation of You Never Know: A Memoir. 2010. 124p. (ENG.). 24.99 *(978-1-4269-2764-5(9))*; pap. 14.99 *(978-1-4269-2654-9(5))* Trafford Publishing.

Solomon, Catherine Leah. Diary of a Terminal Woman: I Had Brain Cancer & Lived. 2011. 798p. 34.99 ***(978-1-4363-6855-1(3))***; pap. 23.99 ***(978-1-4363-6854-4(5))*** Xlibris Corp.

Ward, William. Traveling Light: Walking the Cancer Path. 2008. 240p. pap. 20.00 *(978-1-58420-061-1(8)*, Lindisfarne Bks.) SteinerBooks, Inc.

BRAIN—DISEASES

see also Agraphia; Aphasia; Brain Damage; Cerebral Edema; Cerebral Ischemia; Cerebral Palsy; Cerebrovascular Disease; Dementia; Electroencephalography; Encephalitis; Hepatolenticular Degeneration; Hydrocephalus; Intracranial Tumors; Leucodystrophy; Meningioma; Nervous System—Diseases; Parkinson's Disease; Psychology, Pathological; Thrombosis

Abutalebi, Jubin, et al, eds. Cognitive Neurology. 2008. (ENG., Illus.). 384p. 98.50 *(978-0-19-856927-5(0))* Oxford Univ. Pr., Inc.

Adeli, Hojjat & Ghosh-Dastidar, Samanway. Automated EEG-Based Diagnosis of Neurological Disorders: Inventing the Future of Neurology. 2010. (ENG., Illus.). 423p. 159.95 *(978-1-4398-1531-1(3)*, CRC Press) Taylor & Francis Group GBR. Dist: Taylor & Francis Group.

Adesina, A. M. Atlas of Pediatric Brain Tumors. 2009. 250p. 175.00 *(978-1-60327-182-0(1))* Humana Pr.

Alzheimer, Christian. Molecular & Cellular Biology of Neuroprotection in the CNS. (Neuroscience Intelligence Unit Ser.). 200p. 119.00 *(978-1-58706-104-2(X))* Landes Bioscience.

Aniskiewicz, Albert S. Psychotherapy for Neuropsychological Challenges. 2007. (ENG.). 188p. 73.50 *(978-0-7657-0389-7(0)*, Aronson, Jason) Rowman & Littlefield Publishers, Inc.

Atlas, Scott W., ed. Magnetic Resonance Imaging of the Brain & Spine, 2 vols. 4th rev. ed. 2008. (ENG., Illus.). 2000p. 459.99 *(978-0-7817-6985-3(X))* Lippincott Williams & Wilkins.

Bahn, Sabine & Guest, Paul. Biomarkers of Neurological & Psychiatric Disease. 2011. (ENG., Illus.). 470p. 198.00 ***(978-0-12-387718-5(0)***, Academic Pr.) Elsevier Science & Technology Bks.

Baniel, Anat. Move into Life: The Nine Essentials for Lifelong Vitality. 2009. (ENG., Illus.). 320p. 24.99 *(978-0-307-39529-0(4)*, Harmony) Crown Publishing Group.

Biessels, G. J., et al, eds. Diabetes & the Brain. 2009. (Contemporary Diabetes Ser.). (ENG., Illus.). xii, 474p. 259.00 *(978-1-60327-849-2(4)*, 1603278494) Humana Pr.

Bloom, Floyd E., et al, eds. The Dana Guide to Brain Health: A Practical Family Reference from Medical Experts. 2006. (Illus.). 744p. pap. 25.00 *(978-1-932594-10-2(8))* Dana Pr., The.

Blows, William T. The Biological Basis of Mental Health Nursing. 2nd rev. ed. 2011. (ENG., Illus.). 336p. (C). 140.00 *(978-0-415-57097-8(2))*; pap. 45.95 *(978-0-415-57098-5(0))* Routledge.

Borden, Neil M. & Forseen, Scott E. Pattern Recognition Neuroradiology: Brain & Spine. 2011. (ENG., Illus.). 354p. pap. 79.00 ***(978-0-521-72703-7(0))*** Cambridge Univ. Pr.

Bottiglieri, Teodoro & Bolander-Gouaille, Christina. Homocysteine Related Vitamins & Neuropsychiatric Disorders. 2nd rev. ed. 2007. 224p. pap. 99.00 *(978-2-287-22558-1(7)*, 2287225587) Springer.

Bradley, Walter G. Treating the Brain: What the Best Doctors Know. 2009. (ENG., Illus.). 347p. 25.00 *(978-1-932594-46-1(9))* Dana Pr., The.

Brandson, Curtis M. Brain Research Developments. 2011. *(978-1-61122-066-7(1))* Nova Science Pubs., Inc.

Clagett, Rita H. Killing Mother. 2011. 294p. pap. 15.95 ***(978-1-60594-644-3(3)***, Llumina Pr.) Aeon Publishing Inc.

Clegg, Jim. Addiction: Understanding Fresh Hope Real Healing. 2007. per. 19.99 net. *(978-1-60402-381-7(3))* Independent Pub.

Cohen-Gadol, Aaron A. & Spencer, Dennis D. The Legacy of Harvey Cushing: Profiles of Patient Care. 2007. 139.95 *(978-3-13-141901-9(6))* Thieme Medical Pubs., Inc.

Cohen-Gadol, Aaron A. & Spencer, Dennis D., eds. The Legacy of Harvey Cushing: Profiles of Patient Care. 2007. (ENG., Illus.). 586p. 149.99 *(978-1-58890-389-1(3))* Thieme Medical Pubs., Inc.

Cohen, Ronald & Sweet, Lawrence. Brain Imaging in Behavioral Medicine & Clinical Neuroscience. 2010. (ENG., Illus.). xvi, 404p. 179.00 *(978-1-4419-6371-0(5)*, 1441963715) Springer.

Colman, Carol & Perlmutter, David. Raise a Smarter Child: Raise IQ by up to 30 Points & Turn on Your Child's Smart Genes. 2008. (ENG.). 304p. pap. 14.00 *(978-0-7679-2302-6(2))* Broadway Bks.

Conrad, Cheryl D. The Handbook of Stress: Neuropsychological Effects on the Brain. 2011. 199.95 *(978-1-118-07871-6(3))*; 199.95 *(978-1-118-08320-8(2))* Wiley, John & Sons, Inc. (Wiley-Blackwell).

Cram101 Textbook Reviews & Cram101 Textbook Reviews. Outlines & Highlights for Biopsychology by John P J Pinel. 2011. 426p. pap. 35.95 ***(978-1-61830-474-2(7))*** Cram101 Inc.

—Outlines & Highlights for Lishmans Organic Psychiatry: A Textbook of Neuropsychiatry by Antony David, ISBN. 2011. 216p. pap. 30.95 ***(978-1-61461-260-5(9))*** Cram101 Inc.

Cram101 Textbook Reviews Staff. Outlines & Highlights for Human Neuropsychology by Martin, Isbn: 0131974521. 2008. 204p. pap. 13.95 *(978-1-4288-6043-8(6))* Cram101 Inc.

Cremers, Thomas I. F H., ed. Handbook of Microdialysis: Methods, Applications & Perspectives. 2007. (Handbook of Behavioral Neuroscience Ser.: 16). (ENG., Illus.). 712p. 170.00 *(978-0-444-52276-4(X)*, Academic Pr.) Elsevier Science & Technology Bks.

Cummings, Jeffrey, ed. Progress in Neurotherapeutics & Neuropsychopharmacology. 2007. (ENG., Illus.). 284p. 186.00 *(978-0-521-86254-7(X))* Cambridge Univ. Pr.

—Progress in Neurotherapeutics & Neuropsychopharmacology: Volume 3. 2008. (ENG.). 312p. 162.00 *(978-0-521-86255-4(8))* Cambridge Univ. Pr.

Cummings, Jeffrey L., ed. Progress in Neurotherapeutics & Neuropsychopharmacology: Volume 3 2008. 2009. (ENG.). 312p. pap. 61.00 *(978-0-521-11561-2(2))* Cambridge Univ. Pr.

Danek, Adrian, ed. Neuroacanthocytosis Syndromes. 2010. (ENG.). xvii, 288p. pap. 159.00 *(978-90-481-6743-2(4)* 9048167434) Springer.

David, Antony, et al. Lishman's Organic Psychiatry: A Textbook of Neuropsychiatry. 4th ed. 2012. (ENG.). 952p. pap. 96.95 ***(978-0-470-67507-6(1)***, Wiley-Blackwell) Wiley, John & Sons, Inc.

Davis, Cyndy D. & Sanberg, Paul R., eds. Cell Therapy, Stem Cells & Brain Repair. 2010. (Contemporary Neuroscience Ser.). (Illus.). 408p. pap. 179.00 *(978-1-61737-604-7(3)*, 1617376043) Humana Pr.

Donaghy, Michael, ed. Brain's Diseases of the Nervous System. 12th ed. 2009. (ENG., Illus.). 1376p. 395.00 *(978-0-19-856938-1(6))* Oxford Univ. Pr., Inc.

Dorling Kindersley Publishing Staff & Harrison, James. Brain Training: Boost Memory, Maximize Mental Agility, & Awaken Your Inner Genius. 2009. (ENG.). 192p. (gr. 12). pap. 19.95 *(978-0-7566-5730-7(X))* Dorling Kindersley Publishing, Inc.

du Plessis, Adre J. Fetal Neurology, an Issue of Clinics in Perinatology. 2009. (Clinics: Internal Medicine Ser.: 36-3). (ENG.). 99.00 *(978-1-4377-1259-9(2)*, Saunders) Elsevier - Health Sciences Div.

Evans, Simon J. & Burghardt, Paul R. Brain Fit for Life: A User's Guide to Life-Long Brain Health & Fitness. 2008. (Illus.). 240p. 24.95 *(978-0-9817258-0-2(5))* River Pointe Pubns.

Farooqui, Akhlaq A. & Horrocks, Lloyd A. Glycerophospholipids in the Brain: Phospholipases A2 in Neurological Disorders. 2006. (Illus.). 394p. 159.00 *(978-0-387-36602-9(4)*, 0387366024) Springer.

Farooqui, Akhlaq A., et al. Metabolism & Function of Bioactive Ether Lipids in the Brain. 2008. (ENG., Illus.). xix, 260p. 159.00 *(978-0-387-77400-8(9)*, 0387774009) Springer.

—Metabolism & Functions of Bioactive Ether Lipids in the Brain. 2010. (ENG., Illus.). xix, 260p. pap. 159.00 *(978-1-4419-2652-4(6)*, 1441926526) Springer.

Fatterpekar, Girish, et al. The Teaching Files: Brain & Spine Imaging: Expert Consult - Online & Print. 2011. (ENG., Illus.). 816p. (C). 129.00 ***(978-1-4160-5620-1(3)***, Saunders) Elsevier - Health Sciences Div.

Fields, R. Douglas, ed. Beyond the Synapse: Cell-Cell Signaling in Synaptic Plasticity. 2008. (ENG., Illus.). 320p. 120.00 *(978-0-521-86914-0(5))* Cambridge Univ. Pr.

Figueredo, Benito & Meléndez, and Fidel, eds. Neuroscience Research Advances. 2009. (Neuroscience Research Progress Ser.). 129.00 *(978-1-60692-967-4(4))* Nova Science Pubs., Inc.

Filippi, M. FMRI Techniques & Protocols. 2009. (Illus.). xiii, 843p. ***(978-1-60327-919-2(9))*** Humana Pr.

Filley, Christopher M. The Behavioral Neurology of White Matter, 1 vol. 2nd ed. 2012. (ENG.). 448p. 75.00 ***(978-0-19-974326-1(6))*** Oxford Univ. Pr., Inc.

Filley, Christopher M. Neurobehavioral Anatomy. 3rd ed. 2011. (ENG., Illus.). 304p. (C). pap. 34.95 *(978-1-60732-098-2(3))*; E-Book ***(978-1-60732-099-9(1))*** Univ. Pr. of Colorado.

Fisch, Gene S., ed. Genetics & Genomics of Neurobehavioral Disorders. 2010. (Contemporary Clinical Neuroscience Ser.). (Illus.). 440p. pap. 159.00 *(978-1-61737-322-0(2)*, 1617373222) Humana Pr.

Flores, Steve. Brain Trauma & a Road to Recovery: There Is Hope, 1 vol. 2009. 48p. pap. 16.95 *(978-1-60813-981-1(6))* PublishAmerica, Inc.

Friston, Karl J., et al, eds. Statistical Parametric Mapping: The Analysis of Functional Brain Images. 2006. (ENG., Illus.). 656p. 142.00 *(978-0-12-372560-8(7)*, Academic Pr.) Elsevier Science & Technology Bks.

Gage, Fred H. & Christen, Yves. Retrotransposition, Diversity & the Brain. 2007. (Research & Perspectives in Neurosciences Ser.). (Illus.). 156p. 129.00 *(978-3-540-74965-3(9))* Springer

Gerlach, Manfred, et al, eds. Neuropsychiatric Disorders: An Integrative Approach. 2010. (Journal of Neural Transmission. Supplementa Ser.). (Illus.). ix, 341p. pap. 239.00 *(978-3-211-99906-6(X)*, 321199906X) Springer.

Gilles, Floyd Harry & Nelson, Marvin D. The Developing Human Brain: Growth & Adversities. 2012. (Clinics in Developmental Medicine Ser.). (ENG.). 416p. 170.50 ***(978-1-908316-41-7(1))*** Mac Keith Pr. GBR. Dist: Wiley, John & Sons, Inc.

Gladwin, Thomas. Rhythmic Brain Activity & Cognitive Control. 2008. 212p. pap. *(978-3-639-08821-2(2))* VDM Verlag Dr. Mueller e.K.

Gobbo, Oliviero L. Models of Neurodegeneration in the Hippocampus. 2010. 176p. pap. *(978-3-8383-4597-0(5))* Lambert Academic Publishing.

Gordon, Evian & Koslow, Stephen H. Integrative Neuroscience & Personalized Medicine, 1 vol. 2010. (ENG., Illus.). 320p. 89.95 *(978-0-19-539380-4(5))* Oxford Univ. Pr., Inc.

Grawe, Klaus. Neuropsychotherapy: How the Neurosciences Inform Effective Psychotherapy. 2006. (Counseling & Psychotherapy Investigating Practice from Scientific, Historical, & Cultural Perspectives Ser.). (ENG., Illus.). 504p. 160.95 *(978-0-8058-6121-1(1))*; per. 69.95 *(978-0-8058-6122-8(X))* Routledge.

Greenfield, L. John, Jr. Reading EEGs: A Practical Approach. Geyer, James D. & Carney, Paul R., eds. 2009. (ENG., Illus.). 368p. pap. 94.99 *(978-0-7817-9344-5(0))* Lippincott Williams & Wilkins.

Griffiths, Paul D., et al. Atlas of Fetal & Neonatal Brain Mr Imaging. 2009. (ENG., Illus.). 272p. 174.00 *(978-0-323-05296-2(7)*, Mosby) Elsevier - Health Sciences Div.

Hagan, Jim J., ed. Molecular & Functional Models in Neuropsychiatry. 2011. (Current Topics in Behavioral Neurosciences Ser.). (Illus.). xiv, 392p. 209.00 *(978-3-642-19702-4(7)*, 3642197027) Springer.

Hähnel, Stefan. Inflammatory Diseases of the Brain. 2009. (Medical Radiology / Diagnostic Imaging Ser.). (Illus.). xii, 240p. 129.00 *(978-3-540-76659-9(6))* Springer.

Hassanpour, Hamid. Newborn Eeg Seizure Detection. 2010. 156p. pap. *(978-3-8383-0832-6(8))* Lambert Academic Publishing.

Hathout, Gasser M. Clinical Neuroradiology: A Case-Based Approach. 2008. (ENG., Illus.). 288p. 131.00 *(978-0-521-60054-5(5))* Cambridge Univ. Pr.

Heimer, Lennart, et al. Anatomy of Neuropsychiatry: The New Anatomy of the Basal Forebrain & Its Implications for Neuropsychiatric Illness. 2007. (ENG., Illus.). 200p. (C). 103.00 *(978-0-12-374239-1(0)*, Academic Pr.) Elsevier Science & Technology Bks.

Heine, Vivi M. Induced Pluripotent Stem Cells in Brain Diseases: Understanding the Methods, Epigenetic Basis & Applications for Regenerative Medicine. 2011. (SpringerBriefs in Neuroscience Ser.). (Illus.). xv, 59p. pap. 49.95 ***(978-94-007-2815-8(3)***, 9400728158) Springer.

Hellstrom-Westas, Lena, et al, eds. An Atlas of Amplitude-Integrated EEGS in the Newborn. 2nd rev. ed. 2008. (ENG., Illus.). 180p. 200.00 *(978-1-84184-649-1(X)*, Informa Healthcare) Taylor & Francis Group GBR. Dist: Taylor & Francis Group.

Hodler, Jurg. Diseases of the Brain, Head & Neck, Spine: Diagnostic Imaging & Interventional Techniques. Schulthess, Gustav K. Von & Zollikofer, Christoph L., eds. 2008. (ENG.). xii, 288p. pap. 129.00 *(978-88-470-0839-7(5)*, 8847008395) Springer.

Igbaseimokumo, Usiakimi. Brain CT Scans in Clinical Practice. 2009. (ENG., Illus.). x, 128p. pap. 39.95 *(978-1-84882-364-8(9)*, 1848823649) Springer.

Incagnoli/Puente. Contemporary Neurobehavioral Syndromes: Disorders of Recent Origin. 2011. (ENG.). 328p. 90.00 *(978-0-8058-4985-1(8)*, Psychology Press) Taylor & Francis Group GBR. Dist: Taylor & Francis Group.

Jankovic, Joseph & Morris, John, Jr. Neurological Clinical Examination: A Concise Guide. 3rd ed. 2012. (ENG., Illus.). 134p. pap. 45.00 **(978-1-4441-4538-0(X))** Hodder Arnold Pubs.

Johnstone, Brick. Rehabilitation of Neuropsychological Disorders: A Practical Guide for Rehabilitation Professionals. 2nd rev. ed. 2009. (ENG., Illus.). 304p. 110.00 (978-1-84872-800-4(X), Psychology Press) Taylor & Francis Group GBR. Dist: Taylor & Francis Group.

Jones, Derek K., ed. Diffusion MRI: Theory, Methods, & Applications, 1 vol. 2010. (ENG., Illus.). 784p. 179.50 (978-0-19-536977-9(7)) Oxford Univ. Pr., Inc.

Kaila, Madan & Kaila, Rakhi. Quantum Magnetic Resonance Imaging Diagnostics of Human Brain Disorders. 2010. (ENG., Illus.). 516p. 155.00 (978-0-12-384711-9(7)) Elsevier Science & Technology Bks.

Kalueff, Allan V. & Bergner, Carisa L., eds. Transgenic & Mutant Tools to Model Brain Disorders. 2010. (Neuromethods Ser.). (ENG., Illus.). xiv, 246p. 189.00 (978-1-60761-473-9(1), 1607614731) Humana Pr.

Kassam, A. B. & Gardner, P. A., eds. Endoscopic Approaches to the Skull Base. 2012. (Progress in Neurological Surgery Ser.). (ENG., Illus.). 238p. **(978-3-8055-9210-9(8))** Karger, S. AG.

Ketonen, L. M., et al. Pediatric Brain & Spine: An Atlas of MRI & Spectroscopy. 2010. (Illus.). xiv, 494p. pap. 209.00 (978-3-642-05969-8(4), 3642059694) Springer.

Kidd, Parris M. Phosphatidylserine (PS) Mental Clarity at Any Age. 2007. (Illus.). 32p. 3.95 (978-0-9788031-1-7(6)) Intramedia Publishing LLC.

Kraly, F. Scott. Brain Science & Psychological Disorders: Therapy, Psychotropic Drugs, & the Brain. 2006. (ENG., Illus.). 224p. 23.95 (978-0-393-70465-5(3), 70465) Norton, W. W. & Co., Inc.

Kraly, F. Scott & Kraly. The Unwell Brain: Understanding the Psychobiology of Mental Health. 2009. (ENG., Illus.). 224p. pap. 18.95 (978-0-393-70596-6(X), 70596) Norton, W. W. & Co., Inc.

Kropotov, Juri. Quantitative EEG, Event-Related Potentials & Neurotherapy. 2008. (ENG., Illus.). 600p. 103.00 (978-0-12-374512-5(8), Academic Pr.) Elsevier Science & Technology Bks.

Lagercrantz, Hugo, et al, eds. The Newborn Brain: Neuroscience & Clinical Applications. 2nd ed. 2010. (ENG., Illus.). 426p. 130.00 (978-0-521-88975-9(8)) Cambridge Univ. Pr.

Levene, Malcolm I. & Chervenak, Frank A. Fetal & Neonatal Neurology & Neurosurgery. 4th ed. 2009. (ENG., Illus.). 960p. 549.00 (978-0-443-10407-7(7), Churchill Livingstone) Elsevier - Health Sciences Div.

Lipsett, John. Stroke: Have You Had Yours Yet? 2010. 92p. pap. 11.99 (978-1-4269-2948-9(X)) Trafford Publishing.

Lockhart, Sybil. Mother in the Middle: A Biologist's Story of Caring for Parent & Child. 2009. (ENG.). 320p. 25.00 (978-1-4165-4155-4(1), Touchstone) Touchstone.

Loftus, Christopher M. Neurosurgical Emergencies. 2nd ed. 2007. 139.95 (978-3-13-135052-7(0)) Thieme Medical Pubs., Inc.

Loftus, Christopher M., ed. Neurosurgical Emergencies. 2nd ed. 2007. (ENG.). 408p. 149.99 (978-1-58890-394-5(X)) Thieme Medical Pubs., Inc.

Lovestone, Simon, ed. Biomarkers in Brain Disease. 2009. (Annals of the New York Academy of Sciences Ser.: 38). (ENG., Illus.). 276p. pap. 134.95 (978-1-57331-772-6(1), Wiley-Blackwell) Wiley, John & Sons, Inc.

Lunsford, L. Dade & Sheehan, Jason P., eds. Intracranial Stereotactic Radiosurgery. 2009. (ENG., Illus.). 200p. 179.99 (978-1-60406-200-7(2)) Thieme Medical Pubs., Inc.

Marien, Peter, et al. Neuropsychological Research: A Review. Abutalebi, Jubin, ed. 2008. (ENG., Illus.). 568p. 100.00 (978-1-84169-620-1(X), Psychology Press) Taylor & Francis Group GBR. Dist: Taylor & Francis Group.

McArthur, Robert A. & Borsini, Franco, eds. Animal & Translational Models for CNS Drug Discovery Vol. 2: Neurological Disorders, 3 vols. 2008. (ENG., Illus.). 416p. 91.95 (978-0-12-373855-4(5), Academic Pr.) Elsevier Science & Technology Bks.

McCandless, David W. Metabolic Encephalopathy. 2009. (Illus.). 600p. 179.00 (978-0-387-79109-8(4)) Springer.

McCandless, David W., ed. Metabolic Encephalopathy. 2010. (Illus.). xvi, 585p. pap. 179.00 (978-1-4419-2712-5(3), 1441927123) Springer.

McMahon, Fran. To Love a Stranger: A Caregiver's Perspective. 2007. (ENG.). 160p. per. 15.99 (978-1-4141-0862-9(1)) Pleasant Word.

Meyers, Karen H. & Golden, Robert N. The Truth about ADHD & Other Neurobiological Disorders. 2010. (Truth about Ser.). (Illus.). 192p. (C). (gr. 9-18). 35.00 (978-0-8160-7636-9(7)) Facts On File, Inc.

Minns. Problems Intracranial Children. (Illus.). 458p. (C). (978-0-901260-82-6(7)) Cambridge Univ. Pr.

Mitagvaria, Nodar P. & (Hans) Bicher, Haim I. Cerebral Blood Flow Regulation. 2009. 79.00 (978-1-60692-163-0(0)) Nova Science Pubs., Inc.

Montgomery, Erwin B., Jr. Deep Brain Stimulation Programming: Principles & Practice, 1 vol. 2010. (ENG., Illus.). 208p. 69.95 (978-0-19-973852-6(1)) Oxford Univ. Pr., Inc.

Moritani, Toshio, et al. Diffusion-Weighted MR Imaging of the Brain. 2nd ed. (ENG., Illus.). xx, 402p. 2010. pap. 189.00 **(978-3-642-09760-7(X)**, 364209760X) 2009. 189.00 (978-3-540-78784-6(4), 3540787844) Springer.

Nagami, Pamela. The Woman with a Worm in Her Head: And Other True Stories of Infectious Disease. 2007. 285p. reprint ed. pap. 22.00 (978-1-4223-9022-1(5)) DIANE Publishing Co.

Naidich, Thomas P., et al. Imaging of the Brain: Expert Radiology Series, Expert Consult- Online & Print. 2010. (Illus.). 1398p. 339.00 (978-1-4160-5009-4(4), Saunders) Elsevier - Health Sciences Div.

Nicholson, Anthony. The Neurosciences & the Practice of Aviation Medicine. 2011. (Illus.). 524p. 170.00 **(978-0-7546-7292-0(1))** Ashgate Publishing Co.

Nussbaum, Paul. Your Brain Health Lifestyle: A Proactive Program to Preserve Your Life Story. 2007. pap. 15.00 (978-1-59571-184-7(8)) Word Association Pubs.

Opie, Lionel H. Living Longer: The heart-mind Connection. 2011. (ENG., Illus.). 208p. 36.99 (978-0-19-852567-7(2)) Oxford Univ. Pr., Inc.

Osborn, Anne G., et al. Brain & Spine. 2008. (EXPERTddx™ Ser.). (ENG., Illus.). 1000p. 329.00 (978-1-931884-02-0(1)) Lippincott Williams & Wilkins.

Packer, Lester, et al, eds. Micronutrients & Brain Health. 2009. (Oxidative Stress & Disease Ser.: Vol. 26). (ENG., Illus.). 460p. 174.95 (978-1-4200-7351-5(6), CRC Press) Taylor & Francis Group GBR. Dist: Taylor & Francis Group.

Panayiotopoulos, C. P. A Clinical Guide to Epileptic Syndromes & their Treatment. 2nd ed. 2010. (Illus.). xiv, 578p. 129.00 (978-1-84996-160-8(3), 1849961603) Springer.

Paul, Robert Harris, ed. HIV & the Brain: New Challenges in the Modern Era. 2009. (Current Clinical Neurology Ser.). (Illus.). 350p. 189.00 (978-1-934115-08-4(8)) Humana Pr.

Peters, John C. (John Charles). A Complete Treatise on Headaches & Diseases of the Head 1 the Nature & Treatment of Headaches 2 the Nature & Treatment of Apoplexy 3 the N. 2006. 628p. per. 34.99 (978-1-4255-6608-1(1)) MPublishing.

Pinel, John P. J. Biopsychology. 8th ed. 2010. (ENG.). 608p. (C). 170.67 (978-0-205-83256-9(3), Prentice Hall) Prentice Hall PTR.

—Biopsychology, Books a la Carte Edition. 8th ed. 2010. (ENG.). 608p. (C). ring bd. 111.33 (978-0-205-03607-3(4), Prentice Hall) Prentice Hall PTR.

Piper, Brian. Neurobehavioral Consequences of Adolescent Mdma Exposure in Rats - Effects on Attention, Learning, Memory, Anxiety, Aggression, Physiology, & Neuroc. 2008. 140p. pap. (978-3-639-00356-7(X)) VDM Verlag Dr. Mueller e.K.

Pope, Pauline M. Severe & Complex Neurological Disability: Management of the Physical Condition. 2007. (ENG., Illus.). 300p. pap. 83.95 (978-0-7506-8825-3(4), Butterworth-Heinemann) Elsevier - Health Sciences Div.

Rahman, Shafiqur, ed. The Brain as a Drug Target. 2011. (ENG.). 468p. 161.00 (978-0-12-385506-0(3), Academic Pr.) Elsevier Science & Technology Bks.

Rogers, Mark H. & Anderson, Paul B. Deep Brain Stimulation: Applications, Complications & Side Effects. 2009. (Illus.). xi, 205p. 98.00 (978-1-60692-895-0(3)) Nova Science Pubs., Inc.

Rosenberg, Gary A. Molecular Physiology & Metabolism of the Nervous System: A Clinical Perspective. 2012. (Contemporary Neurology Ser.: 82). (ENG.). 240p. 99.99 **(978-0-19-539427-6(5))** Oxford Univ. Pr., Inc.

Rosenwasser, Robert H. & Jabbour, Pascal. Neuroendovascular Management - Anatomy & Techniques: Neurosurgery Clinics of North America. 2009. (Clinics: Surgery Ser.: 20-3). (ENG., Illus.). 240p. 99.00 (978-1-4377-0507-2(3), Saunders) Elsevier - Health Sciences Div.

Sachdev, Perminder. The Yipping Tiger & Other Tales from the Neuropsychiatric Clinic. 2010. (ENG.). 304p. 26.95 (978-0-8018-9454-1(9)) Johns Hopkins Univ. Pr.

Salvolini, Ugo & Scarabino, T., eds. High Field Brain MRI: Use in Clinical Practice. 2010. (Illus.). xvi, 240p. pap. 169.00 (978-3-642-06866-9(9), 3642068669) Springer.

Sanberg, Paul R. & Davis, Cyndy D., eds. Cell Therapy, Stem Cells & Brain Repair. 2006. (Contemporary Neuroscience Ser.). (Illus.). 408p. 179.00 (978-1-58829-502-6(8), 1588295028) Humana Pr.

Schaller, Bernhard. Neuroscience Imaging Research Trends. 2008. 82.00 (978-1-60456-227-9(7)) Nova Science Pubs., Inc.

Scherer, Marcia J. Assistive Technologies & Other Supports for People with Brain Impairment. 2011. 256p. pap. **(978-0-8261-0645-2(5))** Springer Publishing Co., Inc.

Schmidt, Matthias & Schmidt, Matthias C. Griff nach dem Ich? Ethische Kriterien für die medizinische Intervention in das menschliche Gehirn. 2008. (Studien zu Wissenschaft und Ethik Ser.).Tr. of Ethical Criteria for Medical Intervention in the Human Brain. (GER.). 390p. 147.00 (978-3-11-020817-7(2)) De Gruyter, Walter Inc.

Schmidt, Matthias C. Griff nach dem Ich? Ethische Kriterien far die medizinische Intervention in das menschliche Gehirn. 2008. (Studien zu Wissenschaft und Ethik Ser.).Tr. of Ethical Criteria for Medical Intervention in the Human Brain. (GER.). 390p. 224.00 **(978-3-11-173751-5(9))** De Gruyter, Walter Inc.

Schouenborg, Jens, et al. Brain Machine Interfaces: Implications for science, clinical practice & Society. 2011. (ENG.). 296p. 268.00 (978-0-444-53815-4(1), Elsevier Science) Elsevier Science & Technology Bks.

Schumacher, Martin & Spreer, Joachim. Imaging of Meningeal Diseases. 2010. (ENG., Illus.). 300p. 169.00 (978-3-540-69298-0(3), 3540692983) Springer.

Schwartz, Theodore H. & Anand, Vijay K., eds. Endoscopic Pituitary Surgery: Endocrine, Neuro-Ophthalmologic, & Surgical Management. 2011. (ENG.). 384p. 179.99 (978-1-60406-347-9(5)) Thieme Medical Pubs., Inc.

Sechi, GianPietro, ed. Drug Related Encephalopathies. 2008. 89.00 (978-1-60456-745-8(7)) Nova Science Pubs., Inc.

Seki, Tatsunori, et al, eds. Neurogenesis in the Adult Brain I: Neurobiology. 2011. (ENG., Illus.). xvi, 413p. 209.00 (978-4-431-53932-2(8), 4431539328) Springer.

—Neurogenesis in the Adult Brain II: Clinical Implications. 2011. (ENG., Illus.). xiv, 226p. 189.00 (978-4-431-53944-5(1), 4431539441) Springer.

Shah, Guarang. Intracranial Infections, an Issue of Neuroimaging Clinics. 2012. (Clinics: Radiology Ser.: 22-4). (ENG.). 115.00 (978-1-4557-1109-3(8), Saunders) Elsevier - Health Sciences Div.

Shannon, Joyce, ed. Brain Disorders Sourcebook. 3rd rev. ed. 2010. (Health Reference Ser.). lib. bdg. 93.00 (978-0-7808-1083-9(X)) Omnigraphics, Inc.

Simopoulos, A. P. & Bazan, N. G., eds. Omega-3 Fatty Acids, the Brain & Retina. 2008. (World Review of Nutrition & Dietetics Ser.). (Illus.). 164p. (978-3-8055-9019-8(9)) Karger, S. AG.

Spinelle, Diane E. Brain Mapping & Diseases. 2011. (978-1-61122-065-0(3)) Nova Science Pubs., Inc.

Stevenson, David K., et al, eds. Fetal & Neonatal Brain Injury. 4th ed. 2009. (ENG., Illus.). 642p. 199.00 (978-0-521-88859-2(X)) Cambridge Univ. Pr.

Stones, Mic J. Creutzfeldt-Jakob Disease: New Research. 2006. (Illus.). 158p. 225.00 (978-1-60021-345-8(6)) Nova Science Pubs., Inc.

Surendran, Sankar. Neurochemistry of Metabolic Diseases: Lysosomal Storage Diseases, Phenylketonuria & Canavan Disease. 2011. (Metabolic Diseases - Laboratory & Clinical Research Ser.). 299p. 145.00 (978-1-61209-671-1(9)) Nova Science Pubs., Inc.

Sussler, Robert. A Brain's Battle Against a Stroke: Refocusing My Memory on Earlier Medicine. 2007. (Illus.). 152p. 23.99 (978-1-4259-9784-7(8)); per. 12.99 (978-1-4259-9785-4(6)) AuthorHouse.

Swingle, Paul G. Biofeedback for the Brain: How Neurotherapy Effectively Treats Depression, ADHD, Autism, & More. 2010. (ENG., Illus.). 232p. pap. 21.95 (978-0-8135-4779-4(2)) Rutgers Univ. Pr.

Talan, Jamie & Firstman, Richard. Deep Brain Stimulation: A New Treatment Shows Promise in the Most Difficult Cases. 2009. (Illus.). 200p. 25.00 (978-1-932594-37-9(X)) Dana Pr., The.

Tan, S. & Levison, S. W., eds. Bridging Bench to Bedside in Fetal & Neonatal Brain Injury. 2007. (Illus.). 138p. pap. (978-3-8055-8319-0(2)) Karger, S. AG.

Taylor, Edith Meyer. Psychological Appraisal of Children with Cerebral Defects. 2011. 516p. 60.95 **(978-1-258-09635-9(8))** Literary Licensing, LLC.

Traub, Roger D. & Whittington, Miles A. Cortical Oscillations in Health & Disease, 1 vol. 2010. (ENG., Illus.). 464p. 74.95 (978-0-19-534279-6(8)) Oxford Univ. Pr., Inc.

Trimble, Michael R. The Soul in the Brain: The Cerebral Basis of Language, Art, & Belief. 2007. (ENG., Illus.). 304p. (gr. 17). 38.00 (978-0-8018-8481-8(0)) Johns Hopkins Univ. Pr.

Turkington, Carol & Harris, Joseph. The Encyclopedia of Brain & Brain Disorders. 3rd rev. ed. 2009. (Library of Health & Living). 448p. (C). (gr. 9-18). 75.00 (978-0-8160-6395-6(8)) Facts On File, Inc.

Turner, Marc L. Creutz feld-Jakob Disease Managing the Risk of Transmission by Blood, Plasma & Tissues. 2006. xvi, 319p. (978-1-56395-224-1(6), AABB Pr.) American Assn. of Blood Banks.

Walker, Ruth H., et al, eds. Neuroacanthocytosis Syndromes II. (ENG., Illus.). xxvi, 295p. 2010. pap. 189.00 (978-3-642-09082-0(6), 3642090826) 2007. 189.00 (978-3-540-71692-1(0), 3540716920) Springer.

Webb, Wanda & Adler, Richard K. Neurology for the Speech-Language Pathologist. 5th rev. ed. 2007. (ENG., Illus.). 336p. (C). pap. 68.95 (978-0-7506-7526-0(8), Mosby) Elsevier - Health Sciences Div.

Wildenauer, Dieter. Molecular Biology of Neuropsychiatric Disorders. 2008. (Nucleic Acids & Molecular Biology Ser.). (Illus.). 300p. 219.00 (978-3-540-85382-4(0)) Springer.

Winslow, Forbes. On Obscure Diseases of the Brain & Disorders of the Mind: Their Incipient Symptoms, Pathology, Diagnosis, Treatment & Prophylaxis. 2007. (ENG.). 732p. 66.95 (978-0-548-19874-2(8)); per. 51.95 (978-1-4325-0729-9(X)) Kessinger Publishing, LLC.

Yudofsky, Stuart C. & Hales, Robert E., frwds. Windows to the Brain: Insights from Neuroimaging. 2008. (Illus.). 239p. 89.00 (978-1-58562-302-0(4)) American Psychiatric Publishing, Inc.

Zeman, Adam. A Portrait of the Brain. 2008. (ENG., Illus.). 256p. 27.50 (978-0-300-11416-4(8)) Yale Univ. Pr.

BRAIN—ELECTROMECHANICAL ANALOGIES

Coward, L. Andrew. System Architecture Approach to the Brain: From Neurons to Consciousness. 2009. (Illus.). xiii, 349p. pap. 55.00 (978-1-60456-522-5(5)) Nova Science Pubs., Inc.

BRAIN—EVOLUTION

Aboitiz, Francisco & Montiel, Juan. Origin & Evolution of the Vertebrate Telencephalon, with Special Reference to the Mammalian Neocortex. 2007. (Advances in Anatomy, Embryology & Cell Biology Ser.). (Illus.). VIII, 116p. (C). pap. 169.00 (978-3-540-49760-8(9), 3540497609) Springer.

Allen, John S. The Lives of the Brain: Human Evolution & the Organ of Mind. 2012. (ENG., Illus.). 352p. pap. 19.95 **(978-0-674-06405-8(4)**, Belknap Pr.) Harvard Univ. Pr.

Arbib, Michael A. How the Brain Got Language: The Mirror System Hypothesis, 1 vol. 2012. (ENG., Illus.). 416p. 49.95 **(978-0-19-989668-4(2))** Oxford Univ. Pr., Inc.

Bar, Moshe, ed. Predictions in the Brain: Using Our Past to Generate a Future, 1 vol. 2011. (ENG., Illus.). 400p. 99.95 (978-0-19-539551-8(4)) Oxford Univ. Pr., Inc.

Barrett, Louise. Beyond the Brain: How Body & Environment Shape Animal & Human Minds. 2011. (ENG., Illus.). 304p. (C). 29.95 (978-0-691-12644-9(5)) Princeton Univ. Pr.

Carneiro, Robert L. The Evolution of the Human Mind: From Supernaturalism to Naturalism - an Anthropological Perspective. 2010. (ENG.). 506p. (C). 95.00 (978-0-9797731-1-2(3)); pap. 39.95 (978-0-9797731-2-9(1)) Werner, Eliot Pubns., Inc.

Coolidge, Frederick L., et al. The Rise of Homo Sapiens: The Evolution of Modern Thinking. 2009. (ENG., Illus.). 320p. 104.95 (978-1-4051-5253-2(2), Wiley-Blackwell) Wiley, John & Sons, Inc.

Corballis, Michael. The Recursive Mind - The Origins of Human Thought, Language & Civilization. 2011. (ENG., Illus.). 288p. (C). 29.95 (978-0-691-14547-1(4)) Princeton Univ. Pr.

Cunnane, Stephen & Stewart, Kathlyn, eds. Human Brain Evolution: The Influence of Freshwater & Marine Food Resources. 2010. (ENG., Illus.). 217p. 144.95 (978-0-470-45268-4(4), Wiley-Blackwell) Wiley, John & Sons, Inc.

Damasio, Antonio. Self Comes to Mind: Constructing the Conscious Brain. (Vintage Ser.). (ENG., Illus.). 2012. 416p. pap. 15.95 (978-0-307-47495-7(X), Vintage) 2010. 384p. 28.95 (978-0-307-37875-0(6), Pantheon) Knopf Doubleday Publishing Group.

Deacon, Terrence W. Incomplete Nature: How Mind Emerged from Matter. 2011. (ENG., Illus.). 544p. 29.95 (978-0-393-04991-6(4), 4991) Norton, W. W. & Co., Inc.

DeSalle, Rob & Tattersall, Ian. The Brain: Big Bangs, Behaviors, & Beliefs. 2012. (ENG., Illus.). 368p. 29.95 **(978-0-300-17522-6(1))** Yale Univ. Pr.

Dispenza, Joe. Evolve Your Brain: The Science of Changing Your Mind. 2008. (ENG.). 528p. pap. 16.95 (978-0-7573-0765-2(5)) Health Communications, Inc.

Dunbar, Robin, et al. Social Brain, Distributed Mind. 2010. (Proceedings of the British Academy Ser.). (ENG., Illus.). 400p. 95.00 (978-0-19-726452-2(2)) Oxford Univ. Pr., Inc.

Gooch, Stan. The Neanderthal Legacy: Reawakening Our Genetic & Cultural Origins. 2008. (ENG., Illus.). 1p. pap. 14.95 (978-1-59477-185-9(5)) Inner Traditions International, Ltd.

Herbert, Joe. The Minder Brain: How Your Brain Keeps You Alive, Protects You from Danger, & Ensures That You Reproduce. 2007. 476p. 76.00 (978-981-270-394-1(2)); pap. 44.00 (978-981-270-395-8(0)) World Scientific Publishing Co., Inc.

Heschl, Adolf. The Intelligent Genome: On the Origin of the Human Mind by Mutation & Selection. 2010. (ENG.). 362p. pap. 84.95 (978-3-642-08648-9(9), 3642086489) Springer.

Hoffman, Erik. New Brain, New World. 2012. (ENG.). 250p. pap. 16.95 **(978-1-84850-827-9(1))** Hay Hse., Inc.

Hofman, Michel A. & Falk, Dean. Evolution of the Primate Brain: From Neuron to Behavior. 2012. (ENG., Illus.). 496p. 268.00 **(978-0-444-53860-4(7)**, Elsevier Science) Elsevier Science & Technology Bks.

Kaas, J. H., ed. Diversity in Cortical Organization: 22nd Annual Karger Workshop, San Diego, Calif. , November 2010. Special Topic Issue:'Brain, Behavior & Evolution 2011, Vol. 78, No. 1' 2011. (ENG., Illus.). 128p. pap. **(978-3-8055-9796-8(7))** Karger, S. AG.

Keenan, Julian Paul, et al, eds. Evolutionary Cognitive Neuroscience. 2006. (Cognitive Neuroscience Ser.). (ENG., Illus.). 620p. (gr. 17). 68.00 (978-0-262-16241-8(5)) MIT Pr.

Kurzweil, Ray. The Singularity Is Near: When Humans Transcend Biology. 2006. (ENG., Illus.). 672p. (gr. 12-18). 21.00 (978-0-14-303788-0(9), Penguin (Non-Classics)) Penguin Group (USA) Inc.

Linden, David J. The Accidental Mind: How Brain Evolution Has Given Us Love, Memory, Dreams, & God. 2008. (Illus.). 288p. pap. 21.00 (978-0-674-03058-9(3), Belknap Pr.) Harvard Univ. Pr.

Margulis, Lynn, et al, eds. Chimeras & Consciousness: Evolution of the Sensory Self. 2011. (ENG., Illus.). 344p. (gr. 17). 58.00 (978-0-262-01539-4(0)); pap. 29.00 (978-0-262-51583-2(0)) MIT Pr.

Menger. The Thin Bone Vault. 2009. (Illus.). 312p. 69.00 (978-1-84816-336-2(3)) World Scientific Publishing Co., Inc.

Passingham, Richard. What Is Special about the Human Brain? 2008. (Oxford Portraits in Science Ser.). (ENG., Illus.). 248p. 59.50 (978-0-19-923013-6(7)) Oxford Univ. Pr., Inc.

Passingham, Richard E. & Wise, Steven P. The Neurobiology of the Prefrontal Cortex: Anatomy, Evolution, & the Origin of Insight. 2012. (ENG.). 344p. 89.95 **(978-0-19-955291-7(6))** Oxford Univ. Pr., Inc.

Platek, Steven M., et al, eds. Foundations in Evolutionary Cognitive Neuroscience. 2009. (ENG., Illus.). 232p. 144.00 (978-0-521-88421-1(7)) Cambridge Univ. Pr.

Platek, Steven M. & Shackelford, Todd K., eds. Foundations in Evolutionary Cognitive Neuroscience. 2009. (ENG., Illus.). 232p. pap. 57.99 (978-0-521-71118-0(5)) Cambridge Univ. Pr.

Previc, Fred H. The Dopaminergic Mind in Human Evolution & History. 2011. (ENG.). 226p. pap. 45.00 (978-0-521-36089-0(7)) Cambridge Univ. Pr.

Ramachandran, V. S. The Tell-Tale Brain: A Neuroscientist's Quest for What Makes Us Human. (ENG., Illus.). 2012. 384p. pap. 17.95 **(978-0-393-34062-4(7)**, 34062) 2011. 357p. 26.95 (978-0-393-07782-7(9), 7782) Norton, W. W. & Co., Inc.

Rosa-Molinar, Eduardo & Pritz, Michael B., eds. Hindbrain Evolution, Development, & Organization: 16th Annual Karger Workshop, San Diego, Calif., October 21, 2004. (Brain, Behavior & Evolution Ser.: Vol. 66, No. 4). (Illus.). 68p. (978-3-8055-8032-8(0)) Karger, S. AG.

Schick, Kathy & Toth, Nicholas. The Human Brain Evolving: Paleoneurological Studies in Honor of Ralph L. Holloway. Broadfield, Douglas & Yuan, Michael, eds. 2010. (Stone age institute publication Ser.). (ENG., Illus.). 331p. (C). 74.95 (978-0-9792276-3-9(1)) Stone Age Institute Pr.

Schulkin, Jay, ed. Action, Perception & the Brain: Adaptation & Cephalic Expression. 2012. (New Directions in Philosophy & Cognitive Science Ser.). (ENG., Illus.). 288p. 85.00 **(978-0-230-28258-2(X))** Palgrave Macmillan.

Small, Gary & Vorgan, Gigi. iBrain: Surviving the Technological Alteration of the Modern Mind. 256p. 2009. pap. 16.99 (978-0-06-134034-5(0), Harper Paperbacks) 2008. (ENG., Illus.). 24.95 (978-0-06-134033-8(2), Morrow, William & Co.) HarperCollins Pubs.

Stjernfelt, Frederik, et al, eds. The Symbolic Species Evolved. 2012. (Biosemiotics Ser.: 6). (ENG., Illus.). xiii, 288p. 209.00 **(978-94-007-2335-1(0)**, 9400723350) Springer.

Strausfeld, Nicholas James. Arthropod Brains: Evolution, Functional Elegance, & Historical Significance. 2012. (ENG., Illus.). 848p. 65.00 (978-0-674-04633-7(1), Belknap Pr.) Harvard Univ. Pr.

Striedter, G. F., ed. Evolutionary Developmental Neurobiology: Developmental Mechanisms of Evolutionary Change in Nervous Systems, Paris, July 2010. Special Topic Issue: Brain, Behavior & Evolution 2011, Vol. 78, No. 3 2011. (ENG., Illus.). 66p. pap. **(978-3-8055-9898-9(X))** Karger, S. AG.

Tommasi, Luca, et al, eds. Cognitive Biology: Evolutionary & Developmental Perspectives on Mind, Brain, & Behavior. 2009. (Vienna Series in Theoretical Biology). (ENG., Illus.). 352p. (gr. 17). 52.00 (978-0-262-01293-5(6)) MIT Pr.

Williams, David. The Trickster Brain: Neuroscience, Evolution, & Narrative. 2012. (ENG.). 280p. (gr. 17). 75.00 **(978-0-7391-4397-1(2))** Lexington Bks.

Wolf, Maryanne. Proust & the Squid: The Story & Science of the Reading Brain. 2008. (ENG., Illus.). 320p. pap. 14.99 (978-0-06-093384-5(4), HarperPerennial) HarperCollins Pubs.

Zeigler, H. Philip, et al, eds. New Perspectives on Neurobehavioral Evolution. 2011. (Annals of the New York Academy of Sciences Ser.: 80). (ENG., Illus.). 252p. pap. 130.00 **(978-1-57331-807-5(8)**, Wiley-Blackwell) Wiley, John & Sons, Inc.

BRAIN—GROWTH

Acredolo, Linda & Goodwyn, Susan. Baby Smarts Deck: 50 Brain-Building Games Your Baby Will Love. 2010. 108p. 14.99 (978-0-307-71862-4(X), Potter Style) Crown Publishing Group.

Allen, John S. The Lives of the Brain: Human Evolution & the Organ of Mind. 2012. (ENG., Illus.). 352p. pap. 19.95 **(978-0-674-06405-8(4)**, Belknap Pr.) Harvard Univ. Pr.

Baltes, Paul B., et al, eds. Lifespan Development & the Brain: The Perspective of Biocultural Co-Constructivism. 2010. (ENG.). 444p. pap. 34.99 (978-0-521-17555-5(0)) Cambridge Univ. Pr.

Bangalore, Lakshmi. Brain Development. 2007. (Gray Matter Ser.). (Illus.). 112p. (YA). (gr. 9-12). lib. bdg. 35.00 (978-0-7910-8954-5(1)) Facts On File, Inc.

Bayer, Shirley A. & Altman, Joseph. Atlas of Human Central Nervous System Development -5 Volume Set, 5 vols. 2007. (ENG.). 850.00 (978-1-4200-6800-9(3), CRC Press) Taylor & Francis Group GBR. Dist: Taylor & Francis Group.

Bayer Shirley a Staff. Atlas of Human Central Nervous System Development, 5 vols. 2007. (Atlas of Human Central Nervous System Development Ser.). (ENG., Illus.). 536p. 185.95 (978-0-8493-1424-7(0), CRC Press) Taylor & Francis Group GBR. Dist: Taylor & Francis Group.

Coch, Donna, et al, eds. Human Behavior, Learning, & the Developing Brain: Typical Development. (ENG.). 412p. 2010. pap. 35.00 (978-1-60623-968-1(6)) 2007. (Illus.). 60.00 (978-1-59385-136-1(7)) Guilford Pubns., Inc.

Corbin, Barry. Unleashing the Potential of the Teenage Brain: Ten Powerful Ideas. 2007. 168p. 62.95 (978-1-4129-5762-5(1), B42497C); per. 31.95 (978-1-4129-4249-2(7), B42497P) Corwin Pr.

Cornish, Kim & Wilding, John. Attention, Genes, & Developmental Disorders, 1 vol. 2010. (Oxford Series in Developmental Cognitive Neuroscience Ser.). (ENG., Illus.). 352p. 49.95 (978-0-19-517994-1(3)) Oxford Univ. Pr., Inc.

Dowling, John. The Great Brain Debate: Nature or Nurture? 2007. (Science Essentials Ser.). (ENG., Illus.). 200p. per. 20.95 (978-0-691-13310-2(7)) Princeton Univ. Pr.

Eliot, Lise. Pink Brain, Blue Brain: How Small Differences Grow into Troublesome Gaps — And What We Can Do about It. 2009. (ENG., Illus.). 432p. 25.00 (978-0-618-39311-4(0)) Houghton Mifflin Harcourt Trade & Reference Pubs.

Galinsky, Ellen. Mind in the Making: The Seven Essential Life Skills Every Child Needs. 2010. (ENG., Illus.). 256p. pap. 16.99 (978-0-06-173232-4(X), William Morrow Paperbacks) HarperCollins Pubs.

García-Segura, Luis Miguel. Hormones & Brain Plasticity. 2009. (Series in Behavioral Neuroendocrinology Ser.). (ENG., Illus.). 496p. (C). 65.00 (978-0-19-532661-1(X)) Oxford Univ. Pr., Inc.

Gibson, Kathleen & Petersen, Anne, eds. Brain Maturation & Cognitive Development: Comparative & Cross-Cultural Perspectives. 2010. (ENG., Illus.). 390p. pap. 39.95 (978-0-202-36395-0(3)) Transaction Pubs.

Gilles, Floyd Harry & Nelson, Marvin D. The Developing Human Brain: Growth & Adversities. 2012. (Clinics in Developmental Medicine Ser.). (ENG.). 416p. 170.50 **(978-1-908316-41-7(1))** Mac Keith Pr. GBR. Dist: Wiley, John & Sons, Inc.

Haven, Kendall. Story Proof: The Science Behind the Startling Power of Story, 1 vol. 2007. 164p. per. 25.00 (978-1-59158-546-6(5), LU5465) Libraries Unlimited, Inc.

Hoffelder, Ann McIntosh & Hoffelder, Robert L. How the Brain Grows. 2007. (Brain Works). (Illus.). 120p. (YA). (gr. 5-9). lib. bdg. 32.95 (978-0-7910-8946-0(0)) Facts On File, Inc.

Insausti, Ricardo, et al. Postnatal Development of the Human Hippocampal Formation. 2009. (Advances in Anatomy, Embryology & Cell Biology Ser.). (ENG., Illus.). xvi, 89p. pap. 159.00 (978-3-642-03660-6(0), 3642036600) Springer.

Janigro, Damir, ed. Mammalian Brain Development. 2009. (Contemporary Neuroscience Ser.). (ENG., Illus.). xiv, 227p. 219.00 (978-1-60761-286-5(0), 1607612860) Humana Pr.

Keshavan, Matcheri S., et al, eds. Neurodevelopment & Schizophrenia. 2010. (ENG., Illus.). 516p. pap. 62.00 (978-0-521-12659-5(2)) Cambridge Univ. Pr.

Lagercrantz, Hugo, et al, eds. The Newborn Brain: Neuroscience & Clinical Applications. 2nd ed. 2010. (ENG., Illus.). 426p. 130.00 (978-0-521-88975-9(8)) Cambridge Univ. Pr.

Lee, Ilchi. Power Brain Kids: 12 Easy Lessons to Ignite Your Child's Potential. 2010. 118p. pap. 16.95 (978-1-935127-35-2(7)) BEST Life Media.

—Power Brain Kids: 12 Easy Lessons to Ignite Your Child's Potential. 2007. (Illus.). 118p. per. 18.95 (978-1-932843-19-4(1)) Healing Society, Inc.

Lipina, Sebastián J. & Colombo, Jorge A. Poverty & Brain Development During Childhood: An Approach from Cognitive Psychology & Neuroscience. 2009. (Illus.). 184p. 49.95 (978-1-4338-0445-8(X)) American Psychological Assn.

Medina, John. Brain Rules for Baby: How to Raise a Smart & Happy Child from Zero to Five. 2011. (ENG.). 294p. pap. 15.00 (978-0-9832633-0-2(2)) Pear Pr.

Novartis Foundation Symposium Staff, ed. Cortical Development: Genes & Genetic Abnormalities. 2008. (Novartis Foundation Symposia Ser.). (ENG., Illus.). 302p. 195.00 (978-0-470-06092-6(1), Wiley-Interscience) Wiley, John & Sons, Inc.

O'Rahilly, Ronan R. & Müller, Fabiola. The Embryonic Human Brain: An Atlas of Developmental Stages. 3rd rev. ed. 2006. (ENG., Illus.). 358p. 388.00 (978-0-471-69462-5(2), Wiley-Liss) Wiley, John & Sons, Inc.

Paxinos, George & Watson, Charles. Chemoarchitectonic Atlas of the Mouse Brain. 2009. (ENG., Illus.). 285.00 (978-0-12-374238-4(2), Academic Pr.) Elsevier Science & Technology Bks.

Paxinos, George, et al. Atlas of the Developing Mouse Brain at E17. 5, P0 & P6. 2006. (ENG., Illus.). 356p. spiral bd. 235.00 (978-0-12-547622-5(1), Academic Pr.) Elsevier Science & Technology Bks.

Posner, Michael I. & Rothbart, Mary K. Educating the Human Brain. 2006. (Illus.). 263p. 39.95 (978-1-59147-381-7(0)) American Psychological Assn.

Price, David, et al. Building Brains: An Introduction to Neural Development. 2011. (ENG., Illus.). 348p. 149.95 **(978-0-470-71230-6(9))**; pap. 79.95 **(978-0-470-71229-0(5))** Wiley, John & Sons, Inc. (Wiley).

Rauscher, Francis, ed. Neurosciences in Music Pedagogy. 2007. 79.00 (978-1-60021-834-7(2)) Nova Science Pubs., Inc.

Romer, Daniel & Walker, Elaine F., eds. Adolescent Psychopathology & the Developing Brain: Integrating Brain & Prevention Science. 2007. (Illus.). 544p. (978-0-19-530625-5(2)) Oxford Univ. Pr.

—Adolescent Psychopathology & the Developing Brain: Integrating Brain & Prevention Science. 2007. (ENG., Illus.). 544p. pap. 37.95 (978-0-19-530626-2(0)) Oxford Univ. Pr., Inc.

Schambra, Uta B. Atlas of the Prenatal Mouse Brain. 2nd ed. 2007. (Illus.). 550p. 298.00 (978-0-387-47089-4(1), 0387470891) Springer.

Stibel, Jeffrey M. Wired for Thought: How the Brain Is Shaping the Future of the Internet. 2009. (ENG., Illus.). 256p. 29.95 (978-1-4221-4664-4(2)) Harvard Business Review Pr.

Stiles, Joan. The Fundamentals of Brain Development: Integrating Nature & Nurture. 2008. (Illus.). 440p. 56.50 (978-0-674-02674-2(8)) Harvard Univ. Pr.

Stiles, Joan, et al. Neural Plasticity & Cognitive Development: Insights from Children with Perinatal Brain Injury, 1 vol. 2012. (ENG.). 384p. 79.99 **(978-0-19-538994-4(8))** Oxford Univ. Pr., Inc.

Tan, S. & Levison, S. W., eds. Bridging Bench to Bedside in Fetal & Neonatal Brain Injury. 2007. (Illus.). 138p. pap. (978-3-8055-8319-0(2)) Karger, S. AG.

Technau, Gerhard M. Brain Development in Drosophila Melanogaster. 2008. (Advances in Experimental Medicine & Biology Ser.: Vol. 628). (Illus.). 229.00 (978-0-387-78260-7(5)) Springer.

Wang, Sam & Aamodt, Sandra. Welcome to Your Child's Brain: How the Mind Grows from Conception to College. 2011. (ENG., Illus.). 336p. 26.00 (978-1-59691-649-4(4)) Bloomsbury Publishing.

Wolf, Maryanne. Proust & the Squid: The Story & Science of the Reading Brain. 2008. (ENG., Illus.). 320p. pap. 14.99 (978-0-06-093384-5(4), HarperPerennial) HarperCollins Pubs.

BRAIN—HEMORRHAGE

Carhuapoma, J. Ricardo, et al, eds. Intracerebral Hemorrhage. 2009. (ENG., Illus.). 276p. 125.00 (978-0-521-87331-4(2)) Cambridge Univ. Pr.

Carneado-Ruiz, J., et al, eds. European Society of Neurosonology & Cerebral Hemodynamics: 15th Meeting, Madrid, May 2010: Abstracts. 2010. (Illus.). 66p. pap. (978-3-8055-9480-6(1)) Karger, S. AG.

Fiala, Marie Lawson. Letters from a Distant Shore. 2010. (LaurelBooks Ser.). (ENG.). 338p. pap. 21.00 (978-1-933880-19-8(8)) Cavankerry Pr., Ltd.

Forsting, Michael & Wanke, Isabel. Intracranial Vascular Malformations & Aneurysms: From Diagnostic Work-up to Endovascular Therapy. 2nd ed. 2010. (Medical Radiology / Diagnostic Imaging Ser.). (Illus.). ix, 297p. pap. 119.00 (978-3-642-06946-8(0), 3642069460) Springer.

Itallie, Kathie Van. Kathie's Miracle. 2010. 48p. pap. 15.99 (978-1-4500-5473-7(0)) Xlibris Corp.

Leykam, Britta. Vision Trainer: Rehabilitation von Gesichtsfelddefekten mittels Internettraining. 2011. 146p. pap. **(978-3-8381-2221-2(6))** Südwestdeutscher Verlag für Hochschulschriften AG & Co. KG.

Madajka, Maria. Nitroxidative Stress in Intracerebral Hemorrhage Stroke. 2009. 184p. pap. (978-3-639-17117-4(9)) VDM Verlag Dr. Mueller e.K.

Nutt, Amy E. Shadows Bright as Glass: The Remarkable Story of One Man's Journey from Brain Trauma to Artistic Triumph. 2011. (ENG., Illus.). 288p. 26.00 (978-1-4391-4310-0(2), Free Pr.) Free Pr.

Nutt, Amy Ellis. Shadows Bright As Glass: An Accidental Artist & the Search for the Soul. 2011. pap. (978-1-4391-4311-7(0), Free Pr.) Free Pr.

Rigamonti, Daniele, ed. Cavernous Malformations of the Nervous System. 2011. (ENG., Illus.). 208p. 135.00 (978-0-521-76427-8(0)) Cambridge Univ. Pr.

Shafin, Hafizi. Pattern Recognition of Cerebral Haemorrhage from Ct Images. 2010. 100p. pap. (978-3-8383-0507-3(8)) Lambert Academic Publishing.

Wertheimer, Alison. A Dented Image: Journeys of Recovery from Subarachnoid Haemorrhage. 2008. (ENG.). 272p. 95.00 (978-0-415-38671-5(3)); 27.50 (978-0-415-38672-2(1)) Routledge.

Zhang, John & Colohan, Austin, eds. Intracerebral Hemorrhage Research: From Bench to Bedside. 2011. (Acta Neurochirurgica Supplementum Ser.). (ENG., Illus.). xv, 453p. 299.00 (978-3-7091-0692-1(3), 3709106923) Springer.

Zhou, Liang-Fu. Cerebral Hemorrhage. 2008. (Acta Neurochirurgica Supplementum Ser.). (Illus.). 300p. 319.00 (978-3-211-09468-6(7)) Springer.

Zhou, Liang-Fu, et al, eds. Cerebral Hemorrhage. 2010. (Acta Neurochirurgica Supplementum Ser.). (ENG., Illus.). xiii, 239p. pap. 319.00 (978-3-211-99870-0(5), 3211998705) Springer.

BRAIN—IMAGING

Aizenstein, Howard J., et al. Neuroimaging Research in Geriatric Mental Health. 2010. (Illus.). xiii, 263p. E-Book **(978-0-8261-1116-6(5))** Springer Publishing Co., Inc.

Ames, David & Chiu, Edmond, eds. Neuroimaging & the Psychiatry of Late Life. 2009. (ENG., Illus.). 260p. pap. 56.00 (978-0-521-11247-5(8)) Cambridge Univ. Pr.

Barkhof, Frederik, et al. Neuroimaging in Dementia. 2011. (ENG., Illus.). xix, 278p. 179.00 (978-3-642-00817-7(8), 3642008178) Springer.

Bayer Shirley a Staff. Atlas of Human Central Nervous System Development, 5 vols. 2007. (Atlas of Human Central Nervous System Development Ser.). (ENG., Illus.). 536p. 185.95 (978-0-8493-1424-7(0), CRC Press) Taylor & Francis Group GBR. Dist: Taylor & Francis Group.

Bermudez-Rattoni, Federico. Neural Plasticity & Memory: From Genes to Brain Imaging. 2007. (New Frontiers in Neuroscience Ser.). (ENG., Illus.). 368p. 162.95 (978-0-8493-9070-8(2), CRC Press) Taylor & Francis Group GBR. Dist: Taylor & Francis Group.

Brain Imaging. 2006. (ENG.). 104p. 41.95 (978-0-8058-9350-2(4), Psychology Press) Taylor & Francis Group GBR. Dist: Taylor & Francis Group.

Breznitz, Zvia, ed. Brain Research in Language. (Literacy Studies). (Illus.). 2010. vi, 282p. pap. 179.00 (978-1-4419-4523-5(7), 1441945237) 2007. VI, 282p. (C). 179.00 (978-0-387-74979-2(9), 0387749799) Springer.

Buxton, Richard. Introduction to Functional Magnetic Resonance Imaging: Principles & Techniques. 2nd ed. 2009. (ENG., Illus.). 470p. 215.00 (978-0-521-89995-6(8)) Cambridge Univ. Pr.

Catani, Marco & Thiebaut de Schotten, Michel. Atlas of Human Brain Connections. 2012. (ENG.). 456p. 159.95 (978-0-19-954116-4(7)) Oxford Univ. Pr., Inc.

Cho, Zang Hee, ed. 7.0 Tesla MRI Brain Atlas: In vivo Atlas with Cryomacrotome Correlation. 2010. (ENG., Illus.). ix, 557p. 299.00 (978-1-60761-153-0(8), 1607611538) Humana Pr.

Cohen, Ronald & Sweet, Lawrence. Brain Imaging in Behavioral Medicine & Clinical Neuroscience. 2010. (ENG., Illus.). xvi, 404p. 179.00 (978-1-4419-6371-0(5), 1441963715) Springer.

Creasy, Jeff L. Dating Neurological Injury: A Forensic Guide for Radiologists, Other Expert Medical Witnesses, & Attorneys. 2010. (Illus.). xi, 126p. 189.00 (978-1-60761-249-0(6), 1607612496) Springer.

Deneux, Thomas. Brain Imaging & Hemodynamic Models. 2011. 216p. pap. **(978-3-8433-9086-6(X))** Lambert Academic Publishing.

Drevelegas, Antonios, ed. Imaging of Brain Tumors with Histological Correlations. 2nd ed. 2010. (Illus.). 300p. 179.00 (978-3-540-87648-9(0), 3540876480) Springer.

Ernst, Monique & Rumsey, Judith M., eds. Functional Neuroimaging in Child Psychiatry. 2010. (ENG., Illus.). 456p. pap. 52.00 (978-0-521-12658-8(4)) Cambridge Univ. Pr.

Eswaran, Hari & Singh, Nandini Chatterjee. Developmental Neuro Science & Imaging. 2009. (Illus.). 160p. 100.00 (978-1-84829-024-2(1)) Anshan GBR. Dist: Publishers Storage & Shipping.

Faro, Scott H & Mohamed, Feroze B, eds. Functional MRI: Basic Principles & Clinical Applications. 2010. (ENG., Illus.). xiii, 533p. pap. 199.00 (978-1-4419-1999-1(6), 1441919996) Springer.

Fatterpekar, Girish, et al. The Teaching Files: Brain & Spine Imaging: Expert Consult - Online & Print. 2011. (ENG., Illus.). 816p. (C). 129.00 **(978-1-4160-5620-1(3)**, Saunders) Elsevier - Health Sciences Div.

Filippi, M. FMRI Techniques & Protocols. 2009. (Illus.). xiii, 843p. **(978-1-60327-919-2(9))** Humana Pr.

Filippi, Massimo, ed. FMRI Techniques & Protocols. 2009. (Neuromethods Ser.). (ENG., Illus.). xi, 822p. 229.00 (978-1-60327-918-5(0), 1603279180) Humana Pr.

Forum on Neuroscience and Nervous System Disorders & Institute of Medicine. Future Opportunities to Leverage the Alzheimer's Disease Neuroimaging Initiative: Workshop Summary. 2011. (ENG.). 40p. pap. 15.00 (978-0-309-16188-6(6)) National Academies Pr.

Frostig, Ron. In Vivo Optical Imaging of Brain Function, Second Edition. 2nd rev. ed. 2009. (Frontiers in Neuroscience Ser.). (ENG., Illus.). 428p. 159.95 (978-1-4200-7684-4(1), CRC Press) Taylor & Francis Group GBR. Dist: Taylor & Francis Group.

González, R. Gilberto, et al, eds. Acute Ischemic Stroke: Imaging & Intervention. 2nd ed. 2010. (ENG., Illus.). xiii, 297p. 169.00 (978-3-642-12750-2(9), 3642127509) Springer.

Hathout, Gasser M. Clinical Neuroradiology: A Case-Based Approach. 2008. (ENG., Illus.). 288p. 131.00 (978-0-521-60054-5(5)) Cambridge Univ. Pr.

Helmchen, Fritjof & Konnerth, Arthur, eds. Imaging in Neuroscience: A Laboratory Manual. 2011. (Illus.). 1100p. 287.00 (978-0-87969-937-6(X)); pap. 200.00 (978-0-87969-938-3(8)) Cold Spring Harbor Laboratory Pr.

Hyder, Fahmeed. Dynamic Brain Imaging: Multi-Modal Methods & in Vivo Applications. 2008. (Methods in Molecular Biology Ser.). (Illus.). 296p. 119.00 (978-1-934115-74-9(6)) Humana Pr.

Izzetoglu, Meltem & Onaral, Banu. Optical Brain Imaging. 2009. (Synthesis Lectures on Biomedical Engineering Ser.). pap. 40.00 (978-1-59829-704-1(X)) Morgan & Claypool Pubs.

Jagust, William & D'Esposito, Mark, eds. Imaging the Aging Brain. 2009. (ENG., Illus.). 384p. 125.00 (978-0-19-532987-5(6)) Oxford Univ. Pr., Inc.

Kaufman, Marc J., ed. Brain Imaging in Substance Abuse. 2010. (Forensic Science & Medicine Ser.). (Illus.). 448p. pap. 179.00 (978-1-61737-180-6(7), 1617371807) Humana Pr.

Keenan. Methods of Neuroimaging. 2007. 304p. 95.00 (978-1-84169-463-4(0), Psychology Press) Taylor & Francis Group GBR. Dist: Taylor & Francis Group.

Kraft, Eduard, et al. Neural Correlates of Thinking. 2008. (On Thinking Ser.). (Illus.). 293p. 189.00 (978-3-540-68042-0(X)) Springer.

Law, Meng. State of the Art Brain Tumor Diagnostics, Imagimg, & Therapeutics: Neuroimaging Clinics of North America. 2010. (Clinics: Radiology Ser.: 20-3). (ENG., Illus.). xviii, 259p. 105.00 (978-1-4377-1838-6(8), Saunders) Elsevier - Health Sciences Div.

Lazar, Nicole. The Statistical Analysis of Functional MRI Data. 2010. (Statistics for Biology & Health Ser.). xiv, 299p. pap. 119.00 (978-1-4419-2679-1(8), 1441926798) Springer.

Lazar, Nicole A. The Statistical Analysis of Functional MRI Data. 2008. (Statistics for Biology & Health Ser.). 312p. 119.00 (978-0-387-78190-7(0)) Springer.

Liu, Tianming, et al, eds. Multimodal Brain Image Analysis: First International Workshop, MBIA 2011, Held in Conjunction with MICCAI 2011, Toronto, Canada, September 18, 2011, Proceedings. 2011. (Lecture Notes in Computer Science / Image Processing, Computer Vision, Pattern Recognition, & Graphics Ser.). (ENG., Illus.). x, 162p. pap. 72.00 **(978-3-642-24445-2(9)**, 3642244459) Springer.

Loevner, Laurie A. & Yousem, David M. Brain Imaging. 2nd ed. 2008. (Case Review Ser.). (ENG., Illus.). 432p. 54.95 (978-0-323-03179-0(X), Mosby) Elsevier - Health Sciences Div.

Michel, Christoph M. Electrical Neuroimaging. Michel, Christoph M. et al, eds. 2009. (ENG., Illus.). 248p. 134.00 (978-0-521-87979-8(5)) Cambridge Univ. Pr.

Miller, Karol, ed. Biomechanics of the Brain. 2011. (Biological & Medical Physics, Biomedical Engineering Ser.). (ENG., Illus.). viii, 228p. 129.00 (978-1-4419-9996-2(5), 1441999965) Springer.

Modo, Michel & Bulte, Jeff W. M., eds. Magnetic Resonance Neuroimaging: Methods & Protocols. 2011. (Methods in Molecular Biology Ser.). (ENG., Illus.). xiv, 598p. 159.00 (978-1-61737-991-8(3), 1617379913) Humana Pr.

Monchi, Oury, et al, eds. Recent Advances in Neuroimaging Methodology. 2007. 120p. pap. 19.00 (978-977-454-033-2(6)) Hindawi Publishing Corp.

Moore, Stephen. Computational 3d Modeling of Hemodynamics in the Circle of Willis. 2008. 392p. pap. (978-3-639-10399-1(8)) VDM Verlag Dr. Mueller e.K.

Onozuka, Minoru & Chen-Tung, Yen, eds. Novel Trends in Brain Science: Brain Imaging, Learning & Memory, Stress & Fear, & Pain. 2010. (ENG., Illus.). x, 254p. pap. 159.00 (978-4-431-99828-0(4), 4431998284) Springer.

Orrison, William W. Atlas of Brain Function. 2nd ed. 2008. (ENG., Illus.). 316p. pap. 89.99 (978-1-58890-525-3(X)) Thieme Medical Pubs., Inc.

Osborn, Anne G., et al. Brain. 2nd rev. ed. 2009. (ENG., Illus.). 1266p. 339.00 (978-1-931884-72-3(2)) Lippincott Williams & Wilkins.

Pamir, M. Necmettin, et al, eds. Intraoperative Imaging. 2010. (Acta Neurochirurgica Supplementum Ser.). (Illus.). x, 300p. 249.00 (978-3-211-99650-8(8), 3211996508) Springer.

Paxinos, George & Watson, Charles. The Rat Brain in Stereotaxic Coordinates. 6th ed. 2008. (ENG., Illus.). 400p. spiral bd. 103.00 (978-0-12-374243-8(9), Academic Pr.) Elsevier Science & Technology Bks.

Poldrack, Russell A., et al. Handbook of Functional MRI Data Analysis. 2011. (ENG., Illus.). 238p. 80.00 **(978-0-521-51766-9(4))** Cambridge Univ. Pr.

Rennie, Janet M., et al. Neonatal Cerebral Investigation. 2nd ed. 2008. (ENG., Illus.). 310p. 195.00 (978-0-521-83848-1(7)) Cambridge Univ. Pr.

Roe, Anna, ed. Imaging the Brain with Optical Methods. 2009. (Illus.). xi, 259p. 189.00 (978-1-4419-0451-5(4), 1441904514) Springer.

Roe, Anna Wang. Imaging the Brain with Optical Methods. 2010. (Illus.). xiii, 267p. E-Book (978-1-4419-0452-2(2), 978-1-4419-0451-5) Springer.

Rosen, A. & Adamson, M., eds. Handbook of Imaging the Alzheimer Brain. 2011. 824p. 276.00 **(978-1-60750-792-5(7))** IOS Pr., Inc.

Schaller, B., ed. Neuroscience Imaging Research Compendium: Volume 1. 2008. (978-1-60456-564-5(0)) Nova Science Pubs., Inc.

Schaller, Bernhard. Neuroscience Imaging Research Trends. 2008. 82.00 (978-1-60456-227-9(7)) Nova Science Pubs., Inc.

Schoonover, Carl Edward. Portraits of the Mind: Visualizing the Brain from Antiquity to the 21st Century. 2010. (ENG., Illus.). 240p. 35.00 (978-0-8109-9033-3(4)) Abrams.

Schumacher, Martin & Spreer, Joachim. Imaging of Meningeal Diseases. 2010. (ENG., Illus.). 300p. 169.00 *(978-3-540-69298-0(3),* 3540692983) Springer.

Sibuma, Bernadette. Visual Perceptions of Virtual Characters: How the Brain Processes Graphic Design. 2008. 80p. pap. *(978-3-639-08674-4(0))* VDM Verlag Dr. Mueller e.K.

Stenbacka, Linda. Imaging of Peripheral Vision & Dorsal Visual Stream in Human Cortex. 2011. 100p. pap. ***(978-3-8443-2012-1(1))*** Lambert Academic Publishing.

Stippich, C., ed. Clinical Functional MRI: Presurgical Functional Neuroimaging. 2007. (Medical Radiology / Diagnostic Imaging Ser.). (Illus.). 268p. 219.00 *(978-3-540-24469-1(7),* 3540244697) Springer.

Toga, Arthur W. & Mazziotta, John C. Brain Mapping - the Essentials: A Textbook of NeuroImaging. 2012. (ENG.). 500p. (C). 79.95 *(978-0-12-374222-3(6),* Academic Pr.) Elsevier Science & Technology Bks.

Ulmer, Stephan & Jansen, Olav. FMRI: Basics & Clinical Applications. 2009. (ENG., Illus.). xv, 181p. 149.00 *(978-3-540-68131-1(0),* 3540681310) Springer.

Uttal, William R. Distributed Neural Systems: Beyond the New Phrenology. 2008. (Illus.). 160p. pap. 22.00 net. *(978-1-59738-019-5(9))* Sloan Publishing.

Wagner, Henry N., Jr. Brain Imaging: The Chemistry of Mental Activity. 2009. (ENG., Illus.). xiv, 246p. 169.00 *(978-1-84800-307-1(2),* 1848003072) Springer.

Wagner, Henry N. Jr. Brain Imaging: The Chemistry of Mental Activity. 2009. (ENG., Illus.). xiv, 246p. pap. 49.95 *(978-1-84882-922-0(1),* 1848829221) Springer.

Walker, Matthew T. & Nemeth, Alexander. Emergency Neuroimaging: Radiologic Clinics of North America. 2010. (Clinics: Radiology Ser.: 49-1). (ENG., Illus.). 248p. 110.00 *(978-1-4557-0500-9(4),* Saunders) Elsevier - Health Sciences Div.

Yen, Chen-Tung. Novel Trends in Brain Science: Brain Imaging, Learning & Memory, Stress & Fear, & Pain. Onozuka, Minoru, ed. 2007. (ENG., Illus.). x, 254p. 159.00 *(978-4-431-73241-9(1),* 4431732411) Springer.

Yew, D. T. W. & Chan, W. Y., eds. Imaging of the Developing Brain. 2008. (Illus.). 68p. pap. *(978-3-8055-8546-0(2))* Karger, S. AG.

Yudofsky, Stuart C. & Hales, Robert E., frwds. Windows to the Brain: Insights from Neuroimaging. 2008. (Illus.). 239p. 89.00 *(978-1-58562-302-0(4))* American Psychiatric Publishing, Inc.

Zee, Chi-Shing. Brain & Spine Imaging Patterns. 2010. (ENG., Illus.). 768p. 195.00 *(978-0-07-146541-0(3),* 0071465413) McGraw-Hill Professional Publishing.

BRAIN—LATERALITY

see Cerebral Dominance

BRAIN—LOCALIZATION OF FUNCTIONS

see also Visual Evoked Response

Agam, Galila, et al, eds. The Postmortem Brain in Psychiatric Research. 2010. (Neurobiological Foundation of Aberrant Behaviors Ser.). 416p. pap. 159.00 *(978-1-4419-4921-9(6),* 1441949216) Springer.

Alac, Morana. Handling Digital Brains: A Laboratory Study of Multimodal Semiotic Interaction in the Age of Computers. 2011. (Inside Technology Ser.). (ENG., Illus.). 218p. (gr. 17). 35.00 *(978-0-262-01568-4(4))* MIT Pr.

Anders, Silke, et al. Understanding Emotions. 2006. (Progress in Brain Research Ser.: Vol. 156). (ENG., Illus.). 522p. 268.00 *(978-0-444-52182-8(8),* Elsevier Science) Elsevier Science & Technology Bks.

Arrington, Doris Banowsky. Art, angst, & Trauma: Right Brain Interventions with Developmental Issues. 2007. (Illus.). 278p. *(978-0-398-07733-4(9))* Thomas, Charles C. Pub., Ltd.

—Art, angst, & Trauma: Right Brain Invterventions with Development Issues. 2007. (Illus.). 278p. *(978-0-398-07732-7(0))* Thomas, Charles C. Pub., Ltd.

Ashby, F. Gregory. Statistical Analysis of FMRI Data. 2011. (ENG., Illus.). 352p. (gr. 17). 45.00 *(978-0-262-01504-2(8))* MIT Pr.

Bakker, Lars N. Brain Mapping Research Developments. 2008. (Illus.). (C). 129.00 *(978-1-60456-007-7(X),* Nova Biomedical Bks.) Nova Science Pubs., Inc.

Blakeslee, Sandra & Blakeslee, Matthew. The Body Has a Mind of Its Own: How Body Maps in Your Brain Help You Do (Almost) Everything Better. (ENG., Illus.). 240p. 2008. pap. 16.00 *(978-0-8129-7527-7(8),* Random Hse. Trade Paperbacks) 2007. 24.95 *(978-1-4000-6469-4(4),* Random House) Random House Publishing Group.

Braeckman, Johan, et al, eds. The Moral Brain: Essays on the Evolutionary & Neuroscientific Aspects of Morality. 2008. (Illus.). viii, 275p. 159.00 *(978-1-4020-6286-5(9))* Springer.

Brazis, Paul W., et al. Localization in Clinical Neurology. 6th rev. ed. 2011. (ENG., Illus.). 668p. 209.99 *(978-1-60913-281-1(5))* Lippincott Williams & Wilkins.

Brodmann, K. Brodmann's: Localisation in the Cerebral Cortex. Garey, Laurence J., tr. from GER. 2010. (ENG., Illus.). xv, 298p. pap. 79.95 *(978-1-4419-3895-4(8),* 1441938958) Springer.

Chambers, James J. & Kramer, Richard H., eds. Photosensitive Molecules for Controlling Biological Function. 2011. (Neuromethods Ser.). (ENG., Illus.). xiv, 298p. 119.00 *(978-1-61779-030-0(3),* 1617790303) Humana Pr.

Cherbuin, Nicolas. Left Brain Right Brain Interactions - When & Why Do They Differ? 2008. 168p. pap. *(978-3-639-03487-5(2))* VDM Verlag Dr. Mueller e.K.

Chorost, Michael. World Wide Mind: The Coming Integration of Humans & Machines. 2011. 288p. pap. *(978-1-4391-1916-7(3));* (ENG., Illus.). 256p. 26.00 *(978-1-4391-1914-3(7))* Free Pr. (Free Pr.).

Cram101 Textbook Reviews & Cram101 Textbook Reviews. Outlines & Highlights for Deep Brain Stimulation Management by Jr Marks, Isbn: 9780521514156. 2011. 86p. pap. 27.95 ***(978-1-61461-915-4(8))*** Cram101 Inc.

Deutsch, Diana. Ear & Brain: How We Make Sense of Sounds. 2006. (Illus.). 416p. 35.00 *(978-0-387-95255-0(1),* 0387952551, Copernicus) Springer.

Duffau, Hugues, ed. Brain Mapping: From Neural Basis of Cognition to Surgical Applications. 2011. (ENG., Illus.). xii, 392p. 279.00 *(978-3-7091-0722-5(9),* 3709107229) Springer.

Fallani, Fabrizio De Vico & Babiloni, Fabio. The Graph Theoretical Approach in Brain Functional Networks: Theory & Applications. 2010. (Synthesis Lectures on Biomedical Engineering Ser.). 92p. pap. 35.00 *(978-1-60845-449-5(5))* Morgan & Claypool Pubs.

Filley, Christopher M. Neurobehavioral Anatomy. 3rd ed. 2011. (ENG., Illus.). 304p. (C). pap. 34.95 *(978-1-60732-098-2(3));* E-Book ***(978-1-60732-099-9(1))*** Univ. Pr. of Colorado.

Hanson, Stephen José & Bunzl, Martin. Foundational Issues of Human Brain Mapping. 2010. (ENG., Illus.). 336p. (gr. 17). 76.00 *(978-0-262-01402-1(5));* pap. 38.00 *(978-0-262-51394-4(3))* MIT Pr.

Hardway, Margaret. The Brain, God & Key Thought Processes. 2010. 144p. pap. 18.96 *(978-0-578-04305-0(X))* Firestarter Pubns.

Holmes, Hannah. Quirk: Brain Science Makes Sense of Your Peculiar Personality. 2011. (ENG.). 288p. 26.00 *(978-1-4000-6840-1(1),* Random House) Random House Publishing Group.

Kalenscher, Tobias. Decisions in the Brain. 2008. 192p. pap. *(978-3-639-03996-6(X))* VDM Verlag Dr. Mueller e.K.

Kapur, Narinder, et al. The Paradoxical Brain. 2011. (Illus.). 300p. 105.00 *(978-0-521-11557-5(4))* Cambridge Univ. Pr.

Kellner, Charles, et al. Brain Stimulation in Psychiatry. 2012. (ENG., Illus.). 160p. pap. 55.00 ***(978-0-521-17255-4(1))*** Cambridge Univ. Pr.

Knotkova, Helena, et al, eds. Pain. Brain Stimulation in the Treatment of Pain. 2010. (Disability Studies (Joav Merrick - Series Editor - National Institute of Child Health & Human Development, Ministry of Social Affairs, Jerusalem Ser.). 89.00 *(978-1-60876-690-1(X))* Nova Science Pubs., Inc.

Koelsch, Stefan. Brain & Music. 2012. (ENG.). 322p. 99.95 ***(978-0-470-68340-8(6));*** pap. 44.95 ***(978-0-470-68339-2(2))*** Wiley, John & Sons, Inc. (Wiley-Blackwell).

Kriegeskorte, Nikolaus & Kreiman, Gabriel. Visual Population Codes: Towards a Common Multivariate Framework for Cell Recording & Functional Imaging. 2011. (Computational Neuroscience Ser.). (ENG., Illus.). 632p. (gr. 17). 55.00 ***(978-0-262-01624-7(9))*** MIT Pr.

Liang, Yuanzhu. Research Topics on Brain Mapping. 2008. (Illus.). (C). 129.00 *(978-1-60456-001-5(0),* Nova Biomedical Bks.) Nova Science Pubs., Inc.

Litvin, Chester. Introduction to Brain Stimulation by Psychoconduction: Litvin's Code. 2011. 88p. pap. ***(978-1-4269-7336-9(5))*** Trafford Publishing (UK) Ltd.

Marks, Jr, William J., Jr. Deep Brain Stimulation Management. 2010. (Illus.). 180p. 83.00 *(978-0-521-51415-6(0))* Cambridge Univ. Pr.

Montgomery, Erwin B., Jr. Deep Brain Stimulation Programming: Principles & Practice, 1 vol. 2010. (ENG., Illus.). 208p. 69.95 *(978-0-19-973852-6(1))* Oxford Univ. Pr., Inc.

Nolte, John & Sundsten, John W. The Human Brain: An Introduction to Its Functional Anatomy. 6th ed. 2008. (ENG., Illus.). 736p. (C). pap. 74.95 *(978-0-323-04131-7(0),* Mosby) Elsevier - Health Sciences Div.

Page, Martyn & Carter, Rita. The Human Brain Book. 2009. (ENG.). 256p. 40.00 *(978-0-7566-5441-2(6))* Dorling Kindersley Publishing, Inc.

Principe, Gabrielle F. Your Brain on Childhood: The Unexpected Side Effects of Classrooms, Ballparks, Family Rooms, & the Minivan. 2011. (ENG.). 275p. pap. 17.00 *(978-1-61614-425-8(4))* Prometheus Bks., Pubs.

Puente, Antonio E. & Tonkonogii, I. M. Localization of Clinical Syndromes in Neuropsychology & Neuroscience. 2009. (Illus.). 350p. 125.00 *(978-0-8261-1967-4(0))* Springer Publishing Co., Inc.

Roe, Anna, ed. Imaging the Brain with Optical Methods. 2009. (Illus.). xi, 259p. 189.00 *(978-1-4419-0451-5(4),* 1441904514) Springer.

Roe, Anna Wang. Imaging the Brain with Optical Methods. 2010. (Illus.). xiii, 267p. E-Book *(978-1-4419-0452-2(2),* 978-1-4419-0451-5) Springer.

Rolls, Edmund T. & Deco, Gustavo. The Noisy Brain: Stochastic Dynamics as a Principle of Brain Function. 2010. (ENG., Illus.). 316p. 74.95 *(978-0-19-958786-5(8))* Oxford Univ. Pr., Inc.

Rösler, Frank, et al, eds. Neuroimaging in Human Memory: Linking cognitive processes to neural Systems. 2009. (ENG., Illus.). 424p. 165.00 *(978-0-19-921729-8(7))* Oxford Univ. Pr., Inc.

Siegel, Daniel J. Pocket Guide to Interpersonal Neurobiology: An Integrative Handbook of the Mind. 2012. (Pocket Guides). (ENG.). 224p. pap. 29.95 *(978-0-393-70713-7(X),* 70713) Norton, W. W. & Co., Inc.

Sousa, David A., ed. The Best of Corwin: Educational Neuroscience. 2011. (Best of Corwin Ser.). 200p. pap. 27.95 ***(978-1-4522-1734-5(3),*** B17345P) Corwin Pr.

Sousa, David A., ed. How the Gifted Brain Learns. 2nd ed. 2009. (Illus.). 296p. pap. 41.95 *(978-1-4129-7173-7(X),* B71720P) Corwin Pr.

Spinelle, Diane E. Brain Mapping & Diseases. 2011. ***(978-1-61122-065-0(3))*** Nova Science Pubs., Inc.

Stanton, Angela. Neural Substrates of Decision-Making in Economic Games. 2009. 108p. pap. *(978-3-639-15352-1(9))* VDM Verlag Dr. Mueller e.K.

Stein, Kathleen. The Genius Engine: Where Memory, Reason, Passion, Violence, & Creativity Intersect in the Human Brain. 2007. (ENG., Illus.). 304p. 27.95 *(978-0-471-26239-8(0),* Wiley) Wiley, John & Sons, Inc.

Tarsy, Daniel, et al, eds. Deep Brain Stimulation in Neurological & Psychiatric Disorders. 2010. (Current Clinical Neurology Ser.). (Illus.). xvi, 602p. pap. 199.00 *(978-1-61737-854-6(2),* 1617378542) Humana Pr.

Taylor, Kathleen. Brainwashing: The Science of Thought Control. 2006. (ENG., Illus.). 336p. *(978-0-19-920478-6(0))* Oxford Univ. Pr.

Thomas, Andr & Thomas, Andre. Cerebellar Functions. 2010. 634p. pap. 45.75 *(978-1-148-58436-2(6))* BiblioBazaar.

Thomas, Andre. Cerebellar Functions. 2010. 240p. pap. 26.75 *(978-1-177-13873-4(5))* 2010. 234p. pap. 25.75 *(978-1-146-59378-6(3))* 2009. (ENG.). 230p. pap. 22.99 *(978-1-110-27042-2(9),* BiblioLife) 2009. (ENG.). 230p. pap. 20.99 *(978-1-110-27039-2(9),* BiblioLife) BiblioBazaar.

—Cerebellar Functions. 2010. 306p. pap. 29.69 *(978-1-150-95130-5(3))* General Bks. LLC.

Uttal, William R. Distributed Neural Systems: Beyond the New Phrenology. 2008. (Illus.). 160p. pap. 22.00 net. *(978-1-59738-019-5(9))* Sloan Publishing.

Velazquez, Jose Luis Perez & Wennberg, Richard, eds. Coordinated Activity in the Brain: Measurements & Relevance to Brain Function & Behavior. 2009. (Springer Series in Computational Neuroscience Ser.). (ENG., Illus.). vii, 265p. 209.00 *(978-0-387-93796-0(X),* 038793796X) Springer.

Verplaetse, Jan. The Moral Brain: Neuroscience & the Search for the Cerebral Seat of Morality, 1800-1930. 2009. (ENG., Illus.). xx, 292p. 159.00 *(978-1-4020-6321-3(0),* 1402063210) Springer.

von der Malsburg, Christoph, et al, eds. Dynamic Coordination in the Brain: From Neurons to Mind. 2010. (Strungmann Forum Reports). (ENG., Illus.). 368p. (gr. 17). 40.00 *(978-0-262-01471-7(8))* MIT Pr.

Yao, Yiyu, et al, eds. Brain Informatics: International Conference, BI 2010, Toronto, Canada, August 28-30, 2010, Proceedings. 2010. (Lecture Notes in Computer Science / Lecture Notes in Artificial Intelligence Ser.). xvi, 440p. pap. 95.00 *(978-3-642-15313-6(5),* 3642153135) Springer.

Yoshor, Daniel & Mizrahi, Eli. Clinical Brain Mapping. 2012. (ENG., Illus.). 320p. 159.00 *(978-0-07-148441-1(8),* 0071484418) McGraw-Hill Professional Publishing.

Zeigler, H. Philip, et al, eds. New Perspectives on Neurobehavioral Evolution. 2011. (Annals of the New York Academy of Sciences Ser.: 80). (ENG., Illus.). 252p. pap. 130.00 ***(978-1-57331-807-5(8),*** Wiley-Blackwell) Wiley, John & Sons, Inc.

BRAIN—MATHEMATICAL MODELS

Glimcher, Paul W., et al, eds. Neuroeconomics: Decision Making & the Brain. 2008. (ENG., Illus.). 556p. (C). 72.95 *(978-0-12-374176-9(9),* Academic Pr.) Elsevier Science & Technology Bks.

Hancock, Jonathan & Chapman, Jon. Number-Training Your Brain: A Teach Yourself Guide. 2011. (Teach Yourself: General Reference Ser.). (ENG.). 224p. pap. 15.00 *(978-0-07-176959-4(5),* 0071769595) McGraw-Hill Cos., The.

Ivancevic, Vladimir G. & Ivancevic, Tijana T. Neuro-Fuzzy Associative Machinery for Comprehensive Brain & Cognition Modelling. (Illus.). xii, 730p. 2010. (Studies in Computational Intelligence Ser.). pap. 239.00 *(978-3-642-07998-6(9),* 3642079989) 2007. (Studies in Computational Intelligence: Vol. 45). 239.00 *(978-3-540-47463-0(3))* Springer.

Mitra, Partha & Bokil, Hemant. Observed Brain Dynamics. 2007. (ENG., Illus.). 528p. 67.95 *(978-0-19-517808-1(4))* Oxford Univ. Pr., Inc.

Shadmehr, Reza & Mussa-Ivaldi, Sandro. Biological Learning & Control: How the Brain Builds Representations, Predicts Events, & Makes Decisions. 2012. (Computational Neuroscience Ser.). (ENG., Illus.). 400p. (gr. 17). 40.00 ***(978-0-262-01696-4(6))*** MIT Pr.

BRAIN—METABOLISM

Das, Undurti N. Metabolic Syndrome Pathophysiology: The Role of Essential Fatty Acids. 2010. (ENG., Illus.). 284p. 199.95 *(978-0-8138-1553-4(3),* Wiley-Blackwell) Wiley, John & Sons, Inc.

Farooqui, Akhlaq A. Lipid Mediators & Their Metabolism in the Brain. 2011. (ENG., Illus.). xxiv, 327p. 209.00 *(978-1-4419-9939-9(6),* 1441999396) Springer.

Farooqui, Akhlaq A., et al. Metabolism & Function of Bioactive Ether Lipids in the Brain. 2008. (ENG., Illus.). xix, 260p. 159.00 *(978-0-387-77400-8(9),* 0387774009) Springer.

—Metabolism & Functions of Bioactive Ether Lipids in the Brain. 2010. (ENG., Illus.). xix, 260p. pap. 159.00 *(978-1-4419-2652-4(6),* 1441926526) Springer.

Morser, John, et al. Stem Cells in Reproduction & in the Brain. 2006. (Ernst Schering Research Foundation Workshop: Vol. 60). (Illus.). XIV, 244p. 109.00 *(978-3-540-31436-3(9),* 3540314369) Springer.

Roland, Per E. Brain Activation. 2nd ed. 2010. (ENG., Illus.). 916p. pap. 139.95 *(978-0-471-39630-7(3),* Wiley-Blackwell) Wiley, John & Sons, Inc.

Schmidt, Michael A. Brain-Building Nutrition: How Dietary Fats & Oils Affect Mental, Physical, & Emotional Intelligence. 3rd rev. ed. 2006. (ENG., Illus.). 336p. pap. 18.95 *(978-1-58394-181-2(9),* Frog Ltd.) North Atlantic Bks.

Surendran, Sankar. Neurochemistry of Metabolic Diseases: Lysosomal Storage Diseases, Phenylketonuria & Canavan Disease. 2011. (Metabolic Diseases - Laboratory & Clinical Research Ser.). 299p. 145.00 *(978-1-61209-671-1(9))* Nova Science Pubs., Inc.

Tong, Chi-Kun. The Role of Ph in Brain Function. 2009. 188p. pap. *(978-3-639-09029-1(2))* VDM Verlag Dr. Mueller e.K.

Walz, Wolfgang, ed. The Neuronal Environment: Brain Homeostasis in Health & Disease. 2010. (Contemporary Neuroscience Ser.). (Illus.). 428p. pap. 179.00 *(978-1-61737-235-3(8),* 1617372358) Humana Pr.

BRAIN—MODELS

see also Brain—Electromechanical Analogies; Brain—Mathematical Models

Aur, D. & Jog, M. S., eds. Neuroelectrodynamics: Understanding the Brain Language - Volume 74 Biomedical & Health Research. 2010. 252p. 174.00 *(978-1-60750-091-9(4))* IOS Pr., Inc.

BRAIN—PHYSIOLOGY

Amen, Daniel G. Change Your Brain, Change Your Life Deck: Train Your Brain to Relax, Focus, Let Go, & Be Happy. 2009. (ENG.). 50p. 14.99 *(978-0-307-46457-6(1),* Potter Style) Crown Publishing Group.

Anthes, Emily & Scientific American Staff. Instant Egghead Guide: The Mind. 2008. (ENG., Illus.). 240p. pap., instr.'s gde. ed. 16.99 *(978-0-312-38638-2(9),* St. Martin's Griffin) St. Martin's Pr.

Ashy, Majed. Childhood Experiences, Social Interactions, & Physical Health. 2008. 120p. pap. *(978-3-639-06232-8(9))* VDM Verlag Dr. Mueller e.K.

Badenoch, Bonnie. Being a Brain Wise Therapist: A Practical Guide to Interpersonal Neurobiology. 2008. (Norton Series on Interpersonal Neurobiology Ser.). (ENG., Illus.). 384p. pap. 29.95 *(978-0-393-70554-6(4),* 70554) Norton, W. W. & Co., Inc.

—The Brain-Savvy Therapist's Workbook. 2011. (Norton Series on Interpersonal Neurobiology Ser.). (ENG., Illus.). 288p. pap. 29.95 *(978-0-393-70639-0(7),* 70639) Norton, W. W. & Co., Inc.

Bähr, Mathias, ed. Brain Repair. 2010. (Advances in Experimental Medicine & Biology Ser.). (Illus.). xii, 252p. pap. 189.00 *(978-1-4419-3417-8(0),* 1441934170) Springer.

Bastian, H. Charlton. The Brain As an Organ of Mind. 2009. 546p. pap. *(978-0-217-37985-4(0))* Books LLC.

Bennett, M. R. & Hacker, P. M. S. History of Cognitive Neuroscience. 2008. (ENG., Illus.). 312p. 136.95 *(978-1-4051-8182-2(6),* Wiley-Blackwell) Wiley, John & Sons, Inc.

Bob, Petr. Brain & Dissociated Mind. 2008. viii, 151p. 79.00 *(978-1-60692-035-0(9))* Nova Science Pubs., Inc.

Brizendine, Louann. The Female Brain. 2007. (ENG., Illus.). 304p. pap. 14.95 *(978-0-7679-2010-0(4),* Morgan Road Bks.) Broadway Bks.

Bruni, J. Edward. Human Brain in Dissection. 3rd ed. 2009. (ENG., Illus.). 368p. spiral bd. 39.95 *(978-0-19-537142-0(9))* Oxford Univ. Pr., Inc.

Buonomano, Dean. Brain Bugs: How the Brain's Flaws Shape Our Lives. (ENG., Illus.). 2012. 320p. pap. 16.95 ***(978-0-393-34222-2(0),*** 34222) 2011. 310p. 25.95 *(978-0-393-07602-8(4),* 7602) Norton, W. W. & Co., Inc.

Buzsaki, Gyorgy. Rhythms of the Brain, 1 vol. 2011. (ENG., Illus.). 464p. pap. 39.99 *(978-0-19-982823-4(7))* Oxford Univ. Pr., Inc.

Carroll, Linda & Rosner, David. The Concussion Crisis: Anatomy of a Silent Epidemic. 2011. (ENG., Illus.). 336p. lib. bdg. 26.00 *(978-1-4516-2722-0(X))* Simon & Schuster.

Changeux, Jean-Pierre. The Physiology of Truth: Neuroscience & Human Knowledge. DeBevoise, M. B., tr. from FRE. 2009. (Mind/Brain/Behavior Initiative Ser.). Orig. Title: L' homme de Vérité. (Illus.). 336p. pap. 21.00 *(978-0-674-03260-6(8),* Belknap Pr.) Harvard Univ. Pr.

Chen, Zhe, et al. Correlative Learning: A Basis for Brain & Adaptive Systems. 2007. (Adaptive & Learning Systems for Signal Processing, Communications & Control Ser.: 49). (ENG., Illus.). 480p. 156.00 *(978-0-470-04488-9(8),* Wiley-Interscience) Wiley, John & Sons, Inc.

Chodzko-Zajko, Wojtek, et al. Enhancing Cognitive Functioning & Brain Plasticity. 2009. (ENG., Illus.). 248p. 51.00 *(978-0-7360-5791-2(9))* Human Kinetics Pubs.

Cohen, Gene D. The Mature Mind: The Positive Power of the Aging Brain. 2006. (ENG.). 256p. per. 16.99 *(978-0-465-01204-6(3))* Basic Bks.

Consumer Dummies Staff & Sprenger, Marilee B. The Leadership Brain for Dummies. 2010. (ENG., Illus.). 360p. pap. 21.99 *(978-0-470-54262-0(4),* For Dummies) Wiley, John & Sons, Inc.

Cook, Michelle Schoffro. The Brain Wash: A Powerful, All-Naural Program to Protect Your Brain Against Alzheimer's, Depression, Parkinson's & Other Brain Diseases. annot. ed. 2007. (ENG.). 256p. per. 21.95 *(978-0-470-83928-7(7),* Wiley) Wiley, John & Sons, Inc.

Cotterill, Rodney M. J., ed. Computer Simulation in Brain Science. 2008. (ENG.). 584p. pap. 105.00 *(978-0-521-06118-6(0))* Cambridge Univ. Pr.

Cram101 Textbook Reviews & Cram101 Textbook Reviews. Outlines & Highlights for Biological Psychiatry by Michael Trimble, Isbn: 9780470688946. 2011. 140p. pap. 28.95 ***(978-1-61461-262-9(5))*** Cram101 Inc.

—Outlines & Highlights for Biopsychology by John P J Pinel. 2011. 426p. pap. 35.95 ***(978-1-61830-474-2(7))*** Cram101 Inc.

—Outlines & Highlights for Developmental Cognitive Neuroscience by Mark Johnson, Isbn: 9781444330854. 2011. 94p. pap. 27.95 ***(978-1-61461-297-1(8))*** Cram101 Inc.

Cram101 Textbook Reviews Staff. Outlines & Highlights for Human Brain: An Introduction to its Functional Anatomy by John Nolte, ISBN. 2009. 256p. pap. 31.95 *(978-1-4288-9877-6(8))* Cram101 Inc.

Crasto, Chiquito J., ed. Neuroinformatics. 2010. (Methods in Molecular Biology Ser.). (Illus.). xxiii, 404p. pap. 129.00 *(978-1-61737-740-2(6),* 1617377406) Humana Pr.

Darlington, Cynthia. The Female Brain, Second Edition. 2nd rev. ed. 2009. (Conceptual Advances in Brain Research Ser.). (ENG., Illus.). 266p. 133.95 *(978-1-4200-7744-5(9),* CRC Press) Taylor & Francis Group GBR. Dist: Taylor & Francis Group.

de Haan, Michelle & Gunnar, Megan R., eds. Handbook of Developmental Social Neuroscience. 2009. (ENG., Illus.). 558p. 85.00 *(978-1-60623-117-3(0))* Guilford Pubns., Inc.

Deshmukh, Vinod D., ed. The Astonishing Brain & Holistic Consciousness: Neuroscience & Vedanta Perspectives. 2011. (Series: Health & Human Development Ser.). 165.00 *(978-1-61324-295-7(6))* Nova Science Pubs., Inc.

Dornhege, Guido, et al, eds. Toward Brain-Computer Interfacing. 2007. (Neural Information Processing Ser.). (ENG., Illus.). 520p. (gr. 17). 49.00 *(978-0-262-04244-4(4))* MIT Pr.
Dowling, John. The Great Brain Debate: Nature or Nurture? 2007. (Science Essentials Ser.). (ENG., Illus.). 200p. per. 20.95 *(978-0-691-13310-2(7))* Princeton Univ. Pr.
Edelman, Shimon. Computing the Mind: How the Mind Really Works. 2008. (Illus.). 640p. 69.95 *(978-0-19-532067-1(0))* Oxford Univ. Pr., Inc.
Eichenbaum, Howard. The Cognitive Neuroscience of Memory: An Introduction. 2nd ed. 2011. (ENG., Illus.). 464p. pap. 55.00 ***(978-0-19-977861-4(2))*** Oxford Univ. Pr., Inc.
Einstein, Gillian, ed. Sex & the Brain. 2007. (ENG., Illus.). 856p. (gr. 17). 65.00 *(978-0-262-05087-6(0))* MIT Pr.
Engel, Christoph & Singer, Wolf, eds. Better Than Conscious? Decision Making, the Human Mind, & Implications for Institutions. 2008. (Strüngmann Forum Reports). (ENG., Illus.). 464p. (gr. 17). 43.00 *(978-0-262-19580-5(1))* MIT Pr.
Fields, Ph.D., RDouglas. The Other Brain: The Scientific & Medical Breakthroughs That Will Heal Our Brains & Revolutionize Our Health. 2011. (ENG., Illus.). 384p. pap. 16.00 *(978-0-7432-9142-2(5))* Simon & Schuster.
Fields, R. Douglas. The Other Brain: From Dementia to Schizophrenia, How New Discoveries about the Brain Are Revolutionizing Medicine & Science. 2009. (ENG., Illus.). 384p. 27.00 *(978-0-7432-9141-5(7))* Simon & Schuster.
Filley, Christopher M. The Behavioral Neurology of White Matter, 1 vol. 2nd ed. 2012. (ENG.). 448p. 75.00 ***(978-0-19-974326-1(6))*** Oxford Univ. Pr., Inc.
Fletcher-Janzen, Elaine. The Neuropsychology of Women. 2008. (Issues of Diversity in Clinical Neuropsychology Ser.). (Illus.). 214p. 89.95 *(978-0-387-76907-3(2))* Springer.
Frostig, Ron. In Vivo Optical Imaging of Brain Function, Second Edition. 2nd rev. ed. 2009. (Frontiers in Neuroscience Ser.). (ENG., Illus.). 428p. 159.95 *(978-1-4200-7684-4(1),* CRC Press) Taylor & Francis Group GBR. Dist: Taylor & Francis Group.
Fukuyama, Hidenao & Le Bihan, Denis, eds. Water: The Forgotten Biological Molecule. 2010. (ENG., Illus.). 399p. 99.95 *(978-981-4267-52-6(X))* Pan Stanford Publishing SGP. Dist: Taylor & Francis Group.
Funahashi, Shintaro, ed. Representation & Brain. 2007. (ENG., Illus.). xii, 366p. 179.00 *(978-4-431-73020-0(6),* 4431730206) Springer.
Gage, Fred H., et al, eds. Adult Neurogenesis. 2007. (ENG., Illus.). 673p. 135.00 *(978-0-87969-784-6(9))* Cold Spring Harbor Laboratory Pr.
Gallagher, Shaun. Brainstorming: Views & Interviews on the Mind. 2008. (ENG., Illus.). 276p. pap. 34.90 *(978-1-84540-023-1(2))* Imprint Academic GBR. Dist: Ingram Pub. Services.
García-Segura, Luis Miguel. Hormones & Brain Plasticity. 2009. (Series in Behavioral Neuroendocrinology Ser.). (ENG., Illus.). 496p. (C). 65.00 *(978-0-19-532661-1(X))* Oxford Univ. Pr., Inc.
Gazzaniga, Michael S. Human: The Science Behind What Makes Your Brain Unique. 2009. (ENG.). 464p. pap. 16.99 *(978-0-06-089289-0(7),* HarperPerennial) HarperCollins Pubs.
Gazzaniga, Michael S. Who's in Charge? Free Will & the Science of the Brain. 2012. (ENG.). 352p. pap. 16.99 ***(978-0-06-190611-4(5),*** Ecco) HarperCollins Pubs.
Gazzaniga, Michael S., et al. Cognitive Neuroscience: The Biology of the Mind. 3rd ed. 2008. (ENG.). 752p. (C). 108.00 net. *(978-0-393-92795-5(4),* 92795) Norton, W. W. & Co., Inc.
George, Mark S. & Belmaker, Robert H., eds. Transcranial Magnetic Stimulation in Clinical Psychiatry. 2007. (Illus.). 275p. per. 74.00 *(978-1-58562-197-2(8),* 62197) American Psychiatric Publishing, Inc.
Gibb, Barry J. & Rough Guides Staff. Brain. 2007. (Rough Guide Reference Ser.). (ENG., Illus.). 272p. per. 16.99 *(978-1-84353-664-2(1))* Rough Guides, Ltd. GBR. Dist: Dorling Kindersley Publishing, Inc.
Girard, Ines C. & Andre, Jade S. Brain Mapping Research Progress. 2008. 98.00 *(978-1-60456-784-7(8))* Nova Science Pubs., Inc.
Glanzman, Dennis, et al, eds. The Dynamic Brain: An Exploration of Neuronal Variability & Its Functional Significance, 1 vol. 2011. (ENG., Illus.). 400p. 99.95 *(978-0-19-539379-8(1))* Oxford Univ. Pr., Inc.
Graben, Peter, et al, eds. Lectures in Supercomputational Neuroscience: Dynamics in Complex Brain Networks. 2010. (Understanding Complex Systems Ser.). (Illus.). x, 378p. pap. 129.00 *(978-3-642-09216-9(0),* 3642092160) Springer.
Greenwood, Pamela M. & Parasuraman, Raja. Nurturing the Older Brain & Mind. 2012. (ENG., Illus.). 352p. (gr. 17). 40.00 ***(978-0-262-01714-5(8))*** MIT Pr.
Günaydin, Ozan. Design of a Brain Computer Interface Based on Electroencephalogram. 2011. 136p. pap. ***(978-3-8443-9150-3(9))*** Lambert Academic Publishing.
Hanson, Stephen Jose & Bunzl, Martin. Foundational Issues of Human Brain Mapping. 2010. (ENG., Illus.). 336p. (gr. 17). 76.00 *(978-0-262-01402-1(5));* pap. 38.00 *(978-0-262-51394-4(3))* MIT Pr.
Hass-Cohen, et al. Art Therapy & Clinical Neuroscience. 2008. (ENG., Illus.). 336p. pap. ***(978-1-84310-868-9(2))*** Kingsley, Jessica Ltd.
Hasselmo, Michael E. How We Remember: Brain Mechanisms of Episodic Memory. 2011. (ENG., Illus.). 384p. (gr. 17). 40.00 *(978-0-262-01635-3(4))* MIT Pr.
Hogan, Matthew T. & Altevogt, Bruce. From Molecules to Minds: Challenges for the 21st Century - Workshop Summary. 2008. (ENG.). 90p. pap. 23.00 *(978-0-309-12092-0(6))* National Academies Pr.
Holmes, David Aaron. Psyche's Palace: How the Brain Generates the Light of the Soul. 2008. 284p. pap. 24.95 *(978-0-615-16411-3(0))* Library of Consciousness, The.
Holscher, Christian & Munk, Matthias, eds. Information Processing by Neuronal Populations. 2008. (ENG., Illus.). 488p. 150.00 *(978-0-521-87303-1(7))* Cambridge Univ. Pr.
Hu, Bin, et al, eds. Brain Informatics: International Conference, BI 2011, Lanzhou, China, September 7-9, 2011. Proceedings. 2011. (Lecture Notes in Computer Science / Lecture Notes in Artificial Intelligence Ser.). (ENG., Illus.). ix, 340p. pap. 83.00 ***(978-3-642-23604-4(9),*** 3642236049) Springer.
Hugdahl, Kenneth. The Two Halves of the Brain: Information Processing in the Cerebral Hemispheres. Westerhausen, Rene, ed. 2010. (ENG., Illus.). 704p. (gr. 17). 75.00 *(978-0-262-01413-7(0))* MIT Pr.
Iversen, Leslie L., et al. Dopamine Handbook, 1 vol. 2009. (ENG., Illus.). 640p. 125.00 *(978-0-19-537303-5(0))* Oxford Univ. Pr., Inc.
Jeannerod, Marc. Motor Cognition: What Actions Tell to the Self. 2006. (Oxford Psychology Ser.: No. 42). (ENG., Illus.). 224p. (C). per. 75.00 *(978-0-19-856965-7(3))* Oxford Univ. Pr., Inc.
Kaiser, Jochen & Neumer, Marcus Johannes, eds. Multisensory Object Perception in the Primate Brain. 2010. (ENG., Illus.). xii, 384p. 209.00 *(978-1-4419-5614-9(X),* 144195614X) Springer.
Kalmar, Jessica. Information Processing Speed in Clinical Applications. DeLuca, John, ed. 2007. (Studies on Neuropsychology, Neurology, & Cognition). (ENG., Illus.). 328p. 105.95 *(978-1-84169-476-4(2),* Psychology Press) Taylor & Francis Group GBR. Dist: Taylor & Francis Group.
Klausen, Martina P. Neurogenesis Research Advances. 2007. (C). 129.00 *(978-1-60021-676-3(5))* Nova Science Pubs., Inc.
Korzeniewski, Bernard. From Neurons to Self-Consciousness: How the Brain Generates the Mind. 2010. (Gateway Bks). (ENG., Illus.). 170p. pap. 39.00 *(978-1-61614-227-8(8),* Humanity Bks.) Prometheus Bks., Pubs.
Krepkly, Roman. Brain-Computer Interfaces. 2008. 180p. per. *(978-3-8364-7035-3(7))* VDM Verlag Dr. Mueller e.K.
Kumai, Toshifumi & Yoshiyuki, Shibukawa. Another View of the Brain System. 2008. 79.00 *(978-1-60692-593-5(8))* Nova Science Pubs., Inc.
Lazar, Nicole A. The Statistical Analysis of Functional MRI Data. 2008. (Statistics for Biology & Health Ser.). 312p. 119.00 *(978-0-387-78190-7(0))* Springer.
Linden, David J. The Accidental Mind: How Brain Evolution Has Given Us Love, Memory, Dreams, & God. 2008. (Illus.). 288p. pap. 21.00 *(978-0-674-03058-9(3),* Belknap Pr.) Harvard Univ. Pr.
Locke, Simeon. Consciousness, Self-Consciousness, & the Science of Being Human. 1 vol. 2007. 172p. 34.95 *(978-0-313-35006-1(X),* C35006, Praeger Pubs.) Greenwood Publishing Group, Inc.
MacKinnon, Dean F. Trouble in Mind: An Unorthodox Introduction to Psychiatry. 2011. (ENG., Illus.). 352p. (C). (gr. 13-17). 50.00 *(978-0-8018-9806-8(4));* pap. 25.00 *(978-0-8018-9807-5(2))* Johns Hopkins Univ. Pr.
Marcolin, M. A. & Padberg, F. Transcranial Brain Stimulation for Treatment of Psychiatric Disorders. (Advances in Biological Psychiatry Ser.: Vol. 23). (Illus.). *(978-3-8055-8186-8(6))* Karger, S. AG.
Mathews, Debra J. H., et al, eds. Personal Identity & Fractured Selves: Perspectives from Philosophy, Ethics, & Neuroscience. 2009. (ENG.). 216p. (gr. 17). 57.00 *(978-0-8018-9338-4(0))* Johns Hopkins Univ. Pr.
McCarthy, Margaret. Role of Hormones in Development of Sex Differences in the Brain. 2010. (Colloquium Series on the Developing Nervous System Ser.). 110p. pap. 40.00 *(978-1-61504-060-5(9))* Morgan & Claypool Life Science Publishers.
McGilchrist, Iain. The Master & His Emissary: The Divided Brain & the Making of the Western World. 2010. (Illus.). 544p. pap. 25.00 *(978-0-300-16892-1(6))* Yale Univ. Pr.
Medina, John. Brain Rules: 12 Principles for Surviving & Thriving at Work, Home, & School. 2008. (ENG., Illus.). 301p. 29.95 *(978-0-9797777-0-7(4))* Pear Pr.
Melillo, Robert & Leisman, Gerry. Neurobehavioral Disorders of Childhood: An Evolutionary Perspective. 2009. (ENG.). xii, 447p. pap. 59.95 *(978-1-4419-1232-9(0),* 1441912320) Springer.
Michel, Christoph M. Electrical Neuroimaging. Michel, Christoph M. et al, eds. 2009. (ENG., Illus.). 248p. 134.00 *(978-0-521-87979-8(5))* Cambridge Univ. Pr.
Mitra, Partha & Bokil, Hemant. Observed Brain Dynamics. 2007. (ENG., Illus.). 528p. 67.95 *(978-0-19-517808-1(4))* Oxford Univ. Pr., Inc.
Moller, Aage R. The Malleable Brain: Benefits & Harm from Plasticity of the Brain. 2009. (Illus.). iv, 247p. 79.00 *(978-1-60692-881-3(3))* Nova Science Pubs., Inc.
Moulton, Peter. Brain Agility: Keeping a Healthy & Youthful Brain. 2007. (Illus.). 280p. per. 19.95 *(978-0-615-16166-2(9))* Northwest Border Pubns.
Nicolelis, Miguel. Beyond Boundaries: The New Neuroscience of Connecting Brains with Machines - And How It Will Change Our Lives. 2011. (ENG., Illus.). 368p. 28.00 *(978-0-8050-9052-9(5),* Times Bks.) Holt, Henry & Co.
Nicolelis, Miguel. Beyond Boundaries: The New Neuroscience of Connecting Brains with Machines — and How It Will Change Our Lives. 2012. (ENG.). 368p. pap. 16.99 ***(978-1-250-00261-7(3),*** St. Martin's Griffin) St. Martin's Pr.
Nicolelis, Miguel A. L., ed. Methods for Neural Ensemble Recordings. 2nd rev. ed. 2007. (Frontiers in Neuroscience Ser.). (ENG., Illus.). 296p. 169.95 *(978-0-8493-7046-5(9),* CRC Press) Taylor & Francis Group GBR. Dist: Taylor & Francis Group.
Nolte, John. Essentials of the Human Brain: With STUDENT CONSULT Online Access. 2009. (ENG., Illus.). 256p. (C). pap. 39.95 *(978-0-323-04570-4(7),* Mosby) Elsevier - Health Sciences Div.
Norden, Jeanette. Understanding the Brain. 2007. per. 49.95 *(978-1-59803-363-2(8))* Teaching Co., LLC, The.
Øverli, Ø., ed. Plasticity & Diversity in Behavior & Brain Function: Important Raw Material for Natural Selection? [Bibliography & Price not Definite.]: 18th Annual Karger Workshop, Atlanta, Ga., October 2006: Special Issue: Brain, Behavior & Evolution 2007, Vol. 70, No. 4. 2007. (Illus.). 78p. pap. *(978-3-8055-8367-1(2))* Karger, S. AG.
Page, Martyn & Carter, Rita. The Human Brain Book. 2009. (ENG.). 256p. 40.00 *(978-0-7566-5441-2(6))* Dorling Kindersley Publishing, Inc.
Paris, Ginette. Wisdom of the Psyche: Depth Psychology after Neuroscience. 2007. (ENG.). 256p. 27.50 *(978-0-415-43777-6(6));* 95.00 *(978-0-415-43776-9(8))* Routledge.
Partridge, Kenneth. The Brain. 2009. *(978-0-8242-1088-5(3))* Wilson, H.W.
Pichler, Florian L., ed. Neural Pathways Research. 2008. (C). 89.00 *(978-1-60456-214-9(5),* Nova Biomedical Bks.) Nova Science Pubs., Inc.
Pilling, David J. Tales Told Sometimes in Earnest. 2nd rev. ed. 2011. 640p. pap. 29.32 ***(978-1-4269-7313-0(6))*** Trafford Publishing.
Pinel, John P. J. Biopsychology. 8th ed. (ENG.). (C). 2011. 46.67 *(978-0-205-22637-5(X))* 2010. 608p. 170.67 *(978-0-205-83256-9(3))* 2011. 139.33 *(978-0-205-22638-2(8))* Prentice Hall PTR. (Prentice Hall).
Riddle, David R. Brain Aging: Models, Methods, & Mechanisms. 2007. (Frontiers in Neuroscience Ser.). (ENG., Illus.). 408p. 162.95 *(978-0-8493-3818-2(2),* CRC Press) Taylor & Francis Group GBR. Dist: Taylor & Francis Group.
Rogers, David Ian. It's the Thought That Matters Literally! 2009. 102p. pap. 15.00 *(978-1-60860-032-8(7),* Strategic Bk. Publishing) AEG Literary Publishing Services, Inc.
Rothwell, Nancy J. & Berkenbosch, Frank, eds. Brain Control of Responses to Trauma. 2011. (ENG.). 354p. pap. 70.00 *(978-0-521-33866-0(2))* Cambridge Univ. Pr.
Rumsey, Judith M. & Ernst, Monique, eds. Neuroimaging in Developmental Clinical Neuroscience. 2009. (ENG., Illus.). 472p. 190.00 *(978-0-521-88357-3(1))* Cambridge Univ. Pr.
Salin-Pascual. The Dark Side of the Brain. 2009. 438p. pap. 45.95 *(978-0-557-15637-5(8))* Lulu Enterprises Inc.
Schiff, Steven J. Neural Control Engineering: The Emerging Intersection Between Control Theory & Neuroscience. 2011. (Computational Neuroscience Ser.). (ENG., Illus.). 384p. (gr. 17). 55.00 *(978-0-262-01537-0(4))* MIT Pr.
Seybold, Kevin S. Explorations in Neurosciences Psychology & Religion. 2007. (Ashgate Science & Religion Ser.). (Illus.). 174p. 99.95 *(978-0-7546-5563-3(6))* Ashgate Publishing Co.
Shepherd, Gordon M. Creating Modern Neuroscience: The Revolutionary 1950s. 2009. (ENG., Illus.). 304p. 59.95 *(978-0-19-539150-3(0))* Oxford Univ. Pr., Inc.
Shepherd, Gordon M. Neurogastronomy: How the Brain Creates Flavor & Why It Matters. 2011. (ENG., Illus.). 288p. (gr. 17). 24.95 ***(978-0-231-15910-4(2))*** Columbia Univ. Pr.
Shepherd, Gordon M. & Grillner, Sten. Handbook of Brain Microcircuits, 1 vol. 2010. (ENG., Illus.). 544p. 125.00 *(978-0-19-538988-3(3))* Oxford Univ. Pr., Inc.
Shepherd, Robert K. & Illing, Robert-Benjamin, eds. Cochlear Implants & Brain Plasticity. (Illus.). 48p. *(978-3-8055-7385-6(5))* Karger, S. AG.
Siegel, Allan & Zalcman, Steven. The Neuroimmunological Basis of Behavior & Mental Disorders. 2008. (ENG., Illus.). xvi, 438p. 149.00 *(978-0-387-84850-1(9),* 0387848509) Springer.
Siegel, Allan & Zalcman, Steven S., eds. The Neuroimmunological Basis of Behavior & Mental Disorders. 2010. (ENG., Illus.). xvi, 438p. pap. 149.00 *(978-1-4419-4657-7(8),* 1441946578) Springer.
Siegel, Daniel J. The Mindful Brain. 2007. 26.95 *(978-0-7937-0470-5(7))* Norton, W. W. & Co., Inc.
Small, Gary. The Memory Bible: An Innovative Strategy for Keeping Your Brain Young. 2007. (ENG.). 320p. pap. 16.95 *(978-1-4013-0922-0(4))* Hyperion Pr.
Spear, Linda, et al. The Behavioral Neuroscience of Adolescence. 2009. (ENG., Illus.). 416p. 40.00 *(978-0-393-70542-3(0),* 70542) Norton, W. W. & Co., Inc.
Sporns, Olaf. Networks of the Brain. 2010. (ENG., Illus.). 424p. (gr. 17). 40.00 *(978-0-262-01469-4(6))* MIT Pr.
Stern, Yaakov. Cognitive Reserve: Theory & Applications. 2006. (Studies on Neuropsychology, Neurology, & Cognition). (ENG., Illus.). 368p. 105.95 *(978-1-84169-474-0(6),* Psychology Press) Taylor & Francis Group GBR. Dist: Taylor & Francis Group.
Steyn-Ross, D. Alistair & Steyn-Ross, Moira, eds. Modeling Phase Transitions in the Brain. 2010. (Springer Series in Computational Neuroscience Ser.). (ENG., Illus.). xxv, 350p. 229.00 *(978-1-4419-0795-0(5),* 1441907955) Springer.
Strakowski, Stephen M., ed. The Bipolar Brain: Integrating Neuroimaging & Genetics, 1 vol. 2012. (ENG., Illus.). 296p. 99.99 ***(978-0-19-979760-8(9))*** Oxford Univ. Pr., Inc.
Swanson, Larry W. Brain Architecture: Understanding the Basic Plan, 1 vol. 2nd ed. 2011. (ENG., Illus.). 352p. pap. 39.95 *(978-0-19-537858-0(X))* Oxford Univ. Pr., Inc.
Tancredi, Laurence R. Hardwired Behavior: What Neuroscience Reveals about Morality. 2010. (ENG.). 240p. pap. 19.99 *(978-0-521-12739-4(4))* Cambridge Univ. Pr.
Tapia, Ricardo. Las Celulas de la Mente. (Ciencia para Todos Ser.). (SPA.). pap. 6.99 *(978-968-16-2545-0(5))* Fondo de Cultura Economica USA.
Taupin, Philippe, ed. Hippocampus: Neurotransmission & Plasticity in the Nervous System. 2008. 120.00 *(978-1-60021-914-6(4))* Nova Science Pubs., Inc.
Thaut, Michael. Rhythm, Music, & the Brain: Scientific Foundations & Clinical Applications. 2007. (ENG., Illus.). 272p. 50.95 *(978-0-415-96475-3(X))* Routledge.
Tononi, Giulio. Phi: A Voyage from the Brain to the Soul. 2012. (ENG., Illus.). 384p. 30.00 ***(978-0-307-90721-9(X),*** Pantheon) Knopf Doubleday Publishing Group.
Tseng, Kuei-Yuan. Cortico-Subcortical Dynamics in Parkinsonâ€(tm)s Disease. Tseng, Kuei-Yuan, ed. 2009. (Contemporary Neuroscience Ser.). (ENG., Illus.). x, 316p. 219.00 *(978-1-60327-251-3(8))* Humana Pr.
Ullsperger, Markus & Debener, Stefan. Simultaneous EEG & FMRI: Recording, Analysis, & Application, 1 vol. 2010. (ENG., Illus.). 336p. 125.00 *(978-0-19-537273-1(5))* Oxford Univ. Pr., Inc.
Uttal, William R. Distributed Neural Systems: Beyond the New Phrenology. 2008. (Illus.). 160p. pap. 22.00 net. *(978-1-59738-019-5(9))* Sloan Publishing.
—Mind & Brain: A Critical Appraisal of Cognitive Neuroscience. 2011. (ENG., Illus.). 528p. (gr. 17). 55.00 *(978-0-262-01596-7(X))* MIT Pr.
Velazquez, Jose Luis Perez & Wennberg, Richard, eds. Coordinated Activity in the Brain: Measurements & Relevance to Brain Function & Behavior. 2009. (Springer Series in Computational Neuroscience Ser.). (ENG., Illus.). vi, 265p. 209.00 *(978-0-387-93796-0(X),* 038793796X) Springer.
von der Malsburg, Christoph, et al, eds. Dynamic Coordination in the Brain: From Neurons to Mind. 2010. (Strungmann Forum Reports). (ENG., Illus.). 368p. (gr. 17). 40.00 *(978-0-262-01471-7(8))* MIT Pr.
Webb, Wanda & Adler, Richard K. Neurology for the Speech-Language Pathologist. 5th rev. ed. 2007. (ENG., Illus.). 336p. (C). pap. 68.95 *(978-0-7506-7526-0(8),* Mosby) Elsevier - Health Sciences Div.
Wenk, Gary Lee. Your Brain on Food: How Chemicals Control Your Thoughts & Feelings, 1 vol. 2010. (ENG., Illus.). 192p. 29.95 *(978-0-19-538854-1(2))* Oxford Univ. Pr., Inc.
Wilcoxson, Kent H. The Metamorphosis of Samuel Freeman. 2009. 268p. pap. 24.50 *(978-1-4251-8776-7(5))* Trafford Publishing.
Winner, Paul. 7 Steps to a Healthy Brain. 2008. 228p. pap. 21.95 *(978-1-4357-1068-9(1))* Lulu Enterprises Inc.
Wolf, Maryanne. Proust & the Squid: The Story & Science of the Reading Brain. (ENG., Illus.). 320p. 2008. pap. 14.99 *(978-0-06-093384-5(4),* HarperPerennial) 2007. 25.95 *(978-0-06-018639-5(9))* HarperCollins Pubs.
Wolpaw, Jonathan & Wolpaw, Elizabeth Winter, eds. Brain-Computer Interfaces: Principles & Practice, 1 vol. 2012. (ENG., Illus.). 432p. 135.00 ***(978-0-19-538885-5(2))*** Oxford Univ. Pr., Inc.
Zeki, Semir. Splendors & Miseries of the Brain: Love, Creativity, & the Quest for Human Happiness. 5th ed. 2008. (ENG., Illus.). 256p. 99.95 *(978-1-4051-8558-5(9),* Wiley-Blackwell) Wiley, John & Sons, Inc.
—Splendors & Miseries of the Brain: Love, Creativity, & the Quest for Human Happiness. 5th ed. 2008. (ENG., Illus.). 256p. pap. 31.95 *(978-1-4051-8557-8(0),* Wiley-Blackwell) Wiley, John & Sons, Inc.
Zelazo, Philip David & Paus, Tomas, eds. Developmental Social Neuroscience: A Special Issue of Social Neuroscience. 2011. (Special Issues of Social Neuroscience Ser.). (ENG., Illus.). 160p. 67.00 *(978-1-84872-741-0(0),* Psychology Press) Taylor & Francis Group GBR. Dist: Taylor & Francis Group.

BRAIN—RADIOGRAPHY

Adinoff, Bryon & Stein, Elliot A., eds. Neuroimaging in Addiction. 2012. (ENG., Illus.). 372p. 165.50 ***(978-0-470-66014-0(7),*** Wiley) Wiley, John & Sons, Inc.
Aizenstein, Howard J., et al. Neuroimaging Research in Geriatric Mental Health. 2010. (Illus.). xiii, 263p. E-Book ***(978-0-8261-1116-6(5))*** Springer Publishing Co., Inc.
Biersack, Hans J. & Winkler, Cuno, eds. Amphetamines & pH-shift Agents for Brain Imaging: Basic Research & Clinical Results. (ENG.). VIII, 186p. 210.00 ***(978-3-11-179301-6(X))*** De Gruyter, Walter Inc.
Bradac, Gianni Boris & Boccardi, Edoardo. Cerebral Angiography: Normal Anatomy & Vascular Pathology. 2011. (ENG., Illus.). xiii, 314p. 189.00 *(978-3-642-15677-9(3),* 3642156770) Springer.
Filippi, Massimo, et al. MR Imaging in White Matter Diseases of the Brain & Spinal Cord. 2010. (Medical Radiology / Diagnostic Imaging Ser.). (Illus.). x, 478p. pap. 349.00 *(978-3-642-07298-7(4),* 3642072984) Springer.
Friston, Karl J., et al, eds. Statistical Parametric Mapping: The Analysis of Functional Brain Images. 2006. (ENG., Illus.). 656p. 142.00 *(978-0-12-372560-8(7),* Academic Pr.) Elsevier Science & Technology Bks.
Gallucci, Massimo, et al. Radiographic Atlas of Skull & Brain Anatomy. 2007. (Illus.). 362p. 259.00 *(978-3-540-34190-1(0),* 3540341900) Springer.
Govaert, Paul & De Vries, Linda S. An Atlas of Neonatal Brain Sonography. 2nd rev. ed. 2010. (Clinics in Developmental Medicine Ser.: 11). (ENG., Illus.). 400p. 253.00 *(978-1-898683-56-8(5))* Mac Keith Pr. GBR. Dist: Wiley, John & Sons, Inc.
Hähnel, Stefan. Inflammatory Diseases of the Brain. 2009. (Medical Radiology / Diagnostic Imaging Ser.). (Illus.). xii, 240p. 129.00 *(978-3-540-76659-9(6))* Springer.
Hathout, Gasser M. Clinical Neuroradiology: A Case-Based Approach. 2008. (ENG., Illus.). 288p. 131.00 *(978-0-521-60054-5(5))* Cambridge Univ. Pr.
Kornienko, Valery N. & Pronin, I. N. Diagnostic Neuroradiology. 2008. (Illus.). 1318p. 339.00 *(978-3-540-75652-1(3),* 3540756523) Springer.
Libenson, Mark H. Practical Approach to Electroencephalography. 2009. (ENG., Illus.). 464p. 99.95 *(978-0-7506-7478-2(4),* Saunders) Elsevier - Health Sciences Div.
Moritani, Toshio, et al. Diffusion-Weighted MR Imaging of the Brain. 2nd ed. (ENG., Illus.). xx, 402p. 2010. pap. 189.00 ***(978-3-642-09760-7(X)***, 364209760X) 2009. 189.00 *(978-3-540-78784-6(4),* 3540787844) Springer.

Osborn, Anne G., et al. Brain. 2nd rev. ed. 2009. (ENG., Illus.). 1266p. 339.00 (978-1-931884-72-3(2)) Lippincott Williams & Wilkins.

Stein, Elliot A. Neuroimaging in Addiction. Adinoff, Bryon, ed. 2012. (ENG., Illus.). 372p. 160.00 (978-1-119-99893-8(X), Wiley) Wiley, John & Sons, Inc.

BRAIN—RESEARCH

Abraham, Carolyn. Possessing Genius: The Bizarre Odyssey of Einstein's Brain. 2006. (Illus.). 388p. reprint ed. pap. 22.00 (978-1-4223-5766-8(X)) DIANE Publishing Co.

Agam, Galila, et al, eds. The Postmortem Brain in Psychiatric Research. 2010. (Neurobiological Foundation of Aberrant Behaviors Ser.). 416p. pap. 159.00 (978-1-4419-4921-9(6), 1441949216) Springer.

Benton, Arthur, ed. Brain & Behavior: Research in Clinical Neuropsychology. 2009. (ENG., Illus.). 251p. pap. 29.95 (978-0-202-36318-9(X)) Aldine Transaction.

Bruce, Barbara A. Triangular Teaching: A New Way of Teaching the Bible to Adults. 2007. (Illus.). 192p. per. 15.00 (978-0-687-64352-3(X)) Abingdon Pr.

Cozolino, Louis. The Neuroscience of Psychotherapy: Healing the Social Brain. 2nd ed. 2010. (Norton Series on Interpersonal Neurobiology Ser.). (ENG., Illus.). 480p. 44.95 (978-0-393-70642-0(7), 70642) Norton, W. W. & Co., Inc.

Egolf, Donald B. Human Communication & the Brain: Building the Foundation for the Field of Neurocommunication. 2012. (ENG.). 174p. (gr. 17). 65.00 **(978-0-7391-3963-9(0))**; pap. 26.99 **(978-0-7391-3964-6(9))** Lexington Bks.

Flach, Sabine & Söffner, Jan, eds. Habitus in Habitat II: Other Sides of Cognition. 2010. (Illus.). 266p. pap. (978-3-0343-0531-0(1)) Lang, Peter.

Glannon, Walter. Bioethics & the Brain. (ENG., Illus.). 2008. 256p. pap. 26.95 (978-0-19-537194-9(1)) 2006. 348p. 49.99 (978-0-19-530778-8(X)) Oxford Univ. Pr., Inc.

Greenwood-Robinson, Maggie. Memory, Mind & Emotions: Foolproof Solutions to Boost Your Brainpower in As Little As 10 Minutes. 2007. (978-1-59486-284-7(2)) Rodale Pr., Inc.

Hagner, Michael. Homo Cerebralis. (978-0-8047-3796-8(7)); pap. (978-0-8047-3797-5(5)) Stanford Univ. Pr.

Harris, Jillene. Human Differential Alpha Conditioning: An EEG study. 2008. 248p. pap. (978-3-639-09783-2(1)) VDM Verlag Dr. Mueller e.K.

Hemby, Scott E. & Bahn, Sabine, eds. Functional Genomics & Proteomics in the Clinical Neurosciences. 2006. (Progress in Brain Research Ser.). (ENG., Illus.). 402p. 268.00 (978-0-444-51853-8(3), Elsevier Science) Elsevier Science & Technology Bks.

Henslin, Earl. This Is Your Brain on Joy: A Revolutionary Program for Balancing Mood, Restoring Brain Health, & Nurturing Spiritual Growth. 2011. 258p. pap. 15.99 **(978-0-7852-9837-3(1))** Nelson, Thomas Inc.

Hogan, Matthew T. & Altevogt, Bruce. From Molecules to Minds: Challenges for the 21st Century - Workshop Summary. 2008. (ENG.). 90p. pap. 23.00 (978-0-309-12092-0(6)) National Academies Pr.

Illes, Judy & Sahakian, Barbara J. Oxford Handbook of Neuroethics. 2011. (ENG., Illus.). 1002p. 165.00 (978-0-19-957070-6(1)) Oxford Univ. Pr., Inc.

Kokkinos, Vasileios. Cortical Electrical Stimulation in Epilepsy Surgery. 2010. 132p. pap. (978-3-639-26308-4(1)) VDM Verlag Dr. Mueller e.K.

Laureys, Professor, ed. Coma Science. 2009. (Progress in Brain Research Ser.). (ENG., Illus.). 448p. 268.00 (978-0-444-53432-3(6), Elsevier Science) Elsevier Science & Technology Bks.

Leigh, R. John & Kennard, Christopher, eds. Using Eye Movements as an Experimental Probe of Brain Function: A Symposium in Honor of Jean Büttner-Ennever. 2008. (Progress in Brain Research Ser.). (ENG., Illus.). 652p. 268.00 (978-0-444-53163-6(7), Elsevier Science) Elsevier Science & Technology Bks.

Levy, Neil. Neuroethics: Challenges for the 21st Century. 2007. (ENG.). 360p. 130.00 (978-0-521-86782-5(7)); 364p. per. 61.00 (978-0-521-68726-3(8)) Cambridge Univ. Pr.

Moller, Aage R., ed. Reprogramming the Brain. 2006. (Progress in Brain Research Ser.). (ENG., Illus.). 408p. 268.00 (978-0-444-51602-2(6), Elsevier Science) Elsevier Science & Technology Bks.

Moreno, Jonathan. Mind Wars: Brain Research & National Defense. annot. ed. 2007. 225p. 23.95 (978-1-932594-16-4(7)) Dana Pr., The.

Nothwang, Hans Gerd & Pfeiffer, Steven E., eds. Proteomics of the Nervous System. 2008. (ENG., Illus.). 332p. 189.95 (978-3-527-31716-5(3), Wiley-VCH) Wiley, John & Sons, Inc.

Olsen, Karen D. What Brain Research Can Teach about Cutting School Budgets. Olsen, Karen D., ed. 2010. (Illus.). 224p. pap. 36.95 (978-1-4129-8049-4(6), B80494P) Corwin Pr.

Onozuka, Minoru & Chen-Tung, Yen, eds. Novel Trends in Brain Science: Brain Imaging, Learning & Memory, Stress & Fear, & Pain. 2010. (ENG., Illus.). x, 254p. pap. 159.00 (978-4-431-99828-0(4), 4431998284) Springer.

Paxinos, George & Watson, Charles, eds. BrainNavigator. 2009. 0.02 (978-0-12-374958-1(1), Academic Pr.) Elsevier Science & Technology Bks.

Philipp, Barry. The Fear Factor: Finding Peace in a Desperate Society. 2008. 332p. pap. 17.99 (978-1-60477-444-3(4)) Xulon Pr., Inc.

Raab, Markus, et al, eds. Mind & Motion: the Bidirectional Link between Thought & Action: Progress in Brain Research. 2009. (Progress in Brain Research Ser.). (ENG., Illus.). 374p. 268.00 (978-0-444-53356-2(7), Elsevier Science) Elsevier Science & Technology Bks.

Roth, LaVonna. Brain-Powered Strategies to Engage All Learners. 2011. (N/A Ser.). (ENG.). 344p. (gr. k-8). pap. 99.99 **(978-1-4258-0772-6(0))** Shell Educational Publishing.

Salari, Neda. Brain Waves. 2008. 72p. pap. (978-3-8364-8457-2(9)) VDM Verlag Dr. Mueller e.K.

Schier, Mark. Changes in Brain Visually Evoked Potentials with Attention. 2008. 216p. pap. (978-3-639-03584-1(4)) VDM Verlag Dr. Mueller e.K.

Schouenborg, Jens, et al. Brain Machine Interfaces: Implications for science, clinical practice & Society. 2011. (ENG.). 296p. 268.00 (978-0-444-53815-4(1), Elsevier Science) Elsevier Science & Technology Bks.

Smilkstein, Rita. We're Born to Learn: Using the Brain's Natural Learning Process to Create Today's Curriculum. 2nd ed. 2011. (Illus.). 272p. pap. 39.95 (978-1-4129-7938-2(2), B79382P) Corwin Pr.

Sossin, Wayne S., et al, eds. Essence of Memory. 2008. (Progress in Brain Research Ser.). (ENG., Illus.). 450p. 268.00 (978-0-444-53164-3(5), Elsevier Science) Elsevier Science & Technology Bks.

Stein, Kathleen. The Genius Engine: Where Memory, Reason, Passion, Violence, & Creativity Intersect in the Human Brain. 2007. (ENG., Illus.). 304p. 27.95 (978-0-471-26239-8(0), Wiley) Wiley, John & Sons, Inc.

Strausfeld, Nicholas James. Arthropod Brains: Evolution, Functional Elegance, & Historical Significance. 2012. (ENG., Illus.). 848p. 65.00 (978-0-674-04633-7(1), Belknap Pr.) Harvard Univ. Pr.

Thwaits, Brian. The Big Learn: Smart Ways to Use Your Brain. 2006. (Illus.). 216p. per. 21.50 (978-1-4120-9222-7(1)) Trafford Publishing.

Van Hecke, Madeleine L., et al. The Brain Advantage: Become a More Effective Business Leader Using the Latest Brain Research. 2009. (ENG., Illus.). 250p. pap. 19.00 (978-1-59102-764-5(0)) Prometheus Bks., Pubs.

Van Oosten, Jaap. Realizability: An Introduction to Its Categorical Side. 2008. (Studies in Logic & the Foundations of Mathematics Ser.: 152). (ENG.). 328p. 165.00 (978-0-444-51584-1(4), Elsevier Science) Elsevier Science & Technology Bks.

Van Someren, E. J. Slow Brain Oscillations of Sleep, Resting State & Vigilance. 2011. (ENG., Illus.). 384p. 268.00 (978-0-444-53839-0(9)) Elsevier Science & Technology Bks.

Yen, Chen-Tung. Novel Trends in Brain Science: Brain Imaging, Learning & Memory, Stress & Fear, & Pain. Onozuka, Minoru, ed. 2007. (ENG., Illus.). x, 254p. 159.00 (978-4-431-73241-9(1), 4431732411) Springer.

BRAIN—SURGERY

see also Frontal Lobotomy; Psychosurgery; Stereoencephalotomy

Amundson, James Lange. Unplug Him: A Triumph Against the Odds. 2011. 136p. 22.99 **(978-1-4269-6370-4(X))**; pap. 12.99 **(978-1-4269-6371-1(8))** Trafford Publishing.

Antu-Urias, Mickey. The Other Side of the Rainbow: Memoirs of a Brain Aneurysm Survivor. 2011. pap. 10.99 (978-1-61739-929-9(9)) Tate Publishing & Enterprises, LLC.

Apuzzo, Michael L. J., ed. Surgery of the Human Cerebrum, Pts. 1-3. 2009. (ENG.). 1632p. 299.00 (978-1-60547-133-4(X)) Lippincott Williams & Wilkins.

Baltuch, Gordon H. & Villemure, Jean-Guy. Operative Techniques in Epilepsy Surgery. 2008. 149.95 (978-1-60406-091-1(3)) Thieme Medical Pubs., Inc.

Bambakidis, Nicholas C., et al. Surgery of the Cerebellopontine Angle. 2009. (Illus.). 310p. 149.00 (978-1-60795-001-1(4)) PMPH-USA. Ltd.

Battro, Antonio M. Half a Brain Is Enough: The Story of Nico. 2006. (Cambridge Studies in Cognitive & Perceptual Development Ser.). (ENG.). 136p. (C). pap. 26.99 (978-0-521-03111-0(7)) Cambridge Univ. Pr.

Black, Keith & Mann, Arnold. Brain Surgeon: A Doctor's Inspiring Encounters with Mortality & Miracles. 2011. (ENG.). 240p. pap. 13.99 (978-0-446-19814-1(5), Wellness Central) Grand Central Publishing.

Boggs, Steve. Letters to Dinah. 2011. 224p. pap. 14.03 **(978-1-4634-4288-0(2))** AuthorHouse.

Boswell, Randy Bozo. God's Intervention. 2011. 56p. pap. 15.99 **(978-1-4568-3434-0(7))** Xlibris Corp.

Bullough, Robert V. Adam's Fall: Traumatic Brain Injury-The First 365 Days. 2011. 248p. pap. **(978-0-86534-809-7(X))** Sunstone Pr.

Duffau, Hugues. New Insights into Functional Mapping in Cerebral Tumor Surgery. 2008. pap. 35.00 (978-1-60692-136-4(3)) Nova Science Pubs., Inc.

Firlik, Katrina. Another Day in the Frontal Lobe: A Brain Surgeon Exposes Life on the Inside. annot. ed. 2007. (ENG.). 288p. pap. 16.00 (978-0-8129-7340-2(2), Random Hse. Trade Paperbacks) Random House Publishing Group.

Goel, Atul & Cacciola, Francesco. Craniovertebral Junction: Diagnosis - Pathology - Surgical Techniques. 2011. (ENG., Illus.). 592p. 299.99 (978-3-13-145581-9(0)) Thieme Medical Pubs., Inc.

Grimes, Patricia. Giants in the Land. 2007. 112p. per. 10.99 (978-1-60266-385-5(8)) Xulon Pr., Inc.

Itallie, Kathie Van. Kathie's Miracle. 2010. 48p. pap. 15.99 (978-1-4500-5473-7(0)) Xlibris Corp.

Karinthy, Frigyes. A Journey Round My Skull. Barker, Vernon Duckworth, tr. from HUN. 2008. (New York Review Books Classics). (ENG.). 312p. pap. 17.95 (978-1-59017-258-2(2), NYRB Classics) New York Review of Bks., Inc., The.

Kreutzer, Jeffrey S. & Wehman, Paul H. Community Integration Following Traumatic Brain Injury. (ENG., Illus.). 352p. (978-0-340-53709-1(4), Hodder Arnold) Hodder Education.

Mathew, George. One World Government with 666. 2008. 640p. pap. 39.95 (978-1-60474-493-4(6)) PublishAmerica, Inc.

Nanda, Anil, ed. Principles of Posterior Fossa Surgery: Surgical Management. 2011. (ENG., Illus.). 272p. 139.99 (978-1-58890-663-2(9)) Thieme Medical Pubs., Inc.

Pamir, M. Necmettin, et al, eds. Intraoperative Imaging. 2010. (Acta Neurochirurgica Supplementum Ser.). (Illus.). x, 300p. 249.00 (978-3-211-99650-8(8), 3211996508) Springer.

Proctor, Mark R., ed. Minimally Invasive Neurosurgery. 2010. (Illus.). 448p. pap. 199.00 (978-1-61737-387-9(7), 1617373877) Humana Pr.

Rhoton, Albert L., Jr. Cranial Anatomy & Surgical Approaches. 2007. (ENG.). 225.00 (978-0-7817-9341-4(6)) Lippincott Williams & Wilkins.

Roby, Lynn Christopher. From Darkness to Light: My Journey back from a brain filled with Blood. 2009. (Illus.). 137p. pap. 15.95 (978-1-4327-3689-7(2)) Outskirts Pr., Inc.

Rosenwasser, Robert H. & Jabbour, Pascal. Neuroendovascular Management - Anatomy & Techniques: Neurosurgery Clinics of North America. 2009. (Clinics: Surgery Ser.: 20-3). (ENG., Illus.). 240p. 99.00 (978-1-4377-0507-2(3), Saunders) Elsevier - Health Sciences Div.

Schaller, Bernhard J. Reflexive Autonomic Activation in Skull Base Surgery. 2008. 89.00 (978-1-60456-003-9(7)) Nova Science Pubs., Inc.

Schmidt, Matthias & Schmidt, Matthias C. Griff nach dem Ich? Ethische Kriterien für die medizinische Intervention in das menschliche Gehirn. 2008. (Studien zu Wissenschaft und Ethik Ser.).Tr. of Ethical Criteria for Medical Intervention in the Human Brain. (GER.). 390p. 147.00 (978-3-11-020817-7(2)) De Gruyter, Walter Inc.

Schmidt, Matthias C. Griff nach dem Ich? Ethische Kriterien far die medizinische Intervention in das menschliche Gehirn. 2008. (Studien zu Wissenschaft und Ethik Ser.).Tr. of Ethical Criteria for Medical Intervention in the Human Brain. (GER.). 390p. 224.00 **(978-3-11-173751-5(9))** De Gruyter, Walter Inc.

Schwartz, Theodore H. & Anand, Vijay K., eds. Endoscopic Pituitary Surgery: Endocrine, Neuro-Ophthalmologic, & Surgical Management. 2011. (ENG.). 384p. 179.99 (978-1-60406-347-9(5)) Thieme Medical Pubs., Inc.

Stamm, Aldo C., ed. Transnasal Endoscopic Skull Base & Brain Surgery: Tips & Pearls. 2011. (ENG., Illus.). 448p. 189.99 (978-1-60406-310-3(6)) Thieme Medical Pubs., Inc.

BRAIN—TUMORS

Abrey, Lauren & Mason, Warren. Fast Facts: Brain Tumors: Brain Tumors. 2nd rev. ed. 2011. (ENG., Illus.). 144p. pap. 25.00 **(978-1-905832-87-3(7))** Health Pr., Ltd. GBR. Dist: BookMasters Distribution Services (BDS).

Adesina, Adekunle M. Atlas of Pediatric Brain Tumors. Tihan, Tarik et al, eds. 2010. (ENG., Illus.). x, 400p. 219.00 (978-1-4419-1061-5(1), 1441910611) Springer.

Alice Snow. The Miracle of Me: A Memoir. 2010. 236p. pap. 18.95 (978-1-4502-0119-3(9)) iUniverse, Inc.

Beechem, Kathy. So Far, So Good: A Memoir of a Brain Tumor Patient & His Caregiver. 2011. 278p. pap. 16.95 **(978-1-60976-995-6(3)**, Eloquent Bks.) AEG Literary Publishing Services, Inc.

Bezerra, Marcelo F. & Alve, Claudio R. Glioblastoma: Risk Factors, Diagnosis, & Treatment Options. 2012. (Cancer Etiology, Diagnosis & Treatments Ser.). 277p. 95.00 **(978-1-62100-858-3(4))** Nova Science Pubs., Inc.

Black, Peter M. & Jaaskelainen, Juha, eds. Low Grade Gliomas: Diagnosis & Treatment. 2008. (Illus.). 600p. 235.00 (978-1-58829-259-9(2), 1588292592) Humana Pr.

Black, Peter McLaren & Hogan, Sharon. Living with Brain Tumor: A Guide to Taking Control of Your Treatment. 2006. (ENG., Illus.). 336p. pap. 18.99 (978-0-8050-7968-5(8), Owl Bks.) Holt, Henry & Co.

Bodey, Bela, et al. Molecular Markers of Brain Tumor Cells: Implications for Diagnosis, Prognosis & Anti-Neoplastic Biological Therapy. 2010. (ENG.). xvii, 362p. pap. 99.00 (978-90-481-6721-0(3), 9048167213) Springer.

Bookstaff, Shari. When Life Throws You Lemons Make Cranberry Juice! 2009. 132p. pap. 19.95 (978-1-60749-633-5(X)) PublishAmerica, Inc.

Buff, Keith. Determination: Surviving a Devastating Brain Trauma. 2010. 148p. 24.95 (978-1-4502-2662-2(0)); pap. 14.95 (978-1-4502-2663-9(9)) iUniverse, Inc.

CAT. Love Yourself First. 2011. 80p. pap. 10.97 (978-1-4269-5807-6(2)) Trafford Publishing.

Cram101 Textbook Reviews & Cram101 Textbook Reviews. Outlines & Highlights for Modern Surgical Neuropathology by Douglas C Miller, Isbn: 9780521869324. 2011. 156p. pap. 29.95 **(978-1-61461-821-8(6))** Cram101 Inc.

Drevelegas, Antonios, ed. Imaging of Brain Tumors with Histological Correlations. 2nd ed. 2010. (Illus.). 300p. 179.00 (978-3-540-87648-9(0), 3540876480) Springer.

Duffau, Hugues. New Insights into Functional Mapping in Cerebral Tumor Surgery. 2008. pap. 35.00 (978-1-60692-136-4(3)) Nova Science Pubs., Inc.

Erdmann, Volker A., et al, eds. Therapeutic Ribonucleic Acids in Brain Tumors. 2009. (ENG., Illus.). xvi, 494p. 259.00 (978-3-642-00474-2(1), 3642004741) Springer.

Fisher, James. My Brain Hearts. 2009. (Illus.). 184p. pap. 49.49 (978-1-4389-7310-4(1)) AuthorHouse.

Galvez, Eric Anthony. Reversal: When A Therapist Becomes A Patient. 2010. 280p. pap. 20.95 (978-1-4502-2428-4(8)) iUniverse, Inc.

Gilbert, Mark R., et al, eds. Tumors of the Brain & Spine. 2007. (M. D. Anderson Cancer Care Ser.). (Illus.). 364p. per. 139.00 (978-0-387-29201-4(2), 0387292012) Springer.

Grisold, Wolfgang & Soffietti, Riccardo. Neuro-Oncology, Part II, Vol 105 HCN Series: Handbook of Clinical Neurology (Series editors: Aminoff, Boller, Swaab), 2 vols. 2012. (Handbook of Clinical Neurology Ser.: 105). (ENG., Illus.). 572p. 250.00 **(978-0-444-53502-3(0))** Elsevier Science & Technology Bks.

Gunther, John. Death Be Not Proud. 2007. (P. S. Ser.). 205p. 21.60 (978-0-7569-8228-7(6)) Perfection Learning Corp.

Gunther, John J. Death Be Not Proud. 2007. (P. S. Ser.). 256p. per. 13.99 (978-0-06-123097-4(9), HarperPerennial) HarperCollins Pubs.

Haney, Anessa L. Death Interrupted by Love: A true Story. 2009. 56p. pap. 15.99 (978-1-4500-0504-3(7)) Xlibris Corp.

Haselton, A. Modern Medical Mracle. 2007. pap. (978-1-84747-166-6(8)) Chipmunkapublishing.

Hatch-Taylor, Karen. Mosaic Life: A Memoir in Verse. 2011. 48p. pap. 9.89 **(978-1-4269-5167-1(1))** Trafford Publishing.

Hayat, M. A., ed. Teratoid/Rhabdoid, Brain Tumors, & Glioma, Vol. 2. 2012. (Pediatric Cancer Ser.). (ENG., Illus.). xxii, 332p. 209.00 **(978-94-007-2956-8(1)**, 9400729561) Springer.

—Tumors of the Central Nervous system, Volume 3: Brain Tumors (Part 1), 2 vols. 2011. (Tumors of the Central Nervous System Ser.). (ENG., Illus.). xxii, 382p. 209.00 (978-94-007-1398-7(3), 9400713983) Springer.

—Tumors of the Central Nervous System, Volume 4: Brain Tumors (Part 2), 2 vols. 2011. (Tumors of the Central Nervous System Ser.). (ENG., Illus.). xvi, 383p. 209.00 (978-94-007-1705-3(9), 9400717059) Springer.

—Tumors of the Central Nervous System, Volume 5: Astrocytomas, Hemangioblastomas, & Gangliogliomas. 2011. (Tumors of the Central Nervous System Ser.). (ENG., Illus.). xxv, 290p. 189.00 **(978-94-007-2018-3(1)**, 9400720181) Springer.

—Tumors of the Central Nervous System, Volume 7: Meningiomas & Schwannomas. 2012. (Tumors of the Central Nervous System Ser.). (ENG., Illus.). xxxv, 359p. 209.00 **(978-94-007-2893-6(X)**, 940072893X) Springer.

—Tumors of the Central Nervous System, Volume 8: Astrocytoma, Medulloblastoma, Retinoblastoma, Chordoma, Craniopharyngioma, Oligodendroglioma, & Ependymoma. 2012. (Tumors of the Central Nervous System Ser.: 8). (ENG., Illus.). xv, 311p. 209.00 **(978-94-007-4212-3(6)**, 9400742126) Springer.

Hopley, M. Metronome: Second Edition. 2008. 92p. per. (978-1-84747-459-9(4)) Chipmunkapublishing.

Jiang, Dave. My Fortunate Brain Tumor from God. 2007. 496p. (ENG.). 35.99 (978-1-60266-074-8(3)); per. 23.99 (978-1-60266-073-1(5)) Xulon Pr., Inc.

Karinthy, Frigyes. A Journey Round My Skull. Barker, Vernon Duckworth, tr. from HUN. 2008. (New York Review Books Classics). (ENG.). 312p. pap. 17.95 (978-1-59017-258-2(2), NYRB Classics) New York Review of Bks., Inc., The.

Kathleen Joy. Smile Through It All. 2011. 24p. pap. **(978-1-4269-7066-5(8))** Trafford Publishing (UK) Ltd.

Kaye, Andrew H. & Laws, Edward R. Brain Tumors: An Encyclopedic Approach. 3rd ed. 2011. (ENG., Illus.). 1088p. 365.00 (978-0-443-06967-3(0), Saunders) Elsevier - Health Sciences Div.

Kim, D. G. & Lunsford, L. D., eds. Current & Future Management of Brain Metastasis. 2012. (Progress in Neurological Surgery Ser.). (ENG., Illus.). 314p. **(978-3-8055-9617-6(0))** Karger, S. AG.

Kohler, Deirdre. Brutal Honesty. 2010. 216p. pap. 15.99 (978-1-4520-7894-6(7)) AuthorHouse.

Kristoffersen, Karina. A Functional Study of Notch Signaling in Brain Cancer Stem-Like Cells. 2010. 124p. pap. (978-3-8383-4614-4(9)) Lambert Academic Publishing.

Law, Meng. State of the Art Brain Tumor Diagnostics, Imaginig, & Therapeutics: Neuroimaging Clinics of North America. 2010. (Clinics: Radiology Ser.: 20-3). (ENG., Illus.). xviii, 259p. 105.00 (978-1-4377-1838-6(8), Saunders) Elsevier - Health Sciences Div.

Legnazzi, Elisabeth Zahnd & Look, Ulrich. Chiara - Reise ins Licht: Eine Reise ins Licht. 2009. (GER & ENG., Illus.). 160p. 49.00 (978-3-85881-238-4(2)) Scheidegger und Spiess AG, Verlag CHE. Dist: Antique Collectors' Club.

Liau, Linda M., et al, eds. Brain Tumor Immunotherapy. 2010. (Illus.). 360p. pap. 169.00 (978-1-61737-110-3(6), 1617371106) Humana Pr.

Loebl, Erik. A Light in the Midst of Darkness. 2007. 124p. per. 10.99 (978-1-60266-393-0(9)) Xulon Pr., Inc.

Lomazow, Steven & Fettmann, Eric. FDR's Deadly Secret. (ENG., Illus.). 2011. 304p. pap. 15.95 (978-1-58648-906-9(2)) 2010. 296p. 25.95 (978-1-58648-744-7(2)) PublicAffairs.

Love, Julie Anderson. Disrupted: On Fighting Death & Keeping Faith. 2011. 178p. pap. 20.00 **(978-1-61097-095-2(0)**, Cascade Bks.) Wipf & Stock Pubs.

Markman, Maurie, et al, eds. Molecular Neuro-Oncology: Glioma Methods & Protocols. (Methods in Molecular Medicine Ser.). 400p. 2008. 115.00 (978-1-58829-393-0(9), 1588293939) 2006. 115.00 (978-1-59745-334-9(X)) Humana Pr.

Mee, Benjamin. We Bought a Zoo: The Amazing True Story of a Young Family, a Broken down Zoo, & the 200 Wild Animals that Changed Their Lives Forever. (ENG., 2009, Illus.). 304p. pap. 14.95 (978-1-60286-095-7(5)) 2011. 272p. pap. 14.99 (978-1-60286-157-2(9)) Perseus Bks. Group.

Miller, Douglas C. Modern Surgical Neuropathology. 2009. (ENG., Illus.). 532p. 249.00 incl. cd-rom (978-0-521-86932-4(3)) Cambridge Univ. Pr.

Monaghan, Gerri & Monaghan, Brian. When a Loved One Falls Ill: How to Be an Effective Patient Advocate. 2011. (ENG.). 252p. pap. 14.95 (978-0-7611-6507-1(X), 076116507X) Workman Publishing Co., Inc.

Nimsky, Christopher, et al, eds. Intraoperative MRI-Guided Neurosurgery. 2010. (ENG., Illus.). 272p. 159.99 (978-1-60406-305-9(X)) Thieme Medical Pubs., Inc.

Norden, Andrew, et al. Primary Brain Tumors: Pathogenesis & Therapy. 2011. (Current Clinical Oncology Ser.). (Illus.). 400p. 219.00 (978-1-60761-165-3(1), 1607611651) Humana Pr.

Norden, Andrew D., et al. Primary Central Nervous System Tumors: Pathogenesis & Therapy. 2011. (Illus.). xiii, 568p. E-Book ***(978-1-60761-166-0(X))*** Humana Pr.

Parks, Peggy J. Brain Tumors. 2011. (YA). lib. bdg. *(978-1-60152-138-5(3))* ReferencePoint Pr., Inc.

Parr, Emily. In the Realm of Heroes. 2010. 89p. pap. *(978-1-85756-634-5(3))* Janus Publishing Co.

Patricia Meserve Gauvin And Angel Logan. Hope Through the Eyes of Love. 2011. 124p. 29.99 ***(978-1-4568-6446-0(7))***; pap. 19.99 ***(978-1-4568-6445-3(9))*** Xlibris Corp.

Patterson, Katie L. My Invisible Injury: Living Life with A Traumatic Brain Injury. 2011. 100p. pap. 9.99 ***(978-1-4269-6645-3(8))*** Trafford Publishing.

Pollock, Mike. From Death's Door to Disney World. 2010. pap. 9.95 *(978-0-7414-6101-8(3))* Infinity Publishing.

Prayson, Richard A., et al. Brain Tumors. 2009. 449.00 *(978-1-933864-69-3(9))* Demos Medical Publishing, LLC.

Qureshi, Adnan I., ed. Textbook of Interventional Neurology. 2011. (ENG., Illus.). 506p. 140.00 *(978-0-521-87639-1(7))* Cambridge Univ. Pr.

Raizer, Jeffrey J. & Abrey, Lauren E., eds. Brain Metastases. 2007. (Cancer Treatment & Research Ser.). (Illus.). 239p. 169.00 *(978-0-387-69221-0(5))* Springer.

Rees, Jeremy & Wen, Patrick Y. Neuro-Oncology. 2010. (Blue Books of Neurology Ser.: 36). (ENG.). 484p. 218.00 *(978-0-7506-7516-1(0)*, Saunders) Elsevier - Health Sciences Div.

Said, Harun M., et al. Brain-Cancer Associated Tumor Marker Genes Expression Pattern in Humans. 2010. (Cancer Etiology, Diagnosis & Treatments Ser.). (Illus.). xiii, 52p. pap. 43.00 *(978-1-61728-011-5(9)*, Nova Biomedical Bks.) Nova Science Pubs., Inc.

Saler, Cheryl. Hindrances. 2006. 221p. pap. 24.95 *(978-1-4241-2312-4(7))* PublishAmerica, Inc.

Schott, Evonne Stevenson & Rabinowitz, Ed. One More Dance. 2011. 232p. pap. 16.95 ***(978-1-4685-0066-0(X))*** AuthorHouse.

Stark-Vance, Virginia & Dubay, Mary Louise. Brain Tumors. 2nd rev. ed. 2010. 284p. pap. 22.95 *(978-0-7637-6054-0(4))* Jones & Bartlett Learning, LLC.

Sturgeon Williams, Susan. Clipped Wings. 2011. 88p. ***(978-1-77067-947-4(2))***; pap. ***(978-1-77067-948-1(0))*** FriesenPress.

Sundgren, Pia C. Advanced Imaging Techniques in Brain Tumors, an Issue of Neuroimaging Clinics. 2010. (Clinics: Radiology Ser.: 19-4). (ENG.). 99.00 *(978-1-4377-1837-9(X)*, Saunders) Elsevier - Health Sciences Div.

Taylor, Lynne P., et al. Navigating Life with a Brain Tumor, 1 vol. 2012. (ENG., Illus.). 208p. pap. 19.95 ***(978-0-19-989779-7(4))*** Oxford Univ. Pr., Inc.

Ward, Tim B. Surviving & Thriving: A Brain Tumor Survivor's Story. 2010. 260p. pap. 19.95 *(978-1-4327-5364-1(9))* Outskirts Pr., Inc.

BRAIN—TUMORS—THERAPY

Adesina, A. M. Atlas of Pediatric Brain Tumors. 2009. 250p. 175.00 *(978-1-60327-182-0(1))* Humana Pr.

Ataelmannan, Khalid. Radiosensitizing Glioblastoma in a Rat Model. 2009. 72p. pap. *(978-3-639-12669-3(6))* VDM Verlag Dr. Mueller e.K.

Black, Peter M. & Jaaskelainen, Juha, eds. Low Grade Gliomas: Diagnosis & Treatment. 2008. (Illus.). 600p. 235.00 *(978-1-58829-259-9(2)*, 1588292592) Humana Pr.

Goldman, Stewart & Turner, Christopher. Late Effects of Treatment for Brain Tumors. 2009. (Cancer Treatment & Research Ser.). (Illus.). 400p. 199.00 *(978-0-387-77102-1(6))* Springer.

Kobayashi, T. & Lunsford, L. D., eds. Pineal Region Tumors: Diagnosis & Treatment Options. 2009. (Progress in Neurological Surgery Ser.). (ENG., Illus.). 146p. *(978-3-8055-9077-8(6))* Karger, S. AG.

Quant, Eudocia. Dx/Rx: Brain Tumors. rev. ed. 2010. 214p. pap. 49.95 *(978-0-7637-7372-4(7))* Jones & Bartlett Learning, LLC.

Shlanger, Dafi. Brain Surgeons Don't Do Facelifts: A Woman's Journey Through Brain Surgery. 2008. 264p. pap. 15.95 *(978-1-4343-8697-7(X))* AuthorHouse.

Soriano, Nathaniel. Glioblastoma Treatment with 2, 5-Dimethyl-Celecoxib (Dmc) in Vitro. 2008. 48p. pap. *(978-3-639-02829-4(5))* VDM Verlag Dr. Mueller e.K.

BRAIN—WOUNDS AND INJURIES

see also Brain Damage; Shaken Baby Syndrome

Acimovic, Mary Lou. Mild Traumatic Brain Injury: the Guidebook. 2010. 286p. pap. 22.95 *(978-0-557-52888-2(7))* Lulu Enterprises Inc.

Adams, John P., et al, eds. Neurocritical Care: A Guide to Practical Management. 2010. (Competency-Based Critical Care Ser.). (ENG., Illus.). 128p. pap. 89.95 *(978-1-84882-069-2(0)*, 1848820690) Springer.

Agha, Amar. Hypopituitarism Following Traumatic Brain Injury. 2010. 200p. pap. *(978-3-8383-0443-4(8))* Lambert Academic Publishing.

Anthony-Pillai, Antoinette. The Never Ending Journey: Living with Brain Injury. 2008. 172p. pap. 11.99 *(978-1-4389-0465-8(7))* AuthorHouse.

Ashley, Mark J. Traumatic Brain Injury: Rehabilitation, Treatment, & Case Management. 3rd rev. ed. 2010. (ENG., Illus.). 1079p. 169.95 *(978-1-4200-7194-3(7)*, CRC Press) Taylor & Francis Group GBR. Dist: Taylor & Francis Group.

Baker, Kathryn S. & Edwards, Nelson C., eds. Brain Injuries: New Research. 2012. ***(978-1-62100-503-2(8))*** Nova Science Pubs., Inc.

Beatty, Wayne. Healing, Hope, & Joy: Faith-Based Reflections after A Traumatic Brain Injury. 2011. 204p. 24.59 ***(978-1-4634-4347-4(1))***; pap. 14.03 ***(978-1-4634-4348-1(X))*** AuthorHouse.

Behnish, Sylvia. Rollercoaster Ride with Brain Injury. Taylor, Maggie, ed. 2008. 232p. pap. 19.50 *(978-1-4251-6964-0(3))* Trafford Publishing.

Bennett, Karen. Wounded Head, Wounded Heart: A Mom's Journey through her Son's Traumatic Brain Injury. 2008. 164p. pap. 15.95 *(978-0-595-48827-8(7))* iUniverse, Inc.

Betts, Karen. Lost: Sharing My Life with Brain Injury. 2011. 140p. pap. 14.09 ***(978-1-4567-8583-3(4))*** AuthorHouse.

Bhardwaj, Anish, et al, eds. Acute Brain & Spinal Cord Injury: Evolving Paradigms & Management. 2008. (Neurological Disease & Therapy Ser.: Vol. 95). (ENG., Illus.). 464p. 230.00 *(978-1-4200-4794-3(9)*, Informa Healthcare) Taylor & Francis Group GBR. Dist: Taylor & Francis Group.

Bowen. Relational Approach Rehabilitation: Thinking about Relationships after Brain Injury. 2010. (Brain Injury Ser.). (Illus.). 394p. pap. 49.95 *(978-1-85575-746-6(6))* Karnac Bks. GBR. Dist: Stylus Publishing, LLC.

Brain Trauma Foundation. Guidelines for the Management of Severe Traumatic Brain Injury. Brain Trauma Foundation, ed. 3rd ed. 2007. 106p. 125.00 *(978-0-9703144-2-0(6))* Brain Trauma Foundation.

Brawley, Traver. Finding What Matters: Sometimes We Lose Everything to Find So Much More. Even Ourselves. 2007. 128p. per. 19.95 *(978-1-4241-8778-2(8))* PublishAmerica, Inc.

Bullough, Robert V. Adam's Fall: Traumatic Brain Injury-The First 365 Days. 2011. 248p. pap. ***(978-0-86534-809-7(X))*** Sunstone Pr.

Cassidy, John. Mindstorms: The Complete Guide for Families Living with Traumatic Brain Injury. 2009. (ENG., Illus.). 256p. pap. 18.95 *(978-0-7382-1247-0(4))* Perseus Bks. Group.

Chapman, Jennifer. Acquired Brain Injuries & Working Memory. 2011. 68p. pap. ***(978-3-8443-8403-1(0))*** Lambert Academic Publishing.

Ciafone, Michael Francis. Silent Cries. 2011. 118p. pap. 11.99 ***(978-1-61379-319-7(3))*** Xulon Pr., Inc.

Chu, David X. & Caruso, Deborah. Traumatic Brain Injury. 2010. (Rehabilitation Medicine Quick Reference Ser.). 269.00 *(978-1-933864-61-7(3))* Demos Medical Publishing, LLC.

Cleveland, Lynda/G. Momentum: A Model for Motivation in Rehabilitation for Individuals with Traumatic Brain Injury. 2007. 386p. 39.95 *(978-0-9777795-9-8(9))* Groundbreaking Pr.

Coetzer, Rudi. Anxiety & Mood Disorders Following Traumatic Brain Injury: Clinical Assessment & Psychotherapy. 2010. 180p. pap. 30.95 *(978-1-85575-647-2(1))* Karnac Bks. GBR. Dist: Stylus Publishing, LLC.

—Traumatic Brain Injury Rehabilitation: A Psychotherapeutic Approach to Loss & Grief. 2006. 172p. *(978-1-60021-338-0(3))* Nova Science Pubs., Inc.

Cole, Elliot. Cognitive Prosthetics for Brain Injury: Lessons Learned over Two Decades. 2011. (Synthesis Lectures on Assistive, Rehabilitative, & Life-Preserving Technologies Ser.). 100p. pap. 35.00 *(978-1-60845-643-7(9))* Morgan & Claypool Pubs.

Collicutt McGrath, Joanna. Ethical Practice in Brain Injury Rehabilitation. 2007. (ENG.). 192p. pap. 57.95 *(978-0-19-856899-5(1))* Oxford Univ. Pr., Inc.

Committee on Cognitive Rehabilitation Therapy for Traumatic Brain Injury & Institute of Medicine. Cognitive Rehabilitation Therapy for Traumatic Brain Injury: Evaluating the Evidence. 2011. (ENG.). 280p. pap. 58.25 ***(978-0-309-21818-4(7))*** National Academies Pr.

Committee on Nutrition, Trauma, and the Brain & Institute of Medicine. Nutrition & Traumatic Brain Injury: Improving Acute & Subacute Health Outcomes in Military Personnel. 2011. (ENG.). 444p. pap. 86.00 ***(978-0-309-21008-9(9))*** National Academies Pr.

Connelly, Jim. One More Sunset: A True Story of Commitment, Trust & Love. 222p. pap. 15.00 *(978-0-9708387-0-4(0))* Connelly, James W.

Coskie, Dixie. Unthinkable: Tips for Surviving a Child's Traumatic Brain Injury: Tips. 2011. 94p. pap. 10.00 ***(978-1-936214-41-9(5))*** Wyatt-MacKenzie Publishing.

Courtroom Medicine: Head & Brain, Neck & Low Back Series, 9 Vols. 3rd rev. ed. ring bd. 758.00 *(978-0-8205-4394-9(2))* LexisNexis Matthew Bender.

Cox, Charles S., ed. Progenitor Cell Therapy for Neurological Injury. 2010. (Stem Cell Biology & Regenerative Medicine Ser.). (ENG., Illus.). x, 255p. 189.00 *(978-1-60761-964-2(4)*, 1607619644) Humana Pr.

Cree, Clare. Acquired Brain Injury. 2006. 224p. pap. 41.50 *(978-0-470-02540-6(9)*, Wiley) Wiley, John & Sons, Inc.

Dambinova, Svetlana, et al, eds. Biomarkers for Traumatic Brain Injury. 2012. (RSC Drug Discovery Ser.). (ENG., Illus.). 246p. 175.00 ***(978-1-84973-389-2(9))*** Royal Society of Chemistry, The GBR. Dist: Ingram Pub. Services.

Dennis C. Tanner. The Psychology of Neurogenic Communication Disorders. 2009. 212p. pap. 29.95 *(978-1-4401-8195-5(0))* iUniverse, Inc.

Doroghazi, Cynthia Paddock. Searching for the Open Door: A Woman's Struggle for Survival after A Traumatic Brain Injury. 2007. 160p. per. 14.95 *(978-0-9798227-1-1(8))* New River Pubns., LLC.

Driscoll, Patricia P. & Straus, Celia. Hidden Battles on Unseen Fronts: Stories of American Soldiers with Traumatic Brain Injury & PTSD. 2009. (Illus.). 320p. 27.50 *(978-1-935149-01-9(6))* Casemate Pubs. & Bk. Distributors, LLC.

Eggermont, Jos J. & Lomber, Stephen G., eds. Reprogramming the Cerebral Cortex: Plasticity Following Central & Peripheral Lesions. 2006. (ENG., Illus.). 456p. 185.00 *(978-0-19-852899-9(X))* Oxford Univ. Pr., Inc.

Elbaum, Jean & Benson, Deborah, eds. Acquired Brain Injury: An Integrative Neuro-Rehabilitation Approach. 2007. (ENG., Illus.). viii, 298p. 84.95 *(978-0-387-37574-8(0)*, 0387375740) Springer.

Fahl, Joyce Little. Tbi: Shaken but Not Stirred. 2009. 156p. pap. 14.95 *(978-1-4401-2225-5(3))* iUniverse, Inc.

Finnila, Lori. My Brain Injury: Lori Finnila's Journey after Her Brain Injury. 2009. 48p. pap. 16.95 *(978-1-61582-524-0(X))* PublishAmerica, Inc.

Flynn, Estelle. Head Injury - A Family Nightmare. 2011. 68p. pap. 11.24 ***(978-1-4567-5180-7(8))*** AuthorHouse.

Gosling, Geo. Tbi Hell A Traumatic Brain Injury Reall. 2006. 164p. pap. 14.95 *(978-1-59800-722-0(X))* Outskirts Pr., Inc.

—TBI Purgatory: Comes after Being in TBI Hell. 2010. 159p. pap. 12.95 *(978-1-4327-5845-5(4))* Outskirts Pr., Inc.

Hanson, Mary S. A Moment in Time: A Journey of Faith, Hope, & Love. 2009. 176p. pap. 15.95 *(978-1-4401-2185-2(0))* iUniverse, Inc.

Helm, Gretchen. The Birds Will Sing Again: Facing Life's Challenges Together. 2011. 124p. 23.95 ***(978-1-4620-3057-6(2))***; pap. 13.95 ***(978-1-4620-3056-9(4))*** iUniverse, Inc.

Hotz, Gillian. Pediatric Test of Brain Injury. 2010. (Illus.). ***(978-1-59857-109-7(5))***; ***(978-1-59857-110-3(9))*** Brookes, Paul H. Publishing Co.

Hotz, Gillian. Pediatric Test of Brain Injury (PTBI) Examiner's Manual. 2010. pap. 150.00 *(978-1-59857-111-0(7))* Brookes, Paul H. Publishing Co.

H.R. 6172: Protecting Student Athletes from Concussions: Hearing Before the Committee on Education & Labor, U.S. House of Representatives, One Hundred Eleventh Congress, Second Session, Hearing Held in Washington, DC, September 23, 2010. 2010. (Illus.). iii, 59p. ***(978-0-16-087144-3(1)***, 552-070-419867-0) United States Government Printing Office.

Jallo, Jack & Loftus, Christopher M., eds. Neurotrauma & Critical Care of the Brain. 2009. (ENG.). 496p. 209.99 *(978-1-60406-032-4(8))* Thieme Medical Pubs., Inc.

Jameson, Larry & Jameson, Beth. Brain Injury Survivor's Guide: Welcome to Our World. 2007. 200p. per. 19.95 *(978-1-4327-1620-2(4))* Outskirts Pr., Inc.

John, Sharon. The Road Home. 2007. 52p. per. 9.99 *(978-1-60266-624-5(5))* Xulon Pr., Inc.

Jordan, Barry D. & Herrera, Joseph E., eds. Medical Aspects of Boxing. 2nd ed. 2010. (Musculoskeletal Medicine Ser.). 450p. 165.00 *(978-1-60327-230-8(5))* Humana Pr.

Jordan, Kenneth D., ed. Electroencephalography (EEG) in Acute Brain Injury: Principles & Practice. 2009. (ENG.). 550p. 69.50 *(978-1-934115-03-9(7)*, 1934115037) Humana Pr.

Katzman, Sharon M. Tearing down the Wall. 2010. 98p. pap. 12.95 *(978-1-4327-5554-6(4))* Outskirts Pr., Inc.

Kerpelman, Larry C. Pieces Missing: A Family's Journey of Recovery from Traumatic Brain Injury. 2011. (ENG.). 274p. pap. 16.00 ***(978-1-937293-06-2(8))*** Two Harbors Pr., Inc.

Klonoff, Pamela S. Psychotherapy after Brain Injury: Principles & Techniques. 2010. (ENG.). 288p. 50.00 *(978-1-60623-861-5(2))* Guilford Pubns., Inc.

Lawhorne, Cheryl & Philpott, Don. Combat-Related Traumatic Brain Injury & PTSD: A Resource & Recovery Guide. 2011. (ENG.). 290p. pap. 19.95 *(978-1-60590-766-6(9))* Government Institutes.

Leestma, Jan E. Forensic Neuropathology. 2nd rev. ed. 2008. (ENG., Illus.). 768p. 165.95 *(978-0-8493-9167-5(9)*, CRC Press) Taylor & Francis Group GBR. Dist: Taylor & Francis Group.

Lepore, Franco, et al. Enhancing Performance for Action & Perception Pt. II: Multisensory Integration, Neuroplasticity & Neuroprosthetics. 2011. (ENG.). 323p. 268.00 ***(978-0-444-53355-5(9)***, Elsevier Science) Elsevier Science & Technology Bks.

Levison, Steven W., et al, eds. Developmental Brain Injury, Vol. 27. (Developmental Neuroscience Ser.). (Illus.). 200p. *(978-3-8055-7990-2(X))* Karger, S. AG.

Link, Barbara. Blue Shy. 2009. pap. 19.95 *(978-1-61623-049-4(5))* Independent Pub.

Lorenz, Laura S. Brain Injury Survivors: Narratives of Rehabilitation & Healing. 2010. (Illus.). 200p. 55.00 *(978-1-58826-728-3(8))* Rienner, Lynne Pubs.

Lund, Diana. A Waking Mind. 2008. 248p. pap. 18.95 *(978-1-4357-5057-9(8))* Lulu Enterprises Inc.

Mason, Michael Paul & Mason, Michael. Head Cases: Stories of Brain Injury & Its Aftermath. 2009. (ENG., Illus.). 320p. pap. 16.00 *(978-0-374-53195-9(1))* Farrar, Straus & Giroux.

Mason, Michael Paul & Mason, Michael P. Head Cases: Stories of Brain Injury & Its Aftermath. 2008. (ENG., Illus.). 320p. 25.00 *(978-0-374-13452-5(9))* Farrar, Straus & Giroux.

McCluskey, Annie. Care Management after Brain Injury. 2010. 236p. pap. *(978-3-8383-3499-8(X))* Lambert Academic Publishing.

McCrea, Michael A. Mild Traumatic Brain Injury & Postconcussion Syndrome: The New Evidence Base for Diagnosis & Treatment. 2007. (AACN Workshop Ser.). (ENG., Illus.). 256p. per. 39.95 *(978-0-19-532829-5(9))* Oxford Univ. Pr., Inc.

McKenna, M. C., et al, eds. Pediatric Traumatic Brain Injury: Update 2010 - from Basic Research to Clinical Practice. Special Issue: 'Developmental Neuroscience 2010, Vol. 32, No. 5-6' 2011. (Illus.). 196p. pap. *(978-3-8055-9543-8(3))* Karger, S. AG.

McKenna, M. C. & Robertson, C. L., eds. Pediatric Traumatic Brain Injury [Bibliography & Price not Definite.]. Illus.). 240p. pap. *(978-3-8055-8165-3(3))* Karger, S. AG.

Mochel, Leanna. Eliciting & Evaluating Narratives in Adults with & Without Tbi. 2010. 68p. pap. *(978-3-8383-3561-2(9))* Lambert Academic Publishing.

Moser, Rosemarie Scolaro. Ahead of the Game: The Parents' Guide to Youth Sports Concussion. 2012. (ENG.). 208p. pap. 19.95 ***(978-1-61168-224-3(X)***, Dartmouth College Press) Univ. Pr. of New England.

Mosher, Jennifer. The Smile on My Forehead: Memoir of My Life with a Brain Injury. 2009. 175p. pap. 14.95 *(978-0-578-01304-6(5))* Mosher, Jennifer.

Newhouse, Eric. Faces of Combat, PTSD & TBI: Join One Man's Battle to Improve Treatment for Our Veterans. 2008. *(978-1-930461-06-2(2)*, Issues Pr.) Idyll Arbor, Inc.

Niemeier, Janet P. & Karol, Robert L. Overcoming Grief & Loss after Brain Injury. 2010. (ENG.). 240p. pap. 29.95 *(978-0-19-538895-4(X))* Oxford Univ. Pr., Inc.

Oversight Hearing on Traumatic Brain Injury (TBI) Progress in Treating the Signature Wounds of the Current Conflicts: Hearing Before the Committee on Veterans' Affairs, United States Senate, One Hundred Eleventh Congress, First [i.e. Second] Session, May 5, 2010. 2011. (Illus.). iv, 162p. ***(978-0-16-088322-4(9)***, 552-070-42627-2) United States Government Printing Office.

Papievis, Julie. Go Back & Be Happy: A Devastating Brain Injury Left Julie at the Gates of Heaven..., 1 vol. 2008. (Illus.). 192p. pap. 12.99 *(978-0-8254-6276-4(2)*, Monarch Bks.) Lion Hudson PLC GBR. Dist: Kregel Pubns.

Petrin. Marijuana Motorcycle N' My Injured Brain. 2010. 634p. 34.99 *(978-1-4500-7875-7(3))*; pap. 23.99 *(978-1-4500-7874-0(5))* Xlibris Corp.

Ponsford, Jennie, et al. Traumatic Brain Injury. 2nd ed. 2012. (ENG., Illus.). 426p. 57.50 ***(978-1-84872-027-5(0)***, Psychology Press) Taylor & Francis Group GBR. Dist: Taylor & Francis Group.

Post-Traumatic Stress Disorder & Traumatic Brain Injury As Emerging Trends in Force & Veterans Health: Hearing Before the Committee on Veterans' Affairs, House of Representatives, Subcommittee on Health, One Hundred Ninth Congress, Second Session, September 28, 2006. 2007. iv, 280p. *(978-0-16-078862-8(5)*, 552-070-36007-7) United States Government Printing Office.

Pritchard, Kathleen M. Worthy in His Eyes: Looking Beyond the Reflection in the Mirror. 2012. 256p. pap. ***(978-1-77069-441-5(2))*** Word Alive Pr.

Prowe, Garry. Successfully Surviving a Brain Injury: From the Emergency Room to Selecting a Rehabilitation Facility. 2010. 246p. pap. 17.95 *(978-0-9841974-3-9(5))* Brain Injury Success Bks.

Pruitt, Lois Diane. Favor. 2011. 230p. 29.99 ***(978-1-4568-6178-0(6))***; pap. 19.99 ***(978-1-4568-6177-3(8))*** Xlibris Corp.

Riva, Daria & Benton, Arthur. Localization of Brain Lesions & Developmental Functions. (Illus.). 168p. 68.00 *(978-0-86196-599-1(X))* Libbey, John & Co., Ltd. GBR. Dist: Butterworth-Heinemann.

Rolland, Parker S. & Jack, Ginsberg. Polytraumatic Wounds of War & Terr. 2007. 252p. pap. 125.00 *(978-1-57331-582-8(2))* New York Academy of Sciences.

Schaller, Bernhard. Neuroscience Imaging Research Trends. 2008. 82.00 *(978-1-60456-227-9(7))* Nova Science Pubs., Inc.

Schutz, Larry E., et al, eds. Rehabilitation of the Shaken Soldier Syndrome. 2010. (Neuroscience Research Progress Ser.). 105p. pap. 43.00 *(978-1-61668-192-0(6))* Nova Science Pubs., Inc.

Sherman, Elisabeth M. S. & Brooks, Brian L., eds. Pediatric Forensic Neuropsychology, 1 vol. 2012. (ENG., Illus.). 400p. 79.99 ***(978-0-19-973456-6(9))*** Oxford Univ. Pr., Inc.

Siles, Madonna. Eureka! Memories & Motivations: A Strategy for Creating a Healing Home for the Stroke / Brain Injury Patient & Caregiver. 2010. (ENG., Illus.). 216p. pap. 17.95 *(978-0-9825518-0-6(0))* Third Step Pr.

Silver, Jonathan M., et al. Textbook of Traumatic Brain Injury. 2nd ed. 2011. (ENG., Illus.). 159.00 *(978-1-58562-357-0(1))* American Psychiatric Publishing, Inc.

Smith, Emily A. Confabulation & Traumatic Brain Injury. 2011. 56p. pap. ***(978-3-8443-1923-1(9))*** Lambert Academic Publishing.

Stevenson, David K., et al, eds. Fetal & Neonatal Brain Injury. 4th ed. 2009. (ENG., Illus.). 642p. 199.00 *(978-0-521-88859-2(X))* Cambridge Univ. Pr.

Sullivan, Cheryle. Brain Injury Survival Kit: 365 Tips, Tools & Tricks to Deal with Cognitive Function Loss. 2008. (ENG.). 176p. pap. 16.95 *(978-1-932603-73-6(5))* Demos Medical Publishing, LLC.

Suter, Penelope S. & Harvey, Lisa H., eds. Vision Rehabilitation: Multidisciplinary Care of the Patient Following Brain Injury. 2011. (ENG., Illus.). 532p. 89.95 *(978-1-4398-3655-2(8)*, CRC Press) Taylor & Francis Group GBR. Dist: Taylor & Francis Group.

Tan, S. & Levison, S. W., eds. Bridging Bench to Bedside in Fetal & Neonatal Brain Injury. 2007. (Illus.). 138p. pap. *(978-3-8055-8319-0(2))* Karger, S. AG.

Tanielian, Terri. Invisible Wounds of War: Psychological & Cognitive Injuries, Their Consequences, & Services to Assist Recovery. 2008. 424p. pap. 55.50 *(978-0-8330-4454-9(0)*, mg-720) RAND Corp., The.

Tanielian, Terri, et al. Invisible Wounds of War: Summary & Recommendations for Addressing Psychological & Cognitive Injuries. 2008. 64p. pap. 20.00 *(978-0-8330-4453-2(2)*, mg720.1) RAND Corp., The.

Tate, Robyn L. & Cameron, Ian. A Compendium of Tests, Scales & Questionnaires: The Practitioner's Guide to Measuring Outcomes after Acquired Brain Impairment. 2010. (ENG., Illus.). 768p. 200.00 *(978-1-84169-561-7(0)*, Psychology Press) Taylor & Francis Group GBR. Dist: Taylor & Francis Group.

Terry Smith. Surviving Head Traum: A Guide to Recovery Written by a Traumatic Brain Injury Patient. 2009. 108p. 22.95 *(978-1-4401-7644-9(2))*; pap. 12.95 *(978-1-4401-7642-5(6))* iUniverse, Inc.

Toth, Cory. Sports Neurology, an Issue of Physical Medicine & Rehabilitation Clinics. 2009. (Clinics: Orthopedics Ser.: 20-1). (ENG., Illus.). xviii, 311p. 99.00 *(978-1-4377-0743-4(2)*, Saunders) Elsevier - Health Sciences Div.

Traumatic Brain Injury Related Vision Issues: Hearing Before the Subcommittee on Oversight & Investigations of the Committee on Veterans' Affairs, U.S. House of Representatives, One Hundred Tenth Congress, Second Session,

B

April 2, 2008. 2008. (Illus.). iii, 71p. *(978-0-16-082572-9(5)*, 552-070-38593-2) United States Government Printing Office.

Tyerman, Andy & King, Nigel S., eds. Psychological Approaches to Rehabilitation after Traumatic Brain Injury. 2008. (ENG., Illus.). 528p. 195.00 *(978-1-4051-1167-6(4)*, Wiley-Blackwell) Wiley, John & Sons, Inc.

Vakil, E., et al, eds. Rehabilitation of the Brain Injured: A NeuroPsychological Perspective. *(978-965-294-087-2(9))* Freund Publishing Hse., Ltd.

Valadka, Alex. Handbook of Traumatic Brain Injury. 2007. (Illus.). 280p. pap. 84.95 *(978-1-4051-3808-6(4)*, Wiley-Blackwell) Wiley, John & Sons, Inc.

van Belle-Kusse, Patty & Zadoks, Judith. Supporting Survivors & Caregivers after Brain Injury: A program for psychosocial Support. 2011. 126p. pap. 35.00 ***(978-1-931117-59-3(4))*** Lash & Assocs. Publishing/Training, Inc.

Vandergriff, Rebekah E. & Vandergriff, Rebekah. What Day Is It? A Family's Journey Through Traumatic Brain Injury. 2008. (Illus.). ix, 168p. *(978-0-9820522-0-4(0))* Bear's Nest Pr.

Vannucci, S. J., et al, eds. Developmental Brain Injury: Third Hershey Conference on Developmental Cerebral Blood Flow & Metabolism, Hershey, Pa. , June 2002: Proceedings & Abstracts, Vol. 24. (Illus.). 124p. *(978-3-8055-7572-0(6))* Karger, S. AG.

Varlotta, Gerard P. & Jordan, Barry D. Medical Issues in Boxing, an Issue of Clinics in Sports Medicine. 2009. (Clinics: Orthopedics Ser.: 28-4). (ENG.). 99.00 *(978-1-4377-1276-6(2)*, Saunders) Elsevier - Health Sciences Div.

Vasterling, Jennifer J., et al, eds. PTSD & Mild Traumatic Brain Injury. 2012. (ENG., Illus.). 308p. 60.00 ***(978-1-4625-0338-4(1))*** Guilford Pubns., Inc.

Williams, Lori. My New Brain. 2008. 116p. pap. 11.95 *(978-1-4327-2599-0(8))* Outskirts Pr., Inc.

Willingham, Lisa. Turned Upside Down. 2007. 88p. per. 16.95 *(978-1-4241-8437-8(1))* PublishAmerica, Inc.

Wilson, Barbara A. Memory Rehabilitation: Integrating Theory & Practice. 2009. (ENG., Illus.). 284p. 50.00 *(978-1-60623-287-3(8))* Guilford Pubns., Inc.

Workshop Steering Committee on Systems Engineering Health Care: Tools and Technologies to Maximize the Effectiveness of medical Mission Support to DOD. Systems Engineering to Improve Traumatic Brain Injury Care in the Military Health System: Workshop Summary. Butler, David et al, eds. 2009. (ENG.). 194p. pap. 43.50 *(978-0-309-12758-5(0))* National Academies Pr.

Wyn, Nia. Blue Sky July: A Mother's Story of Hope & Healing. 2008. (ENG.). 176p. pap. 17.95 *(978-1-85411-454-9(9))* Seren Bks. GBR. Dist: Independent Pubs. Group.

Young, G. Bryan. Disorders of Consciousness: Neurologic Clinics. 2011. (Clinics: Internal Medicine Ser.: 29-4). (ENG., Illus.). xiv, 724p. 110.00 ***(978-1-4557-1031-7(8)***, Saunders) Elsevier - Health Sciences Div.

Zamora, Joe R. Tears of a Lost Cowboy. 2009. 120p. pap. 16.49 *(978-1-4389-5318-2(6))* AuthorHouse.

Zasler, Nathan D., et al, eds. Brain Injury Medicine: Principles & Practice. 2006. (Illus.). 1275p. 199.00 *(978-1-888799-93-4(5))* Demos Medical Publishing, LLC.

Zollman, Felise S. Manual of Traumatic Brain Injury Management. 2011. 512p. pap. *(978-1-936287-01-7(3))* Demos Medical Publishing, LLC.

Zoltan, Barbara. Vision, Perception, & Cognition: A Manual for the Evaluation & Treatment of the Adult with Acquired Brain Injury. 4th ed. 2007. (ENG., Illus.). 368p. (C). 52.95 *(978-1-55642-738-1(7))* SLACK, Inc.

Zurek, Jirí & Jurek, Jirí. Biomarkers of Brain Injury in Children-Potential Uses & Limitations. 2011. 120p. pap. ***(978-3-8443-1180-8(7))*** Lambert Academic Publishing.

BRAIN—X-RAY EXAMINATION

see Brain—Radiography

BRAIN-BLOOD BARRIER

see Blood-Brain Barrier

BRAIN CHEMISTRY

Armati, Patricia & Mathey, Emily, eds. The Biology of Oligodendrocytes. 2010. (ENG., Illus.). 304p. 115.00 *(978-0-521-89965-9(6))* Cambridge Univ. Pr.

Arnold, Arthur P., et al, eds. Hormones, Brain & Behavior, 5 vols. 2nd ed. 2009. (ENG., Illus.). 3408p. 1545.00 *(978-0-12-374382-4(6)*, Academic Pr.) Elsevier Science & Technology Bks.

Boulton, Alan A., et al, eds. Voltammetric Methods in Brain Systems. 2010. (Neuromethods Ser.). 365p. pap. 189.00 *(978-1-61737-009-0(6)*, 1617370096) Humana Pr.

Cram101 Textbook Reviews Staff. Outlines & Highlights for Psychopharmacology: Drugs, the Brain & Behavior by Meyer, ISBN. 2008. 268p. pap. 14.95 *(978-1-4288-5839-8(3))* Cram101 Inc.

Denton, Derek. The Primordial Emotions: The Dawning of Consciousness. 2006. (ENG., Illus.). 296p. (C). 69.95 *(978-0-19-920314-7(8))* Oxford Univ. Pr., Inc.

Fields, Ph.D., RDouglas. The Other Brain: The Scientific & Medical Breakthroughs That Will Heal Our Brains & Revolutionize Our Health. 2011. (ENG., Illus.). 384p. pap. 16.00 *(978-0-7432-9142-2(5))* Simon & Schuster.

Fields, R. Douglas. The Other Brain: From Dementia to Schizophrenia, How New Discoveries about the Brain Are Revolutionizing Medicine & Science. 2009. (ENG., Illus.). 384p. 27.00 *(978-0-7432-9141-5(7))* Simon & Schuster.

Fitzgerald, Paul J. Adjust Your Brain: A Practical Theory for Maximizing Mental Health. 2007. (ENG., Illus.). 176p. per. 24.95 *(978-1-84694-055-2(9))* O Bks.,John Hunt.

Freedman, Robert. The Madness Within Us: Schizophrenia as a Neuronal Process. 2009. (ENG., Illus.). 208p. 35.00 *(978-0-19-530747-4(X))* Oxford Univ. Pr., Inc.

Gibson, Gary E. & Dienel, Gerald A., eds. Brain Energetics. Integration of Molecular & Cellular Processes. 3rd rev. ed. 2007. (Handbook of Neurochemistry & Molecular Neurobiology Ser.). (Illus.). 924p. 249.00 *(978-0-387-30366-6(9)*, 0387303669) Springer.

Heller, Samantha. Get Smart: Samantha Heller's Nutrition Prescription for Boosting Brain Power & Optimizing Total Body Health. 2010. (ENG., Illus.). 264p. 43.00 *(978-0-8018-9375-9(5))*; pap. 19.95 *(978-0-8018-9376-6(3))* Johns Hopkins Univ. Pr.

Hooper, Nigel M. & Lendeckel, Uwe, eds. The ADAM Family of Proteases. 2010. (Proteases in Biology & Disease Ser.). xiv, 344p. pap. 179.00 *(978-1-4419-3775-9(7)*, 1441937757) Springer.

Kaiser, Tim F. & Peters, Felix J., eds. Synaptic Plasticity: New Research. 2008. (Illus.). xiii, 407p. 150.00 *(978-1-60456-732-8(5))* Nova Science Pubs., Inc.

Lagercrantz, Hugo, et al, eds. The Newborn Brain: Neuroscience & Clinical Applications. 2nd ed. 2010. (ENG., Illus.). 426p. 130.00 *(978-0-521-88975-9(8))* Cambridge Univ. Pr.

Lendeckel, Uwe & Hooper, Nigel M., eds. Proteases in the Brain. 2010. (Proteases in Biology & Disease Ser.). xvi, 384p. pap. 219.00 *(978-1-4419-3573-1(8)*, 1441935738) Springer.

Maccaro, Janet. Brain Boosting Foods: 50 Ways to Improve Your Memory, Unclutter Your Mind, & Get Your Brain Working at Its Highest Capacity by Eating Right. 2008. (ENG.). 160p. pap. 9.99 *(978-1-59979-225-5(7)*, Siloam Pr.) Charisma Media.

Minagar, Alireza, et al. Functional Plasticity & Genetic Variation: Insights into the Neurobiology of Alcoholism. 2010. (ENG.). 360p. 198.00 *(978-0-12-381276-6(3)*, Academic Pr.) Elsevier Science & Technology Bks.

—International Review of Neurobiology. 2010. (ENG., Illus.). 372p. 198.00 *(978-0-12-381322-0(0)*, Academic Pr.) Elsevier Science & Technology Bks.

—Transcranial Sonography & the Detection of Neurodegenerative Disease. 2010. (ENG., Illus.). 320p. 198.00 *(978-0-12-381330-5(1)*, Academic Pr.) Elsevier Science & Technology Bks.

Minagar, Alireza, ed. Pathophysiology, Pharmacology & Biochemistry of Dyskinesia. 2011. (ENG., Illus.). 664p. 198.00 *(978-0-12-381328-2(X)*, Academic Pr.) Elsevier Science & Technology Bks.

—Science of Awakening. 2010. (ENG., Illus.). 315p. 198.00 *(978-0-12-381324-4(7)*, Academic Pr.) Elsevier Science & Technology Bks.

Pfaff,, Donald W. Man & Woman: An Inside Story. 2010. (ENG., Illus.). 304p. 27.95 *(978-0-19-538884-8(4))* Oxford Univ. Pr., Inc.

Pfaff, Donald W. & Rubin, Robert H., eds. Hormone/Behavior Relations of Clinical Importance: Endocrine Systems Interacting with Brain & Behavior. 2009. (ENG., Illus.). 1182p. 210.00 *(978-0-12-374926-0(3)*, Academic Pr.) Elsevier Science & Technology Bks.

Roland, Per E. Brain Activation. 2nd ed. 2010. (ENG., Illus.). 916p. pap. 139.95 *(978-0-471-39630-7(3)*, Wiley-Blackwell) Wiley, John & Sons, Inc.

Sawyer, Mj. Choosing Sanity: An Unprecedented Guide to Healing Brian Chemistry Disorders without Medications. 2008. 160p. pap. 16.95 *(978-1-59858-700-5(5))* Dog Ear Publishing, LLC.

Schier, Mark. Changes in Brain Visually Evoked Potentials with Attention. 2008. 216p. pap. *(978-3-639-03584-1(4))* VDM Verlag Dr. Mueller e.K.

Simopoulos, A. P. & Bazan, N. G., eds. Omega-3 Fatty Acids, the Brain & Retina. 2008. (World Review of Nutrition & Dietetics Ser.). (Illus.). 164p. *(978-3-8055-9019-8(9))* Karger, S. AG.

Tseng, Kuei-Yuan & Atzori, Marco, eds. Monoaminergic Modulation of Cortical Excitability. 2007. (ENG., Illus.). x, 329p. 179.00 *(978-0-387-72254-2(8)*, 0387722548) Springer.

Woolsey, Thomas A., et al. The Brain Atlas: A Visual Guide to the Human Central Nervous System. 3rd rev. ed. 2007. (ENG., Illus.). 272p. pap. 75.95 *(978-0-470-08476-2(6)*, Wiley-Liss) Wiley, John & Sons, Inc.

Wurtman, Judith J. & Frusztajer, Nina T. The Serotonin Power Diet: Eat Carbs — Nature's Own Appetite Suppressant — to Stop Emotional Overeating & Halt Antidepressant-Associated Weight Gain. 2009. (ENG.). 304p. pap. 15.99 *(978-1-59486-972-3(3))* Rodale Pr., Inc.

BRAIN DAMAGE

see also Cerebral Palsy; Hepatic Encephalopathy

Alzheimer, Christian. Molecular & Cellular Biology of Neuroprotection in the CNS. (Neuroscience Intelligence Unit Ser.). 200p. 119.00 *(978-1-58706-104-2(X))* Landes Bioscience.

Arrington, Doris Banowsky. Art, angst, & Trauma: Right Brain Interventions with Developmental Issues. 2007. (Illus.). 278p. *(978-0-398-07733-4(9))* Thomas, Charles C. Pub., Ltd.

—Art, angst, & Trauma: Right Brain Invterventions with Development Issues. 2007. (Illus.). 278p. *(978-0-398-07732-7(0))* Thomas, Charles C. Pub., Ltd.

Bates, Philip W. & Migotto, Marco, eds. Brain Damage: Medico Legal Aspects. 200p. *(978-1-875114-36-8(X)*, Blackstone Pr.) Oxford Univ. Pr.

Bayles, Kathryn A. & Tomoeda, Cheryl K. Cognitive-Communicative Disorders of Dementia. 2007. (ENG., Illus.). 263p. per. 79.00 *(978-1-59756-111-2(8))* Plural Publishing, Inc.

Bonser, Robert S. Brain Protection in Cardiac Surgery. Bonser, Robert S. et al, eds. 2011. (Illus.). xv, 246p. 189.00 *(978-1-84996-292-6(8)*, 1849962928) Springer.

Cassidy, John. Mindstorms: The Complete Guide for Families Living with Traumatic Brain Injury. 2009. (ENG., Illus.). 256p. pap. 18.95 *(978-0-7382-1247-0(4))* Perseus Bks. Group.

Chiaravalloti, Nancy, ed. Changes in the Brain: Impact on Daily Life. 2010. (ENG.). 200p. 89.95 *(978-0-387-98187-1(X)*, 038798187X) Springer.

Coskie, Dixie. Unthinkable: Tips for Surviving a Child's Traumatic Brain Injury: Tips. 2011. 94p. pap. 10.00 ***(978-1-936214-41-9(5))*** Wyatt-MacKenzie Publishing.

Cram101 Textbook Reviews & Cram101 Textbook Reviews. Outlines & Highlights for Traumatic Brain Injury, an Issue of Psychiatric Clinics by Silvana Riggio, Isbn: 9781437724929. 2011. 188p. pap. 30.95 ***(978-1-61461-207-0(2))*** Cram101 Inc.

Denton, Gail L. Brainlash: Maximize Your Recovery from Mild Brain Injury. 3rd ed. 2008. (ENG., Illus.). 356p. per. 24.95 *(978-1-932603-40-8(9))* Demos Medical Publishing, LLC.

Granacher, Robert P. Traumatic Brain Injury: Methods for Clinical & Forensic Neuropsychiatric Assessment. 2nd rev. ed. 2007. (ENG., Illus.). 584p. 169.95 *(978-0-8493-8138-6(X)*, CRC Press) Taylor & Francis Group GBR. Dist: Taylor & Francis Group.

Herdegen, T. & Delgado-Garcia, J., eds. Brain Damage & Repair: From Molecular Research to Clinical Therapy. 2010. xiv, 721p. pap. 225.00 *(978-90-481-6538-4(5)*, 9048165385) Springer.

Jallo, Jack & Loftus, Christopher M., eds. Neurotrauma & Critical Care of the Brain. 2009. (ENG.). 496p. 209.99 *(978-1-60406-032-4(8))* Thieme Medical Pubs., Inc.

Jandial, Rahul, et al. 100 Questions & Answers about Head & Brain Injuries. 2008. (ENG., Illus.). 118p. pap. 22.95 *(978-0-7637-5572-0(9))* Jones & Bartlett Learning, LLC.

Kapur, Narinder, et al. The Paradoxical Brain. 2011. (Illus.). 300p. 105.00 *(978-0-521-11557-5(4))* Cambridge Univ. Pr.

Laureys, Steven & Tononi, Giulio, eds. The Neurology of Consciousness: Cognitive Neuroscience & Neuropathology. 2008. (ENG., Illus.). 440p. 104.00 *(978-0-12-374168-4(8)*, Academic Pr.) Elsevier Science & Technology Bks.

Maier, Carolina M. & Steinberg, Gary K., eds. Hypothermia & Cerebral Ischemia: Mechanisms & Clinical Applications. 2010. (Illus.). 200p. pap. 125.00 *(978-1-61737-120-2(3)*, 1617371203) Humana Pr.

Manley, Geoffrey, et al, eds. Intracranial Pressure & Brain Monitoring XIII: Mechanisms & Treatment. (Acta Neurochirurgica Supplementum Ser.). (Illus.). x, 448p. 2010. (ENG.). pap. 359.00 *(978-3-211-99942-4(6)*, 3211999426) 2009. 359.00 *(978-3-211-85577-5(7))* Springer.

Marvasti, Jamshid A., ed. War Trauma in Veterans & Their Families: Diagnosis & Management of PTSD, TBI & Comorbidities of Combat Trauma - from Pharmacotherapy to a 12-Step Self-Help Program for Combat Veterans. 2012. 356p. 69.95 ***(978-0-398-08724-1(5))*** Thomas, Charles C. Pub., Ltd.

McCrea, Michael A. Mild Traumatic Brain Injury & Postconcussion Syndrome: The New Evidence Base for Diagnosis & Treatment. 2007. (AACN Workshop Ser.). (ENG., Illus.). 256p. per. 39.95 *(978-0-19-532829-5(9))* Oxford Univ. Pr., Inc.

New, Brandon. Orthodontic Braces Ruin Your Child's Physical Health, Cause Brain Damage, Cause Neurological Damage, Ruin Emotional Health, Reduce Usable I Q , Damage. 2011. 320p. pap. 25.00 ***(978-0-557-55741-7(0))*** Lulu Enterprises Inc.

Newhouse, Eric. Faces of Combat, PTSD & TBI: Join One Man's Battle to Improve Treatment for Our Veterans. 2008. *(978-1-930461-06-2(2)*, Issues Pr.) Idyll Arbor, Inc.

Parker, Rolland S. Concussive Brain Trauma: Neurobehavioral Impairment & Maladaption. 2nd rev. ed. 2011. (ENG., Illus.). 879p. 159.95 *(978-0-8493-8039-6(1)*, CRC Press) Taylor & Francis Group GBR. Dist: Taylor & Francis Group.

Phillips, Joseph R. Hidden Wounds: Traumatic Brain Injury & Post Traumatic Stress Disorder in Service Members. 2011. (Series: Public Health in the 21st Century Ser.). (Illus.). viii, 153p. 115.00 ***(978-1-61122-415-3(2))*** Nova Science Pubs., Inc.

Ramachandran, V. S. The Tell-Tale Brain: A Neuroscientist's Quest for What Makes Us Human. 2011. (ENG., Illus.). 357p. 26.95 *(978-0-393-07782-7(9)*, 7782) Norton, W. W. & Co., Inc.

Riggio, Silvana & Jagoda, Andy. Traumatic Brain Injury - Defining Best Practice: Psychiatric Clinics. 2010. (Clinics: Internal Medicine Ser.: 33-4). (ENG., Illus.). xiv, 742p. 105.00 *(978-1-4377-2492-9(2)*, Saunders) Elsevier - Health Sciences Div.

Roberts, Richard & Roberts, Mary Ann. Mild Traumatic Brain Injury: Episodic Symptoms & Treatment. 2010. 318p. pap. 55.00 *(978-1-59756-423-6(0))* Plural Publishing, Inc.

Russell, Elbert. The Scientific Foundation of Neuropsychological Assessment: With Applications to Forensic Evaluation. 2011. (ENG.). 466p. 74.95 ***(978-0-12-416029-3(8))*** Elsevier Science & Technology Bks.

Silver, Jonathan M., et al. Textbook of Traumatic Brain Injury. 2nd ed. 2011. (ENG., Illus.). 159.00 *(978-1-58562-357-0(1))* American Psychiatric Publishing, Inc.

Starzinski, Donald, ed. The Forensic Evaluation of Traumatic Brain Injury: A Handbook for Clinicians & Attorneys. 2nd rev. ed. 2007. (ENG., Illus.). 200p. 159.95 *(978-0-8493-9075-3(3)*, CRC Press) Taylor & Francis Group GBR. Dist: Taylor & Francis Group.

Sundstrom, Terje, et al, eds. Management of Severe Traumatic Brain Injury: Evidence, Tricks, & Pitfalls. 2012. (ENG., Illus.). xxvi, 411p. 179.00 ***(978-3-642-28125-9(7)***, 3642281257) Springer.

Thacker, Herminia. Coping with the Influx of Dementia Patients - the Need to Involve the Communities & Church Groups with Medical & Social. 2007. pap. *(978-3-8364-2972-6(1))* VDM Verlag Dr. Mueller e.K.

Urschel, Harold. Healing the Addicted Brain. 2009. (ENG.). 288p. pap. 15.99 *(978-1-4022-1844-6(3))* Sourcebooks, Inc.

Wild, Klaus R. H. von, ed. Re-Engineering of the Damaged Brain & Spinal Cord: Evidence-Based Neurorehabilitation. 2010. (Acta Neurochirurgica Supplementum Ser.). (Illus.). xvi, 240p. pap. 249.00 *(978-3-211-99877-9(2)*, 3211998772) Springer.

Zhang, Lu. Bnip3 in Cyanide-Induced Brain Damage. 2010. 188p. pap. *(978-3-8383-5714-0(0))* Lambert Academic Publishing.

Zihl, Josef. Rehabilitation of Visual Disorders after Brain Injury. 2nd rev. ed. 2010. (Neuropsychological Rehabilitation: A Modular Handbook Ser.). (ENG., Illus.). 288p. 70.00 *(978-1-84872-006-0(8)*, Psychology Press) Taylor & Francis Group GBR. Dist: Taylor & Francis Group.

Zollman, Felise S. Manual of Traumatic Brain Injury Management. 2011. 512p. pap. *(978-1-936287-01-7(3))* Demos Medical Publishing, LLC.

BRAIN DAMAGE—PATIENTS

Adamson, Kate. Paralyzed but Not Powerless: Kate's Journey Revisited. 2nd ed. 2008. (Illus.). 262p. pap. 19.95 *(978-0-9741907-0-9(5))* Nosmada Pr.

Ashley, Mark J. Traumatic Brain Injury: Rehabilitation, Treatment, & Case Management. 3rd rev. ed. 2010. (ENG., Illus.). 1079p. 169.95 *(978-1-4200-7194-8(7)*, CRC Press) Taylor & Francis Group GBR. Dist: Taylor & Francis Group.

Bowen. Relational Approach Rehabilitation: Thinking about Relationships after Brain Injury. 2010. (Brain Injury Ser.). (Illus.). 394p. pap. 49.95 *(978-1-85575-748-6(6))* Karnac Bks. GBR. Dist: Stylus Publishing, LLC.

Bullough, Robert V. Adam's Fall: Traumatic Brain Injury-The First 365 Days. 2011. 248p. pap. ***(978-0-86534-809-7(X))*** Sunstone Pr.

Bye, Chris. Crash Test. 2007. pap. *(978-0-9784402-6-8(9))* BPS Bks.

Chadbourne, Earlene Ahlquist. Parenting Myself: Recovery from Traumatic Brain Injury. 2009. *(978-1-892168-13-9(8))* Custom Communications.

Champion, Andrew J. Neuropsychological Rehabilitation: A Resource for Group-Based Education & Intervention. 2006. (ENG.). 192p. per. 70.00 *(978-0-470-02639-7(1)*, Wiley) Wiley, John & Sons, Inc.

Christensen, Anne-Lise & Uzzell, Barbara P., eds. International Handbook of Neuropsychological Rehabilitation. 2010. (Critical Issues in Neuropsychology Ser.). 392p. pap. 209.00 *(978-1-4419-3324-9(7)*, 1441933247) Springer.

Cleveland, Lynda/G. Momentum: A Model for Motivation in Rehabilitation for Individuals with Traumatic Brain Injury. 2007. 386p. 39.95 *(978-0-9777795-9-8(9))* Groundbreaking Pr.

Coetzer, Rudi. Anxiety & Mood Disorders Following Traumatic Brain Injury: Clinical Assessment & Psychotherapy. 2010. 180p. pap. 30.95 *(978-1-85575-647-2(1))* Karnac Bks. GBR. Dist: Stylus Publishing, LLC.

Cram101 Textbook Reviews & Cram101 Textbook Reviews. Outlines & Highlights for Motor Control: Translating Research into Clinical Practice by Anne Shumway-Cook, ISBN. 2011. 622p. pap. 40.95 ***(978-1-61461-239-1(0))*** Cram101 Inc.

—Outlines & Highlights for Neuropsychological Rehabilitation by Barbara a Wilson, Isbn: 9780521841498 0521841496. 2011. 158p. pap. 29.95 ***(978-1-4288-9975-9(8))*** Cram101 Inc.

Cromer, Janet M. Professor Cromer Learns to Read: A Couple's New Life after Brain Injury. 2010. 304p. 25.99 *(978-1-4490-6420-4(5))*; pap. 15.99 *(978-1-4490-6419-8(1))* AuthorHouse.

Crowe, Simon F. The Behavioural & Emotional Complications of Traumatic Brain Injury. 2008. (Studies on Neuropsychology, Neurology, & Cognition). (ENG.). 288p. 99.95 *(978-1-84169-441-2(X)*, Psychology Press) Taylor & Francis Group GBR. Dist: Taylor & Francis Group.

Cusick, Cheryl & Cusick, Jamie Lynn. From Where I Sit: My Life & Struggles with Friedreich's Ataxia. 2011. 52p. pap. 12.95 ***(978-1-4327-7696-1(7))*** Outskirts Pr., Inc.

DiSilvestro, Russell. Human Capacities & Moral Status. 2010. (Philosophy & Medicine Ser.). (ENG.). xiv, 208p. 159.00 *(978-90-481-8536-8(X)*, 904818536X) Springer.

Doidge, Norman. The Brain That Changes Itself: Stories of Personal Triumph from the Frontiers of Brain Science. 2007. (ENG.). 448p. (gr. 12-18). 17.00 *(978-0-14-311310-2(0)*, Penguin (Non-Classics)); 24.95 *(978-0-670-03830-5(X)*, Viking Adult) Penguin Group (USA) Inc.

Dolen, Carolyn E. Brain Injury Rewiring for Loved Ones: A Lifeline to New Connections. 2009. 316p. 19.00 *(978-1-882883-71-4(3))* Idyll Arbor, Inc.

—Brain Injury Rewiring for Survivors: A Lifeline to New Connections. 2009. 322p. 19.00 *(978-1-882883-59-2(4))* Idyll Arbor, Inc.

Doroghazi, Cynthia Paddock. Searching for the Open Door: A Woman's Struggle for Survival after A Traumatic Brain Injury. 2007. 160p. per. 14.95 *(978-0-9798227-1-1(8))* New River Pubns., LLC.

Elbaum, Jean & Benson, Deborah, eds. Acquired Brain Injury: An Integrative Neuro-Rehabilitation Approach. 2010. (ENG., Illus.). viii, 298p. pap. 84.95 *(978-1-4419-2277-9(6)*, 1441922776) Springer.

Elswick, Mark. Padman: A Dad's Guide to Buying — Those & Other Tales. 2011. ***(978-1-61599-116-7(6))***; pap. ***(978-1-61599-115-0(8))***; E-Book ***(978-1-61599-902-6(7))*** Loving Healing Pr., Inc. (Modern History Pr.).

Fahl, Joyce Little. Tbi: Shaken but Not Stirred. 2009. 156p. pap. 14.95 *(978-1-4401-2225-5(3))* iUniverse, Inc.

Gracey, Fergus & Ownsworth, Tamara. The Self & Identity in Rehabilitation: A special issue of Neuropsychological Rehabilitation. 2008. (Special Issues of Neuropsychological Rehabilitation Ser.). (ENG., Illus.). 272p. 110.00 *(978-1-84169-863-2(6)*, Psychology Press) Taylor & Francis Group GBR. Dist: Taylor & Francis Group.

Grimes, Patricia. Giants in the Land. 2007. 112p. pap. 10.99 *(978-1-60266-385-5(8))* Xulon Pr., Inc.

Holland, Gail Bernice. Forget-Me-Not: A Memoir of Anne Bashkiroff's Alzheimer's Crusade. 2006. 193p. per. 19.95 *(978-1-55753-425-5(X))* Purdue Univ. Pr.
Hux, Karen. Assisting Survivors of Traumatic Brain Injury: The Role of Speech-Language Pathologists. 2nd ed. 2010. xv, 438p. 58.00 *(978-1-4164-0488-0(0))* PRO-ED, Inc.
Jacobs, Rick. Life Has Begun. 2007. 260p. per. 19.95 *(978-0-595-38540-9(0))* iUniverse, Inc.
Lewis, Simon. Rise & Shine: The Extraordinary Story of One Man's Journey from near Death to Full Recovery. 2nd ed. 2010. (ENG.). 360p. 24.95 *(978-1-59580-051-0(4))* Santa Monica Pr.
Lorenz, Laura S. Brain Injury Survivors: Narratives of Rehabilitation & Healing. 2010. (Illus.). 200p. 55.00 *(978-1-58826-728-3(8))* Rienner, Lynne Pubs.
Malec, James. New Methodologies for Intervention & Outcome Measurement: A Special Issue of Neuropsychological Rehabilitation. 2010. (Special Issues of Neuropsychological Rehabilitation Ser.). (ENG.). 192p. 59.95 *(978-1-84872-717-5(8)*, Psychology Press) Taylor & Francis Group GBR. Dist: Taylor & Francis Group.
Mason, Michael Paul & Mason, Michael. Head Cases: Stories of Brain Injury & Its Aftermath. 2009. (ENG., Illus.). 320p. pap. 16.00 *(978-0-374-53195-9(1))* Farrar, Straus & Giroux.
McCullagh, Peter. Conscious in a Vegetative State? A Critique of the PVS Concept. 2010. (International Library of Ethics, Law, & the New Medicine Ser.). xix, 354p. pap. 239.00 *(978-90-481-6691-6(8)*, 9048166918) Springer.
Moutsiakis, D. L. The Other Shoe Dropped: A Journey to Hell & Back Again. 2010. 180p. 22.95 *(978-1-4269-3457-5(2))*; pap. 12.95 *(978-1-4269-3456-8(4))* Trafford Publishing.
Niemeier, Janet P. & Karol, Robert L. Overcoming Grief & Loss after Brain Injury. 2010. (ENG.). 240p. pap. 29.95 *(978-0-19-538895-4(X))* Oxford Univ. Pr., Inc.
—Therapists' Guide to Overcoming Grief & Loss after Brain Injury. 2010. (ENG.). 208p. pap. 45.00 *(978-0-19-538896-1(8))* Oxford Univ. Pr., Inc.
Parenté, Rick & Herrmann, Douglas J. Retraining Cognition: Techniques & Applications. 3rd ed. 2010. 70.00 *(978-1-4164-0438-5(4))* PRO-ED, Inc.
Podd, Marvin H. Cognitive Remediation for Brain Injury & Neurological Illness: Real Life Changes. 2011. (Illus.). xiii, 158p. 69.95 ***(978-1-4614-1974-7(3)***, 1461419743) Springer.
Powell, Trevor J. & Malia, Kit. The Brain Injury: Exercises for Cognitive Rehabilitation. (Illus.). 256p. spiral bd., wbk. ed. *(978-0-86388-318-7(4)*, 002-5079) Speechmark Publishing Ltd.
Presley, Todd & Harrison, Romana. Mr. Determination. 2009. 208p. 29.99 *(978-1-4500-0958-4(1))* Xlibris Corp.
Ramachandran, V. S. The Tell-Tale Brain: A Neuroscientist's Quest for What Makes Us Human. 2012. (ENG., Illus.). 384p. pap. 17.95 ***(978-0-393-34062-4(7)***, 34062) Norton, W. W. & Co., Inc.
Raskin, Sarah A., ed. Neuroplasticity & Rehabilitation. 2011. (ENG., Illus.). 351p. 65.00 *(978-1-60918-137-6(9))* Guilford Pubns., Inc.
Rudnick, Eileen. The Glass Between Us. 2011. (Illus.). ix, 193p. pap. ***(978-1-934074-64-0(0))*** Apprentice Hse.
Sanders, Debra. A Matter of Panache: A career in public education. A traumatic brain injury. A memoir of surviving Both. 2008. 344p. pap. 19.95 *(978-1-4327-2616-8(4))* Outskirts Pr., Inc.
Schutz, Larry E. & Schutz, Michael E. Head Injury Recovery in Real Life. 2010. (Illus.). 348p. pap. 39.95 *(978-1-59756-378-9(1))* Plural Publishing, Inc.
Shulman, Alix Kates. To Love What Is: A Marriage Transformed. 2009. (ENG., Illus.). 192p. pap. 14.00 *(978-0-374-53205-5(2))* Farrar, Straus & Giroux.
Sinason, Valerie. Mental Handicap & the Human Condition: An Analytic Approach to Intellectual Disability (Revised Edition) 2nd rev. ed. 2010. 336p. pap. 34.50 *(978-1-85343-202-6(4))* Free Assn. Bks. Ltd. GBR. Dist: International Specialized Bk. Services.
Stone, Sharon Dale. A Change of Plans: Women's Stories of Hemorrhagic Stroke. 2007. (ENG., Illus.). 200p. per. *(978-1-894549-65-3(1)*, Sumach Pr.) Canadian Scholars' Pr., Inc.
Stuss, Donald T., et al, eds. Cognitive Rehabilitation: Evidence & Application. 2nd rev. ed. 2010. (ENG., Illus.). 624p. pap. 83.00 *(978-0-521-69185-7(0))* Cambridge Univ. Pr.
Terry Smith. Surviving Head Traum: A Guide to Recovery Written by a Traumatic Brain Injury Patient. 2009. 108p. 22.95 *(978-1-4401-7644-9(2))*; pap. 12.95 *(978-1-4401-7642-5(6))* iUniverse, Inc.
Traumatic Brain Injury Related Vision Issues: Hearing Before the Subcommittee on Oversight & Investigations of the Committee on Veterans' Affairs, U.S. House of Representatives, One Hundred Tenth Congress, Second Session, April 2, 2008. 2008. (Illus.). iii, 71p. *(978-0-16-082572-9(5)*, 552-070-38593-2) United States Government Printing Office.
Trotter, John. The Burden of Memory. 2009. (Illus.). 196p. *(978-1-904563-26-6(0))* Trolley.
Tsao, Jack W., ed. Traumatic Brain Injury: A Clinician's Guide to Diagnosis, Management, & Rehabilitation. 2012. (ENG., Illus.). xii, 324p. 209.00 ***(978-0-387-87886-7(6)***, 0387878866) Springer.
Vandergriff, Rebekah E. & Vandergriff, Rebekah. What Day Is It? A Family's Journey Through Traumatic Brain Injury. 2008. (Illus.). ix, 168p. *(978-0-9820522-0-4(0))* Bear's Nest Pr.
Welnick, Robin M., et al. Programs Addressing Psychological Health & Traumatic Brain Injury among U. S. Military Servicemembers & Their Families. 2011. 185p. pap. 38.50 ***(978-0-8330-5236-0(5))*** RAND Corp., The.
Wertheimer, Alison. A Dented Image: Journeys of Recovery from Subarachnoid Haemorrhage. 2008. (ENG.). 272p. 27.50 *(978-0-415-38672-2(1))* Routledge.
Wilder, Denise Arrasmith. God's Weakness. 2006. 15.00 *(978-0-8059-8255-8(8))* Dorrance Publishing Co., Inc.
Wilson, Barbara A., et al. Neuropsychological Rehabilitation: Theory, Models, Therapy & Outcome. 2009. (ENG., Illus.). 380p. 117.00 *(978-0-521-84149-8(6))* Cambridge Univ. Pr.
Wilson, Matthew. Tails You Win, Heads You Lose. 2007. (Illus.). 200p. per. *(978-1-84748-133-7(7))* Athena Pr.
Zoltan, Barbara. Vision, Perception, & Cognition: A Manual for the Evaluation & Treatment of the Adult with Acquired Brain Injury. 4th ed. 2007. (ENG., Illus.). 368p. (C). 52.95 *(978-1-55642-738-1(7))* SLACK, Inc.

BRAIN-DAMAGED CHILDREN

see also Cerebral Palsied Children; Minimal Brain Dysfunction in Children

Anderson, Vicki & Beauchamp, Miriam H., eds. Developmental Social Neuroscience & Childhood Brain Insult: Theory & Practice. 2012. (ENG.). 400p. 75.00 ***(978-1-4625-0429-9(9))*** Guilford Pubns., Inc.
Anderson, Vicki & Yeates, Keith Owen, eds. Pediatric Traumatic Brain Injury: New Frontiers in Clinical & Translational Research. 2010. (ENG., Illus.). 244p. 105.00 *(978-0-521-76332-5(0))* Cambridge Univ. Pr.
Baniel, Anat. Kids Beyond Limits: The Anat Baniel Method for Awakening the Brain & Transforming the Life of Your Child with Special Needs. 2012. (ENG.). 288p. (gr. 12). 16.00 ***(978-0-399-53736-3(8)***, Perigee Trade) Penguin Group (USA) Inc.
Dutton, Gordon & Bax, Martin, eds. Visual Impairment in Children Due to Damage to the Brain. 2010. (Clinics in Developmental Medicine Ser.: 10). (ENG., Illus.). 224p. 142.00 *(978-1-898683-86-5(7)*, Wiley-Blackwell) Wiley, John & Sons, Inc.
Griffiths, Paul D., et al. Atlas of Fetal & Neonatal Brain Mr Imaging. 2009. (ENG., Illus.). 272p. 174.00 *(978-0-323-05296-2(7)*, Mosby) Elsevier - Health Sciences Div.
Hartzenberg, Joshua. Harry's Troubled Life. 2006. (ENG.). 96p. pap. 11.95 ***(978-0-85243-869-2(1))*** Y Lolfa GBR. Dist: Dufour Editions, Inc.
Hotz, Gillian. Pediatric Test of Brain Injury. 2010. (Illus.). ***(978-1-59857-110-3(9))***; ***(978-1-59857-109-7(5))*** Brookes, Paul H. Publishing Co.
Hotz, Gillian. Pediatric Test of Brain Injury (PTBI) Examiner's Manual. 2010. pap. 150.00 *(978-1-59857-111-0(7))* Brookes, Paul H. Publishing Co.
McKenna, M. C. & Robertson, C. L., eds. Pediatric Traumatic Brain Injury [Bibliography & Price not Definite.]. (Illus.). 240p. pap. *(978-3-8055-8165-3(3))* Karger, S. AG.
McPherson, Retha & McPherson, Aldo. A Message from God: A 12 Year Old Boy's Experience in Heaven. 2009. pap. 15.99 *(978-0-7684-3051-6(5))* Destiny Image Pubs.
Melillo, Robert. Disconnected Kids: The Groundbreaking Brain Balance Program for Children with Autism, ADHD, Dyslexia, & Other Neurological Disorders. 2010. (ENG.). 288p. (gr. 12-18). 15.95 *(978-0-399-53560-4(8)*, Perigee Trade) Penguin Group (USA) Inc.
—Reconnected Kids: Help Your Child Achieve Physical, Mental, & Emotional Balance. 2011. (ENG.). 336p. (gr. 12). 15.95 *(978-0-399-53648-9(5)*, Perigee Trade) Penguin Group (USA) Inc.
Paneth, Nigel, et al. Brain Damage in the Preterm Infant. 2007. (Clinics in Developmental Medicine Ser.). (ENG., Illus.). 224p. 107.95 *(978-1-898683-00-1(X))* Mac Keith Pr. GBR. Dist: Wiley, John & Sons, Inc.
Player, Mollie. What I Learned from Jane. 2011. (ENG.). 76p. pap. 6.00 ***(978-1-4662-3998-2(0))*** CreateSpace.
Ryan, Joan. The Water Giver: The Story of a Mother, a Son, & Their Second Chance. 2010. (ENG.). 272p. pap. 15.00 *(978-1-4165-7653-2(3))* Simon & Schuster.
Stevenson, David K., et al, eds. Fetal & Neonatal Brain Injury. 4th ed. 2009. (ENG., Illus.). 642p. 199.00 *(978-0-521-88859-2(X))* Cambridge Univ. Pr.
Tan, S. & Levison, S. W., eds. Bridging Bench to Bedside in Fetal & Neonatal Brain Injury. 2007. (Illus.). 138p. pap. *(978-3-8055-8319-0(2))* Karger, S. AG.
Zurek, Jiri´ & Jurek, Jiri. Biomarkers of Brain Injury in Children-Potential Uses & Limitations. 2011. 120p. pap. ***(978-3-8443-1180-8(7))*** Lambert Academic Publishing.

BRAIN-DAMAGED CHILDREN—EDUCATION

Asbell, Shana J. Source for Traumatic Brain Injury. 2007. per. 41.95 *(978-0-7606-0746-6(X))* LinguiSystems, Inc.

BRAIN DEATH

Henderson, D. Scott. Death & Donation: Rethinking Brain Death as a Means for Procuring Transplantable Organs. 2011. 212p. pap. 23.00 ***(978-1-60899-622-3(0)***, Pickwick Pubns.) Wipf & Stock Pubs.
Machado, Calixto. Brain Death: A Reappraisal. 2007. (Illus.). 223p. 171.00 *(978-0-387-38975-2(X)*, 038738975X) Springer.
Martin, Reed. Spirit in the Tears. 2011. 244p. 29.99 ***(978-1-4568-5947-3(1))***; pap. 19.99 ***(978-1-4568-5946-6(3))*** Xlibris Corp.
Spaemann, Robert. Love & the Dignity of Human Life: Issues Concerning Nature & Natural Law in the Present Cultural Situation. 2011. pap. 12.00 ***(978-0-8028-6693-6(X))*** Eerdmans, William B. Publishing Co.
Wijdicks, Eelco F. M. Brain Death, 1 vol. 2nd ed. 2011. (ENG., Illus.). 280p. 59.95 *(978-0-19-979336-5(0))* Oxford Univ. Pr., Inc.

BRAIN DRAIN

Adepoju, Aderanti, ed. International Migration Within, to & from Africa in a Globalised World. 2009. (Illus.). 264p. pap. *(978-9988-647-42-1(5))* Sub-Saharan Pubs. & Traders GHA. Dist: Michigan State Univ. Pr.
D'Costa, Anthony P. International Mobility & the Transformation of Global Capitalism. 2010. (ENG., Illus.). 256p. (C). 135.00 *(978-0-415-56495-3(6)*, Routledge) Taylor & Francis Group GBR. Dist: Taylor & Francis Group.
Fair-Schulz, Axel & Kessler, Andrew. German Scholars in Exile: New Studies in Intellectual History. 2011. (Logos: Perspectives on Modern Society & Culture Ser.). (ENG.). 260p. 70.00 *(978-0-7391-5023-8(5))* Lexington Bks.
Holou, Roland A. A. Y. A Continent in Tears: The Origin of Africa's Collapse & How to Reverse It. 2010. 206p. pap. 18.95 *(978-1-4327-1734-6(0))* Outskirts Pr., Inc.
Patterson, Rubin, ed. African Brain Circulation: Beyond the Drain-Gain Debate. 2007. (International Studies in Sociology & Social Anthropology Ser.). 200p. pap. *(978-90-04-15885-6(5))* BRILL.
Pistone, Michele R. & Hoeffner, John J. Stepping Out of the Brain Drain: Applying Catholic Social Teaching in a New ERA of Migration. 2007. (ENG.). 260p. 76.99 *(978-0-7391-1504-6(9))*; per. 34.99 *(978-0-7391-1505-3(7))* Lexington Bks.
Rogerson, Christian M. Medical Recruiting. 2007. 52p. *(978-1-920118-47-1(0))* IDASA Pubs. ZAF. Dist: Michigan State Univ. Pr.
Sahay, Anjali. Indian Diaspora in the United States: Brain Drain or Gain? 2009. (ENG., Illus.). 262p. 73.50 *(978-0-7391-2106-1(5))* Lexington Bks.
Shah, Rebecca. The International Migration of Health Workers: Ethics, Rights & Justice. Shah, Rebecca, ed. 2010. (ENG., Illus.). 256p. 89.00 *(978-0-230-22441-4(5))* Palgrave Macmillan.
Solimano, Andrés, ed. The International Mobility of Talent: Types, Causes, & Development Impact. 2008. (WIDER Studies in Development Economics Ser.). (ENG., Illus.). 352p. 125.00 *(978-0-19-953260-5(5))* Oxford Univ. Pr., Inc.
Stricker, Kristi. The Geographic Migration of Rural Honor Students. 2009. 100p. pap. *(978-3-639-22056-8(0))* VDM Verlag Dr. Mueller e.K.
Tejada, Gabriela & Bolay, Jean-Claude, eds. Scientific Diasporas As Development Partners: Skilled Migrants from Colombia, India & South Africa in Switzerland: Empirical Evidence & Policy Responses. 2010. (Illus.). 545p. pap. *(978-3-0343-0391-0(2))* Lang, Peter.
Tusa, Timea. Brain Drain with a Brain Gain? 2008. 72p. pap. *(978-3-639-00735-0(2))* VDM Verlag Dr. Mueller e.K.
Yeoh, Brenda & Huang, Shirlena, eds. The Cultural Politics of Talent Migration in East Asia. 2012. (ENG.). 208p. (C). 135.00 ***(978-0-415-52813-9(5))*** Routledge.

BRAIN DYSFUNCTION IN CHILDREN, MINIMAL

see Minimal Brain Dysfunction in Children

BRAIN EDEMA

see Cerebral Edema

BRAIN FUNCTION LOCALIZATION

see Brain—Localization of Functions

BRAIN HEMISPHERES

see Cerebral Hemispheres

BRAIN ISCHEMIA

see Cerebral Ischemia

BRAIN STEM

Duvernoy, Henri M. Human Brain Stem Vessels: Including the Pineal Gland & Information on Brain Stem Infarction. 2nd ed. 2010. (Illus.). x, 261p. pap. 549.00 *(978-3-642-08402-7(8)*, 3642084028) Springer.
Hall, James W., III. New Handbook for Auditory Evoked Responses. 2006. (ENG., Illus.). 736p. 157.40 *(978-0-205-36104-5(8))* Allyn & Bacon, Inc.
Moller, Aage R. Cochlear & Brainstem Implants, Vol. 64. (Advances in Oto-Rhino-Laryngology Ser.: Vol. 64). (Illus.). *(978-3-8055-8157-8(2))* Karger, S. AG.
Naidich, Thomas P., et al. Duvernoy's Atlas of the Human Brain Stem & Cerebellum: High-Field MRI, Surface Anatomy, Internal Structure, Vascularization & 3 D Sectional Anatomy. 2008. (Illus.). 500p. 459.00 *(978-3-211-73970-9(X))* Springer.
Papievis, Julie. Go Back & Be Happy: A Devastating Brain Injury Left Julie at the Gates of Heaven..., 1 vol. 2008. (Illus.). 192p. pap. 12.99 *(978-0-8254-6276-4(2)*, Monarch Bks.) Lion Hudson PLC GBR. Dist: Kregel Pubns.
Paxinos, George, et al, eds. Chemoarchitectonic Atlas of the Rat Brain. 2nd ed. 2008. (ENG., Illus.). 380p. 285.00 *(978-0-12-374237-7(4)*, Academic Pr.) Elsevier Science & Technology Bks.
Salami, Angelo. Neuroplasticity in the Auditory Brainstem from Physiology to the Drug Therapy. 2011. *(978-1-61761-949-6(3))* Nova Science Pubs., Inc.
Urban, Peter, ed. Brainstem Disorders. 2011. (ENG., Illus.). x, 360p. 179.00 *(978-3-642-04202-7(3)*, 3642042023) Springer.

BRAIN STORMING

see Group Problem Solving

BRAIN SYNDROME, ACUTE

see Delirium

BRAIN-WASHING

see Brainwashing

BRAINERD, DAVID, 1718-1747

Brainerd, David. An Account of the Life of the Late Reverend Mr. David Brainerd. 2009. (Amer Philosophy, Religion Ser.). (ENG.). 360p. pap. 22.95 *(978-1-4290-1811-1(9))* Applewood Bks.
—The Journal of David Brainerd. Edwards, Jonathan, ed. 2010. (Cambridge Library Collection - Religion Ser.). (ENG.). 308p. pap. 24.99 *(978-1-108-01438-0(0))* Cambridge Univ. Pr.
Christie, Vance. David Brainerd: A Flame for God. 2009. (History Makers Ser.). (ENG.). 320p. 12.99 *(978-1-84550-478-6(X))* Christian Focus Pubns. GBR. Dist: STL Distribution North America.
Grigg, John A. The Lives of David Brainerd: The Making of an American Evangelical Icon. 2009. (ENG., Illus.). 288p. 65.00 *(978-0-19-537237-3(9))* Oxford Univ. Pr., Inc.
Piper, John. The Hidden Smile of God: The Fruit of Affliction in the Lives of John Bunyan, William Cowper, & David Brainerd. 2008. (Swans Are Not Silent Ser.). 176p. pap. 15.99 *(978-1-4335-0189-0(9))* Crossway.
Pratt, Josiah & Edwards, Jonathan. Life of the Rev. David Brainerd: Missionary to the North American Indians. 2010. (Cambridge Library Collection - Religion Ser.). 416p. pap. 31.99 *(978-1-108-01190-7(X))* Cambridge Univ. Pr.
Serse, Walter. Testimonio Personal de David Brainerd: David Brainerd's Diary. (SPA.). *(978-84-7645-058-1(3)*, 223123) Clie, Editorial.

BRAINWASHING

see also Will

Albarelli, H. P., Jr. A Terrible Mistake: The Murder of Frank Olson & the CIA's Secret Cold War Experiments. 2011. (ENG., Illus.). 856p. pap. 29.95 *(978-1-936296-08-8(X))* Trine Day.
Ault, Caroline, et al. For the Love of My Children: The True Story of One Woman's Struggle to Escape a Brutal British Cult. 2010. (ENG.). 288p. 12.95 *(978-0-00-734092-7(3))* HarperCollins Pubs. Ltd. GBR. Dist: Independent Pubs. Group.
Binhi, V. N., ed. Electromagnetic Mind Control, Fact or Fiction. 2010. 147p. 69.00 *(978-1-60741-431-5(7))* Nova Science Pubs., Inc.
Deadman Switch. Conspiracies & Brainwashing: The Epistle of Napoleon to the Dinosaurs. 2008. 114p. pap. 11.95 *(978-1-4327-2906-6(3))* Outskirts Pr., Inc.
Ellis, J. K. Mind Control 101 - How to Influence the Thoughts & Actions of Others Without Them Knowing or Caring. 2007. 224p. pap. 28.95 *(978-1-4303-1815-6(5))* Lulu Enterprises Inc.
—Perfected Mind Control - the Unauthorized Black Book of Hypnotic Mind Control. 2006. (ENG.). 220p. per. 26.95 *(978-1-84728-750-2(6))* Lulu Enterprises Inc.
Enroth, Ronald M. Sectas y la Juventud: Youth Brainwashing - Extremist. (SPA.). 240p. *(978-84-7228-516-3(2)*, 220807) Clie, Editorial.
Epstein, Badouk, et al, eds. Ritual Abuse & Mind Control: The Manipulation of Attachment Needs. 2011. (Illus.). 200p. pap. 34.95 *(978-1-85575-839-1(3))* Karnac Bks. GBR. Dist: Stylus Publishing, LLC.
Freeman, Pierre S. AMORC Unmasked: The hidden mind control techniques of the Rosicrucian Order. 2009. pap. 23.95 *(978-1-60494-332-0(7))* Wheatmark.
Hunter, Edward. Brainwashing: The Story of Men Who Defied It. 2011. 288p. 48.95 ***(978-1-258-01331-8(2))*** Literary Licensing, LLC.
Huxley, Aldous. Brave New World Revisited. 2006. 144p. per. 11.99 *(978-0-06-089852-6(6)*, HarperPerennial) HarperCollins Pubs.
Lankford, Adam. Human Killing Machines: Systematic Indoctrination in Iran, Nazi Germany, Al Qaeda, & Abu Ghraib. 2010. (ENG.). 202p. pap. 31.50 *(978-0-7391-3416-0(7))* 2009. (ENG., Illus.). 202p. 62.99 *(978-0-7391-3415-3(9))* 2009. (Illus.). xiii, 187p. *(978-0-7391-3417-7(5))* Lexington Bks.
Lung, Haha & Prowant, Christopher. Mind Assassins: The Dark Arts of the Asian Masters. 2010. (ENG.). 256p. pap. 14.95 *(978-0-8065-3141-0(X)*, Citadel Pr.) Kensington Publishing Corp.
Meerloo. The Rape of the Mind: The Psychology of Thought Control, Menticide, & Brainwashing. 2009. 320p. pap. 16.95 *(978-1-61577-376-3(2))* Progressive Pr.
Meerloo, Joost Abraham Maurits. The Rape of the Mind: The Psychology of Thought Control, Menticide & Brainwashing. 2011. 318p. 50.95 ***(978-1-258-00881-9(5))*** Literary Licensing, LLC.
Mitchell, Neil J. Agents of Atrocity: Leaders, Followers, & the Violation of Human Rights in Civil War. 2009. (ENG.). 240p. pap. 33.00 *(978-0-230-61902-9(9))* Palgrave Macmillan.
Powell, Tag. Metodo Silva '90 del Dominio de la Mente.Tr. of Silva Method for Dominating the Mind in the 90's. (SPA.). 19.98 *(978-968-13-2977-8(5))* Editorial Diana, S.A. MEX. Dist: Continental Bk. Co., Inc.
Skedgell, Kristen. Losing the Way: A Memoir of Spiritual Longing, Manipulation, Abuse, & Escape. 2008. (ENG.). 288p. pap. 18.95 *(978-0-9720021-9-6(7))* Bay Tree Publishing.
Smith, Sarah & Snell, Kate. Deceived: A True Story. (ENG., Illus.). 2008. 344p. pap. 14.95 *(978-0-7528-9326-6(2))* 2007. 336p. per. 18.95 *(978-0-7528-8820-0(X))* Orion Publishing Group, Ltd. GBR. Dist: Independent Pubs. Group.
—Deceived: The True Story of a Stolen Life. 2007. (ENG., Illus.). 336p. 25.00 *(978-0-7528-7622-1(8))* Orion Publishing Group, Ltd. GBR. Dist: Independent Pubs. Group.
Streatfeild, Dominic. Brainwash: The Secret History of Mind Control. 2008. (ENG.). 432p. pap. 18.00 *(978-0-312-42792-4(1))* Picador.
—Brainwashing. Date not set. mass mkt. *(978-0-312-99592-8(X))*; pap. *(978-0-312-32573-2(8))* St. Martin's Pr. (St. Martin's Paperbacks).
Tan, Charlene. Islamic Education & Indoctrination. 2011. (Routledge Research in Education Ser.). (ENG., Illus.). 228p. (C). 125.00 *(978-0-415-87976-7(0))* Routledge.
Taylor, Eldon. Mind Programming: From Persuasion & Brainwashing, to Self-Help & Practical Metaphysics. 2009. (ENG., Illus.). 360p. 24.95 *(978-1-4019-2331-0(3)*, 1065) Hay Hse., Inc.

B

—Mind Programming: From Persuasion & Brainwashing to Self-Help & Practical Metaphysics. 2010. (ENG., Illus.). 360p. 15.95 *(978-1-4019-2332-7(1))* Hay Hse., Inc.

Taylor, Kathleen. Brainwashing: The Science of Thought Control. 2006. (ENG., Illus.). 336p. *(978-0-19-920478-6(0))* Oxford Univ. Pr.

BRAJ LANGUAGE

Busch, Allison. Poetry of Kings: The Classical Hindi Literature of Mughal India, 1 vol. 2011. (South Asia Research Ser.). (ENG., Illus.). 368p. 74.00 *(978-0-19-976592-8(8))* Oxford Univ. Pr., Inc.

McGregor, R. S. The Language of Indrajit of Orcha: A Study of Early Braj Bhasa Prose. 2007. (University of Cambridge Oriental Publications). (SAN & ENG.). 280p. pap. 38.00 *(978-0-521-05228-3(9))* Cambridge Univ. Pr.

BRAKES

American Society of Mechanical Engineers Staff, ed. Disc Brakes for Commercial Vehicles. 158p. 76.00 *(978-0-85298-662-2(9))* Professional Engineering Publishing GBR. Dist: SAE Intl.

—Specification & Performance Standard Power Press Brakes. 24p. 30.00 *(978-0-7918-2305-7(9))* ASME Pr.

Norville, Norman. S4 School Bus Brakes: Motor Age Self-Study Guide for ASE Certification. 2006. spiral bd. 22.95 *(978-1-933180-70-0(6))* Advanstar Communications, Inc.

BRAKING RADIATION

see Bremsstrahlung

BRAMSTON FAMILY

Bramston, John. Autobiography of Sir John Bramston. (Camden Society, London, Publications, First Ser.: No. 32). reprint ed. 95.00 *(978-0-404-50132-7(X))* AMS Pr., Inc.

BRANCH BANKS

see Banks and Banking—Branch Banks

BRANCH LIBRARIES

Zdravkovska, Nevenka. Academic Branch Libraries in Changing Times. 2011. (Illus.). 230p. 80.00 *(978-1-84334-630-2(3)*, Chandos Publishing) Woodhead Publishing Ltd. GBR. Dist: Neal-Schuman Pubs., Inc.

BRANCH STORES

see Chain Stores

BRANCHES (BUSINESS ENTERPRISES)

see Chain Stores

BRANCUSI, CONSTANTIN, 1876-1957

Beck, Ernest. Brancusi's Endless Column Ensemble: Targu-Jiu, Romania. 2007. (World Monuments Fund Ser.). (ENG., Illus.). 88p. pap. 14.95 *(978-1-85759-436-2(3))* Scala, Editions FRA. Dist: National Bk. Network.

Brancusi, Constantin & Serra, Richard. Constantin Brancusi & Richard Serra: Resting in Time & Space. 2011. (ENG., Illus.). 244p. 75.00 ***(978-3-7757-2821-8(X))*** Hatje Cantz Verlag GmbH & Co KG DEU. Dist: D.A.P./Distributed Art Pubs.

Cabanne, Pierre. Brancusi. 2006. (Illus.). 255p. pap. 23.50 *(978-2-87939-314-8(0))* Terrail, Pierre Editions FRA. Dist: Perseus-PGW.

Carolyn, Lanchner. Constantin Brancusi. 2010. (ENG., Illus.). 48p. pap. 9.95 *(978-0-87070-787-2(6))* Museum of Modern Art.

Miller, Sanda. Constantin Brancusi. 2010. (Reaktion Books - Critical Lives Ser.). (ENG., Illus.). 192p. pap. 16.95 *(978-1-86189-652-0(2))* Reaktion Bks., Ltd. GBR. Dist: Chicago Distribution Ctr.

Pearson, James. Constantin Brancusi: Sculpting the Essence of Things. 3rd ed. 2010. (Sculptors Ser.). (Illus.). 180p. *(978-1-86171-268-4(5))*; pap. *(978-1-86171-284-4(7))* Crescent Moon Publishing.

BRAND MANAGEMENT

see Product Management

BRAND NAME PRODUCTS

see also Trademarks

Aaker, David A. Brand Relevance: Making Competitors Irrelevant. 2011. (ENG., Illus.). 400p. 32.95 *(978-0-470-61358-0(0)*, Jossey-Bass) Wiley, John & Sons, Inc.

Aaker, David A. & Joachimsthaler, Erich. Brand Leadership: Building Assets in an Information Economy. 2009. (ENG., Illus.). 368p. pap. 23.95 *(978-1-4391-7291-9(9)*, Free Pr.) Free Pr.

Abellán, Miquel. Fashion Branding. Monsa Staff et al, eds. 2010. (ENG & SPA., Illus.). 192p. pap. 57.50 *(978-84-96823-50-1(4))* Instituto Monsa de Ediciones, S.A. ESP. Dist: Trans-Atlantic Pubns., Inc.

Abouzeid, Jessica. City Brand Image. 2011. 116p. pap. ***(978-3-8454-0402-8(7))*** Lambert Academic Publishing.

Adamson, Allen P. BrandDigital: Simple Ways Top Brands Succeed in the Digital World. 2009. (ENG., Illus.). 304p. pap. 17.00 *(978-0-230-61762-9(X))* Palgrave Macmillan.

—BrandSimple: How the Best Brands Keep It Simple & Succeed. 2007. (ENG., Illus.). 256p. pap. 14.95 *(978-1-4039-8490-6(5))* Palgrave Macmillan.

Alexander, Jeffrey C., et al, eds. Iconic Power: Materiality & Meaning in Social Life. 2011. (Cultural Sociology Ser.). (ENG., Illus.). 272p. 95.00 ***(978-0-230-34005-3(9))*** Palgrave Macmillan.

Alt, Dirk & Niefanger, Birgit. Cult Masterpieces: Icons of Our Generation. 2008. (DUT, FRE & ENG., Illus.). 400p. 59.95 *(978-90-76886-64-0(4))* Tectum B.V.B.A. BEL. Dist: Innovative Logistics.

Ambrose, Gavin & Harris, Paul. Packaging the Brand: The Relationship Between Packaging Design & Brand Identity. 2011. (Required Reading Range Ser.). (ENG., Illus.). 208p. (C). pap. 52.50 *(978-2-940411-41-2(7))* Ava Publishing SA CHE. Dist: Ingram Pub. Services.

Andrews, Tim & Chew, Wilson. Building Brands in Asia. 2013. (ENG., Illus.). 256p. (C). pap. 49.95 *(978-0-415-54984-4(1))*; 145.00 *(978-0-415-54983-7(3))* Routledge.

Anholt, Simon & Hildreth, Jeremy. Brand America: The Making, Unmaking & Remaking of the Greatest National Image of All Time. 2010. 192p. pap. 15.95 *(978-1-905736-56-0(8))* Marshall Cavendish GBR. Dist: Midpoint Trade Bks., Inc.

Ashworth, Gregory & Kavaratzis, Mihalis, eds. Towards Effective Place Brand Management: Branding European Cities & Regions. 2010. (Illus.). 296p. 129.00 *(978-1-84844-242-9(4))* Elgar, Edward Publishing, Inc.

Bainbridge, Jane & Dugdale, Karen. Superbrands: An Insight into Some of Britain's Strongest Brands 2010. Cooper, Angela, ed. 2010. (Illus.). 200p. 99.50 *(978-0-9554784-9-9(9))* Superbrands (UK), Ltd. GBR. Dist: Trans-Atlantic Pubns., Inc.

Bainbridge, Jane & Dugdale, Karen. Superbrands Annual 2011: An Insight into Some of Britain's Strongest Brands. Hill, Laura, ed. 2011. (Illus.). 199p. 112.50 ***(978-0-9565334-1-8(8))*** Superbrands (UK), Ltd. GBR. Dist: Trans-Atlantic Pubns., Inc.

Baladi, Joseph. The Brutal Truth about Asian Branding: And How to Break the Vicious Cycle. 2011. (ENG., Illus.). 250p. 29.95 *(978-0-470-82647-8(9)*, Wiley) Wiley, John & Sons, Inc.

Balmer. Corporate Brands an Anthology. 2010. (Illus.). 352p. pap. 45.95 *(978-0-415-37087-5(6))* Routledge.

Bandyopadhyay, Subir, ed. Contemporary Research in E-Branding. 2008. (Illus.). 378p. 195.00 *(978-1-59904-813-0(2))* IGI Global.

Bar-Isaac, Heski & Tadelis, Steven. Seller Reputation. 2008. (ENG.). 88p. pap. 67.00 net. *(978-1-60198-158-5(9))* Now Pubs.

Barlow, Janelle & Stewart, Paul. Branded Customer Service: The New Competitive Edge. 2006. (ENG.). 264p. pap. 22.95 *(978-1-57675-404-7(9))* Berrett-Koehler Pubs., Inc.

Barrera, Rick. Overpromise & Overdeliver: Using TouchPoint Branding to Design & Deliver Extraordinary Customer Experiences. 2008. (ENG.). 240p. (gr. 12). pap. 15.00 *(978-1-59184-251-4(4)*, Portfolio Trade) Penguin Group (USA) Inc.

Baskin, Jonathan Salem. Branding Only Works on Cattle: The New Way to Get Known (and drive your competitors Crazy) 2009. (ENG.). 272p. pap. 16.99 *(978-0-446-17802-0(0)*, Business Plus) Grand Central Publishing.

—Bright Lights & Dim Bulbs: The Year in Marketing Buzz, Brilliance & Buffoonery, So You Don't Have to Repeat It — 2010 Edition. 2009. 200p. pap. 16.95 *(978-1-4401-7840-5(2))* iUniverse, Inc.

Bates, Suzanne. Discover Your CEO Brand: Secrets to Embracing & Maximizing Your Unique Value As a Leader. 2011. (ENG., Illus.). 256p. 25.00 ***(978-0-07-176286-1(8)***, 0071762868) McGraw-Hill Cos., The.

Beaudoin, Tom. Consuming Faith: Integrating Who We Are with What We Buy. 2006. (ENG.). 160p. per. 15.95 *(978-1-58051-208-4(9)*, Sheed & Ward) Rowman & Littlefield Publishers, Inc.

Beckwith, Harry. What Clients Love: A Field Guide to Growing Your Business. 2010. (ENG.). 304p. pap. 14.99 *(978-0-446-55602-6(5)*, Business Plus) Grand Central Publishing.

Bence, Brenda. How You Are Like Shampoo: The Breakthrough Personal Branding System Based on Proven Big-Brand Marketing Methods to Help You Earn More, Do More, & Be More at Work. 2008. (Illus.). 272p. per. 19.95 *(978-0-9799010-2-7(2))* Global Insight Communications, LLC.

—How YOU(tm) Are Like Shampoo: The Breakthrough Personal Branding System Based on Proven Big-Brand Marketing Methods to Help you Earn More, Do More, & Be More at Work. 2008. cd-rom 24.95 *(978-0-9799010-8-9(1))* Global Insight Communications, LLC.

Benett, Andrew, et al. Good for Business: The Rise of the Conscious Corporation. 2010. (ENG.). 256p. pap. 19.00 *(978-0-230-10345-0(6))* Palgrave Macmillan.

Benjamin Cummings. Food Composition Table. 2009. (ENG.). 72p. (C). pap. 20.00 *(978-0-321-66793-9(X))* Benjamin-Cummings Publishing Co.

Bently, Lionel, et al, eds. Trade Marks & Brands: An Interdisciplinary Critique. (Cambridge Intellectual Property & Information Law Ser.). (ENG., Illus.). 2011. 472p. pap. 55.00 *(978-0-521-18792-3(3))* 2008. 480p. 126.00 *(978-0-521-88965-0(0))* Cambridge Univ. Pr.

Berman, Margo & Blakeman, Robyn. The Brains Behind Great Ad Campaigns: Creative Collaboration Between Copywriters & Art Directors. 2009. (ENG.). 224p. 80.00 *(978-0-7425-5550-1(X))*; pap. 33.00 *(978-0-7425-5551-8(8))* Rowman & Littlefield Publishers, Inc.

Beverland, Michael. Building Brand Authenticity: 7 Habits of Iconic Brands. 2009. (ENG., Illus.). 260p. 49.00 *(978-0-230-58031-2(9))* Palgrave Macmillan.

Bis Publishers, creator. British Design 2007/08: Branding & Graphic Design, Packaging Design, New Media Design, Interior, Retail & Event Design, Product Design. 2006. (British Design Ser.). (ENG., Illus.). 248p. 39.00 *(978-90-6369-137-0(8))* Bis B.V., Uitgeverij(BIS Publishers) NLD. Dist: Consortium Bk. Sales & Distribution.

Boiardi, Anna. Delicious Memories: Recipes & Stories from the Chef Boyardee Family. 2011. (ENG., Illus.). 208p. 27.50 *(978-1-58479-906-1(4))* Stewart, Tabori & Chang.

Book Industry Services Publishers Staff. British Design 2009/10. 2009. (ENG., Illus.). 248p. 59.00 *(978-90-6369-202-5(1))* Bis B.V., Uitgeverij(BIS Publishers) NLD. Dist: Consortium Bk. Sales & Distribution.

Boonpaisarnsatit, Nithat. Semantic Analysis of Thai Product Brand Names. 2009. 104p. pap. *(978-3-639-14660-8(3))* VDM Verlag Dr. Mueller e.K.

Boorman, Neil. Bonfire of the Brands: How I Learnt to Live without Labels. Franklin, Dan, ed. 2008. (Illus.). 256p. pap. *(978-1-84767-087-8(3))* Canongate Bks.

Bouchard, Ron A. Patently Innovative: How Pharmaceutical Firms Use Emerging Patent Law to Extend Monopolies on Blockbuster Drugs. 2012. (Woodhead Publishing Series in Biomedicine Ser.). (ENG., Illus.). 296p. 205.00 ***(978-1-907568-12-1(3))*** Woodhead Publishing Ltd. GBR. Dist: Ingram Pub. Services.

Bouchikhi, Hamid & Kimberly, John R. The Soul of the Corporation: How to Manage the Identity of Your Company. 2007. (ENG.). 256p. pap. 32.99 *(978-0-13-259814-9(0))* Wharton Schl. Publishing.

Bradley, John. Purple Reign: The Story Behind Chocolate's Best-Loved Brand. 2008. (ENG., Illus.). 352p. 49.95 *(978-0-470-72524-5(9)*, Wiley) Wiley, John & Sons, Inc.

Brands & Their Companies, 2.0. 35th ed. 2011. 1525.00 *(978-1-4144-5815-1(0))* Cengage Gale.

Breckenfeld, Del. The Cool Factor: Building Your Brand's Image Through Partnership Marketing. 2008. (ENG.). 288p. 24.95 *(978-0-470-37196-1(X)*, Wiley) Wiley, John & Sons, Inc.

Bronner, Kai, et al, eds. (((ABA))) Audio Branding Academy Yearbook 2009/2010. 2010. 142p. pap. 33.00 *(978-3-8329-5531-1(3))* Nomos Verlagsgesellschaft DEU. Dist: International Specialized Bk. Services.

—(((Aba))) Audio Branding Academy Yearbook 2010/2011. 2011. 276p. pap. 55.00 *(978-3-8329-6475-7(4))* Nomos Verlagsgesellschaft DEU. Dist: International Specialized Bk. Services.

Brunner, Conrad. Adidas: All Day I Dream about Sport. 2007. (Great Brand Stories Ser.). (ENG., Illus.). 192p. pap. 12.95 *(978-1-904879-12-1(8))* Cyan Communications GBR. Dist: Independent Pubs. Group.

Buck, Sebastian. Challenges of Brand Management Today. 2010. 120p. pap. *(978-3-639-24763-3(9))* VDM Verlag Dr. Mueller e.K.

Buckingham, Ian P. & Buckingham, Ian. Brand Engagement: How Employees Make or Break Brands. 2008. (ENG., Illus.). 256p. 50.00 *(978-0-230-57306-2(1))* Palgrave Macmillan.

Bueno, B. J. Customers First: Dominate Your Market by Winning Them over Where It Counts the Most. 2012. (ENG., Illus.). 224p. 26.00 ***(978-0-07-178787-1(9)***, 0071787879) McGraw-Hill Cos., The.

Calloway, Joe. Becoming a Category of One: How Extraordinary Companies Transcend Commodity & Defy Comparison. 2nd ed. 2009. (ENG.). 272p. pap. 19.95 *(978-0-470-49635-0(5)*, Wiley) Wiley, John & Sons, Inc.

Campbell Soup Company Staff & Publications International Staff, contrib. by. Campbell's 20-Minute Dishes. 2011. (Illus.). 30p. ***(978-1-4508-2237-4(1))*** Publications International, Ltd.

Carter, Connie. The Law of Trademarks, Brands & Domain Names in China. 2007. 304p. (gr. 13). 150.00 *(978-0-7007-1640-1(8)*, Routledge) Taylor & Francis Group GBR. Dist: Taylor & Francis Group.

Casablanca, Luca. Integration in the Brand Community. 2011. 144p. pap. ***(978-3-8454-0468-4(X))*** Lambert Academic Publishing.

Cato, Mac. Go Logo! - A Handbook to the Art of Global Branding: 12 Keys to Creating Successful Global Brands. 2010. (ENG., Illus.). 208p. instr.'s hndbk. ed. 45.00 *(978-1-59253-517-0(8)*, 1592535178, Rockport Publishers) Quayside.

Chadha, Radha & Husband, Paul. The Cult of the Luxury Brand: Inside Asia's Love Affair with Luxury. 2006. (ENG., Illus.). 300p. 39.95 *(978-1-904838-05-0(7))* Ebsco Publishing.

Charlesworth, Alan. Choosing the Right Domain Name. 2009. 176p. pap. 27.50 *(978-1-4452-0538-0(6))* Lulu Enterprises Inc.

Chernatony, Leslie, et al. Creating Powerful Brands. 4th rev. ed. 2010. (ENG., Illus.). 496p. pap. 49.95 *(978-1-85617-849-5(8))* Routledge.

Chevalier, Michel & Mazzalovo, Gerald. Luxury Brand Management: A World of Privilege. 2008. (ENG., Illus.). 400p. 53.00 *(978-0-470-82326-2(7)*, Wiley) Wiley, John & Sons, Inc.

Chiaravalle, Bill, et al. Branding for Dummies. 2006. (ENG., Illus.). 384p. pap. 21.99 *(978-0-471-77159-3(7)*, For Dummies) Wiley, John & Sons, Inc.

Chimhundu, Ranga. The Brand Management Structure in Consumer Packaged Goods. 2008. 156p. pap. *(978-3-639-01416-7(2))* VDM Verlag Dr. Mueller e.K.

Chung, Yongkuk. Processing Web Ads: The Effects of Animation & Arousing Content. 2007. (ENG.). 132p. (C). 89.95 *(978-1-934043-24-0(9))* Cambria Pr.

Cleary, Andy & Cleary, Cody. Genuis Simple Branding. 2009. 124p. pap. 24.95 *(978-0-557-06572-1(0))* Lulu Enterprises Inc.

Clifton, Rita & Simmons, John. Brands & Branding. 2nd ed. 2009. (Economist Ser.). (ENG.). 284p. 32.95 *(978-1-57660-350-5(4)*, Bloomberg Pr.) Wiley, John & Sons, Inc.

Cocoran, Ian. The Art of Digital Branding. (ENG., Illus.). 272p. 2011. pap. 19.95 *(978-1-58115-876-2(9)*, 115876) 2007. 24.95 *(978-1-58115-488-7(7))* Skyhorse Publishing Co., Inc. (Allworth Pr.).

Companies & Their Brands, 2.0. 35th ed. 2011. 1023.00 *(978-1-4144-5835-9(5))* Cengage Gale.

Conley, Lucas. OBD: Obsessive Branding Disorder - The Illusion of Business & the Business of Illusion. 2009. (ENG.). 240p. pap. 13.95 *(978-1-58648-704-1(3))* PublicAffairs.

Conroy, Michael E. Branded! How the Certification Revolution Is Transforming Global Corporations. 2007. (ENG., Illus.). 320p. per. 19.95 *(978-0-86571-579-0(3)*, 0865715793) New Society Pubs., Ltd. CAN. Dist: Consortium Bk. Sales & Distribution.

Consumer Dummies Staff & Chritton, Susan. Personal Branding for Dummies. 2012. (ENG.). 360p. pap. 24.99 ***(978-1-118-11792-7(1)***, For Dummies) Wiley, John & Sons, Inc.

Coomber, Stephen. Branding. 2nd rev. ed. 2007. 136p. pap. 18.95 *(978-1-84112-706-4(X))* Wiley, John & Sons, Inc.

Cooper, Angela. Kids Superbrands. 2006. (Illus.). 127p. 39.95 *(978-1-905652-01-3(1))* Trans-Atlantic Pubns., Inc.

Copulsky, Jonathan R. Brand Resilience: Managing Risk & Recovery in a High-Speed World. (ENG., Illus.). 256p. 2012. pap. 17.00 ***(978-0-230-39218-2(0))*** 2011. 26.00 *(978-0-230-11138-7(6))* Palgrave Macmillan.

Cram101 Textbook Reviews & Cram101 Textbook Reviews. Outlines & Highlights for Advertising & Integrated Brand Promotion by Thomas Oguinn, Isbn: 9780538473323. 2011. 228p. pap. 31.95 ***(978-1-61461-152-3(1))*** Cram101 Inc.

Cram101 Textbook Reviews Staff. Outlines & Highlights for Balanced Brand: How to Balance the Stakeholder Forces That Can Make or Break Your Business by Foley & Kendrick, ISBN. 2009. 66p. pap. 27.95 *(978-1-4288-3874-1(0))* Cram101 Inc.

—Outlines & Highlights for Balanced Brand: How to Balance the Stakeholder Forces That Can Make or Break Your Business by Foley, ISBN. 2008. 68p. pap. 10.95 *(978-1-4288-6361-3(3))* Cram101 Inc.

—Outlines & Highlights for Brand from the Inside: Eight Essentials to Emotionally Connect Your Employees to Your Business by Sartain, ISBN. 2008. 80p. pap. 10.95 *(978-1-4288-6415-3(6))* Cram101 Inc.

Crocker, Betty. Fix with a Mix Desserts. 2010. (ENG., Illus.). 224p. 19.95 *(978-0-470-61799-1(3)*, Betty Crocker) Wiley, John & Sons, Inc.

Cunningham, Jane & Roberts, Philippa. Inside Her Pretty Little Head: A New Theory of Female Motivation & What It Means for Marketing. 2007. (ENG., Illus.). 256p. 26.95 *(978-1-904879-96-1(9))* Cyan Communications GBR. Dist: Independent Pubs. Group.

Dall'Olmo Riley, Francesca, ed. Brand Management, 4 vols. 2009. (SAGE Library in Marketing Ser.). (Illus.). 1800p. 995.00 *(978-1-84860-208-3(1)*, B02083C) SAGE Pubns., Ltd. GBR. Dist: SAGE Pubns., Inc.

Daly, Anne. Choose Your Foods: Exchange Lists for Diabetics. 2008. (Illus.). 64p. *(978-0-88091-377-5(0))* American Diabetes Assn.

Danesi, Marcel. Why It Sells: Decoding the Meanings of Brand Names, Logos, Ads, & Other Marketing & Advertising Ploys. 2007. (R&L Series in Mass Communication Ser.). (ENG.). 220p. 84.00 *(978-0-7425-5544-0(5))*; per. 29.95 *(978-0-7425-5545-7(3))* Rowman & Littlefield Publishers, Inc.

Davis, John A. The Olympic Games Effect: How Sports Marketing Builds Strong Brands. 2nd ed. 2012. (ENG., Illus.). 256p. pap. 29.95 ***(978-1-118-17168-4(3)***, Wiley) Wiley, John & Sons, Inc.

Davis, John Andrew. Competitive Success: How Branding Adds Value. 2010. (ENG., Illus.). 422p. pap. 70.95 *(978-0-470-99822-9(9)*, Wiley) Wiley, John & Sons, Inc.

Davis, Melissa. Fundamentals of Branding. 2009. (Fundamentals Ser.). (ENG., Illus.). 184p. pap. 34.95 *(978-2-940373-98-7(1))* AVA Publishing GBR. Dist: Ingram Pub. Services.

de Chernatony, Leslie. From Brand Vision to Brand Evaluation: The strategic process of growing & strengthening Brands. 3rd rev. ed. 2010. (ENG., Illus.). 392p. (C). pap. 49.95 *(978-1-85617-773-3(4))* Routledge.

Dearlove, Des. The Unauthorized Guide to Doing Business the Richard Branson Way: 10 Secrets of the World's Greatest Brand Builder. 3rd rev. ed. 2010. (ENG.). 176p. pap. 15.95 *(978-0-85708-061-5(X)*, Capstone) Wiley, John & Sons, Inc.

Del Blanco, Robert Alvarez. Personal Brands: Manage Your Life with Talent & Turn It into a Unique Experience. 2010. (ENG., Illus.). 256p. 42.00 *(978-0-230-25263-9(X))* Palgrave Macmillan.

Delves, Stuart. Scotch Whisky: The Story of Scotland's Greatest Export. 2006. (Great Brand Stories Ser.). (ENG., Illus.). 192p. pap. 14.95 *(978-1-904879-71-8(3))* Cyan Communications GBR. Dist: Independent Pubs. Group.

Deming, Sean & Deming, Scott. The Brand Who Cried Wolf: Deliver on Your Company's Promise & Create Customers for Life. 2010. (ENG.). 224p. pap. 26.50 *(978-1-118-03676-1(X)*, Wiley) Wiley, John & Sons, Inc.

Designer Books. Magic Branding. 2011. (ENG.). 272p. 59.00 *(978-988-18078-0-9(8))* Links International (Leading International Key Services Barcelona, S.A.) ESP. Dist: National Bk. Network.

Dinnie, Keith. Nation Branding: Concepts, Issues, Practice. 2007. (ENG., Illus.). 288p. (C). per. 49.95 *(978-0-7506-8349-4(X))* Routledge.

Doyle, Mona. Package & Brand Likeability. 2007. 415.00 *(978-1-885747-83-9(7))* EPM Communications, Inc.

Duguid, Paul & Lopes, Teresa da Silva, eds. Trade Marks, Brands & Competitiveness. 2010. (Routledge International Studies in Business History Ser.). (ENG., Illus.). 270p. (C). 140.00 *(978-0-415-77693-6(7)*, Routledge) Taylor & Francis Group GBR. Dist: Taylor & Francis Group.

Dutta, Kirti. Brand Management: Principles & Practices. 2012. (ENG., Illus.). 576p. 45.00 ***(978-0-19-806986-7(3))*** Oxford Univ. Pr., Inc.

Ebbers, Lothar. Branding Amsterdam. 2011. 88p. pap. ***(978-3-8443-9111-4(8))*** Lambert Academic Publishing.

Edwards, Helen & Day, Derek. Creating Passion Brands: How to Build Emotional Brand Connection with Customers. 2007. (ENG., Illus.). 244p. per. 27.50 *(978-0-7494-4762-5(1))* Kogan Page, Ltd. GBR. Dist: Ingram Pub. Services.

Elliot, Betsy Rossen. 1000's of Amazing Uses for Everyday Products. 2010. 448p. 15.98 *(978-1-60553-340-7(8)*, Consumer Guide) Publications International, Ltd.

Elliott, Richard H. Brands & Brand Management, 4 vols. Elliott, Richard, ed. 2008. (Critical Perspectives on Business & Management Ser.). (ENG., Illus.). 2208p. (C). 1430.00 *(978-0-415-43324-2(X))* Routledge.

Entrepreneur Press, et al. Million Dollar Web Presence: Leverage Technology to Build & Transform Your Business. 2012. (ENG., Illus.). 240p. pap. 21.95 ***(978-1-59918-434-0(6)***, 1599184346) Entrepreneur Pr. dba Entrepreneur Media, Inc.

Ezrachi, Ariel & Bernitz, Ulf, eds. Private Labels, Branded Goods & Competition Policy: The Changing Landscape of Retail Competition. 2009. (ENG., Illus.). 400p. 245.00 *(978-0-19-955937-4(6))* Oxford Univ. Pr., Inc.

Fanning, John. The Importance of Being Branded: An Irish Perspective. 2006. (ENG.). 355p. 84.95 *(978-1-905785-00-1(3))*; (Illus.). 354p. per. 45.95 *(978-1-904148-93-7(X))* Liffey Pr., The IRL. Dist: Dufour Editions, Inc.

Favorite Brand Name Recipes Editors, ed. The Appetizer Bible. 2010. 256p. 14.98 *(978-1-60553-721-4(7))* Publications International, Ltd.

—Country Cookin' 3 Books In 1. 2010. 288p. 14.98 *(978-1-60553-688-0(1))* Publications International, Ltd.

—Great Tasting Potatoes. 2010. 144p. spiral bd. 10.98 *(978-1-60553-707-8(1))* Publications International, Ltd.

—Hearty Soups & Stews. 2010. 384p. 15.98 *(978-1-60553-713-9(6))* Publications International, Ltd.

—Simple 1-2-3 Chicken Recipes. 2010. 144p. spiral bd. 10.98 *(978-1-60553-118-2(9)*, PIL Kids) Publications International, Ltd.

—Simple 1-2-3 One-Dish Meals. 2010. 144p. spiral bd. 10.98 *(978-1-60553-119-9(7)*, PIL Kids) Publications International, Ltd.

—3 Books In 1: 100 Calorie Snacks, 200 Calorie Desserts, 300 Calorie Main Dishes. 2010. 288p. 14.98 *(978-1-60553-702-3(0))* Publications International, Ltd.

—3 Books In 1: Burger Recipes, Beer Recipes, Wings & More. 2010. 288p. 14.98 *(978-1-60553-701-6(2))* Publications International, Ltd.

—3 Books In 1: Pasta Recipes; Rice Recipes; Bean Recipes. 2010. 288p. 14.98 *(978-1-60553-652-1(0))* Publications International, Ltd.

Feurer. Gepflect: Krass Brandbody & Soul. 2008. pap. 60.00 *(978-3-89955-227-0(X))* Die Gestalten Verlag DEU. Dist: Prestel Publishing.

Finessi, Beppe, intro. How to Break the Rules of Brand Design in 10+8 Easy Exercises. 2009. (ENG., Illus.). 88p. pap. 15.00 *(978-88-7570-164-2(4))* Corraini ITA. Dist: D.A.P./Distributed Art Pubs.

Floor, Ko. Branding a Store: How to Build Successful Retail Brands in a Changing Marketplace. 2010. (ENG., Illus.). 304p. 45.00 *(978-90-6369-122-6(X))* Bis B.V., Uitgeverij(BIS Publishers) NLD. Dist: Consortium Bk. Sales & Distribution.

Foreman, Carol. Made in Scotland: Household Names That Began in Scotland. 2010. (ENG., Illus.). 224p. pap. 20.00 *(978-1-84158-725-7(7))* Birlinn, Ltd. GBR. Dist: Interlink Publishing Group, Inc.

Franzen, Giep & Moriarty, Sandra. The Science & Art of Branding. 2008. (ENG., Illus.). 592p. (C). 104.95 *(978-0-7656-1790-3(0))*; pap. 65.95 *(978-0-7656-1791-0(9))* Sharpe, M.E. Inc.

Fuguo, Yu. Big Brand. Lu, Jican, ed. 2008. (ENG., Illus.). 320p. 70.00 *(978-4-903233-29-1(4))* Azur Corp. JPN. Dist: Antique Collectors' Club.

Gaalan, Anneloes van. Indie Brands. 2012. (ENG., Illus.). 224p. 49.00 ***(978-90-6369-219-3(6))*** Bis B.V., Uitgeverij(BIS Publishers) NLD. Dist: Consortium Bk. Sales & Distribution.

Gaines-Ross, Leslie. Corporate Reputation: 12 Steps to Safeguarding & Recovering Reputation. 2008. (ENG., Illus.). 208p. 39.95 *(978-0-470-17150-9(2)*, Wiley) Wiley, John & Sons, Inc.

George, Peter. Brand Road Map: Your Guide to Greater Profits. 2006. spiral bd. 279.00 *(978-0-9779095-1-3(4)*, 1) Envision Branding.

Gerzema, John & Lebar, Edward. Brand Bubble: The Looming Crisis in Brand Value & How to Avoid It. 2008. (ENG., Illus.). 272p. 27.95 *(978-0-470-18387-3(X)*, Jossey-Bass) Wiley, John & Sons, Inc.

Gilmore, Fiona. Warriors on the High Wire: The Balancing Act of Brand Leadership in the 21st Century. 2006. 264p. reprint ed. pap. 22.00 *(978-1-4223-5796-5(1))* DIANE Publishing Co.

Gimenez, Marc. Branding Logos: From the First Sketch to Final Trademark. Gimenez, Marc & Minguet, Josep Maria, eds. 2011. (ENG & SPA., Illus.). 192p. pap. 62.50 ***(978-84-15223-09-2(9))*** Instituto Monsa de Ediciones, S.A. ESP. Dist: Trans-Atlantic Pubns., Inc.

Global Brand Shop Windows Design. 2008. 306p. *(978-7-5611-3577-8(7))* Dalian Univ. of Technology Electronic & Audio-Visual Pr.

Gobé, Marc. Emotional Branding: The New Paradigm for Connecting Brands to People. rev. ed. 2010. (ENG., Illus.). 352p. pap. 19.95 *(978-1-58115-672-0(3)*, 115672, Allworth Pr.) Skyhorse Publishing Co., Inc.

Goodson, Scott. Uprising: How to Build a Brand — and Change the World — by Sparking Cultural Movements. 2012. (ENG., Illus.). 256p. 26.00 ***(978-0-07-178282-1(6)***, 0071782826) McGraw-Hill Cos., The.

Grainge, Paul. Brand Hollywood: Selling Entertainment in a Global Media Age. 2007. (Illus.). 212p. per. 34.95 *(978-0-415-35405-9(6))*; 224p. 120.00 *(978-0-415-35404-2(8))* Routledge.

Grams, Chris. The Ad-Free Brand: Secrets to Building Successful Brands in a Digital World. rev. ed. 2011. (Que Biz-Tech Ser.). (ENG.). 300p. pap. 24.99 *(978-0-7897-4802-7(9))* Que.

Graphis Inc. Staff. Branding USA No. 2, Vol. 2. 2008. (Illus.). 320p. 50.00 *(978-1-932026-06-1(1))* Graphis, U.S., Inc.

Green, Joey. Joey Green's Amazing Pet Cures: 1,130 Simple Pet Remedies & Treatments Using Brand-Name Products. 2011. (ENG., Illus.). 352p. pap. 17.99 *(978-1-60529-128-4(5))*; ***(978-1-60529-129-1(3))*** Rodale Pr., Inc.

—Joey Green's Cleaning Magic: 2,336 Ingenious Cleanups Using Brand-Name Products. 2010. (ENG., Illus.). 416p. pap. 18.99 *(978-1-60529-745-3(3))* Rodale Pr., Inc.

—Joey Green's Clearing Magic: 2,398 Ingenious Cleanups Using Brand-Name Products. 2010. *(978-1-60529-744-6(5))* Rodale Pr., Inc.

—Joey Green's Fix-It Magic: More Than 1,971 Quick-and-Easy Home Solutions Using Brand-Name Products. 2008. *(978-1-59486-784-2(4))* Rodale Pr., Inc.

—Joey Green's Fix-It Magic: More than 1,971 Quick-and-Easy Household Solutions Using Brand-Name Products. 2008. 14.50 *(978-1-60529-917-4(0))*; (ENG., Illus.). 416p. pap. 17.95 *(978-1-59486-785-9(2))* Rodale Pr., Inc.

Greenman, Barbara & Matlin, Elizabeth, eds. Back of the Box Cooking 30-Minute Meals: 500 Quick & Easy Family Recipes from America's Favorite Brands. 2010. (ENG., Illus.). 352p. 19.95 *(978-1-57912-812-8(2)*, 1579128122) Black Dog & Leventhal Pubs., Inc.

Group work, compiled by. Re-logo: Redesigning the Brand, 1 vol. 2011. (ENG., Illus.). 272p. *(978-84-92810-28-4(9))* Promotora de prensa internacional S.A.

Guitton, Pedro. Packaging Identity, 1 vol. 2009. (ENG.). 354p. 17.95 *(978-84-92643-28-8(5))* Index Bks., Spain ESP. Dist: Innovative Logistics.

Gunelius, Susan. Building Brand Value the Playboy Way. 2009. (ENG., Illus.). 256p. 49.00 *(978-0-230-57789-3(X))* Palgrave Macmillan.

—Harry Potter: The Story of a Global Business Phenomenon. 2008. (ENG., Illus.). 216p. 45.00 *(978-0-230-20323-5(X))* Palgrave Macmillan.

Hackley, Chris. Advertising & Promotion: An Integrated Marketing Communications Approach. 2nd ed. 2010. (Illus.). 360p. (C). pap. 62.00 *(978-1-84920-146-9(3)*, B01452P) SAGE Pubns., Ltd. GBR. Dist: SAGE Pubns., Inc.

Haig, Matt. Brand Failures: The Truth about the 100 Biggest Branding Mistakes of All Time. 2nd rev. ed. 2011. (ENG.). 256p. pap. 19.95 *(978-0-7494-6299-4(X))* Kogan Page, Ltd. GBR. Dist: Ingram Pub. Services.

—Brand Success: How the World's Top 100 Brands Thrive & Survive. 2nd rev. ed. 2011. (ENG.). 304p. pap. 19.95 *(978-0-7494-6287-1(6))* Kogan Page, Ltd. GBR. Dist: Ingram Pub. Services.

Hallward, John. Gimme! the Human Nature of Successful Marketing. 2007. (ENG., Illus.). 240p. 24.95 *(978-0-470-10029-5(X)*, Wiley) Wiley, John & Sons, Inc.

Halve, Anand. Darwin's Brands: Adapting to Succeed. 2012. (Response Bks.). (Illus.). 264p. (C). pap. 33.00 ***(978-81-321-0715-6(2)***, B07156P) SAGE Pubns., Inc.

Hammond James. Branding Your Business: Promoting Your Business Attracting Customers & Standing Out in the Market Place. rev. ed. 2011. (Business Success Ser.). (ENG., Illus.). 272p. pap. 24.95 *(978-0-7494-6296-3(5))* Kogan Page, Ltd. GBR. Dist: Ingram Pub. Services.

Hand, Amy. Enhance Your Training Brand. 2010. (ENG.). 16p. pap. 24.95 *(978-1-56286-726-3(1))* American Society for Training & Development.

Handley, Bill & Cockrum, Jim. Free Marketing: 101 Low & No-Cost Ways to Grow Your Business, Online & Off. 2011. (ENG., Illus.). 352p. 24.95 *(978-1-118-03471-2(6)*, Wiley) Wiley, John & Sons, Inc.

Hatch, Steve & Taylor, Jim. Rigorous Magic: Communication Ideas & Their Application. 2007. (ENG., Illus.). 304p. 49.95 *(978-0-470-02601-4(4)*, Wiley) Wiley John & Sons, Inc.

Healey, Matthew. What Is Branding? (Essential Design Handbooks Ser.). (ENG., Illus.). 256p. 2010. pap. 25.00 *(978-2-88893-135-5(4)*, 2888931354) 2008. 35.00 *(978-2-940361-45-8(2)*, 2940361452) RotoVision SA CHE. Dist: Quayside.

Heding, Tilde, et al. Brand Management: Research, Theory & Practice. 2009. (ENG., Illus.). 288p. (C). 160.00 *(978-0-415-44326-5(1))*; pap. 47.95 *(978-0-415-44327-2(X))* Routledge.

Hegner, Sabrina. Self-Concept & Consumer Behaviour - a Meta-Analysis. 2008. 208p. pap. *(978-3-639-00315-4(2))* VDM Verlag Dr. Mueller e.K.

Hill, Laura. CoolBrands 2009/10: An Insight into Some of Britain's Coolest Brands. Cooper, Angela, ed. 2009. (Illus.). 175p. 112.50 *(978-0-9554784-8-2(0))* Superbrands (UK), Ltd. GBR. Dist: Trans-Atlantic Pubns., Inc.

Hill, Laura, ed. Coolbrands 2011/12. 2011. (Illus.). 150p. 115.00 ***(978-0-9565334-2-5(6))*** Superbrands (UK), Ltd. GBR. Dist: Trans-Atlantic Pubns., Inc.

Hoffmann, Stefanie. Brand Management by Using Special Marketing Strategies. 2008. 72p. pap. *(978-3-639-06448-3(8))* VDM Verlag Dr. Mueller e.K.

Hollis, Nigel. The Global Brand: How to Create & Develop Lasting Brand Value in the World Market. 2010. (ENG., Illus.). 272p. pap. 17.00 *(978-0-230-62056-8(6))* Palgrave Macmillan.

Howard, Jim, et al. Branded for Success: The Entrepreneur's Quick-Start Guide to Making a Profitable, Lasting Impression. 2007. (ENG.). per. 16.95 *(978-1-60037-169-1(8))* Morgan James Publishing.

Ilasco, Meg Mateo & Seto, Catherine. Mom, Inc: The Essential Guide to Running a Successful Business Close to Home. 2012. (ENG., Illus.). 208p. pap. 16.95 ***(978-1-4521-0121-7(3))*** Chronicle Bks. LLC.

Ind, Nicholas. Living the Brand: How to Transform Every Member of Your Organization into a Brand Champion. 3rd rev. ed. 2007. (ENG., Illus.). 200p. 39.95 *(978-0-7494-5083-0(5))* Kogan Page, Ltd. GBR. Dist: Ingram Pub. Services.

Ind, Nicholas & Bjerke, Rune. Branding Governance: A Participatory Approach to the Brand Building Process. 5th ed. 2007. (ENG., Illus.). 288p. 55.00 *(978-0-470-03075-2(5)*, Wiley) Wiley, John & Sons, Inc.

Jiaojiao Chen & Yangjun, Peng. Adidas. 2007. (Brands A to Z Ser.). (Illus.). 240p. *(978-981-245-484-3(5))* Page One Publishing.

John, Daymond. The Brand Within: The Power of Branding from Birth to the Boardroom. 2010. pap. 14.99 *(978-0-9825962-1-0(9))* Sapphire Blue Entertainment Co.

Johnson, Catherine. Branding Television. 2011. (Comedia Ser.). (ENG., Illus.). 224p. (C). 120.00 *(978-0-415-54842-7(X))*; pap. 39.95 *(978-0-415-54843-4(8))* Routledge.

Johnson Phillip. Ambush Marketing & Brand Protection: Law & Practice. 2nd ed. 2012. (ENG.). 472p. 290.00 ***(978-0-19-969645-1(4))*** Oxford Univ. Pr., Inc.

Jones, Nic. Marketing Brands to Children - Ethically. 2009. 96p. pap. 19.95 *(978-1-60860-256-8(7)*, Strategic Bk. Publishing) AEG Literary Publishing Services, Inc.

Kapferer, Jean-Noël. The New Strategic Brand Management: Advanced Insights & Strategic Thinking. 5th ed. 2012. (ENG., Illus.). 512p. pap. 70.00 ***(978-0-7494-6515-5(8))*** Kogan Page, Ltd. GBR. Dist: Ingram Pub. Services.

Kapferer, Jean-Noël & Bastien, Vincent. The Luxury Strategy: Break the Rules of Marketing to Build Luxury Brands. 2009. (ENG., Illus.). 384p. 49.95 *(978-0-7494-5477-7(6))* Kogan Page, Ltd. GBR. Dist: Ingram Pub. Services.

Kapoor, Avinash & Kulshretha, Chinmaya. Branding & Sustainable Competitive Advantage: Building Virtual Presence. 2011. ***(978-1-61350-173-3(0))***; 385p. 185.00 ***(978-1-61350-171-9(4))*** IGI Global.

Kapoor, Jagdeep. Twenty Four Brand Mantras: Finding a Place in the Minds & Hearts of Consumers. 2nd ed. 2009. (Illus.). 116p. (C). pap. 19.95 *(978-81-7829-943-3(7)*, B99433P) SAGE Pubns., Inc.

—9 Brand Shaastras: Nine Successful Brand Strategies to Build Winning Brands. 2nd ed. 2009. (Response Bks.). (Illus.). 108p. (C). pap. 19.95 *(978-81-321-0229-8(0)*, B02298P) SAGE Pubns., Inc.

Karlsson, Ted. Branding Behind the Scenes - Internal Corporate Brand Building in Three Swedish Service Firms. 2008. 172p. pap. *(978-3-639-08450-3(8))* VDM Verlag Dr. Mueller e.K.

Katahn, Martin. Low Fat Supermarket Shoppers Guide. 2080p. pap. 79.80 *(978-0-393-32659-8(4))* Norton, W. W. & Co., Inc.

Kayode, Muyiwa. The Seven Dimensions of Branding: Brand Building from the African Perspective. 2011. 124p. 21.23 ***(978-1-4634-3428-1(6))***; pap. 11.99 ***(978-1-4634-3429-8(4))*** AuthorHouse.

Keller. Strategic Brand Management: Building, Me. 2006. (ENG.). 365p. pap. 16.95 *(978-1-4288-1004-4(8))* Cram101 Inc.

Keller, Kevin Lane. Best Practice Cases in Branding: Lessons from the World's Strongest Brands. 3rd ed. 2007. (ENG., Illus.). 382p. (C). per. 69.33 *(978-0-13-188665-4(X)*, Prentice Hall) Prentice Hall PTR.

—Strategic Brand Management: Building, Measuring, & Managing Brand Equity. 3rd rev. ed. 2007. (ENG., Illus.). 720p. (C). 213.33 *(978-0-13-188859-3(5)*, Prentice Hall) Prentice Hall PTR.

Keller, Kevin Lane, et al. Strategic Brand Management: A European Perspective. (ENG., Illus.). 2008. 856p. pap. 110.00 *(978-0-273-70632-8(2))* 2nd rev. ed. 2011. 940p. pap. 117.50 ***(978-0-273-73787-2(2))*** Pearson Education, Ltd. GBR. Dist: Trans-Atlantic Pubns., Inc.

Kelley Larry D. & Jugenheimer, Donald W. Advertising Media Planning: A Brand Management Approach. 2nd rev. ed. 2008. (Illus.). 188p. 89.95 *(978-0-7656-2032-3(4))*; per. 39.95 *(978-0-7656-2033-0(2))* Sharpe, M.E. Inc.

Kelley, Larry D., et al. Advertising Media Planning: A Brand Management Approach. 3rd ed. 2011. (ENG., Illus.). 304p. (C). 99.95 *(978-0-7656-2535-6(7))*; pap. 49.95 ***(978-0-7656-2636-3(5))*** Sharpe, M.E. Inc.

Kenyon, Andrew, et al, eds. The Law of Reputation & Brands in the Asia Pacific Region. 2012. (Cambridge Intellectual Property & Information Law Ser.: 16). (ENG., Illus.). 298p. 145.00 ***(978-1-107-01772-6(6))*** Cambridge Univ. Pr.

Kimpakorn, Narumon & Narumon, Kimpakorn. Service Brand Equity: The Linkage Between Internal & External Branding. 2011. 168p. pap. ***(978-3-639-31922-4(2))*** VDM Verlag Dr. Mueller e.K.

Klant, Michael. Art Brands: Wenn Hunde Beuys Fressen/When Dogs Eat Beuys. 2008. (GER & ENG., Illus.). 120p. pap. 30.00 *(978-3-7757-2116-5(9))* Hatje Cantz Verlag GmbH & Co KG DEU. Dist: D.A.P./Distributed Art Pubs.

Klein, Naomi. No Logo. 10th anniv. ed. 2009. (ENG., Illus.). 544p. pap. 16.00 *(978-0-312-42927-0(4))* Picador.

Klingmann, Anna. Brandscapes: Architecture in the Experience Economy. (ENG., Illus.). 378p. (gr. 17). 2010. pap. 19.95 *(978-0-262-51503-0(2))* 2007. 31.95 *(978-0-262-11303-8(1))* MIT Pr.

Koris, Riina. Brand Personality As an Image Conveyor. 2010. 96p. pap. *(978-3-8383-6076-8(1))* Lambert Academic Publishing.

Kornberger, Martin. Brand Society: How Brands Transform Management & Lifestyle. 2010. (ENG., Illus.). 328p. 100.00 *(978-0-521-89826-3(9))*; pap. 40.00 *(978-0-521-72690-0(5))* Cambridge Univ. Pr.

Kotler, Philip & Pfoertsch, Waldemar. B2B Brand Management. (ENG.). xvi, 357p. 2010. pap. 49.95 *(978-3-642-06470-8(1)*, 3642064701) 2006. (Illus.). 49.95 *(978-3-540-25360-0(2)*, 3540253602) Springer.

—Ingredient Branding: Making the Invisible Visible. 2010. (ENG., Illus.). xx, 393p. 49.95 *(978-3-642-04213-3(9)*, 3642042139) Springer.

Kremer, Ludger & Ronneberger-Sibold, Elke. Names in Commerce & Industry: Past & Present. 2008. (FRE, GER & ENG., Illus.). 433p. pap. *(978-3-8325-1788-5(X))* Logos Verlag Berlin.

Kumar, Nirmalya & Steenkamp, Jan-Benedict E. M. Private Label Strategy: How to Meet the Store Brand Challenge. 2007. (ENG., Illus.). 270p. 35.00 *(978-1-4221-0167-4(3))* Harvard Business Review Pr.

Lacroix, Jean-Pierre. Belonging Experiences: Designing Engaged Brands. 2010. 136p. 23.95 *(978-1-4502-3050-6(4))*; (ENG.). pap. 13.95 *(978-1-4502-3051-3(2))* iUniverse, Inc.

Lam, Benson & Bin, Xu. Iconic storefronts USA. 2009. (ENG.). 502p. 59.00 *(978-84-96969-63-6(0))* Links International (Leading International Key Services Barcelona, S.A.) ESP. Dist: National Bk. Network.

Land, Bob. America's Greatest Brands. (America's Greatest Brands Ser.). (ENG.). 2011. 116p. 45.00 ***(978-0-9706860-8-4(0))*** 2009. 113p. 45.00 *(978-0-9706860-6-0(4))* America's Greatest Brands.

Land, Bob. America's Greatest Brands: An Insight into Many of America's Strongest & Most Valuable Brands. (America's Greatest Brands Ser.). (ENG., Illus.). 2007. 118p. 60.00 *(978-0-9706860-5-3(6))* 2006. 126p. 75.00 *(978-0-9706860-4-6(8))* America's Greatest Brands.

Land, Bob, ed. America's Greatest Brands: An Insight into Many of America's Strongest & Most Valuable Brands. 2011. (America's Greatest Brands Ser.). (ENG., Illus.). 112p. 45.00 *(978-0-9706860-7-7(2))* America's Greatest Brands.

Lane, Frank. Killer Brands: Create & Market a Brand That Will Annihilate the Competition. 2007. (ENG., Illus.). 224p. per. 14.95 *(978-1-59869-123-8(6))* Adams Media Corp.

Lavric, Eva & Fischer, Fiorenza, eds. People, Products, & Professions: Choosing a Name, Choosing a Language Fachleute, Firmennamen und Fremdsprachen. 2009. (Sprache im Kontext Ser.). (GER & ENG.). 324p. pap. 81.95 *(978-3-631-58556-6(X))* Lang, Peter GmbH, Europaischer Verlag der Wissenschaften DEU. Dist: Lang, Peter.

Lee, Jason W. Branded: Branding in Sport Business. 2010. 370p. pap. 40.00 *(978-1-59460-506-2(8))* Carolina Academic Pr.

Levy, Andrew & Bartkowiak, Judy. Secrets of Success in Brand Licensing. 2011. 206p. pap. ***(978-1-908218-95-7(9))*** MX Publishing, Ltd.

Light, Larry & Kiddon, Joan. Six Rules for Brand Revitalization: Learn How Companies Like Mcdonald's Can Re-Energize Their Brands. 2009. (ENG., Illus.). 240p. 39.99 *(978-0-13-604331-7(3))* Wharton Schl. Publishing.

Lincoln, Keith & Thomassen, Lars. How to Succeed at Retail: Winning Case Studies & Strategies for Retailers & Brands. 2009. (ENG., Illus.). 224p. pap. 27.95 *(978-0-7494-5594-1(2))* Kogan Page, Ltd. GBR. Dist: Ingram Pub. Services.

—Private Label: Turning the Retail Brand Threat into Your Biggest Opportunity. 2009. (ENG., Illus.). 320p. pap. 27.95 *(978-0-7494-5593-4(4))* Kogan Page, Ltd. GBR. Dist: Ingram Pub. Services.

Lincoln, Keith, et al. Retailization: Brand Survival in the Age of Retailer Power. 2009. (ENG., Illus.). 240p. pap. 27.95 *(978-0-7494-5336-7(2))* Kogan Page, Ltd. GBR. Dist: Ingram Pub. Services.

Lindemann, Jan. The Economy of Brands. 2010. (ENG., Illus.). 192p. 47.00 *(978-0-230-23250-1(7))* Palgrave Macmillan.

Lindstrom, Martin. Brand Sense: Sensory Secrets Behind the Stuff We Buy. 2010. (ENG.). 192p. pap. 15.00 *(978-1-4391-7201-8(3)*, Free Pr.) Free Pr.

Loken, Barbara, et al, eds. Brands & Brand Management: Contemporary Research Perspective. 2009. (Marketing & Consumer Psychology Ser.). (ENG., Illus.). 344p. 74.95 *(978-1-84169-759-8(1)*, Psychology Press) Taylor & Francis Group GBR. Dist: Taylor & Francis Group.

Lopes, Teresa da Silva. Global Brands: The Evolution of Multinationals in Alcoholic Beverages. 2007. (Cambridge Studies in the Emergence of Global Enterprise Ser.). (ENG., Illus.). 326p. 60.00 *(978-0-521-83397-4(3))* Cambridge Univ. Pr.

Lu, Pierre Xiao. Elite China: Luxury Consumer Behaviour in China. 2008. (ENG., Illus.). 320p. pap. 38.00 *(978-0-470-82267-8(8)*, Wiley) Wiley, John & Sons, Inc.

MacInnis, Deborah J., et al, eds. Handbook of Brand Relationships. 2009. (Advertising & Consumer Psychology Ser.). (ENG., Illus.). 448p. 89.95 *(978-0-7656-2357-7(9))* Sharpe, M.E. Inc.

Maddock, G. Michael, et al. Brand New: Solving the Innovation Paradox — How Great Brands Invent & Launch New Products, Services, & Business Models. 2011. (ENG., Illus.). 218p. 29.95 *(978-0-470-64359-4(5)*, Wiley) Wiley, John & Sons, Inc.

Martin, Dick. Rebuilding Brand America: What We Must Do to Restore Our Reputation & Safeguard the Future of American Business Abroad. 2007. (ENG., Illus.). 304p. 27.95 *(978-0-8144-7333-7(4))* Amacom.

Mathieson, Rick. The On-Demand Brand: 10 Rules for Digital Marketing Success in an Anytime, Everywhere World, 1 vol. 2010. (ENG., Illus.). 304p. 24.95 *(978-0-8144-1572-6(3))* Amacom.

Mazzalovo, Gerald. Brand Aesthetics. 2012. (ENG., Illus.). 240p. 95.00 ***(978-0-230-33673-5(5))*** Palgrave Macmillan.

McGraw-Hill Companies Staff, contrib. by. Food Composition Table. 2008. (ENG., Illus.). 128p. (C). pap. 8.00 *(978-0-07-340256-7(7)*, 0073402567, McGraw-Hill Science, Engineering & Mathematics) McGraw-Hill Higher Education.

McNally, David & Speak, Karl D. Be Your Own Brand: Achieve More of What You Want by Being More of Who You Are. 2nd ed. 2011. (ENG., Illus.). 168p. pap. 19.95 *(978-1-60509-810-4(8))* Berrett-Koehler Pubs., Inc.

Meister, Sandra. Brand Communities for Fast Moving Consumer Goods: An Empirical Study of Members' Behavior & the Economic Relevance for the Marketer. 2012. (ENG., Illus.). xxiv, 292p. pap. 89.95 ***(978-3-8349-4054-4(2)***, 3834940542) Westdeutscher Verlag GmbH DEU. Dist: Springer.

Middleton, Alan C. & Hanna, J. M. Ikonica: A Field Guide to Canada's Brandscape, 1 vol. 2008. (ENG., Illus.). 224p. pap. 32.95 *(978-1-55365-275-5(4))* D&M Pubs. Inc. CAN. Dist: Perseus-PGW.

Miletsky, Jason & Smith, Genevieve L. Perspectives on Branding. 2009. (ENG., Illus.). 320p. pap. 29.99 *(978-1-59863-872-1(6))* Course Technology.

Milligan, Andy. Brand Beckham: How an English Soccer Player Became a Multi-Million Dollar Brand. 2nd ed. 2008. (ENG.). 192p. 16.95 *(978-1-904879-06-0(3))* Cyan Communications GBR. Dist: Independent Pubs. Group.

—Brand It Like Beckham: Building a Brand with Balls. rev. ed. 2006. (Great Brand Stories Ser.). (ENG., Illus.). 208p. pap. 16.95 (978-1-904879-29-9(2)) Cyan Communications GBR. Dist: Independent Pubs. Group.

—Brand It Like Beckham: The Story of How Brand Beckham Was Built, 1 vol. 2011. (ENG., Illus.). 224p. pap. 17.99 (978-981-4276-93-1(6)) Marshall Cavendish International (Asia) Private Ltd. SGP. Dist: Marshall Cavendish Corp.

Millman, Debbie. Brand Bible: The Complete Guide to Building, Designing, & Sustaining Brands. 2012. (ENG., Illus.). 312p. pap. 45.00 (978-1-59253-726-6(X), 159253726X) Quayside.

—Brand Thinking & Other Noble Pursuits. 2011. (ENG.). 256p. 29.95 (978-1-58115-864-9(5), 115864, Allworth Pr.) Skyhorse Publishing Co., Inc.

Minnick, Fred. The Brand That Changed Beef: How Certified Angus Beef Became a Worldwide Icon of Quality: A Company Biography. 2010. (978-1-59098-485-7(4)) Wooster Bk. Co., The.

Montoya, Peter & Vandehey, Tim. The Brand Called You: Make Your Business Stand Out in a Crowded Marketplace. 2008. (ENG., Illus.). 288p. pap. 16.95 (978-0-07-159750-0(6), 0071597506) McGraw-Hill Cos., The.

Mooney, Kelly & Rollins, Nita. The Open Brand: When Push Comes to Pull in a Web-Made World. 2008. (Voices That Matter Ser.). (ENG., Illus.). 208p. pap. 29.99 (978-0-321-54423-0(4)) New Riders Publishing.

Moor, Liz. The Rise of Brands. 2007. (ENG., Illus.). 192p. pap. 29.95 (978-1-84520-384-9(4)) Berg Pubs. GBR. Dist: Macmillan.

Moore, Anne Elizabeth. Unmarketable: Brandalism, Copyfighting, Mocketing, & the Erosion of Integrity. 2007. (ENG.). 262p. pap. 15.95 (978-1-59558-168-6(5)) New Pr., The.

Mores, Claudio Marenco & Marsilio. From Fiorucci to the Guerrilla Stores: Shop Displays in Architecture, Marketing & Communications. 2007. (Mode Ser.). (ENG., Illus.). 114p. pap. 19.95 (978-88-317-8957-8(0)) Marsilio Editori spa ITA. Dist: Random Hse., Inc.

Morgan, Adam & Morgan. Eating the Big Fish: How Challenger Brands Can Compete Against Brand Leaders. 2nd ed. 2009. (ENG., Illus.). 368p. 29.95 (978-0-470-23827-1(5), Wiley) Wiley, John & Sons, Inc.

Morley, Michael. The Global Corporate Brand Book. 2009. (ENG., Illus.). 256p. 46.00 (978-1-4039-9663-3(6)) Palgrave Macmillan.

Morris, Brenda. History of the Local Grammar School Through Time. 2012. (Illus.). 192p. pap. 22.95 (**978-1-84868-292-4(1)**) Amberley Publishing GBR. Dist: Casemate Pubs. & Bk. Distributors, LLC.

Moss, Giles David. Pharmaceuticals — Where's the Brand Logic? Branding Lessons & Strategies. 2007. (Illus.). 233p. per. 34.00 (978-0-7890-3259-1(7), Informa Healthcare) Taylor & Francis Group.

—Pharmaceuticals — Where's the Brand Logic? Branding Lessons & Strategy. 2007. (Illus.). 223p. 34.00 (978-0-7890-3258-4(9), Informa Healthcare) Taylor & Francis Group.

Moutin. Consumer Behaviour, Branding & Counterfeiting. 2011. 107.00 (978-981-4287-03-6(2)) World Scientific Publishing Co., Inc.

Nadeau, Raymond A. Living Brands: Collaboration + Innovation = Customer Fascination. 2006. (ENG., Illus.). 288p. 29.95 (978-0-07-146614-1(2), 0071466142) McGraw-Hill Cos., The.

Napoletano, Erika. The Power of Un-Popular: A Guide to Building Your Brand for the Audience Who Will Love You (And Why No One Else Matters) 2012. (ENG.). 224p. 24.95 (**978-1-118-13466-5(4)**, Wiley) Wiley, John & Sons, Inc.

Newlin, Kate. Passion Brands: Why Some Brands Are Just Gotta Have, Drive All Night for, & Tell All Your Friends About. 2009. (ENG.). 255p. bds. 24.95 (978-1-59102-687-7(3)) Prometheus Bks., Pubs.

Newton, David & Newton, David C. Trademarked: A History of Well-Known Brands, from Aertex to Wright's Coal Tar. 2008. (ENG., Illus.). 384p. 39.95 (978-0-7509-4590-5(7)) History Pr. Ltd., The GBR. Dist: Independent Pubs. Group.

Nichols, David. Return on Ideas: A Practical Guide to Making Innovation Pay. 2007. (ENG., Illus.). 280p. 55.00 (978-0-470-02857-5(2), Wiley) Wiley, John & Sons, Inc.

Nickles, Liz & Iyer, Savita. Brandstorm: Surviving & Thriving in the Consumer-Driven Marketplace. 2012. (ENG., Illus.). 256p. 26.00 (**978-0-230-34168-5(3)**) Palgrave Macmillan.

Nobre, Helena. Intimate Brand Relationships. 2010. 252p. pap. (978-3-8383-7633-2(1)) Lambert Academic Publishing.

O'Brien, Tim. The Power of Personal Branding: Creating Celebrity Status with Your Target Audience. 2007. 24.95 (978-0-9714589-0-1(1)) Mendham Publishing.

Okonkwo, Uche. Luxury Fashion Branding: Trends, Tactics, Techniques. 2007. (ENG., Illus.). 320p. 53.00 (978-0-230-52167-4(3)) Palgrave Macmillan.

Oliveira, Olivia. Marcas Y Trademarks2. 2006. 928p. 80.00 (978-84-252-2073-9(4)) Trucatriche.

Osterman, Jim & Visual, Reference P. Excellence in Brand Advertising. 2007. (Illus.). 208p. 50.00 (978-1-58471-082-0(9)) Visual Reference Pubns., Inc.

Oswald, Laura R. Marketing Semiotics: Signs, Culture, & Brand Value. 2012. (ENG., Illus.). 304p. 110.00 (**978-0-19-956649-5(6)**); pap. 40.00 (**978-0-19-956650-1(X)**) Oxford Univ. Pr., Inc.

Page, Tom. Emotive Design Methods in Product Branding. 2011. 108p. pap. (**978-3-8443-1067-2(3)**) Lambert Academic Publishing.

Peck, Corey, et al. Pharmaceutical Product Branding Strategies: Simulating Patient Flow & Portfolio Dynamics. 2nd rev. ed. 2009. (ENG., Illus.). 312p. 250.00 (978-1-4200-8770-3(3), Informa Healthcare) Taylor & Francis Group GBR. Dist: Taylor & Francis Group.

Pfoertsch, Waldemar, et al, eds. Business Brand Design Management. 2009. 200p. 99.00 (978-3-540-71495-8(2)) Springer.

Philp, Bruce. Consumer Republic: Using Brands to Get What You Want, Make Corporations Behave, & Maybe Even Save the World. 2012. (ENG.). 288p. pap. 17.95 (**978-0-7710-7004-4(7)**, Emblem Edns) McClelland & Stewart CAN. Dist: Random Hse., Inc.

Pike, Andy. Brands & Branding Geographies. 2011. (Illus.). 384p. 150.00 (**978-1-84980-159-1(2)**) Elgar, Edward Publishing, Inc.

Pillsbury Editors. Easy As Pie: 140 Simple Recipes + 1 Readymade Pie Crust = Sweet Success. 2010. (ENG., Illus.). 208p. 19.95 (978-0-470-48553-8(1), Wiley) Wiley, John & Sons, Inc.

—Pillsbury Savvy Shopper's Cookbook: Hundreds of Simple Strategies for Smart Spending & Inspiring Mealtime Ideas. 2010. (ENG., Illus.). 228p. pap. 17.95 (978-0-470-54397-9(3), Wiley) Wiley, John & Sons, Inc.

Pont, Simon. The Better Mousetrap: Brand Invention in a Media Democracy. 2012. (ENG., Illus.). 272p. pap. 34.95 (**978-0-7494-6621-3(9)**) Kogan Page, Ltd. GBR. Dist: Ingram Pub. Services.

Prinz, Dominik. Cause Branding. 2011. 80p. pap. (**978-3-8433-8964-8(0)**) Lambert Academic Publishing.

Publications International Staff. Chicken Hamburger 3 In 1. 2006. (Illus.). 288p. spiral bd. 10.98 (978-1-4127-2485-2(6), PIL Kids) Publications International, Ltd.

—GCampbell's Recipe COLL 5 Ring Binder. 2009. 512p. 29.95 (978-1-4127-5328-9(7), PIL Kids) Publications International, Ltd.

—Jello Favorite Desserts. 2008. 96p. spiral bd. 9.98 (978-1-4127-2752-5(9)) Publications International, Ltd.

—3 in 1 Church Pot Luck, Sunday Supper, Bake Sale. 2009. 288p. spiral bd. 14.98 (978-1-4127-5697-6(9), PIL Kids) Publications International, Ltd.

—3 in 1 Nabisco, Velveeta, Kraft. 2009. 288p. spiral bd. 14.98 (978-1-4127-7786-5(0), PIL Kids) Publications International, Ltd.

—3 in 1 Weeknight Meals, Pot Luck, Bake Sale. 2008. 288p. spiral bd. 14.98 (978-1-4127-2911-6(4)) Publications International, Ltd.

Publications International Staff, contrib. by. Favorite Brand Name Baking. 2007. (Illus.). 383p. 16.98 (978-1-4127-2602-3(6)) Publications International, Ltd.

Publications International Staff, contrib. by. Slow Cooker: 101 Recipes. 2011. (Illus.). 144p. (**978-1-4508-2164-3(2)**) Publications International, Ltd.

Publications International Staff, creator. Favorite Brand Name Slow Cooker Recipes. 2007. (Favorite Brand Name Ser.). (Illus.). 383p. 15.98 (978-1-4127-2811-9(8)) Publications International, Ltd.

—Incredibly Easy Silly Snacks. 2007. (Favorite Brand Name Ser.). (Illus.). 160p. 9.98 (978-1-4127-2801-0(0)) Publications International, Ltd.

—100 Best Appetizer Recipes. 2007. (100 Best Ser.). (Illus.). 160p. 9.98 (978-1-4127-2871-3(1)) Publications International, Ltd.

—100 Best Cupcake Recipes. 2007. (Favorite Brand Name Ser.). (Illus.). 157p. 9.98 (978-1-4127-9315-5(7)) Publications International, Ltd.

Publications International Staff, ed. Philadelphia. 2009. 256p. 14.98 (978-1-4127-7877-0(8), PIL Kids) Publications International, Ltd.

—Simple 123 Chicken. 2007. 6.83 (978-1-4127-2401-2(5)) Publications International, Ltd.

—100 Best Cupcakes. 2008. spiral bd. 12.98 (978-1-4127-2717-4(0)) Publications International, Ltd.

—100 Best Holiday Cookies. 2007. spiral bd. 12.98 (978-1-4127-2546-0(1)) Publications International, Ltd.

—1000s of Amazing Uses for Everyday Products. 2011. 448p. 15.98 (978-1-4508-1569-7(3)) Publications International, Ltd.

Rai, Mintu Kumar. Market Mapping of Fpd & Mop Tracking: Market Mapping of Flat Pannel Display & Market Operating Price Tracking of Lg's Selected Model of Lcd in Guwahati Market. 2011. 128p. pap. (**978-3-639-33414-2(0)**) VDM Verlag Dr. Mueller e.K.

Ramesh Kumar, S. Marketing & Branding: The Indian Scenario. 2007. (Illus.). xiv, 482p. (978-81-317-0097-6(6)) Dorling Kindersley Pvt Ltd.

Reitzle, Saskia. Markenleasing: Theoretische Fundierung und praxisorientierte Evaluation der Möglichkeiten und Grenzen. 2010. (Strategisches Marketingmanagement Ser.). (GER.). 352p. 89.95 (978-3-631-59441-4(0)) Lang, Peter GmbH, Europaischer Verlag der Wissenschaften DEU. Dist: Lang, Peter.

Ricca, Manfredi & Robins, Rebecca. Meta-Luxury: Brands & the Culture of Excellence. 2012. (ENG., Illus.). 224p. 40.00 (**978-0-230-29357-1(3)**) Palgrave Macmillan.

Riesenbeck, Hajo & Perrey, Jesko. Power Brands: Measuring, Making, & Managing Brand Success. (Illus.). 2007. 274p. 60.00 (978-3-527-50282-0(3)) 2nd ed. 2009. (ENG., 350p. 65.00 (978-3-527-50390-2(0), Wiley-VCH) Wiley, John & Sons, Inc.

Rimmell, Shereen. The Consumer-Brand Relationship Amongst Low-Income Consumers. 2011. 208p. pap. (**978-3-8443-9837-3(6)**) Lambert Academic Publishing.

Room, Adrian. Encyclopedia of Corporate Names Worldwide, 2 vols. alt. ed. 2008. (ENG.). 591p. pap. 65.00 (978-0-7864-3765-8(0)) McFarland & Co., Inc. Pubs.

Rosenbaum-Elliott, Richard, et al. Strategic Brand Management. 2nd ed. 2011. (ENG., Illus.). 326p. (C). pap. 64.95 (978-0-19-956521-4(X)) Oxford Univ. Pr., Inc.

Ross, Maria. Branding Basics for Small Business: How to Create an Irresistible Brand on Any Budget. 2010. 152p. pap. 15.95 (978-1-935254-24-9(3)) Norlightspress.Com.

Rutherford, David & Knowles, Jonathan. Vulcans, Earthlings & Marketing ROI: Getting Finance, Marketing & Advertising onto the Same Planet. 2007. (ENG.). 174p. pap. 34.95 (978-1-55458-031-6(5)) Wilfrid Laurier Univ. Pr. CAN. Dist: Univ. of Toronto Pr.

Ryans, Adrian B. & Ryans. Beating Low Cost Competition: How Premium Brands Can Respond to Cut-Price Rivals. 2009. (ENG., Illus.). 272p. 34.95 (978-0-470-74297-6(6), Wiley) Wiley, John & Sons, Inc.

Salinas, Gabriela. The International Brand Valuation Manual: A Complete Overview & Analysis of Brand Valuation Techniques, & Methodologies & Their Applications. 2009. (ENG., Illus.). 448p. 75.00 (978-0-470-74031-6(0), Wiley) Wiley, John & Sons, Inc.

Sandikci, Ozlem. Handbook of Islamic Marketing. Rice, Gillian, ed. 2011. (Elgar Original Reference Ser.). (Illus.). 544p. 255.00 (**978-1-84980-013-6(8)**) Elgar, Edward Publishing, Inc.

Schmidt, James M. Lincoln's Labels: America's Best Known Brands & the Civil War. 2009. (ENG.). 224p. pap. 19.95 (978-1-889020-28-0(1)); (Illus.). 27.95 (978-1-889020-21-1(4)) Edinborough Pr.

Schmidt, Marco. Interne Markenstärke von B-to-B-Unternehmen: Konzeption-Determinanten-Erfolgsauswirkungen. 2009. (Marktorientierte Unternehmensführung Ser.). (GER.). 312p. 83.95 (978-3-631-59268-7(X)) Lang, Peter GmbH, Europaischer Verlag der Wissenschaften DEU. Dist: Lang, Peter.

Schmitt, Bernd H. & Rogers, David L., eds. Handbook on Brand & Experience Management. 2009. (Elgar Original Reference Ser.). (Illus.). 328p. 210.00 (978-1-84720-007-5(9)) Elgar, Edward Publishing, Inc.

Segreto, Luciano. European Business & Brand Building. 2012. (ENG.). 264p. pap. 48.95 (**978-90-5201-793-8(X)**) PIE - Peter Lang BEL. Dist: Lang, Peter.

Seireeni, Richard & Fields, Scott. The Gort Cloud: The Invisible Force Powering Today's Most Visible Green Brands. 2009. (ENG., Illus.). 240p. pap. 24.95 (978-1-60358-061-8(1)) Chelsea Green Publishing.

Serhanoglu, Suleyman. Branding Technical Services - a Case Study on Sweco's Brand. 2011. 68p. pap. (**978-3-8443-1998-9(0)**) Lambert Academic Publishing.

Shibata, Hirokazu. Global Assembly Quality Methodology. 2009. 140p. pap. (978-3-639-11998-5(3)) VDM Verlag Dr. Mueller e.K.

Siebert, Sebastian. Bewertung von Markenlizenzierungspotenzialen: Ein Modellentwurf als Entscheidungsgrundlage für die Vergabe von Markenlizenzen. 2009. (Strategisches Marketingmanagement Ser.). (GER.). 248p. 72.95 (978-3-631-59238-0(8)) Lang, Peter GmbH, Europaischer Verlag der Wissenschaften DEU. Dist: Lang, Peter.

Simmons, John. Great Brand Stories? Innocent. 2008. (Illus.). 192p. pap. (978-1-905736-57-7(6)) Marshall Cavendish.

Simonson, Alex & Schmitt, Bernd H. Marketing Aesthetics. 2009. (ENG.). 368p. pap. 23.95 (978-1-4391-7292-6(7), Free Pr.) Free Pr.

Simovic, Marko. Brand Equity: Consumer Based Brand Equity in Practice. 2010. 96p. pap. (978-3-639-26420-3(7)) VDM Verlag Dr. Mueller e.K.

Singh, Radhika. The Fabric of Our Lives: The Story of Fabindia. 2011. (ENG., Illus.). 304p. 18.00 (978-0-670-08434-0(4), Penguin Global) Penguin Group (USA) Inc.

SITATI, T. O. M. It's a branded World. 2009. 199p. 38.46 (978-0-557-09380-9(5)) Lulu Enterprises Inc.

Slovinsky, Louis J. Alan Siegel: On Branding & Clear Communications. 2007. Orig. Title: Alan Siegel: on Branding & Clear Communications. (ENG.). 188p. per. (978-0-9790766-4-0(1), Working Biographies) Pinto, Jorge Bks.

Smilansky, Shaz. Experiential Marketing: A Practical Guide to Interactive Brand Experiences. 2009. (ENG., Illus.). 272p. 39.95 (978-0-7494-5275-9(7)) Kogan Page, Ltd. GBR. Dist: Ingram Pub. Services.

Soo, Gwon Young. 21C Hit Design: Hit Brand & Logo. 2009. (ENG., Illus.). 624p. 130.00 (978-89-951034-0-1(X)) Azur Corp. JPN. Dist: Antique Collectors' Club.

Soto J., Tatiana. Methods for Assessing Brand Value a Comparison Between the Interbrand Model & the Bbdo's Brand Equity Evaluator Model. 2008. 108p. pap. (978-3-8366-5872-0(0)) Books on Demand GmbH.

Spence, Roy M., Jr. It's Not What You Sell, It's What You Stand For: Why Every Extraordinary Business Is Driven by Purpose. 2011. (ENG., Illus.). 336p. (gr. 12). 16.00 (978-1-59184-447-1(9), Portfolio Trade) Penguin Group (USA) Inc.

Steward, Geoff. Logos & No Gos: How to Understand & Get the Most from Your Brand IP. 2007. (ENG.). 240p. 70.00 (978-0-470-06037-7(9), Wiley) Wiley, John & Sons, Inc.

Subliminal Branding, Make It Work for You: How to Successfully Market Yourself in a Business Environment. 2008. 24p. pap. (978-0-9786389-3-1(X)) Affinity Communications.

Superbrands (UK) Ltd Staff. CoolBrands 2010/11. 2010. (Illus.). 173p. 112.50 (978-0-9565334-0-1(X)) Superbrands (UK), Ltd. GBR. Dist: Trans-Atlantic Pubns., Inc.

Swystun, Jeff, et al. The Brand Glossary. 2006. (ENG., Illus.). 144p. 59.00 (978-1-4039-9809-5(4)) Palgrave Macmillan.

Taderera, Faustino. Branding. 2010. 364p. pap. (978-3-8383-6647-0(6)) Lambert Academic Publishing.

Tafelmeier, Robert. Markenbilanzierung und Markenbewertung: Analyse und Eignung von Markenbewertungsverfahren in Hinblick auf die bilanzielle Behandlung von Marken nach HGB und IAS/IFRS. 2009. (GER.). 312p. 83.95 (978-3-631-58584-9(5)) Lang, Peter GmbH, Europaischer Verlag der Wissenschaften DEU. Dist: Lang, Peter.

Tai, Jacky & Chew, Wilson. Transforming Your Business into Brand: The 10 Rules of Branding, 1 vol. 2008. (ENG.). 192p. pap. 14.50 (978-981-261-386-8(2)) Marshall Cavendish International (Asia) Private Ltd. SGP. Dist: Marshall Cavendish Corp.

Taylor, David & Nichols, David S. The Brand Gym: A Practical Workout to Gain & Retain Brand Leadership. 2nd ed. 2010. (ENG., Illus.). 256p. 40.00 (978-0-470-68619-5(7), Wiley) Wiley, John & Sons, Inc.

Taylor, David A. Brand Vision: How to Energize Your Team to Drive Business Growth. 2007. (ENG., Illus.). 284p. 49.95 (978-0-470-02835-3(1), Wiley) Wiley, John & Sons, Inc.

—Never Mind the Sizzle... Where's the Sausage? Building Brands Based on Substance Not Spin. 2007. (ENG., Illus.). 162p. pap. 19.95 (978-1-84112-769-9(8), Capstone) Wiley, John & Sons, Inc.

Taylor, Neil. The Name of the Beast: The Process & Perils of Naming Products, Companies & Brands. 2006. (Illus.). 224p. per. 24.95 (978-1-904879-70-1(5)) Cyan Communications GBR. Dist: Independent Pubs. Group.

Tellis, Gerard J. Will & Vision: How Latecomers Grow to Dominate Markets. 2006. (ENG.). 340p. pap. 31.00 (978-1-932800-25-8(5)) Figueroa Pr.

Temporal, Paul. Advanced Brand Management: Managing Brands in a Changing World. 2nd ed. 2010. (ENG., Illus.). 256p. 34.95 (978-0-470-82449-8(2), Wiley) Wiley, John & Sons, Inc.

Titterton, Garry & Fioroni, Michele. Brand Storming: Managing Brands in the Era of Complexity. 2009. (ENG.). 256p. (C). 53.00 (978-0-230-22243-4(9)) Palgrave Macmillan.

Top Management Forum: Corporate Brand Management. 2007. (Illus.). iii, 85p. pap. (978-92-833-2372-3(6)) Asian Productivity Organization.

Trout, Jack. In Search of the Obvious: The Antidote for Today's Marketing Mess. 2008. (ENG.). 224p. 27.95 (978-0-470-28859-7(0), Wiley) Wiley, John & Sons, Inc.

Trout, Jack & Rivkin, Steve. Differentiate or Die: Survival in Our Era of Killer Competition. 2nd ed. 2008. (ENG., Illus.). 272p. 24.95 (978-0-470-22339-0(1), Wiley) Wiley, John & Sons, Inc.

Tungate, Mark. Branded Beauty: How Marketing Changed the Way We Look. 2011. (ENG.). 288p. 29.95 (978-0-7494-6181-2(0)) Kogan Page, Ltd. GBR. Dist: Ingram Pub. Services.

—Branded Male: Marketing to Men. 2008. (ENG., Illus.). 256p. 39.95 (978-0-7494-5011-3(8)) Kogan Page, Ltd. GBR. Dist: Ingram Pub. Services.

—Fashion Brands: Branding Style from Armani to Zara. 3rd ed. 2012. (ENG., Illus.). 272p. pap. 39.95 (**978-0-7494-6446-2(1)**) Kogan Page, Ltd. GBR. Dist: Ingram Pub. Services.

Tungate, Mark. Luxury World: The Past, Present & Future of Luxury Brands. 2009. (ENG., Illus.). 260p. 29.95 (978-0-7494-5263-6(3)) Kogan Page, Ltd. GBR. Dist: Ingram Pub. Services.

Turkel, Bruce. Construyendo Valor de Marca. 2007. (SPA., Illus.). 91p. per. 19.95 net. (978-0-9797084-1-1(9)) TURKEL.

Tuten, Tracy L. Advertising 2. 0: Social Media Marketing in a Web 2. 0 World, 1 vol. 2008. (Illus.). 216p. pap. 24.95 (978-0-313-35296-6(8), B35296, Praeger Pubs.) Greenwood Publishing Group, Inc.

Twitchell, James B. Branded Nation: The Marketing of Megachurch, College Inc., & Museumworld. 2006. (Illus.). 327p. reprint ed. 26.00 (978-1-4223-5762-0(7)) DIANE Publishing Co.

Tyreman, David. World Famous: How to Give Your Business a Kick-Ass Brand Identity. 2009. (ENG.). 240p. pap. 17.95 (978-0-8144-0934-3(2)) Amacom.

van der Grinten, Jaap & Riezebos, Rik. Positioning the Brand: An Inside-Out Approach to Strategic Brand Positioning. (ENG., Illus.). 208p. (C). 2012. 140.00 (978-0-415-66518-6(3)) 2011. pap. 48.95 (978-0-415-66519-3(1)) Routledge.

Van Praet, Douglas. Unconscious Branding: How Neuroscience Can Empower (and Inspire) Marketing. 2012. (ENG.). 288p. 28.00 (**978-0-230-34179-1(9)**) Palgrave Macmillan.

Walker, Rob. Buying In: The Secret Dialogue Between What We Buy & Who We Are. 2008. (ENG.). 320p. 25.00 (978-1-4000-6391-8(4)) Random Hse., Inc.

—Buying In: What We Buy & Who We Are. 2010. (ENG.). 320p. pap. 16.00 (978-0-8129-7409-6(3), Random Hse. Trade Paperbacks) Random House Publishing Group.

Wallace, Margot A. Museum Branding: How to Create & Maintain Image, Loyalty, & Support. 2006. (ENG., Illus.). 208p. 87.50 (978-0-7591-0992-6(3)); per. 30.95 (978-0-7591-0993-3(1)) AltaMira Pr.

Wang, Jing. Brand New China: Advertising, Media, & Commercial Culture. 2010. (Illus.). 432p. pap. 18.95 (978-0-674-04708-2(7)) Harvard Univ. Pr.

Wasmuht, Barbara. Branding & Corporate Identity: A Practical Approach of Brand Management Under the Consideration of Corporate Identity Aspects. 2008. 108p. pap. (978-3-639-09333-9(X)) VDM Verlag Dr. Mueller e.K.

Wenglosky, Alice. Brand Names, Adoption & Diffusion. 2011. 80p. pap. (**978-3-8443-0566-1(1)**) Lambert Academic Publishing.

Wheeler, Alina. Designing Brand Identity: An Essential Guide for the Whole Branding Team. (ENG., 320p. 3rd ed. 2009. Illus.). 45.00 (978-0-470-40142-2(7)) 4th ed. 2012. 45.00 (**978-1-118-09920-9(6)**) Wiley, John & Sons, Inc. (Wiley).

Wheeler, Alina & Katz, Joel. Brand Atlas: Branding Intelligence Made Visible. 2011. (ENG., Illus.). 144p. 29.95 (978-0-470-43342-3(6), Wiley) Wiley, John & Sons, Inc.

Wickstrom, Maurya. Performing Consumers: Global Capital & Its Theatrical Seductions. 2006. (ENG.). 184p. per. 35.95 (978-0-415-33945-2(6)) Routledge.

Wiedemann, Julius. Logo Design Now 02. 2007. (ENG, FRE, GER & SPA., Illus.). 384p. pap. 39.99 (978-3-8228-4622-3(8)) TASCHEN DEU. Dist: Ingram Pub. Services.

Wiedemann, Julius, ed. Brand Identity Now! 2009. (ENG., Illus.). 384p. 39.99 (978-3-8365-1584-9(9)) TASCHEN DEU. Dist: Ingram Pub. Services.

—Logo Design Now 02, Vol. 2. 2009. (FRE, GER & ENG., Illus.). 384p. 39.99 *(978-3-8365-0942-8(3))* TASCHEN DEU. Dist: Ingram Pub. Services.
Winsor, John. Flipped: How Bottom-up Co-Creation Is Replacing Top-down Innovation. 2010. (ENG.). 260p. pap. 16.00 *(978-1-932841-48-0(2))* Agate Publishing, Inc.
Wobben, Carolin. Brand Extensions- Keys to Success in International Marketing. 2007. pap. *(978-3-8364-0629-1(2))* VDM Verlag Dr. Mueller e.K.
Wreden, Nick. Profit Brand: How to Increase the Profitability, Accountability & Sustainability of Brands. 2007. (ENG., Illus.). 240p. pap. 39.50 *(978-0-7494-5018-2(5))* Kogan Page, Ltd. GBR. Dist: Ingram Pub. Services.
Yastrow, Steve. Brand Harmony: Achieving Dynamic Results by Orchestrating Your Customer's Total Experience. 2010. 176p. pap. 16.95 *(978-1-59079-199-8(1))* Select Bks.

BRAND NAME PRODUCTS—COMPOSITION
Borushek, Allan. The CalorieKing Calorie, Fat, & Carbohydrate Counter. 2011. (ENG., Illus.). 287p. pap. 8.99 ***(978-1-930448-36-0(8))*** Family Health Pubns.
Favorite Brand Name Recipes Editors, ed. Simple 1-2-3 Kids Recipes. 2010. 144p. spiral bd. 10.98 *(978-1-60553-121-2(9))*, PIL Kids) Publications International, Ltd.
Natow, Annette B. & Heslin, Jo-Ann. The Complete Food Counter. 3rd ed. 2008. (ENG.). 736p. mass mkt. 7.99 *(978-1-4165-6666-3(X))* Pocket Books.
Netzer, Corinne T. The Complete Book of Food Counts, 9th Edition: The Book That Counts It All. 2011. (ENG.). 912p. mass mkt. 8.99 *(978-0-440-24561-2(3))*, Dell) Random House Publishing Group.

BRANDED MERCHANDISE
see Brand Name Products

BRANDEIS, LOUIS DEMBITZ, 1856-1941
Berk, Gerald. Louis Brandeis & the Making of Regulated Competition, 1900-1932. 2009. (ENG., Illus.). 296p. 92.00 *(978-0-521-42596-4(4))* Cambridge Univ. Pr.
Bosmajian, Haig A. Anita Whitney, Louis Brandeis, & the First Amendment. 2010. 47.50 *(978-0-8386-4267-2(5))* Fairleigh Dickinson Univ. Pr.
De Haas, Jacob. Louis D Brandeis. 2007. 320p. per. *(978-1-4067-3207-8(9))* Read Bks.
Justice Louis Dembitz Brandeis: Commemorating the 150th birthday of the late Supreme Court justice & university namesake: Guided by the Light of Reason. 2007. per. *(978-0-9620545-1-8(8))* Brandeis Univ. Pictorial History Program.
Shogan, Robert. Prelude to Catastrophe: FDR's Jews & the Menance of Nazism. 2010. (ENG.). 312p. 27.95 *(978-1-56663-831-9(3))* Dee, Ivan R. Pub.
Urofsky, Melvin I. Louis D. Brandeis: A Life. 2009. (ENG., Illus.). 976p. 40.00 *(978-0-375-42366-6(4))*, Pantheon) Knopf Doubleday Publishing Group.

BRANDEIS UNIVERSITY
Albom, Mitch. Tuesdays with Morrie: An Old Man, a Young Man, & Life's Greatest Lesson. Lt. ed. 2010. (ENG.). 320p. pap. 20.00 *(978-0-7393-7777-2(9))* Random Hse. Large Print.
Maskas, Emily & Katz, Andrew. Brandeis University 2012: Off the Record. 2011. 188p. pap. 16.95 ***(978-1-4274-0354-4(6))*** College Prowler, Inc.
Von Guggenberg, Miriam. Double Liminality. 2010. 88p. pap. *(978-3-639-26515-4(8))* VDM Verlag Dr. Mueller e.K.

BRANDENBURG (GERMANY)
Friedrich, Karin & Smart, Sara. The Cultivation of Monarchy in Brandenburg-Prussia & the Rise of Berlin, 1700-1701. 2010. (Illus.). 438p. 144.95 *(978-0-7546-0997-1(9))* Ashgate Publishing Co.
Schwikart, Georg. Journey through Brandenburg. 2011. (Journey Through Ser.). (ENG.). 128p. 24.95 *(978-3-8003-1707-3(9))* Verlagshaus Wurzburg GmbH & Co. KG DEU. Dist: Independent Pubs. Group.
Wyatt, Walter James. The History of Prussia V1: from the Earliest Times to the Present. 2007. (ENG.). 516p. per. 40.95 *(978-1-4304-4373-5(1))* Kessinger Publishing, LLC.

BRANDO, MARLON, 1924-2004
Biographiq. Marlon Brando - Actor & Activist. 2008. 56p. pap. 9.99 *(978-1-59986-049-7(X)*, Biographiq) Filiquarian Publishing, LLC.
Duncan, Paul, ed. ICONS Film - Marlon Brando. 2006. (Movie Icons Ser.). (FRE, GER & ENG., Illus.). 192p. per. 9.99 *(978-3-8228-2002-5(4))* TASCHEN DEU. Dist: Ingram Pub. Services.
Grobel, Lawrence. Conversations with Marlon Brando: Lawrence Grobel. 2009. (ENG.). 195p. pap. 25.00 *(978-0-9818056-2-7(0))* Rat Pr.
Kanfer, Stefan. Somebody: The Reckless Life & Remarkable Career of Marlon Brando. 2009. (Vintage Ser.). (ENG., Illus.). 384p. pap. 16.00 *(978-1-4000-7804-2(0))*, Vintage) Knopf Doubleday Publishing Group.
Marchak, Alice. Me & Marlon. 2008. (ENG.). 449p. pap. 19.95 *(978-0-615-22235-6(8))* Marchak, Alice.

BRANDS (COMMERCE)
see Business Names

BRANDT, BILL, 1904-1983
Brandt, Bill, photos by. Bill Brandt. 2007. (Photofile Ser.). (ENG., Illus.). 144p. pap. 15.95 *(978-0-500-41088-2(7)*, 541088) Thames & Hudson.
Riley, Andrew. Let us Face the Future: British Art 1945-1968. 2011. (ENG & SPA.). 283p. 54.95 *(978-84-937610-8-0(7))* Fundacio Joan Miro ESP. Dist: Actar Birkhauser Distribution.

BRANDT, WILLY, 1913-1992
Fink, Carole & Schaefer, Bernd, eds. Ostpolitik, 1969-1974: European & Global Responses. (Publications of the German Historical Institute Ser.). (ENG.). 2011. 322p. pap. 29.99 *(978-0-521-18152-5(6))* 2008. (Illus.). 314p. 90.00 *(978-0-521-89973-3(2))* Cambridge Univ. Pr.
Hofmann, Arne. The Emergence of Detente in Europe: Brandt, Kennedy & the Formation of Ostpolitik. 2007. (Cold War History (Routledge) Ser.). 225p. 160.00 *(978-0-415-38637-1(3))* Routledge.
Michel, Judith. Willy Brandts Amerikabild und -politik 1933 - 1992. 2010. (Internationale Beziehungen. Theorie und Geschichte Ser.). (GER.). 565p. (C). 91.00 *(978-3-89971-626-9(4))* Vandenhoeck & Ruprecht GmbH & Co. KG DEU. Dist: ISD.

BRANDY
Neal, Charles. Armagnac: The Definitive Guide to Frances Premier Brandy. 2011 (ENG., Illus.). 319p. pap. 39.95 ***(978-1-935879-91-6(X))*** Wine Appreciation Guild, Ltd.

BRANDY STATION, BATTLE OF, BRANDY STATION, VA., 1863
McKinney, Joseph W. Brandy Station, Virginia, June 9 1863: The Largest Cavalry Battle of the Civil War. 2006. (ENG., Illus.). 340p. 55.00 *(978-0-7864-2534-6(9))* McFarland & Co., Inc. Pubs.
Wittenberg, Eric J. The Battle of Brandy Station: North America's Largest Cavalry Battle. 2010. (Civil War Sesquicentennial Ser.). (ENG., Illus.). 272p. pap. 24.99 *(978-1-59629-782-1(4))* History Pr., The.

BRANDYWINE CREEK VALLEY (PA. AND DEL.)
Canby, Henry S. Rivers of America: The Brandywine. Date not set. lib. bdg. 23.95 *(978-0-8488-1562-0(4))* Amereon LTD.
Langlieb, David & Langlieb, D. Philadelphia, Brandywine Valley & Bucks County: Includes Lancaster County's Amish Country. 2009. (Explorer's Great Destinations Ser.). (ENG., Illus.). 304p. pap. 19.95 *(978-1-58157-087-8(2)*, 157087) Countryman Pr.
Morris, Roger & Ryan, Cathleen. The Brandywine Book of Food: Exploring the Culinary Landscape of the Brandywine Valley's Country Gardens, Bed-and-Breakfast Inns, Mushroom Barns, & Boutique Wineries. 2009. (ENG., Illus.). 160p. 34.95 *(978-1-58182-700-2(8))*, Cumberland Hse.) Sourcebooks, Inc.
Quillman, Catherine. 100 Artists of the Brandywine Valley. 2011. (Illus.). 240p. 45.00 *(978-0-7643-3674-4(6))* Schiffer Publishing, Ltd.

BRANN, WILLIAM COWPER, 1855-1898
Brann, William Cowper. The Complete Works of Brann the Iconoclast: Volume I. 2008. (GER.). 321p. 36.99 *(978-1-4264-0084-1(5))*; (ENG.). 327p. pap. 24.99 *(978-1-4264-0213-5(9))* BiblioBazaar.
—The Complete Works of Brann the Iconoclast: Volume X. 2008. (GER.). 321p. pap. 24.99 *(978-1-4264-0083-4(7))* BiblioBazaar.
—The Complete Works of Brann the Iconoclast: Volume XII. 2006. (ENG.). 316p. pap. 23.99 *(978-1-4264-0082-7(9))*; 304p. pap. 17.99 *(978-1-4264-0211-1(2))* BiblioBazaar.

BRANNAN, SAMUEL, 1819-1889
Scott, Reva. Samuel Brannan & the Golden Fleece: A Biography. 2007. (ENG.). 486p. 53.95 *(978-0-548-06641-6(8))* Kessinger Publishing, LLC.

BRANSON, RICHARD, 1950-
Branson, Richard. Business Stripped Bare: Adventures of a Global Entrepreneur. 2011. (ENG.). 368p. (gr. 12). 16.00 *(978-1-59184-406-8(1)*, Portfolio Trade) Penguin Group (USA) Inc.
—Business Stripped Bare: Adventures of a Global Entrepreneur. 2009. (ENG.). 320p. pap. 14.95 *(978-0-7535-1961-5(5))*; (Illus.). 384p. pap. *(978-0-7535-1503-7(2))* Virgin Bks. Ltd. GBR. Dist: Independent Pubs. Group.
—Losing My Virginity: The Autobiography. 2011. (ENG., Illus.). 624p. pap. 17.00 *(978-0-307-72074-0(8)*, Crown Business) Crown Publishing Group.
Dearlove, Des. The Unauthorized Guide to Doing Business the Richard Branson Way: 10 Secrets of the World's Greatest Brand Builder. 3rd rev. ed. 2010. (ENG.). 176p. pap. 15.95 *(978-0-85708-061-5(X)*, Capstone) Wiley, John & Sons, Inc.
Redmond, Shirley Raye. Richard Branson: Virgin Mega-brand Mogul. 2011. (Innovators Ser.). 64p. lib. bdg. 28.75 *(978-0-7377-5536-7(9)*, Kidhaven) Cengage Gale.

BRANSON (MO.)
Branson Souvenir Book. pap. *(978-1-56944-020-9(4))*; pap. *(978-1-56944-030-8(1))* Terrell Creative.
Entertainment Publications, Inc. Staff, compiled by. Springfield/Branson 2009 Entertainment Book. 2008. pap. 25.00 *(978-1-59876-715-3(2))* Entertainment Pubns., Inc.
Fodor's Travel Publications, Inc. Staff. Branson. 2nd ed. Date not set. (Fodor's Ser.). pap. 22.00 *(978-0-679-03303-5(3))* Fodor's Travel Pubns.
Pfister, Fred. Branson & the Ozark Mountains. 7th ed. 2009. (Insiders' Guide Ser.). (ENG., Illus.). 320p. pap. 18.95 *(978-0-7627-5028-3(6)*, Insiders' Guide) Globe Pequot Pr., The.
Prosser, Lee. Branson Hauntings. 2010. (Illus.). 160p. pap. 14.99 *(978-0-7643-3402-3(6))* Schiffer Publishing, Ltd.
Sedenko Davis, Julie. Branson: A Guide to America's Live Music Show Capital. 2012. (Tourist Town Guides). 192p. pap. 14.95 *(978-1-935455-11-0(7))* Channel Lake, Inc.
Stacey, Dorothy. Hometown Branson II: 1940 - 2003, 2 vols, II. 2006. (Illus.). 238p. per. 19.95 *(978-0-9720863-1-8(5))* Loafers Glory Pubns.

BRANT, JOSEPH, MOHAWK CHIEF, 1742-1807
Bryant, William Clemen. Captain Brant & the Old King the Trage. 2006. pap. 15.95 *(978-1-4286-5419-8(4))* Kessinger Publishing, LLC.
Paxton, James W. & Paxton, James. Joseph Brant & His World: 18th Century Mohawk Warrior & Statesman. 2008. (ENG., Illus.). 96p. pap. 19.95 *(978-1-55277-023-8(0))* Lorimer, James & Co., Ltd., Pubs. CAN. Dist: Casemate Pubs. & Bk. Distributors, LLC.
Stone, William. Life of Joseph Brant-Thayendanegea. 2010. (Native American Ser.). 519p. pap. 30.95 *(978-1-4290-2257-6(4))* Applewood Bks.
Stone, William L. Life of Joseph Brant-Thayendanegea: Including the Border Wars of the American Revolution & Sketches of the Indian Campaigns of Generals Harmar, St. 2006. 544p. per. 29.99 *(978-1-4255-6033-1(4))* MPublishing.
Wood, Louis Aubrey. The War Chief of the Six Nations. 147p. reprint ed. 88.00 *(978-0-7222-6786-8(X))* Library Reprints, Inc.

BRANT, SEBASTIAN, 1458-1521
Brant, Sebastian. The Ship of Fools. Barclay, Alexander, tr. 2007. (ENG.). 418p. 49.95 *(978-0-548-22654-4(7))*; 420p. per. 34.95 *(978-1-4325-4877-3(8))* Kessinger Publishing, LLC.

BRAQUE, GEORGES, 1882-1963
Kahng, Eik, et al. Picasso & Braque: The Cubist Experiment, 1910-1912. 2011. (Illus.). 136p. 30.00 *(978-0-300-16971-3(X))* Kimbell Art Museum.
Watkins, Nicholas. Behind the Mirror: Miro, Giacometti, Calder, Braque. 2008. (ENG., Illus.). 160p. 65.00 *(978-1-905711-38-3(7))* Royal Academy of Arts GBR. Dist: Hachette Bk. Group.

BRASHER, REX, 1869-1960
Brasher, Milton E. & Brasher, Rex. Rex Brasher, Painter of Birds: A Biography. 2011. 392p. 53.95 ***(978-1-258-09768-4(0))*** Literary Licensing, LLC.

BRASILIA (BRAZIL)
Gautherot, Marcel, photos by. Building Brasilia. 2010. (ENG., Illus.). 192p. 65.00 *(978-0-500-51542-6(5)*, 551542) Thames & Hudson.
Wallpaper Magazine Editors, ed. Brasilia - Wallpaper City Guide. 2011. (ENG.). 128p. pap. 9.95 ***(978-0-7148-6262-0(2))*** Phaidon Pr., Inc.

BRASS
Curnow, James. Two for Easter: 16 Duets for Bb Instruments. 2007. (ENG.). 20p. pap. 7.95 *(978-90-431-2563-5(6)*, 9043125636) Leonard, Hal Corp.
Daugherty, Michael. Asclepius: Fanfare for Brass & Percussion Full Score. 2008. (ENG.). 40p. pap. 17.95 *(978-1-4234-6573-7(3)*, 1423465733) Boosey & Hawkes, Inc.
—Asclepius: Fanfare for Brass & Percussion Score & Parts. 2008. (ENG.). 96p. pap. 50.00 *(978-1-4234-6634-5(9)*, 1423466349) Boosey & Hawkes, Inc.
Hal Leonard Corp., creator. Dixieland Classics: Brass Quintet Tuba. 2010. (ENG.). 16p. pap. 8.99 *(978-1-61774-237-8(6)*, 1617742376) Leonard, Hal Corp.
Hal Leonard Corporation Staff, creator. The Canadian Brass - 14 Collected Intermediate Quintets. 2010. (ENG.). 16p. pap. 8.99 *(978-1-4234-8421-9(5)*, 1423484215) Leonard, Hal Corp.
Hal Leonard Corporation Staff & Canadian Brass Staff, creators. 14 Collected Intermediate Quintets: Brass Quintet Conductor's Score. 2010. (ENG.). 64p. pap. 16.99 *(978-1-4234-8418-9(5)*, 1423484185) Leonard, Hal Corp.
The Canadian Brass. 17 Collected Easy Quintets: Brass Quintet Conductor's Score. 2010. (ENG.). 48p. pap. 16.99 *(978-1-4234-8306-9(5)*, 1423483065) Leonard, Hal Corp.

BRASS BAND MUSIC
see Band Music

BRASS BANDS
see Bands (Music)

BRASS INDUSTRY AND TRADE
see also Copper Industry and Trade
Lathrop, William G. The Development of the Brass Industry in Connecticut. 31p. reprint ed. lib. bdg. 88.00 *(978-0-7222-0468-9(X))* Library Reprints, Inc.

BRASS INSTRUMENTS
see also Bands (Music); Bugle; Cornet; Horn (Musical Instrument); Trombone; Trumpet; Tuba
Ahrens, Christian. Valved Brasses: The History of an Invention. 2008. *(978-1-57647-137-1(3))* Pendragon Pr.
Alexander, Peter Lawrence. Professional Orchestration: Orchestrating the Melody Within the Woodwinds & Brass. 2009. 714p. pap. 64.95 *(978-0-939067-93-0(5))* Alexander Publishing.
Alfred Publishing Staff. Sound Innovations for Concert Band, Bk 2: A Revolutionary Method for Early-Intermediate Musicians (Baritone B. C.), Book, CD & DVD. 2011. (Sound Innovations Ser.). (ENG.). 48p. pap. 8.99 ***(978-0-7390-6756-7(7))*** Alfred Publishing Co., Inc.
—Sound Innovations for Concert Band, Bk 2: A Revolutionary Method for Early-Intermediate Musicians (Baritone T. C.), Book, CD & DVD. 2011. (Sound Innovations Ser.). (ENG.). 48p. pap. 8.99 ***(978-0-7390-6757-4(5))*** Alfred Publishing Co., Inc.
Bailey, Wayne, et al. Teaching Brass: A Resource Manual. 2nd ed. 2006. (ENG., Illus.). 256p. (C). spiral bd. 90.67 *(978-0-07-352658-4(4)*, 0073526584) McGraw-Hill Cos., The.
The Brass Gym: Horn. 2007. spiral bd. 24.95 *(978-0-9748477-0-2(4))* Focus on Excellence.
The Brass Gym: Trumpet. 2007. spiral bd. 24.95 *(978-0-9748477-4-0(7))* Focus on Excellence.
Burba, Malte. Brass Master-Class: Die Methode für alle Blechbläser. 2007. 24.95 *(978-3-7957-6058-8(5)*, 3795760585) Schott Music Corp.
Canadian Brass & Henderson, Luther. The Canadian Brass - Well Tampered Bach. 2011. (ENG.). 28p. pap. 40.00 ***(978-1-4584-1647-6(X)***, 145841647X) Leonard, Hal Corp.
Carter, Stewart. Brass Scholarship in Review: Proceedings of the Historic Brass Society Conference, Cité de la Musique, Paris, 1999. 2006. (C). *(978-1-57647-105-0(5))* Pendragon Pr.
Ellington, Duke. 3 Classic Duke Quintets: Brass Quintet. 2009. (ENG.). 101p. pap. 40.00 *(978-1-4234-8517-9(3)*, 1423485173) Leonard, Hal Corp.
Ely, Mark C. & Van Deuren, Amy E. Wind Talk for Brass: A Practical Guide to Understanding & Teaching Brass Instruments. 2009. (ENG., Illus.). 384p. 99.00 *(978-0-19-532919-3(8))*; pap. 35.00 *(978-0-19-532924-7(4))* Oxford Univ. Pr., Inc.
Embouchure Rehabilitation: A Comprehensive Method for Overcoming Embouchure Overuse Syndrome in Brass Players. 2007. spiral bd. 25.00 *(978-0-9741007-2-2(2)*, Oscar's Hse. Pr.) Embouchures.com, Inc.
Ericson, John Q. A Mello Catechism: A Guide to the World of Mellophones & Marching Horns. 2007. 30p. 15.00 *(978-0-9801030-3-8(7))* Horn Notes Edition LLC.
Hal Leonard Corporation Staff, creator. 10. Bach, Handel & More: The Orchestra Musician's CD-ROM Library - Low Brass. 2008. (ENG.). 8p. cd-rom 19.95 *(978-1-4234-3902-8(3)*, 1423439023) Leonard, Hal Corp.
Oehler, Michael. Die digitale Impulsformung als Werkzeug für die Analyse und Synthese von Blasinstrumentenklängen. 2008. (Systemische Musikwissenschaft Ser.). 256p. pap. 65.95 *(978-3-631-57024-1(4))* Lang, Peter GmbH, Europaischer Verlag der Wissenschaften DEU. Dist: Lang, Peter.
O'Quinn, Keith. Music for Brass Ensemble: For Trombone. 2009. (ENG.). 26p. pap. 24.98 incl. audio compact disk *(978-1-59615-463-6(2)*, 1596154632) Music Minus One.
Pinksterboer, Hugo. Tipbook Trumpet & Trombone, Flugelhorn & Cornet. 2nd ed. 2009. (ENG.). 232p. pap., instr.'s gde. ed. 14.99 *(978-1-4234-6527-0(X)*, 142346527X) Leonard, Hal Corp.
Smith, Nicholas. Don't Miss: Ideas, Concepts, & Excercises designed to increase accuracy on & inaccurate Instruments. 2010. spiral bd. 15.95 *(978-0-578-04922-9(8))* Smith, Nicholas E.
Wagner: Part 1 - Volume 11: The Orchestra Musician's CD-ROM Library - Low Brass. 2009. (ENG.). 8p. cd-rom 19.95 *(978-1-4234-8559-9(9)*, 1423485599) Leonard, Hal Corp.
Wagner: Part 2 - Volume 12: The Orchestra Musician's CD-ROM Library - Low Brass. 2009. (ENG.). 8p. cd-rom 19.95 *(978-1-4234-8573-5(4)*, 1423485734) Leonard, Hal Corp.
Warren, A. E. & Justus, Tim. Amazon Polka: Part(s) 2010. (Heritage of the Cornet Ser.). pap. 6.00 *(978-1-55472-055-2(9))* Alfred Publishing Co., Inc.
Weiner, Howard T. Early Twentieth-Century Brass Idioms: Art, Jazz, & Other Popular Traditions - Proceedings of the International Conference Presented by the Institute of Jazz Studies of Rutgers University & the Historic Brass Society November 4-5, 2005. 2008. (Studies in Jazz Ser.). (ENG.). 186p. 58.00 *(978-0-8108-6245-6(X))* Scarecrow Pr., Inc.

BRASSES
Badham, Sally. Monumental Brasses. 2009. (Shire Library). (ENG., Illus.). 64p. pap. 12.95 *(978-0-7478-0677-6(2))* Shire Pubns., Ltd. GBR. Dist: Random Hse., Inc.
Druitt, Herbert. A Manual of Costume As Illustrated by Monumental Brasses. 2008. (Illus.). 604p. 59.95 *(978-1-4370-1509-6(3))*; pap. 44.95 *(978-1-4367-3829-3(6))* Kessinger Publishing, LLC.
Ward, J. S. M. Brasses. 2012. (ENG., Illus.). 172p. pap. 19.99 ***(978-1-107-64090-0(3))*** Cambridge Univ. Pr.
Wills, Geoffrey. Collecting Copper & Brass. 2008. 168p. *(978-1-4437-3554-4(X))* 2006. 164p. per. *(978-1-4067-9651-3(4))* Read Bks. (Hesperides Pr.).

BRASSEY, THOMAS, 1805-1870
Helps, Arthur. Life & Labours of Mr Brassey 1805-1870 by Sir Arthur Helps, K C B with a Preface to the American Edition, by the Author. 2006. 424p. per. 26.99 *(978-1-4255-4636-6(5))* MPublishing.

BRATIANU, IOAN I. C., 1864-1927
Hitchin, Keith. Ion Bratianu: Romania - The Peace Conferences of 1919-23 & Their Aftermath. 2011. (Makers of the Modern World Ser.). (ENG., Illus.). 220p. 19.95 *(978-1-905791-76-7(3))* Haus Publishing GBR. Dist: Consortium Bk. Sales & Distribution.

BRATTLEBORO (VT.)
Hansen, Fran Lynggaard. Brattleboro: Historically Speaking. 2009. (American Chronicles Ser.). 128p. pap. 21.99 *(978-1-59629-719-7(0))* History Pr., The.

BRAUN, ALBERT, 1889-1967
Cave, Dorothy. God's Warrior: Father Albert Braun, OFM, 1889-1983, Last of the Frontier Priests. 2011. pap. 32.95 ***(978-0-86534-520-1(1))*** Sunstone Pr.

BRAUN, EVA, 1912-1945
Baumann, Hans. The Vanished Life of Eva Braun, 1 vol. 2010. 128p. pap. 19.95 *(978-1-4489-5136-9(4))* PublishAmerica, Inc.
Costelle, Daniel. Eva Braun: Dans L'intimité D'Hitler. 2007. (FRE., Illus.). 189p. *(978-2-84187-925-0(9))* Editions de l'Archipel.
Gortemaker, Heike B. Eva Braun: Life with Hitler. Searls, Damion, tr. from GER. 2011. (ENG., Illus.). 336p. 27.95 *(978-0-307-59582-9(X)*, Knopf) Knopf Doubleday Publishing Group.
—Eva Braun: Life with Hitler. 2012. (Vintage Ser.). (ENG.). 336p. pap. 16.00 *(978-0-307-74260-5(1))* Knopf, Alfred A. Inc.
Lambert, Angela. The Lost Life of Eva Braun. 2008. (ENG., Illus.). 544p. pap. 18.99 *(978-0-312-37865-3(3)*, St. Martin's Griffin) St. Martin's Pr.

B

Segovia, David. Eva Braun. 2007. (Mujeres en la historia Ser.). (ENG., Illus.). 192p. 8.95 (978-84-9764-762-5(9)) Edimat Libros, S. A. ESP. Dist: Independent Pubs. Group.
Taylor, Blaine. Mrs Adolf Hitler: The Eva Braun Photograph Albums 1912-45. 2011. (Illus.). 464p. 99.95 (978-1-907677-43-4(7)) Helion & Co., Ltd. GBR. Dist: Casemate Pubs. & Bk. Distributors, LLC.

BRAWNE, FANNY, 1800-1865

Keats, John. Bright Star: Love Letters & Poems of John Keats to Fanny Brawne. 2009. (ENG.). 144p. (gr. 12). 14.00 (978-0-14-311774-2(2), Penguin (Non-Classics)) Penguin Group (USA) Inc.

BRAUTIGAN, RICHARD, 1935-1984

Barber, John F., ed. Richard Brautigan: Essays on the Writings & Life. 2006. (ENG., Illus.). 314p. per. 39.95 (978-0-7864-2525-9(3)) McFarland & Co., Inc. Pubs.

BRAVERY

see Courage

BRAZIL

Bruce, George J. Brazil & the Brazilians. 307p. reprint ed. 98.00 (978-0-7222-9592-2(8)) Library Reprints, Inc.
Edwards, Todd L. Brazil: A Global Studies Handbook, 1 vol. 2007. (Global Studies: Latin America & the Caribbean Ser.). (Illus.). 333p. 55.00 (978-1-85109-995-5(6), BRAZIL1C) ABC-CLIO, LLC.
Elliott, Lilian E. Brazil Today & Tomarrow. 338p. reprint ed. 98.00 (978-0-7222-9594-6(4)) Library Reprints, Inc.
Hunnicutt, Benjamin H. Brazil - World Frontier. 2007. pap. 31.45 (978-1-4067-5591-6(5)) Hunnicutt Farris Publishing.
Ramos. Viventes das Alagoas. (POR.). pap. 13.25 (978-85-01-00918-0(0)) Distribuidora Record de Servicos de Imprensa SA BRA. Dist: Distribooks, Inc.
Reichmann, Rebecca L. Brazil. 256p. (978-1-85973-263-2(1)); pap. (978-1-85973-268-7(2)) Berg Pubs.

BRAZIL—ANTIQUITIES

Davila, Jerry. Brazil: A Century of Change. Sachs, Ignacy et al, eds. Anderson, Robert N., tr. from POR. 2009. (Latin America in Translation/en Traduccion/n/em Traducao - the Brasiliana Collection). (ENG., Illus.). 392p. 69.95 (978-0-8078-3130-4(1)) Univ. of North Carolina Pr.
—Brazil: A Century of Change. Sachs, Ignacy et al, eds. Anderson, Robert N., tr. from POR. 2009. (Latin America in Translation/en Traduccion/n/em Traducao - the Brasiliana Collection). (ENG., Illus.). 392p. pap. 26.95 (978-0-8078-5927-8(3)) Univ. of North Carolina Pr.
Tindall, Robert. Jaguar That Roams the Mind. 2008. (ENG.). 1p. pap. (978-1-59477-254-2(1), Park Street Pr.) Inner Traditions International, Ltd.
Yound-Sanchez, Margaret & Schaan, Denise Pahl. Marajó: Ancient Ceramics from the Mouth of the Amazon. 2011. (ENG., Illus.). 88p. pap. 25.00 (978-0-914738-73-2(9)) Denver Art Museum.

BRAZIL—BIBLIOGRAPHY

Goldsmith, Peter H. A Brief Bibliography of Books in English, Spanish & Portuguese: The Republics Commonly Called Latin American. 107p. reprint ed. 88.00 (978-0-7222-9523-6(5)) Library Reprints, Inc.

BRAZIL—BIOGRAPHY

Amado, Jorge. A Menino Grapiuna. (POR.). pap. 10.75 (978-85-01-02053-6(2)) Distribuidora Record de Servicos de Imprensa SA BRA. Dist: Distribooks, Inc.
Baquaqua, Mahommah Gardo. The Biography of Mahommah Gardo Baquaqua: His Passage from Slavery to Freedom in Africa & America. 2007. (Illus.). xv, 278p. 69.95 (978-1-55876-429-3(1)) Wiener, Markus Pubs., Inc.
Basbaum, Hersch W. José Renato: Energia Eterna. 2009. (POR., Illus.). 181p. (978-85-7060-772-0(5)) Imprensa Oficial do Estado S/A Imesp.
Bueno, Eduardo. A Viagem Do Descobrimento: A Verdadeira História Da Expedição de Cabral. (POR., Illus.). 137p. (978-85-7302-202-5(7)) Objetiva, Editora Ltda.
Callcott, Maria, et al. Maria Graham's Journal of a Voyage to Brazil. 2010. (978-1-60235-188-2(0)); pap. (978-1-60235-187-5(2)) Parlor Pr.
Campana, Fernando & Campana, Humberto. The Campana Brothers. 2010. (ENG., Illus.). 304p. 75.00 (978-0-8478-3326-9(7)) Rizzoli International Pubns., Inc.
Castroneves, Helio. Victory Road: The Ride of My Life. 2010. (ENG.). 304p. (gr. 12). 24.95 (978-0-451-22737-9(9)) Penguin Group (USA) Inc.
Coelho, Paulo. Palabros Esenciales. 2008.Tr. of Essential Words. (SPA.). 78p. 16.95 (978-987-612-146-0(4)) V & R Editorial ARG. Dist: Baker & Taylor Bks.
Dike, Damian. The Child with Seven Lives: Damian. 2010. (Illus.). 200p. pap. 21.49 (978-1-4490-6273-6(3)) AuthorHouse.
Duarte, Orlando & Bellos, Alex. Pele: Memorias del Mejor Futbolista de Todos los Tiempos. 2007. (SPA.). 353p. pap. 19.95 (978-958-42-1719-6(4)) Planeta Colombiana Editorial S.A. COL. Dist: Planeta Publishing Corp.
Dulles, John W. F. Carlos Lacerda, Brazilian Crusader: Volume II: the Years 1960-1977. 2010. (ENG., Illus.). 795p. pap. 65.00 (978-0-292-72656-7(2)) Univ. of Texas Pr.
Dunsmore, Bob. I Am: A Journey Through Times & Spaces. 2011. 272p. pap. 28.95 (978-1-4620-2432-2(7)) iUniverse, Inc.
Farias, Elson. Claudio Santoro: Cantor Do Sol e Da Paz. 2009. (POR., Illus.). 111p. (978-85-7512-298-3(3)) Valer Livraria Editora e Distribuidora Ltda.
Finger, Anke K., et al. Vilém Flusser: An Introduction. 2011. (Electronic Mediations Ser.). (Illus.). 200p. 63.00 (978-0-8166-7478-7(7)); pap. 21.00 (978-0-8166-7479-4(5)) Univ. of Minnesota Pr.
Freitas, Jose & Moore, David. Luiz Felipe Scolari: The Man, the Manager. 2008. (ENG., Illus.). 192p. pap. (978-1-905928-05-7(X)) Lewis, Dewi Media, Ltd.
Furtado, Júnia Ferreira. Chica da Silva: A Brazilian Slave of the Eighteenth Century. 2008. (New Approaches to the Americas Ser.). (ENG., Illus.). 348p. (C). 75.00 (978-0-521-88465-5(9)) Cambridge Univ. Pr.
Furtado, Júnia Ferreira & Furtado, Júnia Ferreira. Chica Da Silva: A Brazilian Slave of the Eighteenth Century. 2008. (New Approaches to the Americas Ser.). (ENG., Illus.). 348p. (C). pap. 23.99 (978-0-521-71155-5(X)) Cambridge Univ. Pr.
Ginsburg, Solomon L. A Wandering Jew in Brazil: An Autobiography of Solomon L. Ginsburg. 2007. (Illus.). 324p. per. 23.25 (978-1-4251-0851-9(2)) Trafford Publishing.
Goertzel, Ted G. Brazil's Lul: The Most Popular Politician on Earth. 2011. 226p. pap. 26.95 (978-1-61233-505-6(5), Brown Walker Pr.) Universal Pubs.
Hilton, Christopher. Memories of Senna: Anecdotes & Insights from Those Who Knew Him. 2011. (ENG., Illus.). 256p. 24.95 (978-0-85733-229-5(5), 0857332295) Haynes Publishing PLC GBR. Dist: MBI Distribution Services/Quayside Distribution.
Hoffman, Paul. Wings of Madness: Alberto Santos-Dumont & the Invention of Flight. 2008. (ENG.). 369p. pap. 20.00 (978-1-4223-9411-3(5)) DIANE Publishing Co.
Horton, Ron. Peace Corps Syndrome. 2007. 180p. per. 15.00 (978-0-9786366-2-3(7)) Happenstance Bks.
Jobim, Helena. Antonio Carlos Jobim: An Illuminated Man. 2011. (ENG., Illus.). 288p. 27.99 (978-1-61780-343-7(X), 161780343X) Leonard, Hal Corp.
Kropf, Simone & Lacerda, Aline Lopes de. Carlos Chagas: Um Cientista Do Brasil = Scientist of Brazil. 2009. (POR & ENG., Illus.). 306p. (978-85-7541-188-9(8)) Fundacao Oswaldo Cruz.
Leirner, Jac. Jac Leirner in Conversation with Adele Nelson. 2011. (ENG & SPA., Illus.). 220p. 25.00 (978-0-9823544-4-5(4)) Fundacion Cisneros.
Longo, James McMurtry. Isabel Orleans-Braganza: The Brazilian Princess Who Freed the Slaves. 2007. (ENG., Illus.). 300p. per. 39.95 (978-0-7864-3201-1(2)) McFarland & Co., Inc. Pubs.
Lovejoy, Paul & Law, Robin, eds. Biography of Baquaqua: His Passage from Slavery to Freedom in Africa & America. 2nd exp. ed. 2006. (Illus.). 298p. per. 24.95 (978-1-55876-430-9(5)) Wiener, Markus Pubs., Inc.
Lucca, Isa De. With Wings into Life. 2011. 108p. 24.99 (978-1-4568-5406-5(2)); pap. 15.99 (978-1-4568-3798-3(2)) Xlibris Corp.
Magalhães, Rejane Mendes Moreira de Almeida & Senna, Marta de. Rui Barbosa Em Perspectiva: Seleçao de Textos Fundamentais. 2007. (POR., Illus.). 304p. (978-85-7004-278-1(7)) Fundacao Casa De Rui Barbosa.
Mcafee, Steven D. Please God, Be with Us. 2011. 270p. pap. 16.99 (978-1-61379-153-0(4)) Xulon Pr., Inc.
Morais, Fernando. Paulo Coelho: A Warrior's Life - The Authorized Biography. 2009. (ENG.). 608p. 26.99 (978-0-06-171888-5(2), HarperOne); 784p. pap. 26.99 (978-0-06-188588-4(6), HarperLuxe) HarperCollins Pubs.
Moser, Benjamin. Why This World: A Biography of Clarice Lispector. 2009. (ENG., Illus.). 496p. 99.00 (978-0-19-538556-4(X)) Oxford Univ. Pr., Inc.
Murphy, Roseanne. Martyr of the Amazon: The Life of Sister Dorothy Stang. 2007. (Illus.). 168p. per. 18.00 (978-1-57075-735-8(6)) Orbis Bks.
My Journey into Freedom: Confession of an Initiate. 2008. 111p. per. 17.95 (978-0-9815103-2-3(9)) Hallograph Publishing.
Numitor, Gerd, ed. Daniela Mercury. 2011. 116p. pap. (978-613-8-37503-6(3), Flu Pr.) International Book Market Service Ltd.
Osmond, Gordon. Wet Firecrackers: The Unauthorized Autobiography of Gordon Osmond. 2011. 248p. pap. 24.95 (978-1-4512-7585-8(4)) PublishAmerica, Inc.
Overhulser, Josephine. Called According to His Purpose. Ummel, Richard, ed. 2007. 244p. per. 14.99 (978-1-60266-448-7(X)) Xulon Pr., Inc.
Padowicz, Julian. Loves of Yulian Pt. 3: Mother & Me. 2011. (ENG.). 256p. pap. 17.95 (978-0-89733-616-1(X)) Academy Chicago Pubs., Ltd.
Pelé. Pelé: Minha Vida Em Imagens: Fotografias e Itens de Colecionador Sobre o Maior Jogador de Futebol de Todos Os Tempos. 2009. (Illus.). 99p. (978-85-7503-882-6(6)) Cosac & Naify Edicoes Ltda.
Pele. Pelé: The Autobiography. 2007. (ENG., Illus.). 368p. pap. 16.95 (978-1-4165-1121-2(0)) Simon & Schuster, Ltd. GBR. Dist: Independent Pubs. Group.
Pontes, Antonio Rossano Mendes. Amazonia & Other Forests of Brazil. 2010. 272p. pap. (978-1-85756-755-7(2)) Janus Publishing Co.
Popovich, Frances Blok. Forget Not All His Benefits. 2009. pap. (978-1-60178-070-6(2)) Reformation Heritage Bks.
Rodrigues, Gomercindo. Walking the Forest with Chico Mendes: Struggle for Justice in the Amazon. Maybury-Lewis, Biorn, tr. from SPA. 2007. (ENG.). 205p. pap. 22.95 (978-0-292-71706-0(7)) Univ. of Texas Pr.
Sattamini, Lina. A Mother's Cry: A Memoir of Politics, Prison, & Torture under the Brazilian Military Dictatorship. Green, James N., ed. Nielsen, Rex P., tr. 2010. (ENG.). 208p. pap. 22.95 (978-0-8223-4736-1(9)) Duke Univ. Pr.
—A Mother's Cry: A Memoir of Politics, Prison, & Torture under the Brazilian Military Dictatorship. Green, James N., ed. Nielson, Rex P., tr. 2010. (ENG., Illus.). 208p. 79.95 (978-0-8223-4718-7(0)) Duke Univ. Pr.
Smith, Pete & Lovell, Terry. Robinho: King of the City. 2010. (ENG., Illus.). 288p. 24.95 (978-1-84454-829-3(5)) Blake, John Publishing, Ltd. GBR. Dist: Independent Pubs. Group.
Stewart, Dorine Hawkins & Anderson, Frances. Movie Star or Missionary? An Autobiography. 2011. 332p. pap. 22.95 (978-1-61507-657-4(3)) Cross Bks. Publishing.
Vasconcellos, Jorge & Ferreira, Claudiney. Recados Da Bola: Depoimentos de Doze Mestres Do Futebol Brasileiro. 2010. (POR., Illus.). 230p. (978-85-7503-913-7(X)) Cosac & Naify Edicoes Ltda.
Velayas, Kelly M. Odyssey X. 2009. 158p. pap. 12.95 (978-1-60594-318-3(5), Llumina Pr.) Aeon Publishing Inc.
Vincent, Isabel. The Gilded Lily: Lily Safra - The Making of One of the World's Wealthiest Widows. 2010. 336p. 25.99 (978-0-06-113393-0(0)) HarperCollins Pubs.
—Gilded Lily: Lily Safra - The Making of One of the World's Wealthiest Widows. 2011. 352p. pap. 15.99 (978-0-06-113394-7(9), HarperPerennial) HarperCollins Pubs.
Vossia. 2007. (Illus.). 96p. 19.95 (978-0-9778854-5-9(3)) Upper Playground Pubng.
Waldman, Berta. O Teatro Idiche Em São Paulo: Memória. 2010. (POR., Illus.). 84p. (978-85-391-0071-2(1)) Annablume Editora Comunicacao Ltda.
Wilcken, Patrick. Claude Lévi-Strauss: The Father of Modern Anthropology. 2012. (ENG., Illus.). 432p. (gr. 12). 18.00 (978-0-14-312062-9(X), Penguin (Non-Classics)) Penguin Group (USA) Inc.
Wilcken, Patrick. Claude Levi-Strauss: The Poet in the Laboratory. 2010. (ENG., Illus.). 416p. (gr. 12). 29.95 (978-1-59420-273-5(7), Penguin Pr. HC, The) Penguin Group (USA) Inc.
Wilson, Tom, et al, eds. Memories of Paulo. 2010. 210p. (978-94-6091-218-4(4)); pap. (978-94-6091-217-7(6)) Sense Pubs.
Wong, JoySun & Ferreira, Renato. Success Envy Crash Reborn. 2006. (978-0-615-13200-6(6)) JoySun Productions International.
Wright, Jemimah. A Way Beyond Death: A Brazilian Couple's Fight against Fear, Suffering, & Infanticide. 2012. (ENG.). 200p. pap. 13.99 (978-1-57658-430-9(5)) YWAM Publishing.
Wyllie, Brian D. The Long Trip Home: A South American & Caribbean Adventure Through the Past. 2009. (Illus.). xii, 93p. (978-0-595-63025-7(1)) iUniverse, Inc.
Zanardi, Jadir. Benedicto Lacerda: E a Saudade Ficou. 2009. (POR., Illus.). 138p. (978-85-7543-088-0(2)) Muiraquita, Edicoes, Ltda.

BRAZIL—CIVILIZATION

Afolabi, Niyi, et al. The Afro-Brazilian Mind: Contemporary Afro-Brazilian Literary & Cultural Criticism. 2006. (POR & ENG.). (978-1-59221-385-6(5)); 320p. pap. (978-1-59221-386-3(3)) Africa World Pr.
Birle, Peter, et al. Brazil & the Americas: Convergences & Perspectives. 2008. (Illus.). 237p. pap. 29.80 (978-84-8489-375-2(8)) Iberoamericana Vervuert Publishing Corp.
Blake, Stanley E. The Vigorous Core of Our Nationality: Race & Regional Identity in Northeastern Brazil. 2011. (Pitt Latin American Studies). (ENG., Illus.). 360p. pap. 27.95 (978-0-8229-6133-8(4)) Univ. of Pittsburgh Pr.
Bosi, Alfredo & Monteiro, Pedro Meira. Colony, Cult & Culture. 2008. (978-0-9814580-0-7(9)) Univ. of Massachusetts Dartmouth.
Crocitti, John J. & Vallance, Monique. Brazil Today: An Encyclopedia of Life in the Republic. 2011. E-Book (978-0-313-34673-6(9)) ABC-CLIO, LLC.
Davila, Jerry. Brazil: A Century of Change. Sachs, Ignacy et al, eds. Anderson, Robert N., tr. from POR. 2009. (Latin America in Translation/en Traduccion/n/em Traducao - the Brasiliana Collection). (ENG., Illus.). 392p. 69.95 (978-0-8078-3130-4(1)) Univ. of North Carolina Pr.
—Brazil: A Century of Change. Sachs, Ignacy et al, eds. Anderson, Robert N., tr. from POR. 2009. (Latin America in Translation/en Traduccion/n/em Traducao - the Brasiliana Collection). (ENG., Illus.). 392p. pap. 26.95 (978-0-8078-5927-8(3)) Univ. of North Carolina Pr.
Grandin, Greg. Fordlandia: The Rise & Fall of Henry Ford's Forgotten Jungle City. 2009. (ENG., Illus.). 432p. 27.50 (978-0-8050-8236-4(0), Metropolitan Bks.) Holt, Henry & Co.
—Fordlandia: The Rise & Fall of Henry Ford's Forgotten Jungle City. 2010. (ENG., Illus.). 432p. pap. 16.00 (978-0-312-42962-1(2)) Picador.
Hausser, Christian. Auf dem Weg der Zivilisation: Geschichte und Konzepte gesellschaftlicher Entwicklung in Brasilien (1808-1871) 2009. (Beitrage zur Europaischen Uberseegeschichte (BEU) Ser.). (GER.). 349p. (C). pap. 72.00 (978-3-515-09312-5(3)) Steiner, Franz Verlag Wiesbaden GmbH DEU. Dist: Brown, David Bk. Co., The.
Karam, John Tofik. Another Arabesque: Syrian-Lebanese Ethnicity in Neoliberal Brazil. 2007. 232p. 74.50 (978-1-59213-539-4(0)); per. 26.95 (978-1-59213-540-0(4)) Temple Univ. Pr.
Klein, Herbert S. & Luna, Francisco Vidal. Slavery in Brazil. 2009. (ENG., Illus.). 376p. (C). 97.00 (978-0-521-19398-6(2)); pap. 29.99 (978-0-521-14192-5(3)) Cambridge Univ. Pr.
Phaf-Rheinberger, Ineke & Pinto, Tiago de Oliveira. AfricAmericas: Itineraries, Dialogues, & Sounds. 2008. (Illus.). 224p. pap. 29.80 (978-84-8489-380-6(4)) Iberoamericana Vervuert Publishing Corp.
Pinho, Patricia de Santana. Mama Africa: Reinventing Blackness in Bahia. Langdon, Elena, tr. from POR. 2010. (ENG., Illus.). 280p. 84.95 (978-0-8223-4654-8(0)); pap. 23.95 (978-0-8223-4646-3(X)) Duke Univ. Pr.
Preuss, Ori. Bridging the Island: Brazilian's Views of Spanish America & Themselves 1865-1912. 2010. 240p. pap. 29.98 (978-1-936353-02-6(4)) Iberoamericana Vervuert Publishing Corp.
Reis, Manuel Joaquim. A Critica de Arte No ABC. 2009. (POR.). 364p. (978-85-7921-028-0(3)) Terceira Margem Editora Didatica Ltda.
Sadlier, Darlene J. Brazil Imagined: 1500 to the Present. 2008. (William & Bettye Nowlin Series in Art, History, & Culture of the Western Hemisphere). (ENG., Illus.). 408p. 65.00 (978-0-292-71856-2(X)); pap. 24.95 (978-0-292-71857-9(8)) Univ. of Texas Pr.
Sayers, Raymond S., ed. Portugal & Brazil in Transition. 2009. (ENG.). 376p. pap. 60.00 (978-0-8166-5866-4(8)) Univ. of Minnesota Pr.
Souza, Jessz & Sinder, Valter, eds. Imagining Brazil. 2007. (Global Encounters: Studies in Comparative Political Theory Ser.). (ENG.). 318p. per. 34.99 (978-0-7391-1014-0(4)) Lexington Bks.
Tota, Antônio Pedro. The Seduction of Brazil: The Americanization of Brazil during World War II. Ellis, Lorena B., tr. from POR. 2010. (ENG.). 216p. pap. 25.00 (978-0-292-72352-8(0)) Univ. of Texas Pr.

BRAZIL—COMMERCE

Brazil Company Handbook 2006-2007. 2006. pap. 74.95 (978-1-57311-118-8(X)) Hoover's, Inc.
Caetano, Antonio Filipe Pereira. Entre Drogas e Cachaça: A Política Colonial e As Tensões Na América Portuguesa (1640-1710) 2009. (POR.). 362p. (978-85-7177-472-8(2)) Universidade Federal de Alagoas.
Doing Business in Brazil. Date not set. (Doing Business in Regions & Countries Around the World Ser.). 80p. (978-1-882390-53-3(9)) Training Management Corp.
Ebert, Christopher. Between Empires: Brazilian Sugar in the Early Atlantic Economy, 1550-1630. 2008. (Atlantic World Ser.). (Illus.). 220p. (978-90-04-16768-1(4)) BRILL.
Giuliani, Antonio Carlos. Retail in Brazil. 2011. 216p. pap. (978-3-8433-9114-6(9)) Lambert Academic Publishing.
Horn, Carlos Henrique. Collective Bargaining in Brazil. 2009. 224p. pap. (978-3-639-15177-0(1)) VDM Verlag Dr. Mueller e.K.
International Trade Centre. Business Guide to Trade Remedies in Brazil: Anti-dumping, Countervailing & Safeguard Legislation, Practices & Procedures. 2010. (Business & the Multilateral Trading System Ser.). (ENG.). 344p. pap. 70.00 (978-92-9137-370-3(2)) United Nations Pubns.
Kayser, Pedro. The Brazilian Shoe Industry - Competing in International Markets. 2009. 152p. pap. (978-3-639-16644-6(2)) VDM Verlag Dr. Mueller e.K.
Peters, Ina. Interessen und Ideen in multilateralen Handelsbeziehungen: Eine Analyse der Regierungsposition Brasiliens in den DDA- und FTAA-Verhandlungen. 2010. (Europäische Hochschulschriften. Reihe 31: Politikwissenschaft Ser.). 132p. pap. 28.95 (978-3-631-59979-2(X)) Lang, Peter GmbH, Europaischer Verlag der Wissenschaften DEU. Dist: Lang, Peter.
Rogers, Thomas D. The Deepest Wounds: A Labor & Environmental History of Sugar in Northeast Brazil. 2010. (ENG., Illus.). 456p. 65.00 (978-0-8078-3433-6(5)); pap. 25.95 (978-0-8078-7167-6(2)) Univ. of North Carolina Pr.

BRAZIL—COMMERCIAL POLICY

BRAINARD. Brazil as an Economic Superpower? Understanding Brazil's Changing Role in the Global Economy. Brainard, Lael & Martinez-Diaz, Leonardo, eds. 2009. (ENG.). 291p. 52.95 (978-0-8157-0295-5(7)) Brookings Institution Pr.
Brainard, Lael & Martinez-Diaz, Leonardo, eds. Brazil as an Economic Superpower? Understanding Brazil's Changing Role in the Global Economy. 2009. (ENG.). 291p. pap. 24.95 (978-0-8157-0296-2(5)) Brookings Institution Pr.
Brazil Telecom. Date not set. pap. 645.00 (978-1-56851-116-0(7)) Information Gatekeepers, Inc.
Peters, Ina. Interessen und Ideen in multilateralen Handelsbeziehungen: Eine Analyse der Regierungsposition Brasiliens in den DDA- und FTAA-Verhandlungen. 2010. (Europäische Hochschulschriften. Reihe 31: Politikwissenschaft Ser.). 132p. pap. 28.95 (978-3-631-59979-2(X)) Lang, Peter GmbH, Europaischer Verlag der Wissenschaften DEU. Dist: Lang, Peter.

BRAZIL—DESCRIPTION AND TRAVEL

Acuña, Cristóbal de, et al. Nuevo Descubrimiento Del Gran Río de Las Amazonas. 2009. (SPA.). 181p. pap. 22.80 (978-84-8489-445-2(2)) Iberoamericana Vervuert Publishing Corp.
Agassiz, Louis. A Journey in Brazil by Professor & Mrs Louis Agassiz. 2006. (ENG.). 580p. per. 32.99 (978-1-4255-6297-7(3)); 564p. per. 32.99 (978-1-4255-6274-8(4)) MPublishing.
Atkins, John. A Voyage to Guinea, Brazil & the West Indies. 2010. (ENG.). 232p. pap. 17.95 (978-1-897959-67-1(2)) Serif GBR. Dist: Interlink Publishing Group, Inc.
Baxter, David. Big River, Rio Grande. 2009. (ENG., Illus.). 132p. 39.95 (978-0-292-71818-0(7)) Univ. of Texas Pr.
Berts, Jean-Michel, et al. Brazilian Style. 2011. (ENG.). 208p. pap. 65.00 (978-1-61428-013-2(4)) Assouline FRA. Dist: Perseus Distribution.
Bonfato, Antonio Carlos. Macedo Vieira: Ressonâncias Do Modelo Cidade-Jardim. 2008. (Illus.). 245p. (978-85-7359-700-4(3)) Servico Nacional de Aprendizagem Comercial, Senac.
Branco, Sandra. Brazil: The Essential Guide to Customs & Culture. 2006. (Culture Smart! Ser.). (ENG., Illus.). 168p. pap. 9.95 (978-1-85733-323-7(3)) Kuperard Pubs. GBR. Dist: Random Hse., Inc.
Burri, René, et al. René Burri. Brasilia: Fotografien 1960-1993. Rüegg, Arthur, ed. 2011. (GER & ENG., Illus.). 224p. 99.00 (978-3-85881-307-7(9)) Scheidegger und Spiess AG, Verlag CHE. Dist: Antique Collectors' Club.
Callcott, Maria. Journal of a Residence in Chile, during the Year 1822. 2011. (Cambridge Library Collection - Women's Writing Ser.). (ENG., Illus.). 552p. pap. 39.99 (978-1-108-03378-7(4)) Cambridge Univ. Pr.
Callcott, Maria. Journal of a Voyage to Brazil, & Residence There, During Part of the Years 1821, 1822 1823. 2010. (Cambridge Library Collection - Women's

Writing Ser.). (Illus.). 370p. pap. 29.99 *(978-1-108-01828-9(9))* Cambridge Univ. Pr.

Callcott, Maria, et al. Maria Graham's Journal of a Voyage to Brazil. 2010. *(978-1-60235-188-2(0))*; pap. *(978-1-60235-187-5(2))* Parlor Pr.

Codman, John. Ten Months in Brazil: With Notes on the Paraguayan War. by John Codman. 2006. 232p. per. 20.99 *(978-1-4255-1986-5(5))* MPublishing.

Coudreau, Henri Anatole. Voyage á Itaboca et á L'Itacayuna: 1er Juillet, 1897-11 Octobre 1897. 2009. (Cambridge Library Collection - Linguistics Ser.). (FRE., Illus.). 224p. pap. 22.99 *(978-1-108-00692-7(2))* Cambridge Univ. Pr.

—Voyage au Tocantins-Araguaya: 31 Décembre, 1896-23 Mai 1897. 2009. (Cambridge Library Collection - Linguistics Ser.). (FRE., Illus.). 312p. pap. 24.99 *(978-1-108-00740-5(6))* Cambridge Univ. Pr.

—Voyage au Xingú: 30 Mai 1896-26 Octobre 1896. 2009. (Cambridge Library Collection - Linguistics Ser.). (FRE., Illus.). 244p. pap. 22.99 *(978-1-108-00741-2(4))* Cambridge Univ. Pr.

Da Cunha, Euclides. The Amazon: Land Without History. Sa, Lucia, ed. Sousa, Ronald, tr. from POR. 2006. (Library of Latin America Ser.). (ENG.). 128p. per. 19.95 *(978-0-19-517204-1(3))* Oxford Univ. Pr., Inc.

De Mello, Paulo Thiago & Gunti, Reto. At Home in Rio. 2006. (ENG., Illus.). 204p. 50.00 *(978-0-86565-178-4(7))* Vendome Pr., The.

Duffy, Eve M. & Metcalf, Alida C. The Return of Hans Staden: A Go-Between in the Atlantic World. 2011. (ENG., Illus.). 216p. (C). (gr. 13-17). 60.00 *(978-1-4214-0345-8(5))*; pap. 25.00 *(978-1-4214-0346-5(3))* Johns Hopkins Univ. Pr.

Edwards, William H. A Voyage up the River Amazon: Including a Residence at Pará. 2010. (Cambridge Library Collection - Travel & Exploration Ser.). (ENG.). 224p. pap. 24.00 *(978-1-108-01196-9(9))* Cambridge Univ. Pr.

Fawcett, Percy. Exploration Fawcett: Journey to the Lost City of Z. 2010. (ENG.). 356p. (gr. 12). 15.95 *(978-1-59020-430-6(1))* Overlook Pr., The.

Fletcher, James C. & Kidder, Daniel P. Brazil & the Brazilians: Portrayed in Historical & Descriptive Sketches. 8th ed. 2006. (Kegan Paul Travellers Ser.). (Illus.). 650p. 300.00 *(978-0-7103-1146-7(X))* Taylor & Francis Group.

Harris. Amazon Highlights Bradt. 2012. (ENG., Illus.). 208p. pap. 22.99 *(978-1-84162-374-0(1))* Bradt Travel Guides GBR. Dist: Globe Pequot Pr., The.

Hayskar, Bonnie J., ed. Natural Iguassu: Brazil/Brasil & Argentina. 2010. (ENG, POR & SPA., Illus.). 180p. pap. 24.95 *(978-0-9630180-9-0(4))* PANGAEA.

Herndon, William Lewis. Exploration of the Valley of the Amazon, Made under Direction of the Navy Department. 2006. 428p. per. 26.99 *(978-1-4255-4704-2(4))*; 424p. per. 26.99 *(978-1-4255-4621-2(8))* MPublishing.

Hüsch, Anette. ARCHIV UTOPIA ARCHIVE UTOPIA: Das Brasilia-Projekt von Lina Kim und Michael Wesely Project Brasilia by Lina Kim & Michael Wesely. 2012. (ENG., Illus.). 168p. 40.00 *(978-3-86828-221-4(1))* Kehrer Verlag Heidelberg, Klaus Kehrer DEU. Dist: Consortium Bk. Sales & Distribution.

Kidder, Daniel P. Brazil & the Brazilians Portrayed in Historical & Descriptive Sketches. 630p. reprint ed. 128.00 *(978-0-7222-9595-3(2))* Library Reprints, Inc.

Kidder, Daniel P. (Daniel Parish). Brazil & the Brazilians, Portrayed in Historical & Descriptive Sketches by Rev D P Kidder, D D, & Rev J C Fletcher. 2006. 676p. per. 36.99 *(978-1-4255-6805-4(X))* MPublishing.

Koebel, William H. The Great South Land: The River Plate & Southern Brazil of Today. 314p. reprint ed. 98.00 *(978-0-7222-9555-7(3))* Library Reprints, Inc.

Koster, Henry. Travels in Brazil. 2010. 400p. pap. 33.75 *(978-1-142-63502-2(3))* BiblioBazaar.

—Travels in Brazil. 2010. 322p. pap. 24.25 *(978-1-154-11539-0(9))* 2010. (Illus.). 166p. pap. 24.25 *(978-1-154-09400-8(6))* 2009. 172p. pap. 19.99 *(978-1-151-25481-8(9))* General Bks. LLC.

Kuhn, Mona, photos by. Native, 1 vol. 2009. (ENG., Illus.). 88p. 50.00 *(978-3-86521-913-8(6))* Steidl, Gerhard Druckerei und Verlag DEU. Dist: Innovative Logistics.

Landor, Arnold H. S. Across Unknown South America, 2 Vols. reprint ed. 250.00 *(978-0-7222-9556-4(1))* Library Reprints, Inc.

Lange, Algot. The Lower Amazon. 2009. 264p. pap. 19.75 *(978-1-4589-2897-9(7))* General Bks. LLC.

—The Lower Amazon. 2007. 536p. 57.95 *(978-0-548-32991-7(5))*; (ENG.). per. 42.95 *(978-1-4326-8863-9(4))* Kessinger Publishing, LLC.

—The Lower Amazon. 468p. reprint ed. 98.00 *(978-0-7222-6483-6(6))* Library Reprints, Inc.

—The Lower Amazon: A Narrative of Explorations in the Little Known Region of the State of Para. 468p. reprint ed. 98.00 *(978-0-7222-9597-7(9))* Library Reprints, Inc.

Levi-Strauss, Claude. Tristes Tropiques. Weightman, John & Weightman, Doreen, trs. 2012. (ENG., Illus.). 448p. (gr. 12). 20.00 *(978-0-14-310625-8(2)*, Penguin Classics) Penguin Group (USA) Inc.

Locken, E. Travel Journal Brasil. 2010. 192p. pap. 19.99 *(978-0-557-42210-4(8))* Lulu Enterprises Inc.

—Travel Journal Brazil. 2010. 192p. pap. 19.99 *(978-0-557-43276-9(6))* Lulu Enterprises Inc.

—Travel Journal Sao Paulo. 2010. 192p. pap. 19.99 *(978-0-557-42176-3(4))* Lulu Enterprises Inc.

Marjoribanks, Alexander. Travels in South & North America. 2007. (Travel in America Ser.). (ENG.). 504p. 49.95 *(978-1-4290-0314-8(6))*; per. 24.95 *(978-1-4290-0315-5(4))* Applewood Bks.

—Travels in South & North America. 2007. (ENG.). 500p. 53.95 *(978-0-548-32946-7(X))*; per. 38.95 *(978-1-4326-8817-2(0))* Kessinger Publishing, LLC.

Mohlke, Matthew & Strel, Martin. The Man Who Swam the Amazon: 3,274 Miles on the World's Deadliest River. 2007. (ENG., Illus.). 224p. per. 16.95 *(978-1-59921-358-3(3)*, Lyons Pr.) Globe Pequot Pr., The.

Mossinger, Ingrid & Metz, Katharina, eds. Documentary Photography from Brazil 1940-1970. 2009. (ENG., Illus.). 152p. 55.00 *(978-3-86678-163-4(6))* Kerber Verlag DEU. Dist: D.A.P./Distributed Art Pubs.

Page, P. K. Brazilian Journal. 2nd ed. 2011. (Collected Works). (ENG., Illus.). 304p. pap. 27.95 *(978-0-88984-347-9(3))* Porcupine's Quill, Inc. CAN. Dist: Univ. of Toronto Pr.

Parr, Martin & Riedl, Titus. Retratos Pintados. 2010. (Illus.). 66p. *(978-1-59005-267-9(6))* Nazraeli Pr.

Peterson, Joan. Eat Smart in Brazil: How to Decipher the Menu, Know the Market Foods & Embark on a Tasting Adventure. 2nd ed. 2006. (ENG., Illus.). 160p. per. 13.95 *(978-0-9641168-9-4(8))* Ginkgo Pr., Inc.

Ray, T. B. Brazilian Sketches. 2008. 124p. 21.95 *(978-1-4218-9463-8(7))*; pap. 14.95 *(978-1-4218-9363-1(0))* 1st World Publishing, Inc. (1st World Library - Literary Society).

—Brazilian Sketches. 2007. (ENG.). 92p. per. *(978-1-4065-3760-4(8))* Dodo Pr.

—Brazilian Sketches. 2007. (ENG.). 96p. per. *(978-1-4068-3758-2(X))* Echo Library.

Roosevelt, Theodore. Through the Brazilian Wilderness. 2006. (ENG.). 244p. per. 14.95 *(978-1-59818-561-4(6))*; 26.95 *(978-1-59818-192-0(0))* Aegypan.

—Through the Brazilian Wilderness. 2010. 452p. pap. 36.75 *(978-1-143-86622-7(3))* 2010. 510p. pap. 39.75 *(978-1-142-74536-3(8))* 2008. 312p. 28.99 *(978-0-554-33335-9(X))* 2008. 312p. 29.99 *(978-0-554-24032-9(7))* 2007. (ENG.). 276p. pap. 21.99 *(978-1-4264-5538-8(4))* BiblioBazaar.

—Through the Brazilian Wilderness. 2007. (ENG.). 204p. per. *(978-1-4068-4029-2(7))* Echo Library.

—Through the Brazilian Wilderness. 2009. 228p. pap. 26.81 *(978-1-151-25458-0(4))* General Bks. LLC.

—Through the Brazilian Wilderness. 232p. 2009. 34.99 *(978-1-59547-537-4(0))* 2007. (ENG.). per. 15.99 *(978-1-59547-853-5(1))* NuVision Pubns., LLC.

—Through the Brazilian Wilderness. 2011. 216p. pap. 14.99 *(978-1-61203-105-7(6))* Bottom of the Hill Publishing.

—Through the Brazilian Wilderness. l.t. ed. 2007. (ENG.). 308p. pap. 24.99 *(978-1-4264-5646-6(8))* BiblioBazaar.

—Through the Brazilian Wilderness. 383p. reprint ed. 98.00 *(978-0-7222-9600-4(2))* Library Reprints, Inc.

—Through the Brazilian Wilderness: Or My Voyage along the River of Doubt. 2009. 200p. pap. 12.95 *(978-1-60459-618-2(X))* Wilder Pubns., Ltd.

Rushenberger, William, abr. Three Years in the Pacific. 2009. (Military History Ser.). (ENG.). 463p. pap. 27.95 *(978-1-4290-2192-0(6))* Applewood Bks.

Stade, Hans. Captivity of Hans Stade of Hesse in A. D. 1547-1555, among the Wild Tribes of Eastern Brazil. Burton, Richard F., ed. Tootal, Albert, tr. 2010. (Cambridge Library Collection - Travel & Exploration Ser.). (ENG.). 280p. pap. 23.99 *(978-1-108-01237-9(X))* Cambridge Univ. Pr.

Staden, Hans. Hans Staden's True History: An Account of Cannibal Captivity in Brazil. Whitehead, Neil L., ed. Harbsmeier, Michael, tr. from GER. 2008. (Cultures & Practice of Violence Ser.). (ENG., Illus.). 296p. (C). pap. 23.95 *(978-0-8223-4231-1(6))*; 84.95 *(978-0-8223-4213-7(8))* Duke Univ. Pr.

Steinen, Karl. Unter Den Naturvölkern Zentral-Brasiliens: Reiseschilderung und Ergebnisse der Zweiten Schingu-Expedition, 1887 - 1888. (GER.). XIV, 570p. 328.00 *(978-3-11-208802-9(6))* De Gruyter, Walter Inc.

—Unter den Naturvölkern Zentral-Brasiliens: Reiseschilderung und Ergebnisse der Zweiten Schingu-Expedition, 1887 - 1888. (GER.). XIV, 570p. 219.00 *(978-3-11-125492-0(5))* De Gruyter, Walter Inc.

—Unter den Naturvölkern Zentral-Brasiliens: Reiseschilderung und Ergebnisse der Zweiten Schingu-Expedition 1887 - 1888. 2nd ed. (GER.). XVI, 413p. 240.00 *(978-3-11-194279-7(1))*; 161.00 *(978-3-11-111550-4(X))* De Gruyter, Walter Inc.

Steinen, Karl von den. Unter den Naturvölkern Zentral-Brasiliens: Reiseschilderung und Ergebnisse Der Zweiten Schingú-Expedition, 1887-1888. 2009. (Cambridge Library Collection - Linguistics Ser.). (GER., Illus.). 656p. pap. 45.00 *(978-1-108-00686-6(8))* Cambridge Univ. Pr.

Stewart, Charles Samuel. Brazil & la Plata; the Personal Record of a Cruise, by C S Stewart. 2006. 468p. per. 29.99 *(978-1-4255-5179-7(3))* MPublishing.

Stone, Laura. Americans in Brasil. 2008. 207p. pap. 16.95 *(978-0-557-00863-4(2))* Lulu Enterprises Inc.

Tomlinson, H. M. The Sea & the Jungle. 2010. 254p. pap. *(978-1-4099-7378-2(6))* Dodo Pr.

Tomlinson, Henry M. The Sea & the Jungle. 371p. reprint ed. 98.00 *(978-0-7222-9601-1(0))*; 98.00 *(978-0-7222-9568-7(5))* Library Reprints, Inc.

van Baerle, Caspar. The History of Brazil under the Governorship of Count Johan Maurits of Nassau, 1636-1644. 2011. (ENG., Illus.). 448p. 79.95 *(978-0-8130-3664-9(X))* Univ. Pr. of Florida.

Waldecker, Frank. THE BOYS FROM IPANEMA. 2010. (ENG.). 128p. 50.00 *(978-3-03766-598-5(X))* Edition Skylight CHE. Dist: Independent Pubs. Group.

Wallace, Alfred Russel. A Narrative of Travels on the Amazon & Rio Negro, with an Account of the Native Tribes, & Observations on the Climate, Geology, & Natural History of the Amazon. 2010. (Cambridge Library Collection - Travel & Exploration Ser.). (ENG., Illus.). 576p. pap. 39.99 *(978-1-108-00729-0(5))* Cambridge Univ. Pr.

Waterton, Charles. Wanderings in South America. l.t. ed. 2007. (ENG.). 240p. pap. 22.99 *(978-1-4264-2641-4(0))* BiblioBazaar.

BRAZIL—ECONOMIC CONDITIONS

Afonis, Stavros. Brazil's Ethanol Fuel Program. 2010. 64p. pap. *(978-3-8383-1442-6(5))* Lambert Academic Publishing.

Alcoforado, Fernando. The Necessary Conditions of the Economic & Social Development. 2010. 388p. pap. *(978-3-639-24352-9(8))* VDM Verlag Dr. Mueller e.K.

Amann, Edmund & Chang, Ha-Joon. Brazil & South Korea: Economic Crisis & Restructuring. Date not set. (Illus.). 230p. (C). pap. 19.95 *(978-1-900039-51-2(6))* Institute of Latin American Studies GBR. Dist: Brookings Institution Pr.

Arbio, Jan & De Haas, Henning, eds. Supply Chain Management: Brazil as an Emergent Economy. 2011. (Illus.). 146p. pap. 29.00 *(978-87-7674-567-7(6))* Univ. Pr. of Southern Denmark DNK. Dist: International Specialized Bk. Services.

Baer, Werner. The Brazilian Economy: Growth & Development. 6th Edition. 6th ed. 2007. 500p. (C). pap. 29.95 *(978-1-58826-475-6(0))* Rienner, Lynne Pubs.

Baer, Werner & Fleischer, David V. The Economies of Argentina & Brazil: A Comparative Perspective. 2011. (Illus.). 512p. 195.00 *(978-1-84980-996-2(8))* Elgar, Edward Publishing, Inc.

Berg, Janine, et al. Enfrentando el Desafío Del Empleo: Argentina, Brasil y Mexico en una Economía Globalizada. 2009. (SPA., Illus.). 305p. pap. 29.00 *(973-970-722-523-7(8))* Plaza y Valdes, S.A. de C.V. MEX. Dist: Sony Electronics.

Bhatia, Ramesh, et al, eds. Indirect Economic Impacts of Dams: Case Studies from India, Egypt & Brazil. 2009. (ENG., Illus.). 372p. 59.95 *(978-81-7188-681-4(7))* Academic Foundation IND. Dist: Independent Pubs. Group.

Brazil Business Financing Handbook. (Illus.). 70p. (Orig.). pap. 295.00 *(978-0-7605-1182-4(9))* Rector Pr., Ltd.

Bresser-Pereira, Luiz Carlos. Developing Brazil: Overcoming the Failure of the Washington Consensus. 2009. (Illus.). 295p. *(978-1-58826-624-8(9))* Rienner, Lynne Pubs.

Cavalcanti, Marly & de Farias Macedo, Etiene. Flowers Clusters in Brazil: Scenario, market & cold chain Logistics. 2010. 136p. pap. *(978-3-8383-8796-3(1))* Lambert Academic Publishing.

Chilcote, Ronald H. Power & the Ruling Classes in Northeast Brazil: Juazeiro & Petrolina in Transition. 2006. (Cambridge Latin American Studies). (ENG.). 404p. pap. 75.00 *(978-0-521-02881-3(7))* Cambridge Univ. Pr.

Costa, Diogo. Water & War at Pyreneus Mountains. 2011. 192p. pap. *(978-3-8443-0561-6(0))* Lambert Academic Publishing.

Cummings, Barbara J. Dam the Rivers, Damn the People: Development & Resistence in Amazonian Brazil. 2nd ed. 2009. (Sustainable Development Set Ser.). (ENG., Illus.). 148p. 110.00 *(978-1-84407-944-5(9))* Routledge.

Da Rocha Soares Ferreira, Vicente & Souza, Cláudia. Biodiesel in Brazil. 2010. 132p. pap. *(978-3-639-23334-6(4))* VDM Verlag Dr. Mueller e.K.

Davidson, James Dale. Brazil Is the New America: How Brazil Offers Upward Mobility in a Collapsing World. 2012. (ENG.). 336p. 29.95 *(978-1-118-00663-4(1)*, Wiley) Wiley, John & Sons, Inc.

De Moura Engracia Giraldi, Janaina. Brazil's Image & the Attitude Toward Brazilian Products. 2010. 144p. pap. *(978-3-639-23773-3(0))* VDM Verlag Dr. Mueller e.K.

Eveline, Carvalho. Economic Integration: Impacts & Alternative Responses: In Brazil's Northeast. 2011. (Illus.). 160p. pap. *(978-3-639-33251-3(2))* VDM Verlag Dr. Mueller e.K.

Fishlow, Albert. Starting Over: Brazil Since 1985. 2011. (ENG., Illus.). 236p. 34.95 *(978-0-8157-2143-7(9))* Brookings Institution Pr.

Font, Mauricio. The Brazilian State: Debate & Agenda. Randall, Adrian, ed. 2011. (Bildner Western Hemisphere Studies). (ENG.). 434p. (gr. 17). 85.00 *(978-0-7391-6731-1(6))* Lexington Bks.

Font, Mauricio A. & Randall, Laura. The Brazilian State: Debate & Agenda. 2011. *(978-0-7391-6889-9(4))* Lexington Bks.

Franco, Marcelo. Environmental Finances. 2010. 84p. pap. *(978-3-639-24179-2(7))* VDM Verlag Dr. Mueller e.K.

Franklin, Adalberto. Apontamentos e Fontes para a História Econômica de Imperatriz. 2008. (POR., Illus.). 242p. *(978-85-88172-26-5(7))* Etica Servicos Editoriais Ltda.

Furtado, Celso. La formation économique du Brésil: De l'époque coloniale aux temps Modernes. (Civilisations et Sociétés Ser.). (FRE.). 218p. 135.00 *(978-3-11-098596-2(9))* De Gruyter, Mouton DEU. Dist: de Gruyter, Walter GmbH & Co. KG.

Garcia, Vinicius. Rise Reference Model for Software Reuse Adoption. 2011. 212p. pap. *(978-3-8443-1848-7(6))* Lambert Academic Publishing.

Gragnolati, Michele. Growing Old in & Older Brazil: Implications of Population Aging on Growth, Poverty, Public Finance & Service Delivery. 2011. E-Book *(978-0-8213-8803-7(7))* World Bank Pubns.

Gragnolati, Michele, et al. Growing Old in an Older Brazil: Implications of Population Aging on Growth, Poverty, Public Finance & Service Delivery. 2011. (Directions in Development Ser.). (ENG.). 304p. pap. 35.00 *(978-0-8213-8802-0(9))*, 9780821383020) World Bank Pubns.

Hardie, Iain. Financialization & Government Borrowing Capacity in Emerging Markets. 2012. (International Political Economy Ser.). (ENG., Illus.). 232p. 85.00 *(978-0-230-36055-6(6))* Palgrave Macmillan.

Icon Group International, Inc. Staff, compiled by. The 2006 Economic & Product Market Databook for Abaetetuba, Brazil. 2006. 605p. ring bd. 95.00 *(978-0-497-79939-7(1))* Icon Group International, Inc.

—The 2006 Economic & Product Market Databook for Alagoinhas, Brazil. 2006. 618p. ring bd. 95.00 *(978-0-497-80023-9(3))* Icon Group International, Inc.

—The 2006 Economic & Product Market Databook for Altamira, Brazil. 2006. 618p. ring bd. 95.00 *(978-0-497-80040-6(3))* Icon Group International, Inc.

—The 2006 Economic & Product Market Databook for Alvorada, Brazil. 2006. 618p. ring bd. 95.00 *(978-0-497-80041-3(1))* Icon Group International, Inc.

—The 2006 Economic & Product Market Databook for Americana, Brazil. 2006. 618p. ring bd. 95.00 *(978-0-497-80045-1(4))* Icon Group International, Inc.

—The 2006 Economic & Product Market Databook for anápolis, Brazil. 2006. 618p. ring bd. 95.00 *(978-0-497-80068-0(3))* Icon Group International, Inc.

—The 2006 Economic & Product Market Databook for Aparecida de Goiania, Brazil. 2006. 618p. ring bd. 95.00 *(978-0-497-80071-0(3))* Icon Group International, Inc.

—The 2006 Economic & Product Market Databook for Aracaju, Brazil. 2006. 618p. ring bd. 95.00 *(978-0-497-80074-1(8))* Icon Group International, Inc.

—The 2006 Economic & Product Market Databook for Araçatuba, Brazil. 2006. 618p. ring bd. 95.00 *(978-0-497-80078-9(0))* Icon Group International, Inc.

—The 2006 Economic & Product Market Databook for Araguaina, Brazil. 2006. 618p. ring bd. 95.00 *(978-0-497-80075-8(6))* Icon Group International, Inc.

—The 2006 Economic & Product Market Databook for Arapiraca, Brazil. 2006. 618p. ring bd. 95.00 *(978-0-497-80076-5(4))* Icon Group International, Inc.

—The 2006 Economic & Product Market Databook for Araraquara, Brazil. 2006. 618p. ring bd. 95.00 *(978-0-497-80077-2(2))* Icon Group International, Inc.

—The 2006 Economic & Product Market Databook for Bage, Brazil. 2006. 618p. ring bd. 95.00 *(978-0-497-80116-8(7))* Icon Group International, Inc.

—The 2006 Economic & Product Market Databook for Barbacena, Brazil. 2006. 618p. ring bd. 95.00 *(978-0-497-80141-0(8))* Icon Group International, Inc.

—The 2006 Economic & Product Market Databook for Barra Mansa, Brazil. 2006. 618p. ring bd. 95.00 *(978-0-497-80148-9(5))* Icon Group International, Inc.

—The 2006 Economic & Product Market Databook for Barueri, Brazil. 2006. 618p. ring bd. 95.00 *(978-0-497-80151-9(5))* Icon Group International, Inc.

—The 2006 Economic & Product Market Databook for Bauru, Brazil. 2006. 618p. ring bd. 95.00 *(978-0-497-80163-2(9))* Icon Group International, Inc.

—The 2006 Economic & Product Market Databook for Belem, Brazil. 2006. 618p. ring bd. 95.00 *(978-0-497-80174-8(4))* Icon Group International, Inc.

—The 2006 Economic & Product Market Databook for Belford Roxo, Brazil. 2006. 618p. ring bd. 95.00 *(978-0-497-80175-5(2))* Icon Group International, Inc.

—The 2006 Economic & Product Market Databook for Belo Horizonte, Brazil. 2006. 618p. ring bd. 95.00 *(978-0-497-80178-6(7))* Icon Group International, Inc.

—The 2006 Economic & Product Market Databook for Betim, Brazil. 2006. 618p. ring bd. 95.00 *(978-0-497-80193-9(0))* Icon Group International, Inc.

—The 2006 Economic & Product Market Databook for Blumenau, Brazil. 2006. 618p. ring bd. 95.00 *(978-0-497-80210-3(4))* Icon Group International, Inc.

—The 2006 Economic & Product Market Databook for Boa Vista, Brazil. 2006. 618p. ring bd. 95.00 *(978-0-497-80211-0(2))* Icon Group International, Inc.

—The 2006 Economic & Product Market Databook for Bragança Paulista, Brazil. 2006. 618p. ring bd. 95.00 *(978-0-497-80235-6(X))* Icon Group International, Inc.

—The 2006 Economic & Product Market Databook for Brasilia, Brazil. 2006. 618p. ring bd. 95.00 *(978-0-497-80238-7(4))* Icon Group International, Inc.

—The 2006 Economic & Product Market Databook for Cabo, Brazil. 2006. 618p. ring bd. 95.00 *(978-0-497-80279-0(1))* Icon Group International, Inc.

—The 2006 Economic & Product Market Databook for Cachoeiro de Itapemirim, Brazil. 2006. 618p. ring bd. 95.00 *(978-0-497-80280-6(5))* Icon Group International, Inc.

—The 2006 Economic & Product Market Databook for Camacari, Brazil. 2006. 618p. ring bd. 95.00 *(978-0-497-80291-2(0))* Icon Group International, Inc.

—The 2006 Economic & Product Market Databook for Camaragibe, Brazil. 2006. 618p. ring bd. 95.00 *(978-0-497-80293-6(7))* Icon Group International, Inc.

—The 2006 Economic & Product Market Databook for Campina Grande, Brazil. 2006. 618p. ring bd. 95.00 *(978-0-497-80294-3(5))* Icon Group International, Inc.

—The 2006 Economic & Product Market Databook for Campinas, Brazil. 2006. 618p. ring bd. 95.00 *(978-0-497-80295-0(3))* Icon Group International, Inc.

—The 2006 Economic & Product Market Databook for Campo Grande, Brazil. 2006. 618p. ring bd. 95.00 *(978-0-497-80296-7(1))* Icon Group International, Inc.

—The 2006 Economic & Product Market Databook for Campos dos Goytacazes, Brazil. 2006. 618p. ring bd. 95.00 *(978-0-497-80297-4(X))* Icon Group International, Inc.

—The 2006 Economic & Product Market Databook for Canoas, Brazil. 2006. 618p. ring bd. 95.00 *(978-0-497-80302-5(X))* Icon Group International, Inc.

—The 2006 Economic & Product Market Databook for Carapicuiba, Brazil. 2006. 618p. ring bd. 95.00 *(978-0-497-80308-7(9))* Icon Group International, Inc.

—The 2006 Economic & Product Market Databook for Caratinga, Brazil. 2006. 618p. ring bd. 95.00 *(978-0-497-80309-4(7))* Icon Group International, Inc.

—The 2006 Economic & Product Market Databook for Cariacica, Brazil. 2006. 618p. ring bd. 95.00 *(978-0-497-80310-0(0))* Icon Group International, Inc.

—The 2006 Economic & Product Market Databook for Caruaru, Brazil. 2006. 618p. ring bd. 95.00 *(978-0-497-80314-8(3))* Icon Group International, Inc.

—The 2006 Economic & Product Market Databook for Cascavel, Brazil. 2006. 618p. ring bd. 95.00 *(978-0-497-80317-9(8))* Icon Group International, Inc.

B

—The 2006 Economic & Product Market Databook for Castanhal, Brazil. 2006. 618p. ring bd. 95.00 *(978-0-497-80318-6(6))* Icon Group International, Inc.

—The 2006 Economic & Product Market Databook for Caucaia, Brazil. 2006. 618p. ring bd. 95.00 *(978-0-497-80324-7(0))* Icon Group International, Inc.

—The 2006 Economic & Product Market Databook for Caxias, Brazil. 2006. 618p. ring bd. 95.00 *(978-0-497-80326-1(7))* Icon Group International, Inc.

—The 2006 Economic & Product Market Databook for Caxias do Sul, Brazil. 2006. 618p. ring bd. 95.00 *(978-0-497-80325-4(9))* Icon Group International, Inc.

—The 2006 Economic & Product Market Databook for Chapecó, Brazil. 2006. 618p. ring bd. 95.00 *(978-0-497-80338-4(0))* Icon Group International, Inc.

—The 2006 Economic & Product Market Databook for Codó, Brazil. 2006. 618p. ring bd. 95.00 *(978-0-497-80389-6(5))* Icon Group International, Inc.

—The 2006 Economic & Product Market Databook for Colatina, Brazil. 2006. 618p. ring bd. 95.00 *(978-0-497-80392-6(5))* Icon Group International, Inc.

—The 2006 Economic & Product Market Databook for Colombo, Brazil. 2006. 618p. ring bd. 95.00 *(978-0-497-80395-7(X))* Icon Group International, Inc.

—The 2006 Economic & Product Market Databook for Contagem, Brazil. 2006. 618p. ring bd. 95.00 *(978-0-497-80406-0(9))* Icon Group International, Inc.

—The 2006 Economic & Product Market Databook for Cotia, Brazil. 2006. 618p. ring bd. 95.00 *(978-0-497-80416-9(6))* Icon Group International, Inc.

—The 2006 Economic & Product Market Databook for Criciúma, Brazil. 2006. 618p. ring bd. 95.00 *(978-0-497-80421-3(2))* Icon Group International, Inc.

—The 2006 Economic & Product Market Databook for Cuiabá, Brazil. 2006. 618p. ring bd. 95.00 *(978-0-497-80426-8(3))* Icon Group International, Inc.

—The 2006 Economic & Product Market Databook for Curitiba, Brazil. 2006. 618p. ring bd. 95.00 *(978-0-497-80430-5(1))* Icon Group International, Inc.

—The 2006 Economic & Product Market Databook for Diadema, Brazil. 2006. 618p. ring bd. 95.00 *(978-0-497-80457-2(3))* Icon Group International, Inc.

—The 2006 Economic & Product Market Databook for Divinópolis, Brazil. 2006. 618p. ring bd. 95.00 *(978-0-497-80464-0(6))* Icon Group International, Inc.

—The 2006 Economic & Product Market Databook for Dourados, Brazil. 2006. 618p. ring bd. 95.00 *(978-0-497-80477-0(8))* Icon Group International, Inc.

—The 2006 Economic & Product Market Databook for Duque de Caxias, Brazil. 2006. 618p. ring bd. 95.00 *(978-0-497-80489-3(1))* Icon Group International, Inc.

—The 2006 Economic & Product Market Databook for Embu, Brazil. 2006. 618p. ring bd. 95.00 *(978-0-497-80513-5(8))* Icon Group International, Inc.

—The 2006 Economic & Product Market Databook for Feira de Santana, Brazil. 2006. 618p. ring bd. 95.00 *(978-0-497-80530-2(8))* Icon Group International, Inc.

—The 2006 Economic & Product Market Databook for Ferraz de Vasconcelos, Brazil. 2006. 618p. ring bd. 95.00 *(978-0-497-80536-4(7))* Icon Group International, Inc.

—The 2006 Economic & Product Market Databook for Florianópolis, Brazil. 2006. 618p. ring bd. 95.00 *(978-0-497-80543-2(X))* Icon Group International, Inc.

—The 2006 Economic & Product Market Databook for Fortaleza, Brazil. 2006. 618p. ring bd. 95.00 *(978-0-497-80548-7(0))* Icon Group International, Inc.

—The 2006 Economic & Product Market Databook for Foz do Iguaçu, Brazil. 2006. 618p. ring bd. 95.00 *(978-0-497-80550-0(2))* Icon Group International, Inc.

—The 2006 Economic & Product Market Databook for Franca, Brazil. 2006. 618p. ring bd. 95.00 *(978-0-497-80551-7(0))* Icon Group International, Inc.

—The 2006 Economic & Product Market Databook for Garanhuns, Brazil. 2006. 618p. ring bd. 95.00 *(978-0-497-80578-4(2))* Icon Group International, Inc.

—The 2006 Economic & Product Market Databook for Goiânia, Brazil. 2006. 618p. ring bd. 95.00 *(978-0-497-80605-7(3))* Icon Group International, Inc.

—The 2006 Economic & Product Market Databook for Governador Valadares, Brazil. 2006. 618p. ring bd. 95.00 *(978-0-497-80614-9(2))* Icon Group International, Inc.

—The 2006 Economic & Product Market Databook for Gravatai, Brazil. 2006. 618p. ring bd. 95.00 *(978-0-497-80617-0(7))* Icon Group International, Inc.

—The 2006 Economic & Product Market Databook for Guarapuava, Brazil. 2006. 618p. ring bd. 95.00 *(978-0-497-81865-4(5))* Icon Group International, Inc.

—The 2006 Economic & Product Market Databook for Guaratinguita, Brazil. 2006. 618p. ring bd. 95.00 *(978-0-497-81866-1(3))* Icon Group International, Inc.

—The 2006 Economic & Product Market Databook for Guarujá, Brazil. 2006. 618p. ring bd. 95.00 *(978-0-497-80626-2(6))* Icon Group International, Inc.

—The 2006 Economic & Product Market Databook for Guarulhos, Brazil. 2006. 618p. ring bd. 95.00 *(978-0-497-81867-8(1))* Icon Group International, Inc.

—The 2006 Economic & Product Market Databook for Ilhéus, Brazil. 2006. 618p. ring bd. 95.00 *(978-0-497-80674-3(6))* Icon Group International, Inc.

—The 2006 Economic & Product Market Databook for Imperatriz, Brazil. 2006. 618p. ring bd. 95.00 *(978-0-497-81921-7(X))* Icon Group International, Inc.

—The 2006 Economic & Product Market Databook for Indaiatuba, Brazil. 2006. 618p. ring bd. 95.00 *(978-0-497-81923-1(6))* Icon Group International, Inc.

—The 2006 Economic & Product Market Databook for Ipatinga, Brazil. 2006. 618p. ring bd. 95.00 *(978-0-497-81926-2(0))* Icon Group International, Inc.

—The 2006 Economic & Product Market Databook for Itaboraí, Brazil. 2006. 618p. ring bd. 95.00 *(978-0-497-80683-5(5))* Icon Group International, Inc.

—The 2006 Economic & Product Market Databook for Itabuna, Brazil. 2006. 618p. ring bd. 95.00 *(978-0-497-81933-0(3))* Icon Group International, Inc.

—The 2006 Economic & Product Market Databook for Itaguaí, Brazil. 2006. 618p. ring bd. 95.00 *(978-0-497-80684-2(3))* Icon Group International, Inc.

—The 2006 Economic & Product Market Databook for Itaituba, Brazil. 2006. 618p. ring bd. 95.00 *(978-0-497-81934-7(1))* Icon Group International, Inc.

—The 2006 Economic & Product Market Databook for Itajaí, Brazil. 2006. 618p. ring bd. 95.00 *(978-0-497-80685-9(1))* Icon Group International, Inc.

—The 2006 Economic & Product Market Databook for Itapetininga, Brazil. 2006. 618p. ring bd. 95.00 *(978-0-497-81935-4(X))* Icon Group International, Inc.

—The 2006 Economic & Product Market Databook for Itapevi, Brazil. 2006. 618p. ring bd. 95.00 *(978-0-497-81936-1(8))* Icon Group International, Inc.

—The 2006 Economic & Product Market Databook for Itaquaquecetuba, Brazil. 2006. 618p. ring bd. 95.00 *(978-0-497-81937-8(6))* Icon Group International, Inc.

—The 2006 Economic & Product Market Databook for Itu, Brazil. 2006. 618p. ring bd. 95.00 *(978-0-497-81938-5(4))* Icon Group International, Inc.

—The 2006 Economic & Product Market Databook for Jaboatao, Brazil. 2006. 618p. ring bd. 95.00 *(978-0-497-81939-2(2))* Icon Group International, Inc.

—The 2006 Economic & Product Market Databook for Jacareí, Brazil. 2006. 618p. ring bd. 95.00 *(978-0-497-80688-0(6))* Icon Group International, Inc.

—The 2006 Economic & Product Market Databook for Jequié, Brazil. 2006. 618p. ring bd. 95.00 *(978-0-497-80698-9(3))* Icon Group International, Inc.

—The 2006 Economic & Product Market Databook for Ji-Paraná, Brazil. 2006. 618p. ring bd. 95.00 *(978-0-497-80701-6(7))* Icon Group International, Inc.

—The 2006 Economic & Product Market Databook for Joao Pessoa, Brazil. 2006. 618p. ring bd. 95.00 *(978-0-497-81951-4(1))* Icon Group International, Inc.

—The 2006 Economic & Product Market Databook for Joinville, Brazil. 2006. 618p. ring bd. 95.00 *(978-0-497-81954-5(6))* Icon Group International, Inc.

—The 2006 Economic & Product Market Databook for Juazeiro, Brazil. 2006. 618p. ring bd. 95.00 *(978-0-497-81956-9(2))* Icon Group International, Inc.

—The 2006 Economic & Product Market Databook for Juazeiro do Norte, Brazil. 2006. 618p. ring bd. 95.00 *(978-0-497-81955-2(4))* Icon Group International, Inc.

—The 2006 Economic & Product Market Databook for Juiz de Fora, Brazil. 2006. 618p. ring bd. 95.00 *(978-0-497-81957-6(0))* Icon Group International, Inc.

—The 2006 Economic & Product Market Databook for Jundiaí, Brazil. 2006. 618p. ring bd. 95.00 *(978-0-497-79996-0(0))* Icon Group International, Inc.

—The 2006 Economic & Product Market Databook for Lages, Brazil. 2006. 618p. ring bd. 95.00 *(978-0-497-80812-9(9))* Icon Group International, Inc.

—The 2006 Economic & Product Market Databook for Limeira, Brazil. 2006. 618p. ring bd. 95.00 *(978-0-497-80861-7(7))* Icon Group International, Inc.

—The 2006 Economic & Product Market Databook for Linhares, Brazil. 2006. 618p. ring bd. 95.00 *(978-0-497-80865-5(X))* Icon Group International, Inc.

—The 2006 Economic & Product Market Databook for Londrina, Brazil. 2006. 618p. ring bd. 95.00 *(978-0-497-80878-5(1))* Icon Group International, Inc.

—The 2006 Economic & Product Market Databook for Luziania, Brazil. 2006. 618p. ring bd. 95.00 *(978-0-497-80896-9(X))* Icon Group International, Inc.

—The 2006 Economic & Product Market Databook for Macae, Brazil. 2006. 618p. ring bd. 95.00 *(978-0-497-80899-0(4))* Icon Group International, Inc.

—The 2006 Economic & Product Market Databook for Macapá, Brazil. 2006. 618p. ring bd. 95.00 *(978-0-497-80900-3(1))* Icon Group International, Inc.

—The 2006 Economic & Product Market Databook for Maceió, Brazil. 2006. 618p. ring bd. 95.00 *(978-0-497-80902-7(8))* Icon Group International, Inc.

—The 2006 Economic & Product Market Databook for Magé, Brazil. 2006. 618p. ring bd. 95.00 *(978-0-497-80914-0(1))* Icon Group International, Inc.

—The 2006 Economic & Product Market Databook for Manaus, Brazil. 2006. 618p. ring bd. 95.00 *(978-0-497-80937-9(0))* Icon Group International, Inc.

—The 2006 Economic & Product Market Databook for Marabá, Brazil. 2006. 618p. ring bd. 95.00 *(978-0-497-80010-9(1))* Icon Group International, Inc.

—The 2006 Economic & Product Market Databook for Maracanau, Brazil. 2006. 618p. ring bd. 95.00 *(978-0-497-80948-5(6))* Icon Group International, Inc.

—The 2006 Economic & Product Market Databook for Marília, Brazil. 2006. 618p. ring bd. 95.00 *(978-0-497-80963-8(X))* Icon Group International, Inc.

—The 2006 Economic & Product Market Databook for Maringá, Brazil. 2006. 618p. ring bd. 95.00 *(978-0-497-80957-7(5))* Icon Group International, Inc.

—The 2006 Economic & Product Market Databook for Mauá, Brazil. 2006. 618p. ring bd. 95.00 *(978-0-497-80984-3(2))* Icon Group International, Inc.

—The 2006 Economic & Product Market Databook for Moji das Cruzes, Brazil. 2006. 618p. ring bd. 95.00 *(978-0-497-81039-9(5))* Icon Group International, Inc.

—The 2006 Economic & Product Market Databook for Moji-Guaçu, Brazil. 2006. 618p. ring bd. 95.00 *(978-0-497-81040-5(9))* Icon Group International, Inc.

—The 2006 Economic & Product Market Databook for Montes Claros, Brazil. 2006. 618p. ring bd. 95.00 *(978-0-497-81050-4(6))* Icon Group International, Inc.

—The 2006 Economic & Product Market Databook for Mossoró, Brazil. 2006. 618p. ring bd. 95.00 *(978-0-497-81060-3(3))* Icon Group International, Inc.

—The 2006 Economic & Product Market Databook for Natal, Brazil. 2006. 618p. ring bd. 95.00 *(978-0-497-81106-8(5))* Icon Group International, Inc.

—The 2006 Economic & Product Market Databook for Nilópolis, Brazil. 2006. 618p. ring bd. 95.00 *(978-0-497-81128-0(6))* Icon Group International, Inc.

—The 2006 Economic & Product Market Databook for Niterói, Brazil. 2006. 618p. ring bd. 95.00 *(978-0-497-81130-3(8))* Icon Group International, Inc.

—The 2006 Economic & Product Market Databook for Nova Friburgo, Brazil. 2006. 618p. ring bd. 95.00 *(978-0-497-81136-5(7))* Icon Group International, Inc.

—The 2006 Economic & Product Market Databook for Nova Iguaçu, Brazil. 2006. 618p. ring bd. 95.00 *(978-0-497-81137-2(5))* Icon Group International, Inc.

—The 2006 Economic & Product Market Databook for Novo Hamburgo, Brazil. 2006. 618p. ring bd. 95.00 *(978-0-497-81138-9(3))* Icon Group International, Inc.

—The 2006 Economic & Product Market Databook for Olinda, Brazil. 2006. 618p. ring bd. 95.00 *(978-0-497-81158-7(8))* Icon Group International, Inc.

—The 2006 Economic & Product Market Databook for Osasco, Brazil. 2006. 618p. ring bd. 95.00 *(978-0-497-81172-3(3))* Icon Group International, Inc.

—The 2006 Economic & Product Market Databook for Paranagua, Brazil. 2006. 618p. ring bd. 95.00 *(978-0-497-81192-1(8))* Icon Group International, Inc.

—The 2006 Economic & Product Market Databook for Parnaíba, Brazil. 2006. 618p. ring bd. 95.00 *(978-0-497-81195-2(2))* Icon Group International, Inc.

—The 2006 Economic & Product Market Databook for Passo Fundo, Brazil. 2006. 618p. ring bd. 95.00 *(978-0-497-81197-6(9))* Icon Group International, Inc.

—The 2006 Economic & Product Market Databook for Patos de Minas, Brazil. 2006. 618p. ring bd. 95.00 *(978-0-497-81200-3(2))* Icon Group International, Inc.

—The 2006 Economic & Product Market Databook for Paulista, Brazil. 2006. 618p. ring bd. 95.00 *(978-0-497-81202-7(9))* Icon Group International, Inc.

—The 2006 Economic & Product Market Databook for Pelotas, Brazil. 2006. 618p. ring bd. 95.00 *(978-0-497-81206-5(1))* Icon Group International, Inc.

—The 2006 Economic & Product Market Databook for Petrolina, Brazil. 2006. 618p. ring bd. 95.00 *(978-0-497-81214-0(2))* Icon Group International, Inc.

—The 2006 Economic & Product Market Databook for Petrópolis, Brazil. 2006. 618p. ring bd. 95.00 *(978-0-497-81217-1(7))* Icon Group International, Inc.

—The 2006 Economic & Product Market Databook for Pindamonhangaba, Brazil. 2006. 618p. ring bd. 95.00 *(978-0-497-81254-6(1))* Icon Group International, Inc.

—The 2006 Economic & Product Market Databook for Piracicaba, Brazil. 2006. 618p. ring bd. 95.00 *(978-0-497-81258-4(4))* Icon Group International, Inc.

—The 2006 Economic & Product Market Databook for Piraquara, Brazil. 2006. 618p. ring bd. 95.00 *(978-0-497-81260-7(6))* Icon Group International, Inc.

—The 2006 Economic & Product Market Databook for Pocos de Caldas, Brazil. 2006. 618p. ring bd. 95.00 *(978-0-497-81265-2(7))* Icon Group International, Inc.

—The 2006 Economic & Product Market Databook for Ponta Grossa, Brazil. 2006. 618p. ring bd. 95.00 *(978-0-497-81270-6(3))* Icon Group International, Inc.

—The 2006 Economic & Product Market Databook for Pórto Alegre, Brazil. 2006. 618p. ring bd. 95.00 *(978-0-497-81310-9(6))* Icon Group International, Inc.

—The 2006 Economic & Product Market Databook for Pórto Velho, Brazil. 2006. 618p. ring bd. 95.00 *(978-0-497-81311-6(4))* Icon Group International, Inc.

—The 2006 Economic & Product Market Databook for Praia Grande, Brazil. 2006. 618p. ring bd. 95.00 *(978-0-497-81289-8(4))* Icon Group International, Inc.

—The 2006 Economic & Product Market Databook for Presidente Prudente, Brazil. 2006. 618p. ring bd. 95.00 *(978-0-497-81291-1(6))* Icon Group International, Inc.

—The 2006 Economic & Product Market Databook for Queimados, Brazil. 2006. 618p. ring bd. 95.00 *(978-0-497-81318-5(1))* Icon Group International, Inc.

—The 2006 Economic & Product Market Databook for Recife, Brazil. 2006. 618p. ring bd. 95.00 *(978-0-497-81337-6(8))* Icon Group International, Inc.

—The 2006 Economic & Product Market Databook for Ribeirao das Neves, Brazil. 2006. 618p. ring bd. 95.00 *(978-0-497-81349-9(1))* Icon Group International, Inc.

—The 2006 Economic & Product Market Databook for Ribeirao Preto, Brazil. 2006. 618p. ring bd. 95.00 *(978-0-497-81350-5(5))* Icon Group International, Inc.

—The 2006 Economic & Product Market Databook for Rio Branco, Brazil. 2006. 618p. ring bd. 95.00 *(978-0-497-81353-6(X))* Icon Group International, Inc.

—The 2006 Economic & Product Market Databook for Rio Claro, Brazil. 2006. 618p. ring bd. 95.00 *(978-0-497-81354-3(8))* Icon Group International, Inc.

—The 2006 Economic & Product Market Databook for Rio de Janeiro, Brazil. 2006. 618p. ring bd. 95.00 *(978-0-497-81355-0(6))* Icon Group International, Inc.

—The 2006 Economic & Product Market Databook for Rio Grande, Brazil. 2006. 618p. ring bd. 95.00 *(978-0-497-81356-7(4))* Icon Group International, Inc.

—The 2006 Economic & Product Market Databook for Rondonópolis, Brazil. 2006. 618p. ring bd. 95.00 *(978-0-497-81363-5(7))* Icon Group International, Inc.

—The 2006 Economic & Product Market Databook for Salvador, Brazil. 2006. 618p. ring bd. 95.00 *(978-0-497-81409-0(9))* Icon Group International, Inc.

—The 2006 Economic & Product Market Databook for Santa Barbara D'Oeste, Brazil. 2006. 618p. ring bd. 95.00 *(978-0-497-81441-0(2))* Icon Group International, Inc.

—The 2006 Economic & Product Market Databook for Santa Cruz do Sul, Brazil. 2006. 618p. ring bd. 95.00 *(978-0-497-81443-4(9))* Icon Group International, Inc.

—The 2006 Economic & Product Market Databook for Santa Luzia (MA), Brazil. 2006. 618p. ring bd. 95.00 *(978-0-497-81447-2(1))* Icon Group International, Inc.

—The 2006 Economic & Product Market Databook for Santa Luzia (MG), Brazil. 2006. 618p. ring bd. 95.00 *(978-0-497-81448-9(X))* Icon Group International, Inc.

—The 2006 Economic & Product Market Databook for Santa Maria, Brazil. 2006. 618p. ring bd. 95.00 *(978-0-497-81449-6(8))* Icon Group International, Inc.

—The 2006 Economic & Product Market Databook for Santarém, Brazil. 2006. 618p. ring bd. 95.00 *(978-0-497-81454-0(4))* Icon Group International, Inc.

—The 2006 Economic & Product Market Databook for Santo André, Brazil. 2006. 618p. ring bd. 95.00 *(978-0-497-81460-1(9))* Icon Group International, Inc.

—The 2006 Economic & Product Market Databook for Santos, Brazil. 2006. 618p. ring bd. 95.00 *(978-0-497-81463-2(3))* Icon Group International, Inc.

—The 2006 Economic & Product Market Databook for Sao Bernardo do Campo, Brazil. 2006. 618p. ring bd. 95.00 *(978-0-497-81464-9(1))* Icon Group International, Inc.

—The 2006 Economic & Product Market Databook for Sao Caetano do Sul, Brazil. 2006. 618p. ring bd. 95.00 *(978-0-497-81465-6(X))* Icon Group International, Inc.

—The 2006 Economic & Product Market Databook for Sao Carlo, Brazil. 2006. 618p. ring bd. 95.00 *(978-0-497-81466-3(8))* Icon Group International, Inc.

—The 2006 Economic & Product Market Databook for Sao Gonçalo, Brazil. 2006. 618p. ring bd. 95.00 *(978-0-497-81467-0(6))* Icon Group International, Inc.

—The 2006 Economic & Product Market Databook for Sao Joao de Meriti, Brazil. 2006. 618p. ring bd. 95.00 *(978-0-497-81468-7(4))* Icon Group International, Inc.

—The 2006 Economic & Product Market Databook for Sao José, Brazil. 2006. 618p. ring bd. 95.00 *(978-0-497-81233-1(9))* Icon Group International, Inc.

—The 2006 Economic & Product Market Databook for Sao José do Rio Prêto, Brazil. 2006. 618p. ring bd. 95.00 *(978-0-497-81230-0(4))* Icon Group International, Inc.

—The 2006 Economic & Product Market Databook for Sao José dos Campos, Brazil. 2006. 618p. ring bd. 95.00 *(978-0-497-81231-7(2))* Icon Group International, Inc.

—The 2006 Economic & Product Market Databook for Sao José dos Pinhais, Brazil. 2006. 618p. ring bd. 95.00 *(978-0-497-81232-4(0))* Icon Group International, Inc.

—The 2006 Economic & Product Market Databook for Sao Leopoldo, Brazil. 2006. 618p. ring bd. 95.00 *(978-0-497-81234-8(7))* Icon Group International, Inc.

—The 2006 Economic & Product Market Databook for Sao Luís, Brazil. 2006. 618p. ring bd. 95.00 *(978-0-497-81235-5(5))* Icon Group International, Inc.

—The 2006 Economic & Product Market Databook for Sao Paulo, Brazil. 2006. 618p. ring bd. 95.00 *(978-0-497-81469-4(2))* Icon Group International, Inc.

—The 2006 Economic & Product Market Databook for Sao Vicente, Brazil. 2006. 618p. ring bd. 95.00 *(978-0-497-81471-7(4))* Icon Group International, Inc.

—The 2006 Economic & Product Market Databook for Sapucaia, Brazil. 2006. 618p. ring bd. 95.00 *(978-0-497-81473-1(0))* Icon Group International, Inc.

—The 2006 Economic & Product Market Databook for Serra, Brazil. 2006. 618p. ring bd. 95.00 *(978-0-497-81506-6(0))* Icon Group International, Inc.

—The 2006 Economic & Product Market Databook for Sete Lagoas, Brazil. 2006. 618p. ring bd. 95.00 *(978-0-497-81508-0(7))* Icon Group International, Inc.

—The 2006 Economic & Product Market Databook for Sobral, Brazil. 2006. 618p. ring bd. 95.00 *(978-0-497-81551-6(6))* Icon Group International, Inc.

—The 2006 Economic & Product Market Databook for Sumaré, Brazil. 2006. 618p. ring bd. 95.00 *(978-0-497-81584-4(2))* Icon Group International, Inc.

—The 2006 Economic & Product Market Databook for Susano, Brazil. 2006. 618p. ring bd. 95.00 *(978-0-497-81591-2(5))* Icon Group International, Inc.

—The 2006 Economic & Product Market Databook for Taboao da Serra, Brazil. 2006. 618p. ring bd. 95.00 *(978-0-497-81604-9(0))* Icon Group International, Inc.

—The 2006 Economic & Product Market Databook for Taubaté, Brazil. 2006. 618p. ring bd. 95.00 *(978-0-497-81653-7(9))* Icon Group International, Inc.

—The 2006 Economic & Product Market Databook for Teófilo Otoni, Brazil. 2006. 618p. ring bd. 95.00 *(978-0-497-81666-7(0))* Icon Group International, Inc.

—The 2006 Economic & Product Market Databook for Teresina, Brazil. 2006. 618p. ring bd. 95.00 *(978-0-497-81662-9(8))* Icon Group International, Inc.

—The 2006 Economic & Product Market Databook for Teresópolis, Brazil. 2006. 618p. ring bd. 95.00 *(978-0-497-81663-6(6))* Icon Group International, Inc.

—The 2006 Economic & Product Market Databook for Timon, Brazil. 2006. 618p. ring bd. 95.00 *(978-0-497-81683-4(0))* Icon Group International, Inc.

—The 2006 Economic & Product Market Databook for Uberaba, Brazil. 2006. 618p. ring bd. 95.00 *(978-0-497-81742-8(X))* Icon Group International, Inc.

—The 2006 Economic & Product Market Databook for Uberlandia, Brazil. 2006. 618p. ring bd. 95.00 *(978-0-497-81743-5(8))* Icon Group International, Inc.

—The 2006 Economic & Product Market Databook for Umuarama, Brazil. 2006. 618p. ring bd. 95.00 *(978-0-497-81751-0(9))* Icon Group International, Inc.

—The 2006 Economic & Product Market Databook for Uruguaiana, Brazil. 2006. 618p. ring bd. 95.00 *(978-0-497-81758-9(6))* Icon Group International, Inc.

—The 2006 Economic & Product Market Databook for Várzea Grande, Brazil. 2006. 618p. ring bd. 95.00 *(978-0-497-81807-4(8))* Icon Group International, Inc.

—The 2006 Economic & Product Market Databook for Viamao, Brazil. 2006. 618p. ring bd. 95.00 *(978-0-497-81785-5(3))* Icon Group International, Inc.

—The 2006 Economic & Product Market Databook for Vila Velha, Brazil. 2006. 618p. ring bd. 95.00 *(978-0-497-81788-6(8))* Icon Group International, Inc.

—The 2006 Economic & Product Market Databook for Vitoria, Brazil. 2006. 618p. ring bd. 95.00 *(978-0-497-81799-2(3))* Icon Group International, Inc.

—The 2006 Economic & Product Market Databook for Vitoria da Conquista, Brazil. 2006. 618p. ring bd. 95.00 *(978-0-497-81797-8(7))* Icon Group International, Inc.

—The 2006 Economic & Product Market Databook for Vitoria de Santo Antao, Brazil. 2006. 618p. ring bd. 95.00 *(978-0-497-81798-5(5))* Icon Group International, Inc.

—The 2006 Economic & Product Market Databook for Volta Redonda, Brazil. 2006. 618p. ring bd. 95.00 *(978-0-497-81805-0(1))* Icon Group International, Inc.

Jorge T. Almeida, ed. Focus on Brazil. 2008. (C). 89.00 *(978-1-60456-165-4(3))* Nova Science Pubs., Inc.

Klawu, James, et al. Brazil's Cotton Industry: Economic Reform & Development. 2011. 31p. (C). pap. 20.00 ***(978-1-4379-8773-7(7))*** DIANE Publishing Co.

Kinzo, Maria D'Alva G., ed. Brazil under Democracy: Economy, Polity & Society since 1985. Date not set. (Illus.). 248p. (C). pap. 19.95 *(978-1-900039-53-6(2))* Institute of Latin American Studies GBR. Dist: Brookings Institution Pr.

Kunaka, Charles. Logistics in Lagging Regions: Overcoming Local Barriers to Global Connectivity. 2010. (World Bank Studies). (ENG.). 92p. pap. 15.00 *(978-0-8213-8649-1(2))*, 9780821386491) World Bank Pubns.

Latin American Business: Equity Distortion in Regional Resource Allocation in Brazil. 2007. (ENG., Illus.). 242p. 135.00 *(978-0-7890-3535-6(9))*; per. 87.95 *(978-0-7890-3536-3(7))* Routledge.

Leff, Nathaniel H. Underdevelopment & Development in Brazil: Volume II. 2011. (ENG.). 160p. 95.00 *(978-0-415-59508-7(8))* Routledge.

—Underdevelopment & Development in Brazil Vol. 1: Economic Structure & Change, 1822-1947. 2011. 272p. 105.00 *(978-0-415-59507-0(X))* Routledge.

Lemos, Sara. Minimum Wage in Brazil. 2010. 332p. pap. *(978-3-639-21637-0(7))* VDM Verlag Dr. Mueller e.K.

Lohmann, Gui & Dredge, Dianne, eds. Tourism in Brazil: Environment, Management & Segments. 2012. (Contemporary Geographies of Leisure, Tourism & Mobility Ser.). (ENG., Illus.). 224p. (C). 136.00 *(978-0-415-67432-4(8))* Routledge.

Love, Joseph. Brazil under Lula: Economy, Politics, & Society under the Worker-President. Baer, Werner, ed. 2008. (ENG., Illus.). 344p. 110.00 *(978-0-230-60816-0(7))* Palgrave Macmillan.

McCreery, David. Frontier Goias, 1822-1889. 2006. (ENG., Illus.). 312p. 60.00 *(978-0-8047-5179-7(X))* Stanford Univ. Pr.

Merchant, Alexander N. From Barter to Slavery: The Economic Relations of Portuguese & Indians in the Settlement of Brazil, 1500-1580. (Johns Hopkins University. Studies in the Social Sciences, Thirtieth Ser.: 1). reprint ed. 27.50 *(978-0-404-61292-4(X))* AMS Pr., Inc.

Morley, Samuel A. Labor Markets & Inequitable Growth: The Case of Authoritarian Capitalism in Brazil. 2008. (ENG.). 336p. pap. 46.00 *(978-0-521-07469-8(X))* Cambridge Univ. Pr.

Oecd Publishing. Growth & Sustainability in Brazil, China, India, Indonesia & South Afric. 2010. 190p. pap. 75.00 *(978-92-64-09019-4(3))* Organization for Economic Cooperation & Development.

Parkin, Vincent. Chronic Inflation in an Industrializing Economy: The Brazilian Experience. 2010. (ENG.). 332p. pap. 42.00 *(978-0-521-13412-5(9))* Cambridge Univ. Pr.

Pedersen, Jorgen Dige. Globalization, Development & the State: The Performance of India & Brazil since 1990. 2008. (ENG., Illus.). 240p. 89.00 *(978-0-230-20271-9(3))* Palgrave Macmillan.

Pochmann, Marcio. Desenvolvimento e Perspectivas Novas para o Brasil. 2010. (POR., Illus.). 191p. *(978-85-249-1558-1(7))* Cortez Editora e Livraria Ltda.

Ponchio, Mateus. The Influence of Materialism on Consumption Indebtedness. 2010. 144p. pap. *(978-3-8383-1998-8(2))* Lambert Academic Publishing.

Raphael Bar-El Staff. Regional Development & Conflict Management: A Case for Brazil. 2008. (Illus.). xx, 183p. 120.00 *(978-1-84855-190-9(8))* Emerald Group Publishing Ltd. GBR. Dist: Turpin Distribution Services Ltd.

REAL PROPERTY, Brazil. Investing in brazil! istructions. what to do & what... not to Do! 2010. 88p. pap. 26.95 *(978-1-4457-2687-8(4))* Lulu Enterprises Inc.

—Investing in brazil! what to do & what... not to Do! 2010. 182p. pap. 26.95 *(978-1-4461-3436-8(9))* Lulu Enterprises Inc.

RIS & Research and Information System for Developing Countries. Trinity of the South: Potential of India-Brazil-South Africa (IBSA) Partnership. 2008. (ENG.). 202p. pap. 49.95 *(978-81-7188-679-1(5))* Academic Foundation IND. Dist: Independent Pubs. Group.

Roett, Riordan. The New Brazil. (ENG., Illus.). 178p. 2010. 29.95 *(978-0-8157-0423-2(2))* 2nd ed. 2011. pap. 19.95 *(978-0-8157-2168-0(4))* Brookings Institution Pr.

Rohter, Larry. Brazil on the Rise: The Story of a Country Transformed. 2012. (ENG., Illus.). 304p. pap. 17.00 ***(978-0-230-12073-0(3))*** Palgrave Macmillan.

Schelhase, Marc. Globalization, Regionalization & Business: Conflict, Convergence & Influence. 2008. (ENG., Illus.). 224p. 89.00 *(978-0-230-57329-1(0))* Palgrave Macmillan.

Schulz, John. The Financial Crisis of Abolition. 2008. (ENG.). 208p. 55.00 *(978-0-300-13419-3(3))* Yale Univ. Pr.

Selwyn, Ben. Workers State & Development in Brazil: Powers of Labour, Chains of Value. 2012. (ENG., Illus.). 256p. 100.00 ***(978-0-7190-8531-4(4))*** Manchester Univ. Pr. GBR. Dist: Macmillan.

Stefanie, Salomon. Brazil - Opportunities for German Environmental Technology Companies: An Analysis & Overview of the Brazilian Environmental Technology Sector. 2011. 124p. pap. ***(978-3-639-33062-5(5))*** VDM Verlag Dr. Mueller e.K.

Triner, Gail D. Mining & the State in Brazilian Development, 1 vol. 2011. (Perspectives in Economic & Social History Ser.). (ENG., Illus.). 272p. 99.00 *(978-1-84893-066-1(2))* Pickering & Chatto Pubs., Ltd. GBR. Dist: Ashgate Publishing Co.

Van De Rijdt, Karen. Corporate Governance in Emerging Capital Markets. 2010. 76p. pap. *(978-3-639-28161-3(6))* VDM Verlag Dr. Mueller e.K.

Vasconcellos, Ana Maria. A State-Sponsored Socio-Environmental Development Programme in Action. 2010. 168p. pap. *(978-3-639-27503-2(9))* VDM Verlag Dr. Mueller e.K.

Willson, Margaret. Dance Lest We All Fall Down: Breaking Cycles of Poverty in Brazil & Beyond. rev. ed. 2010. (ENG.). 320p. pap. 18.95 *(978-0-295-99058-3(9))* Univ. of Washington Pr.

Wood, Charles H. & Carvalho, Jose Alberto Magno. The Demography of Inequality in Brazil. 2009. (Cambridge Latin American Studies). (ENG., Illus.). 316p. pap. 44.00 *(978-0-521-10246-9(4))* Cambridge Univ. Pr.

BRAZIL—ECONOMIC POLICY

Amann, Edmund & Chang, Ha-Joon. Brazil & South Korea: Economic Crisis & Restructuring. Date not set. (Illus.). 230p. (C). pap. 19.95 *(978-1-900039-51-2(6))* Institute of Latin American Studies GBR. Dist: Brookings Institution Pr.

Arestis, Philip. Political Economy of Brazil: Recent Economic Performance. Arestis, Philip & Saad-Filho, Alfredo, eds. 2007. (ENG., Illus.). 288p. 126.00 *(978-0-230-54277-8(8))* Palgrave Macmillan.

BRAINARD. Brazil as an Economic Superpower? Understanding Brazil's Changing Role in the Global Economy. Brainard, Lael & Martinez-Diaz, Leonardo, eds. 2009. (ENG.). 291p. 52.95 *(978-0-8157-0295-5(7))* Brookings Institution Pr.

Brainard, Lael & Martinez-Diaz, Leonardo, eds. Brazil as an Economic Superpower? Understanding Brazil's Changing Role in the Global Economy. 2009. (ENG.). 291p. pap. 24.95 *(978-0-8157-0296-2(5))* Brookings Institution Pr.

Brazil: Commercial Law. 300p. (Orig.). pap. 295.00 *(978-0-7605-1232-6(9))* Rector Pr., Ltd.

Bresser-Pereira, Luiz Carlos. Developing Brazil: Overcoming the Failure of the Washington Consensus. 2009. (Illus.). 295p. *(978-1-58826-624-8(9))* Rienner, Lynne Pubs.

Da Rocha Soares Ferreira, Vicente & Souza, Cláudia. Biodiesel in Brazil. 2010. 132p. pap. *(978-3-639-23334-6(4))* VDM Verlag Dr. Mueller e.K.

Fan, Qimiao, et al. The Investment Climate in Brazil, India, & South Africa: A Comparison of Approaches for Sustaining Economic Growth in Emerging Economies. 2007. (WBI Learning Resources Ser.). (ENG., Illus.). 117p. per. 20.00 *(978-0-8213-7363-7(3)*, 9780821373637) World Bank Pubns.

Font, Mauricio. The Brazilian State: Debate & Agenda. Randall, Adrian, ed. 2011. (Bildner Western Hemisphere Studies). (ENG.). 434p. (gr. 17). 85.00 ***(978-0-7391-6731-1(6))*** Lexington Bks.

Font, Mauricio A. & Randall, Laura. The Brazilian State: Debate & Agenda. 2011. ***(978-0-7391-6889-9(4))*** Lexington Bks.

Franklin, Adalberto. Apontamentos e Fontes para a História Econômica de Imperatriz. 2008. (POR., Illus.). 242p. *(978-85-88172-26-5(7))* Etica Servicos Editorias Ltda.

Leff, Nathaniel H. Underdevelopment & Development in Brazil: Volume II. 2011. (ENG.). 160p. 95.00 *(978-0-415-59508-7(8))* Routledge.

—Underdevelopment & Development in Brazil Vol. 1: Economic Structure & Change, 1822-1947. 2011. 272p. 105.00 *(978-0-415-59507-0(X))* Routledge.

Organisation for Economic Co-operation and Development Staff. Oecd Reviews of Regulatory Reform Brazil: Improving Governance of Growth. 2008. pap. 63.00 *(978-92-64-04293-3(8))* Organization for Economic Cooperation & Development.

Paula, Luiz Fernando de. Financial Liberalization & Economic Performance: Brazil at the Crossroads. 2010. *(978-0-203-83521-0(2))* Routledge.

Pochmann, Marcio. Desenvolvimento e Perspectivas Novas para o Brasil. 2010. (POR., Illus.). 191p. *(978-85-249-1558-1(7))* Cortez Editora e Livraria Ltda.

Raphael Bar-El Staff. Regional Development & Conflict Management: A Case for Brazil. 2008. (Illus.). xx, 183p. 120.00 *(978-1-84855-190-9(8))* Emerald Group Publishing Ltd. GBR. Dist: Turpin Distribution Services Ltd.

Rodriguez, Alberto. Knowledge & Innovation for Competitiveness in Brazil. 2008. (WBI Development Studies). (ENG., Illus.). 268p. pap. 25.00 *(978-0-8213-7438-2(9)*, 9780821374382) World Bank Pubns.

Roett, Riordan. The New Brazil. 2010. (ENG., Illus.). 178p. 29.95 *(978-0-8157-0423-2(2))* Brookings Institution Pr.

Shaver, Lea, ed. Access to Knowledge in Brazil: New Research in Intellectual Property, Innovation & Development. 2010. (ENG.). 196p. 75.00 *(978-1-84966-009-9(3))* Bloomsbury Publishing.

Silva-Garbade, Caroline. Determinants of National IMF Policy: A Case Study of Brazil & Argentina. 2011. (Hispano-Americana. Geschichte, Sprache, Literatur Ser.). 254p. 75.95 *(978-3-631-60560-8(9))* Lang, Peter GmbH, Europaischer Verlag der Wissenschaften DEU. Dist: Lang, Peter.

Stehnken, Thomas. The Politics of Interaction in Innovation Systems: Evidence from Brazilian Multi-Level-Governance Structures. 2010. 250p. pap. 62.00 *(978-3-8329-5650-9(6))* Nomos Verlagsgesellschaft DEU. Dist: International Specialized Bk. Services.

Zhang, Ming, ed. Competitiveness & Growth in Brazilian Cities: Local Policies & Actions for Innovation. 2009. (Directions in Development Ser.). (ENG., Illus.). 224p. pap. 25.00 *(978-0-8213-8157-1(1)*, 9780821381571) World Bank Pubns.

BRAZIL—FOREIGN RELATIONS

Almeida Filho, João Genésio de. O Forúm de Diálogo Índia, Brasil e África Do Sul (IBAS) Análise e Perpectivas. 2009. (POR.). 159p. pap. *(978-85-7631-159-1(3))* Fundacao Alexandre de Gusmao.

Birle, Peter, et al. Brazil & the Americas: Convergences & Perspectives. 2008. (Illus.). 237p. pap. 29.80 *(978-84-8489-375-2(8))* Iberoamericana Vervuert Publishing Corp.

Bletz, May E. Immigration & Acculturation in Brazil & Argentina: 1890-1929. 2010. (ENG.). 190p. 84.00 *(978-0-230-10019-0(8))* Palgrave Macmillan.

Bodman, Samuel W., et al. Global Brazil & U.S.- Brazil Relations: Independent Task Force Report No.66. 2011. (ENG., Illus.). 80p. pap. 15.00 *(978-0-87609-492-1(2))* Council on Foreign Relations.

Brands, Hal. Dilemmas of Brazilian Grand Strategy. 2010. *(978-1-58487-462-1(7))* Strategic Studies Institute, U.S. Army War College Commandant (AWCC-DSI/Pubns.).

Burges, Sean William. Brazilian Foreign Policy after the Cold War. 2009. (ENG., Illus.). 224p. 65.00 *(978-0-8130-3333-4(0))* Univ. Pr. of Florida.

—Brazilian Foreign Policy after the Cold War. 2011. (ENG., Illus.). 248p. pap. 29.95 *(978-0-8130-3729-5(8))* Univ. Pr. of Florida.

Cepaluni, Gabriel & Vigevani, Tullo. Brazilian Foreign Policy in Changing Times: The Quest for Autonomy from Sarney to Lula. Moura, Leandro, tr. 2012. (ENG.). 190p. (gr. 17). pap. 29.99 ***(978-0-7391-2882-4(5))*** Lexington Bks.

Crandall, Britta. Hemispheric Giants: The Misunderstood History of U. S. -Brazilian Relations. 2011. (ENG.). 230p. 70.00 *(978-1-4422-0787-5(6))* Rowman & Littlefield Publishers, Inc.

Crandall, Britta H. Hemispheric Giants: The Misunderstood History of U.S.-Brazilian Relations. 2010. *(978-1-4422-0789-9(2))* Rowman & Littlefield Publishers, Inc.

Dávila, Jerry. Hotel Tropico: Brazil & the Challenge of African Decolonization, 1950-1980. 2010. (ENG., Illus.). 328p. pap. 23.95 *(978-0-8223-4855-9(1))* Duke Univ. Pr.

—Hotel Tropico: Brazil & the Challenge of African Decolonization, 1950-1980. 2010. (ENG., Illus.). 328p. 84.95 *(978-0-8223-4867-2(5))* Duke Univ. Pr.

Ebert, Christopher. Between Empires: Brazilian Sugar in the Early Atlantic Economy, 1550-1630. 2008. (Atlantic World Ser.). (Illus.). 220p. *(978-90-04-16766-1(4))* BRILL.

Franco, Alvaro da Costa. Documentos Da Política Externa Independente. 2007. (POR.). *(978-85-7631-083-9(X))*; *(978-85-7631-128-7(3))* Fundacao Alexandre de Gusmao.

Green, James. We Cannot Remain Silent: Opposition to the Brazilian Military Dictatorship in the United States. 2010. (Radical Perspectives Ser.). (ENG., Illus.). 472p. pap. 26.95 *(978-0-8223-4735-4(0))*; 94.95 *(978-0-8223-4717-0(2))* Duke Univ. Pr.

Lampreia, Luiz Felipe. O Brasil e Os Ventos Do Mundo: Memórias de Cinco Décadas Na Cena Internacional. 2009. (POR., Illus.). 343p. *(978-85-390-0067-8(9))* Objetiva, Editora Ltda.

Lechini de Alvarez, Gladys, et al. Argentina e Brasil: Vencendo Os Preconceitos: As Várias Arestas de Uma Concepção Estratégica. 2009. (POR & SPA., Illus.). 475p. *(978-85-7106-396-9(6))* Revan, Editora Ltda.

Love, Joseph. Brazil under Lula: Economy, Politics, & Society under the Worker-President. Baer, Werner, ed. 2008. (ENG., Illus.). 344p. 110.00 *(978-0-230-60816-0(7))* Palgrave Macmillan.

Mullins, Martin. In the Shadow of Generals: Foreign Policy Formation in Argentina Brazil & Chile. 2006. (Illus.). 178p. 120.00 *(978-0-7546-4736-2(5))* Ashgate Publishing Co.

Parker, Phyllis R. Brazil & the Quiet Intervention 1964. 2011. (ENG.). 162p. pap. 19.95 *(978-0-292-72950-6(2))* Univ. of Texas Pr.

Peters, Ina. Interessen und Ideen in multilateralen Handelsbeziehungen: Eine Analyse der Regierungsposition Brasiliens in den DDA- und FTAA-Verhandlungen. 2010. (Europäische Hochschulschriften. Reihe 31: Politikwissenschaft Ser.). 132p. pap. 28.95 *(978-3-631-59979-2(X))* Lang, Peter GmbH, Europaischer Verlag der Wissenschaften DEU. Dist: Lang, Peter.

Phaf-Rheinberger, Ineke & Pinto, Tiago de Oliveira. AfricAmericas: Itineraries, Dialogues, & Sounds. 2008. (Illus.). 224p. pap. 29.80 *(978-84-8489-380-6(4))* Iberoamericana Vervuert Publishing Corp.

Preuss, Ori. Bridging the Island: Brazilians Views of Spanish America & Themselves 1865-1912. 2010. 240p. pap. 29.98 *(978-1-936353-02-6(4))* Iberoamericana Vervuert Publishing Corp.

Preuss, Ori. Bridging the Island. Brazilians' Views of Spanish America & Themselves, 1865-1912. 2011. (Tiempo Emulado. Historia de América y España Ser.). (Illus.). 240p. (C). pap. 29.80 ***(978-84-8489-481-0(9))*** Iberoamericana / Vervuert.

Recognizing the Warm Friendship & Expanding Strategic Relationship Between the United States & Brazil, Commending Brazil in Successfully Reducing its Dependence on Oil by Finding Alternative Ways to Satisfy Its Energy Needs, & Recognizing the Importance of the March 9, 2007, United States-Brazil Memorandum of Understanding (MOU) on Biofuels Cooperation: Markup Before the Subcommittee on the Western Hemisphere of the Committee on Foreign Affairs, House of Representatives, One Hundred Tenth Congress, First Session, on H. Res. 651, September 19, 2007. 2007. iii, 9p. *(978-0-16-079561-9(3)*, 552-070-36528-1) United States Government Printing Office.

Roett, Riordan. The New Brazil. (ENG., Illus.). 178p. 2010. 29.95 *(978-0-8157-0423-2(2))* 2nd ed. 2011. pap. 19.95 *(978-0-8157-2168-0(4))* Brookings Institution Pr.

Rottner, Wesley B. Brazil & its Neighbors: Background & U. S. Relations. 2010. (Latin American Political, Economic, & Security Issues Ser.). 115.00 *(978-1-61761-113-1(1))* Nova Science Pubs., Inc.

Schoonmaker, Sara. High-Tech Trade Wars: U. S. Brazilian Conflicts in the Global Economy. 2009. (Pitt Latin American Studies). (ENG.). 232p. (C). pap. 27.95 *(978-0-8229-8595-2(0))* Univ. of Pittsburgh Pr.

Smith, Joseph. Brazil & the United States: Convergence & Divergence. 2010. (United States & the Americas Ser.). (ENG.). 228p. 59.95 *(978-0-8203-2769-3(7))*; pap. 24.95 *(978-0-8203-2770-9(0))* Univ. of Georgia Pr.

—Unequal Giants: Diplomatic Relations between the United States & Brazil, 1889-1930. 2009. (Pitt Latin American Studies). (ENG.). 308p. (C). pap. 27.95 *(978-0-8229-8530-3(6))* Univ. of Pittsburgh Pr.

Vigevani, Tullo & Cepaluni, Gabriel. Brazilian Foreign Policy in Changing Times: The Quest for Autonomy from Sarney to Lula. 2009. (ENG., Illus.). 182p. 68.50 *(978-0-7391-2881-7(7))* Lexington Bks.

BRAZIL—GUIDEBOOKS

Basto, Fernanda. Brasil. 2007. (Illus.). 119p. *(978-1-877339-91-2(1))* NZVP Bks. & Calendars Ltd.

Brazil. 308p. *(978-0-8270-5470-7(X))* Organization of American States.

Candiota, Felipe. Brazil Hotels. 2011. (POR & ENG., Illus.). 416p. 39.99 ***(978-84-9936-865-8(4))*** Loft Pubns. ESP. Dist: Prestel Publishing.

Coates, Rob, et al. Rio de Janeiro. 2009. (ENG., Illus.). 280p. 18.99 *(978-1-84836-190-4(4))* Rough Guides, Ltd. GBR. Dist: Dorling Kindersley Publishing, Inc.

De Fiore, Ottaviano C. Brazil Baedeker Guide. 2012. (Baedeker Guides Ser.). (ENG., Illus.). 484p. pap. 25.00 ***(978-3-8297-6548-0(7))*** Marco Polo Travel Publishing GBR. Dist: Innovative Logistics.

de Vries, Alexandra. Frommer's Rio de Janeiro Day by Day. 2011. (Frommer's Day by Day - Pocket Ser.: 149). (ENG., Illus.). 192p. pap. 13.99 *(978-0-470-88157-6(7)*, Frommers) Wiley, John & Sons, Inc.

de Vries, Alexandra & Blore, Shawn. Frommer's Brazil. 6th ed. 2012. (Frommer's Complete Guides). (ENG., Illus.). 512p. pap. 25.99 ***(978-1-118-08606-3(6)***, Frommers) Wiley, John & Sons, Inc.

Fodor's Travel Publications, Inc. Staff. Rio de Janeiro & Sao Paulo. 2008. (Fodor's Gold Guides). (ENG., Illus.). 256p. pap. 17.95 *(978-1-4000-0681-6(3)*, Fodor's) Fodor's Travel Pubns.

Fullman, Joe. Brazil. 2008. (Travel Through (QEB) Ser.). (Illus.). 32p. (J). (gr. 3-6). lib. bdg. 18.95 *(978-1-59566-355-0(4))* QEB Publishing Inc.

Goslin, Priscilla. How to Be a Carioca: The Alternative Guide for the Tourist in Rio. 2008. (ENG.). pap. 14.95 *(978-1-60037-500-2(6))* Morgan James Publishing.

Heber-Percy, T. & Lohan, Judith. Mr. & Mrs. Smith Boutique Hotel Collection: The Global Shortlist. Purdy, Rufus & Fennings, Lucy, eds. 2008. (ENG.). 360p. pap. 29.95 *(978-0-9544964-7-0(7))* Spy Publishing Ltd. GBR. Dist: Independent Pubs. Group.

Insight Guides. Brazil Insight Guide. 7th ed. 2011. (Insight Guides). (ENG., Illus.). 384p. pap. 22.99 *(978-981-282-318-2(2))* APA Publications Services SGP. Dist: Ingram Pub. Services.

Insight Guides Staff. Brazil. 2006. (Insight Guides). 388p. 26.95 *(978-981-258-583-7(4))* Langenscheidt Publishing Group.

Lonely Planet Staff & Louis, Regis. Rio de Janeiro. 7th rev. ed. 2010. (City Guide Ser.). (ENG., Illus.). 240p. pap. 19.99 *(978-1-74179-590-5(7))* Lonely Planet Pubns.

Louis, Regis. Lonely Planet Brazil. 8th rev. ed. 2011. (Country Guide Ser.). (ENG., Illus.). 760p. pap. 27.99 *(978-1-74179-163-1(4))* Lonely Planet Pubns.

Lowen, James. Pantanal Wildlife: A Visitor's Guide to Brazil's Great Wetland. 2010. (ENG., Illus.). 176p. pap. 25.99 *(978-1-84162-305-4(9))* Bradt Travel Guides GBR. Dist: Globe Pequot Pr., The.

Malathronas, John. Brazil. 2008. (ENG., Illus.). 144p. pap. 19.95 *(978-1-84773-135-7(X))* New Holland Pubs., Ltd. GBR. Dist: Globe Pequot Pr., The.

Marshall, Oliver & Jenkins, Dilwyn. DK Eyewitness Travel Guide: Brazil: Brazil. 2012. (Eyewitness travel Guide Ser.). (ENG.). 464p. pap. 30.00 ***(978-0-7566-8580-5(X))*** Dorling Kindersley Publishing, Inc.

Marshall, Oliver, et al. Brazil. 2010. (Eyewitness Travel Guides). (ENG.). 448p. pap. 30.00 *(978-0-7566-6200-4(1))* Dorling Kindersley Publishing, Inc.

—Brazil. 7th ed. 2009. (ENG., Illus.). 776p. (gr. 12). 27.99 *(978-1-84836-189-8(0))* Rough Guides, Ltd. GBR. Dist: Dorling Kindersley Publishing, Inc.

Nogueira, Cristiano. Rio for Partiers: The Visual Travel Guide to Rio de Janeiro. 2011. 192p. pap. 27.95 *(978-85-89992-07-7(1))* Solcat Publishing.

Poelzl, Volker. Brazil: A Survival Guide to Customs & Etiquette. 2009. 324p. pap. 15.95 *(978-0-7614-5660-5(0))* Marshall Cavendish Corp.

Rice, Christopher. Madeira. 2nd ed. (Illus.). 128p. pap. 14.95 *(978-1-84537-225-5(5))* New Holland Pubs., Ltd. GBR. Dist: Globe Pequot Pr., The.

Robinson, Alex. Bahia: The Heart of Brazil's Northeast. 2011. (Bradt Travel Guide Ser.). (ENG., Illus.). 192p. pap. 25.99 *(978-1-84162-329-0(6))* Bradt Travel Guides GBR. Dist: Globe Pequot Pr., The.

—Bahia & Salvador Footprint Focus. 2011. (Footprint Focus Ser.). (ENG., Illus.). 112p. pap. 11.95 *(978-1-908206-12-1(8))* Footprint Handbooks GBR. Dist: Globe Pequot Pr., The.

—Brazil Handbook. 7th ed. 2011. (Footprint - Handbooks Ser.). (ENG., Illus.). 848p. 27.95 *(978-1-907263-26-2(8))* Footprint Handbooks GBR. Dist: Globe Pequot Pr., The.

—Brazilian Amazon. 2012. (Footprint Focus Ser.). (ENG., Illus.). 128p. pap. 11.95 ***(978-1-908206-65-7(9))*** Footprint Handbooks GBR. Dist: Globe Pequot Pr., The.

—Brazilian Pantanal. 2012. (Footprint Focus Ser.). (ENG., Illus.). 96p. pap. 9.95 ***(978-1-908206-64-0(0))*** Footprint Handbooks GBR. Dist: Globe Pequot Pr., The.

B

—Recife & Northeast Brazil Footprint Focus. 2011. (Footprint Focus Ser.). (ENG.). 112p. pap. 11.95 *(978-1-908206-03-9(9))* Footprint Handbooks GBR. Dist: Globe Pequot Pr., The.
—Rio de Janeiro Footprint Focus. 2011. (Footprint Focus Ser.). (ENG., Illus.). 152p. pap. 12.95 *(978-1-908206-13-8(6))* Footprint Handbooks GBR. Dist: Globe Pequot Pr., The.
—Sao Paolo Footprint Focus. 2011. (Footprint Focus Ser.). (ENG., Illus.). 88p. pap. 8.95 *(978-1-908206-02-2(0))* Footprint Handbooks GBR. Dist: Globe Pequot Pr., The.
—Top 10 Rio de Janeiro. 2011. (Eyewitness top 10 travel Guide Ser.). (ENG.). 128p. 14.00 *(978-0-7566-7053-5(5))* Dorling Kindersley Publishing, Inc.
Runge, Jonathan & Logan, Sam. Rum & Reggae's Rio de Janeiro. 2008. (Rum & Reggae Ser.). (ENG., Illus.). 208p. pap. 14.95 *(978-1-893675-16-2(5))* Rum & Reggae Guidebooks, Inc.
Sommers, Michael. Moon Brazil. 2011. (Moon Handbooks Ser.). (ENG., Illus.). 736p. pap. 21.99 *(978-1-59880-873-5(7))* Avalon Travel Publishing.
—Moon Rio de Janeiro. 2009. (Moon Handbooks). (ENG., Illus.). 324p. pap. 17.95 *(978-1-59880-248-1(8))* Avalon Travel Publishing.
—Salvador & Bahia. 2009. (Moon Spotlight Ser.). (ENG.). 85p. pap. 7.95 *(978-1-59880-538-3(X))* Avalon Travel Publishing.
—São Paulo. 2009. (Moon Spotlight Ser.). (ENG.). 70p. pap. 7.95 *(978-1-59880-537-6(1))* Avalon Travel Publishing.
Storey, Romasa. Going to Live in Brazil. 2009. (Illus.). 192p. pap. 26.00 *(978-1-84528-310-0(4))* How To Books GBR. Dist: Parkwest Pubns., Inc.
Taschen, Angelika, ed. Living in Bahia. 2008. (Taschen's Lifestyle Ser.). (FRE, GER & ENG., Illus.). 200p. 29.99 *(978-3-8365-0478-2(2))* TASCHEN DEU. Dist: Ingram Pub. Services.
Thomas Cook Publishing Staff. Brazil Pocket Guide. 2nd ed. 2010. (Thomas Cook Pocket Guides). (ENG., Illus.). 128p. pap. 9.99 *(978-1-84848-270-8(1))* Cook, Thomas Publishing GBR. Dist: Globe Pequot Pr., The.
Thomas Cook Publishing Staff & Egginton, Jane. Brazil. 2nd ed. 2009. (Travellers - Thomas Cook Ser.). (ENG., Illus.). 176p. pap. 16.95 *(978-1-84848-188-6(8))* Cook, Thomas Publishing GBR. Dist: Globe Pequot Pr., The.
Time Out Guides Staff. Time Out Sao Paulo. 2009. (Time Out Guides). (ENG., Illus.). 256p. 19.95 *(978-1-84670-126-9(0))* Time Out Guides Ltd. GBR. Dist: Perseus-PGW.
Time Out Guides Staff, creator. Time Out Rio de Janeiro. rev. ed. 2007. (Time Out Rio de Janeiro Ser.). (ENG., Illus.). 256p. per. 19.95 *(978-1-84670-045-3(0))* Time Out Guides Ltd. GBR. Dist: Perseus-PGW.
Tingay, Paul. Rio de Janeiro Travel Pack. 2nd ed. 2007. (Globetrotter Travel Packs Ser.). (ENG., Illus.). 128p. pap. 14.95 *(978-1-84537-852-3(0))* New Holland Pubs., Ltd. GBR. Dist: Globe Pequot Pr., The.
Travel, Michelin. Michelin Travel Gd Rio de Janeiro. 2009. (Green Guide/Michelin Ser.). (ENG.). 320p. pap. 19.99 *(978-1-906261-95-5(4))* Michelin Travel & Lifestyle.
Waggoner, John. Brazil Adventure Guide. 2008. (Illus.). 650p. pap. 25.99 *(978-1-58843-639-9(X))* Hunter Publishing, Inc.
Wallpaper Magazine Editors, ed. Brasilia - Wallpaper City Guide. 2011. (ENG.). 128p. pap. 9.95 ***(978-0-7148-6262-0(2))*** Phaidon Pr., Inc.
—Rio de Janeiro 2011 - Wallpaper City Guide. rev. ed. 2011. (Wallpaper* City Guides). (ENG., Illus.). 128p. pap. 9.95 *(978-0-7148-5644-5(4))* Phaidon Pr., Inc.
—Rio de Janeiro 2012 - Wallpaper City Guide. 2012. (ENG., Illus.). 128p. pap. 9.95 ***(978-0-7148-6286-6(X))*** Phaidon Pr. Ltd. GBR. Dist: Hachette Bk. Group.
—Wallpaper* City Guide Sao Paulo 2012. 2011. (ENG.). 128p. pap. 9.95 ***(978-0-7148-6273-6(8))*** Phaidon Pr., Inc.

BRAZIL—HISTORIOGRAPHY

Johnson, Adriana Michele Campos. Sentencing Canudos: Subalternity in the Backlands of Brazil. 2010. (Pitt Illuminations Ser.). (ENG.). 240p. pap. 25.95 *(978-0-8229-6123-9(7))* Univ. of Pittsburgh Pr.
Zir, Alessandro. Dislodging Colonization: An Approach in Terms of Styles of Thinking to the Luso-Brazilian Encounters of the Sixteenth Century. 2011. (ENG.). 128p. 55.00 *(978-1-61147-020-8(X))* Fairleigh Dickinson Univ. Pr.

BRAZIL—HISTORY

Avelar, Idelber & Dunn, Christopher, eds. Brazilian Popular Music & Citizenship. 2011. (ENG., Illus.). 376p. 89.95 *(978-0-8223-4884-9(5))*; pap. 24.95 *(978-0-8223-4906-8(X))* Duke Univ. Pr.
Ba, Gabriel & Moon, Fabio. Daytripper. 2011. (ENG.). 256p. pap. 19.99 *(978-1-4012-2969-6(7)*, Vertigo) DC Comics.
Baan, Iwan. Brasilia-Chandigarh: Living with Modernity. 2010. (Illus.). 240p. pap. *(978-3-03778-228-6(5))* Lars Muller Pubs.
Baggelaar, Kristin. The Copacabana. 2006. (Images of America Ser.). (ENG., Illus.). 128p. per. 21.99 *(978-0-7385-4919-4(3))* Arcadia Publishing.
Bergad, Laird W. Slavery & the Demographic & Economic History of Minas Gerais, Brazil, 1720-1888. 2006. (Cambridge Latin American Studies). (ENG., Illus.). 336p. pap. 61.00 *(978-0-521-02817-2(5))* Cambridge Univ. Pr.
Bonotto, Daniel Marcos & Oliveira, Edson Gomes de, eds. (NON) Conventional Approaches Applied to the Study of Brazilian Aquifers. 2009. (Water Resource Planning, Development & Management Ser.). (Illus.). 65p. pap. 43.00 *(978-1-61668-770-0(3)*, Nova Novinka) Nova Science Pubs., Inc.
Borja-Villel, Manuel J. Drifts & Derivations: Experiences, Journeys & Morphologies. 2011. (ENG.). 301p. pap. 54.95 *(978-84-8026-425-9(X))* Museo Nacional Centro de Arte Reina Sofia ESP. Dist: Actar Birkhauser Distribution.
Bosi, Alfredo & Monteiro, Pedro Meira. Colony, Cult & Culture. 2008. *(978-0-9814580-0-7(9))* Univ. of Massachusetts Dartmouth.
Boxer, C. R. Golden Age Brazil: 1695-1750. (Illus.). 400p. 60.00 *(978-1-85754-100-7(6))* Carcanet Pr., Ltd. GBR. Dist: Paul & Co. Pubs. Consortium, Inc.
Bulmer-Thomas, Victor, ed. Britain & Latin America: A Changing Relationship. 2008. (ENG.). 256p. pap. 37.99 *(978-0-521-05495-9(8))* Cambridge Univ. Pr.
Burgeile, Odete. Um Estudo Sociolinguistico Dos Afro-amazonidas No Brasil: A Imigracao e a Mudanca de Lingual. 2009. (SPA & POR.). 460p. 129.95 *(978-0-7734-4873-5(X))* Mellen, Edwin Pr., The.
Caetano, Antonio Filipe Pereira. Entre Drogas e Cachaça: A Política Colonial e As Tensões Na América Portuguesa (1640-1710) 2009. (POR.). 362p. *(978-85-7177-472-8(2))* Universidade Federal de Alagoas.
Calirman, Claudia. Brazilian Art under Dictatorship: Antonio Manuel, Artur Barrio, & Cildo Meireles. 2012. (ENG., Illus.). 264p. 89.95 ***(978-0-8223-5139-9(0))***; pap. 24.95 ***(978-0-8223-5153-5(6))*** Duke Univ. Pr.
Chauí, Marilena de Souza. Brasil: Mito Fundador e Sociedade Autoritária. (POR., Illus.). 103p. *(978-85-86469-27-5(0))* Fundacao Perseu Abramo Ltda Editora.
Cooper, Clayton S. The Brazilians & Their Country. 403p. reprint ed. 98.00 *(978-0-7222-9593-9(6))* Library Reprints, Inc.
Costa, Cruz. Panorama of the History of Philosophy in Brazil: Pensamiento de America. Sturm, Fred G., tr. 2011. 116p. 39.95 ***(978-1-258-09181-1(X))*** Literary Licensing, LLC.
Craidy, Carmem Maria & Mabilde, Alette. Educação Em Prisões: Direito e Desafio. 2010. (POR & SPA., Illus.). 125p. pap. *(978-85-386-0083-1(4))* Universidade Federal do Rio Grande do Sul. Editora.
Crocitti, John J. Pearl Of The Paraíba No More: The Limits Of Modernity In Brazil. 2008. 272p. pap. *(978-3-639-08597-6(3))* VDM Verlag Dr. Mueller e.K.
Crocitti, John J. & Vallance, Monique, eds. Brazil Today: An Encyclopedia of Life in the Republic, 2 vols. 2011. (Illus.). 741p. 189.00 *(978-0-313-34672-9(0)*, GR4672) Greenwood Publishing Group, Inc.
Cunninghame-Graham, Robert B. A Brazilian Mystic: The Life & Miracles of Antonio Conselheiro. 238p. reprint ed. 98.00 *(978-0-7222-9602-8(9))* Library Reprints, Inc.
Da Costa, Sergio Correa. Every Inch a King: A Biography of Dom Pedro I, First Emperor of Brazil. Putnam, Samuel, tr. 2011. 238p. 46.95 ***(978-1-258-00452-1(6))*** Literary Licensing, LLC.
Da Cunha, Euclides. The Amazon: Land Without History. Sa, Lucia, ed. Sousa, Ronald, tr. from POR. 2006. (Library of Latin America Ser.). (ENG.). 128p. per. 19.95 *(978-0-19-517204-1(3))* Oxford Univ. Pr., Inc.
da Cunha, Euclides & Cunha, Euclides Da. Backlands: The Canudos Campaign. Lowe, Elizabeth, tr. from POR. 2010. (ENG.). 560p. (gr. 12). 18.00 *(978-0-14-310607-4(4)*, Penguin Classics) Penguin Group (USA) Inc.
Da Silva Pires, Cibélia Renata. Formation & Expansion of the Culture & Caipira Dialect. 2010. 312p. pap. *(978-3-639-24423-6(0))* VDM Verlag Dr. Mueller e.K.
de Castro, Eduardo Viveiros. The Inconstancy of the Indian Soul: The Encounter of Catholics & Cannibals in 16th-Century Brazil. 2011. 104p. pap. 12.95 *(978-0-9842010-1-3(7))* Prickly Paradigm Pr., LLC.
Dulles, John W. F. Unrest in Brazil: Political-Military Crises 1955-1964. 2012. 494p. pap. 40.00 ***(978-0-292-74077-8(8))*** Univ. of Texas Pr.
Fishlow, Albert. Starting Over: Brazil Since 1985. 2011. (ENG., Illus.). 236p. 34.95 *(978-0-8157-2143-7(9))* Brookings Institution Pr.
Fletcher, James C. & Kidder, Daniel P. Brazil & the Brazilians: Portrayed in Historical & Descriptive Sketches. 8th ed. 2006. (Kegan Paul Travellers Ser.). (Illus.). 650p. 300.00 *(978-0-7103-1146-7(X))* Taylor & Francis Group.
Foster, David William. Sao Paulo: Perspectives on the City & Cultural Production. 2011. (ENG., Illus.). 176p. 69.95 *(978-0-8130-3665-6(8))* Univ. Pr. of Florida.
Franco, Roberto Kennedy Gomes, et al. Outras Histórias Do Piauí. 2007. (Coleção Diálogos Intempestivos Ser.: Vol. 45). (POR.). 194p. *(978-85-7282-263-3(1))* Universidade Federal do Ceara. Editora.
Franklin, Adalberto. Apontamentos e Fontes para a História Econômica de Imperatriz. 2008. (POR., Illus.). 242p. *(978-85-88172-26-5(7))* Etica Servicos Editoriais Ltda.
Garramuño, Florencia & Kazumi Stahl, Anna. Primitive Modernities: Tango, Samba, & Nation. 2011. (ENG.). 216p. 85.00 *(978-0-8047-6249-6(X))*; pap. 27.95 *(978-0-8047-6250-2(3))* Stanford Univ. Pr.
Gomes, Valéria Severina. Traços de Mudança e de Permanmência em Edetoriais de Jornais Pernambucanos: Da Forma ao Sentido. 2010. (Beihefte Zur Zeitschrift Für Romanische Philologie Ser.). (Illus.). VI, 206p. *(978-3-484-52352-4(2))* Verlag Max Niemeyer.
Green, James. We Cannot Remain Silent: Opposition to the Brazilian Military Dictatorship in the United States. 2010. (Radical Perspectives Ser.). (ENG., Illus.). 472p. pap. 26.95 *(978-0-8223-4735-4(0))*; 94.95 *(978-0-8223-4717-0(2))* Duke Univ. Pr.
Groppo, Luís Antonio, et al. Movimentos Juvenis Na Contemporaneidade. 2008. (POR.). 204p. *(978-85-7315-520-4(5))* Universidade de Pernambuco.
Guimaraes-Iosif, Ranilce. Educação, Pobreza e Desigualdade No Brasil: Impedimentos para a Cidadania Global Emancipada. 2009. (POR., Illus.). 225p. *(978-85-98843-89-6(X))* WEG - ASSESSORIA E CONSULTORIA LTDA.
Harris, Mark. Rebellion on the Amazon: The Cabanagem, Race, & Popular Culture in the North of Brazil, 1798-1840. 2010. (Cambridge Latin American Studies). (ENG., Illus.). 352p. 95.00 *(978-0-521-43723-3(7))* Cambridge Univ. Pr.
Hentschke, Jens. Reconstructing the Brazilian Nation: Public Schooling in the Vargas Era. 2007. 518p. pap. 79.00 *(978-3-8329-3031-8(0))* Nomos Verlagsgesellschaft DEU. Dist: International Specialized Bk. Services.
Hentschke, Jens R. & Hentschke, Jens. Vargas & Brazil: New Perspectives. Hentschke, Jens R., ed. 2006. (Studies of the Americas). (ENG., Illus.). 320p. 95.00 *(978-1-4039-7391-7(1))* Palgrave Macmillan.
Hoffman, Paul. Wings of Madness: Alberto Santos-Dumont & the Invention of Flight. 2008. (ENG.). 369p. pap. 20.00 *(978-1-4223-9411-3(5))* DIANE Publishing Co.
Hollanda, Bernardo Borges Buarque de. O Clube Como Vontade e Representação: O Jornalismo Esportivo e a Formação das Torcidas Organizadas de Futebol Do Rio de Janeiro. 2010. (POR., Illus.). 588p. *(978-85-7577-580-6(4))* Livraria Sette Letras Ltda.
Hüsch, Anette. ARCHIV UTOPIA ARCHIVE UTOPIA: Das Brasilia-Projekt von Lina Kim und Michael Wesely Project Brasilia by Lina Kim & Michael Wesely. 2012. (ENG., Illus.). 168p. 40.00 ***(978-3-86828-221-4(1))*** Kehrer Verlag Heidelberg, Klaus Kehrer DEU. Dist: Consortium Bk. Sales & Distribution.
Israel, Jonathan I. & Schwartz, Stuart B. The Expansion of Tolerance: Religion in Dutch Brazil (1624-1654) 2007. (Amsterdam Studies in the Dutch Golden Age Ser.). (ENG., Illus.). 60p. per. *(978-90-5356-902-3(2)*, Leiden Univ. Pr.) Amsterdam Univ. Pr.
Johnson, Adriana Michele Campos. Sentencing Canudos: Subalternity in the Backlands of Brazil. 2010. (Pitt Illuminations Ser.). (ENG.). 240p. pap. 25.95 *(978-0-8229-6123-9(7))* Univ. of Pittsburgh Pr.
Johnson, Harold & Dutra, Francis A., eds. Pelo Vaso Traseiro: Sodomy & Sodomites in Luso-Brazilian History. 2007. pap. 33.95 *(978-1-58736-658-1(4)*, Fenestra Bks.) Wheatmark.
Jorge T. Almeida, ed. Focus on Brazil. 2008. (C). 89.00 *(978-1-60456-165-4(3))* Nova Science Pubs., Inc.
Kenny, Mary. Hidden Heads of the Households: Child Labor in Urban Northeast Brazil. 2nd ed. 2008. (Teaching Culture: UTP Ethnographies for the Classroom Ser.). (ENG.). 160p. pap. *(978-1-4426-0084-3(5))* Univ. of Toronto Pr.
Kidder, Daniel P. Brazil & the Brazilians Portrayed in Historical & Descriptive Sketches. 630p. reprint ed. 128.00 *(978-0-7222-9595-3(2))* Library Reprints, Inc.
Kidder, Daniel P. (Daniel Parish). Brazil & the Brazilians, Portrayed in Historical & Descriptive Sketches by Rev D P Kidder, D D , & Rev J C Fletcher. 2006. 676p. per. 36.99 *(978-1-4255-6805-4(X))* MPublishing.
Klein, Herbert & Luna, Francisco Vidal. Brazil Since 1980. 2006. (World Since 1980 Ser.). (ENG., Illus.). 282p. 90.00 *(978-0-521-82044-8(8))* Cambridge Univ. Pr.
Krause, Décio & Videira, Antonio. Brazilian Studies in Philosophy & History of Science: An account of recent Works. 2011. (Boston Studies in the Philosophy of Science Ser.). (ENG., Illus.). xiii, 352p. 139.00 *(978-90-481-9421-6(0)*, 9048194210) Springer.
Langfur, Hal. The Forbidden Lands: Colonial Identity, Frontier Violence, & the Persistence of Brazil's Eastern Indians, 1750-1830. (ENG., Illus.). 432p. 2008. pap. 27.95 *(978-0-8047-6338-7(0))* 2006. 70.00 *(978-0-8047-5180-3(3))* Stanford Univ. Pr.
Leal, João. Azorean Identity in Brazil & the United States: Arguments about History, Culture, & Transnational Connections. Graca, Wendy, tr. from POR. 2011. (Portuguese in the Americas Ser.). 192p. pap. 24.95 *(978-1-933227-31-3(1))* Tagus Pr.
Lima, Oliveira. The Evolution of Brazil Compared with That of Spanish & Anglo Saxon America. 159p. reprint ed. 88.00 *(978-0-7222-9599-1(5))* Library Reprints, Inc.
Lockmiller, Alice. Teacher's Guide for Tiago, Explorer of Brazil. 2010. 56p. pap. 13.95 *(978-0-557-36740-5(9))* Lulu Enterprises Inc.
Longo, James McMurtry. Isabel Orleans-Braganza: The Brazilian Princess Who Freed the Slaves. 2007. (ENG., Illus.). 300p. per. 39.95 *(978-0-7864-3201-1(2))* McFarland & Co., Inc. Pubs.
Love, Joseph. The Revolt of the Whip. 2012. (ENG.). 176p. 70.00 ***(978-0-8047-8106-0(0))***; pap. 22.95 ***(978-0-8047-8109-1(5))*** Stanford Univ. Pr.
Machado, Rigan & Fraguas, Jose M. Mastering Brazilian Jiu Jitsu. 2011. (Illus.). 533p. pap. 59.95 ***(978-1-933901-48-0(9))*** Empire Bks.
McCann, Bryan. The Throes of Democracy: Brazil Since 1989. 2008. (Global History of the Present Ser.). (ENG., Illus.). 174p. 80.00 *(978-1-84277-925-5(7))*; pap. 25.95 *(978-1-84277-926-2(5))* Zed Bks., Ltd. GBR. Dist: Macmillan.
McCreery, David. Frontier Goias, 1822-1889. 2006. (ENG., Illus.). 312p. 60.00 *(978-0-8047-5179-7(X))* Stanford Univ. Pr.
Meade, Teresa A. A Brief History of Brazil, Second Edition. 2nd rev. ed. 2009. (Brief History Ser.). 304p. (C). (gr. 9-18). pap. 19.95 *(978-0-8160-7789-2(4)*, Checkmark Bks.); (Illus.). 49.50 *(978-0-8160-7788-5(6))* Facts On File, Inc.
Mendonça, Leila Lobo de, et al. Caminhos Da Modernização: Cronologia Da Energia Elétrica No Brasil (1879-2007) 2007. (POR., Illus.). 130p. *(978-85-85147-75-4(X))* Centro da Memoria da Eletricidade no Brasil.
Monteiro, Adolfo Casais, et al. Cartas Em Família: Correspondência Entre o Escritor e Seus Pais: 1929-1943. 2008. (POR.). 407p. *(978-972-27-1624-6(7))* Imprensa Nacional Casa da Moeda, INCM.
Museo Nacional Centro de Arte Reina Sofia Staff, contrib. by. Desvíos de la Deriva: Experiencias, Travesías y Morfologías. 2010. (SPA., Illus.). 301p. *(978-84-8026-424-2(1))* Museo Nacional Centro de Arte Reina Sofia.
Needell, Jeffrey D. The Party of Order: The Conservatives, the State, & Slavery in the Brazilian Monarchy, 1831-1871. 2006. (ENG., Illus.). 480p. 80.00 *(978-0-8047-5369-2(5))* Stanford Univ. Pr.
Neves, Erivaldo Fagundes. Uma Comunidade Sertaneja: Da Sesmaria Ao Minifúndio: Um Estudo de História Regional e Local. 2nd ed. 2008. (POR., Illus.). 384p. *(978-85-232-0549-2(7))* Universidade Federal da Bahia, Centro Editorial e Didactico.
Oakenfull, J. C. Brazil: Past, Present & Future. 814p. reprint ed. 198.00 *(978-0-7222-9598-4(7))* Library Reprints, Inc.
Oliveira Sobrinho, Reinaldo de. O Negro Açucarou o Nordeste. 2007. (POR., Illus.). 166p. *(978-85-7539-349-9(9))* Ideia Personalizadora e Editora Ltda.
Parker, Phyllis R. Brazil & the Quiet Intervention 1964. 2011. (ENG.). 162p. pap. 19.95 *(978-0-292-72950-6(2))* Univ. of Texas Pr.
Pessoa, Jordania Maria. Entre a Tradição e a Modernidade: A Belle époque Caxiense: Práticas Fabris, Reordenamento Urbano e Padrões Culturais No Final Do Século XIX. 2009. (POR., Illus.). 147p. *(978-85-88172-63-0(1))* Etica Servicos Editoriais Ltda.
Preuss, Ori. Bridging the Island: Brazilian's Views of Spanish America & Themselves 1865-1912. 2010. 240p. pap. 29.98 *(978-1-936353-02-6(4))* Iberoamericana Vervuert Publishing Corp.
Reis, Alda Almeida Miranda & Pereira, Maria Rita Brandão. Carolina: Apogeu, Declínio e Ressurgência. 2nd ed. 2007. (POR., Illus.). 94p. *(978-85-88172-52-4(6))* Etica Servicos Editoriais Ltda.
Reis, Sérgio Rodrigo. Rodrigo Pederneiras e o Grupo Corpo: Dança Universal. 2008. (POR., Illus.). 193p. *(978-85-7060-618-1(4))* Imprensa Oficial do Estado S/A Imesp.
Richardson, Kim. Quebra-Quilos & Peasant: Peasants, Religion, & Politics in Nineteenth-Century Brazil. 2010. (ENG., Illus.). 170p. 57.00 *(978-0-7618-5304-6(9))* Univ. Pr. of America, Inc.
—Quebra-Quilos & Peasant Resistance: Peasants, Religion, & Politics in Nineteenth-Century Brazil. 2010. (ENG., Illus.). 170p. pap. 26.50 *(978-0-7618-5305-3(7))* Univ. Pr. of America, Inc.
Saint-Paul, Ulrich. Mangrove Dynamics & Management in North Brazil. Saint-Paul, Ulrich & Schneider, Horacio, eds. 2010. (Ecological Studies). (Illus.). xviii, 400p. 199.00 *(978-3-642-13456-2(4)*, 3642134564) Springer.
Santana, Charles d'Almeida. Linguagens Urbanas, Memórias Da Cidade: Vivências e Imagens Da Salvador de Migrantes. 2009. (POR., Illus.). 210p. pap. *(978-85-391-0033-0(9))* Annablume Editora Comunicacao Ltda.
Santos, Martha. Cleansing Honor with Blood: Masculinity, Violence, & Power in the Backlands of Northeast Brazil, 1845-1889. 2012. (ENG.). 320p. 65.00 ***(978-0-8047-7456-7(0))*** Stanford Univ. Pr.
Sapiezinskas, Aline. Cultural Heritage in Brazil: The Anthropological Perspective & the Local Point of View. 2011. 144p. pap. 19.99 ***(978-1-4568-8960-9(5))*** Xlibris Corp.
Schwartz, Stuart B., ed. Early Brazil: A Documentary Collection to 1700. 2010. (ENG., Illus.). 346p. (C). 85.00 *(978-0-521-19833-2(X))* Cambridge Univ. Pr.
—Early Brazil: A Documentary Collection To 1700. 2009. (ENG., Illus.). 288p. (C). pap. 27.99 *(978-0-521-12453-9(0))* Cambridge Univ. Pr.
Skidmore, Thomas E. Brazil: Five Centuries of Change. 2nd ed. 2009. (Latin American Histories Ser.). (ENG., Illus.). 304p. (C). pap. 44.95 *(978-0-19-537455-1(X))* Oxford Univ. Pr., Inc.
Somekh, Nadia & Campos, Candido Malta. A Cidade Que Não Pode Parar: Planos Urbanísticos de São Paulo No Século XX. 2008. (POR., Illus.). 192p. *(978-85-89328-01-2(5))* Instituto Presbiteriano Mackenzie.
Southey, Robert. History of Brazil, 3 vols. reprint ed. 375.00 *(978-0-7222-2603-2(9))* Library Reprints, Inc.
Téo, Marcelo, et al. De Arte: Crítica e Crônica Musical N'A Gazeta, Florianópolis, Década de 1930. 2007. (POR., Illus.). 344p. *(978-85-7662-028-0(6))* Livraria e Editora Obra Jurídica Ltda.
Thomas Cochrane. Narrative of Services in the Liberation of Chili Peru & Brazil. l.t. ed. 2007. 260p. pap. 23.99 *(978-1-4264-8275-5(2))*; (ENG.). 298p. pap. 23.99 *(978-1-4264-8312-7(0))* BiblioBazaar.
Tota, Antônio Pedro. The Seduction of Brazil: The Americanization of Brazil During World War II. Ellis, Lorena B., tr. from POR. 2009. (ENG., Illus.). 216p. 55.00 *(978-0-292-71993-4(0))* Univ. of Texas Pr.
—The Seduction of Brazil: The Americanization of Brazil during World War II. Ellis, Lorena B., tr. from POR. 2010. (ENG.). 216p. pap. 25.00 *(978-0-292-72352-8(0))* Univ. of Texas Pr.
van Baerle, Caspar. The History of Brazil under the Governorship of Count Johan Maurits of Nassau, 1636-1644. 2011. (ENG., Illus.). 448p. 79.95 *(978-0-8130-3664-9(X))* Univ. Pr. of Florida.
Vasquez, Manuel A. The Brazilian Popular Church & the Crisis of Modernity. 2008. (Cambridge Studies in Ideology & Religion Ser.). (ENG.). 320p. pap. 44.00 *(978-0-521-09086-5(5))* Cambridge Univ. Pr.
Whitaker, Arthur P., ed. Latin America & the Enlightenment. 2011. 144p. 40.95 ***(978-1-258-08882-8(7))*** Literary Licensing, LLC.
Wiesebron, Marianne. Brazilië in de Nederlandse Archieven (1624-1654) Documenten in Het Koninklijk Huisarchief en in Het Archief Van de Staten-Generaal = o Brasil Em Arquivos Neerlandeses (1624-1654): Documentos No Arquivo Da Casa Real e No Arquivo DOS Estados Gerais. 2008. (CNWS Publications). (POR, DUT & MUL., Illus.). 605p. *(978-90-5789-157-1(3)*, Leiden Univ. Pr.) Amsterdam Univ. Pr.

BRAZIL—POLITICS AND GOVERNMENT

Afolabi, Niyi. Afro-Brazilians: Cultural Production in a Racial Democracy. 2009. (Rochester Studies in African History & the Diaspora Ser.: Volume 39). 443p. 90.00 *(978-1-58046-262-4(6))* Univ. of Rochester Pr.

Arestis, Philip. Political Economy of Brazil: Recent Economic Performance. Arestis, Philip & Saad-Filho, Alfredo, eds. 2007. (ENG., Illus.). 288p. 126.00 *(978-0-230-54277-8(8))* Palgrave Macmillan.

Avritzer, Leonardo. Experiências Nacionais de Participação Social. 2009. (POR.). 159p. pap. *(978-85-249-1550-5(1))* Cortez Editora e Livraria Ltda.

Bailey, Ian & Compston, Hugh, eds. Feeling the Heat: The Politics of Climate Policy in Rapidly Industrializing Countries. 2012. (Energy, Climate & the Environment Ser.). (ENG., Illus.). 264p. 85.00 ***(978-0-230-28040-3(4))*** Palgrave Macmillan.

Bailey, Stanley R. Legacies of Race: Identities, Attitudes, & Politics in Brazil. 2009. (ENG., Illus.). 304p. 70.00 *(978-0-8047-6277-9(5))*; pap. 24.95 *(978-0-8047-6278-6(3))* Stanford Univ. Pr.

Baquero, Marcello & Cremonese, Dejalma. Eleições Municipais 2008: Uma Análise Do Comportamento Eleitoral Brasileiro. 2009. (POR., Illus.). 269p. *(978-85-7429-844-3(1))* Fidene/Unijui Editora.

Bartlett, Lesley. The Word & the World: The Cultural Politics of Literacy in Brazil. 2009. *(978-1-57273-891-1(X))*; *(978-1-57273-890-4(1))* Hampton Pr., Inc.

Bermann, Célio. As Novas Energias No Brasil: Dilemas Da Inclusão Social e Programas de Governo. 2007. (POR., Illus.). 176p. *(978-85-86471-29-2(1))* Federacao de Orgaos P/Assist. Social e Educacional.

Biavaschi, Magda Barros, et al. Memória e Preservação de Documentos: Direitos Do Cidadão. 2007. (POR., Illus.). 160p. *(978-85-361-1055-4(4))* Ltr Editora Ltda.

Bourne, Richard. Lula of Brazil: The Story So Far. (Illus.). 2009. (ENG.). 304p. pap. 21.95 *(978-0-520-26155-6(0))* 2008. 285p. 40.00 *(978-0-520-24663-8(2))* Univ. of California Pr.

—Lula of Brazil: The Story So Far. 2008. (Illus.). 304p. 100.95 *(978-1-84813-010-4(4))*; pap. 31.95 *(978-1-84813-011-1(2))* Zed Bks., Ltd. GBR. Dist: Palgrave Macmillan.

Brandão, Gildo Marçal, et al. Regionalismos, Democracia e Desenvolvimento. 2007. (POR., Illus.). 219p. *(978-85-7732-059-2(6))* Humanitas.

Brands, Hal. Dilemmas of Brazilian Grand Strategy. 2010. *(978-1-58487-462-1(7))* Strategic Studies Institute, U.S. Army War College Commandant (AWCC-DSI/Pubns.)

Brinks, Daniel M. The Judicial Response to Police Killings in Latin America: Inequality & the Rule of Law. 2007. (ENG., Illus.). 302p. 101.00 *(978-0-521-87234-8(0))* Cambridge Univ. Pr.

Cardoso, Fernando Henrique. Accidental President of Brazil: A Memoir. 2007. (ENG., Illus.). 320p. per. 16.00 *(978-1-58648-429-3(X))* PublicAffairs.

Chatterjee, Irani. The Clean Development Mechanism. 2011. 124p. pap. ***(978-3-8443-1287-4(0))*** Lambert Academic Publishing.

Crocitti, John J. & Vallance, Monique. Brazil Today: An Encyclopedia of Life in the Republic. 2011. E-Book ***(978-0-313-34673-6(9))*** ABC-CLIO, LLC.

Czinkota & Uczai, Pedro F. Matematicamente Incorreto. (POR., Illus.). 323p. *(978-0-00-293029-1(3)*, Wiley-Blackwell) Wiley, John & Sons, Inc.

De Oliveira, Frank Marcio. Attache Extraordinaire: Vernon A. Walters in Brazil: Vernon A. Walters in Brazil. National Defense Intelligence College (U.S.), ed. 2010. (ENG., Illus.). 195p. pap. 22.00 *(978-1-932946-22-2(5)*, Defense Dept.) United States Government Printing Office.

Dent, Alexander Sebastian. River of Tears: Country Music, Memory, & Modernity in Brazil. 2009. (ENG., Illus.). 312p. 89.95 *(978-0-8223-4520-6(X))*; pap. 24.95 *(978-0-8223-4537-4(4))* Duke Univ. Pr.

Dickovick, J. Tyler. Decentralization & Recentralization in the Developing World: Comparative Studies from Africa & Latin America. 2011. (ENG.). 232p. 64.95 *(978-0-271-03790-5(3))* Pennsylvania State Univ. Pr.

Domingues Filho, João Batista & Reis, Fábio Wanderley. Planejamento Governamental e Democracia No Brasil. 2007. (POR., Illus.). 217p. *(978-85-7078-137-6(7))* Universidade Federal de Uberlandia, Editora.

Drogus, Carol Ann & Stewart-Gambino, Hannah. Activist Faith: Grassroots Women in Democratic Brazil & Chile. 2008. (ENG.). 272p. pap. 30.00 *(978-0-271-02550-6(9))* Pennsylvania State Univ. Pr.

Dulles, John W. F. Brazilian Communism, 1935-1945: Repression During World Upheaval. 2011. (ENG., Illus.). 300p. pap. 25.00 *(978-0-292-72951-3(0))* Univ. of Texas Pr.

—Carlos Lacerda, Brazilian Crusader: Volume II: the Years 1960-1977. 2010. (ENG., Illus.). 795p. pap. 65.00 *(978-0-292-72656-7(2))* Univ. of Texas Pr.

—Carlos Lacerda, Brazilian Crusader Vol. 1: The Years, 1914-1960. 2010. (ENG., Illus.). 513p. pap. 47.50 *(978-0-292-72373-3(3))* Univ. of Texas Pr.

—Resisting Brazil's Military Regime: An Account of the Battles of Sobral Pinto. 2010. (ENG., Illus.). 324p. pap. 30.00 *(978-0-292-72602-4(3))* Univ. of Texas Pr.

—The Sao Paulo Law School & the Anti-Vargas Resistance (1938-1945) 2011. (ENG.). 274p. pap. 25.00 ***(978-0-292-73968-0(0))*** Univ. of Texas Pr.

—Unrest in Brazil: Political-Military Crises 1955-1964. 2012. 494p. pap. 40.00 ***(978-0-292-74077-8(8))*** Univ. of Texas Pr.

—Vargas of Brazil: A Political Biography. 2012. (ENG., Illus.). 450p. pap. 40.00 ***(978-0-292-74076-5(6))*** Univ. of Texas Pr.

Ferreira, Isabel C. R. Racial Democracy in Literary Works. 2009. 196p. pap. *(978-3-639-12051-6(5))* VDM Verlag Dr. Mueller e.K.

Fischer, Brodwyn. A Poverty of Rights: Citizenship & Inequality in Twentieth-Century Rio de Janeiro. 2010. (ENG., Illus.). 488p. pap. 24.95 *(978-0-8047-7660-8(1))* Stanford Univ. Pr.

Fishlow, Albert. Starting Over: Brazil Since 1985. 2011. (ENG., Illus.). 236p. 34.95 *(978-0-8157-2143-7(9))* Brookings Institution Pr.

Font, Mauricio. The Brazilian State: Debate & Agenda. Randall, Adrian, ed. 2011. (Bildner Western Hemisphere Studies). (ENG.). 434p. (gr. 17). 85.00 ***(978-0-7391-6731-1(6))*** Lexington Bks.

Font, Mauricio A. & Randall, Laura. The Brazilian State: Debate & Agenda. 2011. ***(978-0-7391-6889-9(4))*** Lexington Bks.

Goertzel, Ted G. Brazil's Lula: The Most Popular Politician on Earth. 2011. 226p. pap. 26.95 ***(978-1-61233-505-6(5)***, Brown Walker Pr.) Universal Pubs.

González, Rodrigo Stumpf. Perspectivas Sobre Participação e Democracia No Brasil. 2007. (POR., Illus.). 205p. *(978-85-7429-601-2(5))* Fidene/Unijui Editora.

Grandin, Greg. Fordlandia: The Rise & Fall of Henry Ford's Forgotten Jungle City. 2009. (ENG., Illus.). 432p. 27.50 *(978-0-8050-8236-4(0)*, Metropolitan Bks.) Holt, Henry & Co.

—Fordlandia: The Rise & Fall of Henry Ford's Forgotten Jungle City. 2010. (ENG., Illus.). 432p. pap. 16.00 *(978-0-312-42962-1(2))* Picador.

Green, James. We Cannot Remain Silent: Opposition to the Brazilian Military Dictatorship in the United States. 2010. (Radical Perspectives Ser.). (ENG., Illus.). 472p. pap. 26.95 *(978-0-8223-4735-4(0))*; 94.95 *(978-0-8223-4717-0(2))* Duke Univ. Pr.

Guattari, Felix & Rolnik, Suely. Molecular Revolution in Brazil. Clapshow, Karel & Holmes, Brian, trs. from SPA. 2007. (Semiotext(e) / Foreign Agents Ser.). (ENG.). 496p. (gr. 17). per. 18.95 ***(978-1-58435-051-4(2))*** Semiotexte/Smart Art.

Guedes, Alvaro Martim & Fonseca, Francisco César Pinto da. Controle Social Da Administração Pública: Cenário, Avanços e Dilemas No Brasil. 2007. (Illus.). 287p. *(978-85-98605-29-6(8))* Fundacao para o Desenvolvimento da Unesp. Editora.

Gutierrez, Ricardo A. Between Knowledge & Politics: Experts & Water Policy Reform in Brazil. 2008. 264p. pap. *(978-3-639-08729-1(1))* VDM Verlag Dr. Mueller e.K.

Hagopian, Frances. Traditional Politics & Regime Change in Brazil. 2007. (Cambridge Studies in Comparative Politics). (ENG.). 344p. pap. 69.00 *(978-0-521-03288-9(1))* Cambridge Univ. Pr.

Heyck, Denis. Schools in the Forest: How Grassroots Education Brought Political Empowerment to the Brazilian Amazon. 2010. 196p. 75.00 *(978-1-56549-351-3(6))* Stylus Publishing, LLC.

Hunter, Wendy. The Transformation of the Workers' Party in Brazil, 1989-2009. 2010. (ENG., Illus.). 256p. 85.00 *(978-0-521-51455-2(X))*; pap. 29.99 *(978-0-521-73300-7(6))* Cambridge Univ. Pr.

Irizarry Osorio, Hiram José. Argentina & Brazil's Politics of Taxation: 1980s-1990s. 2008. 300p. pap. *(978-3-639-04754-7(0))* VDM Verlag Dr. Mueller e.K.

Jorge T. Almeida, ed. Focus on Brazil. 2008. (C). 89.00 *(978-1-60456-165-4(3))* Nova Science Pubs., Inc.

Kinzo, Maria D'Alva G., ed. Brazil under Democracy: Economy, Polity & Society since 1985. Date not set. (Illus.). 248p. (C). pap. 19.95 *(978-1-900039-53-6(2))* Institute of Latin American Studies GBR. Dist: Brookings Institution Pr.

Klein, Herbert & Luna, Francisco Vidal. Brazil Since 1980. 2006. (World Since 1980 Ser.). (ENG., Illus.). 282p. 90.00 *(978-0-521-82044-8(8))* Cambridge Univ. Pr.

Krischke, Paulo Jose. Populism & the Catholic Church: Political Crisis in Brazil 1964. 2010. (Religion & Spirituality Ser.). 129.00 *(978-1-61728-296-6(0))* Nova Science Pubs., Inc.

Lampreia, Luiz Felipe. O Brasil e Os Ventos Do Mundo: Memórias de Cinco Décadas Na Cena Internacional. 2009. (POR., Illus.). 343p. *(978-85-390-0067-6(9))* Objetiva, Editora Ltda.

Leal, Victor Nunes. Coronelismo: The Municipality & Representative Government in Brazil. 2009. (Cambridge Latin American Studies). (ENG.). 252p. pap. 36.99 *(978-0-521-10231-5(6))* Cambridge Univ. Pr.

Lima, Solimar Oliveira & Assunção, Rosângela. Governos e Políticas Públicas: A Experiência Do Piauí. 2009. (POR., Illus.). 186p. *(978-85-7729-073-4(5))* Booklink.

Lin, A. H. The Fish Rots from the Head: Brazilians on Corruption, 1 vol. 2010. 276p. pap. 27.95 *(978-1-4489-5735-4(4))* PublishAmerica, Inc.

Lockmiller, Alice. Teacher's Guide for Tiago, Explorer of Brazil. 2010. 56p. pap. 13.95 *(978-0-557-36740-5(9))* Lulu Enterprises Inc.

Love, Joseph. Brazil under Lula: Economy, Politics, & Society under the Worker-President. Baer, Werner, ed. 2008. (ENG., Illus.). 344p. 110.00 *(978-0-230-60816-0(7))* Palgrave Macmillan.

Lyne, Mona. The Voter's Dilemma & Democratic Accountability: Explaining the Democracy-Development Paradox. 2008. (ENG., Illus.). 288p. pap. 60.00 *(978-0-271-03386-0(X))* Pennsylvania State Univ. Pr.

Lyne, Mona M. Voter's Dilemma & Democratic Accountability: Latin America & Beyond. 2008. 288p. pap. 29.95 *(978-0-271-03387-7(8))* Pennsylvania State Univ. Pr.

Macaulay, Fiona. Gender Politics in Brazil & Chile. 2006. (St. Antony's Ser.). (ENG.). 256p. 116.00 *(978-0-333-73614-2(1))* Palgrave Macmillan.

Macaulay, Fiona & Doctor, Mahrukh. Brazil & Globalization. 2008. (Illus.). 208p. 115.00 *(978-0-415-95804-2(0))* Routledge.

Macedo, Miguel, et al. Democracia, Transparência e Desenvolvimento Sustentável. 2007. (POR.). 215p. *(978-85-99995-09-9(X))* Fundacao Konrad-Adenauer-Stiftung E.V.

Magalhães, Rejane Mendes Moreira de Almeida & Senna, Marta de. Rui Barbosa Em Perspectiva: Seleçao de Textos Fundamentais. 2007. (POR., Illus.). 304p. *(978-85-7004-278-1(7))* Fundacao Casa De Rui Barbosa.

Matos, Carolina. Journalism & Political Democracy in Brazil. 2008. (ENG., Illus.). 336p. 89.50 *(978-0-7391-2350-8(5))* Lexington Bks.

Matos, null. Journalism & Political Democracy in Brazil. 2009. (ENG.). 336p. pap. 38.99 *(978-0-7391-2351-5(3))* Lexington Bks.

McCann, Bryan. The Throes of Democracy: Brazil Since 1989. 2008. (Global History of the Present Ser.). (ENG., Illus.). 174p. 80.00 *(978-1-84277-925-5(7))*; pap. 25.95 *(978-1-84277-926-2(5))* Zed Bks., Ltd. GBR. Dist: Macmillan.

McCreery, David. Frontier Goias, 1822-1889. 2006. (ENG., Illus.). 312p. 60.00 *(978-0-8047-5179-7(X))* Stanford Univ. Pr.

Mische, Ann. Partisan Publics: Communication & Contention Across Brazilian Youth Activist Networks. (Princeton Studies in Cultural Sociology Ser.). (Illus.). 2009. (ENG.). 456p. (C). pap. 26.95 *(978-0-691-14104-6(5))* 2007. 432p. 55.00 *(978-0-691-12494-0(9))* Princeton Univ. Pr.

Mosher, Jeffrey Carl. Political Struggle, Ideology, & State Building: Pernambuco & the Construction of Brazil, 1817-1850. 2008. (ENG., Illus.). 360p. (C). 50.00 *(978-0-8032-3247-1(0))* Univ. of Nebraska Pr.

Narlikar, Amrita. New Powers: How to Become One & How to Manage Them. 2010. (Columbia/Hurst Ser.). (ENG.). 208p. (gr. 17). 45.00 *(978-0-231-70202-7(7))* Columbia Univ. Pr.

Nascimento, Elisa Larkin. The Sorcery of Color: Identity, Race, & Gender in Brazil. 2006. (Illus.). 272p. 55.50 *(978-1-59213-350-5(9))* Temple Univ. Pr.

Needell, Jeffrey D. The Party of Order: The Conservatives, the State, & Slavery in the Brazilian Monarchy, 1831-1871. 2006. (ENG., Illus.). 480p. 80.00 *(978-0-8047-5369-2(5))* Stanford Univ. Pr.

Nunn, Amy. The Politics & History of AIDS Treatment in Brazil. 2009. (Illus.). 260p. 79.95 *(978-0-387-09617-9(5))* Springer.

Ondetti, Gabriel. Land, Protest, & Politics: The Landless Movement & the Struggle for Agrarian Reform in Brazil. 2008. (ENG.). 304p. pap. 29.95 *(978-0-271-03354-9(1))* Pennsylvania State Univ. Pr.

Ondetti, Gabriel A. Land, Protest, & Politics: The Landless Movement & the Struggle for Agrarian Reform in Brazil. 2008. (ENG., Illus.). 264p. (C). 60.00 *(978-0-271-03353-2(3))* Pennsylvania State Univ. Pr.

Organisation for Economic Co-operation and Development Staff. Oecd e-Government Studies Belgium. 2008. (Illus.). 248p. pap. 63.00 *(978-92-64-04786-0(7))* Organization for Economic Cooperation & Development.

Ottmann, Goetz. Democracy in the Making: Municipal Reforms, Civil Society, & the Brazilian Workers' Party. 2009. 79.00 *(978-1-60692-592-8(X))* Nova Science Pubs., Inc.

Parker, Phyllis R. Brazil & the Quiet Intervention 1964. 2011. (ENG.). 162p. pap. 19.95 *(978-0-292-72950-6(2))* Univ. of Texas Pr.

Perlman, Janice E. Favela: Four Decades of Living on the Edge in Rio de Janeiro, 1 vol. 2010. (ENG., Illus.). 368p. 29.95 *(978-0-19-536836-9(3))* Oxford Univ. Pr., Inc.

Pessoa, Carlos. Post-Marxism & Politics - the Case of the Brazilian Workers' Party. 2008. 224p. pap. *(978-3-639-09052-9(7))* VDM Verlag Dr. Mueller e.K.

Pochmann, Marcio. Desenvolvimento e Perspectivas Novas para o Brasil. 2010. (POR., Illus.). 191p. *(978-85-249-1558-1(7))* Cortez Editora e Livraria Ltda.

Porto Filho, Carlos Henrique de Oliveira. Contos Da Câmara: Depoimentos de Servidores Nos 180 Anos Do Legislativo, 2 vols. 2007. (Illus.). *(978-85-7365-571-1(2))*; 311p. *(978-85-7365-521-6(6))* Camara dos Deputados Coordenacao de Publicacoes.

Porto, Mauro. Media Power & Democratization in Brazil: TV Globo & the Dilemmas of Political Accountability. 2012. (Routledge Advances in Internationalizing Media Studies). (ENG., Illus.). 200p. (C). 125.00 *(978-0-415-89721-1(1))* Routledge.

Power, Timothy J. & Kingstone, Peter R. Democratic Brazil Revisited. Kingstone, Peter & Power, Timothy J., eds. 2008. (Pitt Latin American Studies). (ENG.). 360p. (C). 65.00 *(978-0-8229-4354-9(9))*; pap. 26.95 *(978-0-8229-6004-1(4))* Univ. of Pittsburgh Pr.

Puff, Jefferson. Online Services to Brazil. 2011. 168p. pap. ***(978-3-8443-1880-7(1))*** Lambert Academic Publishing.

Rebelo, Aldo. Palmeiras Corinthians 1945: O Jogo Vermelho. 2010. (POR., Illus.). 119p. *(978-85-7139-993-8(X))* Fundacao para o Desenvolvimento da Unesp. Editora.

Ricci, Rudá. Lulismo: Da ERA DOS Movimentos Sociais à Ascensão Da Nova Classe Média Brasileira: De Como o Discurso Anti-Institucionalista DOS Anos 80 Deu Lugar Ao Líder Da Conclusão Da Modernização Conservadora Em Nosso País. 2010. (POR., Illus.). 250p. *(978-85-89216-28-9(4))* Fundacao Astrogildo Pereira.

Rohter, Larry. Brazil on the Rise: The Story of a Country Transformed. (ENG., Illus.). 304p. 2012. pap. 17.00 ***(978-0-230-12073-0(3))*** 2010. 27.00 *(978-0-230-61887-9(1))* Palgrave Macmillan.

Romano, Jorge Osvaldo, et al. Olhar Crítico Sobre Participação e Cidadania: Trajetórias de Organização e Luta Pela Redemocratização Da Governanca No Brasil. 2007. (POR.). 323p. *(978-85-7743-056-7(1))* Expressao Popular, Editora, Ltda.

Samuels, David. Ambition, Federalism, & Legislative Politics in Brazil. 2006. (ENG., Illus.). 268p. pap. 53.00 *(978-0-521-03062-5(5))* Cambridge Univ. Pr.

Sattamini, Lina. A Mother's Cry: A Memoir of Politics, Prison, & Torture under the Brazilian Military Dictatorship. Green, James N., ed. Nielsen, Rex P., tr. 2010. (ENG.). 208p. pap. 22.95 *(978-0-8223-4736-1(9))* Duke Univ. Pr.

—A Mother's Cry: A Memoir of Politics, Prison, & Torture under the Brazilian Military Dictatorship. Green, James N., ed. Nielson, Rex P., tr. 2010. (ENG., Illus.). 208p. 79.95 *(978-0-8223-4718-7(0))* Duke Univ. Pr.

Schneider, Ann Christin. Affirmative Action in Higher Education. 2009. 124p. pap. *(978-3-639-11839-1(1))* VDM Verlag Dr. Mueller e.K.

Silva, Itamar & Souto, Anna Luiza Salles, eds. Democracy, Citizenship & Youth: Towards Social & Political Participation in Brazil. 2009. (International Library of Political Studies). (ENG.). 336p. 98.50 *(978-1-84885-048-4(4)*, Tauris Academic Studies) I. B. Tauris & Co., Ltd. GBR. Dist: Macmillan.

Silva, Patricio & Cleuren, Herwig. Widening Democracy: Citizens & Participatory Schemes in Brazil & Chile. 2009. *(978-90-04-17783-3(3))* BRILL.

Skidmore, Thomas E. Politics in Brazil, 1930-1964: An Experiment in Democracy. 40th ed. 2007. (ENG., Illus.). 480p. pap. 29.99 *(978-0-19-533269-8(5))* Oxford Univ. Pr., Inc.

Sluyter-Beltrão, Jeffrey. Rise & Decline of Brazil's New Unionism: The Politics of the Central Única DOS Trabalhadores. 2010. 481p. pap. 84.95 *(978-3-0343-0114-5(6))* Lang, Peter AG GBR. Dist: Lang, Peter.

Souza, Jessz & Sinder, Valter, eds. Imagining Brazil. 2007. (Global Encounters: Studies in Comparative Political Theory Ser.). (ENG.). 318p. per. 34.99 *(978-0-7391-1014-0(4))* Lexington Bks.

Taylor, Matthew M. Judging Policy: Courts & Policy Reform in Democratic Brazil. 2008. (ENG., Illus.). 248p. 55.00 *(978-0-8047-5811-6(5))* Stanford Univ. Pr.

Teles, Edson & Safatle, Vladimir. O Que Resta Da Ditadura: A Exceção Brasileira. 2010. (POR.). 350p. pap. *(978-85-7559-155-0(X))* Jinkings Editores Associados Ltda.

Viteri, Nicholas Coronel. The Conflict over Land Reform in Rural Brazil. 2008. 124p. pap. *(978-3-639-07392-8(4))* VDM Verlag Dr. Mueller e.K.

von Mettenheim, Kurt. The Brazilian Voter: Mass Politics in Democratic Transition, 1974-1986. 2009. (Pitt Latin American Studies). (ENG.). 308p. (C). pap. 27.95 *(978-0-8229-8573-0(X))* Univ. of Pittsburgh Pr.

Wampler, Brian. Participatory Budgeting in Brazil: Contestation, Cooperation, & Accountability. 2007. (ENG.). 264p. pap. 28.00 *(978-0-271-03253-5(7))*; (Illus.). 56.95 *(978-0-271-03252-8(9))* Pennsylvania State Univ. Pr.

Ward, Peter M., et al. Governance in the Americas: Decentralization, Democracy, & Subnational Government in Brazil, Mexico, & the USA. 2008. (ND Kellogg Inst Int'l Studies). (ENG., Illus.). 376p. pap. 35.00 *(978-0-268-04411-4(2))* Univ. of Notre Dame Pr.

Wood, Charles H. & Carvalho, Jose Alberto Magno. The Demography of Inequality in Brazil. 2009. (Cambridge Latin American Studies). (ENG., Illus.). 316p. pap. 44.00 *(978-0-521-10246-9(4))* Cambridge Univ. Pr.

Woodard, James. Place in Politics: São Paulo, Brazil, from Seigneurial Republicanism to Regionalist Revolt. 2009. (ENG.). 424p. 94.95 *(978-0-8223-4346-2(0))*; pap. 26.95 *(978-0-8223-4329-5(0))* Duke Univ. Pr.

BRAZIL—RACE RELATIONS

Alberto, Paulina. Terms of Inclusion: Black Intellectuals in Twentieth-Century Brazil. 2011. (ENG., Illus.). 432p. 69.95 *(978-0-8078-3437-4(8))*; pap. 29.95 *(978-0-8078-7171-3(0))* Univ. of North Carolina Pr.

Blake, Stanley E. The Vigorous Core of Our Nationality: Race & Regional Identity in Northeastern Brazil. 2011. (Pitt Latin American Studies). (ENG., Illus.). 360p. pap. 27.95 *(978-0-8229-6133-8(4))* Univ. of Pittsburgh Pr.

Caldwell, Kia Lilly. Negras in Brazil: Re-Envisioning Black Women, Citizenship, & the Politics of Identity. 2006. (ENG., Illus.). 252p. per. 24.95 *(978-0-8135-3957-7(9))* Rutgers Univ. Pr.

Daniel, G. Reginald. Race & Multiraciality in Brazil & the United States: Converging Paths? 2007. (ENG.). 384p. pap. 25.00 *(978-0-271-03288-7(X))* 2006. (Illus.). 365p. 61.00 *(978-0-271-02883-5(1))* Pennsylvania State Univ. Pr.

Davis, Darién J. & Davis, Darien J. White Face, Black Mask: Africaneity & the Early Social History of Popular Music in Brazil. 2009. (Black American & Diasporic Studies Ser.). (ENG., Illus.). 265p. pap. 29.95 *(978-0-87013-834-8(0))* Michigan State Univ. Pr.

Ferreira, Isabel C. R. Racial Democracy in Literary Works. 2009. 196p. pap. *(978-3-639-12051-6(5))* VDM Verlag Dr. Mueller e.K.

Fredrickson, George M. & Fredrickson, George M. Diverse Nations: Explorations in the History of Racial & Ethnic Pluralism. 2008. (U. S. History in International Perspective Ser.). 240p. (C). 125.00 *(978-1-59451-573-6(5))* Paradigm Pubs.

Mendes Dos Santos, Gildasio. Television in Brazil: A Factor of Racial Divide? 2008. 64p. pap. *(978-3-639-03016-7(8))* VDM Verlag Dr. Mueller e.K.

Reiter, Bernd & Mitchell, Gladys L., eds. Brazil's New Racial Politics. 2009. (Illus.). 270p. 59.95 *(978-1-58826-666-8(4))* Rienner, Lynne Pubs.

Seigel, Micol. Uneven Encounters: Making Race & Nation in Brazil & the United States. 2009. (American Encounters/Global Interactions Ser.). (ENG., Illus.). 408p. 94.95 *(978-0-8223-4426-1(2))*; pap. 26.95 *(978-0-8223-4440-7(8))* Duke Univ. Pr.

Selka, Stephen. Religion & the Politics of Ethnic Identity in Bahia, Brazil. 2009. (New World Diasporas Ser.). (ENG., Illus.). 192p. pap. 29.95 *(978-0-8130-3387-7(X))* Univ. Pr. of Florida.

Sousa, Leone. The Myth of Racial Democracy & National Identity in Brazil. 2009. 196p. pap. *(978-3-639-20473-5(5))* VDM Verlag Dr. Mueller e.K.

Stokland, Ellen. Olodum the Revolt of the Drums. 2009. 132p. pap. *(978-3-639-17240-9(X))* VDM Verlag Dr. Mueller e.K.

BRAZIL—RELIGION

Bastide, Roger. The African Religions of Brazil: Toward a Sociology of the Interpenetration of Civilizations. Sebba, Helen, tr. from FRE. 2007. (Johns Hopkins Studies in Atlantic History & Culture Ser.). (ENG.). 494p. (gr. 17). pap. 26.00 *(978-0-8018-8624-9(4))* Johns Hopkins Univ. Pr.

Berryman, Phillip. Religion in the Megacity: Catholic & Protestant Portraits from Latin America. 2006. 216p. pap. 24.00 *(978-1-59752-903-7(6)*, Wipf and Stock) Wipf & Stock Pubs.

B

Bledsoe, David Allen. Brazilian Neo-Pentecostalism & the Iurd. 2011. 268p. pap. **(978-3-8443-9580-8(6))** Lambert Academic Publishing.
Boff, Clodovis. Feet-on-the-Ground Theology: A Brazilian Journey. Berryman, Phillip, tr. 2008. 204p. pap. 22.00 *(978-1-60608-011-5(3)*, Wipf and Stock) Wipf & Stock Pubs.
Bragdon, Emma. Spiritism & Mental Health: Practices from Spiritist Centers & Spiritist Psychiatric Hospitals in Brazil. Bragdon, Emma, ed. 2011. (ENG.). 304p. *(978-1-84819-059-7(X))* Kingsley, Jessica Ltd.
Brodsky, Barbara. Cosmic Healing: A Spiritual Journey with Aaron & John of God. 2011. (ENG.). 448p. pap. 18.95 *(978-1-55643-966-7(0))* North Atlantic Bks.
Cohen, Emma. The Mind Possessed: The Cognition of Spirit Possession in an Afro-Brazilian Religious Tradition, 1 vol. 2010. (Illus.). 256p. pap. 24.95 *(978-0-19-976744-1(0))* Oxford Univ. Pr., Inc.
Costigan, Lúcia Helena. Through Cracks in the Wall: Modern Inquisitions & New Christian Letrados in the Iberian Atlantic World. 2010. (Atlantic World Ser.). 256p. *(978-90-04-17920-2(8))* BRILL.
Dantas, Beatriz Góis. Nago Grandma & White Papa: Candomble & the Creation of Afro-Brazilian Identity. Berg, Stephen, tr. from POR. 2009. (Latin America in Translation/en Traduccion/em Traducao Ser.). (ENG., Illus.). 208p. 62.95 *(978-0-8078-3177-9(8))*; pap. 26.95 *(978-0-8078-5975-9(3))* Univ. of North Carolina Pr.
Dawson, Andrew. New Era - New Religions: Religious Transformation in Contemporary Brazil. 2007. (Ashgate New Critical Thinking in Religion, Theology & Biblical Studies). 200p. 99.95 *(978-0-7546-5433-9(8))* Ashgate Publishing Co.
Fausto, Carlos. Warfare & Shamanism in Amazonia. 2012. (Cambridge Latin American Studies). (ENG., Illus.). 368p. 99.00 **(978-1-107-02006-1(9))** Cambridge Univ. Pr.
Greenfield, Sidney M. Spirits with Scalpels: The Cultural Biology of Religious Healing in Brazil. 2008. (ENG., Illus.). 240p. 89.00 *(978-1-59874-367-8(8))*; pap. 26.95 *(978-1-59874-368-5(6))* Left Coast Pr., Inc.
Hale, Lindsay. Hearing the Mermaid's Song: The Umbanda Religion in Rio de Janeiro. 2009. (ENG.). 208p. (C). pap. 29.95 *(978-0-8263-4733-6(9))* Univ. of New Mexico Pr.
Hayes, Kelly E. Holy Harlots: Femininity, Sexuality, & Black Magic in Brazil. 2011. (ENG., Illus.). 312p. 65.00 *(978-0-520-26264-5(6))*; pap. 27.95 *(978-0-520-26265-2(4))* Univ. of California Pr.
Labate, Beatriz Caiuby & MacRae, Edward, eds. Ayahuasca, Ritual & Religion in Brazil. 2010. (ENG., Illus.). 256p. (C). pap. 34.95 *(978-1-84553-679-4(7))* Equinox Publishing Ltd. GBR. Dist: ISD.
Lockmiller, Alice. Teacher's Guide for Tiago, Explorer of Brazil. 2010. 56p. pap. 13.95 *(978-0-557-36740-5(9))* Lulu Enterprises Inc.
Mancuso, Lara. Cofradías Mineras:: Religiosidad Popular en México y Brasil, Siglo XVIII. 2007. (Estudios Históricos Ser.). (SPA., Illus.). 249p. pap. 22.99 *(978-968-12-1241-4(X))* El Colegio de México, A.C., Biblioteca Miguel Cosio Villegas MEX. Dist: Fondo de Cultura Economica USA.
Thalhammer, Raphael. Die Neue Evangelikalisierung in Lateinamerika: Fallbeispiel Brasilien: Die Folha Universal und Ihre Bedeutung Für Den Diskurs der Igreja Universal Do Reino de Deus. 2007. (GER.). 61p. pap. *(978-3-86010-906-9(5))* Martin-Luther-Universitat Halle-Wittenberg, Universitats- und Landesbibliothek Sachsen-Anhalt.
Theodoro, Helena. Iansã: Rainha DOS Ventos e das Tempestades. 2010. (POR.). 163p. *(978-85-347-0407-6(4))* Pallas Editora e Distribuidora Ltda.
van de Port, Mattijs. Ecstatic Encounters: Bahian Candomblé & the Quest for the Really Real. 2011. (ENG., Illus.). 300p. pap. *(978-90-8964-298-1(6))* Amsterdam Univ. Pr.
Wadsworth, James E. Agents of Orthodoxy: Honor, Status, & the Inquisition in Colonial Pernambuco, Brazil. 2006. (ENG., Illus.). 288p. 92.00 *(978-0-7425-5445-0(7))* Rowman & Littlefield Publishers, Inc.

BRAZIL—SOCIAL CONDITIONS

Alberto, Paulina. Terms of Inclusion: Black Intellectuals in Twentieth-Century Brazil. 2011. (ENG., Illus.). 432p. 69.95 *(978-0-8078-3437-4(8))*; pap. 29.95 *(978-0-8078-7171-3(0))* Univ. of North Carolina Pr.
Alcoforado, Fernando. The Necessary Conditions of the Economic & Social Development. 2010. 388p. pap. *(978-3-639-24352-9(8))* VDM Verlag Dr. Mueller e.K.
Alves Finco, Marcus Vinicius. Biofuels & Sustainable Development. 2011. 116p. pap. **(978-3-8443-0066-6(X))** Lambert Academic Publishing.
Alves, Maria Helena Moreira & Evanson, Philip. Living in the Crossfire: Favela Residents, Drug Dealers, & Police Violence in Rio de Janeiro. 2011. (Voices of Latin American Life Ser.). (ENG., Illus.). 272p. 74.50 *(978-1-4399-0003-1(5))*; pap. 32.95 *(978-1-4399-0004-8(3))* Temple Univ. Pr.
Avelar, Idelber & Dunn, Christopher, eds. Brazilian Popular Music & Citizenship. 2011. (ENG., Illus.). 376p. pap. 24.95 *(978-0-8223-4906-8(X))* Duke Univ. Pr.
Barbosa, José Carlos. Slavery & Protestant Missions in Imperial Brazil: The Black Does Not Enter the Church, He Peeks in from Outside. Danford, Richard K. & MacHaffie, Fraser G., trs. 2008. (ENG.). 190p. pap. 35.99 *(978-0-7618-4300-9(0))* Univ. Pr. of America, Inc.
Barcinski, Mariana. Women in Drug Trafficking. 2008. 164p. pap. *(978-3-639-08463-4(2))* VDM Verlag Dr. Mueller e.K.
Bastos, Ana Cecilia de Sousa & Rabinovich, Elaine Pedreira. Living in Poverty: Developmental Poetics of Cultural Realities. 2009. 476p. *(978-1-60752-318-5(3))*; pap. *(978-1-60752-317-8(5))* Information Age Publishing, Inc.
Biehl, João. Vita: Life in a Zone of Social Abandonment, with a New Preface. 2nd ed. 2012. (ENG., Illus.). 404p. pap. 29.95 **(978-0-520-27295-8(1))** Univ. of California Pr.
Biehl, João. Will to Live: AIDS Therapies & the Politics of Survival. 2007. (In-Formation Ser.). (Illus.). 466p. 32.95 *(978-0-691-13008-8(6))* Princeton Univ. Pr.
Bonotto, Daniel Marcos. Poços de Caldas Hot Spot: A Big Blast for Nuclear Energy in Brazil. 2010. 160.00 *(978-1-61728-789-3(X))* Nova Science Pubs., Inc.
Burke, Peter & Pallares-Burke, Maria Lucia G. Gilberto Freyre: Social Theory in the Tropics. 2008. (Past in the Present Ser.). 261p. *(978-1-906165-09-3(2))* Lang, Peter AG.
Burton, Guy. Policy-Making & Education Reform in the Development of Latin American Social Democracy: The Role of the Left in Brazil & Chile. 2011. (Illus.). 432p. 139.95 *(978-0-7734-1433-4(9))* Mellen, Edwin Pr., The.
Camara, Maria Clara Coelho, et al. A Critical Analysis of Labeling on Diet, Light & Gmo Food in Brazil. 2010. 60p. pap. *(978-3-639-25171-5(7))* VDM Verlag Dr. Mueller e.K.
Carneiro, Sandra de Sá & Sant'Anna, Maria Josefina Gabriel. Cidade: Olhares e Trajetórias. 2009. (POR., Illus.). 477p. pap. *(978-85-7617-164-5(3))* Garamond, Editora Ltda.
Castilho, Inês, et al. Estrela Nova: Movimento Comunitário Na Região Do Campo Limpo. 2007. (POR., Illus.). 106p. *(978-85-87556-86-8(X))* Terceiro Nome, Editora Ltda.
Cram101 Textbook Reviews & Cram101 Textbook Reviews. Outlines & Highlights for Assault on Paradise by Conrad Phillip Kottak, Isbn: 9780073530864. 2011. 96p. pap. 27.95 **(978-1-61744-953-6(9))** Cram101 Inc.
Crocitti, John J. & Vallance, Monique. Brazil Today: An Encyclopedia of Life in the Republic. 2011. E-Book **(978-0-313-34673-6(9))** ABC-CLIO, LLC.
Crocitti, John J. & Vallance, Monique, eds. Brazil Today: An Encyclopedia of Life in the Republic, 2 vols. 2011. (Illus.). 741p. 189.00 *(978-0-313-34672-9(0)*, GR4672) Greenwood Publishing Group, Inc.
Czinkota & Uczai, Pedro F. Matematicamente Incorreto. (POR., Illus.). 323p. *(978-0-00-293029-1(3)*, Wiley-Blackwell) Wiley, John & Sons, Inc.
de la Dehesa, Rafael. Queering the Public Sphere in Mexico & Brazil: Sexual Rights Movements in Emerging Democracies. 2010. (ENG., Illus.). 320p. 89.95 *(978-0-8223-4707-1(5))*; pap. 24.95 *(978-0-8223-4724-8(5))* Duke Univ. Pr.
de Lima, Renato Sé, et al. Between Words & Numbers. 2010. 200p. pap. *(978-3-639-28838-4(6))* VDM Verlag Dr. Mueller e.K.
De Miranda, Maria Brigida. Playful Training. 2010. 276p. pap. *(978-3-8383-6041-6(9))* Lambert Academic Publishing.
Delgado, Fernando Riberio. Lethal Force: Police Violence & Public Security in Rio de Janeiro & São Paulo. 2009. (Illus.). 122p. **(978-1-56432-578-5(4))** Human Rights Watch.
Diversi, Marcelo & Moreira, Claudio. Betweener Talk: A Dialogue on Decolonizing Class, Knowledge Production, Praxis, & Justice. 2009. (Qualitative Inquiry & Social Justice Ser.). (ENG., Illus.). 236p. pap. 32.95 *(978-1-59874-360-9(0))*; lib. bdg. 94.00 *(978-1-59874-359-3(7))* Left Coast Pr., Inc.
Drogus, Carol Ann & Stewart-Gambino, Hannah. Activist Faith: Grassroots Women in Democratic Brazil & Chile. 2008. (ENG.). 272p. pap. 30.00 *(978-0-271-02550-6(6))* Pennsylvania State Univ. Pr.
Dunn, Ballard S. Brazil, the Home for Southerners: Or, A Practical Account of What the Author, & Others, Who Visited That Country, for the Same Objects, Saw & Did. 2006. 304p. per. 23.99 *(978-1-4255-2912-3(7))* MPublishing.
Edmonds, Alexander. Pretty Modern: Beauty, Sex, & Plastic Surgery in Brazil. 2010. (ENG., Illus.). 312p. 89.95 *(978-0-8223-4785-9(7))*; pap. 24.95 *(978-0-8223-4801-6(2))* Duke Univ. Pr.
Fernandes, Valter & Fernandes, Newton. Criminologia Integrada. 3rd ed. 2010. (POR.). 752p. *(978-85-203-3705-9(8))* Revista dos Tribunais, Editora.
Fischer, Brodwyn. A Poverty of Rights: Citizenship & Inequality in Twentieth-Century Rio de Janeiro. 2010. (ENG., Illus.). 488p. pap. 24.95 *(978-0-8047-7660-8(1))* Stanford Univ. Pr.
Fishlow, Albert. Starting Over: Brazil Since 1985. 2011. (ENG., Illus.). 236p. 34.95 *(978-0-8157-2143-7(9))* Brookings Institution Pr.
Font, Mauricio. The Brazilian State: Debate & Agenda. Randall, Adrian, ed. 2011. (Bildner Western Hemisphere Studies). (ENG.). 434p. (gr. 17). 85.00 **(978-0-7391-6731-1(6))** Lexington Bks.
Font, Mauricio A. & Randall, Laura. The Brazilian State: Debate & Agenda. 2011. **(978-0-7391-6889-9(4))** Lexington Bks.
Frangella, Simone Miziara. Corpos Urbanos Errantes: Uma Etnografia Da Corporalidade de Moradores de Rua Em São Paulo. 2010. (POR., Illus.). 255p. pap. *(978-85-391-0036-1(3))* Annablume Editora Comunicacao Ltda.
French, Jan Hoffman. Legalizing Identities: Becoming Black or Indian in Brazil's Northeast. 2009. (ENG., Illus.). 256p. 65.00 *(978-0-8078-3292-9(8))*; pap. 23.95 *(978-0-8078-5951-3(6))* Univ. of North Carolina Pr.
Freyre. Modos de Homem & Modas de Mulher. (POR.). pap. 11.75 *(978-85-01-02894-5(0))* Distribuidora Record de Servicos de Imprensa SA BRA. Dist: Distribooks, Inc.
Furtado, Júnia Ferreira. Chica da Silva: A Brazilian Slave of the Eighteenth Century. 2008. (New Approaches to the Americas Ser.). (ENG., Illus.). 348p. (C). 75.00 *(978-0-521-88465-5(9))* Cambridge Univ. Pr.
Furtado, Júnia Ferreira & Furtado, Júnia Ferreira. Chica Da Silva: A Brazilian Slave of the Eighteenth Century. 2008. (New Approaches to the Americas Ser.). (ENG., Illus.). 348p. (C). pap. 23.99 *(978-0-521-71155-5(X))* Cambridge Univ. Pr.
Gabara, Esther. Errant Modernism: The Ethos of Photography in Mexico & Brazil. 2008. (ENG., Illus.). 376p. 94.95 *(978-0-8223-4340-0(1))*; pap. 25.95 *(978-0-8223-4323-3(1))* Duke Univ. Pr.
Giambiagi, Fabio & Tafner, Paulo. Demografia: A Ameaça Invisível. 2010. (POR., Illus.). 198p. pap. *(978-85-352-3678-1(3))* Elsevier.
Gioan, Pierre Antoine. Enseignement Superieur en Afrique Francophone: Quels Leviers Pour des Politiques Financierement Soutenables? 2007. (World Bank Working Papers: 103). (FRE., Illus.). 48p. pap. 10.00 *(978-0-8213-7074-2(X)*, 9780821370742) World Bank Pubns.
Gledhill, John & Schell, Patience A., eds. New Approaches to Resistance in Brazil & Mexico. 2012. (ENG.). 424p. 99.95 **(978-0-8223-5173-3(0))**; pap. 28.95 **(978-0-8223-5187-0(0))** Duke Univ. Pr.
Goldman, David. A Father's Love: One Man's Unrelenting Battle to Bring His Abducted Son Home. 2011. (ENG.). 272p. (gr. 12). 26.95 *(978-0-670-02262-5(4)*, Viking Adult) Penguin Group (USA) Inc.
Graham, Richard. Feeding the City: From Street Market to Liberal Reform in Salvador, Brazil, 1780-1860. 2010. (ENG., Illus.). 352p. 60.00 *(978-0-292-72299-6(0))*; pap. 24.95 *(978-0-292-72326-9(1))* Univ. of Texas Pr.
Husain, Saima. In War, Those Who Die Are Not Innocent: Human Rights Implementation, Policing, & Public Security Reform in Rio de Janeiro, Brazil. 2007. 319p. pap. 48.00 *(978-90-5170-757-1(6))* Purdue Univ. Pr.
Isfahani-Hammond, Alexandra. White Negritude: Race, Writing, & Brazilian Cultural Identity. 2007. (New Concepts in Latino American Cultures Ser.). (ENG., Illus.). 208p. 89.00 *(978-1-4039-7595-9(7))* Palgrave Macmillan.
Jasmuheen. Harmonische Heilung. 2008. 212p. pap. 22.00 *(978-1-4092-0175-5(9))* Lulu Enterprises Inc.
Jorge T. Almeida, ed. Focus on Brazil. 2008. (C). 89.00 *(978-1-60456-165-4(3))* Nova Science Pubs., Inc.
Joyce, Samantha Nogu. Brazilian Telenovelas & the Myth of Racial Democracy. 2012. (Critical Studies in Television Ser.). (ENG.). 136p. 60.00 **(978-0-7391-6964-3(5))** Lexington Bks.
Klein, Misha. Kosher Feijoada & Other Paradoxes of Jewish Life in Sao Paulo. 2012. (New World Diasporas Ser.). (ENG.). 240p. 74.95 **(978-0-8130-3987-9(8))** Univ. Pr. of Florida.
Kottak, Conrad Phillip. Prime-Time Society: An Anthropological Analysis of Television & Culture. rev. ed. 2009. (ENG., Illus.). 283p. (C). pap. 29.95 *(978-1-59874-369-2(4))* Left Coast Pr., Inc.
Lin, A. H. The Fish Rots from the Head: Brazilians on Corruption, 1 vol. 2010. 276p. pap. 27.95 *(978-1-4489-5735-4(4))* PublishAmerica, Inc.
Lohmann, Gui & Dredge, Dianne, eds. Tourism in Brazil: Environment, Management & Segments. 2012. (Contemporary Geographies of Leisure, Tourism & Mobility Ser.). (ENG., Illus.). 224p. (C). 136.00 *(978-0-415-67432-4(8))* Routledge.
Lovisi, Giovanni Marcos, et al, eds. The Psychological Impact of Living under Violence & Poverty in Brazil. 2010. (Psychology Research Progress Ser.). (Illus.). xi, 152p. 89.00 *(978-1-60876-587-4(3))* Nova Science Pubs., Inc.
Lucia Sa Staff. Life in the Megalopolis: Mexico City & Sao Paulo. 2007. (Questioning Cities Ser.). (Illus.). 192p. 51.95 *(978-0-415-39272-3(1))* Routledge.
Macaulay, Fiona. Gender Politics in Brazil & Chile. 2006. (St. Antony's Ser.). (ENG.). 256p. 116.00 *(978-0-333-73614-2(1))* Palgrave Macmillan.
Marques, Eduardo Cesar Leão. Opportunities & Deprivation in the Urban South: Poverty Segregation & Social Networks in São Paulo. 2012. (Cities & Society Ser.). (Illus.). 208p. 99.95 **(978-1-4094-4270-7(5))** Ashgate Publishing Co.
Nascimento, Elisa Larkin. The Sorcery of Color: Identity, Race, & Gender in Brazil. 2006. (Illus.). 272p. 55.50 *(978-1-59213-350-5(9))* Temple Univ. Pr.
Nazareno, Claudio. Tecnologias Da Informação e Sociedade: O Panorama Brasileiro. 2007. (POR., Illus.). 187p. *(978-85-7365-478-3(3))* Camara dos Deputados Coordenacao de Publicacoes.
Pardue, Derek. Ideologies of Marginality in Brazilian Hip Hop. 2008. (ENG., Illus.). 224p. 84.00 *(978-0-230-60465-0(X))* Palgrave Macmillan.
Quirk, Patrick. Emotions & the Struggle of Brazil's Landless Social Movement (Mst) 2008. 164p. per. *(978-3-8364-5737-8(7))* VDM Verlag Dr. Mueller e.K.
Read, Ian. The Hierarchies of Slavery in Santos, Brazil, 1822-1888. 2012. (ENG.). 296p. 65.00 **(978-0-8047-7414-7(5))** Stanford Univ. Pr.
Ricci, Rudá. Lulismo: Da ERA DOS Movimentos Sociais à Ascensão Da Nova Classe Média Brasileira: De Como o Discurso Anti-Institucionalista DOS Anos 80 Deu Lugar Ao Líder Da Conclusão Da Modernização Conservadora Em Nosso País. 2010. (POR., Illus.). 250p. *(978-85-89216-28-9(4))* Fundacao Astrogildo Pereira.
Rochester, Julia. Candelaria Massacre: How Wagner dos Santos Survived the Street Children's Killing That Shook Brazil. 2008. (ENG.). 288p. pap. 17.95 *(978-1-905745-26-5(5))* Vision Paperbacks GBR. Dist: Independent Pubs. Group.
Rodrigues, José Honório. The Brazilians: Their Character & Aspirations. Dimmick, Ralph Edward, tr. 2011. (ENG.). 214p. pap. 25.00 *(978-0-292-72985-8(5))* Univ. of Texas Pr.
Rohter, Larry. Brazil on the Rise: The Story of a Country Transformed. (ENG., Illus.). 304p. 2012. pap. 17.00 **(978-0-230-12073-0(3))** 2010. 27.00 *(978-0-230-61887-9(1))* Palgrave Macmillan.
Sa. Life in the Megalopolis: Mexico City & Sao Paulo. 2007. (Questioning Cities Ser.). (Illus.). 192p. 170.00 *(978-0-415-39271-6(3))* Routledge.
Santin, Janaína Rigo, et al. Envelhecimento Humano: Saúde e Qualidade de Vida. 2009. (POR., Illus.). 282p. *(978-85-7515-712-1(4))* Fundacao Universidade de Passo Fundo-Upf Editora.
Silva, Itamar & Souto, Anna Luiza Salles, eds. Democracy, Citizenship & Youth: Towards Social & Political Participation in Brazil. 2009. (International Library of Political Studies). (ENG.). 336p. 98.50 *(978-1-84885-048-4(4))*, Tauris Academic Studies) I. B. Tauris & Co., Ltd. GBR. Dist: Macmillan.
Silva, José Humberto da. Os Filhos Do Desemprego: Jovens Itinerantes Do Primeiro Emprego. 2009. (POR., Illus.). 211p. *(978-85-98843-90-2(3))* WEG - ASSESSORIA E CONSULTORIA LTDA.
Siqueira, Andreia. Climatic Anomalies & Landuse Change on the Fire Occurrence. 2010. 224p. pap. *(978-3-8383-4164-4(3))* Lambert Academic Publishing.
Smith, Tim. In a Window of Prestes Maia 911 Building. 2009. (ENG., Illus.). 80p. 38.00 *(978-1-904587-67-5(4))* Lewis, Dewi Publishing GBR. Dist: Consortium Bk. Sales & Distribution.
Snyder, Shannyn. Access to Water, Sanitation, & Public Health Services among Urban Poor in Maceio, Brazil. 2010. 277p. pap. 19.99 *(978-0-557-32923-6(X))* Lulu Enterprises Inc.
Souza, Diego Beja Inglez de. Reconstruindo Cajueiro Seco: Arquitetura, Política Social e Cultura Popular Em Pernambuco, 1960-64. 2010. (POR., Illus.). 420p. *(978-85-391-0117-7(3))* Fundacao de Amparo a Pesquisa do Est. de Sao Paulo.
Testino, Mario, photos by. Mario Testino - Rio de Janeiro: Rio de Janeiro. 2009. (ENG, FRE & GER., Illus.). 200p. 39.99 *(978-3-8365-1858-1(9))* TASCHEN DEU. Dist: Ingram Pub. Services.
Tyson-Ward, Sue. Complete Brazilian Portuguese: Everything You Need to Speak,Read & Write. 2nd ed. 2010. (Teach Yourself Language Ser.). (ENG., Illus.). 288p. pap. 22.00 *(978-0-07-174828-5(8)*, 0071748288) McGraw-Hill Cos., The.
Watarai, Felipe. Male Teenager Workers in Brazil. 2010. 156p. pap. *(978-3-639-25879-0(7))* VDM Verlag Dr. Mueller e.K.
Wood, Charles H. & Carvalho, Jose Alberto Magno. The Demography of Inequality in Brazil. 2009. (Cambridge Latin American Studies). (ENG., Illus.). 316p. pap. 44.00 *(978-0-521-10246-9(4))* Cambridge Univ. Pr.
Woolcock, Michael & Gacitua Mario, Estanislao, eds. Social Exclusion & Mobility in Brazil. 2008. (Directions in Development Ser.). (ENG., Illus.). 160p. per. 35.00 *(978-0-8213-7219-7(X)*, 9780821372197) World Bank Pubns.
Yazbeck, Dalva Carolina de Menezes & Rocha, Marlos Bessa Mendes da. Cultura e História Da Educação: Intelectuais, Legislação, Cultura Escolar e Imprensa. 2009. (POR.). 251p. *(978-85-7672-045-4(0))* Fundacao de Apoio e Desenvolvimento ao Ens Pesq E.
Zaidan, Michel & Machado, Otavio Luiz. O Pensamento das Juventudes Brasileiras No Século XX. 2010. (POR.). 292p. *(978-85-7315-742-0(9))* Universidade de Pernambuco.
Zerriffi, Hisham. Rural Electrification: Strategies for Distributed Generation. 2010. (ENG., Illus.). xii, 203p. 129.00 *(978-90-481-9593-0(4)*, 9048195934) Springer.

BRAZIL—SOCIAL LIFE AND CUSTOMS

Bates, Henry. The Naturalist on the River Amazons. 2007. 440p. per. *(978-1-905748-57-0(4))*; 376p. per. *(978-1-905748-56-3(6))* Rediscovery Bks.
Beneville, Ed & Cartmell, Tim. Passing the Guard: Brazilian Jiu-Jitsu Details & Techniques. 2nd exp. rev. ed. 2009. 262p. pap. 36.95 *(978-0-9721097-6-5(5))* Grappling Arts Pubns., LLC.
Bletz, May E. Immigration & Acculturation in Brazil & Argentina: 1890-1929. 2010. (ENG.). 190p. 84.00 *(978-0-230-10019-0(8))* Palgrave Macmillan.
Bortoni-Ricardo, Stella Maris. The Urbanization of Rural Dialect Speakers: A Sociolinguistic Study in Brazil. 2008. (Cambridge Studies in Linguistics Ser.). (ENG.). 276p. pap. 37.99 *(978-0-521-10385-5(1))* Cambridge Univ. Pr.
Callcott, Maria, et al. Maria Graham's Journal of a Voyage to Brazil. 2010. *(978-1-60235-188-2(0))*; pap. *(978-1-60235-187-5(2))* Parlor Pr.
Carneiro, Sandra de Sá & Sant'Anna, Maria Josefina Gabriel. Cidade: Olhares e Trajetórias. 2009. (POR., Illus.). 477p. pap. *(978-85-7617-164-5(3))* Garamond, Editora Ltda.
Castro, Ana Claudia Veiga de. A São Paulo de Menotti Del Picchia: Arquitetura, Arte e Cidade Nas Crônicas de Um Modernista. 2008. (POR., Illus.). 296p. *(978-85-98325-77-4(5))* Alameda Casa Editorial Ltda.
Castro, Vanessa de. Das Igrejas Ao Cemitério: Políticas Públicas Sobre a Morte No Recife Do Século XIX. 2007. (POR., Illus.). 312p. *(978-85-7044-176-8(2))* Fundacao De Cultura cidade do Recife.
Chazkel, Amy. Laws of Chance: Brazil's Clandestine Lottery & the Making of Urban Public Life. 2011. (Radical Perspectives Ser.). (ENG., Illus.). 368p. 89.95 *(978-0-8223-4973-0(6))*; pap. 24.95 *(978-0-8223-4988-4(4))* Duke Univ. Pr.
D'Andrea, Moema Selma. A Tradição Re(Des)coberta: O Pensamento de Gilberto Freyre No Contexto das Manifestações Culturais E/Ou Literárias Nordestinas. 2nd ed. 2010. 239p. *(978-85-268-0883-6(4))* Universidade Estadual de Campinas. Editora.
Davis, Darién J. & Davis, Darien J. White Face, Black Mask: Africaneity & the Early Social History of Popular Music in Brazil. 2009. (Black American & Diasporic Studies: Ser.). (ENG., Illus.). 265p. pap. 29.95 *(978-0-87013-834-8(0))* Michigan State Univ. Pr.
de Castro, Eduardo Viveiros. The Inconstancy of the Indian Soul: The Encounter of Catholics & Cannibals in 16th-Century Brazil. 2011. 104p. pap. 12.95 *(978-0-9842010-1-3(7))* Prickly Paradigm Pr., LLC.
Despland, Michel. Bastide on Religion: The Invention of Candomblé. 2008. (Key Thinkers in the Study of Religion Ser.). (ENG.). 224p. (C). 95.00 *(978-1-84553-365-6(8))*; pap. 29.95 *(978-1-84553-366-3(6))* Equinox Publishing Ltd. GBR. Dist: ISD.

Dias, Cleber Augusto Gonçalves & Alves Junior, Edmundo de Drummond. Entre o Mar e a Montanha: Esporte, Aventura e Natureza No Rio de Janeiro. 2007. (POR.). 152p. *(978-85-228-0455-9(9))* Universidade Federal Fluminense. Editora.

Everett, Daniel L. Don't Sleep, There Are Snakes: Life & Language in the Amazonian Jungle. 2009. (Vintage Departures Ser.). (ENG., Illus.). 320p. pap. 16.00 *(978-0-307-38612-0(0)*, Vintage) Knopf Doubleday Publishing Group.

Fausto, Carlos. Warfare & Shamanism in Amazonia. 2012. (Cambridge Latin American Studies). (ENG., Illus.). 368p. 99.00 ***(978-1-107-02006-1(9))*** Cambridge Univ. Pr.

Ferreira, Fernanda L. The Everything Brazilian Portuguese Practice Book with CD: Improve your language skills with inteactive lessons & Exercises. 2012. (ENG & POR.). 336p. pap. 19.95 *(978-1-4405-2854-5(3))* Adams Media Corp.

Fletcher, James C. & Kidder, Daniel P. Brazil & the Brazilians: Portrayed in Historical & Descriptive Sketches. 8th ed. 2006. (Kegan Paul Travellers Ser.). (Illus.). 650p. 300.00 *(978-0-7103-1146-7(X))* Taylor & Francis Group.

George, Terry. Carnival in Rio: Samba, Samba, Samba. 2006. (ENG.). 14.95 incl. lp *(978-3-937406-55-8(7))* Edel Classica Gmbh.

Goslin, Priscilla. How to Be a Carioca: The Alternative Guide for the Tourist in Rio. 2008. (ENG.). pap. 14.95 *(978-1-60037-500-2(6))* Morgan James Publishing.

Graça, Marcos da Silva, et al. Cinema Brasileiro: Três Olhares. (POR., Illus.). 242p. *(978-85-228-0157-2(6))* Universidade Federal Fluminense. Editora.

Greenfield, Sidney M. Spirits with Scalpels: The Cultural Biology of Religious Healing in Brazil. 2008. (ENG., Illus.). 240p. 89.00 *(978-1-59874-367-8(8))*; pap. 26.95 *(978-1-59874-368-5(6))* Left Coast Pr., Inc.

Hale, Lindsay. Hearing the Mermaid's Song: The Umbanda Religion in Rio de Janeiro. 2009. (ENG.). 208p. (C). pap. 29.95 *(978-0-8263-4733-6(9))* Univ. of New Mexico Pr.

Hayes, Kelly E. Holy Harlots: Femininity, Sexuality, & Black Magic in Brazil. 2011. (ENG., Illus.). 312p. 65.00 *(978-0-520-26264-5(6))*; pap. 27.95 *(978-0-520-26265-2(4))* Univ. of California Pr.

Kidder, Daniel P. Brazil & the Brazilians Portrayed in Historical & Descriptive Sketches. 630p. reprint ed. 128.00 *(978-0-7222-9595-3(2))* Library Reprints, Inc.

Kidder, Daniel P. (Daniel Parish). Brazil & the Brazilians, Portrayed in Historical & Descriptive Sketches by Rev D P Kidder, D D , & Rev J C Fletcher. 2006. 676p. per. 36.99 *(978-1-4255-6805-4(X))* MPublishing.

Kiddy, Elizabeth W. Blacks of the Rosary: Memory & History in Minas Gerais, Brazil. 2007. (ENG., Illus.). 328p. pap. 27.00 *(978-0-271-02694-7(4))* Pennsylvania State Univ. Pr.

(Kraakar Shem), Chico Penteado. Talking to the Reptilians-A Report from Brazil. 2010. 130p. pap. 14.49 *(978-0-557-57653-1(9))* Lulu Enterprises Inc.

Labate, Beatriz Caiuby & MacRae, Edward, eds. Ayahuasca, Ritual & Religion in Brazil. 2010. (ENG., Illus.). 256p. (C). pap. 34.95 *(978-1-84553-679-4(7))* Equinox Publishing Ltd. GBR. Dist: ISD.

Lemos, Sara. Minimum Wage in Brazil. 2010. 332p. pap. *(978-3-639-21637-0(7))* VDM Verlag Dr. Mueller e.K.

Lucia Sa Staff. Life in the Megalopolis: Mexico City & Sao Paulo. 2007. (Questioning Cities Ser.). (Illus.). 192p. 51.95 *(978-0-415-39272-3(1))* Routledge.

Mancuso, Lara. Cofradías Mineras:: Religiosidad Popular en México y Brasil, Siglo XVIII. 2007. (Estudios Históricos Ser.). (SPA., Illus.). 249p. pap. 22.99 *(978-968-12-1241-4(X))* El Colegio de México, A.C., Biblioteca Miguel Cosio Villegas MEX. Dist: Fondo de Cultura Economica USA.

Matsuoka, Hideaki. Japanese Prayer below the Equator: How Brazilians Believe in the Church of World Messianity. 2007. (ENG., Illus.). 194p. 62.99 *(978-0-7391-1379-0(8))* Lexington Bks.

Mayblin, Maya. Gender, Catholicism, & Morality in Brazil: Virtuous Husbands, Powerful Wives. 2010. (Contemporary Anthropology of Religion Ser.). (ENG., Illus.). 224p. 84.00 *(978-0-230-62312-5(3))* Palgrave Macmillan.

Moreira, Joe & Beneville, Ed. The Guard, 2E. 2009. 262p. pap. 36.95 *(978-0-9721097-4-1(9))* Grappling Arts Pubns., LLC.

Needell, Jeffrey D. A Tropical Belle Epoque: Elite Culture & Society in Turn-of-the-Century Rio de Janeiro. 2010. (Cambridge Latin American Studies). (ENG.). 372p. pap. 42.00 *(978-0-521-12601-4(0))* Cambridge Univ. Pr.

Oakdale, Suzanne. I Foresee My Life: The Ritual Performance of Autobiography in an Amazonian Community. 2007. (ENG.). 206p. pap. 24.95 *(978-0-8032-2252-6(1))* Univ. of Nebraska Pr.

Pares, Luis Nicolau & Sansi, Roger, eds. Sorcery in the Black Atlantic. 2011. (ENG.). 312p. 75.00 *(978-0-226-64577-3(0))*; pap. 25.00 *(978-0-226-64578-0(9))* Univ. of Chicago Pr.

Parker, Richard G. Bodies, Pleasures, & Passions: Sexual Culture in Contemporary Brazil. 2nd ed. 2009. (ENG.). 232p. pap. 27.95 *(978-0-8265-1675-6(0))* Vanderbilt Univ. Pr.

Perlman, Janice E. Favela: Four Decades of Living on the Edge in Rio de Janeiro, 1 vol. 2010. (ENG., Illus.). 368p. 29.95 *(978-0-19-536836-9(3))* Oxford Univ. Pr., Inc.

Phaf-Rheinberger, Ineke & Pinto, Tiago de Oliveira. AfricAmericas: Itineraries, Dialogues, & Sounds. 2008. (Illus.). 224p. pap. 29.80 *(978-84-8489-380-6(4))* Iberoamericana Vervuert Publishing Corp.

Poelzl, Volker. Brazil: A Survival Guide to Customs & Etiquette. 2009. 324p. pap. 15.95 *(978-0-7614-5660-5(0))* Marshall Cavendish Corp.

—Cultureshock! Brazil. 2007. (Cultureshock Brazil: A Survival Guide to Customs & Etiquette Ser.). (Illus.). 324p. per. 15.95 *(978-0-7614-2490-1(3))* Marshall Cavendish Corp.

Rios, Guilherme. Literacy Discourses. 2009. 284p. pap. *(978-3-639-12848-2(6))* VDM Verlag Dr. Mueller e.K.

Rocha, Angela da & Silva, Jorge Ferreira da. Consumo Na Base Da Pirâmide: Estudos Brasileiros. 2009. (POR., Illus.). 255p. *(978-85-7478-311-6(0))* Mauad Editora Ltda.

Rohter, Larry. Brazil on the Rise: The Story of a Country Transformed. (ENG., Illus.). 304p. 2012. pap 17.00 ***(978-0-230-12073-0(3))*** 2010. 27.00 *(978-0-230-61887-9(1))* Palgrave Macmillan.

Roper Matt. Street Girls: Hope on the Streets of Brazil. 2006. (ENG., Illus.). 176p. per. 10.99 *(978-1-85078-714-3(X))* Authentic Media.

Sa. Life in the Megalopolis: Mexico City & Sao Paulo. 2007. (Questioning Cities Ser.). (Illus.). 192p. 170.00 *(978-0-415-39271-6(3))* Routledge.

Sapiezinskas, Aline. Cultural Heritage in Brazil: The Anthropological Perspective & the Local Point of View. 2011. 144p. pap. 19.99 ***(978-1-4568-8960-9(5))*** Xlibris Corp.

Schlicke, Cindy. Socio-Linguistic Analysis of the Settlers in the Brazilian Amazon. 2008. 124p. per. *(978-3-8364-5959-4(0))* VDM Verlag Dr. Mueller e.K.

Soares, Mariana Cysneiros C. Lampião: A Marca Que Vende o Nordeste. 2007. (POR., Illus.). 102p. *(978-85-907524-0-0(2))* Magyar ISBN Iroda, Orszagos Szechenyi Konyvtar.

Stokland, Ellen. Olodum the Revolt of the Drums. 2009. 132p. pap. *(978-3-639-17240-9(X))* VDM Verlag Dr. Mueller e.K.

Storey, Romasa. Going to Live in Brazil. 2009. (Illus.). 192p. pap. 26.00 *(978-1-84528-310-0(4))* How To Books GBR. Dist: Parkwest Pubns., Inc.

Stroud, Sean. The Defence of Tradition in Brazilian Popular Music: Politics, Culture & the Creation of Musica Popular Brasileira. 2008. (Ashgate Popular & Folk Music Ser.). 222p. 99.95 *(978-0-7546-6343-0(4))* Ashgate Publishing Co.

Talmon-Chvaicer, Maya. The Hidden History of Capoeira: A Collision of Cultures in the Brazilian Battle Dance. 2007. (ENG., Illus.). 249p. 60.00 *(978-0-292-71723-7(7))*; pap. 25.00 *(978-0-292-71724-4(5))* Univ. of Texas Pr.

Taylor, Gerard. Capoeira: The Jogo de Angola from Luanda to Cyberspace, 2 vols. 2007. (Capoeira Ser.). (ENG., Illus.). 560p. pap. 24.95 *(978-1-58394-183-6(5)*, Blue Snake Bks.) North Atlantic Bks.

Waring, Rob. Capoeira: The Fighting Dance. 2008. (ENG.). 24p. (C). pap. 10.95 *(978-1-4240-4471-9(5))* Cengage Heinle.

BRAZILIAN CLOVER

see Alfalfa

BRAZILIAN DRAMA

George, David. The Modern Brazilian Stage. 2011. (ENG., Illus.). 196p. pap. 19.95 *(978-0-292-72976-6(5))* Univ. of Texas Pr.

BRAZILIAN FICTION

see also Short Stories, Brazilian

Lopes, Maria Angélica Guimarães. The Brazilian Short Story in the Late Twentieth Century: A Selection from Nineteen Authors. 2009. 176p. 99.95 *(978-0-7734-4904-6(3))* Mellen, Edwin Pr., The.

BRAZILIAN FICTION—HISTORY AND CRITICISM

Chiappini, Ligia, et al, eds. Studies in the Literary Achievement of João Guimarães Rosa, the Foremost Brazilian Writer of the Twentieth Century. 2011. 460p. 139.95 ***(978-0-7734-3953-5(6))*** Mellen, Edwin Pr., The.

Claudia, Ana & Da Silva, Suriani. Machado de Assis's Philosopher or Dog? From Serial to Book Form. 2010. (Legenda Main Ser.). (ENG., Illus.). 204p. (C). 89.50 *(978-1-906540-45-6(4))* European Humanities Research Ctr. GBR. Dist: Brown, David Bk. Co., The.

Cordeiro Rosa, Debora. Trauma, Memory & Identity in Five Jewish Novels from the Southern Cone. 2012. (ENG.). 202p. (gr. 17). 60.00 ***(978-0-7391-7297-1(2))*** Lexington Bks.

Gordon, Richard A. Cannibalizing the Colony: Cinematic Adaptations of Colonial Literature in Mexico & Brazil. 2008. 288p. pap. 43.95 *(978-1-55753-519-1(1))* Purdue Univ. Pr.

Haywood Ferreira, Rachel. The Emergence of Latin American Science Fiction. 2011. (Early Classics of Science Fiction Ser.). (ENG., Illus.). 320p. (C). 80.00 *(978-0-8195-7081-9(8))*; pap. 29.95 *(978-0-8195-7082-6(6))* Wesleyan Univ. Pr.

Lima, Lucilene Gomes. Ficções Do Ciclo Da Borracha: A Selva, Beiradão, o Amante das Amazonas. 2009. (POR., Illus.). 240p. *(978-85-7401-458-6(3))* Fundacao Universidade do Amazonas.

Nascimento dos Santos, Daiana. Imaginarios literarios politicos en el Brasileno Jorge Amado. 2012. (POR & SPA.). 164p. 109.95 ***(978-0-7734-2590-3(X))*** Mellen, Edwin Pr., The.

Quinlan, Susan Canty, et al. Visões Do Passado, Previsões Do Futuro. (POR., Illus.). 222p. *(978-85-282-0078-2(7))* Tempo Brasileiro Ltda, Edicoes.

Santos, Volnyr. Luiz Antonio de Assis Brasil: Romance e História. 2007. (POR.). 184p. *(978-85-7349-070-1(5))* Rigel, Editora, Ltda.

Schpun, Mônica Raisa. Entre Resistir e Identificar-Se: Para Uma Teoria Da Prática Da Narrativa Brasileira de Autoria Feminina. (POR., Illus.). 203p. *(978-85-86501-04-3(2))* Mulheres, Editora.

BRAZILIAN LITERATURE

see also Brazilian Drama; Brazilian Fiction

Afolabi, Niyi, et al. Cadernos Negros: Movimento Literário Afro-Brasileiro Contemporâneo = Black Notebooks: Contemporary Afro-Brazilian Literary Movement. 2006. (POR & ENG.). *(978-1-59221-454-9(1))*; pap. *(978-1-59221-455-6(X))* Africa World Pr.

Callahan, Monique-Adelle. Between the Lines: Literary Transnationalism & African American Poetics, 1 vol. 2011. (Imagining the Americas Ser.). 208p. 74.00 *(978-0-19-974306-3(1))* Oxford Univ. Pr., Inc.

Goldberg, Isaac. Brazilian Tales. 2009. 50p. pap. *(978-1-151-70687-4(6))* Books LLC.

—Brazilian Tales. 2007. (ENG.). 152p. per. *(978-1-4067-2601-5(X))* Read Bks.

Goldberg, Isaac, ed. Brazilian Tales. 96p. pap. 5.95 *(978-0-8283-1426-8(8))* Branden Bks.

Goldberg, Isaac, tr. Brazilian Tales. 2007. 152p. 36.95 *(978-0-548-52241-7(3))*; (ENG.). per. 21.95 *(978-0-548-45454-1(X))* Kessinger Publishing, LLC.

Sousa, Andréia Aparecida Moreira. Geografia e Literatura: A Representação de Goiânia Em Fragmentos de Viver é Devagar de Brasigóis Felício. 2010. (POR., Illus.). 159p. *(978-85-7766-645-4(X))* Grafica e Editora Kelps Ltda.

Souza, Paulo de. Seara Vermelha: Estética e Ideologia Em Jorge Amado. 2008. (POR.). 151p. *(978-85-7315-483-2(7))* Universidade de Pernambuco.

BRAZILIAN LITERATURE—HISTORY AND CRITICISM

Afolabi, Niyi, et al. The Afro-Brazilian Mind: Contemporary Afro-Brazilian Literary & Cultural Criticism. 2006. (POR & ENG.). *(978-1-59221-385-6(5))*; 320p. pap. *(978-1-59221-386-3(3))* Africa World Pr.

Alencar Brayner, Aquiles. The Literature of the Senses. 2010. 260p. pap. *(978-3-8383-0320-8(2))* Lambert Academic Publishing.

Aragão, Maria do Socorro Silva de, et al. Memorial Augusto DOS Anjos: Um Roteiro Cultural e Poético. 2008. (POR & ENG.). 97p. *(978-85-7539-394-9(4))* Ideia Personalizadora e Editora Ltda.

Arsillo, Vincenzo & Fiorani, Flavio. Sertão - Pampa: Topografie Dell'immaginario Sudamericano. 2007. (ITA & SPA.). 181p. *(978-88-7543-179-2(5))* Libreria Editrice Cafoscarina.

Basto, Márcia Meira & Halliday, Tereza Lúcia. Clarice, Clarear: O Leitor de Si-Mesmo Em Clarice Lispector: Ensaio. 2008. (POR., Illus.). 273p. *(978-85-373-0354-2(2))* Bagaco, Edicoes Ltda.

Choi, Myung. Employing the Grotesque as a Communication Strategy: The History of an Artistic Style. 2009. ii, 120p. *(978-0-7734-3844-6(0))* Mellen, Edwin Pr., The.

Conde, Maite. Consuming Visions: Cinema, Writing, & Modernity in Rio de Janeiro. (Illus.). 2012. xxi, 227p. E-Book ***(978-0-8139-3219-4(X))*** 2011. (ENG.). 248p. (C). (gr. 13-17). pap. 21.50 ***(978-0-8139-3214-9(9))*** 2011. (ENG.). 248p. (gr. 17). 49.50 ***(978-0-8139-3213-2(0))*** Univ. Pr. of Virginia.

D'Andrea, Moema Selma. A Tradição Re(Des)coberta: O Pensamento de Gilberto Freyre No Contexto das Manifestações Culturais E/Ou Literárias Nordestinas. 2nd ed. 2010. 239p. *(978-85-268-0883-6(4))* Universidade Estadual de Campinas. Editora.

Duke, Dawn. Literary Passion, Ideological Commitment: Toward a Legacy of Afro-Cuban & Afro-Brazilian Women Writers. 2008. 280p. (C). 59.50 *(978-0-8387-5706-2(5))* Bucknell Univ. Pr.

Fischer, Luis Augusto. Literatura Ao Sul. 2009. 133p. *(978-85-7515-677-3(2))* Fundacao Universidade de Passo Fundo-Upf Editora.

Foster, David William. Sao Paulo: Perspectives on the City & Cultural Production. 2011. (ENG., Illus.). 176p. 69.95 *(978-0-8130-3665-6(8))* Univ. Pr. of Florida.

Garramuño, Florencia. La Experiencia Opaca: Literatura y Desencanto. 2009. (Tierra Firme Ser.). (SPA.). 280p. pap. 19.99 *(978-950-557-783-5(4))* Fondo de Cultura Económcia.

George, David. The Modern Brazilian Stage. 2011. (ENG., Illus.). 196p. pap. 19.95 *(978-0-292-72976-6(6))* Univ. of Texas Pr.

Goldberg, Isaac. Brazilian Literature. 2010. (ENG.). 326p. pap. 31.75 *(978-1-171-62229-1(5))* 2010. 332p. pap. 31.75 *(978-1-148-96772-1(9))* 2010. 322p. pap. 30.75 *(978-1-142-30765-3(4))* 2009. (ENG.). 318p. 36.99 *(978-1-117-16308-6(3))* 2009. (ENG.). 318p. pap. 23.99 *(978-1-117-16310-9(5)*, BiblioLife) 2009. (ENG.). 318p. pap. 29.75 *(978-1-117-16309-3(1))* BiblioBazaar.

—Brazilian Literature. 2009. 194p. pap. *(978-1-4590-5880-4(1))* Books LLC.

—Brazilian Literature. 316p. 2010. pap. 24.76 *(978-1-163-28041-6(0))* 2007. (ENG.). 45.95 *(978-0-548-22207-2(X))* 2007. (ENG.). per. 30.95 *(978-1-4325-4334-1(2))* Kessinger Publishing, LLC.

Haberly, David T. Three Sad Races: Racial Identity & National Consciousness in Brazilian Literature. 2010. (ENG.). 210p. pap. 30.99 *(978-0-521-15534-2(7))* Cambridge Univ. Pr.

Hammond Matthews, Charlotte. Gender, Race & Patriotism in the Works of Nísia Floresta. 2012. (Monografías A Ser.: Volume 303). 226p. 99.00 ***(978-1-85566-235-3(3)***, Tamesis Bks.) Boydell & Brewer, Ltd. GBR. Dist: Boydell & Brewer, Inc.

Levitin, Alexis, ed. Brazil. 2009. (Travelers Literary Companions Ser.). (ENG., Illus.). 256p. pap. 14.95 *(978-1-883513-21-4(9))* Whereabouts Pr.

Moser, Robert H. The Carnivalesque Defunto: Death & the Dead in Modern Brazilian Literature. 2008. (Ohio RIS Latin America Ser.: No. 46). (ENG.). 344p. pap. 28.00 *(978-0-89680-258-2(2))* Ohio Univ. Pr.

Newcomb, Robert Patrick. Nossa & Nuestra America: Inter-American Dialogues. 2011. (Purdue Studies in Romance Literatures Ser.). 265p. pap. 45.00 *(978-1-55753-603-7(1))* Purdue Univ. Pr.

Oliveira, Emanuella K. F. Writing Identity: The Politics of Afro-Brazilian Literature. 2007. (Purdue Studies in Romance Literatures Ser.). 260p. per. 43.95 *(978-1-55753-485-9(3))* Purdue Univ. Pr.

Piñon, Nélida. La Seducción de la Memoria. 2006. (Cuadernos de la Cátedra Alfonso Reyes Ser.). (SPA.). 176p. pap. 12.95 *(978-968-16-8227-9(0))* Fondo de Cultura Economica USA.

Pinto, Cristina Ferreira & Zilberman, Regina. Clarice Lispector: Novos Aportes Críticos. 2007. (Serie Antonio Cornejo Polar Ser.: Vol. 4). (POR.). 269p. pap. *(978-1-930744-29-5(3))* Instituto Internacional de Literatura Iberoamericana (IILI).

Poeta Movima. Literary Amazonia: Modern Writing by Amazonian Authors. Suarez-Arauz, Nicomedes, ed. 2007. (ENG., Illus.). 216p. 39.95 *(978-0-8130-2728-9(4))* Univ. Pr. of Florida.

Ricciardi, Giovanni. Biografia e Criação Literária. 2008. (POR., Illus.). *(978-85-7884-002-0(X))*; *(978-85-99268-91-9(0))*; *(978-85-86870-84-2(6))*; *(978-85-288-0059-3(8))*; *(978-85-7834-055-6(0))* Arnold-Bergstraesser Institut fur Kulturwissenschaftliche Forschung E. V.

Scarpelli, Marli Fantini & Santiago, Silviano. Machado e Rosa: Leituras Críticas. 2010. 506p. *(978-85-7480-508-5(4))* Atelie Editorial Ltda-Me.

Schlickers, Sabine. Que Yo También Soy Pueta: La Literatura Gauchesca Rioplatense y Brasileña (Siglos XIX-XX) 2007. (SPA.). 264p. pap. 44.00 *(978-84-8489-327-1(8))* Iberoamericana Vervuert Publishing Corp.

Suarez-Arauz, Nicomedes, ed. Literary Amazonia: Modern Writing by Amazonian Authors. 2007. (ENG., Illus.). 216p. per. 24.95 *(978-0-8130-3080-7(3))* Univ. Pr. of Florida.

Surghi, Carlos. Abisinia Exibar: Tres Ensayos Sobre Néstor Perlongher. 2009. 140p. *(978-987-646-120-7(6))* Alcion Editora.

Villares, Lúcia. Examining Whiteness: Reading Clarice Lispector through Bessie Head & Toni Morrison. 2011. (Legenda Main Ser.). (ENG.). 200p. (C). 89.50 *(978-1-906540-47-0(0))* European Humanities Research Ctr. GBR. Dist: Brown, David Bk. Co., The.

Wasserman, Renata R. Central at the Margin: Five Brazilian Women Writers. 2007. (ENG.). 49.50 *(978-1-61148-276-8(3))* Bucknell Univ. Pr.

Wasserman, Renata R. Mautner. Central at the Margin: Five Brazilian Women Writers. 2007. 216p. (C). 49.50 *(978-0-8387-5674-4(3))* Bucknell Univ. Pr.

BRAZILIAN LITERATURE—TRANSLATIONS INTO ENGLISH

Afolabi, Niyi, et al. Cadernos Negros: Literatura Afro-Brasileira Contemporânea = Black Notebooks: Contemporary Afro-Brazilian Literature. 2006. (POR & ENG.). *(978-1-59221-383-2(9))*; pap *(978-1-59221-384-9(7))* Africa World Pr.

Cabral, Astrid. Cage. Levitin, Alexis, tr. from POR. 2008. (ENG & POR.). 91p. pap. 12.00 *(978-0-924047-44-2(5))* Host Pubns., Inc.

Maia Amorim, Lauro. Translation, Blackness, & the Visible. 2010. 188p. pap. *(978-3-8383-6294-6(2))* Lambert Academic Publishing.

Mark J. Curran. Brazil's Folk-Popular Poetry - a Literatura de Cordel: A Bilingual Anthology in English & Portuguese. 2010. 168p. pap. 13.95 *(978-1-4269-2469-9(0))* Trafford Publishing.

Moser, Robert Henry & Tosta, Antonio Luciano de Andrade, eds. Luso-American Literature: Writings by Portuguese-Speaking Authors in North America. 2011. (Multi-Ethnic Literatures of the Americas (MELA) Ser.). (ENG.). 416p. (C). pap. 34.95 *(978-0-8135-5058-9(0))*; (Illus.). 79.00 *(978-0-8135-5057-2(2))* Rutgers Univ. Pr.

Vieira, Nelson H., ed. & tr. from POR. Contemporary Jewish Writing in Brazil: An Anthology. 2010. (Jewish Writing in the Contemporary World Ser.). (ENG.). 386p. 60.00 *(978-0-8032-4562-1(5))* Univ. of Nebraska Pr.

BRAZILIAN NATIONAL CHARACTERISTICS

see National Characteristics, Brazilian

BRAZILIAN POETRY—HISTORY AND CRITICISM

Brandellero, Sara. On a Knife-Edge: The Poetry of João Cabral de Melo Neto. 2011. (Oxford Modern Languages & Literature Monographs). (ENG.). 252p. 110.00 *(978-0-19-958952-4(6))* Oxford Univ. Pr., Inc.

Gullar, Ferreira & Jiménez, Ariel, texts. Ferreira Gullar in Conversation with Ariel Jiménez. 2012. (ENG., Illus.). 272p. 25.00 ***(978-0-9823544-5-2(2))*** Fundacion Cisneros.

Mark J. Curran. Brazil's Folk-Popular Poetry - a Literatura de Cordel: A Bilingual Anthology in English & Portuguese. 2010. 168p. pap. 13.95 *(978-1-4269-2469-9(0))* Trafford Publishing.

Perrone, Charles A. Brazil, Lyric, & the Americas. 2010. (ENG., Illus.). 240p. 69.95 *(978-0-8130-3421-8(3))* Univ. Pr. of Florida.

BRAZILIAN SCULPTURE

see Sculpture—Brazil

BRAZING

see also Solder and Soldering

American Society of Mechanical Engineers Staff, ed. BPVC Section IX - Welding & Brazing Qualifications. 259p. 210.00 *(978-0-7918-2420-7(9))*; 328p. 225.00 *(978-0-7918-2517-4(5))* ASME Pr.

American Welding Society. AWS C3. 3-2008, Recommended Practices for the Design, Manufacture, & Examination of Critical Brazed Components. 2008. *(978-0-87171-092-5(7))* American Welding Society.

—AWS C3. 4M/C3. 4-2007, Specification for Torch Brazing. 2007. *(978-0-87171-038-3(2))* American Welding Society.

—AWS C3. 5M/C3. 5-2007, Specification for Induction Brazing. 2007. *(978-0-87171-069-7(2))* American Welding Society.

—AWS C3. 6M/C3. 6-2008, Specification for Furnace Brazing. 2007. *(978-0-87171-080-2(3))* American Welding Society.

—Brazing Handbook, 5th Edition 2007. 2007. per. *(978-0-87171-046-8(3))* American Welding Society.

—Standard Method for Evaluating the Strength of Brazed Joints. 2008. *(978-0-87171-086-4(2))* American Welding Society.

Campbell, F. C. Joining: Understanding the Basics. 2011. (ENG., Illus.). 260p. 149.00 ***(978-1-61503-825-1(6))*** ASM International.

Materials Science Interantional Team MSIT. Nucelar Materials. 2007. (Landolt-Börnstein: Numerical Data & Functional Relationships in Science &

Technology Ser.). (Illus.). xvii, 493p. 7789.00 (978-3-540-25777-6(2)) Springer.

Technology Research Editors, ed. Brazing: Alloys, Atmospheres, & Fluxes, 2007 Ed. 2007. pap. 128.50 (978-1-60030-607-5(1), Search-In-Print) CSA Journal Division.

—Brazing Techniques, 2007 Ed. 2007. pap. 128.50 (978-1-60030-608-2(X), Search-In-Print) CSA Journal Division.

BRAZOS RIVER AND VALLEY (TEX.)

Ainsworth, Jim H. Biscuits Across the Brazos: A Recollection of a Memorable Horseback & Wagon Journey. 2010. 100p. pap. 14.95 (978-0-86534-754-0(9)) Sunstone Pr.

Kimmel, Jim. Exploring the Brazos River: From Beginning to End. 2011. (River Books, sponsored by the River Systems Institute at Texas State University Ser.). (Illus.). 192p. pap. 24.95 (978-1-60344-432-3(7)) Texas A&M Univ. Pr.

Little, Mike, et al. Biologischer Tabakanbau in Amerika. 2009. 208p. pap. 22.95 (978-0-86534-740-3(9)) Sunstone Pr.

Steele, D. Gentry & Killingsworth, M. Jimmie. Reflections of the Brazos Valley. 2007. (ENG., Illus.). 104p. 25.00 (978-1-58544-615-5(7)) Texas A&M Univ. Pr.

BREACH OF CONTRACT

Anderson, Jane & Shiers, David. The Green Guide to Specifcation. 4th rev. ed. 2009. (ENG., Illus.). 240p. 149.99 (978-1-4051-1961-0(6), Wiley-Blackwell) Wiley, John & Sons, Inc.

Ben-Shahar, Omri & Porat, Ariel, eds. Fault in American Contract Law. 2010. (ENG.). 328p. 90.00 (978-0-521-76985-3(X)) Cambridge Univ. Pr.

Bhadbhade, Nilima. Contract Law in India. 2010. 316p. pap. (978-90-411-3297-0(X)) Kluwer Law International.

Bollenberger, Raimund. Das stellvertretende Commodum: Die Ersatzherausgabe im österreichischen und deutschen Schuldrecht unter Berücksichtigung weiterer Rechtsordnungen. 2011. (GER.). xxi, 467p. **(978-3-211-83356-8(0))** Springer Singapore Pte. Ltd.

Burnett, Rachel. Commercial Litigation: Damages & Other Remedies for Breach of Contract. 2011. (Thorogood Reports). 200p. pap. 240.00 (978-1-85418-748-2(1)) Thorogood GBR. Dist: Stylus Publishing, LLC.

Cappello, A. Barry. Lender Liability: 4th Edition. 2009. 800p. 195.00 (978-1-57823-249-9(X)) Juris Publishing, Inc.

Carter, J. W. Carter's Breach of Contract: [Hart Edition]. 2012. 854p. 280.00 **(978-1-84946-375-1(1))** Hart Publishing Ltd. GBR. Dist: International Specialized Bk. Services.

Chappell, David. Building Contract Claims. 5th ed. 2011. (ENG.). 544p. 135.99 **(978-0-470-65738-6(3)**, Wiley) Wiley, John & Sons, Inc.

Cushman, Robert Frank, et al. Proving & Pricing Construction Claims: Cumulative Supplement. 3rd ed. 2009. 305p. pap. 180.00 (978-0-7355-8149-4(5), Aspen Pubs.) Wolters Kluwer Law & Business.

Eggleston, Brian. Liquidated Damages & Extensions of Time: In Construction Contracts. 3rd ed. 2009. (ENG.). 408p. 149.99 (978-1-4051-1815-6(6), Wiley-Blackwell) Wiley, John & Sons, Inc.

Krasheninnikov, P. V. & Gongalo, B. M. Otvetstvennost Za Narushenie Obiazatelstv: Postateinyi Kommentarii Glavy 25 Grazhdanskogo Kodeksa Rossiiskoi Federatsii. 2010. (RUS.). 92p. (978-5-8354-0684-5(3)) Statut, Izdatel'stvo.

Leisinger, Benjamin. Fundamental Breach Considering Non-Conformity of the Goods. 2007. 162p. 64.00 (978-3-86653-046-1(3)) Sellier - European Law Publishers GmbH DEU. Dist: International Specialized Bk. Services.

Liu, Qiao. Anticipatory Breach. 2011. (ENG.). 278p. 110.00 (978-1-84946-112-2(0)) Hart Publishing Ltd. GBR. Dist: International Specialized Bk. Services.

Meyer, Lars. Non-Performance & Remedies under International Contract Law Principles & Indian Contract Law: A Comparative Survey of the UNIDROIT Principles of International Commercial Contracts, the Principles of European Contract Law, & Indian Statutory Contract Law. 2010. 280p. (978-3-631-60993-4(0)) Lang, Peter GmbH, Europaischer Verlag der Wissenschaften.

Sabbagh-Farshi, Fariba. Die vorvertragliche Haftung im un-Kaufrecht und in den Unidroit- und Lando-Prinzipien unter Einbeziehung des deutschen und englischen Rechts. 2008. (Beiträge zum un-Kaufrecht Ser.). 216p. pap. 56.95 (978-3-631-57273-3(5)) Lang, Peter GmbH, Europaischer Verlag der Wissenschaften DEU. Dist: Lang, Peter.

Schwartzkopf, William & McNamara, John J. Calculating Construction Damages: 2009 Cumulative Supplement. 2nd ed. 2009. 281p. pap. 24.95 (978-0-7355-8074-9(X), Aspen Pubs.) Wolters Kluwer Law & Business.

Scott, Robert E. & Stephan, Paul B. The Limits of Leviathan: Contract Theory & the Enforcement of International Law. 2011. (ENG.). 264p. pap. 50.00 (978-0-521-36797-4(2)) Cambridge Univ. Pr.

Tamez, Jorge Ivan. The Cisg & Mexican Law Remedies for Breach of Sale Contracts. 2008. 192p. pap. (978-3-8364-7351-4(8)) VDM Verlag Dr. Mueller e.K.

Yorio, Edward & Thel, Steve. Contract Enforcement: Specific Performance & Injunctions. 2nd ed. 2011. (978-1-4548-0114-6(X)) Kluwer Law International.

Zeller, Bruno. Damages under the Convention on Contracts for the International Sale of Goods. 2nd ed. 2009. (ENG.). 352p. 180.00 (978-0-19-537186-4(0)) Oxford Univ. Pr., Inc.

BREACH OF THE PEACE

see also Riots

Gracia Martín, Luis, et al. El Delito de Participación en Riña. 2007. (SPA.). 115p. (978-84-8456-683-0(8)) Tirant lo Blanch.

BREAD

see also Automatic Bread Machines; Bagels

Alexander, William. 52 Loaves. 2011. (ENG.). 352p. pap. 15.95 (978-1-61620-050-3(2), 1616200502) Algonquin Bks. of Chapel Hill.

—52 Loaves: One Man's Relentless Pursuit of Truth, Meaning, & a Perfect Crust. 2010. (ENG.). 352p. 23.95 (978-1-56512-583-4(5), 1565125835) Algonquin Bks. of Chapel Hill.

Alford, Jeffrey & Duguid, Naomi. Flatbreads & Flavors: A Baker's Atlas. 2008. (ENG.). 464p. pap. 19.99 (978-0-06-167326-9(9), Morrow, William Cookbooks) HarperCollins Pubs.

Alles, Silke & Janzen, Sieglinde. Healthy Breads with the Breadmaker. 2007. (ENG.). 64p. pap. 11.95 (978-1-55312-014-8(0)) Books Alive.

Baggett, Nancy. The Breadbreakthrough: Easy Recipes, Dough Kneads Itself. 2009. 48p. pap. 9.95 (978-0-470-48558-3(2), Wiley) Wiley, John & Sons, Inc.

Baggett, Nancy. Kneadlessly Simple: Fabulous, Fuss-Free, No-Knead Breads. 2011. (ENG.). 224p. pap. 19.99 **(978-1-118-16943-8(3)**, Wiley) Wiley, John & Sons, Inc.

Baker, C. D. 40 Loaves: Breaking Bread with Our Father Each Day. 2009. (ENG.). 176p. 14.99 (978-0-307-44490-5(2), WaterBrook Pr.) Doubleday Religious Publishing Group, The.

Ballard, Diana. Whole Wheat Bread Making: Secrets of the Masters Made Easy. 2008. 12.99 (978-1-59955-187-6(X)) Cedar Fort, Inc./CFI Distribution.

Baugniet, Rebecca. 500 Pizzas & Flatbreads: The Only Pizza & Flatbread Compendium You'll Ever Need. 2008. (Illus.). 288p. 17.95 (978-1-4162-0522-7(5)) Sellers Publishing, Inc.

Behr, Edmund. In Search of the Perfect Loaf. 2007. (978-0-86547-580-9(6), North Point Pr.) Farrar, Straus & Giroux.

Belderok, Bob, et al. Bread-Making Quality of Wheat: A Century of Breeding in Europe. 2010. 428p. pap. 229.00 (978-90-481-5493-7(6), 9048154936) Springer.

Bertinet, Richard. Crust: Bread to Get Your Teeth Into. 2007. (ENG., Illus.). 159p. 35.00 incl. DVD (978-1-904920-64-9(0)) Cathie, Kyle Ltd. GBR. Dist: National Bk. Network.

Bilderback Leslie. The Everything Bread Cookbook. 2010. (ENG.). 304p. pap. 15.95 (978-1-4405-0031-2(2)) Adams Media Corp.

Bilderback, Leslie. The Everything Bread Cookbook. 2010. viii, 295p. **(978-1-4405-0032-9(0)**, 1319720) Adams Media Corp.

Bobrow-Strain, Aaron. White Bread: A Social History of the Store-Bought Loaf. 2012. (ENG.). 272p. 27.95 **(978-0-8070-4467-4(9))** Beacon Pr.

Brown, Edward Espe. The Tassajara Bread Book. 2011. (ENG., Illus.). 192p. pap. 18.95 (978-1-59030-836-3(0)) Shambhala Pubns., Inc.

Brown, Warren. CakeLove in the Morning: Recipes for Muffins, Scones, Pancakes, Waffles, Biscuits, Frittatas, & Other Breakfast Treats. 2012. (ENG., Illus.). 208p. 24.95 **(978-1-58479-894-1(7))** Stewart, Tabori & Chang.

Caldirola, Manuela, et al. Classic Breads: Delicious Recipes from Around the World. 2008. (ENG., Illus.). 120p. pap. 12.95 (978-1-4027-5616-0(X)) Sterling Publishing Co., Inc.

Cauvain, Stanley P. & Young, Linda S. Technology of Breadmaking. 2nd rev. ed. 2007. (ENG., Illus.). xxii, 398p. 143.00 (978-0-387-38563-1(0), 0387385630) Springer.

Chattman, Lauren. Bread Making: A Home Course - Crafting the Perfect Loaf, from Crust to Crumb. 2nd ed. 2011. (ENG., Illus.). 296p. pap. 16.95 (978-1-60342-791-3(0), 1603427910) Storey Publishing, LLC.

Chovancova, Ilona. Cakes & Loaves: 110 Recipes You Can Make at Home. 2010. (ENG., Illus.). 160p. pap. 24.95 (978-1-55285-954-4(1)) Whitecap Bks., Ltd. CAN. Dist: Midpoint Trade Bks., Inc.

Clayton, Bernard & Clayton, Bernard, Jr. Bernard Clayton's New Complete Book of Breads. 30th ed. 2006. (ENG., Illus.). 704p. pap. 22.00 (978-0-7432-8709-8(6)) Simon & Schuster.

Cohen, Warren Lee. Baking Bread with Children. 2008. (Craft Ser.). (Illus.). 211p. pap. (978-1-903458-60-0(9)) Hawthorn Pr.

Collister, Linda. Bread: From Sourdough to Rye. 2007. (Illus.). 144p. pap. (978-1-84172-986-2(8)) Ryland Peters & Small.

—Quick Breads. 2007. (ENG., Illus.). 64p. (978-1-84597-475-6(1)) Ryland Peters & Small.

Culinary Institute of America Staff. Artisan Breads at Home. 2010. (At Home with the Culinary Institute of America Ser.: 1). (ENG., Illus.). 352p. 34.95 (978-0-470-18260-4(1), Wiley) Wiley, John & Sons, Inc.

Czech This Out. Czech This Out Vol. 2: Authentic Czech Cookies & more, Czech strudel, fruit dumplings, things for kids to make, eat, do, Parenting styles, tips/insights for parenting, Czech proverbs & inspirational Insights. 2007. 163p. spiral bd. 12.95 (978-0-9789012-2-6(3)) Niemann, Carol.

David, Elizabeth. English Bread & Yeast Cookery. 2011. (ENG., Illus.). 624p. 29.95 (978-1-906502-87-4(0)) Grub Street GBR. Dist: Casemate Pubs. & Bk. Distributors, LLC.

DiMuzio, Daniel T. Bread Baking: An Artisan's Perspective. 2009. (ENG., Illus.). 272p. 45.00 (978-0-470-13882-3(3), Wiley) Wiley, John & Sons, Inc.

Dorling Kindersley Publishing Staff. Step-by-Step Bread. 2012. (ENG.). 192p. 18.00 **(978-0-7566-9266-7(0))** Dorling Kindersley Publishing, Inc.

Dumke, Nicolette M. Easy Breadmaking for Special Diets: Use your bread machine, food processor, mixer, or tortilla maker to make the bread YOU need quickly & Easily. 2nd rev. ed. 2007. (ENG.). 230p. pap. 19.95 (978-1-887624-11-4(2)) Adapt Bks.

Eliot, Winslow, ed. The Waldorf Book of Breads. 2009. (Illus.). 64p. spiral bd. 14.95 (978-0-88010-703-7(0)) SteinerBooks, Inc.

Emmanuel Hadjiandreou. How to Make Bread. 2011. (ENG., Illus.). 160p. (978-1-84975-140-7(4)) Ryland Peters & Small.

Farrow, Joanna. 200 Bread Recipes: Hamlyn All Color. 2010. (ENG.). 240p. pap. 7.99 (978-0-600-62014-3(X), Hamlyn) Octopus Publishing Group GBR. Dist: Hachette Bk. Group.

Favorite Recipes Press Staff, contrib. by. Casseroles. 2009. (Illus.). 382p. **(978-0-87197-842-4(3))** FRP.

Fertig, Judith. The Artisan Bread Machine: 250 Recipes for Breads, Rolls, Flatbreads & Pizzas. 2011. (ENG., Illus.). 320p. pap. 24.95 (978-0-7788-0264-8(7)) Rose, Robert Inc. CAN. Dist: Firefly Bks., Ltd.

Fertig, Judith M. Prairie Home Breads: 150 Splendid Recipes from America's Breadbasket. 2011. (ENG., Illus.). 256p. pap. 14.95 (978-1-55832-173-1(X)) Harvard Common Pr.

Field, Carol. The Italian Baker, Revised: The Classic Tastes of the Italian Countryside — Its Breads, Pizza, Focaccia, Cakes, Pastries, & Cookies. 2011. (ENG., Illus.). 432p. 35.00 (978-1-60774-106-0(7)) Ten Speed Pr.

Fiset, Josee & Blais, Eric. Bread, 1 vol. 2012. (ENG., Illus.). 144p. pap. 19.95 **(978-1-55455-204-7(4))** Fitzhenry & Whiteside, Ltd. CAN. Dist: Ingram Pub. Services.

Garramone, Dominic. Bake & Be Blessed. 2nd ed. 2008. pap. 15.95 (978-0-9795944-7-2(2)) Big River Distribution.

Ginsberg, Stanley & Berg, Norman. Inside the Jewish Bakery: Recipes & Memories from the Golden Age of Jewish Baking. 2011. **(978-1-933822-23-5(6))** Camino Bks., Inc.

Goldman, Marcy. The New Best of Betterbaking. Com: 200 Classic Recipes from the Beloved Baker's Website. 2009. (Illus.). 456p. pap. 26.95 (978-1-77050-002-0(2)) Whitecap Bks., Ltd. CAN. Dist: Midpoint Trade Bks., Inc.

Graves, Tomas. Bread & Oil: Majorcan Culture's Last Stand. 2008. (Illus.). 254p. (978-1-904943-52-5(7)) Grub Street.

Greenstein, George. Secrets of a Jewish Baker: Recipes for 125 Breads from Around the World. 2007. (ENG., Illus.). 336p. 29.99 (978-1-58008-844-2(9)) Ten Speed Pr.

Habeeb, Virginia T. Pita the Great. 99.50 (978-0-89480-216-4(X), 92039) Workman Publishing Co., Inc.

Handy, Amy. War-Time Breads & Cakes. 2007. (Cooking in America Ser.). (ENG., Illus.). 80p. per. 9.95 (978-1-4290-1014-6(2)) Applewood Bks.

Hawkins, Kathryn. Bread! Simple & Satisfying Recipes for Your Bread Machine, 1 vol. 2006. (ENG., Illus.). 176p. pap. 15.95 (978-1-56148-540-6(3)); spiral bd. 19.95 (978-1-56148-541-3(1)) Good Bks.

—Pan! Recetas Simples y Satisfactorias para la Maquina de Hacer Pan. 2007. (Illus.). 176p. pap. 15.95 (978-970-718-461-9(2), Degustis) Advanced Marketing, S. de R. L. de C. V. MEX. Dist: Perseus-PGW.

Head, Honor. Bread. 2010. (J). 24.25 (978-1-59920-262-4(X)) Black Rabbit Bks.

—Bread. 2006. (QEB What's for Lunch? Ser.). (Illus.). 32p. (YA). (gr. 1-4). lib. bdg. 19.95 (978-1-59566-198-2(0)) QEB Publishing Inc.

Hertzberg, Jeff & François, Zoë. Artisan Bread in Five Minutes a Day: The Discovery That Revolutionizes Home Baking. 2007. (ENG., Illus.). 256p. 27.99 (978-0-312-36291-1(9), Dunne, Thomas Bks.) St. Martin's Pr.

Hertzberg, Jeff & Francois, Zoe. Artisan Pizza & Flatbread in Five Minutes a Day. 2011. (ENG., Illus.). 320p. 27.99 (978-0-312-64994-4(0), Dunne, Thomas Bks.) St. Martin's Pr.

Hertzberg, Jeff & François, Zoë. Healthy Bread in Five Minutes a Day: 100 New Recipes Featuring Whole Grains, Fruits, Vegetables, & Gluten-Free Ingredients. 2009. (ENG., Illus.). 336p. 27.99 (978-0-312-54552-9(5), Dunne, Thomas Bks.) St. Martin's Pr.

Hitz, Ciril. Baking Artisan Bread: 10 Expert Formulas for Baking Better Bread at Home. 2008. (ENG., Illus.). 176p. pap. 24.99 (978-1-59253-453-1(8), 1592534538, Quarry Books) Quayside.

—Baking Artisan Pastries & Breads: Sweet & Savory Baking for Breakfast, Brunch, & Beyond. 2009. (ENG., Illus.). 176p. pap. 24.99 (978-1-59253-564-4(X), 159253564X) Quayside.

How to Bake Bread: Five Families of Bread. 2011. (Illus.). 525p. pap. 23.95 (978-0-615-23129-7(2)) Red Seal Bks.

Humphries, Carolyn. Gluten-Free Bread & Cakes from Your Breadmaker from Your Breadmaker: With Full Details for Dairy or Lactose Intolerance. 2010. (ENG., Illus.). 160p. pap. 16.95 (978-0-572-03569-3(1)) Foulsham, W. Co., Ltd. GBR. Dist: APG Sales & Distribution Services.

Hunt, Bernice. Great Natural Breads Made Easy: Simple Ways to Make Healthful Bread. 2006. (ENG., Illus.). 224p. pap. 16.95 (978-0-7570-0294-6(3)) Square One Pubs.

Ingram, Christine & Shapter, Jennie. The Bread Bible. 2012. (ENG., Illus.). 256p. 25.00 **(978-0-7548-2406-0(3))** Anness Publishing GBR. Dist: National Bk. Network.

Ingram, Christine & Shapter, Jennie. The Practical Step-by-Step Guide to Baking Bread. 2011. (ENG., Illus.). 128p. pap. 17.99 (978-1-84476-756-4(6)) Anness Publishing GBR. Dist: National Bk. Network.

Jacob, H. E. Six Thousand Years of Bread: Its Holy & Unholy History. Winston, Clara & Winston, Richard, trs. 2007. (ENG., Illus.). 416p. pap. 14.95 (978-1-60239-124-6(6), 239124) Skyhorse Publishing Co., Inc.

Jaine, Tom. Building a Wood-Fired Oven for Bread & Pizza. 13th ed. 2011. (English Kitchen Ser.). (ENG., Illus.). 136p. (C). pap. 19.95 (978-1-903018-80-4(3)) Prospect Bks. GBR. Dist: Brown, David Bk. Co., The.

Kaplan, Steven Laurence. Good Bread Is Back: A Contemporary History of French Bread, the Way It Is Made, & the People Who Make It. Porter, Catherine, tr. from FRE. 2006. (ENG., Illus.). 384p. 32.95 (978-0-8223-3833-8(5)) Duke Univ. Pr.

Kaufman, Sheilah. Upper Crusts: Fabulous Ways to Use Bread - Delectable Recipes for Appetizers, Soups, Salads, Main Courses, Desserts, & More. 2007. (Capital Lifestyles Ser.). (Illus.). 300p. per. 20.00 (978-1-933102-39-9(X)) Capital Bks., Inc.

Kayser, Eric. Beyond the Bread Basket: Recipes for Appetizers, Main Courses, & Desserts. 2008. (ENG., Illus.). 160p. 34.95 (978-2-08-030051-5(2)) Flammarion et Cie FRA. Dist: Random Hse., Inc.

Klivans, Elinor. Fast Breads: 50 Recipes for Easy, Delicious Bread. 2010. (ENG., Illus.). 144p. pap. 19.95 (978-0-8118-6570-8(3)) Chronicle Bks. LLC.

Lahey, Jim. My Bread: The Revolutionary No-Work, No-Knead Method. 2009. (ENG., Illus.). 224p. 29.95 (978-0-393-06630-2(4), 6630) Norton, W. W. & Co., Inc.

Langley, Andrew. The Little Book of Bread Tips. 2008. (Little Book Ser.). (ENG.). 122p. pap. 4.95 (978-1-904573-90-6(8)) Absolute Pr. GBR. Dist: Independent Pubs. Group.

Laskin, Avner. The Easy Way to Artisan Breads & Pastries. 2007. (ENG., Illus.). 160p. pap. 14.95 (978-1-4027-4740-3(3)) Sterling Publishing Co., Inc.

Leader, Daniel. Local Breads. 2007. 35.00 (978-0-7930-5055-0(3)) Norton, W. W. & Co., Inc.

—Local Breads: Sourdough & Whole-Grain Recipes from Europe's Best Artisan Bakers. 2007. (ENG., Illus.). 368p. 35.00 (978-0-393-05055-4(6), 5055) Norton, W. W. & Co., Inc.

—Simply Great Breads: Sweet & Savory Yeasted Treats from America's Premier Artisan Baker. 2011. (ENG., Illus.). 160p. 22.00 (978-1-60085-297-8(1)) Taunton Pr., Inc.

Leisure Arts. Celebrating Quick Breads & Pastries. 2011. (Celebrating Cookbooks Ser.). (ENG., Illus.). 144p. pap. 14.95 (978-1-60900-116-2(8)) Leisure Arts, Inc.

Lewis, Sara. Bread Machine Easy: 70 Delicious Recipes That Make the Most of Your Machine. 2008. 144p. 17.95 (978-0-600-61837-9(4), Hamlyn) Octopus Publishing Group GBR. Dist: Jaguar Bk. Group.

—Bread Machine Easy: 70 Delicious Recipes That Make the Most of Your Machine. 2010. (ENG., Illus.). 144p. pap. 14.99 (978-0-600-62182-9(0), Hamlyn) Octopus Publishing Group GBR. Dist: Hachette Bk. Group.

Mackie, Leslie. Leslie Mackie's Macrina Bakery & Cafe Cookbook: Favorite Breads, Pastries, Sweets & Savories. 2nd ed. 2006. (ENG., Illus.). 304p. per. 19.95 (978-1-57061-504-7(7)) Sasquatch Bks.

Manville, Ron & Reinhart, Peter. Peter Reinhart's Whole Grain Breads: New Techniques, Extraordinary Flavor. 2007. (ENG., Illus.). 320p. 35.00 (978-1-58008-759-9(0)) Ten Speed Pr.

Marchant, John, et al. Bread: A Slice of History. 2009. (ENG., Illus.). 240p. pap. 24.95 (978-0-7524-4748-3(3)) History Pr. Ltd., The GBR. Dist: Independent Pubs. Group.

Ode, Kim. Baking with the St. Paul Bread Club: Recipes, Tips & Stories. 2006. (Illus.). 160p. 24.95 (978-0-87351-567-2(6)) Minnesota Historical Society Pr.

Pare, Jean. Mostly Muffins. 2007. (Company's Coming Ser.). (Illus.). 156p. spiral bd. (978-1-897069-03-5(0)) Company's Coming Publishing, Ltd.

Pellegrini, Matteo. The Art of Baking Bread: What You Really Need to Know to Make Great Bread. 2012. (ENG., Illus.). 192p. 24.95 **(978-1-61608-537-7(1)**, 608537) Skyhorse Publishing Co., Inc.

Peoples, Jerome T. Lee's Bread Machines: The Father of Automated Bread Making. 2011. 67p. pap. 14.95 (978-1-4327-6337-4(7)) Outskirts Pr., Inc.

Preedy, Victor, et al, eds. Flour & Breads & Their Fortification in Health & Disease Prevention. 2011. (ENG., Illus.). 542p. 199.95 (978-0-12-380886-8(3), Academic Pr.) Elsevier Science & Technology Bks.

Prueitt, Elizabeth & Robertson, Chad. Tartine Bread. 2010. (ENG., Illus.). 304p. 40.00 (978-0-8118-7041-2(3)) Chronicle Bks. LLC.

Reinhart, Peter. Artisan Breads Every Day: Fast & Easy Recipes for World-Class Breads. 2009. (ENG., Illus.). 224p. 30.00 (978-1-58008-998-2(4)) Ten Speed Pr.

—Crust & Crumb: Master Formulas for Serious Bread Bakers. 2006. (ENG., Illus.). 224p. pap. 19.99 (978-1-58008-802-2(3)) Ten Speed Pr.

Rubel, William. Bread: A Global History. 2011. (Reaktion Books - Edible Ser.). (Illus.). 160p. 18.00 (978-1-86189-854-8(1)) Reaktion Bks., Ltd. GBR. Dist: Chicago Distribution Ctr.

Ruperti, Yvonne. The Complete Idiot's Guide to Easy Artisan Bread. 2010. (Complete Idiot's Guide Ser.). (ENG.). 256p. (gr. 12). 16.95 (978-1-61564-004-1(5), Alpha Bks.) Penguin Group (USA) Inc.

Sadowski, Laurie. The Allergy-Free Cook Bakes Bread. 2011. E-Book **(978-1-57067-948-3(7))** Book Publishing Co.

Scheele, Charel. Old World Breads & the History of A Flemish Baker. 2011. 104p. pap. 11.95 **(978-1-4620-5471-8(4))** iUniverse, Inc.

Scherber, Amy & Dupree, Toy Kim. The Sweeter Side of Amy's Bread: Cakes, Cookies, Bars, Pastries & More from New York City's Favorite Bakery. 2008. (ENG., Illus.). 272p. 34.95 (978-0-470-17074-8(3), Wiley) Wiley, John & Sons, Inc.

Scherber, Amy, et al. Amy's Bread: Artisan-Style Breads, Sandwiches, Pizzas, & More from New York City's Favorite Bakery. rev. ed. 2010. (ENG., Illus.). 288p. 35.00 (978-0-470-17075-5(1), Wiley) Wiley, John & Sons, Inc.

Septimus, Matthew, photos by. The Fundamental Techniques of Classic Bread Baking. 2011. (ENG., Illus.). 352p. 65.00 (978-1-58479-934-4(X)) Stewart, Tabori & Chang.

Shapter, Jennie. 80 Bread Machine Best-Ever Recipes: Discover the potential of your bread machine with step-by-step recipes from around the world, illustrated in 300 Photographs. 2012. (ENG., Illus.). 128p. pap. 17.99 ***(978-1-84476-870-7(8))*** Anness Publishing GBR. Dist: National Bk. Network.

Shapter, Jenny & Ingram, Christine. 55 Classic Recipes: Bread from Around the World. 2008. (ENG.). 96p. pap. 9.99 *(978-1-84476-614-7(4))* Anness Publishing GBR. Dist: National Bk. Network.

Sheasby, Anne. The Bread Machine Bible: More Than 100 Recipes for Delicious Home Baking with Your Bread Machine. 2009. (ENG., Illus.). 176p. 19.95 *(978-1-84483-795-3(5))* Duncan Baird Pubs. GBR. Dist: Sterling Publishing Co., Inc.

Shu-ling, Chou. Breads. (Illus.). 120p. *(978-957-629-258-3(1))* Hilit Publishing Co., Ltd.

Sidawi, Sam. My Rustic Sandwiches: Great Recipes to Savor Artisan Bread. 2009. (ENG., Illus.). 96p. 18.95 *(978-0-9812935-0-9(6))* Daniel's Rustic Bread CAN. Dist: Independent Pubs. Group.

Sinclair, Donna. The Spirituality of Bread. 2007. (ENG., Illus.). 160p. 34.00 *(978-1-896836-85-0(2))* Northstone Publishing, Inc. CAN. Dist: Westminster John Knox Pr.

Stevens, Daniel. The River Cottage Bread Handbook. 2010. (ENG., Illus.). 224p. 22.00 *(978-1-58008-186-3(X))* Ten Speed Pr.

Stuhlman, Daniel D. Whole Wheat Bread Recipes 2nd Ed. 2008. (Illus.). 25p. 3.50 net. *(978-0-934402-34-7(5))* BYLS Pr.

Suas, Michel. Advanced Bread & Pastry. 2008. (ENG.). 1056p. (C). 92.95 *(978-1-4180-1169-7(X))* Delmar Cengage Learning.

Svanoe, Rolf. Bread for the Journey: A High-Carb, Multi-Sensory Lenten Worship Series. 2007. (Illus.). 84p. per. 9.95 *(978-0-7880-2507-5(4))* CSS Publishing Co.

Swell, Barbara. Aunt Barb's Bread Book. 2011. (ENG., Illus.). 72p. pap. 5.95 ***(978-1-883206-62-8(6))*** Native Ground Music, Inc.

Tiruneh, Dawit & Emire, Shimelis. Optimizing the Formulation & Process Conditions of Gluten-Free Bread. 2011. 116p. pap. ***(978-3-8443-3166-0(2))*** Lambert Academic Publishing.

Tonnac, Jean-Philippe de. Dictionnaire Universel du Pain. (FRE.). xi, 1222p. *(978-2-221-11200-7(8))* Laffont, Robert.

Vondey, Wolfgang. People of Bread: Rediscovering Ecclesiology. 2008. 448p. pap. 29.95 *(978-0-8091-4559-1(6))* Paulist Pr.

Washburn, Donna & Butt, Heather. 125 Best Gluten-Free Bread Machine Recipes. 2010. (ENG., Illus.). 264p. pap. 24.95 *(978-0-7788-0238-9(8))* Rose, Robert Inc. CAN. Dist: Firefly Bks., Ltd.

—300 Best Bread Machine Recipes. 2010. (ENG., Illus.). 448p. pap. 24.95 *(978-0-7788-0244-0(2))* Rose, Robert Inc. CAN. Dist: Firefly Bks., Ltd.

Wenzell, Lori. Creative Bagels & Breads. 2008. 90p. pap. 16.95 *(978-1-4241-9160-4(2))* PublishAmerica, Inc.

Whitley, Andrew. Bread Matters: The State of Modern Bread & a Definitive Guide to Baking Your Own. 2009. (ENG.). 416p. 34.99 *(978-0-7407-7373-0(9))* Andrews McMeel Publishing.

Wood, T b. The Story of a Loaf of Bread. 2012. (ENG.). 150p. pap. 19.99 ***(978-1-107-60606-7(3))*** Cambridge Univ. Pr.

BREAD DOUGH CRAFT

Hughes, Patricia. Making Soft-Bodied Dough Characters. 2006. (Illus.). 146p. pap. 12.95 *(978-1-59764-282-8(7))* New Line Bks.

BREAD MACHINES, AUTOMATIC

see Automatic Bread Machines

BREADSTUFFS

see Flour; Grain; Wheat

BREAKAGE, SHRINKAGE, ETC. (COMMERCE)

Aci, ed. Structural Implications of Shrinkage & Creep of Concrete. 2007. cd-rom *(978-0-87031-250-2(2))* American Concrete Institute.

BREAKDANCING

Peterson, Charles, photos by. Cypher. 2008. (ENG., Illus.). 136p. 35.00 *(978-1-57687-456-1(7))* powerHouse Cultural Entertainment, Inc.

BREAKERS

see Ocean Waves

BREAKFAST FOODS

see Cereals As Food

BREAKFASTS

Allen, Linda. Breakfast Is Not Soda & a Bag of Chips. 2007. 80p. per. 16.95 *(978-1-4241-9063-8(0))* PublishAmerica, Inc.

Barrett, Sharon Kebschull. Morning Glories: Breakfast, Brunch & Light Fare from an Herb Garden. Date not set. pap. *(978-0-312-28570-8(1))*, St. Martin's Griffin) St. Martin's Pr.

Bear, John B. & Fox, Margaret S. Morning Food: Breakfasts, Brunches & More for Savoring the Best Part of the Day. 2nd rev. ed. 2006. (ENG., Illus.). 208p. pap. 19.95 *(978-1-58008-782-7(5))* Ten Speed Pr.

Beckerman, Carol. 500 Breakfast & Brunch Dishes: The Only Compendium of Breakfast & Brunch Dishes You'll Ever Need. 2011. (Illus.). 288p. 16.95 *(978-1-4162-0620-0(5))* Sellers Publishing, Inc.

Brett, Michelle. Best of Country Breakfast & Brunch. 2007. (Illus.). 112p. *(978-0-89821-544-1(7))* Reiman Pubns., L.P.

Brown, Warren. CakeLove in the Morning: Recipes for Muffins, Scones, Pancakes, Waffles, Biscuits, Frittatas, & Other Breakfast Treats. 2012. (ENG., Illus.). 208p. 24.95 ***(978-1-58479-894-1(7))*** Stewart, Tabori & Chang.

Bursey, Michelle & Korgan, Carol. The Lighthouse Breakfast Cookbook: Recipes from Heceta Head Lighthouse Bed & Breakfast. 2009. (ENG., Illus.). 192p. 27.95 *(978-0-88240-743-2(0),* West Winds Pr.) Graphic Arts Ctr. Publishing Co.

Cassidy, Catherine. Breakfast. 2009. (Illus.). 112p. ***(978-0-89821-760-5(1))*** Reiman Pubns., L.P.

Chase, Erin. The $5 Dinner Mom Breakfast & Lunch Cookbook: 200 Recipes for Quick, Delicious, & Nourishing Meals That Are Easy on the Budget & a Snap to Prepare. 2011. (ENG., Illus.). 336p. pap. 14.99 *(978-0-312-60734-0(2),* St. Martin's Griffin) St. Martin's Pr.

Duda, Carlene. Beyond Oatmeal: 101 Breakfast Recipes. 2007. 147p. pap. 14.95 *(978-1-59955-018-3(0))* Cedar Fort, Inc./CFI Distribution.

—Breakfast in a Cookie Jar. 2009. spiral bd. 8.99 *(978-1-59955-337-5(6))* Cedar Fort, Inc./CFI Distribution.

—Completely Breakfast. 2008. 208p. spiral bd. 16.99 *(978-1-59955-102-9(0))* Cedar Fort, Inc./CFI Distribution.

Examining the Costs of Federal Overreach into School Meals: Hearing Before the Subcommittee on Early Childhood, Elementary & Secondary Education, Committee on Education & the Workforce, U.S. House of Representatives, One Hundred Twelfth Congress, First Session, Hearing Held in Washington, DC, May 13, 2011. 2011. (Illus.). iii, 41p. ***(978-0-16-089023-9(3),*** 552-070-43055-5) United States Government Printing Office.

Gooseberry Patch. Breakfast & Brunch Recipes Cookbook. 2007. (ENG., Illus.). 126p. spiral bd. 7.95 *(978-1-933494-13-5(1))* Gooseberry Patch.

James, Laura. Breakfast in Bed. 2010. (ENG., Illus.). 160p. 19.95 *(978-1-906650-00-1(4))* Absolute Pr. GBR. Dist: Independent Pubs. Group.

King, Jonathan, et al. Stonewall Kitchen Breakfast: A Collection of Great Morning Recipes. 2009. (ENG., Illus.). 144p. 19.95 *(978-0-8118-6867-9(2))* Chronicle Bks. LLC.

Lanier, Pamela. Cinnamon Mornings & Savory Nights: Romantic Recipes from America's Inns. (ENG.). 2009. 160p. pap. 19.95 *(978-0-9840850-0-2(9))* 2008. (Illus.). 1p. pap. 19.95 *(978-1-58008-940-1(2))* Ten Speed Pr.

Levine, Sarabeth & Rodgers, Rick. Sarabeth's Bakery: From My Hands to Yours. 2010. (ENG., Illus.). 306p. 39.95 *(978-0-8478-3408-2(5))* Rizzoli International Pubns., Inc.

Main, Sylvia. Easy Elegance from Fabulous Fairholme: Breakfast, Brunch, Lunch. 2012. 144p. 29.95 ***(978-1-77050-110-2(X))*** Whitecap Bks., Ltd. CAN. Dist: Midpoint Trade Bks., Inc.

Main, Sylvia. Fabulous Fairholme: Breakfasts & Brunches. 2010. (ENG., Illus.). 144p. 29.95 *(978-1-55285-932-2(0))* Whitecap Bks., Ltd. CAN. Dist: Midpoint Trade Bks., Inc.

Michalka, Dayna A. & Monroy, Christopher J. Meals in School: Issues & Impacts. 2011. (Food & Beverage Consumption & Health Ser.). 89.00 *(978-1-61209-127-3(X))* Nova Science Pubs., Inc.

Miller, Wayne. Wake Late, Feel Sick, No Time, Don't Eat. 2010. 416p. pap. *(978-3-639-21938-8(4))* VDM Verlag Dr. Mueller e.K.

Moos, Dana. The Art of Breakfast: How to Bring B & B Entertaining Home. 2011. (ENG.). 159p. 28.95 *(978-0-89272-940-1(6))* Down East Bks.

Murrey, Thomas. Breakfast Dainties. 2008. (Cooking in America Ser.). (ENG.). 60p. pap. 9.95 *(978-1-4290-1252-2(8))* Applewood Bks.

Nye, Valerie & Barco, Kathy. Breakfast New Mexico Style: A Fancy, Funky, & Family Friendly Dining Guide to New Mexico Restaurants with over 80 Librarian Recommended Books, 100 Restaurants, & Many Fun Things to Do after Breakfast. 2009. 184p. pap. 22.95 *(978-0-86534-716-8(6))* Sunstone Pr.

Perlman, Michael H. Cookies for Breakfast: A Teen's Not So Bad Guide to Wheat & Gluten-free Baking. 2008. 112p. (YA). pap. 15.95 *(978-0-615-19168-3(1))* Perlman, Michael H.

Phillips, Jill M. The Good Morning Cookbook, 1 vol. 2009. (ENG., Illus.). 132p. pap. 14.95 *(978-1-58980-693-1(X))* Pelican Publishing Co., Inc.

Poppendieck, Janet. Free for All: Fixing School Food in America. 2011. (California Studies in Food & Culture Ser.). (ENG.). 368p. pap. 17.95 *(978-0-520-26988-0(8))* Univ. of California Pr.

Randolph, Carla. The Dutch Oven Breakfast Cookbook. 2008. 83p. pap. 9.99 *(978-1-59955-084-8(9))* Cedar Fort, Inc./CFI Distribution.

Rodgers, Rick. Williams-Sonoma Breakfast Comforts: With Enticing Recipes for the Morning, Including Favorite Dishes from Restaurants Around the Country. 2011. (ENG.). 224p. 34.95 *(978-1-61628-070-3(0))* Weldon Owen, Inc.

Ryland, Peters, ed. Easy Breakfast & Brunch. 2007. (ENG., Illus.). 240p. *(978-1-84597-485-5(9))* Ryland Peters & Small.

Schaefer, Lola M. & Schaefer, Ted. Breakfast. 2006. (What's on Your Plate? Ser.). (ENG., Illus.). 32p. 29.99 *(978-1-4109-2214-4(6),* Raintree Perspectives) Heinemann-Raintree.

Smith, Barbara Brown & Smith, Barbara B. Rise & Dine: Breakfast in Boston. 2007. (ENG., Illus.). 192p. pap. 12.95 *(978-1-55591-607-7(4))* Fulcrum Publishing.

Spendley, Juli. A Study of Factors Influencing Students' Breakfast Routines. 2010. 112p. pap. *(978-3-8383-2122-6(7))* Lambert Academic Publishing.

Stahl, Connie. Breakfast on the Battery: A Charleston Chef's Collection of Breakfast & Tea Recipes. 2007. (Illus.). 148p. 22.95 *(978-0-9791408-0-8(3))* Breakfast on the Battery.

Wurtzel, Claire & Wurtzel, Bill. Funny Food: 365 Fun, Healthy, Silly, Creative Breakfasts. 2012. (ENG., Illus.). 192p. 19.95 ***(978-1-59962-111-1(8),*** Welcome Bks.) Welcome Enterprises, Inc.

BREAKING UP (INTERPERSONAL RELATIONS)

see Seperation (Psychology)

BREAST

Bassett, Lawrence W., et al. Breast Imaging. 2010. (ENG., Illus.). 832p. (C). 262.00 *(978-1-4160-5199-2(6),* Saunders) Elsevier - Health Sciences Div.

Berry, M. G. Adverse Capsular Contracture. 2010. (Surgery - Procedures, Complications, & Results Ser.). pap. 49.00 *(978-1-61728-381-9(9))* Nova Science Pubs., Inc.

Brelum, Sindre Holsboe. Ultrawideband Imaging of Breast Tissue. 2010. 88p. pap. *(978-3-8383-9411-4(9))* Lambert Academic Publishing.

Dershaw, David D., ed. Imaging-Guided Interventional Breast Techniques. 2011. (ENG., Illus.). xv, 212p. pap. 295.00 *(978-1-4419-3007-1(8),* 1441930078) Springer.

Elston. Diagnostic Atlas of Breast Patterns. Date not set. (Illus.). 624p. (C). *(978-0-443-06341-1(9),* Churchill Livingstone) Elsevier - Health Sciences Div.

Gill, Kathryn A. Breast Sonography Review: A Q&A Review for the ARDMS Breast Exam. 2009. spiral bd. 55.00 *(978-0-941022-75-0(7))* Davies Publishing, Inc.

Greenstein, Caren & Manasseh, Donna Marie E. Breast MRI: A Case-Based Approach. 2011. (ENG., Illus.). 344p. 184.95 *(978-1-60913-236-1(X))* Lippincott Williams & Wilkins.

Hanson, Dian. Big Book of Breasts in 3-D. 2011. (FRE, GER & ENG., Illus.). 220p. 39.99 *(978-3-8365-2660-9(3))* TASCHEN DEU. Dist: Ingram Pub. Services.

Hendrick, R. Edward. Breast MRI: Fundamentals & Technical Aspects. 2010. (ENG., Illus.). 254p. pap. 29.95 *(978-1-4419-6520-2(3),* 1441965203) Springer.

Kaiser, Werner A. Signs in MR-Mammography. (Illus.). 2010. xiv, 386p. pap. 179.00 *(978-3-642-09233-6(0),* 3642092330) 2008. 386p. 179.00 *(978-3-540-73292-1(6))* Springer.

Miles, Margaret R. A Complex Delight: The Secularization of the Breast, 1350-1750. 2008. (Illus.). 177p. 45.00 *(978-0-520-25348-3(5))* Univ. of California Pr.

Moy, Linda & Mercado, Cecilia L. Breast MRI, an Issue of Magnetic Resonance Imaging Clinics. 2010. (Clinics: Radiology Ser.: 18-2). (ENG., Illus.). xi, 156p. 105.00 *(978-1-4377-1833-1(7),* Saunders) Elsevier - Health Sciences Div.

Paulsen, Keith D., et al, eds. Alternative Breast Imaging: Four Model-Based Approaches. 2010. (Springer International Series in Engineering & Computer Science Ser.). (Illus.). xv, 253p. pap. 149.00 *(978-1-4419-3616-5(5),* 1441936165) Springer.

Price, Jeremy. Handbook of Breast MRI. 2011. (ENG., Illus.). 230p. pap. 80.00 ***(978-0-521-13966-3(X))*** Cambridge Univ. Pr.

Whitman, Gary. Breast Ultrasound, an Issue of Ultrasound Clinics. 2011. (Clinics: Radiology Ser.: 6-3). (ENG., Illus.). 134p. 83.00 *(978-1-4557-0515-3(2),* Saunders) Elsevier - Health Sciences Div.

Williams, Florence. Breasts: A Natural & Unnatural History. 2012. (ENG., Illus.). 352p. 25.95 ***(978-0-393-06318-9(6),*** 6318) Norton, W. W. & Co., Inc.

BREAST—CANCER

Abel, Emily & Subramanian, Saskia. After the Cure: The Untold Stories of Breast Cancer Survivors. 2010. (ENG.). 208p. pap. 20.00 *(978-0-8147-0735-7(1))* New York Univ. Pr.

Abel, Emily K. & Subramanian, Saskia K. After the Cure: The Untold Stories of Breast Cancer Survivors. 2008. (ENG.). 208p. 50.00 *(978-0-8147-0725-8(4))* New York Univ. Pr.

Abraham, Jame. Breast Cancer: A Clinical Guide. 2006. *(978-0-7817-7099-6(8))* Lippincott Williams & Wilkins.

Agborsangaya, Calypse Bessem. Biomarkers for Risk of Breast Cancer During Pregnancy: A Nested Case Control Study. 2011. (Acta Universitatis Tamperensis Ser.). (Illus.). 129p. pap. 84.50 *(978-951-44-8327-1(8))* Tampere Univ. Pr. FIN. Dist: Coronet Bks.

Akingbade, Olayinka. He Gave Me Beauty for Ashes Again. 2011. 78p. 24.99 ***(978-1-4568-9771-0(3));*** pap. 15.99 ***(978-1-4568-9770-3(5))*** Xlibris Corp.

Allison, Kimberly. Red Sunshine: A Story of Strength & Inspiration from a Doctor Who Survived Stage 3 Breast Cancer. 2011. (ENG.). 192p. pap. 15.95 ***(978-1-57826-407-0(3))*** Hatherleigh Co., Ltd., The.

Ambrose, Greg. Stories of Rell Sunn. 2010. 176p. pap. 22.95 *(978-1-57306-323-4(1))* Bess Pr., Inc.

American Cancer Society Staff. Breast Cancer: The Essential Guide to Your Breast Cancery Journey. 3rd ed. 2009. (ENG.). 400p. pap., instr.'s gde. ed. 24.95 *(978-0-944235-90-4(5),* 0944235905) American Cancer Society, Inc.

—Breast Cancer: What You Need to Know — Now. 2010. (ACS Quick Facts Ser.). 192p. pap. 8.95 *(978-0-944235-74-4(3),* 0944235743) American Cancer Society, Inc.

—QuickFACTS Breast Cancer: What You Need to Know-NOW. 2011. (Quick Facts TM Ser.). (ENG.). 160p. pap. 8.95 *(978-1-60443-031-8(1))* American Cancer Society, Inc.

American Cancer Society Staff, contrib. by. Quick Facts Breast Cancer: What You Need to Know-Now. 2010. pap. *(978-1-60443-030-1(3))* American Cancer Society, Inc.

American Cancer Society Staff, creator. Breast Cancer Clear & Simple: All Your Questions Answered. 2007. (Clear & Simple: All Your Questions Answered Ser.). (ENG., Illus.). 176p. per. 14.95 *(978-0-944235-72-0(7),* 9780944235720) American Cancer Society, Inc.

Anders, Carey K. & Lin, Nancy U. Questions & Answers about Triple Negative Breast Cancer. 2011. 184p. pap. 20.95 *(978-1-4496-0930-6(9))* Jones & Bartlett Learning, LLC.

Anderson, Greg. Breast Cancer: 50 Essential Things to Do. 2011. 304p. pap. 16.95 *(978-1-57324-536-4(4),* Conari Pr.) Red Wheel/Weiser.

Anderson, Greg. Breast Cancer: 50 Essential Things You Can Do. Lt. ed. 2012. (ENG.). 489p. 31.99 ***(978-1-4104-4259-8(4))*** Thorndike Pr.

Anderson, John W. Stand by Her: A Breast Cancer Guide for Men, 1 vol. 2009. (ENG.). 272p. pap. 18.95 *(978-0-8144-1391-3(9))* Amacom.

Anderson, Taffy A. Treasures in Darkness: A Doctor's Personal Journey Through Breast Cancer. 2007. (ENG.). 192p. pap. 13.99 *(978-0-8024-8250-1(3),* Lift Every Voice) Moody Pubs.

Arena, Francis & Manuali, Tanya. Reflections of the Breast. 2010. (ENG.). 120p. pap. 27.95 *(978-1-883283-76-6(0))* Bks., Inc.

Arogo, Grace. Grace under Fire My Journey with Breast Cancer. 2010. 80p. pap. *(978-3-639-26428-9(2))* VDM Verlag Dr. Mueller e.K.

Aronowitz, Robert A. Unnatural History: Breast Cancer & American Society. 2007. (Cambridge Studies in the History of Medicine Ser.). (ENG., Illus.). 378p. 34.99 *(978-0-521-82249-7(1))* Cambridge Univ. Pr.

Astley, S. Digital Mammography: 8th International Workshop, IWDM 2006, Manchester, UK, June 18-21, 2006, Proceedings. 2006. (Lecture Notes in Computer Science Ser.: Vol. 4046). (Illus.). 654p. pap. 129.00 *(978-3-540-35625-7(8),* 3540356258) Springer.

Atallian, Milinda Rose. Mommom's Got a Bip in Her Boop. 2011. 52p. 24.99 ***(978-1-4628-7072-1(4));*** pap. 15.99 ***(978-1-4628-7071-4(6))*** Xlibris Corp.

Balwanz, Patti, et al. Nordie's at Noon: The Personal Stories of Four Women Too Young for Breast Cancer. 2007. (ENG.). 304p. per. 12.95 *(978-0-7382-1112-1(5))* Da Capo Pr., Inc.

Barakat, Richard. Principles & Practice of Gynecologic Oncology. Markman, Maurie & Randall, Marcus E., eds. 5th rev. ed. 2009. (ENG., Illus.). 1088p. 245.99 *(978-0-7817-7845-9(X))* Lippincott Williams & Wilkins.

Barbour, Isabelle. Woman under Construction A Story of Surv. 2007. 81p. pap. 16.95 *(978-1-4241-6513-1(X))* PublishAmerica, Inc.

Barnes, Sally. Better Than New: Insider tips from a glamour girl on surviving breast cancer, mastectomy, & reconstruction. 2011. 86p. pap. 14.95 *(978-1-936401-24-6(X))* Two Harbors Pr., Inc.

Barr, Daniel. Clathrin-Independent Endocytosis of Erbb2 in Human Breast Cancer Cells. 2009. 68p. pap. *(978-3-639-15069-8(4))* VDM Verlag Dr. Mueller e.K.

Batiuk, Tom. Lisa's Story: The Other Shoe. 2007. (Literature & Medicine Ser.). (Illus.). 246p. pap. 18.95 *(978-0-87338-952-5(2));* 27.95 *(978-0-87338-924-2(7))* Kent State Univ. Pr.

Battle, Audrey K. I Fight for Her. 2010. pap. 13.99 *(978-0-578-05327-1(6))* Eagleyes Discounts Co.

Bauman, Ed & Waldman, Helayne L. The Whole-Food Guide for Breast Cancer Survivors: A Nutritional Approach to Preventing Reoccurence. 2012. (New Harbinger Whole-Body Healing Ser.). (ENG., Illus.). 272p. pap. 18.95 ***(978-1-57224-958-5(7))*** New Harbinger Pubns.

Bellenir, Karen, ed. Breast Cancer Sourcebook. 3rd rev. ed. 2009. (Health Reference Ser.). 93.00 *(978-0-7808-1030-3(9))* Omnigraphics, Inc.

—Cancer Sourcebook for Women. 4th rev. ed. 2010. (Health Reference Ser.). 729p. lib. bdg. 93.00 *(978-0-7808-1139-3(9))* Omnigraphics, Inc.

Benson, John R. & Jatoi, Ismail. Management Options in Breast Cancer: Case Histories, Best Practice, & Clinical Decision-Making. 2009. (ENG., Illus.). 256p. 279.95 *(978-0-415-42310-6(4),* Informa Healthcare) Taylor & Francis Group.

Benson, John R. & Nava, Maurizio, eds. Oncoplastic & Reconstructive Surgery of the Breast, Second Edition. 2nd ed. 2009. 319.95 *(978-0-415-47728-4(X),* Informa Healthcare) Taylor & Francis Group.

Berg, Wendie A. Diagnostic Imaging. 2006. (Illus.). *(978-0-8089-2380-0(3))* Harcourt Health Sciences Group.

Berstein, Lev M. & Santen, Richard J., eds. Innovative Endocrinology of Cancer. 2010. (Advances in Experimental Medicine & Biology Ser.). (Illus.). xx, 242p. pap. 209.00 *(978-1-4419-2700-2(X),* 144192700X) Springer.

Bevan, P. & Mala, C., eds. The Role of uPA & uPA Inhibitors in Breast Cancer: Satellite Symposium EBCC6, Berlin, April 2008. 2008. (Illus.). 28p. pap. *(978-3-8055-9045-7(8))* Karger, S. AG.

Bibb, Robert. Deadly Dairy Deception. 2010. pap. 15.99 *(978-1-61566-773-4(3))* Tate Publishing & Enterprises, LLC.

Bick, Ulrich & Diekmann, Felix. Digital Mammography. 2011. (Medical Radiology / Diagnostic Imaging Ser.). (Illus.). xvi, 220p. pap. 119.00 *(978-3-642-17898-6(7),* 3642178987) Springer.

—Digital Mammography: Current Concepts. 2009. (Medical Radiology / Diagnostic Imaging Ser.). (ENG., Illus.). xvi, 220p. 319.00 *(978-3-540-78449-4(7),* 3540784497) Springer.

Birdwell, Robyn L. Breast Imaging, an Issue of Radiologic Clinics of North America. 2010. (Clinics: Radiology Ser.: 48-5). (ENG., Illus.). x, 844p. 105.00 *(978-1-4377-2595-7(3),* Saunders) Elsevier - Health Sciences Div.

Bishop, Leslie. Congratulations, You Have Cancer! An empowering, personal encounter with breast cancer & a positive, good feeling & spiritual approach on how you can look at disease differently & recreate your experience of it! 2006. (ENG.). 120p. per. 11.95 *(978-1-59800-644-5(4))* Outskirts Pr., Inc.

Bissell, Mina J., et al, eds. The Mammary Gland as an Experimental Model. 2011. (Illus.). 550p. 135.00 *(978-0-87969-906-2(X))* Cold Spring Harbor Laboratory Pr.

Blackburn, Amy. Caring for Cynthia. 2008. 96p. pap. 24.95 *(978-0-9773399-1-4(2))* Channe Photographics.

Bland, Kirby I., et al, eds. Surgery in Breast Cancer & Melanoma: Handbooks in General Surgery. 2010. (ENG., Illus.). xvi, 248p. pap. 29.95 *(978-1-84996-434-0(3),* 1849964343) Springer.

Bland, Kirby I., et al. The Breast, 2-Volume Set, Expert Consult Online & Print: Comprehensive Management of Benign & Malignant Diseases, 2 vols., Set. 4th ed. 2009. (ENG., Illus.). 1712p. 395.00 *(978-1-4160-5221-0(6),* Saunders) Elsevier - Health Sciences Div.

Bodach, Diane LaRae. Straw into Gold: Illness, Loss, & Hardship As a Path to Inner Peace. 340p. 2012. E-Book *(978-1-57733-332-6(2))* 2011. pap. 19.95 *(978-1-57733-223-7(7))* Blue Dolphin Publishing, Inc.

B

Bombardieri, E., et al. Breast Cancer: Nuclear Medicine in Diagnosis & Therapeutic Options. Bombardieri, Emilio et al, eds. 2007. (Illus.). 299p. 179.00 *(978-3-540-36780-2(2))* Springer.

Bombardieri, Emilio, et al, eds. Breast Cancer: Nuclear Medicine in Diagnosis & Therapeutic Options. 2010. (Illus.). xiv, 299p. pap. 179.00 *(978-3-642-07186-7(4)*, 3642071864) Springer.

Bonner, Dede. The 10 Best Questions for Surviving Breast Cancer: The Script You Need to Take Control of Your Health. 2008. (ENG.). 336p. pap. 20.99 *(978-1-4165-6050-0(5)*, Touchstone) Touchstone.

Borisch, B. & Jacquemier, J., eds. Translational Research in Breast Cancer. 2008. (Illus.). 98p. pap. *(978-3-8055-8601-6(9))* Karger, S. AG.

Bowcock, Anne M., ed. Breast Cancer: Molecular Genetics, Pathogenesis, & Therapeutics. 2010. (Contemporary Cancer Research Ser.). 608p. pap. 189.00 *(978-1-61737-072-4(X)*, 161737072X) Humana Pr.

Boyages, John. Breast Cancer: Taking Control. 2010. (Illus.). 368p. pap. 34.99 *(978-0-9806311-1-1(4))* BoyCare Pty. Ltd. AUS. Dist: AtlasBooks Distribution.

Boynton, Lora Lee. Goodbye Mommy: Memoirs of a Survivor. 2009. (ENG., Illus.). 296p. *(978-1-84876-110-0(4))* Troubadour Publishing Ltd.

Braddock, Suzanne W., et al. Straight Talk about Breast Cancer: From Diagnosis to Recovery. 4th ed. 2010. (ENG., Illus.). 170p. pap. 19.95 *(978-1-886039-97-1(6))* Addicus Bks.

Branch, Elizabeth. Sisters, You & I. 13.00 *(978-0-9720705-9-1(1))* G M A Publishing & Inspiration Pr.

Brennecke, Cecilia M. Breast Imaging: Case Review Series. 2nd ed. 2012. (Case Review Ser.). (ENG., Illus.). 320p. pap. 49.95 ***(978-0-323-08722-3(1)***, Saunders) Elsevier - Health Sciences Div.

Brinker, Nancy G. Promise Me: How a Sister's Love Launched the Global Movement to End Breast Cancer. l.t. ed. 2010. (Illus.). 646p. 31.99 *(978-1-4104-3149-3(5))* Thorndike Pr.

Brinker, Nancy G. & Rodgers, Joni. Promise Me: How a Sister's Love Launched the Global Movement to End Breast Cancer. 2010. (ENG., Illus.). 368p. 25.99 *(978-0-307-71812-9(3))* Broadway Bks.

—Promise Me: How a Sister's Love Launched the Global Movement to End Breast Cancer. 2011. (ENG.). 368p. pap. 15.00 *(978-0-307-71813-6(1)*, Three Rivers Pr.) Crown Publishing Group.

Brisbois, Maryellen. Why I Hated Pink: Confessions of a Breast Cancer Survivor. 2011. (ENG.). 144p. 17.95 *(978-1-936467-01-3(1)*, vantage*Point) Vantage Pr., Inc.

Brooks, Susan A. & Harris, Adrian, eds. Breast Cancer Research Protocols. 2010. (Methods in Molecular Medicine Ser.). (Illus.). 536p. pap. 179.00 *(978-1-61737-413-5(X)*, 161737413X) Humana Pr.

Brown, Phil. Toxic Exposures: Contested Illnesses & the Environmental Health Movement. 2007. (ENG., Illus.). 392p. (gr. 17). 32.00 *(978-0-231-12948-0(3))* Columbia Univ. Pr.

Brown, Steven G. Living & Loving Through & Past Cancer: A Spouse's Perspective. 2011. pap. 18.99 ***(978-1-61777-290-0(9))*** Tate Publishing & Enterprises, LLC.

Brown, Zora K. & Boatman, Karl. Breast Cancer. 3rd rev. ed. 2008. (ENG., Illus.). 259p. pap. 22.95 *(978-0-7637-6007-6(2))* Jones & Bartlett Learning, LLC.

Brun del Re, Renzo. Minimal Invasive Breast Procedures. 2009. (Recent Results in Cancer Research Ser.). (Illus.). 250p. 189.00 *(978-3-540-31403-5(2))* Springer.

Bueti, Cathy. Breastless in the City: A Young Woman's Story of Love, Loss, & Breast Cancer. 2006. (ENG.). 200p. pap. 14.95 *(978-1-59624-036-0(9))* Cleveland Clinic Pr.

Burstein, Harold J. Targeted Therapies in Breast Cancer. 2011. (Oxford American Pocket Notes Ser.). (ENG., Illus.). 64p. spiral bd. 14.95 *(978-0-19-973567-9(0))* Oxford Univ. Pr., Inc.

Buzdar, Aman U., ed. Endocrine Therapies in Breast Cancer. 2008. (ENG., Illus.). 128p. per. 24.95 *(978-0-19-921814-1(5))* Oxford Univ. Pr., Inc.

Cabot, Sandra & Jasinska ND, Margaret. Breast Cancer Prevention Guide. 2011. (ENG., Illus.). 176p. pap. 19.95 *(978-0-9829336-1-9(4))* SCB International.

Cappello, Mary. Called Back: My Reply to Cancer, My Return to Life. 2009. (ENG.). 220p. pap. 15.95 *(978-1-59350-150-1(1))* Alyson Pubns.

Cardenosa, Gilda. Breast Imaging Companion. 3rd rev. ed. 2007. (Imaging Companion Ser.). (ENG., Illus.). 624p. per. 92.95 *(978-0-7817-6491-9(2))* Lippincott Williams & Wilkins.

Cardiff, R. D. Comparative Pathobiology of Breast Cancer. 2008. pap. 135.00 *(978-1-58603-809-0(5))* IOS Pr., Inc.

Carvalho, Lucia Giuggio & Stewart, James A. The Everything Health Guide to Living with Breast Cancer: An Accessible & Comprehensive Resource for Women. 2009. (ENG., Illus.). 304p. pap. 14.95 *(978-1-59869-921-0(0))* Adams Media Corp.

Casperson, Diane & Wakefield, Cynthia. New Breast Friends: Surviving Cancer... Twice. 2011. 140p. 28.95 ***(978-1-4497-2217-3(2))***; pap. 11.95 ***(978-1-4497-2216-6(4))*** Author Solutions, Inc. (WestBow Pr.).

Castiglione, Monica & Piccart, Martine J., eds. Adjuvant Breast Cancer Treatment. 2008. (Cancer Treatment & Research Ser.). (Illus.). 352p. 199.00 *(978-0-387-75114-6(9)*, 0387751149) Springer.

Castoria, Gabriella & Migliaccio, Antimo, eds. Advances in Rapid Sex-Steroid Action: New Challenges & New Chances in Breast & Prostate Cancers. 2011. (ENG., Illus.). xvii, 268p. 189.00 ***(978-1-4614-1763-7(5)***, 1461417635) Springer.

Chillemi, Stacey. Breast Cancer: Questions, Answers & Self-Help Techniques. 2008. 191p. pap. 23.94 *(978-1-4357-2137-1(3))* Lulu Enterprises Inc.

Clark, Barbara. The Fight of My Life: The Inspiring Story of a Mother's Fight against Breast Cancer. 2007. (ENG., Illus.). 304p. 34.95 *(978-0-340-93809-6(9)*, Hodder & Stoughton) Hodder General Publishing Div. GBR. Dist: Independent Pubs. Group.

Cohen, Deborah A. & Gelfand, Robert M. Just Get Me Through This! - Revised & Updated. 2011. (ENG.). 272p. 15.00 *(978-0-7582-6953-9(6))* Kensington Publishing Corp.

Committee on Breast Cancer and the Environment: The Scientific Evidence, Research Methodology, and Future Directions & Institute of Medicine. Breast Cancer & the Environment: A Life Course Approach. 2012. (ENG.). 468p. pap. 91.00 ***(978-0-309-22069-9(6))*** National Academies Pr.

Cooke, David A., ed. When Your Doctor Says - Breast Cancer: A Guide to Regaining Control over Your Health & Well-Being. 2012. (When Your Doctor Says Ser.). (ENG.). 450p. pap. 24.95 *(978-0-7808-1169-0(0))* KWS Pubs.

Corrigan, Kelly. The Middle Place. 2008. (ENG.). 288p. pap. 14.95 *(978-1-4013-4093-3(8))*; (Illus.). 272p. 23.95 *(978-1-4013-0336-5(6))* Hyperion Pr.

Craig, Eileen. Devotions from the Chemo Room, 1 vol. 2010. 48p. pap. 16.95 *(978-1-4489-4343-2(4))* PublishAmerica, Inc.

Crompvoets, Samantha. Breast Cancer & the Post-Surgical Body: Recovering the Self. 2006. (ENG., Illus.). 224p. 100.00 *(978-1-4039-9900-9(7))* Palgrave Macmillan.

Cubrilo, Branka. The Mosaic of the Broken Soul. 2010. 320p. pap. *(978-1-907211-97-3(7))* Grosvenor Hse. Publishing Ltd.

Cummins, Sherry Taylor. Pink Ribbon Devotions to Go. 2007. pap. 8.95 *(978-0-9789831-3-0(0))* See Media.

Dang, Chau, ed. New Treatment Paradigms in Metastatic Breast Cancer. 2008. (Illus.). 96p. pap. 19.95 *(978-1-891483-61-5(7))* PRR, Inc.

Daniels, Elisha, et al. You Can Do This! Surviving Breast Cancer Without Losing Your Sanity or Your Style. 2009. (ENG.). 192p. pap. 12.99 *(978-0-7407-8575-7(3))* Andrews McMeel Publishing.

Davis, Cindy. Oncology Social Work Practice in the Care of Breast & Ovarian Cancer Survivors. 2008. 79.00 *(978-1-60692-594-2(6))* Nova Science Pubs., Inc.

De Wys, Margaret. Black Smoke: A Woman's Journey of Healing, Wild Love, & Transformation in the Amazon. 2009. (ENG.). 240p. 19.95 *(978-1-4027-4883-7(3))* Sterling Publishing Co., Inc.

DeFrina, Regina H., ed. Aggressive Breast Cancer. 2010. (Cancer Etiology, Diagnosis & Treatments Ser.). 118.62 *(978-1-60876-881-3(3)*, Nova Biomedical Bks.) Nova Science Pubs., Inc.

Delinsky, Barbara. Uplift: Secrets from the Sisterhood of Breast Cancer Survivors. 3rd ed. 2011. (ENG.). 416p. pap. 15.00 *(978-1-4516-5467-7(7)*, Beyond Words/Atria Bks.) Atria Bks.

Derosier, Cynthia Y. H. The Survivor Spirit: The Beauty, Passion, & Power of Breast Cancer Survivors. 2008. 64p. 24.95 *(978-0-9769548-2-8(6))* Good Juju Co., The.

Divine, Debra. My Private Confessions: An Enlightening Journey through Breast Cancer & Sexual Harassment. 2006. 12.00 *(978-0-8059-7311-2(7))* Dorrance Publishing Co., Inc.

Dixon, J. Michael. ABC of Breast Diseases. 4th ed. 2012. (ABC Ser.). (ENG.). 120p. pap. 46.95 ***(978-1-4443-3796-9(3))*** Wiley, John & Sons, Inc.

Douglas, Deborah. Foot Soldiers: Stories from the Breast Cancer 3-Day. 2006. *(978-0-944031-24-7(2))* Aslan Publishing.

Drijarkara, Agustinus Praba. Fuzzy Classification of Microcalcification in Mammograms. 2011. 104p. pap. ***(978-3-8443-2063-3(6))*** Lambert Academic Publishing.

Dwivedi, Alok, et al. Statistical Models for Treatment Delay & Number of Lymph Nodes. 2011. 304p. pap. ***(978-3-8443-2044-2(X))*** Lambert Academic Publishing.

Easter, Sheri. Hear My Heart. 2011. 254p. 36.99 ***(978-1-61379-821-8(0))*** Xulon Pr., Inc.

Ebdell, M. J. Silver Linings: Surviving Breast Cancer. 2007. (Illus.). 88p. per. *(978-1-84401-898-7(9))* Athena Pr.

Edwards, Elizabeth. Resilience: Reflections on the Burdens & Gifts of Facing Life's Adversities. 2010. (ENG.). 256p. pap. 15.00 *(978-0-7679-3156-4(4))* Random Hse., Inc.

—Resilience: Reflections on the Burdens & Gifts of Facing Life's Adversities. l.t. ed. 2009. 31.95 *(978-1-4104-1722-0(0))* Thorndike Pr.

Ehrlich, Ann B. & McMahon, Elizabeth J., eds. Voices of Lymphedema: Stories, advice, & inspiration from patients & Therapists. 2007. 256p. per. *(978-0-9764806-5-5(4))* Lymph Notes.

Elit, Laurie. Compendium of Resources Available for Cervix & Breast Cancer Care in the Majority World. 2007. 89.00 *(978-1-60021-844-6(X))* Nova Science Pubs., Inc.

Elliott, John and Della. Wendy Update:) in HIS HANDS. 2006. pap. 14.99 *(978-1-60034-552-4(2))* Xulon Pr., Inc.

Ellison, Connie & DRG Publishing Staff. Think Pink: Crochet for the Cure. 2008. (ENG.). 66p. pap. 14.95 *(978-1-59635-220-9(5)*, Annie's Attic, LLC) Annie's Publishing, LLC.

Ericksen, Julia A. Taking Charge of Breast Cancer. 2008. 319p. per. 24.95 *(978-0-520-25292-9(6))*; (Illus.). 60.00 *(978-0-520-25291-2(8))* Univ. of California Pr.

Espié, Marc & Gorins, André, eds. The Breast: From Normal to Cancerous. 2011. 800p. 260.00 *(978-2-7472-1651-7(9))* Eska, Editions FRA. Dist: International Publishers Marketing.

Fairchild, Kim. I'D Give My Left Boob for That Oh, Wait, I Already Did. 2009. 156p. 24.95 *(978-1-4401-4978-8(X))*; pap. 14.95 *(978-1-4401-4979-5(8))* iUniverse, Inc.

Faix-Wilkinson, Ph. D Kristin & Faix-Wilkinson. Deaf Women with Breast Cancer. 2011. 140p. pap. ***(978-3-8443-9317-0(X))*** Lambert Academic Publishing.

Farmer, David. The Cancer Diaries, a Journey Through the Crucible. 2009. 200p. pap. 13.95 *(978-1-60693-514-9(3)*, Eloquent Bks.) AEG Literary Publishing Services, Inc.

Favre, Deanna. Don't Bet Against Me! Beating the Odds Against Breast Cancer & in Life. 2008. (ENG.). 296p. pap. 14.99 *(978-1-4143-1908-7(8))* Tyndale Hse. Pubs.

Fenn, Alan J. Breast Cancer Treatment by Focused Microwave Thermotherapy. 2006. (Illus.). 216p. 121.95 *(978-0-7637-4870-8(6))* Jones & Bartlett Learning, LLC.

Fenn, Alan J. & Fenn, A. J. Adaptive Phased Array Thermotherapy for Cancer. 2008. (Illus.). 220p. 139.00 *(978-1-59693-379-8(8))* Artech Hse., Inc.

Ferreira, Melinda. Rays of Grace: A Story of Strength & Spirit. 2010. 148p. pap. 14.99 *(978-0-615-30016-0(2))* Hampton Pr., The.

Fikus, Sandra. Getting It off My Chest: A Journey through Breast Cancer. 2011. 166p. 29.99 ***(978-1-4568-8506-9(5))***; pap. 19.99 ***(978-1-4568-8505-2(7))*** Xlibris Corp.

Filleul, Barbara & Metting, Lucy Crichton. The Healing Handbook. (Illus.). 85p. pap. 10.00 *(978-0-9710319-0-6(8))* Freedom To Heal.

Finkel, Madelon L. Understanding the Mammography Controversy: Science, Politics, & Breast Cancer Screening, 1 vol. 2008. 216p. pap. 19.95 *(978-0-313-36317-7(X)*, B36317, Praeger Trade) Greenwood Publishing Group, Inc.

Fitoussi, A. Oncoplastic & Reconstructive Surgery for Breast Cancer: The Institut Curie Experience. 2009. (Illus.). 150p. *(978-3-642-00144-4(0))* Springer.

Fitoussi, A., et al. Oncoplastic & Reconstructive Surgery for Breast Cancer: The Institut Curie Experience. 2009. (ENG., Illus.). xi, 150p. 159.00 *(978-3-642-00143-7(2)*, 3642001432) Springer.

Fitzal, Florian & Schrenk, Peter, eds. Oncoplastic surgery of the Breast: A guide to clinical Practice. 2010. (ENG., Illus.). xiv, 242p. 369.00 *(978-3-211-99316-3(9)*, 3211993169) Springer.

Fitzpatrick, Andy. Why Mom? A Father's Journal of Mom's Breast Cancer Battle. 2010. 60p. pap. 11.49 *(978-1-4520-7925-7(0))* AuthorHouse.

Fitzpatrick-Nager, Laura. Swimming on My Wedding Day: My Cancer. 2008. 95p. pap. 12.95 *(978-0-595-86983-1(1)*, iUniverse, Inc.) iUniverse, Inc.

Fletcher, Alice. Out of My Valley: A Cancer Survivor's Journey to Meaning & Hope. 2009. 112p. pap. 10.99 *(978-1-60799-427-5(5))* Tate Publishing & Enterprises, LLC.

Floyd, Jeana. An Uninvited Guest: One Woman's Journey from Cancer to Hope. 2007. (Illus.). 128p. 12.99 *(978-0-89221-664-2(6))* New Leaf Pr., Inc.

Flynn, Mary & Barr, Nancy Verde. The Pink Ribbon Diet: A Revolutionary New Weight Loss Plan to Lower Your Breast Cancer Risk. 2010. (ENG.). 288p. pap. 16.95 *(978-0-7382-1394-1(2))* Da Capo Pr., Inc.

Ford, Thomas D. New Cancer Research Developments. 2009. pap. 129.00 *(978-1-60692-447-1(8))* Nova Science Pubs., Inc.

Fortugno, Louis P. Frontiers in Breast Cancer Research. 2007. (Illus.). (C). 129.00 *(978-1-60021-671-8(4))* Nova Science Pubs., Inc.

Fraim, Nalan Linda. Breast Cancer Awareness & Breast Self-Examination in Northern Cyprus. 2010. 156p. pap. *(978-3-8383-5921-2(6))* Lambert Academic Publishing.

Friedman, Sue, et al. Confronting Hereditary Breast & Ovarian Cancer: Identify Your Risk, Understand Your Options, Change Your Destiny. 2012. (Johns Hopkins Press Health Book Ser.). (ENG., Illus.). 288p. pap. 18.95 ***(978-1-4214-0408-0(7))***; (gr. 17). 45.00 ***(978-1-4214-0407-3(9))*** Johns Hopkins Univ. Pr.

Frields, Brenda. Help! I Have Breast Cancer. Tautges, Paul, ed. 2010. (Help! (Day One Publications) Ser.). 58p. pap. *(978-1-84625-216-7(4))* DayOne Pubns.

Fritz, Robert. What's the Next Step? My Journey with Cancer as a Caregiver & then as a Caretaker. 2011. 168p. 25.95 *(978-1-4502-9630-4(0))*; pap. 15.95 *(978-1-4502-9631-1(9))* iUniverse, Inc.

Gabriel, Sarah. Eating Pomegranates: A Memoir of Mothers, Daughters, & the BRCA Gene. 2010. (ENG.). 272p. 25.00 *(978-1-4391-4819-8(8)*, Scribner) Scribner.

Gale, Robert Peter, et al. Blood Stem Cell Transplants. 2011. (ENG.). 200p. pap. 26.99 ***(978-0-521-11693-0(7))*** Cambridge Univ. Pr.

Galgut, Cordelia. The Psychological Impact of Breast Cancer: A Psychologist's Insights As a Patient. 2010. (Illus.). xvi, 187p. pap. *(978-1-84619-303-3(6))* Radcliffe Publishing.

Garbowski, Anthony J. & Shaw, Lorna J. Don't Walk Through the Mirror. 2007. per. 17.95 *(978-1-888223-70-5(7))* McMillen Publishing.

Gasparini, Giampietro & Hayes, Daniel F., eds. Biomarkers in Breast Cancer. 2010. (Cancer Drug Discovery & Development Ser.). (Illus.). 360p. pap. 209.00 *(978-1-61737-436-4(9)*, 1617374369) Humana Pr.

Genetic counseling in breast Cancer. 2007. pap. 163.00 *(978-1-58603-793-2(5))* IOS Pr., Inc.

Ghiassi, Susan E. Thank God I Only Have Two of These! 2009. 103p. pap. 14.62 *(978-0-557-13627-8(X))* Lulu Enterprises Inc.

Gibbon, Sahra. Breast Cancer Genes & the Gendering of Knowledge: Science & Citizenship in the Cultural Context of the 'New' Genetics. 2007. (ENG.). 256p. 100.00 *(978-1-4039-9901-6(5))* Palgrave Macmillan.

Gieber, Jayna. Snatched from the Fire! Breast Cancer, Addiction, & Religious Oppression on the Path to Spiritual Freedom. 2008. 272p. pap. 17.95 *(978-0-595-48460-7(3))* iUniverse, Inc.

Gilsdorf, Janet R. Inside/Outside: A Physician's Journey with Breast Cancer. 2006. (Conversations in Medicine & Society Ser.). (ENG., Illus.). 256p. 29.95 *(978-0-472-11579-2(0))* Univ. of Michigan Pr.

Giordano, Antonio & Normanno, Nicola, eds. Breast Cancer in the Post-Genomic Era. (Current Clinical Oncology Ser.). (ENG., Illus.). xii, 230p. 2010. pap. 99.95 *(978-1-60761-466-1(9)*, 1607614669) 2009. 219.00 *(978-1-60327-944-4(X)*, 160327944X) Humana Pr.

Globe Pequot Press Staff. Pink Ribbon Sisterhood: Courage, Hope, & Inspiration from Women Who Battled Breast Cancer. Norris, Mary, ed. 2009. 224p. pap. 14.95 *(978-1-59921-820-5(8)*, skirt!) Globe Pequot Pr., The.

Gordon, Barbara, et al. Breast Cancer Recurrence & Advanced Disease: Comprehensive Expert Guidance. 2010. (ENG., Illus.). 388p. 74.95 *(978-0-8223-4742-2(3))* Duke Univ. Pr.

Gordon, Barbara L., et al. Breast Cancer Recurrence & Advanced Disease: Comprehensive Expert Guidance. 2010. (ENG., Illus.). 388p. pap. 21.95 *(978-0-8223-4763-7(6))* Duke Univ. Pr.

Gradishar, William J. & Wood, William C., eds. Advances in Breast Cancer Management. 2nd ed. 2007. (Cancer Treatment & Research Ser.). (Illus.). 175p. 139.00 *(978-0-387-73160-5(1)*, 0387731601) Springer.

—Advances in Breast Cancer Management. 2nd ed. 2008. pap. ***(978-0-387-78812-8(3))*** Springer Singapore Pte. Ltd.

Gragg, Ellen Washburn. Lady of Hope: A Journey of Faith with Breast Cancer. 2011. 152p. 30.95 ***(978-1-61507-875-2(4))***; pap. 13.95 ***(978-1-61507-874-5(6))*** Cross Bks. Publishing.

Greene, Diane Tropea. Apron Strings: Inheriting Courage, Wisdom and... Breast Cancer. 2007. (ENG., Illus.). 133p. per. 14.00 *(978-1-56825-108-0(4))* Rainbow Bks., Inc.

Gross, Carolyn. Treatable & Beatable: Healing Cancer Without Surgery. 2007. (Illus.). 200p. per. 19.95 *(978-0-9718064-1-2(1))* Creative Living Pubns.

Grubbs, Ronnie. The Psychological Treatment of Couples Confronting Breast Cancer. 2009. 184p. pap. *(978-3-639-11552-9(X))* VDM Verlag Dr. Mueller e.K.

Guellati-Salcedo, Sophie. Enhanced Benefit Finding in Women with Early Stage Breast Cancer. 2008. 80p. pap. *(978-3-639-07471-0(8))* VDM Verlag Dr. Mueller e.K.

Guscott, Jan. An Uplifting Experience: Cancer Is Not the End of the World It Just Seems Like It. 2009. (Illus.). 240p. pap. 14.49 *(978-1-4490-1217-5(5))* AuthorHouse.

Hall, R. Lee. As Normal As Possible: A Breast Cancer Story. 2009. 132p. 23.95 *(978-1-4401-5083-8(4))*; pap. 13.95 *(978-1-4401-5082-1(6))* iUniverse, Inc.

Hanks, Jerry & Cordova-Hanks, Bobbi de. Lagrimas de Alegria. 2007. 120p. pap. 12.95 *(978-0-7414-3859-1(3))* Infinity Publishing.

Hansen, Mark Victor, et al. Chicken Soup for the Breast Cancer Survivor's Soul: Stories to Inspire, Support & Heal. 2006. (Chicken Soup for the Soul Ser.). (ENG., Illus.). 320p. pap. 14.95 *(978-0-7573-0521-4(0))* Health Communications, Inc.

Hardman, Lizabeth. Breast Cancer. 2010. (Diseases & Disorders Ser.). (ENG.). 120p. 33.45 *(978-1-4205-0279-4(4)*, Lucent Bks.) Cengage Gale.

Harmer, Victoria. Breast Cancer Nursing Care & Management. 2nd ed. 2011. (ENG., Illus.). 384p. pap. 49.99 *(978-1-4051-9866-0(4)*, Wiley-Blackwell) Wiley, John & Sons, Inc.

Harris, Jay R. Diseases of the Breast. Harris, Jay R. et al, eds. 4th rev. ed. 2009. (ENG., Illus.). 1200p. 325.99 *(978-0-7817-9117-5(0))* Lippincott Williams & Wilkins.

Hart, Judy. Love, Judy: Letters of Hope & Healing for Women with Breast Cancer. 2008. (ENG.). 243p. pap. 15.00 *(978-1-4379-5864-5(8))* DIANE Publishing Co.

Hasak, Jan. Mourning Has Broken. 2008. 304p. pap. 17.99 *(978-1-60647-252-1(6))* Xulon Pr., Inc.

Hayat, M. A. Cancer Imaging, 2 vols. 2007. (ENG., Illus.). 672p. 350.00 *(978-0-12-374212-4(9))*; 656p. 225.00 *(978-0-12-370468-9(5))* Elsevier Science & Technology Bks. (Academic Pr.).

—Methods of Cancer Diagnosis, Therapy & Prognosis: Breast Carcinoma. 2008. (Methods of Cancer Diagnosis, Therapy & Prognosis Ser.). (Illus.). 1413p. 309.00 *(978-1-4020-8368-6(8))* Springer.

Hayat, M. A., ed. Methods of Cancer Diagnosis, Therapy, & Prognosis: General Overviews, Head & Neck Cancer & Thyroid Cancer. 2010. (Methods of Cancer Diagnosis, Therapy & Prognosis Ser.). (ENG., Illus.). l, 478p. 319.00 *(978-90-481-3185-3(5)*, 9048131855) Springer.

Hayward, Kate. From Oncology Nursing to Coping with Breast Cancer. 2008. (Patient Narratives Ser.). 160p. pap. *(978-1-84619-273-9(0))* Radcliffe Publishing.

Hazen, Denise & Procell, Jennifer. Treat Her Like a Princess: How to Help Your Girlfriend with Breast Cancer. 2009. (ENG., Illus.). 128p. pap. 14.95 *(978-1-933979-46-5(1))* Bright Sky Pr.

Hildebrandt, Sherri. More Than Enough. 2011. ***(978-1-77069-220-6(7))*** Word Alive Pr.

Hill, Jacquelyn. God's Battle in My Cancer. 2008. 84p. pap. 16.95 *(978-1-60474-591-7(6))* PublishAmerica, Inc.

Hirshaut, Yashar & Pressman, Peter I. Breast Cancer. 5th ed. 2008. (ENG.). 432p. instr.'s gde. ed. 17.00 *(978-0-553-38591-5(7)*, Bantam) Random House Publishing Group.

Hiscox, Stephen, et al, eds. Therapeutic Resistance to Anti-hormonal Drugs in Breast Cancer: New Molecular Aspects & their Potential as Targets. 2009.

(ENG., Illus.). xii, 204p. 159.00 *(978-1-4020-8525-3(7),* 1402085257) Springer.
Hoeppner, Pamela. The Breast Stays Put ~. 2008. 268p. per. 15.99 *(978-1-60477-103-9(8))* Xulon Pr., Inc.
Holmes, Karen L. He Provides the Shoes. 2008. 236p. pap. 15.99 *(978-1-60647-796-0(X))* Xulon Pr., Inc.
Horner, Christine. Waking the Warrior Goddess: Dr. Christine Horner's Program to Protect Against & Fight Breast Cancer. 2nd ed. 2007. (ENG., Illus.). 336p. per. 18.95 *(978-1-59120-215-8(9))* Basic Health Pubns., Inc.
—Waking the Warrior Goddess: Dr. Christine Horner's Program to Protect Against & Fight Breast Cancer. 2007. pap. 18.95 *(978-1-59122-158-6(7))* Gallery Leather Co., Inc.
Horton, Nancy. Hope in the Midst of Darkness: A Breast Cancer Survivor's Journey. 2011. 400p. pap. ***(978-1-77069-194-0(4))*** Word Alive Pr.
Hovda, Penny Meyer. And He Said, Praise Me! An Inspirational Reflection of One Woman's Journey Through Breast Cancer. 2010. pap. 8.99 *(978-1-61566-776-5(8))* Tate Publishing & Enterprises, LLC.
Isaacs, Claudine & Rebbeck, Timothy R., eds. Hereditary Breast Cancer. 2007. (ENG., Illus.). 400p. 230.00 *(978-0-8493-9022-7(2),* Informa Healthcare) Taylor & Francis Group GBR. Dist: Taylor & Francis Group.
Jackisch, C., ed. Treatment Options in ErbB2 (HER2)-Positive Breast Cancer Vol. 3, No. 1: Symposium, Munich, November 2007. 2008. (Illus.). 24p. pap., suppl. ed. *(978-3-8055-8595-8(0))* Karger, S. AG.
Jackisch, C. & Untch, M., eds. Systemic Therapy for Women with Erbb2-Positive Breast Cancer: New Options, New Challenges: Symposium, Munich, October 2009. 2010. (Illus.). 28p. pap. *(978-3-8055-9509-4(3))* Karger, S. AG.
Jackson, Kate. The Smart One. 2013. (ENG., Illus.). 304p. 25.99 *(978-1-4516-2156-3(6))* Gallery Pr., The IRL. Dist: Simon & Schuster, Inc.
Jacobs, Lisa & Finlayson, Christina. Breast Cancer. 2010. (Early Diagnosis in Cancer Ser.). (ENG., Illus.). 408p. 152.00 *(978-1-4160-4932-6(0),* Saunders) Elsevier - Health Sciences Div.
Jarvis, Debra. It's Not about the Hair: And Other Certainties of Life & Cancer. 2008. (ENG.). 256p. pap. 16.95 *(978-1-57061-573-3(X))* Sasquatch Bks.
Jodar, Nannette. Being Held by God: How I Caused My Own Miracle & How You Can Too! 2011. 128p. 23.95 *(978-1-4502-9367-9(0))*; pap. 13.95 *(978-1-4502-9365-5(4))* iUniverse, Inc.
Johnson, Nicole. Stepping into the Ring: Fighting for Hope over Despair in the Battle Against Breast Cancer. 2008. (ENG.). 67p. 11.00 *(978-1-4379-5210-0(0))* DIANE Publishing Co.
Judge, Pamela Morrow. Naming Horses & Other Short Stories & Poems. 2010. pap. 14.99 *(978-1-61566-969-1(6))* Tate Publishing & Enterprises, LLC.
Kaelin, Carolyn M. Living Through Breast Cancer: What a Harvard Doctor & Survivor Wants You to Know about Getting the Best Care While Preserving Your Self-Image. 2006. (ENG., Illus.). 384p. per. 16.95 *(978-0-07-147880-9(9),* 0071478809) McGraw-Hill Cos., The.
Kaelin, Carolyn M., et al. The Breast Cancer Survivor's Fitness Plan: Reclaim Health, Regain Strength, Live Longer. 2006. (Harvard Medical School Guides). (ENG., Illus.). 272p. per. 18.95 *(978-0-07-146578-6(2),* 0071465782) McGraw-Hill Cos., The.
Kahán, Zsuzsanna & Tot, Tibor, eds. Breast Cancer, a Heterogeneous Disease Entity: The Very Early Stages. 2011. (ENG.). x, 313p. 209.00 *(978-94-007-0488-6(7),* 9400704887) Springer.
Kale, Mehmet. Multispectral Co-Occurrence Analysis for Medical Image Processing. 2009. 140p. pap. *(978-3-639-13248-9(3))* VDM Verlag Dr. Mueller e.K.
Kallenbach, JuLee. And Then the Angels Came.... A Teacher's Breast Cancer Story. 2006. per. 5.95 *(978-0-9790529-0-3(4))* Kallenbach, JuLee.
Kantorowicz, Dee. The Handbook of Humor, Survivor Stories, Support, & Hope for People with Inflammatory Breast Cancer: You Are Not Alone. 2007. 52p. per. 8.95 *(978-1-4327-1433-8(3))* Outskirts Pr., Inc.
Kayser, Karen & Scott, Jennifer L. Helping Couples Cope with Women's Cancers: An Evidence-Based Approach for Practitioners. (ENG.). xv, 229p. 2010. pap. 49.95 *(978-1-4419-4514-3(8),* 1441945148) 2008. 49.95 *(978-0-387-74802-3(4),* 0387748024) Springer.
Kedrowski, Karen & Sarow, Marilyn. Cancer Activism: Gender, Media, & Public Policy. 2010. (ENG., Illus.). 320p. pap. 25.00 *(978-0-252-07777-7(6))* Univ. of Illinois Pr.
Keranen, Lisa. Scientific Characters: Rhetoric, Politics, & Trust in Breast Cancer Research. 2nd ed. 2010. (Albma Rhetoric Cult & Soc Crit Ser.). (ENG., Illus.). 248p. 45.00 *(978-0-8173-1704-1(X))* Univ. of Alabama Pr.
Kestner, Patricia. Breast Cancer & God's Word. 2007. 68p. per. 10.99 *(978-0-88144-279-3(8))* Yorkshire Publishing Group.
King, Judy. Breast Cancer Answers: Empowering & Encouraging Patients & Their Caregivers. 2nd ed. 2006. Orig. Title: Breast Cancer Answers: Practical Tips & Personal Advice from a Survivor. (Illus.). 384p. pap. 16.99 *(978-0-9660550-3-0(9))* Listo Pubns.
King, Samantha. Pink Ribbons, Inc: Breast Cancer & the Politics of Philanthropy. 2008. (Illus.). 208p. pap. 18.95 *(978-0-8166-4899-3(9))* Univ. of Minnesota Pr.
Kinney, Trish. Silver Platter Girl. 2009. 380p. 17.95 *(978-0-9822293-9-2(9))* Seven Locks Pr.
Klawiter, Maren. The Biopolitics of Breast Cancer: Changing Cultures of Disease & Activism. 2008. (Illus.). 384p. 75.00 *(978-0-8166-5107-8(8))*; pap. 25.00 *(978-0-8166-5108-5(6))* Univ. of Minnesota Pr.
Knaul, Felicia Marie. Beauty Without the Breast. Knaul, Felicia Marie, ed. adapted ed. 2012. (Women, Health, & Equity Ser.: Women & Health).Tr. of TóMatelo a Pecho. (ENG., Illus.). 375p. pap. 17.95 ***(978-0-9829144-1-0(5))*** Harvard Univ. Pr.
Kneece, Judy C. Breast Cancer Treatment Handbook: Understanding the Disease, Treatments, Emotions & Recovery from Breast Cancer. 7th ed. 2009. (Illus.). xiv, 242p. *(978-1-886665-23-1(0))* NAS/UWT.
Kollak, Ingrid & Utz-Billing, Isabell. Yoga & Breast Cancer: A Journey to Health & Healing. 2010. (ENG.). 224p. pap. 21.95 *(978-1-932603-91-0(3))* Demos Medical Publishing, LLC.
Koohi, Mohammad Kazem. Xenoestrogens. 2010. 132p. pap. *(978-3-639-19080-9(7))* VDM Verlag Dr. Mueller e.K.
Korowlay, Nisaar Ahmed. The Use of Lymphoscintigraphy to Localise the Sentinel Lymph Node/S. 2010. 108p. pap. *(978-3-8383-3914-6(2))* Lambert Academic Publishing.
Krychman. Breast Cancer Sensuality,Sexuality & Intimacy. rev. ed. 2010. 192p. pap. 22.95 *(978-0-7637-7909-2(1))* Jones & Bartlett Learning, LLC.
Kuerer, Henry. Kuerer's Breast Surgical Oncology. 2010. (ENG., Illus.). 1100p. 244.00 *(978-0-07-160176-4(7),* 0071601767) McGraw-Hill Professional Publishing.
Kuerer, Henry Mark. Kuerer's Breast Surgical Oncology. 2010. (Illus.). lii, 1125p. *(978-0-07-160178-8(3))* McGraw-Hill Medical Publishing Div.
Kumar, Amrendar, et al. Reinventing the Breast Cancer. 2011. 148p. pap. ***(978-3-8443-2304-7(X))*** Lambert Academic Publishing.
Kumar, Rakesh, et al. Breast Cancer Imaging II: An Issue of PET Clinics, Pt. 2. 2010. (Clinics: Radiology Ser.: 4-4). (ENG., Illus.). 77.00 *(978-1-4377-1402-9(1),* Saunders) Elsevier - Health Sciences Div.
—Breast Cancer Imaging I, an Issue of PET Clinics, Pt. 1. 2010. (Clinics: Radiology Ser.: 4-3). (ENG., Illus.). 77.00 *(978-1-4377-0964-3(8),* Saunders) Elsevier - Health Sciences Div.
Lacroix, Marc. A Concise History of Breast Cancer. 2011. *(978-1-61122-305-7(9))* Nova Science Pubs., Inc.
—Molecular Therapy of Breast Cancer: Classicism Meets Modernity. 2009. (Cancer Etiology, Diagnosis & Treatments Ser.). 291p. pap. 79.00 *(978-1-60741-593-0(3),* Nova Biomedical Bks.) Nova Science Pubs., Inc.
—Tumor Suppressor Genes in Breast Cancer. 2008. 114p. (C). pap. 39.00 *(978-1-60456-326-9(5),* Nova Biomedical Bks.) Nova Science Pubs., Inc.
Lacroix, Marc, ed. MicroRNAs in Breast Cancer. 2010. (Cancer Etiology, Diagnosis & Treatments Ser.). pap. 43.00 *(978-1-61668-438-9(0),* Nova Biomedical Bks.) Nova Science Pubs., Inc.
Ladun, Brenda. Behind the Scenes of Breast Cancer: A News Anchor Tells Her Story of Body & Soul Recovery. 2007. (ENG.). 208p. pap. 16.99 *(978-1-59669-091-2(7))* New Hope Pubs.
Lake. Dx/Rx: Breast Cancer 2E. 2nd rev. ed. 2010. 142p. pap. 49.95 *(978-0-7637-9433-0(3))* Jones & Bartlett Learning, LLC.
Lamonte, Jean R. Aromatase Inhibitors: Types, Mode of Action & Indications. 2009. (Cancer Etiology, Diagnosis & Treatments Ser.). 89.00 *(978-1-60741-711-8(1),* Nova Biomedical Bks.) Nova Science Pubs., Inc.
Langa, Bek P. Living & Working with Cancer. 2010. (Illus.). 54p. pap. *(978-1-84748-713-1(0))* Athena Pr.
Lange, Vladimir. Be a Survivor. Stankovich, Emily, ed. 2nd rev. ed. pap. 24.95 *(978-0-9663610-9-4(1))* Lange Productions.
—Be a Survivor: Your Guide to Breast Cancer Tratement. 5th ed. 2009. 192p. pap. 24.95 *(978-0-9819489-0-4(1))* Lange Productions.
Ler, Daria & Riederer, Monika. Establishment of a Diagnostic Test for the Detection of Tumor Markers. 2010. 88p. pap. *(978-3-639-23879-2(6))* VDM Verlag Dr. Mueller e.K.
Lester, Susan C. & Hicks, David G. Breast. 2011. (ENG., Illus.). 500p. 299.00 *(978-1-931884-57-0(9))* Lippincott Williams & Wilkins.
Levine, Alice C. Hormones & Cancer: Breast & Prostate, an Issue of Endocrinology Clinics. 2011. (Clinics: Internal Medicine Ser.: 40-3). (ENG.). 110.00 *(978-1-4557-1029-4(6),* Saunders) Elsevier - Health Sciences Div.
Lewis, Jacqueline. Your Guide to Breast Cancer. 2007. (Illus.). 160p. per 19.95 *(978-0-340-90500-5(X))* Hodder Arnold Pubs.
Lewis, Shelley. Five Lessons I Didn't Learn from Breast Cancer (and One Big One I Did) 2009. (Playaway Adult Nonfiction Ser.). (ENG.). 59.99 *(978-1-61545-961-2(8))* Findaway World, LLC.
Ley, Barbara L. From Pink to Green: Disease Prevention & the Environmental Breast Cancer Movement. 2009. (Critical Issues in Health & Medicine Ser.). (ENG., Illus.). 265p. pap. 24.95 *(978-0-8135-4531-8(5))* Rutgers Univ. Pr.
Leyland-Jones, Brian, ed. Pharmacogenetics of Breast Cancer: Towards the Individualization of Therapy. 2008. (Translational Medicine Ser.). 352p. pap. 100.00 *(978-1-4200-8637-9(5))*; (ENG., Illus.). 200.00 *(978-1-4200-5293-0(4))* Taylor & Francis Group GBR. (Informa Healthcare). Dist: Taylor & Francis Group.
Li, Christopher, ed. Breast Cancer Epidemiology. 2009. (ENG., Illus.). xii, 417p. 189.00 *(978-1-4419-0684-7(3),* 1441906843) Springer.
Li, Jonathan J., ed. Hormonal Carcinogenesis 5. 2008. (Advances in Experimental Medicine & Biology Ser.: Vol. 617). (Illus.). 600p. 199.00 *(978-0-387-69078-0(6))* Springer.
Lilia, Antonova. Stress Signalling & Breast Cancer Development: The Roles of Breast Cancer Susceptibility Gene 1 Regulation & Glucocorticoid Receptor Gene Variations in Breast Tumour Development. 2011. 160p. pap. ***(978-3-639-31668-1(1))*** VDM Verlag Dr. Mueller e.K.
Lillé, Shelly L. & Andolina, Valerie F. Mammographic Imaging: A Practical Guide. 3rd rev. ed. 2010. (ENG., Illus.). 608p. 87.95 *(978-1-60547-031-3(7))* Lippincott Williams & Wilkins.
Lober, Cso. Still Bigger Than Pink: Alive & Thriving! 2009. 184p. pap. 18.50 *(978-1-4389-7016-5(1))* AuthorHouse.
Lorde, Audre. The Cancer Journals. 2006. (ENG., Illus.). 104p. per. 12.95 *(978-1-879960-73-2(7))* Aunt Lute Bks.
Lori Lober, Csp Mirm. Still Bigger Than Pink. 2009. 184p. 25.50 *(978-1-4389-7017-2(X))* AuthorHouse.
Loscalzo, Matthew J. For the Women We Love: A Breast Cancer Action Plan & Caregiver's Guide for Men. 2007. (Illus.). 137p. per. 12.50 *(978-0-910155-71-7(2))* Bartleby Pr.
Losken, Albert & Hamdi, Moustapha. Partial Breast Reconstruction: Techniques in Oncoplastic Surgery. 2008. *(978-1-57626-283-2(9))* Quality Medical Publishing, Inc.
Love, Susan M. Dr. Susan Love's Breast Book. 5th ed. 2010. (Merloyd Lawrence Book Ser.). (ENG., Illus.). 752p. pap. 22.00 *(978-0-7382-1359-0(4))* Da Capo Pr., Inc.
Love, Tyesha K. I Am Not My Hair: A Young Woman's Journey & Triumph over Breast Cancer. 2010. 180p. 26.95 *(978-1-4401-9174-9(3))*; (ENG.). pap. 16.95 *(978-1-4401-9172-5(7))* iUniverse, Inc.
Löwy, Ilana. Preventive Strikes: Women, Precancer, & Prophylactic Surgery. 2009. (ENG., Illus.). 344p. (gr. 17). 52.00 *(978-0-8018-9364-3(X))* Johns Hopkins Univ. Pr.
Lyman, Gary H. & Burstein, Harold J., eds. Breast Cancer: Translational Therapeutic Strategies. 2007. (Translational Medicine Ser.: Vol. 2). (ENG., Illus.). 344p. *(978-0-8493-7416-6(2))* Informa Pharmaceuticals & Healthcare.
Mahmud, Khalid. Keeping Abreast: Ways to PREVENT Breast Cancer. 2008. 128p. 22.50 *(978-1-60693-313-8(2),* Strategic Bk. Publishing) AEG Literary Publishing Services, Inc.
Mahon, Suzanne M. Breast Cancer. 2nd ed. 2012. 200p. pap. ***(978-1-935864-07-3(6))*** 2011. ***(978-1-935864-11-0(4))*** Oncology Nursing Society.
Mahon, Suzanne M., ed. Site-Specific Cancer Series Breast Cancer. 2007. (Site-Specific Cancer Ser.). (ENG., Illus.). 178p. per. 49.00 *(978-1-890504-65-6(3))* Oncology Nursing Society.
Maisano, Gina M. Intimacy after Breast Cancer: Dealing with Your Body, Relationships, & Sex. 2009. 256p. pap. 16.95 *(978-0-7570-0324-0(9))* Square One Pubs.
Majumder, Barun. Modulation of Breast Cancer Genes by Conjugated Linoleic Acid. 2011. 244p. pap. ***(978-3-8454-0918-4(5))*** Lambert Academic Publishing.
Malmo, Katherine. Who in This Room: The realities of cancer, fish, & Demolition. 2011. (ENG.). 176p. pap. 14.95 *(978-0-934971-12-6(9))* Calyx Bks.
Mamounas, Terry B. & Mamounas, Eleftherios P. Early-Stage Breast Cancer - New Developments & Controversies: Surgical Oncology Clinics. 2010. (Clinics: Surgery Ser.: 19-3). (ENG., Illus.). xvi, 465p. 105.00 *(978-1-4377-2617-6(8),* Saunders) Elsevier - Health Sciences Div.
Manahan, Nancy & Bohan, Becky. Living Consciously, Dying Gracefully: A Journey with Cancer & Beyond. 2007. (Illus.). 216p. per. 17.00 *(978-1-59298-179-3(8))* Beaver's Pond Pr., Inc.
Manne, Sharon L. & Ostroff, Jamie S. Coping with Breast Cancer: Workbook for Couples. 2008. (Treatments That Work Ser.). (ENG.). 80p. pap. 22.95 *(978-0-19-534291-8(7))* Oxford Univ. Pr., Inc.
Mansel, R. E. Metastasis of Breast Cancer. 2007. (Cancer Metastasis - Biology & Treatment Ser.). xiii, 435p. 229.00 *(978-1-4020-5866-0(7),* 1402058667) Springer.
Mansel, Robert E., et al, eds. Metastasis of Breast Cancer. 2008. 456p. pap. 99.00 *(978-1-4020-8529-1(X))* Springer.
Marchese, Marianne. 8 Weeks of Women's Wellness: The Detoxification Plan for Breast Cancer, Endometriosis, Infertility & Other Women's Health Conditions. 2011. (ENG.). 256p. pap. 16.95 *(978-0-9843635-5-1(6))* Smart Pubns.
Marchetto, Marisa Acocella. Cancer Vixen. 2009. (Illus.). 224p. pap. 16.95 *(978-0-375-71474-0(X),* Pantheon) Knopf Doubleday Publishing Group.
—Cancer Vixen: A True Story. 2006. (ENG., Illus.). 224p. 22.00 *(978-0-307-26357-5(6),* Knopf) Knopf Doubleday Publishing Group.
—Cancer Vixen: A True Story. 2009. (ENG.). 192p. pap. *(978-0-676-97825-4(8),* Vintage Canada) Random Hse. of Canada, Ltd. CAN. Dist: Random Hse., Inc.
Marchionni, Luigi. Impact of Gene Expression Profiling Tests on Breast Cancer Outcomes. 2008. (Illus.). viii, 105p. *(978-1-58763-333-1(7))* Agency for Healthcare Research & Quality.
—Impact of Gene Expression Profiling Tests on Breast Cancer Outcomes. 2009. (ENG.). 221p. (C). pap. 45.00 *(978-1-4379-1104-6(8))* DIANE Publishing Co.
Markes, Martina. Exercise during breast-cancer treatment: A systematic review. 2011. 164p. pap. ***(978-3-8381-2698-2(X))*** Südwestdeutscher Verlag für Hochschulschriften AG & Co. KG.
Matthews, Annie Harmon & Sikora, Karol. Anni's Cancer Companion: An A-Z of Treatments, Therapies & Healing. 2011. (ENG.). 288p. pap. ***(978-1-84819-067-2(0))*** Singing Dragon.
McClain, Catherine. Cancer Dance. 2008. 185p. pap. 24.95 *(978-1-60441-730-2(7))* PublishAmerica, Inc.
McCormick, Sabrina. No Family History: The Environmental Links to Breast Cancer. (New Social Formations Ser.). (ENG.). 2010. 190p. pap. 16.95 *(978-0-7425-6409-1(6))* 2009. (Illus.). 192p. 37.50 *(978-0-7425-6408-4(8))* Rowman & Littlefield Publishers, Inc.
McNeal, Franne. Off My Chest, but on My Mind: Busting the Barriers of Breast Cancer. 2007. 160p. pap. 21.95 *(978-0-9791643-3-0(8))* Significant Business Results LLC.
Mehta, Jai Prakash, et al. Understanding Breast Cancer Dynamics Using Gene Expression Profiling. 2010. 396p. pap. *(978-3-8383-5931-1(3))* Lambert Academic Publishing.
Meinel, Lina Arbash. Breast Cancer Characterization Computer-Aided Diagnostic System for Breast Mri Mass Classification. 2008. 120p. pap. *(978-3-639-08072-8(6))* VDM Verlag Dr. Mueller e.K.
Metz, James M. & Hampshire, Margaret K., eds. Breast Cancer. 2006. (ENG.). 256p. pap. 28.95 *(978-0-7020-2866-3(5),* Saunders) Elsevier - Health Sciences Div.
Meyer, Armin. Alternative Werbung mit Mixed-Reality-Technologie: Konzepte mit Mehrwert für die Kommunikationspolitikdurch den Einsatz von Mixed-Reality-Technologie. 2008. 96p. pap. *(978-3-639-02123-3(1))* VDM Verlag Dr. Mueller e.K.
Michell, Michael J., ed. Breast Cancer. 2010. (Contemporary Issues in Cancer Imaging Ser.). (ENG., Illus.). 282p. 99.00 *(978-0-521-51950-2(0))* Cambridge Univ. Pr.
Miller, Kenneth D., ed. Choices in Breast Cancer Treatment: Medical Specialists & Cancer Survivors Tell You What You Need to Know. 2008. (Johns Hopkins Press Health Book Ser.). (ENG., Illus.). 416p. 47.00 *(978-0-8018-8684-3(8))*; per. 19.95 *(978-0-8018-8685-0(6)),* Johns Hopkins Univ. Pr.
Mirriam-Goldberg, Caryn. The Sky Begins at Your Feet. 2009. 242p. pap. 21.95 *(978-1-888160-43-7(8))* Ice Cube Pr.
Moinfar, Farid. Essentials of Diagnostic Breast Pathology: A Practical Approach. 2007. (Illus.). XVI, 496p. 379.00 *(978-3-540-45117-4(X),* 354045117X) Springer.
Morère, Jean-Francois, et al, eds. Le cancer du Sein. 2008. (Oncologie Pratique Ser.). 314p. pap. 49.95 *(978-2-287-36071-8(9),* 2287360719) Springer.
Morgan. Mastectomy: From Devastation to Resilience. 2009. 368p. 29.99 *(978-1-4490-3343-9(1))*; pap. 19.99 *(978-1-4490-3342-2(3))* AuthorHouse.
Morgan, Christine L. My Sister Has Breast Cancer. 2009. pap. 11.99 *(978-1-60799-030-7(X))* Tate Publishing & Enterprises, LLC.
Morgan, Lindsey & Washington, Linda. Believing That You Belong after Having a Mastectomy: (Follow My Journey, Part 1), 1 vol. 2009. 48p. pap. 16.95 *(978-1-60749-394-5(2))* PublishAmerica, Inc.
Morris, Jol L. & Gordon, Ora K. Positive Results: Making the Best Decisions When You're at High Risk for Breast or Ovarian Cancer. 2010. (ENG., Illus.). 320p. pap. 20.00 *(978-1-59102-776-8(4))* Prometheus Bks., Pubs.
Mozersky, Jessica. Risky Genes: Genetics, Breast Cancer, & Jewish Identity. 2012. (Genetics & Society Ser.). (ENG.). 200p. (C). 135.00 ***(978-0-415-50228-3(4))*** Routledge.
Murphy, Deb, ed. Why We Walk: The Inspirational Journey Toward a Cure for Breast Cancer. 2008. (ENG.). 176p. 30.00 *(978-1-4379-5213-1(5))* DIANE Publishing Co.
Murphy, Diana. A Woman's Initiation: Women's Experiences with Breast Cancer & How It Transformed Their Lives. 2006. 136p. pap. 14.95 *(978-0-9779556-0-2(5))* Synchronicity Bks.
Musser, Robert. The P I N K Primer: For Partners in Need of Koaching. 2009. 116p. pap. 12.95 *(978-1-60844-176-1(8))* Dog Ear Publishing, LLC.
Nahabedian, Maurice & Nahabedian, Maurice Y. Oncoplastic Surgery of the Breast with DVD. 2009. (ENG., Illus.). 200p. 195.00 *(978-0-7020-3181-6(X),* Saunders) Elsevier - Health Sciences Div.
Nathanson, S. David. Ordinary Miracles: Learning from Breast Cancer Survivors, 1 vol. 2007. (Praeger Series on Contemporary Health & Living Ser.). (Illus.). 208p. 49.95 *(978-0-275-99469-3(4),* C9469, Praeger Pubs.) Greenwood Publishing Group, Inc.
Neave, Veronica. Pieces of Me. 2011. pap. 13.99 ***(978-1-59955-851-6(3),*** Bonneville Bks.) Cedar Fort, Inc. CFI Distribution.
Necula, Virgil. Breast Cancer: Women's Killer. 2008. 161p. pap. 14.95 *(978-0-7414-4558-2(1))* Infinity Publishing.
Nelson, Jennifer J., et al. Cancer on the Margins: Method & Meaning in Participatory Research. 2009. (ENG., Illus.). 288p. *(978-0-8020-9169-7(5))*; pap. *(978-0-8020-9434-6(1))* Univ. of Toronto Pr.
Ng, Y. K. Eddie, et al. Performance Evaluation of Breast Cancer: Screening, Diagnosis, & Treatment. 2010. (Illus.). xxiv, 293p. ***(978-1-58883-156-9(6))*** American Scientific Pubs.
Nilon, Cathy. Chemo Cat. 2007. 56p (J). pap. 9.95 *(978-0-9791921-4-2(5))* Ravenna Pr.
Norsa'adah, Bachok, et al. Risk Factors of Female Breast Cancer in Kelantan Malaysi. 2011. 120p. pap. ***(978-3-8443-3498-2(X))*** Lambert Academic Publishing.
Norton, Karen L. Overwhelmed: One Woman's Journey with Breast Cancer. 2011. pap. 10.99 *(978-1-61739-068-5(2))* Tate Publishing & Enterprises, LLC.
Norton, Meredith. Lopsided: A Memoir. 2009. (ENG.). 224p. (gr. 12-18). 15.00 *(978-0-14-311563-2(4),* Penguin (Non-Classics)) Penguin Group (USA) Inc.
Nugent, Andrea. Mommy Is Still Mommy, Cancer Can't Change That. 2011. 20p. pap. 15.99 ***(978-1-4634-3783-1(8))*** AuthorHouse.
O'Brien, Joan & O'Brien, Alyssa. The Quilt of My Life. 2010. 238p. pap. 12.99 *(978-0-557-62696-0(X))* Lulu Enterprises Inc.
O'Hara, Rosie. No More Bingo Dresses: Using NLP to cope with breast cancer & other People. 2011. 224p. pap. ***(978-1-908218-34-6(7))*** MX Publishing, Ltd.
Olopade, Olufunmilayo I. & Falkson, Carla I., eds. Breast Cancer in Women of African Descent. 2010. xxii, 385p. pap. 179.00 *(978-90-481-6929-0(1),* 9048169291) Springer.
Osborn, Lesa Kelley. 365 Daze. 2011. 104p. pap. 13.95 ***(978-1-4567-4572-1(7))*** AuthorHouse.
Papale-Hammontree, Cindy & Hernandez, Sabrina. The Empty Cup Runneth Over: Answers about Breast Cancer from the Experts. 2008. 160p. pap. 26.00 *(978-0-8059-7772-1(4))* Dorrance Publishing Co., Inc.

Pardee, Joel D. Breast Cancer & the Estrogen Receptor. 2011. (Colloquium Series on the Cell Biology of Medicine Ser.). 52p. pap. 35.00 *(978-1-61504-075-9(7))* Morgan & Claypool Life Science Publishers.

Parthasarathy, Shobita. Building Genetic Medicine: Breast Cancer, Technology, & the Comparative Politics of Health Care. (Inside Technology Ser.). (ENG., Illus.). 288p. (gr. 17). 2012. pap. 18.00 ***(978-0-262-51747-8(7))*** 2007. 35.00 *(978-0-262-16242-5(3))* MIT Pr.

Parvin, Elizabeth, ed. Screening for Breast Cancer. 2008. (Introducing Health Science Ser.). (ENG., Illus.). 104p. pap. 52.50 *(978-0-19-923733-3(6))* Oxford Univ. Pr., Inc.

Pasqualini, Jorge R., ed. Breast Cancer: Prognosis, Treatment, & Prevention. 2nd rev. ed. 2008. (ENG., Illus.). 608p. 300.00 *(978-1-4200-5872-7(X)*, Informa Healthcare) Taylor & Francis Group GBR. Dist: Taylor & Francis Group.

Patenaude, Andrea Farkas. Prophylactic Mastectomy: Insights from Women Who Chose to Reduce Their Risk. 2012. E-Book ***(978-0-313-34517-3(1)***, Praeger Pubs.); 227p. 48.00 ***(978-0-313-34516-6(3)***, C34516) Greenwood Publishing Group, Inc.

Patsy McClendon McDonald (Brown). Cancer & Me: My Cure, My Salvation. 2009. 56p. pap. 9.95 *(978-1-4401-6171-1(2))* iUniverse, Inc.

Peart, Olive. Mammography & Breast Imaging PREP. 2012. (ENG., Illus.). 509p. (C). pap. 60.00 ***(978-0-07-174932-9(2)***, 0071749322) McGraw-Hill Medical Publishing Div.

Peart, Olive. Mammography Examination. 2nd ed. 2008. (LANGE Q&a Allied Health Ser.). (ENG., Illus.). 184p. 63.00 *(978-0-07-154835-9(1)*, 007154835l) McGraw-Hill Medical Publishing Div.

Pedicone, Wendi Fox. Hanging Out with Lab Coats: Hope, Humor & Help for Cancer Patients & Their Caregivers. 2007. (Illus.). 348p. 24.95 *(978-0-9768997-0-9(1))*; per. 17.95 *(978-0-9768997-1-6(X))* FoxPress.

Pegg, Jonathan D. Breast Cancer Screening & Prevention. 2011. (Series: Cancer Etiology, Diagnosis & Treatments Ser.). (Illus.). 132p. 59.00 *(978-1-61209-288-1(8)*, Nova Biomedical Bks.) Nova Science Pubs., Inc.

Peltason, Ruth A. I Am Not My Breast Cancer: Women Talk Openly about Love & Sex, Hair Loss & Weight Gain, Mothers & Daughters, & Being a Woman with Breast Cancer. 2008. (ENG.). 400p. pap. 15.95 *(978-0-06-117407-0(6)*, Harper Paperbacks) HarperCollins Pubs.

Peltason, Ruth A. & Peltason, Ruth. I Am Not My Breast Cancer: Women Talk Openly about Love & Sex, Hair Loss & Weight Gain, Mothers & Daughters, & Being a Woman with Breast Cancer. 2008. 400p. 25.95 *(978-0-06-117410-0(6)*, Morrow, William & Co.) HarperCollins Pubs.

Perera, Candida & Camarillo, Ignacio. Mechanisums of Leptin in Breast Cancer Development & Progression. 2010. 128p. pap. *(978-3-8383-7333-1(2))* Lambert Academic Publishing.

Perez, Edith A. Atlas of Breast Cancer. 2007. *(978-1-57340-250-7(8))* Current Medicine Group LLC.

Peters-Smith, Christina. Nothing to See & Nothing to Feel. 2010. 68p. pap. 10.49 *(978-1-4490-0989-2(1))* AuthorHouse.

Peterson, Rosendo D. Breast Pathology: Diagnosis by Needle Core Biopsy. Hoda, Syed A. & Rosen, Paul Peter, eds. 3rd rev. ed. 2010. (ENG., Illus.). 432p. 224.99 *(978-1-60831-670-0(X))* Lippincott Williams & Wilkins.

Photographer Katy Tartakoff. Cup Half Full: Life in the Face of Breast Cancer. 2009. pap. 39.95 *(978-0-615-39083-3(8))* Photographer Katy Tartakoff.

Pollard, Tessa. Western Diseases: An Evolutionary Perspective. 2008. (Cambridge Studies in Biological & Evolutionary Anthropology Ser.). (ENG., Illus.). (C). 236p. 133.99 *(978-0-521-85180-0(7))*; 223p. pap. 66.00 *(978-0-521-61737-6(5))* Cambridge Univ. Pr.

Pontin, Emma. Beating the Blowfish: A candid account of a young yacht skipper's battle with breast Cancer, 1 vol. 2010. (ENG., Illus.). 208p. pap. 19.95 *(978-1-57409-294-3(4))* Sheridan Hse., Inc.

Port, Dina Roth. Previvors: Facing the Breast Cancer Gene & Making Life-Changing Decisions. 2010. (ENG.). 288p. (gr. 12). 16.00 *(978-1-58333-405-8(X)*, Avery) Penguin Group (USA) Inc.

Premium Denim and PrivacyWear, Prvcy. Lives Inspired. 2009. 55p. 44.00 *(978-0-692-00352-7(5))* Diamond Decisions.

Prijatel, Patricia. Surviving Triple Negative Breast Cancer: Hope, Treatment, & Recovery. 2012. 256p. 27.95 ***(978-0-19-538762-9(7))*** Oxford Univ. Pr., Inc.

Queller, Jessica. Pretty Is What Changes: Impossible Choices, the Breast Cancer Gene, & How I Defied My Destiny. 2009. (ENG.). 272p. pap. 14.00 *(978-0-385-52041-6(7))* Spiegel & Grau.

Quinlan, Casey. Cancer for Christmas: Making the Most of a Daunting Gift. 2009. 130p. pap. 12.95 *(978-1-936051-41-0(9))* Peppertree Pr., The.

Raab, Diana. Healing with Words: A Writer's Cancer Journey. 2010. pap. *(978-1-61599-010-8(0))* Loving Healing Pr., Inc.

Raab, Diana M. Healing with Words: A writer's cancer Journey. 2011. 204p. 32.95 ***(978-1-61599-110-5(7))*** Loving Healing Pr., Inc.

Rakoff, Ruth. When My World Was Very Small: A Memoir of Family, Food, Cancer & My Couch. 2010. (ENG.). 224p. 25.95 *(978-0-307-35817-2(8)*, Random Hse CAN) Random Hse. of Canada, Ltd. CAN. Dist: Random Hse., Inc.

Randolph, Margaret & Tewksbury, Cielle. Healing Gifts: Qi Gong in Breast Cancer Recovery. 2009. *(978-1-882883-75-2(6))* Idyll Arbor, Inc.

Rasmussen, Sonja. Doing It with Bling On: Batting Breast Cancer with Style. 2010. 200p. pap. 18.49 *(978-1-4490-8622-0(5))* AuthorHouse.

Ratner, Lynn H. Contemporary Diagnosis & Mangement of Breast Cancer. 2009. 308p. pap. 24.99 *(978-1-935103-06-6(7))* Assocs. in Medical Marketing Co., Inc.

Raval-Nelson, Palak. Breast Cancer Politics: An Evaluation of the Current Research Funding Policies. 2008. 128p. pap. *(978-3-639-09154-0(X))* VDM Verlag Dr. Mueller e.K.

Rawlinson, Mary C. & Lundeen, Shannon, eds. The Voice of Breast Cancer in Medicine & Bioethics. 2010. (Philosophy & Medicine Ser.). (Illus.). xix, 207p. pap. 199.00 *(978-90-481-7139-2(3)*, 9048171393) Springer.

Rayter, Zenon & Mansi, Janine, eds. Medical Therapy of Breast Cancer. 2008. (ENG., Illus.). 416p. pap. 58.00 *(978-0-521-08859-6(3))* Cambridge Univ. Pr.

Reed, Malcolm W. & Audisio, Riccardo A. Management of Breast Cancer in Older Women. 2010. (ENG., Illus.). xvi, 413p. 189.00 *(978-1-84800-264-7(5)*, 1848002645) Springer.

Reed, Malcolm W. & Audisio, Riccardo A., eds. Management of Breast Cancer in Older Women. 2011. (Illus.). xvi, 413p. pap. 89.95 *(978-0-85729-515-6(2)*, 0857295152) Springer.

Reinisch, Nancy. Chemosabee. 2009. 234p. pap. 24.95 *(978-0-615-22963-8(8))* NRR Publishing.

Richardson, Jamie. Letting Go. 2010. 180p. pap. 15.00 *(978-1-4520-0157-9(X))* AuthorHouse.

Robb, Geoffrey L., et al, eds. Breast Cancer. 2nd ed. 2007. (M. D. Anderson Cancer Care Ser.). (Illus.). 561p. per. 89.95 *(978-0-387-34950-3(2))* Springer.

Roderick, Debbie. Scarred for Life: Diary of a Pink Ribbon Princess. 2011. 120p. pap. 12.95 ***(978-1-4575-0140-1(6))*** Dog Ear Publishing, LLC.

Romero, Martin E. & Dashek, Louis M. Breast Cancer: Causes, Diagnosis & Treatment. 2010. (Cancer Etiology, Diagnosis & Treatments Ser.). (Illus.). 228p. 129.00 *(978-1-60876-463-1(X)*, Nova Biomedical Bks.) Nova Science Pubs., Inc.

Ronco, Alvaro Luis & Stéfani, Eduardo de. Nutritional Epidemiology of Breast Cancer. 2011. Orig. Title: Epidemiología Nutricional del Cáncer de Mama. (ENG., Illus.). x, 233p. 189.00 ***(978-94-007-2396-2(2)***, 9400723962) Springer.

Roppe, Laura. Rocking the Pink: Finding Myself on the Other Side of Cancer. 2012. (ENG.). 320p. pap. 17.00 ***(978-1-58005-417-1(X))*** Seal Pr.

Rose, Holly. Live & Give: Facebooking My Way Through Breast Cancer. 2011. (ENG.). 338p. pap. 14.99 *(978-0-615-43869-6(5))* Holly Rose.

Rosu, Claudia A. Race & Patient Perception of Interpersonal Processes of Care. 2008. 300p. pap. *(978-3-639-04834-6(2))* VDM Verlag Dr. Mueller e.K.

Roswell, Eileen C., ed. Encyclopedia of Breast Cancer Research, 2 vols. 2012. (Series: Cancer Etiology, Diagnosis & Treatments Ser.). 638p. 325.00 *(978-1-61324-388-6(X))* Nova Science Pubs., Inc.

Rudden, Jane. If We Must Dance, Then I Will Lead: A Memoir of Breast Cancer Survival. 2010. 180p. (ENG.). 26.95 *(978-1-4502-1176-5(3))*; pap. 16.95 *(978-1-4502-1178-9(X))* iUniverse, Inc.

Russo, Jose, ed. Environment & Breast Cancer. 2011. (ENG., Illus.). xvi, 237p. 209.00 *(978-1-4419-9895-8(0)*, 1441998950) Springer.

Salkowski, Lonie. Breast Imaging. 2012. (ENG., Illus.). 224p. pap. 49.95 *(978-1-60406-191-8(X))* Thieme Medical Pubs., Inc.

Salvador, Sara Marina. Microwave Imaging of Biological Structures. 2010. 144p. pap. *(978-3-8383-6806-1(1))* Lambert Academic Publishing.

Saphron. WHOLE: Women Healing Ourselves with Loving Energy: 12 Principles for Rebuilding Life after Breast Cancer. 2007. (Illus.). 251p. *(978-0-9714219-7-4(8))* Conch Shell Pr.

Sarkeala, Tytti. Performance & Effectiveness of Organised Breast Cancer Screening in Finland. 2009. (Acta Universitatis Tamperensis Ser.). 129p. pap. 72.50 *(978-951-44-7299-2(3))* Tampere Univ. Pr. FIN. Dist: Coronet Bks.

Saunders, Avril Dalziel. Mammograms Save Lives. 2012. (ENG.). 70p. pap. 9.99 ***(978-1-907728-36-5(8)***, PS True Life) Pneuma Springs Publishing GBR. Dist: Lightning Source, Inc.

Saunders, Christobel & Jassal, Sunil. Breast Cancer. 2009. (Facts Ser.). (ENG., Illus.). 160p. pap. 19.95 *(978-0-19-955869-8(8))* Oxford Univ. Pr., Inc.

Sauter, Edward & Daly, Mary B. Breast Cancer Risk Reduction & Early Detection. 2010. (ENG., Illus.). viii, 242p. 189.00 *(978-0-387-87582-8(4)*, 0387875824) Springer.

Schmidt, Leslie D., ed. Effectiveness of Core-Needle & Open Surgical Biopsy in Breast Cancer Evaluation. 2011. ***(978-1-61209-799-2(5))*** Nova Science Pubs., Inc.

Schmitt, Marci A. March Forth: My Journey through Diagnosis, Treatment, & Recovery from Breast Cancer. 2011. (ENG.). 282p. pap. 19.95 ***(978-1-4327-7600-8(2))*** Outskirts Pr., Inc.

Schneider, Andrea. You are Not Alone: Life after a Breast Cancer Diagnosis. 2010. 268p. 29.99 *(978-1-4520-3821-6(X))*; pap. 18.99 *(978-1-4520-3822-3(8))* AuthorHouse.

Schnipper, Hester Hill. After Breast Cancer: A Common-Sense Guide to Life after Treatment. rev. ed. 2006. (ENG.). 320p. pap. 16.00 *(978-0-553-38425-3(2)*, Bantam) Random House Publishing Group.

Schnitt, Stuart J. & Collins, Laura C. Biopsy Interpretation of the Breast. 2008. (Biopsy Interpretation Ser.). (ENG., Illus.). 496p. 164.95 *(978-0-7817-9146-5(4))* Lippincott Williams & Wilkins.

Scott, Catharine Bracken. Only If You Really Want to Know: Breast Cancer: Coping Hints & Treatment Side Effects. 2006. pap. 9.95 *(978-0-9760867-1-0(9))* Fountain City Publishing Co. Enterprise.

Sell, Colleen. Breast Cancer Survivors: Inspiring Stories of Courage & Triumph. 2008. (ENG.). 336p. pap. 9.95 *(978-1-59869-650-9(5))* Adams Media Corp.

—A Cup of Comfort for Breast Cancer Survivors: Inspiring Stories of Courage & Triumph. 2008. (ENG.). 336p. pap. 9.99 *(978-1-60550-644-9(3))* Adams Media Corp.

Sethi, Josephine Caruso. The Faces behind Breast Cancer. 2009. 30.00 net. *(978-1-60402-131-8(4))* Independent Pub.

Sewell, Sue. In the Shadow of Your Wings. 2006. 104p. per. 10.99 *(978-0-9759049-8-5(1))* Master Pr.

Sharma, Garima & Vinita Bhargava. Construals of Stress & Well-Being in Women with Breast Cancer. 2011. 100p. pap. ***(978-3-8443-3067-0(4))*** Lambert Academic Publishing.

Sheldon, Lisa Kennedy & Urquhart, Laura M. A Nurse's Guide to Caring for Cancer Survivors: Breast Cancer. 2009. (ENG.). 230p. spiral bd. 28.95 *(978-0-7637-7258-1(5))* Jones & Bartlett Learning, LLC.

Shelton, Stacy. Me, the Crazy Woman, & Breast Cancer: Strength & Inspiration for the Patient, Survivor, & Those Who Love Them. 2009. 313p. pap. 19.95 *(978-0-9825085-9-6(X))* Enlighten Pr.

Shockney. Breast Cancer Surgery. rev. ed. 2011. 149.95 *(978-0-7637-7910-8(5))* Jones & Bartlett Learning, LLC.

Shockney, Lillie. Becoming a Breast Center Nurse Navigator. rev. ed. 2009. 148p. pap. 28.95 *(978-0-7637-8494-2(X))* Jones & Bartlett Learning, LLC.

—Breast Cancer. 2009. (ENG.). 158p. pap. 11.95 *(978-0-7637-7426-4(X))* Jones & Bartlett Learning, LLC.

—Breast Cancer Survivorship Care. rev. ed. 2009. 226p. pap. 28.95 *(978-0-7637-8496-6(6))* Jones & Bartlett Learning, LLC.

—Navigating Breast Cancer: A Guide for the Newly Diagnosed. 2nd rev. ed. 2010. 116p. pap. 22.95 *(978-0-7637-8683-0(7))* Jones & Bartlett Learning, LLC.

—Stealing Second Base: A Breast Cancer Survivor's Experience & Breast Cancer Expert's Story. 2006. (Illus.). 113p. per. 22.95 *(978-0-7637-4509-7(X))* Jones & Bartlett Learning, LLC.

—Top Concerns about HER2 Positive Breast Cancer. 2012. 128p. pap. 10.95 *(978-1-4496-0125-6(1))* Jones & Bartlett Learning, LLC.

Shockney, Lillie & Shapiro, Gary R. 100 Questions & Answers about Advanced & Metastatic Breast Cancer. 2008. (ENG.). 158p. pap. 22.95 *(978-0-7637-6183-7(4))* Jones & Bartlett Learning, LLC.

—100 Questions & Answers about Advanced & Metastatic Breast Cancer. 2nd ed. 2011. *(978-1-4496-3401-8(X))* Jones & Bartlett Publishers.

Shockney, Lillie D. Navigating Breast Cancer: A Guide for the Newly Diagnosed. 2006. (ENG.). 107p. per. 22.95 *(978-0-7637-4128-0(0))* Jones & Bartlett Learning, LLC.

Shockney, Lillie D. & Shapiro, Gary R. 100 Questions & Answers about Advanced & Metastatic Breast Cancer. 2nd ed. 2011. 152p. pap. 22.95 ***(978-1-4496-4335-5(3))*** Jones & Bartlett Learning, LLC.

Shockney, Lillie D. & Tsangaris, Theodore N. The Johns Hopkins Brest Cancer Handbook for Health Care Professionals. 2007. (Illus.). 312p. pap. 97.95 *(978-0-7637-4992-7(3))* Jones & Bartlett Learning, LLC.

Skarin, Arthur T., et al, eds. Breast Cancer. 2007. (Dana-Farber Cancer Institute Handbooks Ser.). (ENG., Illus.). 176p. pap. 58.95 *(978-0-7234-3432-0(8)*, Mosby) Elsevier - Health Sciences Div.

Smith, Mamie. The Unfolding of a Rose. 2009. 144p. 22.50 *(978-1-60860-058-8(0)*, Strategic Bk. Publishing) AEG Literary Publishing Services, Inc.

Smith, Terry L. Breast Cancer: Current & Emerging Trends in Detection & Treatment. 2009. (Cancer & Modern Science Ser.). 64p. (gr. 5-5). 58.50 *(978-1-61511-771-0(7))* Rosen Publishing Group, Inc., The.

Sokolowski, Nancy & Rossi, Valerie. The Breast Cancer Companion: A Guide for the Newly Diagnosed. 2010. (ENG.). 224p. pap. 16.95 *(978-1-932603-99-6(9))* Demos Medical Publishing, LLC.

Spear, Scott L., ed. Surgery of the Breast: Principles & Art, 2 vols. 3rd rev. ed. 2010. (ENG., Illus.). 1792p. 479.00 *(978-1-60547-577-6(7))* Lippincott Williams & Wilkins.

Springer, Elizabeth M. Struck with Adversity: My Personal Journey with Breast Cancer. 2011. 136p. pap. 24.95 ***(978-1-4560-7059-5(2))*** PublishAmerica, Inc.

St. Onge, Terri. The St. Onge Survivor's Guide: How to Survive Everyday Life While Battling Breast Cancer. 2008. spiral bd. 24.95 *(978-0-615-22542-5(X))* TSO Company.

Sulik, Gayle A. Pink Ribbon Blues. 2012. (ENG., Illus.). 440p. pap. 21.95 ***(978-0-19-993399-0(5))*** Oxford Univ. Pr., Inc.

Sulik, Gayle A. Pink Ribbon Blues: How Breast Cancer Culture Undermines Women's Health, 1 vol. 2010. (ENG.). 400p. 29.95 *(978-0-19-974045-1(3))* Oxford Univ. Pr., Inc.

Sullivan, Ester S. Cancer Is Just Right for God: A Twelve Years Survivor. 2011. 108p. 27.49 *(978-1-4567-4770-1(3))*; pap. 19.99 *(978-1-4567-4771-8(1))* AuthorHouse.

Supernault, Esther. Blue Diamond Journey: The Healing of a Reluctant Seer. 2010. 268p. pap. 19.75 *(978-1-4269-4115-3(3))* Trafford Publishing.

Suri, Jasjit S. Diagnostic & Therapeutic Applications of Breast Imaging. 2012. (Press Monographs). 542p. 125.00 ***(978-0-8194-8789-6(9))*** SPIE.

Suri, Jasjit S., et al. Emerging Technologies in Breast Imaging & Mammography. 2008. (Illus.). xxxiv, 536p. ***(978-1-58883-090-6(X))*** American Scientific Pubs.

Susan G Komen for the Cure. Words for the Cure: Inspiration, Hope, & Comfort for Today & Tomorrow. 2007. (Illus.). 96p. 12.95 *(978-0-696-23812-3(8))* Meredith Bks.

Swanson, Cheryl. Busting Loose: Cancer Survivors Tell You What Your Doctor Won't. 2009. (ENG.). 324p. pap. 17.99 *(978-1-934841-74-7(9))* Zumaya Pubns. LLC.

Swanton, Charles, ed. Handbook of Metastatic Breast Cancer. 2006. (ENG., Illus.). 248p. 170.00 *(978-1-84184-488-6(8))* Taylor & Francis Group.

Syeed, Nidda. Role of Intermediate & Low Penetrance Genes in Breast Cancer. 2011. 316p. pap. ***(978-3-8383-6481-0(3))*** Lambert Academic Publishing.

Tabár, László, et al. Breast Cancer - Early Detection with Mammography: Crushed Stone-Like Calcifications - The Most Frequent Malignant Type. 2008. (Breast Cancer - Early Detection with Mammography Ser.). (ENG., Illus.). 320p. 159.99 *(978-3-13-148531-1(0))* Thieme Medical Pubs., Inc.

Taghian, Alphonse G., et al. Breast Cancer. 2009. 379.00 *(978-1-933864-44-0(3))* Demos Medical Publishing, LLC.

Tan, Antoinette R. Breast Cancer. 2010. 200p. 85.00 *(978-1-936287-14-7(5))* Demos Medical Publishing, LLC.

Tartar, Marie, et al. Breast Cancer Imaging: A Multidisciplinary, Multimodality Approach. 2008. (ENG., Illus.). 632p. 182.00 *(978-0-323-04677-0(0)*, Mosby) Elsevier - Health Sciences Div.

Tavassoli, Fattaneh A. & Eusebi, Vincenzo. Tumors of the Mammary Gland. 2009. (AFIP Atlas of Tumor Pathology: Series 4 Ser.). (Illus.). 418p. 185.50 *(978-1-933477-05-3(9))* American Registry of Pathology.

Taylor, Minister Jewel M. I'm a Survivor. 2011. 62p. pap. 15.99 ***(978-1-4568-2441-9(4))*** Xlibris Corp.

Temple, Susan. Contemporary Issues in Women's Cancers. 2008. (Illus.). 349p. (C). 94.95 *(978-0-7637-2602-7(8)*, 0763726028) Jones & Bartlett Learning, LLC.

The Healing Project, ed. Voices of Breast Cancer: The Healing Companion: Stories for Courage, Comfort & Strength. 2007. (Voices of Ser.). (ENG., Illus.). 300p. per. 16.95 *(978-1-934184-02-8(0))* Lachance Publishing LLC.

Thomas, Patricia, ed. Breast Cancer & Its Precursor Lesions. 2008. (Current Clinical Pathology Ser.). (Illus.). 350p. 139.00 *(978-1-58829-686-3(5)*, 1588296865) Humana Pr.

Thompson, Janet. Dear God, They Say It's Cancer: A Companion Guide for Women on the Breast Cancer Journey. 2006. (ENG.). 400p. pap. 19.99 *(978-1-58229-575-6(1)*, Howard Bks.) Howard Books.

Tjan-Heijnen, V. C. G., ed. Nodal Micrometastases or Isolated Tumor Cells & the Outcome of Breast Cancer - Book Edition of Breast Disease. 2011. 56p. pap. 138.00 ***(978-1-60750-725-3(0))*** IOS Pr., Inc.

Toi, Masakazu & Winer, Eric, eds. Local & Systemic Management of Primary Breast Cancers. 2010. 355p. pap. 74.95 *(978-1-920901-22-6(1))* Trans Pacific Pr. AUS. Dist: International Specialized Bk. Services.

Torosian, Michael H., ed. Breast Cancer. 2010. (Current Clinical Oncology Ser.). (Illus.). 368p. pap. 149.00 *(978-1-61737-216-2(1)*, 1617372161) Humana Pr.

Torran Bagamary, Michelle Iglesias &. The Breast Cancer Survivor's Daily Quote Book. 2009. 162p. pap. 12.95 *(978-0-578-00846-2(7))* CCC Bks.

—Feeling Pink. 2009. 169p. pap. 12.95 *(978-0-578-00801-1(7))* CCC Bks.

Tot, Tibor, ed. Breast Cancer: A Lobar Disease. 2010. (ENG., Illus.). xii, 216p. 139.00 *(978-1-84996-313-8(4)*, 1849963134) Springer.

Tse, Gary M., ed. Magnetic Resonance Spectroscopy of Breast Tumors. 2008. 89.00 *(978-1-60456-882-0(8))* Nova Science Pubs., Inc.

Twellmann, Thorsten. Data-Driven Analysis of Dynamic Contrast-Enhanced Magnetic Resonance. 2007. 184p. per. *(978-3-8364-3316-7(8))* VDM Verlag Dr. Mueller e.K.

Ueno, Naoto T. & Cristofanilli, Massimo, eds. Inflammatory Breast Cancer: an Update: An Update. 2012. (ENG., Illus.). vi, 294p. 189.00 ***(978-94-007-3906-2(0)***, 9400739060) Springer.

Vaidya, Jayant, et al. Fast Facts: Fast Facts: Breast Cancer. 4th rev. ed. 2010. (Illus.). 140p. pap. 25.00 ***(978-1-905832-78-1(8))*** Health Pr., Ltd. GBR. Dist: BookMasters Distribution Services (BDS).

Van Doorn, Margreet Jansen. Row, Row, Row My Boat! A Woman's Incredible Journey with Breast Cancer. 2007. (ENG.). 188p. pap. 20.83 *(978-1-4120-7993-8(4))* Trafford Publishing.

Van, Mo. Singing off Key. 2006. pap. 15.95 *(978-0-9776941-0-5(0))* Sea Wind Publishing.

VanGinhoven, Thais. Moments with God: Diaries of a Cancer Survivor. 2010. pap. 17.99 *(978-1-61663-538-1(X))* Tate Publishing & Enterprises, LLC.

VanNucci, Laura. Gene Therapy for Breast Cancer Treatment. 2011. 80p. pap. ***(978-3-8443-2207-1(8))*** Lambert Academic Publishing.

Vincent, J. Clare Our Story. 2008. 192p. per. *(978-1-84747-591-6(4))* Chipmunkapublishing.

Vonderhaar, B. K. & Smith, G. H., eds. Stem Cells & Breast Cancer - Volume 29 Breast Disease. 2008. 236p. pap. 218.00 *(978-1-58603-912-7(1))* IOS Pr., Inc.

Vuga, Marike. Sequential Therapy in Metastatic Breast Cancer Patients. 2010. 64p. pap. *(978-3-639-20970-9(2))* VDM Verlag Dr. Mueller e.K.

Wagner, Kerstin. Search for Breast Cancer Susceptibility Genes: The Growth Hormone-1 / Insulin-like Growth Factor-1Pathway & its Relationship to Breast Cancer. 2008. 132p. pap. *(978-3-639-02207-0(6))* VDM Verlag Dr. Mueller e.K.

Wahlen Tillema, Renee, ed. Leap of Faith: Stories of Courage from the Leroy Butler Foundation. 2007. (Illus.). 178p. 29.95 *(978-0-9797905-0-8(6))* LeRoy Butler Foundation, Inc., The.

Wakefield, Lalage & Hunter, Kent W. Metastasis. 2007. pap. 182.00 *(978-1-58603-753-6(6))* IOS Pr., Inc.

Walker, Rosemary A. & Thompson, Alastair M., eds. Prognostic & Predictive Factors in Breast Cancer. 2nd rev. ed. 2008. (Illus.). XVI, 192p. 190.00 *(978-0-415-42225-3(6)*, Informa Healthcare) Taylor & Francis Group GBR. Dist: Taylor & Francis Group.

Wazer, Wazer, ed. Accelerated Partial Breast Irradiation: Techniques & Clinical Implementation. 2nd ed. 2009. (ENG., Illus.). xviii, 436p. 199.00 *(978-3-540-88005-9(4)*, 3540880054) Springer.

Weichenthal, Phyllis B. This Is Cancer but You Will Overcome It! 2008. 52p. pap. 10.99 *(978-0-88144-308-0(5))* Yorkshire Publishing Group.

Weiss, Marisa C. & Weiss, Ellen. Living Well Beyond Breast Cancer: A Survivor's Guide for When Treatment Ends & the Rest of Your Life Begins. 2nd ed. 2010. (ENG., Illus.). 528p. pap. 20.00 *(978-0-307-46022-6(3)*, Three Rivers Pr.) Crown Publishing Group.

Welcsh, Piri. The Role of Genetics in Breast & Reproductive Cancers. 2009. (Cancer Genetics Ser.). (Illus.). (ENG.). xiii, 332p. 189.00 (978-1-4419-0476-8(X), 144190476X); xiii, 344p. E-Book (978-1-4419-0477-5(8)) Springer.

Wheeler, Sherry. Welcome to the Pink Side. 2009. 68p. pap. 23.49 (978-1-4343-7050-1(X)) AuthorHouse.

Whitehead-Dickens, Inez. Cancer Kickin' Warrior: The Ultimate Feel-Good Cancer Survivor Book. 2010. 154p. 23.99 (978-1-4520-5503-9(3)); pap. 13.99 (978-1-4520-5504-6(1)) AuthorHouse.

Whittier, Karen. Come, Walk. 2008. pap. 24.95 (978-0-615-19658-9(6)) Whittier, Karen.

Williams-Huw, Michelle. My Mummy Wears a Wig - Does Yours? 2011. (ENG.). 288p. pap. 11.95 (978-1-906125-11-0(2)) Accent Pr. Ltd. GBR. Dist: SCB Distributors.

Williams, Penelope M. Breast Cancer: Biography of an Illness. 2008. 300p. pap. (978-0-9809231-5-5(8)) BPS Bks.

Willis, Jack D. Saving Jack: A Man's Struggle with Breast Cancer. 2008. (ENG.). 208p. pap. 19.95 (978-0-8061-3895-4(5)) Univ. of Oklahoma Pr.

Wilson, Deborah A. Beyond the Boobs: Inspiring & Courageous Stories of Breast Cancer Survival. 2009. (ENG.). 104p. pap. 14.95 (978-0-9841077-3-5(8)) 1 Vision Publishing Co.

Wilson, Jane. A Jar for My Tears: A Journal of Prayer & Healing for Women with Breast Cancer. 2009. pap. 14.99 (978-1-60799-953-9(6)) Tate Publishing & Enterprises, LLC.

Winick, Paul. Cancer Dreams. 2011. 200p. 24.59 **(978-1-4634-1841-0(8))**; pap. 14.03 **(978-1-4634-1842-7(6))** AuthorHouse.

Wolman, Sandra R. & Worsham, Maria J., eds. Benign Breast Disease & Breast Cancer. 2006. 400p. 145.00 (978-1-58829-503-3(6)); 145.00 (978-1-59745-342-4(0)) Humana Pr.

Wood, William C., et al, eds. Breast Cancer Management & Molecular Medicine: Towards Tailored Approaches. 2007. (Illus.). 1027p. 279.00 (978-3-540-28265-5(3), 3540282653) Springer.

Wyatt, Ellie. I Had Two When I Came In. 2011. 50p. 24.99 **(978-1-4653-6044-1(1))**; pap. 15.99 **(978-1-4653-6043-4(3))** Xlibris Corp.

Yarbro, Connie Henke, et al. Breast Care Certification Review. 2012. **(978-1-4496-6740-5(6))** Jones & Bartlett Publishers.

Younis, Tallal, et al. Wait Times in the Management of Early State Breast Cancer. 2011. (Cancer Etiology, Diagnosis & Treatments Ser.). pap. 43.00 (978-1-61209-140-2(7)) Nova Science Pubs., Inc.

Yu, Dihua & Hung, Mien-Chie, eds. Breast Cancer Chemosensitivity. (Advances in Experimental Medicine & Biology Ser.). 2010. xiii, 175p. pap. 189.00 (978-1-4419-2542-8(2), 1441925422) 2007. 190p. 189.00 (978-0-387-74037-9(6)) Springer.

Zaccone, Suzanne. A Random Interruption: Surviving Breast Cancer with Laughter, Vodka, Smoothies & an Attitude: Surviving Breast Cancer with Laughter, Vodka, Smoothies & an Attitude. 2009. 500p. 34.99 (978-1-4415-8057-3(3)); pap. 23.99 (978-1-4415-8056-6(5)) Xlibris Corp.

Zielinski, Christoph C., et al. Drugs for HER2-positive Breast Cancer. 2010. (Milestones in Drug Therapy Ser.). (Illus.). 250p. 139.00 (978-3-0346-0093-4(3), 3034600933) Birkhauser Verlag AG CHE. Dist: Springer.

Zook, Virginia. Ramblings of a Single-Breasted Mattress Thrasher: Or: A Funny Thing Happened to Me on the Way to Chemo. 2008. 84p. pap. 16.95 (978-1-60703-195-6(7)) PublishAmerica, Inc.

BREAST—CARE AND HYGIENE

Ceasar, Sherita T. A Breast Owner's Guide: Situations & Lessons from A to Z. 2006. 70p. per. 8.95 (978-1-59824-311-6(X)) E-BookTime LLC.

Davidson, James West. In Touch with Your Breasts: The Answers to Women's Questions about Breast Care. Date not set. (Illus.). 160p. pap. 9.95 (978-1-56796-128-7(2)) WRS Group, Inc.

Johnson, Ben & Barnes, Kathleen. The Secret of Health: Breast Wisdom. 2008. (ENG.). 167p. pap. 18.95 (978-1-60037-326-8(7)); (Illus.). 28.95 (978-1-60037-327-5(5)) Morgan James Publishing.

The Little Pink Book: What I Say Everyday to my Patients. 2008. (Illus.). 50p. 5.00 (978-0-615-18739-6(0)) Bennett, Kerry G.

Rosen, Paul Peter. Breast Pathology. 3rd rev. ed. 2008. (ENG., Illus.). 1136p. 379.99 (978-0-7817-7137-5(4)) Lippincott Williams & Wilkins.

Shockney, Lillie D. & Tsangaris, Theodore N. The Johns Hopkins Brest Cancer Handbook for Health Care Professionals. 2007. (Illus.). 312p. pap. 97.95 (978-0-7637-4992-7(3)) Jones & Bartlett Learning, LLC.

Wazer, David E., et al, eds. Accelerated Partial Breast Irradiation: Techniques & Clinical Implementation. 2006. (Illus.). 277p. 149.00 (978-3-540-28202-0(5), 3540282025) Springer.

Weiss, Marisa C. & Friedman, Isabel. Taking Care of Your Girls: A Breast Health Guide for Girls, Teens, & In-Betweens. 2008. (ENG., Illus.). 256p. pap. 16.99 (978-0-307-40696-5(2), Three Rivers Pr.) Crown Publishing Group.

BREAST—DISEASES

Appleton, Catherine M. & Wiele, Kimberly N. Breast Imaging Cases, 1 vol. 2011. (Cases in Radiology Ser.). (ENG.). 272p. pap. 59.95 (978-0-19-973192-3(6)) Oxford Univ. Pr., Inc.

Barth, Volker. Diagnosis of Breast Diseases: Integrating the Findings of Clinical Presentation, Mammography, & Ultrasound. 2011. (ENG., Illus.). 448p. 199.99 (978-3-13-143631-7(2)) Thieme Medical Pubs., Inc.

Berstein, Lev M. & Santen, Richard J., eds. Innovative Endocrinology of Cancer. 2008. (Advances in Experimental Medicine & Biology Ser.: Vol. 630). (Illus.). XX, 242p. 209.00 (978-0-387-78817-3(4), 0387788174) Springer.

Boecker, Werner. Preneoplasia of the Breast: A New Conceptual Approach to Proliferative Breast Disease. 2006. (ENG., Illus.). 650p. 286.00 (978-0-7020-2892-2(4), Saunders) Elsevier - Health Sciences Div.

Carlson, Rev. Glenda. Fear Not. 2011. 292p. pap. 16.99 **(978-1-61215-550-0(2))** Xulon Pr., Inc.

Dabbs, David J. Breast Pathology: Expert Consult - Online & Print. 2012. (ENG., Illus.). 816p. 359.00 **(978-1-4377-0604-8(5)**, Saunders) Elsevier - Health Sciences Div.

Dixon, J. Michael. ABC of Breast Diseases. 4th ed. 2012. (ABC Ser.). (ENG.). 120p. pap. 46.95 **(978-1-4443-3796-9(3))** Wiley, John & Sons, Inc.

Dixon, J. Michael. Breast Surgery: A Companion to Specialist Surgical Practice. Dixon, J. Michael, ed. 4th ed. 2009. (Companion to Specialist Surgical Practice Ser.). (ENG., Illus.). 328p. (C). 148.00 (978-0-7020-3012-3(0), Saunders) Elsevier - Health Sciences Div.

Falconieri, Giovanni, et al. Breast Pathology. 2011. 160p. pap. **(978-1-936287-30-7(7))**; E-Book **(978-1-61705-060-2(1))** Demos Medical Publishing, LLC.

Fischer, Uwe, et al. Breast Imaging. 2007. (Direct Diagnosis in Radiology Ser.). (ENG., Illus.). 254p. pap. 64.99 (978-1-60406-041-6(7)) Thieme Medical Pubs., Inc.

Harmer, Victoria. Breast Cancer Nursing Care & Management. 2nd ed. 2011. (ENG., Illus.). 384p. pap. 49.99 (978-1-4051-9866-0(4), Wiley-Blackwell) Wiley, John & Sons, Inc.

Harris, Jay R. Diseases of the Breast. Harris, Jay R. et al, eds. 4th rev. ed. 2009. (ENG., Illus.). 1200p. 325.99 (978-0-7817-9117-5(0)) Lippincott Williams & Wilkins.

Hashimoto, Beverly. Multimodality Breast Imaging: A Correlative Atlas. 2nd ed. 2010. (ENG., Illus.). 664p. 169.99 (978-1-60406-171-0(5)) Thieme Medical Pubs., Inc.

—Practical Digital Mammography. 2007. 94.95 (978-3-13-148041-5(6)); (ENG.). 224p. 99.99 (978-1-58890-620-5(5)) Thieme Medical Pubs., Inc.

Hodler, J., et al. Diseases of the Heart, Chest & Breast: Diagnostic Imaging & Interventional Techniques. 2007. (Illus.). 222p. per. 129.00 (978-88-470-0632-4(5)) Springer.

Hodler, Jarg, et al, eds. Diseases of the Heart, Chest & Breast 2011-2014: Diagnostic Imaging & Interventional Techniques. 2011. (Illus.). 280p. pap. 109.00 (978-88-470-1937-9(0), 8847019370) Springer.

Ikeda, Debra. Breast Imaging: The Requisites. 2nd ed. 2010. (Requisites in Radiology Ser.). (ENG., Illus.). 448p. 110.00 (978-0-323-05198-9(7), Mosby) Elsevier - Health Sciences Div.

Jatoi, Ismail & Kaufmann, Manfred, eds. Management of Breast Diseases. 2009. (ENG., Illus.). xx, 664p. 239.00 (978-3-540-69742-8(X), 354069742X) Springer.

Johnston, Stephen R. D. & Swanton, Charles, eds. Handbook of Metastatic Breast Cancer: Second Edition. 2nd rev. ed. 2011. (ENG., Illus.). 312p. **(978-1-84184-811-2(5))** Informa Pharmaceuticals & Healthcare.

Klimberg, V. Suzanne. Atlas of Breast Surgical Techniques: A Volume in the Surgical Techniques Atlas Series. 2009. (Surgical Techniques Atlas Ser.). (ENG., Illus.). 456p. 274.00 (978-1-4160-4691-2(7), Saunders) Elsevier - Health Sciences Div.

Koerner, Frederick C. Diagnostic Problems in Breast Pathology: Expert Consult: Online & Print. 2008. (ENG., Illus.). 384p. 182.00 (978-1-4160-2612-9(6), Saunders) Elsevier - Health Sciences Div.

Kopans, Daniel B. Breast Imaging. 3rd rev. ed. 2006. (ENG., Illus.). 1136p. 279.00 (978-0-7817-4768-4(6)) Lippincott Williams & Wilkins.

Lawton, Thomas. Breast. 2009. (Cambridge Illustrated Surgical Pathology Ser.). (ENG., Illus.). 256p. 151.99 (978-0-521-88159-3(5)) Cambridge Univ. Pr.

The Little Pink Book: What I Say Everyday to my Patients. 2008. (Illus.). 50p. 5.00 (978-0-615-18739-6(0)) Bennett, Kerry G.

Love, Susan M. Dr. Susan Love's Breast Book. 5th ed. 2010. (Merloyd Lawrence Book Ser.). (ENG., Illus.). 752p. pap. 22.00 (978-0-7382-1359-0(4)) Da Capo Pr., Inc.

Mansel, Robert E., et al. Hughes, Mansel & Webster's Benign Disorders & Diseases of the Breast. 3rd ed. 2009. (ENG., Illus.). 368p. 182.00 (978-0-7020-2774-1(X), Saunders) Elsevier - Health Sciences Div.

Mohsin, Syed K. Frozen Section Library: Breast: Breast. 2011. (Frozen Section Library). (ENG., Illus.). xi, 112p. pap. 139.00 **(978-1-4614-0717-1(6)**, 1461407176) Springer.

Moinfar, Farid. Essentials of Diagnostic Breast Pathology: A Practical Approach. 2007. (Illus.). XVI, 496p. 379.00 (978-3-540-45117-4(X), 354045117X) Springer.

O'Malley, Frances P., et al. Breast Pathology: A Volume in the Foundations in Diagnostic Pathology series (Expert Consult - Online & Print) 2nd ed. 2011. (Foundations in Diagnostic Pathology Ser.). (ENG., Illus.). 400p. (C). 179.00 (978-1-4377-1757-0(8), Saunders) Elsevier - Health Sciences Div.

Palazzo, Juan P. Difficult Diagnosis in Breast Pathology. 2011. 264p. **(978-1-933864-79-2(6))** Demos Medical Publishing, LLC.

Peart, Olive. Mammography Examination. 2nd ed. 2008. (LANGE Q&a Allied Health Ser.). (ENG., Illus.). 184p. 63.00 (978-0-07-154835-9(1), 0071548351) McGraw-Hill Medical Publishing Div.

Pestalozzi, B. C., ed. Infiltrating Lobular Carcinoma of the Breast. 2009. (Breast Disease Ser.). 68p. pap. 150.00 (978-1-60750-063-6(9)) IOS Pr., Inc.

Peterson, Rosendo D. Breast Pathology: Diagnosis by Needle Core Biopsy. Hoda, Syed A. & Rosen, Paul Peter, eds. 3rd rev. ed. 2010. (ENG., Illus.). 432p. 224.99 (978-1-60831-670-0(X)) Lippincott Williams & Wilkins.

Raza, Sughra, et al. Breast MRI: A Comprehensive Imaging Guide. 2009. (ENG., Illus.). 730p. 229.00 (978-1-931884-17-4(X)) Lippincott Williams & Wilkins.

Rosen, Paul Peter. Breast Pathology. 3rd rev. ed. 2008. (ENG., Illus.). 1136p. 379.99 (978-0-7817-7137-5(4)) Lippincott Williams & Wilkins.

Scott-Conner, Carol E. H. & Dirbas, Frederick, eds. Breast Surgery: Office Management & Surgical Techniques. 2010. (Illus.). 440p. 149.00 (978-1-4419-6075-7(9), 1441960759) Springer.

Shah, Biren A., et al. Breast Imaging Review: A Quick Guide to Essential Diagnoses. 2010. (ENG., Illus.). xii, 238p. pap. 69.95 (978-1-4419-1727-0(6), 1441917276) Springer.

Smallwood, J.A. & Taylor, I., eds. Benign Breast Disease. (ENG., Illus.). 208p. (978-0-7131-4579-3(X), Hodder Arnold) Hodder Education.

Tot, Tibor, et al. Casting Type Calcifications - Sign of a Subtype with Deceptive Features. 2007. (Breast Cancer - Early Detection with Mammography Ser.). (ENG., Illus.). 325p. 159.99 (978-1-58890-580-2(2)) Thieme Medical Pubs., Inc.

Wazer, David E., et al, eds. Accelerated Partial Breast Irradiation: Techniques & Clinical Implementation. 2006. (Illus.). 277p. 149.00 (978-3-540-28202-0(5), 3540282025) Springer.

A Woman's Guide to Breast Health. Date not set. (Illus.). 10p. (978-0-945100-69-0(8)) Parlay International.

BREAST—RADIOGRAPHY

Astley, S. Digital Mammography: 8th International Workshop, IWDM 2006, Manchester, UK, June 18-21, 2006, Proceedings. 2006. (Lecture Notes in Computer Science Ser.: Vol. 4046). (Illus.). 654p. pap. 129.00 (978-3-540-35625-7(8), 3540356258) Springer.

Berg, Wendie A. Diagnostic Imaging. 2006. (Illus.). (978-0-8089-2380-0(3)) Harcourt Health Sciences Group.

Berg, Wendie A., et al. Diagnostic Imaging: Breast. 2006. (ENG., Illus.). 860p. 319.00 (978-1-4160-3337-0(8)) Amirsys, Inc.

Berry, Min. Atlas of Diagnostic Radiology: Musculoskeletal & Breast Imaging. 2009. (Anshan Gold Standard Mini Atlas Ser.). (ENG., Illus.). 350p. pap. 34.95 incl. cd-rom (978-1-905740-17-8(4)) Anshan GBR. Dist: Publishers Storage & Shipping.

Bick, Ulrich & Diekmann, Felix. Digital Mammography. 2011. (Medical Radiology / Diagnostic Imaging Ser.). (Illus.). xvi, 220p. pap. 119.00 (978-3-642-17898-6(7), 3642178987) Springer.

Bovik. Digital Mammography. 2007. (Synthesis Lectures on Image, Video, & Multimedia Processing Ser.). 40.00 (978-1-59829-238-1(2)) Morgan & Claypool Pubs.

Cardenosa, Gilda. Breast Imaging Companion. 3rd rev. ed. 2007. (Imaging Companion Ser.). (ENG., Illus.). 624p. per. 92.95 (978-0-7817-6491-9(2)) Lippincott Williams & Wilkins.

—Clinical Breast Imaging: A Patient Focused Teaching File. 2006. (LWW Teaching File Ser.). (ENG., Illus.). 528p. 147.99 (978-0-7817-6267-0(7)) Lippincott Williams & Wilkins.

deParedes, Ellen Shaw. Atlas of Mammography. 3rd rev. ed. 2007. (ENG., Illus.). 704p. 179.95 (978-0-7817-6433-9(5)) Lippincott Williams & Wilkins.

Dixon, Anne-Marie. Breast Ultrasound: How, Why & When. 2007. (How, Why & When Ser.). (ENG., Illus.). 288p. (C). 88.95 (978-0-443-10076-5(4), Churchill Livingstone) Elsevier - Health Sciences Div.

Drijarkara, Agustinus Praba. Fuzzy Classification of Microcalcification in Mammograms. 2011. 104p. pap. **(978-3-8443-2063-3(6))** Lambert Academic Publishing.

Finkel, Madelon L. Understanding the Mammography Controversy: Science, Politics, & Breast Cancer Screening, 1 vol. 2008. 216p. pap. 19.95 (978-0-313-36317-7(X), B36317, Praeger Trade) Greenwood Publishing Group, Inc.

Fischer, Uwe. Practical MR Mammography: High Resolution MRI of the Breast. 2nd ed. 2012. (ENG., Illus.). 300p. 139.95 **(978-3-13-132032-2(X))** Thieme Medical Pubs., Inc.

Fischer, Uwe & Baum, Friedemann. Interventional Breast Imaging: Ultrasound, Mammography, & MR Guidance Techniques. 2010. (ENG., Illus.). 264p. 149.99 (978-3-13-146701-0(0)) Thieme Medical Pubs., Inc.

Fischer, Uwe, et al. Breast Imaging. 2007. (Direct Diagnosis in Radiology Ser.). (ENG., Illus.). 254p. pap. 64.99 (978-1-60406-041-6(7)) Thieme Medical Pubs., Inc.

Fundaro, Gina, et al. Breast MRI Atlas: A Case-Based Guide to Image Interpretation. 2011. (Illus.). 250p. pap. 79.95 (978-1-4419-7016-9(9), 1441970169) Springer.

Gabka, Christian J. & Bohmert, Heinz. Plastic & Reconstructive Surgery of the Breast. 2nd ed. 2008. (ENG., Illus.). 292p. 259.99 (978-3-13-103572-1(2)) Thieme Medical Pubs., Inc.

Ghiassi, Susan E. Thank God I Only Have Two of These! 2009. 103p. pap. 14.62 (978-0-557-13627-8(X)) Lulu Enterprises Inc.

Hashimoto, Beverly. Multimodality Breast Imaging: A Correlative Atlas. 2nd ed. 2010. (ENG., Illus.). 664p. 169.99 (978-1-60406-171-0(5)) Thieme Medical Pubs., Inc.

—Practical Digital Mammography. 2007. 94.95 (978-3-13-148041-5(6)); (ENG.). 224p. 99.99 (978-1-58890-620-5(5)) Thieme Medical Pubs., Inc.

Koerner, Frederick C. Diagnostic Problems in Breast Pathology: Expert Consult: Online & Print. 2008. (ENG., Illus.). 384p. 182.00 (978-1-4160-2612-9(6), Saunders) Elsevier - Health Sciences Div.

Lillé, Shelly L. & Andolina, Valerie F. Mammographic Imaging: A Practical Guide. 3rd rev. ed. 2010. (ENG., Illus.). 608p. 87.95 (978-1-60547-031-3(7)) Lippincott Williams & Wilkins.

Martí, Joan, et al, eds. Digital Mammography: 10th International Workshop, IWDM 2010, Girona, Catalonia, Spain, June 16-18, 2010. Proceedings. 2010. (Lecture Notes in Computer Science / Image Processing, Computer Vision, Pattern Recognition, & Graphics Ser.). xix, 772p. pap. 139.00 (978-3-642-13665-8(6), 3642136656) Springer.

Palmetti, Andrea & Roux, Raphaël, eds. Mammography: Screening, Results & Risks. 2011. (Cancer Etiology, Diagnosis & Treatments Ser.). 95.00 **(978-1-61470-589-5(5)**, Nova Biomedical Bks.) Nova Science Pubs., Inc.

Peart, Olive. Mammography & Breast Imaging PREP. 2012. (ENG., Illus.). 509p. (C). pap. 60.00 **(978-0-07-174932-9(2)**, 0071749322) McGraw-Hill Medical Publishing Div.

Peart, Olive. Mammography Examination. 2nd ed. 2008. (LANGE Q&a Allied Health Ser.). (ENG., Illus.). 184p. 63.00 (978-0-07-154835-9(1), 0071548351) McGraw-Hill Medical Publishing Div.

Rayburn, William F. Diagnostic Imaging in Women's Health, an Issue of Obstetrics & Gynecology Clinics. 2011. (Clinics: Internal Medicine Ser.: 38-1). (ENG., Illus.). 224p. 110.00 (978-1-4557-0837-1(9), Saunders) Elsevier - Health Sciences Div.

Rudman, Jack. ARRT Examination in Mammography (MAM) Date not set. (Admission Test Ser.). 69.95 (978-0-8373-5868-0(X), ATS118); pap. 49.95 (978-0-8373-5818-5(3), ATS118) National Learning Corp.

Sachdev, Rahul, et al. Step by Step: Breast Ultrasound. 2006. (Step by Step Ser.). (Illus.). 172p. pap. 27.99 (978-1-904798-79-8(9)) Anshan GBR. Dist: Publishers Storage & Shipping.

Saunders, Avril Dalziel. Mammograms Save Lives. 2012. (ENG.). 70p. pap. 9.99 **(978-1-907728-36-5(8)**, PS True Life) Pneuma Springs Publishing GBR. Dist: Lightning Source, Inc.

Shah, Biren A., et al. Breast Imaging Review: A Quick Guide to Essential Diagnoses. 2010. (ENG., Illus.). xii, 238p. pap. 69.95 (978-1-4419-1727-0(6), 1441917276) Springer.

Stefanoyiannis, Antonis P. Digital Management of Locally Suboptimal Image Quality in Mammography. 2010. 124p. pap. (978-3-8383-8042-1(8)) Lambert Academic Publishing.

Suri, Jasjit S., et al. Emerging Technologies in Breast Imaging & Mammography. 2008. (Illus.). xxxiv, 536p. **(978-1-58883-090-6(X))** American Scientific Pubs.

Tabár, László, et al. Breast Cancer - Early Detection with Mammography: Crushed Stone-Like Calcifications - The Most Frequent Malignant Type. 2008. (Breast Cancer - Early Detection with Mammography Ser.). (ENG., Illus.). 320p. 159.99 (978-3-13-148531-1(0)) Thieme Medical Pubs., Inc.

—Casting Type Calcifications: Indicators of a Subtype with Unpredictable Outcome. 2007. 149.95 (978-3-13-135391-7(0)) Thieme Medical Pubs., Inc.

Tot, Tibor, et al. Casting Type Calcifications - Sign of a Subtype with Deceptive Features. 2007. (Breast Cancer - Early Detection with Mammography Ser.). (ENG., Illus.). 325p. 159.99 (978-1-58890-580-2(2)) Thieme Medical Pubs., Inc.

Wagner, Jennifer R. & Wight, Erica Koch. Mammography Exam Review. 2007. (Test Preparation Ser.). (ENG., Illus.). 112p. (C). pap. 67.95 (978-1-4180-5079-5(2)) Delmar Cengage Learning.

Yang, Yirong. Quantitative Analysis & Improvement of Retinal Image Quality. 2008. 76p. pap. (978-3-639-05067-7(3)) VDM Verlag Dr. Mueller e.K.

BREAST—SURGERY

see also Mastectomy

Adams, William. Breast Augmentation: An Operative Atlas. 2010. (ENG., Illus.). 300p. 207.00 (978-0-07-160643-1(2), 0071606432) McGraw-Hill Professional Publishing.

Adams, William P., Jr. Breast Augmentation: An Operative Atlas. 2010. (978-0-07-160644-8(0)); (Illus.). xi, 118p. (978-0-07-160641-7(6)) McGraw-Hill Professional Publishing.

Ali, Syed Z. & Parwani, Anil V. Breast Cytopathology. 2007. (Essentials in Cytopathology Ser.). (Illus.). 175p. per. 89.95 (978-0-387-71594-0(0)) Springer.

Ali, Syed Z. & Parwani, Anil V., contrib. by. Breast Cytopathology. 2007. (Illus.). xv, 175p. 59.95 (978-0-387-71595-7(9)) Springer.

Baxter, Richard E. Acellular Dermal Matrices in Breast Surgery, an Issue of Clinics in Plastic Surgery. 2012. (Clinics: Surgery Ser.: 39-2). (ENG.). 115.00 **(978-1-4557-3920-2(0)**, Saunders) Elsevier - Health Sciences Div.

Benson, John R. & Nava, Maurizio, eds. Oncoplastic & Reconstructive Surgery of the Breast, Second Edition. 2nd ed. 2009. 319.95 (978-0-415-47728-4(X), Informa Healthcare) Taylor & Francis Group.

Bland, Kirby I., et al, eds. Surgery in Breast Cancer & Melanoma: Handbooks in General Surgery. 2010. (ENG., Illus.). xvi, 248p. pap. 29.95 (978-1-84996-434-0(3), 1849964343) Springer.

Bland, Kirby I. & Klimberg, V. Suzanne, eds. Breast Surgery. 2010. (ENG., Illus.). 400p. 231.95 (978-1-60547-428-1(2)) Lippincott Williams & Wilkins.

Bucky, Louis P., et al. Aesthetic Breast Surgery. 2009. (Techniques in Aesthetic Surgery Ser.). (ENG., Illus.). 184p. 186.00 (978-0-7020-3091-8(0), Saunders) Elsevier - Health Sciences Div.

Cawthorn, Simon & Michell, Michael, eds. Interventional Ultrasound of the Breast. 2007. (ENG., Illus.). 136p. 109.95 (978-1-84184-416-9(0), Informa Healthcare) Taylor & Francis Group GBR. Dist: Taylor & Francis Group.

Debi, Uma, et al. Directional Vacuum Assisted Breast Biopsy. 2010. 144p. pap. (978-3-8383-7202-0(6)) Lambert Academic Publishing.

B

Dixon, J. Michael. Breast Surgery: A Companion to Specialist Surgical Practice. Dixon, J. Michael, ed. 4th ed. 2009. (Companion to Specialist Surgical Practice Ser.). (ENG., Illus.). 328p. (C). 148.00 *(978-0-7020-3012-3(0),* Saunders) Elsevier - Health Sciences Div.
Fitoussi, A. Oncoplastic & Reconstructive Surgery for Breast Cancer: The Institut Curie Experience. 2009. (Illus.). 150p. *(978-3-642-00144-4(0))* Springer.
Fowler, Lori. Implants for Graduation? Parent & Adolescent Narratives. 2009. 180p. pap. *(978-3-639-14488-8(0))* VDM Verlag Dr. Mueller e.K.
Gabka, Christian J. & Bohmert, Heinz. Plastic & Reconstructive Surgery of the Breast. 2nd ed. 2008. (ENG., Illus.). 292p. 259.99 *(978-3-13-103572-1(2))* Thieme Medical Pubs., Inc.
Hall-Findlay, Elizabeth J. Aesthetic Breast Surgery: Concepts & Techniques. 2010. *(978-1-57626-262-7(6))* Quality Medical Publishing, Inc.
Hall-Findlay, Elizabeth J. & Evans, Gregory R. D. Aesthetic & Reconstructive Surgery of the Breast. 2010. (ENG., Illus.). 696p. 285.00 *(978-0-7020-3180-9(1),* Saunders) Elsevier - Health Sciences Div.
Hamdi, Moustapha, et al, eds. Vertical Scar Mammaplasty. 2010. (Illus.). xvi, 146p. pap. 239.00 *(978-3-642-06045-8(5),* 3642060455) Springer.
Hammond, Dennis C. Atlas of Aesthetic Breast Surgery. 2008. (ENG., Illus.). 236p. 250.00 *(978-1-4160-3184-0(7),* Saunders) Elsevier - Health Sciences Div.
Hendrick, R. Edward. Breast MRI: Fundamentals & Technical Aspects. 2008. (ENG., Illus.). xvi, 254p. 79.95 *(978-0-387-73506-1(2),* 0387735062) Springer.
Jatoi, Ismail, et al. Atlas of Breast Surgery. 2010. (Illus.). x, 134p. pap. 239.00 *(978-3-642-06362-6(4),* 3642063624) Springer.
Jones, Glyn E. & Bostwick, John. Bostwick's Plastic & Reconstructive Breast Surgery. 3rd ed. 2009. *(978-1-57626-233-7(2))* Quality Medical Publishing, Inc.
Klimberg, V. Suzanne. Atlas of Breast Surgical Techniques: A Volume in the Surgical Techniques Atlas Series. 2009. (Surgical Techniques Atlas Ser.). (ENG., Illus.). 456p. 274.00 *(978-1-4160-4691-2(7),* Saunders) Elsevier - Health Sciences Div.
Kuerer, Henry. Kuerer's Breast Surgical Oncology. 2010. (ENG., Illus.). 1100p. 244.00 *(978-0-07-160176-4(7),* 0071601767) McGraw-Hill Professional Publishing.
Kuerer, Henry Mark. Kuerer's Breast Surgical Oncology. 2010. (Illus.). lii, 1125p. *(978-0-07-160178-8(3))* McGraw-Hill Medical Publishing Div.
Morris, Steven M., et al. Cosmetic Breast Surgery & Body Contouring. 2006. (ENG., Illus.). 152p. per. 21.95 *(978-1-886039-75-9(5))* Addicus Bks.
Nahabedian, Maurice. Cosmetic & Reconstructive Breast Surgery. 2008. (ENG., Illus.). 248p. 195.00 *(978-0-7020-2915-8(7),* Saunders) Elsevier - Health Sciences Div.
Nahabedian, Maurice & Nahabedian, Maurice Y. Oncoplastic Surgery of the Breast with DVD. 2009. (ENG., Illus.). 200p. 195.00 *(978-0-7020-3181-6(X),* Saunders) Elsevier - Health Sciences Div.
Nahabedian, Maurice Y. Toolbox for Autologous Breast Reconstruction, an Issue of Clinics in Plastic Surgery. 2011. (Clinics: Surgery Ser.: 38-2). (ENG., Illus.). 184p. 110.00 *(978-1-4557-0982-3(4),* Saunders) Elsevier - Health Sciences Div.
Sabel, Michael S. Essentials of Breast Surgery. 2009. (Surgical Foundations Ser.). (ENG., Illus.). 368p. 113.00 *(978-0-323-03758-7(5),* Mosby) Elsevier - Health Sciences Div.
Scott-Conner, Carol E. H. & Dirbas, Frederick, eds. Breast Surgery: Office Management & Surgical Techniques. 2010. (Illus.). 440p. 149.00 *(978-1-4419-6075-7(9),* 1441960759) Springer.
Shiffman, Melvin A. Mastopexy & Breast Reduction: Principles & Practice. Shiffman, Melvin A., ed. 2009. (ENG., Illus.). xxxii, 694p. 379.00 *(978-3-540-89872-6(7),* 3540898727) Springer.
Shiffman, Melvin A., ed. Breast Augmentation: Principles & Practice. (ENG., Illus.). xxviii, 672p. 2010. pap. 419.00 *(978-3-642-09771-3(5),* 3642097715) 2008. 419.00 *(978-3-540-78947-5(2),* 3540789472) Springer.
Snodgrass, Bethanne. When Less Is More: The Complete Guide for Women Considering Breast Reduction Surgery. 2006. 240p. pap. 14.95 *(978-0-06-113624-5(7))* HarperCollins Pubs.
Spear, Scott L. Breast Augmentation, an Issue of Clinics in Plastic Surgery. 2008. (Clinics: Surgery Ser.: 36-1). (ENG., Illus.). 240p. 99.00 *(978-1-4377-0528-7(6),* Saunders) Elsevier - Health Sciences Div.
Spear, Scott L., ed. Surgery of the Breast: Principles & Art, 2 vols. 3rd rev. ed. 2010. (ENG., Illus.). 1792p. 479.00 *(978-1-60547-577-6(7))* Lippincott Williams & Wilkins.
Tebbetts, John B. Augmentation Mammaplasty with DVD: Redefining the Patient & Surgeon Experience. 2009. (ENG., Illus.). 616p. 342.00 *(978-0-323-04112-6(4),* Mosby) Elsevier - Health Sciences Div.
Thaller, Seth & Panthaki, Zubin, eds. Aesthetic & Reconstructive Breast Surgery: Solving Complications & Avoiding Unfavourable Results. 2012. (ENG., Illus.). 206p. ***(978-1-84184-847-1(6))*** Informa Pharmaceuticals & Healthcare.

BREAST FEEDING
see Breastfeeding

BREAST IN ART
Pluchinotta, A., et al. That Unstable Object of Desire: Images of the Female Breast by Masters of Photography. 2010. (ENG., Illus.). 160p. 60.00 *(978-88-95849-07-2(8))* Alinari 24 Ore spa ITA. Dist: Independent Pubs. Group.
Sigrist, Martin, ed. BOOBMANIA. 2010. (ENG.). 400p. pap. 50.00 *(978-3-03766-585-5(8))* Edition Skylight CHE. Dist: Independent Pubs. Group.
Yalom, Marilyn. Historia del Pecho. (SPA.). 428p. *(978-84-8310-561-0(6),* 6100) Tusquets Editores.

BREAST MILK
see also Lactation
Arnold, Lois D. W. Human Milk in the NICU: Policy into Practice. 2009. 490p. pap. 68.95 *(978-0-7637-6133-2(8))* Jones & Bartlett Learning, LLC.
Clemens, R. A., et al, eds. Milk & Milk Products in Human Nutrition: 67th Nestlé Nutrition Institute Workshop, Pediatric Program, Marrakech, March 2010. 2011. (Nestlé Nutrition Institute Workshop Series: Clinical & Performance Program Ser.). (ENG., Illus.). 220p. *(978-3-8055-9586-5(7))* Karger, S. AG.
Ella, Elijah, et al. Breastmilk Components Bacteriology & Control of Neonatal Septicaemi. 2010. 188p. pap. *(978-3-8383-7817-6(2))* Lambert Academic Publishing.
Hale, Thomas W. Medications & Mothers' Milk 2010. 14th ed. 2010. 1264p. 35.95 *(978-0-9823379-9-8(X))* Hale Publishing.
Hale, Thomas Wright. Medications & Mothers' Milk. 13th ed. 2008. 1276p. pap. 34.95 *(978-0-9815257-2-3(5))* Hale Publishing.
Hausman, Bernice L. Viral Mothers: Breastfeeding in the Age of HIV/AIDS. 2010. (ENG., Illus.). 292p. 90.00 *(978-0-472-07131-9(9));* pap. 37.50 *(978-0-472-05131-1(8))* Univ. of Michigan Pr.
ICRP. Database of Dose Coefficients: Radionuclides in Mothers' Milk. 2007. (International Commission on Radiological Protection Ser.). (ENG.). cd-rom 226.00 *(978-0-08-045076-6(8),* Elsevier) Elsevier - Health Sciences Div.
Long, Shauna. The Pumping Mom. 2010. 165p. pap. 29.97 *(978-0-557-29921-8(7))* Lulu Enterprises Inc.
Lothrop, H. La Lactancia Natural. (SPA.). 296p. 19.00 *(978-84-89920-79-8(6),* 86605) Ediciones Oniro S.A. ESP. Dist: Lectorum Pubns., Inc.
Overton, Linda T. & Ewente, Monica R., eds. Child Nutrition Physiology. 2008. (Illus.). 326p. 120.00 *(978-1-60456-302-3(8))* Nova Science Pubs., Inc.
Robbins, Sandra T. & Meyers, Robin. Infant Feedings: Guidelines for Preparation of Human Milk & Formula in Health Care Facilities. 2nd ed. 2011. ***(978-0-88091-444-4(0))*** Academy of Nutrition & Dietetics.
West, Diana & Marasco, Lisa. The Breastfeeding Mother's Guide to Making More Milk. 2008. (ENG., Illus.). 304p. pap. 17.95 *(978-0-07-159857-6(X),* 007159857X) McGraw-Hill Cos., The.
Wiwanitkit, Viroj, ed. Focus on Milk & Infants. 2009. pap. 43.00 *(978-1-60741-106-2(7))* Nova Science Pubs., Inc.

BREASTED, JAMES HENRY, 1865-1935
Abt, Jeffrey. American Egyptologist: The Life of James Henry Breasted & the Creation of His Oriental Institute. 2012. (ENG., Illus.). 536p. 45.00 *(978-0-226-00110-4(5))* Univ. of Chicago Pr.
Breasted, Charles. Pioneer to the Past: The Story of James Henry Breasted, Archaeologist. 2009. (ENG.). 436p. (C). 24.95 *(978-1-885923-67-7(8))* Oriental Institute of the Univ. of Chicago, The.
Emberling, Geoff, ed. Pioneers to the Past: American Archaeologists in the Middle East, 1919-1920. 2010. (Oriental Institute Museum Publications). (ENG., Illus.). 160p. (C). pap. 34.95 *(978-1-885923-70-7(8))* Oriental Institute of the Univ. of Chicago, The.

BREASTFEEDING
see also Lactation; Wet Nurses
American Academy Of Pediatrics, et al. The American Academy of Pediatrics New Mother's Guide to Breastfeeding. 2nd ed. 2011. (ENG., Illus.). 272p. pap. 15.00 *(978-0-553-38666-0(2))* Random House Publishing Group.
Amy Spangler Lactancia Guia de consulta para los Padres. 2007. per. 12.50 *(978-0-9729988-7-1(X))* Amy's Babies.
Behan, Eileen. Eat Well, Lose Weight, While Breastfeeding: The Complete Nutrition Book for Nursing Mothers. 2007. (ENG.). 288p. pap. 14.95 *(978-0-345-49259-3(5),* Ballantine Bks.) Random House Publishing Group.
Best Medicine: Human Milk in the NICU. 2008. (ENG.). 312p. pap. 32.95 *(978-0-9815257-4-7(1))* Hale Publishing.
Bowen Shea, Sarah & Schlosberg, Suzanne. The Essential Breastfeeding Log: A Feedings Tracker & Baby-Care Organizer for Nursing Moms. 2009. (ENG.). 240p. pap. 15.00 *(978-0-345-50649-8(9),* Ballantine Bks.) Random House Publishing Group.
Breastfeeding & Diseases. 2008. 144p. pap. 24.95 *(978-0-9815257-1-6(7))* Hale Publishing.
Brooks, Elizabeth C. Legal & Ethical Issues for the ILBCLC. 2012. 350p. pap. 52.95 *(978-1-4496-1503-1(1))* Jones & Bartlett Learning, LLC.
Cadwell, Karin & Turner-Maffei, Cindy. Implementing Continuity of Care in Breastfeeding: Best Practices in the Maternity Setting. 2008. 168p. pap. 58.95 *(978-0-7637-5184-5(7))* Jones & Bartlett Learning, LLC.
Cadwell, Karin, et al. 100 Questions & Answers about Breastfeeding. 2007. (ENG., Illus.). 211p. pap. 28.95 *(978-0-7637-5183-8(9))* Jones & Bartlett Learning, LLC.
Carter, Laura V. Child Nutrition Research Advances. 2007. 225.00 *(978-1-60021-849-1(0))* Nova Science Pubs., Inc.
Casemore, Stephanie. Breastfeeding, Take Two: Successful Breastfeeding the Second Time Around. 2011. 284p. pap. ***(978-0-9736142-1-3(8))*** Gray Lion Publishing.
Chamberlain, Kristina. I Can Breastfeed: Visualize Your Way to Breastfeeding Success. 2010. 128p. 23.95 *(978-1-4502-5398-7(9));* pap. 13.95 *(978-1-4502-5397-0(0))* iUniverse, Inc.
Chapagai, Ganesh Prasad. Changing Pattern in Breastfeeding among Migrants. 2011. 60p. pap. ***(978-3-8443-2440-2(2))*** Lambert Academic Publishing.
Coates, Mary-Margaret, et al. Study Guide for Breastfeeding & Human Lactation. 4th rev. ed. 2009. (Illus.). 208p. pap. 61.95 *(978-0-7637-5882-0(5))* Jones & Bartlett Learning, LLC.
Cox, Sue. Breastfeeding with Confidence: A Practical Guide. 2006. (Illus.). xii, 145p. *(978-0-88166-513-0(4))* Meadowbrook Pr.
Crowther, S. M., et al, eds. The Resurgence of Breastfeeding, 1975-2000. 2009. (Illus.). 176p. pap. *(978-0-85484-119-6(9))* Wellcome Institute for the History of Medicine.
Dykes, Fiona. Breastfeeding in Hospital: Mothers, Midwives & the Production Line. 2006. (Illus.). 213p. per. 47.95 *(978-0-415-39576-2(3))* Routledge.
Edwards, Naia. Breast-and Bottle-Feeding. 2008. (Easy-to-Follow Guides). (ENG., Illus.). 64p. pap. 13.95 *(978-0-09-192343-3(3))* Random Hse. GBR. Dist: Independent Pubs. Group.
Ella, Elijah, et al. Breastmilk Components Bacteriology & Control of Neonatal Septicaemi. 2010. 188p. pap. *(978-3-8383-7817-6(2))* Lambert Academic Publishing.
Epstein-Gilboa, Keren. Interaction & Relationships in Breastfeeding Families: Implications & Practice. 2009. (Illus.). 312p. pap. 34.95 *(978-0-9823379-0-5(6))* Hale Publishing.
Evans, Kate. The Food of Love: The Easier Way to Breastfeed Your Baby. 2009. (ENG., Illus.). 192p. pap. 16.95 *(978-1-59376-217-9(8),* Soft Skull Pr.) Counterpoint LLC.
Fredregill, Suzanne & Fredregill, Ray. The Everything Breastfeeding Book: The Helpful, Reassuring Advice & Practical Information You Need for a Comfortable & Confident Nursing Experience. 2nd ed. 2010. (ENG., Illus.). 304p. pap. 15.95 *(978-1-4405-0218-7(8))* Adams Media Corp.
Frischknecht, Kerri & Both, Denise. Breastfeeding: An Atlas of Diagnosis & Treatment. 2008. (ENG., Illus.). 98p. 62.95 *(978-0-7295-3888-6(5),* Mosby) Elsevier - Health Sciences Div.
García Testal, Elena & Testal, Elena García. La Protección de la Lactancia en el Ordenamiento Laboral Español. 2008. (SPA.). 155p. *(978-84-9876-086-6(0))* Tirant lo Blanch.
Gaskin, Ina May. Ina May's Guide to Breastfeeding. 2009. (ENG.). 352p. pap. 18.00 *(978-0-553-38429-1(5))* Random House Publishing Group.
Genna, Catherine Watson. Supporting Sucking Skills in Breastfeeding Infants. 2007. (Illus.). 355p. (C). pap. 66.95 *(978-0-7637-4037-5(3))* Jones & Bartlett Learning, LLC.
Goldberg, Gail, et al, eds. Breast feeding: early influences on later Health: Early influences on later Health. 2008. (Advances in Experimental Medicine & Biology Ser.). (Illus.). xii, 428p. 219.00 *(978-1-4020-8748-6(9))* Springer.
Groer, Maureen & Kendall-Tackett, Kathleen. Clinics in Human Lactation - How Breastfeeding Protects Women's Health Throughout the Lifespan: The Psychoneuroimmunology of Human Lactation. 2011. 130p. pap. 18.95 ***(978-0-9833075-4-9(7))*** Hale Publishing.
Gromada, Karen Kerkhoff. Mother Multiples: Breastfeeding & Caring for Twins or More! 3rd ed. 2007. (Leche League International Book Ser.). (Illus.). 429p. per. 16.95 *(978-0-9768969-3-7(1))* La Leche League International.
Hale, Thomas & Berens, Pamela. Clinical Therapy in Breastfeeding Patients. 3rd ed. 2011. (ENG.). 521p. pap. 29.95 *(978-0-9823379-8-1(1))* Hale Publishing.
Hale, Thomas W. & Hartmann, Peter, eds. Hale & Hartmann's Textbook of Human Lactation. 2007. (Illus.). 680p. lthr. 89.95 *(978-0-9772268-9-4(1))* Hale Publishing.
Hall-Moran, Victoria & Dykes, Fiona, eds. Infant & Young Child Feeding: Challenges to Implementing a Global Strategy. 2009. (ENG., Illus.). 232p. pap. 80.99 *(978-1-4051-8721-3(2),* Wiley-Blackwell) Wiley, John & Sons, Inc.
Hausman, Bernice L. Viral Mothers: Breastfeeding in the Age of HIV/AIDS. 2010. (ENG., Illus.). 292p. 90.00 *(978-0-472-07131-9(9));* pap. 37.50 *(978-0-472-05131-1(8))* Univ. of Michigan Pr.
Hertz, Gail S. The Little Green Book of Breastfeeding Management. 4th ed. 2007. (Illus.). 80p. 8.00 *(978-0-9792699-0-5(3))* Pocket Pubns.
Hormann, Elizabeth. Breastfeeding an Adopted Baby & Relactation. Hormann, Elizabeth, tr. from GER. 2007. (Leche League International Book Ser.). (Illus.). 66p. per. *(978-0-9768969-7-5(4))* La Leche League International.
Huber, Joan. On the Origins of Gender Inequality. 2007. 184p. per. 40.95 *(978-1-59451-362-6(7));* 125.00 *(978-1-59451-361-9(9))* Paradigm Pubs.
Huggins, Kathleen. El Libro Esencial para Madres Lactantes. 6th ed. 2010. (SPA & ENG.). *(978-1-55832-735-1(5))* Harvard Common Pr.
—El Libro Esencial para Madres Lactantes. 25th annot. ed. 2010. (SPA & ENG.). 368p. pap. 14.95 *(978-1-55832-736-8(3))* Harvard Common Pr.
—The Nursing Mother's Companion. 6th ed. 2010. *(978-1-55832-719-1(3))* 2007. (ENG., Illus.). 368p. pap. 16.95 *(978-1-55832-720-7(7))* Harvard Common Pr.
Huggins, Kathleen & Brown, Jan Ellen. The Nursing Mother's Companion Breastfeeding Diary. 2007. (ENG., Illus.). 128p. spiral bd. 12.95 *(978-1-55832-730-6(4))* Harvard Common Pr.
—25 Things Every Nursing Mother Needs to Know. 2009. pap. *(978-1-55832-445-9(3));* (ENG., Illus.). 160p. 12.95 *(978-1-55832-383-4(X))* Harvard Common Pr.
Hunter, Cheryl. I Have a Breasthellip;and I Know How to Use It: Secrets the Experts Wonrsquo;t Sharehellip;but That You Donrsquo;t Want to Be Without! 2007. 48p. per. 16.95 *(978-1-60441-466-0(9))* PublishAmerica, Inc.
Institute of Medicine. Updating the USDA National Breastfeeding Campaign: Workshop Summary. 2011. (ENG.). 124p. pap. 38.75 ***(978-0-309-21919-8(1))*** National Academies Pr.
Ip, Stanley. Breastfeeding & Maternal & Infant Health Outcomes in Developed Countries. 2007. (AHRQ Publication Ser.: No. 153). (Illus.). xi, 186p. *(978-1-58763-242-6(X))* Agency for Healthcare Research & Quality.
Johnson, Vernell & McGruder-Johnson, Anita Kay. Relaxation for Breastfeeding! A Guidebook Journal. 2009. 80p. pap. 11.49 *(978-1-4343-3406-0(6))* AuthorHouse.
Jones, Lisa D. A Guide to Inexpensive Health for You & Baby, 1 vol. 2010. 52p. pap. 16.95 *(978-1-4489-5891-7(1))* PublishAmerica, Inc.
Jordaan, Mimie Margaretha & Saloojee, Haroon. Newborn Feeding Practices & Support in Gauteng, South Afric. 2011. 168p. pap. ***(978-3-8443-8510-6(X))*** Lambert Academic Publishing.
Kalnins, Daina, et al. Better Breastfeeding: A Mother's Guide to Feeding & Nutrition. 2007. (ENG., Illus.). 320p. pap. 19.95 *(978-0-7788-0164-1(0))* Rose, Robert Inc. CAN. Dist: Firefly Bks., Ltd.
Kedrowski, Karen M. & Lipscomb, Michael E. Breastfeeding Rights in the United States, 1 vol. 2007. (Reproductive Rights & Policy Ser.). (Illus.). 192p. 44.95 *(978-0-275-99136-4(9),* C9136, Praeger Pubs.) Greenwood Publishing Group, Inc.
Kimes, Joanne. Breastfeeding Sucks: What to Do When Your Mammaries Make You Miserable. 2008. (ENG., Illus.). 224p. per. 9.95 *(978-1-59337-628-4(6))* Adams Media Corp.
Kippley, Sheila. The Seven Standards of Ecological Breastfeeding: The Frequency Factor. 2008. 116p. pap. 11.99 *(978-1-4357-4622-0(8))* Lulu Enterprises Inc.
Koenig, Debbie. Parents Need to Eat Too: Nap-Friendly Recipes, One-Handed Meals, & Time-Saving Kitchen Tricks for New Parents. 2012. (ENG.). 256p. pap. 16.99 ***(978-0-06-200594-6(4),*** William Morrow Paperbacks) HarperCollins Pubs.
Koletzko, Berthold, et al, eds. Early Nutrition & its Later Consequences: New Opportunities: Perinatal Programming of Adult Health - EC Supported Research. 2010. (Advances in Experimental Medicine & Biology Ser.). xvii, 237p. pap. 189.00 *(978-90-481-6893-4(7),* 9048168937) Springer.
Koren, Gideon. Medication Safety in Pregnancy & Breastfeeding. 2007. (ENG., Illus.). 864p. (C). 125.00 *(978-0-07-144828-4(4),* 0071448284) McGraw-Hill Professional Publishing.
Kujur, Archana. Compatibility of Women's Work & Breast Feeding. 2010. 72p. pap. *(978-3-639-27408-0(3))* VDM Verlag Dr. Mueller e.K.
Kvist, Linda. Mastitis During Breastfeeding. 2008. 80p. pap. *(978-3-639-04872-8(5))* VDM Verlag Dr. Mueller e.K.
La Leche League International. The Womanly Art of Breastfeeding. 8th ed. 2010. (ENG., Illus.). 576p. pap. 20.00 *(978-0-345-51844-6(6),* Ballantine Bks.) Random House Publishing Group.
La Leche League International Staff. Making More Milk: A Nursing Mother's Guide to Milk Supply. 18.95 *(978-0-9768969-4-4(X))* La Leche League International.
La Leche League International Staff, contrib. by. The Womanly Art of Breastfeeding, 1956-2006. 50th ed. 2007. (Illus.). xxix, 447p. *(978-0-9768969-9-9(0))* La Leche League International.
Lauwers, Judith. Quick Reference for the Lactation Professional. 2008. (ENG.). 276p. spiral bd. 54.95 *(978-0-7637-5014-5(X))* Jones & Bartlett Learning, LLC.
Lauwers, Judith & Swisher, Anna. Counseling the Nursing Mother. 5th rev. ed. 2010. 799p. instr.'s gde. ed. 98.95 *(978-0-7637-8052-4(9))* Jones & Bartlett Learning, LLC.
Lawrence, Ruth A. Breastfeeding: A Guide for the Medical Professional. 7th ed. 2010. (ENG., Illus.). 1128p. 96.95 *(978-1-4377-0788-5(2),* Saunders) Elsevier - Health Sciences Div.
Liamputtong, Pranee, ed. Infant Feeding Practices: A Cross-Cultural Perspective. 2010. (ENG.). xxxv, 372p. 169.00 *(978-1-4419-6872-2(5),* 1441968725) Springer.
Lim, Pauline. Succeed at Breastfeeding. 2011. (Teach Yourself Ser.). (ENG., Illus.). 192p. pap. 15.95 *(978-1-4441-0306-9(7),* Hodder & Stoughton) Hodder General Publishing Div. GBR. Dist: Independent Pubs. Group.
—Successful Breastfeeding. 2009. (Teach Yourself: Parenting Ser.). (ENG.). 192p. pap. 12.95 *(978-0-07-158306-0(8),* 0071583068) McGraw-Hill Cos., The.
Long, Shauna. The Pumping Mom. 2010. 165p. pap. 29.97 *(978-0-557-29921-8(7))* Lulu Enterprises Inc.
Mannel, Rebecca, et al, eds. Core Curriculum for Lactation Consultant Practice. 2nd rev. ed. 2007. (Illus.). 774p. per. 84.95 *(978-0-7637-4503-5(0))* Jones & Bartlett Learning, LLC.
Maze, Stephanie. Breastfeeding Around the World? Amamantar Alrededor Del Mundo. 2011. (SPA & ENG.). ***(978-0-9834983-0-8(X),*** Moonstone Pr.) Past Times Publishing Co.
Mcintosh, Alison. Breastfeeding Twins: We Did It! 2011. 24p. pap. 11.50 ***(978-1-4477-5860-0(9))*** Lulu Enterprises Inc.
Michels, Dia L., ed. Breastfeeding Facts for Fathers (Gift Edition) 2nd gif. ed. 2009. (ENG.). 38p. pap. 7.95 *(978-1-930775-49-7(0))* Platypus Media, L.L.C.
Michels, Dia L. & Galanis, Clifford. Breastfeeding Booklet Set. 2009. (ENG.). 24p. 9.95 *(978-1-930775-20-6(2))* Platypus Media, L.L.C.
Mohrbacher, Nancy & Kendall, Tackett. Breastfeeding Made Simple: Seven Natural Laws for Nursing Mothers. 2nd rev. ed. 2010. (ENG., Illus.). 352p. pap. 18.95 *(978-1-57224-861-8(0))* New Harbinger Pubns.
Nathoo, Tasnim & Ostry, Aleck. The One Best Way? Breastfeeding History, Politics, & Policy in Canada. 2009. (Studies in Childhood & Family in Canada Ser.). (ENG., Illus.). 282p. pap. 29.95 *(978-1-55458-147-4(8))* Wilfrid Laurier Univ. Pr. CAN. Dist: Univ. of Toronto Pr.

Neifert, Marianne. Great Expectations: The Essential Guide to Breastfeeding. 2009. (Great Expectations Ser.). (ENG., Illus.). 320p. pap. 14.95 *(978-1-4027-5817-1(0))* Sterling Publishing Co., Inc.
Nice, Frank J. Nonprescription Drugs for the Breastfeeding Mother. 2007. 112p. per. 19.95 *(978-0-9772268-8-7(3))* Hale Publishing.
Nueland, Wilma G., ed. Breastfeeding: Methods, Benefits to the Infant & Mother, & Difficulties. 2009. (Pregnancy & Infants: Medical, Psychological & Social Issues Ser.). 139.00 *(978-1-60741-933-4(5))* Nova Science Pubs., Inc.
O'Brien, Maxine. I Think I Can. 2008. 240p. pap. *(978-3-639-03950-4(5))* VDM Verlag Dr. Mueller e.K.
Overton, Linda T. & Ewente, Monica R., eds. Child Nutrition Physiology. 2008. (Illus.). 326p. 120.00 *(978-1-60456-302-3(8))* Nova Science Pubs., Inc.
Palmer, Gabrielle. Complementary Feeding: Nutrition, Culture & Politics. 2011. (ENG.). 128p. pap. 14.95 *(978-1-905177-42-4(9))* Pinter & Martin Ltd. GBR. Dist: National Bk. Network.
—The Politics of Breastfeeding 2009: When Breasts Are Bad for Business. 3rd rev. ed. 2009. (ENG., Illus.). 352p. pap. 17.95 *(978-1-905177-16-5(X))* Pinter & Martin Ltd. GBR. Dist: National Bk. Network.
Pickering, Larry K., et al, eds. Protecting Infants through Human Milk: Advancing the Scientific Evidence. 2012. (Advances in Experimental Medicine & Biology Ser.). (ENG.). 564p. pap. 249.00 *(978-1-4419-3461-1(8)*, 1441934618) Springer.
Pitman, Teresa & Newman, Jack. The Ultimate Breastfeeding Book of Answers: The Most Comprehensive Problem-Solving Guide to Breastfeeding from the Foremost Expert in North America. rev. ed. 2006. (ENG., Illus.). 352p. per. 19.95 *(978-0-307-34558-5(0)*, Three Rivers Pr.) Crown Publishing Group.
Pollard, Maria. Evidence-Based Care for Breastfeeding Mothers. 2011. (ENG., Illus.). 272p. 135.00 *(978-0-415-49906-4(2))*; pap. 39.95 *(978-0-415-49907-1(0))* Routledge.
Pryor, Gale & Huggins, Kathleen. Nursing Mother, Working Mother: The Essential Guide to Breastfeeding Your Baby Before & after You Return to Work. 2nd rev. ed. 2007. (ENG., Illus.). 256p. per. 14.95 *(978-1-55832-331-5(7))* Harvard Common Pr.
Pugh, Linda C., et al. Breastfeeding the Healthy Newborn. 2nd ed. 2007. *(978-0-86525-119-9(3))* March of Dimes Birth Defects Foundation.
Punger Faafp Ibclc, Denise. Permission to Mother: Going Beyond the Standard-of-Care to Nurture our Children. 2008. 272p. per. 29.95 *(978-1-4327-0385-1(4))* Outskirts Pr., Inc.
Riley, Eileen. Breastfeeding Attitudes - A Comparison Between Junior & Senior Nursing Students. 2008. 52p. pap. *(978-3-639-00425-0(6))* VDM Verlag Dr. Mueller e.K.
Riordan, Jan & Wambach, Karen. Breastfeeding & Human Lactation. 4th rev. ed. 2009. (Illus.). 936p. 140.95 *(978-0-7637-5432-7(3))* Jones & Bartlett Learning, LLC.
Ripudaman, Singh, et al. Rearing a Child: Prenatal & Natal Care. 2011. 112p. pap. ***(978-3-639-33142-4(7))*** VDM Verlag Dr. Mueller e.K.
Roche-Paull, Robyn. Breastfeeding in Combat Boots: A Survival Guide to Successful Breastfeeding While Serving in the Military. 2010. 352p. pap. 29.95 *(978-0-9845039-4-0(3))* Hale Publishing.
Rubin, Stacey H. The ABCs of Breastfeeding: Everything a Mom Needs to Know for a Happy Nursing Experience, 11. 2008. (ENG., Illus.). 288p. pap. 14.95 *(978-0-8144-8057-1(8))* Amacom.
Shubber, Sami. The WHO Code of Marketing of Breast-Milk Substitutes: History & Analysis. 2nd ed. 2011. 320p. pap. 29.95 *(978-1-905177-46-2(1))* Pinter & Martin Ltd. GBR. Dist: National Bk. Network.
Silverman, Andi & Silverman, Andrea. Mama Knows Breast: A Beginner's Guide to Breastfeeding. 2007. (ENG., Illus.). 160p. pap. 14.95 *(978-1-59474-165-4(4))* Quirk Bks.
Sinnott, Ann. Breastfeeding Older Children. 2010. 294p. pap. 34.50 *(978-1-85343-939-1(8))* Free Assn. Bks. Ltd. GBR. Dist: International Specialized Bk. Services.
Smale, M. NCT Book of Breastfeeding. (Illus.). 144p. pap. 17.95 *(978-0-09-177243-7(5))* Random Hse. GBR. Dist: Trafalgar Square Publishing.
Smith, Linda J. Comprehensive Lactation Consultant Exam Review. 2nd rev. ed. 2007. (Illus.). 429p. pap. 89.95 *(978-0-7637-4029-0(2))* 3rd rev. ed. 2010. 310p. pap. 78.95 *(978-0-7637-7616-9(5))* Jones & Bartlett Learning, LLC.
Smith, Linda J. & Kroeger, Mary. Impact of Birthing Practices on Breastfeeding: Protecting the Mother & Baby Continuum. 2nd rev. ed. 2009. (Illus.). 248p. pap. 61.95 *(978-0-7637-6374-9(8))* Jones & Bartlett Learning, LLC.
Smith, Paige Hall, et al, eds. Beyond Health, Beyond Choice: Breastfeeding Constraints & Realities. 2012. (Critical Issues in Health & Medicine Ser.). (ENG., Illus.). 304p. 72.00 ***(978-0-8135-5303-0(2))*** Rutgers Univ. Pr.
Smith, Paige Hall, et al. Beyond Health, Beyond Choice: Breastfeeding Constraints & Realities. 2012. (Critical Issues in Health & Medicine Ser.). (ENG., Illus.). 304p. pap. 25.95 ***(978-0-8135-5304-7(0))*** Rutgers Univ. Pr.
Smith, Sandra. Comprehensive Lactation Consultant Exam Review. 3rd ed. 2010. 310p. pap. 78.95 *(978-1-4496-0346-5(7))* Jones & Bartlett Learning, LLC.
Sullivan, Dana & Connolly, Maureen. Unbuttoned: Women Open up about the Pleasures, Pains, & Politics of Breastfeeding. 2009. (ENG.). 240p. pap. 14.00 *(978-1-55832-397-1(X))* Harvard Common Pr.
Tempelman-Kluit, Annemarie. Healthy Mum, Happy Baby: How to Feed Yourself When You're Breastfeeding Your Baby. 2007. (ENG., Illus.). 192p. pap. 21.00 *(978-0-679-31445-5(8)*, Random Hse CAN) Random Hse. of Canada, Ltd. CAN. Dist: Random Hse., Inc.
Thairu, Lucy. Maternal Care of the Newborn & Breastfeeding in Pemba Island. 2011. 96p. pap. ***(978-3-8433-6314-3(5))*** Lambert Academic Publishing.
Tyree, Nathan. Hydrocephalic Ward. 2008. 114p. pap. 10.81 *(978-0-557-03706-7(5))* Lulu Enterprises Inc.
Walker, Marsha. Breastfeeding Management for the Clinician: Using the Evidence. 2nd rev. ed. 2009. (Illus.). 708p. pap. 72.95 *(978-0-7637-6651-1(8))* Jones & Bartlett Learning, LLC.
—Clinics in Human lactation - Breastfeeding the Late Preterm Infant: Improving Care & Outcomes. 2009. 84p. pap. 18.95 *(978-0-9815257-7-8(6))* Hale Publishing.
Watson Genna, Catherine. Selecting & Using Breastfeeding Tools: Improving Care & Outcomes. 2009. 208p. pap. 32.95 *(978-0-9823379-1-2(4))* Hale Publishing.
Watson Genna, Catherine. Supporting Sucking Skills in Breastfeeding Infants. 2nd ed. 2012. (Illus.). 408p. pap. 65.95 ***(978-1-4496-4736-0(7))*** Jones & Bartlett Learning, LLC.
Weiss, Robin E. The Better Way to Breastfeed: The Latest, Most Effective Ways to Feed & Nurture Your Baby with Comfort & Ease. 2010. (ENG., Illus.). 304p. pap. 19.99 *(978-1-59233-422-3(9)*, 1592334229) Quayside.
Wendkos, Sally, et al. The Complete Book of Breastfeeding. 4th ed. 2010. (ENG., Illus.). 432p. pap. 13.95 *(978-0-7611-5113-5(3)*, 0761151133) Workman Publishing Co., Inc.
West, Diana & Marasco, Lisa. The Breastfeeding Mother's Guide to Making More Milk. 2008. (ENG., Illus.). 304p. pap. 17.95 *(978-0-07-159857-6(X)*, 007159857X) McGraw-Hill Cos., The.
Wilson-Clay, Barbara & Hoover, Kay. The Breastfeeding Atlas. 4th ed. 2008. (Illus.). 206p. spiral bd. 59.00 *(978-0-9672758-5-7(7))* Lactnews Pr.
Wiwanitkit, Viroj, ed. Focus on Milk & Infants. 2009. pap. 43.00 *(978-1-60741-106-2(7))* Nova Science Pubs., Inc.
Woldesenbet, Selamawit. Infant Feeding Strategies & Other Determinants. 2011. 128p. pap. ***(978-3-8443-0926-3(8))*** Lambert Academic Publishing.
Wolf, Joan. Is Breast Best? Taking on the Breastfeeding Experts & the New High Stakes of Motherhood. 2010. (ENG.). 256p. 30.00 *(978-0-8147-9481-4(5))* New York Univ. Pr.

BREATH, BAD
see Bad Breath

BREATHING
see Respiration

BREATHING APPARATUS
see Respirators

BREATHING EXERCISES
see also Respiration

Balancing Active & Receptive Energies. (Breath Ser.). 15p. 3.50 *(978-1-387645-23-2(3)*, RP505MO) Himalayan Institute Pr.
Barth, Virginia Zoros. There Is an Art to Breathing: A Training Course in Conscious Rhythmic Breathing. 2011. 252p. 46.95 ***(978-1-258-06121-0(X))*** Literary Licensing, LLC.
Boston, Jane & Cook, Rena, eds. Breath in Action: The Art of Breath in Vocal & Holistic Practice. 2009. (ENG., Illus.). 256p. pap. *(978-1-84310-942-6(5))* Kingsley, Jessica Ltd.
Bradley, Dinah & Clifton-Smith, Tania. Breathing Works for Asthma. (Illus.). 120p. pap. 19.95 *(978-0-85626-494-5(7))* Cathie, Kyle Ltd. GBR. Dist: Graphic Arts Ctr. Publishing Co.
Bragg, Paul C. & Bragg, Patricia. Super Power Breathing for Super Engery: High Health & Longevity. 23rd ed. 2008. (ENG., Illus.). 200p. per. 11.95 *(978-0-87790-120-4(1))* Health Science.
The Brass Gym: Horn. 2007. spiral bd. 24.95 *(978-0-9748477-0-2(4))* Focus on Excellence.
The Brass Gym: Trumpet. 2007. spiral bd. 24.95 *(978-0-9748477-4-0(7))* Focus on Excellence.
Brown, Richard & Gerbarg, Patricia. The Healing Power of the Breath: Simple Techniques to Reduce Stress & Anxiety, Enhance Concentration, & Balance Your Emotions. 2012. (ENG., Illus.). 240p. pap. 17.95 ***(978-1-59030-902-5(2)***, Trumpeter) Shambhala Pubns., Inc.
Chinese Health Qigong Association Staff. Liu Zi Jue: Six Sounds Approach to Qigong Breathing Exercises. 2008. (ENG., Illus.). 76p. *(978-1-84819-006-1(9))* Kingsley, Jessica Ltd.
Co, Master Stephen, et al. The Power of Prana: Breathe Your Way to Health & Vitality. unabr. ed. 2011. 224p. pap. 15.95 *(978-1-60407-440-6(X))* Sounds True, Inc.
Crum, Thomas. Three Deep Breaths: Finding Power & Purpose in a Stressed-Out World. 2nd ed. 2009. (BK Life Ser.). (ENG.). 98p. pap. 14.00 *(978-1-57675-630-0(0))* Berrett-Koehler Pubs., Inc.
Dimon, Theodore. Your Body, Your Voice: The Key to Natural Singing & Speaking. 2011. (Illus.). 184p. pap. 18.95 *(978-1-58394-320-5(X))* North Atlantic Bks.
Gomieiro, Ludmila Tais Yazbek. Breathing Exercises for Asthmatics Elderly. 2010. 200p. pap. *(978-3-639-22170-1(2))* VDM Verlag Dr. Mueller e.K.
Grof, Stanislav & Grof, Christina. Holotropic Breathwork: A New Approach to Self-Exploration & Therapy. 2010. (Excelsior Editions Ser.). (Illus.). 288p. (ENG.). 60.00 *(978-1-4384-3393-6(X))*; pap. 19.95 *(978-1-4384-3394-3(8))* State Univ. of New York Pr.
Gupta, Subodh. Art of Breathing for Stress Free Life. 2007. 56p. pap. 10.50 *(978-1-84799-047-1(9))* Lulu Enterprises Inc.
Ha'nish, O. Z. A. Power of Breath the Magic Key of SelfDev. 2006. pap. 20.95 *(978-1-4286-5565-2(4))* Kessinger Publishing, LLC
Hirschl, Meta Chaya. Vital Yoga: A Sourcebook for Students & Teachers. 2011. (ENG., Illus.). 320p. pap. 24.95 *(978-1-61519-040-9(6)*, 1615190406); E-Book ***(978-1-61519-144-4(5))*** Experiment LLC, The.
Hooper, James. James Hooper Buteyko Training Kit. 2007. *(978-1-921183-08-9(X))* One-on-One Learning Centre.
Hughes, Louis. The Art of Allowing: The Breath in Meditation & in Life. 2010. (ENG., Illus.). 128p. pap. 22.95 *(978-1-85607-694-4(6))* Columba Pr. IRL. Dist: Dufour Editions, Inc.
Jordan, James, et al. The Musician's Breath: The Role of Breathing in Human Expression. 2011. (ENG.). 226p. 26.95 *(978-1-57999-834-9(8))* G I A Pubns., Inc.
Kim, Sang H. Power Breathing: Breathe Your Way to Inner Power, Stress Reduction, Performance Enhancement, Optimum Health & Fitness. 2008. (Illus.). 160p. pap. 14.95 *(978-1-934903-09-4(4))* Turtle Pr. Corp.
Kohn, Livia. Chinese Healing Exercises: The Tradition of Daoyin. 2008. (C). pap. 27.00 *(978-0-8248-3269-8(8))*; (Illus.). 344p. 62.00 *(978-0-8248-3234-6(5))* Univ. of Hawaii Pr.
Lee, Al & Campbell, Don. Perfect Breathing: Transform Your Life One Breath at a Time. 2009. (ENG.). 240p. 19.95 *(978-1-4027-4388-7(2))* Sterling Publishing Co., Inc.
Lewis, Dennis. Breathe into Being: Awakening to Who You Really Are. 2009. (ENG.). 115p. pap. 16.95 *(978-0-8356-0872-5(7)*, Quest Bks.) Theosophical Publishing Hse.
Lister, Linda. Yoga for Singers: Freeing Your Voice & Spirit Through Yoga. 2011. 164p. pap. 25.00 ***(978-1-257-09212-3(X))*** Lulu Enterprises Inc.
Maisel, Eric. Ten Zen Seconds: Twelve Incantations for Purpose, Power & Calm. 2007. (ENG.). 256p. per. 12.95 *(978-1-4022-0853-9(7))* Sourcebooks, Inc.
McConnell, Alison. Breathe Strong, Perform Better. 2011. (Illus.). 288p. pap. 19.95 *(978-0-7360-9169-5(6))* Human Kinetics Pubs.
Mijares, Sharon G., ed. The Revelation of the Breath: A Tribute to Its Wisdom, Power, & Beauty. 2009. (SUNY Series in Transpersonal & Humanistic Psychology Ser.). 224p. 70.00 *(978-1-4384-2877-2(4))*; pap. 24.95 *(978-1-4384-2876-5(6))* State Univ. of New York Pr. (Suny Pr.).
Ramacharaka, Yogi. Science of Breath. 2007. (ENG.) 96p. per. 9.45 *(978-1-59462-778-1(9)*, Book Jungle) Standard Pubns., Inc.
—Science of Breath. 2011. 60p. pap. 7.45 ***(978-1-61720-332-9(7))*** Wilder Pubns., Ltd.
Ramacharaka, Yogi. Science of Breath: A Complete Manual of the Oriental Breathing Philosophy Of. 2007. 96p. per. 9.45 *(978-1-59462-590-9(5)*, 627, Book Jungle) Standard Pubns., Inc.
Repka, Katrina & Finger, Alan. Breathing Space: Twelve Lessons for the Modern Woman. 2008. (ENG.). 256p. pap. 14.95 *(978-1-4013-0347-1(1))* Hyperion Pr.
Rolfe, Jenny. Breathe Life into Your Riding: Transform Your Riding with Inspirational & Innovative Breathing Techniques. 2012. (ENG., Illus.). 192p. 45.00 ***(978-0-85131-984-1(X)***, Allen, J. A. & Company, Limited) Hale, Robert Ltd. GBR. Dist: Independent Pubs. Group.
Rones, Ramel. Sunset Tai Chi: Simplified Tai Chi for Relaxation & Longevity. 2011. 360p. pap. 20.95 *(978-1-59439-212-2(9))* YMAA Pubn. Ctr.
Rosen, Richard. Pranayama Beyond the Fundamentals: An in-Depth Guide to Yogic Breathing with Instructional CD. 2006. (ENG., Illus.). 224p. pap., tchr. ed. 21.95 *(978-1-59030-298-9(2))* Shambhala Pubns., Inc.
Sabatini, Sandra. Breath. 2007. (ENG., Illus.). 224p. pap. 19.95 *(978-1-905177-09-7(7))* Pinter & Martin Ltd. GBR. Dist: National Bk. Network.
Sivapriyananda, Swami. Secret Power of Tantrik Breathing: Techniques for Attaining Health, Harmony, & Liberation. 2009. (ENG.). 1p. pap. 16.95 *(978-1-59477-289-4(4)*, Destiny Bks.) Inner Traditions International, Ltd.
Star Wolf, Linda. Shamanic Breathwork. 2009. (ENG.). 1p. 20.00 *(978-1-59143-106-0(9))* Bear & Co.
Swartz, Sherwood. Recharging Qi Gong Exercises: A Proven Pathway to Longevity through a Series of Quick, Simple Exercises to Improve Flexibility, Health, & Personal Well Being. 2007. (Illus.). spiral bd. 195.00 *(978-0-9729322-3-3(2))* Golden Skies Productions.
Taylor, Kylea. Considering Holotropic Breathwork: Essays & Articles on the Therapeutic, Sociological, & Spiritual Functions & Effects of Grof Breathwork. 2008. per. 21.95 *(978-1-59275-007-3(9))* Hanford Mead Pubs., Inc.
Thompson, Heidi. Focus: Teaching Children Concentration. 2012. ***(978-0-9698147-4-0(7))*** Coldstream Bks.
Vilga, Edward. Yoga for Suits: 30 No-Sweat Power Poses to Do in Pinstripes. 2006. (ENG., Illus.). 128p. pap. 14.95 *(978-0-7624-2621-8(7))* Running Pr. Bk. Pubs.
Weil, Andrew. Breathing: The Master Key to Self Healing. 2009. (Playaway Adult Nonfiction Ser.). (ENG.). 39.99 *(978-1-60812-774-0(5))* Findaway World, LLC.
Yogani. Asanas, Mudras & Bandhas: Awakening Ecstatic Kundalini. 2006. per. 11.95 *(978-0-9786496-0-9(5))* AYP Publishing.
Yogi Ramacharaka. Science of Breath. 2011. 76p. pap. 3.45 ***(978-1-60386-418-3(0)***, Watchmaker Publishing) Wexford College Pr.

BREATHLESSNESS
see Dyspnoea

BRECHT, BERTOLT, 1898-1956

Bentley, Eric. Bentley on Brecht. 3rd rev ed. 2008. (ENG.). 480p. pap. 29.95 *(978-0-8101-2393-9(2))* Northwestern Univ. Pr.
Bradley, Laura. Brecht & Political Theatre: The Mother on Stage. 2006. (Oxford Modern Languages & Literature Monographs). (ENG., Illus.). 280p. 125.00 *(978-0-19-928658-4(2))* Oxford Univ. Pr., Inc.
Calico, Joy Haslam. Brecht at the Opera. 2008. (California Studies in 20th-Century Music Ser.). (Illus.). 304p. 55.00 *(978-0-520-25482-4(1))* Univ. of California Pr.
Conrad, Wolfgang & Pinkert, Ernst-Ullrich. Brechts Söhne: Topographie, Biographie, Werk. 2008. 136p. pap. 35.95 *(978-3-631-58376-0(1))* Lang, Peter GmbH, Europaischer Verlag der Wissenschaften DEU. Dist: Lang, Peter.
Garde, Ulrike. Brecht & Co: German-Speaking Playwrights on the Australian Stage. 426p. pap. 76.95 *(978-3-03910-832-9(8))* Lang, Peter Publishing, Inc.
Giles, Steve. Bertolt Brecht & Critical Theory: Marxism, Modernity & the Threepenny Lawsuit. Date not set. 202p. (C). pap. 36.95 *(978-0-8204-3400-1(0))* Lang, Peter CHE. Dist: Lang, Peter Publishing, Inc.
Gillett, Robert & Weiss-Sussex, Godela, eds. Verwisch die Spuren! . Bertolt Brecht's Work & Legacy: A Reassessment. 2008. (ENG & GER., Illus.). 364p. 111.60 *(978-90-420-2432-8(1))* Rodopi.
Hayot, Eric R. J. Chinese Dreams: Pound, Brecht, Tel Quel. 2011. (ENG.). 242p. pap. 26.95 ***(978-0-472-03486-4(3))*** Univ. of Michigan Pr.
Hillesheim, Jurgen, et al, eds. Brecht & Death/Brecht und der Tod. 2007. (Brecht Yearbook Ser.). (Illus.). 490p. per. 40.00 *(978-0-9718963-5-2(6))* Univ. of Wisconsin Pr.
Horsman, Yasco. Theaters of Justice: Judging, Staging, & Working Through in Arendt, Brecht, & Delbo. 2010. (Cultural Memory in the Present Ser.). (ENG.). 232p. 55.00 *(978-0-8047-7031-6(X))*; pap. 21.95 *(978-0-8047-7032-3(8))* Stanford Univ. Pr.
Jameson, Fredric. Brecht & Method. 2nd ed. 2011. (Radical Thinkers Ser.). (ENG.). 280p. pap. 15.95 *(978-1-84467-677-4(3)*, 844677) Verso Bks. GBR. Dist: Norton, W. W. & Co., Inc.
Li, Jiefei. Bertolt Brecht und die Peking-Oper: Die Beziehung zwischen Brechts epischem Theater und der Peking-Oper. 2010. 128p. pap. *(978-3-639-21994-4(5))* VDM Verlag Dr. Mueller e.K.
Mumford & Mumford, Meg. Bertolt Brecht. 2008. (Routledge Performance Practitioners Ser.). (Illus.). 144p. 115.00 *(978-0-415-37508-5(8))* Routledge.
Mumford, Meg. Bertolt Brecht. (Routledge Performance Practitioners Ser.). (Illus.). 2009. 208p. pap. 30.95 *(978-0-415-37509-2(6))* 2008. xiv, 188p. 28.95 *(978-0-203-88210-8(5))* Routledge.
Nekimken, Albert. Brecht in Turkey 1955-1977. 2011. 113.96 *(978-1-61719-910-3(9))* Gorgias Pr., LLC.
Pike, David. Lukacs & Brecht. 2011. (ENG.). 360p. pap. 50.00 *(978-0-8078-6581-1(8))* Univ. of North Carolina Pr.
Richardson, Michael D. Revolutionary Theater & the Classical Heritage: Inheritance & Appropriation from Weimar to the GDR. 2007. (Studies in Modern German Literature Ser.: Vol. 108). 257p. pap. 59.95 *(978-0-8204-7987-3(X))* Lang, Peter Publishing, Inc.
Robinson, Douglas. Estrangement & the Somatics of Literature: Tolstoy, Shklovsky, Brecht. 2008. (Parallax: Re#45;visions of Culture & Society Ser.). (ENG.). 344p. (gr. 17). 65.00 *(978-0-8018-8796-3(8))* Johns Hopkins Univ. Pr.
Savage, Robert. Hölderlin after the Catastrophe: Heidegger - Adorno - Brecht. 2008. (Studies in German Literature Linguistics & Culture Ser.: Volume 24). 250p. 80.00 *(978-1-57113-320-5(8))* Camden Hse.
Thomsen, Frank. Von der Taktik zur Tugend. Wandlung des Ethikkonzepts in Brechts marxistischen Dramen Von 1929-1945. 2008. (Hamburger Beiträge zur Germanistik Ser.). (GER.). 340p. pap. 80.95 *(978-3-631-58000-4(2))* Lang, Peter GmbH, Europaischer Verlag der Wissenschaften DEU. Dist: Lang, Peter.
Thomsen, Frank, et al. Ungeheuer Brecht: Eine Biographie seines Werks. 2006. (GER.). 330p. (C). pap. 35.00 *(978-3-525-20846-5(4))* Vandenhoeck & Ruprecht GmbH & Co KG DEU. Dist: ISD.
Thomson, Peter & Sacks, Glendyr, eds. The Cambridge Companion to Brecht. 2nd rev. ed. 2006. (Cambridge Companions to Literature Ser.). (ENG., Illus.). (C). 368p. 100.00 *(978-0-521-85709-3(0))*; 364p. per. 31.00 *(978-0-521-67384-6(4))* Cambridge Univ. Pr.
von Held, Phoebe. Alienation & Theatricality: Cross-Readings of Brecht & Diderot. 2011. (Legenda Studies in Comparative Literature Ser.). (ENG.). 240p. (C). 89.50 *(978-1-906540-12-8(8))* European Humanities Research Ctr. GBR. Dist: Brown, David Bk. Co., The.
Weber, Betty Nance & Heinen, Hubert, eds. Bertolt Brecht: Political Theory & Literary Practice. 2010. (ENG.). 224p. pap. 24.95 *(978-0-8203-3478-3(2))* Univ. of Georgia Pr.
Weidauer, Friedemann, ed. Political Intimacies/Politische Traulichkeiten, Vol. 34. 2009. (Brecht Yearbook Ser.). (ENG.). 250p. pap. 40.00 *(978-0-9718963-7-6(2))* Univ. of Wisconsin Pr.
Weidauer, Friedemann J. Gestus-Musik-Text Vol. 33: Gestus — Musik — Text (Gestus — Music — Text) Weidauer, Freidmann & Intl Brecht Society Staff, eds. 2008. (Brecht Yearbook Ser.). (GER & ENG., Illus.). 300p. pap. 40.00 *(978-0-9718963-6-9(4))* Univ. of Wisconsin Pr.
Weidauer, Friedemann J. & Ostmeier, Dorothee, eds. The Brecht Yearbook / das Brecht Jahrbuch, Volume 35: Brecht-Marxism-Ethics. 2010. (Brecht Yearbook Ser.). (ENG., Illus.). 350p. pap. 44.00 *(978-0-9718963-8-3(0))* Univ. of Wisconsin Pr.
Wekwerth, Manfred. Daring to Play: A Brecht Companion. Hozier, Anthony, ed. 2011. (ENG., Illus.). 264p. pap. 31.95 *(978-0-415-56969-9(9))* Routledge.
White, Ann, et al. Brecht's Furcht und Elend des Dritten Reiches: German Exile Drama & the Struggle Against Fascism. 2010. (Studies in German Literature Linguistics & Culture Ser.: Volume 77). 274p. 75.00 *(978-1-57113-373-1(9))* Camden Hse.

B

Wizisla, Erdmut. Walter Benjamin & Bertolt Brecht: The Story of a Friendship, 1924-1940. Shuttleworth, Christine, tr. from GER. 2009. (ENG., Illus.). 288p. 45.00 *(978-0-300-13695-1(1))* Yale Univ. Pr.

BRECKINRIDGE, MARY, 1881-1965

Goan, Melanie Beals. Mary Breckinridge: The Frontier Nursing Service & Rural Health in Appalachia. 2008. (ENG., Illus.). 360p. 49.95 *(978-0-8078-3211-0(1))* Univ. of North Carolina Pr.

Maher, Marie Bartlett & Bartlett, Marie. The Frontier Nursing Service: America's First Rural Nurse-Midwife Service & School. 2008. (Contributions to Southern Appalachian Studies). (ENG., Illus.). 260p. pap. 39.95 *(978-0-7864-3342-1(6))* McFarland & Co., Inc. Pubs.

BREDESEN, HARALD

Bredesen, Harald. Yes, Lord! 2008. (ENG., Illus.). 224p. 17.99 *(978-0-8307-4535-7(1))* Gospel Light Pubns.

BREEDER REACTORS

Koch, Leonard J. Experimental Breeder Reactor-II: (Ebr-Ii) an Integrated Experimental Fast Reactor Nuclear Power Station. 2008. *(978-0-89448-042-3(1))* American Nuclear Society.

BREEDING

see also Animal Breeding; Genetics; Germplasm Resources; Heredity; Heterosis; Hybridization; Inbreeding; Mendel's Law; Plant Breeding

Benedict, Oyiga. Aspects of Reproductive Biology & Pod Yield in Bambara Groundnut. 2010. 108p. pap. *(978-3-8383-8762-8(7))* Lambert Academic Publishing.

Goncharov, N. P., et al. Metodicheskie Osnovy Selektsii Rastenii. 2nd ed. 2009. (RUS., Illus.). 423p. *(978-5-9747-0169-6(0))* Geo, Wydawnictwo, Migala, P. i S-ka.

Jöchle, W. & Lamond, D. R., eds. Control of Reproductive Functions in Domestic Animals. 2010. (Current Topics in Veterinary Medicine Ser.). 248p. pap. 219.00 *(978-90-481-8263-3(8))*, 9048182638) Springer.

Long, Murray. Breeding Stud Sheep. 2008. (Landlinks Press Ser.). 144p. pap. 39.95 *(978-0-643-09480-2(6))* CSIRO Publishing AUS. Dist: Stylus Publishing, LLC.

Manigbas, Norvie L. & C. Mendoza, Teodoro. Morpho-Physiological Characters Associated with Gxe in Sugarcane. 2010. 156p. pap. *(978-3-639-22123-7(0))* VDM Verlag Dr. Mueller e.K.

Ostrander, Elaine A. & Ruvinsky, Anatoly, eds. The Genetics of the Dog. 2nd ed. 2012. (Illus.). 512p. 220.00 ***(978-1-84593-940-3(9))*** CABI GBR. Dist: Stylus Publishing, LLC.

Pala, Akin. Crossbreeding in Beef Cattle Using Terminal Sires. 2010. 112p. pap. *(978-3-639-23524-1(X))* VDM Verlag Dr. Mueller e.K.

Russell, Nicholas. Like Engend'ring Like: Heredity & Animal Breeding in Early Modern England. 2007. (ENG., Illus.). 284p. per. 58.00 *(978-0-521-03158-5(3))* Cambridge Univ. Pr.

Solomon, Nancy G. & French, Jeffrey A., eds. Cooperative Breeding in Mammals. 2007. (ENG., Illus.). 408p. pap. 79.00 *(978-0-521-03828-7(6))* Cambridge Univ. Pr.

Troiano, Kenny. Gamefowl Breeders Manual & Cockers Guide: Chronicles of Kenny Troiano - Volume Two. 2011. 328p. pap. 19.11 *(978-1-4269-6024-6(7))* Trafford Publishing.

Young, Malachy, et al. Programs for Developing & Feeding the Breeding Herd. 2010. 236p. pap. *(978-3-8383-1730-4(0))* Lambert Academic Publishing.

BREED'S HILL, BATTLE OF, BOSTON, MASS., 1775

see Bunker Hill, Battle of, Boston, Mass., 1775

BREEDS OF CATTLE

see Cattle Breeds

BREEDS OF HORSES

see Horse Breeds

BREHON LAWS

see Law—Ireland

BREMEN

Adams, Bianka J. From Crusade to Hazard: The Denazification of Bremen, Germany. 2010. E-Book *(978-0-8108-7502-9(0))* Scarecrow Pr., Inc.

Buschmann, Ulf. Journey Through Bremen & Bremerhaven. 2011. (Journey Through Ser.). (ENG., Illus.). 140p. 29.95 *(978-3-8003-4037-8(2))* Verlagshaus Wurzburg GmbH & Co. KG DEU. Dist: Independent Pubs. Group.

Fetting, Rainer. Rainer Fetting: Return of the Giants. 2009. (ENG., Illus.). 160p. 55.00 *(978-3-86678-231-0(4))* Kerber Verlag DEU. Dist: D.A.P./Distributed Art Pubs.

BREMSSTRAHLUNG

American Society of Mechanical Engineers Staff, ed. Advances in Automotive Braking Technology. (Illus.). 168p. 83.00 *(978-1-86058-039-0(4))* Professional Engineering Publishing GBR. Dist: SAE Intl.

—Braking on Road Vehicles. (Illus.). 294p. 160.00 *(978-0-85298-853-4(2))* Professional Engineering Publishing GBR. Dist: SAE Intl.

Beaurepaire, Eric, et al, eds. Magnetism: Synchrotron Radiation Approach. 2006. (Lecture Notes in Physics Ser.: Vol. 697). (Illus.). xii, 470p. 159.00 *(978-3-540-33241-1(3)*, 3540332413) Springer.

Jiin-Ju Chang, et al, eds. Biophotons. 2010. 428p. pap. 289.00 *(978-90-481-5033-5(7)*, 9048150337) Springer.

BRENDAN, SAINT, THE VOYAGER, CA. 483-577

Burgess, Glyn S. & Strijbosch, Clara, eds. The Brendan Legend: Texts & Versions. 2006. (Northern World Ser.: Vol. 24). (Illus.). 400p. *(978-90-04-15247-2(4))* BRILL.

Dykstra, Rosemary Kerr. Saint Brendan's Seven Year Voyage. 2007. per. 15.00 *(978-0-9785055-6-1(5))* Dykstra Publishing.

Gregory, Isabella Augusta. The Voyages of St. Brendan: The Navigator & Stories of the Saints of Ireland. pap. 4.95 *(978-0-89979-092-3(5))* British American Bks.

Mackley, Jude S. The Legend of St. Brendan: A Comparative Study of the Latin & Anglo-Norman Versions. 2008. 320p. (C). *(978-90-04-16662-2(9))* BRILL.

BRENNAN, WILLIAM J. (WILLIAM JOSEPH), 1906-1997

Wermiel, Stephen & Stern, Seth. Justice Brennan: Liberal Champion. 2010. (ENG., Illus.). 688p. 35.00 *(978-0-547-14925-7(5))* Houghton Mifflin Harcourt Trade & Reference Pubs.

BRENTANO, CLEMENS, 1778-1842

Benzi, Laura. Resakralisierung und Allegorie im Spatwerk Clemens Brentanos: Das Marchen von Gockel, Hinkel und Gackeleia (1838) und Das Bittere Leiden Unsers Herrn Jesu Christi (1833) (GER.). 265p. 39.95 *(978-3-906769-11-0(9))* Lang, Peter CHE. Dist: Lang, Peter Publishing, Inc.

BRENTANO, FRANZ CLEMENS, 1838-1917

Albertazzi, L., et al, eds. The School of Franz Brentano. 2010. (Nijhoff International Philosophy Ser.). 496p. pap. 379.00 *(978-90-481-4628-4(3)*, 9048146283) Springer.

Albertazzi, Liliana. Immanent Realism: An Introduction to Brentano. 2010. (Synthese Library). (Illus.). xii, 378p. pap. 239.00 *(978-90-481-7070-8(2)*, 9048170702) Springer.

Chisholm, Roderick M. Brentano & Meinong Studies. 2008. 132p. pap. 38.00 *(978-90-6203-724-7(0))* Rodopi.

Chrudzimski, A. Intentionalitätstheorie Beim Frühen Brentano. 2010. (Phaenomenologica Ser.). (ENG & GER., Illus.). 296p. pap. 189.00 *(978-90-481-5670-2(X)*, 904815670X) Springer.

Eaton, Howard Ormsby. The Austrian Philosophy of Values. 2011. 388p. 53.95 ***(978-1-258-04429-9(3))*** Literary Licensing, LLC.

Hickerson, Ryan & Hickerson. History of Intentionality: Theories of Consciousness from Brentano to Husserl. 2007. (Continuum Studies in Philosophy Ser.). (ENG.). 192p. 140.00 *(978-0-8264-8683-7(5))* Continuum International Publishing Group, Ltd. GBR. Dist: National Bk. Network.

Rojszczak, Artur. From the Act of Judging to the Sentence: The Problem of Truth Bearers from Bolzano to Tarski. Wolenski, Jan, ed. 2010. (Synthese Library). xv, 240p. pap. 159.00 *(978-90-481-6853-8(8)*, 9048168538) Springer.

Rollinger, Robin D. Husserl's Position in the School of Brentano. 2010. (Phaenomenologica Ser.). 380p. pap. 239.00 *(978-90-481-5208-7(9)*, 9048152089) Springer.

BRESSON, ROBERT, 1907-1999

Cardullo, Bert. Robert Bresson: A Casebook. 2009. pap. *(978-0-8143-3454-6(7))* Wayne State Univ. Pr.

Pipolo, Tony. Robert Bresson: A Passion for Film. 2010. (ENG., Illus.). 464p. 29.95 *(978-0-19-531979-8(6))* Oxford Univ. Pr., Inc.

Price, Brian. Neither God nor Master: Robert Bresson & Radical Politics. 2011. (Illus.). 264p. 67.50 *(978-0-8166-5461-1(1))*; pap. 22.50 *(978-0-8166-5462-8(X))* Univ. of Minnesota Pr.

Quandt, James. Robert Bresson. 2nd exp. rev. ed. 2012. (Cinematheque Ontario Monographs). (ENG., Illus.). 752p. pap. 39.95 *(978-0-9682969-5-0(5)*, 0968296955) Indiana Univ. Pr.

BREST-LITOVSK, TREATY OF MARCH 3, 1918

Trotsky, Leon. From October to Brest-Litovsk. 2008. 104p. pap. 15.99 *(978-0-559-23442-2(2))* BiblioBazaar.

—From October to Brest-Litovsk. 2008. 104p. pap. 19.95 *(978-1-4368-5452-8(0))* Kessinger Publishing, LLC.

Trotzky, Leon. From October to Brest-Litovsk. 2009. 108p. pap. *(978-1-4099-6979-2(7))* Dodo Pr.

—From October to Brest-Litovsk. 2006. pap. *(978-1-4068-1079-0(7))* Echo Library.

BRETAGNE (FRANCE)

see Brittany (France)

BRETHREN, UNITED

see Moravians

BRETHREN CHURCH

see Church of the Brethren

BRETON, ANDRE, 1896-1966

Brodwer. Andre Breton, Arbiter of Surrealism. 29.95 *(978-0-7859-0637-7(1)*, F89730) French & European Pubns., Inc.

Polizzotti, Mark. Revolution of the Mind, Revised Edition: The Life of Andre Breton. 2009. (ENG.). 680p. pap. 29.95 *(978-0-9795137-8-7(2))* Commonwealth Bks., Black Widow.

BRETON CLUB

see Jacobins

BRETON LANGUAGE

Assimil Staff. Breton Sans Peine Vol. 2: Breton for French Speakers. (BRE & FRE.). 28.95 incl. audio *(978-0-8288-4467-3(4)*, M14495); 28.95 incl. audio *(978-0-8288-4469-7(0)*, M4624) French & European Pubns., Inc.

—Initiation au Breton sans Peine: Introduction to Breton for French Speakers. (BRE & FRE.). 28.95 incl. audio *(978-0-8288-4465-9(8)*, M14799) French & European Pubns., Inc.

Euro Talk. Talk Now! Breton. 2008. 29.99 *(978-1-84352-382-6(5))* TOPICS Entertainment.

Hemon, Roparz & Everson, Michael. Breton Grammar. 3rd ed. 2011. (BRE & ENG., Illus.). 100p. pap. ***(978-1-904808-71-8(9))*** Evertype.

Icon Group International, Inc. Staff, compiled by. Webster's Breton - English Thesaurus Dictionary. 2008. 346p. ring bd. 28.95 incl. audio compact disk *(978-0-497-83452-4(9))* Icon Group International, Inc.

Le Braz, Anatole. The Night of Fires & Other Breton Studies. Gostling, Frances M., tr. from FRE. (Illus.). reprint ed. 45.00 *(978-0-404-16492-8(7))* AMS Pr., Inc.

McKenna, Malachy. A Handbook of Modern Spoken Breton. (Buchreihe der Zeitschrift far celtische Philologie Ser.). (ENG.). VII, 310p. 210.00 ***(978-3-11-183565-5(0))*** De Gruyter, Walter Inc.

Winterstein, David P. Media & Power on the Margins of Europe: The Public Negotiation of the Breton Language & Cultural Identity. (Illus.). 2010. vii, 236p. *(978-1-57273-919-2(3))* 2009. 244p. *(978-1-57273-920-8(7))* Hampton Pr., Inc.

BRETONNE, RESTIF DE LA, 1734-1806

see Restif de La Bretonne, 1734-1806

BREUER, MARCEL, 1902-1981

Thimmesh, Hilary & Breuer, Marcel. Marcel Breuer & the Committee of Twelve Plan a Church: A Monastic Memoir. 2011. 19.95 *(978-0-9740992-7-9(9))* St. John's Univ. Pr.

BREVIARIES

Benedict, Saint. Monastic Breviary Matins: According to the Holy Rule of Saint Benedict. 2007. 1297p. lib. bdg. 45.00 net. *(978-0-9777093-3-5(7))* Lancelot Andrewes Pr.

Hoornaert, Rodolphe. The Breviary & the Laity. 2007. 116p. per. 12.95 *(978-0-9783198-1-6(8))* Catholic Authors Pr.

Hughes, Andrew. Cataloguing Discrepancies: The Printed York Breviary of 1493. 2011. *(978-1-4426-4197-6(5))* Univ. of Toronto Pr.

Quigley, E. J. The Divine Office: A Study of the Roman Breviary. 2006. 232p. pap. 22.99 *(978-1-4264-3974-2(1))* 2007. (ENG.). 214p. pap. 20.99 *(978-1-4264-3916-2(4))* BiblioBazaar.

St. Meinrad's Abbey. The Lessons of the Temporal Cycle & the Principal Feasts of the Sanctoral Cycle According to the Monastic Breviary. 2011. 532p. 60.95 ***(978-1-258-04759-7(4))*** Literary Licensing, LLC.

BREWERIES

see also Microbreweries

Armon, Rick. Ohio Breweries, 1 vol. 2011. (Breweries Ser.). (ENG., Illus.). 192p. pap. 19.95 *(978-0-8117-0868-5(3))* Stackpole Bks.

Baxter, R. Scott & Wooten, Kimberly J. Breweries of the Gold Country. 2012. (Images of America Ser.). (ENG., Illus.). 128p. pap. 21.99 ***(978-0-7385-7621-3(2))*** Arcadia Publishing.

Benson, J. T. & EBC Technology and Engineering Forum, contrib. by. Brewery Utilities. (Illus.). xiv, 200p. *(978-3-418-00756-4(2))* Carl, Hans GmbH & Co. KG.

Bryson, Lew. Pennsylvania Breweries. 4th ed. 2010. (Breweries Ser.). (ENG., Illus.). 304p. pap. 19.95 *(978-0-8117-3641-1(5))* Stackpole Bks.

Bryson, Lew & Haynie, Mark. New Jersey Breweries. 2008. (Breweries Ser.). (ENG., Illus.). 148p. pap. 16.95 *(978-0-8117-3504-9(4))* Stackpole Bks.

Crocker, Ronnie. Houston Beer: A Heady History of Brewing in the Bayou City. 2012. 160p. pap. 19.99 ***(978-1-60949-537-4(3))*** History Pr., The.

Daniels, Ray. The Brewers Association's Guide to Starting Your Own Brewery. 2006. (ENG., Illus.). 200p. per. 80.00 *(978-0-937381-89-2(6))* Brewers Pubns.

Eddings, Bryce. Missouri Breweries. 2012. (Breweries Ser.). (ENG., Illus.). 160p. pap. 19.95 *(978-0-8117-0662-9(1))* Stackpole Bks.

Griffiths, Iorwerth. Beer & Cider in Ireland: The Complete Guide. 2008. (ENG., Illus.). 174p. per. 21.95 *(978-1-905483-17-4(1))* Liberties Pr. IRL. Dist: Dufour Editions, Inc.

Grossman, Ken. Beyond the Pale: The Story of Sierra Nevada Brewing Co. 2012. (ENG.). 240p. 24.95 ***(978-1-118-00736-5(0)**, Wiley)* Wiley, John & Sons, Inc.

Hintz, Martin. A Spirited History of Milwaukee Brews & Booze. 2011. 160p. pap. 19.99 ***(978-1-60949-066-9(5))*** History Pr., The.

Hoil & Schweber, John & Nate. Indiana Breweries. 2011. (Breweries Ser.). (ENG.). 144p. pap. 16.95 *(978-0-8117-0661-2(3))* Stackpole Bks.

Jersey Brew: The Story of Beer in New Jersey. 2009. (Illus.). 160p. 19.95 *(978-0-9765233-1-4(0))* Lake Neepaulin Publishing.

Koeller, Paul D. Brewed with Style. 2007. 264p. 24.95 *(978-0-9605832-2-5(X))* Univ. of Wisconsin-La Crosse Foundation, Inc., The.

Kuderka, Michael & Ench-Kuderka, Catherine A. Essential Reference of Domestic Brewers & Their Bottled Brands, 3rd Edition. 3rd ed. 2007. (Illus.). 574p. 60.00 *(978-0-9774800-1-2(1))* MC Basset, LLC.

Lincoln, Brad & Lincoln, Anda. 21 Questions about Opening a Brewery in the United States. 2009. 80p. pap., pap. 60.00 *(978-0-9825841-0-1(5))* Dark Train LLC.

McFarland, Ben & Sandham, Tom. Good Beer Guide West Coast USA: Including Las Vegas, Alaska & Hawaii. 2008. (Good Beer Guides). (ENG., Illus.). 320p. pap. 27.95 *(978-1-85249-244-1(9))* Camra Bks. GBR. Dist: Independent Pubs. Group.

Mertie, Scott R. Nashville Brewing. 2006. (Images of America Ser.). (ENG., Illus.). 128p. per. 19.99 *(978-0-7385-4347-5(0))* Arcadia Publishing.

Microbreweries Market. 115p. (Orig.). pap. 795.00 *(978-0-7605-2160-1(3))* Rector Pr., Ltd.

Mixed Drink Market. 100p. (Orig.). pap. 1295.00 *(978-0-7605-2168-7(9))* Rector Pr., Ltd.

Morgan, Michael D. Over-the-Rhine: When Beer Was King. 2010. (Food & Drink Ser.). (ENG., Illus.). 184p. pap. 19.99 *(978-1-59629-914-6(2))* History Pr., The.

Moyer, David G. American Breweries of the Past. 2009. 116p. pap. 39.49 *(978-1-4389-7257-2(1))* AuthorHouse.

Myers, Erik Lars. North Carolina Craft Brew & Breweries. 2012. (ENG., Illus.). 304p. pap. 16.95 ***(978-0-89587-571-6(3))*** Blair, John F. Pub.

Noon, Mark A. Yuengling: A History of America's Oldest Brewery. alt. ed. 2007. (ENG., Illus.). 231p. per. 29.95 *(978-0-7864-3758-0(8))* McFarland & Co., Inc. Pubs.

Ostrander, Bob & Morris, Derrick. Hoosier Beer: Tapping into Indiania Brewing History. 2011. 268p. pap. 21.99 ***(978-1-60949-359-2(1))*** History Pr., The.

Pattyn, Joris & Webb, Tim. 100 Belgian Beers to Try Before You Die! 2010. (ENG., Illus.). 160p. pap. 24.95 *(978-1-85249-248-9(1))* Camra Bks. GBR. Dist: Independent Pubs. Group.

Penza, Robert C. Reflections of the Brewmaster. 2010. (Illus.). 175p. pap. 17.95 *(978-1-4327-5786-1(5))* Outskirts Pr., Inc.

Pettigrew, Timmons. Charleston Beer: A High-Gravity History of Lowcountry Brewing. 2011. 128p. pap. 19.99 ***(978-1-60949-244-1(7))*** History Pr., The.

Putman, Roger. Beers & Breweries of Britain. 2008. (Shire Library). (ENG., Illus.). 56p. pap. 12.95 *(978-0-7478-0606-6(3))* Shire Pubns., Ltd. GBR. Dist: Random Hse., Inc.

Renfro, Mike. Shine On: 100 Years of Shiner Beer. 2009. (ENG., Illus.). 187p. pap. 24.95 *(978-1-933979-60-1(7))* Bright Sky Pr.

Ronnenberg, Herman Wiley. Material Culture of Breweries. 2011. (Guides to American Artifacts, Vol. 1 Ser.). (ENG., Illus.). 152p. pap. 24.95 *(978-1-59874-167-4(5))*; lib. bdg. 94.00 *(978-1-59874-166-7(7))* Left Coast Pr., Inc.

Routledge, Christopher, ed. Cains: The Story of Liverpool in a Pint. 2009. (ENG., Illus.). 160p. pap. 35.00 *(978-1-84631-150-5(0))* Liverpool Univ. Pr. GBR. Dist: Chicago Distribution Ctr.

Ruschmann, Paul & Nasiatka, Maryanne. Michigan Breweries. 2006. (Breweries Ser.). (ENG., Illus.). 265p. per. 16.95 *(978-0-8117-3299-4(1))* Stackpole Bks.

Schlafly, Thomas. A New Religion in Mecca: Starting up an Upstart Brewery in St. Louis. 2006. (Illus.). 102p. per. 18.95 *(978-1-891442-42-1(2))* Virginia Publishing Corp.

Sealover, Ed. Mountain Brew: A Guide to Colorado's Breweries. 2011. 208p. pap. 21.99 ***(978-1-60949-177-2(7))*** History Pr., The.

Shepard, Robin. Minnesota's Best Breweries & Brewpubs: Searching for the Perfect Pint. 2011. E-Book *(978-0-299-28243-1(0))*; (ENG., Illus.). 336p. pap. 24.95 *(978-0-299-28244-8(9))* Univ. of Wisconsin Pr.

Stephens, Sarah. Cincinnati's Brewing History. 2010. (Images of America Ser.). (ENG., Illus.). 128p. pap. 21.99 *(978-0-7385-7790-6(1))* Arcadia Publishing.

Webb, Tim. Belgium. 6th ed. 2009. (ENG., Illus.). 352p. pap. 23.95 *(978-1-85249-261-8(9))* Camra Bks. GBR. Dist: Independent Pubs. Group.

Wendler, John. Brewers & Bottlers of California 1860 To 1919. 2007. 208p. per. 39.95 *(978-1-4327-0733-0(7))* Outskirts Pr., Inc.

Wissing, Douglas A. Indiana: One Pint at a Time: A Traveler's Guide to Indiana's Brewpubs. 2010. *(978-0-87195-283-7(1))* Indiana Historical Society.

BREWING

see also Ale; Beer; Enzymes; Liquors; Malt

Alexander, John. A Guide to Craft Brewing. 2006. (ENG., Illus.). 160p. pap. 29.95 *(978-1-86126-899-0(8))* Crowood Pr., Ltd. GBR. Dist: Independent Pubs. Group.

Bailey, R. Douglas. The Brewer's Analyst: A Systematic Handbook of Analysis Relating to Brewing & Malting. 2008. (Cooking in America Ser.). (ENG.). 460p. pap. 28.95 *(978-1-4290-1200-3(5))* Applewood Bks.

Bamforth, Charles. Beer: Tap into the Art & Science of Brewing. 3rd ed. 2009. (ENG., Illus.). 272p. 29.95 *(978-0-19-530542-5(6))* Oxford Univ. Pr., Inc.

Bamforth, Charles W. Beer Is Proof God Loves Us: Reaching for the Soul of Beer & Brewing. 2010. (FT Press Science Ser.). (ENG., Illus.). 304p. 25.99 *(978-0-13-706507-3(8))* FT Press.

—Brewing: New Technologies. Bamforth, C W, ed. 2006. (Illus.). 484p. 269.95 *(978-0-8493-9159-0(8))* CRC Pr. LLC.

—Brewing: New Technologies. Bamforth, C., ed. 2006. (Illus.). 500p. *(978-1-84569-003-8(6))* Woodhead Publishing Ltd.

Beechum, Drew. The Everything Homebrewing Book: All you need to brew the best beer at Home! 2009. (ENG.). 304p. pap. 15.95 *(978-1-60550-122-2(0))* Adams Media Corp.

Bernstein, Joshua M. Brewed Awakening: Behind the Beers & Brewers Leading the World's Craft Beer Revolution. 2011. (ENG., Illus.). 304p. 24.95 *(978-1-4027-7864-3(3)*, Sterling Epicure) Sterling Publishing Co., Inc.

Berry, C. J. J. Homebrewed Beers & Stouts: Full Instructions for All Types of Classic Beers, Stouts, & Lagers. 2011. (ENG., Illus.). 160p. pap. 14.95 *(978-1-56523-601-1(7))* Fox Chapel Publishing Co., Inc.

Bostwick, William & Rymill, Jessi. Beer Craft: A Simple Guide to Making Great Beer. 2011. (ENG., Illus.). 176p. pap. 17.99 *(978-1-60529-133-8(1))* Rodale Pr., Inc.

Bruning, Ted. Home Brewing: A Guide to Making Your Own Beer & Wine. 2011. (ENG., Illus.). 96p. 12.95 *(978-1-907892-03-5(6))* National Trust, Aylesbury GBR. Dist: Independent Pubs. Group.

Calagione, Sam. Extreme Brewing: An Enthusiast's Guide to Brewing Craft Beer at Home. 2006. (ENG., Illus.). 184p. pap. 24.99 (978-1-59253-293-3(4), 1592532934) Quayside.

Chang, Weide & Taylor, Kevin. Automated Beer Fermentation Controller. 2010. 64p. pap. (978-3-8383-4265-8(8)) Lambert Academic Publishing.

Chaston Chapman, A. Brewing. 2012. (ENG.). 144p. pap. 19.99 (978-1-107-60595-4(4)) Cambridge Univ. Pr.

Combrune, Michael. The Theory & Practice of Brewing. 384p. 2008. 48.95 (978-0-548-93599-6(8)) 2007. (ENG.). per. 33.95 (978-0-548-58893-2(7)) Kessinger Publishing, LLC.

The Complete Encyclopedia of Beer. (Complete Encyclopedia Ser.). (Illus.). 304p. (978-90-366-1523-5(2)) Rebo International B.V.

The Complete Guide to Brewing Your Own Beer at Home: Everything You Need to Know Explained Simply. 2012. (Back to Basics Ser.). (ENG.). 288p. pap. 24.95 (978-1-60138-601-4(X)) Atlantic Publishing Co.

Coppinger, Joseph. The American Practical Brewer & Tanner. 2008. 184p. 22.99 (978-0-554-39952-2(0)); 184p. 25.99 (978-0-554-30649-0(2)); (ENG.). 168p. pap. 20.75 (978-1-4375-0827-7(8)); (ENG.). 182p. pap. 22.75 (978-1-4375-0828-4(6)) BiblioBazaar.

Denny, Mark & Denny, M. Froth! The Science of Beer. 2009. (ENG., Illus.). 200p. 25.95 (978-0-8018-9132-8(9)) Johns Hopkins Univ. Pr.

Elkins, Roy. The Wine & Beer Maker's Year: Celebrate Every Season with Classic Wine & Beer Recipes You Can Make at Home. 2012. (ENG., Illus.). 160p. pap. 12.95 (978-1-56523-675-2(0)) Fox Chapel Publishing Co., Inc.

Eßlinger, Hans Michael, ed. Handbook of Brewing: Processes, Technology, Markets. 2009. (ENG., Illus.). 778p. 280.00 (978-3-527-31674-8(4), Wiley-VCH) Wiley, John & Sons, Inc.

Forbes, Kevin. Home Brewing. 2012. (ENG., Illus.). 160p. pap. 12.95 (978-1-56523-701-8(3)) Fox Chapel Publishing Co., Inc.

Gales, Peter W. Brewing Chemistry & Technology in the Americas. 2007. (Illus.). 241p. (978-1-881696-09-4(X)) American Society of Brewing Chemists.

Gately, Iain. Drink: A Cultural History of Alcohol. 2009. (ENG.). 560p. (gr. 12-18). 22.00 (978-1-59240-464-3(2), Gotham) Penguin Group (USA) Inc.

Haudricourt, Tom. Brewers Essential: Everything You Need to Know to Be a Real Fan! 2008. (Essential: Everything You Need to Know to Be a Real Fan Ser.). (ENG., Illus.). 176p. 19.95 (978-1-57243-947-4(5)) Triumph Bks.

Hieronymus, Stan. Brewing with Wheat: The "Wit' & Weizen" of World Wheat Beer Styles. 2010. (ENG.). 295p. pap. 17.95 (978-0-937381-95-3(0)) Brewers Pubns.

Hopkins, R. h. Biochemistry Applied to the Brewing Processes - Malting. 2011. 72p. pap. 26.45 (978-1-4465-4167-8(3)) Thorndike Pr.

Hummel, George. The Complete Homebrew Beer Book: 200 Easy Recipes, from Ales & Lagers to Extreme Beers & International Favorites. 2011. (Illus.). 456p. pap. 24.95 (978-0-7788-0268-6(X)) Rose, Robert Inc. CAN. Dist: Firefly Bks., Ltd.

Koch, Greg & Allyn, Matt. The Brewer's Apprentice: An Insider's Guide to the Art & Craft of Beer Brewing, Taught by the Masters. 2011. (Apprentice Ser.). (ENG., Illus.). 192p. pap. 24.99 (978-1-59253-731-0(6), 1592537316) Quayside.

Koch, Greg, et al. The Craft of Stone Brewing Co: Liquid Lore, Epic Recipes, & Unabashed Arrogance. 2011. (ENG., Illus.). 208p. 25.00 (978-1-60774-055-1(9)) Ten Speed Pr.

Kohn, Rita T. & Arnold, Kris. True Brew: A Guide to Craft Beer in Indiana. 2010. (ENG., Illus.). 288p. pap. 19.95 (978-0-253-22214-5(1), 0253222141, Quarry Bks.) Indiana Univ. Pr.

Kunath, Brian. The Brewer's Bible: How to Brew Delicious Beers at Home. 2011. (ENG.). 224p. spiral bd. 12.99 (978-0-7858-2817-4(6), 0785828176, Chartwell) Book Sales, Inc.

Learn How to Homebrew with Malt Extract Guidebook & DVD. 2nd ed. 2006. 32.50 (978-0-9713645-1-4(7)) Big Beaver Press.

Lebow, Jess. The Beer Devotional: A Daily Celebration of the World's Most Inspiring Beers. 2010. (ENG.). 384p. pap. 14.95 (978-1-4405-0357-3(5)) Adams Media Corp.

Lewis, Michael J. & Bamforth, Charles W. Essays in Brewing Science. 2006. (Illus.). 179p. per. 84.95 (978-0-387-33010-5(0), 0387330100) Springer.

Line, Dave. Big Book of Brewing: The Classic Guide to All-Grain Brewing. 2011. (ENG., Illus.). 256p. pap. 17.95 (978-1-56523-603-5(3)) Fox Chapel Publishing Co., Inc.

Line, Dave. Brewing British-Style Beers: More Than 100 Thirst Quenching Pub Recipes to Brew at Home. 2012. (ENG., Illus.). 160p. pap. 14.95 (978-1-56523-689-9(0)) Fox Chapel Publishing Co., Inc.

Lutz, Henry. Viticulture & Brewing in the Ancient Orient. 2007. (Cooking in America Ser.). (ENG.). 180p. per. 13.95 (978-1-4290-1042-9(8)) Applewood Bks.

Mansfield, Scott. Strong Waters: A Simple Guide to Making Beer, Wine, Cider & Other Spirited Beverages at Home. 2010. (ENG., Illus.). 264p. pap. 18.95 (978-1-61519-010-2(4), 1615190104) Experiment LLC, The.

Meacham, Sarah Hand. Every Home a Distillery: Alcohol, Gender, & Technology in the Colonial Chesapeake. 2009. (Early America: History, Context, Culture Ser.). (ENG., Illus.). 208p. (gr. 17). 50.00 (978-0-8018-9312-4(7)) Johns Hopkins Univ. Pr.

Mosher, Randy. The Brewer's Companion: Being a Complete Compendium of Brewing Knowledge. 2nd rev. ed. Date not set. (Illus.). pap. 19.95 (978-0-9640410-1-1(4)) Alephenalia Pubns.

—Tasting Beer: An Insider's Guide to the World's Greatest Drink. 2009. (ENG., Illus.). 256p. pap. 16.95 (978-1-60342-089-1(4), 1603420894) Storey Publishing, LLC.

Nachel, Marty. Homebrewing for Dummies. 2nd ed. 2008. (ENG., Illus.). 432p. pap. 19.99 (978-0-470-23062-6(2), For Dummies) Wiley, John & Sons, Inc.

Narziß, Ludwig & Back, Werner. Die Bierbrauerei 2: Die Technologie der Würzebereitung, 2 vols. 8th ed. 2009. (GER., Illus.). 820p. (978-3-527-32533-7(6), VCH) Wiley, John & Sons, Ltd.

Owens, Bill & Owen, Bill. How to Build a Small Brewery: Draft Beer in Ten Days. 2010. (ENG.). 68p. pap. 20.00 (978-0-9824055-2-9(9)) White Mule Pr.

Palmer, John. How to Brew: Ingredients, Methods, Recipes & Equipment for Brewing Beer at Home. 400p. pap. 16.95 (978-0-9710579-0-6(7)) Defenestrative Publishing, Co.

Parkes, John. Home Brewing: Self-Sufficiency. 2009. (Self-Sufficiency Ser.). (ENG., Illus.). 128p. 12.95 (978-1-60239-787-3(2), 239787) Skyhorse Publishing Co., Inc.

Peragine, John. The Complete Guide to Growing Your Own Hops, Malts, & Brewing Herbs: Everything You Need to Know Explained Simply. 2011. (ENG.). 336p. pap. 24.95 (978-1-60138-353-2(3)) Atlantic Publishing Co.

Perozzi, Christina & Beaune, Hallie. The Naked Brewer: Fearless Homebrewing, Tips, Tricks & Rule-breaking Recipes. 2012. (ENG.). 336p. (gr. 12). pap. 16.95 (978-0-399-53768-4(6), Perigee Trade) Penguin Group (USA) Inc.

—The Naked Pint: An Unadulterated Guide to Craft Beer. 2012. (ENG.). 336p. (gr. 12). pap. 15.00 (978-0-399-16132-2(5), Perigee Trade) Penguin Group (USA) Inc.

Rouxel, Doug & Paston-Williams, Sara. Home Brew: The Ultimate Guide to Making Your Own Tipple. 2011. (ENG., Illus.). 208p. pap. 24.95 (978-1-86205-882-8(2)) Chrysalis Children's Bks. GBR. Dist: Independent Pubs. Group.

Schiefenhövel, Wulf & Macbeth, Helen, eds. Liquid Bread: Beer & Brewing in Cross-Cultural Perspective. 2011. (AFN Ser.). 264p. 95.00 (978-0-85745-215-3(0)) Berghahn Bks., Inc.

Simpson, William & Downes, Andrew. Brewing Problems Solved. 2013. 320p. (978-1-84569-196-7(2)) Woodhead Publishing Ltd.

Strong, Gordon. Brewing Better Beer: Master Lesson for Advanced Homeowners. 2011. (ENG.). 336p. pap. 17.95 (978-0-937381-98-4(5)) Brewers Pubns.

Sykes, Walter J. The Principles & Practice of Brewing Beer & Ale. 2008. 532p. pap. 37.95 (978-1-934939-23-9(4)) Wexford College Pr.

Szamatulski, Tess and Mark, et al. Clonebrews: Recipes for 200 Brand-Name Beers. 2nd ed. 2010. (ENG., Illus.). 439p. pap. 18.95 (978-1-60342-539-1(X), 160342539X) Storey Publishing, LLC.

Unger, Richard W. Beer in the Middle Ages & the Renaissance. 2007. (Illus.). 344p. (C). per. 24.95 (978-0-8122-1999-9(6)) Univ. of Pennsylvania Pr.

Waller, James. Drinkology Beer: A Book about the Brew. 2011. (ENG., Illus.). 352p. 22.50 (978-1-58479-851-4(3)) Stewart, Tabori & Chang.

Watman, Max. Chasing the White Dog: An Amateur Outlaw's Adventures in Moonshine. 2011. (ENG.). 304p. pap. 15.00 (978-1-4165-7179-7(5)) Simon & Schuster.

Wheeler, Graham. CAMRA's Complete Home Brewing. 3rd ed. 2012. (ENG., Illus.). 400p. pap. 23.95 (978-1-85249-284-7(8)) Camra Bks. GBR. Dist: Independent Pubs. Group.

Wheeler, Graham. Home Brewing: The Camra Guide. (Illus.). 232p. per. 14.99 (978-1-85249-112-3(4)) Camra Bks. GBR. Dist: All About Beer Magazine.

Wheeler, Graham & Campaign for Real Ale Staff. Brew Your Own British Real Ale. 3rd ed. 2010. (ENG.). 208p. pap. 24.95 (978-1-85249-258-8(9)) Camra Bks. GBR. Dist: Independent Pubs. Group.

White, Chris & Zainasheff, Jamil. Yeast: The Practical Guide to Beer Fermentation. 2010. (ENG.). 300p. pap. 19.95 (978-0-937381-96-0(9)) Brewers Pubns.

Wissing, Douglas A. Indiana: One Pint at a Time: A Traveler's Guide to Indiana's Brewpubs. 2010. (978-0-87195-283-7(1)) Indiana Historical Society.

Zainasheff, Jamil. Brewing Classic Styles: 80 Winning Recipes Anyone Can Brew. 2007. (ENG.). 200p. pap. 19.95 (978-0-937381-92-2(6)) Brewers Pubns.

BREWING INDUSTRY

see also Ale; Beer

Alcoholic Drinks Market Latin America: Companies-Products-Services. 200p. (Orig.) pap. 1895.00 (978-0-7605-2172-4(7)) Rector Pr., Ltd.

Arnold, John P. & Penman, Frank. History of the Brewing Industry & Brewing Science in America. 2006. (Illus.). 260p. 29.95 (978-0-9662084-3-6(9)) BeerBooks.com.

Brewers Association. 2011-2012 Brewers' Resource Directory. 2011. 320p. pap. 125.00 (978-0-937381-97-7(7)) Brewers Pubns.

Brewers Association Staff, contrib. by. North American Brewers' Resource Directory. 19th ed. 2007. (North American Brewers' Resource Directory Ser.). (ENG., Illus.). 160p. pap. 99.00 (978-0-937381-90-8(X)) Brewers Pubns.

Brewers Publications. 2009-2010 North American Brewers' Resource Directory. 2009. (ENG.). 224p. pap. 99.00 (978-0-937381-94-6(2)) Brewers Pubns.

Brewing Industry Report: Companies-Products-Services. (Orig.). pap. 395.00 (978-0-7605-2164-9(6)) Rector Pr., Ltd.

Brown, Jared McDaniel & Miller, Anistatia Renard. Spirituous Journey: A History of Drink. 2009. (Illus.). 248p. pap. (978-0-9760937-9-4(0), Mixellany) Mixellany, Ltd.

Burton, Rob. Hops & Dreams: The Story of Sierra Nevada Brewing Co. 2010. (Illus.). (ENG.). 224p. 29.95 (978-1-935807-02-5(1)); 222p. pap. 19.95 (978-1-935807-01-8(3)) Stansbury Publishing.

Cochran, Thomas C. Pabst Brewing Company: The History of an American Business. 2006. (Illus.). 451p. 34.95 (978-0-9662084-5-0(5)) BeerBooks.com.

Corcoran, Tony. The Goodness of Guinness: A Loving History of the Brewery, It's People, & the City of Dublin. 2009. (ENG., Illus.). 154p. 16.95 (978-1-60239-653-1(1), 239653) Skyhorse Publishing Co., Inc.

Coutts, Ian R. Brew North: How Canadians Made Beer & Beer Made Canada, 1 vol. 2010. (ENG., Illus.). 184p. pap. 19.95 (978-1-55365-467-4(6), Greystone Bks.) D&M Pubs. Inc. CAN. Dist: Perseus-PGW.

Crocker, Ronnie. Houston Beer: A Heady History of Brewing in the Bayou City. 2012. 160p. pap. 19.99 (978-1-60949-537-4(3)) History Pr., The.

Dekker, Marjolein van. Brouwen, Branden en Bedienen: Productie en Verkoop Van Drank Door Vrouwen in de Noordelijke Nederlanden, Circa 1500-1800. 2010. (DUT., Illus.). 291p. 43.25 (978-90-5260-361-2(8)) Aksant Academic Pubs. NLD. Dist: Amsterdam Univ. Pr.

The Department of the Treasury Alcohol & Tobacco Tax & Trade Bureau: Hearing Before the Subcommittee on Oversight of the Committee on Ways & Means, U.S. House of Representatives, One Hundred Tenth Congress, Second Session, May 20, 2008. 2009. iii, 117p. (978-0-16-088152-7(8), 552-070-42569-1) United States Government Printing Office.

European Beer Market 1993-97: Companies-Products-Services. 510p. (Orig.). pap. 2295.00 (978-0-7605-2159-5(X)) Rector Pr., Ltd.

Gary, Aaron R. Alcohol Beverages Regulation in Wisconsin. 2012. (978-1-57862-338-9(3)) State Bar of Wisconsin.

Gourvish, T. R. & Wilson, R. G. The British Brewing Industry, 1830-1980. 2008. (ENG., Illus.). 772p. pap. 84.00 (978-0-521-07017-1(1)) Cambridge Univ. Pr.

Grant, Marcus & Leverton, Mark, eds. Working Together to Reduce Harmful Drinking: The Producers' Contribution. 2009. (ENG., Illus.). 224p. 73.95 (978-0-415-80087-7(0)) Routledge.

Guo, Yuantao. Global Big Business & the Chinese Brewing Industry. 2006. (Routledge Studies in the Chinese Economy Ser.). (Illus.). 215p. 160.00 (978-0-415-39918-0(1)) Routledge.

Hindy, Steve & Potter, Tom. Beer School: Bottling Success at the Brooklyn Brewery. 2007. (ENG., Illus.). 304p. per. 16.95 (978-0-470-06867-0(1), Wiley) Wiley, John & Sons, Inc.

Hintz, Martin. A Spirited History of Milwaukee Brews & Booze. 2011. 160p. pap. 19.99 (978-1-60949-066-9(5)) History Pr., The.

Hoverson, Doug. Land of Amber Waters: The History of Brewing in Minnesota. 2007. (Illus.). 352p. 39.95 (978-0-8166-5273-0(2)); (978-0-8166-4797-2(6)) Univ. of Minnesota Pr.

Jackson, Michael. Michael Jackson's Great Beers of Belgium, 6th Edition. 6th ed. 2008. (ENG.). 520p. pap. 36.95 (978-0-937381-93-9(4)) Brewers Pubns.

Jersey Brew: The Story of Beer in New Jersey. 2009. (Illus.). 160p. 19.95 (978-0-9765233-1-4(0)) Lake Neepaulin Publishing.

Keitel, Adolph. Government by the Brewers? 2007. (Illus.). 48p. per. (978-1-4065-1869-6(7)) Dodo Pr.

Kenyon, Alexandra, et al. Ethics in the Alcohol Industry. 2009. (ENG., Illus.). 288p. 95.00 (978-0-230-21988-5(8)) Palgrave Macmillan.

Klous, Kevin. Breweriana. 2012. (Shire Library). (ENG., Illus.). 56p. pap. 9.95 (978-0-7478-1044-5(3)) Shire Pubns., Ltd. GBR. Dist: Random Hse., Inc.

Koeller, Paul D. Brewed with Style. 2007. 264p. 24.95 (978-0-9605832-2-5(X)) Univ. of Wisconsin-La Crosse Foundation, Inc., The.

Kohn, Rita T. & Arnold, Kris. True Brew: A Guide to Craft Beer in Indiana. 2010. (ENG., Illus.). 288p. pap. 19.95 (978-0-253-22214-5(1), 0253222141, Quarry Bks.) Indiana Univ. Pr.

Krebs, Roland & Orthwein, Percy J. Making Friends Is Our Business: 100 Years of Anheuser Busch. 2011. 470p. 57.95 (978-1-258-10364-4(8)) Literary Licensing, LLC.

Legal Issues Concerning State Alcohol Regulation: Hearing Before the Subcommittee on Courts & Competition Policy of the Committee on the Judiciary, House of Representatives, One Hundred Eleventh Congress, Second Session, March 18, 2010. 2010. (Illus.). iv, 240p. (978-0-16-087158-0(1), 552-070-42011-1) United States Government Printing Office.

Mager, Anne Kelk. Beer, Sociability, & Masculinity in South Africa. 2010. (African Systems of Thought Ser.). (ENG.). 248p. pap. 24.95 (978-0-253-22180-3(3), 0253221803) Indiana Univ. Pr.

—Beer, Sociability, & Masculinity in South Africa: Drinking, Sociability, & Masculinity. 2010. (African Systems of Thought Ser.). (ENG.). 248p. 65.00 (978-0-253-35449-5(8), 0253354498) Indiana Univ. Pr.

Meyer, Carrie A. Days on the Family Farm: From the Golden Age Through the Great Depression. 2007. (Illus.). 264p. per. 17.95 (978-0-8166-5033-0(0)) Univ. of Minnesota Pr.

Modern Brewery Age Bluebook. 135.00 (978-0-937506-11-0(7)) Business Journals.

Musson, Robert. Brewing Beer in the Glass City, Volume I: A History of the Brewing Industry in Toledo, Ohio, 2 vols., vol. 1. 2011. (ENG., Illus.). 56p. spiral bd. 19.95 (978-0-9668954-6-9(0)) Zepp Pubns.

—Brewing Beer Since 1829: A Pictorial Saga of the D. G. Yuengling & Son Brewing Company in Pottsville, Pennsylvania. 2010. (ENG., Illus.). 40p. (YA). spiral bd. 17.95 (978-0-9668954-4-5(4)) Zepp Pubns.

Nelson, Max. The Barbarian's Beverage: A History of Beer in Ancient Europe. 2008. pap. 39.95 (978-0-415-48692-7(0)) Routledge.

Neu, Denese. Chicago Beer: A High-Gravity History of Windy City Brewing. 2011. 128p. pap. 19.99 (978-1-60949-125-3(4)) History Pr., The.

Noon, Mark A. Yuengling: A History of America's Oldest Brewery. alt. ed. 2007. (ENG., Illus.). 231p. per. 29.95 (978-0-7864-3758-0(8)) McFarland & Co., Inc. Pubs.

O'Brien, Christopher Mark. Fermenting Revolution: How to Drink Beer & Save the World. 2006. (ENG., Illus.). 288p. per. 18.95 (978-0-86571-556-1(4), 0865715564) New Society Pubs., Ltd. CAN. Dist: Consortium Bk. Sales & Distribution.

Ogle, Maureen. Ambitious Brew: The Story of American Beer. 2007. (ENG., Illus.). 432p. pap. 21.95 (978-0-15-603359-6(3), Mariner Bks.) Houghton Mifflin Harcourt Trade & Reference Pubs.

Priestley, Frank. The Brewer's Tale: Memoirs of a Master Brewer. 2010. (ENG., Illus.). 160p. 18.00 (978-1-906122-17-1(2)) Unwin, Merlin Bks. GBR. Dist: SCB Distributors.

Protz, Roger. Life on the Hop: Memoirs from a Career in Beer. 2009. (ENG., Illus.). 240p. pap. 19.95 (978-1-85249-255-4(2)) Camra Bks. GBR. Dist: Independent Pubs. Group.

Protz, Roger. The Story of Brewing in Burton upon Trent. 2011. (ENG., Illus.). 160p. pap. 24.95 (978-0-7524-6063-5(3)) History Pr. Ltd., The GBR. Dist: Independent Pubs. Group.

Putman, Roger. Beers & Breweries of Britain. 2008. (Shire Library). (ENG., Illus.). 56p. pap. 12.95 (978-0-7478-0606-6(3)) Shire Pubns., Ltd. GBR. Dist: Random Hse., Inc.

Renfro, Mike. Shine On: 100 Years of Shiner Beer. 2009. (ENG., Illus.). 187p. pap. 24.95 (978-1-933979-60-1(7)) Bright Sky Pr.

Ronnenberg, Herman. The Beer Baron of Boise: The Life of John Lemp, Millionaire Brewer of Frontier Idaho. 2009. (Illus.). 464p. 24.95 (978-0-9818408-1-9(7)) Heritage Witness Reflections Publishing.

Salem, Frederick W. Beer: Its History & Its Economic Value as a National Beverage. 2007. (Illus.). 275p. reprint ed. 29.95 (978-0-9662084-7-4(1)) BeerBooks.com.

Schluter, Hermann. The Brewing Industry & the Brewery Workers' Movement in America. 2008. 336p. 45.95 (978-1-4374-0357-2(3)); pap. 30.95 (978-1-4373-1618-6(2)) Kessinger Publishing, LLC.

Skilnik, Bob. Beer: A History of Brewing in Chicago. 2006. 416p. 24.95 (978-1-56980-312-7(9)) Barricade Bks., Inc.

Spicer, John, et al. Intervention in the Modern UK Brewing Industry. 2011. (ENG., Illus.). 344p. 105.00 (978-0-230-29857-6(5)) Palgrave Macmillan.

Stephens, Sarah. Cincinnati's Brewing History. 2010. (Images of America Ser.). (ENG., Illus.). 128p. pap. 21.99 (978-0-7385-7790-6(1)) Arcadia Publishing.

Tames, Richard. The Victorian Public House. 2008. (Shire Library). (Illus.). 40p. pap. 11.95 (978-0-7478-0573-1(3)) Shire Pubns., Ltd. GBR. Dist: Random Hse., Inc.

Tremblay, Victor J. & Tremblay, Carol Horton. The U. S. Brewing Industry: Data & Economic Analysis. 2009. (ENG., Illus.). 400p. (gr. 17). pap. 22.00 (978-0-262-51263-3(7)) MIT Pr.

Wolputte, Steven van & Fumanti, Mattia. Beer As a Local & Transnational Commodity in Africa. 2011. 336p. pap. 49.95 (978-3-8258-1257-7(X)) Lit Verlag DEU. Dist: Transaction Pubs.

Womack, Raven. The Raven's Flight Book of Incense, Oils, Potions & Brews: A Friendly Guide to Magickal Products. 2007. (Illus.). 112p. pap. 10.95 (978-0-9796168-1-5(6)) Pendraig Publishing.

Yaeger, Brian. Red, White, & Brew: An American Beer Odyssey. 2008. (ENG., Illus.). 272p. pap. 14.95 (978-0-312-38314-5(2), St. Martin's Griffin) St. Martin's Pr.

Yenne, Bill. Guinness: The 250-Year Quest for the Perfect Pint. 2007. (ENG., Illus.). 288p. 24.95 (978-0-470-12052-1(5), Wiley) Wiley, John & Sons, Inc.

BREWSTER, DAVID, SIR, 1781-1868

Gordon, Margaret Maria. The Home Life of Sir David Brewster. 2010. (Cambridge Library Collection - Physical Sciences Ser.). (Illus.). 460p. pap. 34.99 (978-1-108-01425-0(9)) Cambridge Univ. Pr.

Higgitt, Rebekah. Recreating Newton: Newtonian Biography & the Making of Nineteenth-Century History of Science, 1 vol. 2007. (Science & Culture in the Nineteenth Century Ser.). (ENG., Illus.). 304p. 99.00 (978-1-85196-906-7(3)) Pickering & Chatto Pubs., Ltd. GBR. Dist: Ashgate Publishing Co.

BREWSTER, WILLIAM, 1566?-1644

Mitchell, John Hanson. Looking for Mr. Gilbert: The Reimagined Life of an African American. 2006. (ENG., Illus.). 288p. per. 16.00 (978-1-59376-142-4(2)) Counterpoint LLC.

Steele, Ashbel. Chief of the Pilgrims: Or, the Life & Time of William Brewster. 2006. 440p. per. 26.99 (978-1-4255-4805-6(9)) MPublishing.

BREZHNEV, LEONID I., 1906-1982

Fleron, Frederic, Jr., et al, eds. Contemporary Issues in Soviet Foreign Policy. 2008. (ENG.). 521p. pap. 39.95 (978-0-202-36326-4(0)) Transaction Pubs.

Nathans, Benjamin, et al, eds. Sedition: Everyday Resistance in the Soviet Union under Khrushchev & Brezhnev. Staklo, Vadim A. & Livshin, Olga, trs. from RUS. 2011. (Annals of Communism Ser.). 414p. 65.00 (978-0-300-11169-9(X)) Yale Univ. Pr.

Ward, Christopher J. Brezhnev's Folly: The Building of BAM & Late Soviet Socialism. 2009. (Pitt Russian East European Ser.). (ENG., Illus.). 232p. pap. 24.95 (978-0-8229-6138-3(5)) Univ. of Pittsburgh Pr.

BRIARD

Scott, Desiree. Briard. 2006. (Comprehensive Owners Guide Ser.). (ENG., Illus.). 155p. 19.95 (978-1-59378-295-5(0)) Kennel Club Bks.

BRIBERY

Abicoff, Kevin, et al. Anti-Corruption Law & Compliance: A Guide to the FCPA & Beyond. 2012. (978-1-61746-005-0(2)) Bureau of National Affairs, Inc., (BNA), The.

Accountability During Contingency Operations: Preventing & Fighting Corruption in Contracting & Establishing & Maintaining Appropriate Controls on Materiel.

2008. iii, 94p. *(978-0-16-082614-6(4)*, 552-070-38632-7) United States Government Printing Office.

Achenbach, Matthias. Strafrechtlicher Schutz des Wettbewerbs? Eine kritische Analyse von Sinn und Zweck der Straftatbestände zum Schutz des Wettbewerbs. 2009. (Frankfurter kriminalwissenschaftliche Studien Ser.). (GER.). 296p. 79.95 *(978-3-631-59514-5(X))* Lang, Peter GmbH, Europaischer Verlag der Wissenschaften DEU. Dist: Lang, Peter.

Biegelman, Martin T. & Biegelman, Daniel R. Foreign Corrupt Practices Act Compliance Guidebook: Protecting Your Organization from Bribery & Corruption. 2010. (Wiley Corporate F&a Ser.: 8). (ENG., Illus.). 384p. 68.50 *(978-0-470-52793-1(5)*, Wiley) Wiley, John & Sons, Inc.

Bisogno, Enrico, ed. Corruption in Afghanistan: Bribery as Reported by the Victims. 2010. 42p. (C). pap. 20.00 *(978-1-4379-2799-3(8))* DIANE Publishing Co.

Callejas, Rodrigo A., et al. Understanding Anti-Corruption Issues in Latin America: An In-Depth Look at Recent Developments & Upcoming Trends. 2010. 41p. pap. *(978-0-314-26812-9(X))* Aspatore Bks.

Cassin, Richard L. Bribery Abroad: Lessons from the Foreign Corrupt Practices Act. 2008. 169p. pap. 18.49 *(978-1-4357-3467-8(X))* Lulu Enterprises Inc.

—Bribery Everywhere: Chronicles from the Foreign Corrupt Practices Act. 2009. 191p. pap. 19.95 *(978-0-557-05348-3(X))* Lulu Enterprises Inc.

Cavico, Frank J. & Mujtaba, Bahaudin G. Baksheesh or Bribe: Cultural Conventions & Legal Pitfalls. 2010. 122p. pap. 17.95 *(978-1-936237-04-3(0))* ILEAD Academy, LLC.

Covington, Joseph P. Practicing under the US Anti Corruption Laws. 2010. ring bd. 385.00 *(978-0-7355-9413-5(9)*, Aspen Pubs.) Wolters Kluwer Law & Business.

Deming, Stuart H. The Foreign Corrupt Practices Act & the New International Norms. 2nd ed. 2011. (ENG.). 425p. pap. 144.95 *(978-1-60442-604-5(7))* American Bar Assn.

Ezoe, Hiromasa. Where Is the Justice: Media Attacks, Prosecutorial Abuse & My 13 Years in Japanese Court, 1 vol. Muroji, Rei, tr. 2010. (ENG., Illus.). 348p. 24.95 *(978-4-7700-3147-1(5))* Kodansha America, Inc.

Greaves, Adam, et al. Understanding Anti-Corruption Issues in the UK: An In-Depth Look at Recent Developments & Upcoming Trends. 2010. 42p. pap. *(978-0-314-26815-0(4))* Aspatore Bks.

Gruetzner, Thomas, et al, eds. Anti-Bribery Risk Assessment: Systematic Overview of 153 countries. Rechtsstand: Juli 2010. 2011. 495p. 436.00 incl. cd-rom *(978-1-84946-129-0(5))* Hart Publishing Ltd. GBR. Dist: International Specialized Bk. Services.

Hamdan, Marwan. Drittmittelforschung in der Medizin: Eine Gratwanderung zwischen strafbarer Vorteilsannahme und verfassungsgarantierter Forschungsfreiheit. 2009. (Schriften zum Strafrecht und Strafprozeßrecht Ser.). (GER.). 152p. pap. 49.95 *(978-3-631-58092-9(4))* Lang, Peter GmbH, Europaischer Verlag der Wissenschaften DEU. Dist: Lang, Peter.

Horrer, Philipp. Bestechung durch deutsche Unternehmen im Ausland: Strafrechtsentwicklung und Probleme. 2011. (Frankfurter kriminalwissenschaftliche Studien Ser.). (GER.). 338p. 89.95 *(978-3-631-61014-5(9))* Lang, Peter GmbH, Europaischer Verlag der Wissenschaften DEU. Dist: Lang, Peter.

Johnson, Graham. Druglord: Guns, Powder & Pay-Offs. 2007. (ENG., Illus.). 352p. pap. 18.95 *(978-1-84596-240-1(0))* Mainstream Publishing Co., Ltd. GBR. Dist: Independent Pubs. Group.

Lawler, David. Frequently Asked Questions in Anti-Bribery & Corruption. 2012. (Wiley Corporate F&a Ser.). (ENG.). 584p. pap. 65.00 ***(978-1-119-97197-9(7)***, Wiley) Wiley, John & Sons, Inc.

Low, Lucinda A., et al. The Foreign Corrupt Practices ACT: Coping with Heightened Enforcement Risks. 2007. (Corporate Law & Practice Course Handbook Ser.: No. 1588). (ENG., Illus.). 443p. ring bd. 295.00 *(978-1-4024-0859-5(5))* Practising Law Institute.

Meyer, Olaf, ed. The Civil Law Consequences of Corruption. 2009. 280p. pap. 85.00 *(978-3-8329-4496-4(6))* Nomos Verlagsgesellschaft DEU. Dist: International Specialized Bk. Services.

Mölders, Simone. Bestechung und Bestechlichkeit im internationalen geschäftlichen Verkehr: Zur Anwendbarkeit des § 299 StGB auf Sachverhalte mit Auslandsbezug. 2009. (Schriften zum Strafrecht und Strafprozeßrecht Ser.). (GER.). 278p. 79.95 *(978-3-631-58615-0(9))* Lang, Peter GmbH, Europaischer Verlag der Wissenschaften DEU. Dist: Lang, Peter.

Murphy, Aaron G. Foreign Corrupt Practices Act: A Practical Resource for Managers & Executives. 2010. (ENG.). 272p. pap., instr.'s gde. ed. 60.00 *(978-0-470-91800-5(4)*, Wiley) Wiley, John & Sons, Inc.

Mwenda, Kenneth. Legal Aspects of Combating Corruption: The Case of Zambia. 2007. 312p. (C). 94.95 *(978-1-934043-84-4(2))* Cambria Pr.

Nicholls QC, Colin, et al. Corruption & Misuse of Public Office. 2nd ed. 2011. (ENG.). 848p. 290.00 *(978-0-19-957727-9(7))* Oxford Univ. Pr., Inc.

Ogino, Masahiro. Scams & Sweeteners: A Sociology of Fraud. 2007. 126p. (C). 79.95 *(978-1-876843-33-5(0))*; pap. 34.95 *(978-1-876843-39-7(X))* Trans Pacific Pr. AUS. Dist: International Specialized Bk. Services.

Organisation for Economic Co-Operation and Development & Asian Development Bank. The Criminalisation of Bribery in Asia & the Pacific: Frameworks & Practices in 28 Jurisdictions; Thematic Review - Final Report. 2011. (Illus.). 522p. pap. ***(978-92-64-09743-8(0))*** Organization for Economic Cooperation & Development.

Organisation for Economic Co-operation and Development & Asian Development Bank. Strategies for business, government & civil society to fight corruption in Asia & the Pacific. 2010. (Illus.). 216p. pap. 63.00 *(978-92-64-07700-3(6))* Organization for Economic Cooperation & Development.

Organisation for Economic Co-operation and Development Staff. Bribery in Public Procurement: A Typology. 2007. pap. 39.00 *(978-92-64-01394-0(6))* Organization for Economic Cooperation & Development.

—Oecd Glossaries Glossary of International Standards for Criminalisation of Corruption: (Bilingual Version)-Glossaires de l'Ocde Glossary of International Standards for Criminalisation of Corruption: (Bilingual Version) 2008. pap. 63.00 *(978-92-64-02740-4(8))* Organization for Economic Cooperation & Development.

Ouyang, Quan & Bai, Xiaoyun. Hu Wen Zhi Jian: Da Jia Sao Huang Shui Shi Zui Hou Ying Jia. 2007. ("Zhongguo Ju Shi" Xi Lie Ser.: Vol. 45). (CHI., Illus.). 421p. *(978-1-932138-58-0(7))* Mirror Bks. USA.

Pierce, Bart. The Bribe of Great Price. 2007. (ENG.). 135p. per. 13.95 *(978-0-9704753-5-0(7))* Gatekeeper Publishing.

Pieth, Mark, ed. Recovering Stolen Assets. 2007. (Illus.). 391p. pap. 81.95 *(978-3-03911-583-9(9))* Lang, Peter Publishing, Inc.

Pieth, Mark, et al, eds. The OECD Convention on Bribery: A Commentary. 2007. (ENG.). 652p. 190.00 *(978-0-521-86817-4(3))* Cambridge Univ. Pr.

Porko, Eero. Corruption & Development in Afric. 2010. 60p. pap. *(978-3-8383-8472-6(5))* Lambert Academic Publishing.

Raphael, Monty. Blackstone's Guide to the Bribery ACT 2010. 2010. (ENG.). 250p. pap. 95.00 *(978-0-19-957978-5(4))* Oxford Univ. Pr., Inc.

Reinhold, Philipp. Amtsträgerbestechung: Unrechtsgehalt und Grenzen der §§ 331 Ff. Stgb. 2011. (Schriften zum Strafrecht und Strafprozeßrecht Ser.). (GER.). 196p. 62.95 ***(978-3-631-62048-9(9))*** Lang, Peter GmbH, Europaischer Verlag der Wissenschaften DEU. Dist: Lang, Peter.

Restoring Key Tools to Combat Fraud & Corruption after the Supreme Court's Skilling Decision: Hearing Before the Committee on the Judiciary, United States Senate, One Hundred Eleventh Congress, Second Session, September 28, 2010. 2011. iii, 72p. ***(978-0-16-088541-9(8)***, 552-070-42718-0) United States Government Printing Office.

Shao, Daosheng. Zhongguo: Zu Ji Fu Bai = China: Anti-Corruption Campaign. 2009. (CHI.). *(978-7-5097-1205-4(X))* China Social Science Documentation Publishing Hse.

Shao, Jingjun. Zhongguo Fan Fu Chang Lian Zhi Lu. 2009. (CHI.). 376p. *(978-7-80216-478-9(8))* China Fangzheng Publishing Hse.

Sherman, Ted & Margolin, Josh. The Jersey Sting: A True Story of Crooked Pols, Money-Laundering Rabbis, Black Market Kidneys, & the Informant Who Brought It All Down. 2011. (ENG., Illus.). 400p. 26.99 *(978-0-312-65417-7(0))* St. Martin's Pr.

Tarun, Robert W. Corporate Counsel's Guide to the Foreign Corrupt Practices ACT. 2nd rev. ed. 2011. (ENG.). 560p. pap. 139.95 *(978-1-60442-951-0(8))* American Bar Assn.

Tarun, Robert W. The Foreign Corrupt Practices Act Handbook: A Practical Guide for Multinational General Counsel & White Collar Criminal Practitioners. 2012. (ENG.). 768p. pap. 149.95 ***(978-1-61438-073-3(2))*** American Bar Assn.

Taylor, Jeffery, et al. Bribery & Corruption: Navigating the Global Risks. 2011. (Wiley Corporate F&a Ser.: 568). (ENG., Illus.). 432p. 75.00 ***(978-1-118-01136-2(8)***, Wiley) Wiley, John & Sons, Inc.

"Urgent Reform Required: Army Expeditionary Contracting" The Report of the Commission on Army Acquisition & Program Management in Expeditionary Operations: Hearing Before the Subcommittee on Readiness & Management Support of the Committee on Armed Services, United States Senate, One Hundred Tenth Congress, First Session, December 6, 2007. 2008. (Illus.). iii, 151p. *(978-0-16-080968-2(1)*, 552-070-37493-1) United States Government Printing Office.

Whiteley, Jason & U. S. Army Staff. Father of Money: Buying Peace in Baghdad. 2011. (Illus.). 208p. 27.50 *(978-1-59797-544-5(3))* Potomac Bks., Inc.

Wrage, Alexandra Addison. Bribery & Extortion: Undermining Business, Governments, & Security, 1 vol. 2007. (Praeger Security International Ser.). 176p. 44.95 *(978-0-275-99649-9(2)*, C9649, Praeger Security International) Greenwood Publishing Group, Inc.

BRIC-A-BRAC

see Art Objects

BRICK BUILDING

see Building, Brick

BRICKLAYING

see also Masonry

Brick Development Association, The. The BDA Guide to Successful Brickwork. 4th rev. ed. 2012. (ENG.). 352p. pap. 52.95 *(978-1-85617-772-6(6)*, Butterworth-Heinemann) Elsevier Science & Technology Bks.

Durkin, Joseph. Brickwork: Electronic Tutor Resource. 2006. (ENG., Illus.). 240p. pap. 49.50 *(978-0-7487-9685-4(1))* Nelson Thornes Ltd. GBR. Dist: Trans-Atlantic Pubns., Inc.

Ham, Robert Benjamin. Residential Construction Academy: Brick, Masonry, & Block Construction. 2007. (ENG.). 144p. (C). pap., wbk. ed. 34.95 *(978-1-4283-2366-7(X))* Delmar Cengage Learning.

Lynch, Gerard. The History of Gauged Brickwork: Conservation, Repair & Modern Application. 2007. (ENG., Illus.). 464p. 70.95 *(978-0-7506-8272-5(8))* Routledge.

Thorpe, Malcolm. Brickwork Level 1: For CAA Construction Diploma & NVQs. 2010. (ENG.). 344p. (C). pap. 34.95 *(978-1-85617-766-5(1))* Routledge.

—Brickwork Level 3: For CAA Construction Diploma & NVQs. 2010. (ENG.). 472p. (C). pap. 41.95 *(978-1-85617-764-1(5))* Routledge.

Thorpe, Malcolm & Hodge, J. C. Brickwork Level 2: For CAA Construction Diploma & NVQs. 2010. (ENG.). 488p. (C). pap. 37.95 *(978-1-85617-765-8(3))* Routledge.

BRICKMAKING

see also Kilns

Bassir, Mouhamadou. Low Temperature Processes. 2011. (Energy Science, Engineering & Technology Ser.). 75.00 ***(978-1-62100-038-9(9))*** Nova Science Pubs., Inc.

Casprini, Massimo. Dizionario delle fornaci da laterizi e da stoviglie nel contado Fiorentino. 2011. (Testi e Studi Ser.). (ITA., Illus.). 224p. (C). pap. 32.00 ***(978-88-596-0897-4(X))*** Polistampa ITA. Dist: Brown, David Bk. Co., The.

Cook, Scott. Handmade Brick for Texas: A Mexican Border Industry, Its Workers, & Its Business. 2010. (ENG.). 290p. 95.00 *(978-0-7391-4797-9(8))*; pap. 39.95 *(978-0-7391-4798-6(6))* Lexington Bks.

Mason, Kelvin. Fuel for Free? Waste Materials in Brick Making. 2007. (ENG., Illus.). 176p. pap. 31.95 *(978-1-85339-625-0(7))* Intermediate Technology Development Group of North America.

Piechocinski, Elizabeth Carpenter. Men of Iron, Men of Stone, Feet of Clay. 2006. (Illus.). xv, 235p. per. 17.95 net. *(978-1-891495-13-7(5))* Oglethorpe Pr., Inc.

BRIDAL CUSTOMS

see Marriage Customs and Rites

BRIDGE (GAME)

see Contract Bridge

BRIDGE CIRCUITS

Eccles. Pragmatic Electrical Engineering: Signals & Systems: Synthesis Lectures on Digital Circuits & Systems. 2011. (Synthesis Lectures on Digital Circuits & Systems Ser.). 143p. pap. 50.00 ***(978-1-60845-671-0(4))*** Morgan & Claypool Pubs.

BRIDGE CONSTRUCTION

see Bridges—Design and Construction

BRIDGE WHIST

see also Contract Bridge

Harkness, Kenneth. Invitation to Bridge. 2008. (Illus.). 340p. per. 19.95 *(978-0-923891-94-7(3))* Ishi Pr. International.

Kantar, Eddie. Bridge for Dummies(R) 2nd Edition. l.t. ed. 2008. 665p. (YA). 31.95 *(978-1-4104-0503-6(6))* Thorndike Pr.

—Take All Your Chances. 2011. (Illus.). 172p. pap. 19.95 *(978-1-897106-70-9(X))* Master Point Pr. CAN. Dist: Strauss Consultants.

Ringel, Howard. Plan Before You Play. 2007. 128p. per. 12.95 *(978-1-58939-975-4(7))* Virtualbookworm.com Publishing, Inc.

Thurston, Paul. Bridge at the Breakfast Table. 2011. (Illus.). 172p. pap. 19.95 *(978-1-897106-71-6(8))* Master Point Pr. CAN. Dist: Strauss Consultants.

BRIDGER, JIM, 1804-1881

Alter, J. Cecil. James Bridger - Trapper, Frontiersman, Scout & Guide - a Historical Narrative. 2007. 632p. per. *(978-1-4067-2213-0(8))* Read Bks.

Dodge, Grenville Mellen. Biographical Sketch of James Bridger. 2009. 48p. pap. *(978-0-217-18100-6(7))* Books LLC.

—Biographical Sketch of James Bridger: Mountainer, Trapper & Guide (1905) 2009. 36p. pap. 15.95 *(978-1-120-26754-2(4))* Kessinger Publishing, LLC.

Lamb, Peter O. The Sign of the Buffalo Skull: The Story of Jim Bridger Frontier Scout. 2007. 298p. 43.95 *(978-0-548-07140-3(3))* Kessinger Publishing, LLC.

Vestal, Stanley. Jim Bridger - Mountain Man. 2007. 348p. per. *(978-1-4067-2452-3(1))* Read Bks.

BRIDGES, ROBERT SEYMOUR, 1844-1930

McKay, George L. Bibliography of Robert Bridges. reprint ed. 20.00 *(978-0-404-04132-8(9))* AMS Pr., Inc.

BRIDGES

see also Arches; Covered Bridges; Girders; Iron and Steel Bridges; Suspension Bridges; Trusses; Wooden Bridges

also names of individual bridges, i.e. Brooklyn Bridge (New York, N.Y.)

Adeli, Hojjat, ed. Historic Bridges: Evaluation, Preservation, & Management. 2008. (ENG., Illus.). 304p. 139.95 *(978-1-4200-7995-1(6)*, CRC Press) Taylor & Francis Group GBR. Dist: Taylor & Francis Group.

Akaro, Cathbert. Long-Term Performance of Epoxy Filled Steel Grate Decking. 2011. 92p. pap. ***(978-3-8443-2765-6(7))*** Lambert Academic Publishing.

Allegheny Bridge Company. The Commonwealth Ex Rel James Todd, vs. the Allegheny Bridge Co'y: Quo warranto, Brief for Defendant. 2011. 18p. pap. 11.99 ***(978-1-4181-8962-4(6))*** MPublishing.

—Paper Book of the Defendants: Commonwealth vs. the president, managers & company, for erecting a bridge over the Allegheny River, opposite the City. 2011. 20p. pap. 11.99 ***(978-1-4181-9121-4(3))*** MPublishing.

American Association of State Highway and Transportation Officials Staff, contrib. by. More Projects & Paychecks: Transportation's Summer of Recovery. 2010. (Illus.). ii, 35p. ***(978-1-56051-498-5(1))*** American Assn. of State Highway & Transportation Officials.

American Association of State Highway and Transportation Officials Staff, contrib. by. Transportation: Invest in Our Future. 2007. (Illus.). 89p. *(978-1-56051-368-1(3))* American Assn. of State Highway & Transportation Officials.

American Welding Society. AASHTO/AWS D1. 5M/D1. 5-2008, Bridge Welding Code. 2008. per. *(978-0-87171-075-8(7))* American Welding Society.

Ashley, Peter. Built for Britain: Bridges to Beach Huts. 2009. (ENG., Illus.). 168p. pap. 19.99 *(978-0-470-74595-3(9)*, Wiley) Wiley, John & Sons, Inc.

Balouchi, Mohammad. Scour Controling Around Bridge Piers by Changing the Shape of Collar. 2010. 80p. pap. *(978-3-639-25766-3(9))* VDM Verlag Dr. Mueller e.K.

Beyer, William E. The History of the Veterans Memorial Bridge. 90th ed. 2009. (Illus.). 612p. *(978-0-692-00126-4(3))* Biddle, Oliver.

Blackman, Jeffrey E., et al. Barns of New England. 2009. (ENG., Illus.). 96p. 19.95 *(978-0-88150-880-2(2)*, 150880) Countryman Pr.

Bottenberg, Ray. Bridges of Portland. 2007. (Images of America Ser.). (ENG., Illus.). 128p. per. 21.99 *(978-0-7385-4876-0(6))* Arcadia Publishing.

Boyd, Donald Edgar. Knox County Bridges. 2008. (Images of America Ser.). (ENG., Illus.). 128p. per. 19.99 *(978-0-7385-5156-2(2))* Arcadia Publishing.

Burk, John S. Massachusetts Covered Bridges. 2010. (Images of America Ser.). (ENG., Illus.). 128p. pap. 21.99 *(978-0-7385-7323-6(X))* Arcadia Publishing.

Burke, Kathryn W. Hudson River Bridges. 2007. (Images of America Ser.). (ENG., Illus.). 128p. pap. 21.99 *(978-0-7385-4986-6(X))* Arcadia Publishing.

Calcada, Rui. Track-Bridge Interaction on High-Speed Railways. 2008. (ENG., Illus.). 222p. 129.95 *(978-0-415-45774-3(2)*, Taylor & Francis) Taylor & Francis Group GBR. Dist: Taylor & Francis Group.

Construction Handbook for Bridge Temporary Works. Date not set. (Bridges & Structures Ser.). (Illus.). 134p. (C). pap. 22.00 *(978-1-56051-035-2(8)*, CHBTW) American Assn. of State Highway & Transportation Officials.

Delgado, Raimundo, et al, eds. Bridges for High-Speed Railways: Revised papers from the Workshop, Porto, Portugal, 3 - 4 June 2004. 2008. (ENG., Illus.). 304p. 144.95 *(978-0-415-47147-3(8)*, Taylor & Francis) Taylor & Francis Group GBR. Dist: Taylor & Francis Group.

—Dynamics of High-Speed Railway Bridges: Selected & Revised Papers from the Advanced Course on 'Dynamics of High-Speed Railway Bridges', Porto, Portugal, 20-23 September 2005. 2008. (ENG., Illus.). 176p. 119.95 *(978-0-415-46767-4(5)*, Taylor & Francis) Taylor & Francis Group GBR. Dist: Taylor & Francis Group.

Della Porta, Donatella. Voices from the Valley, Voices of the Straits: How Protest Creates Communities. 2008. 216p. (C). 35.00 *(978-1-84545-515-6(0))* Berghahn Bks., Inc.

Dickinson, Gene D. The Sheldon Road Project. 2009. 124p. pap. 19.95 *(978-0-578-01099-1(2))* GDT Speedster, LLC.

Duffy, Seán Patrick & Rinkes, Paul. Wheeling. 2010. (Then & Now Ser.). (ENG., Illus.). 96p. pap. 21.99 *(978-0-7385-8593-2(9))* Arcadia Publishing.

Esch, Gregory. Visualization & Design Systems for Road Infrastructure. 2009. 120p. pap. *(978-3-639-14901-2(7))* VDM Verlag Dr. Mueller e.K.

Foster, Norman. Millau Viaduct. 2012. (Illus.). 96p. 29.95 ***(978-3-7913-4687-8(3))*** Prestel Publishing.

Giles, Paul. Hart Crane: The Contexts of the Bridge. 2009. (Cambridge Studies in American Literature & Culture Ser.). (ENG.). 288p. pap. 38.99 *(978-0-521-10700-6(8))* Cambridge Univ. Pr.

Goldberg, Geoffrey H. & Rooney, E. Ashley. Bridges: A Postcard History. 2011. (Illus.). 224p. *(978-0-7643-3792-5(0)*, Schiffer Publishing Ltd) Schiffer Publishing, Ltd.

Guide Design Specifications for Bridge Temporary Works. Date not set. (Bridges & Structures Ser.). (Illus.). 92p. (C). pap. 18.00 *(978-1-56051-034-5(X)*, GSBTW) American Assn. of State Highway & Transportation Officials.

Guidelines for Developing a Bridge Maintenance Program. 28p. 10.00 *(978-0-917084-17-1(9))* American Public Works Assn.

Haché, Jean Didier & Royle, Stephen. Bridging Islands: The Impact of Fixed Links. Baldacchino, Godfrey, ed. 2006. (Illus.). 300p. (C). pap. 24.95 *(978-1-894838-24-5(6))* Acorn Pr., The CAN. Dist: Univ. of Toronto Pr.

Harrison, David. The Bridges of Medieval England: Transport & Society 400-1800. 2008. (Oxford Historical Monographs). (ENG., Illus.). 270p. per. 45.00 *(978-0-19-922685-6(7))* Oxford Univ. Pr., Inc.

Highway Bridge Inspections: Hearing Before the Subcommittee on Highways & Transit of the Committee on Transportation & Infrastructure, House of Representatives, One Hundred Tenth Congress, First Session, October 23, 2007. 2007. (Illus.). xiv, 131p. *(978-0-16-083395-3(7)*, 552-070-39208-4) United States Government Printing Office.

Holth, Nathan. Chicago's Bridges. 2012. (Shire Library). (ENG., Illus.). 64p. pap. 9.95 ***(978-0-7478-1103-9(2))*** Shire Pubns., Ltd. GBR. Dist: Random Hse., Inc.

Hudson, Patrick L. Bridges of New Zealand. (Illus.). 64p. pap. 12.95 *(978-0-908876-81-5(5))* Transpress NZL. Dist: Pacific Island Bks.

Imhof, Daniel. Risk Assessment of Existing Bridge Structures. 2008. 260p. pap. *(978-3-639-05319-7(2))* VDM Verlag Dr. Mueller e.K.

Jacob, Bernard. Hvtt 10. 2009. (Iste Ser.: 338). (ENG., Illus.). iv, 582p. 237.00 *(978-1-84821-058-5(2)*, Wiley-ISTE) Wiley, John & Sons, Inc.

Jervis, John B. Report of John B Jervis in Relation to the Railroad Bridge over the Mississippi River, at Rock Island. 2011. 18p. pap. 11.99 ***(978-1-4181-9086-6(1))*** MPublishing.

Jr., William S. Caswell. Connecticut & Rhode Island Covered Bridges. 2011. (Images of America Ser.). (ENG., Illus.). 128p. pap. 21.99 ***(978-0-7385-7540-7(2))*** Arcadia Publishing.

Kantwell, Evan N., ed. America's Bridges??? 2007. (Illus.). ix, 178p. 69.00 *(978-1-60456-097-8(5))* Nova Science Pubs., Inc.

Karbhari, V. M. Structural Health Monitoring of Civil Infrastructure Systems. 2009. (ENG., Illus.). 552p. 244.95 *(978-1-4398-0131-4(2)*, CRC Press) Taylor & Francis Group GBR. Dist: Taylor & Francis Group.

Karbhari, V. M. & Ansari, F., eds. Structural Health Monitoring of Civil Infrastructure Systems. 2009. (Illus.). 552p. *(978-1-84569-392-3(2))* Woodhead Publishing Ltd.

Khadr, Mosaad, et al. Minimizing of Scour Around Bridge Piers. 2010. 144p. pap. *(978-3-639-24952-1(6))* VDM Verlag Dr. Mueller e.K.

Knapp, Ronald G. Chinese Bridges: Living Architecture from China's Past. 2008. (ENG.). 272p. 49.95 *(978-0-8048-3884-9(4))* Tuttle Publishing.

Koh, Hyun-Moo & Frangopol, Dan M., eds. Bridge Maintenance, Safety Management, Health Monitoring & Informatics: Proceedings of the Fourth International Conference on Bridge Maintenance, Safety & Management, July 13-17 2008, Seoul, Korea - IABMAS '08. 2008. (Bridge Maintenance, Safety & Management Ser.). (ENG., Illus.). 778p. (C). 299.95 *(978-0-415-46844-2(2),* Taylor & Francis) Taylor & Francis Group GBR. Dist: Taylor & Francis Group.

Lander, F. W. Additional Estimate for Fort Kearney, South Pass, & Honey Lake Wagon Road Letter from the Acting Secretary of the Interior, Transmitting a Communic. 2011. 28p. pap. 11.99 ***(978-1-4181-9326-3(7))*** MPublishing.

Leitch, Kenneth. Close-Range Photogrammetric Measurement of Bridge Deformations. 2010. 208p. pap. *(978-3-8383-5018-9(9))* Lambert Academic Publishing.

LePatner, Barry B. Too Big to Fall: America's Failing Infrastructure & the Way Forward. 2010. (Illus.). 268p. 27.95 *(978-0-9844978-0-5(3))* Foster Publishing.

Mahmoud, Khaled M., ed. Advances in Cable-Supported Bridges. 2006. (ENG., Illus.). 261p. 179.95 *(978-0-415-41982-6(4),* Taylor & Francis) Taylor & Francis Group GBR. Dist: Taylor & Francis Group.

Maintaining Our Nation's Highway & Transit Infrastructure: Hearing Before the Subcommittee on Highways & Transit of the Committee on Transportation & Infrastructure, House of Representatives, One Hundred Tenth Congress, Second Session, June 5, 2008. 2008. (Illus.). xiv, 92p. *(978-0-16-083603-9(4),* 552-070-39321-8) United States Government Printing Office.

Mak, Geert. The Bridge: A Journey Between Orient & Occident. Garrett, Sam, tr. from DUT. 2010. (ENG., Illus.). 160p. pap. 14.95 *(978-0-09-953214-9(X))* Random Hse. GBR. Dist: Independent Pubs. Group.

Manbeck, John. Historic Photos of the Brooklyn Bridge. 2009. (Historic Photos Ser.). (ENG.). 206p. 39.95 *(978-1-59652-525-2(8))* Turner Publishing Co.

Markow, Michael J. & Hyman, William A. Bridge Management Systems for Transportation Agency Decision Making. 2009. (Illus.). 126p. pap. *(978-0-309-09835-9(1))* Transportation Research Board.

Martin, George A., ed. Fences, Gates, & Bridges: And How to Build Them. 2011. (ENG., Illus.). 208p. pap. 9.95 *(978-1-61608-129-4(5),* 608129) Skyhorse Publishing Co., Inc.

McCahon, Mary Elizabeth. Guidelines for Historic Bridge Rehabilitation & Replacement. 2008. (Illus.). pap. *(978-1-56051-430-5(2))* American Assn. of State Highway & Transportation Officials.

McCormack, Michael J. Timeless Crossings: Vermont's Covered Bridges. 2011. (Illus.). 144p. 34.99 ***(978-0-7643-3830-4(7),*** Schiffer Publishing Ltd) Schiffer Publishing, Ltd.

McMaster, John Bach. Bridge & Tunnel Centres, by John B Mcmaster. 2006. 128p. per. 16.99 *(978-1-4255-0899-9(5))* MPublishing.

McQuire, Harry & McQuire, Alex. Bridges Between Palm Beach County & Miami, Florid. 2010. 64p. pap. 14.95 *(978-0-89334-466-5(4))* Humanics Publishing Group.

Merriman, Mansfield. On the Theory & Calculation of Continuous Bridges, by Mansfield Merriman. 2006. 132p. per. 16.99 *(978-1-4255-0961-3(4))* MPublishing.

Merritt, Anne. Historic Photos of the Golden Gate Bridge. 2008. (Historic Photos Ser.). (ENG.). 205p. 39.95 *(978-1-59652-445-3(6))* Turner Publishing Co.

Mertz, D. R. Simplified Live Load Distribution Factor Equations. 2007. (Illus.). ix, 127p. 49.00 *(978-0-309-09900-4(5))* Transportation Research Board.

Moore, Elma Lee. Ohio's Covered Bridges. 2010. (Postcard History Ser.). (ENG., Illus.). 128p. pap. 21.99 *(978-0-7385-8430-0(4))* Arcadia Publishing.

Morris, David. Introduction to Bridge Design for Engineers. Date not set. 400p. 76.00 *(978-0-7506-5068-7(0),* Butterworth-Heinemann) Elsevier Science & Technology Bks.

Mort, Mike. A Bridge Worth Saving: A Community Guide to Historic Bridge Preservation. 2008. (ENG., Illus.). 143p. pap. 24.95 *(978-0-87013-828-7(6))* Michigan State Univ. Pr.

NCSEA/ICC. Inspection, Testing, & Monitoring of Buildings & Bridges (Final) 2011. pap. 59.00 ***(978-1-60983-198-1(5))*** International Code Council.

New York (State) Laws, Statutes, etc. Staff. Laws of the State of New York Relating to Highways, Bridges & Ferries, Comprising Chapter Sixteen of the First Part of the Third or Revisers' Editio. 2006. 196p. per. 18.99 *(978-1-4255-1617-8(3))* MPublishing.

Office of the Federal Register (U.S.), compiled by. Code of Federal Regulations, Title 23, Highways, Revised as of April 1 2011. rev. ed. 2011. (ENG.). 639p. pap. 50.00 ***(978-0-16-088405-4(5),*** Office of the Federal Register) United States Government Printing Office.

Pay, Ian J. London's Bridges: Crossing the Royal River. 2009. (ENG., Illus.). 128p. 19.95 *(978-1-904332-90-9(0))* AAPPL Artists & Photographers Pr., Ltd. GBR. Dist: Sterling Publishing Co., Inc.

Proske, Dirk, et al. Safety of historical stone arch Bridges. 2009. (ENG., Illus.). xii, 366p. 129.00 *(978-3-540-77616-1(8),* 3540776168) Springer.

Proulx, Tom. Dynamics of Bridges: Proceedings of the 28th IMAC, A Conference on Structural Dynamics 2010. 2011. (Conference Proceedings of the Society for Experimental Mechanics Ser.). (ENG., Illus.). viii, 187p. 259.00 *(978-1-4419-9824-8(1),* 1441998241) Springer.

Rapley, John. Britannia & Other Tubular Bridges. (Illus.). 176p. 37.50 *(978-0-7524-2753-9(9))* History Pr. Ltd., The GBR. Dist: Trafalgar Square Publishing.

Romanis, Giorgio De. The Bridge on the Adriatic Sea. 2010. (ENG., Illus.). 176p. *(978-88-7685-176-6(3),* Edizioni L'archivolto (Acc)) Antique Collectors' Club.

Ruddock, Ted. Arch Bridges & Their Builders, 1735-1835. 2008. (ENG., Illus.). 272p. pap. 38.99 *(978-0-521-09021-6(0))* Cambridge Univ. Pr.

Ryall, Mike. Bridge Management. 2nd rev. ed. 2009. (ENG., Illus.). 576p. (C). 160.00 *(978-0-7506-8511-5(5),* CRC Press) Taylor & Francis Group GBR. Dist: Taylor & Francis Group.

Rybarz, Beverley. The Bridge Builder. 2006. (ENG., Illus.). 184p. (Orig.). per. 19.95 *(978-1-86254-659-2(2))* Wakefield Pr. Pty, Ltd. AUS. Dist: Independent Pubs. Group.

Sause, Richard, et al, eds. Bridge Maintenance, Safety & Management - IABMAS'10: Proceedings of the Fifth International IABMAS Conference, Philadelphia, USA, 11-15 July 2010. 2010. (Bridge Maintenance, Safety & Management Ser.). (ENG., Illus.). 744p. (C). 259.95 *(978-0-415-87786-2(5),* CRC Press) Taylor & Francis Group GBR. Dist: Taylor & Francis Group.

Scheer, Joachim. Failed Bridges: Case Studies, Causes & Consequences. Wilharm, Linda, tr. 2010. (ENG., Illus.). 321p. 115.00 *(978-3-433-02951-0(2),* Wiley-VCH) Wiley, John & Sons, Inc.

Sheppard, D. M., et al. Scour at Wide Piers & Long Skewed Piers. 2011. (Illus.). 55p. ***(978-0-309-15537-3(1))*** Transportation Research Board.

Sivakumar, Bala, et al. Legal Truck Loads & AASHTO Legal Loads for Posting. 2007. (Illus.). 74p. per. 46.00 *(978-0-309-09881-6(5))* Transportation Research Board.

Structurally Deficient Bridges in the United States: Hearing Before the Committee on Transportation & Infrastructure, House of Representatives, One Hundred Tenth Congress, First Session, September 5, 2007. 2007. (Illus.). xv, 326p. *(978-0-16-083400-4(7),* 552-070-39213-1) United States Government Printing Office.

Technology Research Editors, ed. Bridge Repair Using Composite Materials, 2007 Ed. 2007. pap. 128.50 *(978-1-60030-209-1(2),* Search-In-Print) CSA Journal Division.

—Degradation, Repair, & Rebuilding of Bridges, 2007 Ed. 2007. pap. 128.50 *(978-1-60030-434-7(6),* Search-In-Print) CSA Journal Division.

Truck Weights & Lengths: Assessing the Impact of Existing Laws & Regulations: Hearing Before the Subcommittee on Highways & Transit of the Committee on Transportation & Infrastructure, House of Representatives, One Hundred Tenth Congress, Second Session, July 9, 2008. 2008. (Illus.). xvii, 289p. *(978-0-16-083692-3(1),* 552-070-39404-4) United States Government Printing Office.

Waddell, J. A. L. Memoirs & Addresses of Two Decades. Skinner, Frank W., ed. 2011. 1188p. 89.95 ***(978-1-258-09393-8(6))*** Literary Licensing, LLC.

Wenzel, Helmut. Health Monitoring of Bridges. 2009. (ENG., Illus.). 652p. 150.00 *(978-0-470-03173-5(5),* Wiley) Wiley, John & Sons, Inc.

Whipple, Squire. An Elementary & Practical Treatise on Bridge Building. 2009. 330p. 32.99 *(978-1-110-03969-2(7))* 2009. 330p. pap. 30.75 *(978-1-110-03966-1(2))* 2008. 364p. 29.99 *(978-0-559-73400-7(X))* 2008. 364p. pap. 31.75 *(978-0-559-73395-6(X))* BiblioBazaar.

—An Elementary & Practical Treatise on Bridge Building. 2006. 48p. per. 26.99 *(978-1-4255-4356-3(1));* 340p. per. 23.99 *(978-1-4255-3440-0(6))* MPublishing.

Williamson, Eric B. Blast-Resistant Highway Bridges: Design & Detailing Guidelines. 2010. (Illus.). 142p. pap. ***(978-0-309-11819-4(0))*** Transportation Research Board.

Witczak, M. W. Rotation Limits for Elastomeric Bearings. 2008. (Illus.). 64p. 36.00 *(978-0-309-09918-9(8))* Transportation Research Board.

Woolacott, Amy. Crossing Places of the Upper Thames: A History & Guide. 2009. (ENG., Illus.). 160p. pap. 29.95 *(978-0-7524-4693-6(2))* History Pr. Ltd., The GBR. Dist: Independent Pubs. Group.

Xia, H., et al. Bridge Vibration & Controls: New Research. 2012. ***(978-1-62100-868-2(1))*** Nova Science Pubs., Inc.

Yorke, Trevor. Bridges Explained: Viaducts, Aqueducts. 2008. (Illus.). 160p. (C). pap. 23.95 *(978-1-84674-079-4(7))* Countryside Bks. GBR. Dist: Brown, David Bk. Co., The.

BRIDGES—DESIGN AND CONSTRUCTION

AASHTO LRFD Bridge Design Specifications, 2 Vols. *(978-1-56051-250-9(4))* Bow Historical Bks.

AASHTC/AWS D1. 5M/D1. 5-2010, Bridge Welding Code. 2011. *(978-0-87171-781-8(6))* American Welding Society.

Aci, ed. Seismic Evaluation & Retrofit Techniques for Concrete Bridges. 2007. *(978-0-87031-255-7(3))* American Concrete Institute.

Adeli, Hojjat & Kim, Hongjin. Wavelet-Based Vibration Control of Smart Buildings & Bridges. 2009. (ENG., Illus.). 238p. 133.95 *(978-1-4200-8923-3(4),* CRC Press) Taylor & Francis Group GBR. Dist: Taylor & Francis Group.

Ahmed, Aziz. Suspension Bridge. 2010. 132p. pap. *(978-3-8383-9634-7(0))* Lambert Academic Publishing.

Akesson, Bjorn. Fatigue Life of Riveted Railway Bridges. 2010. (ENG., Illus.). 170p. (C). 89.95 *(978-0-415-87676-6(1),* CRC Press) Taylor & Francis Group GBR. Dist: Taylor & Francis Group.

Allen, Barry. Artifice & Design: Art & Technology in Human Experience. 2008. (Illus.). 264p. 36.95 *(978-0-8014-4682-5(1))* Cornell Univ. Pr.

American Association of State Highway and Transportation Officials, Subcommittee on Bridges and Structures Staff, contrib. by. Guide Specifications for Design of Pedestrian Bridges. Date not set. (Bridges & Structures Ser.). (Illus.). 22p. pap. 15.50 *(978-1-56051-044-4(7))* American Assn. of State Highway & Transportation Officials.

American Association of State Highway and Transportation Officials, Subcommittee on Bridges and Structures Staff, contrib. by. Guide Specifications for Seismic Isolation Design. 3rd ed. 2010. (Illus.). xv, 47p. ***(978-1-56051-456-5(6))*** American Assn. of State Highway & Transportation Officials.

Arginhan, Oktay. Safety Level of Precast Prestressed Concrete Bridge Girders. 2011. 136p. pap. ***(978-3-8443-3178-3(6))*** Lambert Academic Publishing.

Bai, Yong, et al. Highway Bridge Replacement: Processes, Techniques, & Advancements. 2011. (Transportation Infrastructure — Roads, Highways, Bridges, Airports & Mass Transit Ser.). (Illus.). xii, 170p. 69.00 *(978-1-61122-300-2(8),* Nova Biomedical Bks.) Nova Science Pubs., Inc.

Barkdoll, Brian D., et al. Countermeasures to Protect Bridge Abutments from Scour. 2007. (Illus.). 220p. 53.00 *(978-0-309-09895-3(5))* Transportation Research Board.

Barker, Richard M. & Puckett, Jay A. Design of Highway Bridges: An LRFD Approach. 2nd rev. ed. 2006. (ENG., Illus.). 1032p. 175.00 *(978-0-471-69758-9(3),* Wiley) Wiley, John & Sons, Inc.

Biondini, Fabio & Frangopol, Dan M., eds. Bridge Maintenance, Safety & Management - IABMAS'12: Proceedings of the Sixth International IABMAS Conference, Villa Erba, Lake Como, Italy, 8-12 July 2012. 2012. (Bridge Maintenance, Safety & Management Ser.). (ENG.). 1000p. (C). 249.95 ***(978-0-415-62124-3(0),*** CRC Press) Taylor & Francis Group GBR. Dist: Taylor & Francis Group.

Bishop, Peter. Bridge. 2008. (Reaktion Books - Objekt Ser.). (ENG., Illus.). 224p. pap. 27.00 *(978-1-86189-346-8(9))* Reaktion Bks., Ltd. GBR. Dist: Chicago Distribution Ctr.

Blockley, David. Bridges: The Science & Art of the World's Most Inspiring Structures. (ENG., Illus.). 2012. 328p. 19.95 ***(978-0-19-964572-5(8))*** 2010. 288p. 29.95 *(978-0-19-954359-5(3))* Oxford Univ. Pr., Inc.

Bow, Robert. Bracing - with Its Application to Bridges & Other Structures. 2007. 76p. per. 14.95 *(978-1-933998-81-7(4),* Merchant Bks.) Rough Draft Printing.

Brancaleoni, Fabio, et al. The Messina Strait Bridge: A Challenge & a Dream. 2009. (ENG., Illus.). 334p. 104.95 *(978-0-415-46814-5(0),* CRC Press) Taylor & Francis Group GBR. Dist: Taylor & Francis Group.

Bridges, John F. & Unsworth, John F. Design of Modern Steel Railway Bridges. 2010. (ENG., Illus.). 453p. 129.95 *(978-1-4200-8217-3(5),* CRC Press) Taylor & Francis Group GBR. Dist: Taylor & Francis Group.

Building the Benicia-Martinez Bridge. 2007. 29.95 *(978-0-9744124-4-3(9));* pap. 19.95 *(978-0-9744124-5-0(7))* Carquinez Pr.

Burke, Martin P., Jr. Integral & Semi-Integral Bridges. 2009. (ENG., Illus.). 272p. 155.00 *(978-1-4051-9418-1(9),* Wiley-Blackwell) Wiley, John & Sons, Inc.

Buy America: Hearing Before the Subcommittee on Highways & Transit of the Committee on Transportation & Infrastructure, House of Representatives, One Hundred Tenth Congress, First Session, April 24, 2007. 2007. x, 79p. *(978-0-16-080722-0(0),* 552-070-37315-2) United States Government Printing Office.

Caetano, Elsa. Footbridge Vibration Design. Caetano, Elsa et al, eds. 2009. (ENG.). 200p. (C). 87.95 *(978-0-415-49866-1(X),* CRC Press) Taylor & Francis Group GBR. Dist: Taylor & Francis Group.

Carson, Rob. Masters of Suspension: The Men & Women Who Once Again Bridged the Tacoma Narrows. 2007. 29.95 *(978-0-9633035-1-6(1))* News Tribune, The.

Chen, Wai-Fah & Duan, Lian. Handbook of International Bridge Engineering & Design. 2nd ed. 2013. (ENG., Illus.). 1432p. 199.95 ***(978-1-4398-1029-3(X),*** CRC Press) Taylor & Francis Group GBR. Dist: Taylor & Francis Group.

Cleary, Richard L. Bridges. 2007. (Norton/Library of Congress Visual Sourcebooks Ser.). (ENG., Illus.). 336p. 75.00 *(978-0-393-73136-1(7),* 73136) Norton, W. W. & Co., Inc.

Ditran, Marco. Life-Cycle Cost Analysis of Bridges. 2011. 208p. pap. ***(978-3-8443-0411-4(8))*** Lambert Academic Publishing.

Ekesson & Akesson, Bjorn. Understanding Bridge Collapses. 2008. (ENG., Illus.). 276p. (C). 104.95 *(978-0-415-43623-6(0),* CRC Press) Taylor & Francis Group GBR. Dist: Taylor & Francis Group.

Engineers Society of Western Pennsylvania (ESWP) Staff, compiled by. 23rd Annual International Bridge Conference 2006: Advancing Bridge Technology Globally. 2007. 486p. pap. 118.00 *(978-1-60423-336-0(2))* Curran Assocs., Inc.

Erdem, Arda. Seismic Design of Bridges. 2010. 184p. pap. *(978-3-8383-7844-2(X))* Lambert Academic Publishing.

Fardis, Michael N. Seismic Design, Assessment & Retrofitting of Concrete Buildings: Based on En-Eurocode 8. 2009. (Geotechnical, Geological, & Earthquake Engineering Ser.). (ENG., Illus.). xxiii, 743p. 209.00 *(978-1-4020-9841-3(3),* 1402098413) Springer.

Frederick, Gerald R., et al. Engineering Design & Analysis of Highway Bridges. 2009. (Civil & Environmental Engineering Ser.). 350p. 139.95 *(978-0-8493-3803-8(4))* CRC Pr. LLC.

Fujino, Yozo, et al. Wind Resistant Design of Bridges in Japan: Developments & Practices. 2012. (ENG., Illus.). xii, 256p. 129.00 ***(978-4-431-54045-8(8),*** 4431540458) Springer.

Gardner, Denis. Wood, Concrete, Stone & Steel: Minnesota's Historic Bridges. 2008. pap. *(978-0-8166-4667-8(8))* Univ. of Minnesota Pr.

Gardner, Denis P. Wood, Concrete, Stone, & Steel: Minnesota's Historic Bridges. 2008. (Illus.). 344p. 39.95 *(978-0-8166-4666-1(X))* Univ. of Minnesota Pr.

Ger, Jeffrey & Cheng, Franklin Y. Seismic Design Aids for Nonlinear Pushover Analysis for Reinforced Concrete & Steel Bridges. 2011. (Advances in Earthquake Engineering Ser.). (ENG., Illus.). 400p. 119.95 *(978-1-4398-3763-4(5),* CRC Press) Taylor & Francis Group GBR. Dist: Taylor & Francis Group.

Ghosh, Utpal K. Design & Construction of Steel Bridges. 2006. (ENG., Illus.). 458p. 205.95 *(978-0-415-41836-2(4),* Taylor & Francis) Taylor & Francis Group GBR. Dist: Taylor & Francis Group.

González Arestuche, Luis & Recondo Pérez, Ramón. Puentes de Matanzas. 2009. (Illus.). 118p. *(978-959-268-165-1(1))* Matanzas, Ediciones.

Haupt, Herman. General Theory of Bridge Construction: Containing Demonstrations of the Principles of the Art & Th. 2009. (Illus.). 300p. pap. 18.99 *(978-1-103-79365-5(9))* BiblioBazaar.

Haw, Richard. Art of the Brooklyn Bridge: A Visual History. 2008. (Illus.). 280p. 60.00 *(978-0-415-95386-3(3))* Routledge.

Hawkins, Neil Middleton & Kuchma, Daniel A. Application of LRFD Bridge Design Specifications to High-Strength Structural Concrete: Shear Provisions. 2007. (Illus.). 197p. 53.00 *(978-0-309-09886-1(6))* Transportation Research Board.

Hearn, George. Bridge Inspection Practices. 2007. (Illus.). 199p. 53.00 *(978-0-309-09795-6(9))* Transportation Research Board.

Hendy, C. R. & Murphy, C. J. Designers' Guide to en 1993-2 Eurocode 3: Design of Steel Structures Part 2, Steel Bridges. 2007. 332p. *(978-0-7277-3160-9(2))* Telford, Thomas Ltd.

Hobbs, Richard S. Catastrophe to Triumph: Bridges of the Tacoma Narrows. 2006. (Illus.). 200p. pap. 24.95 *(978-0-87422-289-0(3))* Washington State Univ. Pr.

Idelberger, Klaus. The World of Footbridges: From the Utilitarian to the Spectacular. Wilharm, Linda, tr. from GER. 2011. (ENG., Illus.). 183p. 99.00 *(978-3-433-02943-5(1),* Wiley-VCH) Wiley, John & Sons, Inc.

Jackson, Robert W. Rails Across the Mississippi: A History of the St. Louis Bridge. 2006. (Illus.). 312p. pap. 20.95 *(978-0-252-07409-7(2))* Univ. of Illinois Pr.

Jain, Ravi & Lee, Luke, eds. Fiber Reinforced Polymer (FRP) Composites for Infrastructure Applications: Focusing on Innovation, Technology Implementation & Sustainability. 2012. (Strategies for Sustainability Ser.). (ENG., Illus.). xiii, 273p. 179.00 ***(978-94-007-2356-6(3),*** 9400723563) Springer.

Johnson, R. P. Composite Bridges Designed for Eurocodes Vol. 2: Composite Structures of Steel & Concrete. 3rd rev. ed. (ENG.). 336p. *(978-0-632-05411-4(5),* Wiley-Blackwell) Wiley, John & Sons, Ltd.

Khan, Mohiuddin A. Bridge & Highway Structure Rehabilitation & Repair. 2010. (ENG., Illus.). 656p. (C). 125.00 *(978-0-07-154591-4(3),* 0071545913) McGraw-Hill Professional Publishing.

Kimmerling, Robert. Shallow Foundations. 2006. 304p. per. 42.50 *(978-1-4102-2586-3(0))* Univ. Pr. of the Pacific.

Lark, Robert, ed. Bridge Design Construction & Maintenance. 2007. 608p. *(978-0-7277-3593-5(4),* Telford, Thomas Ltd.

Lawler, John S. Guidelines for Concrete Mixtures Containing Supplementary Cementitious Materials to Enhance Durability of Bridge Decks. 2007. (Illus.). 119p. 47.00 *(978-0-309-09897-7(1))* Transportation Research Board.

Mahmoud, Khaled. Safety & Reliability of Bridge Structures. 2009. (ENG., Illus.). 514p. 185.95 *(978-0-415-56484-7(0),* CRC Press) Taylor & Francis Group GBR. Dist: Taylor & Francis Group.

Mahmoud, Khaled, ed. New York Bridge Conference 2011. 2011. (ENG.). 336p. 159.95 ***(978-0-415-68415-6(3),*** CRC Press) Taylor & Francis Group GBR. Dist: Taylor & Francis Group.

Mahmoud, Khaled M. Innovations in Bridge Engineering Technology. Mahmoud, Khaled M., ed. 2007. (ENG., Illus.). 301p. (C). 169.95 *(978-0-415-45337-0(2),* Taylor & Francis) Taylor & Francis Group GBR. Dist: Taylor & Francis Group.

Mannini, Claudio. Flutter Vulnerability Assessment of Flexible Bridges. 2008. 248p. pap. *(978-3-639-01509-6(6))* VDM Verlag Dr. Mueller e.K.

Martin, George. Fences Gates & Bridges: And How to Build Them. 2nd ed. 2008. 186p. pap. 14.95 *(978-1-59921-324-8(9),* Lyons Pr.) Globe Pequot Pr., The.

McCullough, David. The Great Bridge: The Epic Story of the Building of the Brooklyn Bridge. 2012. (ENG., Illus.). 560p. 35.00 ***(978-1-4516-8323-3(5))*** Simon & Schuster.

Mertz, D. R. & Kulicki, J. M. Guide Specifications for Bridges Vulnerable to Coastal Storms. 2008. (Illus.). viii, 55p. ***(978-1-56051-429-9(9))*** American Assn. of State Highway & Transportation Officials.

Mimram, Marc & Desveaux, Delphine. Un Balcon Sur la Loire: Le Pont Léopold-Sédar-Senghor. 2010. (FRE., Illus.). 128p. *(978-2-35733-110-5(0))* Archibooks.

Mondorf, Paul E. Concrete Bridges. 2006. (ENG., Illus.). 1008p. 290.00 *(978-0-415-39362-1(0),* RU3620X, CRC Press) Taylor & Francis Group GBR. Dist: Taylor & Francis Group.

National Research Council (U.S.), Transportation Research Board Subcommittee on Bridge Aesthetics Staff & American Association of State Highway and Transportation Officials, Subcommittee on Bridges and Structures Staff, contrib. by. Bridge Aesthetics Sourcebook: Practical Ideas for Short- & Medium-Span Bridges. 2010. (Illus.). viii, 61p. ***(978-1-56051-485-5(X))*** American Assn. of State Highway & Transportation Officials.

Ohga, Mitao, et al. Condition Assessment & Maintenance of Bridges by Reliability Concept. 2011. 88p. pap. ***(978-3-8443-0226-4(3))*** Lambert Academic Publishing.

Olmos, Bertha. Seismic Response of Isolated Bridges Accouting for Ssi Effects. 2009. 328p. pap. *(978-3-639-17531-8(X))* VDM Verlag Dr. Mueller e.K.

Paikowsky, Samuel G. LRFD Design & Construction of Shallow Foundations for Highway Bridge Structures. 2010. (Illus.). 139p. ***(978-0-309-15467-3(7))*** Transportation Research Board.

Palmer, Robert. Age Well: A Cleveland Clinic Guide. 2007. (Cleveland Clinic Guides). (ENG.). 200p. pap. 14.95 *(978-1-59624-042-1(3))* Cleveland Clinic Pr.

Parkstone Press Staff. Bridges. 2010. (Our Earth Ser.). (ENG., Illus.). 192p. 24.95 *(978-1-84484-773-0(X))* Parkstone International GBR. Dist: Ingram Pub. Services.

Rinke, Mario. Base-Isolated Bridges under Seismic Loads. 2008. 116p. pap. *(978-3-639-02965-9(8))* VDM Verlag Dr. Mueller e.K.

Rizkalla, S. H. Application of the LRFD Bridge Design Specifications to High-Strength Structural Concrete: Flexure & Compression Provisions. 2007. (Illus.). 28p. 32.00 *(978-0-309-09905-9(6))* Transportation Research Board.

Rockland, Michael Aaron. The George Washington Bridge: Poetry in Steel. 2008. (ENG., Illus.). 200p. 22.95 *(978-0-8135-4375-8(4)*, Rivergate Bks.) Rutgers Univ. Pr.

Shi, Xiaomin & Cai, C. S. Approach Slab & Its Effect on Vehicle Induced Bridge Vibration. 2010. 172p. pap. *(978-3-8383-1934-6(6))* Lambert Academic Publishing.

Simiu, Emil, et al. Design of Buildings for Wind: A Guide for ASCE 7-10 Standard Users & Designers of Special Structures. 2nd ed. 2011. (ENG., Illus.). 352p. 140.00 *(978-0-470-46492-2(5)*, Wiley) Wiley, John & Sons, Inc.

Svensson, Holger. Cable-Stayed Bridges. 2012. (ENG.). 458p. 185.00 ***(978-3-433-02992-3(X)***, Wiley-VCH) Wiley, John & Sons, Inc.

Technology Research Editors, ed. Market Developments: Polymer Composites in Bridge Construction, 2007 Ed. 2007. pap. 68.50 *(978-1-60030-221-3(1)*, Search-In-Print) CSA Journal Division.

Tigerman, Stanley. Designing Bridges to Burn: Architectural Memoirs by Stanley Tigerman. 2011. (ENG., Illus.). 240p. pap. 24.95 *(978-1-935935-07-0(0))* Oro Editions.

Toothpick Bridges Getting Started Teacher's Guide. 2007. spiral bd. 24.95 *(978-1-58651-921-6(2))* Pitsco/Pitsco LEGO Dacta.

United States Army Staff. Army Technical Manual TM 5-600 (Bridge Inspection, Maintenance, & Repair) 2007. per. 19.99 *(978-1-4209-2840-2(6))* Digireads.com.

van den Berg, Christa & Nijenhuis, Gerhard. Bridging the Dutch Landscape: Design Guide for Bridges. 2009. (ENG., Illus.). 160p. 38.00 *(978-90-6369-155-4(6))* Bis B.V., Uitgeverij(BIS Publishers) NLD. Dist: Consortium Bk. Sales & Distribution.

van Uffelen, Chris. Masterpieces: Bridge Architecture + Design. 2009. (Masterpieces Ser.). (FRE, GER & ENG., Illus.). 304p. 49.95 *(978-3-03768-025-4(3)*, Braun Publish,Csi) Continental Sales, Inc.

Won, Moon, et al, eds. New Technologies in Construction & Rehabilitation of Portland Cement Concrete Pavement & Bridge Deck Pavement: Selected Papers from the 2009 GeoHunan International Conference, August 3-6, 2009, Changsha, Hunan, China. 2009. pap. 50.00 *(978-0-7844-1048-6(8))* American Society of Civil Engineers.

Xie, Yongli, et al. Gong Lu Han Dong Gong Cheng. 2009. (CHI., Illus.). *(978-7-114-08029-6(8))* People's Communications Publishing Hse., The.

Yanev, Bojidar. Bridge Management. 2007. (ENG., Illus.). 672p. 155.00 *(978-0-471-69162-4(3)*, Wiley) Wiley, John & Sons, Inc.

Zhao, Jim & Tonias, Demetrios. Bridge Engineering 3/E. 3rd ed. 2012. (ENG., Illus.). 544p. (C). 125.00 ***(978-0-07-175249-7(8)***, 0071752498) McGraw-Hill Professional Publishing.

Zhou, Zhengjie. VIBRATION-BASED DAMAGE DETECTION OF BRIDGE SUPERSTRUCTURES: A Tool for Structural Health Monitoring. 2008. 300p. pap. *(978-3-639-09337-7(2))* VDM Verlag Dr. Mueller e.K.

BRIDGES—HISTORY

Adler, Den & Adler, Judy. Janesville. 2010. (Postcard History Ser.). (Illus.). 128p. pap. 21.99 *(978-0-7385-8446-1(0))* Arcadia Publishing.

Blackman, Jeffrey. Covered Bridges of New England. 2008. (ENG.). 96p. 19.95 *(978-0-88150-799-7(7))* Countryman Pr.

Brancaleoni, Fabio, et al. The Messina Strait Bridge: A Challenge & a Dream. 2009. (ENG., Illus.). 334p. 104.95 *(978-0-415-46814-5(0)*, CRC Press) Taylor & Francis Group GBR. Dist: Taylor & Francis Group.

Cleary, Richard L. Bridges. 2007. (Norton/Library of Congress Visual Sourcebooks Ser.). (ENG., Illus.). 336p. 75.00 *(978-0-393-73136-1(7)*, 73136) Norton, W. W. & Co., Inc.

Gardner, Denis P. Wood, Concrete, Stone, & Steel: Minnesota's Historic Bridges. 2008. (Illus.). 344p. 39.95 *(978-0-8166-4666-1(X))* Univ. of Minnesota Pr.

Greater Astoria Historical Society & Roosevelt Island Historical Society. The Queensboro Bridge. 2008. (Images of America Ser.). (ENG., Illus.). 128p. pap. 21.99 *(978-0-7385-5488-4(X))* Arcadia Publishing.

Matthews, Peter. London's Bridges. 2009. (Shire History Ser.). (ENG., Illus.). 160p. pap. 25.95 *(978-0-7478-0679-0(9))* Shire Pubns., Ltd. GBR. Dist: Random Hse., Inc.

Moll, Fred J. Pennsylvania's Historic Bridges. 2007. (Postcard History Ser.). (ENG., Illus.). 127p. per. 21.99 *(978-0-7385-4994-1(0))* Arcadia Publishing.

Nunnally, Andrea & Nunnally, Patrick. The City, the River, the Bridge: Before & after the Minneapolis Bridge Collapse. 2011. (ENG., Illus.). 216p. pap. 22.95 *(978-0-8166-6767-3(5))* Univ. of Minnesota Pr.

Nunnally, Patrick. The City, the River, the Bridge: Before & after the Minneapolis Bridge Collapse. 2011. (ENG., Illus.). 216p. 69.00 *(978-0-8166-6766-6(7))* Univ. of Minnesota Pr.

Wolf, Donald E. Crossing the Hudson: Historic Bridges & Tunnels of the River. 2010. (ENG., Illus.). 288p. 26.95 *(978-0-8135-4708-4(3)*, Rivergate Bks.) Rutgers Univ. Pr.

Zaloga, Steven. Remagen 1945 (CO-ED) Endgame against the Third Reich. 2006. (Illus.). 96p. *(978-1-84603-249-3(0))* Osprey Publishing, Ltd. GBR. Dist: Random Hse., Inc.

BRIDGES—JUVENILE LITERATURE

Latham, Donna. Bridges & Tunnels: Investigate Feats of Engineering with 25 Projects. 2012. (Build It Yourself Ser.). (ENG., Illus.). 128p. (J). (gr. 4-7). pap. 15.95 ***(978-1-936749-51-5(3))*** Nomad Pr.

BRIDGES (COMPUTER NETWORKS)

Bragg, Nigel & Allan, David. 802.1Aq Shortest Path Bridging Design & Evolution: The Architect's Perspective. 2012. (ENG.). 224p. pap. 60.00 ***(978-1-118-14866-2(5))*** IEEE.

BRIDGES, CONCRETE

see Concrete Bridges

BRIDGES, COVERED

see Covered Bridges

BRIDGES, ELECTRIC

see Bridge Circuits

BRIDGES, IRON AND STEEL

see Iron and Steel Bridges

BRIDGES, SUSPENSION

see Suspension Bridges

BRIDGES, WOODEN

see Wooden Bridges

BRIDGES IN ART

Dim, Joan Marans. New York's Golden Age of Bridges. 2011. (ENG., Illus.). 132p. 34.95 ***(978-0-8232-4065-4(7))*** Fordham Univ. Pr.

Harrison, Terry. Rustic Bridge: In Watercolour. 2010. (ENG., Illus.). 12p. pap. 5.95 *(978-1-84448-502-4(1))* Search Pr., Ltd. GBR. Dist: Independent Pubs. Group.

Sousa. The Alfred A. Cunningham Bridge: A Photographic Archive. 2008. (Illus.). 44p. per. 15.95 *(978-0-9707197-1-3(X))* Carolina Comfort Pr.

Wood, John, ed. & intro. Hart Crane's the Bridge. 60th ltd. ed. 2007. *(978-1-892733-37-5(4))* 21st Editions, Inc.

BRIDLE

Esterson, Emily. The Ultimate Book of Horse Bits: What They Are, What They Do, & How They Work. 2010. (ENG., Illus.). 176p. 24.95 *(978-1-60239-959-4(X)*, 239959) Skyhorse Publishing Co., Inc.

Jacobs, Lee C. Ornamental Curb Bits, Fancy Drivers & Bits of Wisdom. 2006. pap. 22.50 *(978-0-9645389-3-1(8))* Jacobs, Lee C.

Sage, E. Helene. Bridle Rosettes: Two Centuries of Equine Adornment. 2011. (Illus.). 256p. 59.99 ***(978-0-7643-3859-5(5))*** Schiffer Publishing, Ltd.

BRIDLE PATHS

see Trails

BRIEF PSYCHOTHERAPY

see also Crisis Intervention (Mental Health Services)

Arntz, Arnoud & van Genderen, Hannie. Schema Therapy for Borderline Personality Disorder. Drost, Jolijn, tr. from DUT. 2009. (ENG., Illus.). 206p. 118.95 *(978-0-470-51080-3(3))*; 216p. pap. 52.95 *(978-0-470-51081-0(1))* Wiley, John & Sons, Inc. (Wiley-Blackwell).

Battino, Rubin. Expectation: The Very Brief Therapy Book. 2006. 208p. *(978-1-84590-028-1(6))* Crown Hse. Publishing.

Binder, Jeffrey L. Key Competencies in Brief Dynamic Psychotherapy: Clinical Practice Beyond the Manual. 2010. (ENG.). 292p. pap. 27.00 *(978-1-60918-168-0(9))* Guilford Pubns., Inc.

Cohen-Posey, Kate. More Brief Therapy Client Handouts. 2010. (ENG., Illus.). 265p. pap. 55.00 *(978-0-470-49985-6(0)*, Wiley) Wiley, John & Sons, Inc.

Coren, Alex. Short-Term Psychotherapy: A Psychodynamic Approach. Frosh, Stephen, ed. 2nd rev. ed. 2009. (Basic Texts in Counselling & Psychotherapy Ser.). (ENG., Illus.). 224p. pap. 34.00 *(978-0-230-55157-2(2))* Palgrave Macmillan.

De Shazer, Steve & Dolan, Yvonne. More Than Miracles: The State of the Art of Solution-Focused Brief Therapy. 2007. (ENG., Illus.). 194p. 125.00 *(978-0-7890-3397-0(6))*; 192p. per. 34.95 *(978-0-7890-3398-7(4))* Routledge.

Dewan, Mantosh J., et al. The Art & Science of Brief Psychotherapies: An Illustrated Guide. 2nd ed. 2012. pap. ***(978-1-58562-396-9(2))*** American Psychiatric Publishing, Inc.

Echterling, Lennis G., et al. Beyond Brief Counseling & Therapy: An Integrative Approach. 2nd ed. 2007. (ENG., Illus.). 368p. (C). per. 47.00 *(978-0-13-230092-6(3)*, Prentice Hall) Prentice Hall PTR.

Franklin, Cynthia, et al, eds. Solution-Focused Brief Therapy: A Handbook of Evidence-Based Practice. 1 vol. 2011. (ENG., Illus.). 448p. 55.00 ***(978-0-19-538572-4(1))*** Oxford Univ. Pr., Inc.

Guggenheim, Frederick G. Prime Time: Maximizing the Therapeutic Experience, A Primer for Psychiatric Clinicians. 2009. (ENG., Illus.). 252p. 125.00 *(978-0-415-80203-1(2))*; pap. 28.95 *(978-0-415-80109-6(5))* Routledge.

Haley, Jay. Ordeal Therapy: Unusual Ways to Change Behavior. 2011. 224p. pap. ***(978-1-935810-05-6(7))*** Crown Hse. Publishing.

Hanton, Paul. Skills in Solution Focused Brief Counselling & Psychotherapy. 2011. (Skills in Counselling & Psychotherapy Ser.). 152p. (C). 104.00 *(978-1-84920-621-1(X)*, B06211C) SAGE Pubns., Ltd. GBR. Dist: SAGE Pubns., Inc.

Iveson, Chris, et al. Brief Coaching: A Solution-Focused Approach. 2012. (Essential Coaching Skills & Knowledge Ser.). (ENG.). 216p. (C). 90.00 *(978-0-415-66746-3(1))*; pap. 28.99 *(978-0-415-66747-0(X))* Routledge.

Kaduson, Heidi Gerard & Schaefer, Charles E., eds. Short-Term Play Therapy for Children. 2nd ed. 2009. (ENG.). 388p. 35.00 *(978-1-60623-353-5(X))* Guilford Pubns., Inc.

Klingberg, Torkel. The Overflowing Brain: Information Overload & the Limits of Working Memory. 2008. (ENG., Illus.). 224p. 21.95 *(978-0-19-537288-5(3))* Oxford Univ. Pr., Inc.

Lemma, Alessandra, et al. Brief Dynamic Interpersonal Therapy: A Clinician's Guide. 2011. (ENG., Illus.). 288p. pap. 37.95 *(978-0-19-960245-2(X))* Oxford Univ. Pr., Inc.

Levenson, Hanna. Brief Dynamic Therapy. 2010. 168p. pap. 24.95 *(978-1-4338-0755-8(6))* American Psychological Assn.

Lines, Dennis. Brief Counselling in Schools: Working with Young People from 11 To 18. 2nd rev. ed. 2006. (Illus.). 224p. (C). 124.00 *(978-1-4129-2400-9(6)*, B24006C) SAGE Pubns., Ltd. GBR. Dist: SAGE Pubns., Inc.

Luquet, Wade. Short-Term Couples Therapy: The Imago Model in Action. 2nd rev. ed. 2006. (ENG., Illus.). 304p. per. 49.95 *(978-0-415-95380-1(4))* Routledge.

Metcalf, Linda. The Field Guide to Counseling Toward Solutions: The Solution-Focused School. 2008. (ENG., Illus.). 144p. per. 24.95 *(978-0-7879-9807-3(9)*, Jossey-Bass) Wiley, John & Sons, Inc.

—Solution Focused Group Therapy: Ideas for Groups in Private Practise, Schools, 2007. (ENG.). 256p. pap. 17.95 *(978-1-4165-8464-3(1)*, Free Pr.) Free Pr.

Monroe, Barbara & Kraus, Frances. Brief Interventions with Bereaved Children. 2nd ed. 2010. (ENG., Illus.). 264p. pap. 59.95 *(978-0-19-956164-3(8))* Oxford Univ. Pr., Inc.

Nelson, Thorana S., ed. Handbook of Solution-Focused Brief Therapy: Clinical Applications. 2007. (ENG., Illus.). 458p. per. 66.95 *(978-0-7890-2395-7(4))* Routledge.

Nelson, Thorana Strever & Thomas, Frank N. Handbook of Solution-Focused Brief Therapy: Clinical Applications. 2007. (ENG., Illus.). 458p. 94.95 *(978-0-7890-2394-0(6))* Routledge.

Oakley, Clare & Malik, Amit. Rapid Psychiatry. 2nd ed. 2010. (Rapid Ser.: 16). (ENG.). 180p. pap. 36.95 *(978-1-4051-9557-7(6)*, Wiley-Blackwell) Wiley, John & Sons, Inc.

O'Farrell, Ursula & McLoughlin, Sarah. Families in Focus: Finding Solutions to Difficult Problems. 2008. (ENG.). 128p. pap. 16.95 *(978-1-84730-048-5(0))* Veritas Pubns. IRL. Dist: Dufour Editions, Inc.

Pichot, Terri. Animal-Assisted Brief Therapy: A Solution-Focused Approach. 2nd rev. ed. 2011. (ENG., Illus.). 312p. 125.00 *(978-0-415-88960-5(X))*; pap. 39.95 *(978-0-415-88961-2(8))* Routledge.

Quick, Ellen K. Core Competencies in the Solution-Focused & Strategic Therapies: Becoming a Highly Competent Solution-Focused & Strategic Therapist. 2011. (Core Competencies in Psychotherapy Ser.). (ENG., Illus.). 203p. pap. 34.95 ***(978-0-415-88530-0(2))*** Routledge.

Quick, Ellen K. Doing What Works in Brief Therapy: A Strategic Solution Focused Approach. 2nd ed. 2007. (Practical Resources for the Mental Health Professional Ser.). (ENG.). 336p. per. 53.95 *(978-0-12-374175-2(0)*, Academic Pr.) Elsevier Science & Technology Bks.

Roberts, Albert R. & Yeager, Kenneth R. Pocket Guide to Crisis Intervention. 2009. (ENG., Illus.). 240p. pap. 29.99 *(978-0-19-538290-7(0))* Oxford Univ. Pr., Inc.

Safran, Muran. Therapeutic Alliance in Brief Psychother. 2006. pap. 8.95 *(978-1-4288-1337-3(3))* Cram101 Inc.

Saitz, Richard & Galanter, Marc. Alcohol/Drug Screening & Brief Intervention: Advances in Evidence-Based Practice. 2008. (ENG., Illus.). 100p. pap. 46.00 *(978-0-7890-3749-7(1)*, Informa Healthcare) Taylor & Francis Group.

Schultheis, Gary M., et al. Couples Therapy Homework Planner. 2nd ed. 2010. (PracticePlanners Ser.: 269). (ENG., Illus.). 256p. pap. 55.00 *(978-0-470-52266-0(6)*, Wiley) Wiley, John & Sons, Inc.

Selekman, Matthew D. Collaborative Brief Therapy with Children. 2nd ed. 2010. (ENG., Illus.). 332p. 40.00 *(978-1-60623-568-3(0))* Guilford Pubns., Inc.

—Pathways to Change, Second Edition: Brief Therapy with Difficult Adolescents. 2nd ed. 2008. (ENG.). 292p. pap. 30.00 *(978-1-59385-979-4(1))* Guilford Pubns., Inc.

Selekman, Matthew D., et al. The Adolescent & Young Adult Self-Harming Treatment Manual: A Collaborative Strengths-Based Brief Therapy Approach. 2009. (ENG., Illus.). 256p. 33.95 *(978-0-393-70567-6(6)*, 70567) Norton, W. W. & Co., Inc.

Sharry, John, et al. Becoming a Solution Detective: Identifying Your Clients' Strengths in Practical Brief Therapy. 2nd rev. ed. 2011. (ENG., Illus.). 184p. 135.00 *(978-0-415-89621-4(5))*; pap. 31.95 *(978-0-415-89622-1(3))* Routledge.

Simon, Joel K. & Nelson, Thorana Strever. Solution-Focused Brief Practice with Long Term Clients in Mental Health Services: I Am More Than My Label. 2007. (ENG.). 196p. 135.00 *(978-0-7890-2794-8(1))*; pap. 44.95 *(978-0-7890-2795-5(X))* Routledge.

Sparrer, Insa. Miracle, Solution & System: Solution Focused Systemic Structural Constellations for Therapy & Organisational Change. Onn, Samuel, tr. from GER. 2007. (Illus.). 384p. per. *(978-0-9549749-5-4(6))* Solutions Bks.

Stadter, null & Stadter, Michael. Object Relations Brief Therapy: The Therapeutic Relationship in Short-Term Work. 2009. (Library of Object Relations Ser.). (ENG.). 384p. pap. 38.99 *(978-0-7657-0690-4(3)*, Aronson, Jason) Rowman & Littlefield Publishers, Inc.

Tudor, Keith, ed. Brief Person-Centred Therapies. 2008. (Brief Therapies Ser.). 216p. (C). 116.00 *(978-1-84787-346-0(4)*, B73460C); pap. 49.00 *(978-1-84787-347-7(2)*, B73460P) SAGE Pubns., Ltd. GBR. Dist: SAGE Pubns., Inc.

Wake. Role of Brief Therapy in Attachment: Disorders. 2010. (Illus.). 210p. pap. 36.95 *(978-1-85575-697-7(8))* Karnac Bks. GBR. Dist: Stylus Publishing, LLC.

Watson, Jeanne C., et al. Case Studies in Emotion-Focused Treatment of Depression: A Comparison of Good & Poor Outcome. 2007. 232p. 49.95 *(978-1-59147-929-1(0))* American Psychological Assn.

Williamson, Anne. Brief Psychological Interventions in Practice. 2008. (ENG., Illus.). 272p. pap. 44.95 *(978-0-470-51306-4(3)*, Wiley) Wiley, John & Sons, Inc.

Wright, Jesse H., et al. High-Yield Cognitive-Behavior Therapy for Brief Sessions. 2010. (ENG., Illus.). pap., instr.'s gde. ed. 74.00 *(978-1-58562-362-4(8))* American Psychiatric Publishing, Inc.

Wyatt, Randall C. & Seid, Erika L. Down Every Year: A Demonstration of Depth Oriented Brief Therapy (Coherence Therapy) (Instructor's Version) 2007. 149.00 *(978-1-60124-057-6(0))* Psychotherapy.net.

Young, Cynthia Y., et al. Schema Therapy. 2010. (CBT Distinctive Features Ser.). (ENG., Illus.). 184p. (C). 90.00 *(978-0-415-46298-3(3))* Routledge.

BRIEFHAND

see Shorthand

BRIEFS

Abbott, Nathan. Brief Making & the Use of Law Books. 2009. 332p. pap. *(978-0-217-18576-9(2))* Books LLC.

Edwards, Linda H. Legal Writing & Analysis. 2nd ed. 2007. 350p. per. 71.00 *(978-0-7355-6229-5(6)*, Aspen Pubs.) Wolters Kluwer Law & Business.

Edwards, Linda Holdeman. Legal Writing & Analysis. 3rd ed. 2011. (Illus.). xix, 356p. ***(978-0-7355-9851-5(7)***, Aspen Pubs.) Wolters Kluwer Law & Business.

Fontham, Michael R., et al. Persuasive Written & Oral Advocacy in Trial & Appellate Courts. 2nd ed. 2007. xxvii, 460p. *(978-0-7355-6394-0(2))* Lippincott Williams & Wilkins.

—Persuasive Written & Oral Advocacy in Trial & Appellate Courts. 2nd ed. 2007. xxvii, 460p. pap. 75.00 *(978-0-7355-6230-1(X)*, Aspen Pubs.) Wolters Kluwer Law & Business.

Miller, Toby & Miller, David W. Practicing Persuasive Written & Oral Advocacy: Case File 4. 2008. pap. 37.50 *(978-0-7355-6422-0(1)*, Aspen Pubs.) Wolters Kluwer Law & Business.

Oates, Laurel Currie. Just Briefs, Second Edition. 2nd ed. 2008. xix, 234p. pap. 59.00 *(978-0-7355-6231-8(8)*, Aspen Pubs.) Wolters Kluwer Law & Business.

Oates, Laurel Currie, et al. Just Briefs. 2nd ed. 2008. xix, 234p. *(978-0-7355-6395-7(0)*, Aspen Pubs.) Wolters Kluwer Law & Business.

Parrish, Austen L. & Yokoyama, Dennis T. Effective Lawyering: A Checklist Approach to Legal Writing & Oral Argument. 2007. 180p. pap. 20.00 *(978-1-59460-348-8(0))* Carolina Academic Pr.

BRIGADA DE ASALTA

de Quesada, Alejandro M. The Bay of Pigs: Cuba 1961. 2009. (Elite Ser.). (ENG., Illus.). 64p. pap. 18.95 *(978-1-84603-323-0(3))* Osprey Publishing, Ltd. GBR. Dist: Random Hse., Inc.

Perez-Cisneros, Pablo, et al. After the Bay of Pigs: Lives & Liberty on the Line. 2007. (Illus.). 240p. 25.00 *(978-0-9796794-3-8(5))* Alexandria Library, Inc.

BRIGADE 2506

see Brigada de Asalta

BRIGANDS AND ROBBERS

see also Bushrangers; Outlaws; Rogues and Vagabonds; Thugs; Train Robberies

Alexander, Bob. Desert Desperadoes: The Banditti of Southwest New Mexico. 2006. pap. 21.95 *(978-0-9765728-2-4(6))*; 34.95 *(978-0-9765728-3-1(4))* Castaway Media. (Gila Bks.).

Barker, Karen. Wave of Change 2012. 2007. 235p. pap. 19.95 *(978-0-7414-3877-5(1))* Infinity Publishing.

Batty, Dane. Wanted- Gentleman Bank Robber: The True Story of Leslie Ibsen Rogge, One of the FBI's Most Elusive Criminals: Gentleman Bank Robber: Gentleman Bank Robber. Beagle Bay, ed. 2010. (Illus.). 218p. 15.95 *(978-0-615-26845-3(5))* Nish Publishing Co.

Brandon, David. Stand & Deliver! A History of Highway Robbery. 2010. (ENG., Illus.). 240p. pap. 16.95 *(978-0-7509-3528-9(6))* History Pr. Ltd.,The GBR. Dist: Independent Pubs. Group.

Broglin, Jana Sloan. Hookers, Crooks, & Kooks, 2 vols. 2007. pap. 21.00 *(978-0-7884-4550-7(2))*; pap. 22.00 *(978-0-7884-4604-7(5))* Heritage Bks.

Carruth, Barbara Woolbright. Rube Burrow Alabama Desperado: Legends of Rube Burrow & Gang. 2007. per. 25.00 *(978-1-59872-781-4(8))* Instant Pub.

Cox, Bruce. Autobiography of a Stagecoach Robber: The Saga of Reimund Holzhey. 2007. 108p. per. 14.95 *(978-1-59858-346-5(8))* Dog Ear Publishing, LLC.

Dacus, Joseph A. Illustrated Lives & Adventures of Frank & Jesse James & the Younger Brothers, the Noted Western Outlaws. (Illus.). 442p. reprint ed. lib. bdg. 98.00 *(978-0-7222-0692-8(5))* Library Reprints, Inc.

DeArment, Robert K. Assault on the Deadwood Stage: Road Agents & Shotgun Messengers. 2011. (ENG.). 272p. 24.95 *(978-0-8061-4182-4(4))* Univ. of Oklahoma Pr.

Doeden, Matt. The World's Most Notorious Crooks, 1 vol. 2006. (Edge Books, the World's Top Tens). (ENG., Illus.). 32p. (gr. 3-4). 27.32 *(978-0-7368-6440-4(7)*, Edge Bks.) Capstone Pr., Inc.

Duncombe, Stephen & Mattson, Andrew. The Bobbed Haired Bandit: A Story of Crime & Celebrity in 1920s New York. 2007. (Mortalis Ser.). (Illus.). 416p. pap. 9.95 *(978-0-8129-7735-6(1)*, Random Hse. Trade Paperbacks) Random House Publishing Group.

Durham, Keith. Border Reiver, 1513-1607. 2011. (Warrior Ser.). (ENG., Illus.). 64p. pap. 18.95 *(978-1-84908-193-1(X))* Osprey Publishing, Ltd. GBR. Dist: Random Hse., Inc.

Enss, Chris. Outlaw Tales of California: True Stories of the Golden State's Most Infamous Crooks, Culprits, & Cutthroats. 2008. (Outlaw Tales Ser.). (Illus.). 128p. per. 12.95 *(978-0-7627-3852-6(9)*, TwoDot) Globe Pequot Pr., The.

Fifer, Barbara C. Bad Boys of the Black Hills. 2008. 200p. pap. 14.95 *(978-1-56037-435-0(7))* Farcountry Pr.

Frazer, Chris. Bandit Nation: A History of Outlaws & Cultural Struggle in Mexico, 1810-1920. 2008. (ENG.). 256p. pap. 24.95 *(978-0-8032-1799-7(4))* Univ. of Nebraska Pr.

Griffith, T. D. South Dakota: True Stories of the Mount Rushmore State's Most Infamous Crooks, Culprits, & Cutthroats. 2008. (Outlaw Tales Ser.). (ENG., Illus.). 128p. pap. 12.95 *(978-0-7627-4342-1(5)*, TwoDot) Globe Pequot Pr., The.

Grunewald, Thomas. Bandits in the Roman Empire: Myth & Reality. Drinkwater, John, tr. 2008. 240p. pap. 39.95 *(978-0-415-48681-1(5))* Routledge.

Holden, Michael. Freney the Robber. 2009. (ENG.). 256p. pap. 22.95 *(978-1-85635-620-6(5))* Mercier Pr., Ltd., The IRL. Dist: Dufour Editions, Inc.

Hume, James B., et al, eds. Wells, Fargo & Co. Stagecoach & Train Robberies, 1870-1884: The Corporate Report of 1885 with Additional Facts about the Crimes & Their Perpetrators. rev. ed. 2010. (ENG., Illus.). 281p. pap. 45.00 *(978-0-7864-4855-5(5))* McFarland & Co., Inc. Pubs.

James, Jesse. The Wild Bandits of the Border: a Thrilling Story of the Adventures. 2007. (ENG.). 412p. per. 34.95 *(978-1-4304-4239-4(5))* Kessinger Publishing, LLC.

Kaufman, Alexander L., ed. British Outlaws of Literature & History: Essays on Medieval & Early Modern Figures from Robin Hood to Twm Shon Catty. 2011. (ENG., Illus.). 272p. pap. 35.00 *(978-0-7864-5877-6(1))* McFarland & Co., Inc. Pubs.

Koblas, John. Ma: The Life & Times of Ma Barker & Her Boys. 2007. pap. 18.95 *(978-0-87839-264-3(5))* North Star Pr. of St. Cloud.

Marshall, Michael L. & Taylor, Jerry L. Wicked Kernersville: Rogues, Robbers, Ruffians, & Rumrunners. 2009. *(978-1-59629-676-3(3))* History Pr., The.

Michael, R. Great Stagecoach Robberies of the Old West. 2006. (ENG., Illus.). 200p. per. 12.95 *(978-0-7627-4127-4(9)*, Falcon Guides) Globe Pequot Pr., The.

—Great Train Robberies of the Old West. 2006. (ENG., Illus.). 176p. per. 12.95 *(978-0-7627-4150-2(3)*, Falcon Guides) Globe Pequot Pr., The.

Miller, Rick. Bloody Bill Longley: The Mythology of a Gunfighter, Second Edition. 2nd ed. 2011. (A. C. Greene Ser.). (Illus.). 384p. 29.95 *(978-1-57441-305-2(8))* Univ. of North Texas Pr.

Modern-Day Bank Robberies. 2007. per. 6.00 net. *(978-0-9795921-1-9(9))* Postmodern Library.

Moffat, Alistair. The Reivers: The Story of the Border Reivers. 2008. (ENG., Illus.). 321p. pap. 18.00 *(978-1-84158-674-8(9))* Birlinn, Ltd. GBR. Dist: Interlink Publishing Group, Inc.

Moxham, Roy. Outlaw: India's Bandit Queen & Me. 2010. (ENG., Illus.). 214p. 27.95 ***(978-1-84604-132-2(1))*** Random Hse. GBR. Dist: Independent Pubs. Group.

Parker, Martin. Cultural Theory & Organizations. 2011. (ENG., Illus.). 192p. (C). 160.00 ***(978-0-415-58547-4(X))***; pap. 46.95 ***(978-0-415-58648-1(8))*** Routledge.

Public Library of Cincinnati & Hamilton County. History of the Lives & Actions of the Most Famous Highwaymen, Street-robbers. 2007. mass mkt. *(978-0-9796997-1-9(1))* Public Library of Cincinnati & Hamilton County.

van Onselen, Charles. Masked Raiders: Irish Banditry in Southern Africa, 1880-1899. 2010. (Illus.). 304p. pap. 25.95 *(978-1-77022-080-5(1))* Random Hse. Struik (Pty.), Ltd. ZAF. Dist: International Publishers Marketing.

Warner, Matt, et al. Last of the Bandit Riders... Revisited. Date not set. (Illus.). 252p. reprint ed. pap. 24.95 *(978-0-9656694-1-2(6))* Big Moon Traders.

Whitehead, C. Lives & Exploits of English Highwaymen. 2006. pap. 37.95 *(978-1-4286-4057-3(6))* Kessinger Publishing, LLC.

BRIGHAM YOUNG UNIVERSITY

Brown, Lance W., et al. The Answered Prayer. 2011. (ENG., Illus.). 20p. 16.95 ***(978-0-615-38794-9(2))*** Last Second Media LLC.

Call, Jeff. Roaring Back to Glory: A Lavish Retrospective of the BYU Football Program's Most Amazing Moments, Most Memorable Quotes, Best Players & Greatest Games. 2003. 224p. pap. 15.95 *(978-1-932898-76-7(X))* Spring Creek Bk. Co.

Cowan, Richard O., ed. Teaching the Word: Religious Education at Brigham Young University. 2008. (Illus.). 96p. 11.95 *(978-0-8425-2708-8(7)*, Brigham Young Univ. Pr.) Brigham Young Univ.

Edwards, LaVell, et al, contrib. by. Loyal, Strong, & True: Speeches by BYU Coaches. 2007. pap. 9.95 *(978-0-8425-2688-3(9)*, BYU Publications & Graphics) Brigham Young Univ.

Hague, Daryl R., ed. A Love of Learning. 2011. pap. *(978-0-8425-2791-0(5)*, Brigham Young Univ. Studies) Brigham Young Univ.

Hinckley, Gordon B., et al, contrib. by. BYU 2006 - 2007 Speeches. 2007. pap. 14.95 *(978-0-8425-2687-6(0)*, BYU Publications & Graphics) Brigham Young Univ.

Tanner, John S. Notes from an Amateur. 2011. (Illus.). 144p. 24.99 ***(978-0-8425-2801-6(6)***, Brigham Young Univ. Religious Studies Ctr.) Brigham Young Univ.

Tittle, Duff. What It Means to Be a Cougar: LaVell Edwards Bronco Mendenhall & BYU's Greatest Players. 2011. (What It Means to Be Ser.). (ENG., Illus.). 336p. 26.95 *(978-1-60078-579-5(4))* Triumph Bks.

Waterstradt, Jean A., ed. They Gladly Taught: Ten BYU Professors, 3 vols. Incl. Vol. 1. They Gladly Taught Vol 1. 1986. 9.95 *(978-0-8425-2242-7(5))*; Vol. 2. They Gladly Taught, Vol 2. 1987. 9.95 *(978-0-8425-2265-6(4))*; Vol. 3. They Gladly Taught Vol 3. 1988. 9.95 *(978-0-8425-2282-3(4))*; (Illus.), Friends of the Library 29.85 *(978-0-8425-2290-8(5))* Brigham Young Univ.

Woodger, Mary Jane & Groberg, Joseph. From the Muddy River to the Ivory Tower: The Journey of George H. Brimhall. 2010. (Illus.). 304p. *(978-0-8425-2765-1(6)*, Brigham Young Univ. Studies) Brigham Young Univ.

BRIGHT, JOHN, 1811-1889

Cash, Bill. John Bright: Statesman, Orator, Agitator. 2011. (ENG., Illus.). 352p. 55.00 ***(978-1-84885-596-8(1))*** I. B. Tauris & Co., Ltd. GBR. Dist: Macmillan.

Robertson, William. Life & Times of the Right Hon John Bri. 2006. pap. 44.95 *(978-1-4286-5449-5(6))* Kessinger Publishing, LLC.

Vince, C. A. John Bright. 2009. 248p. 32.99 *(978-1-115-86742-9(3))*; 28.99 *(978-1-115-86743-6(1))*; pap. 25.75 *(978-1-115-86745-0(8))* BiblioBazaar.

—John Bright. 2007. (ENG.). 244p. 41.95 *(978-0-548-02953-4(9))* Kessinger Publishing, LLC.

BRIGHT CHILDREN

see Gifted Children

BRIGHTNESS (ASTRONOMY)

see Photometry, Astronomical

BRIGHTON (ENGLAND)

Antram, Nicholas, et al. Brighton & Hove. 2008. (Pevsner Architectural Guides). (ENG., Illus.). 256p. pap. 40.00 *(978-0-300-12661-7(1))* Yale Univ. Pr.

Buckley, Adrian. A Murder in Brighton. 2010. (Illus.). 52p. pap. *(978-1-907211-83-6(7))* Grosvenor Hse. Publishing Ltd.

Crisfield, Max & Andrews, Matthew. Brighton & Hove. 2006. (Illus.). 128p. 29.95 *(978-0-7112-2646-3(6))* Lincoln, Frances Ltd. GBR. Dist: Perseus-PGW.

Kraemer-Johnson, Glyn & Bishop, John. Bygone Brighton. 2010. (ENG., Illus.). 80p. 24.95 *(978-0-7110-3279-8(3))* Allan, Ian Publishing GBR. Dist: BookMasters Distribution Services (BDS).

Musgrave, Clifford. Life in Brighton. 2011. (ENG., Illus.). 480p. pap. 29.95 ***(978-0-7524-6047-5(1))*** History Pr. Ltd.,The GBR. Dist: Independent Pubs. Group.

Time Out Guides Staff. Time Out Shortlist Brighton. 2011. (Time Out Shortlist Ser.). (ENG., Illus.). 192p. pap. 12.95 *(978-1-84670-215-0(1))* Time Out Guides Ltd. GBR. Dist: Perseus-PGW.

VisitBritain (Organization) Staff, contrib. by. Brighton Explorer. 2008. (ENG., Illus.). 112p. pap. 7.95 *(978-0-7095-8387-5(7))* VisitBritain GBR. Dist: Globe Pequot Pr., The.

BRIGID, OF IRELAND, SAINT, CA. 453-CA. 524

Bitel, Lisa M. Landscape with Two Saints: How Genovefa of Paris & Brigit of Kildare Built Christianity in Barbarian Europe. 2009. (ENG., Illus.). 336p. 34.95 *(978-0-19-533652-8(6))* Oxford Univ. Pr., Inc.

Meyer, Jane G. The Life of Saint Brigid: Abbess of Kildare. 2009. 32p. (J). pap. 12.95 *(978-0-9822770-0-3(8))* Conciliar Pr.

Wright, Brian. Brigid: Goddess, Druidess & Saint. 2009. (ENG., Illus.). 256p. pap. 32.95 *(978-0-7524-4865-7(X))* History Pr. Ltd.,The GBR. Dist: Independent Pubs. Group.

BRILL'S DISEASE

see Typhus Fever

BRINDLEY, JAMES, 1716-1772

Fisen by Perseverance Lives of SelfMade. 2007. 228p. per. *(978-1-4067-8931-7(3)*, Pomona Pr.) Read Bks.

Smiles, Samuel. Lives of the Engineers Vermuyden Myddelt. 2006. pap. 36.95 *(978-1-4286-5211-8(6))* Kessinger Publishing, LLC.

BRINE

see Salt

BRIQUET'S SYNDROME

see Somatization Disorder

BRISBANE (QLD.)

Carlson, Oliver. Brisbane: A Candid Biography. 384p. 2010. pap. 27.16 *(978-1-163-18239-0(7))* 2008. 48.95 *(978-1-4366-9614-2(3))* 2007. (ENG.). per. 33.95 *(978-1-4325-4227-6(3))* Kessinger Publishing, LLC.

Donald, Darroch. Brisbane & Queensland Footprint Focus. 2012. (Footprint Focus Ser.). (ENG., Illus.). 144p. pap. 12.95 *(978-1-908206-46-6(2))* Footprint Handbooks GBR. Dist: Globe Pequot Pr., The.

Hatherell, William. The Third Metropolis: Imagining Brisbane through Art & Literature 1940 - 1970. 2008. (ENG.). 310p. pap. 36.95 *(978-0-7022-3543-6(1))* Univ. of Queensland Pr. AUS. Dist: Independent Pubs. Group.

BRISSOT DE WARVILLE, JACQUES PIERRE, 1754-1793

Brissot De Warville, Jacques Pierre. New Travels in the United States of America. Performed in 1788. 2007. (Travel in America Ser.). (ENG.). 500p. 49.95 *(978-1-4290-0018-5(X))*; per. 24.95 *(978-1-4290-0019-2(8))* Applewood Bks.

Ellery, Eloise. Brissot de Warville. 2009. 372p. pap. *(978-1-4590-5756-2(2))* Books LLC.

—Brissot de Warville: A Study in the History of the French Revolution. 2010. 554p. pap. 42.75 *(978-1-147-22591-4(5))*; 558p. pap. 42.75 *(978-1-143-53493-5(X))*; 560p. pap. 42.75 *(978-1-144-71034-5(0))* BiblioBazaar.

BRISTOL (ENGLAND)

Arthur, William. The Successful Merchant: Sketches of the Life Mr. Samuel Budgett ... 2006. 340p. per. 23.99 *(978-1-4255-3433-2(3))* MPublishing.

Mowl, Tim & Menneer, Neill. Bristol: City on the Edge. 2007. (Illus.). 128p. 29.95 *(978-0-7112-2570-1(2))* Lincoln, Frances Ltd. GBR. Dist: Perseus-PGW.

BRISTOL (ENGLAND)—DESCRIPTION AND TRAVEL

Foyle, Andrew & Pevsner, Nikolaus. Somerset - North & Bristol. 2011. (Pevsner Architectural Guides). (ENG., Illus.). 800p. 85.00 *(978-0-300-12658-7(1))* Yale Univ. Pr.

Wright, Steve. Banksy's Bristol: Home Sweet Home. 2009. 112p. 24.95 *(978-0-86719-708-2(0))* Last Gasp of San Francisco.

BRISTOL (ENGLAND)—HISTORY

Coles, Sarah. Bristol: A Pocket Miscellany. 2011. (ENG., Illus.). 128p. pap. 14.95 ***(978-0-7524-5976-9(7))*** History Pr. Ltd.,The GBR. Dist: Independent Pubs. Group.

Sly, Nicola. A Grim Almanac of Bristol. 2011. (ENG., Illus.). 192p. pap. 27.95 ***(978-0-7524-5934-9(1))*** History Pr. Ltd.,The GBR. Dist: Independent Pubs. Group.

Wheaton, R. J. Portishead's Dummy. 2011. (33 1/3 Ser.). (ENG., Illus.). 248p. pap. 12.95 *(978-1-4411-9449-7(5))* Continuum International Publishing Group, Ltd. GBR. Dist: National Bk. Network.

BRITAIN, BATTLE OF, GREAT BRITAIN, 1940

Arthur, Max. Last of the Few: The Battle of Britain in the Words of the Pilots Who Won It. 2011. (ENG., Illus.). 304p. 24.95 *(978-1-61608-308-3(5)*, 608308) Skyhorse Publishing Co., Inc.

Barclay, George. Battle of Britain Pilot: Self-Portrait of an RAF Fighter Pilot & Escaper. 2012. (ENG., Illus.). 256p. 40.00 ***(978-0-85733-239-4(2)***, 0857332392) Haynes Publishing PLC GBR. Dist: MBI Distribution Services/Quayside Distribution.

The Battle of Britain. 2011. (ENG., Illus.). 36p. pap. 9.95 *(978-1-4456-0048-2(X))* Amberley Publishing GBR. Dist: Casemate Pubs. & Bk. Distributors, LLC.

Beer, Simon St John. A Salute to One of 'the Few' The Life of Flying Officer Peter Cape Beauchamp St John RAF. 2009. (Illus.). 224p. 39.99 *(978-1-84415-876-8(4))* Pen & Sword Bks. Ltd. GBR. Dist: Casemate Pubs. & Bk. Distributors, LLC.

Birtles, Philip. Battle of Britain Airfields. 2010. (ENG., Illus.). 160p. 32.95 *(978-1-85780-328-0(0))* Midland Publishing Ltd. GBR. Dist: BookMasters Distribution Services (BDS).

Bishop, Patrick. Battle of Britain: A Day-by-Day Chronicle, 10 July 1940 to 31 October 1940. 2009. (ENG., Illus.). 384p. 37.95 *(978-1-84724-984-5(1))* Quercus GBR. Dist: Independent Pubs. Group.

—Battle of Britain: A Day-to-Day Chronicle, 10 July-31 October 1940. 2010. (ENG., Illus.). 542p. pap. 14.95 *(978-1-84916-224-1(7))* Quercus GBR. Dist: Independent Pubs. Group.

—Fighter Boys: The Battle of Britain 1940. 2008. (ENG.). 434p. 27.00 *(978-1-4223-9484-7(0))* DIANE Publishing Co.

Blackah, Paul, et al. Battle of Britain, 3 vols., Set. 2010. (ENG., Illus.). 480p. 90.00 *(978-0-85733-054-3(3)*, 0857330543) Haynes Publishing PLC GBR. Dist: MBI Distribution Services/Quayside Distribution.

Bolitho, Hector & Lack, Katherine. Finest of the Few: The Story of Battle of Britain Fighter Pilot John Simpson. 2011. (ENG., Illus.). 256p. 34.95 *(978-1-4456-0057-4(9))* Amberley Publishing GBR. Dist: Casemate Pubs. & Bk. Distributors, LLC.

Bowyer, Michael. The Battle of Britain: The Fight for Survival in 1940. 2010. (Illus.). 432p. pap. 18.95 *(978-0-85979-147-2(5))* Crecy Publishing GBR. Dist: Crecy Publishing.

Bungay, Stephen. The Most Dangerous Enemy: An Illustrated History of the Battle of Britain. 2010. (ENG., Illus.). 272p. 40.00 *(978-0-7603-3936-7(8)*, 0760339368, Zenith Pr.) MBI Publishing Co. LLC.

—The Most Dangerous Enemy: The Definitive History of the Battle of Britain. 2010. (ENG., Illus.). 512p. pap. 19.95 *(978-1-84513-481-5(8))* Aurum Pr., Ltd. GBR. Dist: Independent Pubs. Group.

Campion, Garry. The Good Fight: Battle of Britain Propaganda & the Few. 2010. (ENG., Illus.). 400p. pap. 37.00 *(978-0-230-27996-4(1))* Palgrave Macmillan.

Darlow, Steve. Five of the Few: Survivors of the Battle of Britain & Blitz tell their Story. 2010. (Illus.). 256p. 18.95 *(978-1-906502-82-9(X))* Grub Street GBR. Dist: Casemate Pubs. & Bk. Distributors, LLC.

Davidson, Martin. Spitfire Pilot. (ENG., Illus.). 256p. 35.00 *(978-0-7522-2511-1(1)*, Boxtree) Pan Macmillan GBR. Dist: Trafalgar Square Publishing.

Dixon, Jack. Dowding & Churchill: The Dark Side of the Battle of Britain. 2009. (Illus.). 320p. 50.00 *(978-1-84415-854-6(3))* Pen & Sword Bks. Ltd. GBR. Dist: Casemate Pubs. & Bk. Distributors, LLC.

Falconer, Jonathan. Life as a Battle of Britain Pilot: 70 Years On. 2010. (ENG.). 96p. pap. 9.95 *(978-0-7524-5788-8(3))* History Pr. Ltd.,The GBR. Dist: Independent Pubs. Group.

Fendrich, Jr. They Did Not Stand Alone: (A Story of God & Man's Role in the Battle of Britain) 2009. 184p. pap. 24.95 *(978-1-60813-270-6(6))* PublishAmerica, Inc.

Fisher, David E. A Summer Bright & Terrible: Winston Churchill, Lord Dowding, Radar, & the Impossible Triumph of the Battle of Britain. 2006. (ENG., Illus.). 304p. per. 16.00 *(978-1-59376-116-5(3))* Counterpoint LLC.

Flintham, K. E. & Moore, Kate. The Battle of Britain. 2010. (General Aviation Ser.). (ENG., Illus.). 200p. 29.95 *(978-1-84603-474-9(4))* Osprey Publishing, Ltd. GBR. Dist: Random Hse., Inc.

Frayn-Turner, John. The Bader Wing. 2007. (Illus.). 153p. 39.95 *(978-1-84415-544-6(7))* Pen & Sword Bks. Ltd. GBR. Dist: Casemate Pubs. & Bk. Distributors, LLC.

Green, Brett. The Luftwaffe in the Battle of Britain 1940, Vol. 1. 2010. (ENG., Illus.). 96p. pap. 27.95 *(978-1-906537-11-1(9))* Classic Pubns. GBR. Dist: BookMasters Distribution Services (BDS).

Hanson, Colin. Why Me? What that long hot summer of 1940 did to Clive Peterson. 2010. 316p. (ENG.). 25.99 *(978-1-4520-0537-9(0))*; pap. 15.49 *(978-1-4520-0536-2(2))* AuthorHouse.

Holland, James. The Battle of Britain: Five Months That Changed History; May—October 1940. 2012. (ENG.). 736p. pap. 21.99 ***(978-1-250-00215-0(X)***, St. Martin's Griffin) St. Martin's Pr.

Holland, James. The Battle of Britain: Five Months That Changed History; May-October 1940. 2011. (ENG., Illus.). 736p. 40.00 *(978-0-312-67500-4(3))* St. Martin's Pr.

Hough, Richard Alexander & Richards, Denis. The Battle of Britain: The Jubilee History. 2008. (Illus.). 420p. pap. 32.35 *(978-1-84415-657-3(5))* Pen & Sword Bks. Ltd. GBR. Dist: Casemate Pubs. & Bk. Distributors, LLC.

Kent, Johnny A. One of the Few: A Triumphant Story of Combat in the Battle of Britain. 2008. (ENG., Illus.). 288p. pap. 23.95 *(978-0-7524-4603-5(7))* History Pr. Ltd.,The GBR. Dist: Independent Pubs. Group.

Korda, Michael. With Wings Like Eagles: A History of the Battle of Britain. 2009. (ENG.). 320p. 25.99 *(978-0-06-112535-5(0))*; 456p. pap. 25.99 *(978-0-06-171971-4(4)*, HarperLuxe) HarperCollins Pubs.

Lambah-Stoate, Edward. Called to Arms: One Family's War, from the Battle of Britain to Burma. 2011. (ENG., Illus.). 224p. pap. 24.95 ***(978-0-7524-5888-5(4))*** History Pr. Ltd.,The GBR. Dist: Independent Pubs. Group.

Lane, Brian. Spitfire! The Experiences of a Battle of Britain Fighter Pilot. 2009. (Illus.). 192p. pap. 19.95 *(978-1-84868-354-9(5))* Amberley Publishing GBR. Dist: Casemate Pubs. & Bk. Distributors, LLC.

MacKenzie, S. P. The Battle of Britain on Screen: 'The Few' in British Film & Television Drama. 2007. (Societies at War Ser.). (ENG., Illus.). 160p. (gr. 17). 90.00 *(978-0-7486-2389-1(2))* Edinburgh Univ. Pr. GBR. Dist: Columbia Univ. Pr.

Mackenzie, S. P. The Battle of Britain on Screen: 'The Few' in British Film & Television Drama. 2007. (Societies at War Ser.). (ENG., Illus.). 160p. (gr. 17). pap. 34.00 *(978-0-7486-2390-7(6))* Edinburgh Univ. Pr. GBR. Dist: Columbia Univ. Pr.

Mosley, Leonard. Battle of Britain. (Illus.) 208p. 24.00 *(978-1-84447-190-4(X))* Time Life Value GBR. Dist: Mercury Bks. Ltd.

Neil, Tom. Gun Button to Fire. 2010. (ENG., Illus.). 320p. 29.95 *(978-1-84868-848-3(2))* Amberley Publishing GBR. Dist: Casemate Pubs. & Bk. Distributors, LLC.

Nesbit, Roy Conyers. The Battle of Britain. 2010. (ENG., Illus.). 272p. pap. 28.95 *(978-0-7524-5652-2(0))* History Pr. Ltd.,The GBR. Dist: Independent Pubs. Group.

North, Richard. The Many Not the Few: The Stolen History of the Battle of Britain. 2012. (ENG.). 456p. 29.95 *(978-1-4411-3151-5(5))* Continuum International Publishing Group, Ltd. GBR. Dist: National Bk. Network.

Orange, Vincent. Dowding of Fighter Command: Victor of the Battle of Britain. 2008. (Illus.). 352p. 45.00 *(978-1-906502-14-0(5))* Grub Street GBR. Dist: Casemate Pubs. & Bk. Distributors, LLC.

Pitchfork, Graham. The Battle of Britain Story. 2010. (Story Ser.). (ENG., Illus.). 128p. 16.95 *(978-0-7524-5682-9(2))* History Pr. Ltd.,The GBR. Dist: Independent Pubs. Group.

Pitchfork, Graham, ed. Battle of Britain. 2010. (Illus.). 272p. pap. 24.95 *(978-1-905615-48-3(5))* National Archives (PRO), The GBR. Dist: International Publishers Marketing.

Price, Alfred. The Hardest Day: The Battle of Britain: 18 August 1940. 2010. (ENG., Illus.). 256p. 34.95 *(978-1-84425-820-8(3)*, 1844258203) Haynes Publishing PLC GBR. Dist: MBI Distribution Services/Quayside Distribution.

Sarkar, Dilip. Duxford 1940. 2009. (Illus.). 192p. pap. 24.95 *(978-1-84868-213-9(1))* Amberley Publishing GBR. Dist: Casemate Pubs. & Bk. Distributors, LLC.

—The Few. 2011. (ENG., Illus.). 320p. pap. 24.95 *(978-1-4456-0050-5(1))* Amberley Publishing GBR. Dist: Casemate Pubs. & Bk. Distributors, LLC.

Sarkar, Dilip. Last of the Few: 18 Battle of Britain Fighter Pilots Tell Their Extraordinary Stories. 2011. (Illus.). 224p. pap. 19.95 ***(978-1-4456-0282-0(2))*** Amberley Publishing GBR. Dist: Casemate Pubs. & Bk. Distributors, LLC.

Sarkar, Dilip & Delaforce, Patrick. How the Spitfire Won the Battle of Britain. 2011. (Illus.). 192p. 29.95 *(978-1-84868-568-1(7))* Amberley Publishing GBR. Dist: Casemate Pubs. & Bk. Distributors, LLC.

Saunders, Andy. Finding the Few: Some Outstanding Mysteries of the Battle of Britain Investigated & Solved. 2009. (Illus.). 192p. 39.95 *(978-1-906502-55-3(2))* Grub Street GBR. Dist: Casemate Pubs. & Bk. Distributors, LLC.

—Finding the Foe: Outstanding Luftwaffe mysteries of the Battle of Britain & beyond investigated & Solved. 2010. (Illus.). 208p. 39.95 *(978-1-906502-85-0(4))* Grub Street GBR. Dist: Casemate Pubs. & Bk. Distributors, LLC.

Storey, Neil. The Battle of Britain. 2012. (Shire Library). (ENG., Illus.). 56p. pap. 12.95 *(978-0-7478-1047-6(8))* Shire Pubns., Ltd. GBR. Dist: Random Hse., Inc.

Sutton, Barry. Fighter Boy. 2010. (ENG., Illus.). 256p. 34.95 *(978-1-84868-849-0(0))* Amberley Publishing GBR. Dist: Casemate Pubs. & Bk. Distributors, LLC.

B

Sutton, Barry. Fighter Boy: Life As a Battle of Britain Pilot. 2nd ed. 2012. (Illus.). 192p. pap. 19.95 ***(978-1-4456-0627-9(5))*** Amberley Publishing GBR. Dist: Casemate Pubs. & Bk. Distributors, LLC.

Taylor, Robert. Robert Taylor's Battle of Britain. 2010. (Illus.). 128p. 34.95 *(978-1-935149-32-3(6))* Casemate Pubs. & Bk. Distributors, LLC.

Thomas, Nick. RAF Top Gun: The Story of Battle of Britain Ace & World Air Speed Holder Air Cdre E. M. "Teddy" Donaldson CB, CBE, DSO, AFC*, LoM (USA) 2008. (Illus.). 256p. 39.95 *(978-1-84415-685-6(0))* Pen & Sword Bks. Ltd. GBR. Dist: Casemate Pubs. & Bk. Distributors, LLC.

Turner, John Frayn. The Battle of Britain. 2010. (Illus.). 256p. pap. 24.95 *(978-1-84884-243-4(0))* Pen & Sword Bks. Ltd. GBR. Dist: Casemate Pubs. & Bk. Distributors, LLC.

Wood, Derek & Dempster, Derek D. Narrow Margin. 2010. (Illus.). 376p. pap. 24.95 *(978-1-84884-314-1(3))* Pen & Sword Bks. Ltd. GBR. Dist: Casemate Pubs. & Bk. Distributors, LLC.

BRITISH

Ben-Srhir, Khalid. Britain & Morocco During the Embassy of John Drummond Hay. 2010. (Illus.). 384p. pap. 39.95 *(978-0-415-58944-4(4))* Routledge.

Bird, Isabella L. My First Travels in North America. 2010. (ENG.). 400p. pap. 14.95 *(978-0-486-47309-3(0))* Dover Pubns., Inc.

Boyes, Roger. To Prussia with Love: Misadventures in Rural East Germany. 2012. (ENG.). 320p. pap. 13.95 ***(978-1-84953-125-2(0))*** Summerdale Pubs. GBR. Dist: Independent Pubs. Group.

Brown, Malcolm. Lawrence of Arabia: The Selected Letters. 2007. (ENG., Illus.). 576p. per. 27.95 *(978-1-904435-74-7(2))* Little Bks., Ltd. GBR. Dist: Independent Pubs. Group.

Burney, James. History of the Buccaneers of America. 2007. (ENG.). 396p. per. 16.75 *(978-1-60206-253-5(6))* Cosimo, Inc.

—History of the Buccaneers of America. 2008. 340p. 46.95 *(978-0-548-93211-7(5))* 2007. (ENG.). 344p. per. 31.95 *(978-0-548-59238-0(1))* Kessinger Publishing, LLC.

Carlson, Jenna K. Culinary Creolization: Subsistence & Cultural Interaction at Fort Michilimackinac, 1730-1761. 2012. pap. ***(978-0-911872-90-3(6))*** Mackinac State Historic Parks.

Colley, Linda. Britons: Forging the Nation, 1707-1837. 3rd rev. ed. 2009. (ENG., Illus.). 469p. pap. 22.00 *(978-0-300-15280-7(9))* Yale Univ. Pr.

Cortazzi, Hugh. Britain & Japan: Biographical Portraits. 2010. (Britain & Japan. Biographical Portraits Ser.). (ENG., Illus.). 700p. *(978-1-906876-26-5(6))* BRILL.

Cross, Anthony. 'by the Banks of the Neva' Chapters from the Lives & Careers of the British in Eighteenth-Century Russia. 2007. (ENG., Illus.). 492p. pap. 90.00 *(978-0-521-03903-1(7))* Cambridge Univ. Pr.

Curry, Ben. Curucucú: The Adventures of a British Ex-Pat in Colombia. 2010. *(978-1-55571-675-2(X),* Hellgate Pr.) L & R Publishing.

Ernst, Waltraud. Mad Tales from the Raj: Colonial Psychiatry in South Asia, 1800-58. 2010. (Anthem South Asian Studies). (ENG., Illus.). 174p. *(978-1-84331-881-1(4))* Anthem Pr.

—Mad Tales from the Raj: Colonial Psychiatry in South Asia, 1800-58. 2010. (Anthem South Asian Studies). (ENG.). 174p. pap. 40.00 *(978-1-84331-868-2(7))* Anthem Pr. GBR. Dist: Books International, Inc.

Hollis, Matthew. Now All Roads Lead to France: A Life of Edward Thomas. 2012. (ENG., Illus.). 416p. 29.95 ***(978-0-393-08907-3(X),*** 8907) Norton, W. W. & Co., Inc.

Langenscheidt. Langenscheidt Pocket Dictionary French: Französisch-Englisch / Englisch-Französisch. 2011. (Langenscheidt Pocket Dictionaries Ser.). (ENG.). 720p. pap. 13.99 *(978-3-468-98134-0(1))* Langenscheidt Publishing Group.

—Langenscheidt Pocket Dictionary Japanese. 2011. (Langenscheidt Pocket Dictionaries Ser.). (ENG.). 672p. pap. 14.99 *(978-3-468-98136-4(8))* Langenscheidt Publishing Group.

MacLeitch, Gail D. Imperial Entanglements: Iroquois Change & Persistence on the Frontiers of Empire. 2011. (Early American Studies). (Illus.). 344p. (C). 45.00 *(978-0-8122-4281-2(5))* Univ. of Pennsylvania Pr.

Mak, Lanver. The British in Egypt: Community, Crime & Crises 1882-1922. 2012. (International Library of Historical Studies). (ENG., Illus.). 320p. 99.00 ***(978-1-84885-709-4(8))*** I. B. Tauris & Co., Ltd. GBR. Dist: Macmillan.

Manning, Jo. My Lady Scandalous: The Amazing Life & Outrageous Times of Grace Dal. 2010. (ENG.). 432p. pap. 25.99 *(978-1-4516-1354-4(7))* Simon & Schuster.

Morgan, M. J. Land of Big Rivers: French & Indian Illinois, 1699-1778. 2010. (ENG., Illus.). 304p. pap. 24.95 *(978-0-8093-2988-5(3))* Southern Illinois Univ. Pr.

Parfitt, Tim. A Load of Bull: An Englishman's Adventures in Madrid. 2008. (ENG.). 288p. 14.95 *(978-1-4050-4620-6(1))* Macmillan Pubs., Ltd. GBR. Dist: Independent Pubs. Group.

Schulting, Sabine, et al. Early Modern Encounters with the Islamic East: Performing Cultures. 2012. (Transculturalisms, 1400ndash;1700 Ser.). (Illus.). 200p. 99.95 ***(978-1-4094-3850-2(3))*** Ashgate Publishing Co.

Watson, William. The Adventures of a Blockade Runner: Trade in Time of War. 324p. reprint ed. 98.00 *(978-0-7222-8215-1(X))* Library Reprints, Inc.

Won-Oh, Choi. An Illustrated Guide to Korean Mythology, Vol. VI. 2007. (Illus.). 317p. *(978-1-905246-60-1(9))* BRILL.

BRITISH—EMPLOYMENT

Ashish, Meera. Live & Work in Dubai: Comprehensive, Up-to-Date, Practical Information about Everyday Life. 2010. (ENG., Illus.). 309p. pap. 34.00 *(978-1-84528-353-7(8))* How To Books GBR. Dist: Parkwest Pubns., Inc.

Blythe, Derek. Live & Work in Brussels. 2008. (Live & Work - Vacation Work Publications). (ENG., Illus.). 320p. pap. 24.95 *(978-1-85458-383-3(2))* Crimson Publishing, Ltd. GBR. Dist: National Bk. Network.

Collins, M. Getting into Australia 3e. 3rd ed. 2008. 194p. pap. 20.00 *(978-1-84528-170-0(5))* How To Books GBR. Dist: Parkwest Pubns., Inc.

Collins Publishers Staff & Neilson, Jeff. Going to Live in New Zealand. 2nd ed. 2008. (Illus.). 224p. 26.00 *(978-1-84528-274-5(4))* How To Books GBR. Dist: Parkwest Pubns., Inc.

Crimson Publishing Staff. Live & Work in India. 2007. (Live & Work - Vacation Work Publications). (Illus.). 320p. pap. 21.95 *(978-1-85458-385-7(9))* Crimson Publishing, Ltd. GBR. Dist: National Bk. Network.

Duman, Roberta. A City by City Guide to Living & Working in Australia. 2006. (Illus.). 274p. per. 26.00 *(978-1-84528-089-5(X))* Parkwest Pubns., Inc.

Explorer Publishing. Abu Dhabi. 8th rev. ed. 2011. (Explorer - Residents' Guides). (ENG., Illus.). 430p. pap. 24.95 ***(978-9948-442-67-7(9))*** Explorer Publishing UAE. Dist: Globe Pequot Pr., The.

Forrester-Atligan, Robbi. Living & Working in Italy, 4th Edition: A Survival Handbook. 4th ed. 2011. (ENG., Illus.). 400p. pap. 25.95 *(978-1-907339-30-1(2))* Survival Bks., Ltd.

Francis, Huw. Living & Working in Turkey. 2009. (Illus.). 170p. 26.00 *(978-1-84528-245-5(0))* How To Books GBR. Dist: Parkwest Pubns., Inc.

Gerrard, Valerie. Getting a Job in Canada. 5th ed. 2006. (Illus.). 243p. per. 22.00 *(978-1-84528-121-2(7))* How To Books GBR. Dist: Parkwest Pubns., Inc.

Griffith, Susan. Summer Jobs Worldwide 2011: Make the Most of the Summer Break. 42nd rev. ed. 2010. (ENG., Illus.). 368p. pap. 21.95 *(978-1-85458-565-3(7))* Crimson Publishing, Ltd. GBR. Dist: National Bk. Network.

Hampshire, David. Living & Working in Australia: A Survival Handbook. 7th ed. 2011. (ENG., Illus.). 400p. pap. 25.95 *(978-1-907339-25-7(6))* Survival Bks., Ltd.

—Living & Working in New Zealand: A Survival Handbook. 5th rev. ed. 2009. (ENG., Illus.). 304p. pap., instr.'s hndbk. ed. 25.95 *(978-1-905303-76-2(9))* Survival Bks., Ltd.

Hampshire, David & Jennings, Sally. Canada. 4th rev. ed. 2009. (ENG., Illus.). 352p. pap., instr.'s hndbk. ed. 25.95 *(978-1-905303-64-9(5))* Survival Bks., Ltd.

Hampshire, David. Living & Working in America, 7th Edition: A Survival Handbook. 7th ed. 2008. (ENG., Illus.). 480p. pap. 25.95 *(978-1-905303-63-2(7))* Survival Bks., Ltd.

Hart, Alan. Going to Live in France 3e. 3rd ed. 2009. (Illus.). 276p. 26.00 *(978-1-84528-219-6(1))* How To Books GBR. Dist: Parkwest Pubns., Inc.

Hobbs, Guy. Jobs & Careers Abroad. 13th ed. 2006. (Directory of Jobs & Careers Abroad Ser.). 444p. per. 21.95 *(978-1-85458-353-6(0),* Vacation Work Pubns.) Crimson Publishing, Ltd. GBR. Dist: National Bk. Network.

Hunt, Deborah. How to Start & Run a BB in Franc. 2nd ed. 2009. (Illus.). 224p. 30.00 *(978-1-84528-272-1(8))* How To Books GBR. Dist: Parkwest Pubns., Inc.

Kelly, Susan. Live & Work in New Zealand. 5th ed. 2008. (ENG., Illus.). 320p. pap. 24.95 *(978-1-85458-392-5(1))* Crimson Publishing, Ltd. GBR. Dist: National Bk. Network.

King, Harry. Spain: Your Guide to a New Life. 2006. (Illus.). 306p. per. 26.00 *(978-1-84528-094-9(6))* Parkwest Pubns., Inc.

Kranc, Benjamin A. & Roman, Karina. Live & Work in Canada: Comprehensive, Up-to-Date, Practical Information about Everyday Life. 4th ed. 2010. (ENG., Illus.). 180p. pap. 22.00 *(978-1-84528-338-4(4))* How To Books GBR. Dist: Parkwest Pubns., Inc.

Laredo, Joe. Living & Working in Ireland: A Survival Handbook. 3rd rev. ed. 2009. (ENG., Illus.). 480p. pap. 25.95 *(978-1-905303-71-7(8))* Survival Bks., Ltd.

Lemon, Frances & Penrith, Deborah. Canada: The Most Accurate, Practical & Comprehensive Guide to Living & Working in Canada. 5th ed. 2009. (ENG., Illus.). 352p. pap. 24.95 *(978-1-85458-427-4(8))* Crimson Publishing, Ltd. GBR. Dist: National Bk. Network.

Mills, Steve. Live & Work in America 7e. 7th ed. 2009. (Illus.). 320p. 26.00 *(978-1-84528-359-9(7))* How To Books GBR. Dist: Parkwest Pubns., Inc.

Neilson, Jeff & Collins Publishers Staff. Going to Live in Australia. 2nd ed. 2008. (Illus.). 258p. 22.00 *(978-1-84528-261-5(2))* How To Books GBR. Dist: Parkwest Pubns., Inc.

Penrith, Deborah. Australia. 5th ed. 2008. (ENG., Illus.). 320p. pap. 24.95 *(978-1-85458-418-2(9))* Crimson Publishing, Ltd. GBR. Dist: National Bk. Network.

Penrith, Deborah & Turner, Eleanor C. USA: The Most Accurate, Practical & Comprehensive Guide to Living & Working in the United States. 5th ed. 2009. (ENG., Illus.). 416p. pap. 24.95 *(978-1-85458-428-1(6))* Crimson Publishing, Ltd. GBR. Dist: National Bk. Network.

Pybus, Victoria. France. 6th ed. 2008. (ENG., Illus.). 416p. pap. 24.95 *(978-1-85458-419-9(7))* Crimson Publishing, Ltd. GBR. Dist: National Bk. Network.

—Working in Ski Resorts: Europe & North America. 6th ed. 2007. (Working in Ski Resorts: Europe & North America Ser.). (Illus.). 344p. per. 19.95 *(978-1-85458-355-0(7),* Vacation Work Pubns.) Crimson Publishing, Ltd. GBR. Dist: National Bk. Network.

Reuvid, Jonathan. Working Abroad: The Complete Guide to Overseas Employment. 28th rev. ed. 2007. 320p. pap. *(978-0-7494-4951-3(9))* Kogan Page, Ltd.

Reynolds, Peter. Going to Live in Greece 5e. 5th ed. 2009. (Illus.). 260p. 22.00 *(978-1-84528-290-5(6))* How To Books GBR. Dist: Parkwest Pubns., Inc.

Storey, Romasa. Going to Live in Brazil. 2009. (Illus.). 192p. pap. 26.00 *(978-1-84528-310-0(4))* How To Books GBR. Dist: Parkwest Pubns., Inc.

Veltman, Laura. Living & Working in Australia: All You Need to Know for Starting a New Life 'down Under' 9th ed. 2007. 430p. pap. 26.00 *(978-1-84528-183-0(7))* Parkwest Pubns., Inc.

Wilson, Pamela, ed. Living & Working in Germany: A Survival Handbook. 4th ed. 2011. (ENG., Illus.). 368p. pap. 25.95 *(978-1-907339-36-3(1))* Survival Bks., Ltd.

Woods, Sarah & Hardy, Felice. Dubai. 2009. (ENG., Illus.). 208p. pap. 19.95 *(978-1-86011-416-8(4))* Cadogan Guides GBR. Dist: Interlink Publishing Group, Inc.

Wright, Rachel. Live & Work in Hong Kong: Comprehensive, Up-to-Date, Practical Information about Everyday Life. 3rd rev. ed. 2011. (ENG., Illus.). 300p. pap. 30.00 *(978-1-84528-429-9(1))* How To Books GBR. Dist: Parkwest Pubns., Inc.

—Living & Working in Hong Kong: The Complete Practical Guide to Expatriate Life in China's Gateway. 2nd ed. 2008. (Illus.). 300p. *(978-1-84528-195-3(0))* How To Books.

BRITISH—AFRICA

Cecil, Veronica. Bongo Bongo Bongo: I Don't Want to Leave the Congo. 2010. 256p. pap. 22.95 *(978-0-7957-0282-2(5))* International Publishers Marketing.

Codrington, Tessa. Spirits of Tangier. 2008. (ENG., Illus.). 360p. pap. 49.95 *(978-1-905147-84-7(8))* Arcadia Bks. Ltd. GBR. Dist: Dufour Editions, Inc.

Denson, Francis R. Abroad in Lesotho. 2010. (Illus.). 135p. pap. *(978-1-907629-06-8(6))* ShieldCrest.

Eshun, Ekow. Black Gold of the Sun: Searching for Home in Africa & Beyond. 2007. (Vintage Ser.). (ENG., Illus.). 240p. pap. 13.95 *(978-0-307-27578-3(7),* Vintage) Knopf Doubleday Publishing Group.

Fuller, Alexandra. Cocktail Hour under the Tree of Forgetfulness. 2012. (ENG.). 256p. (gr. 12). pap. 15.00 ***(978-0-14-312134-3(0),*** Penguin (Non-Classics)) 2011. (ENG.). 256p. (gr. 12). 25.95 *(978-1-59420-299-5(0),* Penguin Pr. HC, The) 2011. (Illus.). 238p. ***(978-1-59420-316-9(4),*** Penguin Pr. HC, The) Penguin Group (USA) Inc.

—Cocktail Hour under the Tree of Forgetfulness. 2011. (Illus.). 361p. ***(978-1-4458-5920-0(3))*** 2011. (Illus.). 361p. ***(978-1-4458-5921-7(1))*** 2012. (ENG.). 360p. pap. 16.99 ***(978-1-59413-545-3(2),*** Large Print Pr.) 2011. (Illus.). 360p. 32.99 ***(978-1-4104-3941-3(0))*** Thorndike Pr.

Fuller, Alexandra. Don't Let's Go to the Dogs Tonight. l.t. ed. 2011. lib. bdg. 33.95 *(978-1-61173-112-5(7))* Ctr. Point Large Print.

Jeal, Tim. Explorers of the Nile: The Triumph & the Tragedy of a Great Victorian Adventure. 2011. (Illus.). 528p. 32.50 *(978-0-300-14935-7(2))* Yale Univ. Pr.

Johnston, Carolyn. Harmattan, a Wind of Change: Life & Letters from Northern Nigeria at the End of Empire. 2010. (ENG., Illus.). 304p. 55.00 *(978-1-84885-143-6(X),* Radcliffe Pr., The) I. B. Tauris & Co., Ltd. GBR. Dist: Macmillan.

Lewis, Simon. British & African Literature in Transnational Context: Beyond Writing Back. 2011. (ENG., Illus.). 256p. 74.95 *(978-0-8130-3602-1(X))* Univ. Pr. of Florida.

Lock, Ron. Zulu Conquered: The March of the Red Soldiers, 1822-1888. 2010. (Illus.). 256p. 39.95 *(978-1-84832-564-7(9),* Frontline) Pen & Sword Bks. Ltd. GBR. Dist: Casemate Pubs. & Bk. Distributors, LLC.

Ochonu, Moses E. Colonial Meltdown: Northern Nigeria in the Great Depression. 2009. (New African Histories Ser.). (ENG., Illus.). 272p. 55.00 *(978-0-8214-1889-5(0));* pap. 24.95 *(978-0-8214-1890-1(4))* Ohio Univ. Pr.

Price, Richard. Making Empire: Colonial Encounters & the Creation of Imperial Rule in Nineteenth-Century Africa. 2008. (ENG., Illus.). 402p. pap. 35.99 *(978-0-521-71819-6(8))* Cambridge Univ. Pr.

Rogers, G. V. Over My Shoulder. 2007. (Illus.). 140p. per. *(978-1-84748-197-9(3))* Athena Pr.

Spicer, Paul. The Temptress: The Scandalous Life of Alice de Janze & the Mysterious Death of Lord Erroll. 2011. (ENG., Illus.). 272p. pap. 14.99 *(978-0-312-58418-4(0),* St. Martin's Griffin) St. Martin's Pr.

St Aubin De Teran, Lisa. Mozambique Mysteries. 2009. (ENG., Illus.). 384p. *(978-1-84408-300-8(4),* Virago Press) Little, Brown Bk. Group Ltd. GBR. Dist: Independent Pubs. Group.

Watt, Julie. Poisoned Lives: The Regency Poet Letitia Elizabeth Landon (L. E. L.) & British Gold Coast Administrator George Maclean. 2010. (ENG., Illus.). 300p. 74.95 *(978-1-84519-420-8(9))* Sussex Academic Pr. GBR. Dist: International Specialized Bk. Services.

Wheeler, Sara. Too Close to the Sun: The Audacious Life & Times of Denys Finch Hatton. 2009. (ENG., Illus.). 336p. pap. 18.00 *(978-0-8129-6892-7(1),* Random Hse. Trade Paperbacks) Random House Publishing Group.

Wills, Walter. AngloAfrican Whos Who & Biographical S. 2006. (Illus.). 492p. per. *(978-0-9553936-3-1(9))* Jeppestown Pr.

BRITISH—AMERICA

Beasley, Nicholas M. Christian Ritual & the Creation of British Slave Societies, 1650-1780. (Race in the Atlantic World, 1700-1900 Ser.). (ENG., Illus.). 240p. 2010. pap. 24.95 *(978-0-8203-3645-9(9))* 2009. lib. bdg. 44.95 *(978-0-8203-3339-7(5))* Univ. of Georgia Pr.

Benton, Obie Folsom. Journey of a Pilgrim Family: The Bentons Come to America: With an Autobiography of Obie Folsom Benton. 2010. vi, 301p. ***(978-0-9741186-8-0(0))*** AAA-Writer's Inkhorn.

Breslin, Thomas A. The Great Anglo-Celtic Divide in the History of American Foreign Relations. 2011. E-Book ***(978-0-313-39794-3(5))***; 411p. 58.00 ***(978-0-313-39793-6(7),*** A3601C) ABC-CLIO, LLC.

Finch, Martha L. Dissenting Bodies: Corporealities in Early New England. 2009. (ENG., Illus.). 296p. (gr. 17). 45.00 *(978-0-231-13946-5(2))* Columbia Univ. Pr.

Gerber, David. Authors of Their Lives: The Personal Correspondence of British Immigrants to North America in the Nineteenth Century. 2008. (ENG.). 432p. pap. 26.00 *(978-0-8147-3200-7(3))* New York Univ. Pr.

Goodwin, Maud W. Dutch & English on the Hudson: A Chronicle of Colonial New York. 243p. reprint ed. 98.00 *(978-0-7222-6621-2(9))*; 98.00 *(978-0-7222-7108-7(5))* Library Reprints, Inc.

Graham-Yooll, Andrew. Goodbye Buenos Aires. 2012. (ENG.). 222p. pap. 29.95 ***(978-1-906011-70-3(2))*** Eland Bks. GBR. Dist: Dufour Editions, Inc.

Haliburton, Thomas Chandler. The English in America, 2 vols. reprint ed. 60.00 *(978-0-404-13720-5(2))* AMS Pr., Inc.

—The English in America. 2008. 376p. 29.99 *(978-0-559-61762-1(3))*; pap. 31.75 *(978-0-559-61760-7(7))* BiblioBazaar.

Hatton, Joseph. Henry Irving's Impressions of America: Narrated in a Series of Sketches, Chronicles, & Conversations. 2007. (Travel in America Ser.). (ENG.). 496p. 49.95 *(978-1-4290-0456-5(8))*; per. 24.95 *(978-1-4290-0457-2(6))* Applewood Bks.

Johnston, Mary. Pioneers of the Old South: A Chronicle of English Colonial Beginnings. 2007. 136p. per. *(978-1-4065-3526-6(5))* Dodo Pr.

Kellogg, Louise P. The British Regime in Wisconsin & the Northwest. 361p. reprint ed. lib. bdg. 98.00 *(978-0-7222-0459-7(0))* Library Reprints, Inc.

Newsome, A. R., ed. Records of Emigrants from England & Scotland to North Carolina: 1774-1775. 2007. 39p. pap. 5.00 *(978-0-86526-327-7(2))* North Carolina Office of Archives & History.

Paine, Thomas, et al. Common Sense, a Summary View of the Rights of British America, Thoughts on Government & the Speeches of Washington: Important Early American Politic. 2010. 116p. pap. 9.95 *(978-0-9826624-0-3(8))* Limitless Pr. LLC.

Pope, Dudley. The Black Ship. 2009. (Illus.). 368p. pap. 25.99 *(978-1-84415-893-5(4))* Pen & Sword Bks. Ltd. GBR. Dist: Casemate Pubs. & Bk. Distributors, LLC.

Powell, Lawrence N. The Accidental City: Improvising New Orleans. 2012. (ENG., Illus.). 448p. 29.95 ***(978-0-674-05987-0(5))*** Harvard Univ. Pr.

Stoddard, Grant. Working Stiff: The Misadventures of an Accidental Sexpert. 2007. (P. S. Ser.). (Illus.). 304p. pap. 13.95 *(978-0-06-087612-8(3),* HarperPerennial) HarperCollins Pubs.

Yearley, Clifton K. Britons in American Labor: A History of the Influence of the United Kingdom Immigrants on American Labor, 1820-1914. (Johns Hopkins University, Studies in the Social Sciences, Seventy-Fifth Ser.: No. 1). reprint ed. 24.50 *(978-0-404-61329-7(2))* AMS Pr., Inc.

BRITISH—ASIA

Cross, J. P. The Call of Nepal: My Life in the Himalayan Homeland of Britain's Gurkha Soldiers. 2009. 496p. pap. 29.95 *(978-1-934840-78-8(5))* Nimble Bks. LLC.

Eade, Philip. Sylvia, Queen of the Headhunters: An Outrageous Englishwoman & Her Lost Kingdom. 2008. (ENG., Illus.). 408p. pap. 17.95 *(978-0-7538-2381-1(0))* Orion Publishing Group, Ltd. GBR. Dist: Independent Pubs. Group.

Hembry, Boris. Malayan Spymaster: Memoirs of a Rubber Planter, Bandit Fighter & Spy. 2012. (ENG., Illus.). 424p. pap. 15.95 ***(978-981-08-5442-3(0))*** Monsoon Bks. Pte. Ltd.

Hill, Samuel C. Bengal in Seventeen Fifty-Six to Seventeen Fifty-Seven: A Selection of Public & Private Papers Dealing with the Affairs of the British in Bengal During the Reign of Siraj-Uddaula, 3 vols. reprint ed. 195.00 *(978-0-404-03310-1(5))* AMS Pr., Inc.

Jarman, Robert L. Shanghai Political & Economic Reports, 1842-1943: British Government Records from the International City, 18 vols. 2008. (ENG., Illus.). 13500p. 9095.00 *(978-1-84097-210-8(6))* Archive Editions, Ltd. GBR. Dist: Cambridge Univ. Pr.

Knowles-Samarraie, Pauline. I Never Said Goodbye: A Mother's Memoir of Love & Brutal Loss Inside Saddam's Regime. 2007. (ENG., Illus.). 264p. 29.95 *(978-0-233-00211-8(1))* Andre Deutsch GBR. Dist: Independent Pubs. Group.

Laisram. The Islamic Orient. 2006. 248p. 110.00 *(978-0-415-40115-9(1))* Routledge.

Leonowens, Anna. The English Governess at the Siamese Court. 2010. (ENG.). 371p. pap. 23.95 *(978-1-4290-4014-3(9))* Applewood Bks.

Leonowens, Anna Harriette. The English Governess at the Siamese Court: Being Recollections of Six Years in the Royal Palace at Bangkok. 2007. (ENG.). 272p. pap. 21.99 *(978-1-4264-3165-4(1))* BiblioBazaar.

—The English Governess at the Siamese Court (large Print Edition) Being Recollections of Six Years in the Royal Palace at Bangkok. l.t. ed. 2007. (ENG.). 298p. pap. 23.99 *(978-1-4264-3258-3(5))* BiblioBazaar.

Loyn, David. In Afghanistan: Two Hundred Years of British, Russian & American Occupation. 2009. (ENG.). 288p. 27.95 *(978-0-230-61403-1(5))* Palgrave Macmillan.

Morgan, Susan. Bombay Anna: The Real Story & Remarkable Adventures of the King & I Governess. 2009. (ENG., Illus.). 296p. pap. 19.95 *(978-0-520-26163-1(1))* Univ. of California Pr.

Rundall, Thomas, ed. Memorials of the Empire of Japon: In the XVI & XVII Centuries. 2010. (Cambridge Library Collection - Travel & Exploration Ser.). (ENG., Illus.). 248p. pap. 24.00 *(978-1-108-00805-1(4))* Cambridge Univ. Pr.

Shennan, Margaret. Cut in the Midday Sun: The British in Malaya, 1880-1960. (Illus.). 45.00 *(978-0-7195-5716-3(X))* Murray, John GBR. Dist: Trafalgar Square Publishing.

Slugett, Peter. Britain in Iraq: Contriving King & Country. 2007. (ENG.). 296p. (gr. 17). 80.00 *(978-0-231-14200-7(5))*; (Illus.). pap. 27.00 *(978-0-231-14201-4(3))* Columbia Univ. Pr.

Spowers, Rory. A Year in Green Tea & Tuk-Tuks: My Unlikely Adventure Creating an Eco Farm in Sri Lanka. 2010. (ENG., Illus.). 320p. pap. 19.95 ***(978-0-00-723309-0(4))*** HarperCollins Pubs. Ltd. GBR. Dist: Independent Pubs. Group.

Thorp, Michael. Elephants, Tigers & Tappers. 2010. (Illus.). 221p. pap. *(978-981-261-745-0(9))* Marshall Cavendish.

Waddell, Laurence. Lhasa & Its Mysteries: With a Record of the Expedition Of 1903-1904. 2007. 740p. per. 32.95 *(978-1-60206-724-0(4))* Cosimo, Inc.

White, Randy Wayne. Hunter's Moon. Lt. ed. 2007. (Doc Ford Ser.: No. 14). 334p. 31.95 *(978-1-58547-935-6(3))* Ctr. Point Large Print.

—Hunter's Moon, 14 vols. 2008. (Doc Ford Ser.: No. 14). (ENG., Illus.). 352p. (gr. 12-18). pap. 9.99 *(978-0-425-22037-5(0), Berkley)* Penguin Group (USA) Inc.

Williams, Sebastian. Send Them to Hell: The Brutal Horrors of Bangkok's Nightmare Jails. 2009. (ENG., Illus.). 301p. 17.95 *(978-1-84018-991-9(6))* Mainstream Publishing Co., Ltd. GBR. Dist: Independent Pubs. Group.

BRITISH—AUSTRALIA

Duman, Roberta. A City by City Guide to Living & Working in Australia. 2006. (Illus.). 274p. per. 26.00 *(978-1-84528-089-5(X))* Parkwest Pubns., Inc.

Hampshire, David. Living & Working in Australia: A Survival Handbook. 7th ed. 2011. (ENG., Illus.). 400p. pap. 25.95 *(978-1-907339-25-7(6))* Survival Bks., Ltd.

Leed, Ida. The Coming of the British to Australia, 1788-1829. 2007. (Illus.). 370p. reprint ed. pap. 34.95 *(978-1-60105-129-5(8), 6D7D)* Scholar's Bookshelf.

Myers, Janet. Antipodal England: Emigration & Portable Domesticity in the Victorian Imagination. 2011. (Illus.). 185p. pap. 23.95 ***(978-1-4384-2714-0(X)***, Suny Pr.) State Univ. of New York Pr.

Neilson, Jeff & Collins Publishers Staff. Going to Live in Australia. 2nd ed. 2008. (Illus.). 258p. 22.00 *(978-1-84528-261-5(2))* How To Books GBR. Dist: Parkwest Pubns., Inc.

Penrith, Deborah. Australia. 5th ed. 2008. (ENG., Illus.). 320p. pap. 24.95 *(978-1-85458-418-2(9))* Crimson Publishing, Ltd. GBR. Dist: National Bk. Network.

Thomson, Alistair. Moving Stories: Migrant Women's Lives & Letters,Britain & Australia 1930-2005. 2011. (ENG., Illus.). 352p. 36.95 *(978-0-7190-7646-6(3))* Manchester Univ. Pr. GBR. Dist: Macmillan.

Veltman, Laura. Living & Working in Australia: All You Need to Know for Starting a New Life 'down Under' 9th ed. 2007. 430p. pap. 26.00 *(978-1-84528-183-0(7))* Parkwest Pubns., Inc.

Wright, Christine. Wellington's Men in Australia: Peninsular War Veterans & the Making of Empire C. 1820-40. 2011. (War, Culture & Society, 1750-1850 Ser.). (ENG., Illus.). 256p. 85.00 *(978-0-230-25230-1(3))* Palgrave Macmillan.

BRITISH—CANADA

Campey, Lucille H. Seeking a Better Future: The English Pioneers of Ontario & Quebec. 2012. (English in Canada Ser.). (ENG., Illus.). 472p. pap. 35.00 ***(978-1-4597-0351-3(0))*** Dundurn CAN. Dist: Ingram Pub. Services.

Christie, Nancy, ed. Transatlantic Subjects: Ideas, Institutions, & Social Experience in Post-Revolutionary British North America. 2008. (ENG., Illus.). 496p. (C). *(978-0-7735-3334-9(6))* McGill-Queen's Univ. Pr.

Gerber, David. Authors of Their Lives: The Personal Correspondence of British Immigrants to North America in the Nineteenth Century. 2008. (ENG.). 432p. pap. 26.00 *(978-0-8147-3200-7(3))* New York Univ. Pr.

Gerrard, Valerie. Getting a Job in Canada. 5th ed. 2006. (Illus.). 243p. per. 22.00 *(978-1-84528-121-2(7))* How To Books GBR. Dist: Parkwest Pubns., Inc.

Hampshire, David & Jennings, Sally. Canada. 4th rev. ed. 2009. (ENG., Illus.). 352p. pap., instr.'s hndbk. ed. 25.95 *(978-1-905303-64-9(5))* Survival Bks., Ltd.

Jarratt, Melynda. War Brides: The Stories of the Women Who Left Everything Behind to Follow the Men They Loved. 2009. (ENG., Illus.). 288p. pap. 28.00 *(978-1-55488-386-6(5), Dundurn Pr.)* Dundurn CAN. Dist: Ingram Pub. Services.

Lemon, Frances & Penrith, Deborah. Canada: The Most Accurate, Practical & Comprehensive Guide to Living & Working in Canada. 5th ed. 2009. (ENG., Illus.). 352p. pap. 24.95 *(978-1-85458-427-4(8))* Crimson Publishing, Ltd. GBR. Dist: National Bk. Network.

Parker, Roy. Uprooted: The Shipment of Poor Children to Canada, 1867-1917. 2010. (Illus.). 376p. pap. 34.95 *(978-1-84742-668-0(9))* Policy Pr. GBR. Dist: Chicago Distribution Ctr.

Salusbury, John & Rompkey, Ronald. Expeditions of Honour: The Journal of John Salusbury in Halifax, Nova Scotia, 1749-53. 2011. (ENG., Illus.). 222p. (C). *(978-0-7735-3869-6(0))* McGill-Queen's Univ. Pr.

BRITISH—EUROPE

Beckford, William. Recollections of an Excursion to the Monasteries of Alcobaça & Batalha. 2009. 86p. pap. 14.14 *(978-0-217-74830-8(9))* General Bks. LLC.

Bending, Stephen & Bygrave, Stephen, eds. Women's Travel Writings in Revolutionary France, Part I, 3 vols., Vols. 1-3. 2007. (Chawton House Library: Women's Travel Writings). (ENG.). 1008p. 495.00 *(978-1-85196-862-5(8))* Pickering & Chatto Pubs., Ltd. GBR. Dist: Ashgate Publishing Co.

—Women's Travel Writings in Revolutionary France, Part II, 4 vols., Vols. 4-7. 2008. (Chawton House Library). (ENG.). 2064p. 625.00 *(978-1-85196-866-4(0))* Pickering & Chatto Pubs., Ltd. GBR. Dist: Ashgate Publishing Co.

Black, Jeremy. The British & the Grand Tour (Routledge Revivals) 2010. (Routledge Revivals Ser.). 288p. 115.00 *(978-0-415-60976-0(3))* Routledge.

Brady, M. Michael. France: A Handbook for New Residents. 2007. (Illus.). 569p. pap. 30.00 *(978-1-84528-132-8(2))* How To Books GBR. Dist: Parkwest Pubns., Inc.

Calder, Martin. A Summer in Gascony: Discovering the Other South of France. 2008. (ENG., Illus.). 256p. pap. 19.95 *(978-1-85788-506-4(6))* Ebsco Publishing.

Clarkson, Wensley. Costa Del Crime. 2006. (Illus.). 288p. pap. 14.95 *(978-1-84454-257-4(2))* Blake, John, Publishing, Ltd. GBR. Dist: Independent Pubs. Group.

Davey, Charles. Going to Live on the French Riviera. 2006. (Illus.). 206p. per. 26.00 *(978-1-84528-118-2(7))* How To Books GBR. Dist: Parkwest Pubns., Inc.

Dear, Helen Alice. My Family Is All I Have: A British Woman's Story of Escaping the Nazis & Surviving the Communists. 2007. (ENG.). 320p. pap. 13.95 *(978-0-09-191223-9(7))* Ebury Publishing GBR. Dist: Independent Pubs. Group.

Francis, Matthew. Ruskie: Beers, Bears & Babushkas. 2011. 268p. pap. 17.09 ***(978-1-4567-8177-4(4))*** AuthorHouse.

Ghiringhelli, Peter. A British Boy in Fascist Italy. 2010. (ENG., Illus.). 192p. pap. 23.95 *(978-0-7524-5343-9(2))* History Pr. Ltd.,The GBR. Dist: Independent Pubs. Group.

Hampshire, David. Retiring in France. 2nd rev. ed. 2008. (ENG., Illus.). 336p. pap. 22.95 *(978-1-905303-61-8(0))* Survival Bks., Ltd.

Harrison, Mark. I Want to Live in Spain. 2007. 256p. per. *(978-1-905796-07-6(2))* Boho Pr., The.

Hunt, Deborah. How to Start & Run a BB in Franc. 2nd ed. 2009. (Illus.). 224p. 30.00 *(978-1-84528-272-1(8))* How To Books GBR. Dist: Parkwest Pubns., Inc.

King, Harry. Spain: Your Guide to a New Life. 2006. (Illus.). 306p. per. 26.00 *(978-1-84528-094-9(6))* Parkwest Pubns., Inc.

Lee, Laurie. As I Walked Out One Midsummer Morning. 2011. 192p. pap. 15.95 *(978-1-56792-392-6(5), Non Pareil Bks.)* Godine, David R. Pub.

Limon, Jerzy. Gentlemen of a Company: English Players in Central & Eastern Europe, 1590-1660. 2009. (ENG., Illus.). 204p. pap. 33.99 *(978-0-521-11509-4(4))* Cambridge Univ. Pr.

Mansfield-Devine, Patricia. Living in France. 2008. (ENG., Illus.). 304p. pap. 25.95 *(978-1-897597-92-7(4))* Harriman Hse. Publishing GBR. Dist: Ingram Pub. Services.

Matthews, Owen. Stalin's Children: Three Generations of Love, War, & Survival. 2009. (ENG., Illus.). 320p. pap. 16.00 *(978-0-8027-1760-3(8))* Walker & Co.

Munson, James & Mullen, Richard. The Smell of the Continent: The British Discover Europe. 2010. (ENG., Illus.). 400p. pap. 13.95 *(978-0-330-44873-4(0))* Macmillan Pubs., Ltd. GBR. Dist: Independent Pubs. Group.

Phipps, Eric & Johnson, Gaynor. Our Man in Berlin: The Diary of Sir Eric Phipps, 1933-1937. 2008. (ENG., Illus.). 320p. 89.00 *(978-0-230-51787-5(0))* Palgrave Macmillan.

Reynolds, Peter. Going to Live in Greece 5e. 5th ed. 2009. (Illus.). 260p. 22.00 *(978-1-84528-290-5(6))* How To Books GBR. Dist: Parkwest Pubns., Inc.

Sanderson, Catherine. Petite Anglaise. 2009. (ENG.). 352p. pap. 15.00 *(978-0-385-52281-6(9))* Spiegel & Grau.

Schoina, Maria. Romantic Anglo-Italians' Configurations of Identity in Byron, the Shelleys, & the Pisan Circle. 2009. (Nineteenth Century Ser.). (Illus.). 202p. 99.95 *(978-0-7546-6292-1(6))* Ashgate Publishing Co.

Souhami, Diana. Edith Cavell. 2010. (Illus.). 432p. *(978-1-84916-359-0(6), Quercus)* Quercus.

Styles, Joanna. Retiring in Spain: A Survival Handbook. 2006. (ENG., Illus.). 300p. per. 19.95 *(978-1-901130-73-7(8))* Survival Bks., Ltd.

Todd, Jackie. Dog Days in Andalucia: Tails from Spain. 2010. (ENG., Illus.). 256p. pap. 14.95 *(978-1-84596-613-3(9))* Mainstream Publishing Co., Ltd. GBR. Dist: Independent Pubs. Group.

Worthington, David. The British & Irish in Central Europe C. 1560-1688. 2012. (Politics & Culture in Europe, 1650ndash;1750 Ser.). (Illus.). 222p. 124.95 ***(978-0-7546-6342-3(6))*** Ashgate Publishing Co.

BRITISH—FOREIGN COUNTRIES

Armitage, David. The British Atlantic World, 1500-1800. Braddick, Michael J., ed. 2nd rev. ed. 2009. (ENG., Illus.). 384p. pap. 32.00 *(978-0-230-20235-1(7))* Palgrave Macmillan.

Armitage, David & Braddick, Michael J., eds. The British Atlantic World, 1500-1800. 2nd rev. ed. 2009. (ENG., Illus.). 384p. 100.00 *(978-0-230-20234-4(3))* Palgrave Macmillan.

Bickers, Robert. Settlers & Expatriates: Britons over the Seas. 2010. (ENG.). 360p. 65.00 *(978-0-19-929767-2(3))* Oxford Univ. Pr., Inc.

Burke-Gaffney, Brian. Nagasaki: The British Experience, 1854-1945. 2010. (ENG., Illus.). 336p. pap. *(978-1-906876-28-9(2))* BRILL.

Candler, Edmund. The Unveiling of Lhasa. 2011. (ENG.). 248p. pap. 19.99 *(978-988-19090-8-4(2))* Earnshaw Bks. HKG. Dist: Independent Pubs. Group.

Canton, James. From Cairo to Baghdad: British Travellers in Arabia. 2011. (ENG., Illus.). 288p. 96.00 *(978-1-84885-696-7(2))* I. B. Tauris & Co., Ltd. GBR. Dist: Macmillan.

Chamberlain, Mary. Empire & Nation-Building in the Caribbean: Barbados, 1937-1966. 2010. (Studies in Imperialism Ser.). (ENG.). 240p. 89.95 *(978-0-7190-7876-7(8))* Manchester Univ. Pr. GBR. Dist: Macmillan.

Chang, Elizabeth H., ed. British Travel Writing from China, 1798-1901, 5 vols., Set. 2009. (ENG.). 1600p. 795.00 *(978-1-85196-625-7(0))* Pickering & Chatto Pubs., Ltd. GBR. Dist: Ashgate Publishing Co.

Collis, Maurice, ed. Siamese White. 2013. (ENG.). 256p. pap. 29.95 *(978-1-906011-12-3(5))* Eland Bks. GBR. Dist: Dufour Editions, Inc.

Corp, Edward. A Court in Exile: The Stuarts in France, 1689-1718. 2009. (Illus.) 404p. pap. 53.00 *(978-0-521-10837-9(3))* Cambridge Univ. Pr.

Edmonds, C. J. East & West of Zagros: Travel, War & Politics in Persia & Iraq 1913-1921. 2009. (Iran Studies). (Illus.). 400p. *(978-90-04-17344-6(7))* BRILL.

Explorer Publishing. Abu Dhabi. 8th rev. ed. 2011. (Explorer - Residents' Guides). (ENG., Illus.). 430p. pap. 24.95 ***(978-9948-442-67-7(9))*** Explorer Publishing UAE. Dist: Globe Pequot Pr., The.

Finch, Tim, et al. Global Brit: Making the Most of the British Diaspora. 2010. (Illus.). 156p. pap. *(978-1-86030-340-1(4))* Institute for Public Policy Research.

Francis, Huw. Living & Working in Turkey. 2009. (Illus.). 170p. 26.00 *(978-1-84528-245-5(0))* How To Books GBR. Dist: Parkwest Pubns., Inc.

Fulford, Tim, et al. Literature, Science & Exploration in the Romantic Era: Bodies of Knowledge. 2007. (Cambridge Studies in Romanticism Ser.). (ENG., Illus.). 348p. pap. 69.00 *(978-0-521-03995-6(9))* Cambridge Univ. Pr.

Gunn, Drewey Wayne. American & British Writers in Mexico, 1556-1973. 2011. (ENG.). 314p. pap. 30.00 *(978-0-292-72943-8(X))* Univ. of Texas Pr.

Hamack, Curtis. Gentlemen on the Prairie: Victorians in Pioneer Iowa. 2011. (Bur Oak Book Ser.). (ENG., Illus.). 262p. pap. 24.00 *(978-1-58729-967-4(4))* Univ. of Iowa Pr.

Hart, Rona. Preparing for Your Move Abroad: Relocating, Settling In, & Managing Culture Shock. 2012. (Culture Smart! Ser.). (ENG.). 220p. pap. 19.95 ***(978-1-85733-644-3(5))*** Kuperard Pubs. GBR. Dist: Random Hse., Inc.

Hobbs, Guy. Jobs & Careers Abroad. 13th ed. 2006. (Directory of Jobs & Careers Abroad Ser.). 444p. per. 21.95 *(978-1-85458-353-6(0), Vacation Work Pubns.)* Crimson Publishing, Ltd. GBR. Dist: National Bk. Network.

Holden, Gay. Brother in Arms: an Englishman in Vietnam. 2008. 240p. pap. 17.95 *(978-0-9558496-1-9(6))* Holden, Gay GBR. Dist: Lulu Enterprises Inc.

Horrell, Steve. Emigrating to New Zealand: An Independent Guide. 2007. (Illus.). 160p. per. 22.00 *(978-1-84528-116-8(0))* How To Books GBR. Dist: Parkwest Pubns., Inc.

—Emigrating to New Zealand: Comprehensive, Up-to-Date, Practical Information about Everyday Life in the Other 'Down-Under' 2nd ed. 2010. (ENG., Illus.). 182p. pap. 26.00 *(978-1-84528-398-8(8))* How To Books GBR. Dist: Parkwest Pubns., Inc.

Hudson, W. H. Far Away & Long Ago: A Childhood in Argentina. reprint ed. 64.50 *(978-0-404-03408-5(X))* AMS Pr., Inc.

—Far Away & Long Ago: A Childhood in Argentina. 2006. (ENG.). 246p. pap. 20.99 *(978-1-4264-1379-7(3))*; 228p. pap. 22.99 *(978-1-4264-1432-9(3))* BiblioBazaar.

—Far Away & Long Ago: A Childhood in Argentina. 332p. reprint ed. 98.00 *(978-0-7222-9581-6(2))* Library Reprints, Inc.

—Far Away & Long Ago: A Childhood in Argentina. 2007. (ENG.). 228p. pap. 12.45 *(978-1-60424-746-6(0), Book Jungle)* Standard Pubns., Inc.

Jacob, Harold F. Kings of Arabia: The Rise & Set of the Turkish Sovranty in the Arabian Peninsula. 2007. (Folios Archive Library Ser.). (Illus.). 294p. pap. 49.50 *(978-1-85964-198-9(9))* Garnet Publishing, Ltd. GBR. Dist: International Specialized Bk. Services.

Kane, Frank & Tilsley, John. In the Shadow of Papillon: Seven Years of Hell in Venezuela's Prison System. 2008. (ENG., Illus.). 287p. per. 14.95 *(978-1-84596-251-7(6))* Mainstream Publishing Co., Ltd. GBR. Dist: Independent Pubs. Group.

Keith, Zak. My Life as a Squint-eyed Chink. 2009. 328p. pap. 24.95 *(978-1-4092-5314-3(7))* Lulu Enterprises Inc.

King, Peter. Student Migration. 2007. 256p. 120.00 *(978-0-415-37826-0(5))* Routledge.

Laurence, Charles. The Social Agent: A True Intrigue of Sex, Spies, & Heartbreak Behind the Iron Curtain. 2010. (ENG.). 240p. 26.00 *(978-1-56663-845-6(3))* Dee, Ivan R. Pub.

Liberman, Sherri. Lynne Reid Banks. 2009. (Library of Author Biographies Ser.). 112p. (gr. 5-8). 63.90 *(978-1-60853-345-3(2), Rosen Central)* Rosen Publishing Group, Inc., The.

MacFarlane, Ben & Simpson, Neil. Holiday SOS: The Life-Saving Adventures of a Travelling Doctor. 2010. (ENG.). 304p. pap. 13.95 *(978-0-340-91976-7(0), Hodder & Stoughton)* Hodder General Publishing Div. GBR. Dist: Independent Pubs. Group.

MacManus, James. Ocean Devil: The Life & Legend of George Hogg. 2008. (ENG., Illus.). 288p. 12.95 *(978-0-00-727075-0(5))* HarperCollins Pubs. Ltd. GBR. Dist: Independent Pubs. Group.

Magee, Gary Bryan & Thompson, Andrew S. Empire & Globalisation: Networks of People, Goods & Capital in the British World, C.1850-1914. 2010. (ENG., Illus.). 314p. 85.00 *(978-0-521-89889-8(7))* Cambridge Univ. Pr.

Melville, Lewis. Lady Mary Wortley Montague: Her Life & Letters (1689-1762) 2007. (ENG.). 276p. pap. 21.99 *(978-1-4264-4239-1(4))*; 308p. pap. 24.99 *(978-1-4264-4303-9(X))* BiblioBazaar.

Montagu, Mary Wortley. The Letters & Works of Lady Mary Wortley Montagu. Wharncliffe, James Archibald Stuart-Wortley-Mackenzie & Thomas, William Moy, eds. 2011. (Cambridge Library Collection - Women's Writing Ser.). (ENG.). 552p. pap. 39.99 *(978-1-108-07316-5(6))*; (Illus.). 544p. pap. 39.99 *(978-1-108-07315-8(8))* Cambridge Univ. Pr.

Mould, Paul, ed. In Drake's Wake: The Later Voyages, 4 vols, Vol. 3. 2009. 268p. pap. 35.00 *(978-1-58690-092-2(7))* Mould, Paul Publishing GBR. Dist: Gazelle Bk.Services Ltd.

Mwangi, Evan Maina. Africa Writes Back to Self: Metafiction, Gender, Sexuality. 2009. 336p. 75.00 *(978-1-4384-2631-5(X))* State Univ. of New York Pr.

Paston, George. Lady Mary Wortley Montagu & Her Times. 2009. 468p. pap. *(978-0-217-01010-8(5))* Books LLC.

Plotz, John. Portable Property: Victorian Culture on the Move. 2009. (ENG., Illus.). 288p. (C). pap. 25.95 *(978-0-691-14662-1(4))* Princeton Univ. Pr.

Power, Angie. Moving to France with Your Children. 2007. (Illus.). 182p. per. 22.00 *(978-1-84528-166-3(7))* How To Books GBR. Dist: Parkwest Pubns., Inc.

Pritchett, V. S. At Home & Abroad. 2012. 344p. pap. ***(978-1-4482-0087-0(3)***, 142605, Bloomsbury Reader) Bloomsbury Publishing Plc.

Provan, Tom. Weve Gone to Spain. 2nd ed. 2008. 235p. pap. 20.00 *(978-1-84528-080-2(6))* How To Books GBR. Dist: Parkwest Pubns., Inc.

Pybus, Victoria. France. 6th ed. 2008. (ENG., Illus.). 416p. pap. 24.95 *(978-1-85458-419-9(7))* Crimson Publishing, Ltd. GBR. Dist: National Bk. Network.

—Working in Ski Resorts: Europe & North America. 6th ed. 2007. (Working in Ski Resorts: Europe & North America Ser.). (Illus.). 344p. per. 19.95 *(978-1-85458-355-0(7), Vacation Work Pubns.)* Crimson Publishing, Ltd. GBR. Dist: National Bk. Network.

Reuvid, Jonathan. Working Abroad: The Complete Guide to Overseas Employment. 28th rev. ed. 2007. 320p. pap. *(978-0-7494-4951-3(9))* Kogan Page, Ltd.

Rose, Susan. Calais: An English Town in France, 1347-1558. 2008. (Illus.). 198p. 90.00 *(978-1-84383-401-4(4), Boydell Press)* Boydell & Brewer, Ltd. GBR. Dist: Boydell & Brewer, Inc.

Rybarz, Beverley. The Bridge Builder. 2006. (ENG., Illus.). 184p. (Orig.). per. 19.95 *(978-1-86254-659-2(2))* Wakefield Pr. Pty, Ltd. AUS. Dist: Independent Pubs. Group.

Schleck, Julia. Telling True Tales of Islamic Lands: Forms of Mediation in English Travel Writing, 1575-1630. 2011. (ENG., Illus.). 218p. 56.00 *(978-1-57591-158-8(2))* Susquehanna Univ. Pr.

Stewart, Rory. The Prince of the Marshes: And Other Occupational Hazards of a Year in Iraq. 2007. (ENG., Illus.). 432p. per. 15.00 *(978-0-15-603279-7(1), Mariner Bks.)* Houghton Mifflin Harcourt Trade & Reference Pubs.

Symonds, Emily. Lady Mary Wortley Montagu & Her Times. 2007. 616p. 59.95 *(978-0-548-05055-2(4))* Kessinger Publishing, LLC.

Turner, Michael. In Drake's Wake: The Early Voyages. 2007. (Illus.). 272p. (gr. 4-12). pap. *(978-1-58690-020-5(X))* Mould, Paul Publishing.

—In Drake's Wake: The Later Voyages, Vol. 3. 2009. (Illus.). pap. 33.00 *(978-1-58690-099-1(4))* Empire Publishing Service.

—In Drake's Wake: The World Voyage, Vol. 2. Mould, Paul, ed. 2007. (Illus.). 298p. (gr. 4-12). pap. *(978-1-58690-036-6(6))* Mould, Paul Publishing.

Wharncliffe, Lord. Letters & Works of Lady Mary Wortley M. 2006. pap. 36.95 *(978-1-4286-4229-4(3))*; pap. 33.95 *(978-1-4286-4230-0(7))* Kessinger Publishing, LLC.

Wilson, Arnold. Persia A Political Officers Diary. 2006. 328p. per. *(978-1-4067-2267-3(7), Hesperides Pr.)* Read Bks.

Wood, Victoria, et al. Victoria's Empire: A Journey Through the British Empire with Victoria Wood. 2007. (ENG., Illus.). 302p. 38.00 *(978-0-340-93801-0(3))* Headline Bk. Publishing GBR. Dist: Independent Pubs. Group.

BRITISH—INDIA

Anderson, Dorothy. An Unlikely Hero. 2008. (ENG., Illus.). 288p. 57.95 *(978-1-86227-462-4(2), History Pr. Ltd.,The)* GBR. Dist: Independent Pubs. Group.

Beaumont, Penny. Imperial Divas,Vicereines of India. 2011. (ENG., Illus.). 328p. 24.95 *(978-1-906598-19-8(3))* Haus Publishing GBR. Dist: Consortium Bk. Sales & Distribution.

Blechynden, Richard & Robb, Peter. Sentiment & Self: Richard Blechynden's Calcutta Diaries, 1791-1822. 2011. (ENG.). 312p. 55.00 ***(978-0-19-807512-7(X))*** Oxford Univ. Pr., Inc.

—Sex & Sensibility: Richard Blechynden's Calcutta Diaries, 1791-1822. 2011. (ENG.). 328p. 55.00 ***(978-0-19-807511-0(1))*** Oxford Univ. Pr., Inc.

Bremner, Fred. My Forty Years in India. 2nd ed. 2007. (Illus.). 70p. reprint ed. pap. *(978-1-904289-07-4(X))* Pagoda Tree Pr.

Brittlebank, Kate, ed. Tall Tales & True: India, Historiography & British Imperial Imaginings. 2008. (Monash Asia Institute Monographes Ser.). 142p. pap. 29.95 *(978-1-876924-61-4(6), Monash Univ. Pr.)* Monash Univ. Publishing AUS. Dist: International Specialized Bk. Services.

Collett, Nigel & Collett. The Butcher of Amritsar: General Reginald Dyer. 2006. (ENG., Illus.). 576p. 29.95 *(978-1-85285-575-8(4), Hambledon Continuum)* Continuum International Publishing Group, Ltd. GBR. Dist: National Bk. Network.

Dinner, Barbara. Mehtars & Marigolds. 2009. 392p. pap. 31.50 *(978-0-9561543-1-6(X))* Perkerren Publishing GBR. Dist: Lulu Enterprises Inc.

Diver, Maud. The Englishwoman in India. 259p. reprint ed. 98.00 *(978-0-7222-1853-2(2))* Library Reprints, Inc.

B

Dyson, Ketaki Kushari. A Various Universe: A Study of the Journals & Memoirs of British Men & Women in the Indian Subcontinent 1765-1856. 2nd ed. 2006. (Illus.). 428p. pap. 30.00 *(978-0-19-568286-1(6))* Oxford Univ. Pr., Inc.

Dyson, Mabel. My Indian Story. 2008. 63p. pap. 16.95 *(978-1-4092-2964-3(5))* Lulu Enterprises Inc.

Fay, Eliza. Original Letters from India. 2010. (ENG., Illus.). 304p. pap. 16.95 *(978-1-59017-336-7(8)*, NYRB Classics) New York Review of Bks., Inc., The.

Franklin, Michael J. Romantic Representations of British India. 2006. (Routledge Studies in Romanticism Ser.). (ENG., Illus.). 304p. (C). 173.00 *(978-0-415-37827-7(3))* Routledge.

Gandhi, Mahatma. Freedom's Battle. 2007. 196p. per. *(978-1-4065-1750-7(X))* Dodo Pr.

Ghandi, Mahatma. Peace: The Words & Inspiration of Mahatma Gandhi. 2007. (Illus.). 95p. 14.95 *(978-1-59842-242-9(1)*, Blue Mountain Pr.) Blue Mountain Arts Inc.

Gibson, Jack & Sharma, Brij. An Indian Englishman. 2008. 419p. pap. 19.76 *(978-1-4357-3461-6(0))* Lulu Enterprises Inc.

Gilmour, David. The Ruling Caste: Imperial Lives in the Victorian Raj. 2007. (ENG., Illus.). 416p. per. 17.00 *(978-0-374-53080-8(7))* Farrar, Straus & Giroux.

Gray, James. Life in Bombay, & the Neighbouring Out-Stations. 2010. 384p. pap. 33.75 *(978-1-148-01440-1(3))* BiblioBazaar.

Harrington, Jack. Sir John Malcolm & the Creation of British India. 2010. (Palgrave Studies in Cultural & Intellectual History Ser.). (ENG.). 266p. 89.00 *(978-0-230-10885-1(7))* Palgrave Macmillan.

Havholm, Peter. Politics & Awe in Rudyard Kipling's Fiction. 2008. (Illus.). 204p. 99.95 *(978-0-7546-6164-1(4))* Ashgate Publishing Co.

Holmes, Richard. Sahib: The British Soldier in India, 1750-1914. 2006. (ENG., Illus.). 572p. pap. 19.95 *(978-0-00-713754-1(0))* HarperCollins Pubs. Ltd. GBR. Dist: Independent Pubs. Group.

Kerr, Gordon. English in Western India. 2006. 420p. per. *(978-1-4067-0430-3(X)*, Hesperides Pr.) Read Bks.

Khorana, Meena G. & Greenwood. The Life & Works of Ruskin Bond. 2009. 188p. pap. 45.99 *(978-1-60752-075-7(3))* Information Age Publishing, Inc.

Kingsmill, Joseph. British Rule & British Christianity in India. 2009. 172p. pap. 19.99 *(978-0-217-91286-0(9))* General Bks. LLC.

—British Rule & British Christianity in India. 2007. pap. 31.95 *(978-1-4304-4988-1(8))* Kessinger Publishing, LLC.

Lassner, Phyllis & Le-Guilcher, Lucy. Rumer Godden: International & Intermodern Storyteller. 2010. (Illus.). 224p. 99.95 *(978-0-7546-6828-2(2))* Ashgate Publishing Co.

Locke, John C., ed. First Englishmen in India. reprint ed. 37.50 *(978-0-404-06615-4(1))* AMS Pr., Inc.

MacMillan, Margaret. Women of the Raj: The Mothers, Wives, & Daughters of the British Empire in India. 2007. (ENG., Illus.). 400p. per. 15.95 *(978-0-8129-7639-7(8)*, Random Hse. Trade Paperbacks) Random House Publishing Group.

Purcell, Hugh. After the Raj: Plain Tales of Those Who Stayed on after Independence. 2008. (ENG., Illus.). 224p. 44.95 *(978-0-7509-4786-2(1))* History Pr. Ltd.,The GBR. Dist: Independent Pubs. Group.

Reich, Leslie M. The White Author's Burden. 2011. 144p. pap. ***(978-3-8443-9288-3(2))*** Lambert Academic Publishing.

Rivett-Carnac, S. Presidential Armies of India. 2010. 477p. 27.95 *(978-1-935501-06-0(2))* Lancer International, Lancer Pr. IND. Dist: Casemate Pubs. & Bk. Distributors, LLC.

Rocher, Ludo & Rocher, Rosane. The Making of Western Ideology: Henry Thomas Colebrooke & the East India Company. 2011. (Royal Asiatic Society Bks.). (ENG., Illus.). 256p. (C). 145.00 *(978-0-415-33601-7(5))* Routledge.

Roy, Parama. Alimentary Tracts: Appetites, Aversions, & the Postcolonial. 2010. (Next Wave: New Directions in Women's Studies). (ENG.). 288p. 84.95 *(978-0-8223-4788-0(1))*; pap. 23.95 *(978-0-8223-4802-3(0))* Duke Univ. Pr.

Sapra, Rahul. The Limits of Orientalism: Seventeenth-Century Representations of India. 2011. *(978-1-936249-00-8(6))* Univ. of Delaware Pr.

—Limits of Orientalism: Seventeenth-Century Representations of India. 2011. (ENG.). 224p. 65.00 *(978-1-61149-014-5(6))* Univ. of Delaware Pr.

Sarila, Narendra Singh. Once a Prince of Sarila: Of Palaces & Tiger Hunts, of Nehrus & Mountbattens. 2008. (ENG., Illus.). 304p. 41.00 *(978-1-84511-707-8(7))* I. B. Tauris & Co., Ltd. GBR. Dist: Macmillan.

Sharma, Jayeeta. Empire's Garden: Assam & the Making of India. 2011. (Radical Perspectives Ser.). (ENG., Illus.). 344p. 94.95 *(978-0-8223-5032-3(7))* Duke Univ. Pr.

Sharma, Jayeeta, et al. Empire's Garden: Assam & the Making of India. 2011. (Radical Perspectives Ser.). (ENG., Illus.). 344p. pap. 25.95 *(978-0-8223-5049-1(1))* Duke Univ. Pr.

Sharrad, Paul. Postcolonial Literary History & Indian English Fiction. 2008. 109.95 *(978-1-60497-560-4(1))* Cambria Pr.

Shields, Nancy K., ed. Birds of Passage: Henrietta Clive's Travels in South India, 1798-1801. 2010. (ENG., Illus.). 328p. 39.95 *(978-1-906011-37-6(0))* Eland Bks. GBR. Dist: Dufour Editions, Inc.

Singh, Khushwant. Sahibs Who Loved India. 2009. (ENG.). 200p. (gr. 12-18). 19.95 *(978-0-670-08241-4(4)*, Penguin Global) Penguin Group (USA) Inc.

Skeen, Andrew. Lessons in Imperial Rule. 2008. 208p. 39.95 *(978-1-84832-507-4(X))* Pen & Sword Bks. Ltd. GBR. Dist: Casemate Pubs. & Bk. Distributors, LLC.

Sramek, Joseph. Gender, Morality, & Race in Company India, 1765-1858. 2011. (ENG., Illus.). 272p. 85.00 *(978-0-230-11693-1(0))* Palgrave Macmillan.

Stark, Herbert Alick. Hostages to India (an Anglo Indian Heritage Book) The Life Story of the Anglo Indian Race. 2007. per. *(978-1-84356-011-1(9))* Wallenberg, Simon Pr.

Wolpert, Stanley. Shameful Flight: The Last Years of the British Empire in India. 2009. (ENG., Illus.). 256p. pap. 17.95 *(978-0-19-539394-1(5))* Oxford Univ. Pr., Inc.

BRITISH—IRELAND

Bennett, Richard. The Black & Tans. 2011. (Illus.). 228p. pap. 24.95 *(978-1-84884-384-4(4))* Pen & Sword Bks. Ltd. GBR. Dist: Casemate Pubs. & Bk. Distributors, LLC.

Bradshaw, Brendan, et al, eds. Representing Ireland: Literature & the Origins of Conflict, 1534-1660. 2010. (ENG.). 264p. pap. 38.99 *(978-0-521-12926-8(5))* Cambridge Univ. Pr.

Brady, Ciaran & Ohlmeyer, Jane, eds. British Interventions in Early Modern Ireland. 2010. (ENG., Illus.). 392p. pap. 36.99 *(978-0-521-15460-4(X))* Cambridge Univ. Pr.

Clare, Linda. On the Edge of the Pale: The Rise & Decline of an Anglo-Irish Community in Co. Meath, 1170-1530. Gillespie, Raymond, ed. 2006. (Maynooth Studies in Local History: No. 66). (Illus.). 64p. pap. 14.95 *(978-1-84682-004-5(9))* Four Courts Pr. IRL. Dist: International Specialized Bk. Services.

Connolly, S. J. Contested Island: Ireland 1460-1630. (Oxford History of Early Modern Europe Ser.). (Illus.). 2009. (ENG.). 440p. pap. 39.95 *(978-0-19-956371-5(3))* 2007. 450p. 85.00 *(978-0-19-820816-7(2))* Oxford Univ. Pr., Inc.

—Divided Kingdom: Ireland 1630-1800. 2010. (ENG., Illus.). 544p. pap. 39.95 *(978-0-19-958387-4(0))* Oxford Univ. Pr., Inc.

Connolly, Sean. Divided Kingdom: Ireland, 1630-1800. 2008. (ENG., Illus.). 530p. 74.00 *(978-0-19-954347-2(X))* Oxford Univ. Pr., Inc.

Coughlin, Patricia, ed. Spenser & Ireland. 127p. pap. *(978-0-902561-55-7(3))* Cork Univ. Pr.

Froude, James A. English in Ireland in the Eighteenth Century, 3 vols. reprint ed. 215.00 *(978-0-404-02640-0(0))* AMS Pr., Inc.

Goff, Annabel. Walled Gardens. 2009. (ENG.). 256p. pap. 36.95 *(978-1-906011-02-4(8))* Eland Bks. GBR. Dist: Dufour Editions, Inc.

Herron, Thomas. Spenser's Irish Work: Poetry Plantation & Colonial Reformation. 2007. (Illus.). 282p. 114.95 *(978-0-7546-5602-9(0))* Ashgate Publishing Co.

Highley, Christopher. Shakespeare, Spenser, & the Crisis in Ireland. 2007. (Cambridge Studies in Renaissance Literature & Culture Ser.). (ENG., Illus.). 264p. pap. 56.00 *(978-0-521-03083-0(8))* Cambridge Univ. Pr.

Jordan, Thomas E. Sir William Petty, 1623-1687: The Genius Entrepreneur of Seventeenth-Century Ireland. 2007. 212p. *(978-0-7734-5368-5(7))* Mellen, Edwin Pr., The.

Klingelhofer, Eric. Castles & Colonists: An Archaeology of Elizabethan Ireland. 2011. (Manchester Spenser Ser.). (ENG., Illus.). 192p. 85.00 *(978-0-7190-8246-7(3))* Manchester Univ. Pr. GBR. Dist: Macmillan.

Malcomson, A. P. W. John Foster (1740-1828) The Politics of Improvement & Prosperity. 2011. 480p. 74.50 *(978-1-84682-230-8(0))* Four Courts Pr. IRL. Dist: International Specialized Bk. Services.

McGowan-Doyle, Valerie. The Book of Howth: Elizabethan Conquest & the Old English. 2011. 300p. 49.00 *(978-1-85918-468-4(5))* Cork Univ. Pr. IRL. Dist: Stylus Publishing, LLC.

Montaño, John Patrick. The Roots of English Colonialism in Ireland. 2011. (Critical Perspectives on Empire Ser.). (ENG., Illus.). 440p. 99.00 *(978-0-521-19828-8(3))* Cambridge Univ. Pr.

Murray, James. Enforcing the English Reformation: State Reform & Clerical Resistance in the Diocese of Dublin, 1534-1590. 2008. (Cambridge Studies in Early Modern British History Ser.). (ENG.). 374p. 116.00 *(978-0-521-77038-5(6))* Cambridge Univ. Pr.

Palmer, Patricia. Language & Conquest in Early Modern Ireland: English Renaissance Literature & Elizabethan Imperial Expansion. 2009. (ENG.). 268p. pap. 38.99 *(978-0-521-12033-3(0))* Cambridge Univ. Pr.

Prendergast, John P. The Cromwellian Settlement of Ireland by John P Prendergast, Esq. 2006. 292p. per. 23.99 *(978-1-4255-2682-5(9))* MPublishing.

Traill, H. D. Lord Strafford. 2007. (ENG.). 212p. 39.95 *(978-0-548-02916-9(4))* Kessinger Publishing, LLC.

Valone, David A. & Bradbury, Jill Marie. Anglo-Irish Identities 1571/1845. 2008. (C). *(978-0-8387-5713-0(8))* Lewisburg United Methodist Church.

White, Randy Wayne. Hunter's Moon. l.t. ed. 2007. (Doc Ford Ser.: No. 14). 334p. 31.95 *(978-1-58547-985-6(3))* Ctr. Point Large Print.

—Hunter's Moon, 14 vols. 2008. (Doc Ford Ser.: No. 14). (ENG., Illus.). 352p. (gr. 12-18). pap. 9.99 *(978-0-425-22037-5(0)*, Berkley) Penguin Group (USA) Inc.

BRITISH—PALESTINE

Ghandour, Zeina Talitha. A Discourse on Domination in Mandate Palestine: Imperialism, Property & Insurgency. 2009. (ENG.). 216p. 140.00 *(978-0-415-48993-5(8)*, Routledge Cavendish) Taylor & Francis Group GBR. Dist: Taylor & Francis Group.

Perry, Yaron & Lev, Efraim. Modern Medicine in the Holy Land: Pioneering British Medical Services in Late Ottoman Palestine. 2007. (International Library of Colonial History Ser.). (ENG., Illus.). 256p. 89.00 *(978-1-84511-489-3(2)*, Tauris Academic Studies) I. B. Tauris & Co., Ltd. GBR. Dist: Macmillan.

BRITISH—UNITED STATES

Abraham, Terry. Mountains So Sublime: Nineteenth-Century British Travellers & the Lure of the Rocky Mountain West. 2007. (Illus.). 224p. per. 29.95 *(978-0-87013-791-4(3))* Michigan State Univ. Pr.

Bell, Jason, photos by. An Englishman in New York. 2011. (ENG., Illus.). 160p. 55.00 ***(978-1-904587-97-2(6))*** Lewis, Dewi Publishing GBR. Dist: Consortium Bk. Sales & Distribution.

Bockstoce, John R. Furs & Frontiers in the Far North: The Contest among Native & Foreign Nations for the Bering Strait Fur Trade. 2009. (Lamar Series in Western History Ser.). (ENG., Illus.). 496p. 35.00 *(978-0-300-14921-0(2))* Yale Univ. Pr.

Byars, Merlene Hutto. Our British Heritage - Volume III: Fight for Independence & Freedom. 2007. (ENG.). 424p. per. 24.99 *(978-1-4257-4813-5(9))* Xlibris Corp.

Cave, Alfred A. Lethal Encounters: Englishmen & Indians in Colonial Virginia, 1 vol. (Native America: Yesterday & Today Ser.). 200p. 34.95 *(978-0-313-39335-8(4)*, A3346C); 2011. xiv, 200p. E-Book ***(978-0-313-39336-5(2))*** Greenwood Publishing Group, Inc. (Praeger Pubs.).

Cole, J. Timothy & Foley, Bradley R. Collett Leventhorpe, the English Confederate: The Life of a Civil War General, 1815-1889. 2006. (ENG., Illus.). 300p. per. 35.00 *(978-0-7864-2649-2(7))* McFarland & Co., Inc. Pubs.

Crowe, Eyre. With Thackeray in Americ. 2010. 190p. pap. 28.45 *(978-1-4455-5827-1(0)*, Kent Pr.) Kent Communications, Ltd.

—With Thackeray in America. 2010. (Cambridge Library Collection - History Ser.). 204p. pap. 22.99 *(978-1-108-00299-8(4))* Cambridge Univ. Pr.

Gigante, Denise. The Keats Brothers: The Life of John & George. 2011. (ENG., Illus.). 552p. 35.00 *(978-0-674-04856-0(3)*, Belknap Pr.) Harvard Univ. Pr.

Gray, Charles D. Saratoga Joe: The Saratoga Sawdust Canary. 2008. 220p. 18.95 *(978-1-4327-3145-8(9))* Outskirts Pr., Inc.

Guinn, Gilbert S. The Arnold Scheme: British Pilots, the American South & the Allies' Daring Plan. 2007. (Illus.). 559p. pap., per. 39.99 *(978-1-59629-042-6(0))* History Pr., The.

Hampshire, David. Living & Working in America, 7th Edition: A Survival Handbook. 7th ed. 2008. (ENG., Illus.). 480p. pap. 25.95 *(978-1-905303-63-2(7))* Survival Bks., Ltd.

Hume, Ivor Noël. Something from the Cellar: More of This & That: Selected Essays from the Colonial Williamsburg Journal. 2008. (Illus.). 163p. per. 29.95 *(978-0-87935-229-5(9))* Colonial Williamsburg Foundation.

Izzo, David Garrett. W. H. Auden Encyclopedia. alt. ed. 2011. (ENG., Illus.). 304p. pap. 55.00 *(978-0-7864-4913-2(6))* McFarland & Co., Inc. Pubs.

LeMaster, Michelle. Brothers Born of One Mother: British-Native American Relations in the Colonial Southeast. 2012. (ENG., Illus.). 304p. (gr. 17). 39.50 ***(978-0-8139-3241-5(6))*** Univ. Pr. of Virginia.

—Brothers Born of One Mother: British Native American Relations in the Colonial Southeast. 2012. E-Book ***(978-0-8139-3242-2(4))*** Univ. Pr. of Virginia.

Living the American Dream? (Press button 2 to continue in English) 2008. 260p. pap. 9.95 *(978-0-615-17859-2(6))* Robson, Nick.

Lumsden, Ian G. Early Views of British North America. (Illus.). 75p. pap. 5.00 *(978-0-920674-38-3(0))* Beaverbrook Art Gallery CAN. Dist: Goose Lane Editions.

McMichael, Andrew. Atlantic Loyalties: Americans in Spanish West Florida, 1785-1810. 2008. (ENG., Illus.). 240p. 59.95 *(978-0-8203-3004-4(3))*; per. 24.95 *(978-0-8203-3023-5(X))* Univ. of Georgia Pr.

Mulvey, Christopher. Anglo-American Landscapes: A Study of Nineteenth-Century Anglo-American Travel Literature. 2009. (ENG.). 312p. pap. 46.00 *(978-0-521-11580-3(9))* Cambridge Univ. Pr.

Pagnamenta, Peter. Prairie Fever: British Aristocrats in the American West, 1830-1890. 2012. (ENG., Illus.). 368p. 27.95 ***(978-0-393-07239-6(8)***, 7239) Norton, W. W. & Co., Inc.

Parker, Hershel. The Powell Papers: A Confidence Man Amok among the Anglo-American Literati. 2011. (ENG.). 360p. 69.95 *(978-0-8101-2703-6(2))* Northwestern Univ. Pr.

Patten, Christopher. Cousins & Strangers: America, Britain, & Europe in a New Century. 2006. (ENG.). 320p. per. 19.00 *(978-0-8050-8257-9(3)*, Owl Bks.) Holt, Henry & Co.

Penrith, Deborah & Turner, Eleanor C. USA: The Most Accurate, Practical & Comprehensive Guide to Living & Working in the United States. 5th ed. 2009. (ENG., Illus.). 416p. pap. 24.95 *(978-1-85458-428-1(6))* Crimson Publishing, Ltd. GBR. Dist: National Bk. Network.

Randall, Will. Limey Gumshoe: The True-Life Adventures of an Undercover Detective. 2010. (ENG.). 304p. pap. 13.95 *(978-0-349-12040-9(4))* Little, Brown Bk. Group Ltd. GBR. Dist: Independent Pubs. Group.

Sweet, Julie Anne. William Stephens: Georgia's Forgotten Founder. 2010. (Southern Biography Ser.). 232p. 42.50 *(978-0-8071-3558-7(5))* Louisiana State Univ. Pr.

van Vugt, William E., ed. British Immigration to the United States, 1736-1914, 4 vols. 2009. (ENG.). 1552p. 625.00 *(978-1-85196-976-0(4))* Pickering & Chatto Pubs., Ltd. GBR. Dist: Ashgate Publishing Co.

Warner, M. /DeLano. The Noble House of Woods: The English Ancestry & Heraldry of the Immigrant John Woods. 2007. spiral bd. *(978-1-886560-04-8(8))* Quintin Pubns.

Wharton, Anne Hollingsworth. English Ancestral Homes of Noted Americans. 2009. 380p. 48.95 *(978-1-104-10920-2(4))*; pap. 33.95 *(978-1-104-08938-2(6))* Kessinger Publishing, LLC.

—English Ancestral Homes of Noted Americans. 313p. reprint ed. 98.00 *(978-0-7222-8420-9(9))* Library Reprints, Inc.

BRITISH ACADEMY

British Academy, ed. The Biographical Memoirs of Fellows, Vol. 6. 2008. (Proceedings of the British Academy Ser.). (ENG., Illus.). 340p. 110.00 *(978-0-19-726423-2(9))* Oxford Univ. Pr., Inc.

—Proceedings of the British Academy, 2006 Lectures, Vol. 151. 2008. (Proceedings of the British Academy Ser.). (ENG., Illus.). 380p. 125.00 *(978-0-19-726424-9(7))* Oxford Univ. Pr., Inc.

BRITISH AIRWAYS

Corke, Alison. British Airways. (Illus.). 145p. *(978-0-86187-635-8(0)*, Burns & Oates) Continuum International Publishing Group, Ltd.

Escolme-Schmidt, Libbie. Glamour in the Skies: The Golden Age of the Air Stewardess. 2009. (ENG., Illus.). 224p. 38.95 *(978-0-7524-4904-3(4))* History Pr. Ltd.,The GBR. Dist: Independent Pubs. Group.

—Glamour in the Skies: The Golden Age of the Air Stewardess. 2010. (ENG., Illus.). 224p. pap. 23.95 *(978-0-7524-5787-1(X))* History Pr. Ltd.,The GBR. Dist: Independent Pubs. Group.

Green, Oliver & Anthony, Scott. British Aviation Posters: Art Design & Flight. 2012. (Illus.). 200p. 70.00 ***(978-1-84822-084-3(7)***, Lund Humphries Pubs.) Ashgate Publishing, Ltd. GBR. Dist: Ashgate Publishing Co.

BRITISH ANTARCTIC EXPEDITION (1907-1909)

Shackleton, E. H. & David, T. W. Edgeworth. The Heart of the Antarctic: Being the Story of the British Antarctic. 2007. (ENG.). 544p. per. 42.95 *(978-1-4304-4235-6(2))* Kessinger Publishing, LLC.

BRITISH ANTARCTIC ("TERRA NOVA") EXPEDITION (1910-1913)

Barczewski, Stephanie & Barczewski. Antarctic Destinies: Scott, Shackleton & the Changing Face of Heroism. 2008. (ENG., Illus.). 412p. 39.95 *(978-1-84725-192-3(7))* Continuum International Publishing Group, Ltd. GBR. Dist: National Bk. Network.

Barczewski, Stephanie L. & Barczewski, Stephanie. Antarctic Destinies: Scott, Shackleton, & the Changing Face of Heroism. 2009. (ENG., Illus.). 412p. 27.95 *(978-0-8264-4562-9(4))* Continuum International Publishing Group, Ltd. GBR. Dist: National Bk. Network.

Cherry-Garrard, Apsley. The Worst Journey in the World. 2009. 712p. 36.99 *(978-0-559-08653-3(9))*; 40.99 *(978-0-559-08642-7(3))*; pap. 48.75 *(978-0-559-08651-9(2))*; pap. 49.75 *(978-0-559-08645-8(8))* BiblioBazaar.

—The Worst Journey in the World. 2008. (Twelve-Point Ser.). lib. bdg. 30.00 *(978-1-58287-471-5(9))* North Bks.

—The Worst Journey in the World: Antarctic 1910-1913. 2007. (ENG.). 436p. per. *(978-1-4068-4534-1(5))* Echo Library.

—The Worst Journey in the World: With Scott in Antarctica 1910-1913. 2010. (ENG.). 528p. pap. 16.95 *(978-0-486-47732-9(0))* Dover Pubns., Inc.

Evans, Edward R. G. R. South with Scott. 2008. 264p. 25.99 *(978-0-554-33179-9(9))* 2008. 264p. 28.99 *(978-0-554-23876-0(4))* 2007. 236p. pap. 20.99 *(978-1-4264-5111-9(3))* 2007. 262p. pap. 23.99 *(978-1-4264-5412-7(0))* BiblioBazaar.

—South with Scott. 2009. 232p. pap. *(978-1-4099-6291-5(1))* Dodo Pr.

Evans, Rear-Admiral E. South with Scott. 2006. pap. *(978-1-4068-0123-1(2))* Echo Library.

Hooper, Meredith. The Longest Winter: Scott's Other Heroes. 2011. (ENG., Illus.). 320p. 26.00 *(978-1-58243-762-0(9)*, Counterpoint) Counterpoint LLC.

—The Longest Winter: Scott's Other Heroes. 2010. (ENG.). 320p. 19.95 *(978-1-84854-306-5(9))*; (Illus.). 358p. 29.95 *(978-0-7195-9580-6(0))* Murray, John GBR. Dist: Independent Pubs. Group.

Langner, Rainer-K. Scott & Amundsen: Duel in the Ice. 2007. (ENG., Illus.). 232p. 24.95 *(978-1-905791-08-8(9))* Haus Publishing GBR. Dist: Consortium Bk. Sales & Distribution.

Raeside, Adrian. Return to Antarctica: The Amazing Adventure of Sir Charles Wright on Robert Scott's Journey to the South Pole. 2011. (ENG., Illus.). 336p. pap. 22.95 *(978-0-470-93215-5(5)*, Wiley) Wiley, John & Sons, Inc.

Scott, Robert Falcon. Journals: Captain Scott's Last Expedition. Jones, Max, ed. 2008. (Oxford World's Classics Ser.). (ENG., Illus.). 592p. pap. 17.95 *(978-0-19-953680-1(5))* Oxford Univ. Pr., Inc.

Turley, Charles. The Voyages of Captain Scott. 2009. 448p. 34.99 *(978-1-113-49437-5(9))*; pap. 35.75 *(978-1-113-49436-8(0))* BiblioBazaar.

Williams, Isobel. Captain Scott's Invaluable Assistant: Edgar Evans. 2012. (ENG., Illus.). 192p. pap. 19.95 ***(978-0-7524-5845-8(0))*** History Pr. Ltd.,The GBR. Dist: Independent Pubs. Group.

BRITISH ARCHITECTURE

see Architecture—Great Britain

BRITISH ART

see Art, British

BRITISH ART POTTERY

see Art Pottery, British

BRITISH BROADCASTING CORPORATION

Aitken, Robin & Aitken. Can We Trust the BBC? (ENG.). 256p. 2008. 19.95 *(978-0-8264-9884-7(1))* 2007. 29.95 *(978-0-8264-9427-6(7))* Continuum International Publishing Group, Ltd. GBR. Dist: National Bk. Network.

Avery, Todd. Radio Modernism: Literature, Ethics, & the Bbc 1922-1938. 2006. (Illus.). 166p. 110.00 *(978-0-7546-5517-6(2))* Ashgate Publishing Co.

Baade, Christina L. Victory Through Harmony: The BBC & Popular Music in World War II. 2011. (ENG., Illus.). 288p. 45.00 *(978-0-19-537201-4(8))* Oxford Univ. Pr., Inc.

Barkho, Leon. News from the BBC, CNN, & Al-Jazeera: How the Three Broadcasters Cover the Middle East. 2010. xii, 185p. *(978-1-57273-975-8(4))*; *(978-1-57273-974-1(6))* Hampton Pr., Inc.

Bennett, Jeremy. British Broadcasting & the Danish Resistance Movement, 1940-1945: A Study of the Wartime Broadcasts of the B. B. C. Danish Service. 2010. (ENG., Illus.). 286p. pap. 17.99 *(978-0-521-15844-2(3))* Cambridge Univ. Pr.

Black, Leo. BBC Music in the Glock Era & After: A Memoir. Wintle, Christopher & Cosman, Milein, eds. 2010. (Illus.). 190p. 70.00 *(978-0-9556087-4-2(0))*; pap. 29.95 *(978-0-9556087-5-9(9))* Plumbago Bks. GBR. Dist: Boydell & Brewer, Inc.

Bloomfield, Ken. The BBC at the Watershed. 2009. (ENG.). 208p. 39.95 *(978-1-84631-160-4(8))* Liverpool Univ. Pr. GBR. Dist: Chicago Distribution Ctr.

Conolly, Leonard & CONOLLY, Leonard. Bernard Shaw & the BBC. 2009. (ENG., Illus.). 256p. *(978-0-8020-8920-5(8))* Univ. of Toronto Pr.

Crisell, Andrew. Liveness & Recording in the Media. 2012. (Key Concerns in Media Studies). (ENG., Illus.). 128p. (C). pap. 22.95 ***(978-0-230-28222-3(9))*** Palgrave Macmillan.

Doctor, Jennifer. The BBC & Ultra-Modern Music, 1922-1936: Shaping a Nation's Tastes. 2007. (Music in the Twentieth Century Ser.). (ENG.). 524p. (C). pap. 70.00 *(978-0-521-03536-6(4))* Cambridge Univ. Pr.

Garner, Ken. The Peel Sessions: A Story of Teenage Dreams & One Man's Love of New Music. 2008. (ENG., Illus.). 352p. pap. 29.95 *(978-1-84607-282-6(4))* BBC Worldwide GBR. Dist: Independent Pubs. Group.

Garnham, Alison. The Selected Letters of Hans Keller. Date not set. (Illus.). 270p. 99.95 *(978-0-7546-0898-1(0))* Ashgate Publishing Co.

Gillespie, Marie & Webb, Alban, eds. Diasporas & Diplomacy: Cosmopolitan contact zones at the BBC World Service (1932ndash;2012) 2013. (Cresc Ser.). (ENG.). 256p. (C). 135.00 ***(978-0-415-50880-3(0))*** Routledge.

Grant, Tony. From Our Foreign Correspondent: A Celebration of Fifty Years of the BBC Radio Programme. 2009. (ENG.). 320p. per. 15.95 *(978-1-86197-747-2(6))* Profile Bks. Ltd. GBR. Dist: Consortium Bk. Sales & Distribution.

Grist, John. Grace Wyndham Goldie, First Lady of Tele. 2006. *(978-0-7552-0248-5(1))* Authors OnLine, Ltd.

Hajkowski, Thomas. The BBC & National Identity in Britain, 1922-53. 2011. (Studies in Popular Culture Ser.). (ENG.). 272p. 89.95 *(978-0-7190-7944-3(5))* Manchester Univ. Pr. GBR. Dist: Macmillan.

Hare, Sam. Dear Auntie Beeb. 2009. 204p. pap. *(978-1-84748-431-4(X))* Athena Pr.

Havers, Richard. Here Is the News: The BBC & the Second World War. 2008. (ENG., Illus.). 288p. 39.95 *(978-0-7509-4121-1(9))* Sutton Publishing.

Hendy, David. Life on Air: A History of Radio Four. (Illus.). 2008. 544p. pap. 29.95 *(978-0-19-955024-1(7))* 2007. (ENG., 500p. 59.99 *(978-0-19-924881-0(8))* Oxford Univ. Pr., Inc.

Hines, Mark. The Story of Broadcasting House: Home of the BBC. 2008. (Illus.). 192p. 54.95 *(978-1-85894-421-0(X))* Merrell Pubs. Ltd. GBR. Dist: Perseus Distribution.

Holmes, Su. Entertaining Television: The BBC & Popular Television Culture in the 1950s. 2008. (ENG., Illus.). 232p. 89.00 *(978-0-7190-7791-3(5))* Manchester Univ. Pr. GBR. Dist: Macmillan.

Inverdale. Seventy Years of BBC Sport. (Illus.). 179p. 40.00 *(978-0-233-99555-7(2))* Andre Deutsch GBR. Dist: Trafalgar Square Publishing.

Irvine, Mat & Tucker, Mike. BBC VFX: The History of the BBC Visual Effects Department, 1954-2003. 2011. (ENG., Illus.). 240p. 44.95 *(978-1-84513-556-0(3))* Aurum Pr., Ltd. GBR. Dist: Independent Pubs. Group.

Launchbury, Claire. Music, Poetry, Propaganda: Constructing French Cultural Soundscapes at the BBC During the Second World War. 2012. (Modern French Identities Ser.: 78). (ENG.). 211p. pap. 49.95 ***(978-3-0343-0239-5(8))*** Lang, Peter AG GBR. Dist: Lang, Peter.

Newton, Darrell M. M. Paving the Empire Road: BBC Television & Black Britons. 2012. (ENG., Illus.). 224p. 80.00 *(978-0-7190-8167-5(X))* Manchester Univ. Pr. GBR. Dist: Macmillan.

Niebur, Louis. Special Sound: The Creation & Legacy of the BBC Radiophonic Workshop, 1 vol. 2010. (Oxford Music/Media Ser.). (ENG., Illus.). 272p. pap. 27.95 *(978-0-19-536841-3(X))* Oxford Univ. Pr., Inc.

North, Richard. 'Scrap the BBC!' Ten Years to Set Broadcasters Free. 2007. 219p. *(978-1-904863-20-5(5))* Social Affairs Unit.

Objective Journalism - Myth or Reality? 2011. 88p. pap. ***(978-3-8443-0197-7(6))*** Lambert Academic Publishing.

Ribeiro, Nelson Costa. BBC Broadcasts to Portugal in World War II: How Radio Was Used as a Weapon of War. 2011. 540p. 149.95 ***(978-0-7734-1487-7(8))*** Mellen, Edwin Pr., The.

Street, Sean. The A to Z of British Radio. 2009. (A to Z Guide Ser.: No. 64). (ENG.). 344p. pap. 34.45 *(978-0-8108-6847-2(4))* Scarecrow Pr., Inc.

Street, Seán. Crossing the Ether: The Untold Story of Pre-War UK Commercial Radio. 2006. (ENG., Illus.). 256p. pap. 29.95 *(978-0-86196-668-4(6), 0861966686)* Indiana Univ. Pr.

Wander, Tim. 2MT Writtle: The Birth of British Broadcasting. 2nd ed. 2010. (Illus.). 548p. pap. *(978-0-7552-0607-0(X))* Authors OnLine, Ltd.

BRITISH COLUMBIA

Elworthy, Terence. Spindrift. 2011. 264p. pap. 17.08 ***(978-1-4269-0106-5(2))*** Trafford Publishing.

Lee, John. British Columbia & the Canadian Rockies. 5th rev. ed. 2011. (Regional Travel Guide Ser.). (ENG., Illus.). 296p. pap. 20.99 *(978-1-74179-804-3(3))* Lonely Planet Pubns.

Martin, Bernice Medbury & Stevenson, Jane. The Railroader's Wife: Letters from the Grand Trunk Pacific Railway. unabr. ed. 2010. (ENG., Illus.). 196p. pap. 24.95 *(978-1-894759-43-4(5))* Caitlin Pr., Inc. CAN. Dist: Partners Pubs. Group, Inc.

Nixon, Bob, et al, eds. Touch Wood: BC Forests at the Crossroads. unabr. ed. (ENG., Illus.). 236p. (Orig.). pap. *(978-1-55017-074-0(0))* Harbour Publishing Co., Ltd.

Wilson, Diana. Heart of the Cariboo-Chilcotin: Stories Worth Keeping, 1 vol. 2010. (ENG., Illus.). 240p. per. *(978-1-894974-08-0(5))* Heritage Hse.

BRITISH COLUMBIA—DESCRIPTION AND TRAVEL

Amos, Robert & Wong, Kileasa. Inside Chinatown: Ancient Culture in a New World, 1 vol. 2010. (ENG., Illus.). 160p. *(978-1-894898-91-5(5))* TouchWood Editions.

Archer, Laurel. Northern British Columbia Canoe Trips, 1 vol. rev. ed. 2009. (ENG., Illus.). 304p. pap. *(978-1-897522-13-4(4))* Rocky Mountain Bks.

—Northern British Columbia Canoe Trips: Volume Two, 1 vol. 2010. (ENG., Illus.). 396p. pap. *(978-1-926855-04-2(3))* Rocky Mountain Bks.

Bartosik, John. Whistler & Blackcomb Country. 3rd unabr. ed. (ENG., Illus.). 48p. reprint ed. pap. 9.95 *(978-1-55017-176-1(3))* Harbour Publishing Co., Ltd. CAN. Dist: Ingram Pub. Services.

Bernhardson, Wayne. Moon Buenos Aires. 2011. (ENG., Illus.). 404p. pap. 18.95 *(978-1-59880-728-8(5))* Avalon Travel Publishing.

Berry, Oliver. Banff, Jasper & Glacier National Parks. 3rd rev. ed. 2012. (National Parks Ser.). (ENG., Illus.). 288p. pap. 19.99 *(978-1-74179-405-2(6))* Lonely Planet Pubns.

Blacklaws, Rick, photos by. Ranchland: British Columbia's Cattle Country. unabr. ed. (ENG., Illus.). 208p. 39.95 *(978-1-55017-232-4(8))* Harbour Publishing Co., Ltd. CAN. Dist: Ingram Pub. Services.

Blanchet, M. Wylie. The Curve of Time. 50th ed. 2011. 178p. 24.95 *(978-1-77050-037-2(5))* Whitecap Bks., Ltd. CAN. Dist: Midpoint Trade Bks., Inc.

Bier, Richard K., compiled by. Hiking Trails 2: South-Central Vancouver Island & the Gulf Islands, 1 vol. 9th ed. 2010. (ENG., Illus.). 192p. pap. 26.00 ***(978-0-9697667-7-3(7))*** Vancouver Island Hiking Trails Society CAN. Dist: Orca Bk. Pubs. USA.

Bodega y Cuadra, Juan de la. Voyage to the Northwest Coast of America, 1792: Juan Francisco de la Bodega y Quadra & the Nootka Sound Controversy. Inglis, Robin & Engstrand, Iris H. W., eds. 2012. (Northwest Historical Ser.). (ENG., Illus.). 192p. 34.95 ***(978-0-87062-408-7(3))***, Clark, Arthur H. Co., The) Univ. of Oklahoma Pr.

Boles, Glen. My Mountain Album: Art & Photography of the Canadian Rockies & Columbia Mountains, 1 vol. 2006. (ENG., Illus.). 168p. *(978-1-894765-78-7(8))* Rocky Mountain Bks.

Bostwick, Mark. The Four-Wheeler's Companion: The Off-Road Guide to Southwestern BC. 3rd rev. ed. (ENG., Illus.). 206p. pap. 24.95 *(978-1-55017-118-1(6))* Harbour Publishing Co., Ltd. CAN. Dist: Ingram Pub. Services.

Bourdon, Marc. Squamish Bouldering. 2nd ed. 2010. (Illus.). 420p. pap. *(978-0-9732593-7-7(X))* Quickdraw Pubns.

Bryan, Liz. Country Roads of British Columbia: Exploring the Interior, 1 vol. rev. ed. 2003. (ENG., Illus.). 192p. pap. *(978-1-894974-43-1(3))* Heritage Hse.

Buente, Gail, ed. Vancouver, Victoria & Whistler Colourguide. 5th rev. ed. 2009. (Colourguide Travel Ser.). (ENG., Illus.). 216p. pap. 19.95 *(978-0-88780-833-3(6))* Formac Publishing Co., Ltd. CAN. Dist: Casemate Pubs. & Bk. Distributors, LLC.

Burke, Michael D. & Burke, Michael. Same River Twice: A Boatman's Journey Home. 2006. (ENG., Illus.). 224p. pap. 16.95 *(978-0-8165-2531-7(5))* Univ. of Arizona Pr.

Cameron, Aaron & Gunn, Matt. Hikes Around Invermere & the Columbia River Valley, 1 vol. 2009. (ENG., Illus.). 208p. pap. *(978-1-897522-51-6(7))* Rocky Mountain Bks.

Cameron, Derek. A Journey to the Retreat Centers of British Columbia: Illustrated with Photographs. 2009. (Illus.). 124p. pap. 10.95 *(978-0-9800817-5-6(0))* Eremitical Pr.

Cameron, June. 26 Feet to the Charlottes: Exploring the Land of the Haida, 1 vol. 2009. (ENG., Illus.). 240p. pap. *(978-1-894974-61-5(1))* Heritage Hse.

Campbell, Colin. Trails of the Southern Cariboo, 1 vol. 2nd rev. ed. 2009. (ENG., Illus.). 144p. pap. *(978-1-897522-44-8(4))* Rocky Mountain Bks.

Cannings, Richard. Roadside Nature Tours through the Okanagan: A Guide to British Columbia's Wine Country, 1 vol. 2009. (ENG., Illus.). 224p. pap. 22.95 *(978-1-55365-288-5(6))*, Greystone Bks.) D&M Pubs. Inc. CAN. Dist: Perseus-PGW.

Casey, Rob. Kayaking Puget Sound & the San Juan Islands: 60 Paddle Trips Including the Gulf Islands. 3rd ed. 2012. (ENG.). 256p. pap. ***(978-1-59485-685-3(0))*** Mountaineers Bks., The.

Cheadle, Chris. Portrait of Greater Victoria & Southern Vancouver Island, 1 vol. 2010. (ENG., Illus.). 64p. pap. *(978-1-894974-95-0(6))* Heritage Hse.

Chittenden, Newton H. Official Report of the Exploration of the Queen Charlotte Islands for the Government of British Columbia. 2007. 80p. per. *(978-1-4065-1361-5(X))* Dodo Pr.

Christie, Jack. Best Weekend Getaways from Vancouver: Favourite Trips & Overnight Destinations, 1 vol. 2009. (ENG., Illus.). 288p. pap. 22.95 *(978-1-55365-256-4(8))*, Greystone Bks.) D&M Pubs. Inc. CAN. Dist: Perseus-PGW.

—The Whistler Book: An All-Season Outdoor Guide, 1 vol. rev. ed. 2009. (ENG., Illus.). 272p. pap. 20.00 *(978-1-55365-447-6(1))*, Greystone Bks.) D&M Pubs. Inc. CAN. Dist: Perseus-PGW.

—52 Best Day Trips from Vancouver, 1 vol. 3rd ed. 2011. (ENG., Illus.). 312p. pap. 19.95 *(978-1-55365-597-8(4))*, Greystone Bks.) D&M Pubs. Inc. CAN. Dist: Perseus-PGW.

Church, Mike & Church, Terri. Pacific Northwest Camping Destinations: RV & Car Camping Destinations in Oregon, Washington, & British Columbia. 3rd ed. 2012. (Camping Destinations Ser.). (ENG., Illus.). 608p. pap. 21.95 ***(978-0-9823101-2-0(9))*** Rolling Homes Pr.

Clapham, Charles. Great Walks of Vancouver: Metro Vancouver Plus Squamish to Whistler. 2nd ed. 2010. (Illus.). 384p. pap. 21.95 *(978-1-894694-75-9(9))* Granville Island Publishing CAN. Dist: Partners Pubs. Group, Inc.

Coffey, Maria & Goering, Dag. Visions of the Wild: A Voyage by Kayak Around Vancouver Island. unabr. ed. (ENG., Illus.). 192p. 36.95 *(978-1-55017-264-5(6))* Harbour Publishing Co., Ltd. CAN. Dist: Ingram Pub. Services.

Coleman, A. P. The Canadian Rockies: New & Old Trails. 2009. (Mountain Classics Collection #1 Ser.). (ENG.). 232p. pap. *(978-1-897522-50-9(9))* Rocky Mountain Bks.

Copeland, Kathy & Copeland, Craig. Don't Waste Your Time in the Canadian Rockies: The Opinionated Hiking Guide. 6th ed. 2009. (Illus.). 544p. *(978-0-9783427-5-3(5))* hikingcamping.com, Inc.

Couper, Jim. The Long & Winding Road: Discovering the Pleasures & Treasures of Highway 97, 1 vol. 2010. (ENG., Illus.). 208p. per. *(978-1-894974-12-7(3))* Heritage Hse.

Daffern, Tony. Popular Day Hikes 2: Canadian Rockies, 1 vol. rev. ed. 2008. (Popular Day Hikes Ser.). (ENG., Illus.). 144p. pap. *(978-1-897522-01-1(0))* Rocky Mountain Bks.

Dombrowski, Theo. Secret Beaches of Greater Victoria: View Royal to Sidney, 1 vol. 2010. (ENG., Illus.). 256p. pap. *(978-1-894974-98-1(0))* Heritage Hse.

Dorst, Adrian. Reflections at Sandhill Creek: Meditations on the Wild West Coast. unabr. ed. 2009. (ENG., Illus.). 112p. 28.95 *(978-1-55017-474-8(6))* Harbour Publishing Co., Ltd. CAN. Dist: Ingram Pub. Services.

Douglass, Don & Hemingway-Douglass, Reanne. Exploring the South Coast of British Columbia: Gulf Islands & Desolation Sound to Broughton Archipelago & Blunden Harbour, 1 vol. 2nd ed. 2009. (ENG.). 480p. pap. *(978-1-932310-23-8(1))* FineEdge.Com LLC.

Entertainment Publications, Inc. Staff, compiled by. Vancouver Island 2009 Entertainment Book. 2008. pap. 35.00 *(978-1-59878-694-1(6))* Entertainment Pubns., Inc.

Ernst, Chloe. Frommer's British Columbia. 7th ed. 2012. (Frommer's Complete Guides). (ENG.). 352p. pap. 20.99 ***(978-1-118-11377-6(2)***, Frommers) Wiley, John & Sons, Inc.

Ernst, Trent. Kootenay Rockies BC, 1 vol. 4th ed. 2008. (Backroad Mapbook Ser.). (ENG., Illus.). 133p. spiral bd. *(978-1-897225-28-8(8))* Mussio Ventures, Ltd.

Ernst, Trent & Mussio, Russell. Southeastern BC Fishing Mapbook: Region 4 - Kootenay, Region 8 - Okanagan, 1 vol. 2008. (Backroad Mapbooks Ser.). (ENG., Illus.). 127p. spiral bd., spiral bd. *(978-1-897225-32-5(6))* Mussio Ventures, Ltd.

Everitt, Nicholas. Round the World in Strange Company: America, British Colombia, & the West. 2007. (Travel in America Ser.). (ENG.). 372p. 49.95 *(978-1-4290-0566-1(1))*; per. 24.95 *(978-1-4290-0567-8(X))* Applewood Bks.

Fodor's. Fodor's Vancouver & Victoria, 3rd Edition: With Whistler, Vancouver Island & the Okanagan Valley. 2012. (Full-color Travel Guide Ser.). (ENG.). 348p. pap. 18.99 ***(978-0-307-92932-7(9))***, Fodor's) Fodor's Travel Pubns.

Fodor's Travel Publications, Inc. Staff. Vancouver & Victoria: With Whistler, Vancouver Island & the Okanagan Valley. 2nd ed. 2010. (Full-Color Gold Guides). (ENG., Illus.). 348p. pap. 18.99 *(978-1-4000-0419-5(5)*, Fodor's) Fodor's Travel Pubns.

Formac Publishing Company Limited Staff. The Canadian Rockies. Inigo-Jones, Terry, ed. 4th rev. ed. 2010. (Colourguide Travel Ser.). (ENG., Illus.). 208p. pap. 19.95 *(978-0-88780-897-5(2))* Formac Publishing Co., Ltd. CAN. Dist: Casemate Pubs. & Bk. Distributors, LLC.

Foster, David. Blisters & Bliss: A Trekker's Guide to the West Coast Trail, 1 vol. 6th ed. 2010. (ENG.). 144p. pap. *(978-1-926613-80-2(5))* Heritage Hse.

Frazer, Neil. Boat Camping Haida Gwaii: A Small Vessel Guide. 2nd unabr. rev. ed. 2010. (ENG., Illus.). 176p. pap. *(978-1-55017-487-8(8))* Harbour Publishing Co., Ltd.

Freeman, Lewis R. & Sanford, Emerson. On the Roof of the Rockies: The Great Columbia Icefield of the Canadian Rockies, 1 vol. 2009. (Mountain Classics Collection #6 Ser.). (ENG., Illus.). 176p. pap. *(978-1-897522-46-2(0))* Rocky Mountain Bks.

Gauthier, Michel. The Nation Lakes Canoe Route: A Paddler's Guide. 2012. (Illus.). 176p. pap. ***(978-0-9865095-2-0(3))*** Dogwood Avenue Bks.

Gayton, Don. Okanagan Odyssey: Journeys through Terrain, Terroir & Culture, 1 vol. 2010. (ENG.). 176p. pap. *(978-1-897522-81-3(9))* Rocky Mountain Bks.

Gazetas, Mary. Around One More Point: A Journal of Paddling Adventures, 1 vol. 2010. (ENG., Illus.). 96p. per. *(978-1-894898-46-1(X))* TouchWood Editions.

Gooch, Jane Lytton. Mount Assiniboine: Images in Art, 1 vol. 2007. (ENG., Illus.). 152p. pap. *(978-1-894765-97-8(4))* Rocky Mountain Bks.

Granander, Hans & Wigle, Michael. Bella Coola: Life in the Heart of the Coast Mountains. unabr. ed. (ENG., Illus.). 160p. 32.95 *(978-1-55017-305-5(7))* Harbour Publishing Co., Ltd. CAN. Dist: Ingram Pub. Services.

Greenfield, Tony. Waterfalls of British Columbia: A Guide to BC's 100 Best Falls. unabr. ed. 2009. (ENG., Illus.). 240p. pap. 26.95 *(978-1-55017-462-5(2))* Harbour Publishing Co., Ltd. CAN. Dist: Ingram Pub. Services.

Hamilton, Jennifer & Hamilton, James. Cruising the Secret Coast: Unexplored Anchorages on British Columbia's Inside Passage, 1 vol. 2008. (ENG., Illus.). 272p. pap. 44.95 *(978-0-935727-29-6(9))* Weatherly Pr.

Hanus, Josef. British Columbia. 2007. (Illus.). 96p. pap. *(978-0-9682498-3-3(3))* Fine, J. H. Art Photo, Ltd.

—Whistler Garibaldi - Sea to Sky. 2007. (Illus.). 80p. pap. *(978-0-9684552-6-5(3))* Fine, J. H. Art Photo, Ltd.

Harbord, Heather. Sea Kayak Nootka & Kyuquot Sounds, 1 vol. 2010. (ENG., Illus.). 176p. pap. *(978-1-894765-52-7(4))* Rocky Mountain Bks.

Hart, E. J. Jimmy Simpson: Legend of the Rockies, 1 vol. 2009. (ENG., Illus.). 224p. pap. *(978-1-897522-25-7(8))* Rocky Mountain Bks.

Harvey, Al. Wild Beauty: A Visual Exploration of BC, 1 vol. 2010. (ENG., Illus.). 128p. pap. *(978-1-894974-93-6(X))* Heritage Hse.

Hempstead, Andrew. Moon British Columbia. 2011. (Moon Handbooks Ser.). (ENG., Illus.). 468p. pap. 19.99 *(978-1-59880-747-9(1))* Avalon Travel Publishing.

—Moon Canadian Rockies: Including Banff & Jasper National Parks. 2010. (Moon Handbooks). (ENG., Illus.). 352p. pap. 17.95 *(978-1-59880-372-3(7))* Avalon Travel Publishing.

—Moon Spotlight Banff National Park. 2010. (Moon Spotlight Ser.). (ENG.). 80p. pap. 7.95 *(978-1-59880-556-7(8))* Avalon Travel Publishing.

—Moon Spotlight Victoria & Vancouver Island. 2011. (Moon Spotlight Ser.). (ENG.). 112p. pap. 9.99 *(978-1-59880-767-7(6))* Avalon Travel Publishing.

—Moon Vancouver & Victoria: Including Whistler & Vancouver Island. 2011. (Moon Handbooks Ser.). (ENG., Illus.). 268p. pap. 17.99 *(978-1-59880-748-6(X))* Avalon Travel Publishing.

Hill, Beth & Converse, Cathy. The Remarkable World of Frances Barkley: 1769-1845, 1 vol. 2nd rev. ed. 2009. (ENG., Illus.). 224p. pap. *(978-1-894898-78-2(8))* TouchWood Editions.

Hill, Kathleen Thompson & Hill, Gerald N. Victoria & Vancouver Island: A Personal Tour of an Almost Perfect Eden. 6th ed. 2007. (Hill Guides). (ENG., Illus.). 368p. per. 14.95 *(978-0-7627-4564-7(9))* Globe Pequot Pr., The.

Hoagland, Edward. Early in the Season: A British Columbia Journal, 1 vol. 2009. (ENG., Illus.). 176p. 22.95 *(978-1-55365-428-5(5))* D&M Pubs. Inc. CAN. Dist: Perseus-PGW.

Holman, John P. Sheep & Bear Trails: A Hunter's Wanderings in Alaska & British Columbia. 2011. 272p. 47.95 ***(978-1-258-09857-5(1))*** Literary Licensing, LLC.

Hornaday, William T. Campfires in the Canadian Rockies. 2007. (ENG.). 492p. 53.95 *(978-0-548-11707-1(1))* Kessinger Publishing, LLC.

Horwood, Dennis. Haida Gwaii: The Queen Charlotte Islands, 1 vol. 3rd rev. ed. 2009. (ENG., Illus.). 256p. pap. *(978-1-894974-82-0(4))* Heritage Hse.

Hughes, Mike. The Northwest Dive Guide: A Scuba Handbook for BC, Washington & Oregon. unabr. ed. 2009. (ENG., Illus.). 272p. pap. 9.95 *(978-1-55017-476-2(2))* Harbour Publishing Co., Ltd. CAN. Dist: Ingram Pub. Services.

Hume, Stephen. Off the Map: Western Travels on Roads Less Taken. unabr. ed. (ENG.). 304p. 32.95 *(978-1-55017-239-3(5))* Harbour Publishing Co., Ltd. CAN. Dist: Ingram Pub. Services.

Island Illustrators Society Staff. Coastal Moments from the Island Illustrators Society: 25th Anniversary Journal. 2011. 128p. spiral bd. 23.95 *(978-0-88982-277-1(8)*, Oolichan Bks. CAN. Dist: Univ. of Toronto Pr.

Jones, Robert H. & Stefanyk, Larry E. Island Halibut Fisherman. unabr. ed. 2007. (ENG., Illus.). 168p. pap. 24.95 *(978-1-55017-414-4(2))* Harbour Publishing Co., Ltd. CAN. Dist: Ingram Pub. Services.

—Island Salmon Fisherman: Vancouver Island Hotspots. unabr. ed. 2008. (ENG., Illus.). 176p. pap. 24.95 *(978-1-55017-425-0(8))* Harbour Publishing Co., Ltd. CAN. Dist: Ingram Pub. Services.

Keller, Betty & Leslie, Rosella. Bright Seas, Pioneer Spirits: A History of the Sunshine Coast, 1 vol. rev. ed. 2009. (ENG., Illus.). 256p. pap. *(978-1-894898-87-4(7))* TouchWood Editions.

Kennedy, Liv. Coastal Villages. unabr. ed. (ENG., Illus.). 176p. *(978-1-55017-057-3(0))* Harbour Publishing Co., Ltd.

Kimantas, John. British Columbia's South Coast & East Vancouver Island, Vol. 1. 2010. (British Columbia Coastal Recreation Kayaking & S Ser.). (ENG., Illus.). 58p. spiral bd. 40.00 *(978-1-55285-864-6(2))* Whitecap Bks., Ltd. CAN. Dist: Midpoint Trade Bks., Inc.

—British Columbia's West Vancouver Island, Vol. 2. 2010. (British Columbia Coastal Recreation Kayaking & S Ser.). (ENG., Illus.). 48p. spiral bd. 40.00 *(978-1-55285-865-3(0))* Whitecap Bks., Ltd. CAN. Dist: Midpoint Trade Bks., Inc.

—A Kayaking, Hiking & Recreation Guide for Bc's South Coast & East Vancouver Island, Vol. 3. 2010. (Wild Coast Ser.). (ENG., Illus.). 344p. pap. 34.95 *(978-1-55285-842-4(1))* Whitecap Bks., Ltd. CAN. Dist: Midpoint Trade Bks., Inc.

—The Wild Coast: A Kayaking & Recreation Guide for the North & Central B. C. Coast. 2010. (Wild Coast Ser.). (ENG., Illus.). 344p. pap. 29.95 *(978-1-55285-786-1(7))* Whitecap Bks., Ltd. CAN. Dist: Midpoint Trade Bks., Inc.

Lamb, W. Kaye, ed. The Letters & Journals of Simon Fraser, 1806-1808. 2007. (ENG., Illus.). 328p. pap. 24.99 *(978-1-55002-713-6(1)*, Dundurn Pr.) Dundurn CAN. Dist: Ingram Pub. Services.

Landers, Rich, et al. Paddling Washington: Flatwater & Whitewater Routes in Washington State & the Inland Northwest. 2008. (ENG., Illus.). 384p. pap. 24.95 *(978-1-59485-056-1(9))* Mountaineers Bks., The.

Leadem, Tim. Hiking the West Coast of Vancouver Island, 1 vol. rev. ed. 2008. (Hiking the West Coast of Vancouver Island Ser.). (ENG., Illus.). 208p. pap.

B

19.95 *(978-1-55365-382-0(3)*, Greystone Bks.) D&M Pubs. Inc. CAN. Dist: Perseus-PGW.

Lee, John. Drinking Vancouver: 100+ Bars in the City & Beyond, 1 vol. 2009. (ENG.). 160p. pap. *(978-1-894898-96-6(6))* TouchWood Editions.

Lee, Norman. Klondike Cattle Drive, 1 vol. 2010. (Classic West Collections). (ENG., Illus.). 96p. per. *(978-1-894898-14-0(1))* TouchWood Editions.

Lee, Virginia. Pacific Flavours: Recipes from the Best Chefs on Canada's West Coast. 3rd rev. ed. 2008. (Flavours Cookbook Ser.). (ENG., Illus.). 160p. pap., instr.'s gde. ed. 24.95 *(978-0-88780-756-5(9))* Formac Publishing Co., Ltd. CAN. Dist: Casemate Pubs. & Bk. Distributors, LLC.

Leiren-Young, Mark. Never Shoot a Stampede Queen: A Rookie Reporter in the Cariboo, 1 vol. rev. ed. 2009. (ENG., Illus.). 224p. pap. *(978-1-894974-52-3(2))* Heritage Hse.

Levinson, Elizabeth. An Edible Journey: Exploring the Islands' Fine Foods, Farms & Vineyards, 1 vol. 3rd rev. ed. 2009. (ENG., Illus.). 312p. pap. *(978-1-894898-90-4(7))* TouchWood Editions.

Lucas, Eric. Victoria & Vancouver Island - Explorer's Guide: A Great Destination. 2011. (Explorer's Guides). (ENG., Illus.). 200p. pap. 19.95 *(978-1-58157-128-8(3)*, 157128) Countryman Pr.

Macaree, David, et al. 103 Hikes in Southwestern British Columbia, 1 vol. 6th ed. 2008. (ENG., Illus.). 256p. pap. 19.95 *(978-1-55365-374-5(2)*, Greystone Bks.) D&M Pubs. Inc. CAN. Dist: Perseus-PGW.

Macaree, Mary & Macaree, David. 109 Walks in British Columbia's Lower Mainland, 1 vol. 6th ed. 2009. (ENG., Illus.). 256p. pap. 19.95 *(978-1-55365-443-8(9)*, Greystone Bks.) D&M Pubs. Inc. CAN. Dist: Perseus-PGW.

McBeath, Chris. Vancouver Island: The Gulf Islands & San Juan Islands. 3rd ed. 2011. (Frommer's Complete Guides). (ENG., Illus.). 288p. pap. 17.99 *(978-0-470-68170-1(5)*, Frommers) Wiley, John & Sons, Inc.

McBeath, Chris & Ernst, Chloe. Frommer's Vancouver & Victoria. 17th ed. 2012. (Frommer's Color Complete Ser.). (ENG., Illus.). 384p. pap. 19.99 ***(978-1-118-09313-9(5)***, Frommers) Wiley, John & Sons, Inc.

McRae, Bill & Olson, Donald. Frommer's British Columbia & the Canadian Rockies. 6th ed. 2010. (Frommer's Complete Guides: 774). (ENG., Illus.). 448p. pap. 20.99 *(978-0-470-59153-6(6)*, Frommers) Wiley, John & Sons, Inc.

Michelin Travel Publications Staff. British Columbia & the Rockies. 2009. (Green Guide Ser.). (ENG., Illus.). 288p. pap. 19.95 *(978-1-906261-54-2(7))* Michelin Travel & Lifestyle.

Mussio, Russell & Ernst, Trent. Southwestern BC Fishing Mapbook: Region 2 - Lower Mainland, Region 3 - Thompson Nicola, 1 vol. 2nd ed. 2008. (Backroad Mapbooks Ser.). (ENG., Illus.). 208p. spiral bd., spiral bd. 27.95 *(978-1-897225-00-4(8))* Backroads.

Mussio, Russell, et al. Vancouver Island BC, 1 vol. Mussio, Wesley, ed. 2008. (Fishing Mapbooks Ser.). (ENG., Illus.). 144p. spiral bd., spiral bd. *(978-1-897225-01-1(6))* Mussio Ventures, Ltd.

Nugara, Andrew W. More Scrambles in the Canadian Rockies, 1 vol. 2007. (ENG., Illus.). 264p. pap. *(978-1-894765-86-2(9))* Rocky Mountain Bks.

Nunuk, David. Natural Light: Visions of British Columbia. unabr. ed. (ENG., Illus.). 120p. 49.95 *(978-1-55017-273-7(5))* Harbour Publishing Co., Ltd. CAN. Dist: Ingram Pub. Services.

Obee, Bruce. Trans Canada Trail: British Columbia. 2010. (ENG., Illus.). 372p. pap. 29.95 *(978-1-55285-928-5(2))* Whitecap Bks., Ltd. CAN. Dist: Midpoint Trade Bks., Inc.

Outram, James. In the Heart of the Canadian Rockies. 2009. 488p. 53.95 *(978-1-104-21783-9(X))*; pap. 38.95 *(978-1-104-18283-0(1))* Kessinger Publishing, LLC.

—In the Heart of the Canadian Rockies, 1 vol. 2007. (Mountain Classics Collection). (ENG.). 312p. per. *(978-1-894765-96-1(6))* Rocky Mountain Bks.

Parker, Gil. Hiking Trails 3, 1 vol. 10th ed. 2009. (ENG., Illus.). 224p. pap. 26.00 *(978-0-9697667-6-6(9))* Vancouver Island Hiking Trails Society CAN. Dist: Orca Bk. Pubs. USA.

Pashby, Christie. Frommer's Banff & the Canadian Rockies Day by Day. 2010. (Frommer's Day by Day - Pocket Ser.: 177). (ENG., Illus.). 184p. pap. 12.99 *(978-0-470-73628-9(3)*, Frommers) Wiley, John & Sons, Inc.

Pashby, Christie, et al. Frommer's Best Hiking Trips in British Columbia. 2009. (Frommer's Best Hiking Trips Ser.: 9). (ENG., Illus.). 288p. pap. 19.99 *(978-0-470-15990-3(1)*, Frommers) Wiley, John & Sons, Inc.

Philipson, Claire Leila & Whitecap Books Staff. The Little Gift Book of Whistler. 2009. (Illus.). 96p. 14.95 *(978-1-55285-991-9(6))* Whitecap Bks., Ltd. CAN. Dist: Midpoint Trade Bks., Inc.

Pole, Graeme. Rogers Pass: A History in Photographs. 2007. (Illus.). 112p. pap. *(978-1-55153-715-3(X))* Altitude Publishing Canada Ltd.

Pratt-Johnson, Betty. 151 Dives in the Protected Waters of Washington State & British Columbia. 2007. (Illus.). 457p. pap. 29.95 *(978-1-59485-043-1(7))* Mountaineers Bks., The.

Proctor, Sharon J. Time Travel in North Vancouver: A Peek into the Past. 2010. (Illus.). 112p. pap. 19.95 ***(978-0-88839-629-7(5))*** Hancock Hse. Pubs.

Randell, Roy. Pictures from Vancouver Island. 2009. 100p. pap. 43.50 *(978-0-557-03797-1(2))* Lulu Enterprises Inc.

Readicker-Henderson, Ed & Readicker-Henderson, Lynn. Adventure Guide Alaska Highway. 4th rev. ed. 2006. (Adventure Guide to the Alaska Highway Ser.). (Illus.). 496p. per. 19.99 *(978-1-58843-571-2(7))* Hunter Publishing, Inc.

Readicker-Henderson, Lynn & Readicker-Henderson, Ed. British Columbia: Adventure Guide. (Adventure Guide Ser.). (Illus.). 384p. pap. 19.99 *(978-1-58843-366-4(8))* Hunter Publishing, Inc.

Reid, D. C. Maximum Salmon: Fishing the West Coast from Alaska to California. unabr. ed. 2007. (ENG., Illus.). 336p. pap. 9.95 *(978-1-55017-403-8(7))* Harbour Publishing Co., Ltd. CAN. Dist: Ingram Pub. Services.

Sandford, Robert. The Columbia Icefield, 1 vol. 2nd ed. 2009. (SuperGuide Ser.). (ENG., Illus.). 64p. pap. *(978-1-897522-37-0(1))* Rocky Mountain Bks.

—The Columbia Icefield: An Altitude SuperGuide. 2007. 96p. pap. *(978-1-55153-719-1(2))* Altitude Publishing Canada Ltd.

Sanford, Emerson & Beck, Janice Sanford. Historic Hikes in Northern Yoho National Park, 1 vol. rev. ed. 2008. (Life of the Trail Ser.). (ENG., Illus.). 216p. pap. *(978-1-897522-00-4(2))* Rocky Mountain Bks.

—Life of the Trail 3: The Historic Route from Old Bow Fort to Jasper, 1 vol. 2009. (ENG., Illus.). 224p. pap. *(978-1-897522-41-7(X))* Rocky Mountain Bks.

—Life of the Trail 5: Historic Hikes Around Mount Assiniboine & in Kananaskis Country, 1 vol. 2010. (ENG., Illus.). 224p. pap. *(978-1-897522-80-6(0))* Rocky Mountain Bks.

Schreiber, John. Stranger Wycott's Place: Stories from the Cariboo - Chilcotin. 2008. (ENG., Illus.). 128p. pap. *(978-1-55420-037-5(7))* New Star Bks., Ltd.

Schreiner, John. John Schreiner's BC Coastal Wine Tour Guide: The Wineries of the Fraser Valley, Vancouver, Vancouver Island, & the Gulf Islands. 2011. 224p. pap. 19.95 *(978-1-77050-042-6(1))* Whitecap Bks., Ltd. CAN. Dist: Midpoint Trade Bks., Inc.

Schreiner, John. John Schreiner's Okanagan Wine Tour Guide, 1 vol. 4th ed. 2012. (ENG.). 320p. pap. 19.95 ***(978-1-77050-096-9(0))*** Whitecap Bks., Ltd. CAN. Dist: Midpoint Trade Bks., Inc.

Shahriari, Shervin. North Vancouver's Lonsdale Neighbourhood. 2009. (Images of America Ser.). (ENG., Illus.). 128p. pap. 21.99 *(978-0-7385-7211-6(X))* Arcadia Publishing.

Sherwood, Jay. Return to Northern British Columbia: A Photojournal of Frank Swannell, 1929-39, 1 vol. 2010. (ENG., Illus.). 192p. pap. *(978-0-7726-6283-5(5))* Royal British Columbia Museum.

Spalding, David A. E. Enchanted Isles: The Southern Gulf Islands. unabr. ed. 2007. (ENG., Illus.). 144p. 34.95 *(978-1-55017-422-9(3))* Harbour Publishing Co., Ltd. CAN. Dist: Ingram Pub. Services.

Stone, Philip. Coastal Hikes: A Guide to West Coast Hiking in British Columbia & Washington State. 2007. (Wild Isle Guide Ser.). (Illus.). 183p. per. *(978-0-9680766-7-5(X))* Wild Isle Pubns.

Strong, Janice. Mountain Footsteps: Hikes in the East Kootenay of Southeastern British Columbia, 1 vol. 3rd rev. ed. 2009. (ENG., Illus.). 280p. pap. *(978-1-897522-43-1(6))* Rocky Mountain Bks.

Stutfield, Hugh E. M. & Collie, J. Norman. Climbs & Exploration in the Canadian Rockies, 1 vol. rev. ed. 2008. (Mountain Classics Collection). (ENG.). 376p. pap. *(978-1-897522-06-6(1))* Rocky Mountain Bks.

Thirkell, Fred & Scullion, Bob. Greetings from British Columbia: A Journey in Vintage Postcards, 1 vol. 6th rev. ed. 2009. (ENG., Illus.). 176p. pap. *(978-1-894974-63-9(8))* Heritage Hse.

Thomas Cook Publishing Staff. Driving Guides Vancouver & British Columbia. 4th ed. 2010. (Drive Around - Thomas Cook Ser.). (ENG., Illus.). 288p. pap. 26.95 *(978-1-84848-331-6(7))* Cook, Thomas Publishing GBR. Dist: Globe Pequot Pr., The.

Truscott, Gerald. Free Spirit: Stories of You, Me & BC, 1 vol. 2010. (ENG.). 180p. pap. *(978-0-7726-5870-8(6))* Royal British Columbia Museum.

Ulysses Travel Guide Staff. Vancouver & Victoria. 4th rev. ed. (Illus.). 336p. pap. 14.95 *(978-2-89464-517-8(1))* Ulysses Travel Guides CAN. Dist: Hunter Publishing, Inc.

Vancouver Island Trails Society Staff, contrib. by. Hiking Trails I: Victoria & Vicinity. 13th ed. 2007. (ENG., Illus.). 176p. per. 24.95 *(978-0-9697667-5-9(0))* Vancouver Island Hiking Trails Society CAN. Dist: Orca Bk. Pubs. USA.

Vancouver/Victoria Whistler 2009. 2009. (CITY GUIDE-INTERNATIONAL Ser.). 192p. 17.95 *(978-0-8416-0884-9(9))* Langenscheidt Publishing Group.

Vogler, Stephen. Top of the Pass: Whistler & the Sea to Sky Country. unabr. ed. 2007. (ENG., Illus.). 144p. 34.95 *(978-1-55017-430-4(4))* Harbour Publishing Co., Ltd. CAN. Dist: Ingram Pub. Services.

Walbran, John T. British Columbia Coast Names, 1 vol. (ENG.). 576p. pap. 29.95 *(978-0-88894-143-5(9))* D&M Pubs. Inc. CAN. Dist: Perseus-PGW.

Walls, John. Celebrating Victoria, 1 vol. 2010. (ENG., Illus.). 32p. pap. *(978-1-926613-76-5(7))* Heritage Hse.

Weiss, Star. Havens in a Hectic World: Finding Sacred Places, 1 vol. 2008. (ENG., Illus.). 240p. pap. *(978-1-894898-69-0(9))* TouchWood Editions.

Wilcox, Walter. The Rockies of Canada: A Revised & Enlarged Edition of Camping in the Canadian Rockies, 1 vol. rev. ed. 2009. (Mountain Classics Collection). (ENG., Illus.). 216p. pap. *(978-1-897522-14-1(2))* Rocky Mountain Bks.

Wild, Paula. The Comox Valley: Courtenay, Comox, Cumberland & Area. unabr. ed. 2006. (ENG., Illus.). 143p. 34.95 *(978-1-55017-408-3(8))* Harbour Publishing Co., Ltd. CAN. Dist: Ingram Pub. Services.

Williams, Huw, ed. Snowfinder Canada. 2008. (ENG.). 400p. pap. 12.95 *(978-0-9775569-3-9(X))* Wavefinder, Ltd. AUS. Dist: SCB Distributors.

Windh, Jacqueline. The Wild Side Guide to Vancouver Island's Pacific Rim: Long Beach, Tofino, Ucluelet, Port Alberni, Nitinat & Bamfield. 2nd unabr. rev. ed. 2010. (ENG., Illus.). 192p. pap. *(978-1-55017-485-4(1))* Harbour Publishing Co., Ltd.

Yeadon-Jones, Anne & Yeadon-Jones, Laurence. Gulf Islands & Vancouver: A Dreamspeaker Cruising Guide, Volume 1. 2010. *(978-1-932310-43-6(6))* FineEdge.Com LLC.

—The West Coast of Vancouver Island. 2008. pap. *(978-1-932310-38-2(X))* FineEdge.Com LLC.

BRITISH COLUMBIA—ECONOMIC CONDITIONS

Hak, Gordon. Capital & Labour in the British Columbia Forest Industry, 1934-74. 2007. (ENG., Illus.). 272p. pap. 29.95 *(978-0-7748-1308-2(3))* UBC Pr. CAN. Dist: Univ. of Washington Pr.

—Capital & Labour in the British Columbia Forest Industry, 1934-74. 2007. (ENG., Illus.). 272p. *(978-0-7748-1307-5(5))* Univ. of British Columbia Pr.

Schnerch, Patrick J. City of Gardens: the Other Side of the Fence. Part 1. 2009. 306p. pap. 25.00 *(978-1-4251-8792-7(7))* Trafford Publishing.

BRITISH COLUMBIA—HISTORY

Amos, Robert & Wong, Kileasa. Inside Chinatown: Ancient Culture in a New World, 1 vol. 2010. (ENG., Illus.). 160p. pap. *(978-1-894898-91-1(5))* TouchWood Editions.

Armitage, Doreen. Tales from the Galley: Stories of the Working Waterfront. unabr. ed. (ENG., Illus.). 198p. 39.95 *(978-1-55017-438-0(X))* Harbour Publishing Co., Ltd. CAN. Dist: Ingram Pub. Services.

Bachusky, Johnnie. Ghost Town Stories of BC: Tales of Hope, Heroism & Tragedy, 1 vol. 2009. (Amazing Stories Ser.). (ENG., Illus.). 136p. pap. *(978-1-894974-73-8(5))* Heritage Hse.

Bancroft, Hubert Howe. History of British Columbia, 1792-1887. 2009. 606p. pap. *(978-1-150-66911-8(X))* Books LLC.

—History of the Pacific States of North America. 2009. 558p. pap. *(978-0-217-00586-9(1))*; 654p. pap. *(978-0-217-00580-7(2))*; 618p. pap. *(978-0-217-00574-6(8))*; 630p. pap. *(978-0-217-00570-8(5))*; 556p. pap. *(978-0-217-69970-9(7))*; 566p. pap. *(978-0-217-95996-4(2))*; 540p. pap. *(978-0-217-93256-1(8))*; 628p. pap. *(978-0-217-93268-4(1))*; 550p. pap. *(978-0-217-93272-1(X))*; 514p. pap. *(978-0-217-00564-7(0))*; 558p. pap. *(978-0-217-22516-8(0))*; 710p. pap. *(978-0-217-22513-7(6))* Books LLC.

—History of the Pacific States of North America. 2009. 612p. pap. 38.14 *(978-0-217-95991-9(1))* General Bks. LLC.

—History of the Pacific States of North America, 34 vol., set. reprint ed. 4250.00 *(978-0-7222-7072-1(0))* Library Reprints, Inc.

Barman, Jean. The West Beyond the West: A History of British Columbia. 3rd rev. ed. 2007. (ENG., Illus.). 480p. *(978-0-8020-9309-7(4))*; pap. *(978-0-8020-9495-7(3))* Univ. of Toronto Pr.

Beck, Janice. Three Towns: A History of Kitimat: Fourth Reprint: 1983. 2010. 100p. pap. 22.00 *(978-1-4269-2629-7(4))* Trafford Publishing.

Belshaw, John Douglas. Becoming British Columbia: A Population History. 2009. (ENG.). 320p. pap. 32.95 *(978-0-7748-1546-8(9))* UBC Pr. CAN. Dist: Univ. of Washington Pr.

—Becoming British Columbia: A Population History. 2009. (ENG., Illus.). 288p. *(978-0-7748-1545-1(0))* Univ. of British Columbia Pr.

Bramham, Daphne. The Secret Lives of Saints: Child Brides & Lost Boys in a Polygamous Mormon Sect. 2009. (ENG., Illus.). 496p. pap. 18.00 *(978-0-307-35589-8(6)*, Vintage Canada) Random Hse. of Canada, Ltd. CAN. Dist: Random Hse., Inc.

Cameron, Derek. A Journey to the Retreat Centers of British Columbia: Illustrated with Photographs. 2009. (Illus.). 124p. pap. 10.95 *(978-0-9800817-5-6(0))* Eremitical Pr.

Cherrington, John A. The Fraser Valley: A History. unabr. ed. (ENG., Illus.). 392p. 46.95 *(978-1-55017-068-9(6))* Harbour Publishing Co., Ltd. CAN. Dist: Ingram Pub. Services.

Coats, Robert Hamilton. Sir James Douglas. (Makers of Canada Ser.). 369p. reprint ed. 98.00 *(978-0-7222-6899-5(8))*; 98.00 *(978-0-7222-6925-1(0))* Library Reprints, Inc.

Dalton, Anthony. The Graveyard of the Pacific: Shipwreck Tales from the Depths of History, 1 vol. 2010. (Amazing Stories Ser.). (ENG., Illus.). 128p. pap. *(978-1-926613-31-4(7))* Heritage Hse.

Dalzell, Kathleen E. The Beloved Island, Vol. 3. unabr. ed. (Queen Charlotte Islands Ser.). (ENG., Illus.). 192p. 26.95 *(978-1-55017-008-5(2))* Harbour Publishing Co., Ltd. CAN. Dist: Ingram Pub. Services.

—The Queen Charlotte Islands Vol. 2: Places & Names. 2nd unabr. ed. (Queen Charlotte Islands Ser.). (ENG., Illus.). 472p. pap. 26.95 *(978-1-55017-011-5(2))* Harbour Publishing Co., Ltd. CAN. Dist: Ingram Pub. Services.

—The Queen Charlotte Islands, 1774-1966, Vol. 1. unabr. ed. (Queen Charlotte Islands Ser.). (ENG., Illus.). 340p. pap. 26.95 *(978-1-55017-312-3(X))* Harbour Publishing Co., Ltd. CAN. Dist: Ingram Pub. Services.

Dawe, Helen. Helen Dawe's Sechelt. unabr. ed. (ENG., Illus.). 152p. *(978-1-55017-027-6(9))* Harbour Publishing Co., Ltd.

Dinwoodie, David W. Reserve Memories: The Power of the Past in a Chilcotin Community. 2007. (Studies in the Anthropology of North American Indians). (ENG., Illus.). 120p. pap. 19.95 *(978-0-8032-2246-5(7))* Univ. of Nebraska Pr.

Doherty, Laura Ricketson. Annie Ricketson¿s Journal:: the Remarkable Voyage of the Only Woman Aboard a Whaling Ship with Her Sea Captain Husband & Crew, 1871-1874. 2010. pap. 17.00 *(978-0-7884-5048-8(4))* Heritage Bks.

Doherty, Laura Ricketson. Annie Ricketson's Journal: The Remarkable Voyage of the Only Woman Aboard a Whaling Ship with Her Sea Captain Husband & Crew, 1871-1874. 2010. (Illus.). xii, 78p. ***(978-0-7884-8312-7(9))*** Heritage Bks.

Downes, David A. Gerard Manley Hopkins: A Study of His Ignatian Spirit. 2011. 192p. 42.95 ***(978-1-258-02802-2(6))*** Literary Licensing, LLC.

Evenden, Matthew D. Fish versus Power: An Environmental History of the Fraser River. 2007. (Studies in Environment & History). (ENG., Illus.). 328p. (C). pap. 42.00 *(978-0-521-04103-4(1))* Cambridge Univ. Pr.

Ferguson, Julie H. James Douglas: Father of British Columbia. 2009. (Quest Biography Ser.). (ENG., Illus.). 240p. pap. 19.99 *(978-1-55488-409-4(8))* Dundurn CAN. Dist: Ingram Pub. Services.

Forsythe, Mark & Dickson, Greg. The Trail Of 1858: British Columbia's Gold Rush Past. unabr. ed. 2007. (ENG., Illus.). 250p. pap. 26.95 *(978-1-55017-424-3(X))* Harbour Publishing Co., Ltd. CAN. Dist: Ingram Pub. Services.

Harbord, Heather. Desolation Sound: A History. unabr. ed. 2007. (ENG., Illus.). 256p. pap. 24.95 *(978-1-55017-407-6(X))* Harbour Publishing Co., Ltd. CAN. Dist: Ingram Pub. Services.

Harris, Yvonne. Everything about British Columbia. 2009. (ENG.). 256p. pap. *(978-1-894864-76-3(X))* Folklore Publishing CAN. Dist: Lone Pine Publishing.

Harvey, Al. Wild Beauty: A Visual Exploration of BC, 1 vol. 2010. (ENG., Illus.). 128p. pap. *(978-1-894974-93-6(X))* Heritage Hse.

Hayes, Derek. Historical Atlas of British Columbia & the Pacific Northwest: Maps of Exploration-British Columbia, Washington, Oregon, Alaska & Yukon. 55.00 *(978-1-55289-900-7(4))* D&M Pubs. Inc. CAN. Dist: Perseus-PGW.

Henry, Tom. Westcoasters: Boats That Built BC. 2nd unabr. ed. (ENG., Illus.). 192p. pap. 28.95 *(978-1-55017-233-1(6))* Harbour Publishing Co., Ltd. CAN. Dist: Ingram Pub. Services.

Hume, Stephen. Simon Fraser: In Search of Modern British Columbia. unabr. ed. 2008. (ENG., Illus.). 336p. 36.95 *(978-1-55017-434-2(7))* Harbour Publishing Co., Ltd. CAN. Dist: Ingram Pub. Services.

Iglauer, Edith. The Strangers Next Door. unabr. ed. (ENG.). 304p. 32.95 *(978-1-55017-054-2(6))* Harbour Publishing Co., Ltd. CAN. Dist: Ingram Pub. Services.

Keddie, Grant. Songhees Pictorial: A History of the Songhees People As Seen by Outsiders,(1790-1912), 1 vol. 2010. (ENG., Illus.). 176p. pap. *(978-0-7726-4964-5(2))* Royal British Columbia Museum.

Keller, Betty & Leslie, Rosella. Bright Seas, Pioneer Spirits: A History of the Sunshine Coast, 1 vol. rev. ed. 2009. (ENG., Illus.). 256p. pap. *(978-1-894898-87-4(7))* TouchWood Editions.

Kennedy, Liv. Coastal Villages. unabr. ed. (ENG., Illus.). 176p. *(978-1-55017-057-3(0))* Harbour Publishing Co., Ltd.

Kutz, David. Burgee Premier Marina Guidebook. 2011. pap. 26.95 *(978-0-9641934-8-2(5))* Pierside Publishing.

Lambert, Barbara Ann. Old-Time Stories: Billy-Goat Smith, a Powell River Co. Xmas, Mr. Dippie, & Others. 2006. (Illus.). 244p. per. 21.74 *(978-1-4251-0039-1(2))* Trafford Publishing.

Laut, Agnes C. The Cariboo Trail: A Chronicle of the Gold-Fields of British Columbia. (Chronicles of Canada Ser.). 115p. reprint ed. 88.00 *(978-0-7222-6770-7(3))* Library Reprints, Inc.

Logan, Don. Canoe Creek B C. 2011. 144p. pap. ***(978-1-4269-5875-5(7))*** Trafford Publishing (UK) Ltd.

Mahood, Ian & Drushka, Ken. Three Men & a Forester. unabr. ed. (ENG., Illus.). 240p. *(978-1-55017-016-0(3))* Harbour Publishing Co., Ltd.

Malanchuk, Terry. Blakeburn-British Columbia's Forgotten Ghost Town-Revised Second Edition. 2008. 228p. pap. 24.95 *(978-0-557-03095-8(1))* Lulu Enterprises Inc.

—It was a good Blakeburn. 2008. 167p. pap. 22.51 *(978-0-557-03094-1(3))* Lulu Enterprises Inc.

Mason, Adrienne. Long Beach Wild: A Celebration of People & Place on Canada's Rugged Western Shore, 1 vol. 2012. (ENG., Illus.). 224p. pap. 22.95 ***(978-1-55365-344-8(0)***, Greystone Bks.) D&M Pubs. Inc. CAN. Dist: Perseus-PGW.

Mather, Ken. Buckaroos & Mud Pups: The Early Days of Ranching in British Columbia, 1 vol. 2010. (ENG., Illus.). 224p. per. *(978-1-894974-09-7(3))* Heritage Hse.

Mawani, Renisa. Colonial Proximities: Crossracial Encounters & Juridical Truths in British Columbia, 1871-1921. 2010. (ENG.). 288p. pap. 35.95 *(978-0-7748-1634-2(1))* Univ. of Washington Pr.

McKirdy, Margaret. The Colour of Gold. unabr. ed. (ENG., Illus.). 208p. pap. *(978-0-920576-66-3(4))* Caitlin Pr., Inc.

Miles, Fraser. Slow Boat on Rum Row. unabr. ed. (ENG., Illus.). 200p. *(978-1-55017-069-6(4))* Harbour Publishing Co., Ltd.

Mindenhall, Dorothy. Unbuilt Victoria. 2012. (ENG., Illus.). 248p. pap. 28.99 ***(978-1-4597-0174-8(7))*** Dundurn CAN. Dist: Ingram Pub. Services.

Mole, Rich. The Chilcotin War: A Tale of Death & Reprisal, 1 vol. 2010. (Amazing Stories Ser.). (ENG., Illus.). 144p. pap. *(978-1-894974-96-7(4))* Heritage Hse.

—Rebel Women of the West Coast: Their Triumphs, Tragedies & Lasting Legacies, 1 vol. 2010. (Amazing Stories Ser.). (ENG., Illus.). 144p. pap. *(978-1-926613-28-4(7))* Heritage Hse.

Murton, James. Creating a Modern Countryside: Liberalism & Land Resettlement in British Columbia. 2007. (Nature, History, Society Ser.). (ENG., Illus.). 280p. *(978-0-7748-1337-2(7))* Univ. of British Columbia Pr.

Nicholson, R. W. Lost Creek Mine: Historical Analysis of the Legendary Gold Deposit of Pitt Lake. 2008. (Illus.). 83p. 51.99 *(978-1-4363-2192-1(1))* Xlibris Corp.

Outram, James. In the Heart of the Canadian Rockies. 2009. 488p. 53.95 *(978-1-104-21783-9(X))*; pap. 38.95 *(978-1-104-18283-0(1))* Kessinger Publishing, LLC.

—In the Heart of the Canadian Rockies, 1 vol. 2007. (Mountain Classics Collection). (ENG.). 312p. per. *(978-1-894765-96-1(6))* Rocky Mountain Bks.

Peterson, Jan. Harbour City: Nanaimo in Transition, 1920-1967, 1 vol. 2006. (ENG., Illus.). 240p. per. *(978-1-894974-20-2(4))* Heritage Hse.

Phillips, Ray. The Little Green Valley: The Kleindale Story. 2010. (ENG., Illus.). 288p. pap. *(978-1-55017-483-0(5))* Harbour Publishing Co., Ltd.

Pole, Graeme. Gravity, Steam & Steel: An Illustrated Railway History of Rogue Pass, 1 vol. 2012. (ENG., Illus.). 128p. pap. 16.95 ***(978-1-897252-46-8(3))*** Fifth Hse. Pubs. CAN. Dist: Ingram Pub. Services.
Pole, Graeme. Rogers Pass: A History in Photographs. 2007. (Illus.). 112p. pap. *(978-1-55153-715-3(X))* Altitude Publishing Canada Ltd.
Rajala, Richard A. & Rajala. Up-Coast: Forests & Industry on British Columbia's North Coast, 1870-2005, 1 vol. 2010. (ENG., Illus.). 304p. *(978-0-7726-5460-1(3))* Royal British Columbia Museum.
Reimer, Chad. Writing British Columbia History, 1784-1958. 2010. (ENG.). 216p. pap. 32.95 *(978-0-7748-1645-8(7))* UBC Pr. CAN. Dist: Univ. of Washington Pr.
Reksten, Terry. Illustrated History of British Columbia. (Illus.). pap. 40.00 *(978-1-55365-111-6(1))* D&M Pubs. Inc. CAN. Dist: Perseus-PGW.
Roberts Creek Historical Committee. Remembering Roberts Creek: 1889 - 1955. unabr. ed. 2008. (ENG., Illus.). 190p. pap. 24.95 *(978-1-55017-457-1(6))* Harbour Publishing Co., Ltd. CAN. Dist: Ingram Pub. Services.
Ross, Becki. Burlesque West: Showgirls, Sex, & Sin in Postwar Vancouver. 2009. (Illus.). 368p. *(978-0-8020-9698-2(0))*; pap. *(978-0-8020-9646-3(8))* Univ. of Toronto Pr.
Roy, Patricia E. Triumph of Citizenship (the) The Japanese & Chinese in Canada, 1941-67. 2007. (ENG., Illus.). 400p. *(978-0-7748-1380-8(6))* Univ. of British Columbia Pr.
Safarik, Norman & Safarik, Allan. Bluebacks & Silver Brights: A Lifetime in the BC Fish Industry from Bounty to Plunder. 2012. (ENG.). 280p. pap. 22.95 ***(978-1-77041-041-1(4))*** ECW Pr. CAN. Dist: Independent Pubs. Group.
Schreiber, John. Stranger Wycott's Place: Stories from the Cariboo - Chilcotin. 2008. (ENG., Illus.). 128p. pap. *(978-1-55420-037-5(7))* New Star Bks., Ltd.
Scott, Andrew. Encyclopedia of Raincoast Place Names: A Complete Reference to Coastal British Columbia. unabr. ed. 2009. (ENG., Illus.). 664p. 49.95 *(978-1-55017-484-7(3))* Harbour Publishing Co., Ltd. CAN. Dist: Ingram Pub. Services.
Shahriari, Shervin. North Vancouver's Lonsdale Neighbourhood. 2009. (Images of America Ser.). (ENG., Illus.). 128p. pap. 21.99 *(978-0-7385-7211-6(X))* Arcadia Publishing.
Sherwood. Surveying Central British Columbia: A Photojournal of Frank Swannell, 1920-1928, 1 vol. Sherwood, Jay, ed. 2010. (ENG., Illus.). 192p. pap. *(978-0-7726-5742-8(4))* Royal British Columbia Museum.
Sherwood, Jay. Return to Northern British Columbia: A Photojournal of Frank Swannell, 1929-39, 1 vol. 2010. (ENG., Illus.). 192p. pap. *(978-0-7726-6283-5(5))* Royal British Columbia Museum.
Smith, Keith D. Liberalism, Surveillance, & Resistance: Indigenous Communities in Western Canada, 1877-1927. 2009. (ENG.). 256p. pap. 37.95 *(978-1-897425-39-8(2))* UBC Pr. CAN. Dist: Univ. of Washington Pr.
Spalding, David A. E. Enchanted Isles: The Southern Gulf Islands. unabr. ed. 2007. (ENG., Illus.). 144p. 34.95 *(978-1-55017-422-9(3))* Harbour Publishing Co., Ltd. CAN. Dist: Ingram Pub. Services.
Stock, Eugene. Metlakahtla & the North Pacific Missio. 2006. pap. *(978-1-4068-3058-3(5))* Echo Library.
Taylor, Jeanette. The Quadra Story: A History of Quadra Island. 2009. (ENG., Illus.). 272p. 32.95 *(978-1-55017-488-5(6))* Harbour Publishing Co., Ltd. CAN. Dist: Ingram Pub. Services.
—Tidal Passages: A History of the Discovery Islands. unabr. ed. 2009. (Illus.). (ENG.). 316p. pap. 24.95 *(978-1-55017-460-1(6))*; 400p. 36.95 *(978-1-55017-435-9(5))* Harbour Publishing Co., Ltd. CAN. Dist: Ingram Pub. Services.
Thirkell, Fred & Scullion, Bob. Greetings from British Columbia: A Journey in Vintage Postcards, 1 vol. 6th rev. ed. 2009. (ENG., Illus.). 176p. pap. *(978-1-894974-63-9(8))* Heritage Hse.
Tickner, Florence. Raincoast Chronicles 14: Fish Hooks & Caulk Boots. (ENG., Illus.). 80p. (Orig.). pap. *(978-1-55017-078-8(3))* Harbour Publishing Co., Ltd.
Truscott, Gerald. Free Spirit: Stories of You, Me & BC, 1 vol. 2010. (ENG.). 180p. pap. *(978-0-7726-5870-8(6))* Royal British Columbia Museum.
Twigg, Alan. Thompson's Highway: British Columbia's Fur Trade, 1800-1850. 2006. (ENG., Illus.). 254p. per. *(978-1-55380-039-2(7))* Ronsdale Pr.
Vancouver Province Staff. The Way We Were: BC's Amazing Journey to the Millennium. unabr. ed. (ENG., Illus.). 160p. pap. *(978-1-55017-230-0(1))* Harbour Publishing Co., Ltd.
Vogler, Stephen. Only in Whistler: Tales of a Mountain Town. unabr. ed. 2009. (ENG., Illus.). 240p. pap. 24.95 *(978-1-55017-504-2(1))* Harbour Publishing Co., Ltd. CAN. Dist: Ingram Pub. Services.
—Top of the Pass: Whistler & the Sea to Sky Country. unabr. ed. 2007. (ENG., Illus.). 144p. 34.95 *(978-1-55017-430-4(4))* Harbour Publishing Co., Ltd. CAN. Dist: Ingram Pub. Services.
White, Bob. Bannock & Beans: A Cowboy's Account of the Bedaux Expedition, 1 vol. Sherwood, Jay, ed. 2010. (ENG., Illus.). 224p. pap. *(978-0-7726-6060-2(3))* Royal British Columbia Museum.
White, Howard. Writing in the Rain. unabr. ed. (ENG.). 256p. pap. 16.95 *(978-1-55017-010-8(4))* Harbour Publishing Co., Ltd. CAN. Dist: Ingram Pub. Services.
White, Howard, ed. Raincoast Chronicles 12. unabr. ed. (Raincoast Chronicles Ser.: Vol. 12). (ENG., Illus.). 76p. pap. *(978-1-55017-028-3(7))* Harbour Publishing Co., Ltd.
—Raincoast Chronicles 13. 13th ed. (ENG., Illus.). 80p. pap. *(978-1-55017-052-8(X))* Harbour Publishing Co., Ltd.
—Raincoast Chronicles 15. unabr. ed. (ENG., Illus.). 80p. (Orig.). pap. *(978-1-55017-091-7(0))* Harbour Publishing Co., Ltd.
—Raincoast Chronicles 18. unabr. ed. (Raincoast Chronicles Ser.). (ENG., Illus.). 80p. pap. 16.95 *(978-1-55017-171-6(2))* Harbour Publishing Co., Ltd. CAN. Dist: Ingram Pub. Services.
—Raincoast Chronicles 19: Stories & History of the British Columbia Coast. unabr. ed. (Raincoast Chronicles Ser.). (ENG., Illus.). 80p. pap. 16.95 *(978-1-55017-316-1(2))* Harbour Publishing Co., Ltd. CAN. Dist: Ingram Pub. Services.
White, Howard & Spilsbury, Jim. Spilsbury's Album: Photographs & Reminiscences of the BC Coast. 2nd unabr. ed. (Spilsbury Saga Ser.). (ENG., Illus.). 178p. reprint ed. pap. 26.95 *(978-1-55017-126-6(7))* Harbour Publishing Co., Ltd. CAN. Dist: Ingram Pub. Services.
Wild, Paula. The Comox Valley: Courtenay, Comox, Cumberland & Area. unabr. ed. 2006. (ENG., Illus.). 143p. 34.95 *(978-1-55017-408-3(8))* Harbour Publishing Co., Ltd. CAN. Dist: Ingram Pub. Services.
—Sointula: An Island Utopia. unabr. ed. 2007. (ENG., Illus.). 224p. per. 24.95 *(978-1-55017-456-4(8))* Harbour Publishing Co., Ltd. CAN. Dist: Ingram Pub. Services.
Wolf, Jim & Owen, Patricia. Yi Fao: Speaking Through Memory - A History of New Westminster's Chinese Community,1858-1980, 1 vol. rev. ed. 2008. (ENG., Illus.). 144p. pap. *(978-1-894974-40-0(9))* Heritage Hse.
Wood, June. Nechako Country: In the Footsteps of Bert Irvine, 1 vol. 2007. (ENG., Illus.). 192p. pap. *(978-1-894974-27-1(1))* Heritage Hse.

BRITISH COLUMBIA—POLITICS AND GOVERNMENT

Cran, Gregory J. Negotiating Buck Naked: Doukhobors, Public Policy, & Conflict Resolution, 1 vol. 2007. (ENG., Illus.). 192p. per. 29.95 *(978-0-7748-1259-7(1))* UBC Pr. CAN. Dist: Univ. of Washington Pr.
Greskiw, Garth East. Communicating 'Forest' 2008. 240p. pap. *(978-3-639-05980-9(8))* VDM Verlag Dr. Mueller e.K.
Herath, R. B. Real Power to the People: A Novel Approach to Electoral Reform in British Columbia. 2007. (ENG., Illus.). 244p. per. 41.99 *(978-0-7618-3685-8(3))* Univ. Pr. of America, Inc.
Mair, Rafe. Over the Mountains: More Thoughts on Things That Matter. 2006. (ENG.). 304p. pap. *(978-1-55017-371-0(5))* Harbour Publishing Co., Ltd.
Mar, Lisa Rose. Brokering Belonging: Chinese in Canada's Exclusion ERA, 1885-1945. 2010. (ENG., Illus.). 256p. 99.00 *(978-0-19-973313-2(9))*; pap. 24.95 *(978-0-19-973314-9(7))* Oxford Univ. Pr., Inc.
Ommer, Rosemary E. Coasts under Stress: Restructuring & Social-Ecological Health. 2007. (ENG., Illus.). 592p. (C). *(978-0-7735-3203-8(X))* McGill-Queen's Univ. Pr.
Ommer, Rosemary E. & Coasts Under Stress Research Project Team Staff. Coasts under Stress: Restructuring & Social-Ecological Health. 2007. (ENG., Illus.). 592p. (C). pap. *(978-0-7735-3225-0(0))* McGill-Queen's Univ. Pr.
Pearse, Hilary & Warren, Mark. Designing Deliberative Democracy: The British Columbia Citizens' Assembly. Warren, Mark E. & Pearse, Hilary, eds. 2008. (Theories of Institutional Design Ser.). (ENG., Illus.). 252p. 90.00 *(978-0-521-88507-2(8))* Cambridge Univ. Pr.
Srikanth, H. Indigenous Peoples in Liberal Democratic States: A Comparative Study of Conflict & Accommodation in Canada & India. 2010. (Illus.). 262p. pap. 24.95 *(978-0-9820467-4-6(X))* Bauu Institute.
Williston, Eileen & Keller, Betty. Forests, Power & Policy: The Legacy of Ray Williston. unabr. ed. (ENG., Illus.). 318p. pap. *(978-0-920576-69-4(9))* Caitlin Pr., Inc.

BRITISH COLUMBIA—SOCIAL LIFE AND CUSTOMS

Belshaw, John Douglas & Purvey, Diane. Private Grief, Public Mourning: The Rise of the Roadside Shrine in British Columbia. 2009. (ENG., Illus.). 160p. pap. 20.00 *(978-1-895636-99-4(X))* Anvil Pr. CAN. Dist: Univ. of Toronto Pr.
Cheng, Pang Guek. Cultureshock Vancouver. 2007. 288p. pap. 15.95 *(978-0-7614-5417-5(9))* Marshall Cavendish Corp.
Cultureshock Staff, ed. Cultureshock Vancouver, 1 vol. 2010. (ENG., Illus.). 240p. pap. 15.95 *(978-0-7614-5879-1(4))* Marshall Cavendish Corp.
Dinwoodie, David W. Reserve Memories: The Power of the Past in a Chilcotin Community. 2007. (Studies in the Anthropology of North American Indians). (ENG., Illus.). 120p. pap. 19.95 *(978-0-8032-2246-5(7))* Univ. of Nebraska Pr.
Lambert, Barbara Ann. Old-Time Stories: Billy-Goat Smith, a Powell River Co. Xmas, Mr. Dippie, & Others. 2006. (Illus.). 244p. per. 21.74 *(978-1-4251-0039-1(2))* Trafford Publishing.
Leiren-Young, Mark. Never Shoot a Stampede Queen: A Rookie Reporter in the Cariboo, 1 vol. rev. ed. 2009. (ENG., Illus.). 224p. pap. *(978-1-894974-52-3(2))* Heritage Hse.
Roth, Christopher Fritz & Roth, Christopher F. Becoming Tsimshian: The Social Life of Names. 2008. (ENG., Illus.). 296p. (C). 60.00 *(978-0-295-98806-1(1))*; pap. 26.95 *(978-0-295-98807-8(X))* Univ. of Washington Pr.
Savard, David. Images from the Likeness House, 1 vol. 2010. (ENG., Illus.). 224p. pap. *(978-0-7726-6150-0(2))* Royal British Columbia Museum.
Schnerch, Patrick J. City of Gardens: the Other Side of the Fence. Part 1. 2009. 306p. pap. 25.00 *(978-1-4251-8792-7(7))* Trafford Publishing.
White, Howard, ed. Raincoast Chronicles 12. unabr. ed. (Raincoast Chronicles Ser.: Vol. 12). (ENG., Illus.). 76p. pap. *(978-1-55017-028-3(7))* Harbour Publishing Co., Ltd.
—Raincoast Chronicles 13. 13th ed. (ENG., Illus.). 80p. pap. *(978-1-55017-052-8(X))* Harbour Publishing Co., Ltd.
—Raincoast Chronicles 15. unabr. ed. (ENG., Illus.). 80p. (Orig.). pap. *(978-1-55017-091-7(0))* Harbour Publishing Co., Ltd.
—Raincoast Chronicles 18. unabr. ed. (Raincoast Chronicles Ser.). (ENG., Illus.). 80p. pap. 16.95 *(978-1-55017-171-6(2))* Harbour Publishing Co., Ltd. CAN. Dist: Ingram Pub. Services.
—Raincoast Chronicles 19: Stories & History of the British Columbia Coast. unabr. ed. (Raincoast Chronicles Ser.). (ENG., Illus.). 80p. pap. 16.95 *(978-1-55017-316-1(2))* Harbour Publishing Co., Ltd. CAN. Dist: Ingram Pub. Services.
White, Howard & Spilsbury, Jim. Spilsbury's Album: Photographs & Reminiscences of the BC Coast. 2nd unabr. ed. (Spilsbury Saga Ser.). (ENG., Illus.). 178p. reprint ed. pap. 26.95 *(978-1-55017-126-6(7))* Harbour Publishing Co., Ltd. CAN. Dist: Ingram Pub. Services.

BRITISH COLUMBIA, UNIVERSITY OF
see University of British Columbia

BRITISH COMMONWEALTH COUNTRIES
see Commonwealth Countries

BRITISH COMMONWEALTH OF NATIONS
see Commonwealth Countries

BRITISH COOKING
see Cooking, British

BRITISH DOMINIONS
see Commonwealth Countries

BRITISH DRAWING
see Drawing, British

BRITISH EMPIRE
see Great Britain—Colonies

BRITISH GUIANA
see Guyana

BRITISH HONDURAS
see Belize

BRITISH IN THE UNITED STATES
see British—United States

BRITISH LEYLAND AUTOMOBILES
see BLMC Automobiles

BRITISH LITERATURE
see English Literature; Irish Literature; Scottish Literature; Welsh Literature

BRITISH MINIATURE PAINTING
see Miniature Painting, British

BRITISH MISSIONARIES
see Missionaries, British

BRITISH MUSEUM

Ambers, Januaryet. Holding it All Together. 2010. (ENG., Illus.). 225p. pap. 90.00 *(978-1-904982-47-5(6))* Archetype Pubns. GBR. Dist: National Bk. Network.
Arlt, C. Deine Seele moge leben fur immer und ewig. Die demotischen Mumienschilder im British Museum. 2011. (Studia Demotica Ser.). (ENG & GER., Illus.). 286p. (C). 80.00 ***(978-90-429-2471-0(3))*** Peeters Pubs. & Booksellers BEL. Dist: Brown, David Bk. Co., The.
Bailey, Donald M. Catalogue of Terracottas in the British Museum IV: Ptolemaic & Roman Terracottas from Egypt. 2008. (ENG., Illus.). 384p. (C). 240.00 *(978-0-7141-2264-9(5))* British Museum Pr. GBR. Dist: Brown, David Bk. Co., The.
Binyon, Laurence. A Catalogue of Japanese & Chinese Woodcuts Preserved in the Sub-Department of Oriental Prints & Drawings in the British Museum. 2009. *(978-1-57898-770-2(9))* Martino Publishing.
Brooks, Robin J. The Portland Vase: The Extraordinary Odyssey of a Mysterious Roman Treasure. 2006. (Illus.). 250p. reprint ed. 25.00 *(978-1-4223-5516-9(0))* DIANE Publishing Co.
Brunton, Guy. British Museum Expedition to Middle Egypt. reprint ed. 45.00 *(978-0-404-16626-7(1))* AMS Pr., Inc.
Budge, E. A. Wallis. By Nile & Tigris: A Narrative of Journeys in Egypt & Mesopotamia on Behalf of the British Museum Between the Years 1886 & 1913. 2009. *(978-1-57898-790-0(3))* Martino Publishing.
Chambers, Neil. Joseph Banks & the British Museum: The World of Collecting, 1770-1830, 1 vol. 2007. (ENG., Illus.). 210p. 99.00 *(978-1-85196-858-9(X))* Pickering & Chatto Pubs., Ltd. GBR. Dist: Ashgate Publishing Co.
Chapman, Hugo & Faletti, Marzia. Fra Angelico to Leonardo: Italian Renaissance Drawings. 2010. (Illus.). 333p. 90.00 *(978-1-84822-058-4(8))*, Lund Humphries Pubs.) Ashgate Publishing Ltd. GBR. Dist: Ashgate Publishing Co.
Coldstream, J. N. Corpus Vasorum Antiquorum, Great Britain Fascicule 25, the British Museum Fascicule 11: Greek Geometric Pottery. 2010. (Corpus Vasorum Antiquorum Ser.). (ENG., Illus.). 168p. (C). 150.00 *(978-0-7141-2263-2(7))* British Museum Pr. GBR. Dist: Brown, David Bk. Co., The.
Cowper, B. Harris. Analecta Nicaena: Fragments relating to the Council of Nice. 2010. pap. 21.28 *(978-1-61719-525-9(1))* Gorgias Pr., LLC.
Dallapiccola, Anna L. South Indian Paintings: A Catalogue of the British Museum's Collections. 2010. (ENG., Illus.). 320p. (C). 120.00 *(978-0-7141-2424-7(9))* British Museum Pr. GBR. Dist: Brown, David Bk. Co., The.
Dawson, Aileen. The Art of Worcester Porcelain, 1751-1788: Masterpieces from the British Museum Collection. 2009. (ENG., Illus.). 248p. 60.00 *(978-1-58465-752-1(9))* Univ. Pr. of New England.
—English & Irish Delftware 1570-1840. 2010. (ENG., Illus.). 320p. (C). 70.00 *(978-0-7141-2810-8(4))* British Museum Pr. GBR. Dist: Brown, David Bk. Co., The.
Dumbrill, Richard. Idiophones of the Ancient near East in the Collections of the British Museum. 2011. 118.75 *(978-1-61143-956-4(6))* Gorgias Pr., LLC.
Edwards, Edward. Lives of the Founders of the British Museum: With Notices of its Chief Augmentors & Other Benefactors, 1570-1870. 2010. (Cambridge Library Collection - Printing & Publishing History Ser.). (ENG., Illus.). 436p. pap. 32.99 *(978-1-108-01495-3(X))* 396p. pap. 31.99 *(978-1-108-01496-0(8))* Cambridge Univ. Pr.
Foster, Norman & Sudjic, Deyan. The Great Court at the British Museum. 2012. (ENG.). 96p. 29.95 ***(978-3-7913-4590-1(7))*** Prestel Publishing.
Gallo, Luciana. Lord Elgin & Ancient Greek Architecture: The Elgin Drawings at the British Museum. 2009. (ENG., Illus.). 362p. (C). 155.00 *(978-0-521-88163-0(3))* Cambridge Univ. Pr.
Garnett, Richard. Essays in Librarianship & Bibliography. 2010. 368p. pap. 32.75 *(978-1-145-03005-3(X))* 2009. 360p. 33.99 *(978-1-113-70874-8(3))* 2009. 360p. pap. 32.75 *(978-1-113-70872-4(7))* 2009. 360p. pap. 31.75 *(978-1-113-70870-0(0))* BiblioBazaar.
—Essays in Librarianship & Bibliography. 2009. 194p. pap. *(978-1-4590-4715-0(X))* Books LLC.
—Essays in Librarianship & Bibliography. 2007. (ENG.). 364p. per. *(978-1-4067-0341-2(9))* Read Bks.
Gere, Charlotte & Rudoe, Judy. Jewellery in the Age of Queen Victoria: A Mirror to the World. 2010. (ENG., Illus.). 552p. (C). 110.00 *(978-0-7141-2819-1(8))* British Museum Pr. GBR. Dist: Brown, David Bk. Co., The.
Graham-Campbell, James. The Cuerdale Hoard & Related Viking-Age Silver & Gold from Britain & Ireland in the British Museum. 2012. (BMP Research Paper Ser.: 185). (ENG., Illus.). 400p. (C). pap. 90.00 *(978-0-86159-185-5(2))* British Museum Pr. GBR. Dist: Brown, David Bk. Co., The.
Hill, J. D., ed. Masterpieces of the British Museum. 2009. (ENG., Illus.). 288p. (C). pap. 35.00 *(978-0-7141-5068-0(1))* British Museum Pr. GBR. Dist: Brown, David Bk. Co., The.
Jacobs, Norman. Behind the Colonnade: Thirty-Seven Years at the British Museum. 2010. (ENG., Illus.). 216p. pap. 16.95 *(978-0-7524-5279-1(7))* History Pr. Ltd., The GBR. Dist: Independent Pubs. Group.
Jerrold, Blanchard. How to See the British Museum in Four Visits. 2007. 160p. per. *(978-1-4065-3468-9(4))* Dodo Pr.
MacGregor, Neil. A History of the World in 100 Objects. 2011. (ENG., Illus.). 736p. (gr. 12). 45.00 *(978-0-670-02270-0(5))*, Viking Adult) Penguin Group (USA) Inc.
McEwan, Colin. Ancient American Art in Detail. 2009. (Art in Detail Ser.). Orig. Title: Ancient American Art in Detail. (Illus.). 144p. 21.95 *(978-0-674-03315-3(9))* Harvard Univ. Pr.
Moser, Stephanie. Wondrous Curiosities: Ancient Egypt at the British Museum. (Illus.). 2012. (ENG.). 360p. pap. 25.00 *(978-0-226-54210-2(6))* 2006. 368p. 37.50 *(978-0-226-54209-6(2))* Univ. of Chicago Pr.
Murphy, Simon. Cox's Fragmenta: An Historical Miscellany. 2011. (ENG., Illus.). 160p. pap. 14.95 ***(978-0-7524-6329-2(2))*** History Pr. Ltd., The GBR. Dist: Independent Pubs. Group.
Piatte, Editha. Bronze Head from Ife. 2010. (Objects in Focus Ser.). (ENG., Illus.). 64p. (C). pap. 10.00 *(978-0-7141-2592-3(X))* British Museum Pr. GBR. Dist: Brown, David Bk. Co., The.
Proctor, Robert & Bowman, J. H. A Critical Edition of the Private Diaries of Robert Proctor: The Life of a Librarian at the British Museum. 2010. (Illus.). xxvii, 373p. 129.95 *(978-0-7734-3634-5(0))* Mellen, Edwin Pr., The.
Read, Charles Hercules & Dalton, O. M. Antiquities from the City of Benin & from Other Parts of West Africa in the British Museum. 2008. (Illus.). 95.00 *(978-1-57898-701-6(6))* Martino Publishing.
Robinson, James. Masterpieces Medieval Art. 2008. (ENG., Illus.). 320p. 39.95 *(978-0-7141-2815-3(5))* British Museum Pr. GBR. Dist: Brown, David Bk. Co., The.
Saunders, David. British Museum Technical Research Bulletin. (ENG., Illus.). 2009. 96p. pap. 40.00 *(978-1-904982-35-7(2))* 2007. 80p. pap. 40.00 *(978-1-904982-27-2(1))* Archetype Pubns. GBR. Dist: National Bk. Network.
—British Museum Technical Research Bulletin, Volume 3. 2010. (ENG., Illus.). 96p. pap. 40.00 *(978-1-904982-43-7(4))* Archetype Pubns. GBR. Dist: National Bk. Network.
Saunders, David. The British Museum Technical Research Bulletin, Volume 5. 2012. (ENG., Illus.). 150p. pap. 40.00 ***(978-1-904982-67-8(0))*** Archetype Pubns. GBR. Dist: National Bk. Network.
Searight, Ann & Mitchell, T. C. Catalogue of the Western Asiatic Seals in the British Museum: Stamp Seals III: Impressions of Stamp Seals on Cuneiform Tablets, Clay Bullae, & Jar Handles. 2007. (Illus.). 314p. *(978-90-04-15615-9(1))* BRILL.
Sloan, Kim. European Visions: American Voices. Sloan, Kim, ed. 2009. (British Museum Research Publication). (ENG., Illus.). 150p. (C). pap. 80.00 *(978-0-86159-172-5(0))* British Museum Pr. GBR. Dist: Brown, David Bk. Co., The.
Sloan, Kim & Lloyd, Stephen. The Intimate Portrait: Drawings, Miniatures & Pastels from Ramsay to Lawrence. 2009. (ENG., Illus.). 272p. pap. *(978-1-906270-14-8(7))* National Galleries of Scotland.
Smith, Rupert. The Museum: Behind the Scenes at the British Museum. 2007. (ENG., Illus.). 192p. 29.95 *(978-0-563-53913-1(5))*, BBC Bks.) Ebury Publishing GBR. Dist: Independent Pubs. Group.
Smith, William. A Stratigraphical System of Organized Fossils: With Reference to the Specimens of the Original Geological Collection in the British Museum. 2010. (Cambridge Library Collection - Earth Science Ser.). (ENG., Illus.). 150p. pap. 19.99 *(978-1-108-02115-9(8))* Cambridge Univ. Pr.
Spencer, Neal & Smoláriková, Kveta. Kom Firin: The Ramesside Temple & the Site Survey. 2008. (Research Paper Ser.). (Illus.). 200p. (C). pap. 90.00

(978-0-86159-170-1(4)) British Museum Pr. GBR. Dist: Brown, David Bk. Co., The.

Strudwick, Nigel. Masterpieces of Ancient Egypt. 2006. (ENG., Illus.). 352p. 35.00 (978-0-292-71662-9(1)) Univ. of Texas Pr.

Thornton, Dora & Wilson, Timothy. Italian Renaissance Ceramics: A Catalogue of the British Museum Collection, 2 vols. 2009. (ENG., Illus.). 826p. (C). 300.00 (978-0-7141-2816-0(3)) British Museum Pr. GBR. Dist: Brown, David Bk. Co., The.

Thorsten, Opper. The Meroe Head of Augustus. 2012. (Objects in Focus Ser.). (ENG., Illus.). 64p. (C). pap. 10.00 (978-0-7141-5091-8(6)) British Museum Pr. GBR. Dist: Brown, David Bk. Co., The.

Wang, Helen. Chairman Mao Badges: Symbols & Slogans of the Cultural Revolution. 2008. (British Museum Research Publication Ser.). (Illus.). 184p. (C). pap. 70.00 (978-0-86159-169-5(0)) British Museum Pr. GBR. Dist: Brown, David Bk. Co., The.

Wheatley, Henry Benjamin. Remarkable Bindings in the British Museum: Selected for their Beauty or Historic Interest. 2010. (Cambridge Library Collection - Printing & Publishing History Ser.). (Illus.). 340p. pap. 28.99 (978-1-108-02151-7(4)) Cambridge Univ. Pr.

Williams, Dyfri. Masterpieces of Classical Art. 2009. (ENG., Illus.). 360p. 45.00 (978-0-292-72147-0(1)) Univ. of Texas Pr.

Williams, Hilary. Rembrandt on Paper. 2009. (Illus.). 96p. 14.95 (978-0-89236-973-7(6)) Oxford Univ. Pr., Inc.

BRITISH MUSEUM (NATURAL HISTORY)

see Natural History Museum (London, England)

BRITISH MUSIC

see Music, British

BRITISH NATIONAL CHARACTERISTICS

see National Characteristics, British

BRITISH NEWSPAPERS

see English Newspapers; Irish Newspapers; Welsh Newspapers

BRITISH NORTH BORNEO

Roth, Henry L. The Natives of Sarawak & British North Borneo, 2 vols., Set. reprint ed. 75.00 (978-0-404-16780-6(2)) AMS Pr., Inc.

BRITISH OPEN (GOLF TOURNAMENT)

Dabell, Norman. One Hand on the Claret Jug: How They Nearly Won the Open. 2007. (ENG., Illus.). 268p. per. 18.95 (978-1-84596-262-3(1)) Mainstream Publishing Co., Ltd. GBR. Dist: Independent Pubs. Group.

Huber, Jim. Four Days in July: Tom Watson, the 2009 Open Championship, & a Tournament for the Ages. 2011. (ENG., Illus.). 304p. 24.99 (978-0-312-66187-8(8), Dunne, Thomas Bks.) St. Martin's Pr.

Royal and Ancient Golf Club of St Andrews Staff. The Open Championship 2009: The Official Story. 2009. (ENG., Illus.). 128p. 32.95 (978-1-84513-456-3(7)) Aurum Pr., Ltd. GBR. Dist: Independent Pubs. Group.

Steel, Donald. The Open: 150 Years of Golf's Oldest Major. 2010. (ENG., Illus.). 304p. 60.00 (978-0-8478-3308-5(9)) Rizzoli International Pubns., Inc.

BRITISH OPEN (WIMBLEDON)

see Wimbledon Championships

BRITISH OPEN GOLF CHAMPIONSHIP

see British Open (Golf Tournament)

BRITISH PAINTING

see Painting, British

BRITISH PERIODICALS

see English Periodicals; Scottish Periodicals

BRITISH POETRY

see English Poetry (Collections); Irish Poetry; Scottish Poetry; Welsh Poetry

BRITISH PORCELAIN

see Porcelain

BRITISH PORTRAITS

see Portraits

BRITISH POTTERY

see Pottery, British

BRITISH PROPAGANDA

see Propaganda, British

BRITISH SCULPTURE

see Sculpture—Great Britain

BRITISH SOUTH AFRICA COMPANY

Gibbs, Peter, et al. Blue & Old Gold: The History of the British South Africa Police, 1889-1980. 2010. 640p. 70.00 (978-1-920143-35-0(1)) 30° South Pubs. ZAF. Dist: International Publishers Marketing.

BRITISH VIRGIN ISLANDS

see also Virgin Gorda Island (V.I.)

Trotman. Developing a Model for a Child-Friendly Church. 2010. 288p. pap. (978-3-639-24740-4(X)) VDM Verlag Dr. Mueller e.K.

BRITISH VIRGIN ISLANDS—DESCRIPTION AND TRAVEL

Acheson, Pamela & Myers, Richard B. The Best of the British Virgin Islands: An Indispensable Guide for Anyone Visiting Tortola, Virgin Gorda, Jost Van Dyke, Anegada, Cooper, Guana, & All Other BVI Destinations. 4th ed. 2006. (ENG., Illus.). 144p. pap. 14.95 (978-1-892285-11-9(8)) 2003 Assocs.

British Virgin Islands. 96p. (978-88-8029-881-6(X)) Casa Editrice Bonechi.

Cohen, Colleen Ballerino. Take Me to My Paradise: Tourism & Nationalism in the British Virgin Islands. 2010. (ENG., Illus.). 292p. (C). 75.00 (978-0-8135-4809-8(8)); pap. 25.95 (978-0-8135-4810-4(1)) Rutgers Univ. Pr.

Colli, Claudia. The British Virgin Islands: An Introduction & Guide. 2006. (MacMillan Caribbean Guides). (ENG., Illus.). 220p. pap. 16.95 (978-1-4050-2862-2(9)) Macmillan Caribbean GBR. Dist: Interlink Publishing Group, Inc.

DK PUBLISHING. Top 10 US & British Virgin Islands. 2012. (Eyewitness top 10 travel Guide Ser.). (ENG.). 128p. pap. 14.00 **(978-0-7566-8548-5(6))** Dorling Kindersley Publishing, Inc.

Fodor's Travel Publications, Inc. Staff. U. S. & British Virgin Islands. 23rd ed. 2011. (Full-Color Gold Guides). (ENG.). 292p. pap. 18.99 (978-0-679-00963-4(9)) Fodor's Travel Pubns.

Porter, Darwin & Prince, Danforth. Frommer's Virgin Islands. 11th ed. 2011. (Frommer's Complete Guides). (ENG., Illus.). 288p. pap. 17.99 (978-1-118-00426-5(4), Frommers) Wiley, John & Sons, Inc.

BRITISH WEST INDIES

see West Indies, British

BRITISH WIT AND HUMOR

see English Wit and Humor

BRITISH WOOD-ENGRAVING

see Wood-Engraving, British

BRITISHERS

see British

BRITONS

Anderson, Graham. King Arthur in Antiquity. 2009. 224p. pap. 39.95 (978-0-415-55500-5(0)) Routledge.

Clarkson, Tim. The Men of the North: The Britons of Southern Scotland. 2011. (ENG., Illus.). 325p. pap. 32.95 (978-1-906566-18-0(6), Donald, John) Birlinn, Ltd. GBR. Dist: Independent Pubs. Group.

Creighton, John. Coins & Power in Late Iron Age Britain. 2009. (New Studies in Archaeology Ser.). (ENG., Illus.). 268p. (C). pap. 38.99 (978-0-521-11451-6(9)) Cambridge Univ. Pr.

Cunliffe, Barry. Iron Age Communities in Britain: An Account of England, Scotland & Wales from the Seventh Century BC until the Roman Conquest. 4th rev. ed. 2009. (ENG., Illus.). 752p. (C). 59.95 (978-0-415-56292-8(9)) Routledge.

Finke, Laurie A. & Shichtman, Martin B. King Arthur & the Myth of History. 2009. (ENG., Illus.). 288p. pap. 29.95 (978-0-8130-3415-7(9)) Univ. Pr. of Florida.

Firth, C. H. Milton. 2006. 156p. per. (978-1-4067-1646-7(4), Hesperides Pr.) Read Bks.

Gidlow, Christopher. Reign of Arthur: From History to Legend. 2007. (ENG., Illus.). 288p. pap. 24.95 (978-0-7509-3419-0(0)) History Pr. Ltd.,The GBR. Dist: Independent Pubs. Group.

Higham, N. J. King Arthur: Myth-Making & History. 2008. (Illus.). X, 310p. 33.95 (978-0-415-48398-8(0)) Routledge.

Nennius. History of the Britons. Giles, J. A., tr. 2007. 48p. per. (978-1-4065-3072-8(7)) Dodo Pr.

—History of the Britons (Historia Brittonum) 48p. 2008. pap. 6.45 (978-1-60597-909-0(0)) 2007. pap. 9.45 (978-1-60424-937-8(4)) Standard Pubns., Inc. (Book Jungle).

Nichols, Ross. The Book of Druidry. 2009. (ENG.). 336p. 9.99 (978-0-7858-2495-4(2), 0785824952, Castle Bks., Inc.) Book Sales, Inc.

O'Hara, Glen. Britain & the Sea: Since 1600. 2010. (ENG., Illus.). 304p. 85.00 (978-0-230-21828-4(8)); pap. 29.00 (978-0-230-21829-1(6)) Palgrave Macmillan.

Reiser, Oliver Leslie. This Holyest Erthe, the Glastonbury Zodiac & King Arthur's Camelot. 2007. pap. (978-1-59731-201-1(0)) Perennis, Sophia.

Reno, Frank D. Arthurian Figures of History & Legend: A Biographical Dictionary. 2010. (ENG., Illus.). 272p. pap. 39.95 (978-0-7864-4420-5(7)) McFarland & Co., Inc. Pubs.

Sealey, Paul R. The Boudican Revolt Against Rome. 2nd ed. 2008. (Shire Archaeology Ser.). (Illus.). 64p. pap. 13.95 (978-0-7478-0618-9(7)) Shire Pubns., Ltd. GBR. Dist: Random Hse., Inc.

Waddell, L. A. British Edda. 333p. 25.00 (978-0-944379-28-8(1)) CPA Bk. Pub.

Williamson, Tom. The Origins of Hertfordshire. 2010. (ENG., Illus.). 256p. pap. 33.95 (978-1-905313-95-2(0)) Univ. of Hertfordshire Pr. GBR. Dist: Independent Pubs. Group.

BRITTANY (FRANCE)

Breton Costumes. 96p. (978-88-8029-542-6(X)) Casa Editrice Bonechi.

McKenna, Malachy. A Handbook of Modern Spoken Breton. (Buchreihe der Zeitschrift far celtische Philologie Ser.). (ENG.). VII, 310p. 210.00 **(978-3-11-183565-5(0))** De Gruyter, Walter Inc.

Michelin Travel Publications Staff. Michelin Green Guide Brittany. 8th ed. 2011. 464p. pap. 21.99 **(978-1-907099-72-4(7))** Michelin Travel & Lifestyle.

Segalen, Martine. Fifteen Generations of Bretons: Kinship & Society in Lower Brittany, 1720-1980. Underwood, J. A., tr. from FRE. 2007. (Cambridge Studies in Social & Cultural Anthropology Ser.). (ENG., Illus.). 356p. pap. 74.00 (978-0-521-04055-6(8)) Cambridge Univ. Pr.

BRITTANY (FRANCE)—DESCRIPTION AND TRAVEL

Anderson, Jane. Brittany with Kids. 2011. (ENG., Illus.). 192p. pap. 21.95 (978-1-907263-38-5(1)) Footprint Handbooks GBR. Dist: Globe Pequot Pr., The.

Andre, Patrick. All of Brittany. Brissonneau, Hubert, ed. Pauli, Erika, tr. from ITA. (Illus.). 128p. pap. (978-88-7009-211-0(9)) Casa Editrice Bonechi.

Barbour, Philippe. Brittany. 4th ed. 2009. (Illus.). 520p. pap. (978-1-86011-417-5(2)) Cadogan Guides GBR. Dist: Globe Pequot Pr., The.

—Brittany. 4th ed. 2009. 520p. pap. 21.95 (978-1-56656-765-7(3)) Interlink Publishing Group, Inc.

Black, Charles Bertram. Touraine, with Normandy & Brittany: Their Celtic Monuments & Ancient Castles, Pleasant Watering-Places & Rocky Islands. 2010. 152p. pap. 21.75 (978-1-141-10780-3(5)) BiblioBazaar.

Carrier, Rhonda. Frommer's Brittany with Your Family. 2nd ed. 2011. (Frommers with Your Family Ser.: 53). (ENG., Illus.). 256p. pap. 18.99 (978-0-470-68387-3(2), Frommers) Wiley, John & Sons, Inc.

Coston, Grace & Shawcross, Paul. Brittany. Cannon, Gwen, ed. 6th rev. ed. 2007. (Michelin Green Guide Brittany Ser.). (Illus.). 469p. 21.95 (978-2-06-712337-3(8)) Michelin.

Dorling Kindersley Publishing Staff. Eyewitness Travel Guide - Brittany. 2011. (Eyewitness Travel Guides). (ENG., Illus.). 288p. 25.00 (978-0-7566-7015-3(2)) Dorling Kindersley Publishing, Inc.

Flaubert, Gustave. Over Strand & Field. 2008. 104p. pap. (978-1-4065-4624-8(0)) Dodo Pr.

Greenside, Mark. I'll Never Be French (No Matter What I Do) Living in a Small Village in Brittany. 2008. (ENG., Illus.). 256p. 24.00 (978-1-4165-8687-6(3), Free Pr.) Free Pr.

—I'll Never Be French (no matter what I Do) Living in a Small Village in Brittany. 2009. (ENG., Illus.). 256p. pap. 14.99 (978-1-4165-8695-1(4), Free Pr.) Free Pr.

Mewes, Wendy. Brittany. 2010. (Footprint - Destination Guides). (ENG., Illus.). 288p. pap. 21.95 (978-1-906098-90-2(5)) Footprint Handbooks GBR. Dist: Globe Pequot Pr., The.

Mewes, Wendy. Brittany West Coast. 2012. (Footprint Focus Ser.). (ENG., Illus.). 128p. pap. 11.95 **(978-1-908206-57-2(8))** Footprint Handbooks GBR. Dist: Globe Pequot Pr., The.

Michelin Travel Publications Staff. Bretagne Green Guide French Edition. (FRE.). pap. 17.95 (978-0-7859-7223-5(4), 2060030943) French & European Pubns., Inc.

Morris, Elisabeth. Brittany. 4th ed. 2009. (Travellers - Thomas Cook Ser.). (ENG., Illus.). 192p. pap. 16.95 (978-1-84848-069-8(5)) Cook, Thomas Publishing GBR. Dist: Globe Pequot Pr., The.

Piette. Brittany. 2008. (University of Wales Press - Histories of Wales Ser.). (ENG.). 65.00 (978-0-7083-2037-2(6)); pap. 35.00 (978-0-7083-2036-5(8)) Univ. of Wales Pr. GBR. Dist: Chicago Distribution Ctr.

Rice, Melanie & Rice, Christopher. Brittany & Normandy. 3rd ed. 2009. (Drive Around - Thomas Cook Ser.). (ENG., Illus.). 288p. pap. 26.95 (978-1-84848-012-4(1)) Cook, Thomas Publishing GBR. Dist: Globe Pequot Pr., The.

Ward, Greg & Rough Guides Staff. Brittany & Normandy. 11th ed. 2010. (ENG., Illus.). 488p. 21.99 (978-1-84836-480-6(6)) Rough Guides, Ltd. GBR. Dist: Dorling Kindersley Publishing, Inc.

BRITTANY (FRANCE)—HISTORY

Anne Douglas Sedgwick. A Childhood in Brittany Eighty Years Ago. 2010. 112p. pap. 3.99 (978-1-60386-301-8(X), Watchmaker Publishing) Wexford College Pr.

Davies, Wendy. Brittany in the Early Middle Ages: Texts & Societies. 2009. (Variorum Collected Studies). (Illus.). 358p. 170.00 (978-0-7546-5970-9(4)) Ashgate Publishing Co.

Everard, J. A. Brittany & the Angevins: Province & Empire 1158-1203. 2006. (Cambridge Studies in Medieval Life & Thought). (ENG., Illus.). 264p. pap. 53.00 (978-0-521-02692-5(X)) Cambridge Univ. Pr.

Locklin, Nancy. Women's Work & Identity in Eighteenth-Century Brittany. 2007. (Illus.). 170p. 114.95 (978-0-7546-5819-1(8)) Ashgate Publishing Co.

Reece, Jack E. & Reece, Jack E. The Bretons Against France: Ethnic Minority Nationalism in Twentieth-Century Brittany. 2011. (ENG.). 285p. pap. 40.00 (978-0-8078-9760-7(4)) Univ. of North Carolina Pr.

Smith, Julia M. H. Province & Empire: Brittany & the Carolingians. 2006. (Cambridge Studies in Medieval Life & Thought). (ENG.). 260p. pap. 53.00 (978-0-521-03030-4(7)) Cambridge Univ. Pr.

Spence, Lewis. Legends & Romances of Brittany. 2009. 364p. 26.99 (978-0-559-07518-6(9)); 31.99 (978-0-559-07504-9(9)); pap. 31.75 (978-0-559-07514-8(6)); pap. 32.75 (978-0-559-07508-7(1)) BiblioBazaar.

BRITTANY (FRANCE)—POLITICS AND GOVERNMENT

Davies, Wendy. Brittany in the Early Middle Ages: Texts & Societies. 2009. (Variorum Collected Studies). (Illus.). 358p. 170.00 (978-0-7546-5970-9(4)) Ashgate Publishing Co.

Gemie, Sharif. Brittany, 1750-1950: The Invisible Nation. 2007. (ENG., Illus.). 224p. 75.00 (978-0-7083-2002-0(3)) Univ. of Wales Pr. GBR. Dist: Chicago Distribution Ctr.

BRITTANY SPANIEL

Boneham, Sheila Webster. Brittany: Breed Lover's Guide, 1 vol. 2011. (ENG., Illus.). 144p. 14.95 (978-0-7938-4182-0(8)) TFH Pubns., Inc.

Rice D.V.M., Dan. Brittanys: Everything about History, Purchase, Care, Nutrition, Training, & Behavior. 2nd ed. 2008. (Complete Pet Owner's Manual Ser.). (ENG., Illus.). 96p. pap. 8.99 (978-0-7641-3772-3(7)) Barron's Educational Series, Inc.

BRITTEN, BENJAMIN, 1913-1976

Brett, Philip. Music & Sexuality in Britten: Selected Essays. Haggerty, George, ed. 2006. (Illus.). 280p. per. 26.95 (978-0-520-24610-2(1)) Univ. of California Pr.

—Music & Sexuality in Britten - Selected Essays. Haggerty, George E., ed. 2006. (Illus.). 256p. 65.00 (978-0-520-24609-6(8)) Univ. of California Pr.

Diana, Barbara A. Benjamin Britten's 'Holy Theatre' from Opera-Oratorio to Theatre-Parable. 2011. 270p. pap. **(978-1-84955-119-9(7)); (978-1-84955-118-2(9))** Travis & Emery Music Bookshop.

English National Opera Staff, contrib. by. A Midsummer Night's Dream. 2011. (Overture Opera Guides). (ENG., Illus.). 150p. pap. 18.95 (978-1-84749-544-0(3)) Alma Classics GBR. Dist: Independent Pubs. Group.

Oliver, Michael. Benjamin Britten. rev. ed. 2008. (ENG., Illus.). 240p. (Orig.). pap. 14.95 (978-0-7148-4771-9(2)) Phaidon Pr. Ltd. GBR. Dist: Hachette Bk. Group.

Reed, Philip, et al, eds. Letters from a Life Vol. 4. 2008. (Selected Letters of Britten Ser.: Volume 4). (Illus.). 676p. 80.00 (978-1-84383-382-6(4), Boydell Press) Boydell & Brewer, Ltd. GBR. Dist: Boydell & Brewer, Inc.

Reed, Philip & Cooke, Mervyn, eds. Letters from a Life: the Selected Letters of Benjamin Britten, 1913-1976: Volume Five: 1958-1965. 2010. (Selected Letters of Britten Ser.: Volume 5). (Illus.). 830p. 80.00 (978-1-84383-591-2(6), Boydell Press) Boydell & Brewer, Ltd. GBR. Dist: Boydell & Brewer, Inc.

Rupprecht, Philip. Britten's Musical Language. 2006. (Music in the Twentieth Century Ser.). (ENG.). 372p. pap. 77.00 (978-0-521-03103-5(6)) Cambridge Univ. Pr.

Tippins, Sherill. February House: The Story of W. H. Auden, Carson McCullers, Jane & Paul Bowles, Benjamin Britten, & Gypsy Rose Lee under One Roof in Brooklyn. 2006. (ENG., Illus.). 336p. pap. 18.95 (978-0-618-71197-0(X)) Houghton Mifflin Harcourt Publishing Co.

Walker, Lucy, ed. Benjamin Britten: New Perspectives on His Life & Work. 2009. (Aldeburgh Studies in Music Ser.: Volume 8). (Illus.). 205p. 90.00 (978-1-84383-516-5(9), Boydell Press) Boydell & Brewer, Ltd. GBR. Dist: Boydell & Brewer, Inc.

Wintle, Christopher. All the Gods: Night-Piece in Context. Littlewood, Julian, ed. 2006. (Poetics of Music Ser.: Volume 2). (Illus.). 136p. 60.00 (978-0-9540123-8-0(0)) Plumbago Bks. GBR. Dist: Boydell & Brewer, Inc.

BRITTLE BONES

see Osteogenesis Imperfecta

BRITTLE-STARS

see Ophiuroidea

BRITTLENESS

see also Fracture Mechanics

also subdivision Brittleness under special materials, e.g. Metals—Brittleness

Bourdin, Blaise, et al. The Variational Approach to Fracture. 2010. (ENG.). x, 164p. pap. 99.00 (978-90-481-7624-3(7), 9048176247) Springer.

Freiman, Stephen & Mecholsky, John J., Jr. The Fracture of Brittle Materials: Testing & Analysis. 2012. (ENG.). 196p. 125.00 **(978-0-470-15586-8(8)**, Wiley-American Ceramic Society) Wiley, John & Sons, Inc.

Morozov, N. & Petrov, Y. Dynamics of Fracture. Stenkin, V. et al, trs. from RUS. 2010. (Foundations of Engineering Mechanics Ser.). (Illus.). viii, 112p. pap. 139.00 (978-3-642-08395-2(1), 3642083951) Springer.

Pluvinage, G. Fracture & Fatigue Emanating from Stress Concentrators. 2010. 242p. pap. 145.00 (978-90-481-6417-2(6), 9048164176) Springer.

Sivakum & Srinivasa, Arun R. Inelasticity of Materials: An Engineering Approach. 2009. (Illus.). 572p. instr.'s gde. ed. 96.00 (978-981-283-749-3(3)) World Scientific Publishing Co., Inc.

BRITTLENESS OF METALS

see Metals—Brittleness

BRITTLENESS OF SOLIDS

see Fracture Mechanics

BROAD, C. D. (CHARLIE DUNBAR), 1887-1971

Oaklander, L. Nathan. C. D. Broad's Philosophy of Time. 2012. (Routledge Studies in Twentieth Century Philosophy Ser.). 256p. (C). 125.00 (978-0-415-99812-3(3)) Routledge.

BROADBAND COMMUNICATION SYSTEMS

see also Asynchronous Transfer Mode

Abate, Zerihun. WiMAX RF Systems Engineering. 2009. (Illus.). 265p. 119.00 (978-1-59693-975-2(3)) Artech Hse., Inc.

Aboul-Magd, Osama S. & Kamal, Ahmed. High Performance Networks. 2010. (ENG.). 500p. 89.95 (978-0-471-65265-6(2), Wiley-Interscience) Wiley, John & Sons, Inc.

Ackerman, Peter & Mabel, Oliver. Networked Nation: Broadband in America. 2009. (Illus.). 107p. pap. 45.00 (978-1-60692-811-0(2)) Nova Science Pubs., Inc.

Acosta-Marum, Guillermo. Measurement, Modeling, & Synchronization for the Mobile Channel. 2008. 268p. pap. (978-3-639-08847-2(6)) VDM Verlag Dr. Mueller e.K.

Agriculture Dept. (US), Rural Utilities Service, ed. Advancing Broadband: A Foundation for Strong Rural Communities: A Foundation for Strong Rural Communities. 2011. (ENG., Illus.). 80p. pap. 19.00 (978-0-16-087745-2(8), Rural Utilities Service) United States Government Printing Office.

Ahmed, Adeel & Asadullah, Salman. Deploying IPv6 in Broadband Access Networks. 2009. (ENG., Illus.). 232p. pap. 66.95 (978-0-470-19338-9(7), Wiley) Wiley, John & Sons, Inc.

Ahmed, Khawza. Channel Estimation of Wireless Channels. 2010. 180p. pap. (978-3-639-27039-6(8)) VDM Verlag Dr. Mueller e.K.

Ahson, Syed A. & Ilyas, Mohammad, eds. VoIP Handbook: Applications, Technologies, Reliability, & Security. 2008. (ENG., Illus.). 440p. 109.95

(978-1-4200-7020-0(7), CRC Press) Taylor & Francis Group GBR. Dist: Taylor & Francis Group.
—WiMAX: Technologies, Performance Analysis, & QoS. 2007. (WiMAX Handbook Ser.). (ENG., Illus.). 296p. 89.95 (978-1-4200-4525-3(3), CRC Press) Taylor & Francis Group GBR. Dist: Taylor & Francis Group.
Ahson Syed a Staff. Wimax Handbook, 3 vols. 2007. (WiMAX Handbook Ser.). (ENG., Illus.). 824p. 205.95 (978-1-4200-4535-2(0), CRC Press) Taylor & Francis Group GBR. Dist: Taylor & Francis Group.
Akujuobi, Cajetan M. & Sadiku, Matthew N. O. Broadband Communication Systems. 2007. (ENG., Illus.). 456p. (C). 115.95 (978-1-4200-6149-9(6), Chapman & Hall/CRC) CRC Pr. LLC.
Al. Multi-Carrier Techniques for Broad. . V3. 2007. 113.00 (978-1-86094-946-3(0)) Imperial College Pr. GBR. Dist: World Scientific Publishing Co., Inc.
Alavi, Bardia. Distance Measurement Error Modeling for Indoor Geolocation. 2011. 200p. pap. (978-3-8454-0943-6(6)) Lambert Academic Publishing.
Anatory, Justinian & Theethayi, Nelson. Broadband Power Line Communication Systems: Theory & Applications. 2010. (Illus.). 192p. 150.00 (978-1-84564-416-1(6)) WIT Pr GBR. Dist: WIT Pr.
Association for Computing Machinery (ACM) Staff, compiled by. Workshop on Broadband Wireless Access for Ubiquitous Networking (BWAN 2006) 2007. (ACM International Conference Proceedings Ser.). 45p. pap. 50.00 (978-1-60423-273-8(0)) Curran Assocs., Inc.
Bader, Faouzi & Zorba, Nizar, eds. Advances on Processing for Multiple Carrier Schemes: OFDM & OFDMA. 2011. (Computer Science, Technology & Applications Ser.). 95.00 (978-1-61470-634-2(4)) Nova Science Pubs., Inc.
Bahai, Ahmad R. S., et al. Multi-Carrier Digital Communications: Theory & Applications of OFDM. 2nd ed. 2012. (Information Technology: Transmission, Processing & Storage Ser.). (ENG.). pap. 139.00 (978-1-4419-3550-2(9), 1441935509) Springer.
Baum, Carl E., et al, eds. Ultra-Wideband Short-Pulse Electromagnetics 8. 2010. (ENG., Illus.). x, 262p. pap. 275.00 (978-1-4419-2507-7(4), 1441925074) Springer.
Bing, Benny. Broadband Video Networking. 2010. (Illus.). 400p. 129.00 (978-1-60807-051-0(4)) Artech Hse., Inc.
Bondarczuk, Krzysztof & P. Barry, Liam. Two-Photon Absorption in a Semiconductor Micro-Cavity. 2011. 124p. pap. (978-3-8443-8161-0(9)) Lambert Academic Publishing.
Broadband Providers & Consumer Privacy: Hearing Before the Committee on Commerce, Science, & Transportation, United States Senate, One Hundred Tenth Congress, Second Session, September 25, 2008. 2009. iii, 37p. (978-0-16-083047-1(8), 552-070-38942-3) United States Government Printing Office.
Carcelle, Xavier. Power Line Communications in Practice. 2009. (Illus.). 370p. 119.00 (978-1-59693-335-4(6)) Artech Hse., Inc.
Cataldo, Andrea, et al. Broadband Reflectometry for Enhanced Diagnostics & Monitoring Applications. 2011. (Lecture Notes in Electrical Engineering Ser.). (Illus.). xviii, 150p. 129.00 (978-3-642-20232-2(2), 3642202322) Springer.
Chang, Yusun. Robust Mobile Networking: Modeling, Implementation, & Performance Evaluation. 2008. 112p. pap. (978-3-639-09475-6(1)) VDM Verlag Dr. Mueller e.K.
Chang, Zhang. Broadband Mobile Multimedia: Techniques & Applications. Mao, Shiwen et al, eds. 2008. (Wireless Networks & Mobile Communications Ser.). (ENG., Illus.). 584p. 109.95 (978-1-4200-5184-1(9)) Auerbach Pubs., Inc.
Chen, Zhi Ning, et al, eds. Ultra Wideband Wireless Communication. 2006. (ENG., Illus.). 520p. 129.00 (978-0-471-71521-4(2), Wiley-Interscience) Wiley, John & Sons, Inc.
Chochliouros, Ioannis P. & Heliotis, George A., eds. Optical Access Networks & Advanced Photonics: Technologies & Deployment Strategies. 2009. 380p. 180.00 (978-1-60566-707-2(2)) IGI Global.
Chong, Chia-Chin, et al, eds. Millimeter-Wave Wireless Communication Systems: Theory & Applications. 2006. 96p. per. 16.00 (978-977-5945-89-1(5)) Hindawi Publishing Corp.
Cohen, Ellen S., ed. Broadband Internet: Access, Regulation & Policy. 2008. (Illus.). (C). pap. 185.00 (978-1-60456-073-2(8)) Nova Science Pubs., Inc.
Communications Forum Staff, compiled by. Broadband World Forum Americas Conference & Exhibition 2006. 2007. 1645p. pap. 618.00 (978-1-60423-788-7(0)) Curran Assocs., Inc.
—Broadband World Forum Europe Conference & Exhibition 2006. 2007. 2336p. pap. 618.00 (978-1-60423-789-4(9)) Curran Assocs., Inc.
The Consumer Wireless Experience: Hearing Before the Committee on Commerce, Science, & Transportation, United States Senate, One Hundred Eleventh Congress, First Session, June 17, 2009. 2010. (Illus.). iii, 87p. (978-0-16-085931-1(X), 552-070-41127-5) United States Government Printing Office.
Consumers, Competition, & Consolidation in the Video & Broadband Market: Hearing Before the Subcommittee on Communications, Technology, & the Internet of the Committee on Commerce, Science, & Transportation, United States Senate, One Hundred Eleventh Congress, Second Session, March 11, 2010. 2011. (Illus.). iv, 155p. (978-0-16-088625-6(2), 552-070-42794-5) United States Government Printing Office.
Côté, Nicolas. Integral & Diagnostic Intrusive Prediction of Speech Quality. 2011. (T-Labs Series in Telecommunication Services Ser.). (Illus.). xvii, 248p. 129.00 (978-3-642-18462-8(6), 3642184626) Springer.
Cotton, Michael. Interference Potential of Ultrawideband Signals. 2006. (Illus.). 318p. (C). 125.00 (978-1-60021-359-5(6)) Nova Science Pubs., Inc.
Cuthbert, Thomas R., Jr. Broadband Direct-Coupled & Matching RF Network. 224p. 69.95 (978-0-9669220-0-4(X)) TRCPEP.
Dahlman, Erik, et al. 3G Evolution: HSPA & LTE for Mobile Broadband, 2 vols. 2nd ed. 2008. (ENG., Illus.). 648p. 130.00 (978-0-12-374538-5(1), Academic Pr.) Elsevier Science & Technology Bks.
—4G: LTE/LTE-Advanced for Mobile Broadband. 2011. (ENG., Illus.). 455p. 125.00 (978-0-12-385489-6(X), Academic Pr.) Elsevier Science & Technology Bks.
Dawy, Zaher & Yaacoub, Elias. Resource Allocation in Uplink OFDMA Wireless Systems: Optimal Solutions & Practical Implementations. 2012. (IEEE Series on Digital & Mobile Communication Ser.: 24). (ENG., Illus.). 296p. 99.95 (978-1-118-07450-3(5), Wiley-IEEE Pr.) Wiley, John & Sons, Inc.
Deal, Tim. Broadband-Enabled Gaming Environments. 2008. (Illus.). 14p. pap. (978-0-937275-57-3(3)) Pike & Fischer.
Deal, Tim & Sleek, Scott. Mobile Broadband Services: 2007 Competitive Analysis & Strategic Outlook. 2007. (Illus.). 36p. pap. (978-0-937275-34-4(4)) Pike & Fischer.
Dingel, Benjamin B., et al. Broadband Access Communication Technologies III: 28-29 January 2009, San Jose, California, United States. 2009. (Proceedings of SPIE Ser.). (Illus.). 172p. pap. 70.00 (978-0-8194-7480-3(0)) SPIE.
Dingel, Benjamin B., et al. Broadband Access Communication Technologies V: 25-27 January 2011, San Francisco, California, United States. 2011. (Proceedings of SPIE Ser.). (Illus.). pap. 70.00 (978-0-8194-8495-6(4)) SPIE.
Dwivedi, Yogesh K. Consumer Adoption & Usage of Broadband. 2007. 332p. 99.95 (978-1-59904-783-6(7), IRM Pr.) IGI Global.
Dwivedi, Yogesh K., ed. Adoption, Usage, & Global Impact of Broadband Technologies: Diffusion, Practice & Policy. 2010. (Illus.). 350p. 180.00 (978-1-60960-011-2(8), Information Science Reference) IGI Global.
Dwivedi, Yogesh K., et al, eds. Handbook of Research on Global Diffusion of Broadband Data Transmission. 2008. 988p. 495.00 (978-1-59904-851-2(5), Information Science Publishing) IGI Global.
Eaton, Thomas N. & Cullen, Robert T., eds. Digital Nation: Broadband Internet Adoption in the United States. 2011. (Media & Communications - Technologies, Policies & Challenges Ser.). (Illus.). 202p. 95.00 (978-1-61324-556-9(4)) Nova Science Pubs., Inc.
Elmezughi, Abdurrezagh S. & S. T. Rowe, Wayne. Broadband Microstrip Patch Antennas. 2010. 120p. pap. (978-3-639-27214-7(5)) VDM Verlag Dr. Mueller e.K.
Engels, Marc & Petre, Frederik. Broadband Fixed Wireless Access: A System Perspective. (Signals & Communication Technology Ser.). (Illus.). 2010. xix, 211p. pap. 129.00 (978-1-4419-4159-6(2), 1441941592) 2006. 211p. 129.00 (978-0-387-33956-6(6), 0387339566) Springer.
Flickenger, Rob, ed. How to Accelerate Your Internet: A practical guide to Bandwidth Management & Optimisation using Open Source Software. 2006. per. (978-0-9778093-1-8(5)) Hacker Friendly LLC.
Fonjallaz, Pierre-Yves & Pearsall, T. P. Workshop on Optical Components for Broadband Communication: 28-29 June 2006, Stockholm, Sweden. 2006. (Proceedings of SPIE Ser.). (Illus.). 176p. pap. 80.00 (978-0-8194-6445-3(7)) SPIE.
Fotheringham, Vern & Sharma, Chetan. Wireless Broadband: Conflict & Convergence. 2008. (IEEE Series on Digital & Mobile Communication Ser.: 18). (ENG., Illus.). 254p. 105.00 (978-0-470-22762-6(1), Wiley-IEEE Pr.) Wiley, John & Sons, Inc.
Full Committee Hearing on Small Business & Broadband: An Engine for Economic Growth & Job Creation: Hearing Before the Committee on Small Business, United States House of Representatives, One Hundred Eleventh Congress, Second Session, Hearing Held May 12, 2010. 2010. v, 59p. (978-0-16-086165-9(9), 552-070-41265-4) United States Government Printing Office.
Full Committee Hearing on the Recovery ACT & Broadband: Evaluation of Broadband Investments on Small Business & Job Creation: Hearing Before the Committee on Small Business, United States House of Representatives, One Hundred Eleventh Congress, First Session, Hearing Held October 28, 2009. 2009. v, 84p. (978-0-16-084891-9(1), 552-070-40287-0) United States Government Printing Office.
Future of Spectrum Policy: Hearing Before the Committee on Commerce, Science, & Transportation, United States Senate, One Hundred Eighth Congress, First Session, March 6, 2003. 2010. iii, 56p. (978-0-16-086757-6(6), 552-070-41678-1) United States Government Printing Office.
The Future of Universal Service: To Whom, by Whom, for What, & How Much?: Hearing Before the Subcommittee on Telecommunications & the Internet of the Committee on Energy & Commerce, House of Representatives, One Hundred Tenth Congress, Second Session, June 24, 2008. 2008. (Illus.). v, 119p. (978-0-16-086895-5(5), 552-070-41805-9) United States Government Printing Office.
Gayraud, Thierry, et al, eds. Broadband Satellite Communication Systems & the Challenges of Mobility: IFIP TC6 Workshops on Broadband Satellite Communication Systems & Challenges of Mobility, World Computer Congress August 22-27, 2004, Toulouse, France. 2010. (IFIP Advances in Information & Communication Technology Ser.). xviii, 247p. pap. 175.00 (978-1-4419-3676-9(9), 1441936769) Springer.
Geerts, Yves, et al. Design of Multi-Bit Delta-Sigma A/D Converters. 2010. (Springer International Series in Engineering & Computer Science Ser.). 240p. pap. 219.00 (978-1-4419-5288-2(8), 1441952888) Springer.
Gharpurey, Ranjit & Kinget, Peter, eds. Ultra Wideband: Circuits, Transceivers & Systems. 2010. (Integrated Circuits & Systems Ser.). (Illus.). x, 199p. pap. 119.00 (978-1-4419-4246-3(7), 1441942467) Springer.
Ghavami, Mohammad, et al. Ultra Wideband Signals & Systems in Communication Engineering. 2nd rev. ed. 2007. (ENG., Illus.). 334p. 110.00 (978-0-470-02763-9(0), Wiley) Wiley, John & Sons, Inc.
Giannakis, Georgios & Yang, Liuqing. Ultra-Wideband Wireless Communications. 2008. 350p. 80.00 (978-0-521-86263-9(9)) Cambridge Univ. Pr.
Ginis, Georgios. Multi-Line Coordinated Communication. 2009. 152p. pap. (978-3-639-12127-8(9)) VDM Verlag Dr. Mueller e.K.
Globecom 2007 - 2007 IEEE Global Telecommunications Conference. 2007. pap. 1052.00 (978-1-4244-1042-2(8), 07CH37886) IEEE.
Grace, David & Mohorcic, Mihael. Broadband Communications Via High Altitude Platforms. 2010. (ENG., Illus.). 398p. 135.00 (978-0-470-69445-9(9), Wiley) Wiley, John & Sons, Inc.
Guo, Mingliang, et al. Wu Xian Jie Ru Yuan Li Ji Ying Yong. 2007. (CHI., Illus.). viii, 238p. (978-7-118-05017-2(2)) National Defence Industry Pr.
Harrison, Alan R. Maximizing Broadband Services to Rural Communities. Haynesworth, Viktor B., ed. 2008. 98.00 (978-1-60692-846-2(5)) Nova Science Pubs., Inc.
Hazlett, Thomas W. The Fallacy of Net Neutrality. 2011. (Encounter Broadsides Ser.). (ENG.). 56p. pap. 5.99 (978-1-59403-592-0(X)) Encounter Bks.
Hearing to Review Rural Broadband Programs Funded by the American Recovery & Reinvestment ACT: Hearing Before the Subcommittee on Rural Development, Biotechnology, Specialty Crops, & Foreign Agriculture of the Committee on Agriculture, House of Representatives, One Hundred Eleventh Congress, First Session, November 19, 2009. 2010. iii, 46p. (978-0-16-084961-7(0), 552-070-40360-4) United States Government Printing Office.
Hearing to Review the Role of Broadband Access in Rural Economic Development: Hearing Before the Subcommittee on Rural Development, Research, Biotechnology, & Foreign Agriculture of the Committee on Agriculture, House of Representatives, One Hundred Twelfth Congress, First Session, September 24, 2011, Springfield, IL. 2011. (Illus.). iii, 48p. (978-0-16-089995-9(8), 552-070-43779-7) United States Government Printing Office.
Hellberg, Chris, et al. Broadband Network Architectures: Designing & Deploying Triple-Play Services. 2007. (Radia Perlman Series in Computer Networking & Security Ser.). (ENG., Illus.). 600p. per. 64.99 (978-0-13-230057-5(5), Prentice Hall) Prentice Hall PTR.
Hendriks, Julie E., ed. Tapping the Television White Space Spectrum: A Revolution in Public Airwave Use. 2009. (Media & Communications - Technologies, Policies & Challenges Ser.). 103.50 (978-1-60692-956-8(9)) Nova Science Pubs., Inc.
Hong, Chin-Gi. Triple Play in Germany. 2008. 124p. pap. (978-3-639-07554-0(4)) VDM Verlag Dr. Mueller e.K.
H.R. ________, a Discussion Draft on Wireless Consumer Protection & Community Broadband Empowerment: Hearing Before the Subcommittee on Telecommunications & the Internet of the Committee on Energy & Commerce, House of Representatives, One Hundred Tenth Congress, Second Session, February 27, 2008. 2008. v, 122p. (978-0-16-083523-0(2), 552-070-39748-5) United States Government Printing Office.
H.R. ________, Draft Legislation Enhancing Access to Broadband Technology & Services for Persons with Disabilities: Hearing Before the Subcommittee on Telecommunications & the Internet of the Committee on Energy & Commerce, House of Representatives, One Hundred Tenth Congress, Second Session, May 1, 2008. 2008. (Illus.). v, 109p. (978-0-16-085780-5(5), 552-070-40998-0) United States Government Printing Office.
H.R. ________ [sic]: A Discussion Draft Addressing Broadband Mapping & Data Collection: Hearing Before the Subcommittee on Telecommunications & the Internet of the Committee on Energy & Commerce, House of Representatives, One Hundred Tenth Congress, First Session, May 17, 2007. 2008. (Illus.). v, 140p. (978-0-16-081222-4(4), 552-070-37620-8) United States Government Printing Office.
Ida, Takanori. Broadband Economics: Lessons from Japan. 2008. (Routledge Studies in Global Competition Ser.). (ENG., Illus.). 320p. (C). 160.00 (978-0-415-47256-2(3)) Routledge.
IEEE Staff. 2008 IEEE International Symposium on Broadband Multimedia Systems & Broadcasting. 2008. pap. 224.00 (978-1-4244-1648-6(5)) IEEE.
Institute of Electrical and Electronics Engineers Staff, contrib. by. 2007 Digest of the LEOS Summer Topical Meetings. 2007. pap. 252.00 (978-1-4244-0926-6(8), 07TH8940) IEEE.
International Engineering Consortium Staff, contrib. by. Beyond the Quadruple Play: Networking, Convergence, & Customer Delivery. 2007. (Comprehensive Report Ser.). (ENG.). 200p. pap. 125.00 (978-1-931695-61-9(X)) International Engineering Consortium.
—Evolving the Access Network. 2006. (Comprehensive Report Ser.). (ENG., Illus.). 267p. pap. 125.00 (978-1-931695-52-7(0)) International Engineering Consortium.
International Engineering Consortium Staff, ed. Broadband Communications, Vol. 2. 2007. (Annual Review Ser.). (ENG., Illus.). 133p. pap. 80.00 (978-1-931695-71-8(7)) International Engineering Consortium.
Iser, Bernd & Schmidt, Gerhard. Bandwidth Extension of Speech Signals. 2010. (Lecture Notes in Electrical Engineering Ser.). (Illus.). x, 190p. pap. 129.00 (978-1-4419-4336-1(6), 1441943366) Springer.
Iser, Bernd, et al. Bandwidth Extension of Speech Signals. 2008. (Lecture Notes in Electrical Engineering Ser.). (Illus.). 182p. 129.00 (978-0-387-68898-5(6)) Springer.
Issues in Telecommunications Competition: Hearing Before the Subcommittee on Telecommunications & the Internet of the Committee on Energy & Commerce, House of Representatives, One Hundred Tenth Congress, Second Session, July 22, 2008. 2010. v, 109p. (978-0-16-087973-9(6), 552-070-42424-5) United States Government Printing Office.
Jain, Raj. Broadband Access Communication Technologies: 2-3 October, 2006, Boston, Massachusetts, USA. 2006. (Proceedings of SPIE Ser.). (Illus.). 224p. pap. 70.00 (978-0-8194-6468-0(0)) SPIE.
—Broadband Access Communication Technologies II: 10-11 September 2007, Boston, Massachusetts, USA. 2007. (Proceedings of SPIE Ser.). (Illus.). 196p. pap. 70.00 (978-0-8194-6936-6(X)) SPIE.
Jubair, Gazi Faisal Ahmed, et al. Performance Evaluation of Mobile Wimax in Ofdm Physical Layer. 2011. 128p. pap. (978-3-8433-9007-1(X)) Lambert Academic Publishing.
Kö, et al. Network Neutrality on the Internet. 2010. 136p. pap. (978-3-8383-5684-6(5)) Lambert Academic Publishing.
Kannu, Arun. Mobile Broadband Communications. 2007. 160p. per. (978-3-8364-2196-6(8)) VDM Verlag Dr. Mueller e.K.
Katz, Marcos. WiMAX Evolution: Emerging Technologies & Applications. Fitzek, Frank, ed. 2009. (ENG., Illus.). 502p. 150.00 (978-0-470-69680-4(X), Wiley) Wiley, John & Sons, Inc.
Kawser, Mohammad T. LTE Air Interface Protocols. 2011. (Illus.). 344p. 129.00 (978-1-60807-201-9(0)) Artech Hse., Inc.
Kazovsky, L. G., et al. Broadband Optical Access Networks. 2011. (ENG., Illus.). 300p. 105.00 (978-0-470-18235-2(0), Wiley-Interscience) Wiley, John & Sons, Inc.
Kelly, Tim & Rossotto, Carlo Maria, eds. Broadband Strategies Handbook. 2011. (ENG.). 404p. pap. 45.00 (978-0-8213-8945-4(9), 9780821389454) World Bank Pubns.
Khan, Engr. Asghar, et al. Channel Estimation for Capacity Maximization in Ofdm Systems. 2011. 92p. pap. (978-3-8443-0632-3(3)) Lambert Academic Publishing.
Kim, Yongsoo, et al. Building Broadband: Strategies & Policies for the Developing World. 2010. (ENG., Illus.). 152p. pap. 40.00 (978-0-8213-8419-0(8), 9780821384190) World Bank Pubns.
Kim, Young-Tak, et al. 2007 2nd IEEE/IFIP Intl Wkshp on Broadband Convergence Networks. 2007. pap. 188.00 (978-1-4244-1297-6(8), 07EX1820) IEEE.
Klein, Alexander. Performance Comparison of Different Wimax Configurations - Impact of Scheduling & Contention Resolution on Quality of Service in Wimax Networks. 2008. 84p. pap. (978-3-8364-9007-8(2)) VDM Verlag Dr. Mueller e.K.
Kleynhans, Waldo. On Channel Estimation for Mobile Wimax. 2009. 84p. pap. (978-3-639-16953-9(0)) VDM Verlag Dr. Mueller e.K.
Kodama, Mitsuru. New Knowledge Creation Through ICT Dynamic Capability Creating Knowledge Communities Using Broadband. 2008. (978-1-59311-875-4(9)); 224p. pap. (978-1-59311-874-7(0)) Information Age Publishing, Inc.
Kong-Pang Pun, et al. Circuit Design for Wireless Communications: Improved Techniques for Image Rejection in Wideband Quadrature Receivers. 2010. (Springer International Series in Engineering & Computer Science Ser.). 217p. pap. 189.00 (978-1-4419-5349-0(3), 1441953493) Springer.
Koranne, Sandeep. Practical Computing on the Cell Broadband Engine. 2009. (ENG., Illus.). xxxv, 485p. 183.00 (978-1-4419-0307-5(0), 1441903070) Springer.
Korea (South), Chongbo Tongsinbu Staff, et al, contrib. by. The 9th International Conference on Advanced Communication Technology: Toward Network Innovation Beyond Evolution: ICACT 2007: Phoenix Park, Korea, Feb. 12-14, 2007. 2007. (Illus.). (978-89-551-9131-8(6)) National Computerization Agency.
Krendzel, Andrey. 3G/4G Mobile Network Planning Aspects: IMS-capable Core Network Dimensioning & Radio Access Network Topological Design for Enabling NGN Services. 2008. 124p. pap. (978-3-639-09011-6(X)) VDM Verlag Dr. Mueller e.K.
Kuchampudi, Venkatanath. Synchronization Techniques for Wimax Systems. 2009. 52p. pap. (978-3-639-13650-0(0)) VDM Verlag Dr. Mueller e.K.
Kumar, Amitabh. Mobile Broadcasting with WiMAX: Principles, Techology, & Applications. 2008. (Focal Press Media Technology Professional Ser.). (ENG., Illus.). 624p. pap. 75.95 (978-0-240-81040-9(6), Focal Pr.) Elsevier Science & Technology Bks.
Lai, Ming-Yee & Etemad, Kamran. WiMAX Technology & Network Evolution. 2010. (ComSoc Guides to Communications Technologies Ser.: 6). (ENG., Illus.). 499p. pap., instr.'s gde. ed. 62.95 (978-0-470-34387-6(7), Wiley-IEEE Pr.) Wiley, John & Sons, Inc.
Lam, Cedric F., ed. Passive Optical Networks: Principles & Practice. 2007. (ENG., Illus.). 368p. 114.00 (978-0-12-373853-0(9), Academic Pr.) Elsevier Science & Technology Bks.
Large, David & Farmer, James. Broadband Cable Access Networks: The HFC Plant. 3rd ed. 2008. (Morgan Kaufmann Series in Networking Ser.). (ENG., Illus.). 432p. 96.95 (978-0-12-374401-2(6), Morgan Kaufmann) Elsevier Science & Technology Bks.
Lee, Byeong Gi & Choi, Sunghyun. Broadband Wireless Access & Local Networks: Mobile Wimax & Wifi. 2008. (Artech House Mobile Communications Ser.). (Illus.). 400p. 159.00 (978-1-59693-293-7(7)) Artech Hse., Inc.

B

Lee, Jae-Beom & Kalva, Hari. The VC-1 & H. 264 Video Compression Standards for Broadband Video Services. 2010. (Multimedia Systems & Applications Ser.). (Illus.). xvi, 496p. pap. 189.00 *(978-1-4419-4376-7(5)*, 1441943765) Springer.

Lee, Kwang-Suk. It Development in Korea. 2011. (Routledge Advances in Korean Studies). (ENG., Illus.). 200p. (C). 125.00 *(978-0-415-58746-4(8))* Routledge.

Lee, Tony T. & Liew, Soung C. Principles of Broadband Switching & Networking. 2010. (Wiley Series in Telecommunications & Signal Processing Ser.: 32). (ENG., Illus.). 454p. 99.95 *(978-0-471-13901-0(7)*, Wiley-Interscience) Wiley, John & Sons, Inc.

Legarda, Jon. Feedforward Amplifiers for Wideband Communication Systems. (ENG.). xvii, 177p. 2010. pap. 145.00 *(978-1-4419-4196-1(7)*, 1441941967) 2006. (Illus.). 145.00 *(978-0-387-35137-7(X)*, 038735137X) Springer.

Li, Rui. Iterative Receiver for Mimo-Ofdm Systems. 2009. 128p. pap. *(978-3-639-21274-7(6))* VDM Verlag Dr. Mueller e.K.

Li, Ye Geoffrey & Stuber, Gordon L., eds. Orthogonal Frequency Division Multiplexing for Wireless Communications. 2010. (Signals & Communication Technology Ser.). xii, 308p. pap. 134.00 *(978-1-4419-3970-8(9)*, 1441939709) Springer.

Lin, Yuan-Pei, et al. Filter Bank Transceivers for OFDM & DMT Systems. 2010. (ENG., Illus.). 372p. 88.00 *(978-1-107-00273-9(7))* Cambridge Univ. Pr.

Liu, K. J. Ray & Siriwongpairat, W. Pam. Ultra-Wideband Communications Systems: Multiband OFDM Approach. 2007. (ENG., Illus.). 229p. 122.00 *(978-0-470-07469-5(8)*, Wiley-IEEE Pr.) Wiley, John & Sons, Inc.

Liu, Wei & Weiss, Stephan. Wideband Beamforming: Concepts & Techniques. 2010. (Wireless Communications & Mobile Computing Ser.). (ENG., Illus.). 302p. 120.00 *(978-0-470-71392-1(5)*, Wiley) Wiley, John & Sons, Inc.

Liu, Yanbing & Tang, Hong. Kuan Dai Wu Xian Yi Dong Tong Xin Wang Luo Ji Shu. 2008. (CHI., Illus.). viii, 411p. *(978-7-03-021385-3(8))* Science Pr.

Liu, Zhiqiang, et al. Space-Time Coding for Broadband Wireless Communications. 2006. (ENG., Illus.). 464p. 111.00 *(978-0-471-21479-3(5)*, Wiley-Interscience) Wiley, John & Sons, Inc.

Lurin, Ely. Broadband Fixed Wireless Access Equipment & Services: Including Wireless Local Loop & Broadband Multipoint, Satellite & Optical Access - 2000-2004 Analysis & Forecasts. 100p. pap. 3400.00 *(978-1-929904-12-9(6))* World Information Technologies, Inc.

Maier, Martin & Ghazisaidi, Navid. FiWi Access Networks. 2011. (ENG., Illus.). 276p. 120.00 ***(978-1-107-00322-4(9))*** Cambridge Univ. Pr.

Maldoom, Dan, et al. Broadband in Europe: How Brussels Can Wire the Information Society. 2010. (ENG.). xiv, 220p. pap. 119.00 *(978-1-4419-3791-9(9)*, 1441937919) Springer.

Maral, Gerard & Restrepo, Joaquin. Broadband Satellite Communications & the Information Society: The Space Bridge for Digital Divide. 2007. (Illus.). 352p. 130.00 *(978-0-470-01927-6(1))* Wiley, John & Sons, Inc.

Marsico, Daniel. Performance Analysis of the WiMAX Tdd Mode. 2008. 100p. pap. *(978-3-8364-9870-8(7))* VDM Verlag Dr. Mueller e.K.

Mitra, Sameer. Inaudible Secrets. 2010. 124p. pap. *(978-3-8383-5770-6(1))* Lambert Academic Publishing.

Morais, Douglas H. Fixed Broadband Wireless Communications: Principles & Practical Applications. 2011. (ENG.). 384p. pap. 120.00 ***(978-0-13-288602-4(2)***, Prentice Hall) Prentice Hall PTR.

Morales, Daniel M. The National Broadband Plan: Analysis & Strategy for Connecting America. 2011. (Series: Media & Communications - Technologies, Policies & Challenges Ser.). (Illus.). viii, 569p. 195.00 *(978-1-61122-024-7(6))* Nova Science Pubs., Inc.

Nekoogar, Faranak. Ultra-Wideband Communications: Fundamentals & Applications. rev. ed. 2011. (Prentice Hall Communications Engineering & Emerging Technologies Ser.). (ENG., Illus.). 240p. pap. 119.00 ***(978-0-13-278223-4(5)***, Prentice Hall) Prentice Hall PTR.

O' Driscoll, Aisling. Deployment, Management & Monitoring of Voice over Ip Services. 2010. 184p. pap. *(978-3-639-25348-1(5))* VDM Verlag Dr. Mueller e.K.

Organisation for Economic Co-operation and Development Staff. Broadband Growth & Policies in Oecd Countries. 2008. pap. 63.00 *(978-92-64-04668-9(2))* Organization for Economic Cooperation & Development.

Oversight of the Broadband Stimulus Programs in the American Recovery & Reinvestment ACT: Hearing Before the Committee on Commerce, Science, & Transportation, United States Senate, One Hundred Eleventh Congress, First Session, October 27, 2009. 2010. iii, 86p. *(978-0-16-086138-3(1)*, 552-070-41243-3) United States Government Printing Office.

Oversight of the Department of Commerce's Broadband Technology Opportunities Program: Hearings Before a Subcommittee of the Committee on Appropriations, United States Senate, One Hundred Eleventh Congress, Second Session, Special Hearing, January 28, 2010, Washington, DC. 2010. iii, 27p. ***(978-0-16-087122-1(0)***, 552-070-41967-5) United States Government Printing Office.

Oversight of the Federal Communications Commission: Hearing Before Subcommittee on Telecommunications & the Internet of the Committee on Energy & Commerce, House of Representatives, One Hundred Tenth Congress, First Session, March 14 & July 24, 2007. 2008. vi, 435p. *(978-0-16-081271-2(2)*, 552-070-37553-1) United States Government Printing Office.

Pagani, Pascal. Ultra Wide Band Radio Propagation Channel. 2009. (Iste Ser.: 364). (ENG., Illus.). 352p. 105.00 *(978-1-84821-084-4(1)*, Wiley-ISTE) Wiley, John & Sons, Inc.

Park, Jonghun. Rf Impairments Compensation for Direct Conversion Ofdm System. 2010. 76p. pap. *(978-3-639-23098-7(1))* VDM Verlag Dr. Mueller e.K.

Pärssinen, Aarno. Direct Conversion Receivers in Wide-Band Systems. 2010. (Springer International Series in Engineering & Computer Science Ser.). 256p. pap. 199.00 *(978-1-4419-4934-9(8)*, 1441949348) Springer.

Perez-Neira, Ana I. & Realp Campalans, Marc. Cross-Layer Resource Allocation in Wireless Communications: Techniques & Models from PHY & MAC Layer Interaction. 2008. (ENG., Illus.). 192p. 109.00 *(978-0-12-374141-7(6)*, Academic Pr.) Elsevier Science & Technology Bks.

Pons, Julien. Turbo Coded Modulation for Multicarrier Communication Systems. 2010. 284p. pap. *(978-3-639-20892-4(7))* VDM Verlag Dr. Mueller e.K.

Prasad, Ramjee & Jha, Uma Shankar. OFDM Towards Fixed & Mobile Broadband Wireless Access. 2007. (Artech House Universal Personal Communications Ser.). (Illus.). 200p. 129.00 *(978-1-58053-641-7(7))* Artech Hse., Inc.

The Present & Future of Public Safety Communications: Hearing Before the Committee on Commerce, Science, & Transportation, United States Senate, One Hundred Tenth Congress, First Session, February 8, 2007. 2010. (Illus.). iv, 123p. *(978-0-16-086818-4(1)*, 552-070-41734-6) United States Government Printing Office.

Quinn, Heather S. Community Information Needs in a Broadband Media Age (with DVD) 2012. (Media & Communications - Technologies Ser.). 171p. 150.00 ***(978-1-61470-953-4(X))*** Nova Science Pubs., Inc.

Radhamani, G. & Radha Krishna Rao, G. S. V. WiMAX: A Wireless Technology Revolution. 2007. (ENG., Illus.). 400p. 79.95 *(978-0-8493-7059-5(0))* Auerbach Pubs., Inc.

Review of Rural Broadband Programs Operated by the U.S. Department of Agriculture's Rural Utilities Service: Hearing Before the Subcommittee on Specialty Crops, Rural Development, & Foreign Agriculture of the Committee on Agriculture, House of Representatives, One Hundred Tenth Congress, First Session, May 1, 2007. 2008. (Illus.). iii, 100p. *(978-0-16-080866-1(9)*, 552-070-37417-5) United States Government Printing Office.

Reviewing the National Broadband Plan: Hearing Before the Committee on Commerce, Science, & Transportation, United States Senate, One Hundred Eleventh Congress, Second Session, April 14, 2010. 2011. (Illus.). iii, 105p. ***(978-0-16-088767-3(4)***, 552-070-42907-7) United States Government Printing Office.

Riddel, Jeff. Packetcable Implementation. 2007. (Networking Technology Ser.). (ENG., Illus.). 1104p. 75.00 *(978-1-58705-181-4(8))* Cisco Pr.

Rogers, Daniel. Broadband Quantum Cryptography. 2010. (Synthesis Lectures on Quantum Computing Ser.). 97p. pap. 35.00 *(978-1-60845-059-6(7))* Morgan & Claypool Pubs.

S. 2686, the Communications, Consumer's Choice, & Broadband Deployment ACT of 2006: Hearing Before the Committee on Commerce, Science, & Transportation, United States Senate, One Hundred Ninth Congress, Second Session, 3 vols. 2011. (Illus.). ***(978-0-16-088718-5(6)***, 552-070-42750-3 (pt. 1)); ***(978-0-16-088574-7(4)***, 552-070-42750-3 (pt. 1)); ***(978-0-16-088571-6(X)***, 552-070-42750-3 (pt. 1)) United States Government Printing Office.

Sabath, Frank. Ultra-Wideband, Short-Pulse Electromagnetics, Vol. 7. 2007. (ENG., Illus.). xvi, 866p. 349.00 *(978-0-387-37728-5(X)*, 038737728X) Springer.

Safarian, Aminghasem & Heydari, Payam. Silicon-Based RF Front-Ends for Ultra Wideband Radios. (Analog Circuits & Signal Processing Ser.). 2010. viii, 100p. pap. 179.00 *(978-90-481-7705-9(7)*, 9048177057) 2008. 160p. 179.00 *(978-1-4020-6721-1(6))* Springer.

Sahena, Begum & Ifiok, Otung. Broadband Satellite-Integrated Network Design: Propagation & Networking Solutions. 2011. 184p. pap. ***(978-3-639-31427-4(1))*** VDM Verlag Dr. Mueller e.K.

Sahinoglu, Zafer, et al. Ultra-Wideband Positioning Systems: Theoretical Limits, Ranging Algorithms, & Protocols. 2008. (ENG., Illus.). 288p. 121.00 *(978-0-521-87309-3(6))* Cambridge Univ. Pr.

Samudra, Pradeep & Cleveland, Joseph. Broadband Access: Technologies, Markets & Players. 2007. 256p. 85.00 *(978-0-470-01776-0(7))* Wiley, John & Sons, Inc.

Sandkuhl, Kurt. Breitbandkommunikation Im Computergestützten Publizieren: Das Bilus-Projekt und Seine Ergebnisse. (Studien zur Wirtschaftsinformatik Ser.). (GER.). XVI, 239p. 210.00 ***(978-3-11-180749-2(5))*** De Gruyter, Walter Inc.

Santos, Gustavo, et al. Video Streaming Optimization in Adsl Architecture. 2010. 116p. pap. *(978-3-8383-6908-2(4))* Lambert Academic Publishing.

Sarkar, Tapan K., et al. Physics of Multiantenna Systems & Broadband Processing. 2008. (Wiley Series in Microwave & Optical Engineering Ser.: 198). (ENG., Illus.). 562p. 141.00 *(978-0-470-19040-1(X)*, Wiley-Interscience) Wiley, John & Sons, Inc.

Settles, Craig. Fighting the Next Good Fight: Bringing True Broadband to Your Community. 2010. (ENG.). 182p. pap. 29.99 *(978-1-58776-905-4(0))* NetSource Distribution.

Shahi, Prakash. Papr Reduction in Ofdm System Using Pulse Shaping Technique. 2011. 76p. pap. ***(978-3-8443-0786-3(9))*** Lambert Academic Publishing.

Shami, Abdallah, et al, eds. Broadband Access Networks: Technologies & Deployments. 2009. (Optical Networks Ser.). (ENG., Illus.). xvii, 379p. 169.00 *(978-0-387-92130-3(3))* Springer.

Shieh, William & Djordjevic, Ivan. Orthogonal Frequency Division Multiplexing for Optical Communications. 2009. (ENG., Illus.). 456p. 124.00 *(978-0-12-374879-9(8)*, Academic Pr.) Elsevier Science & Technology Bks.

Shin, Dong-Hee. The Development of Broadband Community Networks: Two Case Studies. 2008. 364p. pap. *(978-3-639-05868-0(2))* VDM Verlag Dr. Mueller e.K.

Siddiqui, Tauseef. Analysis of Fixed & Mobile Wimax. 2010. 136p. pap. *(978-3-8383-6856-6(8))* Lambert Academic Publishing.

Silva, Francisco. Reviravolta: Do Telefone à Banda Larga. 2007. (POR.). 221p. *(978-972-21-1868-2(4))* Caminho, Editorial.

Soni, Himanshu B., et al. Capacity Enhancement & Interference Mitigation in Multiuser Uwb. 2011. 132p. pap. ***(978-3-8443-2386-3(4))*** Lambert Academic Publishing.

Sridhar, Varadharajan & Saha, Debashis, eds. Recent Advances in Broadband Integrated Network Operations & Services Management. 2011. 350p. 180.00 *(978-1-60960-589-6(6)*, Information Science Reference) IGI Global.

Subcommittee Hearing on Maximizing the Value of Broadband Services to Rural Communities. 2007. (Illus.). iii, 108p. *(978-0-16-080136-5(2)*, 552-070-36876-1) United States Government Printing Office.

Tariq, Faisal. Nonlinear Error in Ofdm Based Systems. 2011. 108p. pap. ***(978-3-8443-2364-1(3))*** Lambert Academic Publishing.

Taylor, James D., ed. Ultraband Radar Technology: Commercial, Security, Medical, & Defense Applications. 2012. (ENG., Illus.). 536p. 149.95 *(978-1-4200-8986-8(2)*, CRC Press) Taylor & Francis Group GBR. Dist: Taylor & Francis Group.

Tepedelenlioglu, Cihan & Banavar, Mahesh. OFDM Systems for Wireless Communications. 2010. (Synthesis Lectures on Algorithms & Software in Engineering Ser.). 78p. pap. 35.00 *(978-1-59829-701-0(5))* Morgan & Claypool Pubs.

Tsui, James B. Y. Special Design Topics in Digital Wideband Receivers. 2009. (Illus.). 450p. 149.00 *(978-1-60807-029-9(8))* Artech Hse., Inc.

Underwood, Caroline D., ed. Spectrum Issues for the New Communications Age. 2010. (Media & Communications - Technologies, Policies & Challenges Ser.). 89.00 *(978-1-61668-544-7(1))* Nova Science Pubs., Inc.

Verhelst, Marian & Dehaene, Wim. Energy Scalable Radio Design: For Pulsed UWB Communication & Ranging. 2009. (Analog Circuits & Signal Processing Ser.). (ENG., Illus.). xiv, 246p. 179.00 *(978-90-481-2693-4(2)*, 9048126932) Springer.

Waleed, Al-Hanafy. Precoding of Broadband Multiple-Input Multiple-Output Systems: Non-Linear Approaches. 2011. 152p. pap. ***(978-3-639-32493-8(5))*** VDM Verlag Dr. Mueller e.K.

Walker, Hermann E., ed. Improving Internet Access to Help Small Business Compete in a Global Economy. 2009. 79.00 *(978-1-60692-515-7(6))* Nova Science Pubs., Inc.

Wang, Jiangzhou. High-Speed Wireless Communications: Ultra-Wideband, 3G Long-Term Evolution, & 4G Broadband Mobile Systems. 2008. (ENG., Illus.). 336p. 99.00 *(978-0-521-88153-1(6))* Cambridge Univ. Pr.

Weber, Joseph M. & Newberry, Tom. IPTV. 2006. (Crash Course Ser.). (ENG., Illus.). 336p. per. 42.95 *(978-0-07-226392-3(X)*, 007226392X) McGraw-Hill Osborne.

Williams, Mark. Broadband for Africa: Developing Backbone Communications Networks in the Region. 2010. (ENG., Illus.). 100p. pap. 15.00 *(978-0-8213-8172-4(5)*, 9780821381724) World Bank Pubns.

Witschnig, Harald. Concepts of Frequency Domain Equalization. 2008. 184p. pap. *(978-3-8364-9285-0(7))* VDM Verlag Dr. Mueller e.K.

Wong, David T., et al. Wireless Broadband Networks. 2009. (ENG., Illus.). 508p. 135.00 *(978-0-470-18177-5(X)*, Wiley) Wiley, John & Sons, Inc.

Wood, Stephen & Aiello, Roberto. Essentials of UWB. 2008. (Cambridge Wireless Essentials Ser.). (ENG., Illus.). 214p. 65.00 *(978-0-521-87783-1(0))* Cambridge Univ. Pr.

Xiao, Yang, ed. WiMAX/MobileFi: Advanced Research & Technology. 2007. (ENG., Illus.). 448p. 99.95 *(978-1-4200-4351-8(X))* Auerbach Pubs., Inc.

Yang, Samuel C. OFDMA System Analysis & Design. 2010. (Illus.). 320p. 139.00 *(978-1-60807-076-3(X))* Artech Hse., Inc.

Yarman, Binboga Siddik. Design of Ultra Wideband Power Transfer Networks. 2010. (ENG., Illus.). 774p. 145.00 *(978-0-470-31989-5(5)*, Wiley) Wiley, John & Sons, Inc.

2007 Fourth International Conference on Broadband Communications, Networks & Systems. 2007. pap. 332.00 *(978-1-4244-1432-1(6)*, 07EX1861) IEEE.

2007 IEEE International Workshop on Radio-Frequency Integration Technology. 2007. pap. 252.00 *(978-1-4244-1307-2(9)*, 07EX1827) IEEE.

BROADCAST JOURNALISM

see also Radio Journalism; Television Broadcasting of News

Barnas, Frank & White, Ted. Broadcast News Writing, Reporting, & Producing. 5th ed. 2010. (ENG., Illus.). 344p. pap. 51.95 *(978-0-240-81183-3(6)*, Focal Pr.) Elsevier Science & Technology Bks.

Block, Mervin. Broadcast Newswriting: The Rtdna Reference Guide. 2nd rev. ed. 2011. 272p. pap. 31.00 *(978-1-60871-416-2(0))* CQ Pr.

—Rewriting Network News: Wordwatching Tips from 345 TV & Radio Scripts, 00 vols. rev. ed. 2010. pap. 28.95 *(978-1-60871-422-3(5))* CQ Pr.

—Writing Broadcast News Shorter, Sharper, Stronger: A Professional Handbook, 00 vols. 3rd rev. ed. 2010. pap. 47.00 *(978-1-60871-417-9(9))* CQ Pr.

Block, Mervin & Durso, Joe, Jr. Writing News for TV & Radio: The New Way to Learn Broadcast Newswriting, 00 vols. rev. ed. 2010. pap. 28.95 *(978-1-60871-421-6(7))* CQ Pr.

Boyd, Andrew, et al. Broadcast Journalism: Techniques of Radio & Television News. 6th ed. 2008. (ENG., Illus.). 400p. pap. 49.95 *(978-0-240-81024-9(4)*, Focal Pr.) Elsevier Science & Technology Bks.

Chapman, Jane. Broadcast Journalism: A Critical Introduction. Chapman, Jane & Kinsey, Marie, eds. 2008. (Illus.). XII, 276p. pap. 41.95 *(978-0-415-44155-1(2))*; 140.00 *(978-0-415-44154-4(4))* Routledge.

Chignell, Hugh. Public Issue Radio: Talks, News & Current Affairs in the Twentieth Century. 2011. (ENG., Illus.). 264p. 85.00 ***(978-0-230-24739-0(3))*** Palgrave Macmillan.

Cram101 Textbook Reviews. Outlines & Highlights for Broadcast News by Stephens. 2011. 148p. pap. 29.95 ***(978-1-61906-195-8(3))*** Cram101 Inc.

Cushion, Stephen. The Rise of 24-Hour News Television: Global Perspectives. 2010. (Illus.). 360p. (C). pap. 34.95 *(978-1-4331-0776-4(7))* Lang, Peter Publishing, Inc.

—The Rise of 24-Hour News Television: Global Perspectives (CB) 2010. (Illus.). 360p. (C). 129.95 *(978-1-4331-0777-1(5))* Lang, Peter Publishing, Inc.

Fenton, Tom. Junk News: The Failure of the Media in the 21st Century. 2009. (Speaker's Corner Ser.). (ENG.). 128p. 14.95 *(978-1-55591-669-5(4))* Fulcrum Publishing.

Geissler, Kyle. Small/Medium Market Models of Media Convergence in the Midwest. 2009. 84p. pap. *(978-3-639-10567-4(2))* VDM Verlag Dr. Mueller e.K.

Gladstone, Brooke. The Influencing Machine: Brooke Gladstone on the Media. 2011. (ENG., Illus.). 192p. 23.95 *(978-0-393-07779-7(9)*, 7779) Norton, W. W. & Co., Inc.

Gladstone, Brooke & Neufeld, Josh. The Influencing Machine: Brooke Gladstone on the Media. 2012. (ENG., Illus.). 192p. pap. 16.95 ***(978-0-393-34246-8(8)***, 34246) Norton, W. W. & Co., Inc.

Haga, Gunnar. Democracy & the Paradoxes of News Medi. 2010. 224p. pap. *(978-3-8383-1801-1(3))* Lambert Academic Publishing.

Harden, Doyle. The Footprints of My Life. 2011. 250p. pap. 19.99 ***(978-1-4568-4348-9(6))*** Xlibris Corp.

Harris, Phillip L. Television Production & Broadcast Journalism. 2nd ed. 2011. (ENG.). 140p. (gr. 8-14). pap., wbk. ed. 20.00 *(978-1-60525-351-0(0))* Goodheart-Willcox Pub.

Heaton, Terry L. Reinventing Local Medi. 2008. 508p. pap. 24.95 *(978-0-9789147-3-8(2))* AR&D.

Henderson, David E. Making News in the Digital Er. 2009. 188p. 21.95 *(978-1-4401-5306-8(X))*; pap. 13.95 *(978-1-4401-5307-5(8))* iUniverse, Inc.

Hewitt, John. Air Words: Writing Broadcast News in the Internet Age, 1 vol. 4th ed. 2011. (ENG.). 240p. (C). pap. 49.95 *(978-0-19-976003-9(9))* Oxford Univ. Pr., Inc.

Heyer, Sandra. True Stories in the News. 3rd ed. 2007. (ENG.). (C). pap. 40.87 *(978-0-13-615481-5(6))* Prentice Hall, ESL Dept.

Hudson, Gary & Rowlands, Sarah. The Broadcast Journalism Handbook. 2007. (ENG., Illus.). 592p. pap. *(978-1-4058-2434-7(4))* Addison-Wesley Longman, Inc.

Kadhim, Kais A. A Discourse Analytical Approach to Stylistic Variations Employed in Arabic Translation of English News Stories: Transmitting Political News Across Linguistic & Cultural Boundaries. 2011. *(978-0-7734-1427-3(4))* Mellen, Edwin Pr., The.

Kolodzy, Janet. Convergence Journalism: An Introduction Cross-Media Storytelling. 2012. (ENG., Illus.). 256p. (C). 150.00 *(978-0-415-89028-1(4))*; pap. 45.00 *(978-0-415-89030-4(6))* Routledge.

McNair, Brian. News & Journalism in the UK. 5th rev. ed. 2008. (Communication & Society Ser.). (Illus.). 288p. 36.95 *(978-0-415-41072-4(X))*; 115.00 *(978-0-415-41071-7(1))* Routledge.

Mellor, Noha. Arab Journalists in Transnational Media. 2011. ***(978-1-61289-019-7(9))***; ***(978-1-61289-018-0(0))*** Hampton Pr., Inc.

Montgomery, Martin. Discourse of Broadcast News. 2007. (ENG., Illus.). 264p. 53.95 *(978-0-415-35872-9(8))*; 133.00 *(978-0-415-35871-2(X))* Routledge.

Morgan, Vivien. Practising Videojournalism. 2007. (Illus.). 192p. 130.00 *(978-0-415-38665-4(9))*; 36.95 *(978-0-415-38666-1(7))* Routledge.

North, Richard. 'Scrap the BBC!' Ten Years to Set Broadcasters Free. 2007. 219p. *(978-1-904863-20-5(5))* Social Affairs Unit.

Papper, Robert A. Broadcast News & Writing Stylebook. 4th ed. 2009. (ENG., Illus.). 304p. (C). pap. 66.80 *(978-0-205-61258-1(X))* Allyn & Bacon, Inc.

Parsons, Tony. A Life in the News. 2009. (ENG., Illus.). 288p. 32.95 *(978-1-55017-461-8(4))* Harbour Publishing Co., Ltd. CAN. Dist: Ingram Pub. Services.

Paterson, Chris. The International Television News Agencies: The World from London. 2011. (Illus.). xiii, 183p. (C). pap. 33.95 ***(978-1-4331-1078-8(4))***; 129.95 ***(978-1-4331-1077-1(6))*** Lang, Peter Publishing, Inc.

Rantanen & Rantanen, Terhi. When News Was New. 2009. (ENG., Illus.). 168p. 99.95 *(978-1-4051-7552-4(4)*, Wiley-Blackwell) Wiley, John & Sons, Inc.

Rantanen, Terhi. When News Was New. 2009. (ENG., Illus.). 168p. pap. 34.95 *(978-1-4051-7551-7(6)*, Wiley-Blackwell) Wiley, John & Sons, Inc.

Seib, Philip, ed. Al Jazeera English: Global News in a Changing World. 2012. (Palgrave Macmillan Series in International Political Communication Ser.). (ENG., Illus.). 224p. 90.00 ***(978-0-230-34020-6(2))***; pap. 24.00 ***(978-0-230-34021-3(0))*** Palgrave Macmillan.

Sevareid, Eric. Not So Wild a Dream. 32.95 *(978-0-8488-0189-2(X))* Amereon LTD.

Sherr, Lynn, ed. Peter Jennings: A Reporter's Life. l.t. ed. 2007. (Thorndike Nonfiction Ser.). (Illus.). 561p. 31.95 *(978-1-4104-0271-4(1))* Thorndike Pr.

Thompson, Rick. Writing for Broadcast Journalists. 2nd rev. ed. 2010. (Media Skills Ser.). (ENG.). 208p. (C). 110.00 *(978-0-415-58167-7(2))*; pap. 30.95 *(978-0-415-58168-4(0))* Routledge.

Thorbrietz, Petra. Vernetztes Denken Im Journalismus: Journalistische Vermittlungsdefizite Am Beispiel Ökologie und Umweltschutz. (Medien in Forschung und Unterricht. Serie A Ser.). (GER.). VIII, 240p. 210.00 **(978-3-11-183795-6(5))** De Gruyter, Walter Inc.
Tompkins, Alan. Aim for the Heart: Write, Shoot, Report & Produce for TV & Multimedia, 00 vols. 2nd rev. ed. 2011. (Illus.). 360p. pap. 32.00 *(978-1-60871-674-6(0))* CQ Pr.
Tuggle, C. A., et al. Broadcast News Handbook. 4th ed. 2010. (ENG., Illus.). 368p. (C). spiral bd. 80.67 *(978-0-07-351196-2(X)*, 007351196X) McGraw-Hill Cos., The.
Wenger, Debora Halpern & Potter, Deborah. Advancing the Story: Broadcast Journalism in a Multimedia World, 00 vols. 2nd rev. ed. 2011. (Illus.). 416p. pap. 39.00 *(978-1-60871-714-9(3))* CQ Pr.
Whitaker, W. Richard. MediaWriting: Print, Broadcast, & Public Relations. 3rd ed. 2008. pap. 63.95 *(978-0-8058-6295-9(1))* Routledge.
Whitaker, W. Richard, et al. Mediawriting. 4th rev. ed. 2012. (ENG., Illus.). 400p. pap. 69.95 **(978-0-415-88803-5(4))** Routledge.
Whitaker, W. Richard, et al. MediaWriting: Print, Broadcast, & Public Relations. 4th rev. ed. 2012. (ENG., Illus.). 400p. 150.00 *(978-0-415-89180-6(9))* Routledge.
Wilkinson, Jeffrey, et al. Principles of Convergent Journalism. 2012. **(978-0-19-983865-3(8))** 2008. (ENG., Illus.). 240p. (C). pap. 44.95 *(978-0-19-533924-6(X))* Oxford Univ. Pr., Inc.
Williams, Bruce A. & Delli Carpini, Michael X. After Broadcast News: Media Regimes, Democracy, & the New Information Environment. 2011. (Communication, Society & Politics Ser.). (ENG., Illus.). 376p. pap. 32.99 *(978-0-521-27983-3(5))* Cambridge Univ. Pr.
Williams, Bruce Alan & Delli Carpini, Michael X. After Broadcast News: Media Regimes, Democracy, & the New Information Environment. 2011. (Communication, Society & Politics Ser.). (ENG., Illus.). 376p. 99.00 *(978-1-107-01031-4(4))* Cambridge Univ. Pr.
Wulfemeyer, K. Tim. Beginning Radio & TV Newswriting: A Self-Instructional Learning Experience. 5th ed. 2009. (ENG.). 160p. pap. 34.95 *(978-1-4051-6042-1(X)*, Wiley-Blackwell) Wiley, John & Sons, Inc.

BROADCAST NEWS
see Broadcast Journalism

BROADCASTERS
see also Disc Jockeys; Sportscasters

Allen, Fred. Treadmill to Oblivion. 252p. 2009. 32.95 *(978-1-4344-5413-3(4))* 2009. pap. 19.95 *(978-1-4344-5412-6(6))* 2007. (ENG.). 35.00 *(978-1-4344-0147-2(2))* 2007. per. 19.95 *(978-1-4344-0142-7(1))* Wildside Pr., LLC.
Ansbro, George. I Have a Lady in the Balcony: Memoirs of a Broadcaster in Radio & Television. alt. ed. 2009. (ENG., Illus.). 245p. pap. 39.95 *(978-0-7864-4318-5(9))* McFarland & Co., Inc. Pubs.
Anthony, George. Starring Brian Linehan: A Life Behind the Scenes. 2008. (ENG., Illus.). 360p. pap. 19.99 *(978-0-7710-0758-3(2)*, Emblem Edns) McClelland & Stewart CAN. Dist: Random Hse., Inc.
Batura, Paul. Good Day! The Paul Harvey Story. 2011. (ENG.). 291p. pap. 16.95 *(978-1-59698-156-0(3))* Regnery Publishing, Inc., An Eagle Publishing Co.
Burgess, Steve. Who Killed Mom? A Delinquent Son's Meditation on Family, Mortality, & Very Tacky Candles, 1 vol. 2012. (ENG.). 264p. pap. 18.95 **(978-1-55365-833-7(7)**, Greystone Bks.) D&M Pubs. Inc. CAN. Dist: Perseus-PGW.
Chafets, Zev. Rush Limbaugh: An Army of One. 2010. (ENG., Illus.). 240p. (gr. 12). 25.95 *(978-1-59523-063-8(7)*, Sentinel) Penguin Group (USA) Inc.
Chasan, Daniel J. On the Air: The King Broadcasting Story. Date not set. (Illus.). 256p. 22.95 *(978-0-9615580-6-2(7))* Island Pubs.
Cox, Jim. Radio Speakers: Narrators, News Junkies, Sports Jockeys, Tattletales, Tipsters, Toastmasters & Coffee Klatch Couples Who Verbalized the Jargon of the Aural Ether from the 1920s to the 1980s — A Biographical Dictionary. alt. ed. 2011. (ENG., Illus.). 368p. pap. 39.95 *(978-0-7864-6086-1(5))* McFarland & Co., Inc. Pubs.
Della Chiesa, Ron. Radio My Way: Featuring Celebrity Profiles from Jazz, Opera, the American Songbook & More. 2011. (ENG., Illus.). 304p. pap. 17.99 **(978-0-205-19078-2(2))** Allyn & Bacon, Inc.
DeLong, Thomas A. Radio Stars: An Illustrated Biographical Dictionary of 953 Performers, 1920 Through 1960. alt. ed. 2006. (ENG., Illus.). 316p. per. 49.95 *(978-0-7864-2834-2(1))* McFarland & Co., Inc. Pubs.
Deters, Eric. Willie-Radio's Great American: The Biography of Bill Cunningham. 2009. *(978-1-935001-31-7(0))* Acclaim Pr., Inc.
Duffy, Joe. Just Joe: My Autobiography. 2012. (ENG., Illus.). 464p. pap. 14.95 **(978-1-84827-100-5(X))** Transworld Publishers Ltd. GBR. Dist: Independent Pubs. Group.
Edwards, Bob. A Voice in the Box: My Life in Radio. 2011. (ENG., Illus.). 236p. 21.95 *(978-0-8131-3450-5(1))* Univ. Pr. of Kentucky.
Evans, Chris. It's Not What You Think. 2010. (ENG.). 352p. pap. 22.95 *(978-0-00-732722-5(6))* HarperCollins Pubs. Ltd. GBR. Dist: Independent Pubs. Group.
Fanning, Dave. The Thing Is... 2010. (ENG., Illus.). 356p. pap. 24.95 *(978-0-00-731075-0(5))* HarperCollins Pubs. Ltd. GBR. Dist: Independent Pubs. Group.
Geller, Valerie. Beyond Powerful Radio: A Communicator's Guide to the Internet Age-News, Talk, Information & Personality for Broadcasting, Podcasting, Internet, Radio. 2nd ed. 2011. (ENG., Illus.). 536p. pap. 44.95 *(978-0-240-52224-1(9)*, Focal Pr.) Elsevier Science & Technology Bks.
German, Ed. Deep down in Brooklyn. 2011. 456p. 35.00 **(978-1-4567-5438-9(6))**; pap. 25.00 **(978-1-4567-5439-6(4))** AuthorHouse.
Ghartey-Tagoe, David Kwesi. David Ghartey-Tagoe. 2010. 228p. 29.99 *(978-1-4535-4206-4(X))*; pap. 19.99 *(978-1-4535-4205-7(1))* Xlibris Corp.
Halper, Donna L. Boston Radio: 1920-2010. 2011. (Images of America Ser.). (Illus.). 128p. pap. 21.99 *(978-0-7385-7410-3(4))* Arcadia Publishing.
Hamilton, Milo & Schlossberg, Dan. Making Airwaves: 60+ Years at Milo's Microphone. 2007. (Illus.). 226p. per. 16.95 *(978-1-59670-218-9(4))* Sports Publishing, LLC
Harwell, Ernie. Breaking 90: Nine decades young & still loving Baseball. Bull, Kevin, ed. 2007. 208p. pap. 14.95 *(978-0-937247-77-8(4))* Detroit Free Pr., Inc.
Hoefling, Larry J. Nils Thor Granlund: Show Business Entrepreneur & America's First Radio Star. 2010. (ENG., Illus.). 243p. pap. 39.95 *(978-0-7864-4849-4(0))* McFarland & Co., Inc. Pubs.
Keller, Ken. Monkey on a Turntable: Living on Love & Leftovers in Local Radio. 2007. (Illus.). 159p. per. 14.95 *(978-1-933197-32-6(3))* Orange Frazer Pr.
King, Larry. My Remarkable Journey. 2010. (ENG.). 288p. pap. 15.95 *(978-1-60286-123-7(4))* 2009. (Illus.). 336p. 27.95 *(978-0-670-06393-2(2)*, Weinstein Bks.) 2009. (ENG., Illus.). 304p. 27.95 *(978-1-60286-086-5(6)*, Weinstein Bks.) Perseus Bks. Group.
—Tell Me More. pap. *(978-0-399-19087-2(2)*, Perigee Trade) Penguin Group (USA) Inc.
—Truth Be Told: Off the Record about Favorite Guests, Memorable Moments, Funniest Jokes, & a Half Century of Asking Questions. 2011. (ENG., Illus.). 248p. 25.00 *(978-1-60286-130-5(7))* Perseus Bks. Group.
Lanpher, Katherine. Leap Days: Chronicles of a Midlife Move. 2006. (ENG.). 240p. 23.99 *(978-0-8212-5830-9(3))* Little Brown & Co.
Lauver, Nelson. Most un Likely to Succeed: The Trails, Travels & Ultimate Triumphs of a Throwaway Kid. 2011. 310p. pap. 14.95 **(978-0-9830403-0-9(3))** Five City Media.
Meindl, Maria. Outside the Box: The Life & Legacy of Writer Mona Gould, the Grandmother I Thought I Knew. 2011. (ENG., Illus.). 304p. (C). **(978-0-7735-3911-2(5))** McGill-Queen's Univ. Pr.
Moyles, Chris. Difficult Second Book, Bk. 2. 2007. (ENG., Illus.). 304p. pap. 15.95 *(978-0-09-192244-3(5))* Ebury Publishing GBR. Dist: Independent Pubs. Group.
—The Gospel According to Chris Moyles: The Story of a Man & His Mouth. 2007. (ENG., Illus.). 304p. pap. 14.95 *(978-0-09-191418-9(3))* Random Hse. GBR. Dist: Independent Pubs. Group.
Murphy, Michael. At Five in the Afternoon. 2010. (ENG.). 272p. 39.95 *(978-0-86322-407-2(5))* Brandon/Mount Eagle Pubns., Ltd. IRL. Dist: Dufour Editions, Inc.
—At Five in the Afternoon: My Battle with Male Cancer. 2010. (ENG., Illus.). 272p. pap. 14.95 *(978-0-86322-426-3(1))* Brandon/Mount Eagle Pubns., Ltd. IRL. Dist: Dufour Editions, Inc.
Pratt, Dave. Dave Pratt: 30 Years in Radio. 2008. 336p. 30.00 net. *(978-1-58985-109-2(5))* Five Star Pubns., Inc.
Putnam, Kathryn Flynn & Putnam, William Lowell. How We Survived in UHF Television: A Broadcasting Memoir, 1953-1984. 2011. (ENG.). 242p. pap. 35.00 **(978-0-7864-6666-5(9))** McFarland & Co., Inc. Pubs.
Quinn, John. Goodnight Ballivor, I'll Sleep in Trim: A Childhood Memoir. 2008. (ENG., Illus.). 196p. pap. 16.95 *(978-1-84730-100-0(2))* Veritas Pubns. IRL. Dist: Dufour Editions, Inc.
Rayburn, John. Cat Whiskers & Talking Furniture: A Memoir of Radio & Television Broadcasting. 2008. (ENG., Illus.). 256p. per. 35.00 *(978-0-7864-3697-2(2))* McFarland & Co., Inc. Pubs.
Rivers, Tomm. Life Was a Radio, but the Rock & Roll Almost Killed Me. 2011. 200p. pap. 24.95 **(978-1-4626-0015-1(8))** PublishAmerica, Inc.
Sayyad, Parviz. Az Har Dari Sukhani. 2007. (PER.). *(978-1-59584-111-7(3))* Ketab Corp.
Smith, Peter. A Cavalcade of Lesser Horrors. 2011. (ENG.). 200p. pap. 17.95 **(978-0-8166-7557-9(0))** Univ. of Minnesota Pr.
Suzuki, David. David Suzuki: The Autobiography, 1 vol. 2007. (ENG., Illus.). 416p. pap. 18.95 *(978-1-55365-281-6(9)*, Greystone Bks.) D&M Pubs. Inc. CAN. Dist: Perseus-PGW.
Terkel, Studs. P. S. Further Thoughts from a Lifetime of Listening. 2008. (ENG.). 230p. pap. 16.95 *(978-1-59558-423-6(4))* New Pr., The.
—Touch & Go: A Memoir. (ENG., 269p. 2008. Illus.). pap. 17.95 *(978-1-59558-411-3(0))* 2007. 24.95 *(978-1-59558-043-6(3))* New Pr., The.
Thiessen, Abe. A Media Pioneer: The Abe Thiessen Story. 2011. 386p. pap. 29.41 **(978-1-4120-5150-7(9))** Trafford Publishing.
Tuccille, Jerome. Dillerland: The Story of Media Mogul Barry Diller. 2009. (ENG.). 296p. 24.95 *(978-1-59350-124-2(2))* Alyson Pubns.

BROADCASTING
see also Broadcast Journalism; Broadcasters; Broadcasting Policy; Public Broadcasting; Radio Broadcasting; Religious Broadcasting; Television Broadcasting

Andrews, Maggie. Domesticating the Airwaves: Broadcasting, Domesticity & Femininity. 2012. (ENG., Illus.). 288p. pap. 34.95 *(978-1-4411-7272-3(6))* Continuum International Publishing Group, Ltd. GBR. Dist: National Bk. Network.
Berg, Jerome S. Broadcasting on the Short Waves, 1945 to Today. 2008. (ENG., Illus.). 496p. 65.00 *(978-0-7864-3674-3(3))* McFarland & Co., Inc. Pubs.
Beutler, Roland. Digital Terrestrial Broadcasting Networks. 2010. (Lecture Notes in Electrical Engineering Ser.). (Illus.). xiv, 282p. pap. 99.00 *(978-1-4419-3500-7(2)*, 1441935002) Springer.
Broadcasting in the Americas Jobern V50#3. 2007. 216p. 45.00 *(978-0-8058-9349-9(2)*, 0805893482, Routledge) Taylor & Francis Group GBR. Dist: Taylor & Francis Group.
Buckley, Steve, et al. Broadcasting, Voice, & Accountability: A Public Interest Approach to Policy, Law, & Regulation. 2008. (New Media World Ser.). (ENG., Illus.). 416p. pap. 28.00 *(978-0-472-03272-3(0))* Univ. of Michigan Pr.
Chasan, Daniel J. On the Air: The King Broadcasting Story. Date not set. (Illus.). 256p. 22.95 *(978-0-9615580-6-2(7))*; pap. 14.95 *(978-0-9615580-7-9(5))* Island Pubs.
Chinn Swartz, Brecken. Strategies in International Broadcasting- Communication Values Across Cultures. 2007. (Illus.). 260p. per. *(978-3-8364-2170-6(4))* VDM Verlag Dr. Mueller e.K.
Cianci, Philip J. & J. Cianci, Philip. Technology & Workflows for Multiple Channel Content Distribution: Infrastructure implementation strategies for converged Production. 2009. (Focal Press Media Technology Professional Ser.). (ENG., Illus.). 360p. pap. 79.95 *(978-0-240-81172-7(0)*, Focal Pr.) Elsevier Science & Technology Bks.
Cram101 Textbook Reviews. Outlines & Highlights for Broadcasting, Cable, the Internet & Beyond: Introduction to Electronic Media by Joseph R. Dominick, ISBN. 2010. 176p. pap. 29.95 *(978-1-4288-9063-3(7))* Cram101 Inc.
—Outlines & Highlights for Broadcasting, Cable, the Internet, & Beyond by Dominick & Messere & Sherman. 2011. 202p. pap. 30.95 **(978-1-61906-221-4(6))** Cram101 Inc.
—Outlines & Highlights for Broadcasting in America by Head, Spann, Mcgregor. 2011. 360p. pap. 34.95 **(978-1-61906-202-3(X))** Cram101 Inc.
—Outlines & Highlights for Broadcasting in America by Head, Sterling, Schofield. 2011. 496p. pap. 37.95 **(978-1-61906-218-4(6))** Cram101 Inc.
—Outlines & Highlights for Only Connect: A Cultural History of Broadcasting in the United States by Hilmes, ISBN. 2011. 478p. pap. 37.95 **(978-1-61812-975-8(9))** Cram101 Inc.
—Outlines & Highlights for Only Connect: A Cultural History of Broadcasting in the United States by Michele Hilmes, ISBN. 2010. 128p. pap. 28.95 *(978-1-61698-237-9(3))* Cram101 Inc.
Cram101 Textbook Reviews. Outlines Starr, Isbn: 9780240808727. 2011. 130p. pap. 28.95 **(978-1-61461-490-6(3))** Cram101 Inc.
Cram101 Textbook Reviews Staff. Outlines & Highlights for Only Connect: A Cultural History of Broadcasting in the United States by Michele Hilmes, ISBN. 2009. 114p. pap. 28.95 *(978-1-4288-9240-8(0))* Cram101 Inc.
Crisell, Andrew. Liveness & Recording in the Media. 2012. (Key Concerns in Media Studies). (ENG., Illus.). 128p. (C). pap. 22.95 **(978-0-230-28222-3(9))** Palgrave Macmillan.
Curran, James. Power Without Responsibility: Press, Broadcasting & the Internet in Britain. 7th rev. ed. 2009. (ENG., Illus.). 448p. 39.95 *(978-0-415-46699-8(7))*; 125.00 *(978-0-415-46698-1(9))* Routledge.
Dominick, Joseph, et al. Broadcasting, Cable, the Internet & Beyond: An Introduction to Modern Electronic Media. 7th ed. 2011. (ENG., Illus.). 352p. (C). pap. 139.67 *(978-0-07-351203-7(6)*, 0073512036) McGraw-Hill Cos., The.
Dover, Bruce. Rupert Murdoch's China Adventures: How the World's Most Powerful Media Mogul Lost a Fortune & Found a Wife. 2008. (ENG., Illus.). 264p. pap. 16.95 *(978-0-8048-3994-5(8))* Tuttle Publishing.
Everitt, David. A Shadow of Red: Communism & the Blacklist in Radio & Television. 2007. (ENG., Illus.). 432p. 27.50 *(978-1-56663-575-2(6))* Dee, Ivan R. Pub.
Gale Directory of Publications & Broadcast Media. 147th ed. 2011. 1297.00 *(978-1-4144-4715-5(9))* Cengage Gale.
Gomery, Douglas. A History of Broadcasting in the United States. 2008. (ENG., Illus.). 376p. 110.95 *(978-1-4051-2281-8(1))*; pap. 44.95 *(978-1-4051-2282-5(X))* Wiley, John & Sons, Inc. (Wiley-Blackwell).
Good, Howard & Borden, Sandra L., eds. Ethics & Entertainment: Essays on Media Culture & Media Morality. 2010. (ENG.). 327p. pap. 39.95 *(978-0-7864-3909-6(2))* McFarland & Co., Inc. Pubs.
Hilliard, Robert L. & Keith, Michael C. The Broadcast Century & Beyond: A Biography of American Broadcasting. 5th ed. 2010. (ENG., Illus.). 387p. pap. 56.95 *(978-0-240-81236-6(0)*, Focal Pr.) Elsevier Science & Technology Bks.
Hilmes, Michele. Only Connect: A Cultural History of Broadcasting in the United States. 3rd ed. 2011. (Illus.). xvi, 496p. 130.95 *(978-1-4240-6928-6(9))* 2010. (ENG.). 512p. (C). pap. 147.95 *(978-0-495-57051-6(6))* Wadsworth.
—Only Connect: A Cultural History of Broadcasting in the United States, International Edition. 3rd ed. 2011. (Illus.). 440p. pap. 130.95 *(978-1-4240-6929-3(7))* Wadsworth.
IEEE Staff. TELSIKS 2007 - 2007 8th International Conference on Telecommunications in Modern Satellite, Cable & Broadcasting Services. 2008. pap. 278.00 *(978-1-4244-1467-3(9))* IEEE.
Ito, Masami, ed. Broadcasting in Japan. 2010. (ENG.). 144p. (Orig.). 100.00 *(978-0-415-58518-7(X)*, Routledge) Taylor & Francis Group GBR. Dist: Taylor & Francis Group.
Johnson, A. Ross & Parta, R. Eugene, eds. Cold War Broadcasting: Impact on the Soviet Union & Eastern Europe - A Collection of Studies & Documents. 2010. (ENG.). 550p. 55.00 *(978-963-9776-80-7(7))* Central European Univ. Pr.
Jones, Janet & O'Malley, Tom. The Peacock Committee & UK Broadcasting Policy. Jones, Janet & O'Malley, Tom, eds. 2009. (ENG.). 272p. 100.00 *(978-0-230-52474-3(5))* Palgrave Macmillan.
Kim, Tai-hoon, et al, eds. Multimedia, Computer Graphics & Broadcasting, Part I: International Conference MulGraB 2011, Held as Part of the Future Generation Information Technology Conference, FGIT 2011, in Conjunction with GDC 2011, Jeju Island, Korea, December 8-10, 2011. Proceedings, Part I, 2 vols. 2011. (Communications in Computer & Information Science Ser.). (ENG., Illus.). 424p. pap. 107.00 **(978-3-642-27203-5(7)**, 3642272037) Springer.
—Multimedia, Computer Graphics & Broadcasting, Part II: International Conference, MulGraB 2011, Held as Part of the Future Generation Information Technology Conference, FGIT 2011, in Conjunction with GDC 2011, Jeju Island, Korea. December 8-10, 2011. Proceedings, Part II, 2 vols. 2011. (Communications in Computer & Information Science Ser.). (ENG., Illus.). xxii, 357p. pap. 95.00 **(978-3-642-27185-4(5)**, 3642271855) Springer.
King, Larry. Truth Be Told: Off the Record about Favorite Guests, Memorable Moments, Funniest Jokes, & a Half Century of Asking Questions. 2011. (ENG., Illus.). 248p. 25.00 *(978-1-60286-130-5(7))* Perseus Bks. Group.
Knauer, Nils. Signal Losses of Outdoor-Indoor Wave Propagation Paths - Signal Fading Through Modern Window Systems. 2007. pap. *(978-3-8364-2530-8(0))* VDM Verlag Dr. Mueller e.K.
Kramer, Leonie. From Fact to Legend: Writing & Broadcasting in Australia. pap. 2.00 *(978-0-909751-75-3(7))* UWA Publishing AUS. Dist: International Specialized Bk. Services.
Kramer, Ronald. Pioneer Mikes: A History of Radio & Television in Oregon. 2009. (Illus.). 480p. pap. 26.95 *(978-0-615-30030-6(8))* JPR Foundation, Inc.
Luff, John A. Centralized Broadcast Operations. 2008. (Focal Press Media Technology Professional Ser.). (Illus.). 275p. pap. 49.95 *(978-0-240-80847-5(9)* Focal Pr.) Elsevier Science & Technology Bks.
McGregor, Michael A., et al. Head's Broadcasting in America: A Survey of Electronic Media. 10th ed. 2009. (ENG.). 360p. (C). pap. 116.80 *(978-0-205-60813-3(2))* Allyn & Bacon, Inc.
Moran, Albert & Keating, Chris. The A to Z of Australian Radio & Television. 2009. (A to Z Guide Ser.: No. 72). (ENG.). 548p. pap. 34.45 *(978-0-8108-6856-4(3))* Scarecrow Pr., Inc.
Muller-Bungart, Michael. Revenue Management with Flexible Products: Models & Methods for the Broadcasting Industry. 2007. (Lecture Notes in Economics & Mathematical Systems Ser.). (Illus.). 297p. per. 139.00 *(978-3-540-72315-8(3))* Springer.
Orlik, Peter B. Broadcast/Broadband Copywriting. 8th ed. 2009. (ENG.). 496p. (C). pap. 127.00 *(978-0-205-67452-7(6))* Allyn & Bacon, Inc.
ProQuest Editorial Staff, ed. Broadcasting & Cable Yearbook 2008. 2007. 245.00 *(978-1-60030-110-0(X))* CSA Journal Division.
ProQuest LLC Staff, ed. Broadcasting & Cable Year Book 2009. 2008. 275.00 *(978-1-60030-121-6(5))* ProQuest LLC.
Radio/TV Station Annual Outlook. 2007. spiral bd. *(978-1-933614-36-6(6))* SNL Kagan.
Rudin, Richard. Broadcasting in the 21st Century. 2011. (ENG., Illus.). 256p. (C). 90.00 *(978-0-230-01317-9(1))*; pap. 30.95 *(978-0-230-01318-6(X))* Palgrave Macmillan.
Ryan E. Moore. Media Industry Programming, Competition & Copyright Issues. 2011. (Series: Media & Communications - Technologies, Policies & Challenges Ser.). 89.00 *(978-1-61122-078-0(5))* Nova Science Pubs., Inc.
Schafer, Kermit. The Best of Bloopers. 20.95 *(978-0-89190-214-0(7))* Amereon LTD.
Seabright, Paul & Von Hagen, Jurgen, eds. The Economic Regulation of Broadcasting Markets: Evolving Technology & Challenges for Policy. 2007. (ENG., Illus.). 368p. 98.00 *(978-0-521-87405-2(X))* Cambridge Univ. Pr.
Singh, Pururaj. Encyclopaedia of Media, Broadcasting & Publishing. 2011. (Illus.). 660p. pap. 52.50 **(978-93-80228-92-1(9))** Global India Pubns. Pvt. Ltd. IND. Dist: Coronet Bks.
Slotten, Hugh Richard. Radio's Hidden Voice: The Origins of Public Broadcasting in the United States. 2009. (History of Communication Ser.). (ENG., Illus.). 344p. 52.00 *(978-0-252-03447-3(3))* Univ. of Illinois Pr.

BROADCASTING—GOVERNMENT POLICY
see Broadcasting Policy

BROADCASTING—LAW AND LEGISLATION

Carter, Barton & Franklin, Marc. The First Amendment & the Fifth Estate, 6th, 2007 Supplement. 7th rev. ed. 2007. (University Casebook Ser.). 187p. pap. 16.00 *(978-1-59941-346-4(9))* Foundation Pr.) West.
Cram101 Textbook Reviews. Outlines & Highlights for Media & Entertainment Law by Sandi Towers, Isbn: 9781418039127 1418039128. 2011. 196p. pap. 30.95 **(978-1-61490-777-0(3))** Cram101 Inc.
Crawford, Michael G. The Journalist's Legal Guide. 5th ed. xxii, 608p. *(978-0-7798-1731-3(1))* Carswell.
Harrison, Jackie & Woods, Lorna. European Broadcasting Law & Policy. 2007. (Cambridge Studies in European Law & Policy Ser.). (ENG.). 392p. pap. 61.00 *(978-0-521-61330-9(2))*; 126.00 *(978-0-521-84897-8(0))* Cambridge Univ. Pr.
Holt, Jennifer. Empires of Entertainment: Media Industries & the Politics of Deregulation, 1980-1996. 2011. (ENG., Illus.). 256p. (C). 72.00 *(978-0-8135-5052-7(1))*; pap. 24.95 *(978-0-8135-5053-4(X))* Rutgers Univ. Pr.
Hyon, Tae-Ho. Kukka Kyongjaengnyok Kanghwa Rul Wihan Pangsong T'ongsin Popche Ui Kaeson Pangan. 2008. 98p. *(978-89-8323-890-0(9))* Korea Legislation Research Institute.

B

Katsirea, Irini. Public Broadcasting & European Law: A Comparative Examination of Public Service Obligations in Six Member States. 2008. (978-90-411-2500-2(0)) Kluwer Law International.

Knorre, Nina. Die Abwicklung des Arbeitsverhältnisses nach erfolgreicher Statusklage im Rundfunk. 2008. (Studien zum deutschen und europäischen Medienrecht Ser.). 266p. pap. 65.95 (978-3-631-57621-2(8)) Lang, Peter GmbH, Europaischer Verlag der Wissenschaften DEU. Dist: Lang, Peter.

Lipschultz, Jeremy H. Broadcast & Internet Indecency: Defining Free Speech. 2007. XII, 412p. 49.95 (978-0-8058-5910-2(1)); 125.00 (978-0-8058-5909-6(8)) Erlbaum, Lawrence Assocs., Inc.

Lipschultz, Jeremy Harris. Broadcast & Internet Indecency: Defining Free Speech. 2008. (978-0-415-96471-5(7)) Routledge.

Niebler, Julia. Die Stärkung der Regionalfensterprogramme im Privaten Rundfunk als Mittel zur Sicherung der Meinungsvielfalt durch den Achten Rundfunkänderungsstaatsvertrag. 2008. (Studien zum deutschen und europäischen Medienrecht Ser.). 302p. pap. 74.95 (978-3-631-58131-5(9)) Lang, Peter GmbH, Europaischer Verlag der Wissenschaften DEU. Dist: Lang, Peter.

Nikolitsis, Nikos Th. EU Competition Law & Regulation in the Converging Telecommunications, Media & IT Sectors. 2006. (International Competition Law Ser.: Vol. 20). (Illus.). 698p. (978-90-411-2469-2(1)) Kluwer Law International.

O'Reilly, Terrance I., ed. Programmer-Distributor Negotiations: Retransmission Consent & Other Federal Rules. 2008. (Illus.). 97p. pap. 39.00 (978-1-60456-279-8(X)) Nova Science Pubs., Inc.

Rosenberg, Marvin. NAB Legal Guide to Broadcast Law & Regulation. 4th ed. 2013. (ENG., Illus.). 740p. 499.95 (978-0-240-81117-8(8), Focal Pr.) Elsevier Science & Technology Bks.

Schejter, Amit M. Muting Israeli Democracy: How Media & Cultural Policy Undermine Free Expression. 2009. (History of Communication Ser.). (ENG., Illus.). 192p. pap. 20.00 (978-0-252-07693-0(1)) Univ. of Illinois Pr.

Velliotis, Harold F., ed. Media Ownership. 2009. pap. 37.00 (978-1-60692-365-8(X)) Nova Science Pubs., Inc.

Voß, Jörg Michael. Pluraler Rundfunk in Europa - ein duales System für Europa? Rahmenbedingungen für den öffentlich-rechtlichen Rundfunk in einer europäischen dualen Rundfunkordnung. 2008. (Studien zum deutschen und europäischen Medienrecht Ser.). 384p. pap. 81.95 (978-3-631-57077-7(5)) Lang, Peter GmbH, Europaischer Verlag der Wissenschaften DEU. Dist: Lang, Peter.

Wagner, Eva Ellen. Abkehr Von der Geräteabhängigen RundfunkgebüHr: Die Neuordnung der Rundfunkfinanzierung. 2011. (Studien zum deutschen und europäischen Medienrecht Ser.). (GER.). 304p. 83.95 **(978-3-631-60654-4(0))** Lang, Peter GmbH, Europaischer Verlag der Wissenschaften DEU. Dist: Lang, Peter.

BROADCASTING—VOCATIONAL GUIDANCE

Dayna Steele. Rock to the Top: What I Learned about Success from the World's Greatest Rock Stars. 2009. 192p. pap. 16.95 (978-1-4401-9606-5(0)) iUniverse, Inc.

Schneider, Chris. Starting Your Career in Broadcasting: Working on & off the Air in Radio & Television. 2007. (ENG., Illus.). 256p. per. 19.95 (978-1-58115-489-4(5), 115489, Allworth Pr.) Skyhorse Publishing Co., Inc.

BROADCASTING AND STATE

see Broadcasting Policy

BROADCASTING AS A PROFESSION

see Broadcasting—Vocational Guidance

BROADCASTING POLICY

Armstrong, Robert & Robert Armstrong. Broadcasting Policy in Canada. 2010. (Illus.). 296p. (978-1-4426-4096-2(0)); pap. (978-1-4426-1035-4(2)) Univ. of Toronto Pr.

Buckley, Steve, et al. Broadcasting, Voice, & Accountability: A Public Interest Approach to Policy, Law, & Regulation. 2008. (New Media World Ser.). (ENG., Illus.). 416p. pap. 28.00 (978-0-472-03272-3(0)) Univ. of Michigan Pr.

—Broadcasting, Voice, & Accountability: A Public Interest Approach to Policy, Law, & Regulation. 2008. (ENG., Illus.). 418p. 35.00 (978-0-8213-7295-1(5), 9780821372951) World Bank Pubns.

Chalaby, Jean K. Transnational Television in Europe: Reconfiguring Global Communications Networks. 2009. (ENG., Illus.). 272p. 94.00 (978-1-84511-953-9(3)); pap. 34.00 (978-1-84511-954-6(1)) I. B. Tauris & Co., Ltd. GBR. Dist: Macmillan.

Choi, Jung-Bong. Digitalization of Television in Japan State, Economy, & Discourse. 2008. 212p. pap. (978-3-639-07834-3(9)) VDM Verlag Dr. Mueller e.K.

Christou, George & Simpson, Seamus. The Eu in Global Electronic Communications. 2014. (Routledge Advances in European Politics Ser.). (ENG.). 240p. (C). 135.00 **(978-0-415-52385-1(0))** Routledge.

Competition in the Sports Programming Marketplace: Hearing Before the Subcommittee on Telecommunications & the Internet of the Committee on Energy & Commerce, House of Representatives, One Hundred Tenth Congress, Second Session, March 5, 2008. 2008. (Illus.). v, 110p. (978-0-16-083860-6(6), 552-070-39555-5) United States Government Printing Office.

D'Haenens, Leen & Saeys, Frieda, eds. Western Broadcast Models: Structure, Conduct & Performance. 2007. (Communications Monograph Ser.). (ENG., Illus.). 524p. (C). 63.00 (978-3-11-019527-9(5)) De Gruyter, Mouton DEU. Dist: de Gruyter, Walter GmbH & Co. KG.

Druick, Zoë, et al, eds. Programming Reality: Perspectives on English-Canadian Television. 2008. (Film & Media Studies). (ENG., Illus.). 354p. pap. 42.95 (978-1-55458-010-1(2)) Wilfrid Laurier Univ. Pr. CAN. Dist: Univ. of Toronto Pr.

Exploring the Scope of Public Performance Rights: Hearing Before the Committee on the Judiciary, United States Senate, One Hundred Tenth Congress, First Session, November 13, 2007. 2008. iii, 63p. (978-0-16-080349-9(7), 552-070-37045-5) United States Government Printing Office.

Farabaugh, Patrick. Carl Mcintire's Crusade Against the Fairness Doctrine. 2010. 204p. pap. (978-3-639-27459-2(8)) VDM Verlag Dr. Mueller e.K.

Hitchens, Lesley. Broadcasting Pluralism & Diversity: A Comparative Study of Policy & Regulation. 2006. 342p. (C). 106.00 (978-1-84113-214-3(4)) Hart Publishing Ltd. GBR. Dist: International Specialized Bk. Services.

Jones, Janet & O'Malley, Tom. The Peacock Committee & UK Broadcasting Policy. Jones, Janet & O'Malley, Tom, eds. 2009. (ENG.). 272p. 100.00 (978-0-230-52474-3(5)) Palgrave Macmillan.

Klinenberg, Eric. Fighting for Air: The Battle to Control America's Media. 2010. 351p. pap. 17.00 (978-1-4379-7415-7(5)) DIANE Publishing Co.

—Fighting for Air: The Battle to Control America's Media. 2008. (ENG.). 368p. pap. 18.99 (978-0-8050-8729-1(X), Holt Paperback) Holt, Henry & Co.

Mickiewicz, Ellen. Television, Power & the Public in Russia. 2008. (ENG., Illus.). 220p. 86.00 (978-0-521-88856-1(5)) Cambridge Univ. Pr.

—Television, Power, & the Public in Russia. 2008. (ENG., Illus.). 220p. pap. 32.00 (978-0-521-71675-8(6)) Cambridge Univ. Pr.

Millwood Hargrave, Andrea, et al. Accountability & the Public Interest in Broadcasting. 2009. (ENG.). 256p. 89.00 (978-0-230-01920-1(X)) Palgrave Macmillan.

Neulander, Joelle. Programming National Identity: The Culture of Radio in 1930s France. 2009. 272p. 40.00 (978-0-8071-3494-8(5)) Louisiana State Univ. Pr.

Niebler, Julia. Die Stärkung der Regionalfensterprogramme im Privaten Rundfunk als Mittel zur Sicherung der Meinungsvielfalt durch den Achten Rundfunkänderungsstaatsvertrag. 2008. (Studien zum deutschen und europäischen Medienrecht Ser.). 302p. pap. 74.95 (978-3-631-58131-5(9)) Lang, Peter GmbH, Europaischer Verlag der Wissenschaften DEU. Dist: Lang, Peter.

Oversight of the Federal Communications Commission: Media Ownership: Hearing Before the Subcommittee on Telecommunications & the Internet of the Committee on Energy & Commerce, House of Representatives, One Hundred Tenth Congress, First Session, December 5, 2007. 2008. (Illus.). vi, 462p. (978-0-16-082397-8(8), 552-070-38443-0) United States Government Printing Office.

Pavarala, Vinod & Malik, Kanchan K. Other Voices: The Struggle for Community Radio in India. 2007. (Illus.). 328p. (C). 49.95 (978-0-7619-3602-2(5), B36022C); 318p. (978-81-7829-765-1(5)) SAGE Pubns., Inc.

Performance Rights ACT: Hearing Before the Subcommittee on Courts, the Internet, & Intellectual Property of the Committee on the Judiciary, House of Representatives, One Hundred Tenth Congress, Second Session, on H.R. 4789, June 11, 2008. 2008. (Illus.). iv, 173p. (978-0-16-082520-0(2), 552-070-38555-0) United States Government Printing Office.

The Performance Rights ACT & Parity among Music Delivery Platforms: Hearing Before the Committee on the Judiciary, United States Senate, One Hundred Eleventh Congress, First Session, August 4, 2009. 2010. (Illus.). iii, 127p. (978-0-16-085243-5(9), 552-070-40585-2) United States Government Printing Office.

Potschka, Christian. Towards a Market in Broadcasting: Communications Policy in the UK & Germany. 2012. (ENG., Illus.). 352p. 85.00 **(978-0-230-29861-3(3))** Palgrave Macmillan.

Ramey, Carl R. Mass Media Unleashed: How Washington Policymakers Shortchanged the American Public. 2007. (ENG.). 346p. 84.00 (978-0-7425-5569-3(0)); per. 32.95 (978-0-7425-5570-9(4)) Rowman & Littlefield Publishers, Inc.

Saeys, Frieda & d'Haenens, Leen, eds. Western Broadcast Models: Structure, Conduct & Performance. 2007. (Communications Monograph Ser.). (Illus.). 445p. 121.00 (978-3-11-019526-2(7)) De Gruyter, Walter Inc.

Schejter, Amit M. Muting Israeli Democracy: How Media & Cultural Policy Undermine Free Expression. 2009. (History of Communication Ser.). (ENG., Illus.). 192p. pap. 20.00 (978-0-252-07693-0(1)) Univ. of Illinois Pr.

Seabright, Paul & von Hagen, Jürgen, eds. The Economic Regulation of Broadcasting Markets: Evolving Technology & Challenges for Policy. 2007. (ENG., Illus.). 368p. pap. 45.99 (978-0-521-69634-0(8)) Cambridge Univ. Pr.

The Status of the Digital Television Transition: Hearings Before the Subcommittee on Telecommunications & the Internet of the Committee on Energy & Commerce, House of Representatives, One Hundred Tenth Congress, First Session, March 28, October 17, 31, 2007. 2008. (Illus.). viii, 655p. (978-0-16-082448-7(6), 552-070-38492-8) United States Government Printing Office.

Upton, Fred, ed. Can You Say That on TV? An Examination of the FCC's Enforcement with Respect to Broadcast Indecency: Congressional Hearing. 2006. 107p. (C). reprint ed. pap. 30.00 (978-1-4223-0654-3(2)) DIANE Publishing Co.

Van Vuuren, Kitty. Participation in Australian Community Broadcasting. 2008. 248p. pap. (978-3-639-03497-4(X)) VDM Verlag Dr. Mueller e.K.

BROADS, THE (ENGLAND)

Matless, D. & Matless, David. In the Nature of Landscape: Cultural Geography on the Norfolk Broads. 2011. (ENG.). 256p. pap. (978-1-4051-9082-4(5), Wiley-Blackwell) Wiley, John & Sons, Ltd.

Matless, David. In the Nature of Landscape: Cultural Geography on the Norfolk Broads. 2011. (ENG.). 256p. (978-1-4051-9081-7(7), Wiley-Blackwell) Wiley, John & Sons, Ltd.

BROADSIDES

see also Playbills

Caemmerer, Christiane & Jungmayr, Jorg, eds. Flugblätter von der frühen Neuzeit bis zur Gegenwart als kulturhistorische Quellen und bibliothekarische Sondermaterialien. 2010. (GER & ENG., Illus.). 302p. pap. 72.95 (978-3-631-56122-5(9)) Lang, Peter GmbH, Europaischer Verlag der Wissenschaften DEU. Dist: Lang, Peter.

Carbonell, John. The Early Printings of Abraham Lincoln's Gettysburg Address & What They Reveal about His Spoken Words. 2008. 19.95 (978-1-58456-256-6(0)) Oak Knoll Pr.

Gilgenast, Trudy. Pennsylvania German Broadsides: A Reflection of Daily Life, 1741-1890. 2009. (978-1-892142-46-7(5)) Cedar Tree Bks.

Paas, Martha White. The Kipper und Wipper Inflation, 1619-23: An Economic History with Contemporary German Broadsheets. Schoolfield, George C., tr. 2012. (Yale Series in Economic & Financial History Ser.). (ENG., Illus.). 192p. 85.00 **(978-0-300-14676-9(0))** Yale Univ. Pr.

Paas, Roger, compiled by. The German Political Broadsheet 1600-1700, Volume 10: 1671-1682. 2010. (German Political Broadsheet 1600-1700 Ser.). (GER & ENG., Illus.). 483p. (C). 1500.00 (978-3-447-06157-5(X)) Harrassowitz, Otto Verlag DEU. Dist: ISD.

Sulmoni, Martina. <Einer Kunst- und Tugendliebenden Jugend Verehrt> Die Bild-Text-Kombinationen in Den Neujahrsblattem der Burgerbibliothek Zurich Von 1645 Bis 1672. (GER., Illus.). 508p. pap. 75.95 (978-3-03911-172-5(8)) Lang, Peter Publishing, Inc.

BROADSIDES—BIBLIOGRAPHY

Lemon, Robert, ed. Catalogue of a Collection of Printed Broadsides in the Possession of the Society of Antiquaries of London. 2007. (ENG.). 244p. per. 26.95 (978-0-548-78331-3(4)) Kessinger Publishing, LLC.

McShane, Angela J. Political Broadside Ballads of Seventeenth-Century England: A Critical Bibliography, 1 vol. 2011. (ENG.). 648p. 260.00 (978-1-84893-014-8(3)) Pickering & Chatto Pubs., Ltd. GBR. Dist: Ashgate Publishing Co.

BROADSIDES—HISTORY AND CRITICISM

Würzbach, Natascha. The Rise of the English Street Ballad, 1550-1650. Walls, Gayna, tr. from GER. 2011. (European Studies in English Literature Ser.). (ENG., Illus.). 372p. pap. 39.99 (978-0-521-17744-3(8)) Cambridge Univ. Pr.

BROCADE

Duits, Rembrandt. Gold Brocade & Renaissance Painting: A Study in Material Culture. 2008. (Illus.). iv, 494p. (C). 300.00 (978-1-904597-42-1(4)) Pindar Pr. GBR. Dist: Brown, David Bk. Co., The.

BROCH, HERMANN, 1886-1951

Broch, Hermann. Briefe an Erich von Kahler (1940-1951) Latzeler, Paul Michael, ed. 2011. (Quellen und Forschungen zur Literatur- und Kulturgeschichte Ser.).Tr. of Letters to Erich von Kahler (1940-1951). (GER., Illus.). XX, 198p. 154.00 **(978-3-11-174995-2(9))** De Gruyter, Walter Inc.

—Briefe an Erich von Kahler (1940-1951) Lützeler, Paul Michael, ed. 2010. (Quellen und Forschungen zur Literatur- und Kulturgeschichte Ser.).Tr. of Letters to Erich von Kahler (1940-1951). (GER.). XX, 198p. 98.00 (978-3-11-022744-4(4)) De Gruyter, Walter Inc.

Dittrich, Andreas. Glauben, Wissen und Sagen: Studien zu Wissen und Wissenskritik im 'Zauberberg', in den 'Schlafwandlern' und im 'Mann ohne Eigenschaften' 2009. (Studien zur deutschen Literatur Ser.).Tr. of Believing, Knowing & Saying. Studies on Knowledge & Critique of Knowledge in 'the Magic mountainâ€(tm), â€˜the Sleepwalkersâ€(tm) & the â€˜the Man Without Qualitiesâ€(tm). (GER.). IX, 365p. 168.00 **(978-3-11-173585-6(0))** De Gruyter, Walter Inc.

—Glauben, Wissen und Sagen: Studien zu Wissen und Wissenskritik im 'Zauberberg', in den 'Schlafwandlern' und im 'Mann ohne Eigenschaften' 2009. (Studien zur deutschen Literatur Ser.).Tr. of Believing, Knowing & Saying. Studies on Knowledge & Critique of Knowledge in 'the Magic mountainâ€(tm), â€˜the Sleepwalkersâ€(tm) & the â€˜the Man Without Qualitiesâ€(tm). (GER.). IX, 365p. pap. (978-3-484-18188-5(5)) Verlag Max Niemeyer.

Fetz, Bernhard. Das unmögliche Ganze: Zur literarischen Kritik der Kultur. 2009. (GER., Illus.). 378p. (978-3-7705-4659-6(8)) Wilhelm/Fink#GmbH & Co. Verlags-KG.

Gay, José María Pérez. The Unfortunate Passion of Hermann Broch. Jiménez, Eduardo, tr. from SPA. 2008. 148p. pap. 24.95 (978-0-9796457-3-0(5)) Floricanto Pr.

Kubik, Silke. Die europäische Ordnung stirbt... - Religion und Geschichtskonstruktion im Angesicht der Katastrophe: Eine vergleichende Untersuchung der Romane Die Schlafwandler von Hermann Broch und das unauslöschliche Siegel von Elisabeth Langgässer. 2008. (Berliner Beiträge zur Literatur- und Kulturgeschichte Ser.). 168p. pap. 56.95 (978-3-631-56293-2(4)) Lang, Peter GmbH, Europaischer Verlag der Wissenschaften DEU. Dist: Lang, Peter.

Stasková, Alice. Nächte der Aufklärung: Studien zur Ästhetik, Ethik und Erkenntnistheorie in 'Voyage au bout de la nuit' von Louis Ferdinand Céline und 'Die Schlafwandler' von Hermann Broch. 2007. (Communicatio Ser.). (GER.). X, 342p. pap. (978-3-484-63039-0(6)) Verlag Max Niemeyer.

Stasková, Alice & Lützeler, Paul Michael, eds. Hermann Broch und die Künste. 2009.Tr. of Hermann Broch & the Arts. (GER.). VI, 263p. 126.00 (978-3-11-020955-6(1)) De Gruyter, Walter Inc.

BROCK, ISAAC, SIR, 1769-1812

Laxer, James. Tecumseh & Brock: The War of 1812. 2012. (ENG., Illus.). 368p. 29.95 **(978-0-88784-261-0(5))** House of Anansi Pr. CAN. Dist: Perseus-PGW.

Nursey, Walter R. The Story of Isaac Brock, Hero, Defender & Saviour of Upper Canada, 1812. 2012. 244p. pap. 26.75 **(978-1-278-73707-2(3))** 2010. (ENG.). 236p. pap. 26.75 (978-1-177-53158-0(5)) 2008. 180p. 25.99 (978-0-554-23852-4(7)) 2007. 160p. pap. 19.99 (978-1-4264-5086-0(9)) 2007. (ENG.). 178p. pap. 21.99 (978-1-4264-5387-8(6)) 2010. (ENG.). 252p. reprint ed. pap. 26.75 (978-1-177-46423-9(3)) 2010. 244p. reprint ed. pap. 26.75 (978-1-149-55700-6(1)) 2008. 180p. reprint ed. 22.99 (978-0-554-33155-3(1)) BiblioBazaar.

—The Story of Isaac Brock, Hero, Defender & Saviour of Upper Canada, 1812. 2009. 112p. reprint ed. pap. (978-1-150-63156-6(2)) Books LLC.

—The Story of Isaac Brock, Hero, Defender & Saviour of Upper Canada, 1812. 2007. 176p. per. (978-1-4065-4048-2(X)) Dodo Pr.

—The Story of Isaac Brock, Hero, Defender & Saviour of Upper Canada, 1812. 2006. pap. (978-1-4068-3567-0(6)) Echo Library.

—The Story of Isaac Brock, Hero, Defender & Saviour of Upper Canada, 1812. 2010. (Illus.). 88p. pap. 7.75 (978-1-77045-066-0(1)); 90p. reprint ed. pap. 7.75 (978-1-152-48510-5(5)) General Bks. LLC.

—The Story of Isaac Brock, Hero, Defender & Saviour of Upper Canada, 1812. 2012. 242p. pap. **(978-1-290-14802-3(3))** HardPr.

—The Story of Isaac Brock, Hero, Defender & Saviour of Upper Canada, 1812. 2010. 230p. pap. 21.56 (978-1-163-97056-0(5)) 2010. 230p. 33.56 **(978-1-164-28057-6(0))** 2008. 228p. 41.95 (978-0-548-97788-0(7)) 2007. (ENG.). 232p. reprint ed. per. 26.95 (978-0-548-66989-1(9)) Kessinger Publishing, LLC.

Nursey, Walter R., creator. The Story of Isaac Brock, Hero, Defender & Saviour of Upper Canada, 1812. 2010. 252p. reprint ed. pap. 26.75 (978-1-175-83227-6(8)) BiblioBazaar.

Riley, Jonathon. A Matter of Honour: The Life, Campaigns & Generalship of Isaac Brock. 2011. 352p. pap. 27.95 (978-1-896941-65-3(6)) Brass, Robin Studio, Inc. CAN. Dist: Midpoint Trade Bks., Inc.

Tupper, Ferdinand Br. The Life & Correspondence of Sir Isaac. 2006. pap. (978-1-4068-3365-2(7)) Echo Library.

Tupper, Ferdinand Brock. The Life & Correspondence of Sir Isaac Brock. 2008. 404p. 32.99 (978-0-554-27082-1(X)) 2007. (ENG.). 352p. pap. 25.99 (978-1-4346-2481-9(1)) 2007. (ENG.). 402p. pap. 28.99 (978-1-4346-2523-6(0)) BiblioBazaar.

Turner, Wesley B. The Astonishing General: The Life & Legacy of Sir Isaac Brock. 2011. (ENG., Illus.). 376p. 35.00 (978-1-55488-777-4(1), Dundurn Pr.) Dundurn CAN. Dist: Ingram Pub. Services.

BROCKTON (MASS.)

Benson, James E. Brockton. 2010. (Images of America Ser.). (ENG., Illus.). 128p. pap. 21.99 (978-0-7385-7308-3(6)) Arcadia Publishing.

Benson, James E. Brockton Revisited. 2012. (Images of America Ser.). (ENG., Illus.). 128p. pap. 21.99 **(978-0-7385-7668-8(9))** Arcadia Publishing.

BRODSKY, JOSEPH, 1940-1996

Eskin, Michael. Poetic Affairs: Celan, Grunbein, Brodsky. 2008. (Verbal Art: Studies in Poetics Ser.). (ENG.). 252p. 60.00 (978-0-8047-5831-4(X)) Stanford Univ. Pr.

Friedberg, Nila. English Rhythms in Russian Verse: On the Experiment of Joseph Brodsky. 2011. (Trends in Linguistics. Studies & Monographs [TiLSM] Ser.). 140.00 **(978-3-11-023808-2(X))** De Gruyter, Mouton DEU. Dist: de Gruyter, Walter GmbH & Co. KG.

Gross, Irena Grudzinska. Czeslaw Milosz & Joseph Brodsky: Fellowship of Poets. 2009. (ENG.). 384p. 40.00 (978-0-300-14937-1(9)) Yale Univ. Pr.

Loseff, Lev. Joseph Brodsky: A Literary Life. Miller, Jane Ann, tr. from RUS. 2012. (ENG.). 352p. pap. 22.00 **(978-0-300-18160-9(4))** Yale Univ. Pr.

Polukhina, Valentina. Brodsky Through the Eyes of His Contemporaries, Vol. I, 2 vols. Jones, Chris et al, trs. 2008. (Studies in Russian & Slavic Literatures, Cultures, & History Ser.: Volume 1). (ENG., Illus.). 360p. 60.00 (978-1-934843-15-4(6)) Academic Studies Pr.

—Brodsky Through the Eyes of His Contemporaries, Vol. II, 2 vols. Retivov, Tatiana et al, trs. 2nd ed. 2008. (Studies in Russian & Slavic Literatures, Cultures, & History Ser.: Volume 2). (ENG., Illus.). 604p. 60.00 (978-1-934843-16-1(4)) Academic Studies Pr.

—Joseph Brodsky: A Poet for our Time. 2009. (Cambridge Studies in Russian Literature Ser.). (ENG., Illus.). 348p. pap. 48.00 (978-0-521-11146-1(3)) Cambridge Univ. Pr.

Turoma, Sanna. Brodsky Abroad: Empire, Tourism, Nostalgia. 2010. (ENG.). 280p. pap. 29.95 (978-0-299-23634-2(X)) Univ. of Wisconsin Pr.

Williams, David-Antoine. Defending Poetry: Art & Ethics in Joseph Brodsky, Seamus Heaney, & Geoffrey Hill. 2010. (ENG.). 264p. 110.00 (978-0-19-958354-6(4)) Oxford Univ. Pr., Inc.

BROILERS (POULTRY)

Aftab, Usama & Ashraf, Muhammad. Protein & Amino Acid Responses of Broilers with Low-Energy Diets. 2010. 144p. pap. (978-3-639-23631-6(9)) VDM Verlag Dr. Mueller e.K.

Akram, Bushra & Shakil Amjid, Syed. Supplementing Fiber-Degrading Enzymes to Broilers. 2011. 80p. pap. **(978-3-8433-8533-6(5))** Lambert Academic Publishing.

Ayyub, Rana Muhammad. Economic & Biological Aspects of Vaccinations: Effects of Ibd Vaccination on Nd Vaccination in Broilers. 2011. 120p. pap. *(978-3-639-32249-1(5))* VDM Verlag Dr. Mueller e.K.
Daigle, Justin M. Transformation of U. S. Animal Agriculture. 2010. (Agriculture Issues & Policies Ser.). 204p. 115.00 *(978-1-60876-938-4(0))* Nova Science Pubs., Inc.
Karki, Surendra. Herbal Immunomodulator Drugs & Broilers. 2011. 68p. pap. *(978-3-8443-3241-4(3))* Lambert Academic Publishing.
Leeson, Steve & Summers, J. D. Broiler Breeder Production. adapted ed. 2010. (ENG.). 338p. pap. 40.95 *(978-1-904761-79-2(8))* Nottingham Univ. Pr. GBR. Dist: Independent Pubs. Group.
Shahzad, Naveed & Haq Nawaz. Efficacy of Feed Additive Probiotic on Broiler Performance. 2011. 96p. pap. *(978-3-8443-1314-7(1))* Lambert Academic Publishing.
Sithambaram, Shanmugavelu. Enzymes & Phytochemicals in Chicken Diets - the Influence of Enzymes & Phytochemicals in Chicken Diets on Performance, Nutrient Utilisation & Gu. 2008. 264p. pap. *(978-3-639-04437-9(1))* VDM Verlag Dr. Mueller e.K

BROKERAGE, MARRIAGE
see Marriage Brokerage

BROKERS
see also Agency (Law); Commission Merchants
Additional Reforms to the Securities Investor Protection ACT: Hearing Before the Subcommittee on Capital Markets, Insurance, & Government Sponsored Enterprises of the Committee on Financial Services, U.S. House of Representatives, One Hundred Eleventh Congress, First Session, December 9, 2009. 2010. v, 274p. *(978-0-16-086323-3(6)*, 552-070-41410-0) United States Government Printing Office.
Aicpa. AICPA Audit & Accounting Guide: Brokers & Dealers in Securities. 2007. pap. 86.25 *(978-0-87051-685-6(X))* American Institute of Certified Public Accountants.
Aikman, J. S. When Prime Brokers Fail: The Unheeded Risk to Hedge Funds, Banks, & the Financial Industry. 2010. (Bloomberg Ser.: 92). (ENG., Illus.). 290p. 49.95 *(978-1-57660-355-0(5)*, Bloomberg Pr.) Wiley, John & Sons, Inc.
Assessing the Limitations of the Securities Investor Protection ACT: Hearing Before the Subcommittee on Capital Markets, Insurance, & Government Sponsored Enterprises of the Committee on Financial Services, U.S. House of Representatives, One Hundred Eleventh Congress, Second Session, September 23, 2010. 2010. v, 165p. *(978-0-16-088084-1(X)*, 552-070-42504-7) United States Government Printing Office.
Bain, Jim. A Financial Tale of Two Cities: Sydney & Melbourne's Remarkable Contest for Commercial Supremacy. 2007. (ENG., Illus.). 336p. per. 35.95 *(978-0-86840-963-4(4)*, UNSW Press) NewSouth Publishing AUS. Dist: Independent Pubs. Group.
Bayer, Christopher A. Beyond Survival: The Stockbroker's Journey. 2008. 100p. pap. *(978-0-615-19621-3(7))* Bayer, Christopher A.
Belfort, Jordan. Catching the Wolf of Wall Street: More Incredible True Stories of Fortunes, Schemes, Parties, & Prison. 2011. 480p. pap. 16.00 *(978-0-553-38544-1(5))* Random House Publishing Group.
—The Wolf of Wall Street. (ENG.). 528p. 2008. pap. 16.00 *(978-0-553-38477-2(5))* 2007. 25.00 *(978-0-553-80546-8(0))* Random House Publishing Group. (Bantam).
Bitner, Richard. Confessions of a Subprime Lender: An Insider's Tale of Greed, Fraud, & Ignorance. 2008. (ENG., Illus.). 208p. pap. 19.95 *(978-0-470-40219-1(9)*, Wiley) Wiley, John & Sons, Inc.
Brigandi, Thomas. Stay Focused: A Nineteen Year Old Stockbroker's Guide to Success in a New Global Age. 2010. 56p. pap. 10.97 *(978-0-557-25473-6(6))* Lulu Enterprises Inc.
Brown, Joshua M. Backstage Wall Street: an Insider’s Guide to Knowing Who to Trust, Who to Run from, & How to Maximize Your Investments. 2012. (ENG., Illus.). 256p. 28.00 *(978-0-07-178232-6(X)*, 007178232X) McGraw-Hill Cos., The.
Butt, Paul D. The Successful Organized Stockbroker, 2 vols., Set. (Illus.). 83p. (Orig.). pap. 125.00 *(978-0-9635346-0-6(2))* Buttonwood Publishing.
Carroll, Terry. NLP for Traders & Investors. 2012. 192p. pap. 24.00 *(978-1-906403-71-3(6))* Global Professional Publishing GBR. Dist: Stylus Publishing, LLC.
Cass, Alden, et al. Bullish Thinking: The Advisor's Guide to Surviving & Thriving on Wall Street. 2008. (ENG., Illus.). 184p. per. 19.95 *(978-0-470-13770-3(3)*, Wiley) Wiley, John & Sons, Inc.
—The Bullish Thinking Guide for Managers: How to Save Your Advisors & Grow Your Bottom Line. 2008. (ENG., Illus.). 215p. 39.95 *(978-0-470-13769-7(X)*, Wiley) Wiley, John & Sons, Inc.
Cch Staff. NASD Manual. 2007. pap. 87.95 *(978-0-8080-1675-5(X))* Wolters Kluwer Law & Business.
Chan, Ernie. Quantitative Trading: How to Build Your Own Algorithmic Trading Business. 2008. (Wiley Trading Ser.: 381). (ENG., Illus.). 208p. 60.00 *(978-0-470-28488-9(9)*, Wiley) Wiley, John & Sons, Inc.
Chapman, Peter. The Last of the Imperious Rich: Lehman Brothers, 1844-2008. 2010. (ENG.). 320p. (gr. 12). 27.95 *(978-1-59184-309-2(X)*, Portfolio (Hardcover)) Penguin Group (USA) Inc.
Coakley, Mark. Tip & Trade: How Two Lawyers Made Millions from Insider Trading. 2011. (ENG., Illus.). 392p. pap. 17.95 *(978-1-55022-986-8(9))* ECW Pr. CAN. Dist: Independent Pubs. Group.
Curley, Michael T. & Walker, Joseph A. Barron's Stockbroker Examination. 3rd rev. ed. 2007. (ENG.). 456p. per. 18.99 *(978-0-7641-2380-1(7))* Barron's Educational Series, Inc.
DeForge, Kristine & Perkovic, Ljubomir. Introduction to Computing Using Python: An Application Development Focus. 2011. (ENG., Illus.). 484p. (C). pap. 95.95 *(978-0-470-61846-2(9)*, Wiley) Wiley, John & Sons, Inc.
Dover a Staff & Ishikawa, Tetsuya. How I Caused the Credit Crunch. 2010. (ENG., Illus.). 368p. pap. 12.95 *(978-1-84831-067-4(6))* Totem Bks. GBR. Dist: Consortium Bk. Sales & Distribution.
DraKoln, Noble. Trade Like a Pro: 15 High-Profit Trading Strategies. 2009. (Wiley Trading Ser.: 383). (ENG., Illus.). 274p. 70.00 *(978-0-470-28735-4(7)*, Wiley) Wiley, John & Sons, Inc.
Gardner, Chris. Pursuit of Happyness. movie tie-in ed. 2006. (ENG., Illus.). 320p. pap. 14.99 *(978-0-06-074487-8(1)*, Amistad) HarperCollins Pubs.
Gasparino, Charles. The Sellout: How Three Decades of Wall Street Greed & Government Mismanagement Destroyed the Global Financial System. 2009. (ENG.). 384p. 27.99 *(978-0-06-169716-6(8)*, Collins) HarperCollins Pubs.
Giannamore, Richard & Osach, Barbara Bordow. The High-Income Mortgage Originator: Sales Strategies & Practices to Build Your Client Base & Become a Top Producer. 2007. (ENG., Illus.). 332p. 29.95 *(978-0-470-13731-4(2)*, Wiley) Wiley, John & Sons, Inc.
Gineris, Peter J. Getting Started as a Commercial Mortgage Broker: How to Get to a Six-Figure Salary in 12 Months. 2008. (ENG., Illus.). 208p. 29.95 *(978-0-470-24653-5(7)*, Wiley) Wiley, John & Sons, Inc.
Goodman, Leah McGrath. The Asylum: The Renegades Who Hijacked the World's Oil Market. 2011. (ENG.). 304p. 27.99 *(978-0-06-176627-5(5)*, Morrow, William & Co.) HarperCollins Pubs.
Gorton, Lars, et al. Shipbroking & Chartering Practice. 7th rev. ed. 2009. (Illus.). 409p. 414.00 *(978-1-84311-806-0(8))* Informa Professional GBR. Dist: International Specialized Bk. Services.
Harrison, Todd A. The Other Side of Wall Street: In Business It Pays to Be an Animal, in Life It Pays to Be Yourself. rev. ed. 2011. (ENG.). 192p. 24.99 *(978-0-13-248966-9(X))* FT Press.
Hazen, Thomas Lee. Broker-Dealer Regulation in A Nutshell, 2D. 2nd rev. ed. 2011. (Nutshell Ser.). 317p. pap. 38.00 *(978-0-314-18957-8(2)*, West Legalworks) West.
Hicks, Tyler G. Discount mortgage brokers cash-out Program. 17th ed. 2007. ring bd. 150.00 *(978-1-56150-811-2(X))* International Wealth Success, Inc.
—Financial Broker/Finder/Business Broker/Business Consultant Kit. 17th ed. 2007. pap. 99.50 *(978-1-56150-821-1(7))* International Wealth Success, Inc.
—Loans by Phone Broker Success Kit. 17th ed. 2007. pap. 100.00 *(978-1-56150-841-9(1))* International Wealth Success, Inc.
Ho, Karen Zouwen. Liquidated: An Ethnography of Wall Street. 2009. (John Hope Franklin Center Book Ser.). (ENG., Illus.). 392p. pap. 25.95 *(978-0-8223-4599-2(4))*; 94.95 *(978-0-8223-4580-0(3))* Duke Univ. Pr.
Hofmann, Alexander. Der Skontroführer an den deutschen Wertpapierbörsen. 2009. (Börsen- und kapitalmarktrechtliche Abhandlungen Ser.). (GRE.). 734p. 159.95 *(978-3-631-58980-9(8))* Lang, Peter GmbH, Europaischer Verlag der Wissenschaften DEU. Dist: Lang, Peter.
Hung, Angela K., et al. Investor & Industry Perspectives on Investment Advisers & Broker-Dealers. 2008. (Illus.). 228p. pap. 48.00 *(978-0-8330-4403-7(5)*, tr-556) RAND Corp., The.
Karasik, Paul. 22 Keys to Sales Success: How to Make it Big in Financial Services. 2009. pap. 30.00 *(978-1-61623-055-5(X))* Independent Pub.
Lawson, Guy. Octopus: Sam Israel, the Secret Market, & Wall Street's Wildest Con. 2012. (ENG.). 368p. 26.00 *(978-0-307-71607-1(4)*, Crown) Crown Publishing Group.
Lefèvre, Edwin & Markman, Jon D. Reminiscences of a Stock Operator: With New Commentary & Insights on the Life & Times of Jesse Livermore. annot. ed. 2009. (ENG., Illus.). 440p. 39.95 *(978-0-470-48159-2(5)*, Wiley) Wiley, John & Sons, Inc.
Lewis, Michael. Liar's Poker. 2010. (ENG.). 310p. pap. 15.95 *(978-0-393-33869-0(X)*, 33869) Norton, W. W. & Co., Inc.
—The Money Culture. 2011. (ENG.). 304p. pap. 15.95 *(978-0-393-33865-2(7)*, 33865) Norton, W. W. & Co., Inc.
Livermore, Samuel. A Treatise on the Law: Relative to Principals, Agents, Factors, Auctioneers, & Brokers. 2007. 95.00 *(978-1-58477-729-8(X))* Lawbook Exchange, Ltd., The.
Lyall, Ian. Street-Smart Investment. 2011. (ENG., Illus.). 160p. pap. 19.99 *(978-1-906659-07-3(9))* Harriman Hse. Publishing GBR. Dist: Ingram Pub. Services.
Miah, Ayna. Stock Brokers: Who Are They & What Do They Do? 2009. 146p. pap. 41.95 *(978-0-9561616-0-4(X))* Miah, Ayna GBR. Dist: Lulu Enterprises Inc.
Morrison Media LLC. Series 7 Exam Secrets. 2007. 49.95 *(978-0-9798971-5-3(7))* Morrison Media LLC.
Naylor, John. London Brokers' Medals. 2008. (Illus.). 52p. pap. 35.00 *(978-0-9802356-0-9(X))* Medal Ventures, Inc.
Parker, Glenn R. Capitol Investments: The Marketability of Political Skills. 2008. (Economics, Cognition & Society Ser.). (ENG., Illus.). 216p. 60.00 *(978-0-472-07037-4(1))* Univ. of Michigan Pr.
Parton, Jim. Buck Stops Here. 2009. (ENG.). v, 234p. pap. 19.99 *(978-1-905641-00-0(1))* Harriman Hse. Publishing GBR. Dist: Ingram Pub. Services.
PASSTRAK Series 24 Premier Set. 245.00 *(978-0-7931-7916-9(5))* Kaplan Publishing.
PASSTRAK Series 26 Premier Set. 185.00 *(978-0-7931-8444-6(4))* Kaplan Publishing.
Patterson, Scott. The Quants: How a New Breed of Math Whizzes Conquered Wall Street & Nearly Destroyed It. (ENG.). 352p. 2011. pap. 16.00 *(978-0-307-45338-9(3)*, Three Rivers Pr.) 2010. 27.00 *(978-0-307-45337-2(5)*, Crown Business) Crown Publishing Group.
Perkins, Edwin J. Wall Street to Main Street: Charles Merrill & Middle-Class Investors. 2006. (ENG.). 308p. pap. 46.00 *(978-0-521-02779-3(9))* Cambridge Univ. Pr.
Person, John L. Forex Conquered: High Probability Systems & Strategies for Active Traders. 2007. (ENG., Illus.). 304p. 90.00 *(978-0-470-09779-3(5)*, Wiley) Wiley, John & Sons, Inc.
Peterson, Richard L. & Murtha, Frank F. MarketPsych: How to Manage Fear & Build Your Investor Identity. 2010. (Wiley Finance Ser.: 661). (ENG., Illus.). 240p. 39.95 *(978-0-470-54358-0(2)*, Wiley) Wiley, John & Sons, Inc.
Plunkett, Jack W. Plunkett's Investment & Securities Industry Almanac 2007: Investment & Securities Industry Market Research, Statistics, Trends & Leading Companies. annuals Plunkett, Jack W., ed. 2007. 487p. pap. 279.99 incl. cd-rom *(978-1-59392-080-7(6))* Plunkett Research, Ltd.
—Plunkett's Investment & Securities Industry Almanac 2007 (E-Book) Investment & Securities Market Research, Statistics, Trends & Leading Companies. annuals Plunkett, Jack W., ed. 2006. 498p. E-Book 499.99 incl. cd-rom *(978-1-59392-422-5(4))* Plunkett Research, Ltd.
Poser, Norman S. & Fanto, James A. Broker-Dealer Law & Regulation. 4th ed. 2007. ring bd. 455.00 *(978-0-7355-6785-6(9)*, Aspen Pubs.) Wolters Kluwer Law & Business.
Price, John. The Conscious Investor: Profiting from the Timeless Value Approach. 20 C. (Wiley Finance Ser.: 586). (ENG., Illus.). 366p. 49.95 *(978-0-470-60436-0(7)*, Wiley) Wiley, John & Sons, Inc.
Ramsaran-Fowdar, Rooma R. & Fowdar, Sooraj. A Study of Service Quality of Stockbrokers in Mauritius. 2010. 148p. pap. *(978-3-8383-3439-4(6))* Lambert Academic Publishing.
Reed, David. Your Successful Career as a Mortgage Broker. 2007. (ENG., Illus.). 240p. pap. 18.95 *(978-0-8144-7370-2(9))* Amacom.
Reingold, Daniel & Reingold, Jennifer. Confessions of a Wall Street Analyst: A True Story of Inside Information & Corruption in the Stock Market. 2007. (ENG., Illus.). 304p. pap. 14.99 *(978-0-06-074770-1(6)*, Harper Paperbacks) HarperCollins Pubs.
Rudman, Jack. Customhouse Brokers' License Examination (CBLE) (Admission Test Ser.: Vol. 7). 69.95 *(978-0-8373-5107-0(3))* National Learning Corp.
—NASD Series 6 Examination: Annuities & Mutual Funds. (Admission Test Ser.: Vol. 97). 59.95 *(978-0-8373-5197-1(9))* National Learning Corp.
—Registered Representative (RR) (Stockbroker) (Admission Test Ser.: Vol. 1). 69.95 *(978-0-8373-5101-8(4))* National Learning Corp.
Schwager, Jack D. Market Wizards: Interviews with Top Traders. rev. ed. 2012 (ENG.). 480p. pap. 24.95 *(978-1-118-27305-0(2)*, Wiley) Wiley, John & Sons, Inc.
—The New Market Wizards: Conversations with America's Top Traders. 2008. *(978-1-59280-337-8(7))* Marketplace Bks., Inc.
—Stock Market Wizards: Interviews with America's Top Stock Traders. 2008. *(978-1-59280-336-1(9))* Marketplace Bks., Inc.
Sheehan, Margaret A., et al. Functional Guide to NASD Regulation. 2006. pap. 95.00 *(978-0-8080-1562-8(1))* Wolters Kluwer Law & Business.
Siebert, Muriel. Changing the Rules: Adventures of a Wall Street Maverick. 2007. (ENG.). 240p. pap. 16.95 *(978-1-4165-7331-9(3)*, Free Pr.) Free Pr.
Steenbarger, Brett N. Enhancing Trader Performance: Proven Strategies from the Cutting Edge of Trading Psychology. 2006. (Wiley Trading Ser.: 276). (ENG., Illus.). 284p. 65.00 *(978-0-470-03866-6(7)*, Wiley) Wiley, John & Sons, Inc.
Straney, Louis L. Investor's Guide to Loss Recovery: Rights, Mediation, Arbitration, & Other Strategies. 2011. (Wiley Finance Ser.: 12). (ENG.). 210p. 75.00 *(978-0-470-93762-4(9)*, Wiley) Wiley, John & Sons, Inc.
Sussex, John. Day One Trader: A Life Story. 2009. (ENG., Illus.). 184p. 27.95 *(978-0-470-74173-3(2)*, Wiley) Wiley, John & Sons, Inc.
Swancoat, Brad. How to Broker Commercial Loans. 2007. per. 39.95 net. *(978-1-60402-310-7(4))* Independent Pub.
U. K. Brokers Yearbook, 1994-95. (DYP Textbook Ser.). 400p. 250.00 *(978-1-870255-32-5(1))* LLP, Inc.
Walker, Robert. Pass The 63: A Training Guide for the NASAA Series 63 Exam. 4th rev. ed. 2010. (First Books Training Library). (ENG.). 312p. pap. 39.95 *(978-0-9823476-0-7(X))* First Bks.
Wilber, W. Kelsea. Selling Internationally - Without a Product: How to Be a Broker & Link Buyers & Sellers Together...for Profit. Friedland, Jennifer, ed. 210p. (Orig.). pap. 14.95 *(978-0-9644778-0-3(7))* International Trade Ctr., Inc.
Zaloom, Caitlin. Out of the Pits: Traders & Technology from Chicago to London. (ENG., Illus.). 240p. 2010. pap. 19.00 *(978-0-226-97814-7(1))* 2006. 29.00 *(978-0-226-97813-0(3))* Univ. of Chicago Pr.

BROKERS, REAL ESTATE
see Real Estate Agents

BROKERS IN PUBLIC CONTRACTS, ETC.
Moss, Timothy, et al, eds. Shaping Urban Infrastructures: Intermediaries & the Governance of Socio-Technical Networks. 2010. (ENG., Illus.). 240p. 99.95 *(978-1-84971-068-8(6))* Routledge.

BROLEY, CHARLES LAVELLE
Broley, Myrtle Jeanne. Eagle Man: Charles L. Broley's Field Adventures with American Eagles. 2011. 232p. 46.95 *(978-1-258-02204-4(4))* Literary Licensing, LLC.

BROME, RICHARD, D. 1652
Brome, Richard. Dramatic Works of Richard Brome, 3 vols. Shepherd, R. H., ed. reprint ed. 165.00 *(978-0-404-01110-9(1))* AMS Pr., Inc.

BROMELIACIAE
Luther, Harry & Benzing, David H. Native Bromeliads of Florida. 2009. (ENG.). 126p. 16.95 *(978-1-56164-448-3(X))* Pineapple Pr., Inc.

BROMFIELD, LOUIS, 1896-1956
Carter, John T. Louis Bromfield & the Malabar Farm Experience. Date not set. lib. bdg. 21.95 *(978-0-8488-1813-5(X))* Amereon LTD.
Geld, Ellen Bromfield. The Heritage: A Daughter's Memories of Louis Bromfield. 2011. 224p. 44.95 *(978-1-258-09452-2(5))* Literary Licensing, LLC.

BROMIDES
Abdel Qader, Abed, et al. Mathematical Modeling of Trihalomethane. 2011. 88p. pap. *(978-3-8443-8140-5(6))* Lambert Academic Publishing.
Baldys, S. Bromide, Chloride, & Sulfate Concentrations & Loads at U.S. Geological Survey Streamflow-Gaging Stations 07331600 Red River at Denison Dam, 07335500 Red River at Arthur City, & 07336820 Red River near DeKalb, Texas, 2007-09. 2010. (Illus.). vi, 30p. *(978-1-4113-2869-3(8))* United States Geological Survey.
Eljarrat, Ethel & Barceló, Damià, eds. Brominated Flame Retardants. 2011. (Handbook of Environmental Chemistry Ser.). (Illus.). xiii, 296p. 309.00 *(978-3-642-19268-5(8)*, 3642192688) Springer.
Gadzuric, Slobodan. Thermodynamic & Transport Properties of Lanthanide Bromide Systems. 2010. 124p. pap. *(978-3-8383-1938-4(9))* Lambert Academic Publishing.
Sánchez-Tovar, Rita, et al. How Do Flowing Conditions Affect Copper/Aisi 304 Galvanic Corrosion? 2011. 76p. pap. *(978-3-8443-1465-6(2))* Lambert Academic Publishing.

BROMINE
Neilson, Alasdair H. Organic Bromine & Iodine Compounds. 2010. (Handbook of Environmental Chemistry / Anthropogenic Compounds Ser.). (Illus.). xiv, 343p. pap. 259.00 *(978-3-642-05700-7(4)*, 3642057004) Springer.
Roza, Greg. Bromine. 2009. (Understanding the Elements of the Periodic Table Ser.). (YA). (gr. 5-9). lib. bdg. 26.50 *(978-1-4358-5068-2(8))* Rosen Publishing Group, Inc., The.
West, Krista. Bromine. 2007. (Elements Ser.). (Illus.). 32p. (gr. 4-7). lib. bdg. 28.50 *(978-0-7614-2685-1(X)*, Benchmark Bks.) Marshall Cavendish Corp.

BRONCHI
see also Bronchodilator Agents
Cagle, Philip T. Transbronchial & Endobronchial Biopsies. Allen, Timothy C., ed. 2008. (ENG., Illus.). 256p. 237.99 *(978-0-7817-8517-4(0))* Lippincott Williams & Wilkins.
Kurimoto, Noriaki, et al, eds. Endobronchial Ultrasonography. 2011. (ENG., Illus.). 176p. 157.95 *(978-1-4051-8272-0(5)*, Wiley-Blackwell) Wiley, John & Sons, Inc.

BRONCHITIS
Smith, Tom. Coping with Bronchitis & Emphysema. (Illus.). 104p. *(978-0-85969-709-5(6)*, Sheldon Press) SPCK Publishing.

BRONCHOCELE
see Goiter

BRONCHODILATOR AGENTS
see also Adrenaline
Cram101 Textbook Reviews & Cram101 Textbook Reviews. Outlines & Highlights for Rau's Respiratory Care Pharmacology by Douglas S Gardenhire. 2011. 252p. pap. 31.95 *(978-1-61830-761-3(4))* Cram101 Inc.
Cram101 Textbook Reviews Staff. Outlines & Highlights for Respiratory Care Pharmacology by Rau, Isbn: 0323016960. 2008. 184p. pap. 12.95 *(978-1-4288-6252-4(8))* Cram101 Inc.
Gardenhire, Douglas S. Rau's Respiratory Care Pharmacology. 8th ed. 2011. (ENG., Illus.). 472p. (C). pap. 72.95 *(978-0-323-07528-2(2)*, Mosby) Elsevier - Health Sciences Div.
Gardenhire, Douglas S. & Harwood, Robert J. Workbook for Rau's Respiratory Care Pharmacology. 8th ed. 2011. (ENG., Illus.). 288p. (C). pap. 31.95 *(978-0-323-08027-9(8)*, Mosby) Elsevier - Health Sciences Div.

BRONCHOSCOPY
Beamis, Jr., John F., John F, et al, eds. Interventional Pulmonary Medicine, Second Edition. 2nd rev. ed. 2009. (ENG., Illus.). 274p. 250.00 *(978-1-4200-8184-8(5)*, Informa Healthcare) Taylor & Francis Group GBR. Dist: Taylor & Francis Group.
Colt, Henri & Murgu, Septimiu. Bronchoscopy & Central Airway Disorders: A Patient-Centered Approach: Expert Consult Online & Print. 2012. (ENG., Illus.). 416p. 149.00 *(978-1-4557-0320-3(6)*, Saunders) Elsevier - Health Sciences Div.
Ernst, Armin. Introduction to Bronchoscopy. Ernst, Armin, ed. 2009. (ENG., Illus.). 176p. 99.00 *(978-0-521-76628-9(1))*; pap. 52.00 *(978-0-521-71109-8(6))* Cambridge Univ. Pr.
Mathur, Praveen, et al. Therapeutic Bronchoscopy. 2009. (Illus.). 249.95 *(978-0-8493-7184-4(8)*, Informa Healthcare) Taylor & Francis Group GBR. Dist: Taylor & Francis Group.
Shah, Pallav. Atlas of Flexible Bronchoscopy. 2012. (ENG.). 224p. 195.00 *(978-0-340-96832-1(X))* Hodder Arnold Pubs.

B

Wagner, Manfred & Ficker, Joachim H. Autofluorescence Bronchoscopy. 2007. (UNI-MED Science Ser.). (Illus.). 96p. (978-3-89599-956-7(3)) UNI-MED Verlag AG.

Wang, KoPen, et al, eds. Flexible Bronchoscopy. 3rd ed. 2012. (ENG., Illus.). 347p. 194.95 (978-1-4051-7587-6(7), Wiley-Blackwell) Wiley, John & Sons, Inc.

BRONENOSETS "POTEMKIN"

Bascomb, Neal. Red Mutiny: Eleven Fateful Days on the Battleship Potemkin. 2007. (ENG., Illus.). 400p. 26.00 (978-0-618-59206-7(7)) Houghton Mifflin Harcourt Publishing Co.

—Red Mutiny: Eleven Fateful Days on the Battleship Potemkin. 2008. (ENG., Illus.). 400p. pap. 15.95 (978-0-547-05352-3(5), Mariner Bks.) Houghton Mifflin Harcourt Trade & Reference Pubs.

BRONSTEIN, DAVID IONOVICH, 1924-2006

Minev, Nikolay. David Bronstein: Fifty Great Short Games. 2008. 97p. pap. 19.49 (978-0-9661889-2-9(6)) Chess Library, The.

BRONTE, ANNE, 1820-1849

Casson, Caryl. A Brontë Bestiary. 2010. 92p. pap. (978-3-8383-5105-6(3)) Lambert Academic Publishing.

Dinsdale, Ann. The Brontes at Haworth. 2006. (ENG., Illus.). 160p. 35.00 (978-0-7112-2572-5(9)) Lincoln, Frances Ltd. GBR. Dist: Perseus-PGW.

Ingham, Patricia. The Brontës. 2008. (Oxford World's Classics Ser.). (ENG., Illus.). 304p. pap. 14.95 (978-0-19-953666-5(X)) Oxford Univ. Pr., Inc.

Jakubowski, Zuzanna. Moors, Mansions, & Museums: Transgressing Gendered Spaces in Novels of the Bronte Sisters. 2009. (Europäische Hochschulschriften. Reihe 14: Angelsächsische Sprache und Literatur Ser.). 122p. pap. 43.95 (978-3-631-59692-0(8)) Lang, Peter GmbH, Europaischer Verlag der Wissenschaften DEU. Dist: Lang, Peter.

Jameson, E. M. The Tenant of Wildfell Hall. 2007. 396p. 29.95 (978-1-4344-9580-8(9)); per. 19.95 (978-1-4344-9579-2(5)) Wildside Pr., LLC.

Thorm+hlen, Marianne & Thormahlen, Marianne. The Brontës & Education. 2010. (ENG.). 318p. pap. 39.99 (978-0-521-15561-8(4)) Cambridge Univ. Pr.

Thormahlen, Marianne. The Brontës & Education. 2007. (ENG.). 320p. 110.00 (978-0-521-83289-2(6)) Cambridge Univ. Pr.

Wells, Juliette & Hagan, Sandra. The Brontës in the World of the Arts. 2008. (Nineteenth Century Ser.). (Illus.). 270p. 114.95 (978-0-7546-5752-1(3)) Ashgate Publishing Co.

Wollaston, Emily & Dale, Sue. The Little Book of Brontë Sisters. 2008. (Little Book Ser.). (ENG., Illus.). 128p. 11.99 (978-1-906229-59-7(7), 1906229597) G2 Entertainment Ltd. GBR. Dist: BookMasters Distribution Services (BDS).

BRONTE, CHARLOTTE, 1816-1855

Adamson, Alan H. Mr. Charlotte Brontë: The Life of Arthur Bell Nicholls. 2008. (ENG., Illus.). 216p. (C). (978-0-7735-3365-3(6)) McGill-Queen's Univ. Pr.

Bailin, Miriam. The Sickroom in Victorian Fiction: The Art of Being Ill. 2007. (Cambridge Studies in Nineteenth-Century Literature & Culture Ser.). (ENG.). 180p. pap. 34.99 (978-0-521-03640-5(2)) Cambridge Univ. Pr.

Brackett, Virginia. Bloom's How to Write about the Brontes. Bloom, Harold, ed. 2008. (Bloom's How to Write about Literature Ser.). 288p. (C). (gr. 9-18). 45.00 (978-0-7910-9794-6(3), Chelsea Hse.) Facts On File, Inc.

Brennan, Zoe. Bronte's Jane Eyre. 2010. (Readers Guide Ser.). (ENG.). 160p. 80.00 (978-1-84706-260-4(1)); pap. 24.95 (978-1-84706-261-1(X)) Continuum International Publishing Group, Ltd. GBR. Dist: National Bk. Network.

Brontë, Charlotte. Jane Eyre. Crow, Anne, ed. 2010. 94p. pap. 24.95 (978-1-4441-1625-0(8)) Hodder Education GBR. Dist: Trans-Atlantic Pubns., Inc.

—Selected Letters. Smith, Margaret, ed. 2010. (Oxford World's Classics Ser.). (ENG.). 320p. pap. 12.95 (978-0-19-957696-8(3)) Oxford Univ. Pr., Inc.

—Selected Letters of Charlotte Brontë. Smith, Margaret, ed. 2007. (ENG., Illus.). 344p. 55.00 (978-0-19-920587-5(6)) Oxford Univ. Pr., Inc.

—The Shakespeare Head Bronte, 19 Vols. (Complete Works of Charlotte Bronte). reprint ed. lib. bdg. 1862.00 (978-0-7426-2195-4(2)) Classic Bks.

Casson, Caryl. A Brontë Bestiary. 2010. 92p. pap. (978-3-8383-5105-6(3)) Lambert Academic Publishing.

Corbett, Mary Jean. Family Likeness: Sex, Marriage, & Incest from Jane Austen to Virginia Woolf. 2010. 280p. pap. 24.95 (978-0-8014-7663-1(1)) 2008. 272p. 57.95 (978-0-8014-4707-5(0)) Cornell Univ. Pr.

Cox, Jessica. Charlotte Bronte. 2011. (Brief Lives Ser.). (ENG.). 112p. pap. 12.95 (978-1-84391-920-9(6)) Hesperus Pr. GBR. Dist: Independent Pubs. Group.

Deathridge, John. Pegasus Pocket Guide to Beethoven. 2010. 352p. pap. 15.75 (978-1-933648-75-0(9)) Pegasus Bks.

Dessner, Lawrence Jay. The homely web of Truth: A study of Charlotte Brontë's Novels. (De Proprietatibus Litterarum. Series Practica Ser.). (ENG.). 126p. 135.00 (978-3-11-099214-4(0)) De Gruyter, Mouton DEU. Dist: de Gruyter, Walter GmbH & Co. KG.

Dinsdale, Ann. The Brontes at Haworth. 2006. (ENG., Illus.). 160p. 35.00 (978-0-7112-2572-5(9)) Lincoln, Frances Ltd. GBR. Dist: Perseus-PGW.

Fraser, Rebecca J. Charlotte Bronte. 2008. 560p. pap. 17.95 (978-1-933648-88-0(0)) Pegasus Bks.

Gaskell, E. C. The Life of Charlotte Bronte. 2010. 738p. pap. 41.56 (978-1-166-34050-6(3)); 53.56 (978-1-166-39200-0(7)) Kessinger Publishing, LLC.

Gaskell, Elizabeth. The Life of Charlotte Bronte. 2010. 374p. pap. 32.75 (978-1-146-89626-9(3)) BiblioBazaar.

—The Life of Charlotte Bronte. 2011. 580p. 58.95 (978-1-169-84143-7(0)) 2010. 580p. 47.16 (978-1-163-21029-1(3)) 2010. 448p. pap. 29.56 (978-1-163-17769-3(5)) 2010. 580p. pap. 35.16 (978-1-162-64556-8(3)) 2010. 450p. 41.56 (978-1-166-13819-6(4)) Kessinger Publishing, LLC.

—The Life of Charlotte Brontë. 2011. 462p. pap. 36.75 (978-1-173-36958-3(9)) 2010. 320p. pap. 30.75 (978-1-178-28250-4(3)) 2010. 304p. pap. 29.75 (978-1-177-72707-5(2)) 2010. 638p. pap. 45.75 (978-1-148-78885-2(9)) 2010. 302p. pap. 29.75 (978-1-149-01816-3(X)) 2010. 588p. pap. 44.75 (978-1-145-92539-7(1)) 2010. 308p. pap. 29.75 (978-1-143-79646-3(2)) 2010. 752p. pap. 52.75 (978-1-143-61817-8(3)) 2010. 454p. pap. 36.75 (978-1-143-39838-4(6)) 2010. 304p. pap. 29.75 (978-1-142-08432-5(9)) 2008. 300p. 25.99 (978-0-559-31894-8(4)) 2008. 300p. pap. 27.75 (978-0-559-31892-4(8)) 2008. 280p. 25.99 (978-0-554-35996-0(0)) 2008. 268p. 25.99 (978-0-554-37843-5(4)) 2008. 280p. 28.99 (978-0-554-26693-0(8)) 2008. 268p. 28.99 (978-0-554-28540-5(1)) BiblioBazaar.

—The Life of Charlotte Brontë. 2009. 316p. pap. (978-1-151-10401-4(9)); 346p. pap. (978-0-217-12575-8(1)); 368p. pap. (978-0-217-09266-1(7)) Books LLC.

—The Life of Charlotte Brontë. 2010. (Cambridge Library Collection - Literary Studies). (Illus.). 368p. pap. 29.99 (978-1-108-02050-3(X)); 340p. pap. 28.99 (978-1-108-02051-0(8)) Cambridge Univ. Pr.

—The Life of Charlotte Brontë. 2009. 280p. pap. 9.99 (978-1-4209-3231-7(4)) Digireads.com.

—The Life of Charlotte Brontë. 2007. (ENG.). 428p. per. (978-1-4065-2799-5(8)) Dodo Pr.

—The Life of Charlotte Brontë. 2010. (Illus.). 158p. pap. 7.84 (978-1-150-93975-4(3)); 298p. pap. 12.03 (978-1-154-13743-9(0)); 290p. pap. 36.84 (978-1-151-52705-9(X)) General Bks. LLC.

—The Life of Charlotte Brontë. 2009. 738p. 66.95 (978-1-120-10739-8(3)) 2009. 738p. pap. 51.95 (978-1-104-99472-3(0)) 2009. 450p. 51.95 (978-1-104-83457-9(X)) 2007. (ENG.). 448p. per. 36.95 (978-1-4325-7651-6(8)) Kessinger Publishing, LLC.

—The Life of Charlotte Brontë. 2007. (Large Print Ser.). lib. bdg. 28.00 (978-1-58287-945-1(1)); lib. bdg. 25.00 (978-1-58287-461-6(1)) North Bks.

—The Life of Charlotte Brontë. Easson, Angus, ed. 2009. (Oxford World's Classics Ser.). (ENG.). 624p. pap. 14.95 (978-0-19-955476-8(5)) Oxford Univ. Pr., Inc.

—Life of Charlotte Bronte. 2010. 176p. pap. (978-1-4076-1803-6(2)) HardPr.

—The Life of Charlotte Bronté. 2010. 594p. pap. 44.75 (978-1-142-41244-9(X)) BiblioBazaar.

—The Life of Charlotte Brontë. 2008. Vol. 1. pap. 9.99 (978-1-60450-500-9(1)) Vol. 2. pap. 9.99 (978-1-60450-501-6(X)) Arc Manor. (Serenity Pubs.).

—The Life of Charlotte Brontë. 2007. 1. (ENG.). 248p. pap. 20.99 (978-1-4346-1639-5(8))1. (ENG.). 276p. pap. 23.99 (978-1-4346-1808-5(0)) Vol. 2. (ENG.). 236p. pap. 20.99 (978-1-4346-5669-8(1)) Vol. 2. 266p. pap. 23.99 (978-1-4346-5670-4(5)) BiblioBazaar.

—The Life of Charlotte Brontë, 2. reprint ed. lib. bdg. 196.00 (978-0-7426-2364-4(5)) Classic Bks.

—The Life of Charlotte Brontë. l.t. ed. 2006. Vol. 1. pap. (978-1-4068-2188-8(8)) Vol. 1A. pap. (978-1-4068-3192-4(1)) Vol. 2. pap. (978-1-4068-2189-5(6)) Echo Library.

Gaskell, Elizabeth & Shorter, Clement King. The Life of Charlotte Brontë. 2010. 758p. pap. 52.75 (978-1-175-97356-6(4)) BiblioBazaar.

Gaskell, Elizabeth, et al. The Life of Charlotte Brontë. 2010. 584p. pap. 43.75 (978-1-148-17896-7(1)) BiblioBazaar.

Gaskell, Elizabeth Cleghorn & Gaskell, Elizabeth. The Life of Charlotte Brontë. 2010. 418p. pap. 34.75 (978-1-178-17496-0(4)); 368p. pap. 32.75 (978-1-146-91675-2(2)); 300p. pap. 28.75 (978-1-147-02057-1(4)); 590p. pap. 44.75 (978-1-147-03078-5(2)); 590p. pap. 44.75 (978-1-147-13566-4(5)); 320p. pap. 30.75 (978-1-147-01820-2(0)); 332p. pap. 31.75 (978-1-144-61655-5(7)) BiblioBazaar.

—The Life of Charlotte Brontë. 2010. (Illus.). 164p. pap. 8.04 (978-1-150-81579-9(5)) General Bks. LLC.

—Life of Charlotte Brontë - 2010. (Illus.). 156p. pap. 24.39 (978-1-153-74409-6(0)) General Bks. LLC.

—Life of Charlotte Bronte - 2010. (Illus.). 140p. pap. 22.91 (978-1-153-74563-5(1)) General Bks. LLC.

Harland, Marion. Charlotte Bronte at Home. 2008. 346p. 46.95 (978-0-548-98790-2(4)) 2007. (ENG.). 348p. per. 31.95 (978-0-548-65956-4(7)) Kessinger Publishing, LLC.

—Charlotte Bronte at Home. 2007. (ENG.). 348p. per. (978-1-4067-8108-3(8)) Read Bks.

Henson, Eithne. Landscape & Gender in the Novels of Charlotte Bronte George Eliot & Thomas Hardy: The Body of Nature. 2011. (Nineteenth Century Ser.). (Illus.). 260p. 114.95 (978-1-4094-3214-2(9)) Ashgate Publishing Co.

Ingham, Patricia. The Brontës. 2008. (Oxford World's Classics Ser.). (ENG., Illus.). 304p. pap. 14.95 (978-0-19-953666-5(X)) Oxford Univ. Pr., Inc.

Jakubowski, Zuzanna. Moors, Mansions, & Museums: Transgressing Gendered Spaces in Novels of the Bronte Sisters. 2009. (Europäische Hochschulschriften. Reihe 14: Angelsächsische Sprache und Literatur Ser.). 122p. pap. 43.95 (978-3-631-59692-0(8)) Lang, Peter GmbH, Europaischer Verlag der Wissenschaften DEU. Dist: Lang, Peter.

Jane Eyre Guide. 16.47 (978-0-13-050214-8(6)) Prentice Hall PTR.

Johnson, Claudia Durst. Women's Search for Independence in Charlotte Bronte's Jane Eyre. 2011. (Social Issues in Literature Ser.). 224p. (J). (ENG.). pap. 26.50 (978-0-7377-5451-3(6)); lib. bdg. 38.45 (978-0-7377-5450-6(8)) Cengage Gale. (Greenhaven Pr., Inc.).

Lodge, Sara. Charlotte Bronte - Jane Eyre. Tredell, Nicolas, ed. 2009. (Readers' Guides to Essential Criticism Ser.). (ENG.). 192p. 85.00 (978-0-230-51815-5(X)); pap. 25.00 (978-0-230-51816-2(8)) Palgrave Macmillan.

Moore, Chantal. Confronting the Monster. 2010. 100p. pap. (978-3-639-22953-0(3)) VDM Verlag Dr. Mueller e.K.

Murray, John Condon. Technologies of Power in the Victorian Period: Print Culture, Human Labor, & New Modes of Critique in Charles Dickens's Hard Times, Charlotte Bronte's Shirley, & George Eliot's Felix Holt. 2010. 176p. (978-1-60497-668-7(3)) Cambria Pr.

Oxford University Press Staff, ed. Bronte Story. 3rd ed. 2008. (ENG.). 80p. 9.38 (978-0-19-479109-0(2)) Oxford Univ. Pr., Inc.

Pyrhönen, Heta. Bluebeard Gothic: Jane Eyre & Its Progeny. 2010. 304p. (978-1-4426-4124-2(X)) Univ. of Toronto Pr.

Rubik, Margarete & Mettinger-Schartmann, Elke, eds. A Breath of Fresh Eyre: Intertextual & Intermedial Reworkings of Jane Eyre. 2007. (Illus.). 420p. (978-90-420-2212-6(4)) Rodopi B.V. Editions.

Scholl, Lesa. Translation Authorship & the Victorian Professional Woman: Charlotte Bronte Harriet Marinea & George Eliot. 2011. 222p. 99.95 (978-1-4094-2653-0(X)) Ashgate Publishing Co.

Searle, Alison. The Eyes of Your Heart: Literary & Theological Trajectories of Imagining Biblically. 2009. (Paternoster Theological Monographs Ser.). 250p. pap. 29.00 (978-1-60608-602-5(2), Wipf and Stock) Wipf & Stock Pubs.

Shorter, Clement K. Charlotte Bronte & Her Circle. 2009. 538p. pap. 39.75 (978-1-113-64873-0(2)); 538p. pap. 40.75 (978-1-113-64875-4(9)); (ENG.). 537p. pap. 30.99 (978-1-113-64869-3(4), BiblioLife); (ENG.). 537p. pap. 31.99 (978-1-113-64871-6(6), BiblioLife) BiblioBazaar.

—Charlotte Bronte & Her Circle. 544p. 2011. 57.95 (978-1-169-89089-3(X)) 2010. 46.36 (978-1-163-39023-8(2)) 2010. pap. 34.36 (978-1-162-92466-3(7)) 2007. (ENG.). 57.95 (978-0-548-08175-4(1)) Kessinger Publishing, LLC.

Shorter, Clement K. Charlotte Bronte & Her Sisters. 2007. (ENG.). 280p. 42.95 (978-0-548-12155-9(9)) Kessinger Publishing, LLC.

Shorter, Clement King. Charlotte Bronte & Her Circle. 2009. 620p. 31.99 (978-0-559-13566-8(1)); 38.99 (978-0-559-13555-2(6)); pap. 45.75 (978-0-559-13559-0(9)); pap. 44.75 (978-0-559-13564-4(5)) BiblioBazaar.

—Charlotte Bronte & Her Circle. 2008. (Illus.). 516p. pap. (978-1-4065-6996-4(8)) Dodo Pr.

—Charlotte Brontë & Her Circle. 2010. 552p. pap. 41.75 (978-1-142-98322-2(6)) BiblioBazaar.

—Charlotte Brontë & Her Circle. 2010. (Illus.). 330p. pap. 40.55 (978-1-4432-1045-4(5)) General Bks. LLC.

—Charlotte Bronte & Her Sisters. 2008. 282p. 43.95 (978-1-4366-4132-6(2)); 284p. pap. 28.95 (978-0-548-87140-9(X)) Kessinger Publishing, LLC.

Shuttleworth, Sally & Ingham, Patricia. Charlotte Bronte. (Writers & Their Work Ser.). (ENG.). 128p. (C). 2012. pap. 26.00 (978-0-7463-0856-1(6)) 2011. 80.00 (978-0-7463-1195-0(8)) Northcote Hse. Publishers, Ltd. GBR. Dist: Brown, David Bk. Co., The.

Taylor, Susan B., ed. The Brontes: A Documentary Volume. 2008. (Dictionary of Literary Biography Ser.). (ENG., Illus.). 464p. 315.00 (978-0-7876-8158-6(X)) Cengage Gale.

Thomas, Sue. Imperialism, Reform & the Making of Englishness in Jane Eyre. 2008. (ENG.). 208p. 89.00 (978-0-230-55425-2(3)) Palgrave Macmillan.

Thormahlen, Marianne. The Brontës & Education. 2007. (ENG.). 320p. 110.00 (978-0-521-83289-2(6)) Cambridge Univ. Pr.

Walter, Hugo. Sanctuaries of Light in Nineteenth-Century European Literature. 2010. (Studies on Themes & Motifs in Literature Ser.). 268p. (C). 77.95 (978-1-4331-0913-3(1)) Lang, Peter Publishing, Inc.

Ward, Ian. Law & the Brontës. 2012. (ENG., Illus.). 208p. 85.00 (978-0-230-25147-2(1)) Palgrave Macmillan.

Wells, Juliette & Hagan, Sandra. The Brontës in the World of the Arts. 2008. (Nineteenth Century Ser.). (Illus.). 270p. 114.95 (978-0-7546-5752-1(3)) Ashgate Publishing Co.

Wilkes, Joanne. Women Reviewing Women in Nineteenth-Century Britain: The Critical Reception of Jane Austen Charlotte Bronte & George Elliot. 2010. (Nineteenth Century Ser.). 194p. 99.95 (978-0-7546-6336-2(1)) Ashgate Publishing Co.

Wollaston, Emily & Dale, Sue. The Little Book of Brontë Sisters. 2008. (Little Book Ser.). (ENG., Illus.). 128p. 11.99 (978-1-906229-59-7(7), 1906229597) G2 Entertainment Ltd. GBR. Dist: BookMasters Distribution Services (BDS).

Zigarovich, Jolene. Narrating Death in Victorian Novels: Absence, Separation, & Displacement. 2012. (ENG., Illus.). 240p. 85.00 (978-1-137-00702-5(8)) Palgrave Macmillan.

BRONTE, EMILY, 1818-1848

Bloom, Harold, ed. Wuthering Heights. annot. ed. 2008. (Bloom's Guides). 96p. (C). (gr. 9). 30.00 (978-0-7910-9831-8(1), Chelsea Hse.) Facts On File, Inc.

Brinton, Ian. Bronte's Wuthering Heights. 2011. (Reader's Guides). (ENG.). 160p. 75.00 (978-1-84706-456-1(6)); pap. 24.95 (978-1-84706-457-8(4)) Continuum International Publishing Group, Ltd. GBR. Dist: National Bk. Network.

Brontë, Emily. Monarch Notes on Bronte's Wuthering Heights. (C). 3.95 (978-0-671-00603-7(7), Arco) Peterson's.

Bryfonski, Dedria, ed. Class Conflict in Emily Bronte's Wuthering Heights. 2011. (Social Issues in Literature Ser.). (Illus.). 224p. pap. 26.50 (978-0-7377-5802-3(3), Greenhaven Pr., Inc.); (YA). (gr. 9-12). 38.45 (978-0-7377-5801-6(5)) Cengage Gale.

Casson, Caryl. A Brontë Bestiary. 2010. 92p. pap. (978-3-8383-5105-6(3)) Lambert Academic Publishing.

Chitham, Edward. A Life of Emily Bronte. 2010. (ENG., Illus.). 224p. pap. 29.95 (978-1-84868-406-5(1)) Amberley Publishing GBR. Dist: Casemate Pubs. & Bk. Distributors, LLC.

Dinsdale, Ann. The Brontes at Haworth. 2006. (ENG., Illus.). 160p. 35.00 (978-0-7112-2572-5(9)) Lincoln, Frances Ltd. GBR. Dist: Perseus-PGW.

Fegan. Wuthering Heights: Character Studies. 2008. (Character Studies). (ENG.). 144p. 90.00 (978-0-8264-9345-3(9)) Continuum International Publishing Group, Ltd. GBR. Dist: National Bk. Network.

Fegan, Melissa & Fegan. Wuthering Heights: Character Studies. 2008. (Character Studies). (ENG.). 144p. 19.95 (978-0-8264-9346-0(7)) Continuum International Publishing Group, Ltd. GBR. Dist: National Bk. Network.

Gezari, Janet. Last Things: Emily Brontë's Poems. Oxford Staff, ed. 2008. (ENG., Illus.). 200p. pap. 25.00 (978-0-19-954329-8(1)) Oxford Univ. Pr., Inc.

Green, Andrew. Wuthering Heights. 2010. (Illus.). 94p. pap. 24.95 (978-1-4441-1620-5(7)) Hodder Education GBR. Dist: Trans-Atlantic Pubns., Inc.

Ingham, Patricia. The Brontës. 2008. (Oxford World's Classics Ser.). (ENG., Illus.). 304p. pap. 14.95 (978-0-19-953666-5(X)) Oxford Univ. Pr., Inc.

Jakubowski, Zuzanna. Moors, Mansions, & Museums: Transgressing Gendered Spaces in Novels of the Bronte Sisters. 2009. (Europäische Hochschulschriften. Reihe 14: Angelsächsische Sprache und Literatur Ser.). 122p. pap. 43.95 (978-3-631-59692-0(8)) Lang, Peter GmbH, Europaischer Verlag der Wissenschaften DEU. Dist: Lang, Peter.

Prentice-Hall Staff. Wuthering Heights. 2nd ed. stu. ed. (978-0-13-716929-0(9)) Prentice Hall (Schl. Div.).

Taylor, Susan B., ed. The Brontes: A Documentary Volume. 2008. (Dictionary of Literary Biography Ser.). (ENG., Illus.). 464p. 315.00 (978-0-7876-8158-6(X)) Cengage Gale.

Thormahlen, Marianne. The Brontës & Education. 2007. (ENG.). 320p. 110.00 (978-0-521-83289-2(6)) Cambridge Univ. Pr.

Wallace, Robert K. Emily Bronte & Beethoven: Romantic Equilibrium in Fiction & Music. 2008. (ENG.). 248p. pap. 22.95 (978-0-8203-3295-6(X)) Univ. of Georgia Pr.

Ward, Ian. Law & the Brontës. 2012. (ENG., Illus.). 208p. 85.00 (978-0-230-25147-2(1)) Palgrave Macmillan.

Wells, Juliette & Hagan, Sandra. The Brontës in the World of the Arts. 2008. (Nineteenth Century Ser.). (Illus.). 270p. 114.95 (978-0-7546-5752-1(3)) Ashgate Publishing Co.

Wollaston, Emily & Dale, Sue. The Little Book of Brontë Sisters. 2008. (Little Book Ser.). (ENG., Illus.). 128p. 11.99 (978-1-906229-59-7(7), 1906229597) G2 Entertainment Ltd. GBR. Dist: BookMasters Distribution Services (BDS).

BRONTE, PATRICK, 1777-1861

Green, Dudley. Patrick Bronte: Father of Genius. 2009. (ENG., Illus.). 284p. 34.95 (978-1-84588-625-7(9)) History Pr. Ltd.,The GBR. Dist: Independent Pubs. Group.

—Patrick Brontë: Father of Genius. 2010. (ENG., Illus.). 384p. pap. 24.95 (978-0-7524-5445-0(5)) History Pr. Ltd.,The GBR. Dist: Independent Pubs. Group.

BRONTE FAMILY

Allott, Miriam. The Brontes: The Critical Heritage. 2010. 476p. pap. 45.00 (978-0-415-56878-4(1)) Routledge.

Barnard, Louise & Barnard, Robert. A Bronte Encyclopedia. 2007. (ENG., Illus.). 416p. 128.95 (978-1-4051-5119-1(6), Wiley-Blackwell) Wiley, John & Sons, Inc.

Bentley, Phyllis, compiled by. The Brontes. 39.00 (978-1-56696-114-1(9)) Jackdaw Pubns.

Bentley, Phyllis Eleano. Bronte Sisters. 2006. 52p. per. (978-1-4067-0992-6(1), Hesperides Pr.) Read Bks.

Bloom, Harold. The Brontes. 2nd rev. ed. 2008. (Modern Critical Views Ser.). 232p. (C). (gr. 9). 45.00 (978-0-7910-9620-8(3), Chelsea Hse.) Facts On File, Inc.

Bloom, Harold & Sparks, Tabitha, eds. The Brontës. 2008. (Bloom's Classic Critical Views Ser.). 288p. (YA). (gr. 9-12). 45.00 (978-1-60413-136-9(5)) Facts On File, Inc.

Brontë, Emily, et al. The Brontë Sisters: Jane Eyre, Wuthering Heights & Agnes Grey. 2009. (Penguin Classics Deluxe Edition Ser.). (ENG.). 672p. (gr. 12-18). pap. 22.00 (978-0-14-310583-1(3), Penguin Classics) Penguin Group (USA) Inc.

Brontes. The Letters of the Brontes: A Selection. Spark, Muriel, ed. 2011. 208p. 44.95 (978-1-258-05018-4(8)) Literary Licensing, LLC.

Buckley, Norman & Buckley, June. Walking with the Brontes in West Yorkshire. 2012. (ENG., Illus.). 144p. pap. 17.95 (978-0-7112-3254-9(7)) Lincoln, Frances Ltd. GBR. Dist: Perseus-PGW.

Cannon, John. The Brontes: A Family History. 2008. (ENG., Illus.). 160p. per. (978-0-7509-4808-1(6)) History Pr. Ltd.,The.

Chadwick, Ellis H. In the Footsteps of the Bront#235;s. 2011. (Cambridge Library Collection - Literary Studies). (ENG., Illus.). 604p. pap. 43.00 (978-1-108-03416-6(0)) Cambridge Univ. Pr.

Cooper, Joseph. The Love Stories of John Wesley. 2011. 108p. 39.95 (978-1-258-05569-1(4)) Literary Licensing, LLC.

Craik, W. A. The Bronte Novels (Routledge Revivals) 2011. (Routledge Revivals Ser.). (ENG.). 274p. 120.00 (978-0-415-68790-4(X)) Routledge.

Gordon, Felicia. Preface to the Brontes. Date not set. (Illus.). 240p. pap. 15.00 (978-0-582-35464-7(1)) Addison-Wesley Longman, Ltd. GBR. Dist: Trans-Atlantic Pubns., Inc.

Green, Dudley. Patrick Brontë: Father of Genius. 2010. (ENG., Illus.). 384p. pap. 24.95 *(978-0-7524-5445-0(5))* History Pr. Ltd.,The GBR. Dist: Independent Pubs. Group.

May Sinclair. The Three Brontës. l.t. ed. 2007. (ENG.). 224p. pap. 22.99 *(978-1-4264-5630-5(1))* BiblioBazaar.

Shorter, Clement K. Charlotte Bronte & Her Circle. 2009. 538p. pap. 40.75 *(978-1-113-64875-4(9))*; pap. 39.75 *(978-1-113-64873-0(2))* BiblioBazaar.

—Charlotte Bronte & Her Circle. 2007. (ENG.). 544p. 57.95 *(978-0-548-08175-4(1))* Kessinger Publishing, LLC.

—Charlotte Bronte & Her Sisters. 2007. (ENG.). 280p. 42.95 *(978-0-548-12155-9(9))* Kessinger Publishing, LLC.

Sinclair, May. The Three Brontes. 2010. 354p. pap. 32.75 *(978-1-175-86351-5(3))* 2009. 328p. 36.99 *(978-1-116-20609-8(9))* 2009. 328p. pap. 30.75 *(978-1-116-20612-8(9))* 2009. 328p. pap. 31.75 *(978-1-116-20611-1(0))* 2009. (ENG.). 327p. pap. 23.99 *(978-1-116-20614-2(5)*, BiblioLife) 2009. (ENG.). 327p. pap. 24.99 *(978-1-116-20613-5(7)*, BiblioLife) 2008. 228p. 27.99 *(978-0-554-24016-9(5))* 2008. 228p. 24.99 *(978-0-554-33319-9(8))* 2007. 188p. pap. 19.99 *(978-1-4264-5582-7(8))* BiblioBazaar.

—The Three Brontes. 2010. 132p. pap. *(978-1-153-17893-8(1))* Books LLC.

—The Three Brontes. 2007. (ENG.). 188p. per. *(978-1-4065-4339-1(X))* Dodo Pr.

—The Three Brontes. 2006. (ENG.). pap. *(978-1-84702-474-9(2))* Echo Library.

—The Three Brontes. 2010. 196p. pap. 18.36 *(978-1-162-71034-1(9))*; 37.95 *(978-1-161-47898-3(1))* Kessinger Publishing, LLC.

Torgerson, Beth. Reading the Brontë Body: Disease, Desire, & the Constraints of Culture. 2010. (ENG.). 208p. pap. 27.00 *(978-0-230-10328-3(6))* Palgrave Macmillan.

Wells, Juliette & Hagan, Sandra. The Brontës in the World of the Arts. 2008. (Nineteenth Century Ser.). (Illus.). 270p. 114.95 *(978-0-7546-5752-1(3))* Ashgate Publishing Co.

Willis, Irene Cooper. Brontes. 2006. 148p. per. *(978-1-4067-2557-5(9)*, Hesperides Pr.) Read Bks.

BRONTE FAMILY—BIBLIOGRAPHY

Taylor, Susan B., ed. The Brontes: A Documentary Volume. 2008. (Dictionary of Literary Biography Ser.). (ENG., Illus.). 464p. 315.00 *(978-0-7876-8158-6(X))* Cengage Gale.

BRONX (NEW YORK, N.Y.)

Carlo, Michele. Fish Out of Agua: My Life on Neither Side of the (Subway) Tracks. 2010. (ENG.). 272p. pap. 15.95 *(978-0-8065-3146-5(0)*, Citadel Pr.) Kensington Publishing Corp.

DeRienzo, Harold. The Concept of Community. 2008. 240p. *(978-88-95145-18-1(6))* Italian Paths of Culture.

Hagstrom Map Company Inc. Bronx, NY Pocket Map. 2008. 4.95 *(978-1-59245-052-7(0))* Hagstrom Map Co., Inc.

Jones, Allen & Naison, Mark. The Rat That Got Away: A Bronx Memoir. 2011. (ENG., Illus.). 224p. pap. 16.95 ***(978-0-8232-3103-4(8))*** Fordham Univ. Pr.

Levitt, Ellen. Lost Synagogues of the Bronx & Queens. 2011. (ENG., Illus.). 168p. 26.00 ***(978-1-886223-48-6(3))*** Avotaynu, Inc.

Mayer, Janet Grossbach. As Bad As They Say? Three Decades of Teaching in the Bronx. 2011. (ENG.). 192p. pap. 16.95 *(978-0-8232-3417-2(7))*; 75.00 *(978-0-8232-3416-5(9))* Fordham Univ. Pr.

McNally, Rand. Map EF Bronx, NY. 2006. 7.95 *(978-0-528-86549-7(8))* Rand McNally.

Sclavi, Marianella. An Italian Lady Goes to the Bronx. 2008. 304p. per. *(978-88-95145-20-4(8))* Italian Paths of Culture.

Yee, Lydia. Urban Mythologies: The Bronx Represented since the 1960s. pap. 30.00 *(978-0-917535-26-0(X))* Bronx Museum of the Arts, The.

BRONX (NEW YORK, N.Y.)—HISTORY

Becker, George. The Restaurant. 2009. pap. *(978-1-61584-425-8(2))* Independent Pub.

De Jesus-Coniglio, Pura M. The Bronx: Exposing Its True DNA & Breaking the Stigma - Discover One of Urban America's Greatest Hidden Truths. 2009. 352p. 32.99 *(978-1-61579-606-9(1))*; pap. 20.99 *(978-1-61579-330-3(5))* Xulon Pr., Inc.

De Kadt, Maarten. The Bronx River: An Environmental & Social History. 2011. (Illus.). 160p. pap. 19.99 ***(978-1-60949-180-2(7))*** History Pr., The.

Gonzalez, Evelyn. The Bronx. 2006. (Columbia History of Urban Life Ser.). (ENG., Illus.). 304p. (gr. 17). pap. 24.95 *(978-0-231-12115-6(6))* Columbia Univ. Pr.

Kahane, Lisa, photos by. Do Not Give Way to Evil: Photographs of the South Bronx,1979-1986. 2008. (ENG.). 144p. 35.00 *(978-1-57687-432-5(X)*, Miss Rosen Editions) powerHouse Cultural Entertainment, Inc.

McAuley, Kathleen A. & Hermalyn, Gary. The Bronx. 2010. (Then & Now Ser.). (ENG., Illus.). 96p. pap. 21.99 *(978-0-7385-7315-1(9))* Arcadia Publishing.

Rosenblum, Constance. Boulevard of Dreams: Heady Times, Heartbreak, & Hope along the Grand Concourse in the Bronx. (ENG., Illus.). 274p. 2011. pap. 19.95 *(978-0-8147-7724-4(4))* 2009. 65.00 *(978-0-8147-7608-7(6))* New York Univ. Pr.

Sartain, Dorthea & Derrick, Peter. Guide to the Collections of the Bronx County Archives. 2007. 72p. *(978-0-941980-54-8(5))* Bronx County Historical Society, The.

Twomey, Bill. The Bronx: In Bits & Pieces. 2007. 289p. per. 19.95 *(978-1-60008-062-3(6)*, Rooftop Publishing) AuthorHouse.

Twomey, Bill & Casey, Thomas X. Northwest Bronx. 2011. (Images of America Ser.). (Illus.). 128p. pap. 21.99 *(978-0-7385-7466-0(X))* Arcadia Publishing.

BRONZE

see also Bronzes; Founding; Metal-Work

Freeman, Kirrily. Bronzes to Bullets: Vichy & the Destruction of French Public Statuary, 1941-1944. 2008. (ENG., Illus.). 264p. 65.00 *(978-0-8047-5889-5(1))* Stanford Univ. Pr.

Gailhard, Nicolas. Transformation du Cuivre Au Moyen-Orient du Neolithique a la Fin du 3eme Millenaire: Etude D'une Chaine Technologique. 2009. (FRE., Illus.). 247p. (C). 117.50 *(978-1-4073-0394-9(5))* British Archaeological Reports Ltd. GBR. Dist: Brown, David Bk. Co., The.

Padilla, Yvonne. Bronze Metal Clay: Explore a New Material with 35 Projects. 2010. (ENG., Illus.). 128p. pap. 17.95 *(978-1-60059-463-2(8))* Lark Bks.

Pryor, Francis. A Catalogue of British & Irish Prehistoric Bronzes in the Royal Ontario Museum. (Illus.). 510p. *(978-0-88854-240-3(2))* BRILL.

BRONZE AGE

see also Copper Age; Iron Age

Alberti, Gianmarco. Ceramica Eoliana Della Facies Del Milazzese. Studio Crono-tipologico e Culturale Sulla Base Dei Dati Editi Da Filicudi, Lipari, Panarea, Salina. 2008. (Bar S Ser.). (ITA & ENG., Illus.). 420p. (C). 160.00 *(978-1-4073-0256-0(6))* British Archaeological Reports Ltd. GBR. Dist: Brown, David Bk. Co., The.

Alessandri, Luca. L'occupazione Costiera Protostorica del Lazio Centromeridionale. 2007. (Bar S Ser.). (ITA., Illus.). 241p. (C). 90.00 *(978-1-4073-0008-5(3))* British Archaeological Reports Ltd. GBR. Dist: Brown, David Bk. Co., The.

Anfinset, Nils & Wrigglesworth, Melanie, eds. Local Societies in Bronze Age Northern Europe. 2012. (ENG., Illus.). 256p. (C). 110.00 ***(978-1-84553-742-5(4))*** Equinox Publishing Ltd. GBR. Dist: ISD.

Anthony, David W. The Horse, the Wheel & Language: How Bronze-Age Riders from the Eurasian Steppes Shaped the Modern World. 2007. (ENG., Illus.). 568p. (C). 45.00 *(978-0-691-05887-0(3))* Princeton Univ. Pr.

—Horse, the Wheel & Language: How Bronze-Age Riders from the Eurasian Steppes Shaped the Modern World. 2010. (ENG., Illus.). 568p. (C). pap. 22.95 *(978-0-691-14818-2(X))* Princeton Univ. Pr.

Arnoldussen, Stijn & Fokkens, Harry, eds. Bronze Age Settlements in the Low Countries. 2008. (ENG., Illus.). 206p. (C). 80.00 *(978-1-84217-307-7(3))* Oxbow Bks., Ltd. GBR. Dist: Brown, David Bk. Co., The.

Ashbee, Paul. Kent: In Prehistoric Times. 2006. (ENG., Illus.). 224p. pap. 39.95 *(978-0-7524-3136-9(6))* History Pr. Ltd.,The GBR. Dist: Independent Pubs. Group.

Bachle, Anna Elisabeth & Deger-Jalkotzy, Sigrid, eds. LH III C Chronology & Synchronisms III: LH III C Late & the transition to the Early Iron Age. Proceedings of the International Workshop held at the Austrian Academy of Sciences at Vienna, February 23rd And 24th 2007. 2009. (Denkschriften der Phil. -Hist. Klasse Ser.). (ENG., Illus.). 408p. (C). pap. 116.00 *(978-3-7001-6598-9(6))* Austrian Academy of Sciences Press AUT. Dist: Brown, David Bk. Co., The.

Badalyan, R. S., et al. Bronze & Early Iron Age Archaeological Sites in Armenia. I. Mt. Aragats & Its Surrounding. 2007. (Bar S Ser.). (ENG., Illus.). 319p. (C). pap. 112.50 *(978-1-4073-0139-6(X))* British Archaeological Reports Ltd. GBR. Dist: Brown, David Bk. Co., The.

Bamforth, Michael & Pryor, Francis. Excavation & Research at Flag Fen, Peterborough 1995-2006. 2010. (ENG., Illus.). 167p. (C). 50.00 *(978-1-84217-414-2(2))* Oxbow Bks., Ltd. GBR. Dist: Brown, David Bk. Co., The.

Barrett, John, et al, eds. Landscape, Monuments & Society: The Prehistory of Cranborne Chase. 2009. (ENG.). 268p. pap. 36.99 *(978-0-521-10922-2(1))* Cambridge Univ. Pr.

Bell, Carol. The Evolution of Long Distance Trading Relationships Across the LBA/Iron Age Transition on the Northern Levantine Coast: Crisis, Continuity & Change, a Study Based on Imported Ceramics, Bronze & Its Constituent Metals. 2006. (BAR International Ser.: Vol. 1574). (ENG., Illus.). 138p. (C). pap. 92.50 *(978-1-84171-999-3(4))* British Archaeological Reports Ltd. GBR. Dist: Brown, David Bk. Co., The.

Bender, Barbara & Hamilton, Sue. Stone Worlds: Narrative & Reflexivity in Landscape Archaeology. Tilley, Christopher, ed. 2008. (University College London Institute of Archaeology Publications). (ENG., Illus.). 464p. 99.00 *(978-1-59874-218-3(3))* Left Coast Pr., Inc.

Bender, Barbara, et al. Stone Worlds: Narrative & Reflexivity in Landscape Archaeology. 2008. (University College London Institute of Archaeology Publications). (ENG., Illus.). 464p. pap. 39.95 *(978-1-59874-219-0(1))* Left Coast Pr., Inc.

Bennet, John, et al, eds. Interweaving Worlds: Systemic Interactions in Eurasia, 7th to the 1st Millennia BC. 2011. (ENG., Illus.). 308p. (C). 110.00 *(978-1-84217-998-7(5))* Oxbow Bks., Ltd. GBR. Dist: Brown, David Bk. Co., The.

Berenger, Daniel & Grunewald, Christoph, eds. Westfalen in der Bronzezeit: Eine Gemeinschaftspublikation der LWL-Archaologie fur Westfalen und der Altertumskommission fur Westfalen. 2008. (GER., Illus.). 180p. (C). pap. 27.00 *(978-3-8053-3932-2(1))* Zabern, Philipp von Verlag, GmbH DEU. Dist: Brown, David Bk. Co., The.

Berg, Ina. Negotiating Island Identities: The Active Use of Pottery in the Middle & Late Bronze Age Cyclades. 2007. (Gorgias Dissertations in Classics: 5). 78.00 *(978-1-59333-725-4(6))* Gorgias Pr., LLC.

Betancourt, Philip. Dams & Water Management Systems of Minoan Pseira. 2012. (ENG., Illus.). 110p. (C). pap. 20.00 ***(978-1-931534-66-6(7))*** Institute for Aegean Prehistory Pr.

Betancourt, Philip P. The Bronze Age Begins: The Ceramics Revolution of Early Minoan I & the New Forms of Wealth That Transformed Prehistoric Society. 2009. (ENG., Illus.). 156p. (C). pap. 36.00 *(978-1-931534-52-9(7))* Institute for Aegean Prehistory Pr.

Bettencourt, Ana M. S., et al, eds. Conceptualising Space & Place: On the Role of Agency, Memory & Identity in the Construction of Space from the Upper Palaeolithic to the Iron Age in Europe. 2010. (Bar S Ser.). (ENG., Illus.). 167p. (C). pap. 90.00 *(978-1-4073-0547-9(6))* British Archaeological Reports Ltd. GBR. Dist: Brown, David Bk. Co., The.

Bevan, Andrew. Stone Logics: Vessels & Values in the Bronze Age Eastern Mediterranean. 2007. (ENG.). 310p. 116.00 *(978-0-521-88080-0(7))* Cambridge Univ. Pr.

Bietak, Manfred & Czerny, Ernst, eds. The Bronze Age in the Lebanon: Studies on the Archaeology & Chronology of Lebanon, Syria & Egypt. 2008. (Contributions to the Chronology of the Eastern Mediterranean Ser.). (Illus.). 256p. (C). pap. 140.00 *(978-3-7001-6136-3(0))* Austrian Academy of Sciences Press AUT. Dist: Brown, David Bk. Co., The.

Bosze, Ildiko. Analysis of the Early Bronze Age Graves in Tell Bi'a (Syria) 2009. (ENG., Illus.). 100p. (C). pap. 72.50 *(978-1-4073-0529-5(8))* British Archaeological Reports Ltd. GBR. Dist: Brown, David Bk. Co., The.

Brandherm, Dirk & Rovira Llorens, Salvador. Las Espadas Del Bronce Final en la Peninsula Iberica y Baleares. 2007. (Prahistorische Bronzefunde (PBF) Ser.). (SPA & ENG., Illus.). xii, 212p. (C). 144.00 *(978-3-515-09166-4(1))* Steiner, Franz Verlag Wiesbaden GmbH DEU. Dist: Brown, David Bk. Co., The.

Brysbaert, Ann. The Power of Technology in the Bronze Age Eastern Mediterranean: The Case of the Painted Plaster. 2008. (Monographs in Mediterranean Archaeology Ser.). (ENG., Illus.). 272p. (C). 100.00 *(978-1-84553-433-2(6))* Equinox Publishing Ltd. GBR. Dist: ISD.

Brysbaert, Ann, ed. Tracing Prehistoric Social Networks Through Technology: A Diachronic Perspective on the Aegean. 2011. (Routledge Studies in Archaeology Ser.). (ENG., Illus.). 228p. (C). 125.00 *(978-0-415-89616-0(9))* Routledge.

Budin, Stephanie Lynn. Images of Woman & Child from the Bronze Age: Reconsidering Fertility, Maternity, & Gender in the Ancient World. 2011. (ENG., Illus.). 390p. 95.00 *(978-0-521-19304-7(4))* Cambridge Univ. Pr.

Bukach, David, et al. An Examination of Prehistoric Stone Bracers from Britain. 2012. (ENG., Illus.). 192p. (C). 90.00 *(978-1-84217-438-8(X))* Oxbow Bks., Ltd. GBR. Dist: Brown, David Bk. Co., The.

Burgess, Christopher. Beyond Stonehenge. 2007. (Illus.). 448p. (C). 180.00 *(978-1-84217-215-5(8))* Oxbow Bks., Ltd. GBR. Dist: Brown, David Bk. Co., The.

Burke, Aaron A. Walled up to Heaven: The Evolution of Middle Bronze Age Fortification Strategies in the Levant. 2008. (Illus.). xix, 362p. 59.50 *(978-1-57506-927-2(X))* Eisenbrauns, Inc.

Cadogan, Gerald & Hood, Sinclair. Knossos Excavations 1957-61: Early Minoan. 2011. (BSA Supplementary Volume Ser.). (ENG., Illus.). 327p. (C). 195.00 ***(978-0-904887-64-8(2))*** British Schl. at Athens GBR. Dist: Brown, David Bk. Co , The.

Carame, Manuel Eleazar Costa. Las Producciones Metalicas del III y II Milenio Ca ANE en el Suroeste de la Peninsula Iberica. 2010. (Bar S Ser.). (ENG & SPA., Illus.). 189p. (C). pap. 92.50 *(978-1-4073-0647-6(2))* British Archaeological Reports Ltd. GBR. Dist: Brown, David Bk. Co., The.

Catling, H. W. Sparta, Menelaion I: The Bronze Age, 2 vols. 2009. (Supplementary Volume Ser.). (ENG., Illus.). 890p. (C). 410.00 *(978-0-904887-59-4(6))* British Schl. at Athens GBR. Dist: Brown, David Bk. Co., The.

Chapman, John, et al, eds. Materialitas: Working Stone, Carving Identity. 2009. (Prehistoric society research Paper Ser.). (ENG., Illus.). 208p. (C). 70.00 *(978-1-84217-377-0(4))* Oxbow Bks., Ltd. GBR. Dist: Brown, David Bk. Co., The.

Chapman, Robert. Emerging Complexity: The Later Prehistory of South-East Spain, Iberia & the West Mediterranean. 2009. (New Studies in Archaeology Ser.). (ENG.). 320p. (C). pap. 42.00 *(978-0-521-10572-9(2))* Cambridge Univ. Pr.

Chesson, Meredith S., et al. Daily Life, Materiality, & Complexity in Early Urban Communities of the Southern Levant: Papers in Honor of Walter E. Rast & R. Thomas Schaub. 2011. ***(978-1-57506-217-4(8))*** Eisenbrauns, Inc.

Chifeng International Collaborative Archaeological Project. Settlement Patterns in the Chifeng Region. 2011. (ENG., Illus.). 161p. pap. 29.00 ***(978-1-877812-91-0(9))*** Univ. of Pittsburgh Ctr. for Comparative Archaeology.

Childe, V. Gordon. The Bronze Age. 2011. (ENG., Illus.). 272p. pap. 23.99 *(978-1-107-62692-8(7))* Cambridge Univ. Pr.

Chowne, Peter, et al. Excavations at Billingborough, Lincolnshire, 1975-8: A Bronze-Iron Age Settlement & Salt-Working Site. (East Anglian Archaeology Ser.: No. 94). (Illus.). x, 102p. pap. *(978-1-874350-32-3(9)*, Orbit Books) Trust for Wessex Archaeology Ltd.

Clarke, D. L. Beaker Pottery of Great Britain & Ireland 2 Part Set, 2 vols. 2011. (Gulbenkian Archaeological Ser.). (ENG.). 614p. pap. 75.00 *(978-1-107-66277-3(X))* Cambridge Univ. Pr.

Cleuziou, S., et al, eds. Protohistoire de l'oasis d'al-Aïn, Travaux de la Mission archéologique française à Abou Dhabi (Emirats arabes unis) 2011. (Bar S Ser.). (ENG & FRE., Illus.) 232p. (C). pap. 105.00 ***(978-1-4073-0789-3(4))*** British Archaeological Reports Ltd. GBR. Dist: Brown, David Bk. Co., The.

Cline, Eric H. The Oxford Handbook of the Bronze Age Aegean, 1 vol. 2012. (Oxford Handbooks Ser.). (ENG., Illus.). 976p. pap. 55.00 ***(978-0-19-987360-9(7))*** Oxford Univ. Pr., Inc.

Cline, Eric H. Sailing the Wine-Dark Sea: International Trade & the Late Bronze Age Aegean Bar S591. 2009. (Bar S Ser.: 591). (ENG., Illus.). 326p. (C). pap. 132.50 *(978-1-4073-0417-5(8))* British Archaeological Reports Ltd. GBR. Dist: Brown, David Bk. Co., The.

Cline, Eric H., ed. Oxford Handbook of the Bronze Age Aegean, 1 vol. 2010. (Oxford Handbooks Ser.). (ENG., Illus.). 976p. 175.00 *(978-0-19-536550-4(X))* Oxford Univ. Pr., Inc.

Cohen, Yoram. The Scribes & Scholars of the City of Emar in the Late Bronze Age. 2009. 44.95 *(978-1-57506-931-9(8))* Eisenbrauns, Inc.

Connor, S. E. A Promethean Legacy: Late Quaternary Vegetation History of Southern Georgia, the Caucasus. 2011. (Ancient near Eastern Studies Supplement Ser.). (ENG.). 419p. (C). 137.00 *(978-90-429-2350-8(4))* Peeters Pubs. & Booksellers BEL. Dist: Brown, David Bk. Co., The.

Cooper, Anwen. Past & Present: Excavations at Broom, Bedfordshire 1996-2005. 2007. (Illus.). 281p. *(978-0-9544824-4-2(1))* Cambridge Archaeological Unit.

Crewe, Lindy. Early Enkomi. 2007. (Bar S Ser.). (Illus.). 301p. (C). 112.50 *(978-1-4073-0150-1(0))* British Archaeological Reports Ltd. GBR. Dist: Brown, David Bk. Co., The.

Cummings, Vicki. From Cairn to Cemetery. 2007. (Bar S Ser.). (Illus.). 188p. (C). pap. 85.00 *(978-1-4073-0039-9(3))* British Archaeological Reports Ltd. GBR. Dist: Brown, David Bk. Co., The.

Deger-Jalkotzy, Sigrid & Zavadil, Michaela, eds. LH III C Chronology & Synchronisms II, LH III C Middle: Proceedings of the International Workshop held at the Austrian Academy of Sciences at Vienna, October 29th And 30th 2004. 2007. (Denkschriften der Phil. -Hist. Klasse Ser.). (GER., Illus.). 356p. (C). pap. 95.00 *(978-3-7001-3787-0(7))* Austrian Academy of Sciences Press AUT. Dist: Brown, David Bk. Co., The.

Demand, Nancy H. The Mediterranean Context of Early Greek History. 2012. (ENG., Illus.). 376p. 134.95 *(978-1-4051-5551-9(5)*, Wiley-Blackwell) Wiley, John & Sons, Inc.

Dever, William G., et al. Confronting the Past: Archaeological & Historical Essays on Ancient Israel in Honor of William G. Dever. 2006. (Illus.). 376p. 69.50 *(978-1-57506-117-7(1))* Eisenbrauns, Inc.

Dickinson, Oliver. The Aegean from Bronze Age to Iron Age: Continuity & Change Between the Twelfth & Eighth Centuries BC. 2007. (Illus.). 298p. 135.00 *(978-0-415-13589-4(3))*; (ENG., 320p. per. 34.95 *(978-0-415-13590-0(7))* Routledge.

Dietz, Ute Luise & Jockenhovel, Albrecht, eds. Bronzen im Spannungsfeld zwischen praktischer Nutzung und symbolischer Bedeutung: Beitrage zum internationalen Kolloquium am 9. und 10. Oktober 2008 in Munster. 2011. (Prahistorische Bronzefunde (PBF) Ser.: 20.13). (GER., Illus.). 324p. (C). 143.00 ***(978-3-515-09918-9(2))*** Steiner, Franz Verlag Wiesbaden GmbH DEU. Dist: Brown, David Bk. Co., The.

Earle, Timothy & Kristiansen, Kristian, eds. Organizing Bronze Age Societies: The Mediterranean, Central Europe, & Scandinavia Compared. 2010. (ENG., Illus.). 328p. pap. 29.99 *(978-0-521-74835-3(6))* Cambridge Univ. Pr.

Eriksen, Berit Valentin. Lithic Technology in Metal-Using Societies: Proceedings of a UISPP Symposium, Lisbon, September 2006. 2010. (Publications of the Jutland Archaeological Socie Ser.). (ENG., Illus.). 260p. (C). 62.00 *(978-87-88415-57-5(0))* Aarhus Universitetsforlag DNK. Dist: ISD.

Eriksson, Kathryn O. The Creative Independence of Late Bronze Age Cyprus: An Account of the Archaeological Importance of White Slip Ware. 2007. (Denkschriften der Gesamtakademie Ser.). (ENG., Illus.). 283p. (C). pap. 132.00 *(978-3-7001-3663-7(3))* Austrian Academy of Sciences Press AUT. Dist: Brown, David Bk. Co., The.

Evans, Helen. Neolithic & Bronze Age Landscapes of Cumbria. 2008. (Bar Ser.). (Illus.). 242p. (C). 102.50 *(978-1-4073-0297-3(3))* British Archaeological Reports Ltd. GBR. Dist: Brown, David Bk. Co., The.

Falconer, Steven E. & Fall, Patricia L. Bronze Age Rural Ecology & Village Life at Tell El-Hayyat, Jordan. 2007. (BAR International Ser.: Vol. 1586). (ENG., Illus.). 274p. (C). pap. 92.50 *(978-1-84171-799-9(1))* Archaeopress GBR. Dist: Brown, David Bk. Co., The.

Fantalkin, Alexander, et al. Bene Israel: Studies in the Archaeology of Israel & the Levant During the Bronze & Iron Ages Offered in Honour of Israel Finkelstein. 2008. *(978-90-04-15282-3(2))* BRILL.

Feder, Yitzhaq. Blood Expiation in Hittite & Biblical Ritual: Origins, Context, & Meaning. 2011. 310p. ***(978-90-04-20259-7(5))*** BRILL.

Field, David. Use of Land in Central Southern England During the Neolithic & Early Bronze Age. 2008. (Bar Ser.). (Illus.). 38p. (C). 95.00 *(978-1-4073-0273-7(6))* British Archaeological Reports Ltd. GBR. Dist: Brown, David Bk. Co., The.

Fillios, Melanie A. Measuring Complexity in Early Bronze Age Greece: The Pig As a Proxy Indicator of Socio-Economic Structures. 2007. (ENG., Illus.). viii, 234p. (C). pap. 112.50 *(978-1-4073-0205-8(1))* British Archaeological Reports Ltd. GBR. Dist: Brown, David Bk. Co., The.

Fink, Amir Sumakai. Late Bronze Age Tell Atchana (Alalakh) 2010. (Bar S Ser.). (ENG., Illus.). 157p. (C). pap. 8[illegible].50 *(978-1-4073-0661-2(8))* British Archaeological Reports Ltd. GBR. Dist: Brown, David Bk. Co., The.

Finkelstein, Israel & Naaman, Nadav. The Fire Signals of Lachish: Studies in the Archaeology & History of Israel in the Late Bronze Age, Iron Age, & Persian Period in Honor of David Ussishkin. 2011. 69.50 *(978-1-57506-205-1(4))* Eisenbrauns, Inc.

Flad, Rowan K. Salt Production & Social Hierarchy in Ancient China: An Archaeological Investigation of Specialization in China's Three Gorges. 2011. (ENG., Illus.). 300p. 90.00 *(978-1-107-00941-7(3))* Cambridge Univ. Pr.

Frachetti, Michael David. Pastoralist Landscapes & Social Interaction in Bronze Age Eurasia. 2009. (ENG., Illus.). 232p. 50.00 *(978-0-520-25689-7(1))* Univ. of California Pr.

B

Frankel, David & Webb, Jennifer M. Bronze Age Cemeteries at Deneia in Cyprus. 2007. (Studies in Mediterranean Archeology Ser.). (Illus.). 266p. 250.00 *(978-91-7081-235-4(7))* Astroms, Paul Forlag SWE. Dist: Coronet Bks.

Frohlich, Bruno & Ortner, Donald J. The Early Bronze Age I Tombs & Burials of Bab edh-Dhra', Jordan. 2008. (Reports of the Expedition to the Dead Sea Plain, Jordan: Vol. 3). (ENG., Illus.). 336p. 200.00 *(978-0-7591-1075-5(1))* AltaMira Pr.

Furestier, Robin. Les Industries Lithiques Campaniformes du Sud-Est de la France. 2007. (FRE., Illus.). 339p. (C). pap. 137.50 *(978-1-4073-0071-9(7))* British Archaeological Reports Ltd. GBR. Dist: Brown, David Bk. Co., The.

Furmánek, Václav & Novotná, Mária. Die Sicheln in der Slowakei. 2006. (Prahistorische Bronzefunde (PBF) Ser.). (GER., Illus.). 124p. (C). 97.00 *(978-3-515-08981-4(0))* Steiner, Franz Verlag Wiesbaden GmbH DEU. Dist: Brown, David Bk. Co., The.

Garfinkel, Yosef & Cohen, Susan, eds. The Middle Bronze Age IIA Cemetery at Gesher: Final Report. 2007. (Annual of ASOR Ser.). (ENG., Illus.). 168p. (C). 74.95 *(978-0-89757-075-6(8))* American Schls. of Oriental Research.

Gauss, Walter, et al, eds. Our Cups Are Full: Pottery & Society in the Aegean Bronze Age. 2011. (ENG., Illus.). 392p. (C). pap. 70.00 ***(978-1-905739-39-4(7))*** Archaeopress GBR. Dist: Brown, David Bk. Co., The.

Gedl, Marek. Die Lanzenspitzen in Polen. 2009. (Prahistorische Bronzefunde (PBF) Ser.). (GER., Illus.). 137p. (C). 169.00 *(978-3-515-09353-8(2))* Steiner, Franz Verlag Wiesbaden GmbH DEU. Dist: Brown, David Bk. Co., The.

Gerloff, Sabine. Atlantic Cauldrons & Buckets of the Late Bronze & Early Iron Ages in Western Europe: With a Review of Comparable Vessels from Central Europe & Italy. 2010. (Prahistorische Bronzefunde Ser.). (ENG., Illus.). 445p. (C). 169.00 *(978-3-515-09195-4(5))* Steiner, Franz Verlag Wiesbaden GmbH DEU. Dist: Brown, David Bk. Co., The.

Ginn, Victoria & Rathbone, Stuart. Corrstown: A Coastal Community. Excavations of a Bronze Age Village in Northern Ireland. 2012. (ENG., Illus.). 301p. (C). pap. 70.00 ***(978-1-84217-464-7(9))*** Oxbow Bks., Ltd. GBR. Dist: Brown, David Bk. Co., The.

Gleba, Margarita. Textile Production in Pre-Roman Italy. 2008. (Ancient Textile Ser.). (Illus.). 280p. (C). 70.00 *(978-1-84217-330-5(8))* Oxbow Bks., Ltd. GBR. Dist: Brown, David Bk. Co., The.

Gossip, James & Jones, Andy M. Archaeological Investigations of a Later Prehistoric & a Romano-British Landscape at Tremough, Penryn, Cornwall. 2007. (ENG., Illus.). 143p. (C). pap. 82.50 *(978-1-4073-0124-2(1))* British Archaeological Reports Ltd. GBR. Dist: Brown, David Bk. Co., The.

Grabbe. Israel in Transition: From Late Bronze II to Iron IIa (C. 1250-850 B.C.E.), 2 vols. Grabbe, Lester L., ed. 2008. (Library of Hebrew Bible/Old Testament Studies, the Ser.: Vol. 491). (ENG., Illus.). 256p. *(978-0-567-02726-9(0)*, T&T Clark Int'l) Continuum International Publishing Group, Ltd.

Grabbe, Lester L. Israel in Transition 2: From Late Bronze II to Iron IIA (C. 1250-850 BCE): the Texts. 2010. (Library of Hebrew Bible/Old Testament Studies, the Ser.). (ENG., Illus.). 272p. 120.00 *(978-0-567-64948-5(2)*, T&T Clark Int'l) Continuum International Publishing Group, Ltd. GBR. Dist: National Bk. Network.

Grimaldi, Stefano, et al. Mountain Environments in Prehistoric Europe, Vol. 26. 2009. (Bar S Ser.). (FRE & ENG., Illus.). 169p. (C). pap. 82.50 *(978-1-4073-0365-9(1))* British Archaeological Reports Ltd. GBR. Dist: Brown, David Bk. Co., The.

Groom, David J. The Identification of British 20th Century Bronze Coin Varieties. 2009. (Illus.). 160p. pap. 27.50 *(978-1-4092-8550-2(2))* Lulu Enterprises Inc.

Grutz, Robert. Late Bronze & Iron Age Chalices in Canaan & Ancient Israel. 2007. (Bar S Ser.). (ENG., Illus.). 240p. (C). pap. 90.00 *(978-1-4073-0106-8(3))* British Archaeological Reports Ltd. GBR. Dist: Brown, David Bk. Co., The.

Guerrero Ayuso, Victor M. Prehistoria de Las Islas Baleares: Registro Arqueológico y Evolución Social Antes de la Edad de Hierro = Prehistory of the Balearic Islands: Archaeological Record & Social Evolution Before the Iron Age. 2007. (Bar S Ser.). (SPA., Illus.). iv, 441p. (C). pap. 117.50 *(978-1-4073-0128-0(4))* British Archaeological Reports Ltd. GBR. Dist: Brown, David Bk. Co., The.

Haerinck, E. & Overlaet, B. Luristan Excavation Documents Vol. VII: The Kalleh Nisar Bronze Age Graveyard in Pusht-i Kuh, Luristan. 2008. (ACTA Iranica Ser.). (ENG.). 224p. (C). 160.00 *(978-90-429-1995-2(7))* Peeters Pubs. & Booksellers BEL. Dist: Brown, David Bk. Co., The.

—Luristan Excavation Documents Volume VIII: Early Bronze Age Graveyards to the West of the Kabir Kuh (Pusht-i Kuh, Luristan) 2010. (ACTA Iranica Ser.). (ENG.). 241p. (C). 160.00 *(978-90-429-2274-7(5))* Peeters Pubs. & Booksellers BEL. Dist: Brown, David Bk. Co., The.

Haggis, Donald & Terrenato, Nicola. Current Issues in State Formation in the Mediterranean. 2011. (ENG., Illus.). 281p. (C). pap. 70.00 *(978-1-84217-967-3(5))* Oxbow Bks., Ltd. GBR. Dist: Brown, David Bk. Co., The.

Hamon, Caroline & Quillies, Benedicte, eds. Hoards from the Neolithic to the Metal Ages. 2008. (Bar S Ser.). (Illus.). 120p. (C). 57.50 *(978-1-4073-0197-6(7))* British Archaeological Reports Ltd. GBR. Dist: Brown, David Bk. Co., The.

Harding, A. F. Warriors & Weapons in Bronze Age Europe. 2007. (Series Minor Ser.). (Illus.). 228p. (C). pap. 50.00 *(978-963-8046-86-4(4))* Archaeolingua Alapitvany HUN. Dist: Brown, David Bk. Co., The.

Hein, Irmgard, ed. Lustrous Wares of Late Bronze Age Cyprus & the Eastern Mediterranean. 2007. (Contributions to the Chronology of the Eastern Mediterranean Ser.). (ENG., Illus.). 209p. (C). pap. 78.00 *(978-3-7001-3786-3(9))* Austrian Academy of Sciences Press AUT. Dist: Brown, David Bk. Co., The.

Hess, Richard S., et al. Critical Issues in Early Israelite History. 2008. 324p. (C). 44.50 *(978-1-57506-804-6(4))* Eisenbrauns, Inc.

Higham, Charles & Thosarat, Rachanee. Early Thailand: From Prehistory to Sukhothai. 2012. (ENG., Illus.). 268p. pap. 25.00 ***(978-974-9863-91-6(7))*** River Bks. THA. Dist: Antique Collectors' Club.

Hofsten, Helène Whittaker von. The Aegean Bronze Age in Relation to the Wider European Context: Papers from a Session at the Eleventh Annual Meeting of the European Association of Archaeologists, Cork, 5-11 September 2005. 2008. (Bar S Ser.). (ENG., Illus.). 170p. (C). pap. 60.00 *(978-1-4073-0187-7(X))* British Archaeological Reports Ltd. GBR. Dist: Brown, David Bk. Co., The.

Hogberg, Anders. Lithics in the Scandinavian Late Bronze Age: Sociotechnical Change & Persistence. 2009. (Illus.). 303p. (C). 122.50 *(978-1-4073-0414-4(3))* British Archaeological Reports Ltd. GBR. Dist: Brown, David Bk. Co., The.

Jackson, Caroline & Wager, Emma C., eds. Vitreous Materials in the Late Bronze Age Aegean: A Window to the East Mediterranean World. 2007. (Sheffield Studies in Aegean Archaeology Ser.). (ENG., Illus.). 255p. (C). pap. 64.00 *(978-1-84217-261-2(1))* Oxbow Bks., Ltd. GBR. Dist: Brown, David Bk. Co., The.

Jasmin, Michael. L' etude de la Transition du Bronze Recent II au Fer I en Palestine Meridionale. 2006. (Bar S Ser.). (FRE., Illus.). 354p. (C). 117.50 *(978-1-84171-926-9(9))* British Archaeological Reports Ltd. GBR. Dist: Brown, David Bk. Co., The.

Johnstone, Andrew. The Prehistoric Peak. 2010. 192p. pap. 73.50 *(978-1-4466-3902-3(9))* Lulu Enterprises Inc.

Jones, Andy M. & Taylor, Sean R. Scarcewater, Pennance, Cornwall: Archaeological excavation of a Bronze Age & Roman landscape. 2010. (Bar Ser.). (ENG., Illus.). 124p. (C). pap. 100.00 *(978-1-4073-0645-2(6))* British Archaeological Reports Ltd. GBR. Dist: Brown, David Bk. Co., The.

Katz, Jill & Katz, Jill Citron. The Archaeology of Cult in Middle Bronze Age Canaan: The Sacred Area at Tel Haror, Israel. 2009. (Illus.). xiii, 251p. *(978-1-59333-791-9(4))* Gorgias Pr., LLC.

Kelder, Jorrit M. The Kingdom of Mycenae: A Great Kingdom in the Late Bronze Age Aegean. 2010. *(978-1-934309-27-8(3)*, CDL Pr.) Univ. Pr. of Maryland.

Kiely, Thomas, ed. Ancient Cyprus in the British Museum: Essays in Honour of Veronica Tatton-Brown. 2009. (British Museum Research Publication). (ENG & FRE., Illus.). 108p. (C). pap. 50.00 *(978-0-86159-180-0(1))* British Museum Pr. GBR. Dist: Brown, David Bk. Co., The.

Kienlin, Tobias L. Traditions & Transformations: Approaches to Eneolithic (Copper Age) & Bronze Age Metalworking & Society in Eastern Central Europe & the Carpathian Basin. 2011. (Bar S Ser.). (ENG., Illus.). 405p. (C). pap. 152.50 *(978-1-4073-0740-4(1))* British Archaeological Reports Ltd. GBR. Dist: Brown, David Bk. Co., The.

Knapp, A. Bernard & Dommelen, Peter van, eds. Material Connections in the Ancient Mediterranean: Mobility, Materiality & Identity. 2010. (ENG., Illus.). 272p. (C). 125.00 *(978-0-415-58668-9(2))* Routledge.

KNAPP, Bernard & Dommelen, P. Van, eds. Material Connections in the Ancient Mediterranean: Mobility, Materiality & Identity. 2010. (ENG., Illus.). 272p. (C). pap. 44.95 *(978-0-415-58669-6(0))* Routledge.

Knappett, Carl. An Archaeology of Interaction: Network Perspectives on Material Culture & Society. 2011. (ENG., Illus.). 264p. 135.00 *(978-0-19-921545-4(6))* Oxford Univ. Pr., Inc.

Koh, Andrew. Wreathed in a Fragrant Cloud. 2008. 304p. pap. *(978-3-639-08654-6(6))* VDM Verlag Dr. Mueller e.K.

Kohl, Philip L. The Making of Bronze Age Eurasia. (Cambridge World Archaeology Ser.). (ENG.). 2009. 322p. pap. 30.99 *(978-0-521-13015-8(8))* 2006. (Illus.). 320p. 106.99 *(978-0-521-84780-3(X))* Cambridge Univ. Pr.

Koryakova, Ludmila N. & Epimakhov, Andrej Vladimirovich. The Urals & Western Siberia in the Bronze & Iron Ages. 2006. (Cambridge World Archaeology Ser.). (ENG., Illus.). 408p. 124.00 *(978-0-521-82928-1(3))* Cambridge Univ. Pr.

Kramer-Hajos, Margaretha. Beyond the Palace: Mycenaean East Lokris. 2008. (Bar S Ser.). (Illus.). 118p. (C). 85.00 *(978-1-4073-0269-0(8))* British Archaeological Reports Ltd. GBR. Dist: Brown, David Bk. Co., The.

Kreiter, Attila. Technological Choices & Material Meanings in Early & Middle Bronze Age Hungary: Understanding the Active Role of Material Culture Through Ceramic Analysis. 2007. (Bar S Ser.). (Illus.). xiii, 251p. pap. 92.50 *(978-1-4073-0021-4(0))* Archaeopress GBR. Dist: Brown, David Bk. Co., The.

Kristiansen, Kristian. Organizing Bronze Age Societies: The Mediterranean, Central Europe, & Scandinavia Compared. Earle, Timothy, ed. 2010. (ENG., Illus.). 328p. 95.00 *(978-0-521-76466-7(1))* Cambridge Univ. Pr.

Krzyszkowska, Olga. Cretan Offerings: Studies in Honour of Peter Warren. 2011. (BSA Studies). (ENG., Illus.). 400p. (C). 158.00 *(978-0-904887-62-4(6))* British Schl. at Athens GBR. Dist: Brown, David Bk. Co., The.

Kuzmina, E E. The Prehistory of the Silk Road. Mair, Victor H., ed. 2007. (Encounters with Asia Ser.). (Illus.). 264p. (C). 65.00 *(978-0-8122-4041-2(3))* Univ. of Pennsylvania Pr.

Last, Jonathan. Beyond the Grave: New Perspectives on Barrows. Last, Jonathan, ed. 2006. (Illus.). 208p. (C). 70.00 *(978-1-84217-258-2(1))* Oxbow Bks., Ltd. GBR. Dist: Brown, David Bk. Co., The.

Leskov, Aleksandr Mikhailovich. The Maikop Treasure. 2008. (Illus.). 304p. (C). 75.00 *(978-1-934536-04-9(0)*, Univ. of Pennsylvania Museum of Archaeology & Anthropology) Univ. Museum Pubns.

Lo Schiavo, Fulvia. Le Fibule dell'Italia meridionale e della Sicilia dall' eta del bronzo recente al VI secolo A. C., 3 vols. 2011. (Prahistorische Bronzefunde (PBF) Ser.). (ITA., Illus.). 1722p. (C). 435.00 *(978-3-515-09823-6(2))* Steiner, Franz Verlag Wiesbaden GmbH DEU. Dist: Brown, David Bk. Co., The.

Long, Jesse C., Jr. Khirbat Iskanda: Final Report on the Early Bronze IV Area C 'Gateway' & Cemeteries. Holdorf, Paul S. et al, eds. 2010. (ASOR Archaeological Reports). (ENG., Illus.). 472p. (C). 89.95 *(978-0-89757-082-4(0))* American Schls. of Oriental Research.

Longworth, Ian H. Collared Urns: Of the Bronze Age in Great Britain & Ireland. 2009. (Gulbenkian Archaeological Ser.). (ENG.). 600p. pap. 69.00 *(978-0-521-10592-7(7))* Cambridge Univ. Pr.

Lupack, Susan M. The Role of the Religious Sector in the Economy of Late Bronze Age Mycenaean Greece. 2008. (Bar S Ser.). (ENG., Illus.). 181p. (C). pap. 85.00 *(978-1-4073-0341-3(4))* British Archaeological Reports Ltd. GBR. Dist: Brown, David Bk. Co., The.

Maeir, Aren M. In the Midst of Jordan: The Jordan Valley during the Middle Bronze Age (circa 2000-1500 BCE). Archaeological & Historical Correlates. 2011. (Contributions to the Chronology of the Eastern Mediterranean Ser.). (ENG.). 298p. (C). pap. 96.00 *(978-3-7001-6602-3(8))* Austrian Academy of Sciences Press AUT. Dist: Brown, David Bk. Co., The.

Maliszewsk, Dariusz. New Light on the Bronze Age Ceramics from H. Schliemann's Excavations at Troy: Studies on the Munich & Poznan Collections Within the Anatolian-Aegean Cultural Context. 2010. (Bar S Ser.). (ENG., Illus.). 402p. (C). pap. 167.50 *(978-1-4073-0482-3(8))* British Archaeological Reports Ltd. GBR. Dist: Brown, David Bk. Co., The.

Marakas, Gemma. Ritual Practice Between the Late Bronze Age & Protogeometric Periods of Greece. 2010. (Bar S Ser.). (ENG., Illus.). 152p. (C). pap. 87.50 *(978-1-4073-0686-5(3))* British Archaeological Reports Ltd. GBR. Dist: Brown, David Bk. Co., The.

Middleton, Guy D. The Collapse of Palatial Society in LBA Greece & the Postpalatial Period. 2010. (Bar S Ser.). (ENG., Illus.). 142p. (C). pap. 85.00 *(978-1-4073-0651-3(0))* British Archaeological Reports Ltd. GBR. Dist: Brown, David Bk. Co., The.

Milevski, Ianir. Early Bronze Age Goods Exchange in the Southern Levant: A Marxist Perspective. 2011. (Approaches to Anthropological Archaeology Ser.). (ENG., Illus.). 294p. (C). 115.00 *(978-1-84553-378-6(X))* Equinox Publishing Ltd. GBR. Dist: ISD.

Mina, Maria. Anthropomorphic Figurines from the Neolithic & Early Bronze Age Aegean: Gender Dynamics & Implications for the Understanding of Early Aegean Prehistory. 2008. (Bar S Ser.). (ENG., Illus.). 204p. (C). pap. 112.50 ***(978-1-4073-0241-6(8))*** British Archaeological Reports Ltd. GBR. Dist: Brown, David Bk. Co., The.

Morris, James & Maltby, Mark, eds. Integrating Social & Environmental Archaeologies: Reconsidering Deposition. 2010. (Bar S Ser.). (ENG., Illus.). 118p. (C). pap. 77.50 *(978-1-4073-0638-4(3))* British Archaeological Reports Ltd. GBR. Dist: Brown, David Bk. Co., The.

Morritt, Robert. Lost Civilisations. 2011. 120p. pap. ***(978-3-8454-0986-3(X))*** Lambert Academic Publishing.

Mudd, Andrew & Pears, Ben. Bronze Age Field System at Tower's Fen, Thorney, Peterboroug. Richmond, Andy & Coates, Gary, eds. 2008. (Bar Ser.). (Illus.). 106p. (C). 75.00 *(978-1-4073-0363-5(5))* British Archaeological Reports Ltd. GBR. Dist: Brown, David Bk. Co., The.

Muehlenbruch, Tobias. Die Synchronisierung der nordlichen Levante und Kilikiens mit der agaischen Spatbronzezeit. 2010. (Denkschriften der Gesamtakademie Ser.). (GER.). 174p. (C). pap. 95.00 *(978-3-7001-6552-1(8))* Austrian Academy of Sciences Press AUT. Dist: Brown, David Bk. Co., The.

Needham, Stuart, et al, eds. Ringlemere, Precious Cups & the Beginning of the Channel Bronze Age. 2006. (British Museum Research Publication). (Illus.). 120p. (C). 46.00 *(978-0-86159-163-3(1))* British Museum Pr. GBR. Dist: Brown, David Bk. Co., The.

Overlaet, B. Bani Surmah: An Early Bronze Age Graveyard in Pusht-I Kuh, Luristan. Haerinck, E., ed. 2006. (Luristan Excavation Documents Ser.: Vol. 6). (ENG.). 188p. (C). 131.00 *(978-90-429-1664-7(8))* Peeters Pubs. & Booksellers BEL. Dist: Brown, David Bk. Co., The.

Parkinson, William A. & Galaty, Michael L. Archaic State Interaction: The Eastern Mediterranean in the Bronze Age. 2010. (ENG., Illus.). 336p. pap. *(978-1-934691-20-5(8))* School for Advanced Research Pr./SAR Pr.

Pearson, Michael Parker. From Machair to Mountains: Archaeological Survey & Excavation in South Uist. 2012. (ENG., Illus.). 428p. (C). 70.00 *(978-1-84217-451-7(7))* Oxbow Bks., Ltd. GBR. Dist: Brown, David Bk. Co., The.

Peltenburg, Edgar, ed. Euphrates River Valley Settlement. 2007. (Levant Supplementary Volume Ser.). (ENG., Illus.). 295p. (C). 120.00 *(978-1-84217-272-8(7))* Oxbow Bks., Ltd. GBR. Dist: Brown, David Bk. Co., The.

Phillips, Jacqueline Sharon. Aegyptiaca on the Island of Crete in Their Chronological Context: A Critical Review, 2 vols. 2008. (Contributions to the Chronology of the Eastern Mediterranean Ser.). (GER., Illus.). 737p. (C). pap. 294.00 *(978-3-7001-6117-2(4))* Austrian Academy of Sciences Press AUT. Dist: Brown, David Bk. Co., The.

Pilafidis-Williams, Korinna. The Sanctuary of Aphaia on Aigina in the Bronze Age. 2006. 274p. 79.95 *(978-3-7774-8010-7(X))* Hirmer Verlag GmbH DEU. Dist: Chicago Distribution Ctr.

Popova, Tzvetana. Plant Environment of Man Between 6000 & 2000 B.C. in Bulgaria. 2010. (Bar S Ser.). (ENG., Illus.). 107p. (C). pap. 107.50 *(978-1-4073-0470-0(4))* British Archaeological Reports Ltd. GBR. Dist: Brown, David Bk. Co., The.

Pullen, Daniel J. The Early Bronze Age Village on Tsoungiza Hill. 2009. (Nemea Valley Archaeological Project I Ser.). (ENG., Illus.). 650p. 150.00 *(978-0-87661-922-3(7))* American Schl. of Classical Studies at Athens.

Pullen, Daniel J., ed. Political Economies of the Aegean Bronze Age. 2010. (ENG., Illus.). 272p. (C). pap. 60.00 *(978-1-84217-392-3(8))* Oxbow Bks., Ltd. GBR. Dist: Brown, David Bk. Co., The.

Randsborg, Klavs. Bronze Age Textiles: Men, Women & Wealth. 2011. (Duckworth Debates in Archaeology Ser.). 160p. pap. 24.95 ***(978-0-7156-4078-4(X))*** Duckworth Publishers GBR. Dist: International Publishers Marketing.

Rosen, Steven A. An Investigation into Early Desert Pastoralism: Excavations at the Camel Site, Negev. 2011. (Monograph Ser.). (ENG., Illus.). 215p. (C). 69.95 *(978-1-931745-83-3(8))*; pap. 39.95 *(978-1-931745-84-0(6))* Cotsen Institute of Archaeology at UCLA.

Ruggles, Clive L. N., ed. Archaeoastronomy & Ethnoastronomy (IAU S278) Building Bridges between Cultures. 2011. (Proceedings of the International Astronomical Union Symposia & Colloquia Ser.). (ENG., Illus.). 430p. 125.00 ***(978-1-107-01978-2(8))*** Cambridge Univ. Pr.

Sagona, A. G. & Abramischwili, Michael. Archaeology in Southern Caucasus: Perspectives from Georgia. 2008. (Ancient near Eastern Studies: Vol. 19). (ENG.). 477p. (C). 136.00 *(978-90-429-1800-9(4))* Peeters Pubs. & Booksellers BEL. Dist: Brown, David Bk. Co., The.

Salvatori, Sandro, et al, eds. The Archaeological Map of the Murghab Delta Vol. 2: The Bronze Age & Early Iron Age in the Margiana Lowlands. 2008. (Bar S Ser.). (ENG., Illus.). 237p. (C). pap. 100.00 *(978-1-4073-0293-5(0))* British Archaeological Reports Ltd. GBR. Dist: Brown, David Bk. Co., The.

Sasson, Aharon. Animal Husbandry in Ancient Israel: A Zooarchaeological Perspective on Livestock Exploitation, Herd Management & Economic Strategies. 2010. (Approaches to Anthropological Archaeology Ser.). (ENG., Illus.). 166p. (C). 165.00 *(978-1-84553-179-9(5))* Equinox Publishing Ltd. GBR. Dist: ISD.

Schloen, J. David & Stager, Lawrence E. Exploring the Longue Durée: Essays in Honor of Lawrence E. Stager. 2009. 69.50 *(978-1-57506-161-0(9))* Eisenbrauns, Inc.

Schmidlin, Clemens. Ornament und Bedeutung: Zur Motivik Mittelminoischer Feinkeramik. 2011. (Bar S Ser.). (GER., Illus.). 83p. (C). pap. 65.00 *(978-1-4073-0728-2(2))* British Archaeological Reports Ltd. GBR. Dist: Brown, David Bk. Co., The.

Singer, Itamar. The Calm Before the Storm: Selected Writings of Itamar Singer on the Late Bronze Age in Anatolia & the Levant. 2011. ***(978-1-58983-558-0(1))***; ***(978-1-58983-559-7(X))*** Society of Biblical Literature.

Sjogren, Karl-Goren, ed. Ecology & economy in Stone Age & Bronze Age Scania. 2006. (ENG., Illus.). 218p. (C). 30.00 *(978-91-7209-445-1(1))* Riksantikvarieambetet och Statens historiska museer SWE. Dist: Brown, David Bk. Co., The.

Smith, Joanna S. Art & Society in Cyprus from the Bronze Age into the Iron Age. 2009. (ENG., Illus.). 416p. 102.00 *(978-0-521-51367-8(7))* Cambridge Univ. Pr.

Sosna, Daniel. Differentiation in the Late Copper Age & the Early Bronze Age in South Moravia (Czech Republic) 2009. (ENG., Illus.). 230p. (C). pap. 105.00 *(978-1-4073-0526-4(3))* British Archaeological Reports Ltd. GBR. Dist: Brown, David Bk. Co., The.

Steel, Louise. Materiality & Consumption in the Bronze Age Mediterranean. 2012. (Routledge Studies in Archaeology Ser.). (ENG.). 220p. (C). 125.00 ***(978-0-415-53734-6(7))*** Routledge.

Tcheremissinoff, Yaramila. Les Sepultures Simples et Plurielles du Campaniforme et du Bronze Ancien dans le Bassin Rhodanien et ses zones D'influences. 2006. (Bar S Ser.). (FRE., Illus.). 155p. (C). 72.50 *(978-1-84171-965-8(X))* British Archaeological Reports Ltd. GBR. Dist: Brown, David Bk. Co., The.

Ur, Jason A. Tell Hamoukar, Volume 1: Urbanism & Cultural Landscapes in Northeastern Syria: the Tell Hamoukar Survey, 1999-2001. 2010. (Oriental Institute Publications). (ENG., Illus.). 384p. (C). 75.00 *(978-1-885923-73-8(2))* Oriental Institute of the Univ. of Chicago, The.

van Gijn, Annelou L. Flint in Focus: Lithic Biographies in the Neolithic & Bronze Age. 2010. (ENG.). 311p. (C). pap. 76.00 *(978-90-8890-033-4(7))* Sidestone Pr. NLD. Dist: Brown, David Bk. Co., The.

Vavouranakis, Giorgos. Funerary Landscapes East of Lasithi, Crete, in the Bronze Age. 2007. (BAR International Ser.: Vol. 1606). (ENG., Illus.). 185p. (C). pap. 95.00 *(978-1-4073-0023-8(7))* British Archaeological Reports Ltd. GBR. Dist: Brown, David Bk. Co., The.

Veber, Cecile. Metallurgie des Depots de Bronzes a la Fin de L'Age du Bronze Final (IXe-VIIIe av. J.-C.) Dans le Domaine Sarre-Lorraine: Essai de Caracterisation D'une Production Bronziere au Travers des Etudes Techniques. 2009. (FRE & ENG., Illus.). 340p. (C). pap. 132.50 *(978-1-4073-0599-8(9))* British Archaeological Reports Ltd. GBR. Dist: Brown, David Bk. Co., The.

Verardi, Virginia. L'introduction et la Diffusion de la Technologie du Bronze en Syrie-Mésopotamie: Genèse D'un Artisanat. 2008. (Bar S Ser.). (FRE., Illus.). 268p. (C). pap. 87.50 *(978-1-4073-0182-2(9))* British Archaeological Reports Ltd. GBR. Dist: Brown, David Bk. Co., The.

Vianello, Andrea, ed. Exotica in the Prehistoric Mediterranean. 2011. (ENG.). 216p. (C). pap. 50.00 *(978-1-84217-424-1(X))* Oxbow Bks., Ltd. GBR. Dist: Brown, David Bk. Co., The.

Von Dassow, Eva. State & Society in the Late Bronze Age: Alalah under the Mittani Empire. 2008. (C). *(978-1-934309-14-8(1)*, CDL Pr.) Univ. Pr. of Maryland.

Wakefield, Jay/Stuart & de Jonge, Reinoud. Rocks & Rows: Sailing Routes across the Atlantic & the Copper Trade. 2009. (Illus.). 416p. pap. *(978-0-917054-20-4(2))* Medical Communications & Services Assn.

Webb, Jennifer M., ed. Bronze Age Cemeteries at Karmi Palealona & Lapatsa in Cyprus: Excavations by J. R. B. Stewart. 2009. (Studies in Mediterranean Archaeology Ser.). 292p. 235.00 *(978-91-7081-241-5(1))* Astroms, Paul Forlag SWE. Dist: Coronet Bks.

Weiberg, Erika. Thinking the Bronze Age: Life & Death in Early Helladic Greece. 2007. (Uppsala Studies in Ancient Mediterranean & near Eastern Civilizations Ser.: 29). (Illus.). 404p. (Orig.). pap. 87.50 *(978-91-554-6782-1(2))* Uppsala Universitet/Acta Universitatis Uppsaliensis SWE. Dist: Coronet Bks.

Weinberger, Susanne. Warfare in the Austrian Weinviertel during the Early Bronze Age. 2008. (Mitteilungen der Prahistorischen Kommission Ser.). (Illus.). 125p. (C). pap. 59.00 *(978-3-7001-3953-9(5))* Austrian Academy of Sciences Press AUT. Dist: Brown, David Bk. Co., The.

Wells, Peter S. How the Ancients Saw the World - Vision, Art & the Shaping Of. 2012. (ENG.). 304p. (C). 35.00 ***(978-0-691-14338-5(2))*** Princeton Univ. Pr.

Wicke, Dirk. Vorderasiatische Pyxiden der Spätbronzezeit und der Früheisenzeit. 2008. (GER., Illus.). xi 461p. *(978-3-934628-74-8(5))* Ugarit-Verlag.

Wickstead, Helen. Theorising Tenure: Land Division & Identity in Later Prehistoric Dartmoor, South-West Britain. 2008. (Bar Ser.). (Illus.). 242p. (C). pap. 107.50 *(978-1-4073-0311-6(2))* British Archaeological Reports Ltd. GBR. Dist: Brown, David Bk. Co., The.

Yasur-Landau, Assaf. The Philistines & Aegean Migration at the End of the Late Bronze Age. 2010. (ENG., Illus.). 412p. (C). 95.00 *(978-0-521-19162-3(9))* Cambridge Univ. Pr.

Zachos, Konstantinos. Ayios Dhimitrios, a Prehistoric Settlement in the Southwestern Peloponnese: The Neolithic & Early Helladic Periods. 2008. (Bar S Ser.). (ENG., Illus.). 141p. (C). pap. 112.50 *(978-1-4073-0259-1(0))* British Archaeological Reports Ltd. GBR. Dist: Brown, David Bk. Co., The.

Zertal, Adam, ed. El-Ahwat, a Fortified Site from the Early Iron Age near Nahal 'Iron, Israel: Excavations, 1993-2000. 2011. (ENG., Illus.). XX, 488p. ***(978-90-04-17645-4(4))*** BRILL.

BRONZE DIABETES

see Hemochromatosis

BRONZES

see also Bronze

Arthur M. Sackler Gallery (Smithsonian Institution) Staff, contrib. by. Gods of Angkor: Bronzes from the National Museum of Cambodia. 2010. pap. *(978-0-934686-17-4(3))* Freer Gallery of Art, Smithsonian Institution.

Avery, Victoria. Vulcan's Forge in Venus' City: The Story of Bronze in Venice, 1350-1650. 2012. (British Academy Postdoctoral Fellowship Monographs). (ENG., Illus.). 700p. 125.00 ***(978-0-19-726496-6(4))*** Oxford Univ. Pr., Inc.

Bagley, Robert W., et al. Max Loehr & the Study of Chinese Bronzes: Style & Classification in the History of Art. 2008. (Illus.). 199p. 55.00 *(978-1-933947-41-9(1))* Cornell Univ. East Asia Program.

Bassett, Jean, et al. The Craftsman Revealed: Adrien de Vries, Sculptor in Bronze. 2008. (Illus.). 352p. 60.00 *(978-0-89236-919-5(1))* Oxford Univ. Pr., Inc.

Boardman, John. The Relief Plaques of Eastern Eurasia & China. 2010. (Bar S Ser.). (ENG., Illus.). 103p. (C). pap. 120.00 *(978-1-4073-0687-2(1))* British Archaeological Reports Ltd. GBR. Dist: Brown, David Bk. Co., The.

Brandherm, Dirk & Rovira Llorens, Salvador. Las Espadas Del Bronce Final en la Peninsula Iberica y Baleares. 2007. (Prahistorische Bronzefunde (PBF) Ser.). (SPA & ENG., Illus.). xii, 212p. (C). 144.00 *(978-3-515-09166-4(1))* Steiner, Franz Verlag Wiesbaden GmbH DEU. Dist: Brown, David Bk. Co., The.

Bunker, Emma C. & Latchford, Douglas. Khmer Bronzes: New Interpretations of the Past. 2011. ***(978-1-58886-111-5(2))*** Art Media Resources, Inc.

Cast in Bronze French Sculpture from Renaissance to Revolution. 2009. 536p. *(978-2-7572-0183-1(2))* Somogy Editions d'Art.

Chen, Fangmei. Shang Ritual Bronzes in the National Palace Museum Collection. (CHI & ENG., Illus.). 608p. *(978-957-562-333-3(9))* National Palace Museum.

Cort, Louise Allison & Jett, Paul, eds. Gods of Angkor: Bronzes from the National Museum of Cambodia. 2010. (ENG., Illus.). 160p. pap. 40.00 *(978-0-295-99042-2(2))* Sackler, Arthur M. Foundation, The.

Falkenhausen, Lothar von. The Lloyd Cotsen Study Collection of Chinese Bronze Mirrors Vol. 1 & Vol. 2: Catalogue - Studies, 2 vols. Cahill, Susan, ed. 2011. (Monumenta Archaeologica Ser.). (ENG., Illus.). 264p. (C). 450.00 ***(978-0-9745168-8-2(0))*** Cotsen Institute of Archaeology at UCLA.

Fetting, Rainer. Rainer Fetting: Return of the Giants. 2009. (ENG., Illus.). 160p. 55.00 *(978-3-86678-231-0(4))* Kerber Verlag DEU. Dist: D.A.P./Distributed Art Pubs.

Freeman, Charles. The Horses of St. Mark's: A Story of Triumph in Byzantium, Paris, & Venice. 2010. (ENG.). 304p. (gr. 12). 27.95 *(978-1-59020-267-8(8))* Overlook Pr., The.

Hu, Philip K. Later Chinese Bronzes: The Saint Louis Art Museum & Robert E. Kresko Collections. Steiner, Mary Ann, ed. 2008. (ENG & CHI., Illus.). 208p. pap. 39.95 *(978-0-89178-092-2(0))* St. Louis Art Museum.

Iozzo, Mario, ed. The Chimaera of Arezzo. 2009. (Illus.). 52p. (C). (ITA.). pap. 15.00 *(978-88-596-0627-7(6))*; (ENG., pap. 15.00 *(978-88-596-0628-4(4))* Polistampa ITA. Dist: Brown, David Bk. Co., The.

Keeble, K. Corey. European Bronzes in the Royal Ontario Museum. (Illus.). 1276p. *(978-0-88854-277-9(1))* BRILL.

Klebinder-Gauss, Gudrun. Bronzefunde aus dem Artemision von Ephesos. 2007. (Forschungen in Ephesos Ser.). (Illus.). 310p. (C). pap. 149.00 *(978-3-7001-3641-5(2))* Austrian Academy of Sciences Press AUT. Dist: Brown, David Bk. Co., The.

Lafli, Ergun & Feugere, Michel. Statues et Statuettes en Bronze de Cilicie avec Deux Annexes sur la Main de Comana et les Figurines en Bronze du Musée de Hatay. 2007. (Bar S Ser.). (FRE., Illus.). 104p. (C). pap. 70.00 *(978-1-84171-797-5(5))* British Archaeological Reports Ltd. GBR. Dist: Brown, David Bk. Co., The.

Leithe-Jasper, Manfred, et al. European Bronzes: From the Quentin Collection. 2006. (ENG., Illus.). *(978-1-85149-472-9(3))* Antique Collectors' Club.

Levy, Thomas E., et al. Masters of Fire: Hereditary Bronze Casters of South India. 2008. (ENG., Illus.). 144p. (C). 60.00 *(978-3-937203-37-9(0))* Deutsches Bergbau-Museum DEU. Dist: Brown, David Bk. Co., The.

Li, Song. Chinese Bronze Ware. 3rd ed. 2011. (Introductions to Chinese Culture Ser.). (ENG., Illus.). 164p. pap. 19.99 *(978-0-521-18685-8(4))* Cambridge Univ. Pr.

McCallum, Donald F. Hakuho Sculpture. 2012. (ENG., Illus.). 176p. 50.00 *(978-0-295-99130-6(5))* Univ. of Washington Pr.

Normand-Romain, Antoinette Le. The Bronzes of Rodin: Catalogue of Works in the Musee Rodin 2 vols. 2007. (Illus.). 800p. 320.00 *(978-2-7118-4939-0(2)*, Lund Humphries Pubs.) Ashgate Publishing, Ltd. GBR. Dist: Ashgate Publishing Co.

Platte, Editha. Bronze Head from Ife. 2010. (Objects in Focus Ser.). (ENG., Illus.). 64p. (C). pap. 10.00 *(978-0-7141-2592-3(X))* British Museum Pr. GBR. Dist: Brown, David Bk. Co., The.

Stibbe, C. M. & Heldring, Barbara. Agalmata: Studien Zur Griechisch-Archaischen Bronzekunst. 2006. (Babesch Supplementa Ser.). (ENG, ITA & GER.). 341p. (C). pap. 128.00 *(978-90-429-1708-8(3))* Peeters Pubs. & Booksellers BEL. Dist: Brown, David Bk. Co., The.

Uhlig, Helmut. On the Path to Enlightenment: The Berti Aschmann Foundation of Tibetan Art at the Museum Rietberg Zürich. 2011. (ENG., Illus.). 226p. (C). 50.00 *(978-3-907070-60-4(7))* Holberton, Paul Publishing GBR. Dist: Univ. of Washington Pr.

Wannenes, Giacomo. Ornamental Bronzes & Objets Montes: From Louis XIV to Napoleon III. 2006. (ENG., Illus.). 456p. 195.00 *(978-0-9700168-9-8(1))* Editions Vausor Llc Dist A/C.

Warren, Jeremy. Beauty & Power: Renaissance & Baroque Bronzes from the Collection of Peter Marino. 2010. (ENG., Illus.). 288p. 90.00 *(978-0-900785-77-1(2))* Holberton, Paul Publishing GBR. Dist: Univ. of Washington Pr.

BROOK, PETER, 1925-

Croyden, Margaret, ed. Conversations with Peter Brook, 1970-2000. 2010. (ENG.). 320p. pap. 16.95 *(978-1-55936-350-1(9))* Theatre Communications Group, Inc.

BROOK FARM PHALANX (WEST ROXBURY, BOSTON, MASS.)

Codman, John Thomas. Brook Farm. 2008. 280p. 25.99 *(978-0-554-31898-1(9))* 2008. 280p. 28.99 *(978-0-554-22595-1(6))* 2006. 278p. pap. 23.99 *(978-1-4264-2728-2(X))* 2006. 258p. pap. 21.99 *(978-1-4264-2671-1(2))* BiblioBazaar.

—Brook Farm. 2009. 194p. pap. *(978-0-217-91299-0(0))* Books LLC.

—Brook Farm. 2007. (ENG.). pap. *(978-1-4065-1334-9(2))* Dodo Pr.

—Brook Farm. 2007. (ENG.). 184p. per. *(978-1-4068-4649-2(X))* Echo Library.

Crowe, Charles Robert. Transcendentalist Support of Brook Farm, a Paradox? the Historian, a Journal of History V21, No 3, May 1959. Rayback, Joseph G., ed. 2011. 18p. 35.95 ***(978-1-258-06556-0(8))*** Literary Licensing, LLC.

Curtis, George William. Early Letters of George Wm. Curtis. 2007. (ENG.). 184p. per. 19.99 *(978-1-4346-7352-7(9))*; 206p. per. 22.99 *(978-1-4346-7353-4(7))* BiblioBazaar.

—Early Letters of George Wm. Curtis. 2007. 172p. per. *(978-1-4065-1502-2(7))* Dodo Pr.

Dwight, Marianne & Orvis, Helen Dwight. Letters from Brook Farm, 1844-1847. Reed, Amy Louise, ed. 2011. 220p. 44.95 ***(978-1-258-09496-6(7))*** Literary Licensing, LLC.

Francis, Richard. Transcendental Utopias: Individual & Community at Brook Farm, Fruitlands, & Walden. 2007. (Illus.). 272p. pap. 24.95 *(978-0-8014-7380-7(2))* Cornell Univ. Pr.

Hawthorne, Nathaniel. Passages from the American Notebooks. 2008. 176p. 22.99 *(978-0-554-31843-1(1))* 2008. 168p. 22.99 *(978-0-554-31842-4(3))* 2008. 168p. 25.99 *(978-0-554-22539-5(5))* 2008. 176p. 25.99 *(978-0-554-22540-1(9))* Vol. 1. 2007. (ENG.). 154p. pap. 19.99 *(978-1-4264-2569-1(4))* Vol. 1. 2007. (ENG.). 164p. pap. 21.99 *(978-1-4264-2610-0(0))* Vol. 2. 2007. (ENG.). 162p. pap. 19.99 *(978-1-4264-2570-7(8))* Vol. 2. 2007. (ENG.). 174p. pap. 21.99 *(978-1-4264-2611-7(9))* BiblioBazaar.

Sams, Henry W., ed. The Autobiography of Brook Farm: A Book of Primary Source Materials. 2011. 280p. 47.95 ***(978-1-258-07650-4(0))*** Literary Licensing, LLC.

Sears, John Van Der Zee. My Friends at Brook Farm. 2007. (ENG.). 86p. per. 16.99 *(978-1-4346-9581-9(6))*; 96p. per. 18.99 *(978-1-4346-9582-6(4))* BiblioBazaar.

—My Friends at Brook Farm. 2009. 84p. pap. *(978-1-4099-6967-9(3))* Dodo Pr.

Swift, Lindsay. Brook Farm. 2009. 172p. pap. *(978-1-4590-5095-2(9))*; 174p. pap. *(978-0-217-69300-4(8))* Books LLC.

BROOKE, EDWARD WILLIAM, 1919-

Brooke, Edward W. Bridging the Divide: My Life. 2006. (ENG., Illus.). 352p. 29.95 *(978-0-8135-3905-6(6))* Rutgers Univ. Pr.

BROOKE, RUPERT, 1887-1915

Brooke, Rupert. Letters from America. 2008. 128p. 24.99 *(978-0-554-29883-3(4))* BiblioBazaar.

—Letters from America. 2008. 104p. pap. *(978-1-4099-1824-0(6))* Dodo Pr.

—Letters from America: Travels in the USA & Canada. 2007. (Modern Voices Ser.) (ENG.). 124p. pap. 15.95 *(978-1-84391-433-4(6))* Hesperus Pr. GBR. Dist: Independent Pubs. Group.

Brooke, Rupert & James, Henry. Letters from America. 2007. (ENG.). 112p. pap. 18.99 *(978-1-4346-6470-9(8))*; 124p. pap. 19.99 *(978-1-4346-6471-6(6))* BiblioBazaar.

de la Mare, Walter. Rupert Brooke & the Intellectual Imagination. 2009. 48p. pap. *(978-0-217-04262-8(7))* Books LLC.

BROOKINGS INSTITUTION

Hagedorn, Hermann. Brookings: A Biography. 334p. reprint ed. lib. bdg. 98.00 *(978-0-7222-0430-6(2))* Library Reprints, Inc.

BROOKLYN (NEW YORK, N.Y.)

Cunningham, Laura Shaine. Sleeping Arrangements. Date not set. 13.95 *(978-0-06-097773-3(6))* HarperCollins Pubs.

Grayson, Richard. The Brooklyn Diaries: 1969-1981. 2010. 623p. pap. 39.99 *(978-0-557-59184-8(8))* Lulu Enterprises Inc.

Is Brooklyn Being Counted? Problems with the 2010 Census: Hearing Before the Committee on Oversight & Government Reform, House of Representatives, One Hundred Eleventh Congress, Second Session, July 19, 2010. 2011. (Illus.). iii, 50p. ***(978-0-16-088290-6(7)***, 552-070-42595-1) United States Government Printing Office.

Keith, Stephanie, text. Vodou Brooklyn: Five Ceremonies with Mambo Marie Carmel. 2010. 35.00 *(978-1-58432-641-0(7))* Educa Vision.

Levitt, Ellen. The Lost Synagogues of Brooklyn: The Stories Behind How & Why Many Brooklyn Synagogues, Now Old Ex-Shuls, Were Converted to Other Uses, Primarily As Christian Churches. 2009. (Illus.). 196p. pap. 26.00 *(978-1-886223-39-4(4))* Avotaynu, Inc.

Marwell, Nicole P. Bargaining for Brooklyn: Community Organizations in the Entrepreneurial City. 2007. (ENG., Illus.). 288p. 60.00 *(978-0-226-50906-8(0))*; per. 25.00 *(978-0-226-50907-5(9))* Univ. of Chicago Pr.

Mueller, Marianne. The Flock, 1 vol. 2008. (ENG., Illus.). 112p. (gr. 13-18). pap. 40.00 *(978-3-88243-969-4(6))* Steidl, Gerhard Druckerei und Verlag DEU. Dist: Innovative Logistics.

Protana, Grace Zolla. As Long As You Can See the Clock, You're Okay: South Brooklyn in The '50s. 2009. 215p. 24.95 *(978-1-4327-3925-6(5))* Outskirts Pr., Inc.

Reeder, Jan. High Style: Masterworks from the Brooklyn Museum Costume Collection at the Metropolitan Museum of Art. 2010. (ENG., Illus.). 256p. 50.00 *(978-0-300-15522-8(0))* Yale Univ. Pr.

Vaughan, Melissa, et al. The New Brooklyn Cookbook: Recipes & Stories from 31 Restaurants That Put Brooklyn on the Culinary Map. 2010. (ENG., Illus.). 272p. 40.00 *(978-0-06-195622-5(8)*, Morrow, William Cookbooks) HarperCollins Pubs.

BROOKLYN (NEW YORK, N.Y.)—DESCRIPTION AND TRAVEL

Crish, Dave, et al. Not for Tourists Guide to Brooklyn. 2007. (Not for Tourists Guide to Brooklyn Ser.). (Illus.). 185p. 12.95 *(978-0-9793945-0-8(3))* Not for Tourists, Inc.

Duer, Stephen C. & Smith, Allan B. Cypress Hills Cemetery. 2010. (Images of America Ser.). (Illus.). 128p. pap. 21.99 *(978-0-7385-7343-4(4))* Arcadia Publishing.

Eisenberg, Sherri. Brooklyn: Best Local Specialties, Markets, Recipes, Restaurants, & Events. 2010. (Food Lovers' Ser.). (ENG., Illus.). 328p. pap. 14.95 *(978-0-7627-5943-9(7)*, 1310033) Globe Pequot Pr., The.

Harrington, Steven P. & Rojo, Jaime. Brooklyn Street Art. 2008. (Illus.). 107p. 14.95 *(978-3-7913-3963-4(X))* Prestel Publishing.

Knutsen, Chris & Steiker, Valerie. Brooklyn Was Mine. 2008. (ENG.). 240p. (gr. 12-18). 15.00 *(978-1-59448-282-3(9)*, Riverhead Trade (Paperbacks)) Penguin Group (USA) Inc.

Koch, Jared. Clean Plates Brooklyn 2012: A Guide to the Healthiest, Tastiest, & Most Sustainable Restaurants for Vegetarians & Carnivores. 2011. (Clean Plates Ser.). (ENG., Illus.). 192p. pap. 14.95 ***(978-0-9821862-5-1(8))*** Craving Wellness.

Leifman, Michael. Brooklyn Bodeg. 2009. 132p. pap. 31.97 *(978-1-4269-1917-6(4))* Trafford Publishing.

Lind, Diana. Brooklyn Modern: Architecture, Interiors & Design. 2008. (ENG., Illus.). 226p. 45.00 *(978-0-8478-3043-5(8))* Rizzoli International Pubns., Inc.

Manbeck, John. Historic Photos of Brooklyn. 2008. (Historic Photos Ser.). (ENG.). 206p. 39.95 *(978-1-59652-435-4(9))* Turner Publishing Co.

Miller's New York As It Is, or Stranger's Guide-Book to the Cities of New York, Brooklyn & Adjacent Places: Comprising Notices of Every Object of In. 2006. 212p. per. 20.99 *(978-1-4255-1727-4(7))* MPublishing.

Not For Tourists. Not for Tourists Guide to Brooklyn, 7th Edition. 7th ed. 2010. (Not for Tourists Ser.). (ENG., Illus.). 236p. pap. 15.99 *(978-0-9825951-1-4(5))* Not For Tourists, Inc.

Not for Tourists Staff. Brooklyn 2009. 5th rev. ed. 2008. (ENG., Illus.). 224p. 14.95 *(978-0-9814887-1-4(4))* Not for Tourists, Inc.

Not For Tourists Staff. Brooklyn 2010. 2009. (Not for Tourists Guidebooks Ser.). (ENG., Illus.). 256p. pap. 14.99 *(978-0-9815591-9-3(0))* Not For Tourists, Inc.

Not For Tourists Staff. Not for Tourists Guide to Brooklyn: 2012. 2011. (ENG., Illus.). 224p. pap. 14.95 ***(978-1-61608-568-1(1)***, 608568, Not For Tourist) Skyhorse Publishing Co., Inc.

Not for Tourists Staff, creator. Not for Tourists Guide to Brooklyn. 3rd ed. 2006. (Not for Tourists Guide to Brooklyn Ser.). (Illus.). 186p. 9.95 *(978-0-9778031-0-1(4)*, Not For Tourists) Not for Tourists, Inc.

Onofri, Adrienne. Walking Brooklyn: 30 Tours Exploring Historical Legacies, Neighborhood Culture, Side Streets, & Waterways. 2007. (Walking Ser.). (ENG., Illus.). 320p. pap. 17.95 *(978-0-89997-430-9(9))* Wilderness Pr.

Regalbuto, Robert J., et al. Brooklyn: 22 Self-Guided Walking Tours from Greenpoint to Coney Island. 2009. (Weekend Walks Ser.). (ENG., Illus.). 256p. pap. 16.95 *(978-0-88150-806-2(3)*, 150806) Countryman Pr.

Roma, Thomas, photos by. Pictures for Books: Photographs by Thomas Roma, 1 vol. 2010. (ENG., Illus.). 136p. pap. 35.00 *(978-1-884919-25-1(1))* Columbia Univ., The Miriam & Ira D. Wallach Art Gallery.

Zagat Survey Staff, creator. Zagat Best of Brooklyn. 2007. (Zagat Survey: Best of Brooklyn Ser.). (ENG., Illus.). 220p. per. 12.95 *(978-1-57006-949-9(2))* Zagat Survey.

Zagat Survey Staff, ed. 2009 Brooklyn. 2008. (ENG.). 176p. pap. 12.95 *(978-1-60478-016-1(9))* Zagat Survey.

BROOKLYN (NEW YORK, N.Y.)—HISTORY

Arth, Diclement & Nino, Langiulli. Brooklyn Existentialism. 2008. (ENG.). 220p. pap. 28.00 *(978-0-929891-06-4(6))* Fidelity Pr.

Benardo, Leonard & Weiss, Jennifer. Brooklyn by Name: How the Neighborhoods, Streets, Parks, Bridges, & More Got Their Names. 2006. (ENG., Illus.). 256p. 65.00 *(978-0-8147-9945-1(0))*; per. 18.95 *(978-0-8147-9946-8(9))* New York Univ. Pr.

Branford Electric Railway Association. Brooklyn Streetcars. 2008. (Images of Rail Ser.). (ENG., Illus.). 128p. pap. 21.99 *(978-0-7385-5761-8(7))* Arcadia Publishing.

Ditta, Joseph. Gravesend, Brooklyn. 2009. (Then & Now Ser.). (ENG., Illus.). 96p. pap. 21.99 *(978-0-7385-6469-2(9))* Arcadia Publishing.

Duer, Stephen C. & Smith, Allan B. Cypress Hills Cemetery. 2010. (Images of America Ser.). (Illus.). 128p. pap. 21.99 *(978-0-7385-7343-4(4))* Arcadia Publishing.

Erenberg, Michael. A Flea Grows in Brooklyn: A Story about Growing up in the Fifties & Sixties. 2010. 182p. pap. 15.95 *(978-1-4327-5283-5(9))* Outskirts Pr., Inc.

Gabrielan, Randall. Greetings from Brooklyn. 2011. (Illus.). 128p. 29.99 ***(978-0-7643-3852-6(8)***, Schiffer Publishing Ltd) Schiffer Publishing, Ltd.

Golenbock, Peter. In the Country of Brooklyn: Inspiration to the World. 2008. (Illus.). 704p. 32.95 *(978-0-06-125381-2(2)*, Morrow, William & Co.) HarperCollins Pubs.

Hamm, Theodore & Cole, William, eds. Pieces of a Decade. 2010. 168p. 20.00 *(978-1-934029-29-9(7)*, Black Square Editions.

Kelly, Wilhelmena Rhodes. Crown Heights & Weeksville. 2009. (Images of America Ser.). (ENG., Illus.). 128p. pap. 21.99 *(978-0-7385-6598-9(9))* Arcadia Publishing.

Maloney, Jack. King for a Day in Brooklyn, New York, 1 vol. 2009. 133p. pap. 24.95 *(978-1-4489-2024-2(8))* PublishAmerica, Inc.

Manbeck, John. Historic Photos of Brooklyn. 2008. (Historic Photos Ser.). (ENG.). 206p. 39.95 *(978-1-59652-435-4(9))* Turner Publishing Co.

Manbeck, John B. Brooklyn, Historically Speaking. 2008. pap. 19.99 *(978-1-59629-500-1(7))* History Pr., The.

McGee, Bob. The Greatest Ballpark Ever: Ebbets Field & the Story of the Brooklyn Dodgers. 2006. (ENG., Illus.). 358p. per. 19.95 *(978-0-8135-3601-9(4))* Rutgers Univ. Pr.

Moorhouse, B-Ann & Silinonte, Joseph M., eds. Kings County, New York, Administration Proceedings 1817-1856. 2006. (Illus.). 360p. 32.50 *(978-1-877692-16-1(6))* New York Genealogical & Biographical Society, The.

Osman, Suleiman. The Invention of Brownstone Brooklyn: Gentrification & the Search for Authenticity in Postwar New York, 1 vol. 2011. (Illus.). 360p. 29.95 *(978-0-19-538731-5(7))* Oxford Univ. Pr., Inc.

Ruocco, Frances. True Love Grows in Brooklyn. 2010. 272p. (ENG.). 30.95 *(978-1-4502-3293-7(0))*; pap. 20.95 *(978-1-4502-3289-0(2))* iUniverse, Inc.

Tippins, Sherill. February House: The Story of W. H. Auden, Carson McCullers, Jane & Paul Bowles, Benjamin Britten, & Gypsy Rose Lee under One Roof in Brooklyn. 2006. (ENG., Illus.). 336p. pap. 18.95 *(978-0-618-71197-0(X))* Houghton Mifflin Harcourt Publishing Co.

Trezza, Frank. Brooklyn Steel-Blood Tenacity. 2007. 192p. per. 24.95 *(978-1-4241-8273-2(5))* PublishAmerica, Inc.

BROOKLYN, BATTLE OF, NEW YORK, N.Y., 1776

see Long Island, Battle of, New York, N.Y., 1776

BROOKLYN BRIDGE (NEW YORK, N.Y.)

Haw, Richard. Art of the Brooklyn Bridge: A Visual History. 2008. (Illus.). 280p. 60.00 *(978-0-415-95386-3(3))* Routledge.

—The Brooklyn Bridge: A Cultural History. 2008. (ENG., Illus.). 320p. pap. 19.95 *(978-0-8135-4350-5(9))* Rutgers Univ. Pr.

Manbeck, John. Historic Photos of the Brooklyn Bridge. 2009. (Historic Photos Ser.). (ENG.). 206p. 39.95 *(978-1-59652-525-2(8))* Turner Publishing Co.

McCullough, David. The Great Bridge: The Epic Story of the Building of the Brooklyn Bridge. 2012. (ENG., Illus.). 560p. 35.00 ***(978-1-4516-8323-3(5))*** Simon & Schuster.

Wood, John, ed. & intro. Hart Crane's the Bridge. 60th ltd. ed. 2007. *(978-1-892733-37-5(4))* 21st Editions, Inc.

B

BROOKLYN DODGERS (BASEBALL TEAM)
see also Los Angeles Dodgers (Baseball Team)

Allen, Maury. Brooklyn Remembered: The 1955 Days of the Dodgers. 2007. (Illus.). 213p. per. 16.95 *(978-1-59670-220-2(6))* Sports Publishing, LLC.

Breslin, Jimmy. Branch Rickey. 2011. (Penguin Lives Ser.). (ENG.). 160p. (gr. 12). 19.95 *(978-0-670-02249-6(7),* Viking Adult) Penguin Group (USA) Inc.

Breslin, Jimmy. Branch Rickey: A Life. 2012. (Penguin Lives Ser.). (ENG.). 160p. (gr. 12). 14.00 ***(978-0-14-312047-6(6),*** Penguin (Non-Classics)) Penguin Group (USA) Inc.

Crosby, Bonnie & D'Agostino, Dennis. Through a Blue Lens: The Brooklyn Dodger Photographs of Barney Stein, 1939-1957. 2007. (ENG., Illus.). 176p. 27.95 *(978-1-57243-952-8(1))* Triumph Bks.

D'Antonio, Michael. Forever Blue: The True Story of Walter O'Malley, Baseball's Most Controversial Owner & the Dodgers of Brooklyn & Los Angeles. 2010. (ENG.). 400p. (gr. 12-18). 16.00 *(978-1-59448-441-4(4),* Riverhead Trade (Paperbacks)) Penguin Group (USA) Inc.

Fornatale, Pete & Biegel, Brian. Miracle Ball: My Hunt for the Shot Heard 'Round the World. 2010. (ENG.). 256p. pap. 15.00 *(978-0-307-45269-6(7),* Three Rivers Pr.) Crown Publishing Group.

Golenbock, Peter. Bums: An Oral History of the Brooklyn Dodgers. 2010. (Dover Baseball Ser.). (ENG.). 544p. pap. 19.95 *(978-0-486-47735-0(5))* Dover Pubns., Inc.

Green, Ron, Jr., et al. 101 Reasons to Love the Dodgers. 2007. (ENG., Illus.). 120p. 15.95 *(978-1-58479-565-0(4))* Stewart, Tabori & Chang.

Gulas, Greg, Sr., told to. My Memories as a Brooklyn Dodger: By George Shotgun Shuba, as told to Greg Gulas. 2007. (Illus.). 230p. per. 20.00 *(978-0-615-15274-5(0))* George Shotgun Shuba Family Enterprise.

Johnson, Rody. The Rise & Fall of Dodgertown: 60 Years of Baseball in Vero Beach. 2008. (ENG., Illus.). 256p. 24.95 *(978-0-8130-3194-1(X))* Univ. Pr. of Florida.

Kahn, Roger. The Boys of Summer. 2011. 14.42 *(978-0-7848-3571-5(3),* Everbind) Marco Bk. Co.

Lanctot, Neil. Campy: The Two Lives of Roy Campanella. 2011. (ENG., Illus.). 528p. 28.00 *(978-1-4165-4704-4(5))* Simon & Schuster.

Lowenfish, Lee. Branch Rickey: Baseball's Ferocious Gentleman. 2009. (ENG., Illus.). 728p. pap. 24.95 *(978-0-8032-2453-7(2),* Bison Bks.) Univ. of Nebraska Pr.

Marzano, Rudy. The Last Years of the Brooklyn Dodgers: A History, 1950-1957. 2007. (ENG., Illus.). 216p. per. 29.95 *(978-0-7864-3006-2(0))* McFarland & Co., Inc. Pubs.

—New York Baseball In 1951: The Dodgers, the Giants, the Yankees & the Telescope. 2011. (ENG., Illus.). 208p. pap. 29.95 *(978-0-7864-4830-2(X))* McFarland & Co., Inc. Pubs.

McGee, Bob. The Greatest Ballpark Ever: Ebbets Field & the Story of the Brooklyn Dodgers. 2006. (ENG., Illus.). 358p. per. 19.95 *(978-0-8135-3601-9(4))* Rutgers Univ. Pr.

Mele, Andrew Paul, ed. A Brooklyn Dodgers Reader. alt. ed. 2010. (ENG., Illus.). 287p. pap. 39.95 *(978-0-7864-6108-0(X))* McFarland & Co., Inc. Pubs.

Nordell, John, Jr. Brooklyn Dodgers: The Last Great Pennant Drive 1957. 2nd ed. 2007. (Illus.). 120p. per. 14.95 *(978-0-9795045-4-9(6))* Tribute Bks.

Nordell, John R. Brooklyn Dodgers: The Last Great Pennant Drive 1957. 2007. 120p. per. 14.95 *(978-0-9765072-9-1(3))* Tribute Bks.

Paper, Lew. Perfect: Don Larsen's Miraculous World Series Game & the Men Who Made It Happen. 2010. (ENG.). 432p. (gr. 12). 15.00 *(978-0-451-23123-9(6),* N A L Trade) Penguin Group (USA) Inc.

Reed, Ted. Carl Furillo, Brooklyn Dodgers All-Star. 2010. (ENG., Illus.). 210p. pap. 29.95 *(978-0-7864-4709-1(5))* McFarland & Co., Inc. Pubs.

Shafer, Ronald G. When the Dodgers Were Bridegrooms: Gunner Mcgunnigle & Brooklyn's Back-to-Back Pennants of 1889 And 1890. 2011. (ENG., Illus.). 212p. pap. 29.95 *(978-0-7864-5899-8(2))* McFarland & Co., Inc. Pubs.

Society for American Baseball Research Staff. The Team That Forever Changed Baseball & America: The 1947 Brooklyn Dodgers. Spatz, Lyle et al, eds. 2012. (Memorable Teams in Baseball History Ser.). (ENG., Illus.). 400p. pap. 26.95 ***(978-0-8032-3992-0(0))*** Univ. of Nebraska Pr.

Travers, Steven. Dodgers Essential: Everything You Need to Know to Be a Real Fan! 2007. (Essential (Triumph) Ser.). (ENG., Illus.). 224p. 19.95 *(978-1-57243-942-9(4))* Triumph Bks.

Vitti, Jim. Brooklyn Dodgers in Cuba. 2011. (Images of Baseball Ser.). (Illus.). 128p. pap. 21.99 *(978-0-7385-7427-1(9))* Arcadia Publishing.

Weisman, Jon. 100 Things Dodgers Fans Should Know & Do Before They Die. 2009. (100 Things... Fans Should Know Ser.). (ENG.). 320p. pap. 14.95 *(978-1-60078-166-7(7))* Triumph Bks.

Ziegel, Vic. Summer in the City: New York Baseball 1947-1957. Guglberger, Claus, ed. 2006. (ENG., Illus.). 192p. 17.98 *(978-0-8109-8257-4(9))* Abrams.

BROOKS, GWENDOLYN, 1917-2000

Brooks, Gwendolyn. Report from Part Two, Vol. 2. 170p. 14.95 *(978-0-88378-164-7(6))* Third World Press.

Kitta, Gergely. Gwendolyn Brooks's Poetry. 2008. 64p. pap. *(978-3-639-00599-8(6))* VDM Verlag Dr. Mueller e.K.

Mickle, Mildred R., ed. Gwendolyn Brooks. 2009. (Critical Insights Ser.). 416p. lib. bdg. 85.00 *(978-1-58765-632-3(9))* Salem Pr., Inc.

Saber, Yomna Mohamed. Brave to Be Involved: Shifting Positions in the Poetry of Gwendolyn Brooks. 2010. 211p. pap. 57.95 *(978-3-0343-0504-4(4))* Lang, Peter Publishing, Inc.

BROOKS, LOUISE, 1905-1985

Wahl, Jan & Brooks, Louise. Dear Stinkpot: Letters from Louise Brooks. 2009. 244p. pap. 21.95 *(978-1-59393-474-3(2))* BearManor Media.

BROTHELS
see Prostitution

BROTHERHOOD
see Brotherhoods; Brotherliness

BROTHERHOODS
see also Monasticism and Religious Orders

Blauner, Andrew, ed. Brothers: 26 Stories of Love & Rivalry. 2010. (ENG.). 304p. pap. 16.95 *(978-0-470-59964-8(2),* Jossey-Bass) Wiley, John & Sons, Inc.

Duncan, Thomas. E Clampus Vitus: Anthology of New Dispensation Lore. 2009. (Illus.). 464p. pap. 40.05 *(978-0-557-03084-2(6))* Lulu Enterprises Inc.

Exama, Aroll. The Colour of the Skin - Between Myth & Science. 2010. 116p. pap. 10.50 *(978-1-60911-799-3(9),* Eloquent Bks.) AEG Literary Publishing Services, Inc.

Kelly, Devon. The Bull Within: A story of brotherhood, growing up, & Running. 2011. 124p. pap. 12.33 ***(978-1-4269-6543-2(5))*** Trafford Publishing.

Kiddy, Elizabeth W. Blacks of the Rosary: Memory & History in Minas Gerais, Brazil. 2007. (ENG., Illus.). 328p. pap. 27.00 *(978-0-271-02694-7(4))* Pennsylvania State Univ. Pr.

Nickless, Rebekah. It's Big Brother Time. 2009. 16p. pap. 8.75 *(978-1-4490-4053-6(5))* AuthorHouse.

Rae, Malcolm. Battle. 2011. 12p. pap. 12.99 ***(978-1-4269-6814-3(0))*** Trafford Publishing.

Roerich, Nicholas. Brotherhood 1937. 2007. (ENG.). 320p. 45.95 *(978-0-548-07729-0(0))* Kessinger Publishing, LLC.

Selassie Star Staff. The Illuminated Holy Spirit: Commentaries of Venerable Wisdom. 2007. (ENG.). 100p. per. 16.95 *(978-1-4137-9493-9(9))* PublishAmerica, Inc.

BROTHERLINESS

Benson, Ezra Taft. The Threat of Communism: World Brotherhood. 2011. 36p. 35.95 ***(978-1-258-00760-7(6))*** Literary Licensing, LLC.

Egziabher, Haile Gebre. Dream for World Unity. 2009. 610p. pap. 34.95 *(978-1-4327-3554-8(3))* Outskirts Pr., Inc.

Goodman, Lenn E. & Goodman, Lenn Evan. Love Thy Neighbor as Thyself. 2008. (ENG.). 256p. 55.00 *(978-0-19-532882-0(5))* Oxford Univ. Pr., Inc.

Linnik, Philip S. Brotherhood of Men: A Fact-Finding Report to Mr. & Mrs. America. 2011. 142p. 40.95 ***(978-1-258-07482-1(6))*** Literary Licensing, LLC.

Podany, Amanda H. Brotherhood of Kings: How International Relations Shaped the Ancient near East, 1 vol. 2010. (ENG., Illus.). 432p. 34.95 *(978-0-19-531398-7(4))* Oxford Univ. Pr., Inc.

Tadros, Mariz & Habib, Akram. The Muslim Brotherhood & Islamist Politics in the Middle East. 2012. (Durham Modern Middle East & Islamic World Ser.). (ENG.). 208p. (C). 145.00 *(978-0-415-46596-0(6))* Routledge.

Weiss, Avraham. Spiritual Activism: A Jewish Guide to Leadership & Repairing the World. 2008. 193p. 24.99 *(978-1-58023-355-2(4))* Jewish Lights Publishing.

BROTHERS

Adams, Max. The Prometheans: John Martin & the generation that stole the Future. 2010. (ENG., Illus.). 336p. pap. 15.95 *(978-1-84916-173-2(9))* Quercus GBR. Dist: Independent Pubs. Group.

Anton, Babette. An East Tennessee Nightmare Lying in Wait. 2008. 184p. 26.95 *(978-0-595-51658-2(0));* pap. 16.95 *(978-0-595-52718-2(3))* iUniverse, Inc.

Backland, Ged. You're a Great Brother Because... 2011. (Suga-Lumps Ser.). (ENG., Illus.). 64p. 8.95 ***(978-0-09-193827-7(9))*** Ebury Publishing GBR. Dist: Independent Pubs. Group.

Banyai, Peter David & Banyai, Louis Kiraly. Stories from the Lou! Stories from the Lives of Two Hungarian-American Brothers. 2007. 172p. 25.95 *(978-0-595-69814-1(X));* per. 15.95 *(978-0-595-45913-1(7))* iUniverse, Inc.

Berrigan, Philip & Wilcox, Fred A. Fighting the Lamb's War: Skirmishes with the American Empire. 2011. 242p. pap. 17.95 ***(978-1-4502-7973-4(2))*** iUniverse, Inc.

Bierdz, Thom. Forgiving Troy. 2009. 288p. pap. 14.95 *(978-1-61539-485-2(0))* Independent Pub.

Bird, Roy. The Better Brother: The Life of Thomas Ward Custer: Tom & George Custer & the Battle for the American West. 2011. (ENG., Illus.). 304p. pap. 19.95 *(978-1-59652-770-6(6))* Turner Publishing Co.

Brian Shawn. Downhill from the Projects. 2009. 528p. pap. 19.86 *(978-1-4269-2130-8(6))* Trafford Publishing.

Brown, Roi. I Am, Roi. 2007. (Illus.). 412p. pap. 33.99 *(978-1-4251-6719-6(5))* Trafford Publishing.

Brown, Roi Joseph. I Am, Roi. 2007. (Illus.). 412p. pap. 25.80 *(978-1-4251-0650-8(1))* Trafford Publishing.

Burket, Joshua. Overcoming the Loss of a Loved One Who Has Truly Inspired. 2011. 90p. pap. 19.95 ***(978-1-4560-5922-4(X))*** PublishAmerica, Inc.

Colle, Jon. Adventures in the Ditch: A Memoir of Family, Navigation, & Discovery on the Intracoastal Waterway. 2011. 208p. pap. 14.95 *(978-1-936236-51-0(6))* iUniverse, Inc.

Conrardy, Galen. Growing up with Roy. 2007. 239p. pap. 14.84 *(978-1-4116-8533-8(4))* Lulu Enterprises Inc.

Danberry, Kenneth. Three Brothers. 2009. 80p. pap. 11.49 *(978-1-4389-4207-0(9))* AuthorHouse.

Dew, Kendra, photos by. Brother: What Would I Do Without You ? 2010. (Illus.). 64p. pap. 9.95 *(978-1-4162-0610-1(8))* Sellers Publishing, Inc.

Dornstein, Ken. The Boy Who Fell Out of the Sky: A True Story. 2007. (Vintage Ser.). (ENG.). 352p. pap. 13.95 *(978-0-375-70769-8(7),* Vintage) Knopf Doubleday Publishing Group.

Dubuc, Jean-Guy. Brother Andre: Friend of the Suffering, Apostle of Saint Joseph. 2010. (Illus.). 260p. pap. 16.95 *(978-1-59471-190-9(9))* Ave Maria Pr.

Duddridge, Lew. The Flying Duddridges of Hanley. 2011. 320p. 29.11 ***(978-1-4269-6654-5(7));*** pap. 19.11 ***(978-1-4269-6653-8(9))*** Trafford Publishing.

Ebard, Peter. The Tales of Fatman's Brother. 2009. 322p. pap. 21.69 *(978-1-4251-8331-8(X))* Trafford Publishing.

Eggers, Dave. A Heartbreaking Work of Staggering Genius: A Memoir Based on a True Story. *(978-0-676-80884-1(0),* Vintage) Knopf Doubleday Publishing Group.

Exley, Helen. To A Very Special Brother. 2009. (ENG., Illus.). 32p. 8.95 *(978-1-84634-290-5(2))* Exley, Helen Giftbooks GBR. Dist: National Bk. Network.

Faulkner, John. My Brother Bill. 2010. pap. 22.50 *(978-1-57003-933-1(X))* Univ. of South Carolina Pr.

Fiennes, William. The Music Room: A Memoir. (ENG.). 2010. 216p. pap. 14.95 *(978-0-393-33878-2(9),* 33878) 2009. 224p. 24.95 *(978-0-393-07258-7(4),* 7258) Norton, W. W. & Co., Inc.

Finn, Mickey. In My Own Words (Still Running) 2011. 228p. pap. 17.09 ***(978-1-4567-7999-3(0))*** AuthorHouse.

Franks, Norman & Muggleto. Raw Courage. 2011. (Illus.). 224p. 39.95 ***(978-1-908117-13-7(3))*** Grub Street GBR. Dist: Casemate Pubs. & Bk. Distributors, LLC.

Garduño, Meg. Immaculate Immigrant: The Virgin of Guadalupe in Los Angeles: Reflections & Meditations. 2010. 136p. pap. 28.72 *(978-1-4269-1660-1(4))* Trafford Publishing.

Giesick, Dalton. Brotherly Love. 2011. 108p. pap. 11.92 ***(978-1-4269-9614-6(4))*** Trafford Publishing.

Gonzales, John. Intimate Grief: My Struggle with ALD. 2011. 224p. pap. 24.95 ***(978-1-4560-7629-0(9))*** PublishAmerica, Inc.

Gossai, Hemchand. A Requiem for Neil. 2009. 124p. 24.95 *(978-1-60860-025-0(4),* Strategic Bk. Publishing) AEG Literary Publishing Services, Inc.

Greenfeld, Karl Taro. Boy Alone: A Brother's Memoir. 2010. (ENG.). 352p. pap. 14.99 *(978-0-06-113667-2(0),* HarperPerennial) 2009. 552p. pap. 25.99 *(978-0-06-177489-8(8),* HarperLuxe) HarperCollins Pubs.

Greenwald, Jeff. Snake Lake. 2010. (ENG.). 384p. 28.00 *(978-1-58243-612-8(6));* pap. 15.95 *(978-1-58243-649-4(5))* Counterpoint LLC. (Counterpoint).

Hada, Ken. The River White: A Confluence of Brush & Quill. 2011. (Illus.). 116p. pap. 30.00 ***(978-0-9833052-6-2(9))*** Mongrel Empire Pr.

Hallwas, John. Dime Novel Desperadoes: The Notorious Maxwell Brothers. 2011. (ENG., Illus.). 448p. pap. 25.00 *(978-0-252-07804-0(7))* Univ. of Illinois Pr.

Himmler, Katrin. The Himmler Brothers: A German Family History. (ENG., Illus.). 2008. 352p. pap. 14.95 *(978-0-330-44814-7(5))* 2007. 334p. 29.95 *(978-0-230-52907-6(0))* Macmillan Pubs., Ltd. GBR. Dist: Independent Pubs. Group.

Keenan, Donal. Brothers in Sport - Gaa. 2011. (ENG., Illus.). 320p. pap. 26.95 *(978-1-85635-695-4(7))* Mercier Pr., Ltd., The IRL. Dist: Dufour Editions, Inc.

Kelsey, Kerck. Remarkable Americans: The Washburn Family. 2010. (Illus.). 402p. 25.95 *(978-0-88448-299-4(5))* Tilbury Hse. Pubs.

L. Waiters, Kevan. Brother to Brother: The Miracle of Family. 2010. pap. 16.99 *(978-1-61663-344-8(1))* Tate Publishing & Enterprises, LLC.

Livingston, David & Livingston, James. Blood over Water. 2011. (ENG.). 320p. 18.50 *(978-1-4088-0119-2(1))* Bloomsbury Publishing.

Lucas, Margaret Jean Lottie. My Brother, My Angel: His Kidney Saved My Life. 2006. 141p. pap. 24.95 *(978-1-4241-3074-0(3))* PublishAmerica, Inc.

Mamburay, Yankuba. The Search for a Lost Brother, 1 vol. 2009. 108p. pap. 16.95 *(978-1-60703-966-2(4))* PublishAmerica, Inc.

Mangieri, M. P. F. My Brother Peter: He Belonged to the Greatest Generation. 2007. 108p. per. 13.00 *(978-1-4120-9967-7(6))* Trafford Publishing.

McGwire, Jay. Mark & Me: Mark McGwire & the Truth Behind Baseball's Worst-Kept Secret. 2010. (ENG.). 208p. 24.95 *(978-1-60078-308-1(2))* Triumph Bks.

Mercer, Bud. Tripping the Light Fantastic: Through the Evolution of Show Business from Vaudeville to MTV. 2007. 204p. per. 18.95 *(978-0-9778311-7-3(5))* Joshua Tree Publishing.

Morgan, Richard L., et al. Dear Brothers: Letters Facing Death. 2009. 72p. pap. 10.00 *(978-1-60899-275-1(6),* Resource Pubns.) Wipf & Stock Pubs.

Motier, Donald. Gerard: The Influence of Jack Kerouac's Brother on His Life & Writing, 1 vol. 2010. 66p. pap. 19.95 *(978-1-4489-5519-0(X))* PublishAmerica, Inc.

Oja, Dan. Ordinary Heroes: Six Stars in the Window. Parsons, June, ed. 2008. (Illus.). 272p. 29.95 *(978-0-9817823-0-0(2))* MediaTechnics Corp.

Pines, Paul. My Brother's Madness: A Memoir. 2007. (ENG.). 318p. per. 15.95 *(978-1-931896-34-4(8))* Curbstone Pr.

Pomper, Philip. Lenin's Brother: The Origins of the October Revolution. 2010. (ENG., Illus.). 304p. 24.95 *(978-0-393-07079-8(4),* 7079) Norton, W. W. & Co., Inc.

Radford, D. Evans. Dry Eyes of Innocence. 2008. 128p. 23.00 *(978-1-934925-27-0(6));* pap. 14.99 *(978-1-934925-19-5(5))* AEG Literary Publishing Services, Inc. (Strategic Bk. Publishing).

Ross, D. Reid. Lincoln's Veteran Volunteers Win the War: The Hudson Valley's Ross Brothers & the Union's Fight for Emancipation. (Illus.). 470p. 2011. pap. 29.95 ***(978-0-7914-7642-0(1),*** Suny Pr.) 2008. 40.00 *(978-0-7914-7641-3(3))* State Univ. of New York Pr.

Seiders-Metz, Margaret. The Four Daredevils. 2010. 84p. pap. 9.25 *(978-1-935125-96-9(6))* Robertson Publishing.

Sharp, Dave. Complete Surrender. 2009. (ENG., Illus.). 264p. pap. 14.95 *(978-1-84454-767-8(1))* Blake, John Publishing, Ltd. GBR. Dist: Independent Pubs. Group.

—Complete Surrender: The True Story of a Family's Dark Secret & the Brothers It Tore Apart at Birth. 2008. (ENG., Illus.). 288p. 29.95 *(978-1-84454-582-7(2))* Blake, John Publishing, Ltd. GBR. Dist: Independent Pubs. Group.

Shelton, Jeanette. In My Brother's Shadow: The Appalachian Way. 2010. 56p. pap. 10.16 *(978-1-4269-3129-1(8))* Trafford Publishing.

Sixta, Stephen, frwd. Our Father's Images: The Photography of Melvin Nelson. 2007. (Illus.). 80p. per. 22.00 *(978-0-9791092-0-1(5))* nxtwo I pr.

Stern, David, et al. Crosley: Two Brothers & a Business Empire That Transformed the Nation. 2008. (ENG.). 504p. pap. 15.95 *(978-1-57860-322-0(6))* Clerisy Pr.

Stowers, Carlton. Oh Brother, How They Played the Game: The Story of Texas' Greatest All-Brothers Baseball Team. 2007. (Texas Heritage Ser.). (ENG., Illus.). 80p. 14.95 *(978-1-933337-13-5(3))* State Hse. Pr.

Thomas, Louisa. Conscience: Two Soldiers, Two Pacifists, One Family — A Test of Will & Faith in World War I. 2011. (ENG., Illus.). 336p. (gr. 12). 25.95 *(978-1-59420-294-0(X),* Penguin Pr. HC, The) Penguin Group (USA) Inc.

Thomas, Louisa. Conscience: Two Soldiers, Two Pacifists, One Family — a Test of Will andFaith in World War I. 2012. (ENG., Illus.). 336p. (gr. 12). pap. 16.00 ***(978-0-14-312099-5(9),*** Penguin (Non-Classics)) Penguin Group (USA) Inc.

Titone, Nora. My Thoughts Be Bloody: The Bitter Rivalry That Led to the Assassination of Abraham Lincoln. 2011. (ENG.). 496p. pap. 16.00 *(978-1-4165-8606-7(7),* Free Pr.) Free Pr.

Toompas, Stephen E. & Toompas, Stanley E. I'm the One the Other Isn't: The Stevie-Stanley Stories. 2011. (ENG., Illus.). 141p. 19.95 ***(978-0-938467-20-5(4))*** Headline Bks.

Ureneck, Lou. Cabin: Two Brothers, a Dream, & Five Acres in Maine. (ENG.). 256p. (gr. 12). 2012. pap. 15.00 ***(978-0-14-312208-1(8),*** Penguin (Non-Classics)) 2011. 25.95 *(978-0-670-02294-6(2),* Viking Adult) Penguin Group (USA) Inc.

Walsh, Michael. Brothers in War. l.t. ed. 2008. 512p. 29.99 *(978-0-7531-9423-2(6))* ISIS Audio Bks. GBR. Dist: Ulverscroft Large Print Bks., Ltd.

Whitney, Catherine. Soldiers Once: My Brother & the Lost Dreams of America's Veterans. (ENG.). 2013. 288p. pap. 16.00 *(978-0-306-81867-7(1))* 2009. (Illus.). 240p. 25.00 *(978-0-306-81788-5(8))* Da Capo Pr., Inc.

Williams, William Carlos & Krivak, Andrew. The Letters of William Carlos Williams to Edgar Irving Williams, 1902-1912. 2009. (Illus.). 400p. 65.00 *(978-0-8386-4148-4(2))* Fairleigh Dickinson Univ. Pr.

BROTHERS AND SISTERS
see also Brothers; Sibling Rivalry; Sisters; Twins

Adams, Elmo. Born in Union Station: Two Sisters & a Brother Remember. 2010. 128p. pap. 10.99 *(978-1-4520-4880-2(0))* AuthorHouse.

Albert, Elisa. Freud's Blind Spot: 23 Original Essays on Cherished, Estranged, Lost, Hurtful, Hopeful, Complicated Siblings. 2010. (ENG.). 288p. pap. 15.00 *(978-1-4391-5472-4(4),* Free Pr.) Free Pr.

Aronoff, Craig E., et al. Making Sibling Teams Work: The Next Generation. 2010. (Family Business Leadership Ser.). (ENG.). 104p. pap. 23.00 *(978-0-230-11108-0(4))* Palgrave Macmillan.

Barnhill, Ann Clinard. At Home in the Land of Oz: Autism, My Sister, & Me. 2007. (ENG., Illus.). 256p. per. *(978-1-84310-859-7(3))* Kingsley, Jessica Ltd.

Barron-Hauwaert, Suzanne. Bilingual Siblings: Language Use in Families. 2010. (Parents' & Teachers' Guides). (ENG., Illus.). 216p. 99.95 *(978-1-84769-327-3(X));* pap. 29.95 *(978-1-84769-326-6(1))* Multilingual Matters GBR. Dist: Univ. of Toronto Pr.

Bell, Debbie. Leave Us Alone & Let Us Shine. 2010. 68p. pap. 10.57 *(978-1-4269-3968-6(X))* Trafford Publishing.

Berman, Claire. When a Brother or Sister Dies: Looking Back, Moving Forward, 1 vol. 2009. 140p. 34.95 *(978-0-313-35528-8(2),* C35528, Praeger Pubs.) Greenwood Publishing Group, Inc.

Bermingham, Lucy. The Rascally Reality of Rosie B. 2011. pap. 8.99 ***(978-1-61777-415-7(4))*** Tate Publishing & Enterprises, LLC.

Bova, Ben. The Immortality Factor. 2012. (ENG.). 480p. pap. 14.99 *(978-0-7653-0642-5(5),* Tor Bks.) Doherty, Tom Assocs., LLC.

Buckle, Jennifer. Parenting after the Death of a Child: A Practitioner's Guide. 2010. (Series in Death, Dying & Bereavement Ser.). (ENG., Illus.). 226p. 41.95 *(978-0-415-99573-3(6))* Routledge.

CAD. Siblings as Agents of Socialization, Number 126, Winter 2009. 2009. pap. 29.00 *(978-0-470-60205-8(8),* Jossey-Bass) Wiley, John & Sons, Inc.

Campbell, Bobbie. Through it All, God Kept Me: A Candid Story of Feeling Unloved. 2007. 280p. per. 20.95 *(978-0-595-43457-2(6))* iUniverse, Inc.

Caspi, Jonathan. Sibling Development: Implications for Mental Health Practitioners Sibling Development: Implications for Mental Health Practitioners. 2010. *(978-0-8261-1752-6(X));* E-Book *(978-0-8261-1753-3(8))* Springer Publishing Co., Inc.

Chadwick, Ellis H. In the Footsteps of the Bront#235;s. 2011. (Cambridge Library Collection - Literary Studies). (ENG., Illus.). 604p. pap. 43.00 ***(978-1-108-03416-6(0))*** Cambridge Univ. Pr.

Christian, Jan. Leave No Brother Behind: A Sister's War Memoir. 2010. (ENG.). 224p. pap. 20.00 *(978-1-936400-49-2(9))* Mill City Pr., Inc.

Cress, Cathy Jo & Peterson, Kali Cress. Mom Loves You Best: Forgiving & Forging Sibling Relationships. 2010. (ENG.). 256p. pap. 14.95 (978-0-88282-321-8(3)) New Horizon Pr. Pubs., Inc.

DeVita-Raeburn, Elizabeth. The Empty Room: Surviving the Loss of a Brother or Sister at Any Age. 2006. 229p. reprint ed. 23.00 (978-1-4223-5484-1(9)) DIANE Publishing Co.

—The Empty Room: Understanding Sibling Loss. 2007. (ENG.). 240p. pap. 15.99 (978-0-7432-0152-0(3), Scribner) Scribner.

Devlin, Carol. What Do You Do with the Yolks? A Happy Childhood on the Prairie of Western Kansas. 2008. 264p. 29.95 (978-1-4401-1038-2(7)); pap. 19.95 (978-1-4401-1036-8(0)) iUniverse, Inc.

Diderich, Monique. Sibling Relationships in Step-Families: A Sociological Study. 2008. iii, 160p. (978-0-7734-4971-8(X)) Mellen, Edwin Pr., The.

Edward, Joyce. The Sibling Relationship: A Force for Growth & Conflict. 2010. xv, 215p. (978-0-7657-0734-5(9)); (ENG.). 214p. 60.00 (978-0-7657-0732-1(2)) Rowman & Littlefield Publishers, Inc. (Aronson, Jason).

Edwards, et al. Sibling Identity & Relationships: Sisters & Brothers. 2006. (Relationships & Resources Ser.). (ENG., Illus.). 144p. (C). 47.95 (978-0-415-33930-8(3)); 160.00 (978-0-415-33929-2(4)) Routledge.

Emery, Le Ann Goodrich. He's the What Now? The True Story of the Four Year Old Father Figure & His Older Daughter/Sister. 2010. 112p. pap. 10.99 (978-1-4520-1291-9(1)) AuthorHouse.

Enrick, Nathan. A True South African Story. 2011. 210p. 29.99 **(978-1-4628-7429-3(0))** Xlibris Corp.

Faber, Adele & Mazlish, Elaine. Siblings Without Rivalry: How to Help Your Children Live Together So You Can Live Too. 2012. (ENG.). 256p. pap. 15.95 **(978-0-393-34221-5(2)**, 34221) Norton, W. W. & Co., Inc.

Fay, Charles. How to Make the Best of Sibling Rivalry: As Seen on Public Television. 2009. 78p. pap. 11.95 (978-1-930429-98-7(3)) Love & Logic Institute, Inc.

Festle, Mary Jo. Second Wind: Oral Histories of Lung Transplant Survivors. 2012. (Palgrave Studies in Oral History Ser.). (ENG., Illus.). 280p. 90.00 **(978-0-230-34091-6(1))** Palgrave Macmillan.

Flannery, Denis. On Sibling Love Queer Attachment & American Writing. 2007. (Illus.). 184p. 114.95 (978-0-7546-5420-9(6)) Ashgate Publishing Co.

Gallagher, Peggy A., et al. Brothers & Sisters: An Special Part of Exceptional Families. 3rd ed. 2006. (Illus.). 367p. per. 24.95 (978-1-55766-719-9(5), 7195) Brookes, Paul H. Publishing Co.

Gandolfi, Claudine. Sisters. 2008. (Charming Petite Ser.). (Illus.). 80p. 5.95 (978-1-59359-894-5(7)) Peter Pauper Pr. Inc.

Geng, Steve. Thick As Thieves: A Brother, a Sister - A True Story of Two Turbulent Lives. 2008. (ENG.). 304p. pap. 15.00 (978-0-8050-8767-3(2), Holt Paperback) Holt, Henry & Co.

Giesick, Dalton. Brotherly Love. 2011. 108p. 21.92 **(978-1-4269-9615-3(2))** Trafford Publishing.

Grumbles, Sally & Stretcher, Virginia. Whoever Is There Decides. 2007. per. 14.99 (978-1-59872-853-8(9)) Instant Pub.

Hanson, Lisa & Kempskie, Heather. The Siblings' Busy Book: 200 Fun Activities for Kids of Different Ages. 2008. (Illus.). 448p. pap. (978-0-88166-530-7(4)) Meadowbrook Pr.

Hemphill, C. Dallett. Siblings: Brothers & Sisters in American History, 1 vol. 2011. (ENG., Illus.). 328p. 34.95 (978-0-19-975405-2(5)) Oxford Univ. Pr., Inc.

Heymann, C. David. American Legacy: The Story of John & Caroline Kennedy. 2008. (ENG., Illus.). 608p. pap. 34.99 (978-0-7434-9739-8(2), Beyond Words/Atria Bks.) Atria Bks.

Hill, Rhonda. Teenage Struggles. 2008. 168p. 29.99 (978-1-4363-7001-1(9)); pap. 19.99 (978-1-4363-7000-4(0)) Xlibris Corp.

Horn, Susan K. Life's B G Little Moments: Sisters & Brothers. 2008. (Life's BIG Little Moments Ser.). (ENG., Illus.). 96p. 9.95 (978-1-4027-5895-9(2)) Sterling Publishing Co., Inc.

Hunting, Jill. Finding Pete: Rediscovering the Brother I Lost in Vietnam. 2009. (ENG., Illus.). 324p. 24.95 (978-0-8195-6923-3(2)) Wesleyan Univ. Pr.

Isay, Jane. Mom Still Likes You Best: Overcoming the Past & Reconnecting with Your Siblings. 2011. 192p. pap. 14.95 (978-0-7679-2864-9(4), Anchor) Knopf Doubleday Publishing Group.

Ittel. Siblings in Adolescence. 2010. 240p. 71.95 (978-1-84169-703-1(6), Psychology Press) Taylor & Francis Group GBR. Dist: Taylor & Francis Group.

Johnson, Christopher H. & Sabean, David Warren. Sibling Relations & the Transformations of European Kinship, 1300-1900. 2011. 356p. 95.00 (978-1-84545-769-3(2)) Berghahn Bks., Inc.

Johnston, Brett A. Close Kids: Connect Your Children for Life. 2010. pap. 13.99 (978-1-61566-080-3(1)) Tate Publishing & Enterprises, LLC.

Kirkman, Rick & Scott, Jerry. Cut! 2011. (ENG.). 128p. pap. 14.99 (978-1-4494-0182-5(1)) Andrews McMeel Publishing.

Kiyosaki, Robert T., et al. Rich Brother - Rich Sister: Two Different Paths to God, Money & Happiness. 2009. (ENG., Illus.). 256p. 24.95 (978-1-59315-493-6(3)) Vanguard Pr.

Kluger, Jeffrey. The Sibling Effect: What the Bonds among Brothers & Sisters Reveal about Us. 2011. (ENG.). 320p. (gr. 12). 26.95 (978-1-59448-831-3(2), Riverhead Bks. (Hardcover)) Penguin Group (USA) Inc.

Kramer, Laurie & Conger, Katherine J., eds. Siblings As Agents of Socialization: New Directions for Child & Adolescent Development, No. 126. 2009. (J-B CAD Single Issue Child & Adolescent Development Ser.: 97). (ENG.). 120p. pap. 29.00 (978-0-470-61459-4(5), Jossey-Bass) Wiley, John & Sons, Inc.

Lang, Gregory E. Brothers & Sisters: 100 Reasons Our Relationship Is Like No Other. 2007. (ENG., Illus.). 128p. 14.95 (978-1-58182-511-4(0), Cumberland Hse.) Sourcebooks, Inc.

Larrinaga, April Faith. Tragedy to Triumph: A Memoir. 2011. 260p. 24.95 **(978-1-4634-3624-7(6))**; pap. 15.99 **(978-1-4634-3625-4(4))** AuthorHouse.

Larson, Beth. Shirley's Garden. 2009. 64p. pap. 19.50 (978-1-60693-095-3(8), Eloquent Bks.) AEG Literary Publishing Services, Inc.

Lehmkuhl, Ulrike. Instanzen Im Schatten: Väter, Geschwister, Bedeutsame Andere. 2006. (Beitrage zur Individualpsychologie Ser.). (GER., Illus.). 175p. (C). pap. 38.00 (978-3-525-45013-0(3)) Vandenhoeck & Ruprecht GmbH & Co. KG DEU. Dist: ISD.

Lewin, Vivienne & Sharp, Belinda, eds. Siblings in Development: A Psychoanalytic View. 2009. 192p. pap. 41.00 (978-1-85575-684-7(6)) Karnac Bks. GBR. Dist: Stylus Publishing, LLC.

Liffrig, Doris Hermundstad. Growing up Rich in A Poor Family: Childhood Memories from the Great Depression. 2011. 120p. pap. 12.95 **(978-1-4620-3209-9(5))** iUniverse, Inc.

Lingenfelter, Pat. For Raymond. 2007. 200p. per. 14.99 (978-1-60266-764-8(0)) Xulon Pr., Inc.

Mackey, Aurora, et al. Family Skeleton: A Brother & Sister's Journey from Murder to Truth. 2008. (ENG., Illus.). 224p. 24.95 (978-0-88282-295-2(0)) New Horizon Pr. Pubs., Inc.

Mae Stephenson Abernathy. We Wanted to Live. 2009. 140p. pap. 14.99 (978-1-4389-4650-4(3)) AuthorHouse.

Mally, Sarah. Making Brothers & Sisters Best Friends Coloring Book. 2008. (Illus.). 64p. (J). 7.00 (978-0-9719405-5-0(X)) Tomorrow's Forefathers, Inc.

Massenet, Ariane, et al. Frères & Soeurs: Ce Que Je Voudrais Te Dire- 2010. (FRE., Illus.). 226p. (978-2-7324-4279-2(8)) Editions de la Martiniere.

McKowen, Dahlynn, et al. Chicken Soup for the Soul Celebrating Brothers & Sisters: Funnies & Favorites about Growing up & Being Grown Up. 2007. (Chicken Soup for the Soul Ser.). (ENG., Illus.). 288p. pap. 14.95 (978-0-7573-0635-8(7)) Health Communications, Inc.

Milevsky, Avidan. Sibling Relationships in Childhood & Adolescence: Predictors & Outcomes. 2011. (ENG.). 176p. (gr. 17). pap. 29.50 (978-0-231-15709-4(6)); (Illus.). 89.50 (978-0-231-15708-7(8)) Columbia Univ. Pr.

Mills, Bruce & Cumberland, Debra, eds. Siblings & Autism: Stories Spanning Generations & Cultures. 2010. (ENG., Illus.). 240p. pap. (978-1-84905-831-5(8)) Kingsley, Jessica Ltd.

Murphy, Frank. Sister + Brother = TROUBLE (A Memoir) 2010. 87p. pap. 14.98 (978-0-557-28404-7(X)) Lulu Enterprises Inc.

Newton, Laura. Brothers & Sisters: Discovering the Psychology of Companionship. 2007. (Illus.). 214p. per. 24.95 (978-1-882670-71-0(X)) Spring Journal.

Nickless, Rebekah. It's Big Brother Time. 2009. 16p. pap. 8.75 (978-1-4490-4053-6(5)) AuthorHouse.

Oris, Michel. Les Fratries: Une Démographie Sociale de la Germanité. (FRE., Illus.). viii, 363p. pap. 66.95 (978-3-03911-255-5(4)) Lang, Peter Publishing, Inc.

Ostlere, Cathy. Lost: A Memoir. 2009. (ENG., Illus.). 256p. pap. 19.95 (978-1-55470-043-1(4)) Key Porter Bks. CAN. Dist: Perseus-PGW.

Pineda, Jon. Sleep in Me. (American Lives Ser.). (ENG.). 168p. 2012. pap. 14.95 **(978-0-8032-4341-5(3))** 2010. 21.95 (978-0-8032-2535-0(0)) Univ. of Nebraska Pr.

Pleasures, Onawa K. It's a Part of Life. 2011. 256p. pap. 16.75 (978-1-4269-3806-1(3)) Trafford Publishing.

Punches, Patricia Christian. Even When Life Doesn't Play Nice: One Child's Journey from Unfavorable Beginnings A Memoir. 2010. 108p. 24.95 (978-1-61507-301-6(9)) Cross Bks. Publishing.

Robbins, Carole Banks, ed. A Railroad Family in the Early 1920s. 2007. pap. (978-0-615-17228-5(8)) Robbins, Carole Banks.

Rowe. My Dearest Enemy, My Dearest Friend: Making & Breaking Sibling Bonds. 2007. 336p. 110.00 (978-0-415-39047-7(8)) Routledge.

Rowe, Dorothy. My Dearest Enemy, My Dangerous Friend: Making & Breaking Sibling Bonds. 2007. (ENG.). 376p. per. 18.00 (978-0-415-39048-4(6)) Routledge.

Safer, Jeanne. Cain's Legacy: Liberating Siblings from a Lifetime of Rage, Shame, Secrecy, & Regret. 2012. (ENG.). 288p. (gr. 9). 25.99 **(978-0-465-01940-3(4))** Basic Bks.

Sardella, Rebecca. My Brother Beth. 2007. pap. 10.00 (978-0-8059-8552-8(2)) Dorrance Publishing Co., Inc.

Schultz, Tori. Zach & Asperger Syndrome: A Sister's View of Her Brother. 2011. 20p. (gr. 1-2). pap. 13.00 **(978-1-4567-5044-2(5))** AuthorHouse.

Smith, Susan Livingston & Silverstein, Deborah N. Siblings in Adoption & Foster Care: Traumatic Separations & Honoured Connections. Silverstein, Deborah & Smith, Susan Livingston, eds. Silverstein, Deborah N., ed. 2008. (Illus.). 216p. 49.95 (978-0-313-35143-3(0), C35143, Praeger Pubs.) Greenwood Publishing Group, Inc.

Strohm, Kate. Being the Other One: Growing up with a Brother or Sister Who Has Special Needs. 2009. (ENG.). 249p. pap. 15.00 (978-1-4379-6612-1(8)) DIANE Publishing Co.

Talbot, David. Brothers: The Hidden History of the Kennedy Years. 2008. (ENG., Illus.). 496p. pap. 15.00 (978-0-7432-6919-3(5), Free Pr.) Free Pr.

Teal, James. The Life of Jimmy. 2011. 80p. pap. 10.95 (978-1-4502-8673-2(9)) iUniverse, Inc.

Thompson, Sue. The Prodigal Brother: Making Peace with Your Parents, Your Past, & the Wayward One in Your Family. 2010. 192p. (ENG.). 30.95 (978-1-4497-0054-6(3)); pap. 13.95 (978-1-4497-0053-9(5)) Author Solutions, Inc. (WestBow Pr.).

Tulcin, Doris F. Memoirs of a Monarch: A Chronicle of My Life. 2008. 120p. 22.95 (978-0-595-50694-1(1)); pap. 12.95 (978-0-595-50654-5(2)) iUniverse, Inc.

Umar, Pastor. How Great Is Your Fall? 2011. 128p. pap. 15.67 **(978-1-4567-8593-2(1))** AuthorHouse.

Vass, Larry Ivan. Hell's too Good for Some People: A Memoir. 2010. 256p. pap. 19.95 (978-1-4502-1663-0(3)) iUniverse, Inc.

Wayne, Mitchell. Used to Bad News. 2008. 136p. pap. 10.99 (978-1-4343-9864-2(1)) AuthorHouse.

Welch, Diana, et al. The Kids Are All Right: A Memoir. 2010. (ENG.). 368p. pap. 15.00 (978-0-307-39605-1(3), Three Rivers Pr.) Crown Publishing Group.

Whitehead, Caroline. Rowland: A Heart of Sunshine. 2011. 216p. pap. **(973-1-897435-54-0(1))** Agio Publishing Hse.

Williams, David. The Return of the Snowman in the Backyard. 2007. (ENG.). 48p. per. 10.00 (978-1-59926-257-4(6)) Xlibris Corp.

York, Sheri Garland. Two Brothers & Me. 2009. 32p. pap. 15.75 (978-1-4389-4682-5(1)) AuthorHouse.

BROTHERS AND SISTERS—JUVENILE LITERATURE

Page, Robin. Sisters & Brothers: Sibling Relationships in the Animal World. 2012. (ENG., Illus.). 32p. (J). (gr. k-3). pap. 6.99 **(978-0-547-72738-7(0)**, Sandpiper) Houghton Mifflin Harcourt Trade & Reference Pubs.

BROTHERS HOSPITALLERS OF SAINT JOHN OF GOD

Phillips, Simon. The Prior of the Knights Hospitaller in Late Medieval England. 2009. (Illus.). 224p. 90.00 (978-1-84383-437-3(5), Boydell Press) Boydell & Brewer, Ltd. GBR. Dist: Boydell & Brewer, Inc.

BROUGHAM AND VAUX, HENRY PETER BROUGHAM, BARON, 1778-1868

Brougham, Henry. Life & Times of Henry Lord Brougham Wr. 2006. pap. 26.99 (978-1-4255-3762-3(6)) MPublishing.

—The Life & Times of Henry, Lord Brougham, Written by Himself. 2006. 376p. per. 26.99 (978-1-4255-3991-7(2)) MPublishing.

—The Works of Henry, Lord Brougham & Vaux. reprint ed. 1375.00 (978-0-7222-9705-6(X)) Library Reprints, Inc.

BROUGHTON, JOHN CAM HOBHOUSE, BARON, 1786-1869

Broughton, John C. Recollections of a Long Life: With Additional Extracts from His Private Diaries, 6 vols., Set. Lady Dorchester, ed. reprint ed. 459.00 (978-0-404-03320-0(2)) AMS Pr., Inc.

BROWN, CAPABILITY, 1716-1783

see Brown, Lancelot, 1715-1783

BROWN, CHARLES BROCKDEN, 1771-1810

Axelrod, Alan. Charles Brockden Brown: An American Tale. 2011. (ENG.). 224p. pap. 25.00 (978-0-292-72954-4(5)) Univ. of Texas Pr.

Clark, David L. Charles Brockden Brown: Pioneer Voice of America. (BCL Ser.). reprint ed. 34.50 (978-0-404-01548-0(4)) AMS Pr., Inc.

Clark, David Lee. Brockden Brown & the Rights of Women. 2009. 52p. pap. 16.75 (978-1-113-63432-0(4)); pap. 17.75 (978-1-113-63433-7(2)) BiblioBazaar.

—Brockden Brown & the Rights of Women. 2007. (ENG.). 52p. per. 16.95 (978-0-548-57416-4(2)) Kessinger Publishing, LLC.

Dunlap, William. The Life of Charles Brockden Brown. 2009. 268p. pap. (978-1-150-76018-1(4)) Books LLC.

—The Life of Charles Brockden Brown. 2009. 314p. pap. 24.86 (978-1-150-18609-7(7)) General Bks. LLC.

Grabo, Norman S. The Coincidental Art of Charles Brockden Brown. 2011. (ENG.). 222p. pap. 40.00 **(978-0-8078-9672-3(1))** Univ. of North Carolina Pr.

Kamrath, Mark L. Historicism of Charles Brockde. 2009. 352p. 65.00 (978-1-60635-032-4(3)) Kent State Univ. Pr.

Levine, Robert S. Conspiracy & Romance: Studies in Brockden Brown, Cooper, Hawthorne, & Melville. 2009. (Cambridge Studies in American Literature & Culture Ser.). (ENG.). 316p. pap. 44.00 (978-0-521-09340-8(6)) Cambridge Univ. Pr.

Vilas, Martin Samuel. Charles Brockden Brown: A Study of Early American Fiction. 2009. 70p. pap. 16.75 (978-1-110-07576-8(6)) BiblioBazaar.

Weinstock, Jeffrey Andrew. Charles Brockden Brown. 2011. (University of Wales Press - Gothic Authors: Critical Revisions Ser.). (ENG.). 224p. pap. 30.00 (978-0-7083-2419-6(3)); 206p. 120.00 (978-0-7083-2420-2(7)) Univ. of Wales Pr. GBR. Dist: Chicago Distribution Ctr.

BROWN, CLAUDE, 1937-2002

Brown, Claude. Manchild in the Promised Land. 2012. (ENG.). 416p. 30.00 (978-1-4516-2667-4(3), Scribner) Scribner.

BROWN, DAN, 1964-

Beyer, Jr., Thomas R., Thomas R. 33 Keys to Unlocking the Lost Symbol: A Reader's Companion to the Dan Brown Novel. 2009. (ENG., Illus.). 176p. pap. 14.95 (978-1-55704-919-3(X), William Morrow Paperbacks) HarperCollins Pubs.

Burstein, Daniel & De Keijzer, Arne. Secrets of the Lost Symbol: The Unauthorized Guide to the Mysteries Behind the Da Vinci Code Sequel. 2010. 432p. pap. 15.99 (978-0-06-196497-8(2), Harper Paperbacks); 25.99 (978-0-06-196495-4(6), Morrow, William & Co.) HarperCollins Pubs.

Collins, Tim. Behind the Lost Symbol. 2010. (ENG., Illus.). 224p. (gr. 12). 15.00 (978-0-425-23721-2(4), Berkley Trade) Penguin Group (USA) Inc.

Cox, Simon. Decoding the Lost Symbol: The Unauthorized Expert Guide to the Facts Behind the Fiction. 2009. (ENG., Illus.). 256p. pap. 14.99 (978-0-7432-8727-2(4), Touchstone) Touchstone.

Greer, John Michael. Secrets of the Lost Symbol: The Unauthorized Guide to Secret Societies, Hidden Symbols & Mysticism. 2010. (ENG.). 240p. pap. 9.95 (978-0-7387-2169-9(7)) Llewellyn Pubns.

Hodapp, Christopher. Deciphering the Lost Symbol: Freemasons, Myths & the Mysteries of Washington D. C. 2010. (ENG., Illus.). 208p. pap. 12.95 (978-1-56975-773-4(9)) Ulysses Pr.

Körber, Joachim & Körber, Joachim. Die Wissenschaft bei Dan Brown. 2009. 307p. pap. (978-3-527-50417-6(6), VCH) Wiley, John & Sons, Ltd.

Loupan, Victor & Noël, Alain. Anges & Démons: L'enquête. 2009. 273p. (978-2-7509-0521-7(4)) Presses de la Renaissance.

Rhodes, Ron. Unlocking the Mysteries of The Lost Symbol. 2009. pap. (978-0-7369-1886-2(8)) Harvest Hse. Pubs.

Thomas, Graham A. The Dan Brown Enigma (Nt) 2011. (ENG., Illus.). 304p. 24.95 (978-1-84358-302-8(X)) Blake, John Publishing, Ltd. GBR. Dist: Independent Pubs. Group.

BROWN, DAN, 1964—DA VINCI CODE

Bell, Shirley. The Da Vinci Code: the Background Explained. 2008. 135p. pap. 15.95 (978-1-84799-638-1(8)) Lulu Enterprises Inc.

Bueno, Lorenzo Fernandez & Urresti, Mariano Fernandez. Keys to the Da Vinci Code: The Hidden Lineage of Jesus & Other Mysteries. 2010. (Illus.). 188p. 19.95 (978-1-59079-101-1(0)) Select Bks.

Dillon, John F. & McKeel, William J. Response to the DaVinci Code As Impression Management. 2007. (ENG.). 172p. (C). 94.95 (978-1-934043-68-4(0)) Cambria Pr.

Ingram, John. Beyond Da Vinci: The True Bride of Christ. 2010. 156p. 22.49 (978-1-4520-2327-4(1)) AuthorHouse.

Nicola, Metropolitan Bishop. The Real Holy Grail: An Orthodox Response to Dan Brown's Deceptions in Angles & Demons & the Da Vinci Code. 2007. 188p. per. 15.95 (978-1-933275-14-7(6), Orthodox Research Institute) Cocheco Falls Publishing.

Persaud, Christopher H. K. The Da Vinci Code Revisited: A conclusive refutation of the sinister, widespread Lie. 2010. 346p. 29.99 (978-1-4500-3488-3(8)); pap. 19.99 (978-1-4500-3487-6(X)) Xlibris Corp.

Plumer, Eric A. The Catholic Church & American Culture: Why the Claims of Dan Brown Strike a Chord. 2009. 340p. pap. 25.00 (978-1-58966-135-6(4)) Univ. of Scranton Pr.

Shugarts, David A. Secrets of the Widow's Son: The Real History Behind the Lost Symbol. Burstein, Dan ed. 2009. (ENG.). 224p. pap. 12.95 (978-1-4027-7729-5(9)) Sterling Publishing Co., Inc.

Theodorou, George. Black & White, & Brown: The Da Vinci Code Deception. 2006. 96p. pap. 15.95 (978-1-59800-577-6(4)) Outskirts Pr., Inc.

BROWN, FORD MADOX, 1821-1893

Ford, Ford Madox. Ford Madox Brown: A Record of His Life & Work. reprint ed. lib. bdg. 98.00 (978-0-7426-3058-1(7)) Classic Bks.

Skinner, Paul, ed. Ford Madox Ford's Literary Contacts. 2007. 271p. pap. 73.00 (978-90-420-2248-5(5)) Rodopi

Thirlwell, Angela. Into the Frame: The Four Loves of Ford Madox Brown. (ENG., Illus.). 2011. 336p. pap. 23.95 **(978-1-84413-914-9(X))** 2010. 328p. 39.95 (978-0-7011-7902-1(3), Chatto & Windus) Random Hse. GBR. Dist: Independent Pubs. Group.

Thirlwell, Angela, et al. Ford Madox Brown: The Unofficial Pre-Raphaelite. 2008. (ENG., Illus.). 72p. pap. 34.95 (978-1-904832-56-0(3)) Giles, D. Ltd. GBR. Dist: Antique Collectors' Club.

Treuherz, Julian. Ford Madox Brown: Pre-Raphaelite Pioneer. 2011. (ENG., Illus.). 336p. 55.00 **(978-0-85667-700-7(0))** Wilson, Philip Pubs., Ltd. GBR. Dist: Macmillan.

BROWN, GORDON, 1951-

Beckett, F. Gordon Brown. 2007. 240p. 30.00 (978-1-84275-213-5(8)) Politico's Publishing Ltd. GBR. Dist: Consortium Bk. Sales & Distribution.

Beckett, Francis. Gordon Brown: Past, Present & Future. 2007. (ENG., Illus.). 240p. pap. 18.95 (978-1-905791-14-9(3)) Haus Publishing GBR. Dist: Consortium Bk. Sales & Distribution.

Beech, Matt & Lee, Simon, eds. The Brown Government: A Policy Evaluation. 2009. 114p. 125.00 (978-0-415-54980-6(9)) Routledge.

Brown, Gordon. The Chance We Choose: Speeches, 2007-2009. 2010. (ENG.). 300p. 36.95 (978-1-84596-632-4(5)) Mainstream Publishing Co., Ltd. GBR. Dist: Independent Pubs. Group.

—Courage: Portraits of Bravery in the Service of Great Causes. 2009. (ENG.). 304p. pap. 15.95 (978-1-60285-075-9(0)) Perseus Bks. Group.

Harvie, Christopher. Broonland: The Last Days of Gordon Brown. 2010. (ENG.). 256p. pap. 17.95 (978-1-84467-439-8(8), 844439) Verso Bks. GBR. Dist: Norton, W. W. & Co., Inc.

Hughes, Colin, ed. What Went Wrong, Gordon Brown? How the Dream Job Turned Sour. 2010. (ENG.). 294p. pap. 16.95 (978-0-85265-219-0(4)) Random Hse. GBR. Dist: Independent Pubs. Group.

Lee, Simon. Best for Britain? The Politics & Legacy of Gordon Brown. 2007. (ENG.). 304p. 29.95 (978-1-85168-537-0(5)) Oneworld Pubns. GBR. Dist: National Bk. Network.

—Boom & Bust: The Politics & Legacy of Gordon Brown. 2009. (ENG.). 328p. pap. 16.95 (978-1-85168-664-3(9)) Oneworld Pubns. GBR. Dist: National Bk. Network.

Radice, Giles. Trio: Inside the Blair, Brown, Mandelson Project. 2010. (ENG., Illus.). 288p. 40.00 (978-1-84885-445-1(5)) I. B. Tauris & Co., Ltd. GBR. Dist: Macmillan.

Rush, Michael & Giddings, Philip James. When Gordon Took the Helm: The Palgrave Review of British Politics 2007-08. Rush, Michael & Giddings, Philip,

B

eds. 2008. (Palgrave Review of British Politics Ser.). (ENG., Illus.). 950p. 100.00 *(978-0-230-00260-9(9))* Palgrave Macmillan.

BROWN, J. GORDON (JAMES GORDON), 1951-
see Brown, Gordon, 1951-

BROWN, JAMES, 1933-2006
Brown, Geoff. The Life of James Brown: A Biography. 2008. (ENG., Illus.). 214p. per. 19.95 *(978-1-84609-958-8(7)*, OP51986) Omnibus Pr.
Danielsen, Anne. Presence & Pleasure: The Funk Grooves of James Brown & Parliament. 2006. (Music Culture Ser.). (ENG., Illus.). 280p. lib. bdg. 65.00 *(978-0-8195-6822-9(8))*; pap. 24.95 *(978-0-8195-6823-6(6))* Wesleyan Univ. Pr.
Munro, Martin. Different Drummers: Rhythm & Race in the Americas. 2010. (Music of the African Diaspora Ser.). (ENG.). 296p. 65.00 *(978-0-520-26282-9(4))*; pap. 27.50 *(978-0-520-26283-6(2))* Univ. of California Pr.
Scannell, John. James Brown. 2012. (Icons of Pop Music Ser.). (ENG., Illus.). 160p. (C). 90.00 ***(978-1-908049-92-6(8))***; pap. 24.95 ***(978-1-84553-743-2(2))*** Equinox Publishing Ltd. GBR. Dist: ISD.
Smith, R. J. The One: The Life & Music of James Brown. 2012. (ENG., Illus.). 464p. (gr. 12). 27.50 *(978-1-59240-657-9(2)*, Gotham) Penguin Group (USA) Inc.
Sullivan, James. The Hardest Working Man: How James Brown Saved the Soul of America. 2009. (ENG.). 256p. (gr. 12-18). 15.00 *(978-1-59240-490-2(1)*, Gotham) Penguin Group (USA) Inc.

BROWN, JIM, 1936-
Freeman, Mike. Jim Brown: The Fierce Life of an American Hero. 2007. (ENG.). 320p. pap. 14.99 *(978-0-06-077683-1(8))* HarperCollins Pubs.
—Jim Brown: The Fierce Life of an American Hero. 2011. cd-rom 29.95 *(978-0-9779883-8-9(4))* Legacy Audio Bks.
Toback, James. Jim: The Author's Self-Centered Memoir on the Great Jim Brown. 2009. (ENG.). 154p. pap. 25.00 *(978-0-9818056-3-4(9))* Rat Pr.

BROWN, JOHN, 1800-1859
see also Harpers Ferry (W. Va.)—History—John Brown's Raid, 1859
Anderson, Osborne Perry. A Voice from Harper's Ferry: A Narrative of Events at Harper's Ferry. 2009. 76p. pap. 16.75 *(978-1-110-11335-4(8))* BiblioBazaar.
—A Voice from Harper's Ferry: A Narrative of Events at Harper's Ferry. 2009. (ENG.). 75p. pap. 16.99 *(978-1-110-11332-3(3))*; pap. 18.99 *(978-1-110-11334-7(X))* BiblioBazaar. (BiblioLife).
—A Voice from Harper's Ferry; a Narrative of Events at Harper's Ferry: With Incidents Prior & Subsequent to Its Capture by Captain Brown And. 2010. (Illus.). 46p. pap. 14.14 *(978-1-154-48742-8(3))* General Bks. LLC.
Anderson, Osborne P[erry], creator. A Voice from Harper's Ferry a Narrative of Events at Harper's Ferry; 2010. 82p. pap. 17.75 *(978-1-176-01014-7(X))* BiblioBazaar.
Anderson, Osborne P[erry] 1830-1872 [F. A Voice from Harper's Ferry a Narrative of Events at Harper's Ferry; 2010. 82p. pap. 17.75 *(978-1-149-57128-6(4))* BiblioBazaar.
Andrew, John Albion. Speeches of John a Andrew at Hingham & Boston, Together with His Testimony Before the Harper's Ferry Committee of the Senate, in Relation to John B. 2011. 18p. pap. 11.99 ***(978-1-4181-9015-6(2))*** MPublishing.
Beck, Janet Kemper. Creating the John Brown Legend: Emerson, Thoreau, Douglass, Child & Higginson in Defense of the Raid on Harpers Ferry. 2009. (ENG., Illus.). 214p. pap. 35.00 *(978-0-7864-3345-2(0))* McFarland & Co., Inc. Pubs.
Biographiq. John Brown - American Abolitionist (Biography) 2008. 76p. pap. 9.99 *(978-1-59986-064-0(3)*, Biographiq) Filiquarian Publishing, LLC.
Brown, G. W. The Truth at Last: History Corrected; Reminiscences of Old John Brown. 80p. reprint ed. lib. bdg. 88.00 *(978-0-7222-4873-7(3))* Library Reprints, Inc.
Brown, John. Life & Letters of John Brown, Liberator of Kansas & Martyr of Virginia. 645p. reprint ed. 128.00 *(978-0-7222-9836-7(6))* Library Reprints, Inc.
Carson, Alexander. Reply to Mr Browns Vindication of the Pr. 2006. 456p. per. 42.00 *(978-1-57978-845-2(9))* Baptist Standard Bearer, Inc.
Carton, Evan. Patriotic Treason: John Brown & the Soul of America. 2009. (ENG., Illus.). 400p. pap. 19.95 *(978-0-8032-1946-5(6)*, Bison Bks.) Univ. of Nebraska Pr.
Chamberlin, Joseph Edgar. John Brown. (Beacon Biographies of Eminent Americans Ser.). 138p. reprint ed. 88.00 *(978-0-7222-8997-6(9))*; 88.00 *(978-0-7222-8522-0(1))* Library Reprints, Inc.
Connelley, William E. John Brown. 426p. reprint ed. lib. bdg. 98.00 *(978-0-7222-4889-8(X))* Library Reprints, Inc.
DeCaro, Louis A., Jr. John Brown: The Cost of Freedom. 2007. (Illus.). 192p. pap. 14.00 *(978-0-7178-0742-0(8))* International Publishers Co., Inc.
Du Bois, W. E. B. John Brown. 406p. reprint ed. 98.00 *(978-0-7222-9835-0(8))*; 98.00 *(978-0-7222-8437-7(3))* Library Reprints, Inc.
—John Brown. 2007. *(978-0-19-532574-4(5))* Oxford Univ. Pr., Inc.
Everhart, William C. & Sullivan, Arthur L. John Brown's Raid. 2009. *(978-1-57864-564-0(6))* Donning Co. Pubs.
Gilpin, Robert B. & Gilpin, R. Blakeslee. John Brown Still Lives! America's Long Reckoning with Violence, Equality, & Change. 2011. (ENG., Illus.). 304p. 30.00 *(978-0-8078-3501-2(3))* Univ. of North Carolina Pr.
Hawkins, Walter. Old John Brown: The Man Whose Soul Is Marching On. 2007. 48p. per. *(978-1-4068-1703-4(1))* Echo Library.
—Old John Brown: The Man whose Soul Is Marching On. 2007. 48p. per. *(978-1-4065-4371-1(3))* Dodo Pr.
Hinton, Richard J. John Brown & His Men; with Some Account of the Roads They Traveled to Reach Harper's Ferry, by Richard J Hinton. 2011. 756p. pap. 40.99 ***(978-1-4181-8929-7(4))*** MPublishing.
Hinton, Richard Josiah. John Brown & his Men. 2011. (ENG.). 756p. pap. 41.95 ***(978-1-4585-0106-6(X))*** Univ. of Michigan Library.
—John Brown & His Men: Accounts of the Roads They Traveled to Reach Harper's Ferry. (American Reformers Ser.). 752p. reprint ed. 148.00 *(978-0-7222-8998-3(7))* Library Reprints, Inc.
—John Brown & His Men: With Some Account of the Roads They Traveled to Reach Harper's Ferry. [Printed in the United States]. (Illus.). 752p. reprint ed. lib. bdg. 148.00 *(978-0-7222-4885-0(7))* Library Reprints, Inc.
Horwitz, Tony. Midnight Rising: John Brown & Raid That Sparked the Civil War. 2011. ***(978-1-4104-4186-7(5))*** Thorndike Pr.
Horwitz, Tony. Midnight Rising: John Brown & the Raid That Sparked the Civil Wa. 2011. (ENG., Illus.). 384p. 29.00 *(978-0-8050-9153-3(X))* Holt, Henry & Co.
John Brown's Raid. 70p. pap. 144.00 *(978-0-16-003422-0(1)*, Interior Dept.) United States Government Printing Office.
Lause, Mark A. Race & Radicalism in the Union Army. 2009. (ENG., Illus.). 216p. 45.00 *(978-0-252-03446-6(5))* Univ. of Illinois Pr.
Malin, James Claude. John Brown & the Legend of Fifty-Six. 2011. 820p. 75.95 ***(978-1-258-03418-4(2))*** Literary Licensing, LLC.
McGinty, Brian. John Brown's Trial. 2009. (Illus.). 384p. 27.95 *(978-0-674-03517-1(8))* Harvard Univ. Pr.
Nelson, Truman. The Old Man: John Brown at Harper's Ferry. 2009. (ENG., Illus.). 324p. pap. 17.00 *(978-1-931859-64-6(7))* Haymarket Bks.
Newton-Howitt, John. Captain John Brown of Harper's Ferry: A Preliminary Incident to the Great Civil War of America. 288p. reprint ed. 98.00 *(978-0-7222-9000-2(4))* Library Reprints, Inc.
Redpath, James. Echoes of Harper's Ferry. 2010. 526p. pap. 40.75 *(978-1-142-48494-1(7))* BiblioBazaar.
—Echoes of Harper's Ferry. 2009. 356p. pap. 25.88 *(978-1-151-11498-3(7))* General Bks. LLC.
—Echoes of Harper's Ferry. 2008. 520p. 55.95 *(978-1-4370-1018-3(0))*; pap. 40.95 *(978-1-4368-2880-2(5))* Kessinger Publishing, LLC.
Reynolds, David S. John Brown, Abolitionist: The Man Who Killed Slavery, Sparked the Civil War, & Seeded Civil Rights. 2006. (Vintage Ser.). (ENG., Illus.). 592p. per. 18.00 *(978-0-375-72615-6(2)*, Vintage) Knopf Doubleday Publishing Group.
Richman, Irving Berdine. John Brown Among the Quakers. 239p. reprint ed. 98.00 *(978-0-7222-9001-9(2))* Library Reprints, Inc.
Ronda, Bruce A. Reading the Old Man: John Brown in American Culture. 2008. (ENG., Illus.). 218p. 39.95 *(978-1-57233-620-9(X))* Univ. of Tennessee Pr.
Sanborn, Franklin Benjamin. John Brown. reprint ed. 150.00 *(978-0-7222-9002-6(0))* Library Reprints, Inc.
—John Brown & His Friends. 25p. reprint ed. 88.00 *(978-0-7222-9003-3(9))* Library Reprints, Inc.
—Recollections of Seventy Years. 2009. 124p. pap. *(978-1-151-27703-9(7))* Books LLC.
—Recollections of Seventy Years. 2009. 246p. pap. 19.99 *(978-0-217-98129-3(1))* General Bks. LLC.
—Recollections of Seventy Years, 2 vol., set. reprint ed. 250.00 *(978-0-7222-9004-0(7))* Library Reprints, Inc.
Stoneham, Michae. John Brown & the Era of Literary Confrontation. 2009. (Studies in American Popular History & Culture Ser.). (ENG.). 240p. 125.00 *(978-0-415-99682-2(1))* Routledge.
Sweets, Judy & DeCaro, Louis A., contrib. by. John Brown Photo Chronology: Catalog of the exhibition at Harpers Ferry 2009. 2009. (Illus.). 96p. pap. 45.00 *(978-0-9773638-7-2(2))* Allies for Freedom Pubs.
Thoreau, Henry David. A Plea for Captain John Brown. 2008. pap. 4.95 *(978-1-60545-129-9(0))* Quiet Vision Publishing.
—A Yankee in Canad: With Anti-Slavery & Reform Papers. 2007. 292p. 43.95 *(978-0-548-09280-4(X))* Kessinger Publishing, LLC.
Villard, Oswald Garrison. John Brown 1800-1859: A Biography after Fifty Years. 738p. reprint ed. 148.00 *(978-0-7222-9005-7(5))* Library Reprints, Inc.
Von Holst, Hermann E. John Brown. 232p. reprint ed. 98.00 *(978-0-7222-8999-0(5))* Library Reprints, Inc.
Warren, Robert Penn. John Brown: The Making of A Martyr. Warren, Robert Penn, ed. 2011. 496p. 58.95 ***(978-1-258-02933-3(2))*** Literary Licensing, LLC.
Wilson, Hill Peebles. John Brown, Soldier of Fortune: A Critique. 2007. 448p. 51.95 *(978-0-548-55684-9(9))*; (ENG.). per. 36.95 *(978-0-548-49337-3(5))* Kessinger Publishing, LLC.
—John Brown, Soldier of Fortune: A Critique. 450p. reprint ed. 98.00 *(978-0-7222-9006-4(3))* Library Reprints, Inc.

BROWN, JOSEPH EMERSON, 1821-1894
Speer, Emory. Lincoln, Lee, Grant, & Other Biographical Addresses. 2008. 284p. pap. *(978-1-4086-8446-7(2))* Read Bks.

BROWN, LANCELOT, 1715-1783
Mayer, Laura. Capability Brown & the English Landscape Garden. 2011. (Shire Library). (ENG., Illus.). 64p. pap. 12.95 *(978-0-7478-1049-0(4))* Shire Pubns., Ltd. GBR. Dist: Random Hse., Inc.

BROWN, LARRY
Cash, Jean W. Larry Brown: A Writer's Life. 2011. (Willie Morris Books in Memoir & Biography Ser.). (ENG., Illus.). 400p. 35.00 *(978-1-60473-980-0(0))* Univ. Pr. of Mississippi.
Cash, Jean W. & Perry, Keith, eds. Larry Brown & the Blue-Collar South. (ENG.). 240p. 2010. pap. 25.00 *(978-1-60473-860-5(X))* 2008. 50.00 *(978-1-934110-75-1(2))* Univ. Pr. of Mississippi.
Watson, Jay, ed. Conversations with Larry Brown. 2007. (ENG.). 202p. 50.00 *(978-1-57806-949-1(1))*; (Illus.). per. 22.00 *(978-1-57806-950-7(5))* Univ. Pr. of Mississippi.

BROWN, MOSES, 1738-1836
Hazelton, Robert Morton & Brown, Moses. Let Freedom Ring! a Biography of Moses Brown. 2011. 286p. 48.95 ***(978-1-258-03105-3(1))*** Literary Licensing, LLC.

BROWN, RITA MAE, 1944-
Brown, Rita Mae. Animal Magnetism: My Life with Creatures Great & Small. 2010. (ENG., Illus.). 256p. pap. 16.00 *(978-0-345-51180-5(8)*, Ballantine Bks.) Random House Publishing Group.
—Animal Magnetism: My Life with Creatures Great & Small. l.t. ed. 2010. (ENG.). 353p. 31.95 *(978-1-4104-2520-1(7))* Thorndike Pr.

BROWN, WILLIAM WELLS, 1814?-1884
Brown, William. Narrative of William W Brown, a Fugitive Slave. 2007. 96p. per. 8.75 *(978-1-60206-736-3(8))* Cosimo, Inc.
Brown, William Wells. Narrative of William W Brown: A Fugitive Slave. 2008. 64p. pap. *(978-1-4099-2556-9(0))* Dodo Pr.
—The Works of William Wells Brown: Using His Strong, Manly Voice. Robbins, Hollis & Garrett, Paula, eds. annot. ed. 2006. (ENG., Illus.). 519p. 115.00 *(978-0-19-530963-8(4))* Oxford Univ. Pr., Inc.
Brown, William Wells & Greenspan, Ezra. William Wells Brown: A Reader. Greenspan, Ezra, ed. 2008. (ENG., Illus.). 488p. pap. 24.95 *(978-0-8203-3224-6(0))*; lib. bdg. 64.95 *(978-0-8203-3223-9(2))* Univ. of Georgia Pr.
Ernest, John, ed. My Southern Home: The South & Its People. 2011. (ENG., Illus.). 288p. 69.95 *(978-0-8078-3511-1(0))*; pap. 27.95 *(978-0-8078-7208-6(3))* Univ. of North Carolina Pr.

BROWN BROTHERS, HARRIMAN & CO.
Brown, John Crosby. A Hundred Years of Merchant Banking. 2009. 246p. pap. *(978-0-217-34141-7(1))* Books LLC.
—A Hundred Years of Merchant Banking: A History of Brown Brothers & Company, Brown, Shipley & Company & the Allied Firms. Alexander Brown & Sons, 2010. 528p. pap. 40.75 *(978-1-146-61706-2(2))* BiblioBazaar.
—A Hundred Years of Merchant Banking, a History of Brown Brothers & Company, Brown, Shipley [and] Company & the Allied Firms, Alexander. 2010. 204p. pap. 28.76 *(978-1-152-32583-8(3))* General Bks. LLC.

BROWN COAL
see Lignite

BROWN FAMILY
Brown, Algie D. & Brown, Bryan T. Brown's Bulletin: Memoirs of a Louisiana Family on the Move, 1876-1973. 2008. (Illus.). 651p. *(978-0-578-00315-3(5))* Bodcau Publishing.
Brown, James. Scull's A Chapter of Family History: Sir William Brown Knight, 1556-1610 & Sir Nathaniel Rich Knight, -1636. Transcription, Notes & Index by James Brown. 2008. pap. 18.00 *(978-0-7884-4560-6(X))* Heritage Bks.
Brown, Joe. Brown Heritage. 2007. 276p. pap. *(978-0-9769106-2-6(4))* Haystack Pr.
Halberstadt, April Hope, et al. John Brown's Family in California: A Journey by Funeral Train, Covered Wagon, Through Archives, to the Valley of Heart's Delight. Libby, Jean, ed. enl. ed. 2006. 15.00 *(978-0-9773638-2-7(1))* Allies for Freedom Pubs.

BROWN-SEQUARD, CHARLES EDOUARD, 1817-1894
Aminoff, Michael J. Brown-Séquard: An Improbable Genius Who Transformed Medicine, 1 vol. 2010. (ENG., Illus.). 352p. 59.95 *(978-0-19-974263-9(4))* Oxford Univ. Pr., Inc.

BROWN UNIVERSITY
Brown University. The Laws of Brown University. 2011. 30p. pap. 11.99 ***(978-1-4181-9362-1(3))*** MPublishing.
Frazer, Colin, et al. Things, All Books May Be Recalled after 7 Days: Date Due, Apr. 9 2011. 2011. (Illus.). 82p. ***(978-0-615-47612-4(0))*** Brown, John Carter Library.
Kim, Justin & Kittay, Matthew. Brown University 2012: Off the Record. 2011. 188p. pap. 16.95 ***(978-1-4274-0357-5(0))*** College Prowler, Inc.
Kingsbury, Henry. The Secret Trial of Brown University: April 26-May 5, 2004. 2008. (Illus.). 135p. pap. ***(978-0-9769269-1-7(1))***, Full Quart Pr.) Holly Hall Pubns., Inc.
Wayland, Francis. A Memoir of the Life & Labors of Francis Wayland. 2009. 284p. pap. *(978-0-217-67251-1(5))*; 260p. pap. *(978-0-217-43242-9(5))*; 286p. pap. *(978-1-4590-2011-5(1))* Books LLC.
—A Memoir of the Life & Labors of Francis Wayland. 2006. 384p. per. 26.99 *(978-1-4255-4165-1(8))* MPublishing.

BROWN UNIVERSITY—HISTORY
Brown University Staff, contrib. by. Brown University in the Civil War: A Memorial. 2006. *(978-1-57898-558-6(7))* Martino Publishing.
Crane, Theodore Rawson. Francis Wayland: Political Economist As Educator. 2011. 48p. 35.95 ***(978-1-258-07802-7(3))*** Literary Licensing, LLC.
Guild, Reuben. Life, Times, & Correspondence of James Manning. 2010. 531p. pap. 31.95 *(978-1-4290-4353-3(9))* Applewood Bks.
Guild, Reuben Aldridge. Life, Times, & Correspondence of James Manning, & the Early History of Brown University by Reuben Aldridge Guild. 2006. 532p. per. 29.99 *(978-1-4255-5926-7(3))* MPublishing.
Harris, Rick. Brown University Baseball: A Legacy of the Game. 2012. 160p. pap. 19.99 ***(978-1-60949-501-5(2))*** History Pr., The.

BROWNE, CHARLES FARRAR, 1834-1867
see Ward, Artemus, 1834-1867

BROWNE, JOHN ROSS, 1821-1875
Browne, J. Ross (John Ross). Yusef; or the Journey of the Frangi a Crusade in the East by J Ross Browne. 2006. 432p. per. 26.99 *(978-1-4255-4742-4(7))* MPublishing.

BROWNE, THOMAS, SIR, 1605-1682
Anderton, Basil. Sketches from a Library Window. 2010. (ENG.). 196p. pap. 23.75 *(978-1-149-48710-5(0))* 2009. 188p. 30.99 *(978-1-116-86677-3(3))* 2009. 188p. 26.99 *(978-1-116-86678-0(1))* 2009. 188p. pap. 21.75 *(978-1-116-86680-3(3))* 2009. (ENG.). 187p. pap. 19.99 *(978-1-116-86682-7(X)*, BiblioLife) 2009. (ENG.). 187p. pap. 21.99 *(978-1-116-86681-0(1)*, BiblioLife) 2009. 188p. pap. 22.75 *(978-1-116-86679-7(X))* BiblioBazaar.
—Sketches from a Library Window. 2010. 122p. pap. 21.14 *(978-1-152-60857-3(6))* General Bks. LLC.
—Sketches from a Library Window. 2008. 192p. 37.95 *(978-1-4366-2971-3(3))*; pap. 22.95 *(978-0-548-87867-5(6))* Kessinger Publishing, LLC.
Barbour, Reid & Preston, Claire, eds. Sir Thomas Browne: The World Proposed. 2009. (ENG., Illus.). 320p. 135.00 *(978-0-19-923621-3(6))* Oxford Univ. Pr., Inc.
Bennett, Joan. Sir Thomas Browne: 'A Man of Achievement in Literature' 2010. (ENG.). 264p. pap. 23.99 *(978-0-521-14823-8(5))* Cambridge Univ. Pr.
Browne, Thomas. Works & Life of Thomas Browne, 4 vols. Wilkin, Simon, ed. reprint ed. 365.00 *(978-0-404-01150-5(0))* AMS Pr., Inc.
Dunn, William P. Sir Thomas Browne: A Study in Religious Philosophy. 2009. (ENG.). 194p. pap. 40.00 *(978-0-8166-5751-3(3))* Univ. of Minnesota Pr.
George, Edward Augustus. Seventeenth Century Men of Latitude: Forerunners of the New. 2007. (ENG.). 220p. per. 24.95 *(978-1-4304-4705-4(2))* Kessinger Publishing, LLC.
Gosse, Edmund. Sir Thomas Browne. 2009. 228p. 23.99 *(978-1-103-82707-7(3))*; 228p. pap. 17.99 *(978-1-103-82702-2(2))*; 224p. 23.99 *(978-1-103-56070-7(0))*; 224p. pap. 17.99 *(978-1-103-56068-4(9))* BiblioBazaar.
—Sir Thomas Browne. 2009. 142p. pap. *(978-0-217-99135-3(1))*; 136p. pap. *(978-0-217-99133-9(5))* Books LLC.
—Sir Thomas Browne. 2007. (ENG.). 228p. 41.95 *(978-0-548-12774-2(3))* 2006. pap. 26.95 *(978-1-4286-3772-6(9))* Kessinger Publishing, LLC.
Guibbory, Achsah. Ceremony & Community from Herbert to Milton: Literature, Religion, & Cultural Conflict in Seventeenth-Century England. 2006. (ENG.). 292p. pap. 58.00 *(978-0-521-03244-5(X))* Cambridge Univ. Pr.
Johnson, Samuel. Sir Thomas Brownes Christian Morals Wit. 2007. 240p. per. *(978-1-4067-8892-1(9)*, Pomona Pr.) Read Bks.
Killeen, Kevin. Biblical Scholarship, Science & Politics in Early Modern England: Thomas Browne & the Thorny Place of Knowledge. 2009. (Literary & Scientific Cultures of Early Modernity Ser.). (Illus.). 268p. 114.95 *(978-0-7546-5730-9(2))* Ashgate Publishing Co.
Marchitello, Howard. Narrative & Meaning in Early Modern England: Browne's Skull & Other Histories. 2007. (Cambridge Studies in Renaissance Literature & Culture Ser.). (ENG.). 248p. pap. 51.00 *(978-0-521-03686-3(0))* Cambridge Univ. Pr.
Murphy, Katherine & Todd, Richard, eds. A man very well Studyed: New Contexts for Thomas Browne. 2008. (Intersections Ser.). (Illus.). 336p. (C). *(978-90-04-17173-2(8))* BRILL.
Preston, Claire. Thomas Browne & the Writing of Early Modern Science. 2009. (ENG., Illus.). 268p. pap. 36.99 *(978-0-521-10779-2(2))* Cambridge Univ. Pr.
Wood, Gareth J. Javier Marías's Debt to Translation: Sterne, Browne, Nabokov. 2012. (Oxford Modern Languages & Literature Monographs). (ENG.). 360p. 110.00 ***(978-0-19-965133-7(7))*** Oxford Univ. Pr., Inc.

BROWNE, WILLIAM, 1590-1645
Browne, William Hand. Browne, William Hand. (Makers of America Ser.). 181p. reprint ed. 88.00 *(978-0-7222-8558-9(2))* Library Reprints, Inc.

BROWNE, WILLIAM MONTAGUE, 1823-1883
Coulter, E. Merton. William Montague Browne: Versatile Anglo-Irish American, 1823-1883. 2010. (ENG.). 346p. pap. 24.95 *(978-0-8203-3533-9(9))* Univ. of Georgia Pr.

BROWNFIELDS
Here are entered works on land and/or buildings that are abandoned or underutilized where expansion or redevelopment is complicated because of the threat of known or potential contamination.
Bargmann, J. Toxic Beauty: A Field Guide to Derelict Terrain. pap. 35.00 *(978-1-56898-369-1(7))* Princeton Architectural Pr.
Brebbia, C. A., ed. Brownfields IV: Prevention, Assessment, Rehabilitation & Development of Brownfield Sites. 2008. (WIT Transactions on Ecology & the Environment Ser.). (Illus.). 250p. 164.00 *(978-1-84564-105-4(1))* WIT Pr GBR. Dist: WIT Pr.
Brownfield's Environmental Law Real Estate. 3rd rev. ed. 1139.00 *(978-0-8205-3894-5(9))* LexisNexis.

Charles, J. A. Brownfield Sites: Ground-Related Risks for Buildings. 2010. (ENG., Illus.). 52p. pap. 65.00 *(978-1-86081-571-3(5))* Building Research Establishment GBR. Dist: Taylor & Francis Group.

Davis, Todd & Sherman, Scott, eds. Brownfields: A Comprehensive Guide to Redeveloping Contaminated Property. 3rd ed. 2011. (ENG., Illus.). 1145p. pap. 219.95 *(978-1-61632-000-3(1))* American Bar Assn.

De Sousa, Christopher. Brownfields Redevelopment & the Quest for Sustainability. 2008. (Current Research in Urban & Regional Studies). 224p. 130.00 *(978-0-08-045358-3(9))* Emerald Group Publishing Ltd. GBR. Dist: Turpin Distribution Services Ltd.

Hollander, Justin B. Polluted & Dangerous: America's Worst Abandoned Properties & What Can Be Done about Them. 2009. (ENG., Illus.). 332p. 30.00 *(978-1-58465-719-4(7))* Univ. Pr. of New England.

Hollander, Justin B., et al. Principles of Brownfield Regeneration: Cleanup, Design, & Reuse of Derelict Land. 2010. (ENG., Illus.). 152p. 50.00 *(978-1-59726-722-9(8))*; pap. 25.00 *(978-1-59726-723-6(6))* Island Pr.

Raco, Mike, et al, eds. Sustainable Brownfield Regeneration: Liveable Places from Problem Spaces. 2007. (ENG., Illus.). 400p. pap. 114.99 *(978-1-4051-4403-2(3))*, Wiley-Blackwell) Wiley, John & Sons, Inc.

The Revitalization of the Environmental Protection Agency's Brownfields Program: Hearing Before the Subcommittee on Water Resources & Environment of the Committee on Transportation & Infrastructure, House of Representatives, One Hundred Tenth Congress, Second Session, February 14, 2008. 2008. (Illus.). xi, 169p. *(978-0-16-083486-8(4)*, 552-070-39226-2) United States Government Printing Office.

Sami, William. Greening Brownfields: Remediation Through Sustainable Development. 2009. (ENG., Illus.). 320p. 79.95 *(978-0-07-160909-8(1)*, 0071609091) McGraw-Hill Professional Publishing.

Syms, Paul. Land, Development & Design. 2nd ed. 2010. (ENG., Illus.). 344p. pap. 80.99 *(978-1-4051-9853-0(2)*, Wiley-Blackwell) Wiley, John & Sons, Inc.

Tonin, Stefania. Measuring the Socio-Economic Benefits of Brownfields Remediation. 2009. 130p. pap. *(978-3-639-14835-0(5))* VDM Verlag Dr. Mueller e.K.

United States, Congress House Committee on Transportation and Infrastructure Subcommittee on Water Resources and Environment Staff, contrib. by. Reauthorizatoni [sic] of the Brownfields Program: Successes & Future Challenges: Hearing Before the Subcommittee on Water Resources & Environment of the Committee on Transportation & Infrastructure, House of Representatives, One Hundred Ninth Congress, Second Session, June 8, 2006. 2007. v, 91p. *(978-0-16-078134-6(5)*, 552-070-35534-1) United States Government Printing Office.

Wilson, Steve. Ground Gas Handbook. 2009. (ENG., Illus.). 192p. 119.95 *(978-1-4398-0883-2(X)*, CRC Press) Taylor & Francis Group GBR. Dist: Taylor & Francis Group.

BROWNIAN MOVEMENTS

Ahmed, Nasir Uddin. Generalized Functionals of Brownian Motion & Their Applications: Nonlinear Functionals of Fundamental Stochastic Processes. 2011. 316p. 88.00 ***(978-981-4366-36-6(6))*** World Scientific Publishing Co., Inc.

Biagini, Francesca, et al. Stochastic Calculus for Fractional Brownian Motion & Applications. 2010. (Probability & Its Applications Ser.). xii, 332p. pap. 109.00 *(978-1-84996-994-9(9)*, 1849969949) Springer.

Chernov, N. & Dolgopyat, D. Brownian Brownian Motion-I. 2009. (Memoirs of the American Mathematical Society Ser.). (Illus.). 193p. pap. 78.00 *(978-0-8218-4282-9(X))* American Mathematical Society.

Chung, Kai Lai & Walsh, John B. Markov Processes, Brownian Motion, & Time Symmetry. 2nd ed. 2010. (Grundlehren der mathematischen Wissenschaften Ser.). (Illus.). xii, 432p. pap. 159.00 *(978-1-4419-1960-1(0)*, 1441919600) Springer.

Cvitanic, Jaka & Zhang, Jianfeng. Contract Theory in Continuous-Time Models. 2011. (Springer Finance Ser.). x, 280p. 99.00 *(978-3-642-14199-7(4)*, 3642141994) Springer.

Earnshaw, Robert C. & Riley, Elizabeth M. Brownian Motion: Theory, Modelling & Applications. 2011. (Mathematics Research Developments Ser.). (Illus.). xii, 386p. 165.00 *(978-1-61209-537-0(2))* Nova Science Pubs., Inc.

Einstein, Albert. Investigations on the Theory of the Brownian Movement. 2011. 132p. pap. ***(978-1-60796-285-4(3))*** Editorial Benei Noaj.

Karatzas, Ioannis & Shreve, Steven E. Methods of Mathematical Finance. 2010. (Stochastic Modelling & Applied Probability Ser.). xv, 415p. pap. 109.00 *(978-1-4419-2852-8(9)*, 1441928529) Springer.

Mansuy, Roger & Yor, Marc. Aspects of Brownian Motion. 2008. (Universitext Ser.). 300p. pap. 59.95 *(978-3-540-22347-4(9)*, 3540223479) Springer.

Mazo, Robert M. Brownian Motion: Fluctuations, Dynamics, & Applications. 2009. (International Series of Monographs on Physics Ser.). (ENG., Illus.). 304p. pap. 75.00 *(978-0-19-955644-1(X))* Oxford Univ. Pr., Inc.

Melehy, Mahmoud A. Introduction to Interfacial Transport: A Generalization of Einstein's Theory of Brownian Motion with Interdisciplinary Applications. 2009. (Illus.). 265p. *(978-1-4490-2038-5(0))*; *(978-1-4490-2037-8(2))* AuthorHouse.

Mezzasalma, Stefano A. Macromolecules in Solution & Brownian Relativity. 2008. (Interface Science & Technology Ser.: 15). (ENG., Illus.). 248p. 240.00 *(978-0-12-373906-3(3)*, Academic Pr.) Elsevier Science & Technology Bks.

Mishura, Yuliya. Stochastic Calculus for Fractional Brownian Motion & Related Processes. 2007. (Lecture Notes in Mathematics Ser.). spiral bd. 79.95 *(978-3-540-75872-3(0)*, 3540758720) Springer.

Osswald, Horst. Malliavin Calculus for Lévy Processes & Infinite-Dimensional Brownian Motion. 2012. (Cambridge Tracts in Mathematics Ser.: 191). (ENG.). 428p. 110.00 ***(978-1-107-01614-9(2))*** Cambridge Univ. Pr.

Peres, Yuval & Mörters, Peter. Brownian Motion. 2010. (Cambridge Series in Statistical & Probabilistic Mathematics Ser.). (Illus.). 416p. 72.00 *(978-0-521-76018-8(6))* Cambridge Univ. Pr.

Rao, B. L. S. Prakasa. Statistical Inference for Fractional Diffusion Processes. 2010. (Wiley Series in Probability & Statistics Ser.). (ENG.). 280p. 112.00 *(978-0-470-66568-8(8)*, Wiley) Wiley, John & Sons, Inc.

Revuz, Daniel & Yor, Marc. Continuous Martingales & Brownian Motion. 3rd ed. 2010. (Grundlehren der mathematischen Wissenschaften Ser.). (Illus.). xi, 606p. pap. 139.00 *(978-3-642-08400-3(1)*, 3642084001) Springer.

Rostek, Stefan. Option Pricing in Fractional Brownian Markets. 2009. (Lecture Notes in Economics & Mathematical Systems Ser.). (ENG., Illus.). xiv, 137p. pap. 109.00 *(978-3-642-00330-1(3))* Springer.

Roynette, Bernard & Yor, Marc. Penalising Brownian Paths. 2009. (Lecture Notes in Mathematics Ser.). (ENG.). xiii, 275p. pap. 79.95 *(978-3-540-89698-2(8))* Springer.

Schweitzer, Frank. Brownian Agents & Active Particles: Collective Dynamics in the Natural & Social Sciences. 2007. (Springer Series in Synergetics Ser.). (ENG., Illus.). xvi, 420p. pap. 79.95 *(978-3-540-73844-2(4)*, 3540738444) Springer.

Snook, Ian. The Langevin & Generalised Langevin Approach to the Dynamics of Atomic, Polymeric & Colloidal Systems. 2007. (ENG., Illus.). 320p. 135.00 *(978-0-444-52129-3(1)*, Elsevier Science) Elsevier Science & Technology Bks.

Stokey, Nancy L. The Economics of Inaction: Stochastic Control Models with Fixed Costs. 2008. (ENG., Illus.). 320p. (C). 55.00 *(978-0-691-13505-2(3))* Princeton Univ. Pr.

Sznitman, Alain-Sol. Brownian Motion, Obstacles & Random Media. 2011. (Springer Monographs in Mathematics Ser.). (ENG., Illus.). xvi, 353p. pap. 109.00 *(978-3-642-08420-1(6)*, 3642084206) Springer.

BROWNING, ELIZABETH BARRETT, 1806-1861

Billington, Josie. Elizabeth Barrett Browning & Shakespeare: 'This Is Living Art' 2012. (Continuum Literary Studies). (ENG., Illus.). 154p. 110.00 *(978-0-8264-9598-3(2))* Continuum International Publishing Group, Ltd. GBR. Dist: National Bk. Network.

Billone, Amy Christine. Little Songs: Women, Silence, & the Nineteenth-Century Sonnet. 2007. x, 199p. cd-rom 14.95 *(978-0-8142-9122-1(8))*; 232p. 54.95 *(978-0-8142-1042-0(2))* Ohio State Univ. Pr.

Bradford, Amory Howe. Spiritual Lessons from the Brownings. 2009. 44p. pap. 12.99 *(978-1-110-79335-8(9))* 2010. 48p. reprint ed. pap. 15.75 *(978-1-176-00031-5(4))* BiblioBazaar.

—Spiritual Lessons from the Brownings. 2010. 30p. pap. 14.14 *(978-1-154-59561-1(7))* General Bks. LLC.

—Spiritual Lessons from the Brownings. 2010. 38p. 24.76 ***(978-1-169-55577-8(2))*** 2010. 40p. pap. 12.76 ***(978-1-165-88088-1(1))*** 2010. 38p. 30.95 *(978-1-161-97901-5(8))* 2009. 40p. pap. 15.95 *(978-1-104-65708-6(2))* Kessinger Publishing, LLC.

Browning, Elizabeth Barrett. The Complete Works of Elizabeth Barrett Browning, 6. reprint ed. lib. bdg. 98.00 *(978-0-7426-2222-7(3))* Classic Bks.

—The Diary of E. B. B. The Unpublished Diary of Elizabeth Barrett Browning. reprint ed. lib. bdg. 98.00 *(978-0-7426-2218-0(5))* Classic Bks.

—The Letters of Elizabeth Barrett Browning. 2008. 460p. 31.99 *(978-0-554-35315-9(6))* 2008. 460p. 33.99 *(978-0-554-26012-9(3))*2. 2007. (ENG.) 456p. pap. 30.99 *(978-1-4346-0290-9(7))* BiblioBazaar.

—The Letters of Elizabeth Barrett Browning. 2009. 216p. pap. *(978-0-217-39241-9(5))*; 114p. pap. *(978-0-217-39242-6(3))* Books LLC.

—The Letters of Elizabeth Barrett Browning. 2007. (ENG.). 292p. per. *(978-1-4068-6064-1(6))*; 272p. per. *(978-1-4068-6065-8(4))* Echo Library.

—The Letters of Elizabeth Barrett Browning Volume II. 2007. (ENG.). 398p. pap. 25.99 *(978-1-4346-0216-9(8))* BiblioBazaar.

Browning Elizabeth Barrett & Browning, Robert. The Brownings' Correspondence, 1849-1851: Vol. 16: Letters 2813-2900, Vol. 16. Kelley, Philip et al, eds. 2007. (Illus.). 110.00 *(978-0-911459-32-6(4))* Wedgestone Pr.

—The Brownings' Correspondence, 1851-1852: Vol. 17; Letters 2901-3000. Kelley, Philip et al, eds. 2010. (Illus.). 432p. 110.00 *(978-0-911459-34-0(0))* Wedgestone Pr.

—The Brownings' Correspondence, 1852-1853: Letters 3001-3173, Vol. 18. Kelley, Philip et al, eds. 2010. (Illus.). 432p. 110.00 *(978-0-911459-35-7(9))* Wedgestone Pr.

—Major Works. Roberts, Adam, ed. 2009. (Oxford World's Classics Ser.). (ENG., Illus.). 864p. pap. 15.95 *(978-0-19-955469-0(2))* Oxford Univ. Pr., Inc.

Browning, Elizabeth Barrett & Browning, Robert. Twenty-Two Unpublished Letters of Elizabeth Barrett Browning & Robert Browning: Addressed to Henrietta & Arabella Moulton-Barrett. 2011. 104p. 39.95 ***(978-1-258-05974-3(6))*** Literary Licensing, LLC.

Browning, Elizabeth Barrett, et al. Florentine Friends: The Letters of Elizabeth Barrett Browning & Robert Browning to Isa Blagden, 1850-1861. 2009. 448p. 145.00 *(978-0-911459-33-3(2))* Wedgestone Pr.

Browning, Robert. Letters of the Brownings to George Barrett. Landis, Paul & Freeman, Ronald E., eds. 2011. 410p. 54.95 ***(978-1-258-03056-8(X))*** Literary Licensing, LLC.

Browning, Robert & Elizabeth Barrett. The Letters of Robert Browning & Elizabeth Barrett, Vol. 1. l.t. ed. 2007. 582p. pap. 32.99 *(978-1-4264-9280-8(4))* BiblioBazaar.

—The Letters of Robert Browning & Elizabeth Barrett Volume 1. 2007. (ENG.). 528p. pap. 30.99 *(978-1-4264-9223-5(5))* BiblioBazaar.

Frederic G. Kenyon. The Letters of Elizabeth Barrett Browning. l.t. ed. 2007. (ENG.). 480p. pap. 30.99 *(978-1-4264-6625-0(0))* BiblioBazaar.

Gaylord Harriet. Pompilia & Her Poet. 2007. (ENG.). 196p. 37.95 *(978-0-548-06546-4(2))* Kessinger Publishing, LLC.

Ingram, John H. Elizabeth Barrett Browning. 2009. 206p. 28.99 *(978-1-110-84493-7(X))*; pap. 23.75 *(978-1-110-84491-3(3))* BiblioBazaar.

—Elizabeth Barrett Browning. 2007. (ENG.). 266p. 42.95 *(978-0-548-19146-0(8))*; 268p. per. 27.95 *(978-1-4304-9647-2(9))* Kessinger Publishing, LLC.

Kelley, Philip & Hudson, Ronald. The Browning's Correspondence Vol. 10: 1845. (Illus.). 450p. *(978-0-485-30030-7(3))* Continuum International Publishing Group, Ltd.

Kelley, Philip & Hudson, Ronald, eds. The Browning's Correspondence: 1809-1826. Vol. 1. 383p. *(978-0-485-30021-5(4))* Vol. 2. 413p. *(978-0-485-30022-2(2))* Continuum International Publishing Group, Ltd.

—The Browning's Correspondence Vol. 3: 1832-1837. 446p. *(978-0-485-30023-9(0))* Continuum International Publishing Group, Ltd.

—The Browning's Correspondence Vol. 4: 1838-1841. 452p. *(978-0-485-30024-6(9))* Continuum International Publishing Group, Ltd.

—The Browning's Correspondence Vol. 5: January 1841-May 1842. 428p. *(978-0-485-30025-3(7))* Continuum International Publishing Group, Ltd.

—The Browning's Correspondence Vol. 6: June 1842-March 1843. (Illus.). 425p. *(978-0-485-30026-0(5))* Continuum International Publishing Group, Ltd.

—The Browning's Correspondence Vol. 7: March 1843-September 1843. (Illus.). 423p. *(978-0-485-30027-7(3))* Continuum International Publishing Group, Ltd.

—The Browning's Correspondence Vol VIII: October 1843-May 1844. (Illus.). 447p. *(978-0-485-30028-4(1))* Continuum International Publishing Group, Ltd.

—The Browning's Correspondence Vol. 9: June 1844-December 1844. (Illus.). 448p. *(978-0-485-30029-1(X))* Continuum International Publishing Group, Ltd.

Kelley, Philip & Lewis, Scott, eds. The Brownings' Correspondence Vol. 13: May-August 1846. (Illus.). 424p. *(978-0-485-30033-8(8))* Continuum International Publishing Group, Ltd.

—The Brownings' Correspondence Vol Xiv: September 1846-December 1847. (Illus.). 424p. *(978-0-485-30034-5(6))* Continuum International Publishing Group, Ltd.

Loth, David. The Brownings: A Victorian Idyll. 2007. (ENG.). 322p. 45.95 *(978-0-548-06817-5(8))* Kessinger Publishing, LLC.

Lubbock, Percy. Elizabeth Barrett Browning in Her Letters. 2010. 182p. pap. 26.71 *(978-1-152-52642-6(1))* General Bks. LLC.

Martinez, Michele. Elizabeth Barrett Browning's 'Aurora Leigh' A Reading Guide. 2012. (Reading Guides to Long Poems Ser.). (ENG., Illus.). 224p. (gr. 17). 95.00 ***(978-0-7486-3971-7(3))***; pap. 27.00 ***(978-0-7486-3972-4(1))*** Edinburgh Univ. Pr. GBR. Dist: Columbia Univ. Pr.

Meredith, Owen. Letters from Owen Meredith, Robert, First Earl of Lytton: To Robert & Elizabeth Barrett Browning. Harlan, Aurelia Brooks & Harlan Jr., J. Lee, eds. 2011. 274p. 47.95 ***(978-1-258-03008-7(X))*** Literary Licensing, LLC.

Morgan, Monique R. Narrative Means, Lyric Ends: Temporality in the Nineteenth-Century British Long Poem. 2009. 47.95 *(978-0-8142-1111-3(9))*; (ENG.). 280p. cd-rom 14.95 *(978-0-8142-9208-2(9))* Ohio State Univ. Pr.

Scheinberg, Cynthia. Women's Poetry & Religion in Victorian England: Jewish Identity & Christian Culture. 2009. (Cambridge Studies in Nineteenth-Century Literature & Culture Ser.). (ENG.). 296p. pap. 41.00 *(978-0-521-09983-7(8))* Cambridge Univ. Pr.

Whiting, Lilian. A Study of Elizabeth Barrett Browning. 2009. 98p. pap. *(978-1-4432-9693-9(7))* Books LLC.

—A Study of Elizabeth Barrett Browning. 2007. (ENG.). 224p. 39.95 *(978-0-548-11338-7(6))* Kessinger Publishing, LLC.

BROWNING, MESHACH, 1781-1859

Browning, Meshach. Forty-Four Years of the Life of a Hunter. 2009. 228p. pap. *(978-1-150-74346-7(8))* Books LLC.

BROWNING, ROBERT, 1812-1889

Berdoe, Edward. Browning & the Christian Faith. 2008. 256p. 25.99 *(978-0-559-61616-7(3))*; pap. 25.75 *(978-0-559-61614-3(7))* BiblioBazaar.

—Browning & the Christian Faith. 2009. 144p. pap. *(978-1-4590-5133-1(5))*; pap. *(978-1-4590-5130-0(0))*; pap. *(978-0-217-69315-8(6))* Books LLC.

—Browning's Message to His Time. 2009. 102p. pap. 14.14 *(978-1-151-34523-3(7))* General Bks. LLC.

—Browning's Message to His Time: His Religion, Philosophy & Science. 2007. (ENG.). 200p. 39.95 *(978-0-548-09524-9(8))* Kessinger Publishing, LLC.

Bloom, Harold, ed. Robert Browning. 2009. (Bloom's Classic Critical Views Ser.). 228p. (C). (gr. 9-18). 45.00 *(978-1-60413-429-2(1)*, Chelsea Hse.) Facts On File, Inc.

Bradford, Amory Howe. Spiritual Lessons from the Brownings. 2009. 44p. pap. 12.99 *(978-1-110-79335-8(9))* 2010. 48p. reprint ed. pap. 15.75 *(978-1-176-00031-5(4))* BiblioBazaar.

—Spiritual Lessons from the Brownings. 2010. 30p. pap. 14.14 *(978-1-154-59561-1(7))* General Bks. LLC.

—Spiritual Lessons from the Brownings. 2010. 38p. 24.76 ***(978-1-169-55577-8(2))*** 2010. 40p. pap. 12.76 ***(978-1-165-88088-1(1))*** 2010. 38p. 30.95 *(978-1-161-97901-5(8))* 2009. 40p. pap. 15.95 *(978-1-104-65708-6(2))* Kessinger Publishing, LLC.

Brooke, Stopford A. Poetry of Robert Browning. reprint ed. 29.50 *(978-0-404-01114-7(4))* AMS Pr., Inc.

Brooke, Stopford Augustus. The Poetry of Robert Browning. 2010. (ENG.). 462p. pap. 37.75 *(978-1-171-56215-3(2))*; (ENG.). 472p. pap. 37.75 *(978-1-178-04382-2(7))*; (ENG.). 458p. pap. 36.75 *(978-1-176-30171-9(3))*; 458p. pap. 36.75 *(978-1-146-87303-1(4))*; 468p. pap. 37.75 *(978-1-144-38238-2(6))*; 470p. pap. 37.75 *(978-1-144-60483-5(4))*; 458p. pap. 36.75 *(978-1-142-05126-6(9))* BiblioBazaar.

—The Poetry of Robert Browning. 2009. 252p. pap. *(978-1-150-19000-1(0))* Books LLC.

Brooke, Stopford Augustus, creator. The Poetry of Robert Browning. 2011. 466p. pap. 37.75 ***(978-1-245-01407-6(2))*** BiblioBazaar.

Browning, Elizabeth Barrett & Browning, Robert. The Brownings' Correspondence, 1849-1851: Vol. 16: Letters 2813-2900, Vol. 16. Kelley, Philip et al, eds. 2007. (Illus.). 110.00 *(978-0-911459-32-6(4))* Wedgestone Pr.

—The Brownings' Correspondence, 1851-1852: Vol. 17; Letters 2901-3000. Kelley, Philip et al, eds. 2010. (Illus.). 432p. 110.00 *(978-0-911459-34-0(0))* Wedgestone Pr.

—The Brownings' Correspondence, 1852-1853: Letters 3001-3173, Vol. 18. Kelley, Philip et al, ed. 2010. (Illus.). 432p. 110.00 *(978-0-911459-35-7(9))* Wedgestone Pr.

Browning, Elizabeth Barrett & Browning, Robert. Twenty-Two Unpublished Letters of Elizabeth Barrett Browning & Robert Browning: Addressed to Henrietta & Arabella Moulton-Barrett. 2011. 104p. 39.95 ***(978-1-258-05974-3(6))*** Literary Licensing, LLC.

Browning, Elizabeth Barrett, et al. Florentine Friends: The Letters of Elizabeth Barrett Browning & Robert Browning to Isa Blagden, 1850-1861. 2009. 448p. 145.00 *(978-0-911459-33-3(2))* Wedgestone Pr.

Browning, Robert. A Browning Calendar. Spender, Constance M., ed. 2007. (ENG.). 108p. 32.95 *(978-0-548-35651-7(3))*; 84p. per. 17.95 *(978-0-548-29916-6(1))* Kessinger Publishing, LLC.

—Complete Poetic & Dramatic Works of Robert Browning. (Collected Works of Robert Browning). reprint ed. lib. bdg. 98.00 *(978-0-7426-2256-2(8))* Classic Bks.

—The Complete Works of Robert Browning, Volume 11: With Variant Readings & Annotations. Bright, Michael, ed. 2008. (Complete Works Robert Browning Ser.). (ENG.). 504p. 79.95 *(978-0-8214-1839-0(4))* Ohio Univ. Pr.

—The Divine Order: Sermons. reprint ed. lib. bdg. 98.00 *(978-0-7426-2263-0(0))* Classic Bks.

—Letters of Robert Browning to Isa Blagden. Armstrong, A. Joseph, ed. 2011. 228p. 46.95 ***(978-1-258-05440-3(X))*** Literary Licensing, LLC.

—Letters of the Brownings to George Barrett. Landis, Paul & Freeman, Ronald E., eds. 2011. 410p. 54.95 ***(978-1-258-03056-8(X))*** Literary Licensing, LLC.

Browning, Robert & Elizabeth Barrett. The Letters of Robert Browning & Elizabeth Barrett, Vol. 1. l.t. ed. 2007. 582p. pap. 32.99 *(978-1-4264-9280-8(4))* BiblioBazaar.

—The Letters of Robert Browning & Elizabeth Barrett Volume 1. 2007. (ENG.). 528p. pap. 30.99 *(978-1-4264-9223-5(5))* BiblioBazaar.

Burt, Mary E. Browning's Women. 2007. (ENG.). 240p. 41.95 *(978-0-548-11828-3(0))* Kessinger Publishing, LLC.

Chapman, John J. Emerson & Other Essays. 2006. pap. *(978-1-4065-1403-2(9))* Dodo Pr.

Chesterton, G. K. Robert Browning. 2008. 172p. 22.99 *(978-0-554-33916-0(1))* 2008. 172p. 25.99 *(978-0-554-24613-0(9))* 2006. (ENG.). 152p. pap. 19.99 *(978-1-4264-6924-4(1))* BiblioBazaar.

—Robert Browning. reprint ed. lib. bdg. 98.00 *(978-0-7426-3006-2(4))* Classic Bks.

—Robert Browning. 2006. (ENG.). pap. *(978-1-4068-0306-8(5))*; pap. *(978-1-4068-2214-4(0))* Echo Library.

Corson, Hiram. An Introduction to the Study of Robert Browning's Poetry. 2008. 400p. 29.99 *(978-0-554-31176-0(3))* 2008. 400p. 31.99 *(978-0-554-21873-1(9))* 2006. (ENG.). 392p. pap. 25.99 *(978-1-4264-1112-0(X))* BiblioBazaar.

—An Introduction to the Study of Robert Browning's Poetry. 2009. 424p. pap. *(978-1-4099-1991-9(9))* Dodo Pr.

—An Introduction to the Study of Robert Browning's Poetry. 2007. (ENG.). 384p. 48.95 *(978-0-548-17059-5(2))*; per. 33.95 *(978-1-4304-6824-0(6))* Kessinger Publishing, LLC.

Douglas, James. Robert Browning. 2007. (ENG.). 48p. per. 15.95 *(978-0-548-79765-5(X))* Kessinger Publishing, LLC.

—Robert Browning. 2008. (ENG.). 43p. per. *(978-1-4086-4087-6(2))* Read Bks.

Dowden, Edward. Robert Browning. 2010. 452p. pap. 36.75 *(978-1-178-35612-0(4))* 2010. 458p. pap. 36.75 *(978-1-143-83019-8(9))* 2010. 456p. pap. 36.75 *(978-1-142-54729-5(9))* 2008. 352p. 29.99 *(978-0-554-24404-4(7))* 2008. 352p. 28.99 *(978-0-554-33707-4(X))* 2007. (ENG.). 312p. pap. 23.99 *(978-1-4264-6422-5(3))* 2007. (ENG.). 350p. pap. 24.99 *(978-1-4264-6436-6(7))* BiblioBazaar.

—Robert Browning. Macfadyen, Dugald, ed. 2009. (Illus.). 314p. pap. *(978-1-4099-7415-4(4))* Dodo Pr.

—Robert Browning. 2007. (ENG.). 224p. per. *(978-1-4068-2587-9(5))* Echo Library.

—Robert Browning. 2010. 208p. pap. 29.13 *(978-1-4432-4822-8(3))* General Bks. LLC.

Dowden, Edward & Duff, Louis Blake. Robert Browning. 2010. 448p. pap. 36.75 *(978-1-177-20030-1(9))* BiblioBazaar.

Flew, Josiah. Studies in Browning. 2010. (ENG.). 260p. pap. 26.75 *(978-1-177-01266-9(9))*; 256p. pap. 26.75 *(978-1-141-25979-3(6))* BiblioBazaar.

B

—Studies in Browning. 2007. (ENG.). 246p. 41.95 (978-0-548-15261-4(6)); 248p. per. 26.95 (978-1-4304-4633-0(1)) Kessinger Publishing, LLC.
Forster, Joseph. Four Great Teachers: John Ruskin, Thomas Carlyle, Ralph Waldo. 2007. pap. 20.95 (978-1-4304-9879-7(X)) Kessinger Publishing, LLC.
Fotheringham, James. Studies in the Poetry of Robert Browning. 2008. 396p. 29.99 (978-0-559-39467-6(5)); pap. 32.75 (978-0-559-39466-9(7)) BiblioBazaar.
—Studies in the Poetry of Robert Browning. 2009. 248p. pap. (978-1-4588-5232-8(6)) Books LLC.
—Studies in the Poetry of Robert Browning. 2007. (ENG.). 444p. 51.95 (978-0-548-12306-5(3)) Kessinger Publishing, LLC.
Gaylord, Harriet. Pompilia & Her Poet. 2007. (ENG.). 196p. 37.95 (978-0-548-06546-4(2)) Kessinger Publishing, LLC.
Herford, C. H. Robert Browning. 2007. (ENG.). 320p. 45.95 (978-0-548-03393-7(5)) Kessinger Publishing, LLC.
Hodell, Charles Wesley. Essay on Robert Brownings the Ring & T. 2006. pap. 15.95 (978-1-4286-6184-4(0)) Kessinger Publishing, LLC.
Jones, Henry. Browning As a Philosophical & Religious Teacher. 2010. 368p. pap. 32.75 (978-1-178-35433-1(4)); 386p. pap. 33.75 (978-1-178-35465-2(2)); (ENG.). 394p. pap. 33.75 (978-1-176-23236-5(3)); 374p. pap. 32.75 (978-1-149-13086-5(5)); 382p. pap. 33.75 (978-1-147-74405-7(X)) BiblioBazaar.
—Browning As a Philosophical & Religious Teacher. 2009. 196p. pap. (978-0-217-91326-3(1)) Books LLC.
—Browning As a Philosophical & Religious Teacher. 2007. (ENG.). 248p. per. (978-1-4065-3543-3(5)) Dodo Pr.
—Browning As a Philosophical & Religious Teacher. 2009. 212p. pap. (978-1-4068-5373-5(9)) Echo Library.
—Browning As a Philosophical & Religious Teacher. 2010. (Illus.). 170p. pap. 9.18 (978-1-4432-0629-7(6)) General Bks. LLC.
—Browning As a Philosophical & Religious Teacher. 2010. 366p. 46.95 (978-1-161-40305-3(1)) Kessinger Publishing, LLC.
Jones, Henry Festing. Browning as a Philosophical & Religious Teacher. 2006. (ENG.). 266p. pap. 21.99 (978-1-4264-7087-5(8)); 300p. pap. 23.99 (978-1-4264-7163-6(7)) BiblioBazaar.
Kelley, Philip & Hudson, Ronald. The Browning's Correspondence Vol. 10: 1845. (Illus.). 450p. (978-0-485-30030-7(3)) Continuum International Publishing Group, Ltd.
Kelley, Philip & Hudson, Ronald, eds. The Browning's Correspondence: 1809-1826. Vol. 1. 383p. (978-0-485-30021-5(4)) Vol. 2. 413p. (978-0-485-30022-2(2)) Continuum International Publishing Group, Ltd.
—The Browning's Correspondence Vol. 3: 1832-1837. 446p. (978-0-485-30023-9(0)) Continuum International Publishing Group, Ltd.
—The Browning's Correspondence Vol. 4: 1838-1841. 452p. (978-0-485-30024-6(9)) Continuum International Publishing Group, Ltd.
—The Browning's Correspondence Vol. 5: January 1841-May 1842. 428p. (978-0-485-30025-3(7)) Continuum International Publishing Group, Ltd.
—The Browning's Correspondence Vol. 6: June 1842-March 1843. (Illus.). 425p. (978-0-485-30026-0(5)) Continuum International Publishing Group, Ltd.
—The Browning's Correspondence Vol. 7: March 1843-September 1843. (Illus.). 429p. (978-0-485-30027-7(3)) Continuum International Publishing Group, Ltd.
—The Browning's Correspondence Vol VIII: October 1843-May 1844. (Illus.). 447p. (978-0-485-30028-4(1)) Continuum International Publishing Group, Ltd.
—The Browning's Correspondence Vol. 9: June 1844-December 1844. (Illus.). 448p. (978-0-485-30029-1(X)) Continuum International Publishing Group, Ltd.
Kelley, Philip & Lewis, Scott, eds. The Brownings' Correspondence Vol. 13: May-August 1846. (Illus.). 424p. (978-0-485-30033-8(8)) Continuum International Publishing Group, Ltd.
—The Brownings' Correspondence Vol Xiv: September 1846-December 1847. (Illus.). 424p. (978-0-485-30034-5(6)) Continuum International Publishing Group, Ltd.
Kenyon, Frederic G. The Working of Robert Browing. 2006. 424p. per. (978-1-4067-3044-9(0), Hesperides Pr.) Read Bks.
Little, Marion. Essays on Robert Browning. 2007. (ENG.). 212p. 39.95 (978-0-548-35064-5(7)); per. 24.95 (978-0-548-29302-7(3)) Kessinger Publishing, LLC.
Lodico, Cheryl. Robert Browning: Idealism & Disillusionment in his Life & Work. 2007. pap. 11.00 (978-0-8059-8461-3(5)) Dorrance Publishing Co., Inc.
Loth, David. The Brownings: A Victorian Idyll. 2007. (ENG.). 322p. 45.95 (978-0-548-06817-5(8)) Kessinger Publishing, LLC.
Martens, Britta. Browning Victorian Poetics & the Romantic Legacy: Challenging the Personal Voice. 2011. (Illus.). 300p. 99.95 (978-1-4094-2303-4(4)) Ashgate Publishing Co.
Mayne, Ethel Colburn. Browning's Heroines. 2008. 304p. 25.99 (978-0-554-38978-3(9)); 28.99 (978-0-554-29675-3(6)) BiblioBazaar.
—Browning's Heroines. 336p. 2008. 45.95 (978-1-4365-8760-0(3)) 2007. (ENG.). per. 30.95 (978-0-548-79832-4(X)) 2007. (ENG.). 45.95 (978-0-548-03073-8(1)) Kessinger Publishing, LLC.
—Browning's Heroines. 2007. (ENG.). 336p. per. (978-1-4067-7923-3(7)) Read Bks.
Mayne, Ethel Colburn & Armfield, Maxwell. Browning's Heroines. 2007. (ENG.). 262p. pap. 21.99 (978-1-4346-8168-3(8)); 300p. pap. 23.99 (978-1-4346-8169-0(6)) BiblioBazaar.
Meredith, Owen. Letters from Owen Meredith, Robert, First Earl of Lytton: To Robert & Elizabeth Barrett Browning. Harlan, Aurelia Brooks & Harlan Jr., J. Lee, eds. 2011. 274p. 47.95 **(978-1-258-03008-7(X))** Literary Licensing, LLC.
Morgan, Monique R. Narrative Means, Lyric Ends: Temporality in the Nineteenth-Century British Long Poem. 2009. 47.95 (978-0-8142-1111-3(9)); (ENG.). 280p. cd-rom 14.95 (978-0-8142-9208-2(9)) Ohio State Univ. Pr.
Nettleship, John T. Robert Browning: Essays & Thoughts. 476p. 2010. 42.36 (978-1-163-40026-5(2)) 2010. pap. 30.36 (978-1-162-92824-1(7)) 2007. (ENG.). 52.95 (978-0-548-09219-4(2)) Kessinger Publishing, LLC.
Orr, Sutherland. A Handbook to the Works of Robert Browning. 2007. (ENG.). 434p. 51.95 (978-0-548-03200-8(9)) Kessinger Publishing, LLC.
—Life & Letters of Robert Browning. 2009. (ENG.). 337p. 36.99 (978-1-117-63411-1(6)) 2009. 338p. pap. 30.75 (978-1-117-63412-8(4)) 2009. (ENG.). 468p. 42.99 (978-1-117-44888-6(6)) 2009. (ENG.). 468p. pap. 36.75 (978-1-117-44889-3(4)) 2008. 336p. 28.99 (978-0-559-32925-8(3)) 2008. 340p. 28.99 (978-0-559-25820-6(8)) 2008. 340p. 28.99 (978-0-559-24298-4(0)) 2008. 336p. pap. 30.75 (978-0-559-32924-1(5)) 2008. 340p. pap. 30.75 (978-0-559-25816-9(X)) 2008. 340p. pap. 30.75 (978-0-559-24296-0(4)) BiblioBazaar.
—Life & Letters of Robert Browning. 2009. 124p. pap. (978-1-150-26859-5(X)) Books LLC.
—Life & Letters of Robert Browning. 2009. 306p. pap. (978-1-4099-7430-7(8)) Dodo Pr.
—Life & Letters of Robert Browning V1. 2007. (ENG.). 336p. 45.95 (978-0-548-15645-2(X)); pap. 30.95 (978-1-4304-5110-5(6)) Kessinger Publishing, LLC.
Phelps, William Lyon. Robert Browning: How to Know Him. 2008. 348p. 28.99 (978-0-554-32237-7(4)) 2007. (ENG.). 346p. pap. 24.99 (978-1-4264-3430-3(8)) 2008. 348p. 29.99 (978-0-554-22934-8(X)) 2007. (ENG.). 298p. pap. 21.99 (978-1-4264-3380-1(8)) BiblioBazaar.
—Robert Browning: How to Know Him. 2006. pap. (978-1-4068-3075-0(5)) Echo Library.
Rain, Thomas. Browning for Beginners. 2010. (ENG.). 246p. pap. 26.75 (978-1-176-28621-4(8)) 2010. (ENG.). 244p. pap. 26.75 (978-1-176-23252-5(5)) 2008. 240p. 24.99 (978-0-559-87665-3(3)) 2008. 240p. pap. 25.75 (978-0-559-87664-6(5)) BiblioBazaar.
—Browning for Beginners. 2009. 114p. pap. 19.99 (978-1-150-76974-0(2)) General Bks. LLC.
—Browning for Beginners. 2010. 238p. 33.56 (978-1-165-35726-0(7)) 2009. 240p. 41.95 (978-1-104-06753-3(6)) 2009. 240p. pap. 26.95 (978-1-104-04324-7(6)) Kessinger Publishing, LLC.
Revell, William F. Browning's Criticism of Life. 2007. (ENG.). 128p. 35.95 (978-0-548-09677-2(5)) Kessinger Publishing, LLC.
Rhys, Ernest. Browning & His Poetry. 2009. (ENG.). 129p. pap. 18.99 (978-1-113-96375-8(1)); pap. 19.99 (978-1-113-96378-9(6)) BiblioBazaar. (BiblioLife).
Ritchie, Anne. Records of Tennyson, Ruskin & Browning. 2007. (ENG.). 318p. 45.95 (978-0-548-01701-2(8)) Kessinger Publishing, LLC.
Sharp, William. Life of Browning. 2006. pap. (978-1-4068-0468-3(1)) Echo Library.
—Life of Robert Browning. 2008. 232p. 27.99 (978-0-554-25020-5(9)) 2008. 232p. 24.99 (978-0-554-34323-5(1)) 2007. (ENG.). 206p. pap. 20.99 (978-1-4264-8019-5(9)) BiblioBazaar.
—The Life of Robert Browning. 2007. (ENG.). 242p. 41.95 (978-0-548-01196-6(6)) Kessinger Publishing, LLC.
—Life of Robert Browning. l.t. ed. 2007. (ENG.). 230p. pap. 22.99 (978-1-4264-8076-8(8)) BiblioBazaar.
Symons, Arthur. An Introduction to the Study of Browning. 2008. 264p. 28.99 (978-0-554-26465-3(X)) 2008. 264p. 25.99 (978-0-554-35768-3(2)) 2007. (ENG.). 228p. pap. 20.99 (978-1-4346-1175-8(2)) 2007. (ENG.). 260p. pap. 23.99 (978-1-4346-1246-5(5)) BiblioBazaar.
—An Introduction to the Study of Browning. 2007. (ENG.). 204p. per. (978-1-4065-6678-9(0)) Dodo Pr.
—An Introduction to the Study of Browning. 2007. 276p. 42.95 (978-0-548-02214-6(3)) Kessinger Publishing, LLC.
Tanner, Aleph. Homage to Robert Browning. 2009. 152p. pap. (978-0-217-22718-6(X)) Books LLC.
—Homage to Robert Browning. 2009. 152p. 36.95 (978-1-120-21864-3(0)); pap. 21.95 (978-1-120-20121-8(7)) Kessinger Publishing, LLC.
Walters, Frank. Studies of Some of Robert Browning's Poems. 2009. 188p. 22.99 (978-1-103-82893-7(2)); pap. 16.99 (978-1-103-82886-9(X)) BiblioBazaar.
—Studies of Some of Robert Browning's Poems. 2009. (Illus.). 114p. pap. 19.99 (978-1-150-48680-7(5)) General Bks. LLC.
Waugh, Arthur. Robert Browning. 2008. 172p. pap. (978-1-4097-1723-2(2)) Read Bks.
Weatherford, Willis Duke. Fundamental Religious Principles in Browning's Poetry. 2007. (ENG.). 154p. 36.95 (978-0-548-15759-6(6)); pap. 21.95 (978-1-4304-5247-8(1)) Kessinger Publishing, LLC.
Westwood, Thomas. A Literary Friendship. 2009. 216p. 32.99 (978-1-113-80444-0(0)); pap. 24.75 (978-1-113-80441-9(6)) BiblioBazaar.
Woolford, John, ed. Robert Browning in Context. (Illus.). 267p. (978-0-485-30041-3(9)) Continuum International Publishing Group, Ltd.

BROWNING, ROBERT, 1812-1889—CRITICISM AND INTERPRETATION

Alexander, William John. An Introduction to the Poetry of Robert Browning. 2009. 224p. 23.99 (978-1-103-45291-0(6)); pap. 17.99 (978-1-103-45290-3(8)); 23.99 (978-1-103-12019-2(0)); pap. 17.99 (978-1-103-12016-1(6)) BiblioBazaar.
—An Introduction to the Poetry of Robert Browning. 2009. 154p. pap. (978-0-217-17306-3(3)) Books LLC.
—An Introduction to the Poetry of Robert Browning. 2009. 152p. pap. 19.99 (978-0-217-77529-8(2)) General Bks. LLC.
—An Introduction to the Poetry of Robert Browning. 2007. (ENG.). 228p. 41.95 (978-0-548-11237-3(1)) Kessinger Publishing, LLC.
BAILEY, Suzanne. Cognitive Style & Perceptual Difference in Browning's Poetry. 2009. (Studies in Major Literary Authors Ser.). (ENG.). 200p. (C). 125.00 (978-0-415-87477-9(7)) Routledge.
Brooke, Stopford A. The Poetry of Robert Browning. 2009. 456p. 35.99 (978-1-115-35216-1(4)) 2009. 456p. 42.99 (978-1-115-35219-2(9)) 2009. 456p. pap. 35.75 (978-1-115-35213-0(X)) 2009. 456p. pap. 36.75 (978-1-115-35214-7(8)) 2008. 384p. 31.99 (978-0-554-27077-7(3)) 2007. (ENG.). 336p. pap. 23.99 (978-1-4346-2430-7(7)) 2007. (ENG.). 382p. pap. 26.99 (978-1-4346-2476-5(5)) BiblioBazaar.
Chesterton, G. K. Robert Browning. l.t. ed. 2006. (ENG.). 170p. pap. 21.99 (978-1-4264-7006-6(1)) BiblioBazaar.
Cooke, George Willis. A Guidebook to the Poetic & Dramatic Works of Robert Browning. 2007. (ENG.). 468p. 52.95 (978-0-548-02029-6(9)); 468p. 52.95 (978-0-548-16822-6(9)); 472p. per. 37.95 (978-1-4304-6546-1(8)) Kessinger Publishing, LLC.
Kennedy, Richard S. & Hair, Donald S. The Dramatic Imagination of Robert Browning: A Literary Life. 2007. (ENG., Illus.). 512p. (C). 54.95 (978-0-8262-1691-5(9)) Univ. of Missouri Pr.
Orr, Sutherland. A Handbook to the Works of Browning. 2008. 412p. 30.99 (978-0-554-34331-0(2)) 2008. 412p. 32.99 (978-0-554-25028-1(4)) 2007. (ENG.). 358p. pap. 25.99 (978-1-4264-8027-0(X)) 2007. 410p. pap. 28.99 (978-1-4264-8084-3(9)) BiblioBazaar.
Woodford, John. Robert Browning. 2006. (Writers & Their Work Ser.). (ENG.). 128p. (C). pap. 26.00 (978-0-7463-0981-0(3)) Northcote Hse. Publishers, Ltd. GBR. Dist: Brown, David Bk. Co., The.

BROWNING, TOD, 1882-1962

Herzogenrath, Bernd, ed. The Cinema of Tod Browning: Essays of the Macabre & Grotesque. 2008. (ENG.). 249p. pap. 35.00 (978-0-7864-3447-3(3)) McFarland & Co., Inc. Pubs.

BROWN'S PARK

Kouris, Diana Allen. Riding the Edge of an ERA: Growing up Cowboy on the Outlaw Trail. 2007. (978-0-931271-84-7(3)); pap. (978-0-931271-85-4(1)) High Plains Pr.

BROWNSON, ORESTES AUGUSTUS, 1803-1876

Brownson, Orestes Augustus. Essays & Reviews. 2009. 346p. pap. 26.99 (978-0-217-71339-9(4)) General Bks. LLC.
—The Spirit-Rapper: An Autobiography. 2010. 426p. pap. 35.75 (978-1-146-15087-3(3)); 446p. pap. 36.75 (978-1-142-25776-7(2)) BiblioBazaar.
Dempsey, Michael James. Separation of Church & State in the Works of Félicité Lamennais & Orestes Brownson: French & American Theories Compared. 2009. iii, 222p. (978-0-7734-4794-3(6)) Mellen, Edwin Pr., The.
Malone, George K. The True Church: A Study in the Apologetics of Orestes Augustus Brownson. 2011. 122p. 39.95 **(978-1-258-06187-6(2))** Literary Licensing, LLC.
Raemers, Sidney A. America's Foremost Philosopher, Orestes Augustine Brownson: Benedictine Historical Monographs No. 5. 2011. 244p. 46.95 **(978-1-258-06928-5(8))** Literary Licensing, LLC.

BROWNSVILLE (TEX.)

Ford, M. H. Fort Brown Military Reservation Investg. 2006. pap. 22.95 (978-1-4286-6286-5(3)) Kessinger Publishing, LLC.
The Ports of Freeport, Port Isabel & Brownsville, Texas. per. 7.00 (978-0-16-001750-6(5)) United States Government Printing Office.

BROWSERS (COMPUTER PROGRAMS)

see also Microsoft Internet Explorer (Computer Program); Netscape (Computer Program)

Ao, Sio-Iong. Data Mining & Applications in Genomics. 2008. (Lecture Notes in Electrical Engineering Ser.). (ENG., Illus.). xii, 152p. 129.00 (978-1-4020-8974-9(0), 1402089740) Springer.
Carroll, Dave, et al. Creating on-Demand Applications with AppExchange: An Introduction. 2006. per. 29.95 (978-0-9789639-0-3(3)) Salesforce.com.
Crowley, Matthew. Pro Internet Explorer 8 & 9 Development: Developing Powerful Applications for the Next Generation of IE. 2010. (Illus.). xxii, 399p. **(978-1-4302-2854-7(7))** Apress L. P.
Feldt, Kenneth C. Programming Firefox: Building Applications in the Browser. 2007. (ENG., Illus.). 512p. per. 59.99 (978-0-596-10243-2(7)) O'Reilly Media, Inc.
Gaskin, Shelley & Lawson, Rebecca. GO! with Internet Explorer 8 Getting Started. 2010. (ENG., Illus.). 96p. (C). pap. 31.00 (978-0-13-508861-6(5), Prentice Hall) Prentice Hall PTR.
—GO! with the Internet, Vol. 1. 2007. (ENG., Illus.). 432p. (C). pap. 81.33 (978-0-13-230002-5(8), Prentice Hall) Prentice Hall PTR.
Kang, Seok. Motivational Use of Web News: Motives, Activity, & Evaluations. 2010. 192p. pap. (978-3-8383-5570-2(9)) Lambert Academic Publishing.
Lawson, Rebecca & Gaskin, Shelley. Go! with the Internet: Comprehensive. 2007. (Go Series for Microsoft Office 2003). (ENG., Illus.). 816p. (C). pap. 111.33 (978-0-13-195695-7(7), Prentice Hall) Prentice Hall PTR.
MacDonald, Matthew. Pro Silverlight 2 in C# 2008. 2008. (ENG., Illus.). 640p. pap. 49.99 (978-1-59059-949-5(7)) Apress L. P.
Mozilla(r) Firefox 3: Introduction: 084034s3. 2008. spiral bd. (978-1-4246-1082-2(6)) Element K Content LLC.
Oshri, Ilan, et al. Standards-Battles in Open Source Software: The Case of Firefox. 2008. (ENG., Illus.). 160p. 105.00 (978-0-230-22072-0(X)) Palgrave Macmillan.
Raasch, Jon. Smashing WebKit. 2011. (Smashing Magazine Book Ser.: 20). (ENG.). 368p. pap. 44.99 **(978-1-119-99913-3(8)**, Wiley) Wiley, John & Sons, Inc.
Ruecker, Stan, et al. Visual Interface Design for Digital Cultural Heritage: A Guide to Rich-Prospect Browsing. 2011. (Illus.). 206p. 99.95 (978-1-4094-0422-4(6)) Ashgate Publishing Co.
Schattner, Peter. Genomes, Browsers & Databases: Data-Mining Tools for Integrated Genomic Databases. 2008. (ENG., Illus.). 344p. 130.00 (978-0-521-88443-3(8)) Cambridge Univ. Pr.
—Genomes, Browsers, & Databases: Data-Mining Tools for Integrated Genomic Databases. 2008. (ENG., Illus.). 344p. pap. 58.99 (978-0-521-71132-6(0)) Cambridge Univ. Pr.
Townsend, Kris. Skills for Success with Internet Explorer 9 Getting Started. 2011. (ENG.). 48p. (C). pap. 31.00 **(978-0-13-293455-8(8)**, Prentice Hall) Prentice Hall PTR.
Watts, David. Implementing IBM Director 5.20. 4th ed. 2007. (Illus.). xxii, 968p. (978-0-7384-8623-9(X)) IBM.
Zavoral, Filip, et al, eds. Networked Digital Technologies, Part I: Second International Conference, NDT 2010, Prague, Czech Republic. 2010. (Communications in Computer & Information Science Ser.). xxiii, 580p. pap. 139.00 (978-3-642-14291-8(5), 3642142915) Springer.
—Networked Digital Technologies, Part II: Second International Conference, NDT 2010, Prague, Czech Republic, July 7-9, 2010 Proceedings. 2010. (Communications in Computer & Information Science Ser.). xxiii, 730p. pap. 149.00 (978-3-642-14305-2(9), 3642143059) Springer.

BRUBECK, DAVE, 1920-

Nelson, Bruce, ed. Simply Brubeck. 2007. (Simply Ser.). (ENG.). 80p. pap. 12.95 (978-0-7390-4496-4(6)) Alfred Publishing Co., Inc.

BRUCE, BLANCHE KELSO, 1841-1898

Graham, Lawrence Otis. The Senator & the Socialite: The True Story of America's First Black Dynasty. (Illus.). 2007. 512p. per. 15.99 (978-0-06-098513-4(5), HarperPerennial) 2006. 816p. per. 27.95 (978-0-06-112079-4(0)) HarperCollins Pubs.

BRUCE, LENNY, 1925-1966

Weaver, Helen. The Awakener: A Memoir of Jack Kerouac & the Fifties. 2009. (ENG.). 180p. pap. 16.95 (978-0-87286-505-1(3)) City Lights Bks.

BRUCELLACEAE

Diptee, Michael. Evaluation of Brucella Abortus Rb51 Vaccine in Water Buffalo. 2009. 140p. pap. (978-3-639-21247-1(9)) VDM Verlag Dr. Mueller e.K.
López-Goñi, Ilgnacio & O'Callaghan, David, eds. Brucella: Molecular Microbiology & Genomics. 2012. 272p. 319.00 **(978-1-904455-93-6(X))** Caister Academic Pr. GBR. Dist: International Specialized Bk. Services.

BRUCELLOSIS

Corbel, M. J. & World Health Organization. Brucellosis in Humans & Animals. 2006. (Nonserial Publications). (ENG., Illus.). 98p. pap. 30.00 (978-92-4-154713-0(8)) World Health Organization.
Ramezani, Amitis. Risk Factors for Human Brucellosis in Iran. 2009. 84p. pap. (978-3-639-21075-0(1)) VDM Verlag Dr. Mueller e.K.
Shrestha, Birochan. Seroprevalence of Brucellosis in Different Species of Animals in Nepal. 2011. 88p. pap. **(978-3-8443-9957-8(7))** Lambert Academic Publishing.
Yellowstone National Park Bison: Oversight Hearing Before the Subcommittee on National Parks, Forests, & Public Lands of the Committee on Natural Resources, U.S. House of Representatives, One Hundred Tenth Congress, First Session, March 20, 2007. 2007. iii, 75p. (978-0-16-078965-6(6), 552-070-36083-2) United States Government Printing Office.

BRUCELLOSIS IN CATTLE

Abd-Elmaksoud, Ahmed. The Bovine Testis. 2010. 232p. pap. (978-3-8383-3617-6(8)) Lambert Academic Publishing.

BRUCKNER, ANTON, 1824-1896

Bruckner, Anton. Symphonies Nos. 6 & 8 in Full Score. 2010. (Dover Music Scores Ser.). (ENG.). 384p. pap. 27.95 (978-0-486-47231-7(0)) Dover Pubns., Inc.
Floros, Constantin & Bernhardt-Kabisch, Ernest. Anton Bruckner: The Man & the Work. 2011. 57.95 (978-3-631-61439-6(X)) Lang, Peter Publishing, Inc.
Gault, Dermot. The New Bruckner: Compositional Developments & the Dynamics of Revision. 2010. (Illus.). 294p. 114.95 (978-1-4094-0091-2(3)) Ashgate Publishing Co.
Hö, et al. Die Rezeption der Kirchenmusik Anton Bruckners: Genese, Tradition und Instrumentalisierung des Vergleichs mit Giovanni Pierluigi da Palestrina. 2011. (Abhandlungen zur Musikgeschichte Ser.). (GER., Illus.). 421p. (C). 74.00 (978-3-89971-601-6(9)) Vandenhoeck & Ruprecht GmbH & Co. KG DEU. Dist: ISD.
Jackson, Timothy L. & Hawkshaw, Paul, eds. Bruckner Studies. 2007. (Cambridge Composer Studies). (ENG., Illus.). 320p. pap. 63.00 (978-0-521-04606-0(8)) Cambridge Univ. Pr.
Kreft, Ekkehard. Die Harmonik Anton Bruckners: Teil 1. 2009. (Beiträge zur europäischen Musikgeschichte Ser.). (GER.). 270p. 67.95 (978-3-631-59730-9(4)) Lang, Peter GmbH, Europäischer Verlag der Wissenschaften DEU. Dist: Lang, Peter.

Newlin, Dika. Bruckner - Mahler - Schoenberg. 2007. pap. ***(978-1-4067-5623-4(7))*** Read Bks.

Stocken, Frederick. Simon Sechter's Fundamental-Bass Theory & Its Influence on the Music of Anton Bruckner. 2009. (Illus.). 296p. 109.95 *(978-0-7734-3879-8(3))* Mellen, Edwin Pr., The.

BRUDERHOF COMMUNITIES

Here are entered works on the communal movement founded by Eberhard Arnold in the early 20th century, known as the Bruderhof, Society of Brothers, or Hutterian Brethren. Works on the Hutterite communities originating in the Anabaptist movement of the 16th century are entered under the name heading Hutterite Brethren.

Arnold, Annemarie, et al. Anni: Letters & Writings of Annemarie Wächter Arnold. 2010. *(978-0-87486-854-8(8))* Plough Publishing Hse.

Arnold, Heini. Discipleship: Living for Christ in the Daily Grind. 2011. ***(978-0-87486-876-0(9)***; ***(978-978-087-486-5(0))*** Plough Publishing Hse.

Barth, Emmy. An Embassy Besieged. 2010. 320p. pap. 35.00 *(978-1-60899-879-1(7)*, Cascade Bks.) Wipf & Stock Pubs.

Kant, Joanita. Hutterites of South Dakota: The Schmiedeleut. 2006. 308p. pap. 49.95 *(978-1-59526-376-6(4)*, Llumina Pr.) Aeon Publishing Inc.

RAUTERT, Timm. No Photographing, 1 vol. 2011. (ENG., Illus.). 156p. 48.00 ***(978-3-86930-322-2(0))*** Steidl, Gerhard Druckerei und Verlag DEU. Dist: Innovative Logistics.

Rhodes, Robert. Nightwatch: An Inquiry into Solitude: Alone on the Prairie with the Hutterites, 1 vol. 2009. (ENG.). 160p. pap. 9.95 *(978-1-56148-666-3(3))* Good Bks.

BRUEGEL, PIETER, CA. 1525-1569

Bonn, Robert L. Painting Life: The Art of Pieter Bruegel, the Elder. 2007. (Illus.). 173p. 29.95 *(978-1-884092-12-1(8)*, Chaucer Pr.) Altschuler, Richard & Assocs., Inc.

Bruegel, Pieter, et al. Bruegel. 2006. (FRE, DUT & ENG., Illus.). 270p. 29.50 ***(978-90-5856-200-5(X))*** Stichting Kunstboek Bvba BEL. Dist: Antique Collectors' Club.

Michel, Emile & Charles, Victoria. The Brueghels. 2012. (Mega Square Ser.). (ENG., Illus.). 256p. 12.95 ***(978-1-906981-42-6(6))*** Parkstone Pr. USA, Ltd.

Richardson, Todd M. Pieter Bruegel the Elder: Art Discourse in the Sixteenth-Century Netherlands. 2011. (Visual Culture in Early Modernity Ser.). (Illus.). 268p. 119.95 ***(978-0-7546-6816-9(9))*** Ashgate Publishing Co.

Roberts-Jones, Francoise & Roberts-Jones, Philippe. Bruegel. 2012. (ENG., Illus.). 352p. 39.95 ***(978-2-08-020106-5(9))*** Flammarion et Cie FRA. Dist: Random Hse., Inc.

Sellink, Manfred. Bruegel: The Complete Paintings, Drawings & Prints. 2007. (ENG., Illus.). 304p. 150.00 *(978-0-8109-9389-1(9))* Abrams.

Silver, Larry. Pieter Bruegel. 2011. (ENG., Illus.). 424p. 150.00 *(978-0-7892-1104-0(1))* Abbeville Pr., Inc.

Sullivan, Margaret A. Bruegel & the Creative Process, 1559-1563. 2010. (Illus.). 268p. 124.95 *(978-0-7546-6979-1(3))* Ashgate Publishing Co.

Vohringer, Christian. Pieter Bruegel: 1525/30-1569. 2008. (Masters of Netherlandish Art Ser.). (Illus.). 140p. pap. 9.95 *(978-0-8416-0076-8(7))* American Map Corp.

BRUGES (BELGIUM)

Brown, Andrew. Civic Ceremony & Religion in Medieval Bruges C. 1300-1520. 2011. (ENG., Illus.). 384p. 99.00 *(978-0-521-76445-2(9))* Cambridge Univ. Pr.

Murray, James M. Bruges, Cradle of Capitalism, 1280-1390. 2009. (ENG., Illus.). 424p. (C). pap. 56.00 *(978-0-521-12053-1(5))* Cambridge Univ. Pr.

BRUGES (BELGIUM)—DESCRIPTION AND TRAVEL

DK Publishing. DK Eyewitness Travel Guide: Brussels, Bruges, Ghent & Antwerp: Brussels, Bruges, Ghent & Antwerp. 2012. (Eyewitness travel Guide Ser.). (ENG.). 208p. pap. 20.00 ***(978-0-7566-9472-2(8))*** Dorling Kindersley Publishing, Inc.

Dorling Kindersley Publishing Staff. Eyewitness Travel Guides - Brussels Bruges Ghent Antwerp. 2011. (Eyewitness Travel Guides). (ENG., Illus.). 208p. 20.00 *(978-0-7566-6958-4(8))* Dorling Kindersley Publishing, Inc.

Evans, Mary Anne. Frommer's Brussels & Bruges Day by Day. 2nd ed. 2011. (Frommer's Day by Day - Pocket Ser.: 144). (ENG., Illus.). 192p. pap. 13.99 *(978-0-470-79422-7(4)*, Frommers) Wiley, John & Sons, Inc.

Gilliat-Smith, Ernest. The Story of Bruges. 2010. 438p. pap. 35.75 *(978-1-144-58692-6(5))*; 444p. pap. 35.75 *(978-1-142-47404-1(6))* BiblioBazaar.

—The Story of Bruges. 2009. 220p. pap. 19.75 *(978-1-150-63139-9(2))* General Bks. LLC.

—The Story of Bruges. 2010. 430p. pap. 29.56 *(978-1-163-29725-4(9))* 2007. (ENG.). 428p. 51.95 *(978-0-548-23167-8(2))* 2007. (ENG.). 432p. per. 36.95 *(978-1-4326-3210-6(8))* Kessinger Publishing, LLC.

Mason, Antony. Bruges. 2nd ed. (City Guides - Cadogan Ser.). (Illus.). 210p. per. 17.95 *(978-1-86011-213-3(7))* Cadogan Guides GBR. Dist: Globe Pequot Pr., The.

Mill, Katharine. Bruges. 2010. (STEP by STEP Ser.). (Illus.). 128p. 16.95 *(978-981-282-104-1(X))* Insight Guides.

Steves, Rick & Openshaw, Gene. Rick Steves' Amsterdam, Bruges & Brussels. 2011. (Rick Steves Ser.). (ENG., Illus.). 648p. pap. 19.99 *(978-1-59880-768-4(4))* Avalon Travel Publishing.

—Rick Steves' Snapshot Bruges & Brussels: Including Antwerp & Ghent. 2011. (Rick Steves Snapshot Ser.). (ENG., Illus.). 272p. pap. 11.99 *(978-1-61238-229-6(0))* Avalon Travel Publishing.

Thomas Cook Publishing. Pocket guides Bruges, 4th. 4th ed. 2012. (Thomas Cook Pocket Guides) (ENG., Illus.). 160p. pap. 9.95 ***(978-1-84848-536-5(0))*** Cook, Thomas Publishing GBR. Dist: Globe Pequot Pr., The.

Turner, Christopher. Bruges. 5th ed. (Illus.). 112p. pap. 10.95 *(978-1-84306-119-9(8))* Hunter Publishing, Inc.

—Bruges. 2nd ed. (Illus.). 112p. pap. 10.95 *(978-1-84306-032-1(9))* Landmark Publishing Ltd. GBR. Dist: Hunter Publishing, Inc.

BRUGGHEN, HENDRIK TER, 1588-1629

Seaman, Natasha T. The Religious Paintings of Hendrick Ter Brugghen: Reinventing Christian Painting after the Reformation in Utrecht. 2012. (Visual Culture in Early Modernity Ser.). (Illus.). 200p. 104.95 ***(978-1-4094-3495-5(8))*** Ashgate Publishing Co.

Slatkes, Leonard J. & Franits, Wayne. The Paintings of Hendrick Ter Brugghen. 2007. 480p. (C). 408.00 *(978-90-272-4961-6(X))* Benjamins, John Publishing Co.

BRUMMELL, GEORGE BRYAN, 1778-1840

Kelly, Ian. Beau Brummell: The Ultimate Man of Style. 2007. (ENG., Illus.). 416p. per. 28.95 *(978-1-4165-8458-2(7)*, Free Pr.) Free Pr.

BRUN, CHARLES FREDERIC, D. 1871

Giono, Jean. Le Deserteur. (FRE.). 23.95 *(978-0-7859-0097-9(7)*, M3496) French & European Pubns., Inc.

BRUNCHES

see also Breakfasts; Luncheons

Bear, John B. & Fox, Margaret S. Morning Food: Breakfasts, Brunches & More for Savoring the Best Part of the Day. 2nd rev. ed. 2006. (ENG., Illus.). 208p. pap. 19.95 *(978-1-58008-782-7(5))* Ten Speed Pr.

Beckerman, Carol. 500 Breakfast & Brunch Dishes: The Only Compendium of Breakfast & Brunch Dishes You'll Ever Need. 2011. (Illus.). 288p. 16.95 *(978-1-4162-0620-0(5))* Sellers Publishing, Inc.

Brettl, Michelle. Best of Country Breakfast & Brunch. 2007. (Illus.). 112p. *(978-0-89821-544-1(7))* Reiman Pubns., L.P.

Cassidy, Catherine. Breakfast. 2009. (Illus.). 112p. ***(978-0-89821-760-5(1))*** Reiman Pubns., L.P.

Gand, Gale & Matheson, Christie. Gale Gand's Brunch! 100 Fantastic Recipes for the Weekend's Best Meal. 2009. (ENG., Illus.). 208p. 27.50 *(978-0-307-40698-9(9)*, Clarkson Potter) Crown Publishing Group.

Gooseberry Patch. Breakfast & Brunch Recipes Cookbook. 2007. (ENG., Illus.). 126p. spiral bd. 7.95 *(978-1-933494-13-5(1))* Gooseberry Patch.

Joseph, Peter. Boozy Brunch: The Quintessential Guide to Daytime Drinking. 2012. (ENG., Illus.). 176p. 16.95 ***(978-1-58979-678-2(0))*** Taylor Trade Publishing.

Lanier, Pamela. Cinnamon Mornings & Savory Nights: Romantic Recipes from America's Inns. (ENG.). 2009. 160p. pap. 19.95 *(978-0-9840850-0-2(9))* 2008. (Illus.). 1p. pap. 19.95 *(978-1-58008-940-1(2))* Ten Speed Pr.

Lee, Rachel. Brunch: Brilliant Ideas for Successful Entertaining. 2008. (ENG., Illus.). 144p. 22.95 *(978-88-89272-66-4(X))* McRae Bks. Srl ITA. Dist: Independent Pubs. Group.

Levine, Sarabeth & Rodgers, Rick. Sarabeth's Bakery: From My Hands to Yours. 2010. (ENG., Illus.). 308p. 39.95 *(978-0-8478-3408-2(5))* Rizzoli International Pubns., Inc.

Main, Sylvia. Easy Elegance from Fabulous Fairholme: Breakfast, Brunch, Lunch. 2012. 144p. 29.95 ***(978-1-77050-110-2(X))*** Whitecap Bks., Ltd. CAN. Dist: Midpoint Trade Bks., Inc.

Main, Sylvia. Fabulous Fairholme: Breakfasts & Brunches. 2010. (ENG., Illus.). 144p. 29.95 *(978-1-55285-932-2(0))* Whitecap Bks., Ltd. CAN. Dist: Midpoint Trade Bks., Inc.

Rosbottom, Betty. Sunday Brunch: Simple, Delicious Recipes for Leisurely Mornings. 2012. (ENG., Illus.). 120p. pap. 19.95 ***(978-1-4521-0535-2(9))*** Chronicle Bks. LLC.

Ryland, Peters, ed. Easy Breakfast & Brunch. 2007. (ENG., Illus.). 240p. *(978-1-84597-485-5(9))* Ryland Peters & Small.

Silver, Ron & Black, Rosemary. Bubby's Brunch Cookbook: Recipes & Menus from New York's Favorite Comfort Food Restaurant. 2009. (ENG., Illus.). 336p. 30.00 *(978-0-345-51163-8(8))*, Ballantine Bks.) Random House Publishing Group.

Taylor, Anne. Alexia Renée's - Brunch. 2007. 103p. pap. 19.95 *(978-1-4357-0468-8(1))* Lulu Enterprises Inc.

BRUNEI

Alexander, James. Malaysia, Brunei & Singapore. (Country & Regional Guides). (Illus.). 475p. per. 24.95 *(978-1-86011-309-3(5))* Cadogan Guides GBR. Dist: Globe Pequot Pr., The.

De Ledesma, Charles, et al. Malaysia, Singapore & Brunei. 6th ed. 2009. (ENG., Illus.). 784p. (gr. 12). pap. 24.99 *(978-1-84836-059-4(2))* Rough Guides, Ltd. GBR. Dist: Dorling Kindersley Publishing, Inc.

Eaton, Peter. Borneo & Beyond: Journey Through a Changing World. 2010. (Illus.). 192p. pap. 27.50 *(978-967-978-959-1(4))* Pelanduk Pubns. Malaysia Sdn. Bhd MYS. Dist: Coronet Bks.

Locken, E. Travel Journal Brunei. 2010. 192p. pap. 19.99 *(978-0-557-43277-6(4))* Lulu Enterprises Inc.

Lonely Planet Staff & Richmond, Simon. Malaysia Singapore & Brunei. 11th rev. ed. 2010. (Country Guide Ser.). (ENG., Illus.). 652p. pap. 24.99 *(978-1-74104-887-2(7))* Lonely Planet Pubns.

Majid, Harun Abdul. Rebellion in Brunei: The 1962 Revolt, Imperialism, Confrontation & Oil. 2007. (ENG., Illus.). 224p. 79.00 *(978-1-84511-423-7(X))* I. B. Tauris & Co., Ltd. GBR. Dist: Macmillan.

Martin, Peter W. & Sercombe, Peter G. Languages in Borneo: Diachronic & Synchronic Perspectives. 2009. (Illus.). x, 328p. *(978-1-929900-11-4(2))* Borneo Research Council, Inc.

Periplus Editors, ed. Malaysia Travel Atlas: Includes Singapore & Brunei. 2011. (ENG., Illus.). 96p. pap. 16.95 *(978-0-8048-4192-4(6))* Tuttle Publishing.

Sidhu, Jatswan S. Historical Dictionary of Brunei Darussalam. 2nd ed. 2009. (Historical Dictionaries of Asia, Oceania, & the Middle East Ser.). (ENG., Illus.). 390p. 95.00 *(978-0-8108-5980-7(7))* Scarecrow Pr., Inc.

Sulaiman Haji Duraman. Kenali Negara Kita. 2009. (MAY., Illus.). v, 64p. *(978-99917-0-638-2(0))* Dewan Bahasa Dan Pustaka.

BRUNEL, ISAMBARD KINGDOM, 1806-1859

Brunel, Isambard. The Life of Isambard Kingdom Brunel, Civil Engineer. 2009. 396p. pap. *(978-0-217-35496-7(3))* Books LLC.

—The Life of Isambard Kingdom Brunel, Civil Engineer. 2011. (Cambridge Library Collection - Travel & Exploration Ser.). (Illus.). 614p. pap. 43.00 *(978-1-108-02630-7(3))* Cambridge Univ. Pr.

Christopher, John. Isambard Kingdom Brunel Through Time. 2010. (Illus.). 96p. pap. 24.95 *(978-1-84868-963-3(2))* Amberley Publishing GBR. Dist: Casemate Pubs. & Bk. Distributors, LLC.

Jones, Robin. Isambard Kingdom Brunel. 2011. (Illus.). 224p. 39.95 *(978-1-84468-121-1(1))* Wharncliffe Bks. GBR. Dist: Casemate Pubs. & Bk. Distributors, LLC.

Pugsley, Alfred. The Works Isambard Kingdom Brunel: An Engineering Appreciation. 2010. (ENG.). 234p. pap. 24.99 *(978-0-521-15778-0(1))* Cambridge Univ. Pr.

Tames, Richard. Isambard Kingdom Brunel. 3rd ed. 2009. (Shire Library) (ENG., Illus.). 48p. pap. 12.95 *(978-0-7478-0758-2(2))* Shire Pubns., Ltd. GBR. Dist: Random Hse., Inc.

Vaughan, Adrian. The Intemperate Engineer: Isambard Kingdom Brunel in His Own Words. 2010. (ENG., Illus.). 288p. 32.95 *(978-0-7110-3280-4(7))* Allan, Ian Publishing GBR. Dist: BookMasters Distribution Services (BDS).

BRUNELLESCHI, FILIPPO, 1377-1446

Fanelli, Giovanni & Fanelli, Michele. Brunelleschi's Cupola: Past & Present of an Architectural Masterpiece. 2006. (ENG., Illus.). 288p. pap. 23.00 *(978-88-85957-91-6(9))* Mandragora ITA. Dist: Antique Collectors' Club.

Holm, Lorens. Brunelleschi, Lacan, le Corbusier: Architecture, Space & the Construction of Subjectivity. 2009. (ENG., Illus.). XIV, 274p. 53.95 *(978-0-415-41969-7(7))*; 274p. 165.00 *(978-0-415-41968-0(9))* Routledge.

Thomas, Paul. Reconfiguring Space. 2009. 168p. pap. *(978-3-639-14088-0(5))* VDM Verlag Dr. Mueller e.K.

Trachtenberg, Marvin. Brunelleschi, Michelozzo, & the Problem of the Pazzi Chapel. 2008. (Illus.). 272p. 60.00 *(978-0-300-11831-5(7))* Yale Univ. Pr.

BRUNER, JEROME S. (JEROME SEYMOUR), 1915-

David Olson Staff. Jerome Bruner: The Cognitive Revolution in Educational Theory. 2008. (Continuum Library of Educational Thought). (ENG.). 224p. 140.00 *(978-0-8264-8402-4(6))* Continuum International Publishing Group, Ltd. GBR. Dist: National Bk. Network.

Smidt, Sandra. Introducing Bruner. 2011. (ENG., Illus.). 144p. (C). 125.00 *(978-0-415-57420-4(X))*; pap. 33.95 *(978-0-415-57421-1(8))* Routledge.

BRUNI, LEONARDO ARETINO, 1369-1444

Botley, Paul. Latin Translation in the Renaissance: The Theory & Practice of Leonardo Bruni, Giannozzo Manetti & Desiderius Erasmus. 2009. (Cambridge Classical Studies). (ENG., Illus.). 220p. pap. 33.00 *(978-0-521-10054-0(2))* Cambridge Univ. Pr.

Regoliosi, Mariangela, ed. Lorenzo Valla e l'Umanesimo Toscano: Traversari, Bruni e Marsuppini: Atti del convegno del Comitato Nazionale VI centenario della nascita di Lorenzo Valla. Prato, 30 Novembre 2007. 2009. (Edizione nazionale delle opere di lorenzo Valla Ser.). (ITA.). 144p. (C). 55.00 *(978-88-596-0682-6(9))* Polistampa ITA. Dist: Brown, David Bk. Co., The.

BRUNNER, HEINRICH EMIL, 1889-1966

Brüning, Franziska. La France et le Chancelier Brüning: Imaginaire et Politique, 1930-1932. 2010. (FRE.). 306p. *(978-2-915611-66-3(1))* Editions universitaires de Dijon.

BRUNNER, JOHN TOMLINSON, SIR, 1842-1919

Koss, Stephen E. Sir John Brunner: Radical Plutocrat 1842-1919. 2008. (Conference on British Studies Biographical Ser.). (ENG., Illus.). 336p. pap. 46.00 *(978-0-521-08564-9(0))* Cambridge Univ. Pr.

BRUNO, GIORDANO, 1548-1600

Besant, Annie W. The Story of Giordano Bruno. 2006. pap. 15.95 *(978-1-4286-7116-4(1))* Kessinger Publishing, LLC.

Brinton, Daniel Garrison & Davidson, Thomas. Giordano Bruno, Philosopher & Martyr: Two Addresses. 2007. 72p. per. 16.95 *(978-1-4304-7516-3(1))* Kessinger Publishing, LLC.

Clucas, Stephen. Magic Memory & Natural Philosophy in the Sixteenth & Seventeenth Centuries. 2011. (Variorum Collected Studies). (Illus.). 332p. 154.95 *(978-1-4094-1975-4(4))* Ashgate Publishing Co.

Gatti, H. Essays on Giordano Bruno. 2010. (ENG., Illus.). 376p. (C). 75.00 *(978-0-691-14574-7(1))* Princeton Univ. Pr.

Gatti, Hilary. Essays on Giordano Bruno. 2010. (ENG., Illus.). 376p. (C). pap. 35.00 *(978-0-691-14839-7(2))* Princeton Univ. Pr.

Greenberg, Sidney. The Infinite in Giordano Bruno: With A Translation of His Dialogue Concerning the Cause, Principle, & One. 2011. 212p. 44.95 ***(978-1-258-01340-0(1))*** Literary Licensing, LLC.

Horowitz, Irving Louis. The Renaissance Philosophy of Giordano Bruno. 2011. 160p. 41.95 ***(978-1-258-01940-2(X))*** Literary Licensing, LLC.

Hufnagel, Henning S. Ein Stück von jeder Wissenschaft: Gattungshybridisierung, Argumentation und Erkenntnis in Giordano Brunos italienischen Dialogen. 2009. (Text und Kontext Ser.). (GER.). 320p. (C). pap. 72.00 *(978-3-515-09605-8(1))* Steiner, Franz Verlag Wiesbaden GmbH DEU. Dist: Brown, David Bk. Co., The.

Magnard, P. Fureurs, Heroisme et Metamorphoses. 2007. (Bibliothèque Philosophique de Louvain Ser.). (ENG.). 178p. (C). pap. 67.00 *(978-90-429-1839-9(X))* Peeters Pubs. & Booksellers BEL. Dist: Brown, David Bk. Co., The.

Olschki, Leonardo. Giordano Bruno. 108p. 2008. 34.95 *(978-1-4366-8066-0(2))* 2007. (ENG.). per. 19.95 *(978-1-4326-2857-4(7))* Kessinger Publishing, LLC.

Pater, Walter. Giordano Bruno, & Aesthetic Poetry. 2007. 48p. per. *(978-1-4065-4129-8(X))* Dodo Pr.

Powers, Alan W. The Worlds of Giordano Bruno: The Man Galileo Plagiarised. 2010. (Illus.). 116p. *(978-0-9549196-4-1(5))* Cortex Design.

Rowland, Ingrid D. Giordano Bruno: Philosopher - Heretic. 2008. (ENG., Illus.). 352p. 27.00 *(978-0-8090-9524-7(6)*, Farrar, Straus & Giroux.

—Giordano Bruno: Philosopher/Heretic. 2009. (ENG.). 352p. pap. 18.00 *(978-0-226-73024-0(7))* Univ. of Chicago Pr.

BRUSH, GEORGE DE FOREST, 1855-1941

Anderson, Nancy K. George de Forest Brush: The Indian Paintings. 2008. (Illus.). vii, 239p. *(978-0-89468-347-3(0))* National Gallery of Art.

Anderson, Nancy K., et al. George de Forest Brush: The Indian Paintings. 2008. (Illus.). 224p. 65.00 *(978-1-84822-006-5(5)*, Lund Humphries Pubs.) Ashgate Publishing, Ltd. GBR. Dist: Ashgate Publishing Co.

BRUSH PAINTING, ORIENTAL

see Ink Painting

BRUSSELS (BELGIUM)

CIVA Staff, ed. BrU Planning a Capital: BrU002, 1 vol. 2011. (ENG & FRE.). 64p. pap. 15.00 *(978-2-930391-24-3(3))* Centre International Pour La Ville, L'Architecture Et Le Paysage BEL. Dist: Innovative Logistics.

Cornaz, Marie. Les éditions musicales publiées à Bruxelles au XVIIIe Siècle (1706-1794) Catalogue descriptif et illustré. 2008. (Etudes de Musicologie / Musicological Studies). (FRE., Illus.). 321p. pap. 49.95 *(978-90-5201-480-7(9))* PIE - Peter Lang BEL. Dist: Lang, Peter.

Gilliat-Smith, Ernest. The Story of Brussels. 2010. 438p. pap. 35.75 *(978-1-143-29408-2(4))* BiblioBazaar.

—The Story of Brussels. 2009. 228p. pap. *(978-0-217-39830-5(8))* Books LLC.

—The Story of Brussels. 2009. 424p. 51.95 *(978-1-104-45131-8(X))*; pap. 36.95 *(978-1-104-40034-7(0))* Kessinger Publishing, LLC.

Pierret, P. Memoires, Mentalites Religieuses, Art Funeraire: La Partie Juive du Cimitiere de Dieweg a Bruxelles, XIXe-XXe Siecles. 2006. (Collection de la Revue des Etudes Juives Ser.). (ENG & FRE.). 334p. (C). pap. 99.00 *(978-90-429-1632-6(X))* Peeters Pubs. & Booksellers BEL. Dist: Brown, David Bk. Co., The.

BRUSSELS (BELGIUM)—DESCRIPTION AND TRAVEL

Beek, Nicolas van & Capart, Nathalie. Secret Brussels. 2008. (Secret Ser.). (ENG., Illus.). 256p. pap. 17.95 *(978-2-915807-08-0(6))* Jonglez Editions FRA. Dist: Globe Pequot Pr., The.

Blyth, Derek. The 500 Hidden Secrets of Brussels. 2012. (ENG., Illus.). 140p. 16.95 ***(978-94-6058-092-5(0))***, Uitgeverij Luster) Antique Collectors' Club GBR. Dist: National Bk. Network.

Blythe, Derek. Live & Work in Brussels. 2008. (Live & Work - Vacation Work Publications). (ENG., Illus.). 320p. pap. 24.95 *(978-1-85458-383-3(2))* Crimson Publishing, Ltd. GBR. Dist: National Bk. Network.

Brussels Marco Polo Guide. 2012. (Marco Polo Guides Ser.). (ENG., Illus.). 140p. pap. 9.99 ***(978-3-8297-0681-0(2))*** Marco Polo Travel Publishing GBR. Dist: Innovative Logistics.

D'Haenens, Tom. Airport. 2007. 224p. 95.00 *(978-90-209-6811-8(4))* Lannoo N. V., Uitgeverij BEL. Dist: Antique Collectors' Club.

DK Publishing. DK Eyewitness Travel Guide: Brussels, Bruges, Ghent & Antwerp: Brussels, Bruges, Ghent & Antwerp. 2012. (Eyewitness travel Guide Ser.). (ENG.). 208p. pap. 20.00 ***(978-0-7566-9472-2(8))*** Dorling Kindersley Publishing, Inc.

Dorling Kindersley Publishing Staff. Eyewitness Travel Guides - Brussels Bruges Ghent Antwerp. 2011. (Eyewitness Travel Guides). (ENG., Illus.). 208p. 20.00 *(978-0-7566-6958-4(8))* Dorling Kindersley Publishing, Inc.

Editors of Wallpaper Magazine, ed. Wallpaper* City Guide Brussels 2013. 2012. (ENG.). 128p. pap. 9.95 ***(978-0-7148-6435-8(8))*** Phaidon Pr., Inc.

Evans, Mary Anne. Frommer's Brussels & Bruges Day by Day. 2nd ed. 2011. (Frommer's Day by Day - Pocket Ser.: 144). (ENG., Illus.). 192p. pap. 13.99 *(978-0-470-79422-7(4)*, Frommers) Wiley, John & Sons, Inc.

Harvard Student Agencies, Inc. Let's Go Amsterdam & Brussels: The Student Travel Guide. 2011. (Let's Go Ser.). (ENG., Illus.). 272p. pap. 14.95 *(978-1-59880-715-8(3)*, Let's Go) Avalon Travel Publishing.

Locken, E. Travel Journal Brussels. 2010. 192p. pap. 19.99 *(978-0-557-44592-9(2))* Lulu Enterprises Inc.

Lonely Planet Staff, et al. Brussels, Bruges, Antwerp & Ghent. 2008. (Best Of Ser.). (ENG., Illus.). 192p. pap. 11.99 *(978-1-74104-921-3(0))* Lonely Planet Pubns.

Marchi, Christina. 365 x Brussels. 2010. (ENG., Illus.). 384p. *(978-2-87386-610-5(1)*, Lannoo Pubs. (Acc)) Antique Collectors' Club.

Mason, Antony & Dorling Kindersley Publishing Staff. Top 10 Brussels. 2011. (Eyewitness top 10 travel Guide Ser.). (ENG.). 144p. 14.00 *(978-0-7566-8446-4(3))* Dorling Kindersley Publishing, Inc.

Steves, Rick & Openshaw, Gene. Rick Steves' Amsterdam, Bruges & Brussels. 2011. (Rick Steves Ser.). (ENG., Illus.). 648p. pap. 19.99 *(978-1-59880-768-4(4))* Avalon Travel Publishing.
—Rick Steves' Snapshot Bruges & Brussels: Including Antwerp & Ghent. 2011. (Rick Steves Snapshot Ser.). (ENG., Illus.). 272p. pap. 11.99 *(978-1-61238-229-6(0))* Avalon Travel Publishing.
Streetwise Maps Inc., des. & rev. Streetwise Brussels Map - Laminated City Street Map of Brussels, Belgium: Folding pocket size travel map with integrated metro map including tram lines & Stations. 2004th rev. ed. 2007. (Streetwise Ser.). (ENG.). 8.95 *(978-1-886705-52-4(6))* Streetwise Maps, Inc.
Thomas Cook Publishing Staff. Brussels Pocket Guide. 3rd ed. 2011. (Thomas Cook Pocket Guides). (ENG., Illus.). 144p. pap. 9.95 *(978-1-84848-350-7(3))* Cook, Thomas Publishing GBR. Dist: Globe Pequot Pr., The.
Time Out Guides Staff. Time Out Brussels: Antwerp, Ghent & Bruges. 7th ed. 2010. (Time Out Guides). (ENG., Illus.). 336p. pap. 19.95 *(978-1-84670-193-1(7))* Time Out Guides Ltd. GBR. Dist: Perseus-PGW.
Trefonides, Steven. Trefonides Sketchbooks: Paris & Brussels 1986. 2008. (Illus.). 110p. 45.54 *(978-0-929228-10-5(3))* Static Image Pr.
—Trefonides Sketchbooks: Paris & Brussels 1986. 2008. (Illus.). 110p. pap. 40.75 *(978-0-929228-11-2(1))* Static Image Pr.
Wallpaper Magazine Editors, ed. Wallpaper* City Guide Brussels. 2009. (ENG., Illus.). 128p. pap. 9.95 *(978-0-7148-4907-2(3))* Phaidon Pr., Inc.

BRUSSELS (BELGIUM)—HISTORY

Detiffe, Marc, photos by. Architectural heritage in the Making: City of Brussels CPAS, 1 vol. 2011. (ENG, DUT & FRE.). 239p. 70.00 *(978-2-930391-38-0(3))* Centre International Pour La Ville, L'Architecture Et Le Paysage BEL. Dist: Innovative Logistics.
Polasky, Janet L. Reforming Urban Labor: Routes to the City, Roots in the Country. 2010. (Illus.). 264p. 55.00 *(978-0-8014-4794-5(1))* Cornell Univ. Pr.
Stéphany, Pierre. La Libre Belgique: Histoire D'un Journal Libre, 1884-1996. (FRE., Illus.). 576p. *(978-2-8011-1140-6(6))* Duculot.
Taghon, Peter & Roba, Jean-Louis. Bruxelles 1940-1945. (Belgique en Guerre Ser.: Tome 2). (FRE., Illus.). 96p. pap. 18.95 *(978-90-72547-95-8(0))* De Krijger BEL. Dist: Casemate Pubs. & Bk. Distributors, LLC.
Tattara, Martino, et al, eds. Brussels: A Manifesto Towards the Capital of Europe, 1 vol. 2007. (ENG., Illus.). 240p. (C). pap. 45.00 *(978-90-5662-552-8(7))* NAi Uitgevers / Publishers Stichting NLD. Dist: D.A.P./Distributed Art Pubs.

BRUSSELS GRIFFON

Sakson, Sharon R. Brussels Griffons: Everything about Purchase, Care, Nutrition, Behavior, & Training. 2007. (Complete Pet Owner's Manual Ser.). (ENG., Illus.). 96p. pap. 8.99 *(978-0-7641-3563-7(5))* Barron's Educational Series, Inc.

BRUTALITY

see Cruelty

BRUTUS, LUCIUS JUNIUS—DRAMA

Payne, John Howard. Brutus or the Fall of Tarquin: A Historical Tragedy, in Five Acts (1818) 2009. 68p. pap. 16.95 *(978-1-104-07735-8(3))* Kessinger Publishing, LLC.

BRUXELLES (BELGIUM)

see Brussels (Belgium)

BRY, THEODOR DE, 1528-1598

Groesen, Michiel van. The Representations of the Overseas World in the de Bry Collection of Voyages (1590-1634) 2008. (Library of the Written Word Ser.). (Illus.). 563p. *(978-90-04-16449-9(9))* BRILL.

BRYAN, WILLIAM JENNINGS, 1860-1925

Bensel, Richard Franklin. Passion & Preferences: William Jennings Bryan & the 1896 Democratic Convention. 2008. (ENG., Illus.). 336p. 93.00 *(978-0-521-88888-2(3))* Cambridge Univ. Pr.
—Passion & Preferences: William Jennings Bryan & the 1896 Democratic National Convention. 2008. (ENG., Illus.). 336p. pap. 33.00 *(978-0-521-71762-5(0))* Cambridge Univ. Pr.
Bryan, William Jennings. Speeches of William Jennings Bryan. 2009. 242p. pap. *(978-0-217-87562-2(9))*; 212p. pap. *(978-0-217-55930-0(1))* Books LLC.
—Speeches of William Jennings Bryan, 2 vol., set. reprint ed. 250.00 *(978-0-7222-9007-1(1))* Library Reprints, Inc.
Hibben, Paxton. The Peerless Leader William Jennings Bryan. 2007. (ENG.). 480p. 53.95 *(978-0-548-02371-6(9))* Kessinger Publishing, LLC.
Kazin, Michael. A Godly Hero: The Life of William Jennings Bryan. 2007. (ENG., Illus.). 432p. pap. 16.95 *(978-0-385-72056-4(4), Anchor)* Knopf Doubleday Publishing Group.
Kohn, Edward P. Hot Time in the Old Town: The Great Heat Wave of 1896 & the Making of Theodore Roosevelt. 2011. (ENG.). 304p. (gr. 9). pap. 16.99 *(978-0-465-02428-5(9))* Basic Bks.
Leinwand, Gerald. William Jennings Bryan: An Uncertain Trumpet. 2006. (American Profiles (Rowman & Littlefield Hardcover) Ser.). (ENG., Illus.). 208p. 38.00 *(978-0-7425-5158-9(X))* Rowman & Littlefield Publishers, Inc.
Magliocca, Gerard N. The Tragedy of William Jennings Bryan: Constitutional Law & the Politics of Backlash. 2011. (Illus.). 248p. 40.00 *(978-0-300-15314-9(7))* Yale Univ. Pr.
Masters, Edgar Lee. The Christian Statesman: American Mercury V3, No. 12, December 1924. Mencken, H. I. & Nathan, George Jean, eds. 2011. 20p. pap. 35.95 ***(978-1-258-04916-4(3))*** Literary Licensing, LLC.
Merriam, Charles Edward. Four American Party Leaders Henry Ward B. 2006. pap. 20.95 *(978-1-4286-5358-0(9))* Kessinger Publishing, LLC.
Newbranch, H. E. Williams Jennings Bryan. reprint ed. 150.00 *(978-0-7222-9009-5(8))* Library Reprints, Inc.
Williams, R. Hal. Realigning America: McKinley, Bryan, & the Remarkable Election of 1896. 2010. 29.95 *(978-0-7006-1721-0(3))* Univ. Pr. of Kansas.

BRYANT, BEAR, 1913-1983

see Bryant, Paul W., 1913-1983

BRYANT, PAUL W., 1913-1983

Barra, Allen. The Last Coach: A Life of Paul Bear Bryant. 2006. (ENG., Illus.). 608p. per. 15.95 *(978-0-393-32897-4(X), 32897)* Norton, W. W. & Co., Inc.
Briley, John David. Career in Crisis: Paul Bear Bryant & the 1971 Season of Change. 2006. (Illus.). 322p. 29.95 *(978-0-88146-025-4(7))* Mercer Univ. Pr.
Bryant, Paul Bear & Underwood, John. Bear: The Hard Life & Good Times of Alabama's Coach Bryant. 2007. (ENG., Illus.). 336p. 24.95 *(978-1-57243-888-0(6))* Triumph Bks.
Krauss, Barry & Moore, Joe M. Ain't Nothin' but a Winner: Bear Bryant, the Goal Line Stand, & a Chance of a Lifetime. 2nd ed. 2006. (ENG., Illus.). 152p. 26.95 *(978-0-8173-1541-2(1))* Univ. of Alabama Pr.
Sikes, Richard. Laughing with the Bear. 2007. 122p. 14.95 *(978-0-9745854-0-6(8))* Old Bay Publishing.

BRYANT, WILLIAM CULLEN, 1794-1878

Bigelow, John. William Cullen Bryant. 2010. 378p. pap. 33.75 *(978-1-145-74875-0(9))* 2010. 368p. pap. 32.75 *(978-1-141-93745-5(X))* 2009. (ENG.). 364p. 38.99 *(978-1-117-59091-2(7))* 2009. (ENG.). 364p. pap. 25.99 *(978-1-117-59093-6(3), BiblioLife)* BiblioBazaar.
—William Cullen Bryant. 2008. 366p. 48.95 *(978-0-548-98962-3(1))* 2007. (ENG.). 368p. per. 33.95 *(978-0-548-65770-6(X))* Kessinger Publishing, LLC.
—William Cullen Bryant. 2007. (ENG.). 364p. per. *(978-1-4067-7631-7(9))* Read Bks.
Bradley, William Aspenwall. William Cullen Bryant. 2009. 240p. 23.99 *(978-1-103-54889-7(1))*; pap. 17.99 *(978-1-103-54886-6(7))* BiblioBazaar.
—William Cullen Bryant: English Men of Letters. 2007. pap. 26.95 *(978-1-4304-8326-7(1))* Kessinger Publishing, LLC.
Bryant, William Cullen, et al. William Cullen Bryant: An American Voice. 2006. (Illus.). 198p. per. 17.95 *(978-1-58465-619-7(0))* Antoca Pr.
Curtis, George William. The Life, Character & Writings of William Cullen Bryant. 2009. 64p. pap. 13.99 *(978-1-103-82751-0(0))* BiblioBazaar.
Godwin, Parke. Biography of William Cullen Bryant with. 2006. pap. 36.95 *(978-1-4286-3462-6(2))*; pap. 37.95 *(978-1-4286-3461-9(4))* Kessinger Publishing, LLC.
Muller, Gilbert H. William Cullen Bryant: Author of America. 2008. (Illus.). 410p. 30.00 *(978-0-7914-7467-9(4))* State Univ. of New York Pr.
Sillen, Samuel. William Cullen Bryant. 16.95 *(978-0-8488-1167-9(4))* Amereon LTD.

BRYANT FAMILY

Bryant, Betty. Here Comes the Showboat! 2010. (Ohio River Valley Ser.). (ENG., Illus.). 216p. pap. 25.00 *(978-0-8131-2967-9(2))* Univ. Pr. of Kentucky.
Bryant, Billy. Children of Ol' Man River: The Life & Times of A Show Boat Trouper. 2011. 354p. 51.95 ***(978-1-258-01811-5(X))*** Literary Licensing, LLC.
Fuller, T. A. The Spear & the Spindle: Ancestors of Sir Francis Bryan 1550. 2008. 146p. (Orig.). pap. 25.50 *(978-1-55613-842-3(3))* Heritage Bks.
Reid, Larry E. My Reid & Harrison Families in North America from their Arrival to Present with Special Section on the Ells, Loss, Smiths of New York. 2006. (Illus.). 8p. (YA). per. *(978-1-59872-533-9(5))* Instant Pub.

BRYCE, JAMES BRYCE, VISCOUNT, 1838-1922

Fisher, H. A. L. James Bryce V2 Viscount Bryce of Dechmon. 2006. pap. 33.95 *(978-1-4286-6129-5(8))* Kessinger Publishing, LLC.
Prochaska, Frank. Eminent Victorians on American Democracy: The View from Albion. 2012. (ENG.). 184p. 45.00 ***(978-0-19-964061-4(0))*** Oxford Univ. Pr., Inc.
Seaman, John T., Jr. & Seaman, John T. A Citizen of the World: The Life of James Bryce. 2006. (ENG., Illus.). 272p. 100.00 *(978-1-84511-126-7(5), Tauris Academic Studies)* I. B. Tauris & Co., Ltd. GBR. Dist: Macmillan.

BRYCE CANYON NATIONAL PARK (UTAH)

Laine, Barbara & Laine, Don. Frommer's Zion & Bryce Canyon National Parks. 7th ed. 2010. (Park Guides). (ENG., Illus.). 192p. pap. 12.99 *(978-0-470-55127-1(5), Frommers)* Wiley, John & Sons, Inc.
Laine, Don & Laine, Barbara. Frommer's Zion & Bryce Canyon National Parks. 8th ed. 2012. (Park Guides: 51). (ENG.). 192p. pap. 12.99 ***(978-1-118-11803-0(0)***, Frommers) Wiley, John & Sons, Inc.
McRae, Bill, et al. Moon Zion & Bryce: Including Arches, Canyonlands, Capitol Reef, Grand Staircase-Escalante & Moab. 2011. (ENG., Illus.). 304p. pap. 17.99 *(978-1-59880-734-9(X))* Avalon Travel Publishing.
Minetor, Randi S. & Crawford, Betty Anne. Zion & Bryce Canyon National Parks Pocket Guide. 2009. (Falcon Pocket Guides Ser.). (ENG., Illus.). 96p. 9.95 *(978-0-7627-4943-0(1), Falcon Guides)* Globe Pequot Pr., The.
Molvar, Erik & Martin, Tamara. Best Easy Day Hikes Zion & Bryce Canyon National Parks. 2007. (Best Easy Day Hikes Ser.). (ENG., Illus.). 112p. per. 9.95 *(978-0-7627-4455-8(3), Falcon Guides)* Globe Pequot Pr., The.
Roos, Constance. The Grand Canyon: With Bryce & Zion Canyons in America's South West. 2nd rev. ed. 2010. (Illus.). 288p. pap. 22.95 *(978-1-85284-453-0(1))* Cicerone Pr. GBR. Dist: Midpoint Trade Bks., Inc.

BRYN MAWR COLLEGE

Baker, Alison. It's Good to Be a Woman: Voices from Bryn Mawr, Class Of '62. 2007. (Illus.). 230p. per. 15.95 *(978-1-933002-33-0(6))* PublishingWorks.
Menza, Kaitlin & Friedman, Sarah. Bryn Mawr College 2012: Off the Record. 2011. 188p. pap. 16.95 ***(978-1-4274-0359-9(7))*** College Prowler, Inc.

BRYOPHYTES

see also Liverworts; Mosses

Engel, John J. & Glenny, David. A Flora of the Liverworts & Hornworts of New Zealand. 2008. (Monographs in Systematic Botany from the Missouri Botanical Garden: Vol. 110). (Illus.). *(978-1-930723-66-5(0))* Missouri Botanical Garden Pr.
—A Flora of the Liverworts & Hornworts of New Zealand, Vol. 1. 2008. (Monographs in Systematic Botany from the Missouri Botanical Garden). (Illus.). 898p. 105.00 *(978-1-930723-67-2(9))* Missouri Botanical Garden Pr.
Goffinet, Bernard. Bryophyte Biology. Shaw, A. Jonathan, ed. 2nd rev. ed. 2008. (ENG., Illus.). 580p. pap. 68.99 *(978-0-521-69322-6(5))* Cambridge Univ. Pr.
Itten, Beatriz Esther. Population Studies on Sphagnum Fimbriatum. 2010. 76p. pap. *(978-3-8383-0483-0(7))* Lambert Academic Publishing.
Longton, R. E. Biology of Polar Bryophytes & Lichens. 2009. (Studies in Polar Research Ser.). (ENG., Illus.). 404p. pap. 69.00 *(978-0-521-09338-5(4))* Cambridge Univ. Pr.
Tuba, Zoltàn, et al, eds. Bryophyte Ecology & Climate Change. 2011. (ENG., Illus.). 528p. 140.00 *(978-0-521-76763-7(6))* Cambridge Univ. Pr.
—Bryophyte Ecology & Climate Change. 2011. (ENG., Illus.). 528p. pap. 60.00 *(978-0-521-75777-5(0))* Cambridge Univ. Pr.
Vanderpoorten, Alain & Goffinet, Bernard. Introduction to Bryophytes. 2009. (ENG., Illus.). 312p. (C). 110.00 *(978-0-521-87712-1(1))*; pap. 49.00 *(978-0-521-70073-3(6))* Cambridge Univ. Pr.
Weber, William A. & Wittmann, Ronald C. Bryophytes of Colorado: Mosses, Liverworts, & Hornworts. 2007. per. 29.95 *(978-0-9790909-1-2(1))* Pilgrims Process, Inc.
Wood, Andrew J., et al, eds. New Frontiers in Bryology: Physiology, Molecular Biology & Functional Genomics. 2010. (ENG.). 216p. pap. 169.00 *(978-90-481-6569-8(5), 9048165695)* Springer.

BRYOZOA

see Polyzoa

BSA MOTORCYCLE

Clymer, Floyd, creator. Book of the Bsa Twins - All 500cc & 650cc Models 1948-1962. 2010. 142p. pap. 24.95 *(978-1-58850-097-7(7))* Veloce Enterprises, Inc.
Henshaw, Peter. BSA 500 & 650 Twins: A7, A10, A50 & A65: 1946 To 1973. 2008. (Essential Buyer's Guide Ser.). (ENG., Illus.). 64p. pap. 19.95 *(978-1-84584-136-2(0), 1845841360)* Veloce Publishing Ltd. GBR. Dist: MBI Distribution Services/Quayside Distribution.
—BSA Bantam: The Essential Buyer's Guide. 2008. (Essential Buyer's Guide Ser.). (ENG., Illus.). 64p. pap. 19.95 *(978-1-84584-165-2(4), 1845841654)* Veloce Publishing Ltd. GBR. Dist: MBI Distribution Services/Quayside Distribution.
—BSA Bantam Bible. 2008. (Bible Ser.). (ENG., Illus.). 160p. 59.95 *(978-1-84584-159-1(X), 184584159X)* Veloce Publishing Ltd. GBR. Dist: MBI Distribution Services/Quayside Distribution.
Lupton, A. Book of the Bsa Ohv & Sv Singles - 250cc 1954-1970. 2011. (Illus.). 132p. pap. 24.95 ***(978-1-58850-158-5(2))*** Veloce Enterprises, Inc.
Vale, Matthew. BSA Unit Singles: The Complete Story Including the Triumph Derivatives. 2006. (ENG., Illus.). 200p. 34.95 *(978-1-86126-843-3(2), 1861268432)* Crowood Pr., Ltd. GBR. Dist: MBI Distribution Services/Quayside Distribution.

BSE (DISEASE)

see Bovine Spongiform Encephalopathy

BSTAN-DZIN-RGYA-MTSHO, DALAI LAMA XIV, 1935-

Chaves-Segura, Alenjandro. A Tibetan Buddhist Approach to International Relations: The Teaching of the Dalai Lama. 2011. 272p. ***(978-0-7734-1608-6(0))*** Mellen, Edwin Pr., The.
Chhaya, Mayank. Dalai Lama: The Revealing Life Story & His Struggle for Tibet. 2007. (ENG., Illus.). 352p. 23.95 *(978-0-385-51945-8(1), Doubleday)* Doubleday Religious Publishing Group, The.
Dalai Lama XIV. All You Ever Wanted to Know from His Holiness the Dalai Lama on Happiness, Life, Living, & Much More: Conversations with Rajiv Mehrotra. 2009. (ENG.). 264p. 19.95 *(978-1-4019-2018-0(7))* Hay Hse., Inc.
Dalai Lama XIV & Ekman, Paul. Emotional Awareness: Overcoming the Obstacles to Psychological Balance. 2009. (ENG., Illus.). 288p. pap. 15.99 *(978-0-8050-9021-5(5), Holt Paperback)* Holt, Henry & Co.
Dalai Lama XIV & Stril-Rever, Sofia. My Spiritual Journey. (ENG.). 2011. 304p. pap. 15.99 *(978-0-06-201809-0(4), HarperOne)* 2010. (Illus.). 304p. 25.99 *(978-0-06-196022-2(5), HarperOne)* 2010. 420p. pap. 25.99 *(978-0-06-200252-5(X), HarperLuxe)* HarperCollins Pubs.
Dalai Lama XIV, et al. Sophia: The Journal of Traditional Studies, 13. 2007. 200p. pap. 17.95 *(978-0-9798429-0-0(5))* Foundation for Traditional Studies.
Designwallas Publishing Staff, creator. HH Cool. 2009. (ICONoclastic Ser.). (ENG.). 128p. 12.95 *(978-81-7436-666-5(0))* Roli Bks. Private, Ltd. IND. Dist: Ingram Pub. Services.
Ekman, Paul & Dalai Lama XIV. Emotional Awareness: Overcoming the Obstacles to Psychological Balance & Compassion. 2008. (ENG., Illus.). 288p. 23.00 *(978-0-8050-8712-3(5), Times Bks.)* Holt, Henry & Co.
Iyer, Pico. The Open Road: The Global Journey of the Fourteenth Dalai Lama. (Vintage Departures Ser.). (ENG.). 288p. 2009. pap. 15.95 *(978-0-307-38755-4(0), Vintage)* 2008. 24.00 *(978-0-307-26760-3(1), Knopf)* Knopf Doubleday Publishing Group.
Lendorfer, Manuel. Soft-Power Resources of the Tibetan Exile Government. 2010. 144p. pap. *(978-3-639-26286-5(7))* VDM Verlag Dr. Mueller e.K.
Levenson, Claude B. Tenzin Gyatso: The Early Life of the Dalai Lama. Rowe, Joseph, tr. 2007. (Illus.). 155p. reprint ed. pap. 15.00 *(978-1-4223-9005-4(5))* DIANE Publishing Co.
Mehotra, Rajiv. Understanding the Dalai Lama: A Simple, Smiling Monk. 2009. 288p. pap. *(978-1-84850-037-2(8), 797)* Hay Hse. UK, Ltd. GBR. Dist: Grantham Bk. Services.
Mehrotra, Rajiv. All You Ever Wanted to Know from His Holiness The Dalai Lama on Happiness, Life, Living, & Much More 2010. (ENG.). 256p. pap. 14.95 *(978-1-4019-2016-6(0))* Hay Hse., Inc.
Mehrotra, Rajiv, ed. Understanding the Dalai Lama. 2009. (ENG., Illus.). 256p. 24.95 *(978-1-4019-2327-3(5))* Hay Hse., Inc.
Saiwai, Tetsu. The 14th Dalai Lama: A Manga Biography. 2010. (ENG., Illus.). 208p. (gr. 12). 15.00 *(978-0-14-311815-2(3), Penguin (Non-Classics))* Penguin Group (USA) Inc.
Thompson, Chris. Felt: Fluxus, Joseph Beuys, & the Dalai Lama. 2011. (Illus.). 320p. 82.50 *(978-0-8166-5354-6(2))*; pap., pap. 27.50 *(978-0-8166-5355-3(0))* Univ. of Minnesota Pr.
Thurman, Robert. Why the Dalai Lama Matters: His Act of Truth as the Solution for China, Tibet, & the World. 2011. (ENG., Illus.). 256p. pap. 14.00 *(978-1-58270-221-6(7), Beyond Words/Atria Bks.)* Atria Bks.
Thurman, Robert & Thurman, Robert A. F. Why the Dalai Lama Matters: His Act of Truth As the Solution for China, Tibet, & the World. 2008. (ENG., Illus.). 256p. 24.00 *(978-1-58270-220-9(9), Beyond Words/Atria Bks.)* Atria Bks.
Vivas, Maxime. Behind the Smile: The Hidden Side of the Dalai Lama. 2012. pap. ***(978-1-59265-140-5(2))*** Long River Pr.
Vyas, Bhaskar & Vyas, Rajni. Experiments with Truth & Non-Violence: The Dalai Lama in Exile from Tibet. 2007. (Illus.). xii, 212p. *(978-81-8069-359-5(7))* Concept Publishing Co.
Western Shugden Society. A Great Deception: The Ruling Lamas' Policies. 2010. (ENG.). 312p. pap. 12.95 *(978-0-615-32924-6(1))* Western Shugden Society US.
White Star, ed. Dalai Lama. 2010. (ENG., Illus.). 280p. pap. 30.00 *(978-88-544-0420-5(9))* White Star ITA. Dist: Random Hse., Inc.

BUBBLES

Ferrari, Michele & Liggieri, L., eds. Drops & Bubbles in Contact with Solid Surfaces. 2012. (Progress in Colloid & Interface Science Ser.). (ENG.). ***(978-90-04-20319-8(2))*** BRILL.
Miller, R. & Liggieri, L. Bubble & Drop Interfaces. 2011. (ENG.). 560p. 277.00 *(978-90-04-17495-5(8), CRC Press)* Taylor & Francis Group GBR. Dist: Taylor & Francis Group.
Nassar, Ahmed F. Single- & Two-Phase Flow in Stirred Vessels. 2011. 112p. pap. ***(978-3-8454-2412-5(5))*** Lambert Academic Publishing.
Penzes, Karen. Bubble Play: Play & Learn with Bubbles! 2007. (ENG., Illus.). 32p. (J). (gr. -1). bds. 16.95 *(978-1-55263-888-0(X))* Key Porter Bks. CAN. Dist: Perseus-PGW.
Tente, Raniska. Microbubbles & Ultrasound. 2011. 240p. pap. ***(978-3-8443-0106-9(2))*** Lambert Academic Publishing.
Young, F. Ronald. Fizzics: The Science of Bubbles, Droplets, & Foams. 2011. (ENG., Illus.). 136p. (gr. 17). 50.00 *(978-0-8018-9891-4(9))*; pap. 25.00 *(978-0-8018-9892-1(7))* Johns Hopkins Univ. Pr.

BUBER, MARTIN, 1878-1965

Chen, Alexander & Meir, Ephraim. Between Heschel & Buber: A Comparative Study. 2012. (Emunot: Jewish Philosophy & Kabbalah Ser.). (ENG.). 270p. 85.00 ***(978-1-936235-72-8(2))*** Academic Studies Pr.
Huston, Phil. Martin Buber's Journey to Presence. 2007. (Abrahamic Dialogues Ser.). (ENG., Illus.). 288p. 70.00 *(978-0-8232-2739-6(1))* Fordham Univ. Pr.
Kramer, Kenneth. Dialogically Speaking: Maurice Friedman's Interdisciplinary Humanism. 2011. xxv, 304p. *(978-1-60599-838-1(9), Pickwick Pubns.)* Wipf & Stock Pubs.
Kramer, Kenneth Paul. Martin Buber's Spirituality: Hasidic Wisdom for Everyday Life. 2011. (ENG.). 200p. 40.00 ***(978-1-4422-1367-8(1))***; E-Book ***(978-1-4422-1369-2(8))*** Rowman & Littlefield Publishers, Inc.
Kramer, Kenneth Paul, ed. Dialogically Speaking: Maurice Friedman's Interdisciplinary Humanism. 2010. 330p. pap. 36.00 *(978-1-60899-838-8(X), Pickwick Pubns.)* Wipf & Stock Pubs.
Lorenz, Michael. Das Wort im Spannungsfeld von Anrede und Interpretation: Erfahrungsbezug und Wirklichkeitsdeutung in der Predigt. 2011. (Arbeiten zur Pastoraltheologie, Liturgik und Hymnologie Ser.). (GER.). 263p. (C). pap. 77.00 *(978-3-525-62415-9(8))* Vandenhoeck & Ruprecht GmbH & Co. KG DEU. Dist: ISD.
Nathan Rotenstreich, ed. Immediacy & Its Limits (Routledge Revivals) 2009. 120p. pap. 39.95 *(978-0-415-57048-0(4))* Routledge.
Polish, Daniel F. Talking about God: Exploring the Meaning of Religious Life with Kierkegaard, Buber, Tillich & Heschel. 2010. (ENG.). 160p. pap. 16.99 *(978-1-59473-272-0(8))* SkyLight Paths Publishing.
Putnam, Hilary. Jewish Philosophy as a Guide to Life: Rosenzweig, Buber, Levinas, Wittgenstein. 2008. (Helen & Martin Schwartz Lectures in Jewish Studies). (ENG.). 136p. 19.95 *(978-0-253-35133-3(2), 0253351332)* Indiana Univ. Pr.
Ress, Jonathan. Understanding Psychotherapy for Trauma with Buber's I-Thou Philosophy. 2010. 96p. pap. *(978-3-8383-4843-8(5))* Lambert Academic Publishing.

Rotenstreich, Nathan, ed. Immediacy & Its Limits: A Study in Martin Buber's Thought. 2009. (Routledge Revivals Ser.). (ENG.). 134p. 100.00 *(978-0-415-56718-3(1))* Routledge.

Scholem, Gershom & Dannhauser, Werner J. On Jews & Judaism in Crisis: Selected Essays. 2012. (ENG.). 306p. pap. 18.95 ***(978-1-58988-074-0(9))*** Dry, Paul Bks., Inc.

Urban, Martina. Aesthetics of Renewal: Martin Buber's Early Representation of Hasidism as Kulturkritik. 2008. (ENG.). 240p. 32.00 *(978-0-226-84270-7(3))* Univ. of Chicago Pr.

Zank, Michael, ed. New Perspectives on Martin Buber. 2006. (Religion in Philosophy & Theology Ser.: Vol. 22). 277p. (C). pap. 89.50 *(978-3-16-148998-3(5))* Mohr Siebeck GmbH & Co. KG DEU. Dist: Coronet Bks.

BUBONIC PLAGUE
see Plague

BUBONIDAE
see Owls

BUBONOCELE
see Hernia

BUCCANEERS
see also Brigands and Robbers; Pirates; Sea Stories

Abbott, John S. C. Captain William Kidd: The Buccaneers. 373p. reprint ed. 98.00 *(978-0-7222-9436-9(0))* Library Reprints, Inc.

—Captain William Kidd: The Pirates or Buccaneers Who Ravaged the Seas, the Islands, And the Continents of America Two Hundred Years Ago. 373p. reprint ed. 98.00 *(978-0-7222-8469-8(1))* Library Reprints, Inc.

—Captain William Kidd, & Others of the Pirates or Buccaneers Who Ravaged the Seas, Islands & Continents of America Two Hundred Years Ago. (American Pioneers & Patriots Ser.). 373p. reprint ed. 98.00 *(978-0-7222-8375-2(X))* Library Reprints, Inc.

—Captain William Kidd, & Others of the Pirates or Buccaneers Who Ravaged the Seas, Islands & Continents of America Two Hundred Years Ago. 373p. reprint ed. 58.00 *(978-0-7950-2557-0(2))* New Library Press LLC.

Beahm, George. Caribbean Pirates: A Treasure Chest of Fact, Fiction, & Folklore. 2009. (ENG.). 233p. pap. 17.00 *(978-1-4379-6549-0(0))* DIANE Publishing Co.

—Caribbean Pirates: A Treasure Chest of Fact, Fiction, & Folklore. 2007. (ENG., Illus.). 256p. (YA). (gr. 4-7). pap. 16.95 *(978-1-57174-541-5(6))* Hampton Roads Publishing Co., Inc.

Beahm, George W. Caribbean Pirates: A Treasure Chest of Fact, Fiction, & Folklore. 2007. (Illus.). xviii, 233p. *(978-1-57174-553-8(X))* Hampton Roads Publishing Co., Inc.

Bowling, Tom. A Brief History of Pirates & Buccaneers. 2010. (ENG.). 256p. pap. 13.95 *(978-0-7624-3852-5(5))* Running Pr. Bk. Pubs.

Brady, Cyrus Townsend. Colonial Fights & Fighters. 2009. 374p. 29.99 *(978-1-116-99569-5(7))*; 31.99 *(978-1-116-99568-8(9))*; pap. 33.75 *(978-1-116-99570-1(0))*; pap. 32.75 *(978-1-116-99571-8(9))* BiblioBazaar.

—Colonial Fights & Fighters. 341p. reprint ed. 98.00 *(978-0-7222-6873-5(4))* Library Reprints, Inc.

Burgess, Douglas R. The Pirates' Pact: The Secret Alliances Between History's Most Notorious Buccaneers & Colonial America. 2008. (ENG., Illus.). 288p. 26.95 *(978-0-07-147476-4(5)*, 0071474765, International Marine/Ragged Mountain Pr.) McGraw-Hill Professional Publishing.

Burney, James. History of the Buccaneers of America. 2010. (Cambridge Library Collection - Travel & Exploration Ser.). (Illus.). 320p. pap. 24.99 *(978-1-108-02524-9(2))* Cambridge Univ. Pr.

—History of the Buccaneers of America. 2007. (ENG.). 396p. per. 16.75 *(978-1-60206-253-5(6))* Cosimo, Inc.

—History of the Buccaneers of America. 2008. 340p. 46.95 *(978-0-548-93211-7(5))* 2007. (ENG.). 344p. per. 31.95 *(978-0-548-59238-0(1))* Kessinger Publishing, LLC.

Carpenter, John Reeve. Pirates: Scourge of the Seas. 2008. (ENG., Illus.). 208p. 9.95 *(978-1-4027-6311-3(5))* Sterling Publishing Co., Inc.

Caygill, Peter. Flying the Buccaneer: Britain's Cold War Warrior. 2008. (Illus.). 256p. 39.95 *(978-1-84415-669-6(9))* Pen & Sword Bks. Ltd. GBR. Dist: Casemate Pubs. & Bk. Distributors, LLC.

Dampier, William. A New Voyage Round the World. 2007. (ENG.). 376p. pap. 19.95 *(978-1-933698-04-5(7))* 1500 Bks.

—A Voyage to New Holland in 1699 with a Continuation of a Voyage to New Holland in 1699 Etc. 2008. (Illus.). 180p. pap. *(978-1-84830-930-2(9)*, Wildhern Pr.) Echo Library.

Esquemeling, John. The Buccaneers of Americ. 2008. 128p. pap. 14.99 *(978-1-60459-520-8(5))* Wilder Pubns., Ltd.

—The Buccaneers of America. 568p. 2010. 47.16 *(978-1-169-35965-9(5))* 2010. 58.95 *(978-1-161-91588-4(5))* 2009. pap. 43.95 *(978-1-104-26704-9(7))* Kessinger Publishing, LLC.

—The Buccaneers of America: A True Account of the Most Remarkable Assaults Committed of Late Years upon the Coasts of the West Indies by the Buccaneers of Jamaica & Tortuga. Powell, Henry, ed. 2010. (Cambridge Library Collection - History Ser.). (Illus.). 566p. pap. 39.99 *(978-1-108-02481-5(5))* Cambridge Univ. Pr.

—The Buccaneers of America: In the Original English Translation Of 1684. 2007. 296p. per. 18.95 *(978-1-60206-100-2(9))* Cosimo, Inc.

Exquemelin, A. O. The Buccaneers of America: A Firsthand Account of Life with the Caribbean Pirates Captain Henry Morgan, Francis Lolonois, & Pierra la Grande. 2009. (Illus.). 192p. pap. *(978-1-934941-72-0(7))* Red & Black Pubs.

Exquemelin, Alexander. The Illustrated Pirate Diaries: A Remarkable Eyewitness Account of Captain Morgan & the Buccaneers. 2008. 192p. 29.95 *(978-0-06-158448-0(7))* HarperCollins Pubs.

Gambrill, Anthony. In Search of the Buccaneers. 2007. (Illus.). 258p. *(978-0-333-97652-4(5))* Macmillan Caribbean.

Gosse, Philip. The Pirates' Who's Who: Giving Particulars of the Lives & Deaths of the Pirates & Buccaneers. 2007. (ENG.). 278p. pap. 21.99 *(978-1-4346-3302-6(0))*; 322p. pap. 24.99 *(978-1-4346-3303-3(9))* BiblioBazaar.

Hakluyt, Richard. The Principal Navigations Voyages Traffiques & Discoveries of the English Nation: Madiera the Canaries Ancient Asia Africa Etc. 6. l.t. ed. 2007. 270p. pap. 23.99 *(978-1-4264-2619-3(4))* BiblioBazaar.

—The Principal Navigations, Voyages, Traffiques & Discoveries of the English Nation, Volume 10: Asia, Part III. 2007. 288p. pap. 21.99 *(978-1-4264-5685-5(9))*; 326p. pap. 24.99 *(978-1-4264-5730-2(8))* BiblioBazaar.

—The Principal Navigations Voyages Traffiques & Discoveries of the English Nation Volume 6: Madiera the Canaries Ancient Asia Africa Etc. 2007. (ENG.). 236p. pap. 20.99 *(978-1-4264-2578-3(3))* BiblioBazaar.

—The Principal Navigations, Voyages, Traffiques & Discoveries of the English Nation, Volume VIII. 2007. (ENG.). 322p. pap. 24.99 *(978-1-4264-3750-2(1))*; 288p. pap. 21.99 *(978-1-4264-3693-2(9))* BiblioBazaar.

Haring, C. H. The Buccaneers in the West Indies in the Xvii Century. 2007. (Illus.). 300p. per. *(978-1-4065-2348-5(8))* Dodo Pr.

Haring, Clarence Henry. The Buccaneers in the West Indies in the XVII Century. 2007. (ENG.). 240p. pap. 20.99 *(978-1-4264-9587-8(0))*; 276p. pap. 23.99 *(978-1-4264-9968-5(X))* BiblioBazaar.

Johnstone, C. I. (Christian Isobel). The Lives & Voyages of Drake, Cavendish, & Dampier; Including an Introductory View of the Earlier Discoveries in the South Sea, & the History Of. 2006. 328p. per. 23.99 *(978-1-4255-3249-9(7))* MPublishing.

Kinkor, Kenneth J. & Simpson, Sharon. Real Pirates: The Untold Story of the Whydah from Slave Ship to Pirate Ship. 2007. (ENG., Illus.). 176p. per. 19.95 *(978-1-4262-0262-9(8))* National Geographic Society.

Konstam, Angus. Scourge of the Seas: Buccaneers, Pirates & Privateers. 2007. (General Military Ser.). (ENG., Illus.). 240p. 24.95 *(978-1-84603-211-0(3))* Osprey Publishing, Ltd. GBR. Dist: Random Hse., Inc.

Kritzler, Edward. Jewish Pirates of the Caribbean: How a Generation of Swashbuckling Jews Carved Out an Empire in the New World in Their Quest for Treasure, Religious Freedom — and Revenge. (ENG.). 2009. 352p. pap. 15.95 *(978-0-7679-1952-4(1)*, Anchor) 2008. (Illus.). 336p. 26.00 *(978-0-385-51398-2(4))* Knopf Doubleday Publishing Group.

Latimer, Jon. Buccaneers of the Caribbean: How Piracy Forged an Empire. 2009. (Illus.). 368p. 27.95 *(978-0-674-03403-7(1))* Harvard Univ. Pr.

Little, Benerson. The Buccaneer's Realm: Pirate Life on the Spanish Main, 1674-1688. 2007. (Illus.). 368p. 29.95 *(978-1-59797-101-0(4))* Potomac Bks., Inc.

—How History's Greatest Pirates Pillaged, Plundered, & Got Away with It: The Stories, Techniques, & Tactics of the Most Feared Sea Rovers From, 1500-1800. 2010. (ENG., Illus.). 272p. pap. 19.99 *(978-1-59233-443-8(1)*, 1592334431) Quayside.

Masefield, John. On the Spanish Main: Or Some English forays on the Isthmus of Darien. 2007. (ENG.). 296p. pap. 21.99 *(978-1-4264-9675-2(3))*; 324p. pap. 24.99 *(978-1-4264-9596-0(X))* BiblioBazaar.

Snow, Edward Rowe. Pirates & Buccaneers of the Atlantic Coast. 2011. 350p. 51.95 ***(978-1-258-03489-4(1))*** Literary Licensing, LLC.

Strong, Ezra, ed. Infamous Pirates: Their Lives & Bloody Exploits. 2007. (Dover Maritime Ser.). (ENG., Illus.). 320p. per. 10.95 *(978-0-486-46185-4(8))* Dover Pubns., Inc.

Thomas, Graham A. Pirate Killers. 2011. (Illus.). 224p. 39.95 ***(978-1-84884-240-3(6))*** Pen & Sword Bks. Ltd. GBR. Dist: Casemate Pubs. & Bk. Distributors, LLC.

BUCER, MARTIN, 1491-1551

de Kroon, Marijn. We Believe in God & in Christ. Not in the Church: The Influence of Wessel Gansfort on Martin Bucer. 2009. (Princeton Theological Seminary Studies in Reformed Theology & History Ser.). (ENG.). 128p. pap. 30.00 *(978-0-664-23293-1(0))* Westminster John Knox Pr.

Eells, Hastings. The Attitudes of Martin Bucer Toward the Bigamy of Philip of Hesse. reprint ed. 32.50 *(978-0-404-19829-9(5))* AMS Pr., Inc.

Friedrich, Reinhold, et al, eds. Martin Bucer: Briefwechsel, Correspondence: Band VI (Mai 1531 - Oktober 1531) 2006. (Studies in Medieval & Reformation Traditions: History, Culture, Religion, Ideas). 336p. *(978-90-04-15494-0(9))* BRILL.

Hamm, Berndt & Friedrich, Reinhold, eds. Martin Bucer: Briefwechsel/Correspondance, Volume 136 Martin Bucer Briefwechsel/Correspondance: Band VII (Oktober 1531 - März 1532) 2008. 650pp.p. *(978-90-04-17132-9(0))* BRILL.

Lawrence, David. Martin Bucer: Unsung Hero of the Reformation. 2008. 268p. per. 19.95 *(978-1-933912-09-7(X))* Westview Publishing Co., Inc.

BUCHAN, JOHN, 1875-1940

Macdonald, Kate. John Buchan: A Companion to the Mystery Fiction. Foxwell, Elizabeth, ed. 2008. (McFarland Companions to Mystery Fiction Ser.). (ENG., Illus.). 229p. pap. 39.95 *(978-0-7864-3489-3(9))* McFarland & Co., Inc. Pubs.

Macdonald, Kate, ed. Reassessing John Buchan: Beyond the Thirty Nine Steps, 1 vol. 2009. (ENG.). 304p. 99.00 *(978-1-85196-998-2(5))* Pickering & Chatto Pubs., Ltd. GBR. Dist: Ashgate Publishing Co.

BUCHANAN, FRANKLIN, 1800-1874

Symonds, Craig L. Confederate Admiral. 2008. 312p. pap. 18.95 *(978-1-59114-846-3(4))* Naval Institute Pr.

BUCHANAN, GEORGE, 1506-1582

Ford, Philip & Green, Roger P. H., eds. George Buchanan: Poet & Dramatist. 2009. (ENG., Illus.). 355p. (C). 100.00 *(978-1-905125-36-4(4))* Classical Pr. of Wales, The GBR. Dist: Brown, David Bk. Co., The.

Henriques, Guilherme J. C. George Buchanan in the Lisbon Inquisitio. 2006. pap. 17.95 *(978-1-4286-4316-1(8))* Kessinger Publishing, LLC.

Mason, Roger & Erskine, Caroline. George Buchanan: Political Thought in Early Modern Europe an the Atlantic World. 2012. (St Andrews Studies in Reformation History Ser.). (Illus.). 286p. 124.95 ***(978-0-7546-6238-9(1))*** Ashgate Publishing Co.

BUCHANAN, JAMES, 1791-1868

Bomberger, C. M. & Buchanan, James. Twelfth Colony Plus: The Formative Years of Pennsylvania & A Biography of James Buchanan. 2011. 244p. 46.95 ***(978-1-258-09548-2(3))*** Literary Licensing, LLC.

Buchanan, James. Letters of James Buchanan: Papers Read Before the Lancaster Historical Society V35, No. 8. Worner, William Frederic, ed. 2011. 28p. 35.95 ***(978-1-258-02951-7(0))*** Literary Licensing, LLC.

Buchanan, James. The Works of James Buchanan: Comprising His Speeches, State Papers; & Private Correspondence, 12 vol., set. reprint ed. 1500.00 *(978-0-7222-8630-2(9))* Library Reprints, Inc.

Buchanan, James M. Economics from the Outside In: Better Than Plowing & Beyond. 2007. (Texas A & M University Economics Ser.: 17). (ENG.). 254p. per. 20.00 *(978-1-58544-603-2(3))* Texas A&M Univ. Pr.

Curtis, George Ticknor. The Life of James Buchanan, 2 vol., set. reprint ed. 250.00 *(978-0-7222-8631-9(7))* Library Reprints, Inc.

Dougherty, Keith L. The Calculus of Consent & Constitutional Design. 2011. (Studies in Public Choice Ser.). (ENG., Illus.). xii, 117p. 119.00 *(978-0-387-98170-3(5)*, 0387981705) Springer.

Horrocks, Thomas A. President James Buchanan & the Crisis of National Leadership. 2012. ***(978-1-62100-476-9(7))*** Nova Science Pubs., Inc.

King, Horatio. Turning on the Light: A Dispassionate Survey of President Buchanan's Administration, from 1860 to Its Close. 419p. reprint ed. 98.00 *(978-0-7222-8632-6(5))* Library Reprints, Inc.

Richardson, James D. A Compilation of the Messages & Papers of the Presidents: James Buchanan, Vol. 5. l.t. ed. 2007. 390p. pap. 26.99 *(978-1-4264-4628-3(4))* BiblioBazaar.

—A Compilation of the Messages & Papers of the Presidents Volume 5: James Buchanan. 2007. 340p. pap. 23.99 *(978-1-4264-4577-4(6))* BiblioBazaar.

BUCHANAN, ROBERT WILLIAMS, 1841-1901

Jay, Harriett. Robert Buchanan. 2009. 224p. pap. 19.99 *(978-0-217-79149-6(2))* General Bks. LLC.

—Robert Buchanan Some Account of His Life. 2006. pap. 26.95 *(978-1-4286-5926-1(9))* Kessinger Publishing, LLC.

BUCHENWALD (CONCENTRATION CAMP)

Kogon, Eugen. The Theory & Practice of Hell: The German Concentration Camps & the System Behind Them. Norden, Heinz, tr. from GER. 2006. (ENG., Illus.). 368p. pap. 16.00 *(978-0-374-52992-5(2))* Farrar, Straus & Giroux.

Lau, Israel Meir. Out of the Depths: The Story of a Child of Buchenwald Who Returned Home at Last. 2011. (ENG., Illus.). 400p. 24.95 *(978-1-4027-8631-0(X))* Sterling Publishing Co., Inc.

Niven, Bill. The Buchenwald Child: Truth, Fiction, & Propaganda. 2007. (Studies in German Literature Linguistics & Culture Ser.: Volume 3). (Illus.). 258p. 45.00 *(978-1-57113-339-7(9))* Camden Hse.

BUCHNER, GEORG, 1813-1837

Büchner, Georg, et al. Georg Büchner: The Major Works. 2012. (Norton Critical Editions Ser.). (ENG.). 432p. (C). pap. 12.00 net. *(978-0-393-93351-2(2)*, 93351) Norton, W. W. & Co., Inc.

Vanecek, Edwin. Auswege aus Literatur: Literarische Vorbereitungen zur musikalisch-künstlerischen Interpretation bei Georg Büchner, Franz Kafka, Lorenzo Da Ponte, Henri Meilhac und Ludovic Halevy. 2009. (Musik und Literatur Ser.). (GER.). 214p. 57.95 *(978-3-631-54819-6(2))* Lang, Peter GmbH, Europäischer Verlag der Wissenschaften DEU. Dist: Lang, Peter.

Wittkowski, Wolfgang. Georg Büchner: Rückblick und Einblick. 2008. 236p. pap. 61.95 *(978-3-631-58574-0(8))* Lang, Peter GmbH, Europaischer Verlag der Wissenschaften DEU. Dist: Lang, Peter.

BUCK, PEARL S. (PEARL SYDENSTRICKER), 1892-1973

Becnel, Kim. The Rise of Corporate Publishing & Its Effects on Authorship in Early Twentieth-Century America. 2007. (Literary Criticism & Cultural Theory Ser.). 149p. 131.00 *(978-0-415-95555-3(6))* Routledge.

Buck, Pearl S. The Child Who Never Grew. 24.95 *(978-0-8488-1250-8(6))* Amereon LTD.

Harker, Jaime. America the Middlebrow: Women's Novels, Progressivism, & Middlebrow Authorship between the Wars. 2007. (Studies in Print Culture & the History of the Book). (Illus.). 208p. lib. bdg. 80.00 *(978-1-55849-596-8(7))* Univ. of Massachusetts Pr.

—America the Middlebrow: Women's Novels, Progressivism, & Middlebrow Authorship Between the Wars. 2007. (Studies in Print Culture & the History of the Book). (Illus.). 182p. per. 24.95 *(978-1-55849-597-5(5))* Univ. of Massachusetts Pr.

Spurling, Hilary. Pearl Buck in China: Journey to the Good Earth. (ENG.). 320p. 2011. pap. 15.00 *(978-1-4165-4043-4(1))* 2010. (Illus.). 27.00 *(978-1-4165-4042-7(3))* Simon & Schuster.

BUCKET-SHOPS
see Speculation

BUCKINGHAM, GEORGE VILLIERS, DUKE OF, 1592-1628

Bellany, Alastair & Cogswell, Tom. England's Assassin: John Felton & the Killing of the Duke of Buckingham. 2007. (ENG., Illus.). 336p. 35.00 *(978-0-300-11849-0(X))* Yale Univ. Pr.

BUCKINGHAM, JAMES SILK, 1786-1855

Buckingham, James Silk. Autobiography of James Silk Buckingham: Including his Voyages, Travels, Adventures, Speculations, Successes & Failures. 2011. (Cambridge Library Collection - Travel & Exploration Ser.). (ENG.). 442p. pap. 32.99 ***(978-1-108-03858-4(1))***; (Illus.). 424p. pap. 31.99 ***(978-1-108-03857-7(3))*** Cambridge Univ. Pr.

BUCKINGHAM PALACE (LONDON, ENGLAND)

Brown, Jane & Sykes, Christopher Simon. The Garden at Buckingham Palace: An Illustrated History. 2005. (Illus.). 55.00 *(978-1-902163-82-6(6))* Royal Collection Enterprises Ltd. GBR. Dist: Antique Collectors' Club.

Jones, Kathryn. For the Royal Table: Dining at the Palace. 2010. (ENG., Illus.). 120p. 15.00 *(978-1-905686-11-7(0))* Royal Collection Enterprises Ltd. GBR. Dist: Chicago Distribution Ctr.

Marsden, Jonathan. Buckingham Palace: Official Souvenir Guide. 2012. (ENG., Illus.). 72p. pap. 10.95 ***(978-1-85759-757-8(5))*** Scala, Editions FRA. Dist: National Bk. Network.

Marsden, Jonathan & Royal Collection Staff. Buckingham Palace: Official Souvenir Guide. 2010. (ENG., Illus.). 96p. per. 7.95 *(978-1-902163-95-5(8))* Royal Collection Enterprises Ltd. GBR. Dist: Chicago Distribution Ctr.

Parsons, Tom & Royal Collection Staff. 100 Treasures of Buckingham Palace. 2010. (Illus.). 224p. pap. 9.95 *(978-1-902163-92-5(3))* Royal Collection Enterprises Ltd. GBR. Dist: Chicago Distribution Ctr.

Royal Collection Publications. Buckingham Palace - Espanol. 2010. (Illus.). 96p. pap. 7.95 *(978-1-902163-38-3(9))* Royal Collection Enterprises Ltd. GBR. Dist: Chicago Distribution Ctr.

—Buckingham Palace - FranCais: Guide-souvenir Officiel. 2010. (Illus.). 96p. pap. 7.95 *(978-1-902163-07-9(9))* Royal Collection Enterprises Ltd. GBR. Dist: Chicago Distribution Ctr.

Vickers, Hugh. The Royal Mews at Buckingham Palace: Official Guidebook. 2010. (ENG.). 56p. pap. 7.95 *(978-1-902163-26-0(5))* Royal Collection Enterprises Ltd. GBR. Dist: Chicago Distribution Ctr.

Wright, Patricia. Strange History of Buckingham Palace. 2009. (ENG., Illus.). 240p. pap. 19.95 *(978-0-7509-4803-6(5))* History Pr. Ltd., The GBR. Dist: Independent Pubs. Group.

BUCKINGHAMSHIRE (ENGLAND)

Dovey, Zillah. Aylesbury Past & Present. (Illus.). 160p. *(978-0-7509-1770-4(9))* Sutton Publishing.

Letters & Papers of the Verney Family down to the End of the Year 1639. 2008. (ENG.). 332p. per. *(978-1-4086-5107-0(6))* Read Bks.

Masefield, Robert. Prehistoric & Later Settlement & Landscape from Chiltern Scarp to Aylesbury Vale. 2009. (Bar Ser.). (Illus.). 234p. (C). 100.00 *(978-1-4073-0374-1(0))* British Archaeological Reports Ltd. GBR. Dist: Brown, David Bk. Co., The.

BUCKINGHAMSHIRE (ENGLAND)—DESCRIPTION AND TRAVEL

Garnett, Oliver. Hughenden Manor (Buckinghamshire) 2006. (National Trust Guidebooks Ser.). (ENG., Illus.). 48p. pap. 11.95 *(978-1-84359-173-3(1))* History Pr. Ltd., The GBR. Dist: Independent Pubs. Group.

Robinson, John Martin. Ascott. 2009. (ENG., Illus.). 64p. pap. 15.00 *(978-1-85759-504-8(1))* Scala, Editions FRA. Dist: National Bk. Network.

BUCKINGHAMSHIRE (ENGLAND)—HISTORY

Farley, Mike. An Illustrated History of Early Buckinghamshire. 2010. (Illus.). 240p. (C). pap. 29.95 *(978-0-9558158-4-3(3))* Buckinghamshire Archaeological Society GBR. Dist: Brown, David Bk. Co., The.

Tinniswood, Adrian. The Verneys: A True Story of Love, War, & Madness in Seventeenth-Century England. 2008. (ENG., Illus.). 592p. (gr. 12-18). 26.00 *(978-1-59443-309-7(4)*, Riverhead Trade (Paperbacks)) Penguin Group (USA) Inc.

BUCKLAND, FRANCIS T. (FRANCIS TREVELYAN), 1826-1880

Bompas, George C. The Life of Frank Buckland. 2007. (ENG.). 444p. 51.95 *(978-0-548-06323-1(0))* Kessinger Publishing, LLC.

Walpole, Francis Caldwell Holland. Essays Political & Biographical. 2009. 346p. 32.99 *(978-1-113-03884-5(5))*; pap. 31.75 *(978-1-113-03882-1(9))* BiblioBazaar.

Walpole, Francis Caldwell Holland, Maud Constance, Spencer, Spencer. Essays Political & Biographical. 2009. 344p. (ENG.). pap. 24.99 *(978-1-113-03881-4(0))*; pap. 23.99 *(978-1-113-03879-1(9))* BiblioBazaar. (BiblioLife).

Walpole, Spencer. Essays Political & Biographical. 2009. 346p. pap. 19.99 *(978-1-115-71227-9(6))*; 344p. 36.99 *(978-1-113-70982-0(0))*; 344p. 32.99 *(978-1-113-70979-0(0))*; (ENG.). 342p. pap. 23.99 *(978-1-113-70972-1(3)*, BiblioLife); (ENG.). 342p. pap. 24.99 *(978-1-113-70974-5(X)*, BiblioLife); 344p. pap. 32.75 *(978-1-113-70977-6(4))*; 344p. pap. 31.75 *(978-1-113-70976-9(6))* BiblioBazaar.

B

—Essays Political & Biographical. 2009. 246p. pap. 19.66 *(978-0-217-71543-0(5))* General Bks. LLC.
—Essays Political & Biographical. Holland, Francis, ed. 2008. 348p. 46.95 *(978-1-4365-6371-0(2))* 2007. 352p. per. 31.95 *(978-0-548-75532-7(9))* Kessinger Publishing, LLC.
—Essays Political & Biographical. 317p. reprint ed. 98.00 *(978-0-7222-7995-3(7))* Library Reprints, Inc.

BUCKLE, HENRY THOMAS, 1821-1862

Buckle, Henry. A Tommy's Sketchbook: Writings & Drawings from the Trenches. Read, David, ed. 2012. (ENG., Illus.). 160p. pap. 18.95 ***(978-0-7524-6605-7(4))*** History Pr. Ltd., The GBR. Dist: Independent Pubs. Group.
Droysen, Johann Gustav. Outline of the Principles of History. 164p. 2009. 16.00 *(978-1-59740-347-4(4))* 2008. pap. 16.00 *(978-1-59740-699-4(6))* ACLS Humanities E-Book.
—Outline of the Principles of History. 2009. 170p. 26.99 *(978-1-110-52272-9(X))*; pap. 20.75 *(978-1-110-52271-2(1))* BiblioBazaar.
—Outline of the Principles of History. 2009. 100p. pap. *(978-0-217-52766-8(3))* Books LLC.

BUCKLES

Meredith, Gillian. Buckles. 2009. (Shire Library). (ENG., Illus.). 56p. pap. 12.95 *(978-0-7478-0691-2(8))* Shire Pubns., Ltd. GBR. Dist: Random Hse., Inc.

BUCKLEY, WILLIAM F. (WILLIAM FRANK), 1925-2008

Biographiq. William F Buckley, Jr - an American Conservative. 2008. 52p. pap. 9.99 *(978-1-59986-067-1(8)*, Biographiq) Filiquarian Publishing, LLC.
Bogus, Carl T. Buckley: William F. Buckley Jr. & the Rise of American Conservatism. 2011. (ENG., Illus.). 416p. 30.00 *(978-1-59691-580-0(3))* Bloomsbury Publishing.
Bridges, Linda & Coyne, John R., Jr. Strictly Right: William F. Buckley Jr. & the American Conservative Movement. 2007. (ENG., Illus.). 368p. 30.00 *(978-0-471-75817-4(5)*, Wiley) Wiley, John & Sons, Inc.
Brookhiser, Richard. Right Time, Right Place: Coming of Age with William F. Buckley Jr. & the Conservative Movement. (ENG.). 272p. (gr. 9). 2011. pap. 16.99 *(978-0-465-02209-0(X))* 2009. 27.50 *(978-0-465-01355-5(4))* Basic Bks.
Buckley, Christopher. Losing Mum & Pup: A Memoir. (ENG.). 2010. 272p. pap. 13.99 *(978-0-446-54095-7(1))* 2009. (Illus.). 272p. 24.99 *(978-0-446-54094-0(3))* 2009. 400p. 29.99 *(978-0-446-55239-4(9))* Grand Central Publishing. (Twelve).
Buckley Jr., William F. Flying High: Remembering Barry Goldwater. 2010. (ENG.). 224p. (gr. 9). pap. 15.00 *(978-0-465-01805-5(X))* Basic Bks.
—The Reagan I Knew. 2009. (ENG.). 312p. pap. 15.95 *(978-0-465-01802-4(5))* Basic Bks.
Buckley, William F., Jr. Cancel Your Own Goddam Subscription: Notes & Asides from National Review. 2009. (ENG.). 304p. pap. 16.00 *(978-0-465-00243-6(9))* Perseus Bks. Group.
—Happy Days Were Here Again: Reflections of a Libertarian Journalist. Bozell, Patricia, ed. 2008. (ENG.). 496p. pap. 18.95 *(978-0-465-00335-8(4))* Perseus Bks. Group.
Edwards, Lee. William F. Buckley Jr: The Maker of a Movement. 2010. (ENG.). 208p. 24.95 *(978-1-935191-73-5(X))* ISI Bks.
Meehan, William F., III, ed. Conversations with William F. Buckley Jr. 2009. (Literary Conversations Ser.). (ENG.). 208p. pap. 22.00 *(978-1-60473-225-2(3))* Univ. Pr. of Mississippi.
—Conversations with William F. Buckley Jr. 2009. (Literary Conversations Ser.). (ENG.). 208p. 50.00 *(978-1-60473-224-5(5))* Univ. Pr. of Mississippi.

BUCKLEY FAMILY

Buckley, Reid. An American Family: The Buckleys. 2009. (ENG., Illus.). 480p. pap. 16.00 *(978-1-4165-7242-8(2)*, Threshold Editions) Threshold Editions.

BUCKLING (MECHANICS)

see also Structural Stability
Akesson, Bjorn, ed. Plate Buckling in Bridges & Other Structures. 2007. (ENG., Illus.). 164p. (C). 83.95 *(978-0-415-43195-8(6)*, Taylor & Francis) Taylor & Francis Group GBR. Dist: Taylor & Francis Group.
Aliabadi, M. H. & Falzon, B. G., eds. Buckling & Postbuckling Structures: Experimental, analytical & Numerical Studies. (Illus.). 450p. 162.00 *(978-1-86094-794-0(8))* Imperial College Pr. GBR. Dist: World Scientific Publishing Co., Inc.
Eglitis, Edgars. Dynamic Buckling of Composite Shells: Behaviour of Plain & Stiffened Composite Shells under Axial Pulse Loadings. 2011. (Illus.). 168p. pap. ***(978-3-8443-1316-1(8))*** Lambert Academic Publishing.
Fatemi, Ali. Buckling & Post-Buckling of Energy Pipelines. 2008. 168p. pap. *(978-3-639-06452-0(6))* VDM Verlag Dr. Mueller e.K.
Leipholz, U. Stability of Elastic Systems. 2010. (Mechanics of Elastic Stability Ser.). 492p. pap. 449.00 *(978-90-481-8463-7(0)*, 9048184630) Springer.
Radu, Adrian George. Dynamic Stability of Composite Laminates. 2009. 160p. pap. *(978-3-639-05379-1(6))* VDM Verlag Dr. Mueller e.K.

BUCKNELL UNIVERSITY

Adams, Jen & Davis, Lauren. Bucknell University 2012: Off the Record. 2011. 188p. pap. 16.95 ***(978-1-4274-0360-5(0))*** College Prowler, Inc.

BUCKS COUNTY (PA.)

Davis, William W. H. A Genealogical & Personal History of Bucks County, Pennsylvania In. Ely, Warren S. & Jordan, John W., eds. 2011. 502p. pap. 39.98 ***(978-0-8063-4864-3(X))***; 476p. pap. 39.97 ***(978-0-8063-4863-6(1))*** Clearfield Co.
Grundy, Martha Paxson. The Evolution of a Quaker Community: Middletown Meeting, Bucks County, Pennsylvania 1750-1850. 2006. (Illus.). 372p. *(978-0-7734-5568-9(X))* Mellen, Edwin Pr., The.
McCullough, Kevin & Meyers, Larry. 2011 Bucks County Data Book. McCullough, Kevin, ed. 2011. (Illus.). 145p. pap. 45.00 *(978-1-58036-709-7(7))* Pennsylvania State Data Ctr.
Myers, Thomas G. Bucks County, Pennsylvania, Miscellaneous Deeds 1687-1910. 2008. pap. 35.00 *(978-0-7884-4555-2(3))* Heritage Bks.
—Bucks County, Pennsylvania, Orphans Court Records: 1685-1852. 2009. 648p. per. 47.00 *(978-1-58549-042-4(3))* Heritage Bks.

BUCKS COUNTY (PA.)—DESCRIPTION AND TRAVEL

ADC, the Map People Staff, creator. Bucks County Pennsylvania Street Altas. 2007. 108p. 12.95 *(978-0-87530-907-1(0))* ADC The Map People.
Phelan, Brenda. East & West Rockhill Townships. 2011. (Images of America Ser.). (ENG., Illus.). 128p. pap. 21.99 ***(978-0-7385-7537-7(2))*** Arcadia Publishing.
Whitacre, Patricia Valentine & Plank, Richard A. Tinicum Township, Bucks County. 2008. (Images of America Ser.). (ENG., Illus.). 128p. pap. 21.99 *(978-0-7385-5753-3(6))* Arcadia Publishing.

BUCOLIC LITERATURE

see Pastoral Literature; Pastoral Poetry

BUDAPEST (HUNGARY)

Amothy, Christine. I Am Fifteen & I Do Not Want to Die: The True Story of a Young Woman's Wartime Survival. 2010. (ENG.). 320p. 12.95 ***(978-0-00-732867-3(2))*** HarperCollins Pubs. Ltd. GBR. Dist: Independent Pubs. Group.
Buza, Peter. Budapest. Date not set. (Illus.). 320p. 19.95 *(978-3-8290-1553-0(4)*, 520597) Konemann.
Csúri, Károly & Orosz, Magdolna, eds. Massenfeste: Ritualisierte Öffentlichkeiten in der mittelosteuropäischen Moderne. 2009. (Budapester Studien zur Literaturwissenschaft Ser.). 288p. 74.95 *(978-3-631-59138-3(1))* Lang, Peter GmbH, Europaischer Verlag der Wissenschaften DEU. Dist: Lang, Peter.
Eber, George F. Pinball Games: Arts of Survival in the Nazi & Communist Eras. 2010. 380p. (ENG.). 31.95 *(978-1-4269-2481-1(X))*; pap. 21.95 *(978-1-4269-2480-4(1))* Trafford Publishing.
Everett, Martyn. War & Revolution: The Hungarian Anarchist Movement in World War I & the Budapest Commune 1919. 2006. (Illus.). 28p. pap. 3.50 *(978-1-873605-38-7(2))* Sharpley, Kate Library GBR. Dist: AK Pr. Distribution.
Gyorgy, Klosz & Laszlo, Lugosi Lugo. Budapest 1900-2000. 2007. (Budapest Ser.). (ENG & HUN., Illus.). 168p. 18.95 *(978-963-9323-20-9(9))* Vince Kiado Kft HUN. Dist: Independent Pubs. Group.
Marton, Kati. Enemies of the People: My Family's Journey to America. 2010. (ENG.). 288p. pap. 16.00 *(978-1-4165-8613-5(X))* Simon & Schuster.
Raj, Tamas & Laszlo, Lugosi Lugo. Budapest Jewish. 2007. (Budapest Ser.). (ENG & HUN., Illus.). 168p. 18.95 *(978-963-9323-68-1(3))* Vince Kiado Kft HUN. Dist: Independent Pubs. Group.
Ungvary, Krisztian. The Siege of Budapest: One Hundred Days in World War II. Lob, Ladislaus, tr. 2006. (ENG., Illus.). 512p. per. 25.00 *(978-0-300-11985-5(2))* Yale Univ. Pr.

BUDAPEST (HUNGARY)—DESCRIPTION AND TRAVEL

Barber, Annabel & Roper-Evans, Emma. Visible Cities Budapest. 4th ed. 2006. (Illus.). 264p. pap. *(978-1-905131-16-7(X))* Blue Guides Ltd.
—Visible Cities Budapest: A City Guide. 4th ed. 2007. (Visible Cities Ser.). (ENG., Illus.). 264p. pap. 27.95 *(978-0-393-33011-3(7)*, 33011) Blue Guides Ltd. GBR. Dist: Norton, W. W. & Co., Inc.
Bisping, Stefanie. Budapest Baedeker Guide. 2012. (Baedeker Guides Ser.). (ENG., Illus.). 274p. pap. 20.00 ***(978-3-8297-6542-8(8))*** Marco Polo Travel Publishing GBR. Dist: Innovative Logistics.
Budapest: Mit extra Cityplan. (Illus.). pap. 4.95 *(978-3-8283-0074-3(X))* Hallwag Verlag GmbH DEU. Dist: Rand McNally.
Budapest Marco Polo Guide. 2012. (Marco Polo Guides Ser.). (ENG., Illus.). 140p. pap. 9.99 ***(978-3-8297-0654-4(5))*** Marco Polo Travel Publishing GBR. Dist: Innovative Logistics.
Dent, Bob. Budapest: A Cultural History. 2007. (Cityscapes Ser.). (ENG.). 256p. 75.00 *(978-0-19-531494-6(8))*; (Illus.). per. 19.99 *(978-0-19-531495-3(6))* Oxford Univ. Pr., Inc.
Dirlis, Tom. Moon Prague & Budapest. 2011. (Moon Handbooks Ser.). (ENG., Illus.). 392p. pap. 17.99 *(978-1-59880-338-9(7))* Avalon Travel Publishing.
DK Publishing. DK Eyewitness Travel Guide: Budapest: Budapest. 2012. (Eyewitness travel Guide Ser.). (ENG.). 272p. pap. 25.00 ***(978-0-7566-9471-5(X))*** Dorling Kindersley Publishing, Inc.
Dorling Kindersley Publishing Staff. Eyewitness Travel Guides - Budapest. 2011. (Eyewitness Travel Guides). (ENG., Illus.). 272p. 25.00 *(978-0-7566-6934-8(0))* Dorling Kindersley Publishing, Inc.
—Top 10 Budapest. 2010. (Eyewitness top 10 travel Guide Ser.). (ENG.). 144p. 14.00 *(978-0-7566-6137-3(4))* Dorling Kindersley Publishing, Inc.
Fallon, Steve. Budapest, 25 vols. 5th rev. ed. 2012. (City Travel Guide Ser.). (ENG., Illus.). 160p. pap. 18.99 *(978-1-74179-690-2(3))* Lonely Planet Pubns.
—Lonely Planet Budapest. 2nd rev. ed. 2007. (Lonely Planet Budapest (Spanish) Ser.). (SPA., Illus.). 232p. per. 26.99 *(978-84-08-06911-9(X))* GeoPlaneta, Editorial, S. A. ESP. Dist: Lonely Planet Pubns.
Fodor's Travel Publications, Inc. Staff. Budapest: With Highlights of Hungary. O'Halloran, Jacinta, ed. 2nd ed. 2007. (Fodor's Gold Guides). (ENG., Illus.). 352p. pap. 17.95 *(978-1-4000-1740-9(8)*, Fodor's) Fodor's Travel Pubns.
Gallager, Mary-Ann, et al. Vienna, Prague & Budapest. 3rd ed. 2011. (ENG.). 336p. pap. 21.95 ***(978-1-56656-871-5(4)***, Cadogan Guides (USA)) Interlink Publishing Group, Inc.
Gerő, András. Public Space in Budapest: The History of Kossuth Square. 2010. (ENG., Illus.). 230p. (gr. 17). 40.00 *(978-0-88033-648-2(X))* Eastern European Monographs.
Harvard Student Agencies, Inc. Let's Go Berlin, Prague & Budapest: The Student Travel Guide. 2010. (Let's Go Ser.). (ENG., Illus.). 280p. pap. 14.95 *(978-1-59880-712-7(9)*, Let's Go) Avalon Travel Publishing.
Hebbert, Charles & Richardson, Dan. The Rough Guide to Budapest. 5th ed. 2012. (Rough Guide To... Ser.). (ENG., Illus.). 256p. 19.99 ***(978-1-4053-8967-9(2))*** Rough Guides, Ltd. GBR. Dist: Dorling Kindersley Publishing, Inc.
Jacobs, Michael. Budapest. 2007. (ENG., Illus.). 256p. per. 17.95 *(978-1-86207-825-3(4))* Granta Bks. GBR. Dist: Independent Pubs. Group.
James, Ryan. Budapest & the Best of Hungary. 8th ed. 2010. (Frommer's Complete Guides: 759). (ENG., Illus.). 310p. pap. 18.99 *(978-0-470-55126-4(7)*, Frommers) Wiley, John & Sons, Inc.
Langenscheidt Publishers Staff. Hungary. Ochterbeck, Cynthia Clayton & Cannon, Gwen, eds. 2nd rev. ed. 2008. (Michelin Green Guide Budapest Hungary Ser.). (ENG., Illus.). 464p. pap. 21.95 *(978-1-906261-18-4(0))* Michelin Travel & Lifestyle.
Locken, E. Travel Journal Budapest. 2010. 192p. pap. 19.99 *(978-0-557-44590-5(6))* Lulu Enterprises Inc.
Lugosi Lugo, László, photos by. A Dunánál Budapest. 2010. (HUN & ENG., Illus.). 168p. 18.95 ***(978-963-9552-62-3(3))*** Vince Kiado Kft HUN. Dist: Independent Pubs. Group.
Meszaros, Laszlo. The Danube. 2009. 256p. 49.95 *(978-963-9705-47-0(0))* Beaufoy, John Publishing GBR. Dist: Midpoint Trade Bks., Inc.
Nicholas, Clapton. Budapest. 2009. (Armchair Traveller Ser.). (ENG.). 250p. 19.95 *(978-1-904950-96-7(5))* Haus Publishing GBR. Dist: Consortium Bk. Sales & Distribution.
Phillips, Adrian & Scotchmer, Jo. Budapest. 2nd ed. 2009. (Bradt Mini Guide Ser.). (ENG., Illus.). 400p. pap. 13.99 *(978-1-84162-185-2(4))* Bradt Travel Guides GBR. Dist: Globe Pequot Pr., The.
Richards, Brian. Globetrotter the Best of Budapest. 2007. (Globetrotter Best of Ser.). (ENG., Illus.). 96p. pap. 8.95 *(978-1-84537-449-5(5))* New Holland Pubs., Ltd. GBR. Dist: Globe Pequot Pr., The.
Richards, Brian & Mead, Rowland. Tenerife. 4th ed. 2011. (Globetrotter Travel Packs Ser.). (ENG., Illus.). 128p. 14.95 *(978-1-84773-850-9(8))* New Holland Pubs., Ltd. GBR. Dist: Globe Pequot Pr., The.
Scotchmer, Jo & Phillips, Adrian. Budapest. 3rd rev. ed. 2012. (ENG., Illus.). 336p. pap. 19.99 ***(978-1-84162-388-7(1))*** Bradt Travel Guides GBR. Dist: Globe Pequot Pr., The.
Smith, Duncan J. D. Only in Budapest: A Guide to Hidden Corners, Little-Known Places & Unusual Objects. 2008. (Illus.). 243p. pap. *(978-963-87090-1-1(4))* JEL-KEP Kft.
Steves, Rick & Hewitt, Cameron. Rick Steves' Budapest. 2011. (Rick Steves Ser.). (ENG., Illus.). 492p. pap. 18.99 *(978-1-59880-771-4(4))* Avalon Travel Publishing.
Thomas Cook Publishing Staff. Traveller Guides Budapest. 4th ed. 2011. (Travellers - Thomas Cook Ser.). (ENG., Illus.). 192p. pap. 16.95 *(978-1-84848-341-5(4))* Cook, Thomas Publishing GBR. Dist: Globe Pequot Pr., The.
Time Out Guides Staff. Time Out Budapest. 7th ed. 2011. (Time Out Guides). (ENG., Illus.). 256p. pap. 19.95 *(978-1-84670-224-2(0))* Time Out Guides Ltd. GBR. Dist: Perseus-PGW.
Turp, Craig. Top 10 Budapest. 2012. (Eyewitness Top 10 Travel Guide Ser.). (ENG.). 128p. 14.00 ***(978-0-7566-8509-6(5))*** Dorling Kindersley Publishing, Inc.
Very, Vamai. Budapest, Walks in the Jewish Quarter. 2006. (Walks Ser.). (ENG.). 232p. pap. 18.95 *(978-963-9552-68-5(2))* Vince Kiado Kft HUN. Dist: Independent Pubs. Group.
Wallpaper Magazine Editors. Wallpaper City Guide: Budapest. Moloney, Rachael, ed. 2007. (ENG., Illus.). 128p. pap. 8.95 *(978-0-7148-4737-5(2))* Phaidon Pr., Inc.
Wallpaper Magazine Editors, ed. Wallpaper* City Guide Budapest 2012. 2011. (ENG.). 128p. pap. 9.95 ***(978-0-7148-6265-1(7))*** Phaidon Pr., Inc.

BUDDHA

see Gautama Buddha

BUDDHISM

see also Buddhist Gods; Buddhist Monasticism and Religious Orders; Buddhist Sociology; Mahayana Buddhism; Meditation—Buddhism; Pali Literature; Tantric Buddhism; Theravada Buddhism; Zen Buddhism
also headings beginning with the word Buddhist
Abeysekara, Ananda. Colors of the Robe: Religion, Identity, & Difference. 2008. (ENG.). 288p. 32.50 *(978-1-57003-787-0(6))* Univ. of South Carolina Pr.
Adi Da Samraj & Adi Da Samraj. The Ancient Reality-Teachings: The Single Transcendental Truth Taught by the Great Sages of Buddhism & Advaitism - As Revealed by the Avataric Great Sage, Adi Da Samraj. 2006. (Perfect Knowledge Ser.). (Illus.). 278p. per. *(978-1-57097-198-3(6))* Dawn Horse Pr.
Akiyama, Aisaburo. Buddhist Hand-Symbol. reprint ed. 39.50 *(978-0-404-17214-5(8))* AMS Pr., Inc.
Al-Sharif, William. Indian Papers. 2010. 103p. pap. 19.95 *(978-1-4457-6521-1(7))* Lulu Enterprises Inc.
Alexander, P. C. Buddhism in Kerala. reprint ed. 37.50 *(978-0-404-17215-2(6))* AMS Pr., Inc.
Allen, G. F. The Buddha's Philosophy: Selections from the Pali Canon & an Introductory Essay. 2008. (Routledge Library Editions: Buddhism Ser.). (ENG., Illus.). 198p. (C). 165.00 *(978-0-415-46088-0(3))* Routledge.
Ananda, Uduhavara. Adi Budusamaye Dakvena Pñña Sankalpaya: Puñña Concept in Early Buddhism. 2009. (PLI.). 232p. *(978-955-30-0663-9(9)*, Library of Congress — New Delhi Overseas Office) Godage, S. & Brothers.
Andersen, Dines & Smith, Helmer, eds. The Sutta-Nipata. reprint ed. 34.00 *(978-0-404-17383-8(7))* AMS Pr., Inc.
Anesaki, Masaharu. Katam Karaniyam: Lectures, Essays & Studies. reprint ed. 32.50 *(978-0-404-17216-9(4))* AMS Pr., Inc.
Angulimalo. Anussati: the Recollections. with quotes from the Pali Canon & Forest Tradition of Theravada Buddhism. 2008. 115p. pap. 22.06 *(978-1-84753-723-2(5))* Lulu Enterprises Inc.
Arnold, Dan. Buddhists, Brahmins, & Belief: Epistemology in South Asian Philosophy of Religion. 2008. (ENG.). 328p. (gr. 17). pap. 26.00 *(978-0-231-13281-7(6))* Columbia Univ. Pr.
Asma, Stephen T. Buddha, A Beginner's Guide, 1 vol. 2009. (ENG., Illus.). 176p. pap. 16.95 *(978-1-57174-595-8(5))* Hampton Roads Publishing Co., Inc.
—Why I Am a Buddhist: No-Nonsense Buddhism with Red Meat & Whiskey. 2010. (ENG.). 192p. 21.95 *(978-1-57174-617-7(X))* Hampton Roads Publishing Co., Inc.
Asvaghosa. The Buddhacarita or Acts of the Buddha, 2 vols. in 1. Johnson, E. H., ed. & tr. by. reprint ed. 33.50 *(978-81-215-0710-3(3))* Coronet Bks.
Atone, Joji, tr. from JPN. The Promise of Amida Buddha: Honen's Path to Bliss. 2011. (ENG.). 456p. pap. 39.95 *(978-0-86171-696-8(5))* Wisdom Pubns.
Bancroft, A., et al. La Palabra del Buda. (Viaje Interior Ser.). (SPA.). 140p. *(978-84-95456-82-3(6)*, 86938) Ediciones Oniro S.A.
Bancroft, Anne, ed. The Buddha Speaks: A Book of Guidance from the Buddhist Scriptures. 2010. (ENG & ABK., Illus.). 176p. pap. 14.00 *(978-1-59030-827-1(1))* Shambhala Pubns., Inc.
Baraz, James & Alexander, Shoshana. Awakening Joy: 10 Steps That Will Put You on the Road to Real Happiness. 2010. (ENG.). 336p. 26.00 *(978-0-553-80703-5(X))* Random House Publishing Group.
Barbic, Bill. Buddhism. 2011. pap. 21.95 ***(978-0-7414-6389-0(X))*** Infinity Publishing.
Barua, Ankur, et al. Applied Buddhism in Modern Science. 2010. 52p. pap. *(978-3-639-25248-4(9))* VDM Verlag Dr. Mueller e.K.
—Self Cultivation Without Self. 2010. 64p. pap. *(978-3-639-24944-6(5))* VDM Verlag Dr. Mueller e.K.
Barua, Dipak Kumar, et al. Glorification of the Buddha & the Bodhisatta: In Therav?Da Buddhism. 2011. 60p. pap. ***(978-3-639-28193-4(4))*** VDM Verlag Dr. Mueller e.K.
Batchelor, Martine. The Spirit of the Buddha. 2010. (Spirit of X Ser.). (ENG.). 192p. pap. 15.00 *(978-0-300-16407-7(6))* Yale Univ. Pr.
Batchelor, Stephen. Confession of a Buddhist Atheist. 2011. (ENG., Illus.). 320p. pap. 16.00 *(978-0-385-52707-1(1))* Spiegel & Grau.
Bays, Jan Chozen. Mindful Eating: A Guide to Rediscovering a Healthy & Joyful Relationship with Food. 2009. (ENG.). 240p. 18.95 *(978-1-59030-531-7(0))* Shambhala Pubns., Inc.
Bell, Randall. QuickMarks: Buddhist. 2006. (Illus.). 6p. vinyl bd. 4.99 *(978-0-9765486-0-7(7))* Owners Manual Pr.
Berkwitz, Stephen C. South Asian Buddhism: A Survey. 2009. (ENG., Illus.). 256p. (C). 115.00 *(978-0-415-45249-6(X))*; XII, 244p. 34.95 *(978-0-415-45248-9(1))* Routledge.
Bhikkhu, Anandapanyo, tr. Ariyapuggala: The Liberated. 2011. pap. 5.95 ***(978-1-935207-05-4(9))*** Ngern, Neecha Thian.
Bhushan, Nalini, et al, eds. TransBuddhism: Transmission, Translation, & Transformation. 2009. (Illus.). 272p. 80.00 net. *(978-1-55849-707-8(2))*; pap. 24.95 net. *(978-1-55849-708-5(0))* Univ. of Massachusetts Pr.
Biddulph, Desmond. 1,001 Pearls of Buddhist Wisdom. 2006. (ENG., Illus.). 384p. pap. 9.95 *(978-0-8118-5612-6(7))* Chronicle Bks. LLC.
Bien, Thomas. Buddhas Way of Happiness: Healing Sorrow, Transforming Negative Emotion, & Finding Well-Being in the Present Moment. 2011. (ENG.). 256p. pap. 17.95 *(978-1-57224-869-4(6))* New Harbinger Pubns.
Bloom, Pamela, ed. The Power of Compassion: Stories That Open the Heart, Heal the Soul, & Change the World. 2010. (ENG.). 256p. pap. 15.95 *(978-1-57174-629-0(3))* Hampton Roads Publishing Co., Inc.
Bodhipaksa. Living As a River: Finding Fearlessness in the Face of Change. 2010. 400p. pap. 18.95 *(978-1-59179-910-8(4))* Sounds True, Inc.
—Vegetarianism: A Buddhist View. 2nd ed. 2010. (Buddhist View Ser.). (ENG.). 104p. pap. 13.95 *(978-1-899579-96-9(6))* Windhorse Pubns. GBR. Dist: Consortium Bk. Sales & Distribution.
Bokenkamp, Stephen R. Ancestors & Anxiety: Daoism & the Birth of Rebirth in China. 2009. (ENG.). 234p. pap. 25.95 *(978-0-520-25988-1(2))* Univ. of California Pr.
Bonk, Jonathan J., ed. The Routledge Encyclopedia of Missions & Missionaries. 2010. (Religion & Society Ser.). 494p. (C). pap. 55.00 *(978-0-415-88089-3(0))* Routledge.
Bose, Monica. The Hill of Fire. 2006. (ENG., Illus.). 23.00 *(978-974-524-003-2(6))* Orchid Pr. THA. Dist: National Bk. Network.
Branson, Alec. Poopsie & the Buddha. 2010. 32p. 19.95 *(978-1-4269-3623-4(0))* Trafford Publishing.
Brinks, Shirley. Into the Fire. 2009. 224p. pap. 19.99 *(978-1-4415-2039-5(2))* Xlibris Corp.

Brown, Sid. A Buddhist in the Classroom. 2008. (Illus.). 160p. 47.50 *(978-0-7914-7597-3(2))*; pap. 19.95 *(978-0-7914-7598-0(0))* State Univ. of New York Pr.

Brunnholzl, Karl. The Heart Attack Sutra: A New Commentary on the Heart Sutra. 2012. (ENG.). 160p. pap. 16.95 ***(978-1-55939-391-1(2))*** Snow Lion Pubns., Inc.

Buddha, Gautama. The Dhammapad. 2008. 64p. pap. 6.99 *(978-1-60459-593-2(0))* Wilder Pubns., Ltd.

Buddhavamsa. The Buddhavamsa & the Cariya-Pitaka, Pt. 1. Morris, Richard, ed. reprint ed. 17.00 *(978-0-404-17249-7(0))* AMS Pr., Inc.

Buddhist Text Translation Society Staff, tr. Flower Adornment (Avatamsaka) Sutra, 22 vols. Set. Incl. Flower Adornment (Avatamsaka) Sutra: Chapter 11, Pure Conduct. Tripitaka Master Hua, comment. (Illus.). 255p. 1983. pap. *(978-0-917512-37-7(5))*; Flower Adornment (Avatamsaka) Sutra: Chapter 15, The Ten Dwellings. Tripitaka Master Hua, comment. (Illus.). 185p. 1981. pap. *(978-0-917512-77-3(4))*; Flower Adornment (Avatamsaka) Sutra: Chapter 17, Merit & Virtue from First Bringing Forth the Mind. Tripitaka Master Hua, comment. (Illus.). 200p. 1982. pap. *(978-0-917512-83-4(9))*; Flower Adornment (Avatamsaka) Sutra: Chapter 22, The Ten Inexhaustible Treasures. Hua, comment. (Illus.). 184p. 1982. pap. *(978-0-917512-38-4(3))*; Flower Adornment (Avatamsaka) Sutra: Chapter 24, Praises in the Tushita Heaven. Tripitaka Master Hua, comment. (Illus.). 123p. 1982. pap. *(978-0-917512-39-1(1))*; Flower Adornment (Avatamsaka) Sutra: Chapter 26, The Ten Grounds, Pt. II. Tripitaka Master Hua, comment. (Illus.). 200p. 1981. pap. *(978-0-917512-74-2(X))*; Flower Adornment (Avatamsaka) Sutra: Chapter 36, Universal Worthy's Conduct. Hua, Tripitaka M., comment. (Illus.). 78p. 1983. pap. *(978-0-88139-011-7(9))*; Flower Adornment (Avatamsaka) Sutra: Chapter 39, Entering the Dharma Realm, Part IV. Tripitaka Master Hua, comment. (Illus.). 173p. 1981. pap. *(978-0-917512-75-6(6))*; Flower Adornment (Avatamsaka) Sutra: Chapter 39, Entering the Dharma Realm, Pt. I. Master Hua Tripitaka, comment. (Illus.). 245p. 1980. pap. *(978-0-917512-68-1(5))*; Flower Adornment (Avatamsaka) Sutra: Chapter 39, Entering the Dharma Realm, Pt. V. Tripitaka Master Hua, comment. (Illus.). 284p. 1981. pap. *(978-0-917512-81-0(2))*; Flower Adornment (Avatamsaka) Sutra: Chapter 39, Entering the Dharma Realm, Pt. VI. Hua, Tripitaka M., comment. (Illus.). 282p. 1982. pap. *(978-0-917512-48-3(0))*; Flower Adornment (Avatamsaka) Sutra: Chapter 39, Entering the Dharma Realm, Pt. VIII. Hua, Tripitaka M., comment. 229p. 1984. pap. *(978-0-88139-055-1(0))*; Flower Adornment (Avatamsaka) Sutra: Chapter 40, Universal Worthy's Conduct & Vows. Tripitaka Master Hua, comment. (Illus.). 277p. 1982. pap. *(978-0-917512-84-1(7))*; Flower Adornment (Avatamsaka) Sutra: Chapter 5, Flower Store Adorned Sea of Worlds, Pt. I & Pt. II. Tripitaka Master Hua, comment. (Illus.). 250p. 1983. pap. *(978-0-917512-54-4(5))*; Flower Adornment (Avatamsaka) Sutra: Chapter 5, Flower Store Adorned Sea of Worlds Pt. III & Chapter 6, Vairocana. Tripitaka Master Hua, comment. (Illus.). 191p. 1985. pap. *(978-0-88139-114-5(X))*; Flower Adornment (Avatamsaka Sutra Chapter 9: Light Enlightenment. Tripitaka Master Hua, comment. (Illus.). 225p. 1983. pap. *(978-0-88139-005-6(4))*; Flower Adornment (Avatamsaka) Sutra Pt. III: Chapter 39, Entering the Dharma Realm. Master Hua, Tripitaka, comment. (Illus.). 284p. 1980. pap. *(978-0-917512-70-4(7))*; Flower Adornment Sutra Prologue Vol. II: The Second Door Pt. I. Ch'Ing Liang. (Illus.). 197p. 1981. pap. 38.00 *(978-0-917512-73-5(1))*; Fower Adornment (Avatamsaka) Sutra: Chapter, 16, Brahma Conduct. Tripitaka Master Hua, comment. (Illus.). 65p. 1981. pap. *(978-0-917512-80-3(4))*; Chapters 7 & 8. Flower Adornment (Avatamsaka) Sutra: Names of Thus Come Ones & the Four Holy Truths, Chapters 7 & 8. Tripitaka Master Hua, comment. 77p. 1983. pap. *(978-0-88139-014-8(3))*; Pt. VII. Flower Adornment (Avatamsaka) Sutra: Chapter 39: Entering the Dharma Realm. Hua, Tripitaka M., comment. 161p. 1983. pap. *(978-0-88139-050-6(X))*; Pt. One. Flower Adornment (Avatamsaka) Sutra: Chapter 26, The Ten Grounds. Master Hua, Tripitaka, comment. (Illus.). 234p 1980. pap. *(978-0-917512-87-2(1))*; Set pap. 174.50 *(978-0-917512-35-3(9))* Buddhist Text Translation Society.

Burnett, David. The Spirit of Buddhism: A Christian Perspective on Buddhist Thought. 2007. (Illus.). 352p. pap. 16.99 *(978-0-8254-6145-3(6)*, Monarch Bks.) Lion Hudson PLC GBR. Dist: Kregel Pubns.

Cantwell, Cathy. Buddhism: The Basics. 2009. (Basics Ser.). (ENG., Illus.). 208p. (C). pap. 19.95 *(978-0-415-40880-6(6))* Routledge.

Carter, John Ross & Palihawadana, Mahinda. The Dhammapada: The Sayings of the Buddha. 2008. (Oxford World's Classics Ser.). (ENG.). 112p. pap. 9.95 *(978-0-19-955513-0(3))* Oxford Univ. Pr., Inc.

Carter, Steven. Upside down Buddha: Parables & Fables. 2010. (ENG.). 226p. pap. 32.50 *(978-0-7618-5405-0(3))* Hamilton Bks.

Carus, Paul. Amitabha: a Story of Buddhist Theology. 2007. (ENG.). 128p. per. 20.95 *(978-1-4304-4708-5(7))* Kessinger Publishing, LLC.

—Buddha, the Gospel. 252p. 2009. 34.99 *(978-1-59547-518-3(4))* 2007. per. 19.99 *(978-1-59547-941-9(4))* NuVision Pubns., LLC.

—Dharma or the Religion of Enlightenment. 2006. pap. 22.95 *(978-1-4286-4301-7(X))* Kessinger Publishing, LLC.

—The Gospel of Buddha. 2010. 296p. pap. 19.95 *(978-0-557-58674-5(7))* Lulu Enterprises Inc.

Cathy Cantwell Staff. Buddhism: the Basics: The Basics. 2009. (Basics Ser.). (ENG., Illus.) 208p. (C). 90.00 *(978-0-415-40879-0(2))* Routledge.

Causton, Richard. The Buddha in Daily Life. 2nd ed. (ENG., Illus.). 368p. pap. 16.95 *(978-0-7126-7456-0(X))* Random Hse. GBR. Dist: Trafalgar Square Publishing.

Cayton, Karuna. The Misleading Mind: How We Create Our Own Problems & How Buddhist Psychology Can Help Us Solve Them. 2012. (ENG.). 224p. pap. 14.95 *(978-1-57731-942-9(7))* New World Library.

Chamberlain-Nyudo, Revered Sylvain. There Is no I. 2010. 104p. pap. 14.96 *(978-0-557-12298-1(8))* Lulu Enterprises Inc.

Chamberland-Nyudo, Sylvain. Quantum Life Buddhism Guidance & Letters. 2009. 220p. pap. 19.95 *(978-1-4357-2921-6(8))* Lulu Enterprises Inc.

—Ultimate Mandala. 2008. 92p. pap. 17.50 *(978-1-4357-3984-0(1))* Lulu Enterprises Inc.

Chaves-Segura, Alenjandro. A Tibetan Buddhist Approach to International Relations: The Teaching of the Dalai Lama. 2011. 272p. ***(978-0-7734-1608-6(0))*** Mellen, Edwin Pr., The.

Chopra, Deepak. La Receta de la Felicidad: Las Siete Claves de la Felicidad y la Iluminación. 2011. (Vintage Espanol Ser.). (SPA.). 144p. pap. 13.95 *(978-0-307-74169-1(9)*, Vintage) Knopf Doubleday Publishing Group.

—The Ultimate Happiness Prescription: 7 Keys to Joy & Enlightenment. 2009. (ENG.). 144p. 19.99 *(978-0-307-58971-2(4)*, Harmony) Crown Publishing Group.

Chung, Paul S. Martin Luther & Buddhism: Aesthetics of Suffering. 2nd ed. 2008. (ENG.). 472p. pap. 53.00 *(978-0-227-17294-0(9))* Clarke, James Co., Ltd. GBR. Dist: Brown, David Bk. Co., The.

—Martin Luther & Buddhism: Aesthetics of Suffering. 2nd ed. 2008. (Princeton Theological Monographs). 472p. pap. 52.00 *(978-1-55635-459-5(2)*, Pickwick Pubns.) Wipf & Stock Pubs.

City of 10,000 Buddhas Recitation Handbook. 250p. 8.00 *(978-0-88139-857-1(8))* Buddhist Text Translation Society.

City of Ten Thousand Buddhas Recitation Handbook. 3rd ed. 240p. (Orig.). pap. 7.00 *(978-0-88139-167-1(0))* Buddhist Text Translation Society.

Conze, Edward. Buddhism: Its Essence & Development. 228p. 2010. 33.56 *(978-1-163-44423-8(5))* 2007. (ENG.). 41.95 *(978-0-548-13762-8(5))* Kessinger Publishing, LLC.

—Buddhism Its Essence & Development. 2006. pap. 26.95 *(978-1-4286-4931-6(X))* Kessinger Publishing, LLC.

Coomaraswamy, Ananda Kentish. Hinduism & Buddhism. 2007. (ENG.). 108p. 33.95 *(978-0-548-12442-0(6))* 2006. pap. 18.95 *(978-1-4286-3399-5(5))* Kessinger Publishing, LLC.

Cooper (Ratnaprabha), Robin. Searching for Mind: A Buddhist View. 2012. (Buddhist View Ser.). (ENG.). 160p. pap. 16.95 ***(978-1-907314-03-2(2))*** Windhorse Pubns. GBR. Dist: Consortium Bk. Sales & Distribution.

Cooper, Paul. Into the Mountain Stream: Psychotherapy & Buddhist Experience. Cooper, Paul C., ed. 2007. (ENG.). 192p. per. 49.50 *(978-0-7657-0465-8(X)*, Aronson, Jason) Rowman & Littlefield Publishers, Inc.

Cooper, Paul C. Into the Mountain Stream: Psychotherapy & Buddhist Experience. 2006. (ENG.). 192p. 86.50 *(978-0-7657-0464-1(1)*, Aronson, Jason) Rowman & Littlefield Publishers, Inc.

Copleston, Reginald S. Buddhism, Primitive & Present in Magdha & in Ceylon. 2nd ed. reprint ed. 42.50 *(978-0-404-17257-2(1))* AMS Pr., Inc.

Cowell, E. B. Jataka V1 or Stories of the Buddhas Form. 2006. pap. 31.95 *(978-1-4286-4527-1(6))* Kessinger Publishing, LLC.

—Jataka V2 or Stories of the Buddhas Form. 2006. pap. 30.95 *(978-1-4286-4528-8(4))* Kessinger Publishing, LLC.

—Jataka V3 or Stories of the Buddhas Form. 2006. pap. 31.95 *(978-1-4286-4529-5(2))* Kessinger Publishing, LLC.

—Jataka V4 or Stories of the Buddhas Form. 2006. pap. 30.95 *(978-1-4286-4530-1(6))* Kessinger Publishing, LLC.

—Jataka V5 or Stories of the Buddhas Form. 2006. pap. 28.95 *(978-1-4286-4531-8(4))* Kessinger Publishing, LLC.

—Jataka V6 or Stories of the Buddhas Form. 2006. pap. 33.95 *(978-1-4286-4532-5(2))* Kessinger Publishing, LLC.

Cram101 Textbook Reviews. Outlines & Highlights for Buddhism by Mitchell. Isbn: 0195139526 0195139518. 2011. 72p. pap. 27.95 ***(978-1-61812-666-5(0))*** Cram101 Inc.

Culture of Peace Press Staff. Voices for a Culture of Peace: Compendium of the SGI-USA Culture of Peace Distinguished Speakers Series. 2010. (Culture of Peace Distinguished Speakers Ser.). (ENG.). 280p. pap. 14.95 *(978-0-9844050-0-8(3))* Culture of Peace Pr.

Dahlke, Paul. Buddhism & Its Place in the Mental Life of Mankind. reprint ed. 29.00 *(978-0-404-17265-7(2))* AMS Pr., Inc.

—Buddhism & Its Place in the Mental Life of Mankind. 2010. 262p. 42.95 *(978-1-161-40722-8(7))* Kessinger Publishing, LLC.

Dalai Lama XIV. All You Ever Wanted to Know from His Holiness the Dalai Lama on Happiness, Life, Living, & Much More: Conversations with Rajiv Mehrotra. 2009. (ENG.). 264p. 19.95 *(978-1-4019-2018-0(7))* Hay Hse., Inc.

—Becoming Enlightened. 2009. (ENG.). 320p. pap. 15.00 *(978-1-4165-6584-0(1)*, Beyond Words/Atria Bks.) Atria Bks.

—El Camino de la Iluminación. Echerri, Vicente, tr. 2010. (ENG & SPA.). 352p. pap. 14.00 *(978-1-4391-3873-1(7)*, Beyond Words/Atria Bks.) Atria Bks.

—Las Cuatro Nobles Verdades.Tr. of Four Noble Truths. (SPA.). 140p. *(978-84-01-01170-2(1))* Plaza & Janes Editories, S.A.

—The Dalai Lama's Little Book of Compassion. 2011. 224p. 12.95 *(978-1-57174-670-2(6))* Hampton Roads Publishing Co., Inc.

—The Middle Way: Faith Grounded in Reason. Jinpa, Geshe Thupten, tr. 2009. (ENG.). 200p. 19.95 *(978-0-86171-552-7(7))* Wisdom Pubns.

—Mind in Comfort & Ease: The Vision of Enlightenment in the Great Perfection. Ricard, Matthieu, tr. from TIB. 2007. (ENG.). 384p. 24.95 *(978-0-86171-493-3(8))* Wisdom Pubns.

—Mundos en Armonia.Tr. of Worlds in Harmony. (SPA.). 184p. *(978-84-95456-50-2(8)*, 86935) Ediciones Oniro S.A.

—Oceano de Sabiduria.Tr. of Ocean of Wisdom. (SPA.). 120p. *(978-84-95456-33-5(8)*, 86931) Ediciones Oniro S.A.

—Pacificar la Mente.Tr. of Pacifier l'esprit. (SPA.). 224p. *(978-84-95456-06-9(0)*, 86925) Ediciones Oniro S.A.

—The Path of Compassion: The Bodhisattva Precepts. Batchelor, Martine, tr. from CHI. 2010. (Sacred Literature Trust Ser.). (ENG.). 144p. pap. 21.95 *(978-0-300-16523-4(4))* Yale Univ. Pr.

—Worlds in Harmony: Compassionate Action for a Better World. 2nd rev. ed. 2008. (ENG.). 160p. pap. 12.95 *(978-1-888375-81-7(7))* Parallax Pr.

—365 Daily Meditations of the Dalai Lama [Persian Language]. Amouzgar, Kuros, tr. from FRE. 2010. (PER.). pap. 12.95 *(978-1-58814-031-9(8))* Ibex Pubs., Inc.

Dalai Lama XIV & Snow Lion Publications Staff. From Here to Enlightenment: Teachings on the Spiritual Path. Newland, Guy, ed. 2012. (ENG., Illus.). 192p. 24.95 *(978-1-55939-382-9(3))* Snow Lion Pubns., Inc.

Das, Lama Surya. The Mind Is Mightier than the Sword: Enlightening the Mind, Opening the Heart. 2009. (ENG.). 432p. pap. 16.99 *(978-0-7679-1864-0(9))* Knopf Doubleday Publishing Group.

—Natural Radiance: Awakening to Your Great Perfection. 2007. 100p. pap. 14.95 incl. audio compact disk *(978-1-59179-612-1(1)*, BK01178D) Sounds True, Inc.

Davids, C. Rhys. Wayfarer's Words, 3 vols. reprint ed. 125.00 *(978-0-404-17600-6(3))* AMS Pr., Inc.

Davids, C. Rhys, ed. Khuddaka-Nikaya: The Minor Anthologies of the Pali Canon, 4 vols. reprint ed. 105.00 *(978-0-404-17640-2(2))* AMS Pr., Inc.

Davids, Carolina A. Buddhism: A Study of the Buddhist Norm. reprint ed. 25.00 *(978-0-404-17269-5(5))* AMS Pr., Inc.

—A Manual of Buddhism for Advanced Students. reprint ed. 32.50 *(978-0-404-17274-9(1))* AMS Pr., Inc.

Davids, Rhys. Buddhism. 2007. pap. *(978-1-4067-5628-9(8))* Read Bks.

—Gotama the Man. 2007. (ENG.). 300p. 43.95 *(978-0-548-00695-5(4))* Kessinger Publishing, LLC.

Davids, T. W. Rhys. Dialogues of the Buddha V1. 2006. pap. 31.95 *(978-1-4286-3500-5(9))* Kessinger Publishing, LLC.

—Dialogues of the Buddha V2. 2006. pap. 33.95 *(978-1-4286-3501-2(7))* Kessinger Publishing, LLC.

—Dialogues of the Buddha V3. 2006. pap. 28.95 *(978-1-4286-3502-9(5))* Kessinger Publishing, LLC.

Davids, T. W. Rhys, tr. Buddhist Suttas. 2007. (ENG.). 368p. 48.95 *(978-0-548-10222-0(8))* Kessinger Publishing, LLC.

—Dialogues of the Buddha V1. 2007. (ENG.). 364p. 46.95 *(978-0-548-12530-4(9))* Kessinger Publishing, LLC.

—Dialogues of the Buddha V2. 2007. (ENG.). 392p. 48.95 *(978-0-548-12531-1(7))* Kessinger Publishing, LLC.

—Dialogues of the Buddha V3. 2007. (ENG.). 284p. 43.95 *(978-0-548-12532-8(5))* Kessinger Publishing, LLC.

Davis, Jimmy. Western Pure Land Buddhism. 2009. 66p. pap. 13.14 *(978-0-557-05048-2(0))* Lulu Enterprises Inc.

Davis, Matthew & Scott, Michael Farrell. Opening the Mountain: Circumabulating Mount Tamalpais, a Ritual Walk. 2006. (ENG., Illus.). 176p. pap. 20.00 *(978-1-59376-127-1(9))* Counterpoint LLC.

De Nebesky-Wojkowitz, Rene. Oracles & Demons of Tibet: The Cult & Iconography of the Tibetan Protective Dieties. (Illus.). 682p. *(978-81-7303-039-0(1))* Book Faith India.

De Sales, Francois. Vive Jesus: Reghelen Ende Oeffeninghen Voor de Gheestelycke Dochters (1723) 2009. 20p. pap. 15.95 *(978-1-120-05303-9(X))* Kessinger Publishing, LLC.

de Silva, Padmasiri et al. An Introduction to Buddhist Psychology. 4th annot. ed. 2006. (Library of Philosophy & Religion Ser.). (ENG.). 216p. 95.00 *(978-0-230-00331-6(1))* Palgrave Macmillan.

Deegalle, Mahinda. Buddhism, Conflict & Violence in Modern Sri Lanka. 2009. 284p. pap. 39.95 *(978-0-415-54441-2(6))* Routledge.

Dematapitiya, Somapala. Discovery of Gods Unseen. 2010. 428p. pap. 20.49 *(978-1-4490-7083-0(3))* AuthorHouse.

Demi. Amitabha Buddha, 1 vol. 2010. (ENG.). 312p. 40.00 *(978-0-9814624-0-0(5))* Demi's Bks.

Derris, Karen & Gummer, Natalie. Defining Buddhism(S) A Reader. Derris, Karen & Gummer, Natalie, eds. 2007. (Critical Categories in the Study of Religion Ser.). (ENG., Illus.). 340p. (C). pap. 29.95 *(978-1-84553-055-6(1))* Equinox Publishing Ltd. GBR. Dist: ISD.

Derris, Karen & Gummer, Natalie, eds. Defining Buddhism(S) A Reader. 2007. (Critical Categories in the Study of Religion Ser.). (ENG., Illus.). 340p. (C). 110.00 *(978-1-84553-231-4(7))* Equinox Publishing Ltd. GBR. Dist: ISD.

Deshi. If You Fall down Seven Times, Get up Eight: Aspects of Practice for Gay & Lesbian Buddhists. 2011. pap. ***(978-1-60864-055-3(8))*** Rebel Satori Pr.

DeVotta, Neil. Sinhalese Buddhist Nationalist Ideology: Implications for Politics & Conflict Resolution in Sri Lanka. 2007. (Policy Studies: 40). 87p. per. *(978-1-932728-64-4(3))* East-West Ctr.

The Dhammapada. 2009. 62p. pap. 9.45 *(978-1-4385-3312-4(8)*, Book Jungle) Standard Pubns., Inc.

Dhivan & Sagaraghosa. Conditionality. 2011. (ENG.). 224p. pap. 20.95 *(978-1-899579-90-7(7))* Windhorse Pubns. GBR. Dist: Consortium Bk. Sales & Distribution.

Dickhoff, Robert Ernst. The Eternal Fountain: A Kaleidoscope of Divine Inspired Thought Sparks 1947. 2007. (ENG.). 128p. 35.95 *(978-0-548-05474-1(6))* Kessinger Publishing, LLC.

Dods, Marcus. Mohammed, Buddha & Christ. 2009. 100p. pap. *(978-1-151-63522-5(3))* Books LLC.

—Mohammed Buddha & Christ Four Lectures. 2006. pap. 27.95 *(978-1-4286-3439-8(8))* Kessinger Publishing, LLC.

Dogen, Eihei. Dogen's Genjo Koan: Three Commentaries. 2012. (JPN & ENG.). 240p. 26.00 *(978-1-58243-743-9(2)*, Counterpoint Pr.) Basic Bks. GBR. Dist: Perseus-PGW.

Drda, Darrin. The Four Global Truths: Awakening to the Peril & Promise of Our Times. 2011. (ENG., Illus.). 352p. pap. 18.95 *(978-1-58394-321-2(8))* North Atlantic Bks.

Duckworth, Douglas S. Mipam on Buddha-Nature: The Ground of the Nyingma Tradition. 2008. xxxiv, 292p. (C). 80.00 *(978-0-7914-7521-8(2))* State Univ. of New York Pr.

Dzogchen Ponlop Rinpoche Staff. Penetrating Wisdom: The Aspiration of Samantabhadra. 2006. (ENG., Illus.). 192p. 22.95 *(978-1-55939-266-2(5))* Snow Lion Pubns., Inc.

Eckel, Malcolm David. Buddhism. 2009. (Understanding Religions Ser.). (Illus.). 112p. (YA). (gr. 7-12). lib. bdg. 33.25 *(978-1-4358-5619-6(8)*, 1300721) Rosen Publishing Group, Inc., The.

—Understanding Buddhism: Origins, Beliefs, Practices, Holy Texts, Sacred Places. 2010. (ENG., Illus.). 112p. pap. 9.95 *(978-1-907486-14-2(3)*, Watkins Publishing) Duncan Baird Pubs. GBR. Dist: Sterling Publishing Co., Inc.

Eddy, Glenys. Becoming Buddhist: Experiences of Socialization & Self-Transformation in Australian Buddhist Centres. 2012. (ENG.). 288p. 120.00 ***(978-1-4411-1846-2(2))*** Continuum International Publishing Group, Ltd. GBR. Dist: National Bk. Network.

Eitel, Ernest J. Buddhism: Its Historical Theoretical & Popular Aspects in Three Lectures. 2007. (ENG.). 126p. 35.95 *(978-0-548-02112-5(0))* Kessinger Publishing, LLC.

Elamatha, John, tr. Budhan. 2010. 208p. pap. 9.99 *(978-1-61667-032-0(0))* Raider Publishing International.

Eliot, Charles. Hinduism & Buddhism. 2007. 444p. per. *(978-1-4065-1793-4(3))* Dodo Pr.

—Hinduism & Buddhism: An Historical Sketch. 2007. Vol. 2. 344p. per. *(978-1-4065-1794-1(1))* Vol. 3. 480p. per. *(978-1-4065-1795-8(X))* Dodo Pr.

Elverskog, Johan. Our Great Qing: The Mongols, Buddhism, & the State in Late Imperial China. 2006. (Illus.). 272p. (C). 52.00 *(978-0-8248-3021-2(0))* Univ. of Hawaii Pr.

Epstein, Mark. Going on Being: Life at the Crossroads of Buddhism & Psychotherapy. 2009. (ENG.). 225p. pap. 16.95 *(978-0-86171-569-5(1))* Wisdom Pubns.

—Psychotherapy Without the Self: A Buddhist Perspective. 2008. (ENG., Illus.). 272p. pap. 14.00 *(978-0-300-14313-3(3))* Yale Univ. Pr.

Erhard, Franz-Karl, et al. A Concise Dictionary of Buddhism & Zen. Kohn, Michael H., tr. 2010. (ENG.). 296p. pap. 24.95 *(978-1-59030-808-0(5))* Shambhala Pubns., Inc.

Evans, D. W. The Buddha Digest: Modern Transcriptions of Pali Texts. 2010. (ENG., Illus.). 238p. pap. *(978-1-85756-741-0(2))* Janus Publishing Co.

Faure, Bernard. Unmasking Buddhism. 2009. (ENG.). 168p. 93.95 *(978-1-4051-8065-8(X))*; pap. 23.95 *(978-1-4051-8064-1(1))* Wiley, John & Sons, Inc. (Wiley-Blackwell).

Ferguson, Gaylon & Ferguson, Gaylon Jules. Natural Wakefulness: Discovering the Wisdom We Were Born With. 2009. (ENG.). 224p. 21.95 *(978-1-59030-657-4(0))* Shambhala Pubns., Inc.

Field, Lloyd M. Business & the Buddha: Doing Well by Doing Good. 2007. (ENG.). 240p. per. 16.95 *(978-0-86171-544-2(6))* Wisdom Pubns.

Fielding-Hall, Harold. The Inward Light. reprint ed. 27.00 *(978-0-404-17294-7(6))* AMS Pr., Inc.

Flanagan, Owen J. The Bodhisattva's Brain: Buddhism Naturalized. 2011. (ENG., Illus.). 280p. (gr. 17). 27.95 *(978-0-262-01604-9(4))* MIT Pr.

Flügel, Peter & Houtman, Gustaaf, eds. Asceticism & Power in South & Southeast Asia. 2013. (Royal Asiatic Society Bks.). (ENG., Illus.). 336p. (C). 145.00 *(978-0-415-42384-7(3))* Routledge.

Gach, Gary. Buddhism - Complete Idiot's Guide. 3rd ed. 2009. (Complete Idiot's Guide Ser.). (ENG.). 416p. (gr. 12-18). pap. 18.95 *(978-1-59257-911-2(6)*, Alpha Bks.) Penguin Group (USA) Inc.

Gard, Richard A., ed. Buddhism. 2007. (ENG.). 260p. 42.95 *(978-0-548-07730-6(4))* Kessinger Publishing, LLC.

Gardiner, Eileen. Buddhist Hell: Visions, Tours & Descriptions of the Infernal Otherworld from Hell-On-Line.org. 2009. pap. *(978-1-59910-131-6(9))* Italica Pr.

Gaudioso, Zan & Martin, Greg. The Buddha Next Door: Ordinary People, Extraordinary Stories. 2007. (ENG.). 224p. pap. 15.95 *(978-0-9779245-1-6(3))* Middleway Pr.

Gellek, Tsering Palmo & Maitland, Padma Dorje, eds. Light of the Valley: Renewing the Sacred Art & Traditions of Svayambhu. 2011. (Illus.). 400p. 99.00 ***(978-0-89800-034-4(3))***; pap. 50.00 ***(978-0-89800-033-7(5))*** Dharma Publishing.

Gerhards, Paul. Mapping the Dharma: A Concise Guide to the Middle Way of the Buddha. 2007. 120p. per. 15.95 *(978-0-9779774-0-6(4))* Parami Pr., LLC.

Giles, H. A., tr. from CHI. The Travels of Fa-hsien (399-414 A. D.), or Record of the Buddhistic Kingdoms. 2012. (ENG.). 116p. pap. 33.99 ***(978-1-107-68532-1(X))*** Cambridge Univ. Pr.

B

Glass, Andrew. Four Gandhari Samyuktagama Sutras: Senior Kharosthi Fragment 5. 2008. (Gandharan Buddhist Texts). (ENG., Illus.). 224p. (978-0-295-98772-9(3)) Univ. of Washington Pr.

Goddard, Dwight, ed. A Buddist Bible, the Favorite Scriptures of the Zen Sect. reprint ed. 65.00 (978-0-404-17297-8(0)) AMS Pr., Inc.

Goddard, Dwight & Kern, H. Essential Writings of Buddhism: The Diamond Sutra & the Lotus Sutra. 2010. 218p. pap. (978-1-934941-84-3(0)) Red & Black Pubs.

Goldstein, Joseph. Abiding in Mindfulness: The Body, Vol. 1. unabr. ed. 2007. (Illus.). 7p. audio compact disk 69.95 (978-1-59179-569-8(9), AF01144D) Sounds True, Inc.

—Abiding in Mindfulness Vol. 2: On Feeling, the Mind & Dhamma. unabr. ed. 2007. (Illus.). 9p. audio compact disk 69.95 (978-1-59179-645-9(8), AF01213) Sounds True, Inc.

Goldstein, Max. Buddhist / Environmentalist: Navigating the Construction of Buddhist and Environmentalist Identity in America. 2008. 104p. pap. (978-3-639-09578-4(2)) VDM Verlag Dr. Mueller e.K.

Goonewardene, Anil. Buddhayana: Living Buddhism. 2010. (ENG., Illus.). 320p. 27.95 (978-1-4411-8795-6(2)); 90.00 (978-0-8264-2310-8(8)) Continuum International Publishing Group, Ltd. GBR. Dist: National Bk. Network.

Gour, Hari S. The Spirit of Buddhism. reprint ed. 57.50 (978-0-404-17299-2(7)) AMS Pr., Inc.

Gray, David B. The Cakrasamvara Tantra: A Study & Annotated Translation. Yarnall, Thomas F., ed. annot. ed. 2007. (Treasury of the Buddhist Sciences Ser.). (ENG.). 472p. (gr. 17). 49.00 (978-0-9753734-6-0(3)) American Institute of Buddhist Studies.

—The Cakrasamvara Tantra (The Discourse of Sri Heruka) Editions of the Sanskrit & Tibetan Texts. 2012. (ENG, TIB & SAN.). 720p. (gr. 17). 62.00 (978-1-935011-04-0(9)) American Institute of Buddhist Studies.

Gray, David B., ed. Tsong Khapa's Illumination of the Hidden Meaning Chs. 1-24: Mandala, Mantra, & the Cult of the Yognis. annot. ed. 2012. (ENG.). 496p. (gr. 17). 49.00 (978-1-935011-09-5(X)) American Institute of Buddhist Studies.

Gray, Stephen. Returning to Sacred World: A Spiritual Toolkit for the Emerging Reality. 2010. (ENG.). 335p. pap. 20.95 (978-1-84694-390-4(6)) O Bks., John Hunt.

The Great Events of 100 Years are Hazy as If aDream. 104p. 3.00 (978-0-88139-552-5(8)) Buddhist Text Translation Society.

Grimes, Pierre. Five Philosophical Dialogues. 2009. 196p. pap. 20.96 (978-0-557-07655-0(2)) Lulu Enterprises Inc.

Grozni, Nikolai. Turtle Feet: The Making & Unmaking of a Buddhist Monk. 2009. (ENG.). 352p. (gr. 12-18). pap. 16.00 (978-1-59448-376-9(0), Riverhead Trade (Paperbacks)) Penguin Group (USA) Inc.

Guest, Roger. The Tender Heart of Sadness. 2009. 194p. pap. 14.95 (978-1-59330-620-5(2)) Aventine Pr.

Guruge, Ananda. Buddhism today & aesthetic Creativity. 2010. 305p. pap. 24.99 (978-0-557-35750-5(0)) Lulu Enterprises Inc.

Gyatso, Geshe Kelsang. Introduction to Buddhism: An Explanation of the Buddhist Way of Life. 2008. (ENG., Illus.). 202p. 17.95 (978-0-9789067-6-4(4)); 212p. per. 12.95 (978-0-9789067-7-1(2)) Tharpa Pubns. GBR. Dist: Ingram Pub. Services.

—Modern Buddhism: The Path of Compassion & Wisdom. 2011. 448p. 19.95 (978-1-61606-005-3(0)); (ENG.). pap. 14.95 (978-1-61606-006-0(9)) Tharpa Pubns. GBR. Dist: Ingram Pub. Services.

Gyatso, Gueshe Kelsang. Esencia del Vajrayana: La Practica del Tantra del Yoga Supremo del Mandala Corporal de Heruka. Libano, Mariana, tr. 2007. (SPA.). 599p. pap. 25.95 (978-84-933148-8-0(9)) Tharpa Pubns. GBR. Dist: Ingram Pub. Services.

—Nuevo Manual de Meditation: Meditaciones para una vida feliz y llena de Significado. Libano, Mariana, tr. 4th rev. ed. 2008. (SPA.). 208p. pap. 12.95 (978-84-933148-5-9(4)) Tharpa Pubns. GBR. Dist: Ingram Pub. Services.

Haggard, H. Rider. The Wanderer's Necklace. 2007. (ENG.). 316p. 29.95 (978-1-4218-4171-7(1)); per. 14.95 (978-1-4218-4269-1(6)) 1st World Publishing, Inc. (1st World Library - Literary Society).

Hall, H. Fielding. The Soul of a People 1920. 2007. (ENG.). 320p. 45.95 (978-0-548-05413-0(4)) Kessinger Publishing, LLC.

Hall, Manly P. Buddha's Sermon on the Mount. pap. 4.95 (978-0-89314-307-7(3)) Philosophical Research Society, Inc.

—Koyasan: Sanctuary of Buddhism. pap. 4.95 (978-0-89314-326-8(X)) Philosophical Research Society, Inc.

Hanh, Thich Nhat. El Corazon de las Ensenanzas de Buda. (SPA.). 356p. (978-84-95456-16-8(8), 86927) Ediciones Oniro S.A.

—For a Future to Be Possible: Buddhist Ethics for Everyday Life. rev. ed. 2007. (ENG.). 160p. per. 12.95 (978-1-888375-66-4(3)) Parallax Pr.

—The Heart of Understanding: Commentaries on the Prajnaparamita Heart Sutra. 2nd rev. ed. 2009. (ENG.). 60p. (Orig.). pap. 10.95 (978-1-888375-92-3(2)) Parallax Pr.

—Volviendo a Casa. (SPA.). 184p. (978-84-95456-47-2(8), 86934) Ediciones Oniro S.A.

—The World We Have: A Buddhist Approach to Peace & Ecology. 2008. (ENG.). 110p. pap. 12.95 (978-1-888375-88-6(4)) Parallax Pr.

—Your True Home: The Everyday Wisdom of Thich Nhat Hanh. McLeod, Melvin, ed. 2011. (ENG.). 400p. pap. 17.95 (978-1-59030-926-1(X)) Shambhala Pubns., Inc.

Hanh, Thich Nhat & Cheung, Lilian. Savor: Mindful Eating, Mindful Life. 2010. (ENG.). 256p. 25.99 (978-0-06-169769-2(9), HarperOne) HarperCollins Pubs.

Hanh, Thich Nhat & Parallax Press Staff. Peaceful Action, Open Heart: Lessons from the Lotus Sutra. 2009. (ENG.). 288p. pap. 16.95 (978-1-888375-93-0(0)) Parallax Pr.

—Present Moment Wonderful Moment: Mindfulness Verses for Daily Living. 2nd rev. ed. 2006. (ENG., Illus.). 120p. per. 14.95 (978-1-888375-61-9(2)) Parallax Pr.

—Transformation & Healing: Sutra on the Four Establishments of Mindfulness. 2nd rev. ed. 2006. (ENG.). 152p. per. 14.95 (978-1-888375-62-6(0)) Parallax Pr.

Harding, John S., et al, eds. Wild Geese: Buddhism in Canada. 2010. (Illus.). 416p. (C). pap. (978-0-7735-3667-8(1)) McGill-Queen's Univ. Pr.

Hardy, R. Spence. The Legends & Theories of the Buddhists Compared with History & Science. 2007. (ENG.). 298p. 43.95 (978-0-548-03652-5(7)) Kessinger Publishing, LLC.

Hardy, Robert S. Eastern Monachism: An Account of the Origin, Laws, Discipline, Sacred Writings, Mysterious Rites, Religious Ceremonies, & Present Circumstances, of the Order of Mendicants Founded by Gotama Budha. reprint ed. 40.00 (978-0-404-17304-3(7)) AMS Pr., Inc.

—A Manual of Buddhism in Its Modern Development. reprint ed. 46.50 (978-0-404-17305-0(5)) AMS Pr., Inc.

Harrington, Anne & Zajonc, Arthur, eds. The Dalai Lama at MIT. 2006. (Illus.). 304p. 24.95 (978-0-674-02319-2(6)) Harvard Univ. Pr.

—The Dalai Lama at Mit. 2008. (Illus.). 304p. pap. 19.50 (978-0-674-02733-6(7)) Harvard Univ. Pr.

Harris, Ian. The Illustrated Encyclopedia of Buddhism: A Comprehensive Guide to Buddhist History & Philosophy, the Traditions & Practices, Magnificently Illustrated with More Than 500 Beautiful Photographs. 2009. (ENG., Illus.). 256p. 35.00 (978-0-7548-1899-1(3)) Anness Publishing GBR. Dist: National Bk. Network.

Harris, Ian Charles. An Illustrated Guide to Buddhism: An Introduction to the Buddhist Faith & Its Practice Worldwide, in over 300 Artworks & Photographs. 2012. (ENG., Illus.). 160p. pap. 16.99 **(978-1-78019-023-5(9))** Anness Publishing GBR. Dist: National Bk. Network.

Harvey, Peter, ed. Themes & Issues in Buddhism. (World Religions Ser.). 224p. pap. (978-0-304-33847-4(8), Burns & Oates) Continuum International Publishing Group, Ltd.

Hearn, Lafcadio. Gleanings in Buddha-Fields. 2009. 188p. 22.99 (978-0-559-05254-5(5)) 2009. 188p. pap. 25.99 (978-0-559-05239-2(1)) 2009. 188p. pap. 21.75 (978-0-559-05250-7(2)) 2009. 188p. pap. 22.75 (978-0-559-05242-2(1)) 2008. 118p. 28.99 (978-0-554-84185-4(1)) 2008. 151p. 25.99 (978-0-554-84192-2(4)) 2008. 151p. pap. 28.75 (978-0-554-84186-1(X)) 2008. 166p. pap. 27.75 (978-0-554-84189-2(4)) BiblioBazaar.

—Gleanings in Buddha-Fields. 2008. 304p. 35.00 (978-1-4344-7111-6(X)); pap. 19.95 (978-1-4344-7110-9(1)) Wildside Pr., LLC. (Borgo Pr.).

—Gleanings in Buddha-Fields: Studies of Hand & Soul in the Far East. 2009. 304p. 25.99 (978-1-103-66309-5(7)); pap. 19.99 (978-1-103-66304-0(6)) BiblioBazaar.

Henry M. Piironen. Divinity: A Portrait of Human Spirituality. 2010. 464p. pap. 28.95 (978-1-4502-1407-0(X)) iUniverse, Inc.

Hershock, Peter D. Buddhisin in the Public Square: Reorienting Global Interdependence. 2006. (Routledge Critical Studies in Buddhism). 229p. 160.00 (978-0-415-77052-1(1), RU521X) Routledge.

—Buddhism in the Public Sphere: Reorienting Global Interdependence. 2009. 230p. pap. 39.95 (978-0-415-54443-6(2)) Routledge.

Hodge, David & Hodge, Hi-Jin Kang. Impermanence: Embracing Change. 2009. (ENG., Illus.). 144p. 29.95 (978-1-55939-307-2(6)) Snow Lion Pubns., Inc.

Holmes, Edmond. The Creed of Buddha. 2008. 120p. pap. 7.99 (978-1-60459-301-3(6)) Wilder Pubns., Ltd.

—The Creed of Buddha 1919. 2007. (ENG.). 270p. 42.95 (978-0-548-05419-2(3)) Kessinger Publishing, LLC.

—The CREED of BUDDHA: How the True Teachings of Buddhism Can Revitalize Western Science & Spirituality. 2008. 172p. pap. 13.95 (978-1-4357-3138-7(7)) Lulu Enterprises Inc.

Holt, John. Spirits of the Place: Buddhism & Lao Religious Culture. 2009. (C). 58.00 (978-0-8248-3327-5(9)) Univ. of Hawaii Pr.

Hookham, Lama Shenpen. There's More to Dying Than Death: A Buddhist Perspective. 2006. (ENG.). 160p. pap. 14.95 (978-1-899579-68-6(0)) Windhorse Pubns. GBR. Dist: Consortium Bk. Sales & Distribution.

Horn, Nils. Buddha Orakel. 2009. 126p. pap. 14.50 (978-1-4092-9515-0(X)) Lulu Enterprises Inc.

Horton, Sarah J. Living Buddhist Statues in Early Medieval & Modern Japan. 2007. (ENG., Illus.). 244p. 89.00 (978-1-4039-6420-5(3)) Palgrave Macmillan.

Hsüan Hua. Secrets of the Five Elements: Age-Old Treasures from China. 2006. (978-0-88139-964-6(7)) Buddhist Text Translation Society.

—Shurangama Syllables Save the World: A Simple Explanation. 2008. (978-1-60103-007-8(X)) Buddhist Text Translation Society.

—Spiritual Practice & Worldly Work: Pearls of Wisdom. 2006. (978-0-88139-870-0(5)) Buddhist Text Translation Society.

—Timely Teachings: Gold Mountain Chan Monastery in the Early 1970s. 2007. (978-0-88139-468-9(8)) Buddhist Text Translation Society.

Hsüan Hua & Buddhist Text Translation Society Staff. Primeros Pasos de un Budista: Tres Refugios y Cinco Preceptos. 2010. (FRE, SPA & ENG.). (978-0-88139-764-2(4), La Sociedad para la Traduccion de Textos Budistas) Buddhist Text Translation Society.

Hsüan Hua, et al. Sutra in Forty-Two Sections Spoken by the Buddha: A General Explanation. 2006. (978-0-88139-957-8(4)) Buddhist Text Translation Society.

Hu, Hsiao-Lan. This-Worldly Nibbana: A Buddhist-Feminist Social Ethic for Peacemaking in the Global Community. 2011. 240p. 75.00 **(978-1-4384-3933-4(4)**, Suny Pr.) State Univ. of New York Pr.

Hua. The Essentials of the Shramena Vinaya & Rules of Deportment. 2nd ed. 5.00 (978-0-917512-86-5(3)) Buddhist Text Translation Society.

—Venerable Master Hua's Talks on Dharma. Vol. 5. 300p. 7.50 (978-0-88139-852-6(7)) Vol. 6. 317p. 7.50 (978-0-88139-853-3(5)) Vol. 7. 300p. 7.50 (978-0-88139-854-0(3)) Vol. 9. 300p. 7.50 (978-0-88139-858-8(6)) Buddhist Text Translation Society.

Humphreys, Christmas. Exploring Buddhism (Routledge Revivals) 2012. (Routledge Revivals Ser.). (ENG.). 196p. 120.00 **(978-0-415-52676-0(0))** Routledge.

Ikeda, Daisaku. Soka Education: For the Happiness of the Individual. 2nd ed. 2010. (ENG.). 256p. pap. 14.95 (978-0-9779245-5-4(6)) Middleway Pr.

Ikeda, Daisaku & Watson, Burton. The First Millennium. Watson, Burton, tr. from JPN. 2009. (Soka Gakkai History of Buddhism Ser.). (ENG.). 150p. pap. 14.95 (978-0-9779245-3-0(X)) Middleway Pr.

Ingram, Daniel. Mastering the Core Teachings of the Buddha: An Unusually Hardcore Dharma Book. 2008. (Illus.). 406p. pap. 38.95 (978-1-904658-40-5(7)) Aeon Bks. Ltd. GBR. Dist: Stylus Publishing, LLC.

Inwood, Kristiaan. Bhikkhu: Disciple of the Buddha. 2006. (ENG., Illus.). 208p. per. 21.95 (978-974-524-059-9(1)) Orchid Pr. THA. Dist: National Bk. Network.

Irons, Edward. Encyclopedia of Buddhism. 2008. (Encyclopedia of World Religions Ser.). 672p. (C). (gr. 9). pap. 21.95 (978-0-8160-7744-1(4), Checkmark Bks.) Facts On File, Inc.

Irons, Edward A. Encyclopedia of Buddhism. 2008. (Encyclopedia of World Religions Ser.). (Illus.). 672p. (C). (gr. 9). 85.00 (978-0-8160-5459-6(2)) Facts On File, Inc.

Itivuttaka & Moore, Justin Hartley. Sayings of Buddha: The Iti-Vuttaka. (Columbia University, Indo-Iranian Ser.: No. 5). reprint ed. 34.50 (978-0-404-50475-5(2)) AMS Pr., Inc.

Jäger, Stefan S. Glaube und Religiöse Rede Bei Tillich und Im Shin-Buddhismus: Eine Religionshermeneutische Studie. 2011. (Tillich Research Ser.). (GER.). XX, 614p. 140.00 **(978-3-11-026875-1(2))** De Gruyter, Walter Inc.

Jagtiani, Suraj. The Incredible World of Nichiren Buddhism. 2011. 140p. pap. 14.88 (978-1-4520-4234-3(9)) AuthorHouse.

Jayatilleke, Kulatissa Nanda. We are Buddhists, 20 vols. 2nd ed. 2008. (Routledge Library Editions). (JPN & ENG., Illus.). 5656p. 2025.00 (978-0-415-44291-6(5)) Routledge.

Jenkins, Sara. This Side of Nirvana: Memoirs of a Spiritually Challenged Buddhist. 2nd ed. 2008. (ENG.). 264p. pap. 13.00 (978-0-9710309-6-1(0)) Keep it Simple Bks.

Jenman, Rodney. The Good Delusion: an Unethical Response to Richard Dawkins the God Delusion. 2010. 72p. pap. 11.98 (978-1-4452-5700-6(9)) Lulu Enterprises Inc.

Jennings, Hargrave. The Mysteries of the Phallus & Its Gnostic, Rosicrucian, And. 2006. pap. 9.95 (978-1-4304-0021-9(8)) Kessinger Publishing, LLC.

—The Round Towers of Ireland & the Adoration of the Vulva - 2006. pap. 9.95 (978-1-4304-0024-0(2)) Kessinger Publishing, LLC.

—The Worship of the Lingam or Phallus & Male Principle in India - 2006. pap. 9.95 (978-1-4304-0023-3(4)) Kessinger Publishing, LLC.

Jennings, Pilar. Mixing Minds: The Power of Relationship in Psychoanalysis & Buddhism. 2010. (ENG.). 320p. pap. 18.95 (978-0-86171-616-6(7)) Wisdom Pubns.

Jensen, Lin. Deep down Things: The Earth in Celebration & Dismay. 2010. (ENG.). 176p. pap. 15.95 (978-0-86171-611-1(6)) Wisdom Pubns.

—Together under One Roof: Making a Home of the Buddha's Household. 2008. (ENG.). 276p. pap. 16.95 (978-0-86171-554-1(3)) Wisdom Pubns.

Jiang, Tao. Contexts & Dialogue: Yogacara Buddhism & Modern Psychology on the Subliminal Mind. 2006. (Monographs of the Society for Asian & Comparative Philosophy Ser.). 198p. per. 22.00 (978-0-8248-3106-6(3)) Univ. of Hawaii Pr.

Jigs-med-glin-pa Ran-byun-rdo-Rje, et al. Yeshe Lama: From the Heart Essence of the Vast Expanse of the Great Perfection, a Practice Manual for the Stages of the Path of the Original Protector Entitled Wisdom Lama. 2007. (978-1-55939-294-5(0)) Snow Lion Pubns., Inc.

Jinapriya, Ginige C. Buddhist Education in Ceylon, & Other Essays. reprint ed. 18.50 (978-0-404-17313-5(6)) AMS Pr., Inc.

Jinsei, Juna. Transforming Human Awareness: Buddhist View of 2012 & Beyond. 2011. 337p. pap. 14.95 (978-1-4327-6697-9(X)) Outskirts Pr., Inc.

Johnson, Charles. Turning the Wheel: Essays on Buddhism & Writing. 2007. (ENG.). 208p. pap. 15.95 (978-1-4165-7243-5(0), Scribner) Scribner.

Jootla, Susan Elbaum. Teacher of the Devas. (Wheel Ser.). 68p. pap. 4.25 (978-955-24-0160-2(7)) Buddhist Publication Society LKA. Dist: Pariyatti Publishing.

Jorgensen, Hans, ed. Vicitrakarnika-Vadanoddhrta: A Collection of Buddhistic Legends. reprint ed. 34.50 (978-0-404-17404-0(3)) AMS Pr., Inc.

K.C., Jose. My Shortness Is My Tallness. 2011. 64p. pap. 22.45 **(978-1-4567-9629-7(1))** AuthorHouse.

Kaklauskas, Francis J., et al, eds. Brilliant Sanity: Buddhist Approaches to Psychotherapy. 2008. 396p. per. 34.95 (978-0-9764638-4-9(9)) Univ. of the Rockies Pr.

Kalupahana, David J. The Buddha & the Conception of Law. 2008. x, 107p. pap. (978-955-663-075-6(9), Library of Congress — New Delhi Overseas Office) Buddhist Cultural Centre, The.

Kasawara, Kenju. The Dharma-Samgraha, an Ancient Collection of Buddhist Technical Terms. Muller, F. Max & Wenzel, H., eds. reprint ed. 27.50 (978-0-404-17286-2(5)) AMS Pr., Inc.

Kawai, Hayao. Buddhism & the Art of Psychotherapy. 2008. (Carolyn & Ernest Fay Series in Analytical Psychology Ser.). (ENG., Illus.). 184p. pap. 19.95 (978-1-60344-053-0(4)) Texas A&M Univ. Pr.

Keith, Arthur B. The Karma-Mimamsa. reprint ed. 27.00 (978-0-404-17318-0(7)) AMS Pr., Inc.

Keown, Damien, ed. Buddhist Studies from India to America. 2010. 320p. pap. 39.95 **(978-0-415-59936-8(9))** Routledge.

Keown, Damien & Prebish, Charles S., eds. Encyclopedia of Buddhism. 2009. 924p. 59.95 (978-0-415-55624-8(4)) Routledge.

Khippapanyo, Acariya Thoon. The Buddha's 16 Prophecies. Thian-Ngern, Neecha, tr. 2011. 3.95 **(978-1-935207-07-8(5))** Ngern, Neecha Thian.

Khong, Chan. Learning True Love: Practicing Buddhism in a Time of War. 2nd rev. ed. 2007. (ENG., Illus.). 300p. per. 16.95 (978-1-888375-67-1(1)) Parallax Pr.

Kipfer, Barbara Ann. 863 Buddhist Ways to Conquer Life's Little Challenges. 2009. (ENG.). 384p. pap. 14.95 (978-1-56975-710-9(0)) Ulysses Pr.

—1325 Buddhist Ways to Be Happy. 2007. (ENG.). 240p. per. 13.95 (978-1-56975-587-7(6)) Ulysses Pr.

Klein, Anne C. Heart Essence of the Vast Expanse: A Story of Transmission. 2010. (TIB & ENG., Illus.). 262p. 29.95 incl. cd-rom (978-1-55939-283-9(5)) Snow Lion Pubns., Inc.

Komarovski, Yaroslav. Visions of Unity: The Golden Pandita Shakya Chokden's New Interpretation of Yogacara & Madhyamaka. 2011. 450p. 90.00 (978-1-4384-3909-9(1)) State Univ. of New York Pr.

Kongtrul, Dzigar Rinpoche. Uncommon Happiness: The Path of the Compassionate Warrior. 2009. (ENG.). 192p. pap. 16.95 (978-962-7341-63-5(0)) North Atlantic Bks.

Konik, A. Buddhism & Transgression: The Appropriation of Buddhism in the Contemporary West. 2009. (Numen Book Ser.). (Illus.). 205p. (978-90-04-17875-5(9)) BRILL.

Kopf, Gereon. Merleau-Ponty & Buddhism. (ENG.). 2010. 322p. pap. 34.95 (978-0-7391-1826-9(9)) 2009. 350p. 89.50 (978-0-7391-1825-2(0)) Lexington Bks.

Kornfield, Jack. Living Dharma: Teachings & Meditation Instructions from Twelve Theravada Masters. 2nd rev. ed. 2010. (ENG., Illus.). 336p. pap. 18.95 (978-1-59030-832-5(8)) Shambhala Pubns., Inc.

—The Wise Heart: A Guide to the Universal Teachings of Buddhist Psychology. (ENG.). 448p. 2009. pap. 20.00 (978-0-553-38233-4(0)) 2008. 28.00 (978-0-553-80347-1(6), Bantam) Random House Publishing Group.

Kosambi, Dharmananda & Kosambi, Meera, intros. Dharmanand Kosambi: The Essential Writings. 2010. xv, 421p. (978-81-7824-303-0(2), Library of Congress — New Delhi Overseas Office) Permanent Black.

Kozak, Arnold & Kozak, Arnie. The Everything Buddhism Book: A Complete Introduction to the History, Traditions, & Beliefs of Buddhism, Past & Present. 2nd ed. 2011. (ENG.). 304p. pap. 15.95 (978-1-4405-1028-1(6)) Adams Media Corp.

Kuzminski, Adrian. Pyrrhonism: How the Ancient Greeks Reinvented Buddhism. (Studies in Comparative Philosophy & Religion Ser.). (ENG.). 170p. 2010. pap. 29.50 (978-0-7391-2507-6(9)) 2008. 68.50 (978-0-7391-2506-9(0)) Lexington Bks.

Kyimo. The Easy Buddah. 2007. 432p. per. (978-1-899820-44-3(2)) Paragon Publishing, Rothersthorpe.

Kyte-Coles, Robin, photos by. The Spirit of Buddha. 2009. 45.00 (978-3-8327-9315-9(1)) teNeues Publishing Co.

Landaw, Jonathan, et al. Buddhism for Dummies. 2nd ed. 2011. (ENG., Illus.). 384p. pap. 21.99 (978-1-118-02379-2(X), For Dummies) Wiley, John & Sons, Inc.

Law, Bimala C. The Buddhist Conception of Spirits. 2nd enl. rev. ed. reprint ed. 32.50 (978-0-404-17334-0(9)) AMS Pr., Inc.

Law, Bimala Churn, ed. Buddhistic Studies. reprint ed. 74.50 (978-0-404-17335-7(7)) AMS Pr., Inc.

—Geography of Early Buddhism. reprint ed. 32.50 (978-0-404-17336-4(5)) AMS Pr., Inc.

—A Study of the Mahavastu. reprint ed. 32.50 (978-0-404-17339-5(X)) AMS Pr., Inc.

Leunk, Thea Nyhoff. Which Way to God? A Christian Look at World Religions. 2008. 106p. pap. 19.95 (978-1-59255-428-7(8)) Faith Alive Christian Resources.

Levine, Marvin. The Positive Psychology of Buddhism & Yoga: Paths to a Mature Happiness. 2nd rev. ed. 2009. (ENG., Illus.). 288p. (C). 78.95 (978-1-84872-850-9(6)); pap. 36.95 (978-1-84872-851-6(4)) Taylor & Francis Group GBR. (Routledge). Dist: Taylor & Francis Group.

Lillie, Arthur. Buddha & Buddhism. 2010. (ENG.). 244p. pap. 26.75 (978-1-176-23317-1(3)) 2009. 236p. 28.99 (978-1-110-41807-7(8)) 2009. 236p. pap. 25.75 (978-1-110-41805-3(1)) 2009. (ENG.). 234p. pap. 22.99 (978-1-110-41804-6(3), BiblioLife) 2009. (ENG.). 234p. pap. 20.99 (978-1-110-41802-2(7), BiblioLife) 2009. 236p. 23.99 (978-1-103-01944-1(9)) 2009. 236p. pap. 17.99 (978-1-103-01942-7(2)) BiblioBazaar.

—Buddha & Buddhism. 2010. (Illus.). 108p. pap. 13.78 (978-1-154-65055-6(3)); 126p. pap. 16.31 (978-1-150-87285-3(3)) General Bks. LLC.

—Buddha & Buddhism. 2010. 236p. 41.95 (978-1-161-36650-1(4)) Kessinger Publishing, LLC.

Longchenpa. You Are the Eyes of the World. Lipman, Kennard & Peterson, Merrill, trs. 2nd ed. 2011. 122p. pap. 18.95 (978-1-55939-367-6(X)) Snow Lion Pubns., Inc.

Lopez, Donald S., Jr., ed. Buddhism in Practice. abr. ed. 2007. (Princeton Readings in Religions Ser.). (ENG.). 480p. (C). per. 32.50 (978-0-691-12968-6(1)) Princeton Univ. Pr.

Lopez, Donald S. & Lopez, Donald S., Jr. Buddhism & Science: A Guide for the Perplexed. 2008. (Buddhism & Modernity Ser.). 278p. 25.00 (978-0-226-49312-1(1)) Univ. of Chicago Pr.

Love, Pat & Carlson, Jon. Never Be Lonely Again: The Way Out of Emptiness, Isolation, & a Life Unfulfilled. 2011. (ENG.). 264p. pap. 14.95 (978-0-7573-1565-7(8)) Health Communications, Inc.

Lowenstein, Tom. Buddhist Inspirations: Essential Philosophy, Truth, & Enlightenment. 2006. (Illus.). 160p. 12.95 (978-1-84483-116-6(7)) Duncan Baird Pubs. GBR. Dist: Sterling Publishing Co., Inc.

—Budismo: Filosofía, verdad e Iluminacion. Portillo Diez, Miguel, tr. 2009. (SPA.). 160p. 6.95 (978-84-9801-186-9(8)) Blume ESP. Dist: Independent Pubs. Group.

Loy, David R. Money, Sex, War, Karma: Notes for a Buddhist Revolution. 2008. (ENG.). 160p. per. 15.95 (978-0-86171-558-9(6)) Wisdom Pubns.

Luisi, Pier Luigi. Mind & Life: Discussions with the Dalai Lama on the Nature of Reality. 2010. (Columbia Series in Science & Religion Ser.). (ENG., Illus.). 232p. (gr. 17). pap. 17.95 (978-0-231-14551-0(9)) Columbia Univ. Pr.

Maberry, John. Waiting for Westmoreland. 2007. 256p. pap. 16.95 (978-0-615-16045-0(X)) Eagle Peak Pr.

Macy, Joanna. Pass It On: Five Stories That Can Change the World. 2010. (ENG.). 140p. pap. 10.95 (978-1-888375-83-1(3)) Parallax Pr.

—World As Lover, World As Self: A Guide to Living Fully in Turbulent Times. 2nd rev. ed. 2007. (ENG.). 260p. pap. 18.95 (978-1-888375-71-8(X)) Parallax Pr.

Madden, Ross McLauran. The Three Poisons: A Buddhist Guide to Resolving Conflict. 2010. (ENG & SPA.). 280p. 25.99 (978-1-4389-8812-2(5)); pap. 17.95 (978-1-4389-8811-5(7)) AuthorHouse.

Madsen, Richard. Democracy's Dharma: Religious Renaissance & Political Development in Taiwan. 2007. (Illus.). 206p. pap., pap., pap. 26.95 (978-0-520-25228-8(4)); 191p. 60.00 (978-0-520-25227-1(6)) Univ. of California Pr.

Mahathera, Ampitiye Rahula, tr. The Buddhist Layman's Code of Discipline. 2011. 42p. 35.95 (978-1-258-04435-0(8)) Literary Licensing, LLC.

Maitriya. The Buddha Mimansa. Maharaja Yogiraja, ed. reprint ed. 23.50 (978-0-404-17347-0(0)) AMS Pr., Inc.

Makransky, John. Awakening Through Love: Unveiling Your Deepest Goodness. 2007. (ENG.). 240p. per. 16.95 (978-0-86171-537-4(3)) Wisdom Pubns.

Mannikka, Eleanor. Hidden Valley, Hidden Mind. 2011. 192p. pap. 15.00 (978-1-257-09704-3(0)) Lulu Enterprises Inc.

Manuel, Zenju Earthlyn. Tell Me Something about Buddhism: Questions & Answers for the Curious Beginner. 2011. (ENG.). 144p. 16.95 (978-1-57174-658-0(7)) Hampton Roads Publishing Co., Inc.

Martin, Rafe. Endless Path: Awakening Within the Buddhist Imagination: Jataka Tales, Zen Practice, & Daily Life. 2010. (ENG., Illus.). 288p. pap. 19.95 (978-1-55643-932-2(6)) North Atlantic Bks.

Mathes, Klaus-Dieter. A Direct Path to the Buddha Within: Go Lotsawa's Mahamudra Interpretation of the Ratnagotravibhaga. 2008. (Studies in Indian & Tibetan Buddhism Ser.). (ENG., Illus.). 608p. per. 32.95 (978-0-86171-528-2(4)) Wisdom Pubns.

Mathiesen, Gaylan Kent. A Theology of Mission: Examining the Challenges & Opportunities in Northeast Asia. 2007. (ENG.). 224p. pap. 16.00 (978-1-932688-26-9(9), Lutheran Univ. Pr.) Kirk Hse. Pubs.

McAra, Sally. Land of Beautiful Vision: Making a Buddhist Sacred Place in New Zealand. 2007. (Topics in Contemporary Buddhism Ser.). (Illus.). 192p. (C). 47.00 (978-0-8248-2996-4(4)) Univ. of Hawaii Pr.

McCabe, Joseph. Asia's Great Atheist Religions: An Account of Confucianism & Buddhism. Haldeman-Julius, E., ed. 2011. 32p. 35.95 (978-1-258-06485-3(5)) Literary Licensing, LLC.

McClintock, Sara. Omniscience & the Rhetoric of Reason: Rationality Argumentation & Religious Authority in Santaraksita's Tattvasamgraha & Kamalasila's Panjika. 2010. (Studies in Indian & Tibetan Buddhism Ser.). (ENG.). 432p. pap. 36.95 (978-0-86171-661-6(2)) Wisdom Pubns.

McCrea, Lawrence J., et al. Buddhist Philosophy of Language in India: Jnanasrimitra on Exclusion. 2010. (SAN & ENG.). 216p. (gr. 17). 82.50 (978-0-231-15094-1(6)); pap. 27.50 (978-0-231-15095-8(4)) Columbia Univ. Pr.

McDaniel, Justin Thomas. Gathering Leaves & Lifting Words: Histories of Buddhist Monastic Education in Laos & Thailand. 2008. (Critical Dialogues in Southeast Asian Studies). (ENG., Illus.). 384p. (C). pap. 30.00 (978-0-295-98849-8(5)) Univ. of Washington Pr.

—Gathering Leaves & Lifting Words: Histories of Buddhist Monastic Education in Laos & Thailand. 2008. (Critical Dialogues in Southeast Asian Studies). (ENG., Illus.). 384p. 70.00 (978-0-295-98848-1(7)) Univ. of Washington Pr.

McLeod, Ken. An Arrow to the Heart: A Commentary on the Heart Sutra. 2007. 156p. 27.95 (978-1-4251-5921-4(4)) Trafford Publishing.

McLeod, Melvin, ed. Mindful Politics: A Buddhist Guide to Making the World a Better Place. 2006. (ENG.). 304p. per. 16.95 (978-0-86171-298-4(6)) Wisdom Pubns.

McLeod, Melvin & Shambhala Sun Editors, eds. The Best Buddhist Writing 2011. 2011. (Shambhala Sun Book Ser.). (ENG.). 336p. pap. 17.95 (978-1-59030-933-9(2)) Shambhala Pubns., Inc.

McMahan, David L. The Making of Buddhist Modernism. 2008. (ENG., Illus.). 304p. 29.95 (978-0-19-518327-6(4)) Oxford Univ. Pr., Inc.

Mdo-snags Bstan-pai-Ñi-Ma. Dbu Ma Bzi Brgya Pai Tshig Don Rnam Par Bsad Pa Klu Dban Dgons Rgyan Bzugs So. 2008. (TIB.). (978-7-5409-3785-0(8)) Sichuan Minzu Chubanshe.

Mehrotra, Rajiv. All You Ever Wanted to Know from His Holiness The Dalai Lama on Happiness, Life, Living, & Much More 2010. (ENG.). 256p. pap. 14.95 (978-1-4019-2016-6(0)) Hay Hse., Inc.

Meinert, Carmen & Zöllner, Hans-Bernd, eds. Buddhist Approaches to Human Rights: Dissonances & Resonances. 2011. (ENG.). 200p. pap. 39.95 (978-3-8376-1263-9(5)) Transcript Verlag DEU. Dist: Transaction Pubs.

Metraux, Daniel Alfred. How Soka Gakkai Became a Global Buddist Movement: The Internationalization of a Japanese Religion. 2010. 152p. 99.95 (978-0-7734-3758-6(4)) Mellen, Edwin Pr., The.

Meynard, Thierry. The Religious Philosophy of Liang Shuming: The Hidden Buddhist. 2010. (Modern Chinese Philosophy Ser.). 226p. (978-90-04-17151-0(7)) BRILL.

Mi-pham-rgya-Mtsho, et al. Essence of Clear Light: An Overview of the Secret Commentary Thorough Dispelling of Darkness Throughout the Ten Directions Entitled Essence of Clear Light. 2010. (978-1-55939-364-5(5)) Snow Lion Pubns., Inc.

Miller, Toby & Mathers, Dale. Self & No-Self: Continuing the Dialogue between Buddhism & Psychotherapy. 2009. (ENG., Illus.). 256p. (C). 37.50 (978-0-415-43606-9(0)) Routledge.

—Self & No-Self: Continuing the Dialogue Between Buddhism & Psychotherapy. 2009. (ENG., Illus.). 256p. (C). 105.00 (978-0-415-43605-2(2)) Routledge.

Mills, Martin A. Identity Ritual & State in Tibetan Buddhism. 2010. (ENG.). 426p. pap. 39.95 (978-0-415-59138-6(4)) Routledge.

Minh Thanh. Communicative English for Buddhism-Elementary & Intermediate Levels. 2009. 568p. pap. 58.76 (978-0-557-09160-7(8)) Lulu Enterprises Inc.

Mnller, Friedrich. Wisdom of the Buddha: The Unabridged Dhammapada. 2007. 64p. per. 9.95 (978-1-60206-254-2(4)) Cosimo, Inc.

Moffitt, Phillip. Dancing with Life: Buddhist Insights for Finding Meaning & Joy in the Face of Suffering. (ENG.). 2012. 368p. pap. 16.99 (978-1-60529-824-5(7)) 2008. 352p. 24.95 (978-1-59486-353-0(9)) Rodale Pr., Inc.

Mone, James. The Sword from the Scabbard. 2007. 189p. pap. 18.95 (978-1-84799-249-9(8)) Lulu Enterprises Inc.

Monier-Williams, Monier. Buddhism: In its Connexion with Brahmanism & Hinduism & in its Contrast with Christianity. 2010. (Cambridge Library Collection - Religion Ser.). (ENG., Illus.). 620p. pap. 43.00 (978-1-108-00797-9(X)) Cambridge Univ. Pr.

—Buddhism, in Its Connection with Brahmanism & Hinduism & in Contrast with Christianity. 2nd ed. reprint ed. 57.50 (978-0-404-17349-4(7)) AMS Pr., Inc.

Morgan, Diane. Essential Buddhism: A Comprehensive Guide to Belief & Practice, 1 vol. 2010. 260p. 44.95 (978-0-313-38452-3(5), A2918C); E-Book (978-0-313-38453-0(3)) Greenwood Publishing Group, Inc. (Praeger Pubs.).

Morisawa, Yoshinobu. Saigoku Sanjusansho Dochu Annai Chizu, 2 vols. 2010. (JPN., Illus.). (978-4-7795-0434-1(1)); (978-4-7795-0435-8(X)) Nakanishiya Shuppan.

—Saigoku Sanjusansho Dochu No Ima to Mukashi, 2 vols. 2010. (JPN., Illus.). (978-4-7795-0433-4(3)); (978-4-7795-0432-7(5)) Nakanishiya Shuppan.

Morris, Richard, ed. The Puggala-Pannatti. reprint ed. 42.50 (978-0-404-17359-3(4)) AMS Pr., Inc.

Morris, Tony. What Do Buddhists Believe? Meaning & Mindfulness in Buddhist Philosophy. 2008. (ENG., Illus.). 112p. per. 9.95 (978-0-8027-1655-2(5)) Walker & Co.

Morton, Kathleen Willis. The Blue Poppy & the Mustard Seed: A Mother's Story of Loss & Hope. 2008. (ENG.). 175p. pap. 15.95 (978-0-86171-565-7(9)) Wisdom Pubns.

Muller, F., tr. The Dhammapada. 2007. 68p. per. 9.99 (978-1-59547-908-2(2)) NuVision Pubns., LLC.

Muller, F. Max. Ancient PalmLeaves Containing the Pragna. 2006. pap. 19.95 (978-1-4286-5101-2(2)) Kessinger Publishing, LLC.

Müller, F. Max. Dhammapada: A Collection of Verses from the Pali Canon of Buddhism Translated from the Pali by F. Max Muller. 2008. 92p. pap. 10.99 (978-1-934941-03-4(4)) Red & Black Pubs.

Muller, F. Max, tr. The Dhammapada. 2009. 56p. pap. (978-1-4099-3417-2(9)) Dodo Pr.

Muller, Friedrich & Davids, T. W., trs. Buddhist Suttas. 2007. 372p. per. 23.95 (978-1-60206-332-7(X)) Cosimo, Inc.

Muller, Friedrich Max, tr. The Dhammapada: The Essential Teachings of the Buddha. annot. ed. 2006. (Sacred Wisdom Ser.). (ENG., Illus.). 192p. 8.95 (978-1-84293-119-6(9), Watkins Publishing) Duncan Baird Pubs. GBR. Dist: Sterling Publishing Co., Inc.

Mus, Paul. India Seen from the East: India & Indigenous Cults in Champa. 2011. 105p. pap. 24.95 (978-1-876924-75-1(6), Monash Univ. Pr.) Monash Univ. Publishing AUS. Dist: International Specialized Bk. Services.

Nagarjuna. She-rab Dong-bu, or Prajnya Danda: A Metrical Translation in Tibetan of a Sanskrit Ethical Work. Campbell, W. L., ed. reprint ed. 27.50 (978-0-404-17354-8(3)) AMS Pr., Inc.

Nagarjuna, Arya. A Strand of Dharma Jewels: A Bodhisattva's Profound Teachings on Happiness, Liberation, & the Path. Dharmamitra, Bhikshu, tr. from CHI. 2009. 240p. pap. 14.95 (978-1-935413-05-9(8)) Kalavinka Pr.

Narasu, P. Lakshmi, tr. The Essence of Buddhism. 2007. (ENG.). 236p. 41.95 (978-0-548-09629-1(5)) Kessinger Publishing, LLC.

Neelis, Jason Emmanuel. Early Buddhist Transmission & Trade Networks: Mobility & Exchange Within & Beyond the Northwestern Borderlands of South Asia. 2010. xviii, 371p. (978-90-04-18159-5(8)) BRILL.

Nemcova, Marcela & Hajek, Karel. Introduction to Satitherapy. 2009. 86p. pap. 12.95 (978-1-4092-5900-8(5)) Lulu Enterprises Inc.

Newland, Guy. Introduction to Emptiness, New Revised Edition. 2nd ed. 2009. (ENG.). 144p. pap. 14.95 (978-1-55939-332-4(7)) Snow Lion Pubns., Inc.

Nguyen, Quang Van. Fourth Uncle in the Mountain. Date not set. mass mkt. (978-0-312-98958-3(X), St. Martin's Paperbacks) St. Martin's Pr.

Nichtern, Ethan. One City: A Declaration of Interdependence. 2007. (ENG.). 224p. per. 15.95 (978-0-86171-516-9(0)) Wisdom Pubns.

Nishitani, Keiji. On Buddhism. Yamamoto, Seisaku & Carter, Robert E., trs. from JPN. 2006. 175p. per. 24.95 (978-0-7914-6786-2(4)) State Univ. of New York Pr.

Nishitani, Keiji, et al. On Buddhism. Yamamoto, Seisaku, tr. from JPN. 2006. xi, 175p. (C). 49.50 (978-0-7914-6785-5(6)) State Univ. of New York Pr.

Nisker, Wes & Gates, Barbara, eds. The Best of Inquiring Mind: 25 Years of Dharma, Drama, & Uncommon Insight. 2008. (ENG.). 400p. pap. 17.95 (978-0-86171-551-0(9)) Wisdom Pubns.

Niwano, Nichiko & Trumbull, Suzanne. Cultivating the Buddhist Heart: How to Find Peace & Fulfillment in a Changing World. Murata, Susan, tr. 2008. (ENG.). 176p. pap. 8.95 (978-4-333-02322-6(X)) Kosei Publishing Co. JPN. Dist: Tuttle Publishing.

Niwano, Nikkyo. Buddhism for Everyday Life: Memorable Dharma Messages from a Long Spiritual Journey. Murata, Susan, tr. 2011. (ENG.). 190p. pap. 12.95 (978-4-333-02483-4(8)) Kosei Publishing Co. JPN. Dist: Tuttle Publishing.

Norbu, Thinley. A Cascading Waterfall of Nectar. 2009. (ENG.). 256p. pap. 18.95 (978-1-59030-526-3(4)) Shambhala Pubns., Inc.

Nukariya, Kaiten. Religion of the Samurai. 2008. 236p. 24.99 (978-0-554-31190-6(9)); 27.99 (978-0-554-21887-8(9)) BiblioBazaar.

—Religion of the Samurai. 2006. pap. (978-1-4068-3566-3(8)) Echo Library.

Numrich, Paul David. North American Buddhists in Social Context. 2008. (Religion & the Social Order Ser.: Vol. 15). 246p. (C). (978-90-04-16826-8(5)) BRILL.

Nyana, U. The Vipassana Dipani: or The Manual of Insight. reprint ed. 22.00 (978-0-404-17357-9(8)) AMS Pr., Inc.

Nyanasobhano, Bhikkhu. Available Truth: Excursions into Buddhist Wisdom & the Natural World. 2007. (ENG.). 224p. per. 16.95 (978-0-86171-519-0(5)) Wisdom Pubns.

Nyi, U. Practical Aspects of Buddhist Ideals. 2010. 280p. pap. 15.49 (978-1-4520-8027-7(5)) AuthorHouse.

Nyunt, Moe. The Essence of Buddhism. 2007. 212p. per. 15.95 (978-1-4327-0413-1(3)) Outskirts Pr., Inc.

O'Connor, Nellie Johnson. How Buddhism Left Indi. 2011. 86p. 38.95 (978-1-258-03230-2(9)) Literary Licensing, LLC.

Øen, Knut Johan. Self As Nature; Nature As Self. 2010. 160p. pap. (978-3-8383-7523-6(8)) Lambert Academic Publishing.

Okumura, Shohaku & Bradley, Philip Shoryu. Realizing Genjokoan: The Key to Dogen's Shobogenzo. 2010. (ENG.). 328p. pap. 16.95 (978-0-86171-601-2(9)) Wisdom Pubns.

Olcott, Henry S. The Buddhist Catechism. 2009. 64p. pap. (978-1-4068-5419-0(0)) Echo Library.

—The Buddhist Catechism. 2010. 122p. 27.96 (978-1-163-31466-1(8)) 2007. (ENG.). 124p. 34.95 (978-0-548-00192-9(8)) Kessinger Publishing, LLC.

Oldenberg, H. Ancient India - Its Language & Religions. 2008. 116p. pap. 26.45 (978-1-4437-8605-8(5)) Barclay Pr., Inc.

Oldenberg, Hermann,. Buddha: His Life, His Doctrine, His Order. 2007. 464p. per. 26.95 (978-1-60206-571-0(3)) Cosimo, Inc.

Olendzki, Andrew. Unlimiting Mind: The Radically Experiential Psychology of Buddhism. 2010. (ENG.). 160p. pap. 15.95 (978-0-86171-620-3(5)) Wisdom Pubns.

Oliver, Paul. Buddhism: Bullet Guides. 2012. (Bullet Guides). (ENG.). 128p. pap. 6.95 (978-1-4441-3491-9(4), Hodder & Stoughton) Hodder General Publishing Div. GBR. Dist: Independent Pubs. Group.

O'Neill, Mark. Tzu Chi: Serving with Compassion. 2010. (ENG.). 320p. pap. 24.95 (978-0-470-82557-9(7), Wiley) Wiley, John & Sons, Inc.

Padmasambhava Staff. Secret Teachings of Padmasambhava: Essential Instructions on Mastering the Energies of Life. Lipman, Kennard, tr. from TIB. 2010. (ENG.). 160p. pap. 18.95 (978-1-59030-774-8(7)) Shambhala Pubns., Inc.

Paramahamsa, K. R. Buddhism in Scripture & Practice. 2007. 212p. per. 24.99 (978-1-59095-892-6(6)) TotalRecall Pubns., Inc.

PARK, Bruce W. Buddha dharma Practice. 2008. 250p. pap. 19.95 (978-0-557-01459-9(7)) Lulu Enterprises Inc.

Parmenter, Ross. A House for Buddha: A Memoir with Drawings. Date not set. (Illus.). 529p. 35.00 (978-1-885241-00-9(3)) Woodstock Mountain Pr.

Pathak, P. Ethical Conflicts in Buddhist Society. 2011. 231p. pap. 35.00 (978-81-7533-316-1(2)) M. D. Pubns. Pvt, Ltd. IND. Dist: Coronet Bks.

Patil, Parimal G. Against a Hindu God: Buddhist Philosophy of Religion in India. 2009. (ENG., Illus.). 400p. (gr. 17). 50.00 (978-0-231-14222-9(6)) Columbia Univ. Pr.

Paul Carus. The Gospel of Buddh. 2011. (Illus.). 336p. pap. 7.89 (978-1-60386-397-1(4), Watchmaker Publishing) Wexford College Pr.

Pha-bon-kha-pa Byams-pa-bstan-dzin-phrin-las-rgya-Mtsho, et al. La Liberación en Nuestras Manos. 2007. (SPA.). (978-0-918753-19-9(8)) Mahayana Sutra & Tantra Pr.

Phillip Moffitt. Dancing with Life: Buddhist Insights for Finding Meaning & Joy in the Face of Suffering. 2008. 17.50 (978-1-60529-896-2(4)) Rodale Pr., Inc.

Pivar, Marjorie & Nguyen, Quang Van. Fourth Uncle in the Mountain: The Remarkable Legacy of a Buddhist Itinerant Doctor in Vietnam. 2006. (ENG., Illus.). 368p. pap. 16.99 (978-0-312-31431-6(0), St. Martin's Paperbacks) St. Martin's Pr.

Piyananda, Bhante Walpola. The Bodhi Tree Grows in L. A.: Tales of a Buddhist Monk in America. 2008. (ENG.). 192p. pap. 14.95 (978-1-59030-568-3(X)) Shambhala Pubns., Inc.

Prasad, Birendra Nath. Monasteries, Shrines, & Society: Buddhist & Brahmanical Religious Institutions in India in Their Socio-Economic Context. 2011. (Illus.). x, 345p. (978-81-7831-231-6(X), Library of Congress — New Delhi Overseas Office) Manak Pubns. Pvt., Ltd.

Prophet, Elizabeth Clare. The Buddhic Essence: Ten Stages to Becoming a Buddha. 2009. (Mystical Paths of the World's Religions Ser.). (ENG.). 160p. pap. 12.95 (978-1-932890-16-7(5)) Summit Univ. Pr.

Puri, Bharati. Engaged Buddhism: The Dalai Lama's Worldview. 2009. (ENG.). 256p. pap. 19.95 (978-0-19-806248-6(6)) Oxford Univ. Pr., Inc.

Rab-Gsal-Zla-Ba, Dil-Mgo Mkhyen-Brtse & Rinpoche, Dilgo Khyentse. Zurchungpa's Testament: A Commentary on Zurchung Sherab Trakpa's Eighty Chapters of Personal Advice. Padmakara Translation Group Staff, tr. from TIB. 2007. (ENG.). 408p. 29.95 (978-1-55939-264-8(9)) Snow Lion Pubns., Inc.

Rabjampa, Ga. To Dispel the Misery of the World: Whispered Teachings of the Bodhisattvas. Translations, Rigpa, tr. from TIB. 2012. (ENG.). 224p. pap. 16.95 (978-1-61429-004-9(0)) Wisdom Pubns.

Raguin, Virginia Chieffo, et al. Pilgrimage & Faith: Buddhism, Christianity & Islam. 2010. (978-1-932476-47-7(4)); pap. (978-1-932476-48-4(2)) Serindia Pubns., Inc.

Ram Kumar Ratnam, M. V. & Srinivas, K. Buddhist Ethics in Impermanence. 2011. xi, 204p. (978-81-246-0562-2(9), Library of Congress — New Delhi Overseas Office) D. K. Print World (P) Ltd.

Ray, Niharranjan. Brahmanical Gods of Burma: A Chapter of Indian Art & Iconography. 2006. (ENG., Illus.). pap. 15.95 (978-974-8299-30-3(9)) Orchid Pr. THA. Dist: National Bk. Network.

—Sanskrit Buddhism in Burma. 2006. (ENG., Illus.). pap. 15.95 (978-974-8299-81-5(3)) Orchid Pr. THA. Dist: National Bk. Network.

Reeves, Gene. The Stories of the Lotus Sutra. 2010. (ENG.). 352p. pap. 18.95 (978-0-86171-646-3(9)) Wisdom Pubns.

Reynolds, John. Self-Liberation through Seeing with Naked Awareness, 2nd Edition. 2nd ed. 2010. (ENG., Illus.). 192p. pap. 18.95 (978-1-55939-352-2(1)) Snow Lion Pubns., Inc.

Rhys Davids. Buddhism: A Study of the Buddhist Norm. 2007. (ENG.). 256p. 42.95 (978-0-548-05418-5(5)) Kessinger Publishing, LLC.

Rinpoche, Anyen. Dying with Confidence: A Tibetan Buddhist Guide to Preparing for Death. 2010. (ENG.). 176p. pap. 16.95 (978-0-86171-656-2(6)) Wisdom Pubns.

Rinpoche, Dudjom. A Torch Lighting the Way to Freedom: Complete Instructions on the Preliminary Practices. Padmakara Translation Group, tr. from TIB. 2011. (ENG., Illus.). 400p. 39.95 (978-1-59030-909-4(X)) Shambhala Pubns., Inc.

Rinpoche, Khenchen Palden Sherab, et al. Tara's Enlightened Activity: Commentary on the Praises to the Twenty-One Taras. 2007. (ENG., Illus.). 128p. pap. 16.95 (978-1-55939-287-7(8)) Snow Lion Pubns., Inc.

Rinpoche, Khenchen Thrangu. The Ninth Karmapa's Ocean of Definitive Meaning. Namgyal, Lama Tashi, ed. 2nd ed. 2011. 152p. pap. 16.95 (978-1-55939-370-6(X)) Snow Lion Pubns., Inc.

Rinpoche, Khenpo. Karma Chakme's Mountain Dharma, Volume Three. 2011. 477p. pap. 29.95 (978-1-934608-01-2(7)) KTD Pubns.

Rinpoche, Khenpo Karthar. Karma Chakmes Mountain Dharma, Vol. 4. 2011. 485p. pap. 24.95 (978-1-934608-07-4(6)) KTD Pubns.

Rinpoche, Sogyal. El Futuro del Budismo.Tr. of Future of Buddhism. (SPA.). 112p. pap. (978-84-7953-576-6(8)) Ediciones Urano S. A.

Rios, Cara. The Road to Whatever: A pop culture approach to Buddhism. 2009. 60p. pap. 9.95 (978-1-4401-2162-3(1)) iUniverse, Inc.

Risk, Main Author Susan Mary. Meeting Ananda Bodhi -Heavenly Enlightenment. 2008. 528p. pap. 27.90 (978-1-4303-2480-5(5)) Lulu Enterprises Inc.

Rma-bya Byang-chub Brtson-Grus & Tsondru, Mabja Jangchub. Ornament of Reason: The Great Commentary to Nagarjuna's Root of the Middle Way. 2011. (ENG.). 612p. 44.95 (978-1-55939-368-3(8)) Snow Lion Pubns., Inc.

Roberts, Peter Alan The Biographies of Rechungpa. 2010. (ENG.). pap. 39.95 (978-0-415-59622-0(X)) Routledge.

Roberts, Peter Alan The Biographies of Rechungpa: The Evolutions of a Tibetan Hagiography. 2007. 290p. 160.00 (978-0-415-76995-2(7)) Routledge.

Roberts, Peter Alan tr. from TIB. Mahamudra & Related Instructions: Core Teachings of the Kagyu Schools. 2011. (Library of Tibetan Classics Ser.). (ENG.). 832p. 59.95 (978-0-86171-444-5(X)) Wisdom Pubns.

Roberts, Stanley (Dyal). Hippie to Mystic. 2009. 204p. pap. 17.95 (978-1-4401-4504-9(0)) iUniverse, Inc.

Rocha, Cristina & Barker, Michelle, eds. Buddhism in Australia: Traditions in Change. 2011. (Routledge Critical Studies in Buddhism Ser.). (ENG., Illus.). 192p. (C). 130.00 (978-0-415-56818-0(8), Routledge) Taylor & Francis Group GBR. Dist: Taylor & Francis Group.

Rockhill, W. Woodville, tr. The Life of the Buddha & the Early History of His Order. 2007. (ENG.). 284p. 43.95 (978-0-548-03600-6(4)) Kessinger Publishing, LLC.

B

Roesler, Ulrike, et al, eds. Lives Lived, Lives Imagined: Biographies of Awakening. 2010. (ENG.). 236p. pap. 24.95 *(978-0-86171-578-7(0))* Wisdom Pubns.

Rokotoff, Natalie & Roerich, Helena. Foundations of Buddhism. 2007. (ENG.). 148p. 35.95 *(978-0-548-07782-5(7))* Kessinger Publishing, LLC.

Ross, Floyd H. The Meaning of Life in Hinduism & Buddhism. 2008. (Routledge Library Editions: Buddhism Ser.). (ENG.). 182p. (C). 165.00 *(978-0-415-46146-7(4))* Routledge.

Rothberg, Donald. The Engaged Spiritual Life: A Buddhist Approach to Transforming Ourselves & the World. 2006. (ENG.). 256p. per. 18.00 *(978-0-8070-7725-2(9))* Beacon Pr.

Rotman, Andy, tr. from SAN. Divine Stories Pt. 1: Divyavadana, Part 1. 2008. (Classics of Indian Buddhism Ser.). (ENG.). 498p. pap. 24.95 *(978-0-86171-295-3(1))* Wisdom Pubns.

Roveda, Vittorio. Buddhist Painting in Cambodia. 2009. (ENG., Illus.). 200p. *(978-974-9863-52-7(6)*, River Bks. Pr. Dist A C) Antique Collectors' Club.

Rubin Museum of Art Staff, contrib. by. The Way of the Buddha: The Illustrated Dhammapada. 2008. (ENG., Illus.). 320p. 16.95 *(978-0-8109-7295-7(6))* Abrams.

Ruegg, David S. The Buddhist Philosophy of the Middle: Essays on Indian & Tibetan Madhyamaka. 2010. (Studies in Indian & Tibetan Buddhism Ser.). (ENG.). 480p. pap. 39.95 *(978-0-86171-590-9(X))* Wisdom Pubns.

Sachs, Robert. The Wisdom of the Buddhist Masters: Common & Uncommon Sense. 2008. (ENG., Illus.). 240p. pap. 17.95 *(978-1-905857-90-6(X)*, Watkins Publishing) Duncan Baird Pubs. GBR. Dist: Sterling Publishing Co., Inc.

Saha, Ranajita Kumara. Sahaja Siddha, 2 vols. 2010. *(978-81-89537-87-6(3)*, Library of Congress — New Delhi Overseas Office) Yash Pubns.

Saint-Hilaire, Jules Barthélemy. Buddha & His Religion. 2006. 380p. per. *(978-1-4067-2665-7(6)*, Hesperides Pr.) Read Bks.

Salzberg, S. El Corazon del Mundo. (SPA.). 240p. 12.00 *(978-84-89920-71-2(0)*, 86919) Ediciones Oniro S.A. ESP. Dist: Lectorum Pubns., Inc.

Samraj, Adi. Reality Is All the God There Is. 2008. (ENG.). 1p. pap. *(978-1-59477-257-3(6)*, Inner Traditions) Inner Traditions International, Ltd.

Samuel, Geoffrey. Introducing Tibetan Buddhism. 2012. (World Religions Ser.). (Illus.). 296p. (C). 125.00 *(978-0-415-45664-7(9))* Routledge.

Sangharakshita. The Buddha's Noble Eightfold Path. 2007. (Buddhist Wisdom for Today Ser.). (ENG.). 176p. per. 16.95 *(978-1-899579-81-5(8))* Windhorse Pubns. GBR. Dist: Consortium Bk. Sales & Distribution.

—Budismo. (Guias de Sabiduria Oriental Ser.). (SPA.). 288p. *(978-84-95456-58-8(3)*, 87205) Ediciones Oniro S.A.

—The Ten Pillars of Buddhism. 2010. (Sangharakshita Classics Ser.). (ENG.). 144p. pap. 13.95 *(978-1-907314-01-8(6))* Windhorse Pubns. GBR. Dist: Consortium Bk. Sales & Distribution.

—Transforming Self & World New Edition: Themes from the Sutra of Golden Light. 2009. (ENG.). 240p. pap. 17.95 *(978-1-899579-95-2(8))* Windhorse Pubns. GBR. Dist: Consortium Bk. Sales & Distribution.

Sangharakshita & Sangharakshita. Precious Teachers: Indian Memoirs of an English Buddhist. 2008. (ENG.). 192p. per. 19.95 *(978-1-899579-78-5(8))* Windhorse Pubns. GBR. Dist: Consortium Bk. Sales & Distribution.

Santideva. The Path of Light. reprint ed. 34.50 *(978-0-404-17374-6(8))* AMS Pr., Inc.

Sarvananda. Solitude & Loneliness: A Buddhist View. 2012. (Buddhist View Ser.). (ENG.). 128p. pap. 16.95 ***(978-1-907314-07-0(5))*** Windhorse Pubns. GBR. Dist: Consortium Bk. Sales & Distribution.

Sasaki, Sokei-Ann. Story of the Giant Disciples of Buddha A. 2006. pap. 15.95 *(978-1-4286-5614-7(6))* Kessinger Publishing, LLC.

Sasson, Vanessa R. Little Buddhas: Children & Childhoods in Buddhist Texts & Traditions. 2012. ***(978-0-19-986026-5(2))*** Oxford Univ. Pr., Inc.

Sativihari, Rishi. Unlearning the Basics: A New Way of Understanding Yourself & the World. 2010. (ENG.). 140p. pap. 14.95 *(978-0-86171-572-5(1))* Wisdom Pubns.

Scherer, Burkhard. Buddhism. 2009. 224p. 24.95 *(978-0-415-45156-7(6))*; 100.00 *(978-0-415-45155-0(8))* Routledge.

Schmidt-Leukel, Perry. Understanding Buddhism. 2006. (Illus.). 180p. pap. 19.95 *(978-1-903765-18-0(8))* Dunedin Academic Pr. GBR. Dist: International Specialized Bk. Services.

Schroeder, Steven. Four Truths. 2011. 74p. pap. 10.00 ***(978-1-61097-449-3(2)***, Wipf and Stock) Wipf & Stock Pubs.

Ses-rab-rgyal-Mtshan. Bka Bsdu Bzi Pai Don Bstan Rtsis Chen Po Zes Bya Ba Bzugs So. 2009. (TIB.). *(978-7-223-02759-5(2))* Tibetan People's Publishing Hse.

Sestito, Joseph. Write for Your Lives: Inspire Your Creative Writing with Buddhist Wisdom. 2009. (ENG.). 192p. pap. 19.95 *(978-1-906787-36-3(0)*, Watkins Publishing) Duncan Baird Pubs. GBR. Dist: Sterling Publishing Co., Inc.

Sgam-po-Pa. Phyag Rgya Chen Po Lna Ldan Gyi Snon Groi Khrid Yig Bka-Brgyud Bla Mai Zal Lun Zes Bya Ba Bzugs So. 2009. (TIB.). *(978-7-223-02611-6(1))* Tibetan People's Publishing Hse.

Shaku, Soyen. Sermons of a Buddhist Abbot. 2009. 152p. pap. *(978-0-217-98826-1(1))*; 154p. pap. *(978-0-217-87108-2(9))* Books LLC.

Shedlock, Marie L. Eastern Stories & Legends. 2009. 88p. pap. *(978-0-217-20299-2(3))* Books LLC.

—Eastern Stories & Legends. 2007. (ENG.). 236p. 41.95 *(978-0-548-12596-0(1))* 2006. pap. 26.95 *(978-1-4286-3574-6(2))* Kessinger Publishing, LLC.

—Eastern Stories & Legends. 2008. 236p. pap. *(978-1-4097-1793-5(3))*; 196p. pap. *(978-1-4097-1220-6(6))* Read Bks.

Shemer, Ze'ev. The Answer: Does Religion Really Matter? 2011. 176p. pap. 15.95 *(978-1-4502-8773-9(5))* iUniverse, Inc.

Shimada, Akira & Hawkes, Jason, eds. Buddhist Stupas in South Asia: Recent Archaeological, Art-Historical, & Historical Perspectives. 2009. (ENG., Illus.). 368p. 60.00 *(978-0-19-569886-2(X))* Oxford Univ. Pr., Inc.

Shonin, Shinran. Buddhist Psalms. 2006. pap. *(978-1-4068-0554-3(8))* Echo Library.

Sidorova, Elena. Psychoanalysis & Buddhism: Echoing in Time. 2008. 395p. pap. 29.95 *(978-1-4357-5062-3(4))* Lulu Enterprises Inc.

Simpson, William. Buddhist Praying Wheel. 2010. 310p. 36.76 *(978-1-169-76298-5(0))*; 45.95 *(978-1-161-37152-9(4))* Kessinger Publishing, LLC.

Singh, Arvind Kumar. Buddhism in Far East Asia. 2009. 285p. 69.50 *(978-81-7533-165-5(8))* M. D. Pubns. Pvt, Ltd. IND. Dist: Coronet Bks.

—Buddhism in Southeast Asia. 2009. 192p. 55.00 *(978-81-7533-166-2(6))* M. D. Pubns. Pvt, Ltd. IND. Dist: Coronet Bks.

Sinnett, A. P. Esoteric Buddhism. 2008. 332p. pap. *(978-1-4086-8066-7(1))* Read Bks.

—Esoteric Buddhism. 2008. (ENG.). 336p. pap. 14.45 *(978-1-4385-0913-6(8))*; pap. 14.46 *(978-1-4385-0365-3(2))* Standard Pubns., Inc. (Book Jungle).

Sivaraksa, Sulak. The Wisdom of Sustainability: Buddhist Economics for the 21st Century. 2009. 192p. pap. 17.95 *(978-0-9821656-1-4(7))* Koa Bks., Inc.

smetham, graham. Quantum Buddhism: Dancing in Emptiness - Reality Revealed at the Interface of Quantum Physics & Buddhist Philosophy. 2010. 650p. pap. 52.50 *(978-1-4452-9430-8(3))* Lulu Enterprises Inc.

Smith, Helmer, ed. The Khuddaka-Patha. reprint ed. 28.50 *(978-0-404-17323-4(3))* AMS Pr., Inc.

Snellgrove, David, tr. The Hevajra Tantra: A Critical Study. 2011. (SAN, ENG & TIB., Illus.). 338p. pap. 50.00 *(978-974-524-128-2(8))* Orchid Pr. THA. Dist: National Bk. Network.

Snyder, Gary & Ginsberg, Allen S. The Selected Letters of Allen Ginsberg & Gary Snyder. Morgan, Bill, ed. 2009. (ENG.). 336p. pap. 16.95 *(978-1-58243-533-6(2)*, Counterpoint Pr.) Basic Bks. GBR. Dist: Perseus-PGW.

Snyder, Gary & Snyder, Gary. A Place in Space: Ethics, Aesthetics, & Watersheds. rev. ed. 2008. (ENG.). 272p. pap. 14.95 *(978-1-58243-412-4(3)*, Counterpoint Pr.) Basic Bks. GBR. Dist: Perseus-PGW.

Snyder, Stephen & Rasmussen, Tina. Practicing the Jhanas: Traditional Concentration Meditation. 2009. (ENG.). 160p. pap. 18.95 *(978-1-59030-733-5(X))* Shambhala Pubns., Inc.

Soucy, Alexander. The Buddha Side: Gender, Power, & Buddhist Practice in Vietnam. 2012. 240p. 49.00 ***(978-0-8248-3598-9(0))*** Univ. of Hawaii Pr.

Sprung, Mervyn. Lucid Exposition of the Middle Way: The Essential Chapters from the Prasannapada of Candrakirti. 2008. (Routledge Library Editions: Buddhism Ser.). (ENG.). 302p. (C). 165.00 *(978-0-415-46150-4(2))* Routledge.

Srivastava, M. Buddhism & Ethics. 2011. 269p. pap. 35.00 ***(978-81-7533-349-9(9))*** M. D. Pubns. Pvt, Ltd. IND. Dist: Coronet Bks.

—Hinayana Buddhism. 2011. 251p. pap. 35.00 ***(978-81-7533-352-9(9))*** M. D. Pubns. Pvt, Ltd. IND. Dist: Coronet Bks.

Stadtner, Donald M. Sacred Sites of Burma: Myths & Folklore in an Evolving Spiritual Realm. 2011. (ENG., Illus.). 300p. pap. *(978-974-9863-60-2(7)*, River Bks. Pr. Dist A C) Antique Collectors' Club.

Stcherbatsky, Th. The conception of Buddhist Nirvana. (Indo-Iranian Reprints Ser.). (ENG.). VI, 246p. 210.00 ***(978-3-11-190396-5(6))***; 135.00 ***(978-3-11-114193-0(4))*** De Gruyter, Mouton DEU. Dist: de Gruyter, Walter GmbH & Co. KG.

Stengs, Irene. Worshipping the Great Moderniser: King Chulalongkorn, Patron Saint of the Thai Middle Class. 2009. (ENG.). 400p. pap. 35.00 *(978-0-295-98917-4(3))* Univ. of Washington Pr.

Stone, Michael, ed. Freeing the Body, Freeing the Mind: Writings on the Connections between Yoga & Buddhism. 2010. (ENG., Illus.). 304p. pap. 18.95 *(978-1-59030-801-1(8))* Shambhala Pubns., Inc.

Strong, D. M., tr. from PLI. The Udana, or the Solemn Utterances of the Buddha. reprint ed. 31.50 *(978-0-404-17399-9(3))* AMS Pr., Inc.

Strong, John S. The Experience of Buddhism: Sources & Interpretations. 3rd rev. ed. 2007. (ENG.). 51p. (C). per. 97.95 *(978-0-495-09486-9(2))* Wadsworth.

Stultz, Sensei. Free Your Mind. 2007. 96p. per. 10.95 *(978-0-595-41953-1(4))* iUniverse, Inc.

Subhuti, Dharmachari & Subhamati. Buddhism & Friendship. 2008. (ENG.). 224p. pap. 14.95 *(978-1-899579-62-4(1))* Windhorse Pubns. GBR. Dist: Consortium Bk. Sales & Distribution.

Subramaniam, Arundhathi. The Book of Buddha. 2010. (ENG.). 152p. pap. 9.99 *(978-0-14-306765-8(6)*, Penguin Global) Penguin Group (USA) Inc.

Sucitto, Ajahn. Turning the Wheel of Truth: Commentary on the Buddha's First Teaching. 2010. (ENG.). 208p. pap. 16.95 *(978-1-59030-764-9(X))* Shambhala Pubns., Inc.

Suttapitaka. Prakrit Dhammapada. reprint ed. 31.50 *(978-0-404-17386-9(1))* AMS Pr., Inc.

Suzuki, Daisetz Teitaro & Suzuki, D. Manual of Zen Buddhism. 2007. (ENG.). 184p. 19.99 *(978-1-59986-828-8(8))* Filiquarian Publishing, LLC.

Syama-Sankara, Hara C. Buddha & His Sayings. reprint ed. 31.50 *(978-0-404-17387-6(X))* AMS Pr., Inc.

Takamori, Kentetsu, et al. You Were Born for a Reason: The Real Purpose of Life. Carpenter, Juliet Winters, tr. from JPN. 2007. 224p. 16.95 *(978-0-9790471-0-7(2))* Ichimannendo Publishing, Inc.

Taye, Jamgon. The Treasury of Knowledge, Books 9 & 10: Journey & Goal. Barron, Richard, tr. from TIB. 2010. (ENG.). 708p. 49.95 *(978-1-55939-360-7(2))* Snow Lion Pubns., Inc.

Taye, Jamgon Kongrul Lodro. The Treasury of Knowledge: Book Six, Parts One & Two: Indo-Tibetan Classical Learning & Buddhist Phenomenology. Dorje, Gyurme, tr. from TIB. 2012. (ENG.). 992p. 49.95 ***(978-1-55939-389-8(0))*** Snow Lion Pubns., Inc.

Taylor, Arnold C., ed. Kathavatthu, 2 vols. in 1. reprint ed. 56.00 *(978-0-404-17317-3(9))* AMS Pr., Inc.

—Patisambhidamagga, 2 vols. in 1. reprint ed. 43.50 *(978-0-404-17358-6(6))* AMS Pr., Inc.

Taylor, Brian. Basic buddhism for a world in Trouble. 2009. (ENG.). 72p. pap. 10.50 *(978-1-4092-8224-2(4))* Lulu Enterprises Inc.

Thakchoe, Sonam. The Two Truths Debate: Tsongkhapa & Gorampa on the Middle Way. 2007. (ENG.). 352p. per. 22.95 *(978-0-86171-501-5(2))* Wisdom Pubns.

The Yeshe De Research Team, compiled by. The Triratna Bell: Remembering the Holy Places of the Buddha. 2011. pap. ***(978-0-89800-007-8(6))*** Dharma Publishing.

Thera, Nyanaponika. Abhidhamma Studies: Research in Buddhist Psychology. Date not set. *(978-955-24-0132-9(1))* Buddhist Publication Society LKA. Dist: Pariyatti Publishing.

Thompson, Ashley. Engendering the Buddhist State: Reconstructions of Cambodian History. 2012. (Routledge Critical Studies in Buddhism Ser.). (ENG.). 240p. (C). 140.00 *(978-0-415-67772-1(6))* Routledge.

Thompson, John M. Understanding Prajna: Sengzhao's 'wild Words' & the Search for Wisdom. 2007. (American University Studies VII: Theology & Religion Ser.). 80.95 *(978-0-8204-8826-4(7))* Lang, Peter Publishing, Inc.

Thompson, Mel. Buddhism. (Illus.). 64p. (YA). (gr. 4-18). lib. bdg. 29.95 *(978-1-59389-130-5(X))* Chrysalis Education.

Thubten, Anam. No Self No Problem. 2009. (ENG.). 144p. pap. 14.95 *(978-1-55939-326-3(2))* Snow Lion Pubns., Inc.

Thurman, Robert A. F. Brilliant Illumination of the Lamp of the Five Stages: Practical Instructions in the King of Tantras, the Glorious Esoteric Community. 2011. (Treasury of the Buddhist Sciences Ser.). (ENG.). 800p. (gr. 17). 62.00 *(978-1-935011-00-2(6))* American Institute of Buddhist Studies.

Thurston, Bonnie Bowman. Merton & Buddhism: Realizing the Self. 2007. (Fons Vitae Thomas Merton Ser.). (ENG., Illus.). 298p. pap. 26.95 *(978-1-887752-84-8(6))* Fons Vitae of Kentucky, Inc.

Tin, Maung, ed. Khudaka Patha. reprint ed. 27.50 *(978-0-404-17385-2(3))* AMS Pr., Inc.

The True Meaning of Taking Refuge. 70p. 3.00 *(978-0-88139-556-3(0))* Buddhist Text Translation Society.

Trungpa, Chogyam. Ocean of Dharma: The Everyday Wisdom of Chogyam Trungpa. Gimian, Carolyn Rose, ed. 2008. (ENG.). 384p. pap. 16.95 *(978-1-59030-536-2(1))* Shambhala Pubns., Inc.

Trungpa, Chogyam & Trungpa, Chögyam. True Perception: The Path of Dharma Art. Lief, Judith L., ed. 2nd rev. ed. 2008. (ENG., Illus.). 224p. pap. 18.95 *(978-1-59030-588-1(4))* Shambhala Pubns., Inc.

Tsering, Geshe Tashi. Buddhist Psychology: The Foundation of Buddhist Thought. McDougall, Gordon, ed. 2006. (Foundation of Buddhist Thought Ser.: Vol. 3). (ENG., Illus.). 192p. per. 14.95 *(978-0-86171-272-4(2))* Wisdom Pubns.

Tseten, Migmar. Treasures of the Sakya Lineage: Teachings from the Masters. 2008. (Paths of Liberation Ser.). (ENG.). 352p. pap. 18.95 *(978-1-59030-488-4(8))* Shambhala Pubns., Inc.

Tsomo, Karma Lekshe. Into the Jaws of Yama, Lord of Death: Buddhism, Bioethics, & Death. 2006. ix, 270p. (C). 83.50 *(978-0-7914-6831-9(3))*; 270p. per. 29.95 *(978-0-7914-6832-6(1))* State Univ. of New York Pr.

Tsongkapa. The Principal Teachings of Buddhism. Tharchin, Geshe L. & Roach, Michael, trs. from TIB. (Classics of Middle Asia Ser.). 216p. pap. 6.95 *(978-0-918753-09-0(0))* Mahayana Sutra & Tantra Pr.

Tulku, Ringu. Confusion Arises As Wisdom: Gampopa's Heart Advice on the Path of Mahamudra. 2012. (ENG.). 256p. pap. 18.95 ***(978-1-59030-995-7(2))*** Shambhala Pubns., Inc.

Unno, Mark, ed. Buddhism & Psychotherapy Across Cultures: Essays on Theories & Practices. 2006. (ENG., Illus.). 350p. per. 19.95 *(978-0-86171-507-7(1))* Wisdom Pubns.

Vajragupta. The Triratna Story: The Story of a Western Buddhist Movement. 2010. (ENG., Illus.). 224p. pap. 13.95 *(978-1-899579-92-1(3))* Windhorse Pubns. GBR. Dist: Consortium Bk. Sales & Distribution.

Varley, Helen. The Buddha & His Teachings: The Essential Introduction to the Origins of Buddhism, from the Life of the Buddha through to the rise of Buddhism as an international Religion. Harris, Ian, ed. 2012. (ENG., Illus.). 96p. pap. 16.99 *(978-1-84476-981-0(X))* Anness Publishing GBR. Dist: National Bk. Network.

Vasubandhu, Shramana. Vasubandhu's Treatise on the Bodhisattva Vow: A Discourse on the Bodhisattva's Vow & the Practices Leading to Buddhahood. 2009. 160p. pap. 13.50 *(978-1-935413-09-7(0))* Kalavinka Pr.

Verma, Sujeet. Communal Stress in Leh. 2010. 72p. pap. *(978-3-8383-7400-0(2))* Lambert Academic Publishing.

Vessantara. A Guide to the Buddhas. 2008. (Meeting the Buddhas Ser.). (ENG., Illus.). 192p. per. 18.95 *(978-1-899579-83-9(4))* Windhorse Pubns. GBR. Dist: Consortium Bk. Sales & Distribution.

Vidhusekhara, Bhattacharya. The Basic Conception of Buddhism. (Adharchandra Mookerjee Lectures). reprint ed. 20.50 *(978-0-404-17405-7(1))* AMS Pr., Inc.

Vikramasimha, Ke Di Pi. Sambudu Sirita. 2010. 328p. *(978-955-551-850-5(5)*, Library of Congress — New Delhi Overseas Office) Dayawansa Jayakody & Co.

Wagiswara, W. C. D. The Buddha's Way of Virtue: A Translatio. 2006. pap. 19.95 *(978-1-4286-3815-0(6))* Kessinger Publishing, LLC.

Wagner, Elizabeth. Tearing Down Strongholds. 4.95 *(978-962-7329-01-5(0))* Living Bks. For All HKG. Dist: CLC Pubns.

Wallace, B. Alan. Contemplative Science: Where Buddhism & Neuroscience Converge. 2006. (Columbia Series in Science & Religion Ser.). (ENG., Illus.). 256p. (gr. 17). 35.00 *(978-0-231-13834-5(2))* Columbia Univ. Pr.

—Hidden Dimensions: The Unification of Physics & Consciousness. (Columbia Series in Science & Religion Ser.). (ENG.). 176p. (gr. 17). 2010. pap. 19.50 *(978-0-231-14151-2(3))* 2007. (Illus.). 24.50 *(978-0-231-14150-5(5))* Columbia Univ. Pr.

—Meditations of a Buddhist Skeptic: A Manifesto for the Mind Sciences & Contemplative Practice. 2011. (ENG.). 304p. (gr. 17). 27.95 *(978-0-231-15834-3(3))* Columbia Univ. Pr.

—Stilling the Mind: Shamatha Teachings from Dudjom Lingpa's Vajra Essence. 2011. (ENG.). 224p. pap. 17.95 *(978-0-86171-690-6(6))* Wisdom Pubns.

Wallace, B. Alan & Wallace, B. A. Contemplative Science: Where Buddhism & Neuroscience Converge. 2009. (Columbia Series in Science & Religion Ser.). (ENG.). 256p. (gr. 17). pap. 22.50 *(978-0-231-13835-2(0))* Columbia Univ. Pr.

Walters, John. The Essence of Buddhism. 2011. 174p. 42.95 ***(978-1-258-04478-7(1))*** Literary Licensing, LLC.

Ward, C.H.S. Outline of Buddhism. 2006. 148p. per. *(978-1-4067-9635-3(2)*, Hesperides Pr.) Read Bks.

Warren, Henry C. Buddhism in Translations. reprint ed. 47.50 *(978-0-404-17408-8(6))* AMS Pr., Inc.

Watters, Thomas. On Yuan Chwang's Travels in India, 629-645 A. D., 2 vols., Set. reprint ed. 67.50 *(978-0-404-06878-3(2))* AMS Pr., Inc.

—On Yuan Chwang's Travels in India, 629-645 A. D. 2009. (ENG.). 418p. pap. 26.99 *(978-1-117-50479-7(4)*, BiblioLife) BiblioBazaar.

Watts, Jonathan S., ed. Rethinking Karma: The Dharma of Social Justice. 2010. (ENG.). 272p. pap. 24.95 *(978-974-9511-78-7(6))* Univ. of Washington Pr.

Wedemeyer, Christian K., tr. from TIB. Aryadeva's Lamp That Integrates the Practices (Caryamelapakapradipa) The Gradual Path of Vajrayana Buddhism According to the Esoteric Community Noble Tradition. 2008. (Treasury of the Buddhist Sciences Ser.). (ENG.). 856p. (gr. 17). 62.00 *(978-0-9753734-5-3(5))* American Institute of Buddhist Studies.

Weerakkody, Wijeratne. God, Science, & the Buddha. 2010. 355p. pap. 40.50 *(978-0-557-50682-8(4))* Lulu Enterprises Inc.

Westerhoff, Jan. Nagarjuna's Madhyamaka: A Philosophical Introduction. 2009. (ENG.). 288p. pap. 24.95 *(978-0-19-538496-3(2))* Oxford Univ. Pr., Inc.

Why Should We Receive & Uphold the Five Precepts? 83p. 3.00 *(978-0-88139-510-5(2))* Buddhist Text Translation Society.

Williams, Duncan Ryuken & Moriya, Tomoe, eds. Issei Buddhism in the Americas. 2010. (Asian American Experience Ser.). (ENG.). 216p. pap. 25.00 *(978-0-252-07719-7(9))*; (Illus.). 70.00 *(978-0-252-03533-3(X))* Univ. of Illinois Pr.

Wilson, Jeff. Mourning the Unborn Dead: A Buddhist Ritual Comes to America. 2009. (ENG., Illus.). 304p. 35.00 *(978-0-19-537193-2(3))* Oxford Univ. Pr., Inc.

With One Heart Bowing to the City of Ten Thousand Buddhas, 9 vols., Set. Incl. Vol. I. Heng Sure & Heng Chau. (Illus.). 180p. 1977. pap. *(978-0-917512-21-6(9))*; Vol. II. Heng Sure & Heng Chau. (Illus.). 322p. 1979. pap. *(978-0-917512-23-0(5))*; Vol. III. Sure, Heng & Chau, Heng. (Illus.). 144p. 1979. pap. *(978-0-917512-89-6(8))*; Vol. IV. Heng Sure & Heng Chau. (Illus.). 130p. 1980. pap. *(978-0-917512-90-2(1))*; Vol. 5. Buddhist Text Translation Society Staff, tr. (Illus.). 234p. 1981. pap. *(978-0-917512-96-4(0))*; Vol. VI. Heng Sure & Heng Chau. (Illus.). 200p. 1981. pap. *(978-0-917512-92-6(8))*; Vol. VII. Sure, Heng & Chau, Heng. (Illus.). 160p. 1982. pap. *(978-0-917512-99-5(5))*; Vol. VIII. Sure, Heng & Chau, Heng. (Illus.). 211p. 1982. pap. *(978-0-917512-53-7(7))*; Vol. IX. Heng Sure & Heng Chau. 215p. 1983. pap. *(978-0-88139-509-9(9))*; Set pap. 63.00 *(978-0-917512-55-1(3))* Buddhist Text Translation Society.

Woo, Edward. Buddhism: The Big Picture Explained. 2008. 172p. pap. 15.95 *(978-0-595-44727-5(9))* iUniverse, Inc.

Woo, Edward P. H. Buddhism: The Big Picture Explained. 2008. 172p. 25.95 *(978-0-595-69137-1(4))* iUniverse, Inc.

Woollard, William. The Reluctant Buddhist. 2007. 296p. per. *(978-1-906210-35-9(7))* Grosvenor Hse. Publishing Ltd.

Wright, Alison. Learning to Breathe: One Woman's Journey of Spirit & Survival. 2009. (ENG., Illus.). 288p. (gr. 12-18). pap. 15.00 *(978-0-452-29535-3(1)*, Plume) Penguin Group (USA) Inc.

Wright, Brooks. Interpreter of Buddhism to the West: Edwin Arnold. 2011. 186p. 42.95 ***(978-1-258-08961-0(0))*** Literary Licensing, LLC.

Xingyun & Kumarajiva. Four Insights for Finding Fulfillment: A Practical Guide to the Buddha's Diamond Sutra. 2012. 268p. 19.95 ***(978-1-932293-54-8(X))*** Buddha's Light Publishing.

—Le Sutra du Diamant. Tran, Le-Binh, tr. from CHI. 2011.Tr. of Diamond Sutra Commentary. 627p. 35.00 ***(978-1-932293-62-3(0))*** Buddha's Light Publishing.

Yogis, Jaimal. Saltwater Buddha: A Surfer's Quest to Find Zen on the Sea. 2009. (ENG.). 200p. pap. 14.95 *(978-0-86171-535-0(7))* Wisdom Pubns.

Yong, Jin & Ikeda, Daisaku. Compassionate Light in Asia: A Dialogue. 2012. (Echoes & Reflections Ser.). (ENG.). 256p. 50.00 *(978-1-84885-198-6(7))* I. B. Tauris & Co., Ltd. GBR. Dist: Macmillan.

Yongun, Han. Selected Writings of Han Yongun: From Social Darwinism to Socialism with a Buddhist Face. Miller, Owen & Tikhonov, Vladimir, trs. from KOR. 2007. (Illus.). 263p. *(978-1-905246-47-2(1))* BRILL.

Yorke, Gerald, et al. Aleister Crowley, the Golden Dawn, & Buddhism. Reminiscences & Writings of Gerald Yorke. Richmond, Keith, ed. 2011. (Illus.). 344p. 45.00 (978-0-933429-23-9(1)) Teitan Pr., Inc., The.

Yun, Hsing. Chan Heart, Chan Art. Lee, Pey-Rong & Dunlap, Dana, trs. from CHI. 2006. (Illus.). 224p. 38.00 (978-1-932293-23-4(X)) Buddha's Light Publishing.

—Life: Politics, Human Rights, & What the Buddha Said about Life. Gill, John & Michon, Nathan, eds. Smitheram, Robert, tr. 2011. 153p. pap. 15.95 (978-1-932293-46-3(9)) Buddha's Light Publishing.

Yun, Hsing & Graham, Tom. The Great Realizations: A Commentary on the Eight Realizations of a Bodhisattva Sutra. 2nd ed. 2010. 150p. 19.95 (978-1-932293-44-9(2)) Buddha's Light Publishing.

Yun, Venerable Master Hsing. Epoch of the Buddha's Light 1: A Letter to Members of the BLIA. Int'l Buddhist Translation Center, tr. 257p. (978-957-543-796-1(9)) Fo Guang Shan Foundation for Buddhist Culture & Education.

Zailckas, Koren. Fury: A Memoir. 2010. (ENG.). 336p. (gr. 12). 25.95 (978-0-670-02230-4(5), Viking Adult) Penguin Group (USA) Inc.

Zailckas, Koren. Fury: True Tales of a Good Girl Gone Ballistic. 2012. (ENG.). 336p. (gr. 12). 16.00 **(978-0-14-312037-7(9)**, Penguin (Non-Classics)) Penguin Group (USA) Inc.

BUDDHISM—DOCTRINES

see also Eightfold Path; Enlightenment (Buddhism); Mysticism—Buddhism; Sunyata

Albahari, Miri. Analytical Buddhism: The Two-Tiered Illusion of Self. 2007. (ENG.). 256p. 100.00 (978-0-230-00712-3(0)) Palgrave Macmillan.

Apple, James B. Stairway to Nirvana: A Study of the Twenty Samghas Based on the Works of Tsong kha Pa. 2009. (Illus.). 287p. pap. 29.95 (978-0-7914-7376-4(7)) State Univ. of New York Pr.

Appleton, Naomi. Jataka Stories in Theravada Buddhism: Narrating the Bodhisatta Path. 2010. (Illus.). 186p. 89.95 (978-1-4094-1092-8(7)) Ashgate Publishing Co.

Arnau, Juan & Arnau Navarro, Juan. Antropologia del Budismo. 2008. (SPA.). 248p. pap. 25.00 (978-84-7245-645-7(5)) Kairós, Editorial S.A. ESP. Dist: Independent Pubs. Group.

Arya Vimuktisena, et al. Abhisamayalamkara with Vrtti & Aloka - Vol. 2, Vol. 2. Sparham, Gareth, tr. from SAN. 2008. 360p. 90.00 (978-0-89581-992-5(9)) Jain Publishing Company, Inc.

Asvaghosa. The Principle & Practice of Mahayana Buddhism: An Interpretation of Professor Suzuki's Translation of Ashvaghosa's Awakening of Faith. Goddard, Dwight, ed. reprint ed. 27.50 (978-0-404-17223-7(7)) AMS Pr., Inc.

Batchelor, Martine. Let Go: A Buddhist Guide to Breaking Free of Habits. 2007. (ENG.). 176p. per. 15.95 (978-0-86171-521-3(7)) Wisdom Pubns.

Bayda, Ezra. Zen Heart: Simple Advice for Living with Mindfulness & Compassion. 2008. (ENG.). 208p. 21.95 (978-1-59030-543-0(4)) Shambhala Pubns., Inc.

Bendall, Cecil & Rouse, W. D., trs. Siksha-Samuccaya: A Compendium of Buddhist Doctrine. reprint ed. 33.50 (978-0-404-17368-5(3)) AMS Pr., Inc.

Berzin, Alexander. Wise Teacher, Wise Student: Tibetan Approaches to a Healthy Relationship. 2010. (ENG.). 272p. pap. 18.95 (978-1-55939-347-8(5)) Snow Lion Pubns., Inc.

Bhadragaka. The Dhammapad: A Collection of Verses on the Doctrine of the Buddha. 2010. 108p. pap. 12.95 (978-1-58509-339-7(4)) Book Tree, The.

Bigelow, William S. Buddhism & Immortality. reprint ed. 32.50 (978-0-404-17228-2(8)) AMS Pr., Inc.

Boon, Marcus. In Praise of Copying. 2010. 304p. 25.95 (978-0-674-04783-9(4)) Harvard Univ. Pr.

Bowden, E. M. The Essence of Buddhism: 400 Dharma Sayings on Compassion. 2008. 85p. pap. 8.95 (978-1-4357-3137-0(9)) Lulu Enterprises Inc.

Brunnholzl, Karl. Luminous Heart: The Third Karmapa on Consciousness, Wisdom, & Buddha Nature. 2009. (ENG.). 512p. 39.95 (978-1-55939-318-8(1)) Snow Lion Pubns., Inc.

—Straight from the Heart: Buddhist Pith Instructions. 2007. (ENG.). 460p. 32.95 (978-1-55939-279-2(7)) Snow Lion Pubns., Inc.

Buddhaghosa. The Path of Purity, 3 vols. Pe Maung Tin, tr. reprint ed. (978-0-404-17570-2(8)) AMS Pr., Inc.

Carus, Paul. Nirvana, a Story of Buddhist Psychology. (Illus.). reprint ed. 32.50 (978-0-404-17254-1(7)); 32.50 (978-0-404-15508-7(1)) AMS Pr., Inc.

Chalmers, Lord. Buddha's Teachings - Being the Sutta Nipata or Discourse Collection. 2007. pap. 30.45 (978-1-4067-5627-2(X)) Chalmers Publishing.

Chamberlain-Nyudo, Sylvain. True Buddhism. 2010. 112p. pap. 17.48 (978-0-557-25856-7(1)) Lulu Enterprises Inc.

Chang, Garma C. C. The Buddhist Teaching of Totality: The Philosophy of Hwa Yen Buddhism. 2008. (Routledge Library Editions: Buddhism Ser.). (ENG.). 298p. (C). 165.00 (978-0-415-46089-7(1)) Routledge.

Cheng, YewChung, tr. from CHI. Crossing the Ocean of Life & Death: The Most Important Event of your Life. 2009. 212p. pap. 12.00 (978-0-9841561-0-8(0)) US Daden Culture LLC.

Chödrön, Pema. Always Maintain a Joyful Mind: And Other Lojong Teachings on Awakening Compassion & Fearlessness. Nalanda Translation Committee, tr. from TIB. 2007. (ENG., Illus.). 128p. 16.00 (978-1-59030-460-0(8)) Shambhala Pubns., Inc.

—Comfortable with Uncertainty: 108 Teachings on Cultivating Fearlessness & Compassion. 2008. (Shambhala Library). (ENG.). 240p. 18.95 (978-1-59030-626-0(0)) Shambhala Pubns., Inc.

Chodron, Pema. Living Beautifully: With Uncertainty & Change. 2012. (ENG.). 128p. 22.95 **(978-1-59030-963-6(4))** Shambhala Pubns., Inc.

Chödrön, Pema. Practicing Peace in Times of War. 2007. (ENG.). 112p. per. 7.95 (978-1-59030-500-3(0)) Shambhala Pubns., Inc.

—Practicing Peace in Times of War: A Buddhist Perspective. Boucher, Sandy, ed. 2006. (ENG.). 128p. 12.95 (978-1-59030-401-3(2)) Shambhala Pubns., Inc.

—Taking the Leap: Freeing Ourselves from Old Habits & Fears. 2009. (ENG.). 128p. 21.95 (978-1-59030-634-5(1)) Shambhala Pubns., Inc.

Chongsan. The Dharma Master Chongsan of Won Buddhism: Analects & Writings. Chung, Bongkil, tr. from KOR. 2012. (SUNY series in Korean Studies). (ENG.). 272p. 80.00 **(978-1-4384-4023-1(5))** State Univ. of New York Pr.

Cleary, J. C. Zen under the Gun: Four Zen Masters from Turbulent Times. 2010. (ENG.). 240p. pap. 16.95 (978-0-86171-592-3(6)) Wisdom Pubns.

Coleman, Graham & Jinpa, Thupten, eds. The Tibetan Book of the Dead: First Complete Translation. Dorje, Gyurme, tr. 2007. (Penguin Classics Deluxe Edition Ser.). (ENG., Illus.). 592p. (gr. 12-18). 21.00 (978-0-14-310494-0(2), Penguin Classics) Penguin Group (USA) Inc.

Collins, Steven. Nirvana: Concept, Imagery, Narrative. 2010. (ENG.). 204p. (C). 74.00 (978-0-521-88198-2(6)); pap. 26.00 (978-0-521-70834-0(6)) Cambridge Univ. Pr.

Condron, Daniel R. The Emptiness Sutra. 2007. 163p. per. 10.00 (978-0-944386-36-5(5)) SOM Publishing Co.

Conze, Edward. Buddhist Meditation. 2011. 182p. 42.95 **(978-1-258-00448-4(8))** Literary Licensing, LLC.

Coomaraswamy, Ananda Kentish & Horner, I. B. The Living Thoughts of Gotama, the Buddha. reprint ed. 34.50 (978-0-404-17256-5(3)) AMS Pr., Inc.

Dalai Lama XIV. The Dalai Lama's Little Book of Inner Peace: The Essential Life & Teachings. 2009. (ENG., Illus.). 400p. 12.95 (978-1-57174-609-2(9)) Hampton Roads Publishing Co., Inc.

—The Dalai Lama's Little Book of Wisdom. 2010. (ENG.). 400p. pap. 10.95 (978-1-57174-628-3(5)) Hampton Roads Publishing Co., Inc.

—For the Benefit of All Beings: A Commentary on the Way of the Bodhisattva. Padmakara Translation Group Staff, tr. from TIB. 2009. (Shambhala Classics Ser.). (ENG.). 160p. 15.95 (978-1-59030-693-2(7)) Shambhala Pubns., Inc.

—In My Own Words: An Introduction to My Teachings & Philosophy. 2011. (ENG.). 224p. pap. 12.95 (978-1-4019-3184-1(7)) Hay Hse., Inc.

—A Profound Mind: Cultivating Wisdom in Everyday Life. Vreeland, Nicholas, ed. 2011. (ENG., Illus.). 160p. 23.00 (978-0-385-51467-5(0), Harmony) Crown Publishing Group.

—The Union of Bliss & Emptiness: Teachings on the Practice of Guru Yoga. 2009. (ENG., Illus.). 192p. pap. 16.95 (978-1-55939-321-8(1)) Snow Lion Pubns., Inc.

Dalai Lama XIV & Cutler, Howard C. The Art of Happiness: A Handbook for Living. 10th anniv. ed. 2009. (ENG.). 352p. (gr. 12-18). 25.95 (978-1-59448-889-4(4), Riverhead Bks. (Hardcover)) Penguin Group (USA) Inc.

—The Art of Happiness in a Troubled World. 2009. (ENG.). 368p. 26.00 (978-0-7679-2064-3(3)) Broadway Bks.

Dalai Lama XIV & Mehrotra, Rajiv. In My Own Words by His Holiness D 2008. 288p. (978-1-84850-043-3(2), 798) Hay Hse. UK, Ltd. GBR. Dist: Grantham Bk. Services.

Dalai Lama XIV, et al. The Essence of Happiness. 2010. (ENG.). 224p. (gr. 12). 19.95 (978-1-59448-789-7(8), Riverhead Bks. (Hardcover)) Penguin Group (USA) Inc.

—Meditation on the Nature of Mind. 2011. (ENG., Illus.). 200p. pap. 16.95 (978-0-86171-628-9(0)) Wisdom Pubns.

D'Amato, Mario, et al. Pointing at the Moon Buddhism, Logic, Analytic Philosophy. 2009. (ENG., Illus.). 200p. pap. 27.95 (978-0-19-538156-6(4)) Oxford Univ. Pr., Inc.

Das, A. N. Buddhist Perspectives on Human Rights. 2010. 253p. 47.50 (978-81-7533-292-8(1)) M. D. Pubns. Pvt. Ltd. IND. Dist: Coronet Bks.

Das, Lama Surya. Buddha Standard Time: Awakening to the Infinite Possibilities of Now. 2012. (ENG.). 224p. pap. 14.99 **(978-0-06-177457-7(X)**, HarperOne) HarperCollins Pubs.

Davids, C. Rhys. What Was the Original Gospel in 'Buddhism'? reprint ed. 17.00 (978-0-404-17277-0(6)) AMS Pr., Inc.

Davids, T. W. Rhys. Early Buddhism. 2007. (ENG.). 108p. 34.95 (978-0-548-00225-4(8)) Kessinger Publishing, LLC.

—Early Buddhism. 2007. pap. (978-1-4067-6400-0(0)) Read Bks.

Derris, Karen & Gummer, Natalie. Defining Buddhism(S) A Reader. Derris, Karen & Gummer, Natalie, eds. 2007. (Critical Categories in the Study of Religion Ser.). (ENG., Illus.). 340p. (C). pap. 29.95 (978-1-84553-055-6(1)) Equinox Publishing Ltd. GBR. Dist: ISD.

Derris, Karen & Gummer, Natalie, eds. Defining Buddhism(S) A Reader. 2007. (Critical Categories in the Study of Religion Ser.). (ENG., Illus.). 340p. (C). 110.00 (978-1-84553-231-4(7)) Equinox Publishing Ltd. GBR. Dist: ISD.

Dge-dun-chos-Phel & Chopel, Gendun. In the Forest of Faded Wisdom. Lopez, Donald S., tr. 2009. (Buddhism & Modernity Ser.). (TIB & ENG.). 199p. 26.00 (978-0-226-10452-2(4)) Univ. of Chicago Pr.

Dhammapada. The Buddha's Path of Virtue. Woodward, F. L., tr. 2nd ed. reprint ed. 21.50 (978-0-404-17283-1(0)) AMS Pr., Inc.

Dharma Flower Sutra. 15.00 (978-0-88139-429-0(7)) Buddhist Text Translation Society.

Dogen. Treasury of the True Dharma Eye: Zen Master Dogen's Shobo Genzo, 2 vols. Tanahashi, Kazuaki, ed. 2011. (ENG.). 1280p. 150.00 (978-1-59030-474-7(8)) Shambhala Pubns., Inc.

Dogen, et al. Shobogenzo: The True Dharma-Eye Treasury, Volume 2. 2007. (C). 30.00 (978-1-886439-36-8(2)) Univ. of Hawaii Pr.

Dogen, Eihei. Shobogenzo: The True Dharma-eye Treasury, 4 vols. Nishijima, Gudo & Cross, Chodo, trs. from JPN. Vol. 1. 2007. (ENG., Illus.). 496p. 30.00 (978-1-886439-35-1(4)) Vol. 3. 2008. 438p. 30.00 (978-1-886439-37-5(0)) Vol. 4. 2008. (ENG.). 414p. 30.00 (978-1-886439-38-2(9)) BDK America.

Dorje, Ogyen Trinley & Gyalwa, Karmapa Ogye. The Future Is Now: Timely Advice for Creating a Better World. 2009. (ENG., Illus.). 256p. pap. 19.95 (978-1-4019-2300-6(3), 902) Hay Hse., Inc.

Dorje, Wangchuk. Middle Way: Commentary on Chandrakirts Madhyamaka. 2008. (Nitartha Institute Ser.). (ENG.). 850p. 59.95 (978-1-55939-289-1(4)) Snow Lion Pubns., Inc.

Drukpa, Gyalwang. Everyday Enlightenment: The Essential Guide to Finding Happiness in the Modern World. 2012. (ENG.). 208p. (gr. 12). 25.95 **(978-1-59448-623-4(9)**, Riverhead Bks. (Hardcover)) Penguin Group (USA) Inc.

Duckworth, Douglas S. Mipam on Buddha-Nature: The Ground of the Nyingma Tradition. 2009. 288p. pap. 27.95 (978-0-7914-7522-5(0), Suny Pr.) State Univ. of New York Pr.

Dudjom Dorjee. Heartfelt Advice. 2010. (ENG., Illus.). 192p. pap. 14.95 (978-1-55939-346-1(7)) Snow Lion Pubns., Inc.

Earth Store Sutra. 10.00 (978-0-88139-974-5(4)) Buddhist Text Translation Society.

Edelglass, William, et al, eds. Buddhist Philosophy: Essential Readings. 2009. (ENG.). 480p. pap. 24.95 (978-0-19-532817-2(5)) Oxford Univ. Pr., Inc.

Edelglass, William & Garfield, Jay L., eds. Buddhist Philosophy: Essential Readings. 2009. (ENG.). 496p. 99.00 (978-0-19-532816-5(7)) Oxford Univ. Pr., Inc.

Ekaku, Hakuin. The Essential Teachings of Zen Master Hakuin: A Translation of the Sokko-Roku Kaien-Fusetsu. Waddell, Norman, tr. from JPN. 2010. (Shambhala Classics Ser.). (ENG., Illus.). 176p. pap. 18.95 (978-1-59030-806-6(9)) Shambhala Pubns., Inc.

Engle, Artemus B. The Inner Science of Buddhist Practice: Vasubandhu's Summary of the Five Heaps with Commentary by Sthiramati. 2009. (TIB, SAN & ENG.). 472p. 34.95 (978-1-55939-322-5(X)) Snow Lion Pubns., Inc.

Erricker, Clive. Buddhism — An Introduction. 5th ed. 2011. (Teach Yourself: Reference Ser.). (ENG.). 240p. pap. 15.00 (978-0-07-175483-5(0), 0071754830) McGraw-Hill Cos., The.

Fisher, Charles. Dismantling Discontent: Buddha's Way Through Darwin's World. 2007. (Illus.). 442p. 26.95 (978-1-60070-031-6(4)); per. 16.95 (978-1-60070-032-3(2)) Author's Publishing Cooperative. (Elite Bks.).

Flower Adornment Dharmas: Bilingual Edition. 170p. 10.00 (978-0-88139-031-5(3)) Buddhist Text Translation Society.

Flower Adornment Sutra. 100.00 (978-0-88139-453-5(X)) Buddhist Text Translation Society.

Geaves, Ron & Vaughan-Williams, Rebecca. Key Words in Buddhism. 2006. (ENG.). 98p. per. 9.95 (978-1-58901-129-8(5)) Georgetown Univ. Pr.

Goddard, Dwight. The Buddha's Golden Path. 2nd rev. ed. reprint ed. 27.00 (978-0-404-17296-1(2)) AMS Pr., Inc.

—Was Jesus Influenced by Buddhism? a Comparative Study of the Lives & Thoughts of Gautama & Jesus. 2007. 260p. per. 19.45 (978-1-60206-281-8(1)) Cosimo, Inc.

Govinda, Lama. Psychocosmic Symbolism. 2007. 120p. pap. (978-0-9735463-6-1(0)) Dills, David R.

Gross, Rita M. A Garland of Feminist Reflections: Forty Years of Religious Exploration. 2009. (ENG.). 352p. 60.00 (978-0-520-25585-2(2)); pap. 26.95 (978-0-520-25586-9(0)) Univ. of California Pr.

Gyatso, Geshe Kelsang. How to Solve Our Human Problems: The Four Noble Truths. 2007. (ENG.). 172p. per. 12.95 (978-0-9789067-1-9(3)) Tharpa Pubns. GBR. Dist: Ingram Pub. Services.

—Introduction to Buddhism: An Explanation of the Buddhist Way of Life. 2008. (ENG., Illus.). 202p. 17.95 (978-0-9789067-6-4(4)); 212p. per. 12.95 (978-0-9789067-7-1(2)) Tharpa Pubns. GBR. Dist: Ingram Pub. Services.

Gyatso, Kelsang Gyatso. How to Solve Our Human Problems: The Four Noble Truths. 2007. (ENG.). 172p. 17.95 (978-0-9789067-0-2(5)) Tharpa Pubns. GBR. Dist: Ingram Pub. Services.

Habito, Ruben L. F., frwd. The Essential Shinran: A Buddhist Path of True Entrusting. 2006. (ENG.). 280p. per. 22.95 (978-1-933316-21-5(7)) World Wisdom, Inc.

Hackett, Paul G. A Catalogue of the Comparative Kangyur (Bka-Gyur Dpe Bsdur Ma) 2012. (ENG.). 390p. (gr. 17). 55.00 **(978-1-935011-14-9(6))** American Institute of Buddhist Studies.

Hanh, Thich Nhat. The Diamond That Cuts Through Illusion. 2nd rev. ed. 2010. (ENG.). 160p. pap. 14.95 (978-1-935209-44-7(2)) Parallax Pr.

—Fear: Essential Wisdom for Getting Through the Storm. 2012. (ENG.). 272p. 25.99 **(978-0-06-200472-7(7)**, HarperOne) HarperCollins Pubs.

—Fidelity: How to Create a Loving Relationship That Lasts. 2011. (ENG.). 144p. 12.95 (978-1-935209-91-1(4)) Parallax Pr.

—True Love: A Practice for Awakening the Heart. Kohn, Sherab Chodzin, tr. (ENG., 2011. Illus.). 128p. pap. 11.00 (978-1-59030-939-1(1)) 2006. 120p. per. 6.99 (978-1-59030-404-4(7)) Shambhala Pubns., Inc.

Hanh, Thich Nhat & Parallax Press Staff. Cultivating the Mind of Love. 2nd rev. ed. 2008. (ENG.). 140p. per. 14.95 (978-1-888375-78-7(7)) Parallax Pr.

—Teachings on Love. 2nd ed. 2006. (ENG.). 195p. per. 16.95 (978-1-888375-00-8(0)) Parallax Pr.

—Two Treasures: Buddhist Teachings on Awakening & True Happiness. 2006. (ENG., Illus.). 72p. per. 8.95 (978-1-888375-68-8(X)) Parallax Pr.

Harding, Sarah. Niguma, Lady of Illusion. 2011. (ENG., Illus.). 418p. 32.95 (978-1-55939-361-4(0)) Snow Lion Pubns., Inc.

Henry M. Piironen. The Transcendental Awareness of Buddh: A Workbook for Interpreting the Teachings in Lankavatara Sutra & Diamond Sutra. 2010. 244p. pap. 19.95 (978-1-4502-1293-9(X)) iUniverse, Inc.

Hiltebeitel, Alf. Dharma: Its Early History in Law, Religion, & Narrative, 1 vol. 2011. (South Asia Research Ser.). (ENG.). 768p. 74.00 (978-0-19-539423-8(2)) Oxford Univ. Pr., Inc.

Ho, Venerable Man, tr. Keeping Busy Is the Best Nourishment. (Hsing Yun's Hundred Saying Ser.). 161p. (978-957-457-068-3(1)) Fo Guang Shan Foundation for Buddhist Culture & Education.

Hopkins, Jeffrey. Nagarjuna's Precious Garland: Buddhist Advice for Living & Liberation. 2007. (ENG.). 284p. pap. 26.95 (978-1-55939-274-7(6)) Snow Lion Pubns., Inc.

—A Truthful Heart: Buddhist Practices for Connecting with Others. 2008. (ENG.). 190p. pap. 14.95 (978-1-55939-290-7(8)) Snow Lion Pubns., Inc.

—Tsong-kha-pa's Final Exposition of Wisdom. Vose, Kevin, ed. 2008. (ENG.). 392p. pap. 29.95 (978-1-55939-297-6(5)) Snow Lion Pubns., Inc.

Hopkins, Jeffrey & Shay-Rap-Gyel-Tsen, Dol-Bo-Ba. Mountain Doctrine: Tibet's Fundamental Treatise on Other-Emptiness & the Buddha Matrix. Vose, Kevin, ed. 2006. (ENG & TIB.). 832p. 79.95 (978-1-55939-238-9(X)) Snow Lion Pubns., Inc.

Horner, Isaline Blew. The Early Buddhist Theory of Man Perfected. 2007. (ENG.). 326p. 45.95 (978-0-548-01207-9(5)) Kessinger Publishing, LLC.

Hsing Yun, Venerable Master. Humanistic Buddhism: A Blueprint for Life. Balcom, John, tr. from CHI. 2008. (Illus.). 231p. pap. 15.00 (978-1-932293-33-3(7)) Buddha's Light Publishing.

Hsuan Hua. Cosmic Magic Syllabes Save the World. 2007. (978-0-88139-905-9(1)) Buddhist Text Translation Society.

—Timely Teachings: Gold Mountain Monastery in the Early 1970s. 2008. (978-0-88139-938-7(8)) Buddhist Text Translation Society.

Hwang, Soonil. Metaphor & Literalism in Buddhism: The Doctrinal History of Nirvana. 2006. (Illus.). 160p. 160.00 (978-0-415-35550-6(8), RU42588) Routledge.

Ikeda, Daisaku. Buddhism Day by Day: Wisdom for Modern Life. 2006. (ENG.). 393p. per. 15.95 (978-0-9723267-5-9(8)) Middleway Pr.

—Learning from the Gosho. 2007. pap. 5.00 (978-1-932911-39-8(1)) World Tribune Pr.

Iyer, Pico. The Open Road: The Global Journey of the Fourteenth Dalai Lama. 2008. (ENG.). 288p. 24.00 (978-0-307-26760-3(1), Knopf) Knopf Doubleday Publishing Group.

Jacobi, Hermann. The Dates of the Philosophical Sutras of the Brahmans. 2010. pap., pap. 19.48 (978-1-61143-150-6(6)) Gorgias Pr., LLC.

Jacobson, Nolan Pliny. Understanding Buddhism. 2010. (ENG., Illus.). 228p. pap. 19.95 (978-0-8093-2985-4(9)) Southern Illinois Univ. Pr.

Jamgon Kongtrul Lodrö, Tayé. The Treasury of Knowledge: Buddhism's Journey to Tibet. 2010. (ENG.). 696p. 49.95 (978-1-55939-345-4(9)) Snow Lion Pubns., Inc.

Jen Chen Buddhists Staff. Tending the Spiritual Land, 9 vols. Shih, Ta L., ed. Date not set. (CHI.). 190p. (Orig.). pap. (978-0-9647369-9-3(3)) Jen Chen Buddhism Houston Mission.

Jerryson, Michael K. & Juergensmeyer, Mark. Buddhist Warfare, 1 vol. 2010. (ENG., Illus.). 272p. pap. 29.95 (978-0-19-539484-9(4)) Oxford Univ. Pr., Inc.

Katagiri, Dainin. Each Moment Is the Universe: Zen & the Way of Being Time. 2008. (ENG.). 256p. 18.95 (978-1-59030-607-9(4)) Shambhala Pubns., Inc.

Kerouac, Jack. Wake Up: A Life of the Buddha. (ENG.). (gr. 12-18). 2009. 224p. 15.00 (978-0-14-311601-1(0), Penguin (Non-Classics)) 2008. 160p. 24.95 (978-0-670-01957-1(7), Viking Adult) Penguin Group (USA) Inc.

Kha Pa, Tsong. Golden Garland of Eloquence - Vol. 2 Vol. 2: Legs Bshad Gser Phreng. Sparham, Gareth, tr. 2008. 230p. 75.00 (978-0-89581-866-9(3)) Jain Publishing Company, Inc.

Khyentse, Dilgo. The Heart of Compassion: The Thirty-Seven Verses on the Practice of a Bodhisattva. Padmakara Translation Group & Ricard, Matthieu, trs. from TIB. 2007. (ENG.). 256p. pr. 16.95 (978-1-59030-457-0(8)) Shambhala Pubns., Inc.

Khyentse, Dzongsar Jamyang. ¿Como saber si no eres budista? (What Makes You Not a Buddhist) 2012. (SPA & ENG.). 168p. pap. 16.95 **(978-1-61180-025-8(0)**, Shambhala Espanol) Shambhala Pubns., Inc.

Khyentse, Dzongsar Jamyang. What Makes You Not a Buddhist. 2008. (ENG.). 144p. pap. 15.95 (978-1-59030-570-6(1)) Shambhala Pubns., Inc.

King, Sallie B. Socially Engaged Buddhism. 2009. (Illus.). 200p. 48.00 (978-0-8248-3335-0(X)); (C). pap. 17.00 (978-0-8248-3351-0(1)) Univ. of Hawaii Pr.

Klon-chen-pa Dri-med-od-Zer & Barron, Richard. The Precious Treasury of Philosophical Systems. 2007. (978-1-881847-44-1(6)) Padma Publishing.

Kongtrul, Dzigar. Light Comes Through: Buddhist Teachings on "Awakening" to Our Natural Intelligence. 2008. (ENG.). 144p. 21.95 (978-1-59030-567-6(1)) Shambhala Pubns., Inc.

—Light Comes Through: Buddhist Teachings on Awakening to Our Natural Intelligence. 2009. (ENG.). 144p. pap. 14.95 (978-1-59030-719-9(4)) Shambhala Pubns., Inc.

Kongtrul, Dzigar & Berliner, Helen. It's up to You: The Practice of Self-Reflection on the Buddhist Path. 2006. (Buddhism Ser.). (ENG., Illus.). 160p. per. 12.95 (978-1-59030-381-8(4)) Shambhala Pubns., Inc.

B

Kornfield, Jack, ed. The Buddha Is Still Teaching: Contemporary Buddhist Wisdom. 2011. (ENG.). 256p. pap. 17.95 *(978-1-59030-922-3(7))* Shambhala Pubns., Inc.

—Teachings of the Buddha. (ENG.). 2012. 232p. pap. 14.95 ***(978-1-59030-897-4(2))*** 2007. 240p. per. 6.99 *(978-1-59030-508-9(6))* Shambhala Pubns., Inc.

Kuan, Tse-fu. Mindfulness in Early Buddhism: New Approaches Through Psychology & Textual Analysis of Pali, Chinese & Sanskrit Sources. 2008. (Routledge Critical Studies in Buddhism Ser.). (ENG., Illus.). 256p. (C). 160.00 *(978-0-415-43737-0(7))* Routledge.

La Vallée Poussin, Louis de. The Way to Nirvana. 2012. (ENG.). 184p. pap. 41.99 ***(978-1-107-64345-1(7))*** Cambridge Univ. Pr.

Lai, Cherry, et al, trs. Where there Is Dharma, there Is a Way. (Hsing Yun's Hundred Saying Ser.). 186p. *(978-957-543-968-2(6))* Fo Guang Shan Foundation for Buddhist Culture & Education.

Lamrimpa. How to Realize Emptiness, 2nd Edition. 2nd ed. 2010. (ENG.). 136p. pap. 15.95 *(978-1-55939-358-4(0))* Snow Lion Pubns., Inc.

Leighton, Taigen Dan. Faces of Compassion: Classic Bodhisattva Archetypes & Their Modern Expression - an Introduction to Mahayana Buddhism. 2nd rev. ed. 2012. (ENG.). 352p. pap. 18.95 ***(978-1-61429-014-8(8))*** Wisdom Pubns.

Levine, Noah. Against the Stream. 2008. 192p. pap. 13.95 *(978-0-06-115794-3(5)*, Harper San Francisco) HarperCollins Pubs.

—Against the Stream: A Buddhist Manual for Spiritual Revolutionaries. 2007. (ENG.). 192p. pap. 13.99 *(978-0-06-073664-4(X)*, HarperOne) HarperCollins Pubs.

—The Heart of the Revolution: The Buddha's Radical Teachings of Forgiveness, Compassion, & Kindness. 2011. (ENG.). 224p. pap. 15.99 *(978-0-06-171124-4(1)*, HarperOne) HarperCollins Pubs.

Liang, Liling. Han Yi Fo Dian Dong Wu Gu Shi Zhi Yan Jiu. 2010. (CHI., Illus.). vi, 370p. *(978-957-668-916-1(3))* Wen Chin Publishing Co, Ltd.

Lingpa, Jigme & Dorje, Longchen Yeshe. Treasury of Precious Qualities. Padmakara Translation Group Staff, tr. from TIB. rev. ed. 2010. (ENG., Illus.). 576p. pap. 29.95 *(978-1-59030-711-3(9))* Shambhala Pubns., Inc.

Loy, David. Lack & Transcendence: The Problem of Death & Life in Psychotherapy, Existentialism & Buddhism. 218p. 69.98 *(978-1-57392-492-4(X)*, Humanity Bks.) Prometheus Bks., Pubs.

Loy, David R. Awareness Bound & Unbound. 2009. 240p. pap. 24.95 *(978-1-4384-2680-8(1))* State Univ. of New York Pr.

—Awareness Bound & Unbound: Buddhist Essays. 2009. 240p. 70.00 *(978-1-4384-2679-2(8))* State Univ. of New York Pr.

Mansfield, Vic. Tibetan Buddhism & Modern Physics: Toward a Union of Love & Knowledge. 2008. (ENG., Illus.). 192p. (C). (gr. 14). per. 19.95 *(978-1-59947-137-2(X))* Templeton Pr.

Masefield, Peter. Divine Revelation in Pali Buddhism. 2nd ed. 2008. (Routledge Library Editions: Buddhism Ser.). (ENG., Illus.). 206p. (C). 165.00 *(978-0-415-46164-1(2))* Routledge.

Master Tran Tam International Associatio, Sr., told to. Pearls of Wisdom 1 (Vietnamese) 2009. (VIE., Illus.). 15.00 *(978-0-9823376-6-0(3))* Master Tran Tam International Assn.

Mdo-snags Bstan-pai-ñi-Ma, et al. Distinguishing the Views & Philosophies: Illuminating Emptiness in a Twentieth-Century Tibetan Buddhist Classic. Samuel, Douglas, tr. from TIB. 2011. (ENG., Illus.). 240p. 80.00 *(978-1-4384-3437-7(5))* State Univ. of New York Pr.

Medicine Master Sutra. 10.00 *(978-0-88139-313-2(4))* Buddhist Text Translation Society.

Menen, Rajendar. The Healing Power of Mudras: The Yoga of the Hands. 2010. (Illus.). 112p. pap. *(978-1-84819-043-6(3))* Singing Dragon.

Michaels, Axel & Luz, Ulrich. Encountering Jesus & Buddha: Their Lives & Teachings. Maloney, Linda M., tr. from GER. 2006. (Illus.). 256p. pap. 17.00 *(978-0-8006-3564-0(7)*, Fortress Pr.) Augsburg Fortress, Pubs.

Michie, David. Buddhism for Busy People: Finding Happiness in an Uncertain World. 2008. (ENG.). 240p. (Orig.). pap. 14.95 *(978-1-55939-298-3(3))* Snow Lion Pubns., Inc.

Mun, Chanju, ed. Mediators & Meditators: Buddhism & Peacemaking. 2007. 409p. pap. 35.00 *(978-0-9777553-3-2(9))* Blue Pine.

Nath, Meeta. Ahimsa: Based on Buddhism & Gandhism. 2011. 343p. *(978-93-80651-17-0(1))* Vidya Nidhi Prakashan.

Ngaosrivathana, Mayoury & Ngaosrivathana, Pheuiphanh. The Enduring Sacred Landscape of the Naga. 2009. (ENG., Illus.). 156p. (C). pap. 25.00 ***(978-974-303-160-1(X))*** Silkworm Bks. THA. Dist: Univ. of Washington Pr.

Nyanaponika, Ven. Pathways of Buddhist Thought: Essays from the Wheel. 2008. (Routledge Library Editions: Buddhism Ser.). 258p. 165.00 *(978-0-415-46132-0(4))* Routledge.

O-rgyan-jigs-med-chos-kyi-dban-Po, et al. Groundless Paths: The Prajnaparamita Sutras, the Ornament of Clear Realization, & Its Commentaries in the Tibetan Nyingma Tradition. 2012. (ENG.). 904p. 54.95 ***(978-1-55939-375-1(0))*** Snow Lion Pubns., Inc.

Olson, Carl & Prebish, Charles S. Historical Dictionary of Buddhism. 2009. (Historical Dictionaries of Religions, Philosophies, & Movements Ser.: 97). (ENG.). 370p. 111.00 *(978-0-8108-5771-1(5))* Scarecrow Pr., Inc.

Ortner, Jon, photos by. Buddha. 2010. (ENG., Illus.). 240p. 29.95 *(978-1-59962-061-9(8)*, Welcome Bks.) Welcome Enterprises, Inc.

Oxford Press University Staff, ed. Sayings of the Buddha: A Selection of Suttas from the Pali Nikayas. Gethin, Rupert, tr. from PLI. & intro. by. 2008. (Oxford World's Classics Ser.). (ENG., Illus.). 336p. pap. 14.95 *(978-0-19-283925-1(X))* Oxford Univ. Pr., Inc.

Palmo, Jetsumna. Into the Heart of Life. 2011. (ENG.). 192p. pap. 18.95 *(978-1-55939-374-4(2))* Snow Lion Pubns., Inc.

Pandit, Moti Lal. The Buddhist View of Knowledge & Reality. 2008. (SAN & ENG.). xx, 314p. 52.50 *(978-81-215-1196-4(8))* Munshiram Manoharlal Pubs. Private, Ltd. IND. Dist: Coronet Bks.

Paraskevopoulos, John. The Way of Shin Buddhism. 2009. 114p. pap. *(978-1-59731-095-6(6))* Perennis, Sophia.

Park, Jin Y. Buddhism & Postmodernity: Zen, Huayan, & the Possibility of Buddhist Postmodern Ethics. 2008. (ENG.). 338p. 83.99 *(978-0-7391-1823-8(4))* Lexington Bks.

Park, Jungnok. How Buddhism Acquired a Soul on the Way to China. 2012. (Oxford centre for buddhist studies Monographs). (ENG.). 256p. (C). 99.95 *(978-1-84553-996-2(6))*; pap. 34.95 *(978-1-84553-997-9(4))* Equinox Publishing Ltd. GBR. Dist: Brown, David Bk. Co., The.

Park, Pori. Trial & Error in Modernist Reforms: Korean Buddhism under Colonial Rule. 2009. *(978-1-55729-094-6(6))* Univ. of California, Institute of East Asian Studies.

Park, Sung Bae. One Korean's Approach to Buddhism: The Mom/Momjit Paradigm. 2009. (SUNY Series in Korean Studies). 144p. 59.50 *(978-0-7914-7697-0(9))* State Univ. of New York Pr.

Park, Sung Bae, et al. One Korean's Approach to Buddh: The Mom/Momjit Paradigm. 2009. (SUNY Series in Korean Studies). 144p. pap. 19.95 *(978-0-7914-7698-7(7))* State Univ. of New York Pr.

Peacock, John. The Tibetan Way of Life, Death & Rebirth: The Illustrated Guide to Tibetan Wisdom. 2009. (ENG., Illus.). 144p. pap. *(978-1-84483-804-2(8))* Duncan Baird Pubs. GBR. Dist: Sterling Publishing Co., Inc.

Pha-bon-kha-pa Byams-pa-bstan-dzin-phrin-las-rgya-Mtsho, et al. La Liberación en Nuestras Manos. 2007. (SPA.). *(978-0-918753-21-2(X))*; *(978-0-918753-23-6(6))* Mahayana Sutra & Tantra Pr.

Piironen, Henry M. Enlightened Life of Buddhism: A workbook for interpreting the 423 teachings of enlightenment in Dhammapada. 2009. 200p. pap. 16.95 *(978-1-4401-8617-2(0))* iUniverse, Inc.

Ponlop, Dzogchen. Mind Beyond Death. 2008. (ENG.). 375p. pap. 18.95 *(978-1-55939-301-0(7))* Snow Lion Pubns., Inc.

—Rebel Buddha: A Guide to a Revolution of Mind. 2011. (ENG.). 224p. pap. 15.95 *(978-1-59030-929-2(4))* Shambhala Pubns., Inc.

Pye, Michael, ed. Beyond Meditation: Expressions of Japanese Shin Buddhist Spirituality. 2011. (Eastern Buddhist Voices Ser.). (ENG., Illus.). 326p. (C). 99.95 *(978-1-84553-918-4(4))*; pap. 34.95 *(978-1-84553-919-1(2))* Equinox Publishing Ltd. GBR. Dist: ISD.

Rabjam, Longchen. Natural Perfection: Lonchenpa's Radical Dzogchen. Dowman, Keith, tr. from TIB. 2010. (ENG.). 300p. pap. 17.95 *(978-0-86171-640-1(X))* Wisdom Pubns.

Rangdrol, Tsele Natsok. The Mirror of Mindfulness, Updated Edition: The Cycle of the Four Bardos. 2010. (ENG.). 176p. pap. 15.95 *(978-962-7341-65-9(7))* North Atlantic Bks.

Ricard, Matthieu. Why Meditate: Working with Thoughts & Emotions. 2010. (ENG.). 200p. 15.95 *(978-1-4019-2663-2(0))* Hay Hse., Inc.

Rinchen, Geshe Sonam. The Three Principal Aspects of the Path, 2nd Edition. Sonam, Ruth, tr. from TIB. 2nd ed. 2010. (ENG., Illus.). 168p. pap. 16.95 *(978-1-55939-350-8(5))* Snow Lion Pubns., Inc.

Rinpoche, Khenchen Thrangu. Everyday Consciousness & Primordial Awareness. Schefczyk, Susanne, tr. 2007. (ENG.). 128p. 19.95 *(978-1-55939-272-3(X))* Snow Lion Pubns., Inc.

Rinpoche, Lama Zopa. How Things Exist: Teachings on Emptiness. Cameron, Ailsa, ed. 2008. (Illus.). 112p. pap. *(978-1-891868-20-7(9))* Lama Yeshe Wisdom Archive.

—Kadampa Teachings. Cameron, Ailsa, ed. 2010. (ENG., Illus.). 260p. pap. *(978-1-891868-24-5(1*, 15410) Lama Yeshe Wisdom Archive.

Rinpoche, Shyalpa Tenzin. Living Fully: Finding Joy in Every Breath. 2012. (ENG.). 296p. 19.95 ***(978-1-60868-075-7(4))*** New World Library.

Robert Epstein With Stacy Taylor. Suffering Buddh: The zen way beyond health & Illness. 2010. 120p. pap. 12.95 *(978-1-4269-2588-7(3))* Trafford Publishing.

Sakashita, Jay, ed. Biography & Disciples. 2008. (Writings of Nichiren Shonin Ser.). 255p. pap. 25.00 *(978-0-8248-3301-5(5))* Univ. of Hawaii Pr.

Sangharakshita. A Guide to the Buddhist Path. Hagel, Sara, ed. 2011. (ENG.). 256p. pap. 23.95 ***(978-1-907314-05-6(9))*** Windhorse Pubns. GBR. Dist: Consortium Bk. Sales & Distribution.

Sangharakshita. The History of My Going for Refuge. 2nd ed. 2010. (Sangharakshita Classics Ser.). (ENG.). 144p. (Orig.). pap. 13.95 *(978-1-907314-00-1(8))* Windhorse Pubns. GBR. Dist: Consortium Bk. Sales & Distribution.

Sangharakshita, Urgyen. Sangharakshita: A Half-Century of Writings from the Founder of the Friends of the Western Buddhist Order. Stout, Vidyadeva Karen, ed. 2009. (ENG.). 792p. pap. 29.95 *(978-0-86171-585-5(3))* Wisdom Pubns.

Sayadaw, Ven. M. A Discourse on Dependent Origination. Date not set. *(978-955-24-0163-3(1))* Buddhist Publication Society LKA. Dist: Pariyatti Publishing.

Sayadaw, Webu. Selected Discourses. Date not set. *(978-955-24-0134-3(8))* Buddhist Publication Society LKA. Dist: Pariyatti Publishing.

Schneider, J., ed. Vagisvarakirtis Mrtuvancanopadesa, eine buddhistische Lehrschrift zur Abwehr des Todes. 2010. (Denkschriften der Phil. -Hist. Klasse Ser.). 299p. (C). pap. 111.00 *(978-3-7001-6722-8(9))* Austrian Academy of Sciences Press AUT. Dist: Brown, David Bk. Co., The.

Seongcheol. Sermon of One Hundred Days. Covill, Linda, ed. Soonil, Hwang, tr. from KOR. 2010. (Oxford centre for buddhist studies Monographs). (ENG., Illus.). 192p. (C). pap. 29.95 *(978-1-84553-631-2(2))*;Pt. 1. 95.00 *(978-1-84553-630-5(4))* Equinox Publishing Ltd. GBR. Dist: ISD.

Shantideva. The Way of the Bodhisattva. Padmakara Translation Group, tr. from SAN. 2008. (Shambhala Library). (ENG.). 384p. 18.95 *(978-1-59030-614-7(7))* Shambhala Pubns., Inc.

Shields, James Mark. Critical Buddhism: Engaging with Modern Japanese Buddhist Thought. 2011. 216p. 89.95 *(978-1-4094-1798-9(0))*; 240p. pap. 34.95 *(978-1-4094-1799-6(9))* Ashgate Publishing Co.

Shinkaku, Kaundinya. Short Talks on Buddhism. 2011. 90p. 38.95 ***(978-1-258-05944-6(4))*** Literary Licensing, LLC.

Shurangama Sutra. 15.00 *(978-0-88139-404-7(1))* Buddhist Text Translation Society.

Siddhartha Gautam, Buddha, + Teacher's Guide. pap. 4.95 *(978-1-878099-10-5(8))* Vidya Bks.

Silk, Jonathan A. Managing Monks: Administrators & Administrative Roles in Indian Buddhist Monasticism. 2008. (South Asia Research Ser.). (TIB, CHI, SAN, PLI & ENG.). 320p. 65.00 *(978-0-19-532684-0(9))* Oxford Univ. Pr., Inc.

Singh, Renuka. Becoming Buddha: Wisdom Culture for a Meaningful Life. 2012. (ENG., Illus.). 208p. (gr. 12). 20.00 *(978-0-670-08537-8(5)*, Library of Congress — New Delhi Overseas Office, Penguin Global) Penguin Group (USA) Inc.

Slater, Robert Lawson. Paradox & Nirvan: A Study of Religious Ultimates with Special Reference to Burmese Buddhism. 2011. 156p. 41.95 ***(978-1-258-03067-4(5))*** Literary Licensing, LLC.

Soeng, Mu. The Heart of the Universe: Exploring the Heart Sutra. 2010. (ENG.). 150p. pap. 15.95 *(978-0-86171-574-9(8))* Wisdom Pubns.

Stanley, John, et al, eds. A Buddhist Response to the Climate Emergency. 2009. (ENG.). 200p. pap. 16.95 *(978-0-86171-605-0(1))* Wisdom Pubns.

Sumedho, Ajahn. The Sound of Silence: The Selected Teachings of Ajahn Sumedho. 2007. (ENG.). 400p. per. 18.95 *(978-0-86171-515-2(2))* Wisdom Pubns.

A Sure Sign of the Proper Dharma. 86p. 3.00 *(978-0-88139-550-1(1))* Buddhist Text Translation Society.

Swanson, Eric & Mingyur, Yongey. Joyful Wisdom: Embracing Change & Finding Freedom. 2010. (ENG.). 304p. pap. 15.00 *(978-0-307-40780-1(2)*, Three Rivers Pr.) Crown Publishing Group.

Taranatha. The Essence of Other-Emptiness. Hopkins, Jeffrey, tr. from TIB. 2007. (ENG.). 148p. pap. 16.95 *(978-1-55939-273-0(8))* Snow Lion Pubns., Inc.

Taye, Jamgon Kongtrul. Treasury of Knowledge: Book 8, Part 3: The Elements of Tantric Practice. 2008. (ENG.). 448p. 34.95 *(978-1-55939-305-8(X))* Snow Lion Pubns., Inc.

Taye, Jamgon Kongtrul Lodro, et al. The Treasury of Knowledge, Book 6, Part 3: Frameworks of Buddhist Philosophy. Callahan, Elizabeth M., tr. from TIB. 2007. (Treasury of Knowledge Ser.). (ENG.). 416p. 34.95 *(978-1-55939-277-8(0))* Snow Lion Pubns., Inc.

Teiser, Stephen F. Readings of the Lotus Sutra. Teiser, Stephen F. & Stone, Jacqueline I., eds. 2009. (Columbia Readings of Buddhist Literature Ser.). (ENG., Illus.). 304p. (gr. 17). pap. 24.50 *(978-0-231-14289-2(7))* Columbia Univ. Pr.

Teiser, Stephen F. & Stone, Jacqueline Ilyse. Readings of the Lotus Sutra. Teiser, Stephen F. & Stone, Jacqueline I., eds. 2009. (Columbia Readings of Buddhist Literature Ser.). (ENG., Illus.). 304p. (gr. 17). 79.50 *(978-0-231-14288-5(9))* Columbia Univ. Pr.

Ten Dharma Realm Are Not Beyond a Single Thought. 135p. 7.50 *(978-0-88139-504-4(8))* Buddhist Text Translation Society.

Thera, Nyanaponika & Bodhi, Bhikkhu. Numerical Discourses of the Buddha: An Anthology of Suttas from the Anguttara Nikaya. 2010. (Sacred Literature Trust Ser.). (ENG.). 356p. pap. 30.95 *(978-0-300-16520-3(X))* Yale Univ. Pr.

Thrangu, Kenchen. Everyday Consciousness & Primordial Awareness. Schefczyk, Susanne, ed. & tr. by. 3rd ed. 2011. (ENG.). 124p. pap. 16.95 *(978-1-55939-379-9(3))* Snow Lion Pubns., Inc.

Thrangu, Khenchen. On Buddha Essence: A Commentary on Rangjung Dorje's Treatise. Johnson, Clark, ed. Roberts, Peter Alan, tr. from TIB. 2006. (ENG.). 200p. per. 29.95 *(978-1-59030-276-7(1))* Shambhala Pubns., Inc.

Thubten Yeshe, et al. Wisdom Energy: Basic Buddhist Teachings. Landaw, Jonathan, ed. 2012. (ENG.). 160p. pap. 15.95 ***(978-1-61429-001-8(6))*** Wisdom Pubns.

Tiwary, K. N. Buddhist Beliefs & Practices. 2010. 267p. 54.50 *(978-81-7533-288-1(3))* M. D. Pubns. Pvt, Ltd. IND. Dist: Coronet Bks.

Tomabechi, Toru. The Adhyardhasatika Prajnaparamita: Sanskrit & Tibetan Texts Critically Edited (Sanskrit Texts from the Tibetan Autonomous Region, No. 5) 2009. (ENG.). 168p. (C). pap. 60.00 *(978-3-7001-6653-5(2))* Austrian Academy of Sciences Press AUT. Dist: Brown, David Bk. Co., The.

Trungpa, Chögyam. The Truth of Suffering & the Path of Liberation. Lief, Judith L., ed. 2010. (ENG.). 176p. pap. 14.95 *(978-1-59030-770-0(4))* Shambhala Pubns., Inc.

—Work, Sex, Money: Real Life on the Path of Mindfulness. Gimian, Carolyn Rose & Kohn, Sherab Chodzin, eds. 2011. (ENG.). 256p. pap. 15.95 *(978-1-59030-596-6(5))* Shambhala Pubns., Inc.

Trungpa, Chögyam & Lief, Judith L. The Truth of Suffering & the Path of Liberation. 2009. (ENG.). 160p. 21.95 *(978-1-59030-668-0(6))* Shambhala Pubns., Inc.

Tsering, Geshe Tashi. Relative Truth, Absolute Truth. 2008. (Foundation of Buddhist Thought Ser.: Vol. 2). (ENG.). 192p. pap. 14.95 *(978-0-86171-271-7(4))* Wisdom Pubns.

Tsering, Geshe Tashi & McDougall, Gordon. Emptiness: The Foundation of Buddhist Thought, Vol. 5. 2009. (Foundation of Buddhist Thought Ser.). (ENG.). 200p. pap. 14.95 *(978-0-86171-511-4(X))* Wisdom Pubns.

Tseten, Migmar. The Tibetan Book of Awakening. 2010. 136p. pap. 14.95 *(978-0-557-38681-9(0))* Lulu Enterprises Inc.

Tulku, Ringu. Daring Steps, 2nd Edition: Traversing the Path of the Buddha. 2nd ed. 2010. (ENG.). 224p. pap. 16.95 *(978-1-55939-354-6(8))* Snow Lion Pubns., Inc.

Vajragupta. Buddhism: Tools for Living Your Life. 2007. (ENG.). 224p. pap. 16.95 *(978-1-899579-74-7(5))* Windhorse Pubns. GBR. Dist: Consortium Bk. Sales & Distribution.

Vasu-Mitra. Origin & Doctrines of Early Indian Buddhist Schools. Masuda, Jiryo, tr. reprint ed. 32.50 *(978-0-404-17403-3(5))* AMS Pr., Inc.

Vecchiotti, Icilio, et al. Storia Del Buddhismo Indiano. 2007. (ITA., Illus.). *(978-88-359-5928-1(4))*; *(978-88-6473-017-2(6))* Editori Riuniti.

Wallace, B. The Four Immeasurables, Third Edition: Practices to Open the Heart. 3rd ed. 2010. (ENG.). 192p. pap. 16.95 *(978-1-55939-353-9(X))* Snow Lion Pubns., Inc.

Wallis, Glenn & Buddha. Basic Teachings of the Buddha: A New Translation & Compilation, with a Guide to Reading the Texts. 2007. (Modern Library Classics Ser.). (ENG., Illus.). 288p. pap. 14.95 *(978-0-8129-7523-9(5)*, Modern Library) Random House Publishing Group.

Webster, David. The Philosophy of Desire in the Buddhist Pali Canon. 2010. (ENG.). pap. 39.95 ***(978-0-415-60000-2(6))*** Routledge.

Wegela, Karen Kissel. The Courage to Be Present: Buddhism, Psychotherapy, & the Awakening of Natural Wisdom. 2010. (ENG & ACE.). 240p. pap. 16.95 *(978-1-59030-830-1(1))* Shambhala Pubns., Inc.

Welter, Albert & Yanshou. Yongming Yanshou's Conception of Chan in the Zongjing Lu: A Special Transmission Within the Scriptures. 2011. (ENG.). 400p. 74.00 *(978-0-19-976031-2(4))* Oxford Univ. Pr., Inc.

Wilkens, Jens. Altturkische Handschriften, Teil 10: Buddhistische Erzahltexte. 2010. (Verzeichnis der Orientalischen Handschriften in Deutschland Ser.). (GER & TUR., Illus.). 389p. (C). 112.00 *(978-3-515-09666-9(3))* Steiner, Franz Verlag Wiesbaden GmbH DEU. Dist: Brown, David Bk. Co., The.

Williams, Paul, et al. Buddhist Thought. 2nd rev. ed. 2012. (ENG., Illus.). 288p. (C). pap. 32.95 *(978-0-415-57179-1(0))*; 110.00 ***(978-0-415-57178-4(2))*** Routledge.

Wright, Dale S. The Six Perfections: Buddhism & the Cultivation of Character. 2009. (ENG.). 304p. 27.95 *(978-0-19-538201-3(3))* Oxford Univ. Pr., Inc.

Yao, Weiqun. Fo Jiao Si Xiang Yu Wen Hua. 2009. (CHI.). *(978-7-301-15625-4(1))* Beijing University Pr.

Yao, Zhihua. The Buddhist Theory of Self-Cognition. 2009. 204p. pap. 39.95 *(978-0-415-54438-2(6))* Routledge.

Yen, Sheng. Orthodox Chinese Buddhism: A Contemporary Chan Master's Answers to Common Questions. Gildow, Douglas, ed. & tr. by. from CHI. Chang, Otto, tr. from CHI. 2007. (ENG., Illus.). 192p. pap. 16.95 *(978-1-55643-657-4(2))* North Atlantic Bks.

Yeshe, Lama. When the Chocolate Runs Out. Bartok, Josh & Ribush, Nicholas, eds. 2011. (ENG.). 176p. 9.95 *(978-0-86171-269-4(2))* Wisdom Pubns.

Yifa. The Tender Heart: A Buddhist Response to Suffering. 2007. (ENG.). 128p. pap. 10.00 *(978-1-59056-111-9(2))* Lantern Bks.

Yun, Hsing. All in a Thought: Between Ignorance & Enlightenment I, 7 vols., Vol. 1. Hsi, Miao & Lai, Cherry, trs. 2008. 128p. pap. 15.00 *(978-1-932293-31-9(0))* Buddha's Light Publishing.

—The Core Teachings. Lee, Pey-Rong & Hsu, Mu-Tzen, trs. 2008. 168p. pap. 15.00 *(978-1-932293-32-6(9))* Buddha's Light Publishing.

—Footprints in the Ganges: The Buddha's Stories on Cultivation & Compassion. 2010. 222p. pap. 14.95 *(978-1-932293-35-7(3))* Buddha's Light Publishing.

—Humble Table, Wise Fare 1, Vol. 1. Fo Guang Shan International Translation Center, ed. Manzo, Tom & Cheng, Shujan, trs. from CHI. 2007. 184p. pap. 9.00 *(978-1-932293-25-8(6))* Buddha's Light Publishing.

—Opening the Mind's Eye: Clarity & Spaciousness in Buddhist Practice. Fo Guang Shan International Translation Center, tr. 2009. 187p. pap. 14.95 *(978-1-932293-38-8(8))* Buddha's Light Publishing.

—Seeking Happiness: Between Ignorance & Enlightenment VII, 7 vols., Vol. 7. 2008. 208p. pap. 15.00 *(978-1-932293-27-2(2))* Buddha's Light Publishing.

Zen Ko, The Reverend John. The Diamond Sutra: Ancient Wisdom in the Age of Terror. 2009. 60p. pap. 19.95 *(978-0-578-00629-1(4))* Mindwhispers Pubns.

Ziegler, Amelia L. The Truth As Non-Foundational According to Zen Buddhism. 2008. 60p. per. *(978-3-8364-6000-2(9))* VDM Verlag Dr. Mueller e.K.

BUDDHISM—DRAMA

Lynn, Kirk. Zen Junior High. 2007. 104p. pap. 6.50 *(978-1-58342-348-6(6))* Dramatic Publishing Co.

BUDDHISM—HISTORY

Adamek, Wendi L. The Mystique of Transmission: On an Early Chan History & Its Contexts. 2007. (CHI & ENG., Illus.). 448p. (gr. 17). 60.00 *(978-0-231-13664-8(1))* Columbia Univ. Pr.

Berkwitz, Stephen C. The History of the Buddha's Relic Shrine: A Translation of the Sinhala Thupavamsa. 2006. (ENG.). 320p. 75.00 *(978-0-19-530139-7(0))* Oxford Univ. Pr., Inc.

Bluck, Robert. British Buddhism: Teachings, Practice & Development. 2008. 234p. 39.95 *(978-0-415-48308-7(5))* Routledge.

Brancaccio, Pia & Behrendt, Kurt, eds. Gandharan Buddhism: Archaeology, Art, & Texts, 1 vol. 2007. (ENG., Illus.). 328p. pap. 34.95 *(978-0-7748-1081-4(5))* UBC Pr. CAN. Dist: Univ. of Washington Pr.

Buescher, Hartmut. The Inception of Yogacara-Vijnanavada. 2008. (Beitrage zur Kultur- und Geistesgeschichte Asiens Ser.). 258p. (C). pap. 74.00 *(978-3-7001-6099-1(2))* Austrian Academy of Sciences Press AUT. Dist: Brown, David Bk. Co., The.

Burnouf, Eugene. Introduction to the History of Indian Buddhism. Buffetrille, Katia & Lopez, Donald S., Jr., trs. from FRE. 2010. (ENG.). 616p. 65.00 *(978-0-226-08123-6(0))* Univ. of Chicago Pr.

Conze, Edward. Buddhism: A Short History. 2007. (ENG., Illus.). 160p. per. 14.95 *(978-1-85168-568-4(5))* Oneworld Pubns. GBR. Dist: National Bk. Network.

Coomaraswamy, Ananda Kentish. Buddha & the Gospel of Buddhism. 2009. 290p. pap. *(978-0-217-18293-5(3))* Books LLC.

—Buddha & the Gospel of Buddhism. 2008. 424p. *(978-1-4437-4004-3(7),* Obscure Pr.) Read Bks.

D. Buddhism. 2009. 3025.00 *(978-0-415-44132-2(3))* Routledge.

Davids, C. Rhys. The Milinda Question: An Inquiry into Its Place in the History of Buddhism with a Theory As to Its Author. reprint ed. 22.50 *(978-0-404-17275-6(X))* AMS Pr., Inc.

—Outlines of Buddhism: A Historical Sketch. reprint ed. 16.50 *(978-0-404-17276-3(8))* AMS Pr., Inc.

Davids, Carolina A. Buddhism: Its Birth & Dispersal. rev. ed. reprint ed. 25.00 *(978-0-404-17268-8(7))* AMS Pr., Inc.

Davids, T. W. Rhys. Buddhism Its History & Literature. 2007. (ENG.). 244p. 41.95 *(978-0-548-03637-2(3))* Kessinger Publishing, LLC.

—Early Buddhism. 2007. (ENG.). 108p. 34.95 *(978-0-548-00225-4(8))* Kessinger Publishing, LLC.

—Early Buddhism. 2007. pap. *(978-1-4067-6400-0(0))* Read Bks.

Dhamma-Kitti. A Manual of Buddhist Historical Traditions - Saddhamma - Sangaha. Law, Bimala Churn, tr. reprint ed. 21.50 *(978-0-404-17279-4(2))* AMS Pr., Inc.

Dutt, Nalinaksha. Early History of the Spread of Buddhism & the Buddhist Schools. reprint ed. 42.00 *(978-0-404-17293-0(8))* AMS Pr., Inc.

Eliot, Charles. Hinduism & Buddhism. 2008. 516p. 35.99 *(978-0-554-25247-6(3))*; 380p. 31.99 *(978-0-554-25248-3(1))*; 532p. 35.99 *(978-0-554-25249-0(X))*; 532p. 32.99 *(978-0-554-34552-9(8))*; 516p. 32.99 *(978-0-554-34550-5(1))*; 380p. 29.99 *(978-0-554-34551-2(X))* BiblioBazaar.

—Hinduism & Buddhism. 2007. (ENG.). 340p. per. *(978-1-4068-6295-9(9))*; 260p. per. *(978-1-4068-6296-6(7))*; 372p. per. *(978-1-4068-6297-3(5))* Echo Library.

—Hinduism & Buddhism: An Historical Sketch. 2007. (ENG.). 1. 456p. pap. 28.99 *(978-1-4264-8544-2(1))*1. 514p. pap. 31.99 *(978-1-4264-8601-2(4))*2. 326p. pap. 23.99 *(978-1-4264-8545-9(X))*3. 464p. pap. 28.99 *(978-1-4264-8546-6(8))* Vol. 2. 376p. pap. 26.99 *(978-1-4264-8602-9(2))* Vol. 3. 530p. pap. 31.99 *(978-1-4264-8603-6(0))* BiblioBazaar.

Elverskog, Johan. Buddhism & Islam on the Silk Road. 2010. (Encounters with Asia Ser.). (Illus.). 384p. (C). 69.95 *(978-0-8122-4237-9(8))* Univ. of Pennsylvania Pr.

Erricker, Clive. Buddhism — An Introduction. 5th ed. 2011. (Teach Yourself: Reference Ser.). (ENG.). 240p. pap. 15.00 *(978-0-07-175483-5(0),* 0071754830) McGraw-Hill Cos., The.

Ford, James L. Jōkei & Buddhist Devotion in Early Medieval Japan. 2006. (ENG., Illus.). 336p. 85.00 *(978-0-19-518814-1(4))* Oxford Univ. Pr., Inc.

Grant, Beata. Eminent Nuns: Women Chan Masters of Seventeenth-Century China. 2008. (Illus.). 241p. (C). 48.00 *(978-0-8248-3202-5(7))* Univ. of Hawaii Pr.

H. H. Dorje Chang Buddha III. 2008. (ENG & CHI., Illus.). 560p. *(978-1-892727-41-1(2))* World Dharma Voice, Inc.

Harris, Elizabeth. Theravada Buddhism & the British Encounter: Religious, Missionary & Colonial Experience in Nineteenth Century Sri Lanka. 2009. 280p. pap. 39.95 *(978-0-415-54442-9(4))* Routledge.

Harris, Ian. Cambodian Buddhism: History & Practice. 2008. (Illus.). 352p. pap. 27.00 *(978-0-8248-3298-8(1))* Univ. of Hawaii Pr.

Heirman, Ann & Bumbacher, Stephan Peter, eds. The Spread of Buddhism. 2007. (Handbook of Oriental Studies). 450p. *(978-90-04-15830-6(8))* BRILL.

Johnson, Donald & Johnson, Jean. Universal Religions in World History: Buddhism, Christianity, & Islam. 2007. (ENG., Illus.). 240p. (C). pap. 35.67 *(978-0-07-295428-9(0),* 0072954280) McGraw-Hill Cos., The.

Kim, Hwansoo Ilmee. Empire of the Dharma: Korean & Japanese Buddhism, 1877-1912. 2012. (Harvard East Asian Monographs: 344). (ENG., Illus.). 350p. 39.95 ***(978-0-674-06575-8(1))*** Harvard Univ. Asia Ctr.

Kimura, Ryukan. A Historical Study of the Terms Hinayana & Mahayana & the Origin of Mahayana Buddhism. reprint ed. 26.50 *(978-0-404-17324-1(1))* AMS Pr., Inc.

Law, Bimala Churn. Historical Gleanings. 2008. 112p. 34.95 *(978-1-4365-0102-5(4))* 2007. (ENG.). 116p. per. 19.95 *(978-0-548-71334-1(0))* Kessinger Publishing, LLC.

—Historical Gleanings. 2008. 112p. pap. *(978-1-4097-0456-0(4))* Read Bks.

Law, Bimala Churn, ed. Historical Gleanings. reprint ed. 20.00 *(978-0-404-17337-1(3))* AMS Pr., Inc.

Lodro Taye, Jamgon Kongtrul. The Hundred Tertons. Gyamtso, Yeshe, tr. 2012. (ENG.). 400p. 32.95 ***(978-1-934608-26-5(2))*** KTD Pubns.

McMahan, David, ed. Buddhism in the Modern World. 2012. (Religions in the Modern World Ser.). (ENG., Illus.). 352p. (C). 125.00 *(978-0-415-78014-8(4))*; pap. 39.95 ***(978-0-415-78015-5(2))*** Routledge.

Mitchell, Donald W. Buddhism: Introducing the Buddhist Experience. 2nd ed. 2007. (ENG., Illus.). 432p. (C). per. 44.95 *(978-0-19-531103-7(5))* Oxford Univ. Pr., Inc.

Montgomery, Robert. The Spread of Religions: A Social Scientific Theory Based on the Spread of Buddhism, Christianity & Islam. 2007. 372p. per. 20.00 *(978-1-59899-086-7(1))* Long Dash Publishing.

Mungekar, Bhalchandra & Rathore, Aakash Singh. Buddhism & the Contemporary World: An Ambedkarian Perspective. 2007. xiv, 218p. *(978-81-89640-30-9(5))* Bookwell Pubns.

Nance, Richard F. Speaking for Buddhas: Scriptural Commentary in Indian Buddhism. 2011. (ENG., Illus.). 312p. (gr. 17). 55.00 ***(978-0-231-15230-3(2))*** Columbia Univ. Pr.

Oldenberg, Hermann., ed. The Dipavamsa: An Ancient Buddhist Historical Record. (ENG & PLI.). reprint ed. 27.00 *(978-0-404-17289-3(X))* AMS Pr., Inc.

—The Dipavamsa: An Ancient Buddhist Historical Record. 2007. (ENG.). 232p. per. 26.95 *(978-1-4304-9982-4(6))* Kessinger Publishing, LLC.

Olson, Carl. The A to Z of Buddhism. 124th ed. 2009. (A to Z Guide Ser.: No. 124). (ENG.). 372p. pap. 34.45 *(978-0-8108-7161-8(0))* Scarecrow Pr., Inc.

Olson, Carl & Prebish, Charles S. Historical Dictionary of Buddhism. 2009. (Historical Dictionaries of Religions, Philosophies, & Movements Ser.: 97). (ENG.). 370p. 111.00 *(978-0-8108-5771-1(5))* Scarecrow Pr., Inc.

Pathak, P. Early Buddhism & Indian Thoughts. 2011. 271p. pap. 35.00 ***(978-81-7533-358-1(8))*** M. D. Pubns. Pvt. Ltd. IND. Dist: Coronet Bks.

Payne, Richard K. Discourse & Ideology in Medieval Japanese Buddhism. 2009. 272p. pap. 39.95 *(978-0-415-54445-0(9))* Routledge.

Prebish, Charles S. & Keown, Damien. Introducing Buddhism. (World Religions (Routledge) Ser.). (Illus.). 2006. 299p. 120.00 *(978-0-415-39234-1(9))* 2006. 299p. per. 36.95 *(978-0-415-39235-8(7))* 2nd rev. ed. 2010. (ENG., 344p. (C). 39.95 *(978-0-415-55001-7(7))* 2nd rev. ed. 2010. (ENG., 344p. (C). 110.00 *(978-0-415-55000-0(9))* Routledge.

Prothero, Stephen R. The White Buddhist: The Asian Odyssey of Henry Steel Olcott. 2010. (Religion in North America Ser.). (ENG., Illus.). 256p. pap. 24.95 *(978-0-253-22276-3(1),* 0253222761) Indiana Univ. Pr.

Rambelli, Fabio. Buddhist Materiality: A Cultural History of Objects in Japanese Buddhism. 2007. (Asian Religions & Cultures Ser.). (ENG., Illus.). 408p. 65.00 *(978-0-8047-5682-2(1))* Stanford Univ. Pr.

Sarao, K. T. S. Origin & Nature of Ancient Indian Buddhism. 3rd ed. 2010. xv, 217p. *(978-81-215-1222-0(0),* Library of Congress — New Delhi Overseas Office) Munshiram Manoharlal Pubs. Private, Ltd.

—Origin & Nature of Ancient Indian Buddhism, 3rd Edition. 3rd ed. 2010. 217p. 55.00 *(978-81-215-1211-4(5),* Library of Congress — New Delhi Overseas Office) Munshiram Manoharlal Pubs. Private, Ltd. IND. Dist: Coronet Bks.

Saunders, Kenneth J. Epochs in Buddhist History: The Haskell Lectures, 1921. reprint ed. 37.50 *(978-0-404-17375-3(6))* AMS Pr., Inc.

Schlagintweit, Emil. Buddhism in Tibet Illustrated by Literar. 2006. pap. 38.95 *(978-1-4286-4999-6(9))* Kessinger Publishing, LLC.

Schlütter, Morten. How Zen Became Zen: The Dispute over Enlightenment & the Formation of Chan Buddhism in Song-Dynasty China. 2008. (Illus.). 340p. (C). 48.00 *(978-0-8248-3255-1(8))* Univ. of Hawaii Pr.

Soucy, Alexander Duncan, et al, eds. Wild Geese: Buddhism in Canada. 2010. (Illus.). 416p. (C). *(978-0-7735-3666-1(3))* McGill-Queen's Univ. Pr.

Tiyavanich, Kamala. Sons of the Buddha: The Early Lives of Three Extraordinary Thai Masters. 2007. (ENG., Illus.). 304p. per. 18.95 *(978-0-86171-536-7(5))* Wisdom Pubns.

Vaziri, Mostafa. Buddhism in Iran: An Anthropological Approach to Traces & Influences. 2012. (ENG., Illus.). 288p. 90.00 ***(978-1-137-02293-6(0))*** Palgrave Macmillan.

Wakabayashi, Haruko Nishioka. The Seven Tengu Scrolls: Evil & the Rhetoric of Legitimacy in Medieval Japanese Buddhism. 2012. 50.00 ***(978-0-8248-3416-6(X))*** Univ. of Hawaii Pr.

Wiltshire, Martin G. Ascetic Figures before & in Early Buddhism: The Emergence of Gautama as the Buddha. (Religion & Reason Ser.). (ENG.). XXXVI, 338p. 314.00 ***(978-3-11-176316-3(1))*** De Gruyter, Walter Inc.

Wright, Arthur F. Buddhism in Chinese History. (Illus.). 144p. reprint ed. pap. 15.00 *(978-957-9482-38-7(1),* PRE012) SMC Publishing, Inc. TWN. Dist: Antique Collectors' Club.

Yakup, Abdurishid, ed. Alttürkische Handschriften: Teil 12: Die uigurischen Blockdrucke der Berliner Turfansammlung Teil 2: Apokryphen, Mahayana-Sutren, Erzahlungen, Magische Texte, Kommentare und Kolophone. 2008. (Verzeichnis der Orientalischen Handschriften in Deutschland (VOHD) Ser.). (GER.). 266p. (C). 102.00 *(978-3-515-09233-3(1))* Steiner, Franz Verlag Wiesbaden GmbH DEU. Dist: Brown, David Bk. Co., The.

Zieme, P., ed. Aspects of Research into Central Asian Buddhism: In Memoriam Kogi Kudara. 2008. (Silk Road Studies). (ENG & GER.). 483p. (C). pap. 94.00 *(978-2-503-52751-2(5))* Brepols Pubs. BEL. Dist: ISD.

BUDDHISM—LITURGY

see Buddhism—Rituals

BUDDHISM—POETRY

Allen, Rc. Emily Dickinson, Accidental Buddhist. 2007. 272p. per. 19.50 *(978-1-4251-0398-9(7))* Trafford Publishing.

Ashvaghosha. Life of the Buddha. Olivelle, Patrick, tr. 2008. (SAN & ENG.). 450p. 22.00 *(978-0-8147-6216-5(6))* New York Univ. Pr.

Asvaghosa. The Fo-Sho-Hing-Tsan-King: A Life of Buddha. 380p. reprint ed. 68.00 *(978-0-7222-9949-4(4))* Library Reprints, Inc.

Fischer, Jason B. 108 Beads: Poems on the Way. 2009. 124p. pap. 10.95 *(978-1-4401-1558-5(3))* iUniverse, Inc.

Joy, Aaron. Within the Eyes of Buddha: 100 Days of Zen Inspired Poetry. 2008. 93p. pap. 9.99 *(978-0-557-02365-3(3))* Lulu Enterprises Inc.

Muller, Friedrich, et al, trs. Buddhist Mahgygna Texts. 2007. 456p. per. 21.95 *(978-1-60206-381-5(8))* Cosimo, Inc.

Sagan, Miriam. Map of the Lost. 2008. (Mary Burritt Christiansen Poetry Ser.). (ENG., Illus.). 152p. 24.95 *(978-0-8263-4160-0(8))* Univ. of New Mexico Pr.

Simmons, Robert aka Azul. Azul. 2008. (ENM., Illus.). 20p. pap. *(978-0-9768148-3-2(8))* Golden Star Productions.

Song, Cathy. Cloud Moving Hands. 2007. (Pitt Poetry Ser.). (ENG.). 104p. per. 14.00 *(978-0-8229-6000-3(1))* Univ. of Pittsburgh Pr.

Stevens, Ikkyu & Stevens, John, eds. Wild Ways: Zen Poems of Ikkyu. 2007. (Companions for the Journey Ser.). (ENG., Illus.). 128p. pap. 14.00 *(978-1-893996-65-6(4))* White Pine Pr.

BUDDHISM—RELATIONS

Alabaster, Henry. Buddha & His Practice of Asceticism. 2006. pap. 12.95 *(978-1-4286-6539-2(0))* Kessinger Publishing, LLC.

—Buddhism & the 32 Characteristics of a Great Man. 2006. pap. 9.95 *(978-1-4286-6530-9(7))* Kessinger Publishing, LLC.

—Buddhism & the Glorious Marriage. 2006. pap. 12.95 *(978-1-4286-6538-5(2))* Kessinger Publishing, LLC.

Borich, Gary. Buddhism from A to Zen: A Westerner's Guide to Key Buddhist Concepts. 2010. 96p. pap. 31.80 *(978-0-557-42763-5(0))* Lulu Enterprises Inc.

Bronkhorst, Johannes. Buddhism in the Shadow of Brahmanism. 2011. 320p. *(978-90-04-20140-8(8))* BRILL.

Elverskog, Johan. Buddhism & Islam on the Silk Road. 2010. (Encounters with Asia Ser.). (Illus.). 384p. (C). 69.95 *(978-0-8122-4237-9(8))* Univ. of Pennsylvania Pr.

Hanh, Thich Nhat. Good Citizens: Creating Enlightened Society. 2012. (ENG.). 144p. pap. 14.95 ***(978-1-935209-89-8(2))*** Parallax Pr.

Kohn, Livia. Laughing at the Dao: Debates among Buddhists & Daoists in Medieval China. 2008. 287p. *(978-1-931483-07-0(8))* Three Pines Pr.

Miller, Andrea, ed. Right Here with You: Bringing Mindful Awareness into Our Relationships. 2011. (Shambhala Sun Book Ser.). (ENG.). 288p. pap. 16.95 *(978-1-59030-904-9(9))* Shambhala Pubns., Inc.

Mitchell, Donald W. & Wiseman, James A., eds. The Spiritual Life: A Dialogue of Buddhist & Christian Monastics. 2010. (Gethsemani Encounters Ser.). 305p. pap. *(978-1-59056-173-7(2))* Lantern Bks.

Moller, Christine. Buddhism & Taoism: Face to Face Scripture, Ritual, & Iconographic Exchange in Medieval China. 2008. (Illus.). 296p. (C). 55.00 *(978-0-8248-3169-1(1))* Univ. of Hawaii Pr.

—Buddhism & Taoism Face to Face: Scripture, Ritual, & Iconographic Exchange in Medieval China. 2009. (Illus.). 241p. pap. 22.00 *(978-0-8248-3411-1(9))* Univ. of Hawaii Pr.

Pathak, P. Early Buddhism & Indian Thoughts. 2011. 271p. pap. 35.00 ***(978-81-7533-358-1(8))*** M. D. Pubns. Pvt. Ltd. IND. Dist: Coronet Bks.

Ruegg, David Seyfort. Symbiosis of Buddhism with Brahmanism/Hinduism in South Asia & of Buddhism with 'local cults' in Tibet & the Himalayan Region. 2008. (Sitzungsberichte der Phil-Klasse Ser.). 197p. (C). pap. 54.00 *(978-3-7001-6057-1(7))* Austrian Academy of Sciences Press AUT. Dist: Brown, David Bk. Co., The.

Schmidt-Leukel, Perry. Buddhism & Religious Diversity. 2012. ***(978-0-415-53567-0(0))***; ***(978-0-415-53566-3(2))***; ***(978-0-415-53568-7(9))***; ***(978-0-415-53565-6(4))*** Routledge.

Schmidt-Leukel, Perry, ed. Buddhism & Religious Diversity, 4 vols. 2012. (Critical Concepts in Religious Studies). (ENG.). 1677p. 1295.00 ***(978-0-415-52534-3(9))*** Routledge.

Shah Kazemi, Reza, et al. Common Ground Between Islam & Buddhism: Spiritual & Ethical Affinities. 2010. (ENG.). 174p. pap. 16.95 *(978-1-891785-62-7(1))* Fons Vitae of Kentucky, Inc.

Soko, Keith. A Mounting East-West Tension: Buddhist-Christian Dialogue on Human Rights, Social Justice & a Global Ethic. 2009. pap. *(978-0-87462-743-5(5))* Marquette Univ. Pr.

Sutin, Lawrence. All Is Change: The Two-Thousand-Year Journey of Buddhism to the West. 2006. (ENG., Illus.). 416p. 25.99 *(978-0-316-74156-9(6))* Little Brown & Co.

Wynne, Alexander. The Origin of Buddhist Meditation. 2007. 169p. 160.00 *(978-0-415-42387-8(2))* Routledge.

Yao, Weiqun. Fo Jiao Si Xiang Yu Wen Hua. 2009. (CHI.). *(978-7-301-15625-4(1))* Beijing University Pr.

BUDDHISM—RELATIONS—CHRISTIANITY

Anonymous. The Dhammapad: With Explanatory Notes & A Short Essay on Buddha's Thought. 2011. 150p. 41.95 ***(978-1-258-04307-0(6))*** Literary Licensing, LLC.

Appleton, George. On the Eightfold Path: Christian Presence amid Buddhism. 2011. 156p. 41.95 ***(978-1-258-00787-4(8))*** Literary Licensing, LLC.

Blackburn, Anne M. Locations of Buddhism: Colonialism & Modernity in Sri Lanka. 2010. (Buddhism & Modernity Ser.). (ENG., Illus.). 256p. 45.00 *(978-0-226-05507-7(8))* Univ. of Chicago Pr.

Burnett, David. The Spirit of Buddhism: A Christian Perspective on Buddhist Thought. 2007. (Illus.). 352p. pap. 16.99 *(978-0-8254-6145-3(6),* Monarch Bks.) Lion Hudson PLC GBR. Dist: Kregel Pubns.

Carter, John Ross. In the Company of Friends: Exploring Faith & Understanding with Buddhists & Christians. 2012. (ENG.). 368p. 85.00 ***(978-1-4384-4279-2(3))*** State Univ. of New York Pr.

Cioccolanti, Steve. From Buddha to Jesus: An Insider's View of Buddhism & Christianity, 1 vol. 2010. (ENG., Illus.). 256p. pap. 13.99 *(978-1-85424-956-2(8),* Monarch Bks.) Lion Hudson PLC GBR. Dist: Kregel Pubns.

De Neui, Paul H. Communicating Christ in Asian Cities: Urban Issues in Buddhist Contexts. 2009. x, 297p. *(978-0-87808-007-6(4))* Carey, William Library Pubs.

—Complexities of Money & Missions in Asia. 2011. ***(978-0-87808-038-0(4))*** Carey, William Library Pubs.

—Family & Faith in Asia: The Missional Impact of Social Networks. 2009. *(978-0-87808-022-9(8))* Carey, William Library Pubs.

—Suffering: Christian Reflectios on Buddhist Dukkha. 2011. *(978-0-87808-024-3(4))* Carey, William Library Pubs.

De Neui, Paul H. & Lim, David. Communicating Christ Through Story & Song: Orality in Buddhist Contexts. 2007. *(978-0-87808-511-8(4))* Carey, William Library Pubs.

Derbolav, Josef, et al. Search for a New Humanity: A Dialogue. Gage, Richard L., ed. 2008. (Echoes & Reflections Ser.). (ENG.). 276p. 42.00 *(978-1-84511-598-2(8))* I. B. Tauris & Co., Ltd. GBR. Dist: Macmillan.

Didier, Hugues. Les Portugais Au Tibet: Les Premières Relations Jésuites, 1624-1635. (FRE., Illus.). 382p. *(978-2-906462-31-1(4))* Chandeigne, Editions.

Drew, Rose. Buddhist & Christian? An Exploration of Dual Belonging. 2011. (Routledge Critical Studies in Buddhism Ser.). (ENG.). 288p. (C). 140.00 *(978-0-415-61123-7(7))* Routledge.

Du Boulay, Shirley, selected by. Swami Abhishiktananda: Essential Writings. 2007. (Modern Spiritual Masters Ser.). 205p. per. 18.00 *(978-1-57075-695-5(3))* Orbis Bks.

Hanh, Thich Nhat. Volviendo a Casa. (SPA.). 184p. *(978-84-95456-47-2(8),* 86934) Ediciones Oniro S.A.

Hardy, R. Spence. Christianity & Buddhism Compared. 2007. (ENG.). 144p. 35.95 *(978-0-548-15542-4(9))*; pap. 20.95 *(978-1-4304-4979-9(9))* Kessinger Publishing, LLC.

Heisig, J. W. & Kim, S., eds. Monasticism Buddhist & Christian: The Korean Experience. 2008. (Louvain Theological & Pastoral Monographs). 201p. (C). pap. 32.00 *(978-90-429-2060-6(2))* Peeters Pubs. & Booksellers BEL. Dist: Brown, David Bk. Co., The.

Ingram, Paul O. Buddhist-Christian Dialogue in an Age of Science. 2007. (ENG.). 168p. per. 19.95 *(978-0-7425-6215-8(8))*; 65.00 *(978-0-7425-6214-1(X))* Rowman & Littlefield Publishers, Inc.

—The Process of Buddhist-Christian Dialogue. 2011. (ENG.). 149p. pap. 36.00 *(978-0-227-17369-5(4))* Clarke, James Co., Ltd. GBR. Dist: Brown, David Bk. Co., The.

—The Process of Buddhist-Christian Dialogue. 2009. 162p. pap. 18.00 *(978-1-60608-554-7(9),* Cascade Bks.) Wipf & Stock Pubs.

Ingram, Paul O. Theological Reflections at the Boundaries. 2011. 188p. pap. 22.00 ***(978-1-61097-405-9(0),*** Cascade Bks.) Wipf & Stock Pubs.

King, Winston L. Buddhism & Christianity: Some Bridges of Understanding. 2008. (Routledge Library Editions: Buddhism Ser.). (ENG.). 4p. (C). 165.00 *(978-0-415-46110-8(3))* Routledge.

Lefebure, Leo D. & Feldmeier, Peter. The Path of Wisdom: A Christian Commentary on the Dhammapada. 2011. x, 379p. ***(978-90-429-2330-0(X))*** Eerdmans, William B. Publishing Co.

Lillie, Arthur. Buddhism in Christendom. 2010. 456p. pap. 26.95 *(978-0-557-50343-8(4))* Lulu Enterprises Inc.

—The Influence of Buddhism on Primitive Christianity. 2009. 108p. pap. 14.14 *(978-0-217-62948-5(2))* General Bks. LLC.

—The Influence of Buddhism on Primitive Christianity. 2007. (ENG.). 192p. 37.95 *(978-0-548-00499-9(4))* Kessinger Publishing, LLC.

—The Influence of Buddhism on Primitive Christianity. 2010. 196p. pap. 19.95 *(978-0-557-47270-3(9))* Lulu Enterprises Inc.

Lim, David & De Neui, Paul H. Communicating Christ in the Buddhist World. 2007. 250p. *(978-0-87808-510-1(6))* Carey, William Library Pubs.

Lounibos, John B. Self-Emptying of Christ & the Christian: Three Essays on Kenosis. 2011. 132p. pap. 16.00 ***(978-1-61097-189-8(2),*** Wipf and Stock) Wipf & Stock Pubs.

MacGregor, Kirk R. A Comparative Study of Adjustments to Social Catastrophes in Christianity & Buddhism: The Black Death in Europe & the Kamakura Takeover in Japan As Causes of Religious Reform. 2011. 400p. 129.95 ***(978-0-7734-1549-2(1))*** Mellen, Edwin Pr., The.

Mitchell, Donald & Skudlarek, William. Green Monasticism: A Buddhist-Catholic Response to an Environmental Calamity. 2010. *(978-1-59056-167-6(8))* Lantern Bks.

Miyamoto, Arata. Embodied Cross: Intercontextual Reading of Theologia Crucis. 2010. 166p. pap. 19.00 *(978-1-60899-149-5(0),* Wipf and Stock) Wipf & Stock Pubs.

Peerman, Gordon. Blessed Relief: What Christians Can Learn from Buddhists about Suffering. 2008. 208p. pap. 16.99 *(978-1-59473-252-2(3))* SkyLight Paths Publishing.

Roach, Michael & McNally, Christie. The Eastern Path to Heaven: A Guide to Happiness from the Teachings of Jesus in Tibet. 2008. 160p. pap. 16.00 *(978-1-59627-097-8(7),* Seabury Bks.) Church Publishing, Inc.

Roebert, Donovan. The Gospel for Buddhists & the Dharma for Christians. 2009. 338p. pap. 37.00 *(978-1-60608-040-5(7),* Resource Pubns.) Wipf & Stock Pubs.

Strand, Clark. How to Believe in God: Whether You Believe in Religion or Not. 2009. (ENG.). 256p. 24.95 *(978-0-7679-2069-8(4))* Knopf Doubleday Publishing Group.

Suzuki, Daisetz Teitaro & Anshen, Ruth Nanda. Mysticism: Christian & Buddhist. 2011. 234p. 46.95 ***(978-1-258-00662-4(6))*** Literary Licensing, LLC.

Thompson, Ross. Buddhist Christianity: A Passionate Openness. 2010. (ENG., Illus.). 313p. pap. 24.95 *(978-1-84694-336-2(1))* Hunt, John Publishing Ltd. GBR. Dist: National Bk. Network.

Zacharias, Ravi. The Lotus & the Cross: Jesus Talks with Buddha. 2010. (Great Conversations Ser.). (ENG.). 96p. pap. 11.99 *(978-1-60142-318-4(7),* Multnomah) Doubleday Religious Publishing Group, The.

BUDDHISM—RELATIONS—JUDAISM

Kamenetz, Rodger. The Jew in the Lotus: A Poet's Rediscovery of Jewish Identity in Buddhist India. 2007. (Plus Ser.). (ENG.). 320p. pap. 14.99 *(978-0-06-136739-7(7),* HarperOne) HarperCollins Pubs.

BUDDHISM—RITUALS

see also Buddhist Chants

Abesirivardhana, Ananda. Maha Pirit Pota: Sanna Sahita. 2009. xi, 205p. *(978-955-1777-96-8(4),* Library of Congress — New Delhi Overseas Office) Dept. of Cultural Affairs.

Cantwell, Cathy & Mayer, Robert. Early Tibetan Documents on Phur pa from Dunhuang. 2008. (Beitrage zur Kultur- und Geistesgeschichte Asiens Ser.). (Illus.). 228p. (C). pap. 99.00 *(978-3-7001-6100-4(X))* Austrian Academy of Sciences Press AUT. Dist: Brown, David Bk. Co., The.

Chaoul, Alejandro. Chod Practice in the Bon Tradition. 2009. (ENG.). 118p. pap. 18.95 *(978-1-55939-292-1(4))* Snow Lion Pubns., Inc.

Dahl, Cortland, intro. Entrance to the Great Perfection: A Guide to the Dzogchen Preliminary Practices. 2010. (ENG.). 260p. pap. 22.95 *(978-1-55939-339-3(4))* Snow Lion Pubns., Inc.

Davids, Carolina A. Psalms of the Early Buddhists, 2 vols., Set. reprint ed. 67.50 *(978-0-404-17590-0(2))* AMS Pr., Inc.

Dorje, Thekchok & Taye, Jamgon Kongtrul Lodro. CHOD Practice Manual & Commentary. Rinpoche, V. V. Lama Lodo, tr. from TIB. 2007. (ENG., Illus.). 128p. pap. 16.95 *(978-1-55939-267-9(3))* Snow Lion Pubns., Inc.

Faure, Bernard, ed. Chan Buddhism in Ritual Context. 2010. 224p. pap. 39.95 ***(978-0-415-60018-7(9))*** Routledge.

Gonsalez, David, et al. The Roar of Thunder: Yamantaka Practice & Commentary. 2011. ***(978-1-55939-387-4(4))*** Snow Lion Pubns., Inc.

Harding. Studying Buddhism in Practice. 2012. (Studying Religions in Practice Ser.). (ENG., Illus.). 200p. 110.00 *(978-0-415-46485-7(4))*; pap. 29.95 *(978-0-415-46486-4(2))* Routledge.

Huang, Kui. Zhongguo Chan Zong Qing Gui: A Study on the Rules of Purity for Chinese Chan Buddhism. 2008. (CHI.). *(978-7-80254-045-3(3))* China Religion and Culture Publishing Hse.

I-Tsing & Muller, F. Max. A Record of the Buddhist Religion As Practised in India & the Malay Archipelago A.D. 671-695. Takakusu, J., tr. 2007. (ENG.). 308p. per. 28.95 *(978-1-4304-4331-5(6))* Kessinger Publishing, LLC.

Kapstein, Matthew & Van Schaik, Sam. Esoteric Buddhism at Dunhuang: Rites & Teachings for This Life & Beyond. 2010. 254p. *(978-90-04-18203-5(9))* BRILL.

Langer, Rita. Buddhist Rituals of Death & Rebirth: Contemporary Sri Lankan Practice & Its Origins. 2009. 246p. pap. 39.95 *(978-0-415-54470-2(X))* Routledge.

Parallax Press Staff. Chanting from the Heart: Buddhist Ceremonies & Daily Practices. 2006. (ENG., Illus.). 360p. pap. 26.95 *(978-1-888375-63-3(9))* Parallax Pr.

Pearce-Glassheim, Elizabeth, ed. Haggadah for Jews & Buddhists: A Passover Ritual. 2007. 70p. pap. 15.00 *(978-0-9773221-2-1(2),* MHD Co.) Modern Haggadah Distribution Co.

Phun-tshogs-tshe-Rin & Nag-Dban. Sku Mkhar Chen Po Yum-Bu-Bla-Sgan Gi Dkar Chag Brin Po Bzugs So. Nan-Wuth Gtsug-Lag Khan Che Moi Dkar Chag Bzugs So. Zwa Lha-Khan Gi Dkar Chag Bzugs So. Phrul-Snan Gtsug-Lag-Khan Gi Nan Mjal Drug Gi Dkar Chag Mkhas Pai Nag Sgron Bzugs So. 2010. (TIB.). 77p. *(978-7-223-02783-0(5))* Tibetan People's Publishing Hse.

Rinpoche, Kyabje Zong. Chod in the Ganden Tradition: The Oral Instructions of Kyabje Zong Rinpoche. Molk, David, ed. 2006. (ENG., Illus.). 216p. pap. 18.95 *(978-1-55939-261-7(4))* Snow Lion Pubns., Inc.

Rinpoche, Tulku Urgyen, et al. Skillful Grace: Tara Practice for Our Times. 2007. (ENG., Illus.). 192p. pap. 15.95 *(978-962-7341-61-1(4))* North Atlantic Bks.

Shakya, YongHua. Buddha Speaks of Amitabha Buddha Sutra: A General Explanation by: Master YongHua. 2011. pap. 15.00 ***(978-0-9835279-1-6(1))*** Bodhi Light International.

Sharkey, Gregory. Buddhist Daily Ritual: The Nitya Puja in Kathmandu Valley Shrines. 2006. (ENG., Illus.). 39.50 *(978-974-8304-80-9(9))* Orchid Pr. THA. Dist: National Bk. Network.

Stone, Jacqueline I. & Cuevas, Bryan J., eds. The Buddhist Dead: Practices, Discourses, Representations. 2007. (Studies in East Asian Buddhism Ser.). (Illus.). 491p. 67.00 *(978-0-8248-3031-1(8))* Univ. of Hawaii Pr.

Vermeersch, Sem. The Power of the Buddhas: The Politics of Buddhism During the Koryo Dynasty (918-1392) 2008. (Harvard East Asian Monographs: 303). (Illus.). 486p. 49.95 *(978-0-674-03188-3(1))* Harvard Univ., Asia Ctr.

Visser, Marinus Willem de. Ancient Buddhism in Japan: Sutras & Ceremonies in Use in the Seventh & Eighth Centuries A. D. & Their History in Later Times. 2006. 850p. 110.00 *(978-1-57898-645-3(1))* Martino Publishing.

BUDDHISM—SACRED BOOKS

Anonymous. The Dhammapada. Roebuck, Valerie, tr. from PLI. & intro. by. rev. ed. 2010. (ENG.). 320p. (gr. 12). 12.00 *(978-0-14-044941-9(8),* Penguin Classics) Penguin Group (USA) Inc.

Beal, Samuel. A Catena of Buddhist Scriptures from the Chinese. 2010. (ENG.). 452p. pap. 36.75 *(978-1-177-39825-1(7))*; 498p. pap. 38.75 *(978-1-176-23354-6(8))* BiblioBazaar.

—A Catena of Buddhist Scriptures from the Chinese. 2010. 326p. pap. *(978-1-151-93706-3(1))* Books LLC.

—A Catena of Buddhist Scriptures from the Chinese. 2010. 452p. 42.36 *(978-1-163-21917-1(7))*; pap. 30.36 *(978-1-162-73125-4(7))* Kessinger Publishing, LLC.

Berkwitz, Stephen C., et al, eds. Buddhist Manuscript Cultures. 2010. (ENG.). pap. 39.95 ***(978-0-415-59613-8(0))*** Routledge.

Buddhaghosa. The Padyacudamani of Buddhaghosacarya. reprint ed. 32.50 *(978-0-404-17248-0(2))* AMS Pr., Inc.

—Papancasudani Majjhimanikayatthakatha of Buddhaghosacariya, 5 vols. in 4. (Indian Life & Customs Ser.). reprint ed. *(978-0-404-17560-3(0))* AMS Pr., Inc.

Carter, Richard Burnett. The Language of Zen: Heart Speaking to Heart. 2010. (ENG., Illus.). 288p. 16.95 *(978-1-4027-4701-4(2))* Sterling Publishing Co., Inc.

Carus, Paul. The Dharma: or The Religious Enlightenment: An Exposition of Buddhism. 5th enl. rev. ed. reprint ed. 29.50 *(978-0-404-17253-4(9))* AMS Pr., Inc.

Chalmers, Lord. Buddha's Teachings: Being the Sutta-Nipata or Discourse Collection. Chalmers, Lord & Lanman, Charles R., eds. 2011. 346p. 51.95 ***(978-1-258-02007-1(6))*** Literary Licensing, LLC.

Conze, Edward, et al, eds. Buddhist Texts Through the Ages. 2010. 326p. pap. 24.76 *(978-1-162-91737-5(7))* Kessinger Publishing, LLC.

Dhammapada. Texts from the Buddhist Canon. Beal, Samuel, tr. from CHI. reprint ed. 22.50 *(978-0-404-17284-8(9))* AMS Pr., Inc.

Dhammapadatthakatha. The Commentary on the Dhammapada, 5 vols. in 4. Norman, H. C., ed. reprint ed. 155.00 *(978-0-404-17620-4(8))* AMS Pr., Inc.

Ensink, Jacob. The Question of Rastrapala. 2007. 162p. per. 30.00 *(978-0-89581-987-1(2))* Jain Publishing Company, Inc.

Fausboll, V., ed. Buddhist Birth Stories: or Jataka Tales, Vol. 1. Davids, Rhys T., tr. reprint ed. 42.50 *(978-0-404-17309-8(8))* AMS Pr., Inc.

Goddard, Dwight. A Buddhist Bible. 2009. 248p. 27.99 *(978-0-559-10985-0(7))*; 24.99 *(978-0-559-10999-7(7))*; pap. 25.75 *(978-0-559-10995-9(4))*; pap. 22.99 *(978-0-559-10988-1(1))* BiblioBazaar.

—A Buddhist Bible. 2007. (ENG.). 284p. 37.95 *(978-1-60206-795-0(3))*; per. 16.50 *(978-1-60206-794-3(5))* Cosimo, Inc.

—A Buddhist Bible. 2007. (ENG.). 284p. 24.99 *(978-1-59986-707-6(9))*; pap. 16.99 *(978-1-59986-878-3(4),* FQ Classics) Filiquarian Publishing, LLC.

—A Buddhist Bible. 2010. 692p. 51.96 *(978-1-163-43139-9(7))* 2010. 694p. pap. 39.96 *(978-1-162-96409-6(X))* 2007. (ENG.). 692p. 64.95 *(978-0-548-12421-5(3))* Kessinger Publishing, LLC.

—A Buddhist Bible: The Favorite Scriptures of the Zen Sect. 2010. 318p. pap. 12.95 *(978-1-57898-857-0(8))* Martino Publishing.

Gooneratne, Edmund R., ed. The Dhatu Katha Pakarana & Its Commentary. reprint ed. 21.50 *(978-0-404-17287-9(3))* AMS Pr., Inc.

Hodge, Stephen. Reading Buddhism Through Chinese: An Introductory Grammar & Reader. 2008. 272p. 170.00 *(978-0-7007-1225-0(9))*; pap. 45.95 *(978-0-7007-1258-8(5))* Taylor & Francis Group. (RoutledgeCurzon).

Judge, William Q. Hit the Mark. 2006. (ENG.). 8p. per. 9.95 *(978-1-4304-0130-8(3))* Kessinger Publishing, LLC.

Kalupahana, David J. A Path of Morals: Dhammapada: Text & Translation of the Dhammapada Together with an Introductory Essay Comparing the Dhammapada & the Bhagavadgta [i.e. Bhagavadgita], & Commentary on the Verses. 2008. (PLI & ENG.). xvii, 290p. pap. *(978-955-663-066-4(X),* Library of Congress — New Delhi Overseas Office) Buddhist Cultural Centre, The.

Kubo, Tsugunari & Yuyama, Akira, trs. The Lotus Sutra. 2nd ed. 2007. (BDK English Tripitaka Ser.). 362p. 35.00 *(978-1-886439-39-9(7))* BDK America.

Nanjio, Bunyiu, compiled by. A Catalogue of the Chinese translation of the Buddhist Tripitaka. 2010. pap. 77.80 *(978-1-61719-053-7(5))*; pap. 77.80 *(978-1-61719-077-3(2))*; pap. 77.80 *(978-1-61719-065-0(9))* Gorgias Pr., LLC.

Park, Jungnok. How Buddhism Acquired a Soul on the Way to China. 2012. (Oxford centre for buddhist studies Monographs). (ENG.). 256p. (C). 99.95 *(978-1-84553-996-2(6))*; pap. 34.95 *(978-1-84553-997-9(4))* Equinox Publishing Ltd. GBR. Dist: Brown, David Bk. Co., The.

Sangharakshita, ed. Puja: The Friends of the Western Buddhist Order Book of Buddhist Devotional Texts. Bennett, A. A. G., tr. 2009. (ENG.). 64p. 19.95 *(978-1-899579-80-8(X))*; pap. 15.95 *(978-1-899579-94-5(X))* Windhorse Pubns. GBR. Dist: Consortium Bk. Sales & Distribution.

Sangharakshita, tr. Dhammapada: The Way of Truth. 2010. (ENG.). 160p. pap. 15.95 *(978-1-899579-93-8(1))* Windhorse Pubns. GBR. Dist: Consortium Bk. Sales & Distribution.

Silacara, Bhikkhu. Lotus Blossoms. 2011. 112p. 39.95 ***(978-1-258-04368-1(8))*** Literary Licensing, LLC.

Suzuki, Daisetz Teitaro. Manual of Zen Buddhism. 2007. pap. 9.99 *(978-1-59986-934-6(9))* Filiquarian Publishing, LLC.

—Manual of Zen Buddhism. 2011. 164p. pap. 15.99 ***(978-1-61279-056-5(9))*** Publishing in Motion.

Thomas, E. J., tr. from SAN. The Quest of Enlightenment: A Selection of the Buddhist Scriptures. reprint ed. 27.50 *(978-0-404-17389-0(6))* AMS Pr., Inc.

Thomas, Edward J. Early Buddhist Scriptures. reprint ed. 41.50 *(978-0-404-17388-3(8))* AMS Pr., Inc.

Thomas, Edward Joseph, ed. Buddhist Scriptures. 2007. (ENG.). 128p. 35.95 *(978-0-548-10401-9(8))* Kessinger Publishing, LLC.

Tucci, Giuseppe, ed. The Nyayanukha of Dignaga. reprint ed. 27.50 *(978-0-404-17288-6(1))* AMS Pr., Inc.

Upham, Edward. The Mahavansi. the Raja-Ratnacari. & the Raja-Vali, Forming the Sacred & Historical Books of Ceylon, 3 vols., Set. reprint ed. 115.00 *(978-0-404-17670-9(4))* AMS Pr., Inc.

Vinaya Texts, 3 Vols. reprint ed. 204.00 *(978-0-7222-9948-7(6))* Library Reprints, Inc.

BUDDHISM—SECTS

see Buddhist Sects

BUDDHISM—BURMA

Bigandet, Paul A. The Life, or Legend of Gaudama: The Buddha of the Burmese, 2 vols., Set. 4th ed. reprint ed. 75.00 *(978-0-404-16800-1(0))* AMS Pr., Inc.

Carbine, Jason A. Sons of the Buddha: Continuities & Ruptures in a Burmese Monastic Tradition. 2011. (Religion & Society Ser.). (ENG., XVIII, 248p. Illus.). 210.00 ***(978-3-11-218915-3(9))***; 140.00 *(978-3-11-025409-9(3))* De Gruyter, Walter Inc.

Maung, E. Burmese Buddhist Law. reprint ed. 25.00 *(978-0-404-16812-4(4))* AMS Pr., Inc.

Min, Moe, photos by. In Buddha's Land: Visions of Buddhist Myanmar. 2007. (ENG., Illus.). 128p. 30.00 *(978-974-524-072-8(9))* Orchid Pr. THA. Dist: National Bk. Network.

Ray, Nihar-Ranjan. An Introduction to the Study of Theravada Buddhism in Burma: A Study of Indo-Burmese Historical & Cultural Relations from the Earliest Times to the British Conquest. reprint ed. 32.50 *(978-0-404-16853-7(1))* AMS Pr., Inc.

BUDDHISM—CHINA

Avis, Yu-Jung L., et al, trs. from CHI. A Sixty-Year Spiritual Voyage on the Ocean of Dharma. 2008. pap. 10.00 *(978-0-9818531-0-9(2))* Noble Path Buddhist Education Fellowship.

Barua, Ankur & BASILIO, M. A. Buddhism Flourishes in Hong Kong. 2010. 60p. pap. *(978-3-639-24029-0(4))* VDM Verlag Dr. Mueller e.K.

Beal, Samuel. Buddhism in China. 2006. (ENG.). pap. 27.95 *(978-1-4286-5146-3(2))* Kessinger Publishing, LLC.

Benn, James A. Burning for the Buddha: Self-Immolation in Chinese Buddhism. 2007. (Studies in East Asian Buddhism Ser.). 360p. 50.00 *(978-0-8248-2992-6(1))* Univ. of Hawaii Pr.

Broughton, Jeffrey L. Zongmi on Chan. 2009. (Translations from the Asian Classics Ser.). (ENG.). 376p. (gr. 17). 50.00 *(978-0-231-14392-9(3))* Columbia Univ. Pr.

Campany, Robert Ford & Wang, Yan. Signs from the Unseen Realm: Buddhist Miracle Tales from Early Medieval China. 2012. 55.00 ***(978-0-8248-3602-3(2))*** Univ. of Hawaii Pr.

Chan/Lo. Philosophy & Religion in Early Medieval China. 2010. (SUNY series in Chinese Philosophy & Culture Ser.). (MUL.). 352p. 80.00 *(978-1-4384-3187-1(2))* State Univ. of New York Pr.

Chen, Huaiyu. The Revival of Buddhist Monasticism. 2007. 252p. (C). 71.95 *(978-0-8204-8624-6(8))* Lang, Peter Publishing, Inc.

Cheng, Wei-Yi. Buddhist Nuns in Taiwan & Sri Lanka: A Critique of the Feminist Perspective. 2006. (Routledge Critical Studies in Buddhism). (ENG., Illus.). 240p. (C). 170.00 *(978-0-415-39042-2(7))* Routledge.

Cheung, Neky Tak-ching. Women's Ritual in China: Jiezhu (Receiving Buddhist Prayer Beads) Performed by Menopausal Women in Ninghua, Western Fujian. 2008. (Illus.). 372p. 119.95 *(978-0-7734-4962-6(0))* Mellen, Edwin Pr., The.

Cristaudo, Wayne. The Church in China. Rule, Paul, ed. 2010. (Interface: A Forum for Theology in the World Ser.). (ENG.). 131p. pap. 19.95 *(978-1-921511-74-5(5))* ATF Pr. AUS. Dist: Brown, David Bk. Co., The.

Cuevas, Bryan J. Travels in the Netherworld: Buddhist Popular Narratives of Death & the Afterlife in Tibet. 2011. (ENG.). 216p. pap. 24.95 ***(978-0-19-989555-7(4))*** Oxford Univ. Pr., Inc.

Edkins, Joseph. Chinese Buddhism: A Volume of Sketches, Historical, Descriptive & Critical. 2007. (ENG.). 488p. 53.95 *(978-0-548-12393-5(4))* Kessinger Publishing, LLC.

—Religion in China: Containing a Brief Account of the Three Religions. 2007. (ENG.). 284p. per. 27.95 *(978-1-4304-4274-5(3))* Kessinger Publishing, LLC.

Foit-Albert, Beverly & Shunxun, Nan. China's Sacred Sites. 2007. (ENG.). 286p. 49.95 *(978-0-89389-262-3(9))* Himalayan Institute Pr.

Forbes, Flores Alexander. Will You Die with Me? My Life & the Black Panther Party. 2007. (ENG., Illus.). 320p. pap. 15.00 *(978-0-7434-8268-4(9),* Washington Square Pr.) Washington Square Pr.

Goossaert, Vincent & Palmer, David A. The Religious Question in Modern China. 2011. 480p. 40.00 *(978-0-226-30416-8(7))* Univ. of Chicago Pr.

Grant, Beata & Idema, Wilt L., trs. from CHI. Escape from Blood Pond Hell: The Tales of Mulian & Woman Huang. 2011. (ENG.). 368p. (C). pap. 35.00 *(978-0-295-99120-7(8))*; 70.00 *(978-0-295-99119-1(4))* Univ. of Washington Pr.

Halperin, Mark. Out of the Cloister: Literati Perspectives on Buddhism in Sung China, 960-1279. 2006. (Harvard East Asian Monographs: 272). (Illus.). 400p. 49.95 *(978-0-674-02265-2(3))* Harvard Univ., Asia Ctr.

Hargett, James M. Stairway to Heaven: A Journey to the Summit of Mount Emei. 2007. (SUNY Series in Chinese Philosophy & Culture). (Illus.). 294p. per. 29.95 *(978-0-7914-6682-7(5))* State Univ. of New York Pr.

He, Mianshan. Taiwan Fo Jiao. 2010. (CHI.). *(978-7-80195-973-7(6))* Jiuzhou Publishing Hse.

Ho, Gary & Tzu Chi Foundation. Challenges: The Life & Teachings of Venerable Master Cheng Yen, 1 vol. 2010. (ENG., Illus.). 208p. pap. 18.95 *(978-1-55365-216-8(9))* D&M Pubs. Inc. CAN. Dist: Perseus-PGW.

Hodous, Lewis. Buddhism & Buddhists in China. reprint ed. 29.50 *(978-0-404-17306-7(3))* AMS Pr., Inc.

Hodus, Lewis. Buddhism & Buddhists in China. 2007. (ENG.). 102p. per. 19.99 *(978-1-4346-9556-7(5))*; 92p. per. 16.99 *(978-1-4346-9555-0(7))* BiblioBazaar.

—Buddhism & Buddhists in China. 2006. (ENG.). 84p. per. 9.99 *(978-1-59547-958-7(9))* NuVision Pubns., LLC.

—Buddhism & Buddhists in China. 2009. (ENG.). 78p. pap. 9.45 *(978-1-4385-2201-2(0),* Book Jungle) Standard Pubns., Inc.

Huang, C. Julia. Charisma & Compassion: Cheng Yen & the Buddhist Tzu Chi Movement. 2009. (Illus.). 354p. 54.50 *(978-0-674-03133-3(4))* Harvard Univ. Pr.

Huang, Kui. Zhongguo Chan Zong Qing Gui: A Study on the Rules of Purity for Chinese Chan Buddhism. 2008. (CHI.). *(978-7-80254-045-3(3))* China Religion and Culture Publishing Hse.

Ikeda, Daisaku. The Flower of Chinese Buddhism. Watson, Burton, tr. from JPN. 2009. (Soka Gakkai History of Buddhism Ser.). (ENG.). 176p. pap. 14.95 *(978-0-9779245-4-7(8))* Middleway Pr.

Index to F. D. Lessing's Lamaist Iconography of the Peking Temple Yung-Ho-Kung. *(978-0-911706-01-7(1))* Mongolia Society, Inc., The.

Johnston, Reginald Fleming. Buddhist China. 2008. 500p. 53.95 *(978-1-4365-4523-5(4))* 2007. (ENG.). 504p. per. 38.95 *(978-0-548-73987-7(0))* Kessinger Publishing, LLC.

—Buddhist China. 2006. *(978-1-57898-564-7(1))* Martino Publishing.

—Buddhist China. 2008. (ENG., Illus.). 308p. per. 22.95 *(978-0-9680459-3-0(6))* Soul Care Publishing CAN. Dist: Ingram Bk. Co.

Kapstein, Matthew. Buddhism Between Tibet & China. 2009. (Studies in Indian & Tibetan Buddhism Ser.). (ENG.). 480p. pap. 34.95 *(978-0-86171-581-7(0))* Wisdom Pubns.

Karcher, Stephen. The Kuan Yin Oracle: The Voice of the Goddess of Compassion. 2010. (ENG.). 304p. pap. 15.95 *(978-0-7499-4133-8(2))* Piatkus Bks. GBR. Dist: Independent Pubs. Group.

Khechog, Nawang. Awakening Kindness: Finding Joy Through Compassion for Others. 2010. (ENG.). 208p. 23.00 *(978-1-58270-252-0(7),* Beyond Words/Atria Bks.) Atria Bks.

Lempert, Michael. Discipline & Debate: The Language of Violence in a Tibetan Buddhist Monastery. 2012. (ENG.). 238p. pap. 26.95 ***(978-0-520-26947-7(0))*** Univ. of California Pr.

Li, Shao-ch'ang. Popular Buddhism in China. lib. bdg. 79.95 *(978-0-87968-539-3(5))* Krishna Pr.

Lo, Chan. Philosophy & Religion in Early Medieval China. Chan, Alan K. L. & Lo, Yuet Keung, eds. 2011. 381p. pap. 26.95 ***(978-1-4384-3188-8(0),*** Suny Pr.) State Univ. of New York Pr.

Madsen, Richard. Democracy's Dharma: Religious Renaissance & Political Development in Taiwan. 2007. (Illus.). 206p. pap., pap., pap. 26.95 *(978-0-520-25228-8(4))*; 191p. 60.00 *(978-0-520-25227-1(6))* Univ. of California Pr.

Ng, Zhiru. The Making of a Savior Bodhisattva: Dizang in Medieval China. 2007. (Studies in East Asian Buddhism Ser.). (Illus.). 305p. 52.00 *(978-0-8248-3045-8(8))* Univ. of Hawaii Pr.

Orzech, Charles D. Politics & Transcendent Wisdom. 2008. pap. 30.95 *(978-0-271-02836-1(X))* Pennsylvania State Univ. Pr.

Palmer, Martin, et al. The Kuan Yin Chronicles: The Myths & Prophecies of the Chinese Goddess of Compassion. 2009. (ENG., Illus.). 156p. pap. 17.95 *(978-1-57174-608-5(0))* Hampton Roads Publishing Co., Inc.

Park, Jungnok. How Buddhism Acquired a Soul on the Way to China. 2012. (Oxford centre for buddhist studies Monographs). (ENG.). 256p. (C). 99.95 *(978-1-84553-996-2(6))*; pap. 34.95 *(978-1-84553-997-9(4))* Equinox Publishing Ltd. GBR. Dist: Brown, David Bk. Co., The.

Porter, Bill & Pine, Red. Zen Baggage: A Pilgrimage to China. 2010. (ENG., Illus.). 352p. pap. 16.95 *(978-1-58243-540-4(5),* Counterpoint Pr.) Basic Bks. GBR. Dist: Perseus-PGW.

Robson, James. Buddhist Monasticism in East Asia: Places of Practice. Benn, James Alexander & Meeks, Lori R., eds. 2009. (Routledge Critical Studies in Buddhism Ser.). (ENG., Illus.). 248p. (C). 135.00 *(978-0-415-48977-5(6))* Routledge.

Rule, Paul, ed. The Church in China. 2010. (Interface Ser.). (ENG.). 123p. (C). pap. 20.00 ***(978-1-921511-96-7(6))*** ATF Theology AUS. Dist: Brown, David Bk. Co., The.

Schlutter, Morten. How Zen Became Zen. 2010. 304p. pap. 27.00 *(978-0-8248-3508-8(5))* Univ. of Hawaii Pr.

Schlütter, Morten. How Zen Became Zen: The Dispute over Enlightenment & the Formation of Chan Buddhism in Song-Dynasty China. 2008. (Illus.). 340p. (C). 48.00 *(978-0-8248-3255-1(8))* Univ. of Hawaii Pr.

Shi, Yongyou. The Diamond Sutra in Chinese Culture. 2009. 283p. 19.95 *(978-1-932293-37-1(X))* Buddha's Light Publishing.

Smyer Ya, Dan. The Spread of Tibetan Buddhism in China: Charisma, Money, Enlightenment. 2011. (Routledge Critical Studies in Buddhism Ser.). (ENG.). 240p. (C). 130.00 *(978-0-415-57532-4(X))* Routledge.

Suzuki, Daisetz Teitaro. Manual of Zen Buddhism. 2011. 164p. pap. 15.99 ***(978-1-61279-056-5(9))*** Publishing in Motion.

Tarocco, Francesca. The Cultural Practices of Modern Chinese Buddhism. 2010. (ENG.). pap. 39.95 *(978-0-415-59617-6(3))* Routledge.

Walsh, Michael J. Sacred Economies: Buddhist Monasticism & Territoriality in Medieval China. 2010. (ENG., Illus.). 256p. (gr. 17). 50.00 *(978-0-231-14832-0(1))* Columbia Univ. Pr.

Wang, Bangwei & Sen, Tansen, compiled by. India & China: Interactions through Buddhism & Diplomacy: A Collection of Essays by Professor Prabodh Chandra Bagchi. 2011. (Anthem Press India Ser.). 272p. 99.00 ***(978-93-80601-17-5(4))*** Anthem Pr. GBR. Dist: Books International, Inc.

Weiming, Tu & Ikeda, Daisaku. New Horizons in Eastern Humanism: Buddhism, Confucianism & the Quest for Global Peace. 2011. (ENG.). 264p. 50.00 *(978-1-84885-592-2(3))*; pap. 25.00 *(978-1-84885-593-9(1))* I. B. Tauris & Co., Ltd. GBR. Dist: Macmillan.

Weinstein, Stanley. Buddhism under the T'ang. 2008. (Cambridge Studies in Chinese History, Literature & Institutions Ser.). (ENG.). 252p. pap. 34.99 *(978-0-521-10348-0(7))* Cambridge Univ. Pr.

Wright, Arthur F. Buddhism in Chinese History. (Illus.). 144p. reprint ed. pap. 15.00 *(978-957-9482-38-7(1),* PRE012) SMC Publishing, Inc. TWN. Dist: Antique Collectors' Club.

Wu, Jiang. Enlightenment in Dispute: The Reinvention of Chan Buddhism in Seventeenth-Century China. 2011. (ENG.). 480p. pap. 24.95 ***(978-0-19-989556-4(2))*** Oxford Univ. Pr., Inc.

Yao, Weiqun. Fo Jiao Si Xiang Yu Wen Hua. 2009. (CHI.). *(978-7-301-15625-4(1))* Beijing University Pr.

Yifa. The Origins of Buddhist Monastic Codes in China: An Annotated Translation & Study of the Chanyuan Qinggui. 2009. (Classics in East Asian Buddhism Ser.). (Illus.). 352p. pap. 28.00 *(978-0-8248-3425-8(9))* Univ. of Hawaii Pr.

Zürcher, E. J. The Buddhist Conquest of China: The Spread & Adaptation of Buddhism in Early Medieval China. 3rd ed. 2006. (Sinica Leidensia Ser.: Vol. 11). (Illus.). 500p. *(978-90-04-15604-3(6))* BRILL.

BUDDHISM—CHINA—TIBET

Arnold, Edward A. As Long as Space Endures: Essays on the Kalacakra Tantra in Honor of H.H. the Dalai Lama. 2009. (ENG., Illus.). 479p. pap. 29.95 *(978-1-55939-330-0(0))* Snow Lion Pubns., Inc.

Baldock, John. The Tibetan Book of the Dead. Dawa-Samdup, Kazi, tr. 2009. (ENG., Illus.). 128p. 8.99 *(978-0-7858-2515-9(0),* 0785825150, Chartwell) Book Sales, Inc.

Berzin, Alexander. Wise Teacher, Wise Student: Tibetan Approaches to a Healthy Relationship. 2010. (ENG.). 272p. pap. 18.95 *(978-1-55939-347-8(5))* Snow Lion Pubns., Inc.

Cabezon, Jose Ignacio, et al. Freedom from Extremes: Gorampa's Distinguishing the Views & the Polemics of Emptiness. annot. ed. 2007. (Studies in Indian & Tibetan Buddhism Ser.). (ENG & TIB.). 576p. per. 32.95 *(978-0-86171-523-7(3))* Wisdom Pubns.

Cantwell & Mayer, Jeffrey J. Tibetan Buddhism. 2007. 242p. 45.95 *(978-0-415-31819-8(X))*; 170.00 *(978-0-415-31818-1(1))* Routledge.

Cantwell, Cathy & Mayer, Robert. The Kilaya Nirvana Tantra & the Vajra Wrath Tantra: Two Texts from the Ancient Tantra Collection. 2007. (Denkschriften der Phil. -Hist. Klasse Ser.). (Illus.). vii, 289p. (C). pap. 98.00 *(978-3-7001-3678-1(1))* Austrian Academy of Sciences Press AUT. Dist: Brown, David Bk. Co., The.

Coleman, Graham & Jinpa, Thupten, eds. The Tibetan Book of the Dead: First Complete Translation. Dorje, Gyurme, tr. 2007. (Penguin Classics Deluxe Edition Ser.). (ENG., Illus.). 592p. (gr. 12-18). 21.00 *(978-0-14-310494-0(2),* Penguin Classics) Penguin Group (USA) Inc.

Cuevas, Bryan J. Travels in the Netherworld: Buddhist Popular Narratives of Death & the Afterlife in Tibet. 2008. (ENG.). 216p. 65.00 *(978-0-19-534116-4(3))* Oxford Univ. Pr., Inc.

Dalai Lama XIV. The Union of Bliss & Emptiness: Teachings on the Practice of Guru Yoga. 2009. (ENG., Illus.). 192p. pap. 16.95 *(978-1-55939-321-8(1))* Snow Lion Pubns., Inc.

—The Universe in a Single Atom: The Convergence of Science & Spirituality. 2006. (ENG.). 224p. pap. 14.95 *(978-0-7679-2081-0(3),* Morgan Road Bks.) Broadway Bks.

Dalton, Jacob P. The Taming of the Demons: Violence & Liberation in Tibetan Buddhism. 2011. (ENG., Illus.). 336p. 40.00 *(978-0-300-15392-7(9))* Yale Univ. Pr.

Davidson, Ronald M. & Wedemeyer, Christian, eds. Tibetan Buddhist Literature & Praxis: Studies in Its Formative Period, 900-1400. 2006. (Brill's Tibetan Studies Library: Vol. 10). 262p. *(978-90-04-15548-0(1))* BRILL.

Dolna, Sonam & Sorensen, Per K. Rare Texts from Tibet: Seven Sources for the Ecclesiastic History of Medieval Tibet. 2008. (Publications of the Lumbini International Research Institute, Nepal Ser.). (ENG. Illus.). 412p. (C). 62.00 *(978-3-89500-660-9(2))* Reichert, Ludwig Dr. DEU. Dist: Brown, David Bk. Co., The.

Dorje, His Holi. The Future Is Now. 2009. 192p. pap. *(978-1-84850-055-6(6),* 902) Hay Hse. UK, Ltd. GBR. Dist: Grantham Bk. Services.

Dorje, Ven. Hung Kar, compiled by. A Book of Common Tibetan Buddhist Prayers: From the Shambhala Prayer Service for Universal Peace. 2008.Tr. of Shambhala mthun sgril smon lam chen mo'i Dral 'don. (Illus.). 324p. (ENG.). per. 15.95 *(978-0-9801730-1-7(9))*; ring bd. 15.95 *(978-0-9801730-0-0(0))* Blazing Wisdom.

Dudjom Dorjee. Heartfelt Advice. 2010. (ENG., Illus.). 192p. pap. 14.95 *(978-1-55939-346-1(7))* Snow Lion Pubns., Inc.

Farrer-Halls, Gill. Tibetan Buddhist Meditation: Insights, Visualizations & Exercises to Help You Find Harmony & Inner Peace. 2011. (ENG., Illus.). 17.95 *(978-1-78028-019-6(X),* Watkins Publishing) Duncan Baird Pubs. GBR. Dist: Sterling Publishing Co., Inc.

Gherwal, Rishi Singh. Great Masters of the Himalayas: Their Lives & Teachings. 2007. (ENG.). 148p. 35.95 *(978-0-548-00155-4(3))* Kessinger Publishing, LLC.

Gold, Jonathan C. The Dharma's Gatekeepers: Sakya Pandita on Buddhist Scholarship in Tibet. 2008. (Illus.). xii, 267p. pap. 29.95 *(978-0-7914-7166-1(7))* 2007. 267p. 65.00 *(978-0-7914-7165-4(9))* State Univ. of New York Pr.

Gouin, Margaret. Tibetan Rituals of Death: Buddhist Funerary Practices. (ENG.). 208p. (C). 2012. pap. 42.95 ***(978-0-415-62619-4(6))*** 2010. 138.00 *(978-0-415-56636-0(3))* Routledge.

Govinda, Lama Anagarika. The Way of the White Clouds. 2006. (ENG., Illus.). 704p. (gr. 12). per. 19.95 *(978-1-58567-785-6(X))* Overlook Pr., The.

Gyatso, Geshe Kelsang. Buddhism in the Tibetan Tradition: A Guide. 2008. (Routledge Library Editions: Buddhism Ser.). 144p. (Orig.). 165.00 *(978-0-415-46099-5(9))* Routledge.

Hamsa, Bhagwan. The Holy Mountain: Being the Story of a Pilgrimage to Lake Manas & of Initiation on Mount Kailas in Tibet. reprint ed. 27.50 *(978-0-404-17303-6(9))* AMS Pr., Inc.

Hopkins, Jeffrey & Shay-Rap-Gyel-Tsen, Dol-Bo-Ba. Mountain Doctrine: Tibet's Fundamental Treatise on Other-Emptiness & the Buddha Matrix. Vose, Kevin, ed. 2006. (ENG & TIB.). 832p. 79.95 *(978-1-55939-238-9(X))* Snow Lion Pubns., Inc.

Jacoby, S. & Terrone, A., eds. Proceedings of the Tenth Seminar of the IATS, 2003, Volume 12 Buddhism Beyond the Monastery: Tantric Practices & their Performers in Tibet & the Himalayas. 2009. (Brill's Tibetan Studies Library: Vol. 10). 224p. *(978-90-04-17600-3(4))* BRILL.

Jagou, Fabienne. The Ninth Panchen Lama (1883-1937) A Life at the Crossroads of Sino-Tibetan Relations. Bisset-Buechel, Rebecca, tr. from FRE. 2012. (ENG., Illus.). 402p. (C). pap. 45.00 *(978-616-215-016-6(X))* Silkworm Bks. THA. Dist: Univ. of Washington Pr.

Jamgon Kongtrul Lodrö, Tayé. The Treasury of Knowledge: Buddhism's Journey to Tibet. 2010. (ENG.). 696p. 49.95 *(978-1-55939-345-4(9))* Snow Lion Pubns., Inc.

Kapstein, Matthew & Van Schaik, Sam. Esoteric Buddhism at Dunhuang: Rites & Teachings for This Life & Beyond. 2010. 254p. *(978-90-04-18203-5(9))* BRILL.

Karmay, Samten Gyaltsen. The Great Perfection (rDzogs Chen) A Philosophical & Meditative Teaching of Tibetan Buddhism. 2nd ed. 2007. (Brill's Tibetan Studies Library). (Illus.). 256p. *(978-90-04-15142-0(7))* BRILL.

Karr, Andy. Contemplating Reality: A Practitioner's Guide to the View in Indo-Tibetan Buddhism. 2007. (ENG., Illus.). 240p. per. 19.95 *(978-1-59030-429-7(2))* Shambhala Pubns., Inc.

Khyentse, Dilgo & Sangye, Padampa. The Hundred Verses of Advice: Tibetan Buddhist Teachings on What Matters Most. Padmakara Translation Group Staff, tr. 2006. (ENG., Illus.). 208p. per. 18.95 *(978-1-59030-341-2(5))* Shambhala Pubns., Inc.

Klein, Anne Carolyn & Klein, Anne C. Meeting the Great Bliss Queen: Buddhists, Feminists, & the Art of the Self. 2008. (ENG.). 328p. pap. 18.95 *(978-1-55939-291-4(6))* Snow Lion Pubns., Inc.

Kon-sprul Blo-gros-mtha-Yas. Zab Moi Gter Dan Gter Ston Grub Thob Ji Ltar Byon Pai lo Rgyus Mdor Bsdus Su Bkod Pa Rin Chen Baiduryai Phren Ba Zes Bya Ba Bzugs So. 2007. (TIB., Illus.). 527p. *(978-7-223-02119-7(5))* Tibetan People's Publishing Hse.

Koppl, Heidi I. Establishing Appearances as Divine: Rongzom Chozang on Reasoning, Madhyamaka, & Purity. 2008. (TIB & ENG.). 152p. 29.95 *(978-1-55939-288-4(6))* Snow Lion Pubns., Inc.

Lingpa, Jigme & Dorje, Longchen Yeshe. Treasury of Precious Qualities. Padmakara Translation Group Staff, tr. from TIB. rev. ed. 2010. (ENG., Illus.). 576p. pap. 29.95 *(978-1-59030-711-3(9))* Shambhala Pubns., Inc.

Lingpa, Traktung Dudjom & Rinpoche, Lama Tarching. A Clear Mirror: The Visionary Autobiography of a Tibetan Master. Drolma, Chonyi, tr. 2011. (ENG.). 352p. pap. 24.95 *(978-962-7341-67-3(3))* North Atlantic Bks.

Longchenpa. Now That I Come To Die. 2007. (ENG.). 157p. pap. 15.95 *(978-0-89800-393-2(8))* Dharma Publishing.

Lopez, Donald S., Jr., ed. Religions of Tibet in Practice. abr. ed. 2007. (Princeton Readings in Religions Ser.). (ENG.). 440p. (C). per. 28.95 *(978-0-691-12972-3(X))* Princeton Univ. Pr.

Mansfield, Vic. Tibetan Buddhism & Modern Physics: Toward a Union of Love & Knowledge. 2008. (ENG., Illus.). 192p. (C). (gr. 14). per. 19.95 *(978-1-59947-137-2(X))* Templeton Pr.

McCurry, Steve, photos by. The Path to Buddha: A Tibetan Pilgrimage. 2012. (ENG.). 144p. pap. 29.95 ***(978-0-7148-6314-6(9))*** Phaidon Pr., Inc.

Mullin, Glenn H. Living in the Face of Death: The Tibetan Tradition. 2009. (ENG.). 240p. pap. 16.95 *(978-1-55939-310-2(6))* Snow Lion Pubns., Inc.

Nagarjuna & Nagarjuna. In Praise of Dharmadhatu. Brunnhoelzl, Karl, tr. from SAN. 2008. (Nitartha Institute Ser.). (ENG.). 304p. 29.95 *(978-1-55939-286-0(X))* Snow Lion Pubns., Inc.

Nes-don Bstan-dzin-bzan-Po. Great Perfection. 2008. *(978-1-55939-316-4(5))* Snow Lion Pubns., Inc.

Norman, Alexander. Secret Lives of the Dalai Lama: The Untold Story of the Holy Men Who Shaped Tibet, from Pre-History to the Present Day. 2010. 448p. pap. 15.00 *(978-0-385-53070-5(6),* Doubleday Religion) Doubleday Religious Publishing Group, The.

Numata Center for Buddhist Translation and Research, creator. Buddha-Dharma: The Way to Enlightenment. 2nd rev. ed. 2006. 829p. per. 25.00 *(978-1-886439-20-7(6))* BDK America.

Nydahl, Lama Ole. The Way Things Are: A Living Approach to Buddhism for Today's World. 2008. (Buddhism (O Books) Ser.). (ENG., Illus.). 240p. pap. 19.95 *(978-1-84694-042-2(7))* Hunt, John Publishing Ltd. GBR. Dist: National Bk. Network.

Nyima, Thuken Chökyi. The Crystal Mirror of Philosophical Systems: A Tibetan Study of Asian Religious Thought. Jackson, Roger, ed. Sopa, Geshe Lhundub, tr. from TIB. 2009. (Library of Tibetan Classics Ser.). (ENG., Illus.). 696p. 59.95 *(978-0-86171-464-3(4))* Wisdom Pubns.

Osho. The Book of Wisdom: The Heart of Tibetan Buddhism. Commentaries on Atisha's Seven Points of Mind Training. rev. ed. 2009. (ENG.). 362p. pap. 19.95 *(978-0-9818341-1-5(6),* OSHO Media International) Osho International.

Pallis, Marco. The Way & the Mountain: Tibet, Buddhism, & Tradition. 2008. (Perennial Philosophy Ser.). (ENG., Illus.). 296p. pap. 21.95 *(978-1-933316-53-6(5))* World Wisdom, Inc.

Peacock, John. The Tibetan Way of Life, Death & Rebirth: The Illustrated Guide to Tibetan Wisdom. 2009. (ENG., Illus.). 144p. pap. *(978-1-84483-804-2(5))* Duncan Baird Pubs. GBR. Dist: Sterling Publishing Co., Inc.

Pha-bon-kha-pa Byams-pa-bstan-dzin-phrin-las-rgya-Mtsho, et al. La Liberación en Nuestras Manos. 2007. (SPA.). *(978-0-918753-23-6(6))* Mahayana Sutra & Tantra Pr.

Phun-tshogs-tshe-Rin & Nag-Dban. Sku Mkhar Chen Po Yum-Bu-Bla-Sgan Gi Dkar Chag Brin Po Bzugs So. Nan-Wuth Gtsug-Lag Khan Che Moi Dkar Chag Bzugs So. Zwa Lha-Khan Gi Dkar Chag Bzugs So. Phrul-Snan Gtsug-Lag-Khan Gi Nan Mjal Drug Gi Dkar Chag Mkhas Pai Nag Sgron Bzugs So. 2010. (TIB.). 77p. *(978-7-223-02783-0(5))* Tibetan People's Publishing Hse.

Pistono, Matteo. In the Shadow of the Buddha: One Man's Journey of Discovery in Tibet. 2012. (ENG., Illus.). 288p. (gr. 12). 16.00 ***(978-0-452-29751-7(6),*** Plume) Penguin Group (USA) Inc.

Ponlop, Dzogchen. Mind Beyond Death. (ENG.). 375p. 2008. pap. 18.95 *(978-1-55939-301-0(7))* 2007. (Illus.). 25.95 *(978-1-55939-276-1(2))* Snow Lion Pubns., Inc.

Powers, John. A Concise Introduction to Tibetan Buddhism. 2008. (ENG.). 160p. pap. 14.95 *(978-1-55939-296-9(7))* Snow Lion Pubns., Inc.

—Introduction to Tibetan Buddhism. rev. ed. 2007. (ENG., Illus.). 512p. pap. 22.95 *(978-1-55939-282-2(7))* Snow Lion Pubns., Inc.

Preece, Rob. Preparing for Tantra: Creating the Psychological Ground for Practice. 2011. (ENG., Illus.). 180p. pap. 18.95 *(978-1-55939-377-5(7))* Snow Lion Pubns., Inc.

—The Wisdom of Imperfection, 2nd Edition: The Challenge of Individuation in Buddhist Life. 2nd ed. 2010. (ENG.). 336p. pap. 18.95 *(978-1-55939-349-2(1))* Snow Lion Pubns., Inc.

Rangdrol, Tsele Natsok. Heart Lamp: The Heart of the Matter & Lamp of Mahamudra. Kunsang, Erik Pema, tr. from TIB. 2009. (ENG.). 224p. pap. 17.95 *(978-962-7341-60-4(6))* North Atlantic Bks.

—The Mirror of Mindfulness, Updated Edition: The Cycle of the Four Bardos. 2010. (ENG.). 176p. pap. 15.95 *(978-962-7341-65-9(7))* North Atlantic Bks.

Rawson, Philip. Sacred Tibet. 2012. (Art & Imagination Ser.). (ENG., Illus.). 128p. pap. 14.95 ***(978-0-500-81049-1(4),*** 581049) Thames & Hudson.

Ray, Reginald A., ed. The Tibetan Buddhism Reader. 2010. (ENG., Illus.). 192p. pap. 14.95 *(978-1-59030-834-9(4))* Shambhala Pubns., Inc.

Ricard, Matthieu. Tibet: An Inner Journey. (ENG., Illus.). 232p. 2012. pap. 19.95 *(978-0-500-28905-1(0),* 528905) 2007. 45.00 *(978-0-500-54332-0(1))* Thames & Hudson.

Rinpoche, Adeu. Freedom in Bondage: The Life & Teachings of Adeu Rinpoche. Wangmo, Marcia Dechen & Schmidt, Marcia Binder, eds. Kunsang, Erik Pema, tr. 2011. (ENG.). 192p. pap. 18.95 *(978-962-7341-66-6(5))* North Atlantic Bks.

Rinpoche, Arjia. Surviving the Dragon: A Tibetan Lama's Account of 40 Years under Chinese Rule. 2010. (ENG., Illus.). 288p. 24.99 *(978-1-60529-754-5(2))* Rodale Pr., Inc.

Rinpoche, Dzogchen. Great Perfection: Outer & Inner Preliminaries. Dahl, Cortland, tr. from TIB. 2008. (Heart Essence Ser.). (ENG., Illus.). 192p. 24.95 *(978-1-55939-285-3(1))* Snow Lion Pubns., Inc.

Rinpoche, Lama Lodu. Bardo Teachings: The Way of Death & Rebirth. 2011. 96p. pap. 14.95 *(978-1-55939-366-9(1))* Snow Lion Pubns., Inc.

Rinpoche, Pabongka. Liberation in the Palm of Your Hand: A Concise Discourse on the Path to Enlightenment. Rinpoche, Trijang, ed. Richards, Michael, tr. from TIB. 2nd ed. 2006. (ENG., Illus.). 980p. per. 24.95 *(978-0-86171-500-8(4))* Wisdom Pubns.

Rinpoche, Patrul & Dalai Lama XIV. The Words of My Perfect Teacher: A Complete Translation of a Classic Introduction to Tibetan Buddhism. 2010. (Sacred Literature Trust Ser.). (ENG., Illus.). 512p. pap. 30.95 *(978-0-300-16532-6(3))* Yale Univ. Pr.

Rinpoche, Samdhong. Tibetan Meditation. 2011. (ENG.). 140p. pap. 9.95 *(978-81-8328-196-6(6))*; 138p. pap. 9.95 ***(978-81-8328-177-5(X))*** Wisdom Tree IND. Dist: SCB Distributors.

Roloff, Carola. Red mda' ba. Buddhist Yogi-Scholar of the Fourteenth Century: The Forgotten Reviver of Madhyamaka Philosophy in Tibet. 2010. (Contributions to Tibetan Studies). 500p. (C). 168.00 *(978-3-89500-693-7(9))* Reichert, Ludwig Dr. DEU. Dist: Brown, David Bk. Co., The.

Ruegg, David Seyfort. Symbiosis of Buddhism with Brahmanism/Hinduism in South Asia & of Buddhism with 'local cults' in Tibet & the Himalayan Region. 2008. (Sitzungsberichte der Phil-Klasse Ser.). 197p. (C). pap. 54.00 *(978-3-7001-6057-1(7))* Austrian Academy of Sciences Press AUT. Dist: Brown, David Bk. Co., The.

Russell, Jeremy. Dharamsala, Tibetan Refuge. 2006. (ENG., Illus.). 93p. pap. 9.95 *(978-81-7436-086-1(7))* Roli Bks. Private, Ltd. IND. Dist: Ingram Pub. Services.

Sawai, Tetsu. The 14th Dalai Lama: A Manga Biography. 2010. (ENG., Illus.). 208p. (gr. 12). 15.00 *(978-0-14-311815-2(3),* Penguin (Non-Classics)) Penguin Group (USA) Inc.

Samuel, Geoffrey. Introducing Tibetan Buddhism. 2012. (World Religions Ser.). (Illus.). 296p. (C). pap. 39.95 *(978-0-415-45665-4(7))* Routledge.

Sangharakshita. Introduccion al Budhismo Tibetano. (SPA.). 214p. 11.50 *(978-84-89920-70-5(2),* 86918) Ediciones Oniro S.A. ESP. Dist: Lectorum Pubns., Inc.

Sangye, Padampa. Lion of Siddhas: The Life & Teachings of Padampa Sangye. 2008. (ENG., Illus.). 362p. pap. 26.95 *(978-1-55939-299-0(1))* Snow Lion Pubns., Inc.

Schettini, Stephen. The Novice: Why I Became a Buddhist Monk, Why I Quit, & What I Learned. 2009. 349p. 24.95 *(978-1-60832-005-9(7),* Greenleaf Book Group Pr.) Greenleaf Book Group.

Schlagintweit, Emil. Buddhism in Tibet Illustrated by Literar. 2006. pap. 38.95 *(978-1-4286-4999-6(9))* Kessinger Publishing, LLC.

Skorupski, Tadeusz. Tibetan Amulets. 2010. (ENG., Illus.). 138p. pap. 25.00 *(978-974-524-120-6(2))* Orchid Pr. THA. Dist: National Bk. Network.

Stein, R. A. & McKeown, Arthur P. Rolf Stein's Tibetica Antiqua: With Additional Materials. 2010. 388p. *(978-90-04-18338-4(8))* BRILL.

Sumegi, A. Dreamworlds of Shamanism & Tibetan Buddhism. 2008. 192p. (C). 65.50 *(978-0-7914-7463-1(1))* State Univ. of New York Pr.

Sumegi, Angela. Dreamworlds & Shamanism & Tibetan Buddhism: The Third Place. 2008. (Illus.). 166p. pap. 24.95 *(978-0-7914-7464-8(X))* State Univ. of New York Pr.

Swift, Dusty. Illusions of Enlightenment: A Story about a Peace Corps Volunteer in Nepal & His Discovery of the Buddhist Teachings. 2011. 444p. 33.95 ***(978-1-4502-9066-1(3))***; pap. 23.95 ***(978-1-4502-9064-7(7))*** iUniverse, Inc.

Taye, Jamgon Kongtrul. Treasury of Knowledge: Book 8, Part 3: The Elements of Tantric Practice. 2008. (ENG.). 448p. 34.95 *(978-1-55939-305-8(X))* Snow Lion Pubns., Inc.

Taye, Jamgon Kongtrul Lodro & Taye, Jamgon. Esoteric Insturctions Pt. 4: A Detailed Presentation of the Process of Meditation in Vajrayana. Harding, Sarah, tr. from TIB. 2008. (Treasury of Knowledge Ser.). (ENG.). 544p. 39.95 *(978-1-55939-284-6(3))* Snow Lion Pubns., Inc.

Taye, Jamgon Kongtrul Lodro, et al. The Treasury of Knowledge, Book 6, Part 3: Frameworks of Buddhist Philosophy. Callahan, Elizabeth M., tr. from TIB. 2007. (Treasury of Knowledge Ser.). (ENG.). 416p. 34.95 *(978-1-55939-277-8(0))* Snow Lion Pubns., Inc.

Thondup, Tulku. Peaceful Death, Joyful Rebirth: A Tibetan Buddhist Guidebook. Talbott, Harold, ed. 2006. (ENG., Illus.). 352p. pap. 24.95 *(978-1-59030-385-6(7))* Shambhala Pubns., Inc.

Thubten Yeshe, Lama. The Essence of Tibetan Buddhism: The Three Principal Aspects of the Path & Introduction to Tantra. Ribush, Nicholas, ed. 2010. (ENG., Illus.). 69p. pap. 0.00 *(978-1-891868-08-5(X),* 18801) Lama Yeshe Wisdom Archive.

Thurman, Robert. Why the Dalai Lama Matters: His Act of Truth as the Solution for China, Tibet, & the World. 2011. (ENG., Illus.). 256p. pap. 14.00 *(978-1-58270-221-6(7),* Beyond Words/Atria Bks.) Atria Bks.

Thurman, Robert & Thurman, Robert A. F. Why the Dalai Lama Matters: His Act of Truth As the Solution for China, Tibet, & the World. 2008. (ENG., Illus.). 256p. 24.00 *(978-1-58270-220-9(9),* Beyond Words/Atria Bks.) Atria Bks.

Trungpa, Chögyam. The Heart of the Buddha: Entering the Tibetan Buddhist Path. 2010. (Shambhala Classics Ser.). (ENG.). 272p. pap. 16.95 *(978-1-59030-766-3(6))* Shambhala Pubns., Inc.

Tseten, Migmar. The Tibetan Book of Awakening. 2010. 136p. pap. 14.95 *(978-0-557-38681-9(0))* Lulu Enterprises Inc.

Tuttle, Gray. Tibetan Buddhists in the Making of Modern China. 2007. (ENG., Illus.). 352p. (gr. 17). pap. 26.00 *(978-0-231-13447-7(9))* Columbia Univ. Pr.

van Schaik, Sam & Galambos, Imre. Manuscripts & Travellers: The Sino-Tibetan Documents of a Tenth-Century Buddhist Pilgrim. 2011. (Studies in Manuscript Cultures Ser.). (ENG., Illus.). VII, 247p. 210.00 ***(978-3-11-174156-7(7))*** De Gruyter, Walter Inc.

Waddell, L. Austine. Lamaism in Sikhim. 2007. (ENG.). 182p. 37.95 *(978-0-548-00564-4(8))* Kessinger Publishing, LLC.

Waddell, Laurence. Lhasa & Its Mysteries: With a Record of the Expedition Of 1903-1904. 2007. 740p. per. 32.95 *(978-1-60206-724-0(4))* Cosimo, Inc.

Waddell, Laurence Austine. The Buddhism of Tibet or Lamaism. 2007. 624p. per. 23.50 *(978-1-60206-137-8(8))* Cosimo, Inc.

Wallace, B. The Four Immeasurables, Third Edition: Practices to Open the Heart. 3rd ed. 2010. (ENG.). 192p. pap. 16.95 *(978-1-55939-353-9(X))* Snow Lion Pubns., Inc.

Walter, M. L. & Walter, Michael L. Buddhism & Empire: The Political & Religious Culture of Early Tibet. 2009. (Brill's Tibetan Studies Library). 400p. *(978-90-04-17584-6(9))* BRILL.

Wangmo, Marcia Dechen. Confessions of a Gypsy Yogini: Experience Through Mistakes. 2010. (ENG., Illus.). 176p. pap. 17.95 *(978-962-7341-64-2(9))* North Atlantic Bks.

Western Shugden Society. A Great Deception: The Ruling Lamas' Policies. 2010. (ENG.). 312p. pap. 12.95 *(978-0-615-32924-6(1))* Western Shugden Society US.

Wolter, Doris, ed. Losing the Clouds, Gaining the Sky: Buddhism & the Natural Mind. 2007. (ENG.). 352p. per. 18.95 *(978-0-86171-359-2(1))* Wisdom Pubns.

Wong, Sylvia. The Karmapa Prophecies. 2010. (Illus.). x, 505p. *(978-81-208-3480-4(1)*, Library of Congress — New Delhi Overseas Office) Motilal Banarsidass Publishers (Pvt. Ltd).

BUDDHISM—EAST ASIA

Ardussi, John A. & Pommaret, Françoise, eds. Proceedings of the Tenth Seminar of the IATS, 2003, Volume 5 Bhutan: Traditions & Changes. 2006. 175p. *(978-90-04-15551-0(1))* BRILL.

Berkwitz, Stephen C., et al. Buddhist Manuscript Cultures: Knowledge, Ritual & Art. Berkwitz, Stephen C. et al, eds. 2009. (Routledge Critical Studies in Buddhism Ser.). (Illus.). 222p. 170.00 *(978-0-415-77616-5(3))* Routledge.

Handley, Paul M. The King Never Smiles: A Biography of Thailand's Bhumibol Adulyadej. 2006. (ENG.). 512p. 39.95 *(978-0-300-10682-4(3))* Yale Univ. Pr.

Jerryson, Michael K. Mongolian Buddhism: The Rise & Fall of the Sangha. 2008. (ENG., Illus.). 240p. pap. 24.95 *(978-974-9511-26-8(3))* Silkworm Bks. THA. Dist: Univ. of Washington Pr.

Jordt, Ingrid. Burma's Mass Lay Meditation Movement: Buddhism & the Cultural Construction of Power. 2007. (Ohio RIS Southeast Asia Ser.). (ENG., Illus.). 272p. per. 28.00 *(978-0-89680-255-1(8))* Ohio Univ. Pr.

Kitinov, Baatr U. The Spread of Buddhism among Western Mongolian Tribes Between the 13th & 18th Centuries: Tibetan Buddhism in the Politics & Ideology of the Oirat People. 2010. 324p. 119.95 *(978-0-7734-1434-1(7))* Mellen, Edwin Pr., The.

Ray, Nihar-Ranjan. Sanskrit Buddhism in Burma. reprint ed. 41.50 *(978-0-404-17367-8(5))* AMS Pr., Inc.

Salomon, Richard. Two Gandhari Manuscripts of the Songs of Lake Anavatapta (Anavatapta-Gatha) British Library Kharosthi Fragment 1 & Senior Scroll 14. 2009. (ENG., Illus.). 496p. 95.00 *(978-0-295-98905-1(X))* Univ. of Washington Pr.

Swearer, Donald K. The Buddhist World of Southeast Asia. 2nd ed. 2010. (SUNY series in Religious Studies). (Illus.). 304p. 75.00 *(978-1-4384-3251-9(8))*; pap. 30.95 *(978-1-4384-3250-2(X))* State Univ. of New York Pr.

BUDDHISM—GREAT BRITAIN

Almond, Philip C. The British Discovery of Buddhism. 2007. (ENG.). 200p. pap. 48.00 *(978-0-521-03385-5(3))* Cambridge Univ. Pr.

Batchelor, Stephen. Confession of a Buddhist Atheist. 2010. (ENG., Illus.). 320p. 26.00 *(978-0-385-52706-4(3))* Spiegel & Grau.

Bluck, Robert. British Buddhism: Teachings, Practice & Development. 2008. 234p. 39.95 *(978-0-415-48308-7(5))* Routledge.

Franklin, J. Jeffrey. The Lotus & the Lion: Buddhism & the British Empire. 2008. 288p. 36.95 *(978-0-8014-4730-3(5))* Cornell Univ. Pr.

Harris, Elizabeth. Theravada Buddhism & the British Encounter: Religious, Missionary & Colonial Experience in Nineteenth Century Sri Lanka. 2009. 280p. pap. 39.95 *(978-0-415-54442-9(4))* Routledge.

BUDDHISM—INDIA

Allen, Charles, adapted by. The Buddha & Dr Führer: An Archaeological Scandal. 2009. (ENG.). 300p. 26.95 *(978-1-905791-93-4(3))* Haus Publishing GBR. Dist: Consortium Bk. Sales & Distribution.

Asher, Frederick M. Bodh Gaya. 2008. (ENG., Illus.). 120p. 35.00 *(978-0-19-569314-0(0))* Oxford Univ. Pr., Inc.

Balikci, Anna. Lamas, Shamans & Ancestors: Village Religion in Sikkim. 2008. (Brill's Tibetan Studies Library Ser.). (Illus.). 400p. *(978-90-04-16706-3(4))* BRILL.

Barber, A. W. & Padma, Sree. Buddhism in the Krishna River Valley of Andhra. 2009. 224p. pap. 24.95 *(978-0-7914-7486-0(0)*, Suny Pr.) State Univ. of New York Pr.

Barua, Ankur & BASILIO, M. A. Disappearance of Buddhism from Indi. 2010. 76p. pap. *(978-3-639-24867-8(8))* VDM Verlag Dr. Mueller e.K.

Boucher, Daniel. Bodhisattvas of the Forest & the Formation of the Mahayana: A Study & Translation of the Rastrapalapariprccha-Sutra. 2008. 352p. (C). 56.00 *(978-0-8248-2881-3(X))* Univ. of Hawaii Pr.

Bronkhorst, Johannes. Buddhism in the Shadow of Brahmanism. 2011. 320p. *(978-90-04-20140-8(8))* BRILL.

—Buddhist Teaching in India. 2009. (ENG.). 260p. pap. 28.95 *(978-0-86171-566-4(7))* Wisdom Pubns.

Burnouf, Eugene. Introduction to the History of Indian Buddhism. Buffetrille, Katia & Lopez, Donald S., Jr., trs. from FRE. 2010. (ENG.). 616p. 65.00 *(978-0-226-08123-6(0))* Univ. of Chicago Pr.

Conze, Edward. Buddhist Thought in India: Three Phases of Buddhist Philosophy. 2008. (Routledge Library Editions: Buddhism Ser.). (ENG.). 302p. (C). 175.00 *(978-0-415-46098-9(0))* Routledge.

Copleston, Reginald. Buddhism Primitive & Present in Magadha & in Ceylon. 2007. (ENG.). 316p. 45.95 *(978-0-548-05188-7(7))* Kessinger Publishing, LLC.

Davids, Carolina A. The Birth of Indian Psychology & Its Development in Buddhism. reprint ed. 37.50 *(978-0-404-17267-1(9))* AMS Pr., Inc.

Davids, T. W. Rhys. Buddhist India. 2009. 356p. 46.95 *(978-1-120-37927-6(X))*; pap. 31.95 *(978-1-120-26874-7(5))* Kessinger Publishing, LLC.

Dorje, Ogyen Trinley. Compassion NOW! 2011. 86p. pap. 9.95 ***(978-1-934608-21-0(1))*** KTD Pubns.

Dwivedi, K. S. Introduction to Indian Buddhism. 2010. 279p. 62.50 *(978-81-7533-304-8(9))* M. D. Pubns. Pvt, Ltd. IND. Dist: Coronet Bks.

Geary, David, et al, eds. Cross-Disciplinary Perspectives on a Contested Buddhist Site: Bodhgaya Jataka. 2012. (Routledge South Asian Religion Ser.). (ENG., Illus.). 224p. (C). 145.00 *(978-0-415-68452-1(8))* Routledge.

Giles, H. A., tr. from CHI. The Travels of Fa-hsien (399-414 A. D.), or Record of the Buddhistic Kingdoms. 2012. (ENG.). 116p. pap. 33.99 ***(978-1-107-68532-1(X))*** Cambridge Univ. Pr.

Giri, Satyananda. Narop. 2011. 300p. pap. 66.95 ***(978-1-61204-448-4(4)**, Strategic Bk. Publishing)* AEG Literary Publishing Services, Inc.

Grunwedel, Albert. Buddhist Art in India. Burgess, James, ed. Gibson, Agnes C., tr. 240p. 2008. 41.95 *(978-1-4365-1611-2(0))* 2007. (ENG.). per. 26.95 *(978-0-548-74617-2(6))* Kessinger Publishing, LLC.

I-Tsing. A Record of the Buddhist Religion As Practised in India & the Malay Archipelago A.D. 671-695. Takakusu, J., tr. reprint ed. 22.50 *(978-0-89644-178-1(4))* Coronet Bks.

Jamgon Kongtrul Lodrö, Tayé. The Treasury of Knowledge: Buddhism's Journey to Tibet. 2010. (ENG.). 696p. 49.95 *(978-1-55939-345-4(9))* Snow Lion Pubns., Inc.

Karr, Andy. Contemplating Reality: A Practitioner's Guide to the View in Indo-Tibetan Buddhism. 2007. (ENG., Illus.). 240p. per. 19.95 *(978-1-59030-429-7(2))* Shambhala Pubns., Inc.

Kerouac, Jack. Wake Up: A Life of the Buddha. 2008. (ENG.). 160p. (gr. 12-18). 24.95 *(978-0-670-01957-1(7)*, Viking Adult) Penguin Group (USA) Inc.

Kinsey, John. The Empty Circle. 2009. 64p. pap. *(978-3-639-16551-7(9))* VDM Verlag Dr. Mueller e.K.

Law, Bimala Churn. Historical Gleanings. 2008. 112p. 34.95 *(978-1-4365-0102-6(4))* 2007. (ENG.). 116p. per. 19.95 *(978-0-548-71334-1(0))* Kessinger Publishing, LLC.

—Historical Gleanings. 2008. 112p. pap. *(978-1-4097-0456-0(4))* Read Bks.

Law, Bimala Churn, ed. Historical Gleanings. reprint ed. 20.00 *(978-0-404-17337-1(3))* AMS Pr., Inc.

Lempert, Michael. Discipline & Debate: The Language of Violence in a Tibetan Buddhist Monastery. 2012. (ENG.). 238p. pap. 26.95 ***(978-0-520-26947-7(0))*** Univ. of California Pr.

Mungekar, Bhalchandra & Rathore, Aakash Singh. Buddhism & the Contemporary World: An Ambedkarian Perspective. 2007. xiv, 218p. *(978-81-89640-30-9(5))* Bookwell Pubns.

Nance, Richard F. Speaking for Buddhas: Scriptural Commentary in Indian Buddhism. 2011. (ENG., Illus.). 312p. (gr. 17). 55.00 ***(978-0-231-15230-3(2))*** Columbia Univ. Pr.

Ohnuma, Reiko. Ties That Bind: Maternal Imagery & Discourse in Indian Buddhism. 2012. (ENG.). 288p. pap. 35.00 ***(978-0-19-991567-5(9))***; (Illus.). 99.00 ***(978-0-19-991565-1(2))*** Oxford Univ. Pr., Inc.

Padma, Sree. Buddhism in the Krishna River Valley of Andhra. Barber, A. W., ed. 2008. (Illus.). xiii, 216p. (C). 65.00 *(978-0-7914-7485-3(2))* State Univ. of New York Pr.

Park, Jungnok. How Buddhism Acquired a Soul on the Way to China. 2012. (Oxford centre for buddhist studies Monographs). (ENG.). 256p. (C). 99.95 *(978-1-84553-996-2(6))*; pap. 34.95 *(978-1-84553-997-9(4))* Equinox Publishing Ltd. GBR. Dist: Brown, David Bk. Co., The.

Powers, John. A Bull of a Man: Images of Masculinity, Sex, & the Body in Indian Buddhism. (Illus.). 336p. 2012. (ENG.). pap. 22.50 ***(978-0-674-06403-4(8))*** 2009. 47.50 *(978-0-674-03329-0(9))* Harvard Univ. Pr.

Rotman, Andy. Thus Have I Seen: Visualizing Faith in Early Indian Buddhism. 2008. (ENG.). 336p. 74.00 *(978-0-19-536615-0(8))* Oxford Univ. Pr., Inc.

Ruegg, David Seyfort. Symbiosis of Buddhism with Brahmanism/Hinduism in South Asia & of Buddhism with 'local cults' in Tibet & the Himalayan Region. 2008. (Sitzungsberichte der Phil-Klasse Ser.). 197p. (C). pap. 54.00 *(978-3-7001-6057-1(7))* Austrian Academy of Sciences Press AUT. Dist: Brown, David Bk. Co., The.

Russell, Jeremy. Dharamsala, Tibetan Refuge. 2006. (ENG., Illus.). 93p. pap. 9.95 *(978-81-7436-086-1(7))* Roli Bks. Private, Ltd. IND. Dist: Ingram Pub. Services.

Silk, Jonathan A. Managing Monks: Administrators & Administrative Roles in Indian Buddhist Monasticism. 2008. (South Asia Research Ser.). (TIB, CHI, SAN, PLI & ENG.). 320p. 65.00 *(978-0-19-532684-0(9))* Oxford Univ. Pr., Inc.

Tsukamoto, Keisho. Source Elements of the Lotus Sutra: Budhist Integration of Religion, Thought, & Culture. 2007. (ENG., Illus.). 496p. per. 26.95 *(978-4-333-02259-5(2))* Kosei Publishing Co. JPN. Dist: Tuttle Publishing.

Williams, Paul, et al. Buddhist Thought. 2nd rev. ed. 2012. (ENG., Illus.). 288p. (C). pap. 32.95 *(978-0-415-57179-1(0))*; 110.00 ***(978-0-415-57178-4(2))*** Routledge.

Yogi Ramacharaka. The Inner Teachings of the Philosophies & Religions of India. 2007. 376p. per. 17.95 *(978-1-60206-628-1(0))* Cosimo, Inc.

BUDDHISM—JAPAN

Adolphson, Mikael S. The Teeth & Claws of the Buddha: Monastic Warriors & Sohei in Japanese History. 2007. (Illus.). 212p. (C). pap. 26.00 *(978-0-8248-3123-3(3))* Univ. of Hawaii Pr.

Armstrong, Robert Cornell. Buddhism & Buddhists in Japan. 2007. (ENG.). 156p. 36.95 *(978-0-548-11051-5(4))* Kessinger Publishing, LLC.

Bowring, Richard. The Religious Traditions of Japan 500-1600. 2008. (ENG., Illus.). 502p. pap. 44.00 *(978-0-521-72027-4(3))* Cambridge Univ. Pr.

Brazier, Caroline. The Other Buddhism: Amida Comes West. 2007. (ENG.). 304p. per. 24.95 *(978-1-84694-052-1(4))* O Bks.,John Hunt.

Chadwick, David. Thank You & Ok! An American Zen Failure in Japan. 2007. (ENG.). 480p. per. 17.95 *(978-1-59030-470-9(5))* Shambhala Pubns., Inc.

Chen, J. Legend & Legitimation: The Formation of Tendai Esoteric Buddhism in Japan. 2009. (Melanges Chinois et Bouddhiques Ser.). 423p. (C). pap. 66.00 *(978-2-9600076-2-6(X))* Peeters Pubs. & Booksellers BEL. Dist: Brown, David Bk. Co., The.

Como, Michael I. Shotoku: Ethnicity, Ritual, & Violence in the Japanese Buddhist Tradition. 2008. (ENG.). 256p. 45.00 *(978-0-19-518861-5(6))* Oxford Univ. Pr., Inc.

Dessì, Ugo, ed. The Social Dimension of Shin Buddhism. 2010. (Numen Book Ser.). (Illus.). 301p. *(978-90-04-18653-8(0))* BRILL.

DuBois, Thomas David. Religion & the Making of Modern East Asia. 2011. (New Approaches to Asian History Ser.). (ENG., Illus.). 272p. (C). 90.00 *(978-1-107-00809-0(3))*; pap. 27.99 *(978-1-107-40040-5(6))* Cambridge Univ. Pr.

Ekaku, Hakuin. Wild Ivy: The Spiritual Autobiography of Zen Master Hakuin. Waddell, Norman, tr. from JPN. 2010. (ENG.). 192p. pap. 22.95 *(978-1-59030-809-7(3))* Shambhala Pubns., Inc.

Eubanks, Charlotte. Miracles of Book & Body: Buddhist Textual Culture & Medieval Japan. 2010. (Buddhisms Ser.). (Illus.). 275p. 49.95 *(978-0-520-26561-5(0))* Univ. of California Pr.

Ford, James L. Jōkei & Buddhist Devotion in Early Medieval Japan. 2006. (ENG., Illus.). 336p. 85.00 *(978-0-19-518814-1(4))* Oxford Univ. Pr., Inc.

Gerhart, Karen M. The Material Culture of Death in Medieval Japan. 2009. (C). 39.00 *(978-0-8248-3261-2(2))* Univ. of Hawaii Pr.

Glassman, Hank. The Face of Jizo: Image & Cult in Medieval Japanese Buddhism. 2012. 52.00 ***(978-0-8248-3443-2(7))***; pap. 25.00 ***(978-0-8248-3581-1(6))*** Univ. of Hawaii Pr.

Graham, Patricia Jane. Faith & Power in Japanese Buddhist Art, 1600-2005. 2007. (Illus.). 353p. (C). pap. 33.00 *(978-0-8248-3191-2(8))* Univ. of Hawaii Pr.

Harding, John S. Mah?y?na Phoenix: Japan's Buddhists at the 1893 World's Parliament of Religions. 2008. (American University Studies VII: Theology & Religion Ser.). (Illus.). 168p. (C). 60.95 *(978-1-4331-0140-3(8))* Lang, Peter Publishing, Inc.

Haukin. Beating the Cloth Drum: Letters of Zen Master Hakuin. Waddell, Norman, tr. from JPN. 2012. (ENG.). 256p. pap. 17.95 ***(978-1-59030-948-3(0))*** Shambhala Pubns., Inc.

Hearn, Lafcadio. In Ghostly Japan. 2009. 120p. pap. *(978-1-150-06924-6(4))* Books LLC.

—In Ghostly Japan. 2007. (ENG.). 252p. per. 12.25 *(978-1-60206-069-2(X))* Cosimo, Inc.

—In Ghostly Japan. 2007. (ENG.). 112p. per. *(978-1-4065-4434-3(5))* Dodo Pr.

—In Ghostly Japan. 2007. (ENG.). 88p. per. *(978-1-4068-1342-5(7))* Echo Library.

Hur, Nam-lin. Death & Social Order in Tokugawa Japan: Buddhism, Anti-Christianity, & the Danka System. 2007. (Harvard East Asian Monographs: 282). (Illus.). 550p. 55.00 *(978-0-674-02503-5(2))* Harvard Univ., Asia Ctr.

Inagaki, Hisao, ed. A Dictionary of Japanese Buddhist Terms. 2007. (ENG.). 548p. 65.00 *(978-1-933330-05-1(8))* Stone Bridge Pr.

Ives, Christopher. Imperial-Way Zen: Ichikawa Hakugen's Critique & Lingering Questions for Buddhist Ethics. 2009. (C). 52.00 *(978-0-8248-3331-2(7))* Univ. of Hawaii Pr.

Jaffe, Richard. Neither Monk nor Layman. 2010. 308p. pap. 25.00 *(978-0-8248-3627-6(8))* Univ. of Hawaii Pr.

Jaffe, Richard M. Neither Monk nor Layman: Clerical Marriage in Modern Japanese Buddhism. 2010. pap. *(978-0-8248-3527-9(1))* Univ. of Hawaii Pr.

Lloyd, Arthur. The Creed of Half Japan: Historical Sketches of Japanese Buddhism. reprint ed. 40.50 *(978-0-404-17344-9(6))* AMS Pr., Inc.

—The Creed of Half Japan: Historical Sketches of Japanese Buddhism. 2007. (ENG.). 400p. 49.95 *(978-0-548-00645-0(8))* Kessinger Publishing, LLC.

MacGregor, Kirk R. A Comparative Study of Adjustments to Social Catastrophes in Christianity & Buddhism: The Black Death in Europe & the Kamakura Takeover in Japan As Causes of Religious Reform. 2011. 400p. 129.95 ***(978-0-7734-1549-2(1))*** Mellen, Edwin Pr., The.

Matsuo, Kenji. A History of Japanese Buddhism. 2008. (Illus.). 264p. *(978-1-905246-41-0(2))*; (ENG., per. *(978-1-905246-59-5(5))* BRILL.

McCallum, Donald F. The Four Great Temples: Buddhist Archaeology, Architecture, & Icons of Seventh-Century Japan. 2008. (Illus.). 360p. (C). 40.00 *(978-0-8248-3114-1(4))* Univ. of Hawaii Pr.

Nonomura, Kaoru. Eat Sleep Sit: My Year at Japan's Most Rigorous Zen Temple, 1 vol. Carpenter, Juliet Winters, tr. from JPN. 2009. (ENG., Illus.). 328p. 24.95 *(978-4-7700-3075-7(4))* Kodansha America, Inc.

Nukariya, Kaiten. The Religion of the Samurai. 2009. (ENG.). 186p. pap. 13.45 *(978-1-4385-2540-2(0)*, Book Jungle) Standard Pubns., Inc.

Ozawa-de Silva, Chikako. Psychotherapy & Religion in Japan: The Japanese Introspection Practice of Naikan. 2009. 216p. pap. 39.95 *(978-0-415-54568-6(4))* Routledge.

Payne, Richard K. Discourse & Ideology in Medieval Japanese Buddhism. 2009. 272p. pap. 39.95 *(978-0-415-54445-0(9))* Routledge.

Porcu. Pure Land Buddhism in Modern Japanese Culture. 2008. (Numen Book Ser.). (Illus.). 300p. (C). *(978-90-04-16471-0(5))* BRILL.

Pussel, Ryofu. A Critical Analysis of the Buddhist 88-Temple Pilgrimage on Shikoku Island, Japan. 2010. 250p. 29.99 *(978-1-4535-3666-7(3))*; pap. 19.99 *(978-1-4535-3665-0(5))* Xlibris Corp.

Rambelli, Fabio. Buddhist Materiality: A Cultural History of Objects in Japanese Buddhism. 2007. (Asian Religions & Cultures Ser.). (ENG., Illus.). 408p. 65.00 *(978-0-8047-5682-2(1))* Stanford Univ. Pr.

Ramirez-Christensen, Esperanza, et al. Murmured Conversations: A Treatise on Poetry & Buddhism. annot. ed. 2008. (ENG.). 432p. 70.00 *(978-0-8047-4863-6(2))* Stanford Univ. Pr.

Reischauer, August Karl. Studies in Japanese Buddhism. 2009. (ENG.). 382p. 38.99 *(978-1-117-04315-9(0))*; 384p. 31.99 *(978-1-116-44380-6(5))*; 384p. pap. 32.75 *(978-1-116-44383-7(X))*; 384p. 33.99 *(978-1-116-44381-3(3))*; 384p. pap. 33.75 *(978-1-116-44382-0(1))*; 372p. 26.99 *(978-0-559-96469-5(2))*; 388p. 26.99 *(978-0-559-93054-6(2))*; 388p. pap. 20.99 *(978-0-559-93050-8(X))*; 372p. pap. 20.99 *(978-0-559-96465-7(X))* BiblioBazaar.

—Studies in Japanese Buddhism. 2009. 256p. pap. 21.42 *(978-1-150-48629-6(5))* General Bks. LLC.

—Studies in Japanese Buddhism. 2007. (ENG.). 380p. 48.95 *(978-0-548-05412-3(6))* Kessinger Publishing, LLC.

Robson, James. Buddhist Monasticism in East Asia: Places of Practice. Benn, James Alexander & Meeks, Lori R., eds. 2009. (Routledge Critical Studies in Buddhism Ser.). (ENG., Illus.). 248p. (C). 135.00 *(978-0-415-48977-5(6))* Routledge.

Rosenfield, J. M. Ch?gen, the Holy One, & the Restoration of Japanese Buddhist Art. 2008. (Japanese Visual Culture Ser.). (Illus.). 240p. *(978-90-04-16864-0(8))* BRILL.

Rowe, Mark Michael. Bonds of the Dead: Temples, Burial, & the Transformation of Contemporary Japanese Buddhism. 2011. (Buddhism & Modernity Ser.). (ENG., Illus.). 256p. 85.00 *(978-0-226-73013-4(1))*; pap. 29.00 *(978-0-226-73015-8(8))* Univ. of Chicago Pr.

Shansky, Albert. Two Trips in Search of the Buddh: A Trip Through the Inland Sea & a Walk Around the Island of Shikoku. 2008. 236p. pap. 14.49 *(978-1-4389-2175-4(6))* AuthorHouse.

Sjoquist, Douglas P. Mii-Dera: The Intersection of Buddhism & Culture in Japan. rev. ed. 2010. (ENG.). 92p. pap. 72.07 *(978-0-7575-5507-7(9))* Kendall Hunt Publishing Co.

Stone, Jacqueline I. & Walter, Mariko Namba. Death & the Afterlife in Japanese Buddhism. 2008. (Illus.). 368p. (C). 54.00 *(978-0-8248-3204-9(3))* Univ. of Hawaii Pr.

Tsang, Carol Richmond. War & Faith: Ikko Ikki in Late Muromachi Japan. 2007. (Harvard East Asian Monographs: 288). (Illus.). 275p. 39.95 *(978-0-674-02509-7(1))* Harvard Univ., Asia Ctr.

Visser, Marinus Willem de. Ancient Buddhism in Japan: Sutras & Ceremonies in Use in the Seventh & Eighth Centuries A. D. & Their History in Later Times. 2006. 850p. 110.00 *(978-1-57898-645-3(1))* Martino Publishing.

Wakabayashi, Haruko Nishioka. The Seven Tengu Scrolls: Evil & the Rhetoric of Legitimacy in Medieval Japanese Buddhism. 2012. 50.00 ***(978-0-8248-3416-6(X))*** Univ. of Hawaii Pr.

Watsuji, Tetsuro. Purifying Zen: Watsuji Tetsuro's Shamon Dogen. 2011. 55.00 *(978-0-8248-3510-1(7))*; pap. 24.00 *(978-0-8248-3556-9(5))* Univ. of Hawaii Pr.

Weiming, Tu & Ikeda, Daisaku. New Horizons in Eastern Humanism: Buddhism, Confucianism & the Quest for Global Peace. 2011. (ENG.). 264p. 50.00 *(978-1-84885-592-2(3))*; pap. 25.00 *(978-1-84885-593-9(1))* I. B. Tauris & Co., Ltd. GBR. Dist: Macmillan.

Woodard, William P. Religions in Japan: Buddhism, Shinto, Christianity. Bunce, William K., ed. 2011. 208p. 44.95 ***(978-1-258-03836-6(6))*** Literary Licensing, LLC.

BUDDHISM—KOREA

Daehaeng, Zen Master & Wisdom Publications Staff. No River to Cross: Trusting the Enlightenment That's Always Right Here. 2007. (ENG.). 144p. per. 14.95 *(978-0-86171-534-3(9))* Wisdom Pubns.

Kim, Hwansoo Ilmee. Empire of the Dharma: Korean & Japanese Buddhism, 1877-1912. 2012. (Harvard East Asian Monographs: 344). (ENG., Illus.). 350p. 39.95 ***(978-0-674-06575-8(1))*** Harvard Univ., Asia Ctr.

Kim, Yong-Tae. Choson Hugi Pulgyosa Yongu: Imje Popt'ong Kwa Kyohak Chont'ong. 2010. (KOR., Illus.). 429p. *(978-89-7668-173-7(8))* Shin-Gu Publishing Co.

McBride, Richard D. Domesticating the Dharma: Buddhist Cults & the Hwaom Synthesis in Silla Korea. 2007. (Illus.). 228p. 54.00 *(978-0-8248-3087-8(3))* Univ. of Hawaii Pr.

Mun, Chanju. Ha Dongsan & Colonial Korean Buddhism: Balancing Sectarianism & Ecumenism. 2009. pap. 40.00 *(978-0-9777553-5-6(5))* Blue Pine.

Park, Jin Y. Makers of Modern Korean Buddhism. 2010. (SUNY series in Korean Studies). 384p. 80.00 *(978-1-4384-2921-2(5))* State Univ. of New York Pr.

Park, Jin Y., ed. Makers of Modern Korean Buddhism. 2010. (SUNY series in Korean Studies). 384p. pap. 29.95 *(978-1-4384-2922-9(3))* State Univ. of New York Pr.

Park, Pori. Trial & Error in Modernist Reforms: Korean Buddhism under Colonial Rule. 2009. *(978-1-55729-094-6(6))* Univ. of California, Institute of East Asian Studies.

Park, Sung Bae. One Korean's Approach to Buddhism: The Mom/Momjit Paradigm. 2009. (SUNY Series in Korean Studies). 144p. 59.50 *(978-0-7914-7697-0(9))* State Univ. of New York Pr.

Park, Sung Bae, et al. One Korean's Approach to Buddh: The Mom/Momjit Paradigm. 2009. (SUNY Series in Korean Studies). 144p. pap. 19.95 *(978-0-7914-7698-7(7))* State Univ. of New York Pr.

Starr, Frederick. Korean Buddhism: History-Condition-Art: 3 Lectures. reprint ed. 37.50 *(978-0-404-17379-1(9))* AMS Pr., Inc.

Sunim, Kusan. The Way of Korean Zen. Fages, Martine & Batchelor, Martine, trs. from KOR. 2nd rev. ed. 2009. (ENG., Illus.). 192p. 17.95 *(978-1-59030-686-4(4),* Weatherhill, Inc.) Shambhala Pubns., Inc.

Vermeersch, Sem. The Power of the Buddhas: The Politics of Buddhism During the Koryo Dynasty (918-1392) 2008. (Harvard East Asian Monographs: 303). (Illus.). 486p. 49.95 *(978-0-674-03188-3(1))* Harvard Univ., Asia Ctr.

BUDDHISM—NEPAL

Leve, Lauren. Ethical Practice, Religious Reform, & the Buddhist Art of Living in Nepal: Seeing Things as They Are. 2013. (Routledge Critical Studies in Buddhism Ser.). (ENG.). 256p. (C). 140.00 *(978-0-415-61734-5(0))* Routledge.

Ramble, Charles. The Navel of the Demoness: Tibetan Buddhism & Civil Religion in Highland Nepal. 2007. (ENG., Illus.). 408p. 89.00 *(978-0-19-515414-6(2))* Oxford Univ. Pr., Inc.

Tuladhar-Douglas, Will. Remaking Buddhism for Medieval Nepal: The Fifteenth-Century Reformation of Newar Buddhism. 2006. (Illus.). 238p. 160.00 *(978-0-415-35919-1(8),* RU42632) Routledge.

BUDDHISM—SRI LANKA

Berkwitz, Stephen C. The History of the Buddha's Relic Shrine: A Translation of the Sinhala Thupavamsa. 2006. (ENG.). 320p. 75.00 *(978-0-19-530139-7(0))* Oxford Univ. Pr., Inc.

Blackburn, Anne M. Locations of Buddhism: Colonialism & Modernity in Sri Lanka. 2010. (Buddhism & Modernity Ser.). (ENG., Illus.). 256p. 45.00 *(978-0-226-05507-7(8))* Univ. of Chicago Pr.

Cheng, Wei-Yi. Buddhist Nuns in Taiwan & Sri Lanka: A Critique of the Feminist Perspective. 2006. (Routledge Critical Studies in Buddhism). (ENG., Illus.). 240p. (C). 170.00 *(978-0-415-39042-2(7))* Routledge.

Copleston, Reginald. Buddhism Primitive & Present in Magadha & in Ceylon. 2007. (ENG.). 316p. 45.95 *(978-0-548-05188-7(7))* Kessinger Publishing, LLC.

De Silva, Wijeyeratne. Nation, Constitutionalism & Buddhism in Sri Lanka. 2012. (Routledge Contemporary South Asia Ser.). (ENG., Illus.). 240p. (C). 145.00 *(978-0-415-46266-2(5))* Routledge.

Grant, Patrick. Buddhism & Ethnic Conflict in Sri Lanka. 2010. (SUNY series in Religious Studies). 160p. pap. 23.95 *(978-0-7914-9354-0(7),* Suny Pr.) State Univ. of New York Pr.

Grant, Patrick & GRANT, P. Buddhism & Ethnic Conflict in Sri Lanka. 2009. (SUNY series in Religious Studies). 176p. 60.00 *(978-0-7914-9353-3(9))* State Univ. of New York Pr.

Harris, Elizabeth. Theravada Buddhism & the British Encounter: Religious, Missionary & Colonial Experience in Nineteenth Century Sri Lanka. 2009. 280p. pap. 39.95 *(978-0-415-54442-9(4))* Routledge.

Harris, Elizabeth J. What Can Buddhism Offer to a Violent World? 2010. (ENG.). 192p. pap. 30.00 *(978-0-7162-0652-1(8))* Epworth Pr., The GBR. Dist: Westminster John Knox Pr.

Langer, Rita. Buddhist Rituals Death & Rebirth: Contemporary Sri Lankan Practice & Its Origins. 2007. (Illus.). 243p. 160.00 *(978-0-415-39496-3(1))* Routledge.

—Buddhist Rituals of Death & Rebirth: Contemporary Sri Lankan Practice & Its Origins. 2009. 246p. pap. 39.95 *(978-0-415-54470-2(X))* Routledge.

Ludowyk, E. F. C. The Footprint of the Buddha. 2008. (Routledge Library Editions: Buddhism Ser.). 216p. 165.00 *(978-0-415-46117-7(0))* Routledge.

Samuels, Jeffrey. Attracting the Heart: Social Relations & the Aesthetics of Emotion in Sri Lankan Monastic Culture. 2010. (C). 36.00 *(978-0-8248-3385-5(6))* Univ. of Hawaii Pr.

BUDDHISM—THAILAND

Buddhism & Postmodern Imaginings in Thailand: The Religiosity of Urban Space. 2008. 252p. 114.95 *(978-0-7546-6247-1(0))* Ashgate Publishing Co.

Darlington, Susan M. The Ordination of a Tree: The Thai Buddhist Environmental Movement. 2012. pap. ***(978-1-4384-4464-2(8))***; (ENG.). 336p. 85.00 ***(978-1-4384-4465-9(6))*** State Univ. of New York Pr.

Engel, David M. & Engel, Jaruwan S. Tort, Custom, & Karma: Globalization & Legal Consciousness in Thailand. 2010. (Cultural Lives of Law Ser.). (ENG., Illus.). 208p. 60.00 *(978-0-8047-6381-3(X))*; pap. 21.95 *(978-0-8047-6382-0(8))* Stanford Univ. Pr.

MacKenzie, Rory. New Buddhist Movements in Thailand: Towards an Understanding of Wat Phra Dhammakaya & Santi Asoke. 2007. (Routledge Critical Studies in Buddhism Ser.). (Illus.). 253p. 150.00 *(978-0-415-40869-1(5))* Routledge.

McDaniel, Justin Thomas. The Lovelorn Ghost & the Magical Monk: Practicing Buddhism in Modern Thailand. 2011. (ENG., Illus.). 384p. (gr. 17). 60.00 *(978-0-231-15376-8(7))* Columbia Univ. Pr.

Reyland, William. Sons of Isan. 2009. 150p. pap. 8.99 *(978-1-935383-64-2(7))* Raider Publishing International.

Scott, Rachelle M. Nirvana for Sale? Buddhism, Wealth, & the Dhammakaya Temple in Contemporary Thailand. 2009. (Illus.). 288p. 70.00 *(978-1-4384-2783-6(2))*; pap. 29.95 *(978-1-4384-2784-3(0))* State Univ. of New York Pr.

Skilling, Peter, et al. Past Lives of the Buddha: Wat Si Chum-Art, Architecture & Inscriptions. 2008. (ENG., Illus.). 296p. 75.00 *(978-974-9863-45-9(3))* River Bks. THA. Dist: Antique Collectors' Club.

Suriyabongs, Luang. The Buddhas' Doctrine of Truth: Dhamma & Buddhist Religion As Practiced by the Holy Brotherhood in Siam. Bunnag, Krachang, tr. reprint ed. 27.50 *(978-0-404-16870-4(1))* AMS Pr., Inc.

Terwiel, Barend Jan. Monks & Magic. 2010. (Illus.). 336p. 50.00 *(978-87-7694-065-2(9))* Nordic Institute of Asian Studies DNK. Dist: Univ. of Hawaii Pr.

Tiyavanich, Kamala. Sons of the Buddha: The Early Lives of Three Extraordinary Thai Masters. 2007. (ENG., Illus.). 304p. per. 18.95 *(978-0-86171-536-7(5))* Wisdom Pubns.

Veidlinger, Daniel M. Spreading the Dhamma: Writing, Orality, & Textual Transmission in Buddhist Northern Thailand. 2006. (Southeast Asia — Politics, Meaning, Memory Ser.). (Illus.). 259p. 54.00 *(978-0-8248-3024-3(5))* Univ. of Hawaii Pr.

BUDDHISM—TIBET

see Buddhism—China—Tibet

BUDDHISM—UNITED STATES

Cheah, Joseph. Race & Religion in American Buddhism: White Supremacy & Immigrant Adaptation, 1 vol. 2011. (Aar academy Ser.). (ENG., Illus.). 192p. 65.00 *(978-0-19-975628-5(7))* Oxford Univ. Pr., Inc.

Friedman, Michael Steven. Confessions of an American Buddhist. 2008. 284p. pap. 16.95 *(978-0-615-18033-5(7))* Friedman, Michael S.

Goddard, Dwight. Followers of Buddh: An American Brotherhood. 2011. 44p. 35.95 ***(978-1-258-02178-8(1))*** Literary Licensing, LLC.

—Followers of Buddh: An American Brotherhood. 2007. 48p. per. 9.95 *(978-1-4344-8542-7(0))* Wildside Pr., LLC.

Hayward, Jeremy. Warrior-King of Shambhala: Remembering Chöyam Trungpa. 2007. (ENG., Illus.). 476p. per. 18.95 *(978-0-86171-546-6(2))* Wisdom Pubns.

Hsüan Hua. Ten Thousand Buddhas City Accomplishes Ten Thousand Buddhas. 2006. *(978-0-88139-869-4(1))* Buddhist Text Translation Society.

Numrich, Paul, et al. Buddhists, Hindus, & Sikhs in America: A Short History. 2007. (Religion in American Life Ser.). (ENG., Illus.). 168p. per. 12.95 *(978-0-19-533311-4(X))* Oxford Univ. Pr., Inc.

Seager, Richard Hughes. Buddhism in America. 2nd rev. ed. 2012. (Columbia Contemporary American Religion Ser.). (ENG.). 384p. (gr. 17). 79.50 ***(978-0-231-15972-2(2))***; pap. 27.50 ***(978-0-231-15973-9(0))*** Columbia Univ. Pr.

Shansky, Albert. An American's Journey into Buddhism. 2008. (ENG., Illus.). 232p. pap. 19.99 *(978-0-7864-3719-1(7))* McFarland & Co., Inc. Pubs.

Storhoff, Gary. American Buddhism as a Way of Life. Whalen-Bridge, John, ed. 2010. (SUNY series in Buddhism & American Culture Ser.). 224p. 75.00 *(978-1-4384-3093-5(0))*; pap. 24.95 *(978-1-4384-3094-2(9))* State Univ. of New York Pr.

Storhoff, Gary & Whalen-Bridge, John, eds. Emergence of Buddhist American Literature. 2010. (SUNY series in Buddhism & American Culture Ser.). 272p. pap. 24.95 *(978-1-4384-2654-9(2),* Suny Pr.) State Univ. of New York Pr.

Tulku, Tarthang. A Garland of Flowers: Beauty of the Odiyan Mandala. 2008. (ENG.). 250p. pap. 24.95 *(978-0-89800-438-0(1))* Dharma Publishing.

Wilson, Jeff. Dixie Dharma: Inside a Buddhist Temple in the American South. 2012. (ENG., Illus.). 304p. 36.95 ***(978-0-8078-3545-6(5))*** Univ. of North Carolina Pr.

Zhuoma, Zhaxi. Dorje Chang Buddha III Is Living in America: Zhaxi Zhuoma Rinpoche Visits the Fifty States of America to Propagate the Buddha-Dharma. 2012. 208p. pap. 18.95 ***(978-0-915556-41-0(3))*** Great River Bks.

BUDDHISM, TANTRIC

see Tantric Buddhism

BUDDHISM AND CHRISTIANITY

see Buddhism—Relations—Christianity; Christianity and Other Religions—Buddhism

BUDDHISM AND STATE

Charney, Michael W. Powerful Learning: Buddhist Literati & the Throne in Burma's Last Dynasty, 1752-1885. 2006. (Illus.). xii, 297p. (C). *(978-0-89148-093-8(5))* Univ. of Michigan, Ctr. for South & Southeast Asian Studies.

Harris, Ian. Buddhism, Power & Political Order. 2009. 242p. pap. 39.95 *(978-0-415-54469-6(6))* Routledge.

Harris, Ian, ed. Buddhism, Power & Political Order. 2007. (Routledge Critical Studies in Buddhism Ser.). (ENG., Illus.). 248p. 160.00 *(978-0-415-41018-2(5))* Routledge.

Ives, Christopher. Imperial-Way Zen: Ichikawa Hakugen's Critique & Lingering Questions for Buddhist Ethics. 2009. (C). 52.00 *(978-0-8248-3331-2(7))* Univ. of Hawaii Pr.

Kuah, Khun Eng. State, Society, & Religious Engineering: Towards a Reformist Buddhism in Singapore. 2nd ed. 2009. (Illus.). xiv, 337p. pap. *(978-981-230-865-8(2))* Institute of Southeast Asian Studies.

Obadia. Buddhism & Modernity. 2009. (ENG.). 304p. pap. *(978-1-4051-6778-9(5),* Wiley-Blackwell) Wiley, John & Sons, Ltd.

Schober, Juliane. Modern Buddhist Conjunct. 2010. 248p. 49.00 *(978-0-8248-3382-4(1))* Univ. of Hawaii Pr.

Sorensen, Per. Rulers of the Celestial Plain: Ecclesiastic & Secular Hegemony in Medieval Tibet. A Study of Tshal Gung-thang, 2 vols. 2007. (VERoFFENTLICHUNGEN ZUR SOZIANLANTHROPOLOGIE Ser.). (ENG.). 988p. (C). 332.00 *(978-3-7001-3828-0(8))* Austrian Academy of Sciences Press AUT. Dist: Brown, David Bk. Co., The.

Soucy, Alexander. The Buddha Side: Gender, Power, & Buddhist Practice in Vietnam. 2012. 240p. 49.00 ***(978-0-8248-3598-9(0))*** Univ. of Hawaii Pr.

Vermeersch, Sem. The Power of the Buddhas: The Politics of Buddhism During the Koryo Dynasty (918-1392) 2008. (Harvard East Asian Monographs: 303). (Illus.). 486p. 49.95 *(978-0-674-03188-3(1))* Harvard Univ., Asia Ctr.

Walter, M. L. & Walter, Michael L. Buddhism & Empire: The Political & Religious Culture of Early Tibet. 2009. (Brill's Tibetan Studies Library). 400p. *(978-90-04-17584-6(9))* BRILL.

BUDDHIST ARCHITECTURE

Cunningham, Alexander. The Bhilsa Topes: or Buddhist Monuments of Central India. reprint ed. 47.50 *(978-0-404-17263-3(6))* AMS Pr., Inc.

—Mahabohdi: Or The Great Buddhist Temple under the Bohdi Tree at Buddha-Gaya. reprint ed. 28.00 *(978-0-404-17264-0(4))* AMS Pr., Inc.

Fraser-Lu, Sylvia. Splendour in Wood: The Buddhist Monasteries of Burma. 2006. (ENG., Illus.). 60.00 *(978-974-8304-16-8(7))* Orchid Pr. THA. Dist: National Bk. Network.

McCallum, Donald F. The Four Great Temples: Buddhist Archaeology, Architecture, & Icons of Seventh-Century Japan. 2008. (Illus.). 360p. (C). 40.00 *(978-0-8248-3114-1(4))* Univ. of Hawaii Pr.

Pant, Mohan & Funo, Shuji. Stupa & Swastika: Historical Urban Planning Principles in Nepal's Kathmandu Valley. 2007. (Illus.). 266p. pap. 30.00 *(978-9971-69-372-5(0))* Univ. of Hawaii Pr.

Rooney, Dawn F. Ancient Sukhothai: Thailand's Cultural Heritage. 2008. (ENG., Illus.). 220p. pap. 30.00 *(978-974-9863-42-8(9))* River Bks. THA. Dist: Antique Collectors' Club.

Sethi, Sunil. Inside Asia Box: 25 Jahre TASCHEN, 2 vols. 2011. (25 Ser.). (ENG., Illus.). 840p. 59.99 ***(978-3-8365-3176-4(3))*** TASCHEN DEU. Dist: Ingram Pub. Services.

Sin, Tae-Hyon. Uri Chol Ul Ch'ajaso: Yoksa Sok Ui Uri Sach'al Iyagi. 2010. (KOR., Illus.). 411p. *(978-89-8494-393-3(2))* Hyean Publishing Co.

Stratton, Carol. What's What in a Wat: Thai Buddhist Temples. 2010. (ENG., Illus.). 104p. pap. 16.95 *(978-974-9511-99-2(9))* Silkworm Bks. THA. Dist: Univ. of Washington Pr.

Tadgell, Christopher. The East: Buddhists, Hindus & the Sons of Heaven. 2007. (ENG., Illus.). 924p. 110.00 *(978-0-415-40752-6(4))* Routledge.

BUDDHIST ART

Agnew, Neville, ed. Ancient Sites on the Silk Road: Proceedings of the Second International Conference on the Conservation of Grotto Sites, Mogao Grottoes, Dunhuang, People's Republic of China, June 28-July 3, 2004. 2010. (ENG., Illus.). pap. 89.00 *(978-1-60606-013-1(9),* Getty Conservation Institute, The) Getty Pubns.

Arthur M. Sackler Gallery (Smithsonian Institution) Staff, contrib. by. Gods of Angkor: Bronzes from the National Museum of Cambodia. 2010. pap. *(978-0-934686-17-4(3))* Freer Gallery of Art, Smithsonian Institution.

Bartholomew, Terese Tse & Johnston, John. The Dragon's Gift: The Sacred Arts of Bhutan. 2008. (Illus.). 400p. *(978-1-932476-35-4(0))*; 390p. pap. *(978-1-932476-36-1(9))* Serindia Pubns., Inc.

Bautze-Picron, Claudine, ed. Miscellanies about the Buddha Image. 2009. (Bar S Ser.). (Illus.). 124p. (C). 70.00 *(978-1-4073-0368-0(6))* British Archaeological Reports Ltd. GBR. Dist: Brown, David Bk. Co., The.

Béguin, Gilles. Buddhist Art: An Historical & Cultural Journey. 2009. (ENG., Illus.). 400p. *(978-974-9863-87-9(9),* River Bks. Pr. Dist A C) Antique Collectors' Club.

Behrendt, Kurt A. The Art of Gandhara in the Metropolitan Museum of Art. 2007. 24.95 *(978-1-58839-224-4(4))* Metropolitan Museum of Art, The.

—The Art of Gandhara in the Metropolitan Museum of Art. 2007. (ENG., Illus.). 128p. pap. 24.95 *(978-0-300-12027-1(3))* Yale Univ. Pr.

Blau, Tatjana. Tibetan Mandalas. 2008. (ENG., Illus.). 64p. pap. 9.95 *(978-1-4027-4620-8(2))* Sterling Publishing Co., Inc.

Brancaccio, Pia. The Caves at Aurangabad: Buddhist Art in Transformation. 2010. (Brill's Indological Library: Vol. 34). (Illus.). 300p. *(978-90-04-18525-8(9))* BRILL.

Brancaccio, Pia & Behrendt, Kurt, eds. Gandharan Buddhism: Archaeology, Art, & Texts, 1 vol. 2007. (ENG., Illus.). 328p. pap. 34.95 *(978-0-7748-1081-4(5))* UBC Pr. CAN. Dist: Univ. of Washington Pr.

Brereton, Bonnie Pacala & Yencheuy, Somroay. Buddhist Murals of Northeast Thailand: Reflections of the Isan Heartland. 2010. (Mekong Press Ser.). (ENG., Illus.). 96p. pap. 35.00 *(978-616-90053-1-5(9))* Silkworm Bks. THA. Dist: Univ. of Washington Pr.

Brinker, Helmut. Secrets of the Sacred: Empowering Buddhist Images in Clear, in Code, & in Cache. 2011. (ENG., Illus.). 224p. (C). 50.00 *(978-0-295-99089-7(9))* Univ. of Washington Pr.

Buddhist Art of Tibet: Companies-Products-Services. (Illus.). 60p. (Orig.). pap. 45.00 *(978-0-7605-1691-1(X))* Rector Pr., Ltd.

Buddhist Suttas. 320p. reprint ed. 68.00 *(978-0-7222-9946-3(X))* Library Reprints, Inc.

Burgess, Jas. Buddhist Art in India. 2007. pap. ***(978-1-4067-5631-9(8))*** Read Bks.

Casey, Jane, et al. Divine Presence: Arts of India & the Himalayas. 2006. (Illus.). *(978-88-7439-022-9(X))* 5 Continents.

Coomaraswamy, Ananda Kentish. Buddhist Primitives. 2006. pap. 15.95 *(978-1-4286-8032-6(2))* Kessinger Publishing, LLC.

Cort, Louise Allison & Jett, Paul, eds. Gods of Angkor: Bronzes from the National Museum of Cambodia. 2010. (ENG., Illus.). 160p. pap. 40.00 *(978-0-295-99042-2(2))* Sackler, Arthur M. Foundation, The.

Coward, Vanessa. Zen Brush Strokes. 2011. 92p. 38.95 ***(978-1-258-06635-2(1))*** Literary Licensing, LLC.

Debreczeny, Karl. The Black Hat Eccentric: Artistic Visions of the Tenth Karmapa. 2012. (ENG., Illus.). 320p. 75.00 ***(978-0-9772131-0-8(2))*** Rubin Museum of Art.

Debreczeny, Karl, ed. The Tenth Karmapa: Tibet's Eccentric Master Revealed. 2012. (ENG.). pap. 60.00 ***(978-0-9772131-6-0(1))*** Rubin Museum of Art.

Epprecht, Katharina, ed. Kannon: Divine Compassion: Early Buddhist Art from Japan. 2007. (Reitberg Museum, Zurich Ser.). (ENG., Illus.). 196p. 50.00 *(978-3-907077-30-6(X))* Holberton, Paul Publishing GBR. Dist: Univ. of Washington Pr.

Fraser-Lu, Sylvia. Splendour in Wood: The Buddhist Monasteries of Burma. 2006. (ENG., Illus.). 60.00 *(978-974-8304-16-8(7))* Orchid Pr. THA. Dist: National Bk. Network.

Fraser, Sarah E., ed. Dunhuang: A Centennial Commemoration of the Discovery of the Cave Library. (Illus.). 188p. 49.95 *(978-7-5054-0716-9(3))* Morning Glory Pr. CHN. Dist: Art Media Resources, Inc.

Gifford, Julie. Buddhist Practice & Visual Culture. 2011. (Routledge Critical Studies in Buddhism Ser.). (ENG., Illus.). 248p. (C). 138.00 *(978-0-415-78098-8(5))* Routledge.

Glassman, Hank. The Face of Jizo: Image & Cult in Medieval Japanese Buddhism. 2012. 52.00 ***(978-0-8248-3443-2(7))***; pap. 25.00 ***(978-0-8248-3581-1(6))*** Univ. of Hawaii Pr.

Graham, Patricia Jane. Faith & Power in Japanese Buddhist Art, 1600-2005. 2007. (Illus.). 353p. (C). pap. 33.00 *(978-0-8248-3191-2(8))* Univ. of Hawaii Pr.

Gray, Basil. Buddhist Cave Paintings at Tun-Huang. 2011. 180p. 42.95 ***(978-1-258-00184-1(5))*** Literary Licensing, LLC.

Grunwedel, Albert. Buddhist Art in India. Burgess, James, ed. Gibson, Agnes C., tr. 240p. 2008. 41.95 *(978-1-4365-1611-2(0))* 2007. (ENG.). per. 26.95 *(978-0-548-74617-2(6))* Kessinger Publishing, LLC.

Gupta, S.P. Elements of Indian Art: Including Temple Architecture, Iconography & Iconometry. 2nd ed. 2007. (SAN & ENG., Illus.). xiv, 146p. *(978-81-246-0214-0(X))* D. K. Print World (P) Ltd.

Harris, Clare. The Museum on the Roof of the World: Art, Politics, & the Representation of Tibet. 2012. (Buddhism & Modernity Ser.). (Illus.). 336p. 45.00 ***(978-0-226-31747-2(1))*** Univ. of Chicago Pr.

Heller, Amy. Hidden Treasures of the Himalayas: Tibetan Manuscripts, Paintings & Sculptures of Dolpo. 2009. *(978-1-932476-44-6(X))* Serindia Pubns., Inc.

Heywood, Denise. Ancient Luang Prabang. 2009. 214p. pap. 30.00 ***(978-974-9863-66-4(6))*** River Bks. THA. Dist: Antique Collectors' Club.

Jackson, David & Jackson, Janice A. Tibetan Thangka Painting: Methods & Materials. 2006. (ENG., Illus.). 208p. pap. 39.95 *(978-1-55939-257-0(6))* Snow Lion Pubns., Inc.

Jackson, David P. Mirror of the Budda: Early Portraits from Tibet, 1 vol. 2011. (ENG., Illus.). 240p. 75.00 *(978-0-9845190-2-6(5))* Rubin Museum of Art.

Jessup, Helen Ibbitson. Masterpieces of the National Museum of Cambodia/An Introduction to the Collection: Chefs D'uvre du Musée National du Cambodge: Introduction Aux Collections. 2006. (JPN, FRE, MUL & ENG., Illus.). 112p. pap. 25.00 *(978-99950-836-0-1(4))* Friends Of Khmer Culture.

Juliano, Annette L. Buddhist Sculpture from China: Selections from the Xi'an Beilin Museum, Fifth through Ninth Centuries. Barrett, J. May Lee & Herrick, Caroline, eds. 2007. (Illus.). lib. bdg. *(978-0-9774054-2-8(7))* China Institute Gallery, China Institute in America.

Kunst- und Ausstellungshalle der Bundesrepublik De, ed. Gandhara: Das buddhistische Erbe Pakistans. Legenden, Klöster und Paradiese. 2008. (Illus.). 384p. (C). 68.00 *(978-3-8053-3916-2(X))* Zabern, Philipp von Verlag, GmbH DEU. Dist: Brown, David Bk. Co., The.

La Violette, Wesley. The Wayfarer: An Interpretation of the Dhammapada. 2011. 138p. 40.95 ***(978-1-258-06326-9(3))*** Literary Licensing, LLC.

Le May, Reginald. A Concise History of Buddhist Art in Siam. 2011. 278p. 47.95 ***(978-1-258-06111-1(2))*** Literary Licensing, LLC.

Lee, Sonya S. Surviving Nirvana: Death of the Buddha in Chinese Visual Culture. 2010. (CHI., Illus.). 372p. ***(978-988-220-744-8(8))*** Hong Kong Univ. Pr.

—Surviving Nirvana: Death of the Buddha in Chinese Visual Culture. 2010. (ENG., Illus.). 372p. (gr. 17). 55.00 *(978-962-209-125-2(3))* Hong Kong Univ. Pr. HKG. Dist: Columbia Univ. Pr.

Leidy, Denise Patry. The Art of Buddhism: An Introduction to Its History & Meaning. 2009. (ENG., Illus.). 352p. pap. 29.95 *(978-1-59030-670-3(3))* Shambhala Pubns., Inc.

Linrothe, Robert N. Holy Madness: Portraits of Tantric Siddhas. (Illus.). 480p. 150.00 *(978-1-932476-26-2(1))* Art Media Resources, Inc.

Lu, Jia, illus. Transcendent: Figurative Art by Jia Lu. 2nd ed. 2009. (ENG.). 160p. 48.00 *(978-1-60109-052-2(8),* Insight Editions) Palace Publishing Group, LP.

McCormick, Melissa & Tokyo National Museum Staff. Elegant Perfection: Masterpieces of Courtly & Religious Art from the Tokyo National Museum. 2012. (ENG., Illus.). 128p. 45.00 ***(978-0-300-17593-6(0))*** Museum of Fine Arts, Houston.

McNair, Amy. Donors of Longmen: Faith, Politics, & Patronage in Medieval Chinese Buddhist Sculpture. 2007. (Illus.). 230p. 58.00 *(978-0-8248-2994-0(8))* Univ. of Hawaii Pr.

Miles, M. R. & Yabuuchi, S. The Vision & Art of Shinjo Ito. Alinari 24 Ore Staff, ed. 2008. (ENG., Illus.). 182p. 75.00 *(978-88-6302-002-1(7),* Art Stock Bks. Ltd/Csi) Continental Sales, Inc.

Mullin, Glenn H. Buddha in Paradise: A Celebration in Himalayan Art. 2007. *(978-0-9772131-1-5(0))* Serindia Pubns., Inc.

Nbc, 1st. Indian Influence on the Art of Japan. 2009. 220p. lib. bdg. *(978-81-7211-269-1(6))* Northern Bk. Ctr.

Pal, Pratapaditya. Buddhist Art Form & Meaning. 2007. (ENG., Illus.). 132p. 66.00 *(978-81-85026-78-7(5))* Marg Pubns. IND. Dist: National Bk. Network.

Pan, An-Yi. Painting Faith: Li Gonglin & Northern Song Buddhist Culture. 2007. (Sinica Leidensia Ser.). (Illus.). 396p. *(978-90-04-16061-3(2))* BRILL.

Proser, Adriana, ed. Pilgrimage & Buddhist Art. 2010. (Illus.). 224p. 65.00 *(978-0-300-15566-2(2))* Yale Univ. Pr.

Rhie. Early Buddhist Art of China & Central Asia, Volume III: The Western Ch'in in Kansu in the Sixteen Kingdoms Period & Inter-relationships with the Buddhist Art of GandhÄra. 2010. (Handbook of Oriental Studies. Section 4 China Ser.). 1032p. *(978-90-04-18400-8(7))* BRILL.

Rhie, Marylin & Thurman, Robert. A Shrine for Tibet: The Alice S. Kandell Collection of Tibetan Sacred Art. 2010. (ENG.). 336p. (gr. 12). 60.00 *(978-1-59020-310-1(0))* Overlook Pr., The.

Rhie, Marylin M. Early Buddhist Art of China & Central Asia. 2007. *(978-90-04-16137-5(6))* BRILL.

Rhie, Marylin M. & Thurman, Robert A. F. A Shrine for Tibet: The Alice S. Kandell Collection. 2009. *(978-0-9670115-7-8(4))* Overlook Pr., The.

Rooney, Dawn F. Ancient Sukhothai: Thailand's Cultural Heritage. 2008. (ENG., Illus.). 220p. pap. 30.00 *(978-974-9863-42-8(9))* River Bks. THA. Dist: Antique Collectors' Club.

Rosenfield, J. M. Ch?gen, the Holy One, & the Restoration of Japanese Buddhist Art. 2008. (Japanese Visual Culture Ser.). (Illus.). 240p. *(978-90-04-16864-0(8))* BRILL.

Sangharakshita. The Religion of Art. 2010. (Sangharakshita Classics Ser.). (ENG.). 144p. pap. 13.95 *(978-1-899579-88-4(5))* Windhorse Pubns. GBR. Dist: Consortium Bk. Sales & Distribution.

Schroeder, Ulrich von. Empowered Masters: Tibetan Wall Paintings of Mahasiddhas at Gyantse. (Illus.). 224p. 85.00 *(978-1-932476-24-8(5))* Art Media Resources, Inc.

Servais, P. W. What Is Your Buddha? 2009. (Illus.). 200p. pap. 18.00 *(978-1-58790-159-1(5))* Regent Pr.

Tartakov, Gary Michael, ed. Dalit Art & Visual Imagery. 2012. (ENG., Illus.). 480p. 99.00 ***(978-0-19-807936-1(2))*** Oxford Univ. Pr., Inc.

Tingley, Nancy. Buddhas. 2009. 120p. 29.95 *(978-0-7649-4800-8(8))* Pomegranate Communications, Inc.

Van Ham, Peter. Heavenly Himalayas: The Murals of Mangyu & Other Discoveries in Ladakh. 2011. (Illus.). 176p. 75.00 *(978-3-7913-4543-7(5))* Prestel Publishing.

Verlag, Hirmer & Hirmer Verlag. Tibet: Kloester oeffnen ihre Schatzkammern. 2006. (GER., Illus.). 664p. (C). pap. 63.00 *(978-3-7774-3115-4(X))* Hirmer Verlag GmbH DEU. Dist: Brown, David Bk. Co., The.

Verma, Archana. Cultural & Visual Flux at Early Historical Bagh in Central India. 2007. (Bar S Ser.). (ENG., Illus.). 76p. (C). pap. 62.50 *(978-1-4073-0151-8(9))* British Archaeological Reports Ltd. GBR. Dist: Brown, David Bk. Co., The.

Vincent, Irene Vongehr. The Sacred Oasis: Caves of the Thousand Buddhas, Tun Huang. 2011. 184p. 42.95 ***(978-1-258-00529-0(8))*** Literary Licensing, LLC.

Yoshizawa, Katsuhiro. The Religious Art of Zen Master Hakuin. 2009. (ENG., Illus.). 256p. 26.00 *(978-1-58243-454-4(9),* Counterpoint Pr.) Basic Bks. GBR. Dist: Perseus-PGW.

BUDDHIST CHANTS

Davids, Carolina A. Psalms of the Early Buddhists, 2 vols., Set. reprint ed. 67.50 *(978-0-404-17590-0(2))* AMS Pr., Inc.

Okumura, Shohaku. Living by Vow: A Practical Introduction to Eight Essential Zen Chants & Texts. 2012. (ENG.). 320p. pap. 18.95 ***(978-1-61429-010-0(5))*** Wisdom Pubns.

Parallax Press Staff. Chanting from the Heart: Buddhist Ceremonies & Daily Practices. 2006. (ENG., Illus.). 360p. pap. 26.95 *(978-1-888375-63-3(9))* Parallax Pr.

BUDDHIST CONVERTS

Eddy, Glenys. Becoming Buddhist: Experiences of Socialization & Self-Transformation in Australian Buddhist Centres. 2012. (ENG.). 288p. 120.00 ***(978-1-4411-1846-2(2))*** Continuum International Publishing Group, Ltd. GBR. Dist: National Bk. Network.

Lienau-Purnell, Amanda. Converts to Buddhism - Interpersonal & Worldview Shifts. 2007. 160p. per. *(978-3-8364-2718-0(4))* VDM Verlag Dr. Mueller e.K.

Rosenzweig, Rosie. A Jewish Mother in Shangri-La. Date not set. 192p. pap. 13.95 *(978-1-57062-459-9(3))* Shambhala Pubns., Inc.

BUDDHIST CONVERTS FROM JUDAISM

Kamenetz, Rodger. The Jew in the Lotus: A Poet's Rediscovery of Jewish Identity in Buddhist India. 2007. (Plus Ser.). (ENG.). 320p. pap. 14.99 *(978-0-06-136739-7(7),* HarperOne) HarperCollins Pubs.

BUDDHIST DOCTRINES

see Buddhism—Doctrines

BUDDHIST GODS

Blofeld, John. Bodhisattva of Compassion: The Mystical Tradition of Kuan Yin. 2009. (Shambhala Classics Ser.). (ENG., Illus.). 160p. pap. 16.95 *(978-1-59030-735-9(6))* Shambhala Pubns., Inc.

Diman, Paz & Serrats, Marta. BUDDHAS, 1 vol. 2010. (FRE, DUT, GER & ENG., Illus.). 480p. pap. 14.95 *(978-94-6065-037-6(6))* booQs Publishers bvba BEL. Dist: Innovative Logistics.

Glassman, Hank. The Face of Jizo: Image & Cult in Medieval Japanese Buddhism. 2012. 52.00 ***(978-0-8248-3443-2(7))***; pap. 25.00 ***(978-0-8248-3581-1(6))*** Univ. of Hawaii Pr.

Hang Trng. Ia Tang Sám: Dizang Chan = Bowing to the Earth Treasury Enlightening Being. 2010. (VIE., Illus.). 101p. pap. ***(978-0-9844419-3-8(X))*** Compassionate Service Society.

Idema, W. L., intro. Personal Salvation & Filial Piety: Two Precious Scroll Narratives of Guanyin & Her Acolytes. 2008. (Classics in East Asian Buddhism Ser.). 256p. (C). 52.00 *(978-0-8248-3215-5(9))* Univ. of Hawaii Pr.

Ng, Zhiru. The Making of a Savior Bodhisattva: Dizang in Medieval China. 2007. (Studies in East Asian Buddhism Ser.). (Illus.). 305p. 52.00 *(978-0-8248-3045-8(8))* Univ. of Hawaii Pr.

Ngaosrivathana, Mayoury & Ngaosrivathana, Pheuiphanh. The Enduring Sacred Landscape of the Naga. 2009. (ENG., Illus.). 156p. (C). pap. 25.00 ***(978-974-303-160-1(X))*** Silkworm Bks. THA. Dist: Univ. of Washington Pr.

Rinpoche, Khenchen Palden. The Dark Red Amulet: Oral Instructions on the Practice of Vajrakilaya. 2009. (ENG., Illus.). 160p. pap. 16.95 *(978-1-55939-311-9(4))* Snow Lion Pubns., Inc.

Rinpoche, Tulku Urgyen, et al. Skillful Grace: Tara Practice for Our Times. 2007. (ENG., Illus.). 192p. pap. 15.95 *(978-962-7341-61-1(4))* North Atlantic Bks.

Schenker, Daniela. Kuan Yin: Accessing the Power of the Divine Feminine. 2007. (Illus.). 160p. 22.95 *(978-1-59179-621-3(0),* BK01187) Sounds True, Inc.

Schroeder, Ulrich von. 108 Buddhist Statues in Tibet: Evolution of Tibetan Sculptures. 2008. (Illus.). 212p. *(978-1-932476-38-5(5))* Serindia Pubns., Inc.

Shaw, Miranda. Buddhist Goddesses of India. 2006. (ENG., Illus.). 602p. 35.00 *(978-0-691-12758-3(1))* Princeton Univ. Pr.

Sponberg, Alan & Hardacre, Helen, eds. Maitreya, the Future Buddha. 2011. (ENG.). 320p. pap. 39.99 *(978-0-521-18010-8(4))* Cambridge Univ. Pr.

Sumali Mahanarongchai. Phrachinnaphuttha Ha Phraong: Phraphutthachao Nai Rup Kaithip Tam Khati Khong Mahayan Læ Watcharayan. 2nd ed. 2009. (THA., Illus.). 13p. *(978-611-7080-00-5(X))* Pum Thai Food Chain Co., Ltd.

Suzuki, Daisetz Teitaro. Manual of Zen Buddhism. 2007. pap. 9.99 *(978-1-59986-934-6(9))* Filiquarian Publishing, LLC.

Vessantara. A Guide to the Buddhas. 2008. (Meeting the Buddhas Ser.). (ENG., Illus.). 192p. per. 18.95 *(978-1-899579-83-9(4))* Windhorse Pubns. GBR. Dist: Consortium Bk. Sales & Distribution.

Vessantara (Tony McMahon). A Guide to the Bodhisattvas. 2008. (Meeting the Buddhas Ser.). (ENG., Illus.). 160p. pap. 18.95 *(978-1-899579-84-6(2))* Windhorse Pubns. GBR. Dist: Consortium Bk. Sales & Distribution.

Vessantara, Tony, et al. A Guide to the Deities of the Tantra. 2008. (Meeting the Buddhas Ser.). (ENG., Illus.). 176p. pap. 18.95 *(978-1-899579-85-3(0))* Windhorse Pubns. GBR. Dist: Consortium Bk. Sales & Distribution.

Woodward, Hiram W. The Sacred Sculpture of Thailand: The Alexander B. Griswold Collection, the Walters Art Gallery. (Illus.). 328p. *(978-0-500-97457-5(8))* Thames & Hudson.

Yeshe, Lama. Universal Love: The Yoga Method of Buddha Maitreya. Ribush, Nicholas, ed. 2008. (Illus.). 149p. pap. 15.00 *(978-1-891868-19-1(5))* Lama Yeshe Wisdom Archive.

BUDDHIST ETHICS

Clairmont, David A. Moral Struggle & Religious Ethics: On the Person as Classic in Comparative Theological Contexts. 2011. (ENG., Illus.). 256p. 109.95 *(978-1-4443-3682-5(7),* Wiley-Blackwell) Wiley, John & Sons, Inc.

Clayton, Barbra R. Moral Theory in Santideva's Siksasamuccaya. 2010. 182p. pap. 39.95 ***(978-0-415-59935-1(0))*** Routledge.

Goodman, Charles. Consequences of Compassion: An Interpretation & Defense of Buddhist Ethics. 2009. (ENG.). 304p. 74.00 *(978-0-19-537519-0(X))* Oxford Univ. Pr., Inc.

Hansen, Anne Ruth. How to Behave: Buddhism & Modernity in Colonial Cambodia, 1860-1930. 2007. (Southeast Asia: Politics, Meaning & Memory Ser.). (Illus.). 254p. 60.00 *(978-0-8248-3032-8(6))* Univ. of Hawaii Pr.

Harris, Elizabeth J. What Can Buddhism Offer to a Violent World? 2010. (ENG.). 192p. pap. 30.00 *(978-0-7162-0652-1(8))* Epworth Pr., The GBR. Dist: Westminster John Knox Pr.

Hershock, Peter D. Valuing Diversity: Buddhist Reflection on Realizing a More Equitable Global Future. 2012. (ENG.). 368p. 90.00 ***(978-1-4384-4459-8(1))*** State Univ. of New York Pr.

Ives, Christopher. Imperial-Way Zen: Ichikawa Hakugen's Critique & Lingering Questions for Buddhist Ethics. 2009. (C). 52.00 *(978-0-8248-3331-2(7))* Univ. of Hawaii Pr.

Loori, John Daido. The Heart of Being: Moral & Ethical Teachings of Zen Buddhism. 2nd ed. 2009. xxv, 237p. pap. *(978-1-882795-22-2(9))* Dharma Communications.

—The Way of Mountains & Rivers: Teachings on Zen & the Environment with Commentary on Zen Master Dogen's Mountains & Rivers Sutra. 2009. xii, 133p. *(978-1-882795-21-5(0))* Dharma Communications.

Madden, Ross McLauran. The Three Poisons: A Buddhist Guide to Resolving Conflict. 2010. (ENG & SPA.). 280p. 25.99 *(978-1-4389-8812-2(5))*; pap. 17.95 *(978-1-4389-8811-5(7))* AuthorHouse.

Mrozik, Susanne. Virtuous Bodies: The Physical Dimensions of Morality in Buddhist Ethics. 2007. (ENG.). 192p. 65.00 *(978-0-19-530500-5(0))* Oxford Univ. Pr., Inc.

Park, Jin. Buddhism & Postmodernity: Zen, Huayan, & the Possibility of Buddhist Postmodern Ethics. 2010. (ENG.). 296p. pap. 32.95 *(978-0-7391-1824-5(2))* Lexington Bks.

Park, Jin Y. Buddhism & Postmodernity: Zen, Huayan, & the Possibility of Buddhist Postmodern Ethics. 2008. (ENG.). 338p. 83.99 *(978-0-7391-1823-8(4))* Lexington Bks.

Prasad, H. Buddhist Aesthetics & Ethics. 2011. 301p. pap. 35.00 ***(978-81-7533-348-2(0))*** M. D. Pubns. Pvt, Ltd. IND. Dist: Coronet Bks.

—Buddhist Metaphysics & Ethics. 2011. 303p. pap. 35.00 ***(978-81-7533-351-2(0))*** M. D. Pubns. Pvt, Ltd. IND. Dist: Coronet Bks.

Sangharakshita. Living Ethically: Advice from Nagarjuna's Precious Garland. 2009. (Buddhist Wisdom for Today Ser.). (ENG.). 224p. pap. 19.95 *(978-1-899579-86-0(9))* Windhorse Pubns. GBR. Dist: Consortium Bk. Sales & Distribution.

Srivastava, M. Buddhism & Ethics. 2011. 269p. pap. 35.00 ***(978-81-7533-349-9(9))*** M. D. Pubns. Pvt, Ltd. IND. Dist: Coronet Bks.

Thompson, Ross. Wounded Wisdom: A Buddhist & Christian Response to Evil, Hurt & Harm. 2011. (ENG.). 348p. pap. 26.95 *(978-1-84694-597-7(6))* Hunt, John Publishing Ltd. GBR. Dist: National Bk. Network.

Trungpa, Chögyam. Meditation in Action. 40th ed. 2010. (ENG.). 112p. pap. 14.00 *(978-1-59030-876-9(X))* Shambhala Pubns., Inc.

Wilson, Jeff. Buddhism of the Heart: Reflections on Shin Buddhism & Inner Togetherness. 2009. (ENG.). 176p. pap. 16.95 *(978-0-86171-583-1(7))* Wisdom Pubns.

Wright, Dale. The Six Perfections: Buddhism & the Cultivation of Character. 2011. (ENG.). 304p. pap. 19.95 ***(978-0-19-989579-3(1))*** Oxford Univ. Pr., Inc.

Wright, Dale S. The Six Perfections: Buddhism & the Cultivation of Character. 2009. (ENG.). 304p. 27.95 *(978-0-19-538201-3(3))* Oxford Univ. Pr., Inc.

Yun, Hsing. Being Good: Buddhist Ethics for Everyday Life. Graham, Tom, tr. 2nd ed. 2009. 195p. pap. 15.95 *(978-1-932293-34-0(5))* Buddha's Light Publishing.

BUDDHIST LEGENDS

Burlingame, Eugene Watson. Buddhist Parables. 2009. (ENG.). 379p. 38.99 *(978-1-117-53702-3(1))*; pap. 32.75 *(978-1-117-53703-0(X))* BiblioBazaar.

Burnouf, Eugene. Legends of Indian Buddhism. 2007. 128p. 35.95 *(978-0-548-11234-2(7))* Kessinger Publishing, LLC.

Campany, Robert Ford & Wang, Yan. Signs from the Unseen Realm: Buddhist Miracle Tales from Early Medieval China. 2012. 55.00 ***(978-0-8248-3602-3(2))*** Univ. of Hawaii Pr.

Dhammapadatthakatha. Buddhist Legends, 3 vols., Set. Burlingame, Eugene W., tr. from PLI. reprint ed. 105.00 *(978-0-404-17610-5(0))* AMS Pr., Inc.

Goto, Akio. Kongoji-Bon "Sanbo Kanno Yoryakuroku" No Kenkyu/Osaka Daigaku Sanbo Kanno Roryakuroku Kenkyukai Hen; Goto Akio Kanshu. 2007. (CHI & JPN., Illus.). 262p. *(978-4-585-03174-1(X))* Bensei Shuppan.

Li, Mingjing. Nihon Bukkyo Setsuwashu No Genryu. 2007. (JPN.). vii, 334p. *(978-4-585-10433-9(X))* Bensei Shuppan.

Stephens, Winifred. Legends of Indian Buddhism. 2008. 132p. pap. *(978-1-4437-0361-1(3))* Read Bks.

Zhang, Qingnian, tr. & compiled by. Buddhist Parables. 2007. (CHI & ENG.). 294p. pap. *(978-1-921099-28-1(3))* Asia-pacific Multiculture Publishing Development Pty Ltd.

BUDDHIST LITERATURE

see also Buddhism—Sacred Books

Appleton, Naomi. Jataka Stories in Theravada Buddhism: Narrating the Bodhisatta Path. 2010. (Illus.). 186p. 89.95 *(978-1-4094-1092-8(7))* Ashgate Publishing Co.

Arya Vimuktisena, et al. Abhisamayalamkara with Vrtti & Aloka - Vol. 2, Vol. 2. Sparham, Gareth, tr. from SAN. 2008. 360p. 90.00 *(978-0-89581-992-5(9))* Jain Publishing Company, Inc.

Beal, Samuel. Abstract of Four Lectures on Buddhist Li. 2006. pap. 24.95 *(978-1-4286-5080-0(6))* Kessinger Publishing, LLC.

Buddhaghosa. The Atthasalini, Buddhaghosa's Commentary on the Dhammasangani. Muller, Edward, ed. reprint ed. 39.50 *(978-0-404-17245-9(8))* AMS Pr., Inc.

—Buddhaghosa's Parables. Rogers, T., tr. from BUR. reprint ed. 37.50 *(978-0-404-17246-6(6))* AMS Pr., Inc.

—Expositor — Atthasalini, 2 vols. in 1. Maung Tin, tr. rev. ed. reprint ed. 49.50 *(978-0-404-17247-3(4))* AMS Pr., Inc.

Conze, Edward, et al, eds. Buddhist Texts Through the Ages. 2010. 326p. pap. 24.76 *(978-1-162-91737-5(7))* Kessinger Publishing, LLC.

Dahlke, Paul. Buddhist Essays. Silicara, Bhikkhu, tr. from GER. reprint ed. 37.50 *(978-0-404-17266-4(0))* AMS Pr., Inc.

—Buddhist Essays. 2009. 190p. pap. 19.99 *(978-1-150-54475-0(9))* General Bks. LLC.

—Buddhist Essays. Silacara, Bhikkhu, tr. 376p. 2010. 39.16 *(978-1-163-43383-6(7))* 2007. (ENG.). 48.95 *(978-0-548-12673-8(9))* Kessinger Publishing, LLC.

—Buddhist Essays. 2006. (ENG.). pap. 33.95 *(978-1-4286-3665-1(X))* Kessinger Publishing, LLC.

D'Amato, Mario. Distinguishing the Middle from the Extremes: A Study & Annotated Translation of the Madhyantavibhaga, along with Its Commentary, the Madhyantavibhaga-Bhasya. 2012. (ENG.). 240p. (gr. 17). 36.00 *(978-1-935011-05-7(7))* American Institute of Buddhist Studies.

Davids, T. W. Dialogues of the Buddha, 3 vols. reprint ed. 375.00 *(978-0-7222-2107-5(X))* Library Reprints, Inc.

Die Ihan kar Ma: Ein fruher Katalog der ins Tibetische ubersetzten buddhistischen Texte. Kritische Neuausgabe mit Einleitung und Materialienby Adelheid Herrmmann-Pfandt. 2008. (Denkschriften der Phil-Klasse Ser.). 531p. (C). pap. 144.00 *(978-3-7001-6041-0(0))* Austrian Academy of Sciences Press AUT. Dist: Brown, David Bk. Co., The.

Dnul-Chu Dharmabhadra, et al. Source of Supreme Bliss: Heruka Chakrasamvara Five Deity Practice & Commentary. 2010. (Illus.). x, 228p. *(978-1-55939-365-2(3))* Snow Lion Pubns., Inc.

Easwaran, Eknath, tr. from PLI. & intro. The Dhammapada. 2nd ed. 2007. (ENG.). 256p. per. 10.95 *(978-1-58638-020-5(6))* Nilgiri Pr.

Eubanks, Charlotte. Miracles of Book & Body: Buddhist Textual Culture & Medieval Japan. 2010. (Buddhisms Ser.). (Illus.). 275p. 49.95 *(978-0-520-26561-5(0))* Univ. of California Pr.

Evans, D. W. The Buddha Digest: Modern Transcriptions of Pali Texts. 2010. (ENG., Illus.). 238p. pap. *(978-1-85756-741-0(2))* Janus Publishing Co.

Flores, Ralph. Buddhist Scriptures as Literature: Sacred Rhetoric & the Uses of Theory. 2009. 232p. pap. 24.95 *(978-0-7914-7340-5(6))* State Univ. of New York Pr.

Franklin, J. Jeffrey. The Lotus & the Lion: Buddhism & the British Empire. 2008. 288p. 36.95 *(978-0-8014-4730-3(5))* Cornell Univ. Pr.

Gill, John & Tidwell, Susan, eds. After Many Autumns: A Collection of Chinese Buddhist Literature. Balcom, John, tr. from CHI. 2011. (CHI & ENG.). 383p. pap. 15.95 *(978-1-932293-49-4(3))* Buddha's Light Publishing.

Hanh, Thich Nhat. Thundering Silence: Sutra on Knowing the Better Way to Catch a Snake. 2nd rev. ed. 2009. (ENG.). 80p. pap. 12.95 *(978-1-888375-98-5(1))* Parallax Pr.

Jamspal, Lozang & Jamspal, L. The Range of the Bodhisattve: The Teachings of the Nirgrantha Satyaka. 2011. (ENG.). 536p. (gr. 17). 49.00 *(978-1-935011-07-1(3))* American Institute of Buddhist Studies.

Jigs-med-bstan-pai-ñi-Ma, et al. Key to the Precious Treasury: A Concise Commentary on the General Meaning of the Glorious Secret Essence Tantra Entitled Key to the Precious Treasury. 2010. *(978-1-55939-351-5(3))* Snow Lion Pubns., Inc.

Kha Pa, Tsong. Golden Garland of Eloquence - Vol. 1 Vol. 1: Legs Bshad Gser Phreng. Kha Pa, Tsong & Sparham, Gareth, trs. from TIB. 2008. 696p. 150.00 *(978-0-89581-865-2(5))* Jain Publishing Company, Inc.

—Golden Garland of Eloquence - Vol. 2 Vol. 2: Legs Bshad Gser Phreng. Sparham, Gareth, tr. 2008. 230p. 75.00 *(978-0-89581-866-9(3))* Jain Publishing Company, Inc.

Kimbrough, R. Keller. Preachers, Poets, Women, & the Way: Izumi Shikibu & the Buddhist Literature of Medieval Japan. 2008. (Illus.). 374p. 75.00 *(978-1-929280-47-6(5))*; (ENG., pap. 29.00 *(978-1-929280-48-3(3))* Univ. of Michigan, Ctr. for Japanese Studies.

Kuan, Tse-fu. Mindfulness in Early Buddhism: New Approaches Through Psychology & Textual Analysis of Pali, Chinese & Sanskrit Sources. 2008. (Routledge Critical Studies in Buddhism Ser.). (ENG., Illus.). 256p. (C). 160.00 *(978-0-415-43737-0(7))* Routledge.

Lenz, Timothy. Gandharan Avadanas: British Library Kharosthi Fragments 1-3 & 21 & Supplementary Fragments A-C. 2010. (Gandharan Buddhist Texts, Volume 6 Ser.). (SAN & ENG., Illus.). 192p. 85.00 *(978-0-295-99013-2(9))* Univ. of Washington Pr.

Lopez, Donald S., Jr., ed. Religions of Tibet in Practice. abr. ed. 2007. (Princeton Readings in Religions Ser.). (ENG.). 440p. (C). per. 28.95 *(978-0-691-12972-3(X))* Princeton Univ. Pr.

Nance, Richard F. Speaking for Buddhas: Scriptural Commentary in Indian Buddhism. 2011. (ENG., Illus.). 312p. (gr. 17). 55.00 ***(978-0-231-15230-3(2))*** Columbia Univ. Pr.

Nariman, Gushtaspshah K. Literary History of Sanskrit Buddhism. reprint ed. 37.50 *(978-0-404-17356-2(X))* AMS Pr., Inc.

Ohnuma, Reiko. Ties That Bind: Maternal Imagery & Discourse in Indian Buddhism. 2012. (ENG.). 288p. pap. 35.00 ***(978-0-19-991567-5(9))***; (Illus.). 99.00 ***(978-0-19-991565-1(2))*** Oxford Univ. Pr., Inc.

Peacock, John. The Tibetan Way of Life, Death & Rebirth: The Illustrated Guide to Tibetan Wisdom. 2009. (ENG., Illus.). 144p. pap. *(978-1-84483-804-2(8))* Duncan Baird Pubs. GBR. Dist: Sterling Publishing Co., Inc.

Pinault, Georges. Chrestomathie Tokharienne: Textes et Grammaire. 2008. (Collection linguistique de la Societe de linguistique de Paris Ser.). (FRE.). 692p. (C). pap. 109.00 *(978-90-429-2168-9(4))* Peeters Pubs. & Booksellers BEL. Dist: Brown, David Bk. Co., The.

Powers, John. A Bull of a Man: Images of Masculinity, Sex, & the Body in Indian Buddhism. (Illus.). 336p. 2012. (ENG.). pap. 22.50 ***(978-0-674-06403-4(8))*** 2009. 47.50 *(978-0-674-03329-0(9))* Harvard Univ. Pr.

Saunders, Kenneth J., ed. The Heart of Buddhism: Being an Anthology of Buddhist Verse. reprint ed. 32.50 *(978-0-404-17377-7(2))* AMS Pr., Inc.

Saunders, Kenneth J., tr. The Heart of Buddhism: Being an Anthology of Buddhist Verse. 2007. (ENG.). 108p. 34.95 *(978-0-548-09477-8(2))* Kessinger Publishing, LLC.

Schaeffer, Kurtis R. The Culture of the Book in Tibet. 2009. (ENG.). 264p. (gr. 17). 45.00 *(978-0-231-14716-3(3))* Columbia Univ. Pr.

Schlingloff, Dieter, et al. From Turfan to Ajanta: Festschrift for Dieter Schlingloff on the Occasion of His Eightieth Birthday, 2 vols. 2010. (ENG & GER., Illus.). 1136p. (C). pap. 252.00 *(978-9937-553-02-5(4))* Lumbini International Research Institute NPL. Dist: Brown, David Bk. Co., The.

Shankman, Richard. The Experience of Samadhi: An In-Depth Exploration of Buddhist Meditation. 2008. (ENG.). 240p. pap. 18.95 *(978-1-59030-521-8(3))* Shambhala Pubns., Inc.

Silk, Jonathan A. Managing Monks: Administrators & Administrative Roles in Indian Buddhist Monasticism. 2008. (South Asia Research Ser.). (TIB, CHI, SAN, PLI & ENG.). 320p. 65.00 *(978-0-19-532684-0(9))* Oxford Univ. Pr., Inc.

—Riven by Lust: Incest & Schism in Indian Buddhist Legend & Historiography. 2008. (Illus.). 376p. (C). 57.00 *(978-0-8248-3090-8(3))* Univ. of Hawaii Pr.

Sobisch, Jan-Ulrich. Hevajra & Lam bras Literature of India & Tibet as Seen Through the Eyes of A-mes-zhab. 2008. (Contributions to Tibetan Studies). (GER, TIB & ENG., Illus.). 264p. (C). 116.00 *(978-3-89500-652-4(1))* Reichert, Ludwig Dr. DEU. Dist: Brown, David Bk. Co., The.

Stein, R. A. & McKeown, Arthur P. Rolf Stein's Tibetica Antiqua: With Additional Materials. 2010. 388p. *(978-90-04-18338-4(8))* BRILL.

Tongguk Taehakkyo, Pusol Han'guk Munhak Yon'guso Staff, contrib. by. Pulga Ui Kul Ssugi Wa Pulgyo Munhak Ui Kanungsong. 2010. 341p. *(978-89-7801-259-1(0))* Dong-guk Univ. Pr.

Waley, Arthur, tr. The Temple, & Other Poems. reprint ed. 31.50 *(978-0-404-17407-1(8))* AMS Pr., Inc.

Wonhyo & Kim, Ho-Gwi. Kumgang Sammaegyong Non. 2010. (KOR.). 537p. *(978-89-26-81439-0(4))* Korean Studies Information Co., Ltd.

Woodward, F. L., tr. from PLI. Buddhist Stories. reprint ed. 31.50 *(978-0-404-17414-9(0))* AMS Pr., Inc.

Wynne, Alexander. The Origin of Buddhist Meditation. 2009. 174p. pap. 39.95 *(978-0-415-54467-2(X))* 2007. 169p. 160.00 *(978-0-415-42387-8(2))* Routledge.

Yixuan & Kirchner, Thomas Yuho. The Record of Linji. 2008. (Nanzan Library of Asian Religion & Culture). (Illus.). xxxii, 485p. pap. 27.00 *(978-0-8248-3319-0(8))*; (CHI., 494p. (C). 55.00 *(978-0-8248-2821-9(6))* Univ. of Hawaii Pr.

BUDDHIST LOGIC

Eltschinger, Vincent & Dharmakirti. Penser L'autorité des écritures: La Polemique de Dharmakirti Contre la Notion Brahmanique Orthodoxe D'un Veda Sans Auteur: Autour de Pramanavarttika I.213-268 et Svavrtti. 2007. (Beitrage zur Kultur- und Geistesgeschichte Asiens Ser.). (TIB, FRE & GER.). 652p. (C). pap. 83.00 *(978-3-7001-3782-5(6))* Austrian Academy of Sciences Press AUT. Dist: Brown, David Bk. Co., The.

Franco, Eli, et al, eds. Religion & Logic in Buddhist Philosophical Analysis. 2012. (Denkschriften der philosophisch-historischen Klasse Ser.). (ENG.). 521p. (C). 104.00 ***(978-3-7001-7000-6(9))*** Austrian Academy of Sciences Press AUT. Dist: Brown, David Bk. Co., The.

Koster, Frits. Buddhist Meditation in Stress Management. Oosterhoff, Marjo, tr. from DUT. 2008. (ENG., Illus.). 199p. pap. 21.00 *(978-974-9511-29-9(8))* Silkworm Bks. THA. Dist: Univ. of Washington Pr.

McCrea, Lawrence J., et al. Buddhist Philosophy of Language in India: Jnanasrimitra on Exclusion. 2010. (SAN & ENG.). 216p. (gr. 17). 82.50 *(978-0-231-15094-1(6))*; pap. 27.50 *(978-0-231-15095-8(4))* Columbia Univ. Pr.

Nagatomo, Shigenori. The Diamondsutra¿s¿ Logic of Not And a Critique of Katz¿s Contextualism: Toward a Non-Dualist Philosophy. 2006. 196p. 99.95 *(978-0-7734-5807-9(7))* Mellen, Edwin Pr., The.

Rogers, Katherine. Tibetan Logic. 2009. (SAN & ENG.). 528p. pap. 39.95 *(978-1-55939-315-7(7))* Snow Lion Pubns., Inc.

Siderits, Mark, et al, eds. Apoha: Buddhist Nominalsim & Human Cognition. 2011. (ENG.). 344p. (gr. 17). 89.50 *(978-0-231-15360-7(0))*; pap. 29.50 *(978-0-231-15361-4(9))* Columbia Univ. Pr.

BUDDHIST MONASTICISM AND RELIGIOUS ORDERS

see also Koen

Benn, James A., et al. Images, Relics, & Legends. 2010. 350p. pap. 25.00 *(978-0-88962-909-7(9))* Mosaic Pr.

Chen, Huaiyu. The Revival of Buddhist Monasticism. 2007. 252p. (C). 71.95 *(978-0-8204-8624-6(8))* Lang, Peter Publishing, Inc.

Claussen, M. A. The Reform of the Frankish Church: Chrodegang of Metz & the Regula canonicorum in the Eighth Century. 2008. (Cambridge Studies in Medieval Life & Thought). (ENG., Illus.). 364p. pap. 42.00 *(978-0-521-06537-5(2))* Cambridge Univ. Pr.

De Visser, Marinus W. The Arhats in China & Japan. reprint ed. 34.50 *(978-0-404-17406-4(X))* AMS Pr., Inc.

Harrison, Peter. Fortress Monasteries of the Himalayas: Tibet, Ladakh, Nepal & Bhutan. 2011. (Fortress Ser.). (ENG., Illus.). 64p. pap. 18.95 *(978-1-84908-396-6(7))* Osprey Publishing, Ltd. GBR. Dist: Random Hse., Inc.

Kim, Sunghae & Heisig, James W., eds. Monasticism, Buddhist, & Christian: The Korean Experience. 2008. 206p. pap. 45.00 *(978-0-8028-6375-1(2))* Eerdmans, William B. Publishing Co.

Lempert, Michael. Discipline & Debate: The Language of Violence in a Tibetan Buddhist Monastery. 2012. (ENG.). 238p. 65.00 ***(978-0-520-26946-0(2))***; pap. 26.95 ***(978-0-520-26947-7(0))*** Univ. of California Pr.

Matsuo, Kenji. A History of Japanese Buddhism. 2008. (Illus.). 264p. *(978-1-905246-41-0(2))*; (ENG., per. *(978-1-905246-59-5(5))* BRILL.

Meeks, Lori Rachelle. Hokkeji & the Reemergence of Female Monasticism in Premodern Japan. 2010. (C). 50.00 *(978-0-8248-3394-7(5))* Univ. of Hawaii Pr.

Merritt, Jane Hamilton. A Meditators Diary. 2012. (ENG., Illus.). 160p. pap. 15.95 ***(978-0-285-64079-5(8))*** Souvenir Pr. Ltd. GBR. Dist: Independent Pubs. Group.

Mills, Martin A. Identity Ritual & State in Tibetan Buddhism. 2010. (ENG.). 426p. pap. 39.95 *(978-0-415-59138-6(4))* Routledge.

Monasticism. 4.95 *(978-81-7120-359-8(0))* Sri Ramakrishna Math IND. Dist: Vedanta Pr.

Okumura, Shohaku, tr. from JPN. Dogen's Extensive Record: A Translation of the Eihei Koroku. 2010. (ENG.). 824p. pap. 26.95 *(978-0-86171-670-8(1))* Wisdom Pubns.

Robson, James. Buddhist Monasticism in East Asia: Places of Practice. Benn, James Alexander & Meeks, Lori R., eds. 2009. (Routledge Critical Studies in Buddhism Ser.). (ENG., Illus.). 248p. (C). 135.00 *(978-0-415-48977-5(6))* Routledge.

Schlagintweit, Emil. Buddhism in Tibet Illustrated by Literar. 2006. pap. 38.95 *(978-1-4286-4999-6(9))* Kessinger Publishing, LLC.

Schroeder, Ulrich von. 108 Buddhist Statues in Tibet: Evolution of Tibetan Sculptures. 2008. (Illus.). 212p. *(978-1-932476-38-5(5))* Serindia Pubns., Inc.

Silk, Jonathan A. Managing Monks: Administrators & Administrative Roles in Indian Buddhist Monasticism. 2008. (South Asia Research Ser.). (TIB, CHI, SAN, PLI & ENG.). 320p. 65.00 *(978-0-19-532684-0(9))* Oxford Univ. Pr., Inc.

Skudlarek, William. Demythologizing Celibacy. 2008. 120p. pap. 14.95 *(978-0-8146-2947-5(4)*, Liturgical Pr. Bks.) Liturgical Pr.

Suzuki, Daisetz Teitaro. Manual of Zen Buddhism. 2011. 164p. pap. 15.99 ***(978-1-61279-056-5(9))*** Publishing in Motion.

Suzuki, Daisetz Teitaro. The Zen Monk's Life. 2006. 148p. per. 13.95 *(978-1-59654-372-0(8))* Disruptive Publishing.

Swami Shri P. Autobiography of an Indian Monk. 20.00 *(978-81-215-0547-5(X))* Munshiram Manoharlal Pubs. Private, Ltd. IND. Dist: Coronet Bks.

Szczepanski, Beth. Buddhist Instrumental Music of Wutaishan: Social & Ritual Contexts. 2012. (SOAS Musicology Ser.). (Illus.). 196p. 89.95 ***(978-1-4094-2743-8(9))*** Ashgate Publishing Co.

Walsh, Michael J. Sacred Economies: Buddhist Monasticism & Territoriality in Medieval China. 2010. (ENG., Illus.). 256p. (gr. 17). 50.00 *(978-0-231-14832-0(1))* Columbia Univ. Pr.

Yun, Hsing. Discipline, Concentration, Sagesse dans le Bouddhisme Humaniste. 2010. (FRE & ENG.). pap. 15.95 net. *(978-1-932293-41-8(8))* Buddha's Light Publishing.

—For All Living Beings: A Guide to Buddhist Practice. Smitheram, Robert, tr. from CHI. 2010. 184p. pap. 15.95 *(978-1-932293-40-1(X))* Buddha's Light Publishing.

Zhuhong. The Essentials of the Shramanera Vinaya & the Rules of Deportment: Vinaya for Daily Use: The Fifty-Three Verses & Mantras. 2011. (CHI.). *(978-0-88139-885-4(3))* Buddhist Text Translation Society.

BUDDHIST PARABLES

Burlingame, Eugene Watson. Buddhist Parables. 2009. (ENG.). 379p. 38.99 *(978-1-117-53702-3(1))*; pap. 32.75 *(978-1-117-53703-0(X))* BiblioBazaar.

Fausboll, V., ed. Buddhist Birth Stories: or Jataka Tales, Vol. 1. Davids, Rhys T., tr. reprint ed. 42.50 *(978-0-404-17309-8(8))* AMS Pr., Inc.

Goto, Akio. Kongoji-Bon "Sanbo Kanno Yoryakuroku" No Kenkyu/Osaka Daigaku Sanbo Kanno Roryakuroku Kenkyukai Hen; Goto Akio Kanshu. 2007. (CHI & JPN., Illus.). 262p. *(978-4-585-03174-1(X))* Bensei Shuppan.

Li, Mingjing. Nihon Bukkyo Setsuwashu No Genryu. 2007. (JPN.). vii, 334p. *(978-4-585-10433-9(X))* Bensei Shuppan.

Zhang, Qingnian, tr. & compiled by. Buddhist Parables. 2007. (CHI & ENG.). 294p. pap. *(978-1-921099-28-1(3))* Asia-pacific Multiculture Publishing Development Pty Ltd.

BUDDHIST PRIESTS

Besserman, Perle & Steger, Manfred. Zen Radicals, Rebels, & Reformers. 2011. (ENG.). 232p. pap. 16.95 *(978-0-86171-691-3(4))* Wisdom Pubns.

Blo-gros-rgya-Mtsho & Don-grub-phun-Tshogs. Slob Dpon Sans Rgyas Gñis Pa Padma-Byun-Gnas Kyi Rnam Thar Yid Kyi Mun Sel Zes Bya Ba Bzugs So. 2010. (TIB., Illus.). 17p. *(978-7-223-02606-2(5))* Tibetan People's Publishing Hse.

Carter, James. Heart of Buddha, Heart of China: The Life & Times of a 20th-Century Chinese Monk, 1 vol. 2010. (ENG., Illus.). 256p. 29.95 *(978-0-19-539885-4(8))* Oxford Univ. Pr., Inc.

Chen, Jinhua. Philosopher, Practitioner, Politician: The Many Lives of Fazang (643-712) 2007. (Sinica Leidensia Ser.). 550p. *(978-90-04-15613-5(5))* BRILL.

Designwallas Publishing Staff, creator. HH Cool. 2009. (ICONoclastic Ser.). (ENG.). 128p. 12.95 *(978-81-7436-666-5(0))* Roli Bks. Private, Ltd. IND. Dist: Ingram Pub. Services.

Dorje, Tulku Hung Kar, frwd. A Path Strewn with Flowers & Bones: A Memoir with the Reflections of Tulku Sherdor. 2009. (Illus.). 305p. pap. 19.95 *(978-0-9801730-2-4(7))* Blazing Wisdom.

Ferguson, Andrew. Zen's Chinese Heritage: The Masters & Their Teachings. 2011. (ENG.). 568p. pap. 26.95 *(978-0-86171-617-3(5))* Wisdom Pubns.

Fu, Zhiying. Bright Star, Luminous Cloud: The Life of a Simple Monk. Smitheram, Robert, tr. from CHI. 2008. 472p. pap. 15.00 *(978-1-932293-29-6(9))* Buddha's Light Publishing.

Gruber, Elmar. From the Heart of Tibet: The Biography of Drikung Chetsang Rinpoche, the Holder of the Drikung Kagyu Lineage. 2010. (ENG., Illus.) 448p. pap. 21.95 *(978-1-59030-765-6(8))* Shambhala Pubns., Inc.

Hua, Hsuan. A Pictorial Biography of the Venerable Master Hsu Yun, 2 vols., Set. Buddhist Text Translation Society Staff, tr. Incl. Vol. 1. Pictorial Biography of the Venerable Hsu Yun. 1983. pap. *(978-0-88139-008-7(9))*; Vol. 2 . Pictorial Biography of the Venerable Hsu Yun. 1985. pap. *(978-0-88139-116-9(6))*; (Illus.). 208p. Set pap. 16.00 *(978-0-917512-40-7(5))* Buddhist Text Translation Society.

Jaffe, Richard. Neither Monk nor Layman. 2010. 308p. pap. 25.00 *(978-0-8248-3627-6(8))* Univ. of Hawaii Pr.

Jaffe, Richard M. Neither Monk nor Layman: Clerical Marriage in Modern Japanese Buddhism. 2010. pap. *(978-0-8248-3527-9(1))* Univ. of Hawaii Pr.

Karma Thinley & O'Sullivan, Adrian. The Telescope of Wisdom: A Condensed Interlinear Commentary on the Great Master Nagarjuna's 'the Letter to a Friend' 2009. (Illus.). 224p. *(978-0-9509119-6-0(8))* Ganesha Pr.

Mukpo, Diana J. & Gimian, Carolyn Rose. Dragon Thunder: My Life with Chogyam Trungpa. 2008. (ENG., Illus.). 432p. per. 19.95 *(978-1-59030-534-8(5))* Shambhala Pubns., Inc.

Nagarjuna, Arya. Letter from a Friend: A Bodhisattva's Advice to an Indian King on Right Living & the Buddhist Path. Dharmamitra, Bhikshu, tr. from CHI. 2009. 184p. pap. 13.95 *(978-1-935413-06-6(6))* Kalavinka Pr.

Ono, Katsutoshi, et al. Ru Tang Qiu Fa Xun Li Xing Ji Jiao Zhu. 2007. (Riben Ru Hua Qiu Fa Seng Ren Xing Ji Jiao Zhu Cong Kan Ser.: Vol. 1). (CHI., Illus.). *(978-7-80755-145-4(3))* Huashan Arts and Literature Publishing Hse.

Porter, Bill & Pine, Red. Road to Heaven: Encounters with Chinese Hermits. 2009. (ENG.). 240p. pap. 15.95 *(978-1-58243-523-7(5)*, Counterpoint Pr.) Basic Bks. GBR. Dist: Perseus-PGW.

Roach, Geshe Michael & Mcnally, Lama Christie. King of the Dharma: The Illustrated Life of Je Tsongkapa, Teacher of the First Dalai Lama. 2012. (ENG.). 472p. pap. 60.00 *(978-0-9765469-6-2(5))* Diamond Cutter Pr., LLC.

Rozenberg, Guillaume. Renunciation & Power: The Quest for Sainthood in Contemporary Burma. Hackett, Jessica, tr. from FRE. 2010. (Monograph Series, Yale Southeast Asia Studies: 59). pap. 20.00 *(978-0-938692-92-8(5))*; (ENG.). lib. bdg. 35.00 *(978-0-938692-93-5(3))* Yale Univ. Southeast Asia Studies.

Seo, Audrey Yoshiko. Enso: Zen Circles of Enlightenment. 2009. (ENG., Illus.). 192p. 16.00 *(978-1-59030-608-6(2)*, Weatherhill, Inc.) Shambhala Pubns., Inc.

Stearns, Cyrus. The Buddha from Dolpo, Revised & Expanded: A Study of the Life & Thought of the Tibetan Master Dolpopa Sherab Gyaltsen. 2010. (ENG., Illus.). 496p. 39.95 *(978-1-55939-343-0(2))* Snow Lion Pubns., Inc.

Thondup, Tulku. Incarnation: The History & Mysticism of the Tulku Tradition of Tibet. 2011. (ENG., Illus.). 128p. pap. 18.95 *(978-1-59030-839-4(5))* Shambhala Pubns., Inc.

BUDDHIST PHILOSOPHY

see also Buddhism—Doctrines; Buddhist Logic; Philosophy, Indic; Sunyata

Anderson, Reb. The Third Turning of the Wheel: Wisdom of the Samdhinirmocana Sutra. 2012. (ENG.). 256p. pap. 18.95 ***(978-1-930485-31-0(X))*** Rodmell Pr.

Anonymous. The Dhammapad: With Explanatory Notes & A Short Essay on Buddha's Thought. 2011. 150p. 41.95 ***(978-1-258-04307-0(6))*** Literary Licensing, LLC.

Arnold, Daniel Anderson. Brains, Buddhas, & Believing: The Problem of Intentionality in Classical Buddhist & Cognitive-Scientific Philosophy of Mind. 2012. (ENG.). 328p. (gr. 17). 50.00 ***(978-0-231-14546-6(2))*** Columbia Univ. Pr.

Athukorala, Don G. Buddha's Principle of Relativity: Mind Body Stress. 2011. 266p. pap. 25.60 ***(978-1-4567-8241-2(X))*** AuthorHouse.

Bazzano, Manu. Buddha Is Dead: Nietzsche & the Dawn of European Zen. 2006. (ENG.). 261p. (C). pap. 35.00 *(978-1-84519-149-8(8))* Sussex Academic Pr. GBR. Dist: International Specialized Bk. Services.

Benedict, Gerald, ed. Buddhist Wisdom: The Path to Enlightenment. 2009. (Sacred Wisdom Ser.). (ENG.). 192p. 8.95 *(978-1-906787-14-1(X)*, Watkins Publishing) Duncan Baird Pubs. GBR. Dist: Sterling Publishing Co., Inc.

Byrd, Nick. Through the Looking Glass: 11 daily meditations & insights on love a philosophy, a truth, a science of Mind. 2009. 396p. pap. 25.95 *(978-1-4401-7200-7(5))* iUniverse, Inc.

Carus, Paul. The Gospel of Buddha. 2007. (ENG.). 296p. per. 15.95 *(978-1-60206-566-6(7))* Cosimo, Inc.

Chang, Garma C. C. The Buddhist Teaching of Totality: The Philosophy of Hwa Yen Buddhism. 2008. (Routledge Library Editions: Buddhism Ser.). (ENG.). 298p. (C). 165.00 *(978-0-415-46089-7(1))* Routledge.

Choi, Dukkyu. Mechanism of Consciousness during Life, Dream & After-death. 2011. (Illus.). 204p. pap. 15.99 *(978-1-4567-7365-6(8))* AuthorHouse.

Coomaraswamy, Ananda Kentish. Buddha & the Gospel of Buddhism. 2009. 290p. pap. *(978-0-217-18293-5(3))* Books LLC.

—Buddha & the Gospel of Buddhism. 2008. 424p. *(978-1-4437-4004-3(7)*, Obscure Pr.) Read Bks.

Coseru, Christian. Perceiving Reality: Consciousness, Intentionality, & Cognition in Buddhist Philosophy. 2nd ed. 2012. (ENG., Illus.). 352p. 74.00 ***(978-0-19-984338-1(4))*** Oxford Univ. Pr., Inc.

Cover, Jennifer. Understanding Bodhasar. 2009. 256p. pap. *(978-3-639-19147-9(1))* VDM Verlag Dr. Mueller e.K.

Cowherds (Authors) Staff, contrib. by. Moonshadows: Conventional Truth in Buddhist Philosophy, 1 vol. 2010. (ENG.). 272p. 99.00 *(978-0-19-975142-6(0))*; pap. 35.00 *(978-0-19-975143-3(9))* Oxford Univ. Pr., Inc.

Craig, Thomas D. A Cup of Buddha. 2011. (ENG.). 232p. pap. 22.95 *(978-1-84694-359-1(0))* O Bks.,John Hunt.

D. Buddhism. 2009. 3025.00 *(978-0-415-44132-2(3))* Routledge.

Dalai Lama XIV. For the Benefit of All Beings: A Commentary on the Way of the Bodhisattva. Padmakara Translation Group Staff, tr. from TIB. 2009. (Shambhala Classics Ser.). (ENG.). 160p. 15.95 *(978-1-59030-693-2(7))* Shambhala Pubns., Inc.

D'Amato, Mario. Distinguishing the Middle from the Extremes: A Study & Annotated Translation of the Madhyantavibhaga, along with Its Commentary, the Madhyantavibhaga-Bhasya. 2012. (ENG.). 240p. (gr. 17). 36.00 *(978-1-935011-05-7(7))* American Institute of Buddhist Studies.

D'Amato, Mario, et al. Pointing at the Moon Buddhism, Logic, Analytic Philosophy. 2009. (ENG., Illus.). 200p. pap. 27.95 *(978-0-19-538156-6(4))* Oxford Univ. Pr., Inc.

Das, Lama Surya. The Big Questions: A Buddhist Response to Life's Most Challenging Mysteries. 2007. (ENG.). 288p. 17.95 *(978-1-59486-208-3(7))* Rodale Pr., Inc.

Dharmachakra Translation Committee Staff, tr. from SAN. Middle Beyond Extremes: Maitreya's Madhyantavibhaga. 2007. (ENG., Illus.). 192p. 22.95 *(978-1-55939-270-9(3))* Snow Lion Pubns., Inc.

Donets, A. M. Problemy Bazovogo Soznaniia V Realnosti Vneshnego V Datsanskoi Filosofii. 2008. (Illus.). 167p. *(978-5-7925-0290-1(0))* Burjatskij Naucnyj Centr Sibirskogo Otdelenija Rossijskoj Akademii Nauk.

Dorje, His Holi. The Future Is Now. 2009. 192p. pap. *(978-1-84850-055-6(6)*, 902) Hay Hse. UK, Ltd. GBR. Dist: Grantham Bk. Services.

Eckel, Malcolm David. Bhaviveka & His Buddhist Opponents: Chapters 4 & 5 of the Verses on the Heart of the Middle Way (Madhyamakahrdayakarikah) with the Commentary Entitled the Flame of Reason (Tarkajvala) 2009. (Harvard Oriental Ser.: 70). (SAN & ENG.). 496p. 60.00 *(978-0-674-03274-3(8))* Harvard Univ., Dept. of Sanskrit & Indian Studies.

Edelglass, William, et al, eds. Buddhist Philosophy: Essential Readings. 2009. (ENG.). 480p. pap. 24.95 *(978-0-19-532817-2(5))* Oxford Univ. Pr., Inc.

Edelglass, William & Garfield, Jay L., eds. Buddhist Philosophy: Essential Readings. 2009. (ENG.). 496p. 99.00 *(978-0-19-532816-5(7))* Oxford Univ. Pr., Inc.

Feldman, Joel, et al. Ratnakirti's Proof of Momentariness by Positive Correlation: Transliteration, Translation, & Philosophica Commentary. 2012. (ENG.). 232p. (gr. 17). 36.00 *(978-1-935011-06-4(5))* American Institute of Buddhist Studies.

Flanagan, Owen J. The Bodhisattva's Brain: Buddhism Naturalized. 2011. (ENG., Illus.). 280p. (gr. 17). 27.95 *(978-0-262-01604-9(4))* MIT Pr.

Franco, Eli, et al, eds. Religion & Logic in Buddhist Philosophical Analysis. 2012. (Denkschriften der philosophisch-historischen Klasse Ser.). (ENG.). 521p. (C). 104.00 ***(978-3-7001-7000-6(9))*** Austrian Academy of Sciences Press AUT. Dist: Brown, David Bk. Co., The.

Genoud, Charles. Gesture of Awareness: A Radical Approach to Time, Space, & Movement. 2006. (ENG.). 224p. per. 16.95 *(978-0-86171-506-0(3))* Wisdom Pubns.

Gherwal, Rishi Singh. Great Masters of the Himalayas: Their Lives & Teachings. 2007. (ENG.). 148p. 35.95 *(978-0-548-00155-4(3))* Kessinger Publishing, LLC.

Giri, Satyananda. Narop. 2011. 300p. pap. 66.95 ***(978-1-61204-448-4(4)***, Strategic Bk. Publishing) AEG Literary Publishing Services, Inc.

Gligor, Mihaela & Sabbarwal, Sherry, eds. Patterns in Philosophy & Sociology of Religions. 2011. (Illus.). 254p. 45.00 *(978-81-316-0388-8(1))* Rawat Pubns. IND. Dist: International Specialized Bk. Services.

Gracián, Baltasar. The Art of Worldly Wisdom. 2006. (ENG.). 208p. per. 6.99 *(978-1-59030-402-0(0))* Shambhala Pubns., Inc.

Gracián y Morales, Baltasar. The Art of Worldly Wisdom. 2009. 102p. pap. *(978-0-217-62043-7(4))* Books LLC.

—The Art of Worldly Wisdom. 2007. (ENG.). 104p. per. 10.99 *(978-1-60459-087-6(4))* Wilder Pubns., Ltd.

Gunasekera, Henry M., tr. Satvotpatti Vinischaya & Nirvana Vibhaga: An Enquiry into the Origin of Beings & Discussions about Nirvana. reprint ed. 17.50 *(978-0-404-17285-5(7))* AMS Pr., Inc.

Hanh, Thich Nhat. Beyond the Self: Teachings on the Middle Way. 2009. (ENG.). 72p. pap. 8.95 *(978-1-935209-41-6(8))* Parallax Pr.

Haycock, Brian. Dharma Road: A Short Cab Ride to Self Discovery. 2010. (ENG.). 256p. pap. 16.95 *(978-1-57174-635-1(8))* Hampton Roads Publishing Co., Inc.

Hsüan Hua. A Home Called Spring Breeze. 2009. *(978-0-88139-963-9(9))* Buddhist Text Translation Society.

Jacobson, Nolan Pliny. The Heart of Buddhist Philosophy. 2010. (ENG.). 208p. pap. 19.95 *(978-0-8093-2984-7(0))* Southern Illinois Univ. Pr.

Jagtiani, Suraj. The Incredible World of Nichiren Buddhism. 2011. 140p. pap. 14.88 *(978-1-4520-4234-3(9))* AuthorHouse.

Jayatilleke, K. N. Early Buddhist Theory of Knowledge. 2008. (Illus.). 524p. 165.00 *(978-0-415-46107-8(3))* Routledge.

Jones, David, ed. Buddha Nature & Animality. 2007. 236p. per. 35.00 *(978-0-89581-860-7(4))* Jain Publishing Company, Inc.

Kardos, Edward G. Zen Master Next Door. 2009. 256p. 29.95 *(978-0-89334-457-3(5))* Humanics Publishing Group.

Kha Pa, Tsong. Golden Garland of Eloquence - Vol. 1 Vol. 1: Legs Bshad Gser Phreng. Kha Pa, Tsong & Sparham, Gareth, trs. from TIB. 2008. 696p. 150.00 *(978-0-89581-865-2(5))* Jain Publishing Company, Inc.

Khu-Byug. Sans Rgyas Chos Lugs Dan Bod Kyi Rig Gnas Las Phros Pai Gnad Don Skor Glen Ba Bden Gtam Yid Kyi Mun Sel Zes Bya Ba Bzugs So. 2009. (TIB.). *(978-7-223-02760-1(6))* Tibetan People's Publishing Hse.

Klon-chen-pa Dri-med-od-Zer & Barron, Richard. The Precious Treasury of Pith Instructions. 2006. *(978-1-881847-42-7(X))* Padma Publishing.

Konik, A. Buddhism & Transgression: The Appropriation of Buddhism in the Contemporary West. 2009. (Numen Book Ser.). (Illus.). 205p. *(978-90-04-17875-5(9))* BRILL.

Kopf, Gereon, ed. Dao Companion to Japanese Buddhist Philosophy. 2012. (Dao Companions to Chinese Philosophy Ser.). (ENG.). 575p. 229.00 *(978-90-481-2923-2(0)*, 9048129230) Springer.

Koppl, Heidi I. Establishing Appearances as Divine: Rongzom Chozang on Reasoning, Madhyamaka, & Purity. 2008. (TIB & ENG.). 152p. 29.95 *(978-1-55939-288-4(6))* Snow Lion Pubns., Inc.

Laumakis, Stephen J. An Introduction to Buddhist Philosophy. 2008. (Cambridge Introductions to Philosophy Ser.). (ENG.). 300p. per. 37.00 *(978-0-521-67008-1(X))*; (C). 96.00 *(978-0-521-85413-9(X))* Cambridge Univ. Pr.

Leighton, Taigen Dan. Visions of Awakening Space & Time: Dogen & the Lotus Sutra. 2008. (ENG.). 208p. pap. 24.95 *(978-0-19-538337-9(0))* Oxford Univ. Pr., Inc.

Liberman, Kenneth. Dialectical Practice in Tibetan Philosophical Culture: An Ethnomethodological Inquiry into Formal Reasoning. 2007. (ENG.). 333p. per. 37.95 *(978-0-7425-5612-6(3))* Rowman & Littlefield Publishers, Inc.

Loizzo, Joseph. Nagarjuna's Reason Sixty: With Candrakirti's Commentary. Thurman, Robert A. F. et al, eds. Loizzo, Joseph, tr. from TIB. annot. ed. 2007. (Treasury of the Buddhist Sciences Ser.). (ENG.). 580p. (gr. 17). 49.00 (978-0-9753734-2-2(0)) American Institute of Buddhist Studies.

Lowenstein, Tom. Budismo: Filosofia, verdad e Iluminacion. Portillo Diez, Miguel, tr. 2009. (SPA.). 160p. 6.95 (978-84-9801-186-9(8)) Blume ESP. Dist: Independent Pubs. Group.

Luisi, P. L., et al. Mind & Life: Discussions with the Dalai Lama on the Nature of Reality. 2008. (Columbia Series in Science & Religion Ser.). (ENG., Illus.). 232p. (gr. 17). 24.95 (978-0-231-14550-3(0)) Columbia Univ. Pr.

Luisi, Pier Luigi. Mind & Life: Discussions with the Dalai Lama on the Nature of Reality. 2010. (Columbia Series in Science & Religion Ser.). (ENG., Illus.). 232p. (gr. 17). pap. 17.95 (978-0-231-14551-0(9)) Columbia Univ. Pr.

MacHovec, Frank. Pocket Buddha. 2008. 80p. pap. 9.95 (978-1-4357-2199-9(3)) Lulu Enterprises Inc.

McGovern, William M. A Manual of Buddhist Philosophy. reprint ed. 27.50 (978-0-404-17346-3(2)) AMS Pr., Inc.

Mipam, Jamgon, et al. Jamgon Mipam: His Life & Teachings. 2011. (ENG.). 272p. pap. 24.95 (978-1-59030-669-7(4)) Shambhala Pubns., Inc.

Mullen, Matt. The Ultimate Distinction: Resolving Our Biggest Philosophical, Spiritual, & Practical Problem. 2011. (ENG., Illus.). 56p. pap. 9.95 (978-1-59181-169-5(4)) Sentient Pubns.

Murthy, Viren. The Political Philosophy of Zhang Taiyan: The Resistance of Consciousness. 2011. VIII, 266p. (978-90-04-20387-7(7)) BRILL.

Murti, T. R. V. The Central Philosophy of Buddhism: A Study of the Madhyamika System. 2008. (Routledge Library Editions: Buddhism Ser.). (ENG.). 388p. (C). 165.00 (978-0-415-46118-4(9)) Routledge.

Nagarjuna & Nagarjuna. In Praise of Dharmadhatu. Brunnholzl, Karl, tr. from SAN. 2008. (Nitartha Institute Ser.). (ENG.). 304p. 29.95 (978-1-55939-286-0(X)) Snow Lion Pubns., Inc.

Nagarjuna & Westerhoff, Jan. The Dispeller of Disputes: Nagarjuna's Vigrahavyavartani. 2010. (ENG., Illus.). 152p. 99.00 (978-0-19-973269-2(8)); pap. 24.95 (978-0-19-973270-8(1)) Oxford Univ. Pr., Inc.

Park, Jin. Buddhism & Postmodernity: Zen, Huayan, & the Possibility of Buddhist Postmodern Ethics. 2010. (ENG.). 296p. pap. 32.95 (978-0-7391-1824-5(2)) Lexington Bks.

Park, Jin Y. Buddhism & Postmodernity: Zen, Huayan, & the Possibility of Buddhist Postmodern Ethics. 2008. (ENG.). 338p. 83.99 (978-0-7391-1823-8(4)) Lexington Bks.

Pathak, P. Early Buddhism & Indian Thoughts. 2011. 271p. pap. 35.00 **(978-81-7533-358-1(8))** M. D. Pubns. Pvt, Ltd. IND. Dist: Coronet Bks.

Pemberton, Harrison J. The Buddha Meets Socrates. 2008. 92p. pap. 15.99 (978-1-4363-0736-9(8)) Xlibris Corp.

Prasad, H. Buddhist Metaphysics & Ethics. 2011. 303p. pap. 35.00 **(978-81-7533-351-2(0))** M. D. Pubns. Pvt, Ltd. IND. Dist: Coronet Bks.

Priest, Graham & Young, Damon A., eds. Martial Arts & Philosophy: Beating & Nothingness. 2010. (Popular Culture & Philosophy Ser.). (ENG., Illus.). 288p. pap. 21.95 (978-0-8126-9684-4(0)) Open Court Publishing Co.

Puligandla, Ramakrishna. Jnana-Yoga: The Way of Knowledge. 2007. 140p. per. 20.00 (978-0-87573-091-2(4)) Jain Publishing Company, Inc.

Raju, P. T. Idealistic Thought of India. 2006. 452p. per. (978-1-4067-3262-7(1), Hesperides Pr.) Read Bks.

—Idealistic Thought of India. 2008. (Routledge Library Editions: Buddhism Ser.). (ENG.). 458p. (C). 165.00 (978-0-415-46120-7(0)) Routledge.

Ram-Prasad, Chakravarthi, et al. Hindu & Buddhist Ideas in Dialogue: Self & No-Self. 2012. (Dialogues in South Asian Traditions: Religion, Philosophy, Literature & History Ser.). 224p. 99.95 **(978-1-4094-4354-4(X))** Ashgate Publishing Co.

Richard, Christophe. Le Bouddhisme: Philosophie Ou Religion? 2010. 143p. pap. (978-2-296-12587-2(5)) Harmattan Pr.

Ronkin, Noa. Early Buddhist Metaphysics. 2010. 288p. pap. 39.95 **(978-0-415-60001-9(4))** Routledge.

Sachs, Robert. The Wisdom of the Buddhist Masters: Common & Uncommon Sense. 2008. (ENG., Illus.). 240p. pap. 17.95 (978-1-905857-90-6(X), Watkins Publishing) Duncan Baird Pubs. GBR. Dist: Sterling Publishing Co., Inc.

Sastri, N. Aiyaswami. Alambanapariksa & Vrtti. 2007. 150p. per. 30.00 (978-0-89581-985-7(6)) Jain Publishing Company, Inc.

Sayadaw, Ven. M. A Discourse on Dependent Origination. Date not set. (978-955-24-0163-3(1)) Buddhist Publication Society LKA. Dist: Pariyatti Publishing.

Sayadaw, Webu. Selected Discourses. Date not set. (978-955-24-0134-3(8)) Buddhist Publication Society LKA. Dist: Pariyatti Publishing.

Scarborough, Milton. Comparative Theories of Nonduality: The Search for a Middle Way. (ENG.). 248p. 2011. pap. 44.95 **(978-1-4411-5902-1(9))** 2009. (Illus.). 130.00 (978-0-8264-3738-9(9)) Continuum International Publishing Group, Ltd. GBR. Dist: National Bk. Network.

Shun'ei, Tagawa. Living Yogacara: An Introduction to Consciousness-Only Buddhism. Muller, Charles, tr. from JPN. 2009. (ENG.). 200p. pap. 18.95 (978-0-86171-589-3(6)) Wisdom Pubns.

Siderits, Mark. Buddhism as Philosophy. 2007. 304p. (C). reprint ed. 55.00 (978-0-87220-874-2(5)); pap. 16.95 (978-0-87220-873-5(7)) Hackett Publishing Co., Inc.

—Buddhism as Philosophy: An Introduction. 2007. (Ashgate World Philosophies Ser.). 242p. pap. (978-0-7546-5369-1(2)) Ashgate Publishing Co.

Singer, Charlie. Reflections in a Mirror: The Nature of Appearance in Buddhist Philosophy. 2011. 80p. pap. 10.95 **(978-1-4620-4656-0(8))** iUniverse, Inc.

Smith, Elihu Genmyo. Everything Is the Way: Ordinary Mind Zen. 2012. (ENG.). 240p. pap. 17.95 **(978-1-59030-972-8(3))** Shambhala Pubns., Inc.

Smith, F. Harold. The Buddhist Way of Life: Its Philosophy & History. 2008. (Routledge Library Editions: Buddhism Ser.). (ENG.). 192p. (C). 165.00 (978-0-415-46147-4(2)) Routledge.

Smith, Rodney. Stepping Out of Self-Deception: The Buddha's Liberating Teaching of No-Self. 2010. (ENG.). 160p. pap. 16.95 (978-1-59030-729-8(1)) Shambhala Pubns., Inc.

Sonam, Ruth. Aryadeva's Four Hundred Stanzas on the Middle Way: With Commentary by Gyel-tsap. 2008. (ENG.). 400p. pap. 29.95 (978-1-55939-302-7(5)) Snow Lion Pubns., Inc.

Taye, Jamgon Kongrul Lodro. The Treasury of Knowledge: Book Six, Parts One & Two: Indo-Tibetan Classical Learning & Buddhist Phenomenology. Dorje, Gyurme, tr. from TIB. 2012. (ENG.). 992p. 49.95 **(978-1-55939-389-8(0))** Snow Lion Pubns., Inc.

Tigunait, Pandit Rajmani. Why We Fight: Practices for Lasting Peace. rev. ed. 2007. (ENG.). 120p. pap. 12.95 (978-0-89389-235-7(1), B212MO) Himalayan Institute Pr.

Tiwary, K. N. Buddhist Beliefs & Practices. 2010. 267p. 54.50 (978-81-7533-288-1(3)) M. D. Pubns. Pvt, Ltd. IND. Dist: Coronet Bks.

Vecchiotti, Icilio, et al. Storia Del Buddhismo Indiano. 2007. (ITA., Illus.). (978-88-6473-017-2(6)); (978-88-359-5928-1(4)) Editori Riuniti.

Wawrytko, Sandra A., ed. Dao Companion to Chinese Buddhist Philosophy: Dharma & Dao. 2009. (Dao Companions to Chinese Philosophy Ser.). (ENG & CHI.). 500p. 229.00 (978-90-481-2938-6(9), 9048129389) Springer.

Westerhoff, Jan. Twelve Examples of Illusion, 1 vol. 2010. (ENG., Illus.). 216p. 29.95 (978-0-19-538735-3(X)) Oxford Univ. Pr., Inc.

Wonhyo, et al. Wonhyo's Philosophy of Mind. 2012. 45.00 **(978-0-8248-3573-6(5))** Univ. of Hawaii Pr.

Yee, Wan Ko. Selected Philosophical Sayings of Master Wan Ko Yee. 31p. pap. 8.00 (978-1-892727-30-5(7)) World Dharma Voice, Inc.

BUDDHIST RITES AND CEREMONIES

see Buddhism—Rituals

BUDDHIST SAINTS

Gordon, Bill. From Boxer to Buddhist: Life as a Spiritual Path. 2009. 308p. pap. 15.49 (978-1-4490-0255-8(2)) AuthorHouse.

Jackson, David P. Mirror of the Buddha: Early Portraits from Tibet. 2011. (ENG., Illus.). pap. 75.00 **(978-0-9845190-3-3(3))** Rubin Museum of Art.

Rozenberg, Guillaume. Renunciation & Power: The Quest for Sainthood in Contemporary Burma. Hackett, Jessica, tr. from FRE. 2010. (Monograph Series, Yale Southeast Asia Studies: 59). pap. 20.00 (978-0-938692-92-8(5)); (ENG.). lib. bdg. 35.00 (978-0-938692-93-5(3)) Yale Univ. Southeast Asia Studies.

Seniff, John C. Awakening Mind: Travels with Myself. 2007. 154p. pap. 13.95 (978-0-7414-3811-9(9)) Infinity Publishing.

BUDDHIST SOCIOLOGY

Bunnag, Jane. Buddhist Monk, Buddhist Layman: A Study of Urban Monastic Organization in Central Thailand. 2007. (Cambridge Studies in Social & Cultural Anthropology Ser.). (ENG.). 232p. pap. 51.00 (978-0-521-04064-8(7)) Cambridge Univ. Pr.

Dalai Lama XIV & Stril-Rever, Sofia. My Spiritual Journey. l.t. ed. 2010. (ENG.). 420p. pap. 25.99 (978-0-06-200252-5(X), HarperLuxe) HarperCollins Pubs.

Ikeda, Daisaku. A New Humanism: The University Addresses of Daisaku Ikeda. 2010. (ENG., Illus.). 320p. 58.00 (978-1-84885-482-6(X)); pap. 18.00 (978-1-84885-483-3(8)) I. B. Tauris & Co., Ltd. GBR. Dist: Macmillan.

Kuah, Khun Eng. State, Society, & Religious Engineering: Towards a Reformist Buddhism in Singapore. 2nd ed. 2009. (Illus.). xiv, 337p. pap. (978-981-230-865-8(2)) Institute of Southeast Asian Studies.

Soucy, Alexander. The Buddha Side: Gender, Power, & Buddhist Practice in Vietnam. 2012. 240p. 49.00 **(978-0-8248-3598-9(0))** Univ. of Hawaii Pr.

BUDDHIST SECTS

see also Bon (Tibetan Religion); Mahayana Buddhism; Theravada Buddhism

Adamek, Wendi Leigh. The Teachings of Master Wuzhu: Zen & Religion of No-Religion. 2011. (Translations from the Asian Classics Ser.). (ENG.). 224p. (gr. 17). 84.50 (978-0-231-15022-4(9)); (ENG.). 224p. (gr. 17). pap. 27.50 (978-0-231-15023-1(7)); x, 208p. **(978-0-231-10522-4(3))** Columbia Univ. Pr.

Armstrong, Robert Cornell. Buddhism & Buddhists in Japan. 2007. (ENG.). 156p. 36.95 (978-0-548-11051-5(4)) Kessinger Publishing, LLC.

Brazier, Caroline. Other-Centred Therapy. 2009. 420p. pap. 34.95 (978-1-86494-237-8(1)) O Bks. GBR. Dist: National Bk. Network.

Brunnholzl, Karl. Luminous Heart: The Third Karmapa on Consciousness, Wisdom, & Buddha Nature. 2009. (ENG.). 512p. 39.95 (978-1-55939-318-8(1)) Snow Lion Pubns., Inc.

Chen, J. Legend & Legitimation: The Formation of Tendai Esoteric Buddhism in Japan. 2009. (Melanges Chinois et Bouddhiques Ser.). 423p. (C). pap. 66.00 (978-2-96006-2-6(X)) Peeters Pubs. & Booksellers BEL. Dist: Brown, David Bk. Co., The.

Dessi, Ugo, ed. The Social Dimension of Shin Buddhism. 2010. (Numen Book Ser.). (Illus.). 301p. (978-90-04-18653-8(0)) BRILL.

Dkon-mchog-yan-Lag & Brunnhölzl, Karl. Gone Beyond: The Prajnaparamita Sutras, the Ornament of Clear Realization, & Its Commentaries in the Tibetan Kagyu Tradition, 2, 2. 2012. (ENG.). 688p. 44.95 (978-1-55939-357-7(2)) Snow Lion Pubns., Inc.

Enji, Torei. The Undying Lamp of Zen: The Testament of Zen Master Torei. Cleary, Thomas, tr. from JPN. 2010. (ENG.). 160p. pap. 16.95 (978-1-59030-792-2(5)) Shambhala Pubns., Inc.

Gonsalez, David, et al. The Roar of Thunder: Yamantaka Practice & Commentary. 2011. **(978-1-55939-387-4(4))** Snow Lion Pubns., Inc.

Gruber, Elmar. From the Heart of Tibet: The Biography of Drikung Chetsang Rinpoche, the Holder of the Drikung Kagyu Lineage. 2010. (ENG., Illus.). 448p. pap. 21.95 (978-1-59030-765-6(8)) Shambhala Pubns., Inc.

Habito, Ruben L. F., frwd. The Essential Shinran: A Buddhist Path of True Entrusting. 2006. (ENG.). 280p. per. 22.95 (978-1-933316-21-5(7)) World Wisdom, Inc.

Hopkins, Jeffrey & Shay-Rap-Gyel-Tsen, Dol-Bo-Ba. Mountain Doctrine: Tibet's Fundamental Treatise on Other-Emptiness & the Buddha Matrix. Vose, Kevin, ed. 2006. (ENG & TIB.). 832p. 79.95 (978-1-55939-238-9(X)) Snow Lion Pubns., Inc.

Jeremiah, Ken. Living Buddhas: The Self-Mummified Monks of Yamagata, Japan. 2010. (ENG., Illus.). 242p. pap. 35.00 (978-0-7864-4880-7(6)) McFarland & Co., Inc. Pubs.

Jordt, Ingrid. Burma's Mass Lay Meditation Movement: Buddhism & the Cultural Construction of Power. 2007. (Ohio RIS Southeast Asia Ser.). (ENG., Illus.). 272p. per. 28.00 (978-0-89680-255-1(8)) Ohio Univ. Pr.

Kunsang, Lama, et al. History of the Karmapas: The Odyssey of the Tibetan Masters with the Black Crown. 2012. (ENG., Illus.). 332p. pap. 21.95 **(978-1-55939-390-4(4))** Snow Lion Pubns., Inc.

Lingpa, Jigme, et al. Deity, Mantra & Wisdom: Development Stage Meditation in Tibetan Buddhist Tantra. 2007. (ENG., Illus.). 270p. 29.95 (978-1-55939-300-3(9)) Snow Lion Pubns., Inc.

Lobsang Tharchin. Esencia Del Lojong Del Mahayana: Comentario de la Mente en Ocho Estrofas de Geshe Langri Tangpa. 2007. (SPA.). (978-0-918753-20-5(1)) Mahayana Sutra & Tantra Pr.

MacKenzie, Rory. New Buddhist Movements in Thailand: Towards an Understanding of Wat Phra Dhammakaya & Santi Asoke. 2007. (Routledge Critical Studies in Buddhism Ser.). (Illus.). 253p. 150.00 (978-0-415-40869-1(5)) Routledge.

Nanjio, Bunyiu, compiled by. A Short History of the Twelve Japanese Buddhist Sects. reprint ed. 37.50 (978-0-404-17355-5(1)) AMS Pr., Inc.

Okusa, Yejitsu, et al. In the Name of the Amida Buddh: Classic Writings from the Pure Land Sect of Buddhism. 2011. 150p. pap. 11.99 **(978-1-61001-007-8(8))** Red & Black Pubs.

Paraskevopoulos, John. The Way of Shin Buddhism. 2009. 114p. pap. (978-1-59731-095-6(6)) Perennis, Sophia.

Pye, Michael, ed. Listening to Shin Buddhism: Starting Points of Modern Dialogue. 2012. (Eastern Buddhist Voices Ser.). (ENG.). 320p. (C). pap. 39.95 **(978-1-908049-17-9(0))**; (Illus.). 110.00 **(978-1-908049-16-2(2))** Equinox Publishing Ltd. GBR. Dist: Brown, David Bk. Co., The.

Rinchen, Geshe Sonam. The Three Principal Aspects of the Path, 2nd Edition. Sonam, Ruth, tr. from TIB. 2nd ed. 2010. (ENG., Illus.). 168p. pap. 16.95 (978-1-55939-350-8(5)) Snow Lion Pubns., Inc.

Rinpoche, Lama Zopa. Kadampa Teachings. Cameron, Ailsa, ed. 2010. (ENG., Illus.). 260p. pap. (978-1-891868-24-5(1), 15410) Lama Yeshe Wisdom Archive.

Sakashita, Jay, ed. Biography & Disciples. 2008. (Writings of Nichiren Shonin Ser.). 255p. 25.00 (978-0-8248-3301-5(5)) Univ. of Hawaii Pr.

Sarao, K. T. S. Urban Centres & Urbanisation, 3rd Edition: As Reflected in the Pali Vinaya & Sutta Pitakas. 2010. 256p. 47.50 (978-81-215-1209-1(3)) Munshiram Manoharlal Pubs. Private, Ltd. IND. Dist: Coronet Bks.

Senzaki, Nyogen. Eloquent Silence: Nyogen Senzaki's Gateless Gate & Other Previously Unpublished Teachings & Letters. Chayat, Roko Sherry, ed. 2008. (ENG., Illus.). 350p. pap. 17.95 (978-0-86171-559-6(4)) Wisdom Pubns.

Silk, Jonathan A. Riven by Lust: Incest & Schism in Indian Buddhist Legend & Historiography. 2008. (Illus.). 376p. (C). 57.00 (978-0-8248-3090-8(3)) Univ. of Hawaii Pr.

Steinilber-Oberlin, E. The Buddhist Sects of Japan: Their History, Philosophical Doctrines & Sanctuaries. Loge, Marc, tr. 2010. (ENG., Illus.). 308p. 130.00 (978-0-415-59351-9(4)) Routledge.

The Surangama Sutra: A New Translation. 2009. (Illus.). 544p. 30.00 (978-0-88139-962-2(0)) Buddhist Text Translation Society.

Suzuki, Daisetz Teitaro, tr. from JPN. Shinran's Kyogyoshinsho: The Collection of Passages Expounding the True Teaching, Living, Faith, & Realizing of the Pure Land, 1 vol. 2012. (ENG.). 352p. 55.00 **(978-0-19-986310-5(5))** Oxford Univ. Pr., Inc.

Taye, Jamgon Kongtrul Lodro, et al. The Treasury of Knowledge, Book 6, Part 3: Frameworks of Buddhist Philosophy. Callahan, Elizabeth M., tr. from TIB. 2007. (Treasury of Knowledge Ser.). (ENG.). 416p. 34.95 (978-1-55939-277-8(0)) Snow Lion Pubns., Inc.

Trizin, Sakya. Freeing the Heart & Mind: Introduction to the Buddhist Path. 2011. (ENG.). 184p. pap. 15.95 (978-0-86171-638-8(8)) Wisdom Pubns.

Tulku, Ringu. Daring Steps, 2nd Edition: Traversing the Path of the Buddha. 2nd ed. 2010. (ENG.). 224p. pap. 16.95 (978-1-55939-354-6(8)) Snow Lion Pubns., Inc.

Williams, Duncan Ryuken. The Other Side of Zen: A Social History of Soto Zen Buddhism in Tokugawa Japan. 2009. (Buddhisms: A Princeton University Press Ser.). (ENG., Illus.). 296p. (C). pap. 22.95 (978-0-691-14429-0(X)) Princeton Univ. Pr.

BUDDHIST TANTRISM

see Tantric Buddhism

BUDDHIST THEOLOGY

see Buddhism—Doctrines

BUDDHIST WOMEN

Arai, Paula Kane Robinson. Bringing Zen Home: The Healing Heart of Japanese Women's Rituals. 2011. 52.00 **(978-0-8248-3535-4(2))** Univ. of Hawaii Pr.

—Women Living Zen: Japanese Soto Buddhist Nuns. 2012. (ENG., Illus.). 268p. pap. 24.95 **(978-0-19-992868-2(1))** Oxford Univ. Pr., Inc.

Bartholomeusz, Tessa J. Women under the Bo Tree: Buddhist nuns in Sri Lanka. 2008. (Cambridge Studies in Religious Traditions Ser.). (ENG.). 308p. pap. 42.00 (978-0-521-07168-0(2)) Cambridge Univ. Pr.

Daehaeng, Zen Master & Wisdom Publications Staff. No River to Cross: Trusting the Enlightenment That's Always Right Here. 2007. (ENG.). 144p. per. 14.95 (978-0-86171-534-3(9)) Wisdom Pubns.

Gregory, Peter N. & Mrozik, Susanne, eds. Women Practicing Buddhism: American Experiences. 2007. (ENG.). 208p. per. 16.95 (978-0-86171-539-8(X)) Wisdom Pubns.

Harding, Sarah. Niguma, Lady of Illusion. 2011. (ENG., Illus.). 418p. 32.95 (978-1-55939-361-4(0)) Snow Lion Pubns., Inc.

Mohr, Thea & Tsedroen, Jampa, eds. Dignity & Discipline: Reviving Full Ordination for Buddhist Nuns. 2010. (ENG.). 350p. pap. 18.95 (978-0-86171-588-6(8)) Wisdom Pubns.

Rahaim, Catherine. Not in God's Image: A Comparative Study of Women's Body Image in Pagan, Jewish, & Buddhist Religions. 2007. 112p. per. 19.95 (978-1-58112-373-9(6), Dissertation.com) Universal Pubs.

Tan, Pamela. The Chinese Factor: An Australian Chinese Woman's Life in China from 1950 to 1979. 2008. (Illus.). 272p. pap. 29.95 (978-1-877058-74-5(2)) Rosenberg Publishing Pty, Ltd. AUS. Dist: International Specialized Bk. Services.

Tisdale, Sallie. Women of the Way: Discovering 2,500 Years of Buddhist Wisdom. 2008. (ENG.). 299p. pap. 15.00 (978-1-4379-6347-2(1)); 25.00 (978-1-4379-5116-5(3)) DIANE Publishing Co.

—Women of the Way: Discovering 2,500 Years of Buddhist Wisdom. 2007. (ENG.). 320p. pap. 14.95 (978-0-06-114659-6(5), HarperOne) HarperCollins Pubs.

Tsomo, Karma. Buddhism Through American Women's Eyes. 2nd ed. 2010. (ENG.). 184p. pap. 16.95 (978-1-55939-363-8(7)) Snow Lion Pubns., Inc.

Van de Belt, J. Ani-la: The Nuns from Redna Menling. 2010. (ENG., Illus.). 94p. (C). pap. 50.00 (978-90-8890-046-4(9)) Sidestone Pr. NLD. Dist: Brown, David Bk. Co., The.

Willis, Jan. Dreaming Me: Black, Baptist, & Buddhist - One Woman's Spiritual Journey. 2008. (ENG.). 330p. pap. 16.95 (978-0-86171-548-0(9)) Wisdom Pubns.

BUDGE, DON, 1915-2000

Fisher, Marshall Jon. A Terrible Splendor: Three Extraordinary Men, a World Poised for War, & the Greatest Tennis Match Ever Played. 2009. (ENG., Illus.). 336p. 25.00 (978-0-307-39394-4(1), Crown) Crown Publishing Group.

BUDGERIGAR

Birmelin, Immanuel. My Parakeet. 2009. (My Pet Ser.). (ENG., Illus.). 144p. pap. 14.99 (978-0-7641-4283-3(6)) Barron's Educational Series, Inc.

Birmelin, Immanuel & Niemann, Hildegard. Budgerigars. 2nd rev. ed. 2008. (Complete Pet Owner's Manual Ser.). (ENG., Illus.). 64p. pap. 8.99 (978-0-7641-3897-3(9)) Barron's Educational Series, Inc.

Davids, Angela. Budgies: A Guide to Caring for Your Parakeet. 2011. (Complete Care Made Easy Ser.). (ENG., Illus.). 160p. pap. 9.95 (978-1-935484-65-3(6)) BowTie Pr.

McAleese, Cheri A. My Name Is Pipsqueak! What's Your Name? My TRUE Story. 2006. (YA). per. 17.95 (978-0-9787229-0-6(6)) Pipsqueak! Pr.

Moustaki, Nikki. Parakeets for Dummies. 2007. (ENG., Illus.). 96p. per. 9.99 (978-0-470-12162-7(9), For Dummies) Wiley, John & Sons, Inc.

T F H Publications, creator. Parakeets. 2007. (Practical Pet Care Ser.). (Illus.). 64p. pap. 7.95 (978-0-7938-1010-9(8)) TFH Pubns., Inc.

BUDGET

see also Budget Deficits; Municipal Budgets; Program Budgeting

The Academic Library Budget & Expenditures Report. Date not set. 125p. pap. 125.00 (978-1-57440-002-1(9)) Primary Research Group.

Agagu, A. A. & Omotoso, 'Femi. Nigerian Public Financial Management: Trends & Issues. 2008. 228p. (978-0-615-22334-6(6)) Nilytops Pubs.

Agger, Eugene E. The Budget in the American Commonwealths. (Columbia University, Studies in the Social Sciences: No. 66). reprint ed. 39.50 (978-0-404-51066-4(3)) AMS Pr., Inc.

—The Budget in the American Commonwealths. 2009. (ENG.). 219p. 32.99 (978-1-117-38085-8(8)); pap. 23.75 (978-1-117-38086-5(6)); pap. 20.99 (978-1-117-38087-2(4), BiblioLife) BiblioBazaar.

Alfred, Andrea L. My (Money) System: Checkbook Budgeting: Pay All Your Bills & Have More Money Between Pay Periods! 2010. 64p. pap. 10.95 (978-1-4502-2362-1(1)) iUniverse, Inc.

Avritzer, Leonardo & Avritzer, L. Participatory Institutions in Democratic Brazil. 2009. (ENG., Illus.). 224p. (C). (gr. 13-17). 49.95 (978-0-8018-9174-8(4)); pap. 24.95 (978-0-8018-9180-9(9)) Johns Hopkins Univ. Pr.

Chambers, Don. Money Basics for Young Adults: High School Edition. 2006. (ENG.). (YA). 16.99 (978-0-9722071-4-0(7)) Healthy Wealth.

Chen, Greg G., et al. Budget Tools: Financial Methods in the Public Sector, 00 vols. rev. ed. 2008. 152p. (C). pap. 47.00 (978-0-87289-539-3(4)) CQ Pr.

Cho, Son-Ju, et al. Song Inji Yesan Chedo Sihaeng e Ttarun Chaejong Saop Ui P'yonik Ch'ujong: CVM Ui Iyong Han Silchung Punsok. 2010. (KOR., Illus.). xx, 155p. *(978-89-8491-351-6(0))* Korean Women's Development Institute.

Cipriani, Gabriele. The EU Budget: Responsibility Without Accountability? 2011. (ENG.). 160p. pap. 30.00 *(978-94-6138-053-1(4))* Ctr. for European Policy Studies BEL. Dist: Brookings Institution Pr.

—Rethinking the EU Budget: Three Unavoidable Reforms. 2007. (ENG., Illus.). 125p. pap. 30.00 *(978-92-9079-735-7(5))* Ctr. for European Policy Studies BEL. Dist: Brookings Institution Pr.

Danner, Kathy Kline. Enjoy Freedom from Financial Stress: Helping Moms Fight the Joy Thief of Financial Stress. 2009. 164p. pap. 14.99 *(978-1-60791-200-2(7))* Xulon Pr., Inc.

Davies, H. The Chancellors' Tales: Managing the British Economy. Davies, Howard, ed. 2007. (ENG., Illus.). 240p. pap. 24.95 *(978-0-7456-3885-0(6))* Polity Pr. GBR. Dist: Wiley, John & Sons, Inc.

Davies, Howard, ed. Chancellors' Tales: Managing the British Economy. 2006. (ENG.). 240p. 69.95 *(978-0-7456-3884-3(8))* Polity Pr. GBR. Dist: Wiley, John & Sons, Inc.

Decker, John. California in the Balance: Why Budgets Matter. 2009. *(978-0-87772-433-9(4))* Univ. of California, Institute of Governmental Studies.

Eckl, Corina & Perez, Arturo. State Budget Actions 2000. 35.00 *(978-1-58024-125-7(3)*, 5101-0119) National Conference of State Legislatures.

Elishaphat, Apostle. Basic Budgeting Work Book: The Help You Need to Build, Rebuild, or Improve Your Credit, & Get Yourself Out of Debt! 2010. 204p. 31.95 *(978-1-4502-4952-2(3))*; pap. 21.95 *(978-1-4502-4951-5(5))* iUniverse, Inc.

Field, Richard. Planning & Budgeting Skills for Health & Social Work Managers. 2012. (ENG., Illus.). 104p. pap. ***(978-0-85725-987-5(3))*** Learning Matters Ltd.

Finkler, Steven A. & McHugh, Mary. Budgeting Concepts for Nurse Managers. 4th rev. ed. 2007. (ENG., Illus.). 520p. (C). per. 80.95 *(978-1-4160-3341-7(6)*, Saunders) Elsevier - Health Sciences Div.

The Fiscal Year 2012 Budget for Veterans' Programs: Hearing Before the Committee on Veterans' Affairs, United States Senate, One Hundred Twelfth Congress, First Session, March 2, 2011. 2011. (Illus.) iii, 452p. ***(978-0-16-089826-6(9)***, 552-070-43675-8) United States Government Printing Office.

Friesen, Dwayne. The Simple Book of Budget & Money Management. 2011. 24p. pap. 12.99 ***(978-0-557-97393-4(7))*** Lulu Enterprises Inc.

Giuberti, Ana Carolina. Public Expenditure & Budget Rule. 2010. 64p. pap. *(978-3-639-25022-0(2))* VDM Verlag Dr. Mueller e.K.

Guess, George M. & LeLoup, Lance T. Comparative Public Budgeting: Global Perspectives on Taxing & Spending. 2010. (Illus.). 352p. 85.00 *(978-1-4384-3309-7(3))* State Univ. of New York Pr.

Hallerberg, Mark, et al. Fiscal Governance in Europe. (Cambridge Studies in Comparative Politics Ser.). (Illus.). 246p. 2010. pap. 29.99 *(978-0-521-13826-0(4))* 2009. (ENG., 88.00 *(978-0-521-85746-8(5))* Cambridge Univ. Pr.

Hartley, Keith. European Market Defence. 2008. (Routledge Studies in Defence & Peace Economics Ser.). (Illus.). 256p. 140.00 *(978-0-415-27132-5(0))* Routledge.

Hoff, Stella. The Minimum Agreed Upon: Consensual Budget Standards for the Netherlands. 2011. (Illus.). 160p. pap. 34.95 *(978-90-377-0472-3(7))* Aksant Academic Pubs. NLD. Dist: Transaction Pubs.

Jackson-Hill, Blanche. Straight to the Point Financing: A Quick & Easy Guide to Managing Your Money. 2010. pap. 7.99 *(978-1-61663-558-9(4))* Tate Publishing & Enterprises, LLC.

Juan Trafton Schmeltanzinger. Pennies-Fun-Heaven! The Priceless Life of a Trailer Park Shrink. 2009. 160p. pap. 12.95 *(978-1-4389-3114-2(X))* AuthorHouse.

Klumpp, Matthias. Modern Public Budgeting: Analyse und Bewertung von Informations- und Risikomanagementsystemen in Öffentlichen Einrichtungen am Beispiel einer Risk-Return-Steuerung für Hochschulen. 2008. (Schriften des Instituts für Finanzen. Universität Leipzig Ser.). (GRE.). 272p. pap. 74.95 *(978-3-631-56751-7(0))* Lang, Peter GmbH, Europaischer Verlag der Wissenschaften DEU. Dist: Lang, Peter.

The Legality & Efficacy of Line-Item Veto Proposals: Hearing Before the Subcommittee on the Constitution of the Committee on the Judiciary, United States Senate, One Hundred Eleventh Congress, Second Session, May 26, 2010. 2010. (Illus.). iii, 118p. *(978-0-16-086863-4(7)*, 552-070-41775-3) United States Government Printing Office.

LeLoup, Lance T. & Guess, George M. Comparative Public Budgeting: Global Perspectives on Taxing & Spending. 2011. (Illus.). 306p. pap. 26.95 ***(978-1-4384-3308-0(5)***, Suny Pr.) State Univ. of New York Pr.

Maier-Bledjian, Larissa. Sondervermögen des Bundes. 2011. (Finanz- und Steuerrecht in Deutschland und Europa Ser.). (GER.). 260p. 72.95 ***(978-3-631-62012-0(8))*** Lang, Peter GmbH, Europaischer Verlag der Wissenschaften DEU. Dist: Lang, Peter.

Manescu, Rare¿. Budgetary Policies in the Economic Development. 2011. 240p. pap. ***(978-3-8433-7799-7(5))*** Lambert Academic Publishing.

McGee, David G. The Budget Process: A Parlimentary Imperative. 2007. (ENG.). 171p. 84.00 *(978-0-7453-2774-7(5))* Pluto Pr. GBR. Dist: Macmillan.

Menifield, Charles E. The Basics of Public Budgeting & Financial Management: A Handbook for Academics & Practitioners. 2008. (ENG.). 250p. pap. 42.99 *(978-0-7618-4165-4(2))* Univ. Pr. of America, Inc.

—Comparative Public Budgeting & Finance. rev. ed. 2010. 392p. pap. 83.95 *(978-0-7637-8010-4(3))* Jones & Bartlett Learning, LLC.

Moravitz, Carl & Breul, Jonathan D. Integrating Performance & Budgets: The Budget Office of Tomorrow. Moravitz, Carl & Breul, Jonathan D., eds. 2007. (IBM Center for the Business of Government Book Ser.). (ENG., Illus.). 496p. 88.95 *(978-0-7425-5831-1(2))*; per. 37.95 *(978-0-7425-5832-8(0))* Rowman & Littlefield Publishers, Inc.

Nakray, Keerty, et al, eds. Gender-based Violence & Public Health: International Perspectives on Budgets & Policies. 2012. (ENG.). 240p. (C). 135.00 ***(978-0-415-50492-8(9))*** Routledge.

Office of Management and Budget (U.S.), ed. Historical Tables: Budget of the U. S. Government, Fiscal Year 2012. 2011. (ENG.). 360p. pap. 49.00 *(978-0-16-087368-3(1)*, Office of Management & Budget) United States Government Printing Office.

Organisation for Economic Co-operation and Development Staff. Evolutions in Budgetary Practice: Allen Schick & the OECD Senior Budget Officials. 2009. (Illus.). 458p. pap. 63.00 *(978-92-64-06087-6(1))* Organization for Economic Cooperation & Development.

Ossa Steer, Alfredo Enrique de la & López Gómez, Pierre Paolo. Análisis de la Imposición Parafiscal en Colombia. 2007. (SPA.). 107p. pap. 13.00 *(978-958-710-214-7(2))* Universidad Externado de Colombia COL. Dist: Siglo del Hombre.

Perera, Koswattage Priyanga & J. Kuruppu, Chamara. Two Worlds of Budgeting. 2010. 96p. pap. *(978-3-639-28195-8(0))* VDM Verlag Dr. Mueller e.K.

Phillips, Mookey Mae. Life on a Budget. 2010. 112p. pap. 12.95 *(978-1-4520-1337-4(3))* AuthorHouse.

Primary Research Group Staff. The Scientific & Technical Library Budget & Expenditure Report, 1995. Date not set. pap. 80.00 *(978-1-57440-001-4(0))* Primary Research Group.

Robinson, Mark. Budgeting for the Poor. 2008. (ENG., Illus.). 240p. 100.00 *(978-0-230-22478-0(4))* Palgrave Macmillan.

Rubin, Irene, ed. Public Budgeting: Policy, Process, & Politics. 2008. (ASPA Classics Ser.). (Illus.). 515p. 94.95 *(978-0-7656-1690-6(4))* Sharpe, M.E. Inc.

Rubin, Irene S., ed. Public Budgeting: Policy, Process, & Politics. 2008. (ASPA Classics Ser.). (ENG., Illus.). 528p. pap. 58.95 *(978-0-7656-1691-3(2))* Sharpe, M.E. Inc.

Rutayisire, Richard. Local Government Budgeting & Poverty Alleviation in Rwand. 2011. 128p. pap. ***(978-3-8433-8975-4(6))*** Lambert Academic Publishing.

Saddleback Educational Publishing, ed. Budgeting & Banking Math. 2011. (Lifeskills Math Ser.). (ENG.). 110p. (gr. 6-12). pap., tchr. ed. 21.95 *(978-1-61651-407-5(8))* Saddleback Educational Publishing.

Seal, W. B. & Ball, Amanda. The Impact of Local Government Modernisation Policies on Local Budgeting-CIMA Research Report: The Impact of Third Way Modernisation on Local Government Budgeting. 2008. (ENG., Illus.). 96p. pap. 78.95 *(978-0-7506-8981-6(1)*, CIMA Publishing) Elsevier Science & Technology Bks.

Shabazz, Bahiyah. Finances Are Linked to Emotions: Live Within Your Means. 2009. 100p. pap. 10.80 *(978-1-4389-5565-0(0))* AuthorHouse.

Shah, Anwar. Local Budgeting. 2007. (Public Sector Governance & Accountability Ser.). (ENG., Illus.). 408p. per. 35.00 *(978-0-8213-6945-6(8)*, 9780821369456) World Bank Pubns.

Shah, Anwar, ed. Budgeting & Budgetary Institutions. 2007. (Public Sector Governance & Accountability Ser.). (ENG., Illus.). 584p. per. 35.00 *(978-0-8213-6939-5(3)*, 9780821369395) World Bank Pubns.

—Participatory Budgeting. 2007. (Public Sector Governance & Accountability Ser.). (ENG., Illus.). 296p. pap. 35.00 incl. cd-rom *(978-0-8213-5923-4(7)*, 9780821369234) World Bank Pubns.

Stapenhurst, Rick. Legislative Oversight & Budgeting: A World Perspective. Stapenhurst, Rick et al, eds. 2008. (WBI Learning Resources Ser.). (ENG., Illus.). 300p. pap. 40.00 *(978-0-8213-7611-9(X)*, 9780821376119) World Bank Pubns.

Stewart, Charles Haynes. Budget Reform Politics: The Design of the Appropriations Process in the House of Representatives, 1865-1921. 2006. (Political Economy of Institutions & Decisions Ser.). (ENG.). 268p. pap. 53.00 *(978-0-521-03115-8(X))* Cambridge Univ. Pr.

Stourm, Rene. The Budget: A Translation. (Brookings Institution Reprint Ser.). reprint ed. lib. bdg. 42.00 *(978-0-697-00169-6(5))* Irvington Pubs.

Sury, M. M. Budgets & Budgetary Procedures in India: 1947-48 To 2009-10. 2009. 589p. 127.50 *(978-81-7708-204-3(3))* New Century Publications IND. Dist: International Specialized Bk. Services.

Verwey, Len & Mukamuri, B. Parliament, the Budget & Poverty in South Africa: A Shift in Power. 2008. 110p. pap. *(978-1-920118-91-4(8))* IDASA Pubs. ZAF. Dist: Michigan State Univ. Pr.

Wang, XiaoHu. Financial Management in the Public Sector: Tools, Applications, & Cases. 2nd rev. ed. 2010. (ENG.). 248p. (C). 99.95 *(978-0-7656-2521-2(0))*; (Illus.). pap. 46.95 *(978-0-7656-2522-9(9))* Sharpe, M.E. Inc.

Wanna, John. The Reality of Budgetary Reform in OECD Nations: Trajectories & Consequences. Wanna, John et al, eds. 2010. 328p. 139.00 *(978-1-84064-689-4(6))* Elgar, Edward Publishing, Inc.

Wehner, Joachim. Legislatures & the Budget Process: The Myth of Fiscal Control. 2010. (ENG., Illus.). 256p. 89.00 *(978-0-230-21972-4(1))* Palgrave Macmillan.

Wilhelm, Vera A. Minding the Gaps: Integrating Poverty Reduction Strategies & Budgets for Domestic Accountability. Krause, Philipp & Renzio, Paolo de, eds. 2007. (Books Ser.). (ENG., Illus.). 200p. pap. 25.00 *(978-0-8213-7205-0(X)*, 9780821372050) World Bank Pubns.

Willoughby, William F. Movement for Budgetary Reform in the States. (Brookings Institution Reprint Ser.). reprint ed. lib. bdg. 37.50 *(978-0-697-00174-0(1))* Irvington Pubs.

BUDGET—CANADA

Beach, Charles M. & Wilson, Thomas A. The 2006 Federal Budget: Rethinking Fiscal Priorities. Smart, Michael, ed. 2007. (John Deutsch Institute Ser.). (ENG., Illus.). 234p. (C). per. 34.95 *(978-1-55339-125-8(X))* Queen's Univ., Schl. of Policy Studies CAN. Dist: McGill-Queen's Univ. Pr.

Beach, Charles M., et al. The 2006 Federal Budget: Rethinking Fiscal Priorities. 2007. (John Deutsch Institute Ser.). (ENG., Illus.). 234p. (C). 95.00 *(978-1-55339-126-5(8))* Queen's Univ., Schl. of Policy Studies CAN. Dist: McGill-Queen's Univ. Pr.

—The 2009 Federal Budget: Challenge, Response & Retrospect. 2010. (John Deutsch Institute Ser.). (ENG.). 366p. (C). *(978-1-55339-166-1(7))*; pap. *(978-1-55339-165-4(9))* McGill-Queen's Univ. Pr.

Doern, G. Bruce, et al. Public Budgeting in Canada: Politics, Economics & Management, No. 147. 256p. pap. *(978-0-88629-069-6(4))* McGill-Queen's Univ. Pr.

Dutil, Patrice. Guardian. 2011. (IPAC Series in Public Management & Governance Ser.). (Illus.). xii, 364p. ***(978-1-4426-4254-6(8))*** Univ. of Toronto Pr.

Flaherty, James M. Canada's Economic Action Plan: The Budget Speech, 2009. 2009. 24p. pap. *(978-1-100-10835-3(1))* Dept. of Finance Canada.

Good, David A. The Politics of Public Money: Spenders, Guardians, Priority Setters, & Financial Watchdogs Inside the Canadian Government. 2007. (IPAC Series in Public Management & Governance Ser.). (ENG.). 352p. *(978-0-8020-9341-7(8))*; pap. *(978-0-8020-9503-9(8))* Univ. of Toronto Pr.

Villard, Harold Garrison. The Canadian Budgetary System. 2010. 214p. pap. *(978-1-151-94789-5(X))* Books LLC.

—The Canadian Budgetary System. 379p. reprint ed. 98.00 *(978-0-7222-6869-8(6))* Library Reprints, Inc.

BUDGET—UNITED STATES

Adams, Gordon. Buying National Security: How America Plans & Pays for Its Global Role & Safety at Home. 2009. (Illus.). 368p. 143.00 *(978-0-415-95439-6(8))* Routledge.

Alderete, Jaime Calleja. Budget Practices & State Expenditures: Lessons for California. 2007. *(978-1-58213-125-2(2))* Public Policy Institute of California.

Ammons, David N. & Fleck, Trevor/A. Budget-Balancing Tactics in Local Government. 2010. pap. 25.00 *(978-1-56011-645-5(5))* Schl. of Government.

Analysis of the President's Fiscal Year 2011 Budget with Treasury Secretary Timothy Geithner: Hearing Before the Committee on Finance, United States Senate, One Hundred Eleventh Congress, Second Session, February 2, 2010. 2010. iii, 162p. ***(978-0-16-089032-1(2)***, 552-070-43064-4) United States Government Printing Office.

Antonellis, Jonathan D. & Barone, Nicholas P., eds. Debt Limit Management & the Government's Role. 2011. (Series: Economic Issues, Problems & Perspectives Ser.). (Illus.). viii, 154p. 95.00 *(978-1-61324-418-0(5))* Nova Science Pubs., Inc.

Arnold, William G. Performance Budgeting: What Works, What Doesn't. 2008. *(978-1-56726-226-1(0))* Management Concepts, Inc.

A Balanced Budget Amendment to the Constitution: Hearing Before the Committee on the Judiciary, House of Representatives, One Hundred Twelfth Congress, First Session, October 4, 2011. 2011. (Illus.). iii, 114p. ***(978-0-16-090127-0(8)***, 552-070-43834-3) United States Government Printing Office.

Bittle, Scott & Johnson, Jean. Where Does the Money Go? Your Guided Tour to the Federal Budget Crisis. 2008. (Illus.). 336p. per. 16.95 *(978-0-06-124187-1(3))* 2011. 368p. pap. 16.99 *(978-0-06-202347-6(0))* HarperCollins Pubs. (Collins).

Bogusz, Christine, ed. The Budget & Economic Outlook, Fiscal Years 2012 To 2022. 2012. (ENG., Illus.). 147p. pap. 29.00 ***(978-0-16-090225-3(8)***, Congressional Budget Office) United States Government Printing Office.

Brenner, Gerard T. & Monroe, Alexander K., eds. United States Federal Budget Process. 2011. (Economic Issues, Problems & Perspectives Ser.). 89.00 *(978-1-61209-844-9(4))* Nova Science Pubs., Inc.

The Budget & Economic Outlook: Hearing Before the Committee on the Budget, House of Representatives, One Hundred Eleventh Congress, Second Session, Hearing Held in Washington, DC, January 27, 2010. 2010. (Illus.). iii, 55p. *(978-0-16-085767-6(8)*, 552-070-40985-8) United States Government Printing Office.

Budget Reform Proposals for the 111th Congress: Hearing Before the Committee on the Budget, House of Representatives, One Hundred Tenth Congress, Second Session, Hearing Held in Washington, DC, September 25, 2008. 2008. iii, 40p. *(978-0-16-082602-3(0)*, 552-070-38620-3) United States Government Printing Office.

Committee on the Fiscal Future of the United States, et al. Choosing the Nation's Fiscal Future. 2010. (ENG., Illus.). 268p. pap. 53.95 *(978-0-309-14723-1(9))* National Academies Pr.

Compilation of Laws & Rules Relating to the Congressional Budget Process: As Amended Through November 30, 2008. 2008. ix, 222p. *(978-0-16-082444-9(3)*, 552-070-38488-0) United States Government Printing Office.

Concurrent Resolution on the Budget Fiscal Year 2011: Hearings Before the Committee on the Budget, United States Senate, One Hundred Eleventh Congress, Second Session. 2010. (Illus.). iv, 525p. ***(978-0-16-088307-1(5)***, 552-070-42612-4) United States Government Printing Office.

Concurrent Resolution on the Budget for Fiscal Year 2009: Hearings Before the Committee on the Budget, United States Senate, One Hundred Tenth Congress, Second Session. 2008. (Illus.). iv, 606p. *(978-0-16-082157-8(5)*, 552-070-38294-1) United States Government Printing Office.

Congress (U.S.), Joint Committee on Taxation Staff, prod. Description of Revenue Provisions Contained in the President's Fiscal Year 2011 Budget Proposal. 2010. (ENG.). 326p. pap. 55.00 *(978-0-16-086327-1(9)*, Joint Committee on Taxation) United States Government Printing Office.

Congressional Budget Office, compiled by. Budget & Economic Outlook: an Update (2009) 2009. (ENG.). 89p. pap. 16.00 *(978-0-16-083881-1(9)*, Congressional Budget Office) United States Government Printing Office.

—Budget Options, Volume I: Health Care. 2008. (ENG.). 233p. pap. 35.00 *(978-0-16-082218-6(1)*, Congressional Budget Office) United States Government Printing Office.

Congressional Budget Office (U.S.), compiled by. Budget & Economic Outlook: Fiscal Years 2010-2021. 2011. (ENG.). 188p. pap. 29.00 *(978-0-16-087764-3(4)*, Congressional Budget Office) United States Government Printing Office.

Congressional Budget Office (U.S.), compiled by. An Analysis of the President's Budgetary Proposals for Fiscal Year 2009. 2008. (ENG.). 72p. pap. 10.00 *(978-0-16-080417-5(5)*, Congressional Budget Office) United States Government Printing Office.

—An Analysis of the President's Budgetary Proposals for Fiscal Year 2011. 2010. (ENG., Illus.). 54p. pap. 11.00 *(978-0-16-085363-0(X)*, Congressional Budget Office) United States Government Printing Office.

—The Long-Term Budget Outlook (June 2009) 2009. (ENG., Illus.). 80p. pap. 15.00 *(978-0-16-083497-4(X)*, Congressional Budget Office) United States Government Printing Office.

Congressional Budget Office (U.S.), ed. CBO's 2011 Long-Term Budget Outlook, June 2011. 2011. (ENG.). 106p. pap. 42.00 ***(978-0-16-088832-8(8)***, Congressional Budget Office) United States Government Printing Office.

Congressional Budget Office (U.S.), prod. Budget & Economic Outlook: Fiscal Years 2008 To 2018. 2008. (ENG.). 197p. pap. 28.00 *(978-0-16-079932-7(5)*, Congressional Budget Office) United States Government Printing Office.

Congressional Budget Office (U.S.) Staff, compiled by. An Analysis of the President's Budgetary Proposals for Fiscal Year 2012. 2011. (ENG., Illus.). 51p. pap. 11.00 ***(978-0-16-088524-2(8)***, Congressional Budget Office) United States Government Printing Office.

—The Budget & Economic Outlook: an Update. 2006. (ENG., Illus.). 200p. pap. 11.50 *(978-0-16-076807-1(1)*, Congressional Budget Office) United States Government Printing Office.

—Budget & Economic Outlook: an Update (2010) 2010. (ENG.). 102p. pap. 19.00 *(978-0-16-086400-1(3)*, Congressional Budget Office) United States Government Printing Office.

The Congressional Budget Office's Long-Term Budget Outlook: Hearing Before the Committee on the Budget, House of Representatives, One Hundred Twelfth Congress, First Session, Hearing Held in Washington, DC, June 23, 2011. 2011. (Illus.). iii, 60p. ***(978-0-16-089709-2(2)***, 552-070-43588-3) United States Government Printing Office.

Council of Economic Advisers (U.S.), compiled by. Economic Report of the President 2008. 2008. (ENG., Illus.). 358p. pap. 34.00 *(978-0-16-079822-1(1)*, Council of Economic Advisers) United States Government Printing Office.

Cram101 Textbook Reviews Staff. Outlines & Highlights for Politics of Public Budgeting by Rubin, Isbn: 9781933116068. 2009. 78p. pap. 26.95 *(978-1-4288-6782-6(1))* Cram101 Inc.

—Outlines & Highlights for Public Budgeting Systems by Lee Jr Robert D , Isbn: 9780763746681. 2009. 240p. pap. 31.95 *(978-1-4288-3311-1(0))* Cram101 Inc.

Crisis in the Future: Long-Run Deficits & Debt: Hearing Before the Committee on Finance, United States Senate, One Hundred Tenth Congress, Second Session, June 17, 2008. 2008. (Illus.). iii, 61p. *(978-0-16-086530-5(1)*, 552-070-41528-9) United States Government Printing Office.

Darling-Hammond, Linda. The Flat World & Education: How America's Commitment to Equity Will Determine Our Future. rev. ed. 2009. (Multicultural Education Ser.). (ENG.). 240p. pap. 21.95 *(978-0-8077-4962-3(1))* Teachers College Pr., Teachers College, Columbia Univ.

The Department of Defense & the Fiscal Year 2008 Budget: Hearing Before the Committee on the Budget, House of Representatives, One Hundred Tenth Congress, First Session, Hearing Held in Washington, DC, March 6, 2007. 2007. (Illus.). iii, 52p. *(978-0-16-079659-3(8)*, 552-070-36611-3) United States Government Printing Office.

Department of the Treasury Fiscal Year 2012 Budget: Hearing Before the Committee on the Budget, House of Representatives, One Hundred Twelfth Congress, First Session, Hearing Held in Washington, DC, February 16, 2011. 2011. iii, 54p. ***(978-0-16-088847-2(6)***, 552-070-42966-2) United States Government Printing Office.

DeSare, Fedro. The Republican Party's Path to Prosperity. 2011. (Congressional Policies, Practices & Procedures Ser.). 284p. 215.00 ***(978-1-61470-178-1(4))*** Nova Science Pubs., Inc.

Executive Office of the President, compiled by. Economic Report of the President. 2011. (Economic Report of the President Ser.). (ENG., Illus.). 318p. pap. 36.00 ***(978-1-60175-844-6(8)***, Executive Office of the President) United States Government Printing Office.

Executive Office of the President, creator. Budget of the U. S. Government Fiscal Year 2011: Analytical Perspectives. 2010. (Budget of the United States Government: Analytical Perspectives Ser.). (Illus.). 461p. pap. 52.00

(978-1-59804-533-8(4), Executive Office of the President) United States Government Printing Office.

—Budget of the United States Government Fiscal Year 2011: Historical Tables. 2010. (Budget of the United States Government: Historical Tables Ser.). (Illus.). 362p. pap. 49.00 *(978-1-59804-532-1(6)*, Executive Office of the President) United States Government Printing Office.

Federal Response to Market Turmoil: What's the Impact on the Budget: Hearing Before the Committee on the Budget, House of Representatives, One Hundred Tenth Congress, Second Session, Hearing Held in Washington, DC, September 24, 2008. 2008. (Illus.). iii, 47p. *(978-0-16-082457-9(5)*, 552-070-38500-2) United States Government Printing Office.

Garrett, Elizabeth, et al. Fiscal Challenges: An Interdisciplinary Approach to Budget Policy. (ENG., Illus.). 2009. 472p. pap. 40.99 *(978-0-521-14009-6(9))* 2007. 468p. 85.00 *(978-0-521-87731-2(8))* Cambridge Univ. Pr.

Gaskin, Jonathan B., ed. Congressional Budget Resolution & Reconciliation. 2011. (Congressional Policies, Practices & Procedures Ser.). 115.00 *(978-1-61209-845-6(2))* Nova Science Pubs., Inc.

Golub. COBRA Handbook 2011e. ring bd. *(978-0-7355-9119-6(9)*, Aspen Pubs.) Wolters Kluwer Law & Business.

Gordon, Tracy M. Fiscal Realities: Budget Tradeoffs in California Government. 2007. (Illus.). xxxiii, 243p. *(978-1-58213-118-4(X))* Public Policy Institute of California.

Gosling, James J. Budgeting Politics in American Governments. 5th ed. 2009. (ENG., Illus.). 302p. pap. 47.95 *(978-0-415-99511-5(6))*; 312p. 143.00 *(978-0-415-80015-0(3))* Routledge.

Groff, Darren & Rutherford, Blaine, eds. Federal Budget Control: A Balanced Budget Amendment or Statutory Limits? 2012. pap. ***(978-1-61942-051-9(1))*** Nova Science Pubs., Inc.

Hallerberg, Mark Stephen, et al. Who Decides the Budget? 2009. (David Rockefeller/Inter-American Development Bank Ser.). (Illus.). 304p. pap. 29.95 *(978-1-59782-089-9(X))* Americas Society.

Halstead, Roger D., ed. Earmarks: Disclosure, Legal Developments & Transportation Funding. 2011. (Congressional Policies, Practices & Procedures Ser.). 109p. pap. 42.00 *(978-1-61324-588-0(2))* Nova Science Pubs., Inc.

Hatchá, Garrett L. Financial Services & General Government Appropriations. 2008. viii, 111p. pap. 45.00 *(978-1-60456-694-9(9))* Nova Science Pubs., Inc.

Hiber, Amanda. The Federal Budget. 2010. (Opposing Viewpoints Ser.). 240p. pap. 26.75 *(978-0-7377-4770-6(6))*; (Illus.). 38.50 *(978-0-7377-4769-0(2))* Cengage Gale. (Greenhaven Pr., Inc.).

H.R. 733, D.C. Budget Autonomy & H.R. 1054, D.C. Legislative Autonomy ACT: Hearing Before the Subcommittee on Federal Workforce, Postal Service, & the District of Columbia of the Committee on Oversight & Government Reform, House of Representatives, One Hundred Tenth Congress, First Session, on H.R. 733 ... & on H.R. 1054 ... June 7, 2007. 2010. iii, 59p. *(978-0-16-085888-8(7)*, 552-070-41084-8) United States Government Printing Office.

H.R. 960, & H.R. 1045, Greater Autonomy for the Nation's Capitol: Hearing Before the Subcommittee on Federal Workforce, Postal Service, & the District of Columbia of the Committee on Oversight & Government Reform, House of Representatives, One Hundred Eleventh Congress, First Session, on H.R. 960 ... H.R. 1045 ... November 18, 2009. 2010. (Illus.). iii, 104p. *(978-0-16-086645-6(6)*, 552-070-41623-4) United States Government Printing Office.

Inhurst, Raymond W. Health Care Costs: Outlook & Options. 2009. (Illus.). 92p. 69.00 *(978-1-60692-151-7(7))* Nova Science Pubs., Inc.

Jessica C. Anderson. The Long-Term Budget Outlook: Federal Budget Spending & Revenue Scenarios. 2011. (Series: Economic Issues, Problems & Perspectives Ser.). 89.00 *(978-1-61122-190-9(0))* Nova Science Pubs., Inc.

Jones, L. R. & McCaffery, Jerry L. Budgeting, Financial Management, & Acquisition Reform in the U S Department of Defense. 2007. 720p. (C). (ENG.). 73.99 *(978-1-59311-871-6(6))*; per. 39.99 *(978-1-59311-870-9(8))* Information Age Publishing, Inc.

Joyce, Philip G. The Congressional Budget Office: Honest Numbers, Power, & Policymaking. 2011. (American Governance & Public Policy Ser.). (ENG.). 264p. pap. 29.95 *(978-1-58901-757-3(9))* Georgetown Univ. Pr.

Krawitz, Natalie. Effective Practice for Academic Leaders: Budgeting for Department Chairs. 2007. (Effective Practices for Academic Leaders Archive Ser.). 16p. pap. 20.00 *(978-1-57922-168-3(8))* Stylus Publishing, LLC.

Leclaire, Jodlle. The Great Deficit Debacle. 2008. 128p. pap. *(978-3-639-03077-8(X))* VDM Verlag Dr. Mueller e.K.

Lee, Mike. The Freedom Agenda: Why a Balanced Budget Amendment Is Necessary to Restore Constitutional Government. 2011. (ENG.). 240p. 24.95 *(978-1-59698-288-8(8))* Regnery Publishing, Inc., An Eagle Publishing Co.

Lee, Robert D., et al. Public Budgeting Systems. 8th rev. ed. 2007. (Illus.). 757p. 135.95 *(978-0-7637-4668-1(1))* Jones & Bartlett Learning, LLC.

Lewis, Carol W. & Hildreth, W Bartley. Budgeting: Politics & Power, 1 vol. 2010. 384p. (C). pap. 49.95 *(978-0-19-538745-2(7))* Oxford Univ. Pr., Inc.

Loizeau, Pierre-Marie. Budget & Economic Outlook: Fiscal Years 2008 To 2018. 2008. 49.00 *(978-1-60456-772-4(4))* Nova Science Pubs., Inc.

Lynch, Christopher G. & McHale, Cory. Budget Control Act Of 2011. 2012. ***(978-1-61942-035-9(X))*** Nova Science Pubs., Inc.

Management and Budget (U.S.) Office, compiled by. Budget of the United States Government Fiscal Year 2008. 2007. (ENG., Illus.). 192p. per. 41.00 *(978-0-16-077508-6(6)*, Office of Management & Budget) United States Government Printing Office.

Mandelbaum, Michael. The Frugal Superpower: America's Global Leadership in a Cash-Strapped Era. (ENG., Illus.). 2011. 256p. pap. 15.99 *(978-1-61039-054-5(7))* 2010. 224p. 23.95 *(978-1-58648-916-8(X))* PublicAffairs.

Melville, Keith, et al. The $9 Trillion Debt: Breaking the Habit of Deficit Spending. Tebbetts, Ilse, ed. 2007. (Illus.). 30p. 3.90 *(978-0-945639-38-1(4))* National Issues Forums Institute.

Members' Day: Hearing Before the Committee on the Budget, House of Representatives, One Hundred Tenth Congress, Second Session, Hearing Held in Washington, DC, February 28, 2008. 2008. iv, 134p. *(978-0-16-081366-5(2)*, 552-070-37744-1) United States Government Printing Office.

Members' Day: Hearing Before the Committee on the Budget, House of Representatives, One Hundred Twelfth Congress, First Session, Hearing Held in Washington, DC, March 30, 2011. 2011. (Illus.). v, 159p. ***(978-0-16-088771-0(2)***, 552-070-42911-5) United States Government Printing Office.

Mikesell, John L. & Mullins, Daniel R., eds. The Evolution of Public Finance & Budgeting: A Quarter Century of Developments. 2006. (ENG., Illus.). 188p. pap. 39.95 *(978-1-4051-5671-4(6)*, Wiley-Blackwell) Wiley, John & Sons, Inc.

Musell, R. Mark. Understanding Government Budgets: A Practical Guide. 2008. (ENG., Illus.). 120p. 36.95 *(978-0-415-99012-7(2))*; 143.00 *(978-0-415-99011-0(4))* Routledge.

Neely, Lawrence P. & Lerner, Patricia V., eds. Economic Policies: Issues & Developments. 2008. (Illus.). 121p. (C). 185.00 *(978-1-60456-260-6(9))* Nova Science Pubs., Inc.

Obama, Barack. A New Era of Responsibility: Renewing America's Promise. 2009. (ENG., Illus.). 140p. pap. 26.00 *(978-0-16-082552-1(0)*, Office of Management & Budget) United States Government Printing Office.

Office of Budget and Managment, creator. Budget of the United States Government Fiscal Year 2012: Historical Tables. 2011. (Budget of the United States Government: Historical Tables Ser.). (Illus.). 354p. pap. 49.00 *(978-1-59804-588-8(1))* Claitor's Publishing Div., Inc.

Office of Management & Budget, creator. Historical Tables: Budget of the U. S. Government. 2007. (Budget of the United States Government: Historical Tables Ser.). (Illus.). 335p. pap. 75.00 *(978-1-59804-387-7(0))* United States Government Printing Office.

Office of Management and Budget. Budget of the U. S. Government: Analytical Perspectives: Fiscal Year. 2009. (Budget of the United States Government: Analytical Perspectives Ser.). (Illus.). 415p. pap. 52.00 *(978-1-59804-489-8(3))* Claitor's Publishing Div., Inc.

—A New Era of Responsibility: Renewing America's Promise. 2009. (Illus.). 134p. pap. 26.00 *(978-1-59804-478-2(8))* Claitor's Publishing Div., Inc.

Office of Management and Budget, creator. Analytical Perspectives: Budget of the United States Government, Fiscal Year 2009. 2008. (Budget of the United States Government: Analytical Perspectives Ser.). (Illus.). 410p. per. 52.00 *(978-1-59804-407-2(9)*, Office of Management & Budget) United States Government Printing Office.

—Budget of the U. S. Government Fiscal Year 2012. 2011. (Budget of the United States Government Ser.). (Illus.). 208p. pap. 37.00 *(978-1-59804-586-4(5))* Claitor's Publishing Div., Inc.

—Historical Tables: Budget of the United States Government, Fiscal Year 2009. 2008. (Budget of the United States Government: Historical Tables Ser.). (Illus.). 335p. per. 49.00 *(978-1-59804-408-9(7)*, Office of Management & Budget) United States Government Printing Office.

Office of Management and Budget (U.S.), compiled by. Analytical Perspectives: Budget of the U. S. Government, Fiscal Year 2012. 2011. (ENG., Illus.). 504p. pap. 52.00 *(978-0-16-087369-0(X)*, Office of Management & Budget) United States Government Printing Office.

—Analytical Perspectives: Budget of the U. S. Government, Fiscal Year 2011. 2010. (ENG., Illus.). 465p. 52.00 *(978-0-16-084798-1(2)*, Office of Management & Budget) United States Government Printing Office.

—Analytical Perspectives: Budget of the United States Government, Fiscal Year 2009. 2008. (ENG.). 414p. pap. 1.00 *(978-0-16-079690-6(3)*, Office of Management & Budget) United States Government Printing Office.

—Appendix, Budget of the United States Government, Fiscal Year 2009. 2008. (ENG.). 1246p. pap. 1.00 *(978-0-16-079687-6(3)*, Office of Management & Budget) United States Government Printing Office.

—Budget of the United States Government, Fiscal Year 2009. 2008. (ENG., Illus.). 184p. pap. 1.00 *(978-0-16-079686-9(5)*, Office of Management & Budget) United States Government Printing Office.

—Budget of the United States Government, Fiscal Year 2011. 2010. (ENG., Illus.). 188p. pap. 39.00 *(978-0-16-084795-0(8)*, Office of Management & Budget) United States Government Printing Office.

—Budget of the United States Government, Fiscal Year 2012. 2011. (ENG., Illus.). 188p. pap. 38.00 *(978-0-16-087366-9(5)*, Office of Management & Budget) United States Government Printing Office.

—The Federal Budget on CD-ROM: Budget of the United States Government, Fiscal Year 2009. 2008. (ENG.). cd-rom 1.00 *(978-0-16-079688-3(1)*, Office of Management & Budget) United States Government Printing Office.

—Fiscal Year 2013 Analytical Perspectives: Budget of the U. S. Government. 2012. (ENG.). 505p. pap. 53.00 ***(978-0-16-090044-0(1)***, Office of Management & Budget) United States Government Printing Office.

—Historical Tables: Budget of the United States Government, Fiscal Year 2009. 2008. (ENG.). 334p. pap. 1.00 *(978-0-16-079689-0(X)*, Office of Management & Budget) United States Government Printing Office.

—Preparation, Submission, & Execution of the Budget, July 2007. rev. ed. 2007. (ENG.). 860p. 66.00 *(978-0-16-078742-3(4)*, Office of Management & Budget) United States Government Printing Office.

—Preparation, Submission, & Execution of the Budget, July 2008 (Paper Edition) 2008. (ENG.). 700p. 73.00 *(978-0-16-081005-3(1)*, Office of Management & Budget) United States Government Printing Office.

Office of Management and Budget (U.S.), ed. Appendix, Budget of the United States Government, Fiscal Year 2011. 2010. (ENG.). 1416p. pap. 73.00 *(978-0-16-084796-7(6)*, Office of Management & Budget) United States Government Printing Office.

—Budget of the U. S. Government, Fiscal Year 2010 (CD-ROM) 2009. (ENG.). cd-rom 24.95 *(978-0-16-082763-1(9)*, Office of Management & Budget) United States Government Printing Office.

—Budget of the U. S. Government, Fiscal Year 2012 (CD-ROM) 2011. (ENG.). cd-rom 27.00 *(978-0-16-087370-6(3)*, Office of Management & Budget) United States Government Printing Office.

—Budget of the U. S. Government, Fiscal Year 2013. 2012. (ENG.). cd-rom 27.00 ***(978-0-16-090045-7(X)***, Office of Management & Budget) United States Government Printing Office.

—Fiscal Year 2013 Appendix, Budget of the United States Government. 2012. (ENG.). 1368p. pap. 76.00 ***(978-0-16-090042-6(5)***, Office of Management & Budget) United States Government Printing Office.

—Fiscal Year 2013 Budget of the U. S. Government. 2012. (ENG.). 255p. pap. 39.00 ***(978-0-16-090041-9(7)***, Office of Management & Budget) United States Government Printing Office.

—Fiscal Year 2013 Historical Tables: Budget of the U. S. Government. 2012. (ENG.). 360p. pap. 50.00 ***(978-0-16-090043-3(3)***, Office of Management & Budget) United States Government Printing Office.

—Historical Tables: Budget of the U. S. Government, Fiscal Year 2011. 2010. (ENG.). 366p. pap. 49.00 *(978-0-16-084797-4(4)*, Office of Management & Budget) United States Government Printing Office.

—Updated Summary Tables: Budget of the U. S. Government, Fiscal Year 2010. 2009. (ENG.). 32p. pap. 9.00 *(978-0-16-083083-9(4)*, Office of Management & Budget) United States Government Printing Office.

Office of Management and Budget (U.S.) Staff, compiled by. Appendix, Budget of the United States Government, Fiscal Year 2008. 2007. (ENG.). 1241p. pap. 73.00 *(978-0-16-077506-2(X)*, Office of Management & Budget) United States Government Printing Office.

Office of Managment and Budget, creator. Budget of the U. S. Government Fiscal Year Appendix 2 Volume Set. 2011. (Budget of the United States Government: Appendix Ser.). pap. 73.00 *(978-1-59804-589-5(X))* Claitor's Publishing Div., Inc.

Okada, Michael S. Federal Budget Outlook & Economic Implications. 2011. (Economic Issues, Problems & Perspectives Ser.). 89.00 *(978-1-61761-769-0(5))* Nova Science Pubs., Inc.

Olsen, Karen D. What Brain Research Can Teach about Cutting School Budgets. Olsen, Karen D., ed. 2010. (Illus.). 224p. pap. 36.95 *(978-1-4129-8049-4(6)*, B80494P) Corwin Pr.

Orszag, Peter R. The President's Fiscal Year 2011 Budget Overview with OMB Director Peter R. Orszag: Hearing Before the Committee on Ways & Means, U.S. House of Representatives, One Hundred Eleventh Congress, Second Session, February 3, 2010. 2011. (Illus.). iii, 55p. ***(978-0-16-088683-6(X)***, 552-070-42847-0) United States Government Printing Office.

Page, Ben. Long-Term Budget Outlook. (ENG.). 20p. (C). 2009. pap. 15.00 *(978-1-4379-0327-0(4))* 2008. pap. 15.00 *(978-1-4379-0131-3(X))* DIANE Publishing Co.

Phillips, Mookey Mae. Life on a Budget. 2010. 112p. 22.50 *(978-1-4520-1338-1(1))* AuthorHouse.

The President's Fiscal Year 2009 Budget: Hearing Before the Committee on the Budget, House of Representatives, One Hundred Tenth Congress, Second Session, Hearing Held in Washington, DC, February 7, 2008. 2008. (Illus.). iii, 39p. *(978-0-16-080905-7(3)*, 552-070-37440-0) United States Government Printing Office.

The President's Fiscal Year 2009 Budget: Hearing Before the Committee on Ways & Means, U.S. House of Representatives, One Hundred Tenth Congress, Second Session, February 13, 2008. 2009. iii, 57p. *(978-0-16-083028-0(1)*, 552-070-38923-7) United States Government Printing Office.

President's Fiscal Year 2009 Budget (Revenue Proposals) Hearing Before the Committee on Finance, United States Senate, One Hundred Tenth Congress, Second Session, February 5, 2008. 2008. iii, 44p. *(978-0-16-085222-0(6)*, 552-070-40564-0) United States Government Printing Office.

The President's Fiscal Year 2010 Budget: Hearing Before the Committee on the Budget, House of Representatives, One Hundred Eleventh Congress, First Session, Hearing Held in Washington, DC, March 3, 2009. 2009. (Illus.). ii, 85p. *(978-0-16-083179-9(2)*, 552-070-39026-0) United States Government Printing Office.

President's Fiscal Year 2010 Budget Overview: Hearing Before the Committee on Ways & Means, U.S. House of Representatives, One Hundred Eleventh Congress, First Session, March 3, 2009. 2009. iii, 63p. *(978-0-16-083700-5(6)*, 552-070-39407-9) United States Government Printing Office.

President's Fiscal Year 2010 Budget Overview: Hearing Before the Committee on Ways & Means, U.S. House of Representatives, One Hundred Eleventh Congress, First Session, March 4, 2009. 2009. iii, 86p. *(978-0-16-083909-2(2)*, 552-070-39598-9) United States Government Printing Office.

President's Fiscal Year 2010 Budget Proposal: Hearing Before the Committee on Finance, United States Senate, One Hundred Eleventh Congress, First Session, March 4, 2009. 2009. (Illus.). iii, 108p. ***(978-0-16-087479-6(3)***, 552-070-42167-0) United States Government Printing Office.

The President's Fiscal Year 2011 Budget: Hearing Before the Committee on the Budget, House of Representatives, One Hundred Eleventh Congress, Second Session, Hearing Held in Washington, DC, February 2, 2010. 2010. (Illus.). iii, 74p. ***(978-0-16-086534-3(4)***, 552-070-41532-7) United States Government Printing Office.

The President's Fiscal Year 2011 Budget: Hearing Before the Committee on Ways & Means, U.S. House of Representatives, One Hundred Eleventh Congress, Second Session, February 3, 2010. 2011. iii, 51p. ***(978-0-16-088657-7(0)***, 552-070-42823-2) United States Government Printing Office.

The President's Fiscal Year 2012 Budget: Hearing Before the Committee on the Budget, House of Representatives, One Hundred Twelfth Congress, First Session, Hearing Held in Washington, DC, February 15, 2011. 2011. (Illus.). iii, 82p. ***(978-0-16-088852-6(2)***, 552-070-42971-9) United States Government Printing Office.

Primo, David M. Rules & Restraint: Government Spending & the Design of Institutions. 2007. (American Politics & Political Economy Ser.). (ENG., Illus.). 216p. 55.00 *(978-0-226-68259-4(5))*; per. 22.50 *(978-0-226-68260-0(9))* Univ. of Chicago Pr.

Ripley. Policy Making in the Federal Executive Branch. 2007. (ENG.). 228p. pap. 16.95 *(978-1-4165-7762-1(9)*, Free Pr.) Free Pr.

Rivlin, Alice M. & Antos, Joseph R., eds. Restoring Fiscal Sanity: The Health Spending Challenge. 2007. (ENG., Illus.). 233p. per. 18.95 *(978-0-8157-7493-8(1))* Brookings Institution Pr.

Roach, Phil & Roach, Sandra, told to. Facing the Financial Disaster Ahead: The Dirty Little Secret Your Government Doesn't Want You to Understand. 2008. 58p. pap. 16.95 *(978-1-60474-806-2(0))* PublishAmerica, Inc.

Rubin, Irene S. The Politics of Public Budgeting: Getting & Spending, Borrowing & Balancing, 6th Edition, 00 vols. 6th rev. ed. 2009. pap. 52.00 *(978-1-60426-461-6(6))* CQ Pr.

Ryu, Jay Eungha. Bounded Bureaucracy & the Budgetary Process in the United States. 2011. (ENG., Illus.). 223p. 49.95 *(978-1-4128-4289-1(1))* Transaction Pubs.

The SAFE Commission ACT (H.R. 3654) & the Long-Term Fiscal Challenge: Hearing Before the Committee on the Budget, House of Representatives, One Hundred Tenth Congress, Second Session, Hearing Held in Washington, DC, June 24, 2008. 2008. (Illus.). iii, 65p. *(978-0-16-081880-6(X)*, 552-070-38055-8) United States Government Printing Office.

Schick, Allen. The Federal Budget: Politics, Policy, Process. 3rd ed. 2007. (ENG., Illus.). 345p. per. 24.95 *(978-0-8157-7735-9(3))* Brookings Institution Pr.

Selee, Andrew D. & Peruzzotti, Enrique, eds. Participatory Innovation & Representative Democracy in Latin America. 2009. (ENG., Illus.). 184p. (gr. 17). 49.95 *(978-0-8018-9406-0(9))*; pap. 24.95 *(978-0-8018-9407-7(7))* Johns Hopkins Univ. Pr.

Singh, Robert P. A Guide to the Economics & Fiscal Performance of the Federal Government (1976-2007) 2008. pap. 29.00 *(978-1-60692-428-0(1))* Nova Science Pubs., Inc.

Spend Less, Owe Less, Grow the Economy: Hearing Before the Joint Economic Committee, Congress of the United States, One Hundred Twelfth Congress, First Session, June 21, 2011. 2011. (Illus.). iii, 101p. ***(978-0-16-089989-8(3)***, 552-070-43773-8) United States Government Printing Office.

Sun, Jinping & Lynch, Thomas D., eds. Government Budget Forecasting: Theory & Practice. 2008. (Public Administration & Public Policy Ser.). (ENG., Illus.). 664p. 109.95 *(978-1-4200-4582-6(2))* Auerbach Pubs., Inc.

Swain, John W. & Reed, B. J. Budgeting for Public Managers. 2010. (ENG.). 240p. (C). 99.95 *(978-0-7656-2524-3(5))*; pap. 57.95 *(978-0-7656-2050-7(2))* Sharpe, M.E. Inc.

Taxes As Part of the Federal Budget: Hearing Before the Subcommittee on Select Revenue Measures of the Committee on Ways & Means, U.S. House of Representatives, One Hundred Tenth [i.e. Eleventh] Congress, Second Session, March 23, 2010. 2010. (Illus.). iii, 164p. ***(978-0-16-089261-5(9)***, 552-070-43257-4) United States Government Printing Office.

Treasury Department Fiscal Year 2010 Budget: Hearing Before the Committee on the Budget, House of Representatives, One Hundred Eleventh Congress, First Session, Hearing Held in Washington, DC, March 5, 2009. 2009. iii, 53p. *(978-0-16-084244-3(1)*, 552-070-39814-7) United States Government Printing Office.

Treasury Department Fiscal Year 2011 Budget: Hearing Before the Committee on the Budget, House of Representatives, One Hundred Eleventh Congress, Second Session, Hearing Held in Washington, DC, February 24, 2010. 2010. (Illus.). iii, 64p. *(978-0-16-085889-5(5)*, 552-070-41085-6) United States Government Printing Office.

United States, Congress House Committee on the Budget Staff, contrib. by. Budgeting for War Costs: Hearing Before the Committee on the Budget, House of Representatives, One Hundred Tenth Congress, First Session, Hearing Held in Washington, DC, January 18, 2007. 2007. (Illus.). iii, 78p. *(978-0-16-078086-8(1)*, 552-070-35499-9) United States Government Printing Office.

—The Congressional Budget Office's Budget & Economic Outlook: Hearing Before the Committee on the Budget, House of Representatives, One Hundred Tenth Congress, First Session, Hearing Held in Washington, DC, January 30, 2007. 2007. (Illus.). iii, 54p. *(978-0-16-078206-0(6)*, 552-070-35590-1) United States Government Printing Office.

—Members' Day: Hearing Before the Committee on the Budget, House of Representatives, One Hundred Tenth Congress, First Session, Hearing Held in Washington, DC, February 14, 2007. 2007. iv, 134p. *(978-0-16-078387-6(9)*, 552-070-35692-4) United States Government Printing Office.

—The President's Fiscal Year 2008 Budget: Hearing Before the Committee on the Budget, House of Representatives, One Hundred Tenth Congress, First Session, Hearing Held in Washington, DC, February 6, 2007. 2007. (Illus.). iii, 81p. *(978-0-16-078643-3(6)*, 552-070-35885-4) United States Government Printing Office.

United States, Congress House Committee on Ways and Means Staff, contrib. by. President's Fiscal Year 2008 Budget with OMB Director Rob Portman: Hearing Before the Committee on Ways & Means, U.S. House of Representatives, One Hundred Tenth Congress, First Session, February 7, 2007. 2007. (Illus.). iii, 51p. *(978-0-16-078746-1(7)*, 552-070-35955-9) United States Government Printing Office.

—President's Fiscal Year 2008 Budget with U.S. Department of the Treasury Secretary Henry Paulson: Hearing Before the Committee on Ways & Means, U.S. House of Representatives, One Hundred Tenth Congress, First Session, February 6, 2007. 2007. iii, 39p. *(978-0-16-078688-4(6)*, 552-070-35917-6) United States Government Printing Office.

United States, Congress Joint Economic Committee Staff contrib. by. The Economic Report of the President: Hearing Before the Joint Economic Committee, Congress of the United States, One Hundred Ninth Congress, Second Session, February 16, 2006. 2007. (Illus.). iii, 31p. *(978-0-16-078128-5(0)*, 552-070-35528-6) United States Government Printing Office.

United States Government Printing Office, creator. Economic Report of the President. 2008. (Economic Report of the President Ser.). (Illus.). 354p. per. 34.00 *(978-1-59804-400-3(1))* United States Government Printing Office.

U.S Department of Veterans Affairs' Vocational Rehabilitation & Employment Program Budget & VRandE National Counseling Contract: Hearing Before the Subcommittee on Economic Opportunity of the Committee on Veterans' Affairs, U.S. House of Representatives, One Hundred Twelfth Congress, First Session, March 31, 2011. 2011. iv, 66p. ***(978-0-16-089514-2(6)***, 552-070-43473-9) United States Government Printing Office.

Using Fiscal Policy to Bolster the U.S. Economy: Hearing Before the Committee on the Budget, House of Representatives, One Hundred Tenth Congress, Second Session, Hearing Held in Washington, DC, January 29, 2008. 2008. iii, 64p. *(978-0-16-080744-2(1)*, 552-070-37348-9) United States Government Printing Office.

Walker, Raleigh E. America's Long-Term Fiscal Outlook. 2009. (America in the 21st Century: Political & Economic Issues Ser.). 69.00 *(978-1-60741-332-5(9))* Nova Science Pubs., Inc.

Whether the Constitution Should Be Amended to Address the Federal Deficit? Hearing Before the Subcommittee on the Constitution of the Committee on the Judiciary, House of Representatives, One Hundred Twelfth Congress, First Session, May 13, 2011. 2011. iii, 55p. ***(978-0-16-089059-8(4)***, 552-070-43091-1) United States Government Printing Office.

White House Historical Association Staff & The Council of Economic Advisors, compiled by. The 2007 Economic Report of the President. 2007. 356p. per. 29.95 *(978-1-60206-399-0(0))* Cosimo, Inc.

Wildavsky, Aaron. Budgeting & Governing. Swedlow, Brendon, ed. 2006. (ENG., Illus.). 393p. (gr. 11). pap. 29.95 *(978-1-4128-0625-1(9))* Transaction Pubs.

BUDGET—UNITED STATES—STATES

Bland, Robert L. A Budgeting Guide for Local Government. 2nd ed. 2007. (ENG.). 199p. 69.00 *(978-0-87326-713-7(3))* International City/County Management Assn.

Clynch, Edward J. & Lauth, Thomas P., eds. Budgeting in the States: Institutions, Processes, & Politics, 1 vol. 2006. (Illus.). 332p. 194.95 *(978-0-275-98013-9(8)*, C8013, Praeger Pubs.) Greenwood Publishing Group, Inc.

Economic Recovery Options & Challenges: Hearing Before the Committee on the Budget, House of Representatives, One Hundred Tenth Congress, Second Session, Hearing Held in Washington, DC, October 20, 2008. 2008. (Illus.). iii, 89p. *(978-0-16-082578-1(4)*, 552-070-38599-1) United States Government Printing Office.

Forsythe, Dall W. & Boyd, Donald J. Memos to the Governor: An Introduction to State Budgeting. 3rd rev. ed. 2012. 112p. (C). pap. 19.95 ***(978-1-58901-924-9(5))*** Georgetown Univ. Pr.

Kelly, Janet M. & Rivenbark, William C. Performance Budgeting for State & Local Government. 2nd rev. ed. 2010. (ENG.). 256p. (C). pap. 54.95 *(978-0-7656-2394-2(3))*; (Illus.). 89.95 *(978-0-7656-2393-5(5))* Sharpe, M.E. Inc.

Walters, Benjamin J. Call for A New Era in the U. S. Budget. 2011. (American Political, Economic, & Security Issues Ser.). 115.00 *(978-1-60741-883-2(5))* Nova Science Pubs., Inc.

BUDGET COOKING, LOW

see Low Budget Cooking

BUDGET DEFICITS

see also Deficit Financing

Beck, Glenn & Balfe, Kevin. Broke: The Plan to Restore Our Trust, Truth & Treasure. (ENG.). 416p. 2012. pap. 19.99 ***(978-1-4516-9344-7(3))*** 2010. (Illus.). 29.99 *(978-1-4391-8719-7(3))* Threshold Editions. (Threshold Editions).

Bergsten, C. Fred. The Long-Term International Economic Position of the United States. 2009. (Illus.). vi, 83p. pap. 17.95 *(978-0-88132-432-7(9))* Peterson Institute for International Economics.

Bittle, Scott & Johnson, Jean. Where Does the Money Go? Your Guided Tour to the Federal Budget Crisis. 2008. (Illus.). 336p. per. 16.95 *(978-0-06-124187-1(3))* 2011. 368p. pap. 16.99 *(978-0-06-202347-6(0))* HarperCollins Pubs. (Collins).

Congressional Budget Office (U.S.), ed. Reducing the Deficit: Spending & Revenue Options: Spending & Revenue Options. 2011. (ENG., Illus.). 260p. pap. 41.00 ***(978-0-16-088156-5(0)***, Congressional Budget Office) United States Government Printing Office.

The Congressional Budget Office's Long-Term Budget Outlook: Hearing Before the Committee on the Budget, House of Representatives, One Hundred Twelfth Congress, First Session, Hearing Held in Washington, DC, June 23, 2011. 2011. (Illus.). iii, 60p. ***(978-0-16-089709-2(2)***, 552-070-43588-3) United States Government Printing Office.

Crisis in the Future: Long-Run Deficits & Debt: Hearing Before the Committee on Finance, United States Senate, One Hundred Tenth Congress, Second Session, June 17, 2008. 2008. (Illus.). iii, 61p. *(978-0-16-086530-5(1)*, 552-070-41528-9) United States Government Printing Office.

Department of the Treasury Fiscal Year 2012 Budget: Hearing Before the Committee on the Budget, House of Representatives, One Hundred Twelfth Congress, First Session, Hearing Held in Washington, DC, February 16, 2011. 2011. iii, 54p. ***(978-0-16-088847-2(6)***, 552-070-42966-2) United States Government Printing Office.

Faloon, William. Pharmocracy: How Corrupt Deals & Misguided Medical Regulations Are Bankrupting America — and What to Do about It. 2011. (ENG.). 381p. 24.00 ***(978-1-60766-011-8(3))*** Axios Pr.

Ferrara, Peter. America's Ticking Bankruptcy Bomb: How the Looming Debt Crisis Threatens the American Dream - And How We Can Turn the Tide Before It's Too Late. 2011. (ENG.). 288p. 25.99 *(978-0-06-202577-7(5))* Broadside Bks. GBR. Dist: HarperCollins Pubs.

Ferrarini, Benno, et al, eds. Sovereign Debt Sustainability in Asia & the Pacific. 2012. (ENG., Illus.). 280p. (C). 152.00 ***(978-0-415-52221-2(8))*** Routledge.

Fisher, Patrick. The Politics of Taxing & Spending. 2009. (Illus.). 200p. (C). 55.00 *(978-1-58826-644-6(3))*; pap. 19.95 *(978-1-58826-619-4(2))* Rienner, Lynne Pubs.

George W. Morse. The Minnesota Response: Cooperative Extension's Money & Mission Crisis. 2009. 428p. pap. 26.95 *(978-1-4401-5541-3(0))* iUniverse, Inc.

Hargis, Frederick C. Federal Spending: A Riddle Wrapped up in an Enigma. 2010. (American Political, Economic, & Security Issues Ser.). 176p. 79.00 *(978-1-60741-728-6(6))* Nova Science Pubs., Inc.

Ihori, Toshihiro & Sato, Masakazu, eds. Government Deficit & Fiscal Reform in Japan. 2010. (Research Monographs in Japan-U. S. Business & Economics Ser.). 184p. pap. 159.00 *(978-1-4419-5292-9(6)*, 1441952926) Springer.

Iley, Richard A. & Lewis, Mervyn K. Untangling the US Deficit: Evaluating Causes, Cures & Global Imbalances. 2007. (Illus.). 288p. (C). 124.00 *(978-1-84542-920-1(6))* Elgar, Edward Publishing, Inc.

Iwan, Morgan. Age of Deficits. 2009. 400p. 34.95 *(978-0-7006-1685-5(3))* Univ. Pr. of Kansas.

Jones, Bryan D. & Williams, Walter. The Politics of Bad Ideas: The Great Tax Cut Delusion & the Decline of Good Government in America. 2007. (Penguin Academics Ser.). (ENG., Illus.). 384p. (C). per. 33.60 *(978-0-205-60079-3(4))* Longman Publishing Group.

Kaizuka, Keimei. Tackling Japan's Fiscal Challenges: Strategies to Cope with High Public Debt & Population Ageing. Kaizuka, Keimei & Krueger, Anne, eds. 2006. (ENG., Illus.). 256p. 110.00 *(978-0-230-00787-1(2))* Palgrave Macmillan.

Kelly, Robert E. The National Debt of the United States 1941 to 2008. 2nd rev. ed. 2008. (ENG., Illus.). 393p. per. 45.00 *(978-0-7864-3233-2(0))* McFarland & Co., Inc. Pubs.

Koesterich, Russ. The Ten Trillion Dollar Gamble: The Coming Deficit Debacle & How to Invest Now - How Deficit Economics Will Change our Global Financial Climate. 2011. (ENG., Illus.). 256p. 28.00 *(978-0-07-175357-9(5)*, 0071753575) McGraw-Hill Cos., The.

Kotlikoff, Laurence J. & Burns, Scott. The Clash of Generations: Saving Ourselves, Our Kids, & Our Economy. 2012. (ENG., Illus.). 288p. (gr. 17). 21.95 ***(978-0-262-01672-8(9))*** MIT Pr.

Kwak, James & Johnson, Simon. White House Burning: The Founding Fathers, Our National Debt, & Why It Matters to You. 2012. (ENG.). 368p. 26.95 ***(978-0-307-90696-0(5)***, Pantheon) Knopf Doubleday Publishing Group.

Leclaire, Jodlle. The Great Deficit Debacle. 2008. 128p. pap. *(978-3-639-03077-8(X))* VDM Verlag Dr. Mueller e.K.

Lifting the Crushing Burden of Debt: Hearing Before the Committee on the Budget, House of Representatives, One Hundred Twelfth Congress, First Session, Hearing Held in Washington, DC, March 10, 2011. 2011. (Illus.). iii, 74p. ***(978-0-16-089223-3(6)***, 552-070-43220-5) United States Government Printing Office.

Lynch, Christopher G. & McHale, Cory. Budget Control Act Of 2011. 2012. ***(978-1-61942-035-9(X))*** Nova Science Pubs., Inc.

Macdonald, Kate, et al, eds. New Visions for Market Governance: Crisis & Renewal. 2012. (Challenges of Globalisation Ser.). (ENG., Illus.). 256p. (C). 130.00 ***(978-0-415-69111-6(7))*** Routledge.

Mauro, Paolo. Chipping Away at Public Debt: Sources of Failure & Keys to Success in Fiscal Adjustment. 2011. (ENG., Illus.). 278p. 45.00 *(978-1-118-04338-7(3)*, Wiley) Wiley, John & Sons, Inc.

Mayer, Julian L. & Lehner, Alexander D., eds. Deficit Reduction: Spending & Revenue Options. 2011. (Economic Issues, Problems & Perspectives Ser.). (Illus.). 277p. 185.00 *(978-1-61324-836-2(9))* Nova Science Pubs., Inc.

Medina, Ignacio T. & Suárez, Mateo S. Advanced Economies & Their Debt. 2012. ***(978-1-62100-581-0(X))*** Nova Science Pubs., Inc.

Melville, Keith, et al. The $9 Trillion Debt: Breaking the Habit of Deficit Spending. Tebbetts, Ilse, ed. 2007. (Illus.). 30p. 3.90 *(978-0-945639-38-1(4))* National Issues Forums Institute.

Morse, George W. The Minnesota Response: Cooperative Extension's Money & Mission Crisis. 2009. 428p. 36.95 *(978-1-4401-5543-7(7))* iUniverse, Inc.

O'Hanlon, Michael. The Wounded Giant: America's Armed Forces in an Age of Austerity. 2011. (ENG.). 256p. (gr. 12). pap. 9.95 ***(978-1-59420-503-3(5)***, Penguin Pr. HC, The) Penguin Group (USA) Inc.

Perry, George L., ed. Brookings Papers on Economic Activity 2. 2007. (Brookings Papers on Economic Activity Ser.). (ENG.). 162p. per. 36.00 *(978-0-8157-1354-8(1))* Brookings Institution Pr.

The President's Fiscal Year 2011 Budget: Hearing Before the Committee on the Budget, House of Representatives, One Hundred Eleventh Congress, Second Session, Hearing Held in Washington, DC, February 2, 2010. 2010. (Illus.). iii, 74p. ***(978-0-16-086534-3(4)***, 552-070-41532-7) United States Government Printing Office.

The President's Fiscal Year 2012 Budget: Hearing Before the Committee on the Budget, House of Representatives, One Hundred Twelfth Congress, First Session, Hearing Held in Washington, DC, February 15, 2011. 2011. (Illus.). iii, 82p. ***(978-0-16-088852-6(2)***, 552-070-42971-9) United States Government Printing Office.

Rasmussen, Scott. The People's Money: How Voters Will Balance the Budget & Eliminate the Federal Debt. 2012. (ENG., Illus.). 288p. 26.00 ***(978-1-4516-6610-6(1)***, Threshold Editions) Threshold Editions.

Rasmussen, Scott W. The People's Money: How Voters Would Balance the Budget & Eliminate the Federal Debt. 2013. (ENG.). 288p. pap. 16.00 ***(978-1-4516-6611-3(X)***, Threshold Editions) Threshold Editions.

Rivlin, Alice M. & Antos, Joseph R., eds. Restoring Fiscal Sanity: The Health Spending Challenge. 2007. (ENG., Illus.). 233p. per. 18.95 *(978-0-8157-7493-8(1))* Brookings Institution Pr.

Shaviro, Daniel N. Taxes, Spending, & the U. S. Government's March Toward Bankruptcy. 2006. (ENG., Illus.). 262p. 82.00 *(978-0-521-86933-1(1))* Cambridge Univ. Pr.

—Taxes, Spending, & the U. S. Government's March Towards Bankruptcy. 2006. (ENG., Illus.). 262p. per. 35.99 *(978-0-521-68958-8(9))* Cambridge Univ. Pr.

Sibhoan, Vanessa C. From Surplus to Deficit: The Impact of Legislation on the Federal Budget. 2011. (Series: Economic Issues, Problems & Perspectives Ser.). 115.00 *(978-1-61728-927-9(2))* Nova Science Pubs., Inc.

State of the Economy: View from the Federal Reserve: Hearing Before the Committee on the Budget, House of Representatives, One Hundred Eleventh Congress, Second Session, Hearing Held in Washington, DC, June 9, 2010. 2010. (Illus.). iii, 61p. ***(978-0-16-086811-5(4)***, 552-070-41727-3) United States Government Printing Office.

The State of the U.S. Economy: Hearing Before the Committee on the Budget, House of Representatives, One Hundred Twelfth Congress, First Session, Hearing Held in Washington, DC, February 9, 2011. 2011. iii, 72p. ***(978-0-16-088823-6(9)***, 552-070-42957-3) United States Government Printing Office.

Sturm, Jan-Egbert & Neck, Reinhard, eds. Sustainability of Public Debt. 2008. (CESifo Seminar Ser.). (ENG., Illus.). 280p. (gr. 17). 38.00 *(978-0-262-14098-0(5))* MIT Pr.

Talpos, Ioan. A New Approach of the Budget Deficit. 2009. 68p. pap. *(978-3-639-20727-9(0))* VDM Verlag Dr. Mueller e.K.

Taxes As Part of the Federal Budget: Hearing Before the Subcommittee on Select Revenue Measures of the Committee on Ways & Means, U.S. House of Representatives, One Hundred Tenth [i.e. Eleventh] Congress, Second Session, March 23, 2010. 2010. (Illus.). iii, 164p. ***(978-0-16-089261-5(9)***, 552-070-43257-4) United States Government Printing Office.

Tools to Combat Deficits & Waste: Expedited Rescission Authority: Hearing Before the Federal Financial Management, Government Information, Federal Services, & International Security Subcommittee of the Committee on Homeland Security & Governmental Affairs, United States Senate of the One Hundred Eleventh Congress, First Session, December 16, 2009. 2010. (Illus.). iii, 93p. ***(978-0-16-087050-7(X)***, 552-070-41907-1) United States Government Printing Office.

Treasury Department Fiscal Year 2010 Budget: Hearing Before the Committee on the Budget, House of Representatives, One Hundred Eleventh Congress, First Session, Hearing Held in Washington, DC, March 5, 2009. 2009. iii, 53p. *(978-0-16-084244-3(1)*, 552-070-39814-7) United States Government Printing Office.

United States, Congress House Committee on the Budget Staff, contrib. by. The President's Fiscal Year 2008 Budget: Hearing Before the Committee on the Budget, House of Representatives, One Hundred Tenth Congress, First Session, Hearing Held in Washington, DC, February 6, 2007. 2007. (Illus.). iii, 81p. *(978-0-16-078643-3(6)*, 552-070-35885-4) United States Government Printing Office.

—Treasury Department Fiscal Year 2008 Budget: Hearing Before the Committee on the Budget, House of Representatives, One Hundred Tenth Congress, First Session, Hearing Held in Washington, DC, February 7, 2007. 2007 (Illus.). iii, 54p. *(978-0-16-078597-9(9)*, 552-070-35845-5) United States Government Printing Office.

—Why Deficits Matter: Hearing Before the Committee on the Budget, House of Representatives, One Hundred Tenth Congress, First Session, Hearing Held in Washington, DC, January 23, 2007. 2007. (Illus.). iii, 69p. *(978-0-16-078361-6(5)*, 552-070-35666-5) United States Government Printing Office.

Wagner, R. E. Deficits, Debt, & Democracy: Wrestling with Tragedy on the Fiscal Commons. 2012. (Illus.). 208p. 99.95 ***(978-0-85793-459-8(7))*** Elgar, Edward Publishing, Inc.

Walker, Raleigh E. America's Long-Term Fiscal Outlook. 2009. (America in the 21st Century: Political & Economic Issues Ser.). 69.00 *(978-1-60741-332-5(9))* Nova Science Pubs., Inc.

Whether the Constitution Should Be Amended to Address the Federal Deficit? Hearing Before the Subcommittee on the Constitution of the Committee on the Judiciary, House of Representatives, One Hundred Twelfth Congress, First Session, May 13, 2011. 2011. iii, 55p. ***(978-0-16-089059-8(4)***, 552-070-43091-1) United States Government Printing Office.

Williams, Walter & Jones, Bryan D. The Politics of Bad Ideas: The Great Tax Cut Delusion & the Decline of Good Government in America. 2008. (Illus.). 388p. pap. 16.95 *(978-0-205-60538-5(9))* Longman Publishing Group.

Wilson, Charlotte G. & Brown, Emily O. The U. S. National Debt: Background, Issues, Significance. 2011. (Economic Issues, Problems & Perspectives Ser.). 115.00 *(978-1-61761-767-6(9))* Nova Science Pubs., Inc.

Xu, Xiongqi & Xie, Fei. A Study of the Macroeconomic Effects of China's Fiscal Deficits: Enrich Series on China's Economic Issues, 5 vols., Vol. 4. 2011. (Enrich Series on China's Economic Issues Ser.). (ENG.). 240p. 88.00 *(978-981-4298-24-7(7))* Enrich Professional Publishing (S)., Ltd. SGP. Dist: Independent Pubs. Group.

Yarrow, Andrew L. Forgive Us Our Debts: The Intergenerational Dangers of Fiscal Irresponsibility. (ENG., Illus.). 184p. 2010. pap. 17.00 *(978-0-300-15863-2(7))* 2008. 25.00 *(978-0-300-12353-1(1))* Yale Univ. Pr.

BUDGET IN BUSINESS

Barrett, Richard. Planning & Budgeting for the Agile Enterprise: A Driver-Based Budgeting Toolkit. 2007. (ENG., Illus.). 240p. (C). pap. 54.95 *(978-0-7506-8327-2(9)*, CIMA Publishing) Elsevier Science & Technology Bks.

Bragg, Steven M. & Roehl-Anderson, Janice M. The Controller's Function: The Work of the Managerial Accountant. 4th ed. 2011. (Wiley Corporate F&a Ser.: 563). (ENG., Illus.). 484p. 95.00 *(978-0-470-93742-6(4)*, Wiley) Wiley, John & Sons, Inc.

Cram101 Textbook Reviews & Cram101 Textbook Reviews. Outlines & Highlights for the Controllers Function: The Work of the Managerial Accountant by Steven Bragg, ISBN. 2011. 70p. pap. 27.95 ***(978-1-61461-234-6(X))*** Cram101 Inc.

Davidson, Israel. Budgetary Control in Modern Organisation. 2009. (Illus.). 470p. pap. *(978-3-639-17802-9(5))* VDM Verlag Dr. Mueller e.K.

Dropkin, Murray, et al. The Budget-Building Book for Nonprofits: A Step-by-Step Guide for Managers & Boards. 2nd rev. ed. 2007. (Jossey-Bass Nonprofit Guidebook Ser.: 5). (ENG.). 240p. pap. 44.95 *(978-0-7879-9603-1(3)*, Jossey-Bass) Wiley, John & Sons, Inc.

Dugdale, David & Lyne, Stephen. Budgeting Practice & Organisational Structure. 2010. 240p. pap. 57.95 *(978-1-85618-005-4(0))*; (ENG., Illus.). 224p. pap. 67.95 *(978-0-08-096590-1(3))* Elsevier Science & Technology Bks. (CIMA Publishing).

Harris, Tim, ed. Improving the Budgeting Process: Benchmarks & Best Practices 2008. 2007. (Illus.). 81p. pap. 299.00 *(978-1-58673-240-0(4))* Institute of Management & Administration, IOMA.

Harvard Business School Press Staff. Preparing a Budget. 2009. (Pocket Mentor Ser.). (ENG., Illus.). 96p. pap. 9.95 *(978-1-4221-2884-8(9))* Harvard Business Review Pr.

Lalli, William R., ed. Handbook of Budgeting. 6th ed. 2012. (Wiley Corporate F&a Ser.: 562). (ENG., Illus.). 846p. 195.00 ***(978-0-470-92045-9(9)***, Wiley) Wiley, John & Sons, Inc.

Mccallion, Robert & Warner, Alan. Improve Your Cash Flow. 2nd ed. 2010. (Teach Yourself Ser.). (ENG.). 304p. pap. 19.95 *(978-1-4441-0863-7(8)*, Hodder & Stoughton) Hodder General Publishing Div. GBR. Dist: Independent Pubs. Group.

McMillan, Edward J. Not-for-Profit Budgeting & Financial Management. 4th ed. 2010. (ENG., Illus.). 220p. pap. 60.00 *(978-0-470-57541-3(7)*, Wiley) Wiley, John & Sons, Inc.

Mucha-Aydlott, Julie. The Quick Guide to Small Business Budgeting 2nd Edition. 2007. per. 29.95 *(978-0-9746093-8-6(2))* San Diego Business Accounting Solutions a Non CPA Firm.

Rudman, Jack. Budget Clerk. (Career Examination Ser.: C-3696). pap. 23.95 *(978-0-8373-3696-1(1))* National Learning Corp.

Secrett, Malcolm. Brilliant Budgets & Forecasts: Your Practical Guide to Preparing & Presenting Financial Information. 2010. (ENG., Illus.). 328p. (C). pap. 19.99 *(978-0-273-73091-0(6))* FT Press.

Shim, Jae K., et al. Budgeting Basics & Beyond. 4th ed. 2011. (Wiley Corporate F&a Ser.: 574). (ENG., Illus.). 544p. 110.00 ***(978-1-118-09627-7(4)***, Wiley) Wiley, John & Sons, Inc.

BUDGETS, FAMILY

see Home Economics—Accounting

BUDGETS, HOUSEHOLD

see Home Economics—Accounting

B

BUDGETS, MUNICIPAL
see Municipal Budgets
BUDGETS, TIME
see Time Management
BUDGIE BIRD
see Budgerigar
BUENOS AIRES (ARGENTINA)
Bao, Sandra. Buenos Aires. 6th rev. ed. 2011. (City Guide Ser.). (ENG., Illus.). 256p. pap. 19.99 *(978-1-74179-578-3(8))* Lonely Planet Pubns.
Benson, Andrew & Rough Guides Staff. The Rough Guide to Buenos Aires. 2nd ed. 2011. (ENG., Illus.). 320p. 19.99 *(978-1-84836-891-0(7))* Rough Guides, Ltd. GBR. Dist: Dorling Kindersley Publishing, Inc.
Bergero, Adriana J. Intersecting Tango: Cultural Geographies of Buenos Aires, 1900-1930. Young, Richard, tr. from SPA. 2008. (Pitt Illuminations Ser.). (ENG., Illus.). 376p. (C). pap. 27.95 *(978-0-8229-5985-4(2))* Univ. of Pittsburgh Pr.
Cousins, Lucy E. Buenos Aires & the Pampas Footprint Focus. 2011. (Footprint Focus Ser.). (ENG., Illus.). 128p. pap. 11.95 *(978-1-908206-26-8(8))* Footprint Handbooks GBR. Dist: Globe Pequot Pr., The.
Cutler, Miriam. Buenos Aires Street Guide. 2011. 80p. pap. 26.50 ***(978-1-59754-653-9(4))*** Editorial Libros en Red.
Dorling Kindersley Publishing Staff. Eyewitness Travel Guides Top Ten Buenos Aires. 2011. (Eyewitness top 10 travel Guide Ser.). (ENG.). 128p. 14.00 *(978-0-7566-7049-8(7))* Dorling Kindersley Publishing, Inc.
Fodor's Travel Publications, Inc. Staff. Buenos Aires. 3rd ed. 2012. (Full-Color Gold Guides). (ENG.). 336p. pap. 19.99 ***(978-0-307-92836-8(5)***, Fodor's) Fodor's Travel Pubns.
Fodor's Travel Publications, Inc. Staff. Buenos Aires: With Side Trips to Gaucho Country, Iguazu, & Uruguay. 2nd ed. 2010. (Full-Color Gold Guides). (ENG., Illus.). 368p. pap. 19.99 *(978-1-4000-0425-6(X*, Fodor's) Fodor's Travel Pubns.
Froggatt, Charles. Buenos Aires. 2007. (Hedonist's Guide to Buenos Aires Ser.). (ENG., Illus.). 208p. im. lthr. 18.95 *(978-1-905428-08-3(1))* Filmer Ltd. GBR. Dist: Perseus-PGW.
González-Bernaldo, Pilar. Civility & Politics in the Origins of the Argentine Nation: Sociabilities in Buenos Aires, 1829-1862. 2007. pap. *(978-0-87903-089-6(5))* Latin American Ctr. of New Music.
Harvard Student Agencies, Inc. Let's Go Buenos Aires: The Student Travel Guide. 2009. (Let's Go Ser.). (ENG., Illus.). 304p. pap. 18.95 *(978-1-59880-311-2(5)*, Let's Go) Avalon Travel Publishing.
Indij, Guido, et al, photos by. Buenos Aires: Out of Series. 2008. (ENG., Illus.). 240p. pap. 25.00 *(978-950-889-165-5(3))* La Marca ARG. Dist: D.A.P./Distributed Art Pubs.
Knopf Guides. Knopf MapGuides: Buenos Aires. 2010. (ENG.). 48p. pap. 9.95 *(978-0-307-26894-5(2)*, Knopf) Knopf Doubleday Publishing Group.
Kogan, Gabriela. The Authentic Bars, Cafes & Restaurants of Buenos Aires. 2008. (ENG., Illus.). 144p. pap. 14.95 *(978-1-892145-55-0(3))* Little Bookroom.
Schlecht, Neil Edward. Frommer's Buenos Aires Day by Day. 2009. (Frommer's Day by Day - Pocket Ser.: 254). (ENG., Illus.). 192p. pap. 12.99 *(978-0-470-16011-4(X*, Frommers) Wiley, John & Sons, Inc.
Stewart, Charles Samuel. Brazil & la Plata; the Personal Record of a Cruise, by C S Stewart. 2006. 468p. per. 29.99 *(978-1-4255-5179-7(3))* MPublishing.
Time Out Guides Staff. Time Out Buenos Aires. (Time Out Shortlist Ser.). (ENG., Illus.). 2009. 192p. pap. 12.95 *(978-1-84670-159-7(7))* 5th ed. 2011. 256p. pap. 19.95 *(978-1-84670-192-4(9))* Time Out Guides Ltd. GBR. Dist: Perseus-PGW.
Time Out Guides Staff, ed. Time Out Selecciones Buenos Aires: Time Out Shortlist Buenos Aires. 2010. (Selecciones Ser.). (SPA.). 184p. pap. 12.95 *(978-84-9801-456-3(5))* Time Out Guides Ltd. GBR. Dist: Perseus-PGW.
Unknow. Buenos Aires 1: 15 000: Buenos Aires Centro, Nunez, Boca, Buenos Aires, Isla Martin Garcia, Gran Buenos Aires, Argentina Central. Metro-Link Linas de Metrovias. 2007. 8.95 *(978-3-86609-300-3(4))* Rand McNally.
Wallpaper Magazine Editors, ed. Wallpaper City Guide - Beunos Aires 2011. 2011. (ENG.). 128p. pap. 9.95 *(978-0-7148-6088-6(3))* Phaidon Pr., Inc.
BUENOS AIRES (ARGENTINA)—HISTORY
Gallo, Klaus. The Struggle for an Enlightened Republic: Buenos Aires & Rivadavia. 2006. (ENG.). 91p. per. 24.95 *(978-1-900039-76-5(1))* Institute of Latin American Studies GBR. Dist: Brookings Institution Pr.
Johnson, Lyman L. Workshop of Revolution: Plebeian Buenos Aires & the Atlantic World, 1776-1810. 2011. (ENG., Illus.). 432p. 94.95 *(978-0-8223-4966-2(3))*; pap. 25.95 *(978-0-8223-4981-5(7))* Duke Univ. Pr.
Komi Kallinikos, Christina. Recorridos Urbanos: La Buenos Aires de Roberto Arlt y Juan Carlos Onetti. 2009. (SPA.). 272p. pap. 29.80 *(978-84-8489-490-2(8))* Iberoamericana Vervuert Publishing Corp.
Locken, E. Travel Journal Buenos Aires. 2010. 192p. pap. 19.99 *(978-0-557-44589-9(2))* Lulu Enterprises Inc.
Luongo, Michael. Frommer's Buenos Aires. 4th ed. 2011. (Frommer's Complete Guides). (ENG., Illus.). 288p. pap. 17.99 *(978-1-118-00964-2(9)*, Frommers) Wiley, John & Sons, Inc.
Ross, Stanley R. & McGann, Thomas F., eds. Buenos Aires: 400 Years. 2011. (ENG., Illus.). 214p. pap. 25.00 *(978-0-292-72952-0(9))* Univ. of Texas Pr.
Schávelzon, Daniel. The Historical Archaeology of Buenos Aires: A City at the End of the World. 2010. (Contributions to Global Historical Archaeology Ser.). 204p. pap. 139.00 *(978-1-4419-3310-2(7)*, 1441933107) Springer.
Socolow, Susan Migden. Merchants of Buenos Aires, 1778-1810: Family & Commerce. 2009. (Cambridge Latin American Studies). (ENG., Illus.). 272p. pap. 36.99 *(978-0-521-10234-6(0))* Cambridge Univ. Pr.
Suriano, Juan. Paradoxes of Utopia: Anarchist Culture & Politics in Buenos Aires, 1890-1910. 2010. (ENG.). 288p. pap. 18.95 *(978-1-84935-006-8(X))* AK Pr. GBR. Dist: Consortium Bk. Sales & Distribution.
Wallpaper Magazine Editors, ed. Wallpaper City Guide - Buenos Aires. 2011. (ENG.). 128p. pap. 9.95 ***(978-0-7148-6281-1(9))*** Phaidon Pr., Inc.
BUERGER, GOTTFRIED AUGUST, 1747-1794
Kertscher, Hans-Joachim, ed. G. A. Bürger und J. W. L. Gleim. (Hallesche Beiträge zur Europäischen Aufklärung Ser.). (GER.). XXVI, 264p. 210.00 ***(978-3-11-187587-3(3))*** De Gruyter, Walter Inc.
BUFFALO (N.Y.)
Bieron, Joseph F. & McCarthy, Paul J. Postcard Views, A Walk down Main Street Buffalo, New York, Circa 1910. 2007. 68p. per. 17.95 *(978-0-9788476-4-7(4))* Buffalo Heritage Unlimited.
Brown, William J. History of the Grain Elevators of Buffalo, New York. 2009. 360p. 119.95 *(978-0-7734-4857-5(8))* Mellen, Edwin Pr., The.
Buffalo Historical Society (Buffalo, N. Y. Certificate of Incorporation, Constitution & by Laws of the Buffalo Historical Society, with the Amendments to 1875 to Which Are Added an Account O. 2011. 36p. pap. 11.99 ***(978-1-4181-9498-7(0))*** MPublishing.
Fargo, Francis F. Memorial of the City & County Hall Opening Ceremonies, Buffalo, N y Ed & Pub by F F Fargo. 2006. 196p. per. 18.99 *(978-1-4255-1564-5(9))* MPublishing.
Fisher, Bruce. Borderland: Essays from Buffalo. 2012. ***(978-1-4384-4223-5(8))*** State Univ. of New York Pr.
Gildiner, Catherine. After the Falls: Coming of Age in the Sixties. 2010. (ENG., Illus.). 368p. (gr. 12). 25.95 *(978-0-670-02205-2(5)*, Viking Adult) Penguin Group (USA) Inc.
Goldman, Mark. City on the Edge: Buffalo, New York. 2007. (ENG., Illus.). 1p. per. 19.98 *(978-1-59102-457-6(9))* Prometheus Bks., Pubs.
Ketchum, William. An Authentic & Comprehensive History of Buffalo, with Some Account of Its Early Inhabitants, Both Savage & Civilized & Historic Notices of the S. 2006. 452p. per. 29.99 *(978-1-4255-5004-2(5))* MPublishing.
Mobarak, Christyn. Buffalo As an Architectural Museum. 2009. 154p. pap. *(978-3-639-17788-6(6))* VDM Verlag Dr. Mueller e.K.
Myers, Stephen G. & Connor, Michael J. Buffalo Railroads. 2011. (Images of Rail Ser.). (ENG., Illus.). 128p. pap. 21.99 *(978-0-7385-7371-7(X))* Arcadia Publishing.
Nyhuis, Philip. Buffalo: A Waterfront City Transformed. 2008. 59.50 *(978-1-882933-10-5(9))* Cherbo Publishing Group, Inc.
Pedersen, Laura. Buffalo Unbound. 2010. (ENG.). 216p. pap. 16.00 *(978-1-55591-735-7(6))* Fulcrum Publishing.
Rifiorgiato, Leonard R. The Life & Times of John Timon, 1797-1867: The First Bishop of Buffalo, New York. Castillo, Dennis, ed. 2006. (Roman Catholic Studies: 27). 524p. (C). 139.95 *(978-0-7734-5943-4(X))* Mellen, Edwin Pr., The.
Rizzo, Michael F. Nine Nine Eight: the Glory Days of Buffalo Shopping. 2007. 168p. pap. 16.95 *(978-1-4303-1386-1(2))* Lulu Enterprises Inc.
Severance, Frank H. Old Trails on the Niagara Frontier. 2007. (ENG.). 288p. 43.95 *(978-0-548-13805-2(2))* 2006. pap. 28.95 *(978-1-4286-4974-3(3))* Kessinger Publishing, LLC.
Severance, Frank Hayward. Studies of the Niagara Frontier. 2009. 444p. reprint ed. pap. 33.00 *(978-0-7884-0845-8(3))* Heritage Bks.
Shaw, Tim. Ghosts of Buffalo. 2011. (Illus.). 192p. pap. 19.99 ***(978-0-7643-3894-6(3)***, Schiffer Publishing Ltd) Schiffer Publishing, Ltd.
BUFFALO, AMERICAN
see American Bison
BUFFALO BILL, 1846-1917
Bartholomew, Ed Ellsworth. Buffalo Bill's Life: An Adventurous Career That Led from the Savagery of Western Life to A Seat Beside Kings & Princes. 2011. 30p. 35.95 ***(978-1-258-01495-7(5))*** Literary Licensing, LLC.
Bonner, Robert E. William F. Cody's Wyoming Empire: The Buffalo Bill Nobody Knows. 2007. (ENG., Illus.). 368p. (C). 32.95 *(978-0-8061-3829-9(7))* Univ. of Oklahoma Pr.
Buffalo Bill, pseud. An Autobiography of Buffalo Bill. 2008. *(978-1-934941-23-2(9))* Red & Black Pubs.
Buffalo Bill, pseud. The Life of Hon. William F. Cody, Known As Buffalo Bill. 2011. (ENG., Illus.). 456p. ***(978-0-8032-3619-6(0))*** Univ. of Nebraska Pr.
Cody, Buffalo Bill. Buffalo Bill's Life Story: An Autobiography. 2010. (ENG., Illus.). 368p. pap. 12.95 *(978-1-60239-752-1(X)*, 239752) Skyhorse Publishing Co., Inc.
Cody, W. F. & Bill, Buffalo. An Autobiography of Buffalo Bill, Colonel W F Cody. 2011. 352p. 51.95 ***(978-1-258-01690-6(7))*** Literary Licensing, LLC.
Cody, William F. An AutoBiography of Buffalo Bill. l.t. ed. 2007. 250p. pap. 22.99 *(978-1-4264-6464-5(9))* BiblioBazaar.
—An AutoBiography of Buffalo Bill: (colonel W. F. Cody) 2006. (ENG.). 222p. pap. 20.99 *(978-1-4264-6390-7(1))* BiblioBazaar.
—Autobiography of Buffalo Bill Colonel W. 2007. (Illus.). pap. *(978-1-4065-1341-7(5))* Dodo Pr.
—The Life of Hon. William F. Cody. l.t. ed. 2007. (ENG.). 246p. pap. 22.99 *(978-1-4264-3906-3(7))*; 274p. pap. 21.99 *(978-1-4264-3838-7(9))* BiblioBazaar.
—The Life of Hon. William F. Cody. 2007. (ENG.). pap. *(978-1-4065-1342-4(3))* Dodo Pr.
—Life of Hon. William F. Cody: Known as Buffalo Bill. Date not set. 384p. 20.95 *(978-0-8488-2476-1(8))* Amereon LTD.
—The Life of Hon. William F. Cody, Known as Buffalo Bill. Christianson, Frank, ed. & intro. by. 2011. (Papers of William F. Buffalo Bill Cody Ser.). (ENG., Illus.). 584p. pap. 27.95 *(978-0-8032-3291-4(8)*, Bison Bks.) Univ. of Nebraska Pr.
Delaney, Michelle Anne. Buffalo Bill's Wild West Warriors: A Photographic History by Gertrude Käsebier. 2007. (ENG., Illus.). 192p. 34.95 *(978-0-06-112977-3(1))* Smithsonian Institution Pr.
Enss, Chris. The Many Loves of Buffalo Bill: The True of Story of Life on the Wild West Show. 2010. (ENG., Illus.). 168p. pap. 16.95 *(978-0-7627-4815-0(X)*, TwoDot) Globe Pequot Pr., The.
Friesen, Steve. Buffalo Bill: Scout, Showman, Visionary. 2010. (ENG., Illus.). 144p. pap. 22.95 *(978-1-55591-719-7(4))* Fulcrum Publishing.
Gallop, Alan. Buffalo Bill's British Wild West. 2009. (ENG., Illus.). 288p. pap. 32.95 *(978-0-7524-5060-5(3))* History Pr. Ltd., The GBR. Dist: Independent Pubs. Group.
Garst, Shannon. The Story of Buffalo Bill. 2011. 262p. 47.95 ***(978-1-258-05459-5(0))*** Literary Licensing, LLC.
Griffin, Charles Eldridge. Four Years in Europe with Buffalo Bill. Dixon, Chris & Dixon, Christopher, eds. 2010. (Papers of William F. Buffalo Bill Cody Ser.). (ENG., Illus.). 200p. pap. 12.95 *(978-0-8032-3465-9(1)*, Bison Bks.) Univ. of Nebraska Pr.
Ingraham, Prentiss. Adventures of Buffalo Bill. 2007. 72p. per. *(978-1-4068-1567-2(5))* Echo Library.
Johnston, Ralph E. Buffalo Bill. 2011. 256p. 47.95 ***(978-1-258-01494-0(7))*** Literary Licensing, LLC.
Leonard, Elizabeth Jane & Goodman, Julia Cody. Buffalo Bill, King of the Old West: Biography of William F. Cody, Pony Express Rider, Buffalo Hunter, Plains Scout & Guide, Master Showman. Hoffman, James Williams, ed. 2011. 348p. 51.95 ***(978-1-258-02194-8(3))*** Literary Licensing, LLC.
Morledge, Phillip J. The 'Real' Wild West. 2009. 438p. pap. 37.95 *(978-0-9559765-0-6(2))* PJM Publishing GBR. Dist: Lulu Enterprises Inc.
Muller, Daniel Cody & Cody, William F. My Life with Buffalo Bill. 2011. 302p. 48.95 ***(978-1-258-03032-2(2))*** Literary Licensing, LLC.
Sagala, Sandra K. Buffalo Bill on Stage. 2008. (ENG., Illus.). 319p. 19.95 *(978-0-8263-4427-4(5))* Univ. of New Mexico Pr.
Spring, Agnes Wright. Buffalo Bill & His Horses. 2011. 28p. 35.95 ***(978-1-258-01521-3(8))*** Literary Licensing, LLC.
Warren, Louis S. Buffalo Bill's America: William Cody & the Wild West Show. 2006. (Vintage Ser.). (ENG., Illus.). 672p. per. 16.95 *(978-0-375-72658-3(6)*, Vintage) Knopf Doubleday Publishing Group.
Wetmore, Helen Cody. Last of the Great Scouts: The Life Story of William F. Cody (Buffalo Bill Cody) 2006. (ENG.). 260p. pap. 21.99 *(978-1-4264-0301-9(1))* BiblioBazaar.
Wilson, R. L. Buffalo Bill's Wild West: An American Legend. 2008. (ENG.). 316p. 29.99 *(978-0-7858-1894-6(4)*, 0785818944) Book Sales, Inc.
BUFFALO BILLS (FOOTBALL TEAM)
Abramoski, Ed. Tale of the Tape: A History of the Buffalo Bills from the Inside. (Illus.). 10.95 *(978-1-879201-41-5(0))* Western New York Wares, Inc.
Crippen, Kenneth R. The Original Buffalo Bills: A History of the All-America Football Conference Team, 1946-1949. 2009. (ENG., Illus.). 327p. pap. 35.00 *(978-0-7864-4619-3(6))* McFarland & Co., Inc. Pubs.
Delamielleure, Joe. Tales from the Buffalo Bills. 2007. (Tales Ser.). (Illus.). 181p. 19.95 *(978-1-59670-070-3(X))* Sports Publishing, LLC.
Gehman, Jim. "Then Levy Said to Kelly..." The Best Buffalo Bills Stories Ever Told. 2008. (Best Sports Stories Ever Told Ser.). (ENG.). 240p. 19.55 *(978-1-60078-055-4(5))* Triumph Bks.
Lazarus, Adam. Super Bowl Monday: From the Persian Gulf to the Shores of West Florida - The New York Giants, the Buffalo Bills & Super Bowl XXV. 2011. (ENG., Illus.). 344p. 24.95 *(978-1-58979-600-3(4))* Taylor Trade Publishing.
Levy, Marv. Marv Levy: Where Else Would You Rather Be? 2012. (ENG., Illus.). 448p. pap. 16.95 ***(978-1-61321-021-5(3)***, 613021) Skyhorse Publishing Co., Inc.
Levy, Marv & Miller, Jeff. Game Changers: The Greatest Plays in Buffalo Bills Football History. 2009. (Game Changers Ser.). (ENG.). 160p. 24.95 *(978-1-60078-275-6(2))* Triumph Bks.
Maiorana, Sal. Buffalo Bills: The Complete Illustrated History. 2010. (ENG., Illus.). 192p. 30.00 *(978-0-7603-3852-0(3)*, 0760338523, MVP Bks.) MBI Publishing Co. LLC.
Miller, Jeffrey J. Rockin' the Rockpile: The Buffalo Bills of the American Football League. 2007. (ENG., Illus.). 592p. 34.95 *(978-1-55022-797-0(1))* ECW Pr. CAN. Dist: Independent Pubs. Group.
Pitoniak, Scott. Buffalo Bills Football Vault. 2010. 144p. pap. 49.95 *(978-0-7948-3047-2(1))* Whitman Publishing LLC.
—The Good, the Bad, & the Ugly - Buffalo Bills: Heart-Pounding, Jaw-Dropping, & Gut-Wrenching Moments from Buffalo Bills History. 2007. (Good, the Bad, & the Ugly Ser.). (ENG., Illus.). 224p. pap. 19.95 *(978-1-60078-008-0(3))* Triumph Bks.
Tasker, Steve. Steve Tasker's Tales from the Buffalo Bills. 2006. (Illus.). 171p. 19.95 *(978-1-59670-092-5(0))* Sports Publishing, LLC.
Tasker, Steve & Pitoniak, Scott. Steve Tasker's Tales from the Buffalo Bills. 2008. (Tales Ser.). (Illus.). 192p. pap. 15.95 *(978-1-59670-337-7(7))* Sports Publishing, LLC.
Thompson, Rob. The Bills Are Due. 2008. 294p. pap. 20.95 *(978-1-4327-2854-0(7))* Outskirts Pr., Inc.
BUFFALO SABRES (HOCKEY TEAM)
Bailey, Budd & Ray, Rob. Rayzor's Edge: Rob Ray's Tough Life on the Ice. 2nd ed. 2011. (ENG., Illus.). 176p. pap. 14.95 *(978-1-61321-025-3(6)*, 613025) Skyhorse Publishing Co., Inc.
Ray, Rob. Rayzor's Edge: Rob Ray's Tough Life on the Ice. (Illus.). 170p. 2008. pap. 15.95 *(978-1-59670-355-1(5))* 2007. 19.95 *(978-1-59670-283-7(4))* Sports Publishing, LLC.
Wieland, Paul. "Then Perreault Said to Rico..." The Best Buffalo Sabres Stories Ever Told. 2008. (Best Sports Stories Ever Told Ser.). (ENG.). 224p. 22.95 *(978-1-60078-095-0(4))* Triumph Bks.
BUFFALOES
Here are entered works on buffaloes of the eastern hemisphere. Works on the American buffalo are entered under American bison.
Abd-Allah, Saber. Laboratory Production of Buffalo Embryos. 2011. 224p. pap. ***(978-3-8443-0815-0(6))*** Lambert Academic Publishing.
Branch, E. Douglas. The Hunting of the Buffalo. 288p. 2008. 43.95 *(978-1-4366-8398-2(X))* 2007. (ENG.). per. 28.95 *(978-1-4325-9296-7(3))* Kessinger Publishing, LLC.
Chandrahasan, C. Follicular Oocytes in Buffaloes. 2011. 96p. pap. ***(978-3-8454-0962-7(2))*** Lambert Academic Publishing.
Das, Gokul & M.C. Yadav. Bull-Biostimulation in Postpartum Buffaloes. 2011. 116p. pap. ***(978-3-8443-0765-8(6))*** Lambert Academic Publishing.
Diptee, Michael. Evaluation of Brucella Abortus Rb51 Vaccine in Water Buffalo. 2009. 140p. pap. *(978-3-639-21247-1(9))* VDM Verlag Dr. Mueller e.K.
Joubert, Dereck & Joubert, Beverly. Relentless Enemies: Lions & Buffalo. 2006. (ENG., Illus.). 176p. 40.00 *(978-1-4262-0004-5(8)*, National Geographic) National Geographic Society.
Khalid, Sumbul. Growth Hormone of Pakistani Buffalo. 2010. 108p. pap. *(978-3-8383-5098-1(7))* Lambert Academic Publishing.
Nili-Ravi, Kundi & Rashid, Saif. Dna Polymorphism a Tool for Molecular Characterization: Dna Fingerprinting of Pakistani Buffalo Breeds Using Microsattelite & Cytochrome B Gene Markers. 2011. 112p. pap. ***(978-3-639-32567-6(2))*** VDM Verlag Dr. Mueller e.K.
Swelum, Ayman. Some Trials for Improving Cryopreservation of Buffalo-Bull Semen. 2011. 156p. pap. ***(978-3-8383-3991-7(6))*** Lambert Academic Publishing.
Tanveer, Hussain & Masroor, Ellahi Babar. Phylogenetic Analysis Based on Snps & Allelic Variations: Genetic Characterization of Pakistani Buffalo Breeds by Mitochondrial D-Loop & Microsatellite Analyses. 2011. 132p. pap. ***(978-3-639-24433-5(8))*** VDM Verlag Dr. Mueller e.K.
BUFFETS (COOKING)
Australian Women's Weekly Staff, contrib. by. New Finger Food. (Illus.). 120p. pap. 12.95 *(978-1-86396-282-7(4))* ACP Publishing Pty, Ltd. AUS. Dist: Graphic Arts Ctr. Publishing Co.
Fraser, Linda. Best-Ever Party Food Cookbook: Tempting recipes for easy Entertaining. 2010. (ENG., Illus.). 96p. pap. 8.99 *(978-1-84476-947-6(X))* Anness Publishing GBR. Dist: National Bk. Network.
Garlough, Robert B. & Campbell, Angus. Modern Garde Manger: A Global Perspective. 2nd ed. 2011. (ENG.). 832p. (C). 120.95 *(978-1-111-30761-5(X))* Delmar Cengage Learning.
Ingram, Christine. Party & Buffet Cookbook: Celebrate in Syle with over 90 Irresistible Recipes for Special Gatherings. 2011. (ENG., Illus.). 128p. pap. 17.99 *(978-1-84476-860-8(0))* Anness Publishing GBR. Dist: National Bk. Network.
Jones, Bridget. The Complete Illustrated Book of Appetizers, Buffets, Finger Food & Party Food: How to Plan the Perfect Celebration with over 400 Inspiring First Course, Nibbles, Finger Foods, Buffet & Party Dishes. 2006. (ENG., Illus.). 512p. 29.99 *(978-0-7548-1688-1(5))* Anness Publishing GBR. Dist: National Bk. Network.
Leonard, Edward G. Modern Buffets: Blueprint for Success. 2011. (ENG., Illus.). 208p. 69.95 *(978-0-470-48466-1(7)*, Wiley) Wiley, John & Sons, Inc.
Murdoch Books, prod. Step by Step Finger Food: More than 250 Recipes. 2011. (ENG., Illus.). 256p. pap. 8.99 ***(978-1-74266-265-7(X)***, 174266265X, Bay Bks.) Murdoch Bks. Pty Ltd. AUS. Dist: Book Sales, Inc.
Taste of Home Magazine Editors & Reader's Digest Editors. Parties, Potlucks, & Barbecues: 368 Recipes for Casual Gatherings. 2008. (ENG.). (gr. 12). pap. 15.95 *(978-0-89821-697-4(4))* Reader's Digest Assn., Inc., The.
BUFFETT, WARREN, 1930-
Brownlee, Adam. Building a Small Business That Warren Buffett Would Love. 2012. (ENG., Illus.). 194p. 24.95 ***(978-1-118-13888-5(0)***, Wiley) Wiley, John & Sons, Inc.
Buffett, Mary & Clark, David. The Tao of Warren Buffett: Warren Buffett's Words of Wisdom: Quotations & Interpretations to Help Guide You to Billionaire Wealth & Enlightened Business Management. 2006. (ENG., Illus.). 192p. 22.95 *(978-1-4165-4132-5(2)*, Scribner) Scribner.
—Warren Buffett & the Art of Stock Arbitrage: Proven Strategies for Arbitrage & Other Special Investment Situations. 2010. (ENG.). 176p. 25.00 *(978-1-4391-9882-7(9)*, Scribner) Scribner.
—Warren Buffett & the Interpretation of Financial Statements: The Search for the Company with a Durable Competitive Advantage. 2008. (ENG., Illus.). 224p. 24.95 *(978-1-4165-7318-0(6)*, Scribner) Scribner.

—The Warren Buffett Stock Portfolio: Warren Buffett's Stock Picks - Why & When He Is Investing in Them. 2011. (ENG.). 240p. 25.00 *(978-1-4516-0648-5(6)*, Scribner) Scribner.

—Warren Buffett's Management Secrets: Proven Tools for Personal & Business Success. 2009. (ENG.). 176p. 25.00 *(978-1-4391-4937-9(2)*, Scribner) Scribner.

Buffett, Peter. Life Is What You Make It: Find Your Own Path to Fulfillment. 2011. (ENG.). 272p. pap. 14.00 *(978-0-307-46472-9(5)*, Three Rivers Pr.) Crown Publishing Group.

Buffett, Warren. Back to School: Question & Answer Session with Business Students. 2008. 160p. pap. *(978-1-60796-055-3(9))* Editorial Benei Noaj.

Chan, Ronald. Behind the Berkshire Hathaway Curtain: Lessons from Warren Buffett's Top Business Leaders. 2010. (ENG., Illus.). 178p. 24.95 *(978-0-470-56062-4(2)*, Wiley) Wiley, John & Sons, Inc.

Connors, Richard J. Warren Buffett on Business: Principles from the Sage of Omaha. 2009. (ENG., Illus.). 259p. 24.95 *(978-0-470-50230-3(4)*, Wiley) Wiley, John & Sons, Inc.

Jain, Prem C. Buffett Beyond Value: Why Warren Buffett Looks to Growth & Management When Investing. 2010. (ENG., Illus.). 304p. 27.95 *(978-0-470-46715-2(0)*, Wiley) Wiley, John & Sons, Inc.

Janjigian, Vahan. Even Buffett Isn't Perfect: What You Can — and Can't — Learn from the World's Greatest Investor. 2009. (ENG., Illus.). 256p. (gr. 12-18). pap. 16.00 *(978-1-59184-270-5(0)*, Portfolio Trade) Penguin Group (USA) Inc.

Labitan, Bud. The Four Filters Invention of Warren Buffett & Charlie Munger. 2009. 148p. pap. 30.47 *(978-0-615-24129-6(8))* Acalmix.

Larsen, Gwyn Davidson. Life Lessons in Business: Wisdom from Warren E. Buffett & L. A. Davy Davidson, 1 volume, Volume 1. 2007. (Illus.). 85p. per. 19.95 *(978-0-9798723-0-3(8))* LAD L.P.

Lowe, Janet C. Warren Buffett Speaks: Wit & Wisdom from the World's Greatest Investor. 2nd rev. ed. 2007. (ENG., Illus.). 288p. 19.95 *(978-0-470-15262-1(1)*, Wiley) Wiley, John & Sons, Inc.

Lowenstein, Roger. Buffett: The Making of an American Capitalist. 2008. (ENG., Illus.). 512p. pap. 19.00 *(978-0-8129-7927-5(3)*, Random Hse. Trade Paperbacks) Random House Publishing Group.

Morris, Charles R. The Sages: Warren Buffett, George Soros, Paul Volcker, & the Maelstrom of Markets. 2010. (ENG.). 224p. pap. 14.95 *(978-1-58648-817-8(1))* PublicAffairs.

Ramaswamy, Srichander & Ramaswamy, Jeeva. Creating a Portfolio Like Warren Buffett: A High Return Investment Strategy. 2012. (ENG.). 284p. 27.95 *(978-1-118-18252-9(9)*, Wiley) Wiley, John & Sons, Inc.

Rittenhouse, L. J. Buffett's Bites: The Essential Investor's Guide to Warren Buffett's Shareholder Letters. 2010. (ENG., Illus.). 224p. 19.95 *(978-0-07-173932-0(7)*, 0071739327) McGraw-Hill Cos., The.

Schroeder, Alice. The Snowball: Warren Buffett & the Business of Life. (ENG., Illus.). 2009. 832p. pap. 20.00 *(978-0-553-38461-1(9))* 2008. 976p. 35.00 *(978-0-553-80509-3(6)*, Bantam) Random House Publishing Group.

—The Snowball: Warren Buffett & the Business of Life. Lt. ed. 2008. (ENG.). 1664p. pap. 35.00 *(978-0-7393-2798-2(4))* Random Hse. Large Print.

Tavakoli, Janet M. Dear Mr. Buffett: What an Investor Learns 1,269 Miles from Wall Street. (ENG., Illus.). 2010. 282p. pap. 16.95 *(978-0-470-63242-0(9))* 2009. 304p. 24.95 *(978-0-470-40678-6(X))* Wiley, John & Sons, Inc. (Wiley).

Train, John. The Midas Touch: The Strategies That Have Made Warren Buffett the World's Most Successful Investor. 2nd ed. 2009. (ENG.). 190p. 19.99 *(978-1-906659-18-9(4))* Harriman Hse. Publishing GBR. Dist: Ingram Pub. Services.

Zitz, Michael. Giving It All Away: The Doris Buffett Story. 2010. 224p. 28.00 *(978-1-57962-209-1(7))* Permanent Pr., The.

BUFFING

see Grinding and Polishing

BUFFON, GEORGES LOUIS LECLERC, COMTE DE, 1707-1788

Dugatkin, Lee Alan. Mr. Jefferson & the Giant Moose: Natural History in Early America. 2009. (ENG., Illus.). 184p. 26.00 *(978-0-226-16914-9(6))* Univ. of Chicago Pr.

Leclerc, Georges-Louis. All the World's Birds: Buffon's Illustrated Natural History General & Particular of Birds. 2008. (ENG., Illus.). 672p. 350.00 *(978-0-8478-3091-6(8))* Rizzoli International Pubns., Inc.

BUGATTI, ETTORE, 1881-1947

Wood, Jonathan. Bugatti: The Man & the Marque. 2007. (ENG., Illus.). 384p. 99.95 *(978-1-85223-364-8(8)*, 1852233648) Crowood Pr., Ltd. GBR. Dist: MBI Distribution Services/Quayside Distribution.

BUGATTI AUTOMOBILE

Bolofo, Koto. Vroom! Vroom! 2010. (ENG., Illus.). 96p. 75.00 *(978-3-86521-961-9(6))* Steidl, Gerhard Druckerei und Verlag DEU. Dist: D.A.P./Distributed Art Pubs.

Brooklands Books & VelocePress, prods. Bugatti - Road Test Portfolio. 2010. 482p. pap. 89.95 *(978-1-58850-099-1(3))* Veloce Enterprises, Inc.

Mead, Syd, frwd. Cosmic Motors: Spaceships, Cars & Pilots of Another Galaxy. 2007. (ENG., Illus.). 171p. 46.95 *(978-1-933492-28-5(7))* Design Studio Pr.

Price, Barrie. Bugatti 46 & 50. rev. ed. (Illus.). 144p. lthr. *(978-1-901295-99-3(0))* Veloce Publishing Ltd. GBR. Dist: MBI Distribution Services/Quayside Distribution.

—Bugatti Type 40. 50th ltd. ed. (Illus.). 128p. lthr. *(978-1-901295-83-2(4))* Veloce Publishing Ltd. GBR. Dist: MBI Distribution Services/Quayside Distribution.

Price, Barrie & Arbey, Jean-Louis. Bugatti: The 8-Cylinder Touring Cars 1920-1934 - Types 28, 30, 38, 38a, 44 & 49. 2007. (ENG., Illus.). 144p. 59.95 *(978-1-901295-95-5(8)*, 1901295958) Veloce Publishing Ltd. GBR. Dist: MBI Distribution Services/Quayside Distribution.

Ratti, Diego. Bugatti Type 32 Tank. 2008. 102p. 126.50 *(978-1-4092-2487-7(2))* Lulu Enterprises Inc.

Wood, Jonathan. Bugatti: The Man & the Marque. 2007. (ENG., Illus.). 384p. 99.95 *(978-1-85223-364-8(8)*, 1852233648) Crowood Pr., Ltd. GBR. Dist: MBI Distribution Services/Quayside Distribution.

BUGAYEV, BORIS NIKOLAYEVICH, 1880-1934

see Bely, Andrey, 1880-1934

BUGGERY

see Sodomy

BUGLE

see also Trumpet

Boy Scouts of America & Boy Scouts Of America. 5-Minute [Five Minute] Guaranteed Bugle Course. 2010. 42p. pap. 7.50 *(978-1-57898-966-9(3))* Martino Publishing.

BUGLIONI, SANTI, 1494-1576

Marquand, Allan. Benedetto & Santi Buglioni. 2008. 296p. pap. 28.95 *(978-1-4367-8730-7(0))* Kessinger Publishing, LLC.

BUICK AUTOMOBILE

Gustin, Lawrence R. David Buick's Marvelous Motor Car: The Men & the Automobile That Launched General Motors. 2008. (Illus.). 231p. (J). 24.95 *(978-0-9786269-0-7(7))* Sloan, Alfred P. Museum.

Olsen, Byron. Buick, 1946-1960. 2006. (Photo Archive Ser.). (ENG., Illus.). 128p. pap. 29.95 *(978-1-58388-178-1(6)*, 1583881786) Iconografix, Inc.

Storer, Jay, et al. Buick Century, 1997 Thru 2005: All Models. 2007. (Haynes Repair Manuals Ser.). (ENG., Illus.). 256p. per. 26.95 *(978-1-56392-628-0(8)*, 1563926288) Haynes Manuals, Inc.

Stubblefield, Mike, et al. Buick, Oldsmobile & Pontiac Full-Size Models 1985 Thru 2005: Front-Wheel Drive. rev. ed. 2007. (Haynes Repair Manuals Ser.). (ENG., Illus.). 256p. per. 26.95 *(978-1-56392-625-9(3)*, 1563926253) Haynes Manuals, Inc.

BUILDER'S PLANT

see Construction Equipment

BUILDING

Here are entered works on the process of construction. General works on structures or edifices are entered under Buildings. Works on the design and style of structures are entered under Architecture.

see also Aluminum Construction; Arches; Architecture; Bricklaying; Building, Stone; Building Fittings; Building Sites; Carpentry; Ceilings; Concrete Construction; Construction Industry; Doors and Doorways; Floors; Foundations; Framing (Building); Glass Construction; House Construction; Industrialized Building; Lightweight Construction; Masonry; Modular Coordination (Architecture); Prestressed Construction; Space Frame Structures; Underground Construction; Underwater Construction; Walls; Windows; Wrecking

Abbs & Freebairn. Building Strategies. Date not set. (Illus.). 48p. per., wbk. ed 24.40 *(978-0-582-57994-1(5))* Addison-Wesley Longman, Ltd. GBR. Dist: Trans-Atlantic Pubns., Inc.

Allen, Edward & Iano, Joseph. Fundamentals of Building Construction: Materials & Methods. 5th ed. 2008. (ENG., Illus.). 1008p. 120.00 *(978-0-470-07468-8(X)*, Wiley) Wiley, John & Sons, Inc.

American Contractors Exam Services. DEWALT Building Contractor's Licensing Exam Guide. 3rd ed. 2010. (ENG.). 240p. pap. 39.95 *(978-1-111-13551-5(7)*, DEWALT) CENGAGE Learning.

Anderson, Dwight. Sustainaility Index. 2010. 60p. pap. *(978-3-639-15493-1(2))* VDM Verlag Dr. Mueller e.K.

Andres, Cameron K. & Smith, R. C. Principles & Practices of Commercial Construction. 8th ed. 2008. (ENG.). 624p. (C). 121.60 *(978-0-13-159923-9(2)*, Prentice Hall) Prentice Hall PTR.

Apostolaki, Stella. The Social Dimension of Stormwater Management Practices in Urban Areas. 2009. 226p. pap. *(978-3-639-17692-6(8))* VDM Verlag Dr. Mueller e.K.

Ariaratnam, Samuel T. & Rojas, Eddy M., eds. Building a Sustainable Future. 2009. 1564p. pap. 259.00 *(978-0-7844-1020-2(8))* American Society of Civil Engineers.

Armpriest, Diane & Mehta, Medan. Homework & Classroom Assignment Manual for Building Construction: Principles, Materials, & Systems 2009. rev. ed. 2009. (ENG.). 146p. (C). pap. 35.80 *(978-0-13-509584-3(0)*, Prentice Hall) Prentice Hall PTR.

ASTM Subcommittee E06.81 on Building Economics Staff, contrib. by. ASTM Standards on Building Economics. 2007. *(978-0-8031-5695-1(2))* American Society for Testing & Materials.

Barritt, C. Building Construction, Vol. 2. Date not set. (Illus.). x, 224p. pap. 181.35 *(978-0-582-41352-8(4))* Addison-Wesley Longman, Ltd. GBR. Dist: Trans-Atlantic Pubns., Inc.

Baudendistel, Robert F. Lawn & Garden Construction. 2011. 268p. 25.00 *(978-1-4567-4247-8(7))*; pap. 15.00 *(978-1-4567-4248-5(5))* AuthorHouse.

Benjamin, Asher. The American Builder's Companion. 2007. (ENG.). 200p. per. 12.50 *(978-1-60206-781-3(3))* Cosimo, Inc.

Better Homes and Gardens Editors & Christian, Vicki, eds. Additions Planner. 2008. (Do It Yourself Ser.). (ENG., Illus.). 160p. pap. 14.95 *(978-0-696-22283-2(3)*, Wiley) Wiley, John & Sons, Inc.

Boussabaine, Halim. Embracing Complexity in the Built Environment. 2008. (ENG., Illus.). 72p. pap. 97.50 *(978-1-84407-640-6(7))* Routledge.

Breeze, Gordon. Dynamic Comfort Criteria for Structures. 2011. (ENG., Illus.). 32p. pap. 49.95 *(978-1-84806-173-6(0))* Building Research Establishment GBR. Dist: Taylor & Francis Group.

Brooks, Alan & Pevsner, Nikolaus. Herefordshire. 2012. (Pevsner Architectural Guides). (ENG., Illus.). 800p. 85.00 **(978-0-300-12575-7(5))** Yale Univ. Pr.

Bruce, Donald A., ed. Specialty Construction Techniques for Dam & Levee Remediation. 2012. (ENG., Illus.). 376p. 165.00 *(978-0-415-78194-7(9)*, CRC Press) Taylor & Francis Group GBR. Dist: Taylor & Francis Group.

Bryan, Tony. Construction Technology: Analysis & Choice. 2nd ed. 2010. (ENG., Illus.). 464p. pap. 50.00 *(978-1-4051-5874-9(3)*, Wiley-Blackwell) Wiley, John & Sons, Inc.

Burchnell, Donald James. Owner Beware! What You Need to Know Before You Build. 2007. (Illus.). 110p. per. 19.95 *(978-0-9796624-2-3(7))* Burchnell, Donald.

Cadwell, Michael. Strange Details. 2007. (Writing Architecture Ser.). (ENG., Illus.). 208p. (gr. 17). pap. 21.95 *(978-0-262-53291-4(3))* MIT Pr.

Charlett, Andrew J. Fundamental Building Technology. (ENG., Illus.). 288p. 2007. 135.00 *(978-0-415-38623-4(3))* 2006. per. 44.95 *(978-0-415-38624-1(1))* Routledge.

Ching, Francis D. K., et al. Building Construction Illustrated. 4th ed. 2008. (ENG., Illus.). 480p. pap. 49.95 *(978-0-470-08781-7(1)*, Wiley) Wiley, John & Sons, Inc.

Chudley, R. Construction Technology. Date not set. (Longman Technician Ser.). (Illus.). Vol. 3. v, 245p. pap. 52.50 *(978-0-582-42028-1(8))* Vol. 4. viii, 292p. pap. 52.50 *(978-0-582-42030-4(X))* Addison-Wesley Longman, Ltd. GBR. Dist: Trans-Atlantic Pubns., Inc.

Cleary, Mark, ed. 21st Century Sustainable Homes. 2011. (ENG., Illus.). 204p. 35.00 *(978-1-86470-428-0(4))* Images Publishing Group AUS. Dist: National Bk. Network.

Co, Us Gr Build. New Construction Reference Guide Version 2.2. 3rd ed. 2007. (Illus.). 422p. *(978-1-932444-06-3(8))* U. S. Green Building Council.

Conran, Terence. Eco House Book. 2009. (ENG., Illus.). 300p. 45.00 *(978-1-84091-522-8(6)*, Conran Octopus) Octopus Publishing Group GBR. Dist: Hachette Bk. Group.

Cooke, Brian. Construction Practice. 2011. (ENG., Illus.). 400p. pap. 48.99 *(978-1-4443-3668-9(1)*, Wiley-Blackwell) Wiley, John & Sons, Inc.

Cooke, Brian & Williams, Peter. Construction Planning, Programming & Control. 3rd ed. 2009. (ENG., Illus.). 504p. pap. 62.99 *(978-1-4051-8380-2(2)*, Wiley-Blackwell) Wiley, John & Sons, Inc.

Cooke, Louise. Conservation Approaches to Earthen Architecture in Archaeological Contexts. 2010. (Bar S Ser.). (ENG., Illus.). 177p. (C). pap. 145.00 *(978-1-4073-0688-9(X))* British Archaeological Reports Ltd. GBR. Dist: Brown, David Bk. Co., The.

Cooke, Robert. Building in the 21st Century. 2007. (ENG., Illus.). 504p. per. 54.99 *(978-1-4051-5655-4(4)*, Wiley-Blackwell) Wiley, John & Sons, Inc.

Cram101 Textbook Reviews. Outlines & Highlights for Construction Planning, Equipment, & Methods by Peurifoy & Schexnayder. 2011. 166p. pap. 29.95 **(978-1-61906-239-9(9))** Cram101 Inc.

—Outlines & Highlights for Construction Principles, Materials, & Methods by Simmons & Olin. 2011. 244p. pap. 31.95 **(978-1-61906-217-7(8))** Cram101 Inc.

—Outlines & Highlights for Principles & Practices of Commercial Construction by Andres & Smith, Isbn: 0130482927. 2011. 158p. pap. 29.95 **(978-1-61830-037-9(7))** Cram101 Inc.

—Outlines & Highlights for Principles & Practices of Light Construction by Ronald C Smith. 2011. 94p. pap. 27.95 **(978-1-61812-804-1(3))** Cram101 Inc.

—Outlines & Highlights for Soils in Construction by W L Schroeder, Isbn: 9780130489173 0130489174. 2011. 108p. pap. 28.95 **(978-1-61490-655-1(6))** Cram101 Inc.

Crochet, Treena M. Designer's Guide to Building Construction & Systems. 2011. (ENG.). 168p. (C). pap. 48.60 *(978-0-13-241428-9(7)*, Prentice Hall) Prentice Hall PTR.

Curtis, Stephen A. Hurricane Katrina Damage Assessment: Louisiana, Alabama, & Mississippi Ports & Coasts. 2007. (Illus.). 133p. pap. 65.00 *(978-0-7844-0931-2(5))* American Society of Civil Engineers.

DeLaOssa, Ralph K. Introduction to Building Constrcution & Firefighting. 2007th ed. 2007. (Illus.). 152p. (C). per. 61.00 *(978-0-9795564-0-1(6))* De La Ossa, Ralph.

Deplazes, Andrea, ed. Constructing Architecture: Materials, Processes, Structures. Söffker, G. H., tr. from GER. 2nd ed. 2008. (Illus.). 555p. pap., instr.'s hndbk. ed. 69.95 *(978-3-7643-8631-3(2)*, 3764386312) Springer.

Doyle, Sophie G. Construction & Building: Design, Materials, & Techniques. 2010. 155.00 **(978-1-61761-211-4(1))** Nova Science Pubs., Inc.

Dutoit, Allison, et al, eds. Quality Out of Control: Standards for Measuring Architecture. 2010. (ENG., Illus.). 240p. 165.00 *(978-0-415-55365-0(2))*; pap. 53.95 *(978-0-415-55366-7(0))* Taylor & Francis Group GBR. (Routledge). Dist: Taylor & Francis Group.

Emmitt, Stephen. Managing Interdisciplinary Projects: A Primer for Architecture, Engineering & Construction. 2010. (ENG., Illus.). 200p. 130.00 *(978-0-415-48170-0(8))*; pap. 44.95 *(978-0-415-48171-7(6))* Routledge.

Emmitt, Stephen & Gorse, Christopher. Introduction to Construction of Buildings, 2 vols., Set. 2nd ed. 2010. (ENG., Illus.). 1360p. pap. 77.95 *(978-1-4443-3576-7(6)*, Wiley-Blackwell) Wiley, John & Sons, Inc.

Emmitt, Stephen & Gorse, Christopher A. Barry's Introduction to Construction of Buildings, 2 vols. 2nd ed. 2010. (ENG., Illus.). 768p. pap. 44.99 *(978-1-4051-8854-8(5)*, Wiley-Blackwell) Wiley, John & Sons, Inc.

Emmitt, Stephen, et al. Barry's Advanced Construction of Buildings, 2 vols. 2nd ed. 2010. (ENG., Illus.). 592p. pap. 47.99 *(978-1-4051-8853-1(7)*, Wiley-Blackwell) Wiley, John & Sons, Inc.

Favorite, Merab-Michal. Palmetto. 2012. (Images of America Ser.). (ENG., Illus.). 128p. pap. 21.99 **(978-0-7385-9104-9(1))** Arcadia Publishing.

Ferguson, Myron R. Drywall: Professional Techniques for Great Results. 4th ed. 2012. (ENG., Illus.). 240p. pap. 21.95 **(978-1-60085-469-9(9))** Taunton Pr., Inc.

Fewings, Peter. Construction Project Management: An Integrated Approach. 2nd rev. ed. 2012. (ENG., Illus.). 536p. 165.00 *(978-0-415-61344-6(2))*; pap. 49.95 *(978-0-415-61345-3(0))* Routledge.

Fickes, Clyde P. & Groben, W. Ellis. Building with Logs. (Shorey Lost Arts Ser.). 56p. reprint ed. pap. 10.00 *(978-0-8466-6030-9(X)*, U30) Shorey's Bookstore.

Forbes, Lincoln Harding & Ahmed, Syed M., eds. Modern Construction: Productive & Lean Practices. 2010. (Industrial Innovation Ser.). (ENG., Illus.). 524p. 129.95 *(978-1-4200-6312-7(X)*, CRC Press) Taylor & Francis Group GBR. Dist: Taylor & Francis Group.

Foster, Jack & Greeno, Roger. Structure & Fabric 1, 2 vols. 7th rev. ed. 2007. (Illus.). 248p. pap. 97.50 *(978-0-13-197094-6(1)*, Prentice Hall) Pearson Education, Ltd. GBR. Dist: Trans-Atlantic Pubns., Inc.

Glover, Peter. Building Surveys. 6th ed. 2006. (ENG., Illus.). 288p. pap. 44.95 *(978-0-7506-8128-5(4)*, Butterworth-Heinemann) Elsevier Science & Technology Bks.

Grant, Richard. Porch, 1 vol. 2011. (ENG.). 72p. 14.95 *(978-0-89272-933-3(3))* Down East Bks.

Greeno, R. Introduction to Building. 4th rev. ed. 2007. (Illus.). 320p. pap. 97.50 *(978-0-13-232571-4(3)*, Prentice Hall) Pearson Education, Ltd. GBR. Dist: Trans-Atlantic Pubns., Inc.

Greeno, Roger & Chudley, Roy. Advanced Construction Technology. 4th rev. ed. 2006. (Illus.). 640p. pap. 77.50 *(978-0-13-201985-9(X))* Pearson Education, Ltd. GBR. Dist: Trans-Atlantic Pubns., Inc.

Haghi, A. K. Advances in Geosciences & the Built Environment. 2009. (Illus.). vi, 194p. 129.00 *(978-1-60741-171-0(7))* Nova Science Pubs., Inc.

Halliday, Sandy. Sustainable Construction. 2008. (ENG., Illus.). 408p. per. 51.95 *(978-0-7506-6394-6(4))* Routledge.

Hersent, Olivier, et al. The Internet of Things: Applications to the Smart Grid & Building Automation. 2nd ed. 2012. (ENG., Illus.). 370p. 105.00 **(978-1-119-99435-0(7)**, Wiley) Wiley, John & Sons, Inc.

Holland, M. Practical Guide to Diagnosing Structural Movement in Buildings. 2012. (ENG.). 240p. pap. 49.95 **(978-0-470-65910-6(6)**, Wiley-Blackwell) Wiley, John & Sons, Inc.

Horowitz, Louis J. & Sparkes, Boyden. The Towers of New York: The Memoirs of A Master Builder. 2011. 310p. 50.95 **(978-1-258-08240-6(3))** Literary Licensing, LLC.

Huth, Mark W. Residential Construction Academy: Basic Principles for Construction. 2nd rev. ed. 2007. (ENG., Illus.). 320p. (C). 84.95 *(978-1-4180-5251-5(5))* Delmar Cengage Learning.

—Residential Construction Academy: Basic Principles for Construction. 2nd ed. 2007. (ENG.). 112p. (C). pap. 34.95 *(978-1-4283-2363-6(5))* Delmar Cengage Learning.

Jaggs, Michael & Scivyer, Chris. Airtightness in Commercial & Public Buildings. 2nd rev. ed. 2011. (ENG., Illus.). 44p. pap. 63.95 *(978-1-84806-174-3(9))* Building Research Establishment GBR. Dist: Taylor & Francis Group.

Jankovic, Ljubomir. Designing Zero Carbon Buildings Using Dynamic Simulation Methods. 2012. (ENG., Illus.). 336p. (C). pap. 59.95 **(978-1-84971-294-1(8))** Routledge.

Jaquin, Paul & Augarde, Charles. Earth Building. 2012. (ENG., Illus.). 120p. pap. 55.95 **(978-1-84806-192-7(7))** Building Research Establishment GBR. Dist: Taylor & Francis Group.

Jergenson, Phil, et al. How to Build with Grid Beam: A Fast, Easy & Affordable System for Constructing Almost Anything. 2008. (ENG., Illus.). 288p. pap. 29.95 *(978-0-86571-613-1(7)*, 9780865716131) New Society Pubs., Ltd. CAN. Dist: Consortium Bk. Sales & Distribution.

Jorgensen, Anna & Keenan, Richard, eds. Urban Wildscapes. 2011. (ENG., Illus.). 272p. (C). 155.00 *(978-0-415-58105-9(2))*; pap. 53.95 *(978-0-415-58106-6(0))* Routledge.

Journal of Light Construction, ed. JLC's Construction Tips & Techniques: Practical Answers to Contractors' Questions. 2006. (Illus.). 348p. per. 32.50 *(978-1-928580-31-7(9)*, Home Planners, LLC) Hanley-Wood, LLC.

Kapfinger, Otto. Haus Rauch. 2010. (Illus.). 160p. 69.95 *(978-3-0346-0110-8(7))* Birkhauser Verlag AG CHE. Dist: Actar Birkhauser Distribution.

Kocatürk, Tuba. Distributed Intelligence in Design. Medjdoub, Benachir, ed. 2011. (ENG., Illus.). 280p. 152.99 *(978-1-4443-3338-1(0)*, Wiley-Blackwell) Wiley, John & Sons, Inc.

Köse, Demir & Ir. Erik Dick, Prof. Prediction of the Pressure Distribution on Buildings with Cfd. 2011. 332p. pap. **(978-3-8443-1716-9(3))** Lambert Academic Publishing.

Kwok, Alison & Grondzik, Walter. The Green Studio Handbook: Environmental Strategies for Schematic Design. 2nd rev. ed. 2011. (ENG., Illus.). 424p. pap. 75.95 *(978-0-08-089052-4(0))* Routledge.

Leppo, RA/CID, LEED AP, Holly Williams & Ballast, David Kent. Construction Documents & Services: ARE Sample Problems & Practice Exam. 2nd ed.

B

2011. (ENG.). 114p. pap. 120.00 *(978-1-59126-323-4(9))* Professional Pubns., Inc.
Liebing, Ralph W. Construction of Architecture: From Design to Built. 2007. (ENG., Illus.). 312p. 90.00 *(978-0-471-78355-8(2),* Wiley) Wiley, John & Sons, Inc.
Loosemore. Corporate Social Strategy in the Construction & Engineering: Doing the Right Thing? 2010. (ENG., Illus.). 192p. (C). 150.00 *(978-0-415-45909-9(5))* Routledge.
Loosemore, Martin & Phua, Florence. Corporate Social Strategy in the Construction & Engineering Industry: Doing the Right Thing? 2010. (ENG., Illus.). 192p. (C). pap. 69.95 *(978-0-415-45910-5(9))* Routledge.
Lstiburek, Joseph. Builder's Guide to Cold Climates: Details for Design & Construction. (Illus.). 352p. pap. *(978-1-56158-387-4(1),* 070519) Taunton Pr., Inc.
Mann, Robert S. Defect-Free Buildings: A Construction Manual for Quality Control & Conflict Resolution. 2006. (ENG., Illus.). 341p. 79.95 *(978-0-07-147959-2(7),* 0071479597) McGraw-Hill Professional Publishing.
Marchand, Trevor. Minaret Building & Apprenticeship in Yemen. 2012. (ENG.). 285p. (C). pap. 39.95 ***(978-0-415-69544-2(9))*** Routledge.
Marsden, P. K. Basic Building Measurement. 158p. pap. *(978-0-86840-133-1(1),* UNSW Press) NewSouth Publishing.
Mc Cormick, Alexander. The MasterBuild Process. 2007. 112p. pap. 59.95 *(978-0-9801733-0-7(2))* Mc Cormick, Alexander.
McAfee, Mark, ed. Principles & Practice of Engineering: Architectural Engineering Sample Questions & Solutions. 2nd ed. 2010. (ENG.). 92p. pap. 49.00 *(978-0-7844-1090-5(9))* American Society of Civil Engineers.
Mehta, Medan, et al. Building Construction: Principles, Materials, & Systems. 2nd rev. ed. 2011. (ENG., Illus.). 976p. (C). 122.67 ***(978-0-13-214869-6(2),*** Prentice Hall) Prentice Hall PTR.
Mehta, Medan, et al. Building Construction: Principles, Materials, & Systems 2009. rev. ed. 2009. (ENG., Illus.). 1024p. (C). 127.60 *(978-0-13-506476-4(7),* Prentice Hall) Prentice Hall PTR.
Meisel, Ari & Princeton Architectural Press Staff. Leed Materials: A Resource Guide to Green Building. 2010. (ENG., Illus.). 224p. pap. 40.00 *(978-1-56898-885-6(0))* Princeton Architectural Pr.
Moe, Kiel & Smith, Ryan E. Building Systems: Technology, Design & Society. 2012. (ENG., Illus.). 272p. (C). 165.00 *(978-0-415-61793-2(6))*; pap. 39.95 *(978-0-415-61794-9(4))* Routledge.
NCCER. Boilermaking Level 1 Annotated Instructor's Guide, Paperback. 2nd ed. 2010. (ENG.). 400p. (C). pap. 86.67 *(978-0-13-213704-1(6),* Prentice Hall) Prentice Hall PTR.
—Boilermaking Level 1 Trainee Guide, Paperback. 2nd ed. 2010. (ENG.). 366p. (C). pap. 86.67 *(978-0-13-213702-7(X),* Prentice Hall) Prentice Hall PTR.
—Careers in Construction — CMEF Houston. 2007. (C). pap. 21.33 *(978-0-13-603733-0(X),* Prentice Hall) Prentice Hall PTR.
—Sheet Metal Level 1 Trainee Guide, Paperback. 3rd ed. 2008. (ENG.). 396p. (C). pap. 86.67 *(978-0-13-604482-6(4),* Prentice Hall) Prentice Hall PTR.
Newton, Peter, et al. Technology, Design & Process Innovation in the Built Environment. 2009. (Spon Research Ser.). (ENG., Illus.). 576p. (C). 175.00 *(978-0-415-46288-4(6))* Routledge.
Nunnally, Stephens W. Construction Methods & Management. 8th ed. 2010. (ENG.). 360p. (C). 117.20 *(978-0-13-500079-3(3),* Prentice Hall) Prentice Hall PTR.
Ofori, George, ed. New Perspectives on Construction in Developing Countries. 2011. (ENG., Illus.). 408p. (C). 125.00 *(978-0-415-58572-9(4))* Routledge.
Peurifoy, Robert L., et al. Construction Planning, Equipment, & Methods. 8th ed. 2010. (ENG., Illus.). 816p. (C). 220.33 *(978-0-07-340112-6(9),* 0073401129, McGraw-Hill Science, Engineering & Mathematics) McGraw-Hill Higher Education.
Pompeu Santos Staff. Enclosure Masonry Wall Systems Worldwide. 2006. *(978-0-415-42171-3(3))* Taylor & Francis Group.
—Enclosure Masonry Wall Systems Worldwide. 2006. (ENG., Illus.). 214p. (C). 107.95 *(978-0-415-42577-3(8),* Taylor & Francis) Taylor & Francis Group GBR. Dist: Taylor & Francis Group.
Preene, Martin. Groundwater Lowering in Construction: A Practical Guide. 2nd rev. ed. 2012. (ENG., Illus.). 678p. 160.00 *(978-0-415-66837-8(9),* CRC Press) Taylor & Francis Group GBR. Dist: Taylor & Francis Group.
Prince, Chris. DEWALT Carpentry Quick Check: Extreme Duty Edition. 2011. (ENG.). 42p. pap. 14.95 *(978-1-111-13587-4(8),* DEWALT) CENGAGE Learning.
Proverbs, David G., et al. Solutions for Climate Change Challenges in the Built Environment. 2012. (Innovation in the Built Environment Ser.: 5). (ENG., Illus.). 368p. 112.99 ***(978-1-4051-9507-2(X),*** Wiley-Blackwell) Wiley, John & Sons, Inc.
Ratay, Robert. Temporary Structures in Construction 3/E. 3rd ed. 2012. (ENG., Illus.). 928p. (C). 125.00 *(978-0-07-175307-4(9),* 0071753079) McGraw-Hill Professional Publishing.
Richards, Ellen H. The Cost of Shelter. 2007. 88p. pap. 16.99 *(978-1-4346-5151-8(7))*; 94p. pap. 18.99 *(978-1-4346-5152-5(5))* BiblioBazaar.
Rumane, Abdul Razzak. Quality Management in Construction Projects. 2010. (Industrial Innovation Ser.). (ENG., Illus.). 464p. 89.95 *(978-1-4398-3871-6(2),* CRC Press) Taylor & Francis Group GBR. Dist: Taylor & Francis Group.
Ryan. Traditional Construction for Sustainable New Building. 2011. (ENG., Illus.). 384p. 165.00 *(978-0-415-46756-8(X))*; pap. 49.95 *(978-0-415-46757-5(8))* Routledge.
Sandler, Michael. Freaky-Strange Buildings. 2011. (So Big Compared to What? Ser.). 24p. (YA). (gr. 1-4). lib. bdg. 22.61 *(978-1-61772-305-6(3))* Bearport Publishing Co., Inc.
Sarkar, Subir K. & Saraswati, Subhajit. Construction Technology. 2008. (ENG., Illus.). 572p. pap. 45.00 *(978-0-19-569483-3(X))* Oxford Univ. Pr., Inc.
Schierle, G. G. Structure & Design. 2008. 624p. pap. 79.95 *(978-1-934269-37-4(9))*; (ENG., Illus.). 620p. pap. 99.95 *(978-1-934269-22-0(0))* Univ. Readers.
Seal, Mark. Hines: A Legacy of Quality in the Built Environment. 2007. *(978-0-9749510-4-1(8))* Fenwick Publishing Group, Inc.
Shaikh, Javeria. Revitalization of Landscape Design at Os Slowackiego. 2010. 68p. pap. *(978-3-639-27480-6(6))* VDM Verlag Dr. Mueller e.K.
Simmons, H. Leslie. Olin's Construction: Principles, Materials, & Methods. 9th ed. 2011. (ENG., Illus.). 1200p. 130.00 ***(978-0-470-54740-3(5),*** Wiley) Wiley, John & Sons, Inc.
Smith, Michael L. Building Construction: Methods & Materials for the Fire Service. 2007. (ENG., Illus.). 240p. (C). 71.33 *(978-0-13-117251-7(4),* Prentice Hall) Prentice Hall PTR.
Standiford, Kevin. RCA: Facilities Maintenance. 2nd ed. 2010. (ENG.). 544p. (C). pap. 101.95 *(978-1-111-31112-4(9))* Delmar Cengage Learning.
Syed, Asif. Advanced Building Technologies for Sustainability. 2012. (Wiley Series in Sustainable Design Ser.: 3). (ENG., Illus.). 256p. 85.00 ***(978-0-470-54603-1(4),*** Wiley) Wiley, John & Sons, Inc.
Trachtenberg, Marvin. Building-in-Time: From Giotto to Alberti & Modern Oblivion. 2010. (ENG., Illus.). 516p. 65.00 *(978-0-300-16592-0(7))* Yale Univ. Pr.
Tragesser, Chris E. & Hirst, Ben A. Exam Prep: Building Construction for the Fire Service. 2007. 110p. per. 39.95 *(978-0-7637-5341-2(6))* Jones & Bartlett Learning, LLC.
Van Gelder, Conny, et al. Inspirational Apartments: Decoration Empire. 2009. (ENG., Illus.). 176p. *(978-90-8989-038-2(6),* Lannoo Pubs. (Acc)) Antique Collectors' Club.
Walker, Frank Ameil. Argyll & Bute. (ENG., Illus.). 688p. 65.00 *(978-0-14-071079-3(5))* Penguin Group (USA) Inc.
Walker, William L. & Felice, Daniel J., Sr. Water-Resistant Design & Construction: An Illustrated Guide to Preventing Water Intrusion, Condensation, & Mold. 2007. (ENG., Illus.). 286p. 49.95 *(978-0-07-149276-8(3),* 0071492763) McGraw-Hill Professional Publishing.
Waltham, Tony, et al. Sinkholes & Subsidence: Karst & Cavernous Rocks in Engineering & Construction. 2010. (Springer Praxis Books / Geophysical Sciences Ser.). (Illus.). xxxi, 382p. pap. 279.00 *(978-3-642-05851-6(5),* 3642058515) Springer.
Watson, Paul & Howarth, Tim. Construction Quality Management: Principles & Practice. 2011. (ENG., Illus.). 336p. (C). 155.00 *(978-0-415-56910-1(9))* Routledge.
Watts, Andrew. Modern Construction Handbook. 2nd ed. 2009. (Modern Construction Ser.). (ENG., Illus.). 504p. 129.00 *(978-3-211-99195-4(6),* 3211991956) Springer.
Webster, Alfred P. & Bright, Kathryn E. Mathematics for Carpentry & the Construction Trades. 3rd ed. 2011. (ENG.). 408p. (C). pap. 107.00 *(978-0-13-511400-1(4),* Prentice Hall) Prentice Hall PTR.
Williams, Alan. Seismic & Wind Forces: Structural Design Examples. 3rd ed. 2007. (Illus.). x, 492p. 72.00 *(978-1-58001-508-0(5))* International Code Council.
Wilsted, Thomas. Planning New & Remodeled Archival Facilities. 2007. *(978-1-931666-25-1(3))* Scarecrow Pr., Inc.
Xie. Innovations in Structural Engineering & Construction: Proceedings of the 4th International Conference on Structural & Construction Engineering, Melbourne, Australia, 26-28 September 2007, 2 vols. 2007. (Illus.). xxviii, 1588p. *(978-0-415-45754-5(8),* Taylor & Francis) Taylor & Francis Group GBR. Dist: Taylor & Francis Group.
—Innovations in Structural Engineering & Construction: Proceedings of the 4th International Conference on Structural & Construction Engineering, Melbourne, Australia, 26-28 September 2007, 2 vols. Patnaikuni, Indubhushan, ed. 2007. (Illus.). xxviii, 1588p. *(978-0-415-45756-9(4),* Taylor & Francis) Taylor & Francis Group GBR. Dist: Taylor & Francis Group.
Zhang, Donia. Courtyard Houses of Beijing. 2010. 240p. pap. *(978-3-639-99630-2(5))* VDM Verlag Dr. Mueller e.K.
Zimmermann, Astrid. Constructing Landscape: Materials, Techniques, Building Elements. 2nd rev. ed. 2011. (ENG., Illus.). 536p. pap. 69.95 *(978-3-0346-0720-9(2))* Birkhauser Verlag AG CHE. Dist: Actar Birkhauser Distribution.
2007-2008 Design/Build Survey: Of Design & Construction Firms. 2007. per. 395.00 *(978-1-934150-19-1(3))* ZweigWhite.

BUILDING—ACCIDENTS
see also Building Failures
Ikpe, Elias & Hammond, Felix. Construction Accident Prevention. 2011. 280p. pap. ***(978-3-8443-0956-0(X))*** Lambert Academic Publishing.

BUILDING—ACCOUNTING
see Construction Industry—Accounting

BUILDING—AMATEURS' MANUALS
see also Building—Handbooks, Manuals, etc.
Conran, Terence. Bathrooms: Home Design, Decoration & Furnishing. 2010. (ENG., Illus.). 112p. 20.00 *(978-1-84091-551-8(X),* Conran Octopus) Octopus Publishing Group GBR. Dist: Hachette Bk. Group.
—Kitchens: The Back to Basics Guide to Home Design, Decoration & Furnishing. 2010. (ENG., Illus.). 112p. 20.00 *(978-1-84091-549-5(8),* Conran Octopus) Octopus Publishing Group GBR. Dist: Hachette Bk. Group.
Kelsey, John, ed. Cabins & Cottages: The Basics of Building a Getaway Retreat for Hunting, Camping, & Rustic Living. 2011. (ENG.). 160p. pap. 19.95 *(978-1-56523-539-7(8))* Fox Chapel Publishing Co., Inc.
Lester, Kent & McGuerty, Dave. The Complete Guide to Contracting Your Home. 4th ed. 2010. (ENG., Illus.). 320p. pap. 24.99 *(978-1-55870-871-6(5),* Betterway Bks.) F&W Media, Inc.
Seiling, Matt. Seiling's Floors Presents: A Unique Step-by-Step Guide. 2009. 104p. pap. 33.95 *(978-1-4490-1336-3(8))* AuthorHouse.
Skinner, Tina & Bannister, Doug. Casting Concrete Countertops. 2008. (Illus.). 128p. pap. 24.95 *(978-0-7643-2865-7(4))* Schiffer Publishing, Ltd.
West, Geoffrey D. Architectural Salvage: A Guide to Selecting, Buying & Using Reclaimed Building Materials, 1 vol. 2010. (ENG., Illus.). 160p. 35.00 *(978-1-84797-207-1(1))* Crowood Pr., Ltd. GBR. Dist: Independent Pubs. Group.
Williamson, Laurie. Building a Garage: A Complete Guide, 1 vol. 2011. (ENG., Illus.). 160p. 32.95 *(978-1-84797-222-4(5))* Crowood Pr., Ltd. GBR. Dist: Independent Pubs. Group.

BUILDING—CONTRACTS AND SPECIFICATIONS
see Buildings—Specifications; Construction Contracts

BUILDING—COSTS
see Building—Estimates

BUILDING—DATA PROCESSING
Akin, Ömer. Embedded Commissioning of Building Systems. 2011. 306p. 129.00 ***(978-1-60807-147-0(2))*** Artech Hse., Inc.
Anumba, Chimay J. & Wang, Xiangyu, eds. Mobile & Pervasive Computing in Construction. 2nd ed. 2012. (ENG.). 352p. 155.00 ***(978-0-470-65801-7(0),*** Wiley-Blackwell) Wiley, John & Sons, Inc.
Aubin, Paul F., et al. The Aubin Academy Master Series: Revit MEP 2011. 2011. (ENG., Illus.). 111p. pap. 86.95 *(978-1-111-13793-9(5),* AutoDesk Pr.) Delmar Cengage Learning.
Barthorpe, Stephen, et al. Managing Construction Logistics. 2010. (ENG., Illus.). 304p. pap. 84.99 *(978-1-4051-5124-5(2),* Wiley-Blackwell) Wiley, John & Sons, Inc.
Cram101 Textbook Reviews & Cram101 Textbook Reviews. Outlines & Highlights for Estimating in Building Construction by Frank R Dagostino. 2011. 126p. pap. 28.95 ***(978-1-61830-841-2(6))*** Cram101 Inc.
Crotty, Ray. The Impact of Building Information Modelling: Transforming Construction. 2011. (ENG., Illus.). 232p. (C). 59.95 *(978-0-415-60167-2(3))* Routledge.
Eastman, Chuck, et al. BIM Handbook: A Guide to Building Information Modeling for Owners, Managers, Designers, Engineers & Contractors. 2nd ed. 2011. (ENG., Illus.). 648p. 85.00 *(978-0-470-54137-1(7),* Wiley) Wiley, John & Sons, Inc.
Epstein, Erika. Building Information Modeling: A Guide to Implementation Around the Globe. 2011. 347p. 129.00 ***(978-1-60807-139-5(1))*** Artech Hse., Inc.
Hauschild, Moritz & Karzel, Rudiger. Detail Practice: Digital Processes: Planning, Designing, Production. 2011. (Illus.). 112p. pap. 54.95 *(978-3-0346-0725-4(3))* Birkhauser Verlag AG CHE. Dist: Actar Birkhauser Distribution.
Li, Heng & Chen, Zhen. Environmental Management in Construction: A Quantitative Approach. 2006. (ENG., Illus.). 232p. 190.00 *(978-0-415-37055-4(8))* Routledge.
Mertic, John. The Definitive Guide to SugarCRM: Better Business Applications. 2009. (ENG.). 280p. pap., instr.'s gde. ed. 59.99 *(978-1-4302-2439-6(8))* Apress L. P.
Peterson, Steven J. & Peterson, Steven. Construction Estimating Using Excel. 2nd rev. ed. 2011. (ENG.). 432p. (C). pap. 129.80 *(978-0-13-800719-5(5),* Prentice Hall) Prentice Hall PTR.
Peterson, Steven J., et al. Estimating in Building Construction. 7th ed. 2010. (ENG., Illus.). 288p. (C). 140.40 *(978-0-13-119952-1(8),* Prentice Hall) Prentice Hall PTR.
—Student Workbook for Estimating in Building Construction. 7th ed. 2010. (ENG.). 160p. (C). pap. 31.60 *(978-0-13-509748-9(7),* Prentice Hall) Prentice Hall PTR.
Sommerville, James. Implementation of It in Construction & Property Enterprises. 2007. (ENG., Illus.). 214p. per. 69.95 *(978-0-415-37052-3(3))* Routledge.
—Implementing IT in Construction. 2007. (ENG., Illus.). 214p. 190.00 *(978-0-415-37051-6(5))* Routledge.
Zarli, Alain. EWork & eBusiness in Architecture, Engineering & Construction: Ecppm 2008. Scherer, Raimar, ed. 2008. (ENG., Illus.). 750p. 289.95 *(978-0-415-48245-5(3),* Taylor & Francis) Taylor & Francis Group GBR. Dist: Taylor & Francis Group.

BUILDING—DETAILS
American Institute of Architects. Architectural Graphic Standards for Residential Construction 1. 0 CD-ROM. 2010. (Ramsey/Sleeper Architectural Graphic Standards Ser.: 15). (ENG.). 325.00 *(978-0-470-54134-0(2),* Wiley) Wiley, John & Sons, Inc.
—Architectural Graphic Standards for Residential Construction 1. 0 CD-ROM Network Version. 2nd ed. 2010. (Ramsey/Sleeper Architectural Graphic Standards Ser.: 16). (ENG., Illus.). 736p. 3498.00 *(978-0-470-54135-7(0),* Wiley) Wiley, John & Sons, Inc.
American Institute of Architects Staff. Architectural Graphic Standards 4. 0 CD-ROM Multi-Seat. 2007. (ENG.). cd-rom 375.00 *(978-0-470-14840-2(3),* Wiley) Wiley, John & Sons, Inc.
American Institute of Architects Staff & Giglio, Nina M. Architectural Graphic Standards for Residential Construction. Hall, Dennis J., ed. 2nd ed. 2010. (Ramsey/Sleeper Architectural Graphic Standards Ser.: 13). (ENG., Illus.). 720p. 199.00 *(978-0-470-39583-7(4),* Wiley) Wiley, John & Sons, Inc.
Ballast, David Kent. Architect's Handbook of Construction Detailing. 2nd ed. 2009. (ENG., Illus.). 480p. 90.00 *(978-0-470-38191-5(4),* Wiley) Wiley, John & Sons, Inc.
—Handbook of Construction Tolerances. 2nd rev. ed. 2007. (ENG., Illus.). 384p. 85.00 *(978-0-471-93151-5(9),* Wiley) Wiley, John & Sons, Inc.
—Interior Construction & Detailing for Designers & Architects. 5th ed. 2011. (ENG.). 592p. pap. 176.00 ***(978-1-59126-337-1(9))*** Professional Pubns., Inc.
Ballast, David Kent. Interior Detailing: Concept to Construction. 2010. (ENG., Illus.). 304p. 85.00 *(978-0-470-50497-0(8),* Wiley) Wiley, John & Sons, Inc.
Bangash, M. Y. H., ed. Structural Detailing in Timber: A Comparative Study of British, European & American Codes & Practices. 2007. (Illus.). x, 211p. 180.95 *(978-1-4200-6834-4(2))* Whittles Publishing GBR. Dist: Taylor & Francis Group.
Binggeli, Corky. Interior Graphic Standards 2. 0 CD-ROM Network Version. 2011. (Ramsey/Sleeper Architectural Graphic Standards Ser.: 14). (ENG.). 3498.00 *(978-0-470-50459-8(5),* Wiley) Wiley, John & Sons, Inc.
Binggeli, Corky & Greichen, Patricia. Interior Graphic Standards. 2nd ed. (ENG.). 2011. (Ramsey/Sleeper Architectural Graphic Standards Ser.: 21). 496p. pap., stu. ed. 110.00 ***(978-0-470-88901-5(2))*** 2010. (Illus.). 992p. 225.00 *(978-0-470-47157-9(3))* Wiley, John & Sons, Inc. (Wiley).
Binggeli, Corky & Greichen, Patricia. Interior Graphic Standards 2. 0 CD-ROM. 2011. (ENG.). 325.00 *(978-0-470-47563-8(3),* Wiley) Wiley, John & Sons, Inc.
Bisharat, Keith A. Construction Graphics: A Practical Guide to Interpreting Working Drawings. 2nd ed. 2008. (ENG., Illus.). 480p. 115.00 *(978-0-470-13750-5(9),* Wiley) Wiley, John & Sons, Inc.
Brookes, Alan J. Building Envelope & Connections. (C). 102.00 *(978-0-8176-2533-7(X))* Birkhauser Boston.
Brown, Walter Charles & Dorfmueller, Daniel P. Print Reading for Construction: Residential & Commercial: Write-In Text with 130 Large Prints. 6th ed. 2012. ***(978-1-60525-802-7(4))*** Goodheart-Willcox Pub.
Diergarten, Gotz, photos by. Götz Diergarten: Photographs. 2010. (ENG & GER., Illus.). 160p. 55.00 *(978-3-7757-2563-7(6))* Hatje Cantz Verlag GmbH & Co KG DEU. Dist: D.A.P./Distributed Art Pubs.
Hall, Dennis J. & Giglio, Nina M. Graphic Standards Field Guide to Residential Construction. 2011. (Graphic Standards Field Guide Ser.: 18). (ENG., Illus.). 496p. pap. 75.00 *(978-0-470-63504-9(5),* Wiley) Wiley, John & Sons, Inc.
ICC. 2009 IBC Q & A: Nonstructural Provisions. 2010. pap. 45.00 *(978-1-58001-632-2(4))* International Code Council.
Kubba, Sam. Blueprint Reading: Construction Drawings for the Building Trades. 2008. (ENG., Illus.). 384p. pap. 49.95 *(978-0-07-154986-8(2),* 0071549862) McGraw-Hill Professional Publishing.
McGrath, Brian. Digital Modelling for Urban Design. 2008. (ENG., Illus.). 272p. 150.00 *(978-0-470-03477-4(7))*; pap. 60.00 *(978-0-470-03478-1(5))* Wiley, John & Sons, Inc. (Wiley).
Moro, José L. Baukonstruktion vom Prinzip zum Detail: Band 1: Grundlagen. 2006. (Illus.). XXX, 666p. pap. 89.95 *(978-3-540-40613-6(1),* 3540406131) Springer.
Moussavi, Farshid & Kubo, Michael, eds. The Function of Ornament. 2006. (Illus.). 186p. pap. 29.95 *(978-84-96540-50-7(2))* Kunst-Werke Berlin e.V. DEU. Dist: Actar Birkhauser Distribution.
Ramsey, Charles George & Sleeper, Harold Reeve. Architectural Graphic Standards 4.0. American Institute of Architects Staff, ed. 2007. (ENG.). 375.00 *(978-0-470-04323-3(7),* Wiley) Wiley, John & Sons, Inc.
Ramsey, Charles George, et al. Architectural Graphic Standards. Bassler, Bruce, ed. 11th ed. 2008. (Ramsey/Sleeper Architectural Graphic Standards Ser.: 8). (ENG., Illus.). 560p. stu. ed., per. 115.00 *(978-0-470-08546-2(0),* Wiley) Wiley, John & Sons, Inc.
Residential Detailed Costs 2003: Contractor's Pricing Guide. 300p. 38.95 *(978-0-87629-686-8(X))* Means, R.S. Co., Inc.
Russell, Ron. Print & Specifications Reading for Construction. 2011. (ENG.). 240p. 95.00 ***(978-0-470-87941-2(6),*** Wiley) Wiley, John & Sons, Inc.
Steiner, Frederick R., et al. Planning & Urban Design Standards. 2006. (Ramsey/Sleeper Architectural Graphic Standards Ser.: 6). (ENG., Illus.). 448p. pap., stu. ed. 99.00 *(978-0-471-76090-0(0),* Wiley) Wiley, John & Sons, Inc.
The American Institute of Architects. Architectural Graphic Standards. Pressman, Andy, ed. 11th rev. ed. 2007. (ENG., Illus.). 1120p. 250.00 *(978-0-471-70091-3(6),* Wiley) Wiley, John & Sons, Inc.
Underwood, Lynn. DEWALT Residential Construction Codes, Complete Handbook. 2012. (ENG.). 275p. pap. 29.95 ***(978-1-133-12953-0(6),*** DEWALT) CENGAGE Learning.

BUILDING—DICTIONARIES
Building Intelligence Group. Intelligent Building Dictionary: Terminology for Smart, Integrated, Green Building Design, Construction, & Management. Ehrlich, Chuck, ed. 2007. (Illus.). 300p. pap. 29.95 *(978-0-9796408-4-1(9))*; *(978-0-9796408-3-4(0))* Hands-On-Guide.
Fenwick Elliot LLP Staff. Dictionary of Construction Terms. 2012. pap. 171.00 *(978-1-84311-794-0(0))* Informa Professional GBR. Dist: International Specialized Bk. Services.

Gorse, Christopher, et al. A Dictionary of Construction, Surveying, & Civil Engineering. 2012. (Oxford Paperback Reference Ser.). (ENG., Illus.). 512p. pap. 21.95 **(978-0-19-953446-3(2))** Oxford Univ. Pr., Inc.

Jokiniemi, Erkki & Davies, Nikolas. Dictionary of Architecture & Building Construction. 2008. (ENG., Illus.). 736p. 59.95 *(978-0-7506-8502-3(6))* Routledge.

McDonald, Roxanna. Illustrated Building Pocket Book. 2nd rev. ed. 2006. (ENG., Illus.). 256p. per. 35.95 *(978-0-7506-8015-8(6))* Routledge.

Quillet Staff. Encyclopédie Pratique de la Construction du Batiment et des Travaux Publics, 3 vols., Set. (FRE.). 3587p. 350.00 *(978-0-7859-0396-3(8),* M6232) French & European Pubns., Inc.

R. S. Means Company Staff, ed. Means Illustrated Construction Dictionary: The Complete Source of Construction Terms & Concept. 4th ed. 2009. (RSMeans Ser.: 8). (ENG.). 880p. 99.95 *(978-0-87629-092-7(6))* Means, R.S. Co., Inc.

Williams, Tara Bradley. ¡A Trabajar! Spanish for Construction Classroom Set. 2007. (SPA.). per. 34.95 *(978-1-934467-08-4(1))* Pronto Spanish Services, LLC.

—Pronto Guide: Spanish for Construction. 2007. (SPA.). 15.95 *(978-1-934467-02-2(2))* Pronto Spanish Services, LLC.

BUILDING—ESTIMATES

see also Quantity Surveying

Andrews, Franklin, ed. Spon's Irish Construction Price Book. 3rd rev. ed. 2008. (Spon's International Price Bks.). (ENG., Illus.). 528p. 290.00 *(978-0-415-45637-1(1),* Spon Pr.) Routledge.

Asdal, William. Defensive Estimating: Protecting Your Profits. 2006. (Illus.). 141p. per. 29.95 *(978-0-86718-620-8(8))* BuilderBooks.

Ashworth, Allan. Pre-Contract Studies: Development Economics, Tendering & Estimating. 3rd ed. 2008. (ENG., Illus.). 376p. pap. 65.00 *(978-1-4051-7700-9(4),* Wiley-Blackwell) Wiley, John & Sons, Inc.

Ashworth, Allan & Hogg, Keith. Willis's Practice & Procedure for the Quantity Surveyor. 12th rev. ed. 2007. (ENG., Illus.). 440p. pap. 69.99 *(978-1-4051-4578-7(1),* Wiley-Blackwell) Wiley, John & Sons, Inc.

Atcheson, Dan. National Concrete & Masonry Estimator. 4th ed. 2008. (National Concrete & Masonry Estimator Ser.). (Illus.). 605p. pap. 64.00 incl. cd-rom *(978-1-57218-207-3(5))* Craftsman Bk. Co.

—National Framing & Finish Carpentry Estimator. annuals (National Framing & Finish Carpentry Estimator Ser.). (Illus.). 402p. 2nd ed. 2007. pap. 57.25 incl. cd-rom *(978-1-57218-192-2(3))* 3rd ed. 2008. pap. 62.95 incl. cd-rom *(978-1-57218-211-0(3))* Craftsman Bk. Co.

Balboni, Barbara, ed. Means Assemblies Cost Data. 33rd ed. 2007. (Means Assemblies Cost Data Ser.). (Illus.). 605p. per. 245.95 *(978-0-87629-019-4(5))* Means, R.S. Co., Inc.

—Means Square Foot Costs. 29th ed. 2007. (Means Square Foot Costs Ser.). (Illus.). 503p. per. 163.95 *(978-0-87629-055-2(1))* Means, R.S. Co., Inc.

Balboni, Barbara, et al, eds. RSMeans Interior Cost Data: Partitions/Ceilings/Finishes/Floors/Furnishings. 25th ed. 2007. (Means Interior Cost Data Ser.). (Illus.). 693p. per. 149.95 *(978-0-87629-032-3(2))* Means, R.S. Co., Inc.

Belcher, Matt. Build Green & Save: Protecting the Earth & Your Bottom Line. 2009. (Illus.). 154p. 21.95 *(978-0-86718-644-4(5))* BuilderBooks.

Bni, creator. Electrical Costbook 2007. 14th ed. 2006. (Building News Electrical Costbook Ser.). 351p. per. 79.95 *(978-1-55701-565-5(1))* BNI Pubns., Inc.

—Facilities Managers Costbook 2007. 13th ed. 2006. (Building News Facilities Manager's Costbook Ser.). (Illus.). 797p. per. 99.95 *(978-1-55701-562-4(7))* BNI Pubns., Inc.

BNI, ed. BNI General Construction 2007 Costbook. 2006. 95.95 *(978-1-55701-561-7(9))* BNI Pubns., Inc.

BNI Building News. Sweets Electrical Cost Guide. 2008. (Sweet's Electrical Cost Guide Ser.). (Illus.). 361p. pap. 96.95 *(978-1-55701-630-0(5))* BNI Pubns., Inc.

—Sweets Facilities Cost Guide. 2008. (Sweet's Facilities Cost Guide Ser.). (Illus.). 714p. pap. 99.95 *(978-1-55701-629-4(1))* BNI Pubns., Inc.

—Sweets Repair & Remodel Cost Guide. 2008. (Sweet's Repair & Remodel Cost Guide Ser.). (Illus.). 547p. pap. 96.95 *(978-1-55701-628-7(3))* BNI Pubns., Inc.

—Sweets Residential Cost Guide. 2008. (Sweet's Residential Cost Guide Ser.). (Illus.). 320p. pap. 96.95 *(978-1-55701-631-7(3))* BNI Pubns., Inc.

—Sweets Unit Cost Guide. 2008. (Sweet's Unit Cost Guide Ser.). (Illus.). 551p. pap. 96.95 *(978-1-55701-627-0(5))* BNI Pubns., Inc.

BNI Building News, creator. Home Builder's Costbook. 15th ed. 2006. (Building News Home Builder's Costbook Ser.). (Illus.). 327p. per. 69.95 *(978-1-55701-566-2(X))* BNI Pubns., Inc.

—Sweets Repair & Remodel Cost Guide. 2009. (McGraw-Hill Construction Ser.). (ENG., Illus.). 548p. pap. 96.95 *(978-1-55701-668-3(2))* BNI Pubns., Inc.

Bni Publications, creator. BNI Facilities Manager's Costbook. 18th ed. 2011. (ENG., Illus.). 798p. pap. 99.95 **(978-1-55701-725-3(5))** BNI Pubns., Inc.

Bourke, Kathryn. Achieving Whole Life Value in Infrastructure & Buildings. 2010. (ENG., Illus.). 60p. pap. 80.00 *(978-1-86081-737-3(3))* Building Research Establishment GBR. Dist: Taylor & Francis Group.

Boussabaine, Abdelhalim. Cost Planning of PFI & PPP Building Projects. 2006. (ENG., Illus.). 336p. 150.00 *(978-0-415-36622-9(4))* Routledge.

Brown, Joseph A. Jab's con$Truction, Co$T Escalation, Engineering & Management, Cpm. 2011. 688p. 34.99 **(978-1-4500-6533-7(3))**; pap. 23.99 **(978-1-4500-6532-0(5))** Xlibris Corp.

Caplehorn, Peter. Whole Life Costing: A New Approach. 2012. (ENG., Illus.). 160p. pap. 55.95 *(978-0-415-43423-2(8))* Routledge.

Chartered Institute of Building Staff. Code of Estimating Practice. 7th rev. ed. 2009. (ENG., Illus.). 176p. pap. 94.99 *(978-1-4051-2971-8(9),* Wiley-Blackwell) Wiley, John & Sons, Inc.

Chiang, John H. & Spencer, Eugene R., eds. RS Means Metric Construction Cost Data. 66th ed. 2007. (Means Metric Construction Cost Data Ser.). 1029p. per. 179.95 *(978-0-87629-049-1(7))* Means, R.S. Co., Inc.

Chipman, Les, et al. Standard Estimating Practice: American Society of Professional Estimators. 6th ed. 2007. (Illus.). 506p. per. 89.00 *(978-1-55701-481-8(7))* BNI Pubns., Inc.

Collier, James. Construction Funding. 3rd ed. 2009. 99.00 *(978-0-471-23242-1(4),* Wiley) Wiley, John & Sons, Inc.

Craftsman Book Company. 2010 National Home Improvement Estimator. Hicks, Ray & Hageman, Constance, eds. 2010. pap. 63.75 *(978-1-57218-229-5(6))* Craftsman Bk. Co.

Craftsman Book Company, ed. 2010 CD Estimator. 2009. (Illus.). cd-rom 98.50 *(978-1-57218-234-9(2))* Craftsman Bk. Co.

—2010 CD Estimator-Heavy. 2009. (Illus.). cd-rom 39.99 *(978-1-57218-235-6(0))* Craftsman Bk. Co.

Cram101 Textbook Reviews & Cram101 Textbook Reviews. Outlines & Highlights for Estimating in Building Construction by Frank R Dagostino. 2011. 126p. pap. 28.95 **(978-1-61830-841-2(6))** Cram101 Inc.

—Outlines & Highlights for Green Construction Project Management & Cost Oversight by Sam Kubb. 2011. 160p. pap. 29.95 **(978-1-61830-831-3(9))** Cram101 Inc.

Dave, Ogershok, ed. 2011 National Building Cost Manual. 2010. 264p. pap. 53.00 incl. cd-rom *(978-1-57218-240-0(7))* Craftsman Bk. Co.

—2011 National Construction Estimator. 2010. 672p. pap. 62.50 incl. cd-rom *(978-1-57218-242-4(3))* Craftsman Bk. Co.

Davis Langdon Seah Staff. Asia-Pacific Construction Costs. 4th ed. 2010. (Spon's International Price Bks.). (ENG., Illus.). 512p. instr.'s hndbk. ed. 210.00 *(978-0-415-46565-6(6),* CRC Press) Taylor & Francis Group GBR. Dist: Taylor & Francis Group.

Davis Langdon, ed. Spon's Architects' & Builders' Price Book 2013. 138th rev. ed. 2012. (ENG.). 912p. 255.00 **(978-0-415-69077-5(3),** Spon Pr.) Routledge.

Davis Langdon Engineering Services. Spon's Mechanical & Electrical Services Price Book 2011. 42nd ed. 2010. (ENG., Illus.). 800p. 255.00 *(978-0-415-55851-5(0),* Spon Pr.) Routledge.

Dawn Romance. Show Well, Sell Well: 103 Simple, Low-Cost Things to do That Will Help Your Property Show & Sell its Best. 2009. 48p. pap. 9.95 *(978-1-4401-7739-2(2))* iUniverse, Inc.

DelPico, Wayne J. Estimating Building Costs for the Residential & Light Commercial Construction Professional. 2nd ed. 2012. (RSMeans Ser.: 80). (ENG.). 528p. pap. 65.00 **(978-1-118-09941-4(9))** Means, R.S. Co., Inc.

Design & Construction Resources, creator. Architects, Contractors, Engineers Guide to Construction Costs, Volume 41. 2010. (Architects, Contractors, & Engineers Guide to Construction Costs Ser.). 176p. pap. *(978-1-58855-104-7(0))* Cyber Classics, Inc.

Design & Construction Resources, ed. Architects Contractors Engineers Guide to Construction Costs 2011. 2010. 176p. 59.95 *(978-1-58855-114-6(8))* Cyber Classics, Inc.

Dickinson, Duo. House on a Budget: Making Smart Choices to Build the Home You Want. 2007. (American Institute Architects Ser.). (ENG., Illus.). 208p. pap. 21.95 *(978-1-56158-923-4(3),* Taunton) Taunton Pr., Inc.

Ding, Adam & American Contractors Educational Services Staff. Construction Estimating Professional Reference. 2006. (DeWalt Ser.). (ENG., Illus.). 384p. per. 19.95 *(978-0-9777183-0-6(1),* DEWALT) CENGAGE Learning.

—HVAC Estimating Professional Reference. 2007. (ENG.). 384p. per. 19.95 *(978-0-9777183-5-1(2),* DEWALT) CENGAGE Learning.

Duff, A Roy & Horner, Malcolm. Improving Productivity: A Contractor's Guide to Leaner Construction. 2009. 224p. pap. 74.99 *(978-1-4051-2380-8(X),* Wiley-Blackwell) Wiley, John & Sons, Inc.

Engineering News-Record Staff, ed. General Contracting Costbook. 2007. 208p. pap. 49.95 *(978-1-58855-708-7(1))* Cyber Classics, Inc.

—Residential Contracting Costbook. 2007. 164p. pap. 49.95 *(978-1-58855-081-1(8))* Cyber Classics, Inc.

Estimating & Tendering for Construction Work. 4th rev. ed. 2008. (ENG., Illus.). 382p. pap. 41.95 *(978-0-7506-8616-7(2))* Routledge.

Fawcett, William & Ellingham, Ian. New Generation Whole-Life Costing: Property & Construction Decision-Making under Uncertainty. 2006. (ENG., Illus.). 224p. (C). 64.95 *(978-0-415-34658-0(4))* Routledge.

—New Generation Whole-Life Costing: Property & Construction Decision-Making under Uncertainty. 2006. (ENG., Illus.). 224p. (C). 170.00 *(978-0-415-34657-3(6))* Routledge.

Gibson, Roger. Construction Delays: Extensions of Time & Prolongation Claims. 2008. (ENG., Illus.). 384p. 150.00 *(978-0-415-34586-6(3))* Routledge.

Gleason, Dennis. 2010 National Painting Cost Estimator. 2010. (Illus.). 448p. pap. 63.00 *(978-1-57218-230-1(X))* Craftsman Bk. Co.

Halpin, Daniel W., et al. Financial Management & Accounting Fundamentals for Construction. 2009. (ENG., Illus.). 320p. 110.00 *(978-0-470-18271-0(7),* Wiley) Wiley, John & Sons, Inc.

Hanscomb, creator. Yardsticks for Costing: Cost Data for the Canadian Construction Industry: Metric & Imperial. 2008. (Illus.). 174p. spiral bd. 149.95 *(978-0-87629-059-0(4))* Means, R.S. Co., Inc.

Kirkham, Richard. Ferry & Brandon's Cost Planning of Buildings. 8th rev. ed. 2007. (ENG., Illus.). 432p. pap. 64.99 *(978-1-4051-3070-7(9),* Wiley-Blackwell) Wiley, John & Sons, Inc.

Knight, Laura, illus. National Building Cost Manual. annuals 32nd ed. 2007. (National Building Cost Manual Ser.). 244p. per. 33.00 *(978-1-57218-187-8(7))* Craftsman Bk. Co.

Landis, Tom. Home Building Consumer's Guide & Video: How to Save Money by Taking Charge of the Design/Build Process. Incl. (Illus.). 1997. pap. *(978-0-9641268-0-0(X))*; 60.00 *(978-0-9641268-1-7(8))* Owner Builder Services.

Landsberg, Dennis R., et al. Energy Efficiency Guide for Existing Commercial Buildings: The Business Case for Building Owners & Managers. 2009. (ENG.). 85p. pap. 39.00 *(978-1-933742-63-2(1))* American Society of Heating, Refrigerating & Air-Conditioning Engineers, Inc.

Langdon, Davis. Spon's Mechanical & Electrical Services Price Book 2013. 44th rev. ed. 2012. (ENG., Illus.). 800p. 255.00 **(978-0-415-69080-5(3),** Spon Pr.) Routledge.

Lee, Sandra, et al. Willis's Elements of Quantity Surveying. 11th ed. 2011. (ENG., Illus.). 360p. pap. 47.50 *(978-1-4443-3500-2(6),* Wiley-Blackwell) Wiley, John & Sons, Inc.

Mahoney, William, ed. Sweets Unit Cost Guide. 2009. (Illus.). 554p. pap. 96.95 *(978-1-55701-667-6(4))* BNI Pubns., Inc.

Mahoney, William D., ed. Bni Building News Remodeling 2010 Costbook. 20th ed. 2010. (Building News Remodeling Costbook Ser.). (Illus.). 522p. pap. *(978-1-55701-665-2(8))* BNI Pubns., Inc.

—Building News Electrical Costbook. 16th ed. 2008. (Building News Electrical Costbook Ser.). (Illus.). 350p. pap. 83.95 *(978-1-55701-623-2(2))* BNI Pubns., Inc.

—Building News Facilities Manager's Costbook. 15th ed. 2008. (Building News Facilities Manager's Costbook Ser.). (Illus.). 794p. pap. 99.95 *(978-1-55701-620-1(8))* BNI Pubns., Inc.

—Building News Home Builder's Costbook. 17th ed. 2008. (Building News Home Builder's Costbook Ser.). (Illus.). 327p. pap. 73.95 *(978-1-55701-624-9(0))* BNI Pubns., Inc.

—Building News Home Remodeler's Costbook. 15th ed. 2008. (Building News Home Remodeler's Costbook Ser.). (Illus.). 370p. pap. 77.95 *(978-1-55701-626-3(7))* BNI Pubns., Inc.

—Building News Mechanical/Electrical 2007 Costbook. 17th ed. 2006. (Building News Mechanical/Electrical Costbook Ser.). (Illus.). 499p. per. 95.95 *(978-1-55701-564-8(3))* BNI Pubns., Inc.

—Building News Mechanical/Electrical Costbook. 19th ed. 2008. (Building News Mechanical/Electrical Costbook Ser.). 498p. pap. 97.95 *(978-1-55701-622-5(4))* BNI Pubns., Inc.

—Building News Remodeling Costbook. 19th ed. 2008. (Building News Remodeling Costbook Ser.). (Illus.). 523p. pap. 95.95 *(978-1-55701-625-6(9))* BNI Pubns., Inc.

MARCH. Finance & Control for Constuction. 2009. (ENG., Illus.). 256p. 150.00 *(978-0-415-37114-8(7))*; pap. 44.95 *(978-0-415-37115-5(5))* Routledge.

Maxim, Korablev. Computer Program Development for House Cost Calculation: Computer Program for House Cost Calculation: How It Is Made? 2011. 68p. pap. **(978-3-639-33080-9(3))** VDM Verlag Dr. Mueller e.K.

McGraw-Hill Staff, ed. Sweets Facilities Cost Guide. 2011. (McGraw-Hill Construction Ser.). (ENG., Illus.). 720p. pap. 99.95 **(978-1-55701-734-5(4))** BNI Pubns., Inc.

Mewis, Robert W., ed. Means Residential Cost Data. 27th ed. 2007. (Means Residential Cost Data Ser.). (Illus.). 693p. per. 128.95 *(978-0-87629-053-8(5))* Means, R.S. Co., Inc.

Mewis, Robert W., et al, eds. Means Residential Repair & Remodeling Costs. 2006. (Means Contractor's Pricing Guide: Residential Repair & Remodeling Ser.). (Illus.). 317p. per. 39.95 *(978-0-87629-873-2(0))* Means, R.S. Co., Inc.

Mitchell, Karen, et al. Contractor's Guide to QuickBooks Pro. 2007. (Illus.). 342p. pap. incl. cd-rom *(978-1-57218-186-1(9))* Craftsman Bk. Co.

—Contractor's Guide to QuickBooks Pro 2008. 2008. (Illus.). 340p. pap. 54.75 incl. cd-rom *(978-1-57218-200-4(8))* Craftsman Bk. Co.

—Contractor's Guide to QuickBooks Pro 2009. 2009. (Illus.). 344p. pap. 56.50 incl. cd-rom *(978-1-57218-221-9(0))* Craftsman Bk. Co.

—Contractor's Guide to Quickbooks Pro 2010. 2010. *(978-1-57218-236-3(9),* Craftsman Bk. Co.

Moskow, Keith. Sustainable Facilities: Green Design, Construction, & Operations. 2008. (ENG., Illus.). 208p. 69.95 *(978-0-07-149474-8(X),* 007149474X) McGraw-Hill Professional Publishing.

Mossman, Melville J., ed. Means Mechanical Cost Data. 31st ed. 2007. (Means Mechanical Cost Data Ser.). (Illus.). 725p. per. 149.95 *(978-0-87629-045-4(9))* Means, R.S. Co., Inc.

—Means Plumbing Cost Data. 31st ed. 2007. (Means Plumbing Cost Data Ser.). 661p. per. 149.95 *(978-0-87629-051-4(9))* Means, R.S. Co., Inc.

Mossman, Melville J., et al, eds. Means Facilities Maintenance & Repair Cost Data. 15th ed. 2007. (Means Facilities Maintenance & Repair Construction Cost Data Ser.). (Illus.). 659p. per. 326.95 *(978-0-87629-030-9(6))* Means, R.S. Co., Inc.

—RSMeans Facilities Construction cost Data. 23rd ed. 2007. (Means Facilities Construction Cost Data Ser.). (Illus.). 1443p. per. 357.95 *(978-0-87629-029-3(2))* Means, R.S. Co., Inc.

Mossman, Melville J. & Plotner, Stephen C., eds. Means Repair & Remodeling Cost Data. 29th ed. 2007. (Means Repair & Remodeling Cost Data Ser.). (Illus.). 773p. per. 128.95 *(978-0-87629-052-1(7))* Means, R.S. Co., Inc.

Mubarak, Saleh A. & Means, R. S. How to Estimate with RSMeans Data: Basic Skills for Building Construction. 4th ed. 2012. (RSMeans Ser.: 91). (ENG., Illus.). 320p. pap. 70.00 **(978-1-118-02528-4(8))** Means, R.S. Co., Inc.

Ogershok, Dave, ed. National Building Cost Manual. (National Building Cost Manual Ser.). (Illus.). 31st ed. 2006. 238p. per. 28.00 *(978-1-57218-174-8(5))* 33rd ed. 2008. 262p. pap. 53.00 incl. cd-rom *(978-1-57218-206-6(7))* Craftsman Bk. Co.

Ogershok, Dave & Pray, Richard. National Construction Estimator. annuals 56th ed. 2007. (National Construction Estimator Ser.). (Illus.). 666p. pap. 57.50 incl. cd-rom *(978-1-57218-189-2(3))* Craftsman Bk. Co.

Ogershok, Dave & Pray, Richard, eds. National Construction Estimator. (National Construction Estimator Ser.). (Illus.). 55th ed. 2006. 653p. pap. 52.50 incl. cd-rom *(978-1-57218-176-2(1))* 57th ed. 2008. 669p. pap. 62.50 incl. cd-rom *(978-1-57218-208-0(3))* Craftsman Bk. Co.

Petty, Robert M. & Denton, Michael A. Lean Operations for Engineering, Procurement, & Construction: Shorten Cycle Time, Eliminate Error, Improve Quality, Reduce Costs. 2009. pap. *(978-1-59942-896-3(2))* Universal Pubs.

Pexton, Albert. 2010 National Repair & Remodeling Estimator. 2010. (Illus.). 496p. pap. 63.50 *(978-1-57218-233-2(4))* Craftsman Bk. Co.

Peterson, Stephen J. Construction Estimating with Excel. 2006. (ENG., Illus.). 560p. (C). pap. 126.00 *(978-0-13-171983-5(1),* Prentice Hall) Prentice Hall PTR.

Peterson, Steven J. & Peterson, Steven. Construction Estimating Using Excel. 2nd rev. ed. 2011. (ENG.). 432p. (C). pap. 129.80 *(978-0-13-800719-5(5),* Prentice Hall) Prentice Hall PTR.

Peterson, Steven J., et al. Estimating in Building Construction. 7th ed. 2010. (ENG., Illus.). 288p. (C). 140.40 *(978-0-13-119952-1(8),* Prentice Hall) Prentice Hall PTR.

—Student Workbook for Estimating in Building Construction. 7th ed. 2010. (ENG.). 160p. (C). pap. 31.60 *(978-0-13-509748-9(7),* Prentice Hall) Prentice Hall PTR.

Plotner, Stephen C., et al, eds. Means Concrete & Masonry Cost Data. (Means Concrete & Masonry Cost Data Ser.). (Illus.). 549p. 25th ed. 2006. per. 124.95 *(978-0-87629-855-8(2))* 26th ed. 2007. per. 136.95 *(978-0-87629-024-8(1))* Means, R.S. Co., Inc.

Pratt. Fundamentals of Construction Estimating. 3rd ed. 2011. 250p. pap. incl. cd-rom **(978-1-4390-5962-3(4))** Wadsworth.

Pratt, David. Estimating for Residential Construction. 2nd ed. 2011. (ENG.). 400p. (C). pap. 121.95 *(978-1-111-30887-2(X))* Delmar Cengage Learning.

—Fundamentals of Construction Estimating. 3rd ed. 2010. (ENG.). 496p. (C). 181.95 *(978-1-4390-5964-7(0))* Delmar Cengage Learning.

R S Means Company. Building Construction Cost Data: Western. 20th ed. 2006. (Means Building Construction Cost Data: Western Edition Ser.). (Illus.). 773p. per. 136.95 *(978-0-87629-854-1(4))* Means, R.S. Co., Inc.

R S Means Company, creator. Means Facilities Construction Cost Data. 22nd ed. 2006. (Means Facilities Construction Cost Data Ser.). (Illus.). 1411p. per. 323.95 *(978-0-87629-858-9(7))* Means, R.S. Co., Inc.

—Means Repair & Remodeling Cost Data. 28th ed. 2006. (Means Repair & Remodeling Cost Data Ser.). (Illus.). 757p. per. 116.95 *(978-0-87629-868-8(4))* Means, R.S. Co., Inc.

—Means Residential Cost Data. 26th ed. 2006. (Means Residential Cost Data Ser.). (Illus.). 677p. per. 116.95 *(978-0-87629-869-5(2))* Means, R.S. Co., Inc.

R. S. Means Company Staff & Mossman, Melville, eds. Mechanical Estimating Methods: Takeoff & Pricing for HVAC & Plumbing. 4th rev. ed. 2007. (RSMeans Ser.: 6). (ENG.). 390p. 64.95 *(978-0-87629-017-0(9))* Means, R.S. Co., Inc.

R S Means Engineering, creator. Mechanical Cost Data: HVAC. Controls. 33rd ed. 2009. (Means Mechanical Cost Data Ser.). (ENG., Illus.). 739p. pap. 169.95 *(978-0-87629-819-0(6))* Means, R.S. Co., Inc.

Reed Construction Data, creator. RSMeans Building Construction Cost Data. 2007. (Means Building Construction Cost Data Ser.). 765p. 187.95 *(978-0-87629-021-7(7))* Means, R.S. Co., Inc.

Remodeling/Repair Construction Costs 2007. 17th ed. 2007. per. 59.95 *(978-1-933461-08-3(X))* Saylor Pubns., Inc.

RS Means, creator. CostWorks: Current Industry-Standard Construction Costs with Point-and-Click Access! 2007. N/Ap. cd-rom 185.95 *(978-0-87629-060-6(8))* Means, R.S. Co., Inc.

RS Means, ed. Informacion de Costos de Construccion. 65th ed. 2006. 1000p. per. 136.95 *(978-0-87629-853-4(6))* Means, R.S. Co., Inc.

RSMeans. Building Construction Cost Data. 765p. pap. 169.95 *(978-0-87629-852-7(8))* Means, R.S. Co., Inc.

—Building Construction Cost Data Spanish. 2008. 765p. pap. 149.95 *(978-0-87629-022-4(5))* Means, R.S. Co., Inc.

—Light Commercial Cost Data. 27th rev. ed. 2008. 800p. pap. 128.95 *(978-0-87629-047-7(0))* Means, R.S. Co., Inc.

—Site Work & Landscape Cost Data. 27th rev. ed. 2008. 750p. pap. 149.95 *(978-0-87629-054-5(3))* Means, R.S. Co., Inc.

Rsmeans, compiled by. Means CPG Residential Detailed Costs. 2007. (Illus.). 403p. per. 39.95 *(978-0-87629-056-9(X))* Means, R.S. Co., Inc.

—Means CPG Residential Repair & Remodeling. 2007. (Means Contractor's Pricing Guide: Residential Repair & Remodeling Ser.). (Illus.). 319p. per. 39.95 *(978-0-87629-057-6(8))* Means, R.S. Co., Inc.

—Means CPG Residential Square Foot Costs. 2007. (Means Residential Square Foot Costs Ser.). (Illus.). 291p. per. 39.95 *(978-0-87629-058-3(6))* Means, R.S. Co., Inc.

RSMeans Engineering Dept., ed. Assemblies Cost Data. 2008. 635p. 254.95 *(978-0-87629-094-1(2))* Means, R.S. Co., Inc.

—Building Construction Cost Data. 2008. 825p. 154.95 *(978-0-87629-095-8(0))* Means, R.S. Co., Inc.

—Concrete/Masonry Cost Data. 2008. 550p. 139.95 *(978-0-87629-123-8(X))* Means, R.S. Co., Inc.
—Contractor's Pricing Guide: Residential Detailed Costs. 2008. 375p. 39.95 *(978-0-87629-135-1(3))* Means, R.S. Co., Inc.
—Contractor's Pricing Guide: Residential Repair & Remodeling. 2008. 315p. 39.95 *(978-0-87629-148-1(5))* Means, R.S. Co., Inc.
—Contractor's Pricing Guide: Residential Square Foot Costs. 2008. 275p. 39.95 *(978-0-87629-149-8(3))* Means, R.S. Co., Inc.
—Cost Works 2009 - Cd Rom (Single File) 2008. 199.95 *(978-0-87629-225-9(2))* Means, R.S. Co., Inc.
—Facilities Construction Cost Data. 2008. 1400p. 368.95 *(978-0-87629-152-8(3))* Means, R.S. Co., Inc.
—Facilities Maintenance & Repair. 2008. 650p. 336.95 *(978-0-87629-175-7(2))* Means, R.S. Co., Inc.
—Heavy Construction Cost Data. 2008. 600p. 154.95 *(978-0-87629-176-4(0))* Means, R.S. Co., Inc.
—Interior Cost Data. 2008. 700p. 154.95 *(978-0-87629-178-8(7))* Means, R.S. Co., Inc.
—Light Commercial Cost Data. 2008. 800p. 132.95 *(978-0-87629-181-8(7))* Means, R.S. Co., Inc.
—Mechanical Cost Data. 2008. 725p. 154.95 *(978-0-87629-183-2(3))* Means, R.S. Co., Inc.
—Open Shop Bccd. 2008. 800p. 154.95 *(978-0-87629-185-6(X))* Means, R.S. Co., Inc.
—Plumbing Cost Data. 2008. 650p. 154.95 *(978-0-87629-186-3(8))* Means, R.S. Co., Inc.
—Repair & Remodeling Cost Data. 2008. 750p. 132.95 *(978-0-87629-206-8(6))* Means, R.S. Co., Inc.
—Residential Cost Data. 2008. 675p. 132.95 *(978-0-87629-207-5(4))* Means, R.S. Co., Inc.
—Site Work & Landscape Cost Data. 2008. 750p. 154.95 *(978-0-87629-208-2(2))* Means, R.S. Co., Inc.
—Square Foot Costs. 2008. 500p. 168.95 *(978-0-87629-209-9(0))* Means, R.S. Co., Inc.
—Yardsticks for Costing - Canadian Construction Cost Data. 2009. (ENG.). 160p. pap. 154.95 *(978-0-87629-221-1(X))* Means, R.S. Co., Inc.
Rudman, Jack. Senior Estimator (Construction) (Career Examination Ser.: C-3689). pap. 39.95 *(978-0-8373-3689-3(9))* National Learning Corp.
Russell, Jonathan. 2010 National Renovation & Insurance Repair Estimator. 2010. (Illus.). 488p. pap. 64.50 *(978-1-57218-232-5(6))* Craftsman Bk. Co.
Russell, Jonathan, ed. National Renovation & Insurance Repair Estimator. (National Renovation & Insurance Repair Estimator Ser.). (Illus.). 2008. 486p. pap. 64.50 incl. cd-rom *(978-1-57218-215-8(6))* 2006. 518p. pap. 54.50 incl. cd-rom *(978-1-57218-181-6(8))* Craftsman Bk. Co.
Schmid, Karl F. Construction Estimating: A Step-by-Step Guide to a Successful Estimate. 2011. 305p. pap. 39.95 ***(978-1-60650-292-1(1))*** Momentum Pr.
Spain. Spon's Estimating Costs Guide to Finishings: Painting, Decorating, Plastering & Tiling. 2nd rev. ed. 2007. (Spon's Estimating Costs Guides). (ENG.). 272p. 64.95 *(978-0-415-43443-0(2)*, Spon Pr.) Routledge.
Spain, Bryan. Minor Works, Alterations & Repairs to Fire, Flood, Gale & Theft Damage: Unit Rates & Project Costs. 4th rev. ed. 2008. (Spon's Estimating Costs Guides). (ENG.). 336p. pap. 64.95 *(978-0-415-46906-7(6)*, Spon Pr.) Routledge.
—Spon's First Stage Estimating Handbook. 3rd rev. ed. 2010. (Spon's Estimating Costs Guides). (ENG.). 256p. pap. 79.95 *(978-0-415-54715-4(6)*, Spon Pr.) Routledge.
—Spon's House Improvements Price Book. 4th rev. ed. 2009. (Spon's Price Bks.). (ENG.). 512p. 99.95 *(978-0-415-54716-1(4)*, Spon Pr.) Routledge.
Spencer, Eugene R., et al, eds. Means Heavy Construction Cost Data. (Means Heavy Construction Cost Data Ser.). (Illus.). 21st ed. 2006. 613p. per. 136.95 *(978-0-87629-860-2(9))* 22nd ed. 2007. 629p. per. 149.95 *(978-0-87629-031-6(4))* Means, R.S. Co., Inc.
Strychaz, Stanley. Commercial Square Foot Building Costs 2007. 17th ed. 2007. per. 59.95 *(978-1-933461-09-0(8))* Saylor Pubns., Inc.
—Current Construction Costs 2007. 44th ed. 2007. per. 74.95 *(978-1-933461-06-9(3))* Saylor Pubns., Inc.
—Residential Construction Costs 2007. 26th ed. 2007. per. 74.95 *(978-1-933461-07-6(1))* Saylor Pubns., Inc.
—Residential Square Foot Building Costs 2007. 2007. per. 39.95 *(978-1-933461-10-6(1))* Saylor Pubns., Inc.
Thomson, James. 2010 National Plumbing & HVAC Estimator. 2010. (Illus.). 464p. pap. 63.25 *(978-1-57218-231-8(8))* Craftsman Bk. Co.
United States, Congress House Committee on Transportation and Infrastructure Subcommittee on Economic Development, Public Buildings, and Emergency Management Staff, contrib. by. The Future of the Federal Courthouse Construction Program: Results of a Government Accountability Office Study on the Judiciary's Rental Obligations: Hearing Before the Subcommittee on Economic Development, Public Buildings, & Emergency Management of the Committee on Transportation & Infrastructure, House of Representatives, One Hundred Ninth Congress, Second Session, Jun3 22, 2006. 2007. (Illus.). v, 296p. *(978-0-16-078034-9(9)*, 552-070-35464-6) United States Government Printing Office.
Waier, Phillip R., ed. Means Building Construction Cost Data. 66th ed. 2007. (Means Building Construction Cost Data Ser.). (Illus.). 837p. per. 149.95 *(978-0-87629-020-0(9))* Means, R.S. Co., Inc.
Waier, Phillip R., et al, eds. Building Construction Cost Data: Western Edition. 21st ed. 2007. (Means Building Construction Cost Data: Western Edition Ser.). (Illus.). 799p. per. 149.95 *(978-0-87629-023-1(3))* Means, R.S. Co., Inc.
—Open Shop Building Construction Cost Data. 24th ed. 2007. (Means Open Shop Building Construction Cost Data Ser.). (Illus.). 821p. per. 149.95 *(978-0-87629-050-7(0))* Means, R.S. Co., Inc.
Waier, Phillip R. & Chiang, John, eds. Unit Price Estimating Methods. 4th ed. 2007. (RSMeans Ser.: 5). (ENG.). 432p. pap. 65.00 *(978-0-87629-016-3(0))* Means, R.S. Co., Inc.
Ware, John. Hanscomb Yardsticks for Costing: Cost Data for the Canadian Construction Industry; Metric & Imperial. Ferguson, John H., ed. 2007. (Illus.). 174p. spiral bd. 126.95 *(978-0-87629-875-6(7))* Means, R.S. Co., Inc.
2003 Building Construction Cost Data. 61st ed. 650p. 104.95 *(978-0-87629-665-3(7))* Means, R.S. Co., Inc.
2003 Square Foot Costs. 24th ed. 450p. 115.95 *(978-0-87629-685-1(1))* Means, R.S. Co., Inc.

BUILDING—HANDBOOKS, MANUALS, ETC.

see also Building—Amateurs' Manuals

Adams, Dave K. The Structural Engineer's Professional Training Manual. 2007. (ENG., Illus.). 405p. 92.95 *(978-0-07-148107-6(9)*, 0071481079) McGraw-Hill Professional Publishing.
American Contractors Exam Services. DeWALT Building Code Reference. 2nd ed. 2010. (ENG.). 84p. spiral bd. 19.95 *(978-1-111-03662-1(4)*, DEWALT) CENGAGE Learning.
American Society of Civil Engineers Staff, contrib. by. Quality in the Constructed Project: A Guide for Owners, Designers, & Constructors. 2012. (Illus.). xxii, 280p. pap. ***(978-0-7844-1189-6(1))***; E-Book ***(978-0-7844-7641-3(1))*** American Society of Civil Engineers.
Atcheson, Dan. National Concrete & Masonry Estimator. 4th ed. 2008. (National Concrete & Masonry Estimator Ser.). (Illus.). 605p. pap. 64.00 incl. cd-rom *(978-1-57218-207-3(5))* Craftsman Bk. Co.
—National Framing & Finish Carpentry Estimator. 3rd ed. 2008. (National Framing & Finish Carpentry Estimator Ser.). (Illus.). 402p. pap. 62.95 incl. cd-rom *(978-1-57218-211-0(3))* Craftsman Bk. Co.
Building Construction Handbook. 8th rev. ed. 2010. (ENG., Illus.). 828p. pap. 49.95 *(978-1-85617-805-1(6))* Routledge.
Building News Staff, ed. Construction Project Log Book. 2008. 416p. pap. 30.95 *(978-1-55701-425-2(6))* BNI Pubns., Inc.
Chudley, Roy. Building Construction Handbook: Xplana Bundle. 2011. pap., pap. 57.44 ***(978-0-08-097108-7(3)***, Butterworth-Heinemann) Elsevier Science & Technology Bks.
Chudley, Roy & Greeno, Roger. Building Construction Handbook, 2 vols. 7th ed. 2008. (ENG., Illus.). 776p. pap. 42.95 *(978-0-7506-8622-8(7)*, Butterworth-Heinemann) Elsevier Science & Technology Bks.
—Building Construction Handbook. 9th rev. ed. 2012. (ENG., Illus.). 884p. (C). pap. 39.95 ***(978-0-08-097061-5(3))*** Routledge.
Cobb, Fiona. Structural Engineer's Eurocode Pocket Book. 2012. (ENG.). pap. 29.00 ***(978-0-08-097121-6(0)***, Butterworth-Heinemann) Elsevier Science & Technology Bks.
Cobb, Fiona. Structural Engineer's Pocket Book. 2nd rev. ed. 2008. (ENG., Illus.). 416p. pap. 35.95 *(978-0-7506-8686-0(3)*, CRC Press) Taylor & Francis Group GBR. Dist: Taylor & Francis Group.
Forde, Mike, ed. ICE Manual of Construction Materials, 2 vols., Vols. I & II. 2009. (Illus.). 928p. *(978-0-7277-3597-3(7))* Telford, Thomas Ltd.
Ghosh, S. K. & Henry, John. 2006 IBC Handbook: Structural Provisions. 2007. 93.00 *(978-1-58001-522-6(0))* International Code Council.
Greeno, Roger. Building Services Handbook: Incorporating Current Building & Construction Regulations. 6th rev. ed. 2011. (ENG., Illus.). 720p. (C). pap. 41.95 *(978-0-08-096982-4(8))* Routledge.
Greeno, Roger & Hall, Fred. Building Services Handbook: Incorporating Current Building & Construction Regulations - Xplana Bundle. 2011. pap., pap. 51.69 ***(978-0-08-097106-3(7)***, Butterworth-Heinemann) Elsevier Science & Technology Bks.
Hall, Dennis J. Graphic Standards Field Guide to Building Construction. 2013. (Graphic Standards Field Guide Ser.). (ENG., Illus.). 496p. pap. 75.00 *(978-0-470-53648-3(9)*, Wiley) Wiley, John & Sons, Inc.
Hardin, Brad. BIM & Construction Management: Proven Tools, Methods, & Workflows. 2009. (ENG., Illus.). 364p. pap. 49.99 *(978-0-470-40235-1(0)*, Sybex) Wiley, John & Sons, Inc.
ICC. Analysis of Changes 2000 IFC to 2006 IFC. 2007. pap. 28.00 *(978-1-58001-538-7(7))* International Code Council.
—2006 IRC Q & A Application Guide. 2008. pap. 45.00 *(978-1-58001-666-7(9))* International Code Council.
Kulczyk, Peter. Disaster Mitigation: A Guide for Building Departments. 2009. (Illus.). vii, 122p. ***(978-1-58001-767-1(3))*** International Code Council.
Marshall, Chris. Roofing Siding & Trim: Protect & Beautify the Exterior of Your Home. 2nd rev. ed. 2008. (Black & Decker Complete Guide Ser.). (ENG., Illus.). 272p. pap. 24.99 *(978-1-58923-418-5(9)*, 1589234189) Quayside.
Meier, Hans W. & Wyatt, David J. Construction Specifications: Principles & Applications. 2007. (ENG.). 416p. 86.95 *(978-1-4283-1861-8(5))* Delmar Cengage Learning.
Neufert, Ernst, et al. Architects' Data. 4th ed. 2012. (ENG., Illus.). 608p. pap. 99.95 ***(978-1-4051-9253-8(4)***, Wiley-Blackwell) Wiley, John & Sons, Inc.
NFPA. National Electical Code 2011. 2010. (ENG.). 1p. spiral bd. 90.00 *(978-1-111-54230-6(9))* Delmar Cengage Learning.
Ogershok, Dave, ed. National Building Cost Manual. 33rd ed. 2008. (National Building Cost Manual Ser.). (Illus.). 262p. pap. 53.00 incl. cd-rom *(978-1-57218-206-6(7))* Craftsman Bk. Co.
Ogershok, Dave & Pray, Richard. National Construction Estimator. annuals 56th ed. 2007. (National Construction Estimator Ser.). (Illus.). 666p. pap. 57.50 incl. cd-rom *(978-1-57218-189-2(3))* Craftsman Bk. Co.
Ogershok, Dave & Pray, Richard, eds. National Construction Estimator. 57th ed. 2008. (National Construction Estimator Ser.). (Illus.). 669p. pap. 62.50 incl. cd-rom *(978-1-57218-208-0(3))* Craftsman Bk. Co.
SEAOC. 2006 IBC Stuctural Seismic Design Manual. 2007. pap. 67.00 *(978-1-58001-404-5(6))* International Code Council.
Spain, Bryan. Spon's First Stage Estimating Handbook. 3rd rev. ed. 2010. (Spon's Estimating Costs Guides). (ENG.). 256p. pap. 79.95 *(978-0-415-54715-4(6)*, Spon Pr.) Routledge.
Wagner, John D. Drywall. 3rd ed. 2010. (Home Improvement Ser.). (ENG., Illus.). 176p. (gr. 5). pap., instr.'s gde. ed. 14.95 *(978-1-58011-500-1(4))* Creative Homeowner.
Wilson, Alex. Green Building Products: The GreenSpec Guide to Residential Building Materials. Malin, Nadav, ed. 3rd ed. 2008. (ENG., Illus.). 352p. pap. 37.95 *(978-0-86571-600-1(5)*, 9780865716001) New Society Pubs., Ltd. CAN. Dist: Consortium Bk. Sales & Distribution.

BUILDING—HISTORY

Cartwright, George. The New Labrador Papers of Captain George Cartwright. Stopp, Marianne P., ed. 2008. (ENG., Illus.). 272p. (C). *(978-0-7735-3382-0(6))* McGill-Queen's Univ. Pr.
Friedman, Donald. Historical Building Construction: Design, Materials, & Technology. 2nd ed. 2010. (ENG., Illus.). 320p. 59.95 *(978-0-393-73268-9(1)*, 73268) Norton, W. W. & Co., Inc.
Garrison, J. Ritchie. Two Carpenters: Architecture & Building in Early New England, 1799-1859. 2006. (Illus.). 240p. 48.95 *(978-1-57233-485-4(1))* Univ. of Tennessee Pr.
Glancey, Jonathan. Lost Buildings: Demolished, Destroyed, Imagined, Reborn. 2009. (ENG.). 256p. (gr. 12). 60.00 *(978-1-59020-316-3(X))* Overlook Pr., The.
Innocent, C. F. The Development of English Building Construction. 2011. (ENG.). 308p. pap. 24.99 *(978-0-521-17860-0(6))* Cambridge Univ. Pr.
Malacrino, Carmelo G. Constructing the Ancient World: Architectural Techniques of the Greeks & Romans. 2010. (Illus.). 224p. 50.00 *(978-1-60606-016-2(3))* Getty Pubns.
Robertson, Charles J., et al. Temple of Invention: The Patent Office Building. 2006. (ENG., Illus.). 112p. pap. 19.95 *(978-1-85759-385-3(5))* Scala, Editions FRA. Dist: National Bk. Network.
Wilkinson, Philip. Great Buildings. 2012. (ENG.). 256p. 30.00 ***(978-0-7566-9829-4(4))*** Dorling Kindersley Publishing, Inc.
Wright. Ancient Building Technology, Volume 3: Construction, 2 vols. 2009. (Technology & Change in History Ser.). (Illus.). *(978-90-04-17745-1(0))* BRILL.
Yockey Jones, L. Beth. Master Builders Association of King & Snohomish Counties: One Hundred Years of Building Community. 2009. (Illus.). 295p. *(978-0-9764839-5-3(5))* Abecedary Pr.
Ziffer, Alfred. Bruno Paul, Haus Friedwart, Wetzlar. 2008. (ENG., Illus.). 56p. 49.00 *(978-3-932565-67-0(3))* Edition Axel Menges GmbH DEU. Dist: National Bk. Network.

BUILDING—INSPECTION

see Building Inspection

BUILDING—JUVENILE LITERATURE

Adamson, Heather. A Day in the Life of a Construction Worker. 2007. (Community Helpers at Work Ser.). (ENG.). 24p. (gr. 1-2). pap. 41.70 *(978-1-4296-1642-3(3)*, First Facts) Capstone Pr., Inc.

BUILDING—LAW AND LEGISLATION

see Building Laws

BUILDING—MATERIALS

see Building Materials

BUILDING—MODULAR COORDINATION

see Modular Coordination (Architecture)

BUILDING—PRICE BOOKS

see Building—Estimates

BUILDING—RESEARCH

Berman, Alan, ed. Jim Stirling & the Red Trilogy: Three Radical Buildings. 2010. (ENG., Illus.). 128p. 45.00 *(978-0-7112-3144-3(3))* Lincoln, Frances Ltd. GBR. Dist: Perseus-PGW.
Cinquemani, Virginia & Prior, Josephine. Integrating Breeam Throughout the Design Process. 2011. (ENG., Illus.). 58p. pap. 59.95 ***(978-1-84806-149-1(8))*** Building Research Establishment GBR. Dist: Taylor & Francis Group.
Cram101 Textbook Reviews. Outlines & Highlights for Advanced Research Methods in T by Knight. 2011. 64p. pap. 27.95 ***(978-1-61905-209-3(1))*** Cram101 Inc.
Crisinel, Michel, et al, eds. EU COST C13 - Final Report: Glass & Interactive Building Envelopes. 2007. (Research in Architectural Engineering Ser.: Vol. 1). 312p. pap. 82.00 *(978-1-58603-709-3(9))* IOS Pr., Inc.
Detwiler, R., et al, eds. Selected Landmark Papers on Concrete Materials Research. 2008. pap. *(978-0-87031-269-4(3))* American Concrete Institute.
Farrell, Peter. Writing a Built Environment Dissertation: Practical Guidance & Examples. 2011. (ENG., Illus.). 280p. pap. 37.95 *(978-1-4051-9851-6(6)*, Wiley-Blackwell) Wiley, John & Sons, Inc.
Fellows, Richard F. & Liu, Anita M. M. Research Methods for Construction. 3rd ed. 2008. (ENG., Illus.). 320p. pap. 42.99 *(978-1-4051-7790-0(X)*, Wiley-Blackwell) Wiley, John & Sons, Inc.
Greider, Katharine. The Archaeology of Home: An Epic Set on a Thousand Square Feet of the Lower East Side. 2011. E-Book 26.99 *(978-1-58648-990-8(9))* PublicAffairs.
Knight, Andrew, et al, eds. Advanced Research Methods in the Built Environment. 2008. (ENG., Illus.). 256p. pap. 84.99 *(978-1-4051-6110-7(8)*, Wiley-Blackwell) Wiley, John & Sons, Inc.
Santamouris, Mat. Advances in Building Energy Research, Vol. 4. 2010. (ENG., Illus.). 336p. 300.00 *(978-1-84971-187-6(9))* Routledge.
Sarja, Asko, ed. Predictive & Optimised Life Cycle Management: Buildings & Infrastructure. 2006. (ENG., Illus.). 688p. 205.00 *(978-0-415-35393-9(9)*, RU939X) Routledge.

BUILDING—SAFETY MEASURES

Banta, John. Extreme Weather Hits Home: Protecting Your Buildings from Climate Change. 2007. (ENG., Illus.). 256p. per. 22.95 *(978-0-86571-593-6(9)*, 9780865715936) New Society Pubs., Ltd. CAN. Dist: Consortium Bk. Sales & Distribution.
Cretu, Ovidiu, et al. Risk Management for Design & Construction. 2011. (RSMeans Ser.: 75). (ENG., Illus.). 288p. 125.00 *(978-0-470-63538-4(X))* Means, R.S. Co., Inc.
Dunlap, Erik Scott. Loss Control Auditing a Guide for Conducting Fire Safety. 2011. (Occupational Safety & Health Guide Ser.). (ENG., Illus.). 255p. pap. 49.95 *(978-1-4398-2886-1(5)*, CRC Press) Taylor & Francis Group GBR. Dist: Taylor & Francis Group.
Goetsch, David L. Construction Safety & the OSHA Standards. 2009. (ENG.). 312p. (C). 129.00 *(978-0-13-502614-4(8)*, Prentice Hall) Prentice Hall PTR.
Hayes, Alastair. Core Competence Leverage & Competitive Advantage. 2010. 104p. pap. *(978-3-639-23457-2(X))* VDM Verlag Dr. Mueller e.K.
Howarth, Tim & Watson, Paul. Construction Safety Management. 2008. (ENG., Illus.). 216p. pap. 52.99 *(978-1-4051-8660-5(7)*, Wiley-Blackwell) Wiley, John & Sons, Inc.
Hughes, Phil & Ferrett, Ed. Introduction to Health & Safety in Construction. 2nd ed. 2006. (ENG., Illus.). 536p. pap. 70.95 *(978-0-7506-8111-7(X)*, Butterworth-Heinemann) Elsevier Science & Technology Bks.
ICC. A Guide to the '06 IRC Wood Wall Bracing Provisions. 2007. pap. 39.00 *(978-1-58001-623-0(5))* International Code Council.
—Quick-Reference Guide to Fire Safety: Occupancy-Based Requirements of the 2009 IBC(r). 2009. pap. 32.00 *(978-1-58001-886-9(6))* International Code Council.
International Code Council. 2012 International Existing Building Code. 2011. (ENG.). pap. 66.00 *(978-1-60983-044-1(X))*; ring bd. 75.00 *(978-1-60983-043-4(1))* International Code Council.
Johnson, Daniel. DeWALT Construction Safety & OSHA Handbook. 2012. (ENG.). 304p. pap. 24.95 ***(978-1-133-13205-9(7)***, DEWALT) CENGAGE Learning.
Joyce, R. CDM Regulations 2007 Explained. 2007. 275p. pap. *(978-0-7277-3496-9(2))* Telford, Thomas Ltd.
Kamardeen, Imriyas. Controlling Accidents & Insurers' Risks in Construction: A Fuzzy Knowledge-Based Approach. 2009. 49.00 *(978-1-60741-368-4(X))* Nova Science Pubs., Inc.
Keller. OSHA Construction Safety Handbook. 6th ed. 2010. (Illus.). 306p. pap. ***(978-1-60287-891-4(9)***, Ohio Univ. Ctr. for International Studies) Keller, J.J. & Assocs., Inc.
Kirk, H. Ray, et al. Construction Industry. 4th rev. ed. 2009. ring bd. 199.50 *(978-0-7355-8033-6(2))* Wolters Kluwer Law & Business.
Kreh, Richard T. Instructor Resources for Kreh's Safety for Masons, 2nd. 2nd ed. 2009. (ENG.). 16p. (C). 176.95 *(978-1-4180-4991-1(3))* Delmar Cengage Learning.
Kulczyk, Peter. Disaster Mitigation: A Guide for Building Departments. 2009. (Illus.). vii, 122p. ***(978-1-58001-767-1(3))*** International Code Council.
MacCollum, David V. Construction Safety Engineering Principles: Designing & Managing Safer Job Sites. 2006. (ENG., Illus.). 416p. 99.95 *(978-0-07-148244-8(X)*, 007148244X) McGraw-Hill Professional Publishing.
Mahmoud, Khaled. Safety & Reliability of Bridge Structures. 2009. (ENG., Illus.). 514p. 185.95 *(978-0-415-56484-7(0)*, CRC Press) Taylor & Francis Group GBR. Dist: Taylor & Francis Group.
McAleenan, Ciaran & Oloke, David. ICE Manual of Health & Safety in Construction. 2010. (Illus.). 280p. *(978-0-7277-4056-4(3))* Telford, Thomas Ltd.
Naik, Nitin. Performance Measurement of Safety Systems in Construction. 2008. 192p. pap. *(978-3-639-10236-9(3))* VDM Verlag Dr. Mueller e.K.
National Association of Home Builders (U.S.), contrib. by. Home Builders' Safety Program. 2007. (ENG., Illus.). 130p. (C). pap. 32.95 *(978-0-86718-630-7(5))* BuilderBooks.
National Association of Home Builders (U.S.) Staff, contrib. by. NAHB Jobsite Safety Handbook. 3rd ed. 2012. ***(978-0-86718-681-9(X))*** BuilderBooks.
NCCER. Sprinkler Fitter Level 1 2007 NFPA Revision Trainee Guide, Perfect Bound. 2007. pap. *(978-0-13-228611-4(4))* Prentice Hall PTR.
—Sprinkler Fitter Level 4, 2007 NFPA Revision Trainee Guide, Perfect Bound. 2008. pap. *(978-0-13-614438-0(1))* Pearson Bks.

OSHA Construction Standards Handbook. 2007. (Illus.). ix, 700p. *(978-1-59042-929-7(X))* Keller, J.J. & Assocs., Inc.

Poon, S. W., et al. Management & Economics of Construction Safety in Hong Kong. 2008. (ENG., Illus.). 180p. (gr. 17). pap. 22.00 *(978-962-209-906-7(8))* Hong Kong Univ. Pr. HKG. Dist: Columbia Univ. Pr.

Summerhayes, Stuart. Design Risk Management: Contribution to Health & Safety. 2010. (ENG., Illus.). 176p. pap. 77.95 *(978-1-4051-3275-6(2),* Wiley-Blackwell) Wiley, John & Sons, Inc.

BUILDING—SPECIFICATIONS

see Buildings—Specifications

BUILDING—STANDARDS

see Building Materials—Standards; Standards, Engineering

BUILDING—SUPERINTENDENCE

Arayici, Yusuf & Aouad, Ghassan. Requirements Engineering for Computer Integrated Environments in Construction. 2010. (ENG., Illus.). 256p. 134.99 *(978-1-4051-8945-3(2),* Wiley-Blackwell) Wiley, John & Sons, Inc.

Atkin, Brian & Borgbrant, Jan, eds. Performance Improvement in Construction Management. 2009. (Spon Research Ser.). (ENG., Illus.). 344p. (C). 130.00 *(978-0-415-54593-3(6))* Routledge.

Bagilhole, Barbara, et al, eds. People & Culture in Construction. 2007. (Spon Research Ser.). (ENG., Illus.). 352p. 170.00 *(978-0-415-34870-6(6))* Routledge.

Barthorpe, Stephen, et al. Managing Construction Logistics. 2010. (ENG., Illus.). 304p. pap. 84.99 *(978-1-4051-5124-5(2),* Wiley-Blackwell) Wiley, John & Sons, Inc.

Bouchlaghem, Dino, ed. Collaborative Working in Construction. 2011. (ENG., Illus.). 248p. (C). 165.00 *(978-0-415-59699-2(8))*; pap., pap. 49.95 *(978-0-415-59700-5(5))* Routledge.

Chartered Institute of Building Staff. Code of Practice for Project Management for Construction & Development. 4th ed. 2010. (ENG., Illus.). 304p. pap. 84.99 *(978-1-4051-9420-4(0),* Wiley-Blackwell) Wiley, John & Sons, Inc.

CIOB (Chartered Institute of Building). Guide to Good Practice in the Management of Time in Complex Projects. 2011. (ENG., Illus.). 170p. pap. 73.50 *(978-1-4443-3493-7(X),* Wiley-Blackwell) Wiley, John & Sons, Inc.

Collins, Robert J. Project Management. 2011. (Construction Materials & Engineering Ser.). (Illus.). x, 210p. 129.00 *(978-1-61761-460-6(2))* Nova Science Pubs., Inc.

Cooke, Robert. Planning, Measurement & Control for Building. 2009. (ENG., Illus.). 280p. pap. 54.99 *(978-1-4051-9139-5(2),* Wiley-Blackwell) Wiley, John & Sons, Inc.

Cram101 Textbook Reviews. Outlines & Highlights for Construction Planning & Scheduling by Hinze. 2011. 72p. pap. 27.95 ***(978-1-61906-252-8(6))*** Cram101 Inc.

—Outlines & Highlights for Construction Project Management by Frederick Gould. 2011. 138p. pap. 28.95 ***(978-1-61906-130-9(9))*** Cram101 Inc.

—Outlines & Highlights for Leed-New Construction Project Management by Vijaya Yellamraju. 2011. 56p. pap. 26.95 ***(978-1-61905-480-6(9))*** Cram101 Inc.

—Outlines & Highlights for Project Management in Construction by Sidney M Levy. 2011. 60p. pap. 26.95 ***(978-1-4672-6914-8(X))*** Cram101 Inc.

Cram101 Textbook Reviews & Cram101 Textbook Reviews. Outlines & Highlights for Construction Planning & Scheduling by Jimmie W Hinze. 2011. 82p. pap. 27.95 ***(978-1-61830-862-7(9))*** Cram101 Inc.

—Outlines & Highlights for Construction Project Administration by Edward R Fisk. 2011. 70p. pap. 27.95 ***(978-1-61830-861-0(0))*** Cram101 Inc.

Deutsch, Randy. BIM & Integrated Design: Strategies for Architectural Practice. 2011. (ENG., Illus.). 272p. 75.00 *(978-0-470-57251-1(5),* Wiley) Wiley, John & Sons, Inc.

Dodds, Jason & Johnson, Scott. Mastering Autodesk Navisworks 2012. 2011. (ENG., Illus.). 480p. pap. 79.99 *(978-1-118-00678-8(X),* Sybex) Wiley, John & Sons, Inc.

Fisk, Edward R. & Reynolds, Wayne. Construction Project Administration. 9th ed. 2009. (ENG.). 648p. (C). 124.00 *(978-0-13-500007-6(6),* Prentice Hall) Prentice Hall PTR.

Frank, George C. Construction Quality: Do it Right or Pay the Price. rev. ed. 2011. (ENG., Illus.). 216p. (C). pap. 20.80 *(978-0-13-217151-9(1),* Prentice Hall) Prentice Hall PTR.

Goldin, Daren. Optimal Construction Jobsite Staffing. 2011. 192p. pap. ***(978-3-8443-9813-7(9))*** Lambert Academic Publishing

Gould, and Joyce. Construction Project Management. 2006. pap. 10.95 *(978-1-4288-0791-4(8))* Cram101 Inc.

Gould, Frederick. Managing the Construction Process. 4th rev. ed. 2010. (ENG., Illus.). 360p. (C). 120.00 *(978-0-13-813596-6(7),* Prentice Hall) Prentice Hall PTR.

Gould, Frederick & Joyce, Nancy. Construction Project Management. 3rd ed. 2008. (ENG., Illus.). 384p. (C). 132.80 *(978-0-13-199623-6(1),* Prentice Hall) Prentice Hall PTR.

Griffin, Joseph. Residential Construction Management: Managing According to the Project Lifecycle. 2010. 288p. pap. *(978-1-60427-022-8(5))* Ross, J. Publishing, Inc.

Hanney, Neil, et al. Surveying & Engineering: Principles & Practice. 2008. (ENG., Illus.). 304p. pap., instr.'s hndbk. ed. 74.99 *(978-1-4051-5923-4(5),* Wiley-Blackwell) Wiley, John & Sons, Inc.

Hinze, Jimmie W. Construction Planning & Scheduling. 4th ed. 2011. (ENG.). 264p. (C). 122.80 *(978-0-13-247398-9(4),* Prentice Hall) Prentice Hall PTR.

ICC. North Carolina State Building Code: Plumbing Code & Commentary 2006. 2007. pap. 88.00 *(978-1-58001-602-5(2))* International Code Council.

—2007 Oregon Structural Specialty Code. 2007. bds. 125.00 *(978-1-58001-517-2(4))* International Code Council.

International Code Council. 2012 International Building Code. 2011. (ENG.). ring bd. 137.00 *(978-1-60983-039-7(3))*; (Illus.). xxx, 690p. pap. 122.00 *(978-1-60983-040-3(7))* International Code Council.

Koch, James Edward, et al. Project Administration for Design-Build Contracts: A Primer for Owners, Engineers, & Contractors. 2010. (ENG.). 298p. pap. 64.00 *(978-0-7844-1075-2(5))* American Society of Civil Engineers.

Lester, Kent & McGuerty, Dave. The Complete Guide to Contracting Your Home. 4th ed. 2010. (ENG., Illus.). 320p. pap. 24.99 *(978-1-55870-871-6(5),* Betterway Bks.) F&W Media, Inc.

Levy, Francois. BIM in Small-Scale Sustainable Design. 2011. (ENG., Illus.). 312p. 85.00 ***(978-0-470-59089-8(0),*** Wiley) Wiley, John & Sons, Inc.

Levy, Sidney. Project Management in Construction 6/E. 6th ed. 2011. (ENG., Illus.). 496p. 90.00 ***(978-0-07-175310-4(9),*** 0071753109) McGraw-Hill Professional Publishing.

Levy, Sidney M. Construction Superintendent's Operations Manual. 2nd ed. 2008. (ENG., Illus.). 447p. 89.95 *(978-0-07-150241-2(6),* 0071502416) McGraw-Hill Professional Publishing.

Lizarralde. Rebuilding after Disasters. 2009. (ENG., Illus.). 296p. (C). 105.00 *(978-0-415-47254-8(7))* Routledge.

London, Kerry. Construction Supply Chain Economics. 2007. (Spon Research Ser.). (ENG., Illus.). 480p. (C). 180.00 *(978-0-415-40971-1(3))* Routledge.

Mincks, William R. & Johnston, Hal. Construction Jobsite Management. 3rd ed. 2010. (ENG.). 496p. (C). 159.95 *(978-1-4390-5573-1(4,)* Delmar Cengage Learning.

Mosey, David. Early Contractor Involvement in Building Procurement: Contracts, Partnering & Project Management. 2009. (ENG.). 328p. 124.99 *(978-1-4051-9645-1(9),* Wiley) Wiley, John & Sons, Inc.

Mubarak, Saleh. Construction Project Scheduling & Control. 2nd ed. 2010. (ENG., Illus.). 480p. 115.00 *(978-0-470-50533-5(8),* Wiley) Wiley, John & Sons, Inc.

Newitt, Jay. Construction Scheduling: Principles & Practices. 2nd ed. 2008. (ENG., Illus.). 384p. (C). 137.60 *(978-0-13-513782-6(9),* Prentice Hall) Prentice Hall PTR.

Noble, Patrick J. Process Plant Construction: A Handbook for Quality Management. 2009. (ENG., Illus.). 232p. 169.99 *(978-1-4051-8725-1(5),* Wiley-Blackwell) Wiley, John & Sons, Inc.

Pompeii, Michael. Build Your Own Home! A Concise Guide to Successfully Subcontracting & Building Your Own New Home. 2006. (ENG.). 160p. per. 49.00 *(978-0-9711954-4-8(7))* Pompeii Engineers.

Rapp, Randy R. Disaster Recovery Project Management: Bringing Order from Chaos. 2011. 265p. 75.00 *(978-1-55753-588-7(4))* Purdue Univ. Pr.

Reddy, K. Pramod. BIM for Building Owners & Developers: Making a Business Case for Using BIM on Projects. 2012. (ENG., Illus.). 240p. 85.00 ***(978-0-470-90598-2(0),*** Wiley) Wiley, John & Sons, Inc.

Rogers, Leon. Basic Construction Management. 5th ed. 2008. 204p. pap. 44.95 *(978-0-86718-645-1(3))* BuilderBooks.

Rounds, Jerald L. & Segner, Robert O. Construction Supervision. 2011. (RSMeans Ser.: 82). (ENG., Illus.). 464p. 95.00 *(978-0-470-61496-9(X))* Means, R.S. Co., Inc.

Senaratne, Sepani & Sexton, Martin. Managing Change in Construction Projects: A Knowledge-Based Approach. 2011. (Innovation in the Built Environment Ser.: 7). (ENG., Illus.). 200p. 124.99 *(978-1-4443-3515-6(4),* Wiley-Blackwell) Wiley, John & Sons, Inc.

Smith, Dana K., et al. Building Information Modeling: A Strategic Implementation Guide for Architects, Engineers, Constructors, & Real Estate Asset Managers. 2009. (ENG., Illus.). 216p. 75.00 *(978-0-470-25003-7(8),* Wiley) Wiley, John & Sons, Inc.

Smith, Mark & Smith, Elaine. The Owner-Builder Book: How You Can Save More than $100,000 in the Construction of Your Custom Home. 4th ed. 2007. (Illus.). 288p. pap. 19.95 *(978-1-932272-04-8(6))* Consensus Group, Inc., The.

Smith, Mark A. & Smith, Elaine M. The Owner-Builder Book: How Owner-Builders Build More for Less. 4th ed. 2007. (Illus.). 312p. spiral bd. 29.95 *(978-1-932272-06-2(2))* Consensus Group, Inc., The.

Sutt, Jüri. Manual of Construction Project Management: For Owners & Clients. 2nd ed. 2011. (ENG.). 168p. pap. 70.00 *(978-0-470-65824-6(X)* Wiley-Blackwell) Wiley, John & Sons, Inc.

Underwood, Jason & Isikdag, Umit, eds. Research on Building Information Modeling & Construction Informatics: Concepts & Technologies. 2009. 567p. instr.'s hndbk. ed. 295.00 *(978-1-60566-928-1(8))* IGI Global.

Winch, Graham M. Managing Construction Projects. 2nd ed. 2010. (ENG., Illus.). 544p. pap. 67.99 *(978-1-4051-8457-1(4),* Wiley-Blackwell) Wiley, John & Sons, Inc.

Woodson, R. Dodge & Woodson, R. 2009 International Building Code Need to Know: The 20% of the Code You Need 80% of the Time. 2009. (ENG., Illus.). 304p. pap. 29.95 *(978-0-07-159257-4(1),* 0071592571) McGraw-Hill Professional Publishing.

BUILDING, ADOBE

see also Adobe Houses

Crews, Carole. Clay Culture: Plasters, Paints & Preservation. 2010. (ENG., Illus.). 224p. pap. 27.00 *(978-0-9842229-0-2(1))* Gourmet Adobe Pr.

Gates, William N. House Born of Mud: A Builder's Story. 2010. (ENG.). 164p. pap. 18.95 *(978-0-86534-751-9(4))* Sunstone Pr.

Rainer, Leslie, et al. Terra 2008: Proceedings of the 10th International Conference on the Study & Conservation of Earthen Architectural Heritage, Bamako, Mali, February 1-5, 2008 = Actes de la 10ème Conférence Internationale Sur L'étude et la Conservation du Patrimoine Bâti en Terre, Bamako, Mali, 1-5 Fevrier 2008. 2011. (Symposium Proceedings Ser.). (FRE & ENG., Illus.). 456p. pap. 80.00 *(978-1-60606-043-8(0))* Getty Pubns.

Sanya, Tom. Living in Earth: The Sustainability of Earth Architecture in Uganda. 2007. (Illus.). *(978-82-547-0208-6(X))* Arkitekthogskolen i Oslo.

BUILDING, BOMBPROOF

see also Blast Effect; Nuclear Bomb Shelters

Bangash, T. Explosion-Resistant Buildings: Design, Analysis, & Case Studies. 2010. (ENG., Illus.). xxi, 784p. pap. 379.00 *(978-3-642-05830-1(2),* 3642058302) Springer.

Colvin, T. F., rev. Design of Structures to Resist the Effects of Explosions & Atomic Weapons - 2007. (ENG.). 164p. per. 59.95 *(978-1-934939-03-1(X))*; 92p. per. 49.95 *(978-1-934939-02-4(1))* Wexford College Pr.

Dusenberry, Donald O., ed. Handbook for Blast Resistant Design of Buildings. 2010. (ENG., Illus.). 512p. 155.00 *(978-0-470-17054-0(9),* Wiley) Wiley, John & Sons, Inc.

Uddin, N., ed. Blast Protection of Civil Infrastructures & Vehicles Using Composites. 2010. (ENG., Illus.). 448p. 219.95 *(978-1-4398-2771-0(0),* CRC Press) Taylor & Francis Group GBR. Dist: Taylor & Francis Group.

—Blast Protection of Civil Infrastructures & Vehicles Using Composites. 2010. (Illus.). 448p. 240.00 *(978-1-84569-399-2(X))* Woodhead Publishing Ltd. GBR. Dist: Taylor & Francis Group.

BUILDING, BRICK

Coffin, L. A. & Holden, A. C. Brick Architecture of the Colonial Period in Maryland & Virginia. (Illus.). 29p. reprint ed. lib. bdg. 88.00 *(978-0-7222-4677-1(3))* Library Reprints, Inc.

Hassanein, Ahmed Taher, et al. Baghdad Arts Deco: Architectural Brickwork, 19201950. 2011. (ENG.). 608p. 39.95 *(978-977-416-356-2(7))* American Univ. in Cairo Pr. EGY. Dist: Oxford Univ. Pr., Inc.

Sanya, Tom. Living in Earth: The Sustainability of Earth Architecture in Uganda. 2007. (Illus.). *(978-82-547-0208-6(X))* Arkitekthogskolen i Oslo.

BUILDING, COMPOSITE

see Composite Construction

BUILDING, CONCRETE

see Concrete Construction

BUILDING, FIREPROOF

see also Fire Testing; Fireproofing

Alvear, Daniel & Capote, Jorge. Fire Safety in High Rise Buildings. 2008. 416p. pap. *(978-3-8364-9336-9(5))* VDM Verlag Dr. Mueller e.K.

Associacao Portuguesa de Staff. Fire Design of Steel Structures Pts. 1-2: Actions on Structures - Actions on Structures Exposed to Fire Eurocode - Design of Steel Structures - Structural Fire Design. European Convention for Constructional Steelwork Staff, ed. 2010. (ENG., Illus.). 452p. pap. 90.00 *(978-3-433-02974-9(1),* Wiley-VCH) Wiley, John & Sons, Inc.

Bangash, T. Explosion-Resistant Buildings: Design, Analysis, & Case Studies. 2010. (ENG., Illus.). xxi, 784p. pap. 379.00 *(978-3-642-05830-1(2),* 3642058302) Springer.

Franssen, Jean Marc. Designing Steel Structures for Fire Safety. 2009. (ENG., Illus.). 182p. 113.95 *(978-0-415-54828-1(4),* CRC Press) Taylor & Francis Group GBR. Dist: Taylor & Francis Group.

International Code Council Staff. 2006 International Building Code Handbook-Fire & Lifesafety Provisions. 2007. (ENG.). 582p. pap. 97.95 *(978-1-58001-507-3(7))* Delmar Cengage Learning.

Moore, D., et al. Designers' Guide to en 1991-1-2, en 1993-1-2 & En 1994-1-2: Fire Engineering (Actions on Steel & Composite Structures) 2007. (Illus.). 200p. pap. *(978-0-7277-3157-9(2))* Telford, Thomas Ltd.

Moore, Francis Cruger. How to Build a Hotel. 2010. (ENG.). 64p. reprint ed. pap. 17.75 *(978-1-171-63952-7(X))* BiblioBazaar.

—How to Build Fireproof. 2009. 138p. 24.99 *(978-1-110-91042-7(8))*; (ENG.). 136p. pap. 18.99 *(978-1-110-91037-3(1),* BiblioLife); 138p. reprint ed. pap. 19.75 *(978-1-110-91040-3(1))* BiblioBazaar.

—How to Build Fireproof & Slow-Burning. 2010. 138p. pap. 20.75 *(978-1-176-71046-7(X))* BiblioBazaar.

—How to Build Fireproof & Slow-Burning. 2009. 54p. pap. 14.14 *(978-1-151-70394-1(X))* General Bks. LLC.

—How to Build Fireproof & Slow-Burning. 136p. 2010. pap. 16.76 *(978-1-163-76135-9(4))* 2010. 28.76 ***(978-1-163-83259-2(6))*** 2007. 35.95 *(978-0-548-52049-9(6))* 2007. (ENG.). per. 20.95 *(978-0-548-48057-1(5))* Kessinger Publishing, LLC.

—How to Build Fireproof & Slow-Burning. 2008. 136p. pap. *(978-1-4097-1589-4(2))* Read Bks.

Nanji, Nawazish Godrej. GIVING ARCHITECTURE TO FIRE: 'ATASH BEHRAM', A PERSIAN FIRE TEMPLE. 2008. 108p. pap. *(978-3-639-09720-7(3))* VDM Verlag Dr. Mueller e.K.

National Fire Protection Association Staff & Society of Fire Protection Engineers Staff, contrib. by. SFPE Engineering Guide to Performance-Based Fire Protection. 2007. (Illus.). xiii, 207p. *(978-0-87765-789-7(0))* National Fire Protection Assn.

Parkinson, David L., et al, eds. Performance-Based Design of Structural Steel for Fire Conditions: ASCE Manuals & Reports on Engineering Practice No. 114. 2008. 124p. pap. 79.00 *(978-0-7844-0963-3(3))* American Society of Civil Engineers.

Purkiss, John A. Fire Safety Engineering: Design of Structures. 2nd rev. ed. 2006. (ENG., Illus.). 424p. 160.00 *(978-0-7506-6443-1(6),* CRC Press) Taylor & Francis Group GBR. Dist: Taylor & Francis Group.

Ramachandran, G. Probabilistic Assessment of Fire Risk. 2009. (Illus.). 25p. 139.98 *(978-0-419-20770-2(8),* Taylor & Francis) Taylor & Francis Group GBR. Dist: Taylor & Francis Group.

—Quantitative Risk Assessment in Fire Safety. 2011. (ENG., Illus.). 384p. 150.00 *(978-0-419-20790-0(2))* Routledge.

Sanchez, Mauricio & Sutton, William H. Radiative Properties of Fire Thermal Barriers. 2008. 140p. pap. *(978-3-639-08283-8(4))* VDM Verlag Dr. Mueller e.K.

Stookey, Scott. Significant Changes to the International Fire Code, 2009 Edition, 1 vol. 2009. (ENG.). 304p. pap. 44.95 *(978-1-4354-0120-4(4))* Delmar Cengage Learning.

Tragesser, Chris E. & Hirst, Ben A. Exam Prep: Building Construction for the Fire Service. 2007. 110p. per. 39.95 *(978-0-7637-5341-2(6))* Jones & Bartlett Learning, LLC.

Wang, Yong, et al. Performance Based Fire Engineering of Structures. 2012. (ENG., Illus.). 393p. (C). 130.00 ***(978-0-415-55733-7(X),*** CRC Press) Taylor & Francis Group GBR. Dist: Taylor & Francis Group.

Yu, Liang. Behavior of Bolted Connections During & after a Fire. 2009. 224p. pap. *(978-3-639-16585-2(3))* VDM Verlag Dr. Mueller e.K.

BUILDING, HOUSE

see House Construction

BUILDING, IRON AND STEEL

see also Composite Construction; Girders; Plates, Iron and Steel; Skyscrapers; Steel, Structural; Strength of Materials; Structures, Theory Of

Aghayere, Abi O. & Vigil, Jason. Structural Steel Design: A Practice Oriented Approach. 2008. (ENG.). 720p. (C). 124.40 *(978-0-13-234018-2(6),* Prentice Hall) Prentice Hall PTR.

Ambrose, James & Tripeny, Patrick. Simplified Design of Steel Structures. 8th rev. ed. 2007. (Parker/Ambrose Series of Simplified Design Guides: 37). (ENG., Illus.). 480p. 95.00 *(978-0-470-08631-5(9),* Wiley) Wiley, John & Sons, Inc.

American Institute of Steel Construction (AISC) Staff, compiled by. North American Steel Construction Conference 2007. 2008. 442p. pap. 95.00 *(978-1-60423-904-1(2))* Curran Assocs., Inc.

—North American Steel Construction Conference NASCC: The Steel Conference Incorporating the Annual Stability Conference 2006. 2007. 532p. pap. 93.00 *(978-1-60423-749-8(X))* Curran Assocs., Inc.

Associacao Portuguesa de Staff. Fire Design of Steel Structures Pts. 1-2: Actions on Structures - Actions on Structures Exposed to Fire Eurocode - Design of Steel Structures - Structural Fire Design. European Convention for Constructional Steelwork Staff, ed. 2010. (ENG., Illus.). 452p. pap. 90.00 *(978-3-433-02974-9(1),* Wiley-VCH) Wiley, John & Sons, Inc.

Baraskar, Manoj. Collapse Evaluation of Steel Structures. 2011. 52p. pap. ***(978-3-8443-2141-8(1))*** Lambert Academic Publishing.

Barton Myers Associates. 3 Steel Houses. 2006. (House Design Ser.: Vol. 2). (ENG., Illus.). 128p. 49.50 *(978-1-876907-89-1(4))* Images Publishing Group AUS. Dist: National Bk. Network.

Be Cool Despite Global Warming: Make Your Home Cooler & Energy Efficient. 2007. per. 9.95 *(978-0-9763274-5-5(7))* I.Form Ink, Publishing.

Beg, Darko, et al. Design of Plated Structures: Design of Steel Structures, Design of Plated Structures. European Convention for Constructional Steelwork, Technical General Secretariat Staff & Associacao Portuguesa de Staff, eds. 2011. (ENG., Illus.). 272p. pap. 70.00 *(978-3-433-02980-0(6),* Wiley-VCH) Wiley, John & Sons, Inc.

Borges, Luis, et al. Fatigue Design of Steel & Composite Structures Pts. 1-9: Eurocode 3 - Design of Steel Structures. Fatigue. Eurocode - Design of Composite Steel & Concrete Structures, Pts. 1-9. ECCS - European Convention & Associacao Portuguesa de, eds. 2011. (ENG., Illus.). 334p. pap. 70.00 *(978-3-433-02981-7(4),* Wiley-VCH) Wiley, John & Sons, Inc.

British Standards Institute Staff. Eurocode 3. Design of steel structures. Plated structures subject to out of plane Loading. 40p. pap. 131.00 *(978-0-580-53282-5(8))* Artech Hse., Inc.

Brookes, Alan J. Building Envelope & Connections. (C). 102.00 *(978-0-8176-2533-7(X))* Birkhauser Boston.

Bruneau, Michel, et al. Ductile Design of Steel Structures. 2nd ed. 2011. (ENG., Illus.). 928p. 115.00 *(978-0-07-162395-7(7),* 0071623957) McGraw-Hill Professional Publishing.

Columbia University Staff. Post-Ductility: Metals in Architecture & Engineering. Bell, Michael & Buckley, Craig, eds. 2012. (ENG.). 272p. 65.00 ***(978-1-61689-046-9(0))*** Princeton Architectural Pr.

Cram101 Textbook Reviews & Cram101 Textbook Reviews. Outlines & Highlights for Steel Structures by Charles G Salmon. 2011. 190p. pap. 30.95 ***(978-1-61830-760-6(6))*** Cram101 Inc.

—Outlines & Highlights for Structural Steel Design: A Practice Oriented Approach by Abi O. Aghayere. 2011. 90p. pap. 27.95 ***(978-1-61830-887-0(4))*** Cram101 Inc.

—Outlines & Highlights for Structural Steel Design by Jack C Mccormac. 2011. 138p. pap. 28.95 ***(978-1-61830-743-9(6))*** Cram101 Inc.

—Outlines & Highlights for Structural Steel Drafting & Design by David C MacLaughlin. 2011. 58p. pap. 26.95 ***(978-1-61830-742-2(8))*** Cram101 Inc.

B

DAAB Media Staff, creator. Steel Design, 1 vol. 2008. (ENG, GER, FRE, SPA & ITA., Illus.). 399p. 37.95 *(978-3-937718-65-1(6))* DAAB Media Gmbh DEU. Dist: Innovative Logistics.

Davies, Michael. Practical Stability of Metal Structures. 2006. 512p. *(978-0-470-84990-3(8)*, Wiley-Blackwell) Wiley, John & Sons, Ltd.

Dubina, D., ed. Steel - A New & Traditional Material for Buil: International Conference in Metal Structures 2006, 20-22 September, Poiana Brasov, Romania. 2006. (ENG., Illus.). 648p. 279.95 *(978-0-415-40817-2(2)*, Taylor & Francis) Taylor & Francis Group GBR. Dist: Taylor & Francis Group.

ECCS - European Convention & Associacao Portuguesa de, eds. Design of Cold-Formed Steel Structures Pts. 1-3: Eurocode 3 - Design of Steel Structures. 2012. (ENG.). 512p. pap. 95.00 *(978-3-433-02979-4(2)*, Wiley-VCH) Wiley, John & Sons, Inc.

El-Reedy, Mohamed A. Construction Management & Design of Industrial Concrete & Ste. 2010. (ENG., Illus.). 576p. 139.95 *(978-1-4398-1599-1(2)*, CRC Press) Taylor & Francis Group GBR. Dist: Taylor & Francis Group.

F M Mazzolani Staff. Behaviour of Steel Structures in Seismic Areas. 2006. (Illus.). xvi, 930p. 167.95 *(978-0-415-40413-6(4)*, Taylor & Francis) Taylor & Francis Group GBR. Dist: Taylor & Francis Group.

Farkas, Jozsef & Jarmai, Karoly. Design & Optimization of Metal Structures. 2008. (ENG.). 328p. 130.00 *(978-1-904275-29-9(X))* Woodhead Publishing Ltd. GBR. Dist: Ingram Pub. Services.

Farkas, Jozsef & Jarmai, Karoly, eds. Design, Fabrication & Economy of Welded Structures: International Conference Proceedings 2008, Miskolc, Hungary, 24-26 April. 2008. (ENG., Illus.). 592p. 130.00 *(978-1-904275-28-2(1)*, Horwood Publishing, Ltd.) Woodhead Publishing Ltd. GBR. Dist: Ingram Pub. Services.

Franssen, Jean Marc. Designing Steel Structures for Fire Safety. 2009. (ENG., Illus.). 182p. 113.95 *(978-0-415-54828-1(4)*, CRC Press) Taylor & Francis Group GBR. Dist: Taylor & Francis Group.

Geschwindner, Louis F. Unified Design of Steel Structures. (ENG., (C). 2007. Illus.). 460p. 197.95 *(978-0-471-47558-3(0))* 2nd ed. 2011. 514p. 161.95 ***(978-0-470-44403-0(7))*** Wiley, John & Sons, Inc. (Wiley).

Ghosh, Karuna Moy. Practical Design of Steel Structures. 2010. (ENG., Illus.). 224p. pap. 79.95 *(978-1-4398-3571-5(3))* Whittles Publishing GBR. Dist: Taylor & Francis Group.

Ghosh, Karuna Moy. Steel Structures: Analysis & Design for Vibrations & Earthquakes. 2011. (ENG.). 224p. pap. 79.95 ***(978-1-4398-8347-1(5))*** Whittles Publishing GBR. Dist: Taylor & Francis Group.

Ghosh, S. K. Seismic Design Guide for Metal Building Systems. 2009. pap. 54.95 *(978-1-58001-792-3(4))* International Code Council.

Gioncu, Victor & Mazzolani, Federico M. Global Analysis of Seismic-Resistant Steel Structures. 2008. (Illus.). 180.00 *(978-0-415-24263-9(0))* Taylor & Francis Group.

Gizejowski. Progress in Steel, Composite & Aluminium Structures. 2006. (Illus.). xx, 408p. cd-rom *(978-0-415-40123-4(2)*, Taylor & Francis) Taylor & Francis Group GBR. Dist: Taylor & Francis Group.

Gorenc, B. & Tinyou, R. Steel Designer's Handbook. 5th ed. (Illus.). 336p. *(978-0-86840-248-2(6)*, UNSW Press) NewSouth Publishing.

Guide for Painting Steel Structures. Date not set. (Bridges & Structures Ser.). (Illus.). 100p. pap. 32.00 *(978-1-56051-043-7(9))* American Assn. of State Highway & Transportation Officials.

Hayward, Alan, et al. Steel Detailers' Manual. 3rd ed. 2011. (ENG., Illus.). 184p. 114.99 *(978-1-4051-7521-0(4)*, Wiley-Blackwell) Wiley, John & Sons, Inc.

Ivanyi, Miklos, ed. Stability & Ductility of Steel Structures: Professor Otto Halasz Memorial Session 2002. (Illus.). 858p. *(978-963-05-7950-6(2))* Akademiai Kiado.

Kharrazi, Mehdi Hadj Karim. Rational Method for Analysis & Design of Steel Plate Walls. 2008. 272p. pap. *(978-3-639-03907-8(6))* VDM Verlag Dr. Mueller e.K.

Kinali, Kursat. Fragility Assessment of Non-Seismically Designed Steel Frames. 2008. 208p. pap. *(978-3-8364-8897-6(3))* VDM Verlag Dr. Mueller e.K.

Kottas, Dimitris. Metal. 2012. (ENG.). 300p. 57.00 *(978-84-15123-27-9(2))* Links International (Leading International Key Services Barcelona, S.A.) ESP. Dist: National Bk. Network.

Leon, Roberto T., et al, eds. Composite Construction in Steel & Concrete VI. 6th ed. 2011. 800p. pap. 130.00 *(978-0-7844-1142-1(5))* American Society of Civil Engineers.

MacLaughlin, David C. & Estrada, Hector. Structural Steel Drafting. 2nd rev. ed. 2009. (ENG.). 256p. (C). pap. 175.95 *(978-1-4018-9032-2(6))* Delmar Cengage Learning.

Maranian, Peter. Reducing Brittle & Fatigue Failures in Steel Structures. 2009. 196p. pap. 70.00 *(978-0-7844-1067-7(4))* American Society of Civil Engineers.

Mazzolani. Behaviour of Steel Structures in Seismic Areas. 2006. (Illus.). xvi, 930p. cd-rom 167.95 *(978-0-415-40823-3(7)*, Taylor & Francis) Taylor & Francis Group GBR. Dist: Taylor & Francis Group.

Mazzolani, Federico, et al, eds. Behaviour of Steel Structures in Seismic Areas. 2009. (ENG.). 998p. 349.00 *(978-0-415-56326-0(7)*, CRC Press) Taylor & Francis Group GBR. Dist: Taylor & Francis Group.

Mazzolani, Federico & Herrera, Ricardo, eds. Behaviour of Steel Structures in Seismic Areas: Stessa 2012. 2011. (ENG.). 1130p. (C). 339.00 ***(978-0-415-62105-2(4)***, CRC Press) Taylor & Francis Group GBR. Dist: Taylor & Francis Group.

McCormac, Jack C. Structural Steel Design: ASD Method. 4th ed. 528p. per. *(978-0-06-500065-8(X))* HarperCollins Pubs.

McCormac, Jack C. & Csernak, Stephen F. Structural Steel Design. 5th rev. ed. 2011. (ENG.). 736p. (C). 185.00 ***(978-0-13-607948-4(2)***, Prentice Hall) Prentice Hall PTR.

Michaleris, P., ed. Minimization of Welding Distortion & Buckling: Modelling & Implementation. 2011. (ENG., Illus.). 316p. 210.00 *(978-1-84569-662-7(X))* Woodhead Publishing Ltd. GBR. Dist: Ingram Pub. Services.

Momement, Adam & Holloway, Simon. Corrugated Iron: Building on the Frontier. 2008. (ENG., Illus.). 224p. 60.00 *(978-0-393-73240-5(1)*, 73240) Norton, W. W. & Co., Inc.

Parkinson, David L., et al, eds. Performance-Based Design of Structural Steel for Fire Conditions: ASCE Manuals & Reports on Engineering Practice No. 114. 2008. 124p. pap. 79.00 *(978-0-7844-0963-3(3))* American Society of Civil Engineers.

Ranzi, Gianluca. Partial Interaction Analysis of Composite Beams. 2009. 480p. pap. *(978-3-639-16629-3(9))* VDM Verlag Dr. Mueller e.K.

Robeck, Ulrike & Robeck. Die älteren Hallen des Bochumer Vereins als Zweckbauten und Denkmale der Eisen- und Stahlindustrie. 2010. (Denkmalpflege und Forschung in Westfalen Ser.). (GER.). (C). 33.00 ***(978-3-8053-4279-7(9))*** Zabern, Philipp von Verlag, GmbH DEU. Dist: Brown, David Bk. Co., The.

Romba, Katherine. Iron Construction & Cultural Discourse. 2008. 180p. pap. *(978-3-8364-6570-0(1))* VDM Verlag Dr. Mueller e.K.

Salmon, Charles G., et al. Steel Structures: Design & Behavior. 5th rev. ed. 2008. (ENG.). 888p. (C). 197.00 *(978-0-13-188556-1(1)*, Prentice Hall) Prentice Hall PTR.

Segui, William T. Steel Design. 5th ed. 2012. (ENG.). 736p. (C). 226.95 ***(978-1-111-57600-4(9))*** Course Technology.

Steel Construction Institute Staff. Steel Designers' Manual. Davison, Buick & Owens, Graham W., eds. 7th ed. 2012. (ENG., Illus.). 1398p. 170.99 ***(978-1-4051-8940-8(1)***, Wiley-Blackwell) Wiley, John & Sons, Inc.

Subramanian, N. Design of Steel Structures: Theory & Practice. 2011. (ENG., Illus.). 864p. pap. 32.95 *(978-0-19-806881-5(6))* Oxford Univ. Pr., Inc.

Tamboli, Akbar R. & Tamboli, Akbar. Steel Connection Design & Details. 2nd ed. 2009. (ENG., Illus.). 656p. (C). instr.'s hndbk. ed. 115.00 *(978-0-07-155005-5(4)*, 0071550054) McGraw-Hill Professional Publishing.

Technology Research Editors, ed. Market Developments: Steel in Residual Construction, 2007 Ed. 2007. pap. 68.50 *(978-1-60030-269-5(6)*, Search-In-Print) CSA Journal Division.

Thomson, Nick. Corrugated Iron Buildings: Churches, Houses, Sheds & Huts. 2011. (Shire Library). (ENG., Illus.). 64p. pap. 12.95 *(978-0-7478-0783-4(3))* Shire Pubns., Ltd. GBR. Dist: Random Hse., Inc.

Trahair, N. S., et al. The Behaviour & Design of Steel Structures to EC3. 4th rev. ed. (ENG., Illus.). 512p. (C). 2008. 200.00 *(978-0-415-41865-2(8))* 2007. 70.00 *(978-0-415-41866-9(6))* Taylor & Francis Group GBR. (CRC Press). Dist: Taylor & Francis Group.

Wang, Y. C. & Choi, Chang-Koon. Steel & Composite Structures: Proceedings of the 3rd International Conference on Steel & Composite Structures (ICSCS07), Manchester, UK, 30 July-1 August 2007. Wang, Y. C. & Choi, C. K., eds. 2007. (ENG., Illus.). 1097p. 369.95 *(978-0-415-45141-3(8)*, Taylor & Francis) Taylor & Francis Group GBR. Dist: Taylor & Francis Group.

Wexler, Donald. Steel & Shade: The Architecture of Donald Wexler. 2011. (ENG., Illus.). 132p. pap. 50.00 ***(978-3-86828-191-0(6))*** Kehrer Verlag Heidelberg, Klaus Kehrer DEU. Dist: Consortium Bk. Sales & Distribution.

Williams, Alan. Steel Structures Design: ASD - LRFD. 2011. (ENG., Illus.). 576p. 125.00 *(978-0-07-163837-1(7)*, 0071638377) McGraw-Hill Professional Publishing.

—Steel Structures Design: ASD/LRFD. 2011. ***(978-0-07-163836-4(9))*** McGraw-Hill Cos., The.

—Structural Steel Design, ASD. 2nd ed. 2007. 366p. pap. 65.00 *(978-1-58001-521-9(2))* International Code Council.

—Structural Steel Design ASD 3rd Edition. 3rd rev. ed. 2010. pap. 65.00 *(978-1-60983-028-1(8))* International Code Council.

—Structural Steel Design, LRFD. 3rd ed. 2007. (Illus.). 376p. pap. 65.00 *(978-1-58001-503-5(4))* International Code Council.

—Structural Steel Design LRFD 4th Edition. 4th rev. ed. 2010. pap. 65.00 *(978-1-60983-027-4(X))* International Code Council.

Williams, Sidney & Weiss Bricker, Lauren. Steel & Shade. 2011. pap. 50.00 *(978-0-9816743-4-6(8))* Palm Springs Art Museum.

Wong, M. Bill. Plastic Analysis & Design of Steel Structures. 2008. (ENG., Illus.). 256p. 109.00 *(978-0-7506-8298-5(1)*, Butterworth-Heinemann) Elsevier Science & Technology Bks.

Yu, Liang. Behavior of Bolted Connections During & after a Fire. 2009. 224p. pap. *(978-3-639-16585-2(3))* VDM Verlag Dr. Mueller e.K.

BUILDING, STONE

Accolella, Alfonso & Turrini, Davide. Travertino Di Siena: Sienese Travertine. 2010. (ITA., Illus.). 297p. *(978-88-6055-513-7(2))* Alinea.

Clarke, Somers. Ancient Egyptian Masonry: The Building Craft. 2009. 352p. 29.95 *(978-1-4344-5212-2(3))*; pap. 14.95 *(978-1-4344-5119-4(4))* Wildside Pr., LLC.

Marmo Studio Staff. Fine Marble in Architecture. Date not set. (Illus.). 192p. *(978-0-393-10411-0(7))* Norton, W. W. & Co., Inc.

Mazet, Sylvain. Les Enceintes Pré- et Protohistoriques de Corse: Essai de Comparaison Avec Quelques Sites de Toscane. 2008. (Bar S Ser.). (FRE., Illus.). viii, 508p. (C). pap. 137.50 *(978-1-4073-0301-7(5))* British Archaeological Reports Ltd. GBR. Dist: Brown, David Bk. Co., The.

Prikryl, Richard & Smith, Bernard J. Building Stone Decay: From Diagnosis to Conservation. 2007. (Geological Society Special Publication Ser.: No. 271). (Illus.). vi, 330p. *(978-1-86239-218-2(8))* Geological Society Publishing Hse.

Saville, Laurel. Outdoor Stonework: The Timeless, Practical, & Aesthetic Value of Stone. 2008. (ENG., Illus.). 160p. pap. 24.99 *(978-1-59253-321-3(3)*, 1592533213, Quarry Books) Quayside.

Stocks, Denys A. Experiments in Egyptian Archaeology: Stoneworking Technology in Ancient Egypt. 2010. 296p. pap. 39.95 *(978-0-415-58894-2(4))* Routledge.

Sunset Books Staff & Wilhite, Tom. Patio & Stone. 2009. (Sunset Design Guide Ser.). (ENG., Illus.). 224p. pap. 22.95 *(978-0-376-01349-1(4)*, Sunset Bks./Sunset Publishing Corp.) Oxmoor Hse., Inc.

BUILDING, UNDERGROUND

see Underground Construction

BUILDING, WOODEN

see also Wooden-Frame Buildings

Aghayere, Abi O. & Vigil, Jason. Structural Wood Design: A Practice-Oriented Approach. 2007. (ENG., Illus.). 416p. 115.00 *(978-0-470-05678-3(9)*, Wiley) Wiley, John & Sons, Inc.

Albano, Giuseppe. Progettazione Esecutiva Di Strutture in Legno Lamellare in Zona Sismica: Prescrizioni, Metodi Di Predimensionamento, Particolari Costruttivi, Progetti Esecutivi Di Cantiere. 2010. (ITA., Illus.). 302p. *(978-88-387-5288-9(5))* Maggioli Editore.

Ambrose, James E., et al. Simplified Design of Wood Structures. 6th ed. 2009. (Parker/Ambrose Series of Simplified Design Guides: 38). (ENG., Illus.). 416p. 95.00 *(978-0-470-18784-5(0)*, Wiley) Wiley, John & Sons, Inc.

American Institute of Timber Construction Staff. Timber Construction Manual. Linville, Jeff D., ed. 6th ed. 2012. (ENG., Illus.). 648p. 125.00 ***(978-0-470-54509-6(7)***, Wiley) Wiley, John & Sons, Inc.

Bachmann, Martin & Tanman, M. Baha. Ahsap Istanbul: Konut Mimarisinden örnekleri = Istanbuls Holzhäuser: Beispiele Seiner Historischen Wohnarchitektur = Wooden Istanbul: Examples from Housing Architecture. 2008. (GER, TUR & ENG., Illus.). 339p. *(978-975-9123-55-0(X))* Suna Ve Inan Kirac Vakfi.

Bangash, M. Y. H., ed. Structural Detailing in Timber: A Comparative Study of British, European & American Codes & Practices. 2007. (Illus.). x, 211p. 180.95 *(978-1-4200-6834-4(2))* Whittles Publishing GBR. Dist: Taylor & Francis Group.

Bodig, J., et al. Reliability-Based Design of Engineered Wood Structures. 2010. (NATO Science Series E: (closed) Ser.). 216p. pap. 219.00 *(978-90-481-4168-5(0)*, 9048141680) Springer.

Breyer, Donald E., et al. Design of Wood Structures-ASD/LRFD. 6th rev. ed. 2006. (ENG., Illus.). 1025p. (C). 99.95 *(978-0-07-145539-8(6)*, 0071455396) McGraw-Hill Professional Publishing.

Broto, Carles. Contemporary Wood Houses. 2008. (ENG.). 240p. 39.95 *(978-84-96969-06-3(1))* Links International (Leading International Key Services Barcelona, S.A.) ESP. Dist: National Bk. Network.

—Superb Wood Houses. 2012. (ENG.). 240p. 45.00 *(978-84-15123-34-7(5))* Links International (Leading International Key Services Barcelona, S.A.) ESP. Dist: National Bk. Network.

—Wood Cabins: Small Wood Houses. 2007. (ENG., Illus.). 192p. 39.95 *(978-84-96424-07-4(3))* Links International (Leading International Key Services Barcelona, S.A.) ESP. Dist: National Bk. Network.

Broto, Charles. Cozy Wood Interiors. 2008. (ENG.). 300p. pap. 24.00 *(978-84-96969-08-7(8))* Links International (Leading International Key Services Barcelona, S.A.) ESP. Dist: National Bk. Network.

Burch, Monte. The Hunting & Fishing Camp Builder's Guide. 2008. (Illus.). 224p. pap. 19.95 *(978-0-88317-365-7(4))* Stoeger Publishing Co.

Campbell, David. Wood in Traditional Architecture. 2011. (Illus.). 224p. 45.00 *(978-0-7643-3581-5(2))* Schiffer Publishing, Ltd.

Carlou, Joel, et al. Sustainable French Timber Houses: L'affaire de Wood. 2006. (ENG., Illus.). 160p. 19.95 *(978-1-86470-179-1(X))* Images Publishing Group AUS. Dist: National Bk. Network.

Coulson, Jim. Wood in Construction: How to Avoid Costly Mistakes. 2012. (ENG., Illus.). 220p. pap. 56.99 ***(978-0-470-65777-5(4)***, Wiley-Blackwell) Wiley, John & Sons, Inc.

Coun, Cdn Wood. Wood Design Manual, 2005: The Complete Reference for Wood Design in Canada. (Illus.). *(978-0-921628-75-0(7))* Canadian Wood Council/Conseil Canadien du Bois.

Heikkinen, Mikka. Zumthor: Spirit of Nature Wood Architecture Award 2006. 2008. (ENG., Illus.). 80p. pap. 66.00 *(978-951-682-807-0(8))* Rakennustieto oy FIN. Dist: Independent Pubs. Group.

Jacobs, Joe. Build It! with Pallets. 2009. (ENG., Illus.). 96p. pap. 12.99 *(978-1-904871-43-9(7)*, 1904871437) Good Life Pr., The GBR. Dist: MBI Distribution Services/Quayside Distribution.

Jodidio, Philip. Architecture Now! Wood. 2011. (FRE, GER & ENG., Illus.). 416p. pap. 39.99 *(978-3-8365-2329-5(9))* TASCHEN DEU. Dist: Ingram Pub. Services.

Kapfinger, Otto. Hermann Kaufmann: WOOD WORKS. 2008. (Illus.). 254p. *(978-3-211-79175-2(2)*, 3211791752) Actar Birkhauser Distribution.

Kapfinger, Otto & Rakennustieto Publishing Staff. Hermann Kaufmann: Spirit of Nature Wood Architecture Award 2010. 2010. (Illus.). 144p. pap. 64.00 *(978-951-682-965-7(1))* Rakennustieto oy FIN. Dist: Independent Pubs. Group.

Kapfinger, Otto & Wieler, Ulrich, eds. Riess Wood³. Modulare Holzbausysteme. Lopez, P. M., tr. 2007. (ENG & GER., Illus.). 159p. *(978-3-211-32771-5(1)*, 3211327711) Actar Birkhauser Distribution.

Karjalainen, Markku & Patokoski, Riko. Wooden Urban Villages. 2008. (ENG.). 168p. 49.00 *(978-951-682-844-5(2))* Rakennustieto oy FIN. Dist: Independent Pubs. Group.

Kaufmann, Hermann, ed. Building with Timber: Paths into the Future. 2012. (Illus.). 224p. 49.95 ***(978-3-7913-5181-0(8))*** Prestel Publishing.

Krauel, Jacobo. Today's Wood Houses. 2010. (ENG., Illus.). 240p. 39.00 *(978-84-92796-53-3(7))* Links International (Leading International Key Services Barcelona, S.A.) ESP. Dist: National Bk. Network.

—Wood Houses. 2010. (ENG., Illus.). 240p. 39.95 *(978-84-92796-45-8(6))* Links International (Leading International Key Services Barcelona, S.A.) ESP. Dist: National Bk. Network.

Larsen, Hans & Enjily, Vahik. Practical Design of Timber Structures to Eurocode 5. 2009. (Illus.). iv, 268p. *(978-0-7277-3609-3(4))* Telford, Thomas Ltd.

Law, Ben. Roundwood Timber Framing: Building Naturally Using Local Resources. 2010. (ENG., Illus.). 172p. 39.95 *(978-1-85623-041-4(4))* Permanent Pubns. GBR. Dist: Chelsea Green Publishing.

McCurry, Chris & Chase, Nan. Bark House Style: Sustainable Designs from Nature, 1 vol. 2008. (ENG., Illus.). 152p. 30.00 *(978-1-4236-0214-9(5))* Gibbs Smith, Publisher.

McLeod, Virginia, et al. Detail in Contemporary Timber Architecture. 2010. (ENG., Illus.). 224p. 50.00 *(978-1-85669-641-8(3))* King, Laurence Publishing GBR. Dist: Hachette Bk. Group.

Meijer, Haiko, et al, texts. Wood Works Onix. 2010. (ENG., Illus.). 320p. 60.00 *(978-90-5662-679-2(5))* NAi Uitgevers / Publishers Stichting NLD. Dist: D.A.P./Distributed Art Pubs.

Miller, Judith. Wooden Houses: From Log Cabins to Beach Houses. 2007. (ENG., Illus.). 144p. pap. *(978-1-84597-347-6(X))* Ryland Peters & Small.

Naza-Dönmez, E. Emine. Wooden Mosques of the Samsun Region, Turkey: From the Past to the Present in the Light of Surveys Carried Out in the Years 2001-2003. 2008. (Bar S Ser.). (Illus.). vi, 159p. (C). pap. 80.00 *(978-1-4073-0306-2(6))* British Archaeological Reports Ltd. GBR. Dist: Brown, David Bk. Co., The.

Owen, Julian. Kit & Modern Timber Frame Homes: The Complete Guide. 2007. (ENG., Illus.). 192p. 42.95 *(978-1-86126-950-8(1))* Crowood Pr., Ltd. GBR. Dist: Independent Pubs. Group.

Ozelton, E. C. & Baird, J. A. Timber Designers' Manual. 3rd ed. 2006. (ENG., Illus.). 560p. pap. 104.99 *(978-1-4051-4671-5(0)*, Wiley-Blackwell) Wiley, John & Sons, Inc.

Pauwels, Wim. Living with Wood. 2008. (ENG., Illus.). 208p. *(978-90-77213-90-2(2)*, Beta-Plus (Acc)) Antique Collectors' Club.

—Wood at Home. 2011. (ENG., Illus.). 200p. 80.00 *(978-90-8944-094-5(1))* Beta-Plus Pubs. BEL. Dist: Antique Collectors' Club.

Pollan, Michael. A Place of My Own: The Architecture of Daydreams. 2008. (ENG.). 352p. (gr. 12-18). 16.00 *(978-0-14-311474-1(3)*, Penguin (Non-Classics)) Penguin Group (USA) Inc.

Rakennustieto Publishing. Jose Cruz Ovalle Spirit of Nature Wood Architecture Award 2008. 2009. (ENG.). 176p. pap. 76.00 *(978-951-682-896-4(5)*, Art Stock Bks. Ltd/Csi) Continental Sales, Inc.

Rooney, Ashley & Brooks, Turner. Shingle Style Homes: Past & Present. 2007. (Illus.). 256p. 39.95 *(978-0-7643-2554-0(X))* Schiffer Publishing, Ltd.

Slavid, Ruth. Wood Houses. 2006. (ENG., Illus.). 208p. 65.00 *(978-0-7892-0888-0(1))* Abbeville Pr., Inc.

Tiainen, Jussi, photos by. Wood Architecture in Finland. 2008. (ENG., Illus.). 144p. 69.00 *(978-951-682-847-6(7))* Rakennustieto oy FIN. Dist: Independent Pubs. Group.

Tostrup, Elizabeth. Norwegian Wood: The Thoughtful Architecture of Wenche Selmer. 2006. (ENG., Illus.). 208p. 45.00 *(978-1-56898-593-0(2))* Princeton Architectural Pr.

Ullmann, H. F., ed. Architecture Compact Wood. 2009. 288p. pap. 22.99 *(978-0-8416-1017-0(7))* American Map Corp.

Waterbolk, H. T. Getimmerd Verleden: Sporen Van Voor- En Vroeghistorische Houtbouw Op de Zand- En Kleigronden Tussen Eems en IJssel. 2009. (Groningen Archaeological Studies). (DUT., Illus.). 229p. (C). 67.00 ***(978-90-77922-47-7(4))*** Barkhuis Publishing NLD. Dist: Brown, David Bk. Co., The.

Wood in Culture Association Staff. Renzo Piano: Spirit of Nature Wood Architecture Award 2000. 2008. (ENG., Illus.). 88p. pap. 34.00 *(978-951-682-606-9(7))* Rakennustieto oy FIN. Dist: Independent Pubs. Group.

Zwerger, Klaus. Wood & Wood Joints: Building Traditions of Europe, Japan & China (Second, Revised & Expanded Edition) 2nd rev. ed. 2012. (ENG., Illus.). 312p. pap. 69.95 *(978-3-0346-0685-1(0))* Birkhauser Verlag AG CHE. Dist: Actar Birkhauser Distribution.

BUILDING AND LOAN ASSOCIATIONS

see Savings and Loan Associations

BUILDING BLOCK DESIGN

see Unit Construction

BUILDING CODES

see Building Laws

BUILDING DYNAMICS

see Structural Dynamics

BUILDING EMPLOYEES

see Building-Service Employees

BUILDING FAILURES

see also Buildings—Protection

Bosher, Lee, ed. Hazards & the Built Environment: Attaining Built-in Resilience. 2008. (ENG., Illus.). 400p. (C). 180.00 *(978-0-415-42729-6(0))*; pap. 68.95 *(978-0-415-42730-2(4))* Routledge.

Brebbia, Carlos A. & Hernandez, S., eds. The Art of Resisting Extreme Natural Forces. 2007. (WIT Transactions on Engineering Sciences Ser.: 58). (Illus.). 144p. 90.00 *(978-1-84564-086-6(1))* WIT Pr GBR. Dist: WIT Pr.

Carper, Kenneth L. & Smilowitz, Robert, eds. Mitigating the Potential for Progressive Disproportionate Structural Collapse. 2006. 116p. pap. 39.00 *(978-0-7844-0892-6(0)*, 40892) American Society of Civil Engineers.

Douglas, James & Ransom, Bill. Understanding Building Failures. 3rd rev. ed. 2007. (ENG., Illus.). 352p. 150.00 *(978-0-415-37082-0(5))* Routledge.

Dunn, Vincent. Collapse of Burning Buildings: A Guide to Fireground Safety. 2nd ed. 2010 (ENG.). 364p. 79.00 *(978-1-59370-233-5(7))* PennWell Corp.

Gage, Richard, et al. 9/11: the Simple Facts. 2011. (ENG.). 112p. pap. 12.00 *(978-1-59376-424-1(3)*, Soft Skull Pr.) Counterpoint LLC.

Holland, M. Practical Guide to Diagnosing Structural Movement in Buildings. 2012. (ENG.). 240p. pap. 49.95 ***(978-0-470-65910-6(6)***, Wiley-Blackwell) Wiley, John & Sons, Inc.

Kulczyk, Peter. Disaster Mitigation: A Guide for Building Departments. 2009. (Illus.). vii, 122p. ***(978-1-58001-767-1(3))*** International Code Council.

Norman, John. Fire Officer's Handbook of Tactics Video Series #18: Structural Collapse. 2010. 59.00 *(978-1-59370-225-0(6))* Fire Engineering Bks. & Videos.

O'Connell, John. Collapse Operations for First Responders. 2011. (ENG.). 206p. 69.00 ***(978-1-59370-263-2(9)***, Fire Engineering Bks. & Videos) PennWell Corp.

Oickle, Alvin F. Disaster in Lawrence. 2008. 128p. pap. 19.99 *(978-1-59629-506-3(6))* History Pr., The.

Ransom, Bill & Douglas, James. Understanding Building Failures. 3rd rev. ed. 2007. (ENG., Illus.). 352p. per. 54.95 *(978-0-415-37083-7(3))* Routledge.

Reimer, Michael T. Rescue Series: Structural Collapse: Awareness & Operations. 2009. 100p. pap. 34.95 *(978-0-7637-6349-7(7))* Jones & Bartlett Learning, LLC.

Smith, Michael. Building Construction: Methods & Materials for the Fire Science & Resource Central Fire Student Access Code Card Package. 2nd ed. 2011. (ENG.). (C). 72.00 ***(978-0-13-283007-2(8)***, Prentice Hall) Prentice Hall PTR.

Smith, Michael. Building Construction: Methods & Materials for the Fire Service. 2nd rev. ed. 2011. (ENG.). 256p. (C). 72.00 *(978-0-13-708378-7(5)*, Prentice Hall) Prentice Hall PTR.

BUILDING FITTINGS

see also Architectural Ironwork; Buildings—Mechanical Equipment

Bailey, Mark and Sally. Restoration Home: Creating Beautiful Interiors with Rescued Treasures. 2007. (ENG., Illus.). 160p. *(978-1-84597-452-7(2))* Ryland Peters & Small.

Decker, Jules. Treasury of Nineteenth-Century Ornamental Metalwork. 2006. (Dover Jewelry & Metalwork Ser.). (ENG., Illus.). 144p. per. 15.95 *(978-0-486-45222-7(0))* Dover Pubns., Inc.

Falk, Bob, et al. Unbuilding: Salvaging the Architectural Treasures of Unwanted Houses. 2007. (ENG., Illus.). 248p. 30.00 *(978-1-56158-825-1(3)*, Taunton) Taunton Pr., Inc.

Forsyth, Michael & White, Lisa. Interior Finishes & Fittings for Historic Building Conservation. 2011. (Historic Building Conservation Ser.). (ENG., Illus.). 232p. 77.99 *(978-1-4051-9022-0(1)*, Wiley-Blackwell) Wiley, John & Sons, Inc.

Matthews, David I., ed. Innovations in Energy: Efficient Technologies for Buildings. 2012. 230p. ***(978-1-61761-976-2(0))*** Nova Science Pubs., Inc.

Monroe, Steve. Selling to Builders. 2nd ed. 2007. (Illus.). 121p. 27.95 *(978-0-86718-631-4(3))* BuilderBooks.

Morris, John T. Stone Designs for the Home, 1 vol. 2008. (ENG., Illus.). 160p. 34.95 *(978-1-4236-0194-4(7))* Gibbs Smith, Publisher.

Residential Detailed Costs 2003: Contractor's Pricing Guide. 300p. 38.95 *(978-0-87629-686-8(X))* Means, R.S. Co., Inc.

Rsmeans, compiled by. Means CPG Residential Detailed Costs. 2007. (Illus.). 403p. per. 39.95 *(978-0-87629-056-9(X))* Means, R.S. Co., Inc.

BUILDING INDUSTRY

see Construction Industry

BUILDING INSCRIPTIONS

see Architectural Inscriptions

BUILDING INSPECTION

see also Building Laws

Arbogast, David H. How to Write a Historic Structure Report. 2011. (ENG., Illus.). 400p. pap. 26.00 *(978-0-393-70614-7(1)*, 70614) Norton, W. W. & Co., Inc.

Becker, Norman. Complete Book of Home Inspection 4/E. 4th rev. ed. 2010. (Complete Book Ser.). (ENG., Illus.). 384p. pap. 19.95 *(978-0-07-170277-5(6)*, 0071702776) McGraw-Hill Professional Publishing.

Caplehorn, Peter. Whole Life Costing: A New Approach. 2012. (ENG., Illus.). 160p. pap. 55.95 *(978-0-415-43423-2(8))* Routledge.

Casey, Michael, et al. Code Check Building: An Illustrated Guide to the Building Codes. 2nd ed. 2007. (Code Check Building Ser.). (ENG., Illus.). 30p. spiral bd. 17.95 *(978-1-56158-912-8(8)*, Taunton) Taunton Pr., Inc.

—Code Check Complete: An Illustrated Guide to Building, Plumbing, Mechanical, & Electrical Codes. 2007. (Code Check Ser.). (ENG., Illus.). 238p. 40.00 *(978-1-56158-911-1(X)*, Taunton) Taunton Pr., Inc.

Chrysler, John. Reinforced Concrete Masonry Construction Inspectors Handbook, 6th Ed. 6th ed. 2007. 39.00 *(978-0-940116-47-4(2))* Masonry Institute of America.

Douglas, James. Building Surveys & Reports. 4th ed. 2011. (ENG., Illus.). 432p. pap. 64.99 *(978-1-4051-9761-8(7)*, Wiley-Blackwell) Wiley, John & Sons, Inc.

Fischetti, David C. & Fischetti. Structural Investigation of Historic Buildings: A Case Study Guide to Preservation Technology for Buildings, Bridges, Towers, & Mills. 2009. (ENG., Illus.). 288p. 110.00 *(978-0-470-18967-2(3)*, Wiley) Wiley, John & Sons, Inc.

Glover, Peter. Building Surveys. 7th rev. ed. 2009. (ENG., Illus.). 366p. pap. 44.95 *(978-1-85617-606-4(1))* Routledge.

Grondzik, Walter T., et al. Principles of Building Commissioning. 2009. (ENG., Illus.). 144p. 110.00 *(978-0-470-11297-7(2)*, Wiley) Wiley, John & Sons, Inc.

Hansen, Douglas & Kardon, Redwood. Code Check Building 3rd Edition: An Illustrated Guide to the Building Codes. 3rd ed. 2011. (Code Check Ser.). (ENG., Illus.). 32p. spiral bd. 19.95 *(978-1-60085-329-6(3))* Taunton Pr., Inc.

Hansen, Douglas, et al. California: An Illustrated Guide to Building a Safe House. 2009. (Code Check Ser.). (ENG., Illus.). 32p. pap. 18.95 *(978-1-60085-084-4(7)*, Taunton) Taunton Pr., Inc.

—Code Check Plumbing & Mechanical 4th Edition: An Illustrated Guide to the Plumbing & Mechanical Codes. 4th ed. 2011. (Code Check Ser.). (ENG., Illus.). 46p. spiral bd. 24.95 *(978-1-60085-339-5(0))* Taunton Pr., Inc.

ICC. Building Department Administration Workbook. 2009. pap. 38.00 *(978-1-58001-793-0(2))* International Code Council.

—Model Program for Special Inspection: Based on 2006 IBC Chapter 17. 2007. pap. 17.50 *(978-1-58001-569-1(7))* International Code Council.

—Model Program for Special Inspection Based on the 2009 IBC Chapter 17: Based on 2009 IBC Chapter 17. 2010. pap. 20.00 *(978-1-58001-911-8(0))* International Code Council.

—Model Program for Special Inspection based on the 2012 IBC Chapter 17. 2011. pap. 22.00 ***(978-1-60983-199-8(3))*** International Code Council.

—Residential Inspector's Guide: Building & Energy - Based on the 2009 International Residential Code Chapters 1-11. 2010. spiral bd. 21.00 *(978-1-58001-883-8(1))* International Code Council.

—Residential Inspector's Guide 2006. 2007. (Illus.). xix, 167p. spiral bd. 21.00 *(978-1-58001-568-4(9))* International Code Council.

ICC/Thrapp. Fire Plan Fire & Inspection Guidelines. 2010. pap. 17.50 *(978-1-58001-881-4(5))* International Code Council.

Kardon, Redwood, et al. Code Check: An Illustrated Guide to Building a Safe House. (Code Check: an Illustrated Guide to Building a Safe House Ser.). (ENG., Illus.). 5th ed. 2007. 30p. spiral bd. 17.95 *(978-1-56158-839-8(3)*, Taunton) 6th ed. 2009. 32p. spiral bd. 18.95 *(978-1-60085-045-5(6))* Taunton Pr., Inc.

—Plumbing: An Illustrated Guide to the Plumbing Codes. 3rd ed. 2006. (Code Check Plumbing: a Field Guide to the Plumbing Codes Ser.). (ENG., Illus.). 30p. spiral bd. 17.95 *(978-1-56158-813-8(X)*, Taunton) Taunton Pr., Inc.

Kitcher, Chris. Practical Guide to Inspection, Testing & Certification of Electrical Installations. 3rd rev. ed. 2013. (ENG.). 248p. (C). pap. 33.95 ***(978-0-08-096907-7(0))*** Routledge.

MCI Exam Secrets Test Prep Staff, ed. Master CREIA Inspector Exam Secrets Study Guide: MCI Test Review for the California Real Estate Inspection Association Examination. 2011. 77.99 *(978-1-61403-516-9(4))* Mometrix Media LLC.

NCSEA/ICC. Inspection, Testing, & Monitoring of Buildings & Bridges (Final) 2011. pap. 59.00 ***(978-1-60983-198-1(5))*** International Code Council.

Pieczynski, Linda. The Building Official's & Inspector's Guide to Codes, Forms, & Complaints. 2007. (ENG., Illus.). 240p. pap. 34.95 *(978-1-4180-4895-2(X))* Delmar Cengage Learning.

—Residential Inspector's Guide to Codes, Forms, & Complaints. 2008. (ENG.). 256p. pap. 34.95 *(978-1-4283-5159-2(0))* Delmar Cengage Learning.

SEAOC. Structural Construction & Special Inspection Manual: A Companion to the 2006 IBC Structural/Seismic Design Manuals. 2009. pap. 59.95 *(978-1-58001-765-7(7))* International Code Council.

Underwood, Lynn. Building Code Compliance for Contractors & Inspectors. 2010. *(978-1-57218-238-7(5))* Craftsman Bk. Co.

Van Note, Steve. Residential Inspector's Guide: Building & Energy- Based on the 2012 IRC Chapters 1-33. 2011. spiral bd. 24.95 ***(978-1-60983-167-7(5))*** International Code Council.

Wells, George. How to Write a Better Home Inspection Report. 2010. 252p. pap. 24.95 *(978-0-557-69363-4(2))* Lulu Enterprises Inc.

—Pricing Concepts & Strategies - A Guide for Home Inspectors. 2010. 81p. pap. 15.98 *(978-0-557-23862-0(5))* Lulu Enterprises Inc.

BUILDING LAWS

see also Architects—Legal Status, Laws, etc.; Building Inspection; Construction Industry—Law and Legislation; Tenement Houses; Zoning Law

Adshead, Julie, ed. Green Buildings & the Law. 2011. (ENG., Illus.). 288p. (C). 115.00 *(978-0-415-55926-3(X))* Routledge.

Al-Mudhei, Ali. Implementation of Building Codes. 2010. 188p. pap. *(978-3-639-25138-8(5))* VDM Verlag Dr. Mueller e.K.

Barker, Bruce. Codes for Homeowners: Electrical Codes - Mechanical Codes - Plumbing Codes - Building Codes. 2010. (Black & Decker Complete Guide Ser.). (ENG., Illus.). 240p. pap. 24.99 *(978-1-58923-479-6(0)*, 1589234790) Quayside.

Building Code Requirements for Structural Concrete & Commentary 2008. per. *(978-0-87031-264-9(2))* American Concrete Institute.

Caufield, Scott. Going Green with the International Residential Code. 2010. (ENG.). 336p. pap. 29.95 *(978-1-4354-9729-0(5))* Delmar Cengage Learning.

Cooke, John R. Building & the Law. (Illus.). 210p. *(978-0-86840-244-4(3)*, UNSW Press) NewSouth Publishing.

Hageman, Jack M. Contractor's Guide to the Building Code: Based on the 2006 IBC & IRC. 6th ed. 2008. (Illus.). 402p. pap. 66.75 incl. cd-rom *(978-1-57218-202-8(4))* Craftsman Bk. Co.

ICC. Conventional Construction Provisions of the 2009 IRC: An Illustrated Guide. 2011. pap. 44.95 *(978-1-60983-061-8(X))* International Code Council.

—IBC Turbo Tabs 2012: Turbocharge Your Code! 2011. (ENG.). ring bd. 16.00 *(978-1-60983-102-8(0))* International Code Council.

—IEBC Turbo Tabs 2012: Turbocharge Your Code! 2011. (ENG.). ring bd. 16.00 *(978-1-60983-114-1(4))*; ring bd. 17.00 *(978-1-60983-113-4(6))* International Code Council.

—IFC Turbo Tabs 2012: Turbocharge Your Code! 2011. (ENG.). ring bd. 16.00 *(978-1-60983-106-6(3))* International Code Council.

—IFGC Turbo Tabs 2012: Turbocharge Your Code! 2011. (ENG.). ring bd. 17.00 *(978-1-60983-111-0(X))* International Code Council.

—International Building Code 2009 New Jersey. 2010. ring bd. 135.00 *(978-1-58001-788-6(6))* International Code Council.

—International Mechanical Code 2012. 2011. (ENG.). ring bd. 17.00 *(978-1-60983-109-7(8))* International Code Council.

—International Residential Code Turbo Tabs 2012. 2011. (ENG.). ring bd. 17.00 *(978-1-60983-103-5(9))* International Code Council.

—Plan Review Manual 2006. 2008. (Illus.). 200p. pap. 48.00 *(978-1-58001-674-2(X))* International Code Council.

—Supplement to the International Codes 2007. 2007. pap. 13.00 *(978-1-58001-616-2(2))* International Code Council.

—UL Standards: As Referenced in the 2006 IBC. 2007. pap. 170.00 *(978-1-58001-544-8(1))* International Code Council.

—2006 IEBC Appendix A Code & Commentary: For Seismic Retrofit of Existing Buildings. 2007. pap. 45.00 *(978-1-58001-658-2(8))* International Code Council.

—2006 International Fire Code with Phoenix Amendments. 2007. bds. 93.00 *(978-1-58001-643-8(X))* International Code Council.

—2009 IBC Checklist - Nonstructural. 2010. pap. 39.00 *(978-1-58001-875-3(0))* International Code Council.

—2009 IBC Checklist - Structural. 2010. pap. 59.00 *(978-1-58001-874-6(2))* International Code Council.

—2009 IBC Structural Q & A. 2010. pap. 45.00 *(978-1-58001-962-0(5))* International Code Council.

—2009 IEBC Q & A. 2010. pap. 40.00 *(978-1-58001-971-2(4))* International Code Council.

—2009 International Fuel Gas Code Study Companion. 2010. pap. 48.00 *(978-1-58001-967-5(6))* International Code Council.

—2009 International Mechanical Code Study Companion. 2009. pap. 52.00 *(978-1-58001-867-8(X))* International Code Council.

—2009 IRC(r) CheckList: Building & Energy Provisions Chapters 1-11. 2010. pap. 39.00 *(978-1-58001-876-0(9))* International Code Council.

—2009 IRC Q & A: Building & Energy Provisions. 2010. pap. 45.00 *(978-1-58001-968-2(4))* International Code Council.

—2009 Plumbing Code Study Companion. 2009. pap. 52.00 *(978-1-58001-868-5(8))* International Code Council.

—2012 collection I-quest-single. 2011. (ENG.). 1000.00 *(978-1-60983-145-5(4))* International Code Council.

—2012 COLLECTION PDF Volume - SINGLE. 2011. (ENG.). 770.00 *(978-1-60983-132-5(2))* International Code Council.

—2012 DESIGNER PDF Volume-SINGLE. 2011. (ENG.). 390.00 *(978-1-60983-134-9(9))* International Code Council.

—2012 ibc i-quest - Single. 2011. (ENG.). 169.00 *(978-1-60983-136-3(5))* International Code Council.

—2012 IBC PDF Volume - SINGLE. 2011. (ENG.). 122.00 *(978-1-60983-126-4(8))* International Code Council.

—2012 IBC Turbo Tabs. 2011. (ENG.). ring bd. 17.00 *(978-1-60983-101-1(2))* International Code Council.

—2012 IFGC Turbo Tabs. 2011. (ENG.). ring bd. 16.00 *(978-1-60983-112-7(6))* International Code Council.

—2012 IMC Turbo Tabs. 2011. (ENG.). ring bd. 16.00 *(978-1-60983-110-3(1))* International Code Council.

—2012 IPC Turbo Tabs. 2011. (ENG.). ring bd. 16.00 *(978-1-60983-108-0(X))* International Code Council.

—2012 irc i-quest - Single. 2011. (ENG.). 144.00 *(978-1-60983-139-4(X))* International Code Council.

—2012 IRC PDF Volume - SINGLE. 2011. (ENG.). 106.00 *(978-1-60983-128-8(4))* International Code Council.

—2012 IRC Turbo Tabs. 2011. (ENG.). ring bd. 16.00 *(978-1-60983-104-2(7))* International Code Council.

ICC Minnesota State. 2009 Minnesota State Mechanical, Fuel Gas, & Plumbing Codes Chapters 1346 And 4715. 2010. pap. 97.00 *(978-1-58001-982-8(X))* International Code Council.

International Code Council. Codigo International de Conservacion de Energia 2006. 2009. (ENG.). pap. 27.00 *(978-1-58001-671-1(5))* International Code Council.

—International Building Code 2009. 2009. (ENG.). ring bd. 137.00 *(978-1-58001-724-4(X))* International Code Council.

—International Building Code Handbook 2009 - Fire- & Life-Safety Provisions. 2009. (ENG.). pap. 99.95 *(978-1-58001-878-4(5))* International Code Council.

—International Existing Building Code 2009. 2009. (ENG.). pap. 66.00 *(978-1-58001-737-4(1))*; ring bd. 75.00 *(978-1-58001-736-7(3))* International Code Council.

—International Residential Code for One-and-Two Family Dwellings 2009. 2009. (ENG.). pap. 106.00 *(978-1-58001-727-5(4))* International Code Council.

—2009 ICC Performance Code for Buildings & Facilities. 2009. (ENG.). pap. 51.00 *(978-1-58001-738-1(X))* International Code Council.

—2009 International Building Code: Softcover Version. 2009. (ENG.). 1p. pap. 122.00 *(978-1-58001-725-1(8))* International Code Council.

—2009 International Energy Conservation Code: Softcover Version. 2009. (ENG.). pap. 40.00 *(978-1-58001-742-8(8))* International Code Council.

—2009 International Fuel Gas Code: Looseleaf Version. 2009. (ENG.). 1p. ring bd. 86.00 *(978-1-58001-734-3(7))* International Code Council.

—2009 International Fuel Gas Code: Softcover Version. 2009. (ENG.). pap. 74.00 *(978-1-58001-735-0(5))* International Code Council.

—2009 International Plumbing Code: Looseleaf Version. 2009. (ENG.). ring bd. 90.00 *(978-1-58001-732-9(0))* International Code Council.

—2009 International Plumbing Code: Softcover Version. 2009. (ENG.). pap. 78.00 *(978-1-58001-733-6(9))* International Code Council.

—2009 International Property Maintenance Code. 2009. (ENG.). pap. 35.00 *(978-1-58001-740-4(1))* International Code Council.

—2009 International Residential Code for One-and-Two Family Dwellings: Looseleaf Version. 2009. (ENG.). 1p. ring bd. 125.00 *(978-1-58001-726-8(6))* International Code Council.

—2009 International Zoning Code. 2009. (ENG.). pap. 33.00 *(978-1-58001-743-5(6))* International Code Council.

—2012 ICC Performance Code for Buildings & Facilities. 2011. (ENG.). 1p. pap. 51.00 *(978-1-60983-047-2(4))* International Code Council.

—2012 International Building Code. 2011. (ENG.). ring bd. 137.00 *(978-1-60983-039-7(3))*; (Illus.). xxx, 690p. pap. 122.00 *(978-1-60983-040-3(7))* International Code Council.

—2012 International Existing Building Code. 2011. (ENG.). pap. 66.00 *(978-1-60983-044-1(X))*; ring bd. 75.00 *(978-1-60983-043-4(1))* International Code Council.

—2012 International Fire Code. 2011. (ENG.). pap. 99.00 *(978-1-60983-046-5(6))*; ring bd. 110.00 *(978-1-60983-045-8(8))* International Code Council.

—2012 International Fuel Gas Code. 2011. (ENG.). pap. 74.00 *(978-1-60983-049-6(0))*; ring bd. 86.00 *(978-1-60983-048-9(2))* International Code Council.

—2012 International Mechanical Code. 2011. (ENG.). pap. 74.00 *(978-1-60983-051-9(2))*; ring bd. 86.00 *(978-1-60983-050-2(4))* International Code Council.

—2012 International Plumbing Code (Includes International Private Sewage Disposal Code) 2011. (ENG.). pap. 78.00 *(978-1-60983-053-3(9))*; ring bd. 90.00 *(978-1-60983-052-6(0))* International Code Council.

—2012 International Residential Code for One- & Two- Family Dwellings. 2011. (ENG.). pap. 106.00 *(978-1-60983-042-7(3))*; ring bd. 125.00 *(978-1-60983-041-0(5))* International Code Council.

—2012 International Zoning Code. 2011. (ENG.). pap. 33.00 *(978-1-60983-060-1(1))* International Code Council.

International Code Council & Thornburg, Doug. Significant Changes to the International Building Code 2012 Edition. 2011. (ENG.). 368p. pap. 44.95 *(978-1-111-54246-7(5))* Delmar Cengage Learning.

International Code Council, (International Code Council (ICC)) & Marinelli, Dominic. Code Source Accessibility: Codes, Standards, & Guidelines. 2011. (ENG.). 64p. spiral bd. 25.95 *(978-1-111-03724-6(8))* Delmar Cengage Learning.

International Code Council Staff. Building Department Administration. 3rd rev. ed. 2009. (ENG.). pap. 101.95 *(978-1-58001-405-2(4))* Delmar Cengage Learning.

—Energy Inspector's Guide: Based on the 2009 IECC & ASHRAE/IESNA 90. 1. 2007. 2011. (ENG.). 146p. pap. 18.75 *(978-1-58001-882-1(3))* International Code Council.

—Energy Inspectors Guide: Commercial & Residential Provisions of the 2006 International Energy Conservation Code. 2009. (ENG.). 76p. pap. 16.50 *(978-1-58001-575-2(1))* Delmar Cengage Learning.

—International Building Code 2006: Code & Commentary. 2006. (ENG.). 908p. pap. 114.50 *(978-1-58001-479-3(8))* Delmar Cengage Learning.

—International Building Code & Commentary 2009, Vol. 1. 2010. (ENG.). pap. 119.75 *(978-1-58001-892-0(0))* International Code Council.

—International Building Code Commentary 2009. 2010. (ENG.). Vol. 2. pap. 124.00 *(978-1-58001-893-7(9))*Vols. 1 & 2. 211.00 *(978-1-58001-891-3(2))* International Code Council.

—International Energy Conservation Code 2009: 90. 1-2007 Energy Standard for Building Except Low-Rise Residential Buildings. 2009. (ENG.). pap. 147.00 *(978-1-58001-799-2(1))* International Code Council.

—International Existing Building Code Commentary 2009. 2010. (ENG.). pap. 80.00 *(978-1-58001-894-4(7))* International Code Council.

—2003 International Residential Code-Spanish Edition. 2006. (ENG.). 702p. pap. 65.00 *(978-1-58001-319-2(8))* Delmar Cengage Learning.

—2006 International Building Code Handbook-Fire & Lifesafety Provisions. 2007. (ENG.). 582p. pap. 97.95 *(978-1-58001-507-3(7))* Delmar Cengage Learning.

—2006 International Existing Building Code: Code & Commentary. 2007. (ENG.). 164p. pap. 76.50 *(978-1-58001-489-2(5))* Delmar Cengage Learning.

B

—2006 International Plumbing Code: Code & Commentary. 2007. (ENG.). 496p. pap. 83.50 *(978-1-58001-485-4(2))* Delmar Cengage Learning.
—2009 Energy Conservation Code Study Companion. 2010. (ENG.). pap. 48.00 *(978-1-58001-869-2(6))* International Code Council.
—2012 IFC Turbo Tabs. 2011. (ENG.). ring bd. 17.00 *(978-1-60983-105-9(5))* International Code Council.
International Code Council Staff. 2012 International Building Code Commentary, Vols. 1 & 2. 2012. (ENG.). 211.00 ***(978-1-60983-075-5(X))*** International Code Council.
International Code Council Staff, creator. International Building Code Vol. 2: Code & Commentary. 2006. (ENG., Illus.). 830p. pap. 114.50 *(978-1-58001-480-9(1))* Delmar Cengage Learning.
—International Building Code 2003. 2006. (ENG., Illus.). 756p. per. 89.00 *(978-1-58001-318-5(X))* Delmar Cengage Learning.
—International Fuel Gas Code: Code & Commentary. 2007. (ENG.). 390p. per. 79.00 *(978-1-58001-486-1(0))* Delmar Cengage Learning.
—International Property Maintenance Code: Code & Commentary. 2007. (ENG.). 88p. per. 37.75 *(978-1-58001-487-8(9))* Delmar Cengage Learning.
—International Residential Code for One- And Two-Family Dwellings 2006: Code & Commentary. 2006. (ENG., Illus.). 632p. per. 114.50 *(978-1-58001-481-6(X))* Delmar Cengage Learning.
Jacks, Ben. Illustrated Residential Wiring by Electricians & Contractors: 2005-2008 Code Cycle. aut. ed. 2008. (Illus.). 134p. spiral bd. 26.00 *(978-0-9752506-4-8(7))* RBJ Pubn.
Kahera, Akel Ismail. Reading the Islamic City: Discursive Practices & Legal Judgment. 2011. ***(978-0-7391-7222-3(0))*** Lexington Bks.
Keller, Kimberley. Nec 2008 Need to Know. 2008. (ENG., Illus.). 268p. pap. 29.95 *(978-0-07-150845-2(7)*, 0071508457) McGraw-Hill Professional Publishing.
London District Surveyors Association Staff & Stephenson, John. Spon's Building Regulations Explained. 8th rev. ed. 2012. (ENG., Illus.). 672p. 160.00 *(978-0-415-43067-8(4)*, Spon Pr.) Routledge.
Olivová, Kveta & Kuba, Bohumil. Byty a Katastr Nemovitostí. 8th ed. 2008. (CZE., Illus.). 542p. *(978-80-7201-727-0(6))* Linde Verlag Wien Ges.m.b.H.
O'Meara, Simon. Space & Muslim Urban Life. 2010. (Illus.). x, 150p. pap. 39.95 *(978-0-415-57670-3(9))* Routledge.
—Space & Muslim Urban Life: At the Limits of the Labyrinth of Fez. 2007. (Culture & Civilization in the Middle East Ser.). (ENG., Illus.). 176p. 160.00 *(978-0-415-38612-8(8))* Routledge.
Pieczynski, Linda. Codes, Forms, & Complaints 2006. 2006. (ENG., Illus.). 336p. pap. 34.95 *(978-1-4180-1609-8(8))* Delmar Cengage Learning.
R. S. Means Company Staff. Residential & Light Commercial Construction Standards: The All-in-One, Authoritaative Reference Compiled from - Major Building Codes - Recognized Trade Customs - Industry Standards. 3rd ed. 2008. (RSMeans Ser.: 1). (ENG.). 554p. pap. 59.95 *(978-0-87629-012-5(8))* Means, R.S. Co., Inc.
Rechberger, Walter, ed. Kommentar zum AußStrG. 2006. 1200p. 139.00 *(978-3-211-23832-5(8)*, 3211238328) Springer.
Spon's Building Regulations Explained. 2012. 140.00 ***(978-0-203-88898-8(7)***, Spon Pr.) Routledge.
Stookey, Scott. 2009 International Fire Code Study Companion. 2009. pap. 55.00 *(978-1-58001-866-1(1))* International Code Council.
Thornburg, Doug & International Code Council Staff. 2009 International Building Code Study Companion. 2009. (ENG.). 524p. pap. 59.00 *(978-1-58001-862-3(9))* International Code Council.
—2009 International Residential Code Study Companion. 2009. (ENG.). 494p. pap. 59.00 *(978-1-58001-865-4(3))* International Code Council.
Thornburg, Douglas & ICC. Accessibility Pocketbook 2012 International Building Code & ICC A117. 1-09. 2011. spiral bd. 29.95 ***(978-1-60983-166-0(7))*** International Code Council.
Understanding the Building Regulations. 4th rev. ed. 2008. (ENG., Illus.). 312p. (C). pap. 39.95 *(978-0-415-45272-4(4))* Routledge.
Underwood, Lynn. Common Code Violations. 2nd ed. 2009. (ENG.). 176p. (C). pap. 29.95 *(978-1-4283-7651-9(8))* Delmar Cengage Learning.
Van Der Heijden, J., ed. Building Regulatory Enforcement Regimes: Comparative Analysis of Private Sector Involvement in the Enforcement of Public Building Regulations. 2009. 274p. pap. 87.00 *(978-1-58603-985-1(7))* IOS Pr., Inc.
—Comparative Analysis of Australian Building Regulatory Enforcement Regimes. 2009. 288p. pap. 87.00 *(978-1-58603-962-2(8))* IOS Pr., Inc.
Van Note, Stephen. 2009 Home Builders' Jobsite Codes: A Quick Guide to the 2009 International Residential Code. 2010. 304p. pap. 28.95 *(978-0-86718-656-7(9))* BuilderBooks.
Van Note, Stephen A. Home Builders' Jobsite Codes: A Pocket Guide to the 2006 International Residential Code. 2007. (Illus.). 281p. spiral bd. 26.95 *(978-0-86718-625-3(9))* BuilderBooks.
Vandenberg, Maritz. An Inclusive Environment: An A-Z Guide to Legislation, Policies & Products. 2008. (ENG., Illus.). 672p. 134.00 *(978-0-7506-8456-9(9))* Routledge.
Wible, Robert C. Architectural Security Codes & Guidelines. 2006. (ENG., Illus.). 360p. 79.95 *(978-0-07-146075-0(6)*, 0071460756) McGraw-Hill Professional Publishing.
Winkel, Steven R., et al. Residential Building Codes Illustrated: A Guide to Understanding the 2009 International Residential Code. 2010. (Building Codes Illustrated Ser.: 4). (ENG., Illus.). 352p. pap. 49.95 *(978-0-470-17359-6(9)*, Wiley) Wiley, John & Sons, Inc.
Woodson, R. Dodge. International Building Code Companion 2006. 2007. (ENG., Illus.). 592p. per. 59.95 *(978-0-07-148429-9(9)*, 0071484299) McGraw-Hill Professional Publishing.
Woodson, R. Dodge & Woodson, R. 2009 International Building Code Need to Know: The 20% of the Code You Need 80% of the Time. 2009. (ENG., Illus.). 304p. pap. 29.95 *(978-0-07-159257-4(1)*, 0071592571) McGraw-Hill Professional Publishing.
Wu nan fa xue yan jiu zhong xin Staff, contrib. by. Ying Jian Fa Gui. 3rd ed. 2007. (CHI.). *(978-957-11-4920-2(9))* Wu-Nan Bk., Inc.

BUILDING LAWS—CALIFORNIA

Hansen, Douglas, et al. California: An Illustrated Guide to Building a Safe House. 2009. (Code Check Ser.). (ENG., Illus.). 32p. pap. 18.95 *(978-1-60085-084-4(7)*, Taunton) Taunton Pr., Inc.
Icbo. 2007 California Building Code, Title 24 Part 2. 2007. 1444p. bds. 274.00 *(978-1-58001-546-2(8))* International Code Council.
ICC. Principle Changes to the 2007 California Plumbing Code. 2007. pap. 26.95 *(978-1-58001-675-9(8))* International Code Council.
—2007 California Administrative Code Title 24 Part 1. 2007. 231p. bds. 49.95 *(978-1-58001-545-5(X))* International Code Council.
—2007 California Energy Code Title 24 Part 6. 2007. (ENG.). 110p. ring bd. 42.95 *(978-1-58001-550-9(6))* International Code Council.
—2007 California Referenced Standards Code Title 24 Part 12. 2007. 178p. bds. 36.95 *(978-1-58001-552-3(2))* International Code Council.
ICC/LA County. 2011 County of Los Angeles Building Code - Amendments & Custom Binders. 2010. ring bd. 59.00 *(978-1-60983-013-7(X))* International Code Council.
—2011 County of Los Angeles Building Code - Complete Code. 2010. ring bd. 145.00 *(978-1-60983-017-5(2))* International Code Council.
—2011 County of Los Angeles Building Code Complete Code. 2010. ring bd. 299.00 *(978-1-60983-014-4(8))* International Code Council.
—2011 County of Los Angeles Green Building Standard Code - Amendments & Custom Binders. 2010. ring bd. 42.00 *(978-1-60983-019-9(9))* International Code Council.
—2011 County of Los Angeles Green Building Standards Code - Complete Code. 2010. ring bd. 79.00 *(978-1-60983-020-5(2))* International Code Council.
—2011 County of Los Angeles Residential Code - Amendments & Custom Binders. 2010. ring bd. 42.00 *(978-1-60983-016-8(4))* International Code Council.
International Code Council Staff. California Building Code 2010, Pt. 2. 2010. (ENG.). 770p. ring bd. 274.00 *(978-1-58001-974-3(9))* International Code Council.
—California Codes 2010. 2010. (ENG.). 780.00 *(978-1-58001-980-4(3))* International Code Council.
—California Green Building Standards Code 2010, Pt. 11. 2010. (ENG.). pap. 54.00 *(978-1-58001-979-8(X))* International Code Council.
—California Residential Code 2010, Pt. 2.5. 2010. (ENG.). 724p. pap. 125.00 *(978-1-58001-975-0(7))* International Code Council.
—Dwelling Construction under the 2007 California Building Code. rev. ed. 2009. (ENG.). 100p. pap. 39.95 *(978-1-4354-8363-7(4))* Delmar Cengage Learning.
—2010 California Administrative Code, Pt. 1. 2010. (ENG.). 234p. pap. 54.00 *(978-1-58001-973-6(0))* International Code Council.
—2010 California Building Turbo Tabs. 2010. (ENG.). pap. 16.00 *(978-1-58001-965-1(X))* International Code Council.
—2010 California Energy Code, Pt. 6. 2010. (ENG.). 127p. pap. 49.00 *(978-1-58001-976-7(5))* International Code Council.
—2010 California Referenced Standards Code, Pt. 12. 2010. (ENG.). pap. 44.00 *(978-1-58001-978-1(1))* International Code Council.
SEAOC. 2006 IBC Structural Seismic Design Manual. 2007. 212p. pap. 67.00 *(978-1-58001-402-1(X))*; pap. 67.00 *(978-1-58001-403-8(8))* International Code Council.
—2009 Seaoc Blue Book. 2009. pap. 94.00 *(978-1-58001-861-6(0))* International Code Council.
State of California. 2008 California Access Compliance Reference Manual: Statutes, Regulation, Policies, Interpretation of Regulations (IRs) & Official Comments (Checklists) 2008. (Illus.). 583p. spiral bd. 49.95 *(978-0-9666265-4-4(0))* That Technical Bookstore, Inc.

BUILDING LAWS—CANADA

BNI Building News. Sweets Electrical Cost Guide. 2008. (Sweet's Electrical Cost Guide Ser.). (Illus.). 361p. pap. 96.95 *(978-1-55701-630-0(5))* BNI Pubns., Inc.
—Sweets Facilities Cost Guide. 2008. (Sweet's Facilities Cost Guide Ser.). (Illus.). 714p. pap. 99.95 *(978-1-55701-629-4(1))* BNI Pubns., Inc.
—Sweets Repair & Remodel Cost Guide. 2008. (Sweet's Repair & Remodel Cost Guide Ser.). (Illus.). 547p. pap. 96.95 *(978-1-55701-628-7(3))* BNI Pubns., Inc.
—Sweets Unit Cost Guide. 2008. (Sweet's Unit Cost Guide Ser.). (Illus.). 551p. pap. 96.95 *(978-1-55701-627-0(5))* BNI Pubns., Inc.
BNI Building News, creator. Sweets Repair & Remodel Cost Guide. 2009. (McGraw-Hill Construction Ser.). (ENG., Illus.). 548p. pap. 96.95 *(978-1-55701-668-3(2))* BNI Pubns., Inc.
RSMeans Engineering Dept., ed. Interior Cost Data. 2008. 700p. 154.95 *(978-0-87629-178-8(7))* Means, R.S. Co., Inc.

BUILDING LAWS—FLORIDA

ICC. 2007 Florida Building Code: Existing Building. 2008. bds. 56.30 *(978-1-58001-588-2(3))* International Code Council.
—2007 Florida Building Code: Fuel Gas. 2008. 162p. bds. 80.00 *(978-1-58001-591-2(3))* International Code Council.
—2007 Florida Building Code: Mechanical. 2008. 132p. bds. 80.00 *(978-1-58001-590-5(5))* International Code Council.
—2007 Florida Building Code: Plumbing. 2008. 176p. bds. 80.00 *(978-1-58001-589-9(1))* International Code Council.
—2007 Florida Building Code: Test Protocols for High-Velocity Hurricane Zones. 2008. bds. 36.00 *(978-1-58001-641-4(3))* International Code Council.
International Code Council Staff, creator. Significant Changes to the Florida Building Code, Residential 2007. 2008. (ENG., Illus.). 208p. pap. 39.95 *(978-1-4354-4015-9(3))* Delmar Cengage Learning.
Stafford, T. Eric, et al. Significant Changes to the Florida Building Code, Building 2007. 2008. (ENG., Illus.). 272p. pap. 39.95 *(978-1-4354-4013-5(7))* Delmar Cengage Learning.

BUILDING LAWS—GERMANY

Feldmann, Ekke. Bauordnungen und Baupolizei: Zur Entwicklungsgeschichte Zwischen 1850 Und 1950. 2011. (GER.). 502p. 114.95 ***(978-3-631-61535-5(3))*** Lang, Peter GmbH, Europaischer Verlag der Wissenschaften DEU. Dist: Lang, Peter.
Heinrich, Roxana. Befristung und Bedingung baulicher und sonstiger Nutzungsrechte nach § 9 Abs. 2 BauGB. 2009. (Studien zum Öffentlichen Recht, Völker- und Europarecht Ser.). (GER.). 286p. 79.95 *(978-3-631-59363-9(5))* Lang, Peter GmbH, Europaischer Verlag der Wissenschaften DEU. Dist: Lang, Peter.
Müller, Alice. Nachhaltigkeit im öffentlichen Baurecht unter besonderer Berücksichtigung energieeffizienten Bauens und des Einsatzes erneuerbarer Energien. 2008. (Schriften zum deutschen und internationalen Baurecht Ser.). 308p. pap. 74.95 *(978-3-631-57163-7(1))* Lang, Peter GmbH, Europaischer Verlag der Wissenschaften DEU. Dist: Lang, Peter.
Puchert, Frank. Entscheidungsfaktoren in der öffentlichen Verwaltung am Beispiel der Windenergie im Landkreis Aurich. 2010. (Recht und Rhetorik Ser.). (GER.). 240p. 69.95 *(978-3-631-60012-2(7))* Lang, Peter GmbH, Europaischer Verlag der Wissenschaften DEU. Dist: Lang, Peter.
Robl, Marion. Das beschleunigte Verfahren für Bebauungspläne der Innenentwicklung: Ein Aspekt des Innenstadtentwicklungsgesetzes (BauGB 2007) 2010. (Regensburger Beiträge zum Staats- und Verwaltungsrecht Ser.). (GER.). 684p. 149.95 *(978-3-631-60014-6(3))* Lang, Peter GmbH, Europaischer Verlag der Wissenschaften DEU. Dist: Lang, Peter.
Walter, Thomas. Der Erschließungsvertrag im System des Erschließungsrechts. 2010. (GER.). 310p. pap. *(978-3-428-13378-9(1))* Duncker & Humblot GmbH.

BUILDING LAWS—GREAT BRITAIN

Ashworth, Allan & Hogg, Keith. Willis's Practice & Procedure for the Quantity Surveyor. 12th rev. ed. 2007. (ENG., Illus.). 440p. pap. 69.99 *(978-1-4051-4578-7(1)*, Wiley-Blackwell) Wiley, John & Sons, Inc.
Bickford-Smith, Stephen, et al. Party Walls. 3rd rev. ed. 2009. (ENG.). 312p. pap. *(978-1-84661-179-7(2))* Jordan Publishing, Ltd.
Bright, Keith, et al. The Building Regulations: Explained & Illustrated. 13th rev. ed. 2007. (ENG., Illus.). 968p. 124.99 *(978-1-4051-5922-7(7)*, Wiley-Blackwell) Wiley, John & Sons, Inc.
Butterworth Staff, compiled by. Butterworths Legislation Service: National Building Regulations & Building Standards Act 103 of 1977. Date not set. *(978-0-409-01440-2(0)*, MICHIE) LEXIS Publishing.
Capper, Phillip, et al, eds. Emden's Construction Law. ring bd. *(978-0-406-99811-8(6)*, ECL8ASET, MICHIE) LEXIS Publishing.
Carr, Helen, et al. Using the Housing ACT 2004. 2008. (ENG.). 624p. pap. *(978-1-84661-100-1(8))* Jordan Publishing, Ltd.
Chappell, David, et al. Building Law Encyclopaedia. 2009. (ENG., Illus.). 592p. 180.00 *(978-1-4051-8724-4(7)*, Wiley-Blackwell) Wiley, John & Sons, Inc.
Cousins, Matthew. Architect's Legal Pocket Book. 2011. (ENG., Illus.). 384p. pap. 34.95 *(978-0-08-096603-8(9))* Routledge.
Elliot, Jon. Guidance Note Four: Protection Against Fire. 5th ed. 2009. (Illus.). 104p. pap. 50.00 *(978-0-86341-858-7(9))* Institution of Engineering & Technology GBR. Dist: Books International, Inc.
Furmston, M. P. & Powell-Smith, Vincent, eds. Construction Law Reports 1985-1996. *(978-0-406-99861-3(2)*, CLRASET, MICHIE) LEXIS Publishing.
Imrie, Rob & Street, Emma. Architectural Design & Regulation. 2011. (ENG., Illus.). 376p. 124.99 *(978-1-4051-7966-9(X)*, Wiley-Blackwell) Wiley, John & Sons, Inc.
Polley, Simon. Understanding the Building Regulations. 5th rev. ed. 2011. (ENG., Illus.). 312p. (C). pap. 33.95 *(978-0-415-60863-3(5))* Routledge.
Quenby, Richard. Sale & Management of Flats. 3rd rev. ed. 2010. 330p. pap. 215.00 incl. cd-rom *(978-1-84766-244-6(7)*, Bloomsbury Professional) Bloomsbury Publishing Plc GBR. Dist: International Specialized Bk. Services.
Smith, Joanna, et al. Built on Commerce: Liverpool's Central Business District. 2008. (Informed Conservation Ser.). (ENG., Illus.). 96p. pap. 16.00 *(978-1-905624-34-8(4))* English Heritage GBR. Dist: Brown, David Bk. Co., The.
Speaight, Anthony, ed. Architect's Legal Handbook: The Law for Architects. 9th rev. ed. 2010. (ENG., Illus.). 432p. pap. 56.95 *(978-1-85617-627-9(4))* Routledge.
Tricker, Ray & Alford, Sam. Building Regulations in Brief. 7th ed. 2012. (ENG., Illus.). 1056p. pap. 46.95 ***(978-0-415-80969-6(X))*** Routledge.
Tricker, Ray & Algar, Rozz. Building Regulations in Brief. 4th ed. 2006. (ENG., Illus.). 856p. per. 36.95 *(978-0-7506-8058-5(X)*, Butterworth-Heinemann) Elsevier Science & Technology Bks.
—Scottish Building Standards in Brief. 2008. (ENG., Illus.). 936p. pap. 59.95 *(978-0-7506-8558-0(1))* Routledge.
Tricker, Ray, et al. Building Regulations in Brief. 6th rev. ed. 2010. (ENG., Illus.). 984p. pap. 44.95 *(978-1-85617-696-5(7))* Routledge.
Wood, Douglas, et al. Law & the Built Environment. 2nd ed. 2011. (ENG.). 352p. pap. 41.50 *(978-1-4051-9760-1(9)*, Wiley-Blackwell) Wiley, John & Sons, Inc.

BUILDING LAWS—MICHIGAN

ICC. Michigan Rehabilitation of Existing Building Code 2006. 2008. pap. 58.00 *(978-1-58001-651-3(0))* International Code Council.
—2006 Michigan Building Code. 2008. pap. 107.00 *(978-1-58001-649-0(9))* International Code Council.
—2006 Michigan Plumbing Code. 2007. pap. 64.00 *(978-1-58001-638-4(3))* International Code Council.

BUILDING LAWS—OHIO

ICC. 2007 Ohio Building Code. 2007. bds. 120.00 *(978-1-58001-526-4(3))* International Code Council.

BUILDING LAWS—OREGON

ICC. 2007 Oregon Structural Specialty Code. 2007. bds. 125.00 *(978-1-58001-517-2(4))* International Code Council.
—2008 Oregon Residential Structural Specialty Code. 2008. bds. 75.00 *(978-1-58001-711-4(8))* International Code Council.
—2010 Oregon Structural Speciality Code. 2010. ring bd. 135.00 *(978-1-58001-955-2(2))* International Code Council.

BUILDING LAWS—NEW YORK (STATE)

ICC. Building Code of New York State 2007. 2007. 654p. bds. 115.00 *(978-1-58001-617-9(0))* International Code Council.
—Energy Conservation Construction Code of New York State 2007. 2007. pap. 34.00 *(978-1-58001-584-4(0))*; bds. 39.00 *(978-1-58001-635-3(9))* International Code Council.
—Existing Building Code of New York State 2007. 2007. 296p. pap. 54.00 *(978-1-58001-634-6(0))*; bds. 57.00 *(978-1-58001-583-7(2))* International Code Council.
—Fire Code & Property Maintenance Code of New York State 2007. 2007. bds. 98.50 *(978-1-58001-620-9(0))* International Code Council.
—Fire Code of New York State 2007. 2007. pap. 85.00 *(978-1-58001-582-0(4))* International Code Council.
—Fuel Gas Code of New York State 2007. 2007. 160p. pap. 69.50 *(978-1-58001-579-0(4))* International Code Council.
—Mechanical Code of New York State 2007. 2007. 124p. pap. 69.50 *(978-1-58001-580-6(8))* International Code Council.
—Plumbing Code of New York State 2007. 2007. pap. 69.50 *(978-1-58001-578-3(6))* International Code Council.
—Property Maintenance of New York State 2007. 2007. 40p. pap. 31.00 *(978-1-58001-581-3(6))* International Code Council.
—Residential Code of New York State 2007. 2007. 604p. pap. 79.50 *(978-1-58001-577-6(8))*; bds. 93.50 *(978-1-58001-618-6(9))* International Code Council.
—User's Guide to the 2010 Energy Conservation Construction Code of New York State. 2011. pap. *(978-1-60983-087-8(3))* International Code Council.
ICC/New York. Building Code of New York State, 2010 Edition. 2010. pap. 111.00 *(978-1-60983-000-7(8))* International Code Council.
—Energy Conservation Construction Code of New York State, 2010 Edition. 2010. pap. 34.50 *(978-1-60983-008-3(3))* International Code Council.
—Existing Building Code of New York State, 2010 Edition. 2010. pap. 60.00 *(978-1-60983-002-1(4))* International Code Council.
—Fire Code of New York State, 2010 Edition. 2010. pap. 90.00 *(978-1-60983-003-8(2))* International Code Council.
—Fuel Gas Code of New York State, 2010 Edition. 2010. pap. 69.00 *(978-1-60983-006-9(7))* International Code Council.
—Mechanical Code of New York State, 2010 Edition. 2010. pap. 69.00 *(978-1-60983-005-2(9))* International Code Council.
—Plumbing Code of New York State, 2010 Edition. 2010. pap. 69.00 *(978-1-60983-004-5(0))* International Code Council.
—Residential Code of New York State, 2010 Edition. 2010. pap. 92.50 *(978-1-60983-001-4(6))* International Code Council.

BUILDING LAWS—NORTH CAROLINA

ICC. North Carolina State Building Code: Plumbing Code & Commentary 2006. 2007. pap. 88.00 *(978-1-58001-602-5(2))* International Code Council.
—North Carolina State Building Code 2006: Administrative Code. 2007. bds. 54.00 *(978-1-58001-536-3(0))* International Code Council.
—2006 North Carolina Fire Code Commentary. 2007. pap. 15.00 *(978-1-58001-598-1(0))* International Code Council.
ICC/North Carolina. North Carolina State Building Code: Administrative Code & Policies 2012. 2011. pap. 58.00 *(978-1-60983-123-3(3))* International Code Council.
—North Carolina State Building Code: Building Code 2012. 2011. pap. 119.00 *(978-1-60983-116-5(0))* International Code Council.
—North Carolina State Building Code: Energy Conservation Code 2012. 2011. pap. 37.00 *(978-1-60983-122-6(5))* International Code Council.
—North Carolina State Building Code: Fire Prevention Code 2012. 2011. pap. 97.00 *(978-1-60983-118-9(7))* International Code Council.
—North Carolina State Building Code: Fuel Gas Code 2012. 2011. pap. 77.00 *(978-1-60983-121-9(7))* International Code Council.
—North Carolina State Building Code: Mechanical Code 2012. 2011. pap. 77.00 *(978-1-60983-120-2(9))* International Code Council.

—North Carolina State Building Code: Residential Code 2012. 2011. pap. 99.00 *(978-1-60983-117-2(9))* International Code Council.
Insurance, North Carolina Department Of, & Insurance, Nc Department Of. North Carolina State Building Code 2006: Residential Code. 2007. 372p. bds. 82.50 *(978-1-58001-476-2(3))* International Code Council.

BUILDING LAWS—UNITED STATES

Aci, ed. Core Requirements for Nuclear Safety-Related Concrete Structures. 2007. *(978-0-87031-251-9(0))* American Concrete Institute.
American Contractors Exam Services. DeWALT Building Code Reference. 2nd ed. 2010. (ENG.). 84p. spiral bd. 19.95 *(978-1-111-03662-1(4),* DEWALT) CENGAGE Learning.
Barker, Bruce A. Everybody's Building Code: Based on the 2003 International Residential Code. 2008. 692p. pap. 59.95 *(978-1-58736-753-3(X))* Wheatmark.
—Everybody's Building Code: Updated & Enhanced Edition. 2009. 644p. pap. 49.95 *(978-1-60494-310-8(6))* Wheatmark.
BNI Building News. Sweets Facilities Cost Guide. 2008. (Sweet's Facilities Cost Guide Ser.). (Illus.). 714p. pap. 99.95 *(978-1-55701-629-4(1))* BNI Pubns., Inc.
—Sweets Repair & Remodel Cost Guide. 2008. (Sweet's Repair & Remodel Cost Guide Ser.). (Illus.). 547p. pap. 96.95 *(978-1-55701-628-7(3))* BNI Pubns., Inc.
—Sweets Unit Cost Guide. 2008. (Sweet's Unit Cost Guide Ser.). (Illus.). 551p. pap. 96.95 *(978-1-55701-627-0(5))* BNI Pubns., Inc.
BNI Building News, creator. Sweets Repair & Remodel Cost Guide. 2009. (McGraw-Hill Construction Ser.). (ENG., Illus.). 548p. pap. 96.95 *(978-1-55701-668-3(2))* BNI Pubns., Inc.
Capital Assets Crisis: Maintaining Federal Real Estate with the Dwindling Federal Building Fund: Hearing Before the Subcommittee on Economic Development, Public Buildings, & Emergency Management of the Committee on Transportation & Infrastructure, House of Representatives, One Hundred Eleventh Congress, Second Session, March 24, 2010. 2010. x, 92p. ***(978-0-16-087006-4(2)***, 552-070-41865-2) United States Government Printing Office.
Casey, Michael, et al. Code Check Building: An Illustrated Guide to the Building Codes. 2nd ed. 2007. (Code Check Building Ser.). (ENG., Illus.). 30p. spiral bd. 17.95 *(978-1-56158-912-8(8),* Taunton) Taunton Pr., Inc.
—Code Check Complete: An Illustrated Guide to Building, Plumbing, Mechanical, & Electrical Codes. 2007. (Code Check Ser.). (ENG., Illus.). 238p. 40.00 *(978-1-56158-911-1(X),* Taunton) Taunton Pr., Inc.
Chen, Gang. Leed Ga Exam Guide: A Must-Have for the LEED Green Associate Exam. 2009. 398p. pap. 73.95 *(978-1-4327-4168-6(3))* Outskirts Pr., Inc.
Code Requirements for Residential Concrete & Commentary. 2008. pap. *(978-0-87031-267-0(7))* American Concrete Institute.
Energy Efficiency of Buildings: Hearing Before the Subcommittee on Energy of the Committee on Energy & Natural Resources, United States Senate, One Hundred Tenth Congress, First Session, to Receive Recommendations on Policies & Programs to Improve the Energy Efficiency of Buildings & to Expand the Role of Electric & Gas Utilities in Energy Efficiency Programs, February 12, 2007. 2007. iii, 62p. *(978-0-16-078935-9(4),* 552-070-36062-0) United States Government Printing Office.
Frieders, Dean. Foundations of Sustainable Development. 2012. ***(978-1-61438-325-3(1))*** American Bar Assn.
Green, Melvyn & Watson, Anne. Building Codes for Existing & Historic Buildings. 2nd ed. 2011. (ENG., Illus.). 264p. 85.00 ***(978-0-470-19591-8(6)***, Wiley) Wiley, John & Sons, Inc.
Gregory, Robert. Virginia Contractor's Law. 3rd ed. 2008. (ENG.). 275p. pap. 85.95 *(978-1-4277-8422-3(1))* Kaplan Publishing.
Hansen, Douglas & Kardon, Redwood. Code Check Building 3rd Edition: An Illustrated Guide to the Building Codes. 3rd ed. 2011. (Code Check Ser.). (ENG., Illus.). 32p. spiral bd. 19.95 *(978-1-60085-329-6(3))* Taunton Pr., Inc.
Hansen, Douglas, et al. Code Check Building for California: An Illustrated Guide to the California Building Code. 2008. (Code Check Building Ser.). (ENG., Illus.). 30p. spiral bd. 18.95 *(978-1-60085-083-7(9),* Taunton) Taunton Pr., Inc.
—Code Check Plumbing & Mechanical 4th Edition: An Illustrated Guide to the Plumbing & Mechanical Codes. 4th ed. 2011. (Code Check Ser.). (ENG., Illus.). 46p. spiral bd. 24.95 *(978-1-60085-339-5(0))* Taunton Pr., Inc.
Harmon, Sharon Koomen & Kennon, Katherine E. The Codes Guidebook for Interiors. 5th ed. 2011. (ENG., Illus.). 544p. 85.00 *(978-0-470-59209-0(5),* Wiley) Wiley, John & Sons, Inc.
—Codes Guidebook for Interiors. 5th ed. 2011. (ENG.). 160p. pap. 40.00 *(978-0-470-59210-6(9),* Wiley) Wiley, John & Sons, Inc.
Howe, J. Cullen. The Law of Green Buildings: Regulatory & Legal Issues in Design, Construction, Operations, & Financing. Gerrard, Michael, ed. 2011. (ENG.). 434p. pap. 109.95 *(978-1-61632-014-0(1))* American Bar Assn.
ICC. Building Department Administration Workbook. 2009. pap. 38.00 *(978-1-58001-793-0(2))* International Code Council.
—Guide to the 2010 California Green Building Standards Code, Non-Residential. 2011. (ENG.). pap. 37.00 *(978-1-60983-115-8(2))* International Code Council.
—International Building Code: New Jersey Edition 2006. 2007. 600p. bds. 120.00 *(978-1-58001-514-1(X))* International Code Council.
—Minnesota State Building Code, Chapter 1305 2007. 2007. bds. 117.00 *(978-1-58001-647-6(2))* International Code Council.
—Minnesota State Residential Code, Chapter 1309 2007. 2008. pap. 79.00 *(978-1-58001-646-9(4))* International Code Council.
—Model Program for Special Inspection: Based on 2006 IBC Chapter 17. 2007. pap. 17.50 *(978-1-58001-569-1(7))* International Code Council.
—Model Program for Special Inspection Based on the 2009 IBC Chapter 17: Based on 2009 IBC Chapter 17. 2010. pap. 20.00 *(978-1-58001-911-8(0))* International Code Council.
—Model Program for Special Inspection based on the 2012 IBC Chapter 17. 2011. pap. 22.00 ***(978-1-60983-199-8(3))*** International Code Council.
—Residential Inspector's Guide: Building & Energy - Based on the 2009 International Residential Code Chapters 1-11. 2010. spiral bd. 21.00 *(978-1-58001-883-8(1))* International Code Council.
—Residential Inspector's Guide: Plumbing, Mechanical & Fuel Gas (Based on the 2009 IRC, Chapters 12-33) 2010. spiral bd. 21.00 *(978-1-58001-885-2(8))* International Code Council.
—Seattle Building Code 2006: As Amended by the City of Seattle. 2007. bds. 121.00 *(978-1-58001-637-7(5))* International Code Council.
—Standard for Bleachers, Folding & Telescopic Seating & Grandstands: Icc 300-2007. 2007. 22p. pap. 20.00 *(978-1-58001-562-2(X))* International Code Council.
—Virginia Statewide Fire Prevention Code 2006. 2008. bds. 90.00 *(978-1-58001-685-8(5))* International Code Council.
—1997 UBC/2006 IBC Nonstructural Comparison & Cross Reference. 2007. pap. 40.00 *(978-1-58001-541-7(7))* International Code Council.
—1997 UBC/2006 IBC Structural Comparison & Cross Reference. 2007. pap. 45.00 *(978-1-58001-542-4(5))* International Code Council.
—2006 International Fire Code City of Seattle. 2007. bds. 97.00 *(978-1-58001-636-0(7))* International Code Council.
—2007 Ohio Update - January 2009. 2009. bds. 31.00 *(978-1-58001-794-7(0))* International Code Council.
—2008 City of Los Angeles Building Code. 2008. bds. 59.00 *(978-1-58001-644-5(8))* International Code Council.
—2009 International Residential Code & Commentary Vol 2. 2010. (ENG.). pap. 124.00 *(978-1-58001-913-2(7))* International Code Council.
—2009 IPC/IMC/IFGC Q & A. 2010. pap. 40.00 *(978-1-58001-889-0(0))* International Code Council.
—2009 Permit Tech Study Companion. 2009. pap. 48.00 *(978-1-58001-870-8(X))* International Code Council.
—2010 Oregon Structural Mechanical Code. 2010. ring bd. 109.00 *(978-1-58001-958-3(7))* International Code Council.
ICC/City of Los Angeles. 2011 City of Los Angeles Building Code (2 Volumes) Complete Code. 2011. ring bd. 299.00 *(978-1-60983-092-2(X))* International Code Council.
—2011 City of Los Angeles Green Building Standards Code - Complete Code. 2011. ring bd. 88.00 *(978-1-60983-096-0(2))* International Code Council.
—2011 City of Los Angeles Residential Code - Complete Code. 2011. ring bd. 155.00 *(978-1-60983-094-6(6))* International Code Council.
ICC/Florida. 2010 Florida Building Code - Accessibility. 2011. pap. 70.00 ***(978-1-60983-190-5(X))*** International Code Council.
—2010 Florida Building Code - Building. 2011. (ENG.). 672p. pap. 131.00 ***(978-1-60983-184-4(5))*** International Code Council.
—2010 Florida Building Code - Energy. 2011. pap. 24.00 ***(978-1-60983-191-2(8))*** International Code Council.
—2010 Florida Building Code - Existing Building. 2011. ring bd. 72.00 ***(978-1-60983-189-9(6))*** International Code Council.
—2010 Florida Building Code - Mechanical. 2011. (ENG.). 672p. pap. 88.00 ***(978-1-60983-187-5(X))*** International Code Council.
—2010 Florida Building Code - Plumbing. 2011. (ENG.). 672p. pap. 88.00 ***(978-1-60983-186-8(1))*** International Code Council.
—2010 Florida Building Code - Residential. 2011. (ENG.). 672p. pap. 115.00 ***(978-1-60983-188-2(8))*** International Code Council.
—2010 Florida Building Code — Test Protocols for High Velocity Hurricane Zone. 2011. ring bd. 33.50 ***(978-1-60983-185-1(3))*** International Code Council.
ICC/New Mexico. 2009 New Mexico Energy Code. 2011. pap. 39.95 *(978-1-60983-149-3(7))* International Code Council.
ICC/New York. New York State Codes, 2010 Edition Complete Collection. 2010. pap. 564.00 *(978-1-60983-011-3(3))* International Code Council.
ICC/North Carolina. North Carolina State Building Code: Plumbing Code 2012. 2011. pap. 77.00 *(978-1-60983-119-6(5))* International Code Council.
ICC/OHIO. 2011 Ohio Building Code. 2011. spiral bd. 123.50 ***(978-1-60983-200-1(0))*** International Code Council.
—2011 Ohio Mechanical Code. 2011. spiral bd. 86.50 ***(978-1-60983-201-8(9))*** International Code Council.
—2011 Ohio Plumbing Code. 2011. spiral bd. 86.50 ***(978-1-60983-202-5(7))*** International Code Council.
ICC/OREGON. 2011 Oregon Reach Code. 2011. pap. 59.95 ***(978-1-60983-205-6(1))*** International Code Council.
ICC/Seattle. 2009 International Building Code, City of Seattle. 2010. ring bd. 130.00 *(978-1-60983-021-2(0))* International Code Council.
—2009 International Fire Code, City of Seattle. 2010. ring bd. 103.00 *(978-1-60983-026-7(1))* International Code Council.
ICC/Vermont. 2010 Vermont Commercial Building Energy Standard. 2011. pap. *(978-1-60983-093-9(8))* International Code Council.
—2010 Vermont Residential Building Energy Standard. 2011. pap *(978-1-60983-095-3(4))* International Code Council.
International Code Council. 2009 International Mechanical Code: Looseleaf Version. 2009. (ENG.). ring bd. 86.00 *(978-1-58001-730-5(4))* International Code Council.
—2009 International Mechanical Code: Softcover Version. 2009. (ENG.). pap. 74.00 *(978-1-58001-731-2(2))* International Code Council.
—2012 International Property Maintenance Code. 2011. (ENG.). pap. 35.00 *(978-1-60983-056-4(3))* International Code Council.
International Code Council & Ghosh, Henry. IBC Handbook Structural Provisions 2009. 2010. (ENG.). pap. 99.95 *(978-1-58001-877-7(7))* International Code Council.
International Code Council Staff. Dwelling Construction under the 2006 International Building Code. 2007. (ENG.). 83p. pap. 36.00 *(978-1-58001-570-7(0))* International Code Council.
—International Mechanical Code & Commentary 2009. 2010. (ENG.). 91.00 *(978-1-58001-903-3(X))* International Code Council.
—International Mechanical Code Commentary 2009. 2010. (ENG.). pap. 91.00 *(978-1-58001-902-6(1))* International Code Council.
—International Property Maintenance Commentary 2009. 2010. (ENG.). pap. 41.00 *(978-1-58001-908-8(0))* International Code Council.
—International Residential Code Commentary 2009, Vols. 1 & 2. 2010. (ENG.). 211.00 *(978-1-58001-910-1(2))* International Code Council.
—International Residential Code Commentery 2009, Vol. 1. 2010. (ENG.). pap. 124.00 *(978-1-58001-912-5(9))* International Code Council.
—2007 Florida Building Code - Building. 2008. (ENG.). 1134p. pap. 127.00 *(978-1-58001-586-8(7))* Delmar Cengage Learning.
—2007 Florida Building Code - Residential. 2008. (ENG.). 866p. ring bd. 103.25 *(978-1-58001-587-5(5))* Delmar Cengage Learning.
International Code Council Staff, creator. International Mechanical Code Commentary 2006. 2007. (ENG., Illus.). 450p. pap. 83.50 *(978-1-58001-484-7(4))* Delmar Cengage Learning.
—International Residential Code for One- & Two-Family Dwellings Vol. 2: Code & Commentary. 2007. (ENG., Illus.). 750p. per. 114.50 *(978-1-58001-482-3(8))* Delmar Cengage Learning.
Ishikawa, Jesse S. & Mullins, Brian W. Drafter's Guide to Wisconsin Condominium Documents. 2nd ed. 2007. pap. *(978-1-57862-206-1(9))* State Bar of Wisconsin.
Kardon, Redwood, et al. Code Check: An Illustrated Guide to Building a Safe House. (Code Check: an Illustrated Guide to Building a Safe House Ser.). (ENG., Illus.). 5th ed. 2007. 30p. spiral bd. 17.95 *(978-1-56158-839-8(3),* Taunton) 6th ed. 2009. 32p. spiral bd. 18.95 *(978-1-60085-045-5(6))* Taunton Pr., Inc.
—Plumbing: An Illustrated Guide to the Plumbing Codes. 3rd ed. 2006. (Code Check Plumbing: a Field Guide to the Plumbing Codes Ser.). (ENG., Illus.). 30p. spiral bd. 17.95 *(978-1-56158-813-8(X),* Taunton) Taunton Pr., Inc.
Mays, Timothy. Guide of Out-of-Plane Wall Anchorage: Based on the 2006/2009 IBC & ASCE/SEI 7-05. 2010. pap. 59.00 *(978-1-58001-989-7(7))* International Code Council.
Merriam, Dwight H. At the Cutting Edge, 2010: Land Use Law from the Urban Lawyer. 2011. *(978-1-61632-823-8(1))* American Bar Assn.
Office of the Federal Register (U.S.), compiled by. Code of Federal Regulations, Title 36, Parks, Forests, & Public Property, Pt. 1-199, Revised as of July 1 2010. rev. ed. 2010. (ENG.). 507p. pap. 42.00 *(978-0-16-086016-4(4),* Office of the Federal Register) United States Government Printing Office.
—Code of Federal Regulations, Title 36, Parks, Forests, & Public Property, Pt. 200-299, Revised as of July 1 2010. rev. ed. 2010. (ENG.). 533p. pap. 39.00 *(978-0-16-086017-1(2),* Office of the Federal Register) United States Government Printing Office.
—Code of Federal Regulations, Title 36, Parks, Forests, & Public Property, Pt. 300-End, Revised as of July 1 2010. rev. ed. 2010. (ENG.). 1054p. pap. 67.00 *(978-0-16-086018-8(0),* Office of the Federal Register) United States Government Printing Office.
Patrick, Lizz. The Annotated Construction Law Glossary. 2010. xxiii, 191p. *(978-1-61632-017-1(6))* American Bar Assn.
Pieczynski, Linda. The Building Official's & Inspector's Guide to Codes, Forms, & Complaints. 2007. (ENG., Illus.). 240p. pap. 34.95 *(978-1-4180-4895-2(X))* Delmar Cengage Learning.
—The Building Process Simplified: A Homeowners & Contractors Guide to Codes, Permits, & Inspections. 2008. (ENG., Illus.). 176p. pap. 34.95 *(978-1-4354-2847-8(1))* Delmar Cengage Learning.
—Residential Inspector's Guide to Codes, Forms, & Complaints. 2008. (ENG.). 256p. pap. 34.95 *(978-1-4283-5159-2(0))* Delmar Cengage Learning.
Underwood, Lynn. Building Code Compliance for Contractors & Inspectors. 2010. *(978-1-57218-238-7(5))* Craftsman Bk. Co.
Van Note, Steve. Residential Inspector's Guide: Building & Energy- Based on the 2012 IRC Chapters 1-33. 2011. spiral bd. 24.95 ***(978-1-60983-167-7(5))*** International Code Council.

BUILDING LEASES

Capital Assets Crisis: Maintaining Federal Real Estate with the Dwindling Federal Building Fund: Hearing Before the Subcommittee on Economic Development, Public Buildings, & Emergency Management of the Committee on Transportation & Infrastructure, House of Representatives, One Hundred Eleventh Congress, Second Session, March 24, 2010. 2010. x, 92p. ***(978-0-16-087006-4(2)***, 552-070-41865-2) United States Government Printing Office.
Too Much for Too Little: Finding the Cost-Risk Balance for Protecting Federal Employees in Leased Facilities: Hearing Before the Subcommittee on Economic Development, Public Buildings, & Emergency Management of the Committee on Transportation & Infrastructure, House of Representatives, One Hundred Eleventh Congress, Second Session, May 20, 2010. 2010. (Illus.). x, 132p. ***(978-0-16-086966-2(8)***, 552-070-41832-6) United States Government Printing Office.
United States, Congress Senate Committee on Veterans' Affairs Staff, contrib. by. Hearing on Construction & Lease Authorization Needs of the Department of Veterans Affairs: Hearing Before the Committee on Veterans' Affairs, One Hundred Ninth Congress, Second Session, April 6, 2006. 2007. iii, 39p. *(978-0-16-078178-0(7),* 552-070-35569-3) United States Government Printing Office.

BUILDING MATERIALS

see also Aggregates (Building Materials); Asbestos; Bituminous Materials; Cement; Ceramics; Concrete; Flooring; Insulating Materials; Plastics; Plastics in Building; Reinforced Concrete; Siding (Building Materials); Steel, Structural; Strength of Materials; Structural Engineering; Tiles; Timber; Wood

Ahmed, Arshad & Sturges, John. Materials Science in Construction: An Introduction. 2013. (ENG.). 416p. pap. 52.95 *(978-1-85617-688-0(6))* Routledge.
Allen, Edward & Iano, Joseph. Exercises in Building Construction. 5th ed. 2008. (ENG., Illus.). 176p. pap. 40.00 *(978-0-470-38100-7(0),* Wiley) Wiley, John & Sons, Inc.
—Fundamentals of Building Construction: Materials & Methods. 5th ed. 2008. (ENG., Illus.). 1008p. 120.00 *(978-0-470-07468-8(X),* Wiley) Wiley, John & Sons, Inc.
Allen, J. R. L. Late Churches & Chapels in Berkshire: A Geological Perspective from the Late Eighteenth Century to the First World War. 2007. (Bar S Ser.). (Illus.). 162p. (C). 90.00 *(978-1-4073-0037-5(7))* British Archaeological Reports Ltd. GBR. Dist: Brown, David Bk. Co., The.
Altenbach, Holm & Eremeyev, Victor A., eds. Shell-like Structures: Non-classical Theories & Applications. 2011. (Advanced Structured Materials Ser.). (Illus.). xi, 750p. 179.00 ***(978-3-642-21854-5(7)***, 3642218547) Springer.
Alternative Framing Materials in Residential Construction: 3 Case Studies. 99p. pap. 45.00 *(978-0-7881-1588-2(X))* DIANE Publishing Co.
Anderson, John. The Strength of Materials & Structures by John Anderson. 2006. 324p. per. 23.99 *(978-1-4255-3160-7(1))* MPublishing.
Aravinthan, Thiru. Futures in Mechanics of Structures & Materials. 2008. (ENG., Illus.). 914p. 349.95 *(978-0-415-49196-9(7),* CRC Press) Taylor & Francis Group GBR. Dist: Taylor & Francis Group.
Baker-Laporte, Paula, et al. Prescriptions for a Healthy House: A Practical Guide for Architects, Builders & Homeowners. 3rd ed. 2008. (ENG., Illus.). 336p. pap. 28.95 *(978-0-86571-604-9(8),* 9780865716049) New Society Pubs., Ltd. CAN. Dist: Consortium Bk. Sales & Distribution.
Benton, W. C., et al. Construction Purchasing & Supply Chain Management. 2009. (ENG., Illus.). 266p. 60.00 *(978-0-07-154885-4(8),* 0071548858) McGraw-Hill Professional Publishing.
Beorkrem, Christopher. Material Strategies in Digital Fabrication. 2012. (ENG., Illus.). 224p. (C). 165.00 ***(978-0-415-53364-5(3))***; pap. 44.95 ***(978-0-415-53366-9(X))*** Routledge.
Berge, Bjorn. The Ecology of Building Materials. 2nd rev. ed. 2009. (ENG., Illus.). 448p. pap. 67.95 *(978-1-85617-537-1(5))* Routledge.
Berman, Alan. Green Design: A Healthy Home Handbook. rev. ed. 2008. (ENG., Illus.). 208p. pap. 24.95 *(978-0-7112-2834-4(5))* Lincoln, Frances Ltd. GBR. Dist: Perseus-PGW.
Beta-Plus, creator. Building with Reclaimed Materials. 2007. (ENG., Illus.). 288p. *(978-90-77213-73-5(2),* Beta-Plus (Acc)) Antique Collectors' Club.
Bevan, Rachel & Woolley, Tom. Hemp Lime Construction: A Guide to Building with Hemp Lime Composites. 2010. (Illus.). 120p. pap. 50.00 *(978-1-84806-033-3(5))* Building Research Establishment GBR. Dist: Taylor & Francis Group.
BIA. Major Building Materials Wholesalers of the World. 6th rev. ed. 2006. 400p. (J). pap. 249.00 *(978-1-4187-4314-7(3))* Business Information Agency.
—Major Concrete Manufacturers. 6th rev. ed. 2006. 400p. (J). pap. 249.00 *(978-1-4187-4287-4(2))* Business Information Agency.
Binggeli, Corky. Materials for Interior Environments. 2007. (ENG., Illus.). 368p. 85.00 *(978-0-470-11428-5(2),* Wiley) Wiley, John & Sons, Inc.
Bingham, Wayne J. & Pfeffer, Jerod. Natural Timber Frame Homes: Building with Wood, Stone, Clay, & Straw. 2007. (ENG., Illus.). 224p. 29.95 *(978-1-58685-860-5(2))* Gibbs Smith, Publisher.
BNI, ed. BNI General Construction 2007 Costbook. 2006. 95.95 *(978-1-55701-561-7(9))* BNI Pubns., Inc.
BNI Building News, creator. Home Builder's Costbook. 15th ed. 2006. (Building News Home Builder's Costbook Ser.). (Illus.). 327p. per. 69.95 *(978-1-55701-566-2(X))* BNI Pubns., Inc.
Bohlin Cywinkski Jackson Architects Staff. Bohlin Cywinski Jackson: The Nature of Circumstance. 2010. (ENG., Illus.). 420p. 95.00 *(978-0-8478-3293-4(7))* Rizzoli International Pubns., Inc.
Borden, G. P. Material Precedent. 2010. (ENG., Illus.). 480p. 85.00 *(978-0-470-47729-8(6),* Wiley) Wiley, John & Sons, Inc.
Borden, Gail Peter & Meredith, Michael, eds. Matter: Material Processes in Architectural Production. 2011. (ENG., Illus.). 520p. (C). 155.00 *(978-0-415-78028-5(4))*; pap. 49.95 *(978-0-415-78029-2(2))* Routledge.
Boshoff, Billy. Advances in Cement-Based Materials: Proc. Int. Conf. Advanced Concrete Materials, 17-19 Nov. 2009, Stellenbosch, South Africa. Van Zijl, Gideon P. A. G., ed. 2009. (ENG.). 300p. (C). 144.95 *(978-0-415-87637-7(0),* CRC Press) Taylor & Francis Group GBR. Dist: Taylor & Francis Group.

Bridgwood, Barry & Lennie, Lindsay. History, Performance & Conservation. 2009. (Technologies of Architecture Ser.). (ENG., Illus.). 352p. (C). 165.00 (978-0-415-43419-5(X)); pap. 49.95 (978-0-415-43420-1(3)) Taylor & Francis Group GBR. (Taylor & Francis). Dist: Taylor & Francis Group.

Broome, Jon. The Green Self-Build Book: How to Design & Build Your Own Eco-Home. 2007. (ENG., Illus.). 256p. per. 50.00 (978-1-903998-73-1(5)) Green Bks. GBR. Dist: Chelsea Green Publishing.

Brownell, Blaine. Material Strategies: Innovative Applications in Architecture. 2011. (ENG.). 160p. pap. 24.95 (978-1-56898-986-0(5)) Princeton Architectural Pr.

Brownell, Blaine. Transmaterial 2: A Catalog of Materials That Redefine Our Physical Environment. 2008. (ENG., Illus.). 248p. pap. 35.00 (978-1-56898-722-4(6)) Princeton Architectural Pr.

Calkins, Meg. Materials for Sustainable Sites: A Complete Guide to the Evaluation, Selection, & Use of Sustainable Construction Materials. 2nd ed. 2008. (ENG., Illus.). 480p. 90.00 (978-0-470-13455-9(0), Wiley) Wiley, John & Sons, Inc.

—Materials for Sustainable Sites & WileyCPE. com Materials for Sustainable Sites Course, Set. 2009. (ENG.). 464p. 99.95 (978-0-470-49038-9(1), Wiley) Wiley, John & Sons, Inc.

Campbell, F. C. Structural Composite Materials. 2010. (Illus.). 630p. 150.00 (978-1-61503-037-8(9)) ASM International.

Chiras, Daniel D. Green Home Improvement. 2008. (RSMeans Ser.: 9). (ENG.). 320p. pap. 34.95 (978-0-87629-093-4(4)) Means, R.S. Co., Inc.

Christiane, Sauer. Made of... New Materials Sourcebook for Architecture & Design. 2010. (Illus.). 280p. 78.00 (978-3-89955-289-8(X)) Die Gestalten Verlag DEU. Dist: Prestel Publishing.

Collings, Janet. The Fixtures & Fittings of Period Houses, 1714 - 1939. 2011. (ENG., Illus.). 240p. 44.95 (978-1-84797-237-8(3)) Crowood Pr., Ltd. GBR. Dist: Independent Pubs. Group.

Cornejo, Donald N. & Haro, Jason L. Building Materials: Properties, Performance & Applications. 2009. (Materials Science & Technologies Ser.). (Illus.). xii, 409p. 98.00 (978-1-60741-082-9(6)) Nova Science Pubs., Inc.

Cram101 Textbook Reviews. Outlines & Highlights for Fundamentals of Building Construction: Materials & Methods by Edward Allen. 2011. 272p. pap. 32.95 (978-1-61906-127-9(9)) Cram101 Inc.

Cram101 Textbook Reviews & Cram101 Textbook Reviews. Outlines & Highlights for Fundamentals of Building Construction by Edward Allen. 2011. 156p. pap. 29.95 (978-1-61830-832-0(7)) Cram101 Inc.

—Outlines & Highlights for Materials for Interior Environments by Corky Binggeli. 2011. 288p. pap. 32.95 (978-1-61830-953-2(6)) Cram101 Inc.

Crawford, Robert. Life Cycle Assessment in the Built Environment. 2011. (ENG., Illus.). 272p. (C). 130.00 (978-0-415-55795-5(X)) Routledge.

Creative Homeowner Press Editors, ed. Roofing. 2nd ed. 2010. (Home Improvement Ser.). (ENG., Illus.). 112p. (gr. 5). pap. 10.95 (978-1-58011-480-6(6)) Creative Homeowner.

Crisinel, Michel, et al, eds. EU COST C13 - Final Report: Glass & Interactive Building Envelopes. 2007. (Research in Architectural Engineering Ser.: Vol. 1). 312p. pap. 82.00 (978-1-58603-709-3(9)) IOS Pr., Inc.

Cristescu, Constantin. Materials with Rheological Properties: Computing of the Structures. 2008. (Iste Ser.: 292). (ENG.). 288p. 174.00 (978-1-84821-012-7(4), Wiley-ISTE) Wiley, John & Sons, Inc.

de Wilde, W. P., et al, eds. High Performance Structure & Materials, 6. 2012. (Illus.). 600p. lib. bdg. 516.00 (978-1-84564-596-0(0)) WIT Pr GBR. Dist: WIT Pr.

de Wilde, W. P., et al, eds. High Performance Structures & Materials V. 2010. (WIT Transactions on the Built Environment Ser.: 112). (Illus.). 608p. 462.00 (978-1-84564-464-2(6)) WIT Pr GBR. Dist: WIT Pr.

Deplazes, Andrea, ed. Constructing Architecture: Materials, Processes, Structures. Söffker, G. H., tr. from GER. 2nd ed. 2008. (Illus.). 555p. pap., instr.'s hdbk. ed. 69.95 (978-3-7643-8631-3(2), 3764386312) Springer.

Didelon, Valery, et al. Rotor Coproduction, 1 vol. 2011. (ENG & FRE.). 80p. pap. 25.00 (978-2-930391-35-9(9)) Centre International Pour La Ville, L'Architecture Et Le Paysage BEL. Dist: Innovative Logistics.

Domone, Peter & Illston, J. M. Construction Materials: Their Nature & Behaviour. 4th rev. ed. 2010. (ENG., Illus.). 584p. (C). 160.00 (978-0-415-46515-1(X), CRC Press) Taylor & Francis Group GBR. Dist: Taylor & Francis Group.

Doran, David K. & Cather, Bob. Construction Materials Reference Book. 2nd rev. ed. 2013. (ENG., Illus.). 768p. 170.00 (978-0-7506-6376-2(6)) Routledge.

Doyle, Sophie G. Construction & Building: Design, Materials, & Techniques. 2010. 155.00 (978-1-61761-211-4(1)) Nova Science Pubs., Inc.

Dvorkin, Leonid, et al. Construction Materials. 2010. (Materials Science & Technologies Ser.). (Illus.). 409p. 195.00 (978-1-61728-693-3(1)) Nova Science Pubs., Inc.

Farrelly, Lorraine. Construction & Materiality. 2009. (Basics Architecture Ser.). (ENG., Illus.). 176p. pap. 29.95 (978-2-940373-83-3(3)) AVA Publishing GBR. Dist: Ingram Pub. Services.

Forde, Mike, ed. ICE Manual of Construction Materials, 2 vols., Vols. I & II. 2009. (Illus.). 928p. (978-0-7277-3597-3(7)) Telford, Thomas Ltd.

Forsyth, Michael. Materials & Skills for Historic Building Conservation. Forsyth, Michael, ed. 2008. (Historic Building Conservation Ser.). (ENG., Illus.). 232p. 99.99 (978-1-4051-1170-6(4), Wiley-Blackwell) Wiley, John & Sons, Inc.

Gagg, Russell. Basics Interior Architecture 05 - Texture + Materials. 2011. (ENG., Illus.). 184p. (C). pap. 34.50 (978-2-940411-53-5(0)) Ava Publishing SA CHE. Dist: Ingram Pub. Services.

Grosse, Christian U., ed. Advances in Construction Materials 2007. (ENG., Illus.). xiv, 784p. 2010. pap. 295.00 (978-3-642-09153-7(9), 3642091539) 2007. 295.00 (978-3-540-72447-6(8), 3540724478) Springer.

Guo, Z., ed. Multiscale materials Modelling: Fundamentals & Applications. 2007. 312p. (978-1-84569-071-7(0)) Woodhead Publishing Ltd.

Hagy, Ference H., ed. Structural Materials & Engineering. 2009. 135.00 (978-1-60692-927-8(5)) Nova Science Pubs., Inc.

Hall, Christopher & Hoff, W. D. Water Transport in Brick, Stone & Concrete. 2nd rev. ed. 2009. (ENG., Illus.). 392p. (C). 170.00 (978-0-415-56467-0(0), CRC Press) Taylor & Francis Group GBR. Dist: Taylor & Francis Group.

Hardt, John. Building Systems Question & Answer 2009. annuals 2008. (ENG.). 48p. pap. 49.95 (978-1-4277-7032-5(8)) Kaplan Publishing.

Harris, Richard. Building a Market: The Rise of the Home Improvement Industry, 1914-1960. 2012. (Historical Studies of Urban America Ser.). (ENG., Illus.). 472p. 45.00 (978-0-226-31766-3(8)) Univ. of Chicago Pr.

Hodge, Brian. Building Your Straw Bale Home: From Foundations to the Roof. 2006. (Landlinks Press Ser.). (Illus.). 280p. pap. 61.95 (978-0-643-09242-6(0)) CSIRO Publishing AUS. Dist: Stylus Publishing, LLC.

Holzman, Malcolm. Stone Work: Designing with Stone. 2006. (Designing with/for Ser.). (ENG., Illus.). 210p. 70.00 (978-1-86470-083-1(1)) Images Publishing Group AUS. Dist: National Bk. Network.

Hornbostel, Caleb & Wertheimer, Lester. Building Design & Construction Systems 2009. 2008. (ENG.). 288p. pap. 111.95 (978-1-4277-7036-3(0)) Kaplan Publishing.

Howe, J. Cullen. The Law of Green Buildings: Regulatory & Legal Issues in Design, Construction, Operations, & Financing. Gerrard, Michael, ed. 2011. (ENG.). 434p. pap. 109.95 (978-1-61632-014-0(1)) American Bar Assn.

Illston, J. M. Construction Materials: Their Nature & Behaviour. Domone, Peter, ed. 4th rev. ed. 2010. (ENG., Illus.). 584p. (C). pap. 62.95 (978-0-415-46516-8(8), CRC Press) Taylor & Francis Group GBR. Dist: Taylor & Francis Group.

Jahren, Per. Concrete: History & Accounts. 2011. 366p. pap. 109.00 (978-82-519-2762-8(5)) Tapir Forlag NOR. Dist: International Specialized Bk. Services.

Jeska, Simone. Transparente Kunststoffe: Technologie und Entwurf. 2007. (Illus.). 159p. 79.95 (978-3-7643-7469-3(1), 3764374691) Birkhauser Boston.

Karbhari, V. M. Durability of composites for civil structural Applications. 2007. 384p. (978-1-84569-035-9(4)) Woodhead Publishing Ltd.

Karbhari, Vistasp M., ed. Durability of Composites for Civil Structural Applications. 2007. (ENG., Illus.). 366p. 309.95 (978-0-8493-9109-5(1), CRC Press) Taylor & Francis Group GBR. Dist: Taylor & Francis Group.

Kaufman JG & McGuire, Michael F. Stainless Steels for Design Engineers. 2008. (Illus.). 304p. (978-0-87170-717-8(9)) ASM International, Inc.

Kellner, Jessica. Housing Relaimed, Sustainable Homes for Next to Nothing. 2011. (ENG., Illus.). 208p. pap. 24.95 (978-0-86571-696-4(X), 9780865716964) New Society Pubs., Ltd. CAN. Dist: Consortium Bk. Sales & Distribution.

Khan, Iqbal Khaleel & H. Abbas. Vulnerability of Low Cost Masonry Buildings to Earthquakes. 2010. 148p. pap. (978-3-8383-7552-6(1)) Lambert Academic Publishing.

Khatib, J., ed. Sustainability of Construction Materials. 2009. (Illus.). 368p. (978-1-84569-349-7(3)) Woodhead Publishing Ltd.

Kinney, Dale & Brilliant, Richard. Reuse Value Erasure: Critical Views on Spolia & Appropriation in Art & Architecture. 2011. (Illus.). 284p. 119.95 (978-1-4094-2422-2(7)) Ashgate Publishing Co.

Klooster, Thorsten & Hochberg, Anette. Smart Surfaces. 2009. (Illus.). 144p. pap. 53.87 (978-3-7643-8812-6(9)) Birkhauser Verlag AG CHE. Dist: Springer.

Komsun, Siripun, et al. Characterisations of Base Course Materials for Flexible Pavements: The Modelling of Unbound Granular Base Course Materials Using Mechanistic Analysis & Design. 2011. 264p. pap. (978-3-639-32314-6(9)) VDM Verlag Dr. Mueller e.K.

Lau, Alan K. T., et al, eds. Multi-Functional Materials & Structures, 2 vols. 2008. (Advanced Materials Research Ser.: Vol. 50). (Illus.). 1612p. pap. (978-0-87849-378-4(6)) Trans Tech Pubns., Ltd.

Leturmy, P. & Robin, C., eds. Limestone in the Built Environment: Present-Day Challenges for the Preservation of the Past. 2010. (Illus.). vi, 257p. (978-1-86239-294-6(3)) Geological Society Publishing Hse.

Levy, Sidney. Construction Databook: Construction Materials & Equipment. 2nd ed. 2010. (ENG., Illus.). 688p. 89.95 (978-0-07-161357-6(9), 0071613579) McGraw-Hill Professional Publishing.

Li, Lijuan. Advances in Building Materials: Selected, Peer-Reviewed Papers from the 2011 International Conference on Structures & Building Materials, (ICSBM 2011), 7-9 January, 2011, Guangzhou, China, 3 vols. 2011. (Illus.). 2625p. pap. (978-0-87849-207-7(0)) Trans Tech Pubns., Ltd.

—Advances in Structures: Selected, Peer-Reviewed Papers from the 2011 International Conference on Structures & Building Materials, (ICSBM 2011), 7-9 January, 2011, Guangzhou, China, 5 vols. 2011. (Illus.). 4200p. pap. (978-0-87849-206-0(2)) Trans Tech Pubns., Ltd.

London, Kerry. Construction Supply Chain Economics. 2007. (Spon Research Ser.). (ENG., Illus.). 480p. (C). 180.00 (978-0-415-40971-1(3)) Routledge.

Loots, Lieven & Degryse, Patrick. Building Materials & Building Techniques at Sagalassos. 2011. (Studies in Eastern Mediterranean Archaeology Ser.). (ENG.). 300p. (C). pap. 128.00 (978-2-503-99113-9(0)) Brepols Pubs. BEL. Dist: Brown, David Bk. Co., The.

Lyons, Arthur. Materials for Architects & Builders. 3rd ed. 2006. (ENG., Illus.). 528p. per. 54.95 (978-0-7506-6940-5(3), Butterworth-Heinemann) Elsevier Science & Technology Bks.

—Materials for Architects & Builders. 4th rev. ed. 2010. (ENG., Illus.). 440p. pap. 56.95 (978-1-85617-519-7(7)) Routledge.

Madge, John. Tomorrows Houses. 2006. 336p. per. (978-1-4067-3470-6(5), Hesperides Pr.) Read Bks.

Mahfuz, Hassan. Nanoparticle Reinforced Composites for Structural Applications. 2011. 250p. 99.00 (978-1-84816-482-6(3)) World Scientific Publishing Co., Inc.

Mahini, Seyed Saeed. Seismic Rehabilitation of RC Beam-Column Joints Using FRPs: An Experimental, Analytical & Numerical Investigation into the Use of Advanced FRP Materials in the Joints of Concrete Structures. 2008. 384p. pap. (978-3-639-03532-2(1)) VDM Verlag Dr. Mueller e.K.

Maiellaro, N., ed. Towards Sustainable Building. 2010. (GeoJournal Library). 265p. pap. 219.00 (978-90-481-5824-9(9), 9048158249) Springer.

Marotta, Theodore, et al. Basic Construction Materials. 8th ed. 2010. (ENG., Illus.). 336p. (C). 94.00 (978-0-13-512969-2(9), Prentice Hall) Prentice Hall PTR.

Meisel, Ari & Princeton Architectural Press Staff. Leed Materials: A Resource Guide to Green Building. 2010. (ENG., Illus.). 224p. pap. 40.00 (978-1-56898-885-6(0)) Princeton Architectural Pr.

Melchers, R. E. & Hough, R., eds. Modeling Complex Engineering Structures. 2007. (Illus.). 384p. 120.00 (978-0-7844-0850-6(5), ASCE Pr.) American Society of Civil Engineers.

Meyhöfer, Dirk, selected by. Magic Metal: Buildings of Steel, Aluminum, Copper & Tin. 2007. (ENG., Illus.). 256p. 49.95 (978-3-938780-31-2(2), Braun Publish,Csi) Continental Sales, Inc.

Min, Christa, et al, eds. Vancouver Matters. 2009. (ENG., Illus.). 176p. pap. 19.95 (978-1-897476-10-9(8)) Simply Read Bks. CAN. Dist: Perseus-PGW.

Moe, Kiel & Princeton Architectural Press Staff. Thermally Active Surfaces in Architecture. 2010. (ENG., Illus.). 240p. 55.00 (978-1-56898-880-1(X)) Princeton Architectural Pr.

Monroe, Steve. Selling to Builders. 2nd ed. 2007. (Illus.). 121p. 27.95 (978-0-86718-631-4(3)) BuilderBooks.

Mouton, Yves. Organic Materials for Sustainable Civil Engineering. 2011. (Iste Ser.: 500). (ENG., Illus.). 688p. 258.00 (978-1-84821-224-4(0), Wiley-ISTE) Wiley, John & Sons, Inc.

Muller, Edward J., et al. Architectural Drawing & Light Construction. 8th ed. 2008. (ENG., Illus.). 792p. (C). 146.00 (978-0-13-513215-9(0), Prentice Hall) Prentice Hall PTR.

Nahar, Nazmun. Implementation of Sustainable Multi-Blended Binders. 2011. 120p. pap. (978-3-8433-8366-0(9)) Lambert Academic Publishing.

Naik. Sustainable Construction Materials & Technologies. 2007. (ENG.). 816p. 259.95 (978-0-415-44689-1(9), Taylor & Francis) Taylor & Francis Group GBR. Dist: Taylor & Francis Group.

Newton, Peter, et al. Technology, Design & Process Innovation in the Built Environment. 2009. (Spon Research Ser.). (ENG., Illus.). 576p. (C). 175.00 (978-0-415-46288-4(6)) Routledge.

Ochshorn, Jonathan. Structural Elements for Architects & Builders: Design of Columns, Beams, & Tension Elements in Wood, Steel, & Reinforced Concrete. 2009. (ENG., Illus.). 400p. 103.00 (978-1-85617-771-9(8), Butterworth-Heinemann) Elsevier Science & Technology Bks.

Ohama, Yoshihiko & Van Gemert, Dionys, eds. Applications of Titanium Dioxide Photocatalysis to Construction Materials: State-of-the-Art Report of the RILEM Technical Committee 194-TDP. 2011. (RILEM State-of-the-Art Reports). (ENG., Illus.). xii, 48p. 129.00 (978-94-007-1296-6(0), 9400712960) Springer.

Ortiz, Oscar, et al. Sustainability Assessment Within the Residential Building Sector. 2010. 160p. pap. (978-3-639-25105-0(9)) VDM Verlag Dr. Mueller e.K.

Pacheco Torgal, Fernando & Jalali, Said. Eco-efficient Construction & Building Materials. 2011. (ENG., Illus.). viii, 247p. 179.00 (978-0-85729-891-1(7), 0857298917) Springer.

Peterson, Chris. Building with Secondhand Stuff: How to Re-Claim, Re-Vamp, Re-Purpose & Re-Use Salvaged & Leftover Building Materials. 2011. (ENG., Illus.). 144p. pap. 19.99 (978-1-58923-662-2(9), 1589236629) Quayside.

Pluvinage, Guy & Sedmak, Aleksandar, eds. Security & Reliability of Damaged Structures & Defective Materials. 2009. (NATO Science for Peace & Security Series C: Environmental Security Ser.). (ENG., Illus.). viii, 418p. pap. 159.00 (978-90-481-2791-7(2), 9048127912); 309.00 (978-90-481-2790-0(4), 9048127904) Springer.

Poikryl, Richard & Török, Akos, eds. Materials, Technologies & Practice in Historic Heritage Structures. 2009. (ENG., Illus.). xvii, 371p. 169.00 (978-90-481-2683-5(5), 9048126835) Springer.

Postell, James (Jim) C. & Gesimondo, Nancy. Materiality & Interior Construction. 2011. (ENG., Illus.). 448p. 80.00 (978-0-470-44544-0(0), Wiley) Wiley, John & Sons, Inc.

Queen, Bill, et al. Green Building & Remodeling - Complete Idiot's Guide. 2009. (Complete Idiot's Guide Ser.). (ENG.). 336p. (gr. 12-18). 19.95 (978-1-59257-828-3(4), Alpha Bks.) Penguin Group (USA) Inc.

R. S. Means Company Staff. Green Building: Project Planning & Cost Estimating. 3rd ed. 2010. (RSMeans Ser.: 24). (ENG., Illus.). 480p. pap. 99.95 (978-0-87629-261-7(9)) Means, R.S. Co., Inc.

Rider, Traci Rose, et al. Understanding Green Building Materials. 2011. (ENG., Illus.). 192p. pap. 24.95 (978-0-393-73317-4(3), 73317) Norton, W. W. & Co., Inc.

Riggs, J. Rosemary. Materials & Components of Interior Architecture. 7th ed. 2007. (ENG., Illus.). 368p. per. 90.73 (978-0-13-158704-5(8), Prentice Hall) Prentice Hall PTR.

Ritter, Axel. Smart Materials: in architektur, innenarchitektur und design. 2006. (Illus.). 191p. 84.93 (978-3-7643-7326-9(1), 3764373261) Birkhauser Boston.

Salazar, Jaime, text. Rhythms, Cycles, Performances: Ceramics in Architecture. 2010. (ENG.). 160p. pap. 39.95 (978-84-613-9405-0(4)) Ico López-Rienda ESP. Dist: Actar Birkhauser Distribution.

Schröpfer, Thomas. Material Design: Informing Architecture by Materiality. 2010. (ENG., Illus.). 216p. 69.95 (978-3-0346-0035-4(6)) Birkhauser Verlag AG CHE. Dist: Actar Birkhauser Distribution.

Siddique, Rafat. Waste Materials & by-Products in Concrete. 2010. (Engineering Materials Ser.). (Illus.). xvi, 414p. pap. 259.00 (978-3-642-09365-4(5), 3642093655) Springer.

Siddique, Rafat & Khan, Mohammad Iqbal. Supplementary Cementing Materials. 2011. (Engineering Materials Ser.). (ENG., Illus.). xv, 350p. 179.00 (978-3-642-17865-8(0), 3642178650) Springer.

Slocombe, Matthew. Traditional Building Materials. 2012. (Shire Library). (ENG., Illus.). 104p. pap. 15.95 (978-0-7478-0840-4(6)) Shire Pubns., Ltd. GBR. Dist: Random Hse., Inc.

Smith, Michael. Building Construction: Methods & Materials for the Fire Science & Resource Central Fire Student Access Code Card Package. 2nd ed. 2011. (ENG.). (C). 72.00 (978-0-13-283007-2(8), Prentice Hall) Prentice Hall PTR.

Smith, Michael. Building Construction: Methods & Materials for the Fire Service. 2nd rev. ed. 2011. (ENG.). 256p. (C). 72.00 (978-0-13-708378-7(5), Prentice Hall) Prentice Hall PTR.

Sovinski, Rob W. Materials & Their Applications in Landscape Design. 2009. (Material in Landscape Architecture & Site Design Ser.: 4). (ENG., Illus.). 208p. 85.00 (978-0-470-11293-9(X), Wiley) Wiley, John & Sons, Inc.

Spence, William P. & Kultermann, Eva. Construction Materials, Methods & Techniques: Building for a Sustainable Future. 3rd ed. 2010. (ENG.). 960p. (C). 176.95 (978-1-4354-8108-4(9)) Delmar Cengage Learning.

Spiegel, Ross & Meadows, Dru. Green Building Materials: A Guide to Product Selection & Specification. 3rd ed. 2010. (ENG., Illus.). 400p. instr.'s gde. ed. 90.00 (978-0-470-53804-3(X), Wiley) Wiley, John & Sons, Inc.

Sprague, Jesse Rainsford. James Read: Building Material Merchant. 2007. (ENG.). 188p. 37.95 (978-0-548-06257-9(9)) Kessinger Publishing, LLC.

Steuteville, Robert, ed. The Directory of the New Urbanism: 2007 Edition. 2007th ed. 2007. 300p. per. 89.00 (978-0-9745021-3-7(8)) New Urban Pubns.

Stoicovici, Dinu Ioan. Screening Critical Humidity Material. 2011. 108p. pap. (978-3-8443-9674-4(8)) Lambert Academic Publishing.

Ternaux, Elodie. Material World 3: Innovative Materials for Architecture & Design. 2011. (ENG., Illus.). 232p. 59.00 (978-90-77174-26-5(5)) Frame Pubs. NLD. Dist: Consortium Bk. Sales & Distribution.

Thomas, Lloyd. Material Matters: Architecture & Material Practice. 2007. (Illus.). 272p. 165.00 (978-0-415-36325-9(X)) Routledge.

The U. S. Market for Green Building Materials. 2006. per. 4250.00 (978-1-59623-225-9(0)) BCC Research.

Uffelen, Van Chris. Fine Fabric: Delicate Materials for Architecture & Interior Design. 2009. (Illus.). 256p. 49.95 (978-3-03768-004-9(0), Braun Publish,Csi) Continental Sales, Inc.

VanDenbergh, Thomas. Optimization at Conceptual Design Stage with Morphological Indicators. 2010. 444p. pap. (978-3-8383-6820-7(7)) Lambert Academic Publishing.

Veer, F., ed. Challenging Glass: Conference on Architectural & Structural Applications of Glass. 2008. 676p. 218.00 (978-1-58603-866-3(4)) IOS Pr., Inc.

Virdi, Surinder Singh. Construction Science & Materials. 2nd ed. 2012. (ENG.). 352p. pap. 39.95 (978-0-470-65888-8(6), Wiley) Wiley, John & Sons, Inc.

Warry, Peter. Tegulae: Manufacture, Typology & Use in Roman Britain. 2006. (Bar S Ser.). (Illus.). 167p. (C). pap. 85.00 (978-1-84171-956-6(0)) British Archaeological Reports Ltd. GBR. Dist: Brown, David Bk. Co., The.

West, Geoffrey D. Architectural Salvage: A Guide to Selecting, Buying & Using Reclaimed Building Materials, 1 vol. 2010. (ENG., Illus.). 160p. 35.00 (978-1-84797-207-1(1)) Crowood Pr., Ltd. GBR. Dist: Independent Pubs. Group.

Wienand, Norman. Materials, Specification & Detailing: Foundations of Building Design. 2008. (Technologies of Architecture Ser.). (ENG., Illus.). 328p. (C). 165.00 (978-0-415-40358-0(8), Taylor & Francis) Taylor & Francis Group GBR. Dist: Taylor & Francis Group.

Wienand, Sean, illus. Materials, Specification & Detailing: Foundations of Building Design. 2008. (Technologies of Architecture Ser.). 309p. per. 45.95 (978-0-415-40359-7(6)) Taylor & Francis Group.

Wilhide, Elizabeth. Materials: A Directory for Home Design. (Illus.). 192p. 34.95 (978-1-84400-042-5(7)) Quadrille Publishing, Ltd. GBR. Dist: Graphic Arts Ctr. Publishing Co.

Wilson, Alex. Green Building Products: The GreenSpec Guide to Residential Building Materials. Malin, Nadav, ed. 3rd ed. 2008. (ENG., Illus.). 352p. pap. 37.95 (978-0-86571-600-1(5), 9780865716001) New Society Pubs., Ltd. CAN. Dist: Consortium Bk. Sales & Distribution.

Wing, Charlie. The Visual Handbook of Building & Remodeling. 3rd ed. 2009. (ENG., Illus.). 640p. pap. 29.95 (978-1-60085-246-6(7)) Taunton Pr., Inc.

Wu, Xingkuan & Xie, Hao, eds. Green Building Technologies & Materials,Proceedings. 2011. 278p. pap. (978-3-03785-091-6(4)) Trans Tech Pubns., Ltd.

Xiao, Yan, et al. Modern Bamboo Structures: Proceedings of First International Conference on Modern Bamboo Structures (ICBS-2007), Changsha, China, 28-30 October 2007. Xiao, Yan et al, eds. 2008. (ENG., Illus.). 312p. 157.95 (978-0-415-47597-6(X), Taylor & Francis) Taylor & Francis Group GBR. Dist: Taylor & Francis Group.

Yu, C W, ed. Durability of Materials & Structures in Building & Civil Engineering. 2006. (Illus.). 462p. 199.95 *(978-0-8493-9239-9(X)*, WH9239) Whittles Publishing GBR. Dist: Taylor & Francis Group.

Zhang, H., ed. Building Materials in Civil Engineering. 2011. (ENG., Illus.). 440p. 245.00 *(978-1-84569-955-0(6))* Woodhead Publishing Ltd. GBR. Dist: Ingram Pub. Services.

Zimmermann, Astrid. Constructing Landscape: Materials, Techniques, Building Elements. 2nd rev. ed. 2011. (ENG., Illus.). 536p. pap. 69.95 *(978-3-0346-0720-9(2))* Birkhauser Verlag AG CHE. Dist: Actar Birkhauser Distribution.

BUILDING MATERIALS—SPECIFICATIONS
see Buildings—Specifications

BUILDING MATERIALS—STANDARDS

Aci, ed. Core Requirements for Nuclear Safety-Related Concrete Structures. 2007. *(978-0-87031-251-9(0))* American Concrete Institute.

—Qualification of Post-Installed Anchors in Concrete & Commentary. 2007. per. *(978-0-87031-247-2(2))* American Concrete Institute.

—Report on Internal & Volume Change Effects on Cracking of Mass Concrete. 2007. *(978-0-87031-258-8(8))* American Concrete Institute.

—Specification for Crack Repair by Epoxy Injection. 2007. per. *(978-0-87031-252-6(9))* American Concrete Institute.

American Institute of Architects. Architectural Graphic Standards for Residential Construction 1. 0 CD-ROM. 2010. (Ramsey/Sleeper Architectural Graphic Standards Ser.: 15). (ENG.). 325.00 *(978-0-470-54134-0(2)*, Wiley) Wiley, John & Sons, Inc.

American Institute of Architects Staff. Architectural Graphic Standards 4. 0 CD-ROM Multi-Seat. 2007. (ENG.). cd-rom 375.00 *(978-0-470-14840-2(3)*, Wiley) Wiley, John & Sons, Inc.

American National Standards Institute Staff, et al, contrib. by. ICC/NSSA Standard for the Design & Construction of Storm Shelters: ICC 500-2008, American National Standard. 2008. (Illus.). x, 42p. 20.00 *(978-1-58001-746-6(0))* International Code Council.

Associacao Portuguesa de Staff. Fire Design of Steel Structures Pts. 1-2: Actions on Structures - Actions on Structures Exposed to Fire Eurocode - Design of Steel Structures - Structural Fire Design. European Convention for Constructional Steelwork Staff, ed. 2010. (ENG., Illus.). 452p. pap. 90.00 *(978-3-433-02974-9(1)*, Wiley-VCH) Wiley, John & Sons, Inc.

ASTM International Staff, contrib. by. ASTM Standards for Whole Building Functionality & Serviceability. 3rd ed. 2009. *(978-0-8031-8006-2(3))* American Society for Testing & Materials.

Bosher, Lee, ed. Hazards & the Built Environment: Attaining Built-in Resilience. 2008. (ENG., Illus.). 400p. (C). 180.00 *(978-0-415-42729-6(0))*; pap. 68.95 *(978-0-415-42730-2(4))* Routledge.

British Standards Institute Staff. Eurocode 3. Design of steel structures. Plated structures subject to out of plane Loading. 40p. pap. 131.00 *(978-0-580-53282-5(8))* Artech Hse., Inc.

Building Code Requirements for Structural Concrete & Commentary (Spanish) 2008. pap. *(978-0-87031-274-8(X))* American Concrete Institute.

Butterworth Staff, compiled by. Butterworths Legislation Service: National Building Regulations & Building Standards Act 103 of 1977. Date not set. *(978-0-409-01440-2(0)*, MICHIE) LEXIS Publishing.

Construction: Concrete & Aggregates, 04.02. 2007. (Annual Book of ASTM Standards Ser.). 928p. 193.00 *(978-0-8031-4108-7(4))* American Society for Testing & Materials.

Cottrell, Michelle. Guide to the LEED AP Building Design & Construction (BD&C) Exam. 2011. (Wiley Series in Sustainable Design Ser.: 20). (ENG., Illus.). 384p. pap. 75.00 *(978-0-470-89042-4(8)*, Wiley) Wiley, John & Sons, Inc.

Doran, Sean. U-Value Conventions in Practice. 2011. (ENG., Illus.). 36p. pap. 44.95 ***(978-1-84806-197-2(8))*** Building Research Establishment GBR. Dist: Taylor & Francis Group.

Fuchs, Manfred. From Legislators to the End-User: Practical Difficulties of Implementing European Directives. 2011. (Illus.). 379p. pap. 59.95 ***(978-3-531-17787-8(7)***, 3531177877) VS Verlag fur Sozialwissenschaften GmbH DEU. Dist: Springer.

Ghosh, S. K. & Henry, John. 2006 IBC Handbook: Structural Provisions. 2007. 93.00 *(978-1-58001-522-6(0))* International Code Council.

Gibbens, Michael. Calcag 2009. 2009. spiral bd. 79.95 *(978-1-58001-783-1(5))* International Code Council.

Guide to the Concrete Capacity Design (CCD) Method: Embedment Design Examples. 2007. *(978-0-87031-263-2(4))* American Concrete Institute.

Gupta, Sachinder. Is That Bridge Safe? Corporate Greed vs. Public Safety. 2010. 280p. pap. 15.49 *(978-1-4490-4471-8(9))* AuthorHouse.

Hall, Dennis J. & Giglio, Nina M. Graphic Standards Field Guide to Residential Construction. 2011. (Graphic Standards Field Guide Ser.: 18). (ENG., Illus.). 496p. pap. 75.00 *(978-0-470-63504-9(5)*, Wiley) Wiley, John & Sons, Inc.

ICC. International Building Code 2009 New Jersey. 2010. ring bd. 135.00 *(978-1-58001-788-6(6))* International Code Council.

—International Residential Code 2009 New Jersey. 2010. ring bd. 109.00 *(978-1-58001-787-9(8))* International Code Council.

—2009 IBC Checklist - Nonstructural. 2010. pap. 39.00 *(978-1-58001-875-3(0))* International Code Council.

—2009 IBC Checklist - Structural. 2010. pap. 59.00 *(978-1-58001-874-6(2))* International Code Council.

—2009 IEBC Q & A. 2010. pap. 40.00 *(978-1-58001-971-2(4))* International Code Council.

International Code Council. International Building Code 2009. 2009. (ENG.). ring bd. 137.00 *(978-1-58001-724-4(X))* International Code Council.

—2009 ICC Performance Code for Buildings & Facilities. 2009. (ENG.). pap. 51.00 *(978-1-58001-736-1(X))* International Code Council.

—2009 International Building Code: Softcover Version. 2009. (ENG.). 1p. pap. 122.00 *(978-1-58001-725-1(8))* International Code Council.

International Code Council Staff. International Energy Conservation Code 2009: 90. 1-2007 Energy Standard for Building Except Low-Rise Residential Buildings. 2009. (ENG.). pap. 147.00 *(978-1-58001-799-2(1))* International Code Council.

International Code Council Staff, contrib. by. Analysis of Changes: 2000 IBC to 2006 IBC. 2007. (Illus.). 164p. 28.00 *(978-1-58001-537-0(9))* International Code Council.

Keller. OSHA Construction Safety Handbook. 6th ed. 2010. (Illus.). 306p. pap. ***(978-1-60287-891-4(9)***, Ohio Univ. Ctr. for International Studies) Keller, J.J. & Assocs., Inc.

Khatib, J. Sustainability of construction Materials. Khatib, J., ed. 2009. (ENG.). 384p. 209.95 *(978-1-4398-0130-7(4)*, CRC Press) Taylor & Francis Group GBR. Dist: Taylor & Francis Group.

Larsen, Hans & Enjily, Vahik. Practical Design of Timber Structures to Eurocode 5. 2009. (Illus.). iv, 268p. *(978-0-7277-3609-3(4))* Telford, Thomas Ltd.

Liu, Feng, et al. Mainstreaming Building Energy Efficiency Codes in Developing Countries: Global Experiences & Lessons from Early Adopters. 2010. (World Bank Working Papers: 204). (ENG., Illus.). 224p. pap. 25.00 *(978-0-8213-8534-0(8)*, 9780821385340) World Bank Pubns.

Mehta, Kishor C. & Coulbourne, William L. Wind Loads: Guide to the Wind Load Provisions of ASCE 7-05. 2010. 163p. pap. 65.00 *(978-0-7844-0858-2(0)*, ASCE Pr.) American Society of Civil Engineers.

Mo. High-Performance Construction Materi. . V1. 2008. 124.00 *(978-981-279-735-3(1))* World Scientific Publishing Co., Inc.

Moore, D., et al. Designers' Guide to en 1991-1-2, en 1993-1-2 & En 1994-1-2: Fire Engineering (Actions on Steel & Composite Structures) 2007. (Illus.). 200p. pap. *(978-0-7277-3157-9(2))* Telford, Thomas Ltd.

Patterson, Terry. Illustrated 2006 Building Code Handbook. 3rd rev. ed. 2006. (ENG., Illus.). 1116p. 125.00 *(978-0-07-145799-6(2)*, 0071457992) McGraw-Hill Professional Publishing.

—Illustrated 2009 Building Code Handbook. 2009. (ENG., Illus.). 1216p. 125.00 *(978-0-07-160618-9(1)*, 0071606181) McGraw-Hill Professional Publishing.

R. S. Means Company Staff. Residential & Light Commercial Construction Standards: The All-in-One, Authoritative Reference Compiled from - Major Building Codes - Recognized Trade Customs - Industry Standards. 3rd ed. 2008. (RSMeans Ser.: 1). (ENG.). 554p. pap. 59.95 *(978-0-87629-012-5(8))* Means, R.S. Co., Inc.

Ramsey, Charles George & Sleeper, Harold Reeve. Architectural Graphic Standards 4.0. American Institute of Architects Staff, ed. 2007. (ENG.). 375.00 *(978-0-470-04323-3(7)*, Wiley) Wiley, John & Sons, Inc.

Report on Measurements of Workability & Rheology of Fresh Concrete. 2008. pap. *(978-0-87031-268-7(5))* American Concrete Institute.

SEAOC. Structural Construction & Special Inspection Manual: A Companion to the 2006 IBC Structural/Seismic Design Manuals. 2009. pap. 59.95 *(978-1-58001-765-7(7))* International Code Council.

Specification for Unbonded Single-Strand Tendon Materials & Commentary. 2007. *(978-0-87031-265-6(0))* American Concrete Institute.

Stafford, T. Eric. Significant Changes to the Wind Load Provisions of ASCE 7-10: An Illustrated Guide. 2010. 160p. pap. 75.00 *(978-0-7844-1116-2(6))* American Society of Civil Engineers.

The American Institute of Architects. Architectural Graphic Standards. Pressman, Andy, ed. 11th rev. ed. 2007. (ENG., Illus.). 1120p. 250.00 *(978-0-471-70091-3(6)*, Wiley) Wiley, John & Sons, Inc.

Thornburg, Doug & International Code Council Staff. 2009 International Building Code Study Companion. 2009. (ENG.). 524p. pap. 59.00 *(978-1-58001-862-3(9))* International Code Council.

Tricker, Ray & Algar, Rozz. Building Regulations in Brief. 4th ed. 2006. (ENG., Illus.). 856p. per. 36.95 *(978-0-7506-8058-5(X)*, Butterworth-Heinemann) Elsevier Science & Technology Bks.

Van Note, Steve. Significant Changes to the International Residential Code 2009. 2009. (ENG.). 304p. pap. 44.95 *(978-1-4354-0122-8(0))* Delmar Cengage Learning.

Winkler, Greg. International Green Construction Code (IGCC) Handbook (GreenSource) 2013. (GreenSource Ser.). (ENG., Illus.). 208p. 60.00 ***(978-0-07-176790-3(8)***, 0071767908) McGraw-Hill Professional Publishing.

BUILDING MATERIALS—TESTING
see also Fire Testing

Desrues, Jacques, et al, eds. Advances in X-Ray Tomography for Geomaterials. 2006. (Iste Ser.: 652). (ENG., Illus.). 452p. 263.00 *(978-1-905209-60-6(6)*, Wiley-ISTE) Wiley, John & Sons, Inc.

Ingham, Jeremy. Geomaterials under the Microscope. 2011. (ENG., Illus.). 192p. 84.95 *(978-1-84076-132-0(6))* Manson Publishing, Ltd. GBR. Dist: Thieme Medical Pubs., Inc.

Volz, Jeffery. The Viability of Partially Post-Tensioned Concrete. 2009. 188p. pap. *(978-3-639-14899-2(1))* VDM Verlag Dr. Mueller e.K.

BUILDING REPAIR
see Buildings—Repair and Reconstruction; Dwellings—Maintenance and Repair

BUILDING RESEARCH
see Building—Research

BUILDING SECURITY
see Buildings—Security Measures; Burglary Protection

BUILDING-SERVICE EMPLOYEES
see also Elevator Operators

Rudman, Jack. Building Services Administrator. (Career Examination Ser.: C-3628). pap. 39.95 *(978-0-8373-3628-2(7))* National Learning Corp.

BUILDING SICKNESS
see Sick Building Syndrome

BUILDING SITES

Alexander, Keith & Price, Ilfryn, eds. Managing Organizational Ecologies: Space, Management, & Organizations. 2012. (ENG., Illus.). 284p. (C). 125.00 *(978-0-415-89699-3(1))* Routledge.

Attali, Erieta & Assonitis, Alessio. Architects' Journeys. 2011. (ENG., Illus.). 160p. 40.00 *(978-1-883584-67-2(1))* Columbia Univ., Graduate Schl. of Architecture.

Banks, Elizabeth C. The Architecture, Settlement, & Stratigraphy of Lerna IV. 2012. (Lerna Ser.). (ENG., Illus.). 400p. (C). 150.00 *(978-0-87661-306-1(7))* American Schl. of Classical Studies at Athens.

Carpenter T.G. Construction in the Landscape: A Handbook for Civil Engineering to Conserve Global Land Resources. 2011. (ENG., Illus.). 544p. 140.00 *(978-1-84407-923-0(6))* Routledge.

Charles, J. Andrew & Watts, K. S. Building on Fill: Geotechnical Aspects. 2nd rev. ed. 2010. (ENG., Illus.). 208p. pap. 135.00 *(978-1-86081-509-6(X))* Building Research Establishment GBR. Dist: Taylor & Francis Group.

Clayden, Andy, et al. Residential Landscape Sustainability: A Checklist Tool. 2007. (ENG., Illus.). 208p. 127.00 *(978-1-4051-5873-2(5)*, Wiley-Blackwell) Wiley, John & Sons, Inc.

Cooke, Brian. Construction Practice. 2011. (ENG., Illus.). 400p. pap. 48.99 *(978-1-4443-3668-9(1)*, Wiley-Blackwell) Wiley, John & Sons, Inc.

Cram101 Textbook Reviews & Cram101 Textbook Reviews. Outlines & Highlights for Site Engineering for Landscape Architects by Steven Strom. 2011. 60p. pap. 26.95 ***(978-1-61830-911-2(0))*** Cram101 Inc.

Dinep, Claudia & Schwab, Kristin. Sustainable Site Design: Criteria, Process, & Case Studies for Integrating Site & Region in Landscape Design. 2009. (ENG., Illus.). 288p. 80.00 *(978-0-470-18783-8(2)*, Wiley) Wiley, John & Sons, Inc.

Elsen, Thomas. To Inhabit a Place. 2006. (ENG & GER., Illus.). 48p. 24.00 *(978-3-936636-75-8(3))* Kehrer Verlag Heidelberg, Klaus Kehrer DEU. Dist: Consortium Bk. Sales & Distribution.

Glaser, Marie Antoinette, ed. Construction Site: Metamorphoses in the City. 2008. (Illus.). 144p. 54.95 *(978-3-03778-112-8(2)*, 3037781122) Springer.

Grissim, John D. The Grissim Buyer's Guide to Manufactured Homes & Land: How to Find a Reputable Dealer & Negotiate a Fair Price on the Best Kept Secret in American Housing. 2nd exp. rev. ed. 2008. Orig. Title: The Complete Buyer's Guide to Manufactured Homes & Land. (Illus.). 192p. per. 29.95 *(978-0-9725436-2-0(7))* Rainshadow Pubns.

Huang, An-Bin & Mayne, Paul W., eds. Geotechnical & Geophysical Site Characterization: Proceedings of the 3rd International Conference on Site Characterization (ISC'3, Taipei, Taiwan, 1-4 April 2008) 2008. (ENG., Illus.). 1516p. 289.95 *(978-0-415-46936-4(8)*, Taylor & Francis) Taylor & Francis Group GBR. Dist: Taylor & Francis Group.

Institute of Transportation Engineers Staff, et al, contrib. by. Promoting Sustainable Transportation Through Site Design: An ITE Recommended Practice. 2010. (Illus.). v, 73p. ***(978-1-933452-54-8(4))*** Institute of Transportation Engineers.

Kavanagh, Barry F. Surveying with Construction Applications. 7th ed. 2009. (ENG.). 704p. (C). 127.40 *(978-0-13-500051-9(3)*, Prentice Hall) Prentice Hall PTR.

Powers, J. Patrick, et al. Construction Dewatering & Groundwater Control: New Methods & Applications. 3rd rev. ed. 2007. (ENG., Illus.). 656p. 195.00 *(978-0-471-47943-7(8)*, Wiley) Wiley, John & Sons, Inc.

Strom, Steven, et al. Site Engineering for Landscape Architects. 5th ed. 2009. (ENG., Illus.). 384p. 95.00 *(978-0-470-13814-4(9))*; 120p. pap., wbk. ed. 35.00 *(978-0-470-13815-1(7))* Wiley, John & Sons, Inc. (Wiley).

Veltkamp, M. Free form structural Design. 2007. pap. 65.00 *(978-1-58603-781-9(1)*, Delft University Pr) IOS Pr., Inc.

Venhaus, Heather L. Designing the Sustainable Site: Integrated Design Strategies for Small Scale Sites & Residential Landscapes. 2012. (ENG.). 256p. pap. 65.00 ***(978-0-470-90009-3(1)***, Wiley) Wiley, John & Sons, Inc.

BUILDING SITES—PLANNING

Ballast, FAIA, NCIDQ-Cert. #9425, David Kent. Site Planning & Design: ARE Sample Problems & Practice Exam. 2nd ed. 2008. (ENG.). 94p. pap. 120.00 *(978-1-59126-154-4(6))* Professional Pubns., Inc.

Brooks, R. Gene & Lestage, David. Before Building: Site Planning in the Digital Age. 2nd ed. 2011. (ENG., Illus.). 312p. (C). pap. 76.40 *(978-0-13-508069-6(X)*, Prentice Hall) Prentice Hall PTR.

Cram101 Textbook Reviews. Outlines & Highlights for Site Analysis by James a Lagro. 2011. 108p. pap. 28.95 ***(978-1-61906-049-4(3))*** Cram101 Inc.

Design Workshop, creator. Toward Legacy. 2007. (ENG., Illus.). 288p. 45.00 *(978-0-9749632-6-6(7))* Spacemaker Pr.

Duggal, Niti. Use of Gis in Retail Location Analysis. 2008. 156p. pap. *(978-3-8364-8586-9(9))* VDM Verlag Dr. Mueller e.K.

Eck, Jeremiah. House in the Landscape: Siting Your Home Naturally. 2010. (ENG., Illus.). 208p. pap. 40.00 *(978-1-56898-823-8(0))* Princeton Architectural Pr.

Gao, Arthur. Residential Landscape. 2011. (ENG., Illus.). 272p. 50.00 *(978-988-19739-4-8(5))* Design Media Publishing Ltd. HKG. Dist: BookMasters Distribution Services (BDS).

International Code Council. Developing Local Green Building Ordinances & Programs. 2007. (ENG.). pap. 22.00 *(978-1-4354-9877-8(1))* Delmar Cengage Learning.

LaGro, James A., Jr. & LaGro, James A. Site Analysis: A Contextual Approach to Sustainable Land Planning & Site Design. 2nd rev. ed. 2007. (ENG., Illus.). 384p. 80.00 *(978-0-471-79798-2(7)*, Wiley) Wiley, John & Sons, Inc.

Littlefair, P. J. Environmental Site Layout Planning: Solar Access, Microclimate & Passive Cooling in Urban Areas. 2010. (ENG., Illus.). 160p. pap. 100.00 *(978-1-86081-339-9(9))* Building Research Establishment GBR. Dist: Taylor & Francis Group.

Mosey, David. Early Contractor Involvement in Building Procurement: Contracts, Partnering & Project Management. 2009. (ENG.). 328p. 124.99 *(978-1-4051-9645-1(9)*, Wiley) Wiley, John & Sons, Inc.

National Association of Home Builders. Green Models for Site Development: Applying the NGBS to Land & Lots. 2010. 98p. pap. 19.95 *(978-0-86718-674-1(7))* BuilderBooks.

Ning, Xin. A Construction Site Layout Planning Decision-Making System. 2010. 336p. pap. *(978-3-639-22792-5(1))* VDM Verlag Dr. Mueller e.K.

Russ, Thomas & Russ, Thomas H. Site Planning & Design. 2nd ed. 2009. (ENG., Illus.). 528p. instr.'s hndbk. ed. 99.95 *(978-0-07-160558-8(4)*, 0071605584) McGraw-Hill Professional Publishing.

Speiregen, Paul & Wertheimer, Lester. Site Planning & Design 2009. 2008. (ENG.). 192p. pap. 111.95 *(978-1-4277-7041-7(7))* Kaplan Publishing.

Winch, Graham M. Managing Construction Projects. 2nd ed. 2010. (ENG., Illus.). 544p. pap. 67.99 *(978-1-4051-8457-1(4)*, Wiley-Blackwell) Wiley, John & Sons, Inc.

BUILDING SOCIETIES
see Savings and Loan Associations

BUILDING STANDARDS
see Building Materials—Standards; Standards, Engineering

BUILDING STONES
see also Masonry; Quarries and Quarrying

Ballard, Julia P. (Julia Perkins). Building Stones. 2006. 264p. per. 23.99 *(978-1-4255-2347-3(1))* MPublishing.

Doehne, Eric Ferguson, et al. Stone Conservation: An Overview of Current Research. 2nd ed. 2011. 164p. pap. 35.00 *(978-1-60606-046-9(5)*, Getty Conservation Institute, The) Getty Pubns.

Emery, Sean. ASTM Standards & Technical Material for Dimension Stone. 2010. *(978-0-8031-8409-1(3))* American Society for Testing & Materials.

Estaire. Preservation of Natural Stone & Rock Weathering. 2007. (ENG.). 228p. (C). pap. 129.95 *(978-0-415-45018-8(7)*, Taylor & Francis) Taylor & Francis Group GBR. Dist: Taylor & Francis Group.

Henry, Alison. Stone Conservation: Principles & Practice. 2006. (Illus.). 352p. *(978-1-873394-78-6(0))* Donhead Publishing Ltd.

Klemm, Dietrich & Klemm, Rosemarie. The Stones of the Pyramids: Provenance of the Building Stones of the Old Kingdom Pyramids of Egypt. 2010. (ENG.). 167p. 98.00 *(978-3-11-022123-7(3))* De Gruyter, Walter Inc.

Kourkoulis, Stavros K., ed. Fracture & Failure of Natural Building Stones: Applications in the Restoration of Ancient Monuments. 2010. xvi, 592p. pap. 249.00 *(978-90-481-7276-4(4)*, 9048172764) Springer.

—Fracture & Failure of Natural Building Stones: Applications in the Restoration of Ancient Monuments. 2006. (Illus.). xvi, 592p. 249.00 *(978-1-4020-5076-3(3)*, 1402050763) Springer.

Marmo Studio Staff. Fine Marble in Architecture. Date not set. (Illus.). 192p. *(978-0-393-10411-0(7))* Norton, W. W. & Co., Inc.

Price, Monica. The Sourcebook of Decorative Stone: An Illustrated Identification Guide. 2007. (ENG., Illus.). 288p. 39.95 *(978-1-55407-254-5(9))* Firefly Bks., Ltd.

Prikryl, R. & Torok, A., eds. Natural Stone Resources for Historical Monuments. 2010. (Illus.). 256p. *(978-1-86239-291-5(9))* Geological Society Publishing Hse.

Siegesmund, Siegfried & Snethlage, Rolf, eds. Stone in Architecture: Properties, Durability. 4th ed. 2011. (ENG., Illus.). xii, 552p. 229.00 *(978-3-642-14474-5(8)*, 3642144748) Springer.

Smith, Bernard, et al. Natural Stone in the Built Environment. 2012. (ENG.). 300p. (C). 99.95 *(978-0-415-54849-6(7)*, CRC Press) Taylor & Francis Group GBR. Dist: Taylor & Francis Group.

Studio Marmo Staff & Campagna, Marco. Stone Sampler. 2nd ed. 2008. (ENG., Illus.). 132p. pap. 55.00 *(978-0-393-73265-8(7)*, 73265) Norton, W. W. & Co., Inc.

Thiel, George A. & Dutton, Carl E. The Architectural, Structural & Monumental Stones of Minnesota. (Illus.). 16p. reprint ed. lib. bdg. 88.00 *(978-0-7222-0530-3(9))* Library Reprints, Inc.

BUILDING SUPERINTENDENCE
see Building—Superintendence

BUILDING TRADES
see also Building; Construction Industry
also Bricklayers, Carpenters, and similar headings

Arayici, Yusuf & Aouad, Ghassan. Requirements Engineering for Computer Integrated Environments in Construction. 2010. (ENG., Illus.). 256p. 134.99 *(978-1-4051-8945-3(2)*, Wiley-Blackwell) Wiley, John & Sons, Inc.

Banfield, John Anthony. My Life, My Times, My Poems. 2009. (Illus.). 416p. 28.49 *(978-1-4389-4999-4(5))*; pap. 17.99 *(978-1-4389-5000-6(4))* AuthorHouse.

B

Braundy, Marcia. Men & Women & Tools: Bridging the Divide. 2012. (Fernwood Basics Ser.). 128p. pap. 17.95 ***(978-1-55266-448-3(1))*** Fernwood Publishing Co., Ltd. CAN. Dist: Independent Pubs. Group.

Breslin, Mark. Survival of the Fittest: How the Future of Union Consturction Depends on Every Journeyman, Evrey Apprentice & You. 2009. (SPA., Illus.). 176p. pap. 19.95 *(978-0-9741662-7-8(8))* McAlly International Pr.

Golland, David Hamilton. Constructing Affirmative Action: The Struggle for Equal Employment Opportunity. 2011. (Civil Rights & the Struggle for Black Equality in the Twentieth Century Ser.). (ENG., Illus.). 280p. 50.00 *(978-0-8131-2997-6(4))* Univ. Pr. of Kentucky.

Leung, Jenny Kwai-Sim & James, Kieran. Sydney's Construction Union Strategy & Immigrant Worker Issues: A Roman Catholic-Marxist Perspective. 2010. 132p. *(978-1-926635-40-8(X))* Adlibbed, Ltd.

Marchand, Trevor. Minaret Building & Apprenticeship in Yemen. 2012. (ENG.). 285p. (C). pap. 39.95 ***(978-0-415-69544-2(9))*** Routledge.

Moccio, Fran. Live Wire: Women & Brotherhood in the Electrical Industry. 2010. (ENG., Illus.). 288p. pap. 28.95 *(978-1-59213-738-1(5))* Temple Univ. Pr.

Moccio, Francine A. Live Wire: Women & Brotherhood in the Electrical Industry. 2009. (ENG., Illus.). 288p. 61.50 *(978-1-59213-737-4(7))* Temple Univ. Pr.

Montelongo, Paul. Be A Big Sales Magnet to Builders. 2007. pap. 49.00 *(978-0-9776910-5-0(5))* Executive Business Pr.

National Association of Home Builders (U.S.) Staff, contrib. by. Profit Building Principles: Business Management Strategies for Home Builders from Start-Up to Growth. 2011. ***(978-0-86718-677-2(1))*** BuilderBooks.

NCCER. Construction Technology Trainee Guide, Hard Cover. 3rd ed. 2009. (ENG.). 936p. (C). 186.67 *(978-0-13-609951-2(3)*, Prentice Hall) Prentice Hall PTR.

—Core Curriculum Trainee Guide 2009 Revision, Hardcover. 4th ed. 2009. (ENG.). 504p. (C). 69.33 *(978-0-13-608636-9(5)*, Prentice Hall) Prentice Hall PTR.

—Core Curriculum Trainee Guide, Paperback 2009. 4th ed. 2009. (ENG.). 504p. (C). pap. 65.33 *(978-0-13-608637-6(3)*, Prentice Hall) Prentice Hall PTR.

Palladino, Grace. Skilled Hands, Strong Spirits: A Century of Building Trades History. 2007. (Illus.). 274p. per. 21.00 *(978-0-8014-7414-9(0)*, ILR Pr.) Cornell Univ. Pr.

Price, Richard. Masters, Unions & Men: Work Control in Building & the Rise of Labour 1830-1914. 2008. (ENG.). 368p. pap. 48.00 *(978-0-521-07871-9(7))* Cambridge Univ. Pr.

Tomasini, Emilio & Jaekle, Urban. Trading Systems: A New Approach to System Optimisation & Portfolio Construction. 2009. (ENG., Illus.). 196p. pap. 34.99 *(978-1-905641-79-6(6))* Harriman Hse. Publishing GBR. Dist: Ingram Pub. Services.

BUILDING TRADES—ACCOUNTING

see Construction Industry—Accounting

BUILDING TRADES—VOCATIONAL GUIDANCE

Harvey, Bethany. Careers in Construction. 2006. (ENG., Illus.). 80p. (C). pap. 20.00 *(978-0-13-228605-3(X))* Prentice Hall PTR.

Kaye, Frances & Ross, Tanya. Snakes & Ladders for Property Professionals: How to Be a Smooth Operator in the Property Industry. 2007. (ENG.). 300p. pap. 48.95 *(978-0-7282-0503-1(3))* Estates Gazette, Ltd. GBR. Dist: Taylor & Francis Group.

NCCER. CIAP Careers in Construction for Careers in Construction. 2008. (C). pap. 22.67 *(978-0-13-610778-1(8)*, Prentice Hall) Prentice Hall PTR.

—Phelps Careers Custom for Careers in Construction. 2008. (C). pap. 21.33 *(978-0-13-610854-2(7)*, Prentice Hall) Prentice Hall PTR.

Sumichrast, Michael & Davitaia, David. Opportunities in Building Construction Careers. 3rd ed. 2007. (ENG.). 160p. per. 14.95 *(978-0-07-148205-9(9)*, 0071482059) McGraw-Hill Cos., The.

BUILDINGS

Here are entered general works on structures or edifices. Works on the design and style of structures are entered under Architecture. Works on the process of construction are entered under Building.

see also Architecture; Basements; Casinos; Commercial Buildings; Dwellings; Farm Buildings; Garages; Garden Structures; Historic Buildings; Industrial Buildings; Joint Occupancy of Buildings; Lofts; Motion Picture Studios; Palaces; Pavilions; Public Buildings; Rooms; Solar Buildings; Sustainable Buildings; Tall Buildings; Towers; Wooden-Frame Buildings

also subdivision Buildings, Structutes, etc. under names of cities; and names of individual buildings

Abramenko, Peter & Brown, Kenneth A. Buildings: Theory & Applications. 2008. (Graduate Texts in Mathematics Ser.: Vol. 251). (Illus.). 794p. 69.95 *(978-0-387-78834-0(4))* Springer.

Abramenko, Peter & Brown, Kenneth S. Buildings: Theory & Applications. 2010. (Graduate Texts in Mathematics Ser.). (Illus.). xxii, 754p. pap. 69.95 *(978-1-4419-2701-9(8)*, 1441927018) Springer.

ABSALOM, B. E. N. & BARDSLEY, S. A. M. 8 X's, 1 vol. 2011. (ENG., Illus.). 96p. 88.00 ***(978-3-86930-341-3(7))*** Steidl, Gerhard Druckerei und Verlag DEU. Dist: Innovative Logistics.

Allenby, Guy. Elements: The Heart of the City. Law, Erica, tr. 2010. (ENG., Illus.). 160p. 50.00 *(978-0-9814628-9-9(8))* Oro Editions.

Aouad, Ghassan, et al. Constructing the Future: ND Modelling. 2006. (ENG., Illus.). 432p. 175.00 *(978-0-415-39171-9(7))* Routledge.

Ashley, Peter. Cross Country: English Buildings & Landscape from Countryside to Coast. 2011. (ENG.). 240p. 45.00 *(978-0-470-68611-9(1)*, Wiley) Wiley, John & Sons, Inc.

Bamonte, Tony G. & Bamonte, Suzanne Schaeffer. Spokane, Our Early History: Under All Is the Land. 2011. (Illus.). 320p. 29.95 ***(978-0-9821529-3-5(0))*** Tornado Creek Pubns.

Baroth, J. Construction Reliability. 2011. (Iste Ser.: 506). (ENG., Illus.). 368p. 130.00 ***(978-1-84821-230-5(5)***, Wiley-ISTE) Wiley, John & Sons, Inc.

Barrett, Peter. Revaluing Construction. Barrett, Peter, ed. 2007. (ENG., Illus.). 296p. 154.99 *(978-1-4051-5919-7(7)*, Wiley-Blackwell) Wiley, John & Sons, Inc.

Bennett, Mark J., et al. Current Critical Issues in Environmental Law: Green Buildings & Sustainable Development. 2008. (Illus.). xii, 54p. pap. *(978-1-4224-2453-7(7))* LexisNexis Matthew Bender.

Berke, Kai-Lee, et al. The Creative Curriculum for Preschool Teaching Guide Featuring the Buildings Study. 2010. *(978-1-60617-384-8(7))* Teaching Strategies, Inc.

—El Currículo Creativo para Educación Preescolar Guía de Enseñanza Estudio de Los Edificios. 2012. (SPA & ENG.). *(978-1-60617-411-1(8))* Teaching Strategies, Inc.

Bettley, James & Pevsner, Nikolaus. Essex: The Buildings of England. Pevsner, Nikolaus, ed. 2007. (Pevsner Architectural Guides). (ENG., Illus.). 960p. 85.00 *(978-0-300-11614-4(4))* Yale Univ. Pr.

Bingham-Hall, Patrick, et al. Recent Malaysian Architecture. Bingham-Hall, Patrick, ed. 2007. (ENG., Illus.). 160p. *(978-1-877015-19-9(9))* Pesaro Publishing.

Bokmiller, Don, et al. Mastering Autodesk Revit MEP 2011. 2010. (ENG., Illus.). 624p. pap. 69.99 *(978-0-470-62637-5(2)*, Sybex) Wiley, John & Sons, Inc.

Bounds, William, ed. Design of Blast-Resistant Buildings in Petrochemical Facilities. 2nd ed. 2010. 300p. pap. 110.00 *(978-0-7844-1088-2(7))* American Society of Civil Engineers.

Bower, John & Bower, Lynn. The Common Good: An Indiana heritage built with taxes, tithes, & Tuition. 2010. pap. 22.00 *(978-0-9745186-6-4(2))* Studio Indiana.

Brooks, Alan & Pevsner, Nikolaus. Worcestershire: The Buildings of England. 2007. (Pevsner Architectural Guides). (Illus.). 848p. 85.00 *(978-0-300-11298-6(X))* Yale Univ. Pr.

Brown, Dan. Bath Then & Now. 2012. (Then & Now Ser.). (ENG., Illus.). 96p. 23.95 ***(978-0-7524-6639-2(9))*** History Pr. Ltd.,The GBR. Dist: Independent Pubs. Group.

Brown, M.E. A Man of No Taste Whatsoever: Joseph Pocklington 1736-1817. 2010. (Illus.). 72p. pap. 24.99 *(978-1-4490-6438-9(8))* AuthorHouse.

Brown, Stewart J. Derelict Britain. 2012. (ENG., Illus.). 128p. 32.95 *(978-0-7110-3513-3(X))* Allan, Ian Publishing GBR. Dist: BookMasters Distribution Services (BDS).

Bruckner, Dietmar. Probabilistic Models in Building Automation. 2008. 144p. per. *(978-3-8364-5720-0(2))* VDM Verlag Dr. Mueller e.K.

Building Green, Saving Green: Constructing Sustainable & Energy-Efficient Buildings: Hearing Before the Select Committee on Energy Independence & Global Warming, House of Representatives, One Hundred Tenth Congress, Second Session, May 14, 2008. 2010. (Illus.). iii, 144p. ***(978-0-16-087419-2(X)***, 552-070-42112-2) United States Government Printing Office.

Carpenter T.G. Construction in the Landscape: A Handbook for Civil Engineering to Conserve Global Land Resources. 2011. (ENG., Illus.). 544p. 140.00 *(978-1-84407-923-0(6))* Routledge.

Cattermole, Paul & Westwell, Ian. Bizarre Buildings. 2007. (ENG., Illus.). 224p. 40.00 *(978-1-55407-308-5(1))* Firefly Bks., Ltd.

Ceulemans, Hadewijch. Belgium's Best Buildings. 2012. (ENG., Illus.). 160p. pap. 24.95 ***(978-94-6058-081-9(5)***, Uitgeverij Luster) Antique Collectors' Club GBR. Dist: National Bk. Network.

Chacon, Hipolitao Rafael. Original Man. 2008. pap. 35.00 *(978-0-9815760-0-8(1))* Farcountry Pr.

Co, Atlantic Publishing. The Complete Guide to Building Classic Barns, Fences, Storage Sheds, Animal Pens, Outbuildings, Greenhouses, Farm Equipment, & Tools: A Step-by-Step Guide to Building Everything You Might Need on a Small Farm. 2012. (ENG.). 288p. pap. 29.95 *(978-1-60138-372-3(X))* Atlantic Publishing Co.

Cook, N. J. Designers' Guide to en 1991-1. 4 Eurocode 1: Wind Actions. 2007. (Illus.). 112p. *(978-0-7277-3152-4(1))* Telford, Thomas Ltd.

Cormie, David, et al, eds. Blast Effects on Buildings: Second Edition. 2nd ed. 2009. (Illus.). 356p. *(978-0-7277-3521-8(7))* Telford, Thomas Ltd.

Cottrell, Michelle. Guide to the Leed AP Operations & Maintenance (O+M) Exam. 2011. (Wiley Series in Sustainable Design Ser.: 18). (ENG., Illus.). 336p. pap. 75.00 *(978-0-470-60830-2(7)*, Wiley) Wiley, John & Sons, Inc.

Coulthard, Sally. Shed Chic: Outdoor Buildings for Work, Rest, & Play. 2009. (ENG., Illus.). 208p. 35.00 *(978-0-7893-1860-2(1))* Universe Publishing.

Cruickshank, Dan. Adventures in Architecture. (ENG., Illus.). 2009. 392p. pap. 14.95 *(978-0-7538-2416-0(7)*, Phoenix) 2008. 288p. 29.95 *(978-0-297-84444-0(X)*, Weidenfeld & Nicolson) Orion Publishing Group, Ltd. GBR. Dist: Sterling Publishing Co., Inc.

Cruzan, Ryan. Manager's Guide to Preventive Building Maintenance. 2009. (ENG.). 300p. 98.00 *(978-1-4398-1431-4(7))* CRC Pr. LLC.

Designing Quality Buildings: A BRE Guide. 2010. (ENG., Illus.). 360p. 110.00 ***(978-1-86081-899-8(4))*** Building Research Establishment GBR. Dist: Taylor & Francis Group.

Dowdle, David, et al, eds. Architectural Engineering & Design Management: Teaching & Learning Building Design & Construction. 2006. (Architectural Engineering & Design Management Ser.). (ENG., Illus.). 160p. per. 94.95 *(978-1-84407-330-6(0))* Routledge.

Dubuque Yesterday & Today. 2008. (Illus.). iv, 156p. ***(978-0-9761125-8-7(2))*** Telegraph Herald.

Fanella, David A. Reinforced Concrete Structures: Analysis & Design. 2010. (ENG., Illus.). 652p. 125.00 *(978-0-07-163834-0(2)*, 0071638342) McGraw-Hill Professional Publishing.

George, Charles & George, Linda. Seminole. 2012. (Images of America Ser.). (ENG., Illus.). 128p. pap. 21.99 ***(978-0-7385-8539-0(4))*** Arcadia Publishing.

Ghosh, S. K., et al. Significant Changes to the Seismic Load Provisions of ASCE 7-10: An Illustrated Guide. 2010. (ENG.). 192p. pap. 85.00 *(978-0-7844-1117-9(4))* American Society of Civil Engineers.

Gössi, Anton, et al. Archivbauten in der Schweiz und Im Fürstentum Liechtenstein 1899-2009. 2007. (FRE & GER., Illus.). 251p. pap. *(978-3-03919-047-8(4))* Hier + Jetzt Pubs.

Greenberg, Stanley. Architecture under Construction. 2010. (ENG., Illus.). 120p. 45.00 *(978-0-226-30642-1(9))* Univ. of Chicago Pr.

Greider, Katharine. The Archaeology of Home: An Epic Set on a 1000 Square Feet of the Lower East Side. 2011. (ENG., Illus.). 352p. 26.99 *(978-1-58648-712-6(4))* PublicAffairs.

Grenier, Bob. Tavares. 2012. (Images of America Ser.). (ENG., Illus.). 128p. pap. 21.99 ***(978-0-7385-9107-0(6))*** Arcadia Publishing.

Haga, Dan. Urban Atrophy. 2011. (Illus.). 176p. 39.99 *(978-0-7643-3738-3(6)*, Schiffer Publishing Ltd) Schiffer Publishing, Ltd.

Hassan, Osama A. B. Train-Induced Groundborne Vibration & Noise in Buildings. 2008. (ENG., Illus.). 537p. pap. 145.00 *(978-0-906522-43-1(9))* Multi Science Publishing Co., Ltd. GBR. Dist: Independent Pubs. Group.

Holmes, John D. Wind Loading of Structures. 2nd rev. ed. 2007. (ENG., Illus.). 392p. (C). 200.00 *(978-0-415-40946-9(2)*, CRC Press) Taylor & Francis Group GBR. Dist: Taylor & Francis Group.

ICC/New York. Property Maintenance Code of New York State, 2010 Edition. 2010. pap. 31.00 *(978-1-60983-007-6(5))* International Code Council.

Jackson, W. P. Estimating Home Building Costs Revised. 2010. (Illus.). 304p. pap. 38.00 *(978-1-57218-205-9(9))* Craftsman Bk. Co.

Jenner, Michael & Morris, Stephen. Bristol's 100 Best Buildings. 2010. (Illus.). 160p. *(978-1-906593-61-2(2))*; *(978-1-906593-67-4(1))* Redcliffe Pr., Ltd.

Kachroo, Pushkin. Pedestrian Dynamics: Feedback Control of Crowd Evacuation. 2008. (Understanding Complex Systems Ser.). (Illus.). 251p. 139.00 *(978-3-540-75559-3(4))* Springer.

Kachroo, Pushkin, et al. Pedestrian Dynamics: Feedback Control of Crowd Evacuation. 2010. (Understanding Complex Systems Ser.). xiv, 246p. pap. 139.00 *(978-3-642-09478-1(3)*, 3642094783) Springer.

Kaelin, Susan. Fife. 2012. (Images of America Ser.). (ENG., Illus.). 128p. pap. 21.99 ***(978-0-7385-8894-0(6))*** Arcadia Publishing.

Kiib, Hans, ed. Performative Urban Design. 2010. (Illus.). 242p. 54.95 *(978-87-7307-982-9(0))* Aalborg Universitetsforlag DNK. Dist: International Specialized Bk. Services.

King, Robert Arthur. Animals in Stone: Architectural Sculpture in New York City. 2009. (ENG., Illus.). 144p. 24.95 *(978-0-393-73286-3(X)*, 73286) Norton, W. W. & Co., Inc.

Kroloff, Reed. Building Community: The Work of Eskew + Dumez + Ripple. 2011. (ENG., Illus.). 220p. 65.00 *(978-0-9826226-2-9(7))* Oro Editions.

Kuhl, Isabel. 50 Buildings You Should Know. 2007. (Illus.). 176p. pap. 19.95 *(978-3-7913-3838-5(2))* Prestel Publishing.

Lau, Alan K. T., et al, eds. Multi-Functional Materials & Structures, 2 vols. 2008. (Advanced Materials Research Ser.: Vol. 50). (Illus.). 1612p. pap. *(978-0-87849-378-4(6))* Trans Tech Pubns., Ltd.

Leach, Peter & Pevsner, Nikolaus. Yorkshire West Riding: Leeds, Bradford & the North. 2009. (Pevsner Architectural Guides). (Illus.). 800p. 85.00 *(978-0-300-12665-5(4))* Yale Univ. Pr.

Mackenzie, Fiona. Energy Efficiency in New & Existing Buildings: Comparative costs & CO2 Savings. 2011. (ENG., Illus.). 32p. pap. 50.95 *(978-1-84806-137-8(4))* Building Research Establishment GBR. Dist: Taylor & Francis Group.

Mallory-Hill, Shauna, et al. Enhancing Building Performance. 2nd ed. 2012. (ENG., Illus.). 360p. pap. 115.00 ***(978-0-470-65759-1(6)***, Wiley-Blackwell) Wiley, John & Sons, Inc.

Marchand, Yves & Meffre, Romain, photos by. The Ruins of Detroit, 1 vol. 2011. (ENG., Illus.). 200p. 125.00 *(978-3-86930-042-9(6))* Steidl, Gerhard Druckerei und Verlag DEU. Dist: Innovative Logistics.

Markon, Sandor A., et al. Control of Traffic Systems in Buildings. 2010. (Advances in Industrial Control Ser.). (Illus.). xxii, 279p. pap. 179.00 *(978-1-84996-604-7(4)*, 1849966044) Springer.

Mehta, Kishor C. & Coulbourne, William L. Wind Loads: Guide to the Wind Load Provisions of ASCE 7-05. 2010. 163p. pap. 65.00 *(978-0-7844-0858-2(0)*, ASCE Pr.) American Society of Civil Engineers.

Mitchell, William Ford. Buildings As History: A Descriptive Catalogue of His Drawings in the Henderson County Public Library: the Architecture of Erle Stillwell. 2006. per. *(978-0-9790753-1-5(9))* Friends of the Henderson County Public Library.

—Builtings as History: A Descriptive Catalogue of His Drawings in the Henderson County Public Library: the Architecture of Erle Stillwell. 2006. *(978-0-9790753-0-8(0))* Friends of the Henderson County Public Library.

Moe, Kiel & Princeton Architectural Press Staff. Thermally Active Surfaces in Architecture. 2010. (ENG., Illus.). 240p. 55.00 *(978-1-56898-880-1(X))* Princeton Architectural Pr.

Moore, Andrew, photos by & text. Andrew Moore: Detroit Disassembled, 1 vol. 2010. (ENG., Illus.). 136p. 50.00 *(978-88-6208-118-4(9))* Damiani ITA. Dist: D.A.P./Distributed Art Pubs.

Momement, Adam. Boathouses. 2010. (ENG., Illus.). 176p. 50.00 *(978-0-7112-2868-9(X))* Lincoln, Frances Ltd. GBR. Dist: Perseus-PGW.

Navigating Green Construction & Energy Initiatives: Government Officials on Responding to LEED Standards, Promoting Sustainable Building Practices, & Improving Energy Efficiency (Inside the Minds) 2009. 148p. pap. 80.00 *(978-0-314-90416-4(6))* Aspatore Bks.

Newman & Pevsner, Nikolaus. West Kent & the Weald. 2nd rev. ed. (Illus.). 688p. 50.00 *(978-0-14-071038-0(8))* Penguin Bks., Ltd. GBR. Dist: Trafalgar Square Publishing.

Newman, John. Glamorgan. (Illus.). 720p. 65.00 *(978-0-14-071056-4(6))* Penguin Bks., Ltd. GBR. Dist: Trafalgar Square Publishing.

Newman, John & Pevsner, Nikolaus. Shropshire. 2006. (Pevsner Architectural Guides). (ENG., Illus.). 787p. 85.00 *(978-0-300-12083-7(4))* Yale Univ. Pr.

O'Corra, Simon. France in Ruins - Buildings in Decay. 2011. (ENG.). 144p. (C). pap. 39.95 *(978-1-906137-23-6(4))* Golden Hse. Pubns. GBR. Dist: Brown, David Bk. Co., The.

Olmert, Michael. Kitchens, Smokehouses, & Privies. 2009. (Illus.). 208p. 27.95 *(978-0-8014-4791-4(7))* Cornell Univ. Pr.

Ormsbee, Renee Richmond Huntley & Ormsbee, Thomas H. If You're Going to Live in the Country. 2008. 188p. 25.99 *(978-0-554-26522-3(2))* 2008. 188p. 22.99 *(978-0-554-35825-3(5))* 2007. (ENG.). 164p. pap. 19.99 *(978-1-4346-1304-2(6))* 2007. (ENG.). 184p. pap. 21.99 *(978-1-4346-1356-1(9))* BiblioBazaar.

Ormsbee, Thomas H. & Huntley, Richmond. If You're Going to Live in the Country: Achieving Your Rural American Dream. 2008. 152p. pap. 13.95 *(978-1-4357-4334-2(2))* Lulu Enterprises Inc.

Parkyn, Neil. Superstructures: The World's Greatest Modern Structures. rev. ed. (Illus.). 192p. *(978-1-85894-238-4(1))* Merrell Pubs. Ltd.

Paterson, Nigel McCullagh. The Vernacular Architecture & Buildings of Stroud & Chalford. 2006. (Illus.). 344p. per. 33.91 *(978-1-4120-9951-6(X))* Trafford Publishing.

Pevsner, Nikolaus. Bedfordshire, Huntingdon Peterborough. (Illus.). 414p. pap. 45.00 *(978-0-14-071034-2(5))* Penguin Bks., Ltd. GBR. Dist: Trafalgar Square Publishing.

—Buildings of England: Norwich & Northeast. 2nd ed. (Illus.). 800p. 65.00 *(978-0-14-071058-8(2))* Penguin Bks., Ltd. GBR. Dist: Trafalgar Square Publishing.

—Leicestershire & Rutland. 2nd ed. (Illus.). 576p. 65.00 *(978-0-14-071018-2(3))* Penguin Bks., Ltd. GBR. Dist: Trafalgar Square Publishing.

—North Lancashire. (Illus.). 320p. 45.00 *(978-0-14-071037-3(X))* Penguin Bks., Ltd. GBR. Dist: Trafalgar Square Publishing.

—Shropshire. (Illus.). 1p. 40.00 *(978-0-14-071016-8(7))* Penguin Bks., Ltd. GBR. Dist: Trafalgar Square Publishing.

—Staffordshire, 1974. (Buildings of England Ser.). (Illus.). 384p. 45.00 *(978-0-14-071046-5(9))* Penguin Bks., Ltd. GBR. Dist: Trafalgar Square Publishing.

—Worcestershire England, 1968. 384p. 40.00 *(978-0-14-071035-9(3))* Penguin Bks., Ltd. GBR. Dist: Trafalgar Square Publishing.

Pevsner, Nikolaus & Newman. Northeast East Kent: Buildings of England. 3rd ed. (Buildings of England Ser.). (Illus.). 564p. pap. 50.00 *(978-0-14-071039-7(6))* Penguin Bks., Ltd. GBR. Dist: Trafalgar Square Publishing.

Randl, Chad. Revolving Architecture: A History of Buildings That Rotate, Swivel, & Pivot. 2008. (ENG., Illus.). 208p. 35.00 *(978-1-56898-681-4(5))* Princeton Architectural Pr.

REDDIN, Patrick. Specifying Minor Works. 2012. (ENG., Illus.). 160p. pap. 47.95 *(978-0-415-58351-0(9))* Routledge.

Rockhill, Dan. Designing & Building: Rockhill & Associates. Cater, Brian, ed. 2011. (Illus.). 120p. pap. *(978-0-929112-59-6(8))* Tuns Pr.

Rogsch, Christian, et al, eds. Pedestrian & Evacuation Dynamics 2008. 2010. (Illus.). xiv, 833p. 219.00 *(978-3-642-04503-5(0)*, 3642045030) Springer.

Rooney, E. Ashley. Boathouses: Architecture at the Water's Edge. 2009. (Illus.). 160p. bds. 49.99 *(978-0-7643-3190-9(6))* Schiffer Publishing, Ltd.

Rudman, Jack. Building Maintenance. (Occupational Competency Examination Ser.: Vol. 8). 49.95 *(978-0-8373-5758-4(6)*, Passbooks) National Learning Corp.

Ruiz-Geli, Encri. Cloud 9. 2012. (ENG., Illus.). 320p. *(978-84-96540-82-8(0))* Actar Birkhauser Distribution.

Ruwanpura, Janaka, et al, eds. Construction Research Congress 2010: Innovation for Reshaping Construction Practice, Vol. 1. 2010. (ENG., Illus.). 1566p. pap. 275.00 *(978-0-7844-1109-4(3))* American Society of Civil Engineers.

Schaller, Matthias Petrus. Matthias Schaller: Controfacciata, 1 vol. 2008. (ENG., Illus.). 68p. 50.00 *(978-3-86521-674-8(9))* Steidl, Gerhard Druckerei und Verlag DEU. Dist: Innovative Logistics.

Schittich, Christian, ed. Small Structures. 2010. (ENG., Illus.). 176p. 99.95 *(978-3-0346-0283-9(9))* Birkhauser Verlag AG CHE. Dist: Actar Birkhauser Distribution.

Schulze, Franz. Building a Masterpiece: Milwaukee Art Museum. 2009. (ENG., Illus.). 240p. pap. 40.00 *(978-1-55595-202-0(X))* Hudson Hills Pr. LLC.

Seidler, Harry. The Grand Tour. 25th ed. 2007. (ENG., Illus.). 575p. pap. 14.99 *(978-3-8228-3780-1(6))* TASCHEN DEU. Dist: Ingram Pub. Services.

Sharma, V. M. & Woods, Richard. Dynamic Effects of Pile Installatio. 2007. (ENG., Illus.). 182p. (C). 113.95 (978-90-5809-243-4(7), Taylor & Francis) Taylor & Francis Group GBR. Dist: Taylor & Francis Group.
Shirley, Frank. New Rooms for Old Houses: Beautiful Additions for the Traditional Home. 2007. (Nat Trust for Historic Preserv Ser.). (ENG., Illus.). 266p. 40.00 (978-1-56158-885-5(7), Taunton) Taunton Pr., Inc.
Simiu, Emil, et al. Design of Buildings for Wind: A Guide for ASCE 7-10 Standard Users & Designers of Special Structures. 2nd ed. 2011. (ENG., Illus.). 352p. 140.00 (978-0-470-46492-2(5), Wiley) Wiley, John & Sons, Inc.
Slavid, Ruth. Micro: Very Small Buildings. (ENG., Illus.). 224p. 2009. pap. 19.95 (978-1-85669-594-7(8)) 2007. 29.95 (978-1-85669-495-7(X)) King, Laurence Publishing GBR. Dist: Hachette Bk. Group.
Stanford, Herb. Effective Building Maintenance: Protection of Capital Assets. 2010. (ENG., Illus.). 300p. instr.'s gde. ed. 99.95 (978-1-4398-4553-0(0)) Fairmont Pr., Inc.
Stathopoulos, Theodore & Baniotopoulos, C. C. Wind Effects on Buildings & Design of Wind-Sensitive Structures. Baniotopoulos, Charalambos C. & Stathopoulos, Ted, eds. 2007. (CISM International Centre for Mechanical Sciences Ser.). (Illus.). 240p. pap. 129.00 (978-3-211-73075-1(3)) Springer.
Sunset Magazine Editors, ed. Sunset Outdoor Design Guide: Backyard Cottages & Gazebos - Fresh Ideas for Outdoor Living. 2011. (ENG., Illus.). 192p. pap. 19.95 (978-0-376-01386-6(9)) Oxmoor Hse., Inc.
Thorpe, Yvonne. Graphing Buildings & Structures. 2008. (Real World Data Ser.). (ENG.). 32p. pap. 7.99 (978-1-4329-1544-5(4), NA-h) Heinemann-Raintree.
Tits, J. Buildings of Spherical Type & Finite Bn-Pairs. 2008. (Lecture Notes in Mathematics Ser.). pap. 59.95 (978-3-540-06757-3(4)) Springer.
Towell, Larry. In the Wake of Katrina. 2006. (Illus.). 96p. 25.00 (978-0-9546894-9-0(6)) Boot, Chris GBR. Dist: D.A.P./Distributed Art Pubs.
Underwood, Jason & Isikdag, Umit, eds. Research on Building Information Modeling & Construction Informatics: Concepts & Technologies. 2009. 567p. instr.'s hndbk. ed. 295.00 (978-1-60566-928-1(8)) IGI Global.
Unwin, Simon. Twenty Buildings Every Architect Should Understand. 2010. (ENG., Illus.). 240p. (C). 165.00 (978-0-415-55251-6(6)); pap. 30.95 (978-0-415-55252-3(4)) Routledge.
Usgbc. Green Building Design & Construction. 2009. (Illus.). xxvi, 645p. (978-1-932444-14-8(9)) U. S. Green Building Council.
Van der Hoorn, Mélanie. Indispensable Eyesores: An Anthropology of Undesired Buildings. 2009. (Illus.). 272p. 90.00 (978-1-84545-530-9(4)) Berghahn Bks., Inc.
Van Rensbergen, Henk. Abandoned Places II. 2010. (ENG., Illus.). 192p. (978-90-209-9083-6(7), Lannoo Pubs. (Acc)) Antique Collectors' Club.
Warr, Anne. Shanghai Architecture. 2008. (Architecture Guides (Watermark Press) Ser.). (Illus.). 338p. pap. 45.00 (978-0-949284-76-1(9)) Watermark Pr., The AUS. Dist: National Bk. Network.
Waterkeyn, Xavier. Grand Visions: Marvels of Building & Engineering. 2010. (ENG., Illus.). 256p. 39.95 (978-1-74110-742-5(3)) New Holland Pubs. Pty, Ltd. AUS. Dist: Tuttle Publishing.
Weiss, Richard M. The Structure of Affine Buildings. 2008. (Annals of Mathematics Studies: No. 168). (ENG., Illus.). 392p. (C). 115.00 (978-0-691-13659-2(9)); pap. 59.95 (978-0-691-13881-7(8)) Princeton Univ. Pr.
Wenzel, Friedemann, ed. Perspectives in Modern Seismology. 2010. (Lecture Notes in Earth Sciences Ser.). (Illus.). xiv, 226p. pap. 179.00 (978-3-642-06263-6(6), 3642062636) Springer.
Wilkins, Helen. The Evolution of the Built Environment: Complexity, Human Agency & Thermal Performance. 2009. (Illus.). 353p. (C). pap. 137.50 (978-1-4073-0595-0(6)) British Archaeological Reports Ltd. GBR. Dist: Brown, David Bk. Co., The.
Williamson, Laurie. Home Extensions: Planning, Managing & Completing Your Extension, 1 vol. 2010. (ENG., Illus.). 160p. 22.95 (978-1-84797-159-3(8)) Crowood Pr., Ltd. GBR. Dist: Independent Pubs. Group.
Wood, Brian. Building Maintenance. 2009. (ENG., Illus.). 328p. pap. 62.99 (978-1-4051-7967-6(8), Wiley-Blackwell) Wiley, John & Sons, Inc.
The World's Greatest Architecture: Past & Present. 2007. (Illus.). 447p. pap. 12.99 (978-0-7858-2239-4(9), Chartwell) Book Sales, Inc.
Yang, Chin S. & Heinsohn, Patricia A. Sampling & Analysis of Indoor Microorganisms. 2007. (ENG., Illus.). 273p. 105.00 (978-0-471-73093-4(9), Wiley-Interscience) Wiley, John & Sons, Inc.
Yankielun, Norbert E. How to Build an Igloo: And Other Snow Shelters. 2007. (ENG., Illus.). 208p. per. 17.95 (978-0-393-73215-3(0), 73215) Norton, W. W. & Co., Inc.
Zehmer, John G., Jr. Hayes: The Plantation, Its People, & Their Papers. 2007. (North Caroliniana Society Imprints Ser.). (ENG., Illus.). 257p. 36.00 (978-0-86526-325-3(6)) North Carolina Office of Archives & History.

BUILDINGS—ACOUSTICS
see Architectural Acoustics

BUILDINGS—CLEANING
see also Industrial Housekeeping

Anderson, Carla. How to Start & Operate a Home-Based Janitorial Business. 2007. 76p. per. 10.95 (978-0-595-43733-7(8)) iUniverse, Inc.
Findley, Mary & Formichelli, Linda. Green Cleaning. 2nd ed. 2009. (Complete Idiot's Guide Ser.). (ENG.). 272p. (gr. 12-18). pap. 14.95 (978-1-59257-856-6(X), Alpha Bks.) Penguin Group (USA) Inc.
Gordon, Robert. Start & Run a Successful Cleaning. 2009. 160p. 30.00 (978-1-84528-284-4(1)) How To Books GBR. Dist: Parkwest Pubns., Inc.
Jorstad, Laura & Morse, Melinda. Housecleaning Business: Organize Your Business - Get Clients & Referrals - Set Rates & Services - Understand Customer Needs - Bill & Renew Contracts - Offer Green Cleaning Options. 3rd ed. 2009. (Home-Based Business Ser.). (ENG., Illus.). 192p. pap. 18.95 (978-0-7627-5014-6(6)) Globe Pequot Pr., The.
Maasberg, Wolfgang. Commercial-Industrial Cleaning, by Pressure-Washing, Hydro-Blasting & UHP-Jetting: The Business Operating Model & How-To Manual for 450 Specific Applications. 2011. (ENG., Illus.). xii, 908p. 279.00 (978-0-85729-834-8(8), 0857298348) Springer.

BUILDINGS—COLOR
see Color in Architecture

BUILDINGS—DETAILS
see Architecture—Details; Building—Details

BUILDINGS—EARTHQUAKE EFFECTS

Abo, Mekonnen. Response of Masonry Infilled Rc Frame under Horizontal Seismic Force. 2010. 120p. pap. (978-3-639-22944-8(4)) VDM Verlag Dr. Mueller e.K.
Albano, Giuseppe. Progettazione Esecutiva Di Strutture in Legno Lamellare in Zona Sismica: Prescrizioni, Metodi Di Predimensionamento, Particolari Costruttivi, Progetti Esecutivi Di Cantiere. 2010. (ITA., Illus.). 302p. (978-88-387-5288-9(5)) Maggioli Editore.
American Society of Civil Engineers Staff, contrib. by. Seismic Rehabilitation of Existing Buildings, ASCE/SEI 41-06. 2007. 416p. pap. 160.00 (978-0-7844-0884-1(X)) American Society of Civil Engineers.
Bali, Ika. Low-Rise Rc Shear Walls. 2008. 236p. pap. (978-3-639-00386-4(1)) VDM Verlag Dr. Mueller e.K.
Bangash, M. Y. H. Earthquake Resistant Buildings: Design, Analysis & Case Studies. 2009. (ENG.). 900p. 489.00 (978-3-540-93817-0(6)) Springer.
Baraskar, Manoj. Collapse Evaluation of Steel Structures. 2011. 52p. pap. (978-3-8443-2141-8(1)) Lambert Academic Publishing.
Boyd, Peter. Why Is L a Ticking? Faultlines & Nukes after Japan. 2011. 90p. pap. 11.95 (978-1-60746-843-1(3)) FastPencil, Inc.
Carpinteri, Alberto & Lacidogna, Giuseppe, eds. Earthquakes & Acoustic Emission. 2007. (ENG., Illus.). 209p. (C). 129.95 (978-0-415-44402-6(0), Taylor & Francis) Taylor & Francis Group GBR. Dist: Taylor & Francis Group.
Celik, Ozan. Probabilistic Seismic Vulnerability Assessment of Concrete Frames. 2008. 152p. pap. (978-3-8364-6415-4(2)) VDM Verlag Dr. Mueller e.K.
Charleson, Andrew. Seismic Design for Architects. 2008. (ENG., Illus.) 296p. pap. 59.95 (978-0-7506-8550-4(6)) Routledge.
F M Mazzolani Staff. Behaviour of Steel Structures in Seismic Areas. 2006. (Illus.). xvi, 930p. 167.95 (978-0-415-40413-6(4), Taylor & Francis) Taylor & Francis Group GBR. Dist: Taylor & Francis Group.
Gatscher, Jeffrey A., et al. Earthquake Protection of Building Equipment & Systems: Bridging the Implementation Gap. 2012. E-Book (978-0-7844-7643-7(8)); (ENG.). pap. 120.00 (978-0-7844-1152-0(2)) American Society of Civil Engineers.
Higashino, Masahiko & Okamoto, Shin. Response Control & Seismic Isolation of Buildings. 2006. (ENG., Illus.). 416p. (C). 210.00 (978-0-415-36623-6(2)) Routledge.
Hussain, Raja Rizwan & Wasim, Mohammad. Seismic Retrofitting of Rc Buildings. 2010. 172p. pap. (978-3-639-25055-8(9)) VDM Verlag Dr. Mueller e.K.
Ilki, Alper, et al, eds. Seismic Risk Assessment & Retrofitting: With Special Emphasis on Existing Low Rise Structures. 2009. (Geotechnical, Geological, & Earthquake Engineering Ser.). (ENG., Illus.). xiii, 495p. 169.00 (978-90-481-2680-4(0), 9048126800) Springer.
Javanpour, Mohsen. Assessment of the Seismic Behavior of the Structures. 2011. 88p. pap. (978-3-8433-8788-0(5)) Lambert Academic Publishing.
—Assessment of the Seismic Vulnerability Behavior of the Structures. 2011. 84p. pap. (978-3-8443-2782-3(7)) Lambert Academic Publishing.
King, S. A., et al, eds. Seismic Hazard & Building Vulnerability in Post-Soviet Central Asian Republics. 2010. (Nato Science Partnership Subseries: 2 (closed) Ser.). (ENG.). 276p. pap. 219.00 (978-90-481-5176-9(7), 9048151767) Springer.
Lacidogna, Giuseppe & Carpinteri, A. Acoustic Emission & Critical Phenomena: From Structural Mechanics to Geophysics. Carpinteri, Alberto & Lacidogna, Giuseppe, eds. 2008. (ENG., Illus.). 282p. 133.95 (978-0-415-45082-9(9), Taylor & Francis) Taylor & Francis Group GBR. Dist: Taylor & Francis Group.
Luca, Antonello De & Serino, Giorgio, eds. Dipartimento della Protezione Civile / Rete dei Laboratori Universitari di Ingegneria Sismica. Tecnologie per l'isolamento ed il controllo di strutture ed infrastrutture: Atti del seminario conclusivo della Linea 7 del progetto di ricerca DPC-ReLUIS 2005-2008. 2009. (ITA & ENG., Illus.). 328p. (C). 65.00 (978-88-596-0656-7(X)) Polistampa ITA. Dist: Brown, David Bk. Co., The.
Matsagar, Vasant & Shyam Jangid, Radhey. Earthquake Base-Isolated Buildings. 2011. 280p. pap. (978-3-8383-8839-7(9)) Lambert Academic Publishing.
Mazzolani. Behaviour of Steel Structures in Seismic Areas. 2006. (Illus.). xvi, 930p. cd-rom 167.95 (978-0-415-40823-3(7), Taylor & Francis) Taylor & Francis Group GBR. Dist: Taylor & Francis Group.
Mazzolani, Federico, et al, eds. Behaviour of Steel Structures in Seismic Areas. 2009. (ENG.). 998p. 349.00 (978-0-415-56326-0(7), CRC Press) Taylor & Francis Group GBR. Dist: Taylor & Francis Group.
Mazzolani, Federico & Herrera, Ricardo, eds. Behaviour of Steel Structures in Seismic Areas: Stessa 2012. 2011. (ENG.). 1130p. (C). 339.00 (978-0-415-62105-2(4), CRC Press) Taylor & Francis Group GBR. Dist: Taylor & Francis Group.
Mazzolani, Federico M., ed. Urban Habitat Constructions under Catastrophic Events: COST C26 Action Final Report. 2010. (ENG.). 478p. 229.00 (978-0-415-60686-8(1), CRC Press) Taylor & Francis Group GBR. Dist: Taylor & Francis Group.
—Urban Habitat Constructions under Catastrophic Events: Proceedings of the COST C26 Action Final Conference. 2010. (ENG.). 1068p. 459.00 (978-0-415-60685-1(3), CRC Press) Taylor & Francis Group GBR. Dist: Taylor & Francis Group.
Mucciarelli, Marco, et al, eds. Increasing Seismic Safety by Combining Engineering Technologies & Seismological Data. 2008. (NATO Science for Peace & Security Series C: Environmental Security Ser.). (Illus.). xviii, 382p. 289.00 (978-1-4020-9193-3(1), 1402091931); pap. 109.00 (978-1-4020-9194-0(X), 140209194X) Springer.
NCSEA. Guide to the Design of Diaphragms, Chords & Collectors. 2009. pap. 59.00 (978-1-58001-790-9(8)) International Code Council.
Podany, Jerry. Advances in the Protection of Museum Collections from Earthquake Damage: Papers from a Conference Held at the J. Paul Getty Museum, May 2006. 2008. (Illus.). 240p. pap. 75.00 (978-0-89236-908-9(6)) Oxford Univ. Pr., Inc.
Rolly, Horst Friedrich. Earthquake Disaster Management: Focussing on the Earthquake of September 30, 1993 in Latur & Osmanabad Districts, Maharashtra, India & the Reconstruction & Rehabilitation Project at Gubal Village where Geodesic Domes were Constructed as Earthquake-Resistant Housing. (Illus.). 239p. pap. 47.95 (978-3-631-56094-5(X)) Lang, Peter Publishing, Inc.
Samsamshariat, Mohammad. Product Development of Earthquake-Safe Houses & Schools. 2011. 144p. pap. (978-3-8381-1837-6(5)) Südwestdeutscher Verlag für Hochschulschriften AG & Co. KG.
SEAOC. 2006 IBC Structural Seismic Design Manual. 2007. 212p. pap. 67.00 (978-1-58001-402-1(X)); pap. 67.00 (978-1-58001-403-8(8)) International Code Council.
—2006 IBC Stuctural Seismic Design Manual. 2007. pap. 67.00 (978-1-58001-404-5(6)) International Code Council.
—2009 Seaoc Blue Book. 2009. pap. 94.00 (978-1-58001-861-6(0)) International Code Council.
Takewaki, Izuru. Building Control with Passive Dampers: Optimal Performance-Based Design for Earthquakes. 2009. (ENG., Illus.). 320p. 175.00 (978-0-470-82491-7(3), Wiley) Wiley, John & Sons, Inc.
Technology Research Editors, ed. Seismic Resistant Metal Structures, 2007 Ed. 2007. pap. 130.50 (978-1-60030-229-9(7), Search-In-Print) CSA Journal Division.
Yanev, Peter & Thompson, Andrew C. T. Peace of Mind in Earthquake Country: How to Save Your Home, Business, & Life. 2009. (ENG.). 256p. pap. 19.95 (978-0-8118-6183-0(X)) Chronicle Bks. LLC.
Zarfam, Panam. Assessment of the Seismic Behavior Structures by Fragility Curves. 2011. 76p. pap. (978-3-8433-7990-8(4)) Lambert Academic Publishing.

BUILDINGS—ELECTRIC EQUIPMENT

Ahuja, Anil. Integrated M/E Design: Building systems Engineering. 2nd ed. 2010. (ENG.). 373p. pap. 155.00 (978-1-4419-4724-6(8), 1441947248) Springer.
Bni, creator. Electrical Costbook 2007. 14th ed. 2006. (Building News Electrical Costbook Ser.). 351p. per. 79.95 (978-1-55701-565-5(1)) BNI Pubns., Inc.
BNI Building News. Sweets Electrical Cost Guide. 2008. (Sweet's Electrical Cost Guide Ser.). (Illus.). 361p. pap. 96.95 (978-1-55701-630-0(5)) BNI Pubns., Inc.
Chamra, Louay M. & Mago, Pedro J. Micro-Chp Power Generation for Residential & Small Commercial Buildings. 2008. (Illus.). 82p. pap. 29.00 (978-1-60456-867-7(4)) Nova Science Pubs., Inc.
Cook, Paul. Commentary on IEE Wiring Regulations: Bs 7671:2008. 17th ed. 2009. (Illus.). 400p. pap. 130.00 (978-0-86341-966-9(6)) Institution of Engineering & Technology GBR. Dist: Books International, Inc.
Cram101 Textbook Reviews. Outlines & Highlights for Mechanical & Electrical Systems in Buildings by Richard R Janis, William K y Tao. 2011. 144p. pap. 28.95 (978-1-61906-132-3(5)) Cram101 Inc.
Cram101 Textbook Reviews & Cram101 Textbook Reviews. Outlines & Highlights for Building Systems for Interior Designers by Corky Binggeli. 2011. 228p. pap. 31.95 (978-1-61830-872-6(6)) Cram101 Inc.
—Outlines & Highlights for Mechanical & Electrical Equipment for Buildings by Walter T Grondzik. 2011. 266p. pap. 31.95 (978-1-61830-808-5(4)) Cram101 Inc.
—Outlines & Highlights for Mechanical & Electrical Systems in Architecture, Engineering & Construction by Frank R Dagostino. 2011. 176p. pap. 29.95 (978-1-61830-947-1(1)) Cram101 Inc.
Dagostino, Frank R. & Wujek, Joseph B. Mechanical & Electrical Systems in Architecture, Engineering & Construction. 5th ed. 2009. (ENG.). 960p. (C). 141.60 (978-0-13-500004-5(1), Prentice Hall) Prentice Hall PTR.
Daneshgari, Perry. Agile Construction for the Electrical Contractor. 2009. (Illus.). 240p. pap. 49.95 (978-0-7637-6562-0(7)) Jones & Bartlett Learning, LLC.
Davis Langdon Engineering Services. Spon's Mechanical & Electrical Services Price Book 2011. 42nd ed. 2010. (ENG., Illus.). 800p. 255.00 (978-0-415-58851-5(0), Spon Pr.) Routledge.
Doyle Bsc (Eng), Bernard & Kevin Kelly. Lighting Controls & Their Associated Problems. 2010. 168p. pap. (978-3-8383-7955-5(1)) Lambert Academic Publishing.
Ferguson, Mitchell B., ed. Renewable Energy Grid Integration: Technical Performance & Requirements. 2011. (Environmental Remediation Technologies, Regulations & Safety Ser.). (Illus.). 249p. 89.00 (978-1-60741-325-7(6)) Nova Science Pubs., Inc.
Fletcher, Greg. Residential Construction Academy: House Wiring. 2nd rev. ed. 2007. (ENG., Illus.). 672p. 111.95 (978-1-4180-1098-0(7)) Delmar Cengage Learning.
Fletcher, Gregory W. Residential Construction Academy: House Wiring - Workbook with Lab Manual. 3rd ed. 2011. (ENG.). 512p. (C). pap. 43.95 (978-1-111-30624-3(9)) Delmar Cengage Learning.
—Residential Construction Academy - House Wiring. 2nd ed. 2011. (ENG.). (C). 1158.95 (978-1-111-30625-0(7)) Delmar Cengage Learning.
Global Sustainable Energy Solutions Pvt Ltd. Staff, et al. Grid-Connected Solar Electric Systems: The Earthscan Expert Handbook for Planning, Design & Installation. 2012. (Earthscan Expert Ser.). (ENG., Illus.). 256p. 59.95 (978-1-84971-344-3(8)) Routledge.
Grondzik, Walter T., et al. Mechanical & Electrical Equipment for Buildings. 11th ed. 2009. (ENG., Illus.). 1792p. 150.00 (978-0-470-19565-9(7), Wiley) Wiley, John & Sons, Inc.
Hauck, John. Electrical Design of Commercial & Industrial Buildings. rev. ed. 2009. 164p. pap. 97.95 (978-0-7637-5828-8(0)) Jones & Bartlett Learning, LLC.
Henke-Konopasek, Nancy & Holzman, Harvey N. Modern Residential Wiring. 9th ed. 2011. (ENG.). 116p. (gr. 9-14). pap. 24.00 (978-1-60525-583-5(1)) Goodheart-Willcox Pub.
Herman, Stephen L. Residential Construction Academy: Electrical Principles. 2nd ed. 2011. (ENG.). (C). 1158.95 (978-1-111-30651-9(6)); 1158.95 (978-1-111-30652-6(4)) Delmar Cengage Learning.
Holzman, Harvey N. Modern Residential Wiring: Based on the 2008 Nec. 8th ed. 2008. (ENG.). 364p. (gr. 9-14). 72.00 (978-1-59070-895-8(4)) Goodheart-Willcox Pub.
Institution of Engineering and Technology. On-Site Guide: BS 7671: 2008 17th Edition. 17th ed. 2008. (Illus.). 183p. ring bd. 40.00 (978-0-86341-854-9(6)) Institution of Engineering & Technology GBR. Dist: Books International, Inc.
Janis, Richard R. & Tao, William K. Y. Mechanical & Electrical Systems in Buildings. 4th ed. 2008. (ENG., Illus.). 672p. (C). 143.60 (978-0-13-513013-1(1), Prentice Hall) Prentice Hall PTR.
Kaminar, Neil. Solar Basics. 2009. pap. 24.95 (978-0-9840510-0-7(7)) McNeill Hill Publishing.
Kissell, Thomas E. Electricity, Electronics, & Control Systems for HVAC. 4th ed. 2007. (ENG., Illus.). 720p. (C). 131.20 (978-0-13-199568-0(5), Prentice Hall) Prentice Hall PTR.
Kitcher, Chris. Practical Guide to Inspection, Testing & Certification of Electrical Installations. 3rd rev. ed. 2013. (ENG.). 248p. (C). pap. 33.95 (978-0-08-096907-7(0)) Routledge.
Lechner, Norbert M. Plumbing, Electricity, Acoustics: Sustainable Design Methods for Architecture. 2011. (ENG., Illus.). 304p. 80.00 (978-1-118-01475-2(8), Wiley) Wiley, John & Sons, Inc.
Litchfield, Michael. Wiring Complete. McAlister, Michael, ed. 2nd rev. ed. 2009. (Taunton's Complete Ser.). (ENG., Illus.). 256p. pap. 21.95 (978-1-60085-256-5(4)) Taunton Pr., Inc.
Litchfield, Michael W. & McAlister, Michael. Wiring Complete. 2008. (Taunton's Quick-Access Guides). (Illus.). 251p. pap. 21.95 (978-1-56158-815-2(6), Taunton) Taunton Pr., Inc.
Locke, Darrell. Guide to the Wiring Regulations: IEE Wiring Regulations. 17th ed. 2008. (ENG., Illus.). 302p. pap., instr.'s gde. ed. 40.00 (978-0-470-51685-0(2), Wiley) Wiley, John & Sons, Inc.
Mahoney, William D., ed. Building News Mechanical/Electrical 2007 Costbook. 17th ed. 2006. (Building News Mechanical/Electrical Costbook Ser.). (Illus.). 499p. per. 95.95 (978-1-55701-564-8(3)) BNI Pubns., Inc.
—Building News Mechanical/Electrical Costbook. 19th ed. 2008. (Building News Mechanical/Electrical Costbook Ser.). 498p. pap. 97.95 (978-1-55701-622-5(4)) BNI Pubns., Inc.
Markell, Jeff. Residential Wiring to the 2008 NEC. 8th ed. 2008. (Illus.). 352p. per. 42.00 (978-1-57218-204-2(0)) Craftsman Bk. Co.
Mcpartland, Brian J., et al. McGraw-Hill's National Electrical Code 2011 Handbook. 27th ed. 2011. (ENG., Illus.). 1662p. 75.00 (978-0-07-174570-3(X), 007174570X) McGraw-Hill Professional Publishing.
McPartland, Brian J., et al. National Electrical Code 2008 Handbook: Based on the Current 2008 National Electrical Code. 26th ed. 2008. (ENG., Illus.). 1583p. 75.00 (978-0-07-154652-2(9), 0071546529) McGraw-Hill Professional Publishing.
Miller, Charles R. & National Fire Protection Association Staff. NEC 2008: Pocket Guide to Residential Electrical Installations. 2007. (ENG., Illus.). 500p. pap. 32.00 (978-0-87765-823-8(4)) Delmar Cengage Learning.
Miller, Rex & Miller, Mark R. Electricity & Electronics for HVAC. 2007. (ENG., Illus.). 380p. (C). pap. 49.95 (978-0-07-149668-1(8), 0071496688) McGraw-Hill Professional Publishing.
Mossman, Melville J., ed. Means Mechanical Cost Data. 31st ed. 2007. (Means Mechanical Cost Data Ser.). (Illus.). 725p. per. 149.95 (978-0-87629-048-4(9)) Means, R.S. Co., Inc.
Mullin, Ray C. Electrical Wiring Residential. 16th ed. 2007. (ENG., Illus.). 752p. 156.95 (978-1-4180-5096-2(2)) Delmar Cengage Learning.
—Electrical Wiring Residential. 16th ed. 2008. (ENG.). 150p. pap., lab manual ed. 38.95 (978-1-4180-5099-3(7)) Delmar Cengage Learning.
—Electrical Wiring Residential. 16th rev. ed. 2007. (ENG., Illus.). 752p. pap. 107.95 (978-1-4180-5095-5(4)) Delmar Cengage Learning.

Mullin, Ray C. & Simmons, J. Philip. Elecrical Wiring Commercial. 14th ed. 2011. (ENG., Illus.). 624p. pap. 113.95 *(978-1-4354-9829-7(1))* Delmar Cengage Learning.

Mullin, Ray C. & Smith, Robert L. Electrical Wiring Commercial. 13th ed. 2008. (ENG., Illus.). 496p. pap. 113.95 *(978-1-4354-3912-2(0))* Delmar Cengage Learning.

NEC. National Electrical Code 2011. 2010. (ENG.). 400p. (C). pap. 92.00 *(978-0-13-237318-0(1)*, Prentice Hall) Prentice Hall PTR.

NFPA. National Electical Code 2011. 2010. (ENG.). 1p. spiral bd. 90.00 *(978-1-111-54230-6(9))* Delmar Cengage Learning.

R S Means Engineering, creator. Mechanical Cost Data: HVAC. Controls. 33rd ed. 2009. (Means Mechanical Cost Data Ser.). (ENG., Illus.). 739p. pap. 169.95 *(978-0-87629-819-0(6))* Means, R.S. Co., Inc.

Rosenberg, Paul. Audel Guide to the 2011 National Electrical Code: All New Edition. 2011. (Audel Technical Trades Ser.: 46). (ENG., Illus.). 696p. pap. 45.00 *(978-1-118-00389-3(6)*, Audel) Wiley, John & Sons, Inc.

RSMeans Engineering Dept., ed. Mechanical Cost Data. 2008. 725p. 154.95 *(978-0-87629-183-2(3))* Means, R.S. Co., Inc.

Smith, Geoffrey B., et al. Green Nanotechnology: Energy for Tomorrow's World. 2010. (ENG., Illus.). 472p. 79.95 *(978-1-4200-8532-7(8)*, CRC Press) Taylor & Francis Group GBR. Dist: Taylor & Francis Group.

Ventre, Jerry. Photovoltaic Systems Engineering, Third Edition. 3rd rev. ed. 2010. (ENG., Illus.). 527p. (C). 104.95 *(978-1-4398-0292-2(0)*, CRC Press) Taylor & Francis Group GBR. Dist: Taylor & Francis Group.

Weller, Bernhard, et al. Detail Practice, Photovoltaics: Technology, Design, Construction. 2010. (Illus.). 112p. pap. 49.95 *(978-3-0346-0369-0(X))* Birkhauser Verlag AG CHE. Dist: Actar Birkhauser Distribution.

Wells, Quentin. Smart Grid Home. 2012. (ENG.). 250p. (C). pap. 55.95 ***(978-1-111-31851-2(4))*** Delmar Cengage Learning.

BUILDINGS—ENERGY CONSERVATION

A S H R A E, et al, contrib. by. Advanced Energy Design Guide for Small Retail Buildings: Achieving 30% Energy Savings over ANSISSHRAE/IESNA Standard 90. 1-1999. 2006. (ENG.). pap. 62.00 *(978-1-933742-06-9(2))* American Society of Heating, Refrigerating & Air-Conditioning Engineers, Inc.

A S H R A E, contrib. by. Advanced Energy Design Guide for Small Warehouses & Self-Storage Buildings: Achieving 30% Energy Savings Toward a Net Zero Energy Building. 2008. (ENG.). 104p. pap. 62.00 *(978-1-933742-22-9(4))* American Society of Heating, Refrigerating & Air-Conditioning Engineers, Inc.

Al-Shemmeri, Tarik. Energy Audits: A Workbook for Energy Management in Buildings. 2011. (ENG.). 320p. pap. 60.00 ***(978-0-470-65608-2(5)***, Wiley) Wiley, John & Sons, Inc.

American Society of Heating, contrib. by. Advanced Energy Design Guide for Small Hospitals & Healthcare Facilities: Achieving 30% Energy Savings Toward a Net Zero Energy Building. 2009. (ENG.). 198p. pap. 62.00 *(978-1-933742-66-3(6))* American Society of Heating, Refrigerating & Air-Conditioning Engineers, Inc.

Beggs, Clive. Energy: Management, Supply & Conservation. 2nd rev. ed. 2009. (ENG., Illus.). 368p. pap. 55.95 *(978-0-7506-8670-9(7))* Routledge.

Capehart, B. L. & Capehart, Lynne C. Web Based Enterprise Energy & Building Automation Systems. 2007. (Illus.). xiii, 423p. *(978-0-88173-536-9(1))* Fairmont Pr., Inc.

Chen, Gang. Leed Ap Exam Guide: Study Materials, Sample Questions, Mock Exam, Building LEED Certification (LEED-NC) & Going Green. 2008. 244p. pap. 69.95 *(978-1-4327-2842-7(3))* Outskirts Pr., Inc.

—Leed Ga Exam Guide: A Must-Have for the LEED Green Associate Exam. 2009. 398p. pap. 73.95 *(978-1-4327-4168-6(3))* Outskirts Pr., Inc.

—LEED ID&C Exam Guide: A Must-Have for the LEED AP ID+C Exam: Study Materials, Sample Questions, Mock Exam, Green Interior Design & Construction, Green Building LEED Certification, & Sustainability. Wenger, Barry, ed. 2010. (Illus.). 248p. pap. 99.95 *(978-0-9843741-0-6(8))* ArchiteG, Inc.

Chiras, Daniel D. Green Home Improvement. 2008. (RSMeans Ser.: 9). (ENG.). 320p. pap. 34.95 *(978-0-87629-093-4(4))* Means, R.S. Co., Inc.

Climate Benefits of Improved Building Energy Efficiency: Hearing Before the Subcommittee on Energy & Air Quality of the Committee on Energy & Commerce, House of Representatives, One Hundred Tenth Congress, Second Session, July 17, 2008. 2011. v, 184p. ***(978-0-16-088086-5(6)***, 552-070-42506-3) United States Government Printing Office.

Covrig, Claudiu. Implementation of Solar Thermal & Photovoltaic Systems. 2011. 72p. pap. ***(978-3-8443-0803-7(2))*** Lambert Academic Publishing.

Cram101 Textbook Reviews. Outlines & Highlights for Air Conditioning Principles & Systems by Pita, Isbn: 0130928720. 2011. 168p. pap. 29.95 ***(978-1-61812-920-8(1))*** Cram101 Inc.

Deru, Michael P. & Kelsey, Jim. Procedures for Commercial Building Energy Audits. 2nd ed. 2011. pap. ***(978-1-936504-09-1(X))*** American Society of Heating, Refrigerating & Air-Conditioning Engineers, Inc.

Doty, Steve. Commercial Energy Auditing Reference Handbook. 2007. *(978-0-88173-567-3(1))* 2nd ed. 2010. *(978-0-88173-648-9(1))* 2nd ed. 2010. *(978-0-88173-649-6(X))* Fairmont Pr., Inc.

Eicker, Ursula & Eicker. Low Energy Cooling for Sustainable Buildings. 2009. (ENG., Illus.). 276p. 100.00 *(978-0-470-69744-3(X)*, Wiley) Wiley, John & Sons, Inc.

Energy Efficiency in Buildings: Hearing Before the Committee on Energy & Natural Resources, United States Senate, One Hundred Eleventh Congress, First Session, to Provide Recommendations for Reducing Energy Consumption in Buildings, February 26, 2009. 2009. iii, 99p. *(978-0-16-083063-1(X)*, 552-070-38958-0) United States Government Printing Office.

Energy Efficiency of Buildings: Hearing Before the Subcommittee on Energy of the Committee on Energy & Natural Resources, United States Senate, One Hundred Tenth Congress, First Session, to Receive Recommendations on Policies & Programs to Improve the Energy Efficiency of Buildings & to Expand the Role of Electric & Gas Utilities in Energy Efficiency Programs, February 12, 2007. 2007. iii, 62p. *(978-0-16-078935-9(4)*, 552-070-36062-0) United States Government Printing Office.

Fullner, Sheryl Kindle. The Shoestring Library, 1 vol. 2010. 139p. pap. 30.00 *(978-1-58683-520-0(3)*, A3072P) Linworth Publishing, Inc.

Gevorkian, Peter. Alternative Energy Systems in Building Design (GreenSource Books) 2009. (ENG., Illus.). 544p. 99.95 *(978-0-07-162147-2(4)*, 0071621474) McGraw-Hill Professional Publishing.

A Growing Capitol Complex & Visitor Center: Needs for Transportation, Security, Greening, Energy, & Maintenance: Hearing Before the Subcommittee on Economic Development, Public Buildings, & Emergency Management of the Committee on Transportation & Infrastructure, House of Representatives, One Hundred Tenth Congress, Second Session, April 1, 2008. 2008. (Illus.). xiii, 158p. *(978-0-16-083842-2(8)*, 552-070-39539-3) United States Government Printing Office.

Hall, M., ed. Materials for Energy Efficiency & Thermal Comfort in Buildings. 2010. (Illus.). 732p. 279.95 *(978-1-4398-2970-7(5))* CRC Pr. LLC.

Haller, Achim. The Performance of a Regenerative Heating & Cooling System: System Analysis Carried out in a Multipurpose Building. 2008. 152p. pap. *(978-3-639-10627-5(X))* VDM Verlag Dr. Mueller e.K.

Harris, Douglas. Energy Management in Buildings. 2011. (ENG., Illus.). 176p. pap. 31.95 *(978-0-415-56649-0(5))*; 165.00 ***(978-0-415-56648-3(7))*** Routledge.

Harvey, L. D. Danny, ed. A Handbook on Low-Energy Buildings & District-Energy Systems: Fundamentals, Techniques, & Examples. 2006. (ENG., Illus.). 720p. 290.00 *(978-1-84407-243-9(6))* Routledge.

Hausladen, Gerhard & Liedl, Petra. Building to Suit the Climate: A Handbook. 2012. (ENG., Illus.). 176p. 69.95 *(978-3-0346-0728-5(8))* Birkhauser Verlag AG CHE. Dist: Actar Birkhauser Distribution.

Hejler Andersen, Helle & Lind Klogborg, Mathias. Solar City. 2011. 216p. pap. ***(978-3-8443-2105-0(5))*** Lambert Academic Publishing.

Henderson, Holley. Becoming a Green Building Professional: A Guide to Careers in Sustainable Architecture, Design, Engineering, Development, & Operations. 2012. (Wiley Series in Sustainable Design Ser.: 33). (ENG., Illus.). 576p. pap. 44.95 ***(978-0-470-95143-9(5)***, Wiley) Wiley, John & Sons, Inc.

Hindrichs, Dirk U. & Daniels, Klaus. Plusminus 20/40 Latitude: Sustainable Building Design in Tropical & Subtropical Regions. 2007. (ENG., Illus.). 448p. 109.00 *(978-3-930698-83-7(8))* Edition Axel Menges GmbH DEU. Dist: National Bk. Network.

Hootman, Thomas. Net Zero Energy Design. 2012. (ENG., Illus.). 432p. 85.00 ***(978-1-118-01854-5(0)***, Wiley) Wiley, John & Sons, Inc.

Horvath, Polly. M Is for Mountie: An RCMP Alphabet. 2008. (ENG., Illus.). 32p. (J). (gr. k-6). 17.95 *(978-1-58536-267-7(0))* Sleeping Bear Pr.

Howlett, Robert J., et al, eds. Sustainability in Energy & Buildings: Results of the Second International Conference in Sustainability in Energy & Buildings (SEB'10) 2010. (Smart Innovation, Systems & Technologies Ser.). (Illus.). xviii, 302p. 259.00 *(978-3-642-17386-8(1)*, 3642173861) Springer.

Hubka, David & Valtcheva-McGee, Vessela. LEED Homes Practice Exam. 2009. (ENG.). 94p. pap. 40.00 *(978-1-59126-183-4(X))* Professional Pubns., Inc.

ICC. Energy Conservation Construction Code of New York State 2007. 2007. pap. 34.00 *(978-1-58001-584-4(0))*; bds. 39.00 *(978-1-58001-635-3(9))* International Code Council.

—International Energy Conservation Code 2006 New Jersey Edition. 2007. 32p. bds. 33.00 *(978-1-58001-516-5(6))* International Code Council.

—International Green Construction Code. 2010. pap. 119.00 *(978-1-58001-630-8(8))* International Code Council.

—International Residential Code New Jersey Edition 2006. 2007. 600p. bds. 105.00 *(978-1-58001-515-8(8))* International Code Council.

—User's Guide to the 2010 Energy Conservation Construction Code of New York State. 2011. pap. *(978-1-60983-087-8(3))* International Code Council.

—2007 California Energy Code Title 24 Part 6. 2007. (ENG.). 110p. ring bd. 42.95 *(978-1-58001-550-9(6))* International Code Council.

ICC/New York. Energy Conservation Construction Code of New York State, 2010 Edition. 2010. pap. 34.50 *(978-1-60983-008-3(3))* International Code Council.

ICC/North Carolina. North Carolina State Building Code: Energy Conservation Code 2012. 2011. pap. 37.00 *(978-1-60983-122-6(5))* International Code Council.

International Code Council. Codigo Internacional de Conservacion de Energia 2006. 2009. (ENG.). pap. 27.00 *(978-1-58001-671-1(5))* International Code Council.

—2009 International Energy Conservation Code: Softcover Version. 2009. (ENG.). pap. 40.00 *(978-1-58001-742-8(8))* International Code Council.

—2012 International Energy Conservation Code. 2011. (ENG.). pap. 40.00 *(978-1-60983-058-8(X))* International Code Council.

—2012 International Energy Conservation Code with ASHRAE Standard. 2011. (ENG.). pap. 147.00 *(978-1-60983-091-5(1))* International Code Council.

International Code Council & Sivigny, Donald J. Code Source: 2012 Energy Conservation Code. 2011. (ENG., Illus.). 64p. spiral bd. 25.95 *(978-1-111-03723-9(X))* Delmar Cengage Learning.

International Code Council Staff. International Energy Conservation Code 2009: 90. 1-2007 Energy Standard for Building Except Low-Rise Residential Buildings. 2009. (ENG.). pap. 147.00 *(978-1-58001-799-2(1))* International Code Council.

—2006 International Energy Conservation Code: Code & Commentary. 2007. (ENG.). 228p. pap. 51.50 *(978-1-58001-488-5(7))* Delmar Cengage Learning.

—2009 Energy Conservation Code Study Companion. 2010. (ENG.). pap. 48.00 *(978-1-58001-869-2(6))* International Code Council.

—2009 International Energy Conservation Code Commentary. 2010. (ENG.). 1p. pap. 55.00 *(978-1-58001-896-8(3))* International Code Council.

—2009 International Energy Conservations Code & Commentary. 2010. (ENG.). 55.00 *(978-1-58001-897-5(1))* International Code Council.

Johnston, David & Gibson, Scott. Green from the Ground Up: Sustainable, Healthy, & Energy-Efficient Home Construction - A Builder's Guide. 2008. (Builder's Guide Ser.). (ENG., Illus.). 330p. pap. 24.95 *(978-1-56158-973-9(X))* Taunton Pr., Inc.

Kabir, Elham. Modeling User Control of Environmental Systems in Office Buildings. 2008. 156p. pap. *(978-3-639-03492-9(9))* VDM Verlag Dr. Mueller e.K.

Kalz, Doreen E. Heating & Cooling Concepts Employing Environmental Energy & Thermo-Active Building Systems: System Analysis & Optimization. 2011. (ENG., Illus.). 219p. pap. 47.72 *(978-3-8396-0176-1(2))* Fraunhofer IRB Verlag DEU. Dist: Silvermine International Bks., LLC.

Krarti, Moncef. Energy Audit Building Systems: An Engineering Approach. 2nd rev. ed. 2010. (Mechanical Engineering Ser.). (ENG., Illus.). 454p. 135.95 *(978-1-4398-2871-7(7)*, CRC Press) Taylor & Francis Group GBR. Dist: Taylor & Francis Group.

Kubba, Sam. LEED Practices, Certification, & Accreditation Handbook. 2009. (ENG., Illus.). 528p. pap. 92.95 *(978-1-85617-691-0(6)*, Butterworth-Heinemann) Elsevier Science & Technology Bks.

Landsberg, Dennis R. Energy Efficiency Guide for Existing Commercial Buildings: Technical Implementation. 2011. pap. ***(978-1-936504-17-6(0))*** American Society of Heating, Refrigerating & Air-Conditioning Engineers, Inc.

Landsberg, Dennis R., et al. Energy Efficiency Guide for Existing Commercial Buildings: The Business Case for Building Owners & Managers. 2009. (ENG.). 85p. pap. 39.00 *(978-1-933742-63-2(1))* American Society of Heating, Refrigerating & Air-Conditioning Engineers, Inc.

LEED Exam Secrets Test Prep Staff, ed. LEED AP Building Design + Construction Exam Flashcard Study System: LEED Test Practice Questions & Review for the Leadership in Energy & Environmental Design Exam. 2011. (C). 62.99 *(978-1-61403-581-7(4))* Mometrix Media LLC.

—LEED AP Building Design + Construction Exam Secrets Study Guide: LEED Test Review for the Leadership in Energy & Environmental Design Exam. 2011. (C). 91.99 *(978-1-61403-580-0(6))* Mometrix Media LLC.

LeedVisual. LeedVisual GA. LeedVisual, ed. 2009. (ENG.). pap. *(978-0-615-33280-2(3))* LeedVisual.

Leppo, RA/CID, LEED AP, Holly Williams. LEED Prep Homes: What You Really Need to Know to Pass the LEED AP Homes Exam. 2009. (ENG.). 360p. pap. 48.00 *(978-1-59126-182-7(1))* Professional Pubns., Inc.

—LEED Prep ID&C: What You Really Need to Know to Pass the LEED AP Interior Design & Construction Exam. 2009. (ENG.). 356p. pap. 48.00 *(978-1-59126-186-5(4))* Professional Pubns., Inc.

Leppo, RA/CID, LEED AP, Holly Williams, et al. LEED Prep BD&C: What You Really Need to Know to Pass the LEED AP Building Design & Construction Exam. 2009. (ENG.). 392p. pap. 48.00 *(978-1-59126-184-1(8))* Professional Pubns., Inc.

Lerum, Vidar. High-Performance Building. 2007. (ENG., Illus.). 304p. 80.00 *(978-0-471-77535-5(5)*, Wiley) Wiley, John & Sons, Inc.

Liu, Feng, et al. Mainstreaming Building Energy Efficiency Codes in Developing Countries: Global Experiences & Lessons from Early Adopters. 2010. (World Bank Working Papers: 204). (ENG., Illus.). 224p. pap. 25.00 *(978-0-8213-8534-0(8)*, 9780821385340) World Bank Pubns.

Lydia, Kallipoliti, ed. EcoRedux: Design Remedies for an Ailing Planet. 2011. (Architectural Design Ser.: 40). (ENG., Illus.). 136p. pap. 40.00 *(978-0-470-74662-2(9)*, Wiley) Wiley, John & Sons, Inc.

Matriti. Epistolae tae V1, 1537-1548: Ex Variis Europae Locis Ab Anno 1537 Ad 1556 Scriptae (1898) 2009. 648p. pap. 45.95 *(978-1-104-12336-9(3))* Kessinger Publishing, LLC.

Matthews, David I., ed. Innovations in Energy: Efficient Technologies for Buildings. 2012. 230p. ***(978-1-61761-976-2(0))*** Nova Science Pubs., Inc.

Meyer, Leo A. & Wray, H. Lynn. The Green Energy Management Book. 2009. (Illus.). 173p. *(978-0-88069-053-9(4))* LAMA Bks.

Miller, Kathryn. Public Libraries Going Green. 2010. (Illus.). 128p. *(978-0-8389-1018-4(1))* American Library Assn.

Mohammadi, Abdolazim. User Interactions with Building Systems & the Energy Implications in Offices. 2008. (Illus.). 124p. pap. *(978-3-8364-5770-5(9))* VDM Verlag Dr. Mueller e.K.

Monfet, Danielle. Development & Calibration of a Model of a University Building. 2008. 96p. pap. *(978-3-639-04242-9(5))* VDM Verlag Dr. Mueller e.K.

Nemecek, Jonas & Schulz, Patrik. Buildings & the Environment. 2009. (Environmental Science, Engineering & Technology Ser.). (Illus.). xv, 330p. 129.00 *(978-1-60876-128-9(2))* Nova Science Pubs., Inc.

Panel on Redesigning the Commercial Buildings and Residential Energy Consumption Surveys of the Energy Information Administration & National Research Council. Effective Tracking of Building Energy Use: Improving the Commercial Buildings & Residential Energy Consumption Surveys. 2012. (ENG.). 133p. pap. 34.50 ***(978-0-309-25401-4(9))*** National Academies Pr.

Papadopoulou, Elena. Energy Management in Buildings Using Photovoltaics. 2012. (Green Energy & Technology Ser.). (ENG., Illus.). xiii, 130p. 129.00 ***(978-1-4471-2382-8(4)***, 1447123824) Springer.

Peot, M Ed, Meghan & Schumacher, LEED AP, Brennan. LEED BD&C Practice Exam: Building Design & Construction. 2009. (ENG.). 112p. pap. 40.00 *(978-1-59126-185-8(6))* Professional Pubns., Inc.

Poikryl, Richard & Török, Akos, eds. Materials, Technologies & Practice in Historic Heritage Structures. 2009. (ENG., Illus.). xvii, 371p. 169.00 *(978-90-481-2683-5(5)*, 9048126835) Springer.

Queen, Bill, et al. Green Building & Remodeling - Complete Idiot's Guide. 2009. (Complete Idiot's Guide Ser.). (ENG.). 336p. (gr. 12-18). 19.95 *(978-1-59257-828-3(4)*, Alpha Bks.) Penguin Group (USA) Inc.

Rabun, John S., et al. Building Evaluation for Adaptive Reuse & Preservation. 2009. (ENG., Illus.). 272p. 120.00 *(978-0-470-10879-6(7)*, Wiley) Wiley, John & Sons, Inc.

Ries, Charles P., et al. Improving the Energy Performance of Buildings: Learning from the European Union & Australia. 2009. 60p. pap. 23.00 *(978-0-8330-4787-8(6)*, tr728) RAND Corp., The.

Robinson, Anthony. High-Performance Buildings: A Guide for Owners & Managers. 2012. (ENG.). 119.95 *(978-1-4398-5199-9(9))* Fairmont Pr., Inc.

Ruiz Geli, Enric & Rifkin, Jeremy. A Green New Deal: From Geopolitics to Biosphere Politics. 2011. (ENG & SPA., Illus.). 96p. pap. *(978-84-92861-58-3(4))* Actar Birkhauser Distribution.

Santamouris, Mat. Advances in Building Energy Research. 2008. (ENG., Illus.). 232p. 360.00 *(978-1-84407-389-4(0))* Routledge.

—Advances in Building Energy Research, Vol. 4. 2010. (ENG., Illus.). 336p. 300.00 *(978-1-84971-187-6(9))* Routledge.

Santamouris, Mat, ed. Advances in Building Energy Research. 2015. (ENG., Illus.). 336p. 300.00 *(978-1-84971-430-3(4))* Earthscan LLC.

—Advances in Building Energy Research, Vol. 2. 2009. (ENG., Illus.). 336p. 296.00 *(978-1-84407-517-1(6))* Routledge.

Santamouris, Mat & Cato, Molly Scott. Advances in Building Energy Research, Vol. 3. Santamouris, Mat, ed. 2007. (ENG., Illus.). 256p. 350.00 *(978-1-84407-752-6(7))* Routledge.

Smith, Geoffrey B., et al. Green Nanotechnology: Energy for Tomorrow's World. 2010. (ENG., Illus.). 472p. 79.95 *(978-1-4200-8532-7(8)*, CRC Press) Taylor & Francis Group GBR. Dist: Taylor & Francis Group.

U.S. Green Building Council Staff, contrib. by. Existing Buildings: Operations & Maintenance Reference Guide. 2008. (Illus.). 532p. pap. ***(978-1-932444-13-1(0))*** U. S. Green Building Council.

U.S. Green Building Council Staff, contrib. by. USGBC LEED AP Operations + Maintenance Study Guide. 2009. (Illus.). 205p. pap. *(978-1-932444-24-7(6))* U. S. Green Building Council.

Utrick, Joseph B., ed. Energy & Buildings: Efficiency, Air Quality, & Conservation. 2009. 115.00 *(978-1-60741-049-2(4))* Nova Science Pubs., Inc.

Vallero, Daniel A. & Brasier, Chris. Sustainable Design: The Science of Sustainability & Green Engineering. 2008. (ENG., Illus.). 352p. 90.00 *(978-0-470-13062-9(8)*, Wiley) Wiley, John & Sons, Inc.

Van Der Like, Robert Neal & Meehan, Peggy. The Paid-From-Savings Guide to Green Existing Buildings. 2009. (Illus.). i, 100p. pap. ***(978-1-932444-29-2(7))*** U. S. Green Building Council.

von Zabeltitz, Christian. Integrated Greenhouse Systems for Mild Climates: Climate Conditions, Design, Construction, Maintenance, Climate Control. 2010. (ENG., Illus.). x, 363p. 209.00 *(978-3-642-14581-0(7)*, 3642145817) Springer.

Voss, Karsten. Net Zero Energy Buildings: International Comparison of Carbon-Neutral Lifestyles. 2011. 184p. pap. 69.95 *(978-3-0346-0780-3(6))* Birkhauser Verlag AG CHE. Dist: Actar Birkhauser Distribution.

Whitton, Kevin J. Green Hawai'i: A Guide to a Sustainable & Energy Efficient Home. 2008. pap. *(978-1-56647-861-8(8))* Mutual Publishing LLC.

Williams, Carter L. A Green United States: Pathways, Policies & Issues. 2011. (Energy Science, Engineering & Technology Ser.). (Illus.). x, 184p. 115.00 *(978-1-61761-599-3(4))* Nova Science Pubs., Inc.

Zira, Christina. Three European Standards for Energy Assessment of Buildings. 2010. 128p. pap. *(978-3-639-26667-2(6))* VDM Verlag Dr. Mueller e.K.

BUILDINGS—ENVIRONMENTAL ENGINEERING

see also Air Conditioning; Architectural Acoustics; Clean Rooms; Interior Decoration; Lighting; Pipe Fitting; Plumbing; Sanitary Engineering; Ventilation

A S H R A E, contrib. by. Best Practices for Datacom Facility Energy Efficiency, Second Edition: Second Edition. 2nd ed. 2009. (ENG.). 254p. pap. 54.00 *(978-1-933742-47-2(X))* American Society of Heating, Refrigerating & Air-Conditioning Engineers, Inc.

Al Satari, Mohamed. Estimation of Seismic Response Demands for R/C Framed Structures. 2008. 172p. pap. *(978-3-639-04424-9(X))* VDM Verlag Dr. Mueller e.K.

American Society of Heating, contrib. by. Advanced Energy Design Guide for Highway Lodging: Achieving 30% Energy Savings Toward a Net Zero Energy Building. 2009. (ENG.). 120p. pap. 62.00 *(978-1-933742-61-8(5))* American Society of Heating, Refrigerating & Air-Conditioning Engineers, Inc.

American Society of Heating, et al, contrib. by. ASHRAE Greenguide: Third Edition: the Design, Construction, & Operation of Sustainable Buildings. 3rd ed. 2010. (Illus.). 464p. lib. bdg. 98.00 *(978-1-933742-85-4(2))* American Society of Heating, Refrigerating & Air-Conditioning Engineers, Inc.

American Society of Heating, contrib. by. Indoor Air Quality Guide: Best Practices for Design, Construction, & Commissioning. 2010. (ENG.). 176p. pap. 29.00

(978-1-933742-59-5(3)) American Society of Heating, Refrigerating & Air-Conditioning Engineers, Inc.

—Thermal Guidelines for Data Processing Environments, 2nd Edition. 2nd ed. 2009. (ENG.). 70p. 54.00 *(978-1-933742-46-5(1))* American Society of Heating, Refrigerating & Air-Conditioning Engineers, Inc.

American Socety of Mechanical Engineers Staff, ed. Practical & Design Aspects of Small-Scale CHP for Building Services' Engineers. 78p. 88.00 *(978-0-85298-842-8(7))* Professional Engineering Publishing GBR. Dist: SAE Intl.

Anderson, Jane & Albury, Kim. Environmental Impact of Materials: Insulation. 2012. (Environmental Impact of Materials Ser.). (ENG., Illus.). 30p. pap. 35.95 ***(978-1-84806-196-5(X))*** Building Research Establishment GBR. Dist: Taylor & Francis Group.

Artmann, Nikolai. Passive Cooling of Buildings by Night-Time Ventilation. 2010. 164p. pap. *(978-3-8383-3993-1(2))* Lambert Academic Publishing.

Ashrae Technical 1.10 Committee, contrib. by. The Design, Construction, & Operation of Sustainable Buildings. 2nd ed. 2006. (ENG., Illus.). 416p. 95.95 *(978-1-933742-07-6(0),* Butterworth-Heinemann) Elsevier Science & Technology Bks.

Aubin, Paul F., et al. The Aubin Academy Master Series: Revit MEP 2011. 2011. (ENG., Illus.). 111p. pap. 86.95 *(978-1-111-13793-9(5),* AutoDesk Pr.) Delmar Cengage Learning.

Bessoudo, Mark. Building façades & thermal comfort: The impacts of climate, solar shading, & glazing onthe indoor thermal environment. 2008. 248p. pap. *(978-3-639-09824-2(2))* VDM Verlag Dr. Mueller e.K.

Bluyssen, Philomena M., et al. Indoor Environment Handbook: How to Make Buildings Healthy & Comfortable. 2009. (ENG., Illus.). 400p. 79.95 *(978-1-84407-787-8(X))* Routledge.

Brebbia, C. A. & Beriatos, E., eds. Sustainable Development & Planning V, Vol. 5. 2011. (Transactions on Ecology & the Environment Ser.: 150). (Illus.). 992p. lib. bdg. 854.00 *(978-1-84564-544-1(8))* WIT Pr GBR. Dist: WIT Pr.

Burroughs, Barney & Hansen, Shirley J. Managing Indoor Air Quality Fifth Edition. 5th rev. ed. 2011. (ENG.). 350p. 119.95 *(978-1-4398-7014-3(4))* Fairmont Pr., Inc.

Burroughs, H. E. & Hansen, Shirley J. Managing Indoor Air Quality. 4th ed. 2008. (Illus.). xii, 359p. *(978-0-88173-569-7(8))* 5th ed. 2011. *(978-0-88173-662-5(7))* 5th ed. 2011. *(978-0-88173-661-8(9))* Fairmont Pr., Inc.

Capehart, Barney L., et al, eds. Web Based Enterprise Energy & Building Automation Systems. 2007. (ENG., Illus.). 423p. 194.95 *(978-0-8493-8235-2(1))* Fairmont Pr., Inc.

Chadderton, David V. Building Services Engineering. (ENG., Illus.). (C). 5th rev. ed. 2007. 448p. 190.00 *(978-0-415-41354-1(0))* 5th rev. ed. 2007. 448p. per. 59.95 *(978-0-415-41355-8(9))* 6th rev. ed. 2012. 368p. 165.00 ***(978-0-415-69931-0(2))*** 6th rev. ed. 2012. 368p. pap. 55.95 ***(978-0-415-69932-7(0))*** Routledge.

Christensen. Introduction Heat Transfer Buildings. 2007. (Synthesis Lectures on Energy & the Environment: Technology, Science, & Society Ser.). 40.00 *(978-1-59829-332-6(X))* Morgan & Claypool Pubs.

Co, Us Gr Build. New Construction Reference Guide Version 2.2. 3rd ed. 2007. (Illus.). 422p. *(978-1-932444-06-3(8))* U. S. Green Building Council.

Construction Research Institute of Canada (CRIC) Staff, compiled by. Cold Regions Engineering & Construction Conference & Expo 2004. 2007. 1972p. pap. 243.00 *(978-1-60423-743-6(0))* Curran Assocs., Inc.

Cram101 Textbook Reviews & Cram101 Textbook Reviews. Outlines & Highlights for Building Systems for Interior Designers by Corky Binggeli. 2011. 228p. pap. 31.95 ***(978-1-61830-872-6(6))*** Cram101 Inc.

—Outlines & Highlights for Mechanical & Electrical Equipment for Buildings by Walter T Grondzik. 2011. 266p. pap. 31.95 ***(978-1-61830-808-5(4))*** Cram101 Inc.

Cusato, Marianne. The Value of Design. 2008. pap. 15.00 *(978-0-9760250-8-5(6),* Plain Paper Pr.) Plain White Pr., LLC.

Davidson, Robert & Blyth, Alastair. Conservation Management in the Built Environment. 2007. (Illus.). 288p. 119.95 *(978-1-4051-4580-0(3),* Wiley-Blackwell) Wiley, John & Sons, Inc.

Doran, Daniel & Anderson, Jane. Environmental Impact of Materials: Vertical Cladding. 2012. (Environmental Impact of Materials Ser.). (ENG., Illus.). 24p. pap. 35.95 ***(978-1-84806-194-1(3))*** Building Research Establishment GBR. Dist: Taylor & Francis Group.

Driscoll, R. & Crilly, Mike. Subsidence Damage to Domestic Buildings: Lessons Learned & Questions Remaining. 2010. (ENG., Illus.). 32p. pap. 65.00 *(978-1-86081-433-4(6))* Building Research Establishment GBR. Dist: Taylor & Francis Group.

Dunster, Bill, et al. The Zed Book: Solutions for a Shrinking World. 2008. (ENG., Illus.). 276p. pap. 63.95 *(978-0-415-39199-3(7),* Taylor & Francis) Taylor & Francis Group GBR. Dist: Taylor & Francis Group.

Duran, Sergi Costa & Liliana, Bollini. New Green Homes: The Latest in Sustainable Living. 2010. (ENG.). 192p. 39.99 *(978-0-06-192799-7(6),* Collins Design) HarperCollins Pubs.

Dutfield, Andrew, et al. Environmental Impact of Materials: Floor Finishes. 2012. (Environmental Impact of Materials Ser.). (ENG., Illus.). 56p. pap. 55.95 ***(978-1-84806-195-8(1))*** Building Research Establishment GBR. Dist: Taylor & Francis Group.

Fernandez-Solis, Jost. Is Building Construction Approaching the Threshold of Becoming Unsustainable? - a System Theoretic Exploration Towards a Post-Forrester Model for Tami. 2008. 408p. pap. *(978-3-8364-6086-6(6))* VDM Verlag Dr. Mueller e.K.

Furuta, Hitoshi. Safety & Reliability of Structures & Infrastructures. Frangopol, Dan, ed. 2009. (ENG., Illus.). 800p. 247.95 *(978-0-415-47557-0(0),* CRC Press) Taylor & Francis Group GBR. Dist: Taylor & Francis Group.

Gissen, David. Subnature: Architecture's Other Environments. 2009. (ENG., Illus.). 240p. pap. 35.00 *(978-1-56898-777-4(3))* Princeton Architectural Pr.

Greeno, Roger. Building Services Handbook: Incorporating Current Building & Construction Regulations. 6th rev. ed. 2011. (ENG., Illus.). 720p. (C). pap. 41.95 *(978-0-08-096982-4(8))* Routledge.

Greeno, Roger & Hall, Fred. Building Services Handbook: Incorporating Current Building & Construction Regulations - Xplana Bundle. 2011. pap., pap. 51.69 ***(978-0-08-097106-3(7),*** Butterworth-Heinemann) Elsevier Science & Technology Bks.

Grondzik, Walter T., et al. Mechanical & Electrical Equipment for Buildings. 11th ed. 2009. (ENG., Illus.). 1792p. 150.00 *(978-0-470-19565-9(7),* Wiley) Wiley, John & Sons, Inc.

Hall, M., ed. Materials for Energy Efficiency & Thermal Comfort in Buildings. 2010. (Illus.). 760p. 290.00 *(978-1-84569-526-2(7))* Woodhead Publishing Ltd. GBR. Dist: Taylor & Francis Group.

Harriman, Lewis G., 3rd. The ASHRAE Guide for Buildings in Hot & Humid Climates: Section 1, Common Issues. 2008. (ENG.). 123p. pap. 116.00 *(978-1-933742-26-7(7))* American Society of Heating, Refrigerating & Air-Conditioning Engineers, Inc.

Hausladen, Gerhard & Liedl, Petra. Building to Suit the Climate: A Handbook. 2012. (ENG., Illus.). 176p. 69.95 *(978-3-0346-0728-5(3))* Birkhauser Verlag AG CHE. Dist: Actar Birkhauser Distribution.

Hens, Hugo S. L. C. Applied Building Physics: Boundary Conditions, Building Performance & Material Properties. 2010. (ENG., Illus.). 322p. pap. 90.00 *(978-3-433-02962-6(8),* Wiley-VCH) Wiley, John & Sons, Inc.

—Building Physics: Heat, Air & Moisture Applied Building Physics. 2010. (ENG.). 572p. pap. 135.00 *(978-3-433-02963-3(6),* Wiley-VCH) Wiley, John & Sons, Inc.

Herschy, Reginald W. & Chen, Yu. Tropical Urban Heat Islands: Climate, Buildings & Greenery. 2008. (Spon Research Ser.). (ENG., Illus.). 272p. (C). 155.00 *(978-0-415-41104-2(1))* Routledge.

Hindrichs, Dirk U. & Daniels, Klaus. Plusminus 20/40 Latitude: Sustainable Building Design in Tropical & Subtropical Regions. 2007. (ENG., Illus.). 448p. 109.00 *(978-3-930698-83-7(8))* Edition Axel Menges GmbH DEU. Dist: National Bk. Network.

Hootman, Thomas. Net Zero Energy Design. 2012. (ENG., Illus.). 432p. 85.00 ***(978-1-118-01854-5(0),*** Wiley) Wiley, John & Sons, Inc.

International Code Council Staff. Developing Green Building Ordinances. 2010. (ENG.). 36.00 *(978-1-58001-934-7(X))* International Code Council.

Isiadinso, Chinwe. Integrating Deconstruction into the Project Delivery Process. 2010. 272p. pap. *(978-3-639-13995-2(X))* VDM Verlag Dr. Mueller e.K.

Jaeger, Falk, ed. Behnisch Architekten. 2009. (ENG., Illus.). 144p. pap. 39.95 *(978-3-939633-83-9(6))* Jovis Verlag GmbH DEU. Dist: D.A.P./Distributed Art Pubs.

Kabir, Elham. Modeling User Control of Environmental Systems in Office Buildings. 2008. 156p. pap. *(978-3-639-03492-9(9))* VDM Verlag Dr. Mueller e.K.

Kemp, Jana M. & Baker, Ken. Building Community in Buildings: The Design & Culture of Dynamic Workplaces, 1 vol. 2006. (Illus.). 224p. 49.95 *(978-0-275-99220-0(9),* C9220, Praeger Pubs.) Greenwood Publishing Group, Inc.

Köhler, Wolfgang. Simulation of a Knx Network with Eibsec Protocol Extensions. 2010. 140p. pap. *(978-3-639-24951-4(8))* VDM Verlag Dr. Mueller e.K.

Lally, Sean, ed. Energies: New Material Boundaries. 2009. (Architectural Design Ser.). (ENG., Illus.). 136p. pap. 55.00 *(978-0-470-75363-7(3),* Wiley) Wiley, John & Sons, Inc.

Lechner, Norbert M. Plumbing, Electricity, Acoustics: Sustainable Design Methods for Architecture. 2011. (ENG., Illus.). 304p. 80.00 ***(978-1-118-01475-2(6),*** Wiley) Wiley, John & Sons, Inc.

Littlefair, Paul. Site Layout Planning for Daylight & Sunlight. 2nd rev. ed. 2012. (ENG., Illus.). 98p. pap. 90.00 ***(978-1-84806-178-1(1))*** Building Research Establishment GBR. Dist: Taylor & Francis Group.

Mcauley, Tavis. Integrated Costing of Sustainable Design. 2008. 308p. per. *(978-3-8364-5423-0(8))* VDM Verlag Dr. Mueller e.K.

Meckler, Milton & Hyman, Lucas. Sustainable On-Site CHP Systems: Design, Construction, & Operations. 2009. (ENG., Illus.). 464p. 89.95 *(978-0-07-160317-1(4),* 0071603174) McGraw-Hill Professional Publishing.

Merz, Hermann, et al. Building Automation: Communication systems with EIB/KNX, LON und BACnet. 2009. (Signals & Communication Technology Ser.). (ENG., Illus.). x, 282p. 109.00 *(978-3-540-88828-4(4),* 3540888284) Springer.

Mumovic, Dejan & Santamouris, Mat, eds. Sustainable Building Design & Engineering: An Integrated Approach to Energy, Health & Operational Performance. 2009. (BEST (Buildings Energy & Solar Technology) Ser.). (ENG., Illus.). 474p. instr.'s hndbk. ed. 146.00 *(978-1-84407-596-6(6))* Routledge.

Nasrollahi, Nazanin. Thermal Environments & Occupant Thermal Comfort. 2009. 268p. pap. *(978-3-639-16978-2(6))* VDM Verlag Dr. Mueller e.K.

National Research Council Staff & Health and Productivity Benefits of Green Schools Staff. Green Schools: Attributes for Health & Learning. 2007. (ENG.). 192p. pap. 43.25 *(978-0-309-10286-5(3))* National Academies Pr.

NCCER. Introduction to Weatherization TG Module. 2010. (ENG.). 64p. (C). pap. 29.33 *(978-0-13-216699-7(2),* Prentice Hall) Prentice Hall PTR.

—Sprinkler Fitter Level 3, 2007 NFPA Revision Trainee Guide, Perfect Bound. 2007. (C). pap. 114.67 *(978-0-13-614436-6(5))* Longman Publishing.

Nemecek, Jonas & Schulz, Patrik. Buildings & the Environment. 2009. (Environmental Science, Engineering & Technology Ser.). (Illus.). xv, 330p. 129.00 *(978-1-60876-128-9(2))* Nova Science Pubs., Inc.

Nicol, Fergus, et al. Adaptive Thermal Comfort: The Physics & Physiology of Field Studies & Comfort. 2012. (ENG., Illus.). 208p. (C). pap. 38.35 ***(978-0-415-69159-8(1))*** Routledge.

Olthuis, Koen & Keuning, David. Float! Building on Water to Combat Urban Congestion & Climate Change. 2010. (ENG., Illus.). 240p. 59.00 *(978-90-77174-29-6(X))* Frame Pubs. NLD. Dist: Consortium Bk. Sales & Distribution.

Orosa Garcia, José A. Indoor Air Ambiences. 2011. (Environmental Science, Engineering & Technology Ser.). pap. 43.00 *(978-1-61209-570-7(4),* Nova Novinka) Nova Science Pubs., Inc.

Orosa, José A. & Oliveira, Armando C. Passive Methods as a Solution for Improving Indoor Environments. 2011. (Green Energy & Technology Ser.). (ENG., Illus.). xi, 147p. 129.00 ***(978-1-4471-2335-4(2),*** 1447123352) Springer.

Pohl, Jens. Building Science: Concepts & Application. 2011. (ENG., Illus.). 280p. pap. 71.99 *(978-0-470-65573-3(9),* Wiley) Wiley, John & Sons, Inc.

Poss, Jeffery S. The International Journal of the Constructed Environment: Volume 1, Number 1. Poss, Jeffery S. & Cope, Bill, eds. 2011. 214p. 0.00 ***(978-1-86335-941-2(9))*** Common Ground Publishing Pty, Ltd.

—The International Journal of the Constructed Environment: Volume 1, Number 2. Poss, Jeffery S. & Cope, Bill, eds. 2011. 228p. 0.00 ***(978-1-86335-964-1(8))*** Common Ground Publishing Pty, Ltd.

Pudasaini, Madhu Sudan. Erosion Modelling under Different Land Use. 2010. 236p. pap. *(978-3-8383-4163-7(5))* Lambert Academic Publishing.

Rice, E. B. Building in the North. 5th ed. 2008. (ENG., Illus.). 100p. pap. 16.95 *(978-1-60223-019-4(6))* Univ. of Alaska Pr.

Robinson, Anthony. High-Performance Buildings: A Guide for Owners & Managers. 2012. (ENG.). 119.95 *(978-1-4398-5199-9(9))* Fairmont Pr., Inc.

Smith, David Lee. Environmental Issues for Architecture. 2011. (ENG., Illus.). 608p. 85.00 *(978-0-470-49709-8(2),* Wiley) Wiley, John & Sons, Inc.

Stiller, Michael. Quality Lighting for High Performance Buildings. 2012. (ENG.). 300p. 129.95 ***(978-1-4665-0130-0(8))*** Fairmont Pr., Inc.

Szokolay, Steven. Introduction to Architectural Science: The Basis of Sustainable Design. 2nd rev. ed. 2008. (ENG., Illus.). 360p. pap. 48.95 *(978-0-7506-8704-1(5))* Routledge.

Thuvander, Liane. Towards Environmental Informatics for Building Stocks: A Conceptual Model for an Environmental BuildingStock Information System. 2008. 184p. pap. *(978-3-639-08392-7(X))* VDM Verlag Dr. Mueller e.K.

U.S. Green Building Council Staff, contrib. by. USGBC LEED AP Operations + Maintenance Study Guide. 2009. (Illus.). 205p. pap. *(978-1-932444-24-7(6))* U. S. Green Building Council.

Utrick, Joseph B., ed. Energy & Buildings: Efficiency, Air Quality, & Conservation. 2009. 115.00 *(978-1-60741-049-2(4))* Nova Science Pubs., Inc.

Van Der Like, Robert Neal & Meehan, Peggy. The Paid-From-Savings Guide to Green Existing Buildings. 2009. (Illus.). i, 100p. pap. ***(978-1-932444-29-2(7))*** U. S. Green Building Council.

Vassigh, Shahin & Chandler, Jason R. Building Systems Integration for Enhanced Environmental Performance. 2011. 168p. *(978-1-60427-015-0(2))* Ross, J. Publishing, Inc.

Wegner, Ramona. Messenger in Built Form & Design. 2007. 64p. per. *(978-3-8364-2359-5(6))* VDM Verlag Dr. Mueller e.K.

Winchip, Susan M. Sustainable Design for Interior Environments. 2nd ed. 2012. (Illus.). 400p. (C). pap. 0.00 *(978-1-60901-081-2(7))* Fairchild Bks.

World Health Organization: Regional Office for Europe. Who Guidelines for Indoor Air Quality: Selected Pollutants. 2011. 479p. pap. 84.00 *(978-92-890-0213-4(1))* World Health Organization.

BUILDINGS—FITTINGS

see Building Fittings

BUILDINGS—MACHINERY

see Buildings—Mechanical Equipment

BUILDINGS—MATERIALS

see Building Materials

BUILDINGS—MECHANICAL EQUIPMENT

see also Buildings—Electric Equipment

Ahuja, Anil. Integrated M/E Design: Building systems Engineering. 2nd ed. 2010. (ENG.). 373p. pap. 155.00 *(978-1-4419-4724-6(8),* 1441947248) Springer.

American Society of Mechanical Engineers Staff, ed. Condition Monitoring of Building Services Systems. (Illus.). 70p. 78.00 *(978-0-85298-816-9(8))* Professional Engineering Publishing GBR. Dist: SAE Intl.

Capehart, B. L. & Capehart, Lynne C. Web Based Enterprise Energy & Building Automation Systems. 2007. (Illus.). xiii, 423p. *(978-0-88173-536-9(1))* Fairmont Pr., Inc.

Chadderton, David V. Building Services Engineering. (ENG., Illus.). (C). 5th rev. ed. 2007. 448p. 190.00 *(978-0-415-41354-1(0))* 5th rev. ed. 2007. 448p. per. 59.95 *(978-0-415-41355-8(9))* 6th rev. ed. 2012. 368p. 165.00 ***(978-0-415-69931-0(2))*** 6th rev. ed. 2012. 368p. pap. 55.95 ***(978-0-415-69932-7(0))*** Routledge.

Cram101 Textbook Reviews. Outlines & Highlights for Mechanical & Electrical Systems in Buildings by Richard R Janis, William K y Tao. 2011. 144p. pap. 28.95 ***(978-1-61906-132-3(5))*** Cram101 Inc.

Cram101 Textbook Reviews & Cram101 Textbook Reviews. Outlines & Highlights for Building Systems for Interior Designers by Corky Binggeli. 2011. 228p. pap. 31.95 ***(978-1-61830-872-6(6))*** Cram101 Inc.

—Outlines & Highlights for Mechanical & Electrical Equipment for Buildings by Walter T Grondzik. 2011. 266p. pap. 31.95 ***(978-1-61830-808-5(4))*** Cram101 Inc.

—Outlines & Highlights for Mechanical & Electrical Systems in Architecture, Engineering & Construction by Frank R Dagostino. 2011. 176p. pap. 29.95 ***(978-1-61830-947-1(1))*** Cram101 Inc.

Dagostino, Frank R. & Wujek, Joseph B. Mechanical & Electrical Systems in Architecture, Engineering & Construction. 5th ed. 2009. (ENG.). 960p. (C). 141.60 *(978-0-13-500004-5(1),* Prentice Hall) Prentice Hall PTR.

D'Amelio, Joseph, ed. Mechanical Estimating Manual: Sheet Metal, Piping & Plumbing. 2006. (ENG., Illus.). 305p. per. 119.95 *(978-0-8493-9210-8(1))* Fairmont Pr., Inc.

Davis Langdon Engineering Services. Spon's Mechanical & Electrical Services Price Book 2011. 42nd ed. 2010. (ENG., Illus.). 800p. 255.00 *(978-0-415-58851-5(0),* Spon Pr.) Routledge.

Gatscher, Jeffrey A., et al. Earthquake Protection of Building Equipment & Systems: Bridging the Implementation Gap. 2012. E-Book ***(978-0-7844-7643-7(8));*** (ENG.). pap. 120.00 ***(978-0-7844-1152-0(2))*** American Society of Civil Engineers.

Grondzik, Walter T., et al. Mechanical & Electrical Equipment for Buildings. 11th ed. 2009. (ENG., Illus.). 1792p. 150.00 *(978-0-470-19565-9(7),* Wiley) Wiley, John & Sons, Inc.

Janis, Richard R. & Tao, William K. Y. Mechanical & Electrical Systems in Buildings. 4th ed. 2008. (ENG., Illus.). 672p. (C). 143.60 *(978-0-13-513013-1(1),* Prentice Hall) Prentice Hall PTR.

Konyndyk, Robert et al. Significant Changes to the International Plumbing Code/International Mechanical Code/International Fuel Gas Code 2009, 8 vols. 2009. (ENG.). 224p. pap. 44.95 *(978-1-4354-0124-2(7))* Delmar Cengage Learning.

Langdon, Davis. Spon's Mechanical & Electrical Services Price Book 2012. 43rd rev. ed. 2011. (ENG., Illus.). 872p. 250.00 ***(978-0-415-68066-0(2),*** Spon Pr.) Routledge.

Mahoney, William D., ed. Building News Mechanical/Electrical 2007 Costbook. 17th ed. 2006. (Building News Mechanical/Electrical Costbook Ser.). (Illus.). 499p. per. 95.95 *(978-1-55701-564-8(3))* BNI Pubns., Inc.

—Building News Mechanical/Electrical Costbook. 19th ed. 2008. (Building News Mechanical/Electrical Costbook Ser.). 498p. pap. 97.95 *(978-1-55701-622-5(4))* BNI Pubns., Inc.

Markon, Sandor A., et al. Control of Traffic Systems in Buildings: Applications of Modern Supervisory & Optimal Control. 2006. (Advances in Industrial Control Ser.). (Illus.). XXII, 279p. 179.00 *(978-1-84628-448-9(1),* 1846284481) Springer.

Mossman, Melville J., ed. Means Mechanical Cost Data. 31st ed. 2007. (Means Mechanical Cost Data Ser.). (Illus.). 725p. per. 149.95 *(978-0-87629-048-4(9))* Means, R.S. Co., Inc.

Peterson, et al. Mastering Autodesk Revit MEP 2012. 2011. (ENG., Illus.). 648p. pap. 69.99 *(978-1-118-06681-2(2),* Sybex) Wiley, John & Sons, Inc.

R. S. Means Company Staff & Mossman, Melville, eds. Mechanical Estimating Methods: Takeoff & Pricing for HVAC & Plumbing. 4th rev. ed. 2007. (RSMeans Ser.: 6). (ENG.). 390p. 64.95 *(978-0-87629-017-0(9))* Means, R.S. Co., Inc.

R S Means Engineering, creator. Mechanical Cost Data: HVAC. Controls. 33rd ed. 2009. (Means Mechanical Cost Data Ser.). (ENG., Illus.). 739p. pap. 169.95 *(978-0-87629-819-0(6))* Means, R.S. Co., Inc.

RSMeans Engineering Dept., ed. Mechanical Cost Data. 2008. 725p. 154.95 *(978-0-87629-183-2(3))* Means, R.S. Co., Inc.

Wang, Shengwei. Intelligent Buildings & Building Automation. 2009. (ENG., Illus.). 264p. (C). 160.00 *(978-0-415-47570-9(8));* pap. 79.95 *(978-0-415-47571-6(6))* Routledge.

Woodward, Jay, et al. Significant Changes to the International Plumbing Code, International Mechanical Code & International Fuel Gas Code 2012. 2011. (ENG.). 224p. pap. 44.95 *(978-1-111-54247-4(3))* Delmar Cengage Learning.

You, Zhong & Chen, Yan. Motion Structures. 2011. (ENG., Illus.). 168p. (C). 130.00 *(978-0-415-55489-3(6),* CRC Press) Taylor & Francis Group GBR. Dist: Taylor & Francis Group.

BUILDINGS—MODELS

see Architectural Models

BUILDINGS—PROTECTION

see also Buildings—Repair and Reconstruction; Dampness in Buildings

American National Standards Institute Staff, et al, contrib. by. ICC/NSSA Standard for the Design & Construction of Storm Shelters: ICC 500-2008, American National Standard. 2008. (Illus.). x, 42p. 20.00 *(978-1-58001-746-6(0))* International Code Council.

Brannigan, Francis L., et al. Building Construction for the Fire Service. 4th rev. ed. 2007. 368p. (C). 89.95 *(978-0-7637-4494-6(8))* Jones & Bartlett Learning, LLC.

Garcia-Jares, Carmen, et al. The Role of Sorbents in Sampling & Analysis of Emerging Pollutants in Indoor Environments. 2010. (Pollution Science, Technology & Abatement Ser.). (Illus.). 108p. pap. 43.00 *(978-1-61761-004-2(6),* Nova Novinka) Nova Science Pubs., Inc.

Hapij, Adam W., ed. Multidisciplinary Assessment of Critical Facility Response to Natural Disasters — the Case of Hurricane Katrina. 2010. 124p. pap. 60.00 *(978-0-7844-1134-6(4))* American Society of Civil Engineers.

Krauthammer, Theodor. Modern Protective Structures. 2008. (ENG., Illus.). 528p. 149.95 *(978-0-8247-2526-6(3),* CRC Press) Taylor & Francis Group GBR. Dist: Taylor & Francis Group.

Kubal, Michael T. Construction Waterproofing Handbook. 2nd ed. 2008. (ENG., Illus.). 576p. 91.00 *(978-0-07-148973-7(8),* 0071489738) McGraw-Hill Professional Publishing.

Kulczyk, Peter. Disaster Mitigation: A Guide for Building Departments. 2009. (Illus.). vii, 122p. ***(978-1-58001-767-1(3))*** International Code Council.

Mazzolani, Federico, ed. Protection of Historical Buildings: Prohitech 09, 2 vols. 2009. (Illus.). xxiv, 1768p. *(978-0-415-55805-1(0)); (978-0-415-55804-4(2))* CRC Pr. LLC.

Murray, Scott. Translucent Skins: Contemporary Innovative Building Enclosure Systems. 2012. (ENG., Illus.). 208p. (C). 165.00 ***(978-0-415-68930-4(9))***; pap. 49.95 ***(978-0-415-68931-1(7))*** Routledge.

Netzel, D. H., ed. Building Response Due to Ground Movements. 2009. 336p. pap. 87.00 *(978-1-58603-995-0(4))* IOS Pr., Inc.

Pasman, Hans & Kirillov, Igor A., eds. Resilience of Cities to Terrorist & Other Threats: Learning from 9/11 & Further Research Issues. 2008. (NATO Science for Peace & Security Series C: Environmental Security Ser.). (Illus.). XIII, 545p. (C). pap. 139.00 *(978-1-4020-8488-1(9),* 1402084889); (ENG., xiii, 545p. 289.00 *(978-1-4020-8487-4(0),* 1402084870) Springer.

Uddin, Nassim, ed. Wind Storm & Storm Surge Mitigation: ASCE Council on Disaster Risk Management Monograph No. 4. 2010. (ENG.). 164p. pap. 65.00 *(978-0-7844-1081-3(X))* American Society of Civil Engineers.

Watt, John, et al, eds. The Effects of Air Pollution on Cultural Heritage. 2009. (ENG., Illus.). xii, 299p. 139.00 *(978-0-387-84892-1(4),* 0387848924) Springer.

BUILDINGS—REMODELING

see Buildings—Repair and Reconstruction

BUILDINGS—REMODELING FOR OTHER USE

Carmassi, Massimo & Carmassi, Gabriella. Senigallia Public Library: Massimo & Gabriella Carmassi. 2006. (ENG & ITA., Illus.). 48p. pap. *(978-0-9544288-0-8(3))* Verba Volant, Ltd.

Christensen, Julia. Big Box Reuse. 2008. (ENG., Illus.). 240p. (gr. 17). 29.95 *(978-0-262-03379-4(8))* MIT Pr.

Corsini, Paolo & Angeli, Giulio. Il Patrimonio Edilizio Dell'Università Di Pisa: Riqualificazione e Nuovi Edifici. 2008. (ITA., Illus.). 118p. *(978-88-8492-579-4(7))* Plus/Pisa University Pr.

Davies, Barrie & Begg, Nigel. Converting Old Buildings into New Homes, 1 vol. 2010. (ENG., Illus.). 192p. 26.95 *(978-1-84797-196-8(2))* Crowood Pr., Ltd. GBR. Dist: Independent Pubs. Group.

Doran, David. Refurbishment & Repair in Construction. 2009. (ENG., Illus.). 480p. 129.95 *(978-1-4398-0871-9(6))* CRC Pr. LLC.

Howard, Maurice. The Building of Elizabethan & Jacobean England. 2008. (ENG., Illus.). 256p. 60.00 *(978-0-300-13543-5(2))* Yale Univ. Pr.

Klanten, R. & Feireiss, L., eds. Build-on: Converted Architectures & Transformed Buildings. 2009. (Illus.). 240p. *(978-3-89955-259-1(8))* Die Gestalten Verlag.

Littlefield, David & Lewis, Saskia. Architectural Voices: Listening to Old Buildings. 2008. (ENG., Illus.). 240p. pap. 60.00 *(978-0-470-01673-2(6),* Wiley) Wiley, John & Sons, Inc.

The New Department of Homeland Security Headquarters at St. Elizabeth's: Local Business Opportunities: Hearing Before the Subcommittee on Economic Development, Public Buildings, & Emergency Management of the Committee on Transportation & Infrastructure, House of Representatives, One Hundred Tenth Congress, First Session, December 12, 2007. 2007. x, 84p. *(978-0-16-083272-7(1),* 552-070-39100-2) United States Government Printing Office.

New Spaces for Old Buildings. 2009. (Illus.). 264p. *(978-981-261-490-2(7))* Marshall Cavendish.

Noelle, Christina. Urban Loft: How Chicago Redefined the Architecture. 2008. (Illus.). 168p. 49.95 *(978-0-9672215-5-7(2))* Bridge Hse. Publishing, Inc.

Owen, Julian. The Complete Loft Conversion Book: Planning, Managing & Completing Your Conversion. 2010. (ENG., Illus.). 224p. 45.00 *(978-1-84797-156-2(3))* Crowood Pr., Ltd. GBR. Dist: Independent Pubs. Group.

Queen, Bill, et al. Green Building & Remodeling - Complete Idiot's Guide. 2009. (Complete Idiot's Guide Ser.). (ENG.). 336p. (gr. 12-18). 19.95 *(978-1-59257-828-3(4),* Alpha Bks.) Penguin Group (USA) Inc.

Sami Kashkooli, Ali Mohammad. Considering Re-Usability in Design of High-Rise Buildings. 2010. 108p. pap. *(978-3-8383-4100-2(7))* Lambert Academic Publishing.

Schleifer, Simone. Converted Spaces. 2006. (Illus.). 380p. pap. 29.99 *(978-3-8228-5147-0(7))* TASCHEN DEU. Dist: Ingram Pub. Services.

van Uffelen, Chris. Re-Use Architecture. 2010. (ENG., Illus.). 424p. 99.95 *(978-3-03768-064-3(4),* Braun Publish,Csi) Continental Sales, Inc.

Wang, Wilfried, ed. & text. Kyriakos Krokos: Fassianos Building, Athens 1990-1995. 2011. (ENG., Illus.). 144p. pap. 40.00 *(978-3-8030-0718-6(6))* Wasmuth, Ernst J. Verlag GmbH & Co. DEU. Dist: D.A.P./Distributed Art Pubs.

Wilsted, Thomas. Planning New & Remodeled Archival Facilities. 2007. *(978-1-931666-25-1(3))* Scarecrow Pr., Inc.

BUILDINGS—REPAIR AND RECONSTRUCTION

see also Architecture—Conservation and Restoration; Dwellings—Maintenance and Repair; Dwellings—Remodeling

Aci, ed. Concrete Repair Basics. 2007. per. *(978-0-87031-249-6(9))* American Concrete Institute.

—Seismic Rehabilitation of Concrete Structures. 2007. per. *(978-0-87031-256-4(1))* American Concrete Institute.

Aci & Icri, eds. Concrete Repair Manual. 2008. pap. *(978-0-87031-262-5(6))* American Concrete Institute.

Alex, Sanchez Vidiella & Francesco, Zamora Mola, eds. Renovated Spaces: New Life for Old Homes. 2010. 420p. pap. 35.00 *(978-84-92463-57-2(0))* Loft Pubns. ESP. Dist: Prestel Publishing.

Amaratunga, Dilanthi & Haigh, Richard. Post-Disaster Reconstruction of the Built Environment: Rebuilding for Resilience. 2011. (ENG., Illus.). 336p. 116.99 *(978-1-4443-3356-5(9),* Wiley-Blackwell) Wiley, John & Sons, Inc.

American Society of Civil Engineers Staff, contrib. by. Seismic Rehabilitation of Existing Buildings, ASCE/SEI 41-06. 2007. 416p. pap. 160.00 *(978-0-7844-0884-1(X))* American Society of Civil Engineers.

Better Homes and Gardens Books Staff. Do It Yourself Kitchens: Stunning Spaces on a Shoestring Budget. 2011. (Better Homes & Gardens Decorating Ser.: 35). (ENG., Illus.). 192p. pap. 19.99 *(978-1-118-03162-9(8),* Wiley) Wiley, John & Sons, Inc.

Bianchina, Paul. Insurance Restoration Contracting: Startup to Success. 2011. (Illus.). 600p. pap. 69.00 ***(978-1-57218-239-4(3))*** Craftsman Bk. Co.

Bloszies, Charles. Old Buildings, New Designs: Architectural Transformations. 2011. (ENG., Illus.). 144p. pap. 24.95 ***(978-1-61689-035-3(5))*** Princeton Architectural Pr.

Bni, creator. Facilities Managers Costbook 2007. 13th ed. 2006. (Building News Facilities Manager's Costbook Ser.). (Illus.). 797p. per. 99.95 *(978-1-55701-562-4(7))* BNI Pubns., Inc.

Bni Publications, creator. BNI Facilities Manager's Costbook. 18th ed. 2011. (ENG., Illus.). 798p. pap. 99.95 ***(978-1-55701-725-3(5))*** BNI Pubns., Inc.

Bottura, Roberto. Renovated Houses in Style. 2010. (ENG., Illus.). 300p. 39.00 *(978-84-96969-09-4(6))* Links International (Leading International Key Services Barcelona, S.A.) ESP. Dist: National Bk. Network.

Breugel, K. van & Koenders, E. A. B. Testing, Modelling & Engineering of Young Concrete: From Fundamentals to Practical Application. 2009. (ENG.). 200p. 109.00 *(978-1-4020-8687-8(3))* Springer.

Chanter, Barrie & Swallow, Peter. Building Maintenance Management. 2nd rev. ed. 2007. (ENG., Illus.). 336p. pap. 79.99 *(978-1-4051-3506-1(9),* Wiley-Blackwell) Wiley, John & Sons, Inc.

Civan, Isilay. Ways to Prevent Office Buildings from Getting Obsolete - a Decision-Tree Approach. 2008. 168p. pap. *(978-3-639-00267-6(9))* VDM Verlag Dr. Mueller e.K.

Clarke, Suzanna. A House in Fez: Building a Life in the Ancient Heart of Morocco. 2008. (ENG., Illus.). 288p. pap. 15.99 *(978-1-4165-7893-2(5))* Gallery Pr., The IRL. Dist: Simon & Schuster, Inc.

Committee on Predicting Outcomes of Investments in Maintenance and Repair for Federal Facilities & National Research Council. Predicting Outcomes from Investments in Maintenance & Repair for Federal Facilities. 2012. (ENG.). 152p. pap. 40.00 ***(978-0-309-22186-3(2))*** National Academies Pr.

Conran, Terence. Bathrooms: Home Design, Decoration & Furnishing. 2010. (ENG., Illus.). 112p. 20.00 *(978-1-84091-551-8(X),* Conran Octopus) Octopus Publishing Group GBR. Dist: Hachette Bk. Group.

—Kitchens: The Back to Basics Guide to Home Design, Decoration & Furnishing. 2010. (ENG., Illus.). 112p. 20.00 *(978-1-84091-549-5(8),* Conran Octopus) Octopus Publishing Group GBR. Dist: Hachette Bk. Group.

Corcuera Aranguiz, Antonio & Minguet, Josep Maria. Remodelling City Apartments. 2007. (POR., Illus.). 192p. 69.50 *(978-84-96429-70-3(9))* Instituto Monsa de Ediciones, S.A. ESP. Dist: Trans-Atlantic Pubns., Inc.

Craftsman Book Company, ed. 2010 CD Estimator. 2009. (Illus.). cd-rom 98.50 *(978-1-57218-234-9(2))* Craftsman Bk. Co.

—2010 CD Estimator-Heavy. 2009. (Illus.). cd-rom 39.99 *(978-1-57218-235-6(0))* Craftsman Bk. Co.

Davies, Barrie & Begg, Nigel. Converting Old Buildings into New Homes, 1 vol. 2010. (ENG., Illus.). 192p. 26.95 *(978-1-84797-196-8(2))* Crowood Pr., Ltd. GBR. Dist: Independent Pubs. Group.

DiLouie, Craig. Lighting Redesign for Existing Buildings. 2011. *(978-0-88173-571-0(X))* Fairmont Pr., Inc.

Doran, David. Refurbishment & Repair in Construction. 2009. (ENG., Illus.). 480p. 129.95 *(978-1-4398-0871-9(6))* CRC Pr. LLC.

Duplex Plan Book: Professional Builder & Remodeler. (Illus.). pap. 29.95 *(978-1-56056-003-6(7))* Reed Business Information.

Durmisevic, Elma. Green Design & Assembly of Buildings & Systems. 2010. 312p. pap. *(978-3-639-11262-7(8))* VDM Verlag Dr. Mueller e.K.

English Heritage Staff. Practical Building Conservation: Mortars Plasters & Renders. 2012. (Practical Building Conservation Ser.). (Illus.). 350p. 124.95 ***(978-0-7546-4559-7(2))*** Ashgate Publishing Co.

Fletcher, Gregory W. Residential Construction Academy: House Wiring - Workbook with Lab Manual. 3rd ed. 2011. (ENG.). 512p. (C). pap. 43.95 *(978-1-111-30624-3(9))* Delmar Cengage Learning.

Foster, Jack & Greeno, Roger. Structure & Fabric, 2 vols., No. 2. 7th rev. ed. 2007. (Illus.). 400p. pap. 99.50 *(978-0-13-197096-0(8),* Prentice Hall) Pearson Education, Ltd. GBR. Dist: Trans-Atlantic Pubns., Inc.

Fountain, Troy. Facadism: Preserving Heritage, Continuing Modernisation. 2010. 60p. pap. *(978-3-8383-4532-1(0))* Lambert Academic Publishing.

Frankl, Lee. Easy Home Repairs from Cellar to Roof. 2011. 148p. 40.95 ***(978-1-258-08404-2(X))*** Literary Licensing, LLC.

Freedman, Philip, et al. Service Charges: Law & Practice. 5th rev. ed. 2012. (ENG.). 450p. pap. *(978-1-84661-247-3(0))* Jordan Publishing, Ltd.

GAO's Analysis of the Gulf Coast Recovery: A Dialogue on Removing the Obstacles to the Recovery Effort: Hearing Before the Ad Hoc Subcommittee on Disaster Recovery of the Committee on Homeland Security & Governmental Affairs, United States Senate, One Hundred Tenth Congress, First Session, April 12, 2007. 2008. (Illus.). iii, 134p. (J). *(978-0-16-080492-2(2),* 552-070-37174-5) United States Government Printing Office.

Gelfand, Lisa & Duncan, Chris. Sustainable Renovation: Strategies for Commercial Building Systems & Envelope. 2011. (Wiley Series in Sustainable Design Ser.: 19). (ENG., Illus.). 304p. 85.00 ***(978-0-470-87261-1(6),*** Wiley) Wiley, John & Sons, Inc.

Gibson, Scott. New Bathroom Ideas that Work. 2012. (Ideas That Work Ser.). (ENG., Illus.). 224p. pap. 19.95 ***(978-1-60085-357-9(9))*** Taunton Pr., Inc.

Gleason, Chris. The Kitchen Makeovers for Any Budget: Layout, Design, Build. 2010. (ENG.). 144p. pap. 24.99 *(978-1-55870-882-2(0),* Betterway Bks.) F&W Media, Inc.

Gorse & Highfield, David. Refurbishment & Upgrading of Buildings. 2nd rev. ed. 2009. (ENG., Illus.). 272p. (C). 62.95 *(978-0-415-44124-7(2),* Spon Pr.) Routledge.

Grantham. Concrete Repair: A Practical Guide. 2011. (ENG., Illus.). 328p. 140.00 *(978-0-415-44734-8(8),* CRC Press) Taylor & Francis Group GBR. Dist: Taylor & Francis Group.

Harrison, H. W. & Trotman, Peter. Building Services: Performance, Diagnosis, Maintenance, Repair & the Avoidance of Defects. 2010. (ENG., Illus.). 270p. pap. 80.00 *(978-1-86081-424-2(7))* Building Research Establishment GBR. Dist: Taylor & Francis Group.

Highfield, David. Refurbishment & Upgrading of Buildings. 2nd rev. ed. 2009. (ENG., Illus.). 272p. (C). 165.00 *(978-0-415-44123-0(4),* Spon Pr.) Routledge.

Holland, M. Practical Guide to Diagnosing Structural Movement in Buildings. 2012. (ENG.). 240p. pap. 49.95 ***(978-0-470-65910-6(6),*** Wiley-Blackwell) Wiley, John & Sons, Inc.

Hubert, Arnold. Resurrection of Fort Lupton. 2011. 112p. 29.99 ***(978-1-4653-3581-4(1))***; pap. 19.99 ***(978-1-4653-3580-7(3))*** Xlibris Corp.

Huth, Mark W. Residential Construction Academy - Basic Principles for Construction. 3rd ed. 2011. (ENG.). 128p. (C). pap. 34.95 *(978-1-111-30721-9(0))* Delmar Cengage Learning.

ICC. Property Maintenance of New York State 2007. 2007. 40p. pap. 31.00 *(978-1-58001-581-3(6))* International Code Council.

ICC/APSP. ICC G2-2010 Guideline for Replicable Buildings. 2010. pap. 29.95 *(978-1-58001-887-6(4))* International Code Council.

ICC/New York. New York State Codes, 2010 Edition Complete Collection. 2010. pap. 564.00 *(978-1-60983-011-3(3))* International Code Council.

IICRC S520 Standard & Reference Guide for Professional Mold Remediation Second Edition. 2nd rev. ed. 2008. 241p. pap. 130.00 *(978-0-9755614-1-6(3))* Institute of Inspection, Cleaning & Restoration.

International Code Council. International Existing Building Code 2009. 2009. (ENG.). pap. 66.00 *(978-1-58001-737-4(1))*; ring bd. 75.00 *(978-1-58001-736-7(3))* International Code Council.

—2012 International Property Maintenance Code. 2011. (ENG.). pap. 35.00 *(978-1-60983-056-4(3))* International Code Council.

International Code Council Staff. 2006 International Existing Building Code: Code & Commentary. 2007. (ENG.). 164p. pap. 76.50 *(978-1-58001-489-2(5))* Delmar Cengage Learning.

Jager, Frank Peter, ed. Old & New: Design Manual for Revitalizing Existing Buildings. 2010. (Illus.). 192p. 99.95 *(978-3-0346-0525-0(0))* Birkhauser Verlag AG CHE. Dist: Actar Birkhauser Distribution.

Jha, Abhas K. Safer Homes, Stronger Communities: A Handbook for Reconstructing after Natural Disasters. 2010. pap. 22.50 *(978-0-8213-8285-1(3))*; (ENG., Illus.). 404p. pap. 29.95 *(978-0-8213-8045-1(1),* 9780821380451) World Bank Pubns.

Jouhara, Hussam, et al. Building Services Design for Energy Efficient Buildings. 2012. (ENG., Illus.). 384p. (C). 180.00 ***(978-0-415-59636-7(X))***; pap. 53.95 ***(978-0-415-59637-4(8))*** Routledge. (Spon Pr.).

Kim, Insung. Use of Cfrp to Provide Continuity in Reinforced Concrete Members. 2009. 504p. pap. *(978-3-639-15982-0(9))* VDM Verlag Dr. Mueller e.K.

Lin, Michael Chew Yit. Maintainability of Facilities: For Building Professionals. 2010. 544p. 73.00 *(978-981-4291-75-0(7))* World Scientific Publishing Co., Inc.

Lleonard, Aitana. Small+Modern+Urban=Home. 2008. (ENG., Illus.). 256p. 29.95 *(978-0-06-154258-9(X),* Collins Design) HarperCollins Pubs.

Loh. Monitoring, Identification & Damage Detection of Structures, Ch. 2010. (ENG.). 250p. 95.90 *(978-0-415-39667-7(0),* Taylor & Francis) Taylor & Francis Group GBR. Dist: Taylor & Francis Group.

Lynn, Abraham C. & Reitherman, Robert, eds. AEI 2011: Building Integration Solutions. 2011. 504p. pap. 99.00 *(978-0-7844-1168-1(9))* American Society of Civil Engineers.

Mahoney, William D., ed. Bni Building News Remodeling 2010 Costbook. 20th ed. 2010. (Building News Remodeling Costbook Ser.). (Illus.). 522p. pap. *(978-1-55701-665-2(8))* BNI Pubns., Inc.

—Building News Facilities Manager's Costbook. 15th ed. 2008. (Building News Facilities Manager's Costbook Ser.). (Illus.). 794p. pap. 99.95 *(978-1-55701-620-1(8))* BNI Pubns., Inc.

—Building News Remodeling Costbook. 19th ed. 2008. (Building News Remodeling Costbook Ser.). (Illus.). 523p. pap. 95.95 *(978-1-55701-625-6(9))* BNI Pubns., Inc.

Mewis, Robert W., et al, eds. Means Residential Repair & Remodeling Costs. 2006. (Means Contractor's Pricing Guide: Residential Repair & Remodeling Ser.). (Illus.). 317p. per. 39.95 *(978-0-87629-873-2(0))* Means, R.S. Co., Inc.

Morassi, Antonino & Vestroni, F. Dynamic Methods for Damage Detection in Structures. 2008. (CISM International Centre for Mechanical Sciences Ser.). (Illus.). 221p. 139.00 *(978-3-211-78776-2(3))* Springer.

Moss, Richard. Bathroom Installations: A Complete Guide Planning, Managing & Completing Your Installation. 2007. (ENG., Illus.). 160p. 45.00 *(978-1-86126-919-5(6))* Crowood Pr., Ltd. GBR. Dist: Independent Pubs. Group.

Mossman, Melville J., et al, eds. Means Facilities Maintenance & Repair Cost Data. 15th ed. 2007. (Means Facilities Maintenance & Repair Construction Cost Data Ser.). (Illus.). 659p. per. 326.95 *(978-0-87629-030-9(6))* Means, R.S. Co., Inc.

Mossman, Melville J. & Plotner, Stephen C., eds. Means Repair & Remodeling Cost Data. 29th ed. 2007. (Means Repair & Remodeling Cost Data Ser.). (Illus.). 773p. per. 128.95 *(978-0-87629-052-1(7))* Means, R.S. Co., Inc.

Mostaedi, Arian. New Perspectives: Renovated Houses. 2007. (ENG., Illus.). 256p. pap. 24.95 *(978-84-96424-48-7(0))* Links International (Leading International Key Services Barcelona, S.A.) ESP. Dist: National Bk. Network.

Necessary Renovations to House Office Buildings: Hearing Before the Committee on House Administration, House of Representatives, One Hundred Eleventh Congress, First Session, Held in Washington, DC, May 6, 2009. 2009. (Illus.). ii, 58p. *(978-0-16-084298-6(0),* 552-070-39853-8) United States Government Printing Office.

Nichols, Al & Laros, Jason. Inside the Civano Project: A Case Study of Large-Scale Sustainable Neighborhood Development. 2009. (ENG., Illus.). 320p. 69.95 *(978-0-07-159931-3(2),* 0071599312) McGraw-Hill Professional Publishing.

Nick, Baker. Sustainable Refurbishment: Non-Domestic Buildings. 2009. (ENG., Illus.). 184p. instr.'s hndbk. ed. 97.50 *(978-1-84407-486-0(2))* Routledge.

Pacifico, Michele F. & Wilsted, Thomas. Archival & Special Collections Facilities: Guidelines for Archivists, Librarians, Architects, & Engineers. 2009. *(978-1-931666-31-2(8))* Scarecrow Pr., Inc.

Peterson, Chris & Creative Publishing Editors. The Complete Guide to Bathrooms: Remodeling on a Budget - Vanities & Cabinets - Plumbing & Fixtures - Showers, Sinks & Tubs. 3rd ed. 2010. (Black & Decker Complete Guide Ser.). (ENG., Illus.). 288p. pap. 24.99 *(978-1-58923-562-5(2),* 1589235622) Quayside.

Prince, Chris & American Contractors Educational Services Staff. Contractor's Daily Logbook & Jobsite Reference. 2010. (ENG.). 400p. spiral bd., instr.'s hndbk. ed. 24.95 *(978-1-4354-9993-5(X),* DEWALT) CENGAGE Learning.

Queen, Bill, et al. Green Building & Remodeling - Complete Idiot's Guide. 2009. (Complete Idiot's Guide Ser.). (ENG.). 336p. (gr. 12-18). 19.95 *(978-1-59257-828-3(4),* Alpha Bks.) Penguin Group (USA) Inc.

R S Means Company, creator. Facilities Maintenance & Repair Cost Data. 14th ed. 2006. (Means Facilities Maintenance & Repair Construction Cost Data Ser.). (Illus.). 659p. per. 296.95 *(978-0-87629-859-6(5))* Means, R.S. Co., Inc.

—Means Repair & Remodeling Cost Data. 28th ed. 2006. (Means Repair & Remodeling Cost Data Ser.). (Illus.). 757p. per. 116.95 *(978-0-87629-868-8(4))* Means, R.S. Co., Inc.

Rabun, John S., et al. Building Evaluation for Adaptive Reuse & Preservation. 2009. (ENG., Illus.). 272p. 120.00 *(978-0-470-10879-6(7),* Wiley) Wiley, John & Sons, Inc.

Ranalli, George. George Ranalli: Saratoga. Ojeda, Oscar Riera, ed. 2009. (ENG., Illus.). 112p. 29.95 *(978-0-9814628-8-2(X))* Oro Editions.

Rebuilding Your Flooded Home: Guidelines for Incorporating Energy Efficiency. 36p. pap. 30.00 *(978-0-7881-4182-9(1))* DIANE Publishing Co.

Reece, Martin B. Strengthening Historic Covered Bridges to Carry Modern Traffic. 2009. (Transportation Infrastructure - Roads, Highways, Bridges, Airports & Mass Transit Ser.). pap. 43.00 *(978-1-60692-581-2(4))* Nova Science Pubs., Inc.

Residential Repair & Remodeling costs 2003: Contractor's Pricing Guide. 250p. 38.95 *(978-0-87629-687-5(8))* Means, R.S. Co., Inc.

Rooney, E. Ashley. Barn Again: Restored & New Barns for the 21st Century. 2010. (Illus.). 176p. 34.99 *(978-0-7643-3431-3(X))* Schiffer Publishing, Ltd.

Rsmeans, compiled by. Means CPG Residential Repair & Remodeling. 2007. (Means Contractor's Pricing Guide: Residential Repair & Remodeling Ser.). (Illus.). 319p. per. 39.95 *(978-0-87629-057-6(8))* Means, R.S. Co., Inc.

RSMeans Engineering Dept., ed. Contractor's Pricing Guide: Residential Detailed Costs. 2008. 375p. 39.95 *(978-0-87629-135-1(3))* Means, R.S. Co., Inc.

—Contractor's Pricing Guide: Residential Repair & Remodeling. 2008. 315p. 39.95 *(978-0-87629-148-1(5))* Means, R.S. Co., Inc.

—Facilities Maintenance & Repair. 2008. 650p. 336.95 *(978-0-87629-175-7(2))* Means, R.S. Co., Inc.

—Repair & Remodeling Cost Data. 2008. 750p. 132.95 *(978-0-87629-206-8(6))* Means, R.S. Co., Inc.

Ruiz Geli, Enric & Rifkin, Jeremy. A Green New Deal: From Geopolitics to Biosphere Politics. 2011. (ENG & SPA., Illus.). 96p. pap. *(978-84-92861-58-3(4))* Actar Birkhauser Distribution.

Russell, Jonathan, ed. National Renovation & Insurance Repair Estimator. (National Renovation & Insurance Repair Estimator Ser.). (Illus.). 2008. 486p.

pap. 64.50 incl. cd-rom *(978-1-57218-215-8(6))* 2006. 518p. pap. 54.50 incl. cd-rom *(978-1-57218-181-6(8))* Craftsman Bk. Co.

Sandu Publishing, creator. Transformer: Reuse, Renewal, & Renovation in Contemporary Architecture. 2010. (Illus.). 267p. 59.95 *(978-1-58423-382-4(6))* Gingko Pr., Inc.

Silberstein, Eugene. Residential Construction Academy. 2nd ed. 2011. (ENG.). (C). 967.95 *(978-1-4390-5598-4(X))* Delmar Cengage Learning.

Smithsimon, Gregory. September 12: Community & Neighborhood Recovery at Ground Zero. 2011. (Illus.). (ENG.). 293p. 79.00 ***(978-0-8147-4084-2(7))***; (ENG., 293p. pap. 24.00 ***(978-0-8147-4085-9(5))***; 304p. E-Book ***(978-0-8147-8671-0(5))*** New York Univ. Pr.

Soria, Sandra S. All New Bathroom Idea Book. 2009. (Taunton Home Idea Bks.). (ENG., Illus.). 224p. pap. 19.95 *(978-1-60085-086-8(3))* Taunton Pr., Inc.

Spain, Bryan. Minor Works, Alterations & Repairs to Fire, Flood, Gale & Theft Damage: Unit Rates & Project Costs. 4th rev. ed. 2008. (Spon's Estimating Costs Guides). (ENG.). 336p. pap. 64.95 *(978-0-415-46906-7(6)*, Spon Pr.) Routledge.

Stanford, Herbert W. Effective Building Maintenance: Protection of Capital Assets. 2010. (Illus.). vi, 426p. *(978-0-88173-638-0(4))* Fairmont Pr., Inc.

Tobias, Leanne. Retrofitting Buildings to Be Green & Energy-Efficient - Optimizing Building Performance, Tenant Satisfaction, & Financial Return. 2010. (ENG., Illus.). 250p. 89.95 *(978-0-87420-133-8(0))* Urban Land Institute.

Triviño, Santi. Eco Refurbishment. Minguet, Josep M. & Triviño, Santi, eds. 2010. (SPA., Illus.). 96p. pap. 22.50 *(978-84-96823-85-3(7))* Instituto Monsa de Ediciones, S.A. ESP. Dist: Trans-Atlantic Pubns., Inc.

U.N. Headquarters Renovation: No Accountability Without Transparency: Hearing Before the Federal Financial Management, Government Information, & International Security Subcommittee of the Committee on Homeland Security & Governmental Affairs, One Hundred Ninth Congress, Second Session, June 20, 2006. 2007. iii, 105p. (YA). *(978-0-16-079442-1(0)*, 552-070-36436-6) United States Government Printing Office.

Valcik, Nicolas A., ed. Space: The Final Frontier for Institutional Research - New Directions for Institutional Research. 2007. (J-B IR Single Issue Institutional Research Ser.: 89). (ENG., Illus.). 120p. per. 29.00 *(978-0-470-25525-4(0)*, Jossey-Bass) Wiley, John & Sons, Inc.

Valigursky, Michelle & Vail, Lisa. Creating Curb Appeal. 2009. (Illus.). 144p. pap. 24.99 *(978-0-7643-3278-4(3))* Schiffer Publishing, Ltd.

van Oudheusden, Kez. The Romance of Renovation. 2010. 161p. pap. 14.56 *(978-1-4452-9446-9(X))* Lulu Enterprises Inc.

Vogel, Steve. The Pentagon: The Untold Story of the Wartime Race to Build the Pentagon — And to Restore It Sixty Years Later. 2008. (ENG., Illus.). 672p. pap. 18.00 *(978-0-8129-7325-9(9)*, Random Hse. Trade Paperbacks) Random House Publishing Group.

Wasim, Muhammad & Toqeer Ahmed, Engr. Computer Aidid Fire Retrofitting Analysis of Existing Rc Buildings. 2010. 112p. pap. *(978-3-639-27383-0(4))* VDM Verlag Dr. Mueller e.K.

West, Geoffrey D. Architectural Salvage: A Guide to Selecting, Buying & Using Reclaimed Building Materials. 1 vol. 2010. (ENG., Illus.). 160p. 35.00 *(978-1-84797-207-1(1))* Crowood Pr., Ltd. GBR. Dist: Independent Pubs. Group.

Westerkamp, Thomas A. Maintenance Manager's Standard Manual. 3rd ed. 2007. (Illus.). 654p. pap. 86.00 incl. cd-rom *(978-1-55701-602-7(X))* BNI Pubns., Inc.

Williams, Andrew R. Spons Practical Guide to Alterations & Extentions. 2nd rev. ed. 2008. (ENG., Illus.). 272p. 51.95 *(978-0-415-43426-3(2))* Routledge.

Woodson, R. Dodge. International Building Code Companion 2006. 2007. (ENG., Illus.). 592p. per. 59.95 *(978-0-07-148429-9(9)*, 0071484299) McGraw-Hill Professional Publishing.

Yudelson, Jerry. Sustainable Retail Development: New Success Strategies. 2009. 309p. pap. 21.80 *(978-90-481-3719-0(5)*, 9048137195) Springer.

Zarfam, Panam. Assessment of the Seismic Behavior Structures by Fragility Curves. 2011. 76p. pap. ***(978-3-8433-7990-8(4))*** Lambert Academic Publishing.

BUILDINGS—SECURITY MEASURES

American Instit. Security Planning & Design: A Guide for Architects & Building Design Professionals Ncarb Edition: A Guide for Architects & Building Design Professionals Ncarb Edition. 2007. 272p. pap. 75.00 *(978-0-941575-52-2(7)*, Wiley) Wiley, John & Sons, Inc.

Condon, Thomas A. Technologies for Facilities Management. 2008. (Illus.). *(978-1-933138-19-0(X))* BOMI Institute.

Government Accountability Office's Review of the Federal Protective Service: Preliminary Findings: Hearing Before the Subcommittee on Economic Development, Public Buildings, & Emergency Management of the Committee on Transportation & Infrastructure, House of Representatives, One Hundred Tenth Congress, Second Session, February 8, 2008. 2008. (Illus.). x, 49p. *(978-0-16-083334-2(5)*, 552-070-39158-4) United States Government Printing Office.

Grassie, Richard P. Building Security Design & Engineering. 2010. (Illus.). 416p. 69.95 *(978-1-4200-8289-0(2))* Auerbach Pubs., Inc.

GuideOne Center for Risk Management Staff, contrib. by. The Missing Ministry: Safety, Risk Management, & Protecting Your Church. 2008. 192p. pap. 17.99 *(978-0-7644-3679-6(1))* Group Publishing, Inc.

Matalucci, Rudolph V., et al. Security Risk Assessment & Management: A Professional Practice Guide for Protecting Buildings & Infrastructures. 2007. (ENG., Illus.). 384p. 99.00 *(978-0-471-79352-6(3)*, Wiley) Wiley, John & Sons, Inc.

Ortmeier, P. J. Introduction to Security: Operations & Management. (ENG., Illus.). 432p. (C). 3rd ed. 2008. per. 76.60 *(978-0-13-512927-2(3))* 4th rev. ed. 2012. pap. 86.67 ***(978-0-13-268295-4(8))*** Prentice Hall PTR. (Prentice Hall).

Prince, Chris & American Contractors Educational Services Staff. Contractor's Daily Logbook & Jobsite Reference. 2010. (ENG.). 400p. spiral bd., instr.'s hndbk. ed. 24.95 *(978-1-4354-9993-5(X)*, DEWALT) CENGAGE Learning.

BUILDINGS—SPECIFICATIONS

American Institute of Architects Staff. The Architecture Student's Handbook of Professional Practice. 14th ed. 2008. (ENG., Illus.). 720p. pap., stu. ed., instr.'s hndbk. ed. 115.00 *(978-0-470-08869-2(9)*, Wiley) Wiley, John & Sons, Inc.

Anderson, Jane & Albury, Kim. Environmental Impact of Materials: Insulation. 2012. (Environmental Impact of Materials Ser.). (ENG., Illus.). 30p. pap. 35.95 ***(978-1-84806-196-5(X))*** Building Research Establishment GBR. Dist: Taylor & Francis Group.

Casey, Michael, et al. Code Check Building: An Illustrated Guide to the Building Codes. 2nd ed. 2007. (Code Check Building Ser.). (ENG., Illus.). 30p. spiral bd. 17.95 *(978-1-56158-912-8(8)*, Taunton) Taunton Pr., Inc.

Ching, Francis D., et al. Building Codes Illustrated: A Guide to Understanding the 2009 International Building Code. 3rd ed. 2009. (Building Codes Illustrated Ser.: 5). (ENG., Illus.). 432p. pap. 55.00 *(978-0-470-19143-9(0)*, Wiley) Wiley, John & Sons, Inc.

Ching, Francis D. K. & Winkel, Steven R. Building Codes Illustrated: A Guide to Understanding the 2012 International Building Code. 4th ed. 2012. (Building Codes Illustrated Ser.: 6). (ENG., Illus.). 432p. pap. 55.00 ***(978-0-470-90357-5(0)***, Wiley) Wiley, John & Sons, Inc.

Dutfield, Andrew, et al. Environmental Impact of Materials: Floor Finishes. 2012. (Environmental Impact of Materials Ser.). (ENG., Illus.). 56p. pap. 55.95 ***(978-1-84806-195-8(1))*** Building Research Establishment GBR. Dist: Taylor & Francis Group.

Emmitt, Stephen & Yeomans, David T. Specifying Buildings: A Design Management Perspective. 2nd rev. ed. 2008. (ENG., Illus.). 272p. pap. 41.95 *(978-0-7506-8450-7(X))* Routledge.

Hansen, Douglas & Kardon, Redwood. Code Check Commercial: An Illustrated Guide to Commercial Building Codes. 2011. (Code Check Ser.). (ENG., Illus.). 46p. spiral bd. 24.95 *(978-1-60085-082-0(0))* Taunton Pr., Inc.

Harmon, Sharon Koomen & Kennon, Katherine E. The Codes Guidebook for Interiors. 5th ed. 2011. (ENG., Illus.). 544p. 85.00 *(978-0-470-59209-0(5)*, Wiley) Wiley, John & Sons, Inc.

—Codes Guidebook for Interiors. 5th ed. 2011. (ENG.). 160p. pap. 40.00 *(978-0-470-59210-6(9)*, Wiley) Wiley, John & Sons, Inc.

Henkiel, Jodi. Conventional Construction Provisions of the 2006 IBC: An Illustrated Guide. 2008. vi, 172p. *(978-1-58001-672-8(3))* International Code Council.

ICC. Model Program for Special Inspection: Based on 2006 IBC Chapter 17. 2007. pap. 17.50 *(978-1-58001-569-1(7))* International Code Council.

—Model Program for Special Inspection Based on the 2009 IBC Chapter 17: Based on 2009 IBC Chapter 17. 2010. pap. 20.00 *(978-1-58001-911-8(0))* International Code Council.

—Plan Review Manual 2006. 2008. (Illus.). 200p. pap. 48.00 *(978-1-58001-674-2(X))* International Code Council.

—UL Standards: As Referenced in the 2006 IBC. 2007. pap. 170.00 *(978-1-58001-544-8(1))* International Code Council.

—2006 Accessibility Study Companion. 2008. 460p. pap. 54.00 *(978-1-58001-698-8(7))* International Code Council.

—2009 Accessibility Study Companion. 2009. pap. 54.00 *(978-1-58001-863-0(7))* International Code Council.

International Code Council. 2009 ICC Performance Code for Buildings & Facilities. 2009. (ENG.). pap. 51.00 *(978-1-58001-738-1(X))* International Code Council.

International Code Council Staff. ICC A117. 1-2009 Accessible & Usable Buildings & Facilities. 2011. (ENG.). 136p. pap. 43.95 *(978-1-58001-918-7(8))* International Code Council.

Kardon, Redwood, et al. Code Check: An Illustrated Guide to Building a Safe House. 5th ed. 2007. (Code Check: an Illustrated Guide to Building a Safe House Ser.). (ENG., Illus.). 30p. spiral bd. 17.95 *(978-1-56158-839-8(3)*, Taunton) Taunton Pr., Inc.

Koch, James Edward, et al. Project Administration for Design-Build Contracts: A Primer for Owners, Engineers, & Contractors. 2010. (ENG.). 298p. pap. 64.00 *(978-0-7844-1075-2(5))* American Society of Civil Engineers.

Kornblut, Arthur & Wertheimer, Lester. Construction Documents & Services 2009. 2008. (ENG.). 336p. pap. 111.95 *(978-1-4277-7038-7(7))* Kaplan Publishing.

Leonard, Donald P. Designer's Illustrated Guide to NFPA 101. 2007. (Illus.). xvi, 447p. *(978-0-87765-632-6(0))* National Fire Protection Assn.

Meier, Hans W. & Wyatt, David J. Construction Specifications: Principles & Applications. 2007. (ENG.). 416p. 86.95 *(978-1-4283-1861-8(5))* Delmar Cengage Learning.

Moore, Francis Cruger. How to Build a Hotel. 2010. 36p. pap. 12.76 *(978-1-163-87795-1(6))* 2010. 50p. reprint ed. 24.76 ***(978-1-168-65816-6(0))*** 2010. 50p. reprint ed. 30.95 *(978-1-161-68990-7(7))* 2007. (ENG.). 48p. reprint ed. per. 15.95 *(978-0-548-58355-5(2))* Kessinger Publishing, LLC.

Moreno, Edgar Ivan. The Home Inspector: The Ultimate Guide to the Greatest Field in the World. 2011. 138p. 29.99 ***(978-1-4628-6588-8(7))***; pap. 19.99 ***(978-1-4628-6587-1(9))*** Xlibris Corp.

Preparing Requests for Proposals & Specifications for Design-Build Projects. 2008. (ENG.). 52p. pap. 45.00 *(978-0-7844-0987-9(0))* American Society of Civil Engineers.

Rosen, Harold J., et al. Construction Specifications Writing: Principles & Procedures. 6th ed. 2010. (ENG., Illus.). 528p. pap. 110.00 *(978-0-470-38036-9(5)*, Wiley) Wiley, John & Sons, Inc.

Russell, Ron. Print & Specifications Reading for Construction. 2011. (ENG.). 240p. 95.00 ***(978-0-470-87941-2(6)***, Wiley) Wiley, John & Sons, Inc.

Shaikh, Javeria, et al. Low Energy House in Lahore. 2010. 152p. pap. *(978-3-639-25765-6(0))* VDM Verlag Dr. Mueller e.K.

Thornburg, Doug & International Code Council Staff. Accessibility Pocketbook 2009 2009. (ENG.). 310p. pap. 28.00 *(978-1-58001-864-7(5))* International Code Council.

Wienand, Norman. Materials, Specification & Detailing: Foundations of Building Design. 2008. (Technologies of Architecture Ser.). (ENG., Illus.). 328p. (C). 165.00 *(978-0-415-40358-0(8)*, Taylor & Francis) Taylor & Francis Group GBR. Dist: Taylor & Francis Group.

Wienand, Sean, illus. Materials, Specification & Detailing: Foundations of Building Design. 2008. (Technologies of Architecture Ser.). 309p. per. 45.95 *(978-0-415-40359-7(6))* Taylor & Francis Group.

Williams, Jane & Williams, Trefor. Construction Management: Emerging Trends & Technologies. 2009. (ENG., Illus.). 288p. (C). pap. 90.95 *(978-1-4283-0518-2(1))* Delmar Cengage Learning.

Winkler, Greg, et al. Construction Administration for Architects. 2009. (ENG., Illus.). 320p. pap. 59.95 *(978-0-07-162231-8(4)*, 0071622314) McGraw-Hill Professional Publishing.

Woodward, Jay & Paarlberg, Kim. Significant Changes to the 2008 Accessibility Standard: Covering 2009 & 2012 International Building Code & the ICC A117. 1 2009 Edition/1st Edition. 2010. (ENG.). 192p. pap. 34.95 *(978-1-4354-9898-3(4))* Delmar Cengage Learning.

BUILDINGS—TESTING

Acceptance Criteria for Special Unbonded Post-Tensioned Precast Structural Walls Based on Validation Testing & Commentary. 2008. pap. *(978-0-87031-270-0(7))* American Concrete Institute.

Becker, Rachel. Physical Performance of Buildings: Integration in the Building Process & Design. 2012. (ENG.). 320p. 90.00 ***(978-0-470-85498-3(7)***, Wiley) Wiley, John & Sons, Inc.

Paik, J. K. & Melchers, R. E., eds. Condition Assessment of Aged Structures. 2008. (Illus.). 552p. *(978-1-84569-334-3(5))* Woodhead Publishing Ltd.

BUILDINGS—WAR DAMAGE

see also Blast Effect; War Damage, Industrial

Bevan, Robert. The Destruction of Memory: Architecture at War. 2007. (ENG., Illus.). 240p. per. 20.00 *(978-1-86189-319-2(1))* Reaktion Bks., Ltd. GBR. Dist: Chicago Distribution Ctr.

Coward, Martin. Urbicide. 2009. 176p. pap. 39.95 *(978-0-415-57356-6(4))* Routledge.

Herscher, Andrew. Violence Taking Place: The Architecture of the Kosovo Conflict. 2010. (Cultural Memory in the Present Ser.). (ENG.). 224p. 55.00 *(978-0-8047-6935-8(4))*; pap. 21.95 *(978-0-8047-6936-5(2))* Stanford Univ. Pr.

Mazzolani, Federico M., ed. Urban Habitat Constructions under Catastrophic Events: COST C26 Action Final Report. 2010. (ENG.). 478p. 229.00 *(978-0-415-60686-8(1)*, CRC Press) Taylor & Francis Group GBR. Dist: Taylor & Francis Group.

—Urban Habitat Constructions under Catastrophic Events: Proceedings of the COST C26 Action Final Conference. 2010. (ENG.). 1068p. 459.00 *(978-0-415-60685-1(3)*, CRC Press) Taylor & Francis Group GBR. Dist: Taylor & Francis Group.

Slavick, Susanne, ed. & text. Out of Rubble. 2011. (ENG., Illus.). 144p. pap. 34.95 ***(978-88-8158-810-7(2))*** Charta ITA. Dist: D.A.P./Distributed Art Pubs.

BUILDINGS—WEATHERING

see Weathering of Buildings

BUILDINGS, COMMERCIAL

see Commercial Buildings

BUILDINGS, DAMPNESS IN

see Dampness in Buildings

BUILDINGS, FARM

see Farm Buildings

BUILDINGS, INDUSTRIAL

see Industrial Buildings

BUILDINGS, LIBRARY

see Library Architecture

BUILDINGS, MOVING OF

see Moving of Buildings, Bridges, etc.

BUILDINGS, OFFICE

see Office Buildings

BUILDINGS, PREFABRICATED

Aeck, Richard. Turnstij Houses & Cannoli Framing. 2008. 116p. pap. *(978-3-639-07847-3(0))* VDM Verlag Dr. Mueller e.K.

Booqs Staff, ed. PREFAB HOUSES. 1 vol. 2011. (FRE, DUT, GER & ENG., Illus.). 620p. (J). pap. 24.95 *(978-94-6065-053-6(8))* booQs Publishers bvba BEL. Dist: Innovative Logistics.

Burkhardt Leitner Staff, ed. Temporary Architecture: Mit Beiträgen von Andrej Kupetz und Kurt Weidemann. 2011. (ENG & GER., Illus.). 280p. 54.00 *(978-3-89986-147-1(7)*, Avedition Gmbh,Csi) Continental Sales, Inc.

Burnside, Kevin & Bentley, Robert. Buying Manufactured Home: How to Get the Most Bang for your Buck in Today's Housing Market. 3rd ed. 2008. 184p. pap. 18.95 *(978-1-392495-58-7(9))* Cycle Publishing/Van Der Plas Pubns.

DAAB Media Staff, creator. Contemporary Prefab Houses. 1 vol. 2008. (ITA, FRE, GER, SPA & ENG., Illus.). 378p. 59.95 *(978-3-86654-022-4(1))* DAAB Media Gmbh DEU. Dist: Innovative Logistics.

Design in Modular Construction. 2012. 100.00 ***(978-0-203-87078-5(6)***, Spon Pr.) Routledge.

Galindo, Michelle. Contemporary Prefab Houses. 2010. (GER & ENG., Illus.). 512p. 89.95 *(978-3-03768-066-7(0)*, Braun Publish,Csi) Continental Sales, Inc.

Ghosh, S. K. Seismic Design Guide for Metal Building Systems. 2009. pap. 54.95 *(978-1-58001-792-3(4))* International Code Council.

Gregory, Daniel P. Cliff May & the Modern Ranch House. 2008. (ENG., Illus.). 256p. 60.00 *(978-0-8478-3047-3(0))* Rizzoli International Pubns., Inc.

Grissim, John D. The Grissim Buyer's Guide to Manufactured Homes & Land: How to Find a Reputable Dealer & Negotiate a Fair Price on the Best Kept Secret in American Housing. 2nd exp. rev. ed. 2008. Orig. Title: The Complete Buyer's Guide to Manufactured Homes & Land. (Illus.). 192p. per. 29.95 *(978-0-9725436-2-0(7))* Rainshadow Pubns.

—The Grissim Ratings Guide to Manufactured Homes: The essential buyer's resource, listing every builder in the U. S. , their histories, products, price ranges, construction ratings, need to know informamtion & much More. 2007. (Illus.). 96p. per. 29.95 *(978-0-9725436-1-3(9))* Rainshadow Pubns.

Huang, Joseph Chuen-Huei. Participatory Design for Prefab House. 2008. (Illus.). 248p. pap. *(978-3-639-07528-1(5))* VDM Verlag Dr. Mueller e.K.

Hunter, Rebecca. Mail-Order Homes: Sears Homes & Other Kit Houses. 2012. (Shire Library). (ENG., Illus.). 64p. pap. 9.95 ***(978-0-7478-1048-3(6))*** Shire Pubns., Ltd. GBR. Dist: Random Hse., Inc.

Jahn, Oliver, et al. PreFab. 2010. (ENG, FRE & GER., Illus.). 432p. 69.99 *(978-3-8365-0753-0(6))* TASCHEN DEU. Dist: Ingram Pub. Services.

Kieran, Stephen & Timberlake, James. Loblolly House: Elements of a New Architecture. 2008. (ENG., Illus.). 176p. 40.00 *(978-1-56898-747-7(1))* Princeton Architectural Pr.

Knaack, Ulrich, et al. Prefabricated Systems: Principles of Construction. 2012. (ENG., Illus.). 136p. pap. 44.95 *(978-3-7643-8747-1(5))* Birkhauser Verlag AG CHE. Dist: Actar Birkhauser Distribution.

Koones, Sheri. Prefabulous + Sustainable: Building & Customizing an Affordable, Energy-Efficient Home. 2010. (ENG., Illus.). 240p. 25.00 *(978-0-8109-8483-7(0))* Abrams.

Koones, Sheri, illus. Prefabulous: The House of Your Dreams, Delivered Fresh from the Factory. 2007. (ENG.). 218p. 25.00 *(978-1-56158-844-2(X)*, Taunton) Taunton Pr., Inc.

Lawson, Mark, et al. Design in Modular Construction. 2012. (ENG., Illus.). 160p. 100.00 ***(978-0-415-55450-3(0)***, CRC Press) Taylor & Francis Group GBR. Dist: Taylor & Francis Group.

McLendon, Sandy. Prefab Elements. 2007. (Illus.). 144p. 29.95 *(978-0-06-115092-0(4)*, Collins Design) HarperCollins Pubs.

Minguet, Josep Maria. Prefab Design. 2006. (CAT, SPA & ENG., Illus.). 256p. pap. 42.50 *(978-84-96429-09-3(1))* Instituto Monsa de Ediciones, S.A. ESP. Dist: Trans-Atlantic Pubns., Inc.

Oshima, Ken, et al. Home Delivery. 2008. (ENG., Illus.). 248p. 45.00 *(978-0-87070-733-9(7))* Museum of Modern Art.

Schneiderman, Deborah. Inside Prefab: The Ready-Made Interior. 2012. (ENG., Illus.). 144p. pap. 24.95 ***(978-1-56898-987-7(3))*** Princeton Architectural Pr.

Siegal, Jennifer, ed. More Mobile: Portable Architecture for Today. 2008. (ENG., Illus.). 144p. pap. 24.95 *(978-1-56898-758-3(7))* Princeton Architectural Pr.

Smith, Ryan E. Prefab Architecture: A Guide to Modular Design & Construction. 2010. (ENG., Illus.). 400p. 75.00 *(978-0-470-27561-0(8)*, Wiley) Wiley, John & Sons, Inc.

Staib, Gerald, et al. Elemente und Systeme: Modulares Bauen: Entwurf, Konstruktion, neue Technologien. 2008. (Detail Ser.). (GER., Illus.). 240p. *(978-3-7643-8655-9(X))* Birkhauser Verlag AG.

Taschen, ed. Prefab Houses. 2009. (FRE, GER & ENG., Illus.). 192p. pap. 14.99 *(978-3-8365-1143-8(6)*, Evergreen) TASCHEN DEU. Dist: Ingram Pub. Services.

Tedesco, Paul H. & Tedesco, James/B. Portable & Prefabricated Houses of the Thirties: E. F. Hodgson Company 1935 & 1939 Catalogs Unabridged Reprint. 2007. 19.95 *(978-0-9792059-1-0(3))* JBT Publishing.

Trulove, James Grayson & Cha, Ray. PreFab Now. 2007. (Illus.). 192p. 39.95 *(978-0-06-114988-7(8)*, Collins Design) HarperCollins Pubs.

BUILDINGS, PUBLIC

see Public Buildings

BUILDINGS, RECONSTRUCTION OF

see Buildings—Repair and Reconstruction

BUILDINGS, RESTORATION OF

see Architecture—Conservation and Restoration

BUILDINGS, SCHOOL

see School Buildings

BUILDINGS IN ART

Here are entered works on buildings as subjects depicted in the fine arts other than architecture.

Coveny, Eloise. The Moving Still. 2010. 116p. pap. *(978-3-8383-6039-3(7))* Lambert Academic Publishing.

Dragset, Ingar & Elmgreen, Michael & Dragset, Ingar. Elmgreen & Dragset: Home Is the Place You Left. 2008. (ENG., Illus.). 196p. pap. 52.00

(978-3-86560-473-6(0)) Verlag der Buchhandlung Walther Konig DEU. Dist: D.A.P./Distributed Art Pubs.

Gardner, Belinda Grace, tr. Kerhaus, 1 vol. 2007. (GER & ENG., Illus.). 80p. 32.00 *(978-3-938025-90-1(5))* Kerber Verlag DEU. Dist: D.A.P./Distributed Art Pubs.

Harrison, Terry. Rustic Buildings & Barns in Watercolour. 2009. (ENG., Illus.). 128p. pap. 19.95 *(978-1-84448-342-6(8))* Search Pr., Ltd. GBR. Dist: Independent Pubs. Group.

Hough, Jessica & Ramirez-Montagut, Monica, eds. Revisiting the Glass House: Contemporary Art & Modern Architecture. 2008. (ENG., Illus.). 134p. pap. 39.95 *(978-0-300-13587-9(4))* Yale Univ. Pr.

Morgan, D., illus. Prayers & Blessings for Your Home. 2008. 32p. 12.99 *(978-0-7369-2157-2(5))* Harvest Hse. Pubs.

Newey, Jonathan. Drawing & Painting Buildings. 2008. (ENG., Illus.). 160p. pap. 37.95 *(978-1-86126-999-7(4))* Crowood Pr., Ltd. GBR. Dist: Independent Pubs. Group.

Robinson. New York, Line by Line: From Broadway to the Battery. 2009. (ENG., Illus.). 64p. 19.95 *(978-0-7893-1836-7(9))* Universe Publishing.

Saint Charles Press, ed. French & Spanish New Orleans: The Pen & Inks of Lola Legier Maduell. 2007. (Illus.). 37p. ring bd. 14.95 net. *(978-0-9796005-1-7(0))* Maduell, Andree.

Simal Lozano, Jesús Ángel. Láminas de Compostela. 2010. (ENG & SPA., Illus.). 102p. *(978-84-9887-286-6(3))* Universidad de Santiago de Compostela, Servicio de Publicaciones e Intercambio Científico.

Slavick, Susanne, ed. & text. Out of Rubble. 2011. (ENG., Illus.). 144p. pap. 34.95 ***(978-88-8158-810-7(2))*** Charta ITA. Dist: D.A.P./Distributed Art Pubs.

Stech, Fabian. Melanie Gugelmann. 2008. (FRE, GER & ENG., Illus.). 150p. 49.00 *(978-3-905770-84-1(9))* JRP Ringier Kunstverlag AG CHE. Dist: D.A.P./Distributed Art Pubs.

Stevens, Janice & Hunter, Pat. Fresno's Architectural Past, Vol. 2. 2007. (ENG., Illus.). 76p. 26.95 *(978-1-933502-13-7(4))* Linden Publishing Co., Inc.

—Fresno's Architectural Past Box Set. 2007. (ENG.). 164p. 49.95 *(978-1-933502-14-4(2))* Linden Publishing Co., Inc.

BUILT-IN FURNITURE

Allen, Sam. Making Cabinets & Built-Ins: Planning, Building, Installing. 2008. (ENG., Illus.). 368p. pap. 17.95 *(978-1-4027-3038-2(1))* Sterling Publishing Co., Inc.

Coleman, Theresa. Custom Shelves & Built-Ins: Build Custom Add-Ons to Create a One-of-a-Kind Home. 2007. (Black & Decker Complete Guides). (ENG., Illus.). 240p. per. 24.95 *(978-1-58923-303-4(4)*, 1589233034) Quayside.

Creative Homeowner Press Editors, ed. Cabinets, Shelves & Home Storage Solutions. 2009. (Home Improvement Ser.). (ENG., Illus.). 224p. (gr. 5). pap. 19.95 *(978-1-58011-436-3(9))* Creative Homeowner.

DeKorne, Clayton. Trim Carpentry. 2008. (Taunton's Build Like a Pro Ser.). (ENG., Illus.). 186p. pap. 19.95 *(978-1-56158-943-2(8))* Taunton Pr., Inc.

Family Handyman Magazine Editors. The Family Handyman's Best Organizing Solutions: Cut Clutter, Store More, & Gain Acres of Closet Space. 2010. (ENG.). 144p. (gr. 12). 14.95 *(978-1-60652-170-0(5))* Reader's Digest Assn., Inc., The.

—Organize Your Whole House. 2009. (ENG.). 192p. (gr. 12). 15.95 *(978-0-7621-0795-7(2))* Reader's Digest Assn., Inc., The.

Rae, Andy. Building Doors & Drawers: A Complete Guide to Design & Construction - Dovetailed Drawers, Utility Drawers, Cabinet Doors, Special Doors, Hardware. 2007. (ENG., Illus.). 186p. per. 24.95 *(978-1-56158-868-8(7)*, Taunton) Taunton Pr., Inc.

Settich, Robert J. Built-Ins. 2009. (Taunton's Build Like a Pro Ser.). (ENG., Illus.). 186p. pap. 19.95 *(978-1-56158-873-2(3))* Taunton Pr., Inc.

Sunset Books Staff & Huber, Jeanne. Built-Ins: Designs to Inspire, Projects to Build. 2009. (ENG., Illus.). 224p. pap. 21.95 *(978-0-376-01117-6(3)*, Sunset Bks./Sunset Publishing Corp.) Oxmoor Hse., Inc.

Woodworker's Journal Editors. Cabinets & Storage Solutions: 17 Space-Saving Projects from Woodworking's Top Experts. 2007. (Best of Woodworker's Journal Ser.). (ENG., Illus.). 151p. pap. 19.95 *(978-1-56523-344-7(1))* Fox Chapel Publishing Co., Inc.

BUILT-IN TEST EQUIPMENT

see Automatic Checkout Equipment

BUKHARA

see Bokhara

BUKHARIN, NIKOLAI IVANOVICH, 1888-1938

Coates, Ken. Who was this Bukharin? 2011. (Illus.). 72p. pap. 24.95 *(978-0-85124-781-6(4))* Spokesman Bks. GBR. Dist: Coronet Bks.

Gregory, Paul R. Politics, Murder, & Love in Stalin's Kremlin: The Story of Nikolai Bukharin & Anna Larina. 2010. (Hoover Inst Press Publication Ser.). xx, 191p. E-Book 19.00 *(978-0-8179-1036-5(0))* Hoover Institution Pr.

Paul, Gregory. Politics, Murder, & Love in Stalin's Kremlin: The Story of Nikolai Bukharin & Anna Larina. 2010. (Hoover inst press Publication). (ENG.). 196p. 29.00 *(978-0-8179-1034-1(4))*; pap. 19.00 *(978-0-8179-1035-8(2))* Hoover Institution Pr.

BUKOWSKI, CHARLES, 1921-1994

Boorman, Neil. Bonfire of the Brands: How I Learned to Live Without Labels. 2007. (Illus.). 256p. pap. *(978-1-84195-987-0(1))* Canongate Bks.

Joyce, William & O'Joyce, Guillermo. Miller, Bukowski & Their Enemies: Essays on Contemporary Culture. 2nd ed. 2011. 160p. pap. 15.00 *(978-1-905177-27-1(5))* Pinter & Martin Ltd. GBR. Dist: National Bk. Network.

Miles, Barry. Charles Bukowski. (ENG.). 2006. 320p. per. 14.95 *(978-0-7535-1102-2(9))* 2011. 352p. 16.95 *(978-0-7535-1818-2(X))* Virgin Bks. Ltd. GBR. Dist: Independent Pubs. Group.

Sounes, Howard. Locked in the Arms of a Crazy Life. 2007. (Illus.). 202p. pap. *(978-1-84195-897-2(2))* Canongate Bks.

Wood, Pamela. Charles Bukowski's Scarlet. 2010. (Illus.). 234p. pap. 15.95 *(978-0-941543-58-3(7))* Sun Dog Pr.

BULBS

Doutt, Richard L. Cape Bulbs. 2009. (ENG.). 254p. pap. 34.95 *(978-1-60469-179-5(4)*, 1604691794) Timber Pr., Inc.

Mathew, Brian. Bulbs: The Four Seasons: A Guide to Selecting & Growing Bulbs All Year Round. (Illus.). 144p. reprint ed. pap. 19.95 *(978-1-86205-200-0(X)*, Pavilion Bks., Ltd.) Anova Bks. GBR. Dist: Trafalgar Square Publishing.

Ogden, Scott. Garden Bulbs for the South. 2nd rev. ed. 2007. (ENG., Illus.). 396p. 34.95 *(978-0-88192-813-6(5)*, 0881928135) Timber Pr., Inc.

Ruksans, Janis. Buried Treasures: Finding & Growing the World's Choicest Bulbs. 2007. (ENG., Illus.). 460p. 39.95 *(978-0-88192-818-1(6)*, 0881928186) Timber Pr., Inc.

Weathers, John. The Bulb Book. 2009. (Gardening in America Ser.). (ENG.). 500p. pap. 29.95 *(978-1-4290-1377-2(X))* Applewood Bks.

Wiesinger, Chris & Colburn, Cherie-Foster. Heirloom Bulbs. 2011. (ENG.). 180p. 34.95 *(978-1-933979-95-3(X))* Bright Sky Pr.

Wolk, Art. Bulb Forcing for Beginners & the Seriously Smitten. 2012. (ENG., Illus.). 255p. 32.95 ***(978-0-9729730-5-2(2))*** AAB Book Publishing LLC.

BULGAKOV, MIKHAIL AFANASEVICH, 1891-1940

Curtis, J. A. E. Bulgakov's Last Decade: The Writer as Hero. 2009. (Cambridge Studies in Russian Literature Ser.). 264p. pap. 38.99 *(978-0-521-10652-8(4))* Cambridge Univ. Pr.

Edwards, T. R. N. Three Russian Writers & the Irrational: Zamyatin, Pil'nyak, & Bulgakov. 2009. (Cambridge Studies in Russian Literature Ser.). (ENG.). 236p. pap. 34.99 *(978-0-521-10985-7(X))* Cambridge Univ. Pr.

Milne, Lesley. Mikhail Bulgakov: A Critical Biography. 2009. (Major European Authors Ser.). (Illus.). 340p. pap. 36.99 *(978-0-521-12246-7(5))* Cambridge Univ. Pr.

Sazontchik, Olga. Zur Problematik des Moskauer Textes der russischen Literatur: Versuch einer Bestimmung anhand von Werken Boris Pasternaks, Michail Bulgakovs, Venedikt Erofeevs, Jurij Trifonovs und Vasilij Aksonovs. 2008. (Slavische Literaturen. Texte und Abhandlungen Ser.). 428p. pap. 99.95 *(978-3-631-57277-1(8))* Lang, Peter GmbH, Europaischer Verlag der Wissenschaften DEU. Dist: Lang, Peter.

Weir, Justin. The Author as Hero: Self & Tradition in Bulgakov, Pasternak, & Nabokov. 2011. (Srlt Ser.). (ENG.). 147p. pap. 24.95 ***(978-0-8101-2807-1(1))*** Northwestern Univ. Pr.

BULGARIA

Miller-Yianni, Martin. Bulgarian History - A Concise Account. 2010. 52p. pap. 8.95 *(978-1-4457-1633-6(X))* Lulu Enterprises Inc.

BULGARIA—BIOGRAPHY

Davies, Chris. Deadly Dimitar: The Biography of Superstriker Dimitar Berbatov. 2009. (ENG., Illus.). 264p. 34.95 *(978-1-84454-569-8(5))* Blake, John Publishing, Ltd. GBR. Dist: Independent Pubs. Group.

Eldurov, Svetlozar. Bulgari, Bulgaria, Bulgarski Sudbi. 2010. (BUL.). 480p. *(978-954-326-118-5(0))* Paradigma.

Jaenke, Ted. Tale of a Short-Term Missionary: Street Ministry in the Balkans:My Faith Journey. 2009. 88p. pap. 11.99 *(978-1-4141-1288-6(2))* Pleasant Word.

Kassabova, Kapka. Street Without a Name: Childhood & Other Misadventures in Bulgaria. 2009. (ENG., Illus.). 348p. 24.95 *(978-1-60239-645-6(0)*, 239645) Skyhorse Publishing Co., Inc.

Stankova, Marietta. Georgi Dimitrov: A Biography. 2010. (Communist Lives Ser.). (ENG.). 256p. 85.00 *(978-1-84511-728-3(X))* I. B. Tauris & Co., Ltd. GBR. Dist: Macmillan.

Todorova, Maria N. Bones of Contention: The Living Archive of Vasil Levski & the Making of Bulgaria's National Hero. 2008. (ENG., Illus.). 500p. 54.95 *(978-963-9776-24-1(6))* Central European Univ. Pr.

Tsatsov, Boris, ed. Chronicle of the Bulgarian Orthodox Church: Volume 1. History & Personalities. 2010. 580p. 250.00 *(978-954-463-124-6(0))* Bulgarian Bestseller - National Museum of Bulgarian Books & Polygraphy BGR. Dist: Coronet Bks.

BULGARIA—COMMERCE

BIA. Essential Bulgarian Manufacturers: Food, Textile, Clothing, & Chemical Companies. 6th rev. ed. 2006. 250p. (J). pap. 219.00 *(978-1-4187-4204-1(X))* Business Information Agency.

Vladimir, Zhechev. General Motors Bulgaria Research Paper: The Penetration of the Crisis & Its Impact on General Motors Bulgaria. 2011. 108p. pap. ***(978-3-639-33421-0(3))*** VDM Verlag Dr. Mueller e.K.

BULGARIA—DESCRIPTION AND TRAVEL

Bousfield, Jonathan & Dorling Kindersley Publishing Staff. Bulgaria - Eyewitness Travel Guide. 2011. (Eyewitness Travel Guides). (ENG., Illus.). 288p. 23.00 *(978-0-7566-7013-9(6))* Dorling Kindersley Publishing, Inc.

Bousfield, Jonathan, et al. Bulgaria. 6th ed. 2008. (Rough Guide Travel Guides). (ENG., Illus.). 480p. (gr. 12). pap. 24.99 *(978-1-85828-068-4(0))* Rough Guides, Ltd. GBR. Dist: Dorling Kindersley Publishing, Inc.

Cultureshock Staff, ed. Cultureshock Bulgaria. 2010. (Illus.). 300p. pap. 15.95 *(978-0-7614-5877-7(8))* Marshall Cavendish Corp.

Egginton, Jane. Buying A Property Bulgaria. (ENG., Illus.). 328p. pap. 19.95 *(978-1-86011-375-8(3))* Cadogan Guides GBR. Dist: Globe Pequot Pr., The.

Kassabova, Kapka. Bulgaria. 2008. (Globetrotter Travel Packs Ser.). (ENG., Illus.). 128p. pap. 14.95 *(978-1-84537-563-8(7))* New Holland Pubs., Ltd. GBR. Dist: Globe Pequot Pr., The.

Kay, Annie. Bulgaria: The Bradt Travel Guide. 2008. (Bradt Travel Guide Ser.). (ENG., Illus.). 320p. pap. 23.99 *(978-1-84162-155-5(2))* Bradt Travel Guides GBR. Dist: Globe Pequot Pr., The.

Locken, E. Travel Journal Borovets. 2010. 192p. pap. 19.99 *(978-0-557-42188-6(8))* Lulu Enterprises Inc.

—Travel Journal Bulgaria. 2010. 192p. pap. 19.99 *(978-0-557-43278-3(2))* Lulu Enterprises Inc.

Perry, Julian. Walking in Bulgaria's National Parks: Pirin, Rila & Central Balkan National Parks. 2010. (Illus.). 256p. pap. 22.95 *(978-1-85284-574-2(0))* Cicerone Pr. GBR. Dist: Midpoint Trade Bks., Inc.

Sachsenroeder, Agnes. Bulgaria, 1 vol. 2008. (CultureShock! Ser.). (ENG.). 256p. pap. 15.95 *(978-0-7614-5505-9(1))* Marshall Cavendish Corp.

Thomas Cook Publishing Staff. Traveller Guides Bulgaria. 4th ed. 2011. (Travellers - Thomas Cook Ser.). (ENG., Illus.). 192p. pap. 16.95 *(978-1-84848-389-7(9))* Cook, Thomas Publishing GBR. Dist: Globe Pequot Pr., The.

Twyman, James. Psychic Children Speak to the World: How Love Creates Miracles. 2011. 176p. pap. 16.95 *(978-1-57174-652-8(8))* Hampton Roads Publishing Co., Inc.

Watkins, Richard, et al. Bulgaria. 3rd rev. ed. 2008. (Lonely Planet Bulgaria Ser.). (ENG., Illus.). 332p. pap. 23.99 *(978-1-74104-474-4(X))* Lonely Planet Pubns.

Zlatkova, Rositsa. Dvoretsut Balchik V Stari Fotografii. 2010. (BUL., Illus.). 72p. *(978-954-337-053-5(2))* Avangard Print.

BULGARIA—ECONOMIC CONDITIONS

Air Power of the Kingdom of Bulgaria Set, 4 vols. *(978-954-9669-79-4(3))* Propeler 92.

Baloutzova, Svetla. Demography & Nation: Social Legislation & Population Policy in Bulgaria, 1918-1944. 2010. (ENG.). 250p. 45.00 *(978-963-9776-66-1(1))* Central European Univ. Pr.

BIA. Essential Bulgarian Manufacturers: Food, Textile, Clothing, & Chemical Companies. 6th rev. ed. 2006. 250p. (J). pap. 219.00 *(978-1-4187-4204-1(X))* Business Information Agency.

Dokov, Pavel. Convergence in Transition Countries. 2011. 52p. pap. ***(978-3-8443-1433-5(4))*** Lambert Academic Publishing.

Evgeniev, Evgeni. Bridge in Transition. 2010. 112p. pap. *(978-3-8383-3411-0(6))* Lambert Academic Publishing.

Garabed, Minassian. Breaking the Bulgarian Economic Model: Reasons & Projections. 2011. 204p. pap. ***(978-3-639-33580-4(5))*** VDM Verlag Dr. Mueller e.K.

GMB Publishing Staff, creator. Bulgaria's Business Environment. 2009. (ENG.). 200p. pap. 75.00 *(978-1-84673-121-1(6)*, GMB Publishing Ltd.) Blue Ibex Ltd. GBR. Dist: Ingram Pub. Services.

Icon Group International, Inc. Staff, compiled by. The 2006 Economic & Product Market Databook for Burgas, Bulgaria. 2006. 618p. ring bd. 95.00 *(978-0-497-80272-1(4))* Icon Group International, Inc.

—The 2006 Economic & Product Market Databook for Pernik, Bulgaria. 2006. 618p. ring bd. 95.00 *(978-0-497-81208-9(8))* Icon Group International, Inc.

—The 2006 Economic & Product Market Databook for Pleven, Bulgaria. 2006. 618p. ring bd. 95.00 *(978-0-497-81261-4(4))* Icon Group International, Inc.

—The 2006 Economic & Product Market Databook for Plovdiv, Bulgaria. 2006. 618p. ring bd. 95.00 *(978-0-497-81263-8(0))* Icon Group International, Inc.

—The 2006 Economic & Product Market Databook for Ruse, Bulgaria. 2006. 618p. ring bd. 95.00 *(978-0-497-81377-2(7))* Icon Group International, Inc.

—The 2006 Economic & Product Market Databook for Shumen, Bulgaria. 2006. 618p. ring bd. 95.00 *(978-0-497-81529-5(X))* Icon Group International, Inc.

—The 2006 Economic & Product Market Databook for Sliven, Bulgaria. 2006. 618p. ring bd. 95.00 *(978-0-497-81550-9(8))* Icon Group International, Inc.

—The 2006 Economic & Product Market Databook for Sofia, Bulgaria. 2006. 618p. ring bd. 95.00 *(978-0-497-81552-3(4))* Icon Group International, Inc.

—The 2006 Economic & Product Market Databook for Stara Zagora, Bulgaria. 2006. 618p. ring bd. 95.00 *(978-0-497-81565-3(6))* Icon Group International, Inc.

—The 2006 Economic & Product Market Databook for Tolbukhin, Bulgaria. 2006. 618p. ring bd. 95.00 *(978-0-497-81697-1(0))* Icon Group International, Inc.

—The 2006 Economic & Product Market Databook for Varna, Bulgaria. 2006. 618p. ring bd. 95.00 *(978-0-497-81778-7(0))* Icon Group International, Inc.

Kressel, Gideon M. Anthropological Studies in Post-Socialist Micro-Economies in the Balkans: Creative Survival Adaptations in Bulgaria & Yugoslavia. 2010. xxiv, 319p. 119.95 *(978-0-7734-3738-8(X))* Mellen, Edwin Pr., The.

BULGARIA—FOREIGN RELATIONS

Asenova, Vera. Money & Power in Bilateral Relations: German-Bulgarian Relations in the Interwar Period. 2008. 56p. pap. *(978-3-639-03389-2(2))* VDM Verlag Dr. Mueller e.K.

Firkatian, Mari A. Diplomats & Dreamers: The Stancioff Family in Bulgarian History. 2008. (ENG., Illus.). 362p. pap. 52.50 *(978-0-7618-4069-5(9))* Univ. Pr. of America, Inc.

Katsikas, Stefanos, ed. Bulgaria & Europe: Shifting Identities. (Anthem Series on Russian, East European & Eurasian Studies). (Illus.). 270p. 2011. pap. 40.00 *(978-0-85728-419-8(3))* 2010. (ENG., 99.00 *(978-1-84331-846-0(6))* Anthem Pr. GBR. Dist: Books International, Inc.

Shepard, Jonathan. Emergent Elites & Byzantium in the Balkans & East-Central Europe. 2011. (Variorum Collected Studies). (Illus.). 434p. 190.00 *(978-1-4094-0364-7(5))* Ashgate Publishing Co.

Sophoulis, Panos. Byzantium & Bulgaria, 775-831. 2011. (East Central & Eastern Europe in the Middle Ages Ser.). (Illus.). 480p. ***(978-90-04-20695-3(7))*** BRILL.

BULGARIA—HISTORY

see also Russo-Turkish War, 1877-1878

Atanasov, Miroslav A. Gypsy Pentecostals: The Growth of the Pentecostal Movement among the Roma in Bulgaria & its Revitalization of Their Communities. 2010. 244p. pap. *(978-1-60947-012-8(5))* Emeth Pr.

Bulgaria: Illustrated History. (Illus.). 161.50 *(978-954-500-091-1(0))* Borina BGR. Dist: Coronet Bks.

Chary, Frederick B. The History of Bulgaria, 1 vol. 2011. (Greenwood Histories of the Modern Nations Ser.). (Illus.). 210p. 49.95 *(978-0-313-38446-2(0)*, A2915C); E-Book *(978-0-313-38447-9(9)*, Greenwood Pr.) Greenwood Publishing Group, Inc.

Crampton, R. J. Bulgaria. 2009. (Oxford History of Modern Europe Ser.). (ENG., Illus.). 536p. pap. 45.00 *(978-0-19-954158-4(2))* Oxford Univ. Pr., Inc.

Detrez, Raymond. The A to Z of Bulgaria. 2010. (A to Z Guide Ser.). (ENG.). 710p. pap. 34.45 *(978-0-8108-7202-8(1))* Scarecrow Pr., Inc.

Gerov, Georgi. Christian Art Icons from Melnik & the Melnik Region, Bulgaria. 2007. (Series Christian Art Ser.). 180p. 110.00 *(978-954-642-285-9(1))* Pensoft Pubs. BGR. Dist: Coronet Bks.

Gjuzelev, Vassil & Petkov, Kiril, eds. State & Church: Studies in Medieval Bulgaria & Byzantium. 2011. (ENG., Illus.). 300p. (C). 39.95 ***(978-954-92571-2-0(6))*** American Research Ctr. in Sofia.

Kralevska-Owens, Nassya. Communism Versus Democracy: Bulgaria 1944 To 1997. 2010. (ENG., Illus.). 432p. (C). 39.95 *(978-954-92571-1-3(8))* American Research Ctr. in Sofia.

MacDonald, John. Czar Ferdinand & His People. 2010. 142p. pap. *(978-1-152-01684-2(9))* Books LLC.

Muir, Stephanie, et al. The Bulgarian Orthodox Church: A Socio-Historical Analysis of the Evolving Relationship Between Church, Nation, & State in Bulgaria. 2009. (ENG., Illus.). 360p. (gr. 17). 55.00 *(978-0-88033-624-6(2))* Eastern European Monographs.

Petkov, Kiril. Voices of Medieval Bulgaria, Seventh-Fifteenth Centuries: The Records of a Bygone Culture. 2008. (East Central & Eastern Europe in the Middle Ages Ser.). (Illus.). 1593p. (C). *(978-90-04-16831-2(1))* BRILL.

Scarboro, Cristofer. The Late Socialist Good Life in Bulgaria: Meaning & Living in a Permanent Present Tense. 2011. (Illus.). x, 244p. ***(978-0-7391-4561-6(4))*** Lexington Bks.

Sophoulis, Panos. Byzantium & Bulgaria, 775-831. 2011. (East Central & Eastern Europe in the Middle Ages Ser.). (Illus.). 480p. ***(978-90-04-20695-3(7))*** BRILL.

Stankova, Marietta. Georgi Dimitrov: A Biography. 2010. (Communist Lives Ser.). (ENG.). 256p. 85.00 *(978-1-84511-728-3(X))* I. B. Tauris & Co., Ltd. GBR. Dist: Macmillan.

Thompson, E. P., et al, contrib. by. Beyond the Frontier: The Politics of a Failed Mission, Bulgaria 1944. (Illus.). 111p. *(978-0-85036-457-6(4))* Merlin Pr. Ltd.

Todorova, Maria N. Bones of Contention: The Living Archive of Vasil Levski & the Making of Bulgaria's National Hero. 2008. (ENG., Illus.). 500p. 54.95 *(978-963-9776-24-1(6))* Central European Univ. Pr.

Yakimov, Radka. Ashes of Wars. 2011. 232p. 28.95 ***(978-1-4620-1984-7(6))***; pap. 18.95 ***(978-1-4620-1982-3(X))*** iUniverse, Inc.

BULGARIA—POLITICS AND GOVERNMENT

Asenova, Vera. Money & Power in Bilateral Relations: German-Bulgarian Relations in the Interwar Period. 2008. 56p. pap. *(978-3-639-03389-2(2))* VDM Verlag Dr. Mueller e.K.

Black, Cyril Edwin. The Establishment of Constitutional Government in Bulgari. 2009. 358p. 53.00 *(978-1-59740-336-8(9))*; 356p. pap. 36.00 *(978-1-59740-338-2(5))* ACLS Humanities E-Book.

Chary, Frederick B. The Bulgarian Jews & the Final Solution, 1940-1944. 2009. (ENG.). 260p. (C). pap. 25.95 *(978-0-8229-8443-6(1))* Univ. of Pittsburgh Pr.

Chiva, Christina & Phinnemore, David, eds. The European Union's 2007 Enlargement. 2011. (ENG.). 136p. (C). 145.00 ***(978-0-415-68965-6(1))*** Routledge.

Crampton, R. J. Bulgaria. 2009. (Oxford History of Modern Europe Ser.). (ENG., Illus.). 536p. pap. 45.00 *(978-0-19-954158-4(2))* Oxford Univ. Pr., Inc.

Crampton, Richard. Aleksandur Stamboliiski: Makers of the Modern World, the Peace Conferences of 1919-23 & Their Aftermath. 2009. (Haus Histories Ser.). (ENG., Illus.). 200p. 19.95 *(978-1-905791-77-4(1))* Haus Publishing GBR. Dist: Consortium Bk. Sales & Distribution.

Engström, Jenny. Democratisation & the Prevention of Violent Conflict: Lessons Learned from Bulgaria & Macedonia. 2009. 188p. 114.95 *(978-0-7546-7434-4(7))* Ashgate Publishing Co.

Evgeniev, Evgeni. Bridge in Transition. 2010. 112p. pap. *(978-3-8383-3411-0(6))* Lambert Academic Publishing.

Ganev, Venelin I. Preying on the State: The Transformation of Bulgaria After 1989. 2007. 222p. 39.95 *(978-0-8014-4564-4(7))* Cornell Univ. Pr.

Katsikas, Stefanos, ed. Bulgaria & Europe: Shifting Identities. 2011. (Anthem Series on Russian, East European & Eurasian Studies). (Illus.). 270p. pap. 40.00 *(978-0-85728-419-8(3))* Anthem Pr. GBR. Dist: Books International, Inc.

MacDonald, John. Czar Ferdinand & His People. 2010. 142p. pap. *(978-1-152-01684-2(9))* Books LLC.

Muir, Stephanie, et al. The Bulgarian Orthodox Church: A Socio-Historical Analysis of the Evolving Relationship Between Church, Nation, & State in Bulgaria. 2009. (ENG., Illus.). 360p. (gr. 17). 55.00 *(978-0-88033-624-6(2))* Eastern European Monographs.

Neuburger, Mary. The Orient Within: Muslim Minorities & the Negotiation of Nationhood in Modern Bulgaria. 2011. (Illus.). 248p. pap. 27.95 *(978-0-8014-7720-1(4))* Cornell Univ. Pr.

Rothschild, Joseph. The Communist Party of Bulgari: Origins & Development 1883-1936. 2011. 364p. 51.95 ***(978-1-258-07638-2(1))*** Literary Licensing, LLC.

Spirova, Maria. Political Parties in Post-Communist Societies: Formation, Persistence, & Change. 2007. (ENG., Illus.). 232p. 89.00 *(978-1-4039-7815-8(8))* Palgrave Macmillan.

BULGARIA—SOCIAL CONDITIONS

Genova, Teodora & Cameron, Lans. A Decade of Roma Inclusion in Bulgarian Society. 2010. 60p. pap. *(978-3-639-26430-2(4))* VDM Verlag Dr. Mueller e.K.

Grunewald, Karsten & Scheithauer, Jörg. Landscape Development & Climate Change in Southwest Bulgaria (Pirin Mountains) 2010. (ENG.). viii, 161p. 129.00 *(978-90-481-9958-7(1),* 9048199581) Springer.

Muir, Stephanie, et al. The Bulgarian Orthodox Church: A Socio-Historical Analysis of the Evolving Relationship Between Church, Nation, & State in Bulgaria. 2009. (ENG., Illus.). 360p. (gr. 17). 55.00 *(978-0-88033-624-6(2))* Eastern European Monographs.

Proykov, Todor. Opening the Pandora's Box: The Child Abuse Discourse. 2010. 132p. pap. *(978-3-8383-5003-5(0))* Lambert Academic Publishing.

Taylor, Karin. Let's Twist Again: Youth & Leisure in Socialist Bulgaria. 2008. (ENG., Illus.). 256p. pap. 49.95 *(978-3-8258-9505-1(X))* Lit Verlag DEU. Dist: Transaction Pubs.

Tejada, Matthew. A History of Bulgaria's Environmental Movement. 2010. 332p. pap. *(978-3-639-22873-1(1))* VDM Verlag Dr. Mueller e.K.

Todorova, Maria N. Balkan Family Structure & the European Pattern: Demographic Developments in Ottoman Bulgaria. 2nd rev. ed. 2006. (Pasts Incorporated Ceu Studies in the Humanities Ser.). (ENG., Illus.). 250p. 41.95 *(978-963-7326-45-5(6))* Central European Univ. Pr.

BULGARIA—SOCIAL LIFE AND CUSTOMS

Creed, Gerald W. Masquerade & Postsocialism: Ritual & Cultural Dispossession in Bulgaria. 2011. (New Anthropologies of Europe Ser.). (ENG., Illus.). 272p. 70.00 *(978-0-253-35557-7(5),* 0253355575); pap. 24.95 *(978-0-253-22261-9(3),* 0253222613) Indiana Univ. Pr.

Kassabova, Kapka. Street Without a Name: Childhood & Other Misadventures in Bulgaria. 2009. (ENG., Illus.). 348p. 24.95 *(978-1-60239-645-6(0),* 239645) Skyhorse Publishing Co., Inc.

Rothschild, Joseph. The Communist Party of Bulgari: Origins & Development 1883-1936. 2011. 364p. 51.95 ***(978-1-258-07638-2(1))*** Literary Licensing, LLC.

Sachsenroeder, Agnes. Bulgaria, 1 vol. 2008. (CultureShock! Ser.). (ENG.). 256p. pap. 15.95 *(978-0-7614-5505-9(1))* Marshall Cavendish Corp.

BULGARIAN BALLADS AND SONGS

see Folk Songs, Bulgarian

BULGARIAN CHURCH SLAVIC LANGUAGE

see Church Slavic Language—Bulgarian Recension

BULGARIAN FOLK SONGS

see Folk Songs, Bulgarian

BULGARIAN LANGUAGE

Alexander, Ronelle & Lonely Planet Staff. Bulgarian. 2008. (Lonely Planet Phrasebook Guides). (BUL & ENG., Illus.). 256p. pap. 8.99 *(978-1-74179-181-5(2))* Lonely Planet Pubns.

Arnaudova, Olga. Focus & Bulgarian Clause Structure. 2010. 232p. pap. *(978-3-639-19981-9(2))* VDM Verlag Dr. Mueller e.K.

Bulgarian/Spanish/Bulgarian Polytechnic Dictionary. (BUL & SPA.). 600p. 59.95 *(978-0-320-01496-3(7))* French & European Pubns., Inc.

Concise Bulgarian-English Technical Dictionary. (BUL & ENG.). 479p. 59.95 *(978-0-320-01493-2(2))* French & European Pubns., Inc.

Concise Bulgarian-French Technical Dictionary. (BUL & FRE.). 59.95 *(978-0-320-01495-6(9))* French & European Pubns., Inc.

Dekova, Rositsa. Lexical Encoding of Verbs in English & Bulgarian. 2011. 256p. pap. ***(978-3-8383-0231-7(1))*** Lambert Academic Publishing.

Euro Talk. Talk Business Bulgarian. 2008. 29.99 *(978-1-84606-227-8(6))* TOPICS Entertainment.

—Talk More Bulgarian. 2008. 29.99 *(978-1-60077-279-5(X))* TOPICS Entertainment.

—Talk Now! Bulgarian. 2008. 29.99 *(978-1-84352-327-7(2))* TOPICS Entertainment.

—Talk the Talk Bulgarian. 2008. 29.99 *(978-1-84606-427-2(9))* TOPICS Entertainment.

Getova, Antoaneta & Novakova, Penka. Bulgarian Verbs. 2009. (BUL & ENG.). 277p. ***(978-1-931546-64-5(9))*** Dunwoody Pr.

Holman, Michael & Kovatcheva, Mira. Complete Bulgarian: A Teach Yourself Guide. 4th ed. 2011. (Teach Yourself Language Ser.). (ENG., Illus.). 336p. pap. 32.00 *(978-0-07-176587-9(5),* 0071765875) McGraw-Hill Cos., The.

—Complete Bulgarian with Two Audio CDs: A Teach Yourself Guide. 4th ed. 2011. (Teach Yourself Language Ser.). (ENG., Illus.). 336p. pap. 46.00 incl. audio compact disk *(978-0-07-176591-6(3),* 0071765913) McGraw-Hill Cos., The.

Icon Group International, Inc. Staff, compiled by. Webster's Bulgarian - English Thesaurus Dictionary. 2008. 647p. ring bd. 28.95 incl. audio compact disk *(978-0-497-83454-6(5))* Icon Group International, Inc.

Kovatcheva, Mira, et al. Harrap's Bulgarian Phrasebook. 2007. (Harrap's Phrasebook Ser.). (ENG., Illus.). 192p. pap. 7.95 *(978-0-07-148627-9(5),* 0071486275) McGraw-Hill Cos., The.

Laskova, Vesselina. The Structure of the Adnominal Modification in Bulgarian. 2010. 144p. pap. *(978-3-8383-7244-0(1))* Lambert Academic Publishing.

Mihaylova, Polia & Thomas Cook Publishing Staff. Bulgarian. 2009. (BUL & ENG., Illus.). 96p. pap. 7.95 *(978-1-84848-105-3(5))* Cook, Thomas Publishing GBR. Dist: Globe Pequot Pr., The.

Mladenova, Olga M. Definiteness in Bulgarian: Modelling the Processes of Language Change. 2007. (Trends in Linguistics. Studies & Monographs). (ENG., Illus.). XI, 472p. 196.00 *(978-3-11-019557-6(7))* De Gruyter, Mouton DEU. Dist: de Gruyter, Walter GmbH & Co. KG.

Novakova, Penka, et al. Bulgarian Reader. 2007. (BUL & ENG.). xxiv, 277p. *(978-1-931546-34-8(7))* Dunwoody Pr.

Stamboliev‌a, Maria. Building up Aspect: A Study of Aspect & Related Categories in Bulgarian with Parallels in English & French. 2008. 243p. pap. 69.95 *(978-3-03910-558-8(2))* Lang, Peter AG GBR. Dist: Lang, Peter.

Stanchev, I. & Ivanov. Bulgarian-German Dictionary. (GER & BUL.). 455p. *(978-0-320-00999-0(8))* French & European Pubns., Inc.

Tisheva, Yovka & Ra Hauge, Kjetil. Colloquial Bulgarian: The Complete Course for Beginners. 2nd rev. ed. 2006. (Colloquial Ser.). (ENG & BUL., Illus.). 284p. per. 29.95 *(978-0-415-31625-5(1),* RU6251X) Routledge.

BULGARIAN LANGUAGE—TO 1100

see Church Slavic Language

BULGARIAN LANGUAGE—MIDDLE BULGARIAN, 1100-1500

see Church Slavic Language—Bulgarian Recension

BULGARIAN LITERATURE—TRANSLATIONS INTO ENGLISH

Mladenov, Ivan & Cooper, Henry R. An Anthology of Bulgarian Literature. 2007. *(978-0-89357-329-4(9))* Slavica Pubs.

BULGARIAN POETRY—TRANSLATIONS INTO ENGLISH

Bernard, Henry. The Shade of the Balkans: Being a Collection of Bulgarian Folksongs & Proverbs. 2009. 332p. 25.99 *(978-1-103-55385-3(2));* pap. 19.99 *(978-1-103-55382-2(8))* BiblioBazaar.

Henry, Bernard. The Shade of the Balkans: Being a Collection of Bulgarian Folksongs & Proverbs. 2009. 330p. 32.99 *(978-1-113-46838-3(6));* pap. 30.75 *(978-1-113-46835-2(1))* BiblioBazaar.

BULGARIAN QUESTION

see Eastern Question (Balkan)

BULGARIANS

Bernard, Henry. The Shade of the Balkans: Being a Collection of Bulgarian Folksongs & Proverbs. 2009. 332p. 25.99 *(978-1-103-55385-3(2));* pap. 19.99 *(978-1-103-55382-2(8))* BiblioBazaar.

Henry, Bernard. The Shade of the Balkans: Being a Collection of Bulgarian Folksongs & Proverbs. 2009. 330p. 32.99 *(978-1-113-46838-3(6));* pap. 30.75 *(978-1-113-46835-2(1))* BiblioBazaar.

BULGARSKA KOMUNISTICHESKA PARTIIA

Kralevska-Owens, Nassya. Communism Versus Democracy: Bulgaria 1944 To 1997. 2010. (ENG., Illus.). 432p. (C). 39.95 *(978-954-92571-1-3(8))* American Research Ctr. in Sofia

BULGE, BATTLE OF THE, 1944-1945

see Ardennes, Battle of the, 1944-1945

BULIMAREXIA

see Bulimia

BULIMIA

Abraham, Suzanne. Eating Disorders. 6th ed. 2008. (ENG., Illus.). 256p. (Orig.). pap. 22.95 *(978-0-19-955101-9(4))* Oxford Univ. Pr., Inc.

Agras, W. Stuart & Apple, Robin. Overcoming Your Eating Disorder: A Cognitive-Behavioral Therapy Approach for Bulimia Nervosa & Binge-Eating Disorder, Guided Self Help Workbook. 2007. (Treatments That Work Ser.). (ENG., Illus.). 112p. pap. 27.95 *(978-0-19-533456-2(6))* Oxford Univ. Pr., Inc.

Astrachan-Fletcher, Ellen & Maslar, Michael. The Dialectical Behavior Therapy Skills Workbook for Bulimia: Using Dbt to Break the Cycle & Regain Control of Your Life. 2009. (Workbook Ser.). (ENG.). 208p. pap. 21.95 *(978-1-57224-619-5(7))* New Harbinger Pubns.

Brisbin, Leigh-Ann. My True Reflection: Freedom from Eating Disorders. 2009. 232p. pap. 14.99 *(978-0-88270-588-0(1))* Bridge-Logos Foundation.

Busche, Rita J. Overcoming the Thin Obsession, 1 vol. 2008. (ENG.). 73p. pap. 14.95 *(978-1-60610-341-8(5))* PublishAmerica, Inc.

Carels, Tiffany Lynn. Shush. 2011. 142p. 29.99 ***(978-1-4568-8922-7(2));*** pap. 19.99 ***(978-1-4568-8921-0(4))*** Xlibris Corp.

Carlton, Pamela & Ashin, Deborah. Take Charge of Your Child's Eating Disorder: A Physician's Step-by-Step Guide to Defeating Anorexia & Bulimia. 2007. (ENG.). 256p. per. 15.95 *(978-1-56924-263-6(1))* Da Capo Pr., Inc.

Chambers, Natalie, ed. Binge Eating: Psychological Factors, Symptoms & Treatment. 2009. 89.00 *(978-1-60692-242-2(4))* Nova Science Pubs., Inc.

Chase, Stephen, ed. Eating Disorder: Complete Handbook. 2011. 136p. pap. 14.95 ***(978-1-937354-05-3(9))*** Rapid Publishing LLC.

Cooper, Myra, et al. Treating Bulimia Nervosa & Binge Eating: An Integrated Metacognitive & Cognitive Therapy Manual. 2008. (ENG., Illus.). 264p. (C). pap. 42.50 *(978-1-58391-945-3(7))* Routledge.

Cooper, Peter. Overcoming Bulimia Nervosa & Binge-Eating: A Self-Help Guide Using Cognitive Behavioral Techniques. 2010. (ENG.). 256p. pap. 14.95 *(978-0-465-01267-1(1))* Basic Bks.

Covington Armstrong, Stephanie. Not All Black Girls Know How to Eat: A Story of Bulimia. 2009. (ENG., Illus.). 272p. pap. 16.95 *(978-1-55652-786-9(1),* Hill, Lawrence Bks.) Chicago Review Pr., Inc.

Day, Merrie. A Phenomenological Psychological Analysis. 2010. 112p. pap. *(978-3-8383-1391-7(7))* Lambert Academic Publishing.

DiGuarde, Kevin I., ed. Binge Drinking Research Progress. 2008. 89.00 *(978-1-60692-065-7(0))* Nova Science Pubs., Inc.

Feigenbaum, Naomi. One Life: Hope, Healing & Inspiration on the Path to Recovery from Eating Disorders. 2009. (ENG.). 160p. pap. *(978-1-84310-912-9(3))* Kingsley, Jessica Ltd.

French, B. La Bulimia. (SPA.). 240p. 12.00 *(978-84-89920-74-3(5),* 87306) Ediciones Oniro S.A. ESP. Dist: Lectorum Pubns., Inc.

Gilhar, Linie. Voiceless, in a Starving Inner World. 2009. 564p. pap. *(978-3-639-17218-3(3))* VDM Verlag Dr. Mueller e.K.

Giordano, Simona. Understanding Eating Disorders: Conceptual & Ethical Issues in the Treatment of Anorexia & Bulimia Nervosa. 2008. (ENG.). 320p. per. 49.95 *(978-0-19-923295-6(4))* Oxford Univ. Pr., Inc.

Gleissner, Greta. Something Spectacular: The True Story of One Rockette's Battle with Bulimia. 2012. (ENG.). 256p. pap. 16.00 ***(978-1-58005-415-7(3))*** Seal Pr.

Golden, Jocelyn. Learning to Be Me: My Twenty-Three-Year Battle with Bulimia. 2007. 196p. per. 16.95 *(978-1-58348-482-1(5),* iUniverse Star) iUniverse, Inc.

Gomez, Joan. How to Cope with Bulimia. (Illus.). 128p. *(978-0-85969-694-4(4),* Sheldon Press) SPCK Publishing.

Hale-Seubert, Barbara. Riptide: Struggling with & Resurfacing from a Daughter's Eating Disorder. 2011. (ENG.). 234p. pap. 17.95 *(978-1-55022-995-0(8))* ECW Pr. CAN. Dist: Independent Pubs. Group.

Hall, Lindsey & Cohn, Leigh. Bulimia: A Guide to Recovery. 25th anniv. ed. 2010. (ENG., Illus.). 288p. pap. 16.95 *(978-0-936077-51-2(4))* Gurze Bks.

Hanson, Lori. It Started with Pop-Tarts(r)... An Alternative Approach to Winning the Battle of Bulimia. 2008. (Illus.). 320p. per. 15.95 *(978-0-9800128-0-4(5))* Shewolf Pr., LLC.

Henke, Paula. Cinderella in the Attic: Bulimia Nervos. 2006. 136p. pap. 24.95 *(978-1-4241-3247-8(9))* PublishAmerica, Inc.

Hunt, Maryjeanne. Eating to Lose: Healing from a Life of Diabulimia. 2012. (ENG.). 192p. pap. 16.95 ***(978-1-936303-27-4(2))*** Demos Medical Publishing, LLC.

Lawrence, Marilyn. The Anorexic Mind. 2008. (Tavistock Clinic Ser.). 143p. pap. *(978-1-85575-383-9(9))* Karnac Bks.

le Grange, Daniel & Lock, James. Treating Bulimia in Adolescents: A Family-Based Approach. 2009. (ENG.). 260p. 25.00 *(978-1-60623-351-1(3))* Guilford Pubns., Inc.

Lock, James & le Grange, Daniel. Treating Bulimia in Adolescents: A Family-Based Approach. 2007. (ENG., Illus.). 260p. 50.00 *(978-1-59385-414-0(5))* Guilford Pubns., Inc.

Mitchell, James E., et al. Binge-Eating Disorder: Clinical Foundations & Treatment. 2007. (ENG., Illus.). 214p. pap. 30.00 *(978-1-59385-594-9(X))* Guilford Pubns., Inc.

Moore-Groarke, Gillian, ed. In Search of Thinness: Treating Anorexia & Bulimia. 2008. (ENG., Illus.). 191p. pap. 28.95 *(978-1-85607-963-1(5))* Currach Pr. IRL. Dist: Dufour Editions, Inc.

Nelson, Tammy. Whats Eating You: A Workbook for Teens with Anorexia, Bulimia, & Other Eating Disorders. 2008. (Instant Help Ser.). 110p. pap. 14.95 *(978-1-931704-44-1(9))* Play2Grow.

Robinson, Paul H. Severe & Enduring Eating Disorder (SEED) Management of Complex Presentations of Anorexia & Bulimia Nervosa. 2009. (ENG., Illus.). 184p. pap. 55.95 *(978-0-470-06207-4(X),* Wiley) Wiley, John & Sons, Inc.

Robinson, Paul H., et al. Severe & Enduring Eating Disorder (SEED) Management of Complex Presentations of Anorexia & Bulimia Nervosa. 2009. (ENG., Illus.). 184p. 144.95 *(978-0-470-06206-7(1),* Wiley) Wiley, John & Sons, Inc.

Ruggiero, Adriane. Bulimia. 2007. (At Issue Ser.). (ENG.). 91p. (gr. 3-7). pap. 22.50 *(978-0-7377-3674-8(7),* Greenhaven Pr., Inc.); (Illus.). 98p. (YA). (gr. 9-12). pap. 31.80 *(978-0-7377-3673-1(9))* Cengage Gale.

Sandoz, Emily, et al. The Mindfulness & Acceptance Workbook for Bulimia: A Guide to Breaking Free from Bulimia Using Acceptance & Commitment Therapy. 2011. (ENG., Illus.). 152p. pap. 21.95 *(978-1-57224-735-2(5))* New Harbinger Pubns.

Schab, Lisa. Bulimia Workbook for Teens: Activities to Help You Stop Bingeing & Purging. 2010. (Instant Help Ser.). (ENG.). 156p. (J). (gr. 6-12). pap. 15.95 *(978-1-57224-807-6(6))* New Harbinger Pubns.

Stavrou, Maria. Bulimics on Bulimia. Stavrou, Maria, ed. 2008. (ENG.). 160p. pap. *(978-1-84310-668-5(X))* Kingsley, Jessica Ltd.

Todd & Wells. Treating Bulimia Nervosa & Binge Eating: An Integrated Metacognitive & Cognitive Therapy Manual. Cooper, Myra, ed. 2008. (ENG., Illus.). 264p. (C). 120.00 *(978-1-58391-944-6(9))* Routledge.

Water, Melissa C. Lady Injury. 2011. 508p. pap. 34.95 ***(978-1-4560-4331-5(5))*** PublishAmerica, Inc.

Wilson, C. Philip. The Fear of Being Fat. 384p. reprint ed. pap. *(978-1-56821-012-4(4),* Aronson, Jason) Rowman & Littlefield Publishers, Inc.

Wilson, Kelly G., et al. Acceptance & Commitment Therapy for Eating Disorders: A Process-Focused Guide to Treating Anorexia & Bulimia. 2011. (Professional Ser.). (ENG., Illus.). 312p. 59.95 *(978-1-57224-733-8(9))* New Harbinger Pubns.

BULIMIA NERVOSA

see Bulimia

BULK SOLIDS

see also Granular Materials; Powders

George, Thomas F., et al. Bulk Metallic Glasses. 2011. (Physics Research & Technology Ser.). 89.00 *(978-1-61122-938-7(3))* Nova Science Pubs., Inc.

Ias, Teodor & Maestas, Ventura, eds. Bulk Materials: Research, Technology & Applications. 2010. (Chemical Engineering Methods & Technology Ser.). 129.00 *(978-1-60692-963-6(1))* Nova Science Pubs., Inc.

Liaw, P. K. & Miller, M. K. Bulk Metallic Glasses: An Overview. Miller, Michael & Liaw, Peter, eds. 2007. (ENG., Illus.). x, 290p. 144.00 *(978-0-387-48920-9(7),* 0387489207) Springer.

Liaw, Peter K. & Buchanan, Raymond A., eds. Bulk Metallic Glasses. (Illus.). 256p. 125.00 *(978-0-87339-573-1(5),* 04-5735) TMS (The Minerals, Metals & Materials Society).

Miller, Michael & Liaw, Peter, eds. Bulk Metallic Glasses: An Overview. 2010. (ENG., Illus.). x, 290p. pap. 144.00 *(978-1-4419-4313-2(7),* 1441943137) Springer.

Schulze, Dietmar. Powders & Bulk Solids: Behavior, Characterization, Storage & Flow. 2010. (ENG., Illus.). xvi, 516p. pap. 159.00 *(978-3-642-09298-5(5),* 3642092985) Springer.

Suryanarayana, Cury & Inoue, A. Bulk Metallic Glasses. 2010. (ENG., Illus.). 565p. 159.95 *(978-1-4200-8596-9(4),* CRC Press) Taylor & Francis Group GBR. Dist: Taylor & Francis Group.

Zehetbauer, Michael J. & Zhu, Yuntian Theodore, eds. Bulk Nanostructured Materials. 2009. (ENG., Illus.). 736p. 330.00 *(978-3-527-31524-6(1),* Wiley-VCH) Wiley, John & Sons, Inc.

Zhao, Yonghao, ed. Advanced Mechanical Properties & Deformation Mechanisms of Bulk Nanostructured Materials: Special Topic Volume With Invited Peer Reviewed Papers Only. 2011. 258p. pap. ***(978-3-03785-105-0(8))*** Trans Tech Pubns., Ltd.

Zhao, Yonghao & Liao, Xiaozhou, eds. Ductility of Bulk Nanostructured Materials. 2010. (Materials Science Forum: 633-634). (Illus.). 734p. pap. 345.00 *(978-0-87849-305-0(0))* Translations for Technology.

BULK SOLIDS FLOW

see also Fluidization

Goddard, Joe, et al, eds. IUTAM-ISIMM Symposium on Mathematical Modeling & Physical Instances of Granular Flows. 2010. (AIP Conference Proceedings Ser.). 458p. 228.00 *(978-0-7354-0772-5(X),* 073540772X, AIP Pr.) Springer.

Hill, James M. & Selvadurai, A. P. S., eds. Mathematics & Mechanics of Granular Materials. 2011. (ENG.). iv, 320p. pap. 149.00 *(978-90-481-6964-1(X),* 904816964X) Springer.

Rosato, Anthony D. & Blackmore, Denis L., eds. IUTAM Symposium on Segregation in Granular Flows. 2010. (Solid Mechanics & Its Applications Ser.). 350p. pap. 219.00 *(978-90-481-5556-9(8),* 9048155568) Springer.

Schulze, Dietmar. Powders & Bulk Solids: Behavior, Characterization, Storage & Flow. 2010. (ENG., Illus.). xvi, 516p. pap. 159.00 *(978-3-642-09298-5(5),* 3642092985) Springer.

—Powders & Bulk Solids: Behavior, Characterization, Storage & Flow. Schulze, Dietmar & Schwedes, Jörg, trs. from GER. 2007. (ENG., Illus.). xvi, 516p. 159.00 *(978-3-540-73767-4(7),* 3540737677) Springer.

BULK SOLIDS HANDLING

see also Earthwork; Silos

Best Bulk A, 94: Silos Hoppers Bins. 130.00 *(978-0-87849-087-5(6))* Trans Tech Pubns., Ltd. CHE. Dist: Enfield Publishing & Distribution Co., Inc.

Best Bulk B, 94: Stacking Blending. 96.00 *(978-0-87849-088-2(4))* Trans Tech Pubns., Ltd. CHE. Dist: Enfield Publishing & Distribution Co., Inc.

Best Bulk C, 94: Bulk Ports. 96.00 *(978-0-87849-089-9(2))* Trans Tech Pubns., Ltd. CHE. Dist: Enfield Publishing & Distribution Co., Inc.

Best Bulk D, 94: Pneumatic Convey. 96.00 *(978-0-87849-090-5(6))* Trans Tech Pubns., Ltd. CHE. Dist: Enfield Publishing & Distribution Co., Inc.

Best Bulk F, 94: Surface Mines. 96.00 *(978-0-87849-091-2(4))* Trans Tech Pubns., Ltd. CHE. Dist: Enfield Publishing & Distribution Co., Inc.

Best Bulk G, 94: Conveying & Process. 96.00 *(978-0-87849-092-9(2))* Trans Tech Pubns., Ltd. CHE. Dist: Enfield Publishing & Distribution Co., Inc.

Best Bulk I, 94: Belt Conveyor Tech. 160.00 *(978-0-87849-093-6(0))* Trans Tech Pubns., Ltd. CHE. Dist: Enfield Publishing & Distribution Co., Inc.

Edwards. Bulk Manufacture. Date not set. (Pharmaceutical Engineering Ser.: No. 7). 256p. 170.00 *(978-0-7506-5147-9(4),* Butterworth-Heinemann) Elsevier Science & Technology Bks.

Klinzing, G. E., et al. Pneumatic Conveying of Solids: A theoretical & practical Approach. 3rd ed. 2010. (Particle Technology Ser.). (Illus.). x, 435p. 169.00 *(978-90-481-3608-7(3),* 9048136083) Springer.

McGlinchey, D. Bulk Solids Handling: Equipment Selection & Operation. 2008. (ENG., Illus.). 304p. 195.00 *(978-1-4051-5825-1(5),* Wiley-Blackwell) Wiley, John & Sons, Inc.

Ortega-Rivas, Enrique. Unit Operations of Particulate Solids. 2011. (ENG., Illus.). 492p. 149.95 *(978-1-4398-4907-1(2),* CRC Press) Taylor & Francis Group GBR. Dist: Taylor & Francis Group.

Schulze, Dietmar. Powders & Bulk Solids: Behavior, Characterization, Storage & Flow. 2010. (ENG., Illus.). xvi, 516p. pap. 159.00 *(978-3-642-09298-5(5),* 3642092985) Springer.

—Powders & Bulk Solids: Behavior, Characterization, Storage & Flow. Schulze, Dietmar & Schwedes, Jörg, trs. from GER. 2007. (ENG., Illus.). xvi, 516p. 159.00 *(978-3-540-73767-4(7),* 3540737677) Springer.

Swinderman, R. Todd. Foundations: The Practical Resource for Cleaner, Safer, More Productive Dust & Material Control. 4th ed. 2009. (Illus.). xi, 562p. *(978-0-9717121-1-9(5))* Martin Engineering.

B

BULL, OLE BORNEMANN, 1810-1880

Acker, Helen. Four Sons of Norway. 256p. 2008. 42.95 *(978-1-4367-1350-4(1))* 2007. (ENG.). per. 27.95 *(978-1-4325-7046-0(3))* Kessinger Publishing, LLC.

BULL-FIGHTERS

see Bullfighters

BULL-FIGHTS

see Bullfights

BULL MASTIFF

see Bullmastiff

BULL RUN, 1ST BATTLE OF, VA., 1861

Cunningham, Horace H. Field Medical Services at the Battles of Manassas. 2008. (ENG.). 130p. pap. 19.95 *(978-0-8203-3355-7(7))* Univ. of Georgia Pr.

le Pautremat, Pascal. First Bull Run: First Victory for the South. 2010. (Men & Battles 7 Ser.). (Illus.). 80p. pap. 19.95 *(978-2-35250-153-4(9))* Histoire et Collections FRA. Dist: Casemate Pubs. & Bk. Distributors, LLC.

Patterson, Robert. A Narrative of the Campaign in the Valley of the Shenandoah In 1861. 2009. (Civil War Ser.). (ENG.). 132p. pap. 11.95 *(978-1-4290-1945-3(X))* Applewood Bks.

BULL RUN, 2ND BATTLE OF, VA., 1862

Anders, Curt. Injustice on Trial. 2009. 549p. pap. 19.95 *(978-0-9824369-4-3(7))* Anders, Curt Bks. LLC.

Cunningham, Horace H. Field Medical Services at the Battles of Manassas. 2008. (ENG.). 130p. pap. 19.95 *(978-0-8203-3355-7(7))* Univ. of Georgia Pr.

Gottfried, Bradley. The Maps of First Bull Run: An Atlas of the First Bull Run (Manassas) Campaign, including the Battle of Ball's Bluff, June - October 1861. 2009. (American Battle Ser.). (Illus.). 144p. 34.95 *(978-1-932714-60-9(X))* Savas Beatie.

Jermann, Donald R. Fitz-John Porter, Scapegoat of Second Manassas: The Rise, Fall & Rise of the General Accused of Disobedience. 2008. (ENG., Illus.). 295p. pap. 39.95 *(978-0-7864-3930-0(0))* McFarland & Co., Inc. Pubs.

Patchan, Scott C. Second Manassas: Longstreet's Attack & the Struggle for Chinn Ridge. 2011. (Illus.). 214p. 26.95 *(978-1-59797-687-9(3))* Potomac Bks., Inc.

Porter, Fitz-John. Reply to the Rejoinder of Maj Gen John Pope, to the Appeal of Maj Gen Fitz John Porter, for a Reexamination of the Proceedings of the Court Marti. 2011. 18p. pap. 11.99 ***(978-1-4181-8953-2(7))*** MPublishing.

Sheppard, Eric William. The Campaign in Virginia & Maryland, June 26th to Sept. 20th, 1862, Cedar Run, Manassas, & Sharpsburg. (Special Campaign Ser.). 306p. reprint ed. 98.00 *(978-0-7222-8042-3(4))*; 98.00 *(978-0-7222-8038-6(6))* Library Reprints, Inc.

BULL TERRIER

Alexander, Carolyn. Bull Terriers. 2006. (Complete Pet Owner's Manual Ser.). (ENG., Illus.). 96p. pap. 8.99 *(978-0-7641-3528-6(7))* Barron's Educational Series, Inc.

Linzy, Jan & Pata, Janae. Bull Terrier Champions, 2002-2006. 2007. (Illus.). 151p. spiral bd. 46.95 *(978-1-55893-223-4(2))* Camino E.E. & Bk. Co.

BULL TERRIER, AMERICAN

see American Pit Bull Terrier

BULL TERRIER, STAFFORDSHIRE

see Staffordshire Bull Terrier

BULL TERRIERS, PIT

see Pit Bull Terriers

BULLDOG

American Kennel Club Staff, contrib. by. The American Kennel Club's Meet the Bulldog: The Responsible Dog Owner's Handbook. 2012. ***(978-1-935484-87-5(7))*** BowTie Pr.

Dawson, Judith. Pet Owner's Guide to the Bulldog. (Illus.). 80p. tchr. ed. 9.95 *(978-1-86054-112-4(7), INT046)* Ringpress Bks., Ltd. GBR. Dist: TFH Pubns., Inc.

Dickerson, Michael. Bulldog. 2009. (Smart Owner's Guide: Ser.). (ENG., Illus.). 176p. 17.95 *(978-1-59378-758-5(8))*; pap. 15.95 *(978-1-59378-771-4(5))* Kennel Club Bks.

Dunn, Joeming & Denham, Brian. Bud: The 1st Dog to Cross the United States. 2011. (Famous Firsts: Animals Making History Ser.). (Illus.). 32p. (J). (gr. 3-6). 28.50 *(978-1-61641-638-6(6))* Magic Wagon.

Gagne, Tammy. Bulldogs, 1 vol. 2007. (Animal Planet Pet Care Library). (ENG., Illus.). 112p. 11.95 *(978-0-7938-3783-0(9))* TFH Pubns., Inc.

Gewirtz, Elaine Waldorf. The Bulldog. 2010. *(978-1-932904-58-1(1))* Eldorado Ink.

Lee, Muriel P. The French Bulldog. 2007. (Kennel Club Classic: Ser.). (ENG., Illus.). 200p. 39.95 *(978-1-59378-680-9(8))* Kennel Club Bks.

Libby, Tracy. Bulldog, 1 vol. 2010. (DogLife Ser.). (ENG., Illus.). 224p. 19.95 *(978-0-7938-3603-1(4), 1320896)* TFH Pubns., Inc.

Linzy, Jan & Pata, Janae. Bulldog Champions, 2003-2006. 2007. (Illus.). 143p. spiral bd. 46.95 *(978-1-55893-221-0(6))* Camino E.E. & Bk. Co.

Linzy, Jan, et al. Bulldog Champions, 2007-2010. 2011. (Illus.). 122p. spiral bd. 46.95 ***(978-1-55893-329-3(8))*** Camino E.E. & Bk. Co.

Linzy, Jan, et al. French Bulldog Champions, 2005-2007. 2008. (Illus.). 105p. spiral bd. 46.95 *(978-1-55893-237-1(2))* Camino E.E. & Bk. Co.

Maggitti, Phil. Bulldogs. 2009. *(978-0-7641-6255-8(1))*; (ENG., Illus.). 192p. 18.99 *(978-0-7641-9653-9(7))* Barron's Educational Series, Inc.

—Bulldogs: Everything about Health, Behavior, Feeding, & Care. 2nd rev. ed. 2007. (Complete Pet Owner's Manual Ser.). (ENG., Illus.). 96p. pap. 8.99 *(978-0-7641-3645-0(3))* Barron's Educational Series, Inc.

Palika, Liz. Bulldog. 2nd ed. 2008. (Happy Healthy Pet Ser.: 150). (ENG., Illus.). 144p. 16.99 *(978-0-470-39054-2(9)*, Howell Bk. Hse.) Wiley, John & Sons, Inc.

Ricciotti, Lisa. Bulldog. 2012. ***(978-0-7938-3725-0(1))*** TFH Pubns., Inc.

Saller-Schneider, Susanne. French Bulldogs. 2012. (Breed Profiles Ser.). (ENG.). 144p. 24.99 *(978-0-7641-6545-0(3))* Barron's Educational Series, Inc.

Willow Creek Press, creator. Bulldog Bad Boys: And Some Pretty Uncontrollabull Girls, Too! 2009. (ENG., Illus.). 96p. 14.95 *(978-1-60755-028-0(8))* Willow Creek Pr., Inc.

Wolfe, R. For Georgia Fans Only. 2011. 256p. 24.95 ***(978-0-9800978-1-8(9))*** Lone Wolfe Pr.

BULLDOGS

see Bulldog

BULLER, REDVERS HENRY, SIR, 1839-1908

Churchill, Winston. London to Ladysmith & Ian Hamilton's March. 2010. (Dover Military History, Weapons, Armor Ser.). (ENG.). 432p. pap. 16.95 *(978-0-486-47543-1(3))* Dover Pubns., Inc.

BULLETIN BOARDS

Beane, Allan L. Bullying Prevention for Schools: A Step-by-Step Guide to Implementing a Successful Anti-Bullying Program. 2009. (ENG., Illus.). 304p. pap. 36.00 *(978-0-470-40701-1(8)*, Jossey-Bass) Wiley, John & Sons, Inc.

Chagnon, Adrienne. Fun & Easy Bulletin Boards. spiral bd. 14.99 *(978-0-89098-220-4(1))* Twentieth Century Christian Bks.

Cheyney, Jeanne & Cheyney, Arnold. More Bulletin Boards for Every Month: Grades K-3. 2007. (Good Year Book Ser.). (Illus.). 120p. per. 12.95 *(978-1-59647-013-2(5))* Good Year Bks.

Gainsley, Suzanne. From Message to Meaning: Using a Daily Message Board in the Preschool Classroom. 2008. *(978-1-57379-355-1(8))* High/Scope Pr.

Gateway Science Bulletin Board. 4th ed. No. 1. 40.83 *(978-0-07-029841-5(6))*No. 2. 40.83 *(978-0-07-029842-2(4))*No. 3. 40.83 *(978-0-07-029843-9(2))*No. 4. 40.83 *(978-0-07-029844-6(0))*No. 5. 40.83 *(978-0-07-029845-3(9))*No. 6. 40.83 *(978-0-07-029846-0(7))* Macmillan/McGraw-Hill Schl. Div.

Riggs, Adrienne. Fun & Easy Bulletin Boards, Vol. 2. (Illus.). spiral bd. 14.99 *(978-0-89098-228-0(7))* Twentieth Century Christian Bks.

Skaggs, Gayle. Look, Its Books! Marketing Your Library with Displays & Promotions. 2008. (ENG., Illus.). 194p. per. 49.95 *(978-0-7864-3132-8(6))* McFarland & Co., Inc. Pubs.

BULLFIGHTERS

Araki, Nobuyoshi, photos by. Dirty Pretty Things. 2007. (ENG., Illus.). 232p. pap. 35.00 *(978-1-57687-358-8(7))* powerHouse Cultural Entertainment, Inc.

Cauwenbergh, Henk van. Rencontre. 2011. (FRE, DUT & ENG., Illus.). 176p. *(978-90-5856-354-5(5)*, Stichting Kunstboak (Acc)) Antique Collectors' Club.

Chaves Nogales, Manuel. Juan Belmonte, Matador de Toros: Su Vida y Sus Hazañas. 2009. (SPA., Illus.). 376p. pap. 21.00 ***(978-84-936597-9-0(7))*** Libros del Asteroide ESP. Dist: Independent Pubs. Group.

Conrad, Barnaby. The Death of Manolete. 2007. (Illus.). 150p. per. 19.95 *(978-0-9787389-1-4(8)*, Pippin Publishing) Little Moose Pr.

—The Death of Manolete. 2007. (Illus.). 155p. 23.95 *(978-1-59777-548-9(7))* Phoenix Bks., Inc.

Corona, Livia, photos by. Enanitos Toreros. 2008. (ENG., Illus.). 176p. 39.95 *(978-1-57687-368-7(4))* powerHouse Cultural Entertainment, Inc.

Crabtree: Memories of a Real Cowboy Hero. 2006. (Illus.). 100p. per. *(978-0-9727759-7-7(8))* Capturing Memories.

Crouser, Michael, photos by. Los Toros. 2007. (Illus.). 200p. 60.00 *(978-1-931885-62-1(1))* Twin Palms Pubs.

Evans, Frank. The Last British Bullfighter. 2009. (ENG., Illus.). 288p. pap. 18.95 *(978-0-230-74330-4(7))* Macmillan Pubs., Ltd. GBR. Dist: Independent Pubs. Group.

Lewine, Edward. Death & the Sun: A Matador's Season in the Heart of Spain. 2007. (ENG.). 272p. pap. 23.95 *(978-0-618-87230-5(2))* Houghton Mifflin Harcourt Trade & Reference Pubs.

Miller, Sandro. Sandro Miller: el Matador. 2010. (ENG., Illus.). 144p. 59.95 *(978-88-8158-771-1(8))* Charta ITA. Dist: D.A.P./Distributed Art Pubs.

Paul, Bart. Double-Edged Sword: The Many Lives of Hemingway's Friend, the American Matador Sidney Franklin. 2009. (ENG.). 336p. 29.95 *(978-0-8032-1129-2(5))* Univ. of Nebraska Pr.

Sherwood, Lyn. Yankees in the Afternoon: An Illustrated History of American Bullfighters. alt. ed. 2008. (ENG., Illus.). 288p. pap. 35.00 *(978-0-7864-3769-6(3))* McFarland & Co., Inc. Pubs.

BULLFIGHTS

see also Bullfighters

Bishop, C. w. & Bishop, C. W. The Ritual Bullfight. 2011. 16p. pap. 35.95 ***(978-1-258-00759-1(2))*** Literary Licensing, LLC.

Evans, Frank. The Last British Bullfighter. 2009. (ENG., Illus.). 288p. pap. 18.95 *(978-0-230-74330-4(7))* Macmillan Pubs., Ltd. GBR. Dist: Independent Pubs. Group.

Hardouin-Fugier, Elisabeth. A History of Bullfighting. Rose, Sue, tr. 2010. (ENG., Illus.). 224p. pap. 35.00 *(978-1-86189-518-9(6))* Reaktion Bks., Ltd. GBR. Dist: Chicago Distribution Ctr.

Lewine, Edward. Death & the Sun: A Matador's Season in the Heart of Spain. 2007. (ENG.). 272p. pap. 23.95 *(978-0-618-87230-5(2))* Houghton Mifflin Harcourt Trade & Reference Pubs.

Mandel, Miriam B. Hemingway's The Dangerous Summer: The Complete Annotations. 2008. (ENG., Illus.). 416p. 125.00 *(978-0-8108-6014-8(7))* Scarecrow Pr., Inc.

Mandel, Miriam B., ed. A Companion to Hemingway's Death in the Afternoon. 2009. (Studies in American Literature & Culture Ser.). (Illus.). 359p. pap. 39.95 *(978-1-57113-409-7(3))* Camden Hse.

Smith, Rex, ed. Biography of the Bulls: An Anthology of Spanish Bullfighting. 2007. (ENG.). 400p. per. 34.95 *(978-0-548-38950-8(0))* Kessinger Publishing, LLC.

Wood, Tristan. How to Watch a Bullfight. 2011. (ENG., Illus.). 224p. 30.00 ***(978-1-906122-27-0(X))*** Mental Gears Pubng. CAN. Dist: SCB Distributors.

BULLFIGHTS—PICTORIAL WORKS

Crouser, Michael, photos by. Los Toros. 2007. (Illus.). 200p. 60.00 *(978-1-931885-62-1(1))* Twin Palms Pubs.

Masats, Ramon, photos by. Ramon Masats: Sanfermines. 2009. (ENG., Illus.). 260p. 65.00 *(978-84-92498-71-0(4))* La Fabrica ESP. Dist: D.A.P./Distributed Art Pubs.

Sherwood, Lyn. Yankees in the Afternoon: An Illustrated History of American Bullfighters. alt. ed. 2008. (ENG., Illus.). 288p. pap. 35.00 *(978-0-7864-3769-6(3))* McFarland & Co., Inc. Pubs.

BULLFIGHTS IN ART

Hardouin-Fugier, Elisabeth. A History of Bullfighting. Rose, Sue, tr. 2010. (ENG., Illus.). 224p. pap. 35.00 *(978-1-86189-518-9(6))* Reaktion Bks., Ltd. GBR. Dist: Chicago Distribution Ctr.

Rebora, Ballo. Carving a Bull Fighter & the Bull. 2008. (Illus.). 64p. pap. 14.95 *(978-0-7643-2910-4(3))* Schiffer Publishing, Ltd.

BULLION

see Precious Metals

BULLOCK, SETH, 1849-1919

Wolff, David A. Seth Bullock: Black Hills Lawman. 2009. (Illus.). x, 206p. pap. 12.95 *(978-0-9798940-5-3(0)*, South Dakota State Historical Society Pr.) South Dakota State Historical Society.

BULLS, IRISH

see Irish Wit and Humor

BULLS AND BEARS

see Stock Exchanges

BULLTERRIER

see Bull Terrier

BULLTERRIERS, PIT

see Pit Bull Terriers

BULLYING

see also Cyberbullying

Alexander, Jenny. When Your Child Is Bullied: An Essential Guide for Parents. 2007. (ENG.). 256p. per. 15.95 *(978-1-4165-2235-5(2))* Simon & Schuster, Ltd. GBR. Dist: Independent Pubs. Group.

Allman, Toney. Cliques. 2010. (Hot Topics Ser.). (ENG.). 96-128p. (YA). (gr. 7-12). 33.45 *(978-1-4205-0308-1(1))* Cengage Gale.

Anderson, Gail. The Impact of Bullying on the Adolescence Sense of Self. 2010. 188p. pap. *(978-3-639-23718-4(8))* VDM Verlag Dr. Mueller e.K.

Anthony, Michelle & Lindert, Reyna. Little Girls Can Be Mean: Four Steps to Bully-proof Girls in the Early Grades. 2010. (ENG., Illus.). 304p. pap. 14.99 *(978-0-312-61552-9(3)*, St. Martin's Griffin) St. Martin's Pr.

Ashworth, Andy. Dogs don't eat Mice. 2010. 50p. pap. 14.95 *(978-1-4092-5782-0(7))* Lulu Enterprises Inc.

Barrow, Lisa M. S. In Darkness Light Dawns: Exposing Workplace Bullying. 2009. 132p. pap. 11.95 *(978-0-615-31142-5(3))* Purple Crown Publishing.

Battaglio, Carol. School Bullying. 2008. 236p. pap. *(978-3-639-00361-1(6))* VDM Verlag Dr. Mueller e.K.

Bauman, Sheri. Cyberbullying: What Counselors Need to Know. 2010. *(978-1-55620-294-0(6))* American Counseling Assn.

Beane, Allan L. Bullying Prevention for Schools: A Step-by-Step Guide to Implementing a Successful Anti-Bullying Program. 2009. (ENG., Illus.). 304p. pap. 36.00 *(978-0-470-40701-1(8)*, Jossey-Bass) Wiley, John & Sons, Inc.

—Protect Your Child from Bullying: Expert Advice to Help You Recognize, Prevent, & Stop Bullying Before Your Child Gets Hurt. 2008. (ENG.). 256p. per. 14.95 *(978-0-7879-9517-1(7)*, Jossey-Bass) Wiley, John & Sons, Inc.

Beaudoin, Marie-Nathalie & Taylor, Maureen E., eds. Responding to the Culture of Bullying & Disrespect: New Perspectives on Collaboration, Compassion, & Responsibility. 2nd ed. 2009. (Illus.). 296p. pap. 39.95 *(978-1-4129-6854-6(2)*, B68539P) Corwin Pr.

Bernard, E. C. Four Minutes a Day: A School Guide to Identifying & Neutralizing Entertainment Bullying A Parent & Teacher Survival Guide for Victims of Entertainment Bullying in School Hallways. 2010. (Illus.). 60p. pap. 12.00 *(978-0-9793200-7-1(0))* Teacher Voice Publishing.

Bevan, Lynda. Stop Being Pushed Around! A Practical Guide. 2007. 128p. per. 14.95 *(978-1-932690-45-3(X))* Loving Healing Pr., Inc.

Bingham, Jane. Taking Action Against Bullying. 2009. 70.50 *(978-1-4358-5471-0(3))*; (ENG.). 48p. (YA). pap. 11.75 *(978-1-4358-5470-3(5))* Rosen Publishing Group, Inc., The. (Rosen Central).

Bissonette, Aimee M. Cyber Law: Maximizing Safety & Minimizing Risk in Classrooms. 2009. (Illus.). 128p. pap. 24.95 *(978-1-4129-6615-3(9)*, B66146P) Corwin Pr.

Blanco, Jodee. Please Stop Laughing at Me... One Woman's Inspirational Story. 2010. (ENG.). 304p. pap. 12.95 *(978-1-4405-0986-5(7))* Adams Media Corp.

—Please Stop Laughing at Us... The Sequel to the New York Times Bestseller Please Stop Laughing at Me... rev. ed. 2011. (ENG.). 504p. pap. 12.95 *(978-1-936661-18-3(7))* BenBella Bks.

Bott, C. J. More Bullies in More Books. 2009. (ENG., Illus.). 208p. pap. 40.00 *(978-0-8108-6654-6(4))* Scarecrow Pr., Inc.

Breakstone, Steve, et al. How to Stop Bullying & Social Aggression: Elementary Grade Lessons & Activities That Teach Empathy, Friendship, & Respect. 2008. (Illus.). 200p. 80.95 *(978-1-4129-5810-3(5)*, B58103C); pap. 36.95 *(978-1-4129-5811-0(3)*, B58103P) Corwin Pr.

Briles, Judith. Stabotage! How to Deal with the Pit Bulls, Skunks, Snakes, Scorpions & Slugs in the Health Care Workplace. 2009. 192p. pap. 29.00 *(978-1-885331-30-4(4))* Mile High Pr., Ltd.

Brown, A. M. C. & Jimerson, Shane R. Bullying in Schools: An International Perspective. Espelage, Dorothy L. & Swearer, Susan M., eds. 2nd ed. 2009. (Illus.). 614p. instr.'s hndbk. ed. 119.95 *(978-0-8058-6393-2(1))* Routledge.

Caponecchia, Carlo & Wyatt, Anne. Preventing Workplace Bullying: An Evidence-Based Guide for Managers & Employees. 2011. (ENG., Illus.). 168p. 80.00 *(978-0-415-66880-4(8))*; pap. 23.95 *(978-0-415-66881-1(6))* Routledge.

Chadwick, Sharlene. They Can't Hurt Me. 2010. 72p. pap. *(978-3-639-24574-5(1))* VDM Verlag Dr. Mueller e.K.

Chavez, Jennifer E. Bee-Ing Bully Free: Bentley's Bullying Behavior Leads to a Solution. 2007. (SPA & ENG.). pap. 16.95 *(978-0-86534-545-4(7))* Sunstone Pr.

Clarkson, Polly. Beating the Bullies: Twenty Inspiring True-Life Stories of Triumph over Violence, Intimidation & Bullying. 2008. (ENG.). 256p. pap. 15.95 *(978-1-84454-511-7(3))* Blake, John Publishing, Ltd. GBR. Dist: Independent Pubs. Group.

Coloroso, Barbara. The Bully, the Bullied, & the Bystander: From Preschool to High School - How Parents & Teachers Can Help Break the Cycle of Violence. rev. ed. 2009. (ENG.). 272p. pap. 14.99 *(978-0-06-174460-0(3)*, William Morrow Paperbacks) HarperCollins Pubs.

The Comfort Zone: Providing a Safe & Bully Free Environment for School-Age Child Care. 2008. (Illus.). pap. 24.95 *(978-0-9773738-1-9(9))* Bryson Taylor Publishing.

Cooper, Cary L. & Zapf, Dieter, eds. Bullying & Emotional Abuse in the Workplace: International Perspectives in Research & Practice. 2nd rev. ed. 2010. (ENG., Illus.). 512p. pap. 83.95 *(978-1-4398-0489-6(3)*, CRC Press) Taylor & Francis Group GBR. Dist: Taylor & Francis Group.

Cowie, Helen & Jennifer, Dawn. New Perspectives on Bullying. 2008. (ENG., Illus.). 176p. (C). instr.'s gde. ed. 117.00 *(978-0-335-22243-8(9)*, 0335222439); pap., instr.'s gde. ed. 43.00 *(978-0-335-22244-5(7)*, 0335222447) McGraw-Hill Education GBR. Dist: McGraw-Hill Cos., The.

Croom, Tina L. Diary of a Bullied Child: The Aftermath I. 2011. 108p. pap. 11.95 ***(978-1-4497-1847-3(7)***, WestBow Pr.) Author Solutions, Inc.

Cross, Donna, et al, eds. Cyberbullying in the Global Playground: Research from International Perspectives. 2012. (ENG., Illus.). 326p. 119.95 ***(978-1-4443-3376-3(3)***, Wiley-Blackwell) Wiley, John & Sons, Inc.

Crothers, Laura M., et al, eds. Understanding Girl Bullying & What to Do about It: Strategies to Help Heal the Divide. 2009. (Illus.). 152p. pap. 28.95 *(978-1-4129-6488-3(1)*, B64876P) Corwin Pr.

Daniel, Teresa A. Stop Bullying at Work: Strategies & Tools for HR & Legal Professionals. 2009. (ENG.). 176p. pap. 22.95 *(978-1-58644-135-7(3))* Society for Human Resource Management.

Darmawan, Darmawan. Bullying in School: A study of forms & motives of Aggression. 2011. 120p. pap. ***(978-3-8433-9276-1(5))*** Lambert Academic Publishing.

Davis, Stan & Davis, Julia. Empowering Bystanders in Bullying Prevention. 2007. 224p. per. 29.95 *(978-0-87822-539-2(0))* Research Pr.

—Schools Where Everyone Belongs: Practical Strategies for Reducing Bullying. 2nd ed. 2007. (ENG.). 292p. pap. 24.95 *(978-0-87822-584-2(6))* Research Pr.

DePino, Catherine. Real Life Bully Prevention for Real Kids: 50 Ways to Help Elementary & Middle School Students. 2009. (ENG.). 150p. 33.00 *(978-1-57886-965-7(X))* Rowman & Littlefield Education.

Dixon, Roz & Smith, Peter. Rethinking School Bullying: Towards an Integrated Model. 2011. (ENG., Illus.). 238p. 90.00 *(978-0-521-88971-1(5))* Cambridge Univ. Pr.

Doll. Resilient Playgrounds. 2009. (School-Based Practice in Action Ser.). (ENG., Illus.). 183p. 125.00 *(978-0-415-96087-8(8))*; pap. 34.95 *(978-0-415-96088-5(6))* Routledge.

Dosani, Sabina. Banish the Bullies. 2008. (52 brilliant ideas Ser.). (Illus.). 256p. 14.99 *(978-1-905940-29-5(7))* Infinite Ideas GBR. Dist: Sony Electronics.

Dragan, Edward F. Bully Action Guide: How to Help Your Child & Get Your School to Listen. 2011. (ENG.). 256p. pap. 16.00 *(978-0-230-11042-7(8))* Palgrave Macmillan.

Drew, Naomi. No Kidding about Bullying: 125 Ready-to-Use Activities to Help Kids Manage Anger, Resolve Conflicts, Build Empathy, & Get Along. 2010. (Bully Free Classroom Ser.). (ENG.). 288p. (gr. 3-6). 39.99 *(978-1-57542-349-4(9))* Free Spirit Publishing, Inc.

Dubin, Nick. Asperger Syndrome & Bullying: Strategies & Solutions. 2007. (ENG.). 16p. per. *(978-1-84310-846-7(1))* Kingsley, Jessica Ltd.

Duffy, Maureen P. & Sperry, Len. Mobbing: Causes, Consequences, & Solutions, 1 vol. 2012. (ENG., Illus.). 320p. 55.00 ***(978-0-19-538001-9(0))*** Oxford Univ. Pr., Inc.

Ellames, David. Workplace Bullying. 2009. 120p. pap. *(978-3-639-12532-0(0))* VDM Verlag Dr. Mueller e.K.

Elliott, Michele. Stop Bullying Pocketbook. 2nd rev. ed. 2010. (Illus.). 128p. pap. *(978-1-906610-26-5(6)*, Teachers' Pocketbooks) Management Pocketbooks GBR. Dist: Ware-Pak, Inc.

Elliott, Michele. Tackling Bullying. rev. ed. 2011. (ENG., Illus.). 219p. pap. 44.50 (978-1-4062-6483-6(8)) Pearson Education, Ltd. GBR. Dist: Trans-Atlantic Pubns., Inc.

Ensuring Student Cyber Safety: Hearing Before the Subcommittee on Healthy Families & Communities, Committee on Education & Labor, U.S. House of Representatives, One Hundred Eleventh Congress, Second Session, Hearing Held in Washington, D.C., June 24, 2010. 2010. iii, 66p. (978-0-16-087768-1(7), 552-070-42279-0) United States Government Printing Office.

Fauteux, Kevin. Defusing Angry People: Practical Tools for Handling Bullying, Threats, & Violence. 2011. (ENG.). 224p. pap. 14.95 (978-0-88282-349-2(3)) New Horizon Pr. Pubs., Inc.

Fevre, Ralph, et al. Trouble at Work. 2012. (ENG., Illus.). 272p. (C). 100.00 (978-1-4081-3703-1(8) 17466) Bloomsbury Publishing.

Field, Evelyn M. Bully Blocking: Six Secrets to Help Children Deal with Teasing & Bullying. 2nd ed. 2007. Orig. Title: Bullybusting. (ENG., Illus.). 176p. per. (978-1-84310-554-1(3)) Kingsley, Jessica Ltd.

Fielder, Randie. Bullies & the Parents Who Raise Them. 2008. 92p. pap. (978-3-639-06095-9(4)) VDM Verlag Dr. Mueller e.K.

Fisher-Blando, Judith. Workplace Bullying: Aggressive Behavior. 2010. 160p. pap. (978-3-8383-6576-3(3)) Lambert Academic Publishing.

Flerx, Vicki Crocker. Class Meetings That Matter: A Year's Worth of Resources for Grades K-5. 2009. viii, 359p. 69.95 (978-1-59285-722-7(1)) Hazelden Publishing & Educational Services.

Flerx, Vicki Crocker, et al. Class Meetings That Matter: A Year's Worth of Resources for Grades 6-8. 2009. (Illus.). vii, 181p. (978-1-59285-831-6(7)) Hazelden Publishing & Educational Services.

Freedman, Jeri. Online Safety. 2011. (J). 167.70 (978-1-4488-4858-4(X), Rosen Central); (Illus.). 48p. (YA). (gr. 5-9). lib. bdg. 27.95 (978-1-4488-4577-4(7)) Rosen Publishing Group, Inc., The.

Frid, Marcia C. I Like You, I Like Me, Too! A Teacher/Parent Guide to Help Children Aged 6-10 Develop Self-Esteem Based on Choice Theory. 2008. (Illus.). 184p. pap. (978-1-894431-25-5(1)) Your Nickel's Worth Publishing.

Fried, Suellen. Banishing Bullying Behavior: Transforming the Culture of Peer Abuse. 2nd ed. 2011. (ENG.). 192p. 45.00 (978-1-61048-432-9(0)) Rowman & Littlefield Education.

García González, Javier & González, Javier García. Ciberacoso: La Tutela Penal de la Intimidad, la Integridad y la Libertad Sexual en Internet. 2010. (SPA.). 220p. (978-84-9876-835-0(7)) Tirant lo Blanch.

Gardner, Olivia, et al. Letters to a Bullied Girl: Messages of Healing & Hope. 2008. (ENG.). 256p. pap. 14.99 (978-0-06-154462-0(0), Harper Paperbacks) HarperCollins Pubs.

Garrett, Anne G. The New Bullying: Understanding & Responding to Cyber Bullying, Punking & Other Assaults on Young People. 2010. (ENG.). [180]p. pap. 35.00 (978-0-7864-4130-3(5)) McFarland & Co., Inc. Pubs.

George, Rosalyn. Girls in a Goldfish Bowl: Moral Regulation, Ritual & the Use of Power amongst Inner City Girls. 2009. 184p. (978-90-8790-186-8(0)) Sense Pubs.

Gerali, Steve. What Do I Do When Teenagers Encounter Bulling & Violence?, 1 vol. 2009. (What Do I Do When Ser.). (ENG.). 128p. pap. 6.99 (978-0-310-29194-7(1)) Zondervan.

Giannetti, Charlene C. & Sagarese, Margaret. Keep Cliques & Bullies from Invading Your School: Six Roads Teachers Can Take to Drive Out a Culture of Cruelty. 2007. (978-1-56090-212-6(4)) National Middle Schl. Assn.

Goldman, Carrie. Bullied: What Every Parent, Teacher, & Kid Needs to Know about Ending the Cycle of Fear. 2012. (ENG.). 320p. 25.99 (978-0-06-210507-3(8), HarperOne) HarperCollins Pubs.

Guillain, Charlotte. Coping with Bullying. 2011. (Real Life Issues Ser.). (ENG.). 48p. (gr. 6-8). pap. 8.99 (978-1-4329-5547-2(0), NA-h) Heinemann-Raintree.

Haber, Joel & Glatzer, Jenna. Bullyproof Your Child for Life: Protect Your Child from Teasing, Taunting, & Bullying for Good. 2007. (ENG.). 288p. (gr. 12-18). 14.95 (978-0-399-53318-1(4), Perigee Trade) Penguin Group (USA) Inc.

Harris, Monica J. Bullying, Rejection, & Peer Victimization a Social Cognitive Neuroscience Perspective. 2009. (Illus.). 400p. (978-0-8261-0378-9(2)) Springer.

Harris, Unice. What's Ailing You Child? Bullying. 2010. 32p. pap. 19.95 (978-0-557-67305-6(4)) Lulu Enterprises Inc.

Haskell, Rebecca & Burtch, Brian E. Get That Freak: Homophobia & Transphobia in High Schools. 2011. (Fernwood Basics Ser.). (ENG.). 128p. pap. 17.95 (978-1-55266-378-3(7)) Fernwood Publishing Co., Ltd. CAN. Dist: Independent Pubs. Group.

Head, Raisin. Religious Bullying. 2009. 80p. pap. 15.99 (978-1-4415-1933-7(5)) Xlibris Corp.

Henry, Sally. Bullying As a Social Pathology: A Peer Group Analysis. 2008. (Illus.). 276p. 109.95 (978-0-7734-5196-4(X)) Mellen, Edwin Pr., The.

Hetu, Sylvie & Elmsater, Mia. Touch in Schools: A Revolutionary Strategy for Replacing Bullying with Respect & for Reducing Violence. 2009. 180p. pap. 14.99 (978-0-9736659-1-8(2)) UR Pubns. & Programmes Inc.

Hogh, Annie. Aggression at Work. 2009. 88p. pap. (978-3-639-17635-3(9)) VDM Verlag Dr. Mueller e.K.

Hoover, John H. & Oliver, Ronald L. The Bullying Prevention Handbook: A Guide for Principals, Teachers, & Counselors. 2nd ed. 2008. (Illus.). 232p. pap. 29.95 incl. audio compact disk (978-1-934009-11-6(3)) Solution Tree.

Horne, Arthur, et al. A Parent's Guide to Understanding & Responding to Bullying: The Bully Buster's Approach. 2008. 164p. pap. 22.95 (978-0-87822-596-5(X)) Research Pr.

Horne, Arthur M., et al. Empowering Teen Peers to Prevent Bullying: The Bully Busters Program for High School. 2012. 194p. pap. 39.95 incl. cd-rom (978-0-87822-664-1(8)) Research Pr.

Jelinske, Jim. Bullying Prevention in Schools: The Adventures of Big Ollie. 2009. 100p. pap. 21.95 (978-1-935551-20-1(5)) Univ. Readers.

Jimerson. International Handbook of Bullying. 2nd ed. 2009. (ENG., Illus.). 614p. 305.00 (978-0-8058-6392-5(3)) Routledge.

Kevorkian, Meline. Tackling Bullying in Athletics: Best Practices for Modeling Appropriate Behavior. 2010. (ENG.). 100p. 60.00 (978-1-60709-379-4(0)); pap. 17.95 (978-1-60709-380-0(4)) Rowman & Littlefield Education.

Kevorkian, Meline M. & D'Antona, Robin. Tackling Bullying in Athletics: Guidelines for Modeling Appropriate Behavior. 2010. 17.95 (978-1-60709-381-7(2)) Rowman & Littlefield Publishers, Inc.

—101 Facts about Bullying: What Everyone Should Know. 2008. (ENG.). 176p. 40.00 (978-1-57886-849-0(1)) Rowman & Littlefield Education.

Khalsa, SiriNam S. Break the Bully Cycle: Intervention Techniques & Activities to Create a Repectful School Community. 2007. (Illus.). 178p. per. 19.95 (978-1-59647-119-1(0)) Good Year Bks.

Kilpatrick, Haley & Joiner, Whitney. The Drama Years: Real Girls Talk about Surviving Middle School — Bullies, Brands, Body Image, & More. 2012. (ENG., Illus.). 288p. pap. 16.00 (978-1-4516-2791-6(2), Free Pr.) Free Pr.

Kiriakidis, Stavros. Bullying among Youth: Issues, Interventions & Theory. 2011. (Education in a Competitive & Globalizing World Ser.). 202p. 69.00 (978-1-61122-869-4(7)) Nova Science Pubs., Inc.

Klein, Jessie. The Bully Society: School Shootings & the Crisis of Bullying in America's Schools. 2012. (ENG.). 304p. 29.95 (978-0-8147-4888-6(0)); xl, 307p. E-Book (978-0-8147-6370-4(7)); xl, 307p. E-Book (978-0-8147-6371-1(5)) New York Univ. Pr.

Kohut, Margaret R. The Complete Guide to Understanding, Controlling, & Stopping Bullies & Bullying: A Complete Guide for Teachers & Parents. 2007. (ENG., Illus.). 288p. per. 24.95 (978-1-60138-021-0(6)) Atlantic Publishing Co.

Kowalski, Robin M., et al. Cyber Bullying: Bullying in the Digital Age. 2008. (ENG., Illus.). 224p. 99.95 (978-1-4051-5991-3(X)); pap. 32.95 (978-1-4051-5992-0(8)) Wiley, John & Sons, Inc. (Wiley-Blackwell).

Kowalski, Robin M., et al. Cyberbullying: Bullying in the Digital Age. 2nd ed. 2012. (ENG.). 294p. 79.95 (978-1-4443-3480-7(8)); (Illus.). pap. 24.95 (978-1-4443-3481-4(6)) Wiley, John & Sons, Inc. (Wiley-Blackwell).

Kraizer, Sherryll. 10 Days to a Bully-Proof Child: The Proven Program to Build Confidence & Stop Bullies for Good. 2007. (ENG.). 240p. per. 14.95 (978-1-56924-253-7(4)) Da Capo Pr., Inc.

Lairson, Pat & King, Patricia. Stop the Bully: Cures for the Bully Epidemic. 2011. 96p. pap. 10.00 (978-1-936101-39-9(4)) XP Publishing.

Lee, Rosalind J. Brantley Goes Home. 2010. 40p. pap. 8.50 (978-1-4457-7951-5(X)) Lulu Enterprises Inc.

Leymann, Heinz. Workplace Mobbing As Psychological Terrorism: How Groups Eliminate Unwanted Members. 2010.Tr. of Fran mobbning till utslagning i Arbetslivet. (Illus.). 163p. 99.95 (978-0-7734-1395-5(2)) Mellen, Edwin Pr., The.

Limber, Sue, et al. Cyber Bullying: A Prevention Curriculum for Grades 3-5. 2009. (Illus.). xi, 110p. 99.00 (978-1-59285-715-9(9)) Hazelden Publishing & Educational Services.

Lines, Dennis. The Bullies: Understanding Bullies & Bullying. 2008. (ENG., Illus.). 16p. per. (978-1-84310-578-7(0)) Kingsley, Jessica Ltd.

Losey, Butch. Bullying, Suicide, & Homicide: Understanding, Assessing, & Preventing Threats to Self & Others for Victims of Bullying. 2011. (ENG., Illus.). 171p. 95.95 (978-0-415-87344-4(4)) Routledge.

—Bullying, Suicide, & Homicide: Understanding, Assessing, & Preventing Threats to Self & Others for Victims of Bullying. 2011. (ENG., Illus.). 171p. pap. 34.95 (978-0-415-87347-5(9)) Routledge.

MacIntyre, Christine. Bullying & Young Children: Understanding the Issues & Tackling the Problem. 2009. (ENG., Illus.). 122p. 33.95 (978-0-415-48496-1(0)) Routledge.

Macklem, Gayle L. Bullying & Teasing: Social Power in Children's Groups. 2010. (ENG.). 210p. pap. 89.95 (978-1-4419-3423-9(5), 1441934235) Springer.

Mah, Ronald, ed. Getting Beyond Bullying & Exclusion, PreK-5: Empowering Children in Inclusive Classrooms. 2009. 152p. pap. 28.95 (978-1-4129-5723-6(0), B57222P); (Illus.). 68.95 (978-1-4129-5722-9(2), B57222C) Corwin Pr.

Marr, Neil & Field, Tim. Bullycide: Death at Playtime. 2nd ed. 2011. (Illus.). 273p. pap. (978-1-906609-97-9(7)) BeWrite Bks.

Martin, Dominic M. St. Joseph Has Lost His Hammer: How Bullying & Hazing Has Swamped Our Nation's Schools & How Best to Stop It. 2011. 184p. pap. 13.95 (978-1-4620-3281-5(8)) iUniverse, Inc.

Martini, Banjo. Expect! 2011. 176p. pap. 15.95 (978-1-4620-6008-5(0)) iUniverse, Inc.

Matteson, Rande. The Bully Behind the Badge. 2010. 236p. pap. (978-3-8383-8139-8(4)) Lambert Academic Publishing.

McCandlish, Tami. Flying Grounded: My Spiritual Triumph over Female Bullying. 2007. 176p. (ENG.). 25.95 (978-0-595-69713-7(5)); per. 15.95 (978-0-595-45839-4(4)) iUniverse, Inc.

McCaw, Donna Sue, et al. Responding to Cyber Bullying: An Action Tool for School Leaders. 2011. 216p. pap. 36.95 (978-1-4129-9484-2(5), B94842P) Corwin Pr.

McGrath, Mary Jo. School Bullying: Tools for Avoiding Harm & Liability. 2006. (Illus.). 248p. 72.95 (978-1-4129-1571-7(6), B15716C); per. 36.95 (978-1-4129-1572-4(4), B15716P) Corwin Pr.

McIntyre Media Staff. Pushed to the Brink: Bullycide on the Rise. 2011. 149.95 (978-1-55548-888-6(9)) Human Relations Media.

McKinney, Elizabeth B. Peer Abuse Know More: Bullying from a Psychological Perspective. 2006. 187p. pap. 13.95 (978-0-7414-3265-0(X)) Infinity Publishing.

McQuade, Samuel C., et al. Cyber Bullying: Protecting Kids & Adults from Online Bullies, 1 vol. 2009. (Illus.). 219p. 39.95 (978-0-313-35193-8(7), C35193, Praeger Pubs.) Greenwood Publishing Group, Inc.

Mellon, Dorene Johnson. Back off Bullies! Bob Back off Bullies. 2011. 88p. pap. 17.99 (978-1-4670-4295-6(1)) AuthorHouse.

Meyer, Elizabeth J. Gender, Bullying, & Harassment: Strategies to End Sexism & Homophobia in Schools. rev. ed. 2009. (ENG., Illus.). 120p. pap. 24.95 (978-0-8077-4953-1(2)); 54.00 (978-0-8077-4954-8(0)) Teachers College Pr., Teachers College, Columbia Univ.

Michael, Susan L. Stop the Bullying Now! An Easy-to-Use Technique That Gives the Victim a Voice. 2007. (Greatest & Latest Teaching Tips Ser.). pap. 6.99 (978-0-86530-705-6(9)) Incentive Pubns., Inc.

Mishna, Faye. Bullying: A Guide to Research, Intervention, & Prevention, 1 vol. 2012. (ENG., Illus.). 224p. 49.99 (978-0-19-979540-6(1)) Oxford Univ. Pr., Inc.

Monks, Claire P. & Coyne, Iain, eds. Bullying in Different Contexts. 2011. (ENG., Illus.). 276p. 99.00 (978-0-521-11481-3(0)); pap. 39.99 (978-0-521-13259-6(2)) Cambridge Univ. Pr.

Monteverde, Matt. Making Smart Choices about Violence, Gangs, & Bullying. (Making Smart Choices Ser.). 48p. (gr. 5-5). 2009. 53.00 (978-1-61514-343-6(2), Rosen Central) 2008. (Illus.). (YA). lib. bdg. 26.50 (978-1-4042-1387-6(2)) Rosen Publishing Group, Inc., The.

Moore, Mona O' & Minton, Stephen James, eds. Cyber-Bullying: The Irish Experience. 2010. (Internet Policies & Issues; Children's Issues, Laws & Programs Ser.). pap. 47.00 (978-1-61728-380-2(0), Nova Novinka) Nova Science Pubs., Inc.

Morrison, Brenda. Restoring Safe School Communities: A Whole School Response to Bullying, Violence & Alienation. 2007. (Illus.). 270p. per. (978-1-86287-477-0(8)) Federation Pr. AUS. Dist: Willan Publishing.

Namie, Gary & Namie, Ruth. The Bully at Work: What You Can Do to Stop the Hurt & Reclaim Your Dignity on the Job. 2nd ed. 2009. (ENG.). 352p. pap. 16.99 (978-1-4022-2426-3(5)) Sourcebooks, Inc.

Namie, Gary & Namie, Ruth F. The Bully-Free Workplace: Stop Jerks, Weasels, & Snakes from Killing Your Organization. 2011. (ENG., Illus.). 190p. 24.95 (978-0-470-94220-8(7), Wiley) Wiley, John & Sons, Inc.

Neft, Deborah. Social & Emotional Profiles of Bullies & Victims. 2008. 100p. pap. (978-3-8364-9496-0(5)) VDM Verlag Dr. Mueller e.K.

Noels, Rodri A. School Bullying & Aggression: Assessment Tools. 2012. (Psychology of Emotions, Motivations & Actions/Children's Issues Ser.). 186p. 95.00 (978-1-61470-883-4(5)) Nova Science Pubs., Inc.

Oade, Aryanne. Managing Workplace Bullying: How to Identify, Respond to & Manage Bullying Behaviour in the Workplace. 2010. (ENG.). 256p. 47.00 (978-0-230-22808-5(9)) Palgrave Macmillan.

O'Brien, Catherine. Bullying Across In-Groups & Out-Groups. 2008. 268p. pap. (978-3-639-01834-9(6)) VDM Verlag Dr. Mueller e.K.

O'Higgins-Norman, James. Homophobic Bullying in Irish Secondary Education. 2008. (Irish Research Ser.: 53). 264p. lib. bdg. (978-1-933146-45-4(1), Maunsel & Co.) Academica Pr., LLC.

Omari, Maryam. Towards Dignity & Respect- an Exploration of the Nature, Causes & Consequences of Workplace Bullying. 2007. 264p. per. (978-3-8364-2861-3(X)) VDM Verlag Dr. Mueller e.K.

O'Moore, Mona. Understanding School Bullying: A Guide for Parents & Teachers. 2011. (ENG., Illus.). 232p. pap. 21.95 (978-1-84730-218-2(1)) Veritas Pubns. IRL. Dist: Dufour Editions, Inc.

Parens, Henri. Taming Aggression in Your Child: How to Avoid Raising Bullies, Delinquents, or Trouble-Makers. 2012. (978-0-7657-0898-4(1)) 2011. (ENG.). 240p. (gr. 17). 70.00 (978-0-7657-0896-0(5)) 2011. (ENG.). 240p. (gr. 17). pap. 29.99 (978-0-7657-0897-7(3)) Rowman & Littlefield Publishers, Inc. (Aronson, Jason).

Patchin, Justin W. & Hinduja, Sameer. Bullying Beyond the Schoolyard: Preventing & Responding to Cyberbullying. 2008. (Illus.). 272p. pap. 39.95 (978-1-4129-6689-4(2), B66887P) Corwin Pr.

—Cyberbullying Prevention & Response: Expert Perspectives. 2011. (ENG., Illus.). 224p. 155.00 (978-0-415-89236-0(8)); pap. 39.95 (978-0-415-89237-7(6)) Routledge.

Patchin, Justin W. & Hinduja, Sameer. School Climate 2. 0: Preventing Cyberbullying & Sexting One Classroom at a Time. 2012. 216p. pap. 29.95 (978-1-4129-9783-6(6), B97836P) Corwin Pr.

Peter, Kamala. When Parents Bully Teachers. 2011. 144p. pap. (978-3-8443-8876-3(1)) Lambert Academic Publishing.

Phillips, Rick, et al. Safe School Ambassadors: Harnessing Student Power to Stop Bullying & Violence. 2008. (ENG., Illus.). 352p. pap. 19.95 (978-0-470-19742-4(0), Jossey-Bass) Wiley, John & Sons, Inc.

Pickhardt, Carl E. Why Good Kids Act Cruel: The Hidden Truth about the Pre-Teen Years. 2010. (ENG.). 320p. pap. 14.99 (978-1-4022-1944-3(X)) Sourcebooks, Inc.

Purnell, A. Through the Eyes of a Dyslexic. 2007. 160p. per. (978-1-84747-194-9(3)) Chipmunkapublishing.

Putnam, Mark S. Respect & Fair Treatment: Facilitator's Guide: Preventing Harassment & Bullying. 2008. 110p. ring bd. 199.00 (978-0-9679729-6-1(5)) Global Ethics Univ.

—Respect & Fair Treatment: Participant Guide. 2008. 48p. per. 19.00 (978-0-9679729-9-2(X)) Global Ethics Univ.

Rahimi, Regina & Liston, Delores D. Pervasive Vulnerabilities: Sexual Harassment in School. 2012. E-Book (978-1-4539-0258-5(9)) Lang, Peter Publishing, Inc.

Randel, Derek. The Stopping School Violence Manual. 2009. 152p. pap. 19.16 (978-0-557-08586-6(1)) Lulu Enterprises Inc.

Reid. Teachers & Parents: The Anti Bully. 2009. 268p. pap. 24.95 (978-1-4389-5594-0(4)) AuthorHouse.

Renner, Nancy K. Trials & Tribulations of Being a Redhead: Bullied, Taunted & Teased for being a Redhead. 2011. 68p. pap. 9.95 (978-1-4497-2028-5(5), WestBow Pr.) Author Solutions, Inc.

Researcher, C. C. Childhood & Adolescence in Society: Selections from CQ Researcher. 2011. (Illus.). 336p. (C). pap. 36.00 (978-1-4129-9434-7(9), B94347P) SAGE Pubns., Inc.

Rickler, David N., ed. Bullying in Schools. 2008. 69.00 (978-1-60692-208-8(4)) Nova Science Pubs., Inc.

Rigby, Ken. Bullying in Schools & What to Do about It: Revised & Updated. 2007. 330p. pap. 39.95 (978-0-86431-447-5(7)) ACER Pr. AUS. Dist: International Specialized Bk. Services.

—Children & Bullying: How Parents & Educators Can Reduce Bullying at School. 2007. (ENG., Illus.). 256p. 99.95 (978-1-4051-6253-1(8)); per. 30.95 (978-1-4051-6254-8(6)) Wiley, John & Sons, Inc. (Wiley-Blackwell).

—The Method of Shared Concern: A Positive Approach to Bullying in Schools. 2011. 193p. pap. 34.95 (978-1-74286-007-7(9)) ACER Pr. AUS. Dist: International Specialized Bk. Services.

Riley, Stephen. Barsteadworth College: How Workplace Bullies Get Away with It. 2010. 250p. pap. (978-1-84991-182-5(7)) Chipmunkapublishing.

Rivers, Ian. Homophobic Bullying: Research & Theoretical Perspectives, 1 vol. 2011. (ENG., Illus.). 248p. 35.00 (978-0-19-516053-6(3)) Oxford Univ. Pr., Inc.

Rivers, Ian & Duncan, Neil, eds. Bullying: Experiences & Discourses of Sexuality & Gender. 2012. (Foundations & Futures of Education Ser.). (ENG.). 208p. (C). 155.00 (978-0-415-50502-4(X)); pap. 44.95 (978-0-415-50503-1(8)) Routledge.

Rivers, Ian, et al. Bullying: A Handbook for Educators & Parents, 1 vol. 2007. (Handbooks for Educators & Parents Ser.). (Illus.). 224p. 49.95 (978-0-313-33850-2(7), GR3850, Praeger Pubs.) Greenwood Publishing Group, Inc.

—Bullying: A Handbook for Educators & Parents. 2009. (ENG.). 222p. pap. 27.95 (978-1-57886-799-8(1)) Rowman & Littlefield Education.

Roberts, Walter B., Jr. Working with Parents of Bullies & Victims. 2007. (Illus.). 152p. 68.95 (978-1-4129-5103-6(8), B51038C) Corwin Pr.

Roberts, Walter B., Jr. & Roberts, Walter B. Working with Parents of Bullies & Victims. 2007. (Illus.). 152p. per. 28.95 (978-1-4129-5104-3(6), B51038P) Corwin Pr.

Robinson, George & Maines, Barbara. Bullying: A Complete Guide to the Support Group Method. 2008. (Lucky Duck Bks.). (Illus.). 168p. pap. 31.00 (978-1-4129-3536-4(9), B35369P) SAGE Pubns., Ltd. GBR. Dist: SAGE Pubns., Inc.

—The Support Group Method Training Pack: Effective Anti-Bullying Intervention. 2010. (Lucky Duck Bks.). 104p. pap. 33.00 (978-1-4129-1176-4(1), B11761P) SAGE Pubns., Ltd. GBR. Dist: SAGE Pubns., Inc.

Rosenthal, Beth & Des Chenes, Elizabeth, eds. Bullying. 2007. (Introducing Issues with Opposing Viewpoints Ser.). (ENG., Illus.). 120p. (YA). (gr. 7-12). lib. bdg. 35.75 (978-0-7377-3801-8(4)) Cengage Gale.

Sampson, Rana. Bullying in Schools. 2010. (ENG.). 60p. reprint ed. pap. 0.00 (978-1-932582-11-6(8)) U.S. Dept. of Justice-COPS.

Savage, Dan & Miller, Terry, eds. It Gets Better: Coming Out, Overcoming Bullying, & Creating a Life Worth Living. (ENG., 352p. 2012. Illus.). (gr. 12). 15.00 (978-0-452-29761-6(3), Plume) 2011. (gr. 8-18). 21.95 (978-0-525-95233-6(0), Dutton Adult) Penguin Group (USA) Inc.

Sawers-Diggins, Lannah. Bullseye. 2010. 104p. 24.99 (978-1-4535-2731-3(1)); pap. 15.99 (978-1-4535-2730-6(3)) Xlibris Corp.

Scaglione, Joanne. Bully-Proofing Children: A Practical, Hands-on Guide to Stop Bullying. 2006. (ENG.). 234p. per. 37.95 (978-1-57886-508-6(5)) Rowman & Littlefield Education.

Scaglione, Joanne & Scaglione, Arrica Rose. Bully-Proofing Children: A Practical, Hands-on Guide to Stop Bullying. 2006. (ENG.). 234p. 74.95 (978-1-57886-507-9(7)) Rowman & Littlefield Education.

Scott-Lennon, Frank & Considine, Margaret. Bullying & Harassment: Values & Best Practice Responses. 2008. (ENG., Illus.). 94p. pap. 14.95 (978-0-9519738-3-7(5)) Management Briefs Ltd.

Seigne, Elizabeth. Personality As a Contributory Factor to Workplace Bullying. 2010. 376p. pap. (978-3-8383-5740-9(X)) Lambert Academic Publishing.

Shariff, Shaheen. Confronting Cyber-Bullying: What Schools Need to Know to Control Misconduct & Avoid Legal Consequences. 2009. (ENG., Illus.). 296p. 89.00 (978-0-521-87723-7(7)); pap. 21.99 (978-0-521-70079-5(5)) Cambridge Univ. Pr.

—Cyber Bullying: Issues & Solutions for the School. 2008. (Illus.). XVIII, 310p. pap. 37.95 (978-0-415-42491-2(7)) Routledge.

SHARP Literacy, compiled by. Bullying: Is Anyone Listening? 2007. (Illus.). 84p. (J). 21.95 (978-0-9770816-5-3(6)) SHARP Literacy, Inc.

—Bullying; Is Anyone Listening? 2007. (ENG & SPA., Illus.). 84p. (J). pap. 15.95 (978-0-9770816-4-6(8)) SHARP Literacy, Inc.

B

Simmons, Rachel. Odd Girl Out: The Hidden Culture of Aggression in Girls. rev. ed. 2011. (ENG.). 432p. (gr. 9-12). pap. 14.95 *(978-0-547-52019-3(0),* Mariner Bks.) Houghton Mifflin Harcourt Trade & Reference Pubs.
Sommers, Donee. Job Harassment in the Department of Public Aid/Welfare Customers. 2007. pap. 10.00 *(978-0-8059-8984-7(6))* Dorrance Publishing Co., Inc.
Spence, Gerry. Bloodthirsty Bitches & Pious Pimps of Power: The Rise & Risks of the New Conservative Hate Culture. 2007. (ENG.). 304p. pap. 16.99 *(978-0-312-37390-0(2),* St. Martin's Griffin) St. Martin's Pr.
Staser, Marcia. Bullies, Beware... Babaloo Bounces Back! A Practical Guide for Kids Who Want to Stop Being Victims of Bullies. 2011. 108p. 21.99 ***(978-1-4567-6367-1(9))***; pap. 13.99 ***(978-1-4567-6368-8(7))*** AuthorHouse.
Stella, N. How Parents Can Help Stop Bullying. 2007. 64p. per. 13.50 *(978-1-84426-411-7(4))* Upfront Publishing Ltd. GBR. Dist: Printondemand-worldwide.com.
Stephenson, Kim & Roxborogh, Tania. No, It's Not Ok: How to Stop the Cycle of Bullying. 2009. (ENG., Illus.). 228p. (gr. 12). 22.00 *(978-0-14-300667-1(3),* Penguin Global) Penguin Group (USA) Inc.
Strauss, Susan. Sexual Harassment & Bullying: A Guide to Keeping Kids Safe & Holding Schools Accountable. 2011. (ENG.). 208p. 34.95 ***(978-1-4422-0162-0(2))***; E-Book ***(978-1-4422-0164-4(9))*** Rowman & Littlefield Publishers, Inc.
Sullivan, Keith. The Anti-Bullying Handbook. 2nd rev. ed. 2010. (Illus.). 280p. 98.00 *(978-1-84920-479-8(9),* B04798C); pap. 41.00 *(978-1-84920-480-4(2),* B04798P) SAGE Pubns., Ltd. GBR. Dist: SAGE Pubns., Inc.
Swearer, Susan M., et al. Bullying Prevention & Intervention: Realistic Strategies for Schools. 2009. (Practical Interventions in the Schools Ser.). (ENG., Illus.). 170p. (gr. k-12). pap. 35.00 *(978-1-60623-021-3(2))* Guilford Pubns., Inc.
Thomas, Michael. Bully the Bully: My Life One Day at A TIme. 2008. 176p. pap. 13.95 *(978-1-59858-685-5(8))* Dog Ear Publishing, LLC.
Thompson, Michael, et al. Mom, They're Teasing Me: Helping Your Chila Solve Social Problems. 2006. 247p. reprint ed. 23.00 *(978-1-4223-5381-3(8))* DIANE Publishing Co.
Thompson, Neil. Tackling Bullying & Harassment in the Workplace: A Learning & Development Manual. 2009. 160p. spiral bd. 99.95 *(978-1-905541-44-7(9))* Russell Hse. Publishing Ltd. GBR. Dist: International Specialized Bk. Services.
Tickle, Anna & Stott, Bettina. Exploring Bullying with Adults with Autism & Asperger Syndrome: A Photocopiable Workbook. 2010. (ENG., Illus.). 320p. pap. *(978-1-84905-035-7(X))* Kingsley, Jessica Ltd.
Train, Alan. The Bullying Problem: How to Deal with Difficult Children. 2nd ed. 2009. (ENG.). 208p. pap. 19.95 *(978-0-285-63829-7(7))* Souvenir Pr. Ltd. GBR. Dist: Independent Pubs. Group.
Trolley, Barbara, et al. Demystifying & Deescalating Cyber Bullying in the Schools: A Resource Guide for Counselors, Educators & Parents. 2006. 120p. pap. 39.95 *(978-1-59113-998-0(8))* Booklocker.com, Inc.
Trolley, Barbara C. & Hanel, Constance, eds. Cyber Kids, Cyber Bullying, Cyber Balance. 2009. (Illus.). 184p. 78.95 *(978-1-4129-7291-8(4),* B72918C); pap. 34.95 *(978-1-4129-7292-5(2),* B72918P) Corwin Pr.
Twale, Darla J. & De Luca, Barbara M. Faculty Incivility: The Rise of the Academic Bully Culture & What to Do about It. 2008. (JB - Anker Ser.: 128). (ENG.). 240p. 42.00 *(978-0-470-19766-0(8),* Jossey-Bass) Wiley, John & Sons, Inc.
Twemlow, Stuart W. & Sacco, Frank C. Preventing Bullying & School Violence. 2011. (ENG., Illus.). 240p. pap. 55.00 *(978-1-58562-384-6(9))* American Psychiatric Publishing, Inc.
—Why School Anti-Bullying Programs Don't Work. 2008. (ENG., Illus.). 178p. 39.95 *(978-0-7657-0475-7(7),* Aronson, Jason) Rowman & Littlefield Publishers, Inc.
Urbanski, Jan & Permuth, Steve. Truth about Bullying: What Educators & Parents Must Know & Do. 2009. (ENG.). 228p. 90.00 *(978-1-60709-410-4(X))*; pap. 34.95 *(978-1-60709-411-1(8))* Rowman & Littlefield Education.
Van der Zande, Irene. Bullying: What Adults Need to Know & Do to Keep Kids Safe. 2011. pap. *(978-0-9796191-6-8(5))* van der Zande, Irene.
Vernberg, Eric M. & Biggs, Bridget K. Preventing & Treating Bullying & Victimization. 2010. (ENG., Illus.). 424p. 59.95 *(978-0-19-533587-3(2))* Oxford Univ. Pr., Inc.
Vitali, Keith & Brouillard, Adam. Bullyproof Your Child: An Expert's Advice on Teaching Children to Defend Themselves. 2007. (Illus.). 176p. pap. 14.95 *(978-1-60239-076-8(2))* Skyhorse Publishing Co., Inc.
Wachs, Sebastian. Bullying unter Schülern: Eine empirisch-quantitative Untersuchung unter besonderer Berücksichtigung des Cyberbullyings. 2009. 144p. pap. *(978-3-639-21358-4(0))* VDM Verlag Dr. Mueller e.K.
Waever, Christina Louise. Bullying & Crime. 2011. 114p. pap. 30.90 ***(978-87-7114-272-3(X))*** Bks. on Demand.
Wambach, Julie Ann. Battles Between Somebodies & Nobodies: Combat Abuse of Rank at Work & at Home. 2008. 196p. pap. 16.95 *(978-0-9814818-0-7(9))* Brookside Pr.
Wardle, Cecile. Bullying... Deal with It!!! A Self-Help Guide Detailing Techniques on HOW to COMBAT the Aftereffect of School Bullying & HOW to DO Home Education Learning. 2007. (ENG.). 112p. pe. 16.95 *(978-1-4241-4438-9(8))* PublishAmerica, Inc.
Watson, Patricia. Workplace Bullying & Harassment: Victim or Victor? 2008. pap. 9.00 *(978-0-8059-7936-7(0))* Dorrance Publishing Co., Inc.
WaVer, Christina Louise. Mobning Og Kriminalitet. 2011. 114p. pap. 31.50 ***(978-87-7114-271-6(1))*** Bks. on Demand.
Westhues, Kenneth, ed. The Anatomy of an Academic Mobbing: Two Cases. 2008. 116p. 89.95 *(978-0-7734-4922-0(1))* Mellen, Edwin Pr., The.
Willard, Nancy. Cyberbullying & Cyberthreats (Book & CD) Responding to the Challenge of Online Social Aggression, Threats, & Distress. 2007. (ENG., Illus.). 320p. pap. 38.95 *(978-0-87822-537-8(4))* Research Pr.
Williams, Michael J. (John) & Winslade, John M. (Maxwell). Safe & Peaceful Schools: Addressing Conflict & Eliminating Violence. 2011. 208p. pap. 36.95 ***(978-1-4129-8675-5(3),*** B86755P) Corwin Pr.
Wilson, Signe & Whitson, Signe. Friendship & Other Weapons: Group Activities to Help Young Girls Aged 5-11 to Cope with Bullying. 2011. 192p. pap. ***(978-1-84905-875-9(X))*** Kingsley, Jessica Ltd.
Withers, Jennie & Hendrickson, Phyllis. Hey, Back Off! Tips for Stopping Teen Harassment. 2011. (ENG.). 224p. pap. 14.95 *(978-0-88282-365-2(5))* New Horizon Pr. Pubs., Inc.
Wood, Faith. The Graduating Bully. 2012. pap. 9.95 ***(978-0-7414-7202-1(3))*** Infinity Publishing.
—Taking the Bully by the Horns. 2012. pap. 9.95 ***(978-0-7414-7211-3(2))*** Infinity Publishing.
Zins, Joseph E., et al. Bullying, Victimization, & Peer Harassment: A Handbook of Prevention & Intervention. 2006. (ENG., Illus.). 450p. 125.00 *(978-0-7890-2218-9(4))*; per. 67.95 *(978-0-7890-2219-6(2))* Routledge.

BULLYING—JUVENILE LITERATURE

Frankel, Erin. Tough! 2012. (Weird! Ser.). (ENG.). 48p. (J). (gr. k-4). 15.99 ***(978-1-57542-400-2(2))*** Free Spirit Publishing, Inc.
—Weird! 2012. (Weird! Ser.). (ENG.). 48p. (J). (gr. k-4). 15.99 ***(978-1-57542-398-2(7))*** Free Spirit Publishing, Inc.
Shirley (Callcut), Marilyn. The BIG Bully. 2011. 28p. (gr. 4-6). pap. 12.03 ***(978-1-4567-6976-5(6))*** AuthorHouse.

BULLMASTIFF

Gunn, Janet. Pet Owner's Guide to the Bullmastiff. (Illus.). 80p. tchr. ed. 9.95 *(978-1-86054-187-2(9),* INT048) Ringpress Bks., Ltd. GBR. Dist: TFH Pubns., Inc.

BULMER, WILLIAM, 1757-1830

Bulmer, William & Timperley, C. H. William Bulmer & the Shakespeare Press: A Biography of William Bulmer from A Dictionary of Printers & Printing. 2011. 42p. 35.95 ***(978-1-258-09554-3(8))*** Literary Licensing, LLC.

BULOW, HANS GUIDO VON, 1830-1894

Bülow, Hans von & Hinrichsen, Hans-Joachim. Hans Von Bülow's Letters to Johannes Brahms: A Research Edition. 2012. E-Book ***(978-0-8108-8216-4(7))*** Scarecrow Pr., Inc.
Hinrichsen, Hans-Joa. Hans Von Bulow's Letters to Johannes Brahms. 2011. (ENG., Illus.). 170p. (gr. 17). 75.00 ***(978-0-8108-8215-7(9))*** Scarecrow Pr., Inc.
Walker, Alan. Hans Von Bülow: A Life & Times. 2009. (ENG., Illus.). 544p. 39.95 *(978-0-19-536868-0(1))* Oxford Univ. Pr., Inc.

BULTMANN, RUDOLF KARL, 1884-1976

Bartels, Cora. Kierkegaard Receptus. 2008. (GER.). 469p. (C). 84.00 *(978-3-89971-436-4(9))* Vandenhoeck & Ruprecht GmbH & Co. KG DEU. Dist: ISD.
—Kierkegaard receptus II: Die theologiegeschichtliche Bedeutung der Kierkegaard-Rezeption Rudolf Bultmanns. 2011. (GER.). 416p. (C). 74.00 *(978-3-89971-516-3(0))* Vandenhoeck & Ruprecht GmbH & Co. KG DEU. Dist: ISD.
Dennison, William D. The Young Bultmann: Context for His Understanding of God, 1884-1925. 2008. (American University Studies VII: Theology & Religion Ser.). 260p. (C). 72.95 *(978-0-8204-8113-5(0))* Lang, Peter Publishing, Inc.
Hammann, Konrad. Rudolf Bultmann: Eine Biographie. 2009. (GER., Illus.). xi, 582p. *(978-3-16-148526-8(2))* Mohr Siebeck GmbH & Co. KG.
—Rudolf Bultmann - Eine Biographie. 2nd ed. 2009. (GER., Illus.). XIII, 582p. *(978-3-16-150204-0(3))* Mohr Siebeck GmbH & Co. KG.
Labron & Labron, Tim. Bultmann Unlocked. 2011. (ENG.). 144p. 110.00 *(978-0-567-03153-2(5),* T&T Clark Int'l) Continuum International Publishing Group, Ltd. GBR. Dist: National Bk. Network.
Robinson, James M. Language, Hermeneutic, & History: Theology after Barth & Bultmann. 2007. 260p. pap. 29.00 *(978-1-59752-881-8(1))* Wipf & Stock Pubs.
Vanhoozer, Kevin J. Remythologizing Theology: Divine Action, Passion, & Authorship. 2010. (Cambridge Studies in Christian Doctrine Ser.). (ENG.). 560p. 131.00 *(978-0-521-47012-4(9))* Cambridge Univ. Pr.
Wedderburn, Alexander J. M. Jesus & the Historians. 2010. (Wissenschaftliche Untersuchungen zum Neuen Testament, No. 269 Ser.). 391p. 197.50 *(978-3-16-150708-3(8))* Mohr Siebeck GmbH & Co. KG DEU. Dist: Coronet Bks.

BULWER-LYTTON, EDWARD GEORGE, 1803-1873

see Lytton, Edward Bulwer Lytton, Baron, 1803-1873

BUMBLEBEES

Chalk, Daniel. Artificially Intelligent Foraging. 2011. 244p. pap. ***(978-3-8454-1515-4(0))*** Lambert Academic Publishing.
Chauhan, Avinash & Raj K Thakur. Bumble Bees: A new pollinator in Indian Agriculture. 2011. 152p. pap. ***(978-3-8443-2035-0(0))*** Lambert Academic Publishing.
Goulson, Dave. Bumblebees: Behaviour, Ecology, & Conservation. 2nd ed. 2009. (ENG., Illus.). 336p. 130.00 *(978-0-19-955306-8(8))*; pap. 55.00 *(978-0-19-955307-5(6))* Oxford Univ. Pr., Inc.
Mader, Eric, et al. Managing Alternative Pollinators: A Handbook for Beekeepers, Growers, & Conservationists. 2009. *(978-1-933395-20-3(6))* Natural Resource, Agricultural, & Engineering Service.
Pr#375;s-Jones, Oliver E. & Corbet, Sally A. Bumblebees (Naturalists' Handbooks 6) 3rd ed. 2011. (Illus.). 130p. pap. *(978-1-907807-06-0(3))* Pelagic Publishing Ltd.
Sabir, A. M., et al. Bumblebees & Utilization of Food Resources in Northern Pakistan. 2011. 224p. pap. ***(978-3-8443-9049-0(9))*** Lambert Academic Publishing.

BUMPER STICKERS

Bowen, Jack. If You Can Read This: The Philosophy of Bumper Stickers. 2010. (ENG., Illus.). 240p. pap. 14.00 *(978-0-8129-8105-6(7),* Random Hse. Trade Paperbacks) Random House Publishing Group.
Kumar, Srini. Sticker Nation Vol. 2. 2009. (ENG.). 64p. pap. 19.95 *(978-1-934708-08-8(9))* Disinformation Co. Ltd., The.

BUMPUS, HERMON CAREY, 1862-1943

Bumpus, Hermon C. Hermon Carey Bumpus, Yankee Naturalist. 2009. (ENG.). 148p. pap. 40.00 *(978-0-8166-5962-3(1))* Univ. of Minnesota Pr.

BUNCHE, RALPH J. (RALPH JOHNSON), 1904-1971

Hill, Robert A. & Keller, Edmond J. Trustee for the Human Community: Ralph J. Bunche, the United Nations, & the Decolonization of Africa. 2010. *(978-0-8214-4344-6(5))* Ohio Univ. Pr.
Hill, Robert A. & Keller, Edmond J., eds. Trustee for the Human Community: Ralph J. Bunche, the United Nations, & the Decolonization of Africa. 2010. (ENG.). 264p. 59.95 *(978-0-8214-1909-0(9))*; pap. 26.95 *(978-0-8214-1910-6(2))* Ohio Univ. Pr.
Lindsay, Beverly, ed. Ralph Johnson Bunche: Public Intellectual & Nobel Peace Laureate. 2008. 216p. 37.00 *(978-0-252-03225-7(X))* Univ. of Illinois Pr.
Miller, Eben. Born along the Color Line: The 1933 Amenia Conference & the Rise of a National Civil Rights Movement, 1 vol. 2012. (ENG., Illus.). 368p. 29.95 *(978-0-19-517455-7(0))* Oxford Univ. Pr., Inc.

BUNDLES, FIBER (MATHEMATICS)

see Fiber Bundles (Mathematics)

BUNKER HILL, BATTLE OF, BOSTON, MASS., 1775

Bunker Hill: Battle, Monument, Memory. 2007. 5.95 *(978-1-59091-066-5(4))* Eastern National.
Frothingham, Richard. History of the Siege of Boston, & of the Battles of Lexington, Concord, & Bunker Hill. 2009. 312p. pap. 25.00 *(978-1-150-74766-3(8))* Books LLC.
—History of the Siege of Boston, & of the Battles of Lexington, Concord, & Bunker Hill. 422p. reprint ed. 98.00 *(978-0-7222-7694-5(X))* Library Reprints, Inc.
Lockhart, Paul Douglas. The Whites of Their Eyes: Bunker Hill, the First American Army, & the Emergence of George Washington. 2011. (ENG.). 352p. 27.99 *(978-0-06-195886-1(7))* HarperCollins Pubs.
Nelson, James L. With Fire & Sword: The Battle of Bunker Hill & the Beginning of the American Revolution. 2011. (ENG., Illus.). 384p. 27.99 *(978-0-312-57644-8(7),* Dunne, Thomas Bks.) St. Martin's Pr.
—With Fire & Sword: The Battle of Bunker Hill & the Beginning of the American Revolution. l.t. ed. 2011. (Illus.). 595p. 31.99 *(978-1-4104-3824-9(4))* Thorndike Pr.

BUNKER HILL MONUMENT (BOSTON, MASS.)

Bunker Hill: Battle, Monument, Memory. 2007. 5.95 *(978-1-59091-066-5(4))* Eastern National.
Pulsifer, David. Account of the Battle of Bunker Hill. 2006. pap. 17.95 *(978-1-4286-5023-7(0))* Kessinger Publishing, LLC.

BUNNER, H. C. (HENRY CUYLER), 1855-1896

Bunner, Henry Cuyler. The Life & Letters of Henry Cuyler Bunner. Jensen, Gerard E., ed. 2011. 264p. 47.95 ***(978-1-258-04878-5(7))*** Literary Licensing, LLC.
Matthews, Brander. Recreations of an Anthologist. 2009. 236p. 23.99 *(978-1-103-59732-1(9))*; pap. 17.99 *(978-1-103-59728-4(0))* BiblioBazaar.
—Recreations of an Anthologist. 2008. 234p. 41.95 *(978-0-548-92095-4(8))* 2007. 236p. per. 26.95 *(978-0-548-59680-7(8))* Kessinger Publishing, LLC.
—Recreations of an Anthologist. 2008. 236p. pap. *(978-1-4097-8779-2(6))* Read Bks.

BUNTING, BASIL, 1900-1981

Stannard, Julian. Basil Bunting. 2012. (Writers & Their Work Ser.). (ENG.). 120p. (C). 80.00 ***(978-0-7463-1048-9(X))***; pap. 26.00 ***(978-0-7463-1006-9(4))*** Northcote Hse. Publishers, Ltd. GBR. Dist: Brown, David Bk. Co., The.

BUNUEL, LUIS, 1900-1983

Edwards, Gwynne. Lorca, Bunuel, Dali: Forbidden Pleasures & Connected Lives. 2009. (ENG., Illus.). 256p. 45.00 *(978-1-84885-007-1(7))* I. B. Tauris & Co., Ltd. GBR. Dist: Macmillan.
Gubern, Roman & Hammond, Paul. Luis Buñuel: The Red Years. 2012. (Wisconsin Film Studies). (ENG., Illus.). 472p. pap. 34.95 *(978-0-299-28474-9(3))* Univ. of Wisconsin Pr.

BUNYAN, JOHN, 1628-1688

Baillie, John. Life-Studies or How to Live: Illustrated by the Biographies of Bunyan, Tersteegen, Montgomery, Perthes & Mrs. Winslow. 2007. pap. 31.95 *(978-1-4304-5041-2(X))* Kessinger Publishing, LLC.
Belmonte, Kevin & Stokes, Mitch. John Bunyan, 0 vols. 2010. (Christian Encounters Ser.). 192p. pap. 12.00 *(978-1-59555-304-1(5))* Nelson, Thomas Inc.
Brittain, Vera. Valiant Pilgrim: The Story of John Bunyan & Puritan England. 2011. 488p. 58.95 ***(978-1-258-06817-2(6))*** Literary Licensing, LLC.
Brown, John. John Bunyan: His Life Times & Work. 3rd ed. 2007. (Illus.). 522p. pap. 45.00 *(978-1-55635-219-5(0),* Wipf and Stock) Wipf & Stock Pubs.
—John Bunyan His Life Times & Work. 2006. (Illus.). pap. 40.95 *(978-1-4286-5050-3(4))* Kessinger Publishing, LLC.
Bunyan, John. All-in-One Curriculum for the Pilgrim's Progress. 2006. (Illus.). 496p. 39.99 incl. cd-rom *(978-1-893345-77-5(7))* Answers in Genesis Ministries.
—Grace Abounding: With Other Spiritual Autobiographies. Stachniewski, John & Pacheco, Anita, eds. 2008. (Oxford World's Classics Ser.). (ENG.). 336p. pap. 11.95 *(978-0-19-955498-0(6))* Oxford Univ. Pr., Inc.
—Grace Abounding to the Chief of Sinners. 2008. 148p. 21.99 *(978-0-559-79474-2(6))*; 148p. pap. 20.75 *(978-0-559-79472-8(X))*; 152p. 21.99 *(978-0-554-37023-1(9))*; 152p. 24.99 *(978-0-554-27720-2(4))* BiblioBazaar.
—Grace Abounding to the Chief of Sinners. 2007. (Authentic Original Classic Ser.). 173p. per. 13.99 *(978-0-7684-2457-7(7))* Destiny Image Pubs.
—Grace Abounding to the Chief of Sinners. 2007. (ENG.). 88p. per. *(978-1-4068-2294-6(9))* Echo Library.
—Grace Abounding to the Chief of Sinners. 2007. (Hendrickson Christian Classics Ser.). 165p. 6.97 *(978-1-59856-206-4(1))*; 9.95 *(978-1-59856-142-5(1))* Hendrickson Pubs. Marketing, LLC.
—Grace Abounding to the Chief of Sinners. 2007. per. 9.99 *(978-1-4245-0793-1(6))* Treasures Media Inc.
—Grace Abounding to the Chief of Sinners: In a Faithful Account of the Life & Death of John Bunyan. 2007. 244p. (ENG.). 24.95 *(978-1-60206-458-4(X))*; per. 10.95 *(978-1-60206-457-7(1))* Cosimo, Inc.
—Memoir of John Bunyan. 2007. 168p. per. *(978-1-4068-2293-9(0))* Echo Library.
Bunyan, John & Edmonson, Robert J. The Most Difficult Journey You'll Ever Make: The Pilgrim's Progress. 2006. 241p. per. 14.95 *(978-1-55725-464-1(8))* Paraclete Pr., Inc.
Bunyan, John Jr. & Bunyan, John. The Life & Death of Mr Badman. 2011. 256p. pap. 10.95 ***(978-1-4474-1765-1(8))*** Audubon Pr. & Christian Bk. Service.
Camden, Vera J., ed. Trauma & Transformation: The Political Progress of John Bunyan. 2007. (ENG.). 200p. 55.00 *(978-0-8047-5785-0(2))* Stanford Univ. Pr.
Cook, Faith. Fearless Pilgrim: The Life & Times of John Bunyan. 2008. (Illus.). 528p. *(978-0-85234-680-8(8))* Evangelical Pr.
Cosby, Brian H. John Bunyan: The Journey of a Pilgrim. 2009. (ENG.). 160p. mass mkt. 8.99 *(978-1-84550-458-8(5))* Christian Focus Pubns. GBR. Dist: STL Distribution North America.
Day, Richard Ellsworth. So Pilgrim Rang the Bells: The Life Story of John Bunyan. 2011. 156p. 41.95 ***(978-1-258-02764-3(X))*** Literary Licensing, LLC.
Dunan-Page, Anne. The Cambridge Companion to Bunyan. 2010. (Cambridge Companions to Literature Ser.). (ENG.). 212p. pap. 29.99 *(978-0-521-73308-3(1))* Cambridge Univ. Pr.
Dunan-Page, Anne, ed. The Cambridge Companion to Bunyan. 2010. (Cambridge Companions to Literature Ser.). (ENG.). 212p. 85.00 *(978-0-521-51526-9(2))* Cambridge Univ. Pr.
Edmund, Venables. Life of John Bunyan. 2006. (ENG.). 132p. pap. 18.99 *(978-1-4264-0622-5(3))*; 124p. pap. 19.99 *(978-1-4264-0664-5(9))* BiblioBazaar.
Ellis, James J. The Life Story of John Bunyan. 2011. 120p. 39.95 ***(978-1-258-06181-4(3))*** Literary Licensing, LLC.
Froude, James. Bunyan. 2007. (ENG.). 188p. 37.95 *(978-0-548-05027-9(9))* Kessinger Publishing, LLC.
Froude, James Anthony. Bunyan. 2011. (Cambridge Library Collection - English Men of Letters Ser.). (ENG.). 194p. pap. 19.99 ***(978-1-108-03466-1(7))*** Cambridge Univ. Pr.
Hamilton, James. Life of Bunyan. 2007. 48p. per. *(978-1-4065-1966-2(9))* Dodo Pr.
John Bunyan. Grace Abounding to the Chief of Sinners. 2007. (ENG.). 136p. pap. 18.99 *(978-1-4346-3844-1(8))* BiblioBazaar.
—Grace Abounding to the Chief of Sinners. 2010. 132p. pap. 4.49 *(978-1-60386-289-9(7),* Merchant Bks.) Rough Draft Printing.
—Grace Abounding to the Chief of Sinners. l.t. ed. 2007. (ENG.). 150p. pap. 19.99 *(978-1-4346-3845-8(6))* BiblioBazaar.
Johnson, Galen. Prisoner of Conscience: John Bunyan on Self, Community, & Christian Faith. 2007. (Studies in Christian History & Thought Ser.). 260p. pap. 27.00 *(978-1-59752-094-2(2),* Wipf and Stock) Wipf & Stock Pubs.
Luebke, Alexandra. The Pilgrim's Progress in American Juvenile Literature 1860-1900. 2007. 84p. per. *(978-3-8364-2300-7(6))* VDM Verlag Dr. Mueller e.K.
McKelvey, Robert J. Histories that Mansoul & Her Wars Anatomize: The Drama of Redemption in John Bunyan's Holy War. 2011. (Reformed Historical Theology Ser.). (ENG.). 336p. (C). 129.00 *(978-3-525-56939-9(4))* Vandenhoeck & Ruprecht GmbH & Co. KG DEU. Dist: ISD.
Olson, Bessie G. John Bunyan - A Great Dreamer. 2006. per. 3.00 *(978-1-60208-024-9(0))* FBC Pubns. & Printing.
Osborn, Ian. Can Christianity Cure Obsessive-Compulsive Disorder? A Psychiatrist Explores the Role of Faith in Treatment. 2008. 208p. pap. 19.99 *(978-1-58743-206-4(4))* Brazos Pr.
Owens, W. R. & Sim, Stuart, eds. Reception,Appropriation, Recollection: Bunyan's Pilgrim's Progress. 2007. (Religious & Discourse Ser.: Vol. 33). 253p. (C). pap. 61.95 *(978-0-8204-7983-5(7))* Lang, Peter Publishing, Inc.

Piper, John. The Hidden Smile of God: The Fruit of Affliction in the Lives of John Bunyan, William Cowper, & David Brainerd. 2008. (Swans Are Not Silent Ser.). 176p. pap. 15.99 *(978-1-4335-0189-0(9))* Crossway.

Rodriguez Garcia, Juan Bunyan: John Bunyan - A Biography. (SPA.). *(978-84-7645-152-6(0),* 223198) Clie, Editorial.

Rosenfeld, Nancy & Stern, Max. The Human Satan in Seventeenth-Century English Literature: From Milton to Rochester. 2008. 224p. 114.95 *(978-0-7546-6468-0(6))* Ashgate Publishing Co.

Searle, Alison. The Eyes of Your Heart: Literary & Theological Trajectories of Imagining Biblically. 2009. (Paternoster Theological Monographs Ser.). 250p. pap. 29.00 *(978-1-60608-602-5(2),* Wipf and Stock) Wipf & Stock Pubs.

Shenton, Tim. Christmas Evans — No Ordinary Preacher: The Story of the 'John Bunyan' of Wales. 2008. (History Today Ser.). (Illus.). 154p. pap. *(978-1-84625-130-6(3))* DayOne Pubns.

Southey, Robert. Oliver Cromwell & John Bunyan. Dowden, Edward, ed. 2007. (ENG.). 188p. 37.95 *(978-0-548-03481-1(8))* Kessinger Publishing, LLC.

Spargo, Tamsin. John Bunyan. 2011. (Writers & Their Work Ser.). (C). (ENG.). 80.00 *(978-0-7463-1049-6(8));* pap. 26.00 *(978-0-7463-0982-7(1))* Northcote Hse. Publishers, Ltd. GBR. Dist: Brown, David Bk. Co., The.

Tulloch, John. English Puritanism & Its Leaders: Cromwell, Milton, Baxter, Bunyan. 2008. 520p. pap. *(978-1-4086-6848-1(3))* Read Bks.

Venables, Edmund. The Life of John Bunyan. 2009. 128p. pap. *(978-1-4099-2628-3(1))* Dodo Pr.

—The Life of John Bunyan. 2007. (ENG.). 96p. per. *(978-1-4068-1540-5(3))* Echo Library.

—Life of John Bunyan. 2008. 236p. 24.99 *(978-0-559-66603-2(9));* 236p. pap. 24.75 *(978-0-559-66601-8(2));* 128p. 24.99 *(978-0-554-21672-0(8));* 128p. 21.99 *(978-0-554-30975-0(0))* BiblioBazaar.

—Life of John Bunyan. 2009. 176p. pap. *(978-0-217-01295-6(5))* Books LLC.

Whyte, Alexander. Bunyan Characters: First Series. 2006. (ENG.). 202p. pap. 20.99 *(978-1-4264-0414-6(X));* 192p. pap. 21.99 *(978-1-4264-0456-6(5))* BiblioBazaar.

—Bunyan Characters: First Series. 2009. 196p. pap. *(978-1-4099-5522-1(2))* Dodo Pr.

BUNYAN, JOHN, 1628-1688—STUDY AND TEACHING

Froude, James A. Bunyan. Morley, John, ed. (English Men of Letters Ser.). reprint ed. lib. bdg. 27.50 *(978-0-404-51711-3(0))* AMS Pr., Inc.

BUNYAN, PAUL (LEGENDARY CHARACTER)

Blair, Eric. Paul Bunyan. 2011. (My First Classic Story Ser.).Tr. of Paul Bunyan. (ENG.). 32p. (gr. k-3). pap. 6.95 ***(978-1-4048-7366-7(X))***; lib. bdg. 21.32 *(978-1-4048-6580-8(2))* Picture Window Bks. (My First Classic Story).

Edmonds, Michael. Out of the Northwoods: The Many Lives of Paul Bunyan, with More Than 100 Logging Camp Tales. 2009. (ENG., Illus.). 304p. 24.95 *(978-0-87020-437-1(8))* Wisconsin Historical Society.

Felton, Harold W. Legends of Paul Bunyan. 2008. (Illus.). 448p. pap. 18.95 *(978-0-8166-5460-4(3))* Univ. of Minnesota Pr.

Laughead, W. B. The Marvelous Exploits of Paul Bunyan. 2009. (ENG.). 48p. pap. 8.45 *(978-1-4385-2284-5(3),* Book Jungle) Standard Pubns., Inc.

Schomp, Virginia, retold by. Paul Bunyan & His Big Blue Ox. 2012. (J). *(978-1-60870-443-9(2))* Marshall Cavendish.

Whiting, Jim. Paul Bunyan. 2007. (What's So Great About...? Ser.). (Illus.). 32p. (YA). (gr. 2-4). lib. bdg. 25.70 *(978-1-58415-574-4(4))* Mitchell Lane Pubs., Inc.

BUONARROTI, FILIPPO MICHELE, 1761-1837

Eisenstein, Elizabeth L. The First Professional Revolutionist: Filippo Michele Buonarroti, 1761-1837. 2011. 224p. 44.95 ***(978-1-258-09100-2(3))*** Literary Licensing, LLC.

BUONARROTI, MICHELANGELO, 1475-1564

see Michelangelo Buonarroti, 1475-1564

BURAKU PEOPLE

Amos, Timothy D. Embodying Difference: The Making of Burakumin in Modern Japan. 2011. 66.00 *(978-0-8248-3578-1(6));* pap. 33.00 *(978-0-8248-3579-8(4))* Univ. of Hawaii Pr.

Gordon, June A. Japan's Outcaste Youth: Education for Liberation. 2008. 168p. pap. 39.95 *(978-1-59451-562-0(X));* 125.00 *(978-1-59451-561-3(1))* Paradigm Pubs.

McKnight, Anne. Nakagami, Japan: Buraku & the Writing of Ethnicity. 2011. (Illus.). 296p. 75.00 *(978-0-8166-7285-1(7));* pap. 25.00 *(978-0-8166-7286-8(5))* Univ. of Minnesota Pr.

Neary, Ian. The Buraku Issue & Modern Japan: The Career of Matsumoto Jiichiro. 2009. (Nissan Institute/Routledge Japanese Studies). (Illus.). 240p. 135.00 *(978-0-415-39082-8(6))* Routledge.

BURAKUMIN (JAPANESE PEOPLE)

see Buraku People

BURBANK, LUTHER, 1849-1926

Haldeman-Julius, E. Miscellaneous Essays. 2006. pap. 16.95 *(978-1-4286-4635-3(3))* Kessinger Publishing, LLC.

Smith, Jane S. The Garden of Invention: Luther Burbank & the Business of Breeding Plants. 2010. (ENG.). 368p. (gr. 12-18). 16.00 *(978-0-14-311689-9(4),* Penguin (Non-Classics)) Penguin Group (USA) Inc.

BURCHFIELD, CHARLES EPHRAIM, 1893-1967

Burlingham, Cynthia & Gober, Robert, eds. Heat Waves in a Swamp: The Paintings by Charles Burchfield. 2009. (Illus.). 176p. 49.95 *(978-3-7913-4380-8(7))* Prestel Publishing.

Moore, Bridget, intro. Charles Burchfield 1920: the Architecture of Painting. 2009. (ENG., Illus.). 120p. 50.00 *(978-0-9815250-5-1(9))* DC Moore Gallery.

—Charles Burchfield: Fifty Years as a Painter. 2010. (ENG., Illus.). 120p. 45.00 *(978-0-9826316-3-6(4))* DC Moore Gallery.

Presenti, Allegra. Rachel Whiteread Drawings. 2010. (Illus.). 224p. 49.95 *(978-3-7913-5038-7(2))* Prestel Publishing.

BURDEN OF PROOF

Ahman, Joachim. Trade Health & the Burden of Proof in WTO Law. 2011. 352p. 189.00 ***(978-90-411-3825-5(0))*** Wolters Kluwer Law & Business.

Ho, H. L. A Philosophy of Evidence Law: Justice in the Search for Truth. 2008. (Oxford Monographs on Criminal Law & Justice Ser.). (ENG.). 320p. 125.00 *(978-0-19-922830-0(2))* Oxford Univ. Pr., Inc.

Kofele-Kale, Ndiva. Combating Economic Crimes: Balancing Competing Rights & Interests in Prosecuting the Crime of Illicit Enrichment. 2011. (Routledge Research in Transnational Crime & Criminal Law Ser.). (ENG.). 248p. 125.00 *(978-0-415-77847-3(6))* Routledge.

Mentz, Dörte. Die Beweislastumkehr in der Rechtsprechung des Reichsgerichts. 2009. (Rechtshistorische Reihe Ser.). (GER.). 456p. 112.95 *(978-3-631-59869-6(6))* Lang, Peter GmbH, Europaischer Verlag der Wissenschaften DEU. Dist: Lang, Peter.

Sundmacher, Julia Susanne. Die unterlassene Befunderhebung des Arztes: Eine Auseinandersetzung mit der Rechtsprechung des BGH. 2008. (Recht & Medizin Ser.). 276p. pap. 74.95 *(978-3-631-57940-4(3))* Lang, Peter GmbH, Europaischer Verlag der Wissenschaften DEU. Dist: Lang, Peter.

Tomkovicz, James J. Constitutional Exclusion: The Rules, Rights, & Remedies That Strike the Balance Between Freedom & Order, 1 vol. 2011. (ENG.). 436p. 95.00 *(978-0-19-536924-3(6))* Oxford Univ. Pr., Inc.

BUREAUCRACY

see also Civil Service; Organizational Sociology

Abdul Majid, Izaidin & Ismail, Kamariah. Entrepreneurial Management & Technology-Based Firms. 2010. 228p. pap. *(978-3-8383-1612-3(6))* Lambert Academic Publishing.

Andreski, Stanislav, ed. Max Weber on Capitalism, Bureaucracy & Religion. 2008. 272p. 39.95 *(978-0-415-48953-9(9))* 2006. 176p. 180.00 *(978-0-415-40214-9(X))* Routledge.

Andrianov, V. D. Biurokratiia, Korruptsiia I Effektivnost Gosudarstvennogo Upravleniia. 2nd ed. 2011. (RUS.). viii, 271p. *(978-5-466-00706-0(4))* Volters Kluver.

Appleby, Paul H. Big Democracy. 2007. (ENG.). 208p. per. *(978-1-4067-5495-7(1))* Read Bks.

Arellano-Gault, David. Community-Based Organizations in Mexico. 2010. 312p. pap. *(978-3-639-27784-5(8))* VDM Verlag Dr. Mueller e.K.

Bachman, David. Bureaucracy, Economy, & Leadership in China: The Institutional Origins of the Great Leap Forward. 2006. (ENG.). 288p. (C). pap. 42.00 *(978-0-521-03233-9(4))* Cambridge Univ. Pr.

Barnes, John, et al, eds. The Politics of Legalism. 2013. (Law, Courts & Politics Ser.). (ENG.). 224p. (C). 130.00 ***(978-0-415-63338-3(9))*** Routledge.

Benveniste, Guy. Bureaucracy. pap. *(978-0-87835-059-9(4))* CENGAGE Learning.

Box, Richard C. Public Administration & Society: Critical Issues in American Governance. 2nd rev. ed. 2009. 312p. (C). (ENG.). pap. 59.95 *(978-0-7656-2359-1(5));* (Illus.). 89.95 *(978-0-7656-2358-4(7))* Sharpe, M.E. Inc.

Bozeman, Barry & Feeney, Mary. Rules & Red Tape: A Prism for Public Administration Theory & Research. 2011. (Illus.). 240p. 79.95 *(978-0-7656-2334-8(X))* Sharpe, M.E. Inc.

Bozeman, Barry & Feeney, Mary K. Rules & Red Tape: A Prism for Public Administration Theory & Research. 2011. (Illus.). 207p. pap. 34.95 ***(978-0-7656-2335-5(3))*** Sharpe, M.E. Inc.

Breton, Albert & Wintrobe, Ronald. The Logic of Bureaucratic Conduct: An Economic Analysis of Competition, Exchange, & Efficiency in Private & Public Organizations. 2008. (ENG., Illus.). 208p. pap. 32.99 *(978-0-521-07172-7(0))* Cambridge Univ. Pr.

Center for Socialist History, compiled by. Neither Capitalism nor Socialism: Theories of Bureaucratic Collectivism. 2007. 349p. pap. 19.99 *(978-0-916695-15-6(8))* Ctr. for Socialist History.

Clegg, Stewart R. & Harris, Martin. Managing Modernity: The End of Bureaucracy? Höpfl, Harro, ed. 2011. (ENG., Illus.). 320p. pap. 45.00 *(978-0-19-956365-4(9))* Oxford Univ. Pr., Inc.

Crozier, Michel. The Bureaucratic Phenomenon. 2009. (ENG.). 342p. pap. 34.95 *(978-1-4128-1158-3(9))* Transaction Pubs.

Cullen, Roy. The Poverty of Corrupt Nations. 2008. (ENG.). 228p. pap. 19.95 *(978-0-9781600-9-8(6))* Dundurn CAN. Dist: Ingram Pub. Services.

Dobbin, Frank R., et al, eds. Institutions in the Making: Identity, Power & the Emergence of New Organizational Forms. 2006. (Topical Issues of American Behavioral Scientist Ser.: 384). 240p. pap. 24.00 *(978-1-4129-4025-2(7),* 201384P) SAGE Pubns., Inc.

Dunsire, Andrew & Hood, Christopher. Cutback Management in Public Bureaucracies: Popular Theories & Observed Outcomes in Whitehall. 2010. (ENG.). 272p. pap. 41.00 *(978-0-521-13075-2(1))* Cambridge Univ. Pr.

Durant, Robert F., ed. The Oxford Handbook of American Bureaucracy. 2010. (Oxford Handbooks Ser.). (ENG., Illus.). 834p. 150.00 *(978-0-19-923895-8(2))* Oxford Univ. Pr., Inc.

Ellinas, Antonis A. & Suleiman, Ezra. Bureaucratic Autonomy & the European Commission: Europe's Custodians. 2012. (ENG., Illus.). 272p. 99.00 ***(978-1-107-02321-5(1))*** Cambridge Univ. Pr.

Etzioni-Halevy, Eva. Bureaucracy & Democracy. 2009. 284p. 122.00 *(978-0-415-55537-1(X))* Routledge.

Farazmand, Ali, ed. Bureaucracy & Administration. 2nd rev. ed. 2009. (Public Administration & Public Policy Ser.). (ENG., Illus.). 652p. instr.'s hndbk. ed. 144.95 *(978-0-8247-2369-9(4),* CRC Press) Taylor & Francis Group GBR. Dist: Taylor & Francis Group.

Francis, Roy G. & Stone, Robert C. Service & Procedures in Bureaucracy: A Case Study. 2009. (ENG.). 207p. pap. 50.00 *(978-0-8166-6019-3(0))* Univ. of Minnesota Pr.

Frausto, Salomon, ed. Hunch 12: Bureaucracy. 2009. (ENG., Illus.). 176p. pap. 35.00 *(978-90-5662-690-7(6))* NAi Uitgevers / Publishers Stichting NLD. Dist: D.A.P./Distributed Art Pubs.

Gormley, William T., Jr. & Balla, Steven J. Bureaucracy & Democracy: Accountability & Performance, 00 vols. 2nd rev. ed. 2007. 220p. (C). pap. 51.00 *(978-0-87289-347-4(2))* 3rd rev. ed. 2012. (Illus.). 336p. pap. 51.00 ***(978-1-60871-717-0(8))*** CQ Pr.

Gortner & Mahler & Nicholson & Cram101 Textbook Reviews Staff. Organization Theory: A Public Perspective. 2007. 84p. per. 10.95 *(978-1-4288-2296-2(8))* Cram101 Inc.

Gould, Phillip. State & Society in Colonial & Postcolonial India. 2010. (Routledge Studies in South Asian History Ser.). (ENG., Illus.). 240p. (C). 140.00 *(978-0-415-77664-6(3))* Routledge.

Gouldner, Alvin W. Metaphysical Pathos & the Theory of Bureaucracy: The American Political Science Review V49, No. 2, June 1955. 2011. 16p. pap. 35.95 ***(978-1-258-03316-3(X))*** Literary Licensing, LLC.

Greenberg, Alan L. Confessions of a Government Man: How to Succeed in Any Bureaucracy. 2010. 320p. pap. 19.95 *(978-1-60844-342-0(6))* Dog Ear Publishing, LLC.

Gregory, Paul R. Restructuring the Soviet Economic Bureaucracy. 2006. (Soviet Interview Project Ser.). (ENG.). 196p. pap. 39.99 *(978-0-521-03268-1(7))* Cambridge Univ. Pr.

Gupta, Akhil. Red Tape: Bureaucracy, Structural Violence, & Poverty in India. 2012. (John Hope Franklin Center Book Ser.). (ENG.). 400p. 94.95 ***(978-0-8223-5098-9(X))***; pap. 26.95 ***(978-0-8223-5110-8(2))*** Duke Univ. Pr.

Handlin, Amy H. Government Grief: How to Help Your Small Business Survive Mindless Regulation, Political Corruption, & Red Tape, 1 vol. 2011. 201p. 34.95 *(978-0-313-39259-7(5),* A3264C) Greenwood Publishing Group, Inc.

Hertog, Steffen. Princes, Brokers, & Bureaucrats: Oil & the State in Saudi Arabia. (Illus.). 312p. 2011. pap. 22.95 ***(978-0-8014-7751-5(4))*** 2010. 35.00 *(978-0-8014-4781-5(X))* Cornell Univ. Pr.

Hill, Michael. The Public Policy Process. 5th ed. 2009. (ENG.). 352p. pap. 87.50 *(978-1-4058-7352-9(3))* Pearson Education, Ltd. GBR. Dist: Trans-Atlantic Pubns., Inc.

Hodder, Rupert. Emotional Bureaucracy. 2011. (ENG., Illus.). 286p. 49.95 *(978-1-4128-1493-5(6))* Transaction Pubs.

Holmes, Larry E. Grand Theater: Regional Governance in Stalin's Russia, 1931-1941. 2009. (ENG., Illus.). 282p. 78.99 *(978-0-7391-3591-4(0))* Lexington Bks.

Hooja, Rakesh, ed. Bureaucracy & Society: IAS at Work. 2009. 272p. 45.00 *(978-81-316-0300-0(8))* Rawat Pubns. IND. Dist: International Specialized Bk. Services.

Howard, Philip K. The Death of Common Sense: How Law Is Suffocating America. 2011. 256p. pap. 15.00 *(978-0-8129-8274-9(6),* Random Hse. Trade Paperbacks) Random House Publishing Group.

Huber, Gregory A. The Craft of Bureaucratic Neutrality: Interests & Influence in Governmental Regulation of Occupational Safety. 2007. (ENG., Illus.). 264p. 95.00 *(978-0-521-87279-9(0))* Cambridge Univ. Pr.

Hull, Matthew S. Government of Paper: The Materiality of Bureaucracy in Urban Pakistan. 2012. (ENG.). 320p. 65.00 ***(978-0-520-27214-9(5))***; pap. 26.95 ***(978-0-520-27215-6(3))*** Univ. of California Pr.

Hummel, Ralph P. The Bureaucratic Experience: The Post-Modern Challenge. 5th rev. ed. 2007. (ENG., Illus.). 288p. (C). 88.95 *(978-0-7656-1010-2(8));* pap. 52.95 *(978-0-7656-1011-9(6))* Sharpe, M.E. Inc.

Huskey, Eugene & Rowney, Don K., eds. Russian Bureaucracy & the State: Officialdom from Alexander III to Vladimir Putin. 2009. (ENG., Illus.). 368p. 116.00 *(978-0-230-22884-9(4))* Palgrave Macmillan.

Kamarck, Elaine C. The End of Government ... As We Know It: Making Public Policy Work. 2007. (Illus.). 175p. (C). pap. 19.95 *(978-1-58826-494-7(7));* lib. bdg. 49.95 *(978-1-58826-469-5(6))* Rienner, Lynne Pubs.

Kaufmann, Franz-Xaver, ed. The Public Sector: Challenge for Coordination & Learning. (De Gruyter Studies in Organization Ser.). (ENG.). XII, 554p. 196.00 ***(978-3-11-178714-5(1))*** De Gruyter, Walter Inc.

Kerner, Lucy. Influence of Bureaucracies on Policy-Making in the Former Soviet Union. 2010. 220p. pap. *(978-3-8383-5065-3(0))* Lambert Academic Publishing.

King, Cheryl Simrell, ed. Government Is Us 2. 0. 2011. (Illus.). 288p. 89.95 *(978-0-7656-2501-4(6));* 241p. pap. 37.95 ***(978-0-7656-2502-1(4))*** Sharpe, M.E. Inc.

Kumar, Praveen. Inside India, 1 vol. 2009. 367p. pap. 29.95 *(978-1-61582-141-9(4))* PublishAmerica, Inc.

Litchfield, R. Burr. Emergence of a Bureaucracy: The Florentine Patricians, 1530-1790. 2008. 440p. pap. 42.00 *(978-1-59740-415-0(2))* ACLS Humanities E-Book.

Locke, Robert R. & Spender, J. C. Confronting Managerialism: How the Business Elite & Their Schools Threw Our Lives Out of Balance. 2011. (Economic Controversies Ser.). (ENG.). 170p. 107.95 ***(978-1-78032-072-4(8))***; pap. 19.95 ***(978-1-78032-071-7(X))*** Zed Bks., Ltd. GBR. Dist: Macmillan.

Lord, Carnes. Losing Hearts & Minds? Public Diplomacy & Strategic Influence in the Age of Terror, 1 vol. 2006. (Praeger Security International Ser.). 152p. 39.95 *(978-0-275-99082-4(6),* C9082, Praeger Security International) Greenwood Publishing Group, Inc.

Ludtke, Alf. Police & State in Prussia, 1815-1850. Burgess, Pete, tr. from GER. 2009. (ENG.). 316p. pap. 46.00 *(978-0-521-11187-4(0))* Cambridge Univ. Pr.

MacDonald, Robert W. Beat the System: 11 Secrets to Building an Entrepreneurial Culture in a Bureaucratic World. 2007. (ENG.). 256p. 24.95 *(978-0-470-17549-1(4),* Wiley) Wiley, John & Sons, Inc.

Meier, Kenneth J. & O'Toole, Laurence J., Jr. Bureaucracy in a Democratic State: A Governance Perspective. 2006. (ENG., Illus.). 200p. (C). (gr. 13-17). per. 22.95 *(978-0-8018-8357-6(1))* Johns Hopkins Univ. Pr.

Meyer, Marshall W. Change in Public Bureaucracies. 2008. (ENG., Illus.). 264p. (C). pap. 37.99 *(978-0-521-06630-3(1))* Cambridge Univ. Pr.

Mimura, Janis. Planning for Empire: Reform Bureaucrats & the Japanese Wartime State. 2011. (Study of the Weatherhead East Asian Institute, Columbia University Ser.). 240p. 39.95 *(978-0-8014-4926-0(X))* Cornell Univ. Pr.

Muramatsu, Michio & Naschold, Frieder, eds. State & Administration in Japan & Germany: A Comparative Perspective on Continuity & Change. (De Gruyter Studies in Organization Ser.). (ENG.). XIV, 349p. 240.00 ***(978-3-11-219085-2(8))*** De Gruyter, Walter Inc.

Murray, Iain. Stealing You Blind: How Government Fat Cats Are Getting Rich off of You. 2011. (ENG.). 256p. 27.95 *(978-1-59698-153-9(9))* Regnery Publishing, Inc., An Eagle Publishing Co.

Niskanen, William A., Jr. & Niskanen, William, Jr. Bureaucracy & Representative Government. 2007. (ENG., Illus.). 251p. pap. 24.95 *(978-0-202-30959-0(2))* Aldine Transaction.

Odom, William E. The Soviet Volunteers: Modernization & Bureaucracy in a Public Mass Organization. 380p. 2009. 30.00 *(978-1-59740-775-5(5))* 2008. pap. 38.00 *(978-1-59740-673-4(2))* ACLS Humanities E-Book.

O'Dwyer, Conor. Runaway State-Building: Patronage Politics & Democratic Development. 2006. (ENG., Illus.). 296p. (gr. 17). 52.00 *(978-0-8018-8365-1(2))* Johns Hopkins Univ. Pr.

Payan, Tony. Cops Soldiers & Diplomats: Exp. 2007. (ENG.). 220p. pap. 29.50 *(978-0-7391-2064-4(6))* Lexington Bks.

Peters, Guy. Politics of Bureaucracy: An Introduction to Comparative Public Administration. 6th rev. ed. 2009. (ENG., Illus.). 400p. (C). 170.00 *(978-0-415-34209-4(0))* Routledge.

—Politics of Bureaucracy Ed6. 6th rev. ed. 2009. (ENG., Illus.). 400p. (C). pap. 49.95 *(978-0-415-34210-0(4))* Routledge.

Petrusevschi, Daniela. Perspectives of Strategic Environmental Assessment in Countries with Communist Past: Perspectives of Implementation of Strategic Environmental Assessment: A comparative Study of Romania & the Republic of Moldova. 2008. 108p. pap. *(978-3-8364-7214-2(7))* VDM Verlag Dr. Mueller e.K.

Phillips, Bernard. Bureaucratic Culture & Escalating World Problems: Advancing the Sociological Imagination, 1 vol. Knottnerus, J. David, ed. (Sociological Imagination Ser.). 208p. 2011. pap. 39.95 *(978-1-59451-654-2(5))* 2009. 125.00 *(978-1-59451-653-5(7))* Paradigm Pubs.

Phillips, Bernard & Christner, David. Saving Society: Breaking Out of Our Bureaucratic Way of Life, 1 vol. (Sociological Imagination Ser.). 286p. 2012. pap. 41.95 ***(978-1-59451-777-8(0))*** 2010. (Illus.). 110.00 *(978-1-59451-776-1(2))* Paradigm Pubs.

Provost, Colin & Teske, Paul. President George W. Bush's Influence over Bureaucracy & Policy: Extraordinary Times, Extraordinary Powers. Provost, Colin & Teske, Paul, eds. 2009. (Evolving American Presidency Ser.). (ENG., Illus.). 288p. 105.00 *(978-0-230-60954-9(6))* Palgrave Macmillan.

Richardson, Steven O. The Political Economy of Bureaucracy. 2010. (Routledge Frontiers of Political Economy Ser.). (ENG., Illus.). 176p. (C). 125.00 *(978-0-415-58856-0(1))* Routledge.

Rist, Ray C., et al. Influencing Change: Capacity Building in Development & Evaluation. 2011. (World Bank Training Ser.). (ENG., Illus.). 302p. 30.00 *(978-0-8213-8403-9(1),* 9780821384039) World Bank Pubns.

—Influencing Change: Evaluation & Capacity Building. 2011. (Illus.). xxi, 275p. *(978-0-8213-8497-8(X))* World Bank Pubns.

Rubin, Edward L. Beyond Camelot: Rethinking Politics & Law for the Modern State. 2007. (ENG.). 480p. (C). per. 37.50 *(978-0-691-13397-3(2))* Princeton Univ. Pr.

Ryu, Jay Eungha. Bounded Bureaucracy & the Budgetary Process in the United States. 2011. (ENG., Illus.). 223p. 49.95 *(978-1-4128-4289-1(1))* Transaction Pubs.

Sarat, Austin & Umphrey, Martha Merrill. Subjects of Responsibility: Framing Personhood in Modern Bureaucracies. Parker, Andrew, ed. 2011. (ENG., Illus.). 224p. pap. 28.00 *(978-0-8232-3323-6(5));* 3rd ed. 80.00 *(978-0-8232-3322-9(7))* Fordham Univ. Pr.

Sasada, Hironori. The Evolution of the Japanese Developmental State. 2012. (Routledge Studies in the Modern History of Asia Ser.). (ENG., Illus.). 220p. (C). 145.00 ***(978-0-415-50346-4(9))*** Routledge.

Schneider, Ben Ross. Politics within the State: Elite Bureaucrats & Industrial Policy in Authoritarian Brazil. 2009. (Pitt Latin American Studies). (ENG.). 366p. (C). pap. 27.95 *(978-0-8229-8536-5(5))* Univ. of Pittsburgh Pr.

B

Sennett, Richard, ed. The Culture of the New Capitalism. 2007. (Castle Lectures in Ethics, Politics, & Economics). (ENG.). 224p. per. 15.00 *(978-0-300-11992-3(5))* Yale Univ. Pr.

Simmons, Randy T. Beyond Politics: The Roots of Government Failure. 2011. (ENG.). 368p. pap. 22.95 ***(978-1-59813-042-3(0))*** Independent Institute, The.

Simmons, Randy T. & Mitchell, William C. Beyond Politics: The Roots of Government Failure. 2011. 368p. 29.95 ***(978-1-59813-050-8(1))*** Independent Institute, The.

Slover, Ron. The Buffet Syndrome: A Wakeup Call for America! 2007. (Illus.). 136p. per. 13.99 *(978-1-891774-00-3(X))* Path Publishing, Inc.

Starr, Greg. Better Living Through Bureaucracy. 2007. (ENG.). 220p. 32.95 *(978-1-59526-634-7(8))*; 176p. per. 15.95 *(978-1-59526-633-0(X))* Aeon Publishing Inc. (Llumina Pr.).

Styhre, Alexander. The Innovative Bureaucracy: Bureaucracy in an Age of Fluidity. (Illus.). 2012. (ENG.). 240p. (C). pap. 42.95 ***(978-0-415-54286-9(3))*** 2007. 233p. 158.00 *(978-0-415-39597-7(6))* Routledge.

Teodoro, Manuel P. Bureaucratic Ambition: Careers, Motives, & the Innovative Administrator. 2011. (Johns Hopkins Studies in Governance & Public Management Ser.). (ENG., Illus.). 240p. (gr. 17). 45.00 *(978-1-4214-0245-1(9))* Johns Hopkins Univ. Pr.

Trondal, Jarle, et al. Unpacking International Organisations: The Dynamics of Compound Bureaucracies. 2010. (European Policy Studies). (ENG., Illus.). 240p. 90.00 *(978-0-7190-8137-8(8))* Manchester Univ. Pr. GBR. Dist: Macmillan.

U, Eddy. Disorganizing China: Counter-Bureaucracy & the Decline of Socialism. 2007. (ENG.). 296p. 55.00 *(978-0-8047-5689-1(9))* Stanford Univ. Pr.

van Rixtel, Adrian. Informality & Monetary Policy in Japan: The Political Economy of Bank Performance. 2007. (ENG.). 420p. pap. 60.00 *(978-0-521-03944-4(4))* Cambridge Univ. Pr.

Vigoda-Gadot, Eran. Building Strong Nations: Improving Governability & Public Management. 2009. (Illus.). 280p. 114.95 *(978-0-7546-7546-4(7))* Ashgate Publishing Co.

von Mises, Ludwig. Bureaucracy. Greaves, Bettina Bien, ed. 2007. (ENG.). 120p. (C). (gr. 12). 22.00 *(978-0-86597-663-4(5))*; pap. 12.00 *(978-0-86597-664-1(3))* Liberty Fund, Inc.

Wesley, David A. State Practices & Zionist Images: Shaping Economic Development in Arab Towns in Israel. 2007. (Illus.). 276p. 34.95 *(978-1-84545-356-5(5))* Berghahn Bks., Inc.

BURGER, GOTTFRIED AUGUST, 1747-1794

see Buerger, Gottfried August, 1747-1794

BURGESS, ANTHONY, 1917-1993

Biswell, Andrew. The Real Life of Anthony Burgess. 2007. (ENG., Illus.). 448p. per. 16.95 *(978-0-330-48171-7(1))* Macmillan Pubs., Ltd. GBR. Dist: Independent Pubs. Group.

di Sandri, Gabriella. The Lure of the Ordinary World. 2008. 80p. pap. *(978-3-639-00588-2(0))* VDM Verlag Dr. Mueller e.K.

Ingersoll, Earl G. & Ingersoll, Mary C., eds. Conversations with Anthony Burgess. 2008. (ENG.). 224p. 50.00 *(978-1-60473-095-1(1))* Univ. Pr. of Mississippi.

—Conversations with Anthony Burgess. 2008. (ENG.). 224p. pap. 22.00 *(978-1-60473-096-8(X))* Univ. Pr. of Mississippi.

Lewis, Roger. Anthony Burgess. Date not set. pap. *(978-0-312-32252-6(6))*; mass mkt. *(978-0-312-99390-0(0))* St. Martin's Pr. (St. Martin's Paperbacks).

Phillips, Paul. Clockwork Counterpoint: The Music & Literature of Anthony Burgess. 2011. (ENG., Illus.). 512p. 89.95 *(978-0-7190-7204-8(2))* Manchester Univ. Pr. GBR. Dist: Macmillan.

Roughley, Alan, ed. Anthony Burgess & Modernity. 2008. (ENG.). 288p. 89.00 *(978-0-7190-7886-6(5))* Manchester Univ. Pr. GBR. Dist: Macmillan.

BURGHLEY, WILLIAM CECIL, BARON, 1520-1598

Alford, Stephen. Burghley: William Cecil at the Court of Elizabeth I. (Illus.). 432p. 2011. pap. 30.00 *(978-0-300-17088-7(2))* 2008. (ENG., 45.00 *(978-0-300-11896-4(1))* Yale Univ. Pr.

Loades, David. Cecils. 2011. (Illus.). 256p. pap. 15.95 ***(978-1-905615-55-1(8))*** National Archives (PRO), The GBR. Dist: International Publishers Marketing.

Maginn, Christopher. William Cecil, Ireland, & the Tudor State. 2012. (ENG., Illus.). 288p. 125.00 ***(978-0-19-969715-1(9))*** Oxford Univ. Pr., Inc.

Martyn, Trea. Queen Elizabeth in the Garden: A Story of Love, Rivalry, & Spectacular Gardens. 2012. (Illus.). 336p. 22.95 *(978-1-933346-36-6(1))* BlueBridge.

BURGHS

see Boroughs

BURGLARY

Crosby, Molly Caldwell. The Great Pearl Heist: London's Greatest Thief & Scotlan Yard's Hunt for the World's Most Valuable Necklace. 2012. (ENG., Illus.). (gr. 12). 25.95 ***(978-0-425-25280-2(9)***, Berkley Hardcover) Penguin Group (USA) Inc.

Shell, Cindy. Overcoming Evil. 2010. pap. 10.99 *(978-1-61663-112-3(0))* Tate Publishing & Enterprises, LLC.

BURGLARY—PREVENTION

see Burglary Protection

BURGLARY PROTECTION

see also Locks and Keys; Security Systems

Conway, Des. The A-Z of Home Security. 2nd ed. 2009. 176p. pap. 20.00 *(978-1-84528-304-9(X))* How To Books GBR. Dist: Parkwest Pubns., Inc.

Conwy, D. G. Home Security: How to Keep Your Home & Family Safe from Crime. 3rd ed. 2010. (ENG.). 149p. pap. 20.00 *(978-1-84528-403-9(8))* How To Books GBR. Dist: Parkwest Pubns., Inc.

Cram101 Textbook Reviews. Outlines & Highlights for Security & Loss Prevention by Philip Purpur. 2011. 532p. pap. 38.95 ***(978-1-61905-639-8(9))*** Cram101 Inc.

Demetis, Dionysios S. Technology & Anti-Money Laundering: A Risk-Based & Systems Theory Approach. 2010. (Illus.). 200p. 112.00 *(978-1-84844-556-7(3))* Elgar, Edward Publishing, Inc.

Fennelly, Lawrence. Handbook of Loss Prevention & Crime Prevention. 5th ed. 2012. (ENG., Illus.). 632p. 94.95 ***(978-0-12-385246-5(3)***, Butterworth-Heinemann) Elsevier Science & Technology Bks.

Fraser, Michael. How Safe Is Your Home. 2008. (Illus.). 174p. pap. 26.00 *(978-1-905862-01-6(6))* How To Books GBR. Dist: Parkwest Pubns., Inc.

Giles, Timothy. How to Develop & Implement a Security Master Plan. 2008. (ENG., Illus.). 352p. 89.95 *(978-1-4200-8625-6(1))* Auerbach Pubs., Inc.

Hilliard, Frank. Home Invasion Prevention. 2009. 75p. pap. 16.00 *(978-0-557-04376-7(X))* Lulu Enterprises Inc.

Mason, Queenie. The Complete DO-IT-YOURSELF Home Security Guide: Burglarproof Your Home. 2008. 96p. per. 14.95 *(978-0-9714878-6-4(3))* Red Triangle Enterprises, Inc.

Mawby, Robert, ed. Burglary. 2007. (International Library of Criminology, Criminal Justice & Penology - Second Ser.). 520p. 300.00 *(978-0-7546-2596-4(6))* Ashgate Publishing Co.

Nemeth, Charles P. Homeland Security: An Introduction to Principles & Practice. 2009. (ENG., Illus.). 542p. (C). 75.95 *(978-1-4200-8567-9(0))* Auerbach Pubs., Inc.

Purpura, Philip. Security & Loss Prevention: An Introduction. 5th ed. 2007. (ENG., Illus.). 600p. 71.95 *(978-0-12-372525-7(9)*, Butterworth-Heinemann) Elsevier Science & Technology Bks.

Rengert, George F. & Groff, Elizabeth. Residential Burglary: How the Urban Environment & Our Lifestyles Play a Contributing Role. 3rd ed. 2011. (Illus.). 254p. 56.95 *(978-0-398-08678-7(8))*; pap. 36.95 *(978-0-398-08679-4(6))* Thomas, Charles C. Pub., Ltd.

BURGOS (SPAIN)

Pérez, Federico. Ensayo de Bibliografía Contemporánea Burgalesa (1808-2007) Estudio de 8.500 Fichas Bibliográficas. 2008. (SPA.). 805p. *(978-84-96606-44-9(9))* Dossoles, Editorial.

BURGOYNE, JOHN, 1722-1792

Albers, Jan. John Burgoyne (1722-1792) (Illus.). 96p. pap. 14.95 *(978-1-884592-13-3(9))* Images from the Past, Inc.

Cubbison, Douglas R. Burgoyne & the Saratoga Campaign: His Papers. 2012. (ENG., Illus.). 408p. 45.00 ***(978-0-87062-409-4(1)***, Clark, Arthur H. Co., The) Univ. of Oklahoma Pr.

De Fonblanque, Edward Barrington. Political & Military Episodes in the L. 2006. pap. 42.95 *(978-1-4286-4756-5(2))* Kessinger Publishing, LLC.

Nickerson, Hoffman. Turning Point of the Revolution or Burgo. 2006. pap. 43.95 *(978-1-4286-3711-5(7))* Kessinger Publishing, LLC.

BURGOYNE'S INVASION, 1777

see also Saratoga Campaign, 1777

Anburey, Thomas. Travels through the Interior Parts of America Set, 2 vols. (Illus.). reprint ed. lib. bdg. 250.00 *(978-0-7222-0906-6(1))* Library Reprints, Inc.

Brandow, John Henry. The Story of Old Saratoga & the Burgoyne Campaign. 396p. reprint ed. 98.00 *(978-0-7222-7696-9(6))* Library Reprints, Inc.

Burgoyne, John. Orderly Book of Lieut. Gen. John Burgoyne: From His Entry into the State of New York until His Surrender at Saratoga, 16th Oct. 1777. O'Callaghan, E. B., ed. 2010. (ENG.). 306p. pap. 29.75 *(978-1-176-51360-0(5))* BiblioBazaar.

—Orderly Book of Lieut. Gen. John Burgoyne: From His Entry into the State of New York until His Surrender at Saratoga, 16th Oct. 1777. 2010. 282p. pap. 28.75 *(978-1-175-98316-9(0))*; 276p. pap. 27.75 *(978-1-146-66954-2(2))* BiblioBazaar.

—Orderly Book of Lieut. Gen. John Burgoyne: From His Entry into the State of New York until His Surrender at Saratoga, 16th Oct. 1777. O'Callaghan, E. B., ed. 2010. 282p. pap. 27.75 *(978-1-144-88360-5(1))* BiblioBazaar.

—Orderly Book of Lieut. Gen. John Burgoyne: From His Entry into the State of New York until His Surrender at Saratoga, 16th Oct. 1777. 2009. (Illus.). 124p. pap. *(978-1-150-69178-2(6))* Books LLC.

Drake, Samuel Adams. Burgoyne's Invasion Of 1777. 2010. 156p. pap. 27.45 *(978-1-4455-3717-7(6))* Thorndike Pr.

Hadden, James. Hadden's Journal & Orderly Books. 2009. (Revolutionary War Ser.). (ENG.). 700p. pap. 40.95 *(978-1-4290-1685-8(X))* Applewood Bks.

Hadden, James M. A Journal Kept in Canada & upon Burgoy. 2006. pap. 50.95 *(978-1-4286-4782-4(1))* Kessinger Publishing, LLC.

Nickerson, Hoffman. Turning Point of the Revolution or Burgo. 2006. pap. 43.95 *(978-1-4286-3711-5(7))* Kessinger Publishing, LLC.

Riedesel, Friederike Cha. Letters & Journals Relating to the War. 2006. pap. 26.95 *(978-1-4286-4888-3(7))* Kessinger Publishing, LLC.

BURGUNDY (FRANCE)

Bouchard, Constance Brittain. Holy Entrepreneurs: Cistercians, Knights, & Economic Exchange in Twelfth-Century Burgundy. 2009. 264p. pap. 25.95 *(978-0-8014-7525-2(2))* Cornell Univ. Pr.

—Sword, Miter, & Cloister: Nobility & the Church in Burgundy, 980-1198. 2009. (Illus.). 463p. pap. 36.95 *(978-0-8014-7526-9(0))* Cornell Univ. Pr.

BURGUNDY (FRANCE)—DESCRIPTION AND TRAVEL

Chase, Sarah Leah. Pedaling Through Burgundy Cookbook. 2008. (ENG.). 192p. pap. 15.00 *(978-1-4223-9437-3(9))* DIANE Publishing Co.

Faith, Nicholas. Burgundy & Its Wines. 2008. (ENG., Illus.). 144p. pap. *(978-1-84483-606-2(1))* Duncan Baird Pubs. GBR. Dist: Sterling Publishing Co., Inc.

Toman, Rolf, ed. Burgundy: Art, Architecture, Landscape. 2008. (Art & Architecture Ser.). (Illus.). 380p. 49.95 *(978-0-8416-0059-1(7))* American Map Corp.

BURGUNDY (FRANCE)—GUIDEBOOKS

Bonechi, Casa. All of Burgundy. 128p. pap. *(978-88-7009-222-6(4))* Casa Editrice Bonechi.

Michelin Travel Publications Staff. Bourgogne Green Guide French Edition. (FRE.). pap. 17.95 *(978-0-7859-7222-8(6)*, 2067003070) French & European Pubns., Inc.

Sanger, Andrew. Burgundy & the Rhone Valley. 3rd ed. 2009. (Drive Around - Thomas Cook Ser.). (ENG., Illus.). 288p. pap. 26.95 *(978-1-84848-013-1(X))* Cook, Thomas Publishing GBR. Dist: Globe Pequot Pr., The.

BURGUNDY (FRANCE)—HISTORY

Hayhoe, Jeremy. Enlightened Feudalism: Seigneurial Justice & Village Society in Eighteenth-Century Northern Burgundy. 2008. (Changing Perspectives on Early Modern Europe Ser.: Volume 10). (Illus.). 321p. 80.00 *(978-1-58046-271-6(5))* Univ. of Rochester Pr.

Kirk, John Foster. History of Charles the Bold, Duke of Burgundy by John Foster Kirk. 2006. 628p. pap. 34.99 *(978-1-4255-6605-0(7))*; 568p. per. 32.99 *(978-1-4255-6212-0(4))* MPublishing.

Marti, Susan. Splendour of the Burgundian Court: Charles the Bold (1433-1477) Borchert, Till-Holger & Keck, Gabriele, eds. 2009. (Illus.). 384p. 80.00 *(978-0-8014-4853-9(0))* Cornell Univ. Pr.

Putnam, Ruth. Charles the Bold: Last Duke of Burgundy 1433-1477. 2007. (ENG.). 348p. pap. 23.99 *(978-1-4264-8026-3(1))*; 396p. pap. 26.99 *(978-1-4264-8083-6(0))* BiblioBazaar.

Small, Graeme & Brown, Andrew. Court & Civic Society in the Burgundian Low Countries C. 1420-1530. 2008. (Manchester Medieval Sources Ser.). (ENG., Illus.). 400p. 89.00 *(978-0-7190-5619-2(5))* Manchester Univ. Pr. GBR. Dist: Macmillan.

Vaughan, Richard. Charles the Bold: The Last Valois Duke of Burgundy. 2011. (History of Valois Burgundy Ser.). (Illus.). 557p. pap. 34.95 *(978-0-85115-918-8(4)*, Boydell Press) Boydell & Brewer, Ltd. GBR. Dist: Boydell & Brewer, Inc.

—The Dukes of Burgundy (4-volume Set) Charles the Bold, John the Fearless, Philip the Bold, Philip the Good. 2008. pap. 90.00 *(978-1-84383-397-0(2)*, Boydell Press) Boydell & Brewer, Ltd. GBR. Dist: Boydell & Brewer, Inc.

Vaughan, Richard & Vale, Malcolm. Philip the Bold: The Formation of the Burgundian State. 2011. (History of Valois Burgundy Ser.). (Illus.). 314p. pap. 34.95 *(978-0-85115-915-7(X)*, Boydell Press) Boydell & Brewer, Ltd. GBR. Dist: Boydell & Brewer, Inc.

BURGUNDY (WINE)

Simon, Andre L. All about Burgundy. (All about Wines Ser.: Vol. 5). 10.50 *(978-0-87559-177-3(9))* Shalom, P. Pubns., Inc.

BURIAL

see also Bog Bodies; Catacombs; Cremation; Cryonics; Embalming; Epitaphs; Funeral Rites and Ceremonies; Funeral Service; Mounds; Mummies; Sepulchral Monuments; Ship Burial; Tombs; Urn Burial

Adams, Ron L. & King, Stacie M., eds. Residential Burial - A Multiregional Exploration, Vol. 20. 2011. (APAZ - Archaeological Papers of the American Anthropological Association Ser.). (ENG.). 146p. pap. 30.00 ***(978-1-4443-5091-3(9)***, Wiley-Blackwell) Wiley, John & Sons, Inc.

Arlt, C. Deine Seele moge leben fur immer und ewig. Die demotischen Mumienschilder im British Museum. 2011. (Studia Demotica Ser.). (ENG & GER., Illus.). 286p. (C). 80.00 ***(978-90-429-2471-0(3))*** Peeters Pubs. & Booksellers BEL. Dist: Brown, David Bk. Co., The.

Bacvarov, Krum, ed. Babies Reborn: Infant/Child Burials in Pre- & Protohistory, Vol. 24. 2008. (Bar S Ser.). (FRE & ENG., Illus.). 213p. (C). pap. 95.00 *(978-1-4073-0316-1(3))* British Archaeological Reports Ltd. GBR. Dist: Brown, David Bk. Co., The.

Barretto-Tesoro, Grace. Identity & Reciprocity in 15th Century Philippines. 2008. (ENG., Illus.). 193p. (C). pap. 112.50 *(978-1-4073-0224-9(8))* British Archaeological Reports Ltd. GBR. Dist: Brown, David Bk. Co., The.

Books, Hephaestus. Articles on Burials, Including: Roman Funerals & Burial, Burial Places of Founders of World Religions, Burial Sites of European Monarchs, Seima-Turb. 2011. 68p. pap. 17.75 ***(978-1-243-34842-5(9)***, Hephaestus Bks.) BiblioBazaar.

Boston, Ceridwen, et al. 'Safe Moor'd in Greenwich Tier' A Study of the Skeletons of Royal Navy Sailors & Marines Excavated at the Royal Hospital Greenwich. 2008. (Oxford Archaeology Monograph Ser.). (Illus.). 168p. (C). pap. 26.00 *(978-0-904220-51-3(6))* Oxford Archaeological Unit GBR. Dist: Brown, David Bk. Co., The.

Bradford, Charles Angell. Heart Burial. 2007. (ENG.). 254p. 42.95 *(978-0-548-00719-8(5))* Kessinger Publishing, LLC.

Brink, Laurie & Green, Deborah. Commemorating the Dead: Texts & Artifacts in Context: Studies of Roman, Jewish, & Christian Burials. 2008. (ENG., Illus.). XIV, 386p. 147.00 *(978-3-11-020054-6(6))* De Gruyter, Walter Inc.

Buckberry, Jo & Cherryson, Annia, eds. Burial in Later Anglo-Saxon England, C. 650-1100 AD. 2010. (Studies in Funerary Archaeology Ser.). (ENG., Illus.). 152p. (C). 60.00 *(978-1-84217-965-9(9))* Oxbow Bks., Ltd. GBR. Dist: Brown, David Bk. Co., The.

Butz, Bob. Going Out Green: One Man's Adventure Planning His Natural Burial. 2009. (ENG.). 148p. pap. 14.95 *(978-0-9818708-1-6(3))* Spirituality & Health Pub.

Castro, Vanessa de. Das Igrejas Ao Cemitério: Políticas Públicas Sobre a Morte No Recife Do Século XIX. 2007. (POR., Illus.). 312p. *(978-85-7044-176-8(2))* Fundacao De Cultura cidade do Recife.

Chaparro, Martina Will de. Death & Dying in New Mexico. 2007. (ENG., Illus.). 285p. 34.95 *(978-0-8263-4163-1(2))* Univ. of New Mexico Pr.

Çiçek, Julius Yeshu, intro. The Rite of Burial for Priests. 2010. (SYR.). 92.72 *(978-1-61143-247-3(2))* Gorgias Pr., LLC.

Çiçek, Julius Yeshu & Gorgis, Amill, eds. The Sacraments of Holy Baptism, Marriage, & Burial of the Dead. Fritsch, Volker, tr. 2010. (SYR.). 126.68 *(978-1-61143-211-4(1))* Gorgias Pr., LLC.

Connell, Brian & Miles, Adrian. The City Bunhill Burial Ground, Golden Lane, London: Excavations at South Islington Schools 2006. 2010. (MoLAS Archaeology Studies Ser.: 21). (ENG., Illus.). 74p. (C). pap. 18.00 *(978-1-901992-91-5(8))* Museum of London Archaeology Service GBR. Dist: Brown, David Bk. Co., The.

Connell, Brian & Miles, Adrian. New Bunhill Fields Burial Ground, Southwark: Excavations at Globe Academy 2008. 2012. (MoLAS Archaeology Studies Ser.). (ENG., Illus.). 120p. (C). pap. 30.00 ***(978-1-907586-09-5(1))*** Museum of London Archaeology Service GBR. Dist: Brown, David Bk. Co., The.

Davies, Rodney. Buried Alive: Horrors of the Undead. (Illus.). 256p. pap. 24.99 *(978-0-7090-6813-6(1))* Hale, Robert Ltd. GBR. Dist: Trafalgar Square Publishing.

Devlin, Zoe. Remembering the Dead in Anglo-Saxon England. 2007. (Bar Bs Ser.). (ENG., Illus.). 148p. (C). pap. 87.50 *(978-1-4073-0144-0(6))* British Archaeological Reports Ltd. GBR. Dist: Brown, David Bk. Co., The.

Dillehay, Tom D., et al. Tombs for the Living: Andean Mortuary Practices. 2011. (Dumbarton Oaks Pre-Columbian Symposia & Colloquia Ser.). (ENG., Illus.). 434p. pap. 40.00 *(978-0-88402-374-6(5))* Dumbarton Oaks.

D'Imperio, Chuck. Great Graves of Upstate New York. 2009. 260p. pap. 19.95 *(978-1-935278-30-6(4))* iUniverse, Inc.

Elder, Emma. A Comparison of the Late Pleistocene & Early Holocene Burials of North Africa & Western Europe. Grim Investigations: Reaping the Dead. 2010. (Bar S Ser.). (ENG., Illus.). 268p. (C). pap. 120.00 *(978-1-4073-0684-1(7))* British Archaeological Reports Ltd. GBR. Dist: Brown, David Bk. Co., The.

Enss, Chris. Tales Behind the Tombstones: The Deaths & Burials of the Old West's Most Nefarious Outlaws, Notorious Women, & Celebrated Lawmen. 2007. (ENG., Illus.). 224p. per. 12.95 *(978-0-7627-3773-4(5)*, Falcon Guides) Globe Pequot Pr., The.

Fahlander, Fredrik & Oestigaard, Terje, eds. The Materiality of Death: Bodies, Burials, Beliefs. 2008. (ENG., Illus.). 160p. (C). pap. 82.50 *(978-1-4073-0257-7(4))* British Archaeological Reports Ltd. GBR. Dist: Brown, David Bk. Co., The.

Faust, Drew Gilpin. This Republic of Suffering: Death & the American Civil War. 2009. (Vintage Civil War Library). (ENG., Illus.). 368p. pap. 16.95 *(978-0-375-70383-6(7)*, Vintage) Knopf Doubleday Publishing Group.

—This Republic of Suffering: Death & the American Civil War. 2008. (ENG., Illus.). 368p. 27.95 *(978-0-375-40404-7(X))* Knopf, Alfred A. Inc.

Fiorato, Veronica, et al. Blood Red Roses: The Archaeology of a Mass Grave from the Battle of Towton AD 1461. Fiorato, Veronica et al, eds. 2nd ed. 2010. (ENG., Illus.). 310p. (C). pap. 50.00 *(978-1-84217-289-6(1))* Oxbow Bks., Ltd. GBR. Dist: Brown, David Bk. Co., The.

Fitzenreiter, Martin & Herb, Michael, eds. Dekorierte Grabanlagen Im Alten Reich: Methodik und Interpretation. 2006. (Internetbeitraege Zur Aegyptologie und Sudanarchaeologie Ser.). (FRE, GER & ENG., Illus.). 334p. per. 70.00 *(978-0-9550256-8-6(0))* Golden Hse. Pubns. GBR. Dist: Brown, David Bk. Co., The.

Fitzpatrick, A. P. The Amesbury Archer & the Boscombe Bowmen: Early Bell Beaker burials at Boscombe down, Amesbury, Wiltshire, Great Britain: Excavations at Boscombe down, Volume 1. 2011. (Wessex Archaeology Reports). (ENG., Illus.). 277p. (C). 60.00 *(978-1-874350-54-5(X))* Trust for Wessex Archaeology Ltd. GBR. Dist: Brown, David Bk. Co., The.

George, Harold. DEAD Soldiers at Gettysburg. 2007. (ENG., Illus.). 60p. 5.95 *(978-0-9728183-3-9(2))* George, H. Publishing.

Gleason, Edward S. Dying We Live. 188p. pap. 2.95 *(978-1-56101-014-1(6)*, 1747) Forward Movement Pubns.

Graham, Emma-Jayne. The Burial of the Urban Poor in Italy in the Late Roman Republic & Early Empire. 2006. (BAR International Ser.: Vol. 1565). (ENG., Illus.). 124p. (C). pap. 80.00 *(978-1-84171-995-5(1))* British Archaeological Reports Ltd. GBR. Dist: Brown, David Bk. Co., The.

Grootboom, Patrick Similo. The Need for a National Policy. 2011. 124p. pap. ***(978-3-8433-9435-2(0))*** Lambert Academic Publishing.

Halsall, Guy. Cemeteries & Society in Merovingian Gaul: Selected Studies in History & Archaeology, 1992-2009. 2009. *(978-90-04-17999-8(2))* BRILL.

Harris, Mark. Grave Matters: A Journey Through the Modern Funeral Industry to a Natural Way of Burial. 2008. (ENG.). 224p. pap. 15.00 *(978-1-4165-6404-1(7)*, Scribner) Scribner.

Jerez-Farran, Carlos & Amago, Samuel, eds. Unearthing Franco's Legacy: Mass Graves & the Recovery of Historical Memory in Spain. 2010. (ND Contemporary European Politics Ser.). (ENG., Illus.). 408p. pap. 40.00 *(978-0-268-03268-5(8))* Univ. of Notre Dame Pr.

Kaiser, Marlene Sophia. Das Keltisch-Römische Gräberfeld von Wederath-Belginum: Die Aschengruben und Aschenfl ächen - Ausgegraben

1954-1985. 2006. (GER., Illus.). 216p. 112.00 *(978-3-8053-3666-6(7))* Zabern, Philipp von Verlag, GmbH DEU. Dist: Brown, David Bk. Co., The.

Kalfel, Jesse. So You're Cremated Now What? Over One Hundred Creative Ways to Scatter Your Ashes & Other Useful Information. 2009. 168p. 25.95 *(978-1-4401-2776-2(X))*; pap. 15.95 *(978-1-4401-2775-5(1))* iUniverse, Inc.

Kammen, Michael G. Digging up the Dead: A History of Notable American Reburials. 2010. (Illus.). 272p. 25.00 *(978-0-226-42329-6(8))* Univ. of Chicago Pr.

Kerrigan, Michael. The History of Death: Burial Customs & Funeral Rites, from the Ancient World to Modern Times. 2007. (ENG., Illus.). 192p. pap. 19.95 *(978-1-59921-201-2(3)*, Lyons Pr.) Globe Pequot Pr., The.

Koutsadelis, Constantinos. Mortuary Practices in the Process of Levantine Neolithisation. 2007. (Bar S Ser.). (ENG., Illus.). 178p. (C). pap. 102.50 *(978-1-4073-0072-6(5))* British Archaeological Reports Ltd. GBR. Dist: Brown, David Bk. Co., The.

Kunat, Abraham, ed. The Rite of Burial for the Order of Priests. 2010. (SYR & MAL.). 122.00 *(978-1-61143-342-5(8))* Gorgias Pr., LLC.

Kunstamt & Heimatmuseum Reinickendorf, eds. Leben mit den Toten: Manifestationen gegenwärtiger Betstattungskultur. 2009. (GER.). 172p. pap. 46.95 *(978-3-631-59124-6(1))* Lang, Peter GmbH, Europaischer Verlag der Wissenschaften DEU. Dist: Lang, Peter.

Lillios, Katina T. Heraldry for the Dead: Memory, Identity, & the Engraved Stone Plaques of Neolithic Iberia. 2008. (ENG., Illus.). 232p. 60.00 *(978-0-292-71822-7(5))* Univ. of Texas Pr.

Mainfort, Robert C. Two Historic Cemeteries in Crawford County, Arkansas. 2006. viii, 261p. *(978-1-56349-101-6(X))* Arkansas Archeological Survey.

Miles, Adrian, et al. St Marylebone Church & Burial Ground in the 18th to19th Centuries: Excavations at St Marylebone School, 1992 & 2004-6. 2008. (MoLAS Monograph Ser.). (ENG., Illus.). 170p. (C). 38.00 *(978-1-901992-79-3(9))* Museum of London Archaeology Service GBR. Dist: Brown, David Bk. Co., The.

Miller, Madeleine. The Funerary Landscape at Knossos: A Diachronic Study of Minoan Burial Customs with Special Reference to the Warrior Graves. 2012. (Bar S Ser.). (ENG., Illus.). 125p. (C). pap. 77.50 ***(978-1-4073-0757-2(6))*** British Archaeological Reports Ltd. GBR. Dist: Brown, David Bk. Co., The.

Morehouse Publishing Staff. Burial of the Dead. pap. 4.95 *(978-0-8192-1766-0(2)*, 6208, Morehouse Publishing) Church Publishing, Inc.

Morris, Ian. Burial & Ancient Society: The Rise of the Greek City-State. 2008. 280p. pap. 27.00 *(978-1-59740-535-5(3))* ACLS Humanities E-Book.

Murphy, Eileen M. Deviant Burial in the Archaeological Record. Murphy, Eileen M., ed. 2008. (Studies in Funerary Archaeology Ser.: 2). (ENG., Illus.). 264p. (C). pap. 60.00 *(978-1-84217-338-1(3))* Oxbow Bks., Ltd. GBR. Dist: Brown, David Bk. Co., The.

Omland, Atle. Stewards & Stakeholders of the Archaeological Record: Archaeologists, Folklore & Burial Mounds in Agder, Southern Norway. 2010. (Bar S Ser.). (Illus.). 266p. (C). pap. 115.00 *(978-1-4073-0695-7(2))* British Archaeological Reports Ltd. GBR. Dist: Brown, David Bk. Co., The.

Papadopoulos, Constantinos. Death Management & Virtual Pursuits: A Virtual Reconstruction of the Minoan Cemetery at Phourni, Archanes. 2010. (Bar S Ser.). (ENG., Illus.). 156p. (C). pap. 115.00 *(978-1-4073-0558-5(1))* British Archaeological Reports Ltd. GBR. Dist: Brown, David Bk. Co., The.

Pariat, Jean-Gabriel. Des Morts Sans Tmbe ? Le Cas des Ossements Humains en Contexte Non Sepulcral en Europe Temperee Entre les 6e et 3e Millenaires av. J. C. 2007. (Bar S Ser.). (FRE., Illus.). 195p. (C). 92.50 *(978-1-4073-0121-1(7))* British Archaeological Reports Ltd. GBR. Dist: Brown, David Bk. Co., The.

Pedersen, Jane Hjar. Cultural Interactions & Social Strategies on the Pontic Shores: Burial Customs in the Northern Black Sea Area C. 550-270 BC. 2010. (Black Sea Studies). (ENG., Illus.). 362p. (C). 60.00 *(978-87-7934-520-1(4))* Aarhus Universitetsforlag DNK. Dist: ISD.

Quiroga, Jorge & Martinez Tejera, A. M. Morir en el Mediterraneo Medieval: Actas Del III Congreso Internacional de Arqueologia, Arte e Historia de la Antigüedad Tardia y Alta Edad Media Peninsular Celebrado en la Universidad Autonoma de Madrid (UAM) y en e Museo de Los Origenes de Madrid (Casa de San Isidro) - 17 y 18 Diciembre de 2007. 2009. (SPA., Illus.). 370p. (C). pap. 145.00 *(978-1-4073-0462-5(3))* British Archaeological Reports Ltd. GBR. Dist: Brown, David Bk. Co., The.

Renshaw, Layla. Exhuming Loss: Memory, Materiality & Mass Graves of the Spanish Civil War. 2011. (Critical Cultural Heritage Ser.). (ENG., Illus.). 259p. 89.00 *(978-1-61132-041-1(0))*; pap. 36.95 *(978-1-61132-042-8(9))* Left Coast Pr., Inc.

Reyher, Ken. Through the Valley of the Shadow of Death: Death & Dying in Early Western Colorado. 2009. pap. 14.95 *(978-1-932738-59-9(2))* Western Reflections Publishing Co.

Reynolds, Andrew. Anglo-Saxon Deviant Burial Customs. 2009. (Medieval History & Archaeology Ser.). (ENG., Illus.). 340p. 145.00 *(978-0-19-954455-4(7))* Oxford Univ. Pr., Inc.

Rigeade, Catherine. Les Sepultures de Catastrophe. 2007. (Bar S Ser.). (FRE., Illus.). 129p. (C). 72.50 *(978-1-4073-0137-2(3))* British Archaeological Reports Ltd. GBR. Dist: Brown, David Bk. Co., The.

Salvatori, Sandro & Usai, Donatella. A Neolithic Cemetery in the Northern Dongola Reach: Excavations at Site R12. 2008. (Bar S Ser.). (Illus.). xxiii, 358p. (C). 125.00 *(978-1-4073-0300-0(7))* British Archaeological Reports Ltd. GBR. Dist: Brown, David Bk. Co., The.

Semple, Sarah. Anglo-Saxon Studies in Archaeology & His. 2007. (Anglo-Saxon Studies). (Illus.). 400p. (C). 100.00 *(978-0-947816-15-5(1))* Oxford Univ. Schl. of Archaeology GBR. Dist: Brown, David Bk. Co., The.

Sledge, Michael. Soldier Dead: How We Recover, Identify, Bury, & Honor Our Military Fallen. 2007. (ENG., Illus.). 376p. (gr. 17). pap. 24.95 *(978-0-231-13515-3(7))* Columbia Univ. Pr.

—Soldier Dead: How We Recover, Identify, Bury, & Honor Our Military Fallen. 2006. (Illus.). 357p. reprint ed. 30.00 *(978-1-4223-5592-3(6))* DIANE Publishing Co.

—Soldier Dead: How We Recover, Identify, Bury, & Honor Our Military Fallen. 2007. (ENG., Illus.). 376p. 75.00 *(978-0-231-13514-6(9))* Univ. of Tokyo Pr. JPN. Dist: Columbia Univ. Pr.

Sluby, Paul E. Burial Ledger of St. Elizabeths Hospital, Washington, D.C: July 5, 1917-August 30, 1983. 2008. (Illus.). ***(978-0-7884-7498-9(7))*** Heritage Bks.

Sluby Sr, Paul E. & Sluby Sr., Paul E. Burial Ledger of St Elizabeths Hospital, Washington, D C , July 5, 1917 - August 30 1983. 2009. 92p. pap. 19.50 *(978-0-7884-4903-1(6))* Heritage Bks.

Smart, Susan. A Better Place: Death & Burial in Nineteenth-Century Ontario. 2011. (ENG.). 208p. pap. 19.00 *(978-1-55488-899-3(9))* Dundurn CAN. Dist: Ingram Pub. Services.

Stone, David L. & Stirling, Lea M., eds. Mortuary Landscapes of North Africa. 2007. (Phoenix Supplementary Volumes Ser.). (ENG., Illus.). 270p. *(978-0-8020-9083-6(4))* Univ. of Toronto Pr.

Taylor, Mark C. Grave Matters. 2006. (Illus.). 192p. reprint ed. pap. 25.00 *(978-1-4223-5349-3(4))* DIANE Publishing Co.

Trinkley, Michael, et al. Son Cemetery: A Bioanthropological Investigation of a Small Lexington County, South Carolina Burial Ground. 2011. (Illus.). xiv, 186p. ***(978-1-58317-076-2(6))*** Chicora Foundation, Inc.

Veit, Richard Francis. New Jersey Cemeteries & Tombstones: History in the Landscape. 2008. (Rivergate Ser.). (ENG., Illus.). 320p. 70.00 *(978-0-8135-4235-5(9))* Rutgers Univ. Pr.

Vokes, Richard. Ghosts of Kanungu: Fertility, Secrecy & Exchange in the Great Lakes of East Africa. 2009. (African Anthropology Ser.). (Illus.). 256p. 95.00 *(978-1-84701-009-4(1)*, Currey, James) Boydell & Brewer, Ltd. GBR. Dist: Boydell & Brewer, Inc.

Watts, Martin, et al. Two Cemeteries from Bristol's Northern Suburbs. 2006. (Bristol & Gloucestershire Archaeological Report). (ENG., Illus.). 96p. (C). pap. 15.95 *(978-0-9553534-0-6(8))* Cotswold Archaeological Trust Ltd GBR. Dist: Brown, David Bk. Co., The.

Weber, Andrzej, et al, eds. Prehistoric Hunter-Gatherers of the Baikal Region, Siberia: Bioarchaeological Studies of Past Life Ways. 2010. (Illus.). 344p. (C). 59.95 *(978-1-934536-11-7(3)*, Univ. of Pennsylvania Museum of Archaeology & Anthropology) Univ. Museum Pubns.

Weeks, Lloyd, ed. Death & Burial in Arabia & Beyond. 2010. (Bar S Ser.). (ENG., Illus.). 372p. (C). pap. 137.50 *(978-1-4073-0648-3(0))* British Archaeological Reports Ltd. GBR. Dist: Brown, David Bk. Co., The.

Will de Chaparro, Martina & Achim, Miruna. Death & Dying in Colonial Spanish America. 2011. (ENG., Illus.). 288p. 55.00 *(978-0-8165-2975-9(2))* Univ. of Arizona Pr.

BURIAL LAWS

Cantor, Norman L. After We Die: The Life & Times of the Human Cadaver. 2010. (ENG.). 384p. 26.95 *(978-1-58901-695-8(5))* Georgetown Univ. Pr.

Kelman, Stuart. CHESED SHEL EMET, 2nd Edition, Guidelines for Taharah: The Truest Act of Kindness. 2nd ed. 2008. 80p. 4.95 *(978-0-939144-60-0(3))* EKS Publishing Co.

Kerin, Charles A. Privation of Christian Burial an Histori. 2006. pap. 28.95 *(978-1-4286-6041-0(0))* Kessinger Publishing, LLC.

O'Reilly, John Anthony. Ecclesiastical Sepulture in the New Code. 2006. pap. 20.95 *(978-1-4286-6135-6(2))* Kessinger Publishing, LLC.

Slocum, Joshua & Carlson, Lisa. Final Rights: Reclaiming the American Way of Death. 2011. 512p. pap. 19.95 *(978-0-942679-34-2(2))* Upper Access, Inc.

United States, Congress Senate Committee on Veterans' Affairs Staff, contrib. by. Preserving Sacred Ground: Should Capital Offenders Be Buried in America's National Cemeteries?: Hearing Before the Committee on Veterans' Affairs, United States Senate, One Hundred Ninth Congress, First Session, September 22, 2005. 2007. iii, 27p. *(978-0-16-078008-0(X)*, 552-070-35429-8) United States Government Printing Office.

BURIAL LAWS—GREAT BRITAIN

Garwood, Paul. Beaker Burials in Britain & North-West Europe 2600-1800 BC: An Ethnography of Death & Identity. 2012. (ENG.). (C). 110.00 *(978-0-415-67476-8(X))*; pap. 39.95 *(978-0-415-67477-5(8))* Routledge.

Hotz, Mary Elizabeth. Literary Remains: Representations of Death & Burial in Victorian England. (SUNY series, Studies in the Long Nineteenth Century Ser.). 2010. 229p. pap. 24.95 *(978-0-7914-7660-4(X)*, Suny Pr.) 2009. 240p. 70.00 *(978-0-7914-7559-8(6))* State Univ. of New York Pr.

BURIAL STATISTICS

see Mortality; Registers of Births, etc.; Vital Statistics

BURIAT LANGUAGE

Brennan, Cathryn. Cultural Upheaval in Revolutionary Russia: The Buriats & the Far Eastern Republic, 1920-1922. 2007. (Illus.). 288p. 150.00 *(978-0-7007-1750-7(1)*, RoutledgeCurzon) Taylor & Francis Group.

BURIED CITIES

see Extinct Cities

BURIED TREASURE

see Treasure Troves

BURKE, EDMUND, 1729-1797

Botting, Eileen Hunt. Family Feuds: Wollstonecraft, Burke, & Rousseau on the Transformation of the Family. 2007. 257p. per. 29.95 *(978-0-7914-6706-0(6))* State Univ. of New York Pr.

Boulton, James T. The Language of Politics. 2009. 300p. 122.00 *(978-0-415-55580-7(9))* Routledge.

Bullard, Paddy. Edmund Burke & the Art of Rhetoric. 2011. (ENG.). 284p. 90.00 *(978-1-107-00657-7(0))* Cambridge Univ. Pr.

Burke, Edmund. Burke, Select Works. 2009. 332p. pap. *(978-0-217-45136-9(5))*; 274p. pap. *(978-0-217-18686-5(6))* Books LLC.

—Reflections on the Revolution in France. 2008. 284p. 25.99 *(978-0-559-17899-3(9))*; pap. 18.99 *(978-0-559-17897-9(2))* BiblioBazaar.

—Reflections on the Revolution in France. 2009. 296p. pap. *(978-0-217-24057-0(8))*; 340p. pap. *(978-0-217-54329-3(4))*; 314p. pap. *(978-0-217-25287-4(7))* Books LLC.

—Reflections on the Revolution in France. Mitchell, L. G., ed. 2009. (Oxford World's Classics Ser.). (ENG.). 352p. pap. 12.95 *(978-0-19-953902-4(2))* Oxford Univ. Pr., Inc.

—Selections from the Speeches & Writing. 2006. pap. *(978-1-4068-0086-9(4))* Echo Library.

—The Works of the Right Honorable Edmund Burke, 12 vols. reprint ed. 895.00 *(978-0-403-04342-2(5))* Somerset Pubs., Inc.

Burke, Edmund & O'Hara, Charles. Edmund Burke, New York Agent: With His Letters to the New York Assembly & Intimate Correspondence with Charles O'Hara, 1761-1776. Hoffman, Ross John Swartz, ed. 2011. 654p. 68.95 ***(978-1-258-02720-9(8))*** Literary Licensing, LLC.

Byrne, William F. Edmund Burke for Our Time: Moral Imagination, Meaning, & Politics. 2011. (ENG.). 246p. 40.00 *(978-0-87580-649-5(X))* Northern Illinois Univ. Pr.

Chaimowicz, Thomas. Antiquity as the Source of Modernity: Freedom & Balance in the Thought of Montesquieu & Burke. 2008. (ENG.). 151p. 49.95 *(978-1-4128-0771-5(9))* Transaction Pubs.

Collings, David. Monstrous Society: Reciprocity, Discipline, & the Political Uncanny, C. 1780/1848. 2009. 61.50 *(978-0-8387-5720-8(0))* Bucknell Univ. Pr.

Dirks, Nicholas B. The Scandal of Empire: India & the Creation of Imperial Britain. 2008. (Illus.). 416p. pap. 22.50 *(978-0-674-02724-4(8)*, Belknap Pr.) Harvard Univ. Pr.

Dwan, David & Insole, Christopher, eds. The Cambridge Companion to Edmund Burke. 2012. (Cambridge Companions to Literature Ser.). (ENG.). 260p. 80.00 ***(978-1-107-00559-4(0))***; pap. 27.99 ***(978-0-521-18331-4(6))*** Cambridge Univ. Pr.

Furniss, Tom. Edmund Burke's Aesthetic Ideology: Language, Gender & Political Economy in Revolution. 2008. (Cambridge Studies in Romanticism Ser.). (ENG.). 324p. (C). pap. 42.00 *(978-0-521-05548-2(2))* Cambridge Univ. Pr.

Garratt, Edmund & MacKintosh, James. James Mackintosh's Vindiciae Gallicae: A Critical Edition. 2008. (Studies in Modern History Ser.). (ENG.). 240p. 84.00 *(978-0-230-52539-9(3))* Palgrave Macmillan.

Gibbons, Luke. Edmund Burke & Ireland: Aesthetics, Politics & the Colonial Sublime. 2009. (ENG., Illus.). 320p. pap. 44.00 *(978-0-521-10094-6(1))* Cambridge Univ. Pr.

Hodson, Jane. Language & Revolution in Burke Wollstonecraft Paine & Godwin. 2007. (Illus.). 226p. 99.95 *(978-0-7546-5403-2(6))* Ashgate Publishing Co.

John Morley. Burke. 2007. 172p. pap. 19.99 *(978-1-4264-6527-7(0))* BiblioBazaar.

Kirk, Russell. Edmund Burke: A Genius Reconsidered. 2009. (ENG.). 300p. pap. 22.00 *(978-1-935191-76-6(4))* ISI Bks.

Lock, F. P. Burke's Reflections on the Revolution in France. 2009. (ENG.). 240p. 122.00 *(978-0-415-55568-5(X))* Routledge.

—Edmund Burke: Volume II: 1784-1797, 2 vols. 2006. (ENG., Illus.). 648p. 225.00 *(978-0-19-820679-8(8))* Oxford Univ. Pr., Inc.

—Edmund Burke, 1730-1784. 2008. (ENG., Illus.). 578p. pap. 74.00 *(978-0-19-922663-4(6))* Oxford Univ. Pr., Inc.

—Edmund Burke, Volume II: 1784-1797, 2 vols. 2009. (ENG., Illus.). 648p. pap. 75.00 *(978-0-19-954153-9(1))* Oxford Univ. Pr., Inc.

MacCunn, John. The Political Philosophy of Burke. 2008. pap. *(978-1-84830-031-6(X)*, Wildhern Pr.) Echo Library.

Maurice, Frederick Denison. The Friendship of Books: And Other Lectures. Hughes, Thomas, ed. 2011. (Cambridge Library Collection - Literary Studies). (ENG.). 426p. pap. 31.99 ***(978-1-108-03186-8(2))*** Cambridge Univ. Pr.

Morley, John. Burke. (English Men of Letters Ser.). reprint ed. 27.50 *(978-0-404-51720-5(X))* AMS Pr., Inc.

—Burke. 2010. (ENG.). 230p. pap. 25.75 *(978-1-177-39722-3(6))* 2010. (ENG.). 336p. pap. 31.75 *(978-1-177-59082-2(4))* 2010. (ENG.). 232p. pap. 25.75 *(978-1-176-23678-3(4))* 2010. 228p. pap. 25.75 *(978-1-145-71250-8(9))* 2010. 240p. pap. 26.75 *(978-1-145-73679-5(3))* 2010. 234p. pap. 25.75 *(978-1-141-45368-9(1))* 2009. 226p. 28.99 *(978-1-115-67112-5(X))* 2009. 326p. 32.99 *(978-1-115-44816-1(1))* 2009. 326p. 36.99 *(978-1-115-44817-8(X))* 2009. 326p. 32.99 *(978-1-115-23194-7(4))* 2009. 326p. 36.99 *(978-1-115-23196-1(0))* 2009. 326p. pap. 29.75 *(978-1-115-44812-3(9))* 2009. 326p. pap. 30.75 *(978-1-115-44813-0(7))* 2009. 226p. pap. 25.75 *(978-1-115-67113-2(8))* 2009. 326p. pap. 30.75 *(978-1-115-23192-3(8))* 2009. 226p. pap. 24.75 *(978-1-115-67114-9(6))* 2009. (ENG.). 225p. pap. 22.99 *(978-1-115-67115-6(4)*, BiblioLife) 2009. (ENG.). 225p. pap. 20.99 *(978-1-115-67116-3(2)*, BiblioLife) 2009. (ENG.). 324p. pap. 23.99 *(978-1-115-23186-2(3)*, BiblioLife) 2009. (ENG.). 324p. pap. 24.99 *(978-1-115-23189-3(8)*, BiblioLife) 2009. (ENG.). 324p. pap. 23.99 *(978-1-115-44808-6(0)*, BiblioLife) 2009. 226p. 28.99 *(978-1-110-41900-5(7))* 2009. 226p. pap. 24.75 *(978-1-110-41897-8(3))* 2009. (ENG.). 225p. pap. 20.99 *(978-1-110-41893-0(0)*, BiblioLife) 2009. (ENG.). 225p. pap. 22.99 *(978-1-110-41894-7(9)*, BiblioLife) 2008. 192p. 25.99 *(978-0-554-24434-1(9))* 2008. 192p. 22.99 *(978-0-554-33737-1(1))* 2006. (ENG.). 190p. pap. 21.99 *(978-1-4264-5586-4(6))* BiblioBazaar.

—Burke. 2009. 124p. pap. *(978-0-217-72931-4(2))* Books LLC.

—Burke. 2011. (Cambridge Library Collection - English Men of Letters Ser.). (ENG.). 230p. pap. 22.99 ***(978-1-108-03474-6(8))*** Cambridge Univ. Pr.

—Burke. 2010. (Illus.). 110p. pap. 20.03 *(978-1-153-59346-5(7))* General Bks. LLC.

—Burke. 2007. (ENG.). 332p. per. *(978-1-4067-7954-7(7))* Read Bks.

—English Men of Letters: Edmund Burke. 2007. (ENG.). 220p. 35.95 *(978-0-548-00527-9(3))* Kessinger Publishing, LLC.

O'Neill, Daniel I. The Burke-Wollstonecraft Debate: Savagery, Civilization, & Democracy. 2007. (ENG.). 304p. 50.00 *(978-0-271-03201-6(4))* Pennsylvania State Univ. Pr.

Paine, Thomas. Common Sense & Rights of Man: Bold-faced thoughts on revolution, reason, & personal Freedom. 2011. (ENG., Illus.). 480p. 12.95 *(978-1-4027-7867-4(8))* Sterling Publishing Co., Inc.

—The Rights of Man. 2010. (Illus.). 158p. pap. 7.87 *(978-1-152-58485-3(5))* General Bks. LLC.

—The Rights of Man. 2010. 158p. 29.56 *(978-1-163-31472-2(2))* Kessinger Publishing, LLC.

—The Rights of Man. 2009. 208p. 32.99 *(978-1-59547-534-3(6))* NuVision Pubns., LLC.

—Rights of Man. 19.95 *(978-0-8488-1443-4(6))* Amereon LTD.

—Rights of Man. 2008. 288p. 25.99 *(978-0-554-38922-6(3))*; 28.99 *(978-0-554-29619-7(5))* BiblioBazaar.

—Rights of Man. 2009. 96p. pap. *(978-0-217-86797-9(9))*; 146p. pap. *(978-0-217-86795-5(2))*; 162p. pap. *(978-0-217-27822-5(1))* Books LLC.

Paine, Thomas & Conway, Moncure Daniel. Rights of Man. 2007. (ENG.). 254p. pap. 21.99 *(978-1-4346-8042-6(8))*; 284p. pap. 23.99 *(978-1-4346-8043-3(6))* BiblioBazaar.

Paine, Thomas & Linebaugh, Peter. The Rights of Man & Common Sense. 2009. (Revolutions Ser.). (ENG.). 314p. pap. 14.95 *(978-1-84467-380-3(4)*, 844380) Verso Bks. GBR. Dist: Norton, W. W. & Co., Inc.

Parkin, Charles. The Moral Basis of Burke's Political Thought: An Essay. 2011. (ENG.). 154p. pap. 19.99 ***(978-0-521-23412-2(3))*** Cambridge Univ. Pr.

Prior, James. Life of the Right Honorable Edmund Burke. 2007. (ENG.). 808p. per. 54.95 *(978-1-4304-4490-9(8))* Kessinger Publishing, LLC.

—Memoir of the Life & Character of the Right Honorable Edmund Burke. 2007. (ENG.). 612p. 59.95 *(978-0-548-04700-2(6))* Kessinger Publishing, LLC.

Stanlis, Peter J. Edmund Burke & the Natural Law. 2011. 326p. 50.95 ***(978-1-258-00343-2(0))*** Literary Licensing, LLC.

Waldron, Jeremy. Nonsense upon Stilts. 2007. 304p. 26.95 *(978-0-415-95678-9(1))*; 95.00 *(978-0-415-95679-6(X))* Routledge.

BURKE, KENNETH, 1897-1993

Bobbitt, David. The Rhetoric of Redemption: Kenneth Burke's Redemption Drama & Martin Luther King, Jr. 's 'I Have a Dream' Speech. 2007. (Communication, Media, & Politics Ser.). (ENG.). 156p. per. 28.95 *(978-0-7425-2928-1(2))* Rowman & Littlefield Publishers, Inc.

George, Ann & Selzer, Jack. Kenneth Burke in The 1930s. 2007. (Studies in Rhetoric/Communication Ser.). (Illus.). 320p. 49.95 *(978-1-57003-700-9(0))* Univ. of South Carolina Pr.

Hawhee, Debra. Moving Bodies: Kenneth Burke at the Edges of Language. 2009. *(978-1-57003-809-9(0))* Univ. of South Carolina Pr.

Holland, L. Virginia. Counterpoint: Kenneth Burke & Aristotle's Theories of Rhetoric. 2011. 144p. 40.95 ***(978-1-258-02387-4(3))*** Literary Licensing, LLC.

Lewis, Camille Kaminski. Romancing the Difference: Kenneth Burke, Bob Jones University, & the Rhetoric of Religious Fundamentalism. 2007. (Studies in Rhetoric & Religion Ser.). 205p. 44.95 *(978-1-60258-003-9(0))* Baylor Univ. Pr.

Selzer, Jack & Wess, Robert. Kenneth Burke & His Circles. 2008. *(978-1-60235-067-0(1))*; 272p. pap. *(978-1-60235-066-3(3))* Parlor Pr.

Weiser, M. Elizabeth. Burke, War, Words: Rhetoricizing Dramatism. 2008. 200p. 34.95 *(978-1-57003-771-9(X))* Univ. of South Carolina Pr.

BURKE, ROBERT O'HARA, 1820-1861

Moorehead, Alan. Cooper's Creek: Tragedy & Adventure in the Australian Outback. 2010. (ENG.). 224p. pap. 14.95 *(978-1-61608-022-8(1)*, 608022) Skyhorse Publishing Co., Inc.

BURKE, THOMAS, 1849-1925

Conover, Charles T., ed. Thomas Burke 1849 To 1925. 2007. (ENG.). 170p. 37.95 *(978-0-548-02926-8(1))* Kessinger Publishing, LLC.

Dunaway, Stewart. Thomas Burke. 2008. 180p. pap. 16.95 *(978-1-4357-1925-5(5))* Lulu Enterprises Inc.

Witchard, Anne. Thomas Burke's Dark Chinoiserie: Limehouse Nights & the Queer Spell of Chinatown. 2009. (Illus.). 302p. 124.95 *(978-0-7546-5864-1(3))* Ashgate Publishing Co.

BURKE AND WILLS EXPEDITION, 1860-1861

Landsborough, William. Journal of Landsborough's Expedition from Carpentaria. 2008. 20p. 25.99 *(978-0-554-27215-3(6))* BiblioBazaar.

—Journal of Landsborough's Expedition from Carpentaria: In Search of Burke & Wills. 2007. (ENG.). 176p. pap. 19.99 *(978-1-4346-2738-4(1))*; 198p. pap. 21.99 *(978-1-4346-2771-1(3))* BiblioBazaar.

—Journal of Landsborough's Expedition from Carpentaria, in Search of Burke & Wills. 2007. 192p. per. *(978-1-4065-2595-3(2))* Dodo Pr.

Moorehead, Alan. Cooper's Creek: Tragedy & Adventure in the Australian Outback. 2010. (ENG.). 224p. pap. 14.95 *(978-1-61608-022-8(1)*, 608022) Skyhorse Publishing Co., Inc.

BURKINA FASO

Bernan Press/ WTO Staff. Trade Policy Review: Benin, Burkina Faso, & Mali 2010. 2011. (ENG.). pap. 75.00 ***(978-1-59888-459-3(X))*** Bernan Assocs.

Icon Group International, Inc. Staff, compiled by. The 2006 Economic & Product Market Databook for Kaya, Burkina Faso. 2006. 618p. ring bd. 95.00 *(978-0-497-81981-1(3))* Icon Group International, Inc.

Locken, E. Travel Journal Burkina Faso. 2010. 192p. pap. 19.99 *(978-0-557-43279-0(0))* Lulu Enterprises Inc.

Pelzer, C., et al, eds. Oursi Hu-beero: A Medieval House Complex in Burkina Faso, West Africa. 2011. (ENG., Illus.). 285p. (C). pap. 80.00 ***(978-90-8890-067-9(1))*** Sidestone Pr. NLD. Dist: Brown, David Bk. Co., The.

Prairie, Michel, ed. & intro. Thomas Sankara Parle: La révolution au Burkina Faso 1983-1987. 2nd rev. exp. ed. 2007.Tr. of Thomas Sankara Speaks: the Burkina Faso Revolution 1983-1987. (FRE., Illus.). 480p. pap. 24.00 *(978-0-87348-987-4(X))* Pathfinder Pr.

Sankara, Thomas. Nous sommes les heritiers des revolutions du Monde: Discours de la revolution au Burkina Faso 1983-1987. 2nd exp. ed. 2008.Tr. of We Are Heirs of the World's Revolutions. (FRE., Illus.). 110p. pap. 10.00 *(978-0-87348-995-9(0))* Pathfinder Pr.

—Thomas Sankara Speaks: The Burkina Faso Revolution 1983-1987. 2nd exp. ed. 2007. (Illus.). 448p. pap. 24.00 *(978-0-87348-986-7(1))* Pathfinder Pr.

—We Are the Heirs of the World's Revolutions: Speeches from the Burkina Faso Revolution 1983-87. 2nd ed. 2007. (Illus.). 108p. pap. 10.00 *(978-0-87348-989-8(6))* Pathfinder Pr.

Schildkrout, Enid. People of the Zongo: The Transformation of Ethnic Identities in Ghana. 2007. (Cambridge Studies in Social & Cultural Anthropology Ser.). (ENG., Illus.). 320p. pap. 61.00 *(978-0-521-04053-2(1))* Cambridge Univ. Pr.

United Nations Development Programme. Assessment of Development Results: Burkina Faso. 2010. 88p. pap. 15.00 *(978-92-1-126274-2(7))* United Nations Pubns.

BURKITT'S LYMPHOMA

Brian, Wills. 10 Hours to Live. 2010. pap. 12.99 *(978-1-60374-243-6(3))* Whitaker Hse.

Molina-París, Carmen & Lythe, Grant. Mathematical Models & Immune Cell Biology. 2011. (Illus.). xvi, 407p. E-Book ***(978-1-4419-7725-0(2))*** Springer.

Stohl, William. B Cell Trophic Factors & B Cell Antagonism in Autoimmune Disease, Vol. 8. (Current Directions in Autoimmunity Ser.: Vol. 8). (Illus.). *(978-3-8055-7851-6(2))* Karger, S. AG.

BURLESQUE (LITERATURE)

see also Farce; Grotesque; Parody

Arellano, Ignacio & Lorente Medina, Antonio. Poesía Satírica y Burlesca en la Hispanoamérica Colonial. 2009. 426p. pap. 36.00 *(978-84-8489-455-1(X))* Iberoamericana Vervuert Publishing Corp.

Willson, Robert Frank. Their form Confounded: Studies in the burlesque play from Udall to Sheridan. (De Proprietatibus Litterarum. Series Practica Ser.). (ENG.). XIV, 170p. 210.00 ***(978-3-11-212241-9(0))***; 135.00 ***(978-3-11-099197-0(7))*** De Gruyter, Mouton DEU. Dist: de Gruyter, Walter GmbH & Co. KG.

BURLESQUE (THEATER)

see also Striptease

Antin, Steve. Burlesque: The Motion Picture. 2010. (ENG., Illus.). 176p. 30.00 *(978-0-7893-2201-2(3))* Universe Publishing.

Barber, Rowland. The Night They Raided Minsky's. 23.95 *(978-0-88411-097-2(4))* Amereon LTD.

Briggman, Jane. Burlesque: A living History. 2009. 444p. pap. 29.95 *(978-1-59393-469-9(6))* BearManor Media.

Davis, Andrew. Baggy Pants Comedy: Burlesque & the Oral Tradition. 2011. (Palgrave Studies in Theatre & Performance History Ser.). (ENG., Illus.). 304p. 90.00 *(978-0-230-11679-5(5))* Palgrave Macmillan.

Goldwyn, Liz. Pretty Things: The Last Generation of American Burlesque Queens. 2010. (ENG., Illus.). 304p. pap. 19.99 *(978-0-06-201181-7(2))* HarperCollins Pubs.

—Pretty Things: The Last Generation of American Burlesque Queens. Augustyn, Jennifer, ed. 2006. (Illus.). 304p. 44.95 *(978-0-06-088944-9(6))* HarperCollins Pubs.

Grondin, Michael & James, Scarlett. Burlesque: The True Art of Seduction. 2011. 335p. pap. 34.95 *(978-1-926893-41-9(7))* Cogito Media Grp. CAN. Dist: Midpoint Trade Bks., Inc.

Klaw, Kittie. This Is Burlesque: The Glitzy Guide. 2011. (ENG.). 256p. pap. 12.99 *(978-0-7858-2832-7(X)*, 078582832X, Chartwell) Book Sales, Inc.

Rosebush, Judson. Burlesque: Exotic Dancers of the 50s And 60s. 2010. (Illus.). 160p. pap. 24.99 *(978-0-7643-3667-6(3))* Schiffer Publishing, Ltd.

Ross, Becki. Burlesque West: Showgirls, Sex, & Sin in Postwar Vancouver. 2009. (Illus.). 368p. *(978-0-8020-9698-2(0))*; pap. *(978-0-8020-9646-3(8))* Univ. of Toronto Pr.

Weldon, Jo. The Burlesque Handbook. 2010. (ENG., Illus.). 272p. 16.99 *(978-0-06-178219-0(X))* HarperCollins Pubs.

BURLINGTON (N.J.)

Stokes, Hon. Edward C. Founders of Burlington. 2006. Orig. Title: The Quakers & Early Citizens of Burlington. (Illus.). 28p. 3.95 *(978-1-58057-531-7(5)*, B28B3) Digital Antiquaria, Inc.

BURLINGTON AND MISSOURI RIVER RAILROAD COMPANY

Davis, Thomas M. Lines West! the Story of George W Holdrege. 2011. 74p. 36.95 ***(978-1-258-03119-0(1))*** Literary Licensing, LLC.

Glick, William L. Business Cars of the Burlington. 2009. (Illus.). 126p. spiral bd. 49.00 *(978-0-940525-01-6(1))* Quincy Hse.

Perkins, Charles Elliott & Perkins, Edith Forbes. Family Letters & Reminiscences, 1865-1907, V1-2: Charles Elliott Perkins & Edith Forbes Perkins. Cunningham, Edith Perkins, ed. 2011. 746p. 71.95 ***(978-1-258-07929-1(1))*** Literary Licensing, LLC.

BURMA

Ferrars, Max & Ferrars, Bertha. Burma. reprint ed. 42.00 *(978-0-404-16818-6(3))* AMS Pr., Inc.

Hubbard, Ethel Daniels. Ann of Ava. 2008. 276p. 42.95 *(978-1-4369-4908-8(4))*; pap. 27.95 *(978-1-4367-7820-6(4))* Kessinger Publishing, LLC.

Kanwar, Amar. Amar Kanwar: the Torn First Pages. 2009. (ENG., Illus.). 260p. 35.00 *(978-3-86560-565-8(6))* Verlag der Buchhandlung Walther Konig DEU. Dist: D.A.P./Distributed Art Pubs.

McMahon, Alexander R. The Karens of the Golden Chersonese. reprint ed. 42.50 *(978-0-404-16840-7(X))* AMS Pr., Inc.

Orr, Kenneth G. Field Notes on the Burmese Standard of Living. reprint ed. 35.00 *(978-0-404-16848-3(5))* AMS Pr., Inc.

Rabinowitz, Alan. Life in the Valley of Death: The Fight to Save Tigers in a Land of Guns, Gold, & Greed. 2010. (ENG., Illus.). 248p. pap. 26.00 *(978-1-59726-824-0(0)*, Shearwater Bks.) Island Pr.

Saul, Jamie. The Naga of Burma: Their Festivals, Customs, & Way of Life. 2006. (ENG., Illus.). 212p. pap. 36.00 *(978-974-524-065-0(6))* Orchid Pr. THA. Dist: National Bk. Network.

Scott, James G. Scott of the Shan Hills: Orders & Impressions. Mitton, Geraldine Edith, ed. reprint ed. 38.50 *(978-0-404-16858-2(2))* AMS Pr., Inc.

Seekins, Donald M. Burma & Japan Since 1940: From Co-Prosperity to Quiet Dialogue. 2006. (Nordic Institute of Asian Studies Monograph Ser.). (Illus.). 181p. 27.00 *(978-87-91114-98-4(5))* Nordic Institute of Asian Studies DNK. Dist: Univ. of Hawaii Pr.

BURMA—BIOGRAPHY

Bengtsson, Jesper. Aung San Suu Kyi: A Biography. 2012. 288p. 27.50 ***(978-1-61234-159-0(4))*** Potomac Bks., Inc.

Bowden, Muriel. Ever Your Loving Mully. 2009. (ENG.). 162p. pap. 33.95 *(978-1-4092-8899-2(4))* Lulu Enterprises Inc.

Campagnac, Charles Haswell & Campagnac-Carney, Ed. Sandra. The Autobiography of a Wanderer in England & Burm. 2011. 420p. pap. 24.99 ***(978-0-557-61503-2(8))*** Lulu Enterprises Inc.

Defolo, Keith. Burma Will Live Again. 2011. 52p. 24.99 ***(978-1-4568-5103-3(9))***; pap. 15.99 ***(978-1-4568-3559-0(9))*** Xlibris Corp.

Felber, Ron. The Hunt for Khun Sa: Drug Lord of the Golden Triangle. 2011. (ENG., Illus.). 240p. pap. 19.95 *(978-1-936296-15-6(2))* Trine Day.

Flory, Derek, et al. Torn Apart: The True Story of Two Sisters Who Found Each Other after Sixty-Five Years. 2008. (ENG., Illus.). 224p. pap. 22.95 *(978-1-84596-368-2(7))* Mainstream Publishing Co., Ltd. GBR. Dist: Independent Pubs. Group.

Hla, Ludu U. The Caged Ones. Tu, Sein, tr. 2006. (Asian Portraits Ser.). (ENG., Illus.). pap. 18.00 *(978-974-8299-15-0(5))* Orchid Pr. THA. Dist: National Bk. Network.

Hough, Jim. Don't Shoot the Mules! 2011. 112p. pap. 14.95 ***(978-1-4670-0033-8(7))*** AuthorHouse.

Kyaw Ma Ma Lay, Journal. A Man Like Him: Portrait of the Burmese Journalist, Journal Kyaw U Chit Maung. Thanegi, Ma, tr. 2009. (Illus.). 205p. 46.95 *(978-0-87727-777-4(X))* Cornell Univ., Southeast Asia Program Pubns.

Kyaw Ma Ma Lay, Journal & Lay, Kyaw Ma Ma. A Man Like Him: Portrait of the Burmese Journalist, Journal Kyaw U Chit Maung. Thanegi, Ma, tr. 2009. (Illus.). 205p. pap. 23.95 *(978-0-87727-747-7(8))* Cornell Univ., Southeast Asia Program Pubns.

Lintner, Bertil. Aung San Suu Kyi & Burma's Struggle for Democracy. 2012. (ENG., Illus.). 200p. pap. 22.50 *(978-616-215-015-9(1))* Silkworm Bks. THA. Dist: Univ. of Washington Pr.

McClelland, Mac. For Us Surrender Is Out of the Question: A Story from Burma's Never-Ending War. 2010. (ENG.). 304p. pap. 15.95 *(978-1-59376-265-0(8)*, Soft Skull Pr.) Counterpoint LLC.

Peter Popham. The Lady & the Peacock: The Life of Aung San Suu Kyi. 2012. (ENG.). 480p. 27.50 ***(978-1-61519-064-5(3)***, 1615190643) Experiment LLC, The.

Phan, Zoya. Undaunted: My Struggle for Freedom & Survival in Burma. 2010. (ENG., Illus.). 304p. 26.00 *(978-1-4391-0286-2(4)*, Free Pr.) Free Pr.

Robinson, H. R. A Modern de Quincey: An Autobiography. 2nd ed. 2006. (ENG., Illus.). pap. 23.00 *(978-974-524-038-4(9))* Orchid Pr. THA. Dist: National Bk. Network.

Rogers, Benedict. Than Shwe: Unmasking Burma's Tyrant. 2010. (ENG., Illus.). 272p. pap. 30.00 *(978-974-9511-91-6(3))* Silkworm Bks. THA. Dist: Univ. of Washington Pr.

A Soldier's Letter about His Adventures on the Burma Road During World War II. 2011. 52p. pap. 9.99 ***(978-1-4634-0843-5(9))*** AuthorHouse.

Taylor, Robert H., compiled by. Dr Maung Maung: Gentleman, Scholar, Patriot. 2008. 616p. *(978-981-230-409-4(6))* Institute of Southeast Asian Studies.

Tooze, George H. The Life & Letters of Emily Chubbic Judson: Volume 1. 2009. 304p. 60.00 *(978-0-88146-131-2(8))* Mercer Univ. Pr.

—The Life & Letters of Emily Chubbic Judson: Volume 2. 2009. (Illus.). 304p. 60.00 *(978-0-88146-149-7(0))* Mercer Univ. Pr.

Tooze, George H., ed. The Life & Letters of Emily Chubbuck Judson: Volume 3; 1846-1847. 2010. (Illus.). 700p. 60.00 *(978-0-88146-156-5(3))* Mercer Univ. Pr.

Wakeman, Carolyn & Tin, San San. No Time for Dreams: Living in Burma under Military Rule. 2009. (Asian Voices Ser.). (ENG.). 256p. 39.95 *(978-0-7425-5703-1(0))* Rowman & Littlefield Publishers, Inc.

Welch, Twilla R. Creative in Struggle. 2007. 244p. per. 18.95 *(978-0-595-43672-9(2))* iUniverse, Inc.

Willson, Arabella M. Stuart. The Lives of Mrs Ann H Judson & Mrs Sarah B Judson, with a Biographical Sketch of Mrs Emily C Judson, Missionaries to Burmah. 2006. 380p. per. 26.99 *(978-1-4255-3975-7(0))* MPublishing.

Wintle, Justin. Perfect Hostage: A Life of Aung San Suu Kyi, Burma's Prisoner of Conscience. 2008. (ENG., Illus.). 480p. 27.95 *(978-1-60239-266-3(8)*, 239266) Skyhorse Publishing Co., Inc.

BURMA—DESCRIPTION AND TRAVEL

Anderson, John. Mandalay to Momien: A Narrative of the Two Expeditions to Western China of 1868 & 1875, under Colonel Edward B. Sladen & Colonel Horace Browne. 2007. *(978-1-57898-673-6(7))* Martino Publishing.

Atlas. Gazetteer of Southern India. 2006. 364p. per. *(978-1-4067-3152-1(8)*, Hesperides Pr.) Read Bks.

Collis, Maurice. The Land of the Great Image. 2008. 300p. (Orig.). *(978-1-4437-2491-3(2)*, Hesperides Pr.) Read Bks.

—Land of the Great Image. 2006. 296p. per. *(978-1-4067-3278-8(8)*, Hesperides Pr.) Read Bks.

—The Land of the Great Image - Being Experiences of Friar Manrique in Arakan. 2007. 264p. per. *(978-1-4067-8986-7(0)*, Pierides Pr.) Read Bks.

Connelly, Karen. Burmese Lessons: A Rrue Love Story. 2010. (ENG.). 400p. 27.95 *(978-0-385-52800-9(0)*, Talese, Nan A.) Knopf Doubleday Publishing Group.

Courtauld, Caroline. Burma. 2nd ed. Date not set. (Illus.). 207p. pap. 16.95 *(978-0-8442-9950-1(2))* McGraw-Hill/Contemporary.

Cultureshock Staff, ed. Cultureshock Myanmar, 1 vol. 2010. (ENG., Illus.). 240p. pap. 15.95 *(978-0-7614-5872-2(7))* Marshall Cavendish Corp.

Delisle, Guy. Burma Chronicles. 2010. (ENG., Illus.). 240p. pap. 16.95 *(978-1-77046-025-6(X))* Drawn & Quarterly Pubns. CAN. Dist: Macmillan.

Edmonds, Paul. Peacocks & Pagodas. (Illus.). reprint ed. 42.50 *(978-0-404-16813-1(2))* AMS Pr., Inc.

Edwardson, Morgan, ed. To Myanmar with Love: A Travel Guide for the Connoisseur. 2009. (To Asia with Love Ser.). (ENG., Illus.). 294p. pap. 21.95 *(978-1-934159-06-4(9))* ThingsAsian Pr.

Ellis, Beth. English Girl's First Impressions of Burmah. 2007. (ENG., Illus.). 248p. 25.00 *(978-974-8299-55-6(4))* Orchid Pr. THA. Dist: National Bk. Network.

Ellis, Elizabeth. An English Girl's First Impressions of Burmah. 2009. 260p. 38.00 *(978-1-59740-368-9(7))*; 258p. pap. 26.00 *(978-1-59740-369-6(5))* ACLS Humanities E-Book.

Enriquez, Collin M. A Burmese Arcady. reprint ed. 25.50 *(978-0-404-16814-8(0))* AMS Pr., Inc.

—A Burmese Loneliness: A Tale of Travel in Burma, the Southern Shan States & Keng Tung. reprint ed. 26.00 *(978-0-404-16815-5(9))* AMS Pr., Inc.

Finger, Hans W. Dhammayangyi: The Pyramid by the Irrawaddy. 2006. (ENG., Illus.). 96p. pap. 17.95 *(978-974-524-045-2(1))* Orchid Pr. THA. Dist: National Bk. Network.

Ganz, Nicholas & Jotow, Elena. Burma. alt. ed. 2009. (ENG., Illus.). 200p. pap. 19.95 *(978-0-500-28787-3(2)*, 528787) Thames & Hudson.

Humphries, Richard. Frontier Mosaic: Voices of Burma from the Lands in Between. 2007. (ENG., Illus.). 200p. pap. 29.95 *(978-974-524-092-6(3))* Orchid Pr. THA. Dist: National Bk. Network.

Kelly. Burma. 2012. (ENG.). 256p. pap. 42.95 ***(978-0-415-54098-8(4))*** Routledge.

Kerr, Gordon. Silken East. 2006. 384p. per. *(978-1-4067-3402-7(0)*, Hesperides Pr.) Read Bks.

Kingdon-Ward, Frank. Burma's Icy Mountains. 2nd ed. 2006. (ENG., Illus.). 296p. pap. 26.95 *(978-974-524-084-1(2))* Orchid Pr. THA. Dist: National Bk. Network.

—In Farthest Burma: The Record of an Arduous Journey of Exploration & Research Through the Unknown Frontier Territory of Burma & Tibet. 2nd ed. 2006. (And Research through the Unknown Frontier Ser.). (ENG., Illus.). 192p. per. 26.95 *(978-974-524-062-9(1))* Orchid Pr. THA. Dist: National Bk. Network.

—Return to the Irrawaddy. 2007. (ENG., Illus.). 224p. pap. 26.00 *(978-974-524-086-5(9))* Orchid Pr. THA. Dist: National Bk. Network.

Kress, W. John. The Weeping Goldsmith: Discoveries in the Secret Land of Myanmar. 2009. (ENG., Illus.). 204p. 45.00 *(978-0-7892-1032-6(0))* Abbeville Pr., Inc.

Larkin, Emma. No Bad News for the King: The True Story of Cyclone Nargis & Its Aftermath in Burma. 2011. (ENG., Illus.). 288p. (gr. 12). 16.00 *(978-0-14-311961-6(3)*, Penguin (Non-Classics)) Penguin Group (USA) Inc.

Locken, E. Travel Journal Burma. 2010. 192p. pap. 19.99 *(978-0-557-43280-6(4))* Lulu Enterprises Inc.

MacLean, Rory. Under the Dragon: A Journey Through Burma. 2008. (ENG., Illus.). 240p. pap. 15.95 *(978-1-84511-622-4(4)*, Tauris Parke Paperbacks) I. B. Tauris & Co., Ltd. GBR. Dist: Macmillan.

Marshall, Andrew. The Trouser People: Burma in the Shadows of the Empire. 2012. (ENG., Illus.). 256p. pap. 17.50 ***(978-616-7339-18-4(X))*** River Bks. THA. Dist: Antique Collectors' Club.

Metford, Beatrix. Where China Meets Burma: Life & Travel in the Burma-China Border Lands. reprint ed. 29.50 *(978-0-404-16844-5(2))* AMS Pr., Inc.

Min, Moe, photos by. In Buddha's Land: Visions of Buddhist Myanmar. 2007. (ENG., Illus.). 128p. 30.00 *(978-974-524-072-8(9))* Orchid Pr. THA. Dist: National Bk. Network.

Myint-U, Thant. Where China Meets India: Burma & the New Crossroads of Asia. 2011. (ENG., Illus.). 384p. 27.00 *(978-0-374-29907-1(2))* Farrar, Straus & Giroux.

Myint-U, Thant. Where China Meets India: Burma & the New Crossroads of Asia, 1 vol. 2012. (ENG., Illus.). 384p. pap. 16.00 ***(978-0-374-53352-6(0))*** Farrar, Straus & Giroux.

O'Hara, Randolph. Fragments from the Past. 2009. (ENG.). 84p. pap. 12.95 *(978-974-524-082-7(6))* Orchid Pr. THA. Dist: National Bk. Network.

Piana, Sergio Loro & Piana, Pier Luigi Loro. The Lotus Flower: A Textile Hidden in the Water. 2011. (ENG., Illus.). 146p. 95.00 *(978-88-572-0887-9(7))* Skira Editore ITA. Dist: Random Hse., Inc.

Roberts, Fredric M., photos by. Humanitas, Vol. 3. 2011. (ENG., Illus.). 120p. 50.00 *(978-0-7892-1109-5(2))* Abbeville Pr., Inc.

Silkworm Books Staff, ed. Historical Walks in Yangon: A Myanmar Heritage Trust Guide Map. 2010. (ENG., Illus.). 1p. pap. 15.00 *(978-974-9511-44-2(1))* Silkworm Bks. THA. Dist: Univ. of Washington Pr.

Tanaka, Yoshitaka & Yee, Tin Tin. Wild Orchids in Myanmar Vol 3, 3 vols. 2008. (JPN & ENG., Illus.). 108p. 45.00 *(978-988-97764-9-7(9))* Orchid Pr. THA. Dist: National Bk. Network.

Tanaka, Yoshitaka, et al. Wild Orchids in Myanmar, 3 vols., Vol. 1. 2008. (JPN & ENG., Illus.). 104p. 45.00 *(978-974-91720-3-2(5))* Orchid Pr. THA. Dist: National Bk. Network.

—Wild Orchids in Myanmar Vol 2, 3 vols. 2008. (JPN & ENG., Illus.). 108p. 45.00 *(978-974-272-910-3(7))* Orchid Pr. THA. Dist: National Bk. Network.

Thanegi, Ma. Defiled on the Ayeyarwaddy: One Woman's Mid-Life Travel Adventures on Myanmar's Great River. 2010. (Illus.). 275p. pap. 12.95 *(978-1-934159-24-8(7))* ThingsAsian Pr.

Visuals Press, photos by. People's Desire. 2010. 128p. pap. 49.95 *(978-0-9795954-5-5(2))* Visuals Pr.

White, Herbert Thirkell. Burma. 2011. (ENG.). 238p. pap. 22.99 *(978-1-107-60067-6(7))* Cambridge Univ. Pr.

Yin, Saw Myat. Cultureshock! Myanmar: A Survival Guide to Customes & Etiquette. 2007. (Cultureshock Myanmar: A Survival Guide to Customs & Etiquette Ser.). (Illus.). 234p. per. 15.95 *(978-0-7614-5410-6(1))* Marshall Cavendish Corp.

BURMA—ECONOMIC CONDITIONS

Adas, Michael. The Burma Delta: Economic Development & Social Change on an Asian Rice Frontier, 1852-1941. 2011. (Illus.). 276p. E-Book *(978-0-299-28353-7(4))*; (ENG., pap. 29.95 *(978-0-299-28354-4(2))* Univ. of Wisconsin Pr.

Cheesman, Nick, et al. Ruling Myanmar: From Cyclone Nargis to National Elections. 2010. (Illus.). xiv, 353p. ***(978-981-4311-47-2(2))*** Institute of Southeast Asian Studies.

Fujita, Koichi, et al. The Economic Transition in Myanmar after 1988: Market Economy Versus State Control. (Illus.). xv, 322p. 28.00 *(978-9971-69-461-6(1))* National Univ. of Singapore Pr. SGP. Dist: Univ. of Hawaii Pr.

Ganesan, N. & Hlaing, Kyaw, eds. Myanmar: State, Society & Ethnicity. 2007. (Illus.). 324p. *(978-981-230-434-6(7))* Institute of Southeast Asian Studies.

Icon Group International, Inc. Staff, compiled by. The 2006 Economic & Product Market Databook for Bassein, Burma. 2006. 618p. ring bd. 95.00 *(978-0-497-80158-8(2))* Icon Group International, Inc.

—The 2006 Economic & Product Market Databook for Pegu, Burma. 2006. 618p. ring bd. 95.00 *(978-0-497-81205-8(3))* Icon Group International, Inc.

—The 2006 Economic & Product Market Databook for Taunggye, Burma. 2006. 618p. ring bd. 95.00 *(978-0-497-81654-4(7))* Icon Group International, Inc.

James, Helen. Governance & Civil Society in Myanmar: Education, Health & Environment. 2009. 208p. pap. 39.95 *(978-0-415-54591-4(9))* Routledge.

Kraas, Frauke, et al, eds. Megacity Yangon: Transformation Processes & Modern Developments. 2008. (ENG., Illus.). 400p. pap. 69.95 *(978-3-8258-0042-0(3))* Lit Verlag DEU. Dist: Transaction Pubs.

Levenstein, Susan. Finding Dollars, Sense & Legitimacy in Burma. 2010. (Illus.). 163p. ***(978-1-933549-85-9(8))*** Woodrow Wilson Interantional Ctr. fo Scholars.

Skidmore, Monique & Wilson, Trevor, eds. Myanmar: The State, Community & the Environment. 2007. (Illus.). (C). pap. *(978-0-7315-3811-9(0))* Asia Pacific Pr.

Than, Tin. State Dominance in Myanmar: The Political Economy of Industrialization. 2006. 500p. *(978-981-230-371-4(5))* Institute of Southeast Asian Studies.

United Nations. Development Partnership Forum: Economic Policies for Growth & Poverty Reduction. 2011. (ENG.). 80p. pap. 52.00 ***(978-92-1-120613-5(8))*** United Nations Pubns.

Wilson, Trevor, ed. Myanmar's Long Road to National Reconciliation. 2006. 310p. (C). pap. *(978-981-230-362-2(6)*, PIC142) Asia Pacific Pr.

BURMA—FOREIGN RELATIONS

Banerjee, Anil C. Annexation of Burma. reprint ed. 34.50 *(978-0-404-16793-6(4))* AMS Pr., Inc.

Bezbaruah, Madhurjya Prasad. Indo-Myanmar Cross-Border Trade. 2010. 124p. pap. *(978-3-639-26188-2(7))* VDM Verlag Dr. Mueller e.K.

Dale, John G. Free Burma: Transnational Legal Action & Corporate Accountability. 2011. (Illus.). 328p. 75.00 *(978-0-8166-4646-3(5))*; pap. 25.00 *(978-0-8166-4647-0(3))* Univ. of Minnesota Pr.

Dittmer, Lowell. Burma or Myanmar? the Struggle for National Identity. 2010. (Illus.). 396p. 98.00 *(978-981-4313-64-3(5))* World Scientific Publishing Co., Inc.

Foley, Matthew. The Cold War & National Assertion in Southeast Asia: Britain, the United States & Burma, 1948-1962. 2010. (ENG.). 228p. 135.00 *(978-0-415-55476-3(4))* Routledge.

Foley, Matthew. The Cold War & National Assertion in Southeast Asia: Britain, the United States & Burma, 1948ndash;1962. 2012. (ENG.). 240p. (C). pap. 42.95 ***(978-0-415-62749-8(4))*** Routledge.

Haacke, Jurgen. Myanmar's Foreign Policy: Domestic Influences & International Implications. 2006. (Adelphi Paper Ser.). (Illus.). 128p. per. 32.50 *(978-0-415-40726-7(5))* Routledge.

Holliday, Ian. Burma Redux: Global Justice & the Quest for Political Reform in Myanmar. 2012. (ENG.). 304p. (gr. 17). 89.50 ***(978-0-231-16126-8(3))***; pap. 29.50 ***(978-0-231-16127-5(1))*** Columbia Univ. Pr.

Pedersen, Morten B. Promoting Human Rights in Burma: A Critique of Western Sanctions Policy. 2007. (ENG.). 312p. 80.00 *(978-0-7425-5559-4(3))* Rowman & Littlefield Publishers, Inc.

Rieffel, Lex, ed. Myanmar / Burma: Inside Challenges, Outside Interests. 2010. (ENG., Illus.). 212p. pap. 26.95 *(978-0-8157-0505-5(0))* Brookings Institution Pr.

Steinberg, David I. & Fan, Hongwei. Modern China-Myanmar Relations: Dilemmas of Mutual Dependence. 2012. (Illus.). 432p. ***(978-87-7694-095-9(0))***; pap. ***(978-87-7694-096-6(9))*** Nordic Institute of Asian Studies.

Stromberg, Brandon E. Bangladesh & Burma: Background & Issues. 2011. (Asian Political, Economic & Security Issues Ser.). 158p. 89.00 *(978-1-61761-219-0(7))* Nova Science Pubs., Inc.

BURMA—HISTORY

Aung Myoe. Building the Tatmadaw: Myanmar Armed Forces since 1948. 2009. 272p. *(978-981-230-848-1(2))* Institute of Southeast Asian Studies.

Aung-Thwin, Michael & Aung-Thwin, Maitrii. A History of Myanmar: Traditions & Transformations. 2012. (Illus.). 304p. 39.00 ***(978-1-86189-901-9(7))*** Reaktion Bks., Ltd. GBR. Dist: Chicago Distribution Ctr.

Banerjee, Anil C. Annexation of Burma. reprint ed. 34.50 *(978-0-404-16793-6(4))* AMS Pr., Inc.

Bigandet, Paul Ambroise. The Catholic Burmese Mission: From the Year 1720 To 1887, Vol. 1. 2006. (Bibliotheca Orientalis Ser.). (ENG., Illus.). pap. 16.00 *(978-974-8299-75-4(9))* Orchid Pr. THA. Dist: National Bk. Network.

Blackburn, Terence. British Humiliation of Burma. 2006. (ENG., Illus.). pap. 23.00 *(978-974-8304-66-3(3))* Orchid Pr. THA. Dist: National Bk. Network.

Bleming, Thomas James. War in Karen Country: Armed Struggle for a Free & Independent Karen State in Southeast Asia. 2007. 212p. (ENG.). 26.95 *(978-0-595-69327-6(X))*; per. 16.95 *(978-0-595-45261-3(2))* iUniverse, Inc.

Browne, Edmond C. The Coming of the Great Queen: A Narrative of the Acquisition of Burma. reprint ed. 38.50 *(978-0-404-16798-1(5))* AMS Pr., Inc.

Butler, John. With the Madras European Regiment in Bur. 2007. pap. *(978-1-84677-138-5(2))* Leonaur Ltd.

—With the Madras European Regiment in Burma - the experiences of An. 2007. (ENG.). 160p. *(978-1-84677-146-0(3))* Leonaur Ltd.

Charney, Michael W. A History of Modern Burma. 2009. (ENG., Illus.). 256p. 75.00 *(978-0-521-85211-1(0))*; pap. 25.99 *(978-0-521-61758-1(8))* Cambridge Univ. Pr.

—Powerful Learning: Buddhist Literati & the Throne in Burma's Last Dynasty, 1752-1885. 2006. (Illus.). xii, 297p. (C). *(978-0-89148-093-8(5))* Univ. of Michigan, Ctr. for South & Southeast Asian Studies.

Flory, Derek, et al. Torn Apart: The True Story of Two Sisters Who Found Each Other after Sixty-Five Years. 2008. (ENG., Illus.). 224p. pap. 22.95 *(978-1-84596-368-2(7))* Mainstream Publishing Co., Ltd. GBR. Dist: Independent Pubs. Group.

Foley, Matthew. The Cold War & National Assertion in Southeast Asia: Britain, the United States & Burma, 1948-1962. 2010. (ENG.). 228p. 135.00 *(978-0-415-55476-3(4))* Routledge.

Foley, Matthew. The Cold War & National Assertion in Southeast Asia: Britain, the United States & Burma, 1948ndash;1962. 2012. (ENG.). 240p. (C). pap. 42.95 ***(978-0-415-62749-8(4))*** Routledge.

Gumaer, Oddny. Displaced Reflections: Refugees & displaced people from Burma shed light on life, love, & Faith. 2nd ed. 2007. 19.99 *(978-0-9777706-0-1(5))* Partners Publishing Hse.

Hall, D.G.E. Burma. 2006. 204p. per. *(978-1-4067-3503-1(5)*, Hesperides Pr.) Read Bks.

John Perry, Peter. Myanmar (Burma) since 1962: The Failure of Development. 2007. (Illus.). 224p. 114.95 *(978-0-7546-4534-4(7))* Ashgate Publishing Co.

Kan Van Man kri & Bagshawe, L. E. The Kinwun Min-Gyi's London Diary: The First Mission of a Burmese Minister in Britain. 2006. (, 1872 Ser.). (ENG., Illus.). 434p. 45.00 *(978-974-524-021-6(4))* Orchid Pr. THA. Dist: National Bk. Network.

Kelly, Claire. The Caged Bird. 2007. (Timeline Ser.). (Illus.). 48p. pap. 8.99 *(978-1-4190-4393-2(5))* Houghton Mifflin Harcourt Supplemental Pubs.

Kraas, Frauke, et al, eds. Megacity Yangon: Transformation Processes & Modern Developments. 2008. (ENG., Illus.). 400p. pap. 69.95 *(978-3-8258-0042-0(3))* Lit Verlag DEU. Dist: Transaction Pubs.

Laurie, William Ferguson Beatson. The Second Burmese War: A Narrative of Operations at Rangoon. 2006. (ENG., Illus.). pap. 19.00 *(978-974-8304-02-1(7))* Orchid Pr. THA. Dist: National Bk. Network.

Marshall, Andrew. The Trouser People: Burma in the Shadows of the Empire. 2012. (ENG., Illus.). 256p. pap. 17.50 ***(978-616-7339-18-4(X))*** River Bks. THA. Dist: Antique Collectors' Club.

Min, Min Sun. Stamps of Burma: A Historical Record Through 1988. 2008. (ENG., Illus.). 84p. pap. 27.00 ***(978-974-8102-43-6(2))*** Silkworm Bks. THA. Dist: Univ. of Washington Pr.

Myanmar Update 2008. 2008. pap. *(978-0-7315-3820-1(X))* Asia Pacific Pr.

Myint-U, Thant. Where China Meets India: Burma & the New Crossroads of Asia. 2011. (ENG., Illus.). 384p. 27.00 *(978-0-374-29907-1(2))* Farrar, Straus & Giroux.

Myint-U, Thant & Myintu, Thant. River of Lost Footsteps: A Personal History of Burma. 2008. (ENG., Illus.). 400p. pap. 15.00 *(978-0-374-53116-4(1))* Farrar, Straus & Giroux.

Oertel, F.O. Note on a Tour in Burma in March & April 1892. 2006. (Itineraria Asiatica: Burma Ser.). (ENG., Illus.). pap. 20.00 *(978-974-8299-73-0(2))* Orchid Pr. THA. Dist: National Bk. Network.

Peters, Anne. Birmanische Handschriften: Die Katalognummern, 1016-1200. 2008. (Verzeichnis der Orientalischen Handschriften in Deutschland Ser.). (ENG.). 370p. (C). 113.00 *(978-3-515-09146-6(7))* Steiner, Franz Verlag Wiesbaden GmbH DEU. Dist: Brown, David Bk. Co., The.

Phasuk, Santanee & Stott, Philip. Royal Siamese Maps: War & Trade in Nineteenth Century Thailand. 2006. (ENG., Illus.). *(978-974-8225-92-0(5)*, River Bks. Pr. Dist A C) Antique Collectors' Club.

Phayre, Arthur P. History of Burma. 2006. (ENG., Illus.). pap. 25.00 *(978-974-8299-00-6(7))* Orchid Pr. THA. Dist: National Bk. Network.

Roycee, Alden T. Burma in Turmoil. 2008. (Horizons in World Cardiovascular Research Ser.). (Illus.). 105p. (C). 145.00 *(978-1-60456-311-5(7))* Nova Science Pubs., Inc.

Sadan, Mandy. A Guide to Colonial Sources on Burma. 2008. (ENG., Illus.). 540p. 50.00 *(978-974-524-106-0(7))* Orchid Pr. THA. Dist: National Bk. Network.

Seekins, Donald M. The A to Z of Burma (Myanmar) 2010. (A to Z Guide Ser.). (ENG.). 570p. pap. 34.45 *(978-0-8108-7635-4(3))* Scarecrow Pr., Inc.

—Historical Dictionary of Burma (Myanmar) 2006. (Historical Dictionaries of Asia, Oceania, & the Middle East Ser.: Vol. 59). (ENG., Illus.). 568p. 115.00 *(978-0-8108-5476-5(7))* Scarecrow Pr., Inc.

Snodgrass. Narrative of the Burmese War. 2009. (Illus.). 345p. 27.95 *(978-1-935501-02-2(X))* Lancer International, Lancer Pr. IND. Dist: Casemate Pubs. & Bk. Distributors, LLC.

Steinberg, David I. & Fan, Hongwei. Modern China-Myanmar Relations: Dilemmas of Mutual Dependence. 2012. (Illus.). 432p. ***(978-87-7694-095-9(0))***; pap. ***(978-87-7694-096-6(9))*** Nordic Institute of Asian Studies.

Syrota, Timothy. Welcome to Burma: And Enjoy the Totalitarian Experience. 2006. (ENG., Illus.). 23.00 *(978-974-524-008-7(7))* Orchid Pr. THA. Dist: National Bk. Network.

Topich, William J. & Leitich, Keith A. The History of Myanmar, 1 vol. (Greenwood Histories of the Modern Nations Ser.). 192p. 58.00 *(978-0-313-35724-4(2)*, GR5724) Greenwood Publishing Group, Inc.

Webb, Paul. The Peacock's Children: Burma Protests, 1885-2000. 2010. (ENG., Illus.). 267p. pap. 25.00 *(978-974-524-069-8(9))* Orchid Pr. THA. Dist: National Bk. Network.

Yawnghwe, Chao Tzang. The Shan of Burm: Memoirs of a Shan Exile. 2010. 296p. pap. *(978-981-230-396-7(0))* Institute of Southeast Asian Studies.

BURMA—POLITICS AND GOVERNMENT

Abbott, Gerry. Back to Mandalay. 2006. (ENG., Illus.). pap. 23.00 *(978-974-524-042-1(7))* Orchid Pr. THA. Dist: National Bk. Network.

Ahmed, S. Z. The Forbidden Misty Mountains. 2008. 107p. pap. 10.95 *(978-0-7414-4469-1(0))* Infinity Publishing.

Aung Myoe. Building the Tatmadaw: Myanmar Armed Forces since 1948. 2009. 272p. *(978-981-230-848-1(2))* Institute of Southeast Asian Studies.

Aung-Thwin, Michael & Aung-Thwin, Maitrii. A History of Myanmar: Traditions & Transformations. 2012. (Illus.). 304p. 39.00 ***(978-1-86189-901-9(7))*** Reaktion Bks., Ltd. GBR. Dist: Chicago Distribution Ctr.

Bengtsson, Jesper. Aung San Suu Kyi: A Biography. 2012. 288p. 27.50 ***(978-1-61234-159-0(4))*** Potomac Bks., Inc.

Bleming, Thomas James. War in Karen Country: Armed Struggle for a Free & Independent Karen State in Southeast Asia. 2007. 212p. (ENG.). 26.95 *(978-0-595-69327-6(X))*; per. 16.95 *(978-0-595-45261-3(2))* iUniverse, Inc.

Boudreau, Vincent. Resisting Dictatorship: Repression & Protest in Southeast Asia. 2009. (ENG., Illus.). 308p. pap. 42.00 *(978-0-521-10961-1(2))* Cambridge Univ. Pr.

Burma in the Aftermath of Cyclone Nargis: Death, Displacement, & Humanitarian Aid: Hearing Before the Subcommittee on Asia, the Pacific, & the Global Environment of the Committee on Foreign Affairs, House of Representatives, One Hundred Tenth Congress, Second Session, May 20, 2008. 2008. (Illus.). iii, 80p. *(978-0-16-082461-6(3)*, 552-070-38504-5) United States Government Printing Office.

Cheesman, Nick, et al. Ruling Myanmar: From Cyclone Nargis to National Elections. 2010. (Illus.). xiv, 353p. ***(978-981-4311-47-2(2))*** Institute of Southeast Asian Studies.

Dale, John G. Free Burma: Transnational Legal Action & Corporate Accountability. 2011. (Illus.). 328p. 75.00 *(978-0-8166-4646-3(5))*; pap. 25.00 *(978-0-8166-4647-0(3))* Univ. of Minnesota Pr.

Delisle, Guy. Burma Chronicles. 2010. (ENG., Illus.). 240p. pap. 16.95 *(978-1-77046-025-6(X))* Drawn & Quarterly Pubns. CAN. Dist: Macmillan.

Dittmer, Lowell. Burma or Myanmar? the Struggle for National Identity. 2010. (Illus.). 396p. 98.00 *(978-981-4313-64-3(5))* World Scientific Publishing Co., Inc.

Fink, Christina. Living Silence in Burma: Surviving under Military Rule. 2nd ed. 2009. (ENG., Illus.) 320p. 120.95 *(978-1-84813-271-9(9))*; pap. 26.95 *(978-1-84813-272-6(7))* Zed Bks., Ltd. GBR. Dist: Macmillan.

Foley, Matthew. The Cold War & National Assertion in Southeast Asia: Britain, the United States & Burma, 1948-1962. 2010. (ENG.). 228p. 135.00 *(978-0-415-55476-3(4))* Routledge.

Foley, Matthew. The Cold War & National Assertion in Southeast Asia: Britain, the United States & Burma, 1948ndash;1962. 2012. (ENG.). 240p. (C). pap. 42.95 ***(978-0-415-62749-8(4))*** Routledge.

Fujita, Koichi, et al. The Economic Transition in Myanmar after 1988: Market Economy Versus State Control. (Illus.). xv, 322p. 28.00 *(978-9971-69-461-6(1))* National Univ. of Singapore Pr. SGP. Dist: Univ. of Hawaii Pr.

Furnivall, J. S. Colonial Policy & Practice: A Comparative Study of Burma & Netherlands India. 2008. 592p. pap. 58.00 *(978-1-59740-602-4(3))* ACLS Humanities E-Book.

Ganesan, N. & Hlaing, Kyaw, eds. Myanmar: State, Society & Ethnicity. 2007. (Illus.). 324p. *(978-981-230-434-6(7))* Institute of Southeast Asian Studies.

Haacke, Jurgen. Myanmar's Foreign Policy: Domestic Influences & International Implications. 2006 (Adelphi Paper Ser.). (Illus.). 128p. per. 32.50 *(978-0-415-40726-7(5))* Routledge.

Hasday, Judy L. Aung San Suu Kyi: Activist for Democracy in Myanmar. 2007. (Modern Peacemakers Ser.). (Illus.). 128p. (YA). (gr 9-12). lib. bdg. 30.00 *(978-0-7910-9435-8(9))* Facts On File, Inc.

Holliday, Ian. Burma Redux: Global Justice & the Quest for Political Reform in Myanmar. 2012. (ENG.). 304p. (gr. 17). 89.50 ***(978-0-231-16126-8(3))***; pap. 29.50 ***(978-0-231-16127-5(1))*** Columbia Univ. Pr.

—Burma Redux: Global Justice & the Quest for Political Reform in Myanmar. 2011. (Illus.). 302p. pap. ***(978-988-8083-74-9(0))*** Hong Kong Univ. Pr.

Horsey, Richard. Ending Forced Labour in Myanmar. 2011. (Routledge Contemporary Southeast Asia Ser.). (ENG.). 256p. (C). 148.00 *(978-0-415-60077-4(4))* Routledge.

Institute of Pacific Relations American Council Staff. The Development of Self-Rule & Independence in Burma, Malaya & the Philippines: An Interim Report in a Study of Progress Toward Self-Government & Independence in Southeast Asia. reprint ed. 37.50 *(978-0-404-16829-2(9))* AMS Pr., Inc.

James, Helen. Governance & Civil Society in Myanmar: Education, Health & Environment. 2009. 208p. pap. 39.95 *(978-0-415-54591-4(9))* Routledge.

—Security & Sustainable Development in Myanmar. 2009. (Illus.). XVIII, 234p. pap. 39.95 *(978-0-415-54574-7(9))* Routledge.

Kyi, Aung San Suu. Freedom from Fear: And Other Writings. Aris, Michael, ed. & intro. by. 2nd rev. ed. 2010. (ENG., Illus.). 416p. (gr. 12). pap. 17.00 *(978-0-14-103949-7(3)*, Penguin (Non-Classics)) Penguin Group (USA) Inc.

—Letters from Burma. rev. ed. 2010. (ENG., Illus.). 224p. (gr. 12). pap. 16.00 *(978-0-14-104144-5(7)*, Penguin (Non-Classics)) Penguin Group (USA) Inc.

—The Voice of Hope: Conversations with Alan Clements. rev. ed. 2008. 336p. pap. 18.95 *(978-1-58322-845-6(4))* Seven Stories Pr.

Larkin, Emma. No Bad News for the King: The True Story of Cyclone Nargis & Its Aftermath in Burma. 2011. (ENG., Illus.). 288p. (gr. 12). 16.00 *(978-0-14-311961-6(3)*, Penguin (Non-Classics)) Penguin Group (USA) Inc.

Leigh, Michael D. Conflict, Politics & Proselytism: Methodist Missionaries in Colonial & Postcolonial Burma, 1887-1966. 2011. (Studies in Imperialism Ser.). (ENG., Illus.). 240p. 95.00 *(978-0-7190-8536-9(5))* Manchester Univ. Pr. GBR. Dist: Macmillan.

Lemere, Maggie & West, Zoe, eds. Nowhere to Be Home: Narratives from Survivors of Burma's Military Regime. 2011. (Voice of Witness Ser.). (ENG.). 500p. pap. 16.00 *(978-1-936365-02-9(2))* McSweeney's Publishing.

Levenstein, Susan. Finding Dollars, Sense & Legitimacy in Burma. 2010. (Illus.). 163p. ***(978-1-933549-85-9(8))*** Woodrow Wilson International Ctr. fo Scholars.

Lintner, Bertil. Aung San Suu Kyi & Burma's Struggle for Democracy. 2012. (ENG., Illus.). 200p. pap. 22.50 *(978-616-215-015-9(1))* Silkworm Bks. THA. Dist: Univ. of Washington Pr.

Pedersen, Morten B. Promoting Human Rights in Burma: A Critique of Western Sanctions Policy. 2007. (ENG.). 312p. 80.00 *(978-0-7425-5559-4(3))* Rowman & Littlefield Publishers, Inc.

Peter Popham. The Lady & the Peacock: The Life of Aung San Suu Kyi. 2012. (ENG.). 480p. 27.50 ***(978-1-61519-064-5(3)***, 1615190643) Experiment LLC, The.

Piercing Burma's Veil of Secrecy: The Truth Behind the Sham Election & the Difficult Road Ahead: Hearing Before the Subcommittee on Asia & the Pacific of the Committee on Foreign Affairs, House of Representatives, One Hundred Twelfth Congress, First Session, June 22, 2011. 2011. (Illus.). iii, 56p. ***(978-0-16-088450-3(6)***, 552-070-43414-3) United States Government Printing Office.

Rieffel, Lex, ed. Myanmar / Burma: Inside Challenges, Outside Interests. 2010. (ENG., Illus.). 212p. pap. 26.95 *(978-0-8157-0505-5(0))* Brookings Institution Pr.

Rogers, Benedict Than Shwe: Unmasking Burma's Tyrant. 2010. (ENG., Illus.). 272p. pap. 30.00 *(978-974-9511-91-6(3))* Silkworm Bks. THA. Dist: Univ. of Washington Pr.

Roycee, Alden T. Burma in Turmoil. 2008. (Horizons in World Cardiovascular Research Ser.). (Illus.). 105p. (C). 145.00 *(978-1-60456-311-5(7))* Nova Science Pubs., Inc.

Sakhong, Lian H. In Defence of Identity: The Ethnic Nationalities' Struggle for Democracy. 2011. (Illus.). 323p. pap. 25.00 *(978-974-524-133-6(4))* Orchid Pr. THA. Dist: National Bk. Network.

Samuels, S. K. Jade & Maw Sit Sit of Burma. 2nd ed. 2009. (ENG.). 160p. pap. 15.00 *(978-0-9725323-2-7(3))* SKS Enterprises, Inc.

Schober, Juliane. Modern Buddhist Conjunct. 2010. 248p. 49.00 *(978-0-8248-3382-4(1))* Univ. of Hawaii Pr.

Seekins, Donald. Struggles for Rangoon. 2010. (Asia's Transformations Ser.). (ENG., Illus.). 272p. (C). 170.00 *(978-0-415-31852-5(1))* Routledge.

Skidmore, Monique & Wilson, Trevor, eds. Myanmar: The State, Community & the Environment. 2007. (Illus.). (C). pap. *(978-0-7315-3811-9(0))* Asia Pacific Pr.

South, Ashley. Ethnic Politics in Burma: States of Conflict. 2008. (Routledge Contemporary Southeast Asia Ser.). (Illus.). XXIV, 280p. 150.00 *(978-0-415-41008-3(8))* Routledge.

Steinberg, David I. Burma/Myanmar: What Everyone Needs to Know. 2009. (What Everyone Needs to Know Ser.). (ENG., Illus.). 192p. pap. 16.95 *(978-0-19-539068-1(7))* Oxford Univ. Pr., Inc.

Suragamika. The Roadmap. 2012. (ENG.). 136p. pap. 18.50 *(978-616-215-017-3(8))* Silkworm Bks. THA. Dist: Univ. of Washington Pr.

Taylor, Robert H., compiled by. Dr Maung Maung: Gentleman, Scholar, Patriot. 2008. 616p. *(978-981-230-409-4(6))* Institute of Southeast Asian Studies.

Thawnghmung, Ardeth Maung. The Karen Revolution in Burm: Diverse Voices, Uncertain Ends. 2008. 96p. pap. *(978-981-230-804-7(0))* Institute of Southeast Asian Studies.

United Nations. Development Partnership Forum: Economic Policies for Growth & Poverty Reduction. 2011. (ENG.). 80p. pap. 52.00 ***(978-92-1-120613-5(8))*** United Nations Pubns.

U.S. Policy Toward Burma: Hearing Before the Committee on Foreign Affairs, House of Representatives, One Hundred Eleventh Congress, First Session, October 21, 2009. 2010. iii, 102p. *(978-0-16-084954-1(3)*, 552-070-40344-2) United States Government Printing Office.

Wakeman, Carolyn & Tin, San San. No Time for Dreams: Living in Burma under Military Rule. 2009. (Asian Voices Ser.). (ENG.). 256p. 39.95 *(978-0-7425-5703-1(0))* Rowman & Littlefield Publishers, Inc.

Webb, Paul. The Peacock's Children: Burma Protests, 1885-2000. 2010. (ENG., Illus.). 267p. pap. 25.00 *(978-974-524-069-8(9))* Orchid Pr. THA. Dist: National Bk. Network.

Wilson, Trevor, ed. Myanmar's Long Road to National Reconciliation. 2006. 310p. (C). pap. *(978-981-230-362-2(6)*, PIC142) Asia Pacific Pr.

Yawnghwe, Chao Tzang. The Shan of Burm: Memoirs of a Shan Exile. 2010. 296p. pap. *(978-981-230-396-7(0))* Institute of Southeast Asian Studies.

Zaw Oo & Win Min. Assessing Burma's Ceasefire Accords. 2007. (Illus.). xiii, 91p. pap. *(978-981-230-495-7(9))* Institute of Southeast Asian Studies.

BURMA—RELIGION

Ananda-Maitreya. The Religion of Burma & Other Papers. reprint ed. 45.00 *(978-0-404-16790-5(X))* AMS Pr., Inc.

Cross, E. B. On the Karens. 2010. pap. 19.24 *(978-1-61719-552-5(9))* Gorgias Pr., LLC.

Hall, H. Fielding. The Soul of a People 1920. 2007. (ENG.). 320p. 45.95 *(978-0-548-05413-0(4))* Kessinger Publishing, LLC.

Ray, Nihar-Ranjan. Brahmanical Gods in Burma: A Chapter of Indian Art & Iconography. reprint ed. 32.50 *(978-0-404-16852-0(3))* AMS Pr., Inc.

Rozenberg, Guillaume. Renunciation & Power: The Quest for Sainthood in Contemporary Burma. Hackett, Jessica, tr. from FRE. 2010. (Monograph Series, Yale Southeast Asia Studies: 59). pap. 20.00 *(978-0-938692-92-8(5))*; (ENG.). lib. bdg. 35.00 *(978-0-938692-93-5(3))* Yale Univ. Southeast Asia Studies.

BURMA—SOCIAL LIFE AND CUSTOMS

Adas, Michael. The Burma Delta: Economic Development & Social Change on an Asian Rice Frontier, 1852-1941. 2011. (Illus.). 276p. E-Book *(978-0-299-28353-7(4))*; (ENG., pap. 29.95 *(978-0-299-28354-4(2))* Univ. of Wisconsin Pr.

Ahmed, S. Z. The Forbidden Misty Mountains. 2008. 107p. pap. 10.95 *(978-0-7414-4469-1(0))* Infinity Publishing.

Aung-Thwin, Maitrii. The Return of the Galon King: History, Law, & Rebellion in Colonial Burma. 2010. (Ohio RIS Southeast Asia Ser.). (ENG., Illus.). 216p. pap. 28.00 *(978-0-89680-276-6(0))* Ohio Univ. Pr.

Cernea, Ruth. Almost Englishmen: Baghdadi Jews in British Burma. 2006. (ENG., Illus.). 202p. 60.99 *(978-0-7391-1646-3(0))* Lexington Bks.

Cernea, Ruth Fredman. Almost Englishmen: Baghdadi Jews in British Burma. 2006. (ENG., Illus.). 202p. pap. 26.50 *(978-0-7391-1647-0(9))* Lexington Bks.

Chit, Khin Myo & Thet, Paw Oo. Festivals & Flowers of the Twelve Burmese Seasons. 2006. (ENG., Illus.). 29.00 *(978-974-8299-56-3(2))* Orchid Pr. THA. Dist: National Bk. Network.

Conway, Susan. The Shan: Culture, Art & Crafts. 2006. (ENG., Illus.). 192p. *(978-974-9863-06-0(2)*, River Bks. Pr. Dist A C) Antique Collectors' Club.

Cultureshock Staff, ed. Cultureshock Myanmar, 1 vol. 2010. (ENG., Illus.). 240p. pap. 15.95 *(978-0-7614-5872-2(7))* Marshall Cavendish Corp.

Dudley, Sandra. Materialising Exile: Material Culture & Embodied Experience among the Karenni Refugees in Thailand. 2010. (SFM Ser.). (Illus.). 204p. 80.00 *(978-1-84545-640-5(8))* Berghahn Bks., Inc.

B

Duguid, Naomi. Burma: Rivers of Flavor. 2012. (ENG.). 384p. 35.00 ***(978-1-57965-413-9(4))*** Artisan.

Finger, Hans W. Dhammayangyi: The Pyramid by the Irrawaddy. 2006. (ENG., Illus.). 96p. pap. 17.95 *(978-974-524-045-2(1))* Orchid Pr. THA. Dist: National Bk. Network.

Ganesan, N. & Hlaing, Kyaw, eds. Myanmar: State, Society & Ethnicity. 2007. (Illus.). 324p. *(978-981-230-434-6(7))* Institute of Southeast Asian Studies.

Gordon, Charles Alexander. Our Trip to Burmah: With Notes on That Country. 2006. (ENG., Illus.). pap. 19.00 *(978-974-524-002-5(8))* Orchid Pr. THA. Dist: National Bk. Network.

Hall, H. Fielding. The Soul of a People 1920. 2007. (ENG.). 320p. 45.95 *(978-0-548-05413-0(4))* Kessinger Publishing, LLC.

Holden, Maggie, et al, eds. Nowhere to Be Home: Narratives from Survivors of Burma's Military Regime. 2011. (Voice of Witness Ser.). (ENG.). 256p. pap. 24.00 *(978-1-934781-95-1(9))* McSweeney's Publishing.

Humphries, Richard. Frontier Mosaic: Voices of Burma from the Lands in Between. 2007. (ENG., Illus.). 200p. pap. 29.95 *(978-974-524-092-6(3))* Orchid Pr. THA. Dist: National Bk. Network.

Kerr, Gordon. Silken East. 2006. 384p. per. *(978-1-4067-3402-7(0),* Hesperides Pr.) Read Bks.

O'Hara, Randolph. The Golden Land: A Burmese Romance. 2009. (ENG.). 132p. pap. 14.95 *(978-974-524-101-5(6))* Orchid Pr. THA. Dist: National Bk. Network.

Phasuk, Santanee & Stott, Philip. Royal Siamese Maps: War & Trade in Nineteenth Century Thailand. 2006. (ENG., Illus.). *(978-974-8225-92-0(5),* River Bks. Pr. Dist A C) Antique Collectors' Club.

Piana, Sergio Loro & Piana, Pier Luigi Loro. The Lotus Flower: A Textile Hidden in the Water. 2011. (ENG., Illus.). 146p. 95.00 *(978-88-572-0887-9(7))* Skira Editore ITA. Dist: Random Hse., Inc.

Rozenberg, Guillaume. Renunciation & Power: The Quest for Sainthood in Contemporary Burma. Hackett, Jessica, tr. from FRE. 2010. (Monograph Series, Yale Southeast Asia Studies: 59). pap. 20.00 *(978-0-938692-92-8(5))*; (ENG.). lib. bdg. 35.00 *(978-0-938692-93-5(3))* Yale Univ. Southeast Asia Studies.

Smeaton, Donald Mackenzie. The Loyal Karens of Burma. 2008. 156p. pap. *(978-1-4099-4807-0(2))* Dodo Pr.

—The Loyal Karens of Burma. 2008. 316p. 45.95 *(978-1-4373-9895-3(2))*; pap. 30.95 *(978-1-4373-1134-1(2))* Kessinger Publishing, LLC.

Smith, Martin. State of Strife: The Dynamics of Ethnic Conflict in Burma. 2007. (Illus.). xii, 95p. pap. *(978-981-230-479-7(7))* Institute of Southeast Asian Studies.

Thanegi, Ma. The Illusion of Life: Burmese Marionettes. 2009. (ENG., Illus.). 108p. pap. 23.00 *(978-974-8304-03-8(5))* Orchid Pr. THA. Dist: National Bk. Network.

Yin, Saw Myat. Cultureshock! Myanmar: A Survival Guide to Customes & Etiquette. 2007. (Cultureshock Myanmar: A Survival Guide to Customs & Etiquette Ser.). (Illus.). 234p. per. 15.95 *(978-0-7614-5410-6(1))* Marshall Cavendish Corp.

BURMA-SIAM RAILROAD

Burton, Reginald. Railway of Hell: War Captivity & Forced Labour at the Hands of the Japanese. 2010. (Illus.). 192p. pap. 24.95 *(978-1-84884-299-1(6))* Pen & Sword Bks. Ltd. GBR. Dist: Casemate Pubs. & Bk. Distributors, LLC.

Crager, Kelly E. Hell under the Rising Sun: Texan POWs & the Building of the Burma-Thailand Death Railway. 2008. (Texas AandM University Military History Ser.). (ENG., Illus.). 216p. 29.95 *(978-1-58544-635-3(1))* Texas A&M Univ. Pr.

Holmes, Linda Goetz. 4000 Bowls of Rice: A Prisoner of War Comes Home. 2007. (ENG., Illus.). 200p. per. 14.95 *(978-1-883283-51-3(5))* IBks., Inc.

Velmans, Loet. Long Way Back to the River Kwai: Memories of World War II. 2011. (ENG., Illus.). 256p. pap. 14.95 *(978-1-61145-185-6(X),* 611185, Arcade Publishing) Skyhorse Publishing Co., Inc.

BURMAN LANGUAGE

see Burmese Language

BURMESE

Piana, Sergio Loro & Piana, Pier Luigi Loro. The Lotus Flower: A Textile Hidden in the Water. 2011. (ENG., Illus.). 146p. 95.00 *(978-88-572-0887-9(7))* Skira Editore ITA. Dist: Random Hse., Inc.

BURMESE ART

see Art, Burmese

BURMESE DRAMA—HISTORY AND CRITICISM

Htin Aung, U. Burmese Drama: A Study of Burmese Plays. reprint ed. 37.50 *(978-0-404-16827-8(2))* AMS Pr., Inc.

BURMESE LANGUAGE

Cunningham, Nance & Soe Min, Aung. Burmese-English English-Burmese Dictionary. 2009. (BUR & ENG.). 934p. pap. 18.00 *(978-1-887521-58-1(5))* Paiboon Publishing.

Euro Talk. Talk Now! Burmese. 2008. 29.99 *(978-1-84352-400-7(7))* TOPICS Entertainment.

Hla Myat Thway. Yinchia Studies: Documentation & Analysis of a Language of Myanmar (Burma) 2010. (Europäische Hochschulschriften. Reihe 21: Linguistik Ser.). 208p. pap. 56.95 *(978-3-631-58498-9(9))* Lang, Peter GmbH, Europaischer Verlag der Wissenschaften DEU. Dist: Lang, Peter.

Hough, G. H. An Anglo-Burmese Dictionary. 2008. (BUR & ENG.). 154p. pap. 22.75 *(978-0-554-95632-9(2))* BiblioBazaar.

Icon Group International, Inc. Staff, compiled by. The 2009-2014 World Outlook for Manufacturing Major Household-Type Appliances Excluding Cooking Equipment, Refrigerators, Upright & Chest Freezers, & Laundry Equipment. 2008. 199p. ring bd. 28.95 incl. audio compact disk *(978-0-497-83678-8(5))* Icon Group International, Inc.

Nolan, Stephen, et al. Pocket Burmese Dictionary: Burmese-English English-Burmese. 2008. (Periplus Pocket Dictionaries Ser.). (BUR & ENG.). 96p. pap. 8.95 *(978-0-7946-0573-5(7),* PeriplusEdition) Tuttle Publishing.

Okell John, et al. Burmese (Myanmar), 4 vols. 2010. (BUR & ENG., Illus.). (C). 264p. pap. 49.95 ***(978-0-87580-645-7(7))***; 454p. pap. 59.95 ***(978-0-87580-644-0(9))***; 300p. pap. 49.95 ***(978-0-87580-643-3(0))***; 302p. pap. 49.95 ***(978-0-87580-642-6(2))*** Northern Illinois Univ. Pr.

Rhoden, T. F. Making Out in Burmese. 2011. (Making Out Bks.). (BUR & ENG.). 96p. pap. 7.95 *(978-0-8048-4173-3(X))* Tuttle Publishing.

Tun, San San Hnin, et al. Burmese. 4th rev. ed. 2008. (Phrasebook Ser.). (BUR & ENG., Illus.). 224p. pap. 8.99 *(978-1-74104-027-2(2))* Lonely Planet Pubns.

BURMESE LITERATURE

Gray, James, ed. Ancient Proverbs & Maxims from Burmese Sources: The Niti Literature of Burma. reprint ed. 32.50 *(978-0-404-16822-3(1))* AMS Pr., Inc.

BURMESE NATIONAL CHARACTERISTICS

see National Characteristics, Burmese

BURN OUT (PSYCHOLOGY)

Borthwick, Paul. Simplify: 106 Ways to Uncomplicate Your Life. 2007. (ENG.). 206p. per. 13.99 *(978-1-934068-01-4(2))* Authentic Media.

Borysenko, Joan Z. Fried: Why You Burn Out & How to Revive. 2011. (ENG.). 200p. 17.95 *(978-1-4019-2550-5(2))* Hay Hse., Inc.

Carter, Sherrie. High-Octane Women: How Superachievers Can Avoid Burnout. 2010. (ENG.). 250p. pap. 18.00 *(978-1-61614-220-9(0))* Prometheus Bks., Pubs.

Case, Steven L. & Case, Steven. Help! I'm a Frustrated Youth Worker! A Practical Guide to Avoiding Burnout in Your Ministry, 1 vol. 2008. (ENG.). 144p. pap. 10.99 *(978-0-310-27888-7(0))* Zondervan.

Cora, Gabriela. ExecutiveHealth. com's Leading under Pressure: Strategies to Avoid Burnout, Increase Energy, & Improve Your Well-Being. 2010. (ENG.). 1p. pap. 15.99 *(978-1-60163-128-2(6))* Career Pr., Inc.

Cordeiro, Wayne. Leading on Empty: Refilling Your Tank & Renewing Your Passion, 1 vol. 2010. (ENG.). 224p. pap. 14.99 *(978-0-7642-0759-4(8))* Bethany Hse. Pubs.

Dengel, Sascha Nicolas. Burnout-Syndrom - Krise oder Chance? ..... oder wie ein Betroffener das Erschöpfungssyndrom erklärt. 2011. 138p. pap. 30.90 ***(978-3-8370-6393-6(3))*** Bks. on Demand.

Eenigenburg, Susan E. & Blyss, Robynn. Expectations & Burnout: Women Surviving the Great Commission. 2010. *(978-0-87808-523-1(8))* Carey, William Library Pubs.

Eklund, Nathan. How Was Your Day at School? Improving Dialogue about Teacher Job Satisfaction. 2009. (ENG., Illus.). 168p. pap. 25.95 *(978-1-57482-264-9(0))* Search Institute.

Epperly, Bruce Gordon & Epperly, Katherine Gould. Feed the Fire! Avoiding Clergy Burnout. 2008. 192p. 22.00 *(978-0-8298-1795-9(6))* Pilgrim Pr., The/United Church Pr.

Farber, Katy. Why Great Teachers Quit: And How We Might Stop the Exodus. 2010. 200p. pap. 29.95 *(978-1-4129-7245-1(0),* B72444P) Corwin Pr.

Fein, Albert H. & Mahoney, Dan. Overload & Collapse in the K-12 System: Essays by Educators on Edge. 2008. 316p. 119.95 *(978-0-7734-5155-1(2))* Mellen, Edwin Pr., The.

Frances, Dee. Twelve Ways to Prevent Burnout. Date not set. pap. 3.00 *(978-1-885519-64-1(8))* DDDD Pubns.

Goodwin, Debbie Salter & Spaite, Daniel. Time Bomb in the Church: Difusing Pastoral Burnout. 2007. 168p. pap. 14.99 *(978-0-8341-2320-5(7))* Nazarene Publishing Hse.

Halbesleben, Jonathon R. B. Handbook of Stress & Burnout in Health Care. Halbesleben, Jonathon R. B., ed. 2008. (Illus.). xiv, 243p. 98.00 *(978-1-60456-500-3(4))* Nova Science Pubs., Inc.

—Managing Stress & Preventing Burnout in the Healthcare Workplace. 2009. 73.00 *(978-1-56793-343-7(2))* Health Administration Pr.

Heugten, Kate van. Social Work under Pressure: How to Overcome Stress, Fatigue & Burnout in the Workplace. 2011. (ENG.). 224p. pap. *(978-1-84905-116-3(X))* Kingsley, Jessica Ltd.

Jackson, Anne. Mad Church Disease: Overcoming the Burnout Epidemic, 1 vol. 2009. (ENG., Illus.). 192p. 16.99 *(978-0-310-28755-1(3))* Zondervan.

Jillings, Ruth & Clarke, Dave. Spotlight on Community Workers. 2011. 432p. pap. ***(978-3-8454-1052-4(3))*** Lambert Academic Publishing.

Johnson, Jeff A. Finding Your Smile Again: A Child Care Professional's Guide to Reducing Stress & Avoiding Burnout. 2007. (ENG., Illus.). 160p. (J). per. 14.95 *(978-1-929610-93-8(9))* Redleaf Pr.

—Keeping Your Smile: Caring for Children with Joy, Love, & Intention. 2010. (ENG.). 184p. pap. 17.95 *(978-1-933653-85-3(X))* Redleaf Pr.

Joint Commission Staff & Joint Commission Resources, Inc Staff, contrib. by. Strategies for Addressing Health Care Worker Fatigue. 2008. (Illus.). vi, 154p. *(978-1-59940-229-1(7))* Joint Commission Resources.

Kemp, Bill. Peter's Boat: Renewing the Vitality of Burned-Out Church Workers. 2007. 104p. per. *(978-0-88177-499-3(5))* Discipleship Resources.

Kennard, David. Staff Support Groups in the Helping Professions: Principles, Practice & Pitfalls. 2009. (ENG., Illus.). 216p. (C). 95.00 *(978-0-415-44773-7(9))*; pap. 34.95 *(978-0-415-44774-4(7))* Routledge.

Kottler, Jeffrey A. The Therapist's Workbook: Self-Assessment, Self-Care, & Self-Improvement Exercises for Mental Health Professionals. 2nd ed. 2011. (ENG.). 197p. pap. 40.00 *(978-1-118-02631-1(4),* Wiley) Wiley, John & Sons, Inc.

Lipman, Frank & Doyle, Mollie. Revive: Stop Feeling Spent & Start Living Again. 2011. (ENG.). 496p. mass mkt. 7.99 *(978-1-4391-9582-6(X))* Pocket Books.

—Revive: Stop Feeling Spent & Start Living Again. 2009. (ENG.). 352p. pap. 15.00 *(978-1-4165-4942-0(0),* Touchstone) Touchstone.

Lipsky, Laura van Dernoot & Burk, Connie. Trauma Stewardship: An Everyday Guide to Caring for Self While Caring for Others. 2007. (Illus.). 263p. *(978-0-615-15206-6(6))* Lipsky, Laura van Dernoot.

Ludgate, John W. Heal Your Self: A CBT Approach to Reducing Therapist Distress & Increasing Therapeutic Effectiveness. 2012. (ENG.). 96p. pap. 24.95 ***(978-1-56887-127-1(9),*** Professional Resource Pr.) Professional Resource Exchange, Inc.

MacKie, Paul. Burnout & Job Satisfaction among Rural & Urban Social Workers. 2008. 180p. pap. *(978-3-639-08173-2(0))* VDM Verlag Dr. Mueller e.K.

McLaughlin, Caitriona D. & Docherty, Jamie N., eds. Nursing Issues: Psychiatric Nursing, Geriatric Nursing & Nursing Burnout. 2010. (Nursing - Issues, Problems & Challenges Ser.). (Illus.). xii, 320p. 145.00 *(978-1-60741-598-5(4))* Nova Science Pubs., Inc.

Meier, Marjorie. The Invisibility of Emotional Labor. 2009. 100p. pap. *(978-3-639-19539-2(6))* VDM Verlag Dr. Mueller e.K.

Merritt, Edward A. The Leadership Trap. 2010. 120p. pap. *(978-3-8383-5552-8(0))* Lambert Academic Publishing.

Norcross, John C., et al. Leaving It at the Office: A Guide to Psychotherapist Self-Care. 2007. (ENG.). 238p. 55.00 *(978-1-59385-490-4(0))*; pap. 28.00 *(978-1-59385-576-5(1))* Guilford Pubns., Inc.

Parrouty, Josiane. Burnout among French Immersion Teachers in British Columbia, Canad. 2010. 164p. pap. *(978-3-639-27512-4(8))* VDM Verlag Dr. Mueller e.K.

Raedeke, Thomas D. & Smith, Alan L. The Athlete Burnout Questionnaire Manual. 2009. 88p. 39.00 *(978-1-885693-88-4(5))* Fitness Information Technology, Inc.

Sachdeva, Ruchi. Ors-Organisational Role Stress. 2011. 88p. pap. ***(978-3-8443-9006-3(5))*** Lambert Academic Publishing.

Sandford, R. Loren. Renewal for the Wounded Warrior: A Burnout Survival Guide for Believers, 1 vol. 2010. (ENG.). 192p. pap. 14.00 *(978-0-8007-9480-4(X))* Chosen Bks.

Schwartzhoffer, Rachel V. Psychology of Burnout: Predictors & Coping Mechanisms. 2009. (Psychology Research Progress Ser.). (Illus.). xiv, 307p. 98.00 *(978-1-60876-010-7(3))* Nova Science Pubs., Inc.

Smith, Winston/Teal. Burned Out? Trusting God with Your to-Do List. 2009. 24p. 3.99 *(978-1-935273-20-2(5))* New Growth Pr.

Spinella, Faith Ann. Principal's Role in Teacher Retention. 2008. 108p. pap. *(978-3-639-07517-5(X))* VDM Verlag Dr. Mueller e.K.

Stone, Charles. Five Ministry Killers & How to Defeat Them: Help for Frustrated Pastors — Including New Research from the Barna Group. 2011. 224p. pap. 15.99 *(978-0-7642-0854-6(3))* Bethany Hse. Pubs.

Transforming Burnout: A simple guide to self Renewal. 2006. per. *(978-0-9787952-0-7(2))* Vibrant Pr.

Trnavská, Tereza. Burnout Syndrom at Andragogical Professions. 2011. 80p. pap. ***(978-3-8454-0138-6(9))*** Lambert Academic Publishing.

Vandenberghe, Roland & Huberman, A. Michael, eds. Understanding & Preventing Teacher Burnout: A Sourcebook of International Research & Practice. 2006. (Jacobs Foundation Series on Adolescence Ser.). (ENG., Illus.). 380p. pap. 39.99 *(978-0-521-02869-1(8))* Cambridge Univ. Pr.

VanSlyke-Briggs, Kjersti. Nurturing Teacher: Managing the Stress of Caring. 2010. (ENG.). 116p. 59.00 *(978-1-60709-397-8(9))*; pap. 25.00 *(978-1-60709-398-5(7))* Rowman & Littlefield Publishers, Inc.

Watkins, Grant. CPR for Caregivers: Connect, Project, & Reflect Through Mind, Body, & Spirit. 2008. 75p. per. 18.95 *(978-1-934690-01-7(5))* Tasora Bks.

Webb, Joan C. The Relief of Imperfection: For Women Who Try Too Hard to Make It Just Right. 2008. (ENG., Illus.). 224p. per. 14.99 *(978-0-8307-4481-7(9))* Gospel Light Pubns.

White, PH.D., Joseph D. Burnout Busters: Stress Management for Ministry. 2007. 63p. pap. 4.95 *(978-1-59276-311-5(1))* Our Sunday Visitor, Publishing Div.

BURNE-JONES, EDWARD COLEY, SIR, 1833-1898

Angelou, Maya. Love's Exquisite Freedom. 2011. (ENG., Illus.). 32p. 19.95 *(978-1-59962-103-6(7),* Welcome Bks.) Welcome Enterprises, Inc.

Arscott, Caroline, et al. William Morris & Edward Burne-Jones: Interlacings. 2008. (ENG., Illus.). 260p. 75.00 *(978-0-300-14093-4(2))* Yale Univ. Pr.

Frehner, Matthias, et al, texts. Edward Burne-Jones: the Earthly Paradise. 2010. (ENG., Illus.). 232p. 60.00 *(978-3-7757-2517-0(2))* Hatje Cantz Verlag GmbH & Co KG DEU. Dist: D.A.P./Distributed Art Pubs.

MacCarthy, Fiona. The Last Pre-Raphaelite: Edward Burne-Jones & the Victorian Imagination. 2012. (Illus.). 656p. 35.00 ***(978-0-674-06579-6(4))*** Harvard Univ. Pr.

Thirkell, Angela. Three Houses: A Victorian Childhood. 2007. (Illus.). 160p. pap. 12.95 *(978-1-55921-389-9(2))* Moyer Bell.

BURNES, ALEXANDER, SIR, 1805-1841

Burnes, Alexander. Travels into Bokhara: A Voyage up the Indus to Lahore & a Journey to Cahool, Tartary & Persia. Hopkirk, Kathleen, ed. 2012. (ENG., Illus.). xii, 240p. pap. 29.95 ***(978-1-906011-71-0(0))*** Eland Bks. GBR. Dist: Dufour Editions, Inc.

BURNET, DAVID GOUVERNEUR, 1788-1870

Burnet, Gilbert. Bishop Burnet's History of His Own Time. 2010. 920p. pap. 60.75 *(978-1-140-83867-8(9),* Gale ECCO, Print Editions); 480p. pap. 37.75 *(978-1-140-79227-7(X),* Gale ECCO, Print Editions); 486p. pap. 37.75 *(978-1-140-79228-4(8),* Gale ECCO, Print Editions); 842p. pap. 56.75 *(978-1-140-83866-1(0),* Gale ECCO, Print Editions); 448p. pap. 35.75 *(978-1-170-63822-4(8),* Gale ECCO, Print Editions); 520p. pap. 39.75 *(978-1-170-63821-7(X),* Gale ECCO, Print Editions); 426p. pap. 34.75 *(978-1-170-66386-8(9),* Gale ECCO, Print Editions); 800p. pap. 54.75 *(978-1-140-92941-3(0),* Gale ECCO, Print Editions); 864p. pap. 57.75 *(978-1-140-92942-0(9),* Gale ECCO, Print Editions); 554p. pap. 41.75 *(978-1-170-63185-0(1),* Gale ECCO, Print Editions); 538p. pap. 40.75 *(978-1-170-63183-6(5),* Gale ECCO, Print Editions); 550p. pap. 41.75 *(978-1-170-63184-3(3),* Gale ECCO, Print Editions); 526p. pap. 39.75 *(978-1-170-63820-0(1),* Gale ECCO, Print Editions); 498p. pap. 38.75 *(978-1-145-32657-6(9))* BiblioBazaar.

—Bishop Burnet's History of His Own Time. 2009. 386p. pap. *(978-1-150-20870-6(8))*; 286p. pap. *(978-0-217-44734-8(1))*; 78p. pap. *(978-0-217-95851-6(6))*; 810p. pap. *(978-0-217-95853-0(2))*; 122p. pap. *(978-0-217-18225-6(9))*; 182p. pap. *(978-0-217-18227-0(5))*; 254p. pap. *(978-1-4588-2476-9(4))*; 176p. pap. *(978-1-4590-5629-9(9))*; 90p. pap. *(978-1-4590-5630-5(2))*; 322p. pap. *(978-1-4590-5632-9(9))*; 72p. pap. *(978-1-4590-5633-6(7))* Books LLC.

—Bishop Burnet's History of His Own Time. 2010. 248p. pap. 24.37 *(978-1-154-03813-2(0))*; (Illus.). 644p. pap. 43.65 *(978-1-154-63935-3(5))* General Bks. LLC.

Burnet, Gilbert & Burnet, Thomas. Bishop Burnet's History of His Own Time. 2010. 502p. pap. 38.75 *(978-1-148-96728-8(1))*; 594p. pap. 44.75 *(978-1-147-15572-3(0))*; 418p. pap. 34.75 *(978-1-144-85668-5(X))*; 582p. pap. 43.75 *(978-1-145-43096-9(1))*; 682p. pap. 47.75 *(978-1-143-31722-4(X))* BiblioBazaar.

Burnet, Gilbert, et al. Bishop Burnet's History of His Own Time. 2010. 424p. pap. 35.75 *(978-1-147-06397-4(4))*; 498p. pap. 38.75 *(978-1-144-36123-3(0))* BiblioBazaar.

BURNETT, FRANCES HODGSON, 1849-1924

Burnett, Frances Hodgson. Collected Works of Frances Hodgson Burnett. 2008. 260p. 28.99 *(978-0-554-27818-6(9))* 2008. 260p. 25.99 *(978-0-554-37121-4(9))* 2008. (ENG.). 94p. per. 18.75 *(978-1-4375-2461-1(3))* 2008. (ENG.). 104p. per. 18.75 *(978-1-4375-2597-7(0))* 2007. 236p. pap. 20.99 *(978-1-4346-4046-8(9))* 2007. 256p. pap. 23.99 *(978-1-4346-4093-2(0))* BiblioBazaar.

Carpenter, Angelica Shirley & Burnett, Frances Hodgson. In the Garden: Essays in Honor of Frances Hodgson Burnett. Carpenter, Angelica Shirley, ed. 2006. (ENG., Illus.). 278p. per. 60.00 *(978-0-8108-5288-4(8))* Scarecrow Pr., Inc.

Horne, Jackie C. & Sanders, Joe Sutliff. Frances Hodgson Burnett's The Secret Garden: A Children's Classic at 100. 2011. (Children's Literature Association Centennial Studies). (ENG.). 312p. 65.00 *(978-0-8108-8187-7(X))* Scarecrow Pr., Inc.

BURNEY, CHARLES, 1726-1814

Anonymous. Memoirs of Doctor Burney: Arranged from His Own Manuscripts, from Family Papers, & from Personal Recollections. 2010. 412p. pap. 34.75 *(978-1-142-12434-2(7))* BiblioBazaar.

Books. Memoirs of Doctor Burney; Arranged from His Own Manuscripts, from Family Papers, & from Personal Recollections. 2010. 174p. pap. 19.99 *(978-1-150-36020-6(8))* General Bks. LLC.

Burney, Charles & Metastasio, Pietro. Memoirs of the Life & Writings of the Abate Metastasio: In which are Incorporated, Translations of his Principal Letters. 2010. (Cambridge Library Collection - Music Ser.). (ENG.). 460p. pap. 34.99 *(978-1-108-01452-6(6))*; 446p. pap. 32.99 *(978-1-108-01466-3(6))*; 458p. pap. 34.99 *(978-1-108-01465-6(8))* Cambridge Univ. Pr.

Burney, Fanny. Memoirs of Doctor Burney. 2010. 456p. pap. 36.75 *(978-1-142-52789-1(1))* 2010. 380p. pap. 33.75 *(978-1-141-96986-9(6))* 2009. 378p. 33.99 *(978-1-116-14521-2(9))* 2009. 378p. 38.99 *(978-1-116-14520-5(0))* 2009. 378p. pap. 32.75 *(978-1-116-14523-6(5))* 2009. 378p. pap. 33.75 *(978-1-116-14522-9(7))* 2008. 380p. 29.99 *(978-0-559-30972-4(4))* 2008. 380p. pap. 32.75 *(978-0-559-30971-7(6))* BiblioBazaar.

—Memoirs of Doctor Burney. 2009. 198p. pap. *(978-0-217-01844-9(0))* Books LLC.

—Memoirs of Doctor Burney. 2009. 198p. pap. 22.37 *(978-1-150-36018-3(6))* General Bks. LLC.

—Memoirs of Doctor Burney: Arr. from His Own Manuscripts, from Family Papers, & from Personal Recollections by Madame d'Arblay, Vol. 3. 2007. 440p. 51.95 *(978-0-548-16315-3(4))*; 444p. per. 36.95 *(978-1-4304-5931-6(X))* Kessinger Publishing, LLC.

—Memoirs of Doctor Burney: Arranged from His Own Manuscripts, from Family Papers, & from Personal Recollections. 2010. 444p. pap. 36.75 *(978-1-142-54374-7(9))* BiblioBazaar.

—Memoirs of Doctor Burney; Arranged from His Own Manuscripts, from Family Papers, & from Personal Recollections. 2009. 196p. pap. 19.99 *(978-1-150-68031-1(8))* General Bks. LLC.

Burney, Fanny, ed. Memoirs of Doctor Burney: Arranged from His Own Manuscripts, from Family Papers, & from Personal Recollections. 2010.

(Cambridge Library Collection - Music Ser.). (ENG.). 444p. pap. 32.99 (978-1-108-01373-4(2)); 408p. pap. 31.99 (978-1-108-01372-7(4)); 380p. pap. 31.99 (978-1-108-01371-0(6)) Cambridge Univ. Pr.

Travis &. Emery, &. Emery. The Present State of Music in France & Italy [Facsimile of 1771 Edition]. 2008. 424p. pap. (978-1-904331-76-6(9)) Travis & Emery Music Bookshop.

BURNEY, FANNY, 1752-1840

Barrett, Charlotte. Diary & Letters of Madame Darblay Vol. 2006. (ENG.). 608p. per. (978-1-4067-3520-8(5), Hesperides Pr.) Read Bks.

Bovill, E. W. & Parisian, Catherine M. Missions to the Niger. 2012. (Ashgate Studies in Publishing History Ser.). (Illus.). 275p. 104.95 **(978-1-4094-1821-4(9))** Ashgate Publishing Co.

Burney, Fanny. The Diary & Letters of Madame D'Arblay. 2009. 532p. 35.99 (978-0-559-08286-3(X)); 32.99 (978-0-559-08302-0(5)); pap. 23.99 (978-0-559-08297-9(5)); pap. 30.99 (978-0-559-08290-0(8)) BiblioBazaar.

—Diary & Letters of Madame d'Arblay (1778-1840), Vol. 1. Dobson, Austin, ed. 2007. 564p. per. 43.95 (978-0-548-76857-0(9)) Kessinger Publishing, LLC.

—Diary & Letters of Madame d'Arblay (1778-1840) Barrett, Charlotte, ed. 2007. Vol. 3. 556p. per. 42.95 (978-0-548-77302-4(5)) Vol. 5. 564p. per. 43.95 (978-0-548-74776-6(8)) Vol. 6. 560p. per. 42.95 (978-0-548-76510-4(3)) Kessinger Publishing, LLC.

Cooke, Stewart. The Court Journals & Letters of Frances Burney: Volume II: 1787. 2011. (Illus.). 416p. 185.00 (978-0-19-926280-9(2)) Oxford Univ. Pr., Inc.

Dobson, Austin. Fanny Burney. 2007. (ENG.). 222p. 39.95 (978-0-548-04225-0(X)) Kessinger Publishing, LLC.

—Fanny Burney. 2006. 216p. per. (978-1-4067-3414-0(4), Hesperides Pr.) Read Bks.

—Fanny Burney, Madame D'Arblay. 2008. 224p. 39.95 (978-0-548-92005-3(2)) 2007. (ENG.). 228p. per. 24.95 (978-0-548-60552-3(1)) Kessinger Publishing, LLC.

Doody, Margaret Anne. Frances Burney: The Life in the Works. 2010. (ENG.). 462p. pap. 34.99 (978-0-521-15892-3(3)) Cambridge Univ. Pr.

Looser, Devoney. Women Writers & Old Age in Great Britain, 1750-1850. 2008. (ENG., Illus.). 252p. (gr. 17). 57.00 (978-0-8018-8705-5(4)) Johns Hopkins Univ. Pr.

Mackie, Erin Skye & Mackie, E. Rakes, Highwaymen, & Pirates: The Making of the Modern Gentleman in the Eighteenth Century. 2009. (ENG.). 248p. (gr. 17). 57.00 (978-0-8018-9088-8(8)) Johns Hopkins Univ. Pr.

Masefield, Muriel. The Story of Fanny Burney: Being an Introduction to the Diary & Letters of Madame D'Arblay. 2011. (ENG.). 190p. pap. 35.00 **(978-1-107-60496-4(6))** Cambridge Univ. Pr.

Parisian, Catherine M. Frances Burney's Cecilia: A Publishing History. 2012. (Ashgate Studies in Publishing History Ser.). (Illus.). 275p. 104.95 **(978-1-4094-1820-7(0))** Ashgate Publishing Co.

Sabor, Peter. The Court Journals & Letters of Frances Burney: Volume I: 1786. 2011. (ENG., Illus.). 400p. 185.00 (978-0-19-926160-4(1)) Oxford Univ. Pr., Inc.

Sabor, Peter, ed. The Cambridge Companion to Frances Burney. 2007. (Cambridge Companions to Literature Ser.). (ENG.). 214p. (C). 90.00 (978-0-521-85034-6(7)); per. 33.99 (978-0-521-61548-8(8)) Cambridge Univ. Pr.

BURNEY FAMILY

Hill, Constance. Fanny Burney at the Court of Queen Charlotte. 2009. 162p. pap. (978-1-151-15192-6(0)) Books LLC.

—Fanny Burney at the Court of Queen Charlotte. 432p. 2008. 51.95 (978-1-4365-9364-9(6)) 2007. (ENG.). per. 36.95 (978-0-548-77810-4(8)) Kessinger Publishing, LLC.

Rogers, D. Laurence. Apostles of Equality: The Birneys, the Republicans, & the Civil War. 2011. (ENG., Illus.). 250p. 39.95 (978-1-61186-015-3(6)) Michigan State Univ. Pr.

BURNHAM, DANIEL HUDSON, 1846-1912

Hines, Thomas S. Burnham of Chicago: Architect & Planner. 2nd ed. 2008. (ENG., Illus.). 474p. pap. 22.50 (978-0-226-34172-9(0)) Univ. of Chicago Pr.

Larson, Erik. The Devil in the White City: Murder, Magic, & Madness at the Fair That Changed America. (Reading Group Guides). (978-1-4000-3552-6(X)) Knopf Doubleday Publishing Group.

Smith, Carl. The Plan of Chicago: Daniel Burnham & the Remaking of the American City. (Chicago Visions & Revisions Ser.). (ENG., Illus.). 2007. 202p. per. 12.00 (978-0-226-76472-6(9)) 2006. 184p. 22.00 (978-0-226-76471-9(0)) Univ. of Chicago Pr.

BURNING OF LAND

see also Shifting Cultivation

Innes, John L., et al, eds. Biomass Burning & Its Inter-Relationships with the Climate System. 2010. (Advances in Global Change Research Ser.). (Illus.). 368p. pap. 229.00 (978-90-481-5375-6(1), 9048153751) Springer.

Russell-Smith, Jeremy, et al, eds. Culture, Ecology & Economy of Fire Management in North Australian Savannas. 2010. 416p. pap. 68.95 (978-0-643-09402-4(4)) CSIRO Publishing AUS. Dist: Stylus Publishing, LLC.

Weir, John Robert. Conducting Prescribed Fires: A Comprehensive Manual. 2009. (ENG., Illus.). 206p. pap. 28.00 (978-1-60344-134-6(4)) Texas A&M Univ. Pr.

BURNING OF THE DEAD

see Cremation

BURNING OF WASTE

see Incineration

BURNOUT (PSYCHOLOGY)

see Burn Out (Psychology)

BURNS, ANTHONY, 1834-1862

Barker, Gordon S. The Imperfect Revolution: Anthony Burns & the Landscape of Race in Antebellum America. 2011. xix, 169p. 39.95 (978-1-60635-069-0(2)) Kent State Univ. Pr.

Dana, Richard Henry. Remarks of Richard H Dana, Jr , Esq Before the Committee on Federal Relations, on the Proposed Removal of Edward G Loring, Esq from the Office Of. 2011. 30p. pap. 11.99 **(978-1-4181-9306-5(2))** MPublishing.

Higginson, Thomas Wentworth. Massachusetts in Mourning a Sermon, Preached in Worcester, on Sunday, June 4 1854. 2011. 18p. pap. 11.99 **(978-1-4181-9001-9(2))** MPublishing.

Hoar, E. R. Charge to the Grand Jury, at the July Term of the Municipal Court, in Boston 1854. 2011. 24p. pap. 11.99 **(978-1-4181-9140-5(X))** MPublishing.

Maltz, Earl M. Fugitive Slave on Trial: The Anthony Burns Case & Abolitionist Outrage. 2010. 192p. 34.95 (978-0-7006-1735-7(3)); pap. 17.95 (978-0-7006-1736-4(1)) Univ. Pr. of Kansas.

BURNS, GEORGE, 1896-1996

Epstein, Lawrence J. George Burns: An American Life. 2011. (ENG.). 212p. pap. 35.00 **(978-0-7864-5849-3(6))** McFarland & Co., Inc. Pubs.

BURNS, ROBERT, 1759-1796

Ainslie, Hew & Latto, Thomas C. A Pilgrimage to the Land of Burns. 2007. (ENG.). 424p. 51.95 (978-0-548-10360-9(7)) Kessinger Publishing, LLC.

Boynton, Henry W. Carlyle: Essay on Burns. 2007. (ENG.). 174p. 37.95 (978-0-548-05909-8(8)) Kessinger Publishing, LLC.

Brooke, Stopford A. Theology in the English Poets: Cowper, Coleridge, Wordsworth & Burns. 356p. 2010. pap. 25.56 (978-1-162-92343-7(1)) 2007. (ENG.). 46.95 (978-0-548-08527-1(7)) Kessinger Publishing, LLC.

Bruce, Wallace. Robert Burns: Poet-Laureate of Lodge Canongate Kilwinning (1893) 2007. 48p. per. 15.95 (978-0-548-73464-3(X)) Kessinger Publishing, LLC.

Burnett, Allan. Robert Burns & All That. 2007. (And All That Ser.). (ENG., Illus.). 105p. per. 6.95 (978-1-84158-573-4(4)) Birlinn, Ltd. GBR. Dist: Interlink Publishing Group, Inc.

Burns, Robert. The Complete Poetical Works of Robert Burns: With Explanatory & Glossarial Notes; & A Life of the Author, by James Currie, M. D. 2006. (Illus.). 288p. per. 23.99 (978-1-4255-2569-9(5)) MPublishing.

—Letters Addressed to Clarinda, &c. 2009. (AccessAble Bks.). 76p. pap. 12.95 (978-1-57003-880-8(5)) Univ. of South Carolina Pr.

—The Letters of Robert Burns. 2008. 396p. 29.99 (978-0-554-32417-3(2)) 2008. 396p. 31.99 (978-0-554-23114-3(X)) 2007. (ENG.). 348p. pap. 23.99 (978-1-4264-3710-6(2)) 2007. (ENG.). 392p. pap. 26.99 (978-1-4264-3767-0(6)) BiblioBazaar.

—The Letters of Robert Burns. 2008. 382p. 48.95 (978-1-4365-9060-0(4)) 2007. (ENG.). 384p. per. 33.95 (978-0-548-78043-5(9)) Kessinger Publishing, LLC.

—A Night Out with Robert Burns: The Greatest Poems. 2009. (ENG.). 224p. pap. 15.00 (978-1-84767-112-7(8)) Canongate Bks. GBR. Dist: Perseus-PGW.

—Robert Burns in Your Pocket. 2009. (Illus.). 288p. 12.95 (978-1-902407-81-4(4)) Waverley Bks. Ltd. GBR. Dist: Interlink Publishing Group, Inc.

Burns, Robert & O'Hagan, Andrew. A Night Out with Robert Burns: The Greatest Poems. 2008. (ENG.). 256p. (978-1-84195-992-4(8)) Canongate Bks.

Carroll, David. Burns Country. 2009. (ENG., Illus.). 128p. pap. 24.95 (978-0-7524-4956-2(7)) History Pr. Ltd.,The GBR. Dist: Independent Pubs. Group

Carruthers, Gerard. The Edinburgh Companion to Robert Burns. 2009. (Edinburgh Companions to Scottish Literature Ser.). (ENG.). 256p. (gr. 17). 95.00 (978-0-7486-3648-8(X)); pap. 32.50 (978-0-7486-3649-5(8)) Edinburgh Univ. Pr. GBR. Dist: Columbia Univ. Pr.

Cody, Sherwin. An Evening with Robert Burns. 2007. (ENG.). 128p. 35.95 (978-0-548-03269-5(6)) Kessinger Publishing, LLC.

Crawford, Robert, et al, eds. The Best Laid Schemes: Selected Poetry & Prose of Robert Burns. 2009. (ENG.). 312p. (C). 67.50 (978-0-691-14294-4(7)); pap. 22.95 (978-0-691-14295-1(5)) Princeton Univ. Pr.

Crichton-Browne, James. Burns from a New Point of View. 2010. 106p. pap. 18.75 (978-1-171-87559-8(2)) BiblioBazaar.

Cuthbertson, John. Complete Glossary to the Poetry & Pros. 2006. pap. 37.95 (978-1-4286-3622-4(6)) Kessinger Publishing, LLC.

—Complete Glossary to the Poetry & Prose of Robert Burns. 476p. 2010. 42.36 (978-1-163-43349-2(7)) 2010. pap. 30.36 (978-1-162-97066-0(9)) 2007. (ENG.). 52.95 (978-0-548-12637-0(2)) Kessinger Publishing, LLC.

Davis, Leith, et al. Robert Burns & Transatlantic Culture. 2012. (Ashgate Ser. in Nineteenth-Century Transatlantic Studies). (Illus.). 290p. 99.95 **(978-1-4094-0576-4(1))** Ashgate Publishing Co.

Douglas, George Brisbane Scott. Robert Burns. 2006. pap. 15.95 (978-1-4286-6412-8(2)) Kessinger Publishing, LLC.

Farrand, Wilson. Carlyle's Essay on Burns- with Selections from Burn's Poems. 2007. pap. (978-1-4067-5705-7(5)) Farrand Pr.

Ferguson, Frank & Holmes, Andrew, eds. Revising Robert Burns & Ulster: Literature, Religion & Politics, C. 1770-1920. 2009. 198p. 65.00 (978-1-84682-197-4(5)) Four Courts Pr. IRL. Dist: International Specialized Bk. Services.

Ferguson John. The Letters of John Ferguson, Early Resident of Western Washington County: The Kansas Historical Quarterly, V12, No. 4, November 1943. 2011. 16p. pap. 35.95 **(978-1-258-04875-4(2))** Literary Licensing, LLC.

Gentz, Natascha. Selected Poems by Robert Burns in Chinese Translation. 2010. (ENG & CHI., Illus.). 64p. (gr. 17). 50.00 (978-0-7486-4111-6(4)) Edinburgh Univ. Pr. GBR. Dist: Columbia Univ. Pr.

Goodwillie, Edward. The World's Memorials of Robert Burns. 2010. 72p. pap. (978-1-151-83707-3(5)); pap. (978-1-151-83705-9(9)) Books LLC.

Hogg, James. Memoir of Burns. Roy, G. Ross et al, eds. 2013. (Collected Works of James Hogg Ser.). (ENG., Illus.). 400p. (gr. 17). 75.00 (978-0-7486-3416-3(9)) Edinburgh Univ. Pr. GBR. Dist: Columbia Univ. Pr.

Hogg, Patrick Scott. Robert Burns: The Patriot Bard. (ENG.). 368p. 2010. pap. 14.95 (978-1-84596-485-6(3)) 2008. 34.95 (978-1-84596-412-2(8)) Mainstream Publishing Co., Ltd. GBR. Dist: Independent Pubs. Group.

Leask, Nigel. Robert Burns & Pastoral: Poetry & Improvement in Late Eighteenth-Century Scotland. 2010. (ENG., Illus.). 336p. 99.00 (978-0-19-957261-8(5)) Oxford Univ. Pr., Inc.

Lockhart, John Gibson. Life of Robert Burns. 2008. 340p. (978-1-4437-3388-5(1), Pomona Pr.) Read Bks.

Lowell, James Russell. My Garden Acquaintance, a Good Word for Winter, a Moosehead Journal by James Russell Lowell the Farmer's Boy by Robert Bloomfield. 2006. 292p. per. 23.99 (978-1-4255-2608-5(X)) MPublishing.

Marshall, Nancy. The Burns Supper Companion. 2007. (ENG., Illus.). 144p. per. 12.95 (978-1-84158-583-3(1)) Birlinn, Ltd. GBR. Dist: Interlink Publishing Group, Inc.

McGinn, Clark. The Ultimate Burns Supper Book: A Practical (But Irreverent) Guide to Scotland's Greatest Celebration. 2007. (ENG., Illus.). 174p. per. 14.95 (978-1-905222-60-5(2)) Luath Pr. Ltd. GBR. Dist: Ingram Pub. Services.

Muir, John. Carlyle on Burns. 2008. 120p. 34.95 (978-1-4368-9066-3(7)); pap. 19.95 (978-1-4367-9768-9(3)) Kessinger Publishing, LLC.

Noble, Andrew. Robert Burns & English Romanticism. Date not set. (19th Century Ser.). 240p. 79.95 (978-0-7546-0203-3(6)) Ashgate Publishing, Ltd. GBR. Dist: Ashgate Publishing, Ltd.

Pittock, Murray. Robert Burns in Global Culture. 2011. (ENG., Illus.). 276p. 75.00 (978-1-61148-030-5(2)) Bucknell Univ. Pr.

Pittock, Murray, ed. Robert Burns in Global Culture. 2011. (Illus.). 269p. (978-0-8387-5748-2(0)) Bucknell Univ. Pr.

Rodgers, Johnny & Carruthers, Gerard, eds. Fickle Man: Robert Burns in the 21st Century. 2009. (ENG., Illus.). 224p. 39.95 (978-1-905207-27-5(1)) Silvermine International Bks., LLC.

Ross, John D. Early Critical Reviews on Robert Burns. 2009. 326p. 32.99 (978-1-113-69365-5(7)); 36.99 (978-1-113-69366-2(5)); pap. 31.75 (978-1-113-69363-1(0)); pap. 30.75 (978-1-113-69361-7(4)) BiblioBazaar.

Setoun, Gabriel. Robert Burns. 2008. 164p. 22.99 (978-0-559-20729-7(8)); pap. 20.75 (978-0-559-20728-0(X)) BiblioBazaar.

—Robert Burns. 2009. 90p. pap. (978-0-217-79152-6(2)) Books LLC.

Shairp, J. C. & Fowler, Thomas. Robert Burns: Also Locke & Bunyan. 2007. (ENG.). 372p. 48.95 (978-0-548-09296-5(6)) Kessinger Publishing, LLC.

Shairp, John C. Robert Burns. Morley, John, ed. (English Men of Letters Ser.). reprint ed. lib. bdg. 27.50 (978-0-404-51727-4(7)) AMS Pr., Inc.

Shairp, John Campbell. Roberts Burns. 2011. (Cambridge Library Collection - English Men of Letters Ser.). (ENG.). 222p. pap. 22.99 **(978-1-108-03472-2(1))** Cambridge Univ. Pr.

Shairp, Principal. Robert Burns. 2009. 218p. 28.99 (978-1-110-59029-2(6)) 2009. 218p. pap. 23.75 (978-1-110-59026-1(1)) 2008. 188p. 22.99 (978-0-554-39043-7(4)) 2008. 188p. 25.99 (978-0-554-29740-8(X)) 2007. (ENG.). 166p. pap. 19.99 (978-1-4346-8318-2(4)) 2007. 186p. pap. 21.99 (978-1-4346-8319-9(2)) BiblioBazaar.

—Robert Burns. 2008. 172p. pap. (978-1-4099-4728-8(9)) Dodo Pr.

Stafford, Fiona. Burns & Other Poets. 2012. (ENG.). 272p. (gr. 17). 105.00 **(978-0-7486-4357-8(5))** Edinburgh Univ. Pr. GBR. Dist: Columbia Univ. Pr.

Stevenson, Robert Louis. Familiar Studies of Men & Books. 2008. 372p. 29.99 (978-0-559-57280-7(8)) 2008. 372p. pap. 31.75 (978-0-559-57276-0(X)) 2008. 232p. 27.99 (978-0-554-21790-1(2)) 2008. 232p. 24.99 (978-0-554-31093-0(7)) 2006. (ENG.). 240p. pap. 20.99 (978-1-4264-0930-1(3)) 2006. 228p. pap. 22.99 (978-1-4264-0917-2(6)) BiblioBazaar.

—Familiar Studies of Men & Books. 2007. (ENG.). 216p. per. (978-1-4065-8207-9(7)) Dodo Pr.

—Familiar Studies of Men & Books. 2008. 428p. pap. (978-1-4097-9111-9(4)) Read Bks.

—Familiar Studies of Men & Books. 2007. (ENG.). 368p. 32.95 (978-1-4344-6829-9(2)); per. 19.95 (978-1-4344-8828-2(4)) Wildside Pr., LLC.

Sudduth, Elizabeth A. & Tarr, Clayton Carlyle, compiled by. The G. Ross Roy Collection of Robert Burns: An Illustrated Catalogue. 2009. (978-1-57003-829-7(5)) Univ. of South Carolina Pr.

Szasz, Ferenc Morton. Abraham Lincoln & Robert Burns: Connected Lives & Legends. 2008. (ENG., Illus.). 256p. 27.95 (978-0-8093-2855-0(0)) Southern Illinois Univ. Pr.

Watkins, Larissa P. Burnsiana: A Bibliography of the William R. Smith Collection in the Library of the Supreme Council, 33[degree Symbol], S. J. 2008. (Illus.). 240p. 65.00 (978-1-58456-246-7(3)) Oak Knoll Pr.

Wilson, John. The Genius & Character of Burns. 2009. 306p. pap. (978-0-217-44645-7(0)) Books LLC.

—The Genius & Character of Burns. 2007. (ENG.). 224p. 39.95 (978-0-548-04848-1(7)) Kessinger Publishing, LLC.

—The Genius & Character of Robert Burns. 2009. 98p. pap. (978-1-4589-1679-2(0)) Books LLC.

BURNS AND SCALDS

Azzopardi, Ernest Anthony, et al. Gram-Negative Burn Wound Infection. 2011. 104p. pap. **(978-3-8383-9025-3(3))** Lambert Academic Publishing.

Cartotto, Robert. Burns, an Issue of Clinics in Plastic Surgery. 2009. (Clinics: Surgery Ser.: 36-4). (ENG.). 99.00 (978-1-4377-1265-0(7), Saunders) Elsevier - Health Sciences Div.

Esselman, Peter C. & Kowalske, Karen J. Burn Rehabilitation, an Issue of Physical Medicine & Rehabilitation Clinics. 2011. (Clinics: Orthopedics Ser.: 22-2). (ENG., Illus.). 184p. 110.00 (978-1-4557-0491-0(1), Saunders) Elsevier - Health Sciences Div.

Fisher, Robin Gaby. After the Fire: A True Story of Friendship & Survival. 2010. (ENG.). 288p. pap. 14.99 (978-0-316-06622-8(2), Back Bay Bks.) Little Brown & Co.

Heat Burn Injuries. 32p. pap. 3.25 (978-0-16-023108-7(6), Labor Dept.) United States Government Printing Office.

Herndon, David N. Total Burn Care. (ENG., Illus.). 3rd rev. ed. 2007. 880p. pap. 299.00 (978-1-4160-3274-8(6)) 4th ed. 2012. 808p. 270.95 **(978-1-4377-2786-9(7))** Elsevier - Health Sciences Div. (Saunders).

Hyakusoku, Hiko et al. Color Atlas of Burn Reconstructive Surgery. Pribaz, Julian J. & Ogawa, Rei, eds. 2010. (ENG., Illus.). xii, 500p. 239.00 (978-3-642-05069-5(7), 3642050697) Springer.

Jeschke, Marc G., et al, eds. Handbook of Burns Vol. 1: Acute Burn Care. 2011. (ENG., Illus.). xii, 493p. 169.00 (978-3-7091-0347-0(9), 3709103479) Springer.

Kamolz, Lars-Peter, et al, eds. Handbook of Burns Volume 2: Reconstruction & Rehabilitation. 2011. (ENG., Illus.). xii, 324p. 169.00 (978-3-7091-0314-2(2), 3709103142) Springer.

Klein, Matthew B. Hand Burns, an Issue of Hand Clinics. 2009. (Clinics: Orthopedics Ser.: 25-4). (ENG., Illus.). viii, 454p. 99.00 (978-1-4377-1224-7(X), Saunders) Elsevier - Health Sciences Div.

McLaughlin, Emily S. & Paterson, Ava O., eds. Burns: Prevention, Causes & Treatment. 2012. **(978-1-62100-446-2(5))** Nova Science Pubs., Inc.

Phillips, Bradley. Pediatric Burns. 2010. (978-1-60497-698-4(5)); (978-1-60497-697-7(7)); 50.00 (978-1-60497-696-0(9)) Cambria Pr.

Piper, Katie. Beautiful: A Beautiful Girl - An Evil Man - One Inspiring True Story of Courage. 2011. (ENG., Illus.). 320p. pap. 13.95 **(978-0-09-194076-8(1))** Ebury Publishing GBR. Dist: Independent Pubs. Group.

Roemer, Suzan van de. Suzan van de Roemer: The Power of Resilience: Survivors of the Volendam Blaze. 2011. (ENG., Illus.). 112p. 50.00 **(978-90-5330-747-2(8))** Mets en Schilt Uitgevers NLD. Dist: Ingram Pub. Services.

Rylah, Lindsey T. A., ed. Critical Care of the Burned Patient. 2007. (ENG.). 224p. pap. 48.00 (978-0-521-04753-1(6)) Cambridge Univ. Pr.

Sarabahi, Sujata & Bajaj, S. P. Step by Step Management of Burns. 2009. (ENG., Illus.). 322p. 39.00 (978-0-07-163430-4(4), 0071634304) McGraw-Hill Professional Publishing.

Schmidt, Christopher W. & Symes, Steven, eds. The Analysis of Burned Human Remains. 2008. (ENG., Illus.). 296p. 142.00 (978-0-12-372510-3(0), Academic Pr.) Elsevier Science & Technology Bks.

Schrage, Norbert, et al. Chemical Ocular Burns: New Understanding & Treatments. 2010. (Illus.). xi, 122p. 139.00 (978-3-642-14549-0(3), 3642145493) Springer.

Sheridan, Robert L. Burns: A Practical Approach. 2011. (ENG., Illus.). 160p. 69.95 (978-1-84076-133-7(4)) Manson Publishing, Ltd. GBR. Dist: Thieme Medical Pubs., Inc.

Transfusion - Think about It. 2010. (Health Care Issues, Costs & Access Ser.). 160.00 (978-1-61668-969-8(2)) Nova Science Pubs., Inc.

Xu, Rong Xiang. Burns Regenerative Medicine & Therapy. Sun, Xia & Weeks, Bradford S., eds. (Illus.). 8;52p. (978-3-8055-7661-1(7)) Karger, S. AG.

BURNS AND SCALDS—PATIENTS—BIOGRAPHY

Bentley, Lisa Misraje. Saving Levi: Left to Die ... Destined to Live. 2006. (ENG., Illus.). 176p. per. 13.99 (978-1-58997-449-4(2)) Tyndale Hse. Pubs.

Caro, Dan. The Gift of Fire: How I Made Adversity Work for Me. 2010. (ENG.). 208p. 19.95 (978-1-4019-2660-1(6)) Hay Hse., Inc.

Caro, Dan & Erwin, Steve. The Gift of Fire: How I Made Adversity Work for Me. 2011. (ENG.). 192p. pap. 14.95 (978-1-4019-2661-8(4)) Hay Hse., Inc.

Fisher, Robin Gaby. After the Fire: A True Story of Friendship & Survival. 2009. 54.99 (978-1-4332-7655-2(0)) Findaway World, LLC.

Fletcher, Carole. Healed by Horses: A Memoir. 2007. (ENG.). 256p. pap. 17.95 (978-1-4165-8296-0(7), Beyond Words/Atria Bks.) Atria Bks.

Gladwin, Peter & Greenough, Jan. Out of the Ashes: The Restoration of a Burned Boy, 1 vol. 2012. 160p. pap. 12.99 **(978-1-85424-992-0(4)**, Monarch Bks.) Lion Hudson PLC GBR. Dist: Kregel Pubns.

Hammer, Dave. From Out of the Flames. 2011. **(978-1-77069-337-1(8))** Word Alive Pr.

McCarthy, Michael. The Sun Farmer: The Story of a Shocking Accident, a Medical Miracle, & a Family's Life-and-Death Decision. 2007. (ENG.). 256p. 24.95 (978-1-56663-700-8(7)) Dee, Ivan R. Pub.

Nielson, Stephanie. Heaven Is Here: An Incredible Story of Hope, Triumph, & Everyday Joy. 2012. (ENG.). 277p. 23.99 **(978-1-4013-4179-4(9))** Hyperion Pr.

BURNT OFFERING

see Sacrifice

BURR, AARON, 1756-1836

Brady, Joseph Plunkett. The Trial of Aaron Burr for High Treason: The Circuit Court of the United States for the District of Virginia, Summer Term 1807. 89p. reprint ed. 88.00 *(978-0-7222-9013-2(6))* Library Reprints, Inc.

Brands, Henry W. The Heartbreak of Aaron Burr. 2012. (ENG.). 192p. pap. 15.00 ***(978-0-307-74326-8(8)***, Anchor) Knopf Doubleday Publishing Group.

Burr, Aaron. Memoirs of Aaron Burr. 2009. 308p. pap. *(978-0-217-96777-8(9))*; 304p. pap. *(978-0-217-51231-2(3))*; 284p. pap. *(978-0-217-01810-4(6))* Books LLC.

—The Private Journal of Aaron Burr, 2 vols., Set. reprint ed. 86.50 *(978-0-404-13710-6(5))* AMS Pr., Inc.

—The Private Journal of Aaron Burr, During His Residence of Four Years in Europe, 2 vol., set. reprint ed. 250.00 *(978-0-7222-9010-1(1))* Library Reprints, Inc.

—The Trial of Aaron Burr for High Treason: The Circuit Court of the United States for the District of Virginia, Summer Term 1807. 392p. reprint ed. 98.00 *(978-0-7222-9011-8(X))* Library Reprints, Inc.

Davis, Matthew L. Memoirs of Aaron Burr, Complete. 2007. 628p. per. *(978-1-4068-1867-3(4))* Echo Library.

Henry, William Wirt. Trial of Aaron Burr & the Trials & T. 2006. pap. 18.95 *(978-1-4286-5761-8(4))* Kessinger Publishing, LLC.

Hoffer, Peter Charles. The Treason Trials of Aaron Burr. 2008. (C). 224p. 35.00 *(978-0-7006-1591-9(1))*; viii, 212p. pap. 16.95 *(978-0-7006-1592-6(X))* Univ. Pr. of Kansas.

Larson, Edward J. A Magnificent Catastrophe: The Tumultuous Election of 1800, America's First Presidential Campaign. 2008. (ENG., Illus.). 352p. pap. 16.99 *(978-0-7432-9317-4(7)*, Free Pr.) Free Pr.

Lewis, Alfred Henry. An American Patrician: The Story of Aaron Burr. 335p. reprint ed. 98.00 *(978-0-7222-9015-6(2))* Library Reprints, Inc.

Merwin, Henry Childs. Aaron Burr. 2007. (ENG.). 172p. 36.95 *(978-0-548-43721-6(1))*; per. 21.95 *(978-0-548-41518-4(8))* Kessinger Publishing, LLC.

—Aaron Burr. (Beacon Biographies Ser.). 150p. reprint ed. 88.00 *(978-0-7222-8535-0(3))*; 88.00 *(978-0-7222-9017-0(9))* Library Reprints, Inc.

Newmyer, R. Kent. The Treason Trial of Aaron Burr: Law, Politics, & the Character Wars of the New Nation. 2012. (Cambridge Studies on the American Constitution Ser.). (ENG.). 232p. pap. 28.99 ***(978-1-107-60661-6(6))***; (Illus.). 90.00 ***(978-1-107-02218-8(5))*** Cambridge Univ. Pr.

Orth, Samuel P. Five American Politicians: A Study in the Evolution of American Politics. 2007. 448p. 51.95 *(978-0-548-55688-7(1))*; (ENG.). per. 36.95 *(978-0-548-50433-8(4))* Kessinger Publishing, LLC.

—Five American Politicians: A Study in the Evolution of American Politics. 447p. reprint ed. 98.00 *(978-0-7222-8401-8(2))* Library Reprints, Inc.

Parton, James. The Life & Times of Aaron Burr. 2009. 446p. 34.99 *(978-1-113-80245-3(6))* BiblioBazaar.

—The Life & Times of Aaron Burr. 2010. 264p. pap. *(978-1-151-52803-2(X))* 2010. 260p. pap. *(978-1-151-52798-1(X))* 2009. 280p. pap. *(978-1-151-11959-9(8))* 2009. 286p. pap. *(978-1-150-62723-1(9))* 2009. 276p. pap. *(978-1-150-31222-9(X))* Books LLC.

—The Life & Times of Aaron Burr. 2009. 278p. pap. 23.37 *(978-1-150-72425-1(0))* General Bks. LLC.

—The Life & Times of Aaron Burr, 2 vol., set. reprint ed. 250.00 *(978-0-7222-9018-7(7))*;Set. (Illus.). lib. bdg. 250.00 *(978-0-7222-0967-7(3))* Library Reprints, Inc.

Reed, V. B. & Williams, J. D. Case of Aaron Burr. Date not set. 216p. 20.95 *(978-0-8488-2644-4(2))* Amereon LTD.

Schachner, Nathan. Aaron Burr: A Biography. (Illus.). reprint ed. 57.50 *(978-0-404-20227-9(6))* AMS Pr., Inc.

Sharp, James Roger. Deadlocked Election of 1800. 2010. (Illus.). 34.95 *(978-0-7006-1742-5(6))* Univ. of Kansas Pubns.

Stewart, David O. American Emperor: Aaron Burr's Challenge to Jefferson's America. (ENG.). 432p. 2012. pap. 17.99 ***(978-1-4391-5720-6(0))*** 2011. (Illus.). 30.00 *(978-1-4391-5718-3(9))* Simon & Schuster.

Todd, Charles Burr. The True Aaron Burr: A Biographical Sketch. 2009. 92p. pap. 13.99 *(978-1-103-01475-0(7))* BiblioBazaar.

—The True Aaron Burr: A Biographical Sketch. 2007. (ENG.). 108p. 33.95 *(978-0-548-37251-7(9))*; 92p. per. 18.95 *(978-0-548-31564-4(7))* Kessinger Publishing, LLC.

—The True Aaron Burr: A Biographical Sketch. 77p. reprint ed. 88.00 *(978-0-7222-9019-4(5))* Library Reprints, Inc.

Tompkins, Hamilton Bullock. Burr Bibliography: A List of Books Relating to Aaron Burr. 89p. reprint ed. 88.00 *(978-0-7222-9012-5(8))* Library Reprints, Inc.

Zellar, Ronald C. A Brave Man Stands Firm: The Historic Battles Between Chief Justice John Marshall & President Thomas Jefferson. 2011. 288p. pap. 23.95 ***(978-0-87586-883-7(5))***; pap. 23.95 ***(978-0-87586-882-0(7))*** Algora Publishing.

BURR, JAMES E.

Thompson, George. Prison Life & Reflections. 2009. 272p. pap. 20.96 *(978-0-217-74332-7(3))* General Bks. LLC.

—Prison Life & Reflections; or, a Narrative of the Arrest, Trial, Conviction, Imprisonment, Treatment, Observations, Reflections, & Deliverance Of. 2006. 380p. per. 26.99 *(978-1-4255-3940-5(8))* MPublishing.

BURR CONSPIRACY, 1805-1807

Bay, William. Reminiscences of the Bench & Bar of Missouri. 611p. reprint ed. lib. bdg. 128.00 *(978-0-7222-0688-1(7))* Library Reprints, Inc.

Brady, Joseph Plunkett. The Trial of Aaron Burr for High Treason: The Circuit Court of the United States for the District of Virginia, Summer Term 1807. 89p. reprint ed. 88.00 *(978-0-7222-9013-2(6))* Library Reprints, Inc.

Burr, Aaron. Reports of the Trials of Colonel Aaron Burr. 2009. 558p. pap. *(978-0-217-86377-3(9))*; 514p. pap. *(978-1-4588-4591-7(5))* Books LLC.

—The Trial of Aaron Burr for High Treason: The Circuit Court of the United States for the District of Virginia, Summer Term 1807. 392p. reprint ed. 98.00 *(978-0-7222-9011-8(X))* Library Reprints, Inc.

Henry, William Wirt. Trial of Aaron Burr & the Trials & T. 2006. pap. 18.95 *(978-1-4286-5761-8(4))* Kessinger Publishing, LLC.

Hill, Frederick Trevor. Decisive Battles of the Law. 2009. 288p. 24.99 *(978-1-103-45849-3(3))*; pap. 18.99 *(978-1-103-45846-2(9))* BiblioBazaar.

—Decisive Battles of the Law. 2009. 106p. pap. 19.99 *(978-0-217-70246-1(5))* General Bks. LLC.

—Decisive Battles of the Law. 278p. reprint ed. 98.00 *(978-0-7222-8722-4(4))* Library Reprints, Inc.

Hoffer, Peter Charles. The Treason Trials of Aaron Burr. 2008. (C). 224p. 35.00 *(978-0-7006-1591-9(1))*; viii, 212p. pap. 16.95 *(978-0-7006-1592-6(X))* Univ. Pr. of Kansas.

McCaleb, Walter Flavius. The Aaron Burr Conspiracy. 2007. (ENG.). 364p. 46.95 *(978-0-548-11696-8(2))* Kessinger Publishing, LLC.

—The Aaron Burr Conspiracy. 377p. reprint ed. 98.00 *(978-0-7222-9016-3(0))* Library Reprints, Inc.

Newmyer, R. Kent. The Treason Trial of Aaron Burr: Law, Politics, & the Character Wars of the New Nation. 2012. (Cambridge Studies on the American Constitution Ser.). (ENG.). 232p. pap. 28.99 ***(978-1-107-60661-6(6))***; (Illus.). 90.00 ***(978-1-107-02218-8(5))*** Cambridge Univ. Pr.

Safford, William Harrison. The Life of Harman Blennerhassett Comprising an Authentic Narrative of the Burr Expedition: And Containing Many Additional Facts Not Heretofore Publi. 2006. 244p. per. 20.99 *(978-1-4255-2050-2(2))* MPublishing.

—The Life of Harman Blennerhassett Comprising an Authentic Narrative of the Burr Expedition: And Containing Many Additional Facts Not Hertofore Publis. 2006. 244p. per. 20.99 *(978-1-4255-2109-7(6))* MPublishing.

BURRI, ALBERTO, 1915-

Burri, Alberto & Ranzi, Gianluca. Cellotex: La Strategia Della Materia = the Strategy of the Matter. 2010. (ITA & ENG., Illus.). 95p. *(978-88-6403-045-6(X)*, Spotlight Poets) Carlo Cambi Editore.

Celant, Germano. Alberto Burri. 2008. (ENG., Illus.). 64p. per. 30.00 *(978-0-9749607-8-4(0))* Mitchell-Innes & Nash.

BURRITT, ELIHU, 1810-1879

Curti, Merle & Burritt, Elihu. The Learned Blacksmith: The Letters & Journals of Elihu Burritt. 2011. 254p. 47.95 ***(978-1-258-04904-1(X))*** Literary Licensing, LLC.

BURRO

see Mules

BURROUGHS, AUGUSTEN, 1965-

Burroughs, Augusten. Dry: A Memoir. Date not set. pap. *(978-0-312-31819-2(7))*; mass mkt. *(978-0-312-99095-4(2))* St. Martin's Pr. (St. Martin's Paperbacks).

—Magical Thinking: True Stories. mass mkt. *(978-0-312-99042-8(1)*, St. Martin's Paperbacks) St. Martin's Pr.

—Possible Side Effects. 2007. (ENG.). 304p. pap. 14.00 *(978-0-312-42681-1(X))* Picador.

—Running with Scissors: A Memoir. 2006. (ENG.). 352p. mass mkt. 7.99 *(978-0-312-93885-7(3)*, St. Martin's Paperbacks) St. Martin's Pr.

—Running with Scissors: A Memoir. 2006. lib. bdg. 18.40 *(978-1-4176-8418-2(6)*, Turtleback) Turtleback Bks.

—This Is How: Help for the Self. 2012. (ENG.). 240p. 24.99 ***(978-0-312-56355-4(8))*** St. Martin's Pr.

—A Wolf at the Table: A Memoir of My Father. 2009. (ENG.). 272p. pap. 14.00 *(978-0-312-42827-3(8))* Picador.

—You Better Not Cry: Stories. 2010. (ENG.). 224p. pap. 14.00 *(978-0-312-43006-1(X))* Picador.

BURROUGHS, EDGAR RICE, 1875-1950

Burroughs, Edgar Rice. The Dream Weaver: An Edgar Rice Burroughs Chapbook. 2011. 24p. 35.95 ***(978-1-258-04776-4(4))*** Literary Licensing, LLC.

DeGraw, Sharon. The Subject of Race in American Science Fiction. 2009. 236p. 39.95 *(978-0-415-80289-5(X))* 2006. 230p. 131.00 *(978-0-415-97901-6(3))* Routledge.

Fenton, Robert W. Edgar Rice Burroughs & Tarzan: A Biography of the Author & His Creation. alt. ed. 2010. (ENG., Illus.). 254p. pap. 38.00 *(978-0-7864-4908-8(X))* McFarland & Co., Inc. Pubs.

Galloway, Stan. The Teenage Tarzan: A Literary Analysis of Edgar Rice Burroughs' Jungle Tales of Tarzan. 2010. (ENG., Illus.). 275p. pap. 35.00 *(978-0-7864-3853-2(3))* McFarland & Co., Inc. Pubs.

Schneider, Jerry L. The Ancestry of Edgar Rice Burroughs. 2008. 296p. pap. 20.00 *(978-1-4357-4972-6(3))* Lulu Enterprises Inc.

—Edgar Rice Burroughs Tells All. 2008. 396p. pap. 29.95 *(978-1-4357-0830-3(X))* Lulu Enterprises Inc.

Vernon, Alex. On Tarzan. 2008. (ENG., Illus.). 240p. pap. 22.95 *(978-0-8203-3205-5(4))*; lib. bdg. 59.95 *(978-0-8203-3183-6(X))* Univ. of Georgia Pr.

Zeuschner, Robert B. Edgar Rice Burroughs: The Exhaustive Scholar's & Collector's Descriptive Bibliography of American Periodical. alt. ed. 2007. (ENG., Illus.). 299p. reprint ed. per. 35.00 *(978-0-7864-3113-7(X))* McFarland & Co., Inc. Pubs.

BURROUGHS, JOHN, 1837-1921

Barrus, Clara. John Burroughs Boy & Man. 2009. 414p. 41.99 *(978-1-117-14460-3(7))*; pap. 33.75 *(978-1-117-14461-0(5))*; 41.99 *(978-1-115-59013-6(8))*; 34.99 *(978-1-115-59014-3(6))*; pap. 34.75 *(978-1-115-59015-0(4))*; pap. 33.75 *(978-1-115-59016-7(2))* BiblioBazaar.

—Our Friend John Burroughs. 2009. 336p. 25.99 *(978-1-103-90315-3(2))* 2009. 336p. pap. 19.99 *(978-1-103-90308-5(X))* 2008. 192p. 25.99 *(978-0-554-23711-4(3))* 2008. 192p. pap. 22.99 *(978-0-554-33014-3(8))* BiblioBazaar.

—Our Friend John Burroughs. 2009. 176p. pap. *(978-0-217-02776-2(8))* Books LLC.

—Our Friend John Burroughs. 2006. (ENG.). pap. *(978-1-4065-1124-6(2))* Dodo Pr.

—Our Friend John Burroughs. 2008. 328p. pap. *(978-1-4097-6964-4(X))* Read Bks.

Burroughs, John. John Burroughs Talks: His Reminiscences & Comments. Johnson, Clifton, ed. 2007. (ENG.). 402p. 49.95 *(978-0-548-02224-5(0))* Kessinger Publishing, LLC.

—My Boyhood. 2008. 112p. per. *(978-1-4065-9013-5(4))* Dodo Pr.

—My Boyhood. 2007. (Large Print Ser.). lib. bdg. 26.00 *(978-1-58287-910-9(9))* North Bks.

—My Boyhood & John James Audobon. 2008. 216p. 24.99 *(978-0-554-35675-4(9))* 2008. 216p. 27.99 *(978-0-554-26372-4(6))* 2007. (ENG.). 214p. pap. 22.99 *(978-1-4346-1081-2(0))* BiblioBazaar.

—Wake-Robin. 2011. 268p. pap. 27.75 ***(978-1-179-62850-9(0))*** 2010. (ENG.). 302p. pap. 29.75 *(978-1-172-33599-2(0))* 2010. (ENG.). 242p. pap. 26.75 *(978-1-178-00781-7(2))* 2010. 264p. pap. 27.75 *(978-1-177-07876-4(7))* 2010. 310p. pap. 29.75 *(978-1-177-19465-5(1))* 2010. 308p. pap. 29.75 ***(978-1-177-19460-0(0))*** 2010. 324p. pap. 30.75 *(978-1-176-11187-5(6))* 2010. 316p. pap. 30.75 *(978-1-175-84924-3(3))* 2010. 272p. pap. 27.75 *(978-1-149-58971-7(X))* 2010. 300p. pap. 29.75 *(978-1-147-29671-6(5))* 2010. 266p. pap. 27.75 *(978-1-143-89988-1(1))* 2010. 280p. pap. 27.75 *(978-1-144-29539-2(4))* 2010. 274p. pap. 27.75 *(978-1-145-20583-3(6))* 2009. 264p. 24.99 *(978-1-103-97429-0(7))* 2009. 264p. pap. 18.99 *(978-1-103-97422-1(X))* 2008. 156p. 25.99 *(978-0-554-21948-6(4))* 2008. 156p. 22.99 *(978-0-554-31251-4(4))* 2006. (ENG.). 160p. pap. 19.99 *(978-1-4264-1319-3(X))* 2006. (ENG.). 152p. pap. 21.99 *(978-1-4264-1343-8(2))* BiblioBazaar.

—Wake-Robin. 2009. 98p. pap. *(978-0-217-41673-3(X))* Books LLC.

—Wake-Robin. 2007. (ENG.). 116p. per. *(978-1-4068-2368-4(6))* Echo Library.

—Wake-Robin. 2010. (Illus.). 98p. pap. 20.00 *(978-1-153-73214-7(9))* 2009. 148p. pap. 19.99 *(978-1-4589-4851-9(X))* General Bks. LLC.

—Wake-Robin. 2010. 156p. pap. 11.95 *(978-1-4385-7440-0(1)*, Book Jungle) Standard Pubns., Inc.

—Wakerobin. 2010. 250p. 32.99 *(978-1-117-96099-9(4))*; pap. 26.75 *(978-1-117-96100-2(1))* BiblioBazaar.

Burroughs, John & Marshall, George. Wake-Robin. 2010. 258p. pap. 26.75 *(978-1-177-07745-3(0))* BiblioBazaar.

Clara Barrus. Our Friend John Burroughs. 2007. (ENG.). 168p. pap. 19.99 *(978-1-4264-4944-4(5))* 2006. 188p. pap. 21.99 *(978-1-4264-5245-1(4))* BiblioBazaar.

John, Burroughs. My Boyhood & John James Audobon. 2007. 190p. pap. 19.99 *(978-1-4346-0982-3(0))* BiblioBazaar.

Sharp, Dallas Lore. The Boys' Life of John Burroughs. 2007. (ENG.). 384p. 48.95 *(978-0-548-09996-4(0))* Kessinger Publishing, LLC.

BURROUGHS, WILLIAM S., 1914-1997

Baker, Phil. William S. Burroughs. 2010. (Reaktion Books - Critical Lives Ser.). (ENG., Illus.). 192p. pap. 16.95 *(978-1-86189-663-6(8))* Reaktion Bks., Ltd. GBR. Dist: Chicago Distribution Ctr.

Burroughs, William S. Cursed from Birth: The Short, Unhappy Life of William S. Burroughs, Jr. Ohle, David, ed. 2006. (ENG.). 256p. per. 13.95 *(978-1-933368-38-2(1))* Counterpoint LLC.

—Everything Lost: The Latin American Notebook of William S. Burroughs. Smith, Geoffrey D. & Bennett, John M., eds. 2007. (ENG.). 224p. 129.95 *(978-0-8142-1080-2(5))* Ohio State Univ. Pr.

—Rub Out the Words: The Letters of William S. Burroughs, 1959-1974. 2012. (ENG.). 448p. 35.00 *(978-0-06-171142-8(X)*, Ecco); 624p. pap. 35.00 *(978-0-06-208886-4(6)*, HarperLuxe) HarperCollins Pubs.

Creighton, David. Ecstasy of the Beats: On the Road to Understanding. 2007. (ENG., Illus.). 320p. pap. 26.99 *(978-1-55002-734-1(4))* Dundurn CAN. Dist: Ingram Pub. Services.

Harris, Oliver. William Burroughs & the Secret of Fascination. 2006. (ENG.). 304p. per. 30.00 *(978-0-8093-2731-7(7))* Southern Illinois Univ. Pr.

Harris, Oliver & MacFadyen, Ian, eds. Naked Lunch @ 50: Anniversary Essays. 2009. (ENG., Illus.). 312p. pap. 22.95 *(978-0-8093-2916-8(6))* Southern Illinois Univ. Pr.

Morgan, Ted. Literary Outlaw: The Life & Times of William S. Burroughs. 2012. (ENG.). 768p. pap. 24.95 ***(978-0-393-34260-4(3)***, 34260) Norton, W. W. & Co., Inc.

O'Hara, Daniel T. Narrating Demons, Transformative Texts: Rereading Genius in Mid-Century Modern Fictional Memoir. 2012. 120p. 42.95 ***(978-0-8142-1179-3(8))***; cd-rom 14.95 ***(978-0-8142-9280-8(1))*** Ohio State Univ. Pr.

Teicher, Hendel. Cut-Outs & Cut-Ups: Hans Christian Andersen & William Seward Burroughs. 2008. (Illus.). 197p. 89.50 *(978-1-903811-81-8(3))* Irish Museum of Modern Art IRL. Dist: Trans-Atlantic Pubns., Inc.

Vale, V., ed. RE/Search 4/5: William S. Burroughs, Throbbing Gristle, Brion Gysin. 3rd ed. 2008. (ENG., Illus.). 140p. pap. 20.00 *(978-1-889307-15-2(7))* RE/Search.

Zappe, Florian. Control Machines und Dispositive: Eine foucaultsche Analyse der Machtstrukturen im Romanwerk von William S. Burroughs zwischen 1959 Und 1968. 2008. (Europäische Hochschulschriften. Reihe 14: Angelsächsische Sprache und Literatur Ser.). (GER.). 112p. pap. 35.95 *(978-3-631-57814-8(8))* Lang, Peter GmbH, Europaischer Verlag der Wissenschaften DEU. Dist: Lang, Peter.

BURTON, RICHARD, 1925-1984

Kashner, Sam & Schoenberger, Nancy. Furious Love: Elizabeth Taylor, Richard Burton, & the Marriage of the Century. (ENG.). 320p. 2011. pap. 16.99 *(978-0-06-156285-3(8)*, Harper Paperbacks) 2010. (Illus.). 27.99 *(978-0-06-156284-6(X))* HarperCollins Pubs.

—Furious Love: Elizabeth Taylor, Richard Burton, & the Marriage of the Century. l.t. ed. 2010. (Illus.). 652p. 32.99 *(978-1-4104-2985-8(7))* Thorndike Pr.

Munn, Michael. Richard Burton: Prince of Players. 2008. (ENG.). 272p. 24.95 *(978-1-60239-355-4(9)*, 239355) Skyhorse Publishing Co., Inc.

Sellers, Robert. Hellraisers: The Life & Inebriated Times of Richard Burton, Richard Harris, Peter O'Toole, & Oliver Reed. 2011. (ENG., Illus.). 320p. pap. 15.99 *(978-0-312-66814-3(7)*, St. Martin's Griffin) St. Martin's Pr.

Sellers, Robert & Jake. Hellraisers. 2013. (Illus.). 160p. pap. 22.95 ***(978-1-906838-36-2(4)***, SelfMadeHero) Metro Media Ltd. GBR. Dist: Abrams.

BURTON, RICHARD FRANCIS, SIR, 1821-1890

Burton, Richard F. The City of the Saints, & across the Rocky Mountains to California. 2011. (Cambridge Library Collection - Travel & Exploration Ser.). (ENG., Illus.). 752p. pap. 48.00 ***(978-1-108-03316-9(4))*** Cambridge Univ. Pr.

—First Footsteps in East Afric. 2009. 368p. 29.99 *(978-0-559-07978-8(8))*; 31.99 *(978-0-559-07965-8(6))*; pap. 32.75 *(978-0-559-07969-6(9))*; pap. 31.75 *(978-0-559-07974-0(5))* BiblioBazaar.

—First Footsteps in East Afric: Or, an Exploration of Harar. 2008. 248p. pap. *(978-1-4097-1864-2(6))* Read Bks.

—First Footsteps in East Africa: Or, an Exploration of Harar. (Illus.). reprint ed. 38.50 *(978-0-404-12010-8(5))* AMS Pr., Inc.

—First Footsteps in East Africa or an Exploration of Harar. 2007. 248p. *(978-1-4068-2259-5(0))* Echo Library.

—First Footsteps in East Africa, or, an Exploration of Harar. 2009. 138p. pap. *(978-0-217-47672-0(4))* Books LLC.

—Personal Narrative of a Pilgrimage to Al-Madinah & Meccah, Vol. II. l.t. ed. 2006. 396p. pap. 24.99 *(978-1-4264-1708-5(X))* BiblioBazaar.

—Personal Narrative of a Pilgrimage to Al-Madinah & Meccah. 2009. 380p. pap. *(978-1-4588-4046-2(8))*; 292p. pap. *(978-0-217-27045-8(X))* Books LLC.

—Personal Narrative of a Pilgrimage to Al-Madinah & Meccah, Volume II. 2007. (ENG.). 338p. pap. 23.99 *(978-1-4264-1620-0(2))* BiblioBazaar.

—Wanderings in Three Continents. 2010. (Folios Archive Library). (Illus.). 328p. pap. 39.95 *(978-1-85964-232-0(2))* Garnet Publishing, Ltd. GBR. Dist: International Publishers Marketing.

—Wanderings in West Africa. 2006. pap. 45.95 *(978-1-4286-4913-2(1))* Kessinger Publishing, LLC.

—Wanderings in West Africa from Liverpool to Fernando Po: By a F. R. G. S. 2011. (Cambridge Library Collection - Travel & Exploration Ser.). (ENG.). 306p. pap. 24.99 *(978-1-108-03052-6(1))*; (Illus.). 322p. pap. 24.99 *(978-1-108-03051-9(3))* Cambridge Univ. Pr.

Dearden, Seton. Burton of Arabia: The Life Story of Sir Richard Francis Burton. 2007. (ENG.). 352p. per. 31.95 *(978-1-4325-7620-2(8))* Kessinger Publishing, LLC.

Grant, Ben. Postcolonialism, Psychoanalysis & Burton: Power Play of Empire. 2012. (Routledge Research in Postcolonial Literatures Ser.). (ENG., Illus.). 222p. pap. 42.95 ***(978-0-415-54197-8(2))*** Routledge.

Grant, Ben Z. Postcolonialism, Psychoanalysis & Burton: Power Play of Empire. 2008. (Routledge Research in Postcolonial Literatures Ser.). (ENG., Illus.). 222p. 149.00 *(978-0-415-45086-7(1))* Routledge.

Kennedy, Dane. The Highly Civilized Man: Richard Burton & the Victorian World. 2007. (Illus.). 368p. per. 21.00 *(978-0-674-02552-3(0))* Harvard Univ. Pr.

McCarthy, James. Selim Aga: A Slave's Odyssey. 2007. (ENG., Illus.). 254p. 26.95 *(978-1-905222-17-9(3))* Luath Pr. Ltd. GBR. Dist: Ingram Pub. Services.

—Selim Aga: A Slave's Odyssey. 2007. 254p. (YA). 26.95 *(978-1-4115-2035-6(1))* Polyglot Pr., Inc.

Newman, James L. Paths Without Glory: Richard Francis Burton in Africa. 2009. (Illus.). 316p. 29.95 *(978-1-59797-287-1(8))* Potomac Bks., Inc.

Ondaatje, Christopher. Journey to the Source of the Nile. 2006. 388p. per. 19.99 *(978-1-59048-225-4(5))* Long Riders' Guild Pr., The.

Wright, Thomas. The Life of Sir Richard Burton. 2008. 496p. 31.99 *(978-0-554-31308-5(1))* 2008. 496p. 33.99 *(978-0-554-22005-5(9))* 2007. (ENG.). 434p. pap. 26.99 *(978-1-4264-1455-8(2))* 2007. (ENG.). 492p. pap. 30.99 *(978-1-4264-1471-8(4))* BiblioBazaar.

BURTON, ROBERT, 1577-1640

Gowland, Angus. The Worlds of Renaissance Melancholy: Robert Burton in Context. 2011. (Ideas in Context Ser.). (ENG.). 358p. pap. 45.00 ***(978-1-107-40301-7(4))*** Cambridge Univ. Pr.

Lerner, Ralph. Playing the Fool: Subversive Laughter in Troubled Times. 2009. (ENG.). 144p. 32.50 *(978-0-226-47315-4(5))* Univ. of Chicago Pr.

Lund, Mary Ann. Melancholy, Medicine & Religion in Early Modern England: Reading 'the Anatomy of Melancholy' 2010. (ENG.). 236p. 95.00 *(978-0-521-19050-3(9))* Cambridge Univ. Pr.

BURUNDI

Beuret, Jean-Eudes & Fino, Daniel. Aide Au Développement et Conflit Armé Au Burundi: Pourquoi Rester, Comment Agir? 2009. (FRE., Illus.). 168p. *(978-2-8111-0173-2(X))* Editions-Diffusion Karthala.

Chretien, Jéan-Pierre. The Great Lakes of Africa: Two Thousand Years of History. Straus, Scott, tr. from FRE. 2006. (ENG., Illus.). 503p. (gr. 17). pap. 25.95 *(978-1-890951-35-1(8))* Zone Bks.

Cunningham, David E. Barriers to Peace in Civil War. 2011. (ENG., Illus.). 296p. 90.00 *(978-1-107-00759-8(3))* Cambridge Univ. Pr.

Eggers, Ellen K. Historical Dictionary of Burundi. 3rd ed. 2006. (Historical Dictionaries of Africa Ser.: Vol. 103). (ENG., Illus.). 224p. 87.00 *(978-0-8108-5302-7(7))* Scarecrow Pr., Inc.

Fuhlrott, Friederike. The Reintegration of Ex-Combatants: A Case Study of Burundi. 2008. 249p. pap. 61.00 *(978-3-8329-3654-9(8))* Nomos Verlagsgesellschaft DEU. Dist: International Specialized Bk. Services.

Icon Group International, Inc. Staff, compiled by. The 2006 Economic & Product Market Databook for Bujumbura, Burundi. 2006. 618p. ring bd. 95.00 *(978-0-497-80259-2(7))* Icon Group International, Inc.

—The 2006 Economic & Product Market Databook for Bururi, Burundi. 2006. 618p. ring bd. 95.00 *(978-0-497-80274-5(0))* Icon Group International, Inc.

Kale Ewusi, Ebenezer Akwanga Jr. Bsc. Burundi's Negative Peace: The Shadow of a Broken Continent in the Era of NEPAD. 2010. 408p. pap. 21.96 *(978-1-4269-2355-5(4))* Trafford Publishing.

Krueger, Robert, et al. From Bloodshed to Hope in Burundi: Our Embassy Years During Genocide. 2007. (Focus on American History Ser.). (ENG., Illus.). 342p. 26.00 *(978-0-292-71486-1(6))* Univ. of Texas Pr.

Locken, E. Travel Journal Burundi. 2010. 192p. pap. 19.99 *(978-0-557-43281-3(2))* Lulu Enterprises Inc.

Mokoena, Benjamin. The Political Economy of Burundi. 2010. 180p. pap. *(978-3-8383-6930-3(0))* Lambert Academic Publishing.

Tuhabonye, Gilbert & Brozek, Gary. This Voice in My Heart: A Runner's Memoir of Genocide, Faith, & Forgiveness. 2007. 272p. (gr. 13). per. 13.99 *(978-0-06-081753-4(4),* Amistad) HarperCollins Pubs.

Uvin, Peter. Life after Violence: A People's Story of Burundi. 2009. (African Arguments Ser.). (ENG.). 224p. pap. 20.95 *(978-1-84813-180-4(1))* Zed Bks., Ltd. GBR. Dist: Macmillan.

Watt, Nigel. Burundi: The Biography of a Small African Country. 2008. (Columbia/Hurst Ser.). (ENG.). 224p. (gr. 17). 55.00 *(978-0-231-70090-0(3))* Columbia Univ. Pr.

BURY ST. EDMUNDS ABBEY

see Abbey of Bury St. Edmunds

BURYING GROUNDS

see Burial; Cemeteries

BUS DRIVERS

Brock, John F., et al. Effectiveness of Commercial Motor Vehicle Driver Training Curricula & Delivery Methods. 2007. (Illus.). 34p. 34.00 *(978-0-309-09883-0(1))* Transportation Research Board.

Calleri, John. Angelo & the Yellow Giant. 2010. 134p. 29.99 *(978-1-4500-4117-1(5));* pap. 19.99 *(978-1-4500-4116-4(7))* Xlibris Corp.

Ehrlich-Klein, Tzvia. On Bus Drivers, Dreidels & Orange Juice: Busdrivers. 128p. 10.99 *(978-1-58330-371-9(5))* Feldheim Pubs.

The Federal Motor Carrier Safety Administration's Progress in Improving Medical Oversight of Commercial Drivers: Hearing Before the Committee on Transportation & Infrastructure, House of Representatives, One Hundred Tenth Congress, Second Session, July 24, 2008. 2008. (Illus.). ix, 116p. *(978-0-16-083633-6(6),* 552-070-39344-7) United States Government Printing Office.

Hickman, Jeffrey Scott. Impact of Behavior-Based Safety Techniques on Commercial Motor Vehicle Drivers. 2007. (Illus.). 67p. 48.00 *(978-0-309-09876-2(9))* Transportation Research Board.

Krueger, Gerald P. Health & Wellness Programs for Commercial Drivers. 2007. (Illus.). 80p. 43.00 *(978-0-309-09887-8(4))* Transportation Research Board.

LearningExpress Editors. Commercial Truck Drivers License Test Prep. 2008. (Complete Preparation Guides). (ENG.). 240p. pap. 26.95 *(978-1-57685-659-8(3))* LearningExpress, LLC.

Maguire, Sean R. Did I Miss My Bus? 2006. 58p. pap. 16.95 *(978-1-4241-2502-9(2))* PublishAmerica, Inc.

Mosher, Matt & Research and Education Association Staff. CDL - Commerical Driver's License Exam. 5th ed. 2011. (CDL Test Preparation Ser.). (ENG.). 336p. pap. 18.95 *(978-0-7386-0907-2(2))* Research & Education Assn.

Olonade, Zaccheaus Olufunminiyi. Driving Behaviour of Intercity Bus Drivers. 2011. 116p. pap. ***(978-3-8454-2040-0(5))*** Lambert Academic Publishing.

BUS LINES

see also Bus Drivers

Baker, Michael. The Routemaster. 2011. (ENG., Illus.). 128p. 16.95 *(978-0-7110-3541-6(5))* Allan, Ian Publishing GBR. Dist: BookMasters Distribution Services (BDS).

Beck, Arne. Competition for Public Transport Services: Institutional Framework & Empirical Evidence of Bus Services in Germany. 2012. (Contributions to Economics Ser.). (ENG., Illus.). xxvi, 235p. 139.00 ***(978-3-7908-2801-6(7),*** 3790828017) Physica-Verlag DEU. Dist: Springer.

Booth, Gavin. BET Buses in the 1960s. 2011. (ENG., Illus.). 112p. 29.95 *(978-0-7110-3464-8(8))* Allan, Ian Publishing GBR. Dist: BookMasters Distribution Services (BDS).

Brein, Michael. Honolulu Bus Map & Guide. 2009. 2p. 5.95 *(978-1-886590-40-3(0))* Brein, Michael Inc.

Brown, Stewart J. Buses Yearbook 2012. 2011. (ENG., Illus.). 128p. 26.95 *(978-0-7110-3553-9(9))* Allan, Ian Publishing GBR. Dist: BookMasters Distribution Services (BDS).

Committee Print: Rail & Public Transportation Security ACT of 2007: Hearing of the Committee on Homeland Security, House of Representatives, One Hundred Tenth Congress, First Session, March 6, 2007. 2009. (Illus.). iv, 168p. *(978-0-16-083485-1(6),* 552-070-39225-4) United States Government Printing Office.

Crawford, Sr Donald. Wheels of Birmingham Civil Rights Movement. 2007. 100p. pap. 18.95 *(978-1-60008-025-8(1),* Rooftop Publishing) AuthorHouse.

Davies, Roger. Barton. 2014. (ENG.). 96p. 32.95 *(978-0-7110-3522-5(9))* Allan, Ian Publishing GBR. Dist: BookMasters Distribution Services (BDS).

Gupta, Sudakshina. Passenger Transport Subsidy in West Bengal: Use or Misuse? 2007. x, 268p. *(978-81-7827-167-5(2))* Manak Pubns. Pvt., Ltd.

Hemily, P. Brendon & King, Rolland D. Uses of Higher Capacity Buses in Transit Service. 2008. (Illus.). 72p. *(978-0-309-09804-5(1))* National Academies Pr.

Hensher, David A. Bus Transport: Economics, Policy & Planning. 2007. (Research in Transportation Economics Ser.). (ENG., Illus.). 538p. 130.00 *(978-0-7623-1408-9(7),* JAI Pr.) Elsevier Science & Technology Bks.

Houston, Ken. The Corporation Bus. 2010. (Illus.). 252p. pap. *(978-1-907211-86-7(1))* Grosvenor Hse. Publishing Ltd.

Ian Allan, ed. The Litte Red Book 2011: The Directory of the UK Bus & Coach Industry. 2010. (ENG., Illus.). 238p. 56.95 *(978-0-7110-3545-4(8))* Allan, Ian Publishing GBR. Dist: BookMasters Distribution Services (BDS).

Ian Allan Publishing Staff. The Little Red Book 2012. 2011. (ENG., Illus.). 240p. 56.95 *(978-0-7110-3660-4(8))* Allan, Ian Publishing GBR. Dist: BookMasters Distribution Services (BDS).

Jones, A. E. North Western. 2008. (ENG., Illus.). 96p. 29.95 *(978-0-7110-3227-9(0))* Allan, Ian Publishing GBR. Dist: BookMasters Distribution Services (BDS).

Keeley, Malcolm & Allan, Ian. West Midlands PTE Buses & Trolleybuses. 2009. (ENG., Illus.). 80p. pap. 29.95 ***(978-0-7110-3422-8(2))*** Allan, Ian Publishing GBR. Dist: BookMasters Distribution Services (BDS).

—Working Days: Midland Red. 2008. (ENG., Illus.). 112p. pap. 27.95 ***(978-0-7110-3316-0(1))*** Allan, Ian Publishing GBR. Dist: BookMasters Distribution Services (BDS).

Kittelson & Associates, et al. Bus Rapid Transit Practitioner's Guide. 2007. (Illus.). 242p. per. 55.00 *(978-0-309-09884-7(X))* Transportation Research Board.

Kraemer-Johnson, Glyn & Bishop, John. Southdown Memories. 2009. (ENG., Illus.). 96p. 26.95 *(978-0-7110-3255-2(6))* Allan, Ian Publishing GBR. Dist: BookMasters Distribution Services (BDS).

Kraemer-Johnson, Glyn, et al. Southdown in NBC Days. 2008. (ENG., Illus.). 80p. 29.95 *(978-0-7110-3254-5(8))* Allan, Ian Publishing GBR. Dist: BookMasters Distribution Services (BDS).

Opus Publishing. Map New Yorkers Manhattan Ny. 2010. 5.95 *(978-0-9729666-0-3(5))* Opus Publishing.

Oversight of Federal Efforts for Rail & Surface Transportation Security: Hearing Before the Committee on Commerce, Science, & Transportation, United States Senate, One Hundred Tenth Congress, First Session, January 18, 2007. 2010. (Illus.). iii, 106p. *(978-0-16-086800-9(9),* 552-070-41716-8) United States Government Printing Office.

Santos, Evandro. Curitiba, Brazil. 2011. 260p. pap. ***(978-3-8443-3299-5(5))*** Lambert Academic Publishing.

Short, Jeffrey. The Role of Safety Culture in Preventing Commercial Motor Vehicle Crashes. 2007. (Illus.). 49p. 36.00 *(978-0-309-09891-5(2))* Transportation Research Board.

Siddique, Abu Bakar. Applications of Gis in Transit Network Development. 2010. 64p. pap. *(978-3-639-27563-6(2))* VDM Verlag Dr. Mueller e.K.

Transit & Rail Security: Joint Hearing Before the Subcommittee on Highways & Transit & the Subcommittee on Railroads, Pipelines, & Hazardous Materials of the Committee on Transportation & Infrastructure, House of Representatives, One Hundred Tenth Congress, First Session, March 7, 2007. 2007. v, 175p. *(978-0-16-079447-6(1),* 552-070-36441-2) United States Government Printing Office.

Weiner, Richard. Integration of Paratransit & Fixed-Route Transit Services. 2008. (Illus.). 48p. pap. *(978-0-309-09816-8(5))* Transportation Research Board.

Yorke, Stan. Fares Please! The Story of Public Transport in Britain. 2010. (Britain's living History Ser.). (Illus.). 64p. pap. 14.95 *(978-1-84674-199-9(8))* Countryside Bks. GBR. Dist: Brown, David Bk. Co., The.

BUS LINES—STATIONS

see Bus Terminals

BUS STATIONS

see Bus Terminals

BUS TERMINALS

Kooi, Brandon R. Policing Public Transportation: An Environmental & Procedural Evaluation of Bus Stops. 2007. (Criminal Justice). 222p. 62.00 *(978-1-59332-146-8(5))* LFB Scholarly Publishing LLC.

Wrenick, Frank E. & Wrenick, Elaine V., eds. The Streamline Era Greyhound Terminals: The Architecture of W. S. Arrasmith. alt. ed. 2011. (ENG., Illus.). 204p. pap. 38.00 *(978-0-7864-6445-6(3))* McFarland & Co., Inc. Pubs.

BUSBY, MATT, SIR, 1909-1994

Meek, David. Legends of United: The Heroes of the Busby Era. 2007. (ENG., Illus.). 312p. pap. 12.95 *(978-0-7528-8140-9(X))* Orion Bks. Ltd. GBR. Dist: Sterling Publishing Co., Inc.

BUSES

see also School Buses

American Society of Mechanical Engineers Staff, ed. Bus: The Expanding Role of Buses Towards the 21st Century. (Illus.). 290p. 176.00 *(978-0-85298-795-7(1))* Professional Engineering Publishing GBR. Dist: SAE Intl.

Baker, Michael. London Transport in The 1920s. 2009. (ENG., Illus.). 96p. 27.95 *(978-0-7110-3367-2(6))* Allan, Ian Publishing GBR. Dist: BookMasters Distribution Services (BDS).

Baker, Michael H. C. London Transport in the 1980s. 2008. (ENG., Illus.). 96p. 31.95 *(978-0-7110-3283-5(1))* Allan, Ian Publishing GBR. Dist: BookMasters Distribution Services (BDS).

Berguer, David. Under the Wires at Tally Ho: Trams & Trolleybuses of North London, 1905-1962. 2011. (ENG., Illus.). 128p. pap. 23.95 ***(978-0-7524-5875-5(2))*** History Pr. Ltd.,The GBR. Dist: Independent Pubs. Group.

Bishop, Richard. Safety Impacts of Speed Limiter Device Installations on Commercial Trucks & Buses: A Synthesis of Safety Practice. 2008. (Illus.). 43p. *(978-0-309-09827-4(0))* Transportation Research Board.

Booth, Gavin. Buses by Design. 2008. (ENG., Illus.). 160p. 46.95 *(978-0-7110-3326-9(9))* Allan, Ian Publishing GBR. Dist: BookMasters Distribution Services (BDS).

—Classic Bus Yearbook 14. 2008. (Illus.). 128p. 29.95 *(978-0-7110-3321-4(8))* Allan, Ian Publishing GBR. Dist: Casemate Pubs. & Bk. Distributors, LLC.

—Daimler Fleetline. 2010. (ENG., Illus.). 96p. 32.95 *(978-0-7110-3456-3(7))* Allan, Ian Publishing GBR. Dist: BookMasters Distribution Services (BDS).

Browand, Fred. Aerodynamics of Heavy Vehicles Ii. 2008. (Lecture Notes in Applied & Computational Mechanics Ser.). (Illus.). 480p. 209.00 *(978-3-540-85069-4(4),* 3540850694) Springer.

Brown, Stewart J. AEC Regent V. 2011. (ENG., Illus.). 96p. 32.95 *(978-0-7110-3539-3(3))* Allan, Ian Publishing GBR. Dist: BookMasters Distribution Services (BDS).

—Buses Yearbook 2012. 2011. (ENG., Illus.). 128p. 26.95 *(978-0-7110-3553-9(9))* Allan, Ian Publishing GBR. Dist: BookMasters Distribution Services (BDS).

Cabrera, Jane. Wheels on the Bus. 2011. (ENG., Illus.). 32p. (YA). 16.95 *(978-0-8234-2350-7(6))* Holiday Hse., Inc.

Clark, Nigel N., et al. Assessment of Hybrid-Electric Transit Bus Technology. 2009. (Illus.). 77p. *(978-0-309-11803-3(4))* Transportation Research Board.

Conway Publishing, ed. The Routemaster Pocket-Book: 1956. 2012. (ENG., Illus.). 128p. 12.95 ***(978-1-84486-152-1(X),*** Conway Maritime Pr.) Anova Bks. GBR. Dist: Sterling Publishing Co., Inc.

Cook, Robert. Red Rover Bus Company. 2007. (ENG.). 96p. pap. 29.95 *(978-0-7524-4442-0(5))* History Pr. Ltd.,The GBR. Dist: Independent Pubs. Group.

Curtis, Martin S. Bristol Lodekka. 2009. (ENG., Illus.). 96p. 29.95 *(978-0-7110-3312-2(9))* Allan, Ian Publishing GBR. Dist: BookMasters Distribution Services (BDS).

Davies, Roger. Barton. 2014. (ENG.). 96p. 32.95 *(978-0-7110-3522-5(9))* Allan, Ian Publishing GBR. Dist: BookMasters Distribution Services (BDS).

—Ribble. 2011. (ENG., Illus.). 112p. 32.95 *(978-0-7110-3484-6(2))* Allan, Ian Publishing GBR. Dist: BookMasters Distribution Services (BDS).

—Wallace Arnold Days. 2010. (ENG., Illus.). 96p. 27.95 *(978-0-7110-3438-9(9))* Allan, Ian Publishing GBR. Dist: BookMasters Distribution Services (BDS).

Delmar Learning Staff. ASE Test Preparation: Transit Bus H5, Suspension & Steering. 2009. (ENG.). 128p. pap. 23.95 *(978-1-4283-4011-4(4))* Delmar Cengage Learning.

—Preventive Maintenance Test H8. 2010. (ENG.). 160p. pap. 23.95 *(978-1-4354-3938-2(4))* Delmar Cengage Learning.

Fedor, John & Delmar Learning Staff. Drive Train Test H3. 2008. (ENG.). 101p. pap. 23.95 *(978-1-4354-5376-0(X))* Delmar Cengage Learning.

Harvey, David. Belfast Trolleybuses from Old Photographs. 2010. (Illus.). 192p. pap. 29.95 *(978-1-84868-466-9(5))* Amberley Publishing GBR. Dist: Casemate Pubs. & Bk. Distributors, LLC.

Heaps, Chris & Eyre, Michael. The Manchester Trolleybus. 2006. (ENG., Illus.). 112p. 29.95 *(978-0-7110-3245-3(9))* Allan, Ian Publishing GBR. Dist: BookMasters Distribution Services (BDS).

Hemily, P. Brendon & King, Rolland D. Uses of Higher Capacity Buses in Transit Service. 2008. (Illus.). 72p. *(978-0-309-09804-5(1))* National Academies Pr.

Hymans, Mick. A History of Eastbourne's Buses. 2011. (ENG.). 160p. pap. 26.95 ***(978-0-7524-5803-8(5))*** History Pr. Ltd.,The GBR. Dist: Independent Pubs. Group.

Jones, A. E. North Western. 2008. (ENG., Illus.). 96p. 29.95 *(978-0-7110-3227-9(0))* Allan, Ian Publishing GBR. Dist: BookMasters Distribution Services (BDS).

Kamonashish, Haldar & Saiful, Azim. Demand Effective Intra-City Bus Service for a Secondary City: A Case Study on Barisal City, Bangladesh. 2011. 80p. pap. ***(978-3-639-32936-0(8))*** VDM Verlag Dr. Mueller e.K.

Kaye, David. Old Buses. 2nd ed. 2008. (Shire Library). (ENG., Illus.). 56p. per. 12.95 *(978-0-7478-0650-9(0))* Shire Pubns., Ltd. GBR. Dist: Random Hse., Inc.

Keeley, Malcolm & Allan, Ian. West Midlands PTE Buses & Trolleybuses. 2009. (ENG., Illus.). 80p. pap. 29.95 ***(978-0-7110-3422-8(2))*** Allan, Ian Publishing GBR. Dist: BookMasters Distribution Services (BDS).

—Working Days: Midland Red. 2008. (ENG., Illus.). 112p. pap. 27.95 ***(978-0-7110-3316-0(1))*** Allan, Ian Publishing GBR. Dist: BookMasters Distribution Services (BDS).

Kraemer-Johnson Glyn & Bishop, John. Southdown Memories. 2009. (ENG., Illus.). 96p. 26.95 *(978-0-7110-3255-2(6))* Allan, Ian Publishing GBR. Dist: BookMasters Distribution Services (BDS).

Lane, Kevin. London Half-Cab Farewell. 2009. (ENG., Illus.). 96p. 27.95 *(978-0-7110-3311-5(0))* Allan, Ian Publishing GBR. Dist: BookMasters Distribution Services (BDS).

The London Bus. 2009. (Shire Library). (ENG., Illus.). 64p. pap. 12.95 *(978-0-7478-0728-5(0))* Shire Pubns., Ltd. GBR. Dist: Random Hse., Inc.

Luke, William A. & Metler, Linda. Buses of Western Flyer & New Flyer Industries Photo Archive. 2009. (Photo Archive Ser.). (ENG., Illus.). 128p. pap. 16.95 *(978-1-58388-229-0(4),* 1583882294) Iconografix, Inc.

—Old Look Buses: Yellow Coach & GM in the '40s And '50s. 2010. (ENG., Illus.). 112p. pap. 29.95 *(978-1-58388-256-6(1),* 1583882561) Iconografix, Inc.

—Trolley Buses Around the World: A Photo Gallery. 2006. (Photo Gallery Ser.). (ENG., Illus.). 160p. pap. 14.95 *(978-1-58388-175-0(1),* 1583881751) Iconografix, Inc.

McCausland, Evan T. Rapid Transit Series Buses: General Motors & Beyond. 2008. (Enthusiast's Reference Ser.). (ENG., Illus.). 160p. pap. 32.95 *(978-1-58388-209-2(X),* 158388209X) Iconografix, Inc.

Mccormack, Kevin. Lost London in Colour. 2008. (ENG., Illus.). 80p. 27.95 *(978-0-7110-3335-1(8))* Allan, Ian Publishing GBR. Dist: BookMasters Distribution Services (BDS).

Millar, A. & Allan, Ian. Abc Bus & Coach Recognition 5th Ed. 5th ed. 2007. (ENG., Illus.). 160p. pap. 16.95 ***(978-0-7110-3136-4(3))*** Allan, Ian Publishing GBR. Dist: BookMasters Distribution Services (BDS).

Morgan, Andrew. Routemaster Bus: 1954 Onwards (All Marks) 2011. (Owners Workshop Manual Ser.). (ENG., Illus.). 160p. 29.95 *(978-1-84425-938-0(2),* 1844259382) Haynes Publishing PLC GBR. Dist: MBI Distribution Services/Quayside Distribution.

Motorcoach Safety: Hearing Before the Subcommittee on Highways & Transit of the Committee on Transportation & Infrastructure, House of Representatives, One Hundred Tenth Congress, First Session, March 20, 2007. 2007. v, 114p. *(978-0-16-079444-5(7),* 552-070-36438-2) United States Government Printing Office.

National Association of Road Transport Museums Staff. Buses Restored 2008. 2008. (Illus.). 128p. 26.95 *(978-0-7110-3319-1(6))* Allan, Ian Publishing GBR. Dist: Casemate Pubs. & Bk. Distributors, LLC.

Paxton, Mark. How to Restore Volkswagen Bus. 2008. (Enthusiast's Restoration Manuals Ser.). (ENG., Illus.). 272p. pap. 74.95 *(978-1-84584-093-8(3),* 1845840933) Veloce Publishing Ltd. GBR. Dist: MBI Distribution Services/Quayside Distribution.

Puvilland, Christophe. Berliet: 1905-1978, toute la gamme autobus et Autocars. 2008. (Illus.). 216p. 75.00 *(978-2-35250-059-9(1))* Histoire et Collections FRA. Dist: Casemate Pubs. & Bk. Distributors, LLC.

Rose, Peter. Luton Corporation Transport. 2009. (ENG., Illus.). 160p. pap. 32.95 *(978-0-7524-4913-5(3))* History Pr. Ltd.,The GBR. Dist: Independent Pubs. Group.

Rozum, Fred A. Streetcars in Kewanee & Galva, Illinois. 2008. 15.00 *(978-0-615-23959-0(5))* Kewanee Historical Society, Inc.

Salvatore, Guiseppe A., ed. Fuel Cell Buses. 2010. (Transportation Infrastructure - Roads, Highways, Bridges, Airports & Mass Transit Ser.). 278p. 115.00 *(978-1-60876-007-7(3))* Nova Science Pubs., Inc.

Singletary, Milly. Honolulu's Famous the Bus. pap. 3.50 *(978-0-941244-07-7(5))* Singletary Pubns.

Smith, Robert L. Motorcoach Milestones. 2010. (ENG., Illus.). 128p. pap. 34.95 *(978-1-58388-260-3(X),* 158388260X) Iconografix, Inc.

Taylor, James. British Buses 1946-1975. 2012. (ENG., Illus.). 192p. 59.95 *(978-1-906133-38-2(7),* 1906133387) Herridge & Sons, Ltd. GBR. Dist: MBI Distribution Services/Quayside Distribution.

Umar Madugu, Yusuf. Commercial Buses & Economic Growth in Kano Metropolis 1967-2003. 2011. 124p. pap. ***(978-3-8443-9664-5(0))*** Lambert Academic Publishing.

Wharmby, Matthew. The London Titan. 2008. (ENG., Illus.). 176p. 36.95 *(978-0-7110-3299-6(8))* Allan, Ian Publishing GBR. Dist: BookMasters Distribution Services (BDS).

Wharmby, Matthew & Rixon, Geoff. Routemaster Omnibus. 2007. (ENG., Illus.). 288p. 37.95 *(978-0-7110-3314-6(5))* Allan, Ian Publishing GBR. Dist: BookMasters Distribution Services (BDS).

BUSES (MICROCOMPUTERS)

see Microcomputers—Buses

BUSH, BARBARA, 1925-

Gutin, Myra G. Barbara Bush: Presidential Matriarch. 2008. (Modern First Ladies Ser.). (Illus.). *(978-0-7006-1583-4(0))* Univ. Pr. of Kansas.

BUSH, GEORGE, 1924-

Alfonsi, Christian. Circle in the Sand: The Bush Dynasty in Iraq. 2007. (Vintage Ser.). (ENG., Illus.). 480p. pap. 15.95 *(978-1-4000-9606-0(5),* Vintage) Knopf Doubleday Publishing Group.

Baker, Russ. Family of Secrets: The Bush Dynasty, the Powerful Forces That Put It in the White House, & What Their Influence Means for America. 2008. (ENG., Illus.). 592p. 30.00 *(978-1-59691-557-2(9))* Bloomsbury Publishing.

B

Borucki, Wesley B. George H.W. Bush in Defense of Principle. 2011. *(978-1-61122-133-6(1))* Nova Science Pubs., Inc.

Castile, George Pierre. Taking Charge: Native American Self-Determination & Federal Indian Policy, 1975-1993. 2006. (ENG.). 168p. 35.00 *(978-0-8165-2542-3(0))* Univ. of Arizona Pr.

Cavazos, Lauro F. A Kineno Remembers: From the King Ranch to the White House. 2008. (Perspectives on South Texas, sponsored by Texas A&M University-Kingsville Ser.). (ENG., Illus.). 300p. per. 19.95 *(978-1-60344-044-8(5))* Texas A&M Univ. Pr.

Cohen, David Elliot. The Bush Legacy: Their Story in Photographs. 2011. (ENG., Illus.). 224p. 24.95 *(978-1-4027-8787-4(1))* Sterling Publishing Co., Inc.

Dieu, Le Tat. Some Words of Advice to the Commander-in-Chief: What you Don't Know Might Hurt your Country. 2009. 118p. 22.95 *(978-1-4401-5667-0(0))*; pap. 12.95 *(978-1-4401-5666-3(2))* iUniverse, Inc.

Duncan, George. Democracy Held Hostage: How neocon arrogance, George Bush's incompetence & Dick Cheney's criminality subverted the Constitution, destroyed Iraq & weakened America. Letters to the Editor 2004-2008. 2009. 224p. pap. 24.00 *(978-1-4269-1343-3(5))* Trafford Publishing.

Engel, Jeffrey A., ed. The China Diary of George H.W. Bush: The Making of a Global President. 2008. (ENG., Illus.). 576p. (C). 29.95 *(978-0-691-13006-4(X))* Princeton Univ. Pr.

Francis, Sandra. George Bush. 2008. (Presidents of the U. S. A. Ser.). (ENG., Illus.). 48p. (YA). (gr. 3-6). 31.36 *(978-1-60253-069-0(6))* Child's World, Inc., The.

Glenn P. Hastedt. The Presidencies of George Herbert Walker Bush & George Walker Bush: Like Father Like Son? Eksterowicz, Anthony J., ed. 2007. 129.00 *(978-1-60456-163-0(7))* Nova Science Pubs., Inc.

Golson, J. Geoffrey & Carlisle, Rodney P., eds. The Reagan Era from the Iran Crisis to Kosovo. 2007. (Turning Points-Actual & Alternate Histories Ser.). (Illus.). 259p. 85.00 *(978-1-85109-885-9(2)*, TPHTRE1C) ABC-CLIO, LLC.

Han, Lori Cox. A Presidency Upstaged: The Public Leadership of George H. W. Bush. 2011. (Joseph V. Hughes Jr. & Holly O. Hughes Series on the Presidency & Leadership Ser.). (Illus.). 224p. 40.00 *(978-1-60344-220-6(0))* Texas A&M Univ. Pr.

Hess, Gary R. Presidential Decisions for War: Korea, Vietnam, the Persian Gulf, & Iraq. 2nd ed. 2009. (American Moment Ser.). (ENG.). 344p. (C). (gr. 13-17). 58.00 *(978-0-8018-9123-6(X))*; pap. 25.95 *(978-0-8018-9124-3(8))* Johns Hopkins Univ. Pr.

Hybel, Alex Roberto & Kaufman, Justin Matthew. The Bush Administrations & Saddam Hussein: Deciding on Conflict. 2006. (Advances in Foreign Policy Analysis Ser.). (ENG.). 208p. 84.00 *(978-1-4039-7578-2(7))* Palgrave Macmillan.

James, Christian, et al. Civil Rights During the Bush Administration: Subject Files of the White House Office of Records Management, 1989-1993. 2008. *(978-0-88692-908-4(3))* ProQuest LLC.

Koch, Doro Bush. My Father, My President: A Personal Account of the Life of George H. W. Bush. 2006. (ENG., Illus.). 608p. 33.99 *(978-0-446-57990-2(4))* Grand Central Publishing.

Mariano, Connie. The White House Doctor: My Patients Were Presidents. 2010. (ENG., Illus.). 320p. 25.99 *(978-0-312-53483-7(3)*, Dunne, Thomas Bks.) St. Martin's Pr.

Matthews, Mark. Lost Years: Bush, Sharon, & Failure in the Middle East. 2007. (ENG.). 480p. 29.95 *(978-1-56858-332-7(X)*, Nation Bks.) Basic Bks.

Maynard, Christopher. Out of the Shadow: George H. W. Bush & the End of the Cold War. 2008. (Foreign Relations & the Presidency Ser.: No. 9). (ENG., Illus.). 192p. 34.95 *(978-1-60344-039-4(9))* Texas A&M Univ. Pr.

McAdams, Dan P. George W. Bush & the Redemptive Dream: A Psychological Portrait, 1 vol. 2010. (Inner Lives Ser.). (ENG.). 352p. 29.95 *(978-0-19-975208-9(7))* Oxford Univ. Pr., Inc.

McGrath, James & Milnes, Arthur. Age of the Offered Hand: The Cross-Border Partnership Between President George H. W. Bush & Prime Minister Brian Mulroney, A Documentary History. 2009. (Library of Political Leadership Ser.). (ENG., Illus.). 144p. (C). pap. *(978-1-55339-232-3(9))* McGill-Queen's Univ. Pr.

McGrath, James & Milnes, Arthur, eds. Age of the Offered Hand: The Cross-Border Partnership Between President George H. W. Bush & Prime Minister Brian Mulroney, A Documentary History. 2009. (Library of Political Leadership Ser.). (ENG., Illus.). 144p. (C). *(978-1-55339-233-0(7))* McGill-Queen's Univ. Pr.

Messerschmidt, James W. Hegemonic Masculinities & Camouflaged Politics: Unmasking the Bush Dynasty & Its War Against Iraq. 2010. 216p. pap. 32.50 *(978-1-59451-818-8(1))*; 107.00 *(978-1-59451-817-1(3))* Paradigm Pubs.

Morman Ph. D., Robert R. Bush's Eighth Year: Vacuous Victory, Iraq Occupation-Dec. 2011. 2009. 504p. pap. 26.49 *(978-1-4389-8216-8(X))* AuthorHouse.

Naftali, Timothy. George H. W. Bush: The 41st President, 1989-1993. Wilentz, Sean & Schlesinger, Arthur M., eds. rev. ed. 2007. (American Presidents Ser.). (ENG., Illus.). 224p. 22.00 *(978-0-8050-6966-2(6)*, Times Bks.) Holt, Henry & Co.

Naftali, Timothy J. George H. W. Bush. l.t. ed. 2008. (American Presidents Ser.). 329p. 30.95 *(978-1-4104-0594-4(X))* Thorndike Pr.

Office of the Federal Register (U.S.), compiled by. Public Papers of the Presidents of the United States, George W. Bush, 2007, Bk. 2. 2012. (ENG., Illus.). 814p. 126.00 ***(978-0-16-079500-8(1)***, Office of the Federal Register) United States Government Printing Office.

O'Neill, William L. A Bubble in Time: America During the Interwar Years, 1989-2001. 2009. (ENG., Illus.). 448p. 27.50 *(978-1-56663-806-7(2))* Dee, Ivan R. Pub.

Otenyo, Eric E. American Promotion of Democracy in Africa, 1988-2000: A Comparison of the Presidential Administrations of George H. W. Bush & William J. Clinton. 2009. (Illus.). 296p. 109.95 *(978-0-7734-4707-3(5))* Mellen, Edwin Pr., The.

Otenyo, Eric E. & Lind, Nancy S. The First World Presidency: George H. W. Bush, 1989-1993. 2009. 260p. pap. 35.00 *(978-1-934844-09-0(8))* Teneo Pr.

Popadiuk, Roman. The Leadership of George Bush: An Insider's View of the Forty-First President. 2009. (Joseph V. Hughes Jr. & Holly O. Hughes Series on the Presidency & Leadership Ser.). (ENG., Illus.). 248p. 30.00 *(978-1-60344-112-4(3))* Texas A&M Univ. Pr.

Risen, James. State of War: The Secret History of the CIA & the Bush Administration. 2006. 240p. 26.00 *(978-1-4223-5680-7(9))* DIANE Publishing Co.

—State of War: The Secret History of the CIA & the Bush Administration. 2006. (ENG., Illus.). 272p. pap. 15.00 *(978-0-7432-7067-0(3)*, Free Pr.) Free Pr.

Sands, Philippe. Torture Team: Rumsfeld's Memo & the Betrayal of American Values. (ENG., 2009. Illus.). 288p. pap. 16.95 *(978-0-230-61443-7(4))* 2008. 272p. 26.95 *(978-0-230-60390-5(4))* Palgrave Macmillan.

Smith, John E. The Beginning & End of What Is Now called America. 2007. 80p. pap. 18.55 *(978-1-4303-0479-1(0))* Lulu Enterprises Inc.

Unger, Craig. House of Bush, House of Saud: The Secret Relationship between the World's Two Most Powerful Dynasties. 2007. (Illus.). 355p. reprint ed. 35.00 *(978-1-4223-9016-0(0))* DIANE Publishing Co.

BUSH, GEORGE W. (GEORGE WALKER), 1946-

Anderson, John. Follow the Money: How George W. Bush & the Texas Republicans Hog-Tied America. 2007. (ENG.). 352p. 26.00 *(978-0-7432-8643-5(X)*, Scribner) Scribner.

Ashbee, Edward. The Bush Administration, Sex & the Moral Agenda. 2007. (ENG., Illus.). 264p. 84.00 *(978-0-7190-7276-5(X))*; 240p. pap. 26.00 *(978-0-7190-7277-2(8))* Manchester Univ. Pr. GBR. Dist: Macmillan.

Baker, Russ. Family of Secrets: The Bush Dynasty, America's Invisible Government, & the Hidden History of the Last Fifty Years. 2009. (ENG., Illus.). 592p. pap. 20.00 *(978-1-60819-006-5(4))* Bloomsbury Publishing.

—Family of Secrets: The Bush Dynasty, the Powerful Forces That Put It in the White House, & What Their Influence Means for America. 2008. (ENG., Illus.). 592p. 30.00 *(978-1-59691-557-2(9))* Bloomsbury Publishing.

Barnes, Fred. Rebel in Chief: Inside the Bold & Controversial Presidency of George W. Bush. 2006. (ENG.). 240p. per. 13.95 *(978-0-307-33650-7(6)*, Three Rivers Pr.) Crown Publishing Group.

Barnett, Thomas P. M. Great Powers: America & the World after Bush. 2010. (ENG.). 496p. (gr. 12-18). 16.00 *(978-0-425-23225-5(5)*, Berkley Trade) Penguin Group (USA) Inc.

Bassiouni, Cherif. Institutionalization of Torture under the Bush Administration. 2010. 351p. pap. 35.00 *(978-94-000-0005-6(7))* Intersentia Uitgevers N.V. BEL. Dist: International Specialized Bk. Services.

Bates, Bill. Bates on Bush. 2007. (Illus.). 64p. pap. 9.95 *(978-0-9799941-0-4(1))* Franklin, Benjamin Pr.

Bayer, Steven. The Brilliant Thoughts & Strategies of George W. Bush: from Diapers to Rashes. 2007. 109p. pap. 9.95 *(978-0-615-18152-3(X))* Bayer, Steven.

Beeson. Bush & Asia. 2007. pap. 41.95 *(978-0-415-44408-8(X))* Routledge.

Begala, Paul. Third Term: Why George W. Bush (Hearts) John McCain. 2008. (ENG., Illus.). 288p. pap. 18.99 *(978-1-4391-0213-8(9))* Simon & Schuster.

Blumenthal, Sidney. How Bush Rules: Chronicles of a Radical Regime. 2006. (ENG.). 416p. (C). 26.95 *(978-0-691-12888-7(X))* Princeton Univ. Pr.

Bonn, Scott A. Mass Deception: Moral Panic & the U. S. War on Iraq. 2010. (Critical Issues in Crime & Society Ser.). (ENG.). 210p. pap. 24.95 *(978-0-8135-4789-3(X))* Rutgers Univ. Pr.

Bostdorff, Denise M. Proclaiming the Truman Doctrine: The Cold War Call to Arms. 2008. (Library of Presidential Rhetoric). (ENG., Illus.). 206p. 34.95 *(978-1-60344-032-5(1))*; pap. 17.95 *(978-1-60344-034-9(8))* Texas A&M Univ. Pr.

Boyle, Francis Anthony. Breaking All the Rules: Palestine, Iraq, Iran & the Case for Impeachment. 2008. (Illus.). 127p. per. 12.95 *(978-0-932863-59-1(0))* Clarity Pr., Inc.

Brasch, Walter M. Sinking the Ship of State: The Presidency of George W. Bush. 2nd ed. 2008. (ENG.). 550p. pap. 24.95 *(978-0-942991-50-5(8))* Greeley & Stone, Pubs.

Brzezinski, Zbigniew. Second Chance: Three Presidents & the Crisis of American Superpower. 2008. (ENG., Illus.). 240p. pap. 15.95 *(978-0-465-00355-6(9))* Basic Bks.

Bugliosi, Vincent. The Prosecution of George Bush for Murder UK Edition. 2008. (Illus.). 376p. pap. 18.95 *(978-1-59315-528-5(X))* Westview Pr.

—The Prosecution of George W. Bush for Murder. 2008. (ENG., Illus.). 352p. 26.95 *(978-1-59315-481-3(X))* Vanguard Pr.

Bumiller, Elisabeth. Condoleezza Rice: an American Life: A Biography. 2009. (ENG., Illus.). 464p. pap. 17.00 *(978-0-8129-7713-4(0)*, Random Hse. Trade Paperbacks) Random House Publishing Group.

Burgan, Michael. George W. Bush. 2008. (Presidents of the U. S. A. Ser.). (ENG., Illus.). 48p. (YA). (gr. 3-6). 31.36 *(978-1-60253-071-3(8))* Child's World, Inc., The.

Burns, Richard Dean. The Missile Defense Systems of George W. Bush: A Critical Assessment, 1 vol. 2010. (Praeger Security International Ser.). (Illus.). 198p. 44.95 *(978-0-313-38466-0(5)*, A2925C, Praeger Pubs.) Greenwood Publishing Group, Inc.

Bush, George W. A Charge Kept: The Record of the Bush Presidency 2001 - 2009. Thiessen, Marc A., ed. 2009. (ENG.). 322p. pap. 12.95 *(978-1-60037-589-7(8))* Morgan James Publishing.

—Decision Points. 2011. (ENG., Illus.). 512p. pap. 18.00 ***(978-0-307-59063-3(1))*** Broadway Bks.

—Decision Points. 2010. (Illus.). 512p. 35.00 *(978-0-307-59061-9(5)*, Crown) Crown Publishing Group.

—Decision Points. l.t. ed. 2010. (Illus.). 768p. pap. 35.00 *(978-0-7393-7782-6(5))* Random Hse. Large Print.

—Highlights of Accomplishments & Results: The Administration of President George W. Bush 2001 - 2009. 2009. (ENG.). pap. 14.95 *(978-1-60037-582-8(0))* Morgan James Publishing.

Bush, Laura. Spoken from the Heart. (ENG.). 464p. 2011. pap. 18.00 *(978-1-4391-5521-9(6))* 2010. 30.00 *(978-1-4391-5520-2(8))* Scribner. (Scribner).

—Spoken from the Heart. l.t. ed. 2011. (ENG.). 822p. pap. 19.99 *(978-1-59413-439-5(1)*, Large Print Pr.) 2010. 32.95 *(978-1-4104-2647-5(5))* Thorndike Pr.

Cafferty, Jack. Now or Never: Getting down to the Business of Saving Our American Dream. 2009. (ENG.). 272p. 24.95 *(978-0-470-37230-2(3)*, Wiley) Wiley, John & Sons, Inc.

Cagle, Daryl & Fairrington, Brian. The Big Book of Campaign 2008 Cartoons. 2008. (ENG., Illus.). 256p. pap. 16.99 *(978-0-7897-3809-7(0))* Que.

Campbell. The George W. Bush Legacy, 00 vols. Rockman, Bert A. & Rudalevige, Andrew, eds. rev. ed. 2007. 348p. (C). pap. 43.95 *(978-0-87289-346-7(4)*, CQ Pr. College) CQ Pr.

Cannon, Lou, et al. Reagan's Disciple: George W. Bush's Troubled Quest for a Presidential Legacy. 2008. (ENG.). 400p. 27.95 *(978-1-58648-448-4(6))* PublicAffairs.

Chernus, Ira. Monsters to Destroy: The Neoconservative War on Terror & Sin. 2006. (ENG.). 258p. 125.00 *(978-1-59451-275-9(2))*; per. 34.95 *(978-1-59451-276-6(0))* Paradigm Pubs.

Chomsky, Noam. Failed States: The Abuse of Power & the Assault on Democracy. 2007. (American Empire Project Ser.). (ENG.). 320p. pap. 17.00 *(978-0-8050-8284-5(0)*, Owl Bks.) Holt, Henry & Co.

—Interventions. 2007. (City Lights Open Media Ser.). (ENG.). 176p. pap. 15.95 *(978-0-87286-483-2(9))* City Lights Bks.

Christie, Ron. Black in the White House: Life Inside George W. Bush's West Wing, 0 vols. 2009. 328p. pap. 14.99 *(978-1-59555-285-3(5))* Nelson, Thomas Inc.

Cobban, Helena. Re-Engage! America & the World after Bush - An Informed Citizen's Guide. 2008. (Illus.). 144p. pap. 24.95 *(978-1-59451-552-1(2))* Paradigm Pubs.

—Re-Engage! America & the World after Bush, an Informed Citizen's Guide. 2008. (Illus.). 144p. 125.00 *(978-1-59451-551-4(4))* Paradigm Pubs.

Coffman, Steve, compiled by. Founders V. Bush: A Comparison in Quotations of the Policies & Politics of the Founding Fathers & George W. Bush. 2007. 192p. pap. 14.95 *(978-0-9797272-0-7(0))* One World Studios Ltd.

Cohen, David Elliot. The Bush Legacy: Their Story in Photographs. 2011. (ENG., Illus.). 224p. 24.95 *(978-1-4027-8787-4(1))* Sterling Publishing Co., Inc.

Cohn, Marjorie. Cowboy Republic: Six Ways the Bush Gang Has Defied the Law. 2007. (ENG.). 191p. per. 14.95 *(978-0-9778253-3-2(7))* PoliPointPress, LLC.

Cole, David, ed. The Torture Memos: Rationalizing the Unthinkable. 2009. (ENG.). 304p. pap. 17.95 *(978-1-59558-492-2(7))* New Pr., The.

Colucci, Lamont. Crusading Realism: The Bush Doctrine & American Core Values after 9/11. 2008. (ENG.). 266p. pap. 42.99 *(978-0-7618-4130-2(X))* Univ. Pr. of America, Inc.

Colvin, Deon D. Congenial Authoritarian: A Psychological Assessment of America's 43rd President. 2010. 204p. 28.95 *(978-1-4490-8671-8(3))*; pap. 18.95 *(978-1-4490-8670-1(5))* AuthorHouse.

Conason, Joe. It Can Happen Here: Authoritarian Peril in the Age of Bush. 2008. (ENG.). 256p. pap. 16.99 *(978-0-312-37930-8(7)*, St. Martin's Griffin) St. Martin's Pr.

Conyers, John C., Jr. Reining in the Imperial Presidency: Lessons & Recommendations Relating to the Presidency of George W. Bush. 2009. (ENG.). 496p. pap. 14.95 *(978-1-60239-930-3(1)*, 239930) Skyhorse Publishing Co., Inc.

Conyers, John C., Jr. & Conyers, John C. The Constitution in Crisis: The High Crimes of the Bush Administration & a Blueprint for Impeachment. 2007. 302p. per. 14.95 *(978-1-60239-009-6(6))* Skyhorse Publishing Co., Inc.

Cooper, David. Absolute Despotism: How False Realities Led to Perpetual War, the Dismantling of Civil Liberties, & the Destruction of a Democracy. 2008. 264p. pap. 27.95 *(978-1-60563-407-4(7))* PublishAmerica, Inc.

Courtney, Ron. A Layman's View: Standing on the Eve of Destruction. 2007. 216p. per. 24.95 *(978-1-4241-9346-2(X))* PublishAmerica, Inc.

Cox, Michael. Rise & Fall of the American Empire. 2012. (ENG.). 224p. 64.95 *(978-0-7456-4446-2(5))*; pap. 24.95 *(978-0-7456-4447-9(3))* Polity Pr. GBR. Dist: Wiley, John & Sons, Inc.

David, Charles-Philippe & Grondin, David. Hegemony or Empire? The Redefinition of US Power under George W. Bush. 2006. (Illus.). 256p. 120.00 *(978-0-7546-4774-4(9))* Ashgate Publishing Co.

Davies, Philip John & Morgan, Iwan W., eds. Assessing George W. Bush's Legacy: The Right Man? 2010. (Evolving American Presidency Ser.). (ENG., Illus.). 240p. 89.00 *(978-0-230-10858-5(X))* Palgrave Macmillan.

De La Vega, Elizabeth & Tomdispatch.com Staff. United States V. George W. Bush et Al. annot. ed. 2006. (ENG.). 256p. per. 14.95 *(978-1-58322-756-5(3))* Seven Stories Pr.

Draper, Robert. Dead Certain: The Presidency of George W. Bush. 2008. (ENG.). 480p. pap. 28.99 *(978-0-7432-7729-7(5)*, Free Pr.) Free Pr.

Dunmire, Patricia L. Projecting the Future Through Political Discourse: The Case of the Bush Doctrine. 2011. (Illus.). ix, 218p. ***(978-90-272-8693-2(0))***; ***(978-90-272-0632-9(5))*** Benjamins, John Publishing Co.

Dyson, Michael Eric. Come Hell or High Water: Hurricane Katrina & the Color of Disaster. 2007. cd-rom 49.95 *(978-0-9779883-5-8(X))* Legacy Audio Bks.

Edwards, George C. & Edwards, George C., III. Governing by Campaigning: The Politics of the Bush Presidency 2007. 2nd rev. ed. 2007. (Great Questions in Politics Ser.). (ENG.). 336p. per. 22.40 *(978-0-205-52962-9(3))* Longman Publishing Group.

Edwards, George C., III & King, Desmond S., eds. The Polarized Presidency of George W. Bush. 2007. (ENG., Illus.). 478p. 60.00 *(978-0-19-921797-7(1))* Oxford Univ. Pr., Inc.

Executive Power & Its Constitutional Limitations: Hearing Before the Committee on the Judiciary, House of Representatives, One Hundred Tenth Congress, Second Session, July 25, 2008. 2009. iv, 466p. *(978-0-16-082841-6(4)*, 552-070-38821-4) United States Government Printing Office.

Federal Register (U.S.) Office, compiled by. Public Papers of the Presidents of the United States, George W. Bush, 2004, Bk. 3, October 1, 2004 to December 31 2004. 2008. (ENG.). 912p. 120.00 *(978-0-16-078479-8(4)*, Office of the Federal Register) United States Government Printing Office.

Federal Register Office, compiled by. Public Papers of the Presidents of the United States, George W. Bush, 2004, Bk. 2, July 1 to September 30 2004. 2008. (ENG., Illus.). 1088p. 138.00 *(978-0-16-078478-1(6)*, Office of the Federal Register) United States Government Printing Office.

Ferguson, Michaele L. & Marso, Lori Jo, eds. W Stands for Women: How the George W. Bush Presidency Shaped a New Politics of Gender. 2007. (ENG., Illus.). 304p. (C). 84.95 *(978-0-8223-4064-5(X))*; per. 23.95 *(978-0-8223-4042-3(9))* Duke Univ. Pr.

Finlay, Barbara. George W. Bush & the War on Women: Turning Back the Clock on Progress. 2006. (ENG.). 288p. 94.95 *(978-1-84277-784-8(X))*; per. 27.95 *(978-1-84277-785-5(8))* Zed Bks., Ltd. GBR. Dist: Macmillan.

Flynn, Matthew J. Contesting History: The Bush Counterinsurgency Legacy in Iraq, 1 vol. 2010. (Praeger Security International Ser.). (Illus.). 164p. 44.95 *(978-0-313-38488-2(6)*, A2937C, Praeger Pubs.) Greenwood Publishing Group, Inc.

Frank, Justin A. Bush on the Couch: Inside the Mind of the President. rev. ed. 2007. (ENG.). 320p. pap. 15.95 *(978-0-06-143065-7(X)*, Harper Paperbacks) HarperCollins Pubs.

Fuqua, Jacques L., Jr. Nuclear Endgame: The Need for Engagement with North Korea, 1 vol. 2007. (Praeger Security International Ser.). (Illus.). 224p. 49.95 *(978-0-275-99074-9(5)*, C9074, Praeger Security International) Greenwood Publishing Group, Inc.

Galbraith, James K. Unbearable Cost: Bush, Greenspan & the Economics of Empire. 2006. (ENG.). 256p. pap. 30.00 *(978-0-230-01901-0(3))*; (Illus.). 240p. 116.00 *(978-0-230-01889-1(0))* Palgrave Macmillan.

Galvin, Daniel. Presidential Party Building: Dwight D. Eisenhower to George W. Bush. 2009. (Princeton Studies in American Politics: Historical, International, & Comparative Perspectives Ser.). (ENG., Illus.). 352p. (C). pap. 28.95 *(978-0-691-13693-6(9))* Princeton Univ. Pr.

Galvin, Daniel J. Presidential Party Building: Dwight D. Eisenhower to George W. Bush. 2009. (Princeton Studies in American Politics: Historical, International, & Comparative Perspectives Ser.). (ENG., Illus.). 352p. (C). 67.50 *(978-0-691-13692-9(0))* Princeton Univ. Pr.

Gawenda, Michael. American Notebook: A Personal & Political Journey. 2007. (ENG.). 288p. 25.00 *(978-0-522-85253-0(X))* Melbourne Univ. Publishing AUS. Dist: Independent Pubs. Group.

—Coming to the Party: Where to Next for Labor? Jones, Barry, ed. 2007. (ENG.). 256p. pap. 19.00 *(978-0-522-85283-7(1))* Melbourne Univ. Publishing AUS. Dist: Independent Pubs. Group.

George W. Bush. Date not set. (American Presidents Ser.). 20.00 *(978-0-8050-6968-6(2)*, Times Bks.) Holt, Henry & Co.

Getting to the Truth Through a Nonpartisan Commission of Inquiry: Hearing Before the Committee on the Judiciary, United States Senate, One Hundred Eleventh Congress, First Session, March 4, 2009. 2009. iv, 236p. *(978-0-16-085165-0(3)*, 552-070-40519-4) United States Government Printing Office.

Gibson, John. How the Left Swiftboated America: The Liberal Media Conspiracy to Make You Think George Bush Was the Worst President in History. 304p. 2010. (ENG.). pap. 15.99 *(978-0-06-179291-5(8)*, Harper Paperbacks) 2009. 26.99 *(978-0-06-179289-2(6))* HarperCollins Pubs.

Gitlin, Todd. The Bulldozer & the Big Tent: Blind Republicans, Lame Democrats, & the Recovery of American Ideals. 2007. (ENG.). 336p. 25.95 *(978-0-471-74853-3(6)*, Wiley) Wiley, John & Sons, Inc.

Glenn P. Hastedt. The Presidencies of George Herbert Walker Bush & George Walker Bush: Like Father Like Son? Eksterowicz, Anthony J., ed. 2007. 129.00 *(978-1-60456-163-0(7))* Nova Science Pubs., Inc.

Goldsmith, Jack. The Terror Presidency: Law & Judgement Inside the Bush Administration. 2007. (ENG.). 256p. 25.95 *(978-0-393-06550-3(2)*, 6550); 24.95 *(978-0-7930-6550-9(X))* Norton, W. W. & Co., Inc.

Goldsmith, Jack & Goldsmith. The Terror Presidency: Law & Judgement Inside the Bush Administration. 2009. (ENG.). 272p. pap. 16.95 *(978-0-393-33533-0(X)*, 33533) Norton, W. W. & Co., Inc.

Golinger, Eva. Bush Versus Chávez: Washington's War on Venezuela. 2007. (ENG., Illus.). 160p. 50.00 *(978-1-58367-166-5(8))*; per. 15.95 *(978-1-58367-165-8(X))* Monthly Review Pr.

Gore, Al. The Assault on Reason. 2008. (ENG.). 320p. (gr. 12-18). 16.00 *(978-0-14-311362-1(3)*, Penguin (Non-Classics)) Penguin Group (USA) Inc.

—The Assault on Reason. Lt. ed. 2008. (ENG.). 540p. pap. 15.95 *(978-1-59413-282-7(8)*, Large Print Pr.) Thorndike Pr.

—The Assault on Reason: How the Politics of Blind Faith Subvert Wise Decision-Making. 2007. (ENG.). 320p. (gr. 12-18). 25.95 *(978-1-59420-122-6(6)*, Penguin Pr. HC, The) Penguin Group (USA) Inc.

Gow, James & Kerr, Rachel, eds. Bush's Foreign & Security Policy: Principle or Partisanship? 2012. (Contemporary Security Studies). (ENG.). 224p. (C). 128.00 *(978-0-415-48661-3(0))* Routledge.

Graham, John D. Bush on the Home Front: Domestic Policy Triumphs & Setbacks. 2010. (ENG.). 440p. 75.00 *(978-0-253-35436-5(6)*, 0253354366); (Illus.). pap. 27.95 *(978-0-253-22215-2(X)*, 025322215X) Indiana Univ. Pr.

Greene, John Robert. The George W. Bush Years. 2010. (Presidential Profiles Ser.). (Illus.). 432p. (C). (gr. 9). 95.00 *(978-0-8160-7765-6(7))* Facts On File, Inc.

Gregg & Rozell & Cram101 Textbook Reviews Staff. Considering the Bush Presidency. 2007. 192p. per. 13.95 *(978-1-4288-2468-3(5))* Cram101 Inc.

Haas, Michael. America's War Crimes Quagmire, from Bush to Obama. 2010. x, 278p. *(978-0-615-39982-9(7))* Morrison Publishing.

Haas, Michael. George W. Bush, War Criminal? The Bush Administration's Liability for 269 War Crimes, 1 vol. 2008. (Illus.). 408p. 39.95 *(978-0-313-36499-0(0)*, C36499, Praeger Pubs.) Greenwood Publishing Group, Inc.

Haass, Richard N. War of Necessity, War of Choice: A Memoir of Two Iraq Wars. 2010. (ENG.). 368p. pap. 16.00 *(978-1-4165-4903-1(X))* Simon & Schuster.

Harwood, William. American Hitler: George W. ShicklBush & the Republicanazi Gestapo. Strozier, M. Stefan & Torke, Kyle, eds. 2008. 200p. per. 20.00 *(978-1-934209-87-5(2))* World Audience Pubs.

Hayden, Joe. A Dubya in the Headlights: President George W. Bush & the Media. 2009. (ENG., Illus.). 294p. 78.99 *(978-0-7391-2571-7(0))* Lexington Bks.

Hayden, Joseph. A Dubya in the Headlights: President George W. Bush & the Media. 2010. (ENG.). 294p. pap. 32.95 *(978-0-7391-2572-4(9))* Lexington Bks.

Healy, Gene. The Cult of the Presidency: America's Dangerous Devotion to Executive Power. rev. ed. 2009. (ENG.). 264p. pap. 15.95 *(978-1-933995-19-9(X))* Cato Institute.

Heinzl, Karin Christine. George W Bush & Tony Blair's Leadership During the War in Iraq. 2010. 104p. pap. *(978-3-639-22269-2(5))* VDM Verlag Dr. Mueller e.K.

Highton, Jake. A Terrible Country. 2008. 234p. *(978-0-9722487-3-0(0))* On-Call Publishing.

Hodges, Adam. The "War on Terror" Narrative: Discourse & Intertextuality in the Construction & Contestation of Sociopolitical Reality. 2011. (Oxford Studies in Sociolinguistics Ser.). (ENG.). 208p. pap. 39.95 *(978-0-19-975958-3(8))* Oxford Univ. Pr., Inc.

Holsinger, Bruce. Neomedievalism, Neoconservatism, & the War on Terror. 2007. 117p. per. 12.95 *(978-0-9761475-9-6(9))* Prickly Paradigm Pr., LLC.

Hoopes, James. Hail to the CEO: The Failure of George W. Bush & the Cult of Moral Leadership, 1 vol. 2007. (Illus.). 144p. 34.95 *(978-0-313-34784-9(0)*, C34784, Praeger Pubs.) Greenwood Publishing Group, Inc.

Huffington, Arianna S. Fanatics & Fools: How Politicians are Betraying the American People. 2008. (Playaway Adult Nonfiction Ser.). 44.99 *(978-1-60640-933-6(6))* Findaway World, LLC.

Hybel, Alex Roberto & Kaufman, Justin Matthew. The Bush Administrations & Saddam Hussein: Deciding on Conflict. 2006. (Advances in Foreign Policy Analysis Ser.). (ENG.). 208p. 84.00 *(978-1-4039-7578-2(7))* Palgrave Macmillan.

Iglesias, David. In Justice: Inside the Scandal That Rocked the Bush Administration. 2008. (ENG.). 256p. 25.95 *(978-0-470-26197-2(8)*, Wiley) Wiley, John & Sons, Inc.

Isikoff, Michael & Corn, David. Hubris: The Inside Story of Spin, Scandal, & the Selling of the Iraq War. 2007. (ENG.). 496p. per. 14.95 *(978-0-307-34682-7(X)*, Three Rivers Pr.) Crown Publishing Group.

Jacobsen, Kurt. Pacification & its Discontents. 2009. (ENG., Illus.). 100p. pap. 12.95 *(978-0-9794057-8-5(5))* Prickly Paradigm Pr., LLC.

Jacobson, Gary C. Divider, A, Not a Uniter. 2nd ed. 2010. (ENG., Illus.). 312p. (C). pap. 37.80 *(978-0-205-77603-0(5))* Longman Publishing Group.

Juhasz, Antonia. The Bush Agenda: Invading the World, One Economy at a Time. 2007. 416p. pap. 15.95 *(978-0-06-087878-8(9)*, HarperPerennial) HarperCollins Pubs.

Kaufman, Robert G. In Defense of the Bush Doctrine. 2008. (ENG.). 264p. per. 24.95 *(978-0-8131-9185-0(8))* Univ. Pr. of Kentucky.

Kaufman, Robert G. & Kaufman, Robert Gordon. In Defense of the Bush Doctrine. 2007. (ENG.). 264p. 50.00 *(978-0-8131-2434-6(4))* Univ. Pr. of Kentucky.

Kelley, Colleen E. Post-9/11 American Presidential Rhetoric: A Study of Protofascist Discourse. 2008. (Lexington Studies in Political Communication Ser.). (ENG.). 340p. pap. 38.99 *(978-0-7391-2925-8(2))* Lexington Bks.

Kelley, Colleen Elizabeth. Post-9/11 American Presidential Rhetoric: A Study of Protofascist Discourse. 2007. (Lexington Studies in Political Communication Ser.). (ENG.). 340p. 78.99 *(978-0-7391-1226-7(0))* Lexington Bks.

Kennedy-Shaffer, Alan. Denial & Deception: A Study of the Bush Administration's Rhetorical Case for Invading Iraq. 2006. (Illus.). 208p. pap. 19.95 *(978-1-58112-934-2(3))* Universal Pubs.

Kitfield, James. War & Destiny: How the Bush Revolution in Foreign & Military Affairs Redefined American Power. 2007. (Illus.). 400p. per. 17.95 *(978-1-59797-000-6(X))* Potomac Bks., Inc.

Knott, Stephen F. George W. Bush, the War on Terror, & His Critics. 2012. ix, 236p. *(978-0-7006-1831-6(7))* Univ. Pr. of Kansas.

Kolin, Andrew. State Power & Democracy: Before & During the Presidency of George W. Bush. 2010. (ENG.). 262p. 89.00 *(978-0-230-10935-3(7))* Palgrave Macmillan.

Kolodziej, Edward A. & Kanet, Roger E., eds. From Superpower to Besieged Global Power: Restoring World Order after the Failure of the Bush Doctrine. 2008. (Studies in Security & International Affairs Ser.). (ENG.). 440p. lib. bdg. 69.95 *(978-0-8203-2977-2(0))*; (Illus.). pap. 24.95 *(978-0-8203-3074-7(4))* Univ. of Georgia Pr.

Konnel, T R. W - Weighed & Found Wanting: The Bush Record. 2006. 322p. per. 19.95 *(978-1-60002-113-8(1)*, 3986) Mountain Valley Publishing, LLC.

Koplowitz, Bradford. Our Brave New World Compilation. 2010. 389p. pap. 20.99 *(978-0-557-33697-5(X))* Lulu Enterprises Inc.

Kucinich, Dennis. The 35 Articles of Impeachment & the Case for Prosecuting George W. Bush. 2008. (ENG.). 180p. pap. 12.00 *(978-1-932595-42-0(2))* Feral Hse.

Lancaster, Carol. George Bush's Foreign Aid: Transformation or Chaos? 2008. (ENG., Illus.). 125p. pap. 18.95 *(978-1-933286-27-3(X))* Ctr. for Global Development.

Lansford, Tom, et al. America's War on Terror. 2nd rev. ed. 2009. (Illus.). 326p. 119.95 *(978-0-7546-7785-7(0))*; pap. 39.95 *(978-0-7546-7787-1(7))* Ashgate Publishing Co.

Leffler, Melvyn P. & Legro, Jeffrey. To Lead the World: American Strategy after the Bush Doctrine. Leffler, Melvyn P. & Legro, Jeffrey W., eds. 2008. (ENG., Illus.). 320p. 99.00 *(978-0-19-533098-4(6))*; pap. 17.95 *(978-0-19-536941-0(6))* Oxford Univ. Pr., Inc.

Leonard, Barry, ed. The Constitution in Crisis: The Downing Street Minutes & Deception, Manipulation, Torture, Retribution, & Coverups in the Iraq War: Congressional Report. 2006. 269p. (C). pap. 45.00 *(978-1-4223-0651-2(8))* DIANE Publishing Co.

Leslie, Craig R. The 2007 Bush-Cheney Impeachments: Year 2008 10th Grade Civics Exam. Berman, Harry F., ed. 2006. (Illus.). x, 165p. per. 17.76 *(978-0-9701904-6-8(8)*, B6I) Layman's Pr., A.

Lester, Paul Martin. On Floods & Photo Ops: How Herbert Hoover & George W. Bush Exploited Catastrophes. 2009. (ENG., Illus.). 240p. 50.00 *(978-1-60473-286-3(5))* Univ. Pr. of Mississippi.

Lind, Nancy S. & Tamas, Bernard Ivan. Controversies of the George W. Bush Presidency: Pro & Con Documents. 2006. 208p. 59.95 *(978-0-313-34011-6(0)*, GR4011, Greenwood Pr.) Greenwood Publishing Group, Inc.

Linker, Damon. The Theocons: Secular America under Siege. 2007. (ENG.). 304p. pap. 14.95 *(978-1-4000-9685-5(5)*, Anchor) Knopf Doubleday Publishing Group.

Macdonald, David B., et al. The Bush Leadership the Power of Ideas & the War on Terror. 2012. 200p. 99.95 *(978-1-4094-4715-3(4))* Ashgate Publishing Co.

Mackiewicz Wolfe, Wojtek. Winning the War of Words: Selling the War on Terror from Afghanistan to Iraq, 1 vol. 2008. (Praeger Security International Ser.). (Illus.). 152p. 75.00 *(978-0-313-34967-6(3)*, C34967, Praeger Security International) Greenwood Publishing Group, Inc.

Magne, Haaland. George W. Bush a Revolutionary President? An Analysis of Political Speeches by George W. Bush & Harry S. Truman. 2011. 144p. pap. *(978-3-639-33556-9(2))* VDM Verlag Dr. Mueller e.K.

Maranto, Robert, et al, eds. Judging Bush. 2009. (Studies in the Modern Presidency Ser.). (ENG.). 360p. pap. 24.95 *(978-0-8047-6069-8(6))*; (Illus.). 75.00 *(978-0-8047-6088-1(8))* Stanford Univ. Pr.

Mcadam, Richard. American Leadership & the Future of the Bush Doctrine. 2008. 140p. pap. *(978-3-639-06135-2(7))* VDM Verlag Dr. Mueller e.K.

McClellan, Scott. What Happened: Inside the Bush White House & Washington's Culture of Deception. (ENG., Illus.). 368p. 2009. pap. 16.95 *(978-1-58648-700-3(0))* 2008. 27.95 *(978-1-58648-556-6(3))* PublicAffairs.

McDaniel, Douglas. Forty Days of Fire, Forty Days of Rain. 2009. 222p. pap. 19.36 *(978-0-557-05432-9(X))* Lulu Enterprises Inc.

McGettigan, Timothy. Adieu Dubya: A Fond Farewell to the Worst President Ever. 2009. 63p. pap. 22.50 *(978-0-557-05110-6(X))* Lulu Enterprises Inc.

Mcmahon, Kevin J. Transformed by Crisis: The Presidency of George W. Bush & American Politics. McMahon, Kevin J. et al, eds. 2007. (ENG.). 226p. pap. 32.00 *(978-0-230-60221-2(5))* Palgrave Macmillan.

McNeely, Dave & Henderson, Jim. Bob Bullock: God Bless Texas. 2008. (Clifton & Shirley Caldwell Texas Heritage Ser.). (ENG., Illus.). 328p. 29.95 *(978-0-292-71454-0(8))* Univ. of Texas Pr.

McWilliam, Neil, ed. Lines of Attack: Conflicts in Caricature. 2010. (ENG., Illus.). 96p. pap. 18.95 *(978-0-938989-32-5(4))* Duke Univ. Pr.

Medhurst, Martin J. The Prospect of Presidential Rhetoric. Aune, James Arnt, ed. 2008. (Presidential Rhetoric Ser.: No. 18). 400p. (ENG.). 50.00 *(978-1-58544-626-1(2))*; (Illus.). per. 29.95 *(978-1-58544-627-8(0))* Texas A&M Univ. Pr.

Messerschmidt, James W. Hegemonic Masculinities & Camouflaged Politics: Unmasking the Bush Dynasty & Its War Against Iraq. 2010. 216p. 107.00 *(978-1-59451-817-1(3))* Paradigm Pubs.

Metz, Steven. Decisionmaking in Operation IRAQI FREEDOM: Removing Saddam Hussein by Force. Martin, John R., ed. 2010. (OIF Key Decisions Ser.). *(978-1-58487-426-3(0))* Strategic Studies Institute, U.S. Army War College Commandant (AWCC-DSI/Pubns.).

—Decisionmaking in Operation Iraqi Freedom: The Strategic Shift Of 2007. 2010. (OIF Key Decisions Ser.). *(978-1-58487-441-6(4))* Strategic Studies Institute, U.S. Army War College Commandant (AWCC-DSI/Pubns.).

Miller, Mark Crispin. Fooled Again: The Real Case for Electoral Reform. annot. ed. 2007. (ENG.). 512p. per. 16.95 *(978-0-465-04580-8(4))* Basic Bks.

—Misunderestimated & Overunderappreciated: The George W. Bush Administration As Seen Through the Eyes of the Tribune's Syndicated Editorial Cartoonists. 2007. (Illus.). 328p. *(978-1-4351-0017-6(4))* Metro Bks.

Miller, T. Christian. Blood Money: Wasted Billions, Lost Lives, & Corporate Greed in Iraq. 2007. (ENG., Illus.). 368p. per. 14.99 *(978-0-316-16628-7(6)*, Back Bay Bks.) Little Brown & Co.

Mondak, Jeffery & Mitchell, Dona-Gene, eds. Fault Lines: Why the Republicans Lost Congress. 2008. (Controversies in Electoral Democracy & Representation Ser.). (Illus.). CLXXVI, 16p. 148.00 *(978-0-415-99361-6(X))*; 35.50 *(978-0-415-99362-3(8))* Routledge.

Montgomery, Bruce P. The Bush-Cheney Administration's Assault on Open Government, 1 vol. 2008. 232p. 49.95 *(978-0-275-99904-9(1)*, C9904, Praeger Pubs.) Greenwood Publishing Group, Inc.

Morgan, Iwan W., et al. The Federal Nation: Perspectives on American Federalism. Morgan, Iwan W. & Davies, Philip J., eds. 2008. (Studies of the Americas Ser.). (ENG., Illus.). 288p. 105.00 *(978-0-230-60940-2(6))* Palgrave Macmillan.

Morgan, William W. The Biblical Flood: Global Warming & Bush's Harvest. 2006. per. 19.95 *(978-0-9778492-3-9(6))* Morgan, William W.

Morman, Robert R. George W Bush Legacy - Dee'Zaster: America Second, National Betrayal. 2009. 504p. pap. 22.99 *(978-1-4490-3209-8(5))* AuthorHouse.

Morris, Christopher, photos by. My America, 1 vol. 2006. (ENG., Illus.). 180p. 40.00 *(978-3-86521-201-6(8))* Steidl, Gerhard Druckerei und Verlag DEU. Dist: Innovative Logistics.

Mycoff, Jason D. & Pika, Joseph A. Confrontation & Compromise: Presidential & Congressional Leadership, 2001-2006. 2007. (ENG.). 282p. 80.00 *(978-0-7425-4059-0(6))*; per. 29.95 *(978-0-7425-4060-6(X))* Rowman & Littlefield Publishers, Inc.

Nautré, Zoé. U. S. Idealism Meets Reality: Democracy Promotion in the Middle East During the George W. Bush Administration. 2010. 216p. pap. 43.00 *(978-3-8329-6000-1(7))* Nomos Verlagsgesellschaft DEU. Dist: International Specialized Bk. Services.

Nichter, Luke A. & Peterson, Barbara Bennett. George W. Bush: Life of Privilege, Leadership in Crisis. 2012. *(978-1-62081-213-6(4))* Nova Science Pubs., Inc.

O'Driscoll, Cian & O'driscoll, Cian. The Renegotiation of the Just War Tradition & the Right to War in the Twenty-First Century. 2008. (ENG.). 244p. 95.00 *(978-0-230-60583-1(4))* Palgrave Macmillan.

Oinstrin. May The Best Man Lose. Date not set. *(978-0-312-00224-4(6))* St. Martin's Pr.

Oliphant, Thomas. Utter Incompetents: Ego & Ideology in the Age of Bush. 2008. (ENG.). 304p. pap. 16.99 *(978-0-312-38566-8(8)*, St. Martin's Griffin) St. Martin's Pr.

Ornstein, Norman J. & Fortier, John C., eds. Second-Term Blues: How George W. Bush Has Governed. 2007. (ENG.). 146p. 24.95 *(978-0-8157-2884-9(0))* Brookings Institution Pr.

Paragoso, Liberacion. Chosen: The Presidency of George Walker Bush, the 43rd President of the United States of America. 2006. pap. 9.00 *(978-0-8059-7186-6(6))* Dorrance Publishing Co., Inc.

Parry, Robert, et al. Neck Deep: The Disastrous Presidency of George Bush. 2007. 428p. 29.95 *(978-1-893517-02-8(0))*; pap. 22.95 *(978-1-893517-03-5(9))* Media Consortium, The.

Paust, Jordan J. Beyond the Law: The Bush Administration's Unlawful Responses in the War on Terror. 2007. (ENG.). 326p. per. 34.00 *(978-0-521-71120-3(7))*; 99.00 *(978-0-521-88426-6(8))* Cambridge Univ. Pr.

Peleg, Ilan. The Legacy of George W. Bush's Foreign Policy: Moving Beyond Neoconservatism. 2009. (ENG.). 224p. pap. 27.00 *(978-0-8133-4446-1(8))* Westview Pr.

Pfiffner, James P. Power Play: The Bush Presidency & the Constitution. (ENG.). 299p. 2009. pap. 22.95 *(978-0-8157-0335-8(X))* 2008. 36.95 *(978-0-8157-7044-2(8))* Brookings Institution Pr.

Phillips, Kevin. American Theocracy: The Peril & Politics of Radical Religion, Oil, & Borrowed Money in the 21st Century. 2007. (ENG.). 480p. (gr. 12-18). 17.00 *(978-0-14-303828-3(1)*, Penguin (Non-Classics)) Penguin Group (USA) Inc.

Phillips, Peter & Loo, Dennis, eds. Impeach the President: The Case Against Bush & Cheney. 2006. (ENG., Illus.). 352p. per. 17.95 *(978-1-58322-743-5(1))* Seven Stories Pr.

Picca, Walter. Why the Reagan & Bush tax-cuts are Unfair. 2nd ed. 2007. 100p. per. 12.95 *(978-0-595-46262-9(6))* iUniverse, Inc.

Piven, Frances Fox. The War at Home: The Domestic Costs of Bush's Militarism. 2006. (ENG.). 165p. per. 14.95 *(978-1-59558-092-4(1))* New Pr., The.

Podhoretz, John. Untitled Biography Of George Bush. Date not set. mass mkt. *(978-0-312-99533-1(4)*, St. Martin's Paperbacks) St. Martin's Pr.

Powers, Thomas. The Military Error: Baghdad & Beyond in America's War of Choice. 2008. (ENG.). 140p. pap. 14.95 *(978-1-59017-299-5(X))* New York Review of Bks., Inc., The.

Presidential Signing Statements under the Bush Administration: A Threat to Checks & Balances & the Rule of Law?: Hearing Before the Committee on the Judiciary, House of Representatives, One Hundred Tenth Congress, First Session, January 31, 2007. 2007. iv, 136p. *(978-0-16-079037-9(9)*, 552-070-36147-2) United States Government Printing Office.

Preston, Thomas. Pandora's Trap: Presidential Decision Making & Blame Avoidance in Vietnam & Iraq. 2011. x, 264p. E-Book *(978-1-4422-1215-2(2))*; (ENG.). 252p. (gr. 17). 75.00 *(978-0-7425-6263-9(8))* Rowman & Littlefield Publishers, Inc.

Provost, Colin & Teske, Paul. President George W. Bush's Influence over Bureaucracy & Policy: Extraordinary Times, Extraordinary Powers. Provost, Colin & Teske, Paul, eds. 2009. (Evolving American Presidency Ser.). (ENG., Illus.). 288p. 105.00 *(978-0-230-60954-9(6))* Palgrave Macmillan.

Record, Jeffrey. Wanting War: Why the Bush Administration Invaded Iraq. 2010. 226p. 24.95 *(978-1-59797-437-0(4))* Potomac Bks., Inc.

Rice, Condoleezza. No Higher Honor: A Memoir of My Years in Washington. 2012. (ENG.). 784p. pap. 18.00 *(978-0-307-98678-8(0))* Broadway Bks.

—No Higher Honor: A Memoir of My Years in Washington. 2011. (ENG., Illus.). 784p. 35.00 *(978-0-307-58786-2(X)*, Crown) Crown Publishing Group.

Rich, Frank. The Greatest Story Ever Sold: The Decline & Fall of Truth in Bush's America. 2007. (ENG.). 352p. (gr. 12-18). 15.00 *(978-0-14-311234-1(1)*, Penguin (Non-Classics)) Penguin Group (USA) Inc.

Risen, James. State of War: The Secret History of the CIA & the Bush Administration. 2006. 240p. 26.00 *(978-1-4223-5680-7(9))* DIANE Publishing Co.

—State of War: The Secret History of the CIA & the Bush Administration. 2006. (ENG., Illus.). 272p. pap. 15.00 *(978-0-7432-7067-0(3)*, Free Pr.) Free Pr.

Ritchie. The Political Road to War with Iraq. 2007. pap. 39.95 *(978-0-415-45950-1(8))* Routledge.

Ritchie, Nick & Rogers, Paul. The Political Road to War with Iraq: Bush, 9/11 & the Drive to Overthrow Saddam. 2006. (Contemporary Security Studies). (ENG.). 240p. 160.00 *(978-0-415-39732-2(4))* Routledge.

Roberts, Alasdair. The Collapse of Fortress Bush: The Crisis of Authority in American Government. 2008. (ENG., Illus.). 272p. 37.00 *(978-0-8147-7606-3(X))* New York Univ. Pr.

Rounds, Frederic. Reflections on the War of the Willing. 2008. 280p. 30.95 *(978-0-595-50977-5(0))*; pap. 20.95 *(978-0-595-52252-1(1))* iUniverse, Inc.

Rountree, Clarke. The Chameleon President: The Curious Case of George W. Bush, 1 vol. 2011. (Illus.). 287p. 48.00 *(978-0-313-39799-8(6)*, A3604C); E-Book *(978-0-313-39800-1(3)*, Praeger Pubs.) Greenwood Publishing Group, Inc.

—George W. Bush: A Biography, 1 vol. 2010. (Greenwood Biographies Ser.). (Illus.). 197p. 35.00 *(978-0-313-38500-1(9)*, A2951C); xxx, 197p. E-Book *(978-0-313-38501-8(7)*, Greenwood Pr.) Greenwood Publishing Group, Inc.

—Judging the Supreme Court: Constructions of Motives in Bush V. Gore. 2007. (Rhetoric & Public Affairs Ser.). (ENG.). 510p. 79.95 *(978-0-87013-809-6(X))* Michigan State Univ. Pr.

Rove, Karl. Courage & Consequence: My Life as a Conservative in the Fight. 2010. (ENG., Illus.). 640p. pap. 18.00 *(978-1-4165-9241-9(5))*; 608p. 30.00 *(978-1-4391-9105-7(0))* Threshold Editions. (Threshold Editions).

Rozell, Mark. Testing the Limits: George W. Bush & the Imperial Presidency. 2009. (ENG.). 280p. 89.00 *(978-1-4422-0039-5(1))* Rowman & Littlefield Publishers, Inc.

Rozell, Mark J. & Whitney, Gleaves. Religion & the Bush Presidency. 2007. (Evolving American Presidency Ser.). (ENG.). 268p. 89.00 *(978-1-4039-8007-6(1))* Palgrave Macmillan.

Rozell/Whitney, ed. Testing the Limits: George W. Bush & the Imperial Presidency. 2009. (ENG.). 280p. pap. 29.95 *(978-1-4422-0040-1(5))* Rowman & Littlefield Publishers, Inc.

Rudolf, Peter. Imperiale Illusionen: Amerikanische Aussenpolitik Unter Präsident George W. Bush. 2007. (GER.). 219p. pap. 36.00 *(978-3-8329-2928-2(2))* Nomos Verlagsgesellschaft DEU. Dist: International Specialized Bk. Services.

Russomanno, Joseph. Tortured Logic: A Verbatim Critique of the George W. Bush Presidency. 2011. (Illus.). 352p. 34.95 *(978-1-59797-513-1(3))* Potomac Bks., Inc.

Sabato, Larry J. The Sixth Year Itch: The Rise & Fall of the George W. Bush Presidency. 2007. (Illus.). 528p. per. 17.40 *(978-0-321-46700-3(0))* Longman Publishing.

Sammon, Bill. The Evangelical President: George Bush's Struggle to Spread a Moral Democracy Throughout the World. 2007. (ENG.). 232p. 27.95 *(978-1-59698-518-6(6))* Regnery Publishing, Inc., An Eagle Publishing Co.

Sanger, David E. The Inheritance: The World Obama Confronts & the Challenges to American Power. 2010. (ENG., Illus.). 544p. pap. 16.00 *(978-0-307-40793-1(4)*, Three Rivers Pr.) Crown Publishing Group.

Scheib, Walter & Friedman, Andrew. White House Chef: Eleven Years, Two Presidents, One Kitchen. 2007. (ENG., Illus.). 336p. 24.95 *(978-0-471-79842-2(8)*, Wiley) Wiley, John & Sons, Inc.

Schier, Steven, ed. Ambition & Division: Legacies of the George W. Bush Presidency. 2009. (ENG.). 320p. (C). pap. 27.95 *(978-0-8229-6049-2(4))* Univ. of Pittsburgh Pr.

Schier, Steven E. Panorama of a Presidency: How George W. Bush Acquired & Spent His Political Capital. 2008. (ENG.). 208p. pap. 31.95 *(978-0-7656-1693-7(9))*; (Illus.). 73.95 *(978-0-7656-1692-0(0))* Sharpe, M.E. Inc.

Schneider, Jonas. The Change toward Cooperation in the George W. Bush Administration's Nuclear Nonproliferation Policy toward North Korea. 2010. (Europäische Hochschulschriften. Reihe 31: Politikwissenschaft Ser.). (Illus.).

B

202p. pap. 50.95 *(978-3-631-60213-3(8))* Lang, Peter GmbH, Europaischer Verlag der Wissenschaften DEU. Dist: Lang, Peter.
Sheehan, Cindy. Peace Mom: A Mother's Journey through Heartache to Activism. 2010. (ENG.). 256p. pap. 16.99 *(978-0-7432-9792-9(X)*, Beyond Words/Atria Bks.) Atria Bks.
Silberhorn, Hubert. Das Ende der Republican Revolution: Die Präsidentschaft George W. Bush und der Neue Konservativismus in der Gesundheits- und Sozialpolitik. 2009. (GER.). 288p. 64.95 *(978-3-631-58548-1(9))* Lang, Peter GmbH, Europaischer Verlag der Wissenschaften DEU. Dist: Lang, Peter.
Skiba, Alexander. The Bush-Administration's Iran Policy & Europe: From «Regime Change» to «Engagement»? 2008. 100p. pap. *(978-3-8364-8773-3(X))* VDM Verlag Dr. Mueller e.K.
Skowronek, Stephen. Presidential Leadership in Political Time. 2nd ed. 2011. 240p. 34.95 *(978-0-7006-1783-8(3))*; pap. 17.95 *(978-0-7006-1762-3(0))* Univ. Pr. of Kansas.
—Presidential Leadership in Political Time: Reprise & Reappraisal. 2008. (Illus.). 192p. *(978-0-7006-1574-2(1))*; per. *(978-0-7006-1575-9(X))* Univ. Pr. of Kansas.
Smith, Charles Anthony. The Rise & Fall of War Crimes Trials: From Charles I to Bush II. 2012. (ENG.). 336p. 99.00 ***(978-1-107-02354-3(8))*** Cambridge Univ. Pr.
Smith, Dane F. U. S. Peacefare: Organizing American Peace-Building Operations, 1 vol. 2010. (Praeger Security International Ser.). (Illus.). 301p. 44.95 *(978-0-313-38262-8(X)*, A2673C, Praeger Pubs.) Greenwood Publishing Group, Inc.
Stramer, Janicke. U. S. Foreign Policy & Religion During the Cold War & the War on Terror: A Study of How Harry S. Truman & George W. Bush Administrations Procured Public Support for Warfare. 2011. 192p. 109.95 ***(978-0-7734-1607-9(2))*** Mellen, Edwin Pr., The.
Strozier, M., ed. Impeaching George W Bush & His Administration; Essays by Different Writers. 2007. 148p. per. 15.99 *(978-1-934209-91-2(0))* World Audience Pubs.
Suedfeld, Peter & Renshon, Stanley A., eds. Understanding the Bush Doctrine: Psychology & Strategy in an Age of Terrorism. 2007. (Illus.). 344p. 145.00 *(978-0-415-95503-4(3))*; per. 43.95 *(978-0-415-95504-1(1))* Routledge.
Sunstein, Cass R. & Epstein, Richard Allen, eds. The Vote: Bush, Gore, & the Supreme Court. Date not set. pap. *(978-0-226-21308-8(0))* Univ. of Chicago Pr.
Swansbrough, Robert. Test by Fire: The War Presidency of George W. Bush. 2008. (Evolving American Presidency Ser.). (ENG.). 304p. 89.00 *(978-0-230-60099-7(9))*; pap. 33.00 *(978-0-230-60100-0(6))* Palgrave Macmillan.
Tabler, Andrew. In the Lion's Den: An Eyewitness Account of Washington's Battle with Syria. 2011. (ENG.). 288p. pap. 16.95 *(978-1-56976-843-3(9)*, Hill, Lawrence Bks.) Chicago Review Pr., Inc.
Tanner, Stephen. Wars of the Bushes: A Legacy Betrayed & the Geopolitical Decline of the New World. 2007. (Illus.). 312p. pap. 18.95 *(978-1-932033-61-8(0))* Casemate Pubs. & Bk. Distributors, LLC.
Termini, Michael. Exceptionalism & the George W Bush Presidency. 2009. 172p. pap. *(978-3-639-12782-9(X))* VDM Verlag Dr. Mueller e.K.
Terrorism Documents of International & Local Control: Volumes 90 And 91. 2008. (Terrorism: Documents of International & Local Control Ser.). 120.00 *(978-0-19-538101-6(7))* Oxford Univ. Pr., Inc.
Thoreau, Jackson. Born to Cheat: How Bush, Cheney, Rove & Co. Broke the Rules - from the Sandlot to the White House. 2007. 256p. per. 19.95 net. *(978-1-881365-53-2(0))* Shay Publications/Random Publishers.
Tripathi, Deepak. Overcoming the Bush Legacy in Iraq & Afghanistan. 2010. (Illus.). 200p. 24.95 *(978-1-59797-503-2(6))* Potomac Bks., Inc.
Ulvin, Hege Kristin. The United States & the Norm of Non-Intervention. 2010. 120p. pap. *(978-3-639-25315-3(9))* VDM Verlag Dr. Mueller e.K.
Unger, Craig. American Armageddon: How the Delusions of the Neoconservatives & the Christian Right Triggered the Descent of America — and Still Imperil Our Future. 2008. (ENG., Illus.). 480p. pap. 16.00 *(978-0-7432-8076-1(8)*, Free Pr.) Free Pr.
—House of Bush, House of Saud: The Hidden Relationship between the World's Two Most Powerful Dynasties. 2007. (Illus.). 355p. reprint ed. 35.00 *(978-1-4223-9016-0(0))* DIANE Publishing Co.
Urban, Hugh B. The Secrets of the Kingdom: Religion & Concealment in the Bush Administration. 2007. (ENG.). 244p. 79.00 *(978-0-7425-5246-3(2))*; per. 25.95 *(978-0-7425-5247-0(0))* Rowman & Littlefield Publishers, Inc.
Velasco, Jesús. Neoconservatives in U. S. Foreign Policy under Ronald Reagan & George W. Bush: Voices behind the Throne. 2010. (ENG.). 320p. (gr. 17). 55.00 *(978-0-8018-9549-4(9))* Johns Hopkins Univ. Pr.
Vidal, Gore. Dreaming War: Blood for Oil & the Cheney-Bush Junta. 2007. (Nation Bks.). (ENG.). 197p. pap. 11.95 *(978-1-56025-502-4(1))* Basic Bks.
Waldherr, Anna. An Evangelical on the Left. 2007. 372p. per. 25.99 *(978-1-59886-941-5(8))* Tate Publishing & Enterprises, LLC.
Wang, Chi. George W. Bush & China: Policies, Problems, & Partnership. 2008. (ENG.). 156p. 47.50 *(978-0-7391-2917-3(1))* Lexington Bks.
Warren, Aiden. Prevention Pre-Emption & the Nuclear Option. 2011. (Routledge Studies in US Foreign Policy Ser.). (ENG.). 264p. 125.00 *(978-0-415-66995-5(2))* Routledge.
Warshaw, Shirley Anne. The Co-Presidency of Bush & Cheney. 2009. (ENG.). 320p. 29.95 *(978-0-8047-5818-5(2))* Stanford Univ. Pr.
Weeks, Albert L. The Choice of War: The Iraq War & the Just War Tradition, 1 vol. 2009. (Ethics of American Foreign Policy Ser.). 200p. 44.95 *(978-0-275-99111-1(3)*, C9111, Praeger Pubs.) Greenwood Publishing Group, Inc.
Weisberg, Jacob. The Bush Tragedy. 2008. (ENG., Illus.). 304p. pap. 16.00 *(978-0-8129-7835-3(8)*, Random House) Random House Publishing Group.
Wickliffe, Richard B. Bush Republicans: Lies & Dirty Tricks. 2008. 104p. pap. 11.49 *(978-1-4389-2675-9(8))* AuthorHouse.
Wilson, Jack L., ed. Imperial Presidency: Reform Lessons from the George W. Bush Era. 2011. (Illus.). vi, 460p. ***(978-1-61728-965-1(5))*** Nova Science Pubs., Inc.
Wilson, Joseph C., intro. George W. Bush Versus the U. S. Constitution: The Downing Street Memos & Deception, Manipulation, Torture, Retribution, Coverups in the Iraq War & Illegal Domestic Spying. 2006. 300p. per. 16.95 *(978-0-89733-550-8(3))* Academy Chicago Pubs., Ltd.
Woodward, Bob. Negar la Evidencia: Bush en la Guerra, Parte III. 2010. (SPA., Illus.). 505p. per. *(978-958-04-9857-5(1))* Norma S.A.
—State of Denial Pt. 3: Bush at War. 2007. (ENG., Illus.). 576p. pap. 16.00 *(978-0-7432-7224-7(2))* Simon & Schuster.
—The War Within: A Secret White House History 2006-2008. 2009. (ENG., Illus.). 512p. pap. 16.00 *(978-1-4165-5898-9(5))* Simon & Schuster.
Wroe, Andrew & Herbert, Jon, eds. Assessing the George W. Bush Presidency. 2010. (ENG.). 256p. (gr. 17). 90.00 *(978-0-7486-2740-0(5))*; pap. 29.50 *(978-0-7486-2741-7(3))* Edinburgh Univ. Pr. GBR. Dist: Columbia Univ. Pr.
Zelden, Charles L. Bush V. Gore: Exposing the Hidden Crisis in American Democracy. 2010. 312p. pap. 19.95 *(978-0-7006-1749-4(3))* 2008. 416p. 34.95 *(978-0-7006-1593-3(8))* Univ. Pr. of Kansas.
Zelizer, Julian E. The Presidency of George W. Bush: A First Historical Assessment. 2010. (ENG.). 398p. (C). 75.00 *(978-0-691-13485-7(5))*; pap. 29.95 *(978-0-691-14901-1(1))* Princeton Univ. Pr.
Zinn, Howard. The Unraveling of the Bush Presidency. 2007. (ENG., Illus.). 48p. per. 7.95 *(978-1-58322-769-5(5))* Seven Stories Pr.
Zylstra, Dick W. Little Hitler. 2009. 272p. pap. 15.49 *(978-1-4389-6037-1(9))* AuthorHouse.

BUSH, LAURA WELCH, 1946-

Bush, Laura. Spoken from the Heart. (ENG.). 464p. 2011. pap. 18.00 *(978-1-4391-5521-9(6))* 2010. 30.00 *(978-1-4391-5520-2(8))* Scribner. (Scribner).
—Spoken from the Heart. l.t. ed. 2011. (ENG.). 822p. pap. 19.99 *(978-1-59413-439-5(1)*, Large Print Pr.) 2010. 32.95 *(978-1-4104-2647-5(5))* Thorndike Pr.
Gerhart, Ann. The Perfect Wife: The Life & Choices of Laura Bush. l.t. ed. 342p. 30.95 *(978-0-7862-6477-3(2)*, Large Print Pr.) Thorndike Pr.
Kessler, Ronald. Laura Bush: An Intimate Portrait of the First Lady. 2007. (ENG., Illus.). 288p. pap. 15.99 *(978-0-7679-2191-6(7)*, Broadway) Broadway Bks.
—Laura Bush: An Intimate Portrait of the First Lady. 2006. (Thorndike Biography Ser.). (Illus.). 401p. 30.95 *(978-0-7862-8871-7(X))* Thorndike Pr.

BUSH FAMILY

Baker, Russ. Family of Secrets: The Bush Dynasty, America's Invisible Government, & the Hidden History of the Last Fifty Years. 2009. (ENG., Illus.). 592p. pap. 20.00 *(978-1-60819-006-5(4))* Bloomsbury Publishing.
—Family of Secrets: The Bush Dynasty, the Powerful Forces That Put It in the White House, & What Their Influence Means for America. 2008. (ENG., Illus.). 592p. 30.00 *(978-1-59691-557-2(9))* Bloomsbury Publishing.
Buick, Robert Clayton. Evil Dynasty. 2011. 144p. pap. 19.99 ***(978-1-4500-0478-7(4))*** Xlibris Corp.
Cohen, David Elliot. The Bush Legacy: Their Story in Photographs. 2011. (ENG., Illus.). 224p. 24.95 *(978-1-4027-8787-4(1))* Sterling Publishing Co., Inc.
Corrigan, Matthew T. American Royalty: The Bush & Clinton Families & the Danger to the American Presidency. 2008. (Evolving American Presidency Ser.). (ENG.). 256p. 89.00 *(978-1-4039-8415-9(8))* Palgrave Macmillan.
Corrigan, Matthew T. & Corrigan, Matthew. American Royalty: The Bush & Clinton Families & the Danger to the American Presidency. 2008. (Evolving American Presidency Ser.). (ENG.). 256p. pap. 31.00 *(978-1-4039-8416-6(6))* Palgrave Macmillan.
McCrary, Patti Sue. Wilson Families in Colonial Virginia & related Mason, Seawell, Goodrich, Boush Families: Ancestors & Kin of Benjamin Wilson (1733-1814) 2007. pap. 28.00 *(978-0-7884-4391-6(7))* Heritage Bks.
Unger, Craig. The Fall of the House of Bush: The Untold Story of How a Band of True Believers Seized the Executive Branch, Started the Iraq War, & Still Imperils America's Future. 2007. (ENG., Illus.). 448p. 27.00 *(978-0-7432-8075-4(X)*, Scribner) Scribner.

BUSH-RANGERS

see Bushrangers

BUSHIDO

Cleary, Thomas. Samurai Wisdom: Lessons from Japan's Warrior Culture. 2009. (ENG.). 256p. 24.95 *(978-0-8048-4008-8(3))* Tuttle Publishing.
—Training the Samurai Mind: A Bushido Sourcebook. 2009. (ENG.). 288p. pap. 18.95 *(978-1-59030-721-2(6))* Shambhala Pubns., Inc.
Hatsumi, Masaaki. The Essence of Budo: The Secret Teachings of the Grandmaster, 1 vol. 2011. (ENG., Illus.). 208p. 35.00 *(978-4-7700-3107-5(6))* Kodansha America, Inc.
Inazo Nitobe. Bushido the Soul of Japan. 2007. 98p. pap. 16.99 *(978-1-4346-3840-3(5))*; (ENG.). 108p. pap. 19.99 *(978-1-4346-3841-0(3))* BiblioBazaar.
Inazo Nitobe, Nitobe & Inazo Nitobe. Bushido: The Soul of Japan. 2009. 96p. pap. 4.95 *(978-1-60386-198-4(X)*, Merchant Bks.) Rough Draft Printing.
Lowry, Dave. The Essence of Budo: A Practitioner's Guide to Understanding the Japanese Martial Ways. 2010. (ENG.). 192p. pap. 16.95 *(978-1-59030-846-2(8))* Shambhala Pubns., Inc.
Martinez, Luis Alberto. Warrior Code: Applying the Tenets of Bushido to the Service of the Master. 2006. 94p. per. 9.99 *(978-1-59886-613-1(3))* Tate Publishing & Enterprises, LLC.
Nakao, Seigo & Sadler, A. L. Code of the Samurai: A Contemporary Translation of the 16th-Century Bushido Shoshishu. 2007. (ENG., Illus.). 144p. per. 10.95 *(978-1-56975-590-7(6))* Ulysses Pr.
Nitobé, Inazô. Bushido: Die Seele Japans. 2008. 96p. pap. 5.99 *(978-1-60459-365-5(2))* Wilder Pubns., Ltd.
—Bushido: The Soul of Japan. 2007. (ENG.). 84p. per. 9.95 *(978-1-60206-318-1(4))* Cosimo, Inc.
—Bushido: The Soul of Japan. 2007. 96p. per. *(978-1-4065-4959-1(2))* Dodo Pr.
—Bushido: The Soul of Japan. 2007. 112p. 19.99 *(978-1-59986-746-5(X))*; pap. 7.99 *(978-1-59986-913-1(6))* Filiquarian Publishing, LLC.
—Bushido: The Soul of Japan. 2008. 84p. pap. 10.99 *(978-1-59547-690-6(3))* NuVision Pubns., LLC.
—Bushido: The Soul of Japan. 2008. pap. 5.95 *(978-1-60545-109-1(6))* Quiet Vision Publishing.
—Bushido the Soul of Japan. 2008. 112p. 24.99 *(978-0-554-27718-9(2))*; 21.99 *(978-0-554-37021-7(2))* BiblioBazaar.
—Bushido the Soul of Japan. 2006. (ENG.). pap. *(978-1-4068-3535-9(8))* Echo Library.
—Bushido, the Soul of Japan. 2008. 100p. pap. 8.95 *(978-1-60597-437-8(4)*, Book Jungle) Standard Pubns., Inc.
—The Way of the Samurai. 2011. (ENG.). 128p. 8.99 *(978-1-84837-722-6(3)*, 1848377223) Arcturus Publishing GBR. Dist: Book Sales, Inc.
Tsunetomo, Yamamoto. Hagakure: The Book of the Samurai. Wilson, William Scott, tr. from JPN. 2012. (ENG.). 208p. 19.95 ***(978-1-59030-985-8(5))*** Shambhala Pubns., Inc.

BUSHINGS

see Bearings (Machinery); Electric Insulators and Insulation

BUSHMEN

see San (African People)

BUSHNELL, DAVID, 1740-1826

Manstan, Roy R. & Frese, Frederic J. Turtle: David Bushnell's Revolutionary Vessel. 2010. (ENG., Illus.). 400p. 29.95 *(978-1-59416-105-6(4))* Westholme Publishing.

BUSHNELL, HORACE, 1802-1876

Addison, Daniel Dulany. Clergy in American Life & Letters. 2006. pap. 34.95 *(978-1-4286-3782-5(6))* Kessinger Publishing, LLC.
Chase, Irah. Infant Baptism an Invention of Men; or, Dr Bushnell's Arguments Reviewed with Articles on Origen's Testimony Respecting the Baptism of Children, And. 2006. 276p. per. 23.99 *(978-1-4255-2451-7(6))* MPublishing.
Crosby, Donald A. Horace Bushnell's theory of Language: In the context of other nineteenth-century philosophies of Language. (Studies in Philosophy Ser.). (ENG.). 300p. 210.00 ***(978-3-11-198052-2(9))*** De Gruyter, Mouton DEU. Dist: de Gruyter, Walter GmbH & Co. KG.
Davis, Andrew Jackson. The Approaching Crisis: Being A Review of Dr. Bushnell's Course of Lectures, on the Bible, Nature, Religion, Skepticism, & the Supernatural. 2006. 304p. per. 23.99 *(978-1-4255-2859-1(7))* MPublishing.
Torbett, David. Theology & Slavery: Charles Hodge & Horace Bushnell. 2006. 230p. *(978-0-88146-032-2(X))* Mercer Univ. Pr.

BUSHONGO (AFRICAN PEOPLE)

see Kuba (African People)

BUSHRANGERS

Bassett, Jennifer. Ned Kelly: A True Story. Oxford University Press Staff, ed. 3rd ed. 2008. (ENG., Illus.). 64p. 9.38 *(978-0-19-478912-7(8))* Oxford Univ. Pr., Inc.
Finger, Charles J. Bushrangers. 2007. 250p. 41.95 *(978-0-548-03872-7(4))* Kessinger Publishing, LLC.
Moore, Laurie & Williams, Stephan. True Story of Jimmy Governor: Killing Us Every Day. (Illus.). 256p. 18.95 *(978-1-86508-481-7(6))* Allen & Unwin AUS. Dist: Independent Pubs. Group.
White, Charles. The History of Australian Bushranging V2: 1863-1880 Ben Hall To. 2007. (ENG.). 408p. per. 34.95 *(978-1-4304-4376-6(6))* Kessinger Publishing, LLC.

BUSHWHACKERS

see Guerillas

BUSHY RUN, BATTLE OF, PA., 1763

Anderson, Niles. Battle of Bushy Run. 2007. (Illus.). 19p. pap. 10.00 *(978-1-4223-1496-8(0))* DIANE Publishing Co.
Bouquet, Henry. Historical Account of Bouquets Expeditio. 2006. pap. 21.95 *(978-1-4286-4788-6(0))* Kessinger Publishing, LLC.
Cort, Cyrus & Smith, William. Bouquet & the Ohio Indian War: Two Accounts of the Campaigns Of 1763-1764. 2008. 264p. *(978-1-84677-584-0(1))*; pap. *(978-1-84677-583-3(3))* Leonaur Ltd.
Parkman, Francis. The Conspiracy of Pontiac & the Indian War after the Conquest of Canada, 2 vol., set. (Everyman's Library). reprint ed. 250.00 *(978-0-7222-6566-6(2))* Library Reprints, Inc.
Smith, William. Historical Account of Bouquet's Expedition Against the Ohio Indians in 1764. 2010. 156p. pap. 11.95 *(978-1-4290-4542-1(6))* Applewood Bks.

BUSINESS

see also Accounting; Advertising; Applications for Positions; Big Business; Bookkeeping; Budget in Business; Business Enterprises; Business Losses; Businesspeople; Businesswomen; Card System in Business; Commerce; Controllership; Creative Ability in Business; Customer Relations; Entrepreneurship; Industrial Management; Mail-Order Business; Mentoring in Business; Minority Business Enterprises; Negotiation in Business; Organization Charts; Profit; Real Estate Business; Selling; Sex-Oriented Business; Small Business; Social Responsibility of Business; Success in Business; Telephone in Business; Wealth

Abbott, Robert M. Conscious Endeavors: Business, Society & the Journey to Sustainability. 2009. (ENG.). 175p. pap. 19.95 *(978-1-397-80971-1(X))* Green Frigate Bks.
Acs, Gregory & Carrington, William. Understanding & Responding to Persistently High Unemployment. 2012. (ENG.). (C). pap. 20.00 ***(978-1-4578-2876-8(6))*** DIANE Publishing Co.
Amatori, Franco. Business History: Complexities & Comparisons. 2011. (ENG., Illus.). 272p. (C). 160.00 *(978-0-415-42396-0(1))* Routledge.
Amatori, Franco & Colli, Andrea. Business History: Complexities & Comparisons. 2011. (ENG., Illus.). 272p. (C). pap. 54.95 *(978-0-415-42397-7(X))* Routledge.
Amatori, Franco & Jones, Geoffrey, eds. Business History around the World. 2011. (Comparative Perspectives in Business History Ser.). (ENG.), 444p. pap. 39.99 *(978-0-521-17223-3(3))* Cambridge Univ. Pr.
Amend, Patricia & Tharrett, Stephen. 101 Strategies for Improving Member Retention in Health/Fitness Clubs. 2012. (ENG., Illus.). 78p. pap. 19.95 ***(978-1-60679-213-1(X))*** Coaches Choice.
Anderson, Angel. Mas Tiempo. 2010. 82p. pap. 12.99 *(978-0-557-50047-5(8))* Lulu Enterprises Inc.
Anderson, Jim. Rentfree Guaranteed. 2009. (Rentfree Guaranteed Org Ser.). 501p. pap. 20.00 *(978-0-932574-18-3(1))* Brun Pr., Inc.
Anderson, Walter. Sweet Nupe: An Unauthorized History of Kappa Alpha Psi. 2006. (C). pap. 18.95 *(978-0-9647596-8-8(3))* Black Adonis Collectibles.
Anthony, Michael Jay & Taylor, Barbara J. Income Without a Job. 2008. 260p. pap. 23.44 *(978-0-557-00377-8(6))* Lulu Enterprises Inc.
Aslett, Don. Barnyard to Boardroom: Business Basics. Cartaino, Carol, ed. 2008. (Illus.). 200p. pap. 14.99 *(978-0-937750-36-0(0))* Marsh Creek Pr.
Azim, Mohammad. Board, Shareholder & Auditor Monitoring. 2010. 360p. pap. *(978-3-8383-7119-1(4))* Lambert Academic Publishing.
Babson, Roger. Fundamentals of Prosperity. 2007. (ENG.). 48p. per. 7.95 *(978-1-4344-8188-7(3))* Wildside Pr., LLC.
Bailey, Andrea. Introduction to Business: Applications & Exercises. rev. ed. 2009. (ENG.). 84p. pap. 35.34 *(978-0-7575-6822-0(X))* Kendall Hunt Publishing Co.
Bankston, Karen, ed. Director Tool Kit. 3rd ed. 2007. (ENG.). 196p. ring bd. 209.00 *(978-1-933081-51-9(1)*, CUES) Credit Union Executives Society.
Bannatyne, Duncan. 37 Questions Everyone in Business Needs to Answer. 2012. (ENG.). 224p. pap. 22.95 ***(978-0-7553-6239-4(X))*** Headline Bk. Publishing GBR. Dist: Independent Pubs. Group.
Barhorst, Warren & Burson, Rusty. Game Plan: The Definitive Playbook for Starting or Growing Your Business. 2010. 196p. (ENG.). 24.99 *(978-1-4520-4610-5(7))*; pap. 15.99 *(978-1-4520-4609-9(3))* AuthorHouse.
Basic Books Staff. Business: The Ultimate Resource. 2nd rev. ed. 2006. (ENG., Illus.). 2032p. 59.95 *(978-0-465-00830-8(5))* Basic Bks.
Bayan, Matthew. CLICK & RETIRE - How Internet Land Trading Can Make You Rich. 2009. 76p. pap. 9.94 *(978-0-557-03699-8(2))* Lulu Enterprises Inc.
Berchicci, Luca. Innovating for Sustainability: Green Entrepreneurship in Personal Mobility. (Illus.). 2012. (ENG.). 256p. (C). pap. 42.95 ***(978-0-415-54145-9(X))*** 2008. XII, 244p. 168.00 *(978-0-415-45464-3(6))* Routledge.
Berg, M. Douglas. The Foundations of Business Analysis: An Introduction to Derivative Calculus & Statistics. 2011. (ENG.). 152p. pap. 48.95 *(978-0-7575-8163-2(3))* Kendall Hunt Publishing Co.
Bernstein, Myron Z. Have You Been Royally Screwed? How to Get What You Deserve by Making People & Companies Deliver on Their Promises, Products, Goods & Services. 2009. 200p. pap. 0.00 *(978-0-9822069-0-4(9))* KAMBS Publishing.
Bertsch, Andrew & Ondracek, James. Doing Business in... Vol. 1. 2010. 120p. pap. 50.00 *(978-0-557-56973-1(7))* Lulu Enterprises Inc.
Bevelacqua, Joan. Working with Business. 116p. 29.95 *(978-0-914951-07-0(6))* Learning Resources Network, Inc.
Bezbaruah, Madhurjya Prasad. Indo-Myanmar Cross-Border Trade. 2010. 124p. pap. *(978-3-639-26188-2(7))* VDM Verlag Dr. Mueller e.K.
Bishop, Bill. The Problem with Penguins: Stand Out in a Crowded Marketplace by Packaging Your BIG Idea. 2010. 196p. 27.95 *(978-1-4502-1202-1(6))*; pap. 17.95 *(978-1-4502-1204-5(2))* iUniverse, Inc.
Bisk Education. Accounting for Business Combinations. 2011. (ENG.). ring bd. 109.00 ***(978-0-88128-001-2(1))*** Bisk Education, Inc.
—Audits of 401(k) Plans. 2012. ring bd. 115.00 ***(978-0-88128-002-9(X))*** Bisk Education, Inc.
—Bisk GAAS Guide. 2012. ring bd. 145.00 ***(978-0-88128-003-6(8))*** Bisk Education, Inc.
—Fraud Prevention for Physicians. 2012. ring bd. 69.00 ***(978-0-88128-004-3(6))*** Bisk Education, Inc.
BizLX. BizLx Software. 2010. (ENG.). (C). 19.95 *(978-0-470-88661-8(7)*, Wiley) Wiley, John & Sons, Inc.

Black, Fischer & Black. Business Cycles & Equilibrium. rev. ed. 2009. (ENG., Illus.). 197p. 49.95 *(978-0-470-49917-7(6)*, Wiley) Wiley, John & Sons, Inc.

Blue, Steven L. Burnarounds: Unlocking the Double Digit Profit Code: Transforming the Small Company into A Global Powerhouse. 2009. 116p. pap. 14.95 *(978-1-60725-252-8(X))* Independent Pub.

Boardman, Calvin, et al. Foundations of Business Thought. 2012. (ENG.). 552p. (C). pap. 73.33 ***(978-0-13-285607-2(7)***, Prentice Hall) Prentice Hall PTR.

Bogle, John C. Enough: True Measures of Money, Business, & Life. (ENG., Illus.). 2010. 328p. pap. 14.95 *(978-0-470-52423-7(5))* 2008. 288p. 24.95 *(978-0-470-39851-7(5))* Wiley, John & Sons, Inc. (Wiley).

Bolland, Eric & Fletcher, Frank. Solutions: Business Problem Solving. 2012. 350p. 89.95 ***(978-1-4094-2687-5(4)***, Gower Publishing Co., Ltd.) Ashgate Publishing, Ltd. GBR. Dist: Ashgate Publishing Co.

Boone & Kurtz. Ie - Contemporary Business. 2007. *(978-0-324-54051-2(5))* Cengage South-Western.

Boone, et al. Contemporary Business, with Audio CD. 12th ed. 2008. (ENG.). 629p. 212.95 *(978-0-470-42467-4(2)*, Wiley) Wiley, John & Sons, Inc.

Boone and, Kurtz. Contemporary Business. 2006. pap. 15.95 *(978-1-4288-0596-5(6))*; pap. 18.95 *(978-1-4288-0718-1(7))* Cram101 Inc.

—Contemporary Business 2003. 2006. pap. 20.95 *(978-1-4288-0589-7(3))* Cram101 Inc.

Boone, Louis E. & Kurtz, David L. Contemporary Business. 12th ed. 2006. 784p. 153.95 incl. audio compact disk *(978-0-324-35929-9(2))* Cengage South-Western.

—Contemporary Business. (ENG.). (C). 13th ed. 2009. 800p. 188.95 *(978-0-470-43368-3(X))* 14th ed. 2011. 768p. 204.95 *(978-0-470-53129-7(0))* Wiley, John & Sons, Inc. (Wiley).

—Contemporary Business 14E for Western District. 14th ed. 2011. 772p. (C). pap. 96.95 ***(978-1-118-11407-0(8)***, Wiley) Wiley, John & Sons, Inc.

—Contemporary Business 14th Edition 2012 Update Binder Ready Version. 14th ed. 2011. 800p. (C). ring bd. 73.95 ***(978-1-118-06167-1(5)***, Wiley) Wiley, John & Sons, Inc.

—Contemporary Business 14th Edition for Anne Arundel Community College. 14th ed. 2011. 738p. (C). pap. 80.95 ***(978-1-118-10445-3(5)***, Wiley) Wiley, John & Sons, Inc.

—Contemporary Business 14th Edition for OCCC Softcover Color. 14th ed. 2011. 772p. (C). pap. 122.95 ***(978-1-118-11808-5(1)***, Wiley) Wiley, John & Sons, Inc.

—Contemporary Business 2012. 14th rev. ed. 2009. (ENG.). 768p. (gr. 9-12). pap. 121.28 ***(978-1-118-01030-3(2)***, Wiley) Wiley, John & Sons, Inc.

Boston, Karen & Hood, Jeff S. Freshman Business Connections. 2nd rev. ed. 2011. (ENG.). 166p. pap. 52.88 *(978-0-7575-8307-0(5))* Kendall Hunt Publishing Co.

Bovee and Thill, Schatzman. Business in Action. 2006. pap. 14.95 *(978-1-4288-0743-3(8))* Cram101 Inc.

Bovee, Court & Thill, John V. Business in Action with Real Time Updates. 4th ed. 2007. (ENG., Illus.). 504p. (C). per. 84.00 *(978-0-13-615408-2(5))* Prentice Hall PTR.

Bovee, Courtland L. & Thill, John V. Business in Action. 5th ed. 2010. (MyBizLab Ser.). (ENG.). 592p. (C). pap. 113.33 *(978-0-13-213965-6(0)*, Prentice Hall) Prentice Hall PTR.

—Business in Action. 6th rev. ed. 2012. (ENG.). 592p. (C). 113.33 ***(978-0-13-282878-9(2)***, Prentice Hall) Prentice Hall PTR.

—Business in Action, Student Value Edition. 6th ed. 2012. (ENG.). 592p. (C). ring bd. 73.67 ***(978-0-13-282881-9(2)***, Prentice Hall) Prentice Hall PTR.

Bovee, Hill. Business in Action. 2006. pap. 15.95 *(978-1-4288-1179-9(6))* Cram101 Inc.

Brady, Chris & Woodward, Orrin. Launching A Leadership Revolution: Mastering the Five Levels of Influence. 2012. pap. 14.99 ***(978-0-9853387-2-5(5))*** Signature Management Team, LLC.

Briggs, Frank D. Seven Recipes for Success in Business: A Gourmet's Guide to Customer Service. 2010. 124p. 23.95 *(978-1-4269-2643-3(X))*; pap. 13.95 *(978-1-4269-2642-6(1))* Trafford Publishing.

Brostek, Michael. IRS Management: Cost Estimate for New Information Reporting System Needs to Be Made More Reliable. 2012. (ENG.). (C). pap. 25.00 ***(978-1-4578-2849-2(9))*** DIANE Publishing Co.

Browning, Guy. The Pocket Guru: Priceless Nuggets of Business Wisdom. rev. ed. 2011. (ENG., Illus.). 176p. pap. 14.99 *(978-0-273-75519-7(6))* FT Press.

Buck, Franklin A. A Yankee Trader in the Gold Rush: The Letters of Franklin A. Buck. White, Katherine A., ed. 2011. 320p. 50.95 ***(978-1-258-01595-4(1))*** Literary Licensing, LLC.

Buckley, Peter, ed. Business History & International Business. 2010. (ENG.). 216p. (C). 125.00 *(978-0-415-60060-6(X))* Routledge.

Buesa, Mikel & Baumert, Thomas. The Economic Repercussions of Terrorism. 2010. (Illus.). 216p. 110.00 *(978-0-19-957770-5(6))* Oxford Univ. Pr., Inc.

Burrow, James L., et al. Business Principles & Management. 12th ed. 2007. (ENG., Illus.). 240p. (C). per., act. bk. ed. 35.95 *(978-0-538-44470-5(3))* Cengage South-Western.

Business and Biodiversity Offset Programme, compiled by. Guidance Notes to the Standard on Biodiversity Offsets: A Tool to Assess Adherence to the BBOP Principles on Biodiversity Offset Design & Implementation. 2012. (ENG.). pap. 0.00 net. ***(978-1-932928-46-4(4))*** Forest Trends.

Business International Atlas: Companies-Products-Services. (Illus.). 300p. (Orig.). pap. *(978-0-7605-0842-8(9))* Rector Pr., Ltd.

Butler, Doug. Six-Figure Shoeing. (Sound Shoeing Ser.). *(978-0-916992-23-1(3))* Butler, Doug Enterprises, Inc.

Byron, Basil Gordon & Coudert, Frederic Rene, eds. America Speaks: A Library of the Best Spoken Thought in Business & the Professions. 2007. (ENG.). 578p. 58.95 *(978-0-548-02346-4(8))* Kessinger Publishing, LLC.

Calhoun, A. R. Business Hints for Men & Women. 2009. 164p. pap. *(978-1-4099-2888-1(8))* Dodo Pr.

Calhoun, Alfred Rochefort. Business Hints for Men & Women. 2007. 116p. per. *(978-1-4068-4164-0(1))* Echo Library.

Carnegie, Andrew. The Empire of Business. 2009. 356p. 31.99 *(978-1-116-45688-2(5))*; pap. 32.75 *(978-1-116-45690-5(7))*; 33.99 *(978-1-116-45689-9(3))*; pap. 31.75 *(978-1-116-45691-2(5))* BiblioBazaar.

—The Empire of Business. 2009. 140p. pap. *(978-1-151-14526-0(2))* Books LLC.

—The Empire of Business. 2007. (ENG.). 360p. per. 21.95 *(978-1-60206-125-5(4))* Cosimo, Inc.

Castellanos, Malu, et al, eds. Enabling Real-Time Business Intelligence: Third International Workshop, BIRTE 2009, Held at the 35th International Conference on Very Large Databases, VLDB 2009, Lyon, France, August 24, 2009, Revised Selected Papers. 2010. (Lecture Notes in Business Information Processing Ser.). iii, 175p. pap. 72.00 *(978-3-642-14558-2(2)*, 3642145582) Springer.

Cengage Learning, (Cengage Learning). Course 360 CLMS Introduction to Business. 2nd ed. 2011. (ENG.). (C). 100.00 *(978-1-111-67308-6(X))* Cengage South-Western.

—Course360 Introduction to Business. 2nd ed. 2011. (ENG.). (C). 90.00 *(978-1-111-67306-2(3))* Cengage South-Western.

Chiarelli, Peter W. & Westphal, Joseph W., eds. U. S. Army Sustainability Report (2010) 2011. (ENG.). (C). pap. 25.00 ***(978-1-4223-1678-8(5)***, Silverwood Institute) DIANE Publishing Co.

Clarke, Paul, et al. Business & Management Course Companion. 2009. (ENG., Illus.). 416p. (YA). pap. 42.00 *(978-0-19-915225-4(X))* Oxford Univ. Pr., Inc.

Colbert, Corinne. A Practical Guide to Business Incubator Marketing. 2007. (ENG.). 104p. per. 65.00 *(978-1-887183-65-9(5)*, NBIA Pubns.) National Business Incubation Assn.

Collins, Karen. Exploring Business. 2006. *(978-0-13-236732-5(7))* Prentice Hall PTR.

Cram101 Textbook Reviews. Outlines & Highlights for Better Business by Michael R Solomon, Isbn: 9780132496698. 2011. 566p. pap. 39.95 ***(978-1-61812-144-8(8))*** Cram101 Inc.

—Outlines & Highlights for Business: Connecting Principles to Practice by William Nickels, ISBN. 2011. 536p. pap. 38.95 ***(978-1-61812-139-4(1))*** Cram101 Inc.

—Outlines & Highlights for Business Information Needs & Strategies by Eileen Abels Deborah Klein, Isbn: 9780123694874. 2011. 102p. pap. 27.95 ***(978-1-61461-468-5(7))*** Cram101 Inc.

—Outlines & Highlights for Business Principles & Management by James L Burrow. 2011. 452p. pap. 36.95 ***(978-1-61905-200-0(8))*** Cram101 Inc.

—Outlines & Highlights for Business Valuation & Bankruptcy by Ian Ratner. 2011. 120p. pap. 28.95 ***(978-1-61905-185-0(0))*** Cram101 Inc.

—Outlines & Highlights for Busn by Marcella Kelly, Isbn: 9781111221461. 2011. 614p. pap. 40.95 ***(978-1-61812-127-1(8))*** Cram101 Inc.

Cram101 Textbook Reviews & Cram101 Textbook Reviews. Outlines & Highlights for Business: Principles, Guidelines & Practices by John Ivancevich. 2011. 680p. pap. 41.95 ***(978-1-61830-253-1(1))*** Cram101 Inc.

—Outlines & Highlights for Business Database Systems by Thomas Connolly. 2011. 82p. pap. 27.95 ***(978-1-61830-444-5(5))*** Cram101 Inc.

Cram101 Textbook Reviews Staff. Business A Changing World. 2006. pap. 9.95 *(978-1-4288-0451-7(X))* Cram101 Inc.

—Outlines & Highlights for Business: A Changing World by Ferrell, Hirt, & Ferrell, ISBN. 2009. 300p. pap. 15.95 *(978-1-4288-6632-4(9))* Cram101 Inc.

—Outlines & Highlights for Business in Action by Bovee, Isbn: 9780136154082. 2009. 348p. pap. 34.95 *(978-1-4288-6756-7(2))* Cram101 Inc.

—Outlines & Highlights for Contemporary Business, 2009 Update by Louis E Boone, Isbn: 9780470425800. 2009. 304p. pap. 32.95 *(978-1-4288-4071-3(0))*; 276p. pap. 32.95 *(978-1-4288-9696-3(1))* Cram101 Inc.

—Outlines & Highlights for Contemporary Business by Louis E Boone, Isbn: 9780470424674. 2009. 300p. pap. 32.95 *(978-1-4288-4069-0(9))*; 276p. pap. 32.95 *(978-1-4288-9725-0(9))* Cram101 Inc.

—Outlines & Highlights for Introduction to Business by Dias, Isbn: 9780073376998. 2008. 304p. pap. 15.95 *(978-1-4288-6514-3(4))* Cram101 Inc.

—Outlines & Highlights for Introduction to Business by Jones, Isbn: 9780073224367. 2008. 164p. pap. 12.95 *(978-1-4288-6519-8(5))* Cram101 Inc.

—Outlines & Highlights for Introduction to Business by les Dlabay, James L Burrow, Brad Kleindl Isbn: 9780538445610. 2009. 232p. pap. 31.95 *(978-1-4288-7328-5(7))* Cram101 Inc.

—Outlines & Highlights for Introduction to Business by Madura, Isbn: 0324407114. 2008. 248p. pap. 14.95 *(978-1-4288-6518-1(7))* Cram101 Inc.

—Outlines & Highlights for Student Achievement Series: Foundations of Business by William M. Pride, ISBN. 2009. 184p. pap. 29.95 *(978-1-4288-4166-6(0))*; 234p. pap. 31.95 *(978-1-4288-8757-2(1))* Cram101 Inc.

Crane, Thomas G. The Heart of Coaching - 4th Edition: Using Transformational Coaching to Create a High-Performance Culture. Patrick, Larissa, ed. 4th ed. 2012.Tr. of Heart of Coaching. (CHI & KOR., Illus.). 224p. per. 24.95 *(978-0-9660874-3-7(7))* F T A Pr.

Crimson Publishing Staff. 50 Best Business Ideas from the Past 50 Years. 2012. (ENG.). 288p. pap. 19.95 *(978-1-85458-690-2(4))* Crimson Publishing, Ltd. GBR. Dist: National Bk. Network.

Dakin, Karl, et al. Everyone's an Expert: How to gain recognition for what you Know. 2011. 50p. per. 19.95 *(978-1-932344-07-3(1))* Thornton Publishing, Inc.

De Bower, Edward W. Business Mans Book of Proverbs Fundament. 2006. pap. 24.95 *(978-1-4286-5277-4(9))* Kessinger Publishing, LLC.

De Ley, Gerd & Potter, David. The Big Book of Business Advice: A Great Resource for Insightful Ideas & Amusing Quotations from the Famous & Infamous. rev. ed. 2011. (ENG.). 188p. pap. 21.95 *(978-1-61110-010-5(0))* Global Management Enterprises.

Deland, Lorin F. Imagination in Business. 2007. (ENG.). 112p. 34.95 *(978-0-548-15157-0(1))*; 116p. per. 19.95 *(978-1-4304-4505-0(X))* Kessinger Publishing, LLC.

Denby, Neil & Hamman, David. AQA Business for GCSE: Growing as a Business. 2009. (Illus.). 156p. pap. 36.50 *(978-0-340-98664-6(6))* Hodder Education GBR. Dist: Trans-Atlantic Pubns., Inc.

—AQA Business Studies for GCSE. 2009. (Illus.). 334p. pap. 49.50 *(978-0-340-98738-4(3))* Hodder Education GBR. Dist: Trans-Atlantic Pubns., Inc.

Dias, Laura & Shah, Amit J. Student Study Guide t/a Introduction to Business. 2008. (ENG.). 352p. (C). pap. 20.67 *(978-0-07-723037-1(X)*, 007723037X, Career Education) McGraw-Hill Higher Education.

Dias, Laura Portolese & Shah, Amit J. Introduction to Business. 2008. (ENG., Illus.). 544p. (C). pap. 92.33 *(978-0-07-337699-8(X)*, 007337699X) McGraw-Hill Higher Education.

Dietrich, Mark, ed. BVR's Guide to Physician Practice Valuation. 2nd ed. 2012. (ENG.). 179.00 ***(978-1-62150-001-8(2))*** Business Valuation Resources, LLC.

Dimoff, Timothy A. The You in Business: How to Build a Strong Business from the Inside Out. 124p. reprint ed. pap. 14.99 *(978-1-58832-028-5(6))* Unlimited Publishing LLC.

Dixon, Patrick. Building a Better Business. 2009. (ENG., Illus.). 256p. pap. 17.95 *(978-1-86197-753-3(0))* Profile Bks. Ltd. GBR. Dist: Consortium Bk. Sales & Distribution.

Dlabay, Les, et al. Intro to Business. 7th rev. ed. 2008. (ENG., Illus.). 624p. (C). 103.95 *(978-0-538-44561-0(0))* Cengage South-Western.

—Principles of Business. 8th ed. 2011. (Marketing (modified) Ser.). (ENG.). 624p. (C). 103.95 *(978-1-111-42694-1(5))* Cengage South-Western.

—Principles of Business - Activities & Projects. 8th ed. 2011. (ENG.). 80p. (C). pap. 27.95 *(978-1-111-57368-3(9))* Cengage South-Western.

Doyle, Michael Scott, et al. Éxito Comercial. 5th ed. 2010. (ENG.). 544p. (C). pap. 134.95 *(978-1-4390-8612-4(5))* Cengage Heinle.

Ducote, Seaon. The New Millenium Self-Publishing Guide: The Eight Step Program to Online Publishing & Marketing. 2009. (ENG., Illus.). 74p. pap. 14.95 *(978-0-9787597-8-0(8))* PureLight Pubns.

Dudley, George W. & Goodson, Shannon L. The Psychology of Sales Call Reluctance: Earning What You're Worth in Sales. 5th ed. 2008. Orig. Title: Psychology of Call Reluctance. (Illus.). 433p. per. 22.95 *(978-0-935907-12-4(2))* Behavioral Science Research Pr., Inc.

Duncan, Kevin. Business Greatest Hits: A Masterclass in Modern Business Ideas. 2010. (ENG., Illus.). 224p. pap. 14.95 *(978-1-4081-2643-1(5))* A & C Black GBR. Dist: Macmillan.

Eastman, George R. Psychology for Business Efficiency. 2009. 158p. pap. *(978-0-217-74750-9(7))* Books LLC.

—Psychology for Business Efficiency. 2007. (ENG.). 276p. 42.95 *(978-0-548-13398-9(0))* 2006. pap. 27.95 *(978-1-4286-4499-1(7))* Kessinger Publishing, LLC.

Eaton, Seymour, ed. Up-to-Date Business. 2007. (Illus.). 352p. per. *(978-1-4065-2543-4(X))* Dodo Pr.

Ebert, Ronald J. & Griffin, Ricky. MyBizLab with Pearson eText for Business Essentials. 7th ed. 2009. (ENG.). 312p. (C). 106.67 *(978-0-13-801888-7(X)*, Prentice Hall) Prentice Hall PTR.

Eggleston, George Cary. How to Make a Living; Suggestions upon the Art of Making, Saving, & Using Money. 2006. 128p. per. 16.99 *(978-1-4255-0880-7(4))* MPublishing.

EPM Communications. Media Use Across Platforms. 2012. 95.00 ***(978-1-935521-24-2(1))*** EPM Communications, Inc.

Falseti, Uirá, et al. Criteria for Funding Models Applicable to Feeder Road Projects. 2010. 192p. pap. *(978-3-639-23562-3(2))* VDM Verlag Dr. Mueller e.K.

Farris, Paul W. & Moore, Michael J., eds. The Profit Impact of Marketing Strategy Project: Retrospect & Prospects. 2009. (ENG., Illus.). 328p. pap. 45.00 *(978-0-521-12345-7(3))* Cambridge Univ. Pr.

Ferrell, O. C., et al. Business: A Changing World. 7th ed. 2008. (ENG., Illus.). 624p. (C). pap. 150.67 *(978-0-07-351172-6(2)*, 0073511722, McGraw-Hill/Irwin) McGraw-Hill Higher Education.

—InBusiness. 2009. (Illus.). viii, 392p. *(978-0-07-351171-9(4))* McGraw-Hill Cos., The.

Ferrell, O. C., et al. M: Business. 3rd ed. 2012. (ENG., Illus.). 416p. (C). pap. 73.33 ***(978-0-07-352458-0(1)***, 0073524581, McGraw-Hill/Irwin) McGraw-Hill Higher Education.

Floyd, William. People vs. Wall Street: A Mock Trial. 2011. 278p. 47.95 ***(978-1-258-03475-7(1))*** Literary Licensing, LLC.

Foulke, Roy Anderson. Relativity of the Moral Hazard. 2011. 62p. 36.95 ***(978-1-258-03767-3(X))*** Literary Licensing, LLC.

Foundations of Business. 3rd ed. 2012. (ENG.). 544p. (C). pap. 71.95 ***(978-1-111-58015-5(4))*** Cengage South-Western.

Fraser, Beau, et al. Death to All Sacred Cows: How Successful Business People Put the Old Rules Out to Pasture. 2008. (Illus.). 224p. 21.95 *(978-1-4013-0331-0(5))* Hyperion Pr.

Freedley, Edwin T. Opportunities for Industry & the Safe Investment of Capital; or, a Thousand Chances to Make Money by Edwin T Freedley. 2006. 424p. per. 26.99 *(978-1-4255-4582-6(3))* MPublishing.

—Practical Treatise on Business. 2006. pap. 26.99 *(978-1-4255-3746-3(4))* MPublishing.

Friedrichs, Ed. Reach Higher: Long-cycle Strategies for a Short-cycle World. 2006. 334p. pap. 39.00 *(978-0-9755654-7-6(8)*, Ostberg) Greenway Communications.

Fritz, Scott. The 40 Hour Work YEAR. 2010. 128p. 29.00 *(978-0-557-38524-9(5))*; pap. 18.00 *(978-0-557-38521-8(0))* Lulu Enterprises Inc.

Fyock, Cathy. The Truth about Hiring the Best: And Nothing but the Truth. 2007. (Prentice Hall Truth about Business Ser.). (ENG.). 224p. pap. 20.99 *(978-0-13-238186-4(9)*, Prentice Hall) Prentice Hall PTR.

Galloway, Lee. Organization & Management. 2009. 726p. pap. *(978-0-217-73768-5(4))* Books LLC.

Garimella, Kiran K. The Power of Process: Unleashing the Source of Competitive Advantage. 2006. pap. 29.95 *(978-0-929652-06-1(1))* Meghan-Kiffer Pr.

Geenhuizen, Marina van, et al, eds. Technological Innovation Across Nations: Applied Studies of Coevolutionary Development. 2011. (ENG., Illus.). xiv, 200p. pap. 129.00 ***(978-3-642-10118-2(6)***, 3642101186) Springer.

Gips & Gips, James. Mastering Excel 2007: A Problem-Solving Approach. 6th ed. 2011. (Illus.). viii, 369p. pap. *(978-0-558-81797-8(1))* Pearson Learning Solutions.

Glencoe, creator. Glencoe Introduction to Business Student Activity Workbook: With Academic Integration Chapters 17-35. 2007. (ENG., Illus.). 350p. (C). per. 30.36 *(978-0-07-877697-7(X)*, 007877697X) McGraw-Hill Higher Education.

Glencoe McGraw-Hill Staff. Glencoe Introduction to Business. 2007. (ENG., Illus.). 350p. (C). per., wbk. ed. 53.00 *(978-0-07-877695-3(3)*, 0078776953) McGraw-Hill Higher Education.

—Glencoe Introduction to Business Student Activity Workbook: With Academic Integration Chapters 1-16. 2007. (ENG., Illus.). 160p. (C). per. 30.36 *(978-0-07-877696-0(1)*, 0078776961) McGraw-Hill Higher Education.

—Introduction to Business Interactive Student Edition CD-ROM. 2007. (ENG.). (C). cd-rom 93.80 *(978-0-07-877704-2(6)*, 0078777046) McGraw-Hill Higher Education.

Goldsmith, Arthur A. Business, Government, Society: The Global Political Economy. 3rd ed. 2007. (Illus.). xiii, 449p. pap. *(978-0-7593-8891-8(1))* Cengage South-Western.

Goldstein, David M. Executive Book of Quotes. 2008. 112p. pap. 29.95 *(978-0-615-20968-5(8))* Bamford Pr.

Goodman, Ted. The Forbes Book of Business Quotations: 10,000 Thoughts on the Business of Life. 2007. (ENG.). 704p. 29.95 *(978-1-57912-721-3(5)*, 1579127215); 90th ed. pap. 17.95 *(978-1-57912-708-4(8)*, 1579127088) Black Dog & Leventhal Pubs., Inc.

Gowin, Enoch Burton. Developing Executive Ability. 2009. 368p. pap. *(978-0-217-46538-0(2))*; pap. *(978-0-217-46536-6(6))* Books LLC.

—Developing Executive Ability. 2007. (ENG.). 512p. 55.95 *(978-0-548-09614-7(7))* Kessinger Publishing, LLC.

Griffin, Ricky E. & Ebert, Ronald J. Business. 7th ed. 2006. 407p. pap. 17.95 *(978-1-4288-1036-5(6))* Cram101 Inc.

Griffiths, Alan & Wall, Stuart. Economics for Business & Management. 3rd rev. ed. 2011. (ENG., Illus.). 592p. pap. 99.50 ***(978-0-273-73524-3(1))*** Pearson Education, Ltd. GBR. Dist: Trans-Atlantic Pubns., Inc.

Gutteridge, Lloyd. Business & Management. 2010. (International Baccalaureate Ser.). (ENG.). 176p. (YA). pap., stu. ed. 42.00 *(978-0-19-913531-8(2))* Oxford Univ. Pr., Inc.

Haan, Jakob de & Berger, Helge, eds. The European Central Bank at Ten. 2010. (ENG., Illus.). xii, 196p. 139.00 *(978-3-642-14236-9(2)*, 3642142362) Springer.

Haas, Alan. Adult Website Business. 2010. 162p. pap. 29.95 *(978-0-557-70094-3(9))* Lulu Enterprises Inc.

Hanratty, Luan. Asymmetric Warfare for Entrepreneurs. 2011. 226p. pap. ***(978-1-78092-200-3(0))*** MX Publishing, Ltd.

Hansjürgens, Bernd & Antes, Ralf, eds. Economics & Management of Climate Change: Risks, Mitigation & Adaptation. 2010. (ENG., Illus.). x, 310p. pap. 134.00 *(978-1-4419-2650-0(X)*, 144192650X) Springer.

Harford, Tim. Adapt: Why Success Always Starts with Failure. 2012. (ENG.). 352p. pap. 17.00 ***(978-1-250-00755-1(0))*** Picador.

Harrop, Thomas. Web 2. 0 for Your Business. 2010. 74p. pap. 14.95 *(978-0-557-43419-0(X))* Lulu Enterprises Inc.

Helgerson, Lonnie. Five Pennies: Ten Rules to Successfully Build a Franchise Mega-Brand & Maximize System Profits. 2012. (ENG.). pap. 19.95 ***(978-0-9851810-1-7(X))*** Helgerson Franchise Group.

Herrera Soler, Honesto & White, Michael, eds. Metaphor & Mills: Figurative Language in Business & Economics. 2012. (Applications of Cognitive Linguistics [ACL] Ser.). (ENG., Illus.). 332p. (gr. 17). 168.00 ***(978-3-11-027296-3(2))*** De Gruyter, Mouton DEU. Dist: de Gruyter, Walter GmbH & Co. KG.

Hesperides. Handy Office Book of System, Form & Method. 2007. 288p. per. *(978-1-4067-6659-2(3)*, Hesperides Pr.) Read Bks.

Hird, Gary. Green IT in Practice: How One Company Is Approaching the Greening of Its IT. 2nd ed. 2010. (Illus.). n/ap. pap. *(978-1-84928-051-8(7))* IT Governance.

B

Hogan, Robert, et al. Hogan Business Reasoning Inventory Manual: Brief Technical Manual. 2008. 37p. pap. 45.00 (978-0-9794448-8-3(8)) Hogan Assessment Systems, Inc.

Horner, Raghee. Thirty Days of Forex Trading: Trades, Tactics, & Techniques. 2006. (Wiley Trading Ser.: 272). (ENG., Illus.). 264p. 85.00 (978-0-471-93441-7(0), Wiley) Wiley, John & Sons, Inc.

Howe, E. W. The Blessing of Business. 2009. 80p. pap. 17.75 (978-1-110-41466-6(8)); (ENG.). 79p. pap. 16.99 (978-1-110-41462-8(5), BiblioLife); (ENG.). 79p. pap. 18.99 (978-1-110-41463-5(3), BiblioLife) BiblioBazaar.

Howie, Luke. Terrorism, the Worker & the City: Simulations & Security in a Time of Terror. 2009. 206p. 114.95 (978-0-566-08889-6(4), Gower Publishing Co., Ltd.) Ashgate Publishing, Ltd. GBR. Dist: Ashgate Publishing Co.

Howlett, Robert J., ed. Innovation through Knowledge Transfer. 2010. (Smart Innovation, Systems & Technologies Ser.). (Illus.). 381p. 299.00 (978-3-642-14593-3(0), 3642145930) Springer.

Hubbard, Elbert. The Romance of Business. 2011. 140p. 40.95 (978-1-258-05610-0(0)) Literary Licensing, LLC.

Hunt, Freeman. Worth & Wealth. 2009. 350p. pap. (978-0-217-66221-5(8)) Books LLC.

—Worth & Wealth: A Collection of Maxims, Morals & Miscellanies for Merchants & Men of Business. by Freeman Hunt. 2006. 504p. per. 29.99 (978-1-4255-5570-2(5)) MPublishing.

International Energy Agency. Energy Policies of Iea Countries: Norway 2011 Review. 2011. (Illus.). 140p. pap. (978-92-64-09815-2(1)) Organization for Economic Cooperation & Development.

Isaca. Security, Audit & Control Features SAP ERP, 3rd Edition. 2009. pap. (978-1-60420-115-4(0)) Information Systems Audit and Control Assn.

Ivancevich, John & Duening, Thomas N. Business: Principles, Guidelines & Practices. 2nd ed. 2006. (ENG.). 658p. (C). pap. 146.95 (978-1-59260-282-7(7)) Delmar Cengage Learning.

Jackson, John Bradley. Déjà New Marketing: Increase Sales with Social Media, Search Marketing, E-mail Marketing, Blogs, & More. 2010. 408p. pap. 24.95 (978-1-60844-464-9(3)) Dog Ear Publishing, LLC.

Jellison, Jerald. Life after Grad School: Getting from A to B, 1 vol. 2010. (ENG.). 240p. pap. 21.95 (978-0-19-973430-6(5)) Oxford Univ. Pr., Inc.

JIST Publishing Editors. Business CareerVision Book & DVD: View What You'd Do. 2008. (ENG.). 256p. 22.95 (978-1-59357-539-7(4), JIST Works) JIST Publishing.

Johnson, Luke. The Maverick: Dispatches from an Unrepentant Capitalist. 2007. (ENG.). 256p. 20.00 (978-1-905641-40-6(0)) Harriman Hse. Publishing GBR. Dist: Ingram Pub. Services.

Jones, Gareth R. Introduction to Business: How Companies Create Value for People. 2007. (Illus.). xv, 507p. (978-0-07-352456-6(5)) McGraw-Hill Cos., The.

Joy, Felicia. Hybrid Entrepreneurship: How the Middle Class Can Beat the Slow Economy, Earn Extra Income & Reclaim the American Dream. 2010. 186p. pap. 19.99 (978-0-9844778-0-7(2)) Joy Group International, LLC.

Kaliski, Burton S. Encyclopedia of Business & Finance, 2 vols. 2nd ed. 2006. (Illus.). xxi, 791p. (978-0-02-866063-9(3)); xxi, 791p. (978-0-02-866062-2(5)); (ENG., 794p. 441.00 (978-0-02-866061-5(7)) Cengage Gale. (Macmillan Reference USA).

Kaufman, Josh. The Personal MBA: Master the Art of Business. 2010. (ENG.). 416p. (gr. 12). 27.95 (978-1-59184-352-8(9), Portfolio (Hardcover)) Penguin Group (USA) Inc.

Kedia, Ben L. Enhancing Global Competitiveness Through Sustainable Environmental Stewardship. Jain, Subhash C., ed. 2011. 256p. 99.95 (978-1-84844-874-2(0)) Elgar, Edward Publishing, Inc.

Keeble, Richard. Ethical Space. Keeble, Richard & Matheson, Donald, eds. 2010. 48p. pap. (978-1-84549-419-3(9), Abramis) arima publishing.

Keeble, Richard & Matheson, Donald, eds. Ethical Space. 2010. 82p. pap. (978-1-84549-429-2(6), Abramis) arima publishing.

Kennedy, Nate & Evans, Mark. The Insider Secrets of the World's Most Successful Mortgage Brokers. 2007. (Illus.). 288p. pap. 16.95 (978-0-615-17270-5(9)) Deal Maker Publishing LLC.

Kennerdell, Peter, et al. OCR Business Studies for GCSE. 2nd rev. ed. 2009. 405p. pap. 56.00 (978-0-340-98349-2(3)) Hodder Education GBR. Dist: Trans-Atlantic Pubns., Inc.

Khalfani-Cox, Lynnette. Investing Success: How to Conquer 30 Costly Mistakes & Multiply Your Wealth. 2011. 236p. pap. 14.95 (978-1-932450-57-6(2)) Advantage World Pr.

Knower, Daniel. The Adventures of a Forty-Niner. 2007. (Illus.). 104p. per. (978-1-4065-2929-6(X)) Dodo Pr.

Kroeker, James L., ed. Consideration of Incorporating International Financial Reporting Standards (IFRS) into the Financial Reporting System for U. S. I. 2011. (ENG.). (C). pap. 25.00 (978-1-4379-4226-2(1)) DIANE Publishing Co.

Kruse, Barbara. Strategic Discourse: Actors — Issues — Arenas. 2011. (COSCO — Cognitive Strategy Concepts Ser.). 273p. pap. (978-3-8325-2856-0(3)) Logos Verlag Berlin.

Kurtz, David L. & Boone, Louis E. Contemporary Business. 12th ed. 2008. 784p. pap. 117.95 incl. cd-rom (978-0-324-65384-7(0)) Cengage South-Western.

—Contemporary Business. 12th ed. 2007. (Illus.). (978-0-324-54052-9(3)) Cengage South-Western.

Kurtz, David L. & Boone, Louis E. Contemporary Business 2012. 14th rev. ed. 2011. (ENG.). 784p. (C). pap. 25.95 (978-1-118-11502-2(3), Wiley) Wiley, John & Sons, Inc.

Labitan, Bud. Decision Framing. 2010. 81p. pap. 19.95 (978-0-557-37307-9(7)) Lulu Enterprises Inc.

Leonard, Barry, ed. Taking the Mystery Out of Retirement Planning. 2012. (ENG.). (C). pap. 25.00 (978-1-4578-2824-9(3)) DIANE Publishing Co.

Leonhard, Gerd. Friction Is Fiction: the Future of Content, Media & Business (Black & White Edition) 2010. (ENG.). 172p. pap. 19.99 (978-0-557-22454-8(3)) Lulu Enterprises Inc.

Levermore, David M. & Hsu, Cheng. Enterprise Collaboration: On-Demand Information Exchange for Extended Enterprises. 2010. (Integrated Series in Information Systems Ser.). (Illus.). xiv, 176p. pap. 129.00 (978-1-4419-4178-7(9), 1441941789) Springer.

Levit, Alexandra. They Don't Teach Corporate in College. rev. ed. 2009. (ENG.). 1p. pap. 15.99 (978-1-60163-058-2(1)) Career Pr., Inc.

Levy, Andrew & Bartkowiak, Judy. Secrets of Success in Brand Licensing. 2011. 206p. pap. (978-1-908218-95-7(9)) MX Publishing, Ltd.

Lewis, Roger & Trevitt, Roger. BTEC National Business, Bk. 1. 2nd rev. ed. 2006. (Illus.). 400p. (YA). pap. 47.50 (978-0-7487-9383-9(6)) Nelson Thornes Ltd. GBR. Dist: Trans-Atlantic Pubns., Inc.

Li, Wei Dong, et al, eds. Collaborative Product Design & Manufacturing Methodologies & Applications. 2010. (Springer Series in Advanced Manufacturing Ser.). (Illus.). xiv, 308p. pap. 239.00 (978-1-84996-649-8(4), 1849966494) Springer.

A Light Shines Bright in Babylon. 2007. per. 10.99 (978-0-9786039-1-5(5)) Lanphier Pr.

Lovejoy, William. A Taxonomy of Process Types. 2010. (C). pap. 20.00 (978-1-61674-527-1(4)) Davidson, William Institute At The Univ. of Michigan, The.

MacCannell, Dean. The Ethics of Sightseeing. 2011. (ENG., Illus.). 256p. 55.00 (978-0-520-25782-5(0)); pap. 22.95 (978-0-520-25783-2(9)) Univ. of California Pr.

MacDivitt, Harry & Wilkinson, Mike. The Challenge of Value. 2010. 74p. pap. (978-1-84549-449-0(0), Abramis) arima publishing.

Madura. Introduction to Business. 2006. pap. 12.95 (978-1-4288-0540-8(0)) Cram101 Inc.

Madura, Jeff. Introduction to Business. 2010. (978-0-314-20557-5(8)) West Publishing Co., College & Schl. Div.

Marcouse, Ian, et al. Building a Business. 2nd rev. ed. 2009. 175p. pap. 39.50 (978-0-340-98582-3(8)) Hodder Education GBR. Dist: Trans-Atlantic Pubns., Inc.

—Business Studies for A Level. 4th ed. 2011. (Hodder Education Publication). (ENG., Illus.). 696p. pap. 60.00 (978-1-4441-2275-6(4)) Hodder Education GBR. Dist: Oxford Univ. Pr., Inc.

Marcouse, Ian, et al. Edexcel Business Studies for GCSE. 2009. 400p. pap. 57.50 (978-0-340-98583-0(6)) Hodder Education GBR. Dist: Trans-Atlantic Pubns., Inc.

Marden, Orison. The Young Man Entering Business. 2007. 232p. per. 14.95 (978-1-60206-192-7(0)) Cosimo, Inc.

Marshall, Alfred. Industry & Trade Volume I. 2006. pap. 29.95 (978-1-59605-965-8(6), Cosimo Classics) Cosimo, Inc.

—Industry & Trade Volume Ii. 2006. pap. 30.95 (978-1-60206-004-3(5), Cosimo Classics) Cosimo, Inc.

Maurer, David C. DHS Human Capital: Senior Leadership Vacancy Rates Generally Declined, but Components' Rates Varied. 2012. (ENG.). (C). pap. 25.00 (978-1-4578-2854-6(5)) DIANE Publishing Co.

Mayhew, Ira. Mayhew's Practical Book-Keeping Embracing Single & Double Entry, Commercial Calculations, & the Philosophy & Morals of Business by Ira Mayhe. 2006. 232p. per. 20.99 (978-1-4255-1922-3(9)) MPublishing.

—Mayhew's Practical Book Keeping Embracing Single & Double Entry, Commercial Calculations, & the Philosophy & Morals of Business by Ira Mayhe. 2006. 228p. per. 20.99 (978-1-4255-1943-8(1)) MPublishing.

—Mayhew's Practical Book-Keeping Key by Ira Mayhew. 2006. 128p. per. 16.99 (978-1-4255-0854-8(5)) MPublishing.

Milady Publishing Company Staff. Financial Analysis & Coaching Tools for the Salon & SPA. 2010. (ENG.). (C). 221.50 (978-1-111-31678-5(3), Milady Publishing Co.) Delmar Cengage Learning.

Miller, Barbara Manning. Marketplace Advocacy Campaigns: Generating Public Support for Business & Industry. 2012. 186p. (978-1-60497-789-9(2)) Cambria Pr.

Mishra, Bishnupriya & Uppal, R., eds. Business Environment in India: Some Aspects. 2009. 307p. 39.75 (978-81-7708-213-5(2)) New Century Publications IND. Dist: International Specialized Bk. Services.

Monroe, Anne. Making a Business Woman. 2006. pap. 19.95 (978-1-59605-257-4(0), Cosimo Classics) Cosimo, Inc.

Montali, Marco. Specification & Verification of Declarative Open Interaction Models: A Logic-Based Approach. 2010. (Lecture Notes in Business Information Processing Ser.). xxii, 411p. pap. 99.00 (978-3-642-14537-7(X), 364214537X) Springer.

Moore, James C. General Equilibrium & Welfare Economics: An Introduction. 2010. (ENG., Illus.). xvi, 576p. pap. 149.00 (978-3-642-06849-2(9), 3642068499) Springer.

Morgan, Clare, et al. What Poetry Brings to Business. 2010. (ENG., Illus.). 280p. 75.00 (978-0-472-07086-2(X)); pap. 27.95 (978-0-472-05086-4(9)) Univ. of Michigan Pr.

Morgan, Glenn & Whitley, Richard, eds. Capitalisms & Capitalism in the Twenty-First Century. 2012. (ENG., Illus.). 400p. 110.00 (978-0-19-969476-1(1)) Oxford Univ. Pr., Inc.

Munsterberg, Hugo. Business Psychology. 2007. (ENG.). 308p. 43.95 (978-0-548-15158-7(X)); 312p. per. 28.95 (978-1-4304-4506-7(8)) Kessinger Publishing, LLC.

—Business Psychology. 2008. 320p. pap. (978-1-4097-9473-8(3)) Read Bks.

Needle, David. Business in Context. 5th ed. 2010. (Illus.). 608p. pap. 61.99 (978-1-84480-613-3(8)) Cengage Learning GBR. Dist: CENGAGE Learning.

Nelson, William D. Advances in Business & Management. 2012. (Advances in Business & Management Ser.). 417p. 185.00 (978-1-62100-510-0(0)) Nova Science Pubs., Inc.

Nelson, William D. Advances in Business & Management. Volume 2. 2011. (Advances in Business & Management Ser.). 89.00 (978-1-61122-898-4(0)) Nova Science Pubs., Inc.

Nickels, et al. Business: Connecting Principles to Practice with ConnectPlus. 2011. (ENG.). (C). 189.67 (978-0-07-749983-9(2), 0077499832, McGraw-Hill/Irwin) McGraw-Hill Higher Education.

Nickels, William, et al. Understanding Business + Student Study Guide. 9th ed. 2009. (ENG.). (C). pap. 204.33 (978-0-07-736493-9(7), 0077364937, McGraw-Hill/Irwin) McGraw-Hill Higher Education.

—Understanding Business with Connect Plus. 10th ed. 2012. (ENG.). (C). 217.66 (978-0-07-763073-7(4), 0077630734, McGraw-Hill/Irwin) McGraw-Hill Higher Education.

Nickels, William, et al. Understanding Business with Premium Content Card. 9th ed. 2009. (ENG.). (C). 227.33 (978-0-07-740599-1(4), 0077405994, McGraw-Hill/Irwin) McGraw-Hill Higher Education.

Nickels, William G. & McHugh, James M. Understanding Business. 2006. pap. 19.95 (978-1-4288-1225-3(3)); pap. 13.95 (978-1-4288-0452-4(8)); 7th ed. pap. 19.95 (978-1-4288-1083-9(8)) Cram101 Inc.

Nickels, William G., et al. Business: Connecting Principles to Practice. 2012. (Illus.). (978-0-07-748206-0(9)) McGraw-Hill Cos., The.

—Business: Connecting Principles to Practice. 2011. (ENG., Illus.). 704p. (C). 174.00 (978-0-07-802312-5(2), 0078023122, McGraw-Hill/Irwin) McGraw-Hill Higher Education.

—Understanding Business. 9th ed. 2012. (ENG., Illus.). 569p. pap. 222.25 (978-0-07-759728-3(1)) McGraw-Hill Cos., The.

—Understanding Business. 10th ed. 2012. (ENG., Illus.). 800p. (C). 202.00 (978-0-07-352459-7(X), 007352459X, Irwin Professional Publishing) McGraw-Hill Higher Education.

—Understanding Business. (Illus.). 8th ed. 2006. (978-0-07-310609-0(7)) 9th ed. 2010. xliii, 569p. (978-0-07-726834-3(2)) McGraw-Hill Schl. Education Group. (Irwin Professional Publishing).

—Understanding Business: Preview Edition. 9th ed. 2010. (Illus.). xliii, 569p. (978-0-07-735546-3(6), Irwin Professional Publishing) McGraw-Hill Schl. Education Group.

Niederman, Derrick. This Is Not Your Father's Stockpicking Book. Date not set. (978-0-8129-2832-7(6), Crown) Crown Publishing Group.

Nomura, Carl. Business Success with Less Stress. 2011. 112p. 29.99 (978-1-4568-1961-3(5)); pap. 19.99 (978-1-4568-1960-6(7)) Xlibris Corp.

Nordstrom, Kjell & Ridderstrale, Jonas. Funky Business Forever: How to Enjoy Capitalism. 3rd rev. ed. 2007. (ENG., Illus.). 256p. (C). pap. (978-0-273-71413-2(9)) Pearson Education Canada.

Nuttall, Chris & Houghton, Medi. Cambridge IGCSE Business Studies Coursebook with CD-ROM. 2nd rev. ed. 2010. (Cambridge International Examinations Ser.). (ENG.). 246p. pap. 23.00 incl. cd-rom (978-0-521-12210-8(4)) Cambridge Univ. Pr.

O'Connor, Peter. Black-Scholes & Augmented Option Pricing Models. 2010. 60p. pap. (978-3-8383-7831-2(8)) Lambert Academic Publishing.

Oecd Publishing, Publishing & Oecd Publishing. Oecd Economic Outlook, Volume 201. 2010. 390p. pap. 25.00 (978-92-64-08521-3(1)) Organization for Economic Cooperation & Development.

Okoronkwo, Daniel. Secrets of Unclaimed $400 Billion Dollars Lost Fortunes Held by the U. S. Government; How to Claim Your Share. 2010. 348p. pap. 39.95 (978-1-4120-7817-7(2)) Trafford Publishing.

Ougaard, Morten & Leander, Anna. Business & Global Governance. Ougaard, Morten & Leander, Anna, eds. 2010. (Warwick Studies in Globalisation Ser.). (ENG., Illus.). 288p. (C). 135.00 (978-0-415-49336-9(6)); pap. 47.95 (978-0-415-49337-6(4)) Taylor & Francis Group GBR. (Routledge). Dist: Taylor & Francis Group.

Owen, Jo. The Mobile MBA: 112 Skills to Take You Further, Faster. rev. ed. 2011. (ENG.). 200p. pap. 19.99 (978-0-273-75021-5(6)) FT Press.

Parhizgar, Kamal Dean & Parhizgar, Fuzhan F. Organizational Behavior: Global Multicultural Perspectives (First Edition) 2012. (ENG.). (C). 0.00 (978-1-62131-101-0(5)); pap. 0.00 (978-1-62131-100-3(7)) Univ. Readers. (Cognella Academic Publishing).

Pegues, Deborah S. Confronting Without Offending. pap. 7.99 (978-0-927936-75-0(5)) Vincom Pubng. Co.

Peter Collin Publishing Staff. Estonian-English Business Glossary. (EST & ENG.). 196p. pap. (978-0-948549-94-6(7), T&AD Poyser) A & C Black.

Picard, Robert G. Media Clusters: Spatial Agglomeration & Content Capabilities. Karlsson, Charlie, ed. 2011. (New Horizons in Regional Science Ser.). (Illus.). 432p. 160.00 (978-0-85793-268-6(3)) Elgar, Edward Publishing, Inc.

Pick, James B. Geo-Business: GIS in the Digital Organization. 2008. (ENG., Illus.). 416p. 115.00 (978-0-471-72998-3(1), Wiley) Wiley, John & Sons, Inc.

Pieth, Mark, et al, eds. The OECD Convention on Bribery: A Commentary. 2007. (ENG.). 652p. 190.00 (978-0-521-86817-4(3)) Cambridge Univ. Pr.

Potts, Chris. Fruition: Creating the Ultimate Corporate Strategy for Information Technology. 2008. (ENG., Illus.). 216p. pap. 18.95 (978-0-9771400-3-9(2)) Technics Pubns., LLC.

Prahalad, C. K., et al. 24/7 Customer: Beyond Call Center Operations. 2010. (C). pap. 20.00 (978-1-61674-004-7(3)); pap. 20.00 (978-1-61674-002-3(7)) Davidson, William Institute At The Univ. of Michigan, The.

Pride, William M. & Hughes, Robert J. Business. 8th ed. 2006. (ENG.). pap. 18.95 (978-1-4288-1080-8(3)) Cram101 Inc.

Proceedings of 7th Global Conference on Business & Economics, October 13-14th, 2007, Association for Business & Economics Research. 2007. cd-rom (978-0-9742114-8-0(6)) Gupta, Atul.

Pulk, Kätlin. Organisational Change Evaluated in Cultural Context. 2010. 92p. pap. (978-3-8383-6110-9(5)) Lambert Academic Publishing.

Puu, Tõnu. Oligopoly: Old Ends - New Means. 2010. (ENG., Illus.). ix, 172p. 119.00 (978-3-642-15963-3(X), 364215963X) Springer.

Quattrone, Paolo, et al, eds. Imagining Business: Performative Imagery in Organizations. 2011. (Routledge Studies in Management, Organizations & Society Ser.). (ENG., Illus.). 274p. (C). 125.00 (978-0-415-88064-0(5)) Routledge.

Rahim, Md Mahbubur & Rahim, Mahbubur. Understanding Adoption of Inter-Organisational Systems. 2011. 324p. pap. (978-3-8443-1241-6(2)) Lambert Academic Publishing.

Rainbow. Introduction to Business. 2009. 480p. pap. 49.95 (978-1-4051-4569-5(2), Wiley-Blackwell) Wiley, John & Sons, Ltd. GBR. Dist: Wiley, John & Sons, Inc.

Rautenstrauch, Walter. The Successful Control of Profits. 2011. 256p. 47.95 (978-1-258-05546-2(5)) Literary Licensing, LLC.

Raval, Vasant & Fichadia, Ashok. Risks, Controls, & Security: Concepts & Applications. 2007. (ENG., Illus.). 432p. (C). 123.95 (978-0-471-48579-7(9), Wiley) Wiley, John & Sons, Inc.

Rees, Nina. Edexcel Business for GCSE: Business Communication. Marcouse, Ian, ed. 2010. (Illus.). 112p. pap. 39.50 (978-1-4441-0791-3(7)) Hodder Education GBR. Dist: Trans-Atlantic Pubns., Inc.

Reeves, Diane Lindsey, et al. Career Ideas for Teens in Business Management & Administration. 2011. (Career Ideas for Teens Ser.). (gr. 6-12). 45.00 (978-0-8160-8265-0(0), Ferguson Publishing Co.) Facts On File, Inc.

Reiner, Gerald, ed. Rapid Modelling & Quick Response: Intersection of Theory & Practice. 2010. (ENG., Illus.). xvi, 348p. 259.00 (978-1-84996-524-8(2), 1849965242) Springer.

Resnick, Lynda & Wilkinson, Francis. Rubies in the Orchard: The POM Queen's Secrets to Marketing Just about Anything. 2010. (ENG., Illus.). 240p. pap. 15.00 (978-0-385-52579-4(6), Broadway Business) Knopf Doubleday Publishing Group.

Richter, Rudolf. New Institutional Economics of Markets. Furubotn, Eirik G., ed. 2010. (International Library of Critical Writings in Economics series Ser.). (Illus.). 688p. 381.00 (978-1-84720-983-2(1)) Elgar, Edward Publishing, Inc.

Ridgway, Bret & Deardurff III, Frank. 50 Biggest Website Mistakes: Secrets to Getting More Traffic, Converting More Customers, & Making More Sales. 2011. (ENG.). 182p. pap. 17.95 (978-1-60037-972-7(9)) Morgan James Publishing.

Rigby, Rhymer. 28 Business Thinkers Who Changed the World: The Management Gurus & Mavericks Who Changed the Way We Think about Business. 2011. (ENG.). 232p. pap. 22.50 (978-0-7494-6239-0(6)) Kogan Page, Ltd. GBR. Dist: Ingram Pub. Services.

Rigobón, Roberto, ed. Economia: Spring 2010 - Journal of the Latin American & Caribbean Economic Association. 2010. (ENG.). 164p. pap. 36.00 (978-0-8157-0470-6(4)) Brookings Institution Pr.

Ring Danzig, Sheila. Invisible Marketing: How to Be Known as an Expert by Becoming an Author (Without Writing a Word) Danzig, William, ed. 2010. (How to Make People Buy Whatever You're Selling Whether They Know They Need It or Not Ser.). (ENG., Illus.). 110p. (Orig.). 39.95 (978-0-9624333-6-8(5), BG Publishing International) National Success Marketing, Inc.

Robinson, Leslie. Hot*Spot: Gross Income, Tax Liabilities & Credits. 4th ed. 2011. 99.00 (978-0-88128-009-8(7)) Bisk Education, Inc.

Rodgers, Paul. Commercial Awareness & Business Decision Making Skills: How to Understand & Analyse Company Financial Information. 2007. (ENG.). 272p. pap. 49.95 (978-0-7506-8384-5(8), CIMA Publishing) Elsevier Science & Technology Bks.

Roper, Maxwell. Consulting Alliance - the Commitment to Team Empowerment: A Case Study of USA Leadership Corps¿ Team Leadership & Management Methodology. 2007. spiral bd. (978-0-9788397-1-0(4)) USA Leadership Corps.

Ross, Celia. Making Sense of Business Reference: A Guide for Librarians & Research Professionals. 2011. 176p. pap. (978-0-8389-1084-9(X)) American Library Assn.

Rubin, Tina, text. Madison: Hub of Innovation. 2012. 59.95 (978-1-882933-93-8(1)) Cherbo Publishing Group, Inc.

Salem Press Staff, contrib. by. Survey of American Industry & Careers. 2011. (978-1-58765-774-0(0)); (978-1-58765-768-9(6)); (978-1-58765-769-6(4)); (978-1-58765-773-3(2)); (978-1-58765-772-6(4)); (978-1-58765-771-9(6)); (978-1-58765-770-2(8)) Salem Pr., Inc.

Samuels, S. G. Get Rich Now on a Secret Multi-Trillion Dollar Market: Trade Money, Not Stock. 2010. 140p. 24.95 (978-1-4502-0164-3(4)) iUniverse, Inc.

Schinkel, Maarten Pieter. Market Oversight Games. 2011. (VOR Economie Ser.). 40p. pap. (978-90-5629-663-6(9), Vossiupers UvA) Amsterdam Univ. Pr.

Schlachter, Gail Ann & Weber, R. David. How to Pay for Your Degree in Business & Related Fields 2010-2012. 4th ed. 2010. 272p. pap. 30.00 *(978-1-58841-214-0(8))* Reference Service Pr.

Schultz, Ron. Adjacent Opportunities: Sparking Emergent Social Action. 2010. 148p. 14.99 *(978-0-9842164-4-4(8))* Emergent Pubns.

Seidl, Immanuel. Data Envelopment Analysis visualisiert in 3D - Diagrammen: Darstellung von Produktionsgebirgen. 2010. 60p. pap. *(978-3-639-23335-3(2))* VDM Verlag Dr. Mueller e.K.

Serletis, Apostolos. The Demand for Money: Theoretical & Empirical Approaches. 2nd ed. 2010. (ENG., Illus.). xxiv, 381p. pap. 149.00 *(978-1-4419-4406-1(0),* 1441944060) Springer.

Sethi, S. Prakash, ed. Globalization & Self-Regulation: The Crucial Role That Corporate Codes of Conduct Play in Global Business. 2011. (ENG.). 312p. 65.00 *(978-0-230-61155-9(9))* Palgrave Macmillan.

Shah, Amit. Business Now. 2nd ed. 2010. (ENG., Illus.). 448p. (C). pap. 96.00 *(978-0-07-337728-5(7),* 0073377287) McGraw-Hill Higher Education.

Shaw, Benjamin. Gdp: A business Perspective. 2010. 96p. pap. *(978-3-639-22913-4(4))* VDM Verlag Dr. Mueller e.K.

Siegel, Andrew F. Practical Business Statistics. 5th ed. 2006. pap. 9.95 *(978-1-4288-1349-6(7))* Cram101 Inc.

Skinner, David C. Introduction to Decision Analysis: A Practitioner's Guide to Improving Decision Quality. 2009. (ENG., Illus.). 368p. 49.95 *(978-0-9647938-6-6(5))* Probabilistic Publishing.

Skrabec, Quentin R., Jr. The 100 Most Significant Events in American Business: An Encyclopedia, 1 vol. 2012. 340p. 89.00 ***(978-0-313-39862-9(3)***, A3638C) Greenwood Publishing Group, Inc.

Skrabec, Quentin R. The 100 Most Significant Events in American Business: An Encyclopedia. 2012. E-Book ***(978-0-313-39863-6(1)***, Greenwood Pr.) Greenwood Publishing Group, Inc.

Smith, Jon. Be #1 on Google: 52 Fast & Easy Search Engine Optimization Tools to Drive Customers to Your Web Site. 2009. (ENG., Illus.). 160p. pap. 16.95 *(978-0-07-162960-7(2),* 0071629602) McGraw-Hill Cos., The.

Solomon, Michael R., et al. Better Business. 2nd rev. ed. 2011. (ENG.). 640p. (C). pap. 146.67 *(978-0-13-249669-8(0),* Prentice Hall) Prentice Hall PTR.

—Study Guide for Better Business. 2nd rev. ed. 2011. (ENG.). 360p. (C). pap. 46.67 *(978-0-13-249675-9(5),* Prentice Hall) Prentice Hall PTR.

Spence, Laura & Painter-Morland, Mollie, eds. Ethics in Small & Medium Sized Enterprises: A Global Commentary. 2010. (International Society of Business, Economics, & Ethics Book Ser.). (Illus.). xxi, 289p. 139.00 *(978-90-481-9330-1(3),* 9048193303) Springer.

Spurgeon, Christina. Advertising & New Media. 2007. (Illus.). 144p. pap. 30.95 *(978-0-415-43035-7(6))*; 120.00 *(978-0-415-43034-0(8))* Routledge.

Spurling, David, et al. Principles of Business & Management. 2006. 600p. per. *(978-1-84549-133-8(5))* arima publishing.

Stimpson, Peter & Farquharson, Alastair. Cambridge International AS & A Level Business Studies Coursebook with CD-ROM. 2nd ed. 2010. (Cambridge International Examinations Ser.). (ENG.). 688p. pap., stu. ed. 34.00 incl. cd-rom *(978-0-521-12656-4(8))* Cambridge Univ. Pr.

Stimpson, Peter & Joyce, Peter. Cambridge International AS & A Level Business Studies. 2012. (Cambridge International Examinations Ser.). (ENG.). 250p. pap. 21.00 ***(978-1-107-60477-3(X))*** Cambridge Univ. Pr.

Stylianou, Yusuf. So You Want to Start A Business. 2009. 52p. pap. 16.95 *(978-1-4092-6325-8(8))* Lulu Enterprises Inc.

Thanaraju, Puvaneswary, et al. Establishing Facilities Management Agreed Service Level. 2011. 88p. pap. ***(978-3-8443-2019-0(9))*** Lambert Academic Publishing.

Tharrett, Stephen & Bedford, Paul. Why People Join, Leave, & Stay with Health/Fitness Clubs: The Ultimate Handbook of Member Retention. 2012. (ENG., Illus.). 217p. pap. 49.95 ***(978-1-60679-216-2(4)***, Healthy Learning) Coaches Choice.

Tharrett, Stephen & Peterson, James. Fitness Management (Third Edition) 3rd ed. 2012. (ENG., Illus.). 583p. pap. 69.95 ***(978-1-60679-215-5(6)***, Healthy Learning) Coaches Choice.

Tharrett, Stephen & Thomason, Teresa. 101 Programming Strategies for Engaging Members in Health/Fitness Clubs. 2012. (ENG., Illus.). 111p. pap. 19.95 ***(978-1-60679-214-8(8)***, Healthy Learning) Coaches Choice.

The Green Sheet Inc., compiled by. Credit Card Processing for Sales Agents. 2012. (ENG.). 640p. pap. 124.99 ***(978-0-9826116-6-1(8))*** C3ET Credit Card Consortia for Education & Training Inc.

Thewlis, Paul. WordPress for Business Bloggers. 2008. (Illus.). 300p. pap. *(978-1-84719-532-6(6))* Packt Publishing, Ltd.

Thomas, Alan Ken, ed. The Business Wisdom of Steve Jobs: 250 Quotes from the Innovator Who Changed the World. 2011. (ENG.). 176p. pap. 12.95 ***(978-1-61608-749-4(8)***, 608749) Skyhorse Publishing Co., Inc.

Thomas, Albert W. If It Doesn't Go up Don't Buy It. 2nd rev. ed. 144p. 29.95 *(978-0-9671553-1-9(2))* Williamsburg Investment Co., Inc.

Thoms, Peg. Battleground: Business, 2 vols. Walden, Michael, ed. 2007. (Battleground Ser.). (Illus.). 704p. 175.00 *(978-0-313-34065-9(X),* GR4065, Greenwood Pr.) Greenwood Publishing Group, Inc.

Towers, Steve & McGregor, Mark. Thrive! How to Succeed in the Age of the Customer. 2006. pap. 19.95 *(978-0-929652-41-2(X))* Meghan-Kiffer Pr.

Trapp, Roger, et al. What You Need to Know about Business. 2011. (ENG., Illus.). 256p. pap. 19.95 *(978-0-85708-115-5(2),* Capstone) Wiley, John & Sons, Inc.

Trippon, James Mark. The Millionaire Physician. 2007. 29.95 *(978-0-9723389-2-9(6))* Woods, Bretton Pr., LLC.

Van Syckle, Barbara & Tietje, Brian. Anybody's Business. 2009. (ENG.). 408p. (C). 106.67 *(978-0-13-213572-6(8),* Prentice Hall) Prentice Hall PTR.

Veblen, Thorstein. The Theory of Business Enterprise. 2009. 236p. pap. *(978-1-4099-6559-6(7))* Dodo Pr.

—The Theory of Business Enterprise. 2007. (ENG.). 416p. per. 24.45 *(978-1-59462-874-0(2),* Book Jungle) Standard Pubns., Inc.

—The Vested Interests. 2009. 194p. 26.99 *(978-1-110-63027-1(1))*; pap. 22.75 *(978-1-110-63026-4(3))* BiblioBazaar.

Vik, David. The Culture King. 2012. 24.95 ***(978-1-935723-56-1(1))*** Motivational Pr., Inc.

Wankel, Charles & Stoner, James A. F., eds. Managing Climate Change Business Risks & Consequences: Leadership for Global Sustainability. 2012. (Global Sustainability Through Business Ser.). (ENG., Illus.). 254p. 95.00 ***(978-0-230-11583-5(7))*** Palgrave Macmillan.

Warren, Waldo Pondray. Thoughts on Business. 2009. 134p. pap. 19.99 *(978-0-217-90143-7(3))*; 118p. pap. 14.14 *(978-0-217-90145-1(X))* General Bks. LLC.

—Thoughts on Business. 2007. (ENG.). 240p. 41.95 *(978-0-548-10397-5(6))* Kessinger Publishing, LLC.

Weatherston, Jamie, et al. The International Business Environment: Challenges & Changes. 2nd rev. ed. 2010. (ENG., Illus.). 376p. pap. 99.50 *(978-0-273-72566-4(1))* FT Press.

Weldon, Gregory T. Gold Trading Boot Camp: How to Master the Basics & Become a Successful Commodities Investor. 2007. (ENG., Illus.). 368p. 34.95 *(978-0-471-72800-9(4),* Wiley) Wiley, John & Sons, Inc.

Wells, Iv. An Economic Model for Swine Production. 2008. 260p. pap. *(978-3-639-05123-0(8))* VDM Verlag Dr. Mueller e.K.

Wetherly, Paul & Otter, Dorron. The Business Environment: Themes & Issues. 2nd ed. 2011. (ENG., Illus.). 535p. (C). pap. 64.95 *(978-0-19-957960-0(1))* Oxford Univ. Pr., Inc.

Weyers, Jonathan. How to Pass Exams, 2 vols. 5th ed. 2007. (Illus.). 208p. pap. 26.50 *(978-0-273-71359-3(0),* Financial Times/Prentice Hall) Pearson Education, Ltd. GBR. Dist: Trans-Atlantic Pubns., Inc.

Whaley, Richard. Manufacturing Cost Accounting: For MS Dynamics GP. 2006. 236p. pap. 150.00 *(978-1-931479-05-9(4))* Accolade Pubns., Inc.

Whitener, Gary Lee. Gary Lee Whitener: My Life & Times. 2010. 112p. 22.95 *(978-1-4502-3188-6(8))* iUniverse, Inc.

Willard, Bob. The Next Sustainability Wave: Building Boardroom Buy-in. (ENG.). 9p. 15.00 *(978-0-86571-495-3(9))* New Society Pubs., Ltd. CAN. Dist: Consortium Bk. Sales & Distribution.

Williams, Brian K., et al. Business: A Practical Introduction. 2012. (ENG.). 696p. (C). 180.00 *(978-0-13-233429-7(1),* Prentice Hall) Prentice Hall PTR.

—Business: A Practical Introduction, Student Value Edition. 2012. (ENG.). 650p. (C). ring bd. 117.00 ***(978-0-13-280715-9(7)***, Prentice Hall) Prentice Hall PTR.

—Mybizlab with Pearson eText Student Access Code Card for Business. 2012. (ENG.). (C). 106.67 ***(978-0-13-280765-4(3)***, Prentice Hall) Prentice Hall PTR.

Williams, H. James & Colby, Marvelle S. Introduction to Business. Pirkle, Kipling M., ed. 2nd ed. 2007. (Collins College Outlines Ser.). (ENG., Illus.). 256p. per. 15.95 *(978-0-06-088149-8(6))* HarperCollins Pubs.

Williams, Hadji. C. R. E. A. M. Principled Principles for Connecting with America's Multi-Trillion Dollar Multicultural Consumer. 2008. (Illus.). 160p. (YA). per. 24.00 *(978-1-932523-02-7(2))* ProdigalPen Publishing, Inc.

Willson, Mark A. Friends & Foes: Your Practical Guide to Identifying, Understanding, & Influencing Project/Task Supporters, Detractors, & champions as well as Building Strong Support from All Those Involved. 2006. (Troubleshooter's Ser.: Bk. 2). pap. 50.00 *(978-0-9749658-6-4(3))* Uncommon Technology Inc.

Witt, Graham. Writing Effective Business Rules. 2012. (ENG.). 360p. pap. 59.95 ***(978-0-12-385051-5(7)***, Morgan Kaufmann) Elsevier Science & Technology Bks.

Witt, Michael B., ed. Asian Business & Management, 8 vols. 2012. (SAGE Library in Business & Management Ser.). 3064p. 1500.00 ***(978-1-4462-0025-4(6)***, B00254C) SAGE Pubns., Ltd. GBR. Dist: SAGE Pubns., Inc.

Wittenberg-Cox, Avivah & Maitland, Alison. Why Women Mean Business + How Women Mean Business Set. 2010. (ENG.). 798p. pap. 39.95 *(978-0-470-66987-7(X),* Wiley) Wiley, John & Sons, Inc.

Wood, David, ed. Linking Enterprise Data. 2010. (ENG.). xxvi, 291p. 129.00 *(978-1-4419-7664-2(7),* 1441976647) Springer.

Woods, William T. Strategic Sourcing: Office Supplies Pricing Study Had Limitations, but New Initiative Shows Potential for Savings. 2011. (ENG.). (C). pap. 20.00 ***(978-1-4223-1675-7(0)***, Silverwood Institute) DIANE Publishing Co.

Woodward, Orrin. Resolved: 13 Resolutions for LIFE. 2012. pap. 21.95 ***(978-0-9853387-3-2(3))*** Signature Management Team, LLC.

Woolf, James D. & Roth, Charles B. How to Use Your Imagination to Make Money. 2011. 200p. pap. 12.95 ***(978-1-61646-066-2(0))*** Coachwhip Pubns.

World Bank. Global Development Horizons 2011. 2011. (Global Development Horizons Ser.). (ENG., Illus.). 180p. pap. 35.00 *(978-0-8213-8692-7(1),* 9780821386927) World Bank Pubns.

World Bank Staff. Doing Business 2009: Comparing Regulation in 181 Economies. rev. ed. 2008. (Doing Business Ser.). (ENG., Illus.). 185p. pap. 35.00 *(978-0-8213-7609-6(8),* 9780821376096) World Bank Pubns.

Yager, Loren. U. S. Export-Import Bank: Actions Needed to Promote Competitiveness & International Cooperation. 2012. (ENG.). (C). pap. 25.00 ***(978-1-4578-2827-0(8))*** DIANE Publishing Co.

Yilmaz, Zozan. Between Recession & Depression. 2010. 110p. pap. *(978-1-84549-424-7(5),* Abramis) arima publishing.

Zendel, Azita. Hollywood Apprentice: How to Break into Hollywood & Survive the Toxic Boss Syndrome. 2006. (Hollywood Apprentice Ser.). 326p. per. 19.95 *(978-0-9759016-4-9(8),* AZ1836) Azita Bks. & Films, Inc.

Zheng, Li & Possel-Dölken, Frank. Strategic Production Networks. 2010. (ENG., Illus.). xv, 489p. pap. 139.00 *(978-3-642-07734-0(X),* 364207734X) Springer.

BUSINESS—ANTHROPOLOGICAL ASPECTS

see Business Anthropology

BUSINESS—AUDIO-VISUAL AIDS

Aik, Chong Tek. Effects of Visual Training & Visual Aids. 2008. 240p. pap. *(978-3-639-00961-3(4))* VDM Verlag Dr. Mueller e.K.

BUSINESS—AUTHORSHIP

see Business Writing

BUSINESS—BIBLIOGRAPHY

see also Business Literature

Basic Books. The Best Business Books Ever: The 100 Most Influential Management Books You'll Never Have Time to Read. 2nd rev. ed. 2011. (ENG.). 280p. (gr. 9). pap. 16.99 *(978-0-465-02236-6(7))* Basic Bks.

Business & Economics. *(978-0-8357-0663-6(X))*; *(978-0-8357-0664-3(8))*; Vol. 16. 941p. *(978-0-8357-0847-0(0))* Univ. Microfilms, Inc.

Covert, Jack & Sattersten, Todd. The 100 Best Business Books of All Time: What They Say, Why They Matter, & How They Can Help You. (ENG., Illus.). (gr. 12). 2011. 368p. 16.00 *(978-1-59184-446-4(0),* Portfolio Trade) 2009. 352p. 25.95 *(978-1-59184-240-8(9),* Portfolio (Hardcover)) Penguin Group (USA) Inc.

Directories in Print, 2.0. 33rd ed. 2011. pap. 920.00 *(978-1-4144-5870-0(3))* Cengage Gale.

Encyclopedia of Business Information Sources, 2.0. 28th ed. 2011. pap. 626.00 *(978-1-4144-5899-1(1))* Cengage Gale.

Forte, Eric & Oppenheim, Michael. The Basic Business Library: Core Resources & Services, 1 vol. 5th rev. ed. 227p. 44.95 *(978-1-59884-611-9(6),* A3137C) Libraries Unlimited, Inc.

Forte, Eric J. & Oppenheim, Michael R. The Basic Business Library: Core Resources & Services. 5th ed. 2011. E-Book ***(978-1-59884-612-6(4))*** Libraries Unlimited, Inc.

Johnson, Stephen K. The Harvard Business Review Annotated Bibliography: All Articles, 1922 Through 2007, with Indexes to Authors, Titles & Subjects. 2010. (ENG.). 472p. pap. 95.00 *(978-0-7864-4182-2(8))* McFarland & Co., Inc. Pubs.

Moss, Rita & Ernsthausen, David G. Strauss's Handbook of Business Information: A Guide for Librarians, Students, & Researchers, 1 vol. 399p. 100.00 ***(978-1-59884-807-6(0)***, A3433C) Pearson Education GBR. Dist: ABC-CLIO, LLC.

BUSINESS—COMMUNICATION SYSTEMS

Agrawal, Manish. Business Data Communications. 2011. (ENG., Illus.). 384p. (C). pap. 114.95 *(978-0-470-48336-7(9),* Wiley) Wiley, John & Sons, Inc.

Brantley & Miller, Toby. Aie Effective Communication for Colleges. 11th ed. 2007. (C). pap. 33.95 *(978-0-324-54336-0(0))* Cengage South-Western.

Cram101 Textbook Reviews. Outlines & Highlights for Effective Communication for Colleges by Clarice Pennebaker Brantley, Isbn: 9780324374766. 2010. 76p. pap. 27.95 *(978-1-61698-003-0(6))* Cram101 Inc.

Cram101 Textbook Reviews Staff. Strategic Planning for Information Syste. 2006. 227p. pap. 12.95 *(978-1-4288-0532-3(X))* Cram101 Inc.

Human Resource Management, Society for. Successfully Transitioning to a Virtual Organization: Challenges, Impact, & Technology. 2010. (Research Quarterly Ser.). (ENG.). 24p. pap. 29.95 *(978-1-58644-194-4(9))* Society for Human Resource Management.

King, William R., ed. Planning for Information Systems, 14 vols. 2009. (Advances in Management Information Systems Ser.). (ENG., Illus.). 528p. 199.95 *(978-0-7656-1950-1(4))* Sharpe, M.E. Inc.

Newman, Aaron, et al. Enterprise 2.0 Implementation: Integrate Web 2.0 Services into Your Enterprise. 2008. (ENG., Illus.). 406p. pap. 49.99 *(978-0-07-159160-7(5),* 0071591605) McGraw-Hill Osborne.

Ramanathan, Jay & Ramnath, Rajiv. Co-Engineering Applications & Adaptive Business Technologies in Practice: Enterprise Service Ontologies, Models, & Frameworks. 2009. (Premier Reference Source Ser.). (Illus.). 426p. 165.00 *(978-1-60566-276-3(3),* Information Science Publishing) IGI Global.

Scott, Joel. GoldMine 8 for Dummies. 2007. (ENG., Illus.). 364p. pap. 24.99 *(978-0-7645-9834-0(1),* For Dummies) Wiley, John & Sons, Inc.

Simionovich, Nir. AsteriskNOW. 2008. pap. *(978-1-84719-288-2(2))* Packt Publishing, Ltd.

Thatcher, Barry, et al, eds. Outsourcing Technical Communication: Issues, Policies & Practice. 2008. (Technical Communication Ser.). (Illus.). 246p. 52.95 *(978-0-89503-334-5(8))* Baywood Publishing Co., Inc.

Ward, Robin. Strategic Planning for Information Systems 4E. 4th ed. 2013. (ENG.). 544p. pap. 77.95 ***(978-0-470-03467-5(X)***, Wiley) Wiley, John & Sons, Inc.

Weatherall, Alan. Getting Results from Electronic Meetings. 2nd ed. 184p. *(978-0-9526525-1-9(X))* Electronic Meeting Solutions, Ltd. GBR. Dist: Vine Hse. Distribution.

BUSINESS—COMPUTER NETWORK RESOURCES

Ahr, Dino. Multiple Postmen Problems- Fundamentals & New Algorithms. 2007. 220p. per. *(978-3-8364-4496-5(8))* VDM Verlag Dr. Mueller e.K.

Applegate and A, McFarlan. Creating Business Advantage in the Infor. 2006. pap. 10.95 *(978-1-4288-0761-7(6))* Cram101 Inc.

Aronson, Bill. Metastorm ProVision 6. 2 Made Easy. 2010. 733p. pap. 79.95 *(978-1-4452-4200-2(1))* Lulu Enterprises Inc.

Arques, Sofia. Network Analysis. 2011. 92p. pap. ***(978-3-8443-1039-9(8))*** Lambert Academic Publishing.

Birch, David, ed. Digital Identity Management: Technological, Business & Social Implications. 2007. (Illus.). 280p. 124.95 *(978-0-566-08679-3(4),* Gower Publishing Co., Ltd.) Ashgate Publishing, Ltd. GBR. Dist: Ashgate Publishing Co.

Boles, Larry & Boles, David W. Google Apps for Your Domain: A Private-Label Web Workspace. 2007. (ENG.). 256p. pap. 29.99 *(978-1-59863-451-8(8))* Course Technology.

Brechner, Eric. I. M. Wright's Hard Code: A Decade of Hard-Won Lessons from Microsoft. 2nd ed. 2011. (ENG.). 450p. pap. 44.99 *(978-0-7356-6170-7(7))* Microsoft Pr.

Butow, Eric & Bollwitt, Rebecca. Blogging to Drive Business: Create & Maintain Valuable Customer Connections. 2010. (Que Biz-Tech Ser.). (ENG., Illus.). 192p. pap. 21.99 *(978-0-7897-4256-8(X))* Que.

Cisco Networking Academy. CCNA Discovery Course Booklet: Networking for Home & Small Businesses, Version 4. 0. 2009. (Course Booklets Ser.). (ENG.). 168p. (C). pap. 24.95 *(978-1-58713-242-1(7))* Cisco Pr.

Couturier, Hervé, et al. Understanding the Future Internet. 2011. (Illus.). 40.00 ***(978-0-9825506-4-9(2))*** Evolved Technologist Pr.

Cram101 Textbook Reviews Staff. Outlines & Highlights for E-Business: Organizational & Technical Foundations by Papazoglou, ISBN. 2008. 132p. pap. 11.95 *(978-1-4288-6322-4(2))* Cram101 Inc.

Cunningham, Peter & öschl, Friedrich. Electronic Business Revolution: Opportunities & Challenges in the 21st Century. 2010. (ENG., Illus.). xviii, 238p. pap. 84.95 *(978-3-642-08549-9(0),* 3642085490) Springer.

de Guise, Preston & De Guise, Preston. Enterprise Systems Backup & Recovery: A Corporate Insurance Policy. 2008. (ENG., Illus.). 308p. 75.95 *(978-1-4200-7639-4(6))* Auerbach Pubs., Inc.

Doom, Claude. An Introduction to Business Information Management. 2010. (ENG., Illus.). 170p. pap. 37.00 *(978-90-5487-609-0(3))* VUB Univ. Pr. BEL. Dist: Independent Pubs. Group.

Forte, Eric & Oppenheim, Michael. The Basic Business Library: Core Resources & Services, 1 vol. 5th rev. ed. 227p. 44.95 *(978-1-59884-611-9(6),* A3137C) Libraries Unlimited, Inc.

Forte, Eric J. & Oppenheim, Michael R. The Basic Business Library: Core Resources & Services. 5th ed. 2011. E-Book ***(978-1-59884-612-6(4))*** Libraries Unlimited, Inc.

Full Committee Hearing on the Recovery ACT & Broadband: Evaluation of Broadband Investments on Small Business & Job Creation: Hearing Before the Committee on Small Business, United States House of Representatives, One Hundred Eleventh Congress, First Session, Hearing Held October 28, 2009. 2009. v, 84p. *(978-0-16-084891-9(1),* 552-070-40287-0) United States Government Printing Office.

Garbade, Michael. M & A, Cooperations & Networks in the E-Business Industry. 2007. 172p. per. *(978-3-8364-2989-4(6))* VDM Verlag Dr. Mueller e.K.

Hartjes, Rudolf. Web Accessibility: Techniken und exemplarische Erfolgsmessung. 2009. (Electronic Business Ser.). (GER.). 118p. 35.95 *(978-3-631-59326-4(0))* Lang, Peter GmbH, Europaischer Verlag der Wissenschaften DEU. Dist: Lang, Peter.

Illing, Gerhard & Peitz, Martin, eds. Industrial Organization & the Digital Economy. 2006. (ENG., Illus.). 344p. (gr. 17). 40.00 *(978-0-262-09041-4(4))* MIT Pr.

Kahonge, Andrew Mwaura. Shared Spaces for Hand Held Devices. 2010. 84p. pap. *(978-3-639-11447-8(7))* VDM Verlag Dr. Mueller e.K.

Krakoff, Patsi & Wakeman, Denise. Build a Better Blog: The Ultimate Guide to Boosting Your Business with a Professional Blog. 2nd ed. 2006. *(978-0-9765153-2-6(6))* Customized Newsletter Services.

Landy, Gene K. & Mastrobattista, Amy J. IT / Digital Legal Companion: A Comprehensive Business Guide to Software, IT, Internet, Media & IP Law. 2008. (ENG., Illus.). 1254p. pap. 69.95 *(978-1-59749-256-0(6),* Syngress Press) Elsevier Science & Technology Bks.

Levitt, Carole & Rosch, Mark. The Cybersleuth's Guide to the Internet: Conducting Effective Investigative & Legal Research on the Web. 9th ed. 2008. Orig. Title: How to Use the Internet for Legal & Investigative Research. (Illus.). 330p. pap. 59.95 *(978-0-9713257-3-9(1))* IFL Pr.

Levy, Evan & Dyché, Jill. Customer Data Integration: Reaching a Single Version of the Truth. 2006. (Wiley & SAS Business Ser.: 7). (ENG., Illus.). 320p. 39.95 *(978-0-471-91697-0(8),* Wiley) Wiley, John & Sons, Inc.

Mair, Karin. Enterprise Resource Planning (ERP) Systeme: Betriebswirtschaftliche Grundlagen. 2010. 100p. pap. *(978-3-639-25122-7(9))* VDM Verlag Dr. Mueller e.K.

Manzer, Ayesha. Integration of Processes Using Formal Methods. 2010. 152p. pap. *(978-3-8383-4503-1(7))* Lambert Academic Publishing.

McNulty, Scott. Building a TypePad Blog People Want to Read. rev. ed. 2010. (ENG., Illus.). 272p. pap. 29.99 *(978-0-321-62451-2(3))* Peachpit Pr.

Mnller, Hendrik. State of the Art in Service-Oriented Architecture. 2008. 168p. per. *(978-3-8364-6226-6(5))* VDM Verlag Dr. Mueller e.K.

Ouellette, L. Paul. I T in Crisis: A New Business Model. 2009. 192p. 31.95 *(978-1-4389-8543-5(6))*; pap. 19.95 *(978-1-4389-8542-8(8))* AuthorHouse.

Podeswa, Howard. UML for the IT Business Analyst. 2nd ed. 2009. (ENG.). 400p. pap. 49.99 *(978-1-59863-868-4(3))* Course Technology.

Raunio, Tommi. Visibility on the Web. 2010. 100p. pap. *(978-3-8383-4298-6(4))* Lambert Academic Publishing.

Robbins, Stuart. Lessons in Grid Computing: The System Is a Mirror. 2006. (ENG., Illus.). 384p. 34.95 *(978-0-471-79010-5(9)*, Wiley) Wiley, John & Sons, Inc.

Rogers, Garett, et al. Google Business Solutions All-in-One for Dummies. 2009. (ENG., Illus.). 792p. pap. 39.99 *(978-0-470-38687-3(8)*, For Dummies) Wiley, John & Sons, Inc.

Russo, Marco, et al. Microsoft Excel Power User's Kit: Microsoft PowerPivot for Excel 2010 & Microsoft Office Excel 2010 - Data Analysis & Business Modeling, 2 vols. 3rd ed. 2011. (ENG., Illus.). 1216p. pap. 59.99 *(978-0-7356-5945-2(1))* Microsoft Pr.

Shevtshenko, Eduard. Intelligent Decision Support System for Industrial Enterprises. 2010. 108p. pap. *(978-3-8383-8958-5(1))* Lambert Academic Publishing.

Singleton, Susan. Computer Contracts. 2007. spiral bd. 99.95 *(978-1-85418-352-1(4))* Thorogood GBR. Dist: National Bk. Network.

Snowden, Michael. The CEO's Guide to Cloud Computing. 2010. 117p. pap. 41.90 *(978-1-4452-4790-8(9))* Lulu Enterprises Inc.

Sparks, David. Mac at Work. 2011. (ENG., Illus.). 368p. pap. 29.99 *(978-0-470-87700-5(6)*, Wiley) Wiley, John & Sons, Inc.

Trivedi, Kunjal. Building or Buying VPNs. 2007. 80p. pap. 40.00 *(978-1-58720-134-9(8))* Cisco Pr.

Vaccaro, Antonino, et al, eds. Impact of Network Ethics on Business Practices. 2010. (Illus.). vi, 242p. 79.95 *(978-94-007-0379-7(1)*, 9400703791) Springer.

Wang, Yao. Dynamic Awareness for Shared Workspaces. 2008. 96p. pap. *(978-3-8364-5529-9(3))* VDM Verlag Dr. Mueller e.K.

Weinberg, Tamar. The New Community Rules: Marketing on the Social Web. 2009. (ENG., Illus.). 370p. pap. 24.99 *(978-0-596-15681-7(2))* O'Reilly Media, Inc.

Wempen, Faithe. Office 2010 eLearning Kit for Dummies. 2011. (ENG.). 416p. pap. 39.99 *(978-1-118-02972-5(0)*, For Dummies) Wiley, John & Sons, Inc.

White, Bruce A., et al. Web 2. 0 for Business. 2009. (ENG., Illus.). 96p. (C). pap. 32.95 *(978-0-470-43618-9(2)*, Wiley) Wiley, John & Sons, Inc.

Williams, Dan. Tales from the Networking Community. 2007. (ENG.). 132p. per. 19.95 *(978-1-60005-053-4(0))* Happy About.

Woessner, Stephen. The Small Business Owner's Handbook to Search Engine Optimization: Increase Your Google Rankings, Double Your Site Traffic... In Just 15-Steps - Guaranteed. 2009. (ENG.). 288p. pap. 24.95 *(978-1-60138-443-0(2))* Atlantic Publishing Co.

Wysocki, Robert K. The Business Analyst/Project Manager: A New Partnership for Managing Complexity & Uncertainty. 2010. (ENG., Illus.). 240p. 49.95 *(978-0-470-76744-3(8)*, Wiley) Wiley, John & Sons, Inc.

BUSINESS—COMPUTER PROGRAMS

Aiello, Joseph L. Rightsizing Inventory. 2007. (Series on Resource Management). (ENG., Illus.). 512p. 89.95 *(978-0-8493-8515-5(6))* Auerbach Pubs., Inc.

Anderson, Chris. Pro Business Applications with Silverlight 4. 2010. (ENG.). 576p. pap. 49.99 *(978-1-4302-7207-6(4))* Apress L. P.

Anderson, George W., et al. SAP Implementation: A Business & Technical Roadmap to Deploying SAP. 2009. (Unleashed Ser.). (ENG., Illus.). 888p. pap. 69.99 *(978-0-672-33004-9(0))* Sams.

Antonovich, Michael. Office & SharePoint 2010 User's Guide: Integrating SharePoint with Excel, Outlook, Access & Word. 2010. (ENG., Illus.). 752p. pap. 44.99 *(978-1-4302-2760-1(5))* Apress L. P.

Appelrath, Hans-Jargen & Ritter, Jörg. SAP R/3 Implementation: Methods & Tools. 2010. (SAP Excellence Ser.). (ENG., Illus.). xii, 188p. pap. 109.00 *(978-3-642-08612-0(8)*, 3642086128) Springer.

Bacon, Jono. The Art of Community: Building the New Age of Participation. 2009. (Theory in Practice Ser.). (ENG., Illus.). 394p. pap. 39.99 *(978-0-596-15671-8(5))* O'Reilly Media, Inc.

Bajaj, Geetesh & Gordon, James. Office 2011 for Mac All-in-One for Dummies. 2011. (ENG.). 840p. pap. 34.99 *(978-0-470-90371-1(6)*, For Dummies) Wiley, John & Sons, Inc.

Ballew, Joli. Brilliant Office 2010 for the over 50s. rev. ed. 2011. (ENG., Illus.). 296p. pap. *(978-0-273-74572-3(7)*, Prentice Hall) Pearson Education, Ltd.

—Office 2010 for the over 50s in Simple Steps. 2010. (ENG., Illus.). 256p. pap. *(978-0-273-74415-3(1))* Prentice Hall PTR.

Banfield, Colin & Walkenbach, John. Excel 2010 for Dummies Quick Reference. 2010. (ENG., Illus.). 240p. pap. 18.99 *(978-0-470-52755-9(2)*, For Dummies) Wiley, John & Sons, Inc.

Barclay, Nick & Downes, Adrian. The Rational Guide to Monitoring & Analyzing with Microsoft Office PerformancePoint Server 2007. 2007. (Rational Guides). (Illus.). 254p. per. 24.99 *(978-1-932577-41-9(6)*, Rational Pr.) Mann Publishing Group.

Beezix, Inc. What's New in Microsoft Office 2003 (from 97) Quick Reference Guide. 2007. 2p. 3.60 *(978-1-934433-27-0(6))* Beezix Quick Reference Cards.

Bellu, Renato. Microsoft Dynamics GP for Dummies. 2008. (ENG., Illus.). 432p. pap. 29.99 *(978-0-470-38835-8(8)*, For Dummies) Wiley, John & Sons, Inc.

Beskeen, David, et al. Microsoft Office 2007. 2008. (Illustrated Ser.). (ENG.). 688p. pap. 124.95 *(978-0-495-80673-8(0))* Course Technology.

Beskeen, David W., et al. Microsoft Office 2010: Illustrated Introductory, First Course. 2010. (Illustrated Ser.). (ENG., Illus.). 688p. spiral bd. 131.95 *(978-0-538-74715-8(3))* Course Technology.

—Microsoft Office 2010 for Medical Professionals Illustrated. 2011. (Illustrated Series: Medical Professionals Ser.). (ENG., Illus.). 528p. (C). pap. 86.95 *(978-1-111-82099-2(6))* Course Technology.

—Microsoft Office 2010 Illustrated Second Course. 2010. (SAM 2010 Compatible Products Ser.). (ENG.). 504p. pap. 125.95 *(978-0-538-74813-1(3))* Course Technology.

Biafore, Bonnie. QuickBooks 2011. 2010. (ENG., Illus.). 724p. pap. 29.99 *(978-1-4493-9245-1(8)*, Pogue Pr.) O'Reilly Media, Inc.

Biheller Bunin, Rachel. Microsoft Outlook 2010: Essentials. 2010. (Illustrated Ser.). (ENG., Illus.). 104p. (C). pap. 26.95 *(978-0-538-74925-1(3))* Course Technology.

Blumohr, Uwe, et al. Variant Configuration with SAP. 2nd exp. ed. 2011. (ENG., Illus.). 660p. 79.95 *(978-1-59229-400-8(6)*, SAP PR.) Galileo Pr., Inc.

Bluttman, Ken & Aitken, Peter G. Excel Formulas & Functions for Dummies. 2nd ed. 2010. (ENG., Illus.). 384p. pap. 24.99 *(978-0-470-56816-3(X)*, For Dummies) Wiley, John & Sons, Inc.

Boles, David W. Picture Yourself Learning Microsoft Office 2008 for Mac. 2008. (Picture Yourself Ser.). (Illus.). 208p. pap. 29.99 *(978-1-59863-515-7(8))* Course Technology.

Bondur, Tom, et al. Integrating & Extending BIRT. 2006. (Eclipse Ser.). (ENG., Illus.). 608p. per. 54.99 *(978-0-321-44385-4(3))* Addison Wesley Professional.

BORNSTEIN. Custom MYITLab with Go! EBook Package CCSF. 2007. (ENG.). (C). pap. 55.13 *(978-0-536-48955-5(6))* Pearson Learning Solutions.

Bott, Ed & Leonhard, Woody. Using Microsoft Office Home & Student. 2007. (Special Edition Using Ser.). (Illus.). 792p. per. 39.99 *(978-0-7897-3518-8(0))* Que.

Bradford, Marianne. Modern ERP: Select, Implement & Use Today's Advanced Business Systems. 2010. 247p. pap. 75.00 *(978-0-557-43407-7(6))* Lulu Enterprises Inc.

Brownfield, Karen, et al. The ABCs of Workflow for E-Business Suite Release 11i & Release 12. 2008. 695p. pap. 69.99 *(978-0-615-24458-7(0))* Reed-Matthews, Inc.

Bunin, Rachel Biheller, et al. Microsoft Office 2007. 2007. (Origins Ser.). (ENG.). 1088p. pap. 117.95 *(978-1-4239-0397-0(8))* Course Technology.

Bunzel, Tom. Easy Microsoft Office 2010. 2010. (Easy Ser.). (ENG., Illus.). 312p. pap. 21.99 *(978-0-7897-4328-2(0))* Que.

—Tools of Engagement: Presenting & Training in a World of Social Media. 2010. (ENG., Illus.). 280p. pap. 45.00 *(978-0-470-57394-5(5)*, Pfeiffer) Wiley, John & Sons, Inc.

Byrd, David & Schauf, Brad. IBM Lotus Notes & Domino 8.5.1. 2010. 336p. pap. *(978-1-84719-928-7(3))* Packt Publishing, Ltd.

Cable, Sandra. Succeeding in Business with Microsoft Office Access 2010: A Problem-Solving Approach. 2010. (New Perspectives Series: Succeeding in Business Ser.). (ENG.). 608p. pap. 128.95 *(978-0-538-75412-5(5))* Course Technology.

Cable, Sandra & Morrison, Connie. Microsoftr Office 2010, Advanced. 2011. (SAM 2010 Compatible Products Ser.). (ENG., Illus.). 1216p. 128.95 *(978-0-538-48129-8(3))*; spiral bd. 122.95 *(978-0-538-48142-7(0))*; pap. 111.95 *(978-0-538-48143-4(9))* Course Technology.

Capachietti, Leslie. QuickBooks 2011 the Official Guide. 2010. (Official Guide Ser.). (ENG., Illus.). 608p. pap. 30.00 *(978-0-07-174859-9(8)*, 0071748598) McGraw-Hill Osborne.

Carlberg, Conrad. Business Analysis: Microsoft Excel 2010. 4th ed. 2010. (MrExcel Library). (ENG., Illus.). 528p. pap. 39.99 *(978-0-7897-4317-6(5))* Que.

Carlberg, Conrad & Carlberg, Conrad George. Business Analysis with Microsoft Excel. 3rd rev. ed. 2007. (Business Solutions Ser.). (Illus.). 504p. per. 39.99 *(978-0-7897-3664-2(0))* Que.

Channelle, Andy. Beginning OpenOffice 3. 2008. (ENG.). 488p. pap. 39.99 *(978-1-4302-1590-5(9))* Apress L. P.

Christofferson, Jay. Estimating with Microsoft Excel, 3rd Edition. 3rd ed. 2009. (Illus.). 175p. pap. 44.95 *(978-0-86718-647-5(X))* BuilderBooks.

Cleeren, Gill & Dockx, Kevin. Microsoft Silverlight 4 Data & Services Cookbook: LITE Edition. 2011. 116p. pap. ***(978-1-84968-384-5(0))*** Packt Publishing, Ltd.

Clemens, Barbara, et al. Upgrading to Microsoft Office 2007. 2007. (Available Titles Skills Assessment Manager (SAM) - Office 2007 Ser.). (ENG., Illus.). 152p. per. 30.95 *(978-1-4239-2566-8(1))* Course Technology.

Cohen, Fred. Enterprise Information Protection. 2008. 336p. 59.00 *(978-1-878109-43-9(X))* ASP Pr.

Cole, Carey, et al. SharePoint for Students. rev. ed. 2010. (ENG., Illus.). 192p. (C). pap. 56.00 *(978-0-13-000009-5(4)*, Prentice Hall) Prentice Hall PTR.

Conner, Nancy. Zoho 4 Everyone. 2008. (Illus.). 432p. pap. 24.99 *(978-0-7897-3937-7(2))* Que.

Course Technology. Microsoft Office Excel 2007, Pack. 2010. (ENG.). (C). 12.95 *(978-0-538-47576-1(5))* Course Technology.

—Microsoft Office Excel 2010. 2010. (CourseNotes Ser.). (ENG.). 6p. 8.95 *(978-0-538-74426-3(X))* Course Technology.

—Microsoft Outlook 2010. 2010. (CourseNotes Ser.). (ENG.). 6p. 8.95 *(978-0-538-74423-2(5))* Course Technology.

Course Technology Staff. Microsoft Office Web Apps. 2010. (CourseNotes Ser.). (ENG.). 6p. pap. 8.95 *(978-0-538-74424-9(3))* Course Technology.

Cowan, Alex. Starting a Tech Business: A Practical Guide for Anyone Creating or Designing Applications or Software. 2012. (ENG.). 258p. pap. 29.95 ***(978-1-118-20555-6(3)***, Wiley) Wiley, John & Sons, Inc.

Cox, Joyce & Lambert, Joan, III. The Microsoft Office Specialist Study Guide. 2008. (ENG., Illus.). 816p. pap., pupil's gde. ed. 39.99 *(978-0-7356-4971-2(5))* Microsoft Pr.

Cram, Carol. Microsoft Office 2010: Illustrated Projects. 2011. (ENG., Illus.). 240p. pap. 49.95 *(978-0-538-74848-3(6))* Course Technology.

Cram, Carol M. Microsoft Office 2007. 2007. (Illustrated Ser.). (ENG., Illus.). 256p. (C). per. 49.95 *(978-1-4239-0546-2(6))* Course Technology.

Cram101 Textbook Reviews. Outlines & Highlights for Model-Driven Design Using Business Patterns by Pavel Hruby, Isbn: 9783540301547. 2011. 60p. pap. 26.95 ***(978-1-4288-2944-2(X))*** Cram101 Inc.

Crews, Thad & Murphy, Chip. Casegrader: Microsoft Office Excel 2007 Casebook with Autograding Technology. 2nd rev. ed. 2007. (ENG.). 72p. per. 40.95 *(978-1-4239-9823-5(5))* Course Technology.

—Microsoft Office Excel 2007. 2009. (CaseGrader Ser.). (ENG.). (C). 27.95 *(978-0-538-75039-4(1))* Course Technology.

Cronan, John & Sandberg, Bobbi. Microsoft Office Access 2007 Quicksteps. 2007. (QuickSteps Ser.). (ENG., Illus.). 226p. per. 20.00 *(978-0-07-226371-8(7)*, 0072263717) McGraw-Hill Osborne.

Daffron, Susan C. Logical Tips for Mastering Microsoft Office: Quick Shortcuts, Tips, Tricks, & Techniques to Help You Use Microsoft Office More Effectively. 2008. 124p. per. 14.95 *(978-0-9749245-6-4(3))* Logical Expressions, Inc.

—Logical Tips for Mastering Microsoft Windows: Quick Shortcuts, Tips, Tricks, & Techniques to Help You Use Microsoft Windows More Effectively. 2008. 132p. per. 14.95 *(978-0-9749245-7-1(1))* Logical Expressions, Inc.

Dalgleish, Debra. Pivot Tables in Excel 2007. 2007. (Expert's Voice Ser.). (ENG., Illus.). 295p. per. 34.99 *(978-1-59059-890-0(3))* Apress L. P.

Davidenkoff, Alexander & Werner, Detlef. Global SAP Systems - Design & Architecture. 2008. (Illus.). 317p. 69.95 *(978-1-59229-183-0(X)*, SAP PR.) Galileo Pr., Inc.

Davis, Glyn & Pecar, Branko. Business Statistics Using Excel. 2010. (ENG., Illus.). 496p. pap. 65.00 *(978-0-19-955689-2(X))* Oxford Univ. Pr., Inc.

Dickens, Risa. No One Knows Everything - Open Source & the Crisis in Public Opinion. 2008. 140p. per. *(978-3-8364-3460-7(1))* VDM Verlag Dr. Mueller e.K.

Dixon, Christopher. Maximize Your Business with MS Publisher 2003. 2007. (Illus.). 167p. per. 55.00 *(978-0-9793796-3-5(6))* Strategic Publishing Group.

Doane, Michael. The New SAP Blue Book. 2006. 256p. pap. 29.95 *(978-1-57579-342-9(3))* Pine Hill Pr., Inc.

Downes, Adrian & Barclay, Nick. The Rational Guide to Planning with Microsoft Office PerformancePoint Server 2007. 2008. (Illus.). 254p. *(978-1-932577-42-6(4))* Mann Publishing Group.

Dyszel, Bill. Outlook 2010 for Dummies. 2010. (ENG., Illus.). 384p. pap. 24.99 *(978-0-470-48771-6(2)*, For Dummies) Wiley, John & Sons, Inc.

EC Technologies. Outlook Quick Reference Guides. 2008. 8.95 *(978-0-9793503-8-2(7))* EC Technologies.

—Project Quick Reference Guides. 2008. 11.95 *(978-0-9793503-4-4(4))* EC Technologies.

Element K Journals Creative Team. Microsoft(r) Office Excel(r) 2007: 084891ie. 2007. spiral bd. *(978-1-4246-0622-1(5))* Element K Content LLC.

—Microsoft(r) Office Excel(r) 2007: 084891s3. 2007. spiral bd. *(978-1-4246-0623-8(3))* Element K Content LLC.

—Microsoft(r) Office Excel(r) 2007: 084892ie. 2007. spiral bd. *(978-1-4246-0630-6(6))* Element K Content LLC.

—Microsoft(r) Office Excel(r) 2007: 084892s3. 2007. spiral bd. *(978-1-4246-0631-3(4))* Element K Content LLC.

Elferdink, Jim. Office 2008 for Macintosh. 4th rev. ed. 2008. (Missing Manual Ser.). (ENG., Illus.). 914p. pap. 34.99 *(978-0-596-51431-0(X)*, Pogue Pr.) O'Reilly Media, Inc.

Elliott, Mark. Survival Guide for Lotus Notes & Domino Administrators. 2009. (ENG., Illus.). 312p. pap. 49.99 *(978-0-13-715331-2(7))* Pearson Education.

Evans, Arthur. FileMaker Pro 8 Business Applications. 2008. (Illus.). 626p. per. 49.95 *(978-1-59822-014-8(4))* Jones & Bartlett Learning, LLC.

Ferrett, Robert, et al. Skills for Success Using Microsoft Office 2007. 2008. (ENG., Illus.). 624p. (C). pap. 126.67 *(978-0-13-502456-0(0)*, Prentice Hall) Prentice Hall PTR.

Ferrett, Robert L., et al. Go! With Office 2010, Vol. 1. 2nd rev. ed. 2012. (ENG., Illus.). 928p. (C). pap. 146.67 ***(978-0-13-284016-3(2)***, Prentice Hall) Prentice Hall PTR.

—Student CD for GO! with Office 2010 Volume 1. 2nd ed. 2012. (ENG.). (C). cd-rom 50.00 ***(978-0-13-284079-8(0)***, Prentice Hall) Prentice Hall PTR.

Fitzgerald, Neil. Crystal Reports 2008 Official Guide. 2nd ed. 2008. (Business Objects Press Ser.). (ENG., Illus.). 576p. pap., instr.'s gde. ed. 54.99 *(978-0-672-32989-0(1))* Sams.

Fletcher, Shayne & Gardner, Christopher. Financial Modelling in Python. 2009. (Wiley Finance Ser.: 467). (ENG., Illus.). 244p. 130.00 *(978-0-470-98784-1(7)*, Wiley) Wiley, John & Sons, Inc.

Forsythe, Kevin & Ubelhor, Laura. HTML for the Business Programmer: With JavaServer Pages, PHP, ASP.NET, CGI, & JavaScript. 2008. (Business Developers Ser.). (ENG., Illus.). 350p. pap. 49.95 *(978-1-58347-079-4(4))* MC Pr., LLC.

Fox, Steve & Sheldon, Bill. Professional Office Business Application Development: Using Microsoft Office SharePoint Server 2007 & VSTO. 2008. (ENG., Illus.). 336p. pap. 49.99 *(978-0-470-37731-4(3)*, Wrox) Wiley, John & Sons, Inc.

Fox, Steve, et al. Professional Microsoft SharePoint 2007 Development Using Microsoft Silverlight 2. 2009. (ENG., Illus.). 312p. pap. 49.99 *(978-0-470-43400-0(7)*, Wrox) Wiley, John & Sons, Inc.

—Programming Microsoft Office Business Applications. 2008. (ENG., Illus.). 256p. pap. 34.99 *(978-0-7356-2536-5(0))* Microsoft Pr.

Fredricks, Karen S. & Orenstein, Lon. Outlook 2007 Business Contact Manager for Dummies. 2007. (ENG., Illus.). 336p. per. 24.99 *(978-0-470-10789-8(8)*, For Dummies) Wiley, John & Sons, Inc.

Fulton, Jennifer. Learning Microsoft Office Excel 2007. 2007. (ENG., Illus.). 499p. (C). spiral bd. 50.00 *(978-0-13-365696-1(9)*, Prentice Hall) Prentice Hall PTR.

Fulton, Jennifer & Fredricks, Karen S. Outlook 2010 All-in-One for Dummies. 2010. (ENG., Illus.). 936p. pap. 34.99 *(978-0-470-48773-0(9)*, For Dummies) Wiley, John & Sons, Inc.

Gaskin, Shelley. Podcasts for GO! with Microsoft Office 2010 Volume 1. 2nd ed. 2012. (ENG.). (C). cd-rom 66.67 ***(978-0-13-289640-5(0)***, Prentice Hall) Prentice Hall PTR.

Gaskin, Shelley & Ferret, Robert. GO! with Office 365 Getting Started. 2012. (ENG.). 72p. (C). pap. 31.00 ***(978-0-13-295574-4(1)***, Prentice Hall) Prentice Hall PTR.

Gaskin, Shelley & Ferrett, Robert L. GO! with Microsoft Office Web Apps Getting Started. 2011. (ENG.). 72p. (C). pap. 31.00 *(978-0-13-254484-9(9)*, Prentice Hall) Prentice Hall PTR.

Gaskin, Shelley & Vargas, Alicia. GO! with Microsoft Excel Brief. 2010. (ENG.). 288p. (C). pap. 52.67 *(978-0-13-509771-7(1)*, Prentice Hall) Prentice Hall PTR.

—Microsoft Excel 2007. 2007. (Go! Ser.). (ENG., Illus.). 320p. (C). spiral bd. 52.67 *(978-0-13-513003-2(4)*, Prentice Hall) Prentice Hall PTR.

Gaskin, Shelley, et al. GO! with Microsoft Excel 2010 Introductory. 2010. (ENG.). 608p. (C). pap. 81.33 *(978-0-13-509814-1(9)*, Prentice Hall) Prentice Hall PTR.

—GO! with Microsoft Office 2007 Introductory. 3rd ed. 2008. (ENG., Illus.). 1104p. (C). pap. 146.67 *(978-0-13-505923-4(2)*, Prentice Hall) Prentice Hall PTR.

—GO! with Microsoft Windows Live & Windows Live Essentials Getting Started. 2011. (ENG.). 72p. (C). pap. 31.00 *(978-0-13-254329-3(X)*, Prentice Hall) Prentice Hall PTR.

—GO! with Office 2007: Introductory. 2nd ed. 2008. (Go! Ser.). (ENG.). 1280p. (C). spiral bd. 146.67 *(978-0-13-241887-4(8)*, Prentice Hall) Prentice Hall PTR.

—GO! with Outlook 2007 Comprehensive. 2008. (ENG., Illus.). 560p. (C). pap. 81.33 *(978-0-13-500124-0(2)*, Prentice Hall) Prentice Hall PTR.

—Microsoft Office 2007. 2007. (Go! Ser.). (ENG.). 928p. (C). pap. 130.67 *(978-0-13-244664-8(2)*, Prentice Hall) Prentice Hall PTR.

—Microsoft Office 2010, Vol. 1. rev. ed. 2010. (ENG.). 1000p. (C). pap. 146.67 *(978-0-13-245446-9(7)*, Prentice Hall) Prentice Hall PTR.

—Microsoft Office 2010: Discipline Specific Projects. 2010. (ENG.). 96p. (C). pap. 31.00 *(978-0-13-703753-7(8)*, Prentice Hall) Prentice Hall PTR.

—With Microsoft Excel 2007, Vol. 1. 2007. (Go! Ser.). (ENG., Illus.). 608p. (C). spiral bd. 81.33 *(978-0-13-512986-9(9)*, Prentice Hall) Prentice Hall PTR.

Gediminas Adomavicius Staff & A. Gupta Staff. Business Computing. 2009. (Illus.). xx, 400p. 244.95 *(978-1-84855-264-7(5))* Emerald Group Publishing Ltd. GBR. Dist: Turpin Distribution Services Ltd.

Gips, James. Mastering Excel 2007: A Problem Solving Approach. 4th ed. 2008. (ENG.). (C). pap. 56.20 *(978-0-558-06528-7(7))* Pearson Learning Solutions.

Glencoe McGraw-Hill Staff. Keyboarding with Computer Applications, Lessons 1-150. 5th ed. 2008. (ENG.). pap., stu. ed. 103.52 *(978-0-07-890833-0(7)*, 0078908337) McGraw-Hill Higher Education.

Grauer, Robert, et al. Exploring Microsoft Office 2007 Vol. 1. 3rd ed. 2008. (ENG.). 1376p. (C). spiral bd. 146.67 *(978-0-13-506250-0(0)*, Prentice Hall) Prentice Hall PTR.

—Exploring Microsoft Office 2010 Getting Started with Web 2. 0. 2011. (ENG.). 96p. (C). pap. 31.00 *(978-0-13-214053-9(5)*, Prentice Hall) Prentice Hall PTR.

—Exploring Microsoft Office 2010, Volume 1. 2nd rev. ed. 2012. (ENG.). 1176p. (C). spiral bd. 146.67 ***(978-0-13-287360-4(5)***, Prentice Hall) Prentice Hall PTR.

Grauer, Robert, et al. Exploring Microsoft Office Excel 2007. 2nd ed. 2009. (ENG., Illus.). 784p. (C). pap. 116.00 *(978-0-13-511980-8(4)*, Prentice Hall) Prentice Hall PTR.

Grauer, Robert T., et al. Exploring Getting Started with Microsoft Outlook 2010. 2011. (ENG.). 96p. (C). pap. 31.00 *(978-0-13-509892-9(0)*, Prentice Hall) Prentice Hall PTR.

—Exploring Microsoft Office Excel 2010 Introductory. 2010. (ENG., Illus.). 352p. (C). pap. 81.33 *(978-0-13-509847-9(5)*, Prentice Hall) Prentice Hall PTR.

—Microsoft Office 2010, Vol. 1. 2010. (ENG., Illus.). 1032p. (C). pap. 146.67 *(978-0-13-612232-6(9)*, Prentice Hall) Prentice Hall PTR.

—Microsoft Office Access 2007. 2nd ed. 2009. (ENG.). 736p. (C). pap. 116.00 *(978-0-13-511988-4(X)*, Prentice Hall) Prentice Hall PTR.

—Microsoft Office Excel 2010 Comprehensive. 2010. (ENG., Illus.). 736p. (C). pap. 116.00 *(978-0-13-509859-2(9)*, Prentice Hall) Prentice Hall PTR.

Griffin, Marilyn. Business Application Development with Excel 2007. rev. ed. 2007. (ENG.). 580p. spiral bd. 113.49 *(978-0-7575-4619-8(6))* Kendall Hunt Publishing Co.

Gross, Debra, et al. Succeeding in Business with Microsoft Excel 2010: A Problem-Solving Approach. 2010. (Spreadsheet Applications Ser.). (ENG.). 720p. pap. 128.95 *(978-0-538-74580-2(0))* Course Technology.

—Succeeding in Business with Microsoft Office Excel 2007: A Problem-Solving Approach. 2007. (Succeeding Ser.). (ENG., Illus.). 696p. (C). per. 128.95 *(978-1-4239-0605-6(5))* Course Technology.

Grover, Chris. Office 2011 for Macintosh: The Missing Manual. 2010. (ENG., Illus.). 816p. pap. 34.99 *(978-1-4493-9335-9(7)*, Pogue Pr.) O'Reilly Media, Inc.

Gunter, Sherry Kinkoph. Office 2010 Visual Quick Tips. 2010. (Visual Quick Tips Ser.: 25). (ENG., Illus.). 368p. pap. 24.99 *(978-0-470-57775-2(4)*, Visual) Wiley, John & Sons, Inc.

Haman, Gerald. Innovation Activater Innovation & Creativity Tool: Innovation & Creativity Tool. 2007. 68.88 *(978-0-929607-05-4(8))* SolutionPeople.

Hambrose, Harold. Wrench in the System: What's Sabotaging Your Business Software & How You Can Release the Power to Innovate. 2009. (ENG., Illus.). 272p. 45.00 *(978-0-470-41343-2(3)*, Wiley) Wiley, John & Sons, Inc.

Hammerle, Patti. Your Office: Getting Started with Computing Concepts. rev. ed. 2012. (ENG., Illus.). 112p. (C). pap. 31.00 ***(978-0-13-262535-7(0)***, Prentice Hall) Prentice Hall PTR.

Hannemann, Alethea, et al. Birt: A Field Guide to Reporting. 2006. (Eclipse Ser.). (Illus.). 704p. per. 54.99 *(978-0-321-44259-8(8))* Addison Wesley Professional.

Hardison, Stephen, et al. IBM Lotus Connections 2.5: Planning & Implementing Social Software for Your Enterprise. 2009. (ENG., Illus.). 456p. pap. 39.99 *(978-0-13-700053-1(7))* Pearson Education.

Harinath, Sivakumar, et al. Professional Microsoft PowerPivot for Excel & SharePoint: 2010. (ENG., Illus.). 384p. pap. 44.99 *(978-0-470-58737-9(7)*, Wrox) Wiley, John & Sons, Inc.

Hart-Davis, Guy. Word 2007 Macros & VBA Made Easy. 2009. (ENG., Illus.). 256p. pap. 21.99 *(978-0-07-161479-5(6)*, 0071614796) McGraw-Hill Osborne.

Hart-Davis, Guy & Mansfield, Richard. Mastering VBA for Office 2010. 2nd ed. 2010. (ENG., Illus.). 912p. pap. 49.99 *(978-0-470-63400-4(6)*, Sybex) Wiley, John & Sons, Inc.

Harvey, Greg. Excel 2007 Workbook for Dummies. 2nd rev. ed. 2007. (ENG., Illus.). 408p. pap. 24.99 *(978-0-470-16937-7(0)*, For Dummies) Wiley, John & Sons, Inc.

—Excel 2010 All-in-One for Dummies. 2010. (ENG., Illus.). 792p. pap. 34.99 *(978-0-470-48959-8(6)*, For Dummies) Wiley, John & Sons, Inc.

—Excel 2010 for Dummies. (ENG.). 2012. 216p. pap. 9.99 ***(978-1-118-31524-8(3))*** 2010. (Illus.). 408p. pap. 24.99 *(978-0-470-48953-6(7))* Wiley, John & Sons, Inc. (For Dummies).

Hawley, David & Hawley, Raina. Excel Hacks: Tips & Tools for Streamlining Your Spreadsheets. 2nd rev. ed. 2007. (Hacks Ser.). (ENG., Illus.). 412p. per. 29.99 *(978-0-596-52834-8(5))* O'Reilly Media, Inc.

Heilman, Rich & Jung, Thomas. Next Generation ABAP Development. 2nd ed. 2010. (Illus.). 716p. 69.95 incl. cd-rom *(978-1-59229-352-0(2)*, SAP PR.) Galileo Pr., Inc.

Held, Bernd. Microsoft Excel Functions & Formulas. 2006. (ENG., Illus.). 397p. per. 29.95 *(978-1-59822-011-7(X))* Jones & Bartlett Learning, LLC.

Hendel, Anja, et al, eds. Rightshore! Successfully Industrialize SAP Projects Offshore. 2008. (Illus.). 292p. 69.95 *(978-3-540-77287-3(1))* Springer.

Henrick, Gavin, et al. Moodle 2.0 for Business: Beginner's Guide. 2011. 303p. pap. ***(978-1-84951-420-0(8))*** Packt Publishing, Ltd.

Hinkle, Deborah. Microsoft Office 2010: A Lesson Approach. 2010. (ENG., Illus.). 1088p. (C). spiral bd. 107.67 *(978-0-07-745489-0(8)*, 0077454898) McGraw-Hill Higher Education.

Hinkle, Deborah, et al. Microsoft Office 2007: A Professional Approach. 2009. (ENG., Illus.). 976p. (C). spiral bd. 107.67 *(978-0-07-351926-5(X)*, 007351926X) McGraw-Hill Higher Education.

Hinkle, Deborah A. Microsoft Office 2007: A Professional Approach. 2008. (Illus.). *(978-0-07-721471-5(4))* McGraw-Hill Cos., The.

Hogendoorn, Roel & LearnWorks.com. BI Publisher for Oracle E-Business Suite. 2007. 134p. pap. 45.95 *(978-1-84799-115-7(7))* Lulu Enterprises Inc.

Holtsnider, Bill, et al. Agile Development & Business Goals: The Six Week Solution. 2010. (ENG., Illus.). 256p. pap. 41.95 *(978-0-12-381520-0(7)*, Morgan Kaufmann) Elsevier Science & Technology Bks.

Holzner, Steven. Special Edition Using Microsoft Office Visio 2007. 2007. (Special Edition Using Ser.). (ENG., Illus.). 672p. per. 49.99 *(978-0-7897-3686-4(1))* Que.

—Zoho for Dummies. 2009. (ENG., Illus.). 336p. pap. 29.99 *(978-0-470-48454-8(3)*, For Dummies) Wiley, John & Sons, Inc.

Hooper, Karen. Ibm Lotus Notes 8 5 User Guide: LITE Edition. 2011. 120p. pap. ***(978-1-84968-386-9(7))*** Packt Publishing, Ltd.

Horngren, Charles T. Excel Manual for Cost Accounting for Cost Accounting & MyAcctgLab Access Code Package. 13th ed. 2008. (ENG.). 144p. (C). pap. 14.00 *(978-0-13-605356-9(4)*, Prentice Hall) Prentice Hall PTR.

Hruby, Pavel. Model-Driven Design Using Business Patterns. 2010. (ENG., Illus.). xvi, 368p. pap. 89.95 *(978-3-642-06765-5(4)*, 3642067654) Springer.

Hunt, Marjorie & Waxer, Barbara M. Microsoft Office 2010: Illustrated Fundamentals. 2010. (Available Titles Skills Assessment Manager (SAM) - Office 2010 Ser.). (ENG., Illus.). 416p. pap. 82.95 *(978-0-538-74944-2(X))* Course Technology.

Hunt, Marjorie S. & Waxer, Barbara. Review Pack for Hunt/Waxer's for Microsoft Office 2007 Illustarted Brief Premium Video Edition. 2009. (ENG.). 12.95 *(978-1-4390-4607-4(7))* Course Technology.

Hunt, Marjorie S., et al. Microsoft Office 2007. 2009. (Available Titles Skills Assessment Manager (SAM) - Office 2007 Ser.). (ENG.). 496p. spiral bd. 82.95 *(978-1-4390-3789-8(2))* Course Technology.

Hyde-Bohn, Mary Kay. IBM Electronic Services: Support Using Automation & Web Tools. 2nd ed. 2007. (Illus.). xii, 186p. *(978-0-7384-8885-1(2))* IBM.

International Business Machines Corporation, International Technical Support Organization Staff, contrib. by. IBM Workplace Forms 2.6: Guide to Building & Integrating a Sample Workplace Forms Application. 2007. (Illus.). xvi, 714p. pap. *(978-0-7384-8638-3(8))* IBM.

Jansen, John. Building Web Applications with Microsoft Office SharePoint Designer 2007. 2009. (ENG.). 336p. pap. 29.99 *(978-0-7356-2632-4(4))* Microsoft Pr.

Janus, Philo. Pro InfoPath 2007. 2007. (Expert's Voice Ser.). (ENG., Illus.). 278p. per. 44.99 *(978-1-59059-730-9(3))* Apress L. P.

Janus, Philo, et al. Pro InfoPath 2010. 2012. (ENG.). 500p. pap. 44.99 *(978-1-4302-3753-2(8))* Apress L. P.

Jayaweera, Prasad M. A Unified Framework for E-Commerce Systems Development - Business Process Pattern Perspective. 2008. 192p. pap. *(978-3-8364-5853-5(5))* VDM Verlag Dr. Mueller e.K.

Jeanandt. Easy Steps to Making More Money Now Using Your Computer. 2008. 20p. pap. 39.95 *(978-0-615-20987-6(4))* investinu.us.

Jelen, Bill. Power Excel 2010 with Mrexcel. 2010. (LiveLessons Ser.). (ENG.). 39.99 *(978-0-7897-4393-0(0))* Que.

Jelen, Bill & Syrstad, Tracy. VBA & Macros for Microsoft Office Excel 2007. 2nd rev. ed. 2007. (Business Solutions Ser.). (ENG., Illus.). 624p. per. 39.99 *(978-0-7897-3682-6(9))* Que.

Johnson, Steve & Perspection, Inc. Staff. Microsoft Office 2007 on Demand. 2006. (On Demand Ser.). (ENG., Illus.). 752p. per. 44.99 *(978-0-7897-3640-6(3))* Que.

—Microsoft Office Excel 2007 on Demand. 2006. (On Demand Ser.). (ENG., Illus.). 560p. pap. 39.99 *(978-0-7897-3642-0(X))* Que.

—Office 2008 for the Mac. 2008. (On Demand Ser.). (ENG., Illus.). 576p. pap. 29.99 *(978-0-7897-3923-0(2))* Que.

Jonasson, Hans. Determining Project Requirements. 2007. (Esi International Project Management Ser.). (ENG., Illus.). 320p. 67.95 *(978-1-4200-4502-4(4))* Auerbach Pubs., Inc.

Khan, Arshad. SAP Transaction Codes: Frequently Used T-Codes. 2010. (ENG.). 310p. *(978-0-9772838-9-7(5))* Khan Consulting & Publishing LLC.

Khan, Zaheer. Bridging the Gap. 2011. 260p. pap. ***(978-3-8433-9098-9(3))*** Lambert Academic Publishing.

Kinser, Amy S. & Cameron, Eric. Your Office: Getting Started with Web 2. 0. 2012. (ENG., Illus.). 96p. (C). pap. 31.00 ***(978-0-13-267545-1(5)***, Prentice Hall) Prentice Hall PTR.

Kinser, Amy S. & Jones, Dorothy. Your Office Getting Started with Business Communication. 2012. (ENG.). 96p. (C). spiral bd. 31.00 ***(978-0-13-267548-2(X)***, Prentice Hall) Prentice Hall PTR.

Kinser, Amy S., et al. Your Office: Microsoft Excel 2010 Comprehensive. 2011. (ENG.). 736p. (C). spiral bd. 116.00 ***(978-0-13-261044-5(2)***, Prentice Hall) Prentice Hall PTR.

Kogent, Inc. Sap Abap: Interview Questions & Answers. 2009. 250p. pap. 40.00 *(978-1-934015-54-4(7))* Jones & Bartlett Learning, LLC.

—SAP ABAP Handbook. 2009. 450p. pap. 44.00 *(978-1-934015-41-4(5))* Jones & Bartlett Learning, LLC.

Korherr, Birgit. Business Process Modelling: Languages, Goals, & Variabilities. 2008. 132p. pap. *(978-3-8364-8716-0(0))* VDM Verlag Dr. Mueller e.K.

Krishan, S. I. Computing with Excel & VBA. 2nd rev. ed. 2008. 298p. pap. 101.95 *(978-0-7637-5668-0(7))* Jones & Bartlett Learning, LLC.

Krishnamoorthy, Venkatesh, et al. SAP Transaction Codes: Your Quick Reference to T-Codes in SAP ERP. 2011. (Illus.). 581p. 49.95 *(978-1-59229-374-2(3)*, SAP PR.) Galileo Pr., Inc.

Kroenke, David & Nilson, Donald. Office 365 in Business. 2011. (ENG.). 312p. pap. 39.99 *(978-1-118-10504-7(4)*, Wiley) Wiley, John & Sons, Inc.

Kushner, Theresa & Villar, Maria C. Managing Your Business Data. 2008. 160p. 32.95 *(978-1-933199-13-9(X))* Racom Communications.

Lambert, Joan, III & Cox, Joyce. Mos 2010 Study Guide for Microsoft Word, Excel, Powerpoint, & Outlook Exams. 2011. (ENG., Illus.). 736p. pap. 44.99 *(978-0-7356-4875-3(1))* Microsoft Pr.

Landrum, Rodney, et al. Pro SQL Server 2008 Reporting Services. 2008. (ENG.). 424p. pap. 39.99 *(978-1-59059-992-1(6))* Apress L. P.

LeVitus, Bob. Office 2008 for Mac for Dummies. 2008. (ENG., Illus.). 432p. pap. 24.99 *(978-0-470-27032-5(2)*, For Dummies) Wiley, John & Sons, Inc.

—Office 2011 for Mac for Dummies. 2011. (ENG., Illus.). 432p. pap. 24.99 *(978-0-470-87869-9(X)*, For Dummies) Wiley, John & Sons, Inc.

Likness, Jeremy. Designing Silverlight Business Applications: Best Practices for Using Silverlight Effectively in the Enterprise. rev. ed. 2012. (Microsoft . NET Development Ser.). (ENG.). 720p. pap. 49.99 ***(978-0-321-81041-0(4))*** Addison Wesley Professional.

Lodhi, Suleman. Voluntary Knowledge Sharing Model. 2009. 108p. pap. *(978-3-639-19848-5(4))* VDM Verlag Dr. Mueller e.K.

Magal. Integrated Business Processes with ERP Systems, No. 1. 2011. (ENG., Illus.). 358p. (C). 138.95 *(978-0-470-47844-8(6)*, Wiley) Wiley, John & Sons, Inc.

Mann, Steven, et al. Microsoft SharePoint 2010 Business Intelligence. rev. ed. 2011. (Unleashed Ser.). (ENG., Illus.). 352p. pap. 39.99 *(978-0-672-33551-8(4))* Sams.

Manning, Cheryl, et al. Microsoft Office Excel 2010: A Skills Approach, Complete. 2011. (ENG., Illus.). 400p. (C). pap. 108.67 ***(978-0-07-739500-1(X)***, 007739500X) McGraw-Hill Higher Education.

Manzo, Joseph & Rhoads, Christine J. Communicating with Microsoft Office Word 2007 in Business, Core. 2007. (ENG., Illus.). 256p. (C). pap. 75.67 *(978-0-13-230761-1(8)*, Prentice Hall) Prentice Hall PTR.

Manzo, Joseph J. Microsoft Office Excel 2007 in Business. 2007. (ENG., Illus.). 592p. (C). pap. 111.40 *(978-0-13-199171-2(X)*, Prentice Hall) Prentice Hall PTR.

—Microsoft Office Excel 2007 in Business, Core. 2007. (ENG., Illus.). 336p. (C). pap. 81.33 *(978-0-13-174344-1(9)*, Prentice Hall) Prentice Hall PTR.

Manzo, Joseph J., et al. Microsoft Office 2007 in Business Core. 2nd ed. 2008. (ENG., Illus.). 1088p. (C). pap. 140.00 *(978-0-13-507320-9(0)*, Prentice Hall) Prentice Hall PTR.

Margolis, Ben. IBM Rational Business Developer with EGL. 2008. (ENG.). 200p. pap. 39.95 *(978-1-58347-066-4(2))* MC Pr., LLC.

—SOA for the Business Developer: Concepts, BPEL, & SCA. 2007. (Business Developers Ser.). (ENG., Illus.). 200p. per. 39.95 *(978-1-58347-065-7(4))* MC Pr., LLC.

Marmel, Elaine. Excel 2010. 2010. (Master VISUALLY Ser.: 745). (ENG., Illus.). 736p. pap. 39.99 *(978-0-470-57769-1(X)*, Visual) Wiley, John & Sons, Inc.

Matthews, Barbara, et al. The Release 12 Primer - Shining a Light on the Release 12 World. 2008. 252p. pap. 29.99 *(978-0-615-23844-9(0))* Reed-Matthews, Inc.

Matthews, Marty. Windows 7 QuickSteps. 2009. (ENG., Illus.). 272p. pap. 19.99 *(978-0-07-163569-1(6)*, 0071635696) McGraw-Hill Osborne.

Matthews, Marty, et al. Microsoft Office 2007 QuickSteps. 2008. (ENG., Illus.). 368p. pap. 29.99 *(978-0-07-159985-6(1)*, 0071599851) McGraw-Hill Osborne.

—Microsoft Office Outlook 2010 QuickSteps. 2nd ed. 2010. (ENG., Illus.). 256p. pap. 19.99 *(978-0-07-163496-0(7)*, 0071634967) McGraw-Hill Osborne.

Mayes, Timothy R. & Shank, Todd M. Financial Analysis with Microsoft Excel. 6th ed. 2011. (ENG.). (C). pap. 92.95 ***(978-1-111-82624-6(2))*** Cengage South-Western.

McCombs, Adam & Banh, Robert. The Definitive Guide to Magento. 2009. (ENG.). 328p. pap. 49.99 *(978-1-4302-7229-8(5))* Apress L. P.

McFedries, Paul. Excel 2010. 2010. (Simplified Ser.: 16). (ENG., Illus.). 256p. pap. 24.99 *(978-0-470-57763-9(0)*, Visual) Wiley, John & Sons, Inc.

—Excel 2010 Visual Quick Tips. 2010. (ENG., Illus.). 304p. pap. 19.99 *(978-0-470-57776-9(2)*, Visual) Wiley, John & Sons, Inc.

—Formulas & Functions: Microsoft Excel 2010. 2010. (Business Solutions Ser.). (ENG., Illus.). 512p. pap. 39.99 *(978-0-7897-4306-0(X))* Que.

—Formulas & Functions with Microsoft Office Excel 2007. 2007. (Business Solutions Ser.). (ENG., Illus.). 552p. per. 39.99 *(978-0-7897-3668-0(3))* Que.

—Microsoft Office Web Apps. 2010. (Using Ser.). (ENG., Illus.). 272p. pap. 24.99 *(978-0-7897-4486-9(4))* Que.

—Teach Yourself VISUALLY Excel 2010. 2010. (Teach Yourself VISUALLY (Tech) Ser.: 63). (ENG., Illus.). 352p. pap. 29.99 *(978-0-470-57764-6(9)*, Visual) Wiley, John & Sons, Inc.

—Tricks of the Microsoft Office 2007 Gurus. 2nd ed. 2007. (Business Solutions Ser.). (ENG., Illus.). 504p. per. 44.99 *(978-0-7897-3666-6(7))* Que.

—VBA for the 2007 Microsoft Office System. 2007. (Business Solutions Ser.). (ENG., Illus.). 432p. per. 44.99 *(978-0-7897-3667-3(5))* Que.

McFedries, Paul & Mcfedries. Office 2008 for Mac. 2009. (Teach Yourself VISUALLY (Tech) Ser.: 53). (ENG., Illus.). 416p. pap. 29.99 *(978-0-470-48503-3(5)*, Visual) Wiley, John & Sons, Inc.

McGraw-Hill Staff & Glencoe McGraw-Hill Staff. Office 2007 Student Manual. 2008. (ENG.). (C). pap. 22.12 *(978-0-07-888764-2(X)*, 007888764X) McGraw-Hill Higher Education.

Mehrwald, Christian, et al. Data Warehousing with SAP BW7 BI in SAP NetWeaver 2004s: Architecture, Concepts, & Implementation. 2009. (ENG., Illus.). 900p. pap. 89.95 *(978-1-933952-40-6(7))* Rocky Nook.

Microsoft Excel 2007 K Card: 030281kc. 2007. *(978-1-4246-0530-9(X))* Element K Content LLC.

Microsoft(r) Office Excel(r) 2007 - Level 3: Nh3165lgeel. 2007. spiral bd. *(978-1-4246-0589-7(X))* Element K Content LLC.

Microsoft(r) Office Excel(r) 2007 - Level 3: Nh84283i. 2007. spiral bd. *(978-1-4246-0587-3(3))* Element K Content LLC.

Microsoft(r) Office Excel(r) 2007 - Level 3: Nh84283s. 2007. spiral bd. *(978-1-4246-0588-0(1))* Element K Content LLC.

Microsoft Office Excel 2007: 084282ie. 2007. spiral bd. *(978-1-4246-0356-5(0))* Element K Content LLC.

Microsoft Office Excel 2007: 084282s3. 2007. spiral bd. *(978-1-4246-0357-2(9))* Element K Content LLC.

Microsoft(r) Office Excel(r) 2007: 084283ie. 2007. spiral bd. *(978-1-4246-0583-5(0))* Element K Content LLC.

Microsoft(r) Office Excel(r) 2007: 084283s3. 2007. spiral bd. *(978-1-4246-0584-2(9))* Element K Content LLC.

Microsoft(r) Office Excel(r) 2007: 084890ie. 2007. spiral bd. *(978-1-4246-0614-6(4))* Element K Content LLC.

Microsoft(r) Office Excel(r) 2007: 084890s3. 2007. spiral bd. *(978-1-4246-0615-3(2))* Element K Content LLC.

Microsoft Office Excel 2007: ET84282IG. 2007. spiral bd. *(978-1-4246-0358-9(7))* Element K Content LLC.

Microsoft Office Excel 2007: ET84282SM. 2007. spiral bd. *(978-1-4246-0359-6(5))* Element K Content LLC.

Microsoft(r) Office Excel(r) 2007: ET84283IG. 2007. spiral bd. *(978-1-4246-0585-9(7))* Element K Content LLC.

Microsoft(r) Office Excel(r) 2007: ET84283SM. 2007. spiral bd. *(978-1-4246-0586-6(5))* Element K Content LLC.

Microsoft Office Excel 2007: NH3164LGEEL. 2007. spiral bd. *(978-1-4246-0363-3(3))* Element K Content LLC.

Microsoft Office Excel 2007: NH84282I. 2007. spiral bd. *(978-1-4246-0360-2(9))* Element K Content LLC.

Microsoft Office Excel 2007: NH84282S. 2007. spiral bd. *(978-1-4246-0361-9(7))* Element K Content LLC.

Microsoft(r) Office Excel(r) 2007 - New Features: Nh3148lgeel. 2007. spiral bd. *(978-1-4246-0488-3(5))* Element K Content LLC.

Microsoft(r) Office Excel(r) 2007 - New Features: Nh84280i. 2007. spiral bd. *(978-1-4246-0479-1(6))* Element K Content LLC.

Microsoft(r) Office Excel(r) 2007 - New Features: Nh84280s. 2007. spiral bd. *(978-1-4246-0480-7(X))* Element K Content LLC.

Microsoft(r) Office Excel(r) 2007: 084280ie. 2007. spiral bd. *(978-1-4246-0475-3(3))* Element K Content LLC.

Microsoft(r) Office Excel(r) 2007: 084280s3. 2007. spiral bd. *(978-1-4246-0476-0(1))* Element K Content LLC.

Microsoft(r) Office Excel(r) 2007: ET84280IG. 2007. spiral bd. *(978-1-4246-0477-7(X))* Element K Content LLC.

Microsoft(r) Office Excel(r) 2007: ET84280SM. 2007. spiral bd. *(978-1-4246-0478-4(8))* Element K Content LLC.

Miller, Roxanne E. The Quest for Software Requirements: Probing Questions to bring nonfunctional requirements into focus; proven techniques to get the right stakeholder Involvement. 2009. (ENG.). 348p. pap. 35.00 *(978-1-59598-067-0(9))* HenschelHAUS Publishing.

MOAC. Office 2010. 2011. (ENG.). 1300p. pap. ***(978-0-470-90850-1(5))*** Wiley, John & Sons, Inc.

Mueller, John Paul. RibbonX for Dummies. 2007. (ENG., Illus.). 404p. per. 29.99 *(978-0-470-16994-0(X)*, For Dummies) Wiley, John & Sons, Inc.

Muir, Nancy & Kimbell, Ian. Discover SAP: Entdecke die Welt von SAP. 2009. (Illus.). 440p. pap. 39.95 *(978-1-59229-320-9(4)*, SAP PR.) Galileo Pr., Inc.

Murray, Katherine. First Look 2007 Microsoft Office System. rev. ed. 2006. (ENG., Illus.). 224p. per. 19.99 *(978-0-7356-2265-4(5))* Microsoft Pr.

Murray, Martin. Maximize Your Warehouse Operations with SAP ERP. 2009. (Illus.). 300p. 69.95 *(978-1-59229-309-4(3)*, SAP PR.) Galileo Pr., Inc.

Nahaboo Solim, Mohammad Zuvair. Computerization of Stock Control & Invoicing. 2010. 100p. pap. *(978-3-8383-9031-4(8))* Lambert Academic Publishing.

Newman, Aaron, et al. Enterprise 2.0 Implementation: Integrate Web 2.0 Services into Your Enterprise. 2008. (ENG., Illus.). 406p. pap. 49.99 *(978-0-07-159160-7(5)*, 0071591605) McGraw-Hill Osborne.

Nickles, David J. & Ogawa, Michael-Brian. Microsoft Office Outlook 2007: A Professional Approach. 2008. (ENG., Illus.). 240p. (C). spiral bd. 71.67 *(978-0-07-337350-8(8)*, 0073373508) McGraw-Hill Higher Education.

Niefert, Wolfgang. SAP Business ONE Implementation. 2009. (Illus.). 377p. pap. *(978-1-84719-638-5(1))* Packt Publishing, Ltd.

Nygard, Michael T. Release It! Design & Deploy Production-Ready Software. 2007. (Pragmatic Programmers Ser.). (ENG., Illus.). 326p. per. 34.95 *(978-0-9787392-1-8(3)*, Pragmatic Bookshelf, The) Pragmatic Programmers, LLC, The.

Oja, Dan, et al. Practical OpenOffice. org. 2006. (Practical Ser.). (ENG., Illus.). 224p. (C). pap. 93.95 *(978-1-4239-0557-8(1))* Course Technology.

O'Leary, Linda . Office 2007 Windows Vista Version. 2009. (ENG., Illus.). 1408p. (C). spiral bd. 141.00 *(978-0-07-351927-2(8)*, 0073519278) McGraw-Hill Higher Education.

O'Leary, Timothy J. & O'Leary, Linda. Microsoft Office 2007. 2007. (ENG., Illus.). 1408p. (C). spiral bd. 121.33 *(978-0-07-351916-6(2)*, 0073519162) McGraw-Hill Higher Education.

O'Leary, Timothy J. & O'Leary, Linda I. Microsoft Office Excel 2007. 2007. (ENG., Illus.). (C). 672p. pap. 74.33 *(978-0-07-329452-0(7)*, 0073294527); 400p. pap. 64.33 *(978-0-07-329451-3(9)*, 0073294519) McGraw-Hill Higher Education.

Palo Alto Software Staff. Business Feasibility Analysis Pro. 2006. (ENG.). (C). 52.00 *(978-0-13-613201-1(4)*, Prentice Hall) Prentice Hall PTR.

Pani, Saroj Kumar. The Effect of Economic & Social Embeddedness of Firms. 2011. 144p. pap. ***(978-3-8433-8312-7(X))*** Lambert Academic Publishing.

Parsons, June Jamrich, et al. Microsoft Excel 2010. 2010. (New Perspectives Ser.). (ENG.). 280p. (C). pap. 68.95 *(978-0-538-74292-4(5))* Course Technology.

—New Perspectives on Microsoft Office Excel 2007, Brief, Premium Video Edition. 2010. (New Perspectives Ser.). (ENG.). 312p. (C). pap. 68.95 *(978-0-538-47561-7(7))* Course Technology.

—New Perspectives on Microsoft Office Excel 2007, Comprehensive, Premium Video Edition. 2010. (New Perspectives Ser.). (ENG.). 952p. (C). pap. 135.95 *(978-0-538-47559-4(5))* Course Technology.

—New Perspectives on Microsoft Office Excel 2007, Introductory, Premium Video Edition. 2010. (New Perspectives Ser.). (ENG.). 600p. (C). pap. 98.95 *(978-0-538-47560-0(9))* Course Technology.

—New Perspectives on Microsoft Office Excel 2010, Introductory. 2010. (New Perspectives Ser.). (ENG.). 616p. (C). pap. 98.95 *(978-0-538-74239-9(9))* Course Technology.

Pasewark. Microsoft Office 2010: Introductory. 2010. 1120p. pap. *(978-0-538-47550-1(1))* Course Technology.

Pasewark and Pasewark Staff & Romer, Robin M. Introductory - Microsoft Office Excel 2010. 2010. (Spreadsheet Applications Ser.). (ENG.). 376p. 68.95 *(978-0-538-47521-1(8))* Course Technology.

—Microsoft Office Excel 2007. 2007. (SAM 2007 Compatible Products Ser.). (ENG.). 328p. spiral bd. 68.95 *(978-1-4239-0411-3(7))* Course Technology.

Pasewark, William R., Sr., et al. Microsoft Office 2007: Introductory. 2007. (Available Titles Skills Assessment Manager (SAM) - Office 2007 Ser.). (ENG., Illus.). 1080p. 129.95 *(978-1-4239-0396-3(X))* Course Technology.

Pearson/Prentice Hall, creator. Essential Office Applications: Custom Edition for University of Pittsburgh at Greensburg. 2007. (Illus.). 991p. spiral bd. *(978-0-536-10133-4(7))* Pearson Education Canada.

Person, Ron. Balanced Scorecards & Operational Dashboards with Microsoft Excel. 2008. (ENG., Illus.). 480p. pap. 49.99 *(978-0-470-38681-1(9)*, Wiley) Wiley, John & Sons, Inc.

Pierce, John. MOS Study Guide for Microsoft(r) Office(r) 365. 2012. (ENG.). 176p. pap. 16.99 (978-0-7356-6903-1(1)) Microsoft Pr.

Piercy, Craig A., et al. Using Microsoft Office 2007: Tutorials & Projects. 2nd ed. 2008. (ENG., Illus.). 600p. (C). pap. 66.95 (978-0-470-22390-1(1), Wiley) Wiley, John & Sons, Inc.

Placeholder, Placeholder & Lawson, Rebecca. Skills for Success with Office 2010 Web Applications Getting Started. rev. ed. 2012. (ENG.). 80p. (C). pap. 31.00 (978-0-13-255004-8(0), Prentice Hall) Prentice Hall PTR.

Powell, Stephen G. & Baker, Kenneth R. Management Science: The Art of Modeling with Spreadsheets, Excel 2007 Update. 2nd rev. ed. 2008. (ENG., Illus.). 528p. (C). 182.95 (978-0-470-39376-5(9), Wiley) Wiley, John & Sons, Inc.

Powell, Stephen G. & Batt, Robert J. Modeling for Insight: A Master Class for Business Analysts. 2008. (ENG., Illus.). 466p. pap. 105.00 (978-0-470-17555-2(9), Wiley) Wiley, John & Sons, Inc.

Pratt, Douglas G. Super-Charge Your Charts! Visually Transform Data into Information. 2007. 112p. per. 24.95 (978-0-9791486-0-6(X)) Thomas, Roscoe International.

Preppernau, Joan, et al. Microsoft Office Home & Student 2007. 2007. (ENG., Illus.). 512p. pap. 24.99 (978-0-7356-2560-0(3)) Microsoft Pr.

Preston, John, et al. Go with Microsoft Office 2003: Brief. Gaskin, Shelley, ed. 2007. (Go! with Microsoft Office Ser.). (Illus.). 1314p. spiral bd. (978-0-536-26359-9(0)) Pearson Education Canada.

Price, Brad, et al. Mastering System Center Operations Manager 2007. 2007. (ENG., Illus.). 456p. per. 59.99 (978-0-470-11930-3(6), Sybex) Wiley, John & Sons, Inc.

Price, Michael. Office 2007 for Seniors: For the over 50s. 2009. (In Easy Steps Ser.). (ENG., Illus.). 244p. pap. 14.99 (978-1-84078-379-7(6)) Computer Step GBR. Dist: Perseus-PGW.

—Office 2010 for Seniors: For the over 50s. 2011. (In Easy Steps Ser.). (ENG., Illus.). 244p. pap. 14.99 (978-1-84078-412-1(1)) Computer Step GBR. Dist: Perseus-PGW.

—Office 2010 in Easy Steps. 2010. (In Easy Steps Ser.). (ENG., Illus.). 240p. pap. 14.99 (978-1-84078-398-8(2)) Computer Step GBR. Dist: Perseus-PGW.

PUEI. Budgeting & Finance Templates. 2007. cd-rom 49.95 (978-1-934147-47-4(8), CareerTrack) Park Univ. Enterprises, Inc.

—Microsoft Excel Pivot Tables Made Easy. 2007. cd-rom 199.00 (978-1-934147-60-3(5), CareerTrack) Park Univ. Enterprises, Inc.

—Unlocking the Secrets of Microsoft Access 2007 Advanced Queries. 2007. cd-rom 89.95 (978-1-934147-36-8(2), CareerTrack) Park Univ. Enterprises, Inc.

—Unlocking the Secrets of Microsoft Access 2007 Macros. 2007. cd-rom 79.95 (978-1-934147-34-4(6), CareerTrack) Park Univ. Enterprises, Inc.

—Unlocking the Secrets of Microsoft Access Advanced Queries. 2007. cd-rom 149.00 (978-1-934147-32-0(X), CareerTrack) Park Univ. Enterprises, Inc.

—Unlocking the Secrets of Microsoft Excel 2007. 2007. cd-rom 199.95 (978-1-934147-38-2(9), CareerTrack) Park Univ. Enterprises, Inc.

—Unlocking the Secrets of Microsoft Excel 2007 Formulas 1. 2007. cd-rom 79.95 (978-1-934147-39-9(7), CareerTrack) Park Univ. Enterprises, Inc.

—Unlocking the Secrets of Microsoft Excel 2007 Formulas 2. 2007. cd-rom 79.95 (978-1-934147-44-3(3), CareerTrack) Park Univ. Enterprises, Inc.

—Unlocking the Secrets of Microsoft Excel 2007 Pivot Tables. 2007. cd-rom 79.95 (978-1-934147-40-5(0), CareerTrack) Park Univ. Enterprises, Inc.

—Unlocking the Secrets of Microsoft Excel 2007 Shortcuts, Tips & Tricks. 2007. cd-rom 79.95 (978-1-934147-35-1(4), CareerTrack) Park Univ. Enterprises, Inc.

—Unlocking the Secrets of Microsoft Office 2007: Shortcuts, Tips, & Tricks. 2007. cd-rom 39.95 (978-1-934147-46-7(X), CareerTrack) Park Univ. Enterprises, Inc.

Rathbone, Andy & Wang, Wallace. Windows 7 & Office 2010. 2011. (Illus.). 352p. pap. (978-0-470-94188-1(X)) Wiley, John & Sons, Inc.

Rathbone, Andy & Wang, Wallace. Windows 7 & Office 2010 for Dummies. 2010. (ENG., Illus.). 352p. pap. 24.99 (978-0-470-92171-5(4), For Dummies) Wiley, John & Sons, Inc.

Reding, Elizabeth & Wermers, Lynn. Microsoft Office Excel 2010. 2010. (Illustrated Ser.). (ENG., Illus.). 520p. pap. 105.95 (978-0-538-74713-4(7)) Course Technology.

—Microsoft Office Excel 2010: Illustrated Introductory. 2010. (Illustrated Ser.). (ENG.). 264p. pap. 53.95 (978-0-538-74929-9(6)) Course Technology.

Reding, Elizabeth Eisner. Microsoft Office Excel 2007. 2008. (Illustrated Ser.). (ENG.). 152p. pap. 31.95 (978-0-495-80675-2(7)) Course Technology.

—Microsoft Office Excel 2010. 2010. (Available Titles Skills Assessment Manager (SAM) - Office 2010 Ser.). (ENG., Illus.). 160p. pap. 31.95 (978-0-538-74928-2(8)) Course Technology.

—Microsoft Office Publisher 2007. 2007. (Illustrated Ser.). (ENG., Illus.). 288p. (C). per. 53.95 (978-1-4239-0528-8(8)) Course Technology.

Refaat, Mamdouh. Credit Risk Scorecards: Development & Implementation Using SAS. 2011. 428p. 19.50 (978-1-4475-1119-9(0)) Lulu Enterprises Inc.

Reynolds, Deanna. Excel 2010: No Problem! 2010. (No Problem Ser.: 2). (ENG., Illus.). 336p. pap. 24.95 (978-0-470-71022-7(5), Wiley) Wiley, John & Sons, Inc.

Reynolds, Garr. Presentation Zen: The Video. 2009. 12p. 24.99 (978-0-321-57389-6(7)) New Riders Publishing.

—Presentation Zen Design: Simple Design Principles & Techniques to Enhance Your Presentations. 2009. (Voices That Matter Ser.). (ENG., Illus.). 264p. pap. 34.99 (978-0-321-66879-0(0)) New Riders Publishing.

Rhoads, C. J. The Entrepreneur's Guide to Managing Information Technology, 1 vol. 2008. (Entrepreneur's Guide Ser.). (Illus.). 208p. 39.95 (978-0-275-99545-4(3), C9545, Praeger Pubs.) Greenwood Publishing Group, Inc.

Rizzo, Tom, et al. Programming Microsoft's Clouds: Azure & Office 365. 2012. (ENG.). 528p. pap. 44.99 (978-1-118-07656-9(7), Wrox) Wiley, John & Sons, Inc.

Roberts, Scott & Green, Hagen. Designing Forms for Microsoft Office InfoPath & Forms Services. 2007. (Microsoft . NET Development Ser.). (ENG., Illus.). 1296p. per. 64.99 (978-0-321-41059-7(9)) Addison Wesley Professional.

Roberts, Scott, et al. Designing Forms for SharePoint & InfoPath: Using Infopath Designer 2010. 2nd rev. ed. 2011. (Microsoft . NET Development Ser.). (ENG., Illus.). 1128p. pap. 59.99 (978-0-321-74360-2(1)) Addison Wesley Professional.

Romer, Robin M., et al. Microsoft Office 2010: Introductory. 2010. (Available Titles Skills Assessment Manager (SAM) - Office 2010 Ser.). (ENG.). 1136p. 129.95 (978-0-538-47539-6(0)) Course Technology.

Rubin, Kenneth S. Scrum: A Manager's Guide: A Non-technical Introduction to the Most Popular Agile Process. rev. ed. 2012. (Addison-Wesley Signature Series (Cohn) Ser.). (ENG.). 504p. pap. 44.99 (978-0-13-704329-3(5)) Addison Wesley Professional.

Rueda, Edwin S. Incorporating Human Experience Quality Attributes in Software Applications. 2008. 160p. pap. (978-3-639-06581-7(6)) VDM Verlag Dr. Mueller e.K.

Russmann, Roland. Collaborative Engineering in Partnernetzwerken der Automobilindustrie: Die Schwierigkeit, verschiedene PDM/CAD-Systeme unterschiedlicher Partner zu verwalten und zu synchronisieren. 2009. 148p. pap. (978-3-639-21511-3(7)) VDM Verlag Dr. Mueller e.K.

Rutkosky, Nita & Roggenkamp, Audrey Rutkosky. Microsoft Excel 2007. 2008. (Benchmark Ser.). (Illus.). 384p. pap. 30.95 (978-0-7638-3066-3(6)) EMC/Paradigm Publishing.

Rutkosky, Nita, et al. Microsoft Office 2007: Windows Vista. 2008. (Marquee Ser.). (Illus.). 688p. 67.95 (978-0-7638-3354-1(1)) EMC/Paradigm Publishing.

Rutkosky, Nita Hewitt, et al. Microsoft Excel 2007: Levels 1 & 2. 2008. (Benchmark Ser.). (Illus.). (978-0-7638-3007-6(0)); (978-0-7638-2992-6(7)) Paradigm Publishing, Inc.

—Microsoft Office 2007: With Windows Vista & Internet Explorer 7.0. 2008. (Illus.). viii, 656p. (978-0-7638-3352-7(5)) Paradigm Pubs.

—Microsoft Office 2007: With Windows XP & Internet Explorer 7.0. 2008. (Illus.). (978-0-03-102324-7(X)); (978-0-7638-2958-2(7)); (978-0-7638-2951-3(X)) Paradigm Pubs.

—Mircrosoft Excel 2007 with Windows XP & Internet Explorer 7.0. 2008. (Illus.). (978-0-7638-2954-4(4)) Paradigm Pubs.

Rutosky, Nita, et al. Microsoft Office 2007: Windows XP. 2008. (Marquee Ser.). (Illus.). 688p. (978-0-7638-3350-3(9)) EMC/Paradigm Publishing.

Sapcookbook. Sap Business Objects Interview Questions: Business Objects Certification Review. 2008. 188p. pap. 64.00 (978-1-60332-023-8(7)) Equity Pr.

Savage, Sam L. Decision Making with Insight (with Insight. xla 2. 0 & Printed Access Card) 3rd ed. 2010. (ENG.). 416p. pap. 97.95 (978-1-4390-4333-2(7)) Cengage South-Western.

Schafer, Marc & Melich, Matthias. SAP Solution Manager. 3rd ed. 2011. (ENG., Illus.). 727p. 69.95 (978-1-59229-388-9(3), SAP PR.) Galileo Pr., Inc.

Schelp, Joachim & Winter, Robert, eds. Auf dem Weg zur Integration Factory: Proceedings der DW2004 - Data Warehousing und EAI. 2006. (GER & ENG., Illus.). XI, 507p. 129.00 (978-3-7908-1564-1(0), 3790815640) Physica-Verlag DEU. Dist: Springer.

Schneider, Thomas. SAP Performance Optimization Guide. 6th ed. 2010.Tr. of SAP(r)-Performanceoptimierung. (Illus.). 789p. 79.95 (978-1-59229-368-1(9), SAP PR.) Galileo Pr., Inc.

Schwartz, Steve. Microsoft Office 2011 for Mac. rev. ed. 2011. (Visual QuickStart Guide Ser.). (ENG., Illus.). 544p. pap. 29.99 (978-0-321-75126-3(4)) Peachpit Pr.

Seguin, Denise & Roggenkamp, Audrey Rutkosky. Microsoft Excel 2007. 2008. (Illus.). xv, 320p. (978-0-7638-3057-1(7)) Paradigm Pubs.

Sens, Maurice. Upgrading SAP. 2008. (ENG., Illus.). 331p. 65.95 (978-1-934015-15-5(6)) Jones & Bartlett Learning, LLC.

Sethi, Sachin. Enhancing Supplier Relationship Management Using SAP SRM. 2nd ed. 2009. (Illus.). 720p. 79.95 (978-1-59229-312-4(3), SAP PR.) Galileo Pr., Inc.

Shadravan, Darvish & Rogers, Laura Derbes. Using Microsoft Infopath 2010 with Microsoft SharePoint 2010. 2011. (ENG., Illus.). 480p. pap. 34.99 (978-0-7356-6206-3(1)) Microsoft Pr.

Shaffer, Kelley. Microsoft Office 2011 for Macintosh, Illustrated Fundamentals. 2nd ed. 2011. (Illustrated Series: MAC Products Ser.). (ENG.). 416p. (C). pap. 77.95 (978-1-111-82431-0(2)) Course Technology.

Shaikh Anwar, Mohd. Sadique. Quantum Leadership for Next Generation Dynamic Business. 2011. 64p. pap. (978-3-8443-2792-2(4)) Lambert Academic Publishing.

Shapiro, Robert, et al. BPMN 2. 0 Handbook: Methods, Concepts, Case Studies & Standards in Business Process Management Notation. 2011. (Illus.). 256p. pap. 75.00 (978-0-9819870-4-0(4)) Future Strategies, Inc.

Sharma, Sunil. Supply Chain Management. 2011. (ENG., Illus.). 540p. 27.95 (978-0-19-568913-6(5)) Oxford Univ. Pr., Inc.

Shelly, Gary B. & Vermaat, Misty E. Microsoft Office 2010. 2010. (Shelly Cashman Office 2010 Ser.). (ENG., Illus.). 1432p. spiral bd. 131.95 (978-1-4390-7841-9(6)) Course Technology.

—Microsoft Office 2010: Essential. 2010. (Available Titles Skills Assessment Manager (SAM) - Office 2010 Ser.). (ENG.). 408p. pap. 89.95 (978-0-538-74870-4(2)) Course Technology.

—Microsoft Office 2010: Introductory. 2010. (Shelly Cashman Series Office 2010 Ser.). (ENG., Illus.). 1176p. pap. 158.95 (978-1-4390-7840-2(8)) Course Technology.

Shelly, Gary B., et al. Microsoft Office 2007: Introductory Concepts & Techniques Windows Vista. (ENG.). 2009. 1368p. ring bd. 119.95 (978-0-324-78988-1(2)) 2007. (Illus.). 1216p. 160.95 (978-1-4239-2713-6(3)) Course Technology.

Shelly, Gary B. (Gary B. Shelly) & Quasney, Jeffrey J. Microsoft Excel 2010: Comprehensive. 2011. (Shelly Cashman Ser.). (ENG.). 920p. pap. 129.95 (978-1-4390-7901-0(3)) Course Technology.

Sideris Courseware Corp. Oracle Database 11g R2 RMAN Backup & Recovery. 3rd ed. 2011. (Sideris Learning Ser.). (Illus.). 560p. pap. 98.00 (978-0-9830445-0-5(3)) Sideris Courseware Corp.

Sideris Courseware Corp. Oracle Database 11g R2 Step-by-Step Installation Guide. 2nd ed. 2011. (Illus.). 304p. pap. 29.00 (978-1-936930-08-1(0)) Sideris Courseware Corp.

Skeete, Kyle. Electronic Document Preparation & Management for CSEC(r) Examinations Coursebook with CD-ROM. 2011. (ENG.). 392p. pap. 31.00 incl. cd-rom (978-0-521-18467-0(3)) Cambridge Univ. Pr.

Sleeter, Doug. Seminar Planning Guide Version 2010 (Printed Book) 2010. spiral bd. (978-1-932487-69-5(7)) Sleeter Group, Inc., The.

Slovak, Ken. Professional Outlook 2007 Programming. 2007. (ENG., Illus.). 454p. per. 49.99 (978-0-470-04994-5(4), Wrox) Wiley, John & Sons, Inc.

Snapp, Shaun. Discover SAP SCM. 2009. (Illus.). 380p. 39.95 (978-1-59229-305-6(0), SAP PR.) Galileo Pr., Inc.

Software & Vendors & Requirements, Oh My! A Project Team's Guide to Evaluating Business Software. 2007. lib. bdg. 34.99 (978-0-9792792-4-9(0)) MB Castle Pr.

Spivey, Dwight. Office for Mac 2011. 2010. (Portable Genius Ser.: 27). (ENG., Illus.). 336p. pap. 30.00 (978-0-470-61019-0(0), Wiley) Wiley, John & Sons, Inc.

Splane, Mike. Business Productivity Tools: Office 2007 - Excel, Powerpoint, Graphics & More. 2nd rev. ed. 2009. (ENG.). 90p. pap. 28.45 (978-0-7575-5879-5(8)) Kendall Hunt Publishing Co.

Stefan, Achleitner. Software Based Planning & Control of Financial Instruments: Financial Instruments Management. 2011. 184p. pap. (978-3-639-27638-1(8)) VDM Verlag Dr. Mueller e.K.

Stephan, Kaleske. SAP Query Reporting - Practical Guide. 2010. (Illus.). 400p. 69.95 (978-1-59229-365-0(4), SAP PR.) Galileo Pr., Inc.

Stephens, Todd. Trademark 2. 0: Defining Your Value in the Web 2. 0 World. 2007. 271p. pap. 19.94 (978-0-615-15688-0(6)) Stephens, R. Todd.

Stewart, Kathleen. Microsoft Excel 2007: A Professional Approach. 2007. (ENG., Illus.). 832p. (C). spiral bd. 98.33 (978-0-07-351921-0(9), 0073519219) McGraw-Hill Higher Education.

—Microsoft Office Excel 2007: A Professional Approach. 2008. (Illus.). (978-0-07-329467-4(5)) McGraw-Hill Cos., The.

Story, Laura & Walls, Dawna. Microsoftr Office 2010 Fundamentals. 2nd ed. 2010. (Origins Ser.). (ENG.). 464p. (C). ring bd. 606.95 (978-0-538-47989-9(2)) Course Technology.

—Review Pack for Story/Walls' Microsoft Office 2007 Fundamentals. 2009. (ENG.). (C). 12.95 (978-0-324-78326-1(4)) Course Technology.

Studio Visual Steps. Microsoft Office 2010 & 2007 for Seniors. 2011. (Computer Books for Seniors Ser.). (ENG.). 400p. pap. 24.95 (978-90-5905-177-5(7)) Visual Steps B.V. NLD. Dist: Independent Pubs. Group.

Targowski, Andrew S., ed. Enterprise Systems Education in the 21st Century. 2006. (Illus.). 369p. 89.95 (978-1-59904-349-4(1), Information Science Publishing) IGI Global.

Tiller, James S. Security Services Management. 2010. (ENG., Illus.). 482p. 79.95 (978-0-8493-7052-6(3)) Auerbach Pubs., Inc.

Toren, Roger & Hancock, John C. Practical Business Intelligence with SQL Server 2005. 2006. (Microsoft Windows Server System Ser.). (ENG., Illus.). 432p. per. 64.99 (978-0-321-35698-7(5)) Addison Wesley Professional.

Townsend, Kris. Go! with Microsoft Office 2003: Brief: Additional End-of-Chapter Projects. 2nd ed. 2007. (Go! with Microsoft Office Ser.). (Illus.). 227p. spiral bd. incl. cd-rom (978-0-13-187877-8(8)) Prentice Hall PTR.

Townsend, Kris, et al. Skills for Success with Excel 2010. 2010. (ENG., Illus.). 400p. (C). spiral bd. 76.00 (978-0-13-510050-9(X), Prentice Hall) Prentice Hall PTR.

—Skills for Success with Microsoft Office 2010, Vol. 1. 2010. (ENG., Illus.). 668p. (C). pap. 126.67 (978-0-13-703257-0(9), Prentice Hall) Prentice Hall PTR.

—Skills for Success with Office 2010, Volume 1. 2nd rev. ed. 2012. (ENG.). 656p. (C). pap. 126.67 (978-0-13-284032-3(4), Prentice Hall) Prentice Hall PTR.

—Student CD for Skills for Success Office 2010, Volume 1. 2nd ed. 2012. (ENG.). (C). cd-rom 50.00 (978-0-13-284057-6(X), Prentice Hall) Prentice Hall PTR.

—Student Video CD for Skills for Success with Office 2010 Volume 1. 2nd ed. 2012. (ENG.). (C). cd-rom 50.00 (978-0-13-288189-0(6), Prentice Hall) Prentice Hall PTR.

Triad Interactive. Office 2007 Working with SimNet. 2009. 1024p. (C). spiral bd. 58.13 (978-0-07-351644-8(9), 9780073516448, Career Education) McGraw-Hill Higher Education.

Umlas, Bob. This isn't Excel, it's Magic! 2nd ed. 2007. per. 14.95 (978-0-9792153-2-2(3)) IIL Publishing NY.

VanHuss, Susie H., et al. Integrated Computer Applications. 6th ed. 2011. (ENG.). 352p. (C). pap. 90.95 (978-1-111-98809-8(9)) Cengage South-Western.

Vargas, Alicia, et al. Student Video CD for Go! All in One: Computer Concepts & Applications. 2012. (ENG.). (C). cd-rom 66.67 (978-0-13-288211-8(6), Prentice Hall) Prentice Hall PTR.

Venkatesan, V. Prasanna & Portchelvi, Venkatachalam. Service Composition & Orchestration: Concepts & Approaches: Goal-Directed Approach to Service Orchestration. 2011. 112p. pap. (978-3-639-33233-9(4)) VDM Verlag Dr. Mueller e.K.

Verschuuren, Gerard. Excel 2007 VBA. 2008. (Visual Training Ser.). (ENG.). 100p. cd-rom 99.00 (978-1-932802-33-7(9), Holy Macro! Bks.) Tickling Keys, Inc.

Walkenbach, John. Excel 2010 Bible. 2010. (Bible Ser.: 593). (ENG., Illus.). 1056p. pap. 44.99 (978-0-470-47487-7(4), Wiley) Wiley, John & Sons, Inc.

—Excel 2010 Formulas. 2010. (Mr. Spreadsheet's Bookshelf Ser.: 7). (ENG., Illus.). 816p. pap. 49.99 (978-0-470-47536-2(6), Wiley) Wiley, John & Sons, Inc.

—Excel VBA Programming for Dummies. 2nd ed. 2010. (ENG.). 408p. pap. 29.99 (978-0-470-50369-0(6), For Dummies) Wiley, John & Sons, Inc.

Wang, Shouhong & Wang, Hai. Programming Languages for Business Problem Solving. 2007. (ENG., Illus.). 384p. (C). 104.95 (978-1-4200-6264-9(6)) Auerbach Pubs., Inc.

Wang Shouhong Staff. Programming Languages for Business Problem Solving - Instructors. 2007. cd-rom (978-1-4200-7431-4(8)) Auerbach Pubs., Inc.

Weimer, John. Statistics for Managers Using Excel(r). 2012. 800p. 69.95 (978-1-936420-19-3(8)) Mercury Learning & Information.

Wempen, Faithe. Office 2010 eLearning Kit for Dummies. 2011. (ENG.). 416p. pap. 39.99 (978-1-118-02972-5(0), For Dummies) Wiley, John & Sons, Inc.

Weverka, Peter. Office Home & Student 2010 All-in-One for Dummies. 2010. (ENG., Illus.). 672p. pap. 29.99 (978-0-470-87951-1(3), For Dummies) Wiley, John & Sons, Inc.

Wicklund, Phil. Deploying Cloud-Based: Learn Ways to Increase Your Organization's ROI Using Cloud Technology. 2011. (ENG.). 474p. pap. 34.99 (978-0-7356-6210-0(X)) Microsoft Pr.

Williams, Fabian, et al. Microsoft SharePoint 2010: Business Connectivity Services. 2012. (ENG.). 400p. pap. 34.99 (978-0-7356-6018-2(2)) Microsoft Pr.

Wolenik, Marc J. & Sinay, Damian. Microsoft Dynamics CRM 4. 0 Unleashed. 2008. (Unleashed Ser.). (ENG., Illus.). 864p. pap. 59.99 (978-0-672-32970-8(0)) Sams.

Wood, Daniel C. Sap Scm: Applications & Modeling for Supply Chain Management. 2007. (ENG., Illus.). 336p. 84.50 (978-0-471-76991-0(6), Wiley) Wiley, John & Sons, Inc.

Wood, J. B., et al. Consumption Economics: The New Rules of Tech. 2011. (ENG., Illus.). 232p. 24.95 (978-0-9842130-3-0(1)) Point B, Inc.

BUSINESS—DATA PROCESSING

see also Computer Networks; Electronic Data Interchange; Local Area Networks (Computer Networks)

Aalst, Wil van der. Handbook of Research on Business Process Modeling. Cardoso, Jorge, ed. 2009. 634p. 265.00 (978-1-60566-288-6(7)) IGI Global.

Aalst, Wil van der & Stahl, Christian. Modeling Business Processes: A Petri Net-Oriented Approach. 2011. (Cooperative Information Systems Ser.). (ENG., Illus.). 400p. (gr. 17). 45.00 (978-0-262-01538-7(2)) MIT Pr.

Abdelnour-Nocera, Jost. The Social Construction of Usefulness. 2007. 264p. per. (978-3-8364-2582-7(3)) VDM Verlag Dr. Mueller e.K.

Abramowicz, Witold. Business Information Systems. 2008. (Lecture Notes in Business Information Processing Ser.). (Illus.). xiv, 484p. spiral bd. 99.00 (978-3-540-79395-3(X), 354079395X) Springer.

—Business Information Systems: 10th International Conference, BIS 2007, Poznan, Poland, April 25-27, 2007, Proceedings. 2007. (Lecture Notes in Computer Science Ser.). (Illus.). 651p. pap. 119.00 (978-3-540-72034-8(0), 3540720340) Springer.

—Business Information Systems: 12th International Conference, BIS 2009, Poznan, Poland, April 27-29, 2009, Proceedings. 2009. (Lecture Notes in Business Information Processing Ser.). (ENG.). xiii, 265p. pap. 69.95 (978-3-642-01189-4(6)) Springer.

Abramowicz, Witold, ed. Business Information Systems: 14th International Conference, BIS 2011, PoznaÅ„, Poland, June 15-17, 2011, Proceedings. 2011. (Lecture Notes in Business Information Processing Ser.). xv, 301p. pap. 83.00 (978-3-642-21829-3(6), 3642218296) Springer.

Abramowicz, Witold, et al, eds. Business Information Systems Workshops: BIS 2010 International Workshop, Berlin, Germany, May 3-5, 2010, Revised Papers. 2010. (Lecture Notes in Business Information Processing Ser.). xvi, 324p. pap. 83.00 (978-3-642-15401-0(8), 3642154018) Springer.

Abramowicz, Witold & Flejter, Dominik. Business Information Systems Workshops: Bis 2009 International Workshops, Poznan, Poland, April 27-29, 2009, revised Papers. 2009. (Lecture Notes in Business Information Processing Ser.). (ENG.). xviii, 388p. pap. 89.95 (978-3-642-03423-7(3), 3642034233) Springer.

Abramowicz, Witold & Mayr, Heinrich C., eds. Technologies for Business Information Systems. 2010. (ENG.). xx, 432p. pap. 149.00 (978-90-481-7415-7(5), 9048174155) Springer.

Abramowicz, Witold & Tolksdorf, Robert, eds. Business Information Systems: 13th International Conference, BIS 2010, Berlin, Germany, May 3-5, 2010, Proceedings. 2010. (Lecture Notes in Business Information Processing Ser.). (Illus.). xi, 305p. pap. 83.00 (978-3-642-12813-4(0), 3642128130) Springer.

The Accountant's Guide to XBRL. (C). 2nd ed. 2006. spiral bd. (978-0-9779525-1-9(7)) 3rd ed. 2008. (ENG.). 225p. spiral bd. 41.00 (978-0-9779525-4-0(1)) SkipWhite.com.

Agrawal, Manish. Business Data Communications. 2011. (ENG., Illus.). 384p. (C). pap. 114.95 (978-0-470-48336-7(9), Wiley) Wiley, John & Sons, Inc.

Alkhalifa, Eshaa M. E-Strategies for Resource Management Systems: Planning & Implementation. 2010. 350p. 180.00 (978-1-61692-016-6(5)) IGI Global.

Allweyer, Thomas. BPMN 2.0 - Business Process Model & Notation: Einführung in den Standard für die Geschäftsprozessmodellierung. 2009. 170p. pap. (978-3-8391-2134-4(5)) Books on Demand GmbH.

Almanza, Alma Lilia Garcia & Tsang, Edward. Evolutionary Applications for Financial Prediction: Classification Methods to Gather Patterns Using Genetic Programming. 2011. 172p. pap. (978-3-639-30767-2(4)) VDM Verlag Dr. Mueller e.K.

Alonso, Gustavo, et al. Business Process Management: 5th International Conference, BPM 2007, Brisbane, Australia, September 24-28, 2007, Proceedings. 2007. (Lecture Notes in Computer Science / Information Systems & Applications, incl. Internet/Web, & HCI Ser.). xiii, 418p. pap. 89.95 (978-3-540-75182-3(3), 3540751823) Springer.

Altan, Gnzide Selin. Triple Graph Grammars for the Transformation of Business Process Models. 2008. 128p. pap. (978-3-8364-7501-3(4)) VDM Verlag Dr. Mueller e.K.

Anderson, Brian & Mutch, John. Preventing Good People from Doing Bad Things: Implementing Least Privilege. 2011. (ENG.). 220p. pap. 29.99 (978-1-4302-3921-5(2)) Apress L. P.

Anderson, Chris. Pro Business Applications with Silverlight 4. 2010. (ENG.). 576p. pap. 49.99 (978-1-4302-7207-6(4)) Apress L. P.

Androutsellis-Theotokis, Stephanos, et al. Open Source Software. 2011. 176p. pap. 99.00 (978-1-60198-484-5(7)) Now Pubs.

Ardagna, Danilo, et al. Business Process Management Workshops: BPM 2008 International Workshops, Milano, Italy, September 1-4, 2008, Revised Papers. 2009. (Lecture Notes in Business Information Processing Ser.). (ENG.). xvi, 725p. pap. 129.00 (978-3-642-00327-1(3), 3642003273) Springer.

Aryan, Anish. Modeling of Production Planning of a Shop Floor. 2011. 80p. pap. (978-3-8383-5395-8(X)) Lambert Academic Publishing.

Association for Computing Machinery (ACM) Staff, compiled by. ACM SIGKDD International Workshop on Domain Driven Data Mining (DDDM 2007) 2007. 60p. pap. 50.00 (978-1-60423-397-1(4)) Curran Assocs., Inc.

Österle, Hubert. Business in the Information Age: Heading for New Processes. 2010. (ENG., Illus.). xvi, 387p. pap. 119.00 (978-3-642-08218-4(1), 3642082181) Springer.

Baker, Stephen R. & Tyler, Cedric G. Business Genetics: Understanding 21st Century Corporations Using XBML. 2007. (ENG., Illus.). 264p. 65.00 (978-0-470-06654-6(7), Wiley) Wiley, John & Sons, Inc.

Bantin, Philip C. Understanding Data & Information Systems for Recordkeeping. 2007. (Archivist's & Records Manager's Bookshelf). 75.00 (978-1-55570-580-0(4)) Neal-Schuman Pubs., Inc.

Barjis, Joseph, ed. Enterprise & Organizational Modeling & Simulation: 6th International Workshop, EOMAS 2010, held at CAiSE 2010, Hammamet, Tunisia, June 7-8, 2010, Selected Papers. 2010. (Lecture Notes in Business Information Processing Ser.). ix, 197p. pap. 72.00 (978-3-642-15722-6(X), 364215722X) Springer.

Barnett, Raymond A., et al. Graphing Calculator & Excel Spreadsheet Manual for Finite Mathematics for Business, Economics, Life Sciences & Social Sciences. 12th ed. 2010. (ENG.). 216p. (C). pap. 24.67 (978-0-321-64541-8(3), Prentice Hall) Prentice Hall PTR.

Beckmann, Jason A. Business Process Modeling: Software Engineering, Analysis & Applications. 2011. (Business Issues, Competition & Entrepreneurship Ser.). (Illus.). 198p. 89.00 (978-1-61209-344-4(2)) Nova Science Pubs., Inc.

Benisis, Apostolos. Business Process Management. 2010. 204p. pap. (978-3-639-22216-6(4)) VDM Verlag Dr. Mueller e.K.

Berry, Tim. The Plan-as-You-Go Business Plan. 2008. (ENG., Illus.). 288p. pap. 19.95 (978-1-59918-190-5(8), 1599181908) Entrepreneur Pr. dba Entrepreneur Media, Inc.

Bider, Ilia, et al, eds. Enterprise, Business-Process & Information Systems Modeling: 11th International Workshop, BPMDS 2010, & 15th International Conference, EMMSAD 2010, held at CAiSE 2010, Hammamet, Tunisia, June 7-8, 2010, Proceedings. 2010. (Lecture Notes in Business Information Processing Ser.). xv, 341p. pap. 83.00 (978-3-642-13050-2(X), 364213050X) Springer.

Bond, Patrick. Communications & Networking in China: 1st International Business Conference, Chinacombiz 2008, Hangzhou China, August 2008, Revised Selected Papers. 2009. (Communications in Computer & Information Science Ser.). vi, 105p. pap. 99.00 (978-3-642-00204-5(8)) Springer.

Boyd, Kevin W. Problem Solver. 2009. (ENG.). 240p. (gr. 12-18). 16.95 (978-1-59257-802-3(0), Alpha Bks.) Penguin Group (USA) Inc.

Boyer, Jérôme & Mili, Hafedh. Agile Business Rule Development: Process, Architecture, & JRules Examples. 2011. xxvi, 567p. 59.95 (978-3-642-19040-7(5), 3642190405) Springer.

Bradford, Marianne. Modern ERP: Select, Implement & Use Today's Advanced Business Systems. 2010. 247p. pap. 75.00 (978-0-557-43407-7(6)) Lulu Enterprises Inc.

Brantley & Miller, Toby. Ale Effective Communication for Colleges. 11th ed. 2007. (C). pap. 33.95 (978-0-324-54336-0(0)) Cengage South-Western.

Breugelmans, Els. Investigating Consumer Behavior in an Online Grocery Context: The Impact of the Adopted Stock-out Policy & Virtual Shelf Placement. 2008. 240p. pap. (978-3-639-09504-3(9)) VDM Verlag Dr. Mueller e.K.

Bridgeland, David M. & Zahavi, Ron. Business Modeling: A Practical Guide to Realizing Business Value. 2008. (MK/OMG Press Ser.). (ENG., Illus.). 408p. pap. 59.95 (978-0-12-374151-6(3), Morgan Kaufmann) Elsevier Science & Technology Bks.

Brooks, Charlotte. IBM System Storage Business Continuity Solutions Overview. 2nd ed. 2007. (Illus.). xii, 172p. (978-0-7384-8971-1(9)) IBM.

Brown, Paul C. TIBCO Architecture Fundamentals. rev. ed. 2011. (TIBCO Press Ser.). (ENG., Illus.). 288p. pap. 39.99 (978-0-321-77261-9(X)) Addison Wesley Professional.

Bücker, Axel. Deployment Guide Series. 2007. (Illus.). xiv, 360p. (978-0-7384-9683-2(9)) IBM.

—Enterprise Security Architecture Using IBM ISS Security Solutions. 2008. (Illus.). xvi, 400p. (978-0-7384-8522-5(5)) IBM.

Bücker, Axel, et al. Deployment Guide Series. 3rd ed. 2008. (Illus.). xvi, 284p. (978-0-7384-3206-9(7)) IBM.

Bunke, Horst, et al. A Graph-Theoretic Approach to Enterprise Network Dynamics. 2007. (Progress in Computer Science & Applied Logic Ser.: Vol. 24). (Illus.). 225p. 98.00 (978-0-8176-4485-7(7), 0817644857) Birkhauser Boston.

Burch, Chuck. Consolidating the Is Success, National Culture, & Global It Story- a Study of Erp & Portal Implementation. 2007. 120p. per. (978-3-8364-2388-5(X)) VDM Verlag Dr. Mueller e.K.

Buresh, Donald. Customer Satisfaction & Agile Methods: Assessing Customer Satisfaction & Agile Project Management Methods. 2008. 208p. pap. (978-3-639-09476-3(X)) VDM Verlag Dr. Mueller e.K.

Burns, Richard & Burns, Robert P. Business Research Methods & Statistics Using SPSS. 2008. (Illus.). 560p. (C). 146.00 (978-1-4129-4529-5(1), B45291C); pap. 79.00 (978-1-4129-4530-1(5), B45291P) SAGE Pubns., Ltd. GBR. Dist: SAGE Pubns., Inc.

Cadman, Dana L. Web 2.0 for Non-Profit Organizations. Anger, Linda & Whitlow, Stephanie, eds. 2009. (Illus.). 112p. pap. 14.99 (978-1-59932-145-5(9)) Advantage Media Group.

Cao, Longbing. Data Mining for Business Applications. 2008. (ENG., Illus.). xx, 302p. 119.00 (978-0-387-79419-8(0), 0387794190) Springer.

Cao, Longbing, et al, eds. Data Mining for Business Applications. 2010. (ENG., Illus.). xx, 302p. pap. 119.00 (978-1-4419-4635-5(7), 1441946357) Springer.

Cao, Longbing, et al. Domain Driven Data Mining. 2010. (Illus.). xiii, 237p. 99.00 (978-1-4419-5736-8(7), 1441957367) Springer.

Cardoso, Jorge, et al, eds. The Semantic Web: Real-World Applications from Industry. 2007. (Semantic Web & Beyond: Computing for Human Experience Ser.). (Illus.). 308p. 119.00 (978-0-387-48530-0(9)) Springer.

Carter, Sandy. The New Language of Business: Soa & Web 2. 0. 2007. (ENG., Illus.). 320p. 29.99 (978-0-13-195654-4(X)) Pearson Education.

Castellanos, Malu, et al. Business Intelligence for the Real-Time Enterprise: Second International Workshop, BIRTE 2008, Auckland, New Zealand, August 24, 2008, Revised Selected Papers. 2009. (Lecture Notes in Business Information Processing Ser.). (ENG.). ix, 123p. pap. 69.95 (978-3-642-03421-3(7), 3642034217) Springer.

Chaffey, Dave & Smith, Paul. EMarketing EXcellence: Planning & optimising your digital Marketing. 3rd rev. ed. 2008. (ENG., Illus.). 528p. (C). pap. 58.95 (978-0-7506-8945-8(5)) Routledge.

Chaney, Paul. The Digital Handshake: Seven Proven Strategies to Grow Your Business Using Social Media. 2009. (ENG., Illus.). 272p. 24.95 (978-0-470-49927-6(3), Wiley) Wiley, John & Sons, Inc.

Clark, Terry. Unofficial Tibco(R) Business WorksT Interview Questions, Answers, & Explanations. 2008. 156p. per. 54.95 (978-1-60332-028-3(8)) Equity Pr.

Clevenger, Nathan. Ipad in the Enterprise: Developing & Deploying Business Applications. 2011. (ENG., Illus.). 408p. pap. 44.99 (978-1-118-02235-1(1), Wiley) Wiley, John & Sons, Inc.

Cole, Ivan, et al. Microsoft Dynamics Ax 2012. 2013. (Unleashed Ser.). (ENG.). 632p. pap. 59.99 (978-0-672-33548-8(4)) Sams.

Connolly, Thomas, et al. Business Database Systems. 2008. (ENG., Illus.). 592p. (C). pap. 177.00 (978-1-4058-7437-3(6)) Addison Wesley.

Constable, Neil. SAS Programming for Enterprise Guide Users. 2007. (SAS Press Ser.). (Illus.). 308p. per. 42.95 (978-1-59994-540-8(1), SAS Pr.) SAS Publishing.

—SAS Programming for Enterprise Guide Users, Second Edition. 2nd ed. 2010. 308p. pap. 42.95 (978-1-60764-528-3(9), SAS Pr.) SAS Publishing.

Cortada, James W. The Digital Hand, Vol 3: How Computers Changed the Work of American Public Sector Industries. 2007. (ENG., Illus.). 496p. 59.95 (978-0-19-516586-9(1)) Oxford Univ. Pr., Inc.

Cram101 Textbook Reviews. Outlines & Highlights for Business Research Methods & Statistics Using Spss by Richard Burns. 2011. 80p. pap. 27.95 (978-1-61905-205-5(9)) Cram101 Inc.

—Outlines & Highlights for Introduction to Information Systems by James a Obrien, Isbn: 9780073402925 0077240588 0073402923. 2011. 348p. pap. 33.95 (978-1-61812-496-8(X)) Cram101 Inc.

—Outlines & Highlights for Introduction to Information Systems by O'Brien. 2011. 412p. pap. 35.95 (978-1-61812-814-0(0)) Cram101 Inc.

—Outlines & Highlights for Mis Essentials by David M Kroenke. 2011. 226p. pap. 30.95 (978-1-61905-755-5(7)) Cram101 Inc.

Cram101 Textbook Reviews & Cram101 Textbook Reviews. Outlines & Highlights for Business Data Communications by Allen Dooley, Isbn: 9780131424296. 2011. 242p. pap. 31.95 (978-1-61461-323-7(0)) Cram101 Inc.

—Outlines & Highlights for Business Data Networks & Telecommunications by Raymond R Panko, Isbn: 9780132214414 0132214415 9780132214414. 2011. 412p. pap. 35.95 (978-1-61461-588-0(8)) Cram101 Inc.

Cram101 Textbook Reviews Staff. Outlines & Highlights for Data Mining for Business Intelligence by Galit Shmueli, Isbn: 9780470084854. 2009. 120p. pap. 28.95 (978-1-4288-3976-2(3)) Cram101 Inc.

—Strategic Planning for Information Syste. 2006. 227p. pap. 12.95 (978-1-4288-0532-3(X)) Cram101 Inc.

Cumberlidge, Matt. Business Process Management with Jboss Jbpm. 2007. 220p. per. (978-1-84719-236-3(X)) Packt Publishing, Ltd.

Cummins, Fred A. Building the Agile Enterprise: With SOA, BPM & MBM. 2008. (MK/OMG Press Ser.). (ENG., Illus.). 336p. pap. 53.95 (978-0-12-374445-6(8), Morgan Kaufmann) Elsevier Science & Technology Bks.

Cummins, Stephen. Pro SharePoint 2010 Disaster Recovery & High Availability. 2011. (ENG.). 276p. pap. 44.99 (978-1-4302-3951-2(4)) Apress L. P.

Cunningham, Peter & Fröschl, Friedrich. Electronic Business Revolution: Opportunities & Challenges in the 21st Century. 2010. (ENG., Illus.). xviii, 238p. pap. 84.95 (978-3-642-08549-9(0), 3642085490) Springer.

Davidrajuh, Reggie. Automating Supplier Selection Procedures. 2009. 148p. pap. (978-3-639-15830-4(X)) VDM Verlag Dr. Mueller e.K.

Davis, Rob. ARIS Design Platform: Advanced Process Modelling & Administration. 2008. (ENG., Illus.). xviii, 408p. pap. 89.95 (978-1-84800-110-7(X), 184800110X) Springer.

Davis, Rob & Brabander, Eric. ARIS Design Platform: Getting Started with BPM. 2007. (ENG., Illus.). xx, 364p. per. 79.95 (978-1-84628-612-4(3), 1846286123) Springer.

Dayal, Umeshwar, et al. Business Process Management: 7th International Conference, BPM 2009, Ulm, Germany, September 8-10, 2009, Proceedings. 2009. (Lecture Notes in Computer Science / Information Systems & Applications, incl. Internet/Web, & HCI Ser.). (Illus.). xiii, 363p. pap. 79.95 (978-3-642-03847-1(6), 3642038476) Springer.

Delwiche, Lora D. & Slaughter, Susan J. The Little SAS Book for Enterprise Guide 4. 1. 2006. (Illus.). 408p. per. 50.95 (978-1-59994-089-2(2), 61054, SAS Pr.) SAS Publishing.

Der, Geoff & Everitt, Brian S. Basic Statistics Using SAS Enterprise Guide: A Primer. 2007. (SAS Press Ser.). (Illus.). 240p. per. 39.95 (978-1-59994-573-6(8), SAS Pr.) SAS Publishing.

Devis, Ricardo. Corporate Social Networking: A Hands-on Guide to Deploy Web 2.0 Initiatives for Organizations & Professionals. 2012. (Advanced & Emerging Communications Technologies Ser.). (ENG., Illus.). 320p. 79.95 (978-1-4398-5312-2(6)) Auerbach Pubs., Inc.

Dickersbach, Jorg Thomas, et al. Production Planning & Control with Sap. 2006. (Illus.). 477p. 69.95 (978-1-59229-106-9(6), SAP PR.) Galileo Pr., Inc.

Dickstein, Dennis I. & Flast, Robert H. No Excuses: A Business Process Approach to Managing Operational Risk. 2008. (ENG., Illus.). 308p. 68.50 (978-0-470-22753-4(2), Wiley) Wiley, John & Sons, Inc.

Ding, Ying. WebSphere Engineering: A Practical Guide for WebSphere Support Managers & Senior Consultants. 2008. (ENG., Illus.). 360p. 49.99 (978-0-13-714225-5(0)) Pearson Education.

Dong, Jing, et al. High Assurance Services Computing. Dong, Jing et al, eds. 2009. (ENG., Illus.). xii, 326p. 129.00 (978-0-387-87657-3(X), 038787657X) Springer.

D'Sena, Bruce P. Cloud Cio Strategy. 2011. 232p. 39.50 (978-1-257-83250-7(6)) Lulu Enterprises Inc.

Dunford II, Terry. Advanced Search Engine Optimization: A Logical Approach. 2008. pap. 16.95 (978-0-615-20506-9(2)) American Creations of Maui.

Dynamic Warehousing: Data Mining Made Easy. 2007. (Illus.). xvi, 532p. (978-0-7384-8886-8(0)) IBM.

Eid, Riyad. Successful Customer Relationship Management Programs & Technologies: Issues & Trends. 2012. (Illus.). xx, 338p. (978-1-4666-0290-8(2)) IGI Global.

Eid, Riyad, ed. Successful Customer Relationship Management Programs & Technologies: Issues & Trends. 2012. (Illus.). 412p. 185.00 (978-1-4666-0288-5(0), Business Science Reference) IGI Global.

Elliot, Trevor & Herbert, Dave. Joined-up Systems: Building the Integrated Business. (ENG., Illus.). 192p. 35.00 (978-0-340-85054-1(X), Coronet) Hodder General Publishing Div. GBR. Dist: Trafalgar Square Publishing.

Elssamadisy, Amr. Agile Adoption Patterns: A Roadmap to Organizational Success. 2008. (Illus.). 408p. pap. 49.99 (978-0-321-51452-3(1)) Addison Wesley Professional.

English, Larry P. Information Quality Applied: Best Practices for Improving Business Information, Processes & Systems. 2009. (ENG., Illus.). 840p. 60.00 (978-0-470-13447-4(X), Wiley) Wiley, John & Sons, Inc.

Ertugrul, Murat. Sap Exchange Infrastructure. 2011. 36p. pap. (978-3-640-82559-2(4)) Hammer, Patrick, Tanja Hammer, Matthias Knoop, Julius Mittenzwei, Georg Steinbach u. Michael Teltscher. GRIN Verlag GbR.

Etzion, Opher & Niblett, Peter. Event Processing in Action. 2010. (ENG., Illus.). 325p. pap. 49.99 (978-1-935182-21-4(8)) Manning Pubns. Co.

Evans, Arthur. FileMaker Pro 8 Business Applications. 2008. (Illus.). 626p. per. 49.95 (978-1-59822-014-8(4)) Jones & Bartlett Learning, LLC.

Eze, Benjamin. Policy-Based Data Sharing for Event-Driven Services in B2b Networks. 2011. 148p. pap. (978-3-8443-0741-2(9)) Lambert Academic Publishing.

Falkowski, Bernd-Jnrgen. Business Computing: Grundlagen und Standardsoftware. 2007. (Springer-Lehrbuch Ser.). (GER.). 328p. per. 34.95 (978-3-540-43187-9(X)) Springer.

Ferreira, E. J., et al. Administrative Management. 2nd ed. 2010. (ENG., Illus.). 480p. pap. 52.00 (978-0-7021-7752-1(0)) Juta Academic ZAF. Dist: Independent Pubs. Group.

FitzGerald, Jerry. Business Data Communications & Networking. 9th ed. 2006. (Wiley Plus Products Ser.). pap. 62.95 (978-0-470-11927-3(6)) Wiley, John & Sons, Inc.

Fleischmann, Albert, et al, eds. Subject-Oriented Business Process Management: Second International Conference, S-BPM ONE 2010, Karlsruhe, Germany, October 14, 2010 Selected Papers. 2011. (Communications in Computer & Information Science Ser.). (ENG., Illus.). xii, 227p. pap. 84.00 (978-3-642-23134-6(9), 3642231349) Springer.

Forbrig, Peter & Günther, Horst, eds. Perspectives in Business Informatics Research: 9th International Conference, BIR 2010, Rostock, Germany, September 29 — October 1, 2010, Proceedings. 2010. (Lecture Notes in Business Information Processing Ser.). viii, 235p. pap. 72.00 (978-3-642-16100-1(6), 3642161006) Springer.

Fortner, Denise, ed. Maturing the Business Continuity Program: Taking the BCP to the Next Level. 2010. (ENG.). 288p. 79.95 (978-1-4200-9062-8(3)) Auerbach Pubs., Inc.

Foster, Mike. The Secure CEO: How to Protect Your Computer Systems, Your Company, & Your Job. 2007. 150p. 27.00 (978-0-9715578-0-2(2), Prime Concepts Publishing) Prime Concepts Group Pr.

Franklin Jr., Curtis. Cloud Computing: Technologies & Strategies of the Ubiquitous Data Center. 2010. (ENG., Illus.). 288p. 69.95 (978-1-4398-0612-8(8), CRC Press) Taylor & Francis Group GBR. Dist: Taylor & Francis Group.

Franz, Peter & Kirchmer, Mathias. Value-Driven Business Process Management. 2012. (ENG., Illus.). 240p. 30.00 (978-0-07-179171-7(X), 007179171X) McGraw-Hill Cos., The.

Fuchshofer, Dominik. Business Process Management, Service-Oriented Architecture, Web 2.0. 2010. 76p. pap. (978-3-639-26834-8(2)) VDM Verlag Dr. Mueller e.K.

Fugere, Peter. Oracle Hyperion Financial Management Tips & Techniques: Design, Implementation & Support. 2011. (Oracle Press Ser.). (ENG., Illus.). 432p. pap. 70.00 (978-0-07-177044-6(5), 0071770445) McGraw-Hill Osborne.

Furness, Anthony, et al. Item-Attendant ICT: Exploiting the Power of Identification. 2010. (ENG., Illus.). 288p. 79.95 (978-1-4200-6951-8(9)) Auerbach Pubs., Inc.

Galic, Michele. Academic Edition. 2007. (Illus.). xvi, 232p. (978-0-7384-8661-1(2)) IBM.

Ganz, Carl, Jr. Pro Crystal Enterprise - BusinessObjects XI Programming. 2006. (Expert's Voice in .NET Ser.). (ENG., Illus.). 488p. 79.99 (978-1-59059-759-0(1)) Apress L. P.

Garbade, Michael. M & A, Cooperations & Networks in the E-Business Industry. 2007. 172p. per. (978-3-8364-2989-4(6)) VDM Verlag Dr. Mueller e.K.

Garnham, Nicholas. Political Economy of the Information Society. 2011. pap. 49.95 (978-0-415-26789-2(7)); pap. 150.00 (978-0-415-26788-5(9)) Routledge.

Garton, Colleen & Wegryn, Kevin. Managing Without Walls: Maximize Success with Virtual, Global, & Cross-Cultural Teams. 2006. (Illus.). 500p. pap. 37.95 (978-1-58347-062-6(X)) MC Pr., LLC.

Gattoufi, Said. Data Envelopment Analysis & Confident-de. 2009. 180p. pap. (978-3-639-13101-7(0)) VDM Verlag Dr. Mueller e.K.

Gediminas Adomavicius Staff & A. Gupta Staff. Business Computing. 2009. (Illus.). xx, 400p. 244.95 (978-1-84855-264-7(5)) Emerald Group Publishing Ltd. GBR. Dist: Turpin Distribution Services Ltd.

Gil-Lafuente, Anna M. Computational Intelligence in Business & Economics - Proceedings of the Ms'10 International Conference. 2010. 836p. 250.00 (978-981-4324-43-4(4)) World Scientific Publishing Co., Inc.

Gitman, Lawrence J. & McDaniel, Carl. The Future of Business: The Essentials. 4th ed. 2008. (ENG.). 528p. (C). pap. 132.95 (978-0-324-59076-0(8)) Cengage South-Western.

Giudici, Paolo & Figini, Silvia. Applied Data Mining for Business & Industry. 2nd ed. 2009. (ENG., Illus.). 258p. 160.00 (978-0-470-05886-2(2), Wiley) Wiley, John & Sons, Inc.

Glencoe. Managing Information in the Workplace. 2006. pap. 8.95 (978-1-4288-0556-9(7)) Cram101 Inc.

Godara, Varuna, ed. Pervasive Computing for Business: Trends & Applications: Trends & Applications. 2010. 414p. 180.00 (978-1-60566-996-0(2), Business Science Reference) IGI Global.

Godfrind, Albert, et al. Pro Oracle Spatial for Oracle Database 11g. 2nd ed. 2007. (Expert's Voice in Oracle Ser.). (ENG., Illus.). 824p. 99.99 (978-1-59059-899-3(7)) Apress L. P.

Goh, Gerald Guan Gan. Knowledge Management Practices in Knowledge-Intensive Firms. 2008. 160p. pap. (978-3-639-03580-3(1)) VDM Verlag Dr. Mueller e.K.

Golfarelli, Matteo & Rizzi, Stefano. Data Warehouse Design: Modern Principles & Methodologies. 2009. (ENG., Illus.). 480p. pap. 49.99 (978-0-07-161039-1(1), 0071610391) McGraw-Hill Osborne.

Gordon, Keith. Principles of Data Management. 2007. (Illus.). xxxii, 226p. pap. 50.99 (978-1-902505-84-8(0)) British Computer Society, The GBR. Dist: Turpin Distribution Services Ltd.

Gorham, Michael & Singh, Nidhi. Electronic Exchanges: The Global Transformation from Pits to Bits. 2009. (ENG., Illus.). 352p. 61.95

B

(978-0-12-374252-0(8), Elsevier Science) Elsevier Science & Technology Bks.

Grabis, Janis & Kirikova, Marite, eds. Perspectives in Business Informatics Research: 10th International Conference, BIR 2011, Riga, Latvia, October 6-8, 2011, Proceedings. 2011. (Lecture Notes in Business Information Processing Ser.). (ENG.). xv, 355p. pap. 83.00 (978-3-642-24510-7(2), 3642245102) Springer.

Graham, Ian. Business Rules Management & Service Oriented Architecture: A Pattern Language. 2007. (ENG., Illus.). 288p. per. 65.00 (978-0-470-02721-9(5), Wiley) Wiley, John & Sons, Inc.

Greer Jr, Melvin B. Software As a Service Inflection Point: Using Cloud Computing to Achieve Business Agility. 2009. 180p. 27.95 (978-1-4401-4195-9(9)); pap. 17.95 (978-1-4401-4196-6(7)) iUniverse, Inc.

Groot, Martijn. Managing Financial Information in the Trade Lifecycle: A Concise Atlas of Financial Instruments & Processes. 2008. (Elsevier & Mondo Visione World Capital Markets Ser.). (ENG., Illus.). 288p. 76.95 (978-0-12-374289-6(7), Academic Pr.) Elsevier Science & Technology Bks.

Gruenberger, Fred & Bliss, Bill. Critical Factors in Data Management. 2nd ed. 2008. (ENG., Illus.). xiii, 146p. (C). pap. 26.60 (978-0-13-193540-2(2)) Prentice Hall, ESL Dept.

Habib, Muhammad Nauman. Role of Training & Teamwork in the Successful Implementation of Bpr: Business Process Re-Engineering a Case of Public Sector of Khyber Pakhtunkhwa (KPK) 2011. 76p. pap. (978-3-639-34011-2(6)) VDM Verlag Dr. Mueller e.K.

Halpin, Terry, et al, eds. Enterprise, Business-Process & Information Systems Modeling: 12th International Conference, BPMDS 2011, & 16th International Conference, EMMSAD 2011, held at CAiSE 2011, London, UK, June 20-21, 2011. Proceedings. 2011. (Lecture Notes in Business Information Processing Ser.). xvii, 538p. pap. 107.00 (978-3-642-21758-6(3), 3642217583) Springer.

Hastings, Brian & McNeal, Justin. The Definitive Guide to Interwoven TeamSite. 2006. (Definitive Guides). (ENG., Illus.). 576p. 119.00 (978-1-59059-611-1(0)) Apress L. P.

Hogendoorn, Roel & LearnWorks.nu. Workflow for Oracle E-Business Suite. 2007. 190p. pap. 53.95 (978-1-84799-087-7(8)) Lulu Enterprises Inc.

—Workflow for Oracle E-Business Suite (Classroom Edition) 2007. 209p. pap. 59.50 (978-1-84799-102-7(5)) Lulu Enterprises Inc.

Holliday, John & Holliday. Professional SharePoint 2007 Records Management Development: Managing Official Records with Microsoft Office SharePoint Server 2007. 2009. (ENG., Illus.). 456p. pap. 49.99 (978-0-470-28762-0(4), Wrox) Wiley, John & Sons, Inc.

Hölzer, Michael & Schramm, Michael. Quality Management with SAP. 3rd ed. 2009. (Illus.). 632p. 79.95 (978-1-59229-262-2(3), SAP PR.) Galileo Pr., Inc.

Huber, Mark W., et al. Introduction to Business Information Systems. (ENG.). 2007. 1p. pap. 109.95 (978-0-470-84030-6(7)) 2nd ed. 2010. 496p. 109.95 (978-0-470-16111-1(6)) Wiley, John & Sons, Inc. (Wiley).

Humphrey, Watts S. Winning with Software: An Executive Strategy. 2nd ed. 2010. (ENG.). 256p. pap. 34.99 (978-0-321-64920-1(6)) Addison Wesley Professional.

Hung, Patrick C. K., ed. Services & Business Computing Solutions with XML: Applications for Quality Management & Best Processes. 2009. (Advances in Database Research (ADR) Book Ser.). 354p. 195.00 (978-1-60566-330-2(1)) IGI Global.

IEEE Computer Society, Technical Community for Services Computing Staff & Institute of Electrical and Electronics Engineers Staff, contrib. by. SCC 2008: 2008 IEEE International Conference on Services Computing: Proceedings, Honolulu, Hawaii, USA, July 8-11, 2008, 2 vols. 2008. (Illus.). (978-0-7695-3283-7(7)) IEEE Computer Society Pr.

Information Resources Management Association Staff, contrib. by. Business Information Systems: Concepts, Methodologies, Tools, & Applications, 4 vols. 2010. 1625p. 1950.00 (978-1-61520-969-9(7)) IGI Global.

International Business Machines Corporation, International Technical Support Organization Staff, contrib. by. Enterprise Security Architecture Using IBM Tivoli Security Solutions. 5th ed. 2007. (Illus.). xxxii, 1038p. (978-0-7384-8641-3(8)) IBM.

International Society for Computers and their Applications (ISCA) Staff, compiled by. 20th International Conference on Computer Applications in Industry & Engineering 2007. 2007. 312p. pap. 125.00 (978-1-60423-986-7(7)) Curran Assocs., Inc.

Isaca. Security, Audit & Control Features SAP ERP, 3rd Edition. 2009. pap. (978-1-60420-115-4(0)) Information Systems Audit and Control Assn.

Jacob, Bart. Deployment Guide Series: Tivoli IT Asset Management Portfolio. 2008. (Illus.). xviii, 304p. (978-0-7384-3116-1(8)) IBM.

Jank, Wolfgang. Business Analytics for Managers. 2011. (Use R Ser.). (ENG., Illus.). xi, 189p. pap. 59.95 (978-1-4614-0405-7(3), 1461404053) Springer.

Janssen, Marijn, et al, eds. E-Government, E-Services & Global Processes: Joint IFIP TC 8 & TC 6 International Conferences, EGES 2010 & GISP 2010, Held as Part of WCC 2010, Brisbane, Australia, September 20-23, 2010, Proceedings. 2010. (IFIP Advances in Information & Communication Technology Ser.). xv, 263p. 109.00 (978-3-642-15345-7(3), 3642153453) Springer.

Jasper, Lisa, et al. Reboot: Competing with Technology Strategy. 2011. (Illus.). 144p. (YA). pap. 19.99 (978-0-9825622-0-8(9)) Inspire on Purpose Bks.

Jelen, Bill & Alexander, Michael. Pivot Table Data Crunching: Microsoft Excel 2010. 2010. (MrExcel Library). (ENG., Illus.). 384p. pap. 34.99 (978-0-7897-4313-8(2)) Que.

—Pivot Table Data Crunching for Microsoft Office Excel 2007. 2006. (Business Solutions Ser.). (ENG., Illus.). 360p. per. 34.99 (978-0-7897-3601-7(2)) Que.

Jimenez, Ray E. Micro-Learning Impacts: Learning, Applying, & Measuring Training Results. 2007. per. (978-0-9791847-1-0(1)) Vignettes for Training, Inc.

Jones, Keith, et al. Executing SOA: A Practical Guide for the Service-Oriented Architect. 2nd rev. ed. 2008. (DeveloperWorks Ser.). (ENG., Illus.). 240p. pap. 49.99 (978-0-13-235374-8(1)) Pearson Education.

Kachinske, Edward, et al. Managing Contacts with Microsoft Outlook 2007: Business Contact Manager. 2007. (ENG., Illus.). 240p. per. 21.99 (978-1-59863-445-7(3)) Course Technology.

Kaplan, Martina & Oehler, Christian. Implementing SAP Enhancement Packages. 2010. (Illus.). 220p. 84.95 (978-1-59229-351-3(4), SAP PR.) Galileo Pr., Inc.

Khatib, Khalid. Banking It Mergers of Equals. 2009. 256p. pap. (978-3-639-15771-0(0)) VDM Verlag Dr. Mueller e.K.

Khoshafian, Setrag. Service Oriented Enterprises. 2006. (ENG., Illus.). 464p. 89.95 (978-0-8493-5360-4(2)) Auerbach Pubs., Inc.

Kilov, Haim & Baclavski, Ken, eds. Practical Foundations of Business System Specifications. 2010. 348p. pap. 145.00 (978-90-481-6367-0(6), 9048163676) Springer.

Kim, Tai-hoon, et al, eds. Software Engineering, Business Continuity, & Education: International Conferences, ASEA, DRBC & el 2011, Held as Part of the Future Generation Information Technology Conference, FGIT 2011, in Conjunction with GDC 2011, Jeju Island, Korea, December 8-10, 2011. Proceedings. 2011. (Communications in Computer & Information Science Ser.). (ENG., Illus.). 736p. pap. 143.00 (978-3-642-27206-6(1), 3642272061) Springer.

—U- & E-Service, Science & Technology: International Conference UNESST 2010, Held as Part of the Future Generation Information Technology Conference, FGIT 2010, Jeju Island, Korea, December 13-15, 2010. Proceedings. 2010. (Communications in Computer & Information Science Ser.). xi, 233p. pap. 84.00 (978-3-642-17643-2(7), 3642176437) Springer.

Kim, Tai-hoon, et al, eds. U- And E-Service, Science & Technology: International Conferences, Unesst 2011, Held As Part of the Future Generation Information Technology Conference, Fgit 2011, Jeju Island, Korea, December 8-10, 2011. Proceedings. 2011. (Communications in Computer & Information Science Ser.). (ENG., Illus.). xiv, 348p. pap. 95.00 (978-3-642-27209-7(6), 3642272096) Springer.

King, P. R. & Simske, Steven J. Proceedings of the 2007 ACM Symposium on Document Engineering:: August 28-31, 2007, Winnipeg, Manitoba, Canada. 2007. (Illus.). x, 225p. (978-1-59593-776-6(5)) ACM Pr.

King, William R., ed. Planning for Information Systems, 14 vols. 2009. (Advances in Management Information Systems Ser.). (ENG., Illus.). 528p. 199.95 (978-0-7656-1950-1(4)) Sharpe, M.E. Inc.

Kirchmer, Mathias. High Performance Through Process Excellence: From Strategy to Operations. 2008. (ENG., Illus.). xiv, 178p. 59.95 (978-3-540-77824-0(1), 3540778241) Springer.

Kissinger, Bryan. Alignment of It & the Business. 2008. 128p. per. (978-3-8364-3674-8(4)) VDM Verlag Dr. Mueller e.K.

Klosterboer, Larry. Implementing ITIL Change & Release Management. 2008. (ENG., Illus.). 240p. 44.99 (978-0-13-815041-9(9)) Pearson Education.

Koch, Tomasz, ed. Lean Business Systems & Beyond: First IFIP TC 5 Advanced Production Management Systems Conference (APMS'2006), Wroclaw, Poland, September 18-20 2006. 2008. (Ifip International Federation for Information Processing Ser.). (Illus.). 504p. 219.00 (978-0-387-77248-6(0)) Springer.

Kodama, Mitsuru. Innovation Networks in Knowledge-Based Firms: Developing Ict-Based Integrative Competences. 2009. (Illus.). 320p. 137.00 (978-1-84720-573-5(9)) Elgar, Edward Publishing, Inc.

Kokinda, Joseph. Building the Information Asset. 2007. pap. 10.95 (978-0-7414-4223-9(X)) Infinity Publishing.

Koop, Reinder & Muris, Ester. Successfully Implementing Microsoft Dynamics: By Using the Regatta Approach for Microsoft Dynamics. 2007. (ENG., Illus.). x, 225p. 69.95 (978-3-540-71592-4(4), 3540715924) Springer.

Kordon, Arthur. Applying Computational Intelligence: How to Create Value. 2009. (ENG., Illus.). xxii, 459p. 89.95 (978-3-540-69910-1(4), 3540699104) Springer.

Kothuri, Ravikanth V., et al. Pro Oracle Spatial for Oracle Database 11g. 2011. (ENG.). 824p. pap. 69.99 (978-1-4302-4287-1(6)) Apress L. P.

Kouzes, James M. & Posner, Barry Z. J2EE Best Practices: Java Design Patterns, Automation, & Performance. 2007. 584p. 80.00 (978-0-470-30643-7(2), Wiley) Wiley, John & Sons, Inc.

Kroenke, David. MIS Essentials. (ENG., (C). 2009. Illus.). 408p. pap. 140.00 (978-0-13-607560-8(6)) 2nd ed. 2011. 384p. 106.67 (978-0-13-247807-6(2)) Prentice Hall PTR. (Prentice Hall).

—MIS Essentials, Student Value Edition. 2nd ed. 2011. (ENG.). 388p. (C). pap. 89.40 (978-0-13-706689-6(9), Prentice Hall) Prentice Hall PTR.

—Using MIS: International Edition. 2nd ed. 2009. (Illus.). 560p. pap. (978-0-13-713029-0(5)) Prentice Hall PTR.

Kroenke, David M. Experiencing MIS. (ENG.). 672p. (C). 2nd ed. 2009. pap. 193.33 (978-0-13-607868-5(0)) 3rd ed. 2010. pap. 186.67 (978-0-13-215794-0(2)) Prentice Hall PTR. (Prentice Hall).

—Experiencing MIS, Student Value Edition. 3rd ed. 2011. (ENG.). 652p. (C). ring bd. 116.80 (978-0-13-215917-3(1), Prentice Hall) Prentice Hall PTR.

—MIS Essentials. 2nd rev. ed. 2011. (ENG.). 384p. (C). pap. 140.00 (978-0-13-801882-5(0), Prentice Hall) Prentice Hall PTR.

Kroenke, David M., et al. Experiencing MIS, First Canadian Edition. 2008. 400p. (C). pap. (978-0-13-239620-2(3)) Pearson Education Canada.

Kumar, B. V., et al. Delivering SOA Using the Java Enterprise Edition Platform. 2009. (ENG., Illus.). 384p. pap. 54.99 (978-0-321-49215-9(3)) Prentice Hall PTR.

Kuong, Javier F. IT Compliance & Governance for Sarbanes-Oxley & Other Regulations. 2006. (Information Technologies Security, Control, Audit & Contingency Planning Ser.). per. 150.00 net. (978-0-940706-69-9(5)) Management Advisory Pubns.

Kyne, Frank. GDPS Family: An Introduction to Concepts & Capabilities. (Illus.). 3rd ed. 2007. xii, 162p. (978-0-7384-8888-2(7)) 4th ed. 2008. xiv, 190p. (978-0-7384-3135-2(4)) 5th ed. 2009. 218p. pap. (978-0-7384-3347-9(0)) IBM.

Lah, Thomas, et al. Building Professional Services: The Sirens' Song. rev. ed. 2011. (Harris Kern's Enterprise Computing Institute Ser.). (ENG.). pap. 69.99 (978-0-13-276210-6(2), Prentice Hall) Prentice Hall PTR.

Landoll, Douglas J. The Security Risk Assessment Handbook: A Complete Guide for Performing Security Risk Assessments, Second Edition. 2nd rev. ed. 2011. (ENG., Illus.). 495p. 79.95 (978-1-4398-2148-0(8), CRC Press) Taylor & Francis Group GBR. Dist: Taylor & Francis Group.

Larsson, Linus & Gonzalez-Rivas, George. Far from the Factory: Lean for the Information Age. 2010. (ENG., Illus.). 325p. pap. 49.95 (978-1-4200-9456-5(4)) Productivity Pr.

Lawrence, Oliver S. The Administrative Assistant's Assistant. 2006. 51p. pap. 16.95 (978-1-4241-5156-1(2)) PublishAmerica, Inc.

Lazo, Diego. Osworkflow: A guide for Java developers & architects to integrating open-source Business Process Management. 2007. 212p. per. (978-1-84719-152-6(5)) Packt Publishing, Ltd.

Lee, Laurence Lock. IT Governance in a Networked World: Multi-Sourcing Strategies & Social Capital for Corporate Computing. 2009. 378p. 165.00 (978-1-60566-084-4(1)) IGI Global.

Lee, Yang W., et al. Journey to Data Quality. 2009. (ENG., Illus.). 240p. (gr. 17). pap. 19.00 (978-0-262-51335-7(8)) MIT Pr.

Leinweber, David J. Nerds on Wall Street: Math, Machines & Wired Markets. 2009. (ENG., Illus.). 353p. 39.95 (978-0-471-36946-2(2), Wiley) Wiley, John & Sons, Inc.

Lemke, Judy, et al. Microsoft Visio 2010: Build Exactly the Skills You Need - Learn at the Pace You Want. 2011. (ENG., Illus.). 480p. pap. 29.99 (978-0-7356-4887-6(5)) Microsoft Pr.

Linenberger, Michael. Seize the Work Day: Using the Tablet PC to Take Total Control of Your Work & Meeting Day. 2009. (ENG., Illus.). 551p. pap. 34.95 (978-0-9749304-0-4(7)) New Academy Pubs.

Loshin, David. Master Data Management. 2008. (MK/OMG Press Ser.). (ENG., Illus.). 304p. pap. 53.95 (978-0-12-374225-4(0), Morgan Kaufmann) Elsevier Science & Technology Bks.

Mackin, J. C. & Russel, Charlie. Windows Essential Business Server 2008 Administrator's Companion. 2009. (ENG.). 768p. pap. 49.99 (978-0-7356-2525-9(5)) Microsoft Pr.

Mahbouli, Hatem. Resolving the ERP Security Headache: The Survival Guide. 2011. 64p. pap. 12.95 (978-1-4327-6698-6(8)) Outskirts Pr., Inc.

Malik, Sahil, et al. Expert SharePoint 2010 Practices. 2011. (ENG.). 760p. pap. 49.99 (978-1-4302-3870-6(4)) Apress L. P.

Marakas, George & O'Brien, James. Introduction to Information Systems, Loose Leaf. 16th ed. 2012. (ENG., Illus.). 768p. (C). ring bd. 122.67 (978-0-07-337688-2(4), 0073376884, McGraw-Hill/Irwin) McGraw-Hill Higher Education.

Maurer, Matthias & Scherzinger, Andy. Business Process Automation - Performance & Capacity Planning with Bpel. 2007. 196p. per. (978-3-8364-2395-3(2)) VDM Verlag Dr. Mueller e.K.

Mayr, Heinrich C., ed. Technologies for Business Information Systems. 2007. (ENG., Illus.). xx, 432p. 149.00 (978-1-4020-5633-8(8), 1402056338) Springer.

McCarthy, Matt. Black & White Business Computing 2010. 2nd ed. 2009. (ENG.). (C). pap. 128.00 (978-0-558-32210-6(7)) Pearson Learning Solutions.

McCombs, Adam & Banh, Robert. The Definitive Guide to Magento. 2009. (ENG.). 328p. pap. 49.99 (978-1-4302-7229-8(5)) Apress L. P.

McLeod, Jordan, Jr. Systems Development A Project Management. 2006. pap. 9.95 (978-1-4288-0645-0(8)) Cram101 Inc.

Meier, Andreas & Stormer, Henrik. EBusiness & ECommerce: Managing the Digital Value Chain. Gosselin, Elizabeth, tr. 2009. (ENG., Illus.). x, 222p. 79.95 (978-3-540-89327-1(X), 354089327X) Springer.

Mendling, Jan. Metrics for Process Models: Empirical Foundations of Verification, Error Prediction, & Guidelines for Correctness. 2008. (Lecture Notes in Business Information Processing Ser.). xix, 193p. pap. 69.95 (978-3-540-89223-6(0)) Springer.

Mertens, Peter, et al. Betriebliche Expertensystem-Anwendungen. 3rd ed. 2007. (GER.). 452p. 111.95 (978-3-540-57269-5(4)) Springer.

Michelson, Bruce. Closed Loop Lifecycle Planning: A Complete Guide to Managing Your PC Fleet. 2007. (ENG.). 336p. pap. 54.99 (978-0-321-76820-9(5)); (Illus.). 49.99 (978-0-321-47714-9(6)) Addison Wesley Professional.

Michelson, Bruce. Closed Loop Lifecycle Planning, Client Computing in the Health Care Industry. 2009. pap. (978-1-61623-045-6(2)) Independent Pub.

Microsoft Press Staff & Krebs, Jochen. Agile Portfolio Management. 2008. (ENG.). 240p. pap. 34.99 (978-0-7356-2567-9(0)) Microsoft Pr.

Mitra, A. & Gupta, A. Creating Agile Business Systems with Reusable Knowledge. 2006. (ENG., Illus.). 404p. 133.99 (978-0-521-85163-3(7)) Cambridge Univ. Pr.

Mnller, Hendrik. State of the Art in Service-Oriented Architecture. 2008. 168p. per. (978-3-8364-6226-6(5)) VDM Verlag Dr. Mueller e.K.

Molluzzo, John C. C++ for Business Programmers. 2nd ed. 2006. pap. (978-0-13-234095-3(X)) Pearson Education Canada.

Morin, Jean-Henry, et al, eds. Exploring Services Science: First International Conference, IESS 2010, Geneva, Switzerland, February 17-19, 2010, Revised Papers. 2010. (Lecture Notes in Business Information Processing Ser.). xi, 301p. pap. 83.00 (978-3-642-14318-2(0), 3642143180) Springer.

Muir, Nancy & Kimbell, Ian. Discover SAP: Entdecke die Welt von SAP. 2009. (Illus.). 440p. pap. 39.95 (978-1-59229-320-9(4), SAP PR.) Galileo Pr., Inc.

Munter, Mary & Paradi, David. Guide to PowerPoint 2007. 2008. (ENG., Illus.). 208p. (C). pap. 36.00 (978-0-13-606871-6(5), Prentice Hall) Prentice Hall PTR.

Murphy, Austin. SIA User's Guide. Bloomquist, Don/Lee, Jr., ed. (C). 2006. 371p. pap. 49.00 net. (978-0-9787344-1-1(6)) 2nd ed. 2007. (ENG.). 359p. pap. 49.00 net. (978-0-9787344-3-5(2)) SIA Publishing, LLC.

Myers, Kenneth N. Business Continuity Strategies: Protecting Against Unplanned Disasters. 3rd rev. ed. 2006. (ENG., Illus.). 224p. 73.95 (978-0-470-04038-6(6), Wiley) Wiley, John & Sons, Inc.

Nguyen, Xuan. The System Builder, Third Edition. 2007. (Illus.). 333p. 20.00 (978-0-9726848-8-0(3)); 3rd ed. per. 20.00 (978-0-9726848-9-7(1)) X Pr.

—The System Builder, Third Edition, Chinese. 2008. (CHI.). pap. (978-0-9726848-6-6(7)) X Pr.

Niefert, Wolfgang. Sap Business One Implementation: LITE Edition. 2011. 112p. pap. (978-1-84968-378-4(6)) Packt Publishing, Ltd.

Norta, Alex. Exploring Dynamic Inter-Organizational Business Process Collaboration. 2008. 296p. pap. (978-3-8364-6239-6(7)) VDM Verlag Dr. Mueller e.K.

Obal, Philip. Selecting Warehouse Software from WMS & ERP Providers: Find the Best Warehouse Module or Warehouse Management System for Inventory Control & Management. 2007. (Illus.). 180p. spiral bd. 125.00 (978-0-9669345-5-7(5)) Industrial Data & Information, Inc. (IDII).

O'Brien, James A., et al. Introduction to Information Systems. 14th ed. 2008. (Illus.). 592p. (978-0-07-340292-5(3)) McGraw-Hill Cos., The.

Okoli, Chitu. Experts Speak on E-Business in Sub-Saharan Afric. 2010. (Illus.). 128p. pap. (978-3-639-23615-6(7)) VDM Verlag Dr. Mueller e.K.

O'Loughlin, Eugene F. M. An Introduction to Business Systems Analysis: Problem Solving Techniques & Strategies. 2010. (ENG.). 306p. pap. 39.95 (978-1-905785-61-2(5)) Liffey Pr., The IRL. Dist: Dufour Editions, Inc.

Oswald, Gerhard & Hommel, Uwe. SAP Enterprise Support: ASAP to Run SAP. 2nd ed. 2010. (Illus.). 371p. 59.95 (978-1-59229-349-0(2), SAP PR.) Galileo Pr., Inc.

Ouellette, Jason. Development with the Force. Com Platform: Building Business Applications in the Cloud. 2nd rev. ed. 2011. (Developer's Library). (ENG., Illus.). 496p. pap. 49.99 (978-0-321-76735-6(7)) Addison Wesley Professional.

Papazafeiropoulou, Anastasia. A Stakeholder Approach to Electronic Commerce Diffusion. 2009. 212p. pap. (978-3-639-20475-9(1)) VDM Verlag Dr. Mueller e.K.

Papows, Jeff. Glitch: The Hidden Impact of Faulty Software. 2010. (ENG., Illus.). 208p. 24.99 (978-0-13-216063-6(3)) Pearson Education Canada CAN. Dist: Pearson Education.

Parry, Dave & Barrall, Martin. Dida Unit 4: Ict in Enterprise. 2006. (Illus.). 240p. pap. 37.50 incl. cd-rom (978-0-340-91531-8(5)); cd-rom 495.00 (978-0-340-92689-5(9)) Hodder Education GBR. (Hodder Arnold). Dist: Trans-Atlantic Pubns., Inc.

Perkonigg, Fidelis. Application of Business Process Management. 2008. 140p. pap. (978-3-639-04430-0(4)) VDM Verlag Dr. Mueller e.K.

Piccoli, Gabe. Information Systems for Managers: Text & Cases. 2nd ed. 2012. (ENG., Illus.). 538p. (C). 147.95 (978-1-118-05761-2(9), Wiley) Wiley, John & Sons, Inc.

Plattner, Hasso & Zeier, Alexander. In-Memory Data Management: An Inflection Point for Enterprise Applications. 2011. (Illus.). xviii, 236p. 59.95 (978-3-642-19362-0(5), 3642193625) Springer.

Polino, Mark. Microsoft Dynamics Gp 2010 Cookbook: LITE Edition. 2011. 116p. pap. (978-1-84968-380-7(8)) Packt Publishing, Ltd.

Popoviciu, Ciprian, et al. Global IPV6 Strategies: From Business Analysis to Operational Planning. 2008. (Network Business Ser.). (ENG., Illus.). 456p. pap. 49.99 (978-1-58705-343-6(8)) Cisco Pr.

Powell, Stephen G. & Baker, Kenneth R. Management Science: The Art of Modeling with Spreadsheets. 3rd ed. 2010. (ENG., Illus.). 528p. (C). 182.95 (978-0-470-53067-2(7), Wiley) Wiley, John & Sons, Inc.

Prentice-Hall Staff. MyITLab for Inbusiness Office 2007. 2007. (C). cd-rom 60.00 (978-0-13-513321-7(1)) Prentice Hall PTR.

Prigmore, Martyn. An Introduction to Databases with Web Applications. 2007. (ENG., Illus.). 712p. pap. 122.50 (978-0-321-26359-9(6)) Pearson Education, Ltd. GBR. Dist: Trans-Atlantic Pubns., Inc.

Priyadarshi, Vaibhav. Global Analysis of Laws Related to Cyber Squatting. 2011. 84p. pap. (978-3-8443-2109-8(8)) Lambert Academic Publishing.

PUEI. Budgeting & Finance Templates. 2007. cd-rom 49.95 (978-1-934147-47-4(8), CareerTrack) Park Univ. Enterprises, Inc.

Rainer & Turban. Introduction to Information Systems: Supporting & Transforming Business. 2nd ed. 2008. (ENG.). 464p. (C). ring bd. 82.95 (978-0-470-27975-5(3), Wiley) Wiley, John & Sons, Inc.

Rakocevic, Veselin, et al. Digital Business: First International ICST Conference, DigiBiz 2009, London, UK, June 17-19, 2009, Revised Selected Papers.

2010. (Lecture Notes of the Institute for Computer Sciences, Social-Informatics & Telecommunications Engineering Ser.). xii, 185p. pap. 72.00 (978-3-642-11531-8(4), 3642115314) Springer.

Ramanathan, Jay & Ramnath, Rajiv. Co-Engineering Applications & Adaptive Business Technologies in Practice: Enterprise Service Ontologies, Models, & Frameworks. 2009. (Premier Reference Source Ser.). (Illus.). 426p. 165.00 (978-1-60566-276-3(3), Information Science Publishing) IGI Global.

Recker, Jan. Evaluations of Process Modeling Grammars: Ontological, Qualitative & Quantitative Analyses Using the Example of BPMN. 2011. (Lecture Notes in Business Information Processing Ser.). xxii, 199p. pap. 72.00 (978-3-642-18359-1(X), 364218359X) Springer.

Refaat, Moustafa. Mastering the BizTalk Technical Interview. 2008. 100p. pap. 44.95 (978-1-4357-1468-7(7)) Lulu Enterprises Inc.

Rehl, Rabea. Change Management. 2008. 56p. pap. (978-3-8364-7961-5(3)) VDM Verlag Dr. Mueller e.K.

Reiff-Marganiec, Stephan & Tilly, Marcel. Handbook of Research on Service-Oriented Systems & Non-Functional Properties: Future Directions. 2011. (Illus.). xxix, 583p. **(978-1-61350-434-5(9))**; **(978-1-61350-432-1(2))**; E-Book **(978-1-61350-433-8(0))** IGI Global.

Reimer, Roger & Dobson, Edward. Understanding RSI. 2007. 29p. pap. 14.95 (978-0-934380-89-8(9), 3250) Traders Pr. Inc.

Reuvid, Jonathan, ed. The Secure Online Business Handbook: A Practical Guide to Risk Management & Business Continuity. 4th rev. ed. 2006. (ENG., Illus.). 152p. 95.00 (978-0-7494-4642-0(0)) Kogan Page, Ltd. GBR. Dist: Ingram Pub. Services.

Reynolds, Ruth & Reynolds, George. Information Technology for Managers. 2009. (ENG.). 400p. pap. 174.95 (978-1-4239-0169-3(X)) Course Technology.

Rinderle-Ma, Stefanie, et al, eds. Business Process Management: 9th International Conference, Bpm 2011, Clermont-Ferrand, France, August - September 2011, Proceedings. 2011. (Lecture Notes in Computer Science / Information Systems & Applications, incl. Internet/Web, & HCI Ser.). (ENG., Illus.). 420p. pap. 95.00 **(978-3-642-23058-5(X)**, 364223058X) Springer.

Rinderle-Ma, Stefanie, et al, eds. Business Process Management Workshops: BPM 2009 International Workshops, Ulm, Germany, September 7, 2009, Revised Papers. 2010. (Lecture Notes in Business Information Processing Ser.). xvi, 708p. pap. 139.00 (978-3-642-12185-2(3), 3642121853) Springer.

Robinson, Glendal. A Mythic Perspective of Commodification on the World Wide Web. 2010. 148p. pap. (978-3-639-28809-4(2)) VDM Verlag Dr. Mueller e.K.

Rodgers, Waymond. Biometric & Auditing Issues Addressed in a Throughput Model. 2012. 374p. **(978-1-61735-654-4(9))**; 374p. pap. **(978-1-61735-653-7(0))**; xi, 361p. E-Book **(978-1-61735-655-1(7))** Information Age Publishing, Inc.

Ross, Jeanne W., et al. Enterprise Architecture As Strategy: Creating a Foundation for Business Execution. 2006. (ENG., Illus.). 256p. 39.95 (978-1-59139-839-4(8)) Harvard Business Review Pr.

Rsssnen, Tomi. Key Challenges of Virtual Teams. 2008. 72p. pap. (978-3-639-03002-0(8)) VDM Verlag Dr. Mueller e.K.

Samarin, Alexander. Improving business process management Systems. 2009. 219p. pap. 70.00 (978-1-4269-0256-7(5)) Trafford Publishing.

Sambamurthy, V. & Fillios, Michael. Extended Enterprise. 2007. 150p. 29.95 (978-0-9788175-3-4(2)) Waterside Publishing.

Sanchez-Clark, Terry. Sap Xi Interview Questions Answers & E. 2006. pap. 54.95 (978-1-933804-68-2(8)) Equity Pr.

Sandler, Corey. Laptops for Dummies. 2nd ed. 2008. (ENG., Illus.). 240p. pap. 16.99 (978-0-470-24056-4(3), For Dummies) Wiley, John & Sons, Inc.

Sarma, Kattamuri S. Predictive Modeling with SAS Enterprise Miner: Practical Solutions for Business Applications. 2007. 384p. pap. 64.95 (978-1-59047-703-8(0), SAS Pr.) SAS Publishing.

Schaeffler, Jimmy. Digital Signage: Software, Networks, Advertising, & Displays - A Primer for Understanding the Business. 2008. (NAB Executive Technology Briefings Ser.). (ENG., Illus.). 296p. pap. 43.95 (978-0-240-81041-6(4), Focal Pr.) Elsevier Science & Technology Bks.

Schafer, Marc & Melich, Matthias. SAP Solution Manager. 3rd ed. 2011. (ENG., Illus.). 727p. 69.95 (978-1-59229-388-9(3), SAP PR.) Galileo Pr., Inc.

Scheck, Reinhold. Create Dynamic Charts in Microsoft Office Excel 2007 & Beyond. 2008. (ENG., Illus.). 608p. pap. 39.99 (978-0-7356-2544-0(1)) Microsoft Pr.

Scheer, August-Wilhelm. Aris: Des processus de gestion au systFme intTgrT D'applications. 2008. VII, 169p. pap. 59.95 (978-2-287-59726-8(3), 2287597263) Springer.

Scheer, August-Wilhelm, et al, eds. Corporate Performance Management: ARIS in Practice. 2010. (ENG., Illus.). xi, 275p. pap. 89.95 (978-3-642-06799-0(9), 3642067999) Springer.

Schmidt, Robert. Web Intelligence XI Vol. 3: Creating Documents with Business Objects. 2010. (Illus.). 420p. pap. 79.99 (978-0-9823352-0-3(5)) Schmidt Ink, Inc.

Schmidt, Robert D. Business Ojects XI - CBT: Designer XI. 2007. 206p. pap. 99.99 (978-0-9722636-3-4(2)) Schmidt Ink, Inc.

—Creating Documents with Business Objects XI-CBT: Web Intelligence XI. 2007. (Illus.). 234p. pap. 99.99 (978-0-9722636-4-1(0)) Schmidt Ink, Inc.

Schönthaler, Frank, et al. Business Processes for Business Communities: Modeling Languages, Methods, Tools. 2012. (ENG., Illus.). xii, 189p. 59.95 **(978-3-642-24790-3(3)**, 3642247903) Springer.

Schratz, Wilhelm. Theory & Practice of Knowledge Management. 2008. 144p. pap. (978-3-639-03659-6(X)) VDM Verlag Dr. Mueller e.K.

Schulz, Olaf. Using SAP: A Guide for Beginners & End Users. 2011.Tr. of SAP-Grundkurs für Einsteiger und Anwender. (ENG., Illus.). 400p. pap. 39.95 **(978-1-59229-408-4(1)**, SAP PR.) Galileo Pr., Inc.

Schurman, Joe, et al. Professional Live Communications Server. 2006. (ENG., Illus.). 302p. pap. 39.99 (978-0-471-77321-4(2), Wrox) Wiley, John & Sons, Inc.

Sexton, Martin Christopher. MDDL & the Quest for a Market Data Standard: Explanation, Rationale, & Implementation. 2007. (Elsevier & Mondo Visione World Capital Markets Ser.). (ENG., Illus.). 320p. 66.95 (978-0-7506-6839-2(3), Butterworth-Heinemann) Elsevier Science & Technology Bks.

Shmueli, Galit, et al. Data Mining for Business Intelligence: Concepts, Techniques, & Applications in Microsoft Office Excel with XLMiner. 2nd ed. 2010. (ENG., Illus.). 428p. 125.00 (978-0-470-52682-8(3), Wiley) Wiley, John & Sons, Inc.

Singleton, Susan. Computer Contracts. 2007. spiral bd. 99.95 (978-1-85418-352-1(4)) Thorogood GBR. Dist: National Bk. Network.

Siropolis. Small Bus Man Computerized Bus Plan. pap. 14.36 (978-0-395-80892-4(8)) CENGAGE Learning.

Smith, Charles. Creating a Trading Floor: The Project Manager's Guide to the Design, Construction & Launch of Trading Floors & Data Centers. 2006. (ENG., Illus.). 497p. 550.00 (978-0-7494-4838-7(5)) Kogan Page, Ltd. GBR. Dist: Ingram Pub. Services.

Smith, Jon. Grow Your Business with Google Adwords: 7 Quick & Easy Secrets for Reaching More Customers with the World's #1 Search Engine. 2009. (ENG., Illus.). 144p. pap. 16.95 (978-0-07-162959-1(9), 0071629599) McGraw-Hill Cos., The.

Soares, Carlos A.Mota. Applications of Data Mining in E-Business & Finance. 2008. (Illus.). x, 143p. pap. 138.00 (978-1-58603-890-8(7)) IOS Pr., Inc.

Sparks, David. iPad at Work. 2011. (ENG., Illus.). 368p. pap. 29.99 (978-1-118-10056-1(5), Wiley) Wiley, John & Sons, Inc.

—Mac at Work. 2011. (ENG., Illus.). 368p. pap. 29.99 (978-0-470-87700-5(6), Wiley) Wiley, John & Sons, Inc.

Ssewanyana, Joseph K. Microsimulation Modeling of Ict Policies at Firm Level. 2011. 104p. pap. **(978-3-8443-2341-2(4))** Lambert Academic Publishing.

Stephan, Kaleske. SAP Query Reporting - Practical Guide. 2010. (Illus.). 400p. 69.95 (978-1-59229-365-0(4), SAP PR.) Galileo Pr., Inc.

Swapnil, Shahriar. Erp System for University Information Functions. 2011. 72p. pap. **(978-3-8443-3295-7(2))** Lambert Academic Publishing.

Tan, Yao-Hua, et al, eds. Accelerating Global Supply Chains with IT-Innovation: ITAIDE Tools & Methods. 2010. (ENG., Illus.). xi, 379p. 189.00 (978-3-642-15668-7(1), 3642156681) Springer.

Thomson NETg Press. Fastcard: Solution Selling. 2007. 4.00 (978-1-4188-6162-9(5)) Course Technology.

Three-Dimensional Analysis: Data Profiling Techniques. 2008. 240p. per. 49.95 (978-0-9800833-0-9(3)) Lindsey, Ed.

Tidrow, Rob. IBM Lotus Symphony for Dummies. 2008. (ENG., Illus.). 380p. pap. 34.99 (978-0-470-29079-8(X), For Dummies) Wiley, John & Sons, Inc.

Torres, Derek, et al. BusinessObjects XI Release 2 for Dummies. 2008. (ENG., Illus.). 344p. pap. 29.99 (978-0-470-18112-6(5), For Dummies) Wiley, John & Sons, Inc.

Tupper, Cheryl. Your Computer System. 2009. 142p. pap. 24.95 (978-0-557-18345-6(6)) Lulu Enterprises Inc.

Ullman, John & West, Tommi. Adobe Business Catalyst: Design Full-Featured Websites Without the Hassles of Development. 2011. (ENG.). 240p. pap. 39.99 **(978-0-321-80957-5(2))** Adobe Pr.

Van Geldern, John. Year 2000 Business Preparedness Guide. pap. 16.95 (978-0-9628923-8-7(6)) Delta-West Publishing, Inc.

van Schewick, Barbara. Internet Architecture & Innovation. 2010. (ENG., Illus.). 592p. (gr. 17). 47.00 (978-0-262-01397-0(5)) MIT Pr.

Van Syckle, Barbara & Tietje, Brian. Anybody's Business. 2009. (ENG.). 408p. (C). pap. 120.00 (978-0-13-608634-5(9), Prentice Hall) Prentice Hall PTR.

van Wencel de Joode, Ruben. Innovation & Organization in Open Source Communities. 2008. 288p. 130.00 (978-0-415-42543-8(3)) Routledge.

Verma, Naresh. Business Process Management: Profiting from Process. 2009. 311p. pap. 24.95 (978-81-907941-7-6(5)) Global India Pubns. Pvt. Ltd. IND. Dist: Coronet Bks.

Vilpola, Inka. User-Centered Design in Erp Implementation Requirements Analysis. 2011. 96p. pap. **(978-3-8433-7798-0(7))** Lambert Academic Publishing.

Voivoda, Jeff. Data Analysis & Harmonization: A Simple Guide. 2011. 156p. 24.95 (978-1-4502-9826-1(5)); pap. 14.95 (978-1-4502-9824-7(9)) iUniverse, Inc.

Von Halle, Barbara. Business Rule Revolution: Running Busine. 2006. (Illus.). xxvii, 286p. pap. (978-1-60005-013-8(1)) Happy About.

Von Halle, Barbara & Goldberg, Larry. The Decision Model: A Business Logic Framework Linking Business & Technology. 2009. (ENG., Illus.). 553p. 59.95 (978-1-4200-8281-4(7)) Auerbach Pubs., Inc.

Wahli, Ueli. Business Process Management: Modeling Through Monitoring Using WebSphere V6.0.2 Products. 2nd ed. 2007. (Illus.). xxiv, 670p. (978-0-7384-8912-4(3)) IBM.

Walsh, Bob & Walsh, Robert. The Web Startup Success Guide. 2009. (ENG.). 440p. pap. 29.99 (978-1-4302-1985-9(8)) Apress L. P.

Ward, Robin. Strategic Planning for Information Systems 4E. 4th ed. 2013. (ENG.). 544p. pap. 77.95 **(978-0-470-03467-5(X)**, Wiley) Wiley, John & Sons, Inc.

Warmer, Jos, ed. Model-Driven Architecture — Foundations & Applications: Second European Conference, ECMDA-FA 2006, Bilbao, Spain, July 10-13, 2006, Proceedings. 2006. (Lecture Notes in Computer Science Ser.: Vol. 4066). (Illus.). XII, 392p. pap. 99.00 (978-3-540-35909-8(5), 3540359095) Springer.

Williams, Mark. Cloud Computing: Moving Your Business into the Cloud. 2010. (ENG., Illus.). 160p. pap. 14.95 (978-0-7494-6130-0(6)) Kogan Page, Ltd. GBR. Dist: Ingram Pub. Services.

Wright, Craig S. The It Regulatory & Standards Compliance Handbook: How to Survive Information Systems Audit & Assessments. 2008. (ENG., Illus.). 750p. pap. 72.95 (978-1-59749-266-9(3), Syngress Press) Elsevier Science & Technology Bks.

Ye, Gewei. Technology-Powered Business Innovation: An Entrepreneur's Guide. 2007. 196p. per. 24.95 (978-1-4241-9048-5(7)) PublishAmerica, Inc.

Yee, George. Privacy Protection Measures & Technologies in Business Organizations: Aspects & Standards. 2011. (Illus.). xxii, 396p. **(978-1-61350-501-4(9))**; **(978-1-61350-503-8(5))**; E-Book **(978-1-61350-502-1(7))** IGI Global.

Young, President Jan. Selecting, Buying, Installing & Using a Modern Warehouse Management System. 2009. 147p. pap. 24.95 (978-0-557-05915-7(1)) Lulu Enterprises Inc.

Zaman, Marzia, et al, eds. E-business Technology & Strategy: International Conference, CETS 2010, Ottawa, Canada, September 29-30, 2010. Proceedings. 2010. (Communications in Computer & Information Science Ser.). xi, 327p. pap. 95.00 (978-3-642-16396-8(3), 3642163963) Springer.

Zanakis, Stelios H., et al, eds. Decision Making: Recent Developments & Worldwide Applications: Recent Developments & Worldwide Applications. 2010. (Applied Optimization Ser.). 508p. pap. 259.00 (978-1-4419-4839-7(2), 1441948392) Springer.

Zhang. Services Computing. 2007. (ENG., Illus.). 452p. 219.00 (978-3-540-38281-2(X), 354038281X) Springer.

zur Muehlen, Michael & Su, Jianwen, eds. Business Process Management Workshops: BPM 2010 International Workshops & Education Track, Hoboken, NJ, USA, September 13-15, 2010, Revised Selected Papers. 2011. (Lecture Notes in Business Information Processing Ser.). xvi, 809p. pap. 143.00 (978-3-642-20510-1(0), 3642205100) Springer.

Zurawski, Richard. Integration Technologies for Industrial Automated Systems. 2006. (Industrial Information Technology Ser.: Vol. 3). (ENG., Illus.). 600p. 124.95 (978-0-8493-9262-7(4), 9262, CRC Press) Taylor & Francis Group GBR. Dist: Taylor & Francis Group.

2007 IEEE International Conference on Services Computing (SCC 2007) Salt Lake City, Utah - 09-13 July 2007. 2007. pap. 287.00 (978-0-7695-2925-7(9)) IEEE Computer Society Pr.

BUSINESS—DICTIONARIES

Agnes, Michael E. Webster's New World Enterprise. 2006. 19.95 (978-0-470-04127-7(7), Webster's New World) Wiley, John & Sons, Inc.

Alon, Ilan & Zhang, Wenxian, eds. Biographical Dictionary of New Chinese Entrepreneurs & Business Leaders. 2009. (Elgar Original Reference Ser.). 296p. 182.00 (978-1-84720-636-7(0)) Elgar, Edward Publishing, Inc.

Anderson, Arthur. Diccionario Espasa Economia y Negocios. 3rd ed. (SPA & ENG., Illus.). 778p. 79.00 (978-84-239-9421-2(X), ECS4921X) Espasa Calpe, S.A. ESP. Dist: Continental Bk. Co., Inc.

Bacal, Robert & Moore, Nancy. Perfect Phrases for Managing Your Small Business. 2008. (Perfect Phrases Ser.). (ENG.). 288p. pap. 9.95 (978-0-07-160052-1(3), 007160052) McGraw-Hill Cos., The.

Baumgartner, Peter. Wörterbuch moderne Wirtschaft / Dictionary of Modern Business: Mit Anwendungsbeispielen / With Model Phrases & Sentences. Deutsch-Englisch / English-German. 22nd ed. 2008. (ENG.). 511p. pap. 45.00 (978-3-89578-309-8(9), Wiley-VCH) Wiley, John & Sons, Inc.

Bayram, Ali & Cankaya, Birsen. The Dictionary of Business Terms. 2010. (TUR & ENG.). 704p. pap. 29.95 (978-1-84059-529-1(9)) Milet Publishing.

Burke, David. Biz Talk 2: More American Business Slang & Jargon. stu. ed. (978-0-87944-019-0(8)) Univ. of Michigan, Institute for Social Research.

Cresson, B. Introduction au Francais Commercial. (FRE.). pap. 24.95 (978-0-7859-7568-7(3)) French & European Pubns., Inc.

Dobson, John. Bulls, Bears, Boom, & Bust: A Historical Encyclopedia of American Business Concepts, 1 vol. 2006. (Illus.). 423p. 95.00 (978-1-85109-553-7(5), BULLSEC) ABC-CLIO, LLC.

Ediciones Deusto Staff. Biblioteca Empresarial Deusto: Deusto Library of Business, 40 vols., Set. (SPA.). 1495.00 (978-0-8288-8256-9(8)) French & European Pubns., Inc.

Friedman C.P.A., Jack P. Dictionary of Business & Economic Terms. 5th rev. ed. 2012. (Barron's Business Dictionaries Ser.). (ENG.). 800p. pap. 14.99 **(978-0-7641-4757-9(9))** Barron's Educational Series, Inc.

Fuertes Olivera, Pedro Antonio & Arribas-Baño, Ascensión. Specialized Lexicography: The Representation of Meaning in Business Dictionaries. 2008. (Illus.). viii, 165p. (C). (978-90-272-2335-7(1)) Benjamins, John Publishing Co.

Gaynor, Frank. International Business Dictionary. (978-0-8022-0573-5(9)) Philosophical Library, Inc.

Ghattas, Nabih. Dictionary of Business & Finance: English - Arabic. (ARA & ENG.). 977p. 45.00 (978-0-86685-271-5(9), LDL2719) International Bk. Ctr., Inc.

Hornak, Kenneth Allen. Dictionary of Economics & Business (English-Spanish Spanish-English) Diccionario de Economy; a y Negocios (Español - Inglés Inglés - Español) 2006.Tr. of Diccionario de Economía y Negocios. (ENG & SPA.). 950p. lib. bdg. 195.00 (978-0-9765947-2-7(2)) Editorial Castilla La Vieja.

Japanese-English Dictionary of Trade & Business. (ENG & JPN.). 125.00 (978-0-7859-9699-6(0)) French & European Pubns., Inc.

Kershaw, F. & Russon, S. German for Business Studies. (GER.). 203p. pap. 14.95 (978-0-582-36186-7(9), M-9203) French & European Pubns., Inc.

Kovalev, Vladimir. Dictionary of Economics & Business: Russian-Italian — Italian-Russian. (ENG, ITA & RUS.) 702p. 150.00 (978-0-7859-8873-1(4)) French & European Pubns., Inc.

Law, Diane & Greenwood, Catriona. The Dictionary of Bull**** A Lexicon of Corporate & Office-Speak. 2009. (ENG.). 192p. 8.99 (978-1-84529-767-1(9), 1845297679, Castle Bks., Inc.) Book Sales, Inc.

Law, Jonathan, ed. A Dictionary of Business & Management. 5th ed. 2009. (Oxford Paperback Reference Ser.). (ENG., Illus.). 608p. pap. 19.99 (978-0-19-923489-9(2)) Oxford Univ. Pr., Inc.

Le Bris, Annie. Phraseological Dictionary of Economics & & Business Terms French-Italian — Italian-French. (FRE & ITA.). 1152p. 125.00 (978-0-7859-8864-9(5)) French & European Pubns., Inc.

Lojac, Anthony. Business & Investing Keywords in English & Japanese: Essential Vocabulary for International Investors & Entrepreneurs. 2009. (ENG & JPN.). 176p. pap. 14.95 (978-0-9818604-1-1(9)) Think More Bks.

Malik, Fredmund. Management: The Essence of the Craft. 2009. (ENG.). 300p. 52.00 (978-3-593-38969-1(X)) Campus Verlag GmbH DEU. Dist: Chicago Distribution Ctr.

Marcousé, Ian, et al. A-Z Business Studies Handbook. 6th rev. ed. 2009. (Illus.). 322p. pap. 36.50 (978-0-340-98729-2(4)) Allan, Philip Updates GBR. Dist: Trans-Atlantic Pubns., Inc.

McGrane, Stephen. Sit Crooked & Speak Straight. 2008. 168p. pap. 13.95 (978-1-60594-031-1(3), Llumina Pr.) Aeon Publishing Inc.

McKay, H. Dean & Shank, P. T. Business Words You Should Know: From Accelerated Depreciation to Zero-Based Budgeting - Learn the Lingo for Any Field. 2008. (ENG.). 256p. per. 9.95 (978-1-59869-146-7(5)) Adams Media Corp.

Picchi, Fernando. Dictionary of Economics & Business & of Modern Language: English-Italian — Italian-English. (ENG & ITA.). 1792p. 100.00 (978-0-7859-8874-8(2)) French & European Pubns., Inc.

Picken, Stuart D. B. The A to Z of Japanese Business. 85th ed. 2009. (A to Z Guide Ser.: No. 85). (ENG.). 448p. pap. 34.45 (978-0-8108-6872-4(5)) Scarecrow Pr., Inc.

—Historical Dictionary of Japanese Business. 2007. (Historical Dictionaries of Professions & Industries Ser.). (ENG.). 448p. 110.00 (978-0-8108-5469-7(4)) Scarecrow Pr., Inc.

Pocket Business Dictionary, Polish/English-English/Polish. Date not set. (ENG & POL.). pap. 59.95 (978-0-7859-9579-1(X)) French & European Pubns., Inc.

Research Wing Of New Century Publications, ed. Dictionary of International Trade & Business. 2008. 295p. 37.00 (978-81-7708-165-7(9)) New Century Publications IND. Dist: International Specialized Bk. Services.

Routledge Staff. Routledge German Dictionary of Business, Commerce & Finance Wor. 3rd rev. ed. 2007. (Routledge Bilingual Specialist Dictionaries Ser.). (GER & ENG.). 1440p. 340.00 (978-0-415-42357-1(0)) Routledge.

Runion, Meryl. Perfect Phrases for Managers & Supervisors. 2nd ed. 2010. (Perfect Phrases Ser.). (ENG.). 208p. pap. 10.95 (978-0-07-174231-3(X), 007174231X) McGraw-Hill Cos., The.

Scott, David L. The American Heritage Dictionary of Business Terms. 2009. (ENG.). 608p. pap. 15.95 (978-0-618-75525-7(X)) Houghton Mifflin Harcourt Trade & Reference Pubs.

Sofer, Morry & Pizarro, MariCarmen. Italian Business Dictionary. 2006. (ENG & ITA.). 344p. per. 24.95 (978-0-88400-319-9(1)) Schreiber Publishing, Inc.

—Portuguese Business Dictionary. 2006. (POR & ENG.). 344p. per. 24.95 (978-0-88400-321-2(3)) Schreiber Publishing, Inc.

Sofer, Morry & Yoon, Peter. Korean Business Dictionary. 2006. (ENG & KOR.). 344p. per. 24.95 (978-0-88400-320-5(5)) Schreiber Publishing, Inc.

Tripathi, Dwijendra & Jumani, Jyoti. The Concise Oxford History of Indian Business. 2006. (Illus.). 280p. per. 24.95 (978-0-19-568429-2(X)) Oxford Univ. Pr., Inc.

Various Authors. QFINANCE: the Pocket Dictionary of Business. 2011. (ENG.). 224p. pap. 19.95 (978-1-84930-013-1(5)) Bloomsbury Publishing.

Von Hoffman, Nicholas. A Devil's Dictionary of Business: Monkey Business - High Finance & Low - Money, the Making, Losing, & Printing Thereof - Commerce - Trade - Clever Tricks - Tours de Force - Globalism & Globaloney - Industry - Invention - The Stock Market - Marvelous Explanations & Clarifications - All Presente. 2006. (ENG., Illus.). 326p. per. 14.95 (978-1-56025-906-0(X)) Basic Bks.

Wankel, Charles, ed. Encyclopedia of Business in Today's World, 4 vols. 2009. (Illus.). 2136p. 520.00 (978-1-4129-6427-2(X), B64272C) SAGE Pubns., Inc.

BUSINESS—DIRECTORIES

BIA. Major Companies of Sweden: Manufacturers, Wholesalers, Banks, Construction Companies. 6th rev. ed. 2006. 450p. (J). pap. 249.00 (978-1-4187-4913-2(3)) Business Information Agency.

Bliss, Kelly. Kelly Bliss's Plus Size Yellow Pages. 2007. 409p. pap. 21.95 (978-0-7414-3872-0(0)) Infinity Publishing.

Directories in Print, 2.0. 33rd ed. 2011. pap. 920.00 (978-1-4144-5870-0(3)) Cengage Gale.

Directory of Business Information Resources. 14th ed. 2007. (Directory of Business Information Resources Ser.). 1747p. per. 195.00 (978-1-59237-146-4(9)) Grey Hse. Publishing.

B

Directory of Minnesota Business & Professional Associations: 1997-1998 Edition. 8th ed. Date not set. 190p. pap. 60.00 *(978-1-891144-00-4(6))* Hill, James J. Reference Library.

European Drinks Marketing Directory: Companies-Products-Services. 650p. (Orig.). pap. 695.00 *(978-0-7605-2175-5(1))* Rector Pr., Ltd.

Grey House Publishing Staff. The Directory of Mail Order Catalogs: With Business to Business Catalogs 2009 Edition. 2008. 1900p. pap. 250.00 *(978-1-59237-396-3(8))* Grey Hse. Publishing.

Hoover's Handbook of World Business. 15th ed. 2008. (Hoover's Handbook of World Business Ser.). (Illus.). 394p. 195.00 *(978-1-57311-122-5(8)*, Hoover's Business Pr.) Hoover's, Inc.

Ibp, Usa. Belgium Industrial & Business Director. 2006. (Illus.). pap. 99.95 *(978-0-7397-9748-8(4))* International Business Pubns., USA.

Law and Business Inc. Staff, ed. Law & Business Directory of Corporate Counsel, 1984-1985. rev. ed. Date not set. 1546p. 125.00 *(978-0-15-004278-5(7))* Harcourt Trade Pubs.

Livingston, Austin. The Everything Green Handbook & Business Directory. 2010. 32p. pap. 17.00 *(978-0-557-42705-5(3))* Lulu Enterprises Inc.

MacKenzie, Leslie & Gottlieb, Richard, eds. The Directory of Business Information Resources. 15th ed. 2008. (Directory of Business Information Resources Ser.). 1747p. per. 195.00 *(978-1-59237-193-8(0))* Grey Hse. Publishing.

Marquis Who's Who Staff. Who's Who in Finance & Business 2008-2009. 36th ed. 2007. 1100p. 349.00 *(978-0-8379-0356-9(4))* Marquis Who's Who, LLC.

Mars, Laura, ed. Directory of Business Information Resources. 2011. 2500p. pap. 195.00 *(978-1-59237-737-4(8))* Grey Hse. Publishing.

Mars-Proietti, Laura, ed. The Directory of Business to Business Catalogs 2007. 2007. 900p. pap. 165.00 *(978-1-59237-157-0(4))* Grey Hse. Publishing.

—Directory of Mail Order Catalogs 2010. 24th rev. ed. 2009. 1500p. pap. 250.00 *(978-1-59237-444-1(1))* Grey Hse. Publishing.

—The Directory of Venture Capital & Private Equity Firms: 2009. 13th rev. ed. 2009. 1100p. pap. 450.00 *(978-1-59237-398-7(4))* Grey Hse. Publishing.

National Register Publishing Co. Staff, ed. Directory of Corporate Affiliations: Who Owns Whom, 5 vols. Incl. International Public & Private Companies. 2016p. pap. *(978-0-87217-207-4(4))*; Master Index II. 2194p. pap. *(978-0-87217-210-4(4))*; U. S. Private Companies. 1446p. pap. *(978-0-87217-206-7(6))*; U. S. Public Companies. 2296p. pap. *(978-0-87217-208-1(2))*; Vol. I. Master Index I. 1920p. pap. *(978-0-87217-209-8(0))*; 1997. 998.00 o.p. *(978-0-87217-211-1(2))* National Register Publishing.

O'Connor, Emily & Fenelon, Mary, compiled by. Business Directory & Buyer's Guide: Orange County, NY. 400p. (Orig.). pap. *(978-0-945965-02-2(8))* Ctrs. Composition.

Peterson's Guides Staff. Bricker's International Directory 2007. 38th ed. 2006. (ENG.). 1608p. 395.00 *(978-0-7689-2174-8(0))* Peterson's.

Ray, Don E., et al. Guide to Dealerships, 2 vols. Incl. Vol. 1. ring bd. *(978-0-7646-0110-1(5))*; Vol. 2. ring bd. *(978-0-7646-0111-8(3))*; 1997. 130.00 *(978-0-7646-0109-5(1))*; 138.00 *(978-0-7646-0390-7(6))* Practitioners Publishing Co.

Spencer, Dorothy A. The Book of Leaders: A Guide to Who's Who in the Philadelphia Business Community. Date not set. (Orig.). pap. 49.95 *(978-0-9657908-0-2(0))* Philadelphia Business Journal.

Uniworld Business Publications, Inc. Staff, ed. Directory of Foreign Firms Operating in the United States. 10th rev. exp. ed. 1216p. 225.00 *(978-0-8360-0044-3(7))* Uniworld Business Pubns., Inc.

Ursery, Prentice N., et al. A Guide to Retail & Service Businesses, 2 vols. Incl. Vol. 1. ring bd. *(978-0-7646-0078-4(8))*; Vol. 2. ring bd. *(978-0-7646-0079-1(6))*; 1996. 150.00 *(978-0-7646-0077-7(X))* Practitioners Publishing Co.

Vault Editors. Vault Guide to the Top Business Services Employers, 2007 Edition. 2008. 176p. pap. 19.95 *(978-1-58131-457-1(4))* Vault.com.

Wingate, Robert. Directory of Green Business Opportunities: 2009 Edition. 2008. 48p. pap. 16.50 *(978-0-557-03530-4(9))* Lulu Enterprises Inc.

BUSINESS—EXAMINATIONS, QUESTIONS, ETC.

see also Graduate Management Admission Test

Adams, Steve, et al. CIMA Official Learning System Fundamentals of Business Economics. 4th ed. 2009. (ENG., Illus.). 406p. (C). pap. 55.95 *(978-1-85617-721-4(1)*, CIMA Publishing) Elsevier Science & Technology Bks.

Brûlé, Glenn R. Cbap(r) Exam. 2nd rev. ed. 2011. (ENG.). 322p. pap. 39.95 ***(978-1-890367-54-1(0))*** ESI International.

Cisco Networking Academy. CCNA Discovery Course Booklet: Networking for Home & Small Businesses, Version 4. 0. 2009. (Course Booklets Ser.). (ENG.). 168p. (C). pap. 24.95 *(978-1-58713-242-1(7))* Cisco Pr.

Cleary, W. Sean. Canadian Securities Exam Fast-Track Study Guide. 3rd ed. 2009. (ENG.). 384p. pap. 54.95 *(978-0-470-16039-8(X)*, Wiley) Wiley, John & Sons, Inc.

Cox, Joyce & Lambert, Joan, III. The Microsoft Office Specialist Study Guide. 2008. (ENG., Illus.). 816p. pap., pupil's gde. ed. 39.99 *(978-0-7356-4971-2(5))* Microsoft Pr.

Davis, Anita Price. GMAT with TestWare. 5th ed. 2011. (GMAT Test Preparation Ser.). (ENG.). 688p. pap. 35.95 *(978-0-7386-0911-9(0))* Research & Education Assn.

Delaney, Patrick R. & Whittington, O. Ray. Wiley CPA Exam Review 2012 Test Bank: Business Environment & Concepts. 17th ed. 2012. (ENG.). 105.00 ***(978-0-470-92386-3(5)**, Wiley)* Wiley, John & Sons, Inc.

Denby, Neil. AQA GCSE Business Studies. rev. ed. 2010. (Illus.). 144p. pap. 17.95 *(978-1-4441-0776-0(3))* Hodder Education GBR. Dist: Trans-Atlantic Pubns., Inc.

—Business Studies. rev. ed. 2010. (Illus.). 143p. pap., instr.'s gde. ed. 22.50 *(978-1-4441-0777-7(1))* Hodder Education GBR. Dist: Trans-Atlantic Pubns., Inc.

Donnelly, Ray. CIM Coursebook: Delivering Customer Value through Marketing, 2 vols. Linton, Colin, ed. 2009. (ENG., Illus.). 286p. (C). pap. 40.95 *(978-1-85617-718-4(1))* Routledge.

Donnelly, Ray & Harrison, Graham. CIM Coursebook: the Marketing Planning Process. Megicks, Phil, ed. 2009. (ENG.). 256p. (C). pap. 40.95 *(978-1-85617-716-0(5))* Routledge.

Eaton, Graham. CIMA Official Learning System Fundamentals of Business Mathematics. 4th ed. 2009. (ENG., Illus.). 528p. (C). pap. 55.95 *(978-1-85617-783-2(1)*, CIMA Publishing) Elsevier Science & Technology Bks.

Graduate Management Admission Council (GMAC) Staff. The Official Guide for GMAT Quantitative Review. 2nd ed. 2009. (ENG.). 216p. pap. 17.95 *(978-0-470-44976-9(4)*, Wiley) Wiley, John & Sons, Inc.

Graduate Management Admission Council Staff. The Official Guide for GMAT Review. 12th ed. 2009. (ENG.). 840p. pap. 32.95 *(978-0-470-44751-2(0))*; pap. 36.95 *(978-0-470-44974-5(8)*, Wiley) Wiley, John & Sons, Inc.

Graduate Management Admission Council & Graduate Management Admissions Council. The Official Guide for GMAT Verbal Review. 2nd ed. 2009. (ENG.). 336p. pap. 17.95 *(978-0-470-44975-2(6)*, Wiley) Wiley, John & Sons, Inc.

Hamman, David & Denby, Neil. Setting up a Business. 2009. (Illus.). 182p. pap. 36.50 *(978-0-340-97492-6(3))* Hodder Education GBR. Dist: Trans-Atlantic Pubns., Inc.

Harris, David & Botten, Neil. CIMAstudy. com Business Strategy. 2009. (ENG.). (C). cd-rom 215.00 *(978-0-08-096453-9(2))* Elsevier Science & Technology Bks.

Hough, Karen & Bentley, Rebecca. OCR Applied Business Studies for GCSE. 2009. 240p. pap. 62.50 *(978-0-340-98739-1(1))* Hodder Education GBR. Dist: Trans-Atlantic Pubns., Inc.

Industrial Hygiene Exam Workbook: 50 Practice Questions Volume II. 2007. spiral bd. 17.00 *(978-0-9792519-3-1(1))* Bowen EHS, Inc.

Kaplan. Kaplan GMAT Verbal Foundations. 2nd ed. 2011. (ENG.). 336p. pap. 24.99 *(978-1-60714-838-8(2))* Kaplan Publishing.

—Kaplan New GMAT Integrative Reasoning Workbook. 2011. 360p. pap. 19.99 *(978-1-60978-211-5(9))* Kaplan Publishing.

Kay, Robin. An APMP Primer. 2009. 217p. pap. 37.95 *(978-1-4092-6707-2(5))* Lulu Enterprises Inc.

LaBrosse, Michelle. Cheetah Accelerated Exam Prep Workbook. 2007. pap. 14.95 *(978-0-9761749-7-4(9))* MAKLAF Pr.

Lambert, Joan, III & Cox, Joyce. Mos 2010 Study Guide for Microsoft Word, Excel, Powerpoint, & Outlook Exams. 2011. (ENG., Illus.). 736p. pap. 44.99 *(978-0-7356-4875-3(1))* Microsoft Pr.

Mead, Larry, et al. CIMA Official Learning System Fundamentals of Ethics, Corporate Governance & Business Law. 4th ed. 2009. (ENG., Illus.). 560p. (C). pap. 55.95 *(978-1-85617-787-0(4)*, CIMA Publishing) Elsevier Science & Technology Bks.

Meek, Helen, et al. Managing Marketing. Sherratt, Andrew, ed. 2009. (ENG.). 288p. (C). pap. 40.95 *(978-1-85617-717-7(3))* Routledge.

Needham, Dave, et al. First Business. 2010. (Illus.). 432p. pap. 57.50 *(978-0-340-99190-9(9))* Hodder Education GBR. Dist: Trans-Atlantic Pubns., Inc.

Parkinson, Lynn, et al. CIM Coursebook: Project Management in Marketing. McKee, Frank, ed. 2009. (ENG.). 256p. (C). pap. 40.95 *(978-1-85617-715-3(7))* Routledge.

Peerless Institute, creator. Peerless Institute Contractors Licensing Courses: Business & Financial Management: Florida Contractors' Exam Study Book. 2009. (Illus.). 496p. pap. 99.95 *(978-1-58855-097-2(4))* BNI Pubns., Inc.

Phillips, Joseph. CBAP - Certified Business Analysis Professional. 2009. (All-in-One Ser.). (ENG., Illus.). 496p. instr.'s gde. ed. 49.99 incl. cd-rom *(978-0-07-162669-9(7)*, 0071626697) McGraw-Hill Osborne.

Pierce, Doug. McGraw-Hills Conquering GMAT Verbal & Writing, 2nd Edition. 2nd ed. 2012. (ENG.). 352p. (C). pap. 17.00 ***(978-0-07-177580-9(3)**,* 0071775803) McGraw-Hill Cos., The.

Princeton Review. Crash Course for the New GMAT, 3rd Edition: Revised & Updated for the New GMAT. 2012. (Graduate School Test Preparation Ser.). (ENG.). 240p. pap. 10.99 ***(978-0-375-42763-3(5)**,* Princeton Review) Random Hse. Information Group.

—Math Workout for the New GMAT, 4th Edition: Revised & Updated for the New GMAT. 2012. (Graduate School Test Preparation Ser.). (ENG.). 304p. pap. 19.99 ***(978-0-375-42749-7(X)**,* Princeton Review) Random Hse. Information Group.

—Verbal Workout for the New GMAT, 3rd Edition: Revised & Updated for the New GMAT. 2012. (Graduate School Test Preparation Ser.). (ENG.). 272p. pap. 19.99 ***(978-0-375-42750-3(3)**,* Princeton Review) Random Hse. Information Group.

Princeton Review Staff. Cracking the GMAT, 2012 Edition. 2011. (Graduate School Test Preparation Ser.). 608p. pap. 22.99 *(978-0-375-42824-1(0)*, Princeton Review) Random Hse. Information Group.

—Cracking the GMAT with DVD, 2012 Edition. 2011. (Graduate School Test Preparation Ser.). 608p. pap. 37.99 *(978-0-375-42825-8(9)*, Princeton Review) Random Hse. Information Group.

Professional Exam Review. Texas Exam Prep for the Mortgage Professional. 2011. (ENG.). 144p. pap. 24.95 *(978-0-324-78356-8(6))* Cengage South-Western.

Royal, Brandon. Chili Hot GMAT: 200 All-Star Problems to Get You a High Score on Your GMAT Exam. 2010. (ENG.). 422p. *(978-1-897393-70-3(9))* Maven Publishing.

Rudman, Jack. Business. (Undergraduate Program Field Tests Ser.: Vol. 3). 49.95 *(978-0-8373-6053-9(6)*, Passbooks) National Learning Corp.

—Business Environment & Strategy. (ACT Proficiency Examination Program Ser.: Vol. 27). (C). 49.95 *(978-0-8373-5577-1(X)*, Passbooks) National Learning Corp.

—Business Policy. (ACT Proficiency Examination Program Ser.: Vol. 23). (C). 49.95 *(978-0-8373-5573-3(7)*, Passbooks) National Learning Corp.

Safety Professional Exam Workbook: 50 Practice Questions Volume II. 2007. spiral bd. 17.00 *(978-0-9792519-4-8(X))* Bowen EHS, Inc.

Skeete, Kyle. Electronic Document Preparation & Management for CSEC(r) Examinations Coursebook with CD-ROM. 2011. (ENG.). 392p. pap. 31.00 incl. cd-rom ***(978-0-521-18467-0(3))*** Cambridge Univ. Pr.

Stimpson, Peter & Smith, Alex. Business & Management for the IB Diploma. 2011. (Ib Ser.). (ENG.). 454p. pap. 48.00 *(978-0-521-14730-9(1))* Cambridge Univ. Pr.

Walker, Janet. CIMA Official Learning System Fundamentals of Management Accounting. 4th ed. 2009. (ENG., Illus.). 504p. (C). pap. 55.95 *(978-1-85617-792-4(0)*, CIMA Publishing) Elsevier Science & Technology Bks.

Welch, Jack & Welch, Suzy. Winning - The Answers: Confronting 74 of the Toughest Questions in Business Today. 2006. (ENG.). 224p. pap. 12.95 *(978-0-06-124149-9(0)*, Harper Paperbacks) HarperCollins Pubs.

BUSINESS—FORMS

see also Business Cards; Letterheads

CCH Tax Editors. Business Expense Log (2009) 2008. 64p. pap. 9.50 *(978-0-8080-1899-5(X))* Toolkit Media Group.

Constance, Smith. Art Office, Second Edition. 2007. (ENG.). 112p. pap. 14.95 *(978-0-940899-28-5(0))* ArtNetwork.

Continuing Education of the Bar (CEB). Selecting & Forming Business Entities: May 2008 Update, 2 vols. 2nd ed. 2008. 678p. ring bd. 91.00 *(978-0-7626-1381-6(5))* Continuing Education of the Bar-California.

Crawford, Tad, ed. Business & Legal Forms for Photographers. 4th rev. ed. 2009. (ENG.). 208p. pap. 29.95 *(978-1-58115-669-0(3)*, 115669, Allworth Pr.) Skyhorse Publishing Co., Inc.

Facts On File, Inc. Forms on File 2010, 2 vols., Set. 2010. (Forms on File Ser.). 280.00 *(978-0-8160-8258-2(8))* Facts On File, Inc.

Facts on File, Inc. Staff. Business Forms on File Collection (1994 Edition) pap. 24.95 *(978-0-8160-3056-9(1))* Facts On File, Inc.

International Business Machines Corporation, International Technical Support Organization Staff, contrib. by. IBM Workplace Forms 2.6: Guide to Building & Integrating a Sample Workplace Forms Application. 2007. (Illus.). xvi, 714p. pap. *(978-0-7384-8638-3(8))* IBM.

Janus, Philo. Pro InfoPath 2007. 2007. (Expert's Voice Ser.). (ENG., Illus.). 278p. per. 44.99 *(978-1-59059-730-9(3))* Apress L. P.

Lanier, Wendy. Maps. 2007. (Kidhaven Science Library Ser.). (ENG., Illus.). 48p. (YA). (gr. 4-7). lib. bdg. 27.50 *(978-0-7377-3632-8(1))* Cengage Gale.

Mitchell, Karen & Savage, Craig. Construction Forms for Contractors. 2010. (Illus.). 360p. pap. 48.50 *(978-1-57218-222-6(9))* Craftsman Bk. Co.

Roberts, Scott & Green, Hagen. Designing Forms for Microsoft Office InfoPath & Forms Services. 2007. (Microsoft . NET Development Ser.). (ENG., Illus.). 1296p. per. 64.99 *(978-0-321-41059-7(9))* Addison Wesley Professional.

Roberts, Scott, et al. Designing Forms for SharePoint & InfoPath: Using Infopath Designer 2010. 2nd rev. ed. 2011. (Microsoft . NET Development Ser.). (ENG., Illus.). 1128p. pap. 59.99 *(978-0-321-74360-2(1))* Addison Wesley Professional.

Rosenberg, Paul & American Contractors Educational Services Staff. Contractor's Forms & Letters. 2008. (DeWalt Ser.). (ENG.). 264p. pap. 24.95 *(978-0-9777183-2-0(8)*, DEWALT) CENGAGE Learning.

Schwesinger, Borries. The Form Book: Creating Forms for Printed & Online Use. 2010. (ENG., Illus.). 324p. 65.00 *(978-0-500-51508-2(5)*, 551508) Thames & Hudson.

Self-Counsel Press Staff. Small Business Forms. 2nd rev. ed. 2010. 100p. 11.95 *(978-1-55180-414-9(X))* Self-Counsel Pr., Inc. CAN. Dist: Midpoint Trade Bks., Inc.

Shadravan, Darvish & Rogers, Laura Derbes. Using Microsoft Infopath 2010 with Microsoft SharePoint 2010. 2011. (ENG., Illus.). 480p. pap. 34.99 ***(978-0-7356-6206-3(1))*** Microsoft Pr.

Smith, Preston. Forms for Business, Vol. I. (Illus.). 50p. 19.95 *(978-0-9624241-4-4(5))* Walker Enterprises.

Thomas, Karen. Ultimate Book of Business & Legal Forms for Startups: 200+ Downloadable Forms & Spreadsheets. 2nd ed. 2010. (ENG., Illus.). 304p. pap. 29.95 *(978-1-59918-389-3(7)*, 1599183897) Entrepreneur Pr. dba Entrepreneur Media, Inc.

BUSINESS—GOVERNMENT POLICY

see Industrial Policy

BUSINESS—GRAPHIC METHODS

Chinese American Literature, Grades 6-12. (Illus.). pap., tchr. ed. 10.50 *(978-0-8359-0538-1(1))* Globe Fearon Educational Publishing.

BUSINESS—HANDBOOKS, MANUALS, ETC.

Africa CD Business. 1400p. 4500.00 *(978-0-7605-4575-1(8))* Rector Pr., Ltd.

Assimil Staff. Allemand des Affaires: German Business for French Speakers. (FRE & GER.). 28.95 incl. audio *(978-0-8288-4479-6(8)*, F46260) French & European Pubns., Inc.

Badiru, Deji. Getting Things Done Through Project Management. 2009. 124p. pap. 13.95 *(978-1-4401-3822-5(2))* iUniverse, Inc.

Berkus, Dave. Berkonomics. 2009. 178p. pap. 24.95 *(978-0-557-14327-6(6))* Lulu Enterprises Inc.

—Berkonomics Workbook. 2009. 102p. pap. 19.95 *(978-0-557-14349-8(7))* Lulu Enterprises Inc.

Bloch, Talia. Doing Business in Eastern Europe. Date not set. (Doing Business in Regions & Countries Around the World Ser.). *(978-1-882390-87-8(3))* Training Management Corp.

—Doing Business in North America. Date not set. (Doing Business in Regions & Countries Around the World Ser.). *(978-1-882390-85-4(7))* Training Management Corp.

Brown, Larry. The official small business owners Manual. 2007. 276p. pap. 19.95 *(978-1-4303-2660-1(3))* Lulu Enterprises Inc.

Business Risk International Country Handbook: Companies-Products-Services. (Illus.). 1200p. (Orig.). pap. *(978-0-7605-1330-9(9))* Rector Pr., Ltd.

Business Strategy Handbook 1995: Companies-Products-Services. (Illus.). 300p. (Orig.). pap. *(978-0-7605-0633-2(7))* Rector Pr., Ltd.

Cameron, Sheila. The Business Student's Handbook: Skills for Study & Employment. 5th ed. 2009. (ENG., Illus.). 464p. pap. 67.50 *(978-0-273-73071-2(1)*, Prentice Hall) Pearson Education, Ltd. GBR. Dist: Trans-Atlantic Pubns., Inc.

Certo, Samuel C. & Certo, Trevis. Modern Management: Concepts & Skills. 11th ed. 2008. (ENG.). 624p. (C). pap. 224.00 *(978-0-13-601016-6(4)*, Prentice Hall) Prentice Hall PTR.

Clay, John R., et al. Guide to Compilation & Review Engagements, 4 vols. Incl. Vol. 4. ring bd. 156.00 *(978-0-7646-0232-0(2))*; Vol. 1. ring bd. 156.00 *(978-0-7646-0229-0(2))*; Vol. 2. ring bd. 156.00 *(978-0-7646-0230-6(6))*; Vol. 3. ring bd. *(978-0-7646-0231-3(4))*; 1997. 156.00 *(978-0-7646-0228-3(4))* Practitioners Publishing Co.

Clifford. Decision Making in Organizations. Date not set. (Illus.). 290p. pap. 15.00 *(978-0-582-35539-2(7))* Addison-Wesley Longman, Ltd. GBR. Dist: Trans-Atlantic Pubns., Inc.

Doing Business in Argentina. Date not set. (Doing Business in Regions & Countries Around the World Ser.). 80p. *(978-1-882390-50-2(4))* Training Management Corp.

Doing Business in Asia. Date not set. (Doing Business in Regions & Countries Around the World Ser.). *(978-1-882390-82-3(2))* Training Management Corp.

Doing Business in Australia. Date not set. (Doing Business in Regions & Countries Around the World Ser.). *(978-1-882390-51-9(2))* Training Management Corp.

Doing Business in Brazil. Date not set. (Doing Business in Regions & Countries Around the World Ser.). 80p. *(978-1-882390-53-3(9))* Training Management Corp.

Doing Business in Chile. Date not set. (Doing Business in Regions & Countries Around the World Ser.). 80p. *(978-1-882390-55-7(5))* Training Management Corp.

Doing Business in China. Date not set. (Doing Business in Regions & Countries Around the World Ser.). 80p. *(978-1-882390-56-4(3))* Training Management Corp.

Doing Business in Hong Kong. Date not set. (Doing Business in Regions & Countries Around the World Ser.). 80p. *(978-1-882390-60-1(1))* Training Management Corp.

Doing Business in Italy. Date not set. (Doing Business in Regions & Countries Around the World Ser.). 80p. *(978-1-882390-63-2(6))* Training Management Corp.

Doing Business in Latin America. Date not set. (Doing Business in Regions & Countries Around the World Ser.). *(978-1-882390-84-7(9))* Training Management Corp.

Doing Business in Mexico. Date not set. (Doing Business in Regions & Countries Around the World Ser.). *(978-1-882390-66-3(0))* Training Management Corp.

Doing Business in Pakistan. Date not set. (Doing Business in Regions & Countries Around the World Ser.). *(978-1-882390-69-4(5))* Training Management Corp.

Doing Business in Saudi Arabia. Date not set. (Doing Business in Regions & Countries Around the World Ser.). *(978-1-882390-72-4(5))* Training Management Corp.

Doing Business in South Africa. Date not set. (Doing Business in Regions & Countries Around the World Ser.). *(978-1-882390-74-8(1))* Training Management Corp.

Doing Business in Switzerland. Date not set. (Doing Business in Regions & Countries Around the World Ser.). *(978-1-882390-77-9(6))* Training Management Corp.

Doing Business in the Philippines. Date not set. (Doing Business in Regions & Countries Around the World Ser.). *(978-1-882390-70-0(9))* Training Management Corp.

Doing Business in Venezuela. Date not set. (Doing Business in Regions & Countries Around the World Ser.). *(978-1-882390-81-6(4))* Training Management Corp.

Duda, Halya. The Executive PowerPak: Maximum Leverage for Your First 90 Days. 53p. 495.00 *(978-1-882474-00-4(7))* Duda, Halya.

Engineer's Guides to Business, Vols. 1-11. pap. 119.95 *(978-0-7803-2303-2(3),* EG114) IEEE.

Ey, Vallabhi. The Art of Taming the Business: Business Essays. 2009. 236p. pap. 18.95 *(978-1-4401-1101-3(4))* iUniverse, Inc.

Gil, Rossina. Doing Business in Colombia. Date not set. (Doing Business in Regions & Countries Around the World Ser.). 80p. *(978-1-882390-57-1(1))* Training Management Corp.

Godette, Jean-Paul. The Complete Visual Guide to Business Objects. 2nd ed. Date not set. pap. *(978-1-893936-04-1(X))* KX Pr.

Goldfinger, Gail. Doing Business in Japan. Date not set. (Doing Business in Regions & Countries Around the World Ser.). 80p. *(978-1-882390-64-9(4))* Training Management Corp.

Greenleaf, Robert. Influencing & Persuading Across Cultures. Date not set. (Management Booklets Ser.). *(978-1-882390-90-8(3))* Training Management Corp.

Harvard Business School Press Staff, compiled by. Creating a Business Plan: Expert Solutions to Everyday Challenges. 2007. (Pocket Mentor Ser.). (ENG., Illus.). 144p. per. 9.95 *(978-1-4221-1885-6(1))* Harvard Business Review Pr.

Hitchner, James R. & Mard, Michael J. Financial Valuation Workbook: Step-by-Step Exercises & Tests to Help You Master Financial Valuation. 3rd ed. 2011. (Wiley Finance Ser.: 546). (ENG., Illus.). 394p. pap., wbk. ed. 65.00 *(978-0-470-50688-2(1),* Wiley) Wiley, John & Sons, Inc.

Hungary. (Illus.). pap. *(978-3-8283-0046-0(4))* Hallwag Verlag GmbH DEU. Dist: Rand McNally.

Hutchinson, Colin. Building to Last: The Challenge for Business Leaders. 2nd ed. 2009. (Earthscan Library Collection: Environmental & Resource Economics Set Ser.). (ENG.). 226p. 110.00 *(978-1-84407-970-4(8))* Earthscan LLC.

International Business Publications Staff & Global Investment and Business Center, Inc. Staff. Global Offshore Business & Investment Contacts Handbook: Business & Investment Contacts for 33 Offshore Countries & Territories. pap. *(978-0-7397-3933-4(6))* International Business Pubns., USA.

Jollimore, Troy. Doing Business in Canada. Date not set. (Doing Business in Regions & Countries Around the World Ser.). 80p. *(978-1-882390-54-0(7))* Training Management Corp.

Lang, Stephan. Hungary. 2009. (Looking at Europe Ser.). (ENG., Illus.). 48p. (YA). (gr. 5-9). lib. bdg. 22.95 *(978-1-881508-88-5(9))* Oliver Pr., Inc.

Malaysia: Business Financing Handbook. (Illus.). 70p. (Orig.). pap. 295.00 *(978-0-7605-1198-5(5))* Rector Pr., Ltd.

Marks, Kenneth H., et al. The Handbook of Financing Growth: Strategies, Capital Structure, & M & A Transactions. 2nd ed. 2009. (Wiley Finance Ser.: 482). (ENG., Illus.). 672p. 95.00 *(978-0-470-39015-3(8),* Wiley) Wiley, John & Sons, Inc.

Middle East CD Business. 1400p. 4500.00 *(978-0-7605-4574-4(X))* Rector Pr., Ltd.

Moss, Rita & Ernsthausen, David G. Strauss's Handbook of Business Information: A Guide for Librarians, Students, & Researchers. 1 vol. 399p. 100.00 ***(978-1-59884-807-6(0),*** A3433C) Pearson Education GBR. Dist: ABC-CLIO, LLC.

Myers, Ray, Jr. Business: Reference for Students & Professionals. 2006. 128p. per. 14.95 net. *(978-0-9786364-0-1(6))* PocketCrib, LLC.

Myers, Ray. Business Tools & Metrics: Reference for Students & Professionals. 2006. 90p. per. 14.95 net. *(978-0-9786364-3-2(0))* PocketCrib, LLC.

Norman. We're in Business. Date not set. (Illus.). 144p. pap., stu. ed. 9.95 *(978-0-582-74872-9(0));* 48p. per., wbk. ed. 9.95 *(978-0-582-74871-2(2))* Addison-Wesley Longman, Ltd. GBR. Dist: Trans-Atlantic Pubns., Inc.

Powers. Sit down Shut up & Hang on Ten. 79.50 *(978-0-87905-813-5(7))* Gibbs Smith, Publisher.

Presenting Across Cultures. Date not set. (Management Booklets Ser.). *(978-1-882390-89-2(X))* Training Management Corp.

Punzo, Richard. Managing Across Cultures. Date not set. (Management Booklets Ser.). *(978-1-882390-94-6(6))* Training Management Corp.

—Managing Global Projects. Date not set. (Management Booklets Ser.). *(978-1-882390-92-2(X))* Training Management Corp.

Reiff-Marganiec, Stephan & Tilly, Marcel. Handbook of Research on Service-Oriented Systems & Non-Functional Properties: Future Directions. 2011. (Illus.). xxx, 583p. ***(978-1-61350-434-5(9)); (978-1-61350-432-1(2));*** E-Book ***(978-1-61350-433-8(0))*** IGI Global.

Rugman, Alan M. The Oxford Handbook of International Business. 2nd ed. 2010. (Oxford Handbooks Ser.). (ENG., Illus.). 880p. pap. 49.95 *(978-0-19-959344-6(2))* Oxford Univ. Pr., Inc.

Sprunt, Hugh H., et al. PPC's 1041 Deskbook, 2 vols. Incl. Vol. 2. 1996. ring bd. *(978-0-7646-0047-0(8));* 150.00 o.p. *(978-0-7646-0045-6(1));* 150.00 *(978-0-7646-0328-0(0))* Practitioners Publishing Co.

Tabah, Albert. Doing Business in Western Europe. Date not set. (Doing Business in Regions & Countries Around the World Ser.). *(978-1-882390-86-1(5))* Training Management Corp.

Vesely, Jeffrey M. & Matsubara, Keme H. O. Distinctions Between Unitary & Non Unitary Business: A Practical Guide. 200p. 75.00 *(978-0-8080-0681-7(9),* 0-5467-200) Toolkit Media Group.

Walker, Tim & Walker, Danielle. Marketing & Sales Across Cultures. Date not set. (Management Booklets Ser.). *(978-1-882390-88-5(1))* Training Management Corp.

Wong, Karina. My First Pot of Gold: An American Business Handbook for Chinese Immigrants. 2006. (ENG & CHI.). per. 29.95 *(978-0-9778469-0-0(3))* Pachira Enterprises.

Wynters, Sharyn & Dorris, Tamara. How to Be a Successful Thinker: Creating the Life of Your Dreams. 2010. 164p. pap. 18.95 *(978-1-4327-5860-8(8))* Outskirts Pr., Inc.

BUSINESS—INFORMATION SERVICES

Bryant, Karen Y. Financial Holdings. 2009. 100p. pap. 19.00 *(978-0-557-08623-8(X))* Lulu Enterprises Inc.

Shemwell, Scott M. Essays on Business & Information II: Maximizing Organizational Performance. 2011. 242p. 29.99 ***(978-1-4568-8376-8(3));*** pap. 19.99 ***(978-1-4568-8375-1(5))*** Xlibris Corp.

BUSINESS—JUVENILE LITERATURE

White, Casey. Sergey Brin & Larry Page: The Founders of Google. 2006. 116p. (gr. 3-7). pap. 31.95 *(978-1-4358-3764-5(9))* Rosen Publishing Group, Inc., The.

BUSINESS—LAW AND LEGISLATION

see Business Law; Commercial Law

BUSINESS—MATHEMATICAL MODELS

Aba-Bulgu, M. & Islam, Sardar M. N. Corporate Crisis & Risk Management: Modelling, Strategies & SME Application. 2006. (International Business & Management Ser.). (Illus.). 358p. 134.95 *(978-0-08-045102-2(0))* Emerald Group Publishing Ltd. GBR. Dist: Turpin Distribution Services Ltd.

Arunachalam, Subramaniam. Supplier Development Using Interpretive Structural Modelling. 2011. 56p. pap. ***(978-3-8443-0732-0(X))*** Lambert Academic Publishing.

Ayres, Ian. Super Crunchers: Why Thinking-by-Numbers Is the New Way to Be Smart. (ENG.). 2008. 320p. pap. 16.00 *(978-0-553-38473-4(2))* 2007. (Illus.). 272p. 26.00 *(978-0-553-80540-6(1))* Random House Publishing Group. (Bantam).

Chatterjee, Arnab & Chakrabarti, Bikas K., eds. Econophysics of Markets & Business Networks: Proceedings of the Econophys-Kolkata III. 2007. (New Economic Windows Ser.). (Illus.). 266p. 119.00 *(978-88-470-0664-5(3))* Springer.

Chen-Burger, Yun-Heh & Robertson, Dave. Automating Business Modelling: A Guide to Using Logic to Represent Informal Methods & Support Reasoning. 2010. (Advanced Information & Knowledge Processing Ser.). (Illus.). xvii, 322p. pap. 139.00 *(978-1-84996-934-5(5),* 1849969345) Springer.

Debelak, Don & Entrepreneur Press Staff. Business Models Made Easy. 2006. (ENG., Illus.). 240p. per. 19.95 *(978-1-59918-041-0(3),* 1599180413) Entrepreneur Pr. dba Entrepreneur Media, Inc.

Digital Actuarial Resources. Digital Actuarial Resources: Practice Test Questions for SOA Exam P / CAS Exam 1. 2007. 132p. spiral bd. 39.00 *(978-0-9798071-6-9(6))* Digital Actuarial Resources, LLC.

Gediminas Adomavicius Staff & A. Gupta Staff. Business Computing. 2009. (Illus.). xx, 400p. 244.95 *(978-1-84855-264-7(5))* Emerald Group Publishing Ltd. GBR. Dist: Turpin Distribution Services Ltd.

Horsti, Aleksi. Revolution of e-Business Models: Electronic Business Models & Their Dynamic Nature. 2008. 216p. pap. *(978-3-639-11158-3(3))* VDM Verlag Dr. Mueller e.K.

Johnson, Mark W. Seizing the White Space: Business Model Innovation for Growth & Renewal. 2010. (ENG., Illus.). 240p. 29.95 *(978-1-4221-2481-9(9))* Harvard Business Review Pr.

Lehr, Michael. Poker: Four Lessons Emphasizing Talent Identification & Development: an Intuitive Business Model. 2007. spiral bd. 14.95 *(978-0-9786613-3-5(9))* Dragon Slayer, LLC.

Mendling, Jan, et al, eds. Business Process Modeling Notation: Second International Workshop, BPMN 2010, Potsdam, Germany, October 13-14, 2010 Proceedings. 2010. (Lecture Notes in Business Information Processing Ser.). vii, 129p. pap. 72.00 *(978-3-642-16297-8(5),* 3642162975) Springer.

Morel, John Henry. Nanogroup Quantum Notebook Series, the Holocomb Theory, Blank Lined. 2009. 130p. pap. 12.99 *(978-1-935436-70-6(8))* Rodaian Pr.

Mullins, John & Komisar, Randy. Getting to Plan B: Breaking Through to a Better Business Model. 2009. (ENG., Illus.). 272p. 32.95 *(978-1-4221-2669-1(2))* Harvard Business Review Pr.

Nelson, Matthew L., et al. Value Creation in E-Business Management: 15th Americas Conference on Information Systems, AMCIS 2009, SIGeBIZ track, San Francisco, CA, USA, August 6-9, 2009, Selected Papers. 2009. (Lecture Notes in Business Information Processing Ser.). (ENG.). ix, 321p. pap. 79.95 *(978-3-642-03131-1(5),* 3642031315) Springer.

Project Management Institute, creator. Organizational Project Management Maturity Model (OPM3) Knowledge Foundation. 2nd ed. 2008. (Illus.). 190p. pap. 95.95 *(978-1-933890-54-8(1))* Project Management Institute.

Quain, Bill. The Quixtar Price Is Right. 2007. 111p. pap. 11.95 *(978-1-891279-12-6(2))* INTI Publishing & Resource Bks., Inc.

Recker, Jan. Evaluations of Process Modeling Grammars: Ontological, Qualitative & Quantitative Analyses Using the Example of BPMN. 2011. (Lecture Notes in Business Information Processing Ser.). xxii, 199p. pap. 72.00 *(978-3-642-18359-1(X),* 364218359X) Springer.

Smith, Martin L. Mine Plan Optimisation. 2012. (ENG.). 350p. (C). 89.95 *(978-0-415-66578-0(7),* CRC Press) Taylor & Francis Group GBR. Dist: Taylor & Francis Group.

Star, Harold. Chickens & Pigs: Business Models & Competitive Strategy. 2007. (Illus.). 120p. pap. 19.95 net. *(978-0-9646962-0-4(7))* EMBA Pr.

BUSINESS—PERIODICALS

BL. Board Leadership Newsletter, Number 86, July/August 2006. 2006. (J-B BL Single Issue Board Leadership Journal Ser.). (ENG.). 8p. pap. 31.00 *(978-0-7879-8888-3(X),* Jossey-Bass) Wiley, John & Sons, Inc.

Bl. Board Leadership Newsletter, Number 87, September/October 2006. 2006. (J-B BL Single Issue Board Leadership Journal Ser.). (ENG.). 8p. pap. 31.00 *(978-0-7879-9457-0(X),* Jossey-Bass) Wiley, John & Sons, Inc.

Business Research Consortium Of Wny. The Brc Academy Journal of Business. 2010. 184p. pap. 29.99 *(978-1-60497-688-5(8))* Cambria Pr.

Corporate Kansas City (2007-2008 Edition) 2008. (YA). 39.95 *(978-0-9749295-4-5(9))* Show Me Publishing Inc.

DIV. Mergent's Dividend Achievers Fall 2007: Featuring Second-Quarter Results For 2007. 2007. (Mergent's Dividend Achievers Ser.). 368p. pap. 50.00 *(978-0-470-11993-8(4),* Wiley) Wiley, John & Sons, Inc.

Encyclopedia of Business Information Sources, 2.0. 28th ed. 2011. pap. 626.00 *(978-1-4144-5899-1(1))* Cengage Gale.

Gorman, Brian, compiled by. Gorman's 2007 Northern California Publicity Guide. 2007. 120p. 59.95 *(978-0-9794959-0-8(3))* Gormans Guides.

Howell, Ocean, ed. Board Leadership Newsletter, Number 90, March/February 2007 No. 90. 2007. (J-B BL Single Issue Board Leadership Journal Ser.). (ENG.). 8p. pap. 31.00 *(978-0-7879-9762-5(5),* Jossey-Bass) Wiley, John & Sons, Inc.

Kimball, Cheryl & Entrepreneur Press Staff. Start Your Own Pet-Sitting Business: Your Step-by-Step Guide to Sucess 2nd ed. 2007. (ENG., Illus.). 146p. per. 17.95 *(978-1-59918-110-3(X),* 159918110X) Entrepreneur Pr. dba Entrepreneur Media, Inc.

Kuada, John. African Journal of Business & Economic. 2006. (ENG.). 160p. per. *(978-1-905068-63-3(8))* Adonis & Abbey Publishers Ltd.

Kuada, John, ed. African Journal of Business & Economic Research. 2007. 124p. per. *(978-1-905068-93-7(X))* Adonis & Abbey Publishers Ltd.

—African Journal of Business & Economic Research, Volume 2, Nos 2 And. 2007. 116p. per. *(978-1-905068-14-2(X))* Adonis & Abbey Publishers Ltd.

Mars, Laura, ed. Directory of Business Information Resources. 2011. 2500p. pap. 195.00 *(978-1-59237-737-4(8))* Grey Hse. Publishing.

—Directory of Business Information Resources 2010. 17th rev. ed. 2010. pap. 195.00 *(978-1-59237-500-4(6))* Grey Hse. Publishing.

Preziosi, Robert C. Management Development 2009. annuals 2008. (J-B Pfeiffer Annual Vol1 Ser.: 45). (ENG.). 256p. 95.00 *(978-0-470-37146-6(3),* Pfeiffer) Wiley, John & Sons, Inc.

Richardson, John E. Marketing. 30th ed. 2007. (Annual Editions Ser.). (Illus.). 203p. per. 28.44 *(978-0-07-336946-4(2),* 9780073369464, McGraw-Hill/Dushkin) McGraw-Hill Higher Education.

Witty, Adam. 21 Ways to Build Your Business with A Magazine: Secrets to Dramatically Grow Your Income, Credibility & Celebrity Power. 2010. 62p. pap. 10.99 *(978-1-59932-176-9(9))* Advantage Media Group.

BUSINESS—PLANNING

see Business Planning

BUSINESS—PUBLIC RELATIONS

see Public Relations

BUSINESS—RECORDS

see Business Records

BUSINESS—RELIGIOUS ASPECTS

Aburdene, Patricia. Megatrends 2010: The Rise of Conscious Capitalism. 2007. (ENG., Illus.). 248p. per. 16.95 *(978-1-57174-539-2(4))* Hampton Roads Publishing Co., Inc.

Acton Institute. The Call of the Entrepreneur. 2011. (ENG.). 35p. pap. 5.00 ***(978-1-880595-24-4(9))*** Acton Institute for the Study of Religion & Liberty.

Addington, Thomas G. & Graves, Stephen R. Behind the Bottom Line: Powering Business Life with Spiritual Wisdom. 2011. (ENG.). 240p. pap. 21.95 *(978-1-118-08589-9(2),* Jossey-Bass) Wiley, John & Sons, Inc.

Agno, Randy. God's Hand. 2008. 148p. 11.99 *(978-1-60462-455-7(8))* Tate Publishing & Enterprises, LLC.

Ananich, B. V., et al. Chastnoe Predprinimatelstvo V Dorevolutsionnoi Rossii: Etnokonfessionalnaia Struktura I Regionalnoe Razvitie, XIX — Nachalo XX V. 2010. (RUS., Illus.). 549p. *(978-5-8243-1505-9(1))* Rossijskaja politiceskaja enciklopedija, Associacija.

Anderson, Dave. How to Run Your Business by the Book: A Biblical Blueprint to Bless Your Business. 2nd rev. expurg. ed. 2011. (ENG.). 252p. pap. 18.95 *(978-1-118-02237-5(8),* Wiley) Wiley, John & Sons, Inc.

Awosika, Ibukun. Business His Way. 2009. 168p. pap. 14.99 *(978-1-60791-506-5(5))* Xulon Pr., Inc.

Baer, Michael R. Business As Mission: The Power of Business in the Kingdom of God. 2006. (ENG.). 157p. per. 12.99 *(978-1-57658-388-3(0))* YWAM Publishing.

Bengtson, Tom. The GEO Principle: God in Every Occupation means purpose for every job - even Yours! 2009. 96p. per. 11.95 *(978-0-9754134-3-2(0))* NFR Communications, Inc.

Biberman, Jerry & Whitty, Mike. At Work: Spirituality Matters. 2007. (Illus.). 292p. pap. 25.00 *(978-1-58966-130-1(3))* Univ. of Scranton Pr.

Biberman, Jerry, et al. Spirituality in Business: Theory, Practice, & Future Directions. 2008. (ENG.). 240p. 95.00 *(978-0-230-60371-4(8))* Palgrave Macmillan.

Blackaby, Henry, et al. God in the Marketplace: 45 Questions Fortune 500 Executives Ask about Faith, Life, & Business. 2008. (ENG.). 288p. 16.99 *(978-0-8054-4688-3(5),* B&H Bks.) B&H Publishing Group.

Bouckaert, Luk & Zsolnai, Laszlo, eds. The Palgrave Handbook of Spirituality & Business. 2011. (ENG., Illus.). 448p. 110.00 ***(978-0-230-23831-2(9))*** Palgrave Macmillan.

Budde, Michael L. & Brimlow, Robert W. Christianity Incorporated: How Big Business Is Buying the Church. 2007. 192p. pap. 22.00 *(978-1-55635-245-4(X),* Wipf and Stock) Wipf & Stock Pubs.

Cabaldon, Larry & Klemmer, Brian. God in the Boardroom: Why Is Christianity losing market Share? 2011. (ENG.). 160p. pap. 13.99 ***(978-1-936417-14-8(6))*** Pilot Communications Group, Inc.

Cahn, Peter S. Direct Sales & Direct Faith in Latin America. 2011. (Contemporary Anthropology of Religion Ser.). (ENG., Illus.). 206p. 85.00 *(978-0-230-11249-0(8))* Palgrave Macmillan.

CBMC Staff. Operation Timothy Bk. 3: Living with Power. rev. ed. (Illus.). wbk. ed. *(978-0-945292-03-6(1))* Christian Business Men's Committee of U.S.A.

Chibanda, Stewart. Entrepreneurship in Africa: The Spiritual Dimension. 2010. 150p. pap. *(978-1-906704-63-6(5))* Adonis & Abbey Publishers Ltd.

Clark, Kontrena. The Business Plan for the Believer. 2006. (Illus.). 79p. per. 8.99 *(978-1-59886-568-4(4))* Tate Publishing & Enterprises, LLC.

Connell, John C. Catholics Mean Business: 30 Days to Managing Your Work Week, God's Way. 2009. 81p. pap. 9.95 *(978-1-4327-2974-5(8))* Outskirts Pr., Inc.

Copeland, Deb. Good Morning Good Night: 99 Days to Your Spiritual Recovery. 2008. 216p. pap. 19.99 *(978-1-4389-1892-1(5))* AuthorHouse.

Cornwall, Jeffrey & Naughton, Michael. Bringing Your Business to Life: The Four Virtues That Will Help You Build a Better Business - And a Better Life. 2008. (ENG.). 208p. 17.99 *(978-0-8307-4593-7(9))* Gospel Light Pubns.

Costa, Ken. God at Work: Ethics, Commerce & Ambition. 2007. (ENG.). 208p. pap. 16.95 *(978-0-8264-9635-5(0))* Continuum International Publishing Group, Ltd. GBR. Dist: National Bk. Network.

Crum, W. Paul "Buddy", Jr. Much More Than a Job: Your 24/7 Mission. 2007. 232p. per. 15.99 *(978-0-88270-232-2(7))* Bridge-Logos Foundation.

Dalai Lama XIV & Van den Muyzenberg, Lauren. The Leader's Way: The Art of Making Right Decisions in Our Lives, Our Organizations, & the Larger World. 2009. (ENG., Illus.). 224p. 25.00 *(978-0-385-52780-4(2),* Broadway Business) Knopf Doubleday Publishing Group.

Davis, Mike. The Christian Entrepreneur. 160p. pap. 10.99 *(978-1-58169-128-3(9),* Evergreen Pr.) Genesis Communications, Inc.

Den Haan, Mia. New Concepts for Business & Humanity: A New Paradigm Shift in Global Consciousness Is Needed for Humanity, in Business & Towards the Environment, to Survive a Future Global Environmental Crisis. 2007. 136p. 30.99 *(978-1-4257-7588-9(8))* Xlibris Corp.

Eldred, Ken. God is at Work: Transforming People & Nations Through Business. 2009. (ENG.). 336p. pap. 14.99 *(978-0-9840911-0-2(6))* Manna Ventures, LLC.

Engelhart, Terces & Engelhart, Matthew. Sacred Commerce: Business as a Path of Awakening. 2008. (ENG.). 136p. pap. 14.95 *(978-1-55643-729-8(3))* North Atlantic Bks.

Fernando, Mario. Spiritual Leadership in the Entrepreneurial Business: A Multifaith Study. 2008. 176p. (C). 119.00 *(978-1-84720-350-2(7))* Elgar, Edward Publishing, Inc.

Fort, Timothy L. Prophets, Profits, & Peace: The Positive Role of Business in Promoting Religious Tolerance. 2008. (ENG.). 224p. 35.00 *(978-0-300-11467-6(2))* Yale Univ. Pr.

Frost, William P. Business Ethics in Catholic Perspectives. Date not set. 136p. (Orig.). (C). pap. *(978-1-881003-05-2(1))* College Pr.

Gabrielle, Rowan & Sawaf, Ayman. Sacred Commerce: The Rise of the Global Citizen. 2008. 156p. 23.00 *(978-0-9801755-5-4(0))* Sacred Commerce Publishing.

Green, Janet. How to Turn Your Talent into a Business Workbook. 2011. (Illus.). 82p. pap. 15.95 ***(978-1-934194-97-3(2))*** Olmstead Publishing LLC.

Griffin, Linda. Christians in Business. 2007. pap. 8.00 *(978-0-8059-7530-7(6))* Dorrance Publishing Co., Inc.

Hall, David W. & Burton, Matthew D. Calvin & Commerce: The Transforming Power of Calvinism in Market Economies. 2009. pap. *(978-1-59638-095-0(0))* P & R Publishing.

Hansen, Mark Victor, et al. Chicken Soup for the Entrepreneur's Soul: Advice & Inspiration on Fulfilling Dreams. 2006. (Chicken Soup for the Soul Ser.). (ENG., Illus.). 320p. pap. 14.95 *(978-0-7573-0261-9(0))* Health Communications, Inc.

Harper, Tom & Broadman and Holman Publishers Staff. Leading from the Lions' Den: Leadership Principles from Every Book of the Bible. 2010. (ENG.). 240p. pap. 12.99 *(978-0-8054-4442-1(4),* B&H Bks.) B&H Publishing Group.

Hill, Alexander. Just Business: Christian Ethics for the Marketplace. rev. ed. 2008. (ENG., Illus.). 276p. per. 18.00 *(978-0-8308-2676-6(9),* IVP Acad.) InterVarsity Pr.

Hutchins, Bob & Stielstra, Greg. Faith-Based Marketing: The Guide to Reaching 140 Million Christian Customers. 2009. (ENG., Illus.). 256p. 27.95 *(978-0-470-42210-6(6),* Wiley) Wiley, John & Sons, Inc.

Hutto, Gary W. The Good Book & Good Business: How to Succeed the Christian Way. 2006. (ENG.). 192p. *(978-1-57587-258-2(7))* Crane Hill Pubs.

Inamori, Kazuo. A Compass to Fulfillment: Passion & Spirituality in Life & Business. 2009. (ENG.). 128p. 21.95 *(978-0-07-161509-9(1),* 0071615091) McGraw-Hill Cos., The.

Kirio, Clayton. An Ayurvedic Approach to Entrepreneurial Health. 2010. 132p. pap. 13.95 *(978-1-60844-252-2(7))* Dog Ear Publishing, LLC.

Kitiarsa, Pattana, ed. Religious Commodifications in Asia: Marketing Gods. 2012. (ENG., Illus.). 288p. (C). pap. 44.95 ***(978-0-415-51460-6(6))*** Routledge.

Maarufu, Pastor Jonathan Gift. Business in Jesus' Name. 2011. 204p. pap. 24.95 ***(978-1-4560-5615-5(8))*** PublishAmerica, Inc.

Manz, Charles C. The Leadership Wisdom of Jesus: Practical Lessons for Today. 2009. (Playaway Adult Nonfiction Ser.). (ENG.). 34.99 *(978-1-60775-721-4(4))* Findaway World, LLC.

Martin, Lillian Hayes. The Business Devotional: 365 Inspirational Thoughts on Management, Leadership & Motivation. 2009. (ENG., Illus.). 384p. 17.95 *(978-1-4027-5642-9(9),* Sterling Innovation) Sterling Publishing Co., Inc.

Martin, Wade A. Spiritual Entrepreneurialism. 2007. 120p. per. 10.99 *(978-1-60477-402-3(9))* Xulon Pr., Inc.

McClymonds, Scott A. Building a Kingdom Business: A View from the Trenches - How You Can Create a Business with Significance & Impact for God. 2009. 208p. 25.99 *(978-1-61579-103-3(5));* pap. 15.99 *(978-1-61579-096-8(9))* Xulon Pr., Inc.

Meaux, Reneé. God's Hands in My Business: Will He Let My Business Fail? 2009. pap. 11.99 *(978-1-60799-663-7(4))* Tate Publishing & Enterprises, LLC.

Medaille, John C. Vocation of Business: Social Justice in the Marketplace. 2007. (ENG.). 374p. pap. 65.00 *(978-0-8264-2809-7(6))* Continuum International Publishing Group, Ltd. GBR. Dist: National Bk. Network.

Mende, Mario. From Fear to Faith: 10 Steps on the Spiritual Path of the Entrepreneur. 2007. 168p. pap. 24.95 *(978-0-9790567-0-3(5))* Mende Media, LLC.

Minus, P. M., ed. The Ethics of Business in a Global Economy. 2010. (Issues in Business Ethics Ser.). 164p. pap. 179.00 *(978-90-481-5795-2(1),* 9048157951) Springer.

Moonwalker, Tu, et al. Business Revolution Through Ancestral Wisdom: The Circle Knowledge of the past comes forward to show us how to create a practical & ethical Process. 2008. 240p. pap. 22.95 *(978-1-4327-1786-5(3))* Outskirts Pr., Inc.

Moreton, Bethany. To Serve God & Wal-Mart: The Making of Christian Free Enterprise. 2010. (ENG., Illus.). 392p. pap. 17.95 *(978-0-674-05740-1(6))* Harvard Univ. Pr.

Morgen, Robert. The Spiritual Entrepreneur. 2011. (Illus.). 268p. pap. 16.95 *(978-0-9790400-3-0(5))* Mystic Wolf Media.

Mosley, Curtis. Raincatcher: Help from above for Entrepreneurs. 2011. pap. 17.99 *(978-1-61777-871-1(0))* Tate Publishing & Enterprises, LLC.

Murphy, Nikita. The Business of Life. 2011. pap. 13.95 ***(978-1-59581-651-1(8),*** Brentwood Christian Pr.) Brentwood Communications Group.

Naughton, Michael & Specht, David. Leading Wisely in Difficult Times: Three Cases of Faith & Business. 2011. 160p. pap. 19.95 ***(978-0-8091-4738-0(6))*** Paulist Pr.

Ogunbekun, Olajumoke. Managing Kingdom Business: Project Management Methodology Based on the Book of Nehemiah. 2010. (Illus.). 56p. pap. 11.99 *(978-1-4490-6408-2(6))* AuthorHouse.

Ouimet, J. -Robert & Semen, Yves. Everything Has Been Loaned to You: The Biography of a Transformational CEO. 2012. ***(978-0-8189-1337-2(1))*** St Pauls.

Paeth, Scott, ed. Religious Perspectives on Business Ethics: An Anthology. 2006. (Religion & Business Ethics Ser.). (ENG.). 381p. 76.00 *(978-0-7425-5010-0(9));* 384p. per. 39.95 *(978-0-7425-5011-7(7))* Rowman & Littlefield Publishers, Inc.

Peacocke, Dennis. Doing Business God's Way. 2nd ed. 2007. (ENG.). 163p. (Orig.). reprint ed. pap. 12.95 *(978-1-887021-02-9(7))* Rebuild.

Percy, Anthony G. Entrepreneurship in the Catholic Tradition. 2010. (Studies in Ethics & Economics Ser.). (ENG.). 192p. 65.00 *(978-0-7391-2513-7(3));* pap. 27.95 *(978-0-7391-2514-4(1))* Lexington Bks.

Phelps, Owen. The Catholic Vision for Leading Like Jesus Leader's Guide: Introducing Leadership S3 Leadership Servant, Steward, Shepherd. 2009. 8p. pap. 2.95 *(978-1-59276-675-8(7))* Our Sunday Visitor, Publishing Div.

Poppe, Jerry L. I'm a Christian even at Work: The Ethics of Business & Economics. 2006. x, 177p. per. *(978-0-8100-1661-3(3))* Northwestern Publishing Hse.

Robinson, Jerry H. Second in Command: We Are All Leaders No Matter What Our Position. 2009. 216p. pap. 15.99 *(978-1-61579-456-0(5))* Xulon Pr., Inc.

Rooyen, Pieter Van. Business Unusual. 2010. 490p. 34.99 *(978-1-4500-5783-7(7));* pap. 23.99 *(978-1-4500-5782-0(9))* Xlibris Corp.

Russell, Mark L. The Missional Entrepreneur: Principles & Practices for Business as Mission. 2009. (ENG.). 320p. pap. 24.99 *(978-1-59669-278-7(2))* New Hope Pubs.

Sandelands, Lloyd. God & Mammon. 2009. (ENG.). 116p. pap. 20.99 *(978-0-7618-4940-7(8))* Univ. Pr. of America, Inc.

Sandelands, Lloyd E. God & Mammon. 2010. vi, 106p. *(978-0-7618-4941-4(6))* Univ. Pr. of America, Inc.

Scheske, Anja. Wu Xing Marketing. 2008. 152p. pap. *(978-3-639-07167-2(0))* VDM Verlag Dr. Mueller e.K.

Seaberg, George H. Where Angels Fear to Tread: One Man's Journey in Starting His Small Business. 2011. 304p. 37.95 ***(978-1-4497-3040-6(X));*** pap. 22.95 ***(978-1-4497-3039-0(6))*** Author Solutions, Inc. (WestBow Pr.).

Silvoso, Ed. Transformation: Change the Marketplace & You Change the World. 2010. (ENG.). 272p. pap. 16.99 *(978-0-8307-4514-2(9))* Gospel Light Pubns.

Sodano, Vincent. Counting Sheep: In the Name of the Beast. 2008. 120p. pap. 11.95 *(978-1-4327-3376-6(1))* Outskirts Pr., Inc.

Standfield, James L. God You Said: Reminding God of His Word on Your Entrepreneurial Journey. 2009. 164p. pap. 19.99 *(978-1-4389-7105-6(2))* AuthorHouse.

Stevens, R. Paul. Doing God's Business: Meaning & Motivation for the Marketplace. 2006. 251p. per. 16.00 *(978-0-8028-3398-3(5))* Eerdmans, William B. Publishing Co.

Traffas, Charlie. Salvation & Sales: A Handbook for Life. 2007. (Illus.). 304p. per. 22.95 *(978-1-4251-0309-5(X))* Trafford Publishing.

Valeri, Mark. Heavenly Merchandize: How Religion Shaped Commerce in Puritan America. 2010. (ENG., Illus.). 354p. (C). 35.00 *(978-0-691-14359-0(5))* Princeton Univ. Pr.

Van Duzer, Jeff. Why Business Matters to God: (and What Still Needs to Be Fixed) 2010. (ENG., Illus.). 206p. pap. 20.00 *(978-0-8308-3888-2(0),* IVP Acad.) InterVarsity Pr.

Varnedoe, Heeth, III. Called to Excellence: Redefining Success in the Marketplace. 2nd ed. 2007. (ENG.). 178p. per. 12.99 *(978-1-58169-243-3(9),* Evergreen Pr.) Genesis Communications, Inc.

Vatel, Karen Wilson. So You're Born Again Now What? 2008. 68p. pap. 9.99 *(978-1-60647-479-2(0))* Xulon Pr., Inc.

Vaughan, Vikkie. Bankruptcy: File with God Not with Man. 2007. (Illus.). 150p. pap. 17.95 *(978-0-9774419-2-1(X))* New Writers' Ink.

Walker, J. D. Godly Ideas: Perceiving & Pursuing God-Given Ideas. 2008. 208p. pap. 29.99 *(978-1-4389-2566-0(2))* AuthorHouse.

White, Bess. Supply-Side Christians. 2007. 72p. per. 9.99 *(978-1-60034-975-1(7))* Xulon Pr., Inc.

Whitlock, David Wesley. Solomon Was a Businessman: Advice from the Wealthiest Man on Earth. Baker, Ardith, ed. 2008. 150p. pap. 17.00 *(978-1-55635-989-7(6))* Wipf & Stock Pubs.

Wong, Kenman L. & Rae, Scott B. Business for the Common Good: A Christian Vision for the Marketplace. 2011. (Christian Worldview Integration Ser.). (ENG.). 288p. pap. 24.00 *(978-0-8308-2816-6(8),* IVP Acad.) InterVarsity Pr.

Zender, Tom. God Goes to Work: New Thought Paths to Prosperity & Profits. 2010. (ENG.). 235p. 24.95 *(978-0-470-56365-6(6),* Wiley) Wiley, John & Sons, Inc.

BUSINESS—RESEARCH

Arbnor, Ingeman & Bjerke, Bjorn. Methodology for Creating Business Knowledge. 3rd ed. 2009. (Illus.). 464p. (C). 135.00 *(978-1-84787-058-2(9),* B70582C); pap. 74.00 *(978-1-84787-059-9(7),* B70582P) SAGE Pubns., Ltd. GBR. Dist: SAGE Pubns., Inc.

Aslam, Sher & Zafar Yab, Mohammad. Comparative Study of Balanced Incomplete Block Designs. 2011. 92p. pap. ***(978-3-8443-1043-6(6))*** Lambert Academic Publishing.

Azzara, Carey V. Questionnaire Design for Business Research: Beyond Linear Thinking-an Interactive Approach. 2010. 361p. pap. 32.99 *(978-1-61566-835-9(7))* Tate Publishing & Enterprises, LLC.

Benito, Gabriel & Greve, Henrich R., eds. Progress in International Business Research: Volume I. 2006. (Progress in International Business Research Ser.). (Illus.). 222p. 111.95 *(978-0-7623-1288-7(2))* Emerald Group Publishing Ltd. GBR. Dist: Turpin Distribution Services Ltd.

Brc. The Brc Academy Journal of Education: Vol. 1, No. 2. 2011. 102p. pap. 16.00 ***(978-1-60497-797-4(3))*** Cambria Pr.

—The Brc Journal of Advances in Business: Vol. 1, No. 2. 2011. 164p. pap. 17.00 ***(978-1-60497-784-4(1))*** Cambria Pr.

—The Brc Journal of Advances in Education: Vol. 1, No. 2. 2011. 126p. pap. 12.00 ***(978-1-60497-771-4(X))*** Cambria Pr.

—Proceedings of the 2010 Business Research Consortium of Western New York. 2011. 478p. pap. 22.00 ***(978-1-60497-809-4(0))*** Cambria Pr.

Bryman, Alan & Bell, Emma. Business Research Methods 3e. 3rd ed. 2011. (ENG., Illus.). 720p. pap. 74.95 *(978-0-19-958340-9(4))* Oxford Univ. Pr., Inc.

Burke, R. J. & Cooper, C. L., eds. Research Companion to Corruption in Organisations. 2009. (New Horizons in Management Ser.). (Illus.). 320p. 210.00 *(978-1-84720-892-7(4))* Elgar, Edward Publishing, Inc.

Burns, Richard & Burns, Robert P. Business Research Methods & Statistics Using SPSS. 2008. (Illus.). 560p. (C). 146.00 *(978-1-4129-4529-5(1),* B45291C); pap. 79.00 *(978-1-4129-4530-1(5),* B45291P) SAGE Pubns., Ltd. GBR. Dist: SAGE Pubns., Inc.

Business Research Consortium Of Wny. The Brc Academy Journal of Business. 2010. 184p. pap. 29.99 *(978-1-60497-688-5(8))* Cambria Pr.

—The Brc Academy Journal of Education: Vol. 1, No. 1. 2010. 142p. pap. 29.99 *(978-1-60497-689-2(6))* Cambria Pr.

—The Brc Journal of Advances in Business: Vol. 1, No. 1. 2010. 140p. pap. 29.99 *(978-1-60497-692-2(6))* Cambria Pr.

—The Brc Journal of Advances in Education: Vol. 1, No. 1. 2010. 108p. pap. 29.99 *(978-1-60497-691-5(8))* Cambria Pr.

—Proceedings of the 2009 Business Research Consortium of Western New York. 2010. 296p. pap. 39.99 *(978-1-60497-681-6(0))* Cambria Pr.

Collis, Jill & Hussey, Roger. Business Research: A Practical Guide for Undergraduate & Postgraduate Students. 3rd rev. ed. 2009. (ENG., Illus.). 420p. pap. 75.00 *(978-1-4039-9247-5(9))* Palgrave Macmillan.

Congregado, Emilio, ed. Measuring Entrepreneurship: Building a Statistical System. 2007. (International Studies in Entrepreneurship Ser.). (Illus.). 338p. 159.00 *(978-0-387-72287-0(4))* Springer.

Cooper and, Schindler. Business Research Methods. 2006. pap. 12.95 *(978-1-4288-0703-7(9))* Cram101 Inc.

Cooper, Donald R. & Schindler, Pamela S. Business Research Methods. 11th ed. 2010. (ENG., Illus.). 784p. (C). 212.33 *(978-0-07-337370-6(2),* 0073373702, McGraw-Hill/Irwin) McGraw-Hill Higher Education.

—Business Research Methods. 10th ed. 2008. (Illus.). xxii, 746p. *(978-0-07-340175-1(7),* Irwin Professional Publishing) McGraw-Hill Schl. Education Group.

Cram101 Textbook Reviews. Outlines & Highlights for Business Research Methods & Statistics Using Spss by Richard Burns. 2011. 80p. pap. 27.95 ***(978-1-61905-205-5(9))*** Cram101 Inc.

Cram101 Textbook Reviews. Outlines & Highlights for Business Research Methods by William G Zikmund, Isbn: 9781439080672. 2010. 110p. pap. 28.95 *(978-1-61654-091-3(5))* Cram101 Inc.

Cram101 Textbook Reviews & Cram101 Textbook Reviews. Outlines & Highlights for Qualitative Methods in Business Research by Paivi Eriksson, Isbn: 9781412903172. 2011. 88p. pap. 27.95 ***(978-1-61461-455-5(5))*** Cram101 Inc.

Crous, Martin. Mission Possible: Strategies & Competencies of Successful Corporate Turnaround Executives. 2007. 244p. per. 19.99 *(978-1-4251-1529-6(2))* Trafford Publishing.

Desarbo, et al. Business Research Methods. 8th ed. 2009. (ENG.). 696p. (C). 243.95 *(978-0-324-32062-6(0))* Cengage South-Western.

Dul, Jan & Hak, Tony. Case Study Methodology in Business Research. 2007. (ENG., Illus.). 328p. (C). per. 45.95 *(978-0-7506-8196-4(9))* Routledge.

EPM's Little Black Book of Research Resources. 2006. pap. 79.95 *(978-1-885747-77-8(2))* EPM Communications, Inc.

Farquhar, Jillian. Case Study Research for Business. 2012. 144p. (C). 120.00 ***(978-1-84920-776-8(3),*** B07768C); pap. 44.95 ***(978-1-84920-777-5(1),*** B07768P) SAGE Pubns., Ltd. GBR. Dist: SAGE Pubns., Inc.

Fenn, Jackie & Raskino, Mark. Mastering the Hype Cycle: How to Choose the Right Innovation at the Right Time. 2008. (Gartner Ser.). (ENG., Illus.). 237p. 29.95 *(978-1-4221-2110-8(0))* Harvard Business Review Pr.

Fifty Lessons Staff, compiled by. Sparking Innovation. 2008. (Lessons Learned: Ser.). (ENG.). 96p. pap. 9.95 *(978-1-4221-2642-4(0))* Harvard Business Review Pr.

Fisher, Colin. Researching & Writing a Dissertation: An Essential Guide for Business Students. 3rd ed. 2010. (ENG., Illus.). 448p. pap. 97.50 *(978-0-273-72343-1(X))* FT Press.

Fisher, James L. & Koch, James V. Born, Not Made: The Entrepreneurial Personality. 1 vol. 2008. (Illus.). 184p. 39.95 *(978-0-313-35050-4(7),* C35050, Praeger Pubs.) Greenwood Publishing Group, Inc.

Ghauri, Pervez & Gronhaug, Kjell. Research Methods in Business Studies. 4th ed. 2010. (ENG., Illus.). 288p. (C). pap. 73.33 *(978-0-273-71204-6(7),* Prentice Hall) Prentice Hall PTR.

Hair, Babin. Essentials of Business Research Methods. 2006. pap. 10.95 *(978-1-4288-0604-7(0))* Cram101 Inc.

Hair, Joseph F., et al. Essentials of Business Research Methods. 2nd rev. ed. 2011. (Illus.). 496p. (C). pap. 99.95 *(978-0-7656-2631-8(4))* Sharpe, M.E. Inc.

Heckman, Lucy. How to Find Business Information: A Guide for Businesspeople, Investors, & Researchers. 2011. (Illus.). 208p. 34.95 *(978-0-313-36280-4(7),* C36280, Praeger Pubs.) Greenwood Publishing Group, Inc.

Israel, D. A Concise Introduction to Business Research Methods: Concepts & Tools Using SPSS. 2012. (ENG.). 210p. 79.95 *(978-1-4398-6109-7(9),* Chapman & Hall/CRC) CRC Pr. LLC.

—Data Analysis in Business Research: A Step-by-Step Nonparametric Approach. 2009. (Response Bks.). (Illus.). 320p. (C). pap. 32.95 *(978-81-7829-875-7(9),* B98757P) SAGE Pubns., Inc.

Karlsson, Charlie, ed. Handbook of Research on Cluster Theory. 2008. (Handbooks of Research on Clusters Ser.). (Illus.). 336p. 210.00 *(978-1-84542-516-6(2))* Elgar, Edward Publishing, Inc.

Kovalainen, Anne & Eriksson, Päivi. Qualitative Methods in Business Research. 2008. (Introducing Qualitative Methods Ser.). 352p. (C). 121.00 *(978-1-4129-0316-5(5),* B03165C); pap. 62.00 *(978-1-4129-0317-2(3),* B03165P) SAGE Pubns., Ltd. GBR. Dist: SAGE Pubns., Inc.

Lee, Nicholas & Lings, Ian. Doing Business Research: A Guide to Theory & Practice. 2008. (Illus.). 448p. (C). pap. 65.00 *(978-1-4129-2879-3(6),* B28786P) SAGE Pubns., Ltd. GBR. Dist: SAGE Pubns., Inc.

Lewin, Arie Y., et al, eds. Thought Leadership in Advancing International Business Research. 2008. (ENG., Illus.). 272p. 105.00 *(978-0-230-21777-5(X))* Palgrave Macmillan.

Lings, Ian & Lee, Nick. Doing Business Research: A Guide to Theory & Practice. 2008. (Illus.). 448p. (C). 119.00 *(978-1-4129-2878-6(8),* B28786C) SAGE Pubns., Ltd. GBR. Dist: SAGE Pubns., Inc.

Lomas, Robert. Mastering Your Business Dissertation. 2011. (ENG., Illus.). 184p. (C). pap. 36.95 *(978-0-415-59679-4(3));* 125.00 *(978-0-415-59678-7(5))* Routledge.

Lussier, Robert N. Research Methods & Statistics for Business. 2011. 468p. (C). pap. 59.95 incl. cd-rom *(978-1-57766-658-5(5))* Waveland Pr., Inc.

Marschan-Piekkari, Rebecca & Welch, Catherine. Rethinking the Case Study in International Business & Management Research. 2011. (Illus.). 576p. 210.00 *(978-1-84844-184-2(3))* Elgar, Edward Publishing, Inc.

Miller, Thomas William. Research & Information Services: An Integrated Approach for Business. 2007. 369p. pap. 50.00 *(978-0-9727297-2-7(0))* Research Pubs. LLC.

Neelankavil, James P. International Business Research. 2007. (ENG., Illus.). 488p. (C). pap. 119.95 *(978-0-7656-1772-9(2))* Sharpe, M.E. Inc.

O'Sullivan, Elizabethann, et al. Practical Research Methods for Nonprofit & Public Administrators. 2010. (ENG.). 272p. (C). pap. 74.00 *(978-0-205-63946-5(1))* Longman Publishing Group.

Pellissier, René. Business Research Made Easy. 2008. (ENG., Illus.). 112p. spiral bd. 26.95 *(978-0-7021-7703-3(2))* Juta Academic ZAF. Dist: Independent Pubs. Group.

Planning Shop, creator. Successful Business Research: Straight to the Numbers You Need - Fast! 2006. (ENG., Illus.). 292p. per. 29.95 *(978-0-9740801-3-0(6))* Planning Shop, The.

Proceedings of 6th Global Conference on Business & Economics, October 15-17th, 2006, Gutman Conference Center, USA: Association for Business & Economics Research. 2006. E-Book incl. cd-rom *(978-0-9742114-6-6(X))* Gupta, Atul.

Proceedings of Oxford Business & Economics Conference, June 22-24th, 2008, Oxford University, Oxford, UK. 2007. E-Book incl. cd-rom *(978-0-9742114-7-3(8))* Gupta, Atul.

Quinlan, Christina. Business Research Methods. 2011. (ENG., Illus.). 528p. pap. 69.99 *(978-1-4080-0779-2(7))* Cengage Learning GBR. Dist: CENGAGE Learning.

Rapoport, Amnon & Zwick, Rami, eds. Experimental Business Research: Volume II: Economic & Managerial Perspectives. 2010. (ENG.). xviii, 267p. pap. 125.00 *(978-1-4419-3702-5(1),* 1441937021) Springer.

Reddy, Prasada. Global Innovation in Emerging Economies. 2010. (ENG., Illus.). 320p. (C). 125.00 *(978-0-415-87966-8(3))* Routledge.

Saunders, Mark & Brown, Reva Berman. Dealing with Statistics: What You Need to Know. 2007. (ENG., Illus.). 152p. (C). pap. 24.00 *(978-0-335-22724-2(4),* 0335227244) McGraw-Hill Education GBR. Dist: McGraw-Hill Cos., The.

Saunders, Mark N. K. & Lewis, Philip. Doing Research in Business & Management: An Essential Guide to Planning Your Project. 2012. (ENG., Illus.). 256p. pap. 67.50 ***(978-0-273-72641-8(2))*** Pearson Education, Ltd. GBR. Dist: Trans-Atlantic Pubns., Inc.

Saunders, Mark N. K., et al. Research Methods for Business Students. 5th ed. 2009. (ENG., Illus.). 656p. (C). pap. 130.00 *(978-0-273-71686-0(7),* Prentice Hall) Prentice Hall PTR.

Sekaran, Uma. Research Methods for Business: A Skill Building Approach. 4th ed. 2006. pap. 8.95 *(978-1-4288-1346-5(2))* Cram101 Inc.

Sekaran, Uma & Bougie, Roger. Research Methods for Business: A Skill Building Approach. 5th ed. 2010. (ENG., Illus.). 488p. pap. 80.95 *(978-0-470-74479-6(0),* Wiley) Wiley, John & Sons, Inc.

Simon, Jon. Business Research Methods: A Structured Approach. 2006. 352p. pap. 45.00 *(978-0-470-02702-8(9))* Wiley, John & Sons, Inc.

Soley, Lawrence C., et al. Projective Techniques for Social Science & Business Research. 2008. (Illus.). 238p. (C). per. 32.95 *(978-0-9720516-1-3(9))* Southshore Pr.

Stanley, T. D. & Doucouliagos, Hristos. Meta-Regression Analysis in Economics & Business. 2012. (Routledge Frontiers of Political Economy Ser.). (ENG., Illus.). 176p. (C). 130.00 *(978-0-415-67078-4(0))* Routledge.

Stokes, Peter. Key Concepts in Business & Management Research Methods. 2011. (Palgrave Key Concepts Ser.). (ENG., Illus.). 256p. pap. 26.00 *(978-0-230-25033-8(5))* Palgrave Macmillan.

Vecchi, Alessandra. Globalisation & the Viability of Industrial Districts. 2008. 376p. pap. *(978-3-639-04165-1(8))* VDM Verlag Dr. Mueller e.K.

Waller, David & Polonsky, Michael J. Designing & Managing a Research Project: A Business Student's Guide. 2nd ed. 2010. (Illus.). 296p. (C). pap. 54.00 *(978-1-4129-7775-3(4),* B77753P) SAGE Pubns., Inc.

Weathington, Bart L., et al. Understanding Business Research. 2012. (ENG.). 508p. 130.00 ***(978-1-118-13426-9(5),*** Wiley) Wiley, John & Sons, Inc.

Welch, Catherine. Rethinking the Case Study in International Business & Management Research. Piekkari, Rebecca, ed. 2012. (Illus.). 576p. pap. 39.95 ***(978-0-85793-333-1(7))*** Elgar, Edward Publishing, Inc.

White, Brian. Writing Your MBA Dissertation. (Illus.). 192p. (C). *(978-0-8264-6012-7(7))* Continuum International Publishing Group, Ltd.

Wilson, Jonathan. Essentials of Business Research: A Guide to Doing Your Research Project. 2010. (Illus.). 336p. (C). pap. 64.00 *(978-1-84860-133-8(6),* B01321P) SAGE Pubns., Ltd. GBR. Dist: SAGE Pubns., Inc.

—Essentials of Business Research: A Guide to Doing Your Research Project. 2010. (Illus.). 336p. (C). 146.00 *(978-1-84860-132-1(8),* B01321C) SAGE Pubns., Ltd. GBR. Dist: SAGE Pubns., Inc.

Zikmund, William G. Business Research Methods. 7th ed. 2006. pap. 12.95 *(978-1-4288-1025-9(0))* Cram101 Inc.

Zikmund, William G., et al. Business Research Methods (with Qualtrics Card) 8th ed. 2009. (ENG., Illus.). 696p. (C). 273.95 *(978-1-4390-8067-2(4))* Cengage South-Western.

Zwick, Rami & Rapoport, Amnon, eds. Experimental Business Research. 2010. (ENG.). 432p. pap. 209.00 *(978-1-4419-4910-3(0),* 1441949100) Springer.

—Experimental Business Research: Volume III: Marketing, Accounting & Cognitive Perspectives. 2010. (ENG.). xviii, 318p. pap. 149.00 *(978-1-4419-3703-2(X),* 144193703X) Springer.

BUSINESS—SOCIAL ASPECTS

see Industries—Social Aspects

BUSINESS—SOCIAL RESPONSIBILITY

see Social Responsibility of Business

BUSINESS—STATISTICAL METHODS

Block, Alex Ben & Wilson, Lucy Autrey. George Lucas's Blockbusting: A Decade-by-Decade Survey of Timeless Movies Including Untold Secrets of Their Financial & Cultural Success. 2010. (ENG.). 944p. pap. 29.99 *(978-0-06-177889-6(3))* HarperCollins Pubs.

Bowerman, Bruce & O'Connell, Richard. Business Statistics in Practice with Connect Plus. 6th ed. 2010. (ENG.). (C). 240.67 *(978-0-07-739821-7(1),* 0077398211, McGraw-Hill/Irwin) McGraw-Hill Higher Education.

Burns, Richard & Burns, Robert P. Business Research Methods & Statistics Using SPSS. 2008. (Illus.). 560p. (C). 146.00 *(978-1-4129-4529-5(1),* B45291C);

pap. 79.00 *(978-1-4129-4530-1(5)*, B45291P) SAGE Pubns., Ltd. GBR. Dist: SAGE Pubns., Inc.
Chen, Chih-hsien, et al. Measuring Service Innovation Performance - Measuring Service Innovation Performance by Diffusion Model: Empirical Evidence on New Festivals of Tourism. 2008. 92p. pap. *(978-3-639-00958-3(4))* VDM Verlag Dr. Mueller e.K.
Cram101 Textbook Reviews. Outlines & Highlights for Business Research Methods & Statistics Using Spss by Richard Burns. 2011. 80p. pap. 27.95 ***(978-1-61905-205-5(9))*** Cram101 Inc.
Fu, Cixiang. Default Prediction of Publicly Traded Companies in Uk. 2010. 72p. pap. *(978-3-639-26272-8(7))* VDM Verlag Dr. Mueller e.K.
Grabovac, David. Are Leaders Born or Made? 2009. 200p. pap. 19.95 *(978-1-4092-4614-5(0))* Lulu Enterprises Inc.
Groebner, David F., et al. Business Statistics: A Decision Making Approach. 7th ed. 2007. (ENG., Illus.). 1072p. (C). 186.67 *(978-0-13-224001-7(7)*, Prentice Hall) Prentice Hall PTR.
Haskins, Mark E. The Secret Language of Financial Reports: The Back Stories That Can Enhance Your Investment Decisions. 2007. (ENG., Illus.). 288p. per. 24.95 *(978-0-07-154553-2(0)*, 0071545530) McGraw-Hill Cos., The.
Human Sciences Research Council (HSRC) Staff. Innovation: Main Results of the South African Innovation Survey 2005. 2009. (ENG.). 200p. pap. 16.95 *(978-0-7969-2240-3(3))* Human Sciences Research Council ZAF. Dist: Independent Pubs. Group.
Jones. Conversational Statistics for Business & Economics. 2nd rev. ed. 2010. pap. 103.95 *(978-0-7575-7758-1(X))* Kendall Hunt Publishing Co.
Keller, Gerald. Statistics W/Management Science. 2007. (C). 161.95 *(978-0-534-46589-6(7))* Cengage South-Western.
Klugman, Stuart A. Loss Models: From Data to Decisions. 3rd ed. 2011. (ENG.). 1p. pap. 225.00 ***(978-1-118-17538-5(7)**, Wiley)* Wiley, John & Sons, Inc.
Levine, David M., et al. Business Statistics. 5th ed. 2009. (ENG.). 384p. (C). pap. 46.67 *(978-0-13-606584-5(8)*, Prentice Hall) Prentice Hall PTR.
Lind, Douglas A., et al. Basic Statistics Using Excel to accompany Statistical Techniques in Business & Economics. 15th ed. 2011. (ENG.). 256p. (C). pap. 60.00 *(978-0-07-732702-6(0)*, 0077327020, McGraw-Hill/Irwin) McGraw-Hill Higher Education.
Lussier, Robert N. Research Methods & Statistics for Business. 2011. 468p. (C). pap. 59.95 incl. cd-rom *(978-1-57766-658-5(5))* Waveland Pr., Inc.
Mendenhall. Statistics for Management & Economics. 3rd ed. Date not set. (Business Statistics Ser.). tchr. ed. 7.25 net. *(978-0-87150-680-1(7)*, Brooks/Cole) Brooks/Cole.
Namusonge, Gregory. Business Statistics. 2010. 300p. pap. *(978-3-639-22966-0(5))* VDM Verlag Dr. Mueller e.K.
Newbold, Paul, et al. Statistics for Business & Economics. 7th ed. 2009. (ENG., Illus.). 1008p. (C). 226.67 *(978-0-13-608536-2(9)*, Prentice Hall) Prentice Hall PTR.
Ravid, Ruth & Haan, Perry. Practical Statistics for Business: An Introduction to Business Statistics. 2007. (ENG., Illus.). 224p. per. 36.99 *(978-0-7618-3884-5(8))* Univ. Pr. of America, Inc.
Richardson, Ronny. Business Applications of Multiple Regression. 2011. 202p. pap. 29.95 ***(978-1-60649-231-4(4))*** Business Expert Pr.
Rogers, Christopher W. Understandable Business Statistics. (ENG.). rev. ed. 2009. 280p. pap. 79.95 *(978-0-7575-6276-1(0))* 2nd rev. ed. 2011. 286p. pap. 86.75 *(978-0-7575-7924-3(1))* Kendall Hunt Publishing Co.
Saunders, Mark & Brown, Reva Berman. Dealing with Statistics: What You Need to Know. 2007. (ENG., Illus.). 152p. (C). pap. 24.00 *(978-0-335-22724-2(4)*, 0335227244) McGraw-Hill Education GBR. Dist: McGraw-Hill Cos., The.
Sharpe, Norean D., et al. Excel Manual for Business Statistics. 2nd ed. 2011. (ENG.). 200p. (C). pap. 24.67 *(978-0-321-71615-6(9))* Addison Wesley.
Waller, Derek L. Statistics for Business. 2011. (ENG., Illus.). 536p. (C). pap. 57.95 *(978-0-7506-8660-0(X))* Routledge.
Wegner, Trevor. Applied Business Statistics: Methods & Excel-Based Applications. 2nd ed. 2010. (ENG., Illus.). 628p. pap. 62.00 *(978-0-7021-7286-1(3))* Juta Academic ZAF. Dist: Independent Pubs. Group.
World Bank. Doing Business 2012. 2011. (Doing Business Ser.). (ENG., Illus.). 264p. pap. 35.00 ***(978-0-8213-8833-4(9)**,* 9780821388334) World Bank Pubns.
Zhu, Zhiwei, et al. Excel Manual for Statistics for Business: Decision Making & Analysis. 2010. (ENG.). 136p. (C). pap. 24.67 *(978-0-321-64534-0(0))* Addison-Wesley Longman, Inc.

BUSINESS—STUDY AND TEACHING

see Business Education

BUSINESS—TAXATION

see Business Tax

BUSINESS—YEARBOOKS

Global Investment and Business Center. Albania Economic & Business Development Policy Handbook: Ultimate Source of Strategic Information, Data & Contacts for Successful Business in the Specific Region. annuals International Business Publications Staff, ed. 2008. (World Investment & Business Guide Library: Vol. 2). (ENG.). 300p. pap. 99.95 *(978-0-7397-4570-0(0))* International Business Pubns., USA.

BUSINESS, CHOICE OF

see Vocational Guidance

BUSINESS ADMINISTRATION

see Industrial Management

BUSINESS AGENTS

see Commercial Agents

BUSINESS AND EDUCATION

Aleckson, Jon D. & Ralston-Berg, Penny. MindMeld: Micro-Collaboration Between ELearning Designers & Instructor Experts. 2011. pap. ***(978-1-891859-85-4(4))*** Atwood Publishing.
Alexander, Dameon. The Imprint of Business Norms on American Education. 2011. 292p. ***(978-1-60497-794-3(9))*** Cambria Pr.
Angel, Dan & Connelly, Terry. Riptide: The New Normal in Higher Education. 2011. 270p. pap. 20.00 ***(978-0-9835095-2-3(2))*** The Publishing Place LLC.
Baker, Geoff & Fisher, Andrew, eds. Arts & Humanities Academics in Schools: Mapping the Pedagogical Interface. 2011. (ENG.). 192p. 140.00 *(978-1-4411-0622-3(7))* Continuum International Publishing Group, Ltd. GBR. Dist: National Bk. Network.
Ball, Stephen J. Global Policy Networks Social Enterprise & Edu-Business. 2012. (ENG., Illus.). 184p. (C). 155.00 ***(978-0-415-68409-5(9))***; pap. 44.95 ***(978-0-415-68410-1(2))*** Routledge.
Beidler, Peter G. Self-Reliance, Inc: A Twentieth-Century Walden Experiment. 2009. 204p. pap. 14.95 *(978-1-60381-002-9(1)*, Coffeetown Pr.) Coffeetown Enterprises, Inc.
Bleak, Jared L. When for-Profit Meets Nonprofit. 2010. 196p. pap. 39.95 *(978-0-415-88246-0(X))* Routledge.
Bolay, Jean-Claude, et al, eds. Technologies & Innovations for Development: Scientific Cooperation for a Sustainable Future. 2012. (ENG., Illus.). xxx, 333p. 179.95 ***(978-2-8178-0267-1(5)**,* 2817802675) Springer.
Bottery, Mike. Lessons for Schools. *(978-0-304-32722-5(0)*, Burns & Oates) Continuum International Publishing Group, Ltd.
—Lessons for Schools. (Illus.). 192p. pap. *(978-0-304-32724-9(7)*, Burns & Oates) Continuum International Publishing Group, Ltd.
Bourrières, Jean-Paul. Proceedings of CEISIE '09. 2010. (Iste Ser.: 414). (ENG., Illus.). 320p. 158.00 *(978-1-84821-134-6(1)*, Wiley-ISTE) Wiley, John & Sons, Inc.
Boyles, Deron. The Corporate Assault on Youth: Commercialism, Exploitation, & the End of Innocence. 2008. (Adolescent Cultures, School & Society Ser.: Vol. 44). 248p. (C). pap. 32.95 *(978-1-4331-0084-0(3))* Lang, Peter Publishing, Inc.
Brc. The Brc Academy Journal of Education: Vol. 1, No. 2. 2011. 102p. pap. 16.00 ***(978-1-60497-797-4(3))*** Cambria Pr.
—The Brc Journal of Advances in Business: Vol. 1, No. 2. 2011. 164p. pap. 17.00 ***(978-1-60497-784-4(1))*** Cambria Pr.
—The Brc Journal of Advances in Education: Vol. 1, No. 2. 2011. 126p. pap. 12.00 ***(978-1-60497-771-4(X))*** Cambria Pr.
—Proceedings of the 2010 Business Research Consortium of Western New York. 2011. 478p. pap. 22.00 ***(978-1-60497-809-4(0))*** Cambria Pr.
Business Research Consortium Of Wny. The Brc Academy Journal of Education: Vol. 1 No. 1. 2010. 142p. pap. 29.99 *(978-1-60497-689-2(6))* Cambria Pr.
—The Brc Journal of Advances in Education: Vol. 1, No. 1. 2010. 108p. pap. 29.99 *(978-1-60497-691-5(8))* Cambria Pr.
Cambridge, Darren. E-Portfolios & Global Diffusion: Solutions for Collaborative Education. 2012. ***(978-1-4666-0145-1(0))***; ***(978-1-4666-0143-7(4))*** IGI Global.
Cheng, Winnie & Kong, Kenneth C. C., eds. Professional Communication: Collaboration Between Academics & Practitioners. 2009. (ENG., Illus.). 256p. (gr. 17). 50.00 *(978-962-209-965-4(3))* Hong Kong Univ. Pr. HKG. Dist: Columbia Univ. Pr.
Chorafas, Dimitris N. Education & Employment in the European Union: The Social Cost of Business. 2011. (Illus.). 328p. 124.95 *(978-0-566-09201-5(8)*, Gower Publishing Co., Ltd.) Ashgate Publishing, Ltd. GBR. Dist: Ashgate Publishing Co.
Cole, David R. Surviving Economic Crises through Education. 2012. (C). pap. 139.95 ***(978-1-4331-1478-6(X))***; (Illus.). xii, 267p. pap. 36.95 ***(978-1-4331-1479-3(8))*** Lang, Peter Publishing, Inc.
—Surviving Economic Crises Through Education. 2012. (Illus.). xii, 267p. E-Book ***(978-1-4539-0523-4(5))*** Lang, Peter GmbH, Europaischer Verlag der Wissenschaften.
Coppin, Dawn, et al. Universities in the Age of Corporate Science: The UC Berkeley-Novartis Controversy. 2007. (Illus.). 256p. 60.50 *(978-1-59213-533-2(1))* Temple Univ. Pr.
Crichton, Jonathan. The Discourse of Commercialization: A Multi-Perspectived Analysis. 2011. (Palgrave Studies in Professional & Organizational Discourse Ser.) (ENG., Illus.). 256p. 84.00 *(978-0-230-57911-8(6))* Palgrave Macmillan.
De Cos, Patricia L., et al. The Careers Project: An Economic Analysis of Ten Industry Clusters in California. 2009. (Illus.). iv, 268p. *(978-1-58703-276-9(7))* California Research Bureau.
Dehaan, Robert L. & Narayan, K. M., eds. Education for Innovation. 2007. 296p. (ENG.). *(978-90-8790-284-1(0))*; per. *(978-90-8790-073-1(2))* Sense Pubs.
Ekman, Marianne, et al, eds. Learning Regional Innovation: Scandinavian Models. 2011. (ENG., Illus.). 288p. 110.00 *(978-0-230-27560-7(5))* Palgrave Macmillan.
Eltis, David, et al, eds. Human Capital & Institutions: A Long-Run View. 2009. (ENG., Illus.). 352p. 90.00 *(978-0-521-76958-7(2))* Cambridge Univ. Pr.
Engineering and Physical Sciences Research Council Staff & IEEE Computer Society Staff, contrib. by. Testing: Academic & Industry Conference — Practice & Research Techniques: TAIC PART 2008: 29-31, August 2008, Windsor, United Kingdom: Sponsored by EPSRC ... [et A.L]. 2008. (Illus.). xi, 106p. *(978-0-7695-3383-4(3))* IEEE Computer Society Pr.
Etzkowitz. Mit & the Rise of Entrepreneurial Science. 2007. 232p. 43.95 *(978-0-415-43505-5(6))* Routledge.
Etzkowitz, Henry. The Triple Helix: University-Industry-Government Innovation in Action. 2008. (Illus.). 164p. 195.00 *(978-0-415-96450-0(4))*; XII, 164p. 38.95 *(978-0-415-96451-7(2))* Routledge.
European Commission Directorate-General XXII, Education, Training, and Youth, contrib. by. Current Situation Regarding Vocational Training in Latin America & the Caribbean. (Illus.). 78p. *(978-92-827-4569-4(4))* European Commission BEL. Dist: Balogh International, Inc.
Fabricant, Michael & Fine, Michelle. Charter Schools & the Corporate Makeover of Public Education: What's at Stake? 2012. (ENG., Illus.). 176p. pap. 25.95 ***(978-0-8077-5285-2(1))*** Teachers College Pr., Teachers College, Columbia Univ.
Fang, Daying. Xiao Qi He Zuo Chuang Xin: Bo Yi, Yan Hua Yu Dui Ce = Cooperative Innovation Between Enterprises & Universities: A Game, Evolution Analysis & Countermeasures Study. 2007. (Illus.). *(978-7-5017-7504-0(4))* China Economics Publishing Hse.
Federal Reserve. Excellence in Education Views on Improvi. 2006. 140p. per. 29.50 *(978-1-4102-2576-4(3))* Univ. Pr. of the Pacific.
Fetters, Michael, et al, eds. The Development of University-Based Entrepreneurship Ecosystems. 2010. (Illus.). 224p. 112.00 *(978-1-84980-263-5(7))* Elgar, Edward Publishing, Inc.
Flicek, Joseph R. & Moses, James. Global Higher Education Technology Transfer Office Benchmarks. 2011. 227p. pap. 279.00 ***(978-1-57440-167-7(X))*** Primary Research Group.
Gary D. Libecap Staff. Measuring the Social Value of Innovation. 2009. (Illus.). xvii, 267p. 124.95 *(978-1-84855-466-5(4))* Emerald Group Publishing Ltd. GBR. Dist: Turpin Distribution Services Ltd.
Giberson, Tom & Giberson, Greg. Knowledge Economy: The Commodification of Knowledge & Information in the Global Academic System. 2009. *(978-1-57273-910-9(X))*; *(978-1-57273-909-3(6))* Hampton Pr., Inc.
Gornitzka, Ase & Langfeldt, Liv, eds. Borderless Knowledge: Understanding the New Internationalisation of Research & Higher Education in Norway. (Higher Education Dynamics Ser.). 2010. x, 198p. pap. 159.00 *(978-90-481-7831-5(2)*, 9048178312) 2008. (Illus.). X, 198p. 159.00 *(978-1-4020-8282-5(7)*, 1402082827) Springer.
Hill, Dave & Hill, Dave. Global Neoliberalism & Education & Its Consequences. 2008. (Routledge Studies in Education & Neoliberalism Ser.). (ENG., Illus.). 282p. 125.00 *(978-0-415-95774-8(5))* Routledge.
Hussey, Matthew, et al, eds. Software Industry-Oriented Education Practices & Curriculum Development: Experiences & Lessons. 2011. 423p. 195.00 *(978-1-60960-797-5(X)*, Engineering Science Reference) IGI Global.
Hussey, Matthew, et al. Software Industry-Oriented Education Practices & Curriculum Development: Experiences & Lessons. 2011. ***(978-1-60960-799-9(6))*** IGI Global.
Innovation in Education Through Business & Educational STEM Partnerships: Hearing Before the Committee on Education & Labor, U.S. House of Representatives, One Hundred Tenth Congress, Second Session, Hearing Held in Washington, DC, July 22, 2008. 2008. (Illus.). iii, 85p. *(978-0-16-082341-1(2)*, 552-070-38398-1) United States Government Printing Office.
Janser, Dorothea, ed. Governance & Performance in the German Public Research Sector: Disciplinary Differences. 2010. (Higher Education Dynamics Ser.). (ENG., Illus.). xxvi, 150p. 159.00 *(978-90-481-9138-3(6)*, 9048191386) Springer.
Jarron, Christina. Corporations As Social Institutions. 2009. 172p. pap. *(978-3-639-19299-5(0))* VDM Verlag Dr. Mueller e.K.
Katzar, Jr. Foundations of Service Science: A Pragmatic Approach. 2008. 220p. pap. 19.95 *(978-1-4401-0653-8(3))* iUniverse, Inc.
Keith, Novella. Engaging in Social Partnerships: A Professional Guide for Successful Collaboration in Higher Education. 2011. (ENG.). 288p. 45.95 *(978-0-415-99637-2(6))* Routledge.
—Engaging in Social Partnerships: Successful Collaboration in Higher Education. 2011. (ENG.). 288p. instr.'s gde. ed. 140.00 *(978-0-415-99636-5(8))* Routledge.
Kenney, Matthew G. Academic Entrepreneurship. 2009. 124p. pap. *(978-3-639-11430-0(2))* VDM Verlag Dr. Mueller e.K.
Kim, Young Choon. The Rise of Organized Transfer Institutional Learning of Technology Transfer in American Research Universities. 2009. 108p. pap. *(978-3-639-10853-8(1))* VDM Verlag Dr. Mueller e.K.
Kingma, Bruce R., ed. Academic Entrepreneurship & Community Engagement: Scholarship in Action & the Syracuse Miracle. 2011. (Illus.). 168p. 99.95 ***(978-1-84980-155-3(X))*** Elgar, Edward Publishing, Inc.
Kock, Ned F., ed. Virtual Team Leadership & Collaborative Engineering Advancements: Contemporary Issues & Implications. 2009. (Advances in E-Collaboration Book Ser.). 396p. 195.00 *(978-1-60566-110-0(4))* IGI Global.
Leatherwood, Jim. Facing the Future Together: Forming Successful School-Business Partnerships. Foley, Michael, ed. 2007. (Illus.). 224p. pap. 17.95 *(978-0-9796245-0-6(9))* Brooke Pr., The.
Lorange, Peter. Thought Leadership Meets Business: How business schools can become more Successful. 2010. (ENG., Illus.). 262p. pap. 34.99 *(978-0-521-15912-8(1))* Cambridge Univ. Pr.
Malerba, Franco. Economic Development As a Learning Process: Variation Across Sectoral Systems. Nelson, R. R., ed. 2012. 320p. 125.00 ***(978-0-85793-788-9(X))*** Elgar, Edward Publishing, Inc.
Marot, Helen. Creative Impulse in Industry. 2009. 60p. pap. *(978-1-4590-7467-5(X))* Books LLC.
Mendoza, Pilar. Academic Capitalism & Doctoral Student Socialization. 2008. 176p. pap. *(978-3-639-06437-7(2))* VDM Verlag Dr. Mueller e.K.
Miller, Robert C., et al. Developing University-Industry Relations: Pathways to Innovation from the West Coast. 2009. (ENG.). 176p. 42.00 *(978-0-470-43396-6(5)*, Jossey-Bass) Wiley, John & Sons, Inc.
Mjelde, Liv. Knowing Work: The Social Relations of Working & Knowing. Weil, Markus & Koski, Leena, eds. 2009. (Studies in Vocational & Continuing Education Ser.). 254p. pap. *(978-3-03911-642-3(8))* Lang, Peter.
Mjelde, Liv & Daly, Richard Heywood. Working Knowledge in a Globalizing World: From Work to Learning, from Learning to Work. 2006. (Illus.). 406p. pap. 96.95 *(978-3-03910-974-6(X))* Lang, Peter Publishing, Inc.
Orcutt, John & Shen, Hong. Shaping China's Innovation Future: University Technology Transfer in Transition. 2011. (Illus.). 320p. 135.00 *(978-1-84980-358-8(7))* Elgar, Edward Publishing, Inc.
Oyelaran-Oyeyinka, Banji & ABIOLA ADEBOWALE, Boladale. University-Industry Linkage in Nigeri. 2010. 72p. pap. *(978-3-8383-8248-7(X))* Lambert Academic Publishing.
Patrinos, Harry Anthony & Sosale, Shobhana, eds. Mobilizing the Private Sector for Public Education: A View from the Trenches. 2007. (Directions in Development Ser.). (ENG., Illus.). 104p. per. 15.00 *(978-0-8213-7199-2(1)*, 9780821371992) World Bank Pubns.
Rickne, Annika, et al, eds. Innovation Governance in an Open Economy: Shaping regional nodes in a globalized World. 2012. (Regions & Cities Ser.). (ENG., Illus.). 304p. (C). 130.00 ***(978-0-415-50493-5(7))*** Routledge.
Rickne, Annika, et al. Innovation Governance in an Open Economy: Shaping Regional Nodes in a Globalized World. 2012. pap. ***(978-0-203-12130-6(9))*** Routledge.
Rimanoczy, Isabel & Turner, Ernie. Action Reflection Learning: Solving Real Business Problems by Connecting Learning with Earning. 2008. (ENG., Illus.). 214p. 36.95 *(978-0-89106-240-0(8))* Ebsco Publishing.
Saad, Mohammed & Zawdie, Girma. Theory & Practice of Triple Helix Model in Developing Countries: Issues & Challenges. 2011. (ENG., Illus.). 336p. (C). 125.00 *(978-0-415-47516-7(3))* Routledge.
Sandler, Michael R. Social Entrepreneurship in Education: Private Ventures for the Public Good. 2010. (New Frontiers in Education Ser.). (ENG.). 170p. 74.95 *(978-1-60709-355-8(3))*; pap. 32.95 *(978-1-60709-356-5(1))* Rowman & Littlefield Education.
Schrecker, Ellen. The Lost Soul of Higher Education: Corporatization, the Assault on Academic Freedom, & the End of the American University. 2010. (ENG.). 304p. 27.95 *(978-1-59558-400-7(5))* New Pr., The.
Sewell, Tony. Power in the Academy. Satterthwaite, Jerome et al, eds. 2009. (Discourse, Power & Resistance Ser.). 210p. pap. 34.95 *(978-1-85856-447-0(6))* Trentham Bks. Ltd. GBR. Dist: Stylus Publishing, LLC.
Siegel, David, ed. Organizing for Social Partnership: Higher Education in Cross-Sector Collaboration. 2010. (ENG., Illus.). 224p. 150.00 *(978-0-415-99498-9(5))*; pap. 40.95 *(978-0-415-99499-6(3))* Routledge.
Slaughter, Sheila & Rhoades, Gary. Academic Capitalism & the New Economy: Markets, State, & Higher Education. 2009. (ENG., Illus.). 384p. (gr. 17). pap. 32.00 *(978-0-8018-9233-2(3))* Johns Hopkins Univ. Pr.
St Leger, Pamela. School-Industry Partnership. 2011. 288p. pap. ***(978-3-8433-8510-7(6))*** Lambert Academic Publishing.
Stabile, Donald R. Economics, Competition & Academia: An Intellectual History of Sophism Versus Virtue. 2007. 160p. 119.00 *(978-1-84720-236-9(5))* Elgar, Edward Publishing, Inc.
Strengthening America's Competitiveness Through Common Academic Standards: Hearing Before the Committee on Education & Labor, U.S. House of Representatives, One Hundred Eleventh Congress, First Session, Hearing Held in Washington, DC, April 29, 2009. 2009. (Illus.). iii, 48p. *(978-0-16-083891-0(6)*, 552-070-39580-6) United States Government Printing Office.
Sweet-Holp, Timothy. Public/Private Partnerships in Education. 2008. 216p. pap. *(978-3-639-06024-9(5))* VDM Verlag Dr. Mueller e.K.
Teichler, Ulrich. Higher Education & the World of Work. 2008. 340p. *(978-90-8790-755-6(9))*; pap. *(978-90-8790-754-9(0))* Sense Pubs.
Thorp, Holden & Goldstein, Buck. Engines of Innovation: The Entrepreneurial University in the Twenty-First Century. 2010. (ENG., Illus.). 192p. 25.00 *(978-0-8078-3438-1(6))* Univ. of North Carolina Pr.
Turk, James, ed. Universities at Risk: How Politics, Special Interests & Corporatization Threaten Academic Integrity. 2008. (ENG.). 416p. pap. 24.95 *(978-1-55277-040-5(0))* Lorimer, James & Co., Ltd., Pubs. CAN. Dist: Casemate Pubs. & Bk. Distributors, LLC.
Viale. The Capitalization of Knowledge a Triple Helix of University-Industry-Government. 2010. (Illus.). 368p. 155.00 *(978-1-84844-114-9(2))* Elgar, Edward Publishing, Inc.
Wang, Jue. Resource Spillover from Academia to High-Tech Industry. 2008. 144p. pap. *(978-3-639-08243-2(5))* VDM Verlag Dr. Mueller e.K.
Wankel, Charles & DeFillippi, Bob. University & Corporate Innovations in Lifelong Learning. 2008. (Research in Management Education & Development Ser.). (Illus.). 288p. (C). *(978-1-59311-810-5(4))*; per. *(978-1-59311-809-9(0))* Information Age Publishing, Inc.
Washburn, Jennifer. University Inc: The Corporate Corruption of Higher Education. 2006. (ENG.). 352p. per. 18.95 *(978-0-465-09052-5(4))* Basic Bks.
Watkins, William H. The Assault on Public Education: Confronting the Politics of Corporate School Reform. 2011. ***(978-0-8077-5255-5(X))*** Teachers College Pr., Teachers College, Columbia Univ.

B

Watkins, William H., ed. The Assault on Public Education: Confronting the Politics of Corporate School Reform. 2011. (ENG., Illus.). 224p. pap. 35.95 ***(978-0-8077-5254-8(1))*** Teachers College Pr., Teachers College, Columbia Univ.

White, Robert E. How Corporate Business Practices are Transforming Education: Case Studies of Five Canadian Secondary Schools. 2009. xii, 433p. *(978-0-7734-3895-8(5))* Mellen, Edwin Pr., The.

Wilson, Alan. Knowledge Power: Interdisciplinary Education for a Complex World. 2010. (ENG., Illus.). 184p. 36.95 *(978-0-415-55311-7(3))* Routledge.

—Knowledge Power: Interdisciplinary Education for a Complex World. 2010. (ENG., Illus.). 184p. 130.00 *(978-0-415-55310-0(5)*, Routledge) Taylor & Francis Group GBR. Dist: Taylor & Francis Group.

Wolf, Alison & Evans, Karen. Improving Literacy at Work. 2010. (Improving Learning Ser.). (ENG., Illus.). 224p. (C). 120.00 *(978-0-415-54868-7(3))* Routledge.

Wong, Poh Kam. Academic Entrepreneurship in Asia: The Role & Impact of Universities in National Innovation Systems. 2012. (New Horizons in Entrepreneurship Ser.). (Illus.). 360p. 135.00 ***(978-1-84980-307-6(2))*** Elgar, Edward Publishing, Inc.

Woodhouse, Howard Robert. Selling Out: Academic Freedom & the Corporate Market. 2009. (ENG.). 350p. (C). *(978-0-7735-3580-0(2))* McGill-Queen's Univ. Pr.

Wright, Tony. University Spin-Outs Processes & Policies. 2007. (Illus.). 240p. (C). pap. 119.00 *(978-1-84542-648-4(7))* Elgar, Edward Publishing, Inc.

Yusuf, Shahid & Nabeshima, Kaoru, eds. How Universities Promote Economic Growth. 2006. (Directions in Development Ser.). (ENG., Illus.). 312p. per. 35.00 *(978-0-8213-6751-3(X)*, 9780821367513) World Bank Pubns.

Zhou, Mark, ed. Advances in Education & Management: International Symposium, ISAEBD 2011, Dalian, China, August 6-7, 2011, Proceedings, Part IV. 2011. (Communications in Computer & Information Science Ser.). (ENG., Illus.). xiii, 627p. pap. 131.00 ***(978-3-642-23061-5(X)***, 364223061X) Springer.

—Education & Management: International Symposium, ISAEBD 2011, Dalian, China, August 6-7, 2011, Proceedings, Part III. 2011. (Communications in Computer & Information Science Ser.). (ENG., Illus.). xiv, 647p. pap. 131.00 ***(978-3-642-23064-6(4)***, 3642230644) Springer.

Zhou, Qingyuan, ed. Advances in Applied Economics, Business & Development: International Symposium, ISAEBD 2011, Dalian, China, August 6-7, 2011, Proceedings, Part II. 2011. (Communications in Computer & Information Science Ser.). (ENG.). xvi, 616p. pap. 131.00 ***(978-3-642-23019-6(9)***, 3642230199) Springer.

—Applied Economics, Business & Development: International Symposium, ISAEBD 2011, Dalian, China, August 6-7, 2011, Proceedings, Part I. 2011. (Communications in Computer & Information Science Ser.). (Illus.). xiv, 616p. pap. 131.00 ***(978-3-642-23022-6(9)***, 3642230229) Springer.

BUSINESS AND POLITICS

An, Wu Xiao. Chinese Business Making Malay. 2010. (Illus.). 239p. pap. 28.00 *(978-9971-69-496-8(4))* National Univ. of Singapore Pr. SGP. Dist: Univ. of Hawaii Pr.

Anderson, Carl. Beyond a House Divided: The Moral Consensus Ignored by Washington, Wall Street, & the Media. 2010. (ENG.). 160p. pap. 12.00 *(978-0-307-88774-0(X)*, Image) Doubleday Religious Publishing Group, The.

Ashton, Robert. The City & the Court 1603-1643. 2008. (ENG.). 264p. pap. 37.99 *(978-0-521-07137-6(2))* Cambridge Univ. Pr.

Baker, Russ. Family of Secrets: The Bush Dynasty, the Powerful Forces That Put It in the White House, & What Their Influence Means for America. 2008. (ENG., Illus.). 592p. 30.00 *(978-1-59691-557-2(9))* Bloomsbury Publishing.

Benjamin, Ed. Cash in on the Obama $3 Trillion Spending Plan! How to Make Large Amounts of Money by Conducting Business with or Receiving Grants from Federal, State, & Local Governments. 2009. 196p. pap. 24.95 *(978-1-4327-4428-1(3))* Outskirts Pr., Inc.

Bernhagen, Patrick. The Political Power of Business: Structure & Information in Public Policymaking. 2008. (Routledge Research in Comparative Politics Ser.). (ENG., Illus.). 192p. (C). 135.00 *(978-0-415-45105-5(1))* Routledge.

Bernstein, Ann. The Case for Business in Developing Economies. (ENG.). 2012. 408p. (gr. 12). pap. 20.00 ***(978-0-14-352799-2(1))*** 2010. 412p. 34.95 *(978-0-14-302652-5(6))* Penguin Group (USA) Inc. (Penguin Global).

Boeri, Tito, et al, eds. The Ruling Class: Management & Politics in Modern Italy. 2010. (ENG., Illus.). 272p. 99.00 *(978-0-19-958828-2(7))* Oxford Univ. Pr., Inc.

Boggs, Carl E. Phantom Democracy: Corporate Interests & Political Power in America. 2011. (ENG.). 320p. 95.00 *(978-0-230-11574-3(8))* Palgrave Macmillan.

Boiardi, Priscilla. Business-Government Relations for the Promotion of R & D & Innovation. 2011. 104p. pap. ***(978-3-8443-8446-8(4))*** Lambert Academic Publishing.

Bremmer, Ian & Keat, Preston. The Fat Tail: The Power of Political Knowledge for Strategic Investing. 2009. (ENG., Illus.). 272p. 27.95 *(978-0-19-532855-4(8))* Oxford Univ. Pr., Inc.

Brodsgaard, Kjeld Erik. Hainan - State, Society, & Business in a Chinese Province. 2012. (China Policy Ser.). (ENG., Illus.). 208p. (C). pap. 42.95 ***(978-0-415-54138-1(7))*** Routledge.

Brooks, Arthur C. The Battle: How the Fight between Free Enterprise & Big Government Will Shape America's Future. 2011. (ENG.). 208p. (gr. 9). pap. 15.99 *(978-0-465-02212-0(X))* Basic Bks.

Brown, Floyd & Troxler, Lee. Killing Wealth, Freeing Wealth: How to Save America's Economy. & Your Own. 2010. 288p. 25.95 *(978-1-935071-81-5(5))* WND Bks, Inc.

Cabrera, Mercedes & Rey, Fernando del. The Powers of Entrepreneurs: Politics & Economy in Contemporary Spain. 2006. 220p. (C). 90.00 *(978-1-84545-185-1(6))* Berghahn Bks., Inc.

Carney, Timothy P. The Big Ripoff: How Big Business & Big Government Steal Your Money. 2006. (ENG.). 285p. 24.95 *(978-0-471-78907-9(0)*, Wiley) Wiley, John & Sons, Inc.

—Obamanomics: How Barack Obama Is Bankrupting You & Enriching His Wall Street Friends, Corporate Lobbyists, & Union Bosses. 2009. (ENG.). 256p. 27.95 *(978-1-59698-612-1(3))* Regnery Publishing, Inc., An Eagle Publishing Co.

Cassis, Youssef. City Bankers, 1890-1914. Rocques, Margaret, tr. from FRE. 2009. (ENG., Illus.). 368p. pap. 38.99 *(978-0-521-10521-7(8))* Cambridge Univ. Pr.

Chua, Christian. Chinese Big Business in Indonesia. 2009. 196p. pap. 39.95 *(978-0-415-57424-2(2))* Routledge.

—Chinese Big Business in Indonesia: The State of Capital. 2008. (Routledge Contemporary Southeast Asia Ser.). (Illus.). XVI, 176p. 150.00 *(978-0-415-45074-4(8))* Routledge.

Clements, Jeffrey D. Corporations Are Not People: Why They Have More Rights Than You Do & What You Can Do about It. 2012. (ENG.). 240p. pap. 17.95 ***(978-1-60994-105-5(5))*** Berrett-Koehler Pubs., Inc.

Coen, David, et al, eds. The Oxford Handbook of Business & Government. 2010. (Oxford Handbooks Ser.). (ENG., Illus.). 750p. 150.00 *(978-0-19-921427-3(1))* Oxford Univ. Pr., Inc.

Coen, David, et al. The Oxford Handbook of Business & Government. 2012. (ENG.). 808p. pap. 49.95 ***(978-0-19-969374-0(9))*** Oxford Univ. Pr., Inc.

Colman, Tyler. Wine Politics: How Governments, Environmentalists, Mobsters, & Critics Influence the Wines We Drink. 2008. (Illus.). 216p. 45.00 *(978-0-520-25521-0(6))* Univ. of California Pr.

Cox, Ronald W., ed. Business Power in US Foreign Policy. 2012. (Routledge Studies in US Foreign Policy Ser.). (ENG., Illus.). 232p. 130.00 *(978-0-415-78196-1(5))* Routledge.

Cram101 Textbook Reviews & Cram101 Textbook Reviews. Outlines & Highlights for Business, Government, & Society. 2011. 680p. pap. 41.95 ***(978-1-61461-283-4(8))*** Cram101 Inc.

Crane, Andrew, et al. Corporations & Citizenship: Business, Responsibility & Society. 2008. (Business Value Creation & Society Ser.). (ENG., Illus.). 264p. pap. 37.00 *(978-0-521-61283-8(7))* Cambridge Univ. Pr.

Crouse, Angie, et al. The Blue Pages: A Directory of Companies Rated by Their Politics & Practices. 2nd ed. 2009. (Blue Pages: A Directory of Companies Rated by Their Politics & Ser.). (ENG.). 320p. pap. 12.95 *(978-0-9817091-4-7(1))* PoliPointPress, LLC.

Deitelhoff, Nicole & Wolf, Klaus Dieter, eds. Corporate Security Responsibility? Corporate Governance Contributions to Peace & Security in Zones of Conflict. 2010. (Global Issues Ser.). (ENG., Illus.). 256p. 95.00 *(978-0-230-24184-8(0))* Palgrave Macmillan.

Duckenfield, Mark. Battles over Free Trade: Anglo-American Experiences with International Trade, 1776-2006, 4 vols. 2008. (ENG.). 1616p. 725.00 *(978-1-85196-935-7(7))* Pickering & Chatto Pubs., Ltd. GBR. Dist: Ashgate Publishing Co.

Edgar, Patrick B. Rational Gridlock. 2011. (ENG.). 176p. pap. 26.99 *(978-0-7618-5165-3(8))* Univ. Pr. of America, Inc.

Eising, Rainer. The Political Economy of State-Business Relations in Europe: Interest Mediation, Capitalism & EU Policy Making. 2009. (Routledge/UACES Contemporary European Studies). (ENG., Illus.). 256p. (C). 128.00 *(978-0-415-46507-6(9))* Routledge.

Falaschetti, Dino. Democratic Governance & Economic Performance: How Accountability Can Go Too Far in Politics & Business. 2009. (Studies in Public Choice Ser.). (ENG., Illus.). xvi, 168p. 159.00 *(978-0-387-78706-0(2))* Springer.

Falck, Oliver, et al, eds. Industrial Policy for National Champions. 2011. (CESifo Seminar Ser.). (ENG., Illus.). 224p. (gr. 17). 35.00 *(978-0-262-01601-8(X))* MIT Pr.

Flohr, Annegret, et al. The Role of Business in Global Governance: Corporations as Norm-Entrepreneurs. 2010. (Global Issues Ser.). (ENG., Illus.). 288p. 100.00 *(978-0-230-24397-2(5))* Palgrave Macmillan.

Florus, Justin. Guerre des Polices et Affaires Corses. 2009. (FRE.). 134p. *(978-2-84736-454-5(4))* Nouveau Monde editions.

Fraser, Jay. The American Publisher: Paying the Cost of Corporatism & Censorship for Writing the Truth about Cuba, Russia, & the War on Terror. 2010. (Illus.). 256p. 28.00 *(978-1-879915-22-0(7))* Signal Peak Pr. LLC.

Fuchs, Doris. Business Power in Global Governance. 2007. (Illus.). 240p. (C). pap. 22.00 *(978-1-58826-468-8(8))*; lib. bdg. 55.00 *(978-1-58826-492-3(0))* Rienner, Lynne Pubs.

Ghosh, D. N. Business & Polity: Dynamics of a Changing Relationship. 2011. 468p. (C). 40.00 *(978-81-321-0531-2(1)*, B05312C) SAGE Pubns., Inc.

Gill, Graeme. Politics in the Russian Regions. Gill, Graeme, ed. 2007. (Studies in Central & Eastern Europe Ser.). (ENG., Illus.). 240p. 105.00 *(978-0-230-51686-1(6))* Palgrave Macmillan.

Gourevitch, Peter Alexis & Shinn, James J. Political Power & Corporate Control: The New Global Politics of Corporate Governance. 2007. (ENG., Illus.). 368p. (C). per. 24.95 *(978-0-691-13381-2(6))* Princeton Univ. Pr.

Gourvish, Terry, ed. Business & Politics in Europe, 1900-1970: Essays in Honour of Alice Teichova. 2011. (ENG., Illus.). 358p. pap. 45.00 *(978-1-107-40274-4(3))* Cambridge Univ. Pr.

Grote, Jrgen R., et al. Organized Business Interests in Changing Environments: The Complexity of Adaptation. Grote, Jrgen R. et al, eds. 2008. (Globalization & Governance Ser.). (ENG., Illus.). 256p. 95.00 *(978-0-230-21665-5(X))* Palgrave Macmillan.

Hartmann, Thom. Unequal Protection: The Rise of Corporate Dominance & the Theft of Human Rights. 2nd ed. 2010. (ENG., Illus.). 360p. pap. 19.95 *(978-1-60509-559-2(1))* Berrett-Koehler Pubs., Inc.

Hayes, Christopher L. Twilight of the Elites: America after Meritocracy. 2012. (ENG.). 304p. 26.00 ***(978-0-307-72045-0(4)***, Crown) Crown Publishing Group.

Hightower, Jim. Swim Against the Current: Even a Dead Fish Can Go with the Flow. 2008. (ENG.). 224p. pap. 14.95 *(978-0-470-42283-0(1))*; (Illus.). 25.95 *(978-0-470-12151-1(3))* Wiley, John & Sons, Inc. (Wiley).

Hoffman, Andrew, et al. Molten Metal Technology. 2010. (C). pap. 7.00 *(978-1-61674-517-2(7))*; pap. 20.00 *(978-1-61674-515-8(0))* Davidson, William Institute At The Univ. of Michigan, The.

Hoopes, James. Corporate Dreams: Big Business in American Democracy from the Great Depression to the Great Recession. 2011. (Ideas in Action Ser.). (ENG., Illus.). 224p. 24.95 *(978-0-8135-5130-2(7))* Rutgers Univ. Pr.

—Hail to the CEO: The Failure of George W. Bush & the Cult of Moral Leadership, 1 vol. 2007. (Illus.). 144p. 34.95 *(978-0-313-34784-9(0)*, C34784, Praeger Pubs.) Greenwood Publishing Group, Inc.

Hughes, Owen E. & O'Neill, Deirdre. Business, Government & Globalisation. 2008. (ENG., Illus.). 288p. pap. 39.00 *(978-0-333-69320-9(5))* Palgrave Macmillan.

Jones, Norman. Main Street vs Wall Street: Wake-up Calls for America's Leaders. 2010. 216p. 27.99 *(978-1-4490-9595-6(X))*; pap. 21.49 *(978-1-4490-9594-9(1))* AuthorHouse.

Ken, Glozer. Great Corn Ethanol Ripoff. 2011. (Hoover Inst Press Publication). (ENG.). 228p. 19.95 *(978-0-8179-4961-7(5))* Hoover Institution Pr.

Kennedy, Scott. The Business of Lobbying in China. 2008. (Illus.). 278p. per. 22.50 *(978-0-674-02744-2(2))* Harvard Univ. Pr.

Komatsu, Keiichiro. Global Politico-Economic Crises: The pragmatic Approach. 2013. (Routledge Studies in the Modern World Economy Ser.). (ENG.). 288p. (C). 125.00 *(978-0-415-47766-6(2))* Routledge.

Kraft, Michael E. & Kamieniecki, Sheldon, eds. Business & Environmental Policy: Corporate Interests in the American Political System. 2007. (American & Comparative Environmental Policy Ser.). (ENG., Illus.). 376p. (gr. 17). 62.00 *(978-0-262-11305-2(8))*; per. 27.00 *(978-0-262-61218-0(6))* MIT Pr.

Krismer, John R. Our Puppet Government. 2008. (Illus.). 300p. pap. *(978-0-9809191-6-5(9)*, CCB Publishing) CCB Publishing.

Ma, Hao, et al. Corporate Political Strategies of Private Chinese Firms. 2011. (ENG., Illus.). 168p. (C). 160.00 *(978-0-415-61479-5(1))* Routledge.

Macdonald, Douglas. Business & Environmental Politics in Canada. 2nd ed. 2007. (ENG.). 240p. pap. *(978-1-4426-0032-4(2))* Univ. of Toronto Pr.

Machan, Tibor R. The Morality of Business: A Profession for Human Wealthcare. 2010. (ENG.). xii, 138p. pap. 124.00 *(978-1-4419-4312-5(9)*, 1441943129) Springer.

—The Morality of Business: A Profession for Human Wealthcare. 2007. (ENG.). xii, 138p. 124.00 *(978-0-387-48906-3(1)*, 0387489061) Springer London, Ltd. GBR. Dist: Springer.

Magnusson, Lars. Nation, State & the Industrial Revolution: The Visible Hand. 2009. (Routledge Explorations in Economic History Ser.). (ENG.). 208p. 135.00 *(978-0-415-46177-1(4))* Routledge.

Manheim, Frank T. The Conflict over Environmental Regulation in the United States: Origins, Outcomes, & Comparisons with the EU & Other Regions. 2009. (ENG., Illus.). xviii, 322p. 59.95 *(978-0-387-75876-3(3)*, 0387758763) Springer.

Markovits, Claude. Merchants, Traders, Entrepreneurs: Indian Business in the Colonial ERA. 2008. (ENG.). 320p. 100.00 *(978-0-230-20598-7(4))* Palgrave Macmillan.

McDermott, John. Restoring Democracy to America: How to Free Markets & Politics from the Corporate Culture of Business & Government. 2010. (ENG.). 456p. 69.95 *(978-0-271-03724-0(5))* Pennsylvania State Univ. Pr.

Mckellar, Robert. A Short Guide to Political Risk. 2010. (Short Guides to Business Risk Ser.). (Illus.). 200p. pap. 34.95 *(978-0-566-09160-5(7)*, Gower Publishing Co., Ltd.) Ashgate Publishing, Ltd. GBR. Dist: Ashgate Publishing Co.

Miller, Raymond C. International Political Economy: Contrasting World Views. 2008. (ENG., Illus.). 296p. 175.00 *(978-0-415-38408-7(7))*; 44.95 *(978-0-415-38409-4(5))* Routledge.

Mitchell, Neil J. Agents of Atrocity: Leaders, Followers, & the Violation of Human Rights in Civil War. 2009. (ENG.). 240p. pap. 33.00 *(978-0-230-61902-9(9))* Palgrave Macmillan.

Moran, Michael. Business, Politics, & Society: An Anglo-American Comparison. 2009. (ENG.). 250p. 125.00 *(978-0-19-920255-3(9))*; pap. 45.00 *(978-0-19-920256-0(7))* Oxford Univ. Pr., Inc.

Morser, Eric J. Hinterland Dreams: The Political Economy of a Midwestern City. 2010. (American Business, Politics, & Society Ser.). (Illus.). 288p. (C). 55.00 *(978-0-8122-4276-8(9))* Univ. of Pennsylvania Pr.

Nedergaard, Peter. Business & Politics in the European Union: Cases in Services, Agriculture & Textiles. 2009. 160p. 59.00 *(978-87-574-2083-8(1))* Djof Publishing DNK. Dist: International Specialized Bk. Services.

Phillips-Fein, Kim & Zelizer, Julian E., eds. What's Good for Business: Business & American Politics since World War II, 1 vol. 2012. (ENG.). 280p. pap. 24.95 ***(978-0-19-975400-7(4))*** Oxford Univ. Pr., Inc.

Reno, William. Corruption & State Politics in Sierra Leone. 2008. (African Studies). (ENG., Illus.). 244p. (C). pap. 31.99 *(978-0-521-10347-3(9))* Cambridge Univ. Pr.

Ringen, Stein. What Democracy Is For: On Freedom & Moral Government. (ENG., Illus.). 334p. (C). 2009. pap. 29.95 *(978-0-691-14116-9(9))* 2007. 52.50 *(978-0-691-12984-6(3))* Princeton Univ. Pr.

Ronit, Karsten, ed. Global Public Policy. 2010. (Illus.). 202p. pap. 39.95 ***(978-0-415-59956-6(3))*** Routledge.

Ronit, Karsten, ed. Global Public Policy: Business & the Countervailing Powers of Civil Society. 2007. (RIPE Series in Global Political Economy). (ENG., Illus.). 202p. (C). 150.00 *(978-0-415-36511-6(2))* Routledge.

Rothkopf, David. Power Inc: The Epic Rivalry Between Big Business & Government-and the Reckoning That Lies Ahead. 2012. (ENG., Illus.). 448p. 30.00 ***(978-0-374-15128-7(8))*** Farrar, Straus & Giroux.

Roy, Jeffrey. Business & Government in Canada. 2007. (Governance Ser.). (ENG., Illus.). 208p. pap. *(978-0-7766-0658-3(1))* Univ. of Ottawa Pr./Presses de l'Universite d'Ottawa.

Salacuse, Jeswald W. Seven Secrets for Negotiating with Government: How to Deal with Local, State, National, or Foreign Governments — And Come Out Ahead. 2008. (ENG.). 224p. 24.95 *(978-0-8144-0908-4(3))* Amacom.

Sasada, Hironori. The Evolution of the Japanese Developmental State. 2012. (Routledge Studies in the Modern History of Asia Ser.). (ENG., Illus.). 220p. (C). 145.00 ***(978-0-415-50346-4(9))*** Routledge.

Saxén, Albert. Symbolic Value in International Politics. 2010. 96p. pap. 12.00 *(978-1-4452-7255-9(5))* Lulu Enterprises Inc.

Schelhase, Marc. Globalization, Regionalization & Business: Conflict, Convergence & Influence. 2008. (ENG., Illus.). 224p. 89.00 *(978-0-230-57329-1(0))* Palgrave Macmillan.

Sell, Axel & Krylov, Alexander N., eds. Government Relations: Interaktionen zwischen Wirtschaft, Politik und Gesellschaft. 2009. (GER.). 308p. pap. 74.95 *(978-3-631-58487-3(3))* Lang, Peter GmbH, Europaischer Verlag der Wissenschaften DEU. Dist: Lang, Peter.

Sirota, David. Hostile Takeover: How Big Money & Corruption Conquered Our Government — and How We Take It Back. 2007. (ENG.). 384p. per. 13.95 *(978-0-307-23735-4(4)*, Three Rivers Pr.) Crown Publishing Group.

—The Uprising: An Unauthorized Tour of the Populist Revolt Scaring Wall Street & Washington. 2009. (ENG., Illus.). 400p. pap. 14.95 *(978-0-307-39564-1(2)*, Three Rivers Pr.) Crown Publishing Group.

Suder, Gabriele. Doing Business in Europe. (C). 2007. 368p. 135.00 *(978-1-4129-1846-6(4)*, B18464C) 2007. (Illus.). 368p. per. 63.00 *(978-1-4129-1847-3(2)*, B18464P) 2nd ed. 2012. 472p. 140.00 ***(978-0-85702-084-0(6)***, B20840C) 2nd ed. 2012. 472p. pap. 56.00 ***(978-0-85702-085-7(4)***, B20840P) SAGE Pubns., Ltd. GBR. Dist: SAGE Pubns., Inc.

Thacker, Strom C. Big Business, the State, & Free Trade: Constructing Coalitions in Mexico. 2006. (ENG.). 256p. pap. 38.99 *(978-0-521-03213-1(0))* Cambridge Univ. Pr.

The World Economic Forum Water Initiative. Water Security: The Water-Food-Energy-Climate Nexus. 2011. (ENG.). 272p. 60.00 *(978-1-59726-735-9(X))* Island Pr.

Tombs, Francis. Power Politics: Political Encounters in Industry & Engineering. 2011. (ENG., Illus.). 192p. 40.00 *(978-1-84885-506-9(0))* I. B. Tauris & Co., Ltd. GBR. Dist: Macmillan.

Torres, Olivier. The Wine Wars: The Mondavi Affair, Globalisation & Terroir. Snaith, Kirsty, tr. from FRE. annot. ed. 2006. (ENG.). 192p. 121.00 *(978-0-230-00210-4(2))* Palgrave Macmillan.

United Nations: Economic Commission for Europe. Assessing Regional Integration in Africa Iv: Enhancing Intra-African Trade. 2010. (ENG.). 524p. pap. 55.00 ***(978-92-1-125114-2(1))*** United Nations Pubns.

Utting, Peter & Marques, José Carlos, eds. Business, Politics & Public Policy Vol. 2: Implications for Inclusive Development. 2010. (International Political Economy Ser.). (ENG., Illus.). 304p. 95.00 *(978-0-230-57645-2(1))* Palgrave Macmillan.

Vigoda-Gadot, Eran & Drory, Amos, eds. Handbook of Organizational Politics. 2008. (Elgar Original Reference Ser.). 392p. pap. 66.00 *(978-1-84720-795-1(2))* Elgar, Edward Publishing, Inc.

Wenger, Andreas. Russian Business Power: The Role of Russian Business in Foreign & Security Relations. 2009. (ENG., Illus.). 288p. (C). pap. 44.95 *(978-0-415-54569-3(2))* Routledge.

Wenger, Andreas, et al, eds. Russian Business Power: The Role of Russian Business in Foreign & Security Relations. 2006. (Routledge Transnational Crime & Corruption Ser.). (ENG., Illus.). 267p. (C). 168.00 *(978-0-415-37478-1(2))* Routledge.

Werner, Timothy. Public Forces & Private Politics in American Big Business. 2012. (ENG., Illus.). 216p. 90.00 ***(978-1-107-02291-1(6))*** Cambridge Univ. Pr.

Yadav, Vineeta. Political Parties, Business Groups, & Corruption in Developing Countries, 1 vol. 2011. (ENG., Illus.). 288p. pap. 29.95 *(978-0-19-973591-4(3))* Oxford Univ. Pr., Inc.

Young, McGee. Developing Interests: Organizational Change & the Politics of Advocacy. 2010. *(978-0-7006-1703-6(5))*; pap. *(978-0-7006-1704-3(3))* Univ. Pr. of Kansas.

BUSINESS AND SOCIAL PROBLEMS

see Industries—Social Aspects

BUSINESS ANTHROPOLOGY

see also Corporate Culture

Bose, Purnima & Lyons, Laura E., eds. Cultural Critique & the Global Corporation. 2010. (Tracking Globalization Ser.). (ENG., Illus.). 248p. 65.00 (978-0-253-30029-4(0), 0253300290); pap. 24.95 (978-0-253-22162-9(5), 0253221625) Indiana Univ. Pr.

Cefkin, Melissa, ed. Ethnography & the Corporate Encounter: Reflections on Research in & of Corporations. (SPAA Ser.). 262p. 2010. 34.95 (978-1-84545-777-8(3)) 2009. 80.00 (978-1-84545-598-9(3)) Berghahn Bks., Inc.

Denny, Rita M. & Sunderland, Patricia L. Doing Anthropology in Consumer Research. 2009. (Critical Cultural Heritage Ser.). (ENG., Illus.). 368p. (C). pap. 29.95 (978-1-59874-091-2(1)) Left Coast Pr., Inc.

Malaby, Thomas M. Making Virtual Worlds: Linden Lab & Second Life. 2009. (Illus.). 192p. 25.95 (978-0-8014-4746-4(1)) Cornell Univ. Pr.

Ostrowski, Pierre & Penner, Gwen. It's All Chinese to Me: An Overview of Culture & Etiquette in China. 2009. (ENG., Illus.). 192p. pap. 16.95 (978-0-8048-4079-8(2)) Tuttle Publishing.

Perin, Constance. Shouldering Risks: The Culture of Control in the Nuclear Power Industry. 2006. (ENG., Illus.). 408p. (C). per. 29.95 (978-0-691-12777-4(8)) Princeton Univ. Pr.

Sedgwick, Mitchell W. Globalization & Japanese Organisational Culture: An Ethnography of a Japanese Corporation in France. 2008. (Japan Anthropology Workshop Ser.). (Illus.). 223p. 160.00 (978-0-415-44678-5(3)) Routledge.

Spillman, Lyn. Solidarity in Strategy: Making Business Meaningful in American Trade Associations. 2012. (ENG.). 512p. pap. 30.00 **(978-0-226-76957-8(7))**; (Illus.). 90.00 **(978-0-226-76956-1(9))** Univ. of Chicago Pr.

Sridhar, Devi, ed. Anthropologists Inside Organisations: South Asian Case Studies. 2008. 228p. (C). 29.95 (978-81-7829-886-3(4), B98863C) SAGE Pubns., Inc.

Sunderland, Patricia L. & Denny, Rita M. Doing Anthropology in Consumer Research. 2009. (Critical Cultural Heritage Ser.). (ENG., Illus.). 368p. (C). 89.00 (978-1-59874-090-5(3)) Left Coast Pr., Inc.

Tian, Robert, et al, eds. Advanced Readings in Business Anthropology. 2011. (Illus.). 248p. pap. 27.95 **(978-0-9828434-8-2(8))** North American Business Pr., Inc.

Yanow, Dvora, et al, eds. Organizational Ethnography: Studying the Complexity of Everyday Life. 2009. 304p. (C). 135.00 (978-1-84787-045-2(7), B70457C); pap. 55.00 (978-1-84787-046-9(5), B70457P) SAGE Pubns., Ltd. GBR. Dist: SAGE Pubns., Inc.

Zaloom, Caitlin. Out of the Pits: Traders & Technology from Chicago to London. 2010. (ENG., Illus.). 240p. pap. 19.00 (978-0-226-97814-7(1)) Univ. of Chicago Pr.

BUSINESS ARITHMETIC

see Business Mathematics

BUSINESS BUDGETING

see Budget in Business

BUSINESS CARDS

see also Advertising Cards

Almon, Harold. Four Errors on Your Business Card Learn the Impact Business Card Errors for College & University Students: Eliminate the 4 Errors in Your Business Card, 8 vols., Vol. 8. 2011. (Illus.). 134p. pap. 19.95 (978-0-917921-68-1(2)) At Ease Pr.

Blackcoffee Design, Inc. Staff, selected by. The Best of Business Card Design 6. 2006. (Best of Business Card Design Ser.). (ENG., Illus.). 232p. pap. 25.00 (978-1-59253-233-9(0), 1592532330) Quayside.

Carter, David E. Big Book of Business Cards. 2008. (Illus.). 384p. pap. 35.00 (978-0-06-114419-6(3), Collins Design) HarperCollins Pubs.

Dorrian, Michael & Farrelly, Liz. Business Cards 2: More Ways of Saying Hello. 2006. (ENG., Illus.). 272p. per. 29.95 (978-1-85669-477-3(1)) King, Laurence Publishing GBR. Dist: Hachette Bk. Group.

Finke, Gail Deibler & Haller, Lynn. Fresh Ideas in Letterhead & Business Card Design. 144p. 29.99 (978-1-56496-156-3(7), Rockport Publishers) Quayside.

Loewy, ed. Best of Business Card Design, No. 7. 2008. (ENG., Illus.). 240p. pap. 30.00 (978-1-59253-435-7(X), 159253435X) Quayside.

Mar, Jam, ed. The Image of Business Card Today: The Most Creative Business Cards All Around the World. 2010. (ENG., Illus.). 320p. 75.00 (978-988-17684-7-6(0)) Azur Corp. JPN. Dist: Antique Collectors' Club.

Nezu, Kayako & Miyazaki, Ami, eds. Smart Designs: Business Cards. 2010. (JPN & ENG., Illus.). 232p. pap. 29.95 (978-4-7562-4003-3(8), PIE Bks.) Rizzoli International Pubns., Inc.

Praquin, Marc. My Own Business Card, 1 vol. 2009. (ENG., Illus.). 210p. pap. 29.95 (978-84-92643-21-9(8)) Index Bks., Spain ESP. Dist: Innovative Logistics.

—My Own Business Card#2. 2011. (ENG., Illus.). 288p. pap. 29.95 (978-84-92643-66-0(8)) Index Bks., Spain ESP. Dist: Innovative Logistics.

Rule29. The Best of Business Card Design 9. 2012. (ENG., Illus.). 240p. 30.00 **(978-1-59253-790-7(1)**, 1592537901) Quayside.

Rule29 Staff. The Best of Business Card Design 9. 2010. (ENG., Illus.). 240p. 45.00 (978-1-59253-596-5(8), 1592535968) Quayside.

Sibley/Peteet Design Austin Staff. Best of Business Card Design 8. 2009. (ENG., Illus.). 240p. pap. 30.00 (978-1-59253-575-0(5), 1592535755) Quayside.

Slomer, Eric M. Business Cards As Communication. 2009. 120p. pap. (978-3-639-16732-0(5)) VDM Verlag Dr. Mueller e.K.

Steff, Steve, et al. The Business Card. 2011. 14.99 **(978-1-934570-17-3(6))** Lanphier Pr.

Victionary, creator. Nice to Meet You: Visual Greeting from Business Cards. 2007. (Illus.). 350p. pap. (978-988-98228-4-2(9)) Victionary.

Victionary Staff. Nice to Meet You Too: Visual Greetings from Business Cards to Identity Packages. 2010. 320p. pap. (978-988-17327-8-1(6)) Victionary.

Witrogen, Ned & Wetzler, Matthew, photos by. The Best of Business Card Design. 2008. (ENG., Illus.). 240p. 45.00 (978-1-59253-403-6(1), 1592534031) Quayside.

BUSINESS COMMUNICATION

Here are entered works on the various forms of oral and written messages used by a business in the conduct of its affairs. Works on the role of communication in effective management are entered under Communication in Management.

see also Business Presentations; Business Writing; Computer Conferencing

Abdelnour-Nocera, Jost. The Social Construction of Usefulness. 2007. 264p. per. (978-3-8364-2582-7(3)) VDM Verlag Dr. Mueller e.K.

Abela, Andrew & Abela, Andrew V. Advanced Presentations by Design: Creating Communication That Drives Action. 2008. (ENG., Illus.). 224p. pap. 50.00 (978-0-7879-9659-8(9), Pfeiffer) Wiley, John & Sons, Inc.

ABORISHADE, Isaac. 101 Reasons Why People Fail in Leadership: An Essential Road Map of Success for Leaders who want to Distinguish Themselves. 2007. 204p. per. 18.95 (978-0-595-45256-9(6)) iUniverse, Inc.

Actis, Ronald. Management's Last Frontier: A Communications System to Focus & Sustain a Culture of Achievement. 2006. (ENG.). (C). 56.60 (978-0-536-27327-7(8)) Pearson Learning Solutions.

Adamchik, Wally. No Yelling: The 9 Secrets of Marine Corps Leadership You Must Know to Win in Business. 2006. (ENG.). 197p. 24.95 (978-0-9779005-0-3(9)) FireStarter Speaking and Consulting.

Adler, Ronald B. & Elmhorst, Jeanne Marquardt. Communicating at Work: Principles & Practices for Business & the Professions. (ENG., Illus.). (C). 9th rev. ed. 2006. 500p. per. 107.19 (978-0-07-351188-7(9), 0073511889) 10th ed. 2009. 544p. pap. 135.67 (978-0-07-338517-4(4), 0073385174) McGraw-Hill Cos., The.

Alamargot, Denis, et al, eds. Written Documents in the Workplace. 2008. (Studies in Writing Ser.: 21). (ENG., Illus.). 336p. 161.00 (978-0-08-047487-8(X), Elsevier Science) Elsevier Science & Technology Bks.

Aliori, Paola Evangelisti & Garzone, Giuliana, eds. Discourse, Identities & Genres in Corporate Communication: Sponsorship, Advertising & Organizational Communication. 2011. (Linguistic Insights. Studies in Language & Communication Ser.). (Illus.). 324p. pap. (978-3-0343-0591-4(5)) Lang, Peter.

Alter, Shannon. Say It with Success: Foolproof Ways to Improve Your Presentation. 2010. pap. 10.95 (978-0-7414-5918-3(3)) Infinity Publishing.

Amernic, Joel & Craig, Russell. CEO-Speak: The Language of Corporate Leadership. 2007. (ENG.). 256p. (C). per. (978-0-7735-3320-2(6)) McGill-Queen's Univ. Pr.

Angell. Business Communication Design. 2006. pap. 10.95 (978-1-4288-0675-7(X)) Cram101 Inc.

Ansell, Jeff. When the Headline Is You: An Insider's Guide to Handling the Media. 2010. (J-B International Association of Business Communicators Ser.: 10). (ENG., Illus.). 256p. 29.95 (978-0-470-54394-8(9), Jossey-Bass) Wiley, John & Sons, Inc.

Argenti, Paul A. & Barnes, Courtney M. Digital Strategies for Powerful Corporate Communications. 2009. (ENG., Illus.). 272p. 34.95 (978-0-07-160602-8(5), 0071606025) McGraw-Hill Cos., The.

Arnold, Bruce M. Hot Tips in Sales Communication. 2010. 144p. pap. 19.99 (978-1-4535-1365-1(5)) Xlibris Corp.

Arredondo, Lani. Communicate Effectively. 2007. (Mcgraw-Hill Professional Education Ser.). (ENG.). 64p. pap. 7.95 (978-0-07-149337-6(9), 0071493379) McGraw-Hill Cos., The.

ASTD Staff. 10 Steps to Successful Presentations. 2008. (ENG.). 126p. pap. 19.95 (978-1-56286-514-6(5)) American Society for Training & Development.

Atlantic Publishing Group. How to Get Your Message Across to Any Personality Type: Be Heard at Work or Home Without Upsetting Others. 2012. (ENG.). 288p. pap. 24.95 (978-1-60138-579-6(X)) Atlantic Publishing Co.

Awang-Shuib, Awang-Rozaimie & Anees, Janee Ali. The Insight of Interpersonal Relation & Communication: A Rule of Thumb. 2011. 56p. pap. **(978-3-639-32685-7(7))** VDM Verlag Dr. Mueller e.K.

Bailey, Edward P. Writing & Speaking at Work. 5th rev. ed. 2010. (ENG., Illus.). 240p. (C). pap. 106.67 (978-0-13-608855-4(4), Prentice Hall) Prentice Hall PTR.

Baker, Stephen R. & Tyler, Cedric G. Business Genetics: Understanding 21st Century Corporations Using XBML. 2007. (ENG., Illus.). 264p. 65.00 (978-0-470-06654-6(7), Wiley) Wiley, John & Sons, Inc.

Balmer. The Corporate Communications Reader. 2007. (Illus.). pap. 53.95 (978-0-415-40313-9(8)) Routledge.

Balmer, John M. T. & Greyser, Stephen A., eds. The Corporate Communications Reader. 2007. (Illus.). 160.00 (978-0-415-40312-2(X)) Routledge.

BarCharts, Inc. Business Communications. 2011. (ENG.). 6p. 5.95 (978-1-4232-1635-3(0)) Barcharts, Inc.

Bargiela-Chiappini, Francesca. The Handbook of Business Discourse. 2009. (ENG., Illus.). 520p. (gr. 17). 150.00 (978-0-7486-2801-8(0)) Edinburgh Univ. Pr. GBR. Dist: Columbia Univ. Pr.

Bargiela-Chiappini, Francesca & Gotti, Maurizio. Asian Business Discourse(S) (Linguistic Insights Ser.: Vol. 29). (Illus.). 350p. 70.95 (978-3-03910-804-6(2)) Lang, Peter CHE. Dist: Lang, Peter Publishing, Inc.

Bargiela-Chiappini, Francesca, et al. Business Discourse. 2007. (Research & Practice in Applied Linguistics Ser.). (ENG.). 288p. pap. 39.00 (978-1-4039-3576-2(9)) Palgrave Macmillan.

Barker, Alan. Improve Your Communication Skills. 2nd ed. 2010. (Creating Success Ser.). (ENG.). 160p. pap. 14.95 (978-0-7494-6036-5(9)); (Illus.). pap. 14.95 (978-0-7494-5627-6(2)) Kogan Page, Ltd. GBR. Dist: Ingram Pub. Services.

Barnard, Alan & Parker, Chris. Campaign It! Achieving Success Through Communication. 2012. (ENG., Illus.). 232p. pap. 34.95 **(978-0-7494-6420-2(8))** Kogan Page, Ltd. GBR. Dist: Ingram Pub. Services.

Barrett, Deborah. Leadership Communication. 3rd ed. 2009. (ENG., Illus.). 464p. (C). 135.00 (978-0-07-337777-3(5), 0073377775, McGraw-Hill/Irwin) McGraw-Hill Higher Education.

Baude, Dawn Michelle. The Executive Guide to E-mail Correspondence: Including Model Letters for Every Situation. 2006. (ENG., Illus.). 1p. per. 15.99 (978-1-56414-910-7(2)) Career Pr., Inc.

Beamer, Linda & Varner, Iris. Intercultural Communication in the Global Workplace. 4th rev. ed. 2006. (ENG., Illus.). 496p. (C). per. 143.33 (978-0-07-352506-8(5), 0073525065, McGraw-Hill/Irwin) McGraw-Hill Higher Education.

Beebe, Steven A. & Mottet, Timothy P. Business & Professional Communication. 2009. (ENG.). 496p. (C). pap. 92.80 (978-0-205-48591-8(X)) Allyn & Bacon, Inc.

Beebe, Steven A. & Mottet, Timothy P. Business & Professional Communication: Principles & Skills for Leadership. 2nd ed. 2012. (ENG.). 464p. (C). 49.33 **(978-0-205-25021-9(1))** Allyn & Bacon, Inc.

—Business & Professional Communication: Principles & Skills for Leadership. 2nd rev. ed. 2012. (ENG., Illus.). 464p. (C). pap. 110.00 **(978-0-205-02899-3(3)**, Prentice Hall) Prentice Hall PTR.

Bell and, Smith. Building Your Network Through Communicat. 2006. pap. 8.95 (978-1-4288-0647-4(4)) Cram101 Inc.

Bell, Arthur H. & Smith, Dayle M. Management Communication. 3rd ed. 2010. (ENG., Illus.). 608p. (C). pap. 140.95 (978-0-470-08445-8(6), Wiley) Wiley, John & Sons, Inc.

Benjamin, Susan F. Perfect Phrases for Dealing with Difficult People: Hundreds of Ready-to-Use Phrases for Handling Conflict, Confrontations, & Challenging Personalities. 2007. (ENG.). 224p. per. 10.95 (978-0-07-149304-8(2), 0071493042) McGraw-Hill Cos., The.

—Quick & Painless Business Writing: An Essential Guide to Clear & Powerful Communication. 2006. (ENG.). 1p. per. 14.99 (978-1-56414-900-8(5)) Career Pr., Inc.

Bennie, Michael. A Guide to Good Business Comm 5e. 5th ed. 2009. (Illus.). 224p. 26.00 (978-1-84528-292-9(2)) How To Books GBR. Dist: Parkwest Pubns., Inc.

Benrazavi, Seyed Rahim, et al. Herzberg's Motivation Factors & Communicative Teamwork. 2011. 152p. pap. **(978-3-8433-9188-7(2))** Lambert Academic Publishing.

Benun, Ilise. Stop Pushing Me Around! A Workplace Guide for the Timid, Shy & Less Assertive. 2006. (ENG.). 224p. per. 14.99 (978-1-56414-882-7(3)) Career Pr., Inc.

Bergman, Gregory. BizzWords: From Ad Creep to Zero Drag, a Guide to Today's Emerging Vocabulary. 2008. (ENG.). 224p. pap. 9.95 (978-1-59869-472-7(3)) Adams Media Corp.

Beynon-Davies, Paul. Significance: Exploring the Nature of Information, Systems & Technology. 2011. (ENG., Illus.). 304p. 110.00 (978-0-230-27519-5(2)) Palgrave Macmillan.

Bhatia, V. K. & Evangelisti Aliori, Paola. Discourse & Identity in the Professions: Legal, Corporate & Institutional Citizenship. 2011. (Linguistic Insights. Studies in Language & Communication Ser.). (ENG.). 352p. pap. **(978-3-0343-1079-6(X))** Lang, Peter.

Bhence, Blaze. The Pounce Theory: How to Create Your Opportunities in Life. 2011. 120p. pap. 12.95 (978-1-4502-9722-6(6)) iUniverse, Inc.

Bianco-Mathis, Virginia, et al. The Dialogue Deck. 2007. (DAK.). 49.95 (978-0-9646642-5-6(X)) Purposeful Pr.

Biemond. Corporate Communications in the Netherlands. 2011. (978-90-411-3195-9(7)) Kluwer Law International.

Bingham, Tony & Jeary, Tony. Presenting Learning. 2007. (ENG.). 224p. 24.95 (978-1-56286-462-0(9)); (Illus.). per. 21.95 (978-1-56286-466-8(1)) American Society for Training & Development.

Bitter, John. Pr Made Easy. 2008. 64p. pap. 13.95 (978-1-4327-3136-6(X)) Outskirts Pr., Inc.

Bjorseth, Lillian D. Breakthrough Networking: Building Relationships That Last (third Edition) 2009. spiral bd. 21.95 (978-0-9648839-4-9(5)) Duoforce Enterprises, Inc.

Black, Ann. Communicating Benefits: Changing Methods & Changing Minds. 2007. 197p. pap. 27.00 (978-0-89154-631-3(6)) International Foundation of Employee Benefit Plans.

Blake, Jacqueline. B2b Communication in the Australian Timber & Wood Products Industry. 2008. 220p. pap. (978-3-639-05311-1(7)) VDM Verlag Dr. Mueller e.K.

The Bliss or the Diss Connection? Email Etiquette for the Business Professional. 2007. 14.95 (978-0-9765970-3-2(9)) ExecuProv.

Bonifer, Mike. GameChangers: Improvisation for Business in the Networked World. 2008. 200p. per. (978-0-9799489-0-9(8)) GameChangers, LLC.

Boross, Paul. The Pitching Bible: The Seven Secrets to a Successful Business Pitch. 2010. (ENG., Illus.). 400p. pap. (978-0-9565358-2-5(8)) CGW Publishing.

Bounds, Andy. The Jelly Effect: How to Make Your Communication Stick. 2010. (ENG., Illus.). 256p. pap. 15.95 (978-0-85708-046-2(6), Capstone) Wiley, John & Sons, Inc.

Bovee and Thill, Schatzman. Business Communication Essentials. 2006. pap. 10.95 (978-1-4288-0716-7(0)) Cram101 Inc.

—Business Communication Today. 2006. pap. 11.95 (978-1-4288-0566-8(4)) Cram101 Inc.

Bovee, Courtland. Study Guide for Business Communication Today. 10th ed. 2009. (ENG.). 300p. (C). pap. 46.67 (978-0-13-815509-4(7), Prentice Hall) Prentice Hall PTR.

Bovee, Courtland & Thill, John V. Business Communication Essentials. 4th ed. 2008. (ENG.). 528p. (C). pap. 146.67 (978-0-13-608441-9(9), Prentice Hall) Prentice Hall PTR.

—Business Communication Today. 11th ed. 2011. (ENG., Illus.). 720p. (C). 193.33 **(978-0-13-253955-5(1)**, Prentice Hall) Prentice Hall PTR.

—Business Communication Today, Student Value Edition. 11th ed. 2011. (ENG.). 720p. (C). ring bd. 124.20 **(978-0-13-253965-4(9)**, Prentice Hall) Prentice Hall PTR.

Bovée, Courtland L. & Thill, John V. Business Communication Essentials. 5th rev. ed. 2010. (ENG.). 528p. (C). pap. 146.67 (978-0-13-253971-5(3), Prentice Hall) Prentice Hall PTR.

Bowden, Mark. Winning Body Language: Control the Conversation, Command Attention, & Convey the Right Message Without Saying a Word. 2010. (ENG., Illus.). 256p. pap. 18.95 (978-0-07-170057-3(9), 0071700579) McGraw-Hill Cos., The.

Bradberry, Travis. Squawk! How to Stop Making Noise & Start Getting Results. 2008. (ENG., Illus.). 144p. 19.95 (978-0-06-156234-1(3), Collins) HarperCollins Pubs.

Brantley & Miller. Toby. Aie Effective Communication for Colleges. 11th ed. 2007. (C). pap. 33.95 (978-0-324-54336-0(0)) Cengage South-Western.

Brantley, Clarice Pennebaker & Miller, Michele Goulet. Effective Communication for Colleges. 11th ed. 2007. (ENG., Illus.). 496p. (C). pap. 174.95 (978-0-324-37476-6(3)) Cengage South-Western.

Brenner, Dean M. Move the World: Persuade Your Audience, Change Minds, & Achieve Your Goals. 2007. (ENG., Illus.). 224p. 24.95 (978-0-470-07318-6(7), Wiley) Wiley, John & Sons, Inc.

Brounstein. Wiley Pathways Business Communication, First Edition. 2009. pap. 54.95 (978-0-470-41515-3(0), Wiley) Wiley, John & Sons, Inc.

Brounstein, Marty & Bell, Arthur H. Wiley Pathways Business Communication. 2008. pap. 54.95 (978-0-470-39033-2(7)) Wiley, John & Sons, Inc.

Brounstein, Marty, et al. Business Communication: Communicate Effectively in Any Business Environment. 2006. (ENG., Illus.). 480p. (C). pap. 71.95 (978-0-471-79077-8(X), Wiley) Wiley, John & Sons, Inc.

Brown, Claire Damken & Nelson, Audrey. Code Switching: How to Talk So Men Will Listen. 2009. (ENG.). 336p. (gr. 12-18). 16.95 (978-1-59257-926-6(4), Alpha Bks.) Penguin Group (USA) Inc.

Brown, M. Katherine, et al. Managing Virtual Teams: Getting the Most from Wikis, Blogs, & Other Collaborative Tools. 2006. (Illus.). 385p. per. 29.95 (978-1-59822-028-5(4)) Jones & Bartlett Learning, LLC.

Brown, Stephen & Lucas, Ceil. Improve Your English: English in the Workplace - Hear & See How English Is Actually Spoken - From Real-Life Speakers. 2008. (ENG., Illus.). 144p. 21.00 (978-0-07-149718-3(8), 0071497188) McGraw-Hill Cos., The.

Budion Devitt, Dianne. What Color Is Your Event: The Art of Bringing People Together. 2010. 187p. pap. 25.00 (978-0-578-04169-8(3)) DND Group.

Burrell, Web. How to Talk Your Talk. 2007. 116p. per. 10.00 (978-1-4257-6434-0(7)) Xlibris Corp.

Business & Professional Communication in a Digital Age. 2012. (ENG.). (C). pap. 95.95 **(978-0-495-80798-8(2))** Wadsworth.

Butterfield, Jeff. Illustrated Course Guides: Verbal Communication - Soft Skills for a Digital Workplace. 2nd ed. 2012. (ENG., Illus.). 150p. (C). pap. 39.95 **(978-1-133-52652-0(7))** Course Technology.

Buzzard, Karen S. F. The Business in Front of the Box. 2012. (ENG.). 192p. pap. 39.95 (978-0-8058-5852-5(0)); 100.00 (978-0-8058-5851-8(2)) Routledge.

Camp, Sue C. & Satterwhite, Marilyn L. College English & Communication. 9th ed. 2007. (Illus.). xvi, 638p. (978-0-07-310651-9(8)) McGraw-Hill Cos., The.

—College English & Communication. 9th ed. 2006. (ENG.). (C). pap. 144.67 (978-0-07-331793-9(4), 0073317934) McGraw-Hill Higher Education.

Canavor, Natalie & Meirowitz, Claire. The Truth about the New Rules of Business Writing. 2009. (Truth About Ser.). (ENG.). 224p. pap. 20.99 (978-0-13-715315-2(5)) FT Press.

Candlin, Christopher & Gotti, Maurizio. Intercultural Aspects of Specialized Communication. 2nd ed. 2006. 369p. pap. 71.95 (978-0-8204-8926-1(3)) Lang, Peter Publishing, Inc.

Candlin, Christopher N. & Sarangi, Srikant, eds. Handbook of Communication in Organisations & Professions. 2011. (Handbooks of Applied Linguistics [HAL] Ser.). (ENG.). XIX, 626p. 257.00 (978-3-11-018831-8(7)) De Gruyter, Mouton DEU. Dist: de Gruyter, Walter GmbH & Co. KG.

Candlin, Christopher N. & Sarangi, Srikant, eds. Handbook of Communication in Organisations & Professions. 2011. (Handbooks of Applied Linguistics [HAL] Ser.). (ENG., Illus.). XIX, 626p. 419.00 **(978-3-11-173738-6(1))** De Gruyter, Mouton DEU. Dist: de Gruyter, Walter GmbH & Co. KG.

Canfield, John. Collaborate: Tools & Techniques for Productive Meetings. 2011. (Illus.). 121p. pap. 12.95 (978-0-9824446-9-6(9)) Black Lake Pr.

Canfield, John. Imagine: Ideation Skills for Improvement & Innovation Today. 2011. (Illus.). 189p. pap. 14.95 **(978-0-9824446-7-2(2))** Black Lake Pr.

Carlson, Doug. Me & Him Are Killing English. 2007. 53p. pap. 5.00 (978-0-9795646-4-2(6)) Comma'aina Communications.

Carte, Penny & Fox, Chris. Bridging the Culture Gap: A Practical Guide to International Business Communication. 2nd ed. 2008. (ENG., Illus.). 192p. pap. 35.00 *(978-0-7494-5274-2(9))* Kogan Page, Ltd. GBR. Dist: Ingram Pub. Services.

Carter, Carol J. Keys to Business Communication. rev. ed. 2010. (ENG.). 608p. (C). pap. 140.00 *(978-0-13-610333-2(2),* Prentice Hall) Prentice Hall PTR.

Cavelzani, Alessandro & Esposito, Mark. Emotional Intelligence & Hospitality. 2010. pap. 12.99 *(978-1-61663-177-2(5))* Tate Publishing & Enterprises, LLC.

Chandler, Robert C. Surviving the Pandemic: A Communication Management Guide for Business. 2009. 338p. pap. 34.95 *(978-1-4327-4893-7(9))* Outskirts Pr., Inc.

Chaney and, Martin. Intercultural Business Communication. 2006. pap. 9.95 *(978-1-4288-0762-4(4))* Cram101 Inc.

Chaney, Lillian & Martin, Jeanette. Intercultural Business Communication. 5th ed. 2010. (ENG., Illus.). 320p. (C). pap. 106.67 *(978-0-13-212790-5(3),* Prentice Hall) Prentice Hall PTR.

Chaney, Lillian Hunt & Martin, Jeanette S. The Essential Guide to Business Etiquette. 1 vol. 2007. 208p. 39.95 *(978-0-275-99714-4(6),* C9714, Praeger Pubs.) Greenwood Publishing Group, Inc.

Chaney, Paul. The Digital Handshake: Seven Proven Strategies to Grow Your Business Using Social Media. 2009. (ENG., Illus.). 272p. 24.95 *(978-0-470-49927-6(3),* Wiley) Wiley, John & Sons, Inc.

Cheesebro, Thomas, et al. Communicating in the Workplace. 2009. (ENG., Illus.). 352p. (C). pap. 103.20 *(978-0-13-613691-0(5),* Prentice Hall) Prentice Hall PTR.

—Communication Skills: Preparing for Career Success. 3rd rev. ed. 2006. (ENG., Illus.). 264p. (C). per. 66.00 *(978-0-13-232796-1(1),* Prentice Hall) Prentice Hall PTR.

—Student Workbook for Communicating in the Workplace. 2010. (ENG.). 150p. (C). pap. 23.00 *(978-0-13-211209-3(4),* Prentice Hall) Prentice Hall PTR.

Christensen, Lars Thoger, et al. Corporate Communications: Convention, Complexity & Critique. 2008. (Illus.). 264p. (C). 121.00 *(978-1-4129-3102-1(9),* B31029C) SAGE Pubns., Ltd. GBR. Dist: SAGE Pubns., Inc.

Chuang, Kai. What's Your Story: A Beginner's Guide to Creating Effective Presentations with PowerPoint 2007. 2007. 119p. pap. 18.95 *(978-0-615-15806-8(4))* PoPo Pr.

Cialdini, Robert B., et al. Yes! 50 Scientifically Proven Ways to Be Persuasive. 2008. (ENG.). 272p. 25.00 *(978-0-4165-7096-7(9),* Free Pr.) Free Pr.

Clark, James L. & Clark, Lyn R. A Handbook for Office Professionals. 12th ed. 2009. (ENG.). 608p. (C). spiral bd. 90.95 *(978-0-324-66239-9(4))* Cengage South-Western.

Cohen, Allan R. & Bradford, David L. Influencing Up. 2012. (ENG.). 256p. 24.95 *(978-1-118-03845-1(2),* Wiley) Wiley, John & Sons, Inc.

Collins, Sandra D. & O'Rourke, James S. Interpersonal Communication Listening & Responding. 2nd ed. 2008. (ENG., Illus.). 90p. (C). pap. 49.95 *(978-0-324-58416-5(4))* Cengage South-Western.

Comm, Joel. Twitter Power 2.0: How to Dominate Your Market One Tweet at a Time. 2nd ed. 2010. (ENG., Illus.). 268p. pap. 16.95 *(978-0-470-56336-6(2),* Wiley) Wiley, John & Sons, Inc.

Condon, John & Masumoto, Tomoko. With Respect to the Japanese: Going to Work in Japan. 2nd ed. 2011. (ENG.). 160p. pap. 24.95 *(978-0-9842471-2-7(2))* Ebsco Publishing.

Coombs, W. Timothy & Holladay, Sherry J. Managing Corporate Social Responsibility: A Communication Approach. 2011. (ENG., Illus.). 200p. pap. 34.95 *(978-1-4443-3645-0(2));* 184p. 84.95 *(978-1-118-10668-6(7))* Wiley, John & Sons, Inc. (Wiley-Blackwell).

Coombs, W. Timothy, et al. Managing Corporate Social Responsibility: A Communication Approach. 2011. (ENG., Illus.). 192p. 84.95 *(978-1-4443-3629-0(0),* Wiley-Blackwell) Wiley, John & Sons, Inc.

Cooper, Franklin. The Bottom Line Handbook. 2010. 118p. pap. 19.95 *(978-1-4327-5691-8(5))* Outskirts Pr., Inc.

Cornelissen, Joep P. Corporate Communication: A Guide to Theory & Practice. 3rd ed. 2011. (Illus.). 296p. (C). 146.00 *(978-0-85702-242-4(3),* B22424C); pap. 57.00 *(978-0-85702-243-1(1),* B22424P) SAGE Pubns., Ltd. GBR. Dist: SAGE Pubns., Inc.

Cram, Carol M. New Perspectives: Portfolio Projects for Business Communication. 2nd ed. 2009. (New Perspectives Ser.). (ENG.). 304p. pap. 82.95 *(978-1-4390-3746-1(9))* Course Technology.

Cram101 Textbook Reviews. Outlines & Highlights for Business & Professional Communication: Keys for Workplace Excellence by Shawn T. Wahl. 2011. 116p. pap. 28.95 ***(978-1-4672-6808-0(9))*** Cram101 Inc.

—Outlines & Highlights for Business & Professional Communication: Plans, Processes, & Performance by James R. Disanza, ISBN. 2011. 182p. pap. 29.95 ***(978-1-61812-077-9(8))*** Cram101 Inc.

—Outlines & Highlights for Business Communication: Process & Product by Mary Ellen Guffey. 2011. 352p. pap. 33.95 ***(978-1-61906-120-0(1))*** Cram101 Inc.

—Outlines & Highlights for Business Communication: Process & Product by Mary Guffey, ISBN. 2011. 266p. pap. 31.95 ***(978-1-61461-862-1(3))*** Cram101 Inc.

—Outlines & Highlights for Business Communication by a C Krizan, Patricia Merrier, Joyce P Logan, Karen Schneiter Williams. 2011. 258p. pap. 31.95 ***(978-1-61906-154-5(6))*** Cram101 Inc.

—Outlines & Highlights for Business Communication by Carol Lehman, Isbn: 9780324782189. 2011. 236p. pap. 31.95 ***(978-1-61461-873-7(9))*** Cram101 Inc.

—Outlines & Highlights for Business Communication by Carol M Lehman. 2011. 202p. pap. 30.95 ***(978-1-61906-152-1(X))*** Cram101 Inc.

—Outlines & Highlights for Business Communication by Locker, Kitty, Isbn: 9780073377728. 2010. 124p. pap. 28.95 *(978-1-61698-101-3(6))* Cram101 Inc.

—Outlines & Highlights for Business Communication by Thomas Means. 2011. 408p. pap. 35.95 ***(978-1-61906-161-3(9))*** Cram101 Inc.

—Outlines & Highlights for Business Communication Essentials by Courtland Bovee, Isbn: 9780136084419 0136084419. 2011. 222p. pap. 30.95 ***(978-1-61490-393-2(X))*** Cram101 Inc.

—Outlines & Highlights for Business Communication Today by Courtland Bovee. 2011. 500p. pap. 37.95 ***(978-1-61906-073-9(6))*** Cram101 Inc.

—Outlines & Highlights for Communicating in Workplace by Thomas Cheesebro. 2011. 174p. pap. 29.95 ***(978-1-61490-972-9(5))*** Cram101 Inc.

—Outlines & Highlights for Communication for Business & the Professions by Patricia Hayes Andrews. 2011. 362p. pap. 34.95 ***(978-1-61490-045-0(0))*** Cram101 Inc.

—Outlines & Highlights for Corporate Communications: Convention, Complexity & Critique by George Cheney, ISBN. 2011. 338p. pap. 27.95 ***(978-1-61490-322-2(0))*** Cram101 Inc.

—Outlines & Highlights for Effective Communication for Colleges by Clarice Pennebaker Brantley, Isbn: 9780324374766. 2010. 76p. pap. 27.95 *(978-1-61698-003-0(6))* Cram101 Inc.

—Outlines & Highlights for Essentials of Business Communication by Mary Ellen Guffey. 2011. 368p. pap. 34.95 ***(978-1-61906-082-1(5))*** Cram101 Inc.

—Outlines & Highlights for Excellence in Business Communication by John V Thill. 2011. 354p. pap. 34.95 ***(978-1-61906-092-0(2))*** Cram101 Inc.

—Outlines & Highlights for Fundamentals of Contemporary Business Communication by Scot Ober. 2011. 194p. pap. 30.95 ***(978-1-61906-162-0(7))*** Cram101 Inc.

—Outlines & Highlights for Fundamentals of Contemporary Financial Management (with Thomson One, Busine by R Charles Moyer. 2011. 456p. pap. 36.95 ***(978-1-4672-6684-0(1))*** Cram101 Inc.

—Outlines & Highlights for Guide to Managerial Communication by Mary Munter. 2011. 56p. pap. 26.95 ***(978-1-4672-6800-4(3))*** Cram101 Inc.

—Outlines & Highlights for Guide to Managerial Communication by Mary Munter, Isbn: 9780131467040 0131467042. 2011. 98p. pap. 27.95 ***(978-1-61812-418-0(8))*** Cram101 Inc.

—Outlines & Highlights for Integrated Business Communication: In a global marketplace by Bonnye E. Stuart. 2011. 260p. pap. 31.95 ***(978-1-61490-808-1(7))*** Cram101 Inc.

—Outlines & Highlights for International Communication: Concepts & Cases by Anokwa, Lin, Salwen, ISBN. 2011. 76p. pap. 27.95 ***(978-1-61830-023-2(7))*** Cram101 Inc.

—Outlines & Highlights for M: Business Communication by Marie Rentz Flatley, ISBN. 2011. 256p. pap. 31.95 ***(978-1-61812-135-6(9))*** Cram101 Inc.

—Outlines & Highlights for M: Business Communications by Marie E. Flatley, Kathryn Rentz. 2011. 228p. pap. 31.95 ***(978-1-4672-7229-2(9))*** Cram101 Inc.

—Outlines & Highlights for Managing Business & Professional Communication by Carley H Dodd, Isbn: 9780205823864. 2011. 270p. pap. 32.95 ***(978-1-61812-116-5(2))*** Cram101 Inc.

—Outlines & Highlights for Strategic Communication in Business & Professions by Dan Ohair, Isbn: 9780205561209. 2010. 102p. pap. 27.95 *(978-1-61654-021-0(4))* Cram101 Inc.

—Outlines & Highlights for Strategic Communication in Business & the Professions by Dan O'Hair. 2011. 78p. pap. 27.95 ***(978-1-61905-361-8(6))*** Cram101 Inc.

—Outlines & Highlights for Strategic Management Communication for Leaders by Robyn Walker. 2011. 56p. pap. 26.95 ***(978-1-61905-564-3(3))*** Cram101 Inc.

—Outlines & Highlights for Workplace Communication by Steven M Gerson, Isbn: 0132288087 9780132288088. 2011. 78p. pap. 27.95 ***(978-1-61812-511-8(7))*** Cram101 Inc.

Cram101 Textbook Reviews & Cram101 Textbook Reviews. Outlines & Highlights for Business Communication: Building Critical Skills by Kitty Locker, ISBN. 2011. 210p. pap. 30.95 ***(978-1-61461-874-4(7))*** Cram101 Inc.

—Outlines & Highlights for Business Communication: Communicate Effectively in Any Business Environment by Marty Brounstein, ISBN. 2011. 106p. pap. 28.95 ***(978-1-61812-014-4(X))*** Cram101 Inc.

—Outlines & Highlights for Business Communication: Polishing Your Professional Presence by Barbara Shwom. 2011. 438p. pap. 36.95 ***(978-1-61830-546-6(8))*** Cram101 Inc.

—Outlines & Highlights for Business Communication Essentials by Courtland L Bovee. 2011. 442p. pap. 36.95 ***(978-1-61830-555-8(7))*** Cram101 Inc.

—Outlines & Highlights for Contemporary Business Communications by Scot Ober, Isbn: 0618472525 9780618472529. 2011. 90p. pap. 27.95 ***(978-1-61461-583-5(7))*** Cram101 Inc.

—Outlines & Highlights for Excellence in Business Communication by John Thill, Isbn: 9780136103769. 2011. 238p. pap. 31.95 ***(978-1-61461-051-9(7))*** Cram101 Inc.

—Outlines & Highlights for Managerial Communication: Strategies & Applications by Geraldine E. Hynes, ISBN. 2011. 98p. pap. 27.95 ***(978-1-61490-781-7(1))*** Cram101 Inc.

—Outlines & Highlights for Workplace Communications: Basics by George J. Searles, ISBN. 2011. 70p. pap. 27.95 ***(978-1-61490-466-3(9))*** Cram101 Inc.

—Outlines Flatley Rentz, Isbn: 9780073377797. 2011. 126p. pap. 28.95 ***(978-1-61461-360-2(5))*** Cram101 Inc.

Cram101 Textbook Reviews Staff. Outlines & Highlights for Business Communications by Lesikar Isbn: 9780073317090. 2008. 100p. pap. 10.95 *(978-1-4288-6030-8(4))* Cram101 Inc.

—Outlines & Highlights for Leadership Communication by Barrett, Isbn: 1428866167. 2009. 80p. pap. 10.95 *(978-1-4288-6616-4(7))* Cram101 Inc.

Craven, Joan. Got It! Twenty-One Communication Tips for Busy, Impatient People. 2011. 100p. pap. 15.00 ***(978-1-60976-690-0(3),*** Eloquent Bks.) AEG Literary Publishing Services, Inc.

Croston, Karen, ed. Business Communication Cases & Concepts. 2007. 114p. (C). pap. 39.99 *(978-0-9786307-3-7(4))* Mustard Seed Publishing, LLC.

Culbert, Samuel. Beyond Bullsh*t: Straight-Talk at Work. 2010. (ENG.). 168p. pap. 17.95 *(978-0-8047-7177-1(4),* Stanford Business Bks.) Stanford Univ. Pr.

Culbert, Samuel A. Beyond Bullsh*t: Straight-Talk at Work. 2008. (ENG.). 168p. 24.95 *(978-0-8047-5885-7(9),* Stanford Business Bks.) Stanford Univ. Pr.

Cullen, Maura. 35 Dumb Things Well-Intended People Say. 2008. (ENG.). 141p. pap. 14.95 *(978-1-60037-491-3(3))* Morgan James Publishing.

Daniel, Carter A. Reader-Friendly Reports: A No-Nonsense Guide to Effective Writing for MBAs, Consultants, & Other Professionals. 2011. (ENG., Illus.). 224p. pap. 20.00 ***(978-0-07-178285-2(0),*** 0071782850) McGraw-Hill Cos., The.

Davin, Doug & Morris, Diana. The Confident Communication Breakthrough Journal: A Celebration of Your Success. 2009. 88p. pap. 18.95 *(978-1-891019-29-6(5))* New Heights Media, Inc.,.

Davis, Kenneth. Business Writing & Communication. 2nd ed. 2010. (McGraw-Hill 36-Hour Courses Ser.). (ENG., Illus.). 256p. pap. 19.95 *(978-0-07-173826-2(6),* 0071738266) McGraw-Hill Cos., The.

Debelak, Don. Meetings: Hundreds of Ready-to-Use Phrases to Get Your Message Across & Advance Your Career. 2008. (Perfect Phrases Ser.). (ENG.). 224p. pap. 9.95 *(978-0-07-154683-6(9),* 0071546839) McGraw-Hill Cos., The.

Decker, Bert. You've Got to Be Believed to Be Heard: Reach the First Brain to Communicate in Business & in Life. 2nd rev. ed. 2008. (ENG., Illus.). 288p. 25.95 *(978-0-312-37469-3(0))* St. Martin's Pr.

Deigh, Robert. How Come No One Knows about Us? The Ultimate Public Relations Guide: Tactics Anyone Can Use to Win High Visibility! 2008. 255p. 24.95 *(978-0-8329-5017-9(3))* New Win Publishing.

Denny, Richard. Communicate to Win: Learn the Secrets of Successful Communication & Presentation. 2nd rev. ed. 2009. (ENG.). 144p. pap. 17.95 *(978-0-7494-5545-0(0))* Kogan Page, Ltd. GBR. Dist: Ingram Pub. Services.

Deterding, Ann Katrin & Meissner, Constantin. Corporate Blogs & Communications in Relationship Management. 2008. 84p. per. *(978-3-8364-3965-7(4))* VDM Verlag Dr. Mueller e.K.

Dew, Angela. Empowering Partnerships. 2009. 220p. pap. *(978-3-639-20812-2(9))* VDM Verlag Dr. Mueller e.K.

Diaz-Ortiz, Claire. Twitter for Good: Change the World One Tweet at a Time. 2011. (ENG., Illus.). 224p. 24.95 *(978-1-118-06193-0(4),* Jossey-Bass) Wiley, John & Sons, Inc.

Dieken, Connie. Communication 3. 0. 2008. (Illus.). 240p. 32.00 *(978-0-9794490-2-4(2))* onPoint Pr.

—Influence 3. 0: The New Rules to Get What You Want. 2008. 275p. *(978-0-9794490-1-7(4))* onPoint Pr.

Dieltjens, Sylvain. Researching Discourse in Business Genres: Cases & Corpora. Gillaerts, Paul, ed. 2012. (Linguistic Insights. Studies in Language & Communication Ser.). (ENG.). 215p. pap. ***(978-3-0343-1092-5(7))*** Lang, Peter.

Dieltjens, Sylvain & Heynderickx, Priscilla, eds. The Language Factor in International Business: New Perspectives on Research, Teaching & Practice. 2012. (Linguistic Insights. Studies in Language & Communication Ser.). (ENG.). 320p. pap. ***(978-3-0343-1090-1(0))*** Lang, Peter.

Dignen, Bob. Communicating Across Cultures Student's Book with Audio CD. 2011. (Cambridge Business Skills Ser.). (ENG., Illus.). 96p. pap. 22.00 incl. audio compact disk *(978-0-521-18198-3(4))* Cambridge Univ. Pr.

Dinnocenzo, Debra A. How to Work Together from a Distance: Building Bridges Within Virtual Teams. 2008. 48p. 9.95 *(978-0-9742902-1-8(1))* Mancini-M'Clintock Pr.

DiSanza, James R. & Legge, Nancy J. Business & Professional Communication: Plans, Processes, & Performance. 5th rev. ed. 2011. (ENG., Illus.). 320p. (C). pap. 101.80 *(978-0-205-72149-8(4))* Allyn & Bacon, Inc.

Dodd, Carley H. Managing Business & Professional Communication. (ENG., (C). 2nd ed. 2007. Illus.). 476p. per. 96.80 *(978-0-205-52486-0(9))* 3rd ed. 2010. 432p. pap. 100.80 *(978-0-205-82386-4(6))* Allyn & Bacon, Inc.

Doleschal, Ursula & Hoffmann, Edgar, eds. Sprache und Diskurs in Wirtschaft und Gesellschaft: Interkulturelle Perspektiven. 2008. (Sprache im Kontext Ser.). 302p. pap. 74.95 *(978-3-631-56032-7(X))* Lang, Peter GmbH, Europaischer Verlag der Wissenschaften DEU. Dist: Lang, Peter.

Dooly, Melinda. Doing Diversity: Teachers' Construction of Their Classroom Reality. 2009. (Linguistic Insights. Studies in Language & Communication Ser.). (Illus.). 176p. *(978-3-03911-688-1(6))* Lang, Peter.

Dorling Kindersley Publishing Staff. Effective Communication. 2009. (DK Essential Managers Ser.). (ENG., Illus.). 72p. (gr. 12). 8.00 *(978-0-7566-5044-5(5))* Dorling Kindersley Publishing, Inc.

Doyle, Michael Scott, et al. Exito Comercial. 5th ed. 2010. (ENG.). (C). 45.95 *(978-0-495-90783-1(9))* Cengage Heinle.

—Éxito Comercial. 5th ed. 2010. (ENG.). 544p. (C). pap. 134.95 *(978-1-4390-8612-4(5))* Cengage Heinle.

Dudinski, Yuri. You've Got Mail, but Have You Got Information? 2010. 116p. pap. *(978-3-8383-9465-7(8))* Lambert Academic Publishing.

DuFrene, Debbie. Communication Strategies for Virtual Teams. 2011. 65p. pap. 29.95 ***(978-1-60649-260-4(8))*** Business Expert Pr.

Durham, Sarah. Brandraising: How Nonprofits Raise Visibility & Money Through Smart Communications. 2009. (ENG., Illus.). 208p. 36.00 *(978-0-470-52753-5(6),* Jossey-Bass) Wiley, John & Sons, Inc.

Earl, Clifford J. How to Build a Business Case: The Practical Guide to Persuasive Business Case Writing. 2007. (Illus.). 182p. spiral bd. 85.00 incl. cd-rom *(978-0-9707733-4-0(X),* RMS-BCP1) Resource Management Systems, Inc.

Edmonds, Graham. Bad Language: Words & Phrases to Avoid in Business. 2009. (ENG.). 194p. pap. 14.95 *(978-1-904915-35-5(3))* Southbank Publishing GBR. Dist: Independent Pubs. Group.

Elearn. Effective Communications: Management Extra. 2007. (Management Extra Ser.). (ENG., Illus.). 128p. (C). pap. 49.95 *(978-0-08-046529-6(3))* Routledge.

Erkas, Eivor. The Importance of Storytelling in Today's Business. 2009. 68p. pap. *(978-3-639-16753-5(8))* VDM Verlag Dr. Mueller e.K.

Ettinger, Blanche & Perfetto, Edda L. Business English: Writing in the Workplace. 4th ed. 2006. (ENG.). 416p. per. 99.40 *(978-0-13-156570-8(2),* Prentice Hall) Prentice Hall PTR.

Facts on File, Inc. Staff. Career Skills Library: Communication Skills, Third Edition. 3rd rev. ed. 2009. (Career Skills Library). (Illus.). 176p. (gr. 6-12). 25.95 *(978-0-8160-7778-6(9),* Ferguson Publishing Co.) Facts On File, Inc.

Featheringham, Richard D. & Csapo, Nancy. Business Communication: Topics & Activities. 3rd rev. ed. 2009. (ENG.). 210p. pap. 70.83 *(978-0-7575-4690-7(0))* Kendall Hunt Publishing Co.

Felber, Terry. Am I Making Myself Clear, 0 vols. 2008. 160p. pap. 12.99 *(978-0-8499-9105-9(6))* Nelson, Thomas Inc.

Fernandez, Delia. Workplace Communication & Conflict Resolution: Workplace Communication Strategies to Help Employees Improve upon Their Skills in One Easy Reading. 2006. per. 9.95 *(978-0-9765241-1-3(2))* New Mark Pr.

Ferrari, Bernard T. Power Listening: Mastering the Most Critical Business Skill of All. 2012. (ENG.). 208p. (gr. 12). 25.95 ***(978-1-59184-462-4(2),*** Portfolio (Hardcover)) Penguin Group (USA) Inc.

Ferreira, Herman S. & Routh, Richard L. How to Build Corporate Politcal Capital — for New Executives. 2008. 234p. pap. 19.95 *(978-0-557-02316-5(5))* Lulu Enterprises Inc.

Fielding, M. Effective Communication in Organizations. 570p. *(978-0-7021-2267-5(X))* Juta & Co., Ltd.

Fifty Lessons Staff, compiled by. Communicating Clearly. 2009. (Lessons Learned Ser.). (ENG.). 96p. pap. 9.95 *(978-1-4221-3983-7(2))* Harvard Business Review Pr.

Fill, Chris & Hughes, Graham. Marketing Communications. 2006. (ENG., Illus.). 318p. (C). pap. 31.95 *(978-0-7506-8010-3(5),* Butterworth-Heinemann) Elsevier Science & Technology Bks.

Finder, Robert L. Finder: Financial Communications. 2012. (Applied Corporate Finance Ser.). (ENG.). 300p. 49.99 ***(978-0-13-301790-8(7))*** FT Press.

Fine, Debra. The Fine Art of the Big Talk: How to Win Clients, Deliver Great Presentations, & Solve Conflicts at Work. 2008. 256p. 16.95 *(978-1-4013-0234-4(3))* Hyperion Pr.

Finkelstein, Sydney, et al. Breakout Strategy: Meeting the Challenge of Double-Digit Growth. 2006. (ENG., Illus.). 352p. 29.95 *(978-0-07-145231-1(1),* 0071452311) McGraw-Hill Cos., The.

Fitzgerald, Dennis. Business Data Communications & Network. 2006. pap. 8.95 *(978-1-4288-0608-5(3))* Cram101 Inc.

Five by Five. The Simple Keys to Effective Communications. 2006. per. 10.00 *(978-1-887934-05-3(7))* Delmax, Inc.

Flatley, Marie, et al. M: Business Communication. 2nd ed. 2011. (ENG., Illus.). 376p. (C). pap. 73.33 *(978-0-07-340316-8(4),* 0073403164, McGraw-Hill/Irwin) McGraw-Hill Higher Education.

Flatley, Marie E. & Rentz, Kathryn. Business Communications. 2009. (ENG., Illus.). (C). pap., pap. 73.33 *(978-0-07-731406-4(9),* 0077314069, McGraw-Hill/Irwin) McGraw-Hill Higher Education.

Flatley, Marie Elizabeth & Rentz, Kathryn. Business Communication. 2010. (Illus.). xi, 322p. *(978-0-07-337781-0(3),* Irwin Professional Publishing) McGraw-Hill Schl. Education Group.

Flynn, Nancy & Flynn, Nanc. Networking for Success: Master the Art of Making Personal Contacts. 2nd ed. 2011. (ENG.). 102p. pap. 14.95 *(978-1-4260-1942-5(4))* Thomson NETg.

Ford, Jeffrey & Ford, Laurie H. The Four Conversations: Daily Communication That Gets Results. 2009. (ENG.). 200p. pap. 20.95 *(978-1-57675-920-2(2))* Berrett-Koehler Pubs., Inc.

Forey, Gail & Lockwood, Jane. Globalization, Communication & the Workplace: Talking Across the World. 2012. (ENG.). 288p. pap. 49.95 ***(978-1-4411-0767-1(3))*** Continuum International Publishing Group, Ltd. GBR. Dist: National Bk. Network.

Forsyth, Patrick. Effective Business Writing. 2009. (Creating Success Ser.). (ENG.). 160p. pap. 17.95 *(978-0-7494-5453-1(9))* Kogan Page, Ltd. GBR. Dist: Ingram Pub. Services.

—How to Write Reports & Proposals. 2nd rev. ed. 2010. (Sunday Times Creating Success Ser.). (ENG., Illus.). 128p. pap. 14.95 *(978-0-7494-5665-8(5))* Kogan Page, Ltd. GBR. Dist: Ingram Pub. Services.

—There's No Need to Shout: 10 Steps to Communicating Your Message Clearly & Effectively. 2007. (Career Makers Ser.). 224p. pap. 19.95 *(978-1-904879-66-4(7))* Cyan Communications GBR. Dist: Independent Pubs. Group.

Forsyth, Patrick & Kay, Frances. The Art of Successful Business Communication. 2008. (Illus.). 184p. pap. 58.00 *(978-0-86341-907-2(0))* Institution of Engineering & Technology GBR. Dist: Books International, Inc.

Freeman, John. The Tyranny of E-Mail: The Four-Thousand-Year Journey to Your Inbox. (ENG., Illus.). 256p. 2011. pap. 16.00 *(978-1-4165-7674-7(6))* 2009. 25.00 *(978-1-4165-7673-0(8))* Scribner. (Scribner).

Freeman, Richard B. & Haynes, Peter. What Workers Say: Employee Voice in the Anglo-American Workplace. Boxall, Peter, ed. 2007. (Illus.). 244p. 57.50 *(978-0-8014-4445-6(4)*, ILR Pr.); per. 22.95 *(978-0-8014-7281-7(4))* Cornell Univ. Pr.

Friedman, Karen. Shut up & Say Something: Business Communication Strategies to Overcome Challenges & Influence Listeners, 1 vol. 2010. (Illus.). 264p. 44.95 *(978-0-313-38585-8(8)*, A3028C, Praeger Pubs.) Greenwood Publishing Group, Inc.

Friedman, Nancy. 54 Golden Nuggets: Quick Tips to Cure Your Business Communication Ills. 2011. (ENG.). 195p. pap. 19.95 ***(978-1-59996-255-9(1))*** Human Resource Development Pr.

Fuller, Edwin D. You Can't Lead with Your Feet on the Desk: Building Relationships, Breaking down Barriers, & Delivering Profits. 2011. (ENG.). 208p. 29.95 *(978-0-470-87961-0(0)*, Wiley) Wiley, John & Sons, Inc.

Gabor, Don. Turn Small Talk into Big Deals: Using 4 Key Conversation Styles to Customize Your Networking Approach, Build Relationships, & Win More Clients. 2009. (ENG., Illus.). 288p. pap. 16.95 *(978-0-07-159965-8(7)*, 0071599657) McGraw-Hill Cos., The.

Gallagher, Kevin. Skills Development for Business & Management Students. 2010. (ENG., Illus.). 400p. pap. 45.00 *(978-0-19-954353-2(1))* Oxford Univ. Pr., Inc.

Gallagher, Richard S. How to Tell Anyone Anything: Breakthrough Techniques for Handling Difficult Conversations at Work, 1 vol. 2009. (ENG.). 224p. pap. 14.95 *(978-0-8144-1015-8(4))* Amacom.

—What to Say to a Porcupine: 20 Humorous Tales That Get to the Heart of Great Customer Service. 2008. (ENG.). 128p. pap. 12.95 *(978-0-8144-1679-2(9))* Amacom.

Gallo, Carmine. Fire Them Up! 7 Simple Secrets to - Inspire Colleagues, Customers, & Clients - Sell Yourself, Your Vision, & Your Values - Communicate with Charisma & Confidence. 2007. (ENG., Illus.). 229p. 21.95 *(978-0-470-16566-9(9)*, Wiley) Wiley, John & Sons, Inc.

—The Presentation Secrets of Steve Jobs: How to Be Insanely Great in Front of Any Audience. 2009. (ENG., Illus.). 256p. 21.95 *(978-0-07-163608-7(0)*, 0071636080) McGraw-Hill Cos., The.

Gargiulo, Terrence L. Once upon a Time: Using Story-Based Activities to Develop Breakthrough Communication Skills. 2007. (ENG., Illus.). 240p. 55.00 *(978-0-7879-8535-6(X)*, Pfeiffer) Wiley, John & Sons, Inc.

Garguilo, Terrance & Ioffreda, Angelo. Putting Stories to Work. 2008. ring bd. *(978-1-888015-58-4(6))* International Assn. of Business Communicators.

Garrido, Carlos. Manual de Correspondencia Comercial Moderna. (SPA., Illus.). 288p. 23.95 *(978-84-315-8455-9(6)*, VE3007) De Vecchi, Editorial, S.A. ESP. Dist: Continental Bk. Co., Inc.

Garzone, G. & Gotti, Maurizio. Discourse, Communication & the Enterprise: Genres & Trends. 2011. (Illus.). 451p. pap. *(978-3-0343-0620-1(2))* Lang, Peter.

Garzone, Giuliana & Ilie, Cornelia, eds. The Use of English in Institutional & Business Settings: An Intercultural Perspective. (Linguistic Insights Ser.: Vol. 34). 379p. pap. 79.95 *(978-3-03910-889-3(1))* Lang, Peter Publishing, Inc.

Gaulke, Sue. 101 Ways to Captivate a Business Audience. 2007. (ENG.). 176p. (Orig.). per. 16.95 *(978-0-8144-0096-8(5))* Amacom.

Gavatorta, Steve. The Reach Out Approach: A Communication Process for Initiating, Developing & Leveraging Mutually Rewarding Relationships. 2009. (ENG.). 232p. pap. 14.99 *(978-1-59932-098-4(3))* Advantage Media Group.

Gee, Val & Gee, Sarah. Business Improv: Experiential Learning Exercises to Train Employees to Handle Every Situation with Success. 2011. (ENG.). 384p. pap. 25.00 *(978-0-07-176821-4(1)*, 0071768211) McGraw-Hill Cos., The.

Geissler, Pete. WordSuccess: Why & How to Express Yourself to the Good Life. 2006. (Illus.). x, 134p. pap. 15.00 *(978-0-87389-699-3(8))* ASQ Quality Pr.

Gendron, Michael. Business Driven Data Communications. 2011. (ENG.). 432p. (C). 146.67 ***(978-0-13-156497-8(8)***, Prentice Hall) Prentice Hall PTR.

Gercik, Patricia. On Track with the Japanese. 2011. 208p. pap. 16.97 ***(978-1-4634-1030-8(1))*** AuthorHouse.

—On Track with the Japanese: An Interactive Workbook for Effective Negotiating & Trust Building with the Japanese. 2011. 84p. pap. 14.00 ***(978-1-4634-0561-8(8))*** AuthorHouse.

Gerson, Sharon J. & Gerson, Steven M. Workplace Communication: Process & Product. 2006. (ENG., Illus.). 352p. per. 77.40 *(978-0-13-228808-8(7)*, Prentice Hall) Prentice Hall PTR.

Gillaerts, P. & Shaw, Philip. The Map & the Landscape: Norms & Practices in Genre. 2006. (Illus.). 256p. pap. 68.95 *(978-3-03911-182-4(5))* Lang, Peter Publishing, Inc.

Gladis, Steve. The Transparent Leader: A Business Fable of Clear & Effective Leadership Communication. 2009. 120p. pap. 19.95 *(978-1-59996-173-6(3))* Human Resource Development Pr.

Glickman, Jodi. Great on the Job: What to Say, How to Say It. the Secrets of Getting Ahead. 2011. (ENG.). 304p. pap. 15.99 *(978-0-312-64146-7(X)*, St. Martin's Griffin) St. Martin's Pr.

Goldstein, Noah J., et al. Yes! 50 Scientifically Proven Ways to Be Persuasive. 2009. (ENG., Illus.). 272p. pap. 15.00 *(978-1-4165-7614-3(2)*, Free Pr.) Free Pr.

Goodall, H. L., Jr., et al. Business & Professional Communication in the Global Workplace. 3rd ed. 2009. (ENG.). 336p. (C). pap. 148.95 *(978-0-495-56738-7(8))* Wadsworth.

Goodall, H. Lloyd, Jr. & Goodall, Sandra. Communicating in Professional Contexts. 2006. pap. 9.95 *(978-1-4288-0849-2(3))* Cram101 Inc.

Goodman, Michael B. Corporate Communication: Tactical Guidelines for Strategic Practice. 2012. 154p. pap. 39.95 ***(978-1-60649-308-3(6))*** Business Expert Pr.

Goodman, Ruth. Victorian Farm. 2010. (ENG., Illus.). 304p. 39.95 *(978-1-86205-871-2(7))* Chrysalis Children's Bks. GBR. Dist: Independent Pubs. Group.

Goulston, Mark. Just Listen: Discover the Secret to Getting Through to Absolutely Anyone, 1 vol. 2009. (ENG., Illus.). 256p. 24.95 *(978-0-8144-1403-3(6))* Amacom.

Granger, Russell H. The 7 Triggers to Yes: The New Science Behind Influencing People's Decisions. 2007. (ENG., Illus.). 240p. 24.95 *(978-0-07-154437-5(2)*, 0071544372) McGraw-Hill Cos., The.

Gray, Jim. How Leaders Speak: Essential Rules for Engaging & Inspiring Others. 2010. (ENG.). 232p. pap. 19.99 *(978-1-55488-701-9(1))* Dundurn CAN. Dist: Ingram Pub. Services.

Gray, Jim. The Young Leader: Timeless Communication for a New Generation of Achievers. 2013. (ENG.). 232p. pap. 19.99 ***(978-1-4597-0404-6(5))*** Dundurn CAN. Dist: Ingram Pub. Services.

Green, Andy. Effective Personal Communication Skills for Public Relations. 2006. (PR in Practice Ser.). (ENG., Illus.). 219p. per. 32.50 *(978-0-7494-4407-5(X))* Kogan Page, Ltd. GBR. Dist: Ingram Pub. Services.

Green, Nigel & Bate, Carl. Lost in Translation: A handbook for information systems in the 21st Century. Safarik, Dan & Woods, Dan, eds. 2007. (Illus.). pap. 40.00 *(978-0-9789218-4-2(4))* Evolved Technologist Pr.

Griffin, Gerry & Lark, Andy. The Message. 2010. 176p. pap. *(978-1-84876-375-3(1))* Troubadour Publishing Ltd.

Griffin, Jack. How to Say It - Be Indispensable at Work: Winning Words & Strategies to Get Noticed, Get Hired, & Get Ahead. 2011. (ENG.). 240p. (gr. 12). 17.95 *(978-0-7352-0454-6(3))* Prentice Hall Pr.

—How to Say It at Work: Power Words, Phrases, & Communication Secrets for Getting Ahead. 2nd ed. 2008. (ENG.). 464p. (gr. 12-18). 17.95 *(978-0-7352-0430-0(6))* Prentice Hall Pr.

—How to Say It for First-Time Managers: Winning Words & Strategies for Earning Your Team's Confidence. 2010. (ENG.). 256p. (gr. 12-18). 16.95 *(978-0-7352-0447-8(0))* Prentice Hall Pr.

Guffey. Business Communication. 2006. pap. 9.95 *(978-1-4288-0472-2(2))* Cram101 Inc.

—Essentials of Business Communication. 2006. pap. 10.95 *(978-1-4288-0839-3(6))* Cram101 Inc.

Guffey, Mary Ellen. Business Communication: Process & Product. 5th ed. 2006. pap. 12.95 *(978-1-4288-1232-1(6))* Cram101 Inc.

—Essentials of Business Communication (with www. meguffey. com Printed Access Card) 8th ed. 2009. (Business Communication Ser.). (ENG.). 560p. (C). pap. 160.95 *(978-0-324-58800-2(3))* Cengage South-Western.

Guffey, Mary Ellen & Loewy, Dana. Business Communication: Process & Product (Book Only) 7th ed. 2010. (ENG., Illus.). 672p. (C). 206.95 *(978-0-538-46626-4(X))* Cengage South-Western.

—Business Communication: Process & Product (with meguffey. com Printed Access Card) 7th ed. 2010. (Business Communication Ser.). (ENG., Illus.). 672p. (C). 206.95 *(978-0-538-46625-7(1))* Cengage South-Western.

Guffey, Mary Ellen & Loewy, Dana. Essentials of Business Communication. 9th ed. 2012.Tr. of Infotrac College Edition. (ENG.). 576p. (C). pap. 160.95 ***(978-1-111-82122-7(4))*** Cengage South-Western.

Gundling & Gundling, Ernest. Working Globesmart: Twelve People Skills for Doing Business Across Borders. 2010. (ENG.). 408p. pap. 34.95 *(978-1-904838-25-8(1))* Ebsco Publishing.

Gurak, Laura J. & Lannon, John M. Strategies for Technical Communication in the Workplace, Books a la Carte Edition. 2nd ed. 2012. (ENG.). 528p. (C). ring bd. 46.00 ***(978-0-205-85127-0(4))*** Longman Publishing Group.

—Strategies for Technical Communication Workplace. 2nd rev. ed. 2012. (ENG.). 528p. (C). pap. 75.33 ***(978-0-205-24552-9(8))*** Longman Publishing Group.

—Strategies for Technical Communication Workplace, Books a la Carte Plus MyTechCommLab. 2nd ed. 2012. (ENG.). (C). ring bd. 52.67 ***(978-0-205-85128-7(2))*** Longman Publishing Group.

Gutierrez, Jairo. Business Data Communications & Networking: A Research Perspective. 2006. (Illus.). 388p. (C). 99.95 *(978-1-59904-274-9(6))* IGI Global.

Gutmann, Joanna. Taking Minutes of Meetings. 2nd rev. ed. 2010. (Creating Success Ser.). (ENG.). 160p. pap. 14.95 *(978-0-7494-6029-7(6))* Kogan Page, Ltd. GBR. Dist: Ingram Pub. Services.

Hamilton, Cheryl M. & Creel, Bonnie. Communicating for Success. 2010. (ENG.). 496p. (C). pap. 119.00 *(978-0-205-52475-4(3))* Allyn & Bacon, Inc.

—Communicating for Success, Books a la Carte Plus MyCommunicationLab. 2010. (ENG.). (C). ring bd. 84.67 *(978-0-205-75793-0(6))* Allyn & Bacon, Inc.

Hamlin, Sonya. How to Talk So People Listen: Connecting in Today's Workplace. 2006. (ENG., Illus.). 336p. pap. 12.99 *(978-0-06-073407-7(8)*, Harper Paperbacks) HarperCollins Pubs.

Hampel, Brenda & Lamont, Erika. New Employee Orientation & Onboarding: Hundreds of Ready-to-Use Phrases to Train & Retain Your Top Talent. 2011. (Perfect Phrases Ser.). (ENG.). 176p. pap. 12.00 *(978-0-07-176650-0(2)*, 0071766502) McGraw-Hill Cos., The.

Harber-Stuart, Colin & Rees, Nina. OCR Business & Communication Systems for GCSE. 2009. 178p. pap. 52.50 *(978-0-340-98443-7(0))* Hodder Education GBR. Dist: Trans-Atlantic Pubns., Inc.

Harvard Business Review. Harvard Business Review on Communicating Effectively. 2011. (ENG., Illus.). 256p. pap. 22.00 *(978-1-4221-6251-4(6))* Harvard Business Review Pr.

Harvey, Bob. Tork & Grunt's Guide to Effective Negotiations. 2008. (Illus.). 92p. pap. 9.95 *(978-0-462-09923-1(7))* Marshall Cavendish GBR. Dist: Midpoint Trade Bks., Inc.

Hatch, Mary Jo & Schultz, Majken. Taking Brand Initiative: How Companies Can Align Strategy, Culture, & Identity Through Corporate Branding. 2008. (Wiley Desktop Editions Ser.). (ENG., Illus.). 288p. 29.95 *(978-0-7879-9830-1(3)*, Jossey-Bass) Wiley John & Sons, Inc.

Havrilla, R. Dynamic Collaboration. 2011. 160p. 26.95 ***(978-0-9820569-3-6(1))*** Third Bridge Pr.

Hawley, Casey. 10 Make-or-Break Career Moments: Navigate, Negotiate, & Communicate for Success. 2010. (ENG., Illus.). 224p. pap. 13.99 *(978-1-58008-723-0(X))* Ten Speed Pr.

Heaton, Gavin & McLellan, Drew. The Age of Conversation. 2008. 116p. pap. 29.95 *(978-1-84799-299-4(4))* Lulu Enterprises Inc.

Hemmings, Robert. Jump-Start Your Career. 2011. (Illus.). 176p. pap. 19.95 *(978-1-933199-27-6(X))* Racom Communications.

Hemphill and, McCormick. Business Communication with Writing Impr. 2006. pap. 9.95 *(978-1-4288-0543-9(5))* Cram101 Inc.

Henry, Carl. The 5 Secrets to Making a Powerful Business Presentation. 2010. 58p. pap. 12.95 *(978-0-9817915-4-8(9))* Henry Assocs.

Hershkowitz-Coore, Sue. How to Say It to Sell It: Key Words, Phrases, & Strategies to Build Relationships, Boost Revenue, & Beat the Competition. 2008. (ENG.). 224p. (gr. 12-18). 11.95 *(978-0-7352-0426-3(8))* Prentice Hall Pr.

Hewett, Beth L. & Robidoux, Charlotte, eds. Virtual Collaborative Writing in the Workplace: Computer-Mediated Communication Technologies & Processes. 2010. (Illus.). 350p. 180.00 *(978-1-60566-994-6(6))* IGI Global.

Hiam, Alexander. I Think You Think. Date not set. (Illus.). ix, 63p. per. 24.40 *(978-0-582-55510-5(8))* Addison-Wesley Longman, Ltd. GBR. Dist: Trans-Atlantic Pubns., Inc.

Hines, Randall & Basso, Joseph. The Writer's Toolbox: A Comprehensive Guide for Public Relations & Business Communication. rev. ed. 2006. (ENG., Illus.). 250p. pap. 69.54 *(978-0-7575-1781-5(1)*, 0757517811) Kendall Hunt Publishing Co.

Hinner, Michael B., ed. The Influence of Culture in the World of Business. 2007. (Illus.). 514p. pap. 88.95 *(978-3-631-54972-8(5))*; pap. 88.95 *(978-0-8204-9864-5(5))* Lang, Peter Publishing, Inc.

—The Interface of Business & Culture. 2010. (Freiberger Beiträge zur interkulturellen und Wirtschaftskommunikation. A Forum for General & Intercultural Business Communication Ser.). 588p. pap. 124.95 *(978-3-631-56339-7(6))* Lang, Peter GmbH, Europaischer Verlag der Wissenschaften DEU. Dist: Lang, Peter.

—The Interrelationship of Business & Communication. 2010. (Freiberger Beiträge zur interkulturellen und Wirtschaftskommunikation. A Forum for General & Intercultural Business Communication Ser.). (Illus.). 530p. pap. 115.95 *(978-3-631-56540-7(2))* Lang, Peter GmbH, Europaischer Verlag der Wissenschaften DEU. Dist: Lang, Peter.

—The Role of Communication in Business Transactions & Relationships. 2007. (Illus.). 462p. pap. 83.95 *(978-3-631-54971-1(7))*; pap. 83.95 *(978-0-8204-9863-8(7))* Lang, Peter Publishing, Inc.

Hoffman, Judith C. Keeping Cool on the Hot Seat: Dealing Effectively with the Media in Times of Crisis. 2008. 256p. pap. 19.95 *(978-0-9709014-2-2(9))* Four C's Publishing Co.

Hofreiter, Birgit. Business Processes & Context-Sensitive Business Documents - Business Collaborations Based on Umm 1 0. 2008. 156p. pap. *(978-3-639-00036-8(6))* VDM Verlag Dr. Mueller e.K.

Hollander, Edwin. Inclusive Leadership: The Essential Leader-Follower Relationship. 2008. (Applied Psychology Ser.). (ENG.). 296p. 60.00 *(978-0-8058-6439-7(3)*, Routledge) Taylor & Francis Group GBR. Dist: Taylor & Francis Group.

HOLLINGSHEAD, Andrea & Poole, Marshall Scott, eds. Research Methods for Studying Groups. 2011. (Routledge Communication Ser.). (ENG., Illus.). 472p. (C). 150.00 *(978-0-415-80632-9(1))* Routledge.

—Research Methods for Studying Groups & Teams. 2011. (Routledge Communication Ser.). (ENG., Illus.). 472p. (C). pap. 49.95 *(978-0-415-80633-6(X))* Routledge.

Holtje, Jim. The Power of Storytelling: Captivate, Convince, or Convert Any Business Audience Using Stories from Top CEOs. 2011. (ENG.). 336p. (gr. 12). 17.00 *(978-0-7352-0460-7(8))* Prentice Hall Pr.

Humphrey, Judith. Speaking As a Leader: How to Lead Every Time You Speak... from Board Rooms to Meeting Rooms, from Town Halls to Phone Calls. 2012. (ENG.). 264p. 27.95 ***(978-1-118-14101-4(6)***, Jossey-Bass) Wiley, John & Sons, Inc.

Hunt, Tara. The Power of Social Networking: Using the Whuffie Factor to Build Your Business. 2010. (ENG.). 320p. pap. 15.00 *(978-0-307-44940-5(8)*, Three Rivers Pr.) Crown Publishing Group.

Hunter, Baye. Business English: Communicating in Today's Business World. 2009. 89p. pap. 19.96 *(978-0-557-05273-8(4))* Lulu Enterprises Inc.

Hynes, Geraldine E. Managerial Communication: Strategies & Applications. 3rd ed. 2006. pap. 10.95 *(978-1-4288-1211-6(3))* Cram101 Inc.

Iapoce, Michael. Art of Using Humor in Business & Personal Communications: A Savvy Guide for Getting What You Want. 2011. (ENG., Illus.). 250p. pap. 16.95 *(978-1-56171-879-5(3))* SPI Bks.

Iarocci, Matthew. The Art of Negotiation, a Practical Guide for Success. 2009. 120p. 22.50 *(978-1-60860-506-4(X)*, Eloquent Bks.) AEG Literary Publishing Services, Inc.

Ihlen, Øyvind, et al, eds. Handbook of Communication & Corporate Social Responsibility. 2011. (Handbooks in Communication & Media Ser.). (ENG.). 608p. 199.95 *(978-1-4443-3634-4(7)*, Wiley-Blackwell) Wiley, John & Sons, Inc.

Ingre, David. Engineering Communication: A Practical Guide to Workplace Communications for Engineering. 2007. (ENG., Illus.). 312p. (C). per. 89.95 *(978-0-495-08256-9(2))* Course Technology.

Insley, Robert G. Communicating in Business in the 21st Century. 3rd ed. 2007. (ENG.). (C). 198p. pap. 92.40 *(978-0-536-52817-9(9))*; (Illus.). 611p. pap. 178.40 *(978-0-536-51499-8(2))* Pearson Learning Solutions.

Irle, Ben M. & Irle, Ben. Convergence of Communications: Implications for Regulating Market Entry. 2009. 393p. pap. 86.00 *(978-3-8329-3688-4(2))* Nomos Verlagsgesellschaft DEU. Dist: International Specialized Bk. Services.

Ishii, Kumi. Social Information During Organizational Change. 2009. 132p. pap. *(978-3-639-14246-4(2))* VDM Verlag Dr. Mueller e.K.

Jacob, Korthuis. Mind-blowing Management: Your Company, Your Mind, Our Technique, Your Success. 2009. Orig. Title: Het Management Support Plan: de volgende generatie Bedrijfsvoering. (ENG., Illus.). 226p. pap. 24.50 net. *(978-0-9786598-4-4(8))* BCE Institute, Inc.

Jacobson, Jennifer L. 42 Rules of Social Media for Small Business: A modern survival guide that answers the question What do I do with Social Media ? Lowell, Laura, ed. 2009. 122p. pap. 19.95 *(978-1-60773-014-9(6)*, Super Star Pr.) Happy About.

Jaffe, Joseph. Join the Conversation: How to Engage Marketing-Weary Consumers with the Power of Community, Dialogue, & Partnership. 2007. (ENG., Illus.). 320p. 29.95 *(978-0-470-13732-1(0)*, Wiley) Wiley, John & Sons, Inc.

Johnson, Brandt. Presentation Skills for Business Professionals. 2007. viii, 72p. per. *(978-0-9785823-0-2(6))* Syntaxis Pr.

Johnson, Lydia. The Jalapeno Handshake. 2010. 186p. 24.95 *(978-1-59930-336-9(1))* LifeSuccess Publishing.

Johnson, Michael. Cracking the Boy's Club Code: The Woman's Guide to Being Heard & Valued in the Workplace. 2009. (ENG.). 272p. pap. 16.95 *(978-1-60037-642-9(8))* Morgan James Publishing.

Johnson-Sheehan, Richard. Technical Communication Strategies for Today. 2010. (ENG., Illus.). 544p. (C). pap. 75.33 *(978-0-205-73941-7(5))* Longman Publishing Group.

—Technical Communication Strategies for Today, Books a la Carte Edition. 2011. (ENG.). 544p. (C). ring bd. 49.33 ***(978-0-205-23867-5(X))*** Longman Publishing Group.

—Technical Communication Strategies for Today, Books a la Carte Plus MyTechCommLab. 2011. (ENG.). (C). ring bd. 56.00 ***(978-0-205-23868-2(8))*** Longman Publishing Group.

Johnson, Steven. The IT Professional's Business & Communications Guide: A Real-World Approach to Comp TIA A+ Soft Skills. 2007. (ENG., Illus.). 240p. per. 24.99 *(978-0-470-12635-6(3)*, Sybex) Wiley, John & Sons, Inc.

Jones, Frances Cole. How to Wow: Proven Strategies for Selling Your [Brilliant] Self in Any Situation. 2009. (ENG.). 224p. pap. 15.00 *(978-0-345-50179-0(9)*, Ballantine Bks.) Random House Publishing Group.

Jones, Leo & Alexander, Richard. New International Business English Student's Book: Communication Skills in English for Business Purposes. 2nd ed. 2011. 176p. pap., stu. ed. 34.00 *(978-1-107-63221-9(8))* Cambridge Univ. Pr.

Kador, John. Effective Apology: Mending Fences, Building Bridges, & Restoring Trust. 2009. (Bk Business Ser.). (ENG.). 273p. pap. 19.95 *(978-1-57675-901-1(6))* Berrett-Koehler Pubs., Inc.

Kahaner, Ellen. Great Communication Skills. (Work Readiness Ser.). 64p. 2009. (gr. 6-6). 58.50 *(978-1-60854-822-4(8))* 2008. (Illus.). (J). (gr. 3-7). lib. bdg. 29.25 *(978-1-4042-1421-7(6))* Rosen Publishing Group, Inc., The.

Kahn-Panni, Phillip. Getting Your Point Across. 3rd ed. 2007. (Illus.). 192p. per. 20.00 *(978-1-84528-191-5(8))* Parkwest Pubns., Inc.

Kallos, Blogger, Consultant Judith, Author. Business E-mail Etiquette: The Manual. 2008. 144p. pap. 19.50 *(978-1-4357-2049-7(0))* Lulu Enterprises Inc.

Karaosmanoglu, Elif & Melewar, T. C. Contemporary Thoughts on Corporate Branding & Corporate Identity Management. Melewar bin Tengku Nasir, Tengku Chik & Karaosmanoglu, Elif, eds. 2008. (ENG., Illus.). 256p. 116.00 *(978-0-230-54314-0(6))* Palgrave Macmillan.

Karen, Berg. Loud & Clear. 2008. (ENG., Illus.). 1p. pap. 14.99 *(978-1-56414-987-9(0))* Career Pr., Inc.

Karen, Brannon. Lead Great: Communicate: How to Motivate Staff & Improve Organizational Effectiveness Through Communication. 2011. 108p. pap. ***(978-3-639-33692-4(5))*** VDM Verlag Dr. Mueller e.K.

Karns, Vicki & Wickelgren, Bruce. Cjn 177: Business Communication: Student Resource Manual. rev. ed. 2008. (ENG.). 128p. ring bd. 28.20 *(978-0-7575-6090-3(3))* Kendall Hunt Publishing Co.

Karr, Douglas & Flannery, Chantelle. Corporate Blogging for Dummies. 2010. (ENG., Illus.). 432p. pap. 24.99 *(978-0-470-60457-1(3)*, For Dummies) Wiley, John & Sons, Inc.

Kay, Frances & Kite, Neilson. Understanding NLP: Strategies for Better Workplace Communication... Without the Jargon. 2nd rev. ed. 2012. (ENG.). 226p. pap. 19.95 *(978-0-7494-6381-6(3))* Kogan Page, Ltd. GBR. Dist: Ingram Pub. Services.

Keiningham, Timothy, et al. Why Loyalty Matters: The Groundbreaking Approach to Rediscovering Happiness, Meaning & Lasting Fulfillment in Your Life & Work. 2009. (ENG.). 224p. 24.95 *(978-1-933771-72-4(0))* BenBella Bks.

Kelly, Patrick D. Rainmaking 101: How to Grow Your Client Base & Maximize Your Income. 2009. 120p. pap. 15.95 *(978-1-4389-5025-9(X))* AuthorHouse.

Kelm, Orlando R. & Risner, Mary E. Brasileiros Que Trabalham Com Americanos: Estudos de Casos Culturais. 2007.Tr. of Brazilians Working with Americans - Cultural Case Studies. (POR & ENG.). 218p. mass mkt. 19.95 *(978-0-292-71473-1(4))* Univ. of Texas Pr.

Kerrigan, Teresa & Sadar, Patricia. Essential Email Do's & Don'ts Kit. 2011. (Train It in Ten Ser.). cd-rom 0.00 *(978-1-936973-19-4(7))* Congrats Books, Inc.

Kindred, Maggie & Kindred, Michael. 500 Tips for Communicating with the Public. 2011. (ENG.). 160p. pap. *(978-1-84905-175-0(5))* Kingsley, Jessica Ltd.

Kinser, Amy S. & Jones, Dorothy. Your Office Getting Started with Business Communication. 2012. (ENG.). 96p. (C). spiral bd. 31.00 ***(978-0-13-267548-2(X)***, Prentice Hall) Prentice Hall PTR.

Kitty O., Locker. Business & Administrative Communicatio. 2006. pap. 10.95 *(978-1-4288-0466-1(8))* Cram101 Inc.

Klaff, Oren. Pitch Anything: An Innovative Method for Presenting, Persuading, & Winning the Deal. 2011. (ENG., Illus.). 240p. 22.00 *(978-0-07-175285-5(4)*, 0071752854) McGraw-Hill Cos., The.

Klaus, Peggy, et al. The Hard Truth about Soft Skills: Workplace Lessons Smart People Wish They'D Learned Sooner. 2008. (ENG.). 208p. pap. 14.99 *(978-0-06-128414-4(9)*, Harper Paperbacks) HarperCollins Pubs.

Klein, Christopher, ed. A/E Branch Office Fitness Plan. 2006. per. 145.00 *(978-1-934150-03-0(7))* ZweigWhite.

Klein, Ron, et al. CPA's Guide to Effective Engagement Letters: Implementing Successful Loss Prevention Practices. 7th ed. 2007. 978p. pap. 137.00 incl. cd-rom *(978-0-8080-9096-0(8))* Toolkit Media Group.

Koegel, Tim. The Exceptional Presenter Goes Virtual. 2010. 208p. 21.95 *(978-1-60832-046-2(4))* Greenleaf Book Group.

Krichko, Marilyn. The Rower's Code: A Business Parable of How to Pull Together as a Team - & Win! 2011. (ENG.). 1p. 19.99 *(978-1-60163-165-7(0))* Career Pr., Inc.

Krizan, A. C. Buddy, et al. Business Communication. 8th ed. 2010. (Business Communication Ser.). (ENG.). 736p. (C). 220.95 *(978-1-4390-8015-3(1))* Cengage South-Western.

Kuzmeski, Maribeth. The Connectors: How the World's Most Successful Businesspeople Build Relationships & Win Clients for Life. 2011. (ENG.). 258p. pap. 18.95 ***(978-1-118-15628-5(5)***, Wiley) Wiley, John & Sons, Inc.

Kyselova&apos, et al. Unconevntional Communication Strategies. 2011. 100p. pap. ***(978-3-8443-9118-3(5))*** Lambert Academic Publishing.

Lamson, Melissa. No Such Thing As Small Talk: 7 Keys to Understanding German Business Culture. 2010. 162p. pap. 19.95 ***(978-1-60005-189-0(8))*** Happy About.

Larsen, Kristian Hedengran. Communication - the Key to Successful Mergers & Acquisitions? 2011. 64p. pap. ***(978-3-8443-3474-6(2))*** Lambert Academic Publishing.

Lauria, Thomas J. Investor Relations: the Art & Philosophy of Effective Corporate Communications. 2008. 122p. pap. 19.95 *(978-0-557-00763-9(1))* Lulu Enterprises Inc.

Lawson, Diana R. & Rudd, Jill E. Communicating in Global Business Negotiations: A Geocentric Approach. 2007. (Illus.). 288p. (C). per. 63.00 *(978-1-4129-1658-5(5)*, B16585P) SAGE Pubns., Inc.

LearningExpress Staff. Office Correspondence Made Easy: Master the Basics of Business Letters, Memos, & E-mail for All Occasions. 4th ed. 2008. (ENG.). 272p. per. 14.95 *(978-1-57685-604-8(6))* LearningExpress, LLC.

Legge, Nancy J. & DiSanza, James R. Business & Professional Communication: Plans, Processes, & Performance. 4th ed. 2008. (ENG., Illus.). 301p. (C). per. 101.80 *(978-0-205-58185-6(4))* Allyn & Bacon, Inc.

Lehman, Carol M. & DuFrene, Debbie D. BCOM. (ENG.). 288p. 3rd ed. 2011. pap. 59.95 *(978-1-111-52777-8(6))* 4th ed. 2012. pap. 64.95 ***(978-1-133-37243-1(0))*** Cengage South-Western.

—BCOM (Book Only) 2nd ed. 2010. (ENG.). (C). pap. 56.95 *(978-0-538-75334-0(X))* Cengage South-Western.

—Building High-Performance Teams. 16th ed. 2010. (ENG.). 74p. (C). pap. 51.95 *(978-0-324-78219-6(5))* Cengage South-Western.

—Business Communication (Book Only) 16th ed. 2010. (ENG.). 656p. (C). 220.95 *(978-0-324-78218-9(7))* Cengage South-Western.

—Business Communication (with Teams Handbook) 16th ed. 2010. (Business Communication Ser.). (ENG.). 656p. (C). 220.95 *(978-0-324-78217-2(9))* Cengage South-Western.

Lehman, Carol M. & Dufrene, Deborah Daniel. Business Communication. 14th ed. 2006. pap. 12.95 *(978-1-4288-1067-9(6))* Cram101 Inc.

Lehman, Carol M. & DuFrene, Deborah Daniel. Business Communication. 16th ed. 2011. (Illus.). *(978-0-324-78230-1(6))* Cengage South-Western.

Lesikar and, Flatley. Basic Business Communication Skills for. 2006. pap. 10.95 *(978-1-4288-0516-3(8))* Cram101 Inc.

Lesikar, Raymond Vincent, et al. Business Communication: Making Connections in a Digital World. 11th ed. 2006. (Illus.). xxvii, 639p. *(978-0-07-305036-2(9))* McGraw-Hill Cos., The.

Lewis, David H. & Mills, G. Riley. The Pin Drop Principle: Captivate, Influence, & Communicate Better Using the Time-Tested Methods of Professional Performers. 2012. (ENG.). 272p. 25.95 ***(978-1-118-28919-8(6)***, Jossey-Bass) Wiley, John & Sons, Inc.

Lindenfield, Stuart. Confident Networking for Career Success. 2010. (ENG., Illus.). 288p. pap. 15.95 *(978-0-7499-4170-3(7))* Piatkus Bks. GBR. Dist: Independent Pubs. Group.

Lindsell-Roberts, Sheryl. New Rules for Today's Workplace: Strategies for Success in the Virtual World. 2011. (ENG.). 304p. pap. 13.95 *(978-0-547-42808-6(1))* Houghton Mifflin Harcourt Trade & Reference Pubs.

—Speaking Your Way to Success. 2010. (ENG.). 272p. pap. 13.95 *(978-0-547-25518-7(7))* Houghton Mifflin Harcourt Trade & Reference Pubs.

—135 Tips on Email & Instant Messages: Plus Blogs, Chatrooms, & Texting. 2008. (ENG.). 160p. pap. 10.95 *(978-0-618-94258-9(0))* Houghton Mifflin Harcourt Publishing Co.

Lips, Cathy Connor. Effective Publications Management: Keeping Print Communications on Time, on Budget, on Message. 2007. (ENG., Illus.). 208p. per. 29.95 *(978-1-58115-486-3(0)*, 115486, Allworth Pr.) Skyhorse Publishing Co., Inc.

Listen & Be Listened To. pap. 155.00 incl. audio *(978-0-7612-0797-9(X)*, 80204) Amacom.

Locker, Kitty & Kaczmarek, Stephen. Loose-Leaf Business Communication: Building Critical Skills. 5th ed. 2010. (ENG.). (C). ring bd. 101.33 *(978-0-07-744398-6(5)*, 0077443985, McGraw-Hill/Irwin) McGraw-Hill Higher Education.

Locker, Kitty & Kienzler, Donna. Business & Administrative Communication with Connect Plus. 10th ed. 2012. (C). 206.66 ***(978-0-07-763040-9(8)***, 0077630408, McGraw-Hill/Irwin) McGraw-Hill Higher Education.

—Loose-leaf Business & Administrative Communication. 10th ed. 2012. (ENG.). (C). ring bd. 134.00 ***(978-0-07-741953-0(7)***, 0077419537, McGraw-Hill/Irwin) McGraw-Hill Higher Education.

Locker, Kitty O. & Kaczmarek, Stephen Kyo. Business Communication. 3rd ed. 2007. (Illus.). 640p. pap. *(978-0-07-293210-2(4))* McGraw-Hill Cos., The.

—Business Communication: Building Critical Skills. 2nd ed. 2006. pap. 28.95 *(978-1-4288-1158-4(3))* Cram101 Inc.

—Business Communication: Building Critical Skills. 5th ed. 2010. (ENG., Illus.). 576p. (C). pap. 144.33 *(978-0-07-340315-1(6)*, 0073403156, McGraw-Hill/Irwin) McGraw-Hill Higher Education.

Locker, Kitty O. & Kienzler, Donna. Business & Administrative Communication. 10th ed. 2012. (ENG., Illus.). 768p. (C). 191.00 ***(978-0-07-340318-2(0)***, 0073403180, McGraw-Hill/Irwin) McGraw-Hill Higher Education.

Lorenzo, Anxo, et al, eds. New Approaches to Discourse & Business Communication. 2009. (ENG., Illus.). 272p. 95.00 *(978-1-4039-4736-9(8))* Palgrave Macmillan.

Luigi Carlo De Micco. Communicational Marketing: How to Communicate Effectively with Competent Consumers. 2010. 168p. 26.95 *(978-0-595-68193-8(X))*; pap. 16.95 *(978-0-595-42867-0(3))* iUniverse, Inc.

Luntz, Frank I. Win: The Key Principles to Take Your Business from Ordinary to Extraordinary. 2011. (ENG.). 320p. 25.99 *(978-1-4013-2399-8(5))* Hyperion Pr.

Lutgen-Sandvik. Destructive Organizational Communication. 2009. (Routledge Communication Ser.). (ENG., Illus.). 424p. pap. 47.95 *(978-0-415-98994-7(9))* Routledge.

Maclay, K. T. Business Writing, Period: A no-sweat, no-stress guide to getting your ideas on Paper. 2006. pap. 26.95 *(978-0-9786435-6-0(9))* Skatekey Productions.

MacLeod, Hugh. Ignore Everybody: And 39 Other Keys to Creativity. 2009. (ENG., Illus.). 176p. (gr. 12-18). 23.95 *(978-1-59184-259-0(X)*, Portfolio (Hardcover)) Penguin Group (USA) Inc.

MacRury, Iain & Macrury, Iain. Advertising. 2009. (Illus.). 318p. 110.00 *(978-0-415-25125-9(7)*, RU22498) Routledge.

Madia, Sherrie A. & Borgese, Paul. The Social Media Survival Guide: Everything You Need to Know to Grow Your Business Exponentially with Social Media. 2010. (Illus.). xiii, 255p. 24.95 *(978-0-9826185-1-6(4)*, Full Court Pr.) Base Camp Communications.

Magnacca, Mark. So What? How to Communicate What Really Matters to Your Audience. 2009. (ENG.). 160p. pap. 14.99 *(978-0-13-715826-3(2))* FT Press.

Magrino, William & Goeller, Michael. Effective Business & Professional Writing: From Project to Proposal. rev. ed. 2011. (ENG.). 208p. pap. 36.98 *(978-0-7575-6773-5(8))* Kendall Hunt Publishing Co.

Magy, Ronna. Working It Out. pap. 40.95 *(978-0-8384-8762-4(9))* Cengage Heinle.

Maraia, Mark. Relationships Are Everything! Growing Your Business One Relationship at a Time. 2009. 232p. 27.95 *(978-0-9724532-2-6(9))* Professional Services Publishing.

Martin, Jeanette S. & Chaney, Lillian H. Global Business Etiquette: A Guide to International Communication & Customs. 2nd ed. 2012. E-Book ***(978-0-313-39718-9(X)***, Praeger Pubs.); 229p. 48.00 ***(978-0-313-39717-2(1)***, A3539C) Greenwood Publishing Group, Inc.

Martin, Steve W. Heavy Hitter Sales Wisdom: Proven Sales Warfare Strategies, Secrets of Persuasion, & Common-Sense Tips for Success. 2006. (ENG., Illus.). 272p. 24.95 *(978-0-470-05231-0(7)*, Wiley) Wiley, John & Sons, Inc.

Martynova, Olga. Sprachwahl in der deutsch-russischen Unternehmenskommunikation. 2010. (Duisburger Arbeiten zur Sprach- und Kulturwissenschaft. Duisburg Papers on Research in Language & Culture Ser.). (GER., Illus.). 264p. 72.95 *(978-3-631-60045-0(3))* Lang, Peter GmbH, Europaischer Verlag der Wissenschaften DEU. Dist: Lang, Peter.

Maslansky, Michael, et al. The Language of Trust: Selling Ideas in a World of Skeptics. (ENG.). 288p. (gr. 12). 2011. 16.00 *(978-0-7352-0456-0(X))* 2010. (Illus.). 25.00 *(978-0-7352-0475-1(6))* Prentice Hall Pr.

Matha, Bob & Boehm, Macy. Beyond the Babble: Leadership Communication That Drives Results. 2008. (ENG., Illus.). 240p. 27.95 *(978-0-470-20048-3(0)*, Jossey-Bass) Wiley, John & Sons, Inc.

Mattus, Thomas J. Boss Talk in the 21st Century: A Leadership Guide. 2008. (ENG.). 202p. pap. 32.95 *(978-0-9745185-9-6(X)*, Arseya Publishing) Arseya, LLC.

Maximo, Rui, et al. Programming for Unified Communications: With Microsoft Office Communications Server 2007. 2009. (ENG.). 416p. pap. 49.99 *(978-0-7356-2623-2(5))* Microsoft Pr.

Mayr, Wolfgang. STORYTELLING: Von den Anforderungen, die Gäste an die Geschichte, die ihnen ein Hotel vermittelt, stellen. 2010. 356p. pap. *(978-3-639-24019-1(7))* VDM Verlag Dr. Mueller e.K.

McCabe, Scott. Marketing Communications in Tourism & Hospitality: Concepts, Strategies & Cases. 2008. (ENG., Illus.). 320p. (C). pap. 55.95 *(978-0-7506-8277-0(9))* Routledge.

McCarney, K. The Secrets of Successful Communication. 2011. 200p. pap. 15.95 ***(978-0-9831244-3-6(4))*** O'Connell Hse.

McClay, Renie & Irwin, LuAnn. The Essential Guide to Training Global Audiences: Your Planning Resource of Useful Tips & Techniques. 2008. (ENG.). 460p. pap. 60.00 *(978-0-7879-9661-1(0)*, Pfeiffer) Wiley, John & Sons, Inc.

McHugh, Damian. Public Relations & Corporate Communications Law in Ireland. 2007. pap. 67.50 *(978-1-904480-38-9(1))* First Law IRL. Dist: Gaunt, Inc.

McIntosh, Perry, et al. Interpersonal Communication Skills in the Workplace. 2nd ed. 2008. xxi, 155p. ***(978-0-7612-1475-5(5))*** American Management Assn.

Means, Thomas. Business Communications. 2nd ed. 2009. (ENG.). 96p. (C). pap., pupil's gde. ed. 38.95 *(978-0-538-44959-5(4))* Cengage South-Western.

Means, Thomas L. Business Communication. 2nd ed. 2009. (Introduction to Business Communication Ser.). (ENG.). 672p. (C). 96.95 *(978-0-538-44947-2(0))* Cengage South-Western.

—Means' English & Communication for Colleges. 4th ed. 2006. (ENG.). 160p. (C). pap. 50.95 *(978-0-538-72994-9(5))* Cengage South-Western.

Means, Thomas L. & Langlois, Elaine. English & Communication for Colleges. 4th rev. ed. 2006. (ENG., Illus.). 640p. (C). 141.95 *(978-0-538-73000-6(5))* Cengage South-Western.

Melewar, T. C. Facets of Corporate Identity, Communication & Reputation. 2008. (Illus.). XVIII, 238p. 175.00 *(978-0-415-40527-0(0))* Routledge.

—Facets of Corporate Identity, Communication & Reputation. Melewar, T. C., ed. 2008. (ENG., Illus.). 256p. (C). 52.95 *(978-0-415-40528-7(9))* Routledge.

Mendell, Brooks. Loving Trees Is Not Enough: Communicatio. 2006. pap. 11.50 *(978-1-59330-428-7(5))* Aventine Pr.

Menke, Julia. The Uk Fast Moving Consumer Good Business. 2007. 76p. per. *(978-3-8364-1629-0(8))* VDM Verlag Dr. Mueller e.K.

Meyer, Carolyn. Communicating for Results: A Canadian Student's Guide. 2006. (Illus.). 384p. per. 60.00 *(978-0-19-541807-1(7))* Oxford Univ. Pr., Inc.

—Communication for Results. 2nd ed. 2010. (ENG., Illus.). 528p. pap., stu. ed. 74.00 *(978-0-19-543164-3(2))* Oxford Univ. Pr., Inc.

Micco, Luigi Carlo De. How You Get What You Want: Dreams Can Change the World. 2010. 282p. 29.99 *(978-1-4535-4638-3(3))*; pap. 19.99 *(978-1-4535-4637-6(5))* Xlibris Corp.

—Wie Sie Bekommen, Was Ihnen Zusteht. 2010. 314p. 29.99 *(978-1-4535-1888-5(6))* Xlibris Corp.

Mikelat, Mark. 50 Tips for Effective Networking. 2007. per. 9.95 *(978-1-934468-00-5(2))* Building Aspirations.

Million Dollar Toolbox. *(978-0-9713742-1-8(X))* Alexa Pr.

Morris, David & Singer, Thom. Some Assembly Required - LinkedIn. Morris, Leslie, ed. 2009. 200p. pap. 22.95 *(978-0-9799885-1-6(9))* New Year Publishing.

Morris, Rebecca A. On the Job with Hearing Loss: Hidden Challenges Successful Solutions. 2007. (ENG., Illus.). 185p. per. 29.95 *(978-1-60037-269-8(4))* Morgan James Publishing.

Morrow, Bruce. The Outcome Model. 2010. pap. *(978-1-61623-922-0(0))* Independent Pub.

Morsing, Mette, et al. Corporate Communications: Convention, Complexity & Critique. 2008. (Illus.). 264p. (C). pap. 61.00 *(978-1-4129-3103-8(7)*, B31029P) SAGE Pubns., Ltd. GBR. Dist: SAGE Pubns., Inc.

Mortensen, Kurt W. Persuasion IQ: The 10 Skills You Need to Get Exactly What You Want, 1 vol. 2008. (ENG., Illus.). 336p. 21.95 *(978-0-8144-0993-0(8))* Amacom.

Mountain, Anita & Davidson, Chris. Orgainizational TA: Using Transactional Analysis for Effective Communication. 2011. (Illus.). 292p. 124.95 *(978-0-566-08846-9(0)*, Gower Publishing Co., Ltd.) Ashgate Publishing, Ltd. GBR. Dist: Ashgate Publishing Co.

Muhney, Mike & Pucher, Max J. Who's in Your Orbit? Beyond Facebook - Creating Relationships That Matter. 2012. (ENG.). 96p. pap. 9.99 ***(978-0-9830415-0-4(4))*** Carpenter's Son Publishing.

Mullins, Chris. Monkey Business for Today's Phone Weary Office. 2010. pap. *(978-1-61623-677-9(9))* Independent Pub.

Munter, Mary M. Guide to Managerial Communication. 9th rev. ed. 2011. (ENG.). 204p. (C). pap. 64.00 *(978-0-13-214771-2(8)*, Prentice Hall) Prentice Hall PTR.

Murray, John. Now That's What I Call Jargon. 2009. (ENG., Illus.). 141p. pap. 21.95 *(978-1-84840-019-1(5))* New Island Books IRL. Dist: Dufour Editions, Inc.

Murray, John E., 3rd. Driving ROI: A Summarized Venture in Storytelling, Listening, & Measuring. 2007. pap. 12.99 *(978-0-9794451-0-1(8))* Story Institute.

Murray State University. Selling Yourself & Your Ideas: A Text/Workbook for Building Presentation Skills. 2nd rev. ed. (ENG.). 2012. 292p. pap. 43.75 ***(978-0-7575-9406-9(9))*** 2010. 270p. pap. 43.75 *(978-0-7575-8121-2(8))* Kendall Hunt Publishing Co.

Naskrent, Julia. Verhaltenswissenschaftliche Determinanten der Spenderbindung: Eine empirische Untersuchung und Implikationen für das Spenderbindungsmanagement. 2010. (Marktorientierte Unternehmensführung Ser.). (GER.). 488p. 118.95 *(978-3-631-60853-1(5))* Lang, Peter GmbH, Europaischer Verlag der Wissenschaften DEU. Dist: Lang, Peter.

Naslund, Amber & Baer, Jay. The NOW Revolution: 7 Shifts to Make Your Business Faster, Smarter & More Social. 2011. (ENG., Illus.). 224p. 24.95 *(978-0-470-92327-6(X)*, Wiley) Wiley, John & Sons, Inc.

Nelson M.S., Carrie. Don't Quit Your Day Job, Learn to Love It. 2009. 150p. 29.95 *(978-1-4401-5288-7(8))*; pap. 19.95 *(978-1-4401-5285-6(3))* iUniverse, Inc.

Niklaus, Eberhard. Successful Selling Unlocked - Relationship Marketing. 2009. 128p. pap. 12.90 *(978-1-4251-7512-2(0))* Trafford Publishing.

Oade, Aryanne. Building Influence in the Workplace: How to Gain & Retain Influence at Work. 2010. (ENG.). 224p. 42.00 *(978-0-230-23773-5(8))* Palgrave Macmillan.

Obenchain Jr. M.B.A., John R. Communicating Your Message to Those Too Busy to Listen. 2009. 272p. 25.99 *(978-1-4389-3122-7(0))*; pap. 16.00 *(978-1-4389-3121-0(2))* AuthorHouse.

Ober. Contemporary Business Communication. 2006. pap. 11.95 *(978-1-4288-0957-4(0))* Cram101 Inc.

—Real Deal Upgrade CD-ROM: Used with ... Ober-Fundamentals of Contemporary Business Communication. cd-rom 2.76 *(978-0-618-07376-4(0)*, 341784) CENGAGE Learning.

Ober, Scot. Student Achievement Series: Fundamentals of Contemporary Business Communication. 2007. (ENG.). 448p. (C). pap. 149.95 *(978-0-618-90093-0(4))* Cengage South-Western.

O'Donovan, Gabrielle. Solvency Ii Stakeholder Communications & Change. 2011. (Illus.). 188p. 134.95 ***(978-1-4094-3152-7(5)***, Gower Publishing Co., Ltd.) Ashgate Publishing, Ltd. GBR. Dist: Ashgate Publishing Co.

O'Hair, Dan, et al. Strategic Communication in Business & the Professions. 7th ed. 2010. (ENG.). 456p. (C). pap. 110.20 *(978-0-205-69311-5(3))* Allyn & Bacon, Inc.

Ojeda-Zapata, Julio. Twitter Means Business: How microblogging can help or hurt your Company. 2008. 152p. pap. 19.95 *(978-1-60005-118-0(9))* Happy About.

Oliu, Walter E., et al. Writing that Works with 2009 MLA & 2010 APA Updates: Communicating Effectively on the Job. 10th ed. 2010. (ENG.). 736p. (C). pap. 84.95 *(978-0-312-69217-9(X))* Bedford/Saint Martin's.

Oliver, Keith. Command Attention. 2009. (Illus.). 192p. 25.95 *(978-1-59114-645-2(3))* Naval Institute Pr.

orford, chris. Communication Skill. 2009. 98p. pap. 31.95 *(978-1-4092-8583-0(9))* Lulu Enterprises Inc.

Ombo, Jens, et al. Experience-Based Communication. 2008. (Illus.). X, 280p. 69.95 *(978-3-540-78711-2(9)*, 3540787119) Springer.

O'Rourke, James S., IV. The Business Communication Casebook: A Notre Dame Collection. 2nd rev. ed. 2007. (ENG.). 368p. (C). per. 72.95 *(978-0-324-54509-8(6))* Cengage South-Western.

Ortiz, Lorelei A. A Practical Course in Business Communication. rev. ed. 2011. (ENG.). 144p. pap. 75.00 ***(978-0-7575-8665-1(1))*** Kendall Hunt Publishing Co.

Owen, Harrison. Open Space Technology: A User's Guide. 3rd rev. ed. 2008. (ENG., Illus.). 198p. pap. 29.95 *(978-1-57675-476-4(6))* Berrett-Koehler Pubs., Inc.

Oxford, Ewan. You've Got Players. 2009. 53p. pap. 16.95 *(978-1-4452-0564-9(5))* Lulu Enterprises Inc.

Pachter, Barbara. When the Little Things Count ... And They Always Count: 601 Essential Things That Everyone in Business Needs to Know. 2nd ed. 2006. (ENG.). 192p. per. 13.95 *(978-1-56924-290-2(9))* Da Capo Pr., Inc.

Palmer-Silveira, Juan Carlos, et al. Intercultural & International Business Communication: Theory, Research & Teaching. 2006. (Illus.). 343p. pap. 86.95 *(978-3-03910-954-8(5))*; Vol. 38. pap. 62.95 *(978-0-8204-8356-6(7))* Lang, Peter Publishing, Inc.

Palomino, M. A. Tecnicas de Correo Comercial. (SPA.). 147p. pap. 24.95 *(978-84-7711-766-7(7)*, EDI1766) Edelsa Grupo Didascalia, S.A. ESP. Dist: Continental Bk. Co., Inc.

Peaker, John. The Call Wizard. 2008. 144p. pap. 18.50 *(978-1-934925-02-7(0)*, Eloquent Bks.) AEG Literary Publishing Services, Inc.

Penrose, Rasberry. Business Communication for Managers. 2006. pap. 10.95 *(978-1-4288-0685-6(7))* Cram101 Inc.

Perkins, P. S. The Art & Science of Communication: Tools for Effective Communication in the Workplace. 2008. (ENG., Illus.). 224p. 31.95 *(978-0-470-24759-4(2)*, Wiley) Wiley, John & Sons, Inc.

Phillips, Jack J., et al. Communication & Implementation: Sustaining the Practice, 7 vols. 2008. (Measurement & Evaluation Ser.: 5). (ENG., Illus.). 224p. pap. 40.00 *(978-0-7879-8722-0(0)*, Pfeiffer) Wiley, John & Sons, Inc.

Phillips, Tim. Talk Normal: Stop the Business Speak, Jargon & Waffle. 2011. (ENG., Illus.). 192p. pap. 19.95 *(978-0-7494-6364-9(3))* Kogan Page, Ltd. GBR. Dist: Ingram Pub. Services.

Pitzl, Marie-Luise. English As a Lingua Franca in International Business. 2010. 192p. pap. *(978-3-639-22507-5(4))* VDM Verlag Dr. Mueller e.K.

Porter, Erin, et al. Communication Matters: Write Speak Succeed: A Collection of Readings in Business Communications. 2nd rev. ed. 2010. (ENG.). 254p. ring bd. 48.23 *(978-0-7575-7376-7(2))* Kendall Hunt Publishing Co.

Powell, Diane L. Written Business Communication: A Learner Centered Approach with Text Addendum. rev. ed. (ENG.). 2010. ring bd. 52.88 *(978-0-7575-7472-6(6))* 2009. ring bd. 52.88 *(978-0-7575-6805-3(X))* Kendall Hunt Publishing Co.

—Written Business Communications: A Learner-Centered Approach. rev. ed. 2008. (ENG.). 150p. ring bd. 52.09 *(978-0-7575-5244-1(7))* Kendall Hunt Publishing Co.

Powell, James Larry. Surviving Group Meetings: Practical Tools for Working in Groups. 2009. 178p. pap. 29.95 *(978-1-59942-521-4(1))*; (Illus.). 176p. E-Book *(978-1-59942-522-1(X))* Universal Pubs. (Brown Walker Pr.).

Prince, Dennis L. Get Rich with Twitter: Harness the Power of the Twitterverse & Reach More Customers Than Ever Before. 2010. (ENG., Illus.). 256p. pap. 19.95 *(978-0-07-163844-9(X)*, 007163844X) McGraw-Hill Cos., The.

Reben, Brent D. & Smulowitz, Stacy M. Core Communication Workbook & Scoring Instructions. 2007. per. 100.00 *(978-1-888015-57-7(8))* International Assn. of Business Communicators.

Redic, Patricia J. Succeed with Style: Make More Sales Faster. 2008. 182p. per. 24.95 *(978-0-9799807-0-1(4))* Millennium Star Publishing.

Reece, Toni. Let the Leaders Steer & the People Drive: Performance Coaching Through the PEOPLE ModelTM. 2007. 88p. per. 11.95 *(978-0-595-42841-0(X))* iUniverse, Inc.

Reiter, Rosina Márquez. Mediated Business Interactions: Intercultural Communication Between Speakers of Spanish. 2011. (ENG., Illus.). 256p. (gr. 17). 100.00 *(978-0-7486-3720-1(6))* Edinburgh Univ. Pr. GBR. Dist: Columbia Univ. Pr.

Remenyi, Dan. How to Prepare Business Cases: An Essential Guide for Accountants. 2009. (ENG.). 268p. pap. 62.95 *(978-1-85617-666-8(5)*, CIMA Publishing) Elsevier Science & Technology Bks.

Richer, Julian. The Richer Way. pap. *(978-0-9526730-0-2(2))* EMAP Business Communications.

—The Richer Way. 4th ed. 256p. *(978-0-9534415-1-8(2))* 5th ed. 2009. (Illus.). 246p. pap. 19.95 *(978-0-9534415-2-5(0))* Richer, Julian Publishing GBR. Dist: Vine Hse. Distribution, Trans-Atlantic Pubns., Inc.

Riel, C. B. M. van. The Alignment Factor: Leveraging the Power of Total Stakeholder Support. 2012. E-Book ***(978-0-203-12453-6(7))*** Routledge.

Rigolosi, Elaine Lamonica. La Monica Empathy Profile-others. rev. ed. 2009. (ENG.). 9p. pap. 44.75 *(978-1-59996-191-0(1))* Human Resource Development Pr.

RoAne, Susan. Face to Face: How to Reclaim the Personal Touch in a Digital World. 2008. (ENG., Illus.). 288p. pap. 14.95 *(978-1-4165-6142-2(0)*, Touchstone) Touchstone.

Roberts, Sherry J. Fundamentals of Business Communication. 2011. (ENG.). (gr. 9-12). pap., wbk. ed. 20.00 *(978-1-60525-473-9(8))* Goodheart-Willcox Pub.

Roebuck, Deborah Britt. Communication Strategies for Today's Managerial Leader. 2011. 200p. pap. 29.95 ***(978-1-60649-199-7(7))*** Business Expert Pr.

Rola, Martin. Email Less Talk More. 2008. 288p. pap. 17.95 *(978-1-59858-702-9(1))* Dog Ear Publishing, LLC.

Rolfes, Rebecca. The Competition Within: How Members Will Reinvent Associations. 2009. 144p. 25.95 *(978-0-595-51477-9(4))*; pap. 15.95 *(978-0-595-52695-6(0))* iUniverse, Inc.

Runion. Perfect Phrases for Icebreakers: Hundreds of Ready-to-Use Phrases to Set the Stage for Productive Conversations, Meeting. 2011. (ENG.). 176p. pap. 12.00 ***(978-0-07-178382-8(2)***, 0071783822) McGraw-Hill Cos., The.

Runion, Meryl. Perfect Phrases for Managers & Supervisors. 2nd ed. 2010. (Perfect Phrases Ser.). (ENG.). 208p. pap. 10.95 *(978-0-07-174231-3(X)*, 007174231X) McGraw-Hill Cos., The.

—Speak Strong: Say what you MEAN. MEAN what you say. Don't be MEAN when you say it. 2010. (ENG.). 308p. pap. 24.95 *(978-1-60037-864-5(1))* Morgan James Publishing.

Runion, Meryl. Virtual Teams: Hundreds of Ready-to-Use Phrases for Implementing & Fostering Collaboration with Off-Site Employees. 2012. (Perfect Phrases Ser.). (ENG.). 176p. pap. 12.00 ***(978-0-07-178384-2(9)***, 0071783849) McGraw-Hill Cos., The.

Runion, Meryl & Brittain, Janelle. How to Say It Performance Reviews: Phrases & Strategies for Painless & Productive Performance Reviews. 2006. (ENG.). 224p. (gr. 12-18). 11.95 *(978-0-7352-0412-6(8))* Prentice Hall Pr.

Runion, Meryl & Fenner, Susan. Office Professionals: Hundreds of Ready-to-Use Phrases for Getting Respect, Recognition, & Results in Today's Workplace. 2011. (Perfect Phrases Ser.). (ENG.). 176p. pap. 12.00 *(978-0-07-176674-6(X)*, 007176674X) McGraw-Hill Cos., The.

Runion, Meryl & Mack, Wendy. Leadership Development: Hundreds of Ready-to-Use Phrases for Guiding Employees to Reach the Next Level. 2010. (Perfect Phrases Ser.). (ENG.). 192p. pap. 12.00 *(978-0-07-175094-3(0)*, 0071750940) McGraw-Hill Cos., The.

Salvi, Rita & Tanaka, Hiromasa. Intercultural Interactions in Business & Management. 2011. (Linguistic Insights. Studies in Language & Communication Ser.). (ENG., Illus.). 304p. pap. ***(978-3-0343-1039-0(0))*** Lang, Peter.

Sampson, Stephen. The Art of Performance Feedback. 2011. (ENG., Illus.). 46p. spiral bd. 14.95 ***(978-1-59996-256-6(X))*** Human Resource Development Pr.

Sanders, Liz & Filkins, Joseph. Effective Reporting, 2nd ed. 2009. (Illus.). 81p. (YA). pap. *(978-1-882393-17-6(1))* Assn. for Institutional Research.

Sarap, Laura. Inside Our Communication of Christian Dior. 2010. 68p. pap. *(978-3-8383-7180-1(1))* Lambert Academic Publishing.

Satterwhite and, Sutton. Business Communication at Work. 2006. pap. 10.95 *(978-1-4286-0609-2(1))* Cram101 Inc.

Satterwhite, Marilyn & Olson-Sutton, Judith. Business Communication. 3rd ed. 2007. (Illus.). xiv, 522p. pap., stu. ed. *(978-0-07-110740-2(1))* McGraw-Hill Cos., The.

Scannell, Mary, et al. Big Book of Virtual Teambuilding Games: Quick, Effective Activities to Build Communication, Trust & Collaboration from Anywhere! 2011. (Big Book Ser.). (ENG., Illus.). 256p. pap. 25.00 ***(978-0-07-177435-2(1)***, 0071774351) McGraw-Hill Cos., The.

Schmidt, Wallace V., et al. Communicating Globally: Intercultural Communication & International Business. 2007. (Illus.). 336p. (C). per. 52.00 *(978-1-4129-1317-1(9)*, B13179P) SAGE Pubns., Inc.

Schnöring, Stefanie. Kommunikation im Spiegel der Unternehmenskultur: Dialogisches Handeln und unternehmerische Zwecke. 2007. (Beiträge Zur Dialogforschung Ser.). (GER.). IX, 207p. pap. *(978-3-484-75035-7(9))* Verlag Max Niemeyer.

Schnurr, Stephanie. Professional Communication. 2012. (Routledge Introductions to Applied Linguistics Ser.). (ENG., Illus.). 256p. pap. 39.95 ***(978-0-415-58483-8(3))***; 150.00 ***(978-0-415-58481-4(7))*** Routledge.

Schober, Johanna. Intercultural Influences in a Strategic Communication Process. 2010. 132p. pap. *(978-3-639-23741-2(2))* VDM Verlag Dr. Mueller e.K.

Schoemaker, Henny & Vos, Marita. Integrated Communication: Concern, Internal & Marketing Communication. 4th ed. 2011. 336p. pap. 61.00 ***(978-90-5931-659-1(2))*** Eleven International Publishing NLD. Dist: International Specialized Bk. Services.

Schrage, Michael. Getting Beyond Ideas: The Future of Rapid Innovation. 2011. (ENG.). 224p. 29.95 *(978-0-470-56364-9(8))* Wiley, John & Sons, Inc.

Schultz, John R. Making It All Work: A Pocket Guide to Sustain Improvement & Anchor Change. 2010. (ENG., Illus.). 168p. pap. 39.95 *(978-0-415-88103-6(X))* Routledge.

—Making It All Work: Sustain Improvement & Anchor Change. 2010. (ENG., Illus.). 168p. 125.00 *(978-0-415-88102-9(1))* Routledge.

Searles, George J. Workplace Communications: The Basics. 5th ed. 2010. (ENG.). 312p. (C). pap. 70.80 *(978-0-205-82809-8(4))* Longman Publishing Group.

—Workplace Communications: The Basics, Book a la Carte Edition. 5th ed. 2011. (ENG.). (C). ring bd. 46.67 ***(978-0-205-23836-1(X))*** Longman Publishing Group.

—Workplace Communications: The Basics, Books a la Carte Plus MyTechCommLab. 5th ed. 2011. (ENG.). (C). ring bd. 53.33 ***(978-0-205-23854-5(8))*** Longman Publishing Group.

Seeley, Monica. Brilliant Email: How to Win Back Time & Increase Your Productivity. rev. ed. 2010. (ENG., Illus.). 280p. (C). pap. 24.99 ***(978-0-273-74255-5(8))*** FT Press.

Seigel, Gary. The Mouth Trap: Strategies, Tips, & Secrets to Keep Your Foot Out of Your Mouth. 2008. (ENG., Illus.). 1p. pap. 14.99 *(978-1-56414-995-4(1))* Career Pr., Inc.

Selby, John. Listening with Empathy: Creating Genuine Connections with Customers & Colleagues. 2007. (ENG.). 240p. 19.95 *(978-1-57174-514-9(9))* Hampton Roads Publishing Co., Inc.

Shipley, David & Schwalbe, Will. Send: Why People Email So Badly & How to Do It Better. 2010. (Vintage Ser.). 288p. pap. 14.95 *(978-0-307-27599-8(X)*, Vintage) Knopf Doubleday Publishing Group.

—Send (Revised Edition) Why People Email So Badly & How to Do It Better. 2nd rev. ed. 2008. (ENG., Illus.). 288p. 19.95 *(978-0-307-27060-3(2)*, Knopf) Knopf Doubleday Publishing Group.

Showalter, Amy. The Underdog Edge: How Ordinary People Change the Minds of the Powerful & Live to Tell about It. 2011. (ENG.). 300p. pap. 19.95 ***(978-1-60037-998-7(2))*** Morgan James Publishing.

Shumba, Milton & Mutonga, Lovemore. Linguistic Strategies Employed in Trading. 2011. 84p. pap. ***(978-3-8443-1284-3(6))*** Lambert Academic Publishing.

Shwom, Barbara & Snyder, Lisa G. Business Communication: Polishing Your Professional Presence, Student Value Edition. 2011. (ENG.). 585p. (C). ring bd. 89.40 *(978-0-13-257392-4(X)*, Prentice Hall) Prentice Hall PTR.

Shwom, Barbara & Snyder, Lisa Gueldenzoph. Business Communication: Polishing Your Professional Presence. 2011. (ENG.). 600p. (C). pap. 140.00 *(978-0-13-607807-4(9)*, Prentice Hall) Prentice Hall PTR.

Shwom, Barbara L., et al. Graphics & Visual Communication for Managers. 2nd ed. 2008. (ENG., Illus.). 128p. per. 49.95 *(978-0-324-58418-9(0))* Cengage South-Western.

Silvers, Julia Rutherford. Professional Event Coordination with Special Events Set: Business Communication. 6th ed. 2011. (Wiley Event Management Ser.). 204.95 *(978-1-118-06343-9(0))* Wiley, John & Sons, Inc.

Simmons, Annette. Whoever Tells the Best Story Wins: How to Use Your Own Stories to Communicate with Power & Impact. 2007. (ENG.). 240p. 22.00 *(978-0-8144-0914-5(8))* Amacom.

Singer, Thom & Barnes, Megan. Batteries Not Included, 1 vol. 2010. (ENG.). 200p. pap. 29.95 *(978-0-9799885-2-3(7))* New Year Publishing.

Singh, Manikant. Communication Management: A Global Perspective for Identification & Corporate Branding. 2011. (Illus.). 376p. pap. 47.50 ***(978-93-80228-87-7(2))*** Global India Pubns. Pvt. Ltd. IND. Dist: Coronet Bks.

Singleton, Susan. E-Mail Legal Issues 2008. 2008. (Thorogood Reports). 130p. spiral bd. 245.00 *(978-1-85418-630-0(2))* Thorogood GBR. Dist: Stylus Publishing, LLC.

Sirgy, M. Joseph & Rahtz, Don. Instructor's Edition Strategic Marketing Communications: A Systems Approach. 2006. (Illus.). 400p. (C). pap. 69.95 *(978-1-59260-283-4(5))* Delmar Cengage Learning.

—Strategic Marketing Communications: A Systems Approach to IMC. 2006. (ENG.). (C). pap. 171.95 *(978-1-59260-284-1(3))* Delmar Cengage Learning.

Slomer, Eric M. Business Cards As Communication. 2009. 120p. pap. *(978-3-639-16732-0(5))* VDM Verlag Dr. Mueller e.K.

Smiciklas, Mark. The Power of Infographics: Using Pictures to Communicate & Connect with Your Audience. 2012. (Que Biz-Tech Ser.). (ENG.). 225p. pap. 29.99 ***(978-0-7897-4949-9(1))*** Que.

Smythe, John. The CEO: Chief Engagement Officer: Turning Hierarchy Upside Down to Drive Performance. 2007. (Illus.). 226p. pap. 49.95 *(978-0-566-08561-1(5)*, Gower Publishing Co., Ltd.) Ashgate Publishing, Ltd. GBR. Dist: Ashgate Publishing Co.

Sobczak, Art. Smart Calling: Eliminate the Fear, Failure, & Rejection from Cold Calling. 2010. (ENG.). 256p. 21.95 *(978-0-470-56702-9(3)*, Wiley) Wiley, John & Sons, Inc.

Sobel, Andrew & Panas, Jerold. Power Questions: Build Relationships, Win New Business, & Influence Others. 2012. (ENG.). 205p. 22.95 ***(978-1-118-11963-1(0)***, Wiley) Wiley, John & Sons, Inc.

Sommer, Dennis. Adviser Secrets How to Become a Top Performer: A Guide to the 13 Most Important Communication Skills Used by Top Performers. 2008. 224p. pap. 27.95 *(978-0-595-52344-3(7))* iUniverse, Inc.

Song, Mike, et al. The Hamster Revolution: How to Manage Your E-Mail Before It Manages You. 2007. (ENG., Illus.). 128p. 19.95 *(978-1-57675-437-5(5))* Berrett-Koehler Pubs., Inc.

Sostrin, Jesse, et al. Cmm Solutions - Workbook. 2011. 38p. pap. 24.94 ***(978-1-4357-6502-3(8))*** Lulu Enterprises Inc.

Sourcebooks. Retire with a Mission: Planning & Purpose for the Second Half of Life. 2008. (ENG.). 320p. pap. 16.95 *(978-1-4022-1474-5(X))* Sourcebooks, Inc.

Southwood, Sue. Lifelines 22: Literacy, Language & Numeracy in the Workplace. 2006. (Illus.). 48p. pap. 12.95 *(978-1-86201-247-9(4))* National Institute of Adult Continuing Education GBR. Dist: International Specialized Bk. Services.

Speedy, Karin. 'Everyone Speaks English, Right?' A Cross-Cultural Postmodern Perspective on Languagein Business. 2008. (FRE & ENG., Illus.). 244p. pap. *(978-3-639-10269-7(X))* VDM Verlag Dr. Mueller e.K.

Stankovich, Peter. Six-Figure Incomes: Profit from America's Best Communicators. 2006. 344p. per. 19.95 *(978-0-9778127-0-7(7))* Wall Street Press, LLC.

Steffel, Frieda. Internal Communication in English. 2010. 128p. pap. *(978-3-639-23998-0(9))* VDM Verlag Dr. Mueller e.K.

Stickel, Gerhard, ed. Language Use in Business & Commerce in Europe: Contributions to the Annual Conference 2008 of EFNIL in Lisbon. 2009. (Duisburger Arbeiten zur Sprach- und Kulturwissenschaft. Duisburg Papers on Research in Language & Culture Ser.). (FRE, GER & ENG., Illus.). 202p. 61.95 *(978-3-631-58803-1(8))* Lang, Peter GmbH, Europaischer Verlag der Wissenschaften DEU. Dist: Lang, Peter.

Stober, Helmut. Der Zusammenhang Von Sprache und Beruf im Kontext Unternehmerischer Praxis. (GER., Illus.). 235p. pap. 54.95 *(978-3-631-56873-5(3))* Lang, Peter GmbH, Europaischer Verlag der Wissenschaften DEU. Dist: Lang, Peter Publishing, Inc.

Stowell, Steven J. & Mead, Stephanie S. The Team Approach: With Teamwork Anything Is Possible. 2007. 208p. *(978-0-9724627-4-7(0))* CMOE Pr.

Strategic Communication Planning: A Guide for Water Utilities; Subject Area: Efficient & Customer-Responsive Organization. 2006. (Illus.). 84p. spiral bd. 143.00 incl. cd-rom *(978-1-58321-444-2(5))* Water Research Foundation.

Stuart, Bonnye E., et al. Integrated Business Communication: In a Global Marketplace. 2007. (ENG., Illus.). 448p. per. 97.95 *(978-0-470-02767-7(3)*, Wiley) Wiley, John & Sons, Inc.

Sutherland, Jonathan & Canwell, Diane. Business & Communication Systems. 2010. (Illus.). 117p. pap., instr.'s gde. ed. 22.50 *(978-1-4441-0775-3(5))* Hodder Education GBR. Dist: Trans-Atlantic Pubns., Inc.

Svendsen, Eric & Svendsen, Virginia. Building Bridges - Using Thinking Styles to Facilitate Communication. Rhoades-Baum, Patrice et al, eds. (Illus.). 35p. (Orig.). pap. *(978-1-57125-053-7(0))* HDI.

Talbot, Fiona. How to Write Effective Business English Bk. 1: The Essential Toolkit for Composing Powerful Letters, E-Mails & More, for Today's Business Needs. 2009. (Better Business English Ser.). (ENG., Illus.). 160p. pap. 17.95 *(978-0-7494-5520-0(9))* Kogan Page Ltd. GBR. Dist: Ingram Pub. Services.

—Make an Impact with Your Written English Bk. 2: How to Use Word Power to Impress in Presentations, Reports, PR & Meetings. 2009. (Better Business English Ser.). (ENG., Illus.). 160p. pap. 17.95 *(978-0-7494-5519-4(5))* Kogan Page, Ltd. GBR. Dist: Ingram Pub. Services.

Taricani, Joseph. The Hello Culture. 2010. 50p. pap. 15.99 *(978-1-4500-5414-0(5))* Xlibris Corp.

Taylor, David & Miles, David. Fusion - the New Way of Marketing. 2011. 182p. pap. ***(978-1-907722-35-6(1))*** Ecademy Pr. Ltd.

Taylor, Shirley & Lester, Alison. Communication: Your Key to Success. 2010. 0208p. pap. 15.99 *(978-981-261-675-3(6))* Marshall Cavendish International (Asia) Private Ltd. SGP. Dist: Marshall Cavendish Corp.

Telofski, Richard. Insidious Competition: The Battle for Meaning & the Corporate Image. 2010. 396p. (ENG.). 36.95 *(978-1-4502-2910-4(7))*; pap. 26.95 *(978-1-4502-2908-1(5))* iUniverse, Inc.

Thaeler, Janet Meiners. I Need a Killer Press Release — Now What??? A Guide to Online PR. Alba, Jason, ed. 2009. (Illus.). 158p. pap. 19.95 *(978-1-60005-154-8(5))* Happy About.

Thatcher, Barry. Intercultural Rhetoric & Professional Communication: Technological Advances & Organizational Behavior. 2011. ***(978-1-61350-452-9(7))***; ***(978-1-61350-450-5(0))***; E-Book ***(978-1-61350-451-2(9))*** IGI Global.

Theaker, Alison & Yaxley, Heather. The Public Relations Strategic Toolkit: An Essential Guide to Successful Public Relations Practice. 2012. (ENG., Illus.). 264p. (C). 130.00 *(978-0-415-67647-2(9))*; pap. 39.95 *(978-0-415-67648-9(7))* Routledge.

Theobald, Theo. Develop Your Presentation Skills. 2011. (Sunday Times Creating Success Ser.). (ENG., Illus.). 176p. pap. 14.95 *(978-0-7494-6278-9(7))* Kogan Page, Ltd. GBR. Dist: Ingram Pub. Services.

Thill, et al. Excellence in Business Communication, Student Value Edition. 9th ed. 2010. (ENG.). 672p. (C). ring bd. 104.60 *(978-0-13-610384-4(7)*, Prentice Hall) Prentice Hall PTR.

Thill and, Bovee. Business Communication. 2006. pap. 11.95 *(978-1-4288-0663-4(6))* Cram101 Inc.

—Excellence in Business Communication. 2006. pap. 11.95 *(978-1-4288-0690-0(3))* Cram101 Inc.

Thill, John V. & Bovee, Courtland. Excellence in Business Communication. 9th ed. 2010. (ENG.). 672p. (C). 106.67 *(978-0-13-702897-9(0)*, Prentice Hall) Prentice Hall PTR.

Thill, John V. & Bovee, Courtland L. Excellence in Business Communication. 8th ed. 2007. (Illus.). 784p. per. 144.33 *(978-0-13-615750-2(5))* 9th ed. 2010. (ENG.). 672p. (C). pap. 162.67 *(978-0-13-610376-9(6)*, Prentice Hall) 10th rev. ed. 2012. (ENG.). 672p. (C). pap. 162.67 ***(978-0-13-271904-9(5)***, Prentice Hall) Prentice Hall PTR.

—Excellence in Business Communication, Student Value Edition. 10th ed. 2012. (ENG.). 672p. (C). ring bd. 105.73 ***(978-0-13-271914-8(2)***, Prentice Hall) Prentice Hall PTR.

Thill, John V. & Bovee, Courtland L. Study Guide for Excellence in Business Communication. 9th ed. 2010. (ENG.). 187p. (C). pap. 46.67 *(978-0-13-610377-6(4)*, Prentice Hall) Prentice Hall PTR.

Thomases, Hollis. Twitter Marketing: An Hour a Day. 2010. (ENG., Illus.). 504p. pap. 29.99 *(978-0-470-56226-0(9)*, Sybex) Wiley, John & Sons, Inc.

Thompson, David. The Magic Blackberry. 2010. 256p. pap. 13.95 *(978-1-905736-43-0(6))* Marshall Cavendish GBR. Dist: Midpoint Trade Bks., Inc.

Thompson, Jo & Bruno-Magdich, Tom. The Energetics of Charisma. 2008. 172p. pap. 31.50 *(978-1-4092-2573-7(9))* Lulu Enterprises Inc.

Thron, Jesko A. Multisensuales Marketing: Eine interdisziplinäre Betrachtung multisensualer Markenführung unter besonderer Berücksichtigung der Wirkung imaginierter Sinneseindrücke. 2009. 84p. pap. *(978-3-639-19583-5(3))* VDM Verlag Dr. Mueller e.K.

Tietze, Susanne. International Management & Language. 2008. (Routledge Studies in International Business & the World Economy Ser.). (ENG., Illus.). 264p. (C). 158.00 *(978-0-415-40393-1(6))* Routledge.

Tofanelli, Dave. Communication in a Business Setting. 2009. 376p. pap. 44.00 *(978-1-4490-2043-9(7))* AuthorHouse.

Toogood, Granville. The New Articulate Executive: Look, Act & Sound Like a Leader. 2nd ed. 2010. (ENG., Illus.). 240p. 21.95 *(978-0-07-174326-6(X)*, 007174326X) McGraw-Hill Cos., The.

Topus, David. Talk to Strangers: How Everyday, Random Encounters Can Expand Your Business, Career, Income & Life. 2012. (ENG.). 208p. 24.95 ***(978-1-118-20347-7(X)***, Wiley) Wiley, John & Sons, Inc.

Troester, Rod & Mester, Cathy Sargent. Civility in Business & Professional Communication. 2007. (Illus.). (C). 278p. 89.95 *(978-0-8204-8653-6(1))*; 280p. pap. 32.95 *(978-0-8204-8652-9(3))* Lang, Peter Publishing, Inc.

Troup, Nicola J. Green Marketing Perceptions & Opinions. 2010. (Illus.). 112p. pap. *(978-3-8383-4566-6(5))* Lambert Academic Publishing.

TSUFIT. Step into the Spotlight! 'Cause All Business Is Show Business!: A Guide to Getting Noticed. 2008. (ENM & ENG., Illus.). 288p. *(978-0-9781913-0-6(7))* Beach View Bks.

Tuleja, Elizabeth A. & O'Rourke, James S. Intercultural Communication for Business. 2nd ed. 2008. (ENG., Illus.). 192p. pap. 49.95 *(978-0-324-58420-2(2))* Cengage South-Western.

Van Raaij, W. F., et al, eds. The Handbook of Economic Psychology. 2010. 700p. pap. 369.00 *(978-90-481-8310-4(3)*, 9048183103) Springer.

Van Riel, Cees & Fombrun, Charles. Essentials of Corporate Communication: Implementing Practices for Effective Reputation Management. 2007. (ENG., Illus.). 328p. (C). 59.95 *(978-0-415-32826-5(8)*, RU27245) Routledge.

Van Riel, Cees B. M. Corporate Persuasion. 2012. (ENG., Illus.). 256p. (C). 160.00 ***(978-0-415-69074-4(9))***; pap. 58.95 ***(978-0-415-69075-1(7))*** Routledge.

Vandome, Nick & McVey, John. Effective Communications in Easy Steps: Get the Right Message Across at Work. 2012. (In Easy Steps Ser.). (ENG., Illus.). 192p. pap. 14.99 ***(978-1-84078-448-0(2))*** Computer Step GBR. Dist: Perseus-PGW.

Verderber, Rudolph F., et al. Essential Speech: Communicating Orally. 2010. (Language Arts Solutions Ser.). (ENG.). 528p. (C). 97.95 *(978-0-538-44990-8(X))* Cengage South-Western.

Vermoortel, P. Bedrijf & taal. Opstellen voor Wilfried Janssens / Business & Language: Essays in Honour of Wilfried Janssens. Jaspers, D., ed. 2009. (DUT, ENG, FRE & GER., Illus.). 677p. (C). 73.00 *(978-90-429-2222-8(2))* Peeters Pubs. & Booksellers BEL. Dist: Brown, David Bk. Co., The.

B

Wahl, Shawn T. & Quintanilla, Kelly M. Business & Professional Communication: KEYS for Workplace Excellence. 2010. (Illus.). 376p. (C). pap. 88.00 *(978-1-4129-6472-2(5)*, B64722P) SAGE Pubns., Inc.

Waldron, Edward E. Communicating as a Professional Engineer: A Guide to Written & Oral Communication in the Business Environment. 2nd rev. ed. 2006. (ENG.). 90p. pap. 66.28 *(978-0-7575-2551-3(2))* Kendall Hunt Publishing Co.

Waldron, Vincent & Kassing, Jeffrey W. Managing Risk in Communication Encounters: Strategies for the Workplace. 2010. (Illus.). 272p. (C). pap. 46.00 *(978-1-4129-6667-2(1)*, B66672P) SAGE Pubns., Inc.

Walker, Robyn. Strategic Management Communication: For Leader. 2nd ed. 2010. (ENG.). 384p. (C). pap. 128.95 *(978-0-538-45134-5(3))* Cengage South-Western.

Wallace, Ed. Business Relationships that Last. 2009. 21.95 *(978-1-60832-001-1(4)*, Greenleaf Book Group Pr.) Greenleaf Book Group.

Wallenius, Dale. Communication Tips for Successful Donor Visits. 2009. 84p. pap. 10.95 *(978-1-4401-1551-6(6))* iUniverse, Inc.

Wang, John X. What Every Engineer Should Know about Business Communication. 2008. (What Every Engineer Should Know Ser.). (ENG., Illus.). 208p. pap. 54.95 *(978-0-8493-8396-0(X)*, CRC Press) Taylor & Francis Group GBR. Dist: Taylor & Francis Group.

Weeks, Barbara. The Job Interview: Communicating for the Business World. 2006. cd-rom 12.95 *(978-0-9787454-1-7(8))* Advanced Marketing Systems, Inc.

Welz, Christian. The European Social Dialogue under Articles 138 & 139 of the EC Treaty: Actors, Processes, Outcomes. 2008. (Illus.). 172.00 *(978-90-411-2744-0(5))* Wolters Kluwer Law & Business.

Whalen, D. Joel. The Professional Communication Toolkit. 2006. (Illus.). 304p. (C). pap. 64.00 *(978-1-4129-2716-1(1)*, B27161P) SAGE Pubns., Inc.

Whaley, Bryan B. & Samter, Wendy, eds. Explaining Communication: Contemporary Theories & Exemplars. 2006. (LEA's Communication Ser.). (Illus.). 467p. per. 65.95 *(978-0-8058-3959-3(3))* Erlbaum, Lawrence Assocs., Inc.

—Explaining Communication: Contemporary Theories & Exemplars. 2006. (LEA's Communication Ser.). (ENG., Illus.). 480p. 157.00 *(978-0-8058-3958-6(5))* Routledge.

Whitlock, Warren & Micek, Deborah. Twitter Revolution: How Social Media & Mobile Marketing Is Changing the Way We Do Business & Market Online. 2008. (Illus.). 277p. pap. 18.97 *(978-1-934275-07-8(7))* Xeno Pr.

Why Did I Say That? Communicating to Keep Your Credibility, Your Cool, & Your Cash! 2007. per. 19.95 *(978-0-9649694-1-4(6))* MC Publishing.

Wichter, Sigurd. Kommunikationsreihen Aus Gesprächen und Textkommunikaten: Zur Kommunikation in und Zwischen Gesellschaften. 2011. (Reihe Germanistische Linguistik Ser.). (GER.). XVI, 427p. 140.00 ***(978-3-11-023409-1(2))*** De Gruyter, Walter Inc.

Williams, Dean. Creating Grade 'A' Business Relationships - Doing the Right Things but Not Always the Most Popular. 2008. 108p. pap. *(978-1-906645-20-5(5))* Grosvenor Hse. Publishing Ltd.

Wiskup, Mark. The It Factor: Be the One People Like, Listen to, & Remember. 2007. (ENG.). 192p. per. 14.95 *(978-0-8144-7437-2(3))* Amacom.

Wollan, Robert, et al. The Social Media Management Handbook: Everything You Need to Know to Get Social Media Working in Your Business. 2011. (ENG., Illus.). 352p. 27.95 *(978-0-470-65124-7(5)*, Wiley) Wiley, John & Sons, Inc.

World Bank Staff, et al. Building Commitment to Reform through Strategic Communication: The Five Key Decisions. 2009. (World Bank Training Ser.). (ENG., Illus.). 148p. pap. 25.00 *(978-0-8213-7621-8(7)*, 9780821376218) World Bank Pubns.

Wort, Carolyn & Petrucke, Fiona. AQA Business & Communication Systems for GCSE. 2009. 200p. pap. 52.50 *(978-0-340-98602-8(6))* Hodder Education GBR. Dist: Trans-Atlantic Pubns., Inc.

Wright, Sylvia. Seven Steps to Grow Green Market Share. 2010. 48p. pap. 14.95 *(978-0-557-70952-6(0))* Lulu Enterprises Inc.

Yaffe, Philip A. The Gettysburg Approach to Writing & Speaking Like a Professional. 2010. 275p. pap. 14.00 *(978-0-9789247-5-1(4)*, INDI Best) INDI, LLC.

Yager, Jan. Productive Relationships: 57 Strategies for Building Stronger Business Connections. 2011. 222p. (ENG.). 31.95 *(978-1-889262-63-5(3))*; pap. 22.95 *(978-1-889262-60-4(9))* Hannacroix Creek Bks., Inc.

Yasko-Mangum, Jamie L. Look, Speak, & Behave for Men: Expert Advice on Image, Etiquette, & Effective Communication for the Professional. 2007. (Illus.). 212p. 19.95 *(978-1-60239-025-6(8))* Skyhorse Publishing Co., Inc.

—Look, Speak, & Behave for Women: Expert Advice on Image, Etiquette, & Effective Communication for the Professional. 2007. (Illus.). 220p. 19.95 *(978-1-60239-026-3(6))* Skyhorse Publishing Co., Inc.

Young, Richard. How Audiences Decide. 2010. (ENG., Illus.). 416p. pap. 69.95 *(978-0-415-87900-2(0))* Routledge.

—How Audiences Decide: A Cognitive Approach to Business Communication. 2010. (ENG., Illus.). 416p. 120.00 *(978-0-415-87899-9(3))* Routledge.

Yung, Moti & Katz, Jonathan. Digital Signatures. 2008. (Advances in Information Security Ser.). (Illus.). 170p. 99.00 *(978-0-387-27711-0(0)*, 0387277110) Springer.

Zachry, Mark, et al, eds. Comunicative Practices in Workplaces & the Professions: Cultural Perspectives on the Regulation of Discourse & Organizations. 2007. (Technical Communication Ser.). (Illus.). 288p. (C). 61.95 *(978-0-89503-372-7(0))* Baywood Publishing Co., Inc.

Zaretskaia, E. N. Rhetoric, the Theory & Practice of Speech Communication. 2007. (Illus.). 416p. *(978-1-893552-45-6(4))* Mir Collection Publishing Hse.

Zoller, Kim & Preston, Kerry. You Did What? The Biggest Mistakes Professionals Make. 2011. 121p. pap. 16.95 ***(978-1-61254-027-6(9))*** Brown Bks. Publishing Group.

178 Communication Facts, Tips & Ideas. 2006. pap. 22.99 *(978-0-9761569-1-8(1))* Communispond.

BUSINESS CONSULTANTS

Adams, Scott. How's That Underling Thing Working Out for You? 2011. (ENG.). 128p. pap. 12.99 *(978-1-4494-0819-0(2))* Andrews McMeel Publishing.

Adams, Susan & Zanzi, Alberto Louis. Preparing Better Consultants: The Role of Academia. 2012. 290p. ***(978-1-61735-615-5(8))***; 290p. pap. ***(978-1-61735-614-8(X))***; xxii, 266p. E-Book ***(978-1-61735-616-2(6))*** Information Age Publishing, Inc.

Albon, Philip, et al. Consulting for Dummies. 2012. (ENG., Illus.). 360p. pap. 27.95 ***(978-0-470-71382-2(8)***, For Dummies) Wiley, John & Sons, Inc.

Andler, Nicolai. Tools for Project Management, Workshops & Consulting: A Must-Have Compendium of Essential Tools & Techniques. 2nd ed. 2011. (ENG., Illus.). 382p. 55.00 *(978-3-89578-370-8(6)*, Wiley) Wiley, John & Sons, Inc.

Anhalt, Karen Nickel, et al. Eastern Europe Consulting: Key Data Trends & Forecasts for Consulting in Eastern Europe, Russia, Ukraine & the Baltics. 2006. (Illus.). 226p. spiral bd. 3495.00 *(978-1-932079-73-9(4))* BNA Subsidiaries, LLC.

Armbrüster, Thomas. The Economics & Sociology of Management Consulting. (ENG., Illus.). 2010. 268p. pap. 30.00 *(978-0-521-14224-3(5))* 2006. 266p. 94.00 *(978-0-521-85715-4(5))* Cambridge Univ. Pr.

Aronoff, Craig E. & Ward, John L. How to Choose & Use Advisors: Getting the Best Professional Family Business Advice. 2010. (Family Business Leadership Ser.). (ENG., Illus.). 100p. pap. 24.00 *(978-0-230-11104-2(1))* Palgrave Macmillan.

Barrington, Gail V. Consulting Start-up & Management: A Guide for Evaluators & Applied Researchers. 2011. 320p. (C). pap. 35.00 ***(978-1-4129-8709-7(1)***, B87097P) SAGE Pubns., Inc.

Beitler, Michael. Strategic Organizational Change, Second Edition: A Practitioner's Guide for Managers & Consultants. 2nd ed. 2006. 242p. per. 39.95 *(978-0-9726064-2-4(4))* Practitioner Pr. International.

Biech, Elaine. The Business of Consulting: The Basics & Beyond. 2nd rev. ed. 2007. (ENG., Illus.). 340p. 55.00 *(978-0-7879-9464-8(2)*, Pfeiffer) Wiley, John & Sons, Inc.

—The Consultant's Quick Start Guide: An Action Plan for Your First Year in Business. 2nd ed. 2008. (ENG., Illus.). 280p. pap. 35.00 *(978-0-470-37231-9(1)*, Pfeiffer) Wiley, John & Sons, Inc.

—Training & Consulting, 2 vols., Set. annuals 2008. (JB 2004 Annuals Set Ser.: 4). (ENG.). 656p. 180.00 *(978-0-470-43118-4(0)*, Pfeiffer) Wiley, John & Sons, Inc.

—The 2008 Pfeiffer Annual Consulting. 2007. (J-B Pfeiffer Annual Looseleaf Vol2 Ser.: 34). (ENG., Illus.). 320p. 95.00 *(978-0-7879-9627-7(0)*, Pfeiffer) Wiley, John & Sons, Inc.

—The 2009 Pfeiffer Annual Consulting. annuals 2008. (J-B Pfeiffer Annual Looseleaf Vol2 Ser.: 41). (ENG.). 320p. 95.00 *(978-0-470-37143-5(9)*, Pfeiffer) Wiley, John & Sons, Inc.

—The 2011 Pfeiffer Annual: Consulting. 2010. (J-B Pfeiffer Annual Looseleaf Vol2 Ser.: 44). (ENG.). 320p. 95.00 *(978-0-470-59237-3(0)*, Pfeiffer) Wiley, John & Sons, Inc.

Biech, Elaine. 2012 Pfeiffer Annual Set. 2011. (JB 2004 Annuals Set Ser.). (ENG.). 672p. 161.50 ***(978-1-118-30166-1(8)***, Pfeiffer) Wiley, John & Sons, Inc.

Biech, Elaine, ed. The 2010 Pfeiffer Annual: Consulting. 2009. (Pfeiffer Annual-Training Ser.). (ENG.). 336p. 95.00 *(978-0-470-90753-5(3)*, Pfeiffer) Wiley, John & Sons, Inc.

Biggs, David. Management Consulting. 2010. (Illus.). xviii, 409p. pap. 81.99 *(978-1-4080-0791-4(6))* CENGAGE Learning.

Birnbaum, Bill. A Lifetime of Small Adventures: Stories of Adventure, Misadventure & Lessons Learned along the Way. 2011. 202p. pap. 14.95 *(978-1-932632-00-2(X))* Douglas Mountain Publishing.

Blank, Uel. Prelude to Greatness: How the Greatest Generation Got That Way. 2007. 300p. per. 16.95 *(978-1-59858-270-3(4))* Dog Ear Publishing, LLC.

Blenkinsopp, Damien & Smith, Derek. The Latin America Consulting Marketplace 2007-2010: Key Trends, Profiles & Forecasts. 2007. spiral bd. 3695.00 *(978-1-932079-87-6(4))* BNA Subsidiaries, LLC.

Blenkinsopp, Damien, et al. Strategy Consulting Marketplace 2006 - 2009: Key Trends, Profiles & Forecasts. 2007. (Illus.). 300p. spiral bd. 4695.00 *(978-1-932079-81-4(5))* BNA Subsidiaries, LLC.

Block, Peter. Flawless Consulting: A Guide to Getting Your Expertise Used. 3rd ed. 2011. (ENG., Illus.). 352p. 55.00 *(978-0-470-62074-8(9)*, Pfeiffer) Wiley, John & Sons, Inc.

Boeckmann, Brent, et al. Marketing & Business Development in Consulting: Trends & Benchmarks. 2007. (Illus.). 98p. spiral bd. 1995.00 *(978-1-932079-82-1(3))* BNA Subsidiaries, LLC.

Bogan, Stephanie. The Power of Practice Management: Best Practices for Building a Better Advisory Business. 2012. (Bloomberg Financial Ser.: 168). (ENG.). 352p. 60.00 ***(978-1-118-12117-7(1)***, Bloomberg Pr.) Wiley, John & Sons, Inc.

Boone, Christopher, et al. High Tech Consulting Marketplace 2006 - 2010: Key Trends, Profiles & Forecasts. 2007. spiral bd. 3695.00 *(978-1-932079-80-7(7))* BNA Subsidiaries, LLC.

Bouwmeester, Onno. Economic Advice & Rhetoric: Why Do Consultants Perform Better Than Academic Advisers? 2010. 320p. 140.00 *(978-1-84844-263-4(7))* Elgar, Edward Publishing, Inc.

Brech, Edward, et al. Lyndall Urwick, Management Pioneer: A Biography. 2010. (ENG., Illus.). 288p. 85.00 *(978-0-19-954196-6(5))* Oxford Univ. Pr., Inc.

Brooks, Ann & Edwards, Kathy. Successful Business Consulting in A Changing World. 2013. (ENG., Illus.). 300p. 130.00 *(978-0-415-80048-8(X))*; pap. 59.95 *(978-0-415-80049-5(8))* Routledge.

Buono, Anthony F. The Changing Paradigm of Consulting: Adjusting to the Fast-Paced World. 2011. 250p. E-Book *(978-1-61735-419-9(8))*; (Illus.). xxi, 440p. *(978-1-61735-418-2(X))*; (Illus.). 250p. pap. *(978-1-61735-417-5(1))* Information Age Publishing, Inc.

—Emerging Trends & Issues in Management Consulting: Consulting As a Janus-Faced Reality. 2009. 296p. *(978-1-60752-052-8(4))*; xx, 272p. pap. *(978-1-60752-051-1(6))* Information Age Publishing, Inc.

Buono, Anthony F. & Jamieson, David. Consultation for Organizational Change. 2010. E-Book *(978-1-61735-088-7(5))*; (Illus.). xviii, 315p. *(978-1-61735-087-0(7))*; (Illus.). 334p. pap. *(978-1-61735-086-3(9))* Information Age Publishing, Inc.

Buono, Anthony F. & Poulfelt, Flemming. Client-Consultant Collaboration: Coping with Complexity & Change. 2009. (Illus.). 276p. pap. *(978-1-60752-208-9(X))* Information Age Publishing, Inc.

Buono, Anthony F. & Poulfelt, Flemming, eds. Client-Consultant Collaboration: Coping with Complexity & Change (HC) 2009. 276p. 85.99 *(978-1-60752-209-6(8))* Information Age Publishing, Inc.

Burchard, Brendon. El Mensajero Millonario: Haga el Bien y una Fortuna Dando Consejos. 2011. (SPA & ENG.). 192p. pap. 14.99 ***(978-1-4516-6644-1(6)***, Free Pr.) Free Pr.

—The Millionaire Messenger: Make a Difference & a Fortune Sharing Your Advice. 2011. (ENG.). 176p. pap. 14.99 ***(978-1-4516-6599-4(7)***, Free Pr.) Free Pr.

Cagney, Penelope & Alliance for Nonprofit Management Staff. Nonprofit Consulting Essentials: What Nonprofits & Consultants Need to Know. 2010. (ENG., Illus.). 272p. 55.00 *(978-0-470-44240-1(9)*, Jossey-Bass) Wiley, John & Sons, Inc.

Carkenord, Barbara A. Seven Steps to Mastering Business Analysis. 2008. 360p. pap. *(978-1-60427-007-5(1))* Ross, J. Publishing, Inc.

Carmichael, Douglas R., et al. Guide to Small Business Consulting Engagements, 3 vols. Incl. Vol. 1. ring bd. 164.00 *(978-0-7646-0415-7(5))*; Vol. 2. ring bd. 164.00 *(978-0-7646-0416-4(3))*; Vol. 3. ring bd. 164.00 *(978-0-7646-0417-1(1))*; 1998. 164.00 *(978-0-7646-0414-0(7))* Practitioners Publishing Co.

—A Guide to Small Business Consulting Engagements, 3 vols. Incl. Vol. 1. Guide to Small Business Consulting Engagements. 1997. ring bd. *(978-0-7646-0149-1(0))*; 156.00 *(978-0-7646-0148-4(2))* Practitioners Publishing Co.

Clark. Management Consulting, 2 vols. 2012. (International Library of Critical Writings on Business & Management Ser.: 20). 1296p. 720.00 ***(978-1-84720-910-8(6))*** Elgar, Edward Publishing, Inc.

Cohen, William A. How to Make It Big as a Consultant, 1 vol. 4th ed. 2009. (ENG.). 320p. pap. 18.95 *(978-0-8144-1032-5(4))* Amacom.

Compensation in Consulting 2007: Benchmarks, Trends & Forecasts of the Profession. 2006. spiral bd. 3495.00 *(978-1-932079-72-2(6))* BNA Subsidiaries, LLC.

Cope, Mick. The Seven Cs of Consulting. 3rd ed. 2010. (ENG., Illus.). 400p. (C). pap. 29.99 *(978-0-273-73108-5(4))* FT Press.

Cosentino, Marc. Case in Point: Complete Case Interview Preparation. 7th ed. 2011. (Illus.). vi, 228p. ***(978-0-9710158-6-9(4))*** Burgee Pr.

Cram101 Textbook Reviews. Outlines & Highlights for Management Consultancy by Joe Omahoney. 2011. 218p. pap. 30.95 ***(978-1-4672-6610-9(8))*** Cram101 Inc.

Cram101 Textbook Reviews Staff. Outlines & Highlights for Designing Solutions for Your Business Problems: A Structured Process for Managers & Consultants by Vandenbosch, ISBN. 2008. 60p. pap. 9.95 *(978-1-4288-6408-5(3))* Cram101 Inc.

Czerniawska, F. & May, Paul. Management Consulting in Practice: A Casebook of International Best Practice. 2006. (ENG., Illus.). 304p. pap. 39.95 *(978-0-7494-4818-9(0))* Kogan Page, Ltd. GBR. Dist: Ingram Pub. Services.

Czerniawska, Fiona. The Trusted Firm: How Consulting Firms Build Successful Client Relationships. 2007. (ENG., Illus.). 260p. 70.00 *(978-0-470-02717-2(7)*, Wiley) Wiley, John & Sons, Inc.

Davis, Miles. Od & Change Management Consultants. 2008. 196p. pap. *(978-3-639-08184-8(6))* VDM Verlag Dr. Mueller e.K.

Davis, Wayne R. Executing Change in the Organization, Kit. 2009. (ENG.). 144p. ring bd. 159.00 *(978-0-470-40000-5(5)*, Pfeiffer) Wiley, John & Sons, Inc.

—A Guide to Executing Change for Individual Contributors. 2009. (ENG.). 112p. pap., wbk. ed. 35.00 *(978-0-470-40002-9(1)*, Pfeiffer) Wiley, John & Sons, Inc.

de Stricker, Ulla. Business Cases for Info Pros: Here's Why, Here's How. 2008. 120p. pap. 39.50 *(978-1-57387-335-2(7))* Information Today, Inc.

DeLong, Thomas J., et al. When Professionals Have to Lead: A New Model for High Performance. 2007. (ENG., Illus.). 256p. 35.00 *(978-1-4221-1737-8(5))* Harvard Business Review Pr.

Donadone, Julio. In the World of Intermediaries. 2010. 104p. pap. *(978-3-639-27280-2(3))* VDM Verlag Dr. Mueller e.K.

Dunning, John H. Seasons of a Scholar: Some Personal Reflections of an International Business Economist. 2009. (Illus.). 232p. 119.00 *(978-1-84844-181-1(9))*; pap. 41.00 *(978-1-84844-188-0(6))* Elgar, Edward Publishing, Inc.

Ekern, C. R. Consultative Brokerage: The Total Cost of Risk Sales Strategy. 2007. (Illus.). xiv, 224p. pap. *(978-0-87218-737-5(3))* National Underwriter Co.

Entrepreneur Press Staff & Sandlin, Eileen. Start Your Own Consulting Business, Third Edition. 3rd ed. 2010. (ENG.). 224p. pap. 19.95 *(978-1-59918-373-2(0)*, 1599183730) Entrepreneur Pr. dba Entrepreneur Media, Inc.

Executive Pay: The Role of Compensation Consultants: Hearing Before the Committee on Oversight & Government Reform, House of Representatives, One Hundred Tenth Congress, First Session, December 5, 2007. 2009. (Illus.). iii, 173p. *(978-0-16-082677-1(2)*, 552-070-38694-7) United States Government Printing Office.

Farrell, John, et al. Risk Management Consulting Marketplace 2008-2011: Key Trends, Profiles & Forecasts. 2007. spiral bd. 3695.00 *(978-1-934717-01-1(0))* BNA Subsidiaries, LLC.

Fees, Utilization & Key Metrics in Consulting 2007. 2007. spiral bd. 3695.00 *(978-1-932079-77-7(7))* BNA Subsidiaries, LLC.

Flanagan, Bob, et al. Operations Management Consulting: Key Data, Trends & Forecasts. 2006. (Illus.). 188p. spiral bd. 3495.00 *(978-1-932079-74-6(2))* BNA Subsidiaries, LLC.

Gitomer, Jeffrey. Trust: How to Earn It, Grow It, & Keep It to Become a Trusted Advisor in Sales, Business & Life. 2008. (Jeffrey Gitomer's Little Bks.). (ENG., Illus.). 208p. 19.99 *(978-0-13-715410-4(0))* FT Press.

Gomez, Pierre-Yves & Moore, Rickie. Board Members & Management Consultants: Redefining the Boundaries of Consulting & Corporate Governance. 2008. *(978-1-59311-806-8(6))*; pap. *(978-1-59311-805-1(8))* Information Age Publishing, Inc.

Gray, Douglas. Start & Run a Consulting Business. 7th rev. ed. 2006. 232p. per. 17.95 *(978-1-55180-737-9(8))* Self-Counsel Pr., Inc. CAN. Dist: Midpoint Trade Bks., Inc.

Gray, Douglas A. Start & Run a Consulting Business. 8th ed. 2008. (Start & Run ... Ser.). 232p. pap. 19.95 *(978-1-55180-824-6(2))* Self-Counsel Pr., Inc. CAN. Dist: Midpoint Trade Bks., Inc.

Greiner, Larry E. Management Consulting Today & Tomorrow: Perspectives & Advice from 20 Leading World Experts. 2009. (ENG., Illus.). XVIII, 510p. 100.00 *(978-0-415-80359-5(4))*; 528p. pap. 49.95 *(978-0-415-80358-8(6))* Routledge.

Greiner, Larry E., et al, eds. Management Consulting Today & Tomorrow Casebook: Enhancing Skills to Become Better Professionals. (ENG., Illus.). 512p. 2010. 100.00 *(978-0-415-80357-1(8))* 2009. 39.95 *(978-0-415-80356-4(X))* Routledge.

Haider, Saba. Vault Career Guide to Consulting, 2nd Edition: European Edition. 2009. 192p. pap. 34.95 *(978-1-58131-691-9(7))* Vault.com.

Hand, D. J. & Everitt, Brian. The Statistical Consultant in Action. 2007. (ENG.). 204p. (C). pap. 48.00 *(978-0-521-04751-7(X))* Cambridge Univ. Pr.

Hedge, Jerry W. & Borman, Walter C. The I/O Consultant: Advice & Insights for Building a Successful Career. 2008. (Illus.). 392p. 69.95 *(978-1-4338-0339-0(9))* American Psychological Assn.

Hicks, Tyler G. Financial Broker/Finder/Business Broker/Business Consultant Kit. 17th ed. 2007. pap. 99.50 *(978-1-56150-821-1(7))* International Wealth Success, Inc.

Higgins, John. Organisational Consulting. 2007. (Management, Policy + Education Ser.). (Illus.). 300p. pap. 45.00 *(978-1-904750-14-7(1))* Libri Publishing Ltd GBR. Dist: Independent Pubs. Group.

Hill, Nadine. The Virtual Assistant Handbook: Insider Secrets for Starting & Running Your Own Profitable VA Business. 2009. (Illus.). 192p. pap. *(978-1-905430-56-7(6))* Lean Marketing Pr.

Hipkiss, Anna. Successful Consulting. 2010. (Teach Yourself Ser.). (ENG., Illus.). 318p. pap. 23.95 *(978-1-4441-0063-1(7)*, Hodder & Stoughton) Hodder General Publishing Div. GBR. Dist: Independent Pubs. Group.

—Teach Yourself Consulting. 2006. (Teach Yourself Ser.). (ENG., Illus.). 256p. per. 12.95 *(978-0-07-148450-3(7)*, 0071484507) McGraw-Hill Cos., The.

The Holmes Report 2007 European Consultancy Report Card. 2007. pap. 69.95 net. *(978-0-9797529-1-9(4))*; pap. 69.95 net. *(978-0-9723645-9-1(5))* Holmes Group, The.

The Holmes Report 2008 Asian Consultancy Report Card. 2008. pap. 69.95 net. *(978-0-9797529-2-6(2))* Holmes Group, The.

Holtje, Bert. How to Start a Home-Based Business. 2009. (Home-Based Business Ser.). (ENG.). 176p. pap. 18.95 *(978-0-7627-5946-0(1))* Globe Pequot Pr., The.

—How to Start a Home-Based Consulting Business: Define Your Specialty Build a Client Base Make Yourself Indispensable. 2010. (Home-Based Business Ser.). (ENG., Illus.). 192p. pap. 18.95 *(978-0-7627-5265-2(3)*, 1302532) Globe Pequot Pr., The.

Horan, James T., Jr. The One Page Business Plan for the Professional Consultant. 2006. (One Page Business Plan Ser.: 2). pap. 34.95 *(978-1-891315-04-6(8))* One Page Business Plan Co., The.

Ingram, Sherrin Ross. Successful Strategic Planning: 10 Things You Absolutely Must Know Before Hiring a Consultant to Prepare a Strategic Plan for Your Business. 2011. 84p. 19.99 *(978-0-9716478-3-1(6))* Jourdan & Brown Publishing, Inc.

Jankowski, Tomek. Recruiting, Retention & Benefits in Consulting 2007: Trends & Benchmarks. 2007. (Illus.). 64p. spiral bd. 1995.00 *(978-1-932079-83-8(1))* BNA Subsidiaries, LLC.

Jankowski, Tomek E., et al. Compensation in Consulting 2007-2008: Benchmarks, Trends & Forecasts of the Profession. 2007. spiral bd. 3695.00 *(978-1-932079-92-0(0))* BNA Subsidiaries, LLC.

Jenkins, Simon, ed. Annual Review of High Performance Coaching & Consulting 2009. 2009. 232p. 45.00 *(978-0-906522-50-9(1))* Multi Science Publishing Co., Ltd. GBR. Dist: Independent Pubs. Group.

Johnson, Thomas D., ed. Bradford's International Directory of Marketing Research Agencies. 30th ed. 2008. Orig. Title: Bradford's Directory of Marketing Research Agencies & Consulting Firms. (ENG.). 420p. pap. 95.00 *(978-0-933527-87-4(X))* Business Research Services, Inc.

Katcher, Bruce L. & Snyder, Adam. An Insider's Guide to Building a Successful Consulting Practice, 1 vol. 2010. (ENG.). 272p. pap. 18.95 *(978-0-8144-1436-1(2))* Amacom.

King, Kathleen & Higgins, John. Organisational Consulting: @ the Edges of Possibility. 2012. (ENG., Illus.). 220p. pap. 44.95 ***(978-1-907471-09-4(X))*** Libri Publishing Ltd GBR. Dist: Independent Pubs. Group.

Kipping, Matthias & Clark, Timothy, eds. The Oxford Handbook of Management Consulting. 2012. (ENG.). 544p. 150.00 ***(978-0-19-923504-9(X))*** Oxford Univ. Pr., Inc.

Kozoll, Charles E. Consulting with Local Organizations. 10.95 *(978-0-914951-08-7(4))* Learning Resources Network Inc.

Krueger, David. The Sage & Scholar's Guide to Coaching Professionals: The Art & Science of Working with Dynamic, Knowledgeable & Coachable Clients. 2006. ring bd. 99.00 *(978-0-9790448-0-9(4))* LearnMore Publishing.

Levitt, Gail. Team Planning for Project Managers & Business Analysts. 2012. (ESI International Project Management Ser.: 13). (ENG., Illus.). 184p. 69.95 *(978-1-4398-5543-0(9))* Auerbach Pubs., Inc.

Lewis, Laurie. What to Charge: Pricing Strategies for Freelancers & Consultants. 2011. 185p. pap. 23.95 *(978-1-4327-6764-8(X))* Outskirts Pr., Inc.

Loo, Y. Kwan. What Clients Don't Tell Management Consultants. 2008. 252p. pap. *(978-0-7552-0438-0(7))* Authors OnLine, Ltd.

Lorette, Kristie. How to Open & Operate a Financially Successful Consulting Business. 2011. (ENG., Illus.). 288p. per. 39.95 *(978-1-60138-016-6(X))* Atlantic Publishing Co.

Luefschuetz, Gary S. Selling Professional Services to the Fortune 500: How to Win in the Billion-Dollar Market of Strategy Consulting, Technology Solutions, & Outsourcing Services. 2010. (ENG., Illus.). 320p. 49.95 *(978-0-07-162282-0(9)*, 0071622829) McGraw-Hill Cos., The.

Lukaszewski, James E. Why Should the Boss Listen to You? The Seven Disciplines of the Trusted Strategic Advisor. 2008. (J-B International Association of Business Communicators Ser.: 13). (ENG., Illus.). 240p. 26.95 *(978-0-7879-9618-5(1)*, Jossey-Bass) Wiley, John & Sons, Inc.

Manns, Emily Caverhill. Executive Recruiting: The State of the Industry 2007. 2007. spiral bd. 995.00 *(978-1-932079-90-6(4))* BNA Subsidiaries, LLC.

Marsh, Sheila. The Feminine in Management Consulting: Power, Emotion & Values in Consulting Interactions. 2009. (ENG., Illus.). 272p. 105.00 *(978-0-230-20716-5(2))* Palgrave Macmillan.

McKenna, Christopher D. The World's Newest Profession: Management Consulting in the Twentieth Century. 2010. (Cambridge Studies in the Emergence of Global Enterprise Ser.). (ENG., Illus.). 392p. pap. 23.99 *(978-0-521-75759-1(2))* Cambridge Univ. Pr.

McKnight, William. 90 Days to Success in Consulting. 2009. (ENG., Illus.). 256p. pap. 19.99 *(978-1-4354-5442-2(1))* Course Technology.

Mulzer, Beatrice & Lim, Mei Ying. Microsoft Small Business Specialist Primer. 2008. (Harry Brelsford's SMB Ser.). (Illus.). per. 59.95 *(978-0-9770949-6-7(0))* SMB Nation Pr.

Nash, Susan. Starting & Running a Successful C. 3rd ec. 2007. 239p. pap. 30.00 *(978-1-84528-216-5(7))* Parkwest Pubns., Inc.

Nelson, Bob & Economy, Peter. Consulting for Dummies. 2nd ed. 2008. (ENG., Illus.). 384p. pap. 21.99 *(978-0-470-17809-6(4)*, For Dummies) Wiley, John & Sons, Inc.

Newman, Pam. Boost Your Bottom Line - Financial Tips for Consultants. 2007. per. 12.95 net. *(978-0-9764408-1-9(4))* Small Business Resource.

Newton, Richard. The Management Consultant: Mastering the Art of Consultancy. 2010. (Financial Times Ser.). (ENG., Illus.). 320p. (C). pap. 25.99 *(978-0-273-73087-3(8))* FT Press.

Nightingale, J. Think Smart - Act Smart: Avoiding the Business Mistakes That Even Intelligent People Make. 2007. (ENG., Illus.). 176p. 27.95 *(978-0-470-17129-5(4)*, Wiley) Wiley, John & Sons, Inc.

O'Connor, Mark F. Consulting Demand Management: Best Practices for Managing Large Organization Spending on Consulting Services. 2007. (Illus.). 72p. pap. *(978-1-932079-91-3(2))* BNA Subsidiaries, LLC.

O'Mahoney, Joe. Management Consultancy. 2010. (ENG., Illus.). 352p. 65.00 *(978-0-19-957718-7(8))* Oxford Univ. Pr., Inc.

Patrick, Donald W. Keep Your Nest Egg from Cracking: What You Need to Know. 2007. per. 15.95 *(978-0-9792566-0-8(7))* Patrick, Donald W.

Perano Vejo, Maria Elisa. Management Consultants As Knowledge Creators. 2008. 148p. pap. *(978-3-639-01540-9(1))* VDM Verlag Dr. Mueller e.K.

Phillips, Jack. How to Build a Successful Consulting Practice. 2006. (ENG., Illus.). 256p. per. 19.95 *(978-0-07-146229-7(5)*, 0071462295) McGraw-Hill Cos., The.

Phillips, Jack & Phillips, Patti. The Consultants Scorecard: Tracking ROI & Bottom-Line Impact of Consulting Projects. 2nd ed. 2010. (ENG., Illus.). 256p. 35.00 *(978-0-07-174282-5(4)*, 0071742824) McGraw-Hill Cos., The.

Rasé, Marie-Anne. The Role of the Business Analyst De-Mystified. 2010. (Illus.). 60p. pap. 15.49 *(978-1-4490-9624-3(7))* AuthorHouse.

Roberson, Mike, et al. Management Consultancy in an Eastern European Context. 184p. *(978-963-224-706-9(X))* Akadémia Kiadó.

Robinson, Dana Gaines & Robinson, James C. Performance Consulting: A Practical Guide for HR & Learning Professionals. 2nd rev. ed. 2008. (ENG., Illus.). 268p. pap. 32.95 *(978-1-57675-435-1(9))* Berrett-Koehler Pubs., Inc.

Rose, Jack. Thanks, Jack - In Need of a Miracle: In Need of a Miracle. 2007. per. 19.95 *(978-0-9789546-5-9(3))* Back Channel Pr.

Russell, George F., Jr. & Sheldon, Michael. Success by Ten: George Russell's Top Ten Elements to Building a Billion-Dollar Business. 2009. (ENG.). 208p. 24.95 *(978-0-470-53727-5(2)*, Wiley) Wiley, John & Sons, Inc.

Sallinen, Risto & Bachman, Christofer. Value Creation in a Process Consultancy Setting. 2009. 104p. pap. *(978-3-639-15062-9(7))* VDM Verlag Dr. Mueller e.K.

Savall, Henri. Mastering Hidden Costs & Socio-Economic Performance. 2008. (Research in Management Consulting Ser.). 376p. (C). 82.95 *(978-1-59311-908-9(9))* Information Age Publishing, Inc.

Savall, Henri & Zardet, V. T. ronique. Mastering Hidden Costs & Socio-Economic Performance. 2008. (Research in Management Consulting Ser.). 376p. (C). per. 45.95 *(978-1-59311-907-2(0))* Information Age Publishing, Inc.

Scott, Beverly & Barnes, B. Consulting on the Inside, 2nd Edition: An Internal Consultant's Guide to Living & Working Inside Organizations. 2nd ed. 2011. (Illus.). 304p. pap. 42.95 *(978-1-56286-745-4(8))* American Society for Training & Development.

Shah, Anwar. Employing Consultants. 2007. (Stand Alones Ser.). 80p. pap. 15.00 *(978-0-8213-6993-7(8))* World Bank Pubns.

Smith, Derek & O'Connor, Mark F. HR Consulting Marketplace 2006 - 2010: Key Data, Trends & Forecasts. 2006. (Illus.). 161p. spiral bd. 3495.00 *(978-1-932079-76-0(9))* BNA Subsidiaries, LLC.

Smith, Derek, et al. Global Consulting Marketplace 2007-2010: Key Trends, Profiles & Forecasts. 2007. spiral bd. 4995.00 *(978-1-932079-88-3(2))* BNA Subsidiaries, LLC.

Stavros, Jacqueline M., et al, eds. Practicing Organization Development: A Guide for Leading Change. 3rd ed. 2009. (J-B O-D (Organizational Development) Ser.: 34). (ENG., Illus.). 704p. 95.00 *(978-0-470-40544-4(9)*, Pfeiffer) Wiley, John & Sons, Inc.

Stryker, Steven C. A Guide to Successful Consulting. 2011. (ENG.). 292p. (gr. 17). 50.00 *(978-1-60590-729-1(4))* Government Institutes.

Sturdy, Andrew, et al. Management Consultancy: Boundaries & Knowledge in Action. (ENG.). 2010. 256p. pap. 34.95 *(978-0-19-959375-0(2))* 2009. 250p. 95.00 *(978-0-19-921264-4(3))* Oxford Univ. Pr., Inc.

Swain, Ann & Brown, Jane Newell. The Professional Recruiter's Handbook: Delivering Excellence in Recruitment Practice. (ENG., Illus.). 2009. 256p. pap. 39.95 *(978-0-7494-5396-1(6))* 2nd ed. 2012. 272p. pap. 39.95 ***(978-0-7494-6541-4(7))*** Kogan Page, Ltd. GBR. Dist: Ingram Pub. Services.

Thomas, Stephen J. Improving Reliability & Maintenance from Within: How to Be an Effective Internal Consultant. 2007. (Web of Change Ser.). (Illus.). 350p. (C). pap. 47.95 *(978-0-8311-3332-0(5))* Industrial Pr., Inc.

Viola, Judah J. & McMahon, Susan D. Consulting & Evaluation with Nonprofit & Community-Based Organizations. 2009. (Illus.). 340p. pap. 81.95 *(978-0-7637-5688-8(1))* Jones & Bartlett Learning, LLC.

Wagner, Terri & Weese, Susan. Cbap/Ccba: Certified Business Analysis. 2011. (ENG., Illus.). 504p. pap., pupil's gde. ed. 59.99 *(978-0-470-93290-2(2)*, Sybex) Wiley, John & Sons, Inc.

Watts, Robert. Development of L a D S Model. 2010. 176p. pap. *(978-3-8383-5554-2(7))* Lambert Academic Publishing.

Weiss, Alan. The Consulting Bible: Everything You Need to Know to Create & Expand a Seven-Figure Consulting Practice. 2011. (ENG., Illus.). 274p. pap. 19.95 *(978-0-470-92908-0(5)*, Wiley) Wiley, John & Sons, Inc.

—How to Establish a Unique Brand in the Consulting Profession: Powerful Techniques for the Successful Practitioner. 2008. (ENG., Illus.). 224p. pap. 55.00 *(978-0-470-43394-2(9)*, Pfeiffer) Wiley, John & Sons, Inc.

—Million Dollar Consulting. 4th ed. 2009. (ENG., Illus.). 400p. pap. 21.95 *(978-0-07-162210-3(1)*, 0071622101) McGraw-Hill Cos., The.

—Million Dollar Consulting Proposals: How to Write a Proposal That's Accepted Every Time. 2011. (ENG., Illus.). 212p. pap. 24.95 ***(978-1-118-09753-3(X)***, Wiley) Wiley, John & Sons, Inc.

Weiss, Alan. Value-Based Fees: How to Charge - & Get - What You're Worth. 2nd ed. 2008. (ENG., Illus.). 288p. 55.00 *(978-0-470-27584-9(7)*, Pfeiffer) Wiley, John & Sons, Inc.

Weiss, Alan & Weiss. Getting Started in Consulting. 3rd ed. 2009. (ENG., Illus.). 320p. pap. 19.95 *(978-0-470-41980-9(6)*, Wiley) Wiley, John & Sons, Inc.

WHITTLE & IZOD. Mind-Ful Consulting. Izod, Karen & Whittle, Sue, eds. 2009. (Illus.). 200p. pap. 41.00 *(978-1-85575-696-0(X))* Karnac Bks. GBR. Dist: Stylus Publishing, LLC.

Wickham, Louise & Wilcock, Jeremy. Management Consulting: Delivering an Effective Project. 4th rev. ed. 2012. (ENG., Illus.). 352p. pap. ***(978-0-273-76874-6(3))*** Pearson Bks.

Wickham, Philip A. & Wickham, Louise. Management Consulting: Delivering an Effective Project. 3rd ed. 2007. (ENG., Illus.). 336p. (C). per. 133.33 *(978-0-273-71184-1(9)*, Prentice Hall) Prentice Hall PTR.

Wysocki, Robert K. The Business Analyst/Project Manager: A New Partnership for Managing Complexity & Uncertainty. 2010. (ENG., Illus.). 240p. 49.95 *(978-0-470-76744-3(8)*, Wiley) Wiley, John & Sons, Inc.

Yeager, Therese F., et al. Global Organization Development: Managing Unprecedented Change. 2006. (Contemporary Trends in Organization Development & Change Ser.). (Illus.). xi, 146p. (C). *(978-1-59311-560-9(1))*; pap. *(978-1-59311-559-3(8))* Information Age Publishing, Inc.

Yurder, Alper. Internationalization of Management Consulting Companies. 2011. 96p. pap. ***(978-3-8443-9160-2(6))*** Lambert Academic Publishing.

BUSINESS CORPORATIONS
see Corporations

BUSINESS CORRESPONDENCE
see Commercial Correspondence

BUSINESS CREATIVITY
see Creative Ability in Business

BUSINESS CYCLES
see also Business Forecasting; Depressions; Economic Forecasting; Economic Stabilization; Financial Crises; Long Waves (Economics); Multiplier (Economics); Recessions

Achinstein, Asher. Buying Power of Labor & Post-War Cycles. (Columbia University, Studies in the Social Sciences: No. 292). reprint ed. 20.00 *(978-0-404-51292-7(5))* AMS Pr., Inc.

Aizenman, Joshua & Pinto, Brian, eds. Managing Economic Volatility & Crises: A Practitioner's Guide. 2011. (ENG.). 614p. pap. 55.00 *(978-0-521-16859-5(7))* Cambridge Univ. Pr.

Allen, Robert G. & Hansen, Mark Victor. Cash in a Flash: Real Money in No Time. 2010. (ENG.). 384p. pap. 15.00 *(978-0-307-45331-0(6)*, Three Rivers Pr.) Crown Publishing Group.

Altug, Sumru G. Business Cycles: Fact, Fallacy & Fantasy. 2009. 160p. 65.00 *(978-981-283-276-4(9))* World Scientific Publishing Co., Inc.

Annunziata, Marco. The Economics of the Financial Crisis: Lessons & New Threats. 2011. (Finance & Capital Markets Ser.). (ENG., Illus.). 240p. 215.00 ***(978-0-230-28281-0(4))*** Palgrave Macmillan.

Ayres, Jeffrey. North America in Question: Regional Integration in an Era of Economic Turbulence. 2011. (Studies in Comparative Political Economy & Public Policy Ser.). (ENG.). *(978-1-4426-4214-0(9))*; pap. *(978-1-4426-1114-6(6))* Univ. of Toronto Pr.

Ayres, Leonard P. The Chief Cause of This & Other Depressions. 2011. 54p. 36.95 ***(978-1-258-00909-0(9))*** Literary Licensing, LLC.

Babson, Roger Ward. Cheer up! Better Times Ahead! 2011. 56p. 36.95 ***(978-1-258-01440-7(8))*** Literary Licensing, LLC.

Batra, Ravi & Batra, Raveendra N. The New Golden Age: A Revolution Against Political Corruption & Economic Chaos. 2009. (ENG.). 256p. pap. 18.00 *(978-0-230-61395-9(0))* Palgrave Macmillan.

Beaton, Charles R. & Maser, Chris. Economics & Ecology: United for a Sustainable World. 2011. (Social Environmental Sustainability Ser.). (ENG., Illus.). 191p. 79.95 *(978-1-4398-5295-8(2)*, CRC Press) Taylor & Francis Group GBR. Dist: Taylor & Francis Group.

Bellofiore, Riccardo. German Monetary Theory Revisited. 2013. (ENG.). 302p. 95.00 *(978-0-333-76113-7(8))* Palgrave Macmillan.

Besomi, Daniele. Crises & Cycles in Economic Dictionaries & Encyclopaedias. 2011. (Routledge Studies in the History of Economics Ser.). (ENG., Illus.). 704p. (C). 195.00 *(978-0-415-49903-3(8))* Routledge.

Black, Fischer. Exploring General Equilibrium. 2010. (ENG.). 360p. (gr. 17). pap. 32.00 *(978-0-262-51409-5(5))* MIT Pr.

Blatt, Dan. Understanding the Great Depression & the Modern Business Cycle. 2009. 397p. (ENG.). 46.03 *(978-0-557-10242-6(1))*; pap. 23.03 *(978-0-557-09889-7(0))* Lulu Enterprises Inc.

Boeckh, J. Anthony. The Great Reflation: How Investors Can Profit from the New World of Money. 2010. (ENG., Illus.). 336p. 34.95 *(978-0-470-53877-7(5)*, Wiley) Wiley, John & Sons, Inc.

Bootle, R. P. The Trouble with Markets: Saving Capitalism from Itself. 2nd ed. 2011. (ENG., Illus.). 256p. pap. 21.99 ***(978-1-85788-558-3(9))*** Ebsco Publishing.

Bootle, Roger. The Trouble with Markets: Saving Capitalism from Itself. 2009. (ENG.). 282p. 29.95 *(978-1-85788-537-8(6))* Ebsco Publishing.

Brown, Clair & Linden, Greg. Chips & Change: How Crisis Reshapes the Semiconductor Industry. 2011. (ENG., Illus.). 282p. (gr. 17). pap. 18.00 ***(978-0-262-51682-2(9))*** MIT Pr.

Brown, Clair, et al. Chips & Change: How Crisis Reshapes the Semiconductor Industry. 2009. (ENG., Illus.). 282p. (gr. 17). 35.00 *(978-0-262-01346-8(0))* MIT Pr.

—Economic Turbulence: Is a Volatile Economy Good for America? 2006. (ENG., Illus.). 212p. 21.00 *(978-0-226-07632-4(6))* Univ. of Chicago Pr.

Calverley, John. When Bubbles Burst: Surviving the Financial Fallout. 2009. (ENG., Illus.). 248p. pap. 19.95 *(978-1-85788-523-1(6))* Ebsco Publishing.

Cantner, Uwe & Malerba, Franco. Innovation, Industrial Dynamics & Structural Transformation: Schumpeterian Legacies. 2007. (ENG., Illus.). viii, 424p. 169.00 *(978-3-540-49464-5(2)*, 3540494642) Springer.

Cassis, Youssef. Crises & Opportunities, 1890-2010: The Shaping of Modern Finance. 2011. (ENG., Illus.). 216p. 45.00 *(978-0-19-960086-1(4))* Oxford Univ. Pr., Inc.

Castilleja-Vargas, Liliana. Valuation Effects on the Business Cycle in Emerging Markets. 2010. 184p. pap. *(978-3-8383-4451-5(0))* Lambert Academic Publishing.

CFA Institute, compiled by. Insights on the Global Financial Crisis. 2009. pap. *(978-1-934667-27-9(7))* Research Foundation of CFA Institute.

Chang, Chun Ping. Political Business Cycles in Developed Countries - Intranational Political Business Cycle. 2008. 124p. pap. *(978-3-639-11495-9(7))* VDM Verlag Dr. Mueller e.K.

Chang, Tse Chun. Cyclical Movements in the Balance of Payments. 2011. (ENG., Illus.). 252p. pap. 23.99 *(978-1-107-51522-9(4))* Cambridge Univ. Pr.

Charpe, Matthieu, et al. Financial Assets, Debt & Liquidity Crises: A Keynesian Approach. 2011. (ENG., Illus.). 456p. 115.00 *(978-1-107-00493-1(4))* Cambridge Univ. Pr.

Chiarella, Carl, et al. Business Fluctuations & Long-Phased Cycles in High Order Macrosystems. 2008. (Illus.). viii, 97p. 87.00 *(978-1-60456-654-3(X))* Nova Science Pubs., Inc.

—Foundations for a Disequilibrium Theory of the Business Cycle: Qualitative Analysis & Quantitative Assessment. 2011. (ENG.). 550p. pap. 65.00 *(978-0-521-36992-3(4))* Cambridge Univ. Pr.

Cowen, Tyler. Risk & Business Cycles. 2010. pap. 42.95 *(978-0-415-78129-9(9))* Routledge.

D'Apice, Vincenzo & Ferri, Giovanni. Financial Instability: Toolkit for Interpreting Boom & Bust Cycles. 2010. (Palgrave Macmillan Studies in Banking & Financial Institutions Ser.). (ENG., Illus.). 256p. 105.00 *(978-0-230-24811-3(X))* Palgrave Macmillan.

Davis, Gerald F. Managed by the Markets: How Finance Re-Shaped America. 2011. (ENG.). 336p. pap. 21.95 ***(978-0-19-969192-0(4))*** Oxford Univ. Pr., Inc.

Dewey, Edward R. & Dakin, Edwin F. Cycles: The Science of Prediction. 268p. 2011. pap. 12.50 ***(978-1-61427-005-8(8))*** 2010. pap. 15.95 *(978-1-57898-874-7(8))* Martino Publishing.

—Cycles the Science of Prediction. 2011. 218p. pap. 12.99 ***(978-1-61720-289-6(4))*** Wilder Pubns., Ltd.

Dumas, Charles-. Globalisation Fractures. 2010. (ENG., Illus.). 256p. pap. 22.95 *(978-1-84668-424-1(2))* Profile Bks. Ltd. GBR. Dist: Consortium Bk. Sales & Distribution.

Dusenberry, James S. Business Cycles & Economic Growth. Harris, Seymour E., ed. 2011. 352p. 51.95 ***(978-1-258-06800-4(1))*** Literary Licensing, LLC.

Eapen, Gill. Flexibility: Flexible Companies for the Uncertain World. 2009. (ENG., Illus.). 192p. 61.95 *(978-1-4398-1632-5(8)*, CRC Press) Taylor & Francis Group GBR. Dist: Taylor & Francis Group.

Easterling, Ed. Probable Outcomes: Secular Stock Market Insights. 2011. (Illus.). 272p. 39.95 *(978-1-879384-82-8(5))* Cypress Hse.

Edmonson, Nathan. Technological Foundations of Cyclical Economic Growth: The Case of the United States Economy. 2009. (ENG., Illus.). 369p. 59.95 *(978-1-4128-1012-8(4))* Transaction Pubs.

Etro, Federico. Endogenous Market Structures & the Macroeconomy. 2009. (ENG., Illus.). xx, 346p. 209.00 *(978-3-540-87426-3(7)*, 3540874267) Springer.

Ferri, Piero. Macroeconomics of Growth Cycles & Financial Instability. 2011. (New Directions in Modern Economics Ser.). (Illus.). 224p. 110.00 *(978-1-84980-916-0(X))* Elgar, Edward Publishing, Inc.

Fisher, Ken. Markets Never Forget (But People Do) How Your Memory Is Costing You Money — And Why This Time Isn't Different. 2011. (ENG., Illus.). 240p. 29.95 *(978-1-118-09154-8(X)*, Wiley) Wiley, John & Sons, Inc.

Fitzgerald, Deborah. Every Farm a Factory: The Industrial Ideal in American Agriculture. 2010. (ENG.). 256p. pap. 26.00 *(978-0-300-11128-6(2))* Yale Univ. Pr.

Flaschel, Peter & Landesmann, Michael A. Mathematical Economics & the Dynamics of Capitalism: Goodwin's Legacy Continued. Flaschel, Peter & Landesmann, Michael A., eds. 2008. (Illus.). CCCII, 18p. 160.00 *(978-0-415-45145-1(0))* Routledge.

Fox, Jeffrey J. How to Be a Fierce Competitor: What Winning Companies & Great Managers Do in Tough Times. 2010. (ENG., Illus.). 176p. 19.95 *(978-0-470-40854-4(5)*, Jossey-Bass) Wiley, John & Sons, Inc.

France, Vaclav. Endogeneity of Credit or Nominal Rigidities? 2011. 92p. pap. ***(978-3-8443-0887-7(3))*** Lambert Academic Publishing.

Frank, Robert. The High-Beta Rich: How the Manic Wealthy Will Take Us to the Next Boom, Bubble, & Bust. 2011. (ENG., Illus.). 256p. 26.00 *(978-0-307-58989-7(7)*, Crown Business) Crown Publishing Group.

Fredriksen, Paula, et al. The Era of Uncertainty: Global Investment Strategies for Inflation, Deflation, & the Middle Ground. 2011. (ENG., Illus.). 256p. 29.95 *(978-1-118-02773-8(6)*, Wiley) Wiley, John & Sons, Inc.

Friedrichs, Ed. Reach Higher: Long-cycle Strategies for a Short-cycle World. 2006. 334p. pap. 39.00 *(978-0-9755654-7-6(8)*, Ostberg) Greenway Communications.

Fuchita, Yasuyuki, et al, eds. After the Crash: The Future of Finance. 2010. (ENG., Illus.). 150p. pap. 26.95 *(978-0-8157-0404-1(6))* Brookings Institution Pr.

Funnell, Warwick, et al. In Government We Trust: Market-Failure & the Delusions of Privatisation. 2009. (ENG.). 336p. pap. 34.00 *(978-0-7453-2907-9(1))* Pluto Pr. GBR. Dist: Macmillan.

Gaffney, Mason. After the Crash: Designing a Depression-Free Economy. 2009. (AJES - Studies in Economic Reform & Social Justice Ser.: 15). (ENG., Illus.). 200p. pap. 44.95 *(978-1-4443-3307-7(0))*; 104.95 *(978-1-4443-3358-9(5))* Wiley, John & Sons, Inc. (Wiley-Blackwell).

Galí, Jordi & Galí, Jordi. Monetary Policy, Inflation, & the Business Cycle: An Introduction to the New Keynesian Framework. 2008. (ENG., Illus.). 224p. (C). 60.00 *(978-0-691-13316-4(5))* Princeton Univ. Pr.

Gerlach, Stefan. Procyclicality of Financial Systems in Asia. Gerlach, Stefan & Gruenwald, Paul, eds. 2007. (ENG., Illus.). 200p. pap. 40.00 *(978-0-230-54700-1(1))* Palgrave Macmillan.

Gerlach, Stefan & Gruenwald, Paul, eds. Procyclicality of Financial Systems in Asia. 2006. (ENG., Illus.). 160p. 116.00 *(978-1-4039-8751-8(3))* Palgrave Macmillan.

Gillman, Max. Inflation Theory in Economics: Welfare, Velocity, Growth & Business Cycles. 2009. (Routledge International Studies in Money & Banking Ser.). (ENG., Illus.). 406p. 160.00 *(978-0-415-47768-0(9))* Routledge.

Goldrian. Handbook of Survey-Based Business Cycle Analysis. 2007. (IFO Economic Policy Ser.). (Illus.). 264p. 182.00 *(978-1-84720-136-2(9))* Elgar, Edward Publishing, Inc.

Granato, Jim & Wong, M. C. Sunny. The Role of Policymakers in Business Cycle Fluctuations. 2011. (ENG.). 318p. pap. 39.99 *(978-0-521-39076-7(1))* Cambridge Univ. Pr.

Gregoriou, Greg N. & Renneboog, Luc. International Mergers & Acquisitions Activity Since 1990: Recent Research & Quantitative Analysis. 2007. (Quantitative Finance Ser.). (ENG., Illus.). 320p. 103.00 *(978-0-7506-8289-3(2),* Academic Pr.) Elsevier Science & Technology Bks.

Gross, Daniel. Pop! Why Bubbles Are Great for the Economy. 2007. (Illus.). 240p. 22.95 *(978-0-06-115154-5(8),* Collins) HarperCollins Pubs.

Haberler, Gottfried. Prosperity & Depression: A Theoretical Analysis of Cyclical Movements. 2011. 530p. pap. 39.95 ***(978-1-4128-4220-4(4))*** Transaction Pubs.

Harrison, Fred. Boom Bust: House Prices, Banking & the Depression of 2010. 2nd ed. 2010. (ENG.). 288p. pap. 29.95 *(978-0-85683-254-3(5))* Shepheard-Walwyn Pubs., Ltd. GBR. Dist: Independent Pubs. Group.

Hasegawa, Harukiyo & Sharpe, Diana Rosemary, eds. New Horizons in Asian Management: Emerging Issues & Critical Perspectives. 2007. (ENG., Illus.). 288p. 110.00 *(978-0-230-01365-0(1))* Palgrave Macmillan.

Hassett, Stephen D. The Risk Premium Factor: A New Model to Understanding the Volatile Forces That Drive Stock Prices. 2011. (Wiley Finance Ser.: 702). (ENG., Illus.). 182p. 85.00 *(978-1-118-09905-6(2),* Wiley) Wiley, John & Sons, Inc.

Hayek, F. A. Business Cycles: Part I. Klausinger, Hansjoerg, ed. 2012. (Collected Works of F. A. Hayek Ser.). (Illus.). 304p. 55.00 ***(978-0-226-32044-1(8))*** Univ. of Chicago Pr.

—Business Cycles: Part II. Klausinger, Hansjoerg, ed. 2012. (Collected Works of F. A. Hayek Ser.). (Illus.). 360p. 65.00 ***(978-0-226-32047-2(2))*** Univ. of Chicago Pr.

Hetzel, Robert L. The Great Recession: Market Failure or Policy Failure? 2012. (Studies in Macroeconomic History Ser.). (ENG., Illus.). 400p. 50.00 ***(978-1-107-01188-5(4))*** Cambridge Univ. Pr.

Hollander, Samuel. The Economics of Karl Marx: Analysis & Application. 2008. (Historical Perspectives on Modern Economics Ser.). (ENG.). 550p. 147.00 *(978-0-521-79078-9(6));* (Illus.). 552p. pap. 75.00 *(978-0-521-79399-5(8))* Cambridge Univ. Pr.

Juglar, Clement. A Brief History of Panics & Their Periodical Occurrence in the United States. 2009. 214p. 28.99 *(978-1-110-41683-7(0));* pap. 23.75 *(978-1-110-41682-0(2))* BiblioBazaar.

—A Brief History of Panics & Their Periodical Occurrence in the United States. 2009. 60p. pap. *(978-1-151-67676-4(4))* Books LLC.

—A Brief History of Panics & Their Periodical Occurrence in the United States. Thom, DeCourcy W., ed. 2009. 164p. 36.95 *(978-1-104-00459-0(3));* pap. 21.95 *(978-1-4374-4751-4(1))* Kessinger Publishing, LLC.

Kalecki. Essays in the Theory of Economic Fluctuations. 2007. 160p. 39.95 *(978-0-415-43465-2(3))* Routledge.

Kalecki, Michal. Theory of Economic Dynamics. 2007. (ENG.). 184p. (C). 205.00 *(978-0-415-31373-5(2))* Routledge.

Karadag, Mehmet Ali & SENTURK, Huseyin. Regime Switching Volatility Models. 2010. 100p. pap. *(978-3-8383-6278-6(0))* Lambert Academic Publishing.

Kiani, Khurshid M. Business Cycle Fluctuations & Economic Policy. 2009. 89.00 *(978-1-60692-341-2(2))* Nova Science Pubs., Inc.

Kindleberger. Financial Crises. 2008. (MSH: Colloques Ser.). (ENG.). 312p. pap. 58.00 *(978-0-521-06871-0(1))* Cambridge Univ. Pr.

Knoop, Todd Alan. Recessions & Depressions. 2nd rev. ed. 2009. (Illus.). 280p. 44.95 *(978-0-313-38163-8(1),* A2590C, Praeger Pubs.) Greenwood Publishing Group, Inc.

Kopitz, Jeffrey S. Down Traders: The Only Guide You Will Ever Need to Make Money on Stocks That Go Down! 2011. (ENG., Illus.). 190p. pap. 24.95 ***(978-1-936782-50-5(2),*** Langdon Street Pr.) Hillcrest Publishing Group, Inc.

Korenok, Oleg, et al. Essays on Dynamics of Output & Prices. 2008. 180p. pap. *(978-3-8364-9988-0(6))* VDM Verlag Dr. Mueller e.K.

Kose, M. Ayhan & Prasad, Eswar S. Emerging Markets: Resilience & Growth amid Global Turmoil. 2010. (ENG., Illus.). 210p. pap. 26.95 *(978-0-8157-0564-2(6))* Brookings Institution Pr.

Kotler, Philip & Caslione, John A. Chaotics: The Business of Managing & Marketing in the Age of Turbulence, 1 vol. 2009. (ENG., Illus.). 224p. 25.00 *(978-0-8144-1521-4(0))* Amacom.

Kourdi, Jeremy. Surviving a Downturn: Building a Successful Business... Without Breaking the Bank. 2011. (Business on a Shoestring Ser.). (ENG.). 208p. pap. 14.95 ***(978-1-4081-3986-8(3))*** A & C Black GBR. Dist: Macmillan.

Krugman, Paul. The Return of Depression Economics & the Crisis of 2008. 2009. (ENG.). 224p. pap. 16.95 *(978-0-393-33780-8(4),* 33780) Norton, W. W. & Co., Inc.

—The Return of Depression Economics & the Crisis Of 2008. 2009. (Next Ser.). (CHI., Illus.). 262p. pap. *(978-957-13-5002-8(8))* China Times Publishing Co.

—The Return of Depression Economics & the Crisis of 2008. rev. ed. 2008. (ENG.). 288p. 24.95 *(978-0-393-07101-6(4),* 7101) Norton, W. W. & Co., Inc.

Kurz, Mordecai, ed. Endogenous Economic Fluctuations: Studies in the Theory of Rational Beliefs. 2011. (Studies in Economic Theory Ser.). (ENG., Illus.). xiv, 356p. pap. 169.00 *(978-3-642-08295-5(5),* 3642082955) Springer.

Lahiri, Kajal & Sadka, Efraim, eds. Transportation Indicators & Business Cycles. 2010. (Contributions to Economic Analysis Ser.). (Illus.). 142p. 114.95 *(978-0-85724-147-4(8))* Emerald Group Publishing Ltd. GBR. Dist: Turpin Distribution Services Ltd.

Link, Robert G. English Theories of Economic Fluctuations, 1815-1848. (Columbia University, Studies in the Social Sciences: No. 598). reprint ed. 27.50 *(978-0-404-51598-0(3))* AMS Pr., Inc.

Litsios, Ioannis. Neoclassical & Keynesian Dynamics for a Small Open Economy. 2011. 220p. pap. ***(978-3-8433-7980-9(7))*** Lambert Academic Publishing.

Maksakovsky, Pavel V. The Capitalist Cycle: Translated with Introduction & Commentary by Richard B. Day. 2009. (Historical Materialism Book Ser.). (ENG.). 152p. pap. 20.00 *(978-1-60846-018-2(5))* Haymarket Bks.

Mansharamani, Vikram. Boombustology: Spotting Financial Bubbles Before They Burst. 2011. (ENG., Illus.). 272p. 29.95 *(978-0-470-87946-7(7),* Wiley) Wiley, John & Sons, Inc.

Marazzi, Christian. Capital & Language: From the New Economy to the War Economy. Conti, Gregory, tr. from ITA. 2008. (Semiotext(e) / Foreign Agents Ser.). (ENG., Illus.). 168p. (gr. 17). pap. 14.95 *(978-1-58435-067-5(9))* Semiotexte/Smart Art.

Matthews, R. C. O. The Business Cycle. 2011. 316p. 50.95 ***(978-1-258-04964-5(3))*** Literary Licensing, LLC.

Matthews, R. C. O. A Study in Trade-Cycle History: Economic Fluctuations in Great Britain 1833-1842. 2011. 242p. pap. 22.99 *(978-1-107-60011-9(1))* Cambridge Univ. Pr.

Mattick, Paul. Business as Usual: The Economic Crisis & the Failure of Capitalism. 2011. (ENG.). 126p. pap. 17.95 *(978-1-86189-801-2(0))* Reaktion Bks., Ltd. GBR. Dist: Chicago Distribution Ctr.

Mauldin, John & Tepper, Jonathan. Endgame: The End of the Debt Supercycle & How It Changes Everything. 2011. (ENG., Illus.). 336p. 27.95 *(978-1-118-00457-9(4),* Wiley) Wiley, John & Sons, Inc.

Mazzi, Gian Luigi & Savio, Giovanni. Growth & Cycle in the Euro-zone. 2007. (ENG., Illus.). 492p. 147.00 *(978-0-230-00790-1(2))* Palgrave Macmillan.

McCandless, George. The ABCs of RBCs: An Introduction to Dynamic Macroeconomic Models. 2008. (Illus.). 448p. 65.50 *(978-0-674-02814-2(7))* Harvard Univ. Pr.

McKean, John. Managing Customers Through Economic Cycles. 2010. (ENG., Illus.). 264p. 45.00 *(978-0-470-68620-1(0),* Wiley) Wiley, John & Sons, Inc.

Montgomery, John. Upwave: City Dynamics & the Coming Capitalist Revival. 2011. (Illus.). 176p. 89.95 *(978-1-4094-2226-6(7))* Ashgate Publishing Co.

Morales Piñero, Jesús Enrique. Essays on Macroeconomic Theory. 2008. 124p. pap. *(978-3-8364-7805-2(6))* VDM Verlag Dr. Mueller e.K.

Motianey, Arun. SuperCycles: The New Economic Force Transforming Global Markets & Investment Strategy. 2010. (ENG.). 304p. 27.95 *(978-0-07-163737-4(0),* 0071637370) McGraw-Hill Cos., The.

Nagakawa, T., ed. Business Fluctuations & Cycles. 2007. (C). 129.00 *(978-1-60021-503-2(3))* Nova Science Pubs., Inc.

Navarro, Armando. Global Capitalist Crisis & the Second Great Depression: Egalitarian Systemic Models for Change. 2012. ***(978-0-7391-7017-5(1))*** 2011. (ENG.). 452p. (gr. 17). 90.00 ***(978-0-7391-7016-8(3))*** Lexington Bks.

Neal, Larry. I Am Not Master of Events: The Speculation of John Law & Lord Londonderry in the Mississippi & South Sea Bubbles. 2012. (Yale Series in Economic & Financial History Ser.). (ENG., Illus.). 232p. 50.00 *(978-0-300-15316-3(3))* Yale Univ. Pr.

Othman, Ayman Ahmed Ezzat. Value & Risk Management for Dynamic Brief Development in Construction. 2010. 484p. pap. *(978-3-8383-9095-6(4))* Lambert Academic Publishing.

Outhwaite, R. William. Critical Theory & Contemporary Europe. 2012. (Critical Theory & Contemporary Society Ser.). (ENG.). 184p. 120.00 *(978-1-4411-1626-0(5))* Continuum International Publishing Group, Ltd. GBR. Dist: National Bk. Network.

Patil, Dhananjay. Life Cycle Cost Analysis of Building Components. 2011. 160p. pap. ***(978-3-8443-9227-2(0))*** Lambert Academic Publishing.

Paul, Biru Paksha. ESSAYS ON INDIAN BUSINESS CYCLES AND INFLATION: An Inquiry into the Indian Economy. 2008. 148p. pap. *(978-3-639-10265-9(7))* VDM Verlag Dr. Mueller e.K.

Pérez, Nerea M. Recessions: Prospects & Developments. 2008. 89.00 *(978-1-60456-866-0(6))* Nova Science Pubs., Inc.

Phillips, Chester Arthur, et al. Banking & the Business Cycle: A Study of the Great Depression in the United States. 2011. 290p. 48.95 ***(978-1-258-03718-5(1))*** Literary Licensing, LLC.

Polak. The Dynamics of Business Cycles. 2007. pap. 39.95 *(978-0-415-43461-4(0))* Routledge.

Pollock, Alex J. Boom & Bust: Financial Cycles & Human Prosperity. 2010. (ENG.). 105p. pap. 9.95 *(978-0-8447-4383-7(6));* E-Book *(978-0-8447-4384-4(4))* American Enterprise Institute for Public Policy Research. (AEI Pr.).

Pont, Muriel Dal. Business Cycles & Growth Theory. 2009. (Illus.). 256p. 140.00 *(978-0-415-32125-9(5))* Routledge.

Read, Colin. The Rise & Fall of an Economic Empire: With Lessons for Aspiring Economies. 2010. (ENG., Illus.). 304p. 44.00 *(978-0-230-27370-2(X))* Palgrave Macmillan.

Reinhart, Carmen & Rogoff, Kenneth. This Time Is Different - Eight Centuries of Financial Folly. 2011. (ENG., Illus.). 512p. pap. 19.95 ***(978-0-691-15264-6(0))*** Princeton Univ. Pr.

Reinhart, Carmen M. & Rogoff, Kenneth S. This Time Is Different: Eight Centuries of Financial Folly. 2009. (ENG., Illus.). 512p. (C). 35.00 *(978-0-691-14216-6(5))* Princeton Univ. Pr.

Rhodes, David & Stelter, Daniel. Accelerating out of the Great Recession: How to Win in a Slow-Growth Economy. 2010. (ENG.). 224p. 22.95 *(978-0-07-171814-1(1),* 0071718141) McGraw-Hill Cos., The.

Rinkunas, Tomas. Business Cycle Synchronization - the Effects of Bilateral Trade Intensity & Economic Development. 2008. 140p. pap. *(978-3-639-05515-3(2))* VDM Verlag Dr. Mueller e.K.

Rostow, W. W. Why the Poor Get Richer & the Rich Slow Down: Essays in the Marshallian Long Period. 2011. (ENG.). 394p. pap. 35.00 *(978-0-292-72963-6(4))* Univ. of Texas Pr.

Rothbard, Murray N. America's Great Depression. 2009. 376p. *(978-1-60796-110-9(5))* 2008. 372p. pap. *(978-1-60796-065-2(6))* Editorial Benei Noaj.

Roubini, Nouriel & Mihm, Stephen. Crisis Economics: A Crash Course in the Future of Finance. (ENG.). 368p. (gr. 12). 2011. 17.00 *(978-0-14-311963-0(X),* Penguin (Non-Classics)) 2010. 27.95 *(978-1-59420-250-6(8),* Penguin Pr. HC, The) Penguin Group (USA) Inc.

Saether, Jan Petter. Market Structure & Cycles. 2011. 140p. pap. ***(978-3-639-33296-4(2))*** VDM Verlag Dr. Mueller e.K.

Safi, Fadi. Expansion of Netiks Lebanon to Dubai. 2010. 116p. pap. *(978-3-8383-6633-3(6))* Lambert Academic Publishing.

Scheiblecker, Marcus. The Austrian Business Cycle in the European Context. 2008. (Forschungsergebnisse der Wirtschaftsuniversität Wien Ser.). 228p. pap. 61.95 *(978-3-631-57607-6(2))* Lang, Peter GmbH, Europaischer Verlag der Wissenschaften DEU. Dist: Lang, Peter.

Schluter, William C. Pre-War Business Cycle, 1907-1914. (Columbia University, Studies in the Social Sciences: No. 243). reprint ed. 20.00 *(978-0-404-51243-9(7))* AMS Pr., Inc.

Schubert, Aurel. The Credit-Anstalt Crisis Of 1931. 2006. (Studies in Macroeconomic History Ser.). (ENG., Illus.). 224p. pap. 48.00 *(978-0-521-03029-8(3))* Cambridge Univ. Pr.

Sherman, Howard J. The Roller Coaster Economy: Financial Crisis, Great Recession, & the Public Option. 2009. (ENG., Illus.). 208p. 79.95 *(978-0-7656-2537-3(7));* pap. 37.95 *(978-0-7656-2538-0(5))* Sharpe, M.E. Inc.

Shimer, Robert. Labor Markets & Business Cycles. 2010. (CREI Lectures in Macroeconomics Ser.). (ENG., Illus.). 208p. (C). 60.00 *(978-0-691-14022-3(7))* Princeton Univ. Pr.

Skarica, David. The Great Super Cycle: Profit from the Coming Inflation Tidal Wave & Dollar Devaluation. 2010. (ENG., Illus.). 272p. 27.95 *(978-0-470-62418-0(3),* Wiley) Wiley, John & Sons, Inc.

Staddon, John. The Malign Hand of the Markets: the Insidious Forces on Wall Street that are Destroying Financial Markets – & What We Can Do about It. 2012. (ENG., Illus.). 304p. 35.00 ***(978-0-07-179740-5(8),*** 0071797408) McGraw-Hill Cos., The.

Stoffaes. Fins de Mondes. Date not set. lib. bdg. 34.95 *(978-0-226-77518-0(6))* Univ. of Chicago Pr.

Sull, Donald. The Upside of Turbulence: Seizing Opportunity in an Uncertain World. 2009. (ENG.). 320p. 27.99 *(978-0-06-177115-6(5),* Collins) HarperCollins Pubs.

Suttles, Gerald D. & Jacobs, Mark D. Front Page Economics. 2011. (ENG., Illus.). 272p. 37.50 *(978-0-226-78198-3(4))* Univ. of Chicago Pr.

Tamura, Hideaki. Human Psychology & Economic Fluctuation: A New Basic Theory of Human Economics. 2006. (ENG., Illus.). 200p. 110.00 *(978-0-230-00482-5(2))* Palgrave Macmillan.

Todrin, Donald. Successfully Navigating the Downturn. 2011. (ENG.). 309p. pap., pap. 19.95 ***(978-1-59918-419-7(2),*** 1599184192) Entrepreneur Pr. dba Entrepreneur Media, Inc.

Tomohara, Akinori & Sherlock, Molly. Financial Crisis in the Global Bubble Economy. 2011. (Global Recession - Causes, Impacts & Remedies Ser.). 187p. pap. 59.00 ***(978-1-61470-597-0(6))*** Nova Science Pubs., Inc.

Tomohara, Akinori & Sherlock, Molly, eds. Financial Crisis in the Global Bubble Economy. 2011. (Global Recession - Causes, Impacts & Remedies Ser.). 187p. 59.00 *(978-1-61668-339-9(2))* Nova Science Pubs., Inc.

von Mises, Ludwig. On the Manipulation of Money & Credit: Three Treatises on Trade-Cycle Theory. 2011. (ENG., Illus.). 250p. (C). (gr. 12). 22.00 *(978-0-86597-761-7(5));* pap. 12.00 *(978-0-86597-762-4(3))* Liberty Fund, Inc.

Wagner, Wayne H., et al. Investment Management: Meeting the Noble Challenges of Funding Pensions, Deficits, & Growth. Wagner, Wayne H. & Rieves, Ralph A., eds. 2009. (Wiley Finance Ser.: 518). (ENG., Illus.). 450p. 140.00 *(978-0-470-45594-4(2),* Wiley) Wiley, John & Sons, Inc.

Webb, Robert I. Trading Catalysts: How Events Move Markets & Create Trading Opportunities. rev. ed. 2006. (ENG.). 368p. pap. 44.99 ***(978-0-13-278205-0(7))*** FT Press.

Whitman, Martin J., et al. Distress Investing: Principles & Technique. 2009. (Wiley Finance Ser.: 397). (ENG., Illus.). 272p. 70.00 *(978-0-470-11767-5(2),* Wiley) Wiley, John & Sons, Inc.

Wiggin, Addison. The Demise of the Dollar... And Why It's Even Better for Your Investments. 2nd rev. ed. 2008. (Agora Ser.: 7). (ENG., Illus.). 197p. pap. 19.95 *(978-0-470-28724-8(1),* Wiley) Wiley, John & Sons, Inc.

Wiggin, Addison & Bonner, William. Financial Reckoning Day Fallout: Surviving Today's Global Depression. 2nd anniv. rev. ed. 2009. (Agora Ser.: 38). (ENG., Illus.). 464p. 27.95 *(978-0-470-48327-5(X),* Wiley) Wiley, John & Sons, Inc.

Wohlrabe, Klaus. Non-Linear Time Series Analysis & the Business Cycle. 2008. (Illus.). 108p. pap. *(978-3-639-00773-2(5))* VDM Verlag Dr. Mueller e.K.

Yogo, Motohiro. Essays on Consumption & Expected Returns. 2008. 164p. pap. *(978-3-639-06856-6(4))* VDM Verlag Dr. Mueller e.K.

Young, Warren. Real Business Cycle Models in Economics. 2012. (Routledge Studies in the History of Economics Ser.). (ENG.). 288p. (C). 140.00 *(978-0-415-47569-3(4))* Routledge.

Zulauf, Roman Felix. Global Financial Market Cycles. 2009. 104p. pap. *(978-3-639-19714-3(3))* VDM Verlag Dr. Mueller e.K.

BUSINESS CYCLES—MATHEMATICAL MODELS

Chen, Ping, ed. Economic Complexity & Equilibrium Illusion: Essays on Market Instability & Macro Vitality. 2010. (Routledge Frontiers of Political Economy Ser.). (ENG., Illus.). 400p. (C). 135.00 *(978-0-415-55475-6(6),* Routledge) Taylor & Francis Group GBR. Dist: Taylor & Francis Group.

Chian, Abraham C.-L. Complex Systems Approach to Economic Dynamics. 2007. (Lecture Notes in Economics & Mathematical Systems Ser.). x, 101p. pap. 109.00 *(978-3-540-39752-6(3),* 3540397523) Springer.

Cram101 Textbook Reviews. Outlines & Highlights for Economic Growth: Theory & Numerical Solution Methods by Alfonso Novales. 2011. 230p. pap. 31.95 ***(978-1-61830-950-1(1))*** Cram101 Inc.

Dietzenbacher, Erik & Lahr, Michael L., eds. Wassily Leontief & Input-Output Economics. 2008. (ENG.). 420p. pap. 56.00 *(978-0-521-04943-6(1))* Cambridge Univ. Pr.

Gatti, Domenico, et al. Emergent Macroeconomics: An Agent-Based Approach to Business Fluctuations. 2010. (New Economic Windows Ser.). (Illus.). xii, 114p. pap. 89.95 *(978-88-470-1561-6(8),* 8847015618) Springer.

Keller, André A. Time-Delay Systems. 2011. 436p. pap. ***(978-3-8433-8848-1(2))*** Lambert Academic Publishing.

Novales, Alfonso, et al. Economic Growth: Theory & Numerical Solution Methods. (ENG., Illus.). xx, 528p. 2010. pap. 69.95 *(978-3-642-11132-7(7),* 3642111327) 2008. 179.00 *(978-3-540-68665-1(7),* 3540686657) Springer.

Sushko, Iryna, ed. Business Cycle Dynamics: Models & Tools. 2010. (ENG., Illus.). viii, 336p. pap. 159.00 *(978-3-642-06879-9(0),* 3642068790) Springer.

Turchin, Peter, et al. Secular Cycles. 2009. (ENG., Illus.). 362p. (C). 37.50 *(978-0-691-13696-7(3))* Princeton Univ. Pr.

BUSINESS DATA INTERCHANGE, ELECTRONIC

see Electronic Data Interchange

BUSINESS DISTRICTS, CENTRAL

see Central Business Districts

BUSINESS ECONOMICS

see Managerial Economics

BUSINESS EDUCATION

see also Bookkeeping; Distributive Education; Master of Business Administration Degree; Shorthand

Adamson, John E. 21st Century Business: Business Law. 2nd ed. 2010. (21st Century Business Ser.). (ENG.). 192p. pap. 38.95 *(978-0-538-74061-6(2))* Cengage South-Western.

Adler, Gordon & Amann, Wolfgang. Case Writing for Executive Education: A Survival Guide. 2011. (Illus.). x, 116p. *(978-1-61735-361-1(2));* pap. *(978-1-61735-360-4(4));* E-Book *(978-1-61735-362-8(0))* Information Age Publishing, Inc.

Allen, Kathleen, et al. Complete MBA for Dummies. 2nd ed. 2007. (ENG., Illus.). 432p. per. 21.99 *(978-0-470-19429-4(4),* For Dummies) Wiley, John & Sons, Inc.

Allmon, Harold. Male Dress & Image: Clothing & Accessories -Things Someone Meant to Tell You When You Bought Your Best-Twenty Percent of Success Is Dress Etiquette on How to Wear It. 2011. (ENG.). 128p. pap. 19.95 *(978-0-917921-81-0(X))* At Ease Pr.

Arbaugh, Ben. Online & Blended Business Education for the 21st Century: Current research & future Directions. 2010. 218p. pap. *(978-1-84334-603-6(6),* Chandos Publishing) Woodhead Publishing Ltd.

Aspatore Books Staff, creator. Business School Management: Top Educational Leaders on Creating a Strong School Reputation, Offering Competitive Programs, & Thriving in the Educational Marketplace. 2008. (Inside the Minds Ser.). (Illus.). 372p. per. 49.95 *(978-0-314-99001-3(1))* Aspatore Bks.

Augier, Mie & March, James G. The Roots, Rituals, & Rhetorics of Change: North American Business Schools after the Second World War. 2011. (ENG.). 376p. 45.00 *(978-0-8047-7616-5(4),* Stanford Business Bks.) Stanford Univ. Pr.

Azim, Tahlil. Entrepreneurship Education & Training. 2010. 168p. pap. *(978-3-639-26399-2(5))* VDM Verlag Dr. Mueller e.K.

Baier, Gundolf & Günther, Gabriele, eds. Aktuelle Herausforderungen der Betriebswirtschaft: Jahrbuch 2008 des Instituts für Betriebswirtschaft der Westsächsischen Hochschule Zwickau. 2008. (Jahrbuch des Instituts für Betriebswirtschaft der Westsächsischen Hochschule Zwickau Ser.). 184p. pap. 52.95 *(978-3-631-57916-9(0))* Lang, Peter GmbH, Europaischer Verlag der Wissenschaften DEU. Dist: Lang, Peter.

Bailey, Jimmy. Teachers Reaching Out: 25 Dedicated Souls who have changed the lives of young entrepreneurs from YEScarolina. 2011. (ENG.). 104p. pap. 12.99 ***(978-1-59932-262-9(5))*** Advantage Media Group.

Barrett, Barbara. Student Assessment & Learning Guide to accompany Understanding Business. 9th ed. 2009. (ENG.). 736p. (C). pap. 61.67 *(978-0-07-726842-8(3),* 0077268423, McGraw-Hill/Irwin) McGraw-Hill Higher Education.

Barsky, Noah P. The Power of Technology for Learning. 2008. (Advances in Business Education & Training Ser.). (ENG., Illus.). x, 226p. 189.00 *(978-1-4020-8746-2(2),* 1402087462) Springer.

Barsky, Noah P., et al, eds. The Power of Technology for Learning. 2010. (Advances in Business Education & Training Ser.). x, 226p. pap. 189.00 *(978-90-481-7977-0(7),* 9048179777) Springer.

Barton, Andrew. Multi-Actor Learning for Sustainable Regional Development in Europe. Barton, Andrew & Dlouh'a, Jana, eds. 2011. 348p. pap. ***(978-1-908105-33-2(X))*** Grosvenor Hse. Publishing Ltd.

Bentzen-Bilkvist, Ann, et al, eds. Educational Innovation in Economics & Business VII: Educating Knowledge Workers for Corporate Leadership: Learning into the Future. 2010. (Educational Innovation in Economics & Business Ser.). 308p. pap. 229.00 *(978-90-481-6195-9(9),* 9048161959) Springer.

Bhatawdekar, Shyam & Bhatawdekar, Kalpana. Classic Management Games, Exercises, Energizers & Icebreakers. 2011. (ENG.). 154p. pap. 19.99 *(978-1-4610-2994-6(5))* CreateSpace.

Bhatia, Bharat. Uncommon Sense: the Other Side of Conventional Thinking. 2009. 182p. pap. 11.26 *(978-0-578-00799-1(1))* Bhatia, Bharat.

Bhatti, Nadeem. Which Mba? 2010. 212p. pap. *(978-3-8383-5189-6(4))* Lambert Academic Publishing.

BIA. Leading Business Schools & Business Libraries. 6th rev. ed. 2006. 350p. (J). pap. 249.00 *(978-1-4187-4390-1(9))* Business Information Agency.

—Leading Universities, Business Schools, & Business Libraries of Russia. 6th rev. ed. 2006. 300p. (J). pap. 249.00 *(978-1-4187-4537-0(5))* Business Information Agency.

Birkin, Jonathan. Business Advantage Intermediate Teacher's Book. 2012. (Business Advantage Ser.). (ENG.). 152p. pap. 39.00 ***(978-1-107-63770-2(8))*** Cambridge Univ. Pr.

—Business Advantage Upper-intermediate Teacher's Book. 2011. (Business Advantage Ser.). (ENG.). 160p. pap., tchr. ed. 39.00 ***(978-1-107-42231-5(0))*** Cambridge Univ. Pr.

Blackman, Stacy & Brookings, Daniel J. The MBA Application Roadmap: The Essential Guide to Getting into a Top Business School. 2008. 256p. pap. 29.95 *(978-0-912301-89-1(9))* First Bks.

Boddewyn. International Business Scholarship: AIB Fellows on the First 50 Years & Beyond. 2008. (Research in Global Strategic Management Ser.: Vol. 14). (Illus.). 252p. 93.95 *(978-0-7623-1470-6(2))* Emerald Group Publishing Ltd. GBR. Dist: Turpin Distribution Services Ltd.

Boersma, Het Magische Egypte Iris. Internet Marketing Voor Beginners. 2010. (DUT.). 76p. pap. 17.50 *(978-1-4457-5189-4(5))* Lulu Enterprises Inc.

Borghans, Lex, et al, eds. Educational Innovation in Economics & Business V: Business Education for the Changing Workplace. 2010. (Educational Innovation in Economics & Business Ser.). 484p. pap. 219.00 *(978-90-481-5558-3(4),* 9048155584) Springer.

Boston, Karen & Hood, Jeff S. Freshman Business Connections. rev. ed. 2010. (ENG.). 180p. pap. 47.36 *(978-0-7575-5321-9(4))* Kendall Hunt Publishing Co.

Bouknight, Omari & Shrum, Scott. Your MBA Game Plan: Proven Strategies for Getting into the Top. rev. ed. 2007. (ENG.). 1p. (Orig.). pap. 17.99 *(978-1-56414-968-8(4))* Career Pr., Inc.

—Your MBA Game Plan, Third Edition: Proven Strategies for Getting into the Top Business Schools. 3rd rev. ed. 2011. (ENG.). 320p. pap. 19.99 *(978-1-60163-182-4(0))* Career Pr., Inc.

Boyles, Deron. The Corporate Assault on Youth: Commercialism, Exploitation, & the End of Innocence. 2008. (Adolescent Cultures, School & Society Ser.: Vol. 44). 248p. (C). pap. 32.95 *(978-1-4331-0084-0(3))* Lang, Peter Publishing, Inc.

Broughton, Philip Delves. Ahead of the Curve: Two Years at Harvard Business School. 2009. (ENG.). 304p. (gr. 12-18). 16.00 *(978-0-14-311543-4(X),* Penguin (Non-Classics)) Penguin Group (USA) Inc.

Brown, Betty J., et al. Introduction to Business. 2007. (ENG., Illus.). 726p. (C). stu. ed. 93.80 *(978-0-07-874768-7(6),* 0078747686) McGraw-Hill Higher Education.

Buchholz, Rogene. Reforming Capitalism: Business & the Scientific Worldview. 2012. (Routledge Studies in Business Ethics Ser.). (ENG.). 360p. (C). 125.00 ***(978-0-415-51738-6(9))*** Routledge.

Burns, Paul. Entrepreneurship & Small Business: Start-Up, Growth & Maturity. 3rd rev. ed. 2010. (ENG., Illus.). 512p. pap. 60.00 *(978-0-230-24780-2(6))* Palgrave Macmillan.

Burrow, James L., et al. Business Principles & Management. 12th rev. ed. 2007. (Management Decision Making Ser.). (ENG., Illus.) 736p. (C). 107.95 *(978-0-538-44468-2(1))* Cengage South-Western.

Business GP, The. Innervention. 2010. 42p. pap. 9.50 *(978-1-4457-7623-1(5))* Lulu Enterprises Inc.

Business Research Consortium Of Wny. Proceedings of the 2009 Business Research Consortium of Western New York. 2010. 296p. pap. 39.99 *(978-1-60497-681-6(0))* Cambria Pr.

Cameron, Sheila. Business Students Handbook. 4th ed. 2007. (Illus.). 464p. pap., stu. ed. 95.00 *(978-0-13-234924-6(8))* Pearson Education, Ltd. GBR. Dist: Trans-Atlantic Pubns., Inc.

—The Business Student's Handbook: Skills for Study & Employment. 5th ed. 2009. (ENG., Illus.). 464p. pap. 67.50 *(978-0-273-73071-2(1),* Prentice Hall) Pearson Education, Ltd. GBR. Dist: Trans-Atlantic Pubns., Inc.

Camiciottoli, Belinda Crawford. The Language of Business Studies Lectures: A Corpus-Assisted Analysis. 229p. 126.00 *(978-90-272-5400-9(1))* Benjamins, John Publishing Co.

Carroll, Thomas H., ed. Business Education for Competence & Responsibility. 2011. (ENG.) 78p. pap. 25.00 ***(978-0-8078-7985-6(1))*** Univ. of North Carolina Pr.

Cavuoto, Jonathan W. The Meltdown of Currency & Paper Assets. 2011. 204p. 29.99 ***(978-1-4568-5884-1(X))***; pap. 19.99 ***(978-1-4568-5883-4(1))*** Xlibris Corp.

Chia, Andrew. Double Your Money: How You Can Accumulate Immense Wealth by Increasing Your Financial Intelligence. 2010. 208p. pap. 15.99 *(978-1-4520-7246-3(9))* AuthorHouse.

Clark, Ruth C. & Mayer, Richard E. E-Learning & the Science of Instruction: Proven Guidelines for Consumers & Designers of Multimedia Learning. 3rd ed. 2011. (ENG., Illus.). 528p. 65.00 *(978-0-470-87430-1(9),* Pfeiffer) Wiley, John & Sons, Inc.

Clark, Ruth Colvin & Kwinn, Ann. The New Virtual Classroom: Evidence-Based Guidelines for Synchronous E-Learning. 2007. (ENG., Illus.). 304p. 60.00 *(978-0-7879-8652-0(6),* Pfeiffer) Wiley, John & Sons, Inc.

Clark, Ruth Colvin & Mayer, Richard E. E-Learning & the Science of Instruction: Proven Guidelines for Consumers & Designers of Multimedia Learning. 2nd rev. ed. 2007. (ENG., Illus.). 496p. 55.00 *(978-0-7879-8683-4(6),* Pfeiffer) Wiley, John & Sons, Inc.

Colby, Anne, et al. Rethinking Undergraduate Business Education: Liberal Learning for the Profession. 2011. (Jossey-Bass/Carnegie Foundation for the Advancement of Teaching Ser.: 20). (ENG., Illus.). 208p. 40.00 *(978-0-470-88962-6(4),* Jossey-Bass) Wiley, John & Sons, Inc.

Comfort, Philip Wesley & Comfort, Jeremy. New Business Course Upper Intermediate-Workbook. 2007. (ENG., Illus.). 80p. (C). pap. 18.95 *(978-1-4240-0066-1(1))* Cengage Heinle.

Cotton & Robbins. Business Class. Date not set. (Illus.). 184p. pap., stu. ed. *(978-0-17-556337-1(3))* Addison-Wesley Longman, Inc.

Cox Aka: Bigg, Randy. Selling Made Simple. 2008. 64p. pap. 16.99 *(978-1-4389-1119-9(X))* AuthorHouse.

Cram101 Textbook Reviews. Outlines & Highlights for E-Learning & Science of Instruction - with Cd by Richard E Mayer, Isbn: 9780787986834. 2010. 56p. pap. 26.95 *(978-1-4288-5407-9(X))* Cram101 Inc.

Crews, Thad & Murphy, Chip. Microsoft Office Excel 2007. 2009. (CaseGrader Ser.). (ENG.). (C). 27.95 *(978-0-538-75039-4(1))* Course Technology.

Dalglish, Carol & Evans, Peter. Teaching in the Global Business Classroom. 2010. 160p. pap. 40.00 *(978-1-84980-052-5(9))* Elgar, Edward Publishing, Inc.

—Teaching in the Global Business Classroom. Evans, Peter, ed. 2008. 160p. 119.00 *(978-1-84720-355-6(9))* Elgar, Edward Publishing, Inc.

Daly, Peter & Gijbels, David, eds. Real Learning Opportunities at Business School & Beyond. 2009. (Advances in Business Education & Training Ser.). (Illus.). xii, 248p. 159.00 *(978-90-481-2972-0(9),* 9048129729) Springer.

Datar, Srikant, et al. Rethinking the MBA: Business Education at a Crossroads. 2010. (ENG., Illus.). 400p. 39.95 *(978-1-4221-3164-0(5))* Harvard Business Review Pr.

DeFillippi, Bob & Wankel, Charles. New Visions of Graduate Management Education. 2006. (Illus.). xxi, 387p. (C). *(978-1-59311-554-8(7))*; pap. *(978-1-59311-553-1(9))* Information Age Publishing, Inc.

Dickie, Laurence & Dickie Carolyn. Mandarin Learning Resources to accompany Cornerstones of Management: Mandarin Glossary; Mandarin Study Guide. 2012. 80p. pap. 22.95 ***(978-0-7346-1118-5(8))*** Tilde Publishing AUS. Dist: International Publishers Marketing.

Duff, Beth. When the Red Horse Spoke: Bringing learning with horses from dream to Reality. 2009. 260p. pap. 21.49 *(978-1-4389-8654-8(8))* AuthorHouse.

Duguid, Paul & Lopes, Teresa da Silva, eds. Trade Marks, Brands & Competitiveness. 2010. (Routledge International Studies in Business History Ser.). (ENG., Illus.). 270p. (C). 140.00 *(978-0-415-77693-6(7),* Routledge) Taylor & Francis Group GBR. Dist: Taylor & Francis Group.

Duska, Ronald F., ed. Education, Leadership & Business Ethics: Essays on the Work of Clarence Walton. 2010. (Issues in Business Ethics Ser.). 344p. pap. 199.00 *(978-90-481-5112-7(0),* 9048151120) Springer.

Edwards, Jacqueline M. Hybrid Organizations: Social Enterprise & Social Entrepreneurship. 2008. (Illus.). 72p. pap. 28.50 *(978-1-4357-0785-6(0))* Lulu Enterprises Inc.

Fayolle, Alain, ed. Handbook of Research in Entrepreneurship Education, 2 vols. 2007. (Elgar Original Reference Ser.). (Illus.). 336p. 210.00 *(978-1-84542-106-9(X))* Elgar, Edward Publishing, Inc.

Fowler, Bruce G. R. Executive Education in Canadian Firms: A Doctoral Dissertation. 2010. 300p. pap. 21.00 *(978-1-4269-2589-4(1))* Trafford Publishing.

Fullerty, Jennifer M. Lifelong Learning Post-Compulsory Education & the University for Industry A Case Study: An Investigation of the Impact of the UK Government Initiative Learndirect on a Changing & Ageing Society with Implications for Policymakers, Researchers & Teachers in Terms of the Supply & Demand of Educational & Training Opportunities. Fullerty, Matt, ed. & des. by. 2011. (ENG.). 242p. pap. 80.00 ***(978-1-937056-57-5(0),*** F Street Bks.) Parkgate Pr.

Geiger, Roger L. & Sá, Creso. Tapping the Riches of Science: Universities & the Promise of Economic Growth. 2009. (Illus.). 262p. 44.00 *(978-0-674-03128-9(8))* Harvard Univ. Pr.

Gijselaers, Wim H., et al, eds. Educational Innovation in Economics & Business Administration: The Case of Problem-Based Learning. 2010. (Educational Innovation in Economics & Business Ser.). 500p. pap. 339.00 *(978-90-481-4504-1(X),* 904814504X) Springer.

Glencoe McGraw-Hill Staff. Marketing Essentials, Student Edition. 5th ed. 2008. (ENG.). (C). 95.24 *(978-0-07-876904-7(3),* 0078769043) McGraw-Hill Higher Education.

Godwin, Joy. Business Advantage Upper-intermediate Personal Study Book with Audio CD. 2011. (Business Advantage Ser.). (ENG.). 96p. pap. 17.00 incl. audio compact disk ***(978-0-521-28130-0(X))*** Cambridge Univ. Pr.

Goetsch, David. Building a Winning Career in Business, 25 Proven St. 2007. 200p. pap. 33.33 *(978-0-13-119015-3(6),* Prentice Hall) Prentice Hall PTR.

Graudins, Chuck. The Technician's Secret Guide to Virus & Malware Computer Repair. Graudins, Chuck, ed. 2010. (ENG., Illus.). 32p. spiral bd. 19.95 *(978-1-929554-15-7(X))* Brevard Marketing.

Grisen, Paul & Wisdom, James. Studying Business at MBA & Masters Level. 2007. (Palgrave Study Guides). (ENG., Illus.). 224p. pap. 30.00 *(978-0-230-50766-1(2))* Palgrave Macmillan.

Groucutt, Jonathan. Business Degree Success. 2008. (Palgrave Study Skills Ser.). (ENG., Illus.). 224p. pap. 23.00 *(978-0-230-50645-9(3))* Palgrave Macmillan.

Gudda. A Guide to Project Monitoring & Evaluation. 2011. 304p. 32.90 ***(978-1-4567-8479-9(X))***; pap. 20.30 ***(978-1-4567-8478-2(1))*** AuthorHouse.

Gupta, Kavita. A Practical Guide to Needs Assessment. 2nd rev. ed. 2007. (ENG., Illus.). 352p. 58.00 *(978-0-7879-8272-0(5),* Pfeiffer) Wiley, John & Sons, Inc.

Hommes, Jeanette, et al, eds. Educational Innovation in Economics & Business IV: Learning in a Changing Environment. 2010. (Educational Innovation in Economics & Business Ser.). 320p. pap. 219.00 *(978-90-481-5278-0(X),* 904815278X) Springer.

Houghton, Medi. Cambridge IGCSE Business Studies Teacher's Resource CD-ROM. 2nd rev. ed. 2011. (Cambridge International Examinations Ser.). cd-rom 48.00 *(978-0-521-12212-2(0))* Cambridge Univ. Pr.

Hsu, Wenhua. Content-Based Instruction, Task-Based Learning: A 3-in-1 Pedagogical Framework for English for Business Purposes. 2008. 360p. pap. *(978-3-639-09411-4(5))* VDM Verlag Dr. Mueller e.K.

Huddlestone, Prue & Stanley, Julian. Work Related Learning in the Secondary School. 2011. (ENG., Illus.). 192p. 128.00 *(978-0-415-57816-5(7))*; pap. 35.95 *(978-0-415-57817-2(5))* Routledge.

Hudson, Bradford T. Academies of Industry. 2008. 328p. per. *(978-3-8364-3504-8(7))* VDM Verlag Dr. Mueller e.K.

Hulsart, Robyn & McCarthy, Victoria. Why the Free Market Must Be an Ethical Market: The Role of Business Schools in Moral Education. 2011. 168p. 109.95 ***(978-0-7734-2562-0(4))*** Mellen, Edwin Pr., The.

Iñiguez de Onzoño, Santiago. The Learning Curve: How Business Schools Are Re-inventing Education. 2011. (IE Business Publishing Ser.). (ENG., Illus.). 256p. 42.00 *(978-0-230-28023-6(4))* Palgrave Macmillan.

Intern Bridge & Bottner, Richard. Total Internship Management: The Employer's Guide to Building the Ultimate Internship Program. Janson, Sean, ed. 2008. 176p. per. 24.95 *(978-0-9799373-9-2(6))* Intern Bridge, Inc.

Ivancevich, John & Duening, Thomas N. Instructor's Edition Business: Principles, Guidelines, & Practices. 2nd ed. 2006. (C). pap. 39.95 *(978-1-59260-281-0(9))* Delmar Cengage Learning.

Jeffcutt. The Foundations of Management Knowledge. 2007. (ENG.). 304p. (C). 44.95 *(978-0-415-43984-8(1))* Routledge.

Johannessen, Tor A., et al, eds. Educational Innovation in Economics & Business VI: Teaching Today the Knowledge of Tomorrow. 2010. (Educational Innovation in Economics & Business Ser.). 352p. pap. 169.00 *(978-90-481-5939-8(8),* 9048159598) Springer.

Kadre, Shailendra. Going Corporate: A Geek's Guide. 2011. (ENG.). 360p. pap. 29.99 *(978-1-4302-3701-3(5))* Apress L. P.

Kaplan, Len. Strategic Innovation. 2009. 440p. pap. 32.84 *(978-0-557-04544-0(4))* Lulu Enterprises Inc.

Karatas. Nascent Entrepreneurship & Learning. 2010. (Illus.). 288p. 125.00 *(978-1-84720-760-9(X))* Elgar, Edward Publishing, Inc.

Kelley, Donna & Thomas, Hugh. Entrepreneurship Education in Asia. 2012. (Illus.). 264p. 115.00 ***(978-1-84980-947-4(X))*** Elgar, Edward Publishing, Inc.

Kourilsky, Marilyn L., et al. The Entrepreneur in Youth: An Untapped Resource for Economic Growth, Social Entrepreneurship, & Education. 2007. (New Horizons in Entrepreneurship Ser.). 192p. 119.00 *(978-1-84542-250-9(3),* Elgar, Edward Publishing, Inc.

Lenssen, Gilbert & Smith, N. Craig, eds. Mainstreaming Corporate Responsibility. 2010. (ENG., Illus.). 600p. pap. 84.95 *(978-0-470-75394-1(3),* Wiley) Wiley, John & Sons, Inc.

Locke, Robert R. & Schöne, Katja E. The Entrepreneurial Shift: Americanization in European High-Technology Management Education. 2011. (ENG.). 266p. pap. 35.99 ***(978-1-107-40339-0(1))*** Cambridge Univ. Pr.

Lorange, Peter. Thought Leadership Meets Business: How business schools can become more Successful. 2010. (ENG., Illus.). 262p. pap. 34.99 *(978-0-521-15912-8(1))* Cambridge Univ. Pr.

Mabey, Christopher & Finch Lees, Tim. Management & Leadership Development. 2007. (Illus.). 280p. (C). per. 60.00 *(978-1-4129-2902-8(4),* B29016P) SAGE Pubns., Ltd. GBR. Dist: SAGE Pubns., Inc.

Marceau, Jane F. A Family Business? The Making of an International Business Elite. 2009. 260p. pap. 38.99 *(978-0-521-12555-0(3))* Cambridge Univ. Pr.

Marques, Joan, et al, eds. Business Administration Education: Changes in Management & Leadership Strategies. 2012. (ENG., Illus.). 256p. 95.00 ***(978-0-230-34103-6(9))*** Palgrave Macmillan.

Mascull, Bill & Comfort, Jeremy. Best Practice Intermediate: Business English in a Global Context. 2007. (Best Practice Ser.). (ENG., Illus.). 176p. (C). pap. 36.95 *(978-1-4130-2185-1(9))* Cengage Heinle.

—Best Practice Upper Intermediate: Business English in a Global Context. 2007. (Best Practice Ser.). (ENG., Illus.). 176p. (C). pap. 36.95 *(978-1-4240-0065-4(3))* Cengage Heinle.

Mauffette-Leenders, Louise A., et al. Apprendre Cas Par Cas. (FRE., Illus.). x, 148p. *(978-0-7714-2496-0(5))* Univ. of Western Ontario.

McAllister, Quentin Oliver. Business Executives & the Humanities. 2011. (ENG.). 126p. pap. 30.00 ***(978-0-8078-6882-9(5))*** Univ. of North Carolina Pr.

McCuddy, Michael K., et al, eds. The Challenges of Educating People to Lead in a Challenging World. 2010. (Educational Innovation in Economics & Business Ser.). xxii, 638p. pap. 309.00 *(978-90-481-7409-6(0),* 9048174090) Springer.

—The Challenges of Educating People to Lead in a Challenging World. 2007. (Educational Innovation in Economics & Business Ser.: Vol. 10). (Illus.). xxii, 638p. 309.00 *(978-1-4020-5611-6(7),* 1402056117) Springer London, Ltd. GBR. Dist: Springer.

Medeni, D. Tunç. Educating Managers for the Global Knowledge Economy. 2009. 218p. pap. *(978-3-639-17433-5(X))* VDM Verlag Dr. Mueller e.K.

Miller, Eugene & Pollack, Neuman F. Barron's Guide to Graduate Business Schools. 15th rev. ed. 2007. (ENG., Illus.). 840p. per. 18.99 *(978-0-7641-3758-7(1))* Barron's Educational Series, Inc.

Milter, Richard G., et al, eds. Educational Innovation in Economics & Business III: Innovative Practices in Business Education. 2010. (Educational Innovation in Economics & Business Ser.). 380p. pap. 219.00 *(978-90-481-5016-8(7),* 9048150167) Springer.

—Educational Innovation in Economics & Business IX: Breaking Boundaries for Global Learning. 2010. (Educational Innovation in Economics & Business Ser.). xxiii, 405p. pap. 309.00 *(978-90-481-6812-5(0),* 9048168120) Springer.

Mintzberg, Henry. Managers, Not Mbas: A Hard Look at the Soft Practice of Managing & Management Development. 2011. 29.95 ***(978-1-60998-572-1(9))***; 69.95 ***(978-0-7927-7119-7(2),*** Sound Library) AudioGO.

Moldoveanu, Mihnea C. & Martin, Roger L. The Future of the MBA: Designing the Thinker of the Future. 2008. (ENG., Illus.). 176p. 39.95 *(978-0-19-534014-3(0))* Oxford Univ. Pr., Inc.

Neubert, Andreas. Leitkategorie: Soziale Kompetenz: Konsequenzen einer Analyse beruflicher Komplexität aus systemtheoretischer Perspektive. 2009. (Europäische Hochschulschriften. Reihe 11: Pädagogik Ser.). (GER.). 232p. pap. 61.95 *(978-3-631-56957-3(2))* Lang, Peter GmbH, Europaischer Verlag der Wissenschaften DEU. Dist: Lang, Peter.

Nickels, William, et al. Loose-Leaf Edition Understanding Business. 10th ed. 2012. (ENG.). (C). ring bd. 141.67 ***(978-0-07-747451-5(1),*** 0077474511, McGraw-Hill/Irwin) McGraw-Hill Higher Education.

Nilsson, Kristina & Bild, Magnus. Teaching & Learning at Business Schools: Transforming Business Education. Mårtensson, Pär, ed. 2008. (Illus.). 330p. 99.95 *(978-0-566-08820-9(7),* Gower Publishing Co., Ltd.) Ashgate Publishing, Ltd. GBR. Dist: Ashgate Publishing Co.

Oade, Aryanne. Starting & Running a Coaching Business. 2009. 176p. pap. 26.00 *(978-1-84528-332-2(5))* How To Books GBR. Dist: Parkwest Pubns., Inc.

O'Sullivan, Arthur, et al. Prentice Hall Economics. 2010. (SPA & ENG., Illus.). xxxii, 96p. *(978-0-13-368018-8(5))* Prentice Hall PTR.

Peacock, Mark A. The Financially Literate Teacher: (or what you can do to get There) 2011. 284p. 24.59 ***(978-1-4567-5787-8(3))***; pap. 18.04 ***(978-1-4567-5788-5(1))*** AuthorHouse.

Perlin, Ross. Intern Nation: How to Earn Nothing & Learn Little in the Brave New Economy. (ENG.). 2012. 258p. pap. 14.95 ***(978-1-84467-883-9(0),*** 844883) 2011. 288p. 22.95 *(978-1-84467-686-6(2),* 844686) Verso Bks. GBR. Dist: Norton, W. W. & Co., Inc.

Peterson's. Competitive Edge: A Guide to Graduate Business Programs. 2011. (ENG.). 704p. (YA). (gr. 7-17). pap. 39.95 *(978-0-7689-3438-0(9))* Peterson's.

—Graduate Programs in Business, Education, Health, Information Studies, Law & Soc. Oram, Fern, ed. 43rd ed. 2008. (ENG.). 2376p. 54.95 *(978-0-7689-2568-5(1))* Peterson's.

—Graduate Programs in Business, Education, Health, Information Studies, Law & Social Work 2012 (Grad 6) 46th ed. 2011. (ENG.). 1944p. (YA). (gr. 7-17). 54.95 ***(978-0-7689-3285-0(8))*** Peterson's.

—MBA Programs: More Than 4,000 Graduate-Level International Business Programs. Snider, Mark D., ed. 15th ed. 2009. (ENG.). 928p. (YA). 44.95 *(978-0-7689-2704-7(8))* Peterson's.

—Peterson's MBA Programs 2009. DeAngelis, Therese, ed. 14th ed. 2008. (ENG.). 928p. 42.95 *(978-0-7689-2553-1(3))* Peterson's.

Peterson's Guides Staff. Bricker's International Directory 2007. 38th ed. 2006. (ENG.). 1608p. 395.00 *(978-0-7689-2174-8(0))* Peterson's.

—Brickers INTL Directo. Seghers, Linda, ed. 2007. (ENG.). 1608p. 395.00 *(978-0-7689-2408-4(1))* Peterson's.

—MBA Programs 2008. Seghers, Linda, ed. 13th ed. 2007. (ENG.). 962p. 42.00 *(978-0-7689-2411-4(1))* Peterson's.

Peterson's Guides Staff, creator. Peterson's Graduate Programs in Business, Education, Health, Information Studies, Law & Social Work. 41st ed. 2006. (ENG., Illus.). 2400p. 54.00 *(978-0-7689-2160-1(0))* Peterson's.

—Peterson's MBA Programs. 12th ed. 2006. (ENG., Illus.). 962p. pap. 42.00 *(978-0-7689-2161-8(9))* Peterson's.

Pfeiff, Andreas. Entstehung und Entwicklung der Handelshochschulen in Deutschland: Empirische Analyse zwischen Kaiserreich, Republik und Diktatur. 2009. (Europäische Hochschulschriften. Reihe 11: Pädagogik Ser.). (GER.). 522p. pap. 122.95 *(978-3-631-59776-7(2))* Lang, Peter GmbH, Europaischer Verlag der Wissenschaften DEU. Dist: Lang, Peter.

Pilbeam, Adrian, et al. New Business Course Intermediate-Workbook. 2007. (ENG., Illus.). 80p. (C). pap. 18.95 *(978-1-4130-2859-1(4))* Cengage Heinle.

Pinkney, Andrea Davis & Rosen, Amy. Teen Business Blasts Off! 2010. (Illus.). 139p. ***(978-0-545-21877-1(2))*** Scholastic, Inc.

Pollock, Mark G. There's A Fine Line. 2011. 220p. 24.59 *(978-1-4567-0082-9(0))*; pap. 14.03 *(978-1-4567-0081-2(2))* AuthorHouse.

Preis, Michael W. & Cabrera, Alfredo. 101 Things I Learned in Business School. 2010. (ENG., Illus.). 212p. 15.00 *(978-0-446-55028-4(0))* Grand Central Publishing.

Price, John & Haddock, David. College Accounting. 2008. 608p. pap. 89.00 *(978-0-07-336549-7(1))* McGraw-Hill Professional Publishing.

Price, John, et al. College Accounting. 12th ed. 2008. (Illus.). (C). 1008p. stu. ed. 132.67 *(978-0-07-336550-3(5)*, 0073365505); 1176p. stu. ed. 151.67 *(978-0-07-340166-9(8)*, 0073401668) McGraw-Hill Professional Publishing.

Pride, William M., et al. Telecourse Guide for Pride/Hughes/Kapoor's Business, 10th. 10th ed. 2009. (ENG.). 256p. (C). ring bd. 67.95 *(978-1-4390-3689-1(6))* Cengage South-Western.

Qiang, Niu & Wolff, Martin. Dissatisfied Customers: Chinese Business Institute Students Speak Out. 2008. pap. 29.00 *(978-1-60456-890-5(9))* Nova Science Pubs., Inc.

Quinn, Rix & Erekson, O. Homer. Major Moments: Life-Changing Lessons of Business Leaders from the Neeley School of Business at TCU. 2012. (ENG.). 240p. 55.00 ***(978-0-87565-488-1(X))*** Texas Christian Univ. Pr.

Radmanesh. The Ultimate Keys to Success in Business & Science: The Modern Blueprint for Prosperity. 2008. 464p. 38.99 *(978-1-4343-2618-8(7))*; pap. 29.99 *(978-1-4343-2619-5(5))* AuthorHouse.

Ramanteba, Mooketsi. The Value of Tacit Knowledge Sharing. 2011. 124p. pap. ***(978-3-8454-1061-6(2))*** Lambert Academic Publishing.

Regni, Rosalie J. & Anderson, Jimmie G. Entrepreneurship in Action: A Retail Store Simulation. 2008. (Illus.). 432p. pap. 88.00 *(978-1-56367-595-9(1))* Fairchild Bks.

Rhodes, Robert T. Graduate Business Law. rev. ed. 2010. (ENG.). 190p. spiral bd. 53.45 *(978-0-7575-4221-3(2))* Kendall Hunt Publishing Co.

—The Legal Environment of Business Undergraduate Edition. rev. ed. 2010. (ENG.). 152p. spiral bd. 53.45 *(978-0-7575-4858-1(X))* Kendall Hunt Publishing Co.

Ristau, Robert A. Intro to Business. 2nd ed. 2010. (21st Century Business Ser.). (ENG.). 192p. pap. 38.95 *(978-0-538-74066-1(3))* Cengage South-Western.

Robert L. Bliss, Ba Ma Littd & Robert L. Bliss, Ba. Are You the Captain of the Love Boat or the Titanic? How to Manage & Succeed in Time of Turmoil & Change. 2009. 104p. pap. 14.00 *(978-1-4389-7959-5(2))* AuthorHouse.

Robinson, Steven T. & Newman, Roberta L. Business & Career Exploration Program for Elementary School-Age Children Curriculum Manual: A Program of the Interfaith Social Change Movement. 2009. 200p. pap. 55.38 *(978-1-4389-7327-2(6))* AuthorHouse.

Royal, Brandon. Secrets to Getting into Business School: 100 Proven Admissions Strategies to Get You Accepted at the MBA Program of Your Dreams. 2010. (ENG.). 308p. *(978-1-897393-80-2(6))* Maven Publishing.

Rutkosky, Nita, et al. Microsoft Office 2007: Windows Vista. 2008. (Marquee Ser.). (Illus.). 688p. 67.95 *(978-0-7638-3354-1(1))* EMC/Paradigm Publishing.

Seguin, Denise & Roggenkamp, Audrey Rutkosky. Microsoft Excel 2007. 2008. (Illus.). xv, 320p. ***(978-0-7638-3057-1(7))*** Paradigm Pubs.

Sijde, Peter van der, et al, eds. Teaching Entrepreneurship: Cases for Education & Training. 2010. (Contributions to Management Science Ser.). (ENG., Illus.). x, 134p. pap. 109.00 *(978-3-7908-2552-7(2)*, 3790825522) Physica-Verlag DEU. Dist: Springer.

Sijde, van der. Teaching Entrepreneurship: Cases for Education & Training. 2008. (Contributions to Management Science Ser.). (ENG., Illus.). x, 134p. 109.00 *(978-3-7908-2037-9(7)*, 3790820377) Physica-Verlag DEU. Dist: Springer.

Silbiger, Steven A. The Ten-Day MBA 4th Ed: A Step-by-Step Guide to Mastering the Skills Taught in America's Top Business Schools. 2012. (ENG.). 448p. pap. 19.99 ***(978-0-06-219957-7(9)***, Collins) HarperCollins Pubs.

Singh, A. Rajmani. Commerce Education in North-East India. 2010. (Illus.). xx, 331p. *(978-81-8324-349-0(5)*, Library of Congress — New Delhi Overseas Office) Mittal Pubns.

Solomon, Michael R., et al. Better Business, Student Value Edition. 2nd ed. 2011. (ENG.). 640p. (C). ring bd. 93.80 *(978-0-13-249673-5(9)*, Prentice Hall) Prentice Hall PTR.

Sousa, Lí, et al. Undergraduate Representations of Management. 2011. 344p. pap. ***(978-3-8383-1633-8(9))*** Lambert Academic Publishing.

Stilliard, Bob, frwd. Executive Education 2007: International Executive Development Programmes. 2007. (Executive Education Ser.). (ENG., Illus.). 203p. per., instr.'s hndbk. ed. 55.00 *(978-1-84673-039-9(2)*, GMB Publishing Ltd.) Blue Ibex Ltd. GBR. Dist: Ingram Pub. Services.

Taderera, Faustino. Branding. 2010. 364p. pap. *(978-3-8383-6647-0(6))* Lambert Academic Publishing.

Targowski, Andrew S., ed. Enterprise Systems Education in the 21st Century. 2006. (Illus.). 369p. 89.95 *(978-1-59904-349-4(1)*, Information Science Publishing) IGI Global.

The\Planning Shop Staff. Passion to Profits: Business for New Entrepreneurs. Abrams, Rhonda, ed. 2009. (ENG., Illus.). 226p. pap. 29.95 *(978-0-9740801-9-2(5))* Planning Shop, The.

Van den Bossche, Piet, et al, eds. Building Learning Experiences in a Changing World. 2011. (Advances in Business Education & Training Ser.). (Illus.). xi, 225p. 139.00 *(978-94-007-0801-3(7)*, 9400708017) Springer.

Van den Bossche, Piet, et al, eds. Learning at the Crossroads of Theory & Practice: Research on Innovative Learning Practices. 2012. (Advances in Business Education & Training Ser.). (ENG., Illus.). viii, 247p. 139.00 ***(978-94-007-2845-5(X)***, 940072845X) Springer.

Vyakarnam, Shailendra. Unlocking the Enterpriser Inside! A Book of Why, What & How! 2010. (Illus.). 200p. 38.00 *(978-981-281-874-4(X))* World Scientific Publishing Co., Inc.

Wankel, Charles, ed. Cutting-Edge Social Media Approaches to Business Education: Teaching with LinkedIn, Facebook, Twitter, Second Life, & Blogs (HC) 2010. 352p. 85.99 *(978-1-61735-117-4(2))* Information Age Publishing, Inc.

—Cutting-Edge Social Media Approaches to Business Education: Teaching with LinkedIn, Facebook, Twitter, Second Life, & Blogs (PB) 2010. 352p. pap. 45.99 *(978-1-61735-116-7(4))* Information Age Publishing, Inc.

Wankel, Charles & DeFillippi, Bob. Being & Becoming a Management Education Scholar. 2010. 194p. *(978-1-60752-347-5(7))*; pap. *(978-1-60752-346-8(9))* Information Age Publishing, Inc.

Wankel, Charles & Stachowicz-Stanusch, Agata. Effectively Integrating Ethical Dimensions into Business Education. 2012. 288p. ***(978-1-61735-579-0(8))***; pap. ***(978-1-61735-578-3(X))***; (Illus.). vii, 279p. E-Book ***(978-1-61735-580-6(1))*** Information Age Publishing, Inc.

Wankel, Charles, et al. Cutting-Edge Social Media Approaches to Business Education: Teaching with LinkedIn, Facebook, Twitter, Second Life, & Blogs. 2010. E-Book *(978-1-61735-118-1(0))* Information Age Publishing, Inc.

Wholihan, Michael R. Educating Entrepreneurs. 2008. 116p. pap. *(978-3-639-01036-7(1))* VDM Verlag Dr. Mueller e.K.

Williams, Allan P.O., ed. The History of UK Business & Management Education. 2010. (Illus.). 160p. 91.95 *(978-1-84950-780-6(5))* Emerald Group Publishing Ltd. GBR. Dist: Turpin Distribution Services Ltd.

Wong, Ken K. More Bucks Annually: Insider's Guide to Getting Your MBA, DBA, & PhD Online. 2011. 112p. pap. 12.95 *(978-1-4620-0022-7(3))* iUniverse, Inc.

BUSINESS EDUCATION—EXAMINATIONS, QUESTIONS, ETC.

see also Graduate Management Admission Test

Albion, Mark. More Than Money: Questions Every MBA Needs to Answer. 2008. (BK Life Ser.). (ENG., Illus.). 105p. 19.95 *(978-1-57675-656-0(4))* Berrett-Koehler Pubs., Inc.

Aluko, Emmanuel. Comprehensive formulas for the CFA(r) Level I Exam. 2009. 84p. pap. 41.95 *(978-1-4092-9519-8(2))* Lulu Enterprises Inc.

Aspen Institute Staff. The Aspen Institute Guide to Socially Responsible MBA Programs: 2008-2009. 2008. (ENG.). 272p. pap. 37.95 *(978-1-57675-765-9(X))* Berrett-Koehler Pubs., Inc.

Crowe, Andy. The PMP Exam: How to Pass on Your First Try. 2009. (ENG., Illus.). 516p. pap. 99.95 *(978-0-9729673-4-1(6))* Velociteach.

Educational Foundation Natl Restaurant Association. Test Prep Managefirst Customer Service. 2008. (ENG.). 48p. (C). pap. 37.47 *(978-0-13-812689-6(5)*, Prentice Hall) Prentice Hall PTR.

The ExamMatrix CPA Exam Review - Business Environment & Concepts. 2007. per. 995.00 net. *(978-1-933366-09-8(5))* ExamMatrix.

Gillespie, Andrew & Surridge, Malcolm. AQA GCSE Business Studies. 2009. (Illus.). 262p. pap. 56.00 *(978-1-84489-414-7(2))* Hodder Education GBR. Dist: Trans-Atlantic Pubns., Inc.

Gmac. GMAT Business Ready All Modules (Accouting, Statistics, Finance, Quantitative Skills) 2011. (ENG.). 199.95 ***(978-1-118-11182-6(6)***, Wiley) Wiley, John & Sons, Inc.

Hasik, James, et al. McGraw-Hill's GMAT 2012-2013. 6th ed. 2012. (ENG., Illus.). 464p. (C). pap. 22.00 ***(978-0-07-176693-7(6)***, 0071766936) McGraw-Hill Cos., The.

—McGraw-Hill's GMAT with CD-ROM, 2012-2013 Edition. 6th ed. 2012. (ENG.). 464p. pap. 36.00 incl. audio compact disk ***(978-0-07-176697-5(9)***, 0071766979) McGraw-Hill Cos., The.

Hasik, James M., et al. McGraw-Hill's GMAT: Graduate Management Admission Test. 2007. (Illus.). xviii, 451p. ***(978-0-07-147596-9(6))*** McGraw-Hill Cos., The.

Jonasson, Hans. Certified Business Analysis Professional Exam Guide. 2009. (ENG., Illus.). 320p. 69.95 *(978-1-4200-6886-3(5))* Auerbach Pubs., Inc.

Manhattan GMAT. Official Guide Companion. 2010. (ENG.). 264p. pap. 24.00 *(978-0-9841780-1-8(5))* Manhattan Prep Publishing.

National Restaurant Association Staff. Food Production. 2008. (ENG.). 64p. (C). pap. 37.47 *(978-0-13-501934-4(6)*, Prentice Hall) Prentice Hall PTR.

NRA Solutions Staff. Test Prep Managefirst Inventory & Purchasing. 2008. (ENG.). 56p. (C). pap. 37.47 *(978-0-13-812690-2(9))* Pearson Education Canada CAN. Dist: Pearson Education.

ORELA Exam Secrets Test Prep Staff, ed. ORELA Business Education Flashcard Study System: ORELA Test Practice Questions & Exam Review for the Oregon Educator Licensure Assessments. 2011. (C). 62.99 *(978-1-61403-634-0(9))* Mometrix Media LLC.

—ORELA Business Education Secrets Study Guide: ORELA Test Review for the Oregon Educator Licensure Assessments. 2011. (C). 62.99 *(978-1-61403-633-3(0))* Mometrix Media LLC.

Praxis II Exam Secrets Test Prep Staff, ed. Praxis II Business Education Content Knowledge (0101) Exam Flashcard Study System: Praxis II Test Practice Questions & Review for the Praxis II Subject Assessments. 2011. (C). 62.99 *(978-1-61403-700-2(0))* Mometrix Media LLC.

BUSINESS EDUCATION—PROBLEMS, EXERCISES, ETC.

see also Graduate Management Admission Test

Koester, Almut, et al. Business Advantage Intermediate Student's Book with DVD. 2012. (Business Advantage Ser.). (ENG.). 192p. pap. 39.00 incl. DVD ***(978-0-521-13220-6(7))*** Cambridge Univ. Pr.

Marcourse, Ian. Answers & Mark Schemes. 2010. (ENG.). 355p. pap. 175.00 *(978-0-340-97578-7(4))* Hodder Education GBR. Dist: Oxford Univ. Pr., Inc.

Rosenberg, Marjorie. Business Advantage Intermediate Personal Study Book with Audio CD. 2012. (Business Advantage Ser.). (ENG.). 96p. pap. 17.00 incl. audio compact disk ***(978-1-107-69264-0(4))*** Cambridge Univ. Pr.

BUSINESS ENGLISH

see English Language—Business English

BUSINESS ENTERPRISES

Here are entered works on business concerns as legal entities, regardless of form of organization.

see also Architectural Firms; Business Tax; Corporations; Corporations, Foreign; Family-Owned Business Enterprises; Government Business Enterprises; International Business Enterprises; Investments, Foreign; New Business Enterprises; Partnership; Trading Companies

Aaron, Shari & Fetzer, Amy V. Climb the Green Ladder: Make Your Company & Career More Sustainable. 2010. (ENG., Illus.). 288p. 29.95 *(978-0-470-74801-5(X)*, Wiley) Wiley, John & Sons, Inc.

Abor, Joshua. Determinants of the Capital Structure of Ghanaian Firms. 2008. 34p. *(978-9966-778-23-9(3))* African Economic Research Consortium.

Abrams, Rhonda. The Successful Business Plan: Secrets & Strategies. 5th ed. 2010. (ENG.). 425p. pap. 44.95 *(978-1-933895-14-7(4))* Planning Shop, The.

Abrams, Rhonda & Barrow, Paul. The Successful Business Plan: Secrets & Strategies. 4th ed. 2008. (Planning Shop Series????? Ser.). (ENG., Illus.). 478p. pap. 32.95 ***(978-1-84112-807-8(4)***, Capstone) Wiley, John & Sons, Inc.

Acharya, Viral, et al. Guaranteed to Fail: Fannie Mae, Freddie Mac & the Debacle of Mortgage Finance. 2011. (ENG., Illus.). 232p. 24.95 *(978-0-691-15078-9(8))* Princeton Univ. Pr.

Al-Hakim, Latif & Jin, Chen, eds. Innovative in Business & Enterprise: Technologies & Frameworks. 2010. 364p. 180.00 *(978-1-61520-643-8(4))* IGI Global.

Al-Qirim, Nabeel. Determinants of Electronic Commerce Adoption. 2010. 360p. pap. *(978-3-8383-2013-7(1))* Lambert Academic Publishing.

Albert, Erin. Single. Women. Entrepreneurs. 2011. 284p. pap. 24.95 net. *(978-1-934922-40-8(4))* IBJ Custom Publishing.

Alessandri, Susan Westcott. Visual Identity: Promoting & Protecting the Public Face of an Organization. 2009. (ENG.). 176p. pap. 42.95 *(978-0-7656-2267-9(X))*; (Illus.). 79.95 *(978-0-7656-2266-2(1))* Sharpe, M.E. Inc.

Anderson, Maggie & Gregory, Ted. Our Black Year: One Family's Quest to Buy Black in America's Racially Divided Economy. 2012. E-Book ***(978-1-61039-025-5(3))*** PublicAffairs.

Anheuser Busch Companies Report: Companies-Products-Services. 60p. (Orig.). pap. *(978-0-7605-2177-9(8))* Rector Pr., Ltd.

Annual Report Production: Companies-Products-Services. 120p. (Orig.). pap. *(978-0-7605-0803-9(8))* Rector Pr., Ltd.

Anti-Infective Market: Companies-Products-Services. 229p. (Orig.). pap. *(978-0-7605-2313-1(4))* Rector Pr., Ltd.

Arthur W. Page Society staff. The Authentic Enterprise: An Arthur W. Page Society Report. 2007. 64p. 8.00 *(978-0-615-23766-4(5))* Page, Arthur W. Society.

Audretsch, David B., et al, eds. Local Heroes in the Global Village: Globalization & the New Entrepreneurship Policies. 2010. (International Studies in Entrepreneurship Ser.). (Illus.). xiv, 202p. pap. 129.00 *(978-1-4419-3630-1(0)*, 1441936300) Springer.

Bachman, Glenn. The Green Business Guide. 2009. (ENG., Illus.). 1p. pap. 15.99 *(978-1-60163-048-3(4))* Career Pr., Inc.

Bacza, Bob. Quality Customer Service Starts Inside Your Business. 2007. 76p. pap. 16.95 *(978-1-60441-678-7(5))* PublishAmerica, Inc.

Bank, Steven A. & Stark, Kirk J. Selected Sections: Corporate & Partnership Income Tax Code & Regulations, 2011-2012. 2011. 836p. pap. 32.00 ***(978-1-59941-949-7(1)***, Foundation Pr.) West.

Barbara Killmeyer. It's Nobody's Business but Yours: A comprehensive guide for the woman who wants to turn her business idea into a Reality. 2010. 108p. 21.95 *(978-1-4269-2187-2(X))*; pap. 11.95 *(978-1-4269-2186-5(1))* Trafford Publishing.

Barnes Reports. 2007 World Industry & Market Outlook. 2007. per. 399.00 *(978-0-9776720-3-5(4))* Barnes Reports.

—2008 World Industry & Market Outlook. 2007. 247p. per. 299.00 net. *(978-0-9776720-6-6(9))* Barnes Reports.

Barwise, Patrick & Meehan, Sean. Beyond the Familiar: Long-Term Growth Through Customer Focus & Innovation. 2011. (ENG., Illus.). 184p. 29.95 *(978-0-470-97631-9(4)*, Jossey-Bass) Wiley, John & Sons, Inc.

Bayley, Stephen, et al. Stanton Williams. 2009. (ENG., Illus.). 256p. 49.95 *(978-1-906155-87-2(9))* Black Dog Publishing Ltd. GBR. Dist: Actar Birkhauser Distribution.

Baynton, Val. Beswick Pottery. 2012. (Shire Library). (ENG., Illus.). 64p. pap. 12.95 ***(978-0-7478-1100-8(8))*** Shire Pubns., Ltd. GBR. Dist: Random Hse., Inc.

Bøllingtoft, Anne, et al, eds. Collaborative Communities of Firms: Purpose, Process, & Design. 2011. (Information & Organization Design Ser.). (ENG., Illus.). viii, 148p. 139.00 ***(978-1-4614-1283-0(8)***, 1461412838) Springer.

Becerra, Manuel. Theory of the Firm for Strategic Management: Economic Value Analysis. 2009. (ENG., Illus.). 310p. 136.99 *(978-0-521-86334-6(1))*; pap. 47.99 *(978-0-521-68194-0(4))* Cambridge Univ. Pr.

Becker, Thomas H. Doing Business in the New Latin America: Keys to Profit in America's Next-Door Markets. 2nd ed. 2011. (Illus.). x, 280p. E-Book *(978-0-313-38382-3(0))*; 280p. 44.95 *(978-0-313-38381-6(2)*, A2872C) Greenwood Publishing Group, Inc. (Praeger Pubs.).

Bellamy, Gartner &, et al. Enterprise! (Book Only) 2009. (ENG.). 592p. (C). pap. 188.95 *(978-0-324-78533-3(X))* CENGAGE Learning.

Bembé Dellinger Architects: Bilder und Pläne pictures & plans 1999 - 2009. 2010. 736p. pap. 69.95 *(978-3-7091-0093-6(3))* Springer Wien AUT. Dist: Actar Birkhauser Distribution.

Bernoff, Josh & Schadler, Ted. Empowered: Unleash Your Employees, Energize Your Customers, & Transform Your Business. 2010. (ENG., Illus.). 272p. 27.95 *(978-1-4221-5563-9(3))* Harvard Business Review Pr.

Bevans, Neal R. Business Organizations & Corporate Law. 2006. (ENG., Illus.). 624p. (C). 144.95 *(978-1-4018-7083-6(X))* Delmar Cengage Learning.

Bhaur, Muhammad Amer & Mulac, Jakub. Dimensions of Enterprise Hypocrisy with Specifics to Recruitment & Selection. 2008. 92p. pap. *(978-3-639-06350-9(3))* VDM Verlag Dr. Mueller e.K.

BIA. Major Companies of the World. 6th rev. ed. 2006. 400p. (J). pap. 249.00 *(978-1-4187-4392-5(5))* Business Information Agency.

Biech, Elaine. Training & Consulting, 2 vols., Set. annuals 2008. (JB 2004 Annuals Set Ser.: 4). (ENG.). 656p. 180.00 *(978-0-470-43118-4(0)*, Pfeiffer) Wiley, John & Sons, Inc.

Bilton, Chris & Cummings, Stephen. Creative Strategy: Reconnecting Business & Innovation. 2010. (Images of Business Strategy Ser.: 3). (ENG., Illus.). 286p. pap. 39.95 *(978-1-4051-8019-1(6)*, Wiley-Blackwell) Wiley, John & Sons, Inc.

Biondi, Yuri, et al, eds. The Firm as an Entity: Implications for Economics, Accounting & the Law. 2007. (Economics of Legal Relationships Ser.). (Illus.). 387p. 160.00 *(978-0-415-41443-2(1))* Routledge.

Bisk, Nathan M. Financial Accounting & Reporting. 40th ed. 2010. (Bisk Comprehensive CPA Review Ser.). pap. 49.95 *(978-1-57961-845-2(6))* Bisk Education, Inc.

Bjuggren, Per-Olof & Mueller, Dennis C., eds. The Modern Firm, Corporate Governance & Investment. 2009. (New Perspectives on the Modern Corporation Ser.). (Illus.). 424p. 173.00 *(978-1-84844-225-2(4))* Elgar, Edward Publishing, Inc.

Bonnin, Jenny, et al. True Green at Work: 100 Ways You Can Make the Environment Your Business. 2008. (ENG., Illus.). 144p. pap. 19.95 *(978-1-4262-0263-6(6))* National Geographic Society.

Börjeson, Mauritz & Pettersson, Andreas. Moving from Practice Towards Science. 2010. 104p. pap. *(978-3-8383-8446-7(6))* Lambert Academic Publishing.

Breiding, James & Schwarz, Gerhard. The Powerhouse: Why Swiss corporations are so Successful. 2013. (ENG., Illus.). 416p. 45.00 ***(978-1-84668-586-6(9))*** Profile Bks. Ltd. GBR. Dist: Consortium Bk. Sales & Distribution.

Brouwer, Maria. Organizations, Individualism & Economic Theory. 2012. (Routledge Frontiers of Political Economy Ser.). (ENG., Illus.). 288p. (C). 130.00 ***(978-0-415-69977-8(0))*** Routledge.

Brown, Fred. The Persistence of Vision: The Denver Metro Chamber of Commerce. 2011. *(978-1-56373-190-7(8))* Fulcrum Publishing.

Bryer, Lanning G., et al. Intellectual Property Strategies for the 21st Century Corporation: A Shift in Strategic & Financial Management. 2011. (ENG., Illus.). 322p. 125.00 *(978-0-470-60175-4(2)*, Wiley) Wiley, John & Sons, Inc.

Buckley, Graeme, et al. The Promotion of Sustainable Enterprises. 2009. (ENG., Illus.). 280p. pap. 50.00 *(978-92-2-121200-3(9))* International Labour Office.

Buckley, Penrose. Producer Organisations. 2007. (Oxfam Skills & Practice Ser.). (ENG.). 200p. pap. 25.95 *(978-0-85598-575-2(5))* Oxfam Publishing GBR. Dist: Stylus Publishing, LLC.

Buono, Anthony F. & Poulfelt, Flemming. Client-Consultant Collaboration: Coping with Complexity & Change. 2009. (Illus.). 276p. pap. *(978-1-60752-208-9(X))* Information Age Publishing, Inc.

Buono, Anthony F. & Poulfelt, Flemming, eds. Client-Consultant Collaboration: Coping with Complexity & Change (HC) 2009. 276p. 85.99 *(978-1-60752-209-6(8))* Information Age Publishing, Inc.

Burchell, Michael & Robin, Jennifer. The Great Workplace: Building Trust & Inspiring Performance Deluxe Set. 2011. (ENG.). ring bd. 250.00 *(978-0-470-59836-8(0)*, Pfeiffer) Wiley, John & Sons, Inc.

Burn Care Products Market: Companies-Products-Services. 241p. (Orig.). pap. *(978-0-7605-2319-3(3))* Rector Pr., Ltd.

Burton, T. Naming Rights. 2008. (ENG.). 256p. 52.50 *(978-0-470-23063-3(0)*, Wiley) Wiley, John & Sons, Inc.

Cafaggi, Fabrizio, ed. Enforcement of Transnational Regulation: Ensuring Compliance in a Global World. 2012. (Private Regulation Ser.). 392p. 150.00 ***(978-1-78100-372-5(6))*** Elgar, Edward Publishing, Inc.

Cainelli, Giulio & Iacobucci, Donato. Agglomeration, Technology & Business Groups. 2007. 160p. (C). 119.00 *(978-1-84542-446-6(8))* Elgar, Edward Publishing, Inc.

Camilleri, Natalie. The Creative City: Reality or Rhetoric? 2010. 104p. pap. *(978-3-8383-7376-8(6))* Lambert Academic Publishing.

Campbell, Christian, Editor. Legal Aspects of Doing Business in Latin America [2009] Volume I. 2009. 392p. pap. 70.00 *(978-0-557-13339-0(4))* Lulu Enterprises Inc.

—Legal Aspects of Doing Business in Latin America [2009] Volume II. 2009. 416p. pap. 70.00 *(978-0-557-13341-3(6))* Lulu Enterprises Inc.

—Legal Aspects of Doing Business in North America [2009] I. 2009. 452p. pap. 110.00 *(978-0-557-20339-0(2))* Lulu Enterprises Inc.

—Legal Aspects of doing Business in North America [2009] II. 2009. 436p. pap. 110.00 *(978-0-557-20365-9(1))* Lulu Enterprises Inc.

—Legal Aspects of Doing Business in North America [2009] III. 2009. 388p. pap. 110.00 *(978-0-557-20370-3(8))* Lulu Enterprises Inc.

Caroleo, Brunella. Complex Industrial Networks. 2010. 88p. pap. *(978-3-639-24748-0(5))* VDM Verlag Dr. Mueller e.K.
Carpenter, Ed. Meaningful Enterprise Metrics Made Simple. 2011. 102p. pap. 9.98 ***(978-0-557-63839-0(9))*** Lulu Enterprises Inc.
Casarez, Vince, et al. Reshaping Your Business with Web 2.0: Using the New Collaborative Technologies to Lead Business Transformation. 2008. (ENG.). 259p. pap. 39.99 *(978-0-07-160078-1(7)*, 0071600787) McGraw-Hill Osborne.
Cavnar, Bob. Disaster on the Horizon: The Deepwater Well Blowout: What Happened & Why. 2010. (ENG., Illus.). 248p. pap. 14.95 *(978-1-60358-316-9(5))* Chelsea Green Publishing.
Chase, Linda & Eigelbach, Kevin R. Cincinnati: Bridges to the Future. 2008. 59.50 *(978-1-882933-88-4(5))* Cherbo Publishing Group, Inc.
Chemeva, Iveta, ed. The Business Case for Sustainable Finance. 2012. (Routledge Studies in Ecological Economics Ser.). (ENG., Illus.). 144p. (C). 140.00 ***(978-0-415-53673-8(1))*** Routledge.
Childrens Food Market: Companies-Products-Services. 208p. (Orig.). pap. *(978-0-7605-2222-6(7))* Rector Pr., Ltd.
Childs, David. Fit for Service: Recycle Inefficiency into Philanthropy. 2007. 183p. per. 12.99 *(978-1-59866-663-6(X))* Tate Publishing & Enterprises, LLC.
Chmura, Alan & Heumann, J. Mark. Logical Data Modeling: What it Is & How to do It. 2010. (Integrated Series in Information Systems Ser.). (Illus.). xi, 228p. pap. 129.00 *(978-1-4419-1989-2(9)*, 1441919899) Springer.
Chunnel Handbook & Atlas: Companies-Products-Services. (Illus.). 60p. (Orig.). pap. *(978-0-7605-0638-7(8))* Rector Pr., Ltd.
CIS Business Reference: Companies-Products-Services. 100p. (Orig.). pap. 125.00 *(978-0-7605-1689-8(8))* Rector Pr., Ltd.
Clark, Leif M. & Glosband, Daniel M. Ancillary & Other Cross-Border Insolvency Cases under Chapter 15 of the Bankruptcy Code. 2008. pap. *(978-1-4224-2421-6(9))* LexisNexis Matthew Bender.
Coad, Alex. The Growth of Firms: A Survey of Theories & Empirical Evidence. 2009. (New Perspectives on the Modern Corporation Ser.). (Illus.). 208p. 119.00 *(978-1-84844-327-3(7))* Elgar, Edward Publishing, Inc.
Coal & Methane Industry International: Companies-Products-Services. (Illus.). 70p. (Orig.). pap. *(978-0-7605-0675-2(2))* Rector Pr., Ltd.
Coal Burning Technologies: Companies-Products-Services. (Illus.). 70p. (Orig.). pap. *(978-0-7605-0676-9(0))* Rector Pr., Ltd.
Cohen, Nevin, ed. Green Business. 2010. (SAGE Reference Series on Green Society: Toward a Sustainable Future-Series Editor: Paul Robbins Ser.: 5). (Illus.). 616p. 110.00 *(978-1-4129-9684-6(8)*, B96846C) SAGE Pubns., Inc.
Confectionary International Market: Companies-Products-Services. 250p. (Orig.). pap. *(978-0-7605-2215-8(4))* Rector Pr., Ltd.
Conway, Mara E. & Conway, Susan D. Essentials of Enterprise Compliance. 2008. (Essentials Ser.: 45). (ENG., Illus.). 160p. pap. 39.95 *(978-0-470-40476-8(0)*, Wiley) Wiley, John & Sons, Inc.
Cope, Bill & Kalantzis, Mary, eds. The International Journal of Knowledge, Culture & Change Management: Volume 10, Number 1. 2010. 602p. 0.00 *(978-1-86335-822-4(6))* Common Ground Publishing Pty, Ltd.
—The International Journal of Knowledge, Culture & Change Management: Volume 10, Number 7. 2011. 180p. 0.00 ***(978-1-86335-910-8(9))*** Common Ground Publishing Pty, Ltd.
—The International Journal of Knowledge, Culture & Change Management: Volume 10, Number 8. 2011. 134p. 0.00 ***(978-1-86335-923-8(0))*** Common Ground Publishing Pty, Ltd.
—The International Journal of Knowledge, Culture & Change Management: Volume 10, Number 9. 2011. 118p. 0.00 ***(978-1-86335-926-9(5))*** Common Ground Publishing Pty, Ltd.
Cope, Bill & Kalantzis, Mary, eds. The International Journal of Knowledge, Culture & Change Management: Volume 9, Number 12. 2010. 188p. 0.00 *(978-1-86335-753-1(X))* Common Ground Publishing Pty, Ltd.
Coughlin, Dan. The Management 500: A High-Octane Formula for Business Success. 1 vol. 2009. (ENG.). 256p. 22.00 *(978-0-8144-1423-1(0))* Amacom.
County Asset-Lien Records Handbook: Companies-Products-Services. 470p. (Orig.). pap. 145.00 *(978-0-7605-1858-8(0))* Rector Pr., Ltd.
Cram101 Textbook Reviews. Outlines & Highlights for Business by William Pride, Isbn: 9780538478083. 2011. 556p. pap. 38.95 ***(978-1-4288-2145-3(7))*** Cram101 Inc.
—Outlines Greve. 2011. 56p. pap. 26.95 ***(978-1-61905-496-7(5))*** Cram101 Inc.
Cram101 Textbook Reviews Staff. Outlines & Highlights for Business by Griffin, Isbn: 9780131495371. 2009. 190p. pap. 30.95 *(978-1-4288-3979-3(8))* Cram101 Inc.
—Outlines & Highlights for Business by Pride, Hughes, & Kapoor, Isbn: 9780324829556. 2009. 232p. pap. 31.95 *(978-1-4288-4116-1(4))*; 264p. pap. 31.95 *(978-1-4288-8905-7(1))* Cram101 Inc.
—Outlines & Highlights for Business by William M Pride, Isbn: 9780618770915. 2009. 252p. pap. 31.95 *(978-1-4288-4073-7(7))* Cram101 Inc.
—Outlines & Highlights for Business by William M Pride, Isbn: 9781439037638. 2009. 260p. pap. 31.95 *(978-1-4288-9077-0(7))* Cram101 Inc.
—Outlines & Highlights for Busn by Marcella Kelly, Jim Mcgowen, Isbn: 9780324569896. 2009. 278p. pap. 32.95 *(978-1-4288-8697-1(4))* Cram101 Inc.
—Outlines & Highlights for Enterprise! by William B Gartner, Isbn: 9780324130850. 2009. 208p. pap. 30.95 *(978-1-4288-8860-9(8))* Cram101 Inc.
—Outlines & Highlights for Student Achievement Series: Foundations of Business by William M. Pride. ISBN. 2009. 184p. pap. 29.95 *(978-1-4288-4166-6(0))*; 234p. pap. 31.95 *(978-1-4288-8757-2(1))* Cram101 Inc.
Cross, Frank B. & Miller, Roger LeRoy. Study Guide for Cross/Miller's the Legal Environment of Business, 8th. 8th ed. 2011. (ENG.). 320p. (C). pap. 46.95 *(978-0-538-46979-1(X))* Cengage South-Western.
Crossan, Kenny. The Theory of the Firm & Corporate Governance. 2010. 188p. pap. *(978-3-8383-4774-5(9))* Lambert Academic Publishing.
Cruz-Cunha, Maria Manuela & Moreira, Fernando, eds. Handbook of Research on Mobility & Computing: Evolving Technologies & Ubiquitous Impacts, 2 vols. 2010. (Illus.). 900p. 475.00 *(978-1-60960-042-6(8)*, Information Science Reference) IGI Global.
Cucer, Stela. Funding Opportunities of the Companies. 2011. 80p. pap. ***(978-3-8443-1018-4(5))*** Lambert Academic Publishing.
Culinary Professional's International Directory: Companies-Products-Services. 320p. (Orig.). pap. *(978-0-7605-0640-0(X))* Rector Pr., Ltd.
Dairy Products International Market: Companies-Products-Services. 325p. (Orig.). pap. *(978-0-7605-2213-4(8))* Rector Pr., Ltd.
Data Acquisition Handbook: Companies-Products-Services. 200p. (Orig.). pap. 125.00 *(978-0-7605-1630-4(0))* Rector Pr., Ltd.
Davidsson, Per, et al. Entrepreneurship & the Growth of Firms. 2008. (Illus.). 240p. pap. 50.00 *(978-1-84720-792-0(8))* Elgar, Edward Publishing, Inc.
Davies, Jeff, et al. The Definitive Guide to SOA: Oracle Service Bus. 2nd ed. 2008. (ENG., Illus.). 550p. pap., instr.'s gde. ed. 79.99 *(978-1-4302-1057-3(5))* Apress L. P.
Davis, Mary E. The Entrepreneurial Mom: Managing for Success in Your Home & Your Business. 2007. (ENG., Illus.). 158p. per. 16.95 *(978-1-58182-591-6(9))* Turner Publishing Co.
de Guitaut, Caroline. Fabergé's Animals: A Royal Farm in Miniature. 2010. (Illus.). 119p. 24.95 *(978-1-905686-12-4(9))* Royal Collection Enterprises Ltd. GBR. Dist: Chicago Distribution Ctr.
De Lange, Deborah E., ed. Research Companion to Green International Management Studies: A Guide for Future Research, Collaboration & Review Writing. (Elgar Original Reference Ser.). 200p. 2012. pap. 29.95 ***(978-1-84980-727-2(2))*** 2011. (Illus.). 145.00 *(978-1-84980-363-2(3))* Elgar, Edward Publishing, Inc.
Dealership Business Management. 17.50 *(978-0-87359-007-5(4)*, AM 104) Northwood Univ. Pr.
Dealership Organization & Management. 22.75 *(978-0-87359-002-0(3)*, AM 101) Northwood Univ. Pr.
The Deepwater Horizon Oil Spill Chain of Command: An Examination of Information Sharing Practices During a Spill of National Significance: Hearing Before the Subcommittee on Management, Investigations, & Oversight of the Committee on Homeland Security, House of Representatives, One Hundred Eleventh Congress, Second Session, July 12, 2010. 2011. (Illus.). iii, 75p. ***(978-0-16-088708-6(9)***, 552-070-42866-6) United States Government Printing Office.
Demirdjian, Z. S. Andrew. Challenges & Opportunities in a Changing World: Insights, Innovations, & Trends. 2009. 202p. 29.99 *(978-1-4415-2015-9(5))*; pap. 19.99 *(978-1-4415-2014-2(7))* Xlibris Corp.
Demographic Market Reports: Companies-Products-Services. 70p. (Orig.). pap. *(978-0-7605-0654-7(X))* Rector Pr., Ltd.
Demographic Zip Code & Area Population & Housing Profiles: Companies-Products-Services. 4000p. (Orig.). pap. *(978-0-7605-0653-0(1))* Rector Pr., Ltd.
Desouza, Kevin C. Managing Knowledge Security: Strategies for Protecting Your Company's Intellectual Assets. 2007. (ENG., Illus.). 200p. 65.00 *(978-0-7494-4961-2(6))* Kogan Page, Ltd. GBR. Dist: Ingram Pub. Services.
Distilled Spirits Market: Companies-Products-Services. 100p. (Orig.). pap. 1295.00 *(978-0-7605-2167-0(0))* Rector Pr., Ltd.
Dixit, Avinash K. Lawlessness & Economics: Alternative Modes of Governance. 2007. (Gorman Lectures). (ENG., Illus.). 184p. (C). per. 30.00 *(978-0-691-13034-7(5))* Princeton Univ. Pr.
Domsch, Michel E. & Hristozova, Elena, eds. Human Resource Management in Consulting Firms. 2010. (ENG., Illus.). x, 225p. pap. 79.95 *(978-3-642-06825-6(1)*, 3642068251) Springer.
East, Roger, et al. The Green Guide for Business: The Ultimate Environment Handbook for Businesses of All Sizes. 2010. (ENG., Illus.). 208p. pap. 14.95 *(978-1-84668-874-4(4))* Profile Bks. Ltd. GBR. Dist: Consortium Bk. Sales & Distribution.
Ebner, Alexander. Embedded Entrepreneurship: The Institutional Dynamics of Innovation. 2011. (Routledge Studies in Global Competition Ser.). (ENG.). 288p. (C). 150.00 *(978-0-415-45976-1(1))* Routledge.
Ebner, Gabriele & Heimerl, Peter. Fehler - Lernen - Unternehmen: Wie Sie die Fehlerkultur und Lernreife Ihrer Organisation wahrnehmen und gestalten. 2008. 316p. pap. 72.95 *(978-3-631-57744-8(3))* Lang, Peter GmbH, Europaischer Verlag der Wissenschaften DEU. Dist: Lang, Peter.
Edelmann, Frederic, et al, texts. Louis Vuitton: Architecture & Interiors. 2011. (ENG., Illus.). 272p. 85.00 *(978-0-8478-3652-9(5))* Rizzoli International Pubns., Inc.
Ehrlich, Donna. Adaptation of Business Processes in Smes. 2011. 120p. pap. ***(978-3-8443-1686-5(8))*** Lambert Academic Publishing.
Eisenberg, Melvin A. Corporations & Other Business Organizations: Cases & Materials 2008. 9th rev. ed. 2008. (University Casebook Ser.). 245p. pap., suppl. ed. 24.00 *(978-1-59941-468-3(6)*, Foundation Pr.) West.
Ekblom, Paul, ed. Design Against Crime: Crime Proofing Everyday Products. 2012. 68.50 ***(978-1-58826-813-6(6))*** Rienner, Lynne Pubs.
Endler, L.z. Creating A Remarkable Business. 2009. 104p. pap. 52.50 *(978-1-4092-9060-5(3))* Lulu Enterprises Inc.
Equipo Staff & Papeti, Dissenys. Gaudí: Dibuixos = Dibujos = Drawings, 1 vol. 2007. (CAT, ENG & SPA., Illus.). 128p. pap. 15.95 ***(978-84-8478-069-4(4))*** Triangle Postals, S.L. ESP. Dist: Innovative Logistics.
Estes, Jonathan & Estes. Smart Green: How to Implement Sustainable Business Practices in Any Industry - And Make Money. 2009. (ENG., Illus.). 224p. 29.95 *(978-0-470-38779-5(3)*, Wiley) Wiley, John & Sons, Inc.
Esty, Daniel C. & Winston, Andrew S. Green to Gold: How Smart Companies Use Environmental Strategy to Innovate, Create Value, & Build a Competitive Advantage. 2009. (ENG., Illus.). 408p. pap. 19.95 *(978-0-470-39374-1(2)*, Wiley) Wiley, John & Sons, Inc.
—Green to Gold: How Smart Companies Use Environmental Strategy to Innovate, Create Value, & Build Competitive Advantage. 2006. (ENG., Illus.). 384p. 27.50 *(978-0-300-11997-8(6))* Yale Univ. Pr.
Fandel, Günter, et al, eds. Modern Concepts of the Theory of the Firm: Managing Enterprises of the New Economy. 2010. (ENG., Illus.). xii, 647p. pap. 179.00 *(978-3-642-07349-6(2)*, 3642073492) Springer.
F&S Index International Subscription. 2007th ed. 2007. (ENG.). 2308.00 *(978-1-4144-0056-3(X))* Cengage Gale.
Favaretto, Irene & Campagnol, Isabella. Rubelli: The Art of Weaving. 2012. (ENG., Illus.). 256p. 65.00 ***(978-88-317-0822-7(8))*** Marsilio Editori spa ITA. Dist: Random Hse., Inc.
Fielden, Sandra L. & Davidson, Marilyn J., eds. International Research Handbook on Successful Women Entrepreneurs. 2010. (Elgar Original Reference Ser.). (Illus.). 256p. 182.00 *(978-1-84720-918-4(1))* Elgar, Edward Publishing, Inc.
Filipe, Joaquim & Obaidat, Mohammad S. E-Business & Telecommunication Networks. 2008. (Communications in Computer & Information Science Ser.). (Illus.). 372p. spiral bd. 99.00 *(978-3-540-70759-2(X))* Springer.
Filtration Markets: Companies-Products-Services. 119p. (Orig.). pap. *(978-0-7605-2314-8(2))* Rector Pr., Ltd.
Fingerhut Companies Report 1994: Companies-Products-Services. 60p. (Orig.). pap. 495.00 *(978-0-7605-2135-9(2))* Rector Pr., Ltd.
Fisher, James L. & Koch, James V. Born, Not Made: The Entrepreneurial Personality, 1 vol. 2008. (Illus.). 184p. 39.95 *(978-0-313-35050-4(7)*, C35050, Praeger Pubs.) Greenwood Publishing Group, Inc.
Fishman, Jay E., et al. Guide to Business, 3 vols. Incl. Vol. 1. Guide to Business Valuations. ring bd. 180.00 *(978-0-7646-0403-4(1))*; Vol. 2. Guide to Business Valuations. ring bd. 180.00 *(978-0-7646-0404-1(X))*; Vol. 3. Guide to Business Valuations. ring bd. 180.00 *(978-0-7646-0405-8(8))*; 1998. 180.00 *(978-0-7646-0402-7(3))* Practitioners Publishing Co.
Folkerts, Thilo. Topotek 1 Martin Rein-Cano / Lorenz Dexler Rosemarie Trockel: Eine Landschaftsskulptur für München/A Landscape Sculpture for Munich. 2010. (Illus.). 128p. 54.95 *(978-3-0346-0591-5(9))* Birkhauser Verlag AG CHE. Dist: Actar Birkhauser Distribution.
Forney, Kristine, et al. The Digital Innovation Playbook: Creating a Transformative Customer Experience. 2011. (ENG., Illus.). 270p. 49.95 *(978-0-470-94479-7(6)*, Wiley) Wiley, John & Sons, Inc.
Foss, Nicolai J. & Klein, Peter G. Organizing Entrepreneurial Judgment: A New Approach to the Firm. 2012. (ENG., Illus.). 312p. 99.00 ***(978-0-521-87442-7(4))***; pap. 36.99 ***(978-0-521-69726-2(3))*** Cambridge Univ. Pr.
Fougeron, Anne. Fougeron Architecture: Opposition/Composition. 2011. (ENG., Illus.). 192p. pap. 40.00 *(978-1-56898-990-7(3))* Princeton Architectural Pr.
Friedrichs, Ed. Reach Higher: Long-cycle Strategies for a Short-cycle World. 2006. 334p. pap. 39.00 *(978-0-9755654-7-6(8)*, Ostberg) Greenway Communications.
Funabashi, Matohisa & Grzech, Adam, eds. Challenges of Expanding Internet: E-Commerce, E-Business, & E-Government: 5th IFIP Conference on e-Commerce, e-Business, & e-Government (I3E'2005), October 28-30 2005, Poznan, Poland. 2010. (IFIP Advances in Information & Communication Technology Ser.). (Illus.). xxiv, 627p. pap. 235.00 *(978-1-4419-3952-4(0)*, 1441939520) Springer.
Galbraith, Sasha. Anatomy of a Business: What It Is, What It Does, & How It Works, 1 vol. 2006. (Illus.). 328p. 75.00 *(978-0-313-33793-2(4)*, GR3793, Greenwood Pr.) Greenwood Publishing Group, Inc.
Gately, Gary M. Maryland: Working Wonders. 2009. 59.95 *(978-1-882933-25-9(7))* Cherbo Publishing Group, Inc.
Gilbert, Joseph. Ethics for Managers. 2012. (ENG., Illus.). 304p. 100.00 ***(978-0-415-80708-1(5))***; pap. 49.95 ***(978-0-415-80709-8(3))*** Routledge.
Giovane, Paolo & Sabbatini, Roberto, eds. The Euro, Inflation & Consumers' Perceptions: Lessons from Italy. 2010. (ENG., Illus.). xvi, 243p. pap. 139.00 *(978-3-642-09709-6(X)*, 364209709X) Springer.
Giulio, Decio & Carugati, Riccardo. Benetti. 2011. (ENG., Illus.). 160p. 85.00 *(978-88-370-6856-1(5))* Electa ITA. Dist: National Bk. Network.
Goldman and, Rawles. Applied Data Communications. 2006. pap. 10.95 *(978-1-4288-0575-0(3))* Cram101 Inc.
Grey, Christopher John. A Very Short Fairly Interesting & Reasonably Cheap Book about Studying Organizations. 2nd ed. 2009. (Very Short, Fairly Interesting & Cheap Bks.). 208p. (C). 97.00 *(978-1-84787-342-2(1)*, B73422C); pap. 31.00 *(978-1-84787-343-9(X)*, B73422P) SAGE Pubns., Ltd. GBR. Dist: SAGE Pubns., Inc.
Griser, William A. Franchise & Business Opportunities: Executive Edition for the Entrepreneur. annuals Griser, William A., ed. 20th ed. Date not set. (Illus.). 200p. pap. 29.95 *(978-0-9645886-0-8(9))*; lib. bdg. 19.95 *(978-0-9645886-1-5(7))* Franchise Business Opportunities Publishing Co.
Hakansson, et al. Use of Science & Technology in Business: Exploring the Impact of Using Activity for Systems, Organizations, & People. 2009. (Illus.). viii, 349p. 134.95 *(978-1-84855-474-0(5))* Emerald Group Publishing Ltd. GBR. Dist: Turpin Distribution Services Ltd.
Halkias, Daphne, et al. Female Immigrant Entrepreneurs: The Economic & Social Impact of a Global Phenomenon. 2010. (Illus.). 324p. 119.95 *(978-0-566-08913-8(0)*, Gower Publishing Co., Ltd.) Ashgate Publishing, Ltd. GBR. Dist: Ashgate Publishing Co.
Harper, Stephen C. The Ever-Evolving Enterprise: Guidelines for Creating Your Company's Future, 1 vol. 2011. 276p. 44.95 *(978-0-313-39183-5(1)*, A3215C); E-Book *(978-0-313-39184-2(X))* Greenwood Publishing Group, Inc. (Praeger Pubs.).
Harrison, Andrew. Business Environment in a Global Context. 2010. (ENG., Illus.). 432p. pap. 65.00 *(978-0-19-921400-6(X))* Oxford Univ. Pr., Inc.
Harvard Business Review. Harvard Business Review on Greening Your Business Profitably. 2011. (ENG., Illus.). 272p. pap. 22.00 *(978-1-4221-6256-9(7))* Harvard Business Review Pr.
Himelstein, Linda. The King of Vodka: The Story of Pyotr Smirnov & the Upheaval of an Empire. 2009. (ENG., Illus.). 416p. 29.99 *(978-0-06-085589-5(4)*, Collins) HarperCollins Pubs.
Hinkelmann, Knut & Thönssen, Barbara, eds. AI for Business Agility: Papers from the AAAI Spring Symposium (SS-11-03) 2011. (Illus.). 80p. spiral bd. 30.00 ***(978-1-57735-495-6(8))*** AAAI Pr.
Hinterleitner, Gudrun. Risk Analysis in Project Management: Ventures when Going International 2008. 96p. pap. *(978-3-639-10010-5(7))* VDM Verlag Dr. Mueller e.K.
Hol, Ana. Etransformation Guide. 2009. 272p. pap. *(978-3-639-20367-7(4))* VDM Verlag Dr. Mueller e.K.
Hollender, Jeffrey & Breen, Bill. The Responsibility Revolution: How the Next Generation of Businesses Will Win. 2010. (ENG.). 240p. 27.95 *(978-0-470-55842-3(3)*, Jossey-Bass) Wiley, John & Sons, Inc.
Howson, Peter. Checklists for Due Diligence. 2008. 150p. pap. 89.95 *(978-0-566-08862-9(2)*, Gower Publishing Co., Ltd.) Ashgate Publishing, Ltd. GBR. Dist: Ashgate Publishing Co.
Hudson, Bradford T. Academies of Industry. 2008. 328p. per. *(978-3-8364-3504-8(7))* VDM Verlag Dr. Mueller e.K.
Huisman, Kuno J. M. Technology Investment: A Game Theoretic Real Options Approach: A Game Theoretic Real Options Approach. 2010. (Theory & Decision Library C Ser.). 276p. pap. 209.00 *(978-1-4419-4911-0(9)*, 1441949119) Springer.
Information Resources Management Association Staff, contrib. by. Green Technologies: Concepts, Methodologies, Tools & Applications. 2010. 1624p. 1845.00 *(978-1-60960-472-1(5))* IGI Global.
João, Maggie. 101 FAQs about Coaching: Everything You Need to know about Coaching to Improve your Practice & Grow Your Business. 2011. 248p. pap. 25.85 ***(978-1-4567-7398-4(4))*** AuthorHouse.
Johnson, C. Neal. Business as Mission: A Comprehensive Guide to Theory & Practice. 2009. (ENG.). 528p. pap. 35.00 *(978-0-8308-3865-3(1)*, IVP Acad.) InterVarsity Pr.
Johnstone. Environmental Policy & Corporate Behaviour. 2007. (Illus.). 288p. (C). 145.00 *(978-1-84720-032-7(X))* Elgar, Edward Publishing, Inc.
Jolly, Adam. Clean Tech Clean Profits: Using Effective Innovation & Sustainable Business Practices to Win in the New Low-Carbon Economy. 2010. (Illus.). xii, 239p. E-Book *(978-0-7494-6118-3(7))* Kogan Page, Ltd.
—Clean Tech Clean Profits: Using Effective Innovation & Sustainable Business Practices to Win in the New Low-Carbon Economy. 2010. (ENG., Illus.). 260p. 55.00 *(978-0-7494-6117-1(9))* Kogan Page, Ltd. GBR. Dist: Ingram Pub. Services.
Jordaan, B., et al, eds. Understanding Broad-Based Black Economic Empowerment. 2010. 190p. pap. 17.50 *(978-0-7021-8187-0(0))* Gaunt, Inc.
Kalantzis, Mary & Cope, Bill, eds. The International Journal of Knowledge, Culture & Change Management: Volume 9, Number 1. 2009. 260p. 0.00 *(978-1-86335-640-4(1))* Common Ground Publishing Pty, Ltd.
Kane, Gareth. The Green Executive: Corporate Leadership in a Low Carbon Economy 2011. (ENG., Illus.). 288p. 39.95 *(978-1-84971-334-4(0))* Routledge.
—The Three Secrets of Green Business: Unlocking Competitive Advantage in a Low Carbon Economy. 2009. (ENG., Illus.). 224p. 96.00 *(978-1-84407-873-8(6))*; pap. 26.95 *(978-1-84407-874-5(4))* Routledge.
Keay, Andrew & Kosmin, Q. C. Directors' Duties. Kosmin, Leslie, ed. 2009. (ENG.). 520p. *(978-1-84661-149-0(0))* Jordan Publishing, Ltd.
Kelly, et al. BUSN (Book Only) 3rd ed. 2010. (ENG.). 288p. (C). pap. 61.95 *(978-1-4390-3963-2(1))* Cengage South-Western.
Kelly, James Floyd. Sams Teach Yourself Mint. com in 10 Minutes. 2011. (Sams Teach Yourself — Minutes Ser.). (ENG., Illus.). 216p. pap. 14.99 *(978-0-672-33566-2(2))* Sams.
Kenis, P. N., et al, eds. Temporary Organizations: Prevalence, Logic & Effectiveness. 2009. (Illus.). 304p. 137.00 *(978-1-84844-085-2(5))* Elgar, Edward Publishing, Inc.
Kennedy, Jackie. Diverse Power: From Light Bulbs to Laptops Building the Electric Co-Op. 2011. (Illus.). 239p. *(978-1-57864-677-7(4))* Donning Co. Pubs.
Kikuchi, Toru. Time Zones Communications Networks & International Trade. 2011. (Routledge Studies in the Modern World Economy Ser.). (ENG., Illus.). 232p. (C). 152.00 *(978-0-415-59312-0(3))* Routledge.
Kingsford, Mark & Vonder. Handmade Tailor-Made. 2011. (ENG & DUT., Illus.). 192p. 75.00 *(978-90-8989-353-6(9))* Lannoo Pubs./Racine.

B

Kim, Stefan, et al, eds. Multiagent Engineering: Theory & Applications in Enterprises. 2010. (International Handbooks on Information Systems Ser.). (Illus.). xiii, 626p. pap. 269.00 *(978-3-642-06848-5(0)*, 3642068480) Springer.

Klein, William A. & Ramseyer, J. Mark. Business Associations-Agency, Partnerships, LLC's & Corporations, 2009 Statutes & Rules. 2009. (Academic Statutes Ser.). 332p. pap. 32.00 *(978-1-59941-696-0(4)*, Foundation Pr.) West.

Klein, William A., et al. Agency, Partnerships, & Limited Liability Entities: Unincorporated Business Associations: Cases & Materials. 2nd ed. 2007. xix, 490p. *(978-1-59941-330-3(2)*, Foundation Pr.) West.

Kooijmans, Alex Louwe. Implementing an ESB Using IBM WebSphere Message Broker V6 & WebSphere ESB V6 on Z/OS. 2007. (Illus.). xii, 336p. pap. *(978-0-7384-8608-6(6))* IBM.

Kozolchyk, Boris & Reyes, Francisco. Latin American Company Law from a Comparative & Economic Perspective, Volume 1. 2011. ***(978-1-61163-124-1(6))*** Carolina Academic Pr.

—Latin American Company Law from a Comparative & Economic Perspective: Reshaping the Closely-Held Landscape, Volume 2. Reyes, Francisco, ed. 2011. ***(978-1-61163-125-8(4))*** Carolina Academic Pr.

Kroszner, Randall S. & Putterman, Louis, eds. The Economic Nature of the Firm: A Reader. 3rd ed. 2009. (ENG., Illus.). 398p. (C). 110.00 *(978-0-521-19394-8(X))*; pap. 39.99 *(978-0-521-14177-2(X))* Cambridge Univ. Pr.

Kupetz, Allen. The Future of Less. 2008. 16.95 *(978-1-934572-09-2(8))* Emerald Bk. Co.

Latorre, Maria C., ed. The Impact of Foreign-Owned Companies on Host Economies. 2010. (Economic Issues, Problems & Perspectives Ser.). (Illus.). xvi, 220p. 79.00 *(978-1-61668-171-5(3))* Nova Science Pubs., Inc.

Lécuyer, Christophe & Brock, David C. Makers of the Microchip: A Documentary History of Fairchild Semiconductor. 2010. (ENG., Illus.). 328p. (gr. 17). 25.95 *(978-0-262-01424-3(6))* MIT Pr.

Lee, Ryan. The Millionaire Workout. 2007. 19.95 *(978-0-9794187-0-9(4))* Okenzie Publishing.

Lingl, Paul, et al. Doing Business in a New Climate: A Guide to Measuring, Reducing & Offsetting Greenhouse Gas Emissions. 2010. (ENG., Illus.). 96p. 136.00 *(978-1-84407-907-0(4))*; pap. 39.95 *(978-1-84407-908-7(2))* Routledge.

Lopez Acevedo, Gladys & Tan, Hong. Impact Evaluation of Small & Medium Enterprise Programs in Latin America & the Caribbean. 2011. ***(978-0-8213-8776-4(6))*** World Bank Pubns.

Lourie, Bruce & Smith, Rick. Slow Death by Rubber Duck: The Secret Danger of Everyday Things. 2010. (ENG.). 336p. 25.00 *(978-1-58243-567-1(7)*, Counterpoint Pr.) Basic Bks. GBR. Dist: Perseus-PGW.

Lucas, Henry C., Jr. The Search for Survival: Lessons from Disruptive Technologies. 1 vol. 2012. 233p. 48.00 ***(978-1-4408-0277-5(7)***, A3836C) Greenwood Publishing Group, Inc.

Lund Petersen, Karen. Corporate Risk & National Security Redefined. 2011. (Routledge Advances in International Relations & Global Politics Ser.). (ENG., Illus.). 176p. (C). 120.00 *(978-0-415-57999-5(6))* Routledge.

Major Companies of Latin America & the Caribbean. 2011th ed. 2010. 1250.00 *(978-1-86099-650-4(7))* Graham & Whiteside, Ltd. GBR. Dist: Cengage Gale.

Malecki, Edward J. & Moriset, Bruno. The Digital Economy: Business Organisation, Production Processes & Regional Developments. 2008. (Illus.). 274p. 180.00 *(978-0-415-39695-0(6))*; 296p. 43.95 *(978-0-415-39696-7(4))* Routledge.

Mann, Leon & Chan, Janet, eds. Creativity & Innovation in Business & Beyond: Social Science Perspectives & Policy Implications. 2010. (ENG., Illus.). 304p. (C). 125.00 *(978-0-415-88010-7(6))* Routledge.

Mäntysaari, Petri. The Law of Corporate Finance - General Principles & EU Law Vol. 1: Cash Flow, Risk, Agency, Information. 2009. (ENG., Illus.). viii, 484p. 179.00 *(978-3-642-02749-9(0)*, 3642027490) Springer.

Marcus, Alfred, et al. Cross-Sector Leadership for the Green Economy: Integrating Research & Practice on Sustainable Enterprise. 2011. (ENG., Illus.). 352p. 120.00 ***(978-0-230-11940-6(9))*** Palgrave Macmillan.

Marer, Paul. Financial Sector Reform & Enterprise Restucturing in Hungary: Policy Study #4. 5.00 *(978-1-55813-052-4(7))* Hudson Institute.

Margot, Olivier. Lacoste Green. 2010. (ENG.). 180p. 50.00 *(978-2-7594-0477-3(3))* Assouline FRA. Dist: Perseus Distribution.

—Lacoste Navy. 2010. (ENG.). 180p. 50.00 *(978-2-7594-0479-7(X))* Assouline FRA. Dist: Perseus Distribution.

—Lacoste Red. 2010. (ENG.). 180p. 50.00 *(978-2-7594-0476-6(5))* Assouline FRA. Dist: Perseus Distribution.

—Lacoste Royal. 2010. (ENG.). 180p. 50.00 *(978-2-7594-0478-0(1))* Assouline FRA. Dist: Perseus Distribution.

Margot, Olivier, frwd. Lacoste. 2010. (ENG.). 180p. 50.00 *(978-2-7594-0455-1(2))* Assouline FRA. Dist: Perseus Distribution.

Markovic, Mirjana Radovic & Kyaruzi, Imani Silver. Women in Business: Theory, Practice & Flexible Approaches. 2010. 164p. *(978-1-906704-44-5(9))*; pap. *(978-1-906704-69-8(4))* Adonis & Abbey Publishers Ltd.

Mason, Roger. Company Articles & Company Constitution. 2011. 200p. pap. 240.00 ***(978-1-85418-752-9(X))*** Thorogood GBR. Dist: Stylus Publishing, LLC.

McCarthy, Killian. The Nature of the New Firm: Beyond the Boundaries of Organisations & Institutions. Fiolet, Maya & Dolfsma, Wilfred, eds. 2011. (Illus.). 264p. 115.00 ***(978-1-84980-393-9(5))*** Elgar, Edward Publishing, Inc.

McGowen, Jim & Kelly, Marcella. BUSN 5. 5th ed. 2012. (ENG.). 352p. pap. 64.95 ***(978-1-111-82673-4(0))*** Cengage South-Western.

McNall, Scott G., et al, eds. The Business of Sustainability: Trends, Policies, Practices, & Stories of Success, 3 vols. 2011. (Illus.). 1059p. 194.00 *(978-0-313-38494-3(0)*, A2947C) Greenwood Publishing Group, Inc.

McNall, Scott G., et al. The Business of Sustainability: Trends, Policies, Practices, & Stories of Success. 2011. E-Book ***(978-0-313-38495-0(9)***, Praeger Pubs.) Greenwood Publishing Group, Inc.

Michael, Shapiro. 50 plus one Best Franchises to Own. 2007. (ENG.). 224p. pap. *(978-1-933766-25-6(5))* Encouragement Pr., 2nd Edition, LLC.

Michel David. Creating the Future: Innovation & Performance Driven Strategic Process. 2009. 140p. pap. 13.95 *(978-1-4401-5837-7(1))* iUniverse, Inc.

Mikami, Kazuhiko. Enterprise Forms & Economic Efficiency: Capitalist, Cooperative & Government Firms. 2011. (Routledge Studies in the Modern World Economy Ser.). (ENG., Illus.). 216p. (C). 152.00 *(978-0-415-61006-3(0))* Routledge.

Miller, Carol D. Niagara Falling: Globalization in a Small Town. 2007. (ENG., Illus.). 134p. 52.50 *(978-0-7391-2168-9(5))* Lexington Bks.

Moda, Shashank. Business Organisations & Corporate Law: A Comparative, Comprehensive & Functional Approach. 2011. (Illus.). 304p. pap. 35.00 ***(978-93-80228-91-4(0))*** Global India Pubns. Pvt. Ltd. IND. Dist: Coronet Bks.

Monahan, William T. Billion Dollar Turnaround: The 3M Spinoff that Became Imation, 1 vol. 2010. 256p. 23.95 *(978-1-892538-22-2(9))* Oaklea Pr., The.

Morgan, Conway Lloyd. häfelinger + wagner design. 2010. (GER & ENG., Illus.). 164p. 65.00 *(978-3-89986-140-2(X)*, Avedition Gmbh,Csi) Continental Sales, Inc.

Murray, Erin Byers. Shucked: Life on a New England Oyster Farm. 2011. (ENG., Illus.). 368p. 25.99 *(978-0-312-68191-3(7))* St. Martin's Pr.

Naik, Anita. Kitchen Table Tycoon: How to Make It Work As a Mother & an Entrepreneur. 2010. (ENG.). 224p. pap. 14.95 *(978-0-7499-2945-9(6))* Piatkus Bks. GBR. Dist: Independent Pubs. Group.

Nair, Suku, et al. Enterprise Security: Compliance V. Competence. 2009. 250p. 39.95 *(978-0-387-74434-6(7))* Springer.

Nambisan, Satish & Sawhney, Mohanbir. The Global Brain: Your Roadmap for Innovating Faster & Smarter in a Networked World. 2007. (ENG.). 304p. pap. 34.99 *(978-0-13-706486-1(1))* Wharton Schl. Publishing.

Newman, Aaron, et al. Enterprise 2.0 Implementation: Integrate Web 2.0 Services into Your Enterprise. 2008. (ENG., Illus.). 406p. pap. 49.99 *(978-0-07-159160-7(5)*, 0071591605) McGraw-Hill Osborne.

Nichols, J. L. The Business Guide: An Outline of Business. 2007. (ENG.). 546p. 57.95 *(978-0-548-06819-9(4))* Kessinger Publishing, LLC.

Nickels, William, et al. Loose-leaf Understanding Business with UBOnline Access Card (Bb/WebCT) 9th ed. 2009. (ENG.). (C). ring bd., ring bd. 164.00 *(978-0-07-740031-6(3)*, 0077400313, McGraw-Hill/Irwin) McGraw-Hill Higher Education.

Novak, David & Boswell, John. The Education of an Accidental CEO: Lessons Learned from the Trailer Park to the Corner Office. 2009. (ENG.). 320p. pap. 15.00 *(978-0-307-45179-8(8)*, Three Rivers Pr.) Crown Publishing Group.

Nsibande, Charles. The Impact of Black Economic Empowerment on Shareprice. 2010. 144p. pap. *(978-3-8383-9225-7(6))* Lambert Academic Publishing.

Oh, Kok-Boon. Innovation & Technology Finance. Ho, Bruce Chien-Ta, ed. 2010. (Financial Institutions & Services Ser.). 129.00 *(978-1-61668-843-1(2))* Nova Science Pubs., Inc.

Oinas, Päivi. The Evolving Firm in Evolving Context: Coordinating Competences. 2006. (Routledge Studies in Global Competition Ser.). 256p. 130.00 *(978-0-415-33966-7(9))* Routledge.

O'Leary, Kevin. Cold Hard Truth: On Business, Money & Life. 2011. (ENG., Illus.). 256p. 25.99 *(978-0-385-67174-3(1)*, Doubleday Can) Doubleday Canada, Ltd. CAN. Dist: Random Hse., Inc.

Olson, Eric G. Better Green Business: Handbook for Environmentally Responsible & Profitable Business Practices. 2009. (ENG., Illus.). 264p. 39.99 *(978-0-13-701017-2(6))* Wharton Schl. Publishing.

Orengo Serra, Karen L. Empresas Puertorriqueñas a la Hora de la Integración Regional: Análisis de Casos de Las Estrategias de Internacionalización de Empresas de Capital Local Puertorriqueño en el Caribe y Centroamérica. 2007. *(978-1-59835-053-1(6)*, CBH Bks.) Cambridge BrickHouse, Inc.

Organisation for Economic Co-operation and Development. SMEs, entrepreneurship & Innovation. 2010. (Illus.). 226p. pap. 54.00 *(978-92-64-08031-7(7))* Organization for Economic Cooperation & Development.

Orts, Eric W. Rethinking the Firm: Theories of the Business Enterprise. 2012. (ENG.). 250p. 49.95 *(978-0-19-921135-7(3))* Oxford Univ. Pr., Inc.

Oswald, Gerhard & Hommel, Uwe. SAP Enterprise Support: ASAP to Run SAP. 2nd ed. 2010. (Illus.). 371p. 59.95 *(978-1-59229-349-0(2)*, SAP PR.) Galileo Pr., Inc.

Pappis, Costas P. Climate Change, Supply Chain Management & Enterprise Adaptation: Implications of Global Warming on the Economy. 2010. (Illus.). 350p. 180.00 *(978-1-61692-800-1(X)*, Information Science Reference) IGI Global.

Paracchini, Gian Luigi. The Prada Life. Shugaar, Antony, tr. 2010. (ENG.). 231p. 26.95 *(978-88-6073-723-6(0))* Baldini Castoldi Dalai Editore ITA. Dist: Independent Pubs. Group.

Parashar, Manu. 8 Steps to Building Innovating Organizations. 2007. (Response Bks.). (Illus.). 142p. (C). per. 32.95 *(978-0-7619-3559-9(2)*, B35592P) SAGE Pubns., Inc.

Pardew, Les & Slade, Brent. Think BIG! An Entrepreneur's Guide to Partnering with Large Companies. 2009. (ENG., Illus.). 216p. pap. 19.99 *(978-1-4354-5475-0(8))* Course Technology.

Park, Frances & Park, Ginger. Chocolate Chocolate: The True Story of Two Sisters, Tons of Treats, & the Little Shop That Could. 2011. (ENG.). 288p. 23.99 *(978-0-312-65293-7(3)*, Dunne, Thomas Bks.) St. Martin's Pr.

Parker, Simon, ed. The Life Cycle of Entrepreneurial Ventures. 2010. (International Handbook Series on Entrepreneurship Ser.). xviii, 585p. pap. 299.00 *(978-1-4419-4072-8(3)*, 1441940723) Springer.

PayPal Press Staff & Miller, Michael. The PayPal Official Insider Guide to Growing Your Business: Make Money the Easy Way. 2011. (PayPal Press Ser.). (ENG., Illus.). 272p. pap. 29.99 *(978-0-321-76852-0(3))* Peachpit Pr.

Pearson. International Corporate Law Compendium. 2010. ring bd. 265.00 *(978-0-7355-9514-9(3)*, Aspen Pubs.) Wolters Kluwer Law & Business.

Pearson, Robert L. Electronic Security Systems: A Manager's Guide to Evaluating & Selecting System Solutions. 2006. (ENG., Illus.). 384p. 59.95 *(978-0-7506-7999-2(9)*, Butterworth-Heinemann) Elsevier Science & Technology Bks.

Pedersen, Torben, 2nd & Asmussen, Christian Geisler, 1st. Dynamics of Globalization: Location-Specific Advantages or Liabilities of Foreignness? Devinney, Timothy, 3rd & Tihanyi, Laszlo, 4th, eds. 2011. (Advances in International Management Ser.). (Illus.). 472p. *(978-0-85724-991-3(6))* Emerald Group Publishing Ltd.

Peitz, Martin & Waldfogel, Joel. The Oxford Handbook of the Digital Economy. 2012. (Oxford Handbooks Ser.). (ENG., Illus.). 560p. 150.00 ***(978-0-19-539784-0(3))*** Oxford Univ. Pr., Inc.

Pollard, Vincent Kelly. State Capitalism, Contentious Politics & Large-Scale Social Change. 2011. 248p. *(978-90-04-19445-8(2))* BRILL.

Pollard, Vincent Kelly, ed. State Capitalism, Contentious Politics & Large-Scale Social Change. 2012. (Studies in Critical Social Sciences Ser.). (ENG., Illus.). 236p. pap. 28.00 ***(978-1-60846-208-7(0))*** Haymarket Bks.

Prabhakar, Rajiv. The Political Economy of the Company. 2013. (ENG.). 224p. 85.00 *(978-1-4039-9869-9(8))* Palgrave Macmillan.

Prentice, Robert, et al, texts. Business Environment & Concepts. 2007th ed. 2008. (ENG.). 420p. per. *(978-0-9746541-0-2(8))* Efficient Learning Systems, Inc.

Prinsloo, Paul & Stoffberg, Hennie. Climate Change: A Guide for Corporates. 2009. 180p. pap. 39.00 *(978-1-86888-564-0(X))* Unisa Press / Uitgewers GBR. Dist: International Specialized Bk. Services.

Qi, Ming, et al. Qi Ye Chuang Xin Biao Gan: Models of Enterprises Innovation. 2009. (Illus.). *(978-7-03-022720-1(4))* Science Pr.

Rademakers, Tijs & Liempd, Ron von. Activiti in Action: Executable business processes in BPMN 2. 0. 2012. (ENG.). 475p. pap. 49.99 ***(978-1-61729-012-1(2))*** Manning Pubns. Co.

Rajak, Dinah. In Good Company: An Anatomy of Corporate Social Responsibility. 2011. (ENG.). 320p. 80.00 ***(978-0-8047-7609-7(1))*** Stanford Univ. Pr.

Ramlogan, Rajendra & Persadie, Natalie. Commonwealth Caribbean Business Law. 2nd rev. ed. 2010. (Commonwealth Caribbean Law Ser.). (ENG., Illus.). 448p. 130.00 *(978-0-415-55049-9(1))* Taylor & Francis Group GBR. Dist: Taylor & Francis Group.

Ramlogan, Rajendra, et al. Commonwealth Caribbean Business Law. 2nd rev. ed. 2010. (Commonwealth Caribbean Law Ser.). (ENG., Illus.). 448p. pap. 90.00 *(978-0-415-55048-2(3))* Taylor & Francis Group GBR. Dist: Taylor & Francis Group.

Rebuilding Haiti's Competitiveness & Private Sector: Hearing Before the Subcommittee on International Monetary Policy & Trade of the Committee on Financial Services, U.S. House of Representatives, One Hundred Eleventh Congress, Second Session, March 16, 2010. 2010. (Illus.). v, 85p. *(978-0-16-086207-6(8)*, 552-070-41305-7) United States Government Printing Office.

Reddy, Prasada. Global Innovation in Emerging Economies. 2010. (ENG., Illus.). 320p. (C). 125.00 *(978-0-415-87966-8(3))* Routledge.

Reed, Kathleen, et al. Business Organizations for Paralegals. 2011. (ENG.). 528p. (C). pap. 124.80 *(978-0-13-510364-7(9)*, Prentice Hall) Prentice Hall PTR.

Richardson, Mark G. & Alfano, Salvatore. How Fit Is Your Business? A Complete Checkup & Prescription for Better Business Health. 2008. (ENG., Illus.). 215p. pap. 19.99 *(978-1-60194-019-3(X))* Advantage Media Group.

Rittgen, Peter. Enterprise Modeling & Computing with UML. 2006. (Illus.). 314p. 94.95 *(978-1-59904-174-2(X))* IGI Global.

Robb, Russell. Buying Your Own Business: Identify Opportunities, Analyze Today's Markets, Negotiate the Best Terms, Close the Deal. 2nd ed. 2008. (ENG.). 352p. pap. 12.95 *(978-1-59869-705-6(6))* Adams Media Corp.

Rodengen, Jeffrey. Commanding the Waterways: The Story of Sea Ray. 2008. (Illus.). 192p. 39.95 *(978-1-932022-33-9(3)*, Write Stuff) Write Stuff Enterprises, Inc.

Rodgers, Waymond. Biometric & Auditing Issues Addressed in a Throughput Model. 2012. 374p. ***(978-1-61735-654-4(9))***; 374p. pap. ***(978-1-61735-653-7(0))***; xi, 361p. E-Book ***(978-1-61735-655-1(7))*** Information Age Publishing, Inc.

Rosenzweig, Phil. The Halo Effect: And the Eight Other Business Delusions That Deceive Managers. 2009. (ENG.). 256p. pap. 16.00 *(978-0-7432-9126-2(3)*, Free Pr.) Free Pr.

Ross, Stephen, et al. Loose-leaf Fundamentals of Corporate Finance Alternate Edition. 10th ed. 2012. (ENG.). (C). ring bd. 163.67 ***(978-0-07-747952-7(1)***, 0077479521, McGraw-Hill/Irwin) McGraw-Hill Higher Education.

Rovell, Darren. First in Thirst: How Gatorade Turned the Science of Sweat into a Cultural Phenomenon. 2009. (ENG.). 243p. 22.00 *(978-1-4379-6598-8(9))* DIANE Publishing Co.

Rundle, Steven & Steffen, Tom A. Great Commission Companies: The Emerging Role of Business in Missions. 2nd rev. ed. 2011. (ENG.). 240p. pap. 20.00 *(978-0-8308-3827-1(9)*, IVP Bks.) InterVarsity Pr.

Sadtler, Carla. Using IBM WebSphere Message Broker As an ESB with WebSphere Process Server. 2008. (Illus.). xiv, 348p. *(978-0-7384-8554-6(3))* IBM.

Sarfaras, Sara. Die Unternehmungsgrenze: Eine Untersuchung der Auswirkungen neuerer Erscheinungsformen der Unternehmung auf die Unternehmungsgrenze und auf das Grenzmanagement. 2010. (Europäische Hochschulschriften. Reihe 5: Volks- und Betriebswirtschaft Ser.). (GER.). 162p. pap. 57.95 *(978-3-631-60301-7(0))* Lang, Peter GmbH, Europaischer Verlag der Wissenschaften DEU. Dist: Lang, Peter.

Sari, Burak. Sme Based Virtual Enterprises. 2009. 332p. pap. *(978-3-639-14163-4(6))* VDM Verlag Dr. Mueller e.K.

Sauter, Joachim, et al. Art+com: Media Spaces & Installations. 2011. (ENG., Illus.). 256p. 60.00 ***(978-3-89955-285-0(7))*** Die Gestalten Verlag DEU. Dist: Prestel Publishing.

Scheer, August-Wilhelm, et al, eds. Business Process Automation: ARIS in Practice. 2011. (ENG., Illus.). viii, 181p. pap. 69.95 *(978-3-642-05869-1(8)*, 3642058698) Springer.

Schmal, Peter Cachola. WOHA: Architektur atmet / Breathing Architecture. Busenkell, Micaela, ed. 2012. (GER & ENG., Illus.). 192p. pap. 60.00 ***(978-3-7913-5186-5(9))*** Prestel Publishing.

Seechurn, Roopesh Kumar Sharma. Barriers to Formal Training in Small & Medium Sized Enterprises. 2008. 88p. pap. *(978-3-639-10312-0(2))* VDM Verlag Dr. Mueller e.K.

Shamamian, Oscar & Ferguson, Mark. New Traditional Architecture: Ferguson & Shamamian Architects - City & Country Residences. 2011. (ENG., Illus.). 248p. 75.00 *(978-0-8478-3545-4(6))* Rizzoli International Pubns., Inc.

Shane, Scott A. From Ice Cream to the Internet. 2010. (ENG.). 256p. pap. 36.99 *(978-0-13-254689-8(2))* FT Press.

Shepard, Aaron. POD for Profit: More on the NEW Business of Self Publishing, or How to Publish Your Books with Online Book Marketing & Print on Demand by Lightning Source. 2010. 282p. pap. 15.00 *(978-0-938497-46-2(4))* Shepard Pubns.

Siedel, George & Haapio, Helena. Proactive Law for Managers: Hidden Source of Competitive Advantage. 2010. (Illus.). 192p. 79.95 *(978-1-4094-0100-1(6)*, Gower Publishing Co., Ltd.) Ashgate Publishing, Ltd. GBR. Dist: Ashgate Publishing Co.

Sigerstad, Thomas. Slack & Munificence. 2008. 224p. pap. *(978-3-639-08471-9(3))* VDM Verlag Dr. Mueller e.K.

Simmons, P. J. & Esty, Daniel C. The Green to Gold Business Playbook: How to Implement Sustainability Practices for Bottom-Line Results in Every Business Function. 2011. (ENG., Illus.). 440p. 27.95 *(978-0-470-59075-1(0)*, Wiley) Wiley, John & Sons, Inc.

Sinofsky, Steven & Iansiti, Marco. One Strategy: Organization, Planning, & Decision Making. 2009. (ENG., Illus.). 304p. 39.95 *(978-0-470-56045-7(2)*, Wiley) Wiley, John & Sons, Inc.

Smith, Rick & Lourie, Bruce. Slow Death by Rubber Duck: The Secret Danger of Everyday Things. 2011. (ENG.). 352p. pap. 15.95 *(978-1-58243-702-6(5)*, Counterpoint) Counterpoint LLC.

Smitha, Elaine. Screwing Mother Nature for Profit: How Corporations Betray Our Trust - & Why the New Biology Offers an Ethical & Sustainable Future. 2011. (ENG.). 256p. pap. 19.95 *(978-1-78028-018-9(1)*, Watkins Publishing) Duncan Baird Pubs. GBR. Dist: Sterling Publishing Co., Inc.

Smolen, Dan. Tailoring the Green Suit: Empowering Yourself for an Executive Career in the New Green Economy. 2011. 136p. pap. 13.99 *(978-1-4490-5979-8(1))* AuthorHouse.

Spadaccini, Michael. Business Structures: How to Form a Corporation, LLC, Partnership, or Sole Proprietorship. 2007. (ENG.). 304p. 32.95 *(978-1-59918-136-3(3)*, 1599181363) Entrepreneur Pr. dba Entrepreneur Media, Inc.

—The Operations Manual for Corporations. 2007. (ENG.). 304p. 32.95 *(978-1-59918-146-2(0)*, 1599181460) Entrepreneur Pr. dba Entrepreneur Media, Inc.

Spector, Robert & McCarthy, Patrick D. The Nordstrom Way to Customer Service Excellence: The Handbook for Becoming the 'Nordstrom' of Your Industry. 2nd ed. 2012. (ENG.). 240p. pap. 19.95 ***(978-1-118-07667-5(2)***, Wiley) Wiley, John & Sons, Inc.

Stachniak, Zbigniew. Inventing the PC: The MCM/70 Story. 2011. (ENG., Illus.). 224p. (C). *(978-0-7735-3852-8(6))* McGill-Queen's Univ. Pr.

Stan. How to Promote Your Business with Little or No Money. 2010. 244p. pap. 19.95 *(978-1-4490-6695-6(X))* AuthorHouse.

Starling, Felipe, et al, eds. Broad Horizons / Larges Horizons: ADPI Architecture & Engineering. 2011. (ENG., Illus.). 176p. 49.95 *(978-1-907317-15-6(5))* Black Dog Publishing Ltd. GBR. Dist: Perseus Distribution.

Steffy, Loren C. Drowning in Oil: Bp & the Reckless Pursuit of Profit. 2010. (ENG., Illus.). 256p. 27.00 *(978-0-07-176081-2(4)*, 0071760814) McGraw-Hill Cos., The.

Steiner, Matthias. Building Extensible Composite Applications with SAP. 2009. (Illus.). 205p. pap. 84.95 *(978-1-59229-287-5(9)*, SAP PR.) Galileo Pr., Inc.

Strasser, Kurt A. Myths & Realities of Business Environmentalism: Good Works, Good Business or Greenwash? 2011. (New Horizons in Environmental & Energy Law Ser.). 224p. 99.95 ***(978-1-84980-066-2(9))*** Elgar, Edward Publishing, Inc.

Sukati, Inda & Bakar Abdul Hamid, Abu. A Study of Firm Integration & Supply Chain Orientation. 2011. 184p. pap. ***(978-3-8443-9734-5(5))*** Lambert Academic Publishing.

Sun, Heshan. Adaptive It Use. 2008. 184p. pap. *(978-3-639-06909-9(9))* VDM Verlag Dr. Mueller e.K.

Sundbo, Jon & Toivonen, Marja. User-Based Innovation in Services. 2012. (Illus.). 432p. 175.00 ***(978-0-85793-195-5(4))*** Elgar, Edward Publishing, Inc.

Sungau, Joseph. Assessment of Financial Forecasting Practices in Smes in Tanzani. 2010. 56p. pap. *(978-3-639-24363-5(3))* VDM Verlag Dr. Mueller e.K.

Teece & Teece, David J. Technological Know-How, Organizational Capabilities, & Strategic Management: Business Strategy & Enterprise Development in Competitive Environments. 2007. (Illus.). 280p. 107.00 *(978-981-256-850-2(6))* World Scientific Publishing Co., Inc.

ter Hofstede, Arthur H. M., et al, eds. Modern Business Process Automation: YAWL & its Support Environment. 2009. (ENG., Illus.). xviii, 676p. 99.00 *(978-3-642-03120-5(X)*, 364203120X) Springer.

Terterov, Marat & Shoult, Anthony. Doing Business with the United Arab Emirates. 2nd rev. ed. 2006. (Global Market Briefings Ser.). (ENG., Illus.). 238p. 115.00 *(978-1-905050-05-5(4)*, GMB Publishing Ltd.) Blue Ibex Ltd. GBR. Dist: Ingram Pub. Services.

Tewodros, Abera Belay. The Effect of Working Capital Policies on Firms' Profitability: The Effect of Working Capital Policies on Firms' Profitability: Evidence from Manufacturing Private Limited Companies in Tigray Region, Ethiopia. 2011. 84p. pap. ***(978-3-639-32495-2(1))*** VDM Verlag Dr. Mueller e.K.

Thompson, Donald H. Castleton, Vermont: Its Industries, Enterprises & Eateries. 2010. (Illus.). 160p. pap. 19.99 *(978-1-60949-096-6(7))* History Pr., The.

Tierney, Gerard. The Public Perception of Auctioneers. 2010. 88p. pap. *(978-3-639-24927-9(5))* VDM Verlag Dr. Mueller e.K.

Tisbury, Jason. 7 Steps to A Lean Business. 2010. 139p. pap. 19.95 *(978-1-4457-6871-7(2))* Lulu Enterprises Inc.

Tonchi, Stefano. The Making of - Gucci. Giannini, Frida & Frisa, Maria Luisa, eds. 2011. (ENG., Illus.). 384p. 85.00 *(978-0-8478-3679-6(7))* Rizzoli International Pubns., Inc.

Tordo, Silvana, et al. National Oil Companies & Value Creation. 2011. ***(978-0-8213-8832-7(0))*** World Bank Pubns.

Townsend, A. K. Green Business: The Five Elements of an Environmentally Responsible Company. 2006. (Illus.). 188p. 29.95 *(978-0-7643-2503-8(5))* Schiffer Publishing, Ltd.

Tracy, Brandon S., et al. National Oil Companies & Value Creation. 2011. (World Bank Working Papers: 218). (ENG.). 144p. pap. 25.00 ***(978-0-8213-8831-0(2)***, 9780821388310) World Bank Pubns.

Tran, Truongsinh & Hoang, Chi-Trung. Information System Adoption. 2011. 104p. pap. ***(978-3-8433-7296-1(9))*** Lambert Academic Publishing.

Tueth, Mattew W. Fundamentals of Sustainable Business: A Guide for the Next 100 Years. 2009. (Illus.). 228p. 58.00 *(978-981-283-932-9(1))* World Scientific Publishing Co., Inc.

Uhrig, John. The Little Book with Big Impact for Day Spas - How to Create Instant Client Promotions & Sales Letters. 2008. 186p. pap. 19.96 *(978-1-4357-0842-6(3))* Lulu Enterprises Inc.

Unhelkar, Bhuvan. Green it Strategies & Applications: Using Environmental Intelligence. 2011. (Advanced & Emerging Communications Technologies Ser.). (ENG., Illus.). 480p. 79.95 *(978-1-4398-3780-1(5)*, CRC Press) Taylor & Francis Group GBR. Dist: Taylor & Francis Group.

Unhelkar, Bhuvan, ed. Handbook of Research on Green Ict: Technology, Business & Social Perspectives, 2 vols. 2010. 900p. 475.00 *(978-1-61692-834-6(4)*, Information Science Reference) IGI Global.

Uphill, Kevin & McMillan, Alex. Buying & Selling a Business for Wealth. 2007. (Illus.). 262p. per. 38.95 *(978-1-85418-394-1(X))* Thorogood GBR. Dist: Stylus Publishing, LLC.

van Bommel, Patrick, et al, eds. The Practice of Enterprise Modeling: Third IFIP WG 8. 1 Working Conference, PoEM 2010, Delft, the Netherlands, November 9-10, 2010, Proceedings. 2010. (Lecture Notes in Business Information Processing Ser.). x, 247p. pap. 94.00 *(978-3-642-16781-2(0)*, 3642167810) Springer.

Van den Branden, Cris & Feldheim, Richard. Form 1120: A Practical Guide. 169.00 incl. audio *(978-0-88128-369-3(X)*, CPE2000) Bisk Education, Inc.

Vault Employer Profile: Proctor & Gamble. pap. *(978-1-58131-260-7(1))* Vault.com.

Veblen, Tom. The Way of Business Revised Edition, vol. 2011. pap. 19.99 ***(978-0-9829273-3-5(9))*** IGI Pr.

Venhoeven, Ton. The Wonderful World of VenhoevenCS Architects. 2009. (Illus.). 296p. *(978-90-5973-073-1(9))* Episode Pubs.

Venkler, Cynthia S. Business Beginnings. 2008. 132p. pap. 14.99 *(978-1-60647-592-8(4))* Xulon Pr., Inc.

Vesterinen, Johanna. Equity Markets & Firm Innovation in Interaction. 2010. 204p. pap. *(978-3-639-22555-6(4))* VDM Verlag Dr. Mueller e.K.

Von Staden Staff. Business - Government Relations in Prewar Japan. 2007. (Routledge Studies in the Modern History of Asia Ser.). (ENG., Illus.). 208p. (C). 158.00 *(978-0-415-39903-6(3))* Routledge.

Warren Hill, Laura & Rabig, Julia, eds. The Business of Black Power: Community Development, Capitalism, & Corporate Responsibility in Postwar America. 2012. (Illus.). 336p. 85.00 ***(978-1-58046-403-1(3))*** Univ. of Rochester Pr.

Wayland, Peter A., ed. The AIG Debacle: Global Impact & the Need for Government Intervention. 2010. (Global Economic Studies). 115.00 *(978-1-60741-990-7(4))* Nova Science Pubs., Inc.

Weiss, Alan. Million Dollar Consulting Proposals: How to Write a Proposal That's Accepted Every Time. 2011. (ENG., Illus.). 212p. pap. 24.95 ***(978-1-118-09753-3(X)***, Wiley) Wiley, John & Sons, Inc.

West. High Court Case Summaries on Business Associations, Keyed to Klein. 7th rev. ed. 2010. (High Court Case Summaries Ser.). 336p. 38.00 *(978-0-314-26565-4(1)*, West Legalworks) West.

Wheeler, Evan. Security Risk Management: Building an Information Security Risk Management Program from the Ground Up. 2011. (ENG., Illus.). 360p. pap. 49.95 *(978-1-59749-615-5(4)*, Syngress Press) Elsevier Science & Technology Bks.

Wilkinghoff, Steve. Found Money: Simple Strategies for Uncovering the Hidden Profit & Cash Flow in Your Business. 2009. (ENG., Illus.). 224p. 21.95 *(978-0-470-45335-0(0)*, Wiley) Wiley, John & Sons, Inc.

Willard, Bob. The New Sustainability Advantage: Seven Business Case Benefits of a Triple Bottom Line. 10th ed. 2012. (ENG., Illus.). 224p. pap. 19.95 ***(978-0-86571-712-1(5)***, 9780865717121) New Society Pubs., Ltd. CAN. Dist: Consortium Bk. Sales & Distribution.

Willard, Bob. The Sustainability Champion's Guidebook: How to Transform Your Company. 2009. (ENG., Illus.). 144p. pap. 19.95 *(978-0-86571-658-2(7)*, 9780865716582) New Society Pubs., Ltd. CAN. Dist: Consortium Bk. Sales & Distribution.

Winkler, Greg. Green Facilities: Industrial & Commercial LEED Certification (GreenSource) 2011. (ENG., Illus.). 256p. 80.00 *(978-0-07-174453-9(3)*, 0071744533) McGraw-Hill Professional Publishing.

Winkler, Matthew. The Bloomberg Way: A Guide for Reporters & Editors. 12th ed. 2011. (Bloomberg Ser.: 149). (ENG., Illus.). 376p. pap. 45.00 ***(978-1-118-03017-2(6)***, Bloomberg Pr.) Wiley, John & Sons, Inc.

World Bank Staff. Doing Business 2007: How to Reform. 2007th rev. ed. 2006. (Doing Business Ser.). (ENG., Illus.). 185p. per. 35.00 *(978-0-8213-6488-8(X)*, 9780821364888) World Bank Pubns.

—Doing Business 2011. 2010. (Doing Business Ser.). (ENG., Illus.). 264p. pap. 35.00 *(978-0-8213-7960-8(7)*, 9780821379608) World Bank Pubns.

Zemlianskii, O. A. Formirovanie Stoimosti Sobstvennosti Promyshlennykh Predpriiatii: Monografiia. 2009. (RUS., Illus.). 144p. *(978-5-215-02231-3(3))* Guu Pr.

BUSINESS ENTERPRISES—COMPUTER NETWORK RESOURCES

Alba, Jason. I'm on Linkedin — Now What??? A Guide to Getting the Most Out of Linkedin. 2011. 154p. pap. 19.95 ***(978-1-60005-197-5(9))*** Happy About.

Baskin, Jonathan Salem. Branding Only Works on Cattle: The New Way to Get Known (and drive your competitors Crazy) 2009. (ENG.). 272p. pap. 16.99 *(978-0-446-17802-0(0)*, Business Plus) Grand Central Publishing.

Bijl, Dik. Anytime, Anyplace: The New Way of Working. 2009. (ENG.). 224p. pap. 24.99 *(978-0-7356-2534-1(4))* Microsoft Pr.

Brunsdon, Terri J., et al. Introduction to Microsoft Dynamics GP 10.0: Focus on Internal Controls. 2nd ed. 2009. (ENG.). 600p. (C). pap. 77.33 *(978-0-13-609804-1(5)*, Prentice Hall) Prentice Hall PTR.

Chaffey, Dave & Smith, Paul. EMarketing EXcellence: Planning & optimising your digital Marketing. 3rd rev. ed. 2008. (ENG., Illus.). 528p. (C). pap. 58.95 *(978-0-7506-8945-8(5))* Routledge.

Cram101 Textbook Reviews Staff. Outlines & Highlights for E-Business & E-Commerce Management by Chaffey, Isbn: 1405847069. 2008. 140p. pap. 11.95 *(978-1-4288-6372-9(9))* Cram101 Inc.

Elwins, Dannie. How to Think Like Successful Internet Entrepreneurs. 2009. 40p. pap. 16.99 *(978-0-557-15707-5(2))* Lulu Enterprises Inc.

Fung, Victor K., et al. Competing in a Flat World: Building Enterprises for a Borderless World. 2007. (ENG.). 272p. pap. 29.99 *(978-0-13-261818-2(4))* Wharton Schl. Publishing.

Gengatharen, Denise. Government Sponsored Online Platforms for Smes. 2008. 336p. pap. *(978-3-639-05866-6(6))* VDM Verlag Dr. Mueller e.K.

Hamilton, Scott. Managing Your Supply Chain using Microsoft Dynamics AX. 2007. 29.95 *(978-0-9792552-0-5(1))* Hamilton, Scott.

Hinchcliffe, Dion & Kim, Peter. Social Business by Design: Transformative Social Media Strategies for the Connected Company. 2012. (ENG.). 256p. 29.95 ***(978-1-118-27321-0(4)***, Jossey-Bass) Wiley, John & Sons, Inc.

Jones, Duane & Cunningham, Jean. Easier, Simpler, Faster: Systems Strategy for Lean IT. 2007. (ENG., Illus.). 192p. 37.95 *(978-1-56327-353-7(5))* Productivity Pr.

Jones, Peter, ed. Handbook of Hospitality Operations & IT. 2008. (ENG., Illus.). 464p. 97.95 *(978-0-7506-8753-9(3))* Routledge.

Kappelman, Leon, ed. The SIM Guide to Enterprise Architecture. 2009. (ENG., Illus.). 330p. 61.95 *(978-1-4398-1113-9(X)*, CRC Press) Taylor & Francis Group GBR. Dist: Taylor & Francis Group.

MacKenzie, Lydia. Fact or Fiction: Are U. S. -based SMEs Advanced in Use of the Internet? - U. S. -based SMEs Have Not Progessed beyond Using Promotional Web Sites to That. 2008. 212p. pap. *(978-3-639-06027-0(X))* VDM Verlag Dr. Mueller e.K.

Martin, James William. Measuring & Improving Performance: Information Technology Applications in Lean Systems. 2009. (ENG., Illus.). 280p. 51.95 *(978-1-4200-8418-4(6)*, CRC Press) Taylor & Francis Group GBR. Dist: Taylor & Francis Group.

Minoli, Dan. Enterprise Architecture A to Z: Frameworks, Business Process Modeling, SOA, & Infrastructure Technology. 2008. (ENG., Illus.). 512p. 79.95 *(978-0-8493-8517-9(2))* Auerbach Pubs., Inc.

Morgen, Robert. Ecommerce 101: The Quick & Easy, down & Dirty Guide to Starting an Online Business TODAY! 2012. per. 16.95 *(978-0-9790400-6-1(X))* Mystic Wolf Media.

Passiante, Giuseppina, ed. Evolving Towards the Internetworked Enterprise: Technological & Organizational Perspectives. 2010. (ENG., Illus.). x, 213p. 99.00 *(978-1-4419-7278-1(1)*, 1441972781) Springer.

Percival, Sean. MySpace Marketing: Creating a Social Network to Boom Your Business. 2008. (ENG., Illus.). 216p. pap. 19.99 *(978-0-7897-3709-0(4))* Que.

Prahalad, C. K. & Krishnan, M. S. The New Age of Innovation: Driving Co-Created Value Through Global Networks. 2008. (ENG., Illus.). 304p. 29.95 *(978-0-07-159828-6(6)*, 0071598286) McGraw-Hill Cos., The.

Reisinger, Thomas. E-Recruiting: Personalbeschaffung über das Internet. 2010. 116p. pap. *(978-3-639-22646-1(1))* VDM Verlag Dr. Mueller e.K.

Richardson, Bruce. The Future of Enterprise Applications. 2006. per. 19.95 *(978-0-9785928-1-3(6))* AMR Research, Inc.

Ruminer, Michael. Team Foundation Server Recipes: A Problem Solution Approach. 600p. pap. 59.99 *(978-1-59059-742-2(7))* Apress L. P.

Rushkoff, Douglas. Get Back in the Box: How Being Great at What You Do Is Great for Business. annot. ed. 2007. (ENG.). 336p. pap. 12.95 *(978-0-06-075870-7(8)*, Collins) HarperCollins Pubs.

Sampson, Michael. Seamless Teamwork: Using Microsoft SharePoint Technologies to Collaborate, Innovate, & Drive Business in New Ways. 2008. (ENG.). 304p. pap. 24.99 *(978-0-7356-2561-7(1))* Microsoft Pr.

Sautter, Ellen & Crompton, Diane. Find a Job Through Social Networking: Use LinkedIn, Twitter, Facebook, Blogs, & More to Advance Your Career. 2nd ed. 2010. 224p. pap. 14.95 *(978-1-59357-817-6(2)*, JIST Works) JIST Publishing.

Seiden, Jason & Gatti, Vincent. Beyond Social: Rethink Your LinkedIn Strategy to Convey Credibility, Connect with Resources & Get Things Done. 2011. 168p. pap. 16.95 ***(978-1-60832-188-9(6))*** Greenleaf Book Group.

Shariff, Munwar. Alfresco Enterprise Content Management I. 2006. pap. *(978-1-904811-11-4(6))* Packt Publishing, Ltd.

Snyder, Mike, et al. Programming Microsoft Dynamics CRM 4.0. 2008. (ENG.). 640p. pap. 59.99 *(978-0-7356-2594-5(8))* Microsoft Pr.

Zarrella, Dan. The Science of Marketing: When to Tweet, What to Post, How to Blog, & Other Proven Strategies. 2012. (ENG.). 240p. 24.95 ***(978-1-118-13827-4(9)***, Wiley) Wiley, John & Sons, Inc.

BUSINESS ENTERPRISES—COMPUTER NETWORKS

see also Intranets (Computer Networks)

Abbott, Martin L. & Fisher, Michael T. The Art of Scalability: Scalable Web Architecture, Processes & Organizations for the Modern Enterprise. 2009. (ENG., Illus.). 592p. pap. 39.99 *(978-0-13-703042-2(8))* Addison Wesley.

Adams, Carlisle & Lloyd, Steve. Understanding PKI: Concepts, Standards, & Deployment Considerations. 2nd ed. 2010. (ENG.). pap. 93.32 *(978-0-321-74309-1(1))* Addison Wesley Professional.

Afsarmanesh, Hamideh, et al, eds. Methods & Tools for Collaborative Networked Organizations. 2008. (ENG.). viii, 532p. 179.00 *(978-0-387-79423-5(9)*, 0387794239) Springer.

Afsarmanesh, Hamideh & Camarinha-Matos, Luis M., eds. Collaborative Networks - Reference Modeling. 2008. (ENG., Illus.). vii, 336p. 149.00 *(978-0-387-79425-9(5)*, 0387794255) Springer.

Agrawal, Manish. Business Data Communications. 2011. (ENG., Illus.). 384p. (C). pap. 114.95 *(978-0-470-48336-7(9)*, Wiley) Wiley, John & Sons, Inc.

Akhmedjanov, Anvar. Security in Sap Netweaver 7 0 Application Server Abap. 2011. 128p. pap. ***(978-3-8443-9883-0(X))*** Lambert Academic Publishing.

Alexander, Philip. Home & Small Business Guide to Protecting Your Computer Network, Electronic Assets, & Privacy, 1 vol. 2009. (Illus.). 160p. 39.95 *(978-0-313-36007-7(3)*, C36007, Praeger Pubs.) Greenwood Publishing Group, Inc.

—Information Security: A Manager's Guide to Thwarting Data Thieves & Hackers, 1 vol. 2008. (PSI Business Security Ser.). (Illus.). 188p. 44.95 *(978-0-313-34558-6(9)*, C34558, Praeger Security International) Greenwood Publishing Group, Inc.

Allen, Paul R. & Bambara, Joseph J. SCEA Sun Certified Enterprise Architect for Java EE Study Guide (Exam 310-051) 2007. (Illus.). xxvii, 643p. *(978-0-07-148862-4(6))*; 2nd ed. *(978-0-07-148863-1(4))* McGraw-Hill Cos., The.

Aronson, Bill. Enterprise Designer - building a conscious Organization. 2008. 200p. pap. 35.95 *(978-1-4092-1624-7(1))* Lulu Enterprises Inc.

—Enterprise Designer Workbook. 2009. 264p. pap. 49.95 *(978-1-4092-3102-8(X))* Lulu Enterprises Inc.

Association for Computing Machinery (ACM) Staff, compiled by. 2nd ACM Workshop on Digital Identity Management (DIM '06) 2007. 78p. pap. 62.00 *(978-1-60423-131-1(9))* Curran Assocs., Inc.

Back, Andrea, et al, eds. Knowledge Networks for Business Growth. 2006. (ENG., Illus.). xii, 226p. 99.00 *(978-3-540-33072-1(0)*, 3540330720) Springer.

—Putting Knowledge Networks into Action: Methodology, Development, Maintenance. 2010. (ENG., Illus.). vi, 196p. pap. 89.95 *(978-3-642-07360-1(3)*, 3642073603) Springer.

Bain, Mark. Sugarcrm Developer's Manual: Customize & extend SugarCRM. 2007. 296p. per. *(978-1-84719-206-6(8))* Packt Publishing, Ltd.

Bajgoric, Nijaz, ed. Always-On Enterprise Information Systems for Business Continuance: Technologies for Reliable & Scalable Operations. 2009. 344p. 180.00 *(978-1-60566-723-2(4))* IGI Global.

Baresi, Luciano, et al. Services-Oriented Computing — ICSOC-ServiceWave 2009: 7th International Joint Conference, Stockholm, Sweden, November 24-27, 2009, Proceedings. 2009. (Lecture Notes in Computer Science / Programming & Software Engineering Ser.). (Illus.). xiv, 637p. pap. 129.00 *(978-3-642-10382-7(0)*, 3642103820) Springer.

Barlow, Mike & Thomas, David B. The Executive's Guide to Enterprise Social Media Strategy: How Social Networks Are Radically Transforming Your Business. 2011. (Wiley & SAS Business Ser.: 42). (ENG., Illus.). 204p. 45.00 *(978-0-470-88602-1(1)*, Wiley) Wiley, John & Sons, Inc.

Bayuk, Jennifer. Enterprise Security for the Executive: Setting the Tone from the Top, 1 vol. 2009. (PSI Business Security Ser.). (Illus.). 163p. 34.95 *(978-0-313-37660-3(3)*, C37660, Praeger Pubs.) Greenwood Publishing Group, Inc.

Belew, Shannon & Elad, Joel. Starting an Online Business All-in-One for Dummies. 3rd ed. 2011. (ENG., Illus.). 888p. pap. 29.99 ***(978-1-118-12319-5(0)***, For Dummies) Wiley, John & Sons, Inc.

Bell, Michael. Service-Oriented Modeling: Service Analysis, Design, & Architecture. 2008. (ENG., Illus.). 384p. 65.00 *(978-0-470-14111-3(5)*, Wiley) Wiley, John & Sons, Inc.

Benyoucef, Lyes & Grabot, Bernard, eds. Artificial Intelligence Techniques for Networked Manufacturing Enterprises Management. 2010. (Springer Series in Advanced Manufacturing Ser.). (ENG., Illus.). xxvi, 510p. 239.00 *(978-1-84996-118-9(2)*, 1849961182) Springer.

Bernus, Peter, et al, eds. Enterprise Architecture, Integration & Interoperability: IFIP TC 5 International Conference, EAI2N 2010, Held as Part of WCC 2010, Brisbane, Australia, September 20-23, 2010, Proceedings. 2010. (IFIP Advances in Information & Communication Technology Ser.). xii, 177p. 109.00 *(978-3-642-15508-6(1)*, 3642155081) Springer.

Bingham, Tony & Conner, Marcia. The New Social Learning: A Guide to Transforming Organizations Through Social Media. 2010. (ENG.). 240p. pap. 18.95 *(978-1-60509-702-2(0))* Berrett-Koehler Pubs., Inc.

Bingham, Tony & Conner, Marcia L. The New Social Learning: A Guide to Transforming Organizations Through Social Media. 2010. 256p. *(978-1-56286-720-1(2))* American Society for Training & Development.

Bond, Patrick. Communications & Networking in China: 1st International Business Conference, Chinacombiz 2008, Hangzhou China, August 2008, Revised Selected Papers. 2009. (Communications in Computer & Information Science Ser.). vi, 105p. pap. 99.00 *(978-3-642-00204-5(8))* Springer.

Bonnet, Pierre, et al. Resilient Information Systems: Progressive Recasting with SOA. 2009. (Iste Ser.: 369). (ENG., Illus.). 384p. 95.00 *(978-1-84821-089-9(2)*, Wiley-ISTE) Wiley, John & Sons, Inc.

Bose, Indranil, ed. Breakthrough Perspectives in Network & Data Communications Security, Design & Applications: Security, Design, & Applications. 2008. (Advances in Business Data Communications & Networking Book Ser.). (Illus.). 356p. 195.00 *(978-1-60566-148-3(1))* IGI Global.

Brand, Koen & Boonen, Harry. IT Governance Based on Cobit 4. 1: A Management Guide. 2008. (ITSM Library). (Illus.). 150p. pap. *(978-90-8753-116-4(8))* Van Haren Publishing.

Breitbarth, Wayne. The Power Formula for LinkedIn Success: Kick-start Your Business, Brand, & Job Search. 2011. (Illus.). 176p. pap. 16.95 *(978-1-60832-093-6(6))* Greenleaf Book Group.

Brown, William A., et al. SOA Governance: Achieving & Sustaining Business & IT Agility. 2008. (ENG., Illus.). 416p. pap. 49.99 *(978-0-13-714746-5(5))* Pearson Education.

Bücker, Axel. Deployment Guide Series. 2008. (Illus.). xii, 232p. *(978-0-7384-3210-6(5))* IBM.

—Identity Management Design Guide with IBM Tivoli Identity Manager. 4th ed. 2009. (Illus.). xvi, 682p. *(978-0-7384-3379-0(9))* IBM.

Bücker, Axel. Identity Management Design Guide with IBM Tivoli Identity Manger. 3rd ed. 2009. (Illus.). xviii, 580p. pap. ***(978-0-7384-3245-8(8))*** IBM.

Burby, Jason & Atchison, Shane. Actionable Web Analytics: Using Data to Make Smart Business Decisions. 2007. (ENG., Illus.). 288p. per. 29.99 *(978-0-470-12474-1(1)*, Sybex) Wiley, John & Sons, Inc.

Butler, Nathan, ed. Service Oriented Architecture: Implementors Guide. 2007. per. *(978-0-9799304-0-9(5))* Composite Software.

Calder, Alan & Watkins, Steve. International IT Governance: An Executive Guide to ISO 17799/ISO 27001. 2006. (Kogan Page Ser.). (ENG., Illus.). 366p. per. 80.00 *(978-0-7494-4748-9(6))* Kogan Page, Ltd. GBR. Dist: Ingram Pub. Services.

—IT Governance: A Manager's Guide to Data Security & ISO 27001/ISO 27002. 4th ed. 2008. (ENG., Illus.). 384p. pap. 90.00 *(978-0-7494-5271-1(4))* Kogan Page, Ltd. GBR. Dist: Ingram Pub. Services.

Camarinha-Matos, Luis, et al, eds. Establishing the Foundation of Collaborative Networks: IFIP TC 5 WG 5. 5 Eighth IFIP WorkingConference on Virtual Enterprises, September 10-12, 2007, Guimaraes, Portugal. 2007. (IFIP Advances in Information & Communication Technology Ser.). xiv, 689p. 139.00 ***(978-0-387-73797-3(9)***, 0387737979) Springer.

Camarinha-Matos, Luis M., ed. Virtual Enterprises & Collaborative Networks. 2012. (IFIP Advances in Information & Communication Technology Ser.). (ENG.). xiv, 609p. pap. 199.00 *(978-1-4419-5485-5(6)*, 1441954856) Springer.

Camarinha-Matos, Luis M., et al, eds. Collaborative Networks for a Sustainable World: 11th IFIP WG 5. 5 Working Conference on Virtual Enterprises, PRO-VE 2010, St. Etienne, France, October 11-13, 2010, Proceedings. 2010. (IFIP Advances in Information & Communication Technology Ser.). xx, 783p. 209.00 *(978-3-642-15960-2(5)*, 3642159605) Springer.

—Methods & Tools for Collaborative Networked Organizations. 2010. (ENG.). viii, 532p. pap. 179.00 *(978-1-4419-4637-9(3)*, 1441946373) Springer.

Carter, Sandy. The New Language of Business: Soa & Web 2. 0. 2007. (ENG., Illus.). 320p. 29.99 *(978-0-13-195654-4(X))* Pearson Education.

Cavanagh, Thomas E. Preparedness in the Private Sector. 2008. (Illus.). 31p. *(978-0-8237-0938-0(8))* Conference Board, Inc., The.

Chaffey, Dave. E-Business & E-Commerce Management: Strategy, Implementation & Practice. 2011. (ENG., Illus.). (C). 4th ed. 800p. pap. 162.67 *(978-0-273-71960-1(2))* 5th rev. ed. 768p. pap. 125.00 ***(978-0-273-75201-1(4))*** Prentice Hall PTR. (Prentice Hall).

Chaitanya, Manish. The Complete Guide to SAP NetWeaver Portal. 2012. (ENG., Illus.). 500p. 69.95 *(978-1-59229-403-9(0),* SAP PR.) Galileo Pr., Inc.

Chang, William Y. Network-Centric Service Oriented Enterprise. (ENG.). xviii, 542p. 2010. pap. 169.00 *(978-90-481-7646-5(8),* 9048176468) 2007. 169.00 *(978-1-4020-6455-5(1),* 1402064551) Springer.

Chapman, Lisa. How to Make Money Online with Social Media: A Step-by-Step Guide for Entrepreneurs. 2010. pap. 9.99 *(978-1-59652-755-3(2))* Turner Publishing Co.

Cheng, Kai. E-Engineering & Digital Enterprise Technology VII, 2 vols. Cheng, Kai et al, eds. 2009. (Applied Mechanics & Materials Ser.: Vol. 19). (Illus.). 1470p. pap. *(978-0-87849-299-2(2))* Trans Tech Pubns., Ltd.

Chilanti, Michele, et al. WebSphere Business Integration Primer: Process Server, BPEL, SCA & SOA. 2007. (DeveloperWorks Ser.). (ENG., Illus.). 456p. per. 54.99 *(978-0-13-224831-0(X))* Pearson Education.

Cisco Networking Academy. Course Booklet for CCNA Discovery Working at a Small-to-Medium Business or ISP, Version 4. 1. 2009. (ENG.). 192p. (C). pap. 24.95 *(978-1-58713-253-7(2))* Cisco Pr.

Coelhas, Helder & Saramago, Mónica, eds. E-Business & Telecommunication Networks. 2007. (Communications in Computer & Information Science Ser.). (Illus.). 292p. per. 79.95 *(978-3-540-75992-8(1))* Springer.

Cohen, Sharon L. & Blozis, Dana. Yahoo Income: How Anyone of Any Age, Location, And/Or Background Can Build a Highly Profitable Online Business with Yahoo. 2009. (ENG.). 336p. per. 24.95 *(978-1-60138-254-2(5))* Atlantic Publishing Co.

Consumer Dummies Staff, et al. Starting an Etsy Business for Dummies. 2011. (ENG.). 384p. pap. 19.99 *(978-0-470-93067-0(5),* For Dummies) Wiley, John & Sons, Inc.

Cramm, Susan. 8 Things We Hate about IT: How to Move Beyond the Frustrations to Form a New Partnership with IT. 2010. (ENG., Illus.). 208p. pap. 16.95 *(978-1-4221-3166-4(1))* Harvard Business Review Pr.

Cram101 Textbook Reviews. Outlines & Highlights for Business Data Networks & Telecommunications by Raymond R Panko. 2011. 72p. pap. 27.95 ***(978-1-61906-155-2(4))*** Cram101 Inc.

Cram101 Textbook Reviews & Cram101 Textbook Reviews. Outlines & Highlights for Business Data Communications by Manish Agrawal, Isbn: 9780470483367. 2011. 132p. pap. 28.95 ***(978-1-61461-308-4(7))*** Cram101 Inc.

—Outlines & Highlights for Business Data Networks & Telecommunications by Raymond Panko, Isbn: 0136100120 9780136100126. 2011. 452p. pap. 36.95 ***(978-1-61461-561-3(6))*** Cram101 Inc.

—Outlines & Highlights for Managing & Using Information Systems by Keri E Pearlson, Isbn: 9780470343814 0470343818. 2011. 226p. pap. 30.95 ***(978-1-61490-782-4(X))*** Cram101 Inc.

—Outlines & Highlights for Working at a Small-to-Medium Business or Isp: CCNA Discovery Learning Guide by Allan Reid, ISBN. 2011. 142p. pap. 28.95 ***(978-1-61490-464-9(2))*** Cram101 Inc.

Cram101 Textbook Reviews Staff. Outlines & Highlights for Electronic Commerce by Gary Schneider, Isbn: 9781423903055. 2009. 206p. pap. 30.95 *(978-1-4288-4197-0(0));* 172p. pap. 29.95 *(978-1-4288-7637-8(5))* Cram101 Inc.

Cunha, Pedro Filipe & Maropoulos, Paul G., eds. Digital Enterprise Technology: Perspectives & Future Challenges. 2010. (ENG., Illus.). xviii, 593p. pap. 195.00 *(978-1-4419-4322-4(6),* 1441943226) Springer.

Dang, Minh Quan. A Framework for Sla-Aware Execution of Grid-Based Workflows. 2008. 184p. pap. *(978-3-8364-8875-4(2))* VDM Verlag Dr. Mueller e.K.

Davies, Saida. Migrating IBM WebSphere Business Integration Server Foundation to WebSphere Process Server V6.1. 2008. (Illus.). xxii, 348p. *(978-0-7384-3169-7(9))* IBM.

Dawson, Ross. Living Networks: Leading Your Company, Customers, & Partners in the Hyper-Connected Economy. anniv. ed. 2008. (Illus.). 247p. pap. 24.95 *(978-1-84799-560-5(8))* Lulu Enterprises Inc.

Demirkan, Haluk, et al, eds. Service Systems Implementation. 2011. (Service Science: Research & Innovations in the Service Economy Ser.). (ENG., Illus.). xxvi, 307p. 99.00 *(978-1-4419-7903-2(4),* 1441979034) Springer.

Di Nitto, Elisabetta, et al, eds. At Your Service: Service-Oriented Computing from an EU Perspective. 2009. (Cooperative Information Systems Ser.). (ENG., Illus.). 576p. (gr. 17). 60.00 *(978-0-262-04253-6(3))* MIT Pr.

Draheim, Dirk. Trends in Enterprise Application Architecture. 2007. (Lecture Notes in Computer Science / Information Systems & Applications, incl. Internet/Web, & HCI Ser.). spiral bd. 79.95 *(978-3-540-75911-9(5))* Springer.

EC-Council. Penetration Testing Bk. 2: Procedures & Methodologies. 2010. (EC-Council Certified Security Analyst (ECSA) Ser.). (ENG.). 256p. pap. 58.95 *(978-1-4354-8367-5(7))* Course Technology.

El-Ghareeb, Haitham. Evaluation of Service Oriented Architecture in E-Learning. 2010. 176p. pap. *(978-3-8383-5538-2(5))* Lambert Academic Publishing.

Elad, Joel. Linkedin for Dummies. 2nd ed. 2011. (ENG., Illus.). 384p. pap. 24.99 *(978-0-470-94854-5(X),* For Dummies) Wiley, John & Sons, Inc.

Erl, Thomas, et al. Soa Governance: Governing Shared Services On-Premise & in the Cloud. 2011. (Prentice Hall Service-Oriented Computing Series from Thomas Erl Ser.). (ENG., Illus.). 704p. 49.99 *(978-0-13-815675-6(1))* Prentice Hall PTR.

Evans, Dave. Social Media Marketing: The Next Generation of Business Engagement. 2010. (ENG., Illus.). 408p. pap. 29.99 *(978-0-470-63403-5(0),* Sybex) Wiley, John & Sons, Inc.

Fairchild, Alea M. Technological Aspects of Virtual Organizations: Enabling the Intelligent Enterprise. 2010. (Illus.). xii, 164p. pap. 149.00 *(978-90-481-6477-6(X),* 904816477X) Springer.

Fajardo, Jose & Dustin, Elfriede. Testing SAP R/3: A Manager's Step-by-Step Guide. 2007. (ENG.). 400p. 84.50 *(978-0-470-05573-1(1),* Wiley) Wiley, John & Sons, Inc.

Fiammante, Marc. Dynamic SOA & BPM: Best Practices for Business Process Management & SOA Agility. 2009. (ENG., Illus.). 216p. 39.99 *(978-0-13-701891-8(6))* Pearson Education.

Fischer-Hübner, Simone, et al. Trust & Privacy in Digital Business: Third International Conference, TrustBus 2006, Krakow, Poland, September 4-8, 2006, Proceedings. 2006. (Lecture Notes in Computer Science Ser.: Vol. 4083). (Illus.). XIII, 243p. pap. 69.95 *(978-3-540-37750-4(6),* 3540377506) Springer.

—Trust, Privacy & Security in Digital Business: 6th International Conference, TrustBus 2009, Linz, Austria, September 3-4, 2009, Proceedings. 2009. (Lecture Notes in Computer Science / Security & Cryptology Ser.). xii, 169p. pap. 64.95 *(978-3-642-03747-4(X),* 364203747X) Springer.

Fischer, Klaus, et al. Agent-Based Technologies & Applications for Enterprise Interoperability: International Workshops, ATOP 2005, Utrecht, the Netherlands, July 25-26, 2005, & ATOP 2008, Estoril, Portugal, May 12-13, 2008, Revised Selected Papers. 2009. (Lecture Notes in Business Information Processing Ser.). x, 257p. pap. 69.95 *(978-3-642-01667-7(7))* Springer.

Fishman, Neal & Whitecar, Don. Viral Data in SOA: An Enterprise Pandemic. 2009. (ENG., Illus.). 288p. pap. 39.99 *(978-0-13-700180-4(0))* Pearson Education.

Fitzgerald, Todd. Information Security Governance Simplified. 2011. (ENG., Illus.). 431p. 79.95 ***(978-1-4398-1163-4(6),*** CRC Press) Taylor & Francis Group GBR. Dist: Taylor & Francis Group.

Fitzsimmons, James & Fitzsimmons, Mona. Service Management with Premium Content Access Card. 7th ed. 2010. (ENG.). (C). 211.67 *(978-0-07-742697-2(5),* 0077426975, McGraw-Hill/Irwin) McGraw-Hill Higher Education.

Foreman, Park. Vulnerability Management. 2009. (ENG., Illus.). 347p. 79.95 *(978-1-4398-0150-5(9))* Auerbach Pubs., Inc.

Forney, Kristine, et al. The Digital Innovation Playbook: Creating a Transformative Customer Experience. 2011. (ENG., Illus.). 270p. 49.95 *(978-0-470-94470-7(6),* Wiley) Wiley, John & Sons, Inc.

Foster, Mike. The Secure CEO: How to Protect Your Computer Systems, Your Company, & Your Job. 2007. 150p. 27.00 *(978-0-9715578-0-2(2),* Prime Concepts Publishing) Prime Concepts Group Pr.

Fulford, Richard. Managing Operational Enterprise Resource Planning Applications. 2009. (Illus.). 304p. pap. *(978-3-639-13983-9(6))* VDM Verlag Dr. Mueller e.K.

Furnell, Steven, et al, eds. Trust, Privacy & Security in Digital Business: 8th International Conference, TrustBus 2011, Toulouse, France, August 29 - September 2, 2011, Proceedings. 2011. (Lecture Notes in Computer Science / Security & Cryptology Ser.). (Illus.). xi, 222p. pap. 72.00 ***(978-3-642-22889-6(5),*** 3642228895) Springer.

Gabhart, Kyle & Bhattacharya, Bibhas. Service Oriented Architecture Field Guide for Executives. 2008. (ENG., Illus.). 228p. 49.95 *(978-0-470-26091-3(2),* Wiley) Wiley, John & Sons, Inc.

Gallaher, Michael P., et al. Cyber Security: Economic Strategies & Public Policy Alternatives. 2008. (Illus.). 288p. (C). 124.00 *(978-1-84720-355-7(8))* Elgar, Edward Publishing, Inc.

Gary Doucet, John Gotze, et al. Coherency Management: Architecting the Enterprise for Alignment, Agility & Assurance. 2009. 544p. pap. 23.99 *(978-1-4389-9606-6(3))* AuthorHouse.

Gelinas and Sut, Fedorowicz. Business Processes & Information Techn. 2006. pap. 11.95 *(978-1-4288-0805-8(1))* Cram101 Inc.

Gelinas, Ulric J., Jr., et al. Business Processes & Information Technology. 2010. (ENG.). 952p. (C). pap. 53.00 *(978-1-61610-146-6(6))* Orange Grove Bks.

Gentile, Michael, et al. CISO Soft Skills: Securing Organizations Impaired by Employee Politics, Apathy, & Intolerant Perspectives. 2008. (ENG., Illus.). 288p. 69.95 *(978-1-4200-8910-3(2))* Auerbach Pubs., Inc.

Georgakopoulos, Dimitrios, et al. Service-Oriented Computing ICSOC 2006: 4th International Conference, Chicago, Il, USA, December 4-7, 2006, Workshop Proceedings. 2007. (Lecture Notes in Computer Science / Programming & Software Engineering Ser.). 200p. pap. 69.95 *(978-3-540-75491-6(1))* Springer.

Gotze, John, et al. Coherency Management: Architecting the Enterprise for Alignment, Agility & Assurance. 2009. (Illus.). 544p. 34.99 *(978-1-4389-9607-3(1))* AuthorHouse.

Gowel, Dave. The Power in a Link: Open Doors, Close Deals, & Change the Way You Do Business Using Linkedin. 2011. (ENG., Illus.). 169p. pap. 19.95 ***(978-1-118-13467-2(2),*** Wiley) Wiley, John & Sons, Inc.

Grabis, Janis & Kirikova, Marite, eds. Perspectives in Business Informatics Research: 10th International Conference, BIR 2011, Riga, Latvia, October 6-8, 2011, Proceedings. 2011. (Lecture Notes in Business Information Processing Ser.). (ENG.). xv, 355p. pap. 83.00 ***(978-3-642-24510-7(2),*** 3642245102) Springer.

Graham, Ian. Requirements Modelling & Specification for Service Oriented Architecture. 2008. (ENG., Illus.). 320p. pap. 65.00 *(978-0-470-77563-9(7),* Wiley) Wiley, John & Sons, Inc.

Graves, Tom. Real Enterprise Architecture. 2008. (Illus.). 135p. pap. ***(978-1-906681-00-5(7))*** Tetradian Bks.

Guerin, Lisa. Smart Policies for Workplace Technologies: Email, Blogs, Cell Phones & More. 2nd ed. 2011. E-Book *(978-1-4133-1352-9(3))* NOLO.

—Smart Policies for Workplace Technology: Email, Blogs, Cell Phones & More, 2 vols. 2nd rev. ed. 2011. (ENG.). 240p. pap. 34.99 *(978-1-4133-1326-0(4))* NOLO.

Gupta, Manish, et al, eds. Threats, Countermeasures & Advances in Applied Information Security. 2012. 421p. 195.00 ***(978-1-4666-0978-5(8),*** Information Science Reference) IGI Global.

Gupta, Manish, et al. Threats, Countermeasures & Advances in Applied Information Security. 2012. ***(978-1-4666-0980-8(X))*** IGI Global.

Gurnani, Anil. Web Development with TIBCO General Interface: Building AJAX Clients for Enterprise SOA. 2009. (Developer's Library). (ENG., Illus.). 384p. pap. 39.99 *(978-0-321-56329-3(8))* Addison Wesley Professional.

Halpert, Ben. Auditing Cloud Computing: A Security & Privacy Guide. 2011. (Wiley Corporate F&a Ser.: 21). (ENG., Illus.). 206p. 65.00 *(978-0-470-87474-5(0),* Wiley) Wiley, John & Sons, Inc.

Hanna, Nagy. Enabling Enterprise Transformation: Business & Grassroots Innovation for the Knowledge Economy. 2010. (Illus.). x, 314p. *(978-1-4419-1508-5(7))* Springer.

Hanna, Nagy K. Enabling Enterprise Transformation: Business & Grassroots Innovation for the Knowledge Economy. (Innovation, Technology, & Knowledge Management Ser.). (Illus.). ix, 311p. 2010. pap. 49.95 *(978-1-4419-7844-8(5),* 1441978445) 2009. (ENG.). 139.00 *(978-1-4419-1507-8(9),* 1441915079) Springer.

Harrington, Jan L. Ethernet Networking for the Small Office & Professional Home Office. 2007. (ENG., Illus.). 352p. per. 43.95 *(978-0-12-373744-1(3),* Morgan Kaufmann) Elsevier Science & Technology Bks.

Hartenauer, Jörg. Introduction to Business Intelligence: Concepts & Tools. 2007. 92p. per. *(978-3-8364-1806-5(1))* VDM Verlag Dr. Mueller e.K.

Hartley, Darin. 10 Steps to Successful Social Networking for Business. 2010. (ENG.). 225p. pap. 19.95 *(978-1-56286-717-1(2))* American Society for Training & Development.

Hausman, Kirk, ed. Sustainable Enterprise Architecture. 2011. (ENG., Illus.). 304p. 79.95 *(978-1-4398-2154-1(2),* CRC Press) Taylor & Francis Group GBR. Dist: Taylor & Francis Group.

Heilig, Loren. Understanding SAP NetWeaver Identity Management. 2010. (Illus.). 300p. 69.95 *(978-1-59229-338-4(7),* SAP PR.) Galileo Pr., Inc.

Heilig, Loren, et al. SAP NetWeaver BW & SAP BusinessObjects: The Comprehensive Guide. 2011.Tr. of SAP NetWeaver BW — das umfassende Handbuch. (ENG., Illus.). 850p. 79.95 *(978-1-59229-384-1(0),* SAP PR.) Galileo Pr., Inc.

Hewitt, Eben. Java SOA Cookbook. 2009. (ENG., Illus.). 742p. pap. 49.99 *(978-0-596-52072-4(7))* O'Reilly Media, Inc.

Hirao, Joey & Wun-Young, Leslie. SAP Security Configuration & Deployment: The IT Administrator's Guide to Best Practices. 2008. (ENG., Illus.). 392p. pap. 72.95 *(978-1-59749-284-3(1),* Syngress Press) Elsevier Science & Technology Bks.

Holden, Greg. Starting an Online Business for Dummies. 6th ed. 2010. (ENG., Illus.). 432p. pap. 24.99 *(978-0-470-60210-2(4),* For Dummies) Wiley, John & Sons, Inc.

Holloman, Christer. The Social Media MBA: Your Competitive Edge in Social Media Strategy Development & Delivery. 2nd ed. 2012. (ENG., Illus.). 276p. 27.95 ***(978-1-119-96323-3(0),*** Wiley) Wiley, John & Sons, Inc.

Honzal, Benjamin. Web Technologies in the Enterprise- Evaluating Their Applicability to a Database Monitoring System. 2007. 136p. per. *(978-3-8364-2401-1(0))* VDM Verlag Dr. Mueller e.K.

Hoogervorst, Jan A. P. Enterprise Governance & Enterprise Engineering. 2009. (Enterprise Engineering Ser.). (Illus.). xxv, 429p. 79.95 *(978-3-540-92670-2(4))* Springer.

Hu, Wen Chen. Handheld Computing for Mobile Commerce: Applications, Concepts & Technologies. Zuo, Yanjun, ed. 2010. (Illus.). 463p. 180.00 *(978-1-61520-761-9(9))* IGI Global.

—Internet-Enabled Handheld Devices, Computing, & Programming: Mobile Commerce & Personal Data Applications. 2008. (Illus.). 414p. (C). 165.00 *(978-1-59140-769-0(9))* IGI Global.

Hughes, Bob. Exploiting It for Business Benefit. 2008. (Illus.). xvii, 192p. pap. 41.99 *(978-1-902505-92-3(1))* British Computer Society, The GBR. Dist: Turpin Distribution Services Ltd.

Hunter, Nick. Social Networking: Big Business on Your Computer. 2012. (Big-Buck Business Ser.). 48p. (gr. 6-8). pap. 14.05 ***(978-1-4339-7768-8(0));*** (Illus.). lib. bdg. 31.95 ***(978-1-4339-7767-1(2))*** Stevens, Gareth Publishing LLLP.

Hyde-Bohn, Mary Kay. IBM Electronic Services: Support Using Automation & Web Tools. 2nd ed. 2007. (Illus.). xii, 186p. *(978-0-7384-8885-1(2))* IBM.

Irwin, David. Exploiting IT in Business: Putting Technology to Work to Grow Your Profits. 2007. 192p. pap. *(978-1-85418-148-0(3))* Thorogood GBR. Dist: Independent Pubs. Group.

Islam, Salekul. Participant Access Control in Ip Multicasting. 2009. 168p. pap. *(978-3-639-21191-7(X))* VDM Verlag Dr. Mueller e.K.

Itami, Hiroyuki. Dynamics of Knowledge, Corporate Systems & Innovation. 2010. (Illus.). x, 355p. E-Book *(978-3-642-04480-9(8))* Springer.

Itcookbook. Lotus Notes Interview Questions Answers. 2006. pap. 54.95 *(978-1-933804-36-1(X))* Equity Pr.

Jacob, Bart. IBM Tivoli Asset Management for IT Portfolio Overview. 2007. (Illus.). xviii, 254p. pap. *(978-0-7384-8878-3(X))* IBM.

—IT Asset Management Processes Using Tivoli Asset Manager for IT. 2008. (Illus.). xiv, 200p. *(978-0-7384-3115-4(X))* IBM.

Jajodia, Sushil, et al, eds. Proceedings of the IFIP TC 11 23rd International Information Security Conference: IFIP 20th World Computer Congress, IFIP SEC'08, September 7-10, 2008, Milano, Italy. 2010. (IFIP Advances in Information & Communication Technology Ser.). xviii, 738p. pap. 269.00 *(978-1-4419-3520-5(7),* 1441935207) Springer.

Jay, Rabi. Sap Netweave Portal Technology. 2008. (ENG., Illus.). 735p. pap. 59.99 *(978-0-07-154853-3(X),* 007154853X) McGraw-Hill Osborne.

Joel, Mitch. Six Pixels of Separation: Everyone Is Connected. Connect Your Business to Everyone. 2010. (ENG.). 304p. pap. 16.99 *(978-0-446-54822-9(7),* Business Plus) Grand Central Publishing.

Johnson, M. Eric. Managing Information Risk & the Economics of Security. Johnson, M. Eric, ed. 2008. (ENG., Illus.). xiv, 347p. 129.00 *(978-0-387-09761-9(9),* 0387097619) Springer.

Juric, Matjaz & Pant, Kapil. Business Process Driven SOA using BPMN & BPEL. 2008. (Illus.). 250p. pap. *(978-1-84719-146-5(0))* Packt Publishing, Ltd.

Juric, Matjaz, et al. Soa Approach to Integration. 2007. 384p. per. *(978-1-904811-17-6(5))* Packt Publishing, Ltd.

Kallinikos. Systems & Institutions New Developments in Work, Technology & Organization. 2007. 224p. (C). 119.00 *(978-1-84542-328-5(3))* Elgar, Edward Publishing, Inc.

Kallinikos, Jannis. The Consequences of Information: Institutional Implications of Technological Change. 2007. (Illus.). 224p. pap. 41.00 *(978-1-84720-500-1(3))* Elgar, Edward Publishing, Inc.

Kar, Els van de & Verbraeck, Alexander. Designing Mobile Service Systems. 2007. (Illus.). x, 236p. pap. 65.00 *(978-1-58603-778-9(1),* Delft University Pr) IOS Pr., Inc.

Katsikas, Sokratis, et al, eds. Trust, Privacy & Security in Digital Business: 7th International Conference, TrustBus 2010, Bilbao, Spain, August 30-31, 2010, Proceedings. 2010. (Lecture Notes in Computer Science / Security & Cryptology Ser.). xii, 252p. pap. 72.00 *(978-3-642-15151-4(5),* 3642151515) Springer.

Kautonen, T & Karjaluoto, H. Trust & New Technologies: Marketing & Management on the Internet & Mobile Media. 2008. 328p. 140.00 *(978-1-84720-568-1(2))* Elgar, Edward Publishing, Inc.

Kerr, Don, et al, eds. Digital Business Security Development: Management Technologies. 2010. 350p. 180.00 *(978-1-60566-806-2(0))* IGI Global.

Khadraoui, Djamel & Herrmann, Francine. Advances in Enterprise Information Technology Security. 2007. (Premier Reference Ser.). (Illus.). 388p. 165.00 *(978-1-59904-090-5(5))* IGI Global.

Khanfar, Mohammad. Assessing the It-Business Alignment Maturity. 2010. 164p. pap. *(978-3-8383-9387-2(2))* Lambert Academic Publishing.

Kock, Ned, ed. Emerging E-Collaboration Concepts & Applications. 2006. (Advances in E-Collaboration, Vol. 1 Ser.). (Illus.). 330p. 94.95 *(978-1-59904-393-7(9))* IGI Global.

Kock, Ned F. E-Collaboration Technologies & Organizational Performance: Current & Future Trends. 2010. 350p. 180.00 *(978-1-60960-466-0(0))* IGI Global.

Koskinen, Ilpo, et al. Design Research Through Practice: From the Lab, Field, & Showroom. 2011. (ENG., Illus.). 224p. pap. 49.95 ***(978-0-12-385502-2(0),*** Morgan Kaufmann) Elsevier Science & Technology Bks.

Kozak-Holland, Mark. Avoiding Project Disaster: Titanic Lessons for IT Executives. 2nd ed. 2006. Orig. Title: On-line, on-time, on-budget: Titanic Lessons for e-business Executives. (Illus.). 312p. per. 49.95 *(978-1-895186-73-4(0),* Lessons From History) Multi-Media Pubns., Inc. CAN. Dist: Ingram Pub. Services.

Krimmel, Mandy & Orb, Joachim. SAP NetWeaver Process Integration. 2nd ed. 2010. (Illus.). 394p. 69.95 *(978-1-59229-344-5(1),* SAP PR.) Galileo Pr., Inc.

Lacey, David. Managing the Human Factor in Information Security: How to Win over Staff & Influence Business Managers. 2009. (ENG., Illus.). 384p. pap. 50.00 *(978-0-470-72199-5(5),* Wiley) Wiley, John & Sons, Inc.

Ladley, John. Making Enterprise Information Management (EIM) Work for Business: A Guide to Understanding Information as an Asset. 2010. (ENG., Illus.). 552p. pap. 61.95 *(978-0-12-375695-4(2),* Morgan Kaufmann) Elsevier Science & Technology Bks.

Lam, Wing & Shankararaman, Venky, eds. Enterprise Architecture & Integration: Methods, Implementation, & Technologies. 2007. (Illus.). 364p. 165.00 *(978-1-59140-887-1(3))* IGI Global.

Laperche, Blandine & Sommers, Paul, eds. Innovation Networks & Clusters: The Knowledge Backbone. 2010. 227p. pap. 55.95 *(978-90-5201-602-3(X))* PIE - Peter Lang BEL. Dist: Lang, Peter.

Lawler, James P. & Howell-Barber, H. Service-Oriented Architecture: SOA Strategy, Methodology, & Technology. 2007. (ENG., Illus.). 288p. 79.95 *(978-1-4200-4500-0(8))* Auerbach Pubs., Inc.

Leibert, Florian. A Service-Oriented Architecture for Social Networks. 2008. 76p. pap. *(978-3-639-06163-5(2))* VDM Verlag Dr. Mueller e.K.

Linkies, Mario & Karin, Horst. SAP Security & Risk Management. 2010. (Illus.). 700p. 69.95 *(978-1-59229-355-1(7),* SAP PR.) Galileo Pr., Inc.

Lytras, Miltiadis D., et al. Web 2.0: The Business Model. 2008. (ENG., Illus.). xii, 324p. 139.00 *(978-0-387-85894-4(6),* 0387858946) Springer.

Magal, Simha R. & Wcrd, Jeffrey. Essentials of Business Processes & Information Systems, 2 vols. 2009. (ENG., Illus.). 200p. (C). pap. 55.95 *(978-0-470-23059-6(2)*, Wiley) Wiley, John & Sons, Inc.
Maglio, Paul P., et al, eds. Service-Oriented Computing: 8th International Conference, ICSOC 2010, San Francisco, CA, USA, December 7-10, 2010. Proceedings. 2010. (Lecture Notes in Computer Science / Programming & Software Engineering Ser.). xx, 737p. pap. 131.00 *(978-3-642-17357-8(8)*, 3642173578) Springer.
Mahmood, Zaigham & Hill, Richard, eds. Cloud Computing for Enterprise Architectures. 2011. (Computer Communications & Networks Ser.). (ENG., Illus.). xvi, 327p. 159.00 ***(978-1-4471-2235-7(6)***, 1447'22356) Springer.
Marks, Eric A. Service-Oriented Architecture (SOA) Governance for the Services Driven Enterprise 2008. (ENG., Illus.). 330p. 65.00 *(978-0-470-17125-7(1)*, Wiley) Wiley, John & Sons, Inc.
Marks, Eric A. & Lozano, Bob. Executive's Guide to Cloud Computing. 2010. (ENG., Illus.). 304p. 49.95 *(978-0-470-52172-4(4)*, Wiley) Wiley, John & Sons, Inc.
Martin, Chuck. The Third Screen: Marketing to Your Customers in a World Gone Mobile. 2011. (ENG., Illus.). 256p. 28.95 *(978-1-85788-564-4(3))* Ebsco Publishing.
McCoy, David. Perimeter Security: Physical & Electronic System Security. 2011. (ENG., Illus.). 256p. 79.95 *(978-1-4200-9180-9(8))* Auerbach Pubs., Inc.
McGuire, Russell. The Power of Mobility: How Your Business Can Compete & Win in the Next Technology Revolution. 2007. (ENG., Illus.). 256p. 27.95 *(978-0-470-17128-8(6)*, Wiley) Wiley, John & Sons, Inc.
Minoli, Dan, et al. Handbook of IPv4 to IPv6 Transition: Methodologies for Institutional & Corporate Networks. 2007. (ENG., Illus.). 248p. 79.95 *(978-0-8493-8516-2(4))* Auerbach Pubs., Inc.
Muller, Gerrit. Systems Architecting: A Business Perspective. 2011. (ENG., Illus.). 263p. 89.95 *(978-1-4398-4762-6(2)*, CRC Press) Taylor & Francis Group GBR. Dist: Taylor & Francis Group.
Mulzer, Beatrice & Lim, Mei Ying. Microsoft Small Business Specialist Primer. 2008. (Harry Brelsford's SMB Ser.). (Illus.). per. 59.95 *(978-0-9770949-6-7(0))* SMB Nation Pr.
Norfolk, David. IT Governance. 2nd rev. ed. 2011. (Thorogood Reports). 200p. pap. 240.00 *(978-1-85418-745-1(7))* Thorogood GBR. Dist: Stylus Publishing, LLC.
Oliver, Grof. From Opensocial to Enterprise 2. 0: Social Software Concepts & Technologies. 2011. 116p. pap. ***(978-3-639-34333-5(6))*** VDM Verlag Dr. Mueller e.K.
Onieva, Jose A., et al. Secure Multi-Party Non-Repudiation Protocols & Applications. 2008. (Advances in Information Security Ser.). (Illus.). 200p. 149.00 *(978-0-387-75629-5(9))* Springer.
Oppenheimer, Priscilla. Top-Down Network Design. 3rd rev. ed. 2010. (Networking Technology Ser.). (ENG., Illus.). 600p. 75.00 *(978-1-58720-283-4(2))* Cisco Pr.
Op't Land, Martin. Enterprise Architecture. 2008. (Enterprise Engineering Ser.). (Illus.). 165p. 59.95 *(978-3-540-85231-5(X))* Springer.
Osunkoya, Ola. Information Security Primer for Managers. 2007. 55p. pap. 20.00 *(978-0-615-17019-0(6))* E-Infoseckonsult.
Ou, Xinming & Singhal, Anoop. Quantitative Security Risk Assessment of Enterprise Networks. 2011. (SpringerBriefs in Computer Science Ser.). (ENG., Illus.). xiii, 28p. pap. 39.95 ***(978-1-4614-1859-7(3)***, 1461418593) Springer.
Palacios. Multinational Corporations & the Emerging Network Economy in Asia & the Pacific. 2007. (PAFTAD (Pacific Trade & Development Conference Series) Ser.). (ENG., Illus.). 336p. (C). 178.00 *(978-0-415-43332-7(0))* Routledge.
Panko, R. R. Business Data Networks & Telecommunications. 8th ed. 2010. *(978-0-13-610015-7(5))* Prentice Hall PTR.
Panko, Raymond R. & Panko, Julia L. Business Data Networks & Telecommunications. 8th rev. ed. 2010. (ENG.). 528p. (C). 200.00 *(978-0-13-610012-6(0)*, Prentice Hall) Prentice Hall PTR.
Papazoglou, Michael P. Web Services: Principles & Technology. 2007. (ENG., Illus.). 784p. (C). pap. 95.00 *(978-0-321-15555-9(6)*, Prentice Hall) Prentice Hall PTR.
Partida, Alberto & Andina, Diego. Setting up an IT Security Function. 2010. (Lecture Notes in Electrical Engineering Ser.). (ENG., Illus.). 270p. 159.00 *(978-90-481-8881-9(4)*, 9048188814) Springer.
Pernul, Gunther, ed. Trust, Privacy & Security in Digital Business: 4th International Conference, Trustbus 2007, Regensburg, Germany, September 3-7, 2007, Proceedings. 2007. (Lecture Notes in Computer Science Ser.). (Illus.). 289p. per. 79.95 *(978-3-540-74408-5(8))* Springer.
Power, Penny & Power, Thomas. Know Me, Like Me, Follow Me: What Online Social Networking Means for You & Your Business. 2009. (ENG.). 256p. pap. 23.95 *(978-0-7553-1951-0(6))* Headline Bk. Publishing GBR. Dist: Independent Pubs. Group.
Protogeros, Nicolaos, ed. Agent & Web Service Technologies in Virtual Enterprises. 2007. (Premier Reference Source Ser.). (Illus.). 407p. 180.00 *(978-1-59904-648-8(2))* IGI Global.
Putnk, M. M., GDCunha. Encyclopedia of networked & virtual Organizations. 2008. 2060p. 895.00 *(978-1-59904-885-7(X))* IGI Global.
Raimondo, Antonio Mario. The Science of the Nikken Business. 2011. 348p. pap. 19.99 ***(978-1-4568-5603-8(0))*** Xlibris Corp.
Ramanathan, Jay & Ramnath, Rajiv. Co-Engineering Applications & Adaptive Business Technologies in Practice: Enterprise Service Ontologies, Models, & Frameworks. 2009. (Premier Reference Source Ser.). (Illus.). 426p. 165.00 *(978-1-60566-276-3(3)*, Information Science Publishing) IGI Global.
Rasmus, Daniel W. Management by Design: Applying Design Principles to the Work Experience. 2010. (ENG., Illus.). 238p. 29.95 *(978-0-470-22751-0(6)*, Wiley) Wiley, John & Sons, Inc.
Rebstock, Michael, et al. Ontologies-Based Business Integration. 2010. (ENG., Illus.). xiv, 268p. pap. 109.00 *(978-3-642-09449-1(X)*, 364209449X) Springer.
Reynolds, Jonathan. E-Business: A Management Perspective. 2010. (ENG., Illus.). 450p. 65.00 *(978-0-19-921648-2(7))* Oxford Univ. Pr., Inc.
Rittgen, Peter. Handbook of Ontologies for Business Interaction. 2007. (Premier Reference Source Ser.). (Illus.). 452p. 210.00 *(978-1-59904-660-0(1))* IGI Global.
Rosen, Michael, et al. Applied SOA: Service-Oriented Architecture & Design Strategies. 2008. (ENG., Illus.). 696p. pap. 44.99 *(978-0-470-22365-9(0)*, Wiley) Wiley, John & Sons, Inc.
Rsssnen, Tomi. Key Challenges of Virtual Teams. 2008. 72p. pap. *(978-3-639-03002-0(8))* VDM Verlag Dr. Mueller e.K.
Rutledge, Patrice-Anne. Sams Teach Yourself Linked in 10 Minutes. 2nd rev. ed. 2011. (Sams Teach Yourself — Minutes Ser.). (ENG., Illus.). 240p. pap. 14.99 *(978-0-672-33544-0(1))* Sams.
—Sams Teach Yourself LinkedIn in 10 Minutes. (Sams Teach Yourself Ser.). (Illus.). 2009. 224p. pap. 14.99 *(978-0-672-33085-8(7))* 3rd rev. ed. 2012. (ENG., 264p pap. 14.99 ***(978-0-672-33598-3(0))*** Sams.
Sachs, Ira. Performance Driven IT Management: Five Practical Steps to Business Success. 2011. (ENG.). 256p. 50.00 *(978-1-60590-702-4(2))* 2010. *(978-1-60590-703-1(0))* Government Institutes.
Salam, A. F. & Stevens, Jason R. Semantic Web Technologies & E-Business: Toward the Integrated Virtual Organization & Business Process Automation. 2006. (Illus.). 450p. 99.95 *(978-1-59904-192-6(8))*; 300p. pap. 99.95 *(978-1-59904-193-3(6))* IGI Global.
Sampson, Geoffrey & British Computer Society Staff. Electronic Business. 2nd ed. 2008. (Illus.). xx, 257p. pap. 41.99 *(978-1-902505-89-3(1))* British Computer Society, The GBR. Dist: Turpin Distribution Services Ltd.
Saxtoft, Christian. Convergence: User Expectations, Communications Enablers & Business Opportunities. 2008. (Telecoms Explained Ser.). (ENG., Illus.). 250p. pap. 60.00 *(978-0-470-72708-9(X)*, Wiley) Wiley, John & Sons, Inc.
Scheuing, Sachiko. A Marketer's Guide to E-CRM: A Strategic, Multi-Channel Approach. 2007. (Emarketing Essentials Ser.). (ENG.). 224p. (C). pap 37.95 *(978-0-7506-6521-6(1)*, Butterworth-Heinemann) Elsevier Science & Technology Bks.
Schmidt, Werner, ed. S-BPM ONE - Learning by Doing - Doing by Learning: Third International Conference S-BPM ONE 2011, Ingolstadt, Germany, September 29-30, 2011, Proceedings. 2011. (Communications in Computer & Information Science Ser.). (ENG., Illus.). xiii, 313p. pap. 95.00 ***(978-3-642-23470-5(4)***, 3642234704) Springer.
Scott, Gini Graham. Top Secrets for Using LinkedIn to Promote Your Business or Yourself: A Complete Step-by-Step Guide to Discover the Power of LinkedIn. 2010. 148p. pap. 12.95 *(978-1-4502-1898-6(9))* iUniverse, Inc.
Scott, Peter R. & Jacka, J. Mike. Auditing Social Media: A Governance & Risk Guide 2011. (ENG.). 187p. 49.95 *(978-1-118-06175-6(6)*, Wiley) Wiley, John & Sons, Inc.
Shah, Rawn. Social Networking for Business: Choosing the Right Tools & Resources to Fit Your Needs. 2010. (ENG.). 192p. pap. 29.99 *(978-0-13-271167-8(2))* Wharton Schl. Publishing.
Shaik, Mohammad Assad. Enterprise Master Data Management Using Sap Netweaver Mdm. 2011. 152p. pap. ***(978-1-4269-5888-5(9))*** Trafford Publishing (UK) Ltd.
Silberman, Louis. Internet: Business Dreams. 2007. 289p. pap. 34.95 *(978-1-4303-1728-9(0))* Lulu Enterprises Inc.
Slezak, Dominik, et al. U- & E-Service, Science & Technology: International Conference, UNESST 2009, Held as Part of the Future Generation Information Technology Conference, FGIT 2009, Jeju Island, Korea, December 10-12, 2009, Proceedings. 2009. (Communications in Computer & Information Science Ser.). xii, 177p. pap. 89.95 *(978-3-642-10579-1(3)*, 3642105793) Springer.
Smit, Michael. Privacy in E-Commerce Software. 2007. 156p. per. *(978-3-8364-2252-9(2))* VDM Verlag Dr. Mueller e.K.
Smith, Jon. Start an Online Business in Easy Steps: Practical Help for Entrepreneurs. 2011. (In Easy Steps Ser.). (ENG., Illus.). 192p. pap. 14.99 *(978-1-84078-413-8(X))* Computer Step GBR. Dist: Perseus-PGW.
Stackpole, Bill & Oksendahl, Eric. Security Strategy: From Requirements to Reality. 2010. (ENG., Illus.). 346p. pap. 79.95 *(978-1-4398-2733-8(8))* Auerbach Pubs., Inc.
Stanoevska-Slabeva, Katarina, et al, eds. Grid & Cloud Computing: A Business Perspective on Technology & Applications. 2009. (ENG., Illus.). x, 274p. 139.00 *(978-3-642-05192-0(8)*, 3642051928) Springer.
Studebaker, David. Programming Microsoft Dynamics Nav. 2007. (Illus.). 480p. per. *(978-1-904811-74-9(4))* Packt Publishing, Ltd.
Sukhija, Piyush. E-Commerce: Opportunities & Challenges. 2011. 317p. pap. 49.50 *(978-93-80228-68-6(6))* Global India Pubns. Pvt. Ltd. IND. Dist: Coronet Bks.
Talukder, Majharul. Virtual Organization. 2011. 88p. pap. ***(978-3-8443-0416-9(9))*** Lambert Academic Publishing.
Thompson, Ken. The Networked Enterprise: Competing for the Future Through Virtual Enterprise Networks. 2008. (ENG., Illus.). 200p. pap. 34.95 *(978-0-929652-45-0(2))* Meghan-Kiffer Pr.
Tiller, James S. CISO's Guide to Penetration Testing: A Framework to Plan, Manage, & Maximize Benefits. 2011. (ENG., Illus.). 389p. 69.95 ***(978-1-4398-8027-2(1))*** Auerbach Pubs., Inc.
Tilley, Shayne & Eley, Brandon. Online Marketing Inside Out. 2009. (ENG., Illus.). 250p. pap. 29.95 *(978-0-9805768-2-5(2))* SitePoint Pty, Ltd. AUS. Dist: Ingram Pub. Services.
Van De Kar, E. A. M. & Verbraeck, A., eds. Designing Mobile Service Systems - Volume 2 Research in Design Series. 2008. 132p. pap. 94.00 *(978-1-58603-919-6(9))* IOS Pr., Inc.
van den Berg, Martin & van Steenbergen, Marlies. Building an Enterprise Architecture Practice: Tools, Tips, Best Practices, Ready-to-Use Insights. 2010. (Enterprise Ser.). xvi, 205p. pap. 69.95 *(978-90-481-7407-2(4)*, 9048174074) Springer.
Vervest, Peter H. M., et al, eds. The Network Experience: New Value from Smart Business Networks. (ENG., Illus.). xiv, 370p. 2010. pap. 89.95 *(978-3-642-09920-5(3)*, 3642099203) 2008. 89.95 *(978-3-540-85580-4(7)*, 3540855807) Springer.
Wagner, Bret & Monk, Ellen. Concepts in Enterprise Resource Planning. 4th ed. 2012. (ENG.). 272p. pap. 75.95 *(978-1-111-82039-8(2))* Course Technology.
Wagner, Bret J. & Monk, Ellen F. Concepts in Enterprise Resource Planning. 3rd ed. 2008. (ENG., Illus.). 272p. per. 75.95 *(978-1-4239-0179-2(7))* Course Technology.
White, Martin S. Making Search Work: Implementing Web, Intranet, & Enterprise Search. 2007. *(978-1-57387-305-5(5))* Information Today, Inc.
Willcocks, Leslie P. & Finnegan, David Jesse. Implementing CRM: From Technology to Knowledge. 2007. (John Wiley Series in Information Systems Ser.: 35). (ENG., Illus.). 342p. 140.95 *(978-0-470-06526-6(5)*, Wiley) Wiley, John & Sons, Inc.
Wood, Theodore A. Understanding Recent Cyberlaw Lawsuits & Developments: An In-Depth Look at New Cyber Security Threats & Their Impact on Digital Business. 2010. 37p. ***(978-0-314-27212-6(7))*** Aspatore Bks.
Wort, Carolyn & Petrucke, Fiona. AQA Business & Communication Systems for GCSE. 2009. 200p. pap. 52.50 *(978-0-340-98602-8(6))* Hodder Education GBR. Dist: Trans-Atlantic Pubns., Inc.

BUSINESS ENTERPRISES—CORRUPT PRACTICES

Adeyeye, Adefolake. Corporate Social Responsibility of Multinational Corporations in Developing Countries: Perspectives on Anti-Corruption. 2012. (ENG.). 246p. 115.00 ***(978-1-107-01362-9(3))*** Cambridge Univ. Pr.
Bower, Tom. Outrageous Fortune: The Rise & Ruin of Conrad & Lady Black. 2006. (Illus.). 448p. 26.95 *(978-0-06-114614-5(5))* HarperCollins Pubs.
Burke, R. J. & Cooper, C. L., eds. Research Companion to Corruption in Organisations. 2009. (New Horizons in Management Ser.). (Illus.) 320p. 210.00 *(978-1-84720-892-7(4))* Elgar, Edward Publishing, Inc.
Cooper, Cynthia & Cooper. Extraordinary Circumstances: The Journey of a Corporate Whistleblower. 2009. (ENG.). 416p. pap. 16.95 *(978-0-470-44331-6(6)*, Wiley) Wiley, John & Sons, Inc.
Dean, Geoff, et al. Organized Crime: Policing Illegal Business Entrepreneurialism. 2010. (ENG., Illus.). 240p. pap. 89.95 *(978-0-19-957843-6(5))* Oxford Univ. Pr., Inc.
Fletcher, Clare & Herrmann, Daniela. Corruption: An International Interdisciplinary & Multi-Sectoral Reader. 2012. (Illus.). 210p. 114.95 ***(978-1-4094-1129-1(X)***, Gower Publishing Co., Ltd.) Ashgate Publishing, Ltd. GBR. Dist: Ashgate Publishing Co.
Gottschalk, Petter. Criminal Entrepreneurship. 2009. 232p. 59.00 *(978-1-60692-019-0(7))* Nova Science Pubs., Inc.
—Entrepreneurship & Organised Crime: Entrepreneurs in Illegal Business. 2009. (Illus.). 224p. 119.00 *(978-1-84844-316-7(1))* Elgar, Edward Publishing, Inc.
—Policing Financial Crime: Intelligence Strategy Implementation. 2009. 282p. pap. 59.95 *(978-1-59942-513-9(0))*; xii, 281p. E-Book 45.00 *(978-1-59942-514-6(9))* Universal Pubs. (Brown Walker Pr.).
Luo, Yadong. Guanxi & Business. 2nd ed 2007. (Asia-Pacific Business Ser.). (Illus.). 397p. 85.00 *(978-981-270-046-9(3))* World Scientific Publishing Co., Inc.
Olsen, William P. The Anti-Corruption Handbook: How to Protect Your Business in the Global Marketplace. 2010. (ENG., Illus.). 192p. 78.95 *(978-0-470-48450-0(0)*, Wiley) Wiley, John & Sons, Inc.
Providing Fairness to Workers Who Have Been Misclassified As Independent Contractors: Hearing Before the Subcommittee on Workforce Protections of the Committee on Education & the Workforce, U.S. House of Representatives, One Hundred Tenth Congress, First Session, Hearing Held in Washington, DC, March 27, 2007. 2007. iii, 36p. *(978-0-16-079474-2(9)*, 552-070-36467-6) United States Government Printing Office.
Roberts, Janine. Glitter & Greed: The Secret World of the Diamond Cartel. 2007. (ENG., Illus.). 384p. per. 15.95 *(978-1-932857-60-3(5))* Disinformation Co. Ltd., The.
Schneider, Friedrich & Enste, Dominik H. The Shadow Economy. 2007. (Illus.) 236p. pap. 51.00 *(978-0-521-89107-3(8))* Cambridge Univ. Pr.
Smith, Rebecca & Emshwiller, John R. 24 Days: How Two Wall Street Journal Reporters Uncovered the Lies that Destroyed Faith in Corporate America. 2006. (Illus.). 400p. reprint ed. pap. 26.00 *(978-1-4223-5746-0(5))* DIANE Publishing Co.
Strader, J. Kelly & Jordan, Sandra D. White Collar Crime: Cases, Materials, & Problems. 2nd ed. 2009. *(978-1-4224-2395-0(6))* LexisNexis Matthew Bender.
Subprime & Predatory Lending: New Regulatory Guidance, Current Market Conditions, & Effects on Regulated Financial Institutions: Hearing Before the Subcommittee on Financial Institutions & Consumer Credit of the Committee on Financial Services, U.S. House of Representatives, One Hundred Tenth Congress, First Session, March 27, 2007. 2007. (Illus.). vi, 510p. *(978-0-16-079160-4(X)*, 552-070-36269-0) United States Government Printing Office.
Transparency International. Global Corruption Report: Corruption in Judicial Systems. 2007. (Transparency International Global Corruption Reports). (ENG., Illus.). 328p. per. 44.99 *(978-0-521-70070-2(1))* Cambridge Univ. Pr.
—Global Corruption Report 2009: Corruption & the Private Sector. 2009. (Transparency International Global Corruption Reports). (ENG., Illus.). 496p. pap. 40.00 *(978-0-521-13240-4(1))* Cambridge Univ. Pr.
Transparency International, compiled by. Global Corruption Report 2008: Corruption in the Water Sector. 2008. (Transparency International Global Corruption Reports). (ENG., Illus.). 398p. pap. 41.99 *(978-0-521-72795-2(2))* Cambridge Univ. Pr.
Ullah, Mamin. Corporate Governance Practices in Bangladesh. 2010. 80p. pap. *(978-3-639-26963-5(2))* VDM Verlag Dr. Mueller e.K.
Verhezen, Peter. Gifts, Corruption, Philanthropy: The Ambiguity of Gift Practices in Business. 2009. (Frontiers of Business Ethics Ser.). 65.95 *(978-3-03911-842-7(0))* Lang, Peter AG GBR. Dist: Lang, Peter.
Wrage, Alexandra Addison. Bribery & Extortion: Undermining Business, Governments, & Security, 1 vol. 2007. (Praeger Security International Ser.). 176p. 44.95 *(978-0-275-99649-9(2)*, C9649, Praeger Security International) Greenwood Publishing Group, Inc.
Yu, Shiping. Xin Tai Zi Shang. 2010. (CHI., Illus.). 517p. *(978-962-8744-32-9(1))* Mirror Bks. USA.

BUSINESS ENTERPRISES—DIRECTORIES

Adonis Abbey, Adonis Abbey Publisher. Directory of African Businesses & Organisations in the United Kingdom 2007. 2007. 236p. *(978-1-905068-78-4(6))* Adonis & Abbey Publishers Ltd.
The Almanac of American Employers 2007. 2006. (Almanac of American Employers Ser.). 704p. pap. 249.99 incl. cd-rom *(978-1-59392-083-8(0))* Plunkett Research, Ltd.
Arden, Lynie. The Work at Home Sourcebook. 2009. (ENG.). 400p. pap. 19.95 *(978-0-911781-20-5(X))* Live Oak Pubns.
Association Meeting & Event Planner 2008-09. 2008. pap. *(978-0-87228-495-1(6))* Douglas Publications, Limited Liability Co.
Bü, et al. Enterprise Directory: Entwurf und Implementierung eines Mitarbeiterverzeichnisses unter Verwendung von Web 2.0 und Enterprise 2.0 Technologien. 2009. 160p. pap. *(978-3-639-21469-7(2))* VDM Verlag Dr. Mueller e.K.
BIA. Major Companies of Italy: Manufacturers, Wholesalers, Banks, Construction Companies. 6th rev. ed. 2006. 400p. (J). pap. 249.00 *(978-1-4187-4786-2(6))* Business Information Agency.
—Major Companies of Japan: Manufacturers, Wholesalers, Banks, Construction Companies. 6th rev. ed. 2006. 250p. (J). pap. 249.00 *(978-1-4187-4403-8(4))* Business Information Agency.
—Major Companies of Latvia: Manufacturers, Wholesalers, Banks, Construction Companies. 6th rev. ed. 2006. 400p. (J). pap. 249.00 *(978-1-4187-4414-4(X))* Business Information Agency.
—Major Companies of Liechtenstein: Manufacturers, Wholesalers, Banks, Construction Companies. 6th rev. ed. 2006. 200p. (J). pap. 219.00 *(978-1-4187-5167-8(7))* Business Information Agency.
—Major Companies of Lithuania: Manufacturers, Wholesalers, Banks, Construction Companies. 6th rev. ed. 2006. 300p. (J). pap. 219.00 *(978-1-4187-4415-1(8))* Business Information Agency.
—Major Companies of Luxembourg: Manufacturers, Wholesalers, Banks, Construction Companies. 6th rev ed. 2006. 300p. (J). pap. 249.00 *(978-1-4187-4804-3(8))* Business Information Agency.
—Major Companies of Mexico: Manufacturers, Wholesalers, Banks, Construction Companies. 6th rev. ed. 2006. 200p. (J). pap. 219.00 *(978-1-4187-4425-0(5))* Business Information Agency.
—Major Companies of Moscow, Volume 1: Manufacturers, Wholesalers & Retailers. 6th rev. ed. 2006. 450p. (J). pap. 249.00 *(978-1-4187-4460-1(3))* Business Information Agency.
—Major Companies of Moscow, Volume 2: Construction & Transportation Companies, & Banks. 6th rev. ed. 2006. 376p. (J). pap. 249.00 *(978-1-4187-4461-8(1))* Business Information Agency.
—Major Companies of Norway: Manufacturers, Wholesalers, Banks, Construction Companies. 6th rev. ed. 2006. 200p. (J). pap. 249.00 *(978-1-4187-5291-0(6))* Business Information Agency.
—Major Companies of Poland: Manufacturers, Wholesalers, Banks, Construction Companies. 6th rev. ed. 2006. 400p. (J). pap. 249.00 *(978-1-4187-4416-8(6))* Business Information Agency.
—Major Companies of Portugal: Manufacturers, Wholesalers, Banks, Construction Companies. 6th rev. ed. 2006. 400p. (J). pap. 249.00 *(978-1-4187-4942-2(7))* Business Information Agency.
—Major Companies of Romania: Manufacturers, Wholesalers, Banks, Construction Companies. 6th rev. ed. 2006. 300p. (J). pap. 219.00 *(978-1-4187-4417-5(4))* Business Information Agency.
—Major Companies of Serbia & Montenegro: Manufacturers, Wholesalers, Banks, Construction Companies. 6th rev. ed. 2006. 400p. (J). pap. 249.00 *(978-1-4187-4419-9(0))* Business Information Agency.

—Major Companies of Singapore: Manufacturers, Wholesalers, Banks, Construction Companies. 6th rev. ed. 2006. 300p. (J). pap. 249.00 *(978-1-4187-4405-2(0))* Business Information Agency.

—Major Companies of Slovakia: Manufacturers, Wholesalers, Banks, Construction Companies. 6th rev. ed. 2006. 300p. (J). pap. 249.00 *(978-1-4187-4420-5(4))* Business Information Agency.

—Major Companies of Slovenia: Manufacturers, Wholesalers, Banks, Construction Companies. 6th rev. ed. 2006. 300p. (J). pap. 249.00 *(978-1-4187-4421-2(2))* Business Information Agency.

—Major Companies of South America: Manufacturers, Wholesalers, Banks, Construction Companies. 6th rev. ed. 2006. 300p. (J). pap. 249.00 *(978-1-4187-4396-3(8))* Business Information Agency.

—Major Companies of South Korea: Manufacturers, Wholesalers, Banks, Construction Companies. 6th rev. ed. 2006. 400p. (J). pap. 249.00 *(978-1-4187-4406-9(9))* Business Information Agency.

—Major Companies of Spain: Manufacturers, Wholesalers, Banks, Construction Companies. 6th rev. ed. 2006. 400p. (J). pap. 249.00 *(978-1-4187-4924-8(9))* Business Information Agency.

—Major Companies of Switzerland: Manufacturers, Wholesalers, Banks, Construction Companies. 6th rev. ed. 2006. 400p. (J). pap. 249.00 *(978-1-4187-4898-2(6))* Business Information Agency.

—Major Companies of Thailand: Manufacturers, Wholesalers, Banks, Construction Companies. 6th rev. ed. 2006. 250p. (J). pap. 219.00 *(978-1-4187-4407-6(7))* Business Information Agency.

—Major Companies of the Central Federal District of Russia: Food, Textile, Clothing, & Chemical Companies. 6th rev. ed. 2006. 400p. (J). pap. 249.00 *(978-1-4187-4492-2(1))* Business Information Agency.

—Major Companies of the Czech Republic: Manufacturers, Wholesalers, Banks, Construction Companies. 6th rev. ed. 2006. 400p. (J). pap. 249.00 *(978-1-4187-4410-6(7))* Business Information Agency.

—Major Companies of the Far Eastern Federal District of Russia: Food, Textile, Clothing, & Chemical Companies. 6th rev. ed. 2006. 400p. (J). pap. 249.00 *(978-1-4187-4493-9(X))* Business Information Agency.

—Major Companies of the Netherlands: Manufacturers, Wholesalers, Banks, Construction Companies. 6th rev. ed. 2006. 400p. (J). pap. 249.00 *(978-1-4187-4808-1(0))* Business Information Agency.

—Major Companies of the Northwestern Federal District of Russia: Food, Textile, Clothing, & Chemical Companies. 6th rev. ed. 2006. 400p. (J). pap. 249.00 *(978-1-4187-4494-6(8))* Business Information Agency.

—Major Companies of the Siberian Federal District of Russia: Food, Textile, Clothing, & Chemical Companies. 6th rev. ed. 2006. 400p. (J). pap. 249.00 *(978-1-4187-4495-3(6))* Business Information Agency.

—Major Companies of the Southern Federal District of Russia: Food, Textile, Clothing, & Chemical Companies. 6th rev. ed. 2006. 400p. (J). pap. 249.00 *(978-1-4187-4496-0(4))* Business Information Agency.

—Major Companies of the United Kingdom: Manufacturers, Wholesalers, Banks, Construction Companies. 6th rev. ed. 2006. 400p. (J). pap. 249.00 *(978-1-4187-4453-3(0))* Business Information Agency.

—Major Companies of the Urals Federal District of Russia: Food, Textile, Clothing, & Chemical Companies. 6th rev. ed. 2006. 400p. (J). pap. 249.00 *(978-1-4187-4497-7(2))* Business Information Agency.

—Major Companies of the USA: Manufacturers, Wholesalers, Banks, Construction Companies. 6th rev. ed. 2006. 400p. (J). pap. 249.00 *(978-1-4187-4426-7(3))* Business Information Agency.

—Major Companies of the Volga Federal District of Russia: Food, Textile, Clothing, & Chemical Companies. 6th rev. ed. 2006. 400p. (J). pap. 249.00 *(978-1-4187-4498-4(0))* Business Information Agency.

—Major Companies of the World. 6th rev. ed. 2006. 400p. (J). pap. 249.00 *(978-1-4187-4392-5(5))* Business Information Agency.

—Major Companies of Turkey: Manufacturers, Wholesalers, Banks, Construction Companies. 6th rev. ed. 2006. 300p. (J). pap. 219.00 *(978-1-4187-4452-6(2))* Business Information Agency.

—Major Companies of Venezuela: Manufacturers, Wholesalers, Banks, Construction Companies. 6th rev. ed. 2006. 250p. (J). pap. 219.00 *(978-1-4187-4444-1(1))* Business Information Agency.

—Major Companies of Western Europe: Manufacturers, Wholesalers, Banks, Construction Companies. 6th rev. ed. 2006. 400p. (J). pap. 249.00 *(978-1-4187-4395-6(X))* Business Information Agency.

—Major Construction Companies of Eastern Europe. 6th rev. ed. 2006. 400p. pap. 249.00 *(978-1-4187-4342-0(9))* Business Information Agency.

—Major Dairy Wholesalers of the World. 6th rev. ed. 2006. 400p. (J). pap. 249.00 *(978-1-4187-4323-9(2))* Business Information Agency.

—Major Drug & Medicine Wholesalers of the World. 6th rev. ed. 2006. 400p. (J). pap. 249.00 *(978-1-4187-4274-4(0))* Business Information Agency.

—Major Electronic & Electrical Equipment Wholesalers of the World. 6th rev. ed. 2006. 400p. (J). pap. 249.00 *(978-1-4187-4316-1(X))* Business Information Agency.

—Major Electronic & Electrical Manufacturers of the World. 6th rev. ed. 2006. 400p. (J). pap. 249.00 *(978-1-4187-4283-6(X))* Business Information Agency.

—Major Farm Products Wholesalers of the World. 6th rev. ed. 2006. 400p. (J). pap. 249.00 *(978-1-4187-4324-6(0))* Business Information Agency.

—Major Fish & Seafood Wholesalers of the World. 6th rev. ed. 2006. 400p. (J). pap. 249.00 *(978-1-4187-4325-3(9))* Business Information Agency.

—Major Footwear Wholesalers of the World. 6th rev. ed. 2006. 300p. (J). pap. 249.00 *(978-1-4187-4326-0(7))* Business Information Agency.

—Major Fruits & Vegetables Wholesalers of the World. 6th rev. ed. 2006. 400p. (J). pap. 249.00 *(978-1-4187-4327-7(5))* Business Information Agency.

—Major Furniture & Fixtures Wholesalers of the World. 6th rev. ed. 2006. 400p. (J). pap. 249.00 *(978-1-4187-4318-5(6))* Business Information Agency.

Business Research Services, creator. National Directory of Minority-Owned Business Firms. 13th ed. 2006. (National Directory of Minority Owned Business Firms Ser.). 876p. per. 295.00 *(978-0-933527-82-9(9))* Business Research Services, Inc.

CER Publishing, ed. China Foreign Enterprise Directory. 6th ed. 2007. 990p. pap. 117.50 *(978-988-17149-8-5(2))* China Economic Review Publishing HKG. Dist: Trans-Atlantic Pubns., Inc.

Clumpner, Bruce, ed. 1999-2000 Irvine Spectrum Business Directory. Date not set. (Illus.). 160p. 39.95 *(978-0-9639578-5-6(6))* Con's Quill.

Djordjevich, Vera. Chicago & Midwest Law Firms 2010. 4th ed. 2009. 256p. pap. 29.95 *(978-1-58131-604-9(6))* Vault.com.

—Texas & Southwest Law Firms 2010. 2009. 208p. pap. 29.95 *(978-1-58131-606-3(2))* Vault.com.

—Vault Guide to the Top 50 United Kingdom Law Firms, 2009 Edition: 3rd Edition. 2008. 450p. pap. 34.95 *(978-1-58131-595-0(3))* Vault.com.

FaxUSA 2007: A Directory of Facsimile Numbers for Businesses & Organizations Nationwide. 14th ed. 2006. pap. 194.00 *(978-0-7808-0929-1(7))* Omnigraphics, Inc.

Gale Editors, ed. International Directory of Company Histories, Vol. 80. 2006. (International Directory of Company Histories Ser.). (ENG.). 700p. 312.00 *(978-1-55862-584-6(4)*, St. James Pr.) Cengage Gale.

Grant, Tina, ed. International Directory of Company Histories: Volume 82, Vol. 82. 2006. (International Directory of Company Histories Ser.). (ENG.). 752p. 312.00 *(978-1-55862-586-0(0)*, St. James Pr.) Cengage Gale.

Headquarters USA 2007: A Directory of Contact Information for Headquarters & Other Central Offices of Major Businesses & Organizations in the United States & Canada, 2. 29th ed. 2006. lib. bdg. 216.00 *(978-0-7808-0927-7(0))* Omnigraphics, Inc.

Headquarters USA 2010. 32nd rev. ed. 2009. 216.00 *(978-0-7808-1095-2(3))* Omnigraphics, Inc.

Hoover's Business Press, creator. Hoover's Handbook of Private Companies. 2008. (Hoover's Handbook of Private Companies Ser.). (Illus.). 589p. 264.00 *(978-1-57311-128-7(7))* Hoover's, Inc.

Hoover's Handbook of World Business 2007. 14th ed. 2007. 190.00 *(978-1-57311-116-4(3))* Hoover's, Inc.

Ibp, Usa. Australia Industrial & Business Direct. 2006. (Illus.). pap. 99.95 *(978-0-7397-6791-7(7))* International Business Pubns., USA.

Intl Dir Co Hist. 2009. (International Directory of Company Histories Ser.). (ENG.). 752p. 312.00 *(978-1-55862-639-3(5))*; 752p. 312.00 *(978-1-55862-640-9(9))*; 720p. 312.00 *(978-1-55862-638-6(7))*; 768p. 312.00 *(978-1-55862-637-9(9))* Cengage Gale.

Johnson, Thomas D., ed. National Directory of Minority Owned Business Firms. 14th ed. 2008. (ENG.). 1314p. pap. 295.00 incl. cd-rom *(978-0-933527-85-0(3))* Business Research Services, Inc.

—National Directory of Woman-Owned Business Firms. 14th rev. ed. 2008. 1288p. pap. 295.00 *(978-0-933527-86-7(1))* Business Research Services, Inc.

Kuderka, Michael & Ench-Kuderka, Catherine A. Essential Reference of Domestic Brewers & Their Bottled Brands, 3rd Edition. 3rd ed. 2007. (Illus.). 574p. 60.00 *(978-0-9774800-1-2(1))* MC Basset, LLC.

Latin American Companies Handbook. 400p. (Orig.). pap. 395.00 *(978-0-7605-1815-1(7))* Rector Pr., Ltd.

Louw, G. N. The Professional Forex Directory. 2008. 80p. pap. *(978-0-620-41062-5(0))* FXTrader.

National Directory of Woman Owned Business Firms 13. 13th ed. 2006. 700p. 295.00 *(978-0-933527-83-6(7))* Business Research Services, Inc.

Omnigraphics, creator. Web Site Source Book: A Guide to Major U. S. Businesses, Organizations, Agencies, Institutions, & Other Information Resources on the World Wide Web. 12th ed. 2007. 2134p. per. 194.00 *(978-0-7808-0931-4(9))* Omnigraphics, Inc.

Pederson, Jay P., ed. International Directory of Company Histories, Vol. 79. 2006. (International Directory of Company Histories Ser.). (ENG., Illus.). 800p. 312.00 *(978-1-55862-583-9(6)*, St. James Pr.) Cengage Gale.

—International Directory of Company Histories, Volume 81, Vol. 81. 2006. (International Directory of Company Histories Ser.). (ENG.). 752p. 312.00 *(978-1-55862-585-3(2)*, St. James Pr.) Cengage Gale.

Plunkett, Jack W. The Almanac of American Employers 2007 (E-Book) Market Research, Statistics & Trends Pertaining to the Leading Corporate Employers in America. Plunkett, Jack W., ed. 2006. 711p. E-Book 499.99 incl. cd-rom *(978-1-59392-425-6(9))* Plunkett Research, Ltd.

—The Almanac of American Employers 2008: Market Research, Statistics & Trends Pertaining to the Leading Corporate Employers in America. annuals Plunkett, Jack W., ed. 2007. 706p. pap. 279.99 incl. cd-rom *(978-1-59392-095-1(4))* Plunkett Research, Ltd.

—E-Book Plunkett's Almanac of Middle Market Companies 2008: Middle Market Research, Statistics & Leading Companies. annuals Plunkett, Jack W., ed. 2007. E-Book 299.99 incl. cd-rom *(978-1-59392-435-5(6))* Plunkett Research, Ltd.

—Plunkett's Almanac of Middle Market Companies 2007: Middle Market Research, Statistics & Leading Companies. Plunkett, Jack W., ed. 2006. 636p. pap. 279.99 incl. cd-rom *(978-1-59392-076-0(8))* Plunkett Research, Ltd.

—Plunkett's Almanac of Middle Market Companies 2007 (E-Book) Middle Market Research, Statistics & Leading Companies. Plunkett, Jack W., ed. 2006. 660p. E-Book 499.99 incl. cd-rom *(978-1-59392-418-8(6))* Plunkett Research, Ltd.

—Plunkett's Almanac of Middle Market Companies 2008: Middle Market Research, Statistics & Leading Companies. annuals Plunkett, Jack W., ed. 2007. pap. 299.99 incl. cd-rom *(978-1-59392-092-0(X))* Plunkett Research, Ltd.

—Plunkett's Companion to the Almanac of American Employers 2007 (E-Book) Market Research, Statistics & Trends Pertaining to America's Leading Mid-Sized Employers. annuals Plunkett, Jack W., ed. 2007. 692p. pap. 299.99 incl. cd-rom *(978-1-59392-426-3(7))* Plunkett Research, Ltd.

—Plunkett's Consulting Industry Almanac 2007: Consulting Industry Market Research, Statistics, Trends & Leading Companies. annuals Plunkett, Jack W., ed. 2007. 408p. pap. 279.99 incl. cd-rom *(978-1-59392-070-8(9))* Plunkett Research, Ltd.

—Plunkett's Consulting Industry Almanac 2007 (E-Book) Consulting Industry Market Research, Statistics, Trends & Leading Companies. annuals Plunkett, Jack W., ed. 2007. 418p. E-Book 279.99 incl. cd-rom *(978-1-59392-412-6(7))* Plunkett Research, Ltd.

Plunkett's Companion to the Almanac of American Employers: Mid-Size Firms: The Only Guide to America's Hottest, Fastest-Growing Mid-Sized Employers. annuals 2007. (Plunkett's Companion to the Almanac of American Employers Ser.). 684p. pap. 249.99 incl. cd-rom *(978-1-59392-084-5(9))* Plunkett Research, Ltd.

Ray, Don E., et al. Guide to Dealerships, 2 vols. Incl. Vol. 1. ring bd. *(978-0-7646-0110-1(5))*; Vol. 2. ring bd. *(978-0-7646-0111-8(3))*; 1997. 130.00 *(978-0-7646-0109-5(1))*; 138.00 *(978-0-7646-0390-7(6))* Practitioners Publishing Co.

Romaniuk, Bobdan, ed. Corporate Giving Directory. 25th ed. 1800p. 550.00 *(978-1-56995-458-4(5))* Taft Group, The.

SM Consulting. The Ultimate Job Directory: Comprehensive Guide to Working at Home. 2010. 379p. pap. 29.95 *(978-1-4327-4184-6(5))* Outskirts Pr., Inc.

TIYM Publishing Company, Inc. Staff, ed. Anuario Hispano-Hispanic Yearbook. 20th ed. 2007. 400p. 29.95 *(978-0-9777254-2-7(1))* TIYM Publishing Co., Inc.

Uniworld Business Publications Inc, creator. Directory of Foreign Firms Operating in the United States. 14th ed. 2008. (Directory of Foreign Firms Operating in the United States Ser.). 2356p. 350.00 *(978-0-8360-0058-0(7))* Uniworld Business Pubns., Inc.

Yorke, Louisa, ed. Guide to the Antique Shops of Britain 2008-2009. 2008. (ENG., Illus.). 584p. *(978-1-85149-554-2(1)*, Antique Collectors Club Dist) Antique Collectors' Club.

Ziegler, Roy. New Hope, Pennsylvani: River Town Passages. 2008. 108p. 22.95 *(978-1-4401-0661-3(4))*; pap. 12.95 *(978-1-4401-0659-0(2))* iUniverse, Inc.

BUSINESS ENTERPRISES—FINANCE

Abor, Joshua. Determinants of the Capital Structure of Ghanaian Firms. 2008. 34p. *(978-9966-778-23-9(3))* African Economic Research Consortium.

Abrams, Rhonda. Six-Week Start-Up: Step-by-Step Program for Starting Your Business, Making Money, & Achieving Your Goals! 2nd rev. ed. 2010. (ENG.). 309p. pap. 19.95 *(978-1-933895-09-3(8))* Planning Shop, The.

Ackerman, Jim. How to Market Your Crap When the Ec , 12 Vital Strategies for Saving. 2009. 150p. 24.97 *(978-1-60860-031-1(9)*, Strategic Bk. Publishing) AEG Literary Publishing Services, Inc.

Advances in Financial Planning & Forecasting, New Series, 2. 2006. *(978-0-9651643-6-8(5))* Ctr. for Pacific Basin Business, Economic & Finance Research.

Advani, Asheesh. Business Loans from Family & Friends: How to Ask, Make It Legal & Make It Work, 2 vols. 2009. (ENG.). 287p. pap. 29.99 *(978-1-4133-1078-8(8))* NOLO.

Advani, Reuben. The Wall Street MBA, Second Edition. 2nd rev. ed. 2011. (ENG., Illus.). 272p. pap. 22.00 ***(978-0-07-178831-1(X)***, 007178831X) McGraw-Hill Cos., The.

Anandarajan, Murugan, et al, eds. Business Intelligence Techniques: A Perspective from Accounting & Finance. 2010. (Illus.). x, 268p. pap. 149.00 *(978-3-642-07403-5(0)*, 3642074030) Springer.

Argentina: Business Financing Handbook. (Illus.). 70p. (Orig.). pap. 295.00 *(978-0-7605-1179-4(9))* Rector Pr., Ltd.

Arnold, Glen. Corporate Financial Management. 4th ed. 2008. (Illus.). 1152p. pap. *(978-0-273-71041-7(9))* Financial Times/Prentice Hall.

Asadullina, Irina. Financial Performance of the U S Forest-Product Companies. 2010. 72p. pap. *(978-3-8383-7849-7(0))* Lambert Academic Publishing.

Aspatore Books Staff, compiled by. Understanding Legal Needs of Technology Companies: Leading Lawyers on Performing a Legal Audit, Managing Financial Risk, & Prioritizing Legal Needs (Inside the Minds) 2009. 216p. pap. 75.00 *(978-0-314-19498-5(3))* Aspatore Bks.

Atlantic Publishing Group. How to Open & Operate a Financially Successful Paralegal Service Business. 2012. (ENG.). 288p. pap. 39.95 *(978-1-60138-627-4(3))* Atlantic Publishing Co.

Australia: Business Financing Handbook. (Illus.). 70p. (Orig.). pap. 295.00 *(978-0-7605-1180-0(2))* Rector Pr., Ltd.

BarCharts Inc., Staff. Business Finance. 2009. (ENG.). 6p. 5.95 *(978-1-4232-0858-7(7))* Barcharts, Inc.

—Finance Equations & Answers. 2009. (ENG.). 6p. 5.95 *(978-1-4232-0859-4(5))* Barcharts, Inc.

Barnes, Robert M. Bad Times, Great Markets: How to Get, Keep, & Grow Money in the New Bull Market. 2011. 136p. 29.99 ***(978-1-4634-2173-1(7))***; pap. 14.99 ***(978-1-4634-2175-5(3))*** AuthorHouse.

Barrett, Richard. Planning & Budgeting for the Agile Enterprise: A Driver-Based Budgeting Toolkit. 2007. (ENG., Illus.). 240p. (C). pap. 54.95 *(978-0-7506-8327-2(9)*, CIMA Publishing) Elsevier Science & Technology Bks.

Barrow, Colin. The 30 Day MBA in Business Finance: Your Fast Track Guide to Business Success. 2011. (ENG., Illus.). 256p. pap. 24.95 *(978-0-7494-6215-4(9))* Kogan Page, Ltd. GBR. Dist: Ingram Pub. Services.

Barrow, Colin, et al. The Business Plan Workbook. 7th ed. 2012. (ENG., Illus.). 348p. pap. 39.95 ***(978-0-7494-6461-5(5))*** Kogan Page, Ltd. GBR. Dist: Ingram Pub. Services.

Barrow, Colin, et al. The Business Plan Workbook: The Definitive Guide to Researching, Writing up & Presenting a Winning Plan. 6th ed. 2008. (ENG., Illus.). 416p. pap., wbk. ed. 39.95 *(978-0-7494-5231-5(5))* Kogan Page, Ltd. GBR. Dist: Ingram Pub. Services.

Bate, Nicholas. Beat the Current Recession: A Blueprint for Business Survival. 2009. (ENG.). 140p. pap. 14.95 *(978-0-9798248-7-6(7))* Easton Studio Pr., LLC.

Baumann, Hans D. Building Lean Companies: How to Keep Companies Profitable as They Grow. 2009. (ENG.). pap. 14.95 *(978-1-60037-488-3(3))* Morgan James Publishing.

Belgium: Business Financing Handbook. (Illus.). 70p. (Orig.). pap. 295.00 *(978-0-7605-1181-7(0))* Rector Pr., Ltd.

Bigelow, Lynette. Lynette Bigelow Business Starter Kit, 1-Video CD. 2009. cd-rom 39.99 *(978-0-914391-62-3(3))* Community People Pr.

Bittlestone, Robert. Financial Management for Business: Cracking the Hidden Code. 2010. (ENG., Illus.). 230p. 36.99 *(978-0-521-76290-8(1))* Cambridge Univ. Pr.

Blackstaff, Michael. Finance for IT Decision Makers: A Practical Handbook for Buyers, Sellers & Managers. 2nd ed. 2006. (Illus.). 344p. pap. 59.99 *(978-1-902505-73-2(5))* British Computer Society, The GBR. Dist: Turpin Distribution Services Ltd.

Bloomfield, Stephen. Venture Capital Funding: A Practical Guide to Raising Finance. 2nd ed. 2008. (ENG.). 256p. pap. 75.00 *(978-0-7494-5230-8(7))* Kogan Page, Ltd. GBR. Dist: Ingram Pub. Services.

Bogenschütz, Nina. Neuausrichtung des Eigenkapitalbegriffs: Dogmatische Überlegungen im Lichte hybrider Finanzierungen. 2008. (Frankfurter wirtschaftsrechtliche Studien Ser.). 244p. pap. 61.95 *(978-3-631-56933-7(5))* Lang, Peter GmbH, Europaischer Verlag der Wissenschaften DEU. Dist: Lang, Peter.

Booth, Laurence D. & Cleary, W. Sean. Introduction to Corporate Finance. 2010. (ENG., Illus.). 955p. 122.95 *(978-0-470-83780-1(2)*, Wiley) Wiley, John & Sons, Inc.

Booth, Laurence D. & Cleary, W. Sean. Introduction to Corporate Finance. 2nd ed. 2010. (ENG.). 992p. 123.25 ***(978-0-470-16110-4(8)***, Wiley) Wiley, John & Sons, Inc.

Bragg, Steven M. Treasury Management: The Practitioner's Guide. 2010. (Wiley Corporate F&a Ser.: 6). (ENG., Illus.). 304p. 78.95 *(978-0-470-49708-1(4)*, Wiley) Wiley, John & Sons, Inc.

Branch, Ben & Ray, Hugh. Bankruptcy Investing - How to Profit from Distressed Companies. 2007. 328p. per. 44.95 *(978-1-58798-291-0(9))* Beard Bks., Inc.

Brazil: Business Financing Handbook. (Illus.). 70p. (Orig.). pap. 295.00 *(978-0-7605-1182-4(9))* Rector Pr., Ltd.

Brent. Applied Cost-Benefit Analysis. 2nd rev. ed. 2007. 496p. (C). 228.00 *(978-1-84376-891-3(7))* Elgar, Edward Publishing, Inc.

Brent, Robert J. Applied Cost-Benefit Analysis. 2nd rev. ed. 2008. 496p. pap. 65.00 *(978-1-84720-623-7(9))* Elgar, Edward Publishing, Inc.

Brigham & Daves. Intermediate Financial Management. 11th ed. 2012. (ENG.). 1072p. (C). 255.95 ***(978-1-111-53026-6(2))*** Cengage South-Western.

Brigham, et al. Fundamentals of Financial Management (Book Only) 12th ed. 2009. 752p. (C). 228.95 *(978-0-324-59771-4(1))* CENGAGE Learning.

Brigham, Daves. Intermediate Financial Management. 2006. pap. 20.95 *(978-1-4288-1199-7(0))* Cram101 Inc.

Brigham, Eugene F. & Daves, Phillip R. Intermediate Financial Management (with Thomson ONE - Business School Edition 6-Month Printed Access Card) 10th ed. 2009. (Available Titles CengageNOW Ser.). (ENG., Illus.). 1072p. (C). 255.95 *(978-0-324-59469-0(0))* Cengage South-Western.

—Study Guide for Brigham/Daves' Intermediate Financial Management, 10th. 10th ed. 2009. (ENG.). 528p. (C). pap. 46.95 *(978-0-324-59697-7(9))* Cengage South-Western.

Brooks, Raymond. Financial Management: Core Concepts. 2nd rev. ed. 2012. (ENG.). 684p. (C). pap. 113.33 ***(978-0-13-267103-3(4)***, Prentice Hall) Prentice Hall PTR.

—Financial Management: Core Concepts, Student Value Edition. 2nd ed. 2012. (ENG.). 684p. (C). ring bd. 73.67 ***(978-0-13-267194-1(8)***, Prentice Hall) Prentice Hall PTR.

Brooks, Raymond. Study Guide for Financial Management: Core Concepts. (ENG.). 264p. (C). 2010. pap. 48.20 *(978-0-321-26665-1(X))* 2nd ed. 2012. pap. 46.67 ***(978-0-13-283513-8(4))*** Prentice Hall PTR. (Prentice Hall).

Brunsdon, Terri J., et al. Introduction to Microsoft Dynamics GP 10.0: Focus on Internal Controls. 2nd ed. 2009. (ENG.). 600p. (C). pap. 77.33 *(978-0-13-609804-1(5)*, Prentice Hall) Prentice Hall PTR.

Bull, Richard. Financial Ratios: How to Use Financial Ratios to Maximise Value & Success for Your Business. 2007. (ENG., Illus.). 192p. pap. 54.95

(978-0-7506-8453-8(4), CIMA Publishing) Elsevier Science & Technology Bks.

Bussgang, Jeffrey. Mastering the VC Game: A Venture Capital Insider Reveals How to Get from Start-up to IPO on Your Terms. 2011. (ENG.). 256p. (gr. 12). 16.00 (978-1-59184-444-0(4), Portfolio Trade) Penguin Group (USA) Inc.

Camerinelli, Enrico. Measuring the Value of Supply Chain: Linking Financial Decisions & Supply Chain Performance. 2009. (Illus.). 236p. 124.95 (978-0-566-08794-3(4), Gower Publishing Co., Ltd.) Ashgate Publishing, Ltd. GBR. Dist: Ashgate Publishing Co.

Canada: Business Financing Handbook. (Illus.). 70p. (Orig.). pap. 295.00 (978-0-7605-1184-8(5)) Rector Pr., Ltd.

Caselli, Stefano. Private Equity & Venture Capital in Europe: Markets, Techniques, & Deals. 2010. (ENG., Illus.). 368p. (C). 83.95 (978-0-12-375026-6(1), Academic Pr.) Elsevier Science & Technology Bks.

Central America: Business Financing Handbook. (Illus.). 70p. (Orig.). pap. 295.00 (978-0-7605-1183-1(7)) Rector Pr., Ltd.

Chakrabarti, Debkumar. Investment Behavior of Firms. 2008. 160p. pap. (978-3-639-04508-6(4)) VDM Verlag Dr. Mueller e.K.

Charles, Nyangara Asaka & Fredrick, Aila. Adding Customer Value Through Effective Distribution Strategy: The Case of Coca-Cola's Equator Bottlers Limited, Kenya. 2011. 96p. pap. **(978-3-639-33885-0(5))** VDM Verlag Dr. Mueller e.K.

China: Business Financing Handbook. (Illus.). 70p. (Orig.). pap. 295.00 (978-0-7605-1186-2(1)) Rector Pr., Ltd.

Churchill, Craig, ed. Protecting the Poor: A Microinsurance Compendium. 2007. (ENG., Illus.). 688p. pap. 80.00 (978-92-2-119254-1(7)) International Labour Office.

Churchill, Craig & Frankiewicz, Cheryl. Making Microfinance Work. 2012. (ENG.). pap. 99.00 (978-92-2-124183-6(1)) International Labour Office.

—Making Microfinance Work: Managing Product Diversification. 2012. (ENG.). 440p. pap. 70.00 (978-92-2-124140-9(8)) International Labour Office.

Cinnamon, Robert & Helweg-Larsen, Brian. How to Understand Business Finance. 2nd ed. 2010. (Creating Success Ser.). (ENG.). 176p. pap. 14.95 (978-0-7494-6041-9(5)) Kogan Page, Ltd. GBR. Dist: Ingram Pub. Services.

Clingman, James. Black Empowerment with an Attitude! You Got a Problem with That? 2007. 318p. per. 17.95 (978-0-9799308-4-3(7)) Milligan Bks.

Cloud, Jeanette. The Business Money Book: Cash, Credit & Collections. 2007. (Business Best Ser.). (ENG., Illus.). 152p. pap. (978-1-933766-18-8(2)) Encouragement Pr., 2nd Edition, LLC.

Colombia: Business Financing Handbook. (Illus.). 70p. (Orig.). pap. 295.00 (978-0-7605-1187-9(X)) Rector Pr., Ltd.

Connolly, Michael B. International Business Finance. 2005. (ENG., Illus.). 232p. 65.00 (978-0-415-70153-2(8)); 170.00 (978-0-415-70152-5(X)) Routledge.

Cornelius, Roschanek & Danya, Li Churanek. Innovation at the Base of Pyramid: How Tata & Godrej Tap the Poor. 2011. 96p. pap. **(978-3-639-33649-8(6))** VDM Verlag Dr. Mueller e.K.

Cornwall, Jeffrey R., et al. Entrepreneurial Financial Management: An Applied Approach. 2nd rev. ed. 2009. (ENG., Illus.). 312p. (C). pap. 75.95 (978-0-7656-2292-1(0)) Sharpe, M.E. Inc.

Cornwall, Vang. Entrepreneurial Financial Management. 2006. pap. 9.95 (978-1-4288-0648-1(2)) Cram101 Inc.

Corthouts, Charles. The Relation Between Csr & Financial Performance. 2011. 64p. pap. **(978-3-8454-1888-9(5))** Lambert Academic Publishing.

Cram101 Textbook Reviews. Outlines & Highlights for Business Planning: Financing the Start-up Business & Venture Capital Financing by Therese Maynard. 2011. 232p. pap. 31.95 **(978-1-4672-6709-0(0))** Cram101 Inc.

—Outlines & Highlights for Cfin2 (with Finance Coursemate by Scott Besley, Isbn: 9781111533731. 2011. 232p. pap. 31.95 **(978-1-4288-3234-3(3))** Cram101 Inc.

—Outlines & Highlights for Contemporary Financial Management by R Charles Moyer. 2011. 132p. pap. 28.95 **(978-1-61905-172-0(9))** Cram101 Inc.

Cram101 Textbook Reviews & Cram101 Textbook Reviews. Outlines & Highlights for Principles of Managerial Finance by Gitman. 2011. 368p. pap. 34.95 **(978-1-61830-390-5(2))** Cram101 Inc.

Cram101 Textbook Reviews Staff. Outlines & Highlights for Contemporary Financial Management by R Charles Moyer, Isbn: 9780324653502. 2009. 322p. pap. 33.95 (978-1-4288-2397-6(2)) Cram101 Inc.

—Outlines & Highlights for Entrepreneurial Finance: Finance & Business Strategies for the Serious Entrepreneur by Steven Rogers, ISBN. 2009. 76p. pap. 27.95 (978-1-4288-2607-6(6)); 106p. pap. 28.95 (978-1-4288-8829-6(2)) Cram101 Inc.

—Outlines & Highlights for Entrepreneurial Finance by Leach, J Chris, Isbn: 9780324561258. 2009. 176p. pap. 29.95 (978-1-4288-3241-1(6)) Cram101 Inc.

—Outlines & Highlights for Financial Reporting for Managers: A Value-Creation Perspective by Jamie Pratt, D. Eric Hirst, ISBN. 2009. 174p. pap. 29.95 (978-1-4288-3319-7(6)) Cram101 Inc.

—Outlines & Highlights for Intermediate Financial Management by Eugene F Brigham, Isbn: 9780324319866. 2009. 376p. pap. 34.95 (978-1-4288-2503-1(7)); 334p. pap. 33.95 (978-1-4288-9142-5(0)) Cram101 Inc.

—Outlines & Highlights for Principles of Managerial Finance, Brief by Lawrence J Gitman, Isbn: 9780321524126. 2009. 218p. pap. 30.95 (978-1-4288-2559-8(2)); 210p. pap. 30.95 (978-1-4288-9120-3(X)) Cram101 Inc.

—Outlines & Highlights for Principles of Managerial Finance by Gitman, Isbn: 0201784793. 2009. 302p. pap. 32.95 (978-1-4288-3956-4(9)) Cram101 Inc.

—Outlines & Highlights for Principles of Managerial Finance by Lawrence J Gitman, Isbn: 9780321557537. 2009. 300p. pap. 32.95 (978-1-4288-2691-5(2)) Cram101 Inc.

Crew, Michael A. & Parker, David, eds. International Handbook on Economic Regulation. 2008. (Elgar Original Reference Ser.). 424p. pap. 75.00 (978-1-84844-172-9(X)) Elgar, Edward Publishing, Inc.

Curnan, Davide. Value Creation in Divisional Buyouts. 2011. 76p. pap. **(978-3-8443-1936-1(0))** Lambert Academic Publishing.

Cuypers, Bart & Parmentier, Guy. Business Valuation: Using Financial Analysis to Measure a Company's Value. 2012. (Illus.). 274p. pap. 111.00 **(978-1-78068-016-3(3))** Intersentia Uitgevers N.V. BEL. Dist: International Specialized Bk. Services.

Cyr, Rob. Co-Sign Language: How Guaranteeing a Debt Can Spell Disaster. 2009. 108p. pap. 12.95 (978-1-60264-497-7(7)) Virtualbookworm.com Publishing, Inc.

Czech & Slovak: Business Financing Handbook. (Illus.). 70p. (Orig.). pap. 295.00 (978-0-7605-1188-6(8)) Rector Pr., Ltd.

Davies, Tony & Crawford, Ian. Business Accounting & Finance. rev. ed. 2011. (ENG., Illus.). 772p. pap. 115.00 **(978-0-273-72312-7(X)**, Financial Times/Prentice Hall) Pearson Education Ltd. GBR. Dist: Trans-Atlantic Pubns., Inc.

De Mtzerac, Edouard. Cost of Capital in Investment Decisions. 2009. 96p. pap. (978-3-639-16184-7(X)) VDM Verlag Dr. Mueller e.K.

Deeds, David. Exploring the Entrepreneurial Finance System. 2009. (ENG.). 250p. (C). pap. 53.33 (978-0-13-157457-1(4), Prentice Hall) Prentice Hall PTR.

Demer, Joanie & Wheeler, Heather. Pick Another Checkout Lane, Honey: Save Big Money & Make the Grocery Aisle your Catwalk. 2009. (Illus.). 248p. pap. 19.99 (978-0-9841497-8-0(3)) Krazy Coupon Lady, The.

Depman, A. How to Build Your Financial Advisory Business & Sell It at a Profit. 2009. (ENG., Illus.). 352p. 59.95 (978-0-07-162157-1(1), 0071621571) McGraw-Hill Cos., The.

Diebold, F. X. Known, the Unknown & the Unknowable in Financial Risk Management: Measurement & Theory Advancing Practice. 2010. (ENG., Illus.). 390p. (C). 62.95 (978-0-691-12883-2(9)) Princeton Univ. Pr.

Dlabay, Les & Burrow, James L. Business Finance. 2007. (ENG.). 64p. (C). pap., wbk. ed. 28.95 (978-0-538-44508-5(4)) Cengage South-Western.

—Business Finance. 2007. (Finance Ser.). (ENG., Illus.). 448p. (C). 94.95 (978-0-538-44507-8(6)) Cengage South-Western.

Draper, William H., III. The Startup Game: Inside the Partnership Between Venture Capitalists & Entrepreneurs. 2011. (ENG.). 272p. 28.00 (978-0-230-10486-0(X)) Palgrave Macmillan.

Draper, William H. H., III. The Startup Game: Inside the Partnership between Venture Capitalists & Entrepreneurs. 2012. (ENG.). 272p. pap. 17.00 **(978-0-230-33994-1(3))** Palgrave Macmillan.

Droms, William G. Finance & Accounting for Nonfinancial Managers: All the Basics You Need to Know. 6th ed. 2010. (ENG.). 320p. (gr. 13). pap. 22.00 (978-0-465-01849-9(1)) Basic Bks.

Eiteman, David K., et al. Multinational Business Finance: Global Edition. 12th ed. 2009. (ENG., Illus.). 784p. pap. (978-0-13-612156-5(X)) Prentice Hall PTR.

El-Gamal, Mahmoud A. Islamic Finance: Law, Economics, & Practice. (ENG., Illus.). 240p. 2008. pap. 31.99 (978-0-521-74126-2(2)) 2006. 74.00 (978-0-521-86414-5(3)) Cambridge Univ. Pr.

Elearn. Financial Management Revised Edition: Management Extra. 2008. (Management Extra Ser.). (ENG.). 128p. (C). pap. 49.95 (978-0-08-055235-4(8)) Routledge.

Els, Gideon & Du Toit, Elda. Corporate Finance: A South African Perspective. 2011. (ENG., Illus.). 608p. pap. 60.00 **(978-0-19-598983-0(X))** Oxford Univ. Pr., Inc.

Epstein, Gene. Econospinning: How to Read Between the Lines When the Media Manipulate the Numbers. 2006. (ENG., Illus.). 246p. 31.50 (978-0-471-73513-7(2), Wiley) Wiley, John & Sons, Inc.

Estrada, Javier. The Essential Financial Toolkit: Everything You Always Wanted to Know about Finance but Were Afraid to Ask. 2011. (ENG., Illus.). 200p. 42.00 (978-0-230-28359-6(4)) Palgrave Macmillan.

—Understanding Finance: A No-Nonsense Companion to Financial Tools & Techniques. 2nd rev ed. 2011. (ENG., Illus.). 432p. (C). pap. 39.99 (978-0-273-73802-2(X)) FT Press.

Eun and, Resnick. International Financial Management. 2006. 415p. pap. 17.95 (978-1-4288-0861-4(2)) Cram101 Inc.

Evans, Vaughan. Writing a Business Plan: How to Win Backing to Start up or Grow Your Business. rev. ed. 2011. (ENG.). 248p. (C). pap. 24.99 **(978-0-273-75798-6(9))** FT Press.

Fabozzi, Frank J. & Markowitz, Harry M., eds. The Theory & Practice of Investment Management: Asset Allocation, Valuation, Portfolio Construction, & Strategies. 2nd ed. 2011. (Wiley Desktop Editions Ser.: 198). (ENG., Illus.). 682p. 95.00 (978-0-470-92990-2(1), Wiley) Wiley, John & Sons, Inc.

Farr, Michael K. The Arrogance Cycle: Think You Can't Lose, Think Again. 2011. (ENG.). 256p. 24.95 (978-0-7627-6435-8(X), Lyons Pr.) Globe Pequot Pr., The.

Fentahun, Tesafa. Informal Land Markets in Rice Production in Ethiopia: The Case of Fogera District in West Amhara Region. 2011. 92p. pap. **(978-3-639-31163-1(9))** VDM Verlag Dr. Mueller e.K.

Financial Technology Cost Management Handbook: Companies-Products-Services. 125p. (Orig.). pap. 595.00 (978-0-7605-1867-0(X)) Rector Pr., Ltd.

Finch, Brian. Critical Finance Issues: Financial Times Briefing. 2011. (Financial Times Ser.). (ENG. Illus.). 176p. (C). pap. 49.99 **(978-0-273-73713-1(9))** FT Press.

Finch, Brian. Effective Financial Management. 2010. (Sunday Times Creating Success Ser.). (ENG.). 160p. pap. 14.95 (978-0-7494-5878-2(X)); pap. 14.95 (978-0-7494-6044-0(X)) Kogan Page, Ltd. GBR. Dist: Ingram Pub. Services.

Fisher Investments Press Staff, et al. Fisher Investments on Consumer Staples. 2009. (Fisher Investments Press Ser.: 3). (ENG., Illus.). 216p. 29.95 (978-0-470-41665-5(3), Wiley) Wiley, John & Sons, Inc.

Fishman, Jay E., et al. Guide to Business Valuations, 3 vols. Incl. Vol. 1. ring bd. (978-0-7646-0123-1(7)); Vol. 2. ring bd. (978-0-7646-0124-8(5)); Vol. 3. ring bd. (978-0-7646-0125-5(3)); 1997. 172.00 (978-0-7646-0122-4(9)) Practitioners Publishing Co.

Fleischmann, Anselm. A Simple Luhmann Economy: Market Mechanisms that lead to the Emergence of the Economy as proposed by Niklas Luhmann are explored by Agent based Modelling. 2008. 124p. pap. (978-3-8364-9565-3(1)) VDM Verlag Dr. Mueller e.K.

France: Business Financing Handbook. (Illus.). 70p. (Orig.). pap. 295.00 (978-0-7605-1189-3(6)) Rector Pr., Ltd.

Fraser-Sampson, Guy. No Fear Finance: An Introduction to Finance & Investment for the Non-Finance Professional. 2011. (MBA Masterclass Ser.). (ENG., Illus.). 264p. pap. 39.95 (978-0-7494-6387-8(2)) Kogan Page, Ltd. GBR. Dist: Ingram Pub. Services.

Frodsham, David & Liechtenstein, Heinrich. Getting Between the Balance Sheets: The Four Things Every Entrepreneur Should Know about Finance 2010. (ENG., Illus.). 224p. 44.00 (978-0-230-25286-8(9)) Palgrave Macmillan.

Full Committee Hearing on SBA's Progress in Implementing the Women's Procurement Program. 2008. v, 127p. (978-0-16-080871-5(5), 552-070-37422-1) United States Government Printing Office.

Full Committee Markup of H.R. 2352, the Job Creation Through Entrepreneurship ACT of 2009: Hearing Before the Committee on Small Business, United States House of Representatives, One Hundred Eleventh Congress, First Session, Hearing Held May 13, 2009. 2009. v, 70p. (978-0-16-083988-7(2), 552-070-39660-8) United States Government Printing Office.

Gasking, Terry. Cash & the Art of Successful Business Management. 2008. 252p. pap. (978-0-9547236-5-1(1)) TwigBooks.

Götze, Uwe, et al. Investment Appraisal: Methods & Models. 2010. (ENG., Illus.). xvi, 391p. pap. 139.00 (978-3-642-07260-4(7), 3642072607) Springer.

Gerber, David. Global Competition: Law, Markets & Globalization. 2010. (ENG.). 350p. 82.50 (978-0-19-922822-5(1)) Oxford Univ. Pr., Inc.

Germany: Business Financing Handbook. (Illus.). 70p. (Orig.). pap. 295.00 (978-0-7605-1190-9(X)) Rector Pr., Ltd.

Gil-Lafuente, Anna Maria. Fuzzy Logic in Financial Analysis. 2010. (Studies in Fuzziness & Soft Computing Ser.). (Illus.). xiii, 450p. pap. 239.00 (978-3-642-06221-6(0), 3642062210) Springer.

Gitman, Lawrence J. Principles of Managerial Finance. 2006. pap. 15.95 (978-1-4288-0830-0(2)) Cram101 Inc.

—Principles of Managerial Finance. 2010. (ENG.). (C). 5th ed. 180.00 (978-0-13-247955-4(9)) 12th ed. 233.33 (978-0-13-247954-7(0)) Pearson Education Canada CAN. Dist: Pearson Education.

—Study Guide for Principles of Managerial Finance. 12th ed. 2008. (ENG.). (C). pap. 48.20 (978-0-321-52523-9(X)) Addison Wesley.

Gitman, Lawrence J. & Zutter, Chad J. Principles of Managerial Finance. 13th ed. 2010. (ENG.). 944p. (C). 233.60 (978-0-13-611946-3(8), Prentice Hall) Prentice Hall PTR.

—Principles of Managerial Finance, Brief. (ENG., Illus.). 704p. (C). 5th ed. 2008. 178.60 (978-0-321-52412-6(8)) 6th rev. ed. 2011. 186.67 (978-0-13-611945-6(X)) Prentice Hall PTR. (Prentice Hall).

—Principles of Managerial Finance, Brief, Student Value Edition. 6th ed. 2011. (ENG.). 764p. (C). ring bd. 121.33 (978-0-13-216573-0(2), Prentice Hall) Prentice Hall PTR.

—Principles of Managerial Finance, Student Value Edition. 13th ed. 2011. (ENG.). 764p. (C). ring bd. 153.33 (978-0-13-216510-5(4), Prentice Hall) Prentice Hall PTR.

—Study Guide for Principles of Managerial Finance. 13th rev. ed. 2011. (ENG.). 250p. (C). pap. 48.20 (978-0-13-255568-5(9), Prentice Hall) Prentice Hall PTR.

Gitman, Lawrence J. & Zutter, Chad J. Study Guide for Principles of Managerial Finance, Brief. 6th rev. ed. 2011. (ENG.). 250p. (C). pap. 46.67 **(978-0-13-216491-7(4)**, Prentice Hall) Prentice Hall PTR.

Goegebeur, Yuri. Statistical Simulation & Inference using R. 2008. (Wiley Series in Computational Statistics Ser.). 352p. (978-0-470-72375-3(0), Wiley-Blackwell) Wiley, John & Sons, Ltd.

Goldman Sachs Staff. Architecture of Wealth: Building Your Practice & Designing Outcome-Based Portfolios. 2009. (Reinvented Wealth Manager Ser.). (ENG.). 208p. 49.95 (978-0-470-28950-1(3), Wiley) Wiley, John & Sons, Inc.

Goldstein, Harvey. Don't Bust the Budget: Toss It! 2007. (Illus.). 148p. per. 15.95 (978-0-9767575-9-7(1)) Topos Bks.

Gorham, Michael & Singh, Nidhi. Electronic Exchanges: The Global Transformation from Pits to Bits. 2009. (ENG., Illus.). 352p. 61.95 (978-0-12-374252-0(8), Elsevier Science) Elsevier Science & Technology Bks.

Grasso, Lawrence P. Practical Lean Accounting: A Proven System for Measuring & Managing the Lean Enterprise. 2nd rev. ed. 2011. (ENG., Illus.). 475p. pap. 59.95 (978-1-4398-1716-2(2)) Productivity Pr.

Greece: Business Financing Handbook. (Illus.). 70p. (Orig.). pap. 295.00 (978-0-7605-1191-6(8)) Rector Pr., Ltd.

Green, Charles. Get Financing Now: How to Navigate Through Bankers, Investors, & Alternative Sources for the Capital Your Business Needs. 2011. (ENG., Illus.). 320p. pap. 18.00 **(978-0-07-178031-5(9)**, 0071780319) McGraw-Hill Cos., The.

Greene, Edward F. US Regulation of International Securities & Derivative Markets. 9th ed. 2008. ring bd. 495.00 (978-0-7355-6816-7(2), Aspen Pubs.) Wolters Kluwer Law & Business.

—U.S. Regulation of the International Securities & Derivative Markets. 9th ed. 2009. (978-0-7355-6817-4(0)); (978-0-7355-6818-1(9)) Wolters Kluwer Law & Business. (Aspen Pubs.).

Grossman, Theodore & Livingstone, John Leslie. The Portable MBA in Finance & Accounting. 4th ed. 2009. (ENG., Illus.). 624p. 34.95 (978-0-470-48130-1(7), Wiley) Wiley, John & Sons, Inc.

Gruber, Alexandra Carina. Biotech Funding Trends: Insights from Entrepreneurs & Investors. 2009. (ENG., Illus.). 210p. 136.95 (978-3-527-32435-4(6), Wiley-VCH) Wiley, John & Sons, Inc.

Hacker, Robert H. Billion Dollar Company. 2010. 116p. pap. (978-3-8383-7331-7(6)) Lambert Academic Publishing.

Haislip, Alexander. Essentials of Venture Capital. 2010. (Essentials Ser.: 52). (ENG., Illus.). 320p. pap. 39.95 (978-0-470-61622-2(9), Wiley) Wiley, John & Sons, Inc.

Hamilton, Robert W. Attorney's Guide to Business & Finance Fundamentals. 2nd ed. 2006. (Illus.). 290.00 (978-0-7355-6058-1(7), Aspen Pubs.) Wolters Kluwer Law & Business.

Hammer, David. No Money - No Mission: Best Practices of Healthcare Revenue Cycle Management. 2012. (ENG.). 475p. 99.95 (978-1-4200-9136-6(0)) Productivity Pr.

Hanf, David. Interdependence & Respect Balanced with Strife & Discord- Analysis of the Relationship Between Venture Capitalists & Angel Investors with Speci. 2007. 108p. per. (978-3-8364-4805-5(X)) VDM Verlag Dr. Mueller e.K.

Harvard Business School Press Staff, compiled by. Creating a Business Plan: Expert Solutions to Everyday Challenges. 2007. (Pocket Mentor Ser.). (ENG., Illus.). 144p. per. 9.95 (978-1-4221-1885-6(1)) Harvard Business Review Pr.

Haslam, Colin, et al. Redefining Business Models: Strategies for a Financialized World. 2012. (ENG., Illus.). 296p. (C). 145.00 (978-0-415-67440-9(9)) Routledge.

Hatcher, Troy A. Collegiate Solutions. 2008. 146p. pap. 29.95 (978-0-615-22427-5(X)) Hatcher, Troy A.

Hawawini, Gabriel & Viallet, Claude. Finance for Executives: Managing for Value Creation. 4th ed. 2010. (ENG., Illus.). 672p. (C). 213.95 (978-0-538-75134-6(7)) Cengage South-Western.

Hawkins, Anne & Turner, Clive. Improving Profitability Pocketbook. 2nd ed. 2009. (ENG., Illus.). 112p. pap. (978-1-903776-94-0(5)) Management Pocketbooks GBR. Dist: Ware-Pak, Inc.

Helweg-Larsen, Brian, et al. How to Understand Business Finance. 2nd ed. 2010. (Sunday Times Creating Success Ser.). (ENG., Illus.). 176p. pap. 14.95 (978-0-7494-6020-4(2)) Kogan Page, Ltd. GBR. Dist: Ingram Pub. Services.

Herold, Cameron. Double Double. 2011. 220p. 22.95 (978-1-60832-099-8(5)) Greenleaf Book Group.

Hettinger, William & Dolan-Heitlinger, John. Finance Without Fear: A Guide to Creating & Managing a Profitable Business. 2010. (ENG.). 25.95 (978-0-9828917-0-4(9)) Institute for Finance & Entrepreneurship.

Hicks, Steven D., compiled by. Sources of Canadian Financing for Business & Real Estate. 2009. pap. 29.50 (978-1-56150-895-2(0)) 17th ed. 2007. pap. 29.50 (978-1-56150-796-2(2)) International Wealth Success, Inc.

Hicks, Tyler G. How to Start & Finance A Business That Works for You. 8th ed. 2007. pap. 24.75 (978-1-56150-868-6(3)) International Wealth Success, Inc.

—Private Loan Money Funding Kit. 2007. ring bd. 100.00 (978-1-56150-814-3(4)) International Wealth Success, Inc.

—Rapid Real Estate & Business Loan-Getting Methods. 2009. (ENG.). pap. 25.00 (978-1-56150-889-1(6)) 17th ed. 2007. pap. 25.00 (978-1-56150-790-0(3)) International Wealth Success, Inc.

—Successful Financing Techniques for Business & Real Estate. 9th ed. 2007. pap. 24.95 (978-1-56150-867-9(5)) International Wealth Success, Inc.

—101 Ways to Get 100+% Financing for Real Estate & Business. 17th ed. 2007. pap. 24.50 (978-1-56150-846-4(2)) International Wealth Success, Inc.

Hoffman, Charles & Watson, Liv. XBRL for Dummies. 2009. (ENG., Illus.). 432p. pap. 29.99 (978-0-470-49979-5(6), For Dummies) Wiley, John & Sons, Inc.

Hofmann, Erik, et al. Ways Out of the Working Capital Trap: Empowering Self-Financing Growth Through Modern Supply Management. 2011. (Advanced Purchasing & SCM Ser.). Orig. Title: Wege aus der Working Capital-Falle. (Illus.). x, 94p. 49.95 (978-3-642-17270-0(9), 3642172709) Springer.

Hofmann, Jennifer. Infoline Blended Learning. 2011. 20p. pap. 24.95 **(978-1-56286-794-2(6))** American Society for Training & Development.

Hommel, Ulrich, et al, eds. The Strategic CFO: Creating Value in a Dynamic Market Environment. 2011. (ENG., Illus.). xv, 315p. 89.95 (978-3-642-04348-2(8), 3642043488) Springer.

Hong Kong: Business Financing Handbook. (Illus.). 70p. (Orig.). pap. 295.00 (978-0-7605-1192-3(6)) Rector Pr., Ltd.

Hoover's, creator. Hoover's Handbook of Emerging Companies. (Hoover's Handbook of Emerging Companies Ser.). (Illus.). 14th ed. 2007. 532p. 150.00

B

(978-1-57311-117-1(1)) 15th ed. 2008. (ENG., 513p. 155.00 (978-1-57311-123-2(6), Hoover's Business Pr.) Hoover's, Inc.

Hoover's Business Press, creator. Hoover's Handbook of Private Companies. 2008. (Hoover's Handbook of Private Companies Ser.). (Illus.). 589p. 264.00 (978-1-57311-128-7(7)) Hoover's, Inc.

Hoover's Incorporated, creator. Hoover's Handbook of Private Companies. 12th ed. 2007. (Hoover's Handbook of Private Companies Ser.). (Illus.). 588p. 175.00 (978-1-57311-115-7(5)) Hoover's, Inc.

Hungary: Business Financing Handbook. (Illus.). 70p. (Orig.). pap. 295.00 (978-0-7605-1193-0(4)) Rector Pr., Ltd.

Im, Yong-Jae & Chon, Song-In. Kiop Chiptan Ui Sunhwan Ch'ulcha: Sijang Kyuyul Kwa Kamdok Kyuyul Ui Yokhal. 2009. (KOR., Illus.). 84p. (978-89-8063-302-9(5)) KDI.

India: Business Financing Handbook. (Illus.). 70p. (Orig.). pap. 295.00 (978-0-7605-1194-7(2)) Rector Pr., Ltd.

Indonesia: Business Financing Handbook. (Illus.). 70p. (Orig.). pap. 295.00 (978-0-7605-1195-4(0)) Rector Pr., Ltd.

Italy: Business Financing Handbook. (Illus.). 70p. (Orig.). pap. 295.00 (978-0-7605-1196-1(9)) Rector Pr., Ltd.

ITT & Gitman, Lawrence J. Principles of Managerial Finance. 2010. (ENG.). (C). pap. 34.68 (978-0-558-75542-3(9)) Pearson Learning Solutions.

Iyengar, Anand. Hotel Finance. 2009. (ENG., Illus.). 324p. pap. 29.95 (978-0-19-569446-8(5)) Oxford Univ. Pr., Inc.

Jacoby, Neil H. Business Finance & Banking. 2007. pap. 28.95 (978-1-4067-5647-0(4)) Jacoby Pr.

Japan: Business Financing Handbook. (Illus.). 70p. (Orig.). pap. 295.00 (978-0-7605-1197-8(7)) Rector Pr., Ltd.

Jarsulic, Marc. Anatomy of a Financial Crisis: A Real Estate Bubble, Runaway Credit Markets, & Regulatory Failure. 2010. (ENG., Illus.). 200p. 68.00 (978-0-230-61568-7(6)) Palgrave Macmillan.

Kaplan CPA Review. CPA Exam Study Manual: Business Environment & Concepts 2009/2010. 2009. (ENG.). 752p. pap. 49.95 (978-1-4277-8861-0(8)) Kaplan Publishing.

Kavaliova, Maria. Foreign Exchange Risk Management- Which Hedging Techniques Can Be Used by a Mid-Size Company. 2007. 120p. per. (978-3-8364-1261-2(6)) VDM Verlag Dr. Mueller e.K.

Keown, Martin. Financial Management Principles & Appl. 2006. pap. 17.95 (978-1-4288-1216-1(4)) Cram101 Inc.

Kibel, Harvey R. How to Turn Around a Financially Troubled Company. Palace, Jon, ed. reprint ed. (978-0-9628399-1-7(4)) HRK & Assocs., Inc.

Kim, Yong-Mi. An Investigation of the Effects of It Investment on Firm Performance. 2008. 196p. pap. (978-3-639-06905-1(6)) VDM Verlag Dr. Mueller e.K.

Klonowski, Darek. Venture Capital Investment Process. 2010. (ENG., Illus.). 288p. 84.00 (978-0-230-61288-4(1)) Palgrave Macmillan.

Kontoghiorghes, Erricos John & Gatu, Cristian, eds. Optimisation, Econometric & Financial Analysis. 2006. (Advances in Computational Management Science Ser.). (Illus.). 277p. 135.00 (978-3-540-36625-6(3), 3540366253) Springer.

Koudal, Peter. Why Finance Transformation Matters in Global Manufacturing. 2007. (978-1-934025-03-1(8)) Deloitte.

Kovacic, Iva. Developing Strategies for Sustainable Planning. 2008. 320p. pap. (978-3-639-01310-8(7)) VDM Verlag Dr. Mueller e.K.

Krishnamurthy, Ravichandran & SELLA, Prabakaran. Financial Management. 2010. 536p. pap. (978-3-639-24565-3(2)) VDM Verlag Dr. Mueller e.K.

Kürsten, Wolfgang & Nietert, Bernhard, eds. Kapitalmarkt, Unternehmensfinanzierung und rationale Entscheidungen: Festschrift für Jochen Wilhelm. (GER., Illus.). XVI, 574p. 159.00 (978-3-540-27691-3(2), 3540276912) Springer.

Laffer, Arthur B., et al. The Private Equity Edge: How Private Equity Players & the World's Top Companies Build Value & Wealth. 2009. (ENG., Illus.). 448p. 34.95 (978-0-07-159078-5(1), 0071590781) McGraw-Hill Cos., The.

Lang, Roger. Operation Enduring Finance. 2010. 366p. pap. 19.99 (978-1-4535-3797-8(X)) Xlibris Corp.

Lasher & Lasher, William R. Practical financial Management. 6th ed. 2010. (ENG.). (C). 177.95 (978-1-4390-8050-4(X)) Cengage South-Western.

Lasher, William. Practical Financial Management. 5th ed. 2007. (ENG., Illus.). 784p. (C). 165.95 (978-0-324-42262-7(8)) Cengage South-Western.

—Practical Financial Management. 4th ed. 2006. pap. 15.95 (978-1-4288-1138-6(9)) Cram101 Inc.

Lasher, William R. Practical Financial Management (with Thomson ONE - Business School Edition 6-Month Printed Access Card) 6th ed. 2010. (Available Titles CengageNOW Ser.). (ENG.). 864p. (C). 206.95 (978-1-4390-8049-8(6)) Cengage South-Western.

Lawrence, Kenneth & Kleinman, Gary. Applications in Multi-Criteria Decision Making, Data Envelopment Analysis, & Finance. 2010. (Applications of Management Science Ser.: Vol. 14). 317p. 135.95 (978-0-85724-469-7(8)) Emerald Group Publishing Ltd. GBR. Dist: Turpin Distribution, Inc., Turpin Distribution Services Ltd.

Lawrence, Kenneth & Kleinman, Gary, eds. Applications of Management Science. 2012. (Applications of Management Science Ser.). 313p. (978-1-78052-100-8(6)) Emerald Group Publishing Ltd.

Leach and, Melicher. Entrepreneurial Finance. 2006. pap. 14.95 (978-1-4288-0897-3(3)) Cram101 Inc.

Leach, Robert. Ratios Made Simple: A beginner's guide to the key financial Ratios. 2010. (ENG.). 196p. pap. 22.99 (978-1-906659-84-4(2)) Harriman Hse. Publishing GBR. Dist: Ingram Pub. Services.

Lee, Alice C., et al. Financial Analysis, Planning & Forecasting: Theory & Application. 2nd ed. 2008. (Illus.). 800p. 153.00 (978-981-270-608-9(9)) World Scientific Publishing Co., Inc.

Lee, Trent & Lee, Chad. Unlimited Business Financing: Learn How to Obtain $250,000 or More in Business Funding Without Harming Your Personal Credit. 2008. 134p. pap. 14.95 (978-1-934275-05-4(0)) Xeno Pr.

Leger, Shane C. Information Sellers & Resellers. 2009. (Financial Institutions & Services Ser.). pap. 79.00 (978-1-60692-228-6(9)) Nova Science Pubs., Inc.

Levin. Structuring Venture Capital 2009. 2009. pap. 286.00 (978-0-7355-8160-9(6)) Wolters Kluwer Law & Business.

—Structuring Venture Capital 2010 Combo (Cd & Print) 2010. pap. (978-0-7355-9377-0(9), Aspen Pubs.) Wolters Kluwer Law & Business.

—Structuring Venture Capital 2010e. 2010. pap. (978-0-7355-9370-1(1), Aspen Pubs.) Wolters Kluwer Law & Business.

Levin, Jack S. Structuring Venture Capital 2009 Combo. 2009. pap. 495.00 (978-0-7355-8286-6(6)) Wolters Kluwer Law & Business.

Libecap, Gary D. & Thursby, Marie. Technological Innovation: Generating Economic Results. 2008. (Illus.). vii, 347p. 99.95 (978-0-7623-1481-2(8)) Emerald Group Publishing Ltd. GBR. Dist: Turpin Distribution Services Ltd.

Library of Congress: Opportunities to Improve General & Financial Management. 12p. pap. 30.00 (978-0-7881-4179-9(1)) DIANE Publishing Co.

Liley, Christopher & Duncan, David. Microsoft Dynamics GP 2010 Reporting. 2011. 333p. pap. (978-1-84968-218-3(6)) Packt Publishing, Ltd.

Livingstone, Les. Finance Made Easy. 2009. 229p. pap. 29.98 (978-0-557-02920-4(1)) Lulu Enterprises Inc.

Lukac, Dusko. Key Success Factors for Foreign Direct Investment in Western Balkan. 2008. 160p. pap. (978-3-639-03807-1(X)) VDM Verlag Dr. Mueller e.K.

Lumby, Steve & Jones, Chris. Corporate Finance: Theory & Practice. 8th ed. 2011. (ENG., Illus.). 752p. pap. 69.99 (978-1-84480-946-2(3)) Cengage Learning GBR. Dist: CENGAGE Learning.

Lyons, Murray & Lyons, Kelly. The 1% Difference: Small Change-Big Impact. 2011. 152p. pap. 17.95 (978-1-4634-1254-8(1)) AuthorHouse.

Madura, Jeff (Jeff Madura). International Financial Management. 11th ed. 2011. (ENG.). 752p. (C). 233.95 (978-0-538-48296-7(6)) Cengage South-Western.

Magoon, Linda M. Dictionary of Financial Formulas & Ratios. 2008. 200p. pap. 35.00 (978-1-906403-03-4(1)) Lessons Professional Publishing GBR. Dist: Stylus Publishing, LLC.

Majcher, Marley. But Are You Making Any Money? Stop Being Busy & Start Creating Cash. 2011. (ENG.). 172p. pap. 19.95 (978-1-60037-776-1(9)) Morgan James Publishing.

Major Donor Game Plan: Rounding 3rd & Heading Home. 2006. 15.00 (978-0-9788585-0-6(6)) Timothy Group, The.

Makki, Muhammad & Lodhi, Suleman. Financial Performance & Intellectual Capital Efficiency. 2010. 116p. pap. (978-3-639-26176-9(3)) VDM Verlag Dr. Mueller e.K.

Maness, Terry S. & Zietlow, John T. Short-Term Financial Management. 2006. pap. 16.95 (978-1-4288-0983-3(X)); 3rd ed. pap. 17.95 (978-1-4288-1100-3(1)) Cram101 Inc.

Marks, Kenneth H., et al. The Handbook of Financing Growth: Strategies, Capital Structure, & M & A Transactions. 2nd ed. 2009. (Wiley Finance Ser.: 482). (ENG., Illus.). 672p. 95.00 (978-0-470-39015-3(8), Wiley) Wiley, John & Sons, Inc.

Marsh, Clive. Financial Management for Non-Financial Managers. 2012. (Strategic Success Ser.). (ENG.). 255p. pap. 39.95 (978-0-7494-6467-7(4)) Kogan Page, Ltd. GBR. Dist: Ingram Pub. Services.

Mason, Roger. Finance for Non-Financial Managers: Learn in a Week, What the Leading Experts Learn in a Lifetime. 2012. (Teach Yourself: General Reference Ser.). (ENG., Illus.). 128p. pap. 12.00 (978-1-4441-5886-1(4), 1444158864) McGraw-Hill Cos., The.

—Finance for Non-Financial Managers 2010. 5th ed. 2010. (ENG., Illus.). 320p. pap. 17.95 (978-1-4441-0492-9(6), Hodder & Stoughton) Hodder General Publishing Div. GBR. Dist: Independent Pubs. Group.

Maude, David John. Global Private Banking & Wealth Management: The New Realities. 2006. (Wiley Finance Ser.: 395). (ENG., Illus.). 360p. 105.00 (978-0-470-85421-1(9), Wiley) Wiley, John & Sons, Inc.

Maynard. Business Planning. 2010. 152.00 (978-0-7355-7727-5(7)) Wolters Kluwer Law & Business.

Maynard, Therese H. & Warren, Dana M. Business Planning: Financing the Start-Up Business & Venture Capital Financing. 2010. xxv, 867p. (978-0-7355-7728-2(5)) Kluwer Law International.

Mayo, Herbert B. Basic Finance: An Introduction to Financial Institutions, Investments & Management. 10th ed. 2011. (ENG.). 720p. (C). pap. 209.95 (978-1-111-82063-3(5)) Cengage South-Western.

McCrary, Stuart A. Mastering Corporate Finance Essentials: The Critical Quantitative Methods & Tools in Finance. 2010. (Wiley Finance Ser.: 486). (ENG., Illus.). 174p. 49.95 (978-0-470-39333-8(5), Wiley) Wiley, John & Sons, Inc.

Mcdermott, Lynda C. Infoline the Power of Peer Coaching. 2011. (ENG.). 20p. pap. 24.95 (978-1-56286-792-8(X)) American Society for Training & Development.

McGrane, Stephen. Sit Crooked & Speak Straight. 2008. 168p. pap. 13.95 (978-1-60594-031-1(3), Llumina Pr.) Aeon Publishing Inc.

McKeever, Mike. How to Write a Business Plan, 2 vols. 10th rev. ed. 2010. (ENG.). 274p. pap. 34.99 (978-1-4133-1280-5(2)) NOLO.

McLaney, Eddie. Business Finance. 8th ed. 2009. (ENG., Illus.). 536p. pap. 115.00 (978-0-273-71768-3(5)) Pearson Education, Ltd. GBR. Dist: Trans-Atlantic Pubns., Inc.

McLaney, Eddie. Business Finance: Theory & Practice. 9th rev. ed. 2011. (ENG., Illus.). 518p. pap. 117.50 (978-0-273-75045-1(3)) Pearson Education, Ltd. GBR. Dist: Trans-Atlantic Pubns., Inc.

Meckin, David. Naked Finance: Business Finance Pure & Simple. 2008. (ENG., Illus.). 286p. per. 24.95 (978-1-85788-394-7(2)) Ebsco Publishing.

Melicher, Ronald W. & Leach, J. Chris. Entrepreneurial Finance. 4th ed. 2011. (ENG.). 688p. (C). 221.95 (978-0-538-47815-1(2)) Cengage South-Western.

Mendez V., David. Proceso de Planeación Financier: La manera simple de tomar control de su dinero y lograr una Independencia Financiera. 2010. 136p. 29.99 (978-1-4490-5130-3(8)) AuthorHouse.

Mexico: Business Financing Handbook. (Illus.). 70p. (Orig.). pap. 295.00 (978-0-7605-1199-2(3)) Rector Pr., Ltd.

Middlebrooks, Gerald. Strategy of Debt Relief. 2011. 130p. pap. 24.95 (978-1-4626-4106-2(7)) PublishAmerica, Inc.

Mikdashi, Zuhayr. Progress-Driven Entrepreneurs: Private Equity Finance & Regulatory Issues. 2010. (ENG., Illus.). 288p. 95.00 (978-0-230-51498-0(7)) Palgrave Macmillan.

Milady Publishing Company Staff. Financial Analysis & Coaching Tools. 2010. (ENG.). (C). 221.50 (978-1-4354-8863-2(6), Milady Publishing Co.) Delmar Cengage Learning.

Mitchell, Stacy. Big-Box Swindle: The True Cost of Mega-Retailers & the Fight for America's Independent Businesses. 2006. 320p. 25.95 (978-0-618-80221-0(5)) Beacon Pr.

Moyer & Moyer, R. Charles. Contemporary Financial Management. 12th ed. 2012. (Illus.). xxvii, 856p. (978-0-538-47916-5(7), Wiley-Blackwell) Cengage South-Western.

Moyer, et al. Contemporary Financial Management. 12th ed. 2011. (ENG.). 960p. (C). 248.95 (978-0-538-47917-2(5)) Cengage South-Western.

Moyer and McGui, Kretlow. Contemporary Financial Management. 2006. pap. 19.95 (978-1-4288-0944-4(9)) Cram101 Inc.

Moyer, R. Charles, et al. Fundamentals of Contemporary Financial Management. 2nd ed. 2007. (Illus.). xxviii, 624p. (978-0-324-40635-1(5)) Cengage South-Western.

Munchau, Wolfgang. The Meltdown Years: The Unfolding of the Global Economic Crisis. 2009. (ENG., Illus.). 256p. 29.95 (978-0-07-163478-6(9), 0071634789) McGraw-Hill Cos., The.

Mwima, Charles. Managing Financial Resources in Organizations. 2011. 68p. pap. (978-3-8433-8666-1(8)) Lambert Academic Publishing.

Nemethy, Les. Business Exit Planning: Options, Value Enhancement, & Transaction Management for Business Owners. 2011. (Wiley Finance Ser.: 9). (ENG., Illus.). 187p. 75.00 (978-0-470-90531-9(X), Wiley) Wiley, John & Sons, Inc.

Newman, Pam. Boost Your Bottom Line - Financial Tips for Consultants. 2007. per. 12.95 net. (978-0-9764408-1-9(4)) Small Business Resource.

Nicoleta, Barbuta-Misu. Analysis & Modelling of the Financial Performance of the Enterprises. 2010. 116p. pap. (978-3-8383-1971-1(0)) Lambert Academic Publishing.

Nikbakht, Ehsan. Finance. 5th ed. 2006. (Barron's Business Review Ser.). (ENG., Illus.). 624p. per. 18.99 (978-0-7641-3420-3(5)) Barron's Educational Series, Inc.

Nordsted, Pete. Mastering Betfair: How to Make Serious Money Trading Betting Exchanges. 2009. (ENG., Illus.). 200p. pap. 34.99 (978-1-906659-02-8(8)) Harriman Hse. Publishing GBR. Dist: Ingram Pub. Services.

Norton, Dewey. The Executive's Guide to Financial Management: Improving Risk, Strategy & Financial Performance. 2012. (ENG.). 388p. 85.00 (978-0-230-34195-1(0)) Palgrave Macmillan.

Oechsli, Matt. How to Build A 21st Century Financial Practice: Attracting, Servicing, & Retaining Affluent Clients. 2007. pap. 29.95 (978-0-9656765-0-2(1)) Wealth Management Pr.

Organisation for Economic Co-operation and Development Staff. Rapport Annuel Sur les Principes Directeurs de l'Ocde à l'Intention des Entreprises Multinationales 2008: Emploi et Relations Industrielles. 2009. pap. 63.00 (978-92-64-01935-5(9)) Organization for Economic Cooperation & Development.

Owsley, Henry. Distressed Investment Banking: To the Abyss & Back. (Illus.). xiii, 219p. 74.95 (978-1-58798-267-5(6)) Beard Bks., Inc.

Pabrai, Mohnish. The Dhandho Investor: The Low-Risk Value Method to High Returns. 2007. (ENG., Illus.). 208p. 27.95 (978-0-470-04389-9(X), Wiley) Wiley, John & Sons, Inc.

Parker, Edmund. Equity Derivatives: Documenting & Understanding Equity Derivative Products. 2009. (Illus.). 437p. (978-1-905783-22-9(1)) Globe Law and Business.

Parks, Steve. How to Fund Your Business: The Essential Guide to Raising Finance to Start & Grow Your Business. 2006. (ENG., Illus.). 224p. pap. 42.50 (978-0-273-70624-3(1), Financial Times/Prentice Hall) Pearson Education, Ltd. GBR. Dist: Trans-Atlantic Pubns., Inc.

Parmenter, David. Winning CFOs: Implementing & Applying Better Practices. 2011. (Wiley Corporate F&a Ser.: 19). (ENG., Illus.). 352p. 60.00 (978-0-470-76750-4(2), Wiley) Wiley, John & Sons, Inc.

Parrat, Frédéric. Reprise et Transmission de L'entreprise: Aspects Stratégiques, Juridiques et Fiscaux. 2010. 591p. (978-2-7178-5827-3(X)) Economica, Editions.

Peer-to-Peer Lending: Back to the Future. 2006. 75.00 net. (978-1-932795-03-5(0)) Filene Research Institute, Inc.

Philippines: Business Financing Handbook. (Illus.). 70p. (Orig.). pap. 295.00 (978-0-7605-1205-0(1)) Rector Pr., Ltd.

Pogue, Michael. Working Capital Management: Principles & Practice. 2011. 145p. pap. 27.00 (978-1-60649-187-4(3)) Business Expert Pr.

Poland: Business Financing Handbook. (Illus.). 70p. (Orig.). pap. 295.00 (978-0-7605-1206-7(X)) Rector Pr., Ltd.

Polino, Mark. Microsoft Dynamics Gp 2010 Cookbook: LITE Edition. 2011. 116p. pap. (978-1-84968-380-7(8)) Packt Publishing, Ltd.

Poll, Edward. The Successful Lawyer-Banker Relationship: A LawBiz Managment Special Report. 2006. 84p. per. 29.00 (978-0-9654948-7-8(X)) Poll, Edward & Assocs., Inc.

Portugal: Business Financing Handbook. (Illus.). 70p. (Orig.). pap. 295.00 (978-0-7605-1207-4(8)) Rector Pr., Ltd.

Pratt, Alexandra. Austerity Business: 39 Tips for Doing More with Less. 2010. (ENG.). 232p. pap. 19.95 (978-0-470-68872-4(6), Wiley) Wiley, John & Sons, Inc.

Protz, Daniel Marc. Das zivilrechtliche Anforderungsprofil mezzaniner Strukturen der Unternehmensfinanzierung. 2009. (Saarbrücker Studien zum Privat- und Wirtschaftsrecht Ser.). (GRE.). 622p. 149.95 (978-3-631-59320-2(1)) Lang, Peter GmbH, Europäischer Verlag der Wissenschaften DEU. Dist: Lang, Peter.

Pyka, Andreas & Burghof, Hans-Peter, eds. Innovation & Finance. 2012. (Routledge Studies in Global Competition Ser.). (ENG., Illus.). 256p. (C). 130.00 (978-0-415-69685-2(2)) Routledge.

Quintyn, Marc & Verdier, Genevieve, eds. African Finance in the 21st Century. 2010. (ENG., Illus.). 176p. 116.00 (978-0-230-58050-3(5)) Palgrave Macmillan.

Quiry, Pascal, et al. Corporate Finance: Theory & Practice. 3rd ed. 2011. (ENG., Illus.). 1024p. pap. 90.00 (978-1-119-97558-8(1), Wiley) Wiley, John & Sons, Inc.

Redic, Patricia, concept & compiled by. Worksite Marketing - A Promise to Deliver: How to turn voluntary benefits into visible Results. 2008. per. 29.95 (978-0-9799807-9-4(8)) Millennium Star Publishing.

Ricketts, Martin, ed. The Economics of Modern Business Enterprise, 3 vols. 2008. (International Library of Critical Writings in Economics Ser.). 1840p. 940.00 (978-1-84064-902-4(X)) Elgar, Edward Publishing, Inc.

Roach, Stephen S. Stephen Roach on the Next Asia: Opportunities & Challenges for a New Globalization. 2009. (ENG., Illus.). 414p. 39.95 (978-0-470-44699-7(4), Wiley) Wiley, John & Sons, Inc.

Robbe. Emerging Market Finance: Law & Practice. 2011. (978-90-411-3244-4(9)) Kluwer Law International.

Robbins, William L. & Lasch, Jonathan G. Seed-Stage Venture Investing, 2nd Edition: An Insider's Guide to Start-Ups for Scientists, Engineers, & Investors. 2011. 304p. pap. 49.95 (978-0-314-27972-9(5)) Aspatore Bks.

Roehl-Anderson, Janice M. IT Best Practices for Financial Managers. 2010. (ENG., Illus.). 352p. 78.95 (978-0-470-50828-2(0), Wiley) Wiley, John & Sons, Inc.

Rogers, Steven. Entrepreneurial Finance: Finance & Business Strategies for the Serious Entrepreneur. 2nd ed. 2009. (ENG., Illus.). 372p. 59.95 (978-0-07-159126-3(5), 0071591265) McGraw-Hill Cos., The.

Rogoff, Edward G. Bankable Business Plans: Second Edition. 2nd rev. ed. 2007. (ENG., Illus.). 275p. per. 24.95 (978-0-9791522-0-7(8)) Rowhouse Publishing.

—Bankable Business Plans for Entrepreneurial Ventures: Textbook Edition. 2007. (ENG., Illus.). 380p. (C). per. 95.00 (978-0-9791522-2-1(4)) Rowhouse Publishing.

Rösler, René. Microfinance on Corporate Level. 2008. 60p. pap. (978-3-8364-9314-7(4)) VDM Verlag Dr. Mueller e.K.

Russia: Business Financing Handbook. (Illus.). 70p. (Orig.). pap. 295.00 (978-0-7605-1208-1(6)) Rector Pr., Ltd.

Ryan, Bob. Finance & Accounting for Business. 2nd ed. 2008. (Illus.). 544p. (C). 64.99 (978-1-84480-897-7(1)) Cengage Learning GBR. Dist: CENGAGE Learning.

Saki, Jacob. Credit Cards Finance System. 2009. 256p. pap. 39.95 (978-1-59330-589-5(3)) Aventine Pr.

Sansone, Alicia, et al. The Handbook of Loan Syndications & Trading. 2006. (ENG., Illus.). 1000p. 129.95 (978-0-07-146898-5(6), 0071468986) McGraw-Hill Cos., The.

SCALO. Credits & Collection Starter Kit. 17th ed. 2007. pap. 29.50 (978-1-56150-838-9(1)) International Wealth Success, Inc.

Schanz, Deborah & Schanz, Sebastian. Business Taxation & Financial Decisions. 2010. (ENG., Illus.). xxi, 401p. 139.00 (978-3-642-03283-7(4), 3642032834) Springer.

Schwenker, Burkhard & Spremann, Klaus. Management Between Strategy & Finance: The Four Seasons of Business. 2008. (ENG., Illus.). xiii, 325p. 79.95 (978-3-540-85274-2(3), 3540852743) Springer.

Seward, James. Corporate Restructurings & Reorganizations. 2013. (ENG.). 425p. 89.95 (978-0-12-637455-1(4), Academic Pr.) Elsevier Science & Technology Bks.

Sg - Strategic Financial Management. 2007. (C). pap. 35.95 (978-0-324-31879-1(0)) Cengage South-Western.

Shah, Syed Muhammad Amir. Determinants of Financing Patterns & Impact on Financial Performance. 2011. 128p. pap. (978-3-8443-9396-5(X)) Lambert Academic Publishing.

Shakespeare, Kevin. Trade for Good - the Essential Guide to Business & Finance in Uk & International Trade. 2011. (Illus.). 368p. pap. ***(978-1-905823-97-0(5))*** Ecademy Pr. Ltd.

Shapiro, Alan C. Multinational Financial Management. 9th ed. 2009. (ENG., Illus.). 762p. (C). 215.95 *(978-0-470-41501-6(0),* Wiley) Wiley, John & Sons, Inc.

Sherman, Andrew J. Raising Capital: Get the Money You Need to Grow Your Business, 1 vol. 3rd ed. 2012. (ENG.). 464p. 34.95 ***(978-0-8144-1703-4(5))*** Amacom.

Shim, Jae, et al. Schaum's Outline of Financial Management, Third Edition. 3rd ed. 2009. (Schaum's Outline Ser.). (ENG., Illus.). 504p. (C). pap. 20.00 *(978-0-07-163531-8(9),* 0071635319) McGraw-Hill Cos., The.

Shim, Jae K., et al. The Vest-Pocket MBA: Fourth Edition. 4th ed. 2011. (ENG., Illus.). 576p. (gr. 12). 22.00 ***(978-1-59184-433-4(9),*** Portfolio Trade) Penguin Group (USA) Inc.

Shoffner, H. George, et al. Finance for NonFinancial Managers. 3rd ed. 2010. (McGraw-Hill 36-Hour Courses Ser.). (ENG., Illus.). 352p. pap. 20.00 *(978-0-07-174955-8(1),* 0071749551) McGraw-Hill Cos., The.

Sloan, Richard & Lundholm, Russell. Equity Valuation & Analysis w/ EVal. 3rd ed. 2009. 384p. 168.44 incl. cd-rom *(978-0-07-352689-8(4))* McGraw-Hill Professional Publishing.

Sloman, John. Economics & the Business Environment with Companion Website with GradeTracker Student Access Card, 2/e. 2nd ed. 2007. (Illus.). pap. 87.50 *(978-1-4058-9250-5(9))* Financial Times/Prentice Hall.

Sloman, John & Jones, Elizabeth. Economics & the Business Environment, Pack. 3rd rev. ed. 2011. (ENG., Illus.). pap. 95.00 ***(978-0-273-73486-4(5))*** Pearson Education, Ltd. GBR. Dist: Trans-Atlantic Pubns., Inc.

Smith, N. R. Understanding Financial Management. 2007. per. 12.95 net. *(978-1-60402-347-3(3))* Independent Pub.

Smith, Richard G. The Law of Entrepreneurial Finance. 2012. *(978-0-7355-4081-1(0),* Aspen Pubs.) Wolters Kluwer Law & Business.

Spulber, Daniel F. Economics & Management of Competitive Strategy. 2009. (Illus.). 520p. 99.00 *(978-981-283-846-9(5))* World Scientific Publishing Co., Inc.

Stancill. Entrepreneurial Finance. 2006. pap. 11.95 *(978-1-4288-1024-2(2))* Cram101 Inc.

Strauss, Steven D. Get Your Business Funded: Creative Methods for Getting the Money You Need. 2011. (ENG., Illus.). 246p. pap. 19.95 *(978-0-470-92811-0(5),* Wiley) Wiley, John & Sons, Inc.

Stutely, Richard. The Definitive Guide to Business Finance: What Smart Managers Do with the Numbers. 2nd rev. ed. 2008. (Financial Times Ser.). (ENG., Illus.). 432p. pap. 44.99 *(978-0-273-71095-0(8))* FT Press.

Takayasu, Misako, et al, eds. New Approaches to the Analysis of Large-Scale Business & Economic Data. 2010. (ENG.). x, 342p. 249.00 *(978-4-431-53852-3(6),* 4431538526) Springer.

Tarantino, Anthony, et al. Risk Management in Finance: Six Sigma & Other Next-Generation Techniques. 2009. (Wiley Finance Ser.: 493). (ENG., Illus.). 360p. 75.00 *(978-0-470-41346-3(8),* Wiley) Wiley, John & Sons, Inc.

Tennent, John. Guide to Financial Management. 2008. (Economist Ser.). (ENG., Illus.). 327p. 29.95 *(978-1-86197-809-7(X),* Bloomberg Pr.) Wiley, John & Sons, Inc.

Tennent, John & Friend, Graham. Guide to Business Modelling. 3rd ed. 2011. (Economist Ser.). (ENG., Illus.). 298p. 45.00 *(978-1-118-09553-9(7),* Wiley) Wiley, John & Sons, Inc.

Thumann, Albert & Woodroof, Eric. Energy Project Financing: Resources & Strategies for Success. 2nd ed. 2008. (ENG.). 450p. 104.95 *(978-1-4200-8386-6(4))* Fairmont Pr., Inc.

Titman, et al. Financial Management: Principles & Applications, Student Value Edition, & MyFinanceLab with Pearson eText Student Access Code Card Package. 11th ed. 2011. (C). ring bd. 154.00 ***(978-0-13-274207-8(1))*** Pearson Education.

Titman, Sheridan, et al. Financial Management: Principles & Applications. 11th ed. 2010. (ENG.). 336p. (C). pap., stu. ed. 48.20 *(978-0-13-234082-3(8),* Prentice Hall) Prentice Hall PTR.

—Financial Management: Principles & Applications plus MyFinanceLab Package. 11th ed. 2010. (ENG.). (C). 242.67 *(978-0-13-216589-1(9),* Prentice Hall) Prentice Hall PTR.

—Financial Management: Principles & Applications, Student Value Edition. 11th ed. 2010. (ENG.). 744p. (C). ring bd. 153.33 *(978-0-13-254433-7(4),* Prentice Hall) Prentice Hall PTR.

Tranter, Kimberly A., et al. An Introduction to Revenue Management for the Hospitality Industry: Principles & Practices for the Real World. 2008. (ENG., Illus.). 352p. (C). per. 103.20 *(978-0-13-188589-9(8),* Prentice Hall) Prentice Hall PTR.

Trapp, Roger, et al. What You Need to Know about Business. 2011. (ENG., Illus.). 256p. pap. 19.95 *(978-0-85708-115-5(2),* Capstone) Wiley, John & Sons, Inc.

Triana, Pablo & Triana. Lecturing Birds on Flying: Can Mathematical Theories Destroy the Financial Markets? 2009. (ENG., Illus.). 400p. 29.95 *(978-0-470-40675-5(5),* Wiley) Wiley, John & Sons, Inc.

Tripathi, Ashutosh. Economics: A Business Management Approach. 2011. 376p. 53.28 *(978-1-4567-7063-1(2))* AuthorHouse.

Trottier, Richard M. & Trottier. Middle Market Strategies: How Private Companies Use the Markets to Create Value. 2009. (ENG., Illus.). 288p. 52.95 *(978-0-470-46457-1(7),* Wiley) Wiley, John & Sons, Inc.

Turner, Geoff. Effective Financial Management: The Cornerstone to Success. 2011. 200p. pap. 27.00 *(978-1-60649-233-8(0))* Business Expert Pr.

Uduk, Paul. The Gods of Quality Strike Back: The Rise & near Fall of an Iconic Bank, How it Flunked the Ultimate Test & Paid a Humiliating Price: the Unauthorised Story & Other Lessons on Excellence. 2011. 160p. pap. 13.69 ***(978-1-4269-7224-9(5))*** Trafford Publishing.

Uvalic, Milica. Investment & Property Rights in Yugoslavia: The Long Transition to a Market Economy. 2009. (Cambridge Russian, Soviet & Post-Soviet Studies). (ENG., Illus.). 276p. pap. 38.99 *(978-0-521-12258-0(9))* Cambridge Univ. Pr.

Van Horne, James C., et al. Fundamentals of Financial Management. 13th ed. 2008. (ENG., Illus.). 760p. (C). pap. 133.33 *(978-0-273-71363-0(9),* Prentice Hall) Prentice Hall PTR.

van Putten II, Paul. Five Dollars to Freedom. 2009. 121p. pap. 21.99 *(978-0-557-11686-7(4))* Lulu Enterprises Inc.

Vause, Bob. Analysing Companies. 5th rev. ed. 2009. (Economist Guide to Analysing Companies Ser.). (ENG.). 336p. 29.95 *(978-1-57660-341-3(5),* Bloomberg Pr.) Wiley, John & Sons, Inc.

, Venture Hacks. Venture Hacks. Pitching Hacks: How to pitch startups to Investors. 2009. 86p. pap. 18.99 *(978-0-557-23559-9(6))* Lulu Enterprises Inc.

Visible Systems Corp Staff. Visible Systems Standard Edition 2008. 2008. (ENG.). (C). 51.95 *(978-0-470-45765-8(1),* Wiley) Wiley, John & Sons, Inc.

Von Bloh, Hannah. Access to & Impact of Microcredit in Rural Northern Vietnam. 2008. 132p. pap. *(978-3-639-06089-8(X))* VDM Verlag Dr. Mueller e.K.

Wall Street Syndicators. 17th ed. 2007. pap. 15.00 *(978-1-56150-782-5(2))* International Wealth Success, Inc.

Walling, Christopher. Financial Strategies for Corporate Executives. 2009. 57p. pap. 14.99 *(978-0-557-09537-7(9))* Lulu Enterprises Inc.

Watson, Denzil & Head, Antony. Corporate Finance Book & MyFinancelab XI, Pack. 5th ed. 2010. (Illus.). 474p. pap. 92.50 *(978-0-273-72534-3(3))* Financial Times/Prentice Hall.

Weaver, Samuel. The Essentials of Financial Analysis. 2011. (ENG., Illus.) 480p. 50.00 ***(978-0-07-176836-8(X),*** 007176836X) McGraw-Hill Cos., The.

Weaver, Samuel C. & Weston, J. Fred. Strategic Financial Management: Applications of Corporate Finance. 2007. (ENG., Illus.). 704p. (C). 236.95 *(978-0-324-31875-3(8))* Cengage South-Western.

Why Finance Transformation Matters in Global Manufacturing. 2007. *(978-1-934025-02-4(X))* Deloitte.

Wiedemann, Lucas. Introduction in Financial Management. 2009. 68p. pap. 17.40 *(978-1-4092-9908-0(2))* Lulu Enterprises Inc.

Willy A. Sussland. Innovate Out of Crisis. 2009. 376p. 49.95 *(978-1-4269-1113-2(0))* Trafford Publishing.

Winston, Andrew S. Green Recovery: Get Lean, Get Smart, & Emerge from the Downturn on Top. 2009. (ENG., Illus.). 208p. 20.00 *(978-1-4221-6654-3(6))* Harvard Business Review Pr.

Woodbine, Steven. Vending Machine Fundamentals Volume II: Success Strategies for Building Your Own Bulk Route. 2009. 108p. pap. 18.95 *(978-0-557-18673-0(0))* Lulu Enterprises Inc.

Woodward, Jim, et al. Great News! We've Sold the Company. 2006. 314p. pap. 29.95 *(978-1-4137-9233-1(2))* PublishAmerica, Inc.

Worsham, C. Bruce. Foundations of Financial Planning: An Overview. 2nd rev. ed. 2009. (ENG.). 500p. (C). 110.00 *(978-1-932819-75-5(4))* American College, The.

Worsham, C. Bruce, et al. Foundations of Financial Planning: An Overview. 2007. 400p. (C). 50.00 *(978-1-932819-28-1(2))* American College, The.

Xu, Qing. Archimedean-Copula-Based Models in Financial Risk Management. 2010. 152p. pap. *(978-3-8383-0293-5(1))* Lambert Academic Publishing.

Yates, Jonathan. Freesourcing: How to Start a Business with No Money. 2010. (ENG.). 240p. pap. 15.95 *(978-1-906465-80-3(0),* Capstone) Wiley, John & Sons, Inc.

Yazdipour, Rassoul. Advances in Entrepreneurial Finance: With Applications from Behavioral Finance & Economics. 2010. (ENG., Illus.). x, 240p. 139.00 *(978-1-4419-7526-3(8),* 1441975268) Springer.

2007 AEC Industry Outlook: Strategy & Insight for Design & Construction Firms. 5th ed. 2006. per. 255.00 ***(978-1-934150-12-2(6))*** ZweigWhite.

BUSINESS ENTERPRISES—HISTORY

Davies, Roger. Wallace Arnold Days. 2010. (ENG., Illus.). 96p. 27.95 *(978-0-7110-3438-9(9))* Allan, Ian Publishing GBR. Dist: BookMasters Distribution Services (BDS).

Gant, Tina. International Directory of Company Histories, 100. 2009. (International Directory of Company Histories Ser.). (ENG.). 704p. 312.00 *(978-1-55862-634-6(4))* Cengage Gale.

—Intl Dir Co Hist. 2008. (International Directory of Company Histories Ser.). (ENG.). 704p. 312.00 *(978-1-55862-619-5(0));* 720p. 312.00 *(978-1-55862-617-1(4));* 800p. 312.00 *(978-1-55862-615-7(8))* Cengage Gale.

Grant, Tina, ed. International Directory of Company Histories, Volume 92. 2008. (International Directory of Company Histories Ser.). (ENG., Illus.). 736p. 312.00 *(978-1-55862-613-3(1))* Cengage Gale.

Higman, B. W. & Monteith, Kathleen E. A., eds. West Indian Business History: Enterprise & Entrepreneurship. 2010. (Illus.). 236p. pap. *(978-976-640-240-2(X))* Univ. of the West Indies Pr.

Imagineers Staff. Walt Disney Imagineering: A Behind the Dreams Look at Making More Magic Real. 2010. (ENG., Illus.). 192p. 60.00 *(978-1-4231-0766-8(7),* Disney Editions) Disney Pr.

International Directory of Company Histories. 2011. (ENG.). 312.00 *(978-1-55862-791-8(X),* St. James Pr.) 2011. (ENG.). 312.00 *(978-1-55862-790-1(1),* St. James Pr.) 2011. (ENG.). 312.00 *(978-1-55862-789-5(8),* St. James Pr.) 2011. (ENG.). 312.00 *(978-1-55862-788-8(X),* St. James Pr.) 2011. 312.00 *(978-1-55862-787-1(1),* St. James Pr.)101. 2009. (ENG.). 736p. 312.00 *(978-1-55862-635-5(2))*102. 2009. (ENG.). 704p. 312.00 *(978-1-55862-636-2(0))* Vol. 108. 2009. (ENG.). 312.00 *(978-1-4144-4104-7(5))* Vol. 109. 2010. (ENG.). 312.00 *(978-1-4144-4105-4(3))* Vol. 110. 2010. (ENG.). 312.00 *(978-1-4144-4106-1(1))* Vol. 111. 2010. (ENG.). 312.00 *(978-1-4144-4107-8(X))* Vol. 112. 2010. (ENG.). 312.00 *(978-1-4144-4108-5(8))* Vol. 113. 2010. (ENG.). 312.00 *(978-1-4144-4109-2(6))* Cengage Gale.

J C Wood Staff & M C Wood Staff. Alfred D Chandler: Critical Evaluations in Business & Mgmt. 2007. (Illus.). 424p. Vol. 1. *(978-0-415-32564-6(1))* Vol. 2. *(978-0-415-32565-3(X))* Routledge.

Jones, Geoffrey & Friedman, Walter A. The Rise of the Modern Firm. 2012. (International Library of Critical Writings in Economics Ser.). (Illus.). 736p. 399.95 ***(978-1-84844-781-3(7))*** Elgar, Edward Publishing, Inc.

Land, Bob. America's Greatest Brands. 2009. (Americas Greatest Brands Ser.). (ENG.). 113p. 45.00 *(978-0-9706860-6-0(4))* America's Greatest Brands.

Llc, Books, ed. Companies Established in 1980: Steve Jackson Games, Psion, Fasa, Taschen, Bmc Software, Whole Foods Market, Stagecoach Group, Ashton-Tate. 2010. 564p. pap. 62.19 *(978-1-156-42779-8(7))* General Bks. LLC.

Maceira de Rosen, Sagra & Goldstein Crowe, Lauren. The Towering World of Jimmy Choo: A Glamorous Story of Power, Profits, & the Pursuit of the Perfect Shoe. 2009. (ENG.). 240p. 26.00 *(978-1-59691-391-2(6))* Bloomsbury Publishing.

Mortimer, Thomas. Every Man his Own Broker: Or, A Guide to Exchange-Alley. 2010. (Cambridge Library Collection - History Ser.). (ENG., Illus.). 214p. pap. 22.99 *(978-1-108-02582-9(X))* Cambridge Univ. Pr.

Orbell, John. Tracing the History of a Business. 2009. (ENG., Illus.). 192p. 37.95 *(978-1-86077-575-8(6))* History Pr. Ltd.,The GBR. Dist: Independent Pubs. Group.

Owen, Gareth. The Shepperton Story: The History of the World-Famous Film Studio. 2009. (ENG., Illus.). 320p. pap. 45.00 *(978-0-7524-4970-8(2))* History Pr. Ltd.,The GBR. Dist: Independent Pubs. Group.

Pederson, Jay P. International Directory of Company Histories, 99. 2009. (International Directory of Company Histories Ser.). (ENG.). 736p. 312.00 *(978-1-55862-633-1(6))* Cengage Gale.

—Intl Dir Co Hist. 2008. (International Directory of Company Histories Ser.). (ENG.). 720p. 312.00 *(978-1-55862-618-8(2));* 768p. 312.00 *(978-1-55862-616-4(6));* 848p. 312.00 *(978-1-55862-612-6(3))* Cengage Gale.

Pederson, Jay P., ed. International Directory of Company Histories: Volume 93. 2008. (International Directory of Company Histories Ser.). (ENG.). 816p. 312.00 *(978-1-55862-614-0(X))* Cengage Gale.

Pinel, Stephen L. Organbuilding along the Erie & Chenango Canals: Alvinza & George N. Andrews of Utica, New York. 2010. (Illus.). xxix, 301p. ***(978-0-913499-30-6(7))*** Organ Historical Society, Inc., The.

Reardon, John. Patek Philippe in America: Marketing the World's Foremost Watch. 2008. (Illus.). 360p. 395.00 *(978-0-9820379-2-8(9))* Cefari Publishing.

Reese, Andrew R. Reese's Peanut Butter Cups: The Untold Story. 2008. (ENG.). 108p. 22.95 *(978-0-595-49107-0(3));* pap. 12.95 *(978-0-595-48707-3(6))* iUniverse, Inc.

Schmidt, James M. Lincoln's Labels: America's Best Known Brands & the Civil War. 2009. (ENG.). 224p. pap. 19.95 *(978-1-889020-28-0(1));* (Illus.). 27.95 *(978-1-889020-21-1(4))* Edinborough Pr.

Sigall, Bob. The Companies We Keep 2: More amazing stories about Hawaii people, places & Companies. 2007. (Illus.). 240p. per. 18.99 *(978-0-9724504-1-6(6))* Small Business Hawaii.

Sluby, Patricia Carter. The Entrepreneurial Spirit of African American Inventors, 1 vol. 2011. (Illus.). 250p. 44.95 *(978-0-313-36335-1(8),* C36335); E-Book *(978-0-313-36336-8(6))* Greenwood Publishing Group, Inc. (Praeger Pubs.).

Teutul, Paul & Teutul. The Ride of a Lifetime: Doing Business the Orange County Choppers Way. 2009. (ENG., Illus.). 208p. 24.95 *(978-0-470-44997-4(7),* Wiley) Wiley, John & Sons, Inc.

Walker, Juliet E. K. The History of Black Business in America: Capitalism, Race, Entrepreneurship: Volume 1, To 1865, 2 vols. 2nd ed. 2009. (ENG., Illus.). 432p. 69.95 *(978-0-8078-3241-7(3));* pap. 26.95 *(978-0-8078-5910-0(9))* Univ. of North Carolina Pr.

Wright, Alex. The Imagineering Field Guide to Magic Kingdom at Walt Disney World — Updated! 2009. (ENG.). 128p. pap. 9.95 *(978-1-4231-2468-9(5),* Disney Editions) Disney Pr.

BUSINESS ENTERPRISES—LOCATION

see Industrial Location

BUSINESS ENTERPRISES—MANAGEMENT

see Industrial Management

BUSINESS ENTERPRISES—PLANNING

see Business Planning

BUSINESS ENTERPRISES—SOCIAL ASPECTS

see Industries—Social Aspects

BUSINESS ENTERPRISES—TAXATION

see also Business Tax; Enterprise Zones

Aujean, Michel & Saint-Etienne, Christian. Stratégies Fiscales des états et des Entreprises: Souveraineté et Concurrence. 2009. (FRE & ENG., Illus.). 184p. *(978-2-13-056897-1(1))* Presses Universitaires de France.

Avi-Yonah, Reuven. International Tax as International Law: An Analysis of the International Tax Regime. 2007. (Cambridge Tax Law Ser.). (ENG.). 224p. 80.00 *(978-0-521-85283-8(8))* Cambridge Univ. Pr.

Avi-Yonah, Reuven S. International Tax as International Law: An Analysis of the International Tax Regime. 2007. (Cambridge Tax Law Ser.). (ENG., Illus.). 224p. per. 36.00 *(978-0-521-61801-4(0))* Cambridge Univ. Pr.

Avi-Yonah, Reuven S. & Ring, Diane M. International Tax, 2nd Edition, 2007 Supplement. 2nd rev. ed. 2007. (University Casebook Ser.). 35p. 21.00 *(978-1-59941-331-0(0),* Foundation Pr.) West.

Ayers, Benjamin, et al. Taxation of Business Entities. 3rd ed. 2011. (ENG., Illus.). 736p. (C). 241.67 *(978-0-07-732841-2(8),* 0077328418, McGraw-Hill/Irwin) McGraw-Hill Higher Education.

—Taxation of Individuals & Business Entities, 2012. 3rd ed. 2011. (ENG., Illus.). 1264p. (C). 243.00 *(978-0-07-811106-8(4),* 0078111064, McGraw-Hill/Irwin) McGraw-Hill Higher Education.

Bank, Steven A. Gilbert Law Summaries on Tax of Business Entities. 14th rev. ed. 2011. 318p. pap. 38.00 ***(978-0-314-27912-5(1))*** West.

Bertram, David, ed. Butterworths Business Tax Service. (Illus.). ring bd. *(978-0-406-99863-7(9),* BBTSASET, MICHIE) LEXIS Publishing.

Borden, Bradley T. Taxation & Business Planning for Real Estate Transactions. 2011. ***(978-1-4224-8230-8(8))*** LexisNexis Matthew Bender.

Brady, Miranda L. & Hansen, Samantha C., eds. International Corporate Taxation: Considerations & Comparisons. 2012. ***(978-1-62100-501-8(1))*** Nova Science Pubs., Inc.

Brookes, David & Kronbergs. Venture Capital Tax Reliefs. 2nd rev. ed. 2011. (Illus.). 616p. pap. 235.00 *(978-1-84766-086-2(X),* Bloomsbury Professional) Bloomsbury Publishing Plc GBR. Dist: International Specialized Bk. Services.

Caldewell, Terrance B., ed. Taxation: 21st Century Issues & Challenges. 2008. 185.00 *(978-1-60456-099-2(1))* Nova Science Pubs., Inc.

Cao, Fuli. Corporate Income Tax Law & Practice in the People's Republic of China, 1 vol. 2011. (ENG., Illus.). 592p. pap. 225.00 *(978-0-19-539339-2(2))* Oxford Univ. Pr., Inc.

CCH Tax Law Editors. Principles of Business Taxation. 2009th ed. 2009. 900p. 149.00 *(978-0-8080-2060-8(9))* Toolkit Media Group.

Cram101 Textbook Reviews Staff. Outlines & Highlights for Business Planning by Franklin a Gevurtz, Isbn: 9781599411491. 2009. 64p. pap. 27.95 *(978-1-4288-3989-2(5))* Cram101 Inc.

—Outlines & Highlights for Taxes & Business Strategy by Myron S Scholes, Mark a Wolfson, Merle M Erickson, Edward L Maydew, Terrence J Shevlin. 2009. 174p. pap. 29.95 *(978-1-4288-3295-4(5))* Cram101 Inc.

German Council of Economic Experts Staff. Dual Income Tax. 2008. (ZEW Economic Studies). pap. 119.00 *(978-3-7908-2051-5(2))* Springer.

Gevurtz, Franklin. Business Planning: Cases & Materials. 4th ed. 2008. xiii, 1182p. pap. *(978-1-59941-619-9(0),* Foundation Pr.) West.

Grimm, Sebastian. Die Negative Konkurrentenklage Im Steuerrecht. 2011. (Finanz- und Steuerrecht in Deutschland und Europa Ser.). (GER.). 302p. 83.95 ***(978-3-631-61583-6(3))*** Lang, Peter GmbH, Europaischer Verlag der Wissenschaften DEU. Dist: Lang, Peter.

Horvath, James L. & Chodikoff, David W., eds. Taxation & Valuation of Technology: Theory Practice, & the Law. 2008. 1004p. *(978-1-55221-152-6(5))* Irwin Law Inc.

Hughes, Peter. Tax Planning for Businesses & Their Owners: A Specially Commissioned Report. 2006. (Thorogood Professional Insights Ser.). (Illus.). 138p. spiral bd. 185.00 *(978-1-85418-334-7(6))* Thorogood GBR. Dist: Stylus Publishing, LLC.

Indian Governments & the Tax Code: Maximizing Tax Incentives for Economic Development: Hearing Before the Committee on Finance, United States Senate, One Hundred Tenth Congress, Second Session, July 22, 2008. 2008. iii, 101p. *(978-0-16-086674-6(X),* 552-070-41652-8) United States Government Printing Office.

James, Malcolm. Taxation of Small Businesses: Fourth Edition. 2011. 498p. pap. 135.00 ***(978-1-907444-39-5(4))*** Spiramus Pr. GBR. Dist: International Specialized Bk. Services.

Kamlana, Unathi. The Taxation of Black Economic Empowerment Transactions. 2010. 100p. pap. *(978-3-8383-4493-5(6))* Lambert Academic Publishing.

Levey, Mark M. & Wrappe, Steven C. Practical Guide to Transfer Pricing Rules & Compliance. 2nd rev. ed. 2007. 500p. pap. 165.00 *(978-0-8080-1656-4(3),* CCH) Wolters Kluwer Tax & Accounting.

McDaniel, Paul R. & McMahon, Martin J. Federal Income Taxation: Cases & Materials. 6th rev. ed. 2011. 96p. pap. 19.00 ***(978-1-59941-984-8(X),*** Foundation Pr.) West.

—Federal Income Taxation of Business Organizations 2008. 4th rev. ed. 2008. (University Casebook Ser.). 80p. pap., suppl. ed. 17.00 *(978-1-59941-477-5(5),* Foundation Pr.) West.

—Federal Income Taxation of Business Organizations 2011. 4th rev. ed. 2011. 112p. pap. 19.00 ***(978-1-59941-982-4(3),*** Foundation Pr.) West.

—Federal Income Taxation of Business Organizations, 4th, 2009 Supplement. 4th rev. ed. 2009. (University Casebook Ser.). 86p. pap. 19.00 *(978-1-59941-782-0(0),* Foundation Pr.) West.

—Federal Income Taxation of Business Organizations, 4th, 2010 Supplement. 4th rev. ed. 2010. (University Casebook Ser.). 78p. pap. 17.00 *(978-1-59941-815-5(0),* Foundation Pr.) West.

—Federal Income Taxation of Corporations, 3d, 2009 Supplement. 3rd rev. ed. 2009. (University Casebook Ser.). 59p. pap. 17.00 (978-1-59941-781-3(2), Foundation Pr.) West.

McDaniel, Paul R., et al. Federal Income Taxation of Business Organizations. 4th rev. ed. 2007. (University Casebook Ser.). 41p. pap. 13.00 (978-1-59941-418-8(X), Foundation Pr.) West.

Meyer-Sandberg, Nils. Die Duale Einkommensteuer als Modell ungleicher Besteuerung von Arbeit und Kapital. 2008. (Finanz- und Steuerrecht in Deutschland und Europa Ser.). 310p. pap. 74.95 (978-3-631-58084-4(3)) Lang, Peter GmbH, Europaischer Verlag der Wissenschaften DEU. Dist: Lang, Peter.

Myers J.D., Terence M. & DeScherer J.D., Dorinda. Business Tax Answer Book 2009. 2008. 760p. pap. 169.00 (978-0-8080-1912-1(0)) Toolkit Media Group.

Myers, Terence M. & Descherer, Dorinda D. Business Tax Answer Book (2012) 2011. 808p. pap. 217.00 (**978-0-8080-2835-2(9)**, CCH) Wolters Kluwer Tax & Accounting.

Nagel, Walter. State Business Taxes. 2009. (978-1-58852-161-3(3), Law Journal Pr.) Incisive Media.

Neslund, Kristofer & Neslund, Nancy. Questions & Answers: Multiple-Choice & Short-Answer Questions & Answers. 2011. iii, 280p. pap. (**978-1-4224-8034-2(8)**, Wiley-Blackwell) LexisNexis Matthew Bender.

Olson, William. Adviser's Guide to the Tax Consequences of the Purchase & Sale of a Business. 2nd ed. 2007. pap. 61.25 (978-0-87051-692-4(2)) American Institute of Certified Public Accountants.

Raabe. West Federal Tax: Essentials of Taxation. 2008. (C). 148.00 (978-0-324-38109-2(3)) Cengage South-Western.

Schanz, Deborah & Schanz, Sebastian. Business Taxation & Financial Decisions. 2010. (ENG., Illus.). xxi, 401p. 139.00 (978-3-642-03283-7(4), 3642032834) Springer.

Scholes, Myron S., et al. Taxes & Business Strategy: A Planning Approach. 4th ed. 2008. (ENG., Illus.). 624p. (C). 173.33 (978-0-13-603315-8(6), Prentice Hall) Prentice Hall PTR.

Smith, James E. West Federal Taxation: Taxation of Business Entities. 2006. pap. 15.95 (978-1-4288-0970-3(8)) Cram101 Inc.

Smith, James E., et al. South-Western Federal Taxation 2011: Taxation of Business Entities, Professional Edition (Book Only) 14th ed. 2010. (ENG.). 928p. (C). pap. 229.95 (978-0-538-78622-5(1)) Cengage South-Western.

—South-Western Federal Taxation 2013: Taxation of Business Entities (with H&R Block @ Home Tax Preparation Software CD-ROM) 16th ed. 2012. (ENG.). 896p. (C). 263.95 incl. cd-rom (**978-1-133-18981-7(4)**) Cengage South-Western.

Smith, James E., et al. Taxation of Business Entities 2008. 11th rev. ed. 2007. (ENG., Illus.). 888p. (C). 246.95 (978-0-324-36664-8(7)) Cengage South-Western.

Smith, Richard G., et al. Prof Version: Wft Taxation of Business Entities (), Vol. 4. 12th ed. 2008. (C). 181.95 (978-0-324-66053-1(7)) Cengage South-Western.

Spilker, Brian, et al. McGraw-Hill's Taxation of Individuals, 2013 Edition. 4th ed. 2012. (ENG., Illus.). 736p. (C). 241.67 (**978-0-07-743411-3(0)**, 0077434110, McGraw-Hill/Irwin) McGraw-Hill Higher Education.

—McGraw-Hill's Taxation of Individuals & Business Entities, 2013 Edition. 4th ed. 2012. (ENG., Illus.). 1216p. (C). 243.00 (**978-0-07-802546-4(X)**, 007802546X, McGraw-Hill/Irwin) McGraw-Hill Higher Education.

Spilker, Brian C., et al. Taxation of Individuals & Business Entities, 2011 Edition. 2nd ed. 2010. (ENG., Illus.). 1280p. (C). 243.00 (978-0-07-813670-2(9), 0078136709, McGraw-Hill/Irwin) McGraw-Hill Higher Education.

State Taxation: The Role of Congress in Developing Apportionment Standards: Hearing Before the Subcommittee on Commercial & Administrative Law of the Committee on the Judiciary, House of Representatives, One Hundred Eleventh Congress, Second Session, May 6, 2010. 2010. iii, 68p. (978-0-16-086186-4(1), 552-070-41284-1) United States Government Printing Office.

Stockdale, John, Jr. BVR's Guide to Canadian Valuation Cases. 2008. ring bd. 279.00 (978-0-9793776-5-5(X)) Business Valuation Resources, LLC.

Streng, William P. Choice of Entity. 2007. (Tax Management Portfolios Ser.: 700-3rd). spiral bd. 400.00 (978-1-55871-579-0(7)) Tax Management, Inc.

VAT Planning 2008/09. 2008. 1304p. pap. 275.00 (978-1-84766-105-0(X), Bloomsbury Professional) Bloomsbury Publishing Plc GBR. Dist: International Specialized Bk. Services.

Westin, Richard A. & Beck, Richard C. E. Federal Income Taxation of Business Enterprises: Cases, Statutes, Rulings. 2007. per. (978-1-60042-024-5(9)) Vandeplas Publishing.

Zuckerman, Jack, et al. The Business Tax Return Handbook. 3rd ed. 2010. (Illus.). ix, 194p. (978-1-60442-801-8(5)) American Bar Assn.

BUSINESS ENTERPRISES—VALUATION

Abrams, Jay B. Quantitative Business Valuation: A Mathematical Approach for Today's Professionals. 2nd ed. 2010. (ENG., Illus.). 672p. 150.00 (978-0-470-39016-0(6), Wiley) Wiley, John & Sons, Inc.

Allman, Keith A. Corporate Valuation Modeling: A Step-by-Step Guide. 2010. (Wiley Finance Ser.: 537). (ENG., Illus.). 275p. pap. 95.00 (978-0-470-48179-0(X), Wiley) Wiley, John & Sons, Inc.

Bauer, Georg. Wertorientierte Steuerung multidivisionaler Unternehmen über Residualgewinne. 2009. (Regensburger Beiträge zur betriebswirtschaftlichen Forschung Ser.). (GER.). 430p. pap. 99.95 (978-3-631-58007-3(X)) Lang, Peter GmbH, Europaischer Verlag der Wissenschaften DEU. Dist: Lang, Peter.

Business Valuation Firm Economics & Best Practices Survey. 2006. ring bd. 279.00 (978-0-9758668-6-3(9)) Business Valuation Resources, LLC.

Business Valuation Resources. BVR's Guide to Personal V. Enterprise Goodwill. 2008. ring bd. 329.00 (978-0-9793776-4-8(1)) Business Valuation Resources, LLC.

Bvr, adapted by. BVR's Guide to Estate & Gift Tax Case Law. 2008. ring bd. 229.00 (978-0-9793776-0-0(9)) Business Valuation Resources, LLC.

BVR's Guide to Discounts for Lack of Marketability. 2008. ring bd. 329.00 (978-0-9758668-9-4(3)) Business Valuation Resources, LLC.

BVR's Guide to Fair Value in Shareholder Dissent, Oppression, & Marital Dissolution. 2007. ring bd. 279.00 (978-0-9758668-8-7(5)) Business Valuation Resources, LLC.

Carver, Lorenzo. Venture Capital Valuation: Case Studies & Methodology. 2011. (Wiley Finance Ser.: 631). (ENG., Illus.). 288p. 95.00 (978-0-470-90828-0(9), Wiley) Wiley, John & Sons, Inc.

Castilleja-Vargas, Liliana. Valuation Effects on the Business Cycle in Emerging Markets. 2010. 184p. pap. (978-3-8383-4451-5(0)) Lambert Academic Publishing.

Cram101 Textbook Reviews & Cram101 Textbook Reviews. Outlines & Highlights for Quantitative Business Valuation: A Mathematical Approach for Today's Professionals by Jay B. Abrams. 2011. 90p. pap. 27.95 (**978-1-61830-240-3(X)**) Cram101 Inc.

Cuypers, Bart & Parmentier, Guy. Business Valuation: Using Financial Analysis to Measure a Company's Value. 2012. (Illus.). 274p. pap. 111.00 (**978-1-78068-016-3(3)**) Intersentia Uitgevers N.V. BEL. Dist: International Specialized Bk. Services.

Damodaran, Aswath. The Dark Side of Valuation: Valuing Young, Distressed, & Complex Businesses. 2nd ed. 2009. (ENG., Illus.). 600p. 74.99 (978-0-13-712689-7(1)) FT Press.

Davidson, Ian & Tippett, Mark. Principles of Equity Valuation. 2012. (ENG., Illus.). 328p. (C). 195.00 (**978-0-415-69602-9(X)**); pap. 90.00 (**978-0-415-69603-6(8)**) Routledge.

Douglas, Deborah L. Ripe: Harvesting the Value of Your Business. 2010. 224p. 24.95 (978-1-59079-193-6(2)) Select Bks.

Dupke, Edward, et al. Business Valuation Standards: Analysis, Application & Reporting. 2008. (ENG.). 256p. 95.00 (978-0-470-24786-0(X), Wiley) Wiley, John & Sons, Inc.

Eschmann, Philippe Olivier. Chancen und Grenzen von Multiples zur Unternehmensbewertung: Vergleich der Sicht von Analysten, Rating-Agenturen und strategischen Investoren. 2009. 72p. pap. (978-3-639-21024-8(7)) VDM Verlag Dr. Mueller e.K.

Fannon, Nancy & Walker, Heidi. The Comprehensive Guide to the Use & Application of the Transaction Databases. 2008. ring bd. 379.00 (978-0-9793776-3-1(3)) Business Valuation Resources, LLC.

Fight, Andrew. Corporate Valuation. 2007. (Essential Capital Markets Ser.). (Illus.). 208p. pap. 40.00 (978-0-7506-6134-8(8), Butterworth-Heinemann) Elsevier Science & Technology Bks.

Grabowski, Roger J., et al. Cost of Capital , Fourth Edition & Financial Valuation, Third Edition Set. 2011. (ENG.). 310.00 (978-0-470-93501-9(4), Wiley) Wiley, John & Sons, Inc.

Grabowski, Roger J., et al. Cost of Capital, Fourth Edition & Financial Valuation, Third Edition Plus Workbooks Set. 2011. (ENG.). 460.00 (**978-0-470-93499-9(9)**, Wiley) Wiley, John & Sons, Inc.

Grace, Robin. Aligning Business Analysis. 2007. 188p. per. (978-1-897312-56-8(3)) Adlibbed Ltd.

Hawkins, George & Paschall, Michael. Business Valuation Guide. 2007. 1500p. pap. 379.00 (978-0-8080-1760-8(8)) Toolkit Media Group.

Hitchner, James R. Financial Valuation: Applications & Models. 3rd ed. 2011. (Wiley Finance Ser.: 545). (ENG., Illus.). 1320p. 150.00 (978-0-470-50687-5(3), Wiley) Wiley, John & Sons, Inc.

Hitchner, James R. & Mard, Michael J. Financial Valuation Workbook: Step-by-Step Exercises & Tests to Help You Master Financial Valuation. 3rd ed. 2011. (Wiley Finance Ser.: 546). (ENG., Illus.). 394p. pap., wbk. ed. 65.00 (978-0-470-50688-2(1), Wiley) Wiley, John & Sons, Inc.

Hoffelner, Matthias. Verfahren Zur Bewertung Mittelständischer Unternehmen Aus Sicht Eines Finanzinvestors. 2011. (Schriften des Instituts für Finanzen. Universität Leipzig Ser.). (GER.). 276p. 79.95 (978-3-631-61179-1(X)) Lang, Peter GmbH, Europaischer Verlag der Wissenschaften DEU. Dist: Lang, Peter.

Holton, Lisa, et al. Business Valuation for Dummies. 2009. (ENG.). 360p. pap. 21.99 (978-0-470-34401-9(6), For Dummies) Wiley, John & Sons, Inc.

Horvath, James L. Valuing a Business in Volatile Markets. 2010. (Illus.). x, 835p. (978-0-7798-2286-7(2)) Carswell.

Horvath, James L. & Chodikoff, David W., eds. Taxation & Valuation of Technology: Theory Practice, & the Law. 2008. 1004p. (978-1-55221-152-6(5)) Irwin Law, Inc.

Howard, Malcolm K. Accounting & Business Valuation Methods: How to Interpret IFRS Accounts. 2007. (ENG., Illus.). 312p. pap. 54.95 (978-0-7506-8468-2(2), CIMA Publishing) Elsevier Science & Technology Bks.

Hyden, Steven D., et al. Business Combinations with SFAS 141 R, 157, & 160: A Guide to Financial Reporting. 2009. (ENG., Illus.). 233p. pap. 210.50 (978-0-470-49755-5(6), Wiley) Wiley, John & Sons, Inc.

Ismail, Issham. Economic Value Added. 2011. 340p. pap. (**978-3-8454-1875-9(3)**) Lambert Academic Publishing.

Kantor, Mark. Valuation for Arbitration: Compensation Standards, Valuation Methods & Expert Evidence. 2008. (Illus.). 172.00 (978-90-411-2735-8(6)) Wolters Kluwer Law & Business.

Kline, Brian. How to Read & Understand Financial Statements: When You Don't Know What You Are Looking At - For Business Owners & Investors. 2007. (ENG., Illus.). 288p. per. 24.95 (978-1-60138-012-8(7)) Atlantic Publishing Co.

Kozberg, Anthony. Explaining Revenues & Valuations for Internet Firms. 2009. 104p. pap. (978-3-639-12804-8(4)) VDM Verlag Dr. Mueller e.K.

Kreutzmann, Daniel. Company Valuation & Information in Analyst Forecasts. 2010. 144p. pap. (978-3-8325-2529-3(7)) Logos Verlag Berlin.

Laro, David & Pratt, Shannon P. Business Valuation & Federal Taxes: Procedure, Law, & Perspective. 2nd ed. 2011. (ENG., Illus.). 482p. 130.00 (978-0-470-60162-4(0), Wiley) Wiley, John & Sons, Inc.

Lee, Timothy R. & Hood, L. Paul. A Reviewer's Handbook to Business Valuation: Practical Guidance to the Use & Abuse of a Business Appraisal. 6th ed. 2011. (ENG., Illus.). 378p. 95.00 (978-0-470-60340-6(2), Wiley) Wiley, John & Sons, Inc.

Lenhhoff, David C. A Business Enterprise Value Anthology. 2nd ed. 2011. (**978-1-935328-20-9(4)**) Appraisal Institute, The.

Long, Michael S. & Bryant, Thomas A. Valuing the Closely Held Firm. 2007. (Financial Management Association Survey & Synthesis Ser.). (ENG., Illus.). 320p. 65.00 (978-0-19-530146-5(3)) Oxford Univ. Pr., Inc.

Lundholm, Russell & Sloan, Richard. Equity Valuation & Analysis with EVal. 2nd ed. 2007. (ENG., Illus.). 342p. (C). 226.67 incl. cd-rom (978-0-07-721985-7(6), 0077219856, McGraw-Hill/Irwin) McGraw-Hill Higher Education.

Madden, Bartley J. Wealth Creation: A Systems Mindset for Building & Investing in Businesses for the Long Term. 2010. (Wiley Finance Ser.: 541). (ENG., Illus.). 178p. 75.00 (978-0-470-48868-3(9), Wiley) Wiley, John & Sons, Inc.

Makoujy, Rick & Amadeo, Paul. How to Read a Balance Sheet: The Bottom Line on What You Need to Know about Cash Flow, Assets, Liquidity, Debt, Equity & Profit... & How It All Comes Together. 2010. (ENG.). 224p. pap. 18.95 (978-0-07-170033-7(1), 0071700331) McGraw-Hill Cos., The.

Meitner, Matthias. The Market Approach to Comparable Company Valuation. 2006. (ZEW Economic Studies: Vol. 35). (Illus.). XII, 241p. pap. 159.00 (978-3-7908-1722-5(8), 3790817228) Physica-Verlag DEU. Dist: Springer.

Mercer, Z. Christopher & Harms, Travis W. Business Valuation: An Integrated Theory. 2nd rev. ed. 2007. (Wiley Series in Finance Ser.: 17). (ENG., Illus.). 288p. 99.95 (978-0-470-14816-7(0), Wiley) Wiley, John & Sons, Inc.

Miller, Warren D. Value Maps: Valuation Tools That Unlock Business Wealth. 2010. (ENG., Illus.). 408p. 110.00 (978-0-470-43756-8(1), Wiley) Wiley, John & Sons, Inc.

Nelling, Edward. Business Valuation Demystified. 2010. (Demystified Ser.). (ENG.). 288p. pap. 22.00 (978-0-07-170274-4(1), 0071702741) McGraw-Hill Cos., The.

Nir Kossovsky. Mission: Intangible. 2010. 228p. 39.95 (978-1-4269-2415-6(1)) Trafford Publishing.

Padua, Donatella. Trust, Social Relations & Engagement: Understanding Customer Behaviour on the Web. 2012. (ENG., Illus.). 240p. 95.00 (**978-0-230-39124-6(9)**) Palgrave Macmillan.

Palepu and Heal, Bernard. Business Analysis & Valuation. 2006. pap. 15.95 (978-1-4288-0942-0(2)) Cram101 Inc.

Palepu, Krishna G. Business Analysis & Valuation: Ifrs Edition - Text & Cases. 2007. (Illus.). xvi, 788p. (C). pap. 92.99 (978-1-84480-492-4(5)) Cengage Learning GBR. Dist: CENGAGE Learning.

—Business Analysis & Valuation: Ifrs Edition - Text Only. 2007. (Illus.). xvi, 572p. (C). pap. 67.99 (978-1-84480-493-1(3)) Cengage Learning GBR. Dist: CENGAGE Learning.

Palepu, Krishna G. & Healy, Paul M. Business Analysis & Valuation: Using Financial Statements, Text & Cases. 4th ed. 2007. (ENG.). (C). 984p. 287.95 (978-0-324-30286-8(X)); (Illus.). 336p. per. 201.95 (978-0-324-30292-9(4)) Cengage South-Western.

—Business Analysis & Valuation: Using Financial Statements: Texts & Cases. 4th ed. 2007. (ENG., Illus.). 1104p. (C). 223.95 (978-0-324-30287-5(8)) Cengage South-Western.

Porras Gonzalez, Eva. The Cost of Capital. 2011. (ENG., Illus.). 250p. 44.00 (978-0-230-20183-5(0)) Palgrave Macmillan.

Pratt, Shannon. Best of Shannon Pratt: A Compilation of Articles. 2006. (ENG.). 240p. per. 239.00 (978-0-9758668-5-6(0)) Business Valuation Resources, LLC.

Pratt, Shannon P. & Grabowski, Roger J. Cost of Capital. 4th ed. 2010. (ENG., Illus.). 255p. pap., suppl. ed., wbk. ed. 85.00 (978-0-470-47606-2(0), Wiley) Wiley, John & Sons, Inc.

—Cost of Capital: Applications & Examples. 4th ed. 2010. (Wiley Finance Ser.: 604). (ENG., Illus.). 754p. 168.00 (978-0-470-47605-5(2), Wiley) Wiley, John & Sons, Inc.

—Cost of Capital in Litigation: Applications & Examples. 4th ed. 2010. (ENG., Illus.). 301p. 100.00 (978-0-470-88094-4(5), Wiley) Wiley, John & Sons, Inc.

Pratt, Shannon P. & Pratt. Business Valuation Discounts & Premiums. 2nd ed. 2009. (ENG., Illus.). 504p. 115.95 (978-0-470-37148-0(X), Wiley) Wiley, John & Sons, Inc.

Ratner, Ian, et al. Business Valuation & Bankruptcy. 2009. (Wiley Finance Ser.: 521). (ENG., Illus.). 262p. 95.00 (978-0-470-46238-6(8), Wiley) Wiley, John & Sons, Inc.

Risius, Jeffrey M. Business Valuation: A Primer for the Legal Professional. 2007. (ENG., Illus.). 256p. per. 89.95 (978-1-59031-746-4(7)) American Bar Assn.

Sallinen, Risto & Bachman, Christofer. Value Creation in a Process Consultancy Setting. 2009. 104p. pap. (978-3-639-15062-9(7)) VDM Verlag Dr. Mueller e.K.

Sample Reports Library Special Edition Volume II. 2006. 198.00 (978-0-9786460-5-9(3)) National Assn. of Certified Valuation Analysts, Inc.

Simmons, Chad. Business Valuation Bluebook: How Successful Entrepreneurs Price, Buy, Sell & Trade Businesses. 4th rev. ed. 2009. (ENG.). 336p. pap. 25.95 (978-1-889150-55-0(X)) Facts on Demand Pr.

Sloan, Richard & Lundholm, Russell. Equity Valuation & Analysis w/ EVal. 2nd ed. 2006. (Illus.). 360p. (C). 158.44 (978-0-07-310026-5(9), 9780073100265, McGraw-Hill/Irwin) McGraw-Hill Higher Education.

Stockdale, John, Jr. BVR's Guide to Canadian Valuation Cases. 2008. ring bd. 279.00 (978-0-9793776-5-5(X)) Business Valuation Resources, LLC.

Venanzi, Daniela. Financial Performance Measures & Value Creation: The State of the Art. 2011. (SpringerBriefs in Business Ser.). (Illus.). xi, 73p. pap. 49.95 (**978-88-470-2450-2(1)**, 8847024501) Springer.

Wahlen, James M., et al. Financial Reporting, Financial Statement Analysis & Valuation: A Strategic Perspective. 7th ed. 2010. (ENG.). 1296p. (C). 246.95 (978-0-324-78942-3(4)) Cengage South-Western.

2007 Valuation Survey: Of Architecture, Engineering, Planning & Environmental Consulting Firms. 17th ed. 2007. per. 445.00 (978-1-934150-15-3(0)) ZweigWhite.

BUSINESS ENTERPRISES—AFRICA

Abate, Gashaw Tadesse & Getnet, Kindie. Determinants of Members Participation in Coffee Marketing Cooperatives. 2010. 120p. pap. (978-3-639-06295-3(7)) VDM Verlag Dr. Mueller e.K.

Abraraw, Chane. Impact of Hiv/Aids on Ethiopian Business: A Managerial Perspective. 2011. 132p. pap. (**978-3-639-32931-5(7)**) VDM Verlag Dr. Mueller e.K.

Africa Business & Political Handbook: Companies-Products-Services. (Illus.). 600p. (Orig.). pap. 2400.00 (978-0-7605-1336-1(8)) Rector Pr., Ltd.

Alasrag, Hussein. Enhancing the Competitiveness of the Smes in the Arab Countries. 2010. 64p. pap. (978-3-639-25108-1(3)) VDM Verlag Dr. Mueller e.K.

Alexander, Max. Two in the Bush: A High-Stakes Adventure with My Crazy Kid Brother. 2012. (ENG.). 400p. 24.99 (**978-1-4013-2417-9(7)**) Hyperion Pr.

Amoako, Samuel & Darkwah, Kwaku Forkuoh. Route Assignment Problem. 2011. 112p. pap. (**978-3-8443-8606-6(8)**) Lambert Academic Publishing.

Bezuidenhout, Jacques & Margie Cullen. The Feasibility of Starting a Dating Company in South Afric. 2011. 168p. pap. (**978-3-8443-2582-9(4)**) Lambert Academic Publishing.

Brink, Annekie & Berndt, Adele. Relationship Marketing & Customer Relationship Management. 2009. (ENG., Illus.). 213p. pap. 34.95 (978-0-7021-7739-2(3)) Juta Academic ZAF. Dist: Independent Pubs. Group.

Cammett, Melani Claire. Globalization & Business Politics in Arab North Africa: A Comparative Perspective. (ENG., Illus.). 286p. 2010. pap. 29.99 (978-0-521-15626-4(2)) 2007. 104.00 (978-0-521-86950-8(1)) Cambridge Univ. Pr.

Campbell, Christian, Editor. Legal Aspects of Doing Business in Africa [2009]. 2009. 652p. pap. 110.00 (978-0-557-13224-9(X)) Lulu Enterprises Inc.

Chao, Emmanuel. Buyer Perceived Opportunism, Contracts & Vertical Coordination. 2011. 140p. pap. (**978-3-8443-3394-7(0)**) Lambert Academic Publishing.

Chibanda, Stewart. Entrepreneurship in Africa: The Spiritual Dimension. 2010. 150p. pap. (978-1-906704-63-6(5)) Adonis & Abbey Publishers Ltd.

Chinunda, Emmanuel Danstan. Practical Insights on Customer Service: An African Perspective. 2011. 136p. pap. (**978-1-906704-85-8(6)**) Adonis & Abbey Publishers Ltd.

Cohen, Douglas. Assessing the Business Value of Cmmi(r) in South Afric. 2010. 204p. pap. (978-3-8383-6800-9(2)) Lambert Academic Publishing.

Committee on Creation of Science-Based Industries in Developing Countries & National Research Council. Mobilizing Science-Based Enterprises for Energy, Water, & Medicines in Nigeria. 2007. (ENG.). 144p. pap. 35.00 (978-0-309-11118-8(8)) National Academies Pr.

Davis, Dennis & Cassim, Farouk. Companies & Other Business Structures 2e. 2011. (ENG.). 416p. pap. 80.00 (978-0-19-599614-2(3)) Oxford Univ. Pr., Inc.

Demie, Muse Gadisa. Dynamic Pattern of Networks & Small Business Development: The Case of Small Enterprises in Addis Ababa, Ethiopia. 2011. 156p. pap. (**978-3-639-34094-5(9)**) VDM Verlag Dr. Mueller e.K.

Doing Business in South Africa. Date not set. (Doing Business in Regions & Countries Around the World Ser.). (978-1-882390-74-8(1)) Training Management Corp.

du Toit, Gawie, et al. Introduction to Business Management. 8th ed. 2011. (ENG., Illus.). 640p. pap. 60.00 (**978-0-19-599251-9(2)**) Oxford Univ. Pr., Inc.

Dzansi, Dennis Yao & Dzansi, Winifred Lineo. Social Responsibility of Smmes in Rural Communities. 2008. 276p. pap. (978-3-639-08880-9(8)) VDM Verlag Dr. Mueller e.K.

Eboreime, Matthew. Oil Multinationals & Social Responsibility in Niger Delta, Nigeri. 2011. 332p. pap. (**978-3-8443-9106-0(1)**) Lambert Academic Publishing.

El-Khazindar Business Research and Case Center, ed. Cases on Business & Management in the MENA Region: New Trends & Opportunities. 2011. 350p. 180.00 (978-1-60960-583-4(7), Business Science Reference) IGI Global.

Emmanuel, Baisie. Meso-Institutions & Endogenous Development in Ghan. 2011. 76p. pap. (**978-3-8433-7306-7(X)**) Lambert Academic Publishing.

Fwatshak, S. U. African Entrepreneurship in Jos, Central Nigeria, 1902-1985. 2010. 264p. pap. 35.00 *(978-1-59460-846-9(6))* Carolina Academic Pr.

Gale. Major Companies of Africa South of the Sahara. 15th ed. 2011. (Major Companies of Africa South of the Sahara Ser.). 910p. lib. bdg. 910.00 ***(978-1-86099-703-7(1))*** Graham & Whiteside, Ltd. GBR. Dist: Cengage Gale.

Grisar-Kasst, Karen. Nationalization of Industrial Management in Afric. 2008. 376p. per. *(978-3-8364-3680-9(9))* VDM Verlag Dr. Mueller e.K.

Hewitt, Magda, et al. Entrepreneurship & New Venture Management. van Aardt, Isa, ed. 4th ed. 2011. (ENG., Illus.). 320p. pap. 65.00 ***(978-0-19-599746-0(8))*** Oxford Univ. Pr., Inc.

Human Sciences Research Council (HSRC) Staff. Innovation: Main Results of the South African Innovation Survey 2005. 2009. (ENG.). 200p. pap. 16.95 *(978-0-7969-2240-3(3))* Human Sciences Research Council ZAF. Dist: Independent Pubs. Group.

Iarossi, Giuseppe. An Assessment of the Investment Climate in Kenya. 2009. (Directions in Development Ser.). (ENG., Illus.). 136p. pap. 15.00 *(978-0-8213-7812-0(0),* 9780821378120) World Bank Pubns.

Ismail, Lubna. Doing Business in the Middle East & North Africa. Date not set. (Doing Business in Regions & Countries Around the World Ser.). *(978-1-882390-83-0(0))* Training Management Corp.

Jack, Bridge, Clow-Wilson, Chris-Chao Wu. Trailblazers: South Africa's Champions of Change. 2009. 256p. pap. 17.95 *(978-1-77013-110-1(8))* Double Storey Bks. ZAF. Dist: International Publishers Marketing.

Kabagabe Byarugaba, Jolly, et al. Manager Development & Self Efficacy in Public Universities in Ugand. 2011. 84p. pap. ***(978-3-8433-9112-2(2))*** Lambert Academic Publishing.

Kariuki, Paul. Can the Inner Cities Be Engines for Small Business Growth? 2011. 60p. pap. ***(978-3-8443-0351-3(0))*** Lambert Academic Publishing.

Kaynak, Erdener & Alozie, Emmanuel. Advertising & Emerging Societies in A Technological & Global Economy: A Cultura: A Cultura. 2009. (Routledge Studies in International Business & the World Economy Ser.). (ENG., Illus.). 144p. 125.00 *(978-0-7890-0141-2(1))* Routledge.

Kayode, Muyiwa. The Seven Dimensions of Branding: Brand Building from the African Perspective. 2011. 124p. 21.23 ***(978-1-4634-3428-1(6))***; pap. 11.99 ***(978-1-4634-3429-8(4))*** AuthorHouse.

Kayode, Remi. Capital Acquisition for Small & Medium Scale Enterprises. 2010. 72p. pap. *(978-3-8383-8931-8(X))* Lambert Academic Publishing.

Kidanu, Embaye, et al. Supply Chain from Gate to Plate. 2011. 160p. pap. ***(978-3-8443-2020-6(2))*** Lambert Academic Publishing.

Kitakule, Sarah & Snyder, Margaret C. Above the Odds: A Decade of Change for Ugandan Women Entrepreneurs. 2010. *(978-1-59221-763-2(X))*; 235p. pap. *(978-1-59221-764-9(8))* Africa World Pr.

Kyaruzi, Imani Silver. African Businesses & Economic Growth. 2008. xvii, 271p. *(978-1-906704-18-6(X))*; pap. *(978-1-906704-19-3(8))* Adonis & Abbey Publishers Ltd.

Mabo, Eric. Emerging ONE Billion Customers in Africa. 2010. 143p. pap. 18.97 *(978-0-557-42124-4(1))* Lulu Enterprises Inc.

Mahajan, Vijay & Gunther, Robert E. Africa Rising: How 900 Million African Consumers Offer More Than You Think. 2008. (ENG., Illus.). 288p. 34.99 *(978-0-13-233942-1(0))* Wharton Schl. Publishing.

Major National Retailers: Europe, Middle East & Africa. rev. ed. 2008. 845.00 *(978-1-84264-443-0(2))* Euromonitor International PLC GBR. Dist: Cengage Gale.

Mangaliso, Mzamo. Strategic Choice under Uncertainty: Multinational Corporations & the Pressure to Disinvest from South Africa. 2010. (Illus.). 212p. E-Book *(978-0-7618-5089-2(9))* Univ. Pr. of America, Inc.

Mangaliso, Mzamo P. Strategic Choice under Uncertainty: Multinational Corporations & the Pressure to Disinvest from South Africa. 2010. (ENG., Illus.). 226p. 62.99 *(978-0-7618-5087-8(2))*; pap. 33.99 *(978-0-7618-5088-5(0))* Univ. Pr. of America, Inc.

Mangcu, Xolela, et al, eds. Visions of Black Economic Empowerment. 2008. (ENG.). 232p. 28.95 *(978-1-77009-358-4(3))* Jacana Media ZAF. Dist: Independent Pubs. Group.

Mbabane, Loyiso (Loy). Broad-Based Black Economic Empowerment in South Afric. 2011. 192p. pap. ***(978-3-8433-8019-5(8))*** Lambert Academic Publishing.

McCormick, Dorothy, et al, eds. Business in Keny. 2007. 360p. (C). pap. *(978-9966-846-95-2(6))* Nairobi University Pr. KEN. Dist: Michigan State Univ. Pr.

Miyambo, Hasani Ronny. South African Listed Private Equity Index. 2011. 68p. pap. ***(978-3-8443-1062-7(2))*** Lambert Academic Publishing.

Mohammed Abdalla, Abdel Gabbar & Abdalla, Abdel Gabbar Mohammed. Markets Cointegration & Competitiveness: Spatial Sudanese Sheep Markets Analysis, & Competitiveness of Sudanese Sheep & Mutton in Export Markets. 2011. 296p. pap. ***(978-3-639-32403-7(X))*** VDM Verlag Dr. Mueller e.K.

Mohammed, Dauda. Business Risk & Capital Structure in Nigerian Listed Firms. 2011. 208p. pap. ***(978-3-8443-3490-6(4))*** Lambert Academic Publishing.

Munene, Gracevasser. Drawing up a Business Plan in Africa Today. 2011. 112p. pap. ***(978-3-8443-9403-0(6))*** Lambert Academic Publishing.

Mussema, Rehima. Analysis of Red Pepper Marketing: Ethiopia. 2011. 172p. pap. ***(978-3-8443-0617-0(X))*** Lambert Academic Publishing.

Nel, Dehlia. Day Labourers on Community Street Corners. 2010. 156p. pap. *(978-3-8383-5536-5(5))* Lambert Academic Publishing.

Nel, René. Puppets or People: People & Organisational Development - An Integrated Approach. 2009. (ENG.). 131p. pap. 26.95 *(978-0-7021-7740-8(7))* Juta Academic ZAF. Dist: Independent Pubs. Group.

Nieuwenhuizen, Cecile, ed. Business Management for Entrepreneurs. 2009. (Illus.). 280p. pap. 35.95 *(978-0-7021-7682-1(6))* Double Storey Bks. ZAF. Dist: International Publishers Marketing.

Okiror, Julius. Impact of Standardization on Product Innovation & Trade in S Afric. 2010. 72p. pap. *(978-3-8383-8465-8(2))* Lambert Academic Publishing.

Olorunsanya, Eniola. Egg Farming Business in Nigeri. 2010. 60p. pap. *(978-3-639-26734-1(6))* VDM Verlag Dr. Mueller e.K.

Ongore, Vincent. Ownership Structure, Board, & Manager Discretion on Performance. 2011. 196p. pap. ***(978-3-8443-0454-1(1))*** Lambert Academic Publishing.

Ramachandran, Vijaya, et al. Africa's Private Sector: What's Wrong with the Business Environment & What to Do about It. 2009. (ENG., Illus.). 110p. pap. 18.95 *(978-1-933286-28-0(8))* Ctr. for Global Development.

Soffiantini, Vic. A Small Business Owners Guidebook. 2010. 112p. pap. 17.51 *(978-1-4461-6737-3(2))* Lulu Enterprises Inc.

Taylor, Scott D. Globalization & the Cultures of Business in Africa. 2012. (ENG., Illus.). 256p. 75.00 ***(978-0-253-00266-2(4),*** 0253002664); pap. 27.00 ***(978-0-253-00573-1(6),*** 0253005736) Indiana Univ. Pr.

Terblanche, Barrie, et al. Starting Your Own Business in South Africa. 12th ed. 2011. (ENG., Illus.). 288p. pap. 40.00 ***(978-0-19-905534-0(3))*** Oxford Univ. Pr., Inc.

Veal, Don-Terry & Grenell, Keenan, eds. Entrepreneurship in South Africa & in the United States: Comparative Studies. 2008. 372p. 119.95 *(978-0-7734-5069-1(6))* Mellen, Edwin Pr., The.

Viggeborn, Anna, et al. Angola, an Emerging Market with Potential & Risk. 2010. 60p. pap. *(978-3-639-17104-4(7))* VDM Verlag Dr. Mueller e.K.

Watkins, Ron. Doing Business in Africa: Myths & Realities. 200p. pap. 15.95 *(978-0-9640480-0-3(0))* Heritage Publishing.

Weldegebriel, Akillu. Analysis of Marketing Practices. 2010. 104p. pap. *(978-3-639-28440-9(2))* VDM Verlag Dr. Mueller e.K.

Wessels, Nelmarie. Supply Chain Management. 2011. 160p. pap. ***(978-3-8443-0883-9(0))*** Lambert Academic Publishing.

Worku, Eshetu. Efficiency & Social Capital in Micro, Small & Medium Enterprises. 2011. 232p. pap. ***(978-3-8443-0924-9(1))*** Lambert Academic Publishing.

World Bank Staff, contrib. by. Industrial Clusters & Micro & Small Enterprises in Africa: From Survival to Growth. 2010. *(978-0-8213-8628-6(X))*; (ENG & ABK.). 208p. pap. 25.00 *(978-0-8213-8627-9(1),* 9780821386279) World Bank Pubns.

Yennict Ndileba, Njinyah. The Challenges of Corporate Social Responsibility in Local Companies. 2011. 128p. pap. ***(978-3-8443-0071-0(6))*** Lambert Academic Publishing.

Zeng, Douglas Zhihua, ed. Knowledge, Technology, & Cluster-based Growth in Africa. 2008. (WBI Development Studies). (ENG.). 144p. (C). pap. 20.00 *(978-0-8213-7306-4(4),* 9780821373064) World Bank Pubns.

BUSINESS ENTERPRISES—ASIA

Ahmad Bashawir, Abdul Ghani. International Strategic Alliances in Malaysi. 2009. 444p. pap. *(978-3-639-19231-5(1))* VDM Verlag Dr. Mueller e.K.

Ahmed, Selim. Ranking of Motivational Factors by Employees & Managers. 2010. 112p. pap. *(978-3-8383-7927-2(6))* Lambert Academic Publishing.

Alasrag, Hussein. Enhancing the Competitiveness of the Smes in the Arab Countries. 2010. 64p. pap. *(978-3-639-25108-1(3))* VDM Verlag Dr. Mueller e.K.

Ali, Anees Janee, et al. Creative Performance of Indonesian Operating Managers. 2010. 168p. pap. *(978-3-8383-5969-4(0))* Lambert Academic Publishing.

Amann, Edmund & Cantwell, John, eds. Innovative Firms in Emerging Market Countries. 2012. (ENG.). 392p. 99.00 ***(978-0-19-964600-5(7))*** Oxford Univ. Pr., Inc.

Asia Business & Political Handbook: Companies-Products-Services. (Illus.). 600p. (Orig.). pap. 2400.00 *(978-0-7605-1337-8(6))* Rector Pr., Ltd.

Asia Business Review: Companies-Products-Services. 100p. (Orig.). pap. 995.00 *(978-0-7605-1993-6(5))* Rector Pr., Ltd.

Asia Yearbook 1995: Companies-Products-Services. (Illus.). 250p. pap. *(978-0-7605-1643-0(X))* Rector Pr., Ltd.

Athukorala. Multinational Enterprises in Asian Development. 2007. (Illus.). 304p. (C). 137.00 *(978-1-84720-102-7(4))* Elgar, Edward Publishing, Inc.

Backman, Michael. The Asian Insider: Unconventional Wisdom for Asian Business. annot. ed. 2006. (ENG.). 352p. pap. 40.00 *(978-0-230-00021-6(5))* Palgrave Macmillan.

BIA. Essential Singaporean Manufacturers: Food, Textile, Clothing, & Chemical Companies. 6th rev. ed. 2006. 250p. (J). pap. 219.00 *(978-1-4187-4196-9(5))* Business Information Agency.

—Essential Turkish Manufacturers: Food, Textile, Clothing, & Chemical Companies. 6th rev. ed. 2006. 400p. (J). pap. 249.00 *(978-1-4187-4232-4(5))* Business Information Agency.

—Essential Uzbek Manufacturers: Food, Textile, Clothing, & Chemical Companies. 6th rev. ed. 2006. 200p. (J). pap. 219.00 *(978-1-4187-4198-3(1))* Business Information Agency.

—Major Companies of Singapore: Manufacturers, Wholesalers, Banks, Construction Companies. 6th rev. ed. 2006. 300p. (J). pap. 249.00 *(978-1-4187-4405-2(0))* Business Information Agency.

—Major Companies of Thailand: Manufacturers, Wholesalers, Banks, Construction Companies. 6th rev. ed. 2006. 250p. (J). pap. 219.00 *(978-1-4187-4407-6(7))* Business Information Agency.

—Major Manufacturers of Asia: Food, Textile, Clothing, & Chemical Companies. 6th rev. ed. 2006. 400p. (J). pap. 249.00 *(978-1-4187-4192-1(2))* Business Information Agency.

—Major Manufacturers of Azerbaijan, Armenia, & Georgia: Food, Textile, Clothing, & Chemical Companies. 6th rev. ed. 2006. 200p. (J). pap. 219.00 *(978-1-4187-4199-0(X))* Business Information Agency.

—Major Manufacturers of Kazakhstan: Food, Textile, Clothing, & Chemical Companies. 6th rev. ed. 2006. 250p. (J). pap. 249.00 *(978-1-4187-4404-5(2))* Business Information Agency.

Campbell, Christian, Editor. Legal Aspects of Doing Business in Asia. 2009. 676p. pap. 115.00 *(978-0-557-20338-3(4))* Lulu Enterprises Inc.

Carney, Michael. Asian Business Groups: Context, Governance & Performance. 2008. (Chandos Asian Studies). (ENG., Illus.). 340p. 110.00 *(978-1-84334-244-1(8),* Chandos Publishing) Woodhead Publishing Ltd. GBR. Dist: Ingram Pub. Services.

Cuttaree, Vickram & Mandri-Perrott, Cledan. Public-Private Partnerships in Europe & Central Asia: Designing crisis-resilient strategies & bankable Projects. 2011. (ENG., Illus.). 138p. pap. 20.00 *(978-0-8213-8703-0(0),* 9780821387030) World Bank Pubns.

Cuttaree, Vickram & Mandri-Perrott, X. Cledan. Public-Private Partnerships in Europe & Central Asia: Designing Crisis-Resilient Strategies & Bankable Projects. 2011. E-Book *(978-0-8213-8704-7(9))* World Bank Pubns.

Dana, L. -P., et al, eds. Handbook of Research on Asian Entrepreneurship. 2009. (Elgar Original Reference Ser.). (Illus.). 464p. 270.00 *(978-1-84720-608-4(5))* Elgar, Edward Publishing, Inc.

Dana, Leo-Paul. Asian Models of Entrepreneurship: From the Indian Union & the Kingdom of Nepal to the Japanese Archipelago. 2007. (Asia-Pacific Business Ser.). (Illus.). 356p. 87.00 *(978-981-256-878-6(6))* World Scientific Publishing Co., Inc.

Debroux, Philippe. Female Entrepreneurship in East & South-East Asia: Opportunities & Challenges. 2010. (Chandos Asian Studies). (ENG.). 260p. 120.00 *(978-1-84334-398-1(3),* Chandos Publishing) Woodhead Publishing Ltd. GBR. Dist: Ingram Pub. Services.

DeKrey, Steven J., et al. Leadership Experiences in Asia: Insight & Inspiration from 20 Innovators. DeKrey, Steven J. & Messick, David M., eds. 2007. (ENG., Illus.). 256p. pap. 29.95 *(978-0-470-82268-5(6),* Wiley) Wiley, John & Sons, Inc.

Dieleman, Marleen. The Rhythm of Strategy: A Corporate Biography of the Salim Group of Indonesia. 2008. (ICAS Publications Ser.). (Illus.). 205p. pap. *(978-90-5356-033-4(5))* Amsterdam Univ. Pr.

Doing Business in Asia. Date not set. (Doing Business in Regions & Countries Around the World Ser.). *(978-1-882390-82-3(2))* Training Management Corp.

Doing Business in Malaysia. Date not set. (Doing Business in Regions & Countries Around the World Ser.). 80p. *(978-1-882390-65-6(2))* Training Management Corp.

Doing Business in Pakistan. Date not set. (Doing Business in Regions & Countries Around the World Ser.). *(978-1-882390-69-4(5))* Training Management Corp.

Doing Business in Singapore. Date not set. (Doing Business in Regions & Countries Around the World Ser.). *(978-1-882390-73-1(3))* Training Management Corp.

Doing Business in Thailand. Date not set. (Doing Business in Regions & Countries Around the World Ser.). *(978-1-882390-78-6(4))* Training Management Corp.

Doing Business in the Philippines. Date not set. (Doing Business in Regions & Countries Around the World Ser.). *(978-1-882390-70-0(9))* Training Management Corp.

Dzever, Sam, et al. Evolving Corporate Structures & Cultures in Asia: Impact of Globalization. 2008. (Iste Ser.: 371). (ENG., Illus.). 320p. 105.00 *(978-1-84821-091-2(4),* Wiley-ISTE) Wiley, John & Sons, Inc.

Englesson, Marie. Lost & Added in Translation. 2010. 92p. pap. *(978-3-639-14492-5(9))* VDM Verlag Dr. Mueller e.K.

Fatima, Mahnaz. Quality Management in Pakistan's Export-Orientated Industries. 2008. 250p. pap. 35.00 *(978-0-19-547644-6(1))* Oxford Univ. Pr., Inc.

Fukukawa, Kyoko, ed. Corporate Social Responsibility in Asia. (ENG., Illus.). 192p. 2011. pap. 42.95 ***(978-0-415-67304-4(6))*** 2009. (C). 138.00 *(978-0-415-45935-8(4))* Routledge.

Gale. Major Companies of Asia & Australasia, 4 vols. 14th ed. 2011. (Major Companies of Asia & Australasia Ser.). 2760p. lib. bdg. 2980.00 ***(978-1-86099-701-3(5))*** Graham & Whiteside, Ltd. GBR. Dist: Cengage Gale.

—Major Companies of Asia & Australasia: Australasia - Australia, New Zealand, Papua New Guinea. 14th ed. 2011. (Major Companies of Asia & Australasia Ser.). 690p. lib. bdg. 670.00 ***(978-1-86099-699-3(X))*** Graham & Whiteside, Ltd. GBR. Dist: Cengage Gale.

—Major Companies of Asia & Australasia: East Asia - East Asia - People's Republic of China, Hong Kong SAR, Japan, South Korea, North Korea, Mongolia, Taiwan. 14th ed. 2011. (Major Companies of Asia & Australasia Ser.). 690p. lib. bdg. 1075.00 ***(978-1-86099-698-6(1))*** Graham & Whiteside, Ltd. GBR. Dist: Cengage Gale.

—Major Companies of Asia & Australasia: South Asia - Bangladesh, Bhutan, India, Iran, Nepal, Pakistan, Sri Lanka. 14th ed. 2011. (Major Companies of Asia & Australasia Ser.). 690p. lib. bdg. 910.00 ***(978-1-86099-700-6(7))*** Graham & Whiteside, Ltd. GBR. Dist: Cengage Gale.

—Major Companies of Asia & Australasia: South East Asia - Brunei, Cambodia, Indonesia, Laos, Malaysia, Myanmar, Philippines, Singapore, Thailand, Vietnam. 14th ed. 2011. (Major Companies of Asia & Australasia Ser.). 690p. lib. bdg. 970.00 ***(978-1-86099-697-9(3))*** Graham & Whiteside, Ltd. GBR. Dist: Cengage Gale.

Gomez, Terence E. Chinese Business in Malaysia: Accumulation, Accommodation & Ascendance. 2012. (ENG.). 234p. pap. 44.95 ***(978-0-415-51737-9(0))*** Routledge.

Guirdham, Maureen. Culture & Business in Asia. 2009. (ENG., Illus.). 320p. pap. 56.00 *(978-0-230-51808-7(7))* Palgrave Macmillan.

Hacker, Robert H. Billion Dollar Company. 2010. 116p. pap. *(978-3-8383-7331-7(6))* Lambert Academic Publishing.

Hasegawa, Harukiyo & Sharpe, Diana Rosemary, eds. New Horizons in Asian Management: Emerging Issues & Critical Perspectives. 2007. (ENG., Illus.). 288p. 110.00 *(978-0-230-01365-0(1))* Palgrave Macmillan.

Hassan, Bushra, et al. Role of Self-Regulation & Decision Making at Organizations. 2010. 96p. pap. *(978-3-8383-8734-5(1))* Lambert Academic Publishing.

Hechanova, Ma Regina M. 1-800-Philippines: Understanding & Managing the Filipino Call Center Worker. 2011. (Illus.). xiv, 124p. 28.00 ***(978-971-8610-59-6(6))*** Ateneo de Manila Univ. Pr. PHL. Dist: Univ. of Hawaii Pr.

Henry, Sebastien. EQ & Leadership in Asia: Using Emotional Intelligence to Lead & Inspire Your People. 2011. (ENG., Illus.). 256p. 29.95 *(978-0-470-82986-8(9),* Jossey-Bass) Wiley, John & Sons, Inc.

Heracleous, Loizos, et al. Flying High in a Competitive Industry: Secrets of the World's Leading Airline. 2nd ed. 2008. (ENG., Illus.). 256p. 29.95 *(978-0-07-128196-6(7),* 0071281967) McGraw-Hill Cos., The.

Hesse, Joachim, et al, eds. The Public Sector in Transition: East Asia & European Union Compared. 2008. 372p. pap. 61.00 *(978-3-8329-3302-9(6))* Nomos Verlagsgesellschaft DEU. Dist: International Specialized Bk. Services.

Hewitt, C. Nick, et al. Leaders & Leadership in Asia. 2006. 250p. pap. 19.95 *(978-0-470-82142-8(6))* Wiley, John & Sons, Inc.

Hipsher, Scott A. Business Practices in Southeast Asia. 2012. (ENG., Illus.). 224p. (C). pap. 42.95 ***(978-0-415-53355-3(4))*** Routledge.

Hipsher, Scott A., et al. The Nature of Asian Firms: An Evolutionary Perspective. 2007. (Chandos Asian Studies). (ENG., Illus.). 228p. 110.00 *(978-1-84334-294-6(4),* Chandos Publishing) Woodhead Publishing Ltd. GBR. Dist: Ingram Pub. Services.

Hodder, R. N. W. Overseas Chinese & Trade Between the Philippines & China: The Intertwining of Family, Social, & Business Interests in Promoting Trade. 2006. (Illus.). 328p. 119.95 *(978-0-7734-5793-5(3))* Mellen, Edwin Pr., The.

HOK. Hok Asia. 2009. (ENG., Illus.). 264p. 80.00 *(978-1-86470-318-4(0))* Images Publishing Group AUS. Dist: National Bk. Network.

The Holmes Report 2008 Asian Consultancy Report Card. 2008. pap. 69.95 net. *(978-0-9797529-2-6(2))* Holmes Group, The.

Ibp, Usa. Mongolia Industrial & Business Directo. 2006. (Illus.). pap. 99.95 *(978-0-7397-9923-9(1))* International Business Pubns., USA.

—Thailand Industrial & Business Directo. 2006. (Illus.). pap. 99.95 *(978-0-7397-9761-7(1))* International Business Pubns., USA.

—Vietnam Industrial & Business Director. 2006. (Illus.). pap. 99.95 *(978-0-7397-9919-2(3))* International Business Pubns., USA.

Im, Yong-Jae & Chon, Song-In. Kiop Chiptan Ui Sunhwan Ch'ulcha: Sijang Kyuyul Kwa Kamdok Kyuyul Ui Yokhal. 2009. (KOR., Illus.). 84p. *(978-89-8063-302-9(5))* KDI.

Iqbal, Mohammed Asif. Growth Factors of Service Based Internet Commerce. 2011. 64p. pap. ***(978-3-8433-9214-3(5))*** Lambert Academic Publishing.

James, S. Major Companies of South West Asia. Date not set. 620p. 395.00 *(978-1-86099-041-0(X),* GML00198-110955) Art Trade Pr. Ltd., The GBR. Dist: Cengage Gale.

Jansson, Hans. International Business Strategy in Emerging Country Markets: The Institutional Network Approach. 2008. 320p. pap. 50.00 *(978-1-84720-960-3(2))* Elgar, Edward Publishing, Inc.

Kavirathna, Eranga & Kapurubandara, M. Factors Affecting E-Commerce Adoption. 2011. (Illus.). 120p. pap. ***(978-3-8443-2815-8(7))*** Lambert Academic Publishing.

Kitiarsa, Pattana, ed. Religious Commodifications in Asia: Marketing Gods. 2012. (ENG., Illus.). 288p. (C). pap. 44.95 ***(978-0-415-51460-6(6))*** Routledge.

Kohpaiboon. Multinational Enterprises & Industrial Transformation Evidence from Thailand. 2007. (Illus.). 304p. (C). 137.00 *(978-1-84720-046-4(X))* Elgar, Edward Publishing, Inc.

Kok Kwon, Chin & Chelliah, Shankar. Marketing & Customer Retention of Herb Coffee in Malaysi. 2010. 112p. pap. *(978-3-8383-6307-3(8))* Lambert Academic Publishing.

Major Companies of Asia & Australasia 2010, 4 Vols., Set. 26th rev. ed. 2009. 2300.00 *(978-1-86099-595-8(0))* Graham & Whiteside, Ltd. GBR. Dist: Cengage Gale.

Major Companies of Asia & Australasia 2010: Australasia-Australia, New Zealand, Papu New Guinea, Vol. 3. 26th rev. ed. 2009. 575.00 *(978-1-86099-593-4(4))* Graham & Whiteside, Ltd. GBR. Dist: Cengage Gale.

Major Companies of Asia & Australasia 2010: Southwest Asia-Bangladesh, Bhutan, India, Nepal, Pakistan, Sri Lanka, Vol. 4. 26th rev. ed. 2009. 780.00 *(978-1-86099-594-1(2))* Graham & Whiteside, Ltd. GBR. Dist: Cengage Gale.

Major National Retailers: Americans & Asia-Pacific. rev. ed. 2008. 845.00 *(978-1-84264-444-7(0))* Euromonitor International PLC GBR. Dist: Cengage Gale.

Meyer, Christian. Leadership Influence & Distance - Energizing an Organization Across Geographical & Ethnic-Cultural Distance. 2007. 88p. per. *(978-3-8364-4611-2(1))* VDM Verlag Dr. Mueller e.K.

Milligan, Andy. Great Asian Brands: Osim. 2010. 192p. pap. *(978-1-905736-13-3(4))* Marshall Cavendish.

B

Moon, Hwy-Chang. Global Business Strategy: Asian Perspective. 2010. 300p. 65.00 *(978-981-4273-19-0(8))* World Scientific Publishing Co., Inc.

Morrison, Terri & Conaway, Wayne A. Kiss, Bow, or Shake Hands - Asia: How to Do Business in 12 Asian Countries. 2006. (ENG., Illus.). 256p. per. 14.95 *(978-1-59869-216-7(X))* Adams Media Corp.

Noronha, Carlos & Hasegawa, Harukiyo, eds. Asian Business & Management: Theory, Practice & Perspectives. 2009. (ENG., Illus.). 432p. pap. 56.00 *(978-0-230-54506-9(8))* Palgrave Macmillan.

Philippines: Business Financing Handbook. (Illus.). 70p. (Orig.). pap. 295.00 *(978-0-7605-1205-0(1))* Rector Pr., Ltd.

Racine, Jean-Louis. Harnessing Quality for Competitiveness in Eastern Europe & Central Asia. 2011. (Eastern Europe & Central Asia Reports). (ENG., Illus.). 356p. pap. 30.00 *(978-0-8213-8509-8(7)*, 9780821385098); E-Book *(978-0-8213-8510-4(0))* World Bank Pubns.

Rao, Purba H. Greening the Supply Chain: A Guide for Asian Managers. 2008. (Illus.). 284p. (C). pap. 24.95 *(978-81-7829-876-4(7)*, B98764P) SAGE Pubns., Inc.

Rashid, Shahidur, et al, eds. From Parastatals to Private Trade: Lessons from Asian Agriculture. 2008. (ENG., Illus.). 280p. (gr. 17). 65.00 *(978-0-8018-8815-1(8))* Johns Hopkins Univ. Pr.

Rowley, Chris. Globalization & Competitiveness. 2009. 280p. pap. 39.95 *(978-0-415-56830-2(7))* Routledge.

Roy, Tirthankar. Company of Kinsmen: Enterprise & Community in South Asian History 1700-1940. 2010. (ENG., Illus.). 264p. 99.00 *(978-0-19-806378-0(4))* Oxford Univ. Pr., Inc.

Schlevogt, Kai-Alexander. Brave New Saw Wave World: Emerging & Submerging Asia in the Global Environment. 2011. 176p. (C). pap. 34.99 *(978-81-317-5403-0(0))* FT Press.

Smyth, Russell & Vicziany, Marika, eds. Business in Asia. 2008. 240p. (C). pap. 29.95 *(978-1-876924-53-9(5)*, Monash Univ. Pr.) Monash Univ. Publishing AUS. Dist: International Specialized Bk. Services.

Stefanac, John. Leadership Style Preferences in Noki. 2010. 176p. pap. *(978-3-8383-6533-6(X))* Lambert Academic Publishing.

Sunaryo, Lenny. Chinese Social-Institutions Imitating Nature? 2011. 304p. pap. ***(978-3-8443-1452-6(0))*** Lambert Academic Publishing.

Taylor, Ranald. Technical Progress & Economic Growth: An Empirical Case Study of Malaysia. 2008. 256p. 119.00 *(978-1-84720-583-4(6))* Elgar, Edward Publishing, Inc.

The A49 Group. A49: An Asian Spirit in Contemporary Design. 2009. (ENG., Illus.). 420p. 85.00 *(978-1-86470-322-1(9))* Images Publishing Group AUS. Dist: National Bk. Network.

Tipton, Frank B. Asian Firms: History, Institutions, & Management. 432p. 2008. pap. 66.00 *(978-1-84720-514-8(3))* 2007. (Illus.). (C). 165.00 *(978-1-84064-334-3(X))* Elgar, Edward Publishing, Inc.

Tuan Hai, Dinh. Value Chain Management. 2010. 164p. pap. *(978-3-8383-0224-9(9))* Lambert Academic Publishing.

Tuncay Çelikel, Asli. Research & Development Collaborations: Turkish Automotive Industry. 2010. 184p. pap. *(978-3-639-23096-3(5))* VDM Verlag Dr. Mueller e.K.

United Nations. Creating Business & Social Value: The Asian Way to Integrate Csr into Business Strategies. 2011. (Studies in Trade & Investment Ser.). (ENG.). 162p. pap. 40.00 ***(978-92-1-120616-6(2))*** United Nations Pubns.

United Nations. Linking Greater Mekong Subregion Enterprises to International Markets: The Role of Global Value Chains, International Production Networks & Enterprise Clusters. 2007. (Studies in Trade & Investment Ser.). (ENG.). 92p. pap. 29.00 *(978-92-1-120492-6(5))* United Nations Pubns.

Walsh, John, ed. The Globalisation of Executives & Economies: Lessons from Thailand. 2006. (Chandos Asian Studies). (ENG.). 270p. 110.00 *(978-1-84334-281-6(2)*, Chandos Publishing) Woodhead Publishing Ltd. GBR. Dist: Ingram Pub. Services.

Werhane, Patricia & Singer, Alan E., eds. Business Ethics in Theory & Practice: Contributions from Asia & New Zealand. 2010. (Issues in Business Ethics Ser.). (Illus.). 256p. pap. 99.00 *(978-90-481-5273-5(9)*, 9048152739) Springer.

Wherry, Frederick F. Global Markets & Local Crafts: Thailand & Costa Rica Compared. 2008. (Themes in Global Social Change Ser.). (ENG., Illus.). 208p. (gr. 17). 57.00 *(978-0-8018-8794-9(1))* Johns Hopkins Univ. Pr.

World Bank. Challenges to Enterprise Performance in the Face of the Financial Crisis: Eastern Europe & Central Asia. 2011. (World Bank Studies). (ENG., Illus.). 144p. pap. 25.00 *(978-0-8213-8800-6(2)*, 9780821388006) World Bank Pubns.

World Bank Staff, contrib. by. Challenges to Enterprise Performance in the Face of the Financial Crisis: Eastern Europe & Central Asia. 2011. ***(978-0-8213-8801-3(0))*** World Bank Pubns.

Wylie, Philip. How to Establish a Successful Business in Thailand. 2007. (Illus.). 258p. per. 19.95 *(978-1-887521-75-8(5))* Paiboon Publishing.

Yeung, Henry Wai-Chung, ed. Globalizing Regional Development in East Asia: Production Networks, Clusters, & Entrepreneurship. 2010. (Regions & Cities Ser.). (ENG., Illus.). 208p. (C). 125.00 *(978-0-415-56053-5(5))* Routledge.

—Handbook of Research on Asian Business. 2008. (Elgar Original Reference Ser.). (Illus.). 512p. pap. 75.00 *(978-1-84844-092-0(8))* Elgar, Edward Publishing, Inc.

Yoneda, Mitaka. English for Business Purposes. 2010. 276p. pap. *(978-3-639-26577-4(7))* VDM Verlag Dr. Mueller e.K.

Yu Chang, Albert Vincent Y. & Thorson, Andrew. A Legal Guide to Doing Business in Asia-Pacific. 2011. (ENG.). 250p. pap. 149.95 *(978-1-60442-843-8(0))* American Bar Assn.

Zhang, Xue. Environmental Scanning & Information Sharing Mechanisms of Smes. 2010. 100p. pap. *(978-3-8383-6195-6(4))* Lambert Academic Publishing.

Zhou, Xiaolin, et al. Doing Business in China: Resolving the Challenges in Today's Environment. 2007. (Corporate Law & Practice Course Handbook Ser.: No. 1626). (Illus.). 375p. *(978-1-4024-0955-4(9))* Practising Law Institute.

BUSINESS ENTERPRISES—AUSTRALIA

Aba-Bulgu, M. & Islam, Sardar M. N. Corporate Crisis & Risk Management: Modelling, Strategies & SME Application. 2006. (International Business & Management Ser.). (Illus.). 358p. 134.95 *(978-0-08-045102-2(0))* Emerald Group Publishing Ltd. GBR. Dist: Turpin Distribution Services Ltd.

Beaton-Wells, Caron & Fisse, Brent. Australian Cartel Regulation: Law, Policy & Practice in an International Context. 2011. (ENG.). 685p. 185.00 *(978-0-521-76089-8(5))* Cambridge Univ. Pr.

Bell, Wendy. A Remote Possibility: The Battle for Imparja Television. 2008. (ENG.). 362p. pap. 25.95 *(978-1-86465-097-5(4))* IAD Pr. AUS. Dist: Independent Pubs. Group.

Blake, Jacqueline. B2b Communication in the Australian Timber & Wood Products Industry. 2008. 220p. pap. *(978-3-639-05311-1(7))* VDM Verlag Dr. Mueller e.K.

Christen, Kimberly A. Aboriginal Business: Alliances in a Remote Australian Town. 2009. pap. 29.95 *(978-1-930618-98-5(0))* School for Advanced Research Pr./SAR Pr.

Crawford, Robert. But Wait, There's More... A History of Australian Advertising, 1900-2000. 2008. (ENG.). 224p. pap. 26.00 *(978-0-522-85322-3(6))* Melbourne Univ. Publishing AUS. Dist: Independent Pubs. Group.

Dick. The Internationalisation Strategies of Firms the Australian Experience in Global Economies. 2007. (New Horizons in International Business Ser.). (Illus.). 416p. (C). 158.00 *(978-1-84542-212-7(0))* Elgar, Edward Publishing, Inc.

Doing Business in Australia. Date not set. (Doing Business in Regions & Countries Around the World Ser.). *(978-1-882390-51-9(2))* Training Management Corp.

Dunn, John. Comeng Vol. 3: A History of Commonwealth Engineering, 1966-1977. 2010. (Illus.). 352p. (C). 69.95 *(978-1-877058-90-5(4))* Rosenberg Publishing Pty, Ltd. AUS. Dist: International Specialized Bk. Services.

Egan, Victor. The Organisational Form of Australian Engineering Design Companies. 2010. 280p. pap. *(978-3-8383-6725-5(1))* Lambert Academic Publishing.

Gale. Major Companies of Asia & Australasia, 4 vols. 14th ed. 2011. (Major Companies of Asia & Australasia Ser.). 2760p. lib. bdg. 2980.00 ***(978-1-86099-701-3(5))*** Graham & Whiteside, Ltd. GBR. Dist: Cengage Gale.

—Major Companies of Asia & Australasia: Australasia - Australia, New Zealand, Papua New Guinea. 14th ed. 2011. (Major Companies of Asia & Australasia Ser.). 690p. lib. bdg. 670.00 ***(978-1-86099-699-3(X))*** Graham & Whiteside, Ltd. GBR. Dist: Cengage Gale.

—Major Companies of Asia & Australasia: South Asia - Bangladesh, Bhutan, India, Iran, Nepal, Pakistan, Sri Lanka. 14th ed. 2011. (Major Companies of Asia & Australasia Ser.). 690p. lib. bdg. 910.00 ***(978-1-86099-700-6(7))*** Graham & Whiteside, Ltd. GBR. Dist: Cengage Gale.

Gill, Robert. Employer of Choice & Csr Reputation in Australi. 2009. 324p. pap. *(978-3-639-13071-3(5))* VDM Verlag Dr. Mueller e.K.

Hilmer, Fred & Drury, Barbara. The Fairfax Experience: What the Management Texts Didn't Teach Me. 2007. (ENG.). xii, 188p. pap. 34.95 *(978-0-7314-0562-6(5)*, Wrightbooks) Wiley, John & Sons Australia, Ltd. AUS. Dist: Wiley, John & Sons, Inc.

Ibp, Usa. Australia Industrial & Business Direct. 2006. (Illus.). pap. 99.95 *(978-0-7397-6791-7(7))* International Business Pubns., USA.

Ipasso, Robert. The Reasons for the Success or Failure of Entrepreneurs. 2009. 220p. pap. *(978-3-639-16582-1(9))* VDM Verlag Dr. Mueller e.K.

Kramer, Bonita & Johnson, Christie. Financial Statements: A Self-Teaching Guide. 2009. (ENG., Illus.). 320p. pap. 19.95 *(978-0-07-154387-3(2)*, 0071543872) McGraw-Hill Cos., The.

Lazarevski, Katie. Isomorphism in Environmental Volunteering Organisations. 2010. 156p. pap. *(978-3-639-21000-2(X))* VDM Verlag Dr. Mueller e.K.

Major Companies of Asia & Australasia 2010, 4 Vols., Set. 26th rev. ed. 2009. 2300.00 *(978-1-86099-595-8(0))* Graham & Whiteside, Ltd. GBR. Dist: Cengage Gale.

Major Companies of Asia & Australasia 2010: Australasia-Australia, New Zealand, Papu New Guinea, Vol. 3. 26th rev. ed. 2009. 575.00 *(978-1-86099-593-4(4))* Graham & Whiteside, Ltd. GBR. Dist: Cengage Gale.

Mooney, Patrick, et al. Enterprise & Venture Capital: A Business Builder's & Investor's Handbook. 5th ed. 2009. (ENG., Illus.). 320p. pap. 39.95 *(978-1-74175-690-6(1))* Allen & Unwin AUS. Dist: Independent Pubs. Group.

Pyke, Joanne. Productive Diversity in Australia- How & Why Companies Make the Most of Diversity. 2007. 260p. per. *(978-3-8364-2917-7(9))* VDM Verlag Dr. Mueller e.K.

Tuck, Robert J. Ethics of Chinese & Australian Business Managers: A Comparative Investigation about Corruption. 2011. (Ethical Issues in the 21st Century Ser.). (Illus.). 690p. 125.00 *(978-1-61668-193-7(4))* Nova Science Pubs., Inc.

Wills-Johnson, Nick. Competition in a Spatial Retail Petroleum Market. 2011. 256p. pap. ***(978-3-8383-3156-0(7))*** Lambert Academic Publishing.

Yip, Shu Wing, et al. Australian SME Readiness to adopt AIFRS: Australian SME Readiness to adopt Australian equivalents of International Financial Reporting Standards. 2008. 120p. pap. *(978-3-639-08913-4(8))* VDM Verlag Dr. Mueller e.K.

BUSINESS ENTERPRISES—BRAZIL

Brazil: Business Financing Handbook. (Illus.). 70p. (Orig.). pap. 295.00 *(978-0-7605-1182-4(9))* Rector Pr., Ltd.

Doing Business in Brazil. Date not set. (Doing Business in Regions & Countries Around the World Ser.). 80p. *(978-1-882390-53-3(9))* Training Management Corp.

Fleury, Afonso Carlos Corrêa & Fleury, Maria Tereza Leme. Brazilian Multinationals: Competencies for Internationalization. 2011. (ENG., Illus.). 460p. 90.00 *(978-0-521-51948-9(9))* Cambridge Univ. Pr.

Franco, Beatriz, et al, eds. International Business Transactions with Brazil. 2008. 584p. 125.00 *(978-1-57823-240-6(6))* Juris Publishing, Inc.

Kobayashi-Hillary, Mark, ed. Building a Future with BRICs: The Next Decade for Offshoring. 2010. (ENG., Illus.). xviii, 219p. pap. 79.95 *(978-3-642-07980-1(6)*, 3642079806) Springer.

Vilaca, Camila. An Analysis of Sustainability in Business. 2009. 140p. pap. *(978-3-639-16508-1(X))* VDM Verlag Dr. Mueller e.K.

BUSINESS ENTERPRISES—CANADA

Armen, Garbis. Prime Markets in Canada: Consumer Demand Prediction & Broadly - Based Selection of Market Location. 2011. 148p. pap. 17.95 ***(978-1-4620-0368-6(0))*** iUniverse, Inc.

Avila D, Jose Antonio, et al. Presente y Futuro de Los Sectores Ganadero, Forestal y de la Pesca Mexicanos en el Contexto Del TLCAN. 2008. (Estudios Económicos Ser.). (SPA., Illus.). 405p. pap. 38.99 *(978-968-12-1337-4(8))* El Colegio de México, A.C., Biblioteca Miguel Cosio Villegas MEX. Dist: Fondo de Cultura Economica USA.

Ávila Dorantes, José Antonio, et al. Presente y Futuro Del Sector Agrícola Mexicano en el Contexto Del TLCAN. 2008. (Estudios Económicos Ser.). (SPA., Illus.). 385p. pap. 39.99 *(978-968-12-1346-6(7))* El Colegio de México, A.C., Biblioteca Miguel Cosio Villegas MEX. Dist: Fondo de Cultura Economica USA.

Bartlett, Steve. The Grit & the Courage: Stories of Success in an Unforgiving Land. 2008. (Illus.). 150p. pap. *(978-1-897174-29-6(2))* Creative Bk. Publishing.

Belanger, Yale D. Gambling with the Future: The Evolution of Aboriginal Gaming in Canada. (Purich's Aboriginal Issues Ser.). (Illus.). 232p. pap. *(978-1-895830-28-6(1))* Purich Publishing.

Bloch, Talia. Doing Business in North America. Date not set. (Doing Business in Regions & Countries Around the World Ser.). *(978-1-882390-85-4(7))* Training Management Corp.

Canada Northern Social Concerns: Companies-Products-Services. (Orig.). 160p. pap. 195.00 *(978-0-7605-1862-5(9))*; 435p. pap. 195.00 *(978-0-7605-1865-6(3))* Rector Pr., Ltd.

Charleson, Mary. 5 Minute Marketing: Five-minute articles on the hottest Canadian topics in marketing Today! 2009. 240p. pap. 25.00 *(978-1-4269-0579-7(3))* Trafford Publishing.

Headquarters USA 2010. 32nd rev. ed. 2009. 216.00 *(978-0-7808-1095-2(3))* Omnigraphics, Inc.

Hicks, Steven D., compiled by. Sources of Canadian Financing for Business & Real Estate. 2009. pap. 29.50 *(978-1-56150-895-2(0))* 17th ed. 2007. pap. 29.50 *(978-1-56150-796-2(2))* International Wealth Success, Inc.

Ibp, Usa. Canada Industrial & Business Directory. 2006. (Illus.). pap. 99.95 *(978-0-7397-9709-9(3))* International Business Pubns., USA.

Jollimore, Troy. Doing Business in Canada. Date not set. (Doing Business in Regions & Countries Around the World Ser.). 80p. *(978-1-882390-54-0(7))* Training Management Corp.

Lapointe-Antunes, Pascale. Causes & Consequences of Transitional Goodwill Impairment Losses. 2010. 92p. pap. *(978-3-8383-5369-2(2))* Lambert Academic Publishing.

Latremoille, Susan & Creaghan, Peter. Who Will Take over the Business? Succession Planning for the Canadian Business Family. 2011. (ENG., Illus.). 160p. 29.95 *(978-1-118-08753-4(4)*, Wiley) Wiley, John & Sons, Inc.

Lobraico, Michael A., et al. Succession Planning for Family Businesses: Preparing for the Next Generation. 2011. 174p. pap. ***(978-1-926645-53-7(7))*** BPS Bks.

Logue, Ann C. & Borzykowski, Bryan. Day Trading for Canadians for Dummies. 2011. (ENG.). 360p. pap. 29.95 *(978-0-470-94503-2(6)*, Wiley) Wiley, John & Sons, Inc.

Mandel-Campbell, Andrea. Why Mexicans Don't Drink Molson: Rescuing Canadian Business from the Suds of Global Obscurity, 1 vol. 2008. (ENG.). 336p. pap. 24.95 *(978-1-55365-406-3(4))* D&M Pubs. Inc. CAN. Dist: Perseus-PGW.

Marchildon, Gregory, ed. Business & Industry: History of the Prairie West #4. 2012. (Hpws Ser.). (ENG.). 440p. 59.95 ***(978-0-88977-238-0(X))*** Canadian Plains Research Ctr. CAN. Dist: Univ. of Toronto Pr.

Margerison, Charles & Smith, Katharine. Amazing Entrepreneurs: Inspirational Stories. Robinson, Kirri, ed. 2010. (ENG.). pap. 16.99 *(978-1-921629-03-7(7))* CJM Publications AUS. Dist: Hachette Bk. Group.

Mars-Proietti, Laura, ed. Food & Beverage Market Place 2010: Suppliers. 9th rev. ed. 2009. 2000p. pap. 250.00 *(978-1-59237-425-0(5))* Grey Hse. Publishing.

Martin, Joe. Relentless Change: A Casebook for the Study of Canadian Business History. 2009. (ENG.). 504p. pap. *(978-0-8020-9559-6(3))* Univ. of Toronto Pr.

McBride, Terry & Ryan, Denise. Nettwerk: 25 Years of Music We Love. 2010. (ENG., Illus.). 256p. pap. 29.95 *(978-0-470-67844-2(5)*, Wiley) Wiley, John & Sons, Inc.

Middleton, Alan C. & Hanna, J. M. Ikonica: A Field Guide to Canada's Brandscape, 1 vol. 2008. (ENG., Illus.). 224p. pap. 32.95 *(978-1-55365-275-5(4))* D&M Pubs. Inc. CAN. Dist: Perseus-PGW.

Ng, Alex. Performance of Stock Market Driven Acquisitions. 2009. 68p. pap. *(978-3-639-13685-2(3))* VDM Verlag Dr. Mueller e.K.

Parker, Marty. Culture Connection: How Developing a Winning Culture Will Give Your Organization a Competitive Advantage. 2011. (ENG., Illus.). 224p. 25.00 ***(978-0-07-178876-2(X)***, 007178876X) McGraw-Hill Cos., The.

Van Valkenburgh, Michael, et al. Grounded: The Work of Phillips Farevaag Smallenberg. 2011. (ENG., Illus.). 288p. 69.95 *(978-1-897476-20-8(5))* Simply Read Bks. CAN. Dist: Perseus-PGW.

BUSINESS ENTERPRISES—CENTRAL AMERICA

Doing Business in Latin America. Date not set. (Doing Business in Regions & Countries Around the World Ser.). *(978-1-882390-84-7(9))* Training Management Corp.

Wherry, Frederick F. Global Markets & Local Crafts: Thailand & Costa Rica Compared. 2008. (Themes in Global Social Change Ser.). (ENG., Illus.). 208p. (gr. 17). 57.00 *(978-0-8018-8794-9(1))* Johns Hopkins Univ. Pr.

BUSINESS ENTERPRISES—CHINA

Agarwala, Rina & Herring, Ronald J., eds. Whatever Happened to Class? Reflections from South Asia. 2008. (Illus.). 240p. 140.00 *(978-0-415-45468-1(9))* Routledge.

Alon, Ilan. Globalization of Chinese Enterprises. Alon, Ilan & McIntyre, John R., eds. 2008. (ENG., Illus.). 256p. 100.00 *(978-0-230-51562-8(2))* Palgrave Macmillan.

Alon, Ilan, et al, eds. China Rules: Globalization & Political Transformation. 2009. (ENG., Illus.). 291p. 105.00 *(978-0-230-57625-4(7))* Palgrave Macmillan.

Alon, Ilan & Zhang, Wenxian. Top 100 Companies in China. 2010. 340p. pap., instr.'s gde. ed. 38.00 *(978-981-4291-46-0(3))* World Scientific Publishing Co., Inc.

Andersen. China Business Guide. Date not set. 233p. pap. 25.95 *(978-0-582-99802-5(6))* Addison-Wesley Longman, Ltd. GBR. Dist: Trans-Atlantic Pubns., Inc.

Aspatore Books Staff, compiled by. Best Practices for International Business Transactions in China, 2011 Ed: Leading Lawyers on Navigating Local Regulations, Overcoming Cultural Barriers, & Advising Clients on Doing Business in China (Inside the Minds) 2011. 212p. pap. 95.00 *(978-0-314-27635-3(1))* Aspatore Bks.

Bapuji, Hari. Not Just China: The Rise of Recalls in the Age of Global Business. 2010. (ENG., Illus.). 204p. 100.00 *(978-0-230-10451-8(7))* Palgrave Macmillan.

Best Practices for International Business Transactions in China: Leading Lawyers on Structuring & Negotiating Trade Transactions, Understanding the Importance of Due Diligence, & Working as a Legal Professional in the International Business Community (Inside the Minds) 2009. 252p. pap. *(978-0-314-19940-9(3))* Aspatore Bks.

Brueckner, M & a in Mainland China. 2007. 108p. per. *(978-3-8364-0238-5(6))* VDM Verlag Dr. Mueller e.K.

Büchelhofer, Christian. Corporate Control & Enterprise Reform in China: An Econometric Analysis of Block Share Trades. 2010. (Contributions to Economics Ser.). (ENG., Illus.). xii, 115p. pap. 109.00 *(978-3-7908-2546-6(8)*, 3790825468) Physica-Verlag DEU. Dist: Springer.

—Corporate Control & Enterprise Reform in China: An Econometric Analysis of Block Share Trades. 2007. (Contributions to Economics Ser.). 128p. (C). 109.00 *(978-3-7908-2019-5(9))* Springer.

Buck, Daniel. Constructing China's Capitalism: Urban-Rural Industries in the Shanghai Region. 2012. (China in Transformation Ser.). (ENG., Illus.). 272p. 85.00 ***(978-0-230-34095-4(4))*** Palgrave Macmillan.

Cao, Fuli. Corporate Income Tax Law & Practice in the People's Republic of China, 1 vol. 2011. (ENG., Illus.). 592p. pap. 225.00 *(978-0-19-539339-2(2))* Oxford Univ. Pr., Inc.

Cao, Xiaoxiao. Internal Strategic Success Factors for Technology Joint Ventures. 2011. 84p. pap. ***(978-3-8433-9058-3(4))*** Lambert Academic Publishing.

CER Publishing, ed. China Foreign Enterprise Directory. 6th ed. 2007. 990p. pap. 117.50 *(978-988-17149-8-5(2))* China Economic Review Publishing HKG. Dist: Trans-Atlantic Pubns., Inc.

Chan, Anita, ed. Walmart in China. 2011. (Illus.). 304p. 65.00 ***(978-0-8014-5020-4(9))***; pap. 24.95 ***(978-0-8014-7731-7(X))*** Cornell Univ. Pr. (ILR Pr.).

Chen, Chao-Chuan & Lee, Yueh-Ting, eds. Leadership & Management in China: Philosophies, Theories, & Practices. 2008. (ENG., Illus.). 324p. 113.00 *(978-0-521-87961-3(2))*; 328p. pap. 41.99 *(978-0-521-70543-1(6))* Cambridge Univ. Pr.

Chen, Yi-Ru Regina. The Business of Corporate Government Affairs in China - Corporate Competitive Advantage in China's Marketization. 2008. 528p. per. *(978-3-8364-3902-2(6))* VDM Verlag Dr. Mueller e.K.

Chen, Yongkui. Min Zu Di Qu Zhong Xiao Qi Ye Rong Zi Yan Jiu. 2009. (CHI., Illus.). *(978-7-105-10452-9(X))* Nationalities Publishing Hse, The.

Cheng, Shaoming. Preference Heterogeneity & Industrial Location: Location choices of Japanese FDI in China. 2007. 196p. per. *(978-3-8364-1650-4(6))* VDM Verlag Dr. Mueller e.K.

Chevalier, Michel & Lu, Pierre Xiao. Luxury China: Market Opportunities & Potential. 2009. (ENG., Illus.). 300p. 34.95 *(978-0-470-82341-5(0),* Wiley) Wiley, John & Sons, Inc.

Chikukutu, Josphat. Transformational Strategies for Companies in Transitional Economies. 2011. 116p. pap. ***(978-3-8443-0483-1(5))*** Lambert Academic Publishing.

Child, John, et al. The Dynamics of Co-Evolution: A Case Study of the Development of China's Port Industry. 2012. (Organisation & Strategy: Case Studies in their Context Ser.). 180p. 110.00 ***(978-1-84980-743-2(4))*** Elgar, Edward Publishing, Inc.

China: Business Financing Handbook. (Illus.). 70p. (Orig.). pap. 295.00 *(978-0-7605-1186-2(1))* Rector Pr., Ltd.

China Business Review: Companies-Products-Services. 100p. (Orig.). pap. 995.00 *(978-0-7605-1992-9(7))* Rector Pr., Ltd.

China Business Risks & Forecasts 1994-1995: Companies-Products-Services. (Illus.). 175p. (Orig.). pap. *(978-0-7605-0661-5(2))* Rector Pr., Ltd.

China Knowledge Press Pte Ltd. Chengdu Business Guide. Wang, Julia, ed. 2007. 352p. pap. *(978-981-4163-45-3(7))* China Knowledge Press Pte Ltd.

China Knowledge Press Staff. Doing Business in Beijing. 2nd ed. 2007. (Illus.). 420p. pap. 49.95 *(978-981-4163-02-6(3),* DOBUBE) China Knowledge Press Pte Ltd SGP. Dist: China Bks. & Periodicals, Inc.

—Doing Business in Shanghai. 2nd ed. 2007. (Illus.). 342p. pap. 49.95 *(978-981-4163-01-9(5),* DOBUSH) China Knowledge Press Pte Ltd SGP. Dist: China Bks. & Periodicals, Inc.

China Knowledge Press Staff & Tong Xiaohu, Tiger. Building a Successful Plant in China. 2007. (Illus.). 729p. pap. 90.00 *(978-981-4163-03-3(1),* BUSUPL) China Knowledge Press Pte Ltd SGP. Dist: Independent Pubs. Group.

China Retailing: Companies-Products-Services. 133p. (Orig.). pap. *(978-0-7605-2124-3(7))* Rector Pr., Ltd.

Ching, Mia Kuang. CFO Guide to Doing Business in China. 2009. (ENG.). 200p. pap. 38.00 *(978-0-470-82373-6(9),* Wiley) Wiley, John & Sons, Inc.

Coates, Rosemary. 42 Rules for Sourcing & Manufacturing in Chin: A practical handbook for doing business in China, special economic zones, factory tours & Manufact. Lowell, Laura, ed. 2009. 134p. pap. 19.95 *(978-1-60773-050-7(2),* Super Star Pr.) Happy About.

Conklin, Lisa. Chinese E-Commerce: A Guide to Selling Online in China. 2008. 84p. pap. *(978-3-639-10617-6(2))* VDM Verlag Dr. Mueller e.K.

Dallas, Nick. How to Do Business in China: 24 Lessons to Make Working in China More Profitable. 2008. (ENG., Illus.). 128p. 12.95 *(978-0-07-159723-4(9),* 0071597239) McGraw-Hill Cos., The.

De Jonge, Alice. Corporate Governance & China's H-Share Market. 2008. (Corporations, Globalisation & the Law Ser.). 328p. 150.00 *(978-1-84720-907-8(6))* Elgar, Edward Publishing, Inc.

Devonshire-Ellis, Chris, et al, eds. Setting up Joint Ventures in China. 3rd ed. 2011. (China Briefing Ser.). Orig. Title: Setting up Joint Ventures in China. (ENG., Illus.). iv, 122p. pap. 59.95 *(978-3-642-16039-4(5),* 3642160395) Springer.

—Setting up Representative Offices in China. 4th ed. 2011. (China Briefing Ser.). Orig. Title: Setting up Representative Offices in China. (ENG., Illus.). vii, 44p. pap. 49.95 *(978-3-642-16070-7(0),* 3642160700) Springer.

—Setting up Wholly Foreign Owned Enterprises in China. 3rd ed. 2011. (China Briefing Ser.). Orig. Title: Setting up Wholly oreign Owned Enterprises in China (Second Edition). (ENG., Illus.). vii, 92p. pap. 59.95 *(978-3-642-15539-0(1),* 3642155391) Springer.

Doing Business in China. Date not set. (Doing Business in Regions & Countries Around the World Ser.). 80p. *(978-1-882390-56-4(3))* Training Management Corp.

Dunne, Robert R. & Dunne, Michael. American Wheels, Chinese Roads: The Story of General Motors in China. 2011. (ENG.). 227p. 29.95 *(978-0-470-82861-8(7),* Wiley) Wiley, John & Sons, Inc.

Fernandez, Juan Antonio & Shengjun, Liu. China CEO: A Case Guide for Business Leaders in China. 2007. (ENG., Illus.). 300p. pap. 24.95 *(978-0-470-82224-1(4),* Wiley) Wiley, John & Sons, Inc.

Fernandez, Juan Antonio & Underwood, Laurie. China Entrepreneur: Voices of Experience from 40 International Business Pioneers. 2009. (ENG., Illus.). 250p. pap. 27.95 *(978-0-470-82321-7(6),* Wiley) Wiley, John & Sons, Inc.

Fraser, Ian. Strategy Formation in Chinese Universities. 2010. 272p. pap. *(978-3-639-22405-4(1))* VDM Verlag Dr. Mueller e.K.

Gallo, Frank T. Business Leadership in China: How to Blend Best Western Practices with Chinese Wisdom. 2008. (ENG.). 240p. pap. 24.95 *(978-0-470-82365-1(8),* Wiley) Wiley, John & Sons, Inc.

—Business Leadership in China: How to Blend Best Western Practices with Chinese Wisdom. 2nd rev. ed. 2011. (ENG.). 280p. pap. 24.95 *(978-0-470-82730-7(0),* Wiley) Wiley, John & Sons, Inc.

Griffiths, Michael. Consumption & Identity in the People's Republic of China. 2012. (Chinese Worlds Ser.). (ENG., Illus.). 272p. (C). 135.00 ***(978-0-415-53572-4(7))*** Routledge.

Grusser Pettersson, Anett. Mei Wenti or You Wenti - Overcoming Cross-Cultural Challenges in the Chinese Working Environment. 2007. 116p. per. *(978-3-8364-5309-7(6))* VDM Verlag Dr. Mueller e.K.

Guo, Li'an & Zong, Fai. Business, Finance & Economics of China. 2010. (China in the 21st Century Ser.). 145.00 *(978-1-60741-299-1(3))* Nova Science Pubs., Inc.

Hagglund, Anders & Bjorksten, Johan. How to Manage a Successful Business in China. 2010. (Illus.). 236p. 27.95 *(978-981-4287-32-1(2))* World Scientific Publishing Co., Inc.

Haley, George T., et al. New Asian Emperors: The Business Strategies of the Overseas Chinese. rev. ed. 2009. (ENG., Illus.). 250p. pap. 24.95 *(978-0-470-82334-7(8),* Wiley) Wiley, John & Sons, Inc.

Hexter, Jimmy & Woetzel, Jonathan. Operation China: From Strategy to Execution. 2007. (ENG., Illus.). 212p. 29.95 *(978-1-4221-1696-8(4))* Harvard Business Review Pr.

Hofer, Markus B. & Ebel, Bernhard, eds. Business Success in China. 2010. (ENG., Illus.). viii, 275p. pap. 74.95 *(978-3-642-07098-3(1),* 3642070981) Springer.

Hoffmann, W. John, et al. China into the Future: Making Sense of the World's Most Dynamic Economy. 2007. (ENG., Illus.). 220p. 34.95 *(978-0-470-82244-9(9),* Wiley) Wiley, John & Sons, Inc.

Hong-Ming Yau, Oliver & Ping-Man Chow, Raymond. Harmony Versus Conflict in Asian Business: Managing in a Turbulent Era. 2007. (ENG., Illus.). 272p. 110.00 *(978-0-230-54292-1(1))* Palgrave Macmillan.

Hsu, Chen-Min, et al. The Business & Investment Environment in Taiwan & Mainland China: A Focus on the It & High-Tech Electronic Industries. 2007. (Illus.). 444p. 150.00 *(978-981-270-366-8(7))* World Scientific Publishing Co., Inc.

Jensen, Hauke. Procurement in China- a Guide for Purchasing Managers. 2007. 116p. per. *(978-3-8364-0612-3(8))* VDM Verlag Dr. Mueller e.K.

Jha, Prem Shankar. Crouching Dragon, Hidden Tiger: Can China & India Dominate the West? 2009. (ENG.). 256p. pap. 16.95 *(978-1-59376-248-3(8),* Soft Skull Pr.) Counterpoint LLC.

Jia, Xinting & Tomasic, Roman. Corporate Governance & Resource Security in China: The Transformation of China's Global Resources Companies. 2009. (Routledge Studies in Corporate Governance). (ENG., Illus.). 190p. (C). 125.00 *(978-0-415-45325-7(9))* Routledge.

Kee, Tan Teng & Xiaofang, Fu, eds. Proceedings of the International Conference on Chinese Enterprise Research 2007. 2008. 548p. pap. 99.00 *(978-981-283-471-3(C))* World Scientific Publishing Co., Inc.

Keister, Lisa A. Chinese Business Groups: The Formation, Structure, & Financial Impact of an Interfirm Network. (Illus.). (C). *(978-0-472-11096-4(9))* Univ. of Michigan Pr.

Kobayashi-Hillary, Mark, ed. Building a Future with BRICs: The Next Decade for Offshoring. 2010. (ENG., Illus.). xviii, 219p. pap. 79.95 *(978-3-642-07980-1(6),* 3642079806) Springer.

Kupper Jd, Samuel Y. Dr China Speaks: Being Successful in China. 2008. 180p. pap. 19.95 *(978-1-4327-3285-1(4))* Outskirts Pr., Inc.

Law, Alice, et al. Leadership Success in China: An Expatriate's Guide. 2008. pap. 30.00 *(978-0-9761514-4-9(8))* Development Dimensions International, Inc.

Leblanc, Jack. Business Republic of China. 2010. (ENG.). 248p. pap. 14.95 *(978-988-99799-0-4(X))* Blacksmith Bks. HKG. Dist: National Bk. Network.

Levenda, Peter & Levenda. The Mao of Business: Guerrilla Trade Techniques for the New China. 2007. (ENG.). 240p. 24.95 *(978-0-8264-2851-6(7))* Continuum International Publishing Group, Ltd. GBR. Dist: National Bk. Network.

Li-Hua, Richard. Competitiveness of Firms in China. 2013. (ENG.). 288p. 94.95 *(978-0-230-22246-5(3))* Palgrave Macmillan.

Li, Qianpin. Consumer Boycotts in Contemporary Chin. 2010. 280p. pap. *(978-3-8383-8082-7(7))* Lambert Academic Publishing.

Liao, Chun. The Governance Structures of Chinese Firms: Innovation, Competitiveness, & Growth in a Dual Economy. 2009. (Innovation, Technology, & Knowledge Management Ser.). (ENG., Illus.). xxvi, 205p. 159.00 *(978-1-4419-0035-7(7),* 1441900357) Springer.

Lieberthal, Kenneth G. Managing the China Challenge: How to Achieve Corporate Success in the People's Republic. 2011. (ENG., Illus.). 149p. 26.95 *(978-0-8157-2204-5(4))* Brookings Institution Pr.

Liu, Binglian. Contemporary Logistics in China: An Introduction. 2011. 252p. 95.00 ***(978-981-4365-88-3(2))*** World Scientific Publishing Co., Inc.

Liu, Hong. Chinese Business: Landscapes & Strategies. 2008. xvii, 206p. (C). 54.95 ***(978-0-203-89084-4(1))***; (Illus.). XVIII, 206p. 165.00 *(978-0-415-40308-5(1))*; (Illus.). XVIII, 206p. pap. 54.95 *(978-0-415-40309-2(X))* Routledge.

Lo, Vai Io & Tian, Xiaowen. Law for Foreign Business & Investment in China. 2009. (Illus.). 432p. 170.00 *(978-0-415-45320-2(8))* Routledge.

Lu, Pierre Xiao. Elite China: Luxury Consumer Behaviour in China. 2008. (ENG., Illus.). 320p. pap. 38.00 *(978-0-470-82267-8(8),* Wiley) Wiley, John & Sons, Inc.

Luo, Jing. Business & Technology in China, 1 vol. 2010. (Understanding China Today Ser.). (Illus.). 234p. 35.00 *(978-0-313-35732-9(3),* GR5732, Greenwood Pr.) Greenwood Publishing Group, Inc.

Ma, Wei. Does China Need a Game Rating System? 2009. 68p. pap. *(978-3-639-20650-0(9))* VDM Verlag Dr. Mueller e.K.

Martin, Sebastian. Acquisitions of Chinese Enterprises- an Alternative Form of Fdi. 2007. 68p. per. *(978-3-8364-0725-0(6))* VDM Verlag Dr. Mueller e.K.

McGregor, James. One Billion Customers: Lessons from the Front Lines of Doing Business in China. 2007. (ENG.). 352p. pap. 15.99 *(978-0-7432-5841-8(X),* Free Pr.) Free Pr.

Meinl, Matthias & Matthias, Meinl. Mergers & Acquisitions in China - Lessons from a Mid-Cap Transaction: A Description of the Takeover Proceedings & Negotiations with a Chinese Mid-Cap Company by an International Investor. 2011. 88p. pap. ***(978-3-639-31818-0(8))*** VDM Verlag Dr. Mueller e.K.

Melvin, Sheila. The Little Red Book of China Business. 2007. (ENG.). 238p. 19.95 *(978-1-4022-0911-6(8))* Sourcebooks, Inc.

Mengkui, Wang. China in the Wake of Asia's Financial Crisis. 2008. (Illus.). 320p. 180.00 *(978-0-415-46469-7(2))* Routledge.

Min, Dai, et al. New China Business Strategies: Chinese & American Companies As Global Partners. 2009. (ENG., Illus.). 351p. 32.95 *(978-1-56171-820-7(3))* SPI Bks.

Miroslawski, Gregor. The International Expansion of Mainland Chinese Businesses. 2008. 284p. pap. *(978-3-8381-0038-8(7))* VDM Verlag Dr. Mueller e.K.

Morgan, Morry. Selling Big to China: Negotiating Principles for the World's Largest Market. 2010. (ENG., Illus.). 224p. pap. 21.95 *(978-0-470-82597-6(9),* Wiley) Wiley, John & Sons, Inc.

Murphy, Rachel. Media, Identity, & Struggle in Twenty-First-Century China. Fong, Vanessa L., ed. 2008. (ENG.). 184p. (C). 150.00 *(978-0-415-46058-3(1))* Routledge.

Nie, Winter & Dowell, William. In The Shadow of the Dragon: The Global Expansion of Chinese Companies - And How It Will Change Business Forever, 1 vol. 2012. (ENG.). 304p. 27.95 ***(978-0-8144-3170-2(4))*** Amacom.

Nie, Winter, et al. Made in China: Secrets of China's Dynamic Entrepreneurs. 2009. (ENG.). 224p. pap. 32.00 *(978-0-470-82436-8(0),* Wiley) Wiley, John & Sons, Inc.

Nocker, Elisabeth. How to Negotiate in China. 2008. 136p. pap. *(978-3-639-01499-3(7))* VDM Verlag Dr. Mueller e.K.

Olukoya, Adeyinka. Corporate Social Responsibility in Chin. 2010. 100p. pap. *(978-3-8383-9309-4(0))* Lambert Academic Publishing.

Ong, Jean Chii. Malaysian Chinese Consumer Behaviour. 2011. 120p. pap. ***(978-3-8454-0955-9(X))*** Lambert Academic Publishing.

Ostertag, Manja. Quality-oriented Procurement in China as a Low-Cost Country. 2008. 104p. pap. *(978-3-8364-8429-9(3))* VDM Verlag Dr. Mueller e.K.

Park, Jacob, et al. Integrating Environmental Goals & Firm Strategy: China Mobile & Climate Change. 2010. (C). pap. 20.00 *(978-1-61674-197-6(X))* Davidson, William Institute At The Univ. of Michigan, The.

Pomp, Remco. Chinese Mnes & Host Countries. 2009. 52p. pap. *(978-3-639-10714-2(4))* VDM Verlag Dr. Mueller e.K.

Quan, Rose. Outward Investment from Emerging Markets: Experiences of Chinese SME Managers. 2010. (Illus.). viii, 260p. pap. *(978-3-8383-4014-2(0))* Lambert Academic Publishing.

Refkin, Alan & Borgia, Daniel. The Wild, Wild East: Lessons for Success in Business in Contemporary Capitalist China. 2011. 200p. pap. 16.95 ***(978-1-4620-4054-4(3))*** iUniverse, Inc.

Reuvid, Jonathan. China: Practical Advice on Operational Strategy & Risk Management. 2nd ed. 2011. (Business Insights Ser.). (ENG., Illus.). 328p. pap. 49.95 *(978-0-7494-5991-8(3))* Kogan Page, Ltd. GBR. Dist: Ingram Pub. Services.

Rui, Huaichuan. China's Multinationals - the Resource Sector. 2010. (ENG., Illus.). 256p. 150.00 *(978-0-415-45508-4(1))* Routledge.

Saxon, Mike. An American's Guide to Doing Business in China: Negotiating Contracts & Agreements; Understanding Culture & Customs; Marketing Products & Services. 2006. (ENG., Illus.). 256p. per. 14.95 *(978-1-59337-730-4(4))* Adams Media Corp.

Schön, Silvia. Cultural Values in Chinese Advertising. 2008. 84p. pap. *(978-3-639-06144-4(6))* VDM Verlag Dr. Mueller e.K.

Shi, Lai. The Balanced Scorecard & Its Applications in Chin. 2008. 68p. pap. *(978-3-639-07881-7(0))* VDM Verlag Dr. Mueller e.K.

Siddharthan, N. S. & Narayanan, K., eds. Indian & Chinese Enterprises: Global Trade, Technology & Investment Regimes. 2009. (Illus.). 268p. 110.00 *(978-0-415-56316-1(X),* Routledge India) Taylor & Francis Group GBR. Dist: Taylor & Francis Group.

Soler, Garrigues Francisco, et al. Doing Business (Safely) in China. 2011. (ENG., Illus.). 206p. pap. 24.99 ***(978-84-8356-395-3(9))*** LID Publishing GBR. Dist: AtlasBooks Distribution.

Stalley, Phillip. Foreign Firms, Investment, & Environmental Regulation in the People's Republic of China. 2010. (ENG., Illus.). 296p. 55.00 *(978-0-8047-7153-5(7))* Stanford Univ. Pr.

Story, Jonathan. China Uncovered: What You Need to Know to Do Business in China. 2010. (Financial Times Ser.). (ENG., Illus.). 248p. (C). pap. 29.99 *(978-0-273-70827-8(9))* FT Press.

Sun, Ted. Inside the Chinese Business Mind: A Tactical Guide for Managers, 1 vol. 2010. (Illus.). 191p. 34.95 *(978-0-313-36519-5(9),* C36519, Praeger Pubs.) Greenwood Publishing Group, Inc.

Sutherland, Dylan. China's Large Enterprises & the Challenge of Late Industrialisation. 2009. 190p. pap. 34.00 *(978-0-415-54625-6(7))* Routledge.

Tadla, Emie. How to Live & Do Business in China: Eight Lessons I Learned from the Communists. 2007. (Illus.). 148p. per. 19.13 *(978-1-4251-0120-6(8))* Trafford Publishing.

Tang, Lei. The Chinese Consumer Market: Opportunities & Risks. 2009. (Chandos Asian Studies). (ENG., Illus.). 250p. 110.00 *(978-1-84334-332-5(0),* Chandos Publishing) Woodhead Publishing Ltd. GBR. Dist: Ingram Pub. Services.

Tang, Yuting. Luxury Retailing in Chin. 2011. 60p. pap. ***(978-3-8443-1482-3(2))*** Lambert Academic Publishing.

Tong, Tiger. China Business Guide, 4th Edition. 2008. 559p. pap. *(978-981-4163-47-7(3))* China Knowledge Press Pte Ltd.

Tse, Edward. The China Strategy: Harnessing the Power of the World's Fastest-Growing Economy. 2010. (ENG.). 256p. (gr. 9). 26.95 *(978-0-465-01825-3(4))* Basic Bks.

Verstappen, Stefan H. Chinese Business Etiquette: The Practical Pocket Guide. 2008. (ENG., Illus.). 148p. pap. 9.95 *(978-1-933330-63-1(5))* Stone Bridge Pr.

Vodicka, Matthias. Guideline for the Development of Chinese Suppliers. 2007. 100p. per. *(978-3-8364-0732-8(9))* VDM Verlag Dr. Mueller e.K.

Walsh, Jean. An American Cookie Seeks Her Fortune in China. 2009. 192p. pap. 69.95 *(978-0-557-05502-9(4))* Lulu Enterprises Inc.

Wang, Barbara Xiaoyu & Chee, Harold. Chinese Leadership. 2011. (ENG., Illus.). 192p. 40.00 *(978-0-230-24818-2(7))* Palgrave Macmillan.

Wang, Huiyao, ed. Globalizing China: The Influence, Strategies & Successes of Chinese Returnees. 2012. 350p. ***(978-1-78052-388-0(2))*** Emerald Group Publishing Ltd.

Wang, Jifu. Strategic Challenges & Strategic Responses: Chinese State-Owned Enterprises. 2007. (Chandos Asian Studies). (ENG., Illus.). 230p. 110.00 *(978-1-84334-222-9(7),* Chandos Publishing) Woodhead Publishing Ltd. GBR. Dist: Ingram Pub. Services.

Wang, Jun & Jun, Wang. Accounting with Heart: China's Role in International Finance & Business. 2010. (ENG.). 256p. pap. 39.95 *(978-0-470-82570-9(7),* Wiley) Wiley, John & Sons, Inc.

Ward, Michael S. How I Ate a Live Scorpion & Survived: Two Decades of Doing Business in China. Kooper, Vivien, ed. 2011. 218p. 26.95 ***(978-1-936780-02-0(X))*** Mill City Pr., Inc.

Warner, M., ed. Management in China: Systems Reform, Human Resources & Emergent Globalization - Book Edition of Human Systems Management. 2011. 122p. pap. 160.00 ***(978-1-60750-696-6(3))*** IOS Pr., Inc.

Warner, Malcolm, ed. In Search of Confucian HRM. 2011. (ENG.). 256p. (C). 125.00 *(978-0-415-60978-4(X))* Routledge.

—Making Sense of Chinese Human Resource Management in China: Economy, Enterprises & Workers. 2010. (ENG.). 272p. (C). 125.00 *(978-0-415-56537-0(5),* Routledge) Taylor & Francis Group GBR. Dist: Taylor & Francis Group.

Wilen-Daugenti, Tracey. China for Businesswomen: A Strategic Guide to Travel, Negotiating, & Cultural Differences. 2007. (ENG., Illus.). 200p. per. 16.95 *(978-1-933330-28-0(7))* Stone Bridge Pr.

Wong, Raymond Sin-Kwok. Chinese Entrepreneurship in a Global Era. 2008. (Chinese Worlds Ser.). (ENG., Illus.). 240p. (C). 158.00 *(978-0-415-46218-1(5))* Routledge.

Wood, David & Johnson, P. Louise, eds. Sporting Cultures: Hispanic Perspectives on Sport, Text & the Body. 2008. (Sport in the Global Society Ser.). (Illus.). XX, 188p. 140.00 *(978-0-415-45762-0(9))* Routledge.

Wu, Xiaobo. Die Dang Yi Bai Nian: Zhongguo Qi Ye, 1870-1977, 2 vols. 2009. (CHI., Illus.). *(978-7-5086-1342-0(2))* CITIC Publishing Hse.

Xiao, Liming & Ruan, Jiawen. Xifeng Shi Jian Hou: Zhongguo Qi Ye Jia Cheng Zhang Zhong de Yi Bu Jing Shi Heng Yan. 2009. (Illus.). 8p. *(978-7-5118-0108-1(0))* Law Publishing Hse., The.

Xu, Tailing. Zhongguo Jia Zu Qi Ye Fa Zhan Tou Shi. 2009. (CHI., Illus.). *(978-7-01-008605-7(2))* People's Publishing Hse., The.

Yu, Shiping. Xin Tai Zi Shang. 2010. (CHI., Illus.). 517p. *(978-962-8744-32-9(1))* Mirror Bks. USA.

Yueh, Linda. Enterprising China: Business, Economic, & Legal Developments Since 1979. 2011. (ENG., Illus.). 336p. 110.00 *(978-0-19-920583-7(3))*; pap. 45.00 *(978-0-19-920582-0(5))* Oxford Univ. Pr., Inc.

Zeng, Ming & Williamson, Peter J. Dragons at Your Door: How Chinese Cost Innovation Is Disrupting Global Competition. 2007. (ENG., Illus.). 239p. 32.00 *(978-1-4221-0208-4(4))* Harvard Business Review Pr.

Zhang, Lin. Venture Capital & the Corporate Governance of Chinese Listed Companies. 2011. (ENG., Illus.). viii, 122p. 139.00 ***(978-1-4614-1280-9(3),*** 1461412803) Springer.

Zhang, Xiaohuan. Npd in Indigenous Chinese Companies and. 2006. 272p. per. 25.95 *(978-1-58112-340-1(X),* Dissertation.com) Universal Pubs.

Zhen, Yong. Globalization & the Chinese Retailing Revolution: Competing in the World's Largest Emerging Market. 2007. (Chandos Asian Studies). (ENG., Illus.). 300p. 110.00 *(978-1-84334-279-3(0),* Chandos Publishing) Woodhead Publishing Ltd. GBR. Dist: Ingram Pub. Services.

Zheng, Congcong. Essays on the Internationalisation of Entrepreneurial Firms. 2010. 284p. pap. *(978-3-8383-8437-5(7))* Lambert Academic Publishing.

Zhou, Xiaolin, et al. Doing Business in China 2008. 2008. (Illus.). 276p. pap. *(978-1-4024-1074-1(3),* 810 7th Ave., New York, NY 10019) Practising Law Institute.

Zhou, Xinmin. Core Capability of Leaders: Exploration & Practice of Chinese State-Owned Enterprises. 2008. *(978-0-9799339-9-8(4))* East West Discovery Pr.

Zhu, Xiaodong, ed. Private Enterprises & China's Economic Development. 2007. (Routledgecurzon Studies in the Growth Economics of Asia Ser.). (ENG., Illus.). 304p. (C). 180.00 *(978-0-415-77147-4(1))* Routledge.

Zimmerman, James M. China Law Deskbook. 3rd ed. 2010. *(978-1-60442-958-9(5))* American Bar Assn.

Zu, Liangrong. Corporate Social Responsibility, Corporate Restructuring & Firm's Performance: Empirical Evidence from Chinese Enterprises. 2008. (ENG., Illus.). xx, 308p. 139.00 *(978-3-540-70895-7(2),* 3540708952) Springer.

BUSINESS ENTERPRISES—CHINA—HONG KONG

China & Hong Kong Law Firm Directory 1994: Companies-Products-Services. 300p. (Orig.). pap. *(978-0-7605-0664-6(7))* Rector Pr., Ltd.

Doing Business in Hong Kong. Date not set. (Doing Business in Regions & Countries Around the World Ser.). 80p. *(978-1-882390-60-1(1))* Training Management Corp.

Hong Kong: Business Financing Handbook. (Illus.). 70p. (Orig.). pap. 295.00 *(978-0-7605-1192-3(6))* Rector Pr., Ltd.

Mapp, Andrew. Hong Kong. 2006. (Illus.). 412p. per. *(978-1-903499-29-0(1))* Liverpool Academic Pr.

BUSINESS ENTERPRISES—COMMUNIST COUNTRIES

Van Grembergen, Wim & De Haes, Steven. Enterprise Governance of Information Technology: Achieving Strategic Alignment & Value. 2009. (ENG., Illus.). xv, 218p. 79.95 *(978-0-387-84881-5(9)*, 0387848819) Springer.

BUSINESS ENTERPRISES—DEVELOPING COUNTRIES

Ackermann, Camilla. Multinational Companies Business Strategies in Developing Countries. 2011. 92p. pap. ***(978-3-8443-0988-1(8))*** Lambert Academic Publishing.

Beck, Adrian, et al. New Loss Prevention: Redefining Shrinkage Management. 2009. (ENG., Illus.). 288p. 100.00 *(978-0-230-57583-7(8))* Palgrave Macmillan.

Beck, T., ed. Entrepreneurship in Developing Countries. 2009. (International Library of Entrepreneurship Ser.). (Illus.). 800p. 400.00 *(978-1-84844-434-8(6))* Elgar, Edward Publishing, Inc.

Brown, Dana L. & Woods, Ngaire, eds. Making Global Self-Regulation Effective in Developing Countries. 2007. (ENG., Illus.). 240p. 125.00 *(978-0-19-923463-9(9))* Oxford Univ. Pr., Inc.

Elegbe, Joel Alemibola. Talent Management in the Developing World: Adopting a Global Perspective. 2010. (Illus.). 248p. 124.95 *(978-1-4094-1813-9(8)*, Gower Publishing Co., Ltd.) Ashgate Publishing, Ltd. GBR. Dist: Ashgate Publishing Co.

Fernandez-Jilberto, Alex E. Big Business & Economic Development: Conglomerates & Economic Groups in Developing Countries & Transition Economies under Globalisation. Hogenboom, Barbara, ed. 2008. (Routledge Studies in International Business & the World Economy Ser.). (ENG., Illus.). 448p. (C). 59.95 *(978-0-415-46461-1(7))* Routledge.

Gebrehiwet Gebremichael, Seifu. Determinants of Market Linkage in Developing Countries. 2010. 112p. pap. *(978-3-639-13386-8(2))* VDM Verlag Dr. Mueller e.K.

Hanna, Nagy. Enabling Enterprise Transformation: Business & Grassroots Innovation for the Knowledge Economy. 2010. (Illus.). x, 314p. *(978-1-4419-1508-5(7))* Springer.

Hanna, Nagy K. Enabling Enterprise Transformation: Business & Grassroots Innovation for the Knowledge Economy. (Innovation, Technology, & Knowledge Management Ser.). (Illus.). ix, 311p. 2010. pap. 49.95 *(978-1-4419-7844-8(5)*, 1441978445) 2009. (ENG., 139.00 *(978-1-4419-1507-8(9)*, 1441915079) Springer.

Hansen. Transnational Corporations & Local Firms in Developing Countries Linking & Upgrading. 2006. (Illus.). 398p. pap. 64.00 *(978-87-630-0175-5(6))* Copenhagen Business Schl. Pr. DNK. Dist: International Specialized Bk. Services.

Harvard Business Review. Harvard Business Review on Thriving in Emerging Markets. 2011. (ENG., Illus.). 272p. pap. 22.00 *(978-1-4221-6263-7(X))* Harvard Business Review Pr.

Hopkins, Michael. Corporate Social Responsibility & International Development: Is Business the Solution? 2008. (ENG., Illus.). 262p. pap. 44.95 *(978-1-84407-610-9(5))* Routledge.

Jansson, Hans. International Business Strategy in Emerging Country Markets: The Institutional Network Approach. 2008. 320p. pap. 50.00 *(978-1-84720-960-3(2))* Elgar, Edward Publishing, Inc.

Johnson, Robert Dean, et al. Developing Global Leaders: A Guide to Managing Effectively in Unfamiliar Places. 2012. (ENG., Illus.). 240p. 35.00 ***(978-0-230-33751-0(1))*** Palgrave Macmillan.

Lutken, Soren Ender & Michaelowa, Axel. Corporate Strategies & the Clean Development Mechanism: Developing Country Financing for Developed Country Commitments? 2008. (Illus.). 192p. 119.00 *(978-1-84720-928-3(9))* Elgar, Edward Publishing, Inc.

Marinov, Marin, ed. The Changing Nature of Doing Business in Transition Economies. 2011. (ENG., Illus.). 336p. 90.00 *(978-0-230-51617-5(3))* Palgrave Macmillan.

Molz, Rick, et al, eds. The Multinational Enterprise in Developing Countries: Local versus Global Logic. 2010. (Routledge Studies in Development Economics Ser.). (ENG., Illus.). 240p. (C). 135.00 *(978-0-415-49252-2(1))* Routledge.

Mujih, Edwin. Regulating Multinationals in Developing Countries: A Conceptual & Legal Framework for Corporate Social Responsibility. 2012. (Corporate Social Responsibility Ser.). 280p. 124.95 ***(978-1-4094-4463-3(5)***, Gower Publishing Co., Ltd.) Ashgate Publishing, Ltd. GBR. Dist: Ashgate Publishing Co.

Naudé, Wim, ed. Entrepreneurship & Economic Development. 2011. (Studies in Development Economics & Policy Ser.). (ENG., Illus.). 304p. 110.00 *(978-0-230-28220-9(2))* Palgrave Macmillan.

Owusu-Manu, De-Graft & Badu, Edward. Capital Structure, Investment Strategy & Financial Decisions. 2011. 340p. pap. ***(978-3-8443-1676-6(0))*** Lambert Academic Publishing.

Ramamurti, Ravi & Singh, Jitendra V. Emerging Multinationals in Emerging Markets. 2010. (ENG., Illus.). 460p. pap. 39.00 *(978-0-521-16018-6(9))* Cambridge Univ. Pr.

Sanni Yaya, Hachimi & Alcius, Gérard Kennedy. La Privatisation des Entreprises Publiques Dans les économies en Développement: L'intérêt Général Peut-Il être Dans la Concurrence? 2008. (FRE.). 344p. *(978-2-7483-4341-0(7))* Publibook.com.

Sumner, Andrew & Rugraff, Eric. Transnational Corporations & Development Policy: Critical Perspectives. Sumner, Andrew & Rugraff, Eric, eds. Sánchez-Ancochea, Diego, ed. 2009. (ENG., Illus.). 288p. 100.00 *(978-0-230-53706-4(5))* Palgrave Macmillan.

Thomley, Daniel & Pacek, Nenad. Emerging Markets: Lessons for Business Success & the Outlook for Different Markets. 2nd rev. ed. 2007. (Economist Ser.). (ENG., Illus.). 245p. 29.95 *(978-1-86197-843-1(X)*, Bloomberg Pr.) Wiley, John & Sons, Inc.

Wheeler, J. W. & Wood, Perry L. Trade Policy in Selected Developing Countries: Key Judgements. 5.00 *(978-1-55813-020-3(9))* Hudson Institute.

BUSINESS ENTERPRISES—EUROPE

Adam, Ioan & Savu, Codrut Nicolae. Legea Societatilor Comerciale: Comentarii Si Explicatii. 2010. ix, 1034p. *(978-973-115-568-5(6))* C. H. Beck'sch Verlagsbuchhandlung.

Ali, Pervaiz. 'Online Shopping' Customer Satisfaction & Loyalty in Norway. 2011. 84p. pap. ***(978-3-8433-8376-9(6))*** Lambert Academic Publishing.

Almond, Phil & Ferner, Anthony, eds. American Multinationals in Europe: Managing Employment Relations across National Borders. 2006. (ENG., Illus.). 368p. 110.00 *(978-0-19-927463-5(0))* Oxford Univ. Pr., Inc.

Anhalt, Karen Nickel, et al. Eastern Europe Consulting: Key Data Trends & Forecasts for Consulting in Eastern Europe, Russia, Ukraine & the Baltics. 2006. (Illus.). 226p. spiral bd. 3495.00 *(978-1-932079-73-9(4))* BNA Subsidiaries, LLC.

Antonelli, Dario & Villa, Agostino, eds. A Road Map to the Development of European SME Networks: Towards Collaborative Innovation. 2008. (ENG., Illus.). xii, 189p. 139.00 *(978-1-84800-341-5(2)*, 1848003412) Springer.

Anwar, Habiba. Business Structures in South East Europe: A Legal Guide. 2008. (ENG.). 48p. pap. 180.00 *(978-1-84673-139-6(9)*, GMB Publishing Ltd.) Blue Ibex Ltd. GBR. Dist: Ingram Pub. Services.

Barth, James R. Corporate Social Responsibility in Europe: Rhetoric & Realities. Barth, Regine & Wolff, Franziska, eds. 2009. (Illus.). 384p. 157.00 *(978-1-84720-764-7(2))* Elgar, Edward Publishing, Inc.

BIA. Complete Business Database of All Companies in Eastern Europe. 6th rev. ed. 2006. 400p. (J). pap. 249.00 *(978-1-4187-4363-5(1))* Business Information Agency.

—Complete Business Database of Eastern European Food Companies. 6th rev. ed. 2006. 400p. (J). pap. 249.00 *(978-1-4187-4369-7(0))* Business Information Agency.

—Complete Business Database of Eastern European Manufacturers. 6th rev. ed. 2006. 300p. (J). pap. 219.00 *(978-1-4187-4366-6(6))* Business Information Agency.

—Essential Norwegian Manufacturers: Food, Textile, Clothing, & Chemical Companies. 6th rev. ed. 2006. 300p. (J). pap. 249.00 *(978-1-4187-4227-0(9))* Business Information Agency.

—Essential Polish Manufacturers: Food, Textile, Clothing, & Chemical Companies. 6th rev. ed. 2006. 400p. (J). pap. 249.00 *(978-1-4187-4209-6(0))* Business Information Agency.

—Essential Portuguese Manufacturers: Food, Textile, Clothing, & Chemical Companies. 6th rev. ed. 2006. 400p. (J). pap. 249.00 *(978-1-4187-4228-7(7))* Business Information Agency.

—Essential Romanian Manufacturers: Food, Textile, Clothing, & Chemical Companies. 6th rev. ed. 2006. 300p. (J). pap. 249.00 *(978-1-4187-4210-2(4))* Business Information Agency.

—Essential Slovenian Manufacturers: Food, Textile, Clothing, & Chemical Companies. 6th rev. ed. 2006. 400p. (J). pap. 219.00 *(978-1-4187-4213-3(9))* Business Information Agency.

—Essential Slowakisch Manufacturers: Food, Textile, Clothing, & Chemical Companies. 6th rev. ed. 2006. 300p. (J). pap. 259.00 *(978-1-4187-4214-0(7))* Business Information Agency.

—Essential Swedish Manufacturers: Food, Textile, Clothing, & Chemical Companies. 6th rev. ed. 2006. 400p. (J). pap. 249.00 *(978-1-4187-4230-0(9))* Business Information Agency.

—Essential Swiss Manufacturers: Food, Textile, Clothing, & Chemical Companies. 6th rev. ed. 2006. 400p. (J). pap. 249.00 *(978-1-4187-4231-7(7))* Business Information Agency.

—Essential Ukrainian & Moldavian Manufacturers: Food, Textile, Clothing, & Chemical Companies. 6th rev. ed. 2006. 400p. (J). pap. 249.00 *(978-1-4187-4422-9(0))* Business Information Agency.

—Essential Western European Manufacturers: Food, Textile, Clothing, & Chemical Companies. 6th rev. ed. 2006. 400p. (J). pap. 249.00 *(978-1-4187-4217-1(1))* Business Information Agency.

—Major Companies of Italy: Manufacturers, Wholesalers, Banks, Construction Companies. 6th rev. ed. 2006. 400p. (J). pap. 249.00 *(978-1-4187-4786-2(6))* Business Information Agency.

—Major Companies of Latvia: Manufacturers, Wholesalers, Banks, Construction Companies. 6th rev. ed. 2006. 400p. (J). pap. 249.00 *(978-1-4187-4414-4(X))* Business Information Agency.

—Major Companies of Liechtenstein: Manufacturers, Wholesalers, Banks, Construction Companies. 6th rev. ed. 2006. 200p. (J). pap. 219.00 *(978-1-4187-5167-8(7))* Business Information Agency.

—Major Companies of Lithuania: Manufacturers, Wholesalers, Banks, Construction Companies. 6th rev. ed. 2006. 300p. (J). pap. 219.00 *(978-1-4187-4415-1(8))* Business Information Agency.

—Major Companies of Luxembourg: Manufacturers, Wholesalers, Banks, Construction Companies. 6th rev. ed. 2006. 300p. (J). pap. 249.00 *(978-1-4187-4804-3(8))* Business Information Agency.

—Major Companies of Norway: Manufacturers, Wholesalers, Banks, Construction Companies. 6th rev. ed. 2006. 200p. (J). pap. 249.00 *(978-1-4187-5291-0(6))* Business Information Agency.

—Major Companies of Poland: Manufacturers, Wholesalers, Banks, Construction Companies. 6th rev. ed. 2006. 400p. (J). pap. 249.00 *(978-1-4187-4416-8(6))* Business Information Agency.

—Major Companies of Portugal: Manufacturers, Wholesalers, Banks, Construction Companies. 6th rev. ed. 2006. 400p. (J). pap. 249.00 *(978-1-4187-4942-2(7))* Business Information Agency.

—Major Companies of Romania: Manufacturers, Wholesalers, Banks, Construction Companies. 6th rev. ed. 2006. 300p. (J). pap. 219.00 *(978-1-4187-4417-5(4))* Business Information Agency.

—Major Companies of Serbia & Montenegro: Manufacturers, Wholesalers, Banks, Construction Companies. 6th rev. ed. 2006. 400p. (J). pap. 249.00 *(978-1-4187-4419-9(0))* Business Information Agency.

—Major Companies of Slovakia: Manufacturers, Wholesalers, Banks, Construction Companies. 6th rev. ed. 2006. 300p. (J). pap. 249.00 *(978-1-4187-4420-5(4))* Business Information Agency.

—Major Companies of Slovenia: Manufacturers, Wholesalers, Banks, Construction Companies. 6th rev. ed. 2006. 300p. (J). pap. 249.00 *(978-1-4187-4421-2(2))* Business Information Agency.

—Major Companies of Sweden: Manufacturers, Wholesalers, Banks, Construction Companies. 6th rev. ed. 2006. 450p. (J). pap. 249.00 *(978-1-4187-4913-2(3))* Business Information Agency.

—Major Companies of Switzerland: Manufacturers, Wholesalers, Banks, Construction Companies. 6th rev. ed. 2006. 400p. (J). pap. 249.00 *(978-1-4187-4898-2(6))* Business Information Agency.

—Major Companies of the Czech Republic: Manufacturers, Wholesalers, Banks, Construction Companies. 6th rev. ed. 2006. 400p. (J). pap. 249.00 *(978-1-4187-4410-6(7))* Business Information Agency.

—Major Companies of Western Europe: Manufacturers, Wholesalers, Banks, Construction Companies. 6th rev. ed. 2006. 400p. (J). pap. 249.00 *(978-1-4187-4395-6(X))* Business Information Agency.

Binda, Veronica. The Dynamics of Big Business: Structure, Strategy, & Impact in Italy & Spain. 2012. (Routledge International Studies in Business History Ser.). (ENG.). 264p. (C). 125.00 *(978-0-415-89614-6(2))* Routledge.

Bird, Emma & Berri, Mario. Starting a Business in Italy: How to Set up & Run a Successful Business in the Bel Paese. 2006. (Illus.). 350p. per. 26.00 *(978-1-84528-128-1(4))* How To Books GBR. Dist: Parkwest Pubns., Inc.

Bloch, Talia. Doing Business in Eastern Europe. Date not set. (Doing Business in Regions & Countries Around the World Ser.). *(978-1-882390-87-8(3))* Training Management Corp.

Borzaga, Carlo & Zandonai, Flaviano. L'impresa Sociale in Italia: Economia e Istituzioni Dei Beni Comuni. 2009. (ITA., Illus.). x, 244p. *(978-88-6036-393-0(4))* Donzelli.

Brandsnes Aurmo, Veslemoy. Sustainable Performance of Business Start-Ups. 2011. 100p. pap. ***(978-3-8433-9458-1(X))*** Lambert Academic Publishing.

Breitschmid, Peter, et al, eds. Doing Succession in Europe: Generational Transfers in Family Businesses in Comparative Perspective. 2011. 412p. pap. 79.95 ***(978-3-940755-88-9(5))*** Budrich-Esser, Barbara DEU. Dist: International Specialized Bk. Services.

Brenner, Barbara. Management Control in Central & Eastern European Subsidiaries. 2008. (ENG., Illus.). 288p. pap. 99.00 *(978-0-230-20140-8(7))* Palgrave Macmillan.

Brewster, Chris, et al, eds. International Human Resource Management: A European Perspective. 2nd rev. ed. 2008. (ENG., Illus.). 344p. (C). 65.95 *(978-0-415-42393-9(7))* Routledge.

Brodbeck & Roulet. Brodbeck & Roulet. 2009. (ENG & FRE., Illus.). 256p. 59.95 *(978-1-86470-244-6(3)*, Images Publishing Dist Ac) Antique Collectors' Club GBR. Dist: National Bk. Network.

Broussky, Salome. Chopard: The Passion for Excellence 1860-2010. 2010. (Illus.). 296p. 95.00 *(978-3-8327-9327-2(5))* teNeues Publishing Co.

Brush, Candida G. The Life Cycle of New Ventures: Emergence, Newness & Growth. Kolvereid, Lars et al, eds. 2010. (New Horizons in Environmental & Energy Law Ser.). (Illus.). 240p. 112.00 *(978-1-84844-697-7(7))* Elgar, Edward Publishing, Inc.

Campbell, Christian, Editor. Legal Aspects of Doing Business in Europe [2009] I. 2009. 428p. pap. 110.00 *(978-0-557-21338-2(X))* Lulu Enterprises Inc.

—Legal Aspects of Doing Business in Europe [2009] II. 2009. 496p. pap. 110.00 *(978-0-557-21337-5(1))* Lulu Enterprises Inc.

—Legal Aspects of Doing Business in Europe [2009] III. 2009. 440p. pap. 110.00 *(978-0-557-21335-1(5))* Lulu Enterprises Inc.

Canfora, Achille Maria. The Evolution & Economic Impact of Software Patents. 2011. 88p. pap. ***(978-3-8454-1471-3(5))*** Lambert Academic Publishing.

Caselli, Stefano. Private Equity & Venture Capital in Europe: Markets, Techniques, & Deals. 2010. (ENG., Illus.). 368p. (C). 83.95 *(978-0-12-375026-6(1)*, Academic Pr.) Elsevier Science & Technology Bks.

Chikan, Attila, et al. National Competitivenes in Global Economy. Roberts, Julian, ed. (Transition, Competitiveness & Economic Growth Ser.: Vol. 4). (Illus.). 292p. *(978-963-05-7867-7(0))* Akademial Kiado.

Colli, Andrea, et al, eds. Mapping European Corporations: Strategy, structure, ownership & performance in a long term Perspective. 2012. (ENG.). 216p. (C). 125.00 ***(978-0-415-69527-5(9))*** Routledge.

Colli, Andrea & Vasta, Michelangelo, eds. Forms of Enterprise in 20th Century Italy: Boundaries, Structures & Strategies. 2010. (Illus.). 352p. 147.00 *(978-1-84720-383-0(3))* Elgar, Edward Publishing, Inc.

Culpepper, Pepper D. Quiet Politics & Business Power: Corporate Control in Europe & Japan. 2010. (Cambridge Studies in Comparative Politics Ser.). (ENG., Illus.). 248p. 90.00 *(978-0-521-11859-0(X))* Cambridge Univ. Pr.

Cuttaree, Vickram & Mandri-Perrott, Cledan. Public-Private Partnerships in Europe & Central Asia: Designing crisis-resilient strategies & bankable Projects. 2011. (ENG., Illus.). 138p. pap. 20.00 *(978-0-8213-8703-0(0)*, 9780821387030) World Bank Pubns.

Cuttaree, Vickram & Mandri-Perrott, X. Cledan. Public-Private Partnerships in Europe & Central Asia: Designing Crisis-Resilient Strategies & Bankable Projects. 2011. E-Book *(978-0-8213-8704-7(9))* World Bank Pubns.

Czech & Slovak: Business Financing Handbook. (Illus.). 70p. (Orig.). pap. 295.00 *(978-0-7605-1188-6(8))* Rector Pr., Ltd.

DAAB Media Staff. Delugan Meissl: Associated Architects, 1 vol. 2008. (ENG, GER, FRE, SPA & ITA., Illus.). 175p. 29.95 *(978-3-937718-87-3(7))* DAAB Media Gmbh DEU. Dist: Innovative Logistics.

Dallago, Bruno & Cvajner, Martina. Youth Entrepreneurship & Local Development in Eastern Europe. Blokker, Paul, ed. 2008. (Illus.). 256p. 124.95 *(978-0-7546-7095-7(3))* Ashgate Publishing Co.

Dana, Leo-Paul, et al, eds. Handbook of Research on European Business & Entrepreneurship: Towards a Theory of Internationalization. 2008. (Elgar Original Reference Ser.). (Illus.). 800p. 335.00 *(978-1-84542-501-2(4))* Elgar, Edward Publishing, Inc.

Dirnberger, Sabina. Granny Moves into a Community Flat. 2010. 124p. pap. *(978-3-639-22627-0(5))* VDM Verlag Dr. Mueller e.K.

Doing Business in Belgium. Date not set. (Doing Business in Regions & Countries Around the World Ser.). *(978-1-882390-52-6(0))* Training Management Corp.

Doing Business in Italy. Date not set. (Doing Business in Regions & Countries Around the World Ser.). 80p. *(978-1-882390-63-2(6))* Training Management Corp.

Doing Business in Norway. Date not set. (Doing Business in Regions & Countries Around the World Ser.). *(978-1-882390-68-7(7))* Training Management Corp.

Doing Business in Sweden. Date not set. (Doing Business in Regions & Countries Around the World Ser.). *(978-1-882390-76-2(8))* Training Management Corp.

Doing Business in Switzerland. Date not set. (Doing Business in Regions & Countries Around the World Ser.). *(978-1-882390-77-9(6))* Training Management Corp.

Doing Business in the Netherlands. Date not set. (Doing Business in Regions & Countries Around the World Ser.). *(978-1-882390-67-0(9))* Training Management Corp.

Dubbink, Wim, et al, eds. European Business Ethics Cases in Context: The Morality of Corporate Decision Making. 2011. (Issues in Business Ethics Ser.). (ENG., Illus.). xviii, 295p. 139.00 *(978-90-481-9333-2(8)*, 9048193338) Springer.

Eggerz, Ambjörn J. S. Early-Stage Venture Capital in Europe: The Case of Germany & Italy. 2008. 112p. pap. *(978-3-639-11523-9(6))* VDM Verlag Dr. Mueller e.K.

F & S Index - Europe. 2008th rev. ed. 2008. (ENG.). 2308.00 *(978-1-4144-0693-0(2))* Cengage Gale.

F&S Index Europe Subscription. 2007th ed. 2007. (ENG.). 2308.00 *(978-1-4144-0041-9(1))* Cengage Gale.

Fico Shehaj, Entela. Ownership Structure & Firm Performance. 2010. 220p. pap. *(978-3-8383-7465-9(7))* Lambert Academic Publishing.

Fink, Matthias, et al. Community-based Entrepreneurship & Rural Development. 2012. (Regions & Cities Ser.). (ENG., Illus.). 224p. (C). 125.00 *(978-0-415-61487-0(2))* Routledge.

Foreman, Carol. Made in Scotland: Household Names That Began in Scotland. 2010. (ENG., Illus.). 224p. pap. 20.00 *(978-1-84158-725-7(7))* Birlinn, Ltd. GBR. Dist: Interlink Publishing Group, Inc.

Gale. Major Companies of Central & Eastern Europe & the Commonwealth of Independent States. 20th ed. 2011. (Major Companies of Central & Eastern Europe & the Commonwealth of Independent States Ser.). 1650p. lib. bdg. 1650.00 ***(978-1-86099-702-0(3))*** Graham & Whiteside, Ltd. GBR. Dist: Cengage Gale.

—Major Companies of Europe 2012, 7 vols. 31st ed. 2011. (Major Companies of Europe Ser.). (ENG.). 2980p. lib. bdg. 3220.00 ***(978-1-86099-696-2(5))*** Graham & Whiteside, Ltd. GBR. Dist: Cengage Gale.

—Major Companies of Europe 2012: Austria, Belgium, Liechtenstein, Luxembourg, the Netherlands, Switzerland. 31st ed. 2011. (Major Companies of Europe Ser.). (ENG.). 640p. lib. bdg. 640.00 ***(978-1-86099-692-4(2))*** Graham & Whiteside, Ltd. GBR. Dist: Cengage Gale.

—Major Companies of Europe 2012: Bulgaria, Czech Republic, Estonia, Hungary, Latvia, Lithuania, Poland, Romania, Slovakia, Slovenia. 31st ed. 2011. (Major Companies of Europe Ser.). 640p. lib. bdg. 640.00 ***(978-1-86099-694-8(9))*** Graham & Whiteside, Ltd. GBR. Dist: Cengage Gale.

—Major Companies of Europe 2012: Cyprus, Greece, Italy, Israel, Malta, Portugal, Spain, Turkey. 31st ed. 2011. (Major Companies of Europe Ser.). 640p. lib. bdg. 640.00 ***(978-1-86099-689-4(2))*** Graham & Whiteside, Ltd. GBR. Dist: Cengage Gale.

—Major Companies of Europe 2012: Denmark, Finland, Iceland, Norway, Sweden. 31st ed. 2011. (Major Companies of Europe Ser.). (ENG.). 640p. lib. bdg. 640.00 ***(978-1-86099-693-1(0))*** Graham & Whiteside, Ltd. GBR. Dist: Cengage Gale.

—Major Companies of Europe 2012: The United Kingdom & the Republic of Ireland. 31st ed. 2011. (Major Companies of Europe Ser.). (ENG.). 640p. lib. bdg. 640.00 ***(978-1-86099-695-5(7))*** Graham & Whiteside, Ltd. GBR. Dist: Cengage Gale.

Goldscheider, Filipp, et al. Goldscheider - Weltmarke der Keramik: Firmengeschichte und Werkverzeichnis. 2008. (GER, ENG & MUL., Illus.). 640p. 225.00 *(978-3-89790-216-9(8))* Arnoldsche Art Pubs. DEU. Dist: Antique Collectors' Club.

Greece: Business Financing Handbook. (Illus.). 70p. (Orig.). pap. 295.00 *(978-0-7605-1191-6(8))* Rector Pr., Ltd.

Handschin, Lukas. Swiss Company Law. 2008. 178p. pap. 49.00 *(978-3-03751-130-5(3))* Dike Verlag AG CHE. Dist: International Specialized Bk. Services.

Hansen, Havard, et al. Consumer Behaviour: A European Outlook. 2nd rev. ed. 2012. (ENG., Illus.). 460p. pap. 120.00 ***(978-0-273-73695-0(7))*** Pearson Education, Ltd. GBR. Dist: Trans-Atlantic Pubns., Inc.

Harapko, Dmitry & Rankou, Kaoutar. International Entrepreneurship in Swedish Well Established Companies. 2010. 96p. pap. *(978-3-8383-8863-2(1))* Lambert Academic Publishing.

Henson, Alica & Curmi, George. Albania's Business Environment. 2009. (ENG.). 280p. pap. 75.00 *(978-1-84673-084-9(8),* GMB Publishing Ltd.) Blue Ibex Ltd. GBR. Dist: Ingram Pub. Services.

Hesse, Joachim, et al, eds. The Public Sector in Transition: East Asia & European Union Compared. 2008. 372p. pap. 61.00 *(978-3-8329-3302-9(6))* Nomos Verlagsgesellschaft DEU. Dist: International Specialized Bk. Services.

The Holmes Report 2007 European Consultancy Report Card. 2007. pap. 69.95 net. *(978-0-9797529-1-9(4))*; pap. 69.95 net. *(978-0-9723645-9-1(5))* Holmes Group, The.

Horvá, et al. E-Procurement. 2009. 204p. pap. *(978-3-639-19226-1(5))* VDM Verlag Dr. Mueller e.K.

Hungary: Business Financing Handbook. (Illus.). 70p. (Orig.). pap. 295.00 *(978-0-7605-1193-0(4))* Rector Pr., Ltd.

Iandoli, Luca, et al, eds. Entrepreneurship, Competitiveness & Local Development: Frontiers in European Entrepreneurship Research. 2007. 296p. (C). 127.00 *(978-1-84720-327-4(2))* Elgar, Edward Publishing, Inc.

Ibp, Usa. Greece Industrial & Business Directory. 2006. (Illus.). pap. 99.95 *(978-0-7397-9743-3(3))* International Business Pubns., USA.

—Sweden Industrial & Business Directory. 2006. (Illus.). pap. 99.95 *(978-0-7397-9773-0(5))* International Business Pubns., USA.

—Switzerland Industrial & Business Dire. 2006. (Illus.). pap. 99.95 *(978-0-7397-9927-7(4))* International Business Pubns., USA.

—Ukraine Export-Import & Business Directo. 2006. (Illus.). pap. 99.95 *(978-0-7397-4243-3(4))* International Business Pubns., USA.

Images Publishing Group. A. 2R. C Architects. 2012. (ENG.). 256p. 59.95 *(978-1-86470-157-9(9))* Images Publishing Group AUS. Dist: National Bk. Network.

Italy: Business Financing Handbook. (Illus.). 70p. (Orig.). pap. 295.00 *(978-0-7605-1196-1(9))* Rector Pr., Ltd.

Iversen, Bent, et al. Danish Business Law. 4th ed. 2010. 584p. pap. 84.00 *(978-87-574-2132-3(3))* Djof Publishing DNK. Dist: International Specialized Bk. Services.

James, Herbert. Patek Philippe Highlights. 2011. (GER & ENG., Illus.). 96p. 19.95 *(978-3-86852-312-6(X))* Heel Verlag GmbH DEU. Dist: Antique Collectors' Club.

Jansson, Hans. International Business Strategy in Emerging Country Markets: The Institutional Network Approach. 2008. 320p. pap. 50.00 *(978-1-84720-960-3(2))* Elgar, Edward Publishing, Inc.

Johnson, Debra & Turner, Colin. European Business. (ENG., Illus.). 480p. (C). 2nd rev. ed. 2006. 200.00 *(978-0-415-35134-8(0))* 3rd rev. ed. 2012. 165.00 *(978-0-415-61716-1(2))* 3rd rev. ed. 2012. pap. 63.95 *(978-0-415-61717-8(0))* Routledge.

Kirpalani, V. H., et al. Successfully Doing Business/Marketing in Eastern Europe. 2008. (Illus.). xvi, 226p. 35.95 *(978-0-203-88570-3(8))* Routledge.

Koslowski, Peter, ed. Contemporary Economic Ethics & Business Ethics. 2010. (Studies in Economic Ethics & Philosophy Ser.). (Illus.). x, 265p. pap. 189.00 *(978-3-642-08591-8(1),* 3642085911) Springer.

Liepina, Sanda, et al. Improving the Business Environment in Latvia: The Impact of FIAS Assistance. 2007. (FIAS Occasional Papers: 2). (ENG., Illus.). 102p. per. 15.00 *(978-0-8213-7189-3(4),* 9780821371893) World Bank Pubns.

Lugosi, Nora & Fotiadis, Anestis. Exploring the Hungarian Culture under Foreign Prism. 2008. 52p. pap. *(978-3-639-03088-4(5))* VDM Verlag Dr. Mueller e.K.

Lukac, Dusko. Key Success Factors for Foreign Direct Investment in Western Balkan. 2008. 160p. pap. *(978-3-639-03807-1(X))* VDM Verlag Dr. Mueller e.K.

Lund, Joachim, ed. Working for the New Order: European Business under German Domination, 1939-1945. 2006. (GER & ENG.). 192p. pap. 34.00 *(978-87-7674-105-1(2))* Univ. Pr. of Southern Denmark DNK. Dist: International Specialized Bk. Services.

Major Companies of Europe 2010, 7 Vols. 29th ed. 2009. Set. 2450.00 *(978-1-86099-590-3(X))* Vol. 3. 550.00 *(978-1-86099-585-9(3))* Vol. 4. 550.00 *(978-1-86099-586-6(1))* Vol. 5. 550.00 *(978-1-86099-587-3(X))* Vol. 6. 550.00 *(978-1-86099-588-0(8))* Vol. 7. 550.00 *(978-1-86099-589-7(6))* Graham & Whiteside, Ltd. GBR. Dist: Cengage Gale.

Marcelli, Enrico. Informal Work in Developed Nations. Marcelli, Enrico et al, eds. 2009. (Routledge Advances in Heterodox Economics Ser.). (ENG., Illus.). 240p. 135.00 *(978-0-415-77779-7(8))* Routledge.

Marchenoir, Julien. Treasures of Vacheron Constantin: A Legacy of Watchmaking Since 1755. 2011. (ENG., Illus.). 204p. 60.00 *(978-0-300-17856-2(5))* Yale Univ. Pr.

Martinussen, Kent. 3xn: Mind your Behaviour. 2010. (Illus.). 276p. pap. *(978-87-993680-0-5(5))* Actar Birkhauser Distribution.

Mercer. The Global Manager's Guide to Living & Working Abroad: Eastern Europe & Asia, 1 vol. 2009. 312p. 49.95 *(978-0-313-37590-3(9),* C37590, Praeger Pubs.) Greenwood Publishing Group, Inc.

—The Global Manager's Guide to Living & Working Abroad: Western Europe & the Americas, 1 vol. 2009. 350p. 49.95 *(978-0-313-35883-8(4),* C35883, Praeger Pubs.) Greenwood Publishing Group, Inc.

Meyer, Christian. Leadership Influence & Distance - Energizing an Organization Across Geographical & Ethnic-Cultural Distance. 2007. 88p. per. *(978-3-8364-4611-2(1))* VDM Verlag Dr. Mueller e.K.

Millward, Robert. Private & Public Enterprise in Europe: Energy, Telecommunications & Transport, 1830-1990. 2008. (Cambridge Studies in Economic History - Second Ser.). (ENG., Illus.). 372p. pap. 48.00 *(978-0-521-06828-4(2))* Cambridge Univ. Pr.

Milo (Lati), Lindita. The Causes & Consequences of Corporate Restructuring in Albania. 2010. 360p. pap. *(978-3-8383-3878-1(2))* Lambert Academic Publishing.

Morrison, Terri & Conaway, Wayne A. Kiss, Bow, or Shake Hands: Europe: How to Do Business in 25 European Countries. 2007. (ENG., Illus.). 336p. per. 14.95 *(978-1-59869-218-1(6))* Adams Media Corp.

Munkert, Michael J., et al, eds. Founding a Company: Handbook of Legal Forms in Europe. 2010. (ENG., Illus.). xv, 280p. 89.95 *(978-3-642-11258-4(7),* 3642112587) Springer.

Munkert, Michael J., et al. Founding a Company: Handbook of Legal Forms in Europe. 2010. (Illus.). xv, 263p. E-Book *(978-3-642-11259-1(5))* Springer.

Museum Fur Gestaltung Zurich, et al, eds. Corporate Diversity: Schweizer Grafik und Werbung für Geigy 1940 -1970. 2009. (GER., Illus.). 208p. pap. *(978-3-03778-161-6(0))* Lars Muller Pubs.

Németh, Zsuzsa. Internationale Sortimentsgestaltung und -steuerung auf Basis von Category Management. 2010. (Europäische Hochschulschriften. Reihe 5: Volks- und Betriebswirtschaft Ser.). (GER.). 366p. pap. 75.95 *(978-3-631-61084-8(X))* Lang, Peter GmbH, Europaischer Verlag der Wissenschaften DEU. Dist: Lang, Peter.

Oecd Publishing, Publishing, et al. OECD Studies on SMEs: Poland 2010. 2010. (OECD studies on SMEs & entrepreneurship Ser.). 230p. pap. 67.00 *(978-92-64-08186-4(0))* Organization for Economic Cooperation & Development.

Oinonen. Does Ec Merger Control Discriminate Against Small Companies. 2010. (Illus.). xxiii, 420p. *(978-90-411-3261-1(9))* Kluwer Law International.

Olsen, Lise Smed. Establishing the Enterprise Europe Network. 2011. 92p. pap. ***(978-3-8443-1934-7(4))*** Lambert Academic Publishing.

Panayiotopoulos, Prodromos. Ethnicity, Migration & Enterprise. 2010. (Migration, Minorities & Citizenship Ser.). (ENG., Illus.). 240p. 89.00 *(978-0-230-22934-1(4))* Palgrave Macmillan.

Pennings. Social Responsibility in Labour Relations: European & Comparative Perspectives. 2008. (Studies in Employment & Social Policy: Vol. 38). (Illus.). xii, 532p. 172.00 *(978-90-411-2783-9(6))* Wolters Kluwer Law & Business.

Poland: Business Financing Handbook. (Illus.). 70p. (Orig.). pap. 295.00 *(978-0-7605-1206-7(X))* Rector Pr., Ltd.

Portugal: Business Financing Handbook. (Illus.). 70p. (Orig.). pap. 295.00 *(978-0-7605-1207-4(8))* Rector Pr., Ltd.

Prouska, Rea & Kapsali, Maria, eds. Business & Management Practices in Greece: A Comparative Context. 2011. (ENG., Illus.). 288p. 95.00 *(978-0-230-24585-3(4))* Palgrave Macmillan.

Racine, Jean-Louis. Harnessing Quality for Competitiveness in Eastern Europe & Central Asia. 2011. (Eastern Europe & Central Asia Reports). (ENG., Illus.). 356p. pap. 30.00 *(978-0-8213-8509-8(7),* 9780821385098); E-Book *(978-0-8213-8510-4(0))* World Bank Pubns.

Reisinger, Thomas. E-Recruiting: Personalbeschaffung über das Internet. 2010. 116p. pap. *(978-3-639-22646-1(1))* VDM Verlag Dr. Mueller e.K.

Rice, Patricia & Drahokoupil, Jan. Globalization & the State in Central & Eastern Europe: The Politics of Foreign Direct Investment. 2008. (BASEES/Routledge Series on Russian & East European Studies). (Illus.). xviii, 237p. pap. 160.00 *(978-0-415-46603-5(2))* Routledge.

Roe, Robert & Zijlstra, Fred. Work Psychology: A European Perspective. 2010. (ENG., Illus.). 300p. 99.95 *(978-1-4051-3570-2(0),* Wiley-Blackwell) Wiley, John & Sons, Inc.

Schadewitz, Hannu. Financial & Nonfinancial Information in Interim Reports. 2010. 276p. pap. *(978-3-8383-0187-7(0))* Lambert Academic Publishing.

Schiffman, Leon G. & Hansen, Havard. Consumer Behaviour: A Global Outlook. 2008. (Illus.). 512p. pap. 97.50 *(978-0-273-70401-0(X))* Pearson Education, Ltd. GBR. Dist: Trans-Atlantic Pubns., Inc.

Schlorhaufer, Bettina, ed. Heinz-Mathoi-Streli Architekten: Buildings & Projects. 2008. (GER & ENG., Illus.). 304p. 59.95 *(978-3-211-75791-8(0),* 3211757910) Springer.

Schroeter, Harm Gustav ed. The European Enterprise: Historical Investigation into a Future Species. 2007. (ENG., Illus.). xiv, 300p. 129.00 *(978-3-540-74036-0(8),* 3540740368) Springer.

Segreto, Luciano. European Business & Brand Building. 2012. (ENG.). 264p. pap. 48.95 ***(978-90-5201-793-8(X))*** PIE - Peter Lang BEL. Dist: Lang, Peter.

Smallbone, David, et al, eds. The Theory & Practice of Entrepreneurship: Frontiers in European Entrepreneurship Research. 2010. (Illus.). 336p. 139.00 *(978-1-84980-379-3(X))* Elgar, Edward Publishing, Inc.

Steffel, Frieda. Internal Communication in English. 2010. 128p. pap. *(978-3-639-23998-0(9))* VDM Verlag Dr. Mueller e.K.

Suder, Gabriele. Doing Business in Europe. (C). 2007. 368p. 135.00 *(978-1-4129-1846-6(4),* B18464C) 2007. (Illus.). 368p. per. 63.00 *(978-1-4129-1847-3(2),* B18464P) 2nd ed. 2012. 472p. 140.00 ***(978-0-85702-084-0(6),*** B20840C) 2nd ed. 2012. 472p. pap. 56.00 ***(978-0-85702-085-7(4),*** B20840P) SAGE Pubns., Ltd. GBR. Dist: SAGE Pubns., Inc.

Tabah, Albert. Doing Business in Western Europe. Date not set. (Doing Business in Regions & Countries Around the World Ser.). *(978-1-882390-86-1(5))* Training Management Corp.

teNeues. Swarovski Crystal Palace: The Art of Light & Crystal. 2010. (ENG., Illus.). 216p. 95.00 *(978-3-8327-9416-3(6))* teNeues Publishing Co.

Thomson, Neil & Baden-Fuller, Charles. Basic Strategy in Context: European Text & Cases. 2010. (ENG., Illus.). 422p. pap. 59.95 *(978-1-4051-6108-4(6),* Wiley-Blackwell) Wiley, John & Sons, Inc.

Turner & Johnson, Steve. European Business. 2nd rev. ed. 2006. (ENG., Illus.). 480p. (C). 69.95 *(978-0-415-35135-5(9))* Routledge.

United Nations Staff. Enhancing the Innovative Performance of Firms: Policy Options & Practical Instruments. 2009. (ENG.). 148p. pap. 32.00 *(978-92-1-116999-7(2))* United Nations Pubns.

United Nations: Economic Commission for Europe. Developing entrepreneurship in the UNECE Region: Country experiences in reducing barriers to enterprise Development. 2009. (ENG., Illus.). 76p. pap. 15.00 *(978-92-1-116996-6(8))* United Nations Pubns.

Van Den Broeck, Ralph. Exploring the Dutch & German Markets for Haka Tours. 2011. 100p. pap. ***(978-3-8443-9088-9(X))*** Lambert Academic Publishing.

Van Gerven, Dirk & Storm, Paul, eds. The European Company Volume 2, 2 vols. 2008. (Law Practitioner Ser.). (ENG.). 524p. 156.00 *(978-0-521-86000-0(8))* Cambridge Univ. Pr.

Vangedal, Susan & VanGedal, Susan. Corporate Social Responsibility. 2011. 188p. pap. ***(978-3-8443-1778-7(3))*** Lambert Academic Publishing.

Vettori, Barbara, et al. I Falsi Di Moda: Le Vulnerabilità Del Mercato Italiano Della Moda Alla Contraffazione. 2008. (ITA., Illus.). 233p. *(978-88-568-0581-9(2))* Angeli.

Villalba, Ernesto. The Uniqueness of Knowledge Management in Small Companies - Managing Knowledge As an Employer Strategy for Lifelong Learning. 2008. 236p. per. *(978-3-8364-5717-0(2))* VDM Verlag Dr. Mueller e.K.

Welter, Friederike & Smallbone, David, eds. The Cutting Edge: Innovation & Entrepreneurship in New Europe. Aidis, Ruta, ed. 2008. 192p. 119.00 *(978-1-84542-974-4(5))* Elgar, Edward Publishing, Inc.

Witte, Sonja. Die soziale Dimension Europas: Soziale Verantwortung öffentlicher Unternehmen. 2009. (Europäische Hochschulschriften. Reihe 31: Politikwissenschaft Ser.). (GER.). 120p. pap. 28.95 *(978-3-631-59830-6(0))* Lang, Peter GmbH, Europaischer Verlag der Wissenschaften DEU. Dist: Lang, Peter.

World Bank. Challenges to Enterprise Performance in the Face of the Financial Crisis: Eastern Europe & Central Asia. 2011. (World Bank Studies). (ENG., Illus.). 144p. pap. 25.00 *(978-0-8213-8800-6(2),* 9780821388006) World Bank Pubns.

World Bank Staff, contrib. by. Challenges to Enterprise Performance in the Face of the Financial Crisis: Eastern Europe & Central Asia. 2011. ***(978-0-8213-8801-3(0))*** World Bank Pubns.

Zhang, Feng & Thar Tran Thi, Minh. Corporate Strategy of Danish Companies Toward Eu Ets. 2011. 84p. pap. ***(978-3-8443-0430-5(4))*** Lambert Academic Publishing.

BUSINESS ENTERPRISES—FRANCE

Bloch, Talia & Rosenberg, Suzanna. Doing Business in France. Date not set. (Doing Business in Regions & Countries Around the World Ser.). 80p. *(978-1-882390-58-8(X))* Training Management Corp.

Croenen, Godfried, et al, eds. Patrons, Authors & Workshops: Books & Book Production in Paris Around 1400. 2006. (Synthema Ser.: Vol. 4). (FRE & ENG., Illus.). 530p. (C). pap. 101.00 *(978-90-429-1707-1(5))* Peeters Pubs. & Booksellers BEL. Dist: Brown, David Bk. Co., The.

Dawson, Catherine. The Mature Student's Study Guide: Essential Skills for Those Returning to Education or Distance Learning. 2nd ed. 2007. 211p. per. 20.00 *(978-1-84528-124-3(1))* How To Books GBR. Dist: Parkwest Pubns., Inc.

de Feydeau, Elisabeth. Diptyque. 2008. (ENG.). 200p. 75.00 *(978-2-262-02803-9(X))* Gourcuff Gradenigo FRA. Dist: National Bk. Network.

Duranton, Gilles, et al. The Economics of Clusters: Lessons from the French Experience. 2011. (ENG., Illus.). 192p. 65.00 *(978-0-19-959220-3(9))* Oxford Univ. Pr., Inc.

Eisler, Eva, et al, texts. Cartier: The Power of Style. 2011. (ENG., Illus.). 320p. 49.95 *(978-2-08-020075-4(5))* Flammarion et Cie FRA. Dist: Random Hse., Inc.

France: Business Financing Handbook. (Illus.). 70p. (Orig.). pap. 295.00 *(978-0-7605-1189-3(6))* Rector Pr., Ltd.

Gale. Major Companies of Europe 2012: France. 31st ed. 2011. (Major Companies of Europe Ser.). 640p. lib. bdg. 640.00 ***(978-1-86099-690-0(6))*** Graham & Whiteside, Ltd. GBR. Dist: Cengage Gale.

Gri, Françoise. Plaidoyer Pour un Emploi Responsable: Un Carnet de Route de Crise Prolongé Par 30 Rencontres Avec des Chefs D'entreprise Engagés. 2010. (FRE.). 211p. *(978-2-234-06490-4(2))* Stock, Editions.

Hartmann, Heinrich. Organisation und Geschaft: Unternehmensorganisation in Frankreich und Deutschland 1890-1914. 2010. (Kritische Studien Zur Geschichtswissenschaft Ser.). (GER., Illus.). 372p. (C). 80.00 *(978-3-525-37003-2(2))* Vandenhoeck & Ruprecht GmbH & Co. KG DEU. Dist: ISD.

Ibp, Usa. France Industrial & Business Directory. 2006. (Illus.). pap. 99.95 *(978-0-7397-9752-5(2))* International Business Pubns., USA.

Kaschefi, Aris. Sachmängelhaftung im französischen Kaufrecht vor und nach Umsetzung der Verbrauchsgüterkaufrichtlinie: Mit rechtsvergleichenden Hinweisen zum deutschen Recht unter besonderer Berücksichtigung von Weiterfressersachverhalten. 2008. (Studien zum vergleichenden und internationalen Recht. Comparative & International Law Studies). 306p. pap. 74.95 *(978-3-631-55576-7(8))* Lang, Peter GmbH, Europaischer Verlag der Wissenschaften DEU. Dist: Lang, Peter.

Lindholm, Jenny. Management in France. 2010. 84p. pap. *(978-3-639-23022-2(1))* VDM Verlag Dr. Mueller e.K.

Parrat, Frédéric. Reprise et Transmission de L'entreprise: Aspects Stratégiques, Juridiques et Fiscaux. 2010. 591p. *(978-2-7178-5827-3(X))* Economica, Editions.

Priester, Charles. Financial Strategies for the Manager. 2009. (Tsinghua University Texts). 210p. 89.95 *(978-3-540-70963-3(0))* Springer.

BUSINESS ENTERPRISES—GERMANY

Akhtar, Mobeena Hamid. Fast Food, Rapid Turnover. 2011. 64p. pap. ***(978-3-8443-2889-9(0))*** Lambert Academic Publishing.

Bettermann, Constantin. Finanzierung von Familiengesellschaften nach Basel II und IFRS: Kautelarjuristische und betriebswirtschaftliche Betrachtung. 2009. (GER.). 328p. 86.95 *(978-3-631-59483-4(6))* Lang, Peter GmbH, Europaischer Verlag der Wissenschaften DEU. Dist: Lang, Peter.

Bogenschütz, Nina. Neuausrichtung des Eigenkapitalbegriffs: Dogmatische Überlegungen im Lichte hybrider Finanzierungen. 2008. (Frankfurter wirtschaftsrechtliche Studien Ser.). 244p. pap. 61.95 *(978-3-631-56933-7(5))* Lang, Peter GmbH, Europaischer Verlag der Wissenschaften DEU. Dist: Lang, Peter.

Borg, Erik A., et al. Succeeding in a Transition Economy: Survival Strategies in Eastern Germany. 2010. 253p. pap. 54.95 *(978-87-7307-980-5(4))* Aalborg Universitetsforlag DNK. Dist: International Specialized Bk. Services.

Burkhardt, Robert. Reputation Management in Small & Medium-Sized Enterprises Analysis & Evaluation of the Use of Reputation Management a Survey of Small & Medium. 2008. 120p. pap. *(978-3-8366-5825-6(9))* Books on Demand GmbH.

Contrepois, Sylvie, et al, eds. Globalizing Employment Relations: Multinational Firms & Central & Eastern Europe Transitions. 2011. (ENG., Illus.). 304p. 110.00 *(978-0-230-25243-1(5))* Palgrave Macmillan.

Crouch, Colin & Voelzkow, Helmut. Innovation in Local Economies: Germany in Comparative Context. 2009. (ENG., Illus.). 256p. 110.00 *(978-0-19-955117-0(0))* Oxford Univ. Pr., Inc.

Dörmer, Thomas. Die Unternehmenspacht: Rechtsstellung der Vertragsparteien unter besonderer Berücksichtigung des Pflicht des Unternehmenspächters zur ordnungsgemäßen Unternehmensführung sowie der Rechtslage bei Vertragsbeendigung. 2010. (Veröffentlichungen des Instituts für deutsches und europäisches Wirtschafts-, Wettbewerbs- und Regulierungsrecht der Freien Universität Berlin Ser.). (GER.). 416p. 101.95 *(978-3-631-59009-6(1))* Lang, Peter GmbH, Europaischer Verlag der Wissenschaften DEU. Dist: Lang, Peter.

Ehring, Philipp. Die Due Diligence im Spannungsverhältnis zwischen kaufrechtlichem Haftungssystem und vertraglicher Gestaltung. 2010. (Saarbrücker Studien zum Privat- und Wirtschaftsrecht Ser.). (GER.). 404p. 98.95 *(978-3-631-60488-5(2))* Lang, Peter GmbH, Europaischer Verlag der Wissenschaften DEU. Dist: Lang, Peter.

Farrell, Henry. The Political Economy of Trust: Institutions, Interests, & Inter-Firm Cooperation in Italy & Germany. 2012. (Cambridge Studies in Comparative Politics Ser.). (ENG., Illus.). 258p. pap. 34.99 ***(978-1-107-40430-4(4))*** Cambridge Univ. Pr.

Fritsch, Michael & Grotz, Reinhold, eds. Empirische Analysen zum Gründungsgeschehen in Deutschland. 2010. (Illus.). 250p. *(978-3-7908-0182-8(8))* Springer Singapore Pte. Ltd.

Fritsch, Michael & Niese, Michael, eds. Gründungsprozess und Gründungserfolg: Interdisziplinäre Beiträge zum Entrepreneurship Research. 2006. (Illus.). VIII, 256p. 119.00 *(978-3-7908-0200-9(X),* 379080200X) Physica-Verlag DEU. Dist: Springer.

Fritsch, Michael & Schmude, Jurgen, eds. Entrepreneurship in the Region. 2010. (International Studies in Entrepreneurship Ser.). (Illus.). xiv, 274p. pap. 159.00 *(978-1-4419-3939-5(3),* 1441939393) Springer.

Furth, Rasmus. Ambush Marketing: Eine rechtsvergleichende Untersuchung im Lichte des deutschen und US-amerikanischen Rechts. 2009. (GER.). xxxv, 562p. *(978-3-452-27190-7(0))* Heymanns, Carl Verlag KG.

Gale. Major Companies of Europe 2012: Germany. 31st ed. 2011. (Major Companies of Europe Ser.). (ENG.). 640p. lib. bdg. 640.00 ***(978-1-86099-691-7(4))*** Graham & Whiteside, Ltd. GBR. Dist: Cengage Gale.

German Council of Economic Experts Staff. Dual Income Tax. 2008. (ZEW Economic Studies). pap. 119.00 *(978-3-7908-2051-5(2))* Springer.

Germany: Business Financing Handbook. (Illus.). 70p. (Orig.). pap. 295.00 *(978-0-7605-1190-9(X))* Rector Pr., Ltd.

Germany Business Strategy with Tape: Companies-Products-Services. 75p. (Orig.). pap. *(978-0-7605-0822-0(4))* Rector Pr., Ltd.

Gerschlauer, Simon. German Multinational Firms in Indi. 2010. 96p. pap. *(978-3-639-25366-5(3))* VDM Verlag Dr. Mueller e.K.

Hartmann, Heinrich. Organisation und Geschaft: Unternehmensorganisation in Frankreich und Deutschland 1890-1914. 2010. (Kritische Studien Zur Geschichtswissenschaft Ser.). (GER., Illus.). 372p. (C). 80.00 *(978-3-525-37003-2(2))* Vandenhoeck & Ruprecht GmbH & Co. KG DEU. Dist: ISD.

Ibp, Usa. Germany Industrial & Business Director. 2006. (Illus.). pap. 99.95 *(978-0-7397-9741-9(7))* International Business Pubns., USA.

Koch, Tobias. Business Knigge Germany. 2009. 6p. cd-rom 29.90 *(978-3-937545-19-6(0))* Koch, Tobias Trivero DEU. Dist: AtlasBooks Distribution.

Kvintradze, Tamar. Minority Shareholder Protection in Georgia & Germany. 2010. 48p. pap. *(978-3-639-22619-5(4))* VDM Verlag Dr. Mueller e.K.

Laeger, Lars M. Deutsch-amerikanisches Internationales Gesellschaftsrecht: Festschreibung der Gründungstheorie durch den deutsch-amerikanischen Freundschaftsvertrag? 2008. (Schriftenreihe zum Gesellschafts- und Kapitalmarktrecht Ser.). 236p. pap. 61.95 *(978-3-631-58276-3(5))* Lang, Peter GmbH, Europaischer Verlag der Wissenschaften DEU. Dist: Lang, Peter.

Lamson, Melissa. No Such Thing As Small Talk: 7 Keys to Understanding German Business Culture. 2010. 162p. pap. 19.95 ***(978-1-60005-189-0(8))*** Happy About.

Lier, Anika. Cultural Diversity Management. 2010. 80p. pap. *(978-3-639-25981-0(5))* VDM Verlag Dr. Mueller e.K.

Lorenzen, Stefanie. Inhaltskontrolle beim Betriebsübergang: Die Anpassung tariflicher Arbeitnehmerpflichten nach Privatisierungen. 2009. (Schriften zum Arbeitsrecht und Wirtschaftsrecht Ser.). (GER.). 254p. pap. 65.95 *(978-3-631-58450-7(4))* Lang, Peter GmbH, Europaischer Verlag der Wissenschaften DEU. Dist: Lang, Peter.

Maier, Michael Thomas. Der Management Approach: Herausforderungen für Controller und Abschlußprüfer im Kontext der IFRS-Finanzberichterstattung. 2009. (Controlling & Business Accounting Ser.). (GRE.). 518p. 122.95 *(978-3-631-59197-0(7))* Lang, Peter GmbH, Europaischer Verlag der Wissenschaften DEU. Dist: Lang, Peter.

Meyer-Sandberg, Nils. Die Duale Einkommensteuer als Modell ungleicher Besteuerung von Arbeit und Kapital. 2008. (Finanz- und Steuerrecht in Deutschland und Europa Ser.). 310p. pap. 74.95 *(978-3-631-58084-4(3))* Lang, Peter GmbH, Europaischer Verlag der Wissenschaften DEU. Dist: Lang, Peter.

Mundelius, Marco. The Reliance of Berlin 's Creative Industries on Milieus: An Organisational & Spatial Analysis. 2008. (Illus.). 156p. pap. *(978-3-8364-8235-6(5))* VDM Verlag Dr. Mueller e.K.

Noelle, Oliver & Strohschein, Alexa. A Useful Guide to Modern Business Etiquette in Germany. 2011. 134p. pap. 22.50 ***(978-3-8423-5229-2(8))*** Bks. on Demand.

Protz, Daniel Marc. Das zivilrechtliche Anforderungsprofil mezzaniner Strukturen der Unternehmensfinanzierung. 2009. (Saarbrücker Studien zum Privat- und Wirtschaftsrecht Ser.). (GRE.). 622p. 149.95 *(978-3-631-59320-2(1))* Lang, Peter GmbH, Europaischer Verlag der Wissenschaften DEU. Dist: Lang, Peter.

Reiche, Stefanie. Die prozessualen Folgen eines Betriebsübergangs nach § 613a BGB. 2009. (Schriften zum Verfahrensrecht Ser.). (GER.). 382p. 93.95 *(978-3-631-59429-2(1))* Lang, Peter GmbH, Europaischer Verlag der Wissenschaften DEU. Dist: Lang, Peter.

Scheffler, Sonja. Das Bild des Unternehmers im Spiegel der Gewerbepolitik im nachnapoleonischen Preußen. 2009. (Volkswirtschaftliche Analysen Ser.). (GER.). 270p. 75.95 *(978-3-631-58757-7(0))* Lang, Peter GmbH, Europaischer Verlag der Wissenschaften DEU. Dist: Lang, Peter.

Schmude, Jnrgen, ed. Neue Unternehmen in Ostdeutschland: Neuaufbau und Umstrukturierung der Unternehmenslandschaft. 2007. (Wirtschaftswissenschaftliche Beiträge Ser.). (GER.). 268p. per. 48.27 *(978-3-7908-1109-4(2))* Springer.

Schneider, Uwe H. & Hommelhoff, Peter, eds. Gesammelte Schriften: Aus Anlass seines 80. Geburtstages am 11. Dezember 2010. 2010. (GER.). 532p. 182.00 *(978-3-89949-795-3(3))* De Gruyter Rechtswissenschaften Verlags GmbH DEU. Dist: de Gruyter, Walter GmbH & Co. KG.

Schöning, Stephan & Richter, Jörg, eds. Mittelstand 2008 Aktuelle Forschungsbeiträge zu gesellschaftlichen und finanzwirtschaftlichen Herausforderungen. 2008. 264p. pap. 65.95 *(978-3-631-57705-9(2))* Lang, Peter GmbH, Europaischer Verlag der Wissenschaften DEU. Dist: Lang, Peter.

Schuck, Frank. Die Doppelstiftung: Instrument zur Gestaltung der Unternehmensnachfolge. 2009. (Bochumer Studien zum Stiftungswesen Ser.). (GER.). 330p. 86.95 *(978-3-631-59332-5(5))* Lang, Peter GmbH, Europaischer Verlag der Wissenschaften DEU. Dist: Lang, Peter.

Smit, Barbara. Sneaker Wars: The Enemy Brothers Who Founded Adidas & Puma & the Family Feud That Forever Changed the Business of Sports. 2009. (ENG.). 400p. pap. 15.99 *(978-0-06-124658-6(1)*, HarperPerennial) HarperCollins Pubs.

Staudt, Erwin, ed. Deutschland online: Standortwettbewerb im Informationszeitalter - Projekte und Strategien für den Sprung an die Spitze. 2007. (GER., Illus.). VIII, 243p. 21.92 *(978-3-540-43435-1(6)*, 3540434356) Springer.

Stolz, Daniel. Der beurlaubte Beamte im Angestelltenverhältnis: Eine Darstellung der Doppelrechtsstellung am Beispiel der Postnachfolgeunternehmen. 2010. (Bonner Schriften zum deutschen und europäischen Recht der Arbeit und der Sozialen Sicherheit Ser.). (GER.). 400p. 98.95 *(978-3-631-60260-7(X))* Lang, Peter GmbH, Europaischer Verlag der Wissenschaften DEU. Dist: Lang, Peter.

von Thunen, Sebastian. Directors' Duty for the Benefit of Creditors: Die Bedeutung der Geschäftsleiterpflicht zur Berücksichtigung der Gläubigerinteressen für den Schutz der Gläubiger einer englischen Limited mit Verwaltungssitz in Deutschland. 2011. (Schriften zum Internationalen Privatrecht und zur Rechtsvergleichung Ser.). (GER.). 463p. (C). 84.00 ***(978-3-89971-864-5(X))*** Vandenhoeck & Ruprecht GmbH & Co. KG DEU. Dist: ISD.

Wallraff, Guenter. Industriereportagen: Als Arbeiter in deutschen Großbetrieben. (GER.). 250p. pap. *(978-3-462-02143-1(5))* Kiepenheuer & Witsch GmbH & Company KG DEU. Dist: International Bk. Import Service, Inc.

Wawra, Daniela. Public Relations im Kulturvergleich: Die Sprache der Geschäftsberichte US-amerikanischer und deutscher Unternehmen. 2008. 458p. pap. 107.95 *(978-3-631-57870-4(9))* Lang, Peter GmbH, Europaischer Verlag der Wissenschaften DEU. Dist: Lang, Peter.

Wildebrand, Hendrik. Kundenindividuelle Massenproduktion zur Bewältigung überkapazitätsbedingter Unternehmenskrisen. 2008. (Wertschöpfungsmanagement Ser.). (GRE.). 270p. pap. 72.95 *(978-3-631-57284-9(0))* Lang, Peter GmbH, Europaischer Verlag der Wissenschaften DEU. Dist: Lang, Peter.

Wortmann, Michael. Komplex und Global: Strategien und Strukturen multinationaler Unternehmen. 2008. (GER., Illus.). 206p. pap. *(978-3-531-16315-4(9))* VS Verlag fur Sozialwissenschaften GmbH.

BUSINESS ENTERPRISES—GREAT BRITAIN

Adonis Abbey, Adonis Abbey Publisher. Directory of African Businesses & Organisations in the United Kingdom 2007. 2007. 236p. *(978-1-905068-78-4(6))* Adonis & Abbey Publishers Ltd.

AKTRIN Furniture Information Center Staff. UK Market for Kitchen Furniture. 2007. (Illus.). 70p. spiral bd. *(978-1-894960-68-7(8))* AKTRIN Group of Information Ctrs.

Anwar, Habiba, ed. The United Kingdom's Business Environment: A Guide to Investment Prospects & Commercial Regulations. 2009. (C). pap. *(978-1-84673-175-4(5)*, GMB Publishing Ltd.) Blue Ibex Ltd.

Arestis, Philip. Critical Essays on the Privatisation Experience. Arestis, Philip & Sawyer, Malcolm, eds. 2008. (International Papers in Political Economy Ser.). (ENG., Illus.). 264p. 105.00 *(978-0-230-22252-6(8))* Palgrave Macmillan.

Armour, John & Payne, Jennifer, eds. Rationality in Company Law: Essays in Honour of DD Prentice. 2009. (ENG., Illus.). 400p. 156.00 *(978-1-84113-806-0(1))* Hart Publishing Ltd. GBR. Dist: International Specialized Bk. Services.

Bainbridge, Jane & Dugdale, Karen. Superbrands: An Insight into Some of Britain's Strongest Brands 2010. Cooper, Angela, ed. 2010. (Illus.). 200p. 99.50 *(978-0-9554784-9-9(9))* Superbrands (UK), Ltd. GBR. Dist: Trans-Atlantic Pubns., Inc.

Beirne, Martin. Empowerment & Innovation: Managers, Principles & Reflective Practice. 2007. (Illus.). 144p. pap. 35.00 *(978-1-84720-499-8(6))* Elgar, Edward Publishing, Inc.

Bennett, Robin. Start-Up Smart: How to Start & Build a Business for £5000. 2010. (ENG.). 200p. pap. 22.99 *(978-1-906659-83-7(4))* Harriman Hse. Publishing GBR. Dist: Ingram Pub. Services.

Bentley, Colin. Prince2: A Practical Handbook. 3rd rev. ed. 2009. (ENG., Illus.). 322p. pap. 64.95 *(978-1-85617-822-8(6))* Routledge.

BIA. Major Companies of the United Kingdom: Manufacturers, Wholesalers, Banks, Construction Companies. 6th rev. ed. 2006. 400p. (J). pap. 249.00 *(978-1-4187-4453-3(0))* Business Information Agency.

Blanchflower, David G. & Shadforth, Chris. Entrepreneurship in the UK. 2007. (Foundations & Trends in Entrepreneurship Ser.: 12). (Illus.). 120p. pap. 85.00 *(978-1-60198-038-0(8))* Now Pubs.

Cameron, Colin. Harrods: Behind the Scenes. (Illus.). 168p. 29.99 *(978-0-233-99617-2(6))* Andre Deutsch GBR. Dist: Trafalgar Square Publishing.

Contrepois, Sylvie, et al, eds. Globalizing Employment Relations: Multinational Firms & Central & Eastern Europe Transitions. 2011. (ENG., Illus.). 304p. 110.00 *(978-0-230-25243-1(5))* Palgrave Macmillan.

Cooper, Rachel E., ed. Legislation for Business Law 2009-2010. 2009. (Blackstone Legal Practice Course Guide Ser.). (ENG.). 1120p. 66.00 *(978-0-19-958065-1(0)*, Blackstone Pr.) Oxford Univ. Pr. GBR. Dist: Oxford Univ. Pr., Inc.

Coopey, Richard & Lyth, Peter, eds. Business in Britain in the Twentieth Century: Decline & Renaissance? 2009. (ENG., Illus.). 352p. 135.00 *(978-0-19-922600-9(8))* Oxford Univ. Pr., Inc.

Derbyshire, Wyn, et al. Tupe: Law & Practice: Transfer of Undertakings (Protection of Employment) Regulations 2006. 2nd ed. 2009. 164p. pap. 95.50 *(978-1-904905-63-9(3))* Spiramus Pr. GBR. Dist: International Specialized Bk. Services.

Dexter, Kenneth. A Fleury Business. 2009. 104p. pap. *(978-1-84748-655-4(X))* Athena Pr.

Djordjevich, Vera. Vault Guide to the Top 50 United Kingdom Law Firms, 2009 Edition: 3rd Edition. 2008. 450p. pap. 34.95 *(978-1-58131-595-0(3))* Vault.com.

Doing Business in the United Kingdom. Date not set. (Doing Business in Regions & Countries Around the World Ser.). *(978-1-882390-79-3(2))* Training Management Corp.

Fu, Cixiang. Default Prediction of Publicly Traded Companies in Uk. 2010. 72p. pap. *(978-3-639-26272-8(7))* VDM Verlag Dr. Mueller e.K.

Gill, Matthew. Accountants' Truth: Knowledge & Ethics in the Financial World. 2009. (ENG.). 200p. 110.00 *(978-0-19-954714-2(9))* Oxford Univ. Pr., Inc.

Harris, Ron. Industrializing English Law: Entrepreneurship & Business Organization, 1720-1844. 2011. (Political Economy of Institutions & Decisions Ser.). (ENG.). 348p. pap. 39.99 *(978-0-521-18252-2(2))* Cambridge Univ. Pr.

Hashemi, Sahar & Hashemi, Bobby. Anyone Can Do It: Building Coffee Republic from Our Kitchen Table - 57 Real-Life Laws on Entrepreneurship. 2nd ed. 2007. (ENG., Illus.). 224p. per. 17.95 *(978-1-84112-765-1(5)*, Capstone) Wiley, John & Sons, Inc.

Hassard, John, et al. Managing in the Modern Corporation: The Intensification of Managerial Work in the USA, UK & Japan. 2009. (ENG., Illus.). 288p. 98.00 *(978-0-521-84582-3(3))* Cambridge Univ. Pr.

Humby, Clive, et al. Scoring Points: How Tesco Continues to Win Customer Loyalty. 2nd ed. 2008. (ENG., Illus.). 304p. pap. 39.95 *(978-0-7494-5338-1(9))* Kogan Page, Ltd. GBR. Dist: Ingram Pub. Services.

James, Malcolm. Taxation of Small Businesses: Fourth Edition. 2011. 498p. pap. 135.00 ***(978-1-907444-39-5(4))*** Spiramus Pr. GBR. Dist: International Specialized Bk. Services.

Jefferson, Lisa. The Medieval Account Books of the Mercers of London: An Edition & Translation, 2 vols. 2009. (LAT, FRO, ENG & FRE., Illus.). 1180p. 375.00 *(978-0-7546-6404-8(X))* Ashgate Publishing Co.

Jenkins, David, ed. Foster + Partners: Catalogue. 2012. (Illus.). 400p. 60.00 ***(978-3-7913-4685-4(7))*** Prestel Publishing.

Jones, Roger. Incorporating a Business. 3rd rev. ed. 2008. 392p. pap. 140.00 *(978-1-84766-131-9(9)*, Bloomsbury Professional) Bloomsbury Publishing Plc GBR. Dist: International Specialized Bk. Services.

Kay, Alison. The Foundations of Female Entrepreneurship: Women in Business in Mid-Victorian London. 2009. (Routledge International Studies in Business History Ser.). (ENG., Illus.). XVI, 186p. 146.00 *(978-0-415-43174-3(3))* Routledge.

Kelly, David, et al. Business Law. 6th ed. 2011. (ENG., Illus.). 656p. (C). pap. 70.00 *(978-0-415-55973-7(1))* Routledge.

Lamb, Harriet. Fighting the Banana Wars & Other Fairtrade Battles. 2009. (ENG., Illus.). 256p. pap. 16.95 *(978-1-84604-084-9(1))* Random Hse. GBR. Dist: Independent Pubs. Group.

Lee, Allison. Starting Your Own Childminding Business: How to Set up High Quality Childcare in Your Own Home. 2006. (Illus.). 180p. per. 26.00 *(978-1-84528-097-0(0))* How To Books GBR. Dist: Parkwest Pubns., Inc.

Lovell, Terry. Bernie Ecclestone: King of Sport. (ENG., Illus.). 2010. 420p. pap. 13.95 *(978-1-84454-826-2(0))* 2008. 288p. 34.95 *(978-1-84454-623-7(3))* Blake, John Publishing, Ltd. GBR. Dist: Independent Pubs. Group.

Maceira de Rosen, Sagra & Goldstein Crowe, Lauren. The Towering World of Jimmy Choo: A Glamorous Story of Power, Profits, & the Pursuit of the Perfect Shoe. 2009. (ENG.). 240p. 26.00 *(978-1-59691-391-2(6))* Bloomsbury Publishing.

Martin, Kathy. Farnell Teddy Bears. 2010. (Illus.). 192p. 39.95 *(978-1-84468-066-5(5))* Pen & Sword Bks. Ltd. GBR. Dist: Casemate Pubs. & Bk. Distributors, LLC.

McClean, Malcolm. To the Edge: Entrepreneurial Secrets from Britain's Richest Square Mile. 2007. (ENG., Illus.). 188p. per. 24.95 *(978-1-84112-782-8(5)*, Capstone) Wiley, John & Sons, Inc.

Miller, Daniel. The Comfort of Things. 2008. (ENG.). 300p. 64.95 *(978-0-7456-4403-5(1))* Polity Pr. GBR. Dist: Wiley, John & Sons, Inc.

Moore, Marc. Company Law Statutes 2011-2012. 3rd rev. ed. 2011. (Routledge Student Statutes Ser.). (ENG.). 592p. (C). pap. 37.95 ***(978-0-415-68745-4(4))*** Routledge.

Moxham, Roy. A Brief History of Tea. 2009. (ENG.). 288p. pap. 13.95 *(978-0-7624-3618-7(2))* Running Pr. Bk. Pubs.

Nurdin, Georges. International Business Control, Reporting & Corporate Governance: Global Business Best Practice Across Cultures, Countries & Organisations. 2008. (ENG., Illus.). 240p. pap. 39.95 *(978-0-7506-8383-8(X)*, CIMA Publishing) Elsevier Science & Technology Bks.

Owen, Gareth. The Shepperton Story: The History of the World-Famous Film Studio. 2009. (ENG., Illus.). 320p. pap. 45.00 *(978-0-7524-4970-8(2))* History Pr. Ltd.,The GBR. Dist: Independent Pubs. Group.

Pie Books Staff & PIE, eds. Shop Image Graphics in London. 2008. (ENG., Illus.). 192p. 69.00 *(978-4-89444-583-3(2))* Rizzoli International Pubns., Inc.

Prince's Trust Staff. Make It Happen: The Prince's Trust Guide to Starting Your Own Business. 3rd ed. 2010. (ENG., Illus.). 240p. pap. 21.95 *(978-0-85708-045-5(8)*, Capstone) Wiley, John & Sons, Inc.

Ratner, Gerald. The Rise & Fall... & Rise Again. (ENG., Illus.). 2008. 385p. pap. 16.95 *(978-1-906465-29-2(0))* 2007. 268p. 39.95 *(978-1-84112-786-6(8))* Wiley, John & Sons, Inc. (Capstone).

Reuvid, Jonathan. Working for Yourself: An Entrepreneur's Guide to the Basics. 23rd rev. ed. 2006. (Illus.). 320p. pap. *(978-0-7494-4757-1(5))* 24th rev. ed. 2007. 304p. pap. *(978-0-7494-4950-6(0))* Kogan Page, Ltd.

Reynolds. Heads: Business Lessons from an Executive Search Pioneer. 2012. (ENG.). 224p. 28.00 ***(978-0-07-179500-5(6)***, 0071795006) McGraw-Hill Cos., The.

Richardson, Mike & Nicholls, Peter, eds. A Business & Labour History of Britain: Case Studies of Britain in the Nineteenth & Twentieth Centuries. 2011. (ENG., Illus.). 224p. 90.00 ***(978-0-230-28092-2(7))*** Palgrave Macmillan.

Roman, Kenneth. The King of Madison Avenue: David Ogilvy & the Making of Modern Advertising. 2009. (ENG., Illus.). 304p. 27.95 *(978-1-4039-7895-0(6))* Palgrave Macmillan.

Sangster, G. How to Start & Run a Holiday Cott. 2nd ed. 2007. 292p. pap. 26.00 *(978-1-84528-193-9(4))* Parkwest Pubns., Inc.

Schoeser, Mary. Sanderson: The Essence of English Decoration. 2010. (ENG., Illus.). 200p. 40.00 *(978-0-500-51519-8(0)*, 551519) Thames & Hudson.

Shakespeare, Kevin. Trade for Good - the Essential Guide to Business & Finance in Uk & International Trade. 2011. (Illus.). 368p. pap. ***(978-1-905823-97-0(5))*** Ecademy Pr. Ltd.

Shoop, Fiona. How to Deal in Antiques. 4th ed. 2009. 320p. pap. 30.00 *(978-1-84528-300-1(7))* 5th rev. ed. 2011. (ENG., Illus.). 313p. pap. 34.00 *(978-1-84528-456-5(9))* How To Books GBR. Dist: Parkwest Pubns., Inc.

Siddiqui, Javed. Regulation of Auditor Independence. 2010. 264p. pap. *(978-3-8383-4775-2(7))* Lambert Academic Publishing.

Singleton, Susan. Beswick & Wine: Buying & Selling Private Companies & Businesses. 8th rev. ed. 2011. 512p. pap. 225.00 incl. cd-rom *(978-1-84766-698-7(1)*, Bloomsbury Professional) Bloomsbury Publishing Plc GBR. Dist: International Specialized Bk. Services.

—Buying & Selling Insolvent Companies & Businesses. 2010. 396p. pap. 198.00 *(978-1-84766-542-3(X)*, Bloomsbury Professional) Bloomsbury Publishing Plc GBR. Dist: International Specialized Bk. Services.

Superbrands (UK) Ltd Staff. CoolBrands 2010/11. 2010. (Illus.). 173p. 112.50 *(978-0-9565334-0-1(X))* Superbrands (UK), Ltd. GBR. Dist: Trans-Atlantic Pubns., Inc.

Sutherland, J. Start & Run a Sandwich & Coffee. 2009. 176p. 26.00 *(978-1-84528-333-9(3))* How To Books GBR. Dist: Parkwest Pubns., Inc.

Talbot, Lorraine. Critical Company Law. 2007. (ENG.). 400p. (C). per. 59.95 *(978-0-415-42542-1(5)*, Routledge Cavendish) Taylor & Francis Group GBR. Dist: Taylor & Francis Group.

Thomas, Steven & Turner, Alwyn W. Welcome to Big Biba: Inside the Most Beautiful Store in the World. 2011. (ENG., Illus.). 96p. 29.95 *(978-1-85149-664-8(5))* Antique Collectors' Club.

Turner, Alwyn W. Biba: The Biba Experience. 2007. (ENG., Illus.). 240p. pap. *(978-1-85149-541-2(X)*, Antique Collectors Club Dist) Antique Collectors' Club.

VAT Planning 2008/09. 2008. 1304p. pap. 275.00 *(978-1-84766-105-0(X)*, Bloomsbury Professional) Bloomsbury Publishing Plc GBR. Dist: International Specialized Bk. Services.

Ward, Robin & Jenkins, Richard, eds. Ethnic Communities in Business: Strategies for economic Survival. 2010. (Comparative Ethnic & Race Relations Ser.). (ENG.). 288p. pap. 42.00 *(978-0-521-12969-5(9))* Cambridge Univ. Pr.

Webb, Sidney & Freeman, Arnold. Seasonal Trades. 2009. (ENG.). 423p. 41.99 *(978-1-117-13754-4(6))* BiblioBazaar.

Weir, William Viscount. History of the Weir Group. 2007. (Illus.). 288p. 36.00 *(978-1-86197-886-8(3))* Profile Bks. Ltd. GBR. Dist: Independent Pubs. Group.

Whittaker, D. Hugh. Comparative Entrepreneurship: The UK, Japan, & the Shadow of Silicon Valley. 2009. (ENG., Illus.). 208p. 95.00 *(978-0-19-956366-1(7))* Oxford Univ. Pr., Inc.

Yorke, Louisa, ed. Guide to the Antique Shops of Britain 2008-2009. 2008. (ENG., Illus.). 584p. *(978-1-85149-554-2(1)*, Antique Collectors Club Dist) Antique Collectors' Club.

Young, Shelagh. How to Be a Successful Life Coach. 2009. 276p. 20.00 *(978-1-84528-296-7(5))* How To Books GBR. Dist: Parkwest Pubns., Inc.

Yurdan, Marilyn. Working Oxfordshire: From Airmen to Wheelwrights. 2011. (ENG., Illus.). 128p. pap. 23.95 *(978-0-7524-5585-3(0))* History Pr. Ltd.,The GBR. Dist: Independent Pubs. Group.

BUSINESS ENTERPRISES—INDIA

Argenti, Paul A. Strategic Corporate Communications: A Global Approach for Doing Business in the New India. 2008. (ENG., Illus.). 360p. 39.95 *(978-0-07-154991-2(9)*, 0071549919) McGraw-Hill Cos., The.

Balasubramanian, S. The Art of Business Leadership: Indian Experiences. 2007. (Illus.). 300p. (C). per. 32.95 *(978-0-7619-3587-2(8)*, B35872P) SAGE Pubns., Inc.

Baskaran, Kamaladevi. Business Plan Analysis of Retail Marketing in Indi. 2011. 100p. pap. ***(978-3-8443-2164-7(0))*** Lambert Academic Publishing.

Chakraborty, Tanupa. Buyback of Shares in India. 2008. (Illus.). 227p. (C). 29.50 *(978-81-7708-161-9(6))* New Century Publications IND. Dist: International Specialized Bk. Services.

Chandrashekhar, Garimalla. Influence of the Founding Conditions on the Growth of Firms. 2011. 216p. pap. ***(978-3-8433-7949-6(1))*** Lambert Academic Publishing.

Das, Niladri. Fundamental Factors Affecting the Indian Index. 2010. 116p. pap. *(978-3-8383-8036-0(3))* Lambert Academic Publishing.

Davies, Paul. The New Business of India Vol. 1: The 21st-Century Opportunity. 2008. 300p. pap. 29.95 *(978-981-279-042-2(X))* World Scientific Publishing Co., Inc.

De Surie, Gita Sud. Knowledge, Organizational Evolution & Market Creation: The Globalization of Indian Firms from Steel to Software. 2008. 232p. (C). 119.00 *(978-1-84720-456-1(2))* Elgar, Edward Publishing, Inc.

Deepak, Jain. Unorganized Retailing in India: an Illustrative Approach: Relationship & Impact of Different Factors of Services on Indian Unorganized Retail Sector. 2011. 560p. pap. ***(978-3-639-34092-1(2))*** VDM Verlag Dr. Mueller e.K.

Dogra, Deepak. Towards Managing Diversity: Cultural Aspects of Business Environment. 2009. 155p. 25.00 *(978-81-8405-047-9(X)*, Reference Pr.) Ess Ess Pubns. IND. Dist: International Specialized Bk. Services.

Gerschlauer, Simon. German Multinational Firms in Indi. 2010. 96p. pap. *(978-3-639-25366-5(3))* VDM Verlag Dr. Mueller e.K.

Ghosal, Sujit. Hotel Engineering. 2011. (ENG., Illus.). 460p. 19.95 *(978-0-19-806291-2(5))* Oxford Univ. Pr., Inc.

Gupta, Hitesh. Internet Influence in It B2b Markets. 2011. 72p. pap. ***(978-3-8443-8156-6(2))*** Lambert Academic Publishing.

India: Business Financing Handbook. (Illus.). 70p. (Orig.). pap. 295.00 *(978-0-7605-1194-7(2))* Rector Pr., Ltd.

India Business Risks & Forecasts 1994-1995: Companies-Products-Services. (Illus.). 175p. (Orig.). pap. *(978-0-7605-0662-2(0))* Rector Pr., Ltd.

Jha, Prem Shankar. Crouching Dragon, Hidden Tiger: Can China & India Dominate the West? 2009. (ENG.). 256p. pap. 16.95 *(978-1-59376-248-3(8),* Soft Skull Pr.) Counterpoint LLC.

Karki, Rajnish. Competing with the Best: Strategic Management of Indian Companies in a Globalizing Arena. 2009. (ENG., Illus.). 256p. (gr. 12). 19.95 *(978-0-670-08178-3(7),* Penguin Global) Penguin Group (USA) Inc.

Kaur, Harjoth. Brand Loyalty-A Study of Cellular Services in Andhra Pradesh, Indi. 2011. 368p. pap. ***(978-3-8433-8960-0(8))*** Lambert Academic Publishing.

Kaushik, Kshama & Dutta, Kaushik. India Means Business: How the Elephant Earned its Stripes. 2012. (ENG., Illus.). 352p. 50.00 ***(978-0-19-807261-4(9))*** Oxford Univ. Pr., Inc.

Kobayashi-Hillary, Mark, ed. Building a Future with BRICs: The Next Decade for Offshoring. 2010. (ENG., Illus.). xviii, 219p. pap. 79.95 *(978-3-642-07980-1(6),* 3642079806) Springer.

Kudaisya, Medha. The Oxford India Anthology of Business History. 2011. (ENG.). 544p. 125.00 *(978-0-19-807019-1(5))* Oxford Univ. Pr., Inc.

Kumar, Nirmalya, et al. India's Global Powerhouses: How They Are Taking on the World. 2009. (ENG., Illus.). 250p. 27.95 *(978-1-4221-4762-7(2))* Harvard Business Review Pr.

Markovits, Claude. Merchants, Traders, Entrepreneurs: Indian Business in the Colonial ERA. 2008. (ENG.). 320p. 100.00 *(978-0-230-20598-7(4))* Palgrave Macmillan.

Mishra, Supriti. Corporate Social Responsibility of Indian Companies. 2010. 100p. pap. *(978-3-8383-4534-5(7))* Lambert Academic Publishing.

Mitra, Meera. It's Only Business! India's Corporate Social Responsiveness in a Globalized World. (ENG.). 2009. 268p. 19.95 *(978-0-19-806026-0(2))* 2007. 215p. 35.00 *(978-0-19-568433-9(8))* Oxford Univ. Pr., Inc.

Nandan, Raghu. Unleashing Your Entrepreneurial Potential. 2009. (Response Bks.). 380p. (C). pap. 44.95 *(978-81-7829-908-2(9),* B99082P) SAGE Pubns., Inc.

Nayak, Amar. Indian Multinationals: The Dynamics of Explosive Firm Growth in a Developing Country Context. 2011. (ENG., Illus.). 308p. 95.00 *(978-0-230-29860-6(5))* Palgrave Macmillan.

Panwar, Vandana. Venture Capital Funding: Global & Indian Experiences. 2009. 314p. 48.25 *(978-81-7708-222-7(1))* New Century Publications IND. Dist: International Specialized Bk. Services.

Prasad, Ashish S. & Shwartz, Mark L. Doing Business in India: Critical Legal Issues for U.S. Companies. 2007. (Corporate Law & Practice Course Handbook Ser.: No. 1587). (Illus.). 312p. pap. *(978-1-4024-0858-8(7))* Practising Law Institute.

Rösler, René. Microfinance on Corporate Level. 2008. 60p. pap. *(978-3-8364-9314-7(4))* VDM Verlag Dr. Mueller e.K.

Roy, Rajeev. Entrepreneurship. 2nd ed. 2011. (ENG., Illus.). 616p. pap. 35.00 ***(978-0-19-807263-8(5))*** Oxford Univ. Pr., Inc.

Sartor, Marco, et al. Sourcing in India: Strategies & Experiences in the Land of Service Offshoring. 2008. (ENG., Illus.). 240p. 100.00 *(978-0-230-20536-9(4))* Palgrave Macmillan.

Sebastian, Thomas. Globalization & Uneven Development: Neocolonialism, Multinational Corporations, Space, & Society. 2007. viii, 296p. *(978-81-316-0058-0(0))* Rawat Pubns.

Sethi, Raunica, et al. Marketing Communications Industry: Entrepreneurial Case Studies. 2008. 212p. (C). pap. 29.95 *(978-81-7829-868-9(6),* B98689P) SAGE Pubns., Inc.

Shah, Janat. Supply Chain Management: Text & Cases. 2009. (ENG., Illus.). 472p. (C). pap. 144.20 *(978-81-317-1517-8(5))* Pearson Education.

Sharma, Sunita Upendra. Corporate Governance in India. 2009. 242p. 42.75 *(978-81-7708-196-1(9))* New Century Publications IND. Dist: International Specialized Bk. Services.

Siddharthan, N. S. & Narayanan, K., eds. Indian & Chinese Enterprises: Global Trade, Technology & Investment Regimes. 2009. (Illus.). 268p. 110.00 *(978-0-415-56316-1(X),* Routledge India) Taylor & Francis Group GBR. Dist: Taylor & Francis Group.

Termenon, Elsa. Cross-Cultural Competence. 2011. 88p. pap. ***(978-3-8433-7721-8(9))*** Lambert Academic Publishing.

Timsina, Suman R. Doing Business in India. Date not set. (Doing Business in Regions & Countries Around the World Ser.). 80p. *(978-1-882390-61-8(X))* Training Management Corp.

Torri, Maria Costanza & Herrmann, Thora Martina. Bridges Between Tradition & Innovation in Ethnomedicine: Fostering Local Development Through Community-Based Enterprises in India. 2011. (ENG., Illus.). xiii, 222p. 129.00 *(978-94-007-1112-9(3),* 9400711123) Springer.

Tripathi, Dwijendra & Jumani, Jyoti. The Concise Oxford History of Indian Business. 2006. (Illus.). 280p. per. 24.95 *(978-0-19-568429-2(X))* Oxford Univ. Pr., Inc.

Verma, Subir. Towards the Next Orbit: Corporate Odyssey. 2011. (Illus.). 492p. (C). 40.00 *(978-81-321-0631-9(8),* B06319C) SAGE Pubns., Inc.

Wilmshö, et al. Offshore Business Process Outsourcing: Eine SWOT-Analyse am Beispiel eines internationalen Dienstleistungsunternehmens in Indien. 2010. 84p. pap. *(978-3-639-24641-4(1))* VDM Verlag Dr. Mueller e.K.

Witzel, Morgen. Tata: The Evolution of a Corporate Brand. 2011. (ENG., Illus.). 256p. 20.00 *(978-0-670-08406-7(9),* Penguin Global) Penguin Group (USA) Inc.

Zubko, Katherine C. & Sahay, Raj R. Inside the Indian Business Mind: A Tactical Guide for Managers. 2010. E-Book *(978-0-313-37830-0(4),* Praeger Pubs.) Greenwood Publishing Group, Inc.

Zubko, Ph.D., Katherine C & Sahay, Raj R. Inside the Indian Business Mind: A Tactical Guide for Managers, 1 vol. 2010. (Illus.). 180p. 34.95 *(978-0-313-37829-4(0),* C37829, Praeger Pubs.) Greenwood Publishing Group, Inc.

BUSINESS ENTERPRISES—IRELAND

Birdthistle, Naomi. Mind Your Own Business. 2009. 116p. pap. *(978-3-639-14801-5(0))* VDM Verlag Dr. Mueller e.K.

Egan & Mckenna, Justin. Buying & Selling Private Companies in Ireland. 2013. 400p. pap. 285.00 *(978-1-84592-300-6(6),* Bloomsbury Professional) Bloomsbury Publishing Plc GBR. Dist: International Specialized Bk. Services.

Fanning, John. The Importance of Being Branded: An Irish Perspective. 2006. (ENG.). 355p. 84.95 *(978-1-905785-00-1(3))* Liffey Pr., The IRL. Dist: Dufour Editions, Inc.

Ibp, Usa. Ireland Industrial & Business Director. 2006. (Illus.). pap. 99.95 *(978-0-7397-6802-0(6))* International Business Pubns., USA.

Jollimore, Troy. Doing Business in Ireland. Date not set. (Doing Business in Regions & Countries Around the World Ser.). 80p. *(978-1-882390-62-5(8))* Training Management Corp.

O'Dowd, John. Organisational Change Through Partnership: Promise, Performance & Prospects for Irish Firms. 2009. 220p. pap. 29.95 *(978-1-905785-58-2(5))* Liffey Pr., The IRL. Dist: Dufour Editions, Inc.

BUSINESS ENTERPRISES—JAPAN

Abegglen, James C. 21st Century Japanese Management: New Systems, Lasting Values. 2006. (ENG., Illus.). 192p. 118.00 *(978-1-4039-9876-7(0))* Palgrave Macmillan.

All Japan News Inc. Japanese Food Business Data Bank 2010. 2009. pap. 5.00 *(978-1-61623-837-7(2))* Independent Pub.

Azur Corporation Editors. New P. O. P. Design 2. 2007. (JPN & ENG., Illus.). 224p. 70.00 *(978-4-86267-015-1(6))* Azur Corp. JPN. Dist: Antique Collectors' Club.

BIA. Major Companies of Japan: Manufacturers, Wholesalers, Banks, Construction Companies. 6th rev. ed. 2006. 250p. (J). pap. 249.00 *(978-1-4187-4403-8(4))* Business Information Agency.

Culpepper, Pepper D. Quiet Politics & Business Power: Corporate Control in Europe & Japan. 2010. (Cambridge Studies in Comparative Politics Ser.). (ENG., Illus.). 248p. 90.00 *(978-0-521-11859-0(X))* Cambridge Univ. Pr.

Dunfee, T. W. & Nagayasu, Y., eds. Business Ethics: Japan & the Global Economy: Japan & the Global Economy. 2010. (Issues in Business Ethics Ser.). 292p. pap. 279.00 *(978-90-481-4309-2(8),* 9048143098) Springer.

Fletcher III, W. Miles & von Staden, Peter W., eds. Japan's 'Lost Decade' Causes, Legacies & Issues of Transformative Change. 2012. (ENG.). 160p. (C). 125.00 *(978-0-415-78320-0(8))* Routledge.

Goldfinger, Gail. Doing Business in Japan. Date not set. (Doing Business in Regions & Countries Around the World Ser.). 80p. *(978-1-882390-64-9(4))* Training Management Corp.

Gunyung, Lee. Business Process Management of Japanese & Korean Companies, Vol. 5. 2009. (Illus.). 188p. 79.00 *(978-981-283-860-5(0))* World Scientific Publishing Co., Inc.

Hassard, John, et al. Managing in the Modern Corporation: The Intensification of Managerial Work in the USA, UK & Japan. 2009. (ENG., Illus.). 288p. 98.00 *(978-0-521-84582-3(3))* Cambridge Univ. Pr.

Helen, Monschein. Complexity of Intercultural Work Processes: A Reflection of Intercultural Complexity Using the Example of Business Experience in Japan. 2011. 76p. pap. ***(978-3-639-34070-9(1))*** VDM Verlag Dr. Mueller e.K.

Heshmati, Almas. Micro-Evidence for the Dynamics of Industrial Evolution: The Case of the Manufacturing Industry in Japan & Korea. Lee, Jeong-Dong, ed. 2008. (Illus.). vi, 206p. (C). 89.00 *(978-1-60456-388-7(5))* Nova Science Pubs., Inc.

Japan: Business Financing Handbook. (Illus.). 70p. (Orig.). pap. 295.00 *(978-0-7605-1197-8(7))* Rector Pr., Ltd.

Japan Business Strategy with Tape. 75p. (Orig.). pap. *(978-0-7605-0821-3(6))* Rector Pr., Ltd.

Japanese Alcoholic Drinks Market. 146p. (Orig.). pap. 3495.00 *(978-0-7605-2176-2(X))* Rector Pr., Ltd.

Kalland, Arne. Japan, 90 vols., Set. 3rd ed. 2010. (ENG & JPN., Illus.). 27000p. 8060.00 *(978-0-415-56498-4(0),* Routledge) Taylor & Francis Group GBR. Dist: Taylor & Francis Group.

Kodama, Mitsuru. The Strategic Community-based Firm. 2007. (ENG.). 256p. 105.00 *(978-0-230-00685-0(X))* Palgrave Macmillan.

Kohlbacher, Florian. The Japanese Mobile Communications Market. 2008. 184p. pap. *(978-3-639-02630-6(6))* VDM Verlag Dr. Mueller e.K.

Lee, Yang-Im & Trim, Peter R.J. Strategic Marketing Decision-Making Within Japanese & South Korean Companies. 2008. (Illus.). 368p. *(978-1-84334-363-9(0),* Chandos Publishing) Woodhead Publishing Ltd.

Long, Brian. Nikon: A Celebration. 2012. (ENG., Illus.). 240p. 69.95 ***(978-1-84797-079-4(6))*** Crowood Pr., Ltd. GBR. Dist: Independent Pubs. Group.

Maekawa, Masao. Basho Management: New Japanese Philosophy of Manufacturing & Empowerment. 2009. 164p. 29.99 *(978-1-4363-3460-0(8));* pap. 19.99 *(978-1-4363-3459-4(4))* Xlibris Corp.

Marutschke, David. Continuous Improvement Strategies: Japanese Convenience Store Systems. 2012. (Palgrave Macmillan Asian Business Ser.). (ENG., Illus.). 224p. 95.00 ***(978-0-230-34793-9(2))*** Palgrave Macmillan.

McNamara, Dennis, et al. Business Innovation in Asia: Knowledge & Technology Networks from Japan. 2009. (Routledge Contemporary Asia Ser.). (ENG., Illus.). 208p. (C). 138.00 *(978-0-415-49935-4(6))* Routledge.

Monden, Yasuhiro. Management of an Inter-Firm Network. 2011. 250p. 85.00 ***(978-981-4324-61-8(2))*** World Scientific Publishing Co., Inc.

Olcott, George. Foreign Ownership & the Japanese Firm. 2009. (ENG., Illus.). 292p. 107.00 *(978-0-521-87870-8(5))* Cambridge Univ. Pr.

Oxley, Mat. Stealing Speed: The Biggest Spy Scandal in Motorsport History. 2010. (ENG., Illus.). 224p. pap. 14.95 *(978-1-84425-975-5(7),* 1844259757) Haynes Publishing PLC GBR. Dist: MBI Distribution Services/Quayside Distribution.

Picken, Stuart D. B. The A to Z of Japanese Business. 85th ed. 2009. (A to Z Guide Ser.: No. 85). (ENG.). 448p. pap. 34.45 *(978-0-8108-6872-4(5))* Scarecrow Pr., Inc.

Rle: Japan Mini-Set A: Economics Business & Management, 20 vols. 2010. (ENG.). 8768p. 2110.00 *(978-0-415-68012-7(3))* Routledge.

Routledge Library Editions: Japan Mini-Set A: Economics Business & Management 20 Vol Set, 20 vols. 2010. (ENG.). 8768p. 2110.00 *(978-0-415-59215-4(1))* Routledge.

Sako, Mari. Shifting Boundaries of the Firm: Japanese Company - Japanese Labour. 2008. (ENG., Illus.). 320p. pap. 45.00 *(978-0-19-954703-6(3))* Oxford Univ. Pr., Inc.

Skouson, Demeron. Becoming Re-Successful. 2008. 234p. pap. 19.96 *(978-0-557-01572-6(3))* Lulu Enterprises Inc.

Tatewaki, Kazuo. Banking & Finance in Japan (RLE Banking & Finance) An Introduction to the Tokyo Market, Volume 32. 2012. (ENG.). 240p. 115.00 ***(978-0-415-53847-3(5))*** Routledge.

von Staden, Peter. Business-Government Relations in Prewar Japan. 2012. (Routledge Studies in the Modern History of Asia Ser.). (ENG., Illus.). 208p. (C). pap. 42.95 ***(978-0-415-54099-5(2))*** Routledge.

Whittaker, D. Hugh. Comparative Entrepreneurship: The UK, Japan, & the Shadow of Silicon Valley. 2009. (ENG., Illus.). 208p. 95.00 *(978-0-19-956366-1(7))* Oxford Univ. Pr., Inc.

Yamazaki, Katsuo. Japanese Global Management: Theory & Practice at Overseas Subsidiaries. 2012. (ENG., Illus.). 224p. 90.00 ***(978-0-230-28015-1(3))*** Palgrave Macmillan.

BUSINESS ENTERPRISES—KOREA

BIA. Essential South Korean Manufacturers: Food, Textile, Clothing, & Chemical Companies. 6th rev. ed. 2006. 450p. (J). pap. 249.00 *(978-1-4187-4197-6(3))* Business Information Agency.

—Major Companies of South Korea: Manufacturers, Wholesalers, Banks, Construction Companies. 6th rev. ed. 2006. 400p. (J). pap. 249.00 *(978-1-4187-4406-9(9))* Business Information Agency.

Cohen, Robert. Turning Around a Bank in Korea, a Business & Cultural Challenge. 2008. 232p. pap. 29.78 *(978-0-557-03772-8(7))* Lulu Enterprises Inc.

Gunyung, Lee. Business Process Management of Japanese & Korean Companies, Vol. 5. 2009. (Illus.). 188p. 79.00 *(978-981-283-860-5(0))* World Scientific Publishing Co., Inc.

Hanson, Mark. Economic Development, Education & Transnational Corporations. 2007. (Routledge Studies in Development Economics Ser.). (ENG., Illus.). 192p. (C). 158.00 *(978-0-415-77116-0(1))* Routledge.

Hemmert, Martin. Korean Companies in World Markets: Tiger Management. 2012. (ENG., Illus.). 256p. (C). 152.00 *(978-0-415-66418-9(7))* Routledge.

Hemmert, Martin. Tiger Management: Korean Companies on World Markets. 2012. (Illus.). 256p. pap. ***(978-0-415-53720-9(7))*** Routledge.

Heshmati, Almas. Micro-Evidence for the Dynamics of Industrial Evolution: The Case of the Manufacturing Industry in Japan & Korea. Lee, Jeong-Dong, ed. 2008. (Illus.). vi, 206p. (C). 89.00 *(978-1-60456-388-7(5))* Nova Science Pubs., Inc.

Kim, Evan. Doing Business in South Korea. Date not set. (Doing Business in Regions & Countries Around the World Ser.). *(978-1-882390-71-7(7))* Training Management Corp.

Kim, Youngmi. Convention Industry Network. 2011. 136p. pap. ***(978-3-8443-1510-3(1))*** Lambert Academic Publishing.

Kim, Zy-He. Managing Diversified Workforces- Korean Multinationals. 2007. 92p. per. *(978-3-8364-1925-3(4))* VDM Verlag Dr. Mueller e.K.

Kwon, O. Yul. International Business in Korea: The Evolution of the Market in the Globalization Era. 2008. 288p. (C). 125.00 *(978-1-84720-570-4(4))* Elgar, Edward Publishing, Inc.

Kwon, Sungmi & Frankl, John M. Essential Korean for Business Use. 2011. (Illus.). 359p. pap. 25.50 ***(978-1-56591-312-7(4))*** Hollym International Corp.

Lee, Yang-Im & Trim, Peter R.J. Strategic Marketing Decision-Making Within Japanese & South Korean Companies. 2008. (Illus.). 368p. *(978-1-84334-363-9(0),* Chandos Publishing) Woodhead Publishing Ltd.

Park, Hun Joo. Diseased Dirigisme: The Political Sources of Financial Policy Toward Small Business in Korea. 2007. (Korea Research Monograph Ser.). *(978-1-55729-090-8(3))* Univ. of California, Institute of East Asian Studies.

BUSINESS ENTERPRISES—MEXICO

Beer Market Mexico: Companies-Products-Services. 200p. (Orig.). pap. 4995.00 *(978-0-7605-2162-5(X))* Rector Pr., Ltd.

BIA. Major Companies of Mexico: Manufacturers, Wholesalers, Banks, Construction Companies. 6th rev. ed. 2006. 200p. (J). pap. 219.00 *(978-1-4187-4425-0(5))* Business Information Agency.

Bloch, Talia. Doing Business in North America. Date not set. (Doing Business in Regions & Countries Around the World Ser.). *(978-1-882390-85-4(7))* Training Management Corp.

Chiapas of Mexico: Companies-Products-Services. 70p. (Orig.). pap. 45.00 *(978-0-7605-1329-3(5))* Rector Pr., Ltd.

Cook, Scott. Handmade Brick for Texas: A Mexican Border Industry, Its Workers, & Its Business. 2010. (ENG.). 290p. 95.00 *(978-0-7391-4797-9(8));* pap. 39.95 *(978-0-7391-4798-6(6))* Lexington Bks.

Doing Business in Mexico. Date not set. (Doing Business in Regions & Countries Around the World Ser.). *(978-1-882390-66-3(0))* Training Management Corp.

Hanson, Mark. Economic Development, Education & Transnational Corporations. 2007. (Routledge Studies in Development Economics Ser.). (ENG., Illus.). 192p. (C). 158.00 *(978-0-415-77116-0(1))* Routledge.

Hernández Elizondo, Roberto. Empresarios Extranjeros, Comercio y Petróleo en Tampico y la Huasteca, 1890-1930. 2009. (SPA., Illus.). 133p. 12.00 *(978-970-722-594-7(7))* Plaza y Valdes, S.A. de C.V. MEX. Dist: Sony Electronics.

Ibp, Usa. Mexico Industrial & Business Directory. 2006. (Illus.). pap. 99.95 *(978-0-7397-9920-8(7))* International Business Pubns., USA.

Mexico: Business Financing Handbook. (Illus.). 70p. (Orig.). pap. 295.00 *(978-0-7605-1199-2(3))* Rector Pr., Ltd.

Mexico Business Strategy with Tape. 75p. (Orig.). pap. *(978-0-7605-0820-6(8))* Rector Pr., Ltd.

Organisation for Economic Co-operation and Development Staff. Review of Sme Issues & Policies in Mexico. 2007. pap. 32.00 *(978-92-64-03178-4(2))* Organization for Economic Cooperation & Development.

Prieto, Leonel. Leaders' Entrepreneurial Behaviors in Mexico. 2009. 112p. pap. *(978-3-639-16081-9(9))* VDM Verlag Dr. Mueller e.K.

BUSINESS ENTERPRISES—MIDDLE EAST

Al Ismaily, Salem Ben Nasser & Tzudiker, Richard. A Cup of Coffee: A Westerner's Guide to Business Culture in the Gulf States. 2008. 208p. pap. 14.95 *(978-1-59858-611-4(4))* Dog Ear Publishing, LLC.

Alasrag, Hussein. Small & Medium Enterprises in the Arab Countries. 2010. 76p. pap. *(978-3-8383-4719-6(6))* Lambert Academic Publishing.

Aschkenazi, Jack. Israeli Expatriate Managers, Knowledge Transfer & Retention. 2008. 204p. pap. *(978-3-639-05851-2(8))* VDM Verlag Dr. Mueller e.K.

Atasoy, Müge. Person-Organization Fit in a Turkish Public Organization. 2010. 96p. pap. *(978-3-8383-8312-5(5))* Lambert Academic Publishing.

BIA. Major Companies of Turkey: Manufacturers, Wholesalers, Banks, Construction Companies. 6th rev. ed. 2006. 300p. (J). pap. 219.00 *(978-1-4187-4452-6(2))* Business Information Agency.

Campbell, Christian, Editor. Legal Aspects of Doing Business in the Middle East [2009]. 2009. 336p. pap. 85.00 *(978-0-557-13229-4(0))* Lulu Enterprises Inc.

Chaddock, David. Qatar: The Business Traveller's Handbook. 2nd ed. 2008. 199p. per. 20.00 *(978-1-56656-697-1(5))* Interlink Publishing Group, Inc.

Dew, Philip. Bahrain's Business Environment. 2008. (ENG.). pap. 75.00 *(978-1-84673-086-3(4),* GMB Publishing Ltd.) Blue Ibex Ltd. GBR. Dist: Ingram Pub. Services.

Doing Business in Saudi Arabia. Date not set. (Doing Business in Regions & Countries Around the World Ser.). *(978-1-882390-72-4(5))* Training Management Corp.

El-Khazindar Business Research and Case Center, ed. Cases on Business & Management in the MENA Region: New Trends & Opportunities. 2011. 350p. 180.00 *(978-1-60960-583-4(7),* Business Science Reference) IGI Global.

Explorer Publishing Staff. Dubai: A Complete Step-by-Step Handbook. 4th ed. 2010. (ENG., Illus.). 336p. pap. 24.95 *(978-9948-8588-2-9(4))* Explorer Publishing UAE. Dist: Globe Pequot Pr., The.

Garfinkle, Steven J. Entrepreneurs & Enterprise in Early Mesopotamia: A Study of Three Archives from the Third Dynasty of Ur (2112-2004 BC) 2012. ***(978-1-934309-41-4(9),*** CDL Pr.) Univ. Pr. of Maryland.

Ghazal, Samir. The Merger of the Two Giants, Saudi Aramco & Samarec. 2011. 78p. pap. 16.50 ***(978-1-4467-3602-9(4))*** Lulu Enterprises Inc.

Hussein, Rania. The Adoption of Web Based Marketing in the Travel & Tourism Industry. 2011. 356p. pap. ***(978-3-8433-7384-5(1))*** Lambert Academic Publishing.

Ismail, Lubna. Doing Business in the Middle East & North Africa. Date not set. (Doing Business in Regions & Countries Around the World Ser.). *(978-1-882390-83-0(0))* Training Management Corp.

Lundberg, Kelly. Success in the City. 2009. pap. *(978-1-61584-145-5(8))* Independent Pub.

Major National Retailers: Europe, Middle East & Africa. rev. ed. 2008. 845.00 *(978-1-84264-443-0(2))* Euromonitor International PLC GBR. Dist: Cengage Gale.

Marsh, Donna. The Middle East Unveiled: A Cultural & Practical Guide for All Western Business Professionals. 2010. (ENG., Illus.). 356p. pap. 34.00 *(978-1-84528-416-9(X))* How To Books GBR. Dist: Parkwest Pubns., Inc.

Metcalfe. Leadership Development in the Middle East. 2012. (Illus.). 448p. 175.00 ***(978-1-84720-615-2(8))*** Elgar, Edward Publishing, Inc.

Middle East Business & Political Handbook. (Illus.). 600p. (Orig.). pap. 2400.00 (978-0-7605-1335-4(X)) Rector Pr., Ltd.

Monelletta-Candemir, Ebru. Business Opportunities in Turkey in the Prospect of Eu Membership. 2008. 164p. per. (978-3-8364-5834-4(9)) VDM Verlag Dr. Mueller e.K.

Rezazadeh Mehrjou, Afsaneh & Tajasom, Adel. Customer Satisfaction in Automobile Market. 2011. 168p. pap. (978-3-8443-8634-9(3)) Lambert Academic Publishing.

Sabri, Nidal Rashid. Arab Financial Institutions. 2008. 69.00 (978-1-60692-430-3(3)) Nova Science Pubs., Inc.

Streather, Adrian. Monsieur Bernar Nahum: A Pioneer of Turkey's Automotive Industry. 2011. (ENG., Illus.). 392p. pap. 22.95 (978-9944-424-85-1(4)) Citlembik/Nettleberry Pubns. TUR. Dist: National Bk. Network.

Suleiman Nawafleh, Abdullah. Law & Investment in Jordan. 2011. 152p. pap. (978-3-8443-0229-5(8)) Lambert Academic Publishing.

Wahab, Samsudin. Electronic Customer Relationship Management in Jordan Mobile Service. 2011. 96p. pap. (978-3-8443-8414-7(6)) Lambert Academic Publishing.

Waring, Rob. Making a Deal. 2008. (ENG.). 24p. (C). pap. 10.95 (978-1-4240-4443-6(X)) Cengage Heinle.

BUSINESS ENTERPRISES—NETHERLANDS

BIA. Major Companies of the Netherlands: Manufacturers, Wholesalers, Banks, Construction Companies. 6th rev. ed. 2006. 400p. (J). pap. 249.00 (978-1-4187-4808-1(0)) Business Information Agency.

Haverkamp, Derk-Jan. Environmental management in the Dutch food & beverage Industry: A longitudinal study into the joint impact of business network & firm characteristics on the adoption of environmental Management, Vol. 1. 2007. (I & S Ser.). (Illus.). 198p. pap. 57.00 (978-90-8686-050-0(8)) Wageningen Academic Publishers NLD. Dist: Enfield Publishing & Distribution Co., Inc.

Ibp, Usa. Netherlands Industrial & Business Dire. 2006. (Illus.). pap. 99.95 (978-0-7397-9904-8(5)) International Business Pubns., USA.

Pols, Laurens. Organizational Career Management in the Netherlands. 2011. 96p. pap. (978-3-8433-9090-3(8)) Lambert Academic Publishing.

Wibier. Financial Restructuring of Business Enterprises in Netherlands. 2011. (978-90-411-3197-3(3)) Kluwer Law International.

BUSINESS ENTERPRISES—RUSSIA (FEDERATION)

Andresen, Frederick. Walking on Ice: An American Businessman in Russia. 2007. 164p. per. 16.95 (978-1-4327-1352-2(3)) Outskirts Pr., Inc.

Asanti, Tomi P. & Cutshaw, Kenneth A. Corporate Counsel's Guide to Doing Business in Russia. 2nd ed. 2008. (Illus.). lvi, 860p. (978-0-314-98473-9(9)) West Publishing Co., College & Schl. Div.

BIA. Business Partners in Russia. 6th rev. ed. 2006. 472p. (J). pap. 249.00 (978-1-4187-4462-5(X)) Business Information Agency.

—Essential Russian Manufacturers: Food, Textile, Clothing, & Chemical Companies. 6th rev. ed. 2006. 400p. (J). pap. 249.00 (978-1-4187-4211-9(2)) Business Information Agency.

—Governmental Authorities of Russia, Federal to Regional. 6th rev. ed. 2006. 350p. (J). pap. 249.00 (978-1-4187-4465-6(4)) Business Information Agency.

—Leading Companies in Kazan City, Russia: Manufacturers, Wholesalers, Banks, Construction Companies. 6th rev. ed. 2006. 200p. (J). pap. 219.00 (978-1-4187-4974-3(5)) Business Information Agency.

—Leading Companies in Krasnodar City, Russia: Manufacturers, Wholesalers, Banks, Construction Companies. 6th rev. ed. 2006. 150p. (J). pap. 219.00 (978-1-4187-4977-4(X)) Business Information Agency.

—Leading Companies in Nizhniy Novgorod City, Russia: Manufacturers, Wholesalers, Banks, Construction Companies. 6th rev. ed. 2006. 350p. (J). pap. 249.00 (978-1-4187-4980-4(X)) Business Information Agency.

—Leading Companies in Novosibirsk City, Russia: Manufacturers, Wholesalers, Banks, Construction Companies. 6th rev. ed. 2006. 250p. (J). pap. 249.00 (978-1-4187-4983-5(4)) Business Information Agency.

—Leading Companies in Rostov City, Russia: Manufacturers, Wholesalers, Banks, Construction Companies. 6th rev. ed. 2006. 200p. (J). pap. 219.00 (978-1-4187-4986-6(9)) Business Information Agency.

—Leading Companies in St. Petersburg, Russia: Manufacturers, Wholesalers, Banks, Construction Companies. 6th rev. ed. 2006. 350p. (J). pap. 249.00 (978-1-4187-4989-7(3)) Business Information Agency.

—Leading Companies in Volgograd City, Russia: Manufacturers, Wholesalers, Banks, Construction Companies. 6th rev. ed. 2006. 180p. (J). pap. 219.00 (978-1-4187-4992-7(3)) Business Information Agency.

—Leading Companies of the Chelyabinsk Region of Russia. 6th rev. ed. 2006. 250p. (J). pap. 249.00 (978-1-4187-4468-7(9)) Business Information Agency.

—Leading Companies of the Krasnodar Region of Russia. 6th rev. ed. 2006. 300p. (J). pap. 249.00 (978-1-4187-4469-4(7)) Business Information Agency.

—Leading Companies of the Krasnoyarsk Region of Russia. 6th rev. ed. 2006. 250p. (J). pap. 249.00 (978-1-4187-4470-0(0)) Business Information Agency.

—Leading Companies of the Moscow Region of Russia. 6th rev. ed. 2006. 250p. (J). pap. 249.00 (978-1-4187-4471-7(9)) Business Information Agency.

—Leading Companies of the Novosibirsk Region of Russia. 6th rev. ed. 2006. 300p. (J). pap. 249.00 (978-1-4187-4472-4(7)) Business Information Agency.

—Leading Companies of the Omsk Region of Russia. 6th rev. ed. 2006. 300p. (J). pap. 249.00 (978-1-4187-4473-1(5)) Business Information Agency.

—Leading Companies of the Sverdlovsk Region of Russia. 6th rev. ed. 2006. 300p. (J). pap. 249.00 (978-1-4187-4474-8(3)) Business Information Agency.

—Leading Companies of the Tatarstan Region of Russia. 6th rev. ed. 2006. 400p. (J). pap. 249.00 (978-1-4187-4475-5(1)) Business Information Agency.

—Leading Companies of the Tyumen Region of Russia. 6th rev. ed. 2006. 300p. (J). pap. 249.00 (978-1-4187-4476-2(X)) Business Information Agency.

—Leading Companies of the Voronezh Region of Russia. 6th rev. ed. 2006. 200p. (J). pap. 249.00 (978-1-4187-4477-9(8)) Business Information Agency.

—Major Companies of Moscow, Volume 1: Manufacturers, Wholesalers & Retailers. 6th rev. ed. 2006. 450p. (J). pap. 249.00 (978-1-4187-4460-1(3)) Business Information Agency.

—Major Companies of Moscow, Volume 2: Construction & Transportation Companies, & Banks. 6th rev. ed. 2006. 376p. (J). pap. 249.00 (978-1-4187-4461-8(1)) Business Information Agency.

—Major Companies of the Central Federal District of Russia: Food, Textile, Clothing, & Chemical Companies. 6th rev. ed. 2006. 400p. (J). pap. 249.00 (978-1-4187-4492-2(1)) Business Information Agency.

—Major Companies of the Far Eastern Federal District of Russia: Food, Textile, Clothing, & Chemical Companies. 6th rev. ed. 2006. 400p. (J). pap. 249.00 (978-1-4187-4493-9(X)) Business Information Agency.

—Major Companies of the Northwestern Federal District of Russia: Food, Textile, Clothing, & Chemical Companies. 6th rev. ed. 2006. 400p. (J). pap. 249.00 (978-1-4187-4494-6(8)) Business Information Agency.

—Major Companies of the Siberian Federal District of Russia: Food, Textile, Clothing, & Chemical Companies. 6th rev. ed. 2006. 400p. (J). pap. 249.00 (978-1-4187-4495-3(6)) Business Information Agency.

—Major Companies of the Southern Federal District of Russia: Food, Textile, Clothing, & Chemical Companies. 6th rev. ed. 2006. 400p. (J). pap. 249.00 (978-1-4187-4496-0(4)) Business Information Agency.

—Major Companies of the Urals Federal District of Russia: Food, Textile, Clothing, & Chemical Companies. 6th rev. ed. 2006. 400p. (J). pap. 249.00 (978-1-4187-4497-7(2)) Business Information Agency.

—Major Companies of the Volga Federal District of Russia: Food, Textile, Clothing, & Chemical Companies. 6th rev. ed. 2006. 400p. (J). pap. 249.00 (978-1-4187-4498-4(0)) Business Information Agency.

Buyske, Gail. Banking on Small Business: Microfinance in Contemporary Russia. 2007. (Illus.). 220p. 40.95 (978-0-8014-4578-1(7)) Cornell Univ. Pr.

Dixon, Sarah. Organizational Transformation in the Russian Oil Industry. 2008. (New Horizons in International Business Ser.). 288p. 127.00 (978-1-84720-592-6(5)) Elgar, Edward Publishing, Inc.

Dolgopyatova, Tatiana, et al, eds. Organization & Development of Russian Business: A Firm-Level Analysis. 2009. (ENG., Illus.). 272p. 105.00 (978-0-230-21728-7(1)) Palgrave Macmillan.

Domsch, Michel E. & Lidokhover, Tatjana, eds. Human Resource Management in Russia. 2007. (Contemporary Employment Relations Ser.). (Illus.). 358p. 134.95 (978-0-7546-4876-5(1)) Ashgate Publishing Co.

Grant, Jonathan A. Big Business in Russia: The Putilov Company in Late Imperial Russia, 1868-1917. 2009. (Pitt Russian East European Ser.). (ENG.). 216p. (C). pap. 27.95 (978-0-8229-8590-7(X)) Univ. of Pittsburgh Pr.

Himelstein, Linda. The King of Vodka: The Story of Pyotr Smirnov & the Upheaval of an Empire. 2010. (P. S. Ser.). (ENG.). 432p. pap. 15.99 (978-0-06-085591-8(6), HarperPerennial) HarperCollins Pubs.

Kamenchuk, Olga. How to Speak the Language of Russian Business? 2011. 116p. pap. (978-3-8443-2659-8(6)) Lambert Academic Publishing.

Krasheninnikov, P. V. Unitarnye Predpriatiia, Uchrezhdeniia, Pravo Khoziaistvennogo Vedeniia I Pravo Operativnogo Upravleniia: Postateinyi Kommentarii K Statiam 113-115, 120 I Glave 19 Grazhdanskogo Kodeksa Rossiiskoi Federatsii. 2010. (RUS.). 122p. (978-5-8354-0683-8(5)) Statut, Izdatel'stvo.

Nell, Julia. Business Integration in Emerging Markets. 2009. 88p. pap. (978-3-639-15949-3(7)) VDM Verlag Dr. Mueller e.K.

Nilsson, Anna. Contemporary Russian Management. 2009. 64p. pap. (978-3-639-16571-5(3)) VDM Verlag Dr. Mueller e.K.

Ransel, David L. A Russian Merchant's Tale: The Life & Adventures of Ivan Alekseevich Tolchënov, Based on His Diary. 2008. (Indiana-Michigan Ser. in Russian & East European Studies). (ENG., Illus.). 352p. 65.00 (978-0-253-35236-1(3), 0253352363); pap. 24.95 (978-0-253-22020-2(3), 0253220203) Indiana Univ. Pr.

Russia: Business Financing Handbook. (Illus.). 70p. (Orig.). pap. 295.00 (978-0-7605-1208-1(6)) Rector Pr., Ltd.

Ulasevich, Roman. State Shareholding & Value of Russian Companies - a Quantitative Study. 2008. 52p. pap. (978-3-639-03717-3(0)) VDM Verlag Dr. Mueller e.K.

Ulianova, Galina. Female Entrepreneurs in Nineteenth-Century Russia, 1 vol. 2009. (Perspectives in Economic & Social History Ser.). (ENG.). 272p. 99.00 (978-1-85196-967-8(5)) Pickering & Chatto Pubs., Ltd. GBR. Dist: Ashgate Publishing Co.

BUSINESS ENTERPRISES—SOUTH AMERICA

Amann, Edmund & Cantwell, John, eds. Innovative Firms in Emerging Market Countries. 2012. (ENG.). 392p. 99.00 (978-0-19-964600-5(7)) Oxford Univ. Pr., Inc.

BIA. Major Companies of South America: Manufacturers, Wholesalers, Banks, Construction Companies. 6th rev. ed. 2006. 300p. (J). pap. 249.00 (978-1-4187-4396-3(8)) Business Information Agency.

—Major Companies of Venezuela: Manufacturers, Wholesalers, Banks, Construction Companies. 6th rev. ed. 2006. 250p. (J). pap. 219.00 (978-1-4187-4444-1(1)) Business Information Agency.

Brennan, James & Rougier, Marcelo. The Politics of National Capitalism: Peronism & the Argentine Bourgeoisie 1946-1947. 2009. (ENG.). 224p. 60.00 (978-0-271-03571-0(4)) Pennsylvania State Univ. Pr.

Champion, Walter T. Business Laws of Colombia. 2009. xx, 224p. pap. (978-0-314-90331-0(3)) West Publishing Co., College & Schl. Div.

Chile: Business Financing Handbook. (Illus.). 70p. (Orig.). pap. 295.00 (978-0-7605-1185-5(3)) Rector Pr., Ltd.

Colombia: Business Financing Handbook. (Illus.). 70p. (Orig.). pap. 295.00 (978-0-7605-1187-9(X)) Rector Pr., Ltd.

Doing Business in Argentina. Date not set. (Doing Business in Regions & Countries Around the World Ser.). 80p. (978-1-882390-50-2(4)) Training Management Corp.

Doing Business in Chile. Date not set. (Doing Business in Regions & Countries Around the World Ser.). 80p. (978-1-882390-55-7(5)) Training Management Corp.

Doing Business in Latin America. Date not set. (Doing Business in Regions & Countries Around the World Ser.). (978-1-882390-84-7(9)) Training Management Corp.

Doing Business in Venezuela. Date not set. (Doing Business in Regions & Countries Around the World Ser.). (978-1-882390-81-6(4)) Training Management Corp.

Dorling Kindersley Publishing Staff. Doing Business in South America. 2009. (DK Essential Managers Ser.). (ENG.). 72p. (gr. 12). pap. 8.00 (978-0-7566-4201-3(9)) Dorling Kindersley Publishing, Inc.

GATT Uruguay Final Documents: Companies-Products-Services. (Illus.). 1500p. (Orig.). pap. (978-0-7605-1340-8(6)) Rector Pr., Ltd.

Gil, Rossina. Doing Business in Colombia. Date not set. (Doing Business in Regions & Countries Around the World Ser.). 80p. (978-1-882390-57-1(1)) Training Management Corp.

Ibp, Usa. Argentina Industrial & Business Direct. 2006. (Illus.). pap. 99.95 (978-0-7397-6792-4(5)) International Business Pubns., USA.

Kuchmann, Sven. Die Haftung des Geschäftsführers einer deutschen GmbH und des Gerente einer argentinischen SRL im Rechtsvergleich. 2008. (Internationalrechtliche Studien. Beiträge zum Internationalen Privatrecht, zum Einheitsrecht und zur Rechtsvergleichung Ser.). 260p. pap. 65.95 (978-3-631-58250-3(1)) Lang, Peter GmbH, Europaischer Verlag der Wissenschaften DEU. Dist: Lang, Peter.

Seynabou Sakho, Yaye, et al, eds. Gender in Bolivian Production: Reducing Differences in Formality & Productivity of Firms. 2009. (Country Studies). (ENG., Illus.). 80p. pap. 25.00 (978-0-8213-8014-7(1), 9780821380147) World Bank Pubns.

BUSINESS ENTERPRISES—SOVIET UNION

Aidis, Ruta, et al, eds. Innovation & Entrepreneurship: Successful Start-ups & Businesses in Emerging Economies. 2008. (Illus.). 144p. (C). 119.00 (978-1-84542-973-7(7)) Elgar, Edward Publishing, Inc.

BUSINESS ENTERPRISES—SPAIN

BIA. Essential Spanish Manufacturers: Food, Textile, Clothing, & Chemical Companies. 6th rev. ed. 2006. 400p. (J). pap. 249.00 (978-1-4187-4229-4(5)) Business Information Agency.

—Key Farms of Spain. 6th rev. ed. 2006. 250p. (J). pap. 219.00 (978-1-4187-4335-2(6)) Business Information Agency.

—Major Companies of Spain: Manufacturers, Wholesalers, Banks, Construction Companies. 6th rev. ed. 2006. 400p. (J). pap. 249.00 (978-1-4187-4924-8(9)) Business Information Agency.

Cabrera, Mercedes & Rey, Fernando del. The Powers of Entrepreneurs: Politics & Economy in Contemporary Spain. 2006. 220p. (C). 90.00 (978-1-84545-185-1(6)) Berghahn Bks., Inc.

Doing Business in Spain. Date not set. (Doing Business in Regions & Countries Around the World Ser.). (978-1-882390-75-5(X)) Training Management Corp.

Guillén, Mauro F. & Garcia-Canal, Esteban. The New Multinationals: Spanish Firms in a Global Context. 2010. (ENG., Illus.). 238p. 59.00 (978-0-521-51614-3(5)) Cambridge Univ. Pr.

Ibp, Usa. Spain Industrial & Business Directory. 2006. (Illus.). pap. 99.95 (978-0-7397-9768-6(9)) International Business Pubns., USA.

Lier, Anika. Cultural Diversity Management. 2010. 80p. pap. (978-3-639-25981-0(5)) VDM Verlag Dr. Mueller e.K.

Ruiz Peris, Juan Ignacio & Peris, Juan Ignacio Ruiz. Hacia un Derecho para Las Redes Empresariales. 2009. (SPA.). 240p. (978-84-9876-677-6(X)) Tirant lo Blanch.

Todo Sociedades Mercantiles 2010. 2009. (SPA.). 1309p. (978-84-8235-894-9(4)) Ciss, S.A., Editorial.

BUSINESS ENTERPRISES—TAIWAN

Chen, I-Pin. The Responsive Actions in Tourism & Amusement Enterprises in Taiwan. 2009. 56p. pap. (978-3-639-18733-5(4)) VDM Verlag Dr. Mueller e.K.

Hsu, Chen-Min, et al. The Business & Investment Environment in Taiwan & Mainland China: A Focus on the It & High-Tech Electronic Industries. 2007. (Illus.). 444p. 150.00 (978-981-270-366-8(7)) World Scientific Publishing Co., Inc.

Ibp, Usa. Taiwan Industrial & Business Directory. 2006. (Illus.). pap. 99.95 (978-0-7397-9775-4(1)) International Business Pubns., USA.

Yang, Hui-O. Human Resource Management in the Hotel Industry in Taiwan: Current & Future. 2008. 344p. pap. (978-3-639-09623-1(1)) VDM Verlag Dr. Mueller e.K.

BUSINESS ENTERPRISES—UNITED STATES

Abshire, Richard. Garland: A Contemporary History. 2009. (Illus.). 110p. (978-1-893619-92-0(3)) Historical Publishing Network.

Adams, Barney. The Wow Factor: How I Turned One Great Idea & My Unbridled Enthusiasm into a Golf Revolution. 2008. (Illus.). 254p. 24.95 (978-1-60239-248-9(X)) Skyhorse Publishing Co., Inc.

Adams Media Corporation Staff, creator. The Colorado Jobbank. 14th ed. 2006. (Colorado JobBank Ser.). 240p. per. 17.95 (978-1-59869-058-3(2)) Adams Media Corp.

Adams Media Corporation Staff, ed. The National Job Bank 2011: The Complete Employment Guide to 20,000 American Companies. 2010. (ENG.). cd-rom 250.00 (978-1-4405-1122-6(5)) Adams Media Corp.

Ahi, Michele Ellie. Outsourcing Everything but the Kitchen Sink. 2009. 194p. pap. 19.97 (978-0-557-06441-0(4)) Lulu Enterprises Inc.

Albert, Erin & Yuspie LLC Staff. Indianapolis: A Young Professional's Guide 2nd Edition. 2010. 420p. pap. 36.99 (978-1-4490-9530-7(5)) AuthorHouse.

Alcoholic Drinks Market Latin America: Companies-Products-Services. 200p. (Orig.). pap. 1895.00 (978-0-7605-2172-4(7)) Rector Pr., Ltd.

Alexander, Dean. Terrorism & Business: Threats, Effects, & Responses. 2010. (Illus.). 256p. 69.95 (978-1-4398-0086-7(3)) Auerbach Pubs., Inc.

Allen, Ronald Jay. Commentaries & Cases Law Business Organization 2009-2010 Stat Sup. 2009. pap. 39.50 (978-0-7355-8410-5(9)) Wolters Kluwer Law & Business.

Allen, William T. Commentaries & Cases on the Law of Business Organizations. 3rd rev. ed. 2009. 152.00 (978-0-7355-8600-0(4)) Wolters Kluwer Law & Business.

Allen, William T., et al. Commentaries & Cases on the Law of Business Organization. 3rd ed. 2009. (Illus.). xxvi, 724p. (978-0-7355-8601-7(2)) Kluwer Law International.

American Bar Association, Section of Litigation Committee on Corporate Counsel Staff, contrib. by. The In-House Counsel's Essential Toolkit. 2008. (ENG.). pap. 225.95 incl. cd-rom (978-1-59031-662-7(2)) American Bar Assn.

American Economy. 2011. pap. 58.00 (978-1-4144-4854-1(6)) Cengage Gale.

Arata, Alexandra. Tu Propia Empresa: La Primera Guía Completa con Todos Los Consehos Necesarios para Tener Tu Propia Empresa en Estados Unidos. 2007. (SPA., Illus.). 196p. (978-0-9796310-6-1(8)); (978-0-9796310-5-4(X)) Hispanic Resources US LLC.

Arden, Lynie. The Work at Home Sourcebook. 2009. (ENG.). 400p. pap. 19.95 (978-0-911781-20-5(X)) Live Oak Pubns.

Asbury, Neal. Conscientious Equity: An American Entrepreneur's Solutions to the World's Greatest Problems. 2010. (ENG.). 240p. 27.00 (978-0-230-10892-9(X)) Palgrave Macmillan.

Aspatore Books Staff, compiled by. Buying & Selling Distressed Businesses: Leading Lawyers on Evaluating Assets & Identifying Buyers, Negotiating Deals, & Advising Directors & Officers on Fiduciary Duties (Inside the Minds) 2009. 452p. pap. 90.00 (978-0-314-20785-2(6)) Aspatore Bks.

—Buying & Selling Distressed Businesses, 2010 Ed: Leading Lawyers on Navigating Recent Distressed Business Transactions, Understanding the Sales Process, & Developing Deal Strategies (Inside the Minds) 2010. (Illus.). 352p. pap. 95.00 (978-0-314-27092-4(2)) Aspatore Bks.

—Understanding Legal Needs of Technology Companies: Leading Lawyers on Performing a Legal Audit, Managing Financial Risk, & Prioritizing Legal Needs (Inside the Minds) 2009. 216p. pap. 75.00 (978-0-314-19498-5(3)) Aspatore Bks.

Audette, Susan T. & Baker, David E. The Old Town Canoe Company: Our First Hundred Years. 2010. (Illus.). 176p. pap. 30.00 (978-0-88448-203-1(0)) Tilbury Hse. Pubs.

Ault, Julie, ed. & text. Show & Tell: A Chronicle of Group Material. 2010. (ENG., Illus.). 272p. pap. 35.00 (978-0-9561928-1-3(5)) Four Corners Bks. GBR. Dist: D.A.P./Distributed Art Pubs.

Babb, Milton. Historic Hunt County: An Illustrated History. 2010. (Illus.). 96p. (978-1-935377-16-0(7)) Historical Publishing Network.

Bagley, Constance E. & Dauchy, Craig E. The Entrepreneur's Guide to Business Law. 4th ed. 2011. (ENG.). 840p. (C). pap. 82.95 (978-0-538-46646-2(4)) Cengage South-Western.

Barriball, Don, 3rd. The History of the Ober Manufacturing Company of Chagrin Falls 1862 - 1959. 2007. (Illus.). 49p. spiral bd. 12.95 (978-0-9753051-6-4(6)) Chagrin Falls Historical Society.

Barry, Benton. Spirit of Collin County. 2007. 103p. 49.95 (978-1-893619-69-2(9)) Historical Publishing Network.

Bauman, Jeffrey D. Corporations & Other Business Associations: Statutes, Rules & Forms, 2009 Ed. 2009th rev. ed. 2009. 1904p. pap. 41.00 (978-0-314-20577-3(2), West Legalworks) West.

Baumer, Poindexter. Legal Environment of Business in the Inf. 2006. pap. 19.95 (978-1-4288-0525-5(7)) Cram101 Inc.

Beard, Patricia. Blue Blood & Mutiny: The Fight for the Soul of Morgan Stanley. 2008. (ENG., Illus.). 464p. pap. 15.95 (978-0-06-088192-4(5), HarperPerennial) HarperCollins Pubs.

Beer Market U. S. A. Companies-Products-Services. 345p. (Orig.). pap. 1595.00 (978-0-7605-2161-8(1)) Rector Pr., Ltd.

Benedict, Margaret. An American Entrepreneur - Mr Joyce Clyde Hall - Founder of Hallmark Cards Inc. 2008. 76p. pap. 19.95 (978-1-4389-0572-3(6)) AuthorHouse.

Bennett, James R. Historic Birmingham & Jefferson County. 2008. (Illus.). 202p. pap. (978-1-893619-91-3(5)) Historical Publishing Network.

—Historic Birmingham & Jefferson County: An Illustrated History. 2008. (Illus.). 312p. (978-1-893619-83-8(4)) Historical Publishing Network.

Best, Harry. The Men's Garment Industry of New York & the Strike of 1913 / by Harry Best. 2011. 34p. pap. 11.99 (978-1-4181-9467-3(0)) MPublishing.

BIA. Major Companies of the USA: Manufacturers, Wholesalers, Banks, Construction Companies. 6th rev. ed. 2006. 400p. (J). pap. 249.00 *(978-1-4187-4426-7(3))* Business Information Agency.

Big Emerging Markets. per. *(978-0-16-063705-6(8))*, Commerce Dept.) United States Government Printing Office.

Biradavolu, Monica Rao. Indian Entrepreneurs in Silicon Valley: The Making of a Transnational Techno-Capitalist Class. 2008. (C). 104.95 *(978-1-60497-527-7(X))* Cambria Pr.

Birchard, Bill. Merchants of Virtue: Herman Miller & the Making of a Sustainable Company. 2011. (ENG., Illus.). 256p. 28.00 *(978-0-230-10660-4(9))* Palgrave Macmillan.

Birnberg, Howard G. Project Management for Designers & Facilities Managers. 3rd ed. 2008. (Illus.). 272p. *(978-1-60427-011-2(X))* Ross, J. Publishing, Inc.

Bisio, Rick & Kohler, Mike. The Educated Franchisee. 2nd ed. 2011. 218p. pap. 18.95 *(978-1-935098-53-9(5))*, Bascom Hill Bks.) Hillcrest Publishing Group, Inc.

Bixby, Michael. The Legal Environment of Business. 4th ed. 2008. (ENG., Illus.). xxiv, 820p. (C). 157.60 *(978-0-536-54498-8(0))* Pearson Learning Solutions.

Bixby, Michael, et al. The Legal Environment of Business. 5th ed. 2011. (ENG.). 850p. (C). ring bd. 106.00 ***(978-1-256-15916-2(6))*** Pearson Learning Solutions.

Blake, Megan K. It Takes a Village. 2008. 140p. pap. *(978-3-639-07938-8(8))* VDM Verlag Dr. Mueller e.K.

Bleak, Jared L. When for-Profit Meets Nonprofit. 2010. 196p. pap. 39.95 *(978-0-415-88246-0(X))* Routledge.

Bloch, Talia. Doing Business in North America. Date not set. (Doing Business in Regions & Countries Around the World Ser.). *(978-1-882390-85-4(7))* Training Management Corp.

Bogle, John C. Don't Count on It! Reflections on Investment Illusions, Capitalism, Mutual Funds, Indexing, Entrepreneurship, Idealism, & Heroes. 2010. (ENG., Illus.). 603p. 29.95 *(978-0-470-64396-9(X))*, Wiley) Wiley, John & Sons, Inc.

Borden, Bradley T. Taxation & Business Planning for Real Estate Transactions. 2011. ***(978-1-4224-8230-8(8))*** LexisNexis Matthew Bender.

Bouchoux, Deborah E. Fundamentals of Business Organizations for Paralegals. 3rd ed. 2010. (Illus.). xxix, 270p. *(978-0-7355-7913-2(X))* Kluwer Law International.

Bourque, Ron. Disturbing Questions: Has God Stopped Blessing America. 2007. (Illus.). 147p. per. 17.50 *(978-0-9795394-0-4(4))* Father's Pr., LLC.

Bowlin, Yvette, des. Impotence in the Boardroom: MySpace Caught an STD. 2008. 105p. per. 24.95 *(978-0-9801253-0-6(8))* In2ideas, LLC.

Bracken, Sharon. Historic McLennan County: An Illustrated History. 2010. (Illus.). 144p. *(978-1-935377-22-1(1))*; *(978-1-893619-72-8(4))* Historical Publishing Network.

Brady, Miranda L. & Hansen, Samantha C., eds. International Corporate Taxation: Considerations & Comparisons. 2012. ***(978-1-62100-501-8(1))*** Nova Science Pubs., Inc.

Braham, Lewis. The House that Bogle Built: How John Bogle & Vanguard Reinvented the Mutual Fund Industry. 2011. (ENG.). 304p. 28.00 *(978-0-07-174906-0(3))*, 0071749063) McGraw-Hill Cos., The.

Branch, Ben & Ray, Hugh. Bankruptcy Investing - How to Profit from Distressed Companies. 2007. 328p. per. 44.95 *(978-1-58798-291-0(9))* Beard Bks., Inc.

Branson, Douglas M. Business Enterprises: Legal Structures, Governance, & Policy: Cases, Materials, & Problems. 2008. 123.00 *(978-0-8205-6467-8(2))* LexisNexis Matthew Bender.

Brc. The Brc Journal of Advances in Business: Vol. 1, No. 2. 2011. 164p. pap. 17.00 ***(978-1-60497-784-4(1))*** Cambria Pr.

—The Brc Journal of Advances in Education: Vol. 1, No. 2. 2011. 126p. pap. 12.00 ***(978-1-60497-771-4(X))*** Cambria Pr.

—Proceedings of the 2010 Business Research Consortium of Western New York. 2011. 478p. pap. 22.00 ***(978-1-60497-809-4(0))*** Cambria Pr.

Brewers Publications. 2009-2010 North American Brewers' Resource Directory. 2009. (ENG.). 224p. pap. 99.00 *(978-0-937381-94-5(2))* Brewers Pubns.

Brewster, Mike & Dalzell, Frederick. Driving Change: The UPS Approach to Business. 2007. (ENG.). 304p. 24.95 *(978-1-4013-0288-7(2))*; pap. *(978-1-4013-0907-7(0))* Hyperion Pr.

Briefs, Casenote Legal. Business Organizations: Allen Kraakman Subramanian 3e. 2009. pap., stu. ed. 35.95 *(978-0-7355-9456-2(2))*, Aspen Pubs.) Wolters Kluwer Law & Business.

Brigante, Brad J. & Magistrale, Jean. Selecting & Forming Business Entities. 2nd ed. 2007. (Illus.). *(978-0-7626-1203-1(7))* Continuing Education of the Bar-California.

Brigham, et al. Fundamentals of Financial Management (Book Only) 12th ed. 2009. 752p. (C). 228.95 *(978-0-324-59771-4(1))* CENGAGE Learning.

Brigham, Eugene & Houston, Joel. Fundamentals of Financial Management. 13th ed. 2012. (ENG.). 816p. (C). 256.95 ***(978-0-538-48212-7(5))*** Cengage South-Western.

Broehl, Wayne G., Jr. Cargill: From Commodities to Customers. 2008. (ENG., Illus.). 368p. 40.00 *(978-1-58465-694-4(8))*, Dartmouth College Press) Univ. Pr. of New England.

Brooks, Arthur C. The Road to Freedom: How to Win the Fight for Free Enterprise. 2012. (ENG.). 224p. (gr. 9). 25.99 ***(978-0-465-02940-2(X))*** Basic Bks.

Brush, Candida G. The Life Cycle of New Ventures: Emergence, Newness & Growth. Kolvereid, Lars et al, eds. 2010. (New Horizons in Environmental & Energy Law Ser.). 240p. 112.00 *(978-1-84844-697-7(7))* Elgar, Edward Publishing, Inc.

Bunker, John P., Jr. Not Far from the Tree: A Brief History of the Apples & the Orchards of Palermo, Maine, 1804-2004. 2007. (Illus.). 200p. pap. 25.00 *(978-1-883957-09-4(6))*, Robin Hood Bks.) Robin Hood Bks. & Little Letterpress.

Burke, Bob & Dabney, Eric. HISTORIC ROGERS COUNTY: An Illustrated History. 2010. (Illus.). 92p. *(978-1-935377-11-5(6))* Historical Publishing Network.

Burnette, O. Lawrence. Historic Baldwin County: A Bicentennial History. 2007. (Illus.). 100p. *(978-1-893619-80-7(X))* Historical Publishing Network.

Business City to City Atlas USA: Companies-Products-Services. (Illus.). 210p. (Orig.). pap. *(978-0-7605-0841-1(0))* Rector Pr., Ltd.

Business Research Consortium Of Wny. The Brc Academy Journal of Education: Vol. 1, No. 1. 2010. 142p. pap. 29.99 *(978-1-60497-689-2(6))* Cambria Pr.

—The Brc Journal of Advances in Education: Vol. 1, No. 1. 2010. 108p. pap. 29.99 *(978-1-60497-691-5(8))* Cambria Pr.

BVR's Guide to Discounts for Lack of Marketability. 2008. ring bd. 329.00 *(978-0-9758568-9-4(3))* Business Valuation Resources, LLC.

Carbasho, Tracy. Nike. 1 vol. 2010. (Corporations That Changed the World Ser.). (Illus.). 132p. 35.00 *(978-1-59884-342-2(7))*, A2578C); xiv, 132p. E-Book *(978-1-59884-343-9(5))*, Greenwood Pr.) Greenwood Publishing Group, Inc.

Carraway, Vince. Depression Investor. 2010. 88p. pap. 12.99 *(978-1-4490-6526-3(0))* AuthorHouse.

Cary, Carolyn C. Historic Fayette County: An Illustrated History. 2009. (Illus.). 96p. *(978-1-935377-03-0(5))* Historical Publishing Network.

Casenotes. Business Organizations: Bauman 7E. 2010. pap., stu. ed. 36.95 *(978-0-7355-9769-3(3))*, Aspen Pubs.) Wolters Kluwer Law & Business.

Cauley, Leslie. End of the Line. 2008. (ENG.). 320p. pap. 21.95 *(978-1-4391-2309-6(8))*, Free Pr.) Free Pr.

Cavanagh, Thomas E. Preparedness in the Private Sector. 2008. (Illus.). 31p. *(978-0-8237-0936-0(8))* Conference Board, Inc., The.

Chalberg, John "Chuck". Bloomington: A Sesquicentennial Celebration. 2007. 59.95 *(978-1-882933-82-2(6))* Cherbo Publishing Group, Inc.

Chasalow, Michael. Business Associations. 2010. (Acing Ser.). (Illus.). 265p. 32.00 *(978-0-314-90673-1(8))*, West Legalworks) West.

Cheeseman, Henry R. Essentials of Business & Online Commerce Law. 2007. (Illus.). 706p. *(978-0-536-55848-0(5))* Prentice Hall PTR.

—Study Guide. 6th ed. 2008. (ENG.). 560p. (C). pap. 46.67 *(978-0-13-601503-1(4))*, Prentice Hall) Prentice Hall PTR.

Chiappinelli. Cases & Materials on Business Entities. 2nd ed. 2010. 158.00 *(978-0-7355-8477-8(X))* Wolters Kluwer Law & Business.

—Ll: Business Entities. 2009. ring bd. 93.50 *(978-0-7355-8883-7(X))* Wolters Kluwer Law & Business.

Chiappinelli, Eric A. Business Associations: With Commentary, 2008-2009 Edition. 2009. pap. 30.50 *(978-0-7355-7230-0(5))* Wolters Kluwer Law & Business.

Chiappinelli, Eric A. Cases & Materials on Business Entities. 2nd ed. 2010. xxxv, 879p. ***(978-0-7355-8478-5(8))***, Aspen Pubs.) Wolters Kluwer Law & Business.

Chilton, Carl S. Historic Brownsville: An Illustrated History. 2010. (Illus.). 92p. ***(978-1-935377-15-3(9))*** Historical Publishing Network.

Chris, E. Fonvielle. Historic Wilmington & Lower Cape Fear. 2007. 96p. 49.95 *(978-1-893619-68-5(0))* Historical Publishing Network.

Clarke, Sally H., et al, eds. The Challenge of Remaining Innovative: Insights from Twentieth-Century American Business. 2009. (Innovation & Technology in the World Economy Ser.). (ENG., Illus.). 368p. 39.95 *(978-0-8047-5892-5(1))* Stanford Univ. Pr.

Classical Collection of Amherst College: Companies-Products-Services. (Illus.). 60p. (Orig.). pap. 45.00 *(978-0-7605-1692-8(8))* Rector Pr., Ltd.

Cochran, Thomas C. The Pabst Brewing Company: The History of an American Business. 2011. 476p. 57.95 ***(978-1-258-05443-4(4))*** Literary Licensing, LLC.

Collyer, John Lyon. B F Goodrich Story of Creative Enterprs. 2006. pap. 15.95 *(978-1-4286-6064-9(X))* Kessinger Publishing, LLC.

Continuing Education of the Bar. Intellectual Property in Business Transactions, 2 vols. 2008. 1168p. ring bd. 239.00 *(978-0-7626-1301-4(7))* Continuing Education of the Bar-California.

Continuing Education of the Bar (CEB). Retail Leasing: Drafting & Negotiating the Lease, 2 vols. 2007. (California Commercial Leasing Ser.). (Illus.). ring bd. 299.00 *(978-0-7626-1204-8(5))* Continuing Education of the Bar-California.

—Selecting & Forming Business Entities: May 2008 Update, 2 vols. 2nd ed. 2008. 678p. ring bd. 91.00 *(978-0-7626-1381-6(5))* Continuing Education of the Bar-California.

Contract Bundling Oversight: Hearing Before the Subcommittee on Economic Opportunity of the Committee on Veterans' Affairs, U.S. House of Representatives, One Hundred Tenth Congress, First Session, July 26, 2007. 2008. iii, 64p. *(978-0-16-081147-0(3))*, 552-070-37569-4) United States Government Printing Office.

Contracts & Contracting Policy at the U.S. Department of Veterans Affairs: Hearing Before the Subcommittee on Economic Opportunity of the Committee on Veterans' Affairs, U.S. House of Representatives, One Hundred Eleventh Congress, First Session, April 23, 2009. 2009. (Illus.). iv, 116p. *(978-0-16-084274-0(3))*, 552-070-39839-2) United States Government Printing Office.

Contrepois, Sylvie, et al, eds. Globalizing Employment Relations: Multinational Firms & Central & Eastern Europe Transitions. 2011. (ENG., Illus.). 304p. 110.00 *(978-0-230-25243-1(5))* Palgrave Macmillan.

County Court Records Handbook: Companies-Products-Services. 540 ED#: 2p. (Orig.). pap. *(978-0-7605-1857-1(2))* Rector Pr., Ltd.

County Locator Locus Handbook: Companies-Products-Services. 930p. (Orig.). pap. 145.00 *(978-0-7605-1861-8(0))* Rector Pr., Ltd.

Covert, Jack & Sattersten, Todd. The 100 Best Business Books of All Time: What They Say, Why They Matter, & How They Can Help You. 2009. (ENG., Illus.). 352p. (gr. 12-18). 25.95 *(978-1-59184-240-8(9))*, Portfolio (Hardcover)) Penguin Group (USA) Inc.

Cram101 Textbook Reviews. Outlines & Highlights for Business Organizations for Paralegals by Deborah E Bouchoux, Isbn: 9780735576285. 2011. 488p. pap. 36.95 ***(978-1-61812-073-1(5))*** Cram101 Inc.

—Outlines & Highlights for Business Organizations for Paralegals by Kathleen Reed, Isbn: 9780135103647. 2011. 466p. pap. 36.95 ***(978-1-61812-140-0(5))*** Cram101 Inc.

—Outlines & Highlights for Business Planning: Financing the Start-up Business & Venture Capital Financing by Therese Maynard. 2011. 232p. pap. 31.95 ***(978-1-4672-6709-0(0))*** Cram101 Inc.

—Outlines & Highlights for Homeland Security & Private Sector Business: Corporations Role in Critical Infrastructure Protection by Elsa Lee, ISBN. 2011. 232p. pap. 31.95 ***(978-1-61812-111-0(1))*** Cram101 Inc.

Cram101 Textbook Reviews. Outlines & Highlights for Law, Business, & Society by Mcadams, Isbn: 9780073377650. 2010. 290p. pap. 32.95 *(978-1-61698-852-4(5))* Cram101 Inc.

Cram101 Textbook Reviews Staff. Outlines & Highlights for Business by William M Pride, Robert J Hughes, Jack R Kapoor, Isbn: 9780618753147. 2009. 276p. pap. 32.95 *(978-1-4288-7708-5(8))* Cram101 Inc.

—Outlines & Highlights for Business Organizations for Paralegals by Deborah E Bouchoux, Isbn: 9780735557505. 2009. 176p. pap. 29.95 *(978-1-4288-399`-5(7))* Cram101 Inc.

—Outlines & Highlights for Law & Ethics in the Business Environment by Halbert, Isbn: 0324657323. 2008. 144p. pap. 11.95 *(978-1-4288-6513-6(6))* Cram101 Inc.

—Outlines & Highlights for Law, Business, & Society by Mcadams, Isbn: 9780073377650. 2009. 232p. pap. 31.95 *(978-1-4288-6769-7(4))* Cram101 Inc.

—Outlines & Highlights for New Business Ventures & the Entrepreneur by Roberts, Isbn: 9780073404974. 2009. 78p. pap. 27.95 *(978-1-4288-6841-0(0))* Cram101 Inc.

Credit Ratings U. S. A. Companies-Products-Services. (Orig.). pap. *(978-0-7605-1864-9(5))* Rector Pr., Ltd.

Crossvolt Low Voltage Handbook: Companies-Products-Services. 200p. (Orig.). pap. 125.00 *(978-0-7605-1823-6(8))* Rector Pr., Ltd.

Crouse, Angie, et al. The Blue Pages: A Directory of Companies Rated by Their Politics & Practices. 2nd ed. 2009. (Blue Pages: A Directory of Companies Rated by Their Politics & Ser.). (ENG.). 320p. pap. 12.95 *(978-0-9817091-4-7(1))* PoliPointPress, LLC.

CSD Architecture, compiled by. People Architecture. 2006. 80p. pap. 29.95 *(978-0-9755654-9-0(4))*, Ostberg) Greenway Communications.

Cuba Trade & Investment Handbook: Companies-Products-Services (Illus.). 100p. (Orig.). pap. *(978-0-7605-1684-3(7))* Rector Pr., Ltd.

Darst, Don R. The Centralia Wizard: The Chance Company Story. 2007. *(978-1-57864-406-3(2))* Donning Co. Pubs.

Daub, Falko. New Whistleblowing Regulations in the Usa. 2007. 80p. per. *(978-3-8364-0730-4(2))* VDM Verlag Dr. Mueller e.K.

Davidson, Daniel V. & Forsythe, Lynn M. The Entrepreneur's Legal Companion. 2010. (ENG.). 336p. (C). pap. 60.00 *(978-0-13-607723-7(4))*, Prentice Hall) Prentice Hall PTR.

Davis, Speaker Gary. Networking in the South. 2008. 108p. pap. 15.95 *(978-0-557-00143-9(9))* Lulu Enterprises Inc.

De Boer, Tycho. Nature, Business, & Community in North Carolina's Green Swamp. 2008. (ENG., Illus.). 256p. 59.95 *(978-0-8130-3248-1(2))* Univ. Pr. of Florida.

Delfeld, Carl T. Red, White & Bold: The New American Century. 2009. 188p. 27.95 *(978-1-4401-5131-6(8))*; pap. 17.95 *(978-1-4401-5130-9(X))* iUniverse, Inc.

Deliyannis, Melina. Powers Brown Architecture. 2007. (Neoarchitecture Ser.). (ENG., Illus.). 124p. 49.50 *(978-1-86470-250-7(8))* Images Publishing Group AUS. Dist: National Bk. Network.

Demographic Business Atlas U S A: Companies-Products-Services. (Illus.). 200p. (Orig.). pap. *(978-0-7605-0839-8(9))* Rector Pr., Ltd.

Demographic U. S. a Zip Code: Companies-Products-Services. (Illus.). 210p. (Orig.). pap. *(978-0-7605-0840-4(2))* Rector Pr., Ltd.

Dennehy, John A. Braintree. 2010. (Images of America Ser.). (ENG., Illus.). 128p. pap. 21.99 *(978-0-7385-7247-5(0))* Arcadia Publishing.

Dennis, Michael. The New Economy & the Modern South. 2009. (Working in the Americas Ser.). (ENG., Illus.). 272p. 75.00 *(978-0-8130-3291-7(1))* Univ. Pr. of Florida.

Dick, Rudolph C. Nathaniel Griffin of Salem & His Naumk. 2006. pap. 15.95 *(978-1-4286-6065-6(8))* Kessinger Publishing, LLC.

DirectoriesUSA, creator. Mississippi Business Directory. 2008. (Mississippi Business Directory Ser.). (Illus.). 940p. per. 1375.00 *(978-0-7687-1201-8(7))* American Business Directories.

Directory of American Firms Operating in Foreign Countries, 4 vols. (ENG.). 20th ed. 2009. 7891p. 435.00 *(978-0-8360-0059-7(5))*4. 19th ed. 2007. 435.00 *(978-0-8360-0057-3(9))* Uniworld Business Pubns., Inc.

Diversifying Native Economies: Oversight Hearing Before the Committee on Natural Resources, U.S. House of Representatives, One Hundred Tenth Congress, First Session, Wednesday, September 19, 2007. 2008. (Illus.). ii, 134p. *(978-0-16-080685-8(2))*, 552-070-37281-4) United States Government Printing Office.

Djordjevich, Vera. Chicago & Midwest Law Firms 2010. 4th ed. 2009. 256p. pap. 29.95 *(978-1-58131-604-9(6))* Vault.com.

—Texas & Southwest Law Firms 2010. 2009. 208p. pap. 29.95 *(978-1-58131-606-3(2))* Vault.com.

Doing Business in the United States. Date not set. (Doing Business in Regions & Countries Around the World Ser.). *(978-1-882390-80-9(6))* Training Management Corp.

Doing Business with the Government: The Record & Goals for Small, Minority, & Disadvantaged Businesses: Hearing Before the Subcommittee on Economic Development, Public Buildings, & Emergency Management of the Committee on Transportation & Infrastructure, House of Representatives, One Hundred Tenth Congress, Second Session, March 6, 2008. 2008. (Illus.). xii, 96p. *(978-0-16-083566-7(6))*, 552-070-38284-0) United States Government Printing Office.

Down A Country Road with the Amish. 2009. (Illus.). 81p. lib. bdg. 12.99 *(978-0-615-27716-5(0))* Brush Creek Publishing.

Downing, Sarah. Vintage Outer Banks: Shifting Sands & Bygone Beaches. 2008. pap. 19.99 *(978-1-59629-508-7(2))* History Pr., The.

Ebert, Griffin. Business Essentials. 2006. pap. 14.95 *(978-1-4288-1180-5(X))* Cram101 Inc.

Ebert, Ronald J. & Griffin, Ricky. Study Guide, Business Essentials. 7th ed. 2009. (ENG.). 252p. (C). pap. 46.67 *(978-0-13-607850-0(8))*, Prentice Hall) Prentice Hall PTR.

—Study Guide for Business Essentials. 8th ed. 2010. 150p. (C). pap. 46.67 *(978-0-13-215267-9(3))*, Prentice Hall) Prentice Hall PTR.

Ebert, Ronald J. & Griffin, Ricky W. Business Essentials. (ENG.). (C). 7th ed. 2008. 312p. pap. 100.00 *(978-0-13-607076-4(0))* 8th ed. 2010. (Illus.). 336p. pap. 100.00 *(978-0-13-705349-0(5))* 9th rev. ed. 2012. (Illus.). 504p. pap. 100.00 ***(978-0-13-266402-8(X))*** Prentice Hall PTR. (Prentice Hall).

—Student Value Edition for Business Essentials. 9th ed. 2012. (ENG.). 504p. (C). ring bd. 65.00 ***(978-0-13-266413-4(5))***, Prentice Hall) Prentice Hall PTR.

—Study Guide for Business Essentials. 9th rev. ed. 2012. (ENG.). 150p. (C). pap. 46.67 ***(978-0-13-266410-3(0))***, Prentice Hall) Prentice Hall PTR.

Ebert, Ronald J., et al. Business Essentials. 5th ed. 2008. (ENG.). 592p. (C). pap. *(978-0-13-240575-1(X))* Pearson Education Canada.

Eckberg, John. The Success Effect: Uncommon Conversations with America's Business Trailblazers. 2008. (ENG.). 300p. pap. 14.95 *(978-0-9779545-8-2(7))* Sterling & Ross Pubs.

Ehrlich, Scott B. & Michael, Douglas C. Business Planning. 2009. *(978-1-4224-1196-4(6))* LexisNexis Matthew Bender.

Eicke, Rolf. Tax Planning with Holding Companies - Repatriation of U.S. Profits from Europe: Concepts, Strategies, Structures. 2008. (Illus.). xxiv, 496p. 185.00 *(978-90-411-2794-5(1))* Wolters Kluwer Law & Business.

Eisenberg, Melvin A. Corporations & Other Business Organizations: Statutes, Rules, Materials & Forms. 2007th rev. ed. 2007. (Academic Statutes Ser.). 2224p. per. 38.00 *(978-1-59941-281-8(0))*, Foundation Pr.) West.

—Corporations & Other Business Organizations: Statutes, Rules, Materials & Forms, 2009 Edition. 2009th rev. ed. 2009. (Academic Statutes Ser Ser.). 2115p. pap. 41.00 *(978-1-59941-598-4(0))*, Foundation Pr.) West.

Eldred, Murray J. The Emperors of Coca Cola. 2008. 88p. pap. 21.13 *(978-1-4092-2815-8(0))* Lulu Enterprises Inc.

Else, Steve. Organization Theory. 2010. 192p. pap. *(978-3-8383-6073-7(7))* Lambert Academic Publishing.

Entrepreneur Press Staff. How to Start a Business in California. 2nd ed. 2007. (ENG., Illus.). 250p. pap. 29.95 *(978-1-59918-068-7(5))*, 1599180685) Entrepreneur Pr. dba Entrepreneur Media, Inc.

—How to Start a Business in Florida. 2nd ed. 2007. (ENG., Illus.). 250p. pap. 29.95 *(978-1-59918-075-5(8))*, 1599180758) Entrepreneur Pr. dba Entrepreneur Media, Inc.

—How to Start a Business in Georgia. 2nd ed. 2007. (ENG., Illus.). 250p. pap. 29.95 *(978-1-59918-090-8(1))*, 1599180901) Entrepreneur Pr. dba Entrepreneur Media, Inc.

—How to Start a Business in Massachusetts. 2nd ed. 2007. (ENG., Illus.). 250p. pap. 29.95 *(978-1-59918-076-2(6))*, 1599180766) Entrepreneur Pr. dba Entrepreneur Media, Inc.

—How to Start a Business in Michigan. 2nd ed. 2007. (ENG., Illus.). 304p. 29.95 *(978-1-59918-134-9(7))*, 1599181347) Entrepreneur Pr. dba Entrepreneur Media, Inc.

—How to Start a Business in Minnesota. 2nd ed. 2007. (ENG., Illus.). 302p. 29.95 *(978-1-59918-156-1(8))*, 1599181568) Entrepreneur Pr. dba Entrepreneur Media, Inc.

—How to Start a Business in Missouri. 2nd ed. 2007. (ENG., Illus.). 250p. pap. 29.95 *(978-1-59918-117-2(7))*, 1599181177) Entrepreneur Pr. dba Entrepreneur Media, Inc.

—How to Start a Business in New York. 2nd ed. 2007. (ENG., Illus.). 250p. pap. 29.95 *(978-1-59918-066-3(9))*, 1599180669) Entrepreneur Pr. dba Entrepreneur Media, Inc.

—How to Start a Business in North Carolina. 2nd ed. 2007. (ENG.). 250p. pap. 29.95 *(978-1-59918-092-2(8))*, 1599180928) Entrepreneur Pr. dba Entrepreneur Media, Inc.

—How to Start a Business in Tennessee. 2nd ed. 2007. (ENG., Illus.). 304p. 29.95 *(978-1-59918-135-6(5))*, 1599181355) Entrepreneur Pr. dba Entrepreneur Media, Inc.

—How to Start a Business in Texas. 2nd ed. 2007. (ENG., Illus.). 250p. pap. 29.95 *(978-1-59918-069-4(3))*, 1599180693) Entrepreneur Pr. dba Entrepreneur Media, Inc.

—How to Start a Business in Virginia. 2nd ed. 2007. (ENG., Illus.). 250p. pap. 29.95 (978-1-59918-067-0(7), 1599180677) Entrepreneur Pr. dba Entrepreneur Media, Inc.

Entrepreneur Press Staff, creator. How to Start a Business in Arizona. 2nd ed. 2007. (ENG., Illus.). 250p. pap. 29.95 (978-1-59918-093-9(6), 1599180936) Entrepreneur Pr. dba Entrepreneur Media, Inc.

—How to Start a Business in Indiana. 2nd ed. 2007. (ENG., Illus.). 250p. pap. 29.95 (978-1-59918-104-2(5), 1599181045) Entrepreneur Pr. dba Entrepreneur Media, Inc.

—How to Start a Business in New Jersey. 2nd ed. 2007. (ENG., Illus.). 250p. pap. 29.95 (978-1-59918-077-9(4), 1599180774) Entrepreneur Pr. dba Entrepreneur Media, Inc.

—How to Start a Business in Pennsylvania. 2nd ed. 2007. (ENG.). 250p. pap. 29.95 (978-1-59918-091-5(X), 159918091X) Entrepreneur Pr. dba Entrepreneur Media, Inc.

—How to Start a Business in South Carolina. 2nd ed. 2007. (ENG., Illus.). 250p. pap. 29.95 (978-1-59918-114-1(2), 1599181142) Entrepreneur Pr. dba Entrepreneur Media, Inc.

—How to Start a Business in Washington. 2nd ed. 2007. (ENG., Illus.). 250p. pap. 29.95 (978-1-59918-074-8(X), 159918074X) Entrepreneur Pr. dba Entrepreneur Media, Inc.

Entrepreneur Press Staff & Mintzer, Rich. Start Your Own Food Truck Business: Carts, Trailers, Kiosks, Standard & Gourmet Trucks, Mobile Catering & Bustaurants. 2011. (ENG., Illus.). 225p. pap. 19.95 (978-1-59918-414-2(1), 1599184141) Entrepreneur Pr. dba Entrepreneur Media, Inc.

Entrepreneur Press Staff & Thomas, Karen. Ultimate Book of Business Forms. 2010. (ENG.). 304p. pap. 29.95 (978-1-59918-379-4(X), 159918379X) Entrepreneur Pr. dba Entrepreneur Media, Inc.

Epstein, David G. & Freer, Richard D. Epstein, Freer, Roberts, & Shepherd's Business Structures, 3d. 3rd rev. ed. 2010. (American Casebook Ser.). (Illus.). 671p. 164.00 (978-0-314-20059-4(2), West Legalworks) West.

Epstein, David G., et al. Business Structures. 2nd rev. ed. 2006. (Illus.). 825p. 145.00 (978-0-314-16803-0(6), West Legalworks) West.

Erpenbach, Mary & Ginsberg-Schutz, Maggie. Wisconsin: A Tradition of Innovation. 2008. 59.50 (978-1-882933-08-2(7)) Cherbo Publishing Group, Inc.

Examining Proposals to Create Jobs & Stimulate Indian Country Economies: Hearing Before the Committee on Indian Affairs, United States Senate, One Hundred Eleventh Congress, First Session, January 15, 2009. 2009. (Illus.). v, 309p. (978-0-16-083587-2(9), 552-070-39305-6) United States Government Printing Office.

Excessive Speculation in the Natural Gas Market: Hearing Before the Permanent Subcommittee on Investigations of the Committee on Homeland Security & Governmental Affairs, United States Senate, One Hundred Tenth Congress, First Session, June 25 & July 9, 2007. 2008. (Illus.). v, 1005p. (978-0-16-080274-4(1), 552-070-37007-1) United States Government Printing Office.

F. W. Woolworth Company. Celebrating Sixty Years of an American Institution. 2011. 48p. pap. 35.95 (**978-1-258-01414-8(9)**) Literary Licensing, LLC.

Fairlie, Robert W. & Robb, Alicia M. Race & Entrepreneurial Success: Black-, Asian-, & White-Owned Businesses in the United States. 2010. (ENG., Illus.). 256p. (gr. 17). pap. 18.00 (978-0-262-51494-1(X)) MIT Pr.

F&S Index United States Subscription. 2007th ed. 2007. (ENG.). 2308.00 (978-1-4144-0071-6(3)) Cengage Gale.

Farmer, Randolph W. From Blackland Prairie to Blacktop: A History of Collin County. 2011. (Illus.). 96p. (**978-1-935377-44-3(2)**) Historical Publishing Network.

FaxUSA 2007: A Directory of Facsimile Numbers for Businesses & Organizations Nationwide. 14th ed. 2006. pap. 194.00 (978-0-7808-0929-1(7)) Omnigraphics, Inc.

Feldman. Representing Foreign Acquirers of US Business. 2010. ring bd. (978-0-7355-9412-8(0), Aspen Pubs.) Wolters Kluwer Law & Business.

Field, Arthur Norman & Smith, Jeffrey M. Legal Opinions in Business Transactions. 2nd rev. ed. 2006. 630p. 280.00 (978-1-4024-0770-3(X)) Practising Law Institute.

Fitzpatrick, Shari. Berried in Chocolate: How I Built a Multimillion-Dollar Business by Doing What I Love to Do & How You Can Too, 1 vol. 2010. (ENG., Illus.). 224p. 23.00 (978-1-58980-881-2(9)) Pelican Publishing Co., Inc.

Fixman, Ben & Roth, Donald. The Ben Fixman Story: From the Ghetto to the Gold. 2009. (978-1-61623-248-1(X)) Independent Pub.

Flanigan, James. Smile Southern California, You're the Center of the Universe: The Economy & People of a Global Region. 2009. (ENG., Illus.). 216p. 27.95 (978-0-8047-5625-9(2), Stanford General Bks.) Stanford Univ. Pr.

Flanigan, Robin L. Rochester: High Performance for 175 Years. 2008. 59.50 (978-1-882933-11-2(7)) Cherbo Publishing Group, Inc.

Florida Bar, Continuing Legal Education Staff, contrib. by. Business Litigation in Florida. 5th ed. 2007. 170.00 (978-0-8205-8670-0(6)) Florida Bar Continuing Legal Education Pubns., The.

Florida Business Entities. 2007. (C). (978-1-934563-12-0(9)) Flood Publishing.

Folsom, Davis. Encyclopedia of American Business, 2 vols., Set. 2nd rev. ed. 2011. (Illus.). 880p. (C). (gr. 9). 150.00 (978-0-8160-8112-7(3)) Facts On File, Inc.

Fournier, Ron, et al. Applebee's America: How Successful Political, Business, & Religious Leaders Connect with the New American Community. 2007. (ENG., Illus.). 272p. pap. 17.99 (978-0-7432-8719-7(3)) Simon & Schuster.

Frye, Dennis E. Historic Washington County: The Story of Hagerstown & Washington County. 2010. (Illus.). 124p. (**978-1-935377-27-6(2)**) Historical Publishing Network.

Full Committee Hearing on SBA's Progress in Implementing the Women's Procurement Program. 2008. v, 127p. (978-0-16-080871-5(5), 552-070-37422-1) United States Government Printing Office.

Full Committee Hearing on Small Business Participation in the Federal Procurement Marketplace: Hearing Before the Committee on Small Business, United States House of Representatives, One Hundred Eleventh Congress, Second Session, Hearing Held March 24, 2010. 2010. (Illus.). v, 361p. (978-0-16-086241-0(8), 552-070-41332-4) United States Government Printing Office.

Full Committee Hearing on the Small Business Administration's Contracting Programs. 2007. v, 94p. (978-0-16-080132-7(X), 552-070-36872-8) United States Government Printing Office.

Full Committee Markup of H.R. 2352, the Job Creation Through Entrepreneurship ACT of 2009: Hearing Before the Committee on Small Business, United States House of Representatives, One Hundred Eleventh Congress, First Session, Hearing Held May 13, 2009. 2009. v, 70p. (978-0-16-083988-7(2), 552-070-39660-8) United States Government Printing Office.

Furth, Rasmus. Ambush Marketing: Eine rechtsvergleichende Untersuchung im Lichte des deutschen und US-amerikanischen Rechts. 2009. (GER.). xxxv, 562p. (978-3-452-27190-7(0)) Heymanns, Carl Verlag KG.

Gale Editors, ed. Global Market Share Planner, 2 vols. 6th ed. 2010. 916p. (C). pap. (978-1-84264-544-4(7)) Euromonitor International PLC.

Garon, Jon M. Own It: The Law & Business Guide to Launching a New Business through Innovation, Exclusivity & Relevance. 2007. (ENG.). 408p. per. 38.00 (978-1-59460-391-4(X)) Carolina Academic Pr.

Gasparino, Charles. Bought & Paid For: The Unholy Alliance Between Barack Obama & Wall Street. 2010. (ENG.). 304p. (gr. 12). 26.95 (978-1-59523-071-3(8), Sentinel) Penguin Group (USA) Inc.

Giancola, Joseph A. Howe to Book: From the Howe Scale Company to the Howe Center, to a Thriving Business Complex, to a Practical Guide Book. Wickman, Don, ed. (ENG., 2008. Illus.). 199p. pap. 34.95 (978-0-9818668-0-2(8)) 2007. 280p. pap. 24.95 (978-0-9772692-5-9(6)) Historical Pages Co.

Gilbert, Richard L. Marching up Madison Avenue: How I Beat the Entrepreneurial Odds Armed with a Pencil & My Imagination. 2008. (ENG.). 200p. pap. 14.95 (978-1-933016-51-1(5)) Behler Pubns., LLC.

Gitman, Lawrence J. The Best of the Future of Business. 2006. pap. 15.95 (978-1-4288-0524-8(9)) Cram101 Inc.

Gitman, Lawrence J. & McDaniel, Carl. The Future of Business. 2006. pap. 18.95 (978-1-4288-0581-1(8)) Cram101 Inc.

—Future of Business. 6th ed. 2007. (Available Titles CengageNOW Ser.). (ENG.). 792p. (C). 213.95 (978-0-324-53744-4(1)) Cengage South-Western.

Glazer, Donald W. Glazer & Fitzgibbon on Legal Opinions: Drafting, Interpreting, & Supporting Closing Opinions in Business. 2008. 300.00 (978-0-7355-6065-9(X), Aspen Pubs.) Wolters Kluwer Law & Business.

Goetz, Robert. Holt Cat, 1933-2008: Seventy-Five Years of Making the Earth Move. 2008. (978-1-893271-47-0(1)) Maverick Publishing Co.

Goldman Sachs Staff. Wealth Creation by Design: The Next Wave in Wealth Management for Financial Advisors. 2009. (Reinvented Wealth Manager Ser.). (ENG.). 320p. 49.95 (978-0-470-28948-8(1), Wiley) Wiley, John & Sons, Inc.

Gonzales, Anne. Stockton: Renewed, Revitalized, Redefined. 2008. 59.50 (978-1-882933-09-9(5)) Cherbo Publishing Group, Inc.

Gordon, Edward E. Winning the Global Talent Showdown: How Businesses & Communities Can Partner to Rebuild the Jobs Pipeline. 2009. (Bk Business Ser.). (ENG., Illus.). 280p. 27.95 (978-1-57675-616-4(5)) Berrett-Koehler Pubs., Inc.

Graffy, Neal. Historic Santa Barbara: An Illustrated History. 2010. (Illus.). 208p. (**978-1-935377-14-6(0)**) Historical Publishing Network.

Grimaldi, Michael. And You Thought Zippo Only Made Lighters: A Collector's Guide to the Other Products Made by Zippo Manufacturing Company, 2 vols., Vol. 1. 2006. (Illus.). 208p. 39.95 (978-0-9777489-0-7(1)) Wolverine Pr.

Grippo, Robert M. Macy's: The Store. the Star. the Story. 2008. (ENG., Illus.). 248p. pap. 27.95 (978-0-7570-0309-7(5)) Square One Pubs.

Gruner, Richard S., et al. Transactional Intellectual Property: From Startups to Public Companies. 2nd ed. 2012. (**978-0-7698-4684-2(X)**) LexisNexis Matthew Bender.

Guy-Halat, Andrea. Historic Fort Bend County: An Illustrated History. 2010. (Illus.). 134p. (**978-1-935377-24-5(8)**) Historical Publishing Network.

Halsey. Practical Business Law. 2011. pap. 80.95 (978-0-7355-6810-5(3), Aspen Pubs.) Wolters Kluwer Law & Business.

Haltiwanger, John & Mackie, Christopher, eds. Understanding Business Dynamics: An Integrated Data System for America's Future. 2007. (ENG.). 200p. per. 36.00 (978-0-309-10492-0(0)) National Academies Pr.

Haman, Edward A. How to Start a Business in Michigan. 5th ed. 2008. (Legal Survival Guides). (ENG., Illus.). 256p. per. 29.95 (978-1-57248-682-9(1), Sphinx Publishing) Sourcebooks, Inc.

Hamilton, Robert W. Attorney's Guide to Business & Finance Fundamentals. 2nd ed. 2006. (Illus.). 290.00 (978-0-7355-6058-1(7), Aspen Pubs.) Wolters Kluwer Law & Business.

Harmon, Jon F. Feeding Frenzy. 2009. 298p. 31.15 (978-1-60860-731-0(3), Eloquent Bks.) AEG Literary Publishing Services, Inc.

Harpster, Jack. King of the Slots: William "Si" Redd. 2010. E-Book (978-0-313-38209-3(3), Praeger Pubs.) Greenwood Publishing Group, Inc.

Harpster, John S. & Harpster, Jack. King of the Slots: William Si Redd, 1 vol. 2010. 273p. 44.95 (978-0-313-38208-6(5), A2632C, Praeger Pubs.) Greenwood Publishing Group, Inc.

Harris. Cases & Material Corporation & Other Business Entities Pract Appr. 2011. (978-0-7355-9636-8(0), Aspen Pubs.) Wolters Kluwer Law & Business.

Harris, Lee. Cases & Materials on Corporations & Other Business Entities. 2011. (Illus.). xxv, 693p. (**978-0-7355-9637-5(9)**) Kluwer Law International.

Harris, Lee. Mastering Corporations & Other Business Entities. 2008. 290p. pap. 30.00 (978-1-59460-444-7(4)) Carolina Academic Pr.

Harrison, E. Bruce. Corporate Greening 2. 0: Create & Communicate Your Company's Climate Change & Sustainability Strategies. 2008. (ENG.). 230p. 24.95 (978-1-933002-70-5(0)) PublishingWorks.

Harvey, Gordon E. Historic Ouachita Parish: An Illustrated History. 2007. (Illus.). 112p. (978-1-893619-70-8(2)) Historical Publishing Network.

Haynes, B. K. Dirt Peddler: How I Turned $50 into $10 Million in Country Property-Part Time. 2008. Orig. Title: How I Turned $50 into $5 Million in Country Property-Part Time & How You Can Do the Same. 540p. pap. 19.95 (978-0-932586-07-0(4)) Greatland Publishing Co.

Headquarters USA 2007: A Directory of Contact Information for Headquarters & Other Central Offices of Major Businesses & Organizations in the United States & Canada, 2. 29th ed. 2006. lib. bdg. 216.00 (978-0-7808-0927-7(0)) Omnigraphics, Inc.

Headquarters USA 2010. 32nd rev. ed. 2009. 216.00 (978-0-7808-1095-2(3)) Omnigraphics, Inc.

Herrington, Rob. Verdict for the Defense: Fighting Jackpot Justice with Firewall Defense Strategies. 2011. (ENG.). 256p. pap. 22.95 (**978-0-9819888-6-3(5)**) Sutton Hart Pr. LLC.

Hicks, Tyler G. Insider's Quick Money Success Sources. 17th ed. 2007. pap. 19.50 (978-1-56150-856-3(X)) International Wealth Success, Inc.

—Million Dollar Guide to Business & Real Estate Loan Sources. 17th ed. 2007. pap. 25.00 (978-1-56150-849-5(7)) International Wealth Success, Inc.

Hoefs, Dennis. Chain of Lakes Country: An Illustrated History of Martin County. 2007. (978-1-57864-452-0(6)) Donning Co. Pubs.

HOK. Hok: A Global Design Portfolio. 2009. (ENG., Illus.). 416p. 85.00 (978-1-86470-314-6(8)) Images Publishing Group AUS. Dist: National Bk. Network.

Holechek, James. Henry Perky: The Shredded Wheat King. 2007. 468p. per. 28.95 (978-0-595-44170-9(X)) iUniverse, Inc.

Holland, Joshua. The Fifteen Biggest Lies about the Economy: And Everything Else the Right Doesn't Want You to Know about Taxes, Jobs, & Corporate America. 2010. (ENG., Illus.). 304p. pap. 16.95 (978-0-470-64392-1(7), Wiley) Wiley, John & Sons, Inc.

Holm, Linda Cooper, et al. Texas City Centennial, 1911-2011: Celebrating Its Past, Present, & Future. 2012. (**978-1-57864-729-3(0)**) Donning Co. Pubs.

Holton, Lisa. For Members Only: A History & Guide to Chicago's Oldest Private Clubs. 2008. (Illus.). 317p. pap. 18.95 (978-1-893121-28-7(3)) Everything Goes Media, LLC.

Hoover's, creator. Hoover's Handbook of Emerging Companies. (Hoover's Handbook of Emerging Companies Ser.). (Illus.). 14th ed. 2007. 532p. 150.00 (978-1-57311-117-1(1)) 15th ed. 2008. (ENG., 513p. 155.00 (978-1-57311-123-2(6), Hoover's Business Pr.) Hoover's, Inc.

Hoover's Business Press, creator. Hoover's Handbook of Private Companies. 2008. (Hoover's Handbook of Private Companies Ser.). (Illus.). 589p. 264.00 (978-1-57311-128-7(7)) Hoover's, Inc.

Hoovers Inc, creator. Hoover's Handbook of American Business. 17th ed. 2006. (Hoover's Handbook of American Business Ser.). (Illus.). 979p. 240.00 (978-1-57311-114-0(7)) Hoover's, Inc.

Hoover's Incorporated, creator. Hoover's Handbook of Private Companies. 12th ed. 2007. (Hoover's Handbook of Private Companies Ser.). (Illus.). 588p. 175.00 (978-1-57311-115-7(5)) Hoover's, Inc.

Hoover's MasterList of U. S. Companies 2007. 13th ed. 2006. 290.00 (978-1-57311-113-3(9), Hoover's Business Pr.) Hoover's, Inc.

Houck, Douglas. Historic Chautauqua County: A Bicentennial History. 2010. (Illus.). 72p. (978-1-935377-20-7(5)) Historical Publishing Network.

House-Soremekun, Bessie. Confronting the Odds: African American Entrepreneurship in Cleveland, Ohio. 2009. (Illus.). 250p. pap. (978-1-60635-006-5(4)) Kent State Univ. Pr.

Howe, Ben Ryder. My Korean Deli: Risking It All for a Convenience Store. 2012. (ENG.). 320p. pap. 15.00 (**978-1-250-00247-1(8)**) Picador.

Hsieh, Lawrence. Business Contracts Handbook. 2010. (ENG.). pap. 29.95 (978-1-55180-856-7(0)) Self-Counsel Pr., Inc. CAN. Dist: Midpoint Trade Bks., Inc.

Huggins, Maryalice. Aesop's Mirror. 2010. (ENG., Illus.). 288p. pap. 15.00 (978-0-312-65532-7(0)) Picador.

Hutzel, Tim & Piechota, Paul. Keeping Your Business in the US: Profit Globally While Operating Locally. 2011. (ENG., Illus.). 135p. 39.95 (978-1-4398-0778-1(7), CRC Press) Taylor & Francis Group GBR. Dist: Taylor & Francis Group.

Hynes, J. Dennis & Loewenstein, Mark J. Agency, Partnership, & the LLC: The Law of Unincorporated Business Enterprises. 7th ed. 2008. xxiv, 504p. pap. (978-1-4224-1153-7(2)) LexisNexis Matthew Bender.

—Agency, Partnership, & the LLC: The Law of Unincorporated Business Enterprises: Cases, Materials, Problems. 7th ed. 2007. xxxvii, 986p. (978-3-00-300007-9(1)) 7th ed. 2007. xxxvii, 986p. 118.00 (978-1-4224-0787-5(X)) 8th ed. 2012. xxiii, 618p. (**978-1-4224-9609-1(0)**) 8th ed. 2011. (**978-1-4224-8531-6(5)**) LexisNexis Matthew Bender.

Ibp, Usa. United States Industrial & Business Di. 2006. (Illus.). pap. 99.95 (978-0-7397-9922-2(3)) International Business Pubns., USA.

Ijseom. International Journal of Social Entrepeneurship: (IJSE) Vol. 1, No. 1 (November 2008) 2008. 148p. pap. 25.00 (978-1-4389-3133-3(6)) AuthorHouse.

Images Publishing Staff, PUBLISHING. Ross Barney Architects: Process + Projects. 2007. (ENG., Illus.). 124p. 65.00 (978-1-86470-229-3(X)) Images Publishing Group AUS. Dist: National Bk. Network.

Insuring Your Business: A Small Businessowners' Guide to Insurance. 2008. 128p. per. 28.00 (978-0-932387-54-7(3)) Insurance Information Institute.

Izard, Mary Beth. BoomerPreneurs: How Baby Boomers Can Start Their Own Business, Make Money & Enjoy Life. 2010. 286p. pap. 25.95 (978-0-9728748-3-0(6)) Acheve Consulting, Inc.

Jackson, Eric M. The PayPal Wars: Battles with eBay, the Media, the Mafia, & the Rest of the Planet Earth. 2nd ed. 2010. 270p. per. 15.95 (978-0-9778984-3-5(1)) WND Bks, Inc.

Jennings, Walter Wilson. A Dozen Captains of American Industry. 2011. 238p. 46.95 (**978-1-258-06023-7(X)**) Literary Licensing, LLC.

John, Stephen. Strategic Learning & Leading Change: How Global Organizations are Reinventing HR. 2008. (ENG., Illus.). 216p. pap. 34.95 (978-0-7506-8288-6(4)) Routledge.

Johnson, Thomas D., ed. National Directory of Minority Owned Business Firms. 14th ed. 2008. (ENG.). 1314p. pap. 295.00 incl. cd-rom (978-0-933527-85-0(3)) Business Research Services, Inc.

—National Directory of Woman-Owned Business Firms. 14th rev. ed. 2008. 1288p. pap. 295.00 (978-0-933527-86-7(1)) Business Research Services, Inc.

Johnson, Todd. Historic Wake County: The Story of Raleigh & Wake County. 2009. (Illus.). 128p. (978-1-935377-10-8(8)) Historical Publishing Network.

Judd, Richard J. & Justis, Robert T. Franchising: An Entrepreneur's Guide. 4th ed. 2007. (ENG., Illus.). 656p. (C). pap. 155.95 (978-0-7593-6705-0(1)) CENGAGE Learning Custom Publishing.

Kaelble, Steve Stackhouse. Indiana: Advancing & Driving the Economy. 2009. 59.95 (978-1-882933-12-9(5)) Cherbo Publishing Group, Inc.

Kakabadse, Andrew & Kakabadse, Nada, eds. Global Boards: One Desire, Many Realities. 2009. (ENG., Illus.). 288p. 105.00 (978-0-230-21212-1(3)) Palgrave Macmillan.

Kaplan CPA Review. CPA Exam Study Manual: Business Environment & Concepts 2009/2010. 2009. (ENG.). 752p. pap. 49.95 (978-1-4277-8861-0(8)) Kaplan Publishing.

Kaufman, William. The Grand American Home. 2008. (ENG., Illus.). 128p. 49.50 (978-1-86470-181-4(1)) Images Publishing Group AUS. Dist: National Bk. Network.

Kealing, Bob. Tupperware, Unsealed: Brownie Wise, Earl Tupper, & the Home Party Pioneers. 2008. (ENG., Illus.). 264p. 28.00 (978-0-8130-3227-6(X)) Univ. Pr. of Florida.

Kemp, Kathryn W. Historic Clayton County: The Sesquicentennial History. 2009. (Illus.). 104p. (978-1-935377-05-4(1)) Historical Publishing Network.

Kemp, Roger L., ed. Homeland Security for the Private Sector: A Handbook. 2007. (ENG.). 355p. per. 39.95 (978-0-7864-2979-0(8)) McFarland & Co., Inc. Pubs.

King, Joseph, ed. Strategic Leadership: Leading Change in a New Age. 2011. 60p. 29.95 (**978-1-4269-7535-6(X)**); pap. 19.95 (**978-1-4269-7534-9(1)**) Trafford Publishing.

Kirkland, Scotty E., et al. Dothan & Houston County Yesterday, Today & Tomorrow. 2011. (Illus.). 156p. (**978-0-9796601-3-9(0)**) Beers & Assocs., LLC.

Klein, et al. Agency, Partnerships, & Limited Liability Entities: Cases & Materials on Unincorporated Business Associations. 3rd rev. ed. 2011. (University Casebook Ser.). 560p. 170.00 (978-1-59941-497-3(X), Foundation Pr.) West.

Klein, William A. & Ramseyer, J. Mark. Business Associations-Agency, Partnerships, LLCs & Corporations, 2011 Statutes & Rules. 2011. 375p. pap. 34.00 (**978-1-59941-965-7(3)**, Foundation Pr.) West.

—Business Associations, Cases & Materials on Agency, Partnership & Corporations, 6th Edition, 2008 Supplement. 6th rev. ed. 2008. (University Casebook Ser.). 86p. pap. 17.00 (978-1-59941-461-4(9), Foundation Pr.) West.

—Business Associations, Cases & Materials on Agency, Partnerships, & Corporations, 7th, 2010 Supplement. 7th rev. ed. 2010. (University Casebook Ser.). 66p. 21.00 (978-1-59941-907-7(6), Foundation Pr.) West.

—Klein, Ramseyer & Bainbridge's Business Associations-Agency, Partnerships, LLC's & Corporations- 2008 Statutes & Rules. 2008. (Academic Statutes Ser.). 332p. pap. 30.00 (978-1-59941-521-5(6), Foundation Pr.) West.

—Klein, Ramseyer & Bainbridge's Business Associations-Agency, Partnerships, LLC's & Corporations, Statutes & Rules 2010. 7th rev. ed. 2010. 328p. pap. 34.00 (978-1-59941-835-3(5), Foundation Pr.) West.

Klein, William A., et al. Agency, Partnerships, & Limited Liability Entities: Unincorporated Business Associations: Cases & Materials. 3rd ed. 2012. xx, 533p. (**978-1-60930-110-1(2)**) West.

—Business Associations: Agency, Partnerships, & Corporations: Cases & Materials. 7th ed. 2009. xxix, 893p. (978-1-59941-702-8(2), Foundation Pr.) West.

—Business Organization & Finance: Legal & Economic Principles. 10th rev. ed. 2007. (Concepts & Insights Ser.). (Illus.). 445p. per. 42.00 (978-1-59941-232-0(2), Foundation Pr.) West.

Koslowski, Peter, ed. Contemporary Economic Ethics & Business Ethics. 2010. (Studies in Economic Ethics & Philosophy Ser.). (Illus.). x, 265p. pap. 189.00 *(978-3-642-08591-8(1)*, 3642085911) Springer.
Kozlowski, Phyllis J. The Chicago River Architecture Tour. 2008. 113p. pap. 12.00 *(978-1-893121-33-1(X))* Everything Goes Media, LLC.
Kubala, Edna. Louisville's Butchertown. 2010. (Images of America Ser.). (ENG., Illus.). 128p. pap. 21.99 *(978-0-7385-6665-8(9))* Arcadia Publishing.
Kvintradze, Tamar. Minority Shareholder Protection in Georgia & Germany. 2010. 48p. pap. *(978-3-639-22619-5(4))* VDM Verlag Dr. Mueller e.K.
Lambert, Stephen & Holzman, Eli. Undercover Boss: Inside the TV Phenomenon That Is Changing Bosses & Employees Everywhere. 2010. (ENG., Illus.). 272p. 24.95 *(978-0-470-91600-1(1)*, Jossey-Bass) Wiley, John & Sons, Inc.
Land, Bob. America's Greatest Brands. 2011. (Americas Greatest Brands Ser.). (ENG.). 116p. 45.00 ***(978-0-9706860-8-4(0))*** America's Greatest Brands.
Land, Bob. America's Greatest Brands: An Insight into Many of America's Strongest & Most Valuable Brands. (America's Greatest Brands Ser.). (ENG., Illus.). 2007. 118p. 60.00 *(978-0-9706860-5-3(6))* 2006. 126p. 75.00 *(978-0-9706860-4-6(8))* America's Greatest Brands.
Land, Bob, ed. America's Greatest Brands: An Insight into Many of America's Strongest & Most Valuable Brands. 2011. (America's Greatest Brands Ser.). (ENG., Illus.). 112p. 45.00 *(978-0-9706860-7-7(2))* America's Greatest Brands.
Laro, David & Pratt, Shannon P. Business Valuation & Federal Taxes: Procedure, Law, & Perspective. 2nd ed. 2011. (ENG., Illus.). 482p. 130.00 *(978-0-470-60162-4(0)*, Wiley) Wiley, John & Sons, Inc.
Larsen, Jack L. 1894-2007 Hawaiian Pineapple Entrepreneurs. 2009. *(978-1-61623-189-7(0))* Independent Pub.
Larson, Agnes Mathilda. The White Pine Industry in Minnesota: A History. 2007. (Fesler-Lampert Minnesota Heritage Ser.). (Illus.). 448p. per. 17.95 *(978-0-8166-5149-8(3))* Univ. of Minnesota Pr.
Larson, Jeanne. Aurora: A City Second to None. 2008. 59.95 *(978-1-882933-85-3(0))* Cherbo Publishing Group, Inc.
Law, Diane & Greenwood, Catriona. The Dictionary of Bull**** A Lexicon of Corporate & Office-Speak. 2009. (ENG.). 192p. 8.99 *(978-1-84529-767-1(9)*, 1845297679, Castle Bks., Inc.) Book Sales, Inc.
Lazell, Carleen & Payne, Melissa. Historic Albuquerque: An Illustrated History. 2007. (Illus.). 112p. *(978-1-893619-75-3(3))* Historical Publishing Network.
Legalines Editorial Staff. Legalines on Business Associations, 6th - Keyed to Klein. 6th rev. ed. 2007. (Legalines Ser.). 251p. pap. 35.00 *(978-0-314-18117-6(2)*, Gilbert Law Publishing) West.
Leinweber, David J. Nerds on Wall Street: Math, Machines & Wired Markets. 2009. (ENG., Illus.). 353p. 39.95 *(978-0-471-36946-2(2)*, Wiley) Wiley, John & Sons, Inc.
Lennhoff, David C. A Business Enterprise Value Anthology. 2nd ed. 2011. ***(978-1-935328-20-9(4))*** Appraisal Institute, The.
Lestz, Gerald S., intro. Lancaster at Work: Business in Lancaster County, Pennsylvania. 2006. (Illus.). 144p. per. 16.95 *(978-0-9740162-3-8(3))* Lancaster County Historical Society.
Levengood, Paul. Virginia: Catalyst of Commerce for Four Centuries. 2007. 59.95 *(978-1-882933-77-8(X))* Cherbo Publishing Group, Inc.
Levin, Rob. An American Mosaic: A Photographic Portrait of Fayetteville & Cumberland County. 2007. *(978-1-883987-33-6(4)*, Riverbend Bks., Ltd.
—Asheville: A Photographic Portrait. 2007. *(978-1-883987-32-9(6))* Riverbend Bks., Ltd.
—Celebrating an American Legacy: A Photographic Journey of Greater Richmond. 2007. (Illus.). 248p. *(978-1-883987-28-2(8))* Riverbend Bks., Ltd.
—Celebrating Springfield: A Photographic Portrait. 2007. *(978-1-883987-30-5(X))* Riverbend Bks., Ltd.
—Kansas City: Unlimited Possibilities. 2007. *(978-1-883987-31-2(8))* Riverbend Bks., Ltd.
—Knoxville: Center of Innovation. 2008. (Illus.). 296p. *(978-1-883987-34-3(2))* Riverbend Bks., Ltd.
—Loudoun, Loudoun County Virginia: A Photographic Portrait. 2007. *(978-1-883987-29-9(6))* Riverbend Bks., Ltd.
—Northwest Treasure: A Photographic Portrait of Tacoma-Pierce County. 2006. 168p. *(978-1-883987-27-5(X))* Riverbend Bks., Ltd.
—St. Petersburg & Tampa Bay: A New View. 2008. *(978-1-883987-37-4(7))* Riverbend Bks., Ltd.
Lewis, Jordan D. Connected Corporation: How Leading Companies Manage Customer-Supplier Alliances. 2007. (ENG.). 368p. pap. 23.95 *(978-1-4165-7336-4(4)*, Free Pr.) Free Pr.
Lionel Sawyer & Collins, text. Doing Business in Nevada: A Practical Guide 2nd Edition. 2nd ed. 2006. 192p. pap. 25.00 *(978-0-9745273-1-4(9))* Lionel Sawyer & Collins.
Lisicky, Michael J. Wanamaker's: Meet Me at the Eagle. 2010. (Landmarks Ser.). (ENG., Illus.). 160p. pap. 19.99 *(978-1-59629-008-2(0))* History Pr., The.
Livesay, Harold C. American Made: Shapers of the American Economy. 3rd rev. ed. 2011. (ENG.). 272p. (C). pap. 53.20 ***(978-0-205-20229-4(2)***, Prentice Hall) Prentice Hall PTR.
Livingston, Jessica. Founders at Work: Stories of Startups' Early Days. 2008. (ENG., Illus.). 488p. pap. 17.99 *(978-1-4302-1078-8(8))* Apress L. P.
Ljungquist, Kent, et al. The History of Woodbury & Company. 2007. (Illus.). 71.95 *(978-0-8204-8108-1(4))* Lang, Peter Publishing, Inc.
Llc, Lake Highland Entrepreneurs. Entrepreneurship: The Bottom Line. 2009. 144p. pap. 15.95 *(978-1-4401-2898-1(7))* iUniverse, Inc.
López-Acevedo, Gladys & Tan, Hong W., eds. Impact Evaluation of Small & Medium Enterprise Programs in Latin America & the Caribbean. 2011. (ENG.). 144p. pap. 20.00 *(978-0-8213-8775-7(8)*, 9780821387757) World Bank Pubns.
Lyda, Hap C. S. Bo — Cherokee: Beyond the Trail. 2012. (ENG., Illus.). 171p. pap. ***(978-0-9816784-2-9(4))*** 21st Century Pr.
Lynch, Margaret C., et al, eds. Hoover's Guide to the Top Texas Companies. 2008. 210p. pap. 83.50 *(978-1-57311-131-7(7))* Hoover's, Inc.
Ma, Wei. Does China Need a Game Rating System? 2009. 68p. pap. *(978-3-639-20650-0(9))* VDM Verlag Dr. Mueller e.K.
Magnuson, Roger. Barracuda Bait: New & growing litigious risks to American Business. 2007. 16.95 *(978-0-9798498-0-0(2))* Dorsey & Whitney LLP.
Major National Retailers: Americans & Asia-Pacific. rev. ed. 2008. 845.00 *(978-1-84264-444-7(0))* Euromonitor International PLC GBR. Dist: Cengage Gale.
Malm, Thomas. Absolutely Vulnerable, the Crisis of Strategic Business Planning in America. 2009. 196p. pap. 15.99 *(978-0-578-01686-3(9))* Malm, T.A. & Assocs.
Mancuso, Anthony. Form Your Own Limited Liability Company, 2 vols. 7th rev. ed. 2011. (ENG.). 267p. pap. 44.99 *(978-1-4133-1624-7(7))* NOLO.
Manresa, Maritza. How to Open & Operate a Financially Successful Import Export Business: With Companion CD-ROM. 2010. (ENG.). 288p. pap. 39.95 *(978-1-60138-226-9(X))* Atlantic Publishing Co.
Marcelli, Enrico. Informal Work in Developed Nations. Marcelli, Enrico et al, eds. 2009. (Routledge Advances in Heterodox Economics Ser.). (ENG., Illus.). 240p. 135.00 *(978-0-415-77779-7(8))* Routledge.
Marquis Who's Who, creator. Who's Who in Corporate America. 2011. (Who's Who in Finance & Business Ser.). 1323p. 412.25 ***(978-0-8379-3575-1(X))*** Marquis Who's Who, LLC.
Mars-Proietti, Laura, ed. Directory of Mail Order Catalogs 2010. 24th rev. ed. 2009. 1500p. pap. 250.00 *(978-1-59237-444-1(1))* Grey Hse. Publishing.
—Food & Beverage Market Place 2010: Suppliers. 9th rev. ed. 2009. 2000p. pap. 250.00 *(978-1-59237-425-0(5))* Grey Hse. Publishing.
Marshall, Walter P. Ezra Cornell His Contributions to Wester. 2006. pap. 15.95 *(978-1-4286-6060-1(7))* Kessinger Publishing, LLC.
Martinello, Marian L. The Search for a Chili Queen: On the Fringes of a Rebozo. 2009. (ENG.). 212p. pap. 17.95 *(978-0-87565-386-0(3))* Texas Christian Univ. Pr.
Maunula, Marko. Guten Tag, Y'all: Globalization & the South Carolina Piedmont, 1950-2000. (Politics & Culture in the Twentieth-Century South Ser.). (ENG.). 176p. 2010. pap. 22.95 *(978-0-8203-3643-5(2))* 2009. lib. bdg. 44.95 *(978-0-8203-2901-7(0))* Univ. of Georgia Pr.
Maynard. Business Planning. 2010. 152.00 *(978-0-7355-7727-5(7))* Wolters Kluwer Law & Business.
Maynard, Therese H. & Warren, Dana M. Business Planning: Financing the Start-Up Business & Venture Capital Financing. 2010. xxv, 867p. *(978-0-7355-7728-2(5))* Kluwer Law International.
McAdams, Tony. Law Business & Society. 7th ed. 2006. pap. 9.95 *(978-1-4288-1731-9(X))* Cram101 Inc.
McAdams, Tony. Law, Business & Society. 10th ed. 2011. (ENG., Illus.). 944p. (C). 216.00 ***(978-0-07-352500-6(6)***, 0073525006, McGraw-Hill/Irwin) McGraw-Hill Higher Education.
McDaniel, Paul R. & McMahon, Martin J. Federal Income Taxation of Business Organizations 2008. 4th rev. ed. 2008. (University Casebook Ser.). 80p. pap., suppl. ed. 17.00 *(978-1-59941-477-5(5)*, Foundation Pr.) West.
—Federal Income Taxation of Business Organizations, 4th, 2009 Supplement. 4th rev. ed. 2009. (University Casebook Ser.). 86p. pap. 19.00 *(978-1-59941-782-0(0)*, Foundation Pr.) West.
—Federal Income Taxation of Business Organizations, 4th, 2010 Supplement. 4th rev. ed. 2010. (University Casebook Ser.). 78p. pap. 17.00 *(978-1-59941-815-5(0)*, Foundation Pr.) West.
—Federal Income Taxation of Corporations, 3d, 2009 Supplement. 3rd rev. ed. 2009. (University Casebook Ser.). 59p. pap. 17.00 *(978-1-59941-781-3(2)*, Foundation Pr.) West.
McDermott, Michael. The 2009-2011 Recession Survival Guide: 414 Actions Businesses Can Take to Weather the Storm & Boost Profits. 2009. 144p. pap. 19.95 *(978-1-892538-51-2(2))* Oaklea Pr., The.
McDonald, Archie P. Water, Rails & Oil: Historic Mid & South Jefferson County. 2008. (Illus.). 100p. *(978-1-893619-60-9(5))* Historical Publishing Network.
McGibbon, Kevin G. American Developer: A Practical Guide to Extending Business Internationally in a World that Is Flat in Places. 2009. 152p. 25.95 *(978-1-4401-2744-1(1))*; pap. 15.95 *(978-1-4401-2742-7(5))* iUniverse, Inc.
McMahon, Mary, et al. South Florida Job Source: The Only Source You Need to Land the Job of Your Choice in South Florida. 2007. (Job Source Guides Ser.). 128p. (C). pap. 12.95 *(978-1-55921-378-3(7)*, Asphodel Pr.) Moyer Bell.
McPherson, Thomas A. & McCall, Walter. Cadillac Fleetwood Seventy-Five Series Limousines 1937-1987 Photo Archive. 2009. (Photo Archive Ser.). (ENG., Illus.). 128p. pap. 32.95 *(978-1-58388-248-1(0)*, 1583882480) Iconografix, Inc.
Medved, Michael. The 5 Big Lies about American Business: Combating Smears Against the Free-Market Economy. 2010. (ENG.). 272p. pap. 15.00 *(978-0-307-58747-3(9)*, Three Rivers Pr.) Crown Publishing Group.
Mercer. The Global Manager's Guide to Living & Working Abroad: Western Europe & the Americas, 1 vol. 2009. 350p. 49.95 *(978-0-313-35883-8(4)*, C35883, Praeger Pubs.) Greenwood Publishing Group, Inc.
Mezzullo, Louis A. An Estate Planner's Guide to Buy-Sell Agreements for the Closely Held Business. 2nd ed. 2008. (Estate Planner's Guide to Buy-Sell Agreements for the Closely Held Ser.). (ENG., Illus.). 135p. pap. 139.95 incl. lp *(978-1-59031-837-9(4))* American Bar Assn.
Miller, Nicole. Outsourcing Through Rentacoder. 2009. 418p. pap. 37.40 *(978-0-557-09544-5(1))* Lulu Enterprises Inc.
Miller, Robert J. Reservation "Capitalism" Economic Development in Indian Country, 1 vol. 2012. (Native America: Yesterday & Today Ser.). 208p. 48.00 ***(978-1-4408-0111-2(8)***, A3778C) Greenwood Publishing Group, Inc.
Min, Dai, et al. New China Business Strategies: Chinese & American Companies As Global Partners. 2009. (ENG., Illus.). 351p. 32.95 *(978-1-56171-820-7(3))* SPI Bks.
Min, Pyong Gap. Ethnic Solidarity for Economic Survival: Korean Greengrocers in New York City. 2008. (Illus.). 193p. 32.50 *(978-0-87154-577-0(2))* Russell Sage Foundation.
Mitchell, Stacy. Big-Box Swindle: The True Cost of Mega-Retailers & the Fight for America's Independent Businesses. 2006. 320p. 25.95 *(978-0-618-80221-0(5))* Beacon Pr.
Morrison & Bauman, Jeffrey D. Corporations & Other Business Associations: Statutes, Rules & Forms 2010. 2010th rev. ed. 2010. 1918p. pap. 43.00 *(978-0-314-26185-4(0)*, West Legalworks) West.
Moskowitz, Marina. Testimonial Advertising in the American Marketplace: Emulation, Identity, Community. Moskowitz, Marina & Schweitzer, Marlis, eds. 2009. (ENG., Illus.). 248p. 89.00 *(978-0-230-61560-1(0))* Palgrave Macmillan.
Murphy, Frederick. Walmart Exposed. 2008. 225p. pap. 22.00 *(978-0-557-01492-7(1))* Lulu Enterprises Inc.
Murrell, Audrey J., et al. Intelligent Mentoring: How IBM Creates Value through People, Knowledge, & Relationships. 2008. (ENG., Illus.). 256p. 29.99 *(978-0-13-713084-9(8))* Pearson Education.
Myers, Jay. Keep Swinging: An Entrepreneur's Story of Overcoming Adversity & Achieving Small Business Success. 2007. (ENG., Illus.). 157p. pap. 14.00 *(978-1-60037-257-5(0))* Morgan James Publishing.
Nagel, Walter. State Business Taxes. 2009. *(978-1-58852-161-3(3)*, Law Journal Pr.) Incisive Media.
National Register Publishing, creator. Direct Marketing Market Place: The Networking Source of the Direct Marketing Industry. 2008. (Direct Marketing Market Place Ser.). (Illus.). 1221p. pap. 456.25 *(978-0-87217-752-9(1))* National Register Publishing.
Neslund, Kristofer & Neslund, Nancy. Questions & Answers: Multiple-Choice & Short-Answer Questions & Answers. 2011. iii, 280p. pap. ***(978-1-4224-8034-2(8)***, Wiley-Blackwell) LexisNexis Matthew Bender.
Noon, Mark A. Yuengling: A History of America's Oldest Brewery. alt. ed. 2007. (ENG., Illus.). 231p. per. 29.95 *(978-0-7864-3758-0(8))* McFarland & Co., Inc. Pubs.
Noon, Ned. American Pipe Dream: A Guide to Surviving Get Rich Quick Opportunities. 2011. 64p. pap. 19.95 ***(978-1-4560-7353-4(2))*** PublishAmerica, Inc.
O'Kelley. Corporations & Other Business Associations: Cases & Materials 6e. 6th ed. 2010. 165.00 *(978-0-7355-8602-4(0))* Wolters Kluwer Law & Business.
O'Kelley, Charles R. & Thompson, Robert B. Corporations & Other Business Associations: Cases & Materials. 6th ed. 2010. xxx, 1212p. *(978-0-7355-8603-1(9)*, Aspen Pubs.) Wolters Kluwer Law & Business.
O'Kelley, E. Corporations & Business Associations Stat Rules Forms 2010 Supp. 2010. pap. 49.50 *(978-0-7355-9062-5(1)*, Aspen Pubs.) Wolters Kluwer Law & Business.
Olsen, William P. The Anti-Corruption Handbook: How to Protect Your Business in the Global Marketplace. 2010. (ENG., Illus.). 192p. 78.95 *(978-0-470-48450-0(0)*, Wiley) Wiley, John & Sons, Inc.
Omnigraphics, creator. Web Site Source Book: A Guide to Major U. S. Businesses, Organizations, Agencies, Institutions, & Other Information Resources on the World Wide Web. 2007. 12th ed. 2134p. per. 194.00 *(978-0-7808-0931-4(9))* 13th ed. 2127p. pap. 194.00 *(978-0-7808-1024-2(4))* Omnigraphics, Inc.
Owsley, Henry. Distressed Investment Banking: To the Abyss & Back. (Illus.). xii, 219p. 74.95 *(978-1-58798-267-5(6))* Beard Bks., Inc.
Pabrai, Mohnish. The Dhandho Investor: The Low-Risk Value Method to High Returns. 2007. (ENG., Illus.). 208p. 27.95 *(978-0-470-04389-9(X)*, Wiley) Wiley, John & Sons, Inc.
Panama: Business Financing Handbook. (Illus.). 70p. (Orig.). pap. 295.00 *(978-0-7605-1204-3(3))* Rector Pr., Ltd.
Pauwels, Cynthia L. Historic Warren County: An Illustrated History. 2009. (Illus.). 80p. *(978-1-935377-09-2(4))* Historical Publishing Network.
Pencak, William. Historic Pennsylvania. 2008. 49.95 *(978-1-893619-88-3(5))* Historical Publishing Network.
Perkins, Edwin & Perkins, Edwin J. Perkins on U. S. Financial History & Related Topics. 2008. (ENG.). 180p. pap. 33.99 *(978-0-7618-4420-4(1))* Univ. Pr. of America, Inc.
Pinel, Stephen L. Organbuilding along the Erie & Chenango Canals: Alvinza & George N. Andrews of Utica, New York. 2010. (Illus.). xxix, 301p. ***(978-0-913499-30-6(7))*** Organ Historical Society, Inc., The.
Pitrone, Jean Maddern. F. W. Woolworth & the American Five & Dime: A Social History. alt. ed. 2007. (ENG., Illus.). 229p. per. 39.95 *(978-0-7864-3024-6(9))* McFarland & Co., Inc. Pubs.
Plunkett, Jack W. The Almanac of American Employers 2008: Market Research, Statistics & Trends Pertaining to the Leading Corporate Employers in America. annuals Plunkett, Jack W., ed. 2007. 706p. pap. 279.99 incl. cd-rom *(978-1-59392-095-1(4))* Plunkett Research, Ltd.
—E-Book Plunkett's Almanac of Middle Market Companies 2008: Middle Market Research, Statistics & Leading Companies. annuals Plunkett, Jack W., ed. 2007. E-Book 299.99 incl. cd-rom *(978-1-59392-435-5(6))* Plunkett Research, Ltd.
—Plunkett's Almanac of Middle Market Companies 2008: Middle Market Research, Statistics & Leading Companies. annuals Plunkett, Jack W., ed. 2007. pap. 299.99 incl. cd-rom *(978-1-59392-092-0(X))* Plunkett Research, Ltd.
—Plunkett's Consulting Industry Almanac 2007: Consulting Industry Market Research, Statistics, Trends & Leading Companies. annuals Plunkett, Jack W., ed. 2007. 408p. pap. 279.99 incl. cd-rom *(978-1-59392-070-8(9))* Plunkett Research, Ltd.
—Plunkett's Consulting Industry Almanac 2007 (E-Book) Consulting Industry Market Research, Statistics, Trends & Leading Companies. annuals Plunkett, Jack W., ed. 2007. 418p. E-Book 279.99 incl. cd-rom *(978-1-59392-412-6(7))* Plunkett Research, Ltd.
Pratt, Shannon P. & Grabowski, Roger J. Cost of Capital. 4th ed. 2010. (ENG., Illus.). 255p. pap., suppl. ed., wbk. ed. 85.00 *(978-0-470-47606-2(0)*, Wiley) Wiley, John & Sons, Inc.
—Cost of Capital in Litigation: Applications & Examples. 4th ed. 2010. (ENG., Illus.). 301p. 100.00 *(978-0-470-88094-4(5)*, Wiley) Wiley, John & Sons, Inc.
Premium, Incentive, & Travel Buyers Guide 2008-09. 2008. pap. *(978-0-87228-497-5(2))* Douglas Publications, Limited Liability Co.
Presser, Stephen B. An Introduction to the Law of Business Organizations: Cases, Notes, & Questions. 2nd ed. 2008. xviii, 491p. *(978-0-314-18781-9(2))* West Publishing Co., College & Schl. Div.
—An Introduction to the Law of Business Organizations: Cases, Notes & Questions. 2nd rev. ed. 2008. 514p. 134.00 *(978-0-314-18780-2(4)*, West Legalworks) West.
Pride, et al. Business. 11th ed. 2011. (ENG.). 704p. (C). ring bd. 135.95 *(978-1-111-52620-7(6))* Cengage South-Western.
Pride Student Achievement Series: Foundations Ofbusiness Dvd First Edition: Foundations Ofbusiness Dvd First Edition. 2008. (YA). 14.76 *(978-0-547-03106-4(8)*, 1033275) CENGAGE Learning.
Pride, William M. & Hughes, Robert J. Business. 8th ed. 2006. (ENG.). pap. 18.95 *(978-1-4288-1080-8(3))* Cram101 Inc.
Pride, William M., et al. Business. 10th ed. 2009. (ENG.). 696p. (C). ring bd. 135.95 *(978-1-4390-3763-8(9))* Cengage South-Western.
Pride, William M. (William M. Pride), et al. Business. 11th ed. 2011. (ENG.). 704p. (C). 225.95 *(978-0-538-47808-3(X))* Cengage South-Western.
Providing Fairness to Workers Who Have Been Misclassified As Independent Contractors: Hearing Before the Subcommittee on Workforce Protections of the Committee on Education & the Workforce, U.S. House of Representatives, One Hundred Tenth Congress, First Session, Hearing Held in Washington, DC, March 27, 2007. 2007. iii, 36p. *(978-0-16-079474-2(9)*, 552-070-36467-6) United States Government Printing Office.
Ragazzo, Robert & Fendler, Frances. Closely Held Business Organizations: Cases, Materials, & Problems 2D. 2nd rev. ed. 2012. (American Casebook Ser.). 1250p. 176.00 ***(978-0-314-27580-6(0))*** West.
Ramseyer, J. Mark, compiled by. Business Associations: Agency, Partnerships, LLCs & Corporations: 2007 Statutes & Rules. 2007. 324p. per. 29.00 *(978-1-59941-287-0(X))* West.
Reardon, Elaine, et al. The Utilization of Women-Owned Small Businesses in Federal Contracting. 2007. 106p. per. 23.00 *(978-0-8330-4166-1(5))* RAND Corp., The.
Reese, Andrew R. Reese's Peanut Butter Cups: The Untold Story. 2008. (ENG.). 108p. 22.95 *(978-0-595-49107-0(3))*; pap. 12.95 *(978-0-595-48707-3(6))* iUniverse, Inc.
Regan, Patrick. Hallmark: A Century of Caring. 2009. (ENG.). 260p. 40.00 *(978-0-7407-9240-3(7))* Andrews McMeel Publishing.
Regehr, Preston C. Utah Limited Liability Company: Forms & Practice Manual. 2nd ed. 2007. *(978-1-57400-119-8(1))* Data Trace Publishing, Co.
Regulatory Barriers to American Indian Job Creation: Hearing Before the Subcommittee on Technology, Information Policy, Intergovernmental Relations, & Procurement Reform of the Committee on Oversight & Government Reform, House of Representatives, One Hundred Twelfth Congress, First Session, April 7, 2011. 2011. (Illus.). iii, 71p. ***(978-0-16-089638-5(X)***, 552-070-43527-1) United States Government Printing Office.
Rehabilitation Equipment Market. 300p. (Orig.). pap. *(978-0-7605-2323-0(1))* Rector Pr., Ltd.
Reich, William L. Colorado Industries of the Past. 2008. 240p. pap. 18.95 *(978-1-55566-416-9(4))* Johnson Bks.
Reynolds, Paul D. & Curtin, Richard T. Business Creation in the United States: Panel Study of Entrepreneurial Dynamics II Initial Assessment. 2007. (ENG.). 172p. pap. 115.00 net. *(978-1-60198-096-0(5))* Now Pubs.
Ribstein, Larry E. & Lipshaw, Jeffrey M. Unincorporated Business Entities. 4th ed. 2009. *(978-1-4224-2960-0(1))* LexisNexis Matthew Bender.
Richardson, John. Annual Editions: Business Ethics 11/12. 23rd ed. 2011. (Annual Editions Ser.). (ENG., Illus.). 176p. (C). pap. 44.00 *(978-0-07-352865-6(X)*, 007352865X, McGraw-Hill/Dushkin) McGraw-Hill Higher Education.
Risius, Jeffrey M. Business Valuation: A Primer for the Legal Professional. 2007. (ENG., Illus.). 256p. per. 89.95 *(978-1-59031-746-4(7))* American Bar Assn.
Rivera, Rebecca, photos by. Valley Places, Valley Faces. 2008. (Illus.). 184p. *(978-1-893619-81-4(8))* Historical Publishing Network.

Robert, Spector. The Legend of Eddie Bauer. 2nd ed. 2011. (Illus.). 120p. 25.00 (978-1-933245-22-5(0)) Documentary Media LLC.
Rogers, W. Sherman. The African American Entrepreneur: Then & Now. 2009. (Illus.). xx, 316p. (978-0-313-35111-2(2), Praeger Pubs.) Greenwood Publishing Group, Inc.
Romley, Valerie. Beyond Translation: The Marketer's Field Guide to Understanding Today's Transcultural Consumer. 2007. 205p. per. 24.95 (978-0-9800121-0-1(4)) Moving Target Pr.
Roosevelt, Ford, et al. Seattle Job Source: The Only Source You Need to Land the Job of Your Choice in Seattle. 2007. (Job Source Guides Ser.). 128p. (C). pap. 12.95 (978-1-55921-376-9(0), Asphodel Pr.) Moyer Bell.
Route 66 St. Louis: From the Bridges to the Diamonds. 2010. 480p. pap. 29.95 (978-0-9823239-1-5(3)) St. Louis Transitions.
Russell, Lynda J. Bristol Business & Industry. 2010. (Images of America Ser.). (ENG., Illus.). 128p. pap. 21.99 (978-0-7385-7337-3(X)) Arcadia Publishing.
Rust, Joe Carroll & Langford, Mark. San Antonio, City Exceptional: Images of Culture & Enterprise. 2010. (Illus.). 127p. **(978-1-935377-21-4(3))** Historical Publishing Network.
Sagner, James S. Is U. S. Business Overregulated? How Government Destroys Our Ability to Compete Globally. 2008. (Illus.). 349p. per. 15.95 (978-0-9791956-1-7(6)) York House Pr., Ltd.
Salterelli, Mary Estelle Gott. Historic Hood County: An Illustrated History. 2009. (Illus.). 126p. (978-1-935377-08-5(6)) Historical Publishing Network.
Sandeen, Sharon K. The Intellectual Property Deskbook for Lawyers: A Transactions-Based Guide to Intellectual Property Law. 2nd ed. 2010. (ENG.). 452p. pap. 109.95 (978-1-60442-448-5(6)) American Bar Assn.
Sandler, Susan F., ed. CPA Firm Statistical Analysis Reference Handbook 2007. 2006. 67p. pap. 379.00 (978-1-58673-204-2(8)) Institute of Management & Administration, IOMA.
Sawler, Harvey. Twenty-First Century Irvings. 2007. (ENG., Illus.). 192p. 29.95 (978-1-55109-608-7(0)) Down East Bks.
Schapiro, Mark. Exposed: the Toxic Chemistry of Everyday Products & What's at Stake for American Power: The Toxic Chemistry of Everyday Products & What's at Stake for American Power. 2009. (ENG.). 216p. pap. 19.95 (978-1-60358-058-8(1)) Chelsea Green Publishing.
Schaut, Scott. Historic Mansfield: A Bicentennial History. 2010. (Illus.). 140p. (978-1-935377-12-2(4)) Historical Publishing Network.
Schmidt, James M. Lincoln's Labels: America's Best Known Brands & the Civil War. 2009. (ENG.). 224p. pap. 19.95 (978-1-889020-28-0(1)); (Illus.). 27.95 (978-1-889020-21-1(4)) Edinborough Pr.
Schneeman. Law of Corporations & Other Business O. 2006. pap. 12.95 (978-1-4288-0903-1(1)) Cram101 Inc.
Schneeman, Angela. Law of Corporations & Other Business Organizations. 5th ed. 2009. (ENG., Illus.). 832p. (C). 176.95 (978-1-4354-2577-4(4)) Delmar Cengage Learning.
Schuster, Randy. Turning Points. 2011. 268p. pap. 14.95 **(978-1-58570-017-2(7))** Indaba Pr.
Scoggins, Michael C. Historic York County: An Illustrated History. 2009. (Illus.). 112p. (978-1-893619-94-4(X)) Historical Publishing Network.
Sherman, Andrew J. Raising Capital: Get the Money You Need to Grow Your Business, 1 vol. 3rd ed. 2012. (ENG.). 464p. 34.95 **(978-0-8144-1703-4(5))** Amacom.
Simon, Richard M. & Draeger, Robert W. Managing the Silent Killer of Businesses: How to Transition A Business Successfully Across Its Lifecycle. 2008. 308p. 33.95 (978-0-595-50059-8(5)); pap. 23.95 (978-0-595-50791-7(3)) iUniverse, Inc.
Sitarz, Daniel. The Business Start-up Toolkit. 2008. (Legal Toolkit Ser.). (ENG.). 384p. pap. 39.95 incl. cd-rom (978-1-892949-43-1(1)) Nova Publishing Co.
—Sole Proprietorship, 3rd Edition: Small Business Start-up Kit. 3rd ed. 2011. (ENG.). pap. 29.95 incl. cd-rom (978-1-892949-59-2(8)) Nova Publishing Co.
SM Consulting. The Ultimate Job Directory: Comprehensive Guide to Working at Home. 2010. 379p. pap. 29.95 (978-1-4327-4184-6(5)) Outskirts Pr., Inc.
Smith, D. Gordon & Williams, Cynthia A. Business Organizations: Cases, Problems, & Case Studies. 2nd ed. 2008. xxi, 1033p. pap. (978-0-7355-7141-9(4), Aspen Pubs.) Wolters Kluwer Law & Business.
Smith, Harold Owens. Historic Smyrna: An Illustrated History. 2010. (Illus.). 168p. **(978-1-935377-28-3(0))** Historical Publishing Network.
Smith, James E. West Federal Taxation: Taxation of Business Entities. 2006. pap. 15.95 (978-1-4288-0970-3(8)) Cram101 Inc.
Smith, James E., et al. South-Western Federal Taxation 2013: Taxation of Business Entities (with H&R Block @ Home Tax Preparation Software CD-ROM) 16th ed. 2012. (ENG.). 896p. (C). 263.95 incl. cd-rom **(978-1-133-18981-7(4))** Cengage South-Western.
Smithersrapra Technology, compiled by. Reach Usa 2010 Conference Proceedings. 2010. (Conference Proceedings Ser.). 152p. pap. (978-1-84735-492-1(0)) iSmithers Rapra Publishing.
Sparks, Edith. Capital Intentions: Female Proprietors in San Francisco, 1850-1920. 2006. (Luther H. Hodges Jr. & Luther H. Hodges Sr. Series on Business, Society, & the State Ser.). (ENG., Illus.). 320p. per. 22.00 (978-0-8078-5775-5(0)) Univ. of North Carolina Pr.
Spector, Stan. Baby Boomers' Official Guide to Retirement Income. 2007. 128p. per. 16.95 (978-1-59858-342-7(5)) Dog Ear Publishing, LLC.
Spilker, Brian C., et al. Taxation of Individuals & Business Entities, 2011 Edition. 2nd ed. 2010. (ENG., Illus.). 1280p. (C). 243.00 (978-0-07-813670-2(9), 0078136709, McGraw-Hill/Irwin) McGraw-Hill Higher Education.
Spillane, Mick & Lorette, Kristie. How to Open & Operate a Financially Successful Notary Business: With Companion CD-ROM. 2011. (ENG.). 288p. pap. 39.95 (978-1-60138-281-8(2)) Atlantic Publishing Co.
Stankovich, Peter. Six-Figure Incomes: Profit from America's Best Communicators. 2006. 344p. per. 19.95 (978-0-9778127-0-7(7)) Wall Street Press, LLC.
Stanley, Jacquelin & Degood, Jeffrey. Start a Business in North Carolina or South Carolina. 2nd rev. ed. 2006. (Legal Survival Guides). 238p. per. 29.95 (978-1-57248-586-0(8), Sphinx Publishing) Sourcebooks, Inc.
Stanton, Maureen. Killer Stuff & Tons of Money: Seeking History & Hidden Gems in Flea-Market America. 2011. (ENG.). 336p. (gr. 12). 26.95 (978-1-59420-293-3(1), Penguin Pr. HC, The) Penguin Group (USA) Inc.
—Killer Stuff & Tons of Money: Seeking History & Hidden Gems in Flea-Market America. l.t. ed. 2011. 483p. 31.99 **(978-1-4104-4124-9(5))** Thorndike Pr.
State Taxation: The Role of Congress in Developing Apportionment Standards: Hearing Before the Subcommittee on Commercial & Administrative Law of the Committee on the Judiciary, House of Representatives, One Hundred Eleventh Congress, Second Session, May 6, 2010. 2010. iii, 68p. (978-0-16-086186-4(1), 552-070-41284-1) United States Government Printing Office.
Stathis, Michael. The Startup Company Bible for Entreprene. 604p. 79.95 (978-0-9755776-0-8(3)) Apex Ventr. Advs.
Steingold, Attorney Fred S. Legal Guide for Starting & Running a Small Business. 12th rev. ed. 2011. (ENG.). 464p. pap. 39.99 (978-1-4133-1381-9(7)) NOLO.
Steingold, Fred. The Complete Guide to Buying a Business. 3rd ed. 2011. (Illus.). 428p. E-Book (978-1-4133-1287-4(X)) NOLO.
Steingold, Fred S. The Complete Guide to Buying a Business, 2 vols. 3rd rev. ed. 2011. (ENG., Illus.). 448p. pap. 29.99 (978-1-4133-1267-6(5)) NOLO.
Steingold, Fred S. & Steingold, Attorney. The Complete Guide to Selling a Business, 2 vols. 3rd rev. ed. 2007. (ENG., Illus.). 496p. pap. 34.99 (978-1-4133-0706-1(X)) NOLO.
Stern, David, et al. Crosley: Two Brothers & a Business Empire That Transformed the Nation. 2008. (ENG.). 504p. pap. 15.95 (978-1-57860-322-0(6)) Clerisy Pr.
Stevens, Phillip G. Chattanooga: The Renaissance of a City. 2008. 49.95 (978-1-882933-86-0(9)) Cherbo Publishing Group, Inc.
Strader, J. Kelly & Jordan, Sandra D. White Collar Crime: Cases, Materials, & Problems. 2nd ed. 2009. (978-1-4224-2395-0(6)) LexisNexis Matthew Bender.
Strauss, Steven D. The Small Business Bible: Everything You Need to Know to Succeed in Your Small Business. 3rd ed. 2012. (ENG., Illus.). 578p. pap. 22.95 **(978-1-118-13594-5(6)**, Wiley) Wiley, John & Sons, Inc.
Streng, William P. Choice of Entity. 2007. (Tax Management Portfolios Ser.: 700-3rd). spiral bd. 400.00 (978-1-55871-579-0(7)) Tax Management, Inc.
Subcommittee Hearing: Is the Veterans Corporation Prepared to Provide Entrepreneurial Development Assistance to Service Men & Women Returning from Iraq & Afghanistan? 2007. iii, 72p. (978-0-16-080168-6(0), 552-070-36905-8) United States Government Printing Office.
Subcommittee Hearing on Federal Government Efforts in Contracting with Women-Owned Businesses. 2007. (Illus.). iii, 86p. (978-0-16-079945-7(7), 552-070-36772-1) United States Government Printing Office.
Subcommittee Hearing on Oversight of the Entrepreneurial Development Programs Implemented by the Small Business Administration & National Veterans Business Development Corporation. 2008. iii, 203p. (978-0-16-080889-0(8), 552-070-37433-7) United States Government Printing Office.
Subcommittee on Contracting & Technology Field Hearing in Norfolk, VA on Veteran Contracting: Preventing Fraud: Hearing Before the Committee on Small Business, United States House of Representatives, One Hundred Eleventh Congress, Second Session, Hearing Held May 24, 2010. 2010. (Illus.). v, 61p. (978-0-16-086562-6(X), 552-070-41560-2) United States Government Printing Office.
Sullivan, Julie. Voices of Lafayette: A Collection of Oral Histories. 2009. 292p. pap. 19.95 (978-0-9745540-3-7(0)) Big Hat Pr.
Sustar, Pamela & Johnson, Matt. Historic Lee County: The Story of Fort Myers & Southwest Florida. 2008. (Illus.). 88p. (978-1-893619-87-6(7)) Historical Publishing Network.
Swaine, Robert T. The Cravath Firm & Its Predecessors, 1819-1947. 2006. 395.00 (978-1-58477-713-7(3)) Lawbook Exchange, Ltd., The.
Swartz, Matt & Lee, Daniel. The Corporate, Securities, & MandA Lawyer's Job: A Survival Guide. 2007. (978-1-59031-824-9(2)) American Bar Assn.
Symonds, Robert L. & O'Toole, Matthew J. Symonds & O'Toole on Delaware Limited Liability Companies. 2006. ring bd. 275.00 (978-0-7355-5598-3(2), Aspen Pubs.) Wolters Kluwer Law & Business.
Tedlow, Richard S. The Watson Dynasty: The Fiery Reign & Troubled Legacy of IBM's Founding Father & Son. 2006. 340p. reprint ed. pap. 16.00 (978-1-4223-5216-8(1)) DIANE Publishing Co.
Thomas, Karen. Ultimate Book of Business & Legal Forms for Startups: 200+ Downloadable Forms & Spreadsheets. 2nd ed. 2010. (ENG., Illus.). 304p. pap. 29.95 (978-1-59918-389-3(7), 1599183897) Entrepreneur Pr. dba Entrepreneur Media, Inc.
Thomas, Lee. Magical Business Solutions: Adventures of a Serial Entrepreneur & Lessons Learned. 2006. 208p. per. 15.95 (978-0-9786807-1-8(5)) Professional Management Group.
Thompson, Shawn & Hunt, Kristy. Elite Sales Gurus: Unlocking the Minds of America's Youngest & Brightest Summer Sales People. 2011. 276p. 25.99 (978-1-4567-4060-3(1)); pap. 17.99 (978-1-4567-4061-0(X)) AuthorHouse.
Thompson Staff, compiled by. HR Guide to Business Continuity Planning. 3rd ed. 2007. 560p. per. (978-1-933807-20-1(2)) Thompson Media Group LLC.
Thomson West, creator. Business Associations: Keyed to Klein's Casebook on Business Associations. 6th rev. ed. 2007. (High Court Case Summaries Ser.). (Illus.). 340p. per. 34.00 (978-0-314-17968-5(2), West Legalworks) West.
Trachtman, Michael G. The Four Mistakes: Avoiding the Legal Landmines that Lead to Business Disaster. 2010. (ENG.). 256p. 19.95 (978-1-4027-6817-0(6)) Sterling Publishing Co., Inc.
Truly, Traci & Warda, Mark. Start Business in TX. 5th rev. ed. 2006. (Legal Survival Guides). 288p. pap. 26.95 (978-1-57248-560-0(4), Sphinx Publishing) Sourcebooks, Inc.
Tucker, Barbara M. & Tucker, Kenneth H. Industrializing Antebellum America: The Rise of Manufacturing Entrepreneurs in the Early Republic. 2008. (ENG.). 272p. 95.00 (978-1-4039-8480-7(8)) Palgrave Macmillan.
Tucker, Debra J. Legal Guide to Illinois Business Organizations. 2007. xxi, 822p. (978-0-314-96769-5(9)) West Publishing Co., College & Schl. Div.
Turley, Hazel B. Narragansett Brewing Company. 2007. (Images of America Ser.). (ENG., Illus.). 128p. per. 21.99 (978-0-7385-4905-7(3)) Arcadia Publishing.
Unemployment on Indian Reservations at 50 Percent: The Urgent Need to Create Jobs in Indian Country: Hearing Before the Committee on Indian Affairs, United States Senate, One Hundred Eleventh Congress, Second Session, January 28, 2010. 2010. (Illus.). iv, 137p. (978-0-16-086608-1(1), 552-070-41596-3) United States Government Printing Office.
United States, Congress House Committee on Financial Services Staff, contrib. by. Oversight Hearing to Examine Recent Treasury & FHA Actions Regarding the Housing GSEs: Hearing Before the Committee on Financial Services, U.S. House of Representatives, One Hundred Tenth Congress, Second Session, September 25, 2008. 2008. iii, 95p. (978-0-16-082579-8(2), 552-070-38600-9) United States Government Printing Office.
United States, Congress House Committee on Oversight and Government Reform Staff, contrib. by. The Role of Fannie Mae & Freddie Mac in the Financial Crisis: Hearing Before the Committee on Oversight & Government Reform, House of Representatives, One Hundred Tenth Congress, Second Session, December 9, 2008. 2009. (Illus.). iii, 351p. (978-0-16-083962-7(9), 552-070-39645-4) United States Government Printing Office.
Uniworld Business Publications Inc, creator. Directory of Foreign Firms Operating in the United States. 14th ed. 2008. (Directory of Foreign Firms Operating in the United States Ser.). 2356p. 350.00 (978-0-8360-0058-0(7)) Uniworld Business Pubns., Inc.
U.S. Department of Veterans Affairs' Center for Veterans Enterprise: Hearing Before the Subcommittee on Economic Opportunity of the Committee on Veterans' Affairs, U.S. House of Representatives, One Hundred Eleventh Congress, Second Session, March 11, 2010. 2010. iv, 55p. (978-0-16-086624-1(3), 552-070-41602-1) United States Government Printing Office.
Valdez, Zulema. The New Entrepreneurs: How Race, Class, & Gender Shape American Enterprise. 2011. (ENG., Illus.). 208p. 65.00 (978-0-8047-7320-1(3)); pap. 21.95 (978-0-8047-7321-8(1)) Stanford Univ. Pr.
Vangedal, Susan & VanGedal, Susan. Corporate Social Responsibility. 2011. 188p. pap. **(978-3-8443-1778-7(3))** Lambert Academic Publishing.
Vassar, Rick. Hide! Here Comes the Insurance Guy: Understanding Business Insurance & Risk Management. 2008. 200p. 28.95 (978-0-595-49811-6(6), iUniverse Star) iUniverse, Inc.
Veal, Don-Terry & Grenell, Keenan, eds. Entrepreneurship in South Africa & in the United States: Comparative Studies. 2008. 372p. 119.95 (978-0-7734-5069-1(6)) Mellen, Edwin Pr., The.
Venkatesan, Sharon. Discrimination: Sam's Club Style. 2007. 336p. per. 25.95 (978-0-9785509-5-0(1)) Magic Valley Pubs.
Veterans Entrepreneurship & Self Employment: Hearing Before the Subcommittee on Economic Opportunity of the Committee on Veterans' Affairs, U.S. House of Representatives, One Hundred Tenth Congress, First Session, May 17, 2007. 2008. iii, 96p. (978-0-16-080862-3(6), 552-070-37414-1) United States Government Printing Office.
Warda, Mark. Como Iniciar su Propio Negocio. 2008. (SPA & ENG., Illus.). 128p. per. 5.95 (978-1-57248-674-4(0), Sphinx Publishing) Sourcebooks, Inc.
—Incorporate in Nevada from Any State, 2E. 2nd ed. 2008. (ENG.). 336p. pap. 26.95 (978-1-57248-662-1(7), Sphinx Publishing) Sourcebooks, Inc.
Warda, Mark & Petrus, Desiree A. Start a Business in Pennsylvania. 4th rev. ed. 2006. (Legal Survival Guides). (ENG., Illus.). 288p. per. 26.95 (978-1-57248-561-7(2), Sphinx Publishing) Sourcebooks, Inc.
Wawra, Daniela. Public Relations im Kulturvergleich: Die Sprache der Geschäftsberichte US-amerikanischer und deutscher Unternehmen. 2008. 458p. pap. 107.95 (978-3-631-57870-4(9)) Lang, Peter GmbH, Europaischer Verlag der Wissenschaften DEU. Dist: Lang, Peter.
Wayhan, Darel. Corporate Bandits. 2008. pap. 12.00 (978-0-8059-7919-0(0)) Dorrance Publishing Co., Inc.
Weeks, Katie & Maurer, Terri. Interior Design in Practice: Case Studies of Successful Business Models. 2010. (ENG., Illus.). 240p. pap. 70.00 (978-0-470-19053-1(1), Wiley) Wiley, John & Sons, Inc.
Weil, Gotshal & Manges Staff & American Bar Association, Section of Business Law Staff, contrib. by. Reorganizing Failing Businesses: A Comprehensive Review & Analysis of Financial Restructuring & Business Reorganization. rev. ed. 2007. (ENG.). 1200p. spiral bd. 290.95 (978-1-59031-714-3(9)) American Bar Assn.
Weinberg, Steve. Taking on the Trust: The Epic Battle of Ida Tarbell & John D. Rockefeller. 2008. (ENG., Illus.). 320p. 25.95 (978-0-393-04935-0(3), 4935) Norton, W. W. & Co., Inc.
Weiser, Paulette J. Historic Hancock County: An Illustrated History. 2007. (Illus.). 120p. (978-1-893619-77-7(X)) Historical Publishing Network.
Weiss, Luise. Small Business & the Public Library: Strategies for a Successful Partnership. 2011. pap. 55.00 **(978-0-8389-9323-1(0))** American Library Assn.
Wells, Gail. A history of Rosboro Lumber Company: How a hardworking Oregon lumber company survived & thrived into the twenty-first Century. 2008. (Illus.). 232p. pap. 25.00 (978-0-9800094-0-8(5)) Dunawi Creek Pr.
Wessel, Ken. Corporations Without Conscience: And Our Responsibility As Would-Be Stakeholders to Cause Them to Change. 2011. 184p. pap. 17.95 **(978-1-4620-4964-6(8))** iUniverse, Inc.
WEST-E Exam Secrets Test Prep Staff, ed. WEST-E Business & Marketing Education (038) Secrets Study Guide: WEST-E Test Review for the Washington Educator Skills Tests-Endorsements. 2011. (C). 62.99 (978-1-61403-763-7(9)) Mometrix Media LLC.
Wickersheim, Laurel Michele & LeBaron, Rawlene Briar. Colorado on the Eve of Statehood: An Edited Business Directory of the Pioneers Who Built the Centennial State. 2008. (Illus.). iv, 246p. (978-0-7884-7314-2(X)) Heritage Bks.
Williams, C. Fred. Historic Little Rock: An Illustrated History. 2008. (Illus.). 148p. (978-1-893619-82-1(6)) Historical Publishing Network.
Wilson, Catherine Kidd. Historic Greene County: An Illustrated History. 2010. (Illus.). 64p. **(978-1-935377-19-1(1))** Historical Publishing Network.
Wilson, Richard L. Historical Encyclopedia of American Business, 3 vols. 2009. (Illus.). 1056p. 364.00 (978-1-58765-518-0(7)); 122.00 (978-1-58765-520-3(9)); 122.00 (978-1-58765-521-0(7)); 122.00 (978-1-58765-519-7(5)) Salem Pr., Inc.
Wingfield, Adia Harvey. Doing Business with Beauty: Black Women, Hair Salons, & the Racial Enclave Economy. 2008. (Perspectives on a Multiracial America Ser.). (ENG.). 176p. 70.00 (978-0-7425-6116-8(X)) Rowman & Littlefield Publishers, Inc.
Wood, John Busey. Cross-Border for Beginners - First U. S. Business Location - Structuring for Success. 2010. 94p. pap. 39.99 (978-0-557-43516-6(1)) Lulu Enterprises Inc.
—Navigating the Dangerous Shoals of a Commercial Lease for Beginners. 2009. 182p. pap. 89.01 (978-0-557-09522-3(0)) Lulu Enterprises Inc.
Woodhead, Lindy. Shopping, Seduction & Mr. Selfridge. 2007. (Illus.). 310p. 35.00 (978-1-86197-888-2(X)) Profile Bks. Ltd. GBR. Dist: Independent Pubs. Group.
—Shopping, Seduction & Mr Selfridge. 2009. (ENG., Illus.). 320p. pap. 15.95 (978-1-86197-169-2(9)) Profile Bks. Ltd. GBR. Dist: Consortium Bk. Sales & Distribution.
Wyly, Sam. 1,000 Dollars & an Idea: Entrepreneur to Billionaire. 2008. (ENG.). 272p. 24.95 (978-1-55704-803-5(7)) Newmarket Pr.
Yaeger, Brian. Red, White, & Brew: An American Beer Odyssey. 2008. (ENG., Illus.). 272p. pap. 14.95 (978-0-312-38314-5(2), St. Martin's Griffin) St. Martin's Pr.
Yetenekian Smith, Liza. Rugged Past, Thriving Future: Lubbock At 100. 2008. 59.50 (978-1-882933-87-7(7)) Cherbo Publishing Group, Inc.
Yockey, L. Beth & Yockey, Ross P. Olympia Federal Savings & Loan: The First Hundred Years. 2006. (Illus.). 165p. (978-0-9764839-1-5(2)) Abecedary Pr.
Zarfes. Corporate Transactional Law: Contracts Cases & Commentary. 2011. (978-0-7355-9819-5(3), Aspen Pubs.) Wolters Kluwer Law & Business.
Zarfes, David & Bloom, Michael L. Contracts & Commercial Transactions. 2011. xxxv, 626p. **(978-0-7355-9820-1(7))** Kluwer Law International.
Ziegler, Roy. New Hope, Pennsylvania: River Town Passages. 2008. 108p. 22.95 (978-1-4401-0661-3(4)); pap. 12.95 (978-1-4401-0659-0(2)) iUniverse, Inc.
101 Power Tips: Great Business Ideas from America's Top Remodeling Companies. 2006. pap. 19.95 (978-0-9648587-8-7(9)) Remodelers Advantage, Inc.

BUSINESS ENTERPRISES, FAMILY-OWNED

see Family-Owned Business Enterprises

BUSINESS ENTERPRISES, SALE OF

see Sale of Business Enterprises

BUSINESS ENTERTAINING

Allen, Judy. The Executive's Guide to Corporate Events & Business Entertaining: How to Choose & Use Corporate Functions to Increase Brand Awareness, Develop New Business, Nurture Customer Loyalty & Drive Growth. 2007. (ENG.). 288p. 41.00 (978-0-470-83848-8(5), Wiley) Wiley, John & Sons, Inc.
CCH Incorporated Staff, creator. Business Expense Log. 2007th rev. ed. 2006. (Illus.). 64p. pap. 8.50 (978-0-8080-1534-5(6)) Toolkit Media Group.
CCH Tax Editors. Business Expense Log (2009) 2008. 64p. pap. 9.50 (978-0-8080-1899-5(X)) Toolkit Media Group.
Cicora, Ken. One Hundred Twenty-Five Ideas for Successful Events. 171p. 24.95 (978-0-914951-74-2(2)) Learning Resources Network, Inc.
Cram101 Textbook Reviews. Outlines & Highlights for Business Protocol: Contemporary American Practice by Robinson, ISBN. 2011. 128p. pap. 28.95 **(978-1-61812-118-9(9))** Cram101 Inc.

RoAne, Susan & Roane, Susan. How to Work a Room: Savvy Socializing. rev. ed. 2007. (ENG., Illus.). 288p. pap. 15.99 *(978-0-06-123867-3(8)*, Harper Paperbacks) HarperCollins Pubs.

Robinson, Amanda. Business Protocol: Contemporary American Practice. 2nd ed. 2006. (ENG.). (C). pap. 62.95 *(978-0-7593-9239-7(0))* CENGAGE Learning Custom Publishing.

Rynecki, David. Deals on the Green: Lessons on Business & Golf from America's Top Executives. 2011. (ENG.). 208p. (gr. 12). 15.00 *(978-1-59184-407-5(X)*, Portfolio Trade) Penguin Group (USA) Inc.

Yager, Jan. Grow Global: Using International Protocol to Expand Your Business Worldwide. 2011. (Illus.). 200p. 31.95 *(978-1-889262-21-5(8))* Hannacroix Creek Bks., Inc.

BUSINESS ESPIONAGE

see Business Intelligence

BUSINESS ETHICS

see also Business Intelligence; Corporations—Corrupt Practices; Social Responsibility of Business; Wealth—Moral and Ethical Aspects

Aburdene, Patricia. Megatrends 2010: The Rise of Conscious Capitalism. 2007. (ENG., Illus.). 248p. per. 16.95 *(978-1-57174-539-2(4))* Hampton Roads Publishing Co., Inc.

Agudelo, Juan & 1st World Publishing. Omega Virus. 2007. 148p. 22.95 *(978-1-4218-9940-4(X))* 1st World Publishing, Inc.

Ahner, Gene. Business Ethics: Making a Life, Not Just a Living. 2007. 249p. per. 25.00 *(978-1-57075-748-8(8))* Orbis Bks.

Alan, Eliabeth. Right to Work. 2007. 196p. per. 24.95 *(978-1-4241-7359-4(0))* PublishAmerica, Inc.

Albuquerque, D. Business Ethics. 2010. (ENG., Illus.). 512p. 24.95 *(978-0-19-569964-7(5))* Oxford Univ. Pr., Inc.

Ali, Ahmed. Prohibition of Usury: Islamic & Jewish Practices. 2009. 200p. pap. 14.95 *(978-1-4327-2322-4(7))* Outskirts Pr., Inc.

Allen, Judy. Event Planning Ethics & Etiquette: A Principled Approach to the Business of Special Event Management. 2009. (ENG.). 320p. pap. 35.00 *(978-0-470-67644-8(2)*, Wiley) Wiley, John & Sons, Inc.

Amann, Wolfgang, et al, eds. Humanism in Business. 2009. (ENG., Illus.). 472p. 116.00 *(978-0-521-89893-5(5))*; 270p. pap. 41.99 *(978-0-521-72762-4(6))* Cambridge Univ. Pr.

Anderson, Max & Escher, Peter. The MBA Oath: Setting a Higher Standard for Business Leaders. 2010. (ENG.). 288p. (gr. 12). 24.95 *(978-1-59184-335-1(9)*, Portfolio (Hardcover)) Penguin Group (USA) Inc.

Arbogast, Steven/V. Resisting Corporate Corruption: Lessons in Practical Ethics from the Enron Wreckage. 2007. (Conflicts & Trends in Business Ethics Ser.). 300p. (C). 64.00 *(978-0-9764041-4-9(1))* M & M Scrivener Pr.

—Solutions Manual to Resisting Corporate Corruption: Lessons in Practical Ethics from the Enron Wreckage. 2007. (C). cd-rom 30.00 *(978-0-9764041-5-6(X))* M & M Scrivener Pr.

Arena, Christine. The High-Purpose Company: The Truly Responsible — And Highly Profitable — Firms That Are Changing Business Now. 2006. (Illus.). 304p. 24.95 *(978-0-06-085207-8(0)*, Collins) HarperCollins Pubs.

Arnold, Chris R. Ethical Marketing & the New Consumer. 2009. (ENG., Illus.). 288p. 29.95 *(978-0-470-74302-7(6)*, Wiley) Wiley, John & Sons, Inc.

Arnold, Denis G., ed. Ethics & the Business of Biomedicine. 2009. (ENG., Illus.). 302p. 93.00 *(978-0-521-76431-5(9))*; pap. 30.99 *(978-0-521-74822-3(4))* Cambridge Univ. Pr.

Asma, Stephen T. Against Fairness. 2012. (Illus.). 200p. 22.50 ***(978-0-226-02986-3(7))*** Univ. of Chicago Pr.

Atienza, Veredigno. Reflections in the Marketplace. 2007. 141p. pap. 16.95 *(978-1-4116-6928-4(2))* Lulu Enterprises Inc.

Audi, Robert. Business Ethics & Ethical Business. 2008. (ENG., Illus.). 176p. (C). 54.95 *(978-0-19-536911-3(4))*; pap. 29.95 *(978-0-19-536910-6(6))* Oxford Univ. Pr., Inc.

Avila, Adrienne & Pockell, Leslie M. MBA in a Book: Fundamental Principles of Business, Sales, & Leadership. 2009. (ENG.). 336p. pap. 19.99 *(978-0-446-53543-4(5)*, Business Plus) Grand Central Publishing.

Baber, Anne & Waymon, Lynne. Make Your Contacts Count: Networking Know-How for Business & Career Success. 2nd rev. ed. 2007. (ENG., Illus.). 272p. pap. 14.95 *(978-0-8144-7402-0(0))* Amacom.

Backhaus, Jürgen G. & Drechsler, Wolfgang, eds. Friedrich Nietzsche (1844-1900) Economy & Society. 2006. (European Heritage in Economics & the Social Sciences Ser.: Vol. 3). (Illus.). xi, 253p. 169.00 *(978-0-387-32979-6(X)*, 038732979X) Springer.

Baer, Michael R. Business As Mission: The Power of Business in the Kingdom of God. 2006. (ENG.). 157p. per. 12.99 *(978-1-57658-388-3(0))* YWAM Publishing.

Bagley. Managers & the Legal Environment. 2006. pap. 26.95 *(978-1-4288-0698-6(9))* Cram101 Inc.

Bagley, Constance E. & Savage, Diane. Managers & the Legal Environment: Strategies for the 21st Century. 6th ed. 2009. (ENG.). 1152p. (C). 264.95 *(978-0-324-58204-8(8))* Cengage South-Western.

Ballenger, Jesse F., et al, eds. Treating Dementia: Do We Have a Pill for It? 2009. (ENG., Illus.). 288p. (gr. 17). 62.00 *(978-0-8018-9365-0(8))* Johns Hopkins Univ. Pr.

Baron, David P. Business & Its Environment. 6th ed. 2009. (ENG.). 832p. (C). 224.00 *(978-0-13-608392-4(7)*, Prentice Hall) Prentice Hall PTR.

Baroutas, Stavros. Conflict & Ethics: Ethical Management in Present Times. 2011. 76p. pap. 15.66 ***(978-1-4567-8650-2(4))*** AuthorHouse.

Barrera, Albino. Market Complicity & Christian Ethics. 2011. (New Studies in Christian Ethics Ser.). (ENG.). 324p. 88.00 *(978-1-107-00315-6(6))* Cambridge Univ. Pr.

Barrett, Marja Wade. Business Manners for Success. 2nd ed. 2007. reprint ed. pap. 25.95 *(978-0-9772720-8-2(7)*, Cincinnati Book Pubs.) Jarndyce & Jarndyce Pr.

Bartos, Judeen, ed. Corporate Corruption. 2011. (At Issue Ser.). 128p. pap. 22.50 *(978-0-7377-5561-9(X)*, Greenhaven Pr., Inc.); (YA). (gr. 9-12). 31.80 *(978-0-7377-5560-2(1))* Cengage Gale.

Bassi, Laurie, et al. Good Company: Business Success in the Worthiness Era. 2011. (Bk Business Ser.). (ENG., Illus.). 264p. 27.95 *(978-1-60994-061-4(X))* Berrett-Koehler Pubs., Inc.

Bazerman, M. Blind Spots: Why We Fail to Do What's Right & What to Do about It. 2011. (ENG., Illus.). 200p. 24.95 *(978-0-691-14750-5(7))* Princeton Univ. Pr.

Beckmann, Suzanne & Morsing, Mette, eds. Strategic CSR Communication. 2006. 301p. pap. 66.00 *(978-87-574-1587-2(0))* Djof Publishing DNK. Dist: International Specialized Bk. Services.

Bell, J. Perry. Doing Business with Integrity: One Man's Story. 70p. (Orig.). pap. 7.95 *(978-0-9628542-1-7(2))* Bell Pr.

Beste, Teresa. The Corporate Ethics Audit As a New Tool for Management by Values. 2008. 84p. pap. *(978-3-639-00023-8(4))* VDM Verlag Dr. Mueller e.K.

Bhandarker, Asha & Singh, Pritam. In Search of Change Maestros. 2011. (Response Bks.). (Illus.). 532p. (C). 50.00 *(978-81-321-0586-2(9)*, B05862C) SAGE Pubns., Inc.

Bhattacharya, C. B., et al. Leveraging Corporate Responsibility: The Stakeholder Route to Maximizing Business & Social Value. 2011. (ENG., Illus.). 340p. 99.00 ***(978-1-107-00917-2(0))***; pap. 34.99 ***(978-1-107-40152-5(6))*** Cambridge Univ. Pr.

Bibb, Sally. The Right Thing: An Everyday Guide to Ethics in Business. 2010. (ENG.). 232p. pap. 24.95 *(978-0-470-68853-3(X)*, Wiley) Wiley, John & Sons, Inc.

Black, Cathie. Women: The Best Business Advice I Ever Received. 2007. 256p. pap. 11.95 *(978-0-06-078789-9(9))* HarperCollins Pubs.

Blank, Jonathan. Turning Ethics into Profits: How Ethical People Succeed in Business. 2007. 19.95 *(978-0-9779835-2-0(8))* Chad Publishing LLC.

Boardman, Henry A. (Henry Augustus). The Bible in the Counting-House: A Course of Lectures to Merchants. by H. A. Boardman, D. D. 2006. 420p. per. 26.99 *(978-1-4255-4524-6(6))* MPublishing.

Boatright. Ethics & the Conduct of Business. 2006. pap. 13.95 *(978-1-4288-0774-7(8))* Cram101 Inc.

Boatright, John & Boatright, John R. Ethics in Finance. 2nd rev. ed. 2007. (Foundations of Business Ethics Ser.). (ENG., Illus.). 232p. 99.95 *(978-1-4051-5599-1(X)*, Wiley-Blackwell) Wiley, John & Sons, Inc.

Boatright, John R. Ethics & the Conduct of Business. 5th ed. 2008. (ENG.). (C). pap. 26.67 *(978-0-558-04956-0(7))* Pearson Learning Solutions.

—Ethics & the Conduct of Business. 7th rev. ed. 2011. (ENG.). 384p. (C). 49.33 ***(978-0-205-21546-1(7))***; pap. 96.00 ***(978-0-205-05313-1(0))*** Prentice Hall PTR. (Prentice Hall).

—Ethics & the Conduct of Business: International Edition. 7th rev. ed. 2012. (ENG.). 384p. pap. ***(978-0-205-20798-5(7))*** Pearson Bks.

—Ethics & the Conduct of Business, Books a la Carte Edition. 7th ed. 2011. (ENG.). 384p. (C). ring bd. 62.67 ***(978-0-205-21447-1(9)***, Prentice Hall) Prentice Hall PTR.

—Ethics in Finance. 2nd rev. ed. 2007. (Foundations of Business Ethics Ser.: 9). (ENG., Illus.). 232p. per. 40.95 *(978-1-4051-5600-4(7)*, Wiley-Blackwell) Wiley, John & Sons, Inc.

—Finance Ethics: Critical Issues in Theory & Practice. 2010. (Robert W. Kolb Ser.: 11). (ENG., Illus.). 592p. 95.00 *(978-0-470-49916-0(8)*, Wiley) Wiley, John & Sons, Inc.

Boje, David M. Critical Theory for Business & Public Administration. 2008. *(978-1-59311-786-3(8))*; pap. *(978-1-59311-785-6(X)*, Information Age Publishing, Inc.

Boldt, Petra. Ethikregeln als verbindlicher Verhaltensmaßstab für die Arbeitsverhältnisse in deutschen Unternehmen. 2008. (Zivilrechtliche Schriften. Beiträge zum Wirtschafts-, Bank- und Arbeitsrecht Ser.). 362p. pap. 81.95 *(978-3-631-58395-1(8))* Lang, Peter GmbH, Europaischer Verlag der Wissenschaften DEU. Dist: Lang, Peter.

Bouckaert, Luk, et al, ecs. Frugality: Rebalancing Material and Spiritual Values in Economic Life. 2008. (Illus.). 336p. pap. 79.95 *(978-3-03911-131-2(3))* Lang, Peter Publishing, Inc.

Bouckaert, Luk & Zsolnai, Laszlo, eds. The Palgrave Handbook of Spirituality & Business. 2011. (ENG., Illus.). 448p. 110.00 ***(978-0-230-23831-2(9))*** Palgrave Macmillan.

Bouillon, Hardy. Business Ethics & the Austrian Tradition in Economics. 2011. (Routledge Frontiers of Political Economy Ser.). (ENG.). 192p. (C). 130.00 *(978-0-415-60025-5(1))* Routledge.

Bowie, Norman E. & Schneider, Meg. Business Ethics for Dummies. 2011. (ENG., Illus.). 364p. pap. 21.99 *(978-0-470-60033-7(0)*, For Dummies) Wiley, John & Sons, Inc.

Bowie, Norman E., et al. Ethical Theory & Business. 8th ed. 2008. (ENG.). 704p. (C). per. 112.20 *(978-0-13-612602-7(2)*, Prentice Hall) Prentice Hall PTR.

Bowles, David & Cooper, Cary. The High Engagement Work Culture. 2012. (ENG., Illus.). 192p. 40.00 ***(978-0-230-30449-9(4))*** Palgrave Macmillan.

Bradley, Ian. Enlightened Entrepreneurs: Business Ethics in Victorian Britain. 2009. (ENG., Illus.). 224p. pap. 19.95 *(978-0-7459-5271-0(2))* Lion Hudson PLC GBR. Dist: Independent Pubs. Group.

Bradshaw, Katherine. Speak up Procedures: IBE Guide to Good Practice. 2007. 45p. pap. *(978-0-9549288-3-4(0))* Institute of Business Ethics.

Branson, Richard. Screw Business As Usual. 2011. (ENG.). 1p. (gr. 12). 26.95 ***(978-1-59184-434-1(7)***, Portfolio (Hardcover)) Penguin Group (USA) Inc.

Bredeson, Dean. Applied Business Ethics: A Skills-Based Approach. 2011. (ENG.). 384p. (C). pap. 139.95 *(978-0-538-45398-1(2))* Cengage South-Western.

Brenkert, George G. & Beauchamp, Tom L., eds. The Oxford Handbook of Business Ethics, 1 vol. (Oxford Handbooks Ser.). (ENG., Illus.). 2012. 746p. pap. 50.00 ***(978-0-19-991622-1(5))*** 2009. 816p. 150.00 *(978-0-19-530795-5(X))* Oxford Univ. Pr., Inc.

Brent, Marvin. Affirmative Exploitation. 2007. 196p. per. 14.95 *(978-1-59858-431-8(6))* Dog Ear Publishing, LLC.

Brink, Alexander, ed. Corporate Governance & Business Ethics. 2011. (Ethical Economy Ser.). (ENG., Illus.). x, 320p. 189.00 *(978-94-007-1587-5(0)*, 9400715870) Springer.

Brooks, Leonard J. & Dunn, Paul. Business & Professional Ethics. 6th ed. 2011. (ENG.). 576p. (C). pap. 118.95 *(978-0-538-47838-0(1))* Cengage South-Western.

Brother Herman Zaccarelli, C. S. C. Integrity at Work. 2009. 108p. pap. 13.95 *(978-1-4401-8196-2(9))* iUniverse, Inc.

Bruni, Luigino & Zamagni, Stefano. Civil Economy: Efficiency, Equity, Public Happiness. (Frontiers of Business Ethics Ser.: Vol. 2). (Illus.). 282p. pap. 67.95 *(978-3-03910-896-1(4))* Lang, Peter Publishing, Inc.

Buckingham, Jane & Nilikant, Venkataraman. Managing Responsibly: Alternative Approaches to Corporate Management & Governance. 2012. ***(978-1-4094-2746-9(3))***; 200p. ***(978-1-4094-2745-2(5))*** Ashgate Publishing, Ltd. (Gower Publishing Co., Ltd.).

Buckner, Michael L. The Abcs of Ethics: A Resource for Leaders, Managers, & Professionals. 2010. 108p. pap. 11.95 *(978-1-935278-49-8(5))* iUniverse, Inc.

By, Rune Todnem & Burnes, Bernard, eds. Organizational Change Leadership & Ethics. 2012. (Understanding Organizational Change Ser.). (ENG., Illus.). 256p. (C). 135.00 *(978-0-415-59244-4(5))* Routledge.

Byron, William J. The Power of Principles: Ethics for the New Corporate Culture. 2006. 235p. per. 18.00 *(978-1-57075-678-8(3))* Orbis Bks.

Caceres, Pedro. The Thundering Voice. 2009. 176p. 24.50 *(978-1-60860-134-9(X)*, Strategic Bk. Publishing) AEG Literary Publishing Services, Inc.

Cardone, Michael, Jr. & Bernard, A. R. Business with Soul: Creating a Workplace Rich in Faith & Values, 0 vols. 2009. 240p. pap. 16.99 *(978-0-7852-2157-9(3))* Nelson, Thomas Inc.

Carroll and, Buchholtz. Business & Society Ethics & Stakehol. 2006. 223p. pap. 12.95 *(978-1-4288-0684-9(9))* Cram101 Inc.

Carroll, Archie B. & Amason, Allen C. Business Ethics: Brief Readings on Vital Topics. 2009. (ENG.). 304p. 110.00 *(978-0-415-80206-2(7))*; (Illus.). pap. 34.95 *(978-0-415-99736-2(4))* Routledge.

Carroll, Archie B. & Buchholtz, Ann K. Business & Society: Ethics & Stakeholder Management. 8th ed. 2011. (ENG.). 768p. (C). 237.95 *(978-0-538-45316-5(8))* Cengage South-Western.

Cavanagh, Gerald F. & Fornacian, Charles. American Business Values. 6th ed. 2009. (ENG.). 384p. (C). pap. 100.00 *(978-0-13-607829-6(X)*, Prentice Hall) Prentice Hall PTR.

Cavico, Frank & Mujtaba, Bahaudin. Legal Challenges for the Global Manager & Entrepreneur. rev. ed. 2008. (ENG.). 840p. pap. 169.55 *(978-0-7575-4037-0(6))* Kendall Hunt Publishing Co.

Cavico, Frank J. & Mujtaba, Bahaudin G. Business Ethics: The Moral Foundation for Effective Leadership, Management, & Entrepreneurship. 2nd ed. 2008. (ENG.). (C). pap. 89.20 *(978-0-555-03606-8(5))* Pearson Learning Solutions.

Centre For Business And Public Sector Ethics Staff. Business Ethics. Thomas, Rosamund M., ed. 2011. (Illus.). 320p. pap. 96.00 *(978-1-871891-04-1(3))* Ethics International Pr. Ltd. GBR. Dist: BookMasters Distribution Services (BDS).

Cernic, Jernej. Human Rights Law & Business: Corporate Responsibility for Fundamental Human Rights. 2010. 346p. pap. 90.00 *(978-90-8952-081-4(3))* Europa Law Publishing, Netherlands NLD. Dist: International Specialized Bk. Services.

Chariri, Anis. The Dynamics of Financial Reporting Practice in an Indonesian Company. 2008. 260p. pap. *(978-3-639-05931-1(X))* VDM Verlag Dr. Mueller e.K.

Church, Dawson. Einstein's Business: Engaging Soul, Imagination, & Excellence in the Workplace. Arnold, Courtney & House, Jeanne, eds. 2007. (Illus.). 483p. 26.95 *(978-1-60070-015-6(2)*, Elite Bks.) Author's Publishing Cooperative.

Cilliers, Paul & Preiser, Rika, eds. Complexity, Difference & Identity: An Ethical Perspective. 2010. (Issues in Business Ethics Ser.). (Illus.). xiv, 273p. 159.00 *(978-90-481-9186-4(6)*, 9048191866) Springer.

Ciulla, Joanne B., et al. Honest Work: A Business Ethics Reader, 1 vol. 2nd ed. 2010. (ENG.). 688p. (C). pap. 79.95 *(978-0-19-538315-7(X))* Oxford Univ. Pr., Inc.

Clarke, Frank & Dean, Graeme. Indecent Disclosure: Gilding the Corporate Lily. 2007. (Illus.). 274p. per. 45.99 *(978-0-521-70183-9(X))* Cambridge Univ. Pr.

Clason, George. El Hombre Mas Rico de Babilonia. 2007. (SPA.). 124p. *(978-956-291-428-4(3))* Editorial Benei Noaj.

—El Hombre Mas Rico de Babilonia: La Vesion Original Renovada y Revisada. 2007. (SPA.). 124p. per. *(978-956-291-381-2(3))* Editorial Benei Noaj.

—Richest Man in Babylon. 2007. 116p. *(978-956-291-393-5(7))* Editorial Benei Noaj.

—The Richest Man in Babylon: Blueprint for Financial Success - Lesson 1. 2007. 108p. per. *(978-956-291-411-6(9))* Editorial Benei Noaj.

—The Richest Man in Babylon: Blueprint for Financial Success - Lesson 2. 2007. 136p. per. *(978-956-291-419-2(4))* Editorial Benei Noaj.

—The Richest Man in Babylon: Now Revised & Updated for the 21st Century. 2007. 124p. (ENG.). *(978-956-291-410-9(0))*; per. *(978-956-291-379-9(1))* Editorial Benei Noaj.

—The Richest Man in Babylon: The Orginal Version, Restored & Revised. 2007. 116p. (ENG.). per. *(978-956-291-378-2(3))*; *(978-956-291-254-9(X))* Editorial Benei Noaj.

—The Richest Man in Babylon - Illustrated. 2007. 200p. (ENG.). *(978-956-291-470-3(4))*; per. *(978-956-291-473-4(9))* Editorial Benei Noaj.

Clason, George S. El Hombre Mas Rico de Babilonia: Los Secretos Del exito de los Antiguos. 9th ed. (SPA.). 159p. pap. *(978-84-7720-371-1(7))* Obelisco, Ediciones S.A.

—The Richest Man in Babylon: The Success Secrets of the Ancients. 2008. 93p. *(978-1-60796-066-9(4))* Meirovich, Igal.

—The Richest Man in Babylon (thINKing Classics) 2011. 108p. pap. *(978-1-907590-12-2(9))* Thinking Ink Limited.

Clegg, Stewart, et al, eds. Business Ethics As Practice: Representation, Reflexivity & Performance. 2007. 256p. (C). 119.00 *(978-1-84542-975-1(3))* Elgar, Edward Publishing, Inc.

Clegg, Stewart R. & Rhodes, Carl, eds. Management Ethics: Contemporary Contexts. 2006. (Illus.). 198p. per. 50.95 *(978-0-415-39336-2(1))* Routledge.

—Management Ethics: Contemporary Contexts. 2006. (ENG., Illus.). 216p. (C). 150.00 *(978-0-415-39335-5(3))* Routledge.

Coles, Robert & LaFarge, Albert, eds. Minding the Store: Great Writing about Business from Tolstoy to Now. 2008. (ENG.). 303p. 25.95 *(978-1-59558-355-0(6))* New Pr., The.

Collins, Denis. Business Ethics: How to Design & Manage Ethical Organizations. 2011. (ENG., Illus.). 600p. (C). pap. 123.95 *(978-0-470-63994-8(6)*, Wiley) Wiley, John & Sons, Inc.

Collins, Denis & Collins. Essentials of Business Ethics: Creating an Organization of High Integrity & Superior Performance. 2009. (Essentials Ser.: 47). (ENG., Illus.). 320p. pap. 44.95 *(978-0-470-44256-2(5)*, Wiley) Wiley, John & Sons, Inc.

Comer, Debra R. & Vega, Gina, eds. Moral Courage in Organizations: Doing the Right Thing at Work. 2011. 256p. (ENG.). 89.95 *(978-0-7656-2409-3(5))*; pap. 39.95 *(978-0-7656-2410-9(9))* Sharpe, M.E. Inc.

Commerce Dept. (U.S.), compiled by Etica Comercial: Manaul Sobre la Administracion de una Empresa Comercial Responsable: Manaul Sobre la Administracion de una Empresa Comercial Responsable. 2009. (SPA.). 161p. pap. 44.00 *(978-0-16-077204-7(4))* United States Government Printing Office.

Conway, Mara E. & Conway, Susan D. Essentials of Enterprise Compliance. 2008. (Essentials Ser.: 45). (ENG., Illus.). 160p. pap. 39.95 *(978-0-470-40476-8(0)*, Wiley) Wiley, John & Sons, Inc.

Cooper, Cary L., et al. Crime & Corruption in Organizations: Why It Occurs & What to Do about It. 2010. (Psychological & Behavioural Aspects of Risk Ser.). (Illus.). 382p. 134.95 *(978-0-566-08981-7(5)*, Gower Publishing Co., Ltd.) Ashgate Publishing, Ltd. GBR. Dist: Ashgate Publishing Co.

Cory, Jacques. Business Ethics for a Sustainable Society: Conquering the Corporate Frankenstein. 2009. x, 729p. *(978-0-7734-3848-4(3))* Mellen, Edwin Pr., The.

Covey, Stephen M. R. The Speed of Trust: The One Thing That Changes Everything. (ENG., Illus.). 384p. 2008. pap. 15.95 *(978-1-4165-4900-0(5))* 2006. 26.99 *(978-0-7432-9730-1(X))* Free Pr. (Free Pr.).

Covey, Stephen M. R., et al. Smart Trust: Creating Prosperity, Energy, & Joy in a Low-Trust World. 2012. (ENG., Illus.). 320p. 27.00 *(978-1-4516-5145-4(7)*, Free Pr.) Free Pr.

Cowton, Christopher & Haase, Michaela. Trends in Business & Economic Ethics. 2010. (Studies in Economic Ethics & Philosophy Ser.). (Illus.). vi, 272p. pap. 149.00 *(978-3-642-09838-3(X)* 364209838X) Springer.

Cram101 Textbook Reviews. Outlines & Highlights for Business: Its Legal, Ethical, & Global Environment by Marianne M. Jennings, ISBN. 2011. 564p. pap. 39.95 ***(978-1-61812-079-3(4))*** Cram101 Inc.

—Outlines & Highlights for Business Ethics, a Teaching & Learning Classroom Edition: Concepts & Cases by Manuel G. Velasquez, ISBN. 2010. 98p. pap. 27.95 *(978-1-61698-771-8(5))* Cram101 Inc.

—Outlines & Highlights for Business Ethics & Values: Individual, Corporate & International Perspectives by Colin Fisher, Alan Lovell, ISBN. 2010. 132p. pap. 28.95 *(978-1-61698-722-0(7))* Cram101 Inc.

—Outlines & Highlights for Business Ethics by Richard Degeorge, Isbn: 9780130991638. 2010. 182p. pap. 29.95 *(978-1-61698-751-0(0))* Cram101 Inc.

—Outlines & Highlights for Business Ethics by William H Shaw, Isbn: 9780495095019. 2010. 114p. pap. 28.95 *(978-1-61698-773-2(1))* Cram101 Inc.

—Outlines & Highlights for Business Ethics Now by Andrew Ghillyer, Isbn: 9780073524696. 2011. 108p. pap. 28.95 ***(978-1-61490-517-2(7))*** Cram101 Inc.

—Outlines & Highlights for Corporate Governance & Ethics by Zabihollah Rezaee, Isbn: 9780471738008. 2010. 38p. pap. 27.95 *(978-1-61654-294-8(2))* Cram101 Inc.

—Outlines & Highlights for Ethics & the Conduct of Business by Boatright. 2010. 170p. pap. 29.95 (978-1-61698-875-3(4)) Cram101 Inc.

—Outlines & Highlights for Ethics in Information Technology by George Reynolds, Isbn: 9781418836313 141883631. 2011. 134p. pap. 28.95 (978-1-61812-271-1(1)) Cram101 Inc.

—Outlines & Highlights for Investment Ethics by Sarah Peck. 2011. 146p. pap. 29.95 (978-1-4672-6638-3(8)) Cram101 Inc.

—Outlines & Highlights for Law, Business, & Society by Mcadams, Isbn: 9780073377650. 2010. 290p. pap. 32.95 (978-1-61698-852-4(5)) Cram101 Inc.

Cram101 Textbook Reviews. Outlines & Highlights for Managing Risks for Corporate Integrity: How to Survive an Ethical Misconduct Disaster by Brewer, Chandler, & Ferrell. 2011. 58p. pap. 26.95 (978-1-61906-178-1(3)) Cram101 Inc.

Cram101 Textbook Reviews & Cram101 Textbook Reviews. Outlines & Highlights for Business Ethics: The Moral Foundation for Effective Leadership, Management, & Entrepreneurship by Frank J. Cavico, ISBN. 2011. 78p. pap. 27.95 (978-1-61490-352-9(2)) Cram101 Inc.

—Outlines & Highlights for Managing Business Ethics by Linda K Trevino, Isbn: 9780470343944. 2011. 166p. pap. 29.95 (978-1-61461-382-4(6)) Cram101 Inc.

—Outlines & Highlights for the Ethics of Management by la Rue Hosmer, Isbn: 9780073530543. 2011. 92p. pap. 27.95 (978-1-61461-401-2(6)) Cram101 Inc.

—Outlines & Highlights for the Ethics of Management by la Rue Tone Hosmer. 2011. 56p. pap. 26.95 (978-1-61830-634-0(0)) Cram101 Inc.

Cram101 Textbook Reviews Staff. Outlines & Highlights for above the Board: How Ethical CEOs Create Honest Corporations by Porrini ISBN. 2009. 78p. pap. 26.95 (978-1-4288-6750-5(3)) Cram101 Inc.

—Outlines & Highlights for American Business Values: A Global Perspective by Cavanagh, ISBN. 2008. 104p. pap. 10.95 (978-1-4288-6363-7(X)) Cram101 Inc.

—Outlines & Highlights for an Introduction to Business Ethics by Desjardins, Isbn: 9780073386584. 2008. 68p. pap. 10.95 (978-1-4288-6221-0(8)) Cram101 Inc.

—Outlines & Highlights for Business: Its Legal, Ethical, & Global Environment by Marianne M. Jennings, ISBN. 2009. 216p. pap. 30.95 (978-1-4288-4104-8(0)) Cram101 Inc.

—Outlines & Highlights for Business & Its Environment by Baron, Isbn: 0131873555. 2008. 200p. pap. 13.95 (978-1-4288-6528-0(4)) Cram101 Inc.

—Outlines & Highlights for Business & Professional Ethics for Directors, Executives & Accountants by Brooks & Dunn, Isbn: 9780324594553. 2009. 108p. pap. 28.95 (978-1-4288-7613-2(8)) Cram101 Inc.

—Outlines & Highlights for Business & Society: Ethics & Stakeholder Management by Carroll, ISBN. 2008. 328p. pap. 16.95 (978-1-4288-6445-0(8)) Cram101 Inc.

—Outlines & Highlights for Business Ethics: A Real World Approach by Ghillyer, ISBN. 2009. 128p. pap. 11.95 (978-1-4288-6675-1(2)) Cram101 Inc.

—Outlines & Highlights for Business Ethics by Andrew W Ghillyer, Isbn: 9780073377100. 2009. 90p. pap. 27.95 (978-1-4288-7643-9(X)) Cram101 Inc.

—Outlines & Highlights for Business Ethics by Richard Degeorge, Isbn: 9780130991638. 2009. 168p. pap. 29.95 (978-1-4288-7392-6(9)) Cram101 Inc.

—Outlines & Highlights for Corporate Management, Governance, & Ethics Best Practices by Vallabhaneni, Isbn: 9780470117231. 2008. 176p. pap. 12.95 (978-1-4288-6273-9(0)) Cram101 Inc.

—Outlines & Highlights for Ethics at Work by Cox, Isbn: 0130450316. 2008. 60p. pap. 9.95 (978-1-4288-6333-0(8)) Cram101 Inc.

—Outlines & Highlights for Ethics in the Workplace by Goree, Isbn: 0538443952. 2008. 60p. pap. 9.95 (978-1-4288-6462-7(8)) Cram101 Inc.

—Outlines & Highlights for Law & Ethics in the Business Environment by Halbert, Isbn: 0324657323. 2008. 144p. pap. 11.95 (978-1-4288-6513-6(6)) Cram101 Inc.

—Outlines & Highlights for Law, Business, & Society by Mcadams, Isbn: 9780073377650. 2009. 232p. pap. 31.95 (978-1-4288-6769-7(4)) Cram101 Inc.

—Outlines & Highlights for Managers & the Legal Environment. 2007. pap. 16.95 (978-1-4288-5717-9(6)) Cram101 Inc.

—Outlines & Highlights for Managers & the Legal Environment: Strategies for the 21st Century by Constance E. Bagley, ISBN. 2009. 458p. pap. 36.95 (978-1-4288-9117-3(X)) Cram101 Inc.

—Outlines & Highlights for Moral Intelligence: Enhancing Business Performance & Leadership Success by Lennick, ISBN. 2008. 80p. pap. 10.95 (978-1-4288-6543-3(8)) Cram101 Inc.

—Outlines & Highlights for Moral Issues in Business by William H Shaw, Isbn: 9780495007173. 2009. 82p. pap. 27.95 (978-1-4288-9631-4(7)) Cram101 Inc.

Crane, Andrew & Matten, Dirk. Business Ethics: Managing Corporate Citizenship & Sustainability in the Age of Globalization. 3rd ed. 2010. (ENG., Illus.). 624p. (Orig.). pap. 59.95 (978-0-19-956433-0(7)) Oxford Univ. Pr., Inc.

Crane, Andrew, et al. Corporate Social Responsibility: Readings & Cases in a Global Context. Crane, Andrew et al, eds. (ENG., Illus.). 544p. (C). 2008. 175.23 (978-0-415-42428-8(3)) 2007. 68.95 (978-0-415-42429-5(1)) Routledge.

Crawford, Micheal & Loyd, D. Scot. CPA's Multistate Guide to Ethics & Professional Conduct 2008. 2008. 600p. pap. 215.00 (978-0-8080-9176-9(X)) Toolkit Media Group.

Cressy, Robert, et al, eds. Entrepreneurship, Governance & Ethics. 2012. (ENG.). vi, 266p. 99.00 (978-94-007-2925-4(1), 9400729251) Springer.

Crowther, David & Davila Gomez, Ana Maria. Human Dignity & Managerial Responsibility: Diversity Rights & Sustainability. 2012. (Corporate Social Responsibility Ser.). (Illus.). 236p. 104.95 (978-1-4094-2311-9(5), Gower Publishing Co., Ltd.) Ashgate Publishing, Ltd. GBR. Dist: Ashgate Publishing Co.

Daly, Frank & Oliver, Carl. Business Ethics: Business Ethics. 2012. 300p. pap. 59.95 (978-0-7346-1129-1(3)) Tilde Publishing AUS. Dist: International Publishers Marketing.

Daniels, Vincent. International Sales: How to Excel in Gloval Selling. 2007. 102p. pap. 15.00 (978-0-9768522-3-0(3)) DISC.

Darrough, Odessa. Trust & Commitment in Organizations. 2008. 112p. pap. (978-3-8364-6337-9(7)) VDM Verlag Dr. Mueller e.K.

Das Gupta, Ananda, ed. Ethics, Business & Society: Managing Responsibly. 2010. (Response Bks.). (Illus.). 244p. (C). pap. 25.95 (978-81-321-0402-5(1), B04025P) SAGE Pubns., Inc.

Daub, Falko. New Whistleblowing Regulations in the Usa. 2007. 80p. per. (978-3-8364-0730-4(2)) VDM Verlag Dr. Mueller e.K.

De Cremer, David & Tenbrunsel, Ann E. Behavioral Business Ethics. 2011. (Series in Organization & Management Ser.). (ENG., Illus.). 280p. 62.95 (978-0-415-87324-6(X), Routledge) Taylor & Francis Group GBR. Dist: Taylor & Francis Group.

De Graaf, Gjalt. Contextual Morality. 2009. 268p. pap. (978-3-639-15970-7(5)) VDM Verlag Dr. Mueller e.K.

DeGeorge, Richard. Business Ethics. 7th ed. 2009. (ENG.). 576p. (C). pap. 115.80 (978-0-205-73193-0(7), Prentice Hall) Prentice Hall PTR.

DeMars, Nan. You've Got to Be Kidding! How to Keep Your Job Without Losing Your Integrity. 2011. (ENG., Illus.). 288p. 24.95 (978-0-470-94751-7(9), Wiley) Wiley, John & Sons, Inc.

DeMartino, George F. The Economist's Oath: On the Need for & Content of Professional Economic Ethics, 1 vol. 2011. (ENG.). 288p. 35.00 (978-0-19-973056-8(3)) Oxford Univ. Pr., Inc.

DesJardins, Joseph. An Introduction to Business Ethics. 4th ed. 2010. (ENG., Illus.). 320p. (C). pap. 74.67 (978-0-07-353581-4(8), 0073535818) McGraw-Hill Cos., The.

DesJardins, Joseph R. Business, Ethics, & the Environment: Imagining a Sustainable Future. 2006. (Basic Ethics in Action Ser.). (ENG.). 224p. (C). per. 39.60 (978-0-13-189174-6(X), Prentice Hall) Prentice Hall PTR.

Dethomasis, Louis & St Anthony, Neal. Doing Right in a Shrinking World: How Corporate America Can Balance Ethics & Profit in a Changing Economy. 2006. 162p. 21.95 (978-1-929774-39-5(7), Greenleaf Book Group Pr.) Greenleaf Book Group.

Developing a Corporate Ethics Strategy: Leading CEOs on Building a Culture of Trust, Addressing Ethical Dilemmas, & Ensuring Company Consistency (Inside the Minds) 2009. 104p. pap. (978-0-314-20614-5(0)) Aspatore Bks.

Dierksmeier, Claus, et al, eds. Humanistic Ethics in the Age of Globality. 2011. (ENG., Illus.). 304p. 105.00 (978-0-230-27327-6(0)) Palgrave Macmillan.

Djelic, Marie-Laure & Vranceanu, R., eds. Moral Foundations of Management Knowledge. 2009. (Illus.). 304p. pap. 66.00 (978-1-84844-705-9(1)) Elgar, Edward Publishing, Inc.

Djelic, Marie-Laure & Vranceanu, Radu. Moral Foundations of Management Knowledge. 2007. (Illus.). 304p. 130.00 (978-1-84720-477-6(5)) Elgar, Edward Publishing, Inc.

Dubbink, W. Assisting the Invisible Hand: Contested Relations Between Market, State & Civil Society. 2010. (Issues in Business Ethics Ser.). 240p. pap. 179.00 (978-90-481-6353-3(6), 9048163536) Springer.

Dubbink, Wim, et al, eds. European Business Ethics Casebook: The Morality of Corporate Decision Making. 2011. (Issues in Business Ethics Ser.). (ENG., Illus.). xvi, 182p. pap. 49.95 (978-90-481-8965-6(9), 9048189659) Springer.

—European Business Ethics Cases in Context: The Morality of Corporate Decision Making. 2011. (Issues in Business Ethics Ser.). (ENG., Illus.). xviii, 295p. 139.00 (978-90-481-9333-2(8), 9048193338) Springer.

Duncan, Jeremy S. Perspectives on Ethics. 2011. (Series: Ethical Issues in the 21st Century Ser.). 195.00 (978-1-61761-677-8(X)) Nova Science Pubs., Inc.

Dunfee, T. W. & Nagayasu, Y., eds. Business Ethics: Japan & the Global Economy: Japan & the Global Economy. 2010. (Issues in Business Ethics Ser.). 292p. pap. 279.00 (978-90-481-4309-2(8), 9048143098) Springer.

Duska, Brenda Shay, et al. Accounting Ethics. 2nd ed. 2011. (CourseSmart Ser.: 21). (ENG.). 256p. pap. 39.95 (978-1-4051-9613-0(0), Wiley-Blackwell) Wiley, John & Sons, Inc.

Duska, Ronald F. Contemporary Reflections on Business Ethics. (Issues in Business Ethics Ser.). xxii, 268p. 2010. pap. 179.00 (978-90-481-7244-3(6), 9048172446) 2006. (Illus.). (C). 179.00 (978-1-4020-4983-5(8), 1402049838) Springer.

Duska, Ronald F., ed. Education, Leadership & Business Ethics: Essays on the Work of Clarence Walton. 2010. (Issues in Business Ethics Ser.). 344p. pap. 199.00 (978-90-481-5112-7(0), 9048151120) Springer.

Edesess, Michael. The Big Investment Lie: What Your Financial Advisor Doesn't Want You to Know. 2007. (BK Life Ser.). (ENG., Illus.). 298p. 24.95 (978-1-57675-407-8(3)) Berrett-Koehler Pubs., Inc.

Edmonds, Graham. Lying in Business: The Truth. 2008. (ENG.). 194p. pap. 17.95 (978-1-904915-34-8(5)) Southbank Publishing GBR. Dist: Independent Pubs. Group.

Eldred, Ken. God Is at Work: Transforming People & Nations Through Business. 2009. (ENG.). 336p. pap. 14.99 (978-0-9840911-0-2(6)) Manna Ventures, LLC.

Ethics Resource Center Staff. Ethics Resource Center's 2007 National Business Ethics Survey: An Inside View of Private Sector Ethics. 2007. 32p. (978-0-916152-11-6(1)) Ethics Resource Ctr., Inc.

—Ethics Resource Center's 2007 National Government Ethics Survey: An Inside View of Public Sector Ethics. 2008. 30p. (978-0-916152-12-3(X)) Ethics Resource Ctr., Inc.

—National Nonprofit Ethics Survey: An Inside View of Civil Society Ethics. 2008. 30p. (978-0-916152-13-0(8)) Ethics Resource Ctr., Inc.

Ethics Resource Center Staff & Ethics Resource Center Staff. Leading Corporate Integrity: Defining the Role of the Chief Ethics & Compliance Officer (CECO) 2007. 40p. spiral bd. (978-0-916152-10-9(3)) Ethics Resource Ctr., Inc.

Everton, Michael J. The Grand Chorus of Complaint: Authors & the Business Ethics of American Publishing, 1 vol. 2011. (ENG., Illus.). 256p. 65.00 (978-0-19-975178-5(1)) Oxford Univ. Pr., Inc.

Facts on File, Inc. Staff. Career Skills Library: Professional Ethics & Etiquette. 3rd rev. ed. 2009. (Career Skills Library). (Illus.). 174p. (gr. 6-12). 25.95 (978-0-8160-7772-4(X), Ferguson Publishing Co.) Facts On File, Inc.

Faulkner, Robert R. Corporate Wrongdoing & the Art of the Accusation. 2011. (Tracts for Our Times Ser.). 202p. 99.00 (978-0-85728-791-5(5)); (ENG.). pap. 32.95 (978-0-85728-794-6(X)) Anthem Pr. GBR. Dist: Books International, Inc.

Ferdowsian, M. C. Ethical Solutions. 2009. 602p. 34.99 (978-1-4415-4503-9(4)); pap. 23.99 (978-1-4415-4502-2(6)) Xlibris Corp.

Ferrato, Elio. Developing Ethical Corporate Cultures. 2010. 156p. pap. (978-3-8383-4337-2(9)) Lambert Academic Publishing.

Ferrell, O. C., et al. Business Ethics: Ethical Decision Making & Cases. 8th ed. 2010. (Available Titles CourseMate Ser.). (ENG.). 544p. (C). pap. 135.95 (978-1-4390-4223-6(3)) Cengage South-Western.

—Ethical Business. 2009. (DK Essential Managers Ser.). (ENG.). 72p. (gr. 12-18). 8.00 (978-0-7566-4200-6(0)) Dorling Kindersley Publishing, Inc.

Fifty Lessons Staff, compiled by. Doing Business Ethically. 2009. (Lessons Learned Ser.). (ENG.). 112p. pap. 9.95 (978-1-4221-3985-1(9)) Harvard Business Review Pr.

Finser, Torin M. Initiative: A Rosicrucian Path of Leadership. 2011. 144p. pap. 15.00 (978-0-88010-734-1(0)) SteinerBooks, Inc.

—Organizational Integrity: How to Apply the Wisdom of the Body to Develop Healthy Organizations. 2007. (Illus.). 246p. 30.00 (978-0-88010-582-8(8)); per. 25.00 (978-0-88010-578-1(X)) SteinerBooks, Inc.

Fisher and, Phillips. Legal Ethical & Regulatory Environment. 2006. pap. 18.95 (978-1-4288-0549-1(4)) Cram101 Inc.

Fort, Timothy L. Business, Integrity, & Peace: Beyond Geopolitical & Disciplinary Boundaries. (Business, Value Creation, & Society Ser.). (ENG.). 270p. 2011. pap. 35.99 (978-1-107-40289-8(1)) 2007. (Illus.). 118.00 (978-0-521-86298-1(1)) Cambridge Univ. Pr.

—Prophets, Profits, & Peace: The Positive Role of Business in Promoting Religious Tolerance. 2008. (ENG.). 224p. 35.00 (978-0-300-11467-6(2)) Yale Univ. Pr.

Fox, Lawrence & Martyn, Susan J. The Ethics of Representing Organizations Legal Fictions for Clients. 2009. (ENG., Illus.). 256p. pap. 135.00 (978-0-19-537154-3(2)) Oxford Univ. Pr., Inc.

Frank, Robert H. What Price the Moral High Ground? How to Succeed Without Selling Your Soul. 2010. (ENG., Illus.). 224p. pap. 16.95 (978-0-691-14694-2(2)) Princeton Univ. Pr.

Franklin, Thomas F. Leadership: Where Business Ethics Begin. Serey, Jody, ed. 2007. 204p. 37.95 (978-1-881276-08-1(2)); pap. 27.95 (978-1-881276-07-4(4)) Serey/Jones Pubs.

—Leadership: Where Business Ethics Begin - Instructor's Edition. Serey, Jody, ed. 2009. 222p. pap. 37.95 (978-1-881276-10-4(4)) Serey/Jones Pubs.

—Leadership: Where Business Ethics Begin - Student's Edition. Serey, Jody, ed. 2009. 210p. pap. 27.95 (978-1-881276-11-1(2)) Serey/Jones Pubs.

Freeman, R. Edward. Managing for Stakeholders: Survival Reputation & Success. 2007. 284p. per. 35.00 (978-0-300-13848-1(2)) Yale Univ. Pr.

Freeman, R. Edward, et al. Managing for Stakeholders: Survival, Reputation, & Success. 2007. (Business Roundtable Institute for Corporate Ethics Series in Ethics & Lead). (ENG., Illus.). 200p. 26.00 (978-0-300-12528-3(3)) Yale Univ. Pr.

—Stakeholder Theory: The State of the Art. 2010. (ENG., Illus.). 362p. 99.00 (978-0-521-19081-7(9)); pap. 42.00 (978-0-521-13793-5(4)) Cambridge Univ. Pr.

Friedland, Julian. Doing Well & Good: The Human Face of the New Capitalism. 2009. 258p. (978-1-59311-788-7(4)) Information Age Publishing, Inc.

Friedland, Julian, ed. Doing Well & Good: The Human Face of the New Capitalism (PB) 2009. 260p. pap. 45.99 (978-1-59311-787-0(6)) Information Age Publishing, Inc.

Fritzsche, David J. Business Ethics: A Global & Managerial Perspective. 2nd ed. 2006. pap. 9.95 (978-1-4288-1217-8(2)) Cram101 Inc.

Frost, William P. Business Ethics in Catholic Perspectives. Date not set. 136p. (Orig.). (C). pap. (978-1-881003-05-2(1)) College Pr.

Fryer, Mick. Ethics & Organizational Leadership: Developing a Normative Model. 2011. (ENG.). 224p. 85.00 (978-0-19-959018-6(4)) Oxford Univ. Pr., Inc.

Gaffney, Steven & Francis, Colleen. Honesty Sells: How to Make More Money & Increase Business Profits. 2009. (ENG., Illus.). 224p. 24.95 (978-0-470-41153-7(6), Wiley) Wiley, John & Sons, Inc.

Galford, Robert M. & Drapeau, Anne Seibold. The Trusted Leader. 2011. (ENG.). 288p. pap. 18.99 (978-0-7432-3540-2(1), Free Pr.) Free Pr.

Galindo, Linda. The Accountability Experience Deluxe Set. 2010. (ENG.). 256p. ring bd. 240.00 (978-0-470-61022-0(0), Pfeiffer) Wiley, John & Sons, Inc.

—The Accountability Experience Facilitator's Guide, Set. 2010. (ENG.). ring bd. 225.00 (978-0-470-60710-7(6), Pfeiffer) Wiley, John & Sons, Inc.

—The Accountability Experience Fg Flashdrive. 2010. (ENG.). 50.00 (978-0-470-60460-1(3), Pfeiffer) Wiley, John & Sons, Inc.

—The Accountability Experience Participant Workbook. 2010. (ENG.). 80p. pap. 39.00 (978-0-470-60461-8(1), Pfeiffer) Wiley, John & Sons, Inc.

—The Accountability Experience Participant Workbook & Self Assessemnt. 2011. (ENG.). pap., wbk. ed. 45.00 (978-0-470-90365-0(1), Pfeiffer) Wiley, John & Sons, Inc.

—The Accountability Experience Poster. 2010. (ENG.). 1p. pap. 10.00 (978-0-470-60478-6(6), Pfeiffer) Wiley, John & Sons, Inc.

—The Accountability Experience Self-Assessment. 2010. (ENG.). 16p. pap. 12.00 (978-0-470-60462-5(X), Pfeiffer) Wiley, John & Sons, Inc.

—The 85% Solution: How Personal Accountability Guarantees Success — No Nonsense, No Excuses. 2009. (ENG., Illus.). 256p. 22.95 (978-0-470-50016-3(6), Jossey-Bass) Wiley, John & Sons, Inc.

Gall, Gregor, ed. The Future of Union Organizing: Building for Tomorrow. 2009. (ENG., Illus.). 288p. 100.00 (978-0-230-22242-7(0)) Palgrave Macmillan.

Gardner, Howard, ed. Responsibility at Work: How Leading Professionals Act (or Don't Act) Responsibly. 2007. (ENG.). 368p. 29.95 (978-0-7879-9475-4(8), Jossey-Bass) Wiley, John & Sons, Inc.

Garsten, Christina & Hernes, Tor. Ethical Dilemmas in Management. 2008. (Illus.). 184p. (ENG.). (C). pap. 44.95 (978-0-415-43760-8(1)); 175.00 (978-0-415-43759-2(8)) Routledge.

Gaulden, Dorothea E. Right Makes Might: Reviving Ethics to Improve Your Business. 2007. 75p. 19.95 (978-1-933538-86-0(4)) Bridgeway Bks.

Gehrcke, Robert. Independent Sri Rating Agencies. 2007. 80p. per. (978-3-8364-3212-2(9)) VDM Verlag Dr. Mueller e.K.

Gentile, Mary C. Giving Voice to Values: How to Speak Your Mind When You Know What's Right. 320p. 2012. (ENG.). pap. 18.00 (978-0-300-18156-2(6)) 2010. 26.00 (978-0-300-16118-2(2)) Yale Univ. Pr.

Ghate, Debi & Ralston, Richard E., eds. Why Businessmen Need Philosophy: The Capitalist's Guide to the Ideas Behind Ayn Rand's Atlas Shrugged. 2011. (ENG.). 336p. (gr. 12). 15.00 (978-0-451-23269-4(0), N A L Trade) Penguin Group (USA) Inc.

Ghillyer, Andrew. Business Ethics Now. 3rd ed. 2011. (ENG., Illus.). 256p. (C). pap. 96.00 (978-0-07-352469-6(7), 0073524697) McGraw-Hill Higher Education.

Ghillyer, Andrew W. Business Ethics. 2nd ed. 2009. (ENG., Illus.). 384p. (C). pap. 96.00 (978-0-07-337710-0(4), 0073377104) McGraw-Hill Higher Education.

Gibson, Kevin. Ethics & Business: An Introduction. 2007. (Cambridge Applied Ethics Ser.). (ENG.). 274p. (C). pap. 37.00 (978-0-521-68245-9(2)); 105.00 (978-0-521-86379-7(1)) Cambridge Univ. Pr.

Gilbert, Joseph. Ethics for Managers. 2012. (ENG., Illus.). 304p. 100.00 (978-0-415-80708-1(5)); pap. 49.95 (978-0-415-80709-8(3)) Routledge.

Gill, David W. It's about Excellence: Building Ethically Healthy Organizations. 2011. 222p. pap. 25.00 (978-1-61097-609-1(6), Wipf and Stock) Wipf & Stock Pubs.

Gilliland, Stephen, et al. Emerging Perspectives on Organizational Justice & Ethics. 2012. 296p. (978-1-61735-582-0(8)); pap. (978-1-61735-581-3(X)); E-Book (978-1-61735-583-7(6)) Information Age Publishing, Inc.

Gini, Al & Marcoux, Alexei. The Ethics of Business: A Concise Introduction. 2011. (Elements of Philosophy Ser.). (ENG.). 164p. (C). (gr. 13-17). 75.00 (978-0-7425-6161-8(5)) Rowman & Littlefield Publishers, Inc.

Gini, Al & Marcoux, Alexei, eds. The Ethics of Business: A Concise Introduction. 2011. (Elements of Philosophy Ser.). (ENG.). 164p. (C). (gr. 13-17). pap. 24.95 (978-0-7425-6162-5(3)) Rowman & Littlefield Publishers, Inc.

—The Ethics of How to Do Business: Competitions, Entrepreneurship, & Risk. 2012. (Elements of Philosophy Ser.). (ENG.). pap. 58.00 (978-0-7425-6164-9(X)) Rowman & Littlefield Publishers, Inc.

Gini, Al & Marcoux, Alexei M. Case Studies in Business Ethics. 6th ed. 2008. (ENG., Illus.). 448p. (C). per. 90.40 (978-0-13-242432-5(0), Prentice Hall) Prentice Hall PTR.

Gini, Al & Marcoux, Alexei M. The Ethics of Business: A Concise Introduction. 2011. E-Book (978-1-4422-1434-7(1)) Rowman & Littlefield Publishers, Inc.

Gitlow, Abraham L. Corruption in Corporate America: Who Is Responsible? Who Will Protect the Public Interest? 2nd ed. 2007. (ENG.). 244p. 62.99 (978-0-7618-3811-1(2)); per. 39.99 (978-0-7618-3812-8(0)) Univ. Pr. of America, Inc.

Gladis, Stephen D. The Trusted Leader: Trust. 2010. 139p. pap. 19.95 (978-1-59996-204-7(7)) Human Resource Development Pr.

Glautier, Michel. The Social Conscience: Can a Caring Society Exist in a Market Economy? 2007. (ENG.). 384p. 37.95 (978-0-85683-248-2(0)) Shepheard-Walwyn Pubs., Ltd. GBR. Dist: Independent Pubs. Group.

Global Business: Managing Risk & Responsibility Across Borders. 2nd rev. ed. 2011. (Illus.). 480p. (C). 175.23 (978-0-415-60035-4(9)); pap. 72.95 (978-0-415-60037-8(5)) Routledge.

Global Economics Crisis Resource Center. Global Economic Crisis: Impact on Business Ethics & Society. 2009. (ENG.). 32p. (C). pap. 20.95 (978-0-538-74330-3(1)) Cengage South-Western.

Goldman, Stephen M. Temptations in the Office: Ethical Choices & Legal Obligations, 1 vol. 2008. 224p. 39.95 *(978-0-275-99675-8(1)*, C9675, Praeger Pubs.) Greenwood Publishing Group, Inc.

Goodpaster, Nash. Business Ethics Policies & Persons. 2006. pap. 12.95 *(978-1-4288-1201-7(6))* Cram101 Inc.

Goree, Keith. Ethics in the Workplace. 3rd ed. 2011. (ENG., Illus.). 250p. (C). pap. 61.95 *(978-0-538-49777-0(7))* Cengage South-Western.

Goree, Keith & Addis, Donald G. Education Ethics Applied. 2nd ed. 2007. (Illus.). xxxv, 387p. 67.20 *(978-0-536-32228-9(7))* Pearson Education.

Green, Charles H. & Howe, Andrea P. The Trusted Advisor Fieldbook: A Comprehensive Toolkit for Leading with Trust. 2011. (ENG., Illus.). 270p. pap. 27.95 ***(978-1-118-08564-6(7)***, Wiley) Wiley, John & Sons, Inc.

Greenberg, Michael D. Directors As Guardians of Compliance & Ethics Within the Corporate Citadel: What the Policy Community Should Know. 2010. 74p. pap. 20.00 *(978-0-8330-5032-8(X)*, cf-277) RAND Corp., The.

—Perspectives of Chief Ethics & Compliance Officers on the Detection & Prevention of Corporate Misdeeds: What the Policy Community Should Know. 2009. 74p. pap. 23.00 *(978-0-8330-4726-7(4)*, CF-258) RAND Corp., The.

Greene, Francis J., et al. Three Decades of Enterprise Culture? Entrepreneurship, Economic Regeneration & Public Policy. 2008. (ENG., Illus.). 288p. 100.00 *(978-1-4039-4102-2(5))* Palgrave Macmillan.

Gregg, Samuel & Stoner, James. Profit, Prudence & Virtue: Essays in Ethics, Business & Management. Gregg, Samuel & Stoner, James, eds. 2009. (St. Andrews Studies in Philosophy & Public Affairs Ser.). (ENG.). 300p. 80.00 *(978-1-84540-158-0(1))*; pap. 34.90 *(978-1-84540-159-7(X))* Imprint Academic GBR. Dist: Ingram Pub. Services.

Gregg, Samuel & Stoner, James Reist. Rethinking Business Management: Examining the Foundations of Business Education. 2008. (ENG.). x, 220p. (C). 25.00 *(978-0-9814911-0-3(3))* ISI Bks.

Griseri. Business Ethics. 2010. (Illus.). xxiv, 471p. pap. 69.99 *(978-1-4080-0743-3(6))* CENGAGE Learning.

Grudzewski, Wieslaw M., et al. Trust Management in Virtual Organizations: A Human Factors Perspective. 2008. (ENG., Illus.). 256p. 97.95 *(978-1-4200-6890-0(3)*, CRC Press) Taylor & Francis Group GBR. Dist: Taylor & Francis Group.

Gupta, Dipankar. Ethics Incorporated: Top Priority & Bottom Line. rev. ed. 2006. (Response Bks.). 216p. (C). 71.00 *(978-0-7619-3470-7(7)*, B34707C); per. 31.95 *(978-0-7619-3471-4(5)*, B34707P) SAGE Pubns., Inc.

Gupta, Nishang. Investing for the Fair-Weather Fan. 2003. 76p. pap. 16.95 *(978-1-60610-867-3(0))* PublishAmerica, Inc.

Guy, Mary E. Ethical Decision Making in Everyday Work Situations, 1 vol. 206p. pap. 20.00 ***(978-0-313-36052-7(9)***, BGYE/) Greenwood Publishing Group, Inc.

Haase, Michaela & Cowton, Christopher, eds. Trends in Business & Economic Ethics. 2008. (Ethical Economy Ser.). (ENG., Illus.). vi, 272p. 149.00 *(978-3-540-79471-4(9)*, 3540794719) Springer.

Hadley, Arthur Twining. Standards of Public Morality. 2010. (ENG.). 180p. pap. 22.75 *(978-1-176-99222-1(8))* 2010. (ENG.). 176p. pap. 22.75 *(978-1-177-97598-8(X))* 2010. 180p. pap. 22.75 *(978-1-146-07612-8(6))* 2010. 172p. pap. 21.75 *(978-1-141-41252-5(7))* 2009. 168p. 26.99 *(978-1-113-90388-4(0))* 2009. 168p. 30.99 *(978-1-113-90390-7(2))* 2009. (ENG.). 167p. pap. 19.99 *(978-1-113-90380-8(5)*, BiblioLife) 2009. 168p. pap. 16.99 *(978-1-113-90384-6(8))* 2009. 168p. pap. 21.75 *(978-1-113-90386-0(4))* BiblioBazaar.

—Standards of Public Morality. 168p. 2010. 29.56 *(978-1-163-39784-8(9))* 2010. pap. 17.56 *(978-1-162-92944-6(8))* 2007. (ENG.). 36.95 *(978-0-548-08968-2(X))* Kessinger Publishing, LLC.

Hafrey, Leigh. The Story of Success: Five Steps to Mastering Ethics in Business. 2009. (ENG.). 270p. pap. 21.00 *(978-1-59051-354-5(1))* Other Pr., LLC.

Halbert, Terry & Ingulli, Elaine. Law & Ethics in the Business Environment. 7th ed. 2011. (ENG.). 416p. (C). pap. 158.95 *(978-0-538-47351-4(7))* Cengage South-Western.

Hamington, Maurice & Sander-Staudt, Maureen, eds. Applying Care Ethics to Business. 2011. (Issues in Business Ethics Ser.). 300p. 189.00 *(978-90-481-9306-6(0)*, 9048193060) Springer.

Hanekamp, G., ed. Business Ethics of Innovation. 2007. (Ethics of Science & Technology Assessment Ser.). (Illus.). 110p. 69.95 *(978-3-540-72309-7(9))* Springer.

Hanekamp, Gerd, ed. Business Ethics of Innovation. 2010. (Ethics of Science & Technology Assessment Ser.). (Illus.). xvi, 110p. pap. 69.95 *(978-3-642-09140-7(7)*, 3642091407) Springer.

Harper, Tom & Broadman and Holman Publishers Staff. Leading from the Lions' Den: Leadership Principles from Every Book of the Bible. 2010. (ENG.). 240p. pap. 12.99 *(978-0-8054-4442-1(4)*, B&H Bks.) B&H Publishing Group.

Hartman, Laura P. The Global Corporation: Sustainable, Effective & Ethical Practices. 2009. (ENG., Illus.). VIII, 432p. 110.00 *(978-0-415-80161-4(3))* Routledge.

—The Global Corporation: Sustainable, Effective & Ethical Practices, A Case Book. 2009. (ENG., Illus.). 440p. pap. 69.95 *(978-0-415-80160-7(5))* Routledge.

—Perspectives in Business Ethics. 3rd ed. 2006. pap. 14.95 *(978-1-4288-1223-9(7))* Cram101 Inc.

Hartman, Laura P. & DesJardins, Joe. Business Ethics: Decision-Making for Personal Integrity & Social Responsibility. 2nd ed. 2010. (ENG., Illus.). 624p. (C). pap. 124.00 *(978-0-07-813713-6(6)*, 0078137136, McGraw-Hill/Irwin) McGraw-Hill Higher Education.

Hawthorne, Fran. Ethical Chic: The Inside Story of the Companies We Think We Love. 2012. (ENG.). 224p. 25.95 ***(978-0-8070-0094-6(9))*** Beacon Pr.

Heal, Geoffrey. When Principles Pay: Corporate Social Responsibility & the Bottom Line. 2008. (Columbia Business School Publishing Ser.). (ENG., Illus.). 288p. (gr. 17). 29.95 *(978-0-231-14400-1(8))* Columbia Univ. Pr.

Heller, Victor. Ethical Dilemmas: How Do You Measure Up? 2007. 234p. pap. 52.95 *(978-0-7575-3900-8(9))* Kendall Hunt Publishing Co.

Henn, Stephen K. & Henn. Business Ethics: A Case Study Approach. 2009. (ENG., Illus.). 192p. 60.00 *(978-0-470-45067-3(3)*, Wiley) Wiley, John & Sons, Inc.

Henriques, Adrian. Corporate Truth: The Limits to Transparency. 2007. (ENG., Illus.). 180p. 44.95 *(978-1-84407-390-0(4))* Routledge.

Hicks, Stephen. Ayn Rand & Contemporary Business Ethics. 2007. 30p. 5.95 *(978-0-9794270-3-9(7))* Ctr. for Ethics & Entrepreneurship.

Higginson, Thomas Wentworth. Merchants: A Sunday evening Lecture ... 2011. 32p. pap. 11.99 ***(978-1-4181-9437-6(9))*** MPublishing.

Hill, Napoleon & Clason, George. Think & Grow Rich by Napoleon Hill & the Richest Man in Babylon by George S Clason. 2007. 264p. per. *(978-956-291-511-3(5))* Editorial Benei Noaj.

Hodgson, Tim. Jump Start Your Coaching Business. 2007. 240p. pap. 41.95 *(978-1-4303-2524-6(0))* Lulu Enterprises Inc.

Hoffman, Andrew. Hank Thaler: Ethics of Disclosure. 2010. (C). pap. 7.00 *(978-1-61674-501-1(0))*; pap. 7.00 *(978-1-61674-503-5(7))* Davidson, William Institute At The Univ. of Michigan, The.

Holden, Phillip. Etica para Managers.Tr. of Ethics for Managers. (SPA.). 300p. *(978-84-493-1156-1(6))* Ediciones Paidos Iberica, S.A. ESP. Dist: I S H K.

Holland and Knight, LLP Staff. Corporate Compliance Answer Book 2009. Myers, Christopher, ed. 2009. 1145p. pap. 295.00 *(978-1-4024-1126-7(X))* Practising Law Institute.

Hollender, Jeffrey. What Matters Most: How a Small Group of Pioneers Is Teaching Social Responsibility to Big Business, & Why Big Business Is Listening. 2011. (ENG.). 326p. pap. 17.00 ***(978-1-4379-7773-8(1))*** DIANE Publishing Co.

Holzer, B. Moralizing the Corporation: Transnational Activism & Corporate Accountability. 2010. (Illus.). 192p. 112.00 *(978-1-84844-759-2(0))* Elgar, Edward Publishing, Inc.

Hongladaram, Soraj & Ess, Charles. Information Technology Ethics: Cultural Perspectives. 2006. (Premier Reference Source Ser.). pap. 165.00 *(978-1-59904-311-1(4))* IGI Global.

Honiball, George. The Relationship Between Spirituality & Work Performance. 2010. 132p. pap. *(978-3-8383-5333-3(1))* Lambert Academic Publishing.

Hooker, John. Business Ethics as Rational Choice. 2010. (ENG., Illus.). 120p. (C). pap. 44.00 *(978-0-13-611867-1(4))* Prentice Hall PTR.

Hoover, Robert Shannon. Ethical Climate, Organizational Support & Affective Well-Being. 2008. 116p. pap. *(978-3-639-05021-9(5))* VDM Verlag Dr. Mueller e.K.

Hosmer, La Rue Tone. The Ethics of Management. (ENG., Illus.). (C). 6th ed. 2007. 204p. pap. 96.67 *(978-0-07-340503-2(5)*, 0073405035) 7th ed. 2010. 208p. pap. 96.67 *(978-0-07-353054-3(9)*, 0073530549) McGraw-Hill Higher Education. (McGraw-Hill/Irwin).

Howard, Ronald A., et al. Ethics for the Real World: Creating a Personal Code to Guide Decisions in Work & Life. 2008. (ENG., Illus.). 224p. 27.00 *(978-1-4221-2106-1(2))* Harvard Business Review Pr.

Hoyk, Robert & Hersey, Paul. The Ethical Executive: Becoming Aware of the Root Causes of Unethical Behavior - 45 Psychological Traps That Every One of Us Falls Prey To. 2010. (ENG.). 152p. pap. 17.95 *(978-0-8047-7178-8(2)*, Stanford Business Bks.) Stanford Univ. Pr.

Huffman, Robert K. & Levy, Frederic M. Guide to the Mandatory Disclosure Rule: Issues, Guidelines, & Best Practices: Report of the Task Force on Implementation of the Contractor Code of Business Ethics & Conduct & Mandatory Disclosure Rule. 2010. (Illus.). ***(978-1-60442-782-0(5))*** American Bar Assn.

Huntsman, Jon M. & Beck, Glenn. Winners Never Cheat: Even in Difficult Times. exp. ed. 2008. (ENG.). 256p. 22.99 *(978-0-13-700903-9(8))* Wharton Schl. Publishing.

Hutchens, David & Rellaford, Barry. Slice of Trust: The Leadership Secret with the Hot & Fruity Filling, 1 vol. 2011. (ENG., Illus.). 112p. 16.99 *(978-1-4236-2118-8(2))* Gibbs Smith, Publisher.

Hyndman, Maxine. The Organic Entrepreneur: Cultivating the Conscious Capitalist. 2007. (ENG., Illus.). 192p. per. *(978-1-897178-28-7(X))* Insomniac Pr.

International Trade Centre. Consumer Conscience: How Environment & Ethics are Influencing Exports. 2010. (ENG.). 72p. pap. 50.00 *(978-92-9137-379-6(6))* United Nations Pubns.

Jackall, Robert. Moral Mazes: The World of Corporate Managers. 20th rev. ed. 2009. (ENG.). 320p. pap. 19.95 *(978-0-19-972988-3(3))* Oxford Univ. Pr., Inc.

Jackson, Kevin T. Virtuosity in Business: Invisible Law Guiding the Invisible Hand. 2011. 376p. (C). 79.95 ***(978-0-8122-4376-5(5))*** Univ. of Pennsylvania Pr.

Jackson, Terence. International Management Ethics: A Critical, Cross-Cultural Perspective. 2011. (ENG., Illus.). 308p. 99.00 *(978-0-521-85344-6(3))*; pap. 36.99 *(978-0-521-61865-6(7))* Cambridge Univ. Pr.

Jasso, Sean D. The New Corporation - Aristotle, Sarbanes-Oxley, & the Future Manager. 2008. 152p. pap. *(978-3-639-07521-2(8))* VDM Verlag Dr. Mueller e.K.

Jennings. Business Ethics. 2006. (ENG.). pap. 12.95 *(978-1-4288-0624-5(5))* Cram101 Inc.

—Im-Business: Legal, Ethical, & Global Environment. 2009. *(978-0-324-65542-1(8))* Cengage South-Western.

Jennings, Marianne M. Business: It's Legal, Ethical & Global Environment. 6th ed. 2006. pap. 20.95 *(978-1-4288-1060-0(9))* Cram101 Inc.

—Business: Its Legal, Ethical, & Global Environment. 9th ed. 2010. (ENG.). 896p. (C). 264.95 *(978-0-538-47054-4(2))* Cengage South-Western.

—Business Ethics: Case Studies & Selected Readings. 7th ed. 2011. (ENG.). 640p. (C). pap. 153.95 *(978-0-538-47353-8(3))* Cengage South-Western.

Jennings, Marianne Moody. Business: Its Legal, Ethical, & Global Environment. 8th ed. 2008. (ENG., Illus.). 896p. (C). 264.95 *(978-0-324-65554-4(1))* Cengage South-Western.

—Business Ethics: Case Studies & Selected Readings. 6th ed. 2008. (ENG., Illus.). 640p. (C). per. 158.95 *(978-0-324-65774-6(9))* Cengage South-Western.

Johnson, Craig E. Ethics in the Workplace: Tools & Tactics for Organizational Transformation. 2006. (Illus.). 368p. (C). per. 55.00 *(978-1-4129-0539-8(7)*, B05389P) SAGE Pubns., Inc.

Johnson, Craig E. Organizational Ethics: A Practical Approach. 2nd ed. 2011. (Illus.). 480p. (C). pap. 55.00 ***(978-1-4129-8796-7(2)***, B87967P) SAGE Pubns., Inc.

Johnson, W. Brad, et al. Elements of Ethics: For Professionals. 2008. (ENG., Illus.). 240p. 22.95 *(978-0-230-60391-2(2))* Palgrave Macmillan.

Johnston, Herbert. Business Ethics. 2011. 320p. 50.95 ***(978-1-258-07119-6(3))*** Literary Licensing, LLC.

Johnston, Jessica R. Technological Turf Wars: A Case Study of the Computer Antivirus Industry. 2008. (ENG.). 232p. 69.00 *(978-1-59213-881-4(0))*; pap. 24.95 *(978-1-59213-882-1(9))* Temple Univ. Pr.

Johnston, Phil. Biscuitville: The Secret Recipe for Building a Sustainable Competitive Advantage. 2009. (ENG.). 208p. 21.95 *(978-1-935212-05-8(2))* Easton Studio Pr., LLC.

Kanes, Clive, ed. Elaborating Professionalism: Studies in Practice & Theory. 2010. (Innovation & Change in Professional Education Ser.). (ENG., Illus.). 205p. 139.00 *(978-90-481-2604-0(5)*, 9048126045) Springer.

Kavaliauskas, Tomas. The Individual in Business Ethics: An American Cultural Perspective. 2011. (ENG., Illus.). 192p. 95.00 *(978-0-230-28553-8(8))* Palgrave Macmillan.

Keeble, Richard Lance. Ethical Space. Keeble, Richard Lance & Mattheson, Donald, eds. 2011. 74p. pap. ***(978-1-84549-480-3(6)***, Abramis) arima publishing.

Kerf, Raoul de. De Juiste Prijs in de Laatmiddeleeuwse Stad: Een Onderzoek Naar Middeleeuwse Economische Ethiek Op de Ambachtelijke Markt en in Moralistische Lekenliteratuur. 2010. (Studies Stadsgeschiedenis Ser.). (DUT.). 197p. 36.00 ***(978-90-5260-366-7(9))*** Aksant Academic Pubs. NLD. Dist: Amsterdam Univ. Pr.

Kettles, Nick, et al. Working Ethically. . . on a Shoestring: Creating a Sustainable Business Without Breaking the Bank. 2007. (Business on a Shoestring Ser.). (ENG.). 168p. per. 12.95 *(978-0-7136-7548-1(9))* A & C Black GBR. Dist: Macmillan.

Khalsa, Mahan & Illig, Randy. Let's Get Real or Let's Not Play: Transforming the Buyer/Seller Relationship. 2008. (ENG.). 256p. (gr. 12-18). 27.95 *(978-1-59184-226-2(3)*, Portfolio (Hardcover)) Penguin Group (USA) Inc.

Kitson, Alan & Campbell, Robert. The Ethical Organisation. 2nd rev. ed. 2008. (ENG., Illus.). 280p. pap. 49.00 *(978-0-333-99421-4(3))* Palgrave Macmillan.

Klemmer, Brian. The Compassionate Samurai: Being Extraordinary in an Ordinary World. 2007. 24.95 *(978-0-9779452-9-0(4))* Foghorn Pubs.

Kliem, PMP, Ralph L., Ralph L. Ethics & Project Management. 2011. (ENG., Illus.). 244p. 69.95 *(978-1-4398-5261-3(8))* Auerbach Pubs., Inc.

Klikauer, Thomas. Critical Management Ethics. 2010. (ENG., Illus.). 240p. 100.00 *(978-0-230-23825-1(4))* Palgrave Macmillan.

Kline, John. Ethics for International Business: Decision-Making in a Global Political Economy. 2nd ed. 2010. (ENG., Illus.). 296p. (C). 190.00 *(978-0-415-99942-7(1))*; pap. 64.95 *(978-0-415-99943-4(X))* Routledge.

Kliukinskaite Vigil, Virginija. Individual Decision Making Process Related to Ethical Issues. 2009. 122p. pap. *(978-3-639-18513-3(7))* VDM Verlag Dr. Mueller e.K.

Knapp, John C., ed. For the Common Good: The Ethics of Leadership in the 21st Century, 1 vol. 2006. 192p. 44.95 *(978-0-275-99259-0(4)*, C9259, Praeger Pubs.) Greenwood Publishing Group, Inc.

—Leaders on Ethics: Real-World Perspectives on Today's Business Challenges, 1 vol. 2007. 136p. 39.95 *(978-0-275-99671-0(9)*, C9671, Praeger Pubs.) Greenwood Publishing Group, Inc.

Kolb, Robert W., ed. Encyclopedia of Business Ethics & Society, 5 vols., Set. 2007. 2592p. 835.00 *(978-1-4129-1652-3(6)*, B16526C) SAGE Pubns., Inc.

Kolk, Ans & Pinkse, Jonatan. International Business & Global Climate Change. 2009. (ENG., Illus.). 216p. (C). 160.00 *(978-0-415-41552-1(7))* Routledge.

—International Business & Global Climate Change. 2008. (ENG., Illus.). 216p. (C). pap. 54.95 *(978-0-415-41553-8(5))* Routledge.

Komisarjevsky, Chris. The Power of Reputation: Strengthen the Asset That Will Make or Break Your Career, 1 vol. 2012. (ENG.). 224p. 22.00 ***(978-0-8144-1797-3(3))*** Amacom.

Koslowski, Peter, et al, eds. Business Ethics & the Electronic Economy. 2010. (Studies in Economic Ethics & Philosophy Ser.). (Illus.). ix, 248p. pap. 179.00 *(978-3-642-06055-7(2)*, 3642060552) Springer.

Koslowski, Peter. The Ethics of Banking: Conclusions from the Financial Crisis. 2011. (Issues in Business Ethics Ser.). (ENG.). xv, 214p. 139.00 *(978-94-007-0655-2(3)*, 9400706553) Springer.

Koslowski, Peter, ed. Contemporary Economic Ethics & Business Ethics. 2010. (Studies in Economic Ethics & Philosophy Ser.). (Illus.). x, 265p. pap. 189.00 *(978-3-642-08591-8(1)*, 3642085911) Springer.

—Shareholder Value und die Kriterien des Unternehmenserfolgs. 2007. (Ethische Ökonomie: Beiträge zur Wirtschaftsethik und Wirtschaftskultur Ser.). (GER., Illus.). X, 261p. pap. 61.00 *(978-3-7908-1179-7(3)*, 3790811793) Springer.

Kothari, Vinay B. Executive Greed: Examining Business Failures that Contributed to the Economic Crisis. 2010. (ENG.). 208p. 68.00 *(978-0-230-10401-3(0))* Palgrave Macmillan.

Kraemer, Harry M. From Values to Action: The Four Principles of Values-Based Leadership. 2011. (ENG., Illus.). 224p. 27.95 *(978-0-470-88125-5(9)*, Jossey-Bass) Wiley, John & Sons, Inc.

Kramer, Roderick M. & Cook, Karen S., eds. Trust & Distrust in Organizations: Dilemmas & Approaches. 2007. (Russell Sage Foundation Series on Trust). (Illus.). 381p. per. 24.95 *(978-0-87154-486-5(5))* Russell Sage Foundation.

Kuhns, John D. China Fortunes: A Tale of Business in the New World. 2011. (ENG.). 592p. 34.95 *(978-0-470-92804-2(2)*, Wiley) Wiley, John & Sons, Inc.

Kumar, Brij Nino & Steinmann, Horst, eds. Ethics in International Management. (De Gruyter Studies in Organization Ser.). (ENG.). XXII, 463p. 84.00 ***(978-3-11-187044-1(8))*** De Gruyter, Walter Inc.

Lakhani, Salim. How to Select a Vendor for Web Development. 2008. 136p. pap. 99.95 *(978-1-4303-2586-4(0))* Lulu Enterprises Inc.

Lane, Bill. Losing It: Behaviors & Mindsets That Ruin Careers - Lessons on Protecting Yourself from Avoidable Mistakes. 2012. (ENG.). 176p. 27.99 ***(978-0-13-304024-1(0))*** FT Press.

Lange, Heiko, et al, eds. Working Across Cultures: Ethical Perspectives for Intercultural Management. 2010. (Issues in Business Ethics Ser.). 364p. pap. 279.00 *(978-90-481-4893-6(6)*, 9048148936) Springer.

Languilaire, Jean-Charles. Experiencing Work/Non-Work. 2010. 528p. pap. *(978-3-8383-5130-8(4))* Lambert Academic Publishing.

Lecker, Martin J. D., ed. Conducting Business Ethically: A Philosophical Approach. rev. ed. 2011. (ENG.). 258p. pap. 54.95 *(978-0-7575-7497-9(1))* Kendall Hunt Publishing Co.

Ledeneva, Alena V. How Russia Really Works: The Informal Practices That Shaped Post-Soviet Politics & Business. 2006. (Culture & Society after Socialism Ser.). (Illus.). 270p. 75.50 *(978-0-8014-4346-6(6))* Cornell Univ. Pr.

—How Russia Really Works: The Informal Practices That Shaped Post-Soviet Politics & Bussiness. 2006. (Culture & Society after Socialism Ser.). (Illus.). 270p. per. 24.95 *(978-0-8014-7352-4(7))* Cornell Univ. Pr.

Lennick, Doug & Kiel, Fred. Moral Intelligence: Enhancing Business Performance & Leadership Success. 2007. (ENG., Illus.). 336p. per. 18.99 *(978-0-13-234986-4(8))* Wharton Schl. Publishing.

—Moral Intelligence 2. 0: Enhancing Business Performance & Leadership Success in Turbulent Times. rev. ed. 2011. (ENG.). 336p. 25.99 *(978-0-13-249828-9(6))* Wharton Schl. Publishing.

Levitt, Evan. Honest Business People: Top Advocates, Consultants & Lwayers! 2009. 270p. pap. 16.95 *(978-1-4327-3479-4(2))* Outskirts Pr., Inc.

Lipman, Frederick D. Whistleblowers: Incentives, Disincentives, & Protection Strategies. 2011. (Wiley Corporate F&a Ser.: 575). (ENG., Illus.). 272p. 65.00 ***(978-1-118-09403-7(4)***, Wiley) Wiley, John & Sons, Inc.

Long, Deborah H. Ethics for the Real Estate Professional. 3rd ed. 2007. (ENG.). 80p. (C). pap. 13.95 *(978-0-324-65100-3(7))* Cengage South-Western.

Lorne Cummings Chris Pate Staff. Determining Stakeholder Prominence: An Empirical Study in Asia. 2009. (Illus.). xi, 219p. 114.95 *(978-1-84855-254-8(8))* Emerald Group Publishing Ltd. GBR. Dist: Turpin Distribution Services Ltd.

Lorsch, Jay W., ed. The Future of Boards: Leading HBS Thinkers on Meeting the Governance Challenges of the 21st Century. 2012. (ENG.). 208p. 35.00 ***(978-1-4221-8321-2(1))*** Harvard Business Review Pr.

Lovas, Michael & Holloway, Pam. Axis of Influence: How Credibility & Likeability Intersect to Drive Success. 2009. (ENG., Illus.). viii, 182p. pap. 16.95 *(978-1-60037-534-7(0))* Morgan James Publishing.

Lozano, Josep M. The Relational Company: Responsibility, Sustainability, Citizenship. 2009. (Frontiers of Business Ethics Ser.). 188p. pap. 48.95 *(978-3-03911-940-0(0))* Lang, Peter AG GBR. Dist: Lang, Peter.

Luetge, Chrisoph, et al, eds. Globalisation & Business Ethics. 2007. (Law, Ethics & Economics Ser.). (Illus.). 256p. 114.95 *(978-0-7546-4817-8(6))* Ashgate Publishing Co.

Luetge, Christoph, et al. Corporate Citizenship, Contractarianism & Ethical Theory: On Philosophical Foundations of Business Ethics. Conill, Jesus & Luetge, Christoph, eds. Schoenwaelder-Kuntze, Tatjana, ed. 2008. (Law, Ethics & Economics Ser.). (Illus.). 206p. 124.95 *(978-0-7546-7383-5(9))* Ashgate Publishing Co.

Luyk, Angella. Wisdom in a Traffic Jam: The Secrets Nobody Tells You about Owning an Amazing Successful Business. 2011. (ENG.). 140p. pap. 14.95 *(978-1-60037-976-5(1))* Morgan James Publishing.

Machan, Tibor R. The Morality of Business: A Profession for Human Wealthcare. 2010. (ENG.). xii, 138p. pap. 124.00 *(978-1-4419-4312-5(9)*, 1441943129) Springer.

—The Morality of Business: A Profession for Human Wealthcare. 2007. (ENG.). xii, 138p. 124.00 *(978-0-387-48906-3(1)*, 0387489061) Springer London, Ltd. GBR. Dist: Springer.

Manz. The Virtuous Organization. 2008. 69.00 *(978-981-281-859-1(6))* World Scientific Publishing Co., Inc.

B

Marburger, Ari. Business Halachah: A Practical Halachic Guide to Modern Business. 2008. (ArtScroll Halachah Ser.). 287p. (978-1-4226-0547-9(7)) Mesorah Pubns., Ltd.

Marr, Steve. Integrity in the Workplace: Blueprint for Today's Business Success. 2007. 196p. per. 9.99 (978-0-88270-339-8(0)) Bridge-Logos Foundation.

Matten, Dirk & Crane, Andy, eds. New Directions in Business Ethics, 4 vols. 2012. (SAGE Library in Business & Management Ser.). (Illus.). 1720p. 895.00 (978-0-85702-988-1(6), B02988C) SAGE Pubns., Ltd. GBR. Dist: SAGE Pubns., Inc.

Mawere, Munyaradzi. Moral Degeneration in Contemporary Zimbabwean Business Practices. 2011. 188p. pap. (978-9956-726-97-4(4)) Langaa Research & Publishing Common Initiative Group.

McAdams, Tony. Law Business & Society. 7th ed. 2006. pap. 9.95 (978-1-4288-1731-9(X)) Cram101 Inc.

McAdams, Tony. Law, Business & Society. 10th ed. 2011. (ENG., Illus.). 944p. (C). 216.00 (978-0-07-352500-6(6), 0073525006, McGraw-Hill/Irwin) McGraw-Hill Higher Education.

McCallister, Bill. Your Business & Your Life. 2009. 220p. pap. 16.95 (978-0-9820938-6-3(1)) Hillcrest Publishing Group, Inc.

McCloskey, Deirdre N. The Bourgeois Virtues: Ethics for an Age of Commerce. (Illus.). 634p. 2007. pap. 22.50 (978-0-226-55664-2(6)) 2006. 32.50 (978-0-226-55663-5(8)) Univ. of Chicago Pr.

McCoy, Bowen H. Living into Leadership: A Journey in Ethics. 2007. (ENG.). 232p. 24.95 (978-0-8047-5576-4(0)) Stanford Univ. Pr.

Mccreadie, Karen. George S. Clason's the Richest Man. 2008. 128p. 14.00 (978-1-905940-97-4(1)) Infinite Ideas GBR. Dist: Sony Electronics.

McKibben, W. T. Play Nice, Make Money. 2007. per. 19.95 net. (978-1-60402-412-8(7)) Independent Pub.

McKinley, Mary M., ed. Ethics in Marketing & Communications: Towards a Global Perspective. 2012. (ENG., Illus.). 144p. 90.00 (978-0-230-35855-3(1)) Palgrave Macmillan.

McLachlan, Jane-Ann. Ethics in Theory & Practice. 2008. (ENG., Illus.). 336p. (C). pap. (978-0-13-206496-5(0)) Pearson Education Canada.

McMahon, Christopher. Public Capitalism: The Political Authority of Corporate Executives. 2012. (Haney Foundation Ser.). 208p. (C). 39.95 (978-0-8122-4444-1(3)) Univ. of Pennsylvania Pr.

Mele, Domenec. Business Ethics in Action: Seeking Human Excellence in Organizations. 2009. (ENG., Illus.). 320p. pap. 51.00 (978-0-230-57310-9(X)) Palgrave Macmillan.

Melé, Domènec. Management Ethics: Placing Ethics at the Core of Good Management. 2011. (IESE Business Collection). (ENG., Illus.). 192p. 40.00 (978-0-230-24630-0(3)) Palgrave Macmillan.

Mellahi, Kamel, et al. The Ethical Business: Challenges & Controversies. 2nd rev. ed. 2010. (ENG., Illus.). 352p. pap. 50.00 (978-0-230-54693-6(5)) Palgrave Macmillan.

Merrill. Muddy Boots: Ethical in the Construction Field. 33.00 net. (978-0-534-55169-8(6)) CENGAGE Learning.

Merz, Robert L. A Declaration of American Business Values: Ethics, Equity & Efficiency in the New Millennium. 2006. 148p. per. (978-0-9765868-1-4(9)) Values of America Co.

Michalos, Alex C. & Poff, Deborah C., eds. Citation Classics from the Journal of Business Ethics: Celebrating the First Thirty Years of Publication. 2012. (Advances in Business Ethics Research Ser.). (ENG., Illus.). viii, 682p. pap. 279.00 (978-94-007-4125-6(1), 9400741251) Springer.

Millar, Carla & Poole, Eve, eds. Ethical Leadership: Global Challenges & Perspectives. 2011. (ENG., Illus.). 208p. 95.00 (978-0-230-27546-1(X)) Palgrave Macmillan.

Miller, Allan. Determinants of Ethical Behaviour of Managers in Malaysi. 2009. 136p. pap. (978-3-639-16064-2(9)) VDM Verlag Dr. Mueller e.K.

Minkler, Alanson. Integrity & Agreement: Economics When Principles Also Matter. 2008. (Economics, Cognition & Society Ser.). (ENG., Illus.). 184p. 80.00 (978-0-472-11643-0(6)) Univ. of Michigan Pr.

Minus, P. M., ed. The Ethics of Business in a Global Economy. 2010. (Issues in Business Ethics Ser.). 164p. pap. 179.00 (978-90-481-5795-2(1), 9048157951) Springer.

Mitchell, Lawrence. Corporate Governance. 2009. (Library of Corporate Responsibilities Ser.). (Illus.). 590p. 325.00 (978-0-7546-2839-2(6)) Ashgate Publishing Co.

Monych, Bonnie D. Get Your Shift Together: The Secret to Working with Multiple Generations in the Workplace. 2010. 115p. pap. (978-1-58169-349-2(4)) Genesis Communications, Inc.

Moon. Glovemance & Business Ethics. Moon, Jeremy et al, eds. 2010. (Corporate Governance in the New Global Economy Ser.). (Illus.). 576p. 304.00 (978-1-84844-200-9(9)) Elgar, Edward Publishing, Inc.

Morgan, Thomas. The Loan Officer's Practical Guide to Compliance: Federal Laws, Fraud, Predatory Lending & Ethics. 2nd ed. 2007. pap. 55.00 (978-0-9718205-4-8(6)) QuickStart Pubns.

Morris, Matthew. International Buyer-Supplier Relationships. 2007. 144p. per. (978-3-8364-2871-2(7)) VDM Verlag Dr. Mueller e.K.

Mueller, Barbara. Communicating with the Ethnic Consumer: Theoretical & Practical Perspectives. 2007. 352p. (C). pap. 49.95 (978-0-8204-8119-7(X)) Lang, Peter Publishing, Inc.

—Communicating with the Multicultural Consumer: Theoretical & Practical Perspectives. 2007. 350p. (C). 129.95 (978-1-4331-0204-2(8)) Lang, Peter Publishing, Inc.

Muhr, Sara Louise, et al, eds. Ethics & Organizational Practice: Questioning the Moral Foundations of Management. 2010. (Illus.). 232p. 112.00 (978-1-84844-168-2(1)) Elgar, Edward Publishing, Inc.

Mujtaba, Bahaudin Ghulam. Business Ethics of Retail Employees: How Ethical Are Modern Workers? 2009. 128p. pap. 18.95 (978-0-9774211-8-3(X)) ILEAD Academy, LLC.

Munyaradzi, Mawere. Business & Ethics in a Country with Political, Socio-Economic Crisis: Business & Business Ethics in Time of Crisis: A Zimbabwean Case Study. 2011. 172p. pap. (978-3-639-33413-5(2)) VDM Verlag Dr. Mueller e.K.

Murphy, Aaron G. Foreign Corrupt Practices Act: A Practical Resource for Managers & Executives. 2010. (ENG.). 272p. pap., instr.'s gde. ed. 60.00 (978-0-470-91800-5(4), Wiley) Wiley, John & Sons, Inc.

Murphy, Joseph E. & Leet, Joshua H. Building a Career in Compliance & Ethics: Find your place in the business world's hottest new Field. 2007. 193p. per. 29.95 (978-0-9792210-0-2(5)) Society of Corporate Compliance and Ethics.

Murthy, N. R. Narayana. A Better India: A Better World. 2009. (ENG.). 320p. 24.95 (978-0-670-08283-4(X), Penguin Global) Penguin Group (USA) Inc.

Myint, Thant Lwin & Kruaechaipinit, Sasinan. Ethical Climate & Job Attitudes. 2008. 80p. pap. (978-3-639-00586-8(4)) VDM Verlag Dr. Mueller e.K.

Naskrent, Julia. Marketing Activities- a Critical Analysis from an Ethical Point of View. 2007. 116p. per. (978-3-8364-0627-7(6)) VDM Verlag Dr. Mueller e.K.

National Restaurant Association Staff. Hospitality & Restaurant Management: Competency Guide. 2006. (ENG., Illus.). 272p. (C). per. 44.40 (978-0-13-241465-4(1), Prentice Hall) Prentice Hall PTR.

Nelson, Katherine A. & Trevino, Linda Klebe. Managing Business Ethics: Straight Talk about How to Do It Right. 4th rev. ed. 2006. (ENG., Illus.). 432p. (C). pap. 125.95 (978-0-471-75525-8(7), Wiley) Wiley, John & Sons, Inc.

Newton, Lisa, et al. Clashing Views in Business Ethics & Society. 11th ed. 2009. (Taking Sides Ser.). (ENG.). 448p. (C). pap. 48.00 (978-0-07-352731-4(9), 0073527319, McGraw-Hill/Dushkin) McGraw-Hill Higher Education.

Newton, Lisa H. Permission to Steal: Revealing the Roots of Corporate Scandal — an Address to My Fellow Citizens. 2006. (Wiley Desktop Editions Ser.: 7). (ENG.). 112p. pap. 20.95 (978-1-4051-4540-4(4), Wiley-Blackwell) Wiley, John & Sons, Inc.

—Permission to Steal: Revealing the Roots of Corporate Scandal — An Address to My Fellow Citizens. 2006. (Blackwell Public Philosophy Ser.: 23). (ENG.). 112p. 87.95 (978-1-4051-4539-8(0), Wiley-Blackwell) Wiley, John & Sons, Inc.

Newton, Lisa H., et al. Taking Sides: Clashing Views in Business Ethics & Society. 12th ed. 2011. (Taking Sides Ser.). (ENG.). 400p. (C). pap. 48.00 (978-0-07-352735-2(1), 0073527351, McGraw-Hill/Dushkin) McGraw-Hill Higher Education.

Nowak, Mark. Shut Up, Shut Down. 2008. (ENG., Illus.). 161p. pap. 16.00 (978-1-56689-163-9(9)) Coffee Hse. Pr.

Nyquist, Greg. Visions of Reality: New Ways of Conceiving Old Problems. 2009. 304p. pap. 21.95 (978-1-4401-0756-6(4)) iUniverse, Inc.

O'Brien, Justin. Corporate Business Responsibility. 2009. (Library of Corporate Responsibilities Ser.). 566p. 325.00 (978-0-7546-2845-3(0)) Ashgate Publishing Co.

O'Brien, William J. Character at Work: Building Prosperity Through the Practice of Virtue. 2008. (Illus.). 176p. pap. 18.95 (978-0-8091-4588-1(X)) Paulist Pr.

Olsen, William P. The Anti-Corruption Handbook: How to Protect Your Business in the Global Marketplace. 2010. (ENG., Illus.). 192p. 78.95 (978-0-470-48450-0(0), Wiley) Wiley, John & Sons, Inc.

O'Sullivan, Patrick, et al, eds. Business Ethics: Integrating Ethics Across the Business World. 2012. (ENG., Illus.). 384p. (C). 215.00 (978-0-415-66356-4(3)); pap. 71.95 (978-0-415-66358-8(X)) Routledge.

Ouimet, J. -Robert & Semen, Yves. Everything Has Been Loaned to You: The Biography of a Transformational CEO. 2012. (978-0-8189-1337-2(1)) St Pauls.

Paeth, Scott, ed. Religious Perspectives on Business Ethics: An Anthology. 2006. (Religion & Business Ethics Ser.). (ENG.). 381p. 76.00 (978-0-7425-5010-0(9)); 384p. per. 39.95 (978-0-7425-5011-7(7)) Rowman & Littlefield Publishers, Inc.

Painter-Morland, Mollie. Business Ethics as Practice: Ethics as the Everyday Business of Business. (Business, Value Creation, & Society Ser.). (ENG.). 2011. 322p. pap. 39.99 (978-0-521-17456-5(2)) 2008. (Illus.). 320p. 99.00 (978-0-521-87745-9(8)) Cambridge Univ. Pr.

Painter-Morland, Mollie & ten Bos, Rene, eds. Business Ethics & Continental Philosophy. 2011. (ENG., Illus.). 392p. (C). 110.00 (978-0-521-19904-9(2)); pap. 45.00 (978-0-521-13756-0(X)) Cambridge Univ. Pr.

Painter-Morland, Mollie & Werhane, Patricia, eds. Cutting-edge Issues in Business Ethics: Continental Challenges to Tradition & Practice. 2010. (Issues in Business Ethics Ser.). xiv, 230p. pap. 149.00 (978-90-481-7868-1(1), 9048178681) Springer.

Palmer, Daniel E., ed. Ethical Issues in E-Business: Models & Frameworks. 2010. 362p. 180.00 (978-1-61520-615-5(9)) IGI Global.

Palmer, Donald. Normal Organizational Wrongdoing: A Critical Analysis of Theories of Misconduct in & by Organizations. 2012. (ENG., Illus.). 352p. 85.00 (978-0-19-957359-2(X)) Oxford Univ. Pr., Inc.

Parboteeah, K. Praveen & Cullen, J. B. Business Ethics. 2012. (ENG., Illus.). 400p. 120.00 (978-0-415-89368-8(2)); pap. 89.95 (978-0-415-89369-5(0)) Routledge.

Parhizgar Kamal Dean. Multicultural Business Ethics & Global Managerial Moral Reasoning. 2006. (ENG., Illus.). 730p. per. 94.50 (978-0-7618-3428-1(1)) Univ. Pr. of America, Inc.

Parker, Glenn. Team Empowerment: 20 Ways to Get There (PTTE) Ptte. 2010. (Illus.). 39p. pap. 9.95 (978-1-59996-201-6(2)) Human Resource Development Pr.

Parrish, Laura A. Business Ethics in Focus. 2007. (Illus.). (C). 89.00 (978-1-60021-684-8(6)) Nova Science Pubs., Inc.

Peacocke, Dennis. Doing Business God's Way. 2nd ed. 2007. (ENG.). 163p. (Orig.). reprint ed. pap. 12.95 (978-1-887021-02-9(7)) Rebuild.

Peck, Sarah. Investment Ethics. 2010. (ENG., Illus.). 304p. (C). pap. 93.95 (978-0-470-43453-6(8), Wiley) Wiley, John & Sons, Inc.

Peppers, Don & Rogers, Martha. Extreme Trust: Honesty as a Competitive Advantage. 2012. (ENG.). 256p. (gr. 12). 27.95 (978-1-59184-467-9(3), Portfolio (Hardcover)) Penguin Group (USA) Inc.

Petersen, Peter B. From Inkwell to Internet: 90 Years of Teaching Business Administration at Johns Hopkins University (1916-2006) 2009. 520p. 42.95 (978-0-595-51211-9(9)); pap. 32.95 (978-0-595-52478-5(8)) iUniverse, Inc.

Peus, Claudia, et al, eds. Ethics & Economic Success. 2011. 60p. pap. 89.00 (978-0-88937-392-1(2)) Hogrefe Publishing.

Pies, Ingo & Koslowski, Peter, eds. Corporate Citizenship & New Governance: The Political Role of Corporations. 2011. (Ethical Economy Ser.). (ENG., Illus.). ix, 193p. 139.00 (978-94-007-1660-5(5), 9400716605) Springer.

Pollock, Mark G. There's A Fine Line. 2011. 220p. 24.59 (978-1-4567-0082-9(0)); pap. 14.03 (978-1-4567-0081-2(2)) AuthorHouse.

Pontiff, Susie. Ethical Choices - How Managers Perceive Their Decision-Making Experiences in the Face of Ethical Dilemmas. 2008. 164p. pap. (978-3-639-09325-4(9)) VDM Verlag Dr. Mueller e.K.

Poppe, Jerry L. I'm a Christian even at Work: The Ethics of Business & Economics. 2006. x, 177p. per. (978-0-8100-1661-3(3)) Northwestern Publishing Hse.

Porrini, Patrizia, et al. Above the Board: How Ethical CEOs Create Honest Corporations. 2008. (ENG.). 240p. 27.95 (978-0-07-149631-5(9), 0071496319) McGraw-Hill Cos., The.

Poulston, Jill. Ethical Issues & Workplace Problems in Commercial Hospitality. 2009. 376p. pap. (978-3-639-13206-9(8)) VDM Verlag Dr. Mueller e.K.

Provis, Chris. Individuals, Groups, & Business Ethics. 2011. (Routledge Studies in Business Ethics Ser.). (ENG.). 186p. (C). 125.00 (978-0-415-89194-3(9)) Routledge.

Quatro, Scott A. & Sims, Ronald R. Executive Ethics: Ethical Dilemmas & Challenges for the C-Suite. 2008. 340p. (978-1-59311-784-9(1)); pap. (978-1-59311-783-2(3)) Information Age Publishing, Inc.

Radin, Max. The Lawful Pursuit of Gain. 156p. 2008. 36.95 (978-1-4366-8718-8(7)) 2007. (ENG.). per. 21.95 (978-1-4325-6851-1(5)) Kessinger Publishing, LLC.

Ragatz, Julie. Ethics for the Financial Services Professional. 4th rev. ed. 2011. 215p. (C). 65.00 (978-1-58293-038-1(4)) American College, The.

Ramsden, Jeremy. Spiritual Motivation: New Thinking for Business & Management. Ramsden, Jeremy et al, eds. 2007. (ENG., Illus.). 384p. 126.00 (978-0-230-54291-4(3)) Palgrave Macmillan.

Rendtorff, Jacob Dahl. Responsibility, Ethics & Legitimacy of Corporations. 2009. 514p. pap. 68.00 (978-87-630-0220-2(5)) Copenhagen Business Schl. Pr. DNK. Dist: International Specialized Bk. Services.

Rendtorff, Jacob Dahl, ed. Power & Principle in the Market Place: On Ethics & Economics. 2010. (Law, Ethics & Economics Ser.). (Illus.). 302p. 124.95 (978-1-4094-0717-1(9)) Ashgate Publishing Co.

Renz, Patrick S. Project Governance: Implementing Corporate Governance & Business Ethics in Nonprofit Organizations. 2007. (Contributions to Economics Ser.). (Illus.). XVI, 260p. (C). pap. 139.00 (978-3-7908-1926-7(3), 3790819263) Springer.

Ressler, Peter & Mitchell Ressler, Monika. Spiritual Capitalism: How 9/11 Gave Us Nine Spiritual Lessons of Work & Business. rev. ed. 2007. 282p. per. 16.95 (978-0-9761984-2-0(8)) Chilmark Bks.

Rezaee, Zabihollah & Swanson, Diane L. Corporate Governance & Ethics. 2008. (ENG., Illus.). 464p. (C). pap. 123.95 (978-0-471-73800-8(X), Wiley) Wiley, John & Sons, Inc.

Richardson, John. Annual Editions: Business Ethics 11/12. 23rd ed. 2011. (Annual Editions Ser.). (ENG., Illus.). 176p. (C). pap. 44.00 (978-0-07-352865-6(X), 007352865X, McGraw-Hill/Dushkin) McGraw-Hill Higher Education.

—Business Ethics 10/11. 22nd ed. 2010. (Annual Editions Ser.). (ENG., Illus.). 192p. (C). pap. 44.00 (978-0-07-352861-8(7), 0073528617, McGraw-Hill/Dushkin) McGraw-Hill Higher Education.

Richardson, John & Kehoe, William. Annual Editions: Business Ethics 12/13. 24th ed. 2012. (Annual Editions Ser.). (ENG., Illus.). 224p. (C). pap. 44.00 (978-0-07-352872-4(2), 0073528722, McGraw-Hill/Dushkin) McGraw-Hill Higher Education.

Rima, Samuel D. Spiritual Capital & Economic Transformation: A Us Perspective. 2012. (Transformation & Innovation Ser.). 230p. 119.95 (978-1-4094-0484-2(6), Gower Publishing Co., Ltd.) Ashgate Publishing, Ltd. GBR. Dist: Ashgate Publishing Co.

Robinson, Simon, et al. Engineering, Business & Professional Ethics. 2007. (ENG., Illus.). 256p. pap. 53.95 (978-0-7506-6741-8(9)) Routledge.

Rogers, Catherine. Ethics in International Arbitration. 2013. (ENG.). 350p. 95.00 (978-0-19-533769-3(7)) Oxford Univ. Pr., Inc.

Ronnegard, David. Corporate Moral Agency & the Role of the Corporation in Society. 2007. 268p. pap. 30.95 (978-1-84753-580-1(1)) Lulu Enterprises Inc.

Rossouw. Business Ethics. 4th ed. 2010. (Illus.). 352p. pap. 29.95 (978-0-19-598269-5(X)) Oxford Univ. Pr., Inc.

Rossouw, Deon, et al. Ethics for Accountants & Auditors. 2nd ed. 2010. (Illus.). 352p. pap. 29.95 (978-0-19-599046-1(3)) Oxford Univ. Pr., Inc.

Rossouw, G. J. & Sison, Alejo José G. Global Perspectives on Ethics of Corporate Governance. 2006. (ENG., Illus.). 240p. 89.00 (978-1-4039-7584-3(1)) Palgrave Macmillan.

Roth, James. Best Practices: Evaluating the Corporate Culture. 2010. (Illus.). xi, 258p. pap. (978-0-89413-682-5(8)) Institute of Internal Auditors, Inc.

Rotta, Carlo Patetta. A Short Guide to Ethical Risk. 2010. (Short Guides to Business Risk Ser.). (Illus.). 168p. pap. 34.95 (978-0-566-09172-8(0), Gower Publishing Co., Ltd.) Ashgate Publishing, Ltd. GBR. Dist: Ashgate Publishing Co.

Russo, Michael V. Companies on a Mission: Entrepreneurial Strategies for Growing Sustainably, Responsibly, & Profitably. 2010. (ENG., Illus.). 272p. 27.95 (978-0-8047-6162-8(0), Stanford Business Bks.) Stanford Univ. Pr.

Sage, Martin. Zentrepreneurship. Blake, Diana, ed. 2006. per. (978-0-9789443-0-8(5)) Phoenix Publishing.

Sage Publications Staff. Marketing Ethics. 2011. 232p. (C). pap. 31.00 (978-1-4129-9514-6(0), B95146P) SAGE Pubns., Inc.

—SAGE Brief Guide to Business Ethics. 2011. 408p. (C). pap. 31.00 (978-1-4129-9721-8(6), B97218P) SAGE Pubns., Inc.

Salomon, Margot E., et al, eds. Casting the Net Wider: Human Rights, Development & New Duty-Bearers. 2007. 462p. (C). 110.75 (978-90-5095-718-2(8)) Intersentia Uitgevers N.V. BEL. Dist: International Specialized Bk. Services.

Salter, Malcolm S. Innovation Corrupted: The Origins & Legacy of Enron's Collapse. 2008. (Illus.). 544p. 38.50 (978-0-674-02825-8(2)) Harvard Univ. Pr.

Sandbu, Martin. Just Business: Arguments in Business Ethics. rev. ed. 2011. (ENG.). 224p. (C). pap. 56.80 (978-0-205-69775-5(5), Prentice Hall) Prentice Hall PTR.

Sandelands, Lloyd. God & Mammon. 2009. (ENG.). 116p. pap. 20.99 (978-0-7618-4940-7(8)) Univ. Pr. of America, Inc.

Sandelands, Lloyd E. God & Mammon. 2010. vi, 106p. (978-0-7618-4941-4(6)) Univ. Pr. of America, Inc.

Sanders, Dan J., et al. Built to Serve: How to Drive the Bottom Line with People-First Practices. 2007. (ENG., Illus.). 200p. 24.95 (978-0-07-149792-3(7), 0071497927) McGraw-Hill Cos., The.

Sansbury, George. The Employment Relationship & Integrated Theory. 2008. 248p. pap. (978-3-639-05172-8(6)) VDM Verlag Dr. Mueller e.K.

Santoro, Michael A. China 2020: How Western Business Can-and Should-Influence Social & Political Change in the Coming Decade. 2009. 176p. 21.95 (978-0-8014-4695-5(3)) Cornell Univ. Pr.

Saunders, Mark N. K., et al, eds. Organizational Trust: A Cultural Perspective. 2010. (Cambridge Companions to Management Ser.). (ENG., Illus.). 456p. 110.00 (978-0-521-49291-1(2)) Cambridge Univ. Pr.

Sayles, Leonard R. & Smith, Cynthia J. The Rise of the Rogue Executive: How Good Companies Go Bad & How to Stop the Destruction. 2011. (ENG.). 288p. pap. 32.99 (978-0-13-290616-6(3)) FT Press.

Schminke, Marshall, ed. Managerial Ethics: Managing the Psychology of Morality. 2nd ed. 2010. (ENG., Illus.). 334p. 55.95 (978-1-84872-833-2(6), Routledge) Taylor & Francis Group GBR. Dist: Taylor & Francis Group.

Schuett, Robert. The Realist & Business Ethics: Leadership Challenges in the Global Struggle for Power, Money, & Morality. 2012. (ENG., Illus.). 256p. 90.00 (978-0-230-10727-4(3)) Palgrave Macmillan.

Seglin, Jeffrey L. The Good, the Bad, & Your Business: Choosing Right When Ethical Dilemmas Pull You Apart. 2007. (ENG.). 224p. per. 24.00 (978-0-9786899-3-3(3)) Smith/Kerr Assoc.

Sethi, S. Prakash, ed. Globalization & the Good Corporation. 2010. (Illus.). vi, 366p. 89.95 (978-94-007-0239-4(6), 9400702396) Springer.

Shaw, Peter. Defining Moments: Navigating through Business & Organizational Life. 2010. (ENG.). 256p. 44.00 (978-0-230-57720-6(2)) Palgrave Macmillan.

Shaw, William H. Business Ethics: A Textbook with Cases. 7th ed. 2010. (Available Titles CourseMate Ser.). (ENG.). 512p. (C). pap. 110.95 (978-0-495-80876-3(8)) Wadsworth.

Shibusawa, Eiichi, et al. Lun Yu Yu Suan Pan. 2010. (CHI.). 325p. (978-986-6274-10-7(1)) Asian Culture Co., Ltd.

SHRM Society for Human Resource Management Staff. The Ethics Landscape in American Business: Sustaining a Strong Ethical Work Environment. 2010. (ENG.). 50p. pap. 99.95 (978-1-58644-132-6(9)) Society for Human Resource Management.

Shulman, David. From Hire to Liar: The Role of Deception in the Workplace. annot. ed. 2006. (Illus.). 213p. 60.95 (978-0-8014-4473-9(X)); per. 20.95 (978-0-8014-7331-9(4)) Cornell Univ. Pr. (Comstock Publishing Assocs.).

Simons, Tony. The Integrity Dividend: Leading by the Power of Your Word. 2008. (ENG., Illus.). 256p. 27.95 (978-0-470-18566-7(X), Jossey-Bass) Wiley, John & Sons, Inc.

Sims, Ronald R. & Sauser, William I. Experiences in Teaching Business Ethics. 2011. 290p. (978-1-61735-470-0(8)); 290p. pap. (978-1-61735-469-4(4)); E-Book (978-1-61735-471-7(6)) Information Age Publishing, Inc.

Singer, Alan E. Integrating Ethics with Strategy: Selected Papers of Alan E Singer. 2007. (Illus.). 405p. 113.00 (978-981-270-145-9(1)) World Scientific Publishing Co., Inc.

Singer, Alan E., ed. Business Ethics & Strategy, 2 vols., Vols. 1-2. 2007. (International Library of Essays in Public & Professional Ethics Ser.). (Illus.). 1160p. 675.00 (978-0-7546-2609-1(1)) Ashgate Publishing Co.

Sisodia, Rajendra S., et al. Firms of Endearment: How World-Class Companies Profit from Passion & Purpose. 2007. (ENG., Illus.). 320p. 39.99 (978-0-13-187372-8(5)) Wharton Schl. Publishing.

Sison, Alejo José G. Corporate Governance & Ethics: An Aristotelian Perspective. Escola Gil, Rafae , ed. 2008. (New Horizons in Leadership Studies). (Illus.). 256p. 119.00 (978-1-84542-746-7(7)) Elgar, Edward Publishing, Inc.
Sison, Alejo Jose G. Corporate Governance & Ethics: An Aristotelian Perspective. 2010. (New Horizons in Leadership Studies). (Illus.). 256p. pap. 45.00 (978-1-84980-061-7(8)) Elgar, Edward Publishing, Inc
Sivak, Martin. Evo Morales: The Extraordinary Rise of the First Indigenous President of Bolivia. 2010. (ENG., Illus.). 256p. 27.00 (978-0-230-62305-7(0)) Palgrave Macmillan.
Smith, Bradley M. What Do You Think? Preparing for the Question That All Clients Ask. 2010. (978-0-9759337-4-9(4)) Society of Actuaries.
Smith, Jeffery D. Normative Theory & Business Ethics. 2008. (New Perspectives in Business Ethics Ser.). (ENG.). 240p. 75.00 (978-0-7425-4842-8(2)); pap. 29.95 (978-0-7425-4841-1(4)) Rowman & Littlefield Publishers, Inc.
Smith, Lamar & Kling, Tammy. There's More to Life Than the Corner Office. 2009. (ENG.). 144p. 17.95 (978-0-07-160930-2(X), 007160930X) McGraw-Hill Cos., The.
Smith, Roger D. & Smith, Roger. In the Footsteps of Franklin. 2nd ed. 2008. (Illus.). 89p. pap. (978-0-9823040-0-6(5)) Modelbenders Pr.
Smitha, Elaine. Screwing Mother Nature for Profit: How Corporations Betray Our Trust - & Why the New Biology Offers an Ethical & Sustainable Future. 2011. (ENG.). 256p. pap. 19.95 (978-1-78028-018-9(1), Watkins Publishing) Duncan Baird Pubs. GBR. Dist: Sterling Publishing Co., Inc.
Society for Human Resource Management Staff. 2007 Corporate Social Responsibility: United States, Australia, India, China, Canada, Mexico & Brazil: A Pilot Study. 2008. (ENG.). 40p. pap. 99.95 (978-1-58644-097-8(7)) Society for Human Resource Management.
Soraj Hongladarom & Ess, Charles. Information Technology Ethics: Cultural Perspectives. 2006. (Premier Reference Source Ser.). (Illus.). 260p. 165.00 (978-1-59904-310-4(6)) IGI Global.
Spence, Laura & Painter-Morland, Mollie, eds. Ethics in Small & Medium Sized Enterprises: A Global Commentary. 2010. (International Society of Business, Economics, & Ethics Book Ser.). (Illus.). xxi, 289p. 139.00 (978-90-481-9330-1(3), 9048193303) Springer.
Stachowicz-Stanusch, Agata, ed. Organizational Immunity to Corruption: Building Theoretical & Research Foundations (PB) 2010. 482p. pap. 45.99 (978-1-61735-050-4(8)) Information Age Publishing, Inc.
Stanwick, Peter & Stanwick, Sarah. Understanding Business Ethics. 2008. (ENG., Illus.). 504p. (C). per. 120.00 (978-0-13-173542-2(X), Prentice Hall) Prentice Hall PTR.
Stehr, Nico, et al, eds. The Moralization of Markets. 2009. (ENG., Illus.). 378p. pap. 34.95 (978-1-4128-1089-0(2)) Transaction Pubs.
Stoll, Mary Lyn. Stakeholder Theory: Essential Readings in Ethical Leadership & Management. Zakhem, Abe J., ed. 2007. (ENG., Illus.). 1p. pap. 31.98 (978-1-59102-526-9(5)) Prometheus Bks., Pubs.
Stolle, Ron. White-Collar Crime & Punishment - Corporate Codes & the Sarbanes-Oxley Act. 2008. 228p. pap. (978-3-639-07857-2(8)) VDM Verlag Dr. Mueller e.K.
Sucher, Sandra J. The Moral Leader. 2007. (Illus.). 264p. 58.95 (978-0-415-40064-0(3)) Routledge.
Svensson, Göran & Wood, Greg, eds. Business Ethics: Through Time & Across Contexts. 2009. 426p. pap. (978-91-44-05540-4(4)) Utbildningshuset/Studentlitteratur.
Swanson, Diane L. & Fisher, Dann G. Advancing Business Ethics Education. 2008. 356p. (978-1-59311-544-9(X)); (Illus.). pap. (978-1-59311-543-2(1)) Information Age Publishing, Inc.
—Toward Assessing Business Ethics Education. 2010. (978-1-61735-163-1(6)); pap. (978-1-61735-162-4(8)); E-Book (978-1-61735-164-8(4)) Information Age Publishing, Inc.
Swenson, Michael J., et al. Boom Start: Super Laws of Successful Entrepreneurs. rev. ed. 2009. (ENG.). 244p. pap. 54.50 (978-0-7575-6623-3(5)) Kendall Hunt Publishing Co.
Swift, Crystal Lane. This House Would Ethically Engage. 2008. 224p. pap. (978-3-639-05589-4(6)) VDM Verlag Dr. Mueller e.K.
Taderera, Faustino. Leadership. 2010. 464p. pap. (978-3-8383-6602-9(6)) Lambert Academic Publishing.
—Principles & Practice of Purchasing. 2010. 236p. pap. (978-3-8383-6143-7(1)) Lambert Academic Publishing.
—Trappings of Power, Leadership & Empire. 2010. 44Cp. pap. (978-3-8383-6788-0(X)) Lambert Academic Publishing.
Talukder, Majharul. Virtual Organization. 2011. 88p. pap. (978-3-8443-0416-9(9)) Lambert Academic Publishing.
Taylor, Jim & Haneberg, Lisa. Connecting Top Managers: Developing Executive Teams for Business Success. rev. ed. 2010. (ENG., Illus.). 272p. 34.99 (978-0-13-707156-2(6)) FT Press.
Tencati, Antonio & Perrini, Francesco. Business Ethics & Corporate Sustainability. Tencati, Antonio & Perrini, Francesco, eds. 2011. (Studies in TransAtlantic Business Ethics Ser.). 264p. 135.00 (978-1-84980-371-7(4)) Elgar, Edward Publishing, Inc.
Thyssen, Ole. Business Ethics & Organizational Values: A Systems Theoretical Analysis. 2009. (ENG., Illus.). 264p. 105.00 (978-0-230-23035-4(0)) Palgrave Macmillan.
Tillquist, Kristin. Capitalizing on Kindness: Why 21st Century Professionals Need to Be Nice. 2008. (ENG.). 1p. pap. 15.99 (978-1-60163-038-4(7)) Career Pr., Inc.
Trevino, Linda K. & Nelson, Katherine A. Managing Business Ethics. 5th ed. 2010. (ENG.). 480p. (C). pap. 125.95 (978-0-470-34394-4(X), Wiley) Wiley, John & Sons, Inc.
Triskatis, Claudiana. Ethikrichtlinien im Arbeitsrecht. 2008. (Schriften zum Arbeitsrecht und Wirtschaftsrecht Ser.). 272p. pap. 65.95 (978-3-631-57509-3(2)) Lang, Peter GmbH, Europaischer Verlag der Wissenschaften DEU. Dist: Lang, Peter.
Turning Ethics into Profits: How Ethical People Succeed in Business. 2007. pap. 14.95 (978-0-9779835-3-7(6)) Chad Publishing LLC.
Udemezue, Chike. Societal Development: Concerns for Humans, Systems, Strategies, Skills, & Social Change. 2007. 220p. per. 15.95 (978-1-4327-1628-8(X)) Outskirts Pr., Inc.
Udemezue, Chike C. The Role & Obligations of Accountants in the Development of Nigeria. 2006. 118p. per. 10.95 (978-1-59824-424-3(8)) E-BookTime LLC.
Ulrich, Peter. Integrative Economic Ethics: Foundations of a Civilized Market Economy. Fearns, James, tr. from GER. 2010. (ENG.). 500p. pap. 45.00 (978-0-521-17242-4(X)) Cambridge Univ. Pr.
United Nations. Doing Business While Advancing Development & Peace. 2011. (ENG.). 66p. pap. 17.00 (978-92-1-104606-9(8)) United Nations Pubns.
United Nations University Staff. The Business of Sustainable Development in Africa: Human Rights, Partnerships, Alternative Business Models. Hamann, Ralph et al, eds. 2009. (ENG., Illus.). 376p. pap. 37.00 (978-92-808-1168-1(1)) United Nations Univ. Pr. JPN. Dist: Brookings Institution Pr.
Velasquez, Manuel G. Business Ethics. 7th rev. ed. 2011. (ENG.). 504p. (C). 82.67 (978-0-205-21416-7(9), Prentice Hall) Prentice Hall PTR.
—Business Ethics: Concepts & Cases. 7th rev. ed. 2011. (ENG.). (C). 46.67 (978-0-205-21406-8(1)); (Illus.). 504p. pap. 107.20 (978-0-205-01766-9(5)) Prentice Hall PTR. (Prentice Hall).
—Business Ethics: Concepts & Cases, Books a la Carte Edition. 7th ed. 2011. (ENG.). 504p. (C). ring bd. 70.20 (978-0-205-01809-3(2), Prentice Hall) Prentice Hall PTR.
—Business Ethics: Concepts & Cases, Books a la Carte Plus MyThinkingLab. 7th ed. 2011. (ENG.). (C). ring bd. 76.87 (978-0-205-01810-9(6), Prentice Hall) Prentice Hall PTR.
Verhezen, Peter. Gifts, Corruption, Philanthropy: The Ambiguity of Gift Practices in Business. 2009. (Frontiers of Business Ethics Ser.). 65.95 (978-3-03911-842-7(0)) Lang, Peter AG GBR. Dist: Lang, Peter.
Vilcox, Mary W. & Mohan, Thomas O. Contemporary Issues in Business Ethics. 2007. (C). 89.00 (978-1-60021-773-9(7)) Nova Science Pubs., Inc.
Vogel, David. The Market for Virtue: The Potential & Limits of Corporate Social Responsibility. rev. annot. ed. 2006. (ENG.). 222p. per. 20.95 (978-0-8157-9077-8(5)) Brookings Institution Pr.
Voronovich, Zoya A. & Larsen, Kai R., eds. Privacy in a Transparent World. 2007. 244p. per. (978-0-9764284-4-2(X)) Ethica Publishing.
Walters, Diane & McPhail, Ken. Accounting & Business Ethics. (Illus.). 2009. (ENG.). 240p. (C). 45.95 (978-0-415-36236-8(9)) 2007. 320p. 155.00 (978-0-415-36235-1(0)) Routledge.
Wang, Yuan, et al. China Business Culture: Strategies for Success. 2007. 280p. 35.00 (978-981-04-9158-1(1)) Thorogood GBR. Dist: Stylus Publishing, LLC.
Wankel, Charles & Stachowicz-Stanusch, Agata. Effectively Integrating Ethical Dimensions into Business Education. 2012. 288p. (978-1-61735-579-0(8)); pap. (978-1-61735-578-3(X)); (Illus.). vii, 279p. E-Book (978-1-61735-580-6(1)) Information Age Publishing, Inc.
—Handbook of Research on Teaching Ethics in Business & Management Education. 2011. (978-1-61350-510-6(8)); (978-1-61350-512-0(4)); E-Book (978-1-61350-511-3(6)) IGI Global.
Wankel, Charles & Stachowicz-Stanusch, Agata, eds. Management Education for Integrity: Ethically Educating Tomorrow's Business Leaders. 2011. (Illus.). 300p. (978-1-78052-068-1(9)) Emerald Group Publishing Ltd.
Watts, Theresa. Business leaders' values & beliefs regarding decision making Ethics. 2008. 227p. pap. 23.50 (978-1-4357-4768-5(2)) Lulu Enterprises Inc.
Weckert & Lucas, Richard. An Integrity System for ICT: Incorporating Ethics into Industry Practice. 2013. (Information & Communication Technology Series, Ser.) (ENG.). 220p. 110.00 (978-0-470-54357-3(4), Wiley) Wiley, John & Sons, Inc.
Weinstein, Bruce. Ethical Intelligence: Five Principles for Untangling Your Toughest Problems at Work & Beyond. 2011. (ENG.). 248p. pap. 14.95 (978-1-60868-054-2(1)) New World Library.
Weiss, Joseph W. Business Ethics: A Stakeholder & Issues Management Approach. 5th ed. 2008. (ENG.). 552p. (C). pap. 156.95 (978-0-324-58973-3(5)) Cengage South-Western.
—Cram101 Textbook Outlines to Accompany Business Ethics - a Stakeholder & Issues Management Approach, Weiss, 3rd Edition. 2006. (ENG.). 179p. pap. 11.95 (978-1-4288-0530-9(3)) Cram101 Inc.
Werhane, Patricia & Singer, Alan E., eds. Business Ethics in Theory & Practice: Contributions from Asia & New Zealand. 2010. (Issues in Business Ethics Ser.). (Illus.). 256p. pap. 99.00 (978-90-481-5273-5(9), 9048152739) Springer.
Werhane, Patricia H. Cutting-Edge Issues in Business Ethics. 2008. (Issues in Business Ethics Ser.). (C). 149.00 (978-1-4020-8400-3(5)) Springer.
Werhane, Patricia H. & Freeman, R. Edward, eds. Business Ethics, 13 vols., Volume 2. 2nd rev. ed. 2006. (Blackwell Encyclopaedia of Management Ser.: 3). (ENG., Illus.). 600p. 165.00 (978-1-4051-0013-7(3), Wiley-Blackwell) Wiley, John & Sons, Inc.
Werhane, Patricia Hogue, ed. Ethical Issues in Business: A Philosophical Approach. 8th ed. 2007. (ENG., Illus.). 640p. (C). per. 117.40 (978-0-13-184619-7(1), Prentice Hall) Prentice Hall PTR.
West, Jonathan P. & Berman, Evan M. The Ethics Edge. 2nd ed. 2006. (ENG.). 232p. 65.00 (978-0-87326-710-6(9)) International City/County Management Assn.
Whitlock, David W. Opportunity: Introducing Free Enterprise & Business. 2007. (Illus.). 326p. pap. 36.00 (978-1-55635-148-8(8), Resource Pubns.) Wipf & Stock Pubs.
Whitlock, David Wesley & Dutile, Gordon, eds. A Noble Calling: Devotions & Essays for Business Professionals. 2008. 228p. pap. 25.00 (978-1-55635-536-3(X), Resource Pubns.) Wipf & Stock Pubs.
Wicks, Andrew, et al. Business Ethics. 2009. (ENG., Illus.). 448p. (C). pap. 120.00 (978-0-13-142792-1(X), Prentice Hall) Prentice Hall PTR.
Wieland, Josef, ed. Standards & Audits for Ethics Management Systems: The European Perspective. 2010. (Ethical Economy Ser.). (Illus.). viii, 253p. pap. 189.00 (978-3-642-07292-5(5), 3642072925) Springer.
Williams, C.S.C., Oliver F, CSC, ed. Peace Through Commerce: Responsible Corporate Citizenship & the Ideals of the United Nations Global Compact. 2008. (ND Houck Series Business Ethics Ser.). (ENG.). 536p. pap. 37.00 (978-0-268-04414-5(7)) Univ. of Notre Dame Pr.
Williams, Rowan, et al. Crisis & Recovery: Ethics, Economics & Justice. 2010. (ENG.). 256p. 37.00 (978-0-230-25214-1(1)) Palgrave Macmillan.
Wincel, Jeffrey. Defying the Trend: Business Ethics & Corporate Morality from a Faith Perspective. 2010. 147p. pap. 18.95 (978-0-557-32835-2(7), Lulu Enterprises Inc.
Wirtenberger, Henry J. Morality & Business. 2011. 320p. 50.95 (978-1-258-02462-8(4)) Literary Licensing, LLC.
Wong, Kenman L. & Rae, Scott B. Business for the Common Good: A Christian Vision for the Marketplace. 2011. (Christian Worldview Integration Ser.). (ENG.). 288p. pap. 24.00 (978-0-8308-2816-6(8), IVP Acad.) InterVarsity Pr.
Wong, Peter. A Study of Business Ethical Practices in Australian Organisations: A Multiple Case Study Using Critical Incidence to Measure how Ethical Decisions are Made. 2008. 296p. pap. (978-3-639-10035-8(2)) VDM Verlag Dr. Mueller e.K.
Wood, Donna J. Business Ethics: Text & Workbook. 2007. (C). spiral bd. 35.00 net. (978-1-934481-00-4(9)) Woodhaven Pr., LLC.
Zakhem, Abe J. A Manager's Guide for Ethical Decision Making: Doing Right, Doing Good. 2012. 131p. pap. 39.95 (978-1-60649-157-7(1)) Business Expert Pr.
Zanda, Gianfranco. Corporate Management in a Knowledge-Based Economy. 2011. (ENG., Illus.). 280p. 100.00 (978-0-230-29425-7(1)) Palgrave Macmillan.
Zaphiropoulos, Renn. Entrepreneurial Wisdom: Philosophical Thoughts for an Uncluttered Life. 2010. 156p. 24.95 (978-1-4401-8300-3(7)); pap. 14.95 (978-1-4401-8299-0(X)) iUniverse, Inc.
Zimmerli, Walther C., et al, eds. Corporate Ethics & Corporate Governance. (ENG., Illus.). viii, 332p. 2010. pap. 129.00 (978-3-642-08976-3(3), 3642089763) 2007. 129.00 (978-3-540-70817-9(0), 3540708170) Springer.
Zsolnai, Laszlo. The Collaborative Enterprise: Creating Values for a Sustainable World. Tencati, Antonio, ed. 2010. (ENG.). 415p. pap. 44.95 (978-3-0343-0159-6(6)) Lang, Peter AG GBR. Dist: Lang, Peter.
Zsolnai, Laszlo, ed. Ethical Principles & Economic Transformation - A Buddhist Approach. 2011. (Issues in Business Ethics Ser.). (ENG., Illus.). xi, 213p. 139.00 (978-90-481-9309-7(5), 9048193095) Springer.
—Ethics in the Economy: Handbook of Business Ethics. 3rd ed. 2006. xiii,331p. pap. (978-0-8204-9326-8(0)) Lang, Peter AG.
—Interdisciplinary Yearbook of Business Ethics: Volume 1 2006. 2006. (Interdisciplinary Yearbook for Business Ethics Ser.). 228p. pap. 47.95 (978-0-8204-8010-7(X)) Lang, Peter Publishing, Inc.
—Spirituality & Ethics in Management. 2nd ed. 2011. (Issues in Business Ethics Ser.). (Illus.). xii, 227p. 139.00 (978-94-007-1152-5(2), 9400711522) Springer.
Zsolnai, Laszlo, ed. Ethical Prospects: Economy, Society & Environment. 2009. (ENG., Illus.). xxviii, 316p. 119.00 (978-1-4020-9820-8(0), 1402098200) Springer.
Zsolnai, László, ed. Spirituality & Ethics in Management. 2010. (Issues in Business Ethics Ser.). xi, 221p. pap. 139.00 (978-90-481-6648-0(9), 9048166489) Springer.
Zumbuehl, Martin. Justice, Ethics & Morals in Switzerland & Abroad: Version 2008. 2009. 108p. pap. 13.95 (978-1-4401-2617-8(8)) iUniverse, Inc.

BUSINESS ETIQUETTE

Al Barrak, Saad. Dark Horse: Zain & the Art of Leadership. 2012. (ENG.). 272p. 30.00 (978-99921-94-67-6(7)) Bloomsbury Publishing.
Allen, Judy. Event Planning Ethics & Etiquette: A Principled Approach to the Business of Special Event Management. 2009. (ENG.). 320p. pap. 35.00 (978-0-470-67644-8(2), Wiley) Wiley, John & Sons, Inc.
Almon, Harold. Business Dining Etiquette Lessons for College & University Students Climbing the Ladder Advanced Table Manners Rules for Business Dining. 2012. (ENG., Illus.). 129p. (C). pap. 19.95 (978-0-917921-80-3(1)) At Ease Pr.
—Male Care Matters Etiquette for College & University Students: Everyday Business Social Etiquette Surviving the Parent Company Male Personal Grooming Things Someone Will Tell a Son. 2011. (ENG.). 169p. pap. 19.95 (978-0-917921-44-5(5)) At Ease Pr.
Axtell, Roger E. Essential Do's & Taboos: The Complete Guide to International Business & Leisure Travel. 2007. (ENG., Illus.). 308p. pap. 16.95 (978-0-471-74050-6(0), Wiley) Wiley, John & Sons, Inc.
Becker, Thomas H. Doing Business in the New Latin America: Keys to Profit in America's Next-Door Markets. 2nd ed. 2011. (Illus.). x, 280p. E-Book (978-0-313-38382-3(0)); 280p. 44.95 (978-0-313-38381-6(2), A2872C) Greenwood Publishing Group, Inc. (Praeger Pubs.).
Bernstein, Albert & Bernstein, Albert J. Am I the Only Sane One Working Here? 101 Solutions for Surviving Office Insanity. 2009. (ENG.). 304p. pap. 16.95 (978-0-07-160872-5(9), 0071608729) McGraw-Hill Cos., The.
The Bliss or the Diss Connection? Email Etiquette for the Business Professional. 2007. 14.95 (978-0-9765970-3-2(9)) ExecuProv.
Block, Carson & Collins, Robert. Doing Business in China for Dummies. 2007. (ENG., Illus.). 384p. per. 21.99 (978-0-470-04929-7(4), For Dummies) Wiley, John & Sons, Inc.
The Blue Book of Stationery: The Definitive Guide to Social & Business Correspondence Etiquette. 2009. (Illus.). (YA). pap. (978-0-615-27921-3(X)) Crane & Co.
Bosrock, Mary Murray. Asian Business Customs & Manners: A Country-by-Country Guide. 2007. (Illus.). 450p. pap. (978-0-88166-525-3(8)) Meadowbrook Pr.
Bowman, Judith. Don't Take the Last Donut: New Rules of Business Etiquette. (ENG.). 2009. 1p. pap. 14.99 (978-1-60163-087-2(5)) 2007. (Illus.). 224p. pap. 19.99 (978-1-56414-929-9(3)) Career Pr., Inc.
Carte, Penny & Fox, Chris. Bridging the Culture Gap: A Practical Guide to International Business Communication. 2nd ed. 2008. (ENG., Illus.). 192p. pap. 35.00 (978-0-7494-5274-2(9)) Kogan Page, Ltd. GBR. Dist: Ingram Pub. Services.
Chaddock, David. Qatar 2008. 3rd ed. 2008. (Illus.). 168p. 63.95 (978-1-905299-90-4(7), Stacey International) Stacey Publishing GBR. Dist: Midpoint Trade Bks., Inc.
Chaney and, Martin. Intercultural Business Communication. 2006. pap. 9.95 (978-1-4288-0762-4(4)) Cram101 Inc.
Chaney, Lillian & Martin, Jeanette. Intercultural Business Communication. 5th ed. 2010. (ENG., Illus.). 320p. (C). pap. 106.67 (978-0-13-212790-5(3), Prentice Hall) Prentice Hall PTR.
Chaney, Lillian Hunt & Martin, Jeanette S. The Essential Guide to Business Etiquette, 1 vol. 2007. 208p. 39.95 (978-0-275-99714-4(6), C9714, Praeger Pubs.) Greenwood Publishing Group, Inc.
Chee, Harold. Myths about Doing Business in China. 2nd rev. ed. 2007. (ENG., Illus.). 176p. pap. 43.00 (978-0-230-55118-3(1)) Palgrave Macmillan.
Chung, Mona. Doing Business Successfully in China. 2011. (Chandos Asian Studies). 246p. 120.00 (978-0-85709-155-0(7), Chandos Publishing) Woodhead Publishing Ltd. GBR. Dist: Ingram Pub. Services.
Cook, Roy A., et al. Guide to Business Etiquette. 2nd ed. 2010. (ENG., Illus.). 144p. (C). pap. 36.00 (978-0-13-707504-1(9), Prentice Hall) Prentice Hall PTR.
Corday, Kathy. The Networking Field Guide: Essential Social Skills for Business. 2010. (ENG., Illus.). 150p. pap. 13.95 (978-0-9843897-0-4(9)) Alchemy Media Group, Inc.
Cram101 Textbook Reviews. Outlines & Highlights for Business Protocol: Contemporary American Practice by Robinson, ISBN. 2011. 128p. pap. 28.95 (978-1-61812-118-9(9)) Cram101 Inc.
Davies, Paul. What's This India Business? Offshoring, Outsourcing & the Global Services Revolution. 2008. (ENG.). 233p. pap. (978-1-904838-21-0(9), Brealey, Nicholas International) Brealey, Nicholas Publishing Ltd.
Dulek, Ron. Who Killed Keyboard? A Lighthearted Business Mystery about Leading Through E-Mails. 2011. pap. 12.99 (978-1-61739-179-8(4)) Tate Publishing & Enterprises, LLC.
Dummies Press Staff, et al. Cross-Cultural Selling for Dummies. 2008. (ENG., Illus.). 384p. pap. 21.99 (978-0-470-37701-7(1), For Dummies) Wiley, John & Sons, Inc.
Facts on File, Inc. Staff. Career Skills Library: Professional Ethics & Etiquette. 3rd rev. ed. 2009. (Career Skills Library). (Illus.). 174p. (gr. 6-12). 25.95 (978-0-8160-7772-4(X), Ferguson Publishing Co.) Facts On File, Inc.
Flocker, Michael E. Death by PowerPoint: A Modern Office Survival Guide. 2006. (ENG., Illus.). 224p. pap. 12.95 (978-0-306-81512-6(5)) Da Capo Pr., Inc.
Fox, Jeffrey J. How to Get to the Top: Business Lessons Learned at the Dinner Table. 2007. (Fox Business Library). 224p. 17.95 (978-1-4013-0330-3(7)) Hyperion Pr.
Fox, Sue. Business Etiquette for Dummies. 2nd ed. 2008. (ENG., Illus.). 360p. pap. 21.99 (978-0-470-14709-2(1), For Dummies) Wiley, John & Sons, Inc.
Gama, Noel. Culture Wise India. 2009. (ENG., Illus.). 224p. pap. 17.95 (978-1-905303-47-2(5)) Survival Bks., Ltd.
Gerson, Donna & Gerson, David. The Modern Rules of Business Etiquette. 2008. (Modern Rules Ser.). (ENG.). 100p. per. 29.95 (978-1-59031-922-2(2)) American Bar Assn.
Gesteland, Mary & Gesteland, Richard R. India - Cross-Cultural Business Behavior - For Business People, Expatriates & Scholars. 2010. 192p. pap. 47.00 (978-87-630-0222-6(1)) Copenhagen Business Schl. Pr. DNK. Dist: International Specialized Bk. Services.
Goldman, Lynda. You're Hired... Now What? An Immigrant's Guide to Success in the Canadian Workplace. 2011. (Canadian Newcomer Ser.). (ENG., Illus.). 384p. 24.95 (978-0-19-543218-3(5)) Oxford Univ. Pr., Inc.
Gupta, Subodh. Understanding Indian Culture & Bridging the Communication Gap. 2008. 100p. pap. (978-0-5556882-5-6(6)) Gupta, Subodh.

B

Hagglund, Anders & Bjorksten, Johan. How to Manage a Successful Business in China. 2010. (Illus.). 236p. 27.95 *(978-981-4287-82-1(2))* World Scientific Publishing Co., Inc.

Hamilton, Stewart & Zhang, Jinxuan. Doing Business with China: Avoiding the Pitfalls. 2012. (ENG., Illus.). 208p. 40.00 *(978-0-230-22265-6(X))* Palgrave Macmillan.

Henderson, Sylvia. ProfEtiquette: Profitable Etiquette - What to Do & Say to Excel at Work & Pay. 2007. 112p. 14.97 *(978-1-932197-30-3(3))*, Springboard Pr.) Springboard Training.

Hipsher, Scott A. Business Practices in Southeast Asia. 2012. (ENG., Illus.). 224p. (C). pap. 42.95 ***(978-0-415-53355-3(4))*** Routledge.

Hipsher, Scott A. Business Practices in Southeast Asia: An Interdisciplinary Analysis of Theravada Buddhist Countries. 2010. (Routledge Studies in the Growth Economies of Asia Ser.). (ENG., Illus.). 224p. (C). 135.00 *(978-0-415-56202-7(3))* Routledge.

Horton, Stephanie. Are Bad Manners Driving Your Clients CRAZY? 2008. 160p. pap. 17.00 *(978-0-615-20162-7(8))* Top Dog Etiquette.

Johnston, Laura. Mastering Business Etiquette. (CliffsNotes Ser.). pap. 8.99 *(978-0-7645-8618-7(1))* Wiley, John & Sons, Inc.

Jovin, Ellen. E-Mail Etiquette for Business Professionals. 2007. x, 129p. per. *(978-0-9785823-3-3(0))* Syntaxis Pr.

Jovin, Ellen & Johnson, Brandt. Syntaxis Communication Guides. 2007. per. *(978-0-9785823-4-0(9))* Syntaxis Pr.

Kallos, Blogger, Consultant Judith, Author. Business E-mail Etiquette: The Manual. 2008. 144p. pap. 19.50 *(978-1-4357-2049-7(0))* Lulu Enterprises Inc.

Kelm, Orlando R. & Risner, Mary E. Brasileiros Que Trabalham Com Americanos: Estudos de Casos Culturais. 2007.Tr. of Brazilians Working with Americans - Cultural Case Studies. (POR & ENG.). 218p. mass mkt. 19.95 *(978-0-292-71473-1(4))* Univ. of Texas Pr.

Kerrigan, Teresa & Sadar, Patricia. Essential Email Do's & Don'ts Kit. 2011. (Train It in Ten Ser.). cd-rom 0.00 *(978-1-936973-19-4(7))* Congrats Books, Inc.

Kobayashi-Hillary, Mark. Outsourcing to India: The Offshore Advantage. 2nd ed. 2010. xxii, 321p. pap. 99.00 *(978-3-642-06299-5(7)*, 3642062997) Springer.

Koch, Tobias. Business Knigge Germany. 2009. 6p. cd-rom 29.90 *(978-3-937545-19-6(0))* Koch, Tobias Trivero DEU. Dist: AtlasBooks Distribution.

Lamson, Melissa. No Such Thing As Small Talk: 7 Keys to Understanding German Business Culture. 2010. 162p. pap. 19.95 ***(978-1-60005-189-0(8))*** Happy About.

Lannoo Publishers Editors. Growing Abroad: No Business as Usual. 2012. (ENG.). 188p. pap. 50.00 *(978-90-209-6729-6(0))* Lannoo Pubs./Racine.

Levenda, Peter & Levenda. The Mao of Business: Guerrilla Trade Techniques for the New China. 2007. (ENG.). 240p. 24.95 *(978-0-8264-2851-6(7))* Continuum International Publishing Group, Ltd. GBR. Dist: National Bk. Network.

Lewis, Kate T. The Civilized Minute. 2010. pap. *(978-0-7414-6209-1(5))* Infinity Publishing.

Manian, Ranjini. Doing Business in India for Dummies. 2007. (ENG., Illus.). 342p. per. 24.99 *(978-0-470-12769-8(4)*, For Dummies) Wiley, John & Sons, Inc.

Margulis, Alexander R. How to Rise to the Top... & Stay There! A Leadership Manual. 2011. (ENG., Illus.). xiv, 167p. pap. 34.95 *(978-1-4419-7502-7(0)*, 1441975020) Springer.

Marsh, Donna. The Middle East Unveiled: A Cultural & Practical Guide for All Western Business Professionals. 2010. (ENG., Illus.). 356p. pap. 34.00 *(978-1-84528-416-9(X))* How To Books GBR. Dist: Parkwest Pubns., Inc.

Martin, Jeanette S. & Chaney, Lillian H. Global Business Etiquette: A Guide to International Communication & Customs. 2nd ed. 2012. E-Book ***(978-0-313-39718-9(X)***, Praeger Pubs.); 229p. 48.00 ***(978-0-313-39717-2(1)***, A3539C) Greenwood Publishing Group, Inc.

Martin, Jeanette S. & Chaney, Lillian H. Passport to Success: The Essential Guide to Business Culture & Customs in America's Largest Trading Partners, 1 vol. 2008. 304p. 39.95 *(978-0-275-99716-8(2)*, C9716, Praeger Pubs.) Greenwood Publishing Group, Inc.

Millar, Roderick. Doing Business with India. 3rd ed. 2009. (Doing Business With Ser.). (ENG., Illus.). 300p. pap. 170.00 *(978-1-84673-113-6(5)*, GMB Publishing Ltd.) Blue Ibex Ltd. GBR. Dist: Ingram Pub. Services.

Morrison, Terri & Conaway, Wayne A. Kiss, Bow, or Shake Hands: The Bestselling Guide to Doing Business in More Than 60 Countries. 2nd ed. 2006. (ENG., Illus.). 592p. per. 24.95 *(978-1-59337-368-9(6))* Adams Media Corp.

Morrison, Terri & Conway, Wayne A. Kiss, Bow, or Shake Hands: Sales & Marketing - The Essential Cultural Guide-From Presentations & Promotions to Communicating & Closing. 2011. (ENG.). 304p. pap. 20.00 ***(978-0-07-171404-4(9)***, 0071714049) McGraw-Hill Cos., The.

National Centre for Language Training Staff & University of New South Wales Press Staff. Doing Business in China: A Guide for Australians. 2008. (ENG.). 128p. pap. 25.95 *(978-1-921410-34-5(5)*, UNSW Press) NewSouth Publishing AUS. Dist: Independent Pubs. Group.

Noelle, Oliver & Strohschein, Alexa. A Useful Guide to Modern Business Etiquette in Germany. 2011. 134p. pap. 22.50 ***(978-3-8423-5229-2(8))*** Bks. on Demand.

Oliver, Vicky. 301 Smart Answers to Tough Business Etiquette Questions. 2010. (ENG.). 384p. pap. 12.95 *(978-1-61608-141-6(4)*, 608141) Skyhorse Publishing Co., Inc.

Pachter, Barbara. When the Little Things Count ... And They Always Count: 601 Essential Things That Everyone in Business Needs to Know. 2nd ed. 2006. (ENG.). 192p. per. 13.95 *(978-1-56924-290-2(9))* Da Capo Pr., Inc.

Pachter, Barbara & Coleman, Ellen Schneid. New Rules @ Work: 79 Etiquette Tips, Tools, & Techniques to Get Ahead & Stay Ahead. 2006. (ENG., Illus.). 272p. (gr. 12-18). 15.00 *(978-0-7352-0407-2(1))* Prentice Hall Pr.

Pagana, Kathleen Deska. The Nurse's Etiquette Advantage: How Professional Etiquette Can Advance Your Nursing Career. 2008. *(978-1-930538-80-1(4))* Sigma Theta Tau International, Ctr. for Nursing Pr.

Peters, James. The Arab World. 3rd ed. 2009. (ARA & ENG., Illus.). 150p. pap., instr.'s hndbk. ed. 18.95 ***(978-1-906768-03-4(X)***, Stacey International) Stacey Publishing GBR. Dist: Midpoint Trade Bks., Inc.

Poerner, Michael. Business-Knigge China: Die Darstellung Chinas in interkultureller Ratgeberliteratur. 2009. (FASK - Publikationen des Fachbereichs Angewandte Sprach- und Kulturwissenschaft der Johannes-Gutenberg-Universität Mainz in Germersheim. Reihe A: Abhandlungen und Sammelbände Ser.). (GER., Illus.). 146p. pap. 49.95 *(978-3-631-58475-0(X))* Lang, Peter GmbH, Europaischer Verlag der Wissenschaften DEU. Dist: Lang, Peter.

Professional Presence: The Total Program for Gaining That Extra Edge in Business by America's Top Corporate Image Consultant. 288p. 23.00 *(978-0-7881-9125-1(X))* DIANE Publishing Co.

Ramsey, Lydia. Manners That Sell: Adding the Polish That Builds Profits, 1 vol. 2008. (ENG., Illus.). 192p. 23.00 *(978-1-58980-637-5(9))* Pelican Publishing Co., Inc.

Riley, Donna Paige. What Is Executive Etiquette Anyway? Key Ingredients for Building Successful Working Relationships. 2006. per. 14.95 *(978-0-9785166-0-4(5))* Courteous Pubns.

RoAne, Susan & Roane, Susan. How to Work a Room: Savvy Socializing. rev. ed. 2007. (ENG., Illus.). 288p. pap. 15.99 *(978-0-06-123867-3(8)*, Harper Paperbacks) HarperCollins Pubs.

Robinson, Amanda. Business Protocol: Contemporary American Practice. 2nd ed. 2006. (ENG.). (C). pap. 62.95 *(978-0-7593-9239-7(0))* CENGAGE Learning Custom Publishing.

Sabath, Ann Marie. Business Etiquette: 101 Ways to Conduct Business with Charm & Savvy. 3rd ed. 2010. 13.99 *(978-1-60163-749-9(7))* Career Pr., Inc.

—Business Etiquette, Third Edition: 101 Ways to Conduct Business with Charm & Savvy. 3rd ed. 2010. (ENG.). 1p. pap. 13.99 *(978-1-60163-120-6(0))* Career Pr., Inc.

Schulz, Andrea. Chinese Business Culture- Theories, Examples, Figures. 2007. 136p. per. *(978-3-8364-0487-7(7))* VDM Verlag Dr. Mueller e.K.

Seligson, Hannah. New Girl on the Job: How Not to Cry at Work & Other Advice from the Trenches & Beyond. 2007. (ENG.). 256p. 19.95 *(978-0-8065-2811-3(7)*, Citadel Pr.) Kensington Publishing Corp.

Shinomiya, Sue & Szepkouski, Brian. Business Passport to Japan. rev. ed. 2007. (ENG., Illus.). 248p. per. 14.95 *(978-1-933330-47-1(3))* Stone Bridge Pr.

Shutt, Robert A. Shine While You Dine: Business Dining Etiquette for the Virtual Age. 2011. 132p. pap. 14.95 *(978-1-4567-1329-4(9))* AuthorHouse.

Sokolosky, Valerie. Do It Right! The New Book of Business Etiquette. 2007. per. 14.95 *(978-0-9788137-8-9(2))* CornerStone Leadership Institute.

Stoberl, Helmut. Der Zusammenhang Von Sprache und Beruf im Kontext Unternehmerischer Praxis. (GER., Illus.). 235p. pap. 54.95 *(978-3-631-56870-5(3))* Lang, Peter GmbH, Europaischer Verlag der Wissenschaften DEU. Dist: Lang, Peter Publishing, Inc.

Story, Jonathan. China Uncovered: What You Need to Know to Do Business in China. 2010. (Financial Times Ser.). (ENG., Illus.). 248p. (C). pap. 29.99 *(978-0-273-70827-8(9))* FT Press.

Sun, Ted. Inside the Chinese Business Mind: A Tactical Guide for Managers, 1 vol. 2010. (Illus.). 191p. 34.95 *(978-0-313-36519-5(9)*, C36519, Praeger Pubs.) Greenwood Publishing Group, Inc.

Turley, Joan. Connecting with China: Business Success Through Mutual Benefit & Respect. 2010. (ENG.). 278p. 35.00 *(978-0-470-74841-1(9)*, Wiley) Wiley, John & Sons, Inc.

Verstappen, Stefan H. Chinese Business Etiquette: The Practical Pocket Guide. 2008. (ENG., Illus.). 148p. pap. 9.95 *(978-1-933330-63-1(5))* Stone Bridge Pr.

Vieira, Walter. World Passport for Global Managers: The comprehensive guide to style, manners & etiquette in different Cultures. 2010. 168p. pap. 6.00 *(978-81-7806-184-9(8))* Unicorn Bks. Pvt Ltd. IND. Dist: Mahal, Pustak Pubs., Booksellers & Order Suppliers.

Waitzman, Michelle. Moon Living Abroad in New Zealand. 2011. (Living Abroad Ser.). (ENG., Illus.). 384p. pap. 19.99 ***(978-1-59880-887-2(7))*** Avalon Travel Publishing.

Wang, Yuan, et al. China Business Culture: Strategies for Success. 2008. 280p. pap. 35.00 *(978-981-04-8704-1(5))* Thorogood GBR. Dist: Stylus Publishing, LLC.

Weingarten, Rachel. Career & Corporate Cool: How to Look, Dress, & Act the Part — At Every Stage in Your Career... 2007. (ENG., Illus.). 272p. 21.95 *(978-0-470-12034-7(7)*, Wiley) Wiley, John & Sons, Inc.

Whitmore, Jacqueline. How to Become an Etiquette & Image Consultant Home Study Course. 2007. 495.00 incl. cd-rom *(978-0-9789330-2-9(8))* Protocol Schl. of Palm Beach, Inc., The.

Yager, Jan. Grow Global: Using International Protocol to Expand Your Business Worldwide. 2011. (Illus.). 200p. 31.95 *(978-1-889262-21-5(8))* Hannacroix Creek Bks., Inc.

Zoller, Kim & Preston, Kerry. You Did What? The Biggest Mistakes Professionals Make. 2011. 121p. pap. 16.95 ***(978-1-61254-027-6(9))*** Brown Bks. Publishing Group.

Zubko, Katherine C. & Sahay, Raj R. Inside the Indian Business Mind: A Tactical Guide for Managers. 2010. E-Book *(978-0-313-37830-0(4)*, Praeger Pubs.) Greenwood Publishing Group, Inc.

Zubko, Ph.D., Katherine C & Sahay, Raj R. Inside the Indian Business Mind: A Tactical Guide for Managers, 1 vol. 2010. (Illus.). 180p. 34.95 *(978-0-313-37829-4(0)*, C37829, Praeger Pubs.) Greenwood Publishing Group, Inc.

BUSINESS EXECUTIVES

see Executives

BUSINESS FAILURES

see also Bankruptcy; Success in Business

Acharya, Viral, et al. Guaranteed to Fail: Fannie Mae, Freddie Mac & the Debacle of Mortgage Finance. 2011. (ENG., Illus.). 232p. 24.95 *(978-0-691-15078-9(8))* Princeton Univ. Pr.

Aspatore Books Staff, compiled by. Buying & Selling Distressed Businesses: Leading Lawyers on Evaluating Assets & Identifying Buyers, Negotiating Deals, & Advising Directors & Officers on Fiduciary Duties (Inside the Minds) 2009. 452p. pap. 90.00 *(978-0-314-20785-2(6))* Aspatore Bks.

—Buying & Selling Distressed Businesses, 2010 Ed: Leading Lawyers on Navigating Recent Distressed Business Transactions, Understanding the Sales Process, & Developing Deal Strategies (Inside the Minds) 2010. (Illus.). 352p. pap. 95.00 *(978-0-314-27092-4(2))* Aspatore Bks.

Bennett, Andrew E. 25 Business Stories: A Practical Guide for English Learners. 2008. (ENG.). 144p. (gr. 7). 16.95 *(978-0-87779-683-1(1))* Merriam-Webster, Inc.

Branch, Ben & Ray, Hugh. Bankruptcy Investing - How to Profit from Distressed Companies. 2007. 328p. per. 44.95 *(978-1-58798-291-0(9))* Beard Bks., Inc.

Brewer, Lynn. House of Cards: Confessions of an Enron Executive. Date not set. 336p. 25.95 *(978-0-06-051852-3(9)*, ReganBooks) HarperCollins Pubs.

Bruner, Robert F. Deals from Hell: M & A Lessons That Rise above the Ashes. 2009. (ENG., Illus.). 432p. pap. 16.95 *(978-0-470-45259-2(5)*, Wiley) Wiley, John & Sons, Inc.

Byrd, Bill & Page, George. Under the Gun: How to start & lose a business in six Months. 2009. 184p. 25.99 *(978-1-4389-9561-8(X))*; pap. 15.99 *(978-1-4389-9562-5(8))* AuthorHouse.

Carroll, Paul B, et al. Billion Dollar Lessons: What You Can Learn from the Most Inexcusable Business Failures of the Last 25 Years. 2009. (ENG.). 336p. (gr. 12-18). 16.00 *(978-1-59184-289-7(1)*, Portfolio Trade) Penguin Group (USA) Inc.

Chapman, Peter. The Last of the Imperious Rich: Lehman Brothers, 1844-2008. 2010. (ENG.). 320p. (gr. 12). 27.95 *(978-1-59184-309-2(X)*, Portfolio (Hardcover)) Penguin Group (USA) Inc.

Clarke, Frank & Dean, Graeme. Indecent Disclosure: Gilding the Corporate Lily. 2007. (Illus.). 274p. per. 45.99 *(978-0-521-70183-9(X))* Cambridge Univ. Pr.

The Collapse & Federal Rescue of AIG & What It Means for the U.S. Economy: Hearing Before the Committee on Oversight & Government Reform, House of Representatives, One Hundred Eleventh Congress, First Session, April 2, 2009. 2009. (Illus.). iii, 83p. *(978-0-16-084114-9(3)*, 552-070-39721-3) United States Government Printing Office.

Collins, Jim. How the Mighty Fall: And Why Some Companies Never Give In. 2009. (ENG.). 256p. 23.99 *(978-0-9773264-1-9(1)*, JimCollins) Collins, Jim.

Cram101 Textbook Reviews Staff. Outlines & Highlights for Big Winners & Big Losers: The 4 Secrets of Long-Term Business Success & Failure by Marcus, ISBN. 2008. 108p. pap. 11.95 *(978-1-4288-6359-0(1))* Cram101 Inc.

Davis, Kristin R. Your Business Failed You Did Not! Defining & Living Your Well-lived Life. 2011. 78p. pap. 19.95 ***(978-1-4626-2934-3(2))*** PublishAmerica, Inc.

Delmar, Frederic & Wennberg, Karl. Knowledge Intensive Entrepreneurship: The Birth, Growth & Demise of Entrepreneurial Firms. 2010. (Illus.). 208p. 112.00 *(978-1-84844-990-9(9))* Elgar, Edward Publishing, Inc.

Drummond, Helga. The Dynamics of Organizational Collapse: The Case of Barings Bank. (Routledge International Studies in Money & Banking Ser.). 2012. (ENG.). 160p. (C). pap. 42.95 ***(978-0-415-54270-8(7))*** 2007. XVI, 144p. 143.00 *(978-0-415-39961-6(0))* Routledge.

Eisner, Howard. Failure, Inc: 52 Ways to Go under in Business. 2007. (Capital Ideas for Business & Personal Development Ser.). 156p. 18.95 *(978-1-933102-40-5(3))* Capital Bks., Inc.

Enyi, Enyi. Detecting, Predicting & Preventing Corporate Failure. 2010. 140p. pap. *(978-3-8383-4863-6(X))* Lambert Academic Publishing.

Finch, Vanessa. Corporate Insolvency Law: Perspectives & Principles. 2nd ed. 2009. (ENG.). 918p. 205.00 *(978-0-521-87810-4(1))*; pap. 84.00 *(978-0-521-70182-2(1))* Cambridge Univ. Pr.

Finn, Paul. Insolvency in Business. (ENG., Illus.). 1p. *(978-0-304-31797-4(7)*, Burns & Oates) Continuum International Publishing Group, Ltd.

Gibb, Alistair. How to Beat the Recession: Make Sure Your Business Prospers While Others Struggle. 2009. 122p. pap. *(978-1-904608-96-7(5))* Taxcafe UK Ltd.

GM & Chrysler Dealership Closures: Protecting Dealers & Consumers: Hearing Before the Committee on Commerce, Science, & Transportation, United States Senate, One Hundred Eleventh Congress, First Session, June 3, 2009. 2010. (Illus.). iv, 130p. ***(978-0-16-087147-4(6)***, 552-070-41990-0) United States Government Printing Office.

Hamilton, Stewart & Micklethwait, Alicia. Greed & Corporate Failure: The Lessons from Recent Disasters. 2006. (ENG.). 256p. 59.00 *(978-1-4039-8636-8(3))* Palgrave Macmillan.

Heath, Ralph. Celebrating Failure. 2009. (ENG.). 1p. pap. 14.99 *(978-1-60163-064-3(6))* Career Pr., Inc.

Henderson, Gordon D. & Goldring, Stuart J. Tax Planning for Troubled Corporations (2012) 2011. 1090p. pap. 397.50 ***(978-0-8080-2787-4(5)***, CCH) Wolters Kluwer Tax & Accounting.

Johnston, Ronnie. View from the Tower: Business & Entrepreneurship in Depression Scotland. 2013. (ENG.). 256p. 50.00 ***(978-1-84519-284-6(2))*** Sussex Academic Pr. GBR. Dist: International Specialized Bk. Services.

Kaplan, Philip J. F'd Companies: Spectacular Dot-com Flameouts. 2007. (ENG.). 208p. pap. 15.95 *(978-1-4165-7793-5(9))* Simon & Schuster.

Kato, Mushumbusi Paul & Dominick Mushi, Lawrencia. Learning from Entrepreneurial Failure. 2010. 92p. pap. *(978-3-639-18920-9(5))* VDM Verlag Dr. Mueller e.K.

Keough, Donald R. The Ten Commandments for Business Failure. 2011. (ENG.). 208p. (gr. 12). 15.00 *(978-1-59184-413-6(4)*, Portfolio Trade) Penguin Group (USA) Inc.

Lehman Brothers, Sharper Image, Bennigan's & Beyond: Is Chapter 11 Bankruptcy Working?: Hearing Before the Subcommittee on Commercial & Administrative Law of the Committee on the Judiciary, House of Representatives, One Hundred Tenth Congress, Second Session, September 26, 2008. 2009. (Illus.). iii, 74p. *(978-0-16-083314-4(0)*, 552-070-39139-8) United States Government Printing Office.

Maharaj, Jyothi. Symptoms of Small Business Failure. 2011. 168p. pap. ***(978-3-8443-1507-3(1))*** Lambert Academic Publishing.

Marcus, Alfred. Big Winners & Big Losers: The 4 Secrets of Long-Term Business Success & Failure. rev. ed. 2011. (ENG.). 300p. pap. 34.99 *(978-0-13-276231-1(5))* FT Press.

McLean, Bethany & Elkind, Peter. Smartest Guys in the Room: The Amazing Rise & Scandalous Fall of Enron. 2006. (Illus.). 435p. reprint ed. 27.00 *(978-1-4223-5468-1(7))* DIANE Publishing Co.

Miles, D. Anthony. Entrepreneurship & Risk: the Five Forces of Entrepreneurial Risk: Forces That Cause Business Failure & Discontinuance. 2011. 240p. pap. ***(978-3-639-33790-7(5))*** VDM Verlag Dr. Mueller e.K.

—Risk Factors & Business Models: Understanding the Five Forces of Entrepreneurial Risk & the Causes of Business Failure. 2011. 198p. pap. 25.95 ***(978-1-59942-388-3(X)***, Dissertation.com) Universal Pubs.

Moltz, Barry J. Bounce! Failure, Resiliency, & Confidence to Achieve Your Next Great Success. 11th ed. 2008. (ENG., Illus.). 256p. 24.95 *(978-0-470-22408-3(8)*, Wiley) Wiley, John & Sons, Inc.

Morris, Piers. Risk in Business: The Impact of People & Events. 2010. 162p. pap. *(978-0-7552-1247-7(9))* Authors OnLine, Ltd.

Oliver, Jamie & Goodwin, Tony. How They Blew It: The CEO's & Entrepreneurs Behind Some of the World's Most Catastrophic Business Failures. 2010. (ENG.). 224p. pap. 19.95 *(978-0-7494-6065-5(2))* Kogan Page, Ltd. GBR. Dist: Ingram Pub. Services.

Ormerod, Paul. Why Most Things Fail: Evolution, Extinction & Economics. 2007. (ENG., Illus.). 272p. per. 16.95 *(978-0-470-08919-4(9)*, Wiley) Wiley, John & Sons, Inc.

Owen, Jo. Tribal Business School: Lessons in Business Survival & Success from the Ultimate Survivors. 2008. (ENG., Illus.). 144p. 34.95 *(978-0-470-72781-2(0)*, Jossey-Bass) Wiley, John & Sons, Inc.

Pehn, Franz. Financial Distress & Bankruptcy. 2009. 76p. pap. *(978-3-639-12921-2(0))* VDM Verlag Dr. Mueller e.K.

Phillips, Tim. Fit to Bust: How Great Companies Fail. 2011. (ENG.). 216p. pap. 19.95 *(978-0-7494-6013-6(X))* Kogan Page, Ltd. GBR. Dist: Ingram Pub. Services.

Ramifications of Auto Industry Bankruptcies: Hearing Before the Committee on the Judiciary, House of Representatives, One Hundred Eleventh Congress, First Session, May 21, 2009. 2009. iv, 178p. *(978-0-16-084379-2(0)*, 552-070-39922-4) United States Government Printing Office.

Ramifications of Auto Industry Bankruptcies: Hearing Before the Subcommittee on Commercial & Administrative Law of the Committee on the Judiciary, House of Representatives, One Hundred Eleventh Congress, First Session, July 21, 2009. 2010. iv, 71p. *(978-0-16-085264-0(1)*, 552-070-40605-1) United States Government Printing Office.

Ramifications of Auto Industry Bankruptcies: Hearing Before the Subcommittee on Commercial & Administrative Law of the Committee on the Judiciary, House of Representatives, One Hundred Eleventh Congress, First Session, July 22, 2009. 2010. (Illus.). iv, 282p. *(978-0-16-085324-1(9)*, 552-070-40654-9) United States Government Printing Office.

Rohrbeck, René & Rohrbeck, René. Corporate Foresight: Towards a Maturity Model for the Future Orientation of a Firm. 2010. (Contributions to Management Science Ser.). (ENG., Illus.). xxiii, 220p. 139.00 *(978-3-7908-2625-8(1)*, 3790826251) Physica-Verlag DEU. Dist: Springer.

Rudzki, Robert. Beat the Odds: Avoid Corporate Death & Build a Resilient Enterprise. 2007. (Illus.). 248p. per. *(978-1-932159-68-4(1))* Ross, J. Publishing, Inc.

Samet, Joseph. Recent Developments in Distressed Debt, Restructurings & Workouts: Fallout from the Credit Crunch 2008. 2008. (Illus.). 674p. pap. *(978-1-4024-1188-5(X))* Practising Law Institute.

Schoemaker, Paul J. H. Brilliant Mistakes: Finding Success on the Far Side of Failure. 2011. (ENG.). 144p. pap. 15.99 ***(978-1-61363-012-9(3))*** Wharton Digital Pr.

Shepherd, Dean A. From Lemons to Lemonade: Squeeze Every Last Drop of Success Out of Your Mistakes. 2009. (ENG., Illus.). 224p. 22.99 *(978-0-13-136273-4(9))* Wharton Schl. Publishing.

Sheth, Jagdish N. The Self-Destructive Habits of Good Companies. 2007. (ENG., Illus.). 304p. pap. 29.99 *(978-0-13-611741-4(4))* Wharton Schl. Publishing.
Singleton, Susan. Buying & Selling Insolvent Companies & Businesses. 2010. 396p. pap. 198.00 *(978-1-84766-542-3(X),* Bloomsbury Professional) Bloomsbury Publishing Plc GBR. Dist: International Specialized Bk. Services.
Smith, Rebecca & Emshwiller, John R. 24 Days: How Two Wall Street Journal Reporters Uncovered the Lies that Destroyed Faith in Corporate America. 2006. (Illus.). 400p. reprint ed. pap. 26.00 *(978-1-4223-5746-0(5))* DIANE Publishing Co.
Sutton, Gary. Corporate Canaries: Avoid Business Disasters with a Coal Miner's Secrets, 0 vols. 2007. 160p. pap. 12.99 *(978-0-7852-3849-7(X))* Nelson, Thomas Inc.
Taylor, Alex, III. Sixty to Zero: An Inside Look at the Collapse of General Motors — and the Detroit Auto Industry. 2011. (ENG.). 272p. pap. 17.00 *(978-0-300-17151-8(X))* Yale Univ. Pr.
Tedlow, Richard S. Denial: Why Business Leaders Fail to Look Facts in the Face - And What to Do about It. 2010. (ENG., Illus.). 272p. (gr. 12-18). 26.95 *(978-1-59184-313-9(8),* Portfolio (Hardcover)) Penguin Group (USA) Inc.
—Denial: Why Business Leaders Fail to Look Facts in the Face — And What to Do about It. 2011. (ENG., Illus.). 288p. (gr. 12). 16.00 *(978-1-59184-391-7(X),* Portfolio Trade) Penguin Group (USA) Inc.
Too Big to Fail? The Role of Antitrust Law in Government-Funded Consolidation in the Banking Industry: Hearing Before the Subcommittee on Courts & Competition Policy of the Committee on the Judiciary, House of Representatives, One Hundred Eleventh Congress, First Session, March 17, 2009. 2009. (Illus.). iii, 87p. *(978-0-16-084890-2(3),* 552-070-40286-1) United States Government Printing Office.
Torres, Olivier. The Wine Wars: The Mondavi Affair, Globalisation & Terroir. Snaith, Kirsty, tr. from FRE. annot. ed. 2006. (ENG.). 192p. 121.00 *(978-0-230-00210-4(2))* Palgrave Macmillan.
Turner, Marcia Layton. Kmart's Deadly Sins: How Incompetence Tainted an American Icon. 2006. 256p. reprint ed. 25.00 *(978-1-4223-5571-8(3))* DIANE Publishing Co.
Warner, Ralph & Laurence, Bethany K. Save Your Small Business: 10 Crucial Strategies to Survive Hard Times or Close down & Move On. 2009. (ENG.). 316p. pap. 29.99 *(978-1-4133-1041-2(9))* NOLO.
Weil, Gotshal & Manges Staff & American Bar Association, Section of Business Law Staff, contrib. by. Reorganizing Failing Businesses: A Comprehensive Review & Analysis of Financial Restructuring & Business Reorganization. rev. ed. 2007. (ENG.). 1200p. spiral bd. 290.95 *(978-1-59031-714-3(9))* American Bar Assn.
Zopounidis, Constantin & Dimitras, A. I. Multicriteria Decision Aid Methods for the Prediction of Business Failure. 2010. (Applied Optimization Ser.). 204p. pap. 169.00 *(978-1-4419-4787-1(6),* 1441947876) Springer.

BUSINESS FILMS
see Industrial Films

BUSINESS FORECASTING
see also Business Planning; Sales Forecasting; Stock Price Forecasting
Abramowicz, Michael. Predictocracy: Market Mechanisms for Public & Private Decision Making. 2008. (ENG., Illus.). 368p. 50.00 *(978-0-300-11599-4(7))* Yale Univ. Pr.
Advances in Financial Planning & Forecasting, New Series, 2. 2006. *(978-0-9651643-6-8(5))* Ctr. for Pacific Basin Business, Economic & Finance Research.
Backman, Michael. Asia Future Shock: Business Crisis & Opportunity in the Coming Years. 2007. (ENG.). 200p. 59.00 *(978-0-230-00677-5(9))* Palgrave Macmillan.
Baumohl, Bernard. The Secrets of Economic Indicators: Hidden Clues to Future Economic Trends & Investment Opportunities. 3rd ed. 2012. (ENG.). 480p. pap. 29.99 ***(978-0-13-293207-3(5))*** Wharton Schl. Publishing.
Bisconti, Robert. An Exploration of Approaches to Forecasting Company Earnings Using the Neural Network Paradigm. 2010. 232p. pap. *(978-3-8383-5165-0(7))* Lambert Academic Publishing.
BVR Staff, compiled by. The Use of Management Projections in Valuations. 2011. pap. 129.00 ***(978-1-935081-78-4(0))*** Business Valuation Resources, LLC.
Canduela, Jesus. Forecasting in Fast Moving Consumer Goods Organisations: A Case Study. 2010. 264p. pap. *(978-3-8383-0092-4(0))* Lambert Academic Publishing.
Chase, Charles & Chase. Demand-Driven Forecasting: A Structured Approach to Forecasting. 2009. (Wiley & SAS Business Ser.: 19). (ENG., Illus.). 288p. 60.00 *(978-0-470-41502-3(9),* Wiley) Wiley, John & Sons, Inc.
Christensen, Clayton M., et al. Disrupting Class: How Disruptive Innovation Will Change the Way the World Learns. 2008. (ENG., Illus.). 288p. 32.95 *(978-0-07-159206-2(7),* 0071592067) McGraw-Hill Cos., The.
Constable, Simon & Wright, Robert. The WSJ Guide to the 50 Economic Indicators That Really Matter: From Big Macs to Zombie Banks, the Indicators Smart Investors Watch to Beat the Market. 2011. (ENG.). 208p. pap. 15.99 *(978-0-06-200138-2(8),* Harper Paperbacks) HarperCollins Pubs.
Cont, Rama, ed. Frontiers in Quantitative Finance: Volatility & Credit Risk Modeling. 2008. (Wiley Finance Ser.: 463). (ENG., Illus.). 300p. 75.00 *(978-0-470-29292-1(X),* Wiley) Wiley, John & Sons, Inc.
Cram101 Textbook Reviews. Outlines & Highlights for Business Forecasting by Wilson & Keating, Isbn: 9780077309305. 2010. 62p. pap. 27.95 *(978-1-61698-855-5(X))* Cram101 Inc.
Cram101 Textbook Reviews Staff. Outlines & Highlights for Business Forecasting by John E Hanke, Dean Wichern, Isbn: 9780132301206. 2009. 92p. pap. 27.95 *(978-1-4288-7394-0(5))* Cram101 Inc.
Crusie, Jennifer, pseud, et al. Business Forecasting: With ForecastX? 6th ed. 2008. (Illus.). 528p. (C). 159.38 *(978-0-07-337364-5(8),* 9780073373645) McGraw-Hill Professional Publishing.
Dewey, Edward R. & Dakin, Edwin F. Cycles: The Science of Prediction. 268p. 2011. pap. 12.50 ***(978-1-61427-005-8(8))*** 2010. pap. 15.95 *(978-1-57898-874-7(8))* Martino Publishing.
—Cycles the Science of Prediction. 2011. 218p. pap. 12.99 ***(978-1-61720-289-6(4))*** Wilder Pubns., Ltd.
Diebold, Francis X. Elements of Forecasting. 4th ed. 2006. (ENG., Illus.). 384p. (C). 256.95 *(978-0-324-35904-6(7));* 256.95 *(978-0-324-32359-7(X))* Cengage South-Western.
Disney, Stephen M. & Lambrecht, Marc R. On Replenishment Rules, Forecasting & the Bullwhip Effect in Supply Chains. 2008. (ENG.). 88p. pap. 70.00 net. *(978-1-60198-132-5(5))* Now Pubs.
Donohue Group Inc. Encyclopedia of Emerging Industries. 5th ed. 2007. (Encyclopedia of Emerging Industries Ser.). 1022p. 325.00 *(978-1-59237-242-3(2))* Grey Hse. Publishing.
Encyclopedia of Emerging Industries. 6th ed. 2011. 1400p. 520.00 *(978-1-4144-8687-1(1))* Cengage Gale.
Ferrell, O. C., et al. Business: A Changing World. 8th ed. 2010. (ENG., Illus.). 640p. (C). pap. 150.67 *(978-0-07-351175-7(7),* 0073511757, McGraw-Hill/Irwin) McGraw-Hill Higher Education.
Fildes, Robert A. & Allen, Geoff, eds. Forecasting, 5 vols. 2011. (SAGE Benchmarks in Social Research Methods Ser.). (Illus.). 2104p. 1195.00 *(978-1-84850-782-8(2),* B07828C) SAGE Pubns., Ltd. GBR. Dist: SAGE Pubns., Inc.
Gerwick, Madeline C. Good Timing Guide 2007: An Astrological Business Planner. 2010. spiral bd. 24.50 *(978-1-60070-011-8(X),* Elite Bks.) Author's Publishing Cooperative.
Gilliland, Michael & Platt, Julie. The Business Forecasting Deal: Exposing Myths, Eliminating Bad Practices, Providing Practical Solutions. 2010. (Wiley & SAS Business Ser.: 27). (ENG., Illus.). 272p. 49.95 *(978-0-470-57443-0(7),* Wiley) Wiley, John & Sons, Inc.
Hanke, John E. & Wichern, Dean W. Business Forecasting. 9th ed. 2008. (ENG., Illus.). 576p. (C). pap. 173.33 *(978-0-13-230120-6(2),* Prentice Hall) Prentice Hall PTR.
Hordeski, Michael F. Alternative Fuels: The Future of Hydrogen. 2nd ed. 2008. x, 286p. *(978-0-88173-595-6(7))* Fairmont Pr., Inc.
Hoshmand, A. Reza. Business Forecasting: A Practical Approach. 2nd ed. 2009. (ENG., Illus.). 384p. (C). 180.00 *(978-0-415-98855-1(1));* pap. 52.95 *(978-0-415-98856-8(X))* Routledge.
Hyndman, Rob, et al. Forecasting with Exponential Smoothing: The State Space Approach. 2008. (Springer Series in Statistics Ser.). (Illus.). 350p. pap. 69.95 *(978-3-540-71916-8(4))* Springer.
Johansen, Bob. Get There Early: Sensing the Future to Compete in the Present. 2007. (ENG., Illus.). 258p. 27.95 *(978-1-57675-440-5(5))* Berrett-Koehler Pubs., Inc.
Johar, Khalid L. Venture Appraisal. 2010. 240p. pap. *(978-3-8383-8607-2(8))* Lambert Academic Publishing.
K. D. Lawrence R. Klimberg Staff. Advances in Business & Management Forecasting. 2009. 114.95 *(978-1-84855-548-8(2))* Emerald Group Publishing Ltd. GBR. Dist: Turpin Distribution Services Ltd.
Kanter, Rosabeth Moss. SuperCorp: How Vanguard Companies Create Innovation, Profits, Growth, & Social Good. 2009. (ENG.). 336p. 27.50 *(978-0-307-38235-1(4),* Crown Business) Crown Publishing Group.
Katsaros, John & Christy, Peter. Getting It Right the First Time: How Innovative Companies Anticipate Demand, 1 vol. 2008. 176p. pap. 19.95 *(978-0-313-35154-9(6),* B35154, Praeger Trade) Greenwood Publishing Group, Inc.
Landrum, Gene. Cover Your Assets & Become Your Own Liability: Self-Serving Destroys from Within. 2009. (ENG.). 288p. 29.95 *(978-1-60037-658-0(4));* pap. 19.95 *(978-1-60037-657-3(6))* Morgan James Publishing.
Lawrence, Kenneth D. & Geurts, Michael D., eds. Advances in Business & Management Forecasting. 2008. (Advances in Business & Management Forecasting Ser.). (Illus.). 291p. 99.95 *(978-0-7623-1478-2(8))* Emerald Group Publishing Ltd. GBR. Dist: Turpin Distribution Services Ltd.
Lawrence, Kenneth D. & Klimberg, Ronald, eds. Advances in Business & Management Forecasting. (Advances in Business & Management Forecasting Ser.). (Illus.). 2011. 208p. ***(978-0-85724-959-3(2))*** 2010. 256p. *(978-0-85724-201-3(6))* Emerald Group Publishing Ltd.
Lee, Alice C., et al. Financial Analysis, Planning & Forecasting: Theory & Application. 2nd ed. 2008. (Illus.). 800p. 153.00 *(978-981-270-608-9(9))* World Scientific Publishing Co., Inc.
Lee, Migi. Economic & Political Impacts of Business Improvement District. 2011. 76p. pap. ***(978-3-8443-0770-2(2))*** Lambert Academic Publishing.
Maital, Shlomo & Seshadri, D. V. R. Global Risk, Global Opportunity: Ten Essential Tools for Tracking Minds, Markets & Money. 2010. (Response Bks.). (Illus.). 320p. (C). pap. 32.95 *(978-81-321-0443-8(9),* 88196) SAGE Pubns., Inc.
Malunga, Chiku. Oblivion or Utopia: The Prospects for Africa. 2009. (ENG., Illus.). 148p. 52.50 *(978-0-7618-4985-8(8));* pap. 26.50 *(978-0-7618-4986-5(6))* Univ. Pr. of America, Inc.
Martinsky, Ondrej. Intelligent Trading Systems: Applying Artificial Intelligence to Financial Markets. 2010. (Illus.). 212p. pap. 110.00 *(978-1-906659-53-0(2))* Harriman Hse. Publishing GBR. Dist: Ingram Pub. Services.
McGough, Tony & Tsolacos, Sotiris. Real Estate Market Analysis & Forecasting. 2008. (Illus.). 248p. pap. 89.95 *(978-1-4051-2122-4(X),* Wiley-Blackwell) Wiley, John & Sons, Inc.
Morlidge, Steve & Player, Steve. Future Ready: How to Master Business Forecasting. 2010. (ENG., Illus.). 328p. 34.95 *(978-0-470-74705-6(6),* Wiley) Wiley, John & Sons, Inc.
Olamade, Olumuyiwa Owolabi. Ict for Business Environmental Scanning. 2010. 428p. pap. *(978-3-8383-9335-3(X))* Lambert Academic Publishing.
Ord, Keith & Fildes, Robert. Principles of Business Forcasting. 2012. (ENG.). 480p. (C). 149.95 ***(978-0-324-31127-3(3))*** Cengage South-Western.
Passikoff, Robert. Predicting Market Success: New Ways to Measure Customer Loyalty & Engage Consumers with Your Brand. 2006. (ENG., Illus.). 256p. 29.95 *(978-0-470-04022-5(X),* Wiley) Wiley, John & Sons, Inc.
Plunkett, Jack W. The Next Boom: What You Absolutely, Positively Have to Know about the World Between Now And 2025. Plunkett, Jack W., ed. 2011. (ENG.). 274p. 29.99 *(978-1-60879-999-2(9))* Plunkett Research, Ltd.
Ramo, Simon & Sugar, Ronald. Strategic Business Forecasting: A Structured Approach to Shaping the Future of Your Business. 2009. (ENG.). 240p. 34.95 *(978-0-07-162126-7(1),* 0071621261) McGraw-Hill Cos., The.
Salzman, Marian & Matathia, Ira. Next Now: Trends for the Future. 2007. (ENG.). 320p. pap. 16.95 *(978-0-230-60001-0(8))* Palgrave Macmillan.
Secrett, Malcolm. Brilliant Budgets & Forecasts: Your Practical Guide to Preparing & Presenting Financial Information. 2010. (ENG., Illus.). 328p. (C). pap. 19.99 *(978-0-273-73091-0(6))* FT Press.
Shim, Jae K. Management of Insurance Operations. 2009. 402p. pap. 49.95 *(978-1-906403-34-8(1))* Lessons Professional Publishing GBR. Dist: Stylus Publishing, LLC.
SPANOTES Mathematics - Bilingual Hardcopy: A bilingual study aid for secondary school Mathematics. 2009. (ENG & SPA., Illus.). 224p. pap. 24.95 *(978-1-884730-00-9(0),* Interlingua Publishing) InterLingua.com, Inc.
Tanous, Peter J. & Cox, Jeff. Debt, Deficits, & the Demise of the American Economy. 2011. (ENG., Illus.). 207p. 27.95 *(978-1-118-02151-4(7),* Wiley) Wiley, John & Sons, Inc.
Tertzakian, Peter. A Thousand Barrels a Second: The Coming Oil Break Point & the Challenges Facing an Energy Dependent World. 2007. (ENG., Illus.). 238p. per. 16.95 *(978-0-07-149260-7(7),* 0071492607) McGraw-Hill Cos., The.
Vaughan Williams, Leighton, ed. Prediction Markets. 2011. (Routledge International Studies in Money & Banking Ser.). (ENG., Illus.). 288p. (C). 150.00 *(978-0-415-57286-6(X))* Routledge.
Wade, Pamela A. & Wade, Woody. Scenario Planning: A Field Guide to the Future. 2012. (ENG.). 204p. pap. 29.95 ***(978-1-118-17015-1(6),*** Wiley) Wiley, John & Sons, Inc.
Wenzelburger, Jan. Learning in Economic Systems with Expectations Feedback. 2006. (Lecture Notes in Economics & Mathematical Systems Ser.). (Illus.). x, 176p. pap. 109.00 *(978-3-540-24322-9(4),* 3540243224) Springer.
Wilson, J. Holton, et al. Business Forecasting with Student CD. 6th ed. 2008. (ENG.). (C). 212.33 incl. cd-rom *(978-0-07-730930-5(8),* 0077309308, McGraw-Hill/Irwin) McGraw-Hill Higher Education.
Wilson, K. Business Forecasting. 2006. pap. 8.95 *(978-1-4288-0649-8(0))* Cram101 Inc.

BUSINESS FORECASTING—DATA PROCESSING
Bojadziev, George & Bojadziev, Maria. Fuzzy Logic for Business, Finance, & Management. 2nd ed. (Illus.). 230p. 121.00 *(978-981-270-649-2(6))* World Scientific Publishing Co., Inc.
Lawrence, K. & Klimberg. Fundamentals of Forecasting Using Excel. 2009. 300p. (C). pap. 39.95 *(978-0-8311-3335-1(X))* Industrial Pr., Inc.
Linzer, Richard S. & Linzer, Anna O. The Cash Flow Forecaster. 2007. cd-rom 60.00 *(978-0-7879-8626-1(7))* Wiley, John & Sons, Inc.

BUSINESS GAMES
see Management Games

BUSINESS GRAPHICS SOFTWARE
see Presentation Graphics Software

BUSINESS INFORMATION SERVICES
Abdelnour-Nocera, Jost. The Social Construction of Usefulness. 2007. 264p. per. *(978-3-8364-2582-7(3))* VDM Verlag Dr. Mueller e.K.
Directory of Business Information Resources. 14th ed. 2007. (Directory of Business Information Resources Ser.). 1747p. per. 195.00 *(978-1-59237-146-4(9))* Grey Hse. Publishing.
Encyclopedia of Business Information Sources, 2.0. 28th ed. 2011. pap. 626.00 *(978-1-4144-5899-1(1))* Cengage Gale.
Euromonitor International Staff, contrib. by. World Database of Business Information Sources, 2 vols. 2nd ed. 2010. xxxviii, 1500p. *(978-1-84264-528-4(5))* Euromonitor International PLC.
Forte, Eric & Oppenheim, Michael. The Basic Business Library: Core Resources & Services, 1 vol. 5th rev. ed. 227p. 44.95 *(978-1-59884-611-9(6),* A3137C) Libraries Unlimited, Inc.
Forte, Eric J. & Oppenheim, Michael R. The Basic Business Library: Core Resources & Services. 5th ed. 2011. E-Book ***(978-1-59884-612-6(4))*** Libraries Unlimited, Inc.
Foster, Pamela, ed. Business Information Basics 2000. (ENG.). 190p. ***(978-3-11-183267-8(8))*** Saur, K. G. Verlag GmbH & Co.
Giraud, Laurent & Fichet, Hugues. Information Flow in Project-Based Companies. 2011. 80p. pap. ***(978-3-8443-2571-3(9))*** Lambert Academic Publishing.
Heinzl, Armin, et al, eds. Theory-Guided Modeling & Empiricism in Information Systems Research. 2011. (ENG., Illus.). x, 258p. pap. 109.00 ***(978-3-7908-2780-4(0),*** 3790827800) Physica-Verlag DEU. Dist: Springer.
Heuser, Lutz, et al. International Research Forum 2007. 2008. (Illus.). 304p. per. 40.00 *(978-0-9789218-3-5(6))* Evolved Technologist Pr.
Hirao, Joey & Wun-Young, Leslie. SAP Security Configuration & Deployment: The IT Administrator's Guide to Best Practices. 2008. (ENG., Illus.). 392p. pap. 72.95 *(978-1-59749-284-3(1),* Syngress Press) Elsevier Science & Technology Bks.
Hosack, Bryan. Putting Values in It. 2008. 116p. pap. *(978-3-8364-3495-9(4))* VDM Verlag Dr. Mueller e.K.
Lopez-Catalan, Blanca, et al. Gis for Business & Social Decisions. 2011. 56p. pap. ***(978-3-8443-2471-6(2))*** Lambert Academic Publishing.
MacDonald, Karen & Kirkwood, Hal, eds. Business Librarianship & Entrepreneurship Outreach. 2011. (ENG., Illus.). 120p. (C). 145.00 ***(978-0-415-68976-2(7))*** Routledge.
MacKenzie, Leslie & Gottlieb, Richard, eds. The Directory of Business Information Resources. 15th ed. 2008. (Directory of Business Information Resources Ser.). 1747p. per. 195.00 *(978-1-59237-193-8(0))* Grey Hse. Publishing.
Macoustra, Jane. Global Research Without Leaving Your Desk: Travelling the World with Your Mouse as Companion. 2009. 200p. pap. 80.00 *(978-1-84334-366-0(5),* Chandos Publishing) Woodhead Publishing Ltd. GBR. Dist: Neal-Schuman Pubs., Inc.
Magal, Simha R. & Word, Jeffrey. Integrated Business Processes with ERP Systems, Preliminary Edition. 2010. (ENG., Illus.). 240p. (C). pap. 51.95 *(978-0-470-88424-9(X),* Wiley) Wiley, John & Sons, Inc.
Mahlke, Sascha. User Experience of Interaction with Technical Systems. 2008. 144p. pap. *(978-3-639-02970-3(4))* VDM Verlag Dr. Mueller e.K.
Mars, Laura, ed. Directory of Business Information Resources. 2011. 2500p. pap. 195.00 *(978-1-59237-737-4(8))* Grey Hse. Publishing.
—Directory of Business Information Resources 2010. 17th rev. ed. 2010. pap. 195.00 *(978-1-59237-500-4(6))* Grey Hse. Publishing.
Mars-Proietti, Laura, ed. Directory of Business Information Resources: 2009. 16th rev. ed. 2009. 1800p. pap. 195.00 *(978-1-59237-399-4(2))* Grey Hse. Publishing.
McCarthy, Nigel. Economic & Business News on Television - How Political & Business Leaders Connect with Journalists & Why Television News Is Addicted to Leaders. 2008. 316p. pap. *(978-3-639-00881-4(2))* VDM Verlag Dr. Mueller e.K.
Miller, David. Business Focused It & Service Excellence. 2nd ed. 2008. (Illus.). xvii, 176p. pap. 41.99 *(978-1-902505-88-6(3))* British Computer Society, The GBR. Dist: Turpin Distribution Services Ltd.
Miller, Thomas William. Research & Information Services: An Integrated Approach for Business. 2007. 369p. pap. 50.00 *(978-0-9727297-2-7(0))* Research Pubs. LLC.
Moss, Rita & Ernsthausen, David G. Strauss's Handbook of Business Information: A Guide for Librarians, Students, & Researchers, 1 vol. 399p. 100.00 ***(978-1-59884-807-6(0),*** A3433C) Pearson Education GBR. Dist: ABC-CLIO, LLC.
Ogc. Service Operation, 5 vols. (Illus.). xi, 263p. pap. 225.00 *(978-0-11-331046-3(3))* Stationery Office, The GBR. Dist: Bernan Assocs.
—Service Strategy, 5 vols. (Illus.). xii, 264p. pap. 185.00 *(978-0-11-331045-6(5))* Stationery Office, The GBR. Dist: Bernan Assocs.
—Service Transition, 5 vols. (Illus.). xi, 261p. pap. 225.00 *(978-0-11-331048-7(X))* Stationery Office, The GBR. Dist: Bernan Assocs.
Okolita, Patricia, ed. Building an Enterprise Business Continuity Program. 2009. (ENG., Illus.). 344p. 82.95 *(978-1-4200-8864-9(5))* Auerbach Pubns., Inc.
Phelps, Marcy. Research on Main Street: Using the Web to Find Local Business & Market Information. 2011. (ENG.). 240p. pap. 29.95 *(978-0-910965-88-0(9),* CyberAge Bks.) Information Today, Inc.
Ramachandran, Anand. Getting Clarity: The 7 Fundamental Skills to Conquer Information Overload, 1. 2006. 208p. 24.95 *(978-0-9788958-0-8(0),* 1) Ramachandran, Anand.
Richter, Sam. Take the Cold Out of Cold Calling: Web Search Secrets for the Inside Info on Companies, Industries, & People. 2008. (Illus.). 290p. pap. 34.95 incl. cd-rom *(978-1-59298-209-7(3))* Beaver's Pond Pr., Inc.
Sifleet, Jean D. Ishift- Innovation Shift. 2010. pap. 13.95 *(978-0-7414-6139-1(0))* Infinity Publishing.
Webb, Jela. Strategic Information Management (SIM) A Practitioner's Guide Jela Webb, Azione Consulting. 2008. 248p. *(978-1-84334-377-6(0));* pap. *(978-1-84334-376-9(2))* Woodhead Publishing Ltd. (Chandos Publishing).
Weiss, Luise. Small Business & the Public Library: Strategies for a Successful Partnership. 2011. pap. 55.00 ***(978-0-8389-9323-1(0))*** American Library Assn.
Weiss, Luise. Small Business & the Public Library: Strategies for a Successful Partnership. (Illus.). 176p. pap. 55.00 *(978-0-8389-0993-5(0))* American Library Assn.

BUSINESS INFORMATION WAREHOUSE FOR SAP
see SAP Business Information Warehouse

BUSINESS INSURANCE
see also Bank Insurance
Alexander, Frank S. D. Closing the Gap: A Model for Commercial Underwriting. 2007. x, 165p. pap. *(978-0-87218-738-2(1))* National Underwriter Co.

B

ASIS International. ASIS Information Asset Protection Guideline. 2007. (ENG.). 43p. 10.00 *(978-1-887056-70-0(X))* ASIS International.

Bregman, Robert A. & Feldhaus, William R. RPLU — 2006 Professional Liability: Medical Text & Course Guide. 2006. 29.00 *(978-1-933686-07-3(3))* International Risk Management Institute, Inc.

Business Insurance. 50.00 *(978-0-7931-4448-8(5))* Kaplan Publishing.

Costante, Fabio. Principles of Entrepreneurship: Building a Resilient Windsor-Essex Economy One Entrepreneur at a Time. 2011. 80p. pap. 11.91 ***(978-1-4269-0041-9(4))*** Trafford Publishing.

Franklin, T. R. Cyber Liability & Insurance: Managing the Risks of Intangible Assets: Commercial Lines Coverage Guide. 2009. (Illus.). xi, 276p. ***(978-0-87218-828-0(0))*** National Underwriter Co.

Gauntlett, David A. IP Attorney's Handbook for Insurance Coverage in Intellectual Property Disputes. 2011. (ENG.). 339p. pap. 129.95 *(978-1-60442-509-3(1))* American Bar Assn.

Glaser, Kevin L. Inside the Insurance Industry. 2010. 107p. pap. 17.99 *(978-0-557-30029-7(0))* Lulu Enterprises Inc.

Insuring Your Business: A Small Businessowners' Guide to Insurance. 2008. 128p. per. 28.00 *(978-0-932387-54-7(3))* Insurance Information Institute.

Jasper, Margaret C. Protecting Your Business: Disaster Preparation & the Law. 2007. (Legal Almanac Ser.). (ENG., Illus.). 224p. 47.00 *(978-0-19-533903-1(7))* Oxford Univ. Pr., Inc.

Kain, Cole Stephen & Glovach, Lana M. Annotated Commercial Crime Policy. 2nd ed. 2006. xiii, 818p. *(978-1-59031-791-4(2))* American Bar Assn.

Malecki, Donald S., et al. Commercial Liability Risk Management & Insurance. 7th ed. 2008. (ENG.). 624p. 110.00 *(978-0-89463-360-7(0))* Insurance Institute of America, Inc.

National Underwriter Company Staff, contrib. by. FCandS QandA Book. 2007. vi, 132p. pap. *(978-0-87218-736-8(5))* National Underwriter Co.

Pablolledo. Project Manager: How to Pass the Pmp(r) Exam Without Dying in the Attempt. 2011. 436p. pap. 24.90 ***(978-1-4269-7158-7(3))*** Trafford Publishing.

Pasich, Kirk A. Complex Insurance Coverage Litigation Handbook. 2011. (ENG.). xxix, 276p. pap. 139.95 incl. cd-rom *(978-1-60442-931-2(3))* American Bar Assn.

Pierre, Sr. Increase Your Insurance Sales, Retention & Referrals Now!!! 2009. 168p. pap. 19.95 *(978-1-4389-4774-7(7))* AuthorHouse.

Professional Liability Underwriting Society, prod. Commercial General Liability Insurance: Overview. 2006. ring bd. 100.00 *(978-1-934279-05-2(6))* Professional Liability Underwriting Society.

—Fiduciary Liability Insurance: In Focus. 2006. ring bd. 145.00 *(978-1-934279-03-8(X))* Professional Liability Underwriting Society.

—Professional Liability Insurance Claims: In Focus. 2007. ring bd. 105.00 *(978-1-934279-09-0(9))* Professional Liability Underwriting Society.

—Professional Liability Reinsurance: In Focus. 2006. ring bd. 100.00 *(978-1-934279-01-4(3))* Professional Liability Underwriting Society.

Smith, Kim. Auto Dealerships. 2009. v, 228p. pap. *(978-0-87218-833-4(7))* National Underwriter Co.

Stevick, Glenn E., Jr. Essentials of Business Insurance. 2nd ed. 2007. 560p. (C). 50.00 *(978-1-932819-30-4(4))* American College, The.

Stevick, Glenn E. Essentials of Business Insurance. 2nd rev. ed. 2010. (Financial Advisor Series: Product Esssentials). 614p. (C). 65.00 *(978-1-932819-98-4(3))* American College, The.

United States, Congress House Committee on Financial Services Subcommittee on Capital Markets, Insurance, and Government Sponsored Enterprises Staff, contrib. by. Commercial Insurance Modernization: Hearing Before the Subcommittee on Capital Markets, Insurance, & Government Sponsored Enterprises of the Committee on Financial Services, U.S. House of Representatives, One Hundred Ninth Congress, Second Session, June 21, 2006. 2007. (Illus.). v, 107p. *(978-0-16-078040-0(3)*, 552-070-35448-4) United States Government Printing Office.

Vassar, Rick. Hide! Here Comes the Insurance Guy: Understanding Business Insurance & Risk Management. 2008. 200p. 28.95 *(978-0-595-49811-6(6))*; pap. 18.95 *(978-1-60528-020-2(8))* iUniverse, Inc. (iUniverse Star).

BUSINESS INTELLIGENCE

Here are entered works on the systematic accumulation of information regarding business competitors and their products, including trade secrets.

see also Trade Secrets

Abzaltynova, Zhanna & Williams, Janice. Business Intelligence Software. 2010. 104p. pap. *(978-3-8383-6779-8(0))* Lambert Academic Publishing.

Amos, D. Competitive Intelligence & Decision Problems. 2011. (Iste Ser.: 512). (ENG., Illus.). 368p. 125.00 ***(978-1-84821-237-4(2)**,* Wiley-ISTE) Wiley, John & Sons, Inc.

Anandarajan, Murugan, et al, eds. Business Intelligence Techniques: A Perspective from Accounting & Finance. 2010. (Illus.). x, 268p. pap. 149.00 *(978-3-642-07403-5(0)*, 3642074030) Springer.

Antelo, Manel & Loureiro, Maria L. Taxing a Polluting Monopoly with Private Information. 2010. (Business Issues, Competition & Entrepreneurship Ser.). pap. 43.00 *(978-1-61728-954-5(X)*, Nova Novinka) Nova Science Pubs., Inc.

Audas, Thierry, et al. Discover SAP BusinessObjects. 2010. (Illus.). 374p. pap. 39.95 *(978-1-59229-315-5(8)*, SAP PR.) Galileo Pr., Inc.

Bates, Pat, et al. New Intelligence for a Smarter Planet: Driving Business Innovation with IBM Analytic Solutions. 2009. (ENG.). 112p. pap. 14.95 *(978-1-58347-086-2(7))* MC Pr., LLC.

Bell, Peter & Zaric, Gregory. Analytics for Managers. 2012. (ENG., Illus.). 248p. 100.00 ***(978-0-415-62269-1(7))***; pap. 59.95 ***(978-0-415-62268-4(9))*** Routledge.

Bens. Staying Ahead of the Competition. 2007. pap. 122.00 *(978-981-277-906-9(X))* World Scientific Publishing Co., Inc.

Bensoussan, Babette E. Analysis Without Paralysis: 10 Tools to Make Better Strategic Decisions. 2008. (ENG.). 240p. pap. 29.99 *(978-0-13-261957-8(1))* FT Press.

Bensoussan, Babette E. & Fleisher, Craig S. Analysis for Managers: Effective Planning Tools & Techniques. 2009. (ENG., Illus.). 216p. pap. 69.50 *(978-0-273-72201-4(8))* Pearson Education, Ltd. GBR. Dist: Trans-Atlantic Pubns., Inc.

Berkman, Robert. The Art of Strategic Listening: Finding Market Intelligence in Blogs & Social Media. 2008. (Illus.). 264p. pap. 39.95 *(978-0-9786602-7-7(7))* Paramount Market Publishing, Inc.

Berube, David. Practical Reporting with Ruby & Rails. 2008. (Expert's Voice in Open Source Ser.). (ENG., Illus.). 312p. per. 42.99 *(978-1-59059-933-4(0))* Apress L. P.

Bianco, Anthony. The Big Lie: Spying, Scandal, & Ethical Collapse at Hewlett Packard. 2010. (ENG., Illus.). 368p. 26.95 *(978-1-58648-803-1(1))* PublicAffairs.

Biere, Mike. The New Era of Enterprise Business Intelligence: Using Analytics to Achieve a Global Competitive Advantage. 2010. (ENG., Illus.). 320p. pap. 44.99 *(978-0-13-707542-3(1))* Pearson Education.

Botha, Deonie. Creating a Competitive Intelligence Capability: Developing the Intelligent Organisation. 2013. 200p. pap. 85.00 *(978-1-84334-297-7(9)*, Chandos Publishing) Woodhead Publishing Ltd. GBR. Dist: Neal-Schuman Pubs., Inc.

—Creating a Competitive Intelligence Capability: Developing the intelligent Organisation. 2012. (ENG.). 200p. pap. 85.00 *(978-0-85709-158-1(1)*, Chandos Publishing) Woodhead Publishing Ltd. GBR. Dist: Ingram Pub. Services.

Bouman, Roland & van Dongen, Jos. Pentaho Solutions: Business Intelligence & Data Warehousing with Pentaho & MySQL. 2009. (ENG., Illus.). 648p. pap. 50.00 *(978-0-470-48432-6(2)*, Wiley) Wiley, John & Sons, Inc.

Boyer, John, et al. Business Intelligence Strategy: A Practical Guide for Achieving BI Excellence. 2010. (ENG.). 136p. pap. 14.95 *(978-1-58347-362-7(9))* MC Pr., LLC.

Brady, Chris & Moeller, Scott. Intelligent M&A: Navigating the Mergers & Acquisitions Minefield. 2007. (ENG., Illus.). 328p. 39.95 *(978-0-470-05812-1(9)*, Wiley) Wiley, John & Sons, Inc.

Brijs, Bert. Business Analysis & Business Intelligence. 2012. (ENG., Illus.). 328p. 89.95 *(978-1-4398-5834-9(9))* Auerbach Pubs., Inc.

Brogden, Jim, et al. SAP BusinessObjects Web Intelligence. 2010. (Illus.). 583p. 79.95 *(978-1-59229-322-3(0)*, SAP PR.) Galileo Pr., Inc.

Brown, Mark Graham. Beyond the Balanced Scorecard: Improving Business Intelligence with Analytics. 2007. (ENG., Illus.). 240p. 41.95 *(978-1-56327-346-9(2))* Productivity Pr.

Burgess, Christopher & Power, Richard. Secrets Stolen, Fortunes Lost: Preventing Intellectual Property Theft & Economic Espionage in the 21st Century. 2008. (ENG., Illus.). 300p. per. 72.95 *(978-1-59749-255-3(8)*, Syngress Press) Elsevier Science & Technology Bks.

Bussler, Christoph. Business Intelligence for the Real-Time Enterprises: First International Workshop, BIRTE 2006, Seoul, Korea, September 11, 2006, Revised Selected Papers. 2007. (Lecture Notes in Computer Science Ser.). (Illus.). 156p. per. 69.95 *(978-3-540-73949-4(1))* Springer.

Caravajal, Steve, et al. Professional SharePoint 2010 Business Intelligence Administration. 2013. (ENG.). 504p. pap. 44.99 *(978-1-118-00374-9(8)*, Wrox) Wiley, John & Sons, Inc.

Castellanos, Malu, et al. Business Intelligence for the Real-Time Enterprise: Second International Workshop, BIRTE 2008, Auckland, New Zealand, August 24, 2008, Revised Selected Papers. 2009. (Lecture Notes in Business Information Processing Ser.). (ENG.). ix, 123p. pap. 69.95 *(978-3-642-03421-3(7)*, 3642034217) Springer.

Castellanos, Malu, et al, eds. Enabling Real-Time Business Intelligence: 4th International Workshop, BIRTE 2010, Held at the 36th International Conference on Very Large Databases, VLDB 2010, Singapore, September 13, 2010, Revised Selected Papers. 2011. (Lecture Notes in Business Information Processing Ser.). (ENG.). ix, 133p. pap. 72.00 ***(978-3-642-22969-5(7)**,* 3642229697) Springer.

Cates, James, et al. Climbing the Ladder of Business Intelligence: Happy about Creating Excellence through Enabled Intuition. 2007. (ENG.). 192p. per. *(978-1-60005-043-5(3))* Happy About.

Chiu, Susan & Tavella, Domingo. Data Mining & Market Intelligence for Optimal Marketing Returns. 2011. (ENG., Illus.). 296p. 65.95 *(978-0-7506-8234-3(5))* Routledge.

Cohen, Corine, et al. Business Intelligence: The Effective of Strategic Intelligence & Its Impact on the Performance of Organizations. 2009. (Iste Ser.: 394). (ENG., Illus.). 304p. 132.00 *(978-1-84821-114-8(7)*, Wiley-ISTE) Wiley, John & Sons, Inc.

Collier, Ken W. Agile Analytics: A Value-Driven Approach to Business Intelligence & Data Warehousing. rev. ed. 2011. (Agile Software Development Ser.). (ENG., Illus.). 368p. pap. 49.99 *(978-0-321-50481-4(X))* Addison Wesley Professional.

Cram101 Textbook Reviews. Outlines & Highlights for Business Intelligence by Rajiv Sabherwal, Isbn: 9780470461709. 2011. 72p. pap. 27.95 ***(978-1-61812-091-5(3))*** Cram101 Inc.

—Outlines & Highlights for Tapping into Unstructured Dat: Integrating Unstructured Data & Textual Analytics into Business Intelligence by William H. 2011. 56p. pap. 26.95 ***(978-1-61905-512-4(0))*** Cram101 Inc.

Cram101 Textbook Reviews & Cram101 Textbook Reviews. Outlines & Highlights for Business Intelligence: Data Mining & Optimization for Decision Making by Carlo Vercellis. 2011. 132p. pap. 28.95 ***(978-1-61830-552-7(2))*** Cram101 Inc.

Cram101 Textbook Reviews Staff. Outlines & Highlights for Business Intelligence by Efraim Turban, David King, Ramesh Sharda, Jay E Aronson, Jay Aronson, Isbn: 9780132347617. 2009. 78p. pap. 27.95 *(978-1-4288-7389-6(9))* Cram101 Inc.

Data Analysis with Microsoft Access 2010: From Simple Queries to Business Intelligence. 2011. (ENG., Illus.). 304p. pap. 29.99 ***(978-1-4354-6010-2(3))*** Course Technology.

Davenport, Thomas H. & Harris, Jeanne G. Competing on Analytics: The New Science of Winning. 2007. (ENG., Illus.). 240p. 29.95 *(978-1-4221-0332-6(3))* Harvard Business Review Pr.

Davenport, Thomas H., et al. Analytics at Work: Smarter Decisions, Better Results. 2010. (ENG., Illus.). 240p. 29.95 *(978-1-4221-7769-3(6))* Harvard Business Review Pr.

E-technologies; Proceedings: International MCETECH Conference on E-Technologies (2008: Quebec, Canada) 2007. 262p. pap. 178.00 *(978-0-7695-3082-6(6))* IEEE Computer Society Pr.

Earnest, Peter & Karinch, Maryann. Business Confidential: Lessons for Corporate Success from Inside the CIA, 1 vol. 2010. (ENG.). 240p. 24.95 *(978-0-8144-1448-4(6))* Amacom.

El Sheikh, Asim Abdel Rahman & Alnoukari, Mouhib. Business Intelligence & Agile Methodologies for Knowledge-Based Organizations: Cross-Disciplinary. 2011. ***(978-1-61350-052-1(1))*** IGI Global.

Fink, Andreas, et al, eds. Advances in Data Analysis, Data Handling & Business Intelligence: Proceedings of the 32nd Annual Conference of the Gesellschaft für Klassifikation E. V., Joint Conference with the British Classification Society (BCS) & the Dutch/Flemish Classification Society (VOC), Helmut-Schmidt-University, Hamburg, July 16-18 2008. 2009. (Studies in Classification, Data Analysis, & Knowledge Organization Ser.). (ENG., Illus.). xxvi, 695p. pap. 199.00 *(978-3-642-01043-9(1)*, 3642010431) Springer.

Fisher, Tony. The Data Asset: How Smart Companies Govern Their Data for Business Success. 2009. (Wiley & SAS Business Ser.: 24). (ENG., Illus.). 240p. 45.00 *(978-0-470-46226-3(4)*, Wiley) Wiley, John & Sons, Inc.

Fleisher, Craig S. & Bensoussan, Babette E. Business & Competitive Analysis: Effective Application of New & Classic Methods. 2007. (ENG.). 528p. pap. 89.99 *(978-0-13-216158-9(3))* FT Press.

Fouche, Guy & Langit, Lynn. Foundations of SQL Server 2008 R2 Business Intelligence. 2nd ed. 2011. (ENG.). 448p. pap. 49.99 *(978-1-4302-3324-4(9))* Apress L. P.

Fuld, Leonard M. The Secret Language of Competitive Intelligence: How to see through & stay ahead of business disruptions, distortions, rumors & smoke Screens. 2010. 326p. pap. 19.95 *(978-1-60844-553-0(4))* Dog Ear Publishing, LLC.

Gladysz, Margean. A Spy on the Bus: Memoir of a Company Rat. 2008. (Illus.). 272p. pap. 16.95 *(978-1-933926-07-0(4))* Arbutus Pr.

Gluchowski, Peter, et al. Management Support Systeme und Business Intelligence: Computergestützte Informationssysteme für Fach- und Führungskräfte. 2nd ed. 2006. 420p. pap. 39.95 *(978-3-540-23543-9(4)*, 3540235434) Springer.

Grabis, Janis & Kirikova, Marite, eds. Perspectives in Business Informatics Research: 10th International Conference, BIR 2011, Riga, Latvia, October 6-8, 2011, Proceedings. 2011. (Lecture Notes in Business Information Processing Ser.). (ENG.). xv, 355p. pap. 83.00 ***(978-3-642-24510-7(2)**,* 3642245102) Springer.

Gragido, Will & Pirc, John. Cybercrime & Espionage: An Analysis of Subversive Multi-Vector Threats. 2011. (ENG., Illus.). 272p. pap. 59.95 *(978-1-59749-613-1(8)*, Syngress Press) Elsevier Science & Technology Bks.

Hall, Wayne Michael & Citrenbaum, Gary. Intelligence Collection: How to Plan & Execute Intelligence Collection in Complex Environments, 1 vol. 2012. (Praeger Security International Ser.). 512p. 63.00 ***(978-0-313-39817-9(8)**,* A3614C) Greenwood Publishing Group, Inc.

Halpin, Terry, et al. Enterprise, Business-Process & Information Systems Modeling: 10th International Workshop, BPMDS 2009, & 14th International Conference, EMMSAD 2009, held at CAiSE 2009, Amsterdam, the Netherlands, June 8-9, 2009, Proceedings. 2009. (Lecture Notes in Business Information Processing Ser.). xvi, 420p. pap. 89.95 *(978-3-642-01861-9(0))* Springer.

Harding, Rodger Nevill. Corporate Intelligence Awareness: Securing the Competitive Edge. 2006. (Illus.). 300p. 43.95 *(978-1-895186-42-0(0))* Multi-Media Pubns., Inc. CAN. Dist: Baker & Taylor Bks.

Hartenauer, Jörg. Introduction to Business Intelligence: Concepts & Tools. 2007. 92p. per. *(978-3-8364-1806-5(1))* VDM Verlag Dr. Mueller e.K.

Harts, Doug, et al. Microsoft SQL Server 2008 R2 Analytics & Data Visualization. 2010. (ENG., Illus.). 576p. pap. 49.99 *(978-0-07-160143-6(0)*, 0071601430) McGraw-Hill Osborne.

Heesen, Bernd. Effective Strategy Execution: Improving Performance with Business Intelligence. 2012. (Management for Professionals Ser.). (ENG., Illus.). xvi, 228p. 69.95 *(978-3-642-19204-3(1)*, 3642192041) Springer.

Heilig, Loren, et al. SAP NetWeaver BW & SAP BusinessObjects: The Comprehensive Guide. 2011.Tr. of SAP NetWeaver BW — das umfassende Handbuch. (ENG., Illus.). 850p. 79.95 *(978-1-59229-384-1(0)*, SAP PR.) Galileo Pr., Inc.

Herschel, Richard T. Organizational Applications of Business Intelligence Management: Emerging Trends. 2012. (Illus.). xxv, 319p. ***(978-1-4666-0281-6(3))*** IGI Global.

Herschel, Richard T., ed. Organizational Applications of Business Intelligence Management: Emerging Trends. 2012. (Illus.). 312p. 185.00 ***(978-1-4666-0279-3(1)**,* Business Science Reference) IGI Global.

Hilgefort, Ingo. Inside SAP BusinessObjects Explorer. 2010. (Illus.). 307p. 69.95 *(978-1-59229-340-7(9)*, SAP PR.) Galileo Pr., Inc.

—Reporting & Analytics with SAP BusinessObjects. 2009. (Illus.). 500p. 79.95 *(978-1-59229-310-0(7)*, SAP PR.) Galileo Pr., Inc.

Hirvensalo, Irmeli, et al. The Handbook of Market Intelligence: Understand, Compete & Grow in Global Markets. 2011. (ENG., Illus.). 256p. 65.00 ***(978-1-119-99364-3(4)**,* Wiley) Wiley, John & Sons, Inc.

Howson, Cindi. Successful Business Intelligence: Secrets to Making BI a Killer App. 2007. (ENG., Illus.). 244p. 39.95 *(978-0-07-149851-7(6)*, 0071498516) McGraw-Hill Osborne.

Inmon, William H. & Nesavich, Anthony. Tapping into Unstructured Data: Integrating Unstructured Data & Textual Analytics into Business Intelligence. 2007. (ENG., Illus.). 264p. per. 49.99 *(978-0-13-236029-6(2))* Prentice Hall PTR.

Ishikawa, Akira. An Introduction to Knowledge Information Strategy: From Business Intelligence to Knowledge Sciences. 2012. 300p. 65.00 ***(978-981-4324-42-7(6))*** World Scientific Publishing Co., Inc.

Javers, Eamon. Broker, Trader, Lawyer, Spy: The Secret World of Corporate Espionage. 320p. 2011. (ENG.). pap. 15.99 *(978-0-06-169721-0(4)*, Harper Paperbacks) 2010. 26.99 *(978-0-06-169720-3(6)*, Collins) HarperCollins Pubs.

Khaitan, Debashish. Efficient SAP NetWeaver BW Implementation & Upgrade Guide. 2nd ed. 2010. (Illus.). 532p. 79.95 *(978-1-59229-336-0(0)*, SAP PR.) Galileo Pr., Inc.

Khan, Arshad. Business Intelligence & Data Warehousing Simplified: 500 Questions, Answers, & Tips. 2011. 250p. pap. 35.95 ***(978-1-936420-32-2(5))*** Mercury Learning & Information.

Kimball, Ralph & Ross, Margy. The Kimball Group Reader: Relentlessly Practical Tools for Data Warehousing & Business Intelligence. 2010. (ENG., Illus.). 744p. pap. 50.00 *(978-0-470-56310-6(9)*, Wiley) Wiley, John & Sons, Inc.

Klostermann, Olaf. SAP NetWeaver Business Warehouse: Administration & Monitoring. 2009. (Illus.). 600p. 79.95 *(978-1-59229-330-8(1)*, SAP PR.) Galileo Pr., Inc.

Knight, Brian, et al. Knight's 24-Hour Trainer: Microsoft SQL Server 2008 Integration Services. 2009. (ENG., Illus.). 384p. pap. 49.99 *(978-0-470-49692-3(4)*, Wrox) Wiley, John & Sons, Inc.

Laberge, Robert. The Data Warehouse Mentor: Practical Data Warehouse & Business Intelligence Insights. 2011. (ENG., Illus.). 416p. pap. 50.00 *(978-0-07-174532-1(7)*, 0071745327) McGraw-Hill Osborne.

Lachev, Teo. Applied Microsoft SQL Server 2011 Analysis Services: Tabular Modeling. 2012. (ENG.). 500p. pap. 49.95 ***(978-0-9766353-5-2(6))*** Prologika.

Lai, David & Hacking, Xavier. SAP BusinessObjects Dashboards 4. 0 Cookbook. 2011. 333p. pap. ***(978-1-84968-178-0(3))*** Packt Publishing, Ltd.

Lampard, Liz, ed. Business Information from Government 2000. (ENG.). ***(978-3-11-183268-5(6))*** Saur, K. G. Verlag GmbH & Co.

Landry, Nat. Iterative & Agile Implementation Methodologies in Business Intelligence Software Development. 2011. 172p. pap. 29.99 ***(978-0-557-24758-5(6))*** Lulu Enterprises Inc.

Langit, Lynn. Foundations of SQL Server 2005 Business Intelligence. 2007. (Books for Professionals by Professionals). (ENG., Illus.). 396p. per. 49.99 *(978-1-59059-834-4(2))* Apress L. P.

Langit, Lynn, et al. Smart Business Intelligence Solutions with Microsoft SQL Server 2008. 2009. (ENG.). 800p. pap. 49.99 *(978-0-7356-2580-8(8))* Microsoft Pr.

Larson, Brian. Delivering Business Intelligence with Microsoft SQL Server 2008. 2nd ed. 2008. (ENG., Illus.). 792p. pap. 49.99 *(978-0-07-154944-8(7)*, 0071549447) McGraw-Hill Osborne.

Larson, Brian. Delivering Business Intelligence with Microsoft SQL Server XXXX 3/E. 3rd ed. 2012. (ENG., Illus.). 832p. pap. 50.00 ***(978-0-07-175938-0(7)**,* 0071759387) McGraw-Hill Osborne.

Laursen, Gert & Thorlund, Jesper. Business Analytics for Managers: Taking Business Intelligence Beyond Reporting. 2010. (Wiley & SAS Business Ser.). (ENG., Illus.). 272p. 49.95 *(978-0-470-89061-5(4)*, Wiley) Wiley, John & Sons, Inc.

Laursen, Gert H. N. Business Analytics for Sales & Marketing Managers: How to Compete in the Information Age. 2011. (Wiley & SAS Business Ser.: 41). (ENG., Illus.). 256p. 49.95 *(978-0-470-91286-7(3)*, Wiley) Wiley, John & Sons, Inc.

Lesca, Nicolas. Environmental Scanning & Sustainable Development. 2011. (Iste Ser.: 552). (ENG., Illus.). 336p. 125.00 *(978-1-84821-284-8(4)*, Wiley-ISTE) Wiley, John & Sons, Inc.

Loshin, David. Master Data Management. 2008. (MK/OMG Press Ser.). (ENG., Illus.). 304p. pap. 53.95 *(978-0-12-374225-4(0)*, Morgan Kaufmann) Elsevier Science & Technology Bks.

Marcet, Rick C. Win/Loss Reviews: A New Knowledge Model for Competitive Intelligence. 2011. (Microsoft Executive Leadership Ser.: 23). (ENG., Illus.). 202p. 39.95 *(978-1-118-00741-9(7)*, Wiley) Wiley, John & Sons, Inc.

Martin, Steve. Business Intelligence & Corporate Espionage. 2006. 720p. (C). pap. 73.33 *(978-0-13-233142-5(X)*, Prentice Hall) Prentice Hall PTR.

McDowell, Don. Strategic Intelligence: A Handbook for Practitioners, Managers, & Users. rev. ed. 2008. (Scarecrow Professional Intelligence Education Ser.). (ENG.). 286p. pap. 42.00 *(978-0-8108-6184-8(4))* Scarecrow Pr., Inc.

Mendell, Ronald L. The Quiet Threat: Fighting Industrial Espionage in America. 2nd ed. 2010. 272p. 59.95 *(978-0-398-07962-8(5))*; pap. 39.95 *(978-0-398-07963-5(3))* Thomas, Charles C. Pub., Ltd.

Michaeli, Rainer. Competitive Intelligence: Competitive Advantage through Analysis of Competition, Markets & Technologies. 2009. 400p. 89.95 *(978-3-540-72758-3(2))* Springer.

Michalewicz, Zbigniew, et al. Adaptive Business Intelligence. (ENG., Illus.). xiii, 246p. 2010. pap. 59.95 *(978-3-642-06948-2(7)*, 3642069487) 2006. 59.95 *(978-3-540-32928-2(5)*, 3540329285) Springer.

Monger, Jodie & Perkins, Debra. Survey Pain Relief: Transforming Customer Insights into Action. 2008. (Illus.). 276p. pap. 34.95 *(978-1-932558-13-5(6))* Call Center Pr.

Munro. Information Warfare in Business. 2007. (Illus.). 216p. 42.50 *(978-0-415-43990-9(6))* Routledge.

Naarits, Tiina. Information Management & Business Intelligence. 2010. 64p. pap. *(978-3-8383-6355-4(8))* Lambert Academic Publishing.

Neumeier, Marty. The Designful Company: How to Build a Culture of Nonstop Innovation. 2008. (Voices That Matter Ser.). (ENG., Illus.). 208p. pap. 29.99 *(978-0-321-58006-1(0))* Peachpit Pr.

Nilton Bonder. Boundaries of Intelligence: Senses & Spirituality in Management. 2010. 160p. 24.00 *(978-1-4269-2618-1(9))* Trafford Publishing.

Niu, Li, et al. Cognition-Driven Decision Support for Business Intelligence: Models, Techniques, Systems & Applications. 2009. (Studies in Computational Intelligence Ser.). (ENG., Illus.). xii, 244p. 179.00 *(978-3-642-03207-3(9)*, 3642032079) Springer.

Oxley, Mat. Stealing Speed: The Biggest Spy Scandal in Motorsport History. 2010. (ENG., Illus.). 224p. pap. 14.95 *(978-1-84425-975-5(7)*, 1844259757) Haynes Publishing PLC GBR. Dist: MBI Distribution Services/Quayside Distribution.

Padilla, Juan. Cognos 8 BI for Consumers: A step-by-step introductory guide to Cognos Connection. 2007. 248p. per. 29.99 *(978-0-9796920-0-0(8))* Technology Partners Bks.

Paredes, John. The Multidimensional Data Modeling Toolkit: Making Your Business Intelligence Applications Smart Using Oracle OLAP. 2009. (Illus.). 375p. pap. 65.00 *(978-0-9817753-0-2(6))* OLAP World Pr.

Pareek, Deepak. Business Intelligence for Telecommunications. 2006. (Informa Telecoms & Media Ser.). (ENG., Illus.). 312p. 95.95 *(978-0-8493-8792-0(2))* Auerbach Pubs., Inc.

Patel, Bharat, et al. A Practical Guide to SAP Business Warehouse (BW) 7. 0. 2009. (Illus.). 600p. 69.95 *(978-1-59229-323-0(9)*, SAP PR.) Galileo Pr., Inc.

Quoniam, L. Competitive Intelligence 2. 0: Organization, Innovation, Territory. 2011. (Iste Ser.: 573). (ENG., Illus.). 400p. 175.00 ***(978-1-84821-305-0(0)***, Wiley-ISTE) Wiley, John & Sons, Inc.

Rittman, Mark. Oracle Business Intelligence Suite Developer's Guide. 2013. (ENG., Illus.). 672p. pap. 60.00 *(978-0-07-149575-2(4)*, 0071495754) McGraw-Hill Osborne.

Roche, Edward M. Corporate Spy. 2008. 437p. 53.95 *(978-0-615-20608-0(5))* Barraclough Ltd.

Rodenberg, Joseph H. A M. Competitive Intelligence & Senior Management: The Best Solution to Where to Place the Office of Competitive Intelligence Is on a Par with Functions That Report Directly to the Board. 2008. (Illus.). 284p. 49.00 *(978-90-5972-192-0(6))* Eburon Academic Pubs. NLD. Dist: Chicago Distribution Ctr.

Rokach, Lior & Maimon, Oded. Data Mining with Decision Trees: Theory & Applications. 2008. (Series in Machine Perception & Artificial Intelligence). (Illus.). 244p. 111.00 *(978-981-277-171-1(9))* World Scientific Publishing Co., Inc.

Rose, Sarah. For All the Tea in China: How England Stole the World's Favorite Drink & Changed History. (ENG.). 272p. (gr. 12). 2011. 15.00 *(978-0-14-311874-9(9)*, Penguin (Non-Classics)) 2010. 25.95 *(978-0-670-02152-9(0)*, Viking Adult) Penguin Group (USA) Inc.

Rousseau, Denise M., ed. The Oxford Handbook of Evidence-Based Management. 2012. (Oxford Library of Psychology Ser.). (ENG.). 480p. 150.00 ***(978-0-19-976398-6(4))*** Oxford Univ. Pr., Inc.

Rud, Olivia Parr. Business Intelligence Success Factors: Tools for Aligning Your Business in the Global Economy. 2009. (Wiley & SAS Business Ser.: 18). (ENG., Illus.). 283p. 49.95 *(978-0-470-39240-9(1)*, Wiley) Wiley, John & Sons, Inc.

Sackett, Larry. MDX Reporting & Analytics with SAP NetWeaver BW. 2009. (Illus.). 384p. 69.95 *(978-1-59229-249-3(6)*, SAP PR.) Galileo Pr., Inc.

SAS Publishing, creator. Moving & Accessing SAS 9 2 Files. 2008. 136p. per. 18.95 *(978-1-59994-322-0(0))* SAS Publishing.

Sauter, Vicki L. Decision Support Systems for Business Intelligence. 2nd ed. 2011. (ENG., Illus.). 453p. pap. 121.00 *(978-0-470-43374-4(4)*, Wiley) Wiley, John & Sons, Inc.

Sayeed, Ruhan. High Performance Analytics with the R3-Cache. 2010. 104p. pap. *(978-3-8383-7612-7(9))* Lambert Academic Publishing.

Scharpff, Joris, et al. I M D E a D. 2010. 172p. pap. *(978-3-8383-5428-6(1))* Lambert Academic Publishing.

Scheps, Swain. Business Intelligence for Dummies. 2008. (ENG., Illus.). 384p. per. 24.99 *(978-0-470-12723-0(6)*, For Dummies) Wiley, John & Sons, Inc.

Schiuma, Giovanni, ed. Managing Knowledge Assets & Business Value Creation in Organizations: Measures & Dynamics. 2010. (Illus.). 350p. 180.00 *(978-1-60960-071-6(1)*, Business Science Reference) IGI Global.

Schmidt, Robert D. Creating Documents with Business Objects XI-CBT: Web Intelligence XI. 2007. (Illus.). 234p. pap. 99.99 *(978-0-9722636-4-1(0))* Schmidt Ink, Inc.

Sharp, Seena. Competitive Intelligence Advantage: How to Minimize Risk, Avoid Surprises, & Grow Your Business in a Changing World. 2009. (ENG., Illus.). 304p. 39.95 *(978-0-470-29317-1(9)*, Wiley) Wiley, John & Sons, Inc.

Sheikh, Asim Abdel Rahman El & Alnoukari, Mouhib, eds. Business Intelligence & Agile Methodologies for Knowledge-Based Organizations: Cross-Disciplinary Applications. 2011. 375p. 185.00 *(978-1-61350-050-7(5)*, Business Science Reference) IGI Global.

Silber, Kenneth H. & Kearny, Lynn. Organizational Intelligence: A Guide to Understanding the Business of Your Organization for HR, Training, & Performance Consulting. 2009. (ENG., Illus.). 320p. 55.00 *(978-0-470-47231-6(6)*, Pfeiffer) Wiley, John & Sons, Inc.

Society of Management Science of China, Academic Committee Staff & IEEE Computer Society Staff, contrib. by. ECBI 2009: 2009 International Conference on Electronic Commerce & Business Intelligence: Proceedings, 6-7 June 2009, Beijing, China. 2009. (Illus.). xvii, 537p. *(978-0-7695-3661-3(1))* IEEE Computer Society Pr.

Spangler, Scott & Kreulen, Jeffrey. Mining the Talk: Unlocking the Business Value in Unstructured Information. 2007. (IBM Press Ser.). (ENG., Illus.). 240p. per. 49.99 *(978-0-13-233953-7(6)*, IBM Pr.) Pearson Higher Education & Professional Group.

Stackowiak, Robert, et al. Oracle Data Warehousing & Business Intelligence Solutions. 2007. (ENG., Illus.). 408p. pap. 55.00 *(978-0-471-91921-6(7)*, Wiley) Wiley, John & Sons, Inc.

Surma, Jerzy. Business Intelligence: Making Decisions Through Data Analytics. 2011. 150p. pap. 27.00 *(978-1-60649-185-0(7))* Business Expert Pr.

Tennick, Art. Practical PowerPivot & DAX Formulas for Excel 2010. 2010. (ENG., Illus.). 464p. pap. 39.99 *(978-0-07-174685-4(4)*, 0071746854) McGraw-Hill Osborne.

Tennick, Arthur. Practical MDX Queries: For Microsoft SQL Server Analysis Services 2008. 2010. (ENG., Illus.). 304p. pap. 49.99 *(978-0-07-171336-8(0)*, 0071713360) McGraw-Hill Osborne.

Thorlund, Jesper. The Lost-Trade System. 2008. 168p. 23.50 *(978-1-60693-263-6(2)*, Strategic Bk. Publishing) AEG Literary Publishing Services, Inc.

Turban, Efraim, et al. Business Intelligence. 2nd rev. ed. 2010. (ENG.). 312p. (C). pap. 66.67 *(978-0-13-610066-9(X)*, Prentice Hall) Prentice Hall PTR.

—Decision Support & Business Intelligence Systems. 9th ed. 2010. (ENG.). 720p. (C). 213.33 *(978-0-13-610729-3(X)*, Prentice Hall) Prentice Hall PTR.

Veerman, Erik, et al. Microsoft SQL Server 2008 Kit: Business Intelligence Development & Maintenance. 2nd ed. 2009. (ENG.). 688p. pap. 69.99 *(978-0-7356-2636-2(7))* Microsoft Pr.

Vitt, Elizabeth, et al. Business Intelligence. 2008. (ENG., Illus.). 220p. pap. 24.99 *(978-0-7356-2660-7(X))* Microsoft Pr.

Wang, John. Intelligence Methods & Systems Advancements for Knowledge-Based Business. 2012. ***(978-1-4666-1875-6(2))*** IGI Global.

Wang, John, ed. Intelligence Methods & Systems Advancements for Knowledge-Based Business. 2012. 406p. 175.00 ***(978-1-4666-1873-2(6)***, Information Science Reference) IGI Global.

Wang, Jue & Wang, Shouyang, eds. Business Intelligence in Economic Forecasting: Technologies & Techniques. 2010. 401p. 180.00 *(978-1-61520-629-2(9))* IGI Global.

Waters, T. J. Hyperformance: Using Competitive Intelligence for Better Strategy & Execution. 2010. (ENG., Illus.). 272p. 27.95 *(978-0-470-53364-2(1)*, Jossey-Bass) Wiley, John & Sons, Inc.

Welch, William, ed. Introduction to Competitive Intelligence Study Guide. 2007. 214p. (C). pap. *(978-0-9773881-0-3(7))* CIRAT.

Wells, John. Strategic IQ: Creating Smarter Corporations. 2012. (ENG.). 328p. 29.95 *(978-0-470-97828-3(7)*, Jossey-Bass) Wiley, John & Sons, Inc.

Williams, Steve & Williams, Nancy. The Profit Impact of Business Intelligence. 2006. (ENG., Illus.). 240p. per. 48.95 *(978-0-12-372499-1(6)*, Morgan Kaufmann) Elsevier Science & Technology Bks.

Wise, Lyndsay. Using Open Source Platforms for Business Intelligence: Avoid Pitfalls & Maximize ROI. 2012. (ENG., Illus.). 284p. pap. 39.95 ***(978-0-12-415811-5(0)***, Morgan Kaufmann) Elsevier Science & Technology Bks.

Wolf, Frank Kevin & Yamada, Stefan. Data Modeling in SAP NetWeaver BW 7. 1. 2010. (Illus.). 450p. pap. 79.95 *(978-1-59229-346-9(8)*, SAP Pr.) Galileo Pr., Inc.

Wood, Robert T. Physical Security for Information Protection. 2009. 93p. pap. 14.22 *(978-0-557-10545-8(5))* Lulu Enterprises Inc.

Wouters, Thomas L., ed. Progress in Economics Research, Vol. 20. 2010. (Progress in Economics Research Ser.). 165.00 *(978-1-61761-112-4(3))* Nova Science Pubs., Inc.

Xu, Mark, ed. Managing Strategic Intelligence: Techniques & Technologies. 2007. (Premier Reference Ser.). 323p. 165.00 *(978-1-59904-243-5(6))* IGI Global.

Zorrilla, Marta E. Business Intelligence Applications & the Web: Models, Systems & Technologies. 2011. ***(978-1-61350-040-8(8))*** IGI Global.

Zorrilla, Marta E., et al, eds. Business Intelligence Applications & the Web: Models, Systems & Technologies. 2011. 362p. 185.00 *(978-1-61350-038-5(6)*, Business Science Reference) IGI Global.

BUSINESS INTELLIGENCE—COMPUTER PROGRAMS

Alexander, Michael & Walkenbach, John. Excel Dashboards & Reports. 2010. (Mr. Spreadsheet's Bookshelf Ser.: 12). (ENG., Illus.). 456p. pap. 39.99 *(978-0-470-62012-0(9)*, Wiley) Wiley, John & Sons, Inc.

Aziza, Bruno, et al. Microsoft Office PerformancePoint Server 2007. 2008. (ENG., Illus.). 417p. pap. 49.99 *(978-0-470-22907-1(1)*, Wiley) Wiley, John & Sons, Inc.

Bappoo, Paul. BIRT for Beginners. 2010. 241p. pap. 39.95 *(978-1-4457-4886-3(X))* Lulu Enterprises Inc.

Bellissimo, Lisette. SAP Certified Application Associate: SAP Netweaver Business Warehouse 7. 0. 2010. (Illus.). 318p. pap. 69.95 *(978-1-59229-353-7(0)*, SAP PR.) Galileo Pr., Inc.

Bruni, Paolo. Leveraging IBM Cognos 8 BI for Linux on IBM System Z. 2010. (Illus.). xx, 192p. pap. ***(978-0-7384-3375-2(6))*** IBM.

Bulusu, Lakshman, ed. Open Source Data Warehousing & Business Intelligence. 2012. (ENG., Illus.). 368p. 79.95 *(978-1-4398-1640-0(9)*, CRC Press) Taylor & Francis Group GBR. Dist: Taylor & Francis Group.

Czernicki, Bart. Next-Generation Business Intelligence Software with Silverlight 3. 2009. (ENG., Illus.). 576p. pap. 64.99 *(978-1-4302-2487-7(8))* Apress L. P.

De Ville, Barry. Decision Trees for Business Intelligence & Data Mining: Using SAS Enterprise Miner. 2007. (SAS Press Ser.). (Illus.). 240p. per. 49.95 *(978-1-59047-567-6(4)*, 57587, SAS Pr.) SAS Publishing.

Gautam, Sangeeta. Unleashing the Power of IBM Cognos Business Intelligence V10. 2012. (ENG.). 700p. pap. 69.99 ***(978-0-13-272472-2(3))*** Pearson Education.

Hahne, Michael. SAP Business Information Warehouse: Mehrdimensionale Datenmodellierung. 2007. (Illus.). X, 218p. 54.95 *(978-3-540-22015-2(1)*, 3540220151) Springer.

Hammergren, Thomas C., et al. Microsoft PerformancePoint 2007 for Dummies. 2008. (ENG., Illus.). 408p. pap. 29.99 *(978-0-470-23966-7(2)*, For Dummies) Wiley, John & Sons, Inc.

Harts, Doug. Microsoft Office 2007 Business Intelligence: Reporting, Analysis, & Measurement from the Desktop. 2007. (ENG., Illus.). 444p. per. 39.99 *(978-0-07-149424-3(3)*, 0071494243) McGraw-Hill Osborne.

Hilgefort, Ingo. Inside SAP BusinessObjects Advanced Analysis. 2010. (Illus.). 343p. 69.95 *(978-1-59229-371-1(9)*, SAP PR.) Galileo Pr., Inc.

—Integrating SAP BusinessObjects XI 4. X Tools with SAP NetWeaver. 2011. (ENG., Illus.). 325p. 79.95 *(978-1-59229-395-7(6)*, SAP PR.) Galileo Pr., Inc.

—Reporting & Analysis with SAP BusinessObjects. 2nd ed. 2011. (ENG., Illus.). 675p. 79.95 *(978-1-59229-387-2(5)*, SAP PR.) Galileo Pr., Inc.

Howson, Cindi. Successful Business Intelligence: Secrets to Making BI a Killer App. 2007. (ENG., Illus.). 244p. 39.95 *(978-0-07-149851-7(6)*, 0071498516) McGraw-Hill Osborne.

Howson, Cindi, et al. SAP BusinessObjects BI 4. 0 the Complete Reference 3/E. 3rd ed. 2012. (Complete Reference Ser.). (ENG., Illus.). 752p. pap. 70.00 ***(978-0-07-177312-6(6)***, 0071773126) McGraw-Hill Osborne.

International Business Machines Corporation, International Technical Support Organization Staff, contrib. by. Infrastructure Solution: Design, Manage, & Optimize a 20 TB SAP NetWeaver BI Data Warehouse. 2007. (Illus.). xii, 324p. pap. *(978-0-7384-8607-9(8))* IBM.

Janus, Philo. Pro PerformancePoint Server 2007: Building Business Intelligence Solutions. 2008. (ENG.). 472p. pap. 49.99 *(978-1-59059-961-7(6))* Apress L. P.

Janus, Philo & Misner, Stacia. Building Integrated Business Intelligence Solutions with SQL Server 2008 R2 & Office 2010. 2011. (ENG., Illus.). 496p. pap. 50.00 *(978-0-07-171673-4(4)*, 0071716734) McGraw-Hill Osborne.

Jelen, Bill. PowerPivot for the Data Analyst: Microsoft Excel 2010. 2010. (MrExcel Library). (ENG., Illus.). 336p. pap. 34.99 *(978-0-7897-4315-2(9))* Que.

Jhingran, Anant, et al. IBM Business Analytics & Cloud Computing: Best Practices for Deploying Cognos Business Intelligence to the IBM Cloud. 2010. (ENG.). 128p. pap. 19.95 *(978-1-58347-363-4(7))* MC Pr., LLC.

Jones, Peter. SAP Business Information Warehouse Reporting: Building Better BI with SAP BI 7. 0. 2008. (ENG., Illus.) 894p. per. 70.00 *(978-0-07-149616-2(5)*, 0071496165) McGraw-Hill Osborne.

Jorgensen, Adam, et al. SharePoint 2010 Business Intelligence 24-Hour Trainer. 2011. (ENG., Illus.). 432p. pap. 44.99 *(978-1-118-02642-7(X)*, Wrox) Wiley, John & Sons, Inc.

Knight, Brian, et al. Knight's Microsoft Business Intelligence 24-Hour Trainer: Leveraging Microsoft SQL Server Integration, Analysis, & Reporting Services with Excel. 2010. (ENG., Illus.). 432p. pap. 44.99 *(978-0-470-88963-3(2)*, Wrox) Wiley, John & Sons, Inc.

Larson, Brian, et al. Visualizing Data with Microsoft Crescent (SET 2) 2012. (ENG.). pap. 30.00 incl. audio compact disk ***(978-0-07-178082-7(3)***, 0071780823) McGraw-Hill Osborne.

Magal. Integrated Business Processes with ERP Systems. 2011. (C). pap. 63.95 *(978-0-470-92362-7(8)*, Wiley) Wiley, John & Sons, Inc.

Malik, Sahil, et al. Pro SharePoint 2010 Business Intelligence Solutions. 2010. (ENG.). 432p. pap. 59.99 *(978-1-4302-3285-8(4))* Apress L. P.

Mann, Steven, et al. Microsoft SharePoint 2010 Business Intelligence. rev. ed. 2011. (Unleashed Ser.). (ENG., Illus.). 352p. pap. 39.99 *(978-0-672-33551-8(4))* Sams.

Pareek, Deepak. Business Intelligence for Telecommunications. 2006. (Informa Telecoms & Media Ser.). (ENG., Illus.). 312p. 95.95 *(978-0-8493-8792-0(2))* Auerbach Pubs., Inc.

Parziale, Lydia. Best Practices for SAP BI Using DB2 9 for Z/OS. 2nd ed. 2007. (Illus.). xiv, 306p. *(978-0-7384-8921-6(2))* IBM.

Ralston, Barry. PowerPivot for Business Intelligence Using Excel & SharePoint. 2011. (ENG.). 304p. pap. 39.99 *(978-1-4302-3380-0(X))* Apress L. P.

Sabherwal, Rajiv & Becerra-Fernandez, Irma. Business Intelligence. 2010. (ENG., Illus.). 295p. (C). pap. 75.95 *(978-0-470-46170-9(5)*, Wiley) Wiley, John & Sons, Inc.

Taniar, David, ed. Progressive Methods in Data Warehousing & Business Intelligence: Concepts & Competitive Analytics. 2009. (Advances in Data Warehousing & Mining Book Ser.). (Illus.). 390p. 195.00 *(978-1-60566-232-9(1))* IGI Global.

Tjung, Luna. The Art & Science of Predicting Stock Prices. 2010. 133p. pap. 54.94 *(978-0-557-60248-3(3))* Lulu Enterprises Inc.

Utley, Craig. Business Intelligence with Microsoft Office PerformancePoint Server 2007. 2008. (ENG., Illus.). 358p. per. 49.99 *(978-0-07-149370-3(0)*, 0071493700) McGraw-Hill Osborne.

Volitich, Dan. IBM Cognos 8 Business Intelligence. 2008. (ENG., Illus.). 700p. pap. 69.99 *(978-0-07-149852-4(4)*, 0071498524) McGraw-Hill Osborne.

Volitich, Dan & Ruppert, Gerard. IBM Cognos 10 Business Intelligence the Official Guide. 2012. (Official Guide Ser.). (ENG., Illus.). 802p. pap. 70.00 ***(978-0-07-177593-9(5)***, 0071775935) McGraw-Hill Osborne.

Warren, Norm, et al. Business Intelligence in Microsoft SharePoint 2010. 2011. (ENG., Illus.). 416p. pap. 44.99 *(978-0-7356-4340-6(7))* Microsoft Pr.

Withee, Ken. Microsoft Business Intelligence for Dummies. 2010. (ENG., Illus.). 432p. pap. 34.99 *(978-0-470-52693-4(9)*, For Dummies) Wiley, John & Sons, Inc.

BUSINESS ITALIAN

see Italian Language—Business Italian

BUSINESS JOURNALISM

see Journalism, Commercial

BUSINESS LAW

Here are entered popular works on commercial law for use by persons in business. General works on commercial law are entered under Commercial Law.

Abbott, Keith, et al. Business Law. 8th ed. 2007. (ENG., Illus.). 720p. pap. 51.99 *(978-1-84480-461-0(5))* Cengage Learning GBR. Dist: CENGAGE Learning.

Adamson, John E. Law for Business & Personal Use. (C). 18th rev. ed. 2008. (ENG.). 688p. 111.95 *(978-0-538-44588-7(2))* 19th ed. 2011. 25.95 *(978-1-111-42649-1(X))* 19th ed. 2011. (ENG.). 341.95 *(978-0-8400-6861-3(1))* Cengage South-Western.

—Law for Business & Personal Use Law for Business & Personal Use. 19th ed. 2011. (ENG.). 208p. (C). pap. 31.95 *(978-0-8400-6851-4(4))* Cengage South-Western.

—21st Century Business: Business Law. 2nd ed. 2010. (21st Century Business Ser.). (ENG.). 192p. pap. 38.95 *(978-0-538-74061-6(2))* Cengage South-Western.

Adamson, John E. & Morrison, Amanda. Law for Business & Personal Use. 19th ed. 2011. (Business Law Ser.). (ENG.). 688p. (C). 111.95 *(978-0-538-49690-2(8))* Cengage South-Western.

Adeyeye, Adefolake. Corporate Social Responsibility of Multinational Corporations in Developing Countries: Perspectives on Anti-Corruption. 2012. (ENG.). 246p. 115.00 ***(978-1-107-01362-9(3))*** Cambridge Univ. Pr.

Alghamdi, Abdulhadi M. The Law of E-Commerce: E-Contracts, E-Business. 2011. 260p. pap. 28.14 ***(978-1-4678-8603-1(3))*** AuthorHouse.

Allen, William T. Commentaries & Cases on the Law of Business Organizations. 3rd rev. ed. 2009. 152.00 *(978-0-7355-8600-0(4))* Wolters Kluwer Law & Business.

American Library Association Staff. ALA Guide to Economics & Business Reference. 2010. 280p. pap. *(978-0-8389-1024-5(6))* American Library Assn.

Anson, Weston. The Attorney's Guide to the Business Mind: An Expert Explains Corporate Clients, Finance, & the Instincts of an MBA. 2008. (ENG., Illus.). 272p. pap. 18.95 *(978-1-4277-9836-7(2))* Kaplan Publishing.

Ashcroft, John D. & Ashcroft, Janet. Journal of Legal Studies in Business, Vol. 14. 14th ed. 2009. (ENG.). (C). 13.95 *(978-0-538-46696-7(0))* Cengage South-Western.

—Law for Business. 17th ed. 2010. (ENG.). (C). 368p. pap., wbk. ed., pupil's gde. ed. 46.95 *(978-0-324-82924-2(8))*; (Illus.). 592p. pap. 171.95 *(978-0-324-78653-8(0))* Cengage South-Western.

Ashcroft, John D. & Ashcroft, Janet E. Law for Business. 16th rev. ed. 2007. (ENG., Illus.). 621p. (C). per. 153.95 *(978-0-324-38157-3(3))* Cengage South-Western.

Aspatore Books Staff, compiled by. Analyzing VC Deal Terms: Leading Lawyers on Structuring Term Sheets, Developing Negotiation Strategies, And. 2008. 312p. pap. 110.00 *(978-0-314-99172-0(7))* Aspatore Bks.

—Driving Business Results with Your Marketing Strategy: Leading Marketing Executives on Adapting to Evolving Market Conditions, Leveraging New Technologies, & Embracing Global Markets (Inside the Minds) 2010. (Illus.). 120p. pap. 70.00 *(978-0-314-26861-7(8))* Aspatore Bks.

Bagley. Managers & the Legal Environment. 2006. pap. 26.95 *(978-1-4288-0698-6(9))* Cram101 Inc.

Bagley, Constance E. & Dauchy, Craig E. The Entrepreneur's Guide to Business Law. 4th ed. 2011. (ENG.). 840p. (C). pap. 82.95 *(978-0-538-46646-2(4))* Cengage South-Western.

Bagley, Constance E. & Savage, Diane. Managers & the Legal Environment: Strategies for the 21st Century. 6th ed. 2009. (ENG.). 1152p. (C). 264.95 *(978-0-324-58204-8(6))* Cengage South-Western.

BarCharts, Inc. Business Contracts: Tips & Terminology. 2011. (ENG.). 6p. 5.95 *(978-1-4232-1636-0(9))* Barcharts, Inc.

Barnes and Dwor, Richards. Law for Business. 2006. pap. 22.95 *(978-1-4288-0771-6(3))* Cram101 Inc.

Barreca, Hugo, et al. Business Owner's Guide to the Internet: How to Build a Strong Web Presence for Your Business. 2nd ed. 2008. (ENG.). 208p. pap. 16.95 *(978-1-57248-657-7(0),* Sphinx Publishing) Sourcebooks, Inc.

Battersby, Gregory J. & Simon, Danny. Basics of Licensing: How to Extend Brand & Entertainment Properties for Profit. 2011. (ENG., Illus.). 268p. pap. 24.95 ***(978-0-9830963-0-6(9),*** Kent Pr.) Kent Communications, Ltd.

Beatty & Samuelson. Instructor Edition-Business Law & the Legal Environ: Stndrd. 4th ed. 2007. (Illus.). *(978-0-324-37989-1(7))* West Publishing Co., College & Schl. Div.

Beatty and, Samuelson. Business Law & the Legal Environment. 2006. pap. 20.95 *(978-1-4288-0620-7(2))* Cram101 Inc.

—Essentials of Business Law. 2006. pap. 18.95 *(978-1-4288-0560-6(5))* Cram101 Inc.

Beatty, Jeffrey & Samuelson, Susan. Cengage Advantage Books: Introduction to Business Law. 4th ed. 2012. (ENG.). 600p. (C). pap. 136.95 ***(978-1-133-18815-5(X))*** Cengage South-Western.

Beatty, Jeffrey F. & Samuelson, Susan S. Business Law & the Legal Environment. 5th ed. 2010. (Illus.). xxxi, 1167p. *(978-0-324-58201-7(3))* Cengage South-Western.

—Business Law & the Legal Environment, Standard Edition. 6th ed. 2012. (ENG., Illus.). 1392p. (C). 278.95 ***(978-1-111-53060-0(2))*** Cengage South-Western.

—Cengage Advantage Books: Essentials of Business Law. 4th ed. 2011. (ENG., Illus.). 1040p. (C). pap. 149.95 *(978-0-538-47380-4(0))* Cengage South-Western.

—Introduction to Business Law. 3rd ed. 2009. (ENG.). 600p. (C). pap. 136.95 *(978-0-324-82699-9(0))* Cengage South-Western.

—Sg, Business Law & the Legal Environment. 4th ed. 2006. (ENG.). 400p. (C). pap. 46.95 *(978-0-324-37519-0(0))* Cengage South-Western.

Beller, Anthony, ed. Business Law in California. 12th rev. ed. Date not set. (Illus.). 516p. 47.50 *(978-0-914504-12-2(6))* General Educational Pubns.

Bennett-Alexander, Dawn & Harrison, Linda. Legal Environment of Business with Connect Plus. 2011. (ENG.). (C). 219.67 ***(978-0-07-751243-9(X),*** 007751243X, McGraw-Hill/Irwin) McGraw-Hill Higher Education.

Bennett-Alexander, Dawn, et al. The Legal, Ethical, & Regulatory Environment of Business in a Diverse Society. 2011. (ENG., Illus.). 544p. (C). 204.00 *(978-0-07-352492-4(1),* 0073524921, McGraw-Hill/Irwin) McGraw-Hill Higher Education.

Bixby, Michael. The Legal Environment of Business. 4th ed. 2008. (ENG., Illus.). xxiv, 820p. (C). 157.60 *(978-0-536-54498-8(0))* Pearson Learning Solutions.

Bixby, Michael, et al. The Legal Environment of Business. 5th ed. 2011. (ENG.). 850p. (C). ring bd. 106.00 ***(978-1-256-15916-2(6))*** Pearson Learning Solutions.

Bonnice and, Liuzzo. Essentials of Business Law. 2006. pap. 29.95 *(978-1-4288-0671-9(7))* Cram101 Inc.

Bouchoux, Deborah E. Business Organizations for Paralegals. 4th ed. 2007. (Illus.). xxxvii, 735p. *(978-0-7355-5751-2(9),* Aspen Pubs.) Wolters Kluwer Law & Business.

—Business Organizations for Paralegals, Fifth Edition. 5th rev. ed. 2009. pap. 126.95 *(978-0-7355-7628-5(9))* Wolters Kluwer Law & Business.

—Fundamentals of Business Organizations for Paralegals. 2nd ed. 2007. (Illus.). xxix, 262p. *(978-0-7355-5844-1(2),* Aspen Pubs.) Wolters Kluwer Law & Business.

—Fundamentals of Business Organizations for Paralegals, Third Edition. 3rd rev. ed. 2009. pap. 86.95 *(978-0-7355-7912-5(1))* Wolters Kluwer Law & Business.

Boundy, Charles. A Business Guide to Contracts. 2010. 442p. pap. 144.95 *(978-0-566-08856-8(8),* Gower Publishing Co., Ltd.) Ashgate Publishing, Ltd. GBR. Dist: Ashgate Publishing Co.

Branson, Douglas M. Business Enterprises: Legal Structures, Governance, & Policy: Cases, Materials, & Problems. 2008. 123.00 *(978-0-8205-6467-8(2))* LexisNexis Matthew Bender.

Brown, Gordon & Sukys, Paul. Business Law with Connect Plus. 13th ed. 2012. (ENG.). (C). 207.33 ***(978-0-07-763042-3(4),*** 0077630424, McGraw-Hill/Irwin) McGraw-Hill Higher Education.

—Loose-Leaf for Brown Business Law. 13th ed. 2012. (ENG.). (C). ring bd. 134.33 ***(978-0-07-748882-6(2),*** 0077488822, McGraw-Hill/Irwin) McGraw-Hill Higher Education.

Browne, Irving. Elements of the Law of Domestic Relations & of Employer & Employed. 2009. 114p. pap. *(978-1-150-55010-2(4))* Books LLC.

Browne, M. Neil & Kubasek, Nancy K. Business Law. 2008. (Roundtable Viewpoints Ser.). (ENG.). 600p. (C). pap. 45.00 *(978-0-07-352729-1(7),* 0073527297, McGraw-Hill/Dushkin) McGraw-Hill Higher Education.

Buskop, Wendy, JD. Patents, Trademarks, Copyrights, & Trade Secrets: What Automation Professionals, Manufacturers, & Business Owners Need to Know. 2008. (ENG.). 134p. pap. 49.00 *(978-1-934394-53-3(X))* ISA.

Buying & Selling a Massachusetts Business. *(978-1-57589-199-6(9))* Massachusetts Continuing Legal Education, Inc.

Campbell, Dennis. Comparative Law Yearbook of International Business. Vol. 30a. 2009. 211.00 *(978-90-411-2800-3(X))* Vol. 31a. 2010. 176.00 *(978-90-411-2802-7(6))* Wolters Kluwer Law & Business.

Carte, Milton V., ed. Advanced Business Issues: Taxation, Executive Compensation & Antitrust Laws. 2009. 82.00 *(978-1-60456-512-6(8))* Nova Science Pubs., Inc.

Cavico, Frank J. & Mujtaba, Bahaudin G. Business Law for the Entrepreneur & Manager. 2010. 458p. 88.95 *(978-1-936237-02-9(4))* ILEAD Academy, LLC.

Cengage Learning. Course360 Business Organizations on CLMS Printed Access Code. 2011. (ENG.). (C). 100.00 ***(978-1-111-54530-7(8))*** Delmar Cengage Learning.

Chatterjee, Charles. Law of International Business. 2006. (ENG.). 320p. 170.00 *(978-1-85743-383-8(1))* Routledge.

Cheeseman. Contemporary Business & ECommerce Law. 2006. pap. 25.95 *(978-1-4288-0613-9(X))* Cram101 Inc.

Cheeseman, Henry R. Business Law. (ENG.). (C). 7th ed. 2009. 984p. 220.00 *(978-0-13-608554-6(7))* 8th rev. ed. 2012. (Illus.). 1056p. 220.00 ***(978-0-13-289041-0(0))*** Prentice Hall PTR. (Prentice Hall).

—Business Law: Legal Environment, Online Commerce, Business Ethics, & International Issues. 2007. (Illus.). xx, 143p. pap. *(978-0-536-27320-8(0))* Pearson Learning Solutions.

—Contemporary Business & Online Commerce Law. 5th ed. 2006. pap. 23.95 *(978-1-4288-1185-0(0))* Cram101 Inc.

—Contemporary Business & Online Commerce Law. 7th ed. 2011. (ENG.). 1104p. (C). ring bd. 134.33 *(978-0-13-266444-8(5),* Prentice Hall) Prentice Hall PTR.

—Contemporary Business & Online Commerce Law: Legal, Internet, Ethical, & Global Environments. (ENG., Illus.). (C). 6th ed. 2008. 1376p. 193.33 *(978-0-13-601500-0(X))* 7th ed. 2011. 1104p. 206.67 *(978-0-13-266437-0(2))* Prentice Hall PTR. (Prentice Hall).

—Contemporary Essentials of Business Law. 2006. pap. 21.95 *(978-1-4288-1054-9(4))* Cram101 Inc.

—Essentials of Business & Online Commerce Law. 2007. (Illus.). 706p. *(978-0-536-55848-0(5))* Prentice Hall PTR.

—Legal Environment of Business & Online. 4th ed. 2006. pap. 20.95 *(978-1-4288-1183-6(4))* Cram101 Inc.

—The Legal Environment of Business & Online Commerce. 6th ed. 2009. (ENG.). 600p. (C). 126.67 *(978-0-13-608568-3(7),* Prentice Hall) Prentice Hall PTR.

—Legal Environment of Business & Online Commerce. 6th ed. 2009. (ENG.). 450p. (C). pap., stu. ed. 46.67 *(978-0-13-608574-4(1),* Prentice Hall) Prentice Hall PTR.

—The Legal Environment of Business & Online Commerce. 7th ed. 2012. (ENG.). 648p. (C). 126.67 ***(978-0-13-287088-7(6),*** Prentice Hall) Prentice Hall PTR.

—Study Guide. 6th ed. 2008. (ENG.). 560p. (C). pap. 46.67 *(978-0-13-601503-1(4),* Prentice Hall) Prentice Hall PTR.

—Study Guide for Business Law. 8th ed. 2012. (ENG.). 744p. (C). pap. 46.67 ***(978-0-13-296998-7(X),*** Prentice Hall) Prentice Hall PTR.

—Study Guide for Legal Environment of Business & Online Commerce. 7th ed. 2012. (ENG.). 236p. (C). pap. 46.67 ***(978-0-13-296994-9(7),*** Prentice Hall) Prentice Hall PTR.

Cheeseman, Henry R., et al. The Legal Environment of Business & Online Commerce. 2007. (Illus.). v, 273p. *(978-0-536-39231-2(5))* Pearson Learning Solutions.

Chiappinelli, Eric A. Business Associations: With Commentary, 2008-2009 Edition. 2009. pap. 30.50 *(978-0-7355-7230-0(5))* Wolters Kluwer Law & Business.

Chomsky, Carol L. & Kunz, Christina L. Selected Commercial Statutes for Sales & Contracts Courses 2008. 2008. (Academic Statutes Ser.). 1149p. pap. 40.00 *(978-0-314-19016-1(3),* West Legalworks) West.

Cilliers, H. S. Entrepreneurial Law. 459p. *(978-0-409-01978-0(X),* SA, MICHIE) LEXIS Publishing.

Clarkson, et al. Study Guide for Clarkson/Cross/Miller's Business Law: Text & Cases - Legal, Ethical, Global, & Corporate Environment, 12th. 12th ed. 2011. (ENG.). 528p. (C). pap. 44.95 *(978-0-538-47277-7(4))* Cengage South-Western.

Clarkson, Kenneth W., et al. Business Law: Text & Cases - Legal, Ethical, Global, & Corporate Environment. 12th ed. 2010. (ENG., Illus.). 1392p. (C). 275.95 *(978-0-538-47082-7(8))* Cengage South-Western.

—Business Law: Text & Cases: Legal, Ethical, Global, & Corporate Environment. 12th ed. 2012. (Illus.). xxxiv, 1041p. *(978-0-538-47081-0(X))* Cengage South-Western.

—Journal of Legal Studies in Business. 13th ed. 2008. (C). pap. 13.95 *(978-0-324-78944-7(0))* Cengage South-Western.

CLEP Exam Secrets Test Prep Staff, ed. CLEP Introductory Business Law Exam Flashcard Study System: CLEP Test Practice Questions & Review for the College Level Examination Program. 2011. 62.99 *(978-1-61403-505-3(9))* Mometrix Media LLC.

—CLEP Introductory Business Law Exam Secrets Study Guide: CLEP Test Review for the College Level Examination Program. 2011. 62.99 *(978-1-61403-504-6(0))* Mometrix Media LLC.

Cody, Tom, et al, eds. Guide to Limited Liability Companies. 9th rev. ed. 2007. (Illus.). 376p. per. 58.00 *(978-0-8080-1784-4(5))* Toolkit Media Group.

Continuing Education of the Bar (CEB). Selecting & Forming Business Entities: May 2008 Update, 2 vols. 2nd ed. 2008. 678p. ring bd. 91.00 *(978-0-7626-1381-6(5))* Continuing Education of the Bar-California.

Conway, Mara E. & Conway, Susan D. Essentials of Enterprise Compliance. 2008. (Essentials Ser.: 45). (ENG., Illus.). 160p. pap. 39.95 *(978-0-470-40476-8(0),* Wiley) Wiley, John & Sons, Inc.

Cooter, Robert D. & Schäfer, Hans-Bernd. Solomon's Knot: How Law Can End the Poverty of Nations. 2011. (Kauffman Foundation Series on Innovation & Entrepreneurship Ser.). (ENG., Illus.). 344p. (C). 35.00 ***(978-0-691-14792-5(2))*** Princeton Univ. Pr.

Cram101 Textbook Reviews. Outlines & Highlights for Business: Its Legal, Ethical, & Global Environment by Marianne M. Jennings, ISBN. 2011. 564p. pap. 39.95 ***(978-1-61812-079-3(4))*** Cram101 Inc.

—Outlines & Highlights for Business Law: Ethical, Global, & E-Commerce Environment - with 2 DVDS by Jane P. Mallor, ISBN. 2010. 538p. pap. 38.95 *(978-1-61654-044-9(3))* Cram101 Inc.

—Outlines & Highlights for Business Law: Principles for Todays Commerical Environment by Twomey & Jennings, ISBN. 2011. 516p. pap. 37.95 ***(978-1-61830-045-4(8))*** Cram101 Inc.

—Outlines & Highlights for Business Law: Text & Exercises by Roger Leroy Miller, ISBN. 2011. 102p. pap. 27.95 ***(978-1-61490-426-7(X))*** Cram101 Inc.

—Outlines & Highlights for Business Law: Text & Exercises by Roger Leroy Miller, William E. Hollowell, ISBN. 2010. 458p. pap. 36.95 *(978-1-61698-768-8(5))* Cram101 Inc.

—Outlines & Highlights for Business Law: The Ethical, Global, & E-Commerce Environment by A. James Barnes, ISBN. 2010. 540p. pap. 38.95 *(978-1-61698-102-0(4))* Cram101 Inc.

—Outlines & Highlights for Business Law & Regulation of Business by Mann, Isbn: 9780324652895 0324652895. 2011. 338p. pap. 33.95 ***(978-1-61490-409-0(X))*** Cram101 Inc.

—Outlines & Highlights for Business Law & Regulation of Business by Richard a Mann, Barry S Roberts, Isbn: 9780324537130. 2010. 454p. pap. 36.95 *(978-1-61698-761-9(8))* Cram101 Inc.

—Outlines & Highlights for Dynamic Business Law: The Essentials by Linda Barkacs, ISBN. 2010. 290p. pap. 32.95 *(978-1-61698-099-3(0))* Cram101 Inc.

—Outlines & Highlights for Essentials of Business Law & Legal Environment by Richard a Mann, Isbn: 9780324303957 0324303955. 2011. 232p. pap. 31.95 ***(978-1-61812-405-0(6))*** Cram101 Inc.

—Outlines & Highlights for Essentials of Business Law by Jeffrey F Beatty, Susan S Samuelson, Isbn: 9780324537123. 2010. 324p. pap. 33.95 *(978-1-61698-758-9(8))* Cram101 Inc.

—Outlines & Highlights for Fundamentals of Business Law: Summarized Cases by Roger Leroy Miller, Gaylord A. Jentz, ISBN. 2010. 526p. pap. 38.95 *(978-1-61698-756-5(1))* Cram101 Inc.

—Outlines & Highlights for Law for Businessadvantage Series: Law for Business by John D. Ashcroft, Janet Ashcroft, ISBN. 2010. 180p. pap. 29.95 *(978-1-61698-760-2(X))* Cram101 Inc.

—Outlines & Highlights for Smith & Robersons Business Law by Richard a Mann, Barry S Roberts, Isbn: 9780324655520. 2010. 272p. pap. 32.95 *(978-1-61698-757-2(X))* Cram101 Inc.

—Outlines & Highlights for the Legal, Ethical, & Regulatory Environment of Business in a Diverse Society by Dawn Bennett-Alexander, Isbn: 97800735249. 2011. 434p. pap. 35.95 ***(978-1-61812-090-8(5))*** Cram101 Inc.

—Outlines & Highlights for Wests Business Law, Alternate Edition - Text by Gaylord a Jentz, Isbn: 9780324364996 0324364997. 2011. 500p. pap. 38.95 ***(978-1-61490-458-8(8))*** Cram101 Inc.

Cram101 Textbook Reviews & Cram101 Textbook Reviews. Outlines & Highlights for Business & Personal Law: Real-World Connections by Brown, ISBN. 2011. 424p. pap. 35.95 ***(978-1-61461-636-8(1))*** Cram101 Inc.

—Outlines & Highlights for Foundations of Business Law & Legal Environment by Phillip J Scaletta, Isbn: 9781426631184 1426631189. 2011. 562p. pap. 38.95 ***(978-1-61490-685-8(8))*** Cram101 Inc.

—Outlines & Highlights for Fundamentals of Business Law: Excerpted Cases by Miller, ISBN. 2011. 194p. pap. 30.95 ***(978-1-61461-793-8(7))*** Cram101 Inc.

—Outlines & Highlights for Fundamentals of Business Law: Summarized Cases by Roger Leroy Miller; Gaylord A. Jentz;, ISBN. 2011. 586p. pap. 39.95 ***(978-1-61461-787-7(2))*** Cram101 Inc.

—Outlines & Highlights for Legal Environment Today - Text by Roger Leroy Miller, Isbn: 9780324640977 0324640978. 2011. 430p. pap. 36.95 ***(978-1-61490-055-9(8))*** Cram101 Inc.

—Outlines & Highlights for Smith & Robersons Business Law by Richard a Mann, Isbn: 9780324204865 0324204868. 2011. 432p. pap. 35.95 ***(978-1-61490-667-4(X))*** Cram101 Inc.

—Outlines & Highlights for the Legal Environment of Business: A Managerial Approach. 2011. 420p. pap. 35.95 ***(978-1-61461-177-6(7))*** Cram101 Inc.

—Outlines & Highlights for the Legal Environment Today: Business in Its Ethical, Regulatory, E-Commerce, & Global Setting by Roger Leroy Miller; Fra. 2011. 526p. pap. 38.95 ***(978-1-61461-729-7(5))*** Cram101 Inc.

Cram101 Textbook Reviews Staff. Outlines & Highlights for Business: Its Legal, Ethical, & Global Environment by Marianne M. Jennings, ISBN. 2009. 216p. pap. 30.95 *(978-1-4288-4104-8(0))* Cram101 Inc.

—Outlines & Highlights for Business Law: Principles for Todays Commercial Environment by David, ISBN. 2009. 476p. pap. 37.95 *(978-1-4288-6771-0(6))* Cram101 Inc.

—Outlines & Highlights for Business Law: Text & Exercises by Roger Leroy Miller, William E. Hollowell, ISBN. 2009. 380p. pap. 34.95 *(978-1-4288-7751-1(7))* Cram101 Inc.

—Outlines & Highlights for Business Law: Text by Kenneth W. Clarkson, ISBN. 2009. 488p. pap. 37.95 *(978-1-4288-9578-2(7))* Cram101 Inc.

—Outlines & Highlights for Business Law & Regulation of Business by Richard a Mann, Barry S Roberts, Isbn: 9780324537130. 2009. 386p. pap. 34.95 *(978-1-4288-7965-2(X))* Cram101 Inc.

—Outlines & Highlights for Business Law Today: Essentials by Roger Leroy Miller, ISBN. 2009. 408p. pap. 35.95 *(978-1-4288-8895-1(0))* Cram101 Inc.

—Outlines & Highlights for Business Law Today: Standard by Roger Leroy Miller, ISBN. 2009. 492p. pap. 37.95 *(978-1-4288-8994-1(9))* Cram101 Inc.

—Outlines & Highlights for Business Organizations for Paralegals by Deborah E Bouchoux, Isbn: 9780735557505. 2009. 176p. pap. 29.95 *(978-1-4288-3991-5(7))* Cram101 Inc.

—Outlines & Highlights for Contemporary Business & Online Commerce Law: Legal, Internet, Ethical, & Global Environments by Cheeseman, ISBN. 2009. 248p. pap. 31.95 *(978-1-4288-6752-9(X))* Cram101 Inc.

—Outlines & Highlights for Essentials of Business Law by Anthony Liuzzo, Joseph Bonnice, Isbn: 9780073377056. 2009. 174p. pap. 29.95 *(978-1-4288-8782-4(2))* Cram101 Inc.

—Outlines & Highlights for Essentials of Business Law by Liuzzo, Isbn: 9780073054278. 2009. 130p. pap. 28.95 *(978-1-4288-6870-0(4))* Cram101 Inc.

—Outlines & Highlights for Essentials of Legal Environment by Roger Leroy Miller, Isbn: 9780324400403. 2009. 256p. pap. 31.95 *(978-1-4288-9805-9(0))* Cram101 Inc.

—Outlines & Highlights for Introduction to Business Law by Jeffrey F Beatty, Isbn: 9780324826999. 2009. 168p. pap. 29.95 *(978-1-4288-9571-3(X))* Cram101 Inc.

—Outlines & Highlights for Law for Business by Barnes Isbn: 9780073524931. 2009. 278p. pap. 32.95 *(978-1-4288-6840-3(2))* Cram101 Inc.

—Outlines & Highlights for Legal Environment of Business & Online Commerce, the by Henry R Cheeseman, Isbn: 9780136085683. 2009. 196p. pap. 30.95 *(978-1-4288-9103-6(X))* Cram101 Inc.

—Outlines & Highlights for Legal Environment of Business by Nancy K Kubasek, Isbn: 9780136059172. 2009. 248p. pap. 31.95 *(978-1-4288-8748-0(2))* Cram101 Inc.

—Outlines & Highlights for Managers & the Legal Environment. 2007. pap. 16.95 *(978-1-4288-5717-9(6))* Cram101 Inc.

—Outlines & Highlights for Managers & the Legal Environment: Strategies for the 21st Century by Constance E. Bagley, ISBN. 2009. 458p. pap. 36.95 *(978-1-4288-9117-3(X))* Cram101 Inc.

—Outlines & Highlights for Marketing & E-Commerce by Miller & Jentz, Isbn: 0324122756. 2009. 106p. pap. 28.95 *(978-1-4288-3960-1(7))* Cram101 Inc.

—Outlines & Highlights for Smith & Robersons Business Law by Richard a Mann, Barry S Roberts, Isbn: 9780324655520. 2009. 234p. pap. 31.95 *(978-1-4288-7906-5(4))* Cram101 Inc.

—Outlines & Highlights for the Legal & Regulatory Environment of Business by Jere W Morehead, Isbn: 9780073377667. 2009. 194p. pap. 30.95 *(978-1-4288-9569-0(8))* Cram101 Inc.

Crew, Michael A. & Parker, David, eds. International Handbook on Economic Regulation. 2008. (Elgar Original Reference Ser.). 424p. pap. 75.00 *(978-1-84844-172-9(X))* Elgar, Edward Publishing, Inc.

Cross, Frank B. & Miller, Roger LeRoy. West's Legal Environment of Business. 5th ed. 2006. pap. 19.95 *(978-1-4288-1061-7(7))* Cram101 Inc.

Cushway, Barry. The Employer's Handbook: An Essential Guide to Employment Law Personnel Policies & Procedures. 4th ed. 2006. (Illus.). 336p. *(978-0-7494-4700-7(1))* Kogan Page, Ltd.

Dance, E. Leigh, ed. Bright Ideas: Insights from Legal Luminaries Worldwide. 2009. 212p. pap. 24.95 *(978-1-934937-78-5(9))* Mill City Pr., Inc.

Drake, Dwight J. Business Planning: Closely Held Enterprises. 2nd rev. ed. 2008. (American Casebook Ser.). 831p. 109.00 *(978-0-314-18508-2(9),* West Legalworks) West.

DSST Exam Secrets Test Prep Staff, ed. DSST Business Law II Exam Secrets Study Guide: DSST Test Review for the Dantes Subject Standardized Tests. 2011. 62.99 *(978-1-61403-518-3(0))* Mometrix Media LLC.

DuBoff, Leonard D. Law (in Plain English) for Small Business. 2nd ed. 2007. (ENG.). 320p. pap. 18.95 *(978-1-57248-599-0(X),* Sphinx Publishing) Sourcebooks, Inc.

Dworkin, Terry M., et al. Law for Business. 11th ed. 2011. (ENG., Illus.). 1056p. (C). 233.67 *(978-0-07-337771-1(6),* 0073377716, McGraw-Hill/Irwin) McGraw-Hill Higher Education.

Edelman, Lauren & Suchman, Mark C. Legal Lives of Private Organizations. 2007. (International Library of Essays in Law & Society Ser.). 564p. 325.00 *(978-0-7546-2526-1(5))* Ashgate Publishing Co.

Eisenberg, Melvin A. Corporations & Other Business Organizations: Statutes, Rules, Materials & Forms 2010. 2010th rev. ed. 2010. 2128p. pap. 43.00 *(978-1-59941-832-2(0),* Foundation Pr.) West.

Elias, Stephen. The Foreclosure Survival Guide: Keep Your House or Walk Away with Money in Your Pocket. 3rd rev. ed. 2011. (ENG.). 303p. pap. 24.99 *(978-1-4133-1626-1(3))* NOLO.

Elias, Stephen, et al. How to File for Chapter 7 Bankruptcy. 17th rev. ed. 2011. (ENG.). 458p. pap. 39.99 *(978-1-4133-1633-9(6))* NOLO.

Ellis, Howard C. & Cheeseman, Henry R. Legal Environment of Business. 2008. *(978-0-536-06084-6(3))* Pearson Learning Solutions.

Emerson, Robert W. Business Law. 5th rev. ed. 2009. (Barron's Business Review Ser.). (ENG.). 768p. pap. 18.99 *(978-0-7641-4240-6(2))* Barron's Educational Series, Inc.

Entrepreneur Press Staff. How to Start a Business in California. 2nd ed. 2007. (ENG., Illus.). 250p. pap. 29.95 *(978-1-59918-068-7(5),* 1599180685) Entrepreneur Pr. dba Entrepreneur Media, Inc.

—How to Start a Business in Florida. 2nd ed. 2007. (ENG., Illus.). 250p. pap. 29.95 *(978-1-59918-075-5(8),* 1599180758) Entrepreneur Pr. dba Entrepreneur Media, Inc.

—How to Start a Business in Georgia. 2nd ed. 2007. (ENG., Illus.). 250p. pap. 29.95 *(978-1-59918-090-8(1),* 1599180901) Entrepreneur Pr. dba Entrepreneur Media, Inc.

—How to Start a Business in Massachusetts. 2nd ed. 2007. (ENG., Illus.). 250p. pap. 29.95 (978-1-59918-076-2(6), 1599180766) Entrepreneur Pr. dba Entrepreneur Media, Inc.
—How to Start a Business in New York. 2nd ed. 2007. (ENG., Illus.). 250p. pap. 29.95 (978-1-59918-066-3(9), 1599180669) Entrepreneur Pr. dba Entrepreneur Media, Inc.
—How to Start a Business in North Carolina. 2nd ed. 2007. (ENG.). 250p. pap. 29.95 (978-1-59918-092-2(8), 1599180928) Entrepreneur Pr. dba Entrepreneur Media, Inc.
—How to Start a Business in Texas. 2nd ed. 2007. (ENG., Illus.). 250p. pap. 29.95 (978-1-59918-069-4(3), 1599180693) Entrepreneur Pr. dba Entrepreneur Media, Inc.
—How to Start a Business in Virginia. 2nd ed. 2007. (ENG., Illus.). 250p. pap. 29.95 (978-1-59918-067-0(7), 1599180677) Entrepreneur Pr. dba Entrepreneur Media, Inc.
Entrepreneur Press Staff, creator. How to Start a Business in Arizona. 2nd ed. 2007. (ENG., Illus.). 250p. pap. 29.95 (978-1-59918-093-9(6), 1599180936) Entrepreneur Pr. dba Entrepreneur Media, Inc.
—How to Start a Business in New Jersey. 2nd ed. 2007. (ENG., Illus.). 250p. pap. 29.95 (978-1-59918-077-9(4), 1599180774) Entrepreneur Pr. dba Entrepreneur Media, Inc.
—How to Start a Business in Pennsylvania. 2nd ed. 2007. (ENG.). 250p. pap. 29.95 (978-1-59918-091-5(X), 159918091X) Entrepreneur Pr. dba Entrepreneur Media, Inc.
—How to Start a Business in Washington. 2nd ed. 2007. (ENG., Illus.). 250p. pap. 29.95 (978-1-59918-074-8(X), 159918074X) Entrepreneur Pr. dba Entrepreneur Media, Inc.
Epstein, David G., et al. Business Structures. 2nd rev. ed. 2006. (Illus.). 825p. 145.00 (978-0-314-16803-0(6), West Legalworks) West.
Eroglu, Muzaffer & Eroglu, M. Multinational Enterprises & Tort Liabilities: An Inter-Disciplinary & Comparative Examination. 2008. (Corporations, Globalisation & the Law Ser.). 352p. 150.00 (978-1-84844-031-9(6)) Elgar, Edward Publishing, Inc.
Fairfax, Lisa M. CLEP Introductory Business Law. 2007. (CLEP Test Preparation Ser.). (ENG.). 288p. pap. 34.95 (978-0-7386-0316-2(3)); pap. 27.95 (978-0-7386-0315-5(5)) Research & Education Assn.
Field, Arthur Norman & Smith, Jeffrey M. Legal Opinions in Business Transactions. 2nd rev. ed. 2006. 630p. 280.00 (978-1-4024-0770-3(X)) Practising Law Institute.
Florida Bar, Continuing Legal Education Staff, contrib. by. Business Litigation in Florida. 5th ed. 2007. 170.00 (978-0-8205-8670-0(6)) Florida Bar Continuing Legal Education Pubns., The.
Flynn, Nancy. Blog Rules: A Business Guide to Managing Policy, Public Relations, & Legal Issues. 2006. (ENG.). 224p. per. 19.95 (978-0-8144-7355-9(5)) Amacom.
Folsom, Ralph H. & Gordon, Michael Wallace. Principles of International Business Transactions, 2d. 2nd rev. ed. 2010. (Concise Hornbook Ser.). 839p. 46.00 (978-0-314-90683-0(5), West Legalworks) West.
Friedland, Jerold A. Understanding International Business & Financial Transactions. 3rd ed. 2010. (978-1-4224-7841-7(6)) LexisNexis Matthew Bender.
Georgas, M. Stephen. Incorporation & Business Guide for Ontario. 17th ed. 136p. pap. (978-1-55180-340-1(2)) Self-Counsel Pr., Inc.
Glencoe McGraw-Hill Staff. Business & Personal Law. 2007. (ENG., Illus.). 210p. (C). stu. ed., per., wbk. ed. 28.12 (978-0-07-877944-2(8), 0078779448) McGraw-Hill Higher Education.
Global Economics Crisis Resource Center. Global Economic Watch: Impact on Business Law. 2009. (ENG.). 32p. (C). 22.95 (978-0-538-75445-3(1)) Cengage South-Western.
Goldman and, Sigismond. Business Law. 2006. pap. 16.95 (978-1-4288-0824-9(8)) Cram101 Inc.
Goldman, Arnold J. & Sigismond, William D. Business Law. 8th ed. 2010. (ENG.). (C). 312p. pap., wbk. ed., pupil's gde. ed. 43.95 (978-1-4390-7975-1(7)); 768p. pap. 194.95 (978-1-4390-7922-5(6)) Cengage South-Western.
Gough, W. Michael. Guide to Business Law. rev. ed. 2010. (ENG.). 162p. pap. 44.02 (978-0-7872-6706-3(6)) Kendall Hunt Publishing Co.
Greene, Edward F. U.S. Regulation of the International Securities & Derivative Markets. 9th ed. 2009. (978-0-7355-6817-4(0)); (978-0-7355-6818-1(9)) Wolters Kluwer Law & Business. (Aspen Pubs.)
Gupta, Udayan. The Entrepreneurial Lawyer: Richard Testa & the Massachusetts High-Tech Dream. 2007. 180p. pap. (978-1-896209-95-1(5)) Bayeux Arts, Inc.
Halbert, Terry & Ingulli, Elaine. Law & Ethics in the Business Environment. 7th ed. 2011. (ENG.). 416p. (C). pap. 158.95 (978-0-538-47351-4(7)) Cengage South-Western.
Halsey. Practical Business Law. 2011. pap. 80.95 (978-0-7355-6810-5(3), Aspen Pubs.) Wolters Kluwer Law & Business.
Hamilton, Robert W. Attorney's Guide to Business & Finance Fundamentals. 2nd ed. 2006. (Illus.). 290.00 (978-0-7355-6058-1(7), Aspen Pubs.) Wolters Kluwer Law & Business.
Hansen, Bradley A. Institutions, Entrepreneurs, & American Economic History: How the Farmers' Loan & Trust Company Shaped the Laws of Business from 1822-1929. 2009. (ENG.). 240p. 95.00 (978-0-230-60392-9(0)) Palgrave Macmillan.
Hardy, Stephen T. & Butler, Mark, eds. International Themes in Business Law, 4 vols. 2007. (SAGE Library in Business & Management Ser.). (Illus.). 1704p. 1195.00 (978-1-4129-2900-4(8), B29008C) SAGE Pubns., Ltd. GBR. Dist: SAGE Pubns., Inc.
Harris, Lee. Mastering Corporations & Other Business Entities. 2008. 290p. pap. 30.00 (978-1-59460-444-7(4)) Carolina Academic Pr.
Heines, M. Henry. Patents for Business: The Manager's Guide to Scope, Strategy, & Due Diligence, 1 vol. 2007. (Illus.). 216p. 54.95 (978-0-275-99337-5(X), C9337, Praeger Pubs.) Greenwood Publishing Group, Inc.
Herrington, Rob. Verdict for the Defense: Fighting Jackpot Justice with Firewall Defense Strategies. 2011. (ENG.). 256p. pap. 22.95 **(978-0-9819888-6-3(5))** Sutton Hart Pr. LLC.
Hopt, Klaus J. & Grundmann, Stefan. Festschrift Für Klaus J. Hopt Zum 70. Geburtstag Am 24. August 2010: Unternehmen, Markt und Verantwortung, 2 vols. 2010. (GER., Illus.). xxix, 3447p. 839.00 **(978-3-89949-628-4(0))**; E-Book 839.00 **(978-3-89949-632-1(9))** De Gruyter, Walter Inc.
Howard, Michael & Knott, John. Foreign Currency & the Law. 2012. 396.00 (978-1-84311-813-8(0)) Informa Professional GBR. Dist: International Specialized Bk. Services.
Intermediate Business Law. (ACT Proficiency Examination Program Ser.). (C). 49.95 (978-0-8373-5567-2(2), PEP-17, Passbooks) National Learning Corp.
International Business Publications Staff & Global Investment and Business Center, Inc. Staff. Global Offshore Business Laws & Regulations Handbook. pap. 99.95 (978-0-7397-3934-1(4)) International Business Pubns., USA.
James, Noie. A Victim of Boards of Directors: Based on A True Story. 2011. 56p. pap. 9.95 **(978-1-4620-6145-7(1))** iUniverse, Inc.
Jennings. Im-Business: Legal, Ethical, & Global Environment. 2009. (978-0-324-65542-1(8)) Cengage South-Western.
Jennings, Marianne M. Business: It's Legal, Ethical & Global Environment. 6th ed. 2006. pap. 20.95 (978-1-4288-1060-0(9)) Cram101 Inc.
—Business: Its Legal, Ethical, & Global Environment. 9th ed. 2010. (ENG.). 896p. (C). 264.95 (978-0-538-47054-4(2)) Cengage South-Western.
—Study Guide for Jennings' Business: Its Legal, Ethical, & Global Environment, 9th. 9th ed. 2011. (ENG.). 224p. (C). pap. 44.95 (978-0-538-47219-7(7)) Cengage South-Western.
Jennings, Marianne Moody. Business: Its Legal, Ethical, & Global Environment. 8th ed. 2008. (ENG., Illus.). 896p. (C). 264.95 (978-0-324-65554-4(1)) Cengage South-Western.
Jentz, Gaylord A., et al. West's Business Law: Alternate Edition: Text Summarized Cases Legal, Ethical, International, & E-Commerce Environment. 10th ed. 2007. (Illus.). (978-0-324-36499-6(7)) West Publishing Co., College & Schl. Div.
Johnson, Kevin. Legal Issues in Business. rev. ed. 2008. (ENG.). 394p. pap. 116.47 (978-0-7575-5515-2(2)) Kendall Hunt Publishing Co.
Kahn, Randolph, et al. Information Nation: Seven Keys to Information Management Compliance. 2nd ed. 2009. (ENG.). 272p. pap. 50.00 (978-0-470-45311-7(7), Wiley) Wiley, John & Sons, Inc.
Kaplan CPA Review. CPA Exam Study Manual: Regulation 2009/2010. 2009. (ENG.). 688p. pap. 49.95 (978-1-4277-8865-8(0)) Kaplan Publishing.
Kennedy, Charles H. The Business Privacy Law Handbook. 2008. (Artech House Telecommunications Ser.). 312p. 119.00 (978-1-59693-176-3(0)) Artech Hse., Inc.
Khuzami, Robert. Mortgage Fraud, Securities Fraud, & the Financial Meltdown: Prosecuting Those Responsible: Congressional Testimony. 2010. 17p. (C). pap. 15.00 (978-1-4379-2828-0(5)) DIANE Publishing Co.
Kim, In-Suk & Son, Hui-Du. Han-Mi FTA T'uja Hyopsang e Ttarun Kungnae Popche Ui Chongbi Pangan. 2007. (KOR.). 317p. (978-89-8323-598-5(5)) Korea Legislation Research Institute.
Kim, Jasper. Fundamentals of International Economics. 2012. **(978-1-61438-300-0(6))** American Bar Assn.
King, W. J. The Unwritten Laws of Business. 2007. (ENG.). 112p. 16.00 (978-0-385-52126-0(X), Broadway Business) Knopf Doubleday Publishing Group.
Klein, William A. & Coffee, John C. Klein, Coffee & Partnoy's Business Organization & Finance, Legal & Economic Principles. 11th rev. ed. 2010. (Concepts & Insights Ser.). 476p. 47.00 (978-1-59941-449-2(X), Foundation Pr.) West.
Klein, William A., et al. Agency, Partnerships, & Limited Liability Entities: Unincorporated Business Associations: Cases & Materials. 2nd ed. 2007. xix, 490p. (978-1-59941-330-3(2), Foundation Pr.) 3rd ed. 2012. xx, 533p. **(978-1-60930-110-1(2))** West.
Krois-Lindner, Amy & TransLegal. International Legal English Student's Book with Audio CDs (3) A Course for Classroom or Self-study Use. 2nd ed. 2011. (ENG.). 344p. pap. 56.00 incl. audio compact disk (978-0-521-27945-1(3)) Cambridge Univ. Pr.
Krois-Lindner, Amy, et al. Introduction to International Legal English Student's Book with Audio CDs (2) A Course for Classroom or Self-Study Use. 2008. 160p. pap. 45.00 incl. audio compact disk (978-0-521-71899-8(6)) Cambridge Univ. Pr.
Kubasek, Brennan. Legal Environment of Business. 2006. pap. 14.95 (978-1-4288-0504-0(4)) Cram101 Inc.
Kubasek, Nancy & Browne, M. Neil. Dynamic Business Law with ConnectPlus. 2nd ed. 2011. (ENG.). (C). ring bd. 249.33 **(978-0-07-750392-5(9)**, 0077503929, McGraw-Hill/Irwin) McGraw-Hill Higher Education.
Kubasek, Nancy, et al. Dynamic Business Law. 2nd ed. 2011. (ENG., Illus.). 1430p. (C). 233.67 (978-0-07-337767-4(8), 0073377678, McGraw-Hill/Irwin) McGraw-Hill Higher Education.
—Dynamic Business Law: Summarized Cases. 2012. (ENG., Illus.). 1328p. (C). 233.67 **(978-0-07-802377-4(7)**, 0078023777, McGraw-Hill/Irwin) McGraw-Hill Higher Education.
—Dynamic Business Law: The Essentials. (ENG., Illus.). (C). 2009. 672p. pap. 157.67 (978-0-07-337768-1(6), 0073377686) 2nd ed. 2012. 688p. pap. 157.67 **(978-0-07-352497-9(2)**, 0073524972) McGraw-Hill Higher Education. (McGraw-Hill/Irwin).
—Dynamic Business Law: Summarized Cases with Connect Plus. 2012. (ENG.). (C). 249.33 **(978-0-07-763045-4(9)**, 0077630459, McGraw-Hill/Irwin) McGraw-Hill Higher Education.
—Dynamic Business Law: the Essentials with Connect Plus. 2nd ed. 2012. (ENG.). (C). pap. 173.33 **(978-0-07-763043-0(2)**, 0077630432, McGraw-Hill/Irwin) McGraw-Hill Higher Education.
—The Legal Environment of Business: A Critical Thinking Approach. 6th ed. 2011. (ENG., Illus.). 864p. (C). 206.67 (978-0-13-266484-4(4), Prentice Hall) Prentice Hall PTR.
—Loose-Leaf Business Law: The Essentials. 2nd ed. 2012. (ENG.). (C). ring bd. 110.67 **(978-0-07-743742-8(X)**, 007743742X, McGraw-Hill/Irwin) McGraw-Hill Higher Education.
—Loose-Leaf Dynamic Business Law: Summarized Cases. 2012. (ENG., Illus.). (C). ring bd. 122.75 **(978-0-07-759948-5(9)**, 0077599489, McGraw-Hill/Irwin) McGraw-Hill Higher Education.
Kubasek, Nancy K., et al. Legal Environment of Business: International Edition. 5th ed. 2009. (Illus.). 896p. pap. (978-0-13-715498-2(4)) Prentice Hall PTR.
—Legal Environment of Business, the, Student Value Edition. 6th ed. 2011. (ENG.). 864p. (C). ring bd. 134.33 (978-0-13-266668-8(5), Prentice Hall) Prentice Hall PTR.
Lahcenper&aumi, et al. The Intellectual Property Rights Protection of Service Concepts. 2011. 92p. pap. **(978-3-8454-1116-3(3))** Lambert Academic Publishing.
Levin. Structuring Venture Capital 2009. 2009. pap. 286.00 (978-0-7355-8160-9(6)) Wolters Kluwer Law & Business.
—Structuring Venture Capital 2010 Combo (Cd & Print) 2010. pap. (978-0-7355-9377-0(9), Aspen Pubs.) Wolters Kluwer Law & Business.
—Structuring Venture Capital 2010e. 2010. pap. (978-0-7355-9370-1(1), Aspen Pubs.) Wolters Kluwer Law & Business.
Levin, Jack S. Structuring Venture Capital 2009 Combo. 2009. pap. 495.00 (978-0-7355-8286-6(9)) Wolters Kluwer Law & Business.
Lionel Sawyer & Collins, text. Doing Business in Nevada: A Practical Guide 2nd Edition. 2nd ed. 2006. 192p. pap. 25.00 (978-0-9745273-1-4(5)) Lionel Sawyer & Collins.
Liuzzo, Anthony. Essentials of Business Law. 8th ed. 2012. (ENG., Illus.). 718p. (C). pap. 85.67 **(978-0-07-351185-6(4)**, 0073511854) McGraw-Hill Higher Education.
Liuzzo, Anthony & Bonnice, Joseph. Essentials of Business Law. 7th ed. 2009. (ENG., Illus.). 576p. (C). pap. 89.33 (978-0-07-337705-6(8), 0073377058) McGraw-Hill Higher Education.
Loefton, Erolye P., ed. Emerging Business Issues. 2008. (Illus.). 244p. (C). 98.00 (978-1-60456-511-9(X)) Nova Science Pubs., Inc.
LYON. Regulation. 2007. (Business Economics Ser.). 704p. (C). 340.00 (978-1-84376-620-9(5)) Elgar, Edward Publishing, Inc.
Magnuson, Roger. Barracuda Bait: New & growing litigious risks to American Business. 2007. 16.95 (978-0-9798498-0-0(2)) Dorsey & Whitney LLP.
Mailänder, Peter O. Festschrift Für Karl Peter Mailänder Zum 70. Geburtstag Am 23. Oktober 2006. Geiss, Karlmann et al, eds. 2006. (GER., Illus.). XIV, 653p. 335.00 (978-3-89949-316-0(8)) De Gruyter, Walter Inc.
Mallor, Jane, et al. Business Law. 15th ed. 2012. (ENG., Illus.). 1696p. (C). 233.67 **(978-0-07-352498-6(0)**, 0073524980, Irwin Professional Publishing) McGraw-Hill Higher Education.
—Loose-Leaf for Business Law. 15th ed. 2012. (ENG.). (C). ring bd. 163.67 **(978-0-07-741945-5(6)**, 0077419456, McGraw-Hill/Irwin) McGraw-Hill Higher Education.
Mallor, Jane P. Business Law: The Ethical, Global, & E-Commerce Environment. 13th ed. 2007. (Illus.). (978-0-07-327064-7(4)) McGraw-Hill Cos., The.
Mallor, Jane P., et al. Business Law: The Ethical, Global, & E-Commerce Environment. 14th ed. 2009. (ENG., Illus.). 1600p. (C). 233.67 (978-0-07-337764-3(3), 0073377643, McGraw-Hill/Irwin) McGraw-Hill Higher Education.
Mann, Richard A. & Roberts, Barry S. Business Law & the Regulation of Business. 10th ed. 2010. (ENG., Illus.). 1296p. (C). 275.95 (978-0-324-78660-6(3)) Cengage South-Western.
—Essentials of Business Law & the Legal Environment. 10th ed. 2009. (ENG.). 648p. (C). pap., pupil's gde. ed. 46.95 (978-0-324-59366-2(X)) Cengage South-Western.
—Smith & Roberson's Business Law. 15th ed. 2011. (ENG., Illus.). 1296p. (C). 278.95 (978-0-538-47363-7(0)) Cengage South-Western.
Mann, Richard A. & Roberts, Barry S. Smith & Roberson's Business Law - Study Guide. 15th ed. 2011. (ENG.). (C). pap. 42.95 **(978-0-538-47580-8(3))** Cengage South-Western.
McGraw-Hill Staff. Business & Personal Law Interactive Student Edition CD-ROM. 2007. (C). cd-rom 88.68 (978-0-07-877952-7(9), 9780078779527) Glencoe/McGraw-Hill.
Melvin, Sean. The Legal Environment of Business: A Managerial Approach. 2010. (ENG., Illus.). 800p. (C). 214.00 (978-0-07-337769-8(4), 0073377694, McGraw-Hill/Irwin) McGraw-Hill Higher Education.
Miller & Cross. The Legal Env Today Bus in Its Ethical Regul e Comm Global. 7th ed. 2012. (ENG.). 848p. (C). 237.95 **(978-1-111-53061-7(0))** Cengage South-Western.
Miller and, Hollowell. Business Law. 2006. pap. 15.95 (978-1-4288-0669-6(5)) Cram101 Inc.
Miller, Roger, et al. Business Law. 12th ed. 2012. (ENG.). 1344p. (C). 268.95 **(978-1-111-53059-4(9))** Cengage South-Western.
Miller, Roger LeRoy. ESeries: Business Law. 2010. (ENG.). (C). pap. 69.95 (978-0-538-46737-7(1)); ring bd. 29.95 (978-0-538-47013-1(5)) Cengage South-Western.
—Modern Principles of Business Law Cengage Advantage Books. 2011. (ENG., Illus.). 576p. (C). pap. 145.95 (978-1-111-53117-1(X)) Cengage South-Western.
Miller, Roger LeRoy & Cross, Frank B. The Legal Environment Today: Business in Its Ethical, Regulatory, E-Commerce, & Global Setting. 6th ed. 2008. (Available Titles CengageNOW Ser.). (ENG.). 976p. (C). 237.95 (978-0-324-59925-1(0)) Cengage South-Western.
—The Legal Environment Today: Business in Its Ethical, Regulatory, E-Commerce, & International Setting. 6th ed. 2010. (Illus.). xxxvi, 802p. (978-0-324-78421-3(X)) Cengage South-Western.
—Study Guide for Miller/Cross' the Legal Environment Today: Business in Its Ethical, Regulatory, E-Commerce, & Global Setting, 6th. 6th ed. 2008. (ENG.). 248p. (C). pap. 37.95 (978-0-324-78420-6(1)) Cengage South-Western.
Miller, Roger LeRoy & Hollowell, William E. Business Law. 5th ed. 2008. (Illus.). pap. (978-0-324-64095-3(1)) West Publishing Co., College & Schl. Div.
—Business Law: Text & Exercises. 6th ed. 2010. (ENG., Illus.). 656p. (C). pap. 149.95 (978-0-324-78616-3(6)) Cengage South-Western.
Miller, Roger LeRoy & Jentz, Gaylord A. Business Law Today. 8th rev. ed. 2007. (ENG.). 1376p. (C). 246.95 (978-0-324-65455-4(3)) Cengage South-Western.
—Business Law Today: Comprehensive. 9th ed. 2011. (ENG., Illus.). 1224p. (C). 278.95 (978-0-538-45280-9(3)) Cengage South-Western.
—Business Law Today: Comprehensive Edition: Text & Cases: E-Commerce, Legal, Ethical, & Global Environment. 8th ed. 2010. (Illus.). xxix, 1132p. (978-0-324-78257-8(8)) Cengage South-Western.
—Business Law Today: Comprehensive Edition: Text & Cases: E-Commerce, Legal, Ethical, & International Environment. 7th ed. 2007. xxiii, 1196p. (978-0-324-37721-7(5)) West Publishing Co., College & Schl. Div.
—Business Law Today: The Essentials. 9th ed. 2010. (ENG., Illus.). 864p. (C). pap. 171.95 (978-0-324-78615-6(8)) Cengage South-Western.
—Business Law Today: The Essentials. 7th ed. 2006. pap. 18.95 (978-1-4288-1145-4(1)) Cram101 Inc.
—Business Law Today: Comprehensive. 8th ed. 2009. (C). 208.95 (978-0-324-59575-8(1)) Cengage South-Western.
—Business Law Today Comprehensive Edition. 2006. pap. 25.95 (978-1-4288-0616-0(4)) Cram101 Inc.
—Business Law Today, Standard Edition. 9th ed. 2010. (Available Titles CengageNOW Ser.). (ENG., Illus.). 1176p. (C). 277.95 (978-0-324-78652-1(2)) Cengage South-Western.
—Fundamentals of Business Law: Excerpted Cases. 2007. (Illus.). pap. (978-0-324-37707-1(X)) West Publishing Co., College & Schl. Div.
—Fundamentals of Business Law: Summarized Cases. 7th ed. 2007. (Illus.). (978-0-324-38172-6(7)) West.
—Study Guide for Miller/Jentz's Business Law Today: Comprehensive, 9th. 9th ed. 2011. (ENG.). 464p. (C). pap. 44.95 (978-0-538-46631-8(6)) Cengage South-Western.
—Study Guide for Miller/Jentz's Business Law Today, Standard Edition. 9th ed. 2010. (ENG.). 400p. (C). pap. 46.95 (978-0-324-78678-1(6)) Cengage South-Western.
—Study Guide for Miller/Jentz's Business Law Today: the Essentials. 9th ed. 2010. (ENG.). 304p. (C). pap. 43.95 (978-0-324-78634-7(4)) Cengage South-Western.
Miller, Roger LeRoy, et al. Essentials of the Legal Environment. 3rd ed. 2010. (ENG., Illus.). 648p. (C). pap. 149.95 (978-0-324-78614-9(X)) Cengage South-Western.
Mitra Majumdar, Supriya. When Management Overlap with Law. 2010. 104p. pap. (978-3-639-26843-0(1)) VDM Verlag Dr. Mueller e.K.
Moens. International Trade & Business Law Review. 2007. (ENG.). 336p. (C). 99.95 (978-0-415-41965-9(4), Routledge Cavendish) Taylor & Francis Group GBR. Dist: Taylor & Francis Group.
Monti, Mario, et al, eds. Economic Law & Justice in Times of Globalisation: Festschrift fur Carl Baudenbacher. 2007. 916p. 199.00 (978-3-8329-2875-9(8)) Nomos Verlagsgesellschaft DEU. Dist: International Specialized Bk. Services.
Mujih, Edwin. Regulating Multinationals in Developing Countries: A Conceptual & Legal Framework for Corporate Social Responsibility. 2012. (Corporate Social Responsibility Ser.). 280p. 124.95 **(978-1-4094-4463-3(5)**, Gower Publishing Co., Ltd.) Ashgate Publishing, Ltd. GBR. Dist: Ashgate Publishing Co.
Myers J.D., Terence M. & DeScherer J.D., Dorinda. Business Tax Answer Book 2009. 2008. 760p. pap. 169.00 (978-0-8080-1912-1(0)) Toolkit Media Group.
Neipert. Law of Global Commerce A Tour. 2006. pap. 10.95 (978-1-4288-0561-3(3)) Cram101 Inc.
Nolo Press Editors, et al. Nolo's Plain-English Law Dictionary. 2009. (ENG.). 477p. pap. 29.99 (978-1-4133-1037-5(0)) NOLO.

O'Dowd, John. Organisational Change Through Partnership: Promise, Performance & Prospects for Irish Firms. 2009. 220p. pap. 29.95 *(978-1-905785-58-2(5))* Liffey Pr., The IRL. Dist: Dufour Editions, Inc.

O'Leary, Arthur F. & Acret, James. Construction Nightmares: Jobs from Hell & How to Avoid Them. 3rd ed. 2007. 461p. per. 64.95 *(978-1-55701-603-4(8))* BNI Pubns., Inc.

Oswald. Law of Marketing. 2006. pap. 11.95 *(978-1-4288-0677-1(6))* Cram101 Inc.

Otto, Lucas. Dictionary of International Business Law. 2008. 196p. pap. 40.00 *(978-0-85297-658-6(5))* Financial World Publishing GBR. Dist: Stylus Publishing, LLC.

Patterson, Thomas E. Handling the Business Emergency: Temporary Restraining Orders & Preliminary Injunctions. 2009. *(978-1-60442-490-4(7))* American Bar Assn.

Penn, Ana D. & Arias, Martha L. Global E-Business Law & Taxation. 2009. (ENG., Illus.). 560p. 235.00 *(978-0-19-536721-8(9))* Oxford Univ. Pr., Inc.

Picciotto, Sol. Regulating Global Corporate Capitalism. 2011. (International Corporate Law & Financial Market Regulation Ser.). (ENG., Illus.). 602p. 130.00 *(978-1-107-00501-3(9))*; pap. 65.00 *(978-0-521-18196-9(8))* Cambridge Univ. Pr.

Plimpton, Laura. Business Contracts: Turn Any Business Contract to Your Advantage. 2007. (ENG.). 320p. 32.95 *(978-1-59918-072-4(3)*, 1599180723) Entrepreneur Pr. dba Entrepreneur Media, Inc.

PLI's GT the Sarbanes-Oxley Act for Business Professionals. pap. 24.95 *(978-1-4024-0480-1(8))* Practising Law Institute.

Prentice, Robert A. & Jentz, Gaylord A., texts. Regulation - Business Law, 2 vols. 2007th ed. 2008. 304p. per. *(978-0-9746541-1-9(6))* Efficient Learning Systems, Inc.

Putman, Cara C. The Complete Idiot's Guide to Business Law. 2009. (Complete Idiot's Guide Ser.). (ENG.). 352p. (gr. 12-18). pap. 21.00 *(978-1-59257-852-8(7)*, Alpha Bks.) Penguin Group (USA) Inc.

Ramseyer, J. Mark, compiled by. Business Associations: Agency, Partnerships, LLCs & Corporations 2006 Statutes & Rules. rev. ed. 2007. 307p. per. 29.00 *(978-1-59941-095-1(8))* West.

Rawal, Radhakishan. The Taxation of Permanent Establishments: An International Perspective. 2006. 551p. (C). pap. 135.00 *(978-1-904905-45-5(5))* Spiramus Pr. GBR. Dist: International Specialized Bk. Services.

Reed, O. Lee, et al. The Legal & Regulatory: Environment of Business. 16th ed. 2012. (ENG., Illus.). 816p. (C). 216.00 ***(978-0-07-352499-3(9)**, 0073524999, McGraw-Hill/Irwin) McGraw-Hill Higher Education.

Reed, O. Lee, et al. The Legal & Regulatory Environment of Business. (Illus.). 704p. 14th rev. ed. 2006. 165.94 *(978-0-07-304849-9(6)*, 9780073048499) 15th ed. 2009. (ENG., (C). 216.00 *(978-0-07-337766-7(X)*, 007337766X) McGraw-Hill Higher Education. (McGraw-Hill/Irwin).

Rhodes, Robert T. Graduate Business Law. rev. ed. 2010. (ENG.). 190p. spiral bd. 53.45 *(978-0-7575-4221-3(2))* Kendall Hunt Publishing Co.

Ribstein, Larry E. & Lipshaw, Jeffrey M. Unincorporated Business Entities. 4th ed. 2009. *(978-1-4224-2960-0(1))* LexisNexis Matthew Bender.

Richmond Law & Tax Ltd., ed. Financial Services Regulators in Emerging Markets. 2nd rev. ed. 2006. 600p. pap. *(978-1-904501-74-9(5))* Richmond Law & Tax Ltd.

—Financial Services Regulators in Major Financial Centres. 2nd rev. ed. 2006. 500p. pap. *(978-1-904501-73-2(7))* Richmond Law & Tax Ltd.

Rosen, Eric A. Buyout Agreements Line by Line: A Detailed Look at Buyout Agreements & How to Change Them to Meet Your Clients¿ Needs. 2011. (ENG.). 116p. pap. 95.00 incl. cd-rom ***(978-0-314-27890-6(7))*** Aspatore Bks.

Samuelson & Beatty. Im-Surv Bus Law/Legl Environ. 2nd ed. 2007. (Illus.). pap. *(978-0-324-31144-0(3))* West Publishing Co., College & Schl. Div.

Savage, Marc. The Dirty Secrets the Mortgage Industry Doesn't Want You to Know. 2008. 78p. pap. 26.17 *(978-0-615-18516-3(9))* Savage, Marc.

Schulz, Martin & Wasmeier, Oliver. The Law of Business Organizations: A Concise Overview of the German Corporate Law. 2012. (ENG., Illus.). xi, 204p. 69.95 *(978-3-642-17792-7(1)*, 3642177921) Springer.

Singh, Arun. Business & Contract Law. 2010. (Thorogood Reports). 250p. spiral bd. 290.00 *(978-1-85418-653-9(1))* Thorogood GBR. Dist: Stylus Publishing, LLC.

Smith, D. Gordon. Business Organizations: Case Problems & Case Studies. 2nd ed. 2008. xxi, 1033p. 154.00 *(978-0-7355-7140-2(6))* Wolters Kluwer Law & Business.

Smith, D. Gordon & Williams, Cynthia A. Business Organizations: Cases, Problems, & Case Studies. 2nd ed. 2008. xxi, 1033p. pap. *(978-0-7355-7141-9(4)*, Aspen Pubs.) Wolters Kluwer Law & Business.

Smith, James E. West Federal Taxation: Taxation of Business Entities. 2006. pap. 15.95 *(978-1-4288-0970-3(8))* Cram101 Inc.

Smith, Richard G. The Law of Entrepreneurial Finance. 2012. *(978-0-7355-4081-1(0)*, Aspen Pubs.) Wolters Kluwer Law & Business.

Spadaccini, Michael. The Operations Manual for Corporations. 2007. (ENG.). 304p. 32.95 *(978-1-59918-146-2(0)*, 1599181460) Entrepreneur Pr. dba Entrepreneur Media, Inc.

Stickney, Albert. State Control of Trade & Commerce by National or State Authority. 2009. 148p. pap. 19.99 *(978-1-150-38158-4(2))* General Bks. LLC.

Stoneman, Mark L. Understanding the Use of Financial Accounting Provisions in Private Acquisition Agreements. 2012. ***(978-1-61438-319-2(7))*** American Bar Assn.

Story, Joseph. Commentaries on the Law of Partnership. 2009. 480p. pap. *(978-1-150-43546-1(1))* Books LLC.

Swink, Dawn. Midwest Law Journal: Volume 23, Spring 2009, Number 1. 2011. 136p. pap. 19.95 *(978-1-58909-866-4(8))* Bookstand Publishing.

Theiselmann, Ruediger, ed. Governance: Legal Guidelines for International Management Practice. 2012. (ENG., Illus.). 672p. 145.00 ***(978-1-137-00440-6(1))*** Palgrave Macmillan.

Thomas, Karen. Ultimate Book of Business & Legal Forms for Startups: 200+ Downloadable Forms & Spreadsheets. 2nd ed. 2010. (ENG., Illus.). 304p. pap. 29.95 *(978-1-59918-389-3(7)*, 1599183897) Entrepreneur Pr. dba Entrepreneur Media, Inc.

Trachtman, Michael G. The Four Mistakes: Avoiding the Legal Landmines that Lead to Business Disaster. 2010. (ENG.). 256p. 19.95 *(978-1-4027-6817-0(6))* Sterling Publishing Co., Inc.

Trotter, Mary. Business Law & Society. Date not set. (C). *(978-0-395-35229-8(0))* CENGAGE Learning.

Twomey, David P. & Jennings, Marianne M. Business Law: Principles for Today's Commerical Environment. 3rd ed. 2010. (ENG., Illus.). 1248p. (C). 288.95 *(978-0-324-78669-9(7))* Cengage South-Western.

—Business Law & the Legal Environment. 21st ed. 2010. (ENG.). 1528p. (C). 264.95 *(978-0-324-78666-8(2))* Cengage South-Western.

United Nations. Uncitral. 2006. (ENG.). 62p. pap. 75.00 *(978-92-1-133753-2(4))* United Nations Pubns.

Van Dyke, William A. How to Protect Your Intellectual Property & Make a Profit: A Comprehensive How-to Guide on Patents, Copyrights, Trademarks, & Other Legal Business Affairs. 2009. pap. 27.99 *(978-1-60696-434-7(8))* Tate Publishing & Enterprises, LLC.

von Thunen, Sebastian. Directors' Duty for the Benefit of Creditors: Die Bedeutung der Geschäftsleiterpflicht zur Berücksichtigung der Gläubigerinteressen für den Schutz der Gläubiger einer englischen Limited mit Verwaltungssitz in Deutschland. 2011. (Schriften zum Internationalen Privatrecht und zur Rechtsvergleichung Ser.). (GER.). 463p. (C). 84.00 ***(978-3-89971-864-5(X))*** Vandenhoeck & Ruprecht GmbH & Co. KG DEU. Dist: ISD.

Vroman, Margaret. Business Law. rev. ed. 2011. (ENG.). 264p. pap. 91.04 *(978-0-7575-6338-6(4))* Kendall Hunt Publishing Co.

Warda, Mark. Como Iniciar su Propio Negocio. 2008. (SPA & ENG., Illus.). 128p. per. 5.95 *(978-1-57248-674-4(0)*, Sphinx Publishing) Sourcebooks, Inc.

—Incorporate in Nevada from Any State, 2E. 2nd ed. 2008. (ENG.). 336p. pap. 26.95 *(978-1-57248-662-1(7)*, Sphinx Publishing) Sourcebooks, Inc.

Warda, Mark & Robertson, Charles T., II. How to Start a Business in Georgia. 5th ed. 2008. (Legal Survival Guides). (ENG., Illus.). 304p. per. 34.99 *(978-1-57248-642-3(2)*, Sphinx Publishing) Sourcebooks, Inc.

Warendorf. Company & Business Legislation of the Netherlands. 2008. (Illus.). 1676p. ring bd. 537.00 *(978-90-411-2739-6(9))* Wolters Kluwer Law & Business.

Wessels & Wessels, B. Cross-Border Insolvency Law: International Instruments & Commentary. 2007. *(978-90-411-2526-2(4))* Kluwer Law International.

West Virginia Business Organizations Laws Annotated: 1997 Edition. 757p. pap. 40.00 *(978-1-55834-626-0(0))* LEXIS Publishing.

Willes and Will, Q. C. International Business Law. 2006. pap. 15.95 *(978-1-4288-0577-4(X))* Cram101 Inc.

World Bank. Reforming Through Difficult Times 2010. 2009. (Doing Business Ser.). (ENG., Illus.). 228p. pap. 35.00 *(978-0-8213-7961-5(5)*, 9780821379615) World Bank Pubns.

World Bank Staff. Celebrating Reform 2007: Doing Business Case Studies. 2007. (ENG., Illus.). 90p. per. 25.00 *(978-0-8213-7293-7(9)*, 9780821372937) World Bank Pubns.

—Doing Business 2009: Comparing Regulation in 181 Economies. rev. ed. 2008. (Doing Business Ser.). (ENG., Illus.). 185p. pap. 35.00 *(978-0-8213-7609-6(8)*, 9780821376096) World Bank Pubns.

Yin, George K. Taxation of Partnerships. 2009. (Illus.). xxi, 392p. 130.00 *(978-0-7355-2632-7(X)*, Aspen Pubs.) Wolters Kluwer Law & Business.

Zuckerman, Jack, et al. The Business Tax Return Handbook. 3rd ed. 2010. (Illus.). ix, 194p. *(978-1-60442-801-8(5))* American Bar Assn.

BUSINESS LAW—AFRICA

Handley, Antoinette. Business & the State in Africa: Economic Policy-Making in the Neo-Liberal Era. 2008. (ENG., Illus.). 304p. 92.00 *(978-0-521-88605-5(8))*; pap. 40.00 *(978-0-521-71371-9(4))* Cambridge Univ. Pr.

Keith, Don. Understanding Sectoral Determination 9: The Wholesale & Retail Sector. 2010. (Juta's Pocket Companions Ser.). 166p. pap. 20.50 ***(978-0-7021-8520-5(5))*** Gaunt, Inc.

Kopel, Shawn. Guide to Business Law. 4th ed. 2010. 448p. pap. 55.00 *(978-0-19-598908-3(2))* Oxford Univ. Pr., Inc.

Martor, Boris, et al. Business Law in Africa: OHADA & the Harmonization Process. 2nd ed. 2009. (ARA & ENG.). 284p. pap. 140.00 *(978-1-84673-190-7(9)*, GMB Publishing Ltd.) Blue Ibex Ltd. GBR. Dist: Ingram Pub. Services.

—OHADA & the Harmonization Process Business Law in Africa. 2nd ed. 2007. (ENG.). 347p. pap. 140.00 *(978-1-84673-072-6(4)*, GMB Publishing Ltd.) Blue Ibex Ltd. GBR. Dist: Ingram Pub. Services.

Richmond Law & Tax Ltd., ed. Financial Services Regulation in the Middle East & Africa. 2nd rev. ed. 2006. 300p. *(978-1-904501-83-1(4))* Richmond Law & Tax Ltd.

—Financial Services Regulators in the Middle East & Africa. 2nd rev. ed. 2006. 400p. pap. *(978-1-904501-72-5(9))* Richmond Law & Tax Ltd.

Simo Tumndé, Martha, et al. Unified Business Laws for Africa: Common Law Perspectives on OHADA. 2009. (ENG.). 148p. pap. 110.00 *(978-1-84673-150-1(X)*, GMB Publishing Ltd.) Blue Ibex Ltd. GBR. Dist: Ingram Pub. Services.

BUSINESS LAW—ASIA

Doyle, Michael. Doyle's Practical Guide to Business Law in Emerging Countries in Asia. 2010. 324p. pap. 30.00 *(978-1-59460-777-6(X))* Carolina Academic Pr.

Gillespie, John. Transplanting Commercial Law Reform: Developing a 'Rule of Law' in Vietnam. 2006. 362p. 130.00 *(978-0-7546-4704-1(8))* Ashgate Publishing Co.

Richmond Law & Tax Ltd., ed. Financial Services Regulation in Asia Pacific. 2nd rev. ed. 2006. 400p. *(978-1-904501-82-4(6))* Richmond Law & Tax Ltd.

—Financial Services Regulators in Asia Pacific. 2006. 500p. pap. *(978-1-904501-71-8(0))* Richmond Law & Tax Ltd.

Yu Chang, Albert Vincent Y. & Thorson, Andrew. A Legal Guide to Doing Business in Asia-Pacific. 2011. (ENG.). 250p. pap. 149.95 *(978-1-60442-843-8(0))* American Bar Assn.

BUSINESS LAW—AUSTRALIA

Broeckelmann, Philipp. Austrian Economics as a Basis for a General Marketing Theory: Potentials & Limitations. 2008. 92p. pap. *(978-3-8364-8291-2(6))* VDM Verlag Dr. Mueller e.K.

Carvan, John, et al. A Guide to Business Law. 12th ed. *(978-0-455-21419-1(0))* LBC Information Services.

BUSINESS LAW—CANADA

Mallor, Jane, et al. Student Study Guide to accompany Business Law: the Ethical, Global, & E-Commerce Environment. 14th ed. 2009. (ENG.). 384p. (C). pap. 74.33 *(978-0-07-336179-6(8)*, 0073361798, McGraw-Hill/Irwin) McGraw-Hill Higher Education.

Michalos, Alex C. Trade Barriers to the Public Good: Free Trade & Environmental Protection. 2008. (ENG.). 432p. (C). *(978-0-7735-3352-3(4))* McGill-Queen's Univ. Pr.

BUSINESS LAW—CARIBBEAN AREA

Ramlogan, Rajendra & Persadie, Natalie. Commonwealth Caribbean Business Law. 2nd rev. ed. 2010. (Commonwealth Caribbean Law Ser.). (ENG., Illus.). 448p. 130.00 *(978-0-415-55049-9(1))* Taylor & Francis Group GBR. Dist: Taylor & Francis Group.

Ramlogan, Rajendra, et al. Commonwealth Caribbean Business Law. 2nd rev. ed. 2010. (Commonwealth Caribbean Law Ser.). (ENG., Illus.). 448p. pap. 90.00 *(978-0-415-55048-2(3))* Taylor & Francis Group GBR. Dist: Taylor & Francis Group.

BUSINESS LAW—CHINA

Aspatore Books Staff, compiled by. Best Practices for International Business Transactions in China, 2011 Ed: Leading Lawyers on Navigating Local Regulations, Overcoming Cultural Barriers, & Advising Clients on Doing Business in China (Inside the Minds) 2011. 212p. pap. 95.00 *(978-0-314-27635-3(1))* Aspatore Bks.

—Best Practices for Mergers & Acquisitions in China: Leading Lawyers on Understanding Changing Laws & Trends, Navigating the Review & Approval Process, & Identifying the Key Steps in a Successful M&A Transaction. 2008. (Inside the Minds Ser.). 264p. pap. 110.00 *(978-0-314-19996-6(9))* Aspatore Bks.

Best Practices for International Business Transactions in China: Leading Lawyers on Structuring & Negotiating Trade Transactions, Understanding the Importance of Due Diligence, & Working as a Legal Professional in the International Business Community (Inside the Minds) 2009. 252p. pap. *(978-0-314-19940-9(3))* Aspatore Bks.

Best Practices for International Business Transactions in China, 2010 Ed: Leading Lawyers on Negotiating in China, Meeting the Changing Needs of Corporate Clients, & Understanding the Impact of the Economic Downturn (Inside the Minds) 2010. 456p. pap. 100.00 *(978-0-314-26525-8(2))* Aspatore Bks.

Bu, Yianshi & Mota, Carlos Esplugues. Chinese Business Law. 2010. (Illus.). 412p. 210.00 *(978-1-84946-058-3(2))* Hart Publishing Ltd. GBR. Dist: International Specialized Bk. Services.

CCH Asia. China Master Business Law Guide: Legislation. 2009. 218.00 *(978-90-411-3176-8(0))* Wolters Kluwer Law & Business.

Chen, Jianfu. China Master Business Law Guide: Commentary & Analysis. 2009. 319.00 *(978-90-411-3155-3(8))* Wolters Kluwer Law & Business.

China & Hong Kong Law Firm Directory 1994: Companies-Products-Services. 300p. (Orig.). pap. *(978-0-7605-0664-6(7))* Rector Pr., Ltd.

Chong, Seung. The Law & Practice of Mergers & Acquisitions in the People's Republic of China. 2007. (ENG., Illus.). 504p. 440.00 *(978-0-19-927799-5(0))* Oxford Univ. Pr., Inc.

Haan, Arjan de. How the Aid Industry Works: An Introduction to International Development. 2009. 256p. 65.00 *(978-1-56549-288-2(9))*; pap. 24.95 *(978-1-56549-287-5(0))* Stylus Publishing, LLC.

Lo, Vai Io & Tian, Xiaowen. Law for Foreign Business & Investment in China. 2009. (Illus.). 432p. 170.00 *(978-0-415-45320-2(8))* Routledge.

Martin, Sebastian. Acquisitions of Chinese Enterprises- an Alternative Form of Fdi. 2007. 68p. per. *(978-3-8364-0725-0(6))* VDM Verlag Dr. Mueller e.K.

Moser. Managing Business Disputes in Today's China: Duelling with Dragons. 2007. (Illus.). 319p. *(978-90-411-2462-3(4))* Kluwer Law International.

Zhou, Xiaolin, et al. Doing Business in China: Resolving the Challenges in Today's Environment. 2007. (Corporate Law & Practice Course Handbook Ser.: No. 1626). (Illus.). 375p. *(978-1-4024-0955-4(9))* Practising Law Institute.

—Doing Business in China 2008. 2008. (Illus.). 276p. pap. *(978-1-4024-1074-1(3)*, 810 7th Ave., New York, NY 10019) Practising Law Institute.

Zimmerman, James M. China Law Deskbook. 3rd ed. 2010. *(978-1-60442-958-9(5))* American Bar Assn.

BUSINESS LAW—EUROPE

Adam, Ioan & Savu, Codrut Nicolae. Legea Societatilor Comerciale: Comentarii Si Explicatii. 2010. ix, 1034p. *(978-973-115-568-5(6))* C. H. Beck'sch Verlagsbuchhandlung.

Arvanitopoulos, Constantine, ed. Reforming Europe: The Role of Central Right. 2010. (Constantinos Karamanlis Institute for Democracy Series on European & International Affairs Ser.). (ENG., Illus.). xxiv, 295p. 139.00 *(978-3-642-00559-6(4)*, 3642005594) Springer.

Bettermann, Constantin. Finanzierung von Familiengesellschaften nach Basel II und IFRS: Kautelarjuristische und betriebswirtschaftliche Betrachtung. 2009. (GER.). 328p. 86.95 *(978-3-631-59483-4(6))* Lang, Peter GmbH, Europaischer Verlag der Wissenschaften DEU. Dist: Lang, Peter.

Bogenschütz, Nina. Neuausrichtung des Eigenkapitalbegriffs: Dogmatische Überlegungen im Lichte hybrider Finanzierungen. 2008. (Frankfurter wirtschaftsrechtliche Studien Ser.). 244p. pap. 61.95 *(978-3-631-56933-7(5))* Lang, Peter GmbH, Europaischer Verlag der Wissenschaften DEU. Dist: Lang, Peter.

Cox, Joanne. Business Law. 5th ed. 2012. (ENG.). 512p. pap. 100.00 ***(978-0-19-960341-1(3))*** Oxford Univ. Pr., Inc.

Egan, Paul & Hayes+Curran, Mason. Irish Corporate Procedures. 3rd rev. ed. 2007. (ENG.). 272p. pap. *(978-1-84661-063-9(X))* Jordan Publishing, Ltd.

Hö, et al. Abuse of Market Dominance. 2009. 128p. pap. *(978-3-639-14141-2(5))* VDM Verlag Dr. Mueller e.K.

Heijden, M. -J van der. Transnational Corporations & Human Rights Liabilities. 2012. 460p. pap. 125.00 ***(978-94-000-0195-4(9))*** Intersentia Uitgevers N.V. BEL. Dist: International Specialized Bk. Services.

Iversen, Bent, et al. Danish Business Law. 4th ed. 2010. 584p. pap. 84.00 *(978-87-574-2132-3(3))* Djof Publishing DNK. Dist: International Specialized Bk. Services.

Junker, Abbo, ed. Betriebsübergang in Europa: Symposium aus Anlass des 10-jährigen Bestehens der Schriften zum Arbeitsrecht und Wirtschaftsrecht. 2009. (Schriften zum Arbeitsrecht und Wirtschaftsrecht Ser.). (GER.). 110p. pap. 35.95 *(978-3-631-58264-0(1))* Lang, Peter GmbH, Europaischer Verlag der Wissenschaften DEU. Dist: Lang, Peter.

Keessen, Andrea. European Administrative Decisions: How the EU Regulates Products on the Internal Market. 2009. 271p. 112.00 *(978-90-8952-056-2(2))* Europa Law Publishing, Netherlands NLD. Dist: International Specialized Bk. Services.

Körner, Pavel. Three Essays on Corporate Governance & Corporate Finance: Theoretical Approaches & Czech Empirical Evidence. 2008. 112p. pap. *(978-3-639-10330-4(0))* VDM Verlag Dr. Mueller e.K.

Kroes. E Business Law European Union. 2nd rev. ed. 2010. (Illus.). xii, 429p. pap. *(978-90-411-2636-8(8))* Kluwer Law International.

Leenen, Detlef. BGB Allgemeiner Teil: Rechtsgeschäftslehre. 2011. (De Gruyter Studium Ser.).Tr. of Theory of Legal Acts. (GER., Illus.). XL, 462p. (C). pap. 56.00 *(978-3-89949-434-1(2))* De Gruyter, Walter Inc.

Marson, James. Business Law. 2nd ed. 2011. (ENG., Illus.). 640p. pap. 70.00 *(978-0-19-960870-6(9))* Oxford Univ. Pr., Inc.

Nagel, Bernhard, et al. Beteiligung der Arbeitnehmer im Unternehmen auf der Grundlage des europäischen Rechts: Kommentar zum: SE-Beteiligungsgesetz - SEBG, SCE-Beteiligungsgesetz - SCEBG, Gesetz über die Mitbestimmung der Arbeitnehmer bei einer grenzüberschreitenden Verschmelzung - MgVG. 2nd ed. 2009. (De Gruyter Kommentar Ser.).Tr. of Negotiated Employee Participation According to EU Guidelines. (GER., Illus.). XXX, 621p. 109.00 *(978-3-89949-498-3(9))* De Gruyter, Walter Inc.

Nagel, Bernhard, et al. Beteiligung der Arbeitnehmer im Unternehmen auf der Grundlage des europäischen Rechts: Kommentar zum SE-Beteiligungsgesetz â€" SEBG. SCE-Beteiligungsgesetz â€" SCEBG. Gesetz aber die Mitbestimmung der Arbeitnehmer bei einer grenzaberschreitenden Verschmelzung â€" MgVG. 2nd ed. 2009. (De Gruyter Kommentar Ser.).Tr. of Negotiated Employee Participation According to EU Guidelines. (GER.). XXX, 621p. 168.00 ***(978-3-11-173553-5(2))*** De Gruyter, Walter Inc.

Oinonen. Does Ec Merger Control Discriminate Against Small Companies. 2010. (Illus.). xxiii, 420p. *(978-90-411-3261-1(9))* Kluwer Law International.

Pennings. Social Responsibility in Labour Relations: European & Comparative Perspectives. 2008. (Studies in Employment & Social Policy: Vol. 38). (Illus.). xlii, 532p. 172.00 *(978-90-411-2783-9(6))* Wolters Kluwer Law & Business.

Richmond Law & Tax Ltd., ed. Financial Services Regulation in Europe. 2nd rev. ed. 2006. 750p. *(978-1-904501-80-0(X))* Richmond Law & Tax Ltd.

—Financial Services Regulators in Europe. 2nd rev. ed. 2006. 1100p. pap. *(978-1-904501-69-5(9))* Richmond Law & Tax Ltd.

Schulze, Reiner, ed. Compensation of Private Losses: The Evolution of Torts in European Business Law. 2011. 258p. pap., pap. 89.00 *(978-3-86653-175-8(3))* Sellier - European Law Publishers GmbH DEU. Dist: International Specialized Bk. Services.

Wendler, Michael, et al, eds. Key Aspects of German Business Law: A Practical Manual. 4th ed. 2010. (ENG.). xxiv, 522p. pap. 139.00 *(978-3-642-08811-7(2)*, 3642088112) Springer.

Wendler, Michael, et al. Key Aspects of German Business Law: A Practical Manual. 4th ed. 2008. (ENG., Illus.). xxiv, 522p. 139.00 *(978-3-540-68574-6(X)*, 354068574X) Springer.

Wiener, Jonathan B. & Hammitt, James K. The Reality of Precaution: Comparing Risk Regulation in the United States & Europe. Rogers, Michael D. & Sand,

Peter H., eds. 2010. (ENG., Illus.). 602p. 150.00 *(978-1-933115-86-3(6))*; pap. 69.95 *(978-1-933115-85-6(8))* Earthscan LLC. (RFF Pr.).

BUSINESS LAW—GREAT BRITAIN

Adams, Alix. Law for Business Students. (Illus.). 4th rev. ed. 2007. 464p. pap. 68.50 *(978-1-4058-3262-5(2))* 7th rev. ed. 2012. (ENG., 672p. pap. ***(978-1-4082-8701-9(3))*** Pearson Education.

Brock, Amanda, et al. E-Business: The Practical Guide to the Laws. 2nd ed. 2009. 353p. pap. 52.50 *(978-1-904905-87-5(0))* Spiramus Pr. GBR. Dist: International Specialized Bk. Services.

Cooper, Rachel E., ed. Legislation for Business Law 2009-2010. 2009. (Blackstone Legal Practice Course Guide Ser.). (ENG.). 1120p. 66.00 *(978-0-19-958065-1(0)*, Blackstone Pr.) Oxford Univ. Pr. GBR. Dist: Oxford Univ. Pr., Inc.

Coutts, Ken & Rowthorn, Robert. Prospects for the Uk Balance of Payments. 2010. (Illus.). 30p. pap. 12.50 *(978-1-906837-12-9(0))* Civitas:Institute for the Study of Civil Society GBR. Dist: Coronet Bks.

Denoncourt, Janice. Q & A Business Law. 2nd rev. ed. 2012. (Questions & Answers Ser.). (ENG., Illus.). 232p. (C). pap. 24.95 ***(978-0-415-68842-0(6))*** Routledge.

Kelly, David, et al. Business Law. 6th ed. 2011. (ENG., Illus.). (C). 656p. pap. 70.00 *(978-0-415-55973-7(1))*; 640p. 160.00 *(978-0-415-58366-4(7))* Routledge.

King, Anthony & Barlow, John. Business Law Vol. 1: 1994-95. (Legal Practice Course Guides Ser.). 332p. pap. *(978-1-85431-366-9(5)*, Blackstone Pr.) Oxford Univ. Pr.

Lang, Yvonne. Accounts & Audits of Limited Liability Partnerships: Third Edition. 3rd ed. 2009. 223p. pap. 145.00 *(978-1-84766-503-4(9))*, Bloomsbury Professional) Bloomsbury Publishing Plc GBR. Dist: International Specialized Bk. Services.

Macintyre, Ewan. Business Law. 3rd rev. ed. 2007. (Illus.). 896p. pap. 99.50 *(978-1-4058-4617-2(8))* Pearson Education, Ltd. GBR. Dist: Trans-Atlantic Pubns., Inc.

Marson, James. Business Law. 2nd ed. 2011. (ENG., Illus.). 640p. pap. 70.00 *(978-0-19-960870-6(9))* Oxford Univ. Pr., Inc.

—Business Law Concentrate. 2010. (ENG., Illus.). 224p. pap. 30.00 *(978-0-19-957946-4(6))* Oxford Univ. Pr., Inc.

Mead, Larry & Bampton, Kevin. CIMA Official Exam Practice Kit Fundamentals of Ethics, Corporate Governance & Business Law Kit: Certificate in Business Accounting. 4th ed. 2010. (ENG., Illus.). 208p. (C). pap. 28.95 *(978-1-85617-709-2(2)*, CIMA Publishing) Elsevier Science & Technology Bks.

Mead, Larry, et al. CIMA Official Learning System Fundamentals of Ethics, Corporate Governance & Business Law. 4th ed. 2009. (ENG., Illus.). 560p. (C). pap. 55.95 *(978-1-85617-787-0(4)*, CIMA Publishing) Elsevier Science & Technology Bks.

Mellor, John. Practical Corporate Governance: For Smaller Quoted Companies & Private Companies. 2008. (ENG.). 326p. incl. cd-rom *(978-1-84661-126-1(1))* Jordan Publishing, Ltd.

Riches, Sarah & Keenan, Denis. Business Law. 8th rev. ed. 2008. (Illus.). 640p. pap. 75.00 *(978-1-4058-4697-4(6))* Pearson Education.

Roach, Lee. Card & James' Business Law for Business, Accounting, & Finance Students. 2nd ed. 2012. (ENG., Illus.). 960p. pap. 75.00 ***(978-0-19-969805-9(8))*** Oxford Univ. Pr., Inc.

Sanders, Tim & Ridgway, Philip. Tax Indemnities & Warranties. 3rd ed. 2009. 445p. 210.00 *(978-1-84592-127-9(5)*, Bloomsbury Professional) Bloomsbury Publishing Plc GBR. Dist: International Specialized Bk. Services.

Singleton, Susan. Buying & Selling Insolvent Companies & Businesses. 2010. 396p. pap. 198.00 *(978-1-84766-542-3(X)*, Bloomsbury Professional) Bloomsbury Publishing Plc GBR. Dist: International Specialized Bk. Services.

BUSINESS LAW—INDIA

Haan, Arjan de. How the Aid Industry Works: An Introduction to International Development. 2009. 256p. 65.00 *(978-1-56549-288-2(9))*; pap. 24.95 *(978-1-56549-287-5(0))* Stylus Publishing, LLC.

Prasad, Ashish S. & Shwartz, Mark L. Doing Business in India: Critical Legal Issues for U.S. Companies. 2007. (Corporate Law & Practice Course Handbook Ser.: No. 1587). (Illus.). 312p. pap. *(978-1-4024-0858-8(7))* Practising Law Institute.

BUSINESS LAW—MIDDLE EAST

Richmond Law & Tax Ltd., ed. Financial Services Regulation in the Middle East & Africa. 2nd rev. ed. 2006. 300p. *(978-1-904501-83-1(4))* Richmond Law & Tax Ltd.

—Financial Services Regulators in the Middle East & Africa. 2nd rev. ed. 2006. 400p. pap. *(978-1-904501-72-5(9))* Richmond Law & Tax Ltd.

BUSINESS LAW—RUSSIA (FEDERATION)

Douma, Wybe Th. & Mucklow, Fiona M., eds. Environmental Finance & Socially Responsible Business in Russia: Legal & Practical Trends. 2010. (Illus.). 372p. 99.00 *(978-90-6704-330-4(3))* T.M.C. Asser Pr. NLD. Dist: Springer.

Ledeneva, Alena V. How Russia Really Works: The Informal Practices That Shaped Post-Soviet Politics & Business. 2006. (Culture & Society after Socialism Ser.). (Illus.). 270p. 75.50 *(978-0-8014-4346-6(6))* Cornell Univ. Pr.

—How Russia Really Works: The Informal Practices That Shaped Post-Soviet Politics & Bussiness. 2006. (Culture & Society after Socialism Ser.). (Illus.). 270p. per. 24.95 *(978-0-8014-7352-4(7))* Cornell Univ. Pr.

Lidings Law Firm. An Introduction to Russian Business Law. 2010. (Illus.). 216p. pap. 95.00 *(978-0-314-26864-8(2))* Aspatore Bks.

Orlov, Vladimir. Introduction to Business Law in Russia. 2011. (Markets & the Law Ser.). 334p. 165.00 *(978-0-7546-7755-0(9))* Ashgate Publishing Co.

Terterov, Marat. Russia During President Putin's Second Term: A Business & Investment Review. 2006. (Business & Investment Review Ser.). (ENG.). 97p. pap. 290.00 *(978-1-84673-008-5(2)*, GMB Publishing Ltd.) Blue Ibex Ltd. GBR. Dist: Ingram Pub. Services.

BUSINESS LAW—SOUTH AMERICA

Barretto, Ricardo, et al. A Legal Guide to Doing Business in South America. 2012. (ENG.). 300p. pap. 149.95 *(978-1-61632-957-0(2))* American Bar Assn.

Champion, Walter T. Business Laws of Colombia. 2009. xx, 224p. pap. *(978-0-314-90331-0(3))* West Publishing Co., College & Schl. Div.

Dorling Kindersley Publishing Staff. Doing Business in South America. 2009. (DK Essential Managers Ser.). (ENG.). 72p. (gr. 12). pap. 8.00 *(978-0-7566-4201-3(9))* Dorling Kindersley Publishing, Inc.

Franco, Beatriz, et al, eds. International Business Transactions with Brazil. 2008. 584p. 125.00 *(978-1-57823-240-6(6))* Juris Publishing, Inc.

Scaletta, Phillip J. & Cameron, George Dana. Foundations of Business Law & Legal Environment. 7th ed. 2009. (Illus.). xxii, 855p. *(978-1-4266-3118-4(9))* Course Technology.

BUSINESS LEASES

see Commercial Leases

BUSINESS LETTERS

see Commercial Correspondence

BUSINESS LIBRARIES

see also Information Storage and Retrieval Systems—Business

Bergart, Robin & Lewis, Vivian. Sudden Selector's Guide to Business Resources. 2007. xv, 70p. 28.50 *(978-0-8389-8414-7(2))* American Library Assn.

BIA. Leading Business Schools & Business Libraries. 6th rev. ed. 2006. 350p. (J). pap. 249.00 *(978-1-4187-4390-1(9))* Business Information Agency.

—Leading Business Schools & Business Libraries of the USA. 6th rev. ed. 2006. 350p. (J). pap. 249.00 *(978-1-4187-4439-7(5))* Business Information Agency.

—Leading Universities, Business Schools, & Business Libraries of Russia. 6th rev. ed. 2006. 300p. (J). pap. 249.00 *(978-1-4187-4537-0(5))* Business Information Agency.

Forte, Eric & Oppenheim, Michael. The Basic Business Library: Core Resources & Services, 1 vol. 5th rev. ed. 227p. 44.95 *(978-1-59884-611-9(6)*, A3137C) Libraries Unlimited, Inc.

Forte, Eric J. & Oppenheim, Michael R. The Basic Business Library: Core Resources & Services. 5th ed. 2011. E-Book ***(978-1-59884-612-6(4))*** Libraries Unlimited, Inc.

BUSINESS LIFE INSURANCE

see also Stock Purchase Agreements (Close Corporations)

Business Buy-Sell Agreements: August 2006 Update. 2006. 340p. ring bd. 74.00 *(978-0-7626-1145-4(6)*, BU-31496) Continuing Education of the Bar-California.

Continuing Education of the Bar. Business Buy-Sell Agreements: August 2007 Update. 2007. 322p. ring bd. 79.00 *(978-0-7626-1279-6(7))* Continuing Education of the Bar-California.

Slevick, Glenn E. Essentials of Business Insurance. 2nd rev. ed. 2010. (Financial Advisor Series: Product Esssentials). 614p. (C). 65.00 *(978-1-932819-98-4(3))* American College, The.

BUSINESS LITERATURE

see also Business—Bibliography

Coria-Sanchez, Carlos M. & Torres, German. Temas del Comercio y la Economia en la Narrativa Hispana. 2007. (SPA & ENG.). 288p. per. 46.00 *(978-0-300-10955-9(5))* Yale Univ. Pr.

Fierce, Jon L. & Newstrom, John. The Manager's Bookshelf: A Mosaic of Contemporary Views. 8th ed. 2007. (ENG.). 416p. (C). per. 106.67 *(978-0-13-230165-7(2)*, Prentice Hall) Prentice Hall PTR.

ProQuest LLC Staff, ed. News Media Directory 2009: Magazine & Newsletter Directory, Vol. 2. 2008. 385.00 *(978-1-60030-118-6(5))*, ProQuest LLC.

—News Media Directory 2009: Newspaper Directory, Vol. 1. 2008. 385.00 *(978-1-60030-117-9(7))* ProQuest LLC.

—News Media Directory 2009: TV & Radio Directory, Vol. 3. 2008. 385.00 *(978-1-60030-119-3(3))* ProQuest LLC.

Stanley, T. D. & Doucouliagos, Hristos. Meta-Regression Analysis in Economics & Business. 2012. (Routledge Frontiers of Political Economy Ser.). (ENG., Illus.) 176p. (C). 130.00 *(978-0-415-67078-4(0))* Routledge.

BUSINESS LITERATURE SEARCHING

see Information Storage and Retrieval Systems—Business

BUSINESS LOCATION

see Industrial Location

BUSINESS LOGISTICS

Here are entered works on the system of managing the flow of materials (raw materials, supplies, purchased parts, etc.) from the suppliers, through the company processes, to the customers.

see also Inventory Control; Marketing—Management; Materials Management; Physical Distribution of Goods; Shipment of Goods

Agrawal, Narendra & Smith, Stephen A., eds. Retail Supply Chain Management: Quantitative Models & Empirical Studies. 2010. (International Series in Operations Research & Management Science Ser.). (Illus.). xii, 340p. pap. 149.00 *(978-1-4419-4627-0(6)*, 1441946276) Springer.

Agrawal, Narendra M. & Smith, Stephen A. Retail Supply Chain Management: Quantitative Models & Empirical Studies. 2008. (International Series in Operations Research & Management Science Ser.). (Illus.). 352p. 149.00 *(978-0-387-78902-6(2))* Springer.

Ahr, Dino. Multiple Postmen Problems- Fundamentals & New Algorithms. 2007. 220p. per. *(978-3-8364-4496-5(8))* VDM Verlag Dr. Mueller e.K.

Ait-Kadi, D., et al. Recycling & Inverse Manufacturing. 2012. (Iste Ser.: 577). (ENG.). 125.00 ***(978-1-84821-310-4(7)***, Wiley-ISTE) Wiley, John & Sons, Inc.

Albekov, A. U. Logistika Kak Faktor Povysheniia Konkurentosposobnosti Predpriiatii Regiona V Usloviiakh Globalnogo Ekonomicheskogo Krizisa: Nauchno-Prakticheskoe Posobie. 2009. (RUS.). 204p. *(978-5-7972-1444-1(X))* Rostovskij Gosudarstvennyj Ekonomiceskij Universitet RINH.

Albrecht, Martin. Supply Chain Coordination Mechanisms: New Approaches for Collaborative Planning. 2009. (Lecture Notes in Economics & Mathematical Systems Ser.). (ENG., Illus.). xxii, 211p. pap. 109.00 *(978-3-642-02832-8(2)*, 3642028322) Springer.

Alfonso, Cristina M. & Sullivan, Jason P. Cargo Containers & Supply Chain Security: Issues & Developments. 2011. (Defense, Security & Strategies Ser.). 195.00 *(978-1-61209-271-3(3))* Nova Science Pubs., Inc.

Ali, Mohammad M. Centralised Demand Information Sharing in Supply Chains: A Consumer Centric Approach. 2011. (Illus.). 284p. pap. ***(978-3-639-28435-5(6))*** VDM Verlag Dr. Mueller e.K.

Ameri, Farhad. Supply Chain Standardization- an Ontological Approach. 2007. 216p. pap. *(978-3-8364-2120-1(8))* VDM Verlag Dr. Mueller e.K.

An, Chae & Fromm, Hansjörg, eds. Supply Chain Management on Demand: Strategies & Technologies, Applications. 2010. (ENG., Illus.). xviii, 331p. pap. 99.00 *(978-3-642-06373-2(X)*, 364206373X) Springer.

Anderson, Roger N., et al. Computer-Aided Lean Management for the Energy Industry. 2008. (Illus.). 245p. 89.00 *(978-1-59370-157-4(8))* PennWell Corp.

Arkes, Jeremy & Chenoweth, Mary E. Estimating the Benefits of the Air Force Purchasing & Supply Chain Management Initiative. 2007. 70p. pap. 21.00 *(978-0-8330-4188-3(6)*, mg-584) RAND Corp., The.

Arlbjo, Jan, et al, eds. Supply Chain Management: Business Operations in India. 2010. 169p. pap. 20.25 *(978-87-7674-484-7(1))* Univ. Pr. of Southern Denmark DNK. Dist: International Specialized Bk. Services.

Arlbjo, Jan & De Haas, Henning, eds. Supply Chain Management: Brazil as an Emergent Economy. 2011. (Illus.). 146p. pap. 29.00 ***(978-87-7674-567-7(8))*** Univ. Pr. of Southern Denmark DNK. Dist: International Specialized Bk. Services.

Arvis, Jean Francois, et al. The Cost of Being Landlocked: Logistics Costs & Supply Chain Reliability. 2010. (Directions in Development Ser.). (ENG., Illus.). 120p. pap. 25.00 *(978-0-8213-8408-4(2)*, 9780821384084) World Bank Pubns.

ASEAN Secretariat, et al. Trusting Trade & the Private Sector for Food Security in Southeast Asia. 2011. (Directions in Development Ser.). (ENG., Illus.). 286p. pap. 35.00 *(978-0-8213-8626-2(3)*, 9780821386262) World Bank Pubns.

ASEAN, Secretariat Staff, contrib. by. Trusting Trade & the Private Sector for Food Security in Southeast Asia. 2011. 400p. ***(978-0-8213-8648-4(4))*** World Bank Pubns.

Asian Development Bank Staff & International Food Policy Research Institute Staff, contrib. by. High-Value Crops & Marketing: Strategic Options for Development in Uttarakhand. 2010. (ENG., Illus.). 132p. pap. 49.95 *(978-81-7188-758-3(9))* Academic Foundation IND. Dist: Independent Pubs. Group.

Assessing the Resiliency of the Nation's Supply Chain: Hearing Before the Subcommittee on Border, Maritime, & Global Counterterrorism of the Committee on Homeland Security, House of Representatives, One Hundred Tenth Congress, Second Session, May 7, 2008. 2008. iii, 41p. *(978-0-16-082100-4(2)*, 552-070-38247-0) United States Government Printing Office.

Ayers, James B. Supply Chain Project Management. Second Edition: A Structured Collaborative & Measurable Approach. 2nd rev. ed. 2009. (ENG., Illus.). 430p. 87.95 *(978-1-4200-8392-7(9)*, CRC Press) Taylor & Francis Group GBR. Dist: Taylor & Francis Group.

Ayers, James B. & Odegaard, Mary Ann. Retail Supply Chain Management. 2007. (ENG., Illus.). 448p. 99.95 *(978-0-8493-9052-4(4)*, AU9052) Auerbach Pubs., Inc.

Ballou. Business LogisticsSupply Chain Managemen. 2006. pap. 13.95 *(978-1-4288-0775-4(6))* Cram101 Inc

Baluch, Issa & Edwards, Charles H. W. Transport Logistics: The Wheel of Commerce. 2010. 340p. 50.00 *(978-1-57197-508-9(X)*, Ivy House Publishing Group) Pentland Pr., Inc.

Bansal, Sam & Bansal. Technology Scorecards: Aligning IT Investments with Business Performance. 2009. (ENG., Illus.). 336p. 49.95 *(978-0-470-46456-4(9)*, Wiley) Wiley, John & Sons, Inc.

Bartholdi Iii John J Staff & Goldsman, Dave. Humanitarian Logistics & Supply Chains: Case Studies & Research Issues. 2012. (Integrated Supply Chain Management Ser.). (ENG., Illus.). 288p. 89.95 *(978-1-4200-4290-0(4))* Auerbach Pubs., Inc.

Barthorpe, Stephen, et al. Managing Construction Logistics. 2010. (ENG., Illus.). 304p. pap. 84.99 *(978-1-4051-5124-5(2)*, Wiley-Blackwell) Wiley, John & Sons, Inc.

Basu, Ron. Managing Project Supply Chains' 2011. (Advances in Project Management Ser.). (Illus.). 168p. pap. 49.95 ***(978-1-4094-2515-1(0)***, Gower Publishing Co., Ltd.) Ashgate Publishing, Ltd. GBR. Dist: Ashgate Publishing Co.

Belt, Bill. Five Basic Principles of Production & Supply Chain Management. 2009. 160p. 29.99 *(978-1-4415-0035-9(9))*; pap. 19.99 *(978-1-4415-0034-2(0))* Xlibris Corp.

Benton, W. C., et al. Construction Purchasing & Supply Chain Management. 2009. (ENG., Illus.). 266p. 80.00 *(978-0-07-154885-4(8)*, 0071548858) McGraw-Hill Professional Publishing.

Bertazzi, Luca, et al. Innovations in Distribution Logistics. Bertazzi, Luca et al, eds. 2009. (Lecture Notes in Economics & Mathematical Systems Ser.). (ENG., Illus.). x, 281p. pap. 109.00 *(978-3-540-92943-7(6))* Springer.

Beste, Teresa. Greening the Supply Chain in Public Procurement. 2008. 60p. pap. *(978-3-8364-8901-0(5))* VDM Verlag Dr. Mueller e.K.

Bevilacqua, Maurizio, et al. Design for Environment as a Tool for the Development of a Sustainable Supply Chain. 2012. (ENG., Illus.). x, 373p. 179.00 ***(978-1-4471-2460-3(X)***, 144712460X) Springer.

Bian, Wenliang. Wu Liu Xin Xi Wang Luo: Gou Jian Yu Yun Zuo = Logistics Information Network: Establishment & Operation. 2008. (CHI., Illus.). 235p. *(978-7-5097-0273-4(9))* China Social Science Documentation Publishing Hse.

Binder, Mario & Clegg, Ben, eds. Sustainable Supplier Management in the Automotive Industry: Leading the 3rd Revolution through Collaboration. 2010. (Transportation Issues, Policies & R&D Ser.). 158p. pap. 38.70 *(978-1-61668-675-8(8))* Nova Science Pubs., Inc.

Blanchard, David. Supply Chain Management Best Practices. 2nd ed. 2010. (ENG., Illus.). 304p. 60.00 *(978-0-470-53188-4(6)*, Wiley) Wiley, John & Sons, Inc.

Bolstorff, Peter & Rosenbaum, Robert. Supply Chain Excellence: A Handbook for Dramatic Improvement Using the SCOR Model, 1 vol. 3rd ed. 2011. (ENG., Illus.). 304p. 45.00 ***(978-0-8144-1771-3(X))*** Amacom.

Bonacich, Edna & Wilson, Jake B. Getting the Goods: Ports, Labor, & the Logistics Revolution. 2008. 336p. 75.50 *(978-0-8014-4572-9(8))*; 273p. per. 24.95 *(978-0-8014-7425-5(6))* Cornell Univ. Pr.

Bookbinder, James H., ed. Global Logistics. 2011. (International Series in Operations Research & Management Science Ser.). 300p. 139.00 ***(978-1-4419-6131-0(3)***, 1441961313) Springer.

Boomsma, Marije J. Sustainable Procurement from Developing Countries: Practices & Challenges for Business & Support Agencies. 2009. (Bulletins of the Royal Tropical Institute Ser.). 64p. pap. 35.00 *(978-90-6832-745-8(3))* Royal Tropical Institute Pr. (KIT (Koninklijk Instituut voor de Tropen) NLD. Dist: Stylus Publishing, LLC.

Boone, Tonya, et al, eds. Sustainable Supply Chains: Models, Methods, & Public Policy Implications. 2011. (International Series in Operations Research & Management Science Ser.). (ENG.). 480p. 179.00 *(978-1-4419-6104-4(6)*, 1441961046) Springer.

Booth, Caroline. Strategic Procurement: Organising Suppliers & Supply Chains for Competitive Advantage. 2010. (ENG., Illus.). 192p. pap. 39.95 *(978-0-7494-6022-8(9))* Kogan Page, Ltd. GBR. Dist: Ingram Pub. Services.

Böse, Jürgen W., et al, eds. Computational Logistics: Second International Conference, ICCL 2011, Hamburg, Germany, September 19-22, 2011, Proceedings. 2011. (Lecture Notes in Computer Science / Theoretical Computer Science & General Issues Ser.). (ENG., Illus.). xi, 371p. pap. 83.00 ***(978-3-642-24263-2(4)***, 3642242634) Springer.

Botta-Genoulaz, Valérie, et al. Supply Chain Performance: Collaboration, Alignment, & Coordination. 2010. (Iste Ser.: 497). (ENG., Illus.). xxii, 369p. 158.00 *(978-1-84821-219-0(4)*, Wiley-ISTE) Wiley, John & Sons, Inc.

Bourlakis, Michael, et al, eds. Intelligent Agrifood Chains & Networks. 2011. (ENG., Illus.). 312p. 209.95 *(978-1-4051-8299-7(7)*, Wiley-Blackwell) Wiley, John & Sons, Inc.

Bowersox and Cl, Cooper. Supply Chain Logistics Management. 2006. pap. 15.95 *(978-1-4288-0559-0(1))* Cram101 Inc.

Bowersox, Donald, et al. Supply Chain Logistics Management. 3rd ed. 2009. (ENG., Illus.). 480p. (C). 211.67 *(978-0-07-337787-2(2)*, 0073377872, McGraw-Hill/Irwin) McGraw-Hill Higher Education.

Bowersox, Donald, et al. Supply Chain Logistics Management. 4th ed. 2012. (ENG., Illus.). 496p. (C). 211.67 ***(978-0-07-802405-4(6)***, 0078024056, McGraw-Hill/Irwin) McGraw-Hill Higher Education.

Bowersox, Donald J. & LaHowchic, Nicholas J. Start Pulling Your Chain: Leading Responsive Supply Chain Tranformation. 2008. (ENG., Illus.). 360p. 49.95 *(978-0-9800896-0-8(3))* OGI Enterprises LLC.

Boyer, Kenneth Karel & Verma, Rohit. Operations & Supply Chain Management for the 21st Century. 2009. (Available Titles CengageNOW Ser.). (ENG., Illus.). 720p. (C). 164.95 *(978-0-618-74933-1(0)*, South-Western) Cengage South-Western.

Bozarth, Cecil & Handfield, Robert B. Introduction to Operations & Supply Chain Management. 3rd rev. ed. 2011. (ENG., Illus.). 512p. (C). 200.00 ***(978-0-13-274732-5(4)***, Prentice Hall) Prentice Hall PTR.

Bozarth, Cecil C. & Handfield, Robert B. Introduction to Operations & Supply Chain Management. 2007. pap. incl. cd-rom *(978-0-13-600041-9(X))* Pearson Education Canada.

Bozarth, Handfield. Introduction to Operations & Supply Ch. 2006. (Illus.). 175p. pap. 11.95 *(978-1-4288-1277-2(6))* Cram101 Inc.

Branch, Alan. Global Supply Chain Management & International Logistics. 2008. (ENG., Illus.). 192p. (C). pap. 65.95 *(978-0-415-39845-9(2))* Routledge.

Branch, Alan E. & Branch, Alan. Global Supply Chain Management & International Logistics. 2008. (Illus.). XIV, 178p. 170.00 *(978-0-415-39844-2(4))* Routledge.

B

Brandimarte, Paolo & Zotteri, Giulio. Introduction to Distribution Logistics. 2007. (Statistics in Practice Ser.: 21). (ENG., Illus.). 587p. 140.00 *(978-0-471-75044-4(1)*, Wiley-Interscience) Wiley, John & Sons, Inc.

Brown, Alan. Enterprise Software Delivery: Bringing Agility & Efficiency to the Global Software Supply Chain. 2012. (ENG.). 352p. pap. 39.99 ***(978-0-321-80301-6(9))*** Addison Wesley Professional.

Brown, George F., Jr. & Pope, Atlee Valentine. CoDestiny: Overcome Your Growth Challenges by Helping Your Customers Overcome Theirs. 2010. (Illus.). 264p. 23.95 *(978-1-60832-053-0(7))* Greenleaf Book Group.

Burges, Dan. Cargo Theft, Loss Prevention, & Supply Chain Security. 2012. (ENG.). 400p. 74.95 ***(978-0-12-416007-1(7)***, Butterworth-Heinemann) Elsevier Science & Technology Bks.

Burritt, Roger, et al, eds. Environmental Management Accounting & Supply Chain Management. 2011. (Eco-Efficiency in Industry & Science Ser.). (ENG., Illus.). xxi, 376p. 209.00 *(978-94-007-1389-5(4)*, 9400713894) Springer.

Burt, David, et al. Proactive Purchasing in the Supply Chain: the Key to World-Class Procurement. 2011. (ENG., Illus.). 784p. 75.00 ***(978-0-07-177061-3(5)***, 0071770615) McGraw-Hill Professional Publishing.

Cagliano, Anna Corinna. Understanding Supply Chain Complexity. 2010. 292p. pap. *(978-3-639-24435-9(4))* VDM Verlag Dr. Mueller e.K.

Camerinelli, Enrico. Measuring the Value of Supply Chain: Linking Financial Decisions & Supply Chain Performance. 2009. (Illus.). 236p. 124.95 *(978-0-566-08794-3(4)*, Gower Publishing Co., Ltd.) Ashgate Publishing, Ltd. GBR. Dist: Ashgate Publishing Co.

Campuzano, Francisco & Mula, Josefa. Supply Chain Simulation: A System Dynamics Approach for Improving Performance. 2011. (ENG., Illus.). vii, 106p. 129.00 *(978-0-85729-718-1(X)*, 085729718X) Springer.

Caramia, Massimiliano & Dell'Olmo, Paolo. Multi-Objective Management in Freight Logistics: Increasing Capacity, Service Level & Safety with Optimization Algorithms. 2008. (ENG., Illus.). xvi, 187p. 159.00 *(978-1-84800-381-1(1)*, 1848003811) Springer.

Carter, Joseph R. & Choi, Thomas Y. Foundation of Supply Management. 2008. (Illus.). xxiv, 354p. *(978-0-9815770-2-9(4))* Institute for Supply Management.

Carter, M. Brian, et al. SAP Extended Warehouse Management: Processes, Functionality, & Configuration. 2010. (Illus.). 550p. 79.95 *(978-1-59229-304-9(2)*, SAP PR.) Galileo Pr., Inc.

catalbas, sevtap & Catalbas, Sevtap. Supply Chain Management. 2011. 100p. pap. ***(978-3-8443-9231-9(9))*** Lambert Academic Publishing.

CER Publishing, ed. China Logistics Directory 2007/2008. 2007. 804p. pap. 57.50 *(978-988-99633-7-8(X))* China Economic Review Publishing HKG. Dist: Trans-Atlantic Pubns., Inc.

Cetinkaya, Balkan, et al. Sustainable Supply Chain Management: Practical Ideas for Moving Towards Best Practice. 2011. (ENG., Illus.). xviii, 283p. pap. 69.95 *(978-3-642-12022-0(9)*, 3642120229) Springer.

Chaib-draa, Brahim & Müller, Jëorg, eds. Multiagent-Based Supply Chain Management. 2006. (Studies in Computational Intelligence Ser.). (Illus.). xix, 450p. 269.00 *(978-3-540-33875-8(6)*, 3540338756) Springer.

Chaib-Draa, Brahim & Müller, Jörg P., eds. Multiagent based Supply Chain Management. 2012. (Studies in Computational Intelligence Ser.). (ENG., Illus.). 472p. pap. 269.00 *(978-3-642-07043-3(4)*, 3642070434) Springer.

Chandra, Charu & Grabis, Janis. Supply Chain Configuration: Concepts, Solutions, & Applications. (ENG., Illus.). xx, 348p. 2010. pap. 169.00 *(978-1-4419-3778-0(1)*, 1441937781) 2007. 169.00 *(978-0-387-25190-5(1)*, 0387251901) Springer.

Chaovalitwongse, Wanpracha, et al, eds. Optimization & Logistics Challenges in the Enterprise. 2009. (Springer Optimization & Its Applications Ser.). (ENG., Illus.). xvi, 432p. 139.00 *(978-0-387-88616-9(8)*, 0387886168) Springer.

Cheng, T. C. E. Postponement Strategies in Supply Chain Management. 2010. (Illus.). xviii, 166p. E-Book ***(978-1-4419-5837-2(1))*** Springer.

Cheng, T. C. Edwin & Choi, Tsan-Ming, eds. Innovative Quick Response Programs in Logistics & Supply Chain Management. 2010. (International Handbooks on Information Systems Ser.). (ENG., Illus.). xv, 468p. 269.00 *(978-3-642-04312-3(7)*, 3642043127) Springer.

Cheng, T. C. Edwin, et al. Postponement Strategies in Supply Chain Management. 2010. (International Series in Operations Research & Management Science Ser.). (ENG., Illus.). xviii, 166p. 159.00 *(978-1-4419-5836-5(3)*, 1441958363) Springer.

Chew, Ek Peng, et al. Advances in Maritime Logistics & Supply Chain Systems. 2011. 332p. 98.00 ***(978-981-4329-85-9(1))*** World Scientific Publishing Co., Inc.

Choi, Tsan-Ming. Fashion Supply Chain Management: Industry & Business Analysis. 2011. (Illus.). xix, 392p. ***(978-1-60960-758-6(9))*** IGI Global.

Choi, Tsan-Ming, ed. Fashion Supply Chain Management: Industry & Business Analysis. 2011. 373p. 195.00 *(978-1-60960-756-2(2)*, Business Science Reference) IGI Global.

Choi, Tsan-Ming & Cheng, T. C. Edwin, eds. Supply Chain Coordination under Uncertainty. 2011. (International Handbooks on Information Systems Ser.). (ENG., Illus.). xiv, 652p. 189.00 *(978-3-642-19256-2(4)*, 3642192564) Springer.

Christopher, Martin, et al. Humanitarian Logistics: Meeting the Challenge of Preparing for & Responding to Disasters. 2011. (ENG., Illus.). 298p. pap. 70.00 *(978-0-7494-6246-8(9))* Kogan Page, Ltd. GBR. Dist: Ingram Pub. Services.

Christou, Ioannis T. Quantitative Methods in Supply Chain Management: Models & Algorithms. 2011. (ENG., Illus.). xiv, 397p. 179.00 *(978-0-85729-765-5(1)*, 0857297651) Springer.

Cimorelli, Stephen. Kanban for the Supply Chain: Fundamental Practices for Manufacturing Management. 2nd rev. ed. 2012. (ENG., Illus.). 175p. pap. 59.95 ***(978-1-4398-9549-8(X))*** Productivity Pr.

Coff, Christian, et al, eds. Ethical Traceability & Communicating Food. 2010. (International Library of Environmental, Agricultural & Food Ethics Ser.). xxvi, 318p. pap. 189.00 *(978-90-481-7900-8(9)*, 9048179009) Springer.

Cole, Ivan, et al. Microsoft Dynamics Ax 2012. 2013. (Unleashed Ser.). (ENG.). 632p. pap. 59.99 *(978-0-672-33548-8(4))* Sams.

Collier, David A. & Evans, James R. OM. 2009. (Illus.). viii, 371p. *(978-0-324-66256-6(4))*; *(978-0-324-66295-5(5))*; *(978-0-324-66293-1(9))* Cengage South-Western.

—Operations Management: Goods, Services & Value Chains. 2nd ed. 2007. (Illus.). xxviii, 830p. *(978-0-324-18470-9(0))* Cengage South-Western.

Collier, James & Evans. Ie Operations Management Goods, Services & Value Chains. 2nd ed. 2007. (Illus.). xxviii, 830p. *(978-0-324-36076-9(2))* Cengage South-Western.

Commonwealth Secretariat Staff, contrib. by. Potential Supply Chains in the Textiles & Clothing Sector in South Asia: An Exploratory Study. 2012. (ENG.). 200p. pap. 24.95 ***(978-1-84929-076-0(8))*** Commonwealth Secretariat GBR. Dist: Stylus Publishing, LLC.

Cook, Thomas A. Global Sourcing Logistics: How to Manage Risk & Gain Competitive Advantage in a Worldwide Marketplace. 2006. (ENG., Illus.). 464p. 69.95 *(978-0-8144-0892-6(3))* Amacom.

—Managing Global Supply Chains: Compliance, Security, & Dealing with Terrorism. 2008. (ENG., Illus.). 320p. 85.95 *(978-1-4200-6456-8(8))* Auerbach Pubs., Inc.

—Mastering Purchasing Management for Inbound Supply Chains. 2010. (ENG., Illus.). 417p. 79.95 *(978-1-4200-8619-5(7)*, CRC Press) Taylor & Francis Group GBR. Dist: Taylor & Francis Group.

Cooper, Kevin, et al. Lean Printing: Pathway to Success. 2007. (Illus.). per. 30.00 *(978-0-88362-586-5(5))* Printing Industries Pr.

Cordón, Carlos, et al. Strategic Supply Chain Management. 2012. (ENG., Illus.). 288p. (C). pap. 63.95 ***(978-0-415-59176-8(7))***; 160.00 ***(978-0-415-59175-1(9))*** Routledge.

Cox, Andrew, et al. Strategies for Supply Chains & Markets: Optimising Business Performance in the Food & Farming Industry. 2013. (ENG.). 256p. 79.95 *(978-0-230-54316-4(2))* Palgrave Macmillan.

Coyle & Bardi. Management of Business Logistics. 6th ed. 2009. *(978-0-314-20439-4(3))* West Publishing Co., College & Schl. Div.

Coyle, Bardi. Management of Business Logistics. 2006. pap. 12.95 *(978-1-4288-0652-8(0))* Cram101 Inc.

Coyle, John J., et al. Supply Chain Management: A Logistics Perspective. 8th ed. 2008. (ENG.). 736p. (C). 253.95 *(978-0-324-22433-7(8))* Cengage South-Western.

—Supply Chain Management: A Logistics Perspective. 9th ed. 2012. (ENG.). 736p. (C). 240.95 *(978-0-538-47919-6(1))* Cengage South-Western.

—Supply Chain Management: A Logistics Perspective (with Printed Access Card) 9th ed. 2011. 736p. (C). 216.95 *(978-0-538-47918-9(3))* Cengage South-Western.

—Transportation: A Supply Chain Perspective. 7th ed. 2010. (ENG., Illus.). 528p. (C). 255.95 *(978-0-324-78919-5(X))* Cengage South-Western.

Coyle, John Joseph, et al. Supply Chain Management: A Logistics Perspective. 8th ed. 2008. (ENG., Illus.). xxvii, 705p. (C). 66.95 *(978-0-324-59478-2(X))* Cengage South-Western.

Cram101 Textbook Reviews. Outlines & Highlights for Introduction to Distribution Logistics by Paolo Brandimarte, Isbn: 9780471750444. 2011. 100p. pap. 27.95 ***(978-1-4288-6807-6(0))*** Cram101 Inc.

—Outlines & Highlights for Supply Chain Science by Wallace J Hopp. 2011. 68p. pap. 27.95 ***(978-1-61905-635-0(6))*** Cram101 Inc.

Cram101 Textbook Reviews & Cram101 Textbook Reviews. Outlines & Highlights for Facility Logistics: Approaches & Solutions to Next Generation Challenges by Maher Lahmar (Editor) 2011. 66p. pap. 27.95 ***(978-1-61830-363-9(5))*** Cram101 Inc.

—Outlines & Highlights for Fundamentals of Production Logistics by Peter Nyhuis. 2011. 58p. pap. 26.95 ***(978-1-61830-715-6(0))*** Cram101 Inc.

—Outlines & Highlights for Logistics & Transportation by Raja G Kasilingam. 2011. 84p. pap. 27.95 ***(978-1-61830-352-3(X))*** Cram101 Inc.

—Outlines & Highlights for Quantitative Measurements for Logistics by Philip T Frohne, Isbn: 9780071494151. 2011. 56p. pap. 26.95 ***(978-1-61461-445-6(8))*** Cram101 Inc.

—Outlines & Highlights for Strategic Supply Management: Principles, theories & practice by Paul; Lamming Cousins. 2011. 80p. pap. 27.95 ***(978-1-61830-623-4(5))*** Cram101 Inc.

Cram101 Textbook Reviews Staff. Outlines & Highlights for Introduction to Operations & Supply Chain Management by Cecil Bozarth, Isbn: 9780131791039. 2009. 82p. pap. 27.95 *(978-1-4288-2467-6(7))* Cram101 Inc.

—Outlines & Highlights for Om 2008 by David Alan Collier, Isbn: 9780324662559. 2009. 80p. pap. 27.95 *(978-1-4288-4155-0(5))*; 112p. pap. 28.95 *(978-1-4288-8791-6(1))* Cram101 Inc.

—Outlines & Highlights for Operations Management by Andrew Greasley, Isbn: 9780470997611. 2009. 96p. pap. 27.95 *(978-1-4288-4210-6(1))* Cram101 Inc.

—Outlines & Highlights for Principles of Supply Chain Management by Joel D Wisner, Isbn: 9780324657913. 2009. 320p. pap. 33.95 *(978-1-4288-4135-2(0))*; 416p. pap. 35.95 *(978-1-4288-8846-3(2))* Cram101 Inc.

—Outlines & Highlights for Supply Chain Logistics Management by Donald Bowersox, Isbn: 9780072947885. 2009. 144p. pap. 29.95 *(978-1-4288-4176-5(8))*; 196p. pap. 30.95 *(978-1-4288-9045-9(9))* Cram101 Inc.

—Outlines & Highlights for Supply Chain Management: A Logistics Perspective by Cecil Bozarth, ISBN. 2009. 196p. pap. 30.95 *(978-1-4288-4164-2(4))*; 234p. pap. 31.95 *(978-1-4288-8753-4(9))* Cram101 Inc.

Crandall, Richard E., et al. Principles of Supply Chain Management. 2009. (Resource Management Ser.). (ENG., Illus.). 645p. (C). 96.95 *(978-1-4200-9107-6(7)*, CRC Press) Taylor & Francis Group GBR. Dist: Taylor & Francis Group.

Crespo Márquez, Adolfo. Dynamic Modelling for Supply Chain Management: Dealing with Front-End, Back-End & Integration Issues. 2010. (ENG., Illus.). xviii, 297p. 169.00 *(978-1-84882-680-9(X)*, 184882680X) Springer.

Cudney, Elizabeth A. & Kestle, Rodney. Implementing Lean Six Sigma Throughout the Supply Chain: The Comprehensive & Transparent Case Study. 2010. (ENG., Illus.). 280p. pap. 59.95 *(978-1-4398-2814-4(8))* Productivity Pr.

Daganzo, Carlos F. Logistics Systems Analysis. 4th ed. 2010. (ENG., Illus.). xviii, 296p. pap. 109.00 *(978-3-642-06294-0(6)*, 3642062946) Springer.

Dangelmaier, Wilhelm, et al, eds. Advanced Manufacturing & Sustainable Logistics: 8th International Heinz Nixdorf Symposium, IHNS 2010, Paderborn, Germany, April 21-22, 2010, Proceedings. 2010. (Lecture Notes in Business Information Processing Ser.). xii, 444p. pap. 99.00 *(978-3-642-12461-7(5)*, 3642124615) Springer.

D'Apice, Ciro, et al. Modeling, Simulation, & Optimization of Supply Chains: A Continuous Approach. 2010. (ENG.). 216p. pap. ***(978-0-89871-700-6(0))*** Society for Industrial and Applied Mathematics.

Datta, Partha Priya. Agent-based simulation for improving resillence of supply chains: A guide to manage uncertainty in supply chains. 2008. 456p. pap. *(978-3-639-10718-0(7))* VDM Verlag Dr. Mueller e.K.

David, Pierre A. & Stewart, Richard D. Instructor's Edition: International Logistics. 2nd ed. 2006. 414p. (C). pap. 59.95 *(978-0-7593-9143-7(2))* CENGAGE Learning Custom Publishing.

De Koster Staff. Managing Supply Chains Challenges & Opportunities. 2007. (Illus.). 248p. pap. 48.00 *(978-87-630-0178-6(0))* Copenhagen Business Schl. Pr. DNK. Dist: International Specialized Bk. Services.

Deepen, Jan M. Logistics Outsourcing Relationships: Measurement, Antecedents, & Effects of Logistics Outsourcing Performance. 2007. (Contributions to Management Science Ser.). (ENG., Illus.). xiv, 350p. pap. 169.00 *(978-3-7908-1916-8(6)*, 3790819166) Physica-Verlag DEU. Dist: Springer.

Dekker, Rommert, et al, eds. Reverse Logistics: Quantitative Models for Closed-Loop Supply Chains. 2010. (ENG., Illus.). viii, 436p. pap. 149.00 *(978-3-642-07380-9(8)*, 3642073808) Springer.

Dekkers, Rob, ed. Dispersed Manufacturing Networks: Challenges for Research & Practice. 2009. (ENG., Illus.). x, 257p. 159.00 *(978-1-84882-467-6(X)*, 184882467X) Springer.

Dickersbach, Jörg T. Service Parts Planning with Mysap SCM: Processes, Structures, & Functions. 2010. (ENG., Illus.). xii, 296p. pap. 64.95 *(978-3-642-06911-6(8)*, 3642069118) Springer.

Dickersbach, Jörg Thomas. Characteristic Based Planning with MySAP SCM: Scenarios, Processes, & Functions. 2010. (SAP Excellence Ser.). (Illus.). x, 161p. pap. 89.95 *(978-3-642-06516-3(3)*, 3642065163) Springer.

Dickersbach, Jorg Thomas. Service Parts Planning with mySAP SCM: Processes, Structures, & Functions. 2007. (ENG., Illus.). xii, 296p. 64.95 *(978-3-540-32650-2(2)*, 3540326502) Springer.

Dickersbach, Jörg Thomas. Supply Chain Management with APO: Structures, Modelling Approaches & Implementation of SAP SCM 2008. 3rd ed. 2009. (ENG., Illus.). xvi, 504p. 89.95 *(978-3-540-92941-3(X)*, 354092941X) Springer.

Disney, Stephen M. & Lambrecht, Marc R. On Replenishment Rules, Forecasting & the Bullwhip Effect in Supply Chains. 2008. (ENG.). 88p. pap. 70.00 net. *(978-1-60198-132-5(5))* Now Pubs.

Dolgui, Alexandre & Proth, Jean-Marie. Supply Chain Engineering: Useful Methods & Techniques. 2010. (ENG., Illus.). xx, 539p. 209.00 *(978-1-84996-016-8(X)*, 184996016X) Springer.

Doukidis, Georgios I. & Vrechopoulos, Adam P., eds. Consumer Driven Electronic Transformation: Applying New Technologies to Enthuse Consumers & Transform the Supply Chain. 2010. (ENG., Illus.). x, 250p. pap. 119.00 *(978-3-642-06149-3(4)*, 3642061494) Springer.

Drake, Matt. Global Supply Chain Management. 2011. 122p. pap. 29.95 ***(978-1-60649-276-5(4))*** Business Expert Pr.

Drechsel, Julia. Cooperative Lot Sizing Games in Supply Chains. 2010. (Lecture Notes in Economics & Mathematical Systems Ser.). (Illus.). xiv, 167p. pap. 109.00 *(978-3-642-13724-2(5)*, 3642137245) Springer.

Dubey, Jayashree & Sai Kumar, M. L., eds. Supply Chain Management. 2007. 310p. (C). 44.75 *(978-81-7708-142-8(X))* New Century Publications IND. Dist: International Specialized Bk. Services.

Dudek, Gregor. Collaborative Planning in Supply Chains: A Negotiation-Based Approach. 2nd ed. (ENG., Illus.). xiv, 234p. 2010. pap. 119.00 ***(978-3-642-10072-7(4)***, 3642100724) 2009. 119.00 *(978-3-540-92175-2(3)*, 3540921753) Springer.

Dwivedi, Ashish & Butcher, Tim, eds. Supply Chain Management & Knowledge Management: Integrating Critical Perspectives in Theory & Practice. 2008. (ENG., Illus.). 336p. 126.00 *(978-0-230-57343-7(6))* Palgrave Macmillan.

Dyckhoff, Harald, et al, eds. Supply Chain Management & Reverse Logistics. 2010. (ENG., Illus.). xviii, 426p. pap. 169.00 *(978-3-642-07346-5(8)*, 3642073468) Springer.

Emmett, Stuart. Excellence in Supply Chain Management. 2008. (Illus.). 218p. pap. *(978-1-903499-39-9(9))* Liverpool Academic Pr.

Emmett, Stuart & Sood, Vivek. Green Supply Chains: An Action Manifesto. 2010. (ENG., Illus.). 316p. 60.00 *(978-0-470-68941-7(2)*, Wiley) Wiley, John & Sons, Inc.

Enarsson. Future Logistics Challenges. 2006. (Illus.). 400p. pap. 64.00 *(978-87-630-0170-0(5))* Copenhagen Business Schl. Pr. DNK. Dist: International Specialized Bk. Services.

Engell, Sebastian, ed. Logistic Optimization of Chemical Production Processes. 2008. (ENG., Illus.). 298p. 340.00 *(978-3-527-30830-9(X)*, Wiley-VCH) Wiley, John & Sons, Inc.

Evangelista, Pietro, et al, eds. Supply Chain Innovation for Competing in Highly Dynamic Markets: Challenges & Solutions. 2011. 350p. 180.00 *(978-1-60960-585-8(3)*, Business Science Reference) IGI Global.

Eyob, Ephrem & Tetteh, Edem. Customer-Oriented Global Supply Chains: Concepts for Effective Management. 2012. ***(978-1-4666-0248-9(1))*** IGI Global.

Eyob, Ephrem & Tetteh, Edem, eds. Customer-Oriented Global Supply Chains: Concepts for Effective Management. 2012. 432p. 180.00 ***(978-1-4666-0246-5(5)***, Information Science Reference) IGI Global.

Fahimnia, Behnam. Planning & Optimisation of Complex Supply Chains. 2011. 304p. pap. ***(978-3-8443-1864-7(X))*** Lambert Academic Publishing.

Farahani, Reza, et al, eds. Logistics Operations & Management: Concepts & Models. 2011. (ENG.). 486p. 130.00 *(978-0-12-385202-1(1))* Elsevier Science & Technology Bks.

Fawcett, Stanley E., et al. Supply Chain Management: From Vision to Implementation. 2006. (ENG., Illus.). 600p. (C). 153.33 *(978-0-13-101504-3(4)*, Prentice Hall) Prentice Hall PTR.

Ferguson, Mark E. & Souza, Gilvan C., eds. Closed Loop Supply Chains: New Developments to Improve the Sustainability of Business Practices. 2010. (Supply Chain Integration Modeling, Optimization & Application Ser.). (ENG., Illus.). 257p. 79.95 *(978-1-4200-9525-8(0))* Auerbach Pubs., Inc.

Fernie, John & Sparks, Leigh. Logistics & Retail Management: Emerging Issues & New Challenges in the Retail Supply Chain. 3rd ed. 2009. (ENG., Illus.). 256p. 75.00 *(978-0-7494-5407-4(5))* Kogan Page, Ltd. GBR. Dist: Ingram Pub. Services.

Fink, Andreas & Rothlauf, Franz, eds. Advances in Computational Intelligence in Transport, Logistics, & Supply Chain Management. 2009. (Studies in Computational Intelligence Ser.). (Illus.). xii, 278p. 159.00 *(978-3-540-69024-5(7))* Springer.

Fisher, Marshall & Raman, Ananth. The New Science of Retailing: How Analytics are Transforming the Supply Chain & Improving Performance. 2010. (ENG., Illus.). 272p. 29.95 *(978-1-4221-1057-7(5))* Harvard Business Review Pr.

Flapper, Simme D. P., et al, eds. Managing Closed-Loop Supply Chains. 2010. (ENG., Illus.). xii, 214p. pap. 89.95 *(978-3-642-07381-6(6)*, 3642073816) Springer.

Flores, Erick & Jenkin, Tristan. Integrating Environmental Costs in Logistics Network Management. 2011. 144p. pap. ***(978-3-8383-8303-3(6))*** Lambert Academic Publishing.

Foti, Christopher & Chimni, Jessie. Demand Management with SAP. 2009. (Illus.). 398p. 69.95 *(978-1-59229-267-7(4)*, SAP PR.) Galileo Pr., Inc.

Franks, Steven M. Rare Earth Minerals: Policies & Issues. 2011. (Series: Earth Sciences in the 21st Century Ser.). 115.00 *(978-1-61122-310-1(5))* Nova Science Pubs., Inc.

Fung, Victor K., et al. Competing in a Flat World: Building Enterprises for a Borderless World. 2007. (ENG.). 272p. pap. 29.99 *(978-0-13-261818-2(4))* Wharton Schl. Publishing.

Garg, Miti & Gupta, Sumeet. Cases on Supply Chain & Distribution Management: Issues & Principles. 2011. ***(978-1-4666-0065-2(9))***; ***(978-1-4666-0067-6(5))***; E-Book ***(978-1-4666-0066-9(7))*** IGI Global.

Garrett, Jack & Shepard, Steven. Managing Supply Chain Technology: Bridging the Gap Between the Supply Chain & the Technology That Supports It. 2006. 444p. 149.95 *(978-1-59622-592-3(0))* Aspatore Bks.

Gassner, Stefan. Deriving Maintenance Strategies for Cooperative Alliances — A Value Chain Approach. 2009. 117p. pap. 82.95 *(978-1-4092-8773-5(4))* Lulu Enterprises Inc.

Gattorna, John. Dynamic Supply Chain Alignment: A New Business Model for Peak Performance in Enterprise Supply Chains Across All Geographies. 2009. (Illus.). 440p. 124.95 *(978-0-566-08822-3(3)*, Gower Publishing Co., Ltd.) Ashgate Publishing, Ltd. GBR. Dist: Ashgate Publishing Co.

—Dynamic Supply Chains: Delivering Value Through People. 2nd rev. ed. 2010. (Financial Times Ser.). (ENG., Illus.). 528p. (C). 59.99 *(978-0-273-73040-8(1))* FT Press.

Geunes, Joseph, et al. Applications of Supply Chain Management & E-Commerce Research. 2010. (Applied Optimization Ser.). (Illus.). x, 478p. pap. 179.00 *(978-1-4419-3623-3(8)*, 1441936238) Springer.

Geunes, Joseph. Demand Flexibility in Supply Chain Planning. 2012. (SpringerBriefs in Optimization Ser.). (ENG., Illus.). xiii, 90p. pap. 49.95 *(978-1-4419-9346-5(0)*, 1441993460) Springer.

Geunes, Joseph, et al, eds. Supply Chain Management: Models, Applications, & Research Directions: Models, Applications, & Research Directions. 2011. (Applied Optimization Ser.). (ENG.). 396p. pap. 259.00 *(978-1-4419-5211-0(X)*, 144195211X) Springer.

Geunes, Joseph & Pardalos, Panos M., eds. Supply Chain Optimization. 2010. (Applied Optimization Ser.). x, 413p. pap. 189.00 *(978-1-4419-3880-0(X)*, 144193880X) Springer.

Goetschalckx, Marc. Supply Chain Engineering. 2011. (International Series in Operations Research & Management Science Ser.). (ENG., Illus.). x, 682p. 129.00 *(978-1-4419-6511-0(4)*, 1441965114) Springer.

Golinska, Paulina, ed. EcoProduction & Logistics: Emerging Trends & Business Practices. 2012. (EcoProduction Ser.). (ENG., Illus.). x, 347p. 179.00 ***(978-3-642-23552-8(2)***, 3642235522) Springer.

Golinska, Paulina & Romano, Carlos Andres, eds. Environmental Issues in Supply Chain Management: New Trends & Applications. 2012. (EcoProduction. Environmental Issues in Logistics & Manufacturing Ser.). (ENG., Illus.). xi, 307p. 179.00 ***(978-3-642-23561-0(1)***, 3642235611) Springer.

Gonçalves, Patricia. Interfaces Between End-Users in Agile & Virtual Enterprises. 2009. 336p. pap. *(978-3-639-18780-9(6))* VDM Verlag Dr. Mueller e.K.

Gorbett, Dallas W. The Inventory Book. 2009. 150p. pap. 13.95 *(978-1-936107-20-9(1))* Mill City Pr., Inc.

Gray, Deborah M. How to Import Wine: An Insider's Guide. 2011. (ENG., Illus.). 288p. pap. 29.95 *(978-1-934259-61-0(6))* Wine Appreciation Guild, Ltd.

Greasley, Andrew. Operations Management. 2007. (SAGE Course Companions Ser.). (Illus.). 176p. (C). per. 31.00 *(978-1-4129-1883-1(9)*, B18824P) SAGE Pubns., Ltd. GBR. Dist: SAGE Pubns., Inc.

Greasley, Andrew & Greasley. Operations Management, 2 vols. 2nd ed. 2009. (ENG., Illus.). 584p. pap. 91.95 *(978-0-470-99761-1(3)*, Wiley) Wiley, John & Sons, Inc.

Groot, Martijn. Managing Financial Information in the Trade Lifecycle: A Concise Atlas of Financial Instruments & Processes. 2008. (Elsevier & Mondo Visione World Capital Markets Ser.). (ENG., Illus.). 288p. 76.95 *(978-0-12-374289-6(7)*, Academic Pr.) Elsevier Science & Technology Bks.

Groothedde, Bas. Logistics Network Design & Collaboration: Design, Theory, & Practice. 2009. 250p. 129.00 *(978-3-7908-2047-8(4))* Physica-Verlag DEU. Dist: Springer.

Günther, Hans-Otto & Beek, Paul van, eds. Advanced Planning & Scheduling Solutions in Process Industry. 2010. (GOR-Publications). (ENG., Illus.). vi, 426p. pap. 219.00 *(978-3-642-05528-7(1)*, 3642055281) Springer.

Günther, Hans-Otto & Kim, Kap Hwan, eds. Container Terminals & Automated Transport Systems: Logistics Control Issues & Quantitative Decision Support. 2010. (ENG.). xv, 374p. pap. 189.00 *(978-3-642-06102-8(8)*, 3642061028) Springer.

Günther, Oliver P., et al. RFID in Manufacturing. 2010. (ENG., Illus.). xvi, 163p. pap. 59.95 *(978-3-642-09531-3(3)*, 3642095313) Springer.

Gupta, Anil Kumar. Quality Assurance for Dynamics Ax-Based Erp Solutions. 2008. 168p. per. *(978-1-84719-291-2(2))* Packt Publishing, Ltd.

Gupta, Surendra M., et al. Strategic Planning Models for Reverse & Closed-Loop Supply Chains. 2008. (ENG., Illus.). 292p. 85.95 *(978-1-4200-5478-1(3)*, CRC Press) Taylor & Francis Group GBR. Dist: Taylor & Francis Group.

Gurnani, Haresh, et al, eds. Supply Chain Disruptions: Theory & Practice of Managing Risk. 2011. (ENG., Illus.). x, 336p. 179.00 *(978-0-85729-777-8(5)*, 0857297775) Springer.

Gustafsson, Kerstin, et al. Retailing Logistics & Fresh Food Packaging: Managing Change in the Supply Chain. 2009. (ENG., Illus.). 224p. pap. 44.95 *(978-0-7494-5517-0(9))* Kogan Page, Ltd. GBR. Dist: Ingram Pub. Services.

Haasis, Hans-Dietrich, et al, eds. Dynamics in Logistics: First International Conference, LDIC 2007 Bremen, Germany, August 2007 Proceedings. 2008. (ENG., Illus.). xxii, 465p. 159.00 *(978-3-540-76861-6(0)*, 3540768610) Springer.

—Dynamics in Logistics: First International Conference, LDIC 2007, Bremen, Germany, August 2007. Proceedings. 2010. (ENG., Illus.). xxii, 465p. pap. 159.00 *(978-3-642-09555-9(0)*, 3642095550) Springer.

Haksoz, Cagri, et al, eds. Managing Supply Chains on the Silk Road: Strategy, Performance, & Risk. 2011. (ENG., Illus.). 323p. 69.95 *(978-1-4398-6720-4(8)*, CRC Press) Taylor & Francis Group GBR. Dist: Taylor & Francis Group.

Halldórsson, Árni, et al. Northern Lights in Logistics & Supply Chain Management. Arlbjorn, Jan, ed. 2008. 285p. pap. 45.00 *(978-87-630-0218-9(3))* Copenhagen Business Schl. Pr. DNK. Dist: International Specialized Bk. Services.

Hamilton, Scott. Managing Lean Manufacturing using Microsoft Dynamics AX 2009. 2009. 29.95 *(978-0-9792552-1-2(X))* Hamilton, Scott.

—Managing Your Supply Chain using Microsoft Dynamics AX 2009. 2008. 400p. pap. 39.95 *(978-0-9792552-2-9(8))* Hamilton, Scott.

Hamm, Steve. Bangalore Tiger: How Indian Tech Upstart Wipro Is Rewriting the Rules of Global Competition. 2006. (ENG., Illus.). 288p. 24.95 *(978-0-07-147478-8(1)*, 0071474781) McGraw-Hill Cos., The.

Handfield, Robert B. & Bozarth, Cecil C. Introduction to Operations & Supply Chain Management. 2nd ed. 2007. (ENG., Illus.). 600p. (C). 200.00 *(978-0-13-179103-9(6)*, Prentice Hall) Prentice Hall PTR.

Handfield, Robert B. & Nichols, Ernest L., Jr. Supply Chain Redesign: Transforming Supply Chains into Integrated Value Systems. 2008. (ENG.). 400p. pap. 41.99 *(978-0-7686-8221-2(5))* FT Press.

Hansen, Wolf-Ruediger & Gillert, Frank. RFID for the Optimization of Business Processes. 2008. (ENG., Illus.). 298p. 90.00 *(978-0-470-72422-4(6)*, Wiley) Wiley, John & Sons, Inc.

Harrington, Lisa H., et al. X-Treme Supply Chains: The New Science of Extreme Supply Chain Management. 2010. (ENG., Illus.). 312p. 200.00 *(978-0-415-87355-0(X))*; pap. 71.95 *(978-0-415-87356-7(8))* Routledge.

Harris, Chris, et al. Lean Supplier Development: Establishing Partnerships & True Costs Throughout the Supply Chain. 2010. (ENG., Illus.). 218p. 49.95 *(978-1-4398-1125-2(3))* Productivity Pr.

Harrison, Alan & Van Hoek, Remko. Logistics Management & Strategy: Competing Through the Supply Chain. 4th rev. ed. 2011. (ENG., Illus.). 384p. (C). pap. 160.00 *(978-0-273-73022-4(3)*, Prentice Hall) Prentice Hall PTR.

Harvard Business Review. Harvard Business Review on Managing Supply Chains. 2011. (ENG.). 240p. pap. 22.00 *(978-1-4221-6260-6(5))* Harvard Business Review Pr.

Hazen, J. Kenneth & Lynch, Clifford F. The Role of Transportation in the Supply Chain. 2008. (Illus.). 340p. 69.95 *(978-0-9744167-4-8(6))* Lynch, C.F. & Assocs.

Höhn, Michaela Isabel. Relational Supply Contracts: Optimal Concessions in Return Policies for Continuous Quality Improvements. 2009. (Lecture Notes in Economics & Mathematical Systems Ser.). (ENG., Illus.). xvi, 124p. pap. 109.00 *(978-3-642-02790-1(3)*, 3642027903) Springer.

Hellström, Daniel. Integrating Packaging & Logistics. 2008. 228p. pap. *(978-3-639-08083-4(2))* VDM Verlag Dr. Mueller e.K.

Hertel, Joachim, et al. Supply-Chain-Management und Warenwirtschaftssysteme im Handel. 2007. (Illus.). XII, 442p. 89.95 *(978-3-540-21916-3(1)*, 3540219161) Springer.

Higuchi, Toru & Troutt, Marvin. Life Cycle Management in Supply Chains: Identifying Innovations Through the Case of the VCR. 2008. (Illus.). 300+p. 99.95 *(978-1-59904-555-9(9)*, CyberTech Publishing) IGI Global.

Hill, Arthur V. The Encyclopedia of Operations Management: A Field Manual & Glossary of Operations Management Terms & Concepts. 2011. (FT Press Operations Management Ser.). (ENG.). 408p. pap. 49.99 ***(978-0-13-288370-2(8))*** FT Press.

Hines, Tony. Supply Chain Strategies. 2012. (ENG.). 400p. (C). pap. 72.95 *(978-0-415-68319-7(X))*; 160.00 *(978-0-415-68317-3(3))* Routledge.

Hofmann, Erik & Belin, Oliver. Supply Chain Finance Solutions: Relevance - Propositions - Market Value. 2011. (SpringerBriefs in Business Ser.). (ENG., Illus.). xiii, 85p. pap. 49.95 *(978-3-642-17565-7(1)*, 3642175651) Springer.

Hogendoorn, Roel & LearnWorks.nu. System Administration for Oracle E-Business Suite (Classroom Edition) 2007. 200p. pap. 59.50 *(978-1-4357-0079-6(1))* Lulu Enterprises Inc.

—System Administration for Oracle E-Business Suite (Personal Edition) 2007. 184p. pap. 47.51 *(978-1-4357-0075-8(9))* Lulu Enterprises Inc.

Horvá, et al. E-Procurement. 2009. 204p. pap. *(978-3-639-19226-1(5))* VDM Verlag Dr. Mueller e.K.

Huang, George. RFID-Enabled Real-Time Manufacturing. 2012. (ENG.). 400p. 145.00 *(978-0-470-90165-6(9)*, Wiley-Scrivener) Wiley, John & Sons, Inc.

Huang, George & Maropoulos, Paul G., eds. Proceedings of the 6th CIRP-Sponsored International Conference on Digital Enterprise Technology. 2009. (Advances in Intelligent & Soft Computing Ser.). (Illus.). xviii, 1800p. pap. 399.00 *(978-3-642-10429-9(0)*, 3642104290) Springer.

Hübner, Reinhard. Strategic Supply Chain Management in Process Industries: An Application to Specialty Chemicals Production Network Design. 2007. (Lecture Notes in Economics & Mathematical Systems Ser.). (Illus.). xii, 243p. pap. 129.00 *(978-3-540-72180-2(0))* Springer.

Hugos, Michael H. Essentials of Supply Chain Management. 3rd ed. 2011. (Essentials Ser.: 62). (ENG., Illus.). 348p. pap. 39.95 *(978-0-470-94218-5(5)*, Wiley) Wiley, John & Sons, Inc.

Hülsmann, Michael, et al, eds. Autonomous Cooperation & Control in Logistics: Contributions & Limitations - Theoretical & Practical Perspectives. 2011. (ENG., Illus.). viii, 350p. 179.00 *(978-3-642-19468-9(0)*, 3642194680) Springer.

Hülsmann, Michael & Windt, Katja, eds. Understanding Autonomous Cooperation & Control in Logistics: The Impact of Autonomy on Management, Information, Communication & Material Flow. 2010. (ENG., Illus.). xxviii, 417p. pap. 219.00 *(978-3-642-07996-2(2)*, 3642079962) Springer.

Husby, Paul. Fix Your Supply Chain: How to Create a Sustainable Lean Improvement Roadmap. 2009. (ENG., Illus.). 214p. 51.95 *(978-1-56327-381-0(0))* Productivity Pr.

IEEE Staff. 2007 International Symposium on Logistics & Industrial Informatics. 2007. pap. 224.00 *(978-1-4244-1440-6(7))* IEEE.

Ijioui, Raschid, et al, eds. Strategies & Tactics in Supply Chain Event Management. (ENG., Illus.). xii, 368p. 2010. pap. 89.95 *(978-3-642-09297-8(7)*, 3642092977) 2007. 89.95 *(978-3-540-73765-0(0)*, 3540737650) Springer.

Itcookbook, Www. Itcookbook. Com. Microsoft« Dynamics Ax« Interview Questions: Unofficial Microsoft Dynamics AX Axapta Certification Review. 2007. 196p. per. 54.95 *(978-1-60332-004-7(0))* Equity Pr.

Ivanov, Dmitry & Sokolov, B. V. Adaptive Supply Chain Management. 2010. (Illus.). xxxii, 269p. ***(978-1-84882-952-7(3))*** Springer.

Ivanov, Dmitry & Sokolov, Boris. Adaptive Supply Chain Management. 2009. (ENG., Illus.). xxxii, 269p. 169.00 *(978-1-84882-951-0(5)*, 1848829515) Springer.

Iyer, Ananth. Orchestrating Supply Chain Opportunities: Achieving Stretch Goals, Efficiently. 2011. 200p. pap. 27.95 *(978-1-60649-223-9(3))* Business Expert Pr.

Iyer, Ananth, et al. Toyota Supply Chain Management: A Strategic Approach to Toyota's Renowned System. 2009. (ENG., Illus.). 240p. 34.95 *(978-0-07-161549-5(0)*, 0071615490) McGraw-Hill Cos., The.

Jacoby, David. Guide to Supply Chain Management: How Getting It Right Boosts Corporate Performance. 2009. (Economist Ser.). (ENG.). 272p. 29.95 *(978-1-57660-345-1(8)*, Bloomberg Pr.) Wiley, John & Sons, Inc.

Jain, Ankit. Impact of Supply Uncertainty in Supply Chain. 2010. 84p. pap. *(978-3-8383-8878-6(X))* Lambert Academic Publishing.

Javaheri, Shirin. The Fundamentals of Low-Cost Country Sourcing. 2009. 134p. pap. *(978-3-639-17789-3(4))* VDM Verlag Dr. Mueller e.K.

Jin, Yue. Essays on Supply Chain Management - Integration, Information, & Customer. 2008. 72p. pap. *(978-3-639-02385-5(4))* VDM Verlag Dr. Mueller e.K.

Jodlbauer, Herbert, et al, eds. Modelling Value: Selected Papers of the 1st International Conference on Value Chain Management. 2012. (Contributions to Management Science Ser.). (ENG., Illus.). xxi, 418p. 189.00 ***(978-3-7908-2746-0(0)***, 3790827460) Physica-Verlag DEU. Dist: Springer.

Joint Transport Research Centre. Integration & Competition Between Transport & Logistics Businesses. 2010. (Illus.). 184p. pap. 91.00 *(978-92-821-0259-6(9))* Organization for Economic Cooperation & Development.

Józefowska, Joanna. Just-in-Time Scheduling: Models & Algorithms for Computer & Manufacturing Systems. 2007. (International Series in Operations Research & Management Science (eBooks) Ser.). (Illus.). 255p. 149.00 *(978-0-387-71717-3(X))* Springer.

Jozefowska, Joanna. Just-in-Time Scheduling: Models & Algorithms for Computer & Manufacturing Systems. 2010. (International Series in Operations Research & Management Science Ser.). (Illus.). xiv, 258p. pap. 149.00 *(978-1-4419-4403-0(6)*, 1441944036) Springer.

Jung, Hosang, et al, eds. Trends in Supply Chain Design & Management: Technologies & Methodologies. (Springer Series in Advanced Manufacturing Ser.). (Illus.). 2010. xiv, 451p. pap. 199.00 *(978-1-84996-627-6(3)*, 1849966273) 2007. XIV, 451p. 199.00 *(978-1-84628-606-3(9)*, 1846286069) Springer.

Kannegiesser, Matthias. Value Chain Management in the Chemical Industry: Global Value Chain Planning of Commodities. (Contributions to Management Science Ser.). (ENG., Illus.). xvi, 270p. 2010. pap. 139.00 *(978-3-7908-2550-3(6)*, 3790825506) 2008. 139.00 *(978-3-7908-2031-7(8)*, 3790820318) Physica-Verlag DEU. Dist: Springer.

Kappauf, Jens, et al. Logistic Core Operations with SAP: Inventory Management, Warehousing, Transportation, & Compliance. 2012. (ENG., Illus.). 304p. 89.95 *(978-3-642-18201-3(1)*, 3642182011) Springer.

—Logistic Core Operations with SAP: Procurement, Production & Distribution Logistics. 2011. (ENG., Illus.). viii, 264p. 89.95 *(978-3-642-18203-7(8)*, 3642182038) Springer.

Katz, Norman. Detecting & Reducing Supply Chain Fraud. 2012. 200p. 119.95 ***(978-1-4094-0732-4(2)***, Gower Publishing Co., Ltd.) Ashgate Publishing, Ltd. GBR. Dist: Ashgate Publishing Co.

Katzorke, Michael & Lee, William B. Leading Effective Supply Chain Transformation. 2010. 280p. *(978-1-932159-91-2(6))* Ross, J. Publishing, Inc.

Kenaroglu, Bahar. Erp Systems Selection Process. 2009. 108p. pap. *(978-3-639-09964-5(8))* VDM Verlag Dr. Mueller e.K.

Kerber, Bill & Dreckshage, Brian J. Lean Supply Chain Management Essentials: A Framework for Materials Managers. 2011. (ENG., Illus.). 274p. pap. 59.95 *(978-1-4398-4082-5(2)*, CRC Press) Taylor & Francis Group GBR. Dist: Taylor & Francis Group.

Khan, Omera & Zsidisin, George A. Handbook for Supply Chain Risk Management. Khan, Dr Omera & Zsidisin, George, eds. 2011. (Illus.). 360p. ***(978-1-60427-038-9(1))*** Ross, J. Publishing, Inc.

Kidanu, Embaye, et al. Supply Chain from Gate to Plate. 2011. 160p. pap. ***(978-3-8443-2020-6(2))*** Lambert Academic Publishing.

Kiesel, Jens. Dictionary of Logistics & Supply Chain Management / Fachwörterbuch Logistik und Supply Chain Management: English - German / Deutsch - Englisch. 2009. (ENG.). 75.00 *(978-3-89578-326-5(9)*, Wiley-VCH) Wiley, John & Sons, Inc.

—Dictionary of Logistics & Supply Chain Management / Wörterbuch Logistik und Supply Chain Management: English - German / Deutsch - Englisch. 16th ed. 2010. (ENG & GER., Illus.). 739p. pap. 60.00 *(978-3-89578-365-4(X)*, Wiley-VCH) Wiley, John & Sons, Inc.

Kikuchi, Toru. Time Zones Communications Networks & International Trade. 2011. (Routledge Studies in the Modern World Economy Ser.). (ENG., Illus.). 232p. (C). 152.00 *(978-0-415-59312-0(3))* Routledge.

Kildow, Betty A. A Supply Chain Management Guide to Business Continuity, 1 vol. 2011. (ENG.). 272p. 35.00 *(978-0-8144-1645-7(4))* Amacom.

Killingsworth, William R. Design, Analysis & Optimization of Supply Chains: A System Dynamics Approach. 2011. (Illus.). 228p. pap. 29.95 *(978-1-60649-251-2(9))* Business Expert Pr.

Klaus, Peter & Müller, Stefanie, eds. The Roots of Logistics: A Reader of Classical Contributions to the History & Conceptual Foundations of the Science of Logistics. 2012. (ENG., Illus.). ix, 427p. 179.00 ***(978-3-642-27921-8(X)***, 364227921X) Springer.

Kletti, Wolfhard, et al. RFID in Manufacturing. 2008. (ENG., Illus.). xvi, 163p. 59.95 *(978-3-540-76453-3(4)*, 3540764534) Springer London, Ltd. GBR. Dist: Springer.

Kleyner, Andre. Determining Optimal Reliability Targets. 2010. 216p. pap. *(978-3-8383-4062-3(0))* Lambert Academic Publishing.

Knolmayer, Gerhard F., et al. Supply Chain Management Based on SAP Systems: Architecture & Planning Processes. 2008. (SAP Excellence Ser.). (Illus.). xi, 207p. 69.95 *(978-3-540-68737-5(8))* Springer.

—Supply Chain Management Based on SAP Systems: Order Management in Manufacturing Companies. 2010. (SAP Excellence Ser.). (Illus.). xi, 244p. pap. 79.95 *(978-3-642-08625-0(X)*, 364208625X) Springer.

Koch, Daniel. Supply Chain Fitness: Bewertung der Supply Chain Management-Kompetenz mittelständischer Unternehmen. 2010. 116p. pap. *(978-3-639-02528-6(8))* VDM Verlag Dr. Mueller e.K.

Kogan, Konstantin & Tapiero, Charles S. Supply Chain Games: Operations Management & Risk Valuation. 2007. (International Series in Operations Research & Management Science Ser.). (Illus.). 510p. 179.00 *(978-0-387-72775-2(2))* Springer.

—Supply Chain Games: Operations Management & Risk Valuation: Operations Management & Risk Valuation. 2010. (International Series in Operations Research & Management Science Ser.). (Illus.). xii, 513p. pap. 179.00 *(978-1-4419-4448-1(6)*, 1441944486) Springer.

Kolmogorovs, Vadims. Logistics Outsourcing- a Way to Increase Efficiency. 2007. 76p. per. *(978-3-8364-0554-6(7))* VDM Verlag Dr. Mueller e.K.

Koop, Reinder & Muris, Ester. Successfully Implementing Microsoft Dynamics: By Using the Regatta Approach for Microsoft Dynamics. 2010. (ENG., Illus.). x, 225p. pap. 69.95 *(978-3-642-09078-3(8)*, 3642090788) Springer.

Kosalka, Tomasz. CENTRALIZED AND DECENTRALIZED DISTRIBUTION STORAGESYSTEMS: DECISION MAKING THROUGH THE SIMULATION OF CENTRALIZEDAND DECENTRALIZED DISTRIBUTION STORAGE SYSTEMS. 2008. 168p. pap. *(978-3-639-10620-6(2))* VDM Verlag Dr. Mueller e.K.

Kouvelis, Panos. The Structure of Global Supply Chains: The Design & Location of Sourcing, production & Distribution Facility Networks for Global Markets. 2008. (ENG.). 152p. pap. 99.00 net. *(978-1-60198-098-4(1))* Now Pubs.

Krajewski, Lee & Weiss, Howard J. Operations Management: Process & Value Chains. 8th rev. ed. 2009. (ENG., Illus.). xv, 728p. (C). cd-rom 6.67 ***(978-0-13-187305-6(9)***, Prentice Hall) Prentice Hall PTR.

Kreowski, Hans-Jorg, et al, eds. Dynamics in Logistics: Second International Conference, LDIC 2009, Bremen, Germany, August 2009. Proceedings. 2011. (ENG., Illus.). xiii, 500p. 259.00 *(978-3-642-11995-8(6)*, 3642119956) Springer.

Kruger, David & Ramphal, Roy. Operations Management. 2nd ed. 2009. (ENG., Illus.). 424p. pap. 50.00 *(978-0-19-598477-4(3))* Oxford Univ. Pr., Inc.

Kumar, Sameer, ed. Connective Technologies in the Supply Chain. 2007. (Supply Chain Integration Ser.). (ENG., Illus.). 296p. 89.95 *(978-1-4200-4349-5(8))* Auerbach Pubs., Inc.

Kumar, Sameer & Krob, William A. Managing Product Life Cycle in a Supply Chain: Context: A Prescription Based on Empirical Research. 2010. xii, 160p. pap. 129.00 *(978-1-4419-2007-2(2)*, 1441920072) Springer.

Kumar, Sameer & Meade David. Financial Models & Tools for Managing Lean Manufacturing. 2006. (Supply Chain Integration Modeling, Optimization & Applications Ser.: No. 1). (ENG., Illus.). 197p. 95.95 *(978-0-8493-9185-9(7))* Auerbach Pubs., Inc.

Kutlu, S. Fourth Party Logistics: Is It the Future of Supply Chain Outsourcing? 2007. 136p. per. *(978-1-84693-057-7(X))* Best Global Publishing Ltd.

Lai, Kee-Hung & Cheng, T. C. E. Just-in-Time Logistics. 2009. 206p. 114.95 *(978-0-566-08900-8(9)*, Gower Publishing Co., Ltd.) Ashgate Publishing, Ltd. GBR. Dist: Ashgate Publishing Co.

Lamb, Robert. Improving Your Bottom Line Through the Contact Center. 2010. 154p. pap. 14.98 *(978-0-557-46348-0(3))* Lulu Enterprises Inc.

Langabeer, James R. Health Care Operations Management: A Quantitative Approach to Business & Logistics. 2007. (Illus.). 438p. 115.95 *(978-0-7637-5051-0(4))* Jones & Bartlett Learning, LLC.

Langevin, Andre & Riopel, Diane, eds. Logistics Systems: Design & Optimization: Design & Optimization. 2010. (ENG., Illus.). xx, 388p. pap. 115.00 *(978-1-4419-3763-6(3)*, 1441937633) Springer.

Lawrence, Kenneth & Kleinman, Gary, eds. Applications of Management Science. 2012. (Applications of Management Science Ser.). 313p. ***(978-1-78052-100-8(6))*** Emerald Group Publishing Ltd.

Lawrence, Kenneth D., et al. The Supply Chain in Manufacturing, Distribution & Transportation: Modeling, Optimization, & Applications. 2010. (ENG., Illus.). 330p. (C). 94.95 *(978-1-4200-7945-6(X))* Auerbach Pubs., Inc.

Ledlow, Gerald R., et al. Optimize Your Healthcare Supply Chain Performance: A Strategic Approach. 2007. 70p. 46.00 *(978-1-56793-950-7(3))* Health Administration Pr.

Lee, Hau L. & Lee, Chung-Yee, eds. Building Supply Chain Excellence in Emerging Economies. (International Series in Operations Research & Management Science Ser.). (Illus.). 2010. xviii, 470p. pap. 159.00 *(978-1-4419-4261-6(0)*, 1441942610) 2006. 465p. 159.00 *(978-0-387-38428-3(6)*, 0387384286) Springer.

Lee, William B. Creating Entrepreneurial Supply Chains. 2012. 320p. ***(978-1-60427-062-4(4))*** Ross, J. Publishing, Inc.

Leinbach, Thomas R. & Capineri, Cristina, eds. Globalized Freight Transport: Intermodality, E-commerce, Logistics & Sustainability. 2007. (Transport Economics, Management & Policy Ser.). (Illus.). 304p. (C). 137.00 *(978-1-84542-502-9(2))* Elgar, Edward Publishing, Inc.

Lenart, Annika. I Changed My Mind. 2009. 120p. pap. *(978-3-639-16254-7(4))* VDM Verlag Dr. Mueller e.K.

Levesque, Peter J. The Shipping Point: The Rise of China & the Future of Retail Supply Chain Management. 2011. (ENG., Illus.). 300p. 49.95 *(978-0-470-82453-5(0)*, Wiley) Wiley, John & Sons, Inc.

Li. Supply Chain Management: Concepts... 2007. (Illus.). 112.00 *(978-981-270-072-8(2))* World Scientific Publishing Co., Inc.

Li, Jian, et al. Risk Management of Supply & Cash Flows in Supply Chains. 2011. (International Series in Operations Research & Management Science Ser.).

B

(ENG., Illus.). xvii, 202p. 139.00 ***(978-1-4614-0510-8(6)***, 1461405106) Springer.

Liu, Binglian. Contemporary Logistics in China: An Introduction. 2011. 252p. 95.00 ***(978-981-4365-88-8(2))*** World Scientific Publishing Co., Inc.

Liu, John. Supply Chain & Transport Logistics: Integrated Logistics of Navigation, Aviation & Transportation. 2011. (ENG., Illus.). 560p. (C). 160.00 *(978-0-415-61895-3(9))*; pap. 71.95 *(978-0-415-61896-0(7))* Routledge.

Lo, Sonia M. & Power, Damien J. Competitive Strategy in the Supply Chain. 2008. 300p. pap. *(978-3-639-05217-6(X))* VDM Verlag Dr. Mueller e.K.

London, Kerry. Construction Supply Chain Economics. 2007. (Spon Research Ser.). (ENG., Illus.). 480p. (C). 180.00 *(978-0-415-40971-1(3))* Routledge.

Lun, Y. H. Venus, et al. Shipping & Logistics Management. 2010. (ENG., Illus.). iv, 356p. 169.00 *(978-1-84882-996-1(5)*, 1848829965) Springer.

Luo, Zongwei. Innovations in Logistics & Supply Chain Management Technologies for Dynamic Economies. 2012. ***(978-1-4666-0269-4(4))*** IGI Global.

Luo, Zongwei, ed. Innovations in Logistics & Supply Chain Management Technologies for Dynamic Economies. 2012. 460p. 185.00 ***(978-1-4666-0267-0(8)***, Business Science Reference) IGI Global.

Luo, Zongwei, ed. Service Science & Logistics Informatics: Innovative Perspectives. 2010. 382p. 180.00 *(978-1-61520-603-2(5)*, Business Science Reference) IGI Global.

Luyster, Tom & Tapping, Don. Creating Your Lean Future State: How to Move from Seeing to Doing. 2006. (ENG., Illus.). 144p. pap. 54.95 *(978-1-56327-248-6(2))* Productivity Pr.

Lyons, Andrew C., et al. Customer-driven Supply Chains. 2010. (Decision Engineering Ser.). (Illus.). 220p. 129.00 *(978-1-84628-875-3(4)*, 1846288754) Springer.

Ma, Hongze. Design of Distribution Chain. 2009. 168p. pap. *(978-3-639-15397-2(9))* VDM Verlag Dr. Mueller e.K.

Mamic, Ivanka. Implementing Codes of Conduct: How Businesses Manage Social Performance in Global Supply Chains. 2007. (ENG., Illus.). 336p. 65.00 *(978-92-2-116270-4(2))* International Labour Office.

Mangan, John, et al. Global Logistics & Supply Chain Management. 2nd ed. 2011. (ENG., Illus.). 446p. pap. 83.95 ***(978-1-119-99884-6(0)***, Wiley) Wiley, John & Sons, Inc.

Manzira, Francis Mungofa. Supply Chain Resilience. 2011. 92p. pap. ***(978-3-8433-8729-3(X))*** Lambert Academic Publishing.

Manzoni, Alex & Islam, Sardar M. N. Performance Measurement in Corporate Governance: DEA Modelling & Implications for Organisational Behaviour & Supply Chain Management. 2009. (Contributions to Management Science Ser.). (Illus.). xxi, 232p. 139.00 *(978-3-7908-2169-7(1))* Physica-Verlag DEU. Dist: Springer.

Martichenko, Robert & von Grabe, Kevin. Building a Lean Fulfillment Stream. 2010. (Illus.). 111p. spiral bd. 50.00 *(978-1-934109-19-9(3))* Lean Enterprise Institute, Inc.

Martin, James W. Lean Six Sigma for Supply Chain Management: The 10-Step Solution Process. 2006. (ENG., Illus.). 432p. 37.00 *(978-0-07-147942-4(2)*, 0071479422) McGraw-Hill Professional Publishing.

Martin, James William. Operational Excellence: Using Lean Six Sigma to Translate Customer Value Through Global Supply Chains. 2007. (ENG., Illus.). 664p. 99.95 *(978-1-4200-6250-2(6))* Auerbach Pubs., Inc.

Martin, Pinar. Remanufacturing As a Supply Chain Strategy. 2010. 88p. pap. *(978-3-639-24739-8(6))* VDM Verlag Dr. Mueller e.K.

Massi. Guidebook for Supporting Decision Maki. . 2008. 300p. 47.00 *(978-981-270-803-8(0))* World Scientific Publishing Co., Inc.

Maurno, Dann Anthony & Sirico, Louis. Thin Air: How Wireless Technology Supports Lean Initiatives. 2010. (ENG., Illus.). 251p. 59.95 *(978-1-4398-0439-1(7))* Productivity Pr.

McDonald, Stan, et al. Materials Management: An Executive's Supply Chain Guide. 2009. (ENG., Illus.). 208p. 49.95 *(978-0-470-43757-5(X)*, Wiley) Wiley, John & Sons, Inc.

McKinnon, Alan, et al. Green Logistics: Improving the Environmental Sustainability of Logistics. 2010. (ENG., Illus.). 384p. 55.00 *(978-0-7494-5678-8(7))* Kogan Page, Ltd. GBR. Dist: Ingram Pub. Services.

McLaughlin, Stephen. Effective Knowledge Transfer in Complex Organizations. 2010. 292p. pap. *(978-3-8383-4561-1(4))* Lambert Academic Publishing.

Meier, Andreas & Stormer, Henrik. Ebusiness & Ecommerce. 2nd ed. 2009. 296p. pap. *(978-3-540-85016-8(3))* Springer Singapore Pte. Ltd.

—EBusiness & ECommerce: Managing the Digital Value Chain. Gosselin, Elizabeth, tr. 2009. (ENG., Illus.). x, 222p. 79.95 *(978-3-540-89327-1(X)*, 354089327X) Springer.

Meisel, Robert M. The Executive Guide to Understanding & Implementing Lean Six Sigma: The Financial Impact. 2007. (Illus.). xiv, 90p. 32.00 *(978-0-87389-711-2(0))* ASQ Quality Pr.

Mejía, Gonzalo & Velasco, Nubia, eds. Production Systems & Supply Chain Management in Emerging Countries: Best Practices - Selected Papers from the International Conference on Production Research (ICPR) Americas. 2012. (ENG., Illus.). viii, 282p. 179.00 ***(978-3-642-26003-2(9)***, 3642260039) Springer.

Mena, C. & Stevens, G., eds. Delivering Performance in Food Supply Chains. 2010. (Illus.). 576p. 265.00 *(978-1-84569-471-5(6))* Woodhead Publishing Ltd. GBR. Dist: Taylor & Francis Group.

Mendes, Paulo. Demand Driven Supply Chain: A Structured & Practical Roadmap to Increase Profitability. 2011. (ENG., Illus.). xiii, 185p. 129.00 *(978-3-642-19991-2(7)*, 3642199917) Springer.

Mensah, Solomon. Globalized Supply Chains & U. S. Policy. 2010. (America in the 21st Century: Political & Economic Issues Ser.). pap. 43.00 *(978-1-60876-133-3(9))* Nova Science Pubs., Inc.

Mestrini, Guy. Supply Chain Integration in the Dutch Manufacturing Industry. 2011. 68p. pap. ***(978-3-8433-8882-5(2))*** Lambert Academic Publishing.

Meyr, Herbert & Günther, Hans Otto. Supply Chain Planning: Quantitative Decision Support & Advanced Planning Solutions. Günther, Hans-Otto & Meyr, Herbert, eds. 2009. (ENG., Illus.). x, 392p. 159.00 *(978-3-540-93774-6(9)*, 3540937749) Springer.

Milanato, Damiano. Demand Planning. 2010. 618p. pap. *(978-88-470-0821-2(2))* Springer Singapore Pte. Ltd.

Miller, Donald, et al. New Principles in Planning Evaluation. 2008. (Urban Planning & Environment Ser.). (Illus.). 344p. 134.95 *(978-0-7546-7507-5(6))* Ashgate Publishing Co.

Min. Supply Chain Management: Text & Cases. 2008. (C). 151.95 *(978-0-324-37841-2(6))* Cengage South-Western.

Minis, Ioannis, et al, eds. Supply Chain Optimization, Design, & Management: Advances & Intelligent Methods. 2010. (Illus.). 350p. 180.00 *(978-1-61520-633-9(7)*, Business Science Reference) IGI Global.

Mitra, Amit & Gupta, Amar. Knowledge Reuse & Agile Processes: Catalysts for Innovation. 2008. (Premier Reference Source Ser.). (Illus.). 424p. 180.00 *(978-1-59904-921-2(X))* IGI Global.

Montoya, Gabriel. Assessing Resilience As a Particular Case of Supply Chain Management. 2011. 184p. pap. ***(978-3-8443-2857-8(2))*** Lambert Academic Publishing.

Moore, Nancy Y., et al. Developing Tailored Supply Strategies. 2007. (Illus.). 150p. pap. 28.00 *(978-0-8330-4120-3(7)*, mg572) RAND Corp., The.

Morán, Lucas G. Manufacturing Trends in the United States. 2012. ***(978-1-62100-583-4(6))*** Nova Science Pubs., Inc.

Morris, Peter & Pinto, Jeffrey K., eds. The Wiley Guide to Project Technology, Supply Chain & Procurement Management. 2007. (Wiley Guides to the Management of Projects Ser.: 4). (ENG., Illus.). 408p. pap. 65.00 *(978-0-470-22682-7(X)*, Wiley) Wiley, John & Sons, Inc.

Mulcahy, David E. Eaches or Pieces Order Fulfillment, Design, & Operations Handbook. 2007. (ENG., Illus.). 952p. 99.95 *(978-0-8493-3522-8(1))* Auerbach Pubs., Inc.

Mulcahy, David E. & Sydow, Joachim. Supply Chain Logistics for Warehouse Management. 2008. (ENG., Illus.). 552p. 97.95 *(978-0-8493-0575-7(6))* Auerbach Pubs., Inc.

Murphy, Paul R., Jr. & Wood, Donald. Contemporary Logistics. 10th rev. ed. 2010. (ENG.). 336p. (C). pap. 204.00 *(978-0-13-611077-4(0)*, Prentice Hall) Prentice Hall PTR.

Murray, Martin. Materials Management with SAP ERP: Functionality & Technical Configuration. 3rd ed. 2010. (Illus.). 652p. 69.95 *(978-1-59229-358-2(1)*, SAP PR.) Galileo Pr., Inc.

—Maximize Your Warehouse Operations with SAP ERP. 2009. (Illus.). 300p. 69.95 *(978-1-59229-309-4(3)*, SAP PR.) Galileo Pr., Inc.

Murray, Martin. Warehouse Management with SAP ERP: Functionality & Technical Configuration. 2nd ed. 2011. (ENG., Illus.). 581p. 79.95 ***(978-1-59229-409-1(X)***, SAP PR.) Galileo Pr., Inc.

Myers, Matthew B. & Stank, Theodore P. Handbook of Global Supply Chain Management. Mentzer, John T. et al, eds. 2006. (Illus.). 600p. 150.00 *(978-1-4129-1805-3(7)*, B18057C) SAGE Pubns., Inc.

Nag, Barin, ed. Intelligent Systems in Operations: Methods, Models & Applications in the Supply Chain. 2010. 350p. 180.00 *(978-1-61520-605-6(1))* IGI Global.

Narayanan, Srivathsan. Optimizing Reverse Logistics with SAP ERP. 2010. (Illus.). 303p. 84.95 *(978-1-59229-325-4(5)*, SAP PR.) Galileo Pr., Inc.

Nassimbeni, Guido & Sartor, Marco. Sourcing in China: Strategies, Methods & Experiences. 2006. (ENG., Illus.). 320p. 126.00 *(978-1-4039-9855-2(8))* Palgrave Macmillan.

Nekolar, Alexander-Philip. e-Procurement. 2007. (GER., Illus.). XIV, 163p. 49.95 *(978-3-540-43980-6(3)*, 3540439803) Springer.

New, Steve, ed. Supply Chain Management, 4 vols. 2008. (Critical Perspectives on Business & Management Ser.). (ENG., Illus.). 1600p. (C). 1395.00 *(978-0-415-41678-8(7))* Routledge.

—Supply Chain Management, 4 vols. 2008. (Illus.). *(978-0-415-41682-5(5))*; 488p. *(978-0-415-41679-5(5))*; *(978-0-415-41681-8(7))*; 488p. *(978-0-415-41680-1(9))* Routledge.

Newbold, Robert. The Billion Dollar Solution: Secrets of Prochain Project Management. 2008. (Illus.). 289p. 29.95 *(978-1-934979-05-1(8))* ProChain Solutions, Inc.

Nyhuis, Peter & Wiendahl, Hans-Peter. Fundamentals of Production Logistics: Theory, Tools & Applications. 2008. (ENG., Illus.). xix, 312p. 159.00 *(978-3-540-34210-6(9)*, 3540342109) Springer.

Oberegger, Markus. Supply Chain Management und Risikominimierung in Krisenzeiten: Die Integration von SCM auf strategischer und operativer Ebene zur Risikominimierung in Krisenzeiten. 2010. 180p. pap. *(978-3-639-26584-2(X))* VDM Verlag Dr. Mueller e.K.

O'Brien, Jonathan. Category Management in Purchasing: A Strategic Approach to Maximize Business Profitability. (ENG., Illus.). 320p. 2009. 70.00 *(978-0-7494-5257-5(9))* 2nd ed. 2012. 80.00 ***(978-0-7494-6498-1(4))*** Kogan Page, Ltd. GBR. Dist: Ingram Pub. Services.

Ochoa Ortiz Zezzatti, Carlos Alberto. Logistics Management & Optimization Through Hybrid Artificial Intelligence Systems. 2012. ***(978-1-4666-0299-1(6))*** IGI Global.

Olsen, Lars Dragheim, et al. Inside Microsoft Dynamics AX 2009. 2nd ed. 2009. (ENG.). 720p. pap. 69.99 *(978-0-7356-2645-4(6))* Microsoft Pr.

Olson, David. Supply Chain Information Technology. 2011. 140p. pap. 29.95 ***(978-1-60649-360-1(4))*** Business Expert Pr.

Olson, David L. & Wu, Desheng. Enterprise Risk Management Models. 2010. (ENG., Illus.). x, 200p. 119.00 *(978-3-642-11473-1(3)*, 3642114733) Springer.

Organisation for Economic Co-operation and Development Staff. Enhancing the Role of SMEs in Global Value Chains. 2008. (Illus.). 100p. pap. 32.00 *(978-92-64-05095-2(7))* Organization for Economic Cooperation & Development.

Ortiz Zezzati, Carlos Alberto Ochoa & Chira, Carmelia, eds. Logistics Management & Optimization through Hybrid Artificial Intelligence Systems. 2012. 422p. 195.00 ***(978-1-4666-0297-7(X)***, Information Science Reference) IGI Global.

Ostertag, Manja. Quality-oriented Procurement in China as a Low-Cost Country. 2008. 104p. pap. *(978-3-8364-8429-9(3))* VDM Verlag Dr. Mueller e.K.

Palevich, Robert. The Lean Sustainable Supply Chain: How to Create a Green Infrastructure with Lean Technologies. 2012. (FT Press Operations Management Ser.). (ENG., Illus.). 448p. 99.99 ***(978-0-13-283761-3(7))*** FT Press.

Pandit, Kirit, et al. Spend Analysis: The Window into Strategic Sourcing. 2008. (Illus.). 249p. *(978-1-932159-93-6(2))* Ross, J. Publishing, Inc.

Pani, Ashis K., ed. E-Procurement in Emerging Economies: Theory & Cases. 2007. (Illus.). 360p. 99.95 *(978-1-59904-153-7(7))* IGI Global.

Pani, Ashis Kumar & Agrahari, Amit. E-Procurement in Emerging Economies: Theory & Cases. 2007. (Illus.). xiv, 342p. pap. 99.95 *(978-1-59904-154-4(5))* IGI Global.

Papageorgiou, Lazaros, ed. Process Systems Engineering: Supply-Chain Optimization. 2007. (Process Systems Engineering Ser.). (ENG.). 368p. 235.00 *(978-3-527-31906-0(9)*, Wiley-VCH) Wiley, John & Sons, Inc.

Pappis, Costas P. Climate Change, Supply Chain Management & Enterprise Adaptation: Implications of Global Warming on the Economy. 2010. (Illus.). 350p. 180.00 *(978-1-61692-800-1(X)*, Information Science Reference) IGI Global.

Pardalos, Panos M. & Tsitsiringos, Vassilis, eds. Financial Engineering, E-commerce & Supply Chain. 2010. (Applied Optimization Ser.). 412p. pap. 179.00 *(978-1-4419-5222-6(5)*, 1441952225) Springer.

Parlier, Greg. Transforming US Army Supply Chains: Strategies for Management Innovation. 2011. 275p. pap. 32.95 *(978-1-60649-235-2(7))* Business Expert Pr.

Parthasarathy, S., ed. Enterprise Information Systems & Implementing IT Infrastructures: Challenges & Issues. 2010. 399p. 180.00 *(978-1-61520-625-4(6))* IGI Global.

Payne, Joseph, et al. Managing Indirect Spend: Enhancing Profitability Through Strategic Sourcing. 2011. (Wiley Corporate F&a Ser.: 557). (ENG., Illus.). 446p. 95.00 ***(978-0-470-88688-5(9)***, Wiley) Wiley, John & Sons, Inc.

Peace Jr, William D. & Peace Jr., William D. Supply Chain Management: The Real WOW Factor. 2011. 242p. pap. 39.95 ***(978-0-557-28296-8(9))*** Lulu Enterprises Inc.

Perret Francis-Luc Staff. The Essentials of Logistics & Management. 2007. 550p. 99.95 *(978-1-4200-4619-9(5))* CRC Pr. LLC.

Piccirillo, Ettore & Noro, Massimo G. Guidebook for Supporting Decision-Making under Uncertainties: Today's Managers, Tomorrow's Business. 2008. 300p. pap. *(978-981-270-804-5(9))* World Scientific Publishing Co., Inc.

Pistikopoulos, Efstratios, et al, eds. Supply-Chain Optimization, Vol. 3, Pt.1. 2007. (Process Systems Engineering Ser.). (ENG.). 367p. 235.00 *(978-3-527-31693-9(0)*, Wiley-VCH) Wiley, John & Sons, Inc.

Platt, Jan Hendrik. Strategische Früherkennung für Supply Chains: Ein Ansatz auf Basis des Fließsystemmodells. 2008. (Europäische Hochschulschriften. Reihe 5: Volks- und Betriebswirtschaft Ser.). 494p. pap. 107.95 *(978-3-631-58075-2(4))* Lang, Peter GmbH, Europaischer Verlag der Wissenschaften DEU. Dist: Lang, Peter.

Plunkett, Jack W. Plunkett's Transportation, Supply Chain & Logistics Industry Almanac 2007: Transportation, Supply Chain & Logistics Industry Market Research, Statistics, Trends & Leading Companies. annuals Plunkett, Jack W., ed. 2007. 684p. pap. 299.99 incl. cd-rom *(978-1-59392-085-2(7))* Plunkett Research, Ltd.

—Plunkett's Transportation, Supply Chain & Logistics Industry Almanac 2007 (E-Book) Transportation, Supply Chain & Logistics Industry Market Research, Statistics, Trends & Leading Companies. annuals Plunkett, Jack W., ed. 2007. 695p. E-Book 299.99 incl. cd-rom *(978-1-59392-427-0(5))* Plunkett Research, Ltd.

Poiger, Martin. Improving Performance of Supply Chains by Reducing Variability. 2011. 108p. pap. ***(978-3-8381-2749-1(8))*** Südwestdeutscher Verlag für Hochschulschriften AG & Co. KG.

Poirier, Charles C., et al. Diagnosing Greatness: Ten Traits of the Best Supply Chains. 2009. 280p. *(978-1-60427-026-6(8))* Ross, J. Publishing, Inc.

Poluha, Rolf G. Application of the SCOR Model in Supply Chain Management. 2007. (Illus.). 480p. 109.95 *(978-1-934043-23-3(0))* Cambria Pr.

Ponis, Stavros, ed. Managing Risk in Virtual Enterprise Networks: Implementing Supply Chain Principles. 2010. 351p. 180.00 *(978-1-61520-607-0(8)*, Business Science Reference) IGI Global.

Pradhan, Sandeep. Implementing & Configuring SAP Event Management. 2010. (Illus.). 407p. 79.95 *(978-1-59229-316-2(6)*, SAP PR.) Galileo Pr., Inc.

Pradhan, Sandeep & Pavan, Verma. Global Available to Promise with SAP: Functionality & Configuration. 2011. (ENG., Illus.). 300p. 84.95 *(978-1-59229-385-8(9)*, SAP PR.) Galileo Pr., Inc.

Pryke, Stephen & Pryke. Construction Supply Chain Management. 2009. (Innovation in the Built Environment Ser.: 2). (ENG., Illus.). 248p. 149.99 *(978-1-4051-5844-2(1)*, Wiley-Blackwell) Wiley, John & Sons, Inc.

Rachmayani, Novianti. Success on Logistical Outsourcing. 2010. 132p. pap. *(978-3-639-23589-0(4))* VDM Verlag Dr. Mueller e.K.

Ramachandra, Manjunath. Web-Based Supply Chain Management & Digital Signal Processing: Methods for Effective Information Administration & Transmission. 2009. 316p. 180.00 *(978-1-60566-888-8(5))* IGI Global.

Rao, Purba H. Greening the Supply Chain: A Guide for Asian Managers. 2008. (Illus.). 284p. (C). pap. 24.95 *(978-81-7829-876-4(7)*, B98764P) SAGE Pubns., Inc.

Reyes, Pedro M. Rfid in the Supply Chain. 2011. (ENG., Illus.). 176p. 60.00 *(978-0-07-163497-7(5)*, 0071634975) McGraw-Hill Professional Publishing.

Richards, Gwynne. Warehouse Management: A Complete Guide to Improving Efficiency & Minimizing Costs in the Modern Warehouse. 2011. (ENG., Illus.). 352p. pap. 70.00 *(978-0-7494-6074-7(1))* Kogan Page, Ltd. GBR. Dist: Ingram Pub. Services.

Robeson, James F. Logistics Handbook. 2011. (ENG.). 974p. pap. 72.99 ***(978-1-4516-6569-7(5)***, Free Pr.) Free Pr.

Rogers, Stephen C. The Supply-Based Advantage: How to Link Suppliers to Your Organization's Corporate Strategy, 1 vol. 2009. (ENG., Illus.). 368p. 39.95 *(978-0-8144-0155-2(4))* Amacom.

Ross, David F. The Intimate Supply Chain: Leveraging the Supply Chain to Manage the Customer Experience. 2008. (ENG., Illus.). 304p. 85.95 *(978-1-4200-6497-1(5))* Auerbach Pubs., Inc.

—Introduction to Supply Chain Management Technologies. 2nd ed. 2010. (Resource Management Ser.). (ENG., Illus.). 424p. 79.95 *(978-1-4398-3752-8(X)*, CRC Press) Taylor & Francis Group GBR. Dist: Taylor & Francis Group.

Ross, David Frederick. Competing Through Supply Chain Management. 2010. (ENG.). 320p. pap. 189.00 *(978-1-4419-4727-7(2)*, 1441947272) Springer.

Rudzki, Robert A. & Trent, Robert. Next Level Supply Management Excellence H/C: Your Straight Bottom Line Roadmap. 2011. 352p. pap. ***(978-1-60427-059-4(4))*** Ross, J. Publishing, Inc.

Ruffa, Stephen A. The Going Lean Fieldbook: A Practical Guide to Lean Transformation & Sustainable Success, 1 vol. 2010. (ENG.). 224p. 27.95 *(978-0-8144-1558-0(X))* Amacom.

Rushton, Alan & Walker, Steve. International Logistics Supply Chain Outsourcing: From Local to Global. 2007. (ENG., Illus.). 424p. 80.00 *(978-0-7494-4814-1(8))* Kogan Page, Ltd. GBR. Dist: Ingram Pub. Services.

Sabri, Ehap H. & Shaikh, Salim. Lean & Agile Value Chain Management: A Guide to the Next Level of Improvement. 2010. 264p. *(978-1-60427-025-9(X))* Ross, J. Publishing, Inc.

Sabri, Ehap H., et al. Purchase Order Management Best Practices: Process, Technology, & Change Management. 2006. (Illus.). 219p. *(978-1-932159-63-9(0))* Ross, J. Publishing, Inc.

Sadler, Ian. Logistics & Supply Chain Integration. 2007. (Illus.). 288p. (C). 114.00 *(978-1-4129-2978-3(4)*, B29784C); per. 62.00 *(978-1-4129-2979-0(2)*, B29784P) SAGE Pubns., Ltd. GBR. Dist: SAGE Pubns., Inc.

Samson, Regina M., ed. Supply-Chain Management: Theories, Activities/Functions & Problems. 2010. (Business Issues, Competition & Entrepreneurship Ser.). (Illus.). xiv, 359p. 129.00 *(978-1-61668-284-2(1))* Nova Science Pubs., Inc.

Sanderson, Ian & Sanders, Nada R. Supply Chain Management: A Global Perspective. 2011. (ENG., Illus.). 428p. (C). 199.95 *(978-0-470-14117-5(4)*, Wiley) Wiley, John & Sons, Inc.

Sarkis, Joseph, ed. Greening the Supply Chain. (ENG., Illus.). xxiv, 407p. 2010. pap. 159.00 *(978-1-84996-572-9(2)*, 1849965722) 2006. 159.00 *(978-1-84628-298-0(5)*, 1846282985) Springer.

Sawik, Tadeusz. Scheduling in Supply Chains Using Mixed Integer Programming. 2011. (ENG., Illus.). 492p. 125.00 *(978-0-470-93573-6(1)*, Wiley) Wiley, John & Sons, Inc.

Schönberger, Jö. Model-Based Control of Logistics Processes in Volatile Environments: Decision Support for Operations Planning in Supply Consortia. 2011. (Operations Research Computer Science Interfaces Ser.). (ENG., Illus.). xii, 181p. 119.00 *(978-1-4419-9681-7(8)*, 1441996818) Springer.

Schönsleben, Paul. Integral Logistics Management. 4th rev. ed. 2011. (Resource Management Ser.). (ENG., Illus.). 1064p. 99.95 *(978-1-4398-7823-1(4))* Auerbach Pubs., Inc.

Schimmelpfennig, Andrt. Relational Factors in Supply Chain Performance Measurement. 2008. 152p. pap. *(978-3-639-02706-8(X))* VDM Verlag Dr. Mueller e.K.

Schneller, Eugene S. & Smeltzer, Larry R. Strategic Management of the Health Care Supply Chain. 2011. (ENG.). 328p. pap. 78.00 ***(978-1-118-19342-6(3)***, Jossey-Bass) Wiley, John & Sons, Inc.

Schniederjans, Marc J. Topics in Lean Supply Chain Management. 2009. 368p. 88.00 *(978-981-281-855-3(3))* World Scientific Publishing Co., Inc.

Schoenfeldt, Thomas I. A Practical Application of Supply Chain Management Principles. 2008. 55.00 *(978-0-87389-736-5(6))* ASQ Quality Pr.

Schuldt, Arne. Multiagent Coordination Enabling Autonomous Logistics. 2011. (ENG., Illus.). xvi, 272p. 129.00 *(978-3-642-20091-5(5)*, 3642200915) Springer.

Scott, Colin, et al. Guide to Supply Chain Management. 2011. (ENG., Illus.). xviii, 189p. 69.95 *(978-3-642-17675-3(5)*, 3642176755) Springer.

Scott-Sabic, Vanessa. Logistik-Wörterbuch Dictionary of Logistics: Deutsch-Englisch/Englisch-Deutsch. German-English/English-German. 2nd ed. 2006. (VDI-Buch Ser.). (Illus.). X, 480p. pap. 69.95 *(978-3-540-20553-1(5)*, 3540205535) Springer.

Sehested, Claus & Sonnenberg, Henrik. Lean Innovation: A Fast Path from Knowledge to Value. 2010. (ENG., Illus.). x, 189p. 59.95 *(978-3-642-15894-0(3)*, 3642158943) Springer.

Sehgal, Vivek. Supply Chain As Strategic Asset: The Key to Reaching Business Goals. 2011. (Wiley Corporate F&a Ser.: 22). (ENG., Illus.). 305p. 60.00 *(978-0-470-87477-6(5)*, Wiley) Wiley, John & Sons, Inc.

Sehgal, Vivek & Sehgal. Enterprise Supply Chain Management: Integrating Best in Class Processes. 2009. (ENG., Illus.). 206p. 49.95 *(978-0-470-46545-5(X)*, Wiley) Wiley, John & Sons, Inc.

Seitz. Supply Chain Performance, Collaboration, & Stability Measurement: Development of a Model for the Automotive Industry. 2007. 100p. per. *(978-3-8364-0242-2(4))* VDM Verlag Dr. Mueller e.K.

Sen, Dipankar, et al. RFID for Energy & Utility Industries. 2009. 240p. 89.00 *(978-1-59370-105-5(5))* PennWell Corp.

Sethi, Sachin. Enhancing Supplier Relationship Management Using SAP SRM. 2nd ed. 2009. (Illus.). 720p. 79.95 *(978-1-59229-312-4(3)*, SAP PR.) Galileo Pr., Inc.

Sethi, Suresh P., et al, eds. Industrial Engineering: Innovative Networks: 5th International Conference on Industrial Engineering & Industrial Management CIO 2011, Cartagena, Spain, September 2011, Proceedings. 2012. (ENG., Illus.). xiv, 396p. 259.00 ***(978-1-4471-2320-0(4)***, 1447123204) Springer.

Sethi, Suresh P., et al. Inventory & Supply Chain Management with Forecast Updates. 2010. (International Series in Operations Research & Management Science Ser.). (Illus.). xviii, 292p. pap. 139.00 *(978-1-4419-5481-7(3)*, 1441954813) Springer.

Seuring, Stefan, et al, eds. Strategy & Organization in Supply Chains. 2010. (ENG., Illus.). x, 420p. pap. 169.00 *(978-3-7908-2451-3(8)*, 3790824518) Physica-Verlag DEU. Dist: Springer.

Seuring, Stefan & Goldbach, Maria, eds. Cost Management in Supply Chains. 2010. (ENG., Illus.). xii, 435p. pap. 169.00 *(978-3-7908-2515-2(8)*, 3790825158) Physica-Verlag DEU. Dist: Springer.

Shah, Janat. Supply Chain Management: Text & Cases. 2009. (ENG., Illus.). 472p. (C). pap. 144.20 *(978-81-317-1517-8(5))* Pearson Education.

Shapiro, Jeremy F. Modeling the Supply Chain. 2nd ed. 2006. (ENG., Illus.). 624p. (C). 206.95 *(978-0-495-12609-6(8))* Brooks/Cole.

Sharma, Sunil. Supply Chain Management. 2011. (ENG., Illus.). 540p. 27.95 *(978-0-19-568913-6(5))* Oxford Univ. Pr., Inc.

Sharma, Vikram & Sahay, B. S. Supply Chain Management for Enhancing Competitive Potential. 2010. 216p. pap. *(978-3-8383-8361-3(3))* Lambert Academic Publishing.

Sheffi, Yossi. The Resilient Enterprise: Overcoming Vulnerability for Competitive Advantage. 2007. (ENG., Illus.). 352p. (gr. 17). per. 20.95 *(978-0-262-69349-3(6))* MIT Pr.

Sheldon, Donald. Lean Materials Planning & Execution: A Guide to Internal & External Supply Management Excellence. 2007. (Illus.). 252p. *(978-1-932159-65-3(7))* Ross, J. Publishing, Inc.

Shuler, James. Using Performance Information to Facilitate Decisionmaking in Transportation Logistics. 2009. 372p. pap. 40.10 *(978-0-557-09643-5(X))* Lulu Enterprises Inc.

Simchi-Levi, David, et al. Designing & Managing the Supply Chain. 3rd rev. ed. 2007. (Mcgraw-Hill/Irwin Series Operations & Decision Sciences). 528p. (C). 105.94 *(978-0-07-298239-8(X)*, 9780072982398, McGraw-Hill/Irwin) McGraw-Hill Higher Education.

—Designing & Managing the Supply Chain: Concepts, Strategies, & Case Studies. 3rd ed. 2007. (ENG., Illus.). 544p. (C). 157.00 incl. cd-rom *(978-0-07-334152-1(5)*, 0073341525, McGraw-Hill/Irwin) McGraw-Hill Higher Education.

—The Logic of Logistics: Theory, Algorithms, & Applications for Logistics & Supply Chain Management. 2nd ed. 2010. (Springer Series in Operations Research & Financial Engineering Ser.). (Illus.). xx, 355p. pap. 79.95 *(978-1-4419-1970-0(8)*, 1441919708) Springer.

Skjott-Larsen, et al. Managing the Global Supply Chain. 2007. 459p. pap. 77.00 *(978-87-630-0171-7(3))* Copenhagen Business Schl. Pr. DNK. Dist: International Specialized Bk. Services.

Slater, Jeffrey. The Global Lean Supply Chain. 2012. (ENG., Illus.). 175p. pap. 39.95 *(978-1-4398-6235-3(4))* Productivity Pr.

Slone, Reuben, et al. New Supply Chain Agenda: The 5 Steps That Drive Real Value. 2010. (ENG., Illus.). 224p. 35.00 *(978-1-4221-4936-2(6))* Harvard Business Review Pr.

Smith, Wynet. From Chainsaw to Chainstore. 2008. 236p. pap. *(978-3-639-02276-6(9))* VDM Verlag Dr. Mueller e.K.

Smock, Douglas A., et al. On-Demand Supply Management: World Class Strategies, Practices, & Technology. 2007. (Illus.). 309p. *(978-1-932159-62-2(2))* Ross, J. Publishing, Inc.

Smyth, Hedley & Pryke, Stephen, eds. Collaborative Relationships in Construction: Developing Frameworks & Networks. 2008. (ENG., Illus.). 272p. 139.99 *(978-1-4051-8041-2(2)*, Wiley-Blackwell) Wiley, John & Sons, Inc.

Snapp, Shaun. Discover SAP SCM. 2009. (Illus.). 380p. 39.95 *(978-1-59229-305-6(0)*, SAP PR.) Galileo Pr., Inc.

Snyder, Lawrence V. & Shen, Zuo-Jun Max. Fundamentals of Supply Chain Theory. 2011. (ENG., Illus.). 400p. 110.00 *(978-0-470-52130-4(9)*, Wiley) Wiley, John & Sons, Inc.

Sodhi, ManMohan S. & Tang, Christopher S. Managing Supply Chain Risk. 2012. (International Series in Operations Research & Management Science Ser.). (ENG., Illus.). xx, 331p. 179.00 ***(978-1-4614-3237-1(5)***, 1461432375) Springer.

Solis, William M. DoD's High-Risk Areas: Progress Made Implementing Supply Chain Management Recommendations, but Full Extent of Improvement Unknown. 2007. 159p. (C). pap. 25.00 *(978-1-4223-1534-7(7))* DIANE Publishing Co.

Sollish, Fred & Semanik, John. Strategic Global Sourcing Best Practices. 2011. (ENG., Illus.). 229p. 65.00 *(978-0-470-49440-0(9)*, Wiley) Wiley, John & Sons Inc.

Song, Dong-Wook & Panayides, Photis M. Maritime Logistics: A Complete Guide to Effective Shipping & Port Management. 2012 (ENG.). 344p. pap. 75.00 ***(978-0-7494-6369-4(4))*** Kogan Page, Ltd. GBR. Dist: Ingram Pub. Services.

Song, Haiyan. Tourism Supply Chain Management. (Advances in Tourism Ser.). (ENG., Illus.). 216p. (C). 2012. 152.00 *(978-0-415-58155-4(9))* 2011. pap. 45.95 *(978-0-415-58156-1(7))* Routledge.

Song, Jing-Sheng & Yao, David D., eds. Supply Chain Structures: Coordination, Information & Optimization. 2010. (International Series in Operations Research & Management Science Ser.). 456p. pap. 199.00 *(978-1-4419-4917-2(8)*, 1441949178) Springer.

Srinivasan, Mandyam. Building Lean Supply Chains with the Theory of Constraints. 2011. (ENG., Illus.). 384p. 60.00 ***(978-0-07-177121-4(2)***, 0071771212) McGraw-Hill Professional Publishing.

Stadtler, Hartmut & Kilger, Christoph, eds. Supply Chain Management & Advanced Planning: Concepts, Models, Software, & Case Studies. 4th ed. (ENG., Illus.). xviii, 556p. 2010. pap. 89.95 *(978-3-642-09392-0(2)*, 3642093922) 2007. 89.95 *(978-3-540-74511-2(4)*, 3540745114) Springer.

Stadtler, Hartmut, et al. Advanced Planning in Supply Chains: Illustrating the Concepts Using an SAP(r) APO Case Study. 2011. (Management for Professionals Ser.). (ENG., Illus.). x, 303p. 79.95 ***(978-3-642-24214-4(3)***, 3642242146) Springer.

Stalk, George & Butman, John. Five Future Strategies You Need Right Now. 2008. (Memo to the CEO: Ser.). (ENG., Illus.). 120p. 18.00 *(978-1-4221-2126-9(7))* Harvard Business Review Pr.

Stock, Lambert. Strategic Logistics Management. 2006. pap. 16.95 *(978-1-4288-1280-2(6))* Cram101 Inc.

Studebaker, David. Programming Microsoft Dynamics Nav. 2007. (Illus.). 480p. per. *(978-1-904811-74-9(4))* Packt Publishing, Ltd.

Supporting the Warfighter: Assessing the Department of Defense Supply Chain Management Plan: Hearing Before the Oversight of Government Management, the Federal Workforce, & the District of Columbia Subcommittee of the Committee on Homeland Security & Governmental Affairs, United States Senate, One Hundred Ninth Congress, Second Session, July 25, 2006. 2007. iii, 57p. *(978-0-16-079022-5(0)*, 552-070-36132-4) United States Government Printing Office.

Swink, Morgan, et al. Loose-leaf Managing Operations Across the Supply Chain. 2010. (ENG.). (C). ring bd. 157.33 *(978-0-07-740362-1(2)*, 0077403622, McGraw-Hill/Irwin) McGraw-Hill Higher Education.

—Managing Operations Across the Supply Chain. 2010. (ENG., Illus.). 608p. (C). 224.67 *(978-0-07-340331-1(8)*, 0073403318, McGraw-Hill/Irwin) McGraw-Hill Higher Education.

—Managing Operations Across the Supply Chain with Connect Plus. 2010. (ENG.). (C). 240.33 *(978-0-07-739829-3(7)*, 0077398297, McGraw-Hill/Irwin) McGraw-Hill Higher Education.

Swinnen, J. F. M., ed. Global Supply Chains, Standards & the Poor. 2007. (Illus.). 320p. 145.00 *(978-1-84593-185-8(8))* CABI GBR. Dist: Stylus Publishing, LLC.

Taderera, Faustino. International Purchasing Strategy. 2010. 584p. pap. *(978-3-8383-6484-1(8))* Lambert Academic Publishing.

—Logistics & Supply Chain Management. 2010. (Illus.). 624p. pap. *(978-3-8383-6769-9(3))* Lambert Academic Publishing.

—Practice of Management. 2010. 572p. pap. *(978-3-8383-8601-0(9))* Lambert Academic Publishing.

—Shipping Management & Logistics Strategy. 2010. 232p. pap. *(978-3-8383-6169-7(5))* Lambert Academic Publishing.

Taderera, Faustino & Mahachi, Zebert. International Logistics. 2010. 696p. pap. *(978-3-8383-7944-9(6))* Lambert Academic Publishing.

Tan, Yang. Optimal Deteriorating Inventory Control & Price Theory. 2011. 228p. pap. ***(978-3-8443-3346-6(0))*** Lambert Academic Publishing.

Tan, Yao-Hua, et al, eds. Accelerating Global Supply Chains with IT-Innovation: ITAIDE Tools & Methods. 2010. (ENG., Illus.). xi, 379p. 189.00 *(978-3-642-15668-7(1)*, 3642156681) Springer.

Tang, Christopher S., et al, eds. Supply Chain Analysis: A Handbook on the Interaction of Information, System & Optimization. (International Series in Operations Research & Management Science Ser.). (Illus.). 2010. x, 283p. pap. 179.00 *(978-1-4419-4526-6(1)*, 1441945261) 2007. 312p. 179.00 *(978-0-387-75239-6(0))* Springer.

Taniguchi, Eiichi & Thompson, Russell G., eds. Recent Advances in City Logistics: Proceedings of the 4th International Conference on City Logistics (Langkawi, Malaysia, 12-14 July, 2005) 2006. (Illus.). 538p. 184.95 *(978-0-08-044799-5(6))* Emerald Group Publishing Ltd. GBR. Dist: Turpin Distribution Services Ltd.

Tavana, Madjid. Enterprise Information Systems & Advancing Business Solutions: Emerging Models. 2012. ***(978-1-4666-1763-6(2))*** IGI Global.

Tavana, Madjid, ed. Enterprise Information Systems & Advancing Business Solutions: Emerging Models. 2012. 356p. 185.00 ***(978-1-4666-1761-2(6)***, Business Science Reference) IGI Global.

Taylor, David A. Supply Chains: A Manager's Guide. 2010. (ENG.). 384p. pap. 54.99 *(978-0-321-72069-6(5))* Addison Wesley Professional.

Thierry, Caroline, et al, eds. Simulation for Supply Chain Management. 2008. (Iste Ser.: 370). (ENG., Illus.). 360p. 158.00 *(978-1-84821-090-5(6)*, Wiley-ISTE) Wiley, John & Sons, Inc.

Thomas, Andrew R. Supply Chain Security: International Practices & Innovations in Moving Goods Safely & Efficiently, 2 vols. 2010. (Illus.). E-Book *(978-0-313-36421-1(4)*, Praeger Pubs.) Greenwood Publishing Group, Inc.

Thornton, Frank, et al. How to Cheat at Deploying & Securing RFID. 2007. (How to Cheat Ser.). (ENG., Illus.). 362p. per. 51.95 *(978-1-59749-230-0(2)*, Syngress Press) Elsevier Science & Technology Bks.

Tiffin, John & Kissling, Chris. Transport Communications: Understanding Global Networks Enabling Transport Services. 2007. (ENG., Illus.). 256p. 75.00 *(978-0-7494-5070-0(3))* Kogan Page, Ltd. GBR. Dist: Ingram Pub. Services.

Tomasini, Rolando & van Wassenhove, Luk. Humanitarian Logistics. 2009. (INSEAD Business Press Ser.). (ENG., Illus.). 256p. (C). 53.00 *(978-0-230-20575-8(5))* Palgrave Macmillan.

Trent, Robert J. End-To-End Lean Management: A Guide to Complete Supply Chain Improvement. 2008. 312p. *(978-1-932159-92-9(4))* Ross, J. Publishing, Inc.

—Strategic Supply Management: Creating the Next Source of Competitive Advantage. 2007. (Illus.). 302p. *(978-1-932159-67-7(3))* Ross, J. Publishing, Inc.

Trent, Robert J. & Roberts, Llewellyn R. Managing Global Supply & Risk: Best Practices, Concepts, & Strategies. 2009. 336p. *(978-1-60427-014-3(4))* Ross, J. Publishing, Inc.

Trienekens, Jacques, et al, eds. European pork Chains: Diversity & quality challenges in consumer-oriented production & Distribution. 2009. (Illus.). 286p. 96.00 *(978-90-8686-103-3(2))* Wageningen Academic Publishers NLD. Dist: Enfield Publishing & Distribution Co., Inc.

Turner, Robert W. Supply Management & Procurement. 2011. 264p. ***(978-1-60427-063-1(2))*** Ross, J. Publishing, Inc.

United Nations. Linking Greater Mekong Subregion Enterprises to International Markets: The Role of Global Value Chains, International Production Networks & Enterprise Clusters. 2007. (Studies in Trade & Investment Ser.). (ENG.). 92p. pap. 29.00 *(978-92-1-120492-6(5))* United Nations Pubns.

—Logistics Sector Developments: Planning Models for Enterprises & Logistics Clusters. 2009. (ENG.). 154p. pap. 52.00 *(978-92-1-120517-6(4))* United Nations Pubns.

van Weele, Arjan. Purchasing & Supply Chain Management: Analysis, Strategy, Planning & Practice. 5th ed. 2009. (ENG., Illus.). 448p. pap. 59.99 *(978-1-4080-1896-5(9))* Cengage Learning GBR. Dist: CENGAGE Learning.

Veeke, Hans. Advanced Modeling & Simulation for Industrial Logistics. 2009. 264p. pap. *(978-3-639-10674-9(1))* VDM Verlag Dr. Mueller e.K.

Villa, Agostino, ed. Managing Cooperation in Supply Network Structures & Small or Medium-sized Enterprises: Main Criteria & Tools for Managers. 2011. (ENG., Illus.). ix, 108p. 129.00 *(978-0-85729-242-1(0)*, 0857292420) Springer.

Voß, Stefan & Woodruff, David L. Introduction to Computational Optimization Models for Production Planning in a Supply Chain. 2nd ed. 2010. (ENG., Illus.). xii, 257p. pap. 129.00 *(978-3-642-06755-6(7)*, 3642067557) Springer.

Voigt, Guido. Supply Chain Coordination in Case of Asymmetric Information: Information Sharing & Contracting in a Just-in-Time Environment. 2011. (Lecture Notes in Economics & Mathematical Systems Ser.). (ENG., Illus.). xxvii, 181p. pap. 89.95 *(978-3-642-20131-8(8)*, 3642201318) Springer.

Walden, Joseph L. Modeling & Benchmarking Supply Chain Leadership: Setting the Conditions for Excellence. 2009. (Resource Management Ser.). (ENG., Illus.). 216p. 82.95 *(978-1-4200-8397-2(X)*, CRC Press) Taylor & Francis Group GBR. Dist: Taylor & Francis Group.

Wallace, Carol, et al. Food Safety for the 21st Century: Managing HACCP & Food Safety throughout the Global Supply Chain. 2010. (ENG., Illus.). 352p. 209.99 *(978-1-4051-8911-8(8)*, Wiley-Blackwell) Wiley, John & Sons, Inc.

Wander, Carsten H. Logistik und Wettbewerb: Zur Rolle logistischer (Re-)Organisation in einer wettbewerbsbasierten Marktwirtschaft. 2009. (Hohenheimer volkswirtschaftliche Schriften Ser.). (GRE.). 508p. 122.95 *(978-3-631-59000-3(8))* Lang, Peter GmbH, Europaischer Verlag der Wissenschaften DEU. Dist: Lang, Peter.

Wang, Hsiao-Fan, ed. Web-Based Green Products Life Cycle Management Systems: Reverse Supply Chain Utilization. 2008. (Illus.). 488p. 195.00 *(978-1-60566-114-8(7))* IGI Global.

Wang, Hsiao-Fan & Gupta, Surendra M. Green Supply Chain Management: Product Life Cycle Approach. 2011. (ENG., Illus.). 320p. 130.00 *(978-0-07-162283-7(7)*, 0071622837) McGraw-Hill Professional Publishing.

Wang, James, et al, eds. Ports, Cities, & Global Supply Chains. 2007. (Transport & Mobility Ser.). (Illus.). 294p. 114.95 *(978-0-7546-7054-4(6))* Ashgate Publishing Co.

Wang, John. Information Technologies, Methods, & Techniques of Supply Chain Management. 2012. (Illus.). xxxiii, 415p. ***(978-1-4666-0920-4(6))*** IGI Global.

Wang, John, ed. Information Technologies, Methods, & Techniques of Supply Chain Management. 2012. (Illus.). 412p. 185.00 ***(978-1-4666-0918-1(4)***, Business Science Reference) IGI Global.

Wang, William Y. C., et al, eds. Supply Chain Management: Issues in the New Era of Collaboration & Competition. 2006. (Illus.). 428p. 94.95 *(978-1-59904-231-2(2))* IGI Global.

Waters, Donald. Global Logistics: New Directions in Supply Chain Management. 6th rev. ed. 2010. (ENG., Illus.). 536p. pap. 70.00 *(978-0-7494-5703-7(1))* Kogan Page, Ltd. GBR. Dist: Ingram Pub. Services.

—Supply Chain Management: An Introduction to Logistics. 2nd rev. ed. 2009. (ENG., Illus.). 384p. pap. 76.00 *(978-0-230-20052-4(4))* Palgrave Macmillan.

—Supply Chain Risk Management: Vulnerability & Resilience in Logistics. 2nd ed. 2011. (ENG., Illus.). 262p. pap. 60.00 *(978-0-7494-6393-9(7))* Kogan Page, Ltd. GBR. Dist: Ingram Pub. Services.

Weber, Ingo M. Semantic Methods for Execution-level Business Modeling: Modeling Support Through Process Verification & Service Composition. 2009. (Lecture Notes in Business Information Processing Ser.). xii, 292p. pap. 83.00 *(978-3-642-05084-8(0)*, 3642050840) Springer.

Webster, Scott. Principles & Tools for Supply Chain Management. 2006. (Illus.). 450p. pap., stu. ed. 121.56 incl. cd-rom *(978-0-07-287268-2(3)*, 9780072872682, McGraw-Hill/Irwin) McGraw-Hill Higher Education.

Webster, Scott Taggart. Principles & Tools for Supply Chain Management. 2008. (Illus.). xiii, 450p. *(978-0-07-282791-0(2))* McGraw-Hill Cos., The.

Wenzel, Sigrid, et al. Qualitätskriterien für die Simulation in Produktion und Logistik: Planung und Durchführung von Simulationsstudien. 2007. (VDI-Buch Ser.). (Illus.). XII, 220p. pap. 89.95 *(978-3-540-35272-3(4)*, 3540352724) Springer.

—Verifikation und Validierung für die Simulation in Produktion und Logistik: Vorgehensmodelle und Techniken. 2008. (VDI-Buch Ser.). 240p. pap. 89.95 *(978-3-540-35281-5(3)*, 3540352813) Springer.

Wessels, Nelmarie. Supply Chain Management. 2011. 160p. pap. ***(978-3-8443-0883-9(0))*** Lambert Academic Publishing.

Wieck, Ingo, et al. Switchpoints for the Future of Logistics. 2011. (SpringerBriefs in Business Ser.). (ENG., Illus.). x, 86p. pap. 49.95 ***(978-3-642-23492-7(5)***, 3642234925) Springer.

Wiehenbrauk, Daniela. Collaborative Promotions: Optimizing Retail Supply Chains with Upstream Information Sharing. 2010. (Lecture Notes in Economics & Mathematical Systems Ser.). (Illus.). xx, 153p. pap. 109.00 *(978-3-642-13392-3(4)*, 3642133924) Springer.

Wisma, Michael. Supply Chain Modeling. 2010. 252p. pap. *(978-3-8383-6012-6(5))* Lambert Academic Publishing.

Wisner and Leon, Tan. Principles of Supply Chain Management A. 2006. pap. 14.95 *(978-1-4288-0562-0(1))* Cram101 Inc.

Wisner, Joel D., et al. Principles of Supply Chain Management: A Balanced Approach. 3rd ed. 2011. (ENG.). 592p. (C). 194.95 *(978-0-538-47548-8(X))* Cengage South-Western.

Wood, Daniel C. Sap Scm: Applications & Modeling for Supply Chain Management. 2007. (ENG., Illus.). 336p. 84.50 *(978-0-471-76991-0(6)*, Wiley) Wiley, John & Sons, Inc.

Wu, Desheng Dash, ed. Modeling Risk Management in Sustainable Construction. 2010. (Computational Risk Management Ser.). xxi, 450p. 189.00 *(978-3-642-15242-9(2)*, 3642152422) Springer.

Wu, Teresa & Blackhurst, Jennifer, eds. Managing Supply Chain Risk & Vulnerability: Tools & Methods for Supply Chain Decision Makers. 2009. (ENG., Illus.). xi, 232p. 209.00 *(978-1-84882-633-5(8)*, 1848826338) Springer.

Yang, Liu. Evaluation of Flexible Capacity Strategy under Demand Uncertainties. 2010. 160p. pap. *(978-3-8383-7662-2(5))* Lambert Academic Publishing.

Young, President Jan. Selecting, Buying, Installing & Using a Modern Warehouse Management System. 2009. 147p. pap. 24.95 *(978-0-557-05915-7(1))* Lulu Enterprises Inc.

—Supply Chain Metrics. 2009. 72p. pap. 17.95 *(978-0-557-07351-1(0))* Lulu Enterprises Inc.

Yucesan, Enver. Competitive Supply Chains: A Value-Based Management Perspective. 2007. (ENG., Illus.). 144p. 105.00 *(978-0-230-51567-3(3))* Palgrave Macmillan.

Zanjirani Farahani, Reza, et al. Supply Chain & Logistics in National, International & Governmental Environment: Concepts & Models. Zanjirani Farahani, Reza et al, eds. 2009. (Contributions to Management Science Ser.). (ENG., Illus.). xviii, 316p. 159.00 *(978-3-7908-2155-0(1)*, 3790821551) Physica-Verlag DEU. Dist: Springer.

Zanjirani Farahani, Reza, et al. Supply Chain Sustainability & Raw Material Management: Concepts & Processes. 2011. ***(978-1-61350-506-9(X))***; ***(978-1-61350-504-5(3))***; E-Book ***(978-1-61350-505-2(1))*** IGI Global.

Zäpfel, Günther, et al. Metaheuristic Search Concepts: A Tutorial with Applications to Production & Logistics. 2010. (ENG., Illus.). x, 316p. 139.00 *(978-3-642-11342-0(7)*, 3642113427) Springer.

Zelbst, Pamela. RFID for the Supply Chain & Operations Professional. 2012. 150p. pap. 29.95 ***(978-1-60649-268-0(3))*** Business Expert Pr.

Zhang, Qingyu. E-Supply Chain Technologies & Management. 2007. (Illus.). 312p. 165.00 *(978-1-59904-255-8(X))* IGI Global.

Zsidisin, George & Ritchie, Robert. Supply Chain Risk: A Handbook of Assessment, Management & Performance. 2008. (International Series in Operations Research & Management Science Ser.). (Illus.). 360p. (C). 179.00 *(978-0-387-79933-9(8)*, 0387799338) Springer.

Zsidisin, George A. & Ritchie, Bob, eds. Supply Chain Risk: A Handbook of Assessment, Management, & Performance. 2010. (International Series in Operations Research & Management Science Ser.). (Illus.). xvi, 349p. pap. 179.00 *(978-1-4419-4645-4(4)*, 1441946454) Springer.

2007 IEEE International Conference on Service Operations & Logistics & Informatics. 2007. pap. 234.00 *(978-1-4244-1117-7(3)*, 07EX1741) IEEE.

BUSINESS LOSSES

Cauley, Richard F. Winning the Patent Damages Case: A Litigator's Guide to Economic Models & Other Damage Strategies, 1 vol. 2nd ed. 2011. (ENG.). 186p. pap. 225.00 (978-0-19-976756-4(4)) Oxford Univ. Pr., Inc.

Combating Organized Retail Crime: The Role of Federal Law Enforcement: Hearing Before the Subcommittee on Crime, Terrorism, & Homeland Security of the Committee on the Judiciary, House of Representatives, One Hundred Eleventh Congress, First Session, November 5, 2009. 2010. (Illus.). iii, 72p. (978-0-16-086299-1(X), 552-070-41386-3) United States Government Printing Office.

Cram101 Textbook Reviews Staff. Outlines & Highlights for Loss Prevention in the Retail Business by Kimieck & Thomas, Isbn: 1428866124. 2009. 80p. pap. 10.95 (978-1-4288-6612-6(4)) Cram101 Inc.

E-Fencing Enforcement ACT of 2008, the Organized Retail Crime ACT of 2008, & the Combating Organized Retail Crime ACT of 2008: Hearing Before the Subcommittee on Crime, Terrorism, & Homeland Security of the Committee on the Judiciary, House of Representatives, One Hundred Tenth Congress, Second Session, on H.R. 6713, H.R. 6491 & S. 3434, September 22, 2008. 2009. iii, 107p. (978-0-16-082618-4(7), 552-070-38636-0) United States Government Printing Office.

Filler, Mark. A Quantitative Approach to Commercial Damages: Applying Statistics to the Measurement of Lost Profits. 2012. (ENG.). 352p. 125.00 **(978-1-118-07259-2(6)**, Wiley) Wiley, John & Sons, Inc.

Gaughan, Patrick A. Measuring Business Interruption Losses & Other Commercial Damages. 2nd ed. 2009. (ENG., Illus.). 509p. 150.00 (978-0-470-40014-2(5), Wiley) Wiley, John & Sons, Inc.

Goodman, Fred. Fortune's Fool: Edgar Bronfman, Jr., Warner Music, & an Industry in Crisis. 2010. (ENG., Illus.). 336p. 28.00 (978-0-7432-6998-8(5)) Simon & Schuster.

Greggo, Alan & Kresevich, Millie. Retail Security & Loss Prevention Solutions: Problems & Solutions. 2010. (ENG., Illus.). 274p. 79.95 (978-1-4200-9006-2(2)) Auerbach Pubs., Inc.

Laskey, Herman Otis. Secrets of A Successful Loss Prevention Career. 2011. 112p. 23.95 **(978-1-4620-3221-1(4))**; pap. 13.95 **(978-1-4620-3220-4(6))** iUniverse, Inc.

Organized Retail Theft Prevention: Fostering a Comprehensive Public-Private Response: Hearing Before the Subcommittee on Crime, Terrorism, & Homeland Security of the Committee on the Judiciary, House of Representatives, One Hundred Tenth Congress, First Session, October 25, 2007. 2008. iii, 59p. (978-0-16-082014-4(6), 552-070-38175-9) United States Government Printing Office.

Petrov, Ivan. Loss Given Default - Empirical Observations & Models. 2009. 80p. pap. (978-3-639-17808-1(4)) VDM Verlag Dr. Mueller e.K.

Schulze, Reiner, ed. Compensation of Private Losses: The Evolution of Torts in European Business Law. 2011. 258p. pap., pap. 89.00 (978-3-86653-175-8(3)) Sellier - European Law Publishers GmbH DEU. Dist: International Specialized Bk. Services.

Turner, Dana. Loss Prevention Techniques & Training Manual. Bond, Kris, ed. 2nd ed. 320p. pap. 125.00 (978-0-8080-0492-9(1)) Toolkit Media Group.

Wilson, R. Michael. Wells, Fargo & Co. Report of Losses from Train & Stagecoach Robbers, 1870-1884. 2007. (Illus.). **(978-0-9665925-8-0(1)**, StageCoach Bks.) Rama Pr.

BUSINESS MACHINES

see Electronic Office Machines; Office Equipment and Supplies

BUSINESS MANAGEMENT

see Industrial Management

BUSINESS MATHEMATICS

see also Business—Mathematical Models; Industrial Management—Mathematical Models; Insurance—Mathematics; Marketing—Mathematical Models; Ready-Reckoners

also subdivision Tables, etc. under economic subjects; also subdivision Tables and Ready-Reckoners under names of industries

Alhabeeb, M. J. Mathematical Finance. 2012. (ENG., Illus.). 536p. 115.00 (978-0-470-64184-2(3), Wiley) Wiley, John & Sons, Inc.

Allan, Walter, contrib. by. Fundamentals of Business Mathematics, Kit. 3rd ed. 2010. (ENG., Illus.). xx, 236p. (C). pap. 28.95 (978-1-85617-780-1(7), CIMA Publishing) Elsevier Science & Technology Bks.

Bangert, Patrick. Optimization for Industrial Problems. 2012. (ENG., Illus.). xxii, 246p. pap. 99.00 **(978-3-642-24973-0(6)**, 3642249736) Springer.

Bäuerle, Nicole & Rieder, Ulrich. Markov Decision Processes with Applications to Finance. 2011. (Universitext Ser.). (Illus.). xvi, 388p. pap. 74.95 (978-3-642-18323-2(9), 3642183239) Springer.

Biehler, Timothy. HM Virtual to accompany the Mathematics of Money. 2007. (C). pap. 15.00 (978-0-07-325911-6(X), 9780073259116, McGraw-Hill/Irwin) McGraw-Hill Higher Education.

Biehler, Timothy J. The Mathematics of Money: Math for Business & Personal Finance Decisions. 2008. (Illus.). xviii, 670p. (978-0-07-325907-9(1)) McGraw-Hill Cos., The.

—The Mathematics of Money: Math for Business & Personal Finance Decisions. 2007. (ENG., Illus.). 688p. (C). per. 162.33 (978-0-07-352482-5(4), 0073524824, McGraw-Hill/Irwin) McGraw-Hill Higher Education.

Björk, Tomas. Arbitrage Theory in Continuous Time. 3rd ed. 2009. (Oxford Finance Ser.). (ENG., Illus.). 512p. 85.00 (978-0-19-957474-2(X)) Oxford Univ. Pr., Inc.

Bluhm Christian & Overbeck Ludger. Structured Credit Portfolio Analysis, Baskets & CDOs. 2006. (Chapman & Hall/CRC Financial Mathematics Ser.). (ENG., Illus.). 376p. 92.95 (978-1-58488-647-1(1), Chapman & Hall/CRC) CRC Pr. LLC.

Bolten, Randall. Painting with Numbers: Presenting Financials & Other Numbers So People Will Understand You. 2012. (ENG.). 322p. 39.95 **(978-1-118-17257-5(4)**, Wiley) Wiley, John & Sons, Inc.

Bradley, Teresa. Essential Mathematics for Economics & Business, 2 vols. 3rd ed. 2008. (ENG., Illus.). 682p. pap. 74.95 (978-0-470-01856-9(9), Wiley) Wiley, John & Sons, Inc.

Bragg, Steven M. Business Ratios & Formulas: A Comprehensive Guide. 3rd ed. 2012. (Wiley Corporate F&a Ser.: 577). (ENG.). 355p. 85.00 **(978-1-118-16996-4(4)**, Wiley) Wiley, John & Sons, Inc.

Broverman, Samuel A. Mathematics of Investment & Credit. 4th ed. 2008. (978-1-56698-657-1(5)) Actex Pubns.

Brown, Mark Graham. Beyond the Balanced Scorecard: Improving Business Intelligence with Analytics. 2007. (ENG., Illus.). 240p. 41.95 (978-1-56327-346-9(2)) Productivity Pr.

Bryce, T. A. The American Commercial Arithmetic, for the Use of Commercial Colleges, Private Students, Schools & Counting-Houses Together with the Laws of Th. 2006. 284p. per. 26.99 (978-1-4255-3700-5(6)) MPublishing.

—The American Commercial Arithmetic, for the Use of the Grand Rapids Business College, Grand Rapids, Michigan, & Also for the Use of Universities, Pr. 2006. 372p. per. 26.99 (978-1-4255-3871-2(1)) MPublishing.

Buchanan, J. Robert. An Undergraduate Introduction to Financial Mathematics. 2008. 61.00 (978-981-283-535-2(0)) World Scientific Publishing Co., Inc.

Burton, Sharon & Shelton, Nelda. Business Math Using Excel, Pack. 2nd ed. 2011. (Business Math Ser.). (ENG.). 640p. (C). spiral bd. 133.95 (978-0-538-73119-5(2)) Cengage South-Western.

Byleen, Karl E., et al. Calculus: For Business, Economics, Life Sciences, & Social Sciences. 11th ed. 2007. (ENG., Illus.). 704p. (C). 153.33 (978-0-13-232818-0(6), Prentice Hall) Prentice Hall PTR.

Capiski, Marek & Zastawniak, Tomasz. Mathematics for Finance: An Introduction to Financial Engineering. 2nd ed. 2010. (Springer Undergraduate Mathematics Ser.). (Illus.). xiii, 336p. pap. 49.95 (978-0-85729-081-6(9), 0857290819) Springer.

Carmona, Rene A., et al. Paris-Princeton Lectures on Mathematical Finance 2004. Ekeland, Ivar et al, eds. 2007. (Lecture Notes in Mathematics Ser.). (Illus.). x, 248p. pap. 69.95 (978-3-540-73326-3(4)) Springer.

Chandra Shil, Nikhil & Parvez, Mahbub. Life Cycle Costing: Techniques & Applications. 2010. 80p. pap. (978-3-639-23430-5(8)) VDM Verlag Dr. Mueller e.K.

Chen, Bo, ed. Algorithmic Aspects in Information & Management: 6th International Conference, AAIM 2010, Weihai, China, July 19-21, 2010. Proceedings. 2010. (Lecture Notes in Computer Science / Information Systems & Applications, incl. Internet/Web, & HCI Ser.). xi, 336p. pap. 83.00 (978-3-642-14354-0(7), 3642143547) Springer.

Cleaves, Cheryl & Hobbs, Margie. Business Math. 8th ed. 2008. (ENG.). (C). 102p. pap. 35.40 (978-0-13-513863-2(9)); (Illus.). 896p. pap. 183.40 (978-0-13-159121-9(5)); 656p. pap. 132.80 (978-0-13-515010-8(8));Pack. pap., pap. 187.40 (978-0-13-605493-1(5)) Prentice Hall PTR. (Prentice Hall).

Cleaves, Cheryl, et al. Business Mathematics. 9th ed. 2011. (ENG., Illus.). 880p. (C). pap. 183.47 (978-0-13-510817-8(9), Prentice Hall) Prentice Hall PTR.

—Student Solutions Manual for Business Mathematics Complete & Brief Editions. 9th ed. 2011. (ENG.). 110p. (C). pap. 29.00 (978-0-13-217999-7(7), Prentice Hall) Prentice Hall PTR.

Cleaves, Cheryl S., et al. Business Math: Brief Edition. 9th ed. 2011. (ENG., Illus.). 672p. (C). pap. 141.47 (978-0-13-211174-4(8), Prentice Hall) Prentice Hall PTR.

Cleaves, PH.D., Cheryl, et al. Quick Reference Tables for Business Mathematics. 9th ed. 2011. (ENG.). 90p. (C). pap. 14.40 (978-0-13-218000-9(6), Prentice Hall) Prentice Hall PTR.

—Study Guide for Business Mathematics Complete & Brief Editions. 9th ed. 2011. (ENG.). 96p. (C). pap. 21.80 (978-0-13-211173-7(X), Prentice Hall) Prentice Hall PTR.

Clendenen, Gary, et al. Business Mathematics. 12th rev. ed. 2011. (ENG., Illus.). 800p. (C). pap. 183.47 (978-0-13-510978-6(7)) Addison Wesley.

Clodfelter, Richard. Making Buying Decisions 3rd Edition: Using the Computer as a Tool. 3rd rev. ed. 2008. (Illus.). 192p. pap. 80.00 (978-1-56367-699-4(0)) Fairchild Bks.

Cooper, Daryl. Calculus & Mathematical Reasoning for Social & Life Sciences. rev. ed. 2010. (ENG.). 330p. pap. 34.81 (978-0-7872-8698-9(2)) Kendall Hunt Publishing Co.

Cram101 Textbook Reviews. Outlines & Highlights for Business Math by Cleaves, Isbn: 9780135056271. 2011. 120p. pap. 28.95 **(978-1-61812-143-1(X))** Cram101 Inc.

—Outlines & Highlights for Business Mathematics by Gary Clendenen. 2011. 290p. pap. 32.95 **(978-1-61905-036-5(6))** Cram101 Inc.

—Outlines & Highlights for Contemporary Mathematics for Business & Consumers by Robert Brechner, Isbn: 9780538481250. 2011. 264p. pap. 31.95 **(978-1-61812-128-8(6))** Cram101 Inc.

—Outlines & Highlights for Essential Quantitative Methods: For Business, Management & Finance by les Oakshott. 2011. 178p. pap. 29.95 **(978-1-4672-6689-5(2))** Cram101 Inc.

—Outlines & Highlights for Essential Quantitative Methods for Business, Management & Finance by les Oakshott. 2011. 198p. pap. 30.95 **(978-1-4672-6685-7(X))** Cram101 Inc.

—Outlines & Highlights for Finite Mathematics: An Applied Approach by Michael Sullivan. 2011. 218p. pap. 30.95 **(978-1-61830-134-5(9))** Cram101 Inc.

—Outlines & Highlights for Finite Mathematics: For Business, Economics, Life Sciences & Social Sciences by Raymond A. Barnett. 2011. 126p. pap. 28.95 **(978-1-61830-160-4(8))** Cram101 Inc.

Cram101 Textbook Reviews & Cram101 Textbook Reviews. Outlines & Highlights for Fundamentals of Actuarial Mathematics by S David Promislow. 2011. 76p. pap. 27.95 **(978-1-61830-183-3(7))** Cram101 Inc.

Cram101 Textbook Reviews Staff. Outlines & Highlights for Business Math, Brief Version by Cheryl Cleaves, Margie Hobbs, Isbn: 9780135150108. 2009. 114p. pap. 28.95 (978-1-4288-3557-3(1)) Cram101 Inc.

—Outlines & Highlights for Business Math by Hansen, Isbn: 9780538448734. 2009. 134p. pap. 28.95 (978-1-4288-4151-2(2)); 174p. pap. 29.95 (978-1-4288-8812-8(8)) Cram101 Inc.

—Outlines & Highlights for Business Math by Robert Schultheis, Isbn: 9780538440523. 2009. 126p. pap. 28.95 (978-1-4288-2031-9(0)) Cram101 Inc.

—Outlines & Highlights for Business Mathematics by Charles D Miller, Stanley a Salzman, Gary Clendenen, Isbn: 9780321500120. 2009. 96p. pap. 27.95 (978-1-4288-3507-8(5)) Cram101 Inc.

—Outlines & Highlights for Contemporary Business Mathematics for Colleges, Brief Edition by James E Deitz, Isbn: 9780324595475. 2009. 56p. pap. 26.95 (978-1-4288-9066-4(1)) Cram101 Inc.

—Outlines & Highlights for Finite Mathematics: An Applied Approach 10e by Michael Sullivan, ISBN. 2009. 156p. pap. 29.95 (978-1-4288-3569-6(5)) Cram101 Inc.

—Outlines & Highlights for Introductory Mathematical Analysis for Business, Economics & the Life & Social Sciences by Ernest F Haeussler, Richard. 2009. 268p. pap. 31.95 (978-1-4288-3545-0(8)) Cram101 Inc.

—Outlines & Highlights for Practical Business Mathematics Procedure by Jeffrey Slater, Isbn: 9780073137674. 2009. 84p. pap. 27.95 (978-1-4288-2649-6(1)); 80p. pap. 27.95 (978-1-4288-8750-3(4)) Cram101 Inc.

Curwin. Quantitative Methods for Business Decisions 6e. 6th ed. 2007. (Illus.). 808p. 59.99 (978-1-84480-574-7(3)) Cengage Learning GBR. Dist: CENGAGE Learning.

Cushman. A Practical Approach to Merchandising Mathematics, Revised 1st Edition. 2011. (Illus.). 320p. (C). pap. 0.00 (978-1-60901-300-4(X)) Fairchild Bks.

Cushman, Linda M. A Practical Approach to Merchandising Mathematics. 2009. 400p. pap. 88.00 (978-1-56367-624-6(9)) Fairchild Bks.

Davenport, Thomas H. & Harris, Jeanne G. Competing on Analytics: The New Science of Winning. 2007. (ENG., Illus.). 240p. 29.95 (978-1-4221-0332-6(3)) Harvard Business Review Pr.

Davis, Mark H. A., et al, eds. Mathematical Finance. 2010. (IMA Volumes in Mathematics & its Applications Ser.). xix, 133p. pap. 79.95 (978-1-4419-2845-0(6), 1441928456) Springer.

Day, Alastair L. Mastering Financial Mathematics in Microsoft Excel: A Practical Guide for Business Calculations. 2nd ed. 2010. (Financial Times Ser.). (ENG., Illus.). 384p. (C). pap. 79.99 (978-0-273-73033-0(9)) FT Press.

Deitz, James E. & Southam, James L. Contemporary Business Mathematics for Colleges, Brief (with Printed Access Card) 16th ed. 2012. (ENG.). 384p. (C). pap. 171.95 **(978-1-133-19114-8(2))** Cengage South-Western.

—Contemporary Business Mathematics for Colleges (with CD-ROM) 15th ed. 2008. (ENG.). 560p. (C). pap. 212.95 (978-0-324-66316-7(1)) Cengage South-Western.

—Contemporary Business Mathematics for Colleges (with CD-ROM) 16th ed. 2012. (ENG.). 560p. (C). pap. 212.95 (978-1-111-82132-6(1)) Cengage South-Western.

Di Nunno, Guilia & Øksendal, Bernt, eds. Advanced Mathematical Methods for Finance. 2011. (Illus.). viii, 536p. 119.00 (978-3-642-18411-6(1), 3642184111) Springer.

Dimitric, Radoslav. Mathematics for Financial Engineering. 3rd rev. ed. 2007. 237p. (978-0-9788256-1-4(6)) Helios Publishing Co.

Dworsky, Lawrence N. Understanding the Mathematics of Personal Finance: An Introduction to Financial Literacy. 2009. (ENG., Illus.). 242p. pap. 62.95 (978-0-470-49780-7(7), Wiley) Wiley, John & Sons, Inc.

Eaton, Graham. CIMA Official Learning System Fundamentals of Business Mathematics. 4th ed. 2009. (ENG., Illus.). 528p. (C). pap. 55.95 (978-1-85617-783-2(1), CIMA Publishing) Elsevier Science & Technology Bks.

Embrechts, Paul, et al. Modelling Extremal Events: For Insurance & Finance. 2011. (Stochastic Modelling & Applied Probability Ser.). (ENG., Illus.). xvi, 648p. pap. 107.00 (978-3-642-08242-9(4), 3642082424) Springer.

Fabozzi, Frank J. & Drake, Pamela Peterson. Foundations & Applications of the Time Value of Money. 2009. (Frank J. Fabozzi Ser.: 179). (ENG., Illus.). 298p. 60.00 (978-0-470-40736-3(0), Wiley) Wiley, John & Sons, Inc.

Farlow & Cram101 Textbook Reviews Staff. Finite Mathematics & Its Applications. 2007. 112p. per. 11.95 (978-1-4288-3640-2(3)) Cram101 Inc.

Gerber, Leon. Algebra & Calculus with Excel for Business & Economics. 2007. (C). per. (978-0-9792926-0-6(3)) Gerber, Leon.

Gerver, Robert K. & Sgroi, Richard J. Financial Algebra. 2010. (ENG.). 160p. (C). pap., wbk. ed. 30.95 (978-0-538-44970-0(5)) Cengage South-Western.

Glencoe McGraw-Hill Staff. Mathematics: For Business & Personal Finance. 2009. (ENG.). 896p. (C). stu. ed. 95.24 (978-0-07-880505-9(8), 0078805058) McGraw-Hill Higher Education.

Gmac. GMAT Business Ready, Quantitative Skills. 2011. (ENG.). 89.95 **(978-1-118-11186-4(9)**, Wiley) Wiley, John & Sons, Inc.

Goldberg, Andrew & Zhou, Yunhong. Algorithmic Aspects in Information & Management: 5th International Conference, AAIM 2009, San Francisco, CA, USA, June 15-17, 2009, Proceedings. 2009. (Lecture Notes in Computer Science / Information Systems & Applications, incl. Internet/Web, & HCI Ser.). x, 327p. pap. 74.95 (978-3-642-02157-2(3), 3642021573) Springer.

Gough, Leo. Business Numeracy: How to Check the Figures for Yourself. 2nd ed. 2011. (ENG., Illus.). 240p. pap. 39.99 **(978-0-273-74643-0(X))** FT Press.

Groesbeck, John. The Crittenden Commercial Arithmetic & Business Manual. 2008. 416p. 30.99 (978-0-559-78632-7(8)); 416p. pap. 33.75 (978-0-559-78629-7(8)); 348p. 28.99 (978-0-559-54290-9(9)); 348p. pap. 31.75 (978-0-559-54287-9(9)); 352p. 29.99 (978-0-559-22919-0(4)); 220p. 24.99 (978-0-559-43853-0(2)); 352p. pap. 31.75 (978-0-559-22917-6(8)); 220p. pap. 23.75 (978-0-559-43851-6(6)) BiblioBazaar.

—The Crittenden Commercial Arithmetic & Business Manual. 2006. 352p. per. 23.99 (978-1-4255-3561-2(5)) MPublishing.

—The Crittenden Commercial Arithmetic & Business Manual Designed for the Use of Merchants, Business Men, Academies, & Commercial Colleges by John. 2006. 220p. per. 20.99 (978-1-4255-1837-0(0)) MPublishing.

Guiasu, Silviu. Probablistic Models in Operations Research. 2009. 89.00 (978-1-60692-233-0(5)) Nova Science Pubs., Inc.

Gusak, D. V. Theory of Stochastic Processes: With Applications to Financial Mathematics & Risk Theory. 2010. (Illus.). xii, 375p. **(978-0-387-87862-1(9))** Springer.

Haeussler, Ernest F., et al. Introductory Mathematical Analysis for Business, Economics, & the Life & Social Sciences. 13th ed. 2010. (ENG.). 888p. (C). 154.67 (978-0-321-64372-8(0), Prentice Hall) Prentice Hall PTR.

—Introductory Mathematical Analysis for Business, Economics, & the Life & Social Sciences, Books a la Carte Edition. 13th ed. 2010. (ENG.). (C). ring bd. 92.80 (978-0-321-69156-9(3)) Addison Wesley.

—Student's Solutions Manual for Introductory Mathematical Analysis for Business, Economics, & the Life & Social Sciences. 13th ed. 2010. (ENG.). 384p. (C). pap. 36.67 (978-0-321-64530-2(8), Prentice Hall) Prentice Hall PTR.

Haghighi, Aliakbar Montazer & Mishev, Dimitar P. Queuing Models in Industry & Business. 2008. 79.00 (978-1-60456-189-0(0)) Nova Science Pubs., Inc.

Hands, Krista. The Business Calculus Gmt. 2008. 192p. pap. (978-3-639-07443-7(2)) VDM Verlag Dr. Mueller e.K.

Hansen, et al. Business Math. 17th ed. 2009. (Business Math Ser.). (ENG.). 688p. (C). 98.95 (978-0-538-44873-4(3)) Cengage South-Western.

—Workbook for Hansen's Business Math. 17th ed. 2009. (ENG.). 192p. (C). pap. 32.95 (978-0-538-44884-0(9)) Cengage South-Western.

Hansen, Mary. Master Math: Business & Personal Finance Math. 2011. (ENG.). 304p. pap. 19.99 (978-1-4354-5788-1(9)) Course Technology.

Harshbarger, Reynolds & Cram101 Textbook Reviews Staff. Mathematical Applications for the Management, Life, & Social Sciences. 2007. 148p. per. 12.95 (978-1-4288-3694-5(2)) Cram101 Inc.

Hawkins, Anne. Smart Skills: Mastering the Numbers, 1 vol. 2011. (ENG., Illus.). 130p. pap. 14.99 (978-1-908248-06-0(8)) Legend Pr. GBR. Dist: Innovative Logistics.

INTELECOM - Intelligent Telecommunications, text. By the Numbers Study Guide. 2007. (C). pap. (978-1-58370-024-2(2)) INTELECOM - Intelligent Telecommunication.

Jacques, Ian. Mathematics for Economics & Business, 2 vols. 6th ed. 2010. (ENG., Illus.). 584p. (C). pap. 110.00 (978-0-273-72216-8(6), Prentice Hall) Prentice Hall PTR.

Janssen, Jacques, et al. Mathematical Finance 2: Stochastic Models. 2008. 352p. 150.00 (978-1-905209-85-9(1)) ISTE/Hermes Science Publishing GBR. Dist: Independent Pubs. Group.

Joshi, M. S. C++ Design Patterns & Derivatives Pricing. 2nd ed. 2008. (Mathematics, Finance & Risk Ser.). (ENG.). 308p. pap. 58.99 (978-0-521-72162-2(8)) Cambridge Univ. Pr.

Kabanov, Yu., et al. From Stochastic Calculus to Mathematical Finance: The Shiryaev Festschrift. 2010. (ENG., Illus.). xxxviii, 634p. pap. 119.00 (978-3-642-06803-4(0), 3642068030) Springer.

Kaminsky, Kenneth. Financial Literacy: Introduction to the Mathematics of Interest, Annuities, & Insurance. 2nd ed. 2010. (ENG.). 388p. pap. 50.00 (978-0-7618-5309-1(X)) Univ. Pr. of America, Inc.

Kindsfather & Parish & Cram101 Textbook Reviews Staff. Business Mathematics. 2007. 92p. per. 10.95 (978-1-4288-2690-8(4)) Cram101 Inc.

Kotsiopoulos, Antigone, et al. Merchandising Mathematics. 2008. (Illus.). 214p. pap. 78.00 (978-1-56367-675-8(3)) Fairchild Bks.

Larson, Ron & Hodgkins, Anne V. College Algebra with Applications for Business & Life Sciences. 2nd ed. 2012. (Textbooks Available with Cengage YouBook Ser.). (ENG.). 768p. (C). 200.95 **(978-1-133-10849-8(0))** Brooks/Cole.

LearningExpress Staff. Office Financials Made Easy. 4th ed. 2008. (ENG., Illus.). 272p. per. 14.95 (978-1-57685-603-1(8)) LearningExpress, LLC.

Lerner, Joel J., et al. Basic Business Mathematics: More Than 700 Fully Solved Problems. 2nd ed. 2009. (Schaum's Outline Ser.). (ENG.). 272p. (C). pap. 18.95 (978-0-07-161158-9(4), 0071611584) McGraw-Hill Cos., The.

Lial, Greenwell & Cram101 Textbook Reviews Staff. Finite Mathematics & Calculus with Applications. 2007. 196p. per. 13.95 (978-1-4288-3608-2(X)) Cram101 Inc.

Lisa, Schönenberger. Nonstandard Methods in Stochastics: Nonstandard Stochastics & Applications to Mathematical Finance. 2011. 60p. pap. ***(978-3-639-32407-5(2))*** VDM Verlag Dr. Mueller e.K.

Lorimer, Dawn E. & Rayhorn, Charles R. Financial Modeling for Managers. 2nd ed. 2006. pap. 8.95 *(978-1-4288-1041-9(2))* Cram101 Inc.

Ma, Jeffrey. The House Advantage: Playing the Odds to Win Big in Business. 2012. (ENG., Illus.). 272p. pap. 16.00 ***(978-0-230-12053-1(6))*** Palgrave Macmillan.

Macarthur, Kelly. Business Algebra. 2nd rev. ed. 2011. (ENG.). 410p. spiral bd. 60.00 ***(978-0-7575-9166-2(3))*** Kendall Hunt Publishing Co.

Magoon, Linda M. Dictionary of Financial Formulas & Ratios. 2008. 200p. pap. 35.00 *(978-1-906403-03-4(1))* Lessons Professional Publishing GBR. Dist: Stylus Publishing, LLC.

Marino, Anthony I. & Fawcett, Harold P. Arithmetic for Successful Living. 2011. 610p. 64.95 ***(978-1-258-06603-1(3))*** Literary Licensing, LLC.

Mautner, Karin. Black-Scholes Variational Inequalities. 2008. 132p. pap. *(978-3-8364-9328-4(4))* VDM Verlag Dr. Mueller e.K.

McCauley, Joseph L. Dynamics of Markets: The New Financial Economics. 2nd ed. 2009. (ENG., Illus.). 286p. 75.00 *(978-0-521-42962-7(5))* Cambridge Univ. Pr.

McKenzie, Jimmy C., et al. Office Machines: With Excel Applications. 7th rev. ed. 2007. 336p. (C). pap. 63.00 *(978-0-13-170094-9(4)*, Prentice Hall) Prentice Hall PTR.

Meckin, David. Naked Finance: Business Finance Pure & Simple. 2008. (ENG., Illus.). 286p. per. 24.95 *(978-1-85788-394-7(2))* Ebsco Publishing.

Miller, et al. Student's Solutions Manual for Business Mathematics. 12th rev. ed. 2011. (ENG.). 182p. (C). pap. 38.60 *(978-0-13-254565-5(9)*, Prentice Hall) Prentice Hall PTR.

Miller, Charles David, et al. Business Mathematics. 11th ed. 2007. *(978-0-321-51805-7(5))* Addison-Wesley Longman, Inc.

Morris, Clare. Essential Mathematics for Business & Management. 2006. (ENG.). 416p. 80.00 *(978-1-4039-1609-9(8))* Palgrave Macmillan.

Morris, Clare & Thanassoulis, Emmanuel. Essential Maths for Business & Management. 2007. (ENG., Illus.). 416p. pap. 49.00 *(978-1-4039-1610-5(1))* Palgrave Macmillan.

Mumba, Cryford. Understanding Financial Mathematics: Concepts & Practice. 2011. 260p. pap. 17.50 ***(978-1-4269-7391-8(8))*** Trafford Publishing.

Nefzi, Emna. Valuation of Continuous Asian Options. 2011. 60p. pap. ***(978-3-8454-0768-5(9))*** Lambert Academic Publishing.

Oakshott, Les. Essential Quantitative Methods: For Business, Management & Finance. 5th rev. ed. 2012. (ENG., Illus.). 512p. (C). pap. 60.00 ***(978-0-230-30266-2(1))*** Palgrave Macmillan.

Perna, Cira & Sibillo, Marilena, eds. Mathematical & Statistical Methods in Insurance & Finance. 2008. (Illus.). 208p. 79.95 *(978-88-470-0703-1(8))* Springer.

Qian, Maijian. Business Calculus. 2010. (ENG.). pap. 115.00 *(978-0-7575-5331-8(1))* Kendall Hunt Publishing Co.

Rout-Hoolash, Sweta & Lai, Choi-Hong. Computing Financial Derivatives: A Finite-Difference Approach. 2012. (Chapman & Hall/CRC Numerical Analysis & Scientific Computing Ser.). (ENG., Illus.). 268p. 89.95 *(978-1-4200-8264-7(7)*, Chapman & Hall/CRC) CRC Pr. LLC.

Salzman, Stanley A., et al. Business Mathematics. 11th ed. 2008. (ENG., Illus.). 804p. (C). per. 187.80 *(978-0-321-50012-0(1))* Addison Wesley.

—Mathematics for Business. 9th ed. 2009. *(978-0-13-506562-4(3))* Prentice Hall PTR.

Sandmann, Klaus & Schönbucher, Philip J., eds. Advances in Finance & Stochastics: Essays in Honour of Dieter Sondermann. 2010. (ENG., Illus.). xix, 312p. pap. 89.95 *(978-3-642-07792-0(7)*, 3642077927) Springer.

Sarychev, Andrey, et al, eds. Mathematical Control Theory & Finance. 2008. (ENG., Illus.). xiv, 420p. 169.00 *(978-3-540-69531-8(1)*, 3540695311) Springer.

Shim, Jae K. The Art of Mathematics in Business. 2009. 416p. pap. 45.00 *(978-1-906403-32-4(5))* Lessons Professional Publishing GBR. Dist: Stylus Publishing, LLC.

Shiryaev, Albert N., et al, eds. Stochastic Finance. 2010. (Illus.). xiv, 370p. pap. 115.00 *(978-1-4419-3932-6(6)*, 1441939326) Springer.

Slavin, Steve. Business Math: Essential Math Concepts for Any Business Environment. 2006. (ENG., Illus.). 312p. (C). per. 71.95 *(978-0-470-00719-8(2)*, Wiley) Wiley, John & Sons, Inc.

Steele, J. Michael. Stochastic Calculus & Financial Applications. 2010. (Stochastic Modelling & Applied Probability Ser.). (Illus.). ix, 300p. pap. 99.00 *(978-1-4419-2862-7(6)*, 1441928626) Springer.

Steiner, Bob. Mastering Financial Calculations: A Step-by-Step Guide to the Mathematics of Financial Market Instruments. (Financial Times Ser.). (ENG., Illus.). (Orig.). 2nd rev. ed. 2007. 504p. pap. 79.99 *(978-0-273-70444-7(3))* 3rd rev. ed. 2012. 616p. pap. 79.99 ***(978-0-273-75058-1(5))*** FT Press.

Steland, A. Financial Statistics & Mathematical Finance: Methods, Models & Applications. 2012. (ENG.). 400p. 90.00 ***(978-0-470-71058-6(6)***, Wiley) Wiley, John & Sons, Inc.

Sterling, Mary Jane. Business Math for Dummies. 2008. (ENG., Illus.). 388p. pap. 21.99 *(978-0-470-23331-3(1)*, For Dummies) Wiley, John & Sons, Inc.

Stull. Marketing Math. 4th ed. Date not set. (SB - Marketing Education Ser.). (C). pap., tchr. ed. 40.95 *(978-0-538-68114-8(4))* Cengage South-Western.

Sullivan, Michael. Finite Mathematics: An Applied Approach. 9th ed. 2006. pap. 62.95 *(978-0-470-07967-6(3))* 10th ed. 2007. (ENG.). (C). 201.95 *(978-0-470-28754-5(3)*, Wiley) 11th ed. 2010. (ENG.). 864p. (C). 170.95 *(978-0-470-45827-3(5)*, Wiley) 11th ed. 2010. (ENG.). 294p. (C). pap. 48.95 *(978-0-470-45828-0(3)*, Wiley) Wiley, John & Sons, Inc.

—Finite Mathematics: An Applied Approach 10th Edition Binder Ready Version with Binder & Student Solutions Manual Set. 2007. (ENG.). (C). ring bd. 154.95 *(978-0-470-28752-1(7)*, Wiley) Wiley, John & Sons, Inc.

—Finite Mathematics: An Applied Approach 10th Edition Binder Ready Version with Student Solutions Manual Set. 2007. (ENG.). (C). ring bd. 147.95 *(978-0-470-28753-8(5)*, Wiley) Wiley, John & Sons, Inc.

—Finite Mathematics: An Applied Approach, Binder Ready Book. 10th ed. 2007. (ENG.). 864p. (C). ring bd. 113.95 *(978-0-470-27992-2(3)*, Wiley) Wiley, John & Sons, Inc.

—Finite Mathematics: An Applied Approach with Wiley Plus WebCT Powerpack Set. 9th ed. 2006. (Wiley Plus Products Ser.). 111.95 *(978-0-470-11567-1(X)*, Wiley) Wiley, John & Sons, Inc.

Sullivan, Michael & Mizrahi, Abe. Finite Mathematics: An Applied Approach. 9th rev. ed. 2006. (Wiley Plus Products Ser.). 1p. pap. 151.95 *(978-0-470-12830-5(5))* Wiley, John & Sons, Inc.

Sullivan, Mizrahi & Cram101 Textbook Reviews Staff. Finite Mathematics an Applied Approach. 2007. 104p. per. 10.95 *(978-1-4288-3666-2(7))* Cram101 Inc.

Talbott, John L. The Western Practical Arithmetic Containing a Great Variety of Exercises, Particularly Adapted to the Currency of the United States: To Which Is A. 2006. 260p. per. 23.99 *(978-1-4255-2270-4(X))* MPublishing.

Tepper, Bette K. Mathematics for Retail Buying. 5th rev. ed. 134p. pap. *(978-1-56367-196-8(4))* Fairchild Bks.

—Mathematics for Retail Buying 6th Edition. 6th rev. ed. 2008. (Illus.). 368p. pap. 110.00 *(978-1-56367-588-1(9))* Fairchild Bks.

Thomsett, Michael C. The Manager's Pocket Calculator: A Quick Guide to Essential Business Formulas & Ratios, 1 vol. 2010. (ENG.). 288p. pap. 18.95 *(978-0-8144-1635-8(7))* Amacom.

—The Stock Investor's Pocket Calculator: A Quick Guide to All the Formulas & Ratios You Need to Invest Like a Pro. 2007. (ENG., Illus.). 272p. per. 17.95 *(978-0-8144-7460-0(8))* Amacom.

Todorova, Tamara. Problems Book to Accompany Mathematics for Economists. 2010. (ENG.). 614p. (C). pap. 39.95 *(978-0-470-59181-9(1)*, Wiley) Wiley, John & Sons, Inc.

Treviño, Regina. PreMBA Analytical Primer: Essential Quantitative Concepts for Business Math. 2008. (ENG., Illus.). 224p. pap. 38.00 *(978-0-230-60913-6(9))* Palgrave Macmillan.

Treviño, Regina & Trevilo, Regina. PreMBA Analytical Primer: Essential Quantitative Concepts for Business Math. 2008. (ENG., Illus.). 224p. 105.00 *(978-0-230-60912-9(0))* Palgrave Macmillan.

Truchon, Richard P. Basic Business Math: Add New Skills & Multiply Your Success. 3rd ed. 2011. (ENG.). 152p. pap. 14.95 *(978-1-4260-1952-4(1))* Thomson NETg.

Ummer, E. K. Basic Mathematics with Mathematica for Economics Business & Finance. 2012. (ENG., Illus.). 496p. (C). 120.00 *(978-0-415-66419-6(5))*; pap. 71.95 *(978-0-415-66420-2(9))* Routledge.

Virdi, Surinder Singh & Baker, Roy T. Construction Mathematics. 2006. (ENG., Illus.). 296p. (C). per. 33.95 *(978-0-7506-6792-0(3))* Routledge.

Walsh, Thomas P. & Goozner, Calman. E-Z Business Math. 4th rev. ed. 2009. (Barron's E-Z Ser.). (ENG.). 336p. pap. 14.99 *(978-0-7641-4259-8(3))* Barron's Educational Series, Inc.

Whigham, David. Business Data Analysis using Excel. 2010. (ENG., Illus.). 312p. (C). 59.95 *(978-0-19-929628-6(6))* Oxford Univ. Pr., Inc.

White, Emerson Elbridge. Bryant & Stratton's Commercial Arithmetic by E E White G B Meriam & H B Bryant, & H D Stratton. 2006. 332p. per. 23.99 *(978-1-4255-3380-9(9))* MPublishing.

Wilson, Frank C. Finite Mathematics & Applied Calculus. 2007. (Illus.). xi, 964p. *(978-0-618-73265-4(9))* Houghton Mifflin Harcourt Publishing Co.

Wilson, Steven J. Business Math: Using Percents. 2nd rev. ed. 2011. (ENG.). 380p. pap. 89.84 *(978-0-7575-2605-3(5))* Kendall Hunt Publishing Co.

Winslow, Ezra S. The Universal Modern Cambist, & Foreign & Domestic Commercial Calculator; 2006. 256p. per. 23.99 *(978-1-4255-2226-1(2))* MPublishing.

Yor, Marc, ed. Aspects of Mathematical Finance. Qechar, K., tr. 2010. (Illus.). viii, 80p. pap. 49.95 *(978-3-642-09452-1(X)*, 364209452X) Springer.

—Aspects of Mathematical Finance. 2008. 100p. 49.95 *(978-3-540-75258-5(7)*, 3540752587) Springer.

2010 International Conference on Financial Theory & Engineering: ICFTE 2010: Proceedings: 18-20 June 2010, Dubai, United Arab Emirates. 2010. (Illus.). xiv, 364p. pap. ***(978-1-4244-7758-6(1))*** IEEE Computer Society Pr.

BUSINESS MATHEMATICS—PROBLEMS, EXERCISES, ETC.

Brechner, Robert. Contemporary Mathematics for Business & Consumers. 6th ed. 2011. (ENG.). 528p. (C). pap. 156.95 *(978-1-111-52937-6(X))* Cengage South-Western.

—Contemporary Mathematics for Business & Consumers (with Student Resource CD with MathCue. Business) 6th ed. 2011. (ENG.). 816p. (C). pap. 209.95 *(978-0-538-48125-0(0))* Cengage South-Western.

Brown, Robert & Zima, Petr. Mathematics of Finance. 2nd ed. 2011. (Schaum's Outline Ser.). (ENG., Illus.). 304p. (C). pap. 19.00 *(978-0-07-175605-1(1)*, 0071756051) McGraw-Hill Cos., The.

Cleaves, Cheryl & Hobbs, Margie. Business Math. 8th ed. 2008. (ENG.). 76p. (C). pap., pupil's gde. ed. 28.80 *(978-0-13-515011-5(6)*, Prentice Hall) Prentice Hall PTR.

Cram101 Textbook Reviews & Cram101 Textbook Reviews. Outlines & Highlights for Practical Business Math Procedures by Jeffrey Slater. 2011. 80p. pap. 27.95 ***(978-1-61830-548-0(4))*** Cram101 Inc.

Cram101 Textbook Reviews Staff. Outlines & Highlights for Contemporary Mathematics for Business & Consumers, Brief Edition by Robert Brechner, Isbn: 9780324658644. 2009. 106p. pap. 28.95 *(978-1-4288-3541-2(5))*; 86p. pap. 27.95 *(978-1-4288-7680-4(4))* Cram101 Inc.

—Outlines & Highlights for Contemporary Mathematics for Business & Consumers by Robert Brechner, Isbn: 9780324568493. 2009. 142p. pap. 28.95 *(978-1-4288-2229-0(1))* Cram101 Inc.

Dowling, Edward & Dowling, Edward T. Schaum's Outline of Mathematical Methods for Business & Economics. 2009. (Schaum's Outline Ser.). (ENG.). 408p. (C). pap. 20.00 *(978-0-07-163532-5(7)*, 0071635327) McGraw-Hill Cos., The.

Easterling, Cynthia R., et al. Merchandising Mathematics for Retailing. 4th ed. 2007. (ENG., Illus.) 384p. (C). per. 99.40 *(978-0-13-193643-0(3)*, Prentice Hall) Prentice Hall PTR.

Laughbaum, Edward D. & Seidel, Ken. Business Math Excel Applications for Business Mathematics. 2nd ed. 2008. (ENG.). 80p. (C). pap. 23.00 *(978-0-13-607184-6(8)*, Prentice Hall) Prentice Hall PTR.

Pasewark, William R. Calculators: Printing & Display. 5th ed. 2011. (FBLA - All Ser.). (ENG.). 144p. (C). pap. 44.95 *(978-0-8400-6535-3(3))* Cengage South-Western.

Slater & Cram101 Textbook Reviews Staff. Practical Business Math Procedures. 2007. 96p. per. 10.95 *(978-1-4288-3688-4(8))* Cram101 Inc.

Slater, Jeffrey. Loose-leaf Practical Business Math Procedures. 10th ed. 2010. (C). ring bd. 113.44 *(978-0-07-740363-8(0)*, 0077403630, McGraw-Hill/Irwin) McGraw-Hill Higher Education.

—Loose-leaf Practical Business Math Procedures Brief Edition. 10th ed. 2010. (C). ring bd. 91.88 *(978-0-07-740364-5(9)*, 0077403649, McGraw-Hill/Irwin) McGraw-Hill Higher Education.

—Practical Business Math Procedures. 9th ed. 2008. (Illus.). *(978-0-07-313767-4(7))* 9th ed. 2008. (Illus.). *(978-0-07-327863-6(7))* 9th ed. 2008. (Illus.). *(978-0-07-327849-0(1))* 9th ed. 2008. (Illus.). *(978-0-07-327867-4(X))* 10th ed. 2011. *(978-0-07-732793-4(4))* 10th ed. 2011. *(978-0-07-732785-9(3))* 10th ed. 2011. (Illus.). *(978-0-07-732784-2(5))* 10th ed. 2011. (Illus.). 752p. pap. *(978-0-07-337753-7(8))* McGraw-Hill Cos., The.

Varner, Iris & Beamer, Linda. Intercultural Communication in the Global Workplace. 5th ed. 2010. (ENG., Illus.). 528p. (C). pap. 143.33 *(978-0-07-337774-2(0)*, 0073377740, McGraw-Hill/Irwin) McGraw-Hill Higher Education.

Varner, Iris, et al. Intercultural Communication in the Global Workplace. 3rd ed. 2010. (ENG.). 384p. (C). pap. 43.44 *(978-0-07-730167-5(6)*, 0077301676, McGraw-Hill/Irwin) McGraw-Hill Higher Education.

Warren, Amos W. The Young Man's Best Companion, or, Mathematica Compendium, Containing a Great Variety of Very Useful Rules & Examples in Mathematics for the Merch. 2006. 188p. per. 18.99 *(978-1-4255-1504-1(5))* MPublishing.

BUSINESS MATHEMATICS—PROGRAMMED INSTRUCTION

Clendenen, Gary, et al. Business Mathematics. 12th ed. 2012. (Illus.). *(978-0-13-254564-8(0))* Prentice Hall PTR.

—Business Mathematics Brief. 12th ed. 2011. (ENG.). 688p. (C). pap. 141.60 *(978-0-13-254587-7(X))* Addison Wesley.

Miller, Charles David, et al. Business Mathematics. 11th ed. 2007. *(978-0-321-51805-7(5))* Addison-Wesley Longman, Inc.

Miller, Salzman & Cram101 Textbook Reviews Staff. Business Mathematics. 2007. 80p. per. 10.95 *(978-1-4288-3536-8(9))* Cram101 Inc.

BUSINESS MATHEMATICS—REAL ESTATE BUSINESS

Friedman, Jack P., et al. Real Estate Handbook. 7th rev. ed. 2009. (ENG., Illus.). 784p. 39.99 *(978-0-7641-6110-0(5))* Barron's Educational Series, Inc.

BUSINESS MEN

see Businesspeople

BUSINESS MERGERS

see Consolidation and Merger of Corporations

BUSINESS MORTALITY

see Business Failures

BUSINESS NAMES

see also Brand Name Products; Trademarks

Adamson, Allen P. BrandSimple: How the Best Brands Keep It Simple & Succeed. 2007. (ENG., Illus.). 256p. pap. 14.95 *(978-1-4039-8490-6(5))* Palgrave Macmillan.

Balmer. Revealing the Corporation. 2nd ed. 2009. pap. 55.95 *(978-0-415-77346-1(6))* 2008. (ENG.). 352p. 160.00 *(978-0-415-77345-4(8))* Routledge.

Barlow, Janelle & Stewart, Paul. Branded Customer Service: The New Competitive Edge. 2006. (ENG.). 264p. pap. 22.95 *(978-1-57675-404-7(9))* Berrett-Koehler Pubs., Inc.

Basini, Justin. Why Should Anyone Buy from You? Earn Customer Trust to Drive Business Success. rev. ed. 2011. (Financial Times Ser.). (ENG.). 224p. pap. 24.99 *(978-0-273-74551-8(4))* FT Press.

Bouchikhi, Hamid & Kimberly, John R. The Soul of the Corporation: How to Manage the Identity of Your Company. 2007. (ENG.). 256p. pap. 32.99 *(978-0-13-259814-9(0))* Wharton Schl. Publishing.

Brands & Their Companies, 2.0. 35th ed. 2011. 1525.00 *(978-1-4144-5815-1(0))* Cengage Gale.

Burton, T. Naming Rights. 2008. (ENG.). 256p. 52.50 *(978-0-470-23063-3(0)*, Wiley) Wiley, John & Sons, Inc.

Companies & Their Brands, 2.0. 35th ed. 2011. 1023.00 *(978-1-4144-5835-9(5))* Cengage Gale.

Conley, Lucas. OBD: Obsessive Branding Disorder. 2008. (ENG.). 240p. 22.95 *(978-1-58648-468-2(0))* PublicAffairs.

Coomber, Stephen. Branding. 2nd rev. ed. 2007. 136p. pap. 18.95 *(978-1-84112-706-4(X))* Wiley, John & Sons, Inc.

Dvorak, Doug. Build Your Own Brand, 1 vol. 2010. (ENG., Illus.). 160p. 23.00 *(978-1-58980-699-3(9))* Pelican Publishing Co., Inc.

Elias, Stephen & Stim, Richard. Trademark: Legal Care for Your Business & Product Name. 9th rev. ed. 2010. (ENG., Illus.). 464p. pap. 39.99 *(978-1-4133-1256-0(X))* NOLO.

Fuguo, Yu. Big Brand. Lu, Jican, ed. 2008. (ENG., Illus.). 320p. 70.00 *(978-4-903233-29-1(4))* Azur Corp. JPN. Dist: Antique Collectors' Club.

Howard, Jim, et al. Branded for Success: The Entrepreneur's Quick-Start Guide to Making a Profitable, Lasting Impression. 2007. (ENG.). per. 16.95 *(978-1-60037-169-1(8))* Morgan James Publishing.

Ind, Nicholas. Living the Brand: How to Transform Every Member of Your Organization into a Brand Champion. 3rd rev. ed. 2007. (ENG., Illus.). 200p. 39.95 *(978-0-7494-5083-0(5))* Kogan Page, Ltd. GBR. Dist: Ingram Pub. Services.

Klaming, Gunnar. Brands Versus Information- the Changing Role of Brands in the Age of Empowered Consumers. 2007. 144p. per. *(978-3-8364-0709-0(4))* VDM Verlag Dr. Mueller e K.

Komaitis, Konstantinos. The Current State of Domain Name Regulation: Domain Names as Second Class Citizens in a Mark-Dominated World. 2012. (ENG.). 296p. pap. 44.95 ***(978-0-415-63153-7(0))*** Routledge.

Land, Bob. America's Greatest Brands. (Americas Greatest Brands Ser.). (ENG.). 2011. 116p. 45.00 ***(978-0-9706860-8-4(0))*** 2009. 113p. 45.00 *(978-0-9706860-6-0(4))* America's Greatest Brands.

Land, Bob. America's Greatest Brands: An Insight into Many of America's Strongest & Most Valuable Brands. (America's Greatest Brands Ser.). (ENG., Illus.). 2007. 118p. 60.00 *(978-0-9706860-5-3(6))* 2006. 126p. 75.00 *(978-0-9706860-4-6(8))* America's Greatest Brands.

Land, Bob, ed. America's Greatest Brands: An Insight into Many of America's Strongest & Most Valuable Brands 2011. (America's Greatest Brands Ser.). (ENG., Illus.). 112p. 45.00 *(978-0-9706860-7-7(2))* America's Greatest Brands.

Lindemann, Jan. The Economy of Brands. 2010. (ENG., Illus.). 192p. 47.00 *(978-0-230-23250-1(7))* Palgrave Macmillan.

Novak, David & Boswell, John. The Education of an Accidental CEO: Lessons Learned from the Trailer Park to the Corner Office. 2009. (ENG.). 320p. pap. 15.00 *(978-0-307-45179-8(8)*, Three Rivers Pr.) Crown Publishing Group.

Picker, Ursula. Zur Instrumentalisierung von Geschichte in der Franzosischen Ergonymik. (Bonner Romanistische Arbeiten Ser.: Vol. 82). (GER., Illus.). 252p. 37.95 *(978-3-631-50770-4(4))* Lang, Peter Publishing, Inc.

Praninskas, Jean. Trade name Creation: Processes & Patterns. (Janua Linguarum. Series Practica Ser.). (ENG.). 115p. 210.00 ***(978-3-11-197712-6(9))***; 135.00 ***(978-3-11-100079-4(6))*** De Gruyter, Mouton DEU. Dist: de Gruyter, Walter GmbH & Co. KG.

Room, Adrian. Encyclopedia of Corporate Names Worldwide, 2 vols. alt. ed. 2008. (ENG.). 591p. pap. 65.00 *(978-0-7864-3765-8(0))* McFarland & Co., Inc. Pubs.

Taylor, Neil. The Name of the Beast: The Process & Perils of Naming Products, Companies & Brands. 2006. (Illus.). 224p. per. 24.95 *(978-1-904879-70-1(5))* Cyan Communications GBR. Dist: Independent Pubs. Group.

Vallaster, Christine & Fisher, Claudia. Connective Branding: Building Brand Equity in a Demanding World. 2008. (ENG., Illus.). 380p. 60.00 *(978-0-470-51240-1(7)*, Wiley) Wiley, John & Sons, Inc.

Van Tongeren, Michel. Retail Branding: From Stopping Power to Shopping Power. 2nd ed. 2008. (ENG., Illus.). 160p. 55.00 *(978-90-6369-043-4(6))* Bis B.V., Uitgeverij(BIS Publishers) NLD. Dist: Consortium Bk. Sales & Distribution.

Wallace, Margot A. Museum Branding: How to Create & Maintain Image, Loyalty, & Support. 2006. (ENG., Illus.). 208p. 87.50 *(978-0-7591-0992-6(3))*; per. 30.95 *(978-0-7591-0993-3(1))* AltaMira Pr.

Weinberger, Ralf. Cultural Differences in Sensory Brands. 2008. 120p. pap. *(978-3-639-02577-4(6))* VDM Verlag Dr. Mueller e.K.

Wow Branding Staff, ed. Logo Savvy: Top Brand-Design Firms Share Their Naming & Identity Strategies. 2007. (ENG., Illus.). 192p. 40.00 *(978-1-59253-304-6(3)*, 1592533043) Quayside.

Yastrow, Steve. Brand Harmony: Achieving Dynamic Results by Orchestrating Your Customer's Total Experience. 2010. 176p. pap. 16.95 *(978-1-59079-199-8(1))* Select Bks.

BUSINESS NETWORKS

Here are entered works on groupings of organizations or individuals who combine, either intermittently or on a longer term basis, to achieve specific business objectives.

see also Strategic Alliances (Business)

Abraham, Joel. Hired! Networking to Land the Job YOU Want. 2011. 100p. pap. 14.99 ***(978-1-4567-4564-6(6))*** AuthorHouse.

Achwan, Rochman. Weaving Business Networks in Indonesi. 2011. 224p. pap. ***(978-3-8443-2250-7(7))*** Lambert Academic Publishing.

Afsarmanesh, Hamideh, et al, eds. Network-Centric Collaboration & Supporting Frameworks: IFIP TC5 WG 5. 5, Seventh IFIP Working Conference on Virtual Enterprises, 25-27 September 2006, Helsinki, Finland. 2006. (IFIP International Federation for Information Processing Ser.). (Illus.). 653p. 229.00 (978-0-387-38266-1(6), 0387382666) Springer.

Alba, Jason. I'm on Linkedin — Now What??? A Guide to Getting the Most Out of LinkedIn. 2011. 154p. pap. 19.95 **(978-1-60005-197-5(9))** Happy About.

Ali, Mohammad M. Centralised Demand Information Sharing in Supply Chains: A Consumer Centric Approach. 2011. (Illus.). 284p. pap. **(978-3-639-28435-5(6))** VDM Verlag Dr. Mueller e.K.

An, Wu Xiao. Chinese Business Making Malay. 2010. (Illus.). 239p. pap. 28.00 (978-9971-69-496-8(4)) National Univ. of Singapore Pr. SGP. Dist: Univ. of Hawaii Pr.

Anklam, Patti. Net Work: A Practical Guide to Creating & Sustaining Networks at Work & in the World. 2011. (ENG., Illus.). 288p. per. 36.95 (978-0-7506-8297-8(3)) Routledge.

Antonelli, Dario & Villa, Agostino, eds. A Road Map to the Development of European SME Networks: Towards Collaborative Innovation. 2008. (ENG., Illus.). xii, 189p. 139.00 (978-1-84800-341-5(2), 1848003412) Springer.

Association for Computing Machinery (ACM) Staff, compiled by. Workshop on Game Theory for Communications & Networks (GameNets 2006) 2007. (ACM International Conference Proceedings Ser.). 103p. pap. 75.00 (978-1-60423-266-0(8)) Curran Assocs., Inc.

Baber, Anne & Waymon, Lynne. Make Your Contacts Count: Networking Know-How for Business & Career Success. 2nd rev. ed. 2007. (ENG., Illus.). 272p. pap. 14.95 (978-0-8144-7402-0(0)) Amacom.

Back, Andrea, et al, eds. Knowledge Networks for Business Growth. 2010. (ENG., Illus.). xii, 226p. pap. 99.00 (978-3-642-06960-4(6), 3642069606) Springer.

Baudry, Bernard & Dubrion, Benjamin. Analyses et Transformations de la Firme: Une Approche Pluridisciplinaire. 2009. (FRE., Illus.). 375p. (978-2-7071-5801-7(1)) La Decouverte Editions.

Baxter, Roger, ed. Interfirm Networks: Theory, Strategy, & Behavior. 2011. (Advances in Business Marketing & Purchasing Ser.). 496p. (978-1-78052-024-7(7)) Emerald Group Publishing Ltd.

Behnken, Edda. Innovationsmanagement in Netzwerken: Analyse und Handlungskonzept zur kollektiven Innovationsgenerierung. 2010. (Strukturwandel und Strukturpolitik. Structural Change & Structural Policies. Ser.). 424p. 101.95 (978-3-631-61282-8(6)) Lang, Peter GmbH, Europaischer Verlag der Wissenschaften DEU. Dist: Lang, Peter.

Bell and, Smith. Building Your Network Through Communicat. 2006. pap. 8.95 (978-1-4288-0647-4(4)) Cram101 Inc.

Belussi, Fiorenza. Business Networks in Clusters & Industrial Districts: The Governance of the Global Value Chain. Sammarra, Alessia, ed. 2009. (Regions & Cities Ser.). (ENG., Illus.). 418p. 160.00 (978-0-415-45784-2(X)) Routledge.

Belussi, Fiorenza & Sammarra, Alessia, eds. Business Networks in Clusters & Industrial Districts: The Governance of the Global Value Chain. 2012. (ENG., Illus.). 418p. (C). pap. 43.56 **(978-0-415-53985-2(4))** Routledge.

Belussi, Fiorenza & STABER, U. D. O. Hermann, eds. Managing Networks of Creativity. 2011. (ENG., Illus.). 396p. (C). 125.00 (978-0-415-88764-9(X)) Routledge.

Benjamin, Susan. Professional Networking: Hundreds of Ready-to-Use Phrases for Meeting & Keeping Helpful Contacts Everywhere You Go. 2009. (Perfect Phrases Ser.). (ENG.). 208p. pap. 10.95 (978-0-07-162916-4(5), 0071629165) McGraw-Hill Cos., The.

Bettison, Tina. Social Networking for Rookies. 2009. (Illus.). 192p. pap. (978-0-462-09954-5(7)) Marshall Cavendish.

Bhat, Sushma Seth. Inter-Organisational Cooperation & Networks in Destination Marketing. 2010. 292p. pap. (978-3-639-13753-8(1)) VDM Verlag Dr. Mueller e.K.

Bhattacharya, Jayati. Beyond the Myth: Indian Business Communities in Singapore. 2011. (Illus.). xxv, 371p. **(978-981-4345-27-9(X))** Institute of Southeast Asian Studies.

Binder, Mario & Clegg, Ben, eds. Sustainable Supplier Management in the Automotive Industry: Leading the 3rd Revolution through Collaboration. 2010. (Transportation Issues, Policies & R&D Ser.). 158p. pap. 38.70 (978-1-61668-675-8(8)) Nova Science Pubs., Inc.

Bing, Benny. Broadband Video Networking. 2010. (Illus.). 400p. 129.00 (978-1-60807-051-0(4)) Artech Hse., Inc.

Bjorseth, Lillian D. Breakthrough Networking: Building Relationships That Last (third Edition) 2009. spiral bd. 21.95 (978-0-9648839-4-9(5)) Duoforce Enterprises, Inc.

Blien, Uwe & Maier, Gunther. The Economics of Regional Clusters: Networks, Technology, & Policy. Blien, Uwe, ed. 2008. (New Horizons in Regional Science Ser.). (Illus.). 320p. (C). 137.00 (978-1-84720-515-5(1)) Elgar, Edward Publishing, Inc.

Boothman, Nicholas. Convince Them in 90 Seconds: How to Connect in Business. 2010. (ENG.). 295p. pap. 12.95 (978-0-7611-5855-4(3), 0761158553) Workman Publishing Co., Inc.

Borgo, Stefano & Lesmo, Leonardo. Formal Ontologies Meet Industry. 2008. (Illus.). x, 157p. 116.00 (978-1-58603-871-7(0)) IOS Pr., Inc.

Borras, Susana & Tsagdis, Dimitrios. Cluster Policies in Europe: Firms, Institutions & Governance. 2009. 304p. 130.00 (978-1-84542-758-0(0)) Elgar, Edward Publishing, Inc.

Brand, Jason. The Crowdsourcing Handbook - Everything you need to know about Crowdsourcing. 2011. (Illus.). 219p. pap. (978-1-74304-095-9(4), Tebbo) Emereo Pty Ltd.

Bratvold, David. Crowdsourcing for Dummies. 2012. (ENG.). 384p. pap. 19.99 **(978-1-119-94040-1(0)**, For Dummies) Wiley, John & Sons, Inc.

Brown, Mike, et al. Intelligent Information Integration in B2B Electronic Commerce. 2010. (Springer International Series in Engineering & Computer Science Ser.). 160p. pap. 159.00 (978-1-4419-5305-6(1), 1441953051) Springer.

Burghouwt, Guillaume. Airline Network Development in Europe & its Implications for Airport Planning. 2007. (Illus.). 300p. 124.95 (978-0-7546-4506-1(1)) Ashgate Publishing Co.

Burt, Ronald S. Brokerage & Closure: An Introduction to Social Capital. 2007. (Clarendon Lectures in Management Studies). (ENG., Illus.). 304p. pap. 34.99 (978-0-19-924915-2(6)) Oxford Univ. Pr., Inc.

Burt, Ronald S. Neighbor Networks: Competitive Advantage Local & Personal. 2011. (ENG.). 416p. pap. 29.95 **(978-0-19-969191-3(6))** Oxford Univ. Pr., Inc.

Camarinha-Matos, Luis M., et al, eds. Adaptation & Value Creating Collaborative Networks: 12th IFIP WG 5. 5 Working Conference on Virtual Enterprises, PRO-VE 2011, Sao Paulo, Brazil, October 17-19, 2011, Proceedings. 2011. (IFIP Advances in Information & Communication Technology Ser.). (ENG., Illus.). xvii, 566p. 169.00 **(978-3-642-23329-6(5)**, 3642233295) Springer.

Camarinha-Matos, Luis M., et al, eds. Network-Centric Collaboration & Supporting Frameworks: IFIP TC 5 WG 5. 5, Seventh IFIP Working Conference on Virtual Enterprises, 25-27 September 2006, Helsinki, Finland. 2010. (IFIP Advances in Information & Communication Technology Ser.). xiv, 653p. pap. 229.00 (978-1-4419-4257-9(2), 1441942572) Springer.

Cappellin, Riccardo & Wink, Rudiger. International Knowledge & Innovation Networks: Knowledge Creation & Innovation in Medium-technology Clusters. 2009. (New Horizons in Regional Science Ser.). (Illus.). 288p. 127.00 (978-1-84844-441-6(9)) Elgar, Edward Publishing, Inc.

Carayannis, Elias G. & Formica, Piero, eds. Knowledge Matters: Technology, Innovation & Entrepreneurship in Innovation Networks & Knowledge Clusters. 2008. (ENG., Illus.). 288p. 95.00 (978-1-4039-9872-9(8)) Palgrave Macmillan.

Casson, Mark & Giusta, Marina Della, eds. The Economics of Networks, 2 vols. 2008. (International Library of Critical Writings in Economics Ser.). (Illus.). 432p. (C). 210.00 (978-1-84720-365-6(5)) Elgar, Edward Publishing, Inc.

Chambers, John, ed. The Truth about Networking: Strategic Business Networking, the Facts You Should Know. 2009. 209p. pap. (978-1-74244-160-3(2), Tebbo) Emereo Pty Ltd.

Chu, Sam. Managing Knowledge for Global & Collaborative Innovations. 2009. 432p. 135.00 (978-981-4299-85-5(5)) World Scientific Publishing Co., Inc.

Ciravegna, Luciano. Promoting Silicon Valleys in Latin America. 2012. (Illus.). xv, 156p. **(978-0-203-12728-5(5))** Routledge.

Clegg, Stewart R., et al. Business Networks & Strategic Alliances in China. 2007. 352p. (C). 150.00 (978-1-84542-306-3(2)) Elgar, Edward Publishing, Inc.

Cooke, Philip & Piccaluga, Andrea, eds. Regional Development in the Knowledge Economy. 2009. 278p. pap. 39.60 (978-0-415-57863-9(9)) Routledge.

Corallo, Angelo, et al, eds. The Digital Business Ecosystem. 2007. (Illus.). 264p. 119.00 (978-1-84720-043-3(5)) Elgar, Edward Publishing, Inc.

Corday, Kathy. The Networking Field Guide: Essential Social Skills for Business. 2010. (ENG., Illus.). 150p. pap. 13.95 (978-0-9843897-0-4(9)) Alchemy Media Group, Inc.

Cram101 Textbook Reviews Staff. Outlines & Highlights for Achieving Success Through Social Capital by Baker, Isbn: 1428865942. 2009. 80p. pap. 10.95 (978-1-4288-6594-5(2)) Cram101 Inc.

—Outlines & Highlights for Network Challenge: Strategy, Profit, & Risk in an Interlinked World by Paul R. Kleindorfer, ISBN. 2009. 202p. pap. 30.95 (978-1-4288-8985-9(X)) Cram101 Inc.

Cross, Robert L. & Thomas, Robert J. Driving Results Through Social Networks: How Top Organizations Leverage Networks for Performance & Growth. 2009. (J-B US Non-Franchise Leadership Ser.: 35). (ENG., Illus.). 240p. 29.95 (978-0-470-39249-2(5), Jossey-Bass) Wiley, John & Sons, Inc.

Cross, Robert L., et al. The Organizational Network Fieldbook: Best Practices, Techniques & Exercises to Drive Organizational Innovation & Performance. 2010. (ENG., Illus.). 384p. pap. 50.00 (978-0-470-54220-0(9), Jossey-Bass) Wiley, John & Sons, Inc.

Cruz-Cunha, Maria Manuela. Handbook of Research on Business Social Networking: Organizational, Managerial & Technological Dimensions. 2011. **(978-1-61350-170-2(6))**; 956p. pap. 495.00 **(978-1-61350-168-9(4))** IGI Global.

Cumbers, Andy, ed. Clusters in Urban & Regional Development. 2009. 252p. pap. 39.95 (978-0-415-56841-8(2)) Routledge.

Cummings, Tom & Keen, Jim. Leadership Landscapes. 2008. (ENG., Illus.). 200p. 50.00 (978-0-230-52569-6(5)) Palgrave Macmillan.

Curtis, Gordon S. Well Connected: An Unconventional Approach to Building Genuine, Effective Business Relationships. 2010. (ENG.). 240p. 26.95 (978-0-470-57794-3(0), Jossey-Bass) Wiley, John & Sons, Inc.

Darling, Diane. The Networking Survival Guide: Practical Advice to Help You Gain Confidence, Approach People, & Get the Success You Want. 2nd ed. 2010. (ENG.). 288p. pap. 16.95 (978-0-07-171758-8(7), 0071717587) McGraw-Hill Cos., The.

Das, T. K. Behavioral Perspectives on Strategic Alliances. 2011. **(978-1-61735-539-4(9))**; pap. **(978-1-61735-538-7(0))**; E-Book **(978-1-61735-540-0(2))** Information Age Publishing, Inc.

Dauser, Regina. Informationskultur und Beziehungswissen: Das Korrespondenznetz Hans Fuggers, 1531-1598. 2008. (Studia Augustana Ser.). (GER., Illus.). IX, 458p. (978-3-484-16516-8(2)) Verlag Max Niemeyer.

Davies, Chris. Winning Client Trust. 2011. 250p. pap. **(978-1-907722-46-2(7))** Ecademy Pr. Ltd.

Dawson, Ross. Living Networks: Leading Your Company, Customers, & Partners in the Hyper-Connected Economy. anniv. ed. 2008. (Illus.). 247p. pap. 24.95 (978-1-84799-560-5(8)) Lulu Enterprises Inc.

Dezell, Tom. Networking for the Novice, Nervous, or Naïve Job Seeker. 2009. 112p. 23.95 (978-1-4401-6611-2(0)); pap. 13.95 (978-1-4401-6609-9(9)) iUniverse, Inc.

Doerges, David. Master Networker's Manual. 2007. 42p. pap. 8.95 (978-0-9790768-3-1(8)) Jimsam Inc. Publishing.

Donaldson, Bill & O'Toole, Tom. Strategic Market Relationships: From Strategy to Implementation. 2nd rev. ed. 2007. (ENG., Illus.). 288p. per. 70.95 (978-0-470-02880-3(7), Wiley) Wiley, John & Sons, Inc.

Doyle, Alison. Internet Your Way to a New Job: How to Really Find a Job Online. 2011. 152p. pap. 19.95 **(978-1-60005-199-9(5))** Happy About.

D'Souza, Steven. Brilliant Networking: What the Best Networkers Know, Say & Do. 2nd ed. 2011. (ENG., Illus.). 288p. (C). pap. 19.99 (978-0-273-74321-7(X)) FT Press.

Dulworth, Michael. The Connect Effect: Building Strong Personal, Professional, & Virtual Networks. 2008. (ENG., Illus.). 220p. 22.95 (978-1-57675-462-7(6)) Berrett-Koehler Pubs., Inc.

Duranton, Gilles, et al. The Economics of Clusters: Lessons from the French Experience. 2011. (ENG., Illus.). 192p. 65.00 (978-0-19-959220-3(9)) Oxford Univ. Pr., Inc.

Dyker, David A. Network Dynamics in Emerging Regions of Europe. 2010. 350p. 111.00 (978-1-84816-373-7(8)) Imperial College Pr. GBR. Dist: World Scientific Publishing Co., Inc.

Elwins, Dannie. How to Think Like Successful Internet Entrepreneurs. 2009. 40p. pap. 16.99 (978-0-557-15707-5(2)) Lulu Enterprises Inc.

Entrepreneur Press, et al. Business Networking & Sex Not What You Think. 2011. (ENG.). 256p. pap. 21.95 **(978-1-59918-424-1(9)**, 1599184249) Entrepreneur Pr. dba Entrepreneur Media, Inc.

Fardanesh, Bagher. Global Communications & Misunderstanding. 2009. (Illus.). 156p. pap. 16.95 (978-0-7414-5341-9(X)) Infinity Publishing.

Farrell, Henry. The Political Economy of Trust: Institutions, Interests, & Inter-Firm Cooperation in Italy & Germany. 2012. (Cambridge Studies in Comparative Politics Ser.). (ENG., Illus.). 258p. pap. 34.99 **(978-1-107-40430-4(4))** Cambridge Univ. Pr.

Farrell, Henry. The Political Economy of Trust: Institutions, Interests, & Inter-Firm Cooperation in Italy & Germany. 2009. (Cambridge Studies in Comparative Politics Ser.). (ENG., Illus.). 256p. 98.00 (978-0-521-88649-9(X)) Cambridge Univ. Pr.

Faulkner, Michael L. & Nierenberg, Andrea. Networking for College Students (and Recent Graduates) Nonstop Business Networking That Will Change Your Life. 2010. (ENG.). 114p. (C). pap. 14.93 (978-0-558-85687-8(X)) Pearson Learning Solutions.

Fernández Pérez, Paloma. Innovation & Entrepreneurial Networks in Europe. Rose, Mary, ed. 2009. (Routledge International Studies in Business History Ser.). (ENG., Illus.). 230p. (C). 125.00 (978-0-415-45451-3(4)) Routledge.

Fernandez, Sonia & Fernández, Sonia. Two Degrees of Separation: Creating a Truly Effective Network of Contacts. 2007. (ENG., Illus.). 256p. pap. 15.95 (978-1-904879-92-3(6)) Marshall Cavendish GBR. Dist: Midpoint Trade Bks., Inc.

Ferrario, R. & Oltramari, A., eds. Formal Ontologies Meet Industry. 2009. (Ambient Intelligence & Smart Environments Ser.). 144p. 145.00 (978-1-60750-047-6(7)) IOS Pr., Inc.

Fischer, Manfred M. Innovation, Networks, & Knowledge Spillovers: Selected Essays. 2010. (ENG., Illus.). viii, 272p. pap. 159.00 (978-3-642-07150-8(3), 3642071503) Springer.

Flynn, Nancy & Flynn, Nanc. Networking for Success: Master the Art of Making Personal Contacts. 2nd ed. 2011. (ENG.). 102p. pap. 14.95 (978-1-4260-1942-5(4)) Thomson NETg.

Ford, David, et al. The Business Marketing Course: Managing in Complex Networks. 2nd rev. ed. 2006. (ENG., Illus.). 288p. per. 65.95 (978-0-470-03450-7(5), Wiley) Wiley, John & Sons, Inc.

Ford, David I., et al. Business in Networks. 2010. (ENG., Illus.). 318p. pap. 74.95 (978-0-470-74963-0(6), Wiley) Wiley, John & Sons, Inc.

Fornahl, Dirk, et al. Emerging Clusters: Theoretical, Empirical & Political Perspectives on the Initial Stage of Cluster Evolution. Fornahl, Dirk et al, eds. 2010. (Industrial Dynamics, Entrepreneurship & Innovation Ser.). (Illus.). 384p. 155.00 (978-1-84844-522-2(9)) Elgar, Edward Publishing, Inc.

Fortanier, Fabienne & van Tulder, Rob. Networking for Development. 2006. (Illus.). 224p. 49.95 (978-0-415-33916-2(2)); 160.00 (978-0-415-33915-5(4)) Routledge.

Fouquet, Gerhard & Gilomen, Hans-Jörg. Netzwerke im europäischen Handel des Mittelalters: Herausgegeben vom Konstanzer Arbeitskreis für mittelalterliche Geschichte. 2010. (Illus.). 397p. (978-3-7995-6872-2(7)) Thorbecke, Jan Verlag Gmbh & Co.

Fraser, George C. & Fraser, George MacDonald. Click: Ten Truths for Building Extraordinary Relationships. 2009. (ENG.). 256p. pap. 16.95 (978-0-07-162712-2(X), 007162712X) McGraw-Hill Cos., The.

Fraser, Matthew & Dutta, Soumitra. Throwing Sheep in the Boardroom: How Online Social Networking Will Transform Your Life, Work & World. 2008. (ENG., Illus.). 344p. 29.95 (978-0-470-74014-9(0), Wiley) Wiley, John & Sons, Inc.

Fung, Victor K., et al. Competing in a Flat World: Building Enterprises for a Borderless World. 2007. (ENG.). 272p. pap. 29.99 (978-0-13-261818-2(4)) Wharton Schl. Publishing.

Ganne, Bernard. Asian Industrial Clusters, Global Competitiveness & New Policy Initiatives. 2009. 600p. 130.00 (978-981-4280-12-9(7)) World Scientific Publishing Co., Inc.

Gérard, Cliquet, et al, eds. Economics & Management of Networks: Franchising, Strategic Alliances, & Cooperatives. 2007. (Contributions to Management Science Ser.). (ENG., Illus.). viii, 465p. pap. 169.00 (978-3-7908-1757-7(0), 3790817570) Physica-Verlag DEU. Dist: Springer.

Gerson, Donna. Building Career Connections: Networking Tools for Law Students & New Lawyers. 2007. pap. 25.00 (978-1-55733-052-9(2)) National Assn. for Law Placement.

Gibbert, Michael & Durand, Thomas, eds. Strategic Networks: Learning to Compete. 2007. (Strategic Management Society Ser.). (ENG., Illus.). 216p. 95.00 (978-1-4051-3585-6(9), Wiley-Blackwell) Wiley, John & Sons, Inc.

Glaeser, Edward L., ed. Agglomeration Economics. 2010. (National Bureau of Economic Research Conference Report). (ENG., Illus.). 376p. 99.00 (978-0-226-29789-7(6)) Univ. of Chicago Pr.

Glavee-Geo, Richard. Organizational Buying Behavior. 2009. 100p. pap. (978-3-639-22199-2(0)) VDM Verlag Dr. Mueller e.K.

Gossling, Tobias, et al. Inside Networks: A Process View on Multi-Organisational Partnerships, Alliances & Networks. 2007. (Illus.). 320p. 137.00 (978-1-84542-784-9(X)) Elgar, Edward Publishing, Inc.

Graen, George B. & Graen, Joni A. Knowledge-Driven Corporation: Complex Creative Destruction. 2008. (LMX Leadership Ser.). (Illus.). 264p. (C). (978-1-59311-942-3(9)); pap. (978-1-59311-941-6(0)) Information Age Publishing, Inc.

—New Multinational Network Sharing. 2007. (LMX Leadership Ser.). (ENG.). 248p. (978-1-59311-772-6(8)); per. (978-1-59311-771-9(X)) Information Age Publishing, Inc.

Graf, Margarete. Networks in the Innovation Process Local & Regional Interactions. 2007. 224p. (C). 119.00 (978-1-84542-930-0(3)) Elgar, Edward Publishing, Inc.

Grewal, David Singh. Network Power: The Social Dynamics of Globalization. 2009. (ENG.). 416p. pap. 18.00 (978-0-300-15134-3(9)) 2008. 760p. pap. 45.00 (978-0-300-14442-0(3)) Yale Univ. Pr.

Groothedde, Bas. Logistics Network Design & Collaboration: Design, Theory, & Practice. 2009. 250p. 129.00 (978-3-7908-2047-8(4)) Physica-Verlag DEU. Dist: Springer.

Grünberg-Bochard, Jutta. Die Entwicklung Eines Profils Erfolgreicher Governance FüR Interorganisatorische Wissensproduktionsnetzwerke Mit Akteursdiversität: Eine Theoretische Betrachtung Aus Sicht des Wissensgovernanceansatzes. 2011. (Europäische Hochschulschriften. Reihe 5: Volks- und Betriebswirtschaft Ser.). (GER.). 434p. pap. 101.95 **(978-3-631-61669-7(4))** Lang, Peter GmbH, Europaischer Verlag der Wissenschaften DEU. Dist: Lang, Peter.

Guest, Robert. Borderless Economics: Chinese Sea Turtles, Indian Fridges & the New Fruits of Global Capitalism. 2011. (ENG., Illus.). 256p. 27.00 (978-0-230-11382-4(6)) Palgrave Macmillan.

Guilmette, Jean-H. The Power of Peer Learning: Networks & Development Cooperation. 2008. (ENG., Illus.). 276p. 41.95 (978-81-7188-622-7(1)) Academic Foundation IND. Dist: Independent Pubs. Group.

Gulati, Ranjay. Managing Network Resources: Alliances, Affiliations, & Other Relational Assets. 2007. (ENG., Illus.). 342p. per. 39.95 (978-0-19-929985-0(4)) Oxford Univ. Pr., Inc.

Haddad, Bassam. Business Networks in Syria: The Political Economy of Authoritarian Resilience. 2011. (Stanford Studies in Middle Eastern & Islamic Societies & Cultures). (ENG.). 280p. 45.00 (978-0-8047-7332-4(7)) Stanford Univ. Pr.

Hall, Starr & Rosenberg, Chadd. Get Connected: The Social Networking Toolkit for Business. 2009. (ENG.). 288p. pap. 21.95 (978-1-59918-358-9(7), 1599183587) Entrepreneur Pr. dba Entrepreneur Media, Inc.

Harryson. Know-Who Based Entrepreneurhip from Knowledge Creation to Business Implementation. 2007. (Illus.). 424p. (C). 162.00 (978-1-84542-115-1(9)) Elgar, Edward Publishing, Inc.

Harryson, Sigvald J. Know-Who Based Entrepreneurship: From Knowledge Creation to Business Implementation. 2008. (Illus.). 424p. pap. 66.00 (978-1-84844-311-2(0)) Elgar, Edward Publishing, Inc.

Hatch, Walter. Asia's Flying Geese: How Regionalization Shapes Japan. 2010. (Cornell Studies in Political Economy Ser.). (Illus.). 304p. 65.00 (978-0-8014-4868-3(9)) Cornell Univ. Pr.

Hatch, Walter F. Asia's Flying Geese: How Regionalization Shapes Japan. 2010. (Cornell Studies in Political Economy Ser.). (Illus.). 304p. pap. 24.95 (978-0-8014-7647-1(X)) Cornell Univ. Pr.

Hawryszkiewycz, Igor. Knowledge Management: Organizing Knowledge Based Enterprises. 2009. (ENG., Illus.). 232p. pap. 51.00 (978-0-230-23027-9(X)) Palgrave Macmillan.

Hay, Fraser. How to Make Money on Ecademycom. 2006. pap. (978-1-905823-01-7(0)) Ecademy Pr. Ltd.

Hendrikse, George, et al, eds. Strategy & Governance of Networks: Cooperatives, Franchising, & Strategic Alliances. (Contributions to Management Science Ser.). (Illus.). xii, 391p. 2010. (ENG.). pap. 189.00 (978-3-7908-2559-6(X), 379082559X) 2008. 189.00 (978-3-7908-2057-7(1), 3790820571) Physica-Verlag DEU. Dist: Springer.

Hinchcliffe, Dion & Kim, Peter. Social Business by Design: Transformative Social Media Strategies for the Connected Company. 2012. (ENG.). 256p. 29.95 **(978-1-118-27321-0(4)**, Jossey-Bass) Wiley, John & Sons, Inc.

Hinner, Michael B., ed. The Role of Communication in Business Transactions & Relationships. 2007. (Illus.). 462p. pap. 83.95 *(978-3-631-54971-1(7))*; pap. 83.95 *(978-0-8204-9863-8(7))* Lang, Peter Publishing, Inc.

Hiratsuka, Daisuke & Uchida, Yoko, eds. Input Trade & Production Networks in East Asia. 2010. (Illus.). 224p. 112.00 *(978-1-84980-069-3(3))* Elgar, Edward Publishing, Inc.

Hocker, Gero. Market - Hierarchy - Networking: Cooperation in Times of Globalization, Fragmentation, & Uncertainty. 2008. (Strukturwandel und Strukturpolitik Ser.). 242p. pap. 61.95 *(978-3-631-57528-0(2))* Lang, Peter GmbH, Europaischer Verlag der Wissenschaften DEU. Dist: Lang, Peter.

Hodgkinson, Ann T., ed. Small Business Clustering Technologies: Applications in Marketing, Management, IT & Economics. 2006. (Illus.). 332p. 94.95 *(978-1-59904-126-1(X))* IGI Global.

Hoffman, Reid & Casnocha, Ben. The Start-Up of You: Adapt to the Future, Invest in Yourself, & Transform Your Career. 2012. ***(978-0-307-88891-4(6))***; (ENG.). 272p. 26.00 ***(978-0-307-88890-7(8))*** Crown Publishing Group. (Crown Business).

Huang, Yukon & Bocchi, Alessandro Magnoli, eds. Reshaping Economic Geography in East Asia. 2008. (ENG., Illus.). 408p. pap. 40.00 *(978-0-8213-7641-6(1)*, 9780821376416) World Bank Pubns.

Hunt, Tara. The Whuffie Factor: Using the Power of Social Networks to Build Your Business. 2009. (ENG.). 320p. 25.00 *(978-0-307-40950-8(3)*, Crown Business) Crown Publishing Group.

Ivens, Sarah. A Modern Girl's Guide to Networking: How to Win Friends & Influence People - From the Office to the Party, from the Boardroom to the Bedroom. 2007. (Modern Girl's Guide Ser.). (ENG., Illus.). 224p. pap. 12.95 *(978-0-7499-2758-5(5))* Piatkus Bks. GBR. Dist: Independent Pubs. Group.

James, Larry. Ten Commitments of Networking: Creative Ways to Maximize Your Personal Connections. 2010. 175p. per. 12.95 *(978-1-931741-70-5(0))* Reed, Robert D. Pubs.

Jansson, Hans. International Business Marketing in Emerging Country Markets: The Third Wave of Internationalization of Firms. 2007. 264p. (C). 127.00 *(978-1-84720-251-2(9))* Elgar, Edward Publishing, Inc.

Jayachandran, C., et al, eds. Business Clusters: Partnering for Strategic Advantage. 2011. (ENG.). (C). 130.00 *(978-0-415-60231-0(9)*, Routledge India) Taylor & Francis Group GBR. Dist: Taylor & Francis Group.

Johanson, Martin & Lundberg, Helne, eds. Network Strategies for Regional Growth. 2011. (ENG., Illus.). 240p. 100.00 *(978-0-230-27330-6(0))* Palgrave Macmillan.

Jones-Kaminski, Sandy. I'm at a Networking Event — Now What??? A Guide to Getting the Most Out of Any Networking Event. Alba, Jason, ed. 2009. 102p. pap. 19.95 *(978-1-60005-166-1(9))* Happy About.

Jue, Arthur L., et al. Social Media at Work: How Networking Tools Propel Organizational Performance. 2009. (ENG., Illus.). 240p. 29.95 *(978-0-470-40543-7(0)*, Jossey-Bass) Wiley, John & Sons, Inc.

Julien, Pierre-André. A Theory of Local Entrepreneurship in the Knowledge Economy. 2008. 336p. 144.00 *(978-1-84720-388-5(4))* Elgar, Edward Publishing, Inc.

Kahn, Lynn Sandra. Performance Networks: Transforming Governance for the 21st Century. 2009. xxii, 164p. pap. 44.00 *(978-1-56726-242-1(2))* Management Concepts, Inc.

Kamp, Bart. Location Behaviour & Relationship Stability in International Business Networks: Evidence from the Automotive Industry. 2006. (Routledge Studies in Business Organization & Networks Ser.). (Illus.). 219p. 168.00 *(978-0-415-39962-3(9))* Routledge.

Karlsson, Charlie. Handbook of Research on Cluster Theory. 2010. (Handbooks of Research on Clusters Ser.). 336p. pap. 53.00 *(978-1-84980-086-0(3))* Elgar, Edward Publishing, Inc.

—Handbook of Research on Innovation & Clusters: Cases & Policies. 2010. (Handbooks of Research on Clusters Ser.). (Illus.). 488p. pap. 61.00 *(978-1-84980-087-7(1))* Elgar, Edward Publishing, Inc.

Karlsson, Charlie, ed. Handbook of Research on Cluster Theory. 2008. (Handbooks of Research on Clusters Ser.). (Illus.). 336p. 210.00 *(978-1-84542-516-6(2))* Elgar, Edward Publishing, Inc.

—Handbook of Research on Innovation & Clusters: Cases & Policies. 2009. (Handbooks of Research on Clusters Ser.). (Illus.). 488p. 235.00 *(978-1-84720-842-2(8))* Elgar, Edward Publishing, Inc.

Kase, Larina. Clients, Clients, & More Clients: Create an Endless Stream of New Business with the Power of Psychology. 2012. (Illus.). xxv, 228p. E-Book ***(978-0-07-177100-9(X))*** McGraw-Hill Cos., The.

—Clients, Clients, & More Clients: Create an Endless Stream of New Business with the Power of Psychology. 2011. (ENG.). 256p. pap. 20.00 ***(978-0-07-177075-0(5)***, 0071770755) McGraw-Hill Cos., The.

Kay, Frances. How to Build Successful Business Relationships. 2009. 200p. pap. 58.00 *(978-0-86341-956-0(9))* Institution of Engineering & Technology GBR. Dist: Books International, Inc.

—Successful Networking: How to Build New Networks for Career & Company Progression. 2010. (ENG.). 208p. pap. 17.95 *(978-0-7494-5879-9(8))* Kogan Page, Ltd. GBR. Dist: Ingram Pub. Services.

Keister, Lisa A. Chinese Business Groups: The Formation, Structure, & Financial Impact of an Interfirm Network. (Illus.). (C). *(978-0-472-11096-4(9))* Univ. of Michigan Pr.

Kettl, Donald F. Unlocking the Power of Networks: Keys to High-Performance Government. Goldsmith, Stephen & Kettl, Donald F., eds. 2009. (Brookings / Ash Institute Series, Innovative Governance in the 21st Century Ser.). (ENG., Illus.). 252p. pap. 29.95 *(978-0-8157-3187-0(6))* Brookings Institution Pr.

Klein, Stefan & Poulymenakou, Angeliki, eds. Managing Dynamic Networks: Organizational Perspectives of Technology Enabled Inter-firm Collaboration. 2010. (ENG., Illus.). viii, 308p. pap. 149.00 *(978-3-642-06472-2(8)*, 3642064728) Springer.

Kleindorfer, Paul R., et al. The Network Challenge: Strategy, Profit, & Risk in an Interlinked World. 2009. (ENG.). 592p. pap. 64.99 *(978-0-13-706920-0(0))* Wharton Schl. Publishing.

Knoben, Joris. Firm Mobility & Organizational Networks: Innovation, Embeddedness & Economic Geography. 2008. (New Horizons in Regional Science Ser.). (Illus.). 192p. (C). 119.00 *(978-1-84720-245-1(4))* Elgar, Edward Publishing, Inc.

Kock, Ned, ed. Emerging E-Collaboration Concepts & Applications. 2006. (Advances in E-Collaboration, Vol. 1 Ser.). (Illus.). 330p. 94.95 *(978-1-59904-393-7(9))* IGI Global.

Kock, Ned F. E-Collaboration Technologies & Organizational Performance: Current & Future Trends. 2010. 350p. 180.00 *(978-1-60960-466-0(0))* IGI Global.

Kodama, Mitsuru. Interactive Business Communities: Accelerating Corporate Innovation Through Boundary Networks. 2011. (Illus.). 232p. 124.95 ***(978-0-566-08928-2(9)***, Gower Publishing Co., Ltd.) Ashgate Publishing, Ltd. GBR. Dist: Ashgate Publishing Co.

Kodama, Mitsuru. The Strategic Community-based Firm. 2007. (ENG.). 256p. 105.00 *(978-0-230-00685-0(X))* Palgrave Macmillan.

Koput, Kenneth W. & Broschak, Joseph P., eds. Social Capital in Business. 2011. (Illus.). 552p. 299.95 *(978-1-84980-758-6(2))* Elgar, Edward Publishing, Inc.

Kornberger. Only Connect Neat Words, Networks & Identities. 2006. (Illus.). 256p. pap. 54.00 *(978-87-630-0189-2(6))* Copenhagen Business Schl. Pr. DNK. Dist: International Specialized Bk. Services.

Kuchiki, Akifumi & Tsuji, Masatsugu, eds. Industrial Clusters, Upgrading & Innovation in East Asia. 2011. (Illus.). 320p. 125.00 ***(978-0-85793-512-0(7))*** Elgar, Edward Publishing, Inc.

Kuroiwa, Ikuo & Toh, Mun-Heng. Production Networks & Industrial Clusters Integrating Economies in Southeast Asia. 2008. (Illus.). xix, 363p. *(978-981-230-763-7(X))* Institute of Southeast Asian Studies.

Langenberg, Elke A. Guanxi & Business Strategy: Theory & Implications for Multinational Companies in China. 2007. (Contributions to Management Science Ser.). (Illus.). 226p. per. 119.00 *(978-3-7908-1955-7(7)*, 3790819557) Physica-Verlag DEU. Dist: Springer.

Ledeneva, Alena V. How Russia Really Works: The Informal Practices That Shaped Post-Soviet Politics & Business. 2006. (Culture & Society after Socialism Ser.). (Illus.). 270p. 75.50 *(978-0-8014-4346-6(6))* Cornell Univ. Pr.

—How Russia Really Works: The Informal Practices That Shaped Post-Soviet Politics & Business. 2006. (Culture & Society after Socialism Ser.). (Illus.). 270p. per. 24.95 *(978-0-8014-7352-4(7))* Cornell Univ. Pr.

Lederman, Michelle. The 11 Laws of Likability: Relationship Networking ... Because People Do Business with People They Like, 1 vol. 2011. (ENG.). 240p. pap. 16.95 ***(978-0-8144-1637-2(3))*** Amacom.

Li. Supply Chain Management: Concepts... 2007. (Illus.). 112.00 *(978-981-270-072-8(2))* World Scientific Publishing Co., Inc.

Li, Yi. Zhongguo Xin Xi Chan Ye Ji Qun Fa Zhan Yan Jiu: Research on China's Information Industry Cluster Development. 2010. (Illus.). *(978-7-80745-627-8(2))* Shanghai Academy of Social Sciences Pr.

Liebowitz, Jay. Social Networking: The Essence of Innovation. 2007. (ENG., Illus.). 136p. per. 45.00 *(978-0-8108-5857-2(6))* Scarecrow Pr., Inc.

Lincoln, James R. & Gerlach, Michael L. Japan's Network Economy: Structure, Persistence, & Change. 2007. (Structural Analysis in the Social Sciences Ser.). (ENG., Illus.). 430p. (C). pap. 44.00 *(978-0-521-71189-0(4))* Cambridge Univ. Pr.

Lindenfield, Stuart. Confident Networking for Career Success. 2010. (ENG., Illus.). 288p. pap. 15.95 *(978-0-7499-4170-3(7))* Piatkus Bks. GBR. Dist: Independent Pubs. Group.

Lonkila, Markku. Networks in the Russian Market Economy. 2010. (ENG., Illus.). 208p. 95.00 *(978-0-230-25239-4(7))* Palgrave Macmillan.

Lopata, Andy. Recommended: How to Sell Through Networking & Referrals. rev. ed. 2011. (Financial Times Ser.). (ENG., Illus.). 304p. pap. 24.99 ***(978-0-273-75796-2(2))*** FT Press.

Lopata, Andy & Roper, Peter. And Death Came Third! 2nd ed. 2011. 280p. pap. ***(978-1-907722-30-1(0))*** Ecademy Pr. Ltd.

Lundberg, Helene. Geographical Proximity Effects & Regional Strategic Networks. 2010. 160p. pap. *(978-3-8383-2181-3(2))* Lambert Academic Publishing.

Luo, Yadong. Guanxi & Business. 2nd ed. 2007. (Asia-Pacific Business Ser.). (Illus.). 397p. 85.00 *(978-981-270-046-9(3))* World Scientific Publishing Co., Inc.

Lynch, Liz. Smart Networking: Attract a Following in Person & Online. 2008 (ENG., Illus.). 288p. pap. 16.95 *(978-0-07-160294-5(1)*, 0071602941) McGraw-Hill Cos., The.

Malerba, Franco. Innovation Networks in Industries. Malerba, Franco & Vonortas, Nicholas S., eds. 2009. (Illus.). 272p. 127.00 *(978-1-84720-376-2(0))* Elgar, Edward Publishing, Inc.

Malerba, Franco & Vonortas, Nicholas S. Innovation Networks in Industries Malerba, Franco & Vonortas, Nicholas S., eds. 2011. (Illus.). 272p. pap. 40.00 *(978-1-84844-801-8(5))* Elgar, Edward Publishing, Inc.

Man, Adrianus Pieter de. Knowledge Management & Innovation in Networks. de Man, A. -P., ed. 2008. (Illus.). 232p. 119.00 *(978-1-84720-230-7(6))* Elgar, Edward Publishing, Inc.

Marala, Mark. Relationships Are Everything! Growing Your Business One Relationship at a Time. 2009. 232p. 27.95 *(978-0-9724532-2-6(9))* Professional Services Publishing.

Marschall, Daniel. The Company We Keep: Occupational Community in the High-Tech Network Society. 2012. (ENG.). 204p. 69.50 ***(978-1-4399-0755-9(2))***; E-Book ***(978-1-4399-0757-3(9))*** Temple Univ. Pr.

McClain, Annette. Creating Meaningful Relationships with Volunteers. 2007. 52p. per. 16.95 *(978-1-4241-7806-3(1))* PublishAmerica, Inc.

McNamara, Dennis, et al. Business Innovation in Asia: Knowledge & Technology Networks from Japan. 2009. (Routledge Contemporary Asia Ser.). (ENG., Illus.). 208p. (C). 138.00 *(978-0-415-49935-4(6))* Routledge.

Mehandjiev, Nikolay & Grefen, Paul W. P. J. Dynamic Business Process Formation for Instant Virtual Enterprises: The CrossWork Project. 2010. (Advanced Information & Knowledge Processing Ser.). (ENG., Illus.). ix, 266p. 119.00 *(978-1-84882-690-8(7)*, 1848826907) Springer.

Meshel, Jeffrey W. The Opportunity Magnet: Attract Success in Every Aspect of Your Life. 2010. (ENG.). 272p. pap. 15.00 *(978-1-57826-367-7(0))* Hatherleigh Co., Ltd., The.

Miron, John R. Firms, Prices, & Localization: The Geography of Competition. 2010. (ENG., Illus.). xiii, 428p. 189.00 *(978-1-4419-5625-5(5)*, 1441956255) Springer.

Misner, Ivan R. & Donovan, Michelle R. The 29% Solution: 52 Weekly Networking Success Strategies. 2008. 286p. 21.95 *(978-1-929774-54-8(0))* Greenleaf Book Group.

Misner, Ivan R., et al. Networking Like a Pro: Turning Contacts into Connections. 2009. (ENG., Illus.). 288p. pap. 21.95 *(978-1-59918-356-5(0)*, 1599183560) Entrepreneur Pr. dba Entrepreneur Media, Inc.

Monden, Yasuhiro. Management of an Inter-Firm Network. 2011. 250p. 85.00 ***(978-981-4324-61-8(2))*** World Scientific Publishing Co., Inc.

Muccio, Chris, et al. 42 Rules for 24-Hour Success on LinkedIn: Practical ideas to help you quickly achieve your desired business Success. 2008. 128p. pap. 19.95 *(978-1-60773-018-7(9)*, Super Star Pr.) Happy About.

Mulholland, Andy & Earle, Nick. Mesh Collaboration: Creating new business value in the network of Everything. Woods, Dan, ed. 2008. (ENG., Illus.). 406p. per. 40.00 *(978-0-9789218-5-9(2))* Evolved Technologist Pr.

Nambisan, Satish & Sawhney, Mohanbir. The Global Brain: Your Roadmap for Innovating Faster & Smarter in a Networked World. 2007. (ENG.). 304p. pap. 34.99 *(978-0-13-706486-1(1))* Wharton Schl. Publishing.

Networks of Business. (Illus.). 175p. *(978-0-7605-0642-4(6))* Rector Pr., Ltd.

Neves, Marcos Fava. Demand Driven Strategic Planning. 2012. (ENG., Illus.). 196p. pap. 39.99 ***(978-0-415-62639-2(0))*** Routledge.

Newman, Charles H. Beyond the Chicken Dance. 2009. 126p. 29.99 *(978-1-4415-3548-1(9))*; pap. 19.99 *(978-1-4415-3547-4(0))* Xlibris Corp.

Nour, David. Relationship Economics: Transform Your Most Valuable Business Contacts into Personal & Professional Success. 2011. (ENG., Illus.). 320p. pap. 19.95 *(978-1-118-05712-4(0)*, Wiley) Wiley, John & Sons, Inc.

Organisation for Economic Co-operation and Development Staff. Clusters, Innovation & Entrepreneurship. Miranda, Gabriela & Potter, Jonathan, eds. 2009. (Illus.). 233p. pap. 63.00 *(978-92-64-04442-5(6))* Organization for Economic Cooperation & Development.

Palacios. Multinational Corporations & the Emerging Network Economy in Asia & the Pacific. 2007. (PAFTAD (Pacific Trade & Development Conference Series) Ser.). (ENG., Illus.). 336p. (C). 178.00 *(978-0-415-43332-7(0))* Routledge.

Parinello, Anthony. Secrets of VITO: Think & Sell Like a CEO. 2006. (ENG.). 288p. per. 17.95 *(978-1-59918-033-5(2)*, 1599180332) Entrepreneur Pr. dba Entrepreneur Media, Inc.

Pentland, Alex. Honest Signals: How They Shape Our World. 2010. (ENG.). 208p. (gr. 17). pap. 15.95 *(978-0-262-51512-2(1))* MIT Pr.

Pentland, Alex (Sandy). Honest Signals: How They Shape Our World. 2008. (ENG.). 208p. (gr. 17). 23.95 *(978-0-262-16256-2(3))* MIT Pr.

Perry, Chris. Business Clusters: An International Perspective. 2007. (Illus.). 256p. 42.50 *(978-0-415-43991-6(4))* Routledge.

Picard, Robert G. Media Clusters: Spatial Agglomeration & Content Capabilities. Karlsson, Charlie, ed. 2011. (New Horizons in Regional Science Ser.). (Illus.). 432p. 160.00 ***(978-0-85793-268-6(3))*** Elgar, Edward Publishing, Inc.

Pierson, Orville. Highly Effective Networking: Meet the Right People & Get a Great Job. 2009. (ENG.). 1p. pap. 15.99 *(978-1-60163-050-6(6))* Career Pr., Inc.

Piperopoulos, Panos G. Entrepreneurship Innovation & Business Clusters. 2012. 240p. 124.95 ***(978-1-4094-3443-6(5)***, Gower Publishing Co., Ltd.) Ashgate Publishing, Ltd. GBR. Dist: Ashgate Publishing Co.

Pourmohammadi, Hamid. GREEN LOGISTICS FOR REGIONAL INDUSTRIAL WASTE MATERIALS AND BYPRODUCTS: A Closed Supply Chain Management Model. 2009. 144p. pap. *(978-3-639-04911-4(X))* VDM Verlag Dr. Mueller e.K.

Powell, Juliette. 33 Million People in the Room. 2012. (ENG.). 176p. pap. 21.99 *(978-0-13-138095-0(8))* FT Press.

Prussakov, Evgenii. A Practical Guide to Affiliate Marketing: Quick Reference for Affiliate Managers & Merchants. 2007. (ENG.). 208p. per. 29.99 *(978-0-9791927-0-8(6))* AM Navigator LLC.

Pyka, Andreas & Scharnhorst, Andreas, eds. Innovation Networks: New Approaches in Modelling & Analyzing. 2009. (Understanding Complex Systems Ser.). (ENG., Illus.). x, 330p. 159.00 *(978-3-540-92266-7(0)*, 3540922660) Springer.

Querejeta, Mari Jose Aranguren, et al, eds. Networks, Governance & Economic Development: Bridging Disciplinary Frontiers. 2008. (Illus.). 288p. (C). 135.00 *(978-1-84720-271-0(3))* Elgar, Edward Publishing, Inc.

Ramaswamy, Venkat & Gouillart, Francis. The Power of Co-Creation: Build It with Them to Boost Growth, Productivity, & Profits. 2010. (ENG., Illus.). 288p. 28.00 *(978-1-4391-8104-1(7)*, Free Pr.) Free Pr.

Ramos, Pedro Pablo. Network Models for Organizations: The Flexible Design of 21st Century Companies. 2011. (ENG., Illus.). 192p. 40.00 *(978-0-230-32016-1(3))* Palgrave Macmillan.

Randel, Jim. The Skinny on Networking: Maximizing the Power of Numbers. 2010. (Skinny On Ser.). (ENG., Illus.). 150p. (YA). pap. 14.95 *(978-0-9844418-1-5(6)*, Skinny On (tm), The) Rand Media Co.

Rauch, James E. The Missing Links: Formation & Decay of Economic Networks. 2007. (Illus.). 244p. *(978-0-87154-709-5(0))* Russell Sage Foundation.

Reinders, Adrie & Freijsen, Marion. The N Factor: How Efficient Networking Can Change the Dynamics of Your Business. 2007. 148p. per. 19.95 *(978-0-8329-5006-3(8)*, WBusiness Bks.) New Win Publishing.

Rizova, Polly & Rizova, Polly S. The Secret of Success: The Double Helix of Formal & Informal Structures in an RandD Laboratory. 2007. (ENG., Illus.). 200p. 60.00 *(978-0-8047-5570-2(1))* Stanford Univ. Pr.

RoAne, Susan. Face to Face: How to Reclaim the Personal Touch in a Digital World. 2008. (ENG., Illus.). 288p. pap. 14.95 *(978-1-4165-6142-2(0)*, Touchstone) Touchstone.

Robert-Ribes, Jordi. Connecting Forward: Advanced networking for executives changing jobs, company, industry or Country. 2011. (ENG.). 136p. pap. ***(978-1-78088-049-5(9))*** Troubadour Publishing Ltd.

Rogers, David L. The Network Is Your Customer: Five Strategies to Thrive in a Digital Age. 2011. (Illus.). 336p. 24.00 *(978-0-300-16587-6(0))* Yale Univ. Pr.

Romano, Aldo & Secundo, Giustina, eds. Dynamic Learning Networks: Models & Cases in Action. 2009. (ENG., Illus.). xxii, 178p. 149.00 *(978-1-4419-0250-4(3)*, 1441902503) Springer.

Rosen, Lucy & Gryvatz Copquin, Claudia. Fast Track Networking: Turning Conversations into Contacts. 2010. (ENG.). 1p. pap. 14.99 *(978-1-60163-121-3(9))* Career Pr., Inc.

Ruiz Peris, Juan Ignacio & Peris, Juan Ignacio Ruiz. Hacia un Derecho para Las Redes Empresariales. 2009. (SPA.). 240p. *(978-84-9876-677-6(X))* Tirant lo Blanch.

Ruth, Matthias & Davidsdottir, Brynhildur, eds. The Dynamics of Regions & Networks in Industrial Ecosystems. 2009. (Illus.). 264p. 119.00 *(978-1-84720-742-5(1))* Elgar, Edward Publishing, Inc.

Rutledge, Patrice-Anne. LinkedIn. 2010. (Using Ser.). (ENG., Illus.). 288p. pap. 24.99 *(978-0-7897-4459-3(7))* Que.

—Sams Teach Yourself LinkedIn in 10 Minutes. 2009. (Sams Teach Yourself Ser.). (Illus.). 224p. pap. 14.99 *(978-0-672-33085-8(7))* Sams.

Rynecki, David. Deals on the Green: Lessons on Business & Golf from America's Top Executives. 2011. (ENG.). 208p. (gr. 12). 15.00 *(978-1-59184-407-5(X)*, Portfolio Trade) Penguin Group (USA) Inc.

Sachsenmeier, Peter & Schottenloher, Martin, eds. Challenges Between Competition & Collaboration: The Future of the European Manufacturing Industry. 2010. (ENG., Illus.). viii, 326p. pap. 119.00 *(978-3-642-07278-9(X)*, 364207278X) Springer.

Salpeter, Miriam M. Social Networking for Career Success. 2011. (ENG.). 368p. pap. 18.95 *(978-1-57685-782-3(4))* LearningExpress, LLC.

Sautter, Ellen & Crompton, Diane. Find a Job Through Social Networking: Use LinkedIn, Twitter, Facebook, Blogs, & More to Advance Your Career. 2nd ed. 2010. 224p. pap. 14.95 *(978-1-59357-817-6(2)*, JIST Works) JIST Publishing.

Savar, Sheila. The Power of Networking: A How-to Networking Guide for Your Career & Business Success! 2008. 130p. pap. 14.95 *(978-0-9798533-0-2(3))* Savar & Assocs.

Saz-Carranza, Angel. Managing Networks in the Public & Nonprofit Sectors. 2012. (Routledge Studies in Business Organizations & Networks Ser.). (ENG., Illus.). 160p. (C). 125.00 ***(978-0-415-69902-4(8))*** Routledge.

Schemm-Gregory, Reto. Europa als ein Club voller Clubs: Eine clubtheoretische Betrachtung des politischen Systems der Europäischen Union. 2010. (Schriften zur Wirtschaftstheorie und Wirtschaftspolitik Ser.). (GER.). 534p. 122.95 *(978-3-631-60184-6(0))* Lang, Peter GmbH, Europaischer Verlag der Wissenschaften DEU. Dist: Lang, Peter.

Scherm, Michael. Kleine und mittelständische Betriebe in unternehmerischen Netzwerken: Die Reidemeister auf der Vollme im vor- und frühindustriellen Metallgewerbe der Grafschaft Mark. 2009. (Beiträge zur Wirtschafts- und Sozialgeschichte (BWSG) Ser.). (GER., Illus.). 691p. (C). pap. 124.00 *(978-3-515-09432-0(6))* Steiner, Franz Verlag Wiesbaden GmbH DEU. Dist: Brown, David Bk. Co., The.

Schiuma, Giovanni, ed. Managing Knowledge Assets & Business Value Creation in Organizations: Measures & Dynamics. 2010. (Illus.). 350p. 180.00 *(978-1-60960-071-6(1)*, Business Science Reference) IGI Global.

Schlögl, Gerhard. Regional Business Networks. 2010. 72p. pap. *(978-3-639-26164-6(X))* VDM Verlag Dr. Mueller e.K.

Schneider, Cheryl. A Beginner's Fundamentals Guide: for an Easy Online Affiliate Business. 2010. 245p. pap. 15.99 *(978-0-557-13451-9(X))* Lulu Enterprises Inc.

Scott, Allen J. & Garofoli, Gioacchino, eds. Development on the Ground: Clusters, Networks & Regions in Emerging Economies. 2012. (Routledge Advances in Management & Business Studies). (ENG., Illus.). 368p. (C). pap. 42.95 ***(978-0-415-51276-3(X))*** Routledge.

Scott, Gini Graham. Top Secrets for Using LinkedIn to Promote Your Business or Yourself: A Complete Step-by-Step Guide to Discover the Power of LinkedIn. 2010. 148p. pap. 12.95 *(978-1-4502-1898-6(9))* iUniverse, Inc.

Scott, Noel & Laws, Eric, eds. Advances in Service Network Analysis. 2011. (ENG., Illus.). 208p. (C). 125.00 (978-0-415-68664-8(4)) Routledge.

Seger, Linda Th. D. The Better Way to Win. 2011. 174p. 29.99 (978-1-4568-5680-9(4)); pap. 19.99 (978-1-4568-5679-3(0)) Xlibris Corp.

Sharp, Julien. Design & Launch an Online Social Networking Business in a Week. 2009. (ENG., Illus.). 200p. pap. 17.95 (978-1-59918-268-1(8), 1599182688) Entrepreneur Pr. dba Entrepreneur Media, Inc.

Sherman, Aliza. The Complete Idiot's Guide to Crowdsourcing. 2011. (Complete Idiot's Guide Ser.). (ENG.). 336p. (gr. 12). 19.95 (978-1-61564-092-8(4), Alpha Bks.) Penguin Group (USA) Inc.

Singer, Thom. Some Assembly Required: A Networking Guide for Graduates. Morris, Leslie, ed. 2010. (ENG.). 200p. pap. 15.95 (978-1-935547-08-2(9)) New Year Publishing.

Smallbone, D., et al, eds. Cross-Border Entrepreneurship & Economic Development in Europe's Border Regions. 2012. 224p. 110.00 (978-1-84844-768-4(X)) Elgar, Edward Publishing, Inc.

Snehota, Ivan, et al. Managing Business Relationships. 3rd ed. 2011. (ENG., Illus.). 256p. pap. 69.95 (978-0-470-72109-4(X), Wiley) Wiley, John & Sons, Inc.

Spulber, Daniel F. & Yoo, Christopher S. Networks in Telecommunications: Economics & Law. 2009. (ENG., Illus.). 510p. 120.00 (978-0-521-85710-9(4)); pap. 55.00 (978-0-521-67386-0(0)) Cambridge Univ. Pr.

Stelzner, Michael A. Launch: How to Quickly Propel Your Business Beyond the Competition. 2011. (ENG., Illus.). 255p. 24.95 (978-1-118-02723-3(X), Wiley) Wiley, John & Sons, Inc.

Sundquist, Viktoria. Intermediation in Business Networks. 2011. 148p. pap. (978-3-8443-9502-0(4)) Lambert Academic Publishing.

Sweeney, Joe. Networking Is a Contact Sport: How Staying Connected & Serving Others Will Help You Grow Your Business, Expand Your Influence — or Even Land Your Next Job. 2011. (ENG.). 256p. pap. 14.95 (978-1-936661-17-6(9)) BenBella Bks.

Taplin, Ian M. The Modern American Wine Industry: Market Formation & Growth in North Carolina, 1 vol. 2011. (Studies in Business History Ser.). (ENG., Illus.). 224p. 99.00 (978-1-84893-136-7(0)) Pickering & Chatto Pubs., Ltd. GBR. Dist: Ashgate Publishing Co.

Tapscott, Don & Williams, Anthony D. Macrowikinomics: Rebooting Business & the World. 2010. (ENG.). 432p. (gr. 12). 27.95 (978-1-59184-356-6(1), Portfolio (Hardcover)) Penguin Group (USA) Inc.

—Wikinomics: How Mass Collaboration Changes Everything. 2010. (ENG.). 368p. (gr. 12). 17.00 (978-1-59184-367-2(7), Portfolio Trade) Penguin Group (USA) Inc.

Teubner, Gunther. Networks as Connected Contracts: Edited with an Introduction by Hugh Collins. Collins, Hugh, ed. 2011. (ENG.). 314p. 100.00 (978-1-84946-174-0(0)) Hart Publishing Ltd. GBR. Dist: International Specialized Bk. Services.

Timperley, John. Network Your Way to Success: The Secrets of Successful Business Relationships. 2010. (ENG., Illus.). 272p. pap. 15.95 (978-0-7499-5263-1(6)) Piatkus Bks. GBR. Dist: Independent Pubs. Group.

Todeva. Business Networks: Strategy & Structure. 2006. (Routledge Studies in Business Organizations & Networks Ser.). (ENG., Illus.). 272p. (C). 168.00 (978-0-415-36838-4(3), RU8383X) Routledge.

Todeva, Emanuela. Management of International Business Networks. 2009. (Routledge Studies in Business Organizations & Networks Ser.). 256p. 150.00 (978-0-415-36839-1(1)) Routledge.

Townsend, Heather. FT Guide to Business Networking: How to use the power of online & offline networking for business Success. rev. ed. 2011. (ENG., Illus.). 224p. pap. 24.99 (978-0-273-74582-2(4)) FT Press.

Tsuji, Masatsugu & Kuchiki, Akifumi, eds. From Agglomeration to Innovation: Upgrading Industrial Clusters in Emerging Economies. 2009. (ENG., Illus.). 288p. 121.00 (978-0-230-23310-2(4)) Palgrave Macmillan.

Tuunanen, Mika. New Developments in the Theory of Networks: Franchising, Alliances & Cooperatives. Tuunanen, Mika et al, eds. 2011. (Contributions to Management Science Ser.). (Illus.). xi, 390p. 189.00 (978-3-7908-2614-2(6), 3790826146) Physica-Verlag DEU. Dist: Springer.

Ulin, Jeff. The Business of Media Distribution: Monetizing Film, TV & Video Content in an Online World. 2009. (ENG., Illus.). 528p. pap. 34.95 (978-0-240-81200-7(X), Focal Pr.) Elsevier Science & Technology Bks.

United Nations. Linking Greater Mekong Subregion Enterprises to International Markets: The Role of Global Value Chains, International Production Networks & Enterprise Clusters. 2007. (Studies in Trade & Investment Ser.). (ENG.). 92p. pap. 29.00 (978-92-1-120492-6(5)) United Nations Pubns.

Vaghult, Anna Löfmarck. The Quest for Stability. 2009. 248p. pap. (978-3-639-13159-8(2)) VDM Verlag Dr. Mueller e.K.

Varol, Çigdem. Entrepreneurial Networks in Local Industrial Development. 2009. 172p. pap. (978-3-639-13345-5(5)) VDM Verlag Dr. Mueller e.K.

Vermaas, P. E. & Dignum, V., eds. Formal Ontologies Meet Industry: Proceedings of the 5th International Workshop (FOMI 2011) 2011. 136p. 145.00 (978-1-60750-784-0(6)) IOS Pr., Inc.

Vermeiren, Jan. Let's Connect! A Practical Guide for Highly Effective Professional Networking. 2007. (ENG.). 274p. per. 19.95 (978-1-60037-261-2(9)) Morgan James Publishing.

Villa, Agostino, ed. Managing Cooperation in Supply Network Structures & Small or Medium-sized Enterprises: Main Criteria & Tools for Managers. 2011. (ENG., Illus.). ix, 108p. 129.00 (978-0-85729-242-1(0), 0857292420) Springer.

Vincent, Aaltje & Valkenburg, Jacco. Career Management via LinkedIn. 2011. (ENG., Illus.). 128p. pap. (978-90-491-0439-9(8), Lannoo Pubs. (Acc)) Antique Collectors' Club.

Vitale, Joe & Hibbler, Bill. Meet & Grow Rich: How to Easily Create & Operate Your Own Mastermind Group for Health, Wealth, & More. 2006. (ENG.). 240p. 24.95 (978-0-470-04548-0(5), Wiley) Wiley, John & Sons, Inc.

Vitasek, Kate & Manrodt, Karl. Vested: How P&G, Microsoft, & Mcdonald's are Redefining Winning in Business Relationships. 2012. (ENG.). 240p. 30.00 (978-0-230-34170-8(5)) Palgrave Macmillan.

Von Saldern, Adelheid. Netzwerkökonomie im frühen 19. Jahrhundert: Das Beispiel der Schoeller-Häuser. 2009. (Beitrage zur Unternehmensgeschichte (BZUG) Ser.). (GER., Illus.). 363p. (C). pap. 75.00 (978-3-515-09369-9(9)) Steiner, Franz Verlag Wiesbaden GmbH DEU. Dist: Brown, David Bk. Co., The.

Waite, Michael E. Networking Fuel: Who Needs to Know You? 2008. 56p. pap. 16.95 (978-1-60474-627-3(0)) PublishAmerica, Inc.

Wallace, Ed. Business Relationships that Last. 2009. 21.95 (978-1-60832-001-1(4), Greenleaf Book Group Pr.) Greenleaf Book Group.

Warner, Jon. The Networking Pocketbook. 2nd ed. 2008. (Illus.). 112p. pap. (978-1-903776-89-6(9)) Management Pocketbooks GBR. Dist: Ware-Pak, Inc.

Weber, Steve. Wired for Work: Get a Job Fast Using LinkedIn, Facebook or Twitter. 2010. 112p. pap. 13.95 (978-0-9772406-7-8(3)) Weber Bks.

Weiss, Alan. Million Dollar Referrals: The Secrets to Building a Perpetual Client List for a Seven-Figure Income. 2011. (ENG.). 288p. pap. 22.00 (978-0-07-176927-3(7), 0071769277) McGraw-Hill Cos., The.

Wenger, Diane E. & Wenger, Diane. A Country Storekeeper in Pennsylvania: Creating Economic Networks in Early America, 1790-1807. 2008. (ENG.). 232p. 55.00 (978-0-271-03412-6(2)) Pennsylvania State Univ. Pr.

Whelan, Chad. Networks & National Security: Dynamics Effectiveness & Organisation. 2012. 182p. 99.95 (978-1-4094-3123-7(1)) Ashgate Publishing Co.

Whitener, Michael L. Creating Software Alliances: A Detailed Look at Establishing Partnerships in the Software Industry, Structuring Agreements, & Managing Relationships. 2007. 165p. per. 249.95 (978-1-59622-621-0(8)) Aspatore Bks.

Wilkinson, Ian. Business Relating Business: Managing Organisational Relations & Networks. 304p. 2010. pap. 45.00 (978-1-84980-022-8(7)) 2008. (Illus.). (C). 140.00 (978-1-84542-539-5(1)) Elgar, Edward Publishing, Inc.

Woodside, Arch G., ed. & contrib. by. Organizational Culture, Business-to-Business Relationships, & Interfirm Networks. 2010. (Advances in Business Marketing & Purchasing Ser.). 520p. (978-0-85724-305-8(5)) Emerald Group Publishing Ltd.

Word, Jeffrey. Business Network Transformation: Strategies to Reconfigure Your Business Relationships for Competitive Advantage. 2009. (ENG., Illus.). 304p. 40.00 (978-0-470-52834-1(6), Jossey-Bass) Wiley, John & Sons, Inc.

World Bank Staff, contrib. by. Industrial Clusters & Micro & Small Enterprises in Africa: From Survival to Growth. 2010. (978-0-8213-8628-6(X)); (ENG & ABK.). 208p. pap. 25.00 (978-0-8213-8627-9(1), 9780821386279) World Bank Pubns.

Yeung, Henry Wai-Chung, ed. Globalizing Regional Development in East Asia: Production Networks, Clusters, & Entrepreneurship. 2010. (Regions & Cities Ser.). (ENG., Illus.). 208p. (C). 125.00 (978-0-415-56053-5(5)) Routledge.

Yeung, Rob. Networking: The Rules, 1 vol. 2009. (ENG.). 176p. pap. 18.50 (978-981-261-616-6(0)) Marshall Cavendish International (Asia) Private Ltd. SGP. Dist: Marshall Cavendish Corp.

—Networking? The Rules Of. 2009. 192p. pap. (978-1-905736-30-0(4)) Marshall Cavendish.

Zabora, Theodore J. N-E-T-Working: A Step-by-Step, Time-Tested, & Proven Strategy to Find Your New Job: Now Everything the Working Public Needs to Know. 2008. (ENG.). 100p. pap. 19.95 (978-1-58982-423-2(7), American Business Pr.) American Bk. Publishing Group.

Zack, Devora. Networking for People Who Hate Networking: A Field Guide for Introverts, the Overwhelmed, & the Underconnected. 2010. (ENG., Illus.). 192p. pap. 16.95 (978-1-60509-522-6(2)) Berrett-Koehler Pubs., Inc.

Zeng, Douglas Zhihua, ed. Building Engines for Growth & Competitiveness in China: Experience with Special Economic Zones & Industrial Clusters. 2010. (Directions in Development Ser.). (ENG., Illus.). 256p. pap. 35.00 (978-0-8213-8432-9(5), 9780821384329) World Bank Pubns.

Zheng, Li & Possel-Dölken, Frank. Strategic Production Networks. 2010. (ENG., Illus.). xv, 489p. pap. 139.00 (978-3-642-07734-0(X), 364207734X) Springer.

BUSINESS OBJECTS (COMPUTER PROGRAM)

see BusinessObjects (Computer Program)

BUSINESS PATRONAGE OF THE ARTS

see Art Patronage

BUSINESS PLANNING

see also Business Forecasting; Corporate Planning; New Business Enterprises—Planning; Small Business—Planning

Abid, Ellahi, et al. International Marketing Plan for Sanono Egg Group in Pakistan: Learn How to Enter in a Unknown Land. 2011. 68p. pap. (978-3-639-34243-7(7)) VDM Verlag Dr. Mueller e.K.

Abraham, Jay. The Sticking Point Solution: 9 Ways to Move Your Business from Stagnation to Stunning Growth in Tough Economic Times. (ENG.). 2010. 288p. pap. 15.95 (978-1-59315-575-9(1)) 2009. 272p. 25.95 (978-1-59315-510-0(7)) Vanguard Pr.

Abraham, Joe. Entrepreneurial DNA: The Breakthrough Discovery That Aligns Your Business to Your Unique Strengths. 2011. (ENG., Illus.). 256p. 25.00 (978-0-07-175451-4(2), 0071754512) McGraw-Hill Cos., The.

Abrams, Rhonda. Business Plan in a Day: Get It Done Right, Get It Done Fast. 2nd rev. ed. 2009. (ENG.). 183p. pap. 19.95 (978-1-933895-07-9(1)) Planning Shop, The.

—The Successful Business Plan: Secrets & Strategies. 5th ed. 2010. (ENG.). 425p. pap. 44.95 (978-1-933895-14-7(4)) Planning Shop, The.

Abrams, Rhonda & Barrow, Paul. The Successful Business Plan: Secrets & Strategies. 4th ed. 2008. (Planning Shop Series????? Ser.). (ENG., Illus.). 478p. pap. 32.95 (978-1-84112-807-8(4), Capstone) Wiley, John & Sons, Inc.

Adams, Rob. If You Build It Will They Come? Three Steps to Test & Validate Any Market Opportunity. 2010. (ENG.). 224p. 24.95 (978-0-470-56363-2(X), Wiley) Wiley, John & Sons, Inc.

Ahmed, Rachdi, et al. My Business Plan. rev. ed. 2011. (ENG.). 68p. spiral bd., wbk. ed. 25.27 (978-0-7575-8117-5(X)) Kendall Hunt Publishing Co.

Akoto, Michael. Rethinking Business Strategy. 2008. 41p. pap. 11.95 (978-0-7414-4331-1(7)) Infinity Publishing.

Aleksandrova, Dina. Business Plan Evaluation. 2011. 92p. pap. (978-3-8454-0450-9(7)) Lambert Academic Publishing.

Allen, Kathleen. Entrepreneurship for Scientists & Engineers. 2009. (ENG., Illus.). 256p. (C). pap. 60.00 (978-0-13-235727-2(5), Prentice Hall) Prentice Hall PTR.

Allen, Kathleen R. Growing & Managing a Small Business: An Entrepreneurial Perspective. 2nd ed. 2006. (ENG., Illus.). 560p. (C). 242.95 (978-0-618-70509-2(0), 302315) CENGAGE Learning.

—Launching New Ventures: An Entrepreneurial Approach (with Management CourseMate with eBook Printed Access Card) 6th ed. 2011. (ENG.). 608p. (C). 227.95 (978-0-538-48179-3(X)) Cengage South-Western.

Anthony, Scott D. The Little Black Book of Innovation: How It Works, How to Do It. 2011. (ENG.). 304p. 25.00 (978-1-4221-7172-1(8)) Harvard Business Review Pr.

Aronoff, Craig E., et al. Developing Family Business Policies: Your Guide to the Future. 2010. (Family Business Leadership Ser.). (ENG.). 112p. pap. 23.00 (978-0-230-11109-7(2)) Palgrave Macmillan.

Aspatore Books Staff, compiled by. Analyzing VC Deal Terms: Leading Lawyers on Structuring Term Sheets, Developing Negotiation Strategies, And. 2008. 312p. pap. 110.00 (978-0-314-99172-0(7)) Aspatore Bks.

—Capitalizing on Marketing Trends: Leading CMOs on Assessing New Trends, Analyzing Changing Demographics, & Incorporating Global Trends into Your Marketing Strategy (Inside the Minds) 2008. 96p. pap. 65.00 (978-0-314-98679-5(0)) Aspatore Bks.

—Health Care Venture Capital Best Practices: Top VCs & CEOs on Company Growth Plans, Valuations, Exit Strategies, & Raising Rounds of Capital. 2008. 92p. pap. 125.00 (978-0-314-98976-5(5)) Aspatore Bks.

Augusto De Carvalho, Luiz & Naude, Benjamin. Planning, Negotiating, Implementing, & Managing Wide Area Networks: A Practical Guide. 2009. 280p. 31.95 (978-1-4401-6391-3(X)); pap. 21.95 (978-1-4401-6390-6(1)) iUniverse, Inc.

Autio, James. The Digital Mantrap: An Operating System for the Human Organism. 55.00 (978-0-9678487-0-9(9)) eBola Communications.

Axson, David A. J. Best Practices in Planning & Performance Management: Radically Rethinking Management for a Volatile World. 3rd ed. 2010. (ENG., Illus.). 320p. 65.00 (978-0-470-53979-8(8), Wiley) Wiley, John & Sons, Inc.

Babson, Harold C., et al. Business Policy & Strategy: The Art of Competition. 7th rev. ed. 2007. (ENG., Illus.). 264p. (C). 87.95 (978-0-8493-8324-3(2)) Auerbach Pubs., Inc.

Backman, Michael & Buttler, Charlotte. Big in Asia: 30 Strategies for Business Success. 2nd rev. ed. 2007. (ENG., Illus.). 380p. pap. 41.00 (978-0-230-00027-8(4)) Palgrave Macmillan.

Badiru, Adedeji B. Statistical Techniques for Project Control. 2012. (Industrial Innovation Ser.). (ENG., Illus.). 412p. 99.95 (978-1-4200-8317-0(1), CRC Press) Taylor & Francis Group GBR. Dist: Taylor & Francis Group.

Balanko-Dickson, Greg. Tips & Traps for Writing an Effective Business Plan. 2006. (Tips & Traps Ser.). (ENG.). 368p. per. 18.95 (978-0-07-146751-3(3), 0071467513) McGraw-Hill Cos., The.

Ball, Wes. The Alpha Factor Project: A Revolutionary New Look at What Really Creates Market Dominance & Self-Sustaining Success. 2008. (Illus.). 212p. 27.95 (978-0-9800031-0-9(5)) Westlyn Publishing.

Bangs, David H., Jr. & Entrepreneur Press Staff. Nonprofits Made Easy. 2006. (ENG., Illus.). 288p. per. 19.95 (978-1-932531-73-2(4), 1932531734) Entrepreneur Pr. dba Entrepreneur Media, Inc.

Barney, Jay & Hesterly, William. Concepts, Strategic Management & Competitive Advantage. 3rd ed. 2010. (Illus.). 380p. pap. (978-0-13-215168-9(5)) Prentice Hall PTR.

Barney, Jay & Hesterly, William S. Strategic Management & Competitive Advantage. 3rd ed. 2009. (ENG.). 656p. (C). 213.33 (978-0-13-609458-6(9), Prentice Hall) Prentice Hall PTR.

Barney, Jay & Hesterly, William S. Strategic Management & Competitive Advantage: Concepts. 4th ed. 2011. (ENG., Illus.). 408p. (C). pap. 146.67 (978-0-13-254634-8(5), Prentice Hall) Prentice Hall PTR.

Barney, Jay B. & Hesterly, William S. Strategic Management & Competitive Advantage. 4th rev. ed. 2011. (ENG., Illus.). 624p. (C). 213.33 (978-0-13-255550-0(6), Prentice Hall) Prentice Hall PTR.

—Strategic Management & Competitive Advantage: Concepts. 4th ed. 2012. (978-0-13-254639-3(6)) Pearson Bks.

Barnum, Diana. Map: Move Ahead Plan - A Complete Business Plan Kit with Marketing & Advertising Plans, Downloadable Templates & More. 2006. 132p. pap. 12.95 (978-1-60145-087-6(7)) Booklocker.com, Inc.

Barringer, Bruce R. Preparing Effective Business Plans: An Entrepreneurial Approach. 2008. (Entrepreneurship Ser.). (ENG.). 288p. (C). per. 60.00 (978-0-13-231832-7(6), Prentice Hall) Prentice Hall PTR.

Barrow, Colin. Business Plans Kit for Dummies. 2012. (ENG., Illus.). 378p. pap. 36.99 (978-0-470-74381-2(6), For Dummies) Wiley, John & Sons, Inc.

—Business Success for Dummies, 3 vols., Set. 2012. (ENG., Illus.). 1152p. pap. 49.99 (978-0-470-74537-3(1), For Dummies) Wiley, John & Sons, Inc.

Barrow, Colin, et al. The Business Plan Workbook. 7th ed. 2012. (ENG., Illus.). 348p. pap. 39.95 (978-0-7494-6461-5(5)) Kogan Page, Ltd. GBR. Dist: Ingram Pub. Services.

Barrow, Colin, et al. The Business Plan Workbook: The Definitive Guide to Researching, Writing up & Presenting a Winning Plan. 6th ed. 2008. (ENG., Illus.). 416p. pap., wbk. ed. 39.95 (978-0-7494-5231-5(5)) Kogan Page, Ltd. GBR. Dist: Ingram Pub. Services.

Barrow, Colin C., et al. Business Plans for Dummies. 2nd ed. 2011. 272p. pap. 21.50 (978-1-119-97442-0(9), For Dummies) Wiley, John & Sons, Inc.

Bate, Nicholas. Beat the Recession: A Blueprint for Business Survival. 2009. 192p. pap. 14.00 (978-1-905940-72-1(6)) Infinite Ideas GBR. Dist: Sony Electronics.

Battell, Christina M. & Miller, Deborah C. Wow Change Cards Five Volume Set. 2008. 250p. 84.95 net. (978-0-9787335-8-2(4)) Miller, Deborah C. Inc.

—Wow Change Cards Volume 1: Leading. 2008. 50p. 24.95 net. (978-0-9787335-3-7(3)) Miller, Deborah C. Inc.

—Wow Change Cards Volume 2: Leading. 2008. 50p. 24.95 net. (978-0-9787335-4-4(1)) Miller, Deborah C. Inc.

—Wow Change Cards Volume 3: Leading. 2008. 50p. 24.95 net. (978-0-9787335-5-1(X)) Miller, Deborah C. Inc.

—Wow Change Cards Volume 4: Inspiring. 2008. 50p. 24.95 net. (978-0-9787335-6-8(8)) Miller, Deborah C. Inc.

—Wow Change Cards Volume 5: Inspiring. 2008. 50p. 24.95 net. (978-0-9787335-7-5(6)) Miller, Deborah C. Inc.

Bazerman, Max H., et al. Predictable Surprises: The Disasters You Should Have Seen Coming, & How to Prevent Them. 2008. (Center for Public Leadership Ser.). (ENG., Illus.). 336p. pap. 18.00 (978-1-4221-2287-7(5)) Harvard Business Review Pr.

Beaulieu, Alan N. & Beaulieu, Brian L. Make Your Move: Change the Way You Look at Your Business & Increase Your Bottom Line. 2010. (ENG.). 224p. pap. 18.95 (978-1-60037-719-8(X)) Morgan James Publishing.

Bell, Randall. Strategy 360: 10 Steps to Creating a Complete Game Plan for Business & Life. 2008. (ENG., Illus.). 261p. 21.95 (978-1-933969-16-9(4)) Owners Manual Pr.

Benn, Suzanne, et al. Organizational Change for Corporate Sustainability: A Guide for Leaders & Change Agents of the Future. 2nd rev. ed. 2007. (Understanding Organizational Change Ser.). (ENG., Illus.). 368p. (C). per. 59.95 (978-0-415-39330-0(2)) Routledge.

Bensoussan, Babette E. Analysis Without Paralysis: 10 Tools to Make Better Strategic Decisions. 2008. (ENG.). 240p. pap. 29.99 (978-0-13-261957-8(1)) FT Press.

Bensoussan, Babette E. & Fleisher, Craig S. Analysis for Managers: Effective Planning Tools & Techniques. 2009. (ENG., Illus.). 216p. pap. 69.50 (978-0-273-72201-4(8)) Pearson Education, Ltd. GBR. Dist: Trans-Atlantic Pubns., Inc.

Benun, Ilise & Top, Peleg. The Designer's Guide to Marketing & Pricing: How to Win Clients & What to Charge Them. 2008. (ENG., Illus.). 288p. pap. 24.99 (978-1-60061-008-0(0), HOW Bks.) F&W Media, Inc.

Berry, Tim. The Plan-as-You-Go Business Plan. 2008. (ENG., Illus.). 288p. pap. 19.95 (978-1-59918-190-5(8), 1599181908) Entrepreneur Pr. dba Entrepreneur Media, Inc.

Berry, Timothy J. Hurdle: The Book on Business Planning. 6th sensomatic ed. 2006. (Illus.). 280p. pap. 19.95 (978-0-9712185-0-5(1), PA-1145) Palo Alto Software, Inc.

Beyer, Philip Paul. System Busters: How to Stop Them in Your Business. 2007. (Illus.). 154p. per. 14.95 (978-0-9764822-3-9(1)) Beyer Printing, Inc.

Bing, Gordon. Due Diligence: Planning, Questions, Issues, 1 vol. 2007. 224p. 44.95 (978-0-313-34540-1(6), C34540, Praeger Pubs.) Greenwood Publishing Group, Inc.

Blanchard, Ken & Stoner, Jesse. Full Steam Ahead! Unleash the Power of Vision in Your Company & Your Life. 2nd ed. 2011. (Bk Business Ser.). (ENG.). 216p. 22.95 (978-1-60509-875-3(2)) Berrett-Koehler Pubs., Inc.

Blyth, Michael. Business Continuity Management: Building an Effective Incident Management Plan Course Guide. 2011. pap. 59.00 (978-1-118-06581-5(6), Wiley) Wiley, John & Sons, Inc.

—Business Continuity Management: Building an Effective Incident Management Plan Course Guide Custom Set. 2011. (ENG.). 384p. 134.00 (978-1-118-06687-4(1), Wiley) Wiley, John & Sons, Inc.

Blyth, Michael & Blyth. Business Continuity Management: Building an Effective Incident Management Plan. 2009. (ENG., Illus.). 362p. 75.00 (978-0-470-43034-7(6), Wiley) Wiley, John & Sons, Inc.

Boons, F. Creating Ecological Value: An Evolutionary Approach to Business Strategies & the Natural Environment. 2010. 224p. 112.00 (978-1-84720-972-6(6)) Elgar, Edward Publishing, Inc.

Boons, Frank. Creating Ecological Value: An Evolutionary Approach to Business Strategies & the Natural Environment. 2011. (Illus.). 224p. pap. 29.95 *(978-1-84980-883-5(X))* Elgar, Edward Publishing, Inc.

Bower, Joseph L. & Gilbert, Clark G., eds. From Resource Allocation to Strategy. 2007. (ENG., Illus.). 496p. per. 39.95 *(978-0-19-927745-2(1))* Oxford Univ. Pr., Inc.

Bowhill, Bruce. Business Planning & Control: Integrating Accounting, Strategy, & People. 2008. (ENG., Illus.). 634p. pap. 65.95 *(978-0-470-06177-0(4),* Wiley) Wiley, John & Sons, Inc.

Bradford, Marianne. Modern ERP: Select, Implement & Use Today's Advanced Business Systems. 2009. 270p. pap. 75.00 *(978-0-557-01291-6(0))* Lulu Enterprises Inc.

Braun, Gerry Cole. Fresh Start. 2011. 306p. 29.99 ***(978-1-4628-7920-5(9))***; pap. 19.99 ***(978-1-4628-7919-9(5))*** Xlibris Corp.

Bridger, Steve. Success Before Start-up: How to prepare for business, avoid mistakes, succeed. Get it Right before You Start. 2011. 202p. pap. ***(978-1-908218-75-9(4))*** MX Publishing, Ltd.

Brinkman, John, et al. Understanding the Business Environment. 2010. (ENG., Illus.). 304p. pap. 49.95 *(978-0-340-94207-9(X))* Hodder Education GBR. Dist: Oxford Univ. Pr., Inc.

Briskey, Richard. Money Agency Planning Guide. 17th ed. 2007. pap. 25.00 *(978-1-56150-859-4(4))* International Wealth Success, Inc.

Brooks, Charlotte. IBM System Storage Business Continuity Solutions Overview. 2nd ed. 2007. (Illus.). xii, 172p. *(978-0-7384-8971-1(9))* IBM.

Brown, Rebel. Defy Gravity: Propel Your Business to High-Velocity Growth. 2010. 221p. 24.95 *(978-1-60832-054-7(5))* Greenleaf Book Group.

Brown, John H. Cash Out, Move On: Get Top Dollar, & More, Selling Your Business. 2008. *(978-0-9655731-2-2(5))*; pap. *(978-0-9655731-3-9(3))* Business Enterprise Pr.

Bruce, Anne. Employee Development Plans. 2010. (Perfect Phrases Ser.). (ENG., Illus.). 176p. pap. 10.95 *(978-0-07-171509-6(6),* 0071715096) McGraw-Hill Cos., The.

Brûlé, Glenn R. Business Analysis Terms. 2011. (ENG.). 220p. pap. 29.95 ***(978-1-890367-51-0(6))*** ESI International.

Bungay Stanier, Michael. End Malaria: Bold Innovation, Limitless Generosity, & the Opportunity to Save a Life. 2011. (Illus.). 208p. pap. ***(978-1-936719-28-0(2),*** Orbit Books) Domino Project, The.

Bungay, Stephen. The Art of Action: How Leaders Close the Gaps Between Plans, Actions & Results. 2011. (ENG., Illus.). 304p. 29.95 *(978-1-85788-559-0(7))* Ebsco Publishing.

Burgess, Jonny. You Can Too: How an Aflac Rookie Built the Business in A Year. 2011. 116p. 23.95 ***(978-1-4620-3971-5(5))***; pap. 13.95 ***(978-1-4620-3969-2(3))*** iUniverse, Inc.

Burtles, Jim & British Standards Institute Staff. Principles & Practice of Business Continuity: Tools & Techniques. 2007. (Illus.). pap. 99.00 *(978-1-931332-39-2(8),* DR800) Rothstein Assocs., Inc.

Business Marketing Association. Advice from the Top: The Expert Guide to B2B Marketing. 2011. 228p. pap. 29.95 ***(978-1-4575-0219-4(4))*** Dog Ear Publishing, LLC.

Business Plans Handbook. 20th ed. 2011. 231.00 *(978-1-4144-6832-7(6))* 21st ed. 2011. (ENG.). 231.00 *(978-1-4144-6833-4(4))* Vol. 17. 17th rev. ed. 2010. (ENG.). 231.00 *(978-1-4144-4571-7(7))* Cengage Gale.

Business Valuation Firm Economics & Best Practices Survey. 2006. ring bd. 279.00 *(978-0-9758668-6-3(9))* Business Valuation Resources, LLC.

Cadle, James, et al. Business Analysis Techniques: 77 Essential Tools for Success. 2010. (ENG., Illus.). 256p. pap. 50.99 *(978-1-906124-23-6(X))* British Computer Society, The GBR. Dist: Turpin Distribution Services Ltd.

Cadotte and, Bruce. Management of Strategy in the Marketplac. 2006. pap. 14.95 *(978-1-4288-0593-4(1))* Cram101 Inc.

Cagan, Michele. Streetwise Business Plans with CD: Create a Business Plan to Supercharge Your Profits! 2006. (ENG., Illus.). 384p. pap. 29.95 *(978-1-59337-620-8(0))* Adams Media Corp.

Calhoon, Joe. The One Hour Plan for Growth: How a Single Sheet of Paper Can Take Your Business to the Next Level. 2010. (ENG., Illus.). 194p. pap. 19.95 *(978-0-470-88096-8(1),* Wiley) Wiley, John & Sons, Inc.

Calkins, Tim. Breakthrough Marketing Plans: How to Stop Wasting Time & Start Driving Growth. 2008. (ENG., Illus.). 184p. 95.00 *(978-0-230-60756-9(X))*; pap. 25.00 *(978-0-230-60757-6(8))* Palgrave Macmillan.

Campisi, Gabriel. The Independent Filmmaker's Guide to Writing A Business Plan for Investors, 2D Ed. 2nd rev. ed. 2012. (ENG., Illus.). 280p. pap. 45.00 ***(978-0-7864-6285-8(X))*** McFarland & Co., Inc. Pubs.

Cannon Concepts for Professionals: A Complete Library of Financial Concepts. 2008th ed. 2008. (Illus.). 908p. pap. 55.00 *(978-0-9702186-5-0(6))* Cannon Financial Institute, Inc.

Capezio, Peter J. Manager's Guide to Business Planning. 2009. (ENG., Illus.). 240p. pap. 16.95 *(978-0-07-162800-6(2),* 0071628002) McGraw-Hill Cos., The.

Capon, Claire. Understanding Strategic Management. 2008. (ENG., Illus.). 448p. pap. *(978-0-273-69498-4(7))* Prentice Hall PTR.

Carkenord, Barbara A. Seven Steps to Mastering Business Analysis. 2008. 360p. pap. *(978-1-60427-007-5(1))* Ross, J. Publishing, Inc.

Carlberg, Conrad. Business Analysis: Microsoft Excel 2010. 4th ed. 2010. (MrExcel Library). (ENG., Illus.). 528p. pap. 39.99 *(978-0-7897-4317-6(5))* Que.

Carvalho, Rogério Atem de & Johansson, Bjorn. Free & Open Source Enterprise Planning: Systems & Strategies. 2011. ***(978-1-61350-486-8(8))***; ***(978-1-61350-486-4(1))***; E-Book ***(978-1-61350-487-1(X))*** IGI Global.

Cassingena, Brian. The Mother of All Marketing Systems Volume 1. 2009. 230p. pap. 29.97 *(978-1-4092-5425-6(9))* Lulu Enterprises Inc.

—The Mother of All Marketing Systems Volume 2. 2009. 224p. pap. 29.91 *(978-1-4092-5439-3(9))* Lulu Enterprises Inc.

—The Mother of All Marketing Systems Volume 3. 2009. 183p. pap. 29.97 *(978-1-4092-5453-9(4))* Lulu Enterprises Inc.

Ceci, Federica. The Business of Solutions. 2009. (Illus.). 192p. 119.00 *(978-1-84844-185-9(1))* Elgar, Edward Publishing, Inc.

Cengage Learning. Online Interactive Business Plan Printed Access Card. 10th ed. 2009. (ENG.). (C). 42.95 *(978-1-4390-4183-3(0))* Cengage South-Western.

Chang, Felicia Yuwei. Lotus - Fashion & Wine Bar Business. 2010. 104p. pap. *(978-3-639-23325-4(5))* VDM Verlag Dr. Mueller e.K.

Chen, Te Fu, ed. Implementing New Business Models in for-Profit & Non-Profit Organizations: Technologies & Applications. 2010. 350p. 180.00 *(978-1-60960-129-4(7),* Business Science Reference) IGI Global.

Chibaya Mbuya, John. The Strategists' Survival Handbook. 2010. 152p. pap. *(978-3-8383-8668-3(X))* Lambert Academic Publishing.

Chien, Chia-Li. Show Me the Money: Run Your Business like a Prosperous Investor. 2010. 184p. 28.00 *(978-1-4502-1521-3(1))* iUniverse, Inc.

—Show Me the Money: Run Your Business like a Prosperous Investor. 2010. 184p. pap. 18.00 *(978-1-4502-1519-0(X))* iUniverse, Inc.

Chowdhury, Lutfun Nahar, et al. Study on the Relationship Between Formal Business Planning & Smes. 2011. 72p. pap. ***(978-3-8443-9760-4(4))*** Lambert Academic Publishing.

Chrisopher, Paul. The Entrepreneur's Starter Kit: 50 Things to Know Before Starting a Business. 2012. (ENG.). 240p. pap. 19.95 ***(978-1-937589-02-8(1),*** Huron Street Pr.) American Library Assn.

Cichelli, David J. The Sales Growth Imperative: How World Class Sales Organizations Successfully Manage the Four Stages of Growth. 3rd ed. 2010. (ENG., Illus.). 320p. 27.00 *(978-0-07-173903-0(3),* 0071739033) McGraw-Hill Cos., The.

Clark, Kontrena. The Business Plan for the Believer. 2006. (Illus.). 79p. per. 8.99 *(978-1-59886-568-4(4))* Tate Publishing & Enterprises, LLC.

Clark, Terry. Microsoft Nav Interview Questions: Unofficial Microsoft Navision Business Solution Certification Review. 2008. 120p. pap. 54.95 *(978-1-60332-005-4(9))* Equity Pr.

Clutterbuck, David. The Talent Wave: Why Succession Planning Fails & What to Do about It. 2012. (ENG.). 256p. pap. 39.95 ***(978-0-7494-5697-9(3))*** Kogan Page, Ltd. GBR. Dist: Ingram Pub. Services.

Cochran, Alice Collier. QuickStart Guide to Roberta's Rules of Order. 2009. 104p. pap. 18.95 *(978-0-578-00893-6(9))* Cochran, Alice Collier.

Concato, Cynthia. The Business Plan: A Workbook for the Entrepreneur to Plan the Start-Up of a Business Venture. (Illus.). xvii, 220p. spiral bd., wbk. ed. 99.95 *(978-0-9664029-4-0(4))*; ring bd., wbk. ed. 99.95 *(978-0-9664029-3-3(6))*; 2nd ed. ring bd., wbk. ed. 29.95 *(978-0-9664029-2-6(8))* Bks. & WorkBooks, Corp.

Cones, John W. Business Plans for Filmmakers. 2010. (Illus.). 192p. pap. 29.95 *(978-0-8093-2994-6(8))* Southern Illinois Univ. Pr.

Constant, Paul C. Readying a Company for a Catastrophic Event: A Template for Success. 2010. 206p. 27.99 *(978-1-4520-0588-1(5))*; pap. 17.99 *(978-1-4520-0587-4(7))* AuthorHouse.

Corporate Meeting & Event Planner 2008-09. 2008. pap. *(978-0-87228-493-7(X))* Douglas Publications, Limited Liability Co.

Corrigan Philip & White Michael. Barthes. 2007. 160p. pap. 45.95 *(978-0-415-06419-4(8),* RU9677) Routledge.

Cortez, Annetta. The Complete Idiot's Guide to Risk Management. 2010. (Complete Idiot's Guide Ser.). (ENG.). 368p. (gr. 12-18). 19.95 *(978-1-59257-958-7(2),* Alpha Bks.) Penguin Group (USA) Inc.

Cowher, Salene & Dickson, Larry S. Effective Planning Strategies & Proposal Writing: A Workbook for Helping Professionals. 2009. (ENG.). 102p. pap. 19.99 *(978-0-7618-4976-6(9))* Univ. Pr. of America, Inc.

Cram101 Textbook Reviews. Outlines & Highlights for Project Management by Jeffery K Pinto. 2011. 110p. pap. 28.95 ***(978-1-61905-658-9(5))*** Cram101 Inc.

Cram101 Textbook Reviews & Cram101 Textbook Reviews. Outlines an Activity Based Approach by Paula Jarzabkowski, Isbn: 9780761944379. 2011. 60p. pap. 26.95 ***(978-1-61461-311-4(7))*** Cram101 Inc.

—Outlines & Highlights for Definitive Hdbk of Business Continui by Hiles. 2011. 110p. pap. 28.95 ***(978-1-61830-263-2(9))*** Cram101 Inc.

—Outlines & Highlights for the Wiley Guide to Organization & Project Management Competencies by Peter Morris, Isbn: 9780470226834. 2011. 56p. pap. 26.95 ***(978-1-61461-349-7(4))*** Cram101 Inc.

—Outlines & Highlights for the Wiley Guide to Project, Program, & Portfolio Management by Peter Morris, Isbn: 9780470226858 9780470226827. 2011. 114p. pap. 28.95 ***(978-1-61461-389-3(3))*** Cram101 Inc.

—Outlines & Highlights for Understanding Business Strategy Concepts Plus by R Duane Ireland. 2011. 272p. pap. 32.95 ***(978-1-61830-544-2(1))*** Cram101 Inc.

—Outlines Jeanette C Lauer, Isbn: 9780073528281. 2011. 166p. pap. 29.95 ***(978-1-4288-6491-7(1))*** Cram101 Inc.

Cram101 Textbook Reviews Staff. Outlines & Highlights for Corporate Strategy by Collis,Isbn: 0072312866. 2008. 104p. per. 10.95 *(978-1-4288-5743-8(5))* Cram101 Inc.

—Outlines & Highlights for Entrepreneurial Finance: Finance & Business Strategies for the Serious Entrepreneur by Steven Rogers, ISBN. 2009. 76p. pap. 27.95 *(978-1-4288-2607-6(6))*; 106p. pap. 28.95 *(978-1-4288-8829-6(2))* Cram101 Inc.

—Outlines & Highlights for Essentials of Strategic Management by Charles Hill, Isbn: 9780547194325. 2009. 116p. pap. 28.95 *(978-1-4288-4152-9(0))*; 146p. pap. 29.95 *(978-1-4288-8810-4(1))* Cram101 Inc.

—Outlines & Highlights for Launching New Ventures by Kathleen R Allen, Isbn: 9780547014562. 2009. 188p. pap. 30.95 *(978-1-4288-4188-8(1))*; 184p. pap. 29.95 *(978-1-4288-7911-9(0))* Cram101 Inc.

—Outlines & Highlights for Preparing Effective Business Plans: An Entrepreneurial Approach by Bruce R. Barringer, ISBN. 2009. 66p. pap. 27.95 *(978-1-4288-2805-6(2))* Cram101 Inc.

—Outlines & Highlights for Strategic Management & Competitive Advantage: Concepts by Jay Barney, ISBN. 2009. 166p. pap. 29.95 *(978-1-4288-3998-4(4))* Cram101 Inc.

—Outlines & Highlights for Strategic Management & Competitive Advantage: Concepts by Jay Barney, William Hesterly, ISBN. 2009. 184p. pap. 29.95 *(978-1-4288-4184-0(9))*; 142p. pap. 28.95 *(978-1-4288-8695-7(8))* Cram101 Inc.

—Outlines & Highlights for Strategic Management Theory by Charles Hill, Isbn: 9780618894765. 2009. 200p. pap. 30.95 *(978-1-4288-4075-1(3))*; 90p. pap. 27.95 *(978-1-4288-9641-3(4))* Cram101 Inc.

Cross, Stuart. The Ceo's Strategy Handbook. 2011. 212p. pap. 29.95 ***(978-1-906403-66-9(X))*** Global Professional Publishing GBR. Dist: Stylus Publishing, LLC.

Crossan, Mary, et al. Strategic Analysis & Action. 7th ed. 2009. (ENG.). (C). pap. 70.00 *(978-0-13-206142-1(2),* Prentice Hall) Prentice Hall PTR.

Crystal, Michael. Succeeding in Your Sandbox. 2010. 100p. pap. 16.95 *(978-0-557-34109-2(4))* Lulu Enterprises Inc.

Cullen, Brian. The Bottom Line: The Entrepreneur's Guide to Financial Management. 2009. 70p. pap. 39.95 *(978-1-4327-4451-9(8))* Outskirts Pr., Inc.

Dadamo, Dick. Planning: As Exciting As It Gets or Plans Were Born to Be Changed. 2007. 132p. per. 14.95 *(978-0-595-45338-2(4),* Authors Choice Pr.) iUniverse, Inc.

Daehn, Michael. 188 Business Tips (and 300 Questions) to Get Your Brain Juices Flowing. 2010. 167p. pap. 12.95 *(978-0-557-47823-1(5))* Lulu Enterprises Inc.

Day, Adrian. Investing in Resources: How to Profit from the Outsized Potential & Avoid the Risks. 2010. (ENG., Illus.). 341p. 39.95 *(978-0-470-61326-9(2),* Wiley) Wiley, John & Sons, Inc.

Dayal, Umeshwar, et al. Business Process Management: 7th International Conference, BPM 2009, Ulm, Germany, September 8-10, 2009, Proceedings. 2009. (Lecture Notes in Computer Science / Information Systems & Applications, incl. Internet/Web, & HCI Ser.). (Illus.). xiii, 363p. pap. 79.95 *(978-3-642-03847-1(6),* 3642038476) Springer.

De Puy, John. Gaining the Edge: Building Business in the 21st Century. 2008. 144p. *(978-0-9799879-9-1(7))* Palm Tree Pubns.

Dennis, Pascal. Conseguindo que as coisas certas sejam Executadas. 2007. (POR.). 40.00 *(978-1-934109-14-4(2))* Lean Enterprise Institute, Inc.

Dent, Julian. Distribution Channels. 2nd rev. ed. 2011. (ENG.). 432p. pap. 65.00 *(978-0-7494-6269-7(8))* Kogan Page, Ltd. GBR. Dist: Ingram Pub. Services.

DeThomas, Arthur R. & Derammelaere, Stephanie A. Writing a Convincing Business Plan. 3rd rev. ed. 2008. (Barron's Business Library Ser.). (ENG.). 272p. pap. 18.99 *(978-0-7641-3934-5(7))* Barron's Educational Series, Inc.

Dorsey, Thomas J., et al. Commodity Strategies: High-Profit Techniques for Investors & Traders. 2007. (Wiley Trading Ser.: 313). (ENG., Illus.). 208p. 60.00 *(978-0-470-12631-8(0),* Wiley) Wiley, John & Sons, Inc.

Drake, Dwight J. Business Planning: Closely Held Enterprises. 2nd rev. ed. 2008. (American Casebook Ser.). 831p. 109.00 *(978-0-314-18508-2(9))* West Legalworks) West.

Drewitt, Tony. A Manager's Guide to BS25999. 2008. (Illus.). 216p. pap. *(978-1-905356-51-5(X))* IT Governance.

Dringoli, Angelo. Corporate Strategy & Firm Growth: Creating Value for Shareholders. 2012. (New Perspectives on the Modern Corporation Ser.). (Illus.). 272p. 115.00 ***(978-0-85793-827-5(4))*** Elgar, Edward Publishing, Inc.

Du Toit, Angelique. Corporate Strategy & Feminism. 2006. (Routledge Research in Strategic Management Ser.). 144p. 158.00 *(978-0-415-36561-1(9))* Routledge.

Duff, Beth. When the Red Horse Spoke: Bringing learning with horses from dream to Reality. 2009. 260p. pap. 21.49 *(978-1-4389-8654-8(8))* AuthorHouse.

Dumitrescu, Delia. Road Trip to Innovation: How I Came to Understand Future Thinking. 2012. (ENG., Illus.). 280p. pap. 39.95 ***(978-3-00-035736-7(X))*** Vivays Pubng. Ltd. GBR. Dist: Innovative Logistics.

Duncan, Kevin. So What? The Definitive Guide to the Only Business Questions That Matter. 2008. (ENG., Illus.). 260p. per. 24.95 *(978-1-84112-793-4(0),* Capstone) Wiley, John & Sons, Inc.

Dunphy, Dexter, et al. Organizational Change for Corporate Sustainability. 3rd rev. ed. 2012. (Understanding Organizational Change Ser.). (ENG., Illus.). 368p. (C). 160.00 ***(978-0-415-69548-0(1))***; pap. 62.95 ***(978-0-415-69549-7(X))*** Routledge.

Dunphy, Dexter C., et al. Organizational Change for Corporate Sustainability: A Guide for Leaders & Change Agents of the Future. 2nd rev. ed. 2007. (Understanding Organizational Change Ser.). (ENG., Illus.). 368p. (C). 185.00 *(978-0-415-39329-4(9))* Routledge.

Dutta, Anirban & Folden, Hetze W. Winning Strategies: Secrets to Clinching Multimillion-Dollar Deals. 2010. (ENG., Illus.). 224p. 34.95 *(978-0-470-82466-5(2),* Wiley) Wiley, John & Sons, Inc.

Dykes, Brent. Web Analytics Action Hero: Using Analysis to Gain Insight & Optimize Your Business. 2011. (ENG., Illus.). 256p. pap. 49.99 ***(978-0-321-79401-7(X))*** Adobe Pr.

Earl, Clifford J. How to Build a Business Case: The Practical Guide to Persuasive Business Case Writing. 2007. (Illus.). 182p. spiral bd. 85.00 incl. cd-rom *(978-0-9707733-4-0(X),* RMS-BCP1) Resource Management Systems, Inc.

El-Homsi, Anwar & Slutsky, Jeff. Corporate Sigma: Optimizing the Health of Your Company with Systems Thinking. 2009. (ENG., Illus.). 288p. 45.95 *(978-1-4398-0394-3(3))* Productivity Pr.

Elkin, Paul. Mastering Business Planning & Strategy. 2nd rev. ed. 2007. (Illus.). 184p. pap. 27.95 *(978-1-85418-325-3(X))* Thorogood GBR. Dist: Stylus Publishing, LLC.

Elliott, Ord. The Future Is Fluid Form: Practical Steps for Designing Flat, Flexible Organizations. 2009. 156p. 25.95 *(978-1-4401-1539-4(7))*; pap. 15.95 *(978-1-4401-1537-0(0))* iUniverse, Inc.

Elssamadisy, Amr. Patterns of Agile Practice Adoption. 2007. 184p. per. 24.95 *(978-1-4303-1488-2(5))* Lulu Enterprises Inc.

Elwins, Dannie. How to Get Business Grants for Your Business. 2009. 40p. pap. 16.99 *(978-0-557-15542-2(8))* Lulu Enterprises Inc.

—How to Start A Business in Car Detailing. 2009. 44p. pap. 16.99 *(978-0-557-15565-1(7))* Lulu Enterprises Inc.

Entrepreneur Press Staff & Kimball, Cheryl. Start Your Own Event Planning Business 3/E: Your Step-by-Step Guide to Success. 3rd ed. 2011. (ENG., Illus.). 224p. pap. 19.95 *(978-1-59918-415-9(X),* 159918415X) Entrepreneur Pr. dba Entrepreneur Media, Inc.

Espejo, Raul & Reyes, Alfonso. Organizational Systems: Managing Complexity with the Viable System Model. 2011. (Illus.). xii, 264p. 139.00 *(978-3-642-19108-4(8),* 3642191088) Springer.

Esteves, José, et al. Handbook of Research in Enterprise Systems. 2011. (Response Bks.). (Illus.). 324p. (C). 60.00 *(978-81-321-0509-1(5),* B05091C) SAGE Pubns., Inc.

Evans, James R. Business Analytics. 2012. (ENG.). 688p. (C). 166.67 ***(978-0-13-295061-9(8),*** Prentice Hall) Prentice Hall PTR.

Evans, Vaughan. Writing a Business Plan: How to Win Backing to Start up or Grow Your Business. rev. ed. 2011. (ENG., Illus.). 248p. (C). pap. 24.99 ***(978-0-273-75798-6(9))*** FT Press.

Evarts, Jeff. Making Good Money in A Bad Economy: 35 Self-Employed Options. 2011. 168p. 25.95 ***(978-1-4502-8988-7(6))*** iUniverse, Inc.

Excellence: The Drive to Competitive Advantage: The General Plan for Dominance. 2007. (C). pap. 75.00 *(978-0-9761491-6-3(8))* Eagles Publishing.

Feigin, Gerald. Operational Challenges in Supply Chain Planning: The Right Product in the Right Place at the Right Time. 2011. 150p. pap. 29.95 ***(978-1-60649-245-1(4))*** Business Expert Pr.

Fernandez, Elizabeth F. The Investor's Bible. 2008. 73p. pap. 16.95 *(978-1-4092-3307-7(3))* Lulu Enterprises Inc.

Ferrell, Mike. Ultimate Breakthrough Planning: The Business Funnel Approach. 2008. (ENG.). 216p. pap. 18.95 *(978-0-9798249-0-6(7))* Scarletta Pr.

Fife, Lynn. The Guaranteed Profit System. 2008. 268p. per. 39.95 *(978-1-4327-1948-7(3))* Outskirts Pr., Inc.

Finch, Brian. How to Write a Business Plan. 3rd rev. ed. 2010. (Creating Success Ser.). (ENG.). 184p. pap. 14.95 *(978-0-7494-6030-3(X))*; (Illus.). 160p. pap. 14.95 *(978-0-7494-5582-8(9))* Kogan Page, Ltd. GBR. Dist: Ingram Pub. Services.

Fligel, Robert. Supercharge Your Cpa Firm. 2011. 36p. pap. 21.99 ***(978-1-4568-6495-8(5))*** Xlibris Corp.

Ford, Brian R., et al. The Ernst & Young Business Plan Guide. 3rd rev. ed. 2007. (ENG., Illus.). 256p. per. 19.95 *(978-0-470-11269-4(7),* Wiley) Wiley, John & Sons, Inc.

Forsyth, Patrick & Kay, Frances. Tough Tactics for Tough Times: How to Maintain Business Success in Difficult Economic Conditions. 2009. (ENG., Illus.). 160p. pap. 17.95 *(978-0-7494-5521-7(7))* Kogan Page, Ltd. GBR. Dist: Ingram Pub. Services.

Fortner, Denise, ed. Maturing the Business Continuity Program: Taking the BCP to the Next Level. 2010. (ENG.). 288p. 79.95 *(978-1-4200-9062-8(3))* Auerbach Pubs., Inc.

Fox, Jeffrey J. How to Be a Fierce Competitor: What Winning Companies & Great Managers Do in Tough Times. 2010. (ENG., Illus.). 176p. 19.95 *(978-0-470-40854-4(5),* Jossey-Bass) Wiley, John & Sons, Inc.

Franklin, Burke, et al. BizPlanBuilder Express: A Guide to Creating a Business Plan with BizPlanBuilder. 3rd ed. 2007. (Illus.). viii, 184p. *(978-0-324-42117-0(6))* Cengage South-Western.

Freeman, R. Edward. Strategic Management: A Stakeholder Approach. 2010. (ENG., Illus.). 292p. pap. 35.00 *(978-0-521-15174-0(0))* Cambridge Univ. Pr.

Friedman, Pirjo. Pushing Your Boundaries: The Feminine Principle in Business. 2007. 108p. per. 16.95 *(978-1-4241-6334-2(X))* PublishAmerica, Inc.

Friend, Graham & Zehle, Stefan. Guide to Business Planning. 2nd ed. 2009. (Economist Ser.). (ENG., Illus.). 282p. 29.95 *(978-1-57660-326-4(8),* Bloomberg Pr.) Wiley, John & Sons, Inc.

Fulford, Richard. Managing Operational Enterprise Resource Planning Applications. 2009. (Illus.). 304p. pap. *(978-3-639-13983-9(6))* VDM Verlag Dr. Mueller e.K.

Furuhata, Junpei & Inoue, Osamu. Nintendo Magic: Winning the Videogame Wars. Starr, Paul, tr. from JPN. 2010. (ENG., Illus.). 224p. 19.95 *(978-1-934287-22-4(9))* Vertical, Inc.

Gale Editor, ed. Business Plans Handbook. 22nd ed. 2011. 459p. lib. bdg. 231.00 *(978-1-4144-6834-1(2))* Cengage Gale.

Gale Editors, ed. Business Plan Handbook, Vol. 12. 12th ed. 2006. (Business Plans Handbook Ser.). (ENG.). 368p. 231.00 *(978-0-7876-6682-8(3))* Cengage Gale.

Gamble, John & Peteraf, Margaret. Essentials of Strategic Management: The Quest for Competitive Advantage. 3rd ed. 2012. (ENG., Illus.). 560p. (C). pap. 143.33 ***(978-0-07-802928-8(7)***, 0078029287, McGraw-Hill/Irwin) McGraw-Hill Higher Education.

Gamble, John, et al. Crafting & Executing Strategy: Concepts & Readings. 18th ed. 2011. (ENG., Illus.). 688p. (C). pap. 147.33 *(978-0-07-732517-6(6)*, 0077325176, McGraw-Hill/Irwin) McGraw-Hill Higher Education.

Gamble, John, et al. Loose-Leaf Essentials of Strategic Management. 3rd ed. 2012. (ENG., Illus.). (C). ring bd. 100.33 ***(978-0-07-749271-7(4)***, 0077492714, McGraw-Hill/Irwin) McGraw-Hill Higher Education.

Gamble, John E. & Thompson, Arthur A., Jr. Essential of Strategic Management: The Quest for Competitive Advantage. 2nd ed. 2010. (ENG., Illus.). 592p. (C). pap. 143.33 *(978-0-07-813714-3(4)*, 0078137144, McGraw-Hill/Irwin) McGraw-Hill Higher Education.

Gambles, Ian. Making the Business Case: Proposals That Succeed for Projects That Work. 2009. (Illus.). 198p. pap. 49.95 *(978-0-566-08745-5(6)*, Gower Publishing Co., Ltd.) Ashgate Publishing, Ltd. GBR. Dist: Ashgate Publishing Co.

Gandellini, Giorgio, et al. Strategy for Action - I: The Logic & Context of Strategic Management. 2012. (SpringerBriefs in Business Ser.). (ENG., Illus.). xi, 84p. pap. 49.95 ***(978-88-470-2486-1(2)***, 8847024862) Springer.

Garson, Jack. How to Build a Business & Sell It for Millions. 2010. (ENG.). 272p. 25.99 *(978-0-312-38311-4(8))* St. Martin's Pr.

Gbadegesin, Saheed Adebayo & Khan, Younas. Analysis of Innovation Process. 2011. 96p. pap. ***(978-3-8433-9311-9(7))*** Lambert Academic Publishing.

Gerwick, Madeline C. Good Timing Guide 2007: An Astrological Business Planner. 2010. spiral bd. 24.50 *(978-1-60070-011-8(X)*, Elite Bks.) Author's Publishing Cooperative.

Ghalili, Farid. I Am in Business with My: Money Matters. 2009. 128p. pap. 14.95 *(978-1-4401-1291-1(6))* iUniverse, Inc.

Gibbert, Michael. Strategy Making in a Crisis: From Analysis to Imagination. 2010. (Illus.). 240p. 112.00 *(978-1-84844-240-5(8))* Elgar, Edward Publishing, Inc.

Ginsberg. Entrepreneurship Strategy. 2010. (International Library of Entrepreneurship Ser.). (Illus.). 784p. 389.00 *(978-1-84720-982-5(3))* Elgar, Edward Publishing, Inc.

Gione, M. Employees Your Money-Making MacHine: The ability to listen, motivate, communicate, & passionately implement Is the difference between a Successfu. 2008. 128p. pap. 15.95 *(978-1-4389-1486-2(5))* AuthorHouse.

Go, Frank & Govers, Robert, eds. International Place Branding Yearbook 2010: Place Branding in the New Age of Innovation. 2010. (ENG., Illus.). 256p. 42.00 *(978-0-230-27954-4(6))* Palgrave Macmillan.

Goldman Sachs Staff. Architecture of Wealth: Building Your Practice & Designing Outcome-Based Portfolios. 2009. (Reinvented Wealth Manager Ser.). (ENG.). 208p. 49.95 *(978-0-470-28950-1(3)*, Wiley) Wiley, John & Sons, Inc.

Goldsmith, Walter & Clutterbuck, David. The Winning Streak. (Illus.). xviii, 302p. 40.00 *(978-0-7528-0778-2(1))* Orion Bks. Ltd. GBR. Dist: Trafalgar Square Publishing.

Goldstein, Arnold S. Turnaround: How to Turn Your Business into a Debt-Free Money Machine. 2006. 322p. 24.95 *(978-1-880539-65-1(9))* Garrett Publishing, Inc.

Gorchels, Linda. Business Model Renewal: How to Grow & Prosper by Defying Best Practices & Reinventing Your Strategy. 2012. (ENG., Illus.). 256p. 30.00 ***(978-0-07-178403-0(9)***, 0071784039) McGraw-Hill Cos., The.

Gorman, Tom. Execution: Create the Vision, Implement the Plan, Get the Job Done. 2007. (ENG.). 192p. per. 9.95 *(978-1-59869-118-4(X)*, Adams Business) Adams Media Corp.

Graham, Gerald "Sandy". See the Greens: Achieving your entrepreneurial Dream. 2010. 128p. pap. 19.95 *(978-1-934899-21-2(6)*, Logos Pr.) ThinkBiotech, LLC.

Granger, Michele & Sterling, Tina. Fashion Entrepreneurship: Retail Business Planning. 2nd ed. 2011. (Illus.). 448p. (C). pap. 0.00 *(978-1-60901-134-5(1))* Fairchild Bks.

Greene, Cynthia L. Entrepreneurship: Ideas in Action. 4th rev. ed. 2008. (ENG., Illus.). 432p. (C). 84.95 *(978-0-538-44626-6(9))* Cengage South-Western.

Greenwald, Bruce C. & Kahn, Judd. Competition Demystified: A Radically Simplified Approach to Business Strategy. 2007. (ENG.). 416p. (gr. 12-18). 18.00 *(978-1-59184-180-7(1)*, Portfolio Trade) Penguin Group (USA) Inc.

Grensing-Pophal, Lin. The Complete Idiot's Guide to Strategic Planning. 2011. (Complete Idiot's Guide Ser.). (ENG.). 336p. (gr. 12). 19.95 *(978-1-61564-059-1(2)*, Alpha Bks.) Penguin Group (USA) Inc.

Griffin, Darrell. Business with a Purpose: Starting, building, managing & protecting your new Business. 2010. 614p. pap. 34.95 *(978-1-4327-3565-4(9))* Outskirts Pr., Inc.

Grit, Roel. Making a Business Plan. 2nd rev. ed. 2011. (ENG.). 108p. (C). pap. 34.95 ***(978-90-01-79098-1(4))*** Routledge.

Grüne, Guido, et al. Business Process Management within the Chemicals Industry & the Pharmaceuticals Industry. 2010. (ENG.). 250p. 89.95 *(978-3-642-11716-9(3)*, 3642117163) Springer.

Grünig, Rudolf & Kühn, Richard. Process-based Strategic Planning. Clark, Anthony, tr. 6th ed. 2010. (Illus.). xxiv, 358p. 69.95 *(978-3-642-16714-0(4)*, 3642167144) Springer.

Gunasekaran, Angappa & Shea, Timothy, eds. Organizational Advancements through Enterprise Information Systems: Emerging Applications & Developments: Emerging Applications & Developments. 2009. 388p. 180.00 *(978-1-60566-968-7(7)*, Business Science Reference) IGI Global.

Günes, Nazif, et al, eds. Business-Plan-Guide: Grundlagen — Anschauungsbeispiele — Vorgehensmodell. 2010. (GER.). 457p. pap. *(978-3-8325-2303-9(0))* Logos Verlag Berlin.

Gunyung, Lee. Business Process Management of Japanese & Korean Companies, Vol. 5. 2009. (Illus.). 188p. 79.00 *(978-981-283-860-5(0))* World Scientific Publishing Co., Inc.

Hagel, John, III, et al. The Power of Pull: How Small Moves, Smartly Made, Can Set Big Things in Motion. 2010. (ENG.). 288p. (gr. 9). 27.50 *(978-0-465-01935-9(8))* Basic Bks.

Hall, Richard E. Business Model Designer. 2008. 86p. pap. 16.95 *(978-0-7414-4758-6(4))* Infinity Publishing.

—The Good Idea & Good Resources Business Plan Workbook. 2010. pap. 16.95 *(978-0-7414-5694-6(X))* Infinity Publishing.

Hambleton, Lynne. Treasure Chest of Six Sigma Growth Methods, Tools, & Best Practices. rev. ed. 2007. (Prentice Hall Six Sigma for Innovation & Growth Ser.). (ENG.). 864p. pap. 99.00 ***(978-0-13-282405-7(1)***, Prentice Hall) Prentice Hall PTR.

Hampson, Steve. Certifying Your Aftermarket Maintenance Program Class. 2008. 268p. pap. 44.95 *(978-0-615-20319-5(1))* Hampson, Steve.

—Certifying Your Maintenance First Class - Facilities. 2008. 248p. pap. 44.96 *(978-0-615-20318-8(3))* Hampson, Steve.

—Certifying Your Owner Maintained Fleet Maintenance Program Class. 2008. 244p. pap. 44.95 *(978-0-615-20320-1(5))* Hampson, Steve.

Harrington, H. James & Voehl, Frank. The Organizational Masterplan Handbook: A Catalyst for Performance Planning & Results. 2012. (ENG., Illus.). 275p. 49.95 ***(978-1-4398-7877-4(3))*** Productivity Pr.

Harris, Gerald. The Art of Quantum Planning: Lessons from Quantum Physics for Breakthrough Strategy, Innovation, & Leadership. 2009. (ENG., Illus.). 168p. pap. 18.95 *(978-1-60509-265-2(7))* Berrett-Koehler Pubs., Inc.

Harvard Business Review. Harvard Business Review on Rebuilding Your Business Model. 2011. (ENG., Illus.). 288p. pap. 22.00 *(978-1-4221-6262-0(1))* Harvard Business Review Pr.

Harvard Business School Press Staff, compiled by. Creating a Business Plan: Expert Solutions to Everyday Challenges. 2007. (Pocket Mentor Ser.). (ENG., Illus.). 144p. per. 9.95 *(978-1-4221-1885-6(1))* Harvard Business Review Pr.

Harvey, Jean. Complex Service Delivery Processes: Strategy to Operations. 2nd ed. 2010. (Illus.). xxxi, 428p. *(978-0-87389-800-3(1))* ASQ Quality Pr.

Hass, Kathleen B. Professionalizing Business Analysis: Breaking the Cycle of Challenged Projects. 2007. (ENG.). pap. 24.00 *(978-1-56726-208-7(2))* Management Concepts, Inc.

Hass, Kathleen B., et al. Getting It Right: Business Requirement Analysis Tools & Techniques. 2007. (ENG.). pap. 24.00 *(978-1-56726-211-7(2))* Management Concepts, Inc.

Hax, Arnoldo C. The Delta Model: Reinventing Your Business Strategy. (Illus.). 2010. xx, 235p. *(978-1-4419-1480-4(3))* 2009. (ENG., xx, 248p. 49.95 *(978-1-4419-1479-8(X)*, 144191479X) Springer.

Hayzlett, Jeffrey W. The Mirror Test: Is Your Business Really Breathing? 2011. (ENG.). 256p. pap. 16.99 *(978-0-446-55981-2(4)*, Business Plus) Grand Central Publishing.

Head, Keith. Elements of Multinational Strategy. 2007. (ENG., Illus.). xii, 208p. per. 49.95 *(978-3-540-74438-2(X)*, 354074438X); 109.00 *(978-3-540-44765-8(2)*, 3540447652) Springer.

Heene, Aime & Sanchez, Ron, eds. Managing Firm Growth & Diversification. 2010. (Advances in Applied Business Strategy Ser.). (Illus.). 275p. 124.95 *(978-1-84855-876-2(7))* Emerald Group Publishing Ltd. GBR. Dist: Turpin Distribution Services Ltd.

Hess, Edward D. Smart Growth: Building an Enduring Business by Managing the Risks of Growth. 2010. (Columbia Business School Publishing Ser.). (ENG., Illus.). 248p. (gr. 17). 27.95 *(978-0-231-15050-7(4))* Columbia Univ. Pr.

Hess, Edward D. & Goetz, Charles F. So, You Want to Start a Business? 8 Steps to Take Before Making the Leap. 2008. (ENG., Illus.). 224p. pap. 21.99 *(978-0-13-712667-5(0))* FT Press.

Hicks, Tyler G. Business Plan Kit. 2009. pap. 29.50 *(978-1-56150-880-8(2))* 17th ed. 2007. pap. 29.50 *(978-1-56150-781-8(4))* International Wealth Success, Inc.

Hiles, Andrew. The Definitive Handbook of Business Continuity Management. 3rd ed. 2010. (ENG., Illus.). 832p. 57.95 *(978-0-470-67014-9(2)*, Wiley) Wiley, John & Sons, Inc.

Hill and, Jones. Strategic Management an Integrated Appro. 2006. pap. 15.95 *(978-1-4288-0786-0(1))*; pap. 11.95 *(978-1-4288-0506-4(0))* Cram101 Inc.

Hill, Charles & Jones, Gareth. Strategic Management: An Integrated Approach. 9th ed. 2009. (Strategic Management Ser.). (ENG.). 936p. (C). 251.95 *(978-0-538-74856-8(7))* Cengage South-Western.

—Strategic Management Theory: An Integrated Approach. 9th ed. 2009. (Strategic Management Ser.). (ENG.). 524p. (C). pap. 175.95 *(978-0-538-75107-0(X))* Cengage South-Western.

Hill, Dave, et al. Strategic Management Theory: An Integrated Approach. 8th ed. 2007. (Illus.). (YA). pap., pap., pap. 138.36 *(978-0-547-11818-5(X)*, 1047030) CENGAGE Learning.

Hillier, Jean & Healey, Patsy. Foundations of the Planning Enterprise, 3 vols., Vol. 1. 2008. (Critical Essays in Planning Theory Ser.). 540p. 300.00 *(978-0-7546-2719-7(5))* Ashgate Publishing Co.

Hilse, Lars. Adding the E to your Business Strategy. 2009. 148p. pap. 19.99 *(978-0-557-08080-9(0))* Lulu Enterprises Inc.

Hirata, Thomas T. Customer Satisfaction Planning: Ensuring Product Quality & Safety Within Your MRP/ERP Systems. 2008. (ENG., Illus.). 120p. 44.95 *(978-1-4200-8381-1(3))* Productivity Pr.

Hoffman, Andrew J. & Woody, John G. Climate Change: What's Your Business Strategy? 2008. (Memo to the CEO: Ser.). (ENG.). 115p. 18.00 *(978-1-4221-2105-4(4))* Harvard Business Review Pr.

Hogan, Daniel R. $$$ the Entrepreneur Manager: The Business Man's Business Plan. 2009. 312p. pap. 39.99 *(978-1-4490-1135-2(7))* AuthorHouse.

Holbeche, Linda. Aligning Human Resources & Business Strategy. 2nd rev. ed. 2009. (ENG., Illus.). 496p. pap. 44.95 *(978-0-7506-8017-2(2))* Routledge.

Holloman, Christer & Donnelly, William. First Time Entrepreneur Series: How to Write A Professional Business Plan Quickly. 2010. 127p. pap. 62.95 *(978-1-4092-9977-6(5))* Lulu Enterprises Inc.

Holm, Sheila. Seven Step Business Plan, 1 vol. 2007. (ENG., Illus.). 128p. 19.95 *(978-1-58980-471-5(6))* Pelican Publishing Co., Inc.

Holt, Jon. Pragmatic Guide to Business Process Mode. 2nd ed. 2009. (Illus.). 248p. pap. 50.99 *(978-1-906124-12-0(4))* British Computer Society, The GBR. Dist: Turpin Distribution Services Ltd.

Hooley, Graham, et al. Marketing Strategy & Competitive Positioning. 5th rev. ed. 2012. (ENG., Illus.). 578p. pap. 125.00 ***(978-0-273-74093-3(8)***, Financial Times/Prentice Hall) Pearson Education, Ltd. GBR. Dist: Trans-Atlantic Pubns., Inc.

Hopkins, Richard & Jenkins, Kevin. Eating the IT Elephant: Moving from Greenfield Development to Brownfield. 2008. (ENG., Illus.). 256p. pap. 39.99 *(978-0-13-713012-2(0))* Pearson Education.

Horan, James T., Jr. The One Page Business Plan for the Professional Consultant. 2006. (One Page Business Plan Ser.: 2). pap. 34.95 *(978-1-891315-04-6(8))* One Page Business Plan Co., The.

Horan, Jim. The One Page Business Plan: The Fastest, Easiest Way to Write a Business Plan. 2008. (Illus.). 92p. pap. 28.50 *(978-1-906465-31-5(2)*, Wiley) Wiley, John & Sons, Inc.

—The One Page Business Plan Financial Services Edition: The Fastest, Easiest Way to Write a Business Plan!: Financial Services Edition. 2007. (Illus.). 100p. pap. 34.95 incl. cd-rom *(978-1-891315-05-3(6))* One Page Business Plan Co., The.

—The One Page Business Plan for Financial Services Professionals. 2011. (ENG.). 104p. pap. 34.95 ***(978-1-59996-223-8(3))*** Human Resource Development Pr.

—The One Page Business Plan for Non-Profit Organizations. 2011. (ENG.). 120p. pap. 34.95 ***(978-1-59996-221-4(7))*** Human Resource Development Pr.

—The One Page Business Plan for Non-Profit Organizations: The Fastest, Easiest Way to Write a Business Plan! 2006. (One Page Business Plan Ser.: 3). (Illus.). 117p. pap. 34.95 incl. cd-rom *(978-1-891315-02-2(1))* One Page Business Plan Co., The.

—The One Page Business Plan for the Creative Entrepreneur. 2011. (ENG.). 98p. pap. 34.95 ***(978-1-59996-219-1(5))*** Human Resource Development Pr.

—The One Page Business Plan for the Creative Entrepreneur - Spanish Version. 2011. (ENG.). 92p. pap. 34.95 ***(978-1-59996-224-5(1))*** Human Resource Development Pr.

—The One Page Business Plan for the Professional Consultant. 2011. (ENG.). 80p. pap. 34.95 ***(978-1-59996-222-1(5))*** Human Resource Development Pr.

—The One Page Business Plan for Women in Business. 2011. (ENG.). 128p. pap. 34.95 ***(978-1-59996-220-7(9))*** Human Resource Development Pr.

Hossenlopp, Rosemary & Hass, Kathleen B. Unearthing Business Requirements: Elicitation Tools & Techniques. 2007. pap. 24.00 *(978-1-56726-210-0(4))* Management Concepts, Inc.

Hotchkiss, Stuart. Business Continuity Management: In Practice. 2010. (ENG., Illus.). 128p. pap. 34.99 ***(978-1-906124-72-4(8))*** British Computer Society, The GBR. Dist: Turpin Distribution Services Ltd.

Howe, Jeff. Crowdsourcing: Why the Power of the Crowd Is Driving the Future of Business. 2009. (ENG.). 336p. pap. 15.00 *(978-0-307-39621-1(5)*, Three Rivers Pr.) Crown Publishing Group.

Howell, Marvin T. Critical Success Factors: The Measurable Path to Success. 2009. (ENG., Illus.). 156p. 40.95 *(978-1-4398-1117-7(2))* Productivity Pr.

Hunter, M. Gordon. Contemporary Chief Information Officers: Management Experiences. 2007. 303p. 99.95 *(978-1-59904-078-3(6))* IGI Global.

Ireland, R. Duane, et al. Understanding Business Strategy: Concepts & Cases. 3rd ed. 2011. (ENG.). 272p. (C). pap. 151.95 *(978-0-538-47681-2(8))* Cengage South-Western.

Jackson, Carl. Business Resumption Planning. Wrobel, Leo A., ed. 2nd rev. ed. 2008. (ENG., Illus.). 512p. 104.95 *(978-0-8493-1459-9(3))* Auerbach Pubs., Inc.

Jacobs, Andrew C. No Road Is Ever Straight. 2011. 240p. pap. 14.95 ***(978-0-9823699-8-2(0))*** Ideal Jacobs Corp.

Jansen, Wendy, et al. New Business Models for the Knowledge Economy. 2007. (Illus.). 160p. 114.95 *(978-0-566-08788-2(X)*, Gower Publishing Co., Ltd.) Ashgate Publishing, Ltd. GBR. Dist: Ashgate Publishing Co.

Japan Business Strategy with Tape. 75p. (Orig.). pap. *(978-0-7605-0821-3(6))* Rector Pr., Ltd.

Jauk, Renate. Operatives Controlling in Bauunternehmen: Voraussetzungen, Instrumente, Kennzahlen des Projektcontrollings. 2010. 180p. pap. *(978-3-639-23876-1(1))* VDM Verlag Dr. Mueller e.K.

Jeffery, Mark. Data-Driven Marketing: The 15 Metrics Everyone in Marketing Should Know. 2010. (ENG., Illus.). 320p. 29.95 *(978-0-470-50454-3(4)*, Wiley) Wiley, John & Sons, Inc.

Jeffs, Chris. Strategic Management. 2008. (SAGE Course Companions Ser.). (Illus.). 232p. (C). 93.00 *(978-1-4129-4768-8(5)*, B47688C); pap. 32.00 *(978-1-4129-4769-5(3)*, B47688P) SAGE Pubns., Ltd. GBR. Dist: SAGE Pubns., Inc.

Jenkins, Mark & Collier, Nardine. Advanced Strategic Management: A Multi-Perspective Approach. Ambrosini, Veronique, ed. 2nd rev. ed. 2007. (ENG., Illus.). 416p. pap. 61.00 *(978-1-4039-8592-7(8))* Palgrave Macmillan.

Jeston, John & Nelis, Johan. Business Process Management: Practical Guidelines to Successful Implementations. 2nd rev. ed. 2008. (ENG., Illus.). 504p. (C). pap. 43.95 *(978-0-7506-8656-3(1))* Routledge.

—Management by Process: A Practical Road-Map to Sustainable Business Process Management. 2008. (ENG., Illus.). 322p. pap. 41.95 *(978-0-7506-8761-4(4))* Routledge.

Johnson, Gerry, et al. Exploring Corporate Strategy. 8th ed. 2008. (ENG., Illus.). 664p. (C). per. 129.33 *(978-0-273-71191-9(1))* Prentice Hall PTR.

—Exploring Corporate Strategy: Text & Cases. 8th ed. 2008. (ENG., Illus.). 920p. (C). per. 150.40 *(978-0-273-71192-6(X))* Prentice Hall Higher Education.

—Exploring Corporate Strategy with MyStrategyLab. 8th ed. 2010. (ENG., Illus.). (C). pap. 113.00 *(978-0-273-73155-9(6)*, Prentice Hall) Prentice Hall PTR.

—Exploring Strategy. 9th rev. ed. 2011. (ENG.). 600p. (C). pap. 118.00 ***(978-0-273-73549-6(7)***, Prentice Hall) Prentice Hall PTR.

—Exploring Strategy: Text & Cases. 9th rev. ed. 2011. (ENG.). 808p. (C). pap. 146.00 ***(978-0-273-73202-0(1)***, Prentice Hall) Prentice Hall PTR.

—Fundamentals of Strategy. 2nd ed. 2011. (ENG., Illus.). 304p. pap., stu. ed. ***(978-0-273-75725-2(3))*** Pearson Education, Ltd.

—Fundamentals of Strategy. 2008. (Illus.). 320p. pap. *(978-0-273-71310-4(8))* Prentice Hall PTR.

—Strategy as Practice: Research Directions & Resources. 2007. (ENG., Illus.). 258p. 135.00 *(978-0-521-86293-6(0))* Cambridge Univ. Pr.

Johnson, John E. & Smith, Anne Marie. 60 Minute Strategic Plan: 2 Stages, 12 Steps, 300 Words. 2nd rev. ed. 2006. cd-rom 149.00 *(978-0-9786452-1-2(9))* 60 Minute Strategic Plan.

—60 Minute Strategic Plan: 2 Stages, 12 Steps, 300 Words... Planning & Problem Solving for the Real Worls. 2006. (Illus.). x, 147p. per. 24.95 *(978-0-9786452-0-5(0))* 60 Minute Strategic Plan.

Johnson, Mark W. Seizing the White Space: Business Model Innovation for Growth & Renewal. 2010. (ENG., Illus.). 240p. 29.95 *(978-1-4221-2481-9(9))* Harvard Business Review Pr.

Jones, Jeffrey L. Business Start up Essentials. 2009. 120p. 29.99 *(978-1-4500-1278-2(7))*; pap. 19.99 *(978-1-4500-1277-5(9))* Xlibris Corp.

Jones, Nada & Briody, Michelle. 16 Weeks to Your Dream Business: A Weekly Planner for Entrepreneurial Women. 2008. (ENG., Illus.). 272p. spiral bd. 22.00 *(978-0-07-158836-2(1)*, 0071588361) McGraw-Hill Cos., The.

Jones, Sally & Rhoades-Catanach, Shelley. Principles of Taxation for Business & Investment Planning, 2012 Edition. 15th ed. 2011. (ENG., Illus.). 640p. (C). 229.67 *(978-0-07-811094-8(7)*, 0078110947, McGraw-Hill/Irwin) McGraw-Hill Higher Education.

Kadin, Ellen R. & Solovic, Susan Wilson. It's Your Biz: The Complete Guide to Becoming Your Own Boss, 1 vol. 2011. (ENG.). 240p. 22.95 ***(978-0-8144-1671-6(3))*** Amacom.

Kannegiesser, Matthias. Value Chain Management in the Chemical Industry: Global Value Chain Planning of Commodities. 2008. (Contributions to Management Science Ser.). (ENG., Illus.). xvi, 270p. 139.00 *(978-3-7908-2031-7(8)*, 3790820318) Physica-Verlag DEU. Dist: Springer.

Kapil, Kanwal. Strategic Business Practices of Small Scale Companies. 2011. 204p. pap. ***(978-3-8443-0185-4(2))*** Lambert Academic Publishing.

Kaplan, Len. The Mind of the OutCompete Strategist. 2009. 220p. pap. 24.92 *(978-0-557-04498-6(7))* Lulu Enterprises Inc.

Kaplan, Robert S. & Norton, David P. The Execution Premium: Linking Strategy to Operations for Competitive Advantage. 2008. (ENG., Illus.). 336p. 39.95 *(978-1-4221-2116-0(X))* Harvard Business Review Pr.

Kaplan, Steve. Be the Elephant: Build a Bigger, Better Business. 2007. (ENG., Illus.). 208p. 19.95 *(978-0-7611-4448-9(X)*, 076114448X) Workman Publishing Co., Inc.

Katsaros, John & Christy, Peter. Getting It Right the First Time: How Innovative Companies Anticipate Demand, 1 vol. 2008. 176p. pap. 19.95 *(978-0-313-35154-9(6)*, B35154, Praeger Trade) Greenwood Publishing Group, Inc.

Kaufman, Roger. The Manager's Pocket Guide to Mega Thinking & Planning. 2011. (ENG.). 168p. pap. 14.95 ***(978-1-59996-251-1(9))*** Human Resource Development Pr.

Kazanjian, Kirk, et al. High Growth Strategy. 2009. (Global Dimensions of Business Ser.). 288p. pap. 45.00 *(978-1-4051-8575-2(9)*, Wiley-Blackwell) Wiley, John & Sons, Inc.

Kelly, Kevin & Hayes, Gary. Leading in Turbulent Times. 2010. (Financial Times Ser.). (ENG.). 192p. 25.99 *(978-0-273-72753-8(2))* FT Press.

Kelly, Kevin, et al. Leading in Turbulent Times. 2010. (ENG.). 250p. 19.95 *(978-1-60509-540-0(0))* Berrett-Koehler Pubs., Inc.

Kelly, Patrick D. Rainmaking 101: How to Grow Your Client Base & Maximize Your Income. 2009. 120p. pap. 15.95 *(978-1-4389-5025-9(X))* AuthorHouse.

Kenny, Ivor. Freedom & Order: Studies in Strategic Leadership. 288p. *(978-1-86076-120-1(8))* Oak Tree Pr.

Kerr, Margaret & Kurtz, JoAnn. Canadian Small Business Kit for Dummies. 3rd ed. 2011. (ENG., Illus.). 480p. pap. 38.95 *(978-0-470-93652-8(5)*, For Dummies) Wiley, John & Sons, Inc.

Kiechel, Walter. Lords of Strategy: The Secret Intellectual History of the New Corporate World. 2010. (ENG., Illus.). 368p. 26.95 (978-1-59139-782-3(0)) Harvard Business Review Pr.

King, Gary. Getting Business Fit: How to Survive in These Tough Economic Times. 2009. 132p. pap. 13.95 (978-1-4401-3668-9(8)) iUniverse, Inc.

Kirchmer, Mathias. High Performance Through Process Excellence: From Strategy to Execution with Business Process Management. 2nd ed. 2011. (ENG., Illus.). xviii, 178p. 59.95 (978-3-642-21164-5(X), 364221164X) Springer.

Klososky, Scott. The Velocity Manifesto: Harnessing Technology, Vision, & Culture to Future-Proof Your Organization. 2011. 277p. 24.95 (978-1-60832-085-1(5)) Greenleaf Book Group.

Koch, Richard. Strategy: How to Create & Deliver a Winning Strategy. 3rd rev. ed. 2009. (Financial Times Ser.). (ENG., Illus.). 352p. (C). pap. 39.99 (978-0-273-70877-3(5)) FT Press.

Kono, Toyohiro & Lynn, Leonard. Strategic New Product Development in the Global Economy. 2007. (ENG., Illus.). 288p. 110.00 (978-0-230-00199-2(8)) Palgrave Macmillan.

Kotler, Philip, et al. The Quintessence of Strategic Management: What You Really Need to Know to Survive in Business. 2010. Orig. Title: Quintessenz des strategischen Managements. (Illus.). vi, 132p. 29.95 (978-3-642-14543-8(4), 3642145434) Springer.

Koudal, Peter. Why Finance Transformation Matters in Global Manufacturing. 2007. (978-1-934025-03-1(8)) Deloitte.

Kourdi, Jeremy. Business, 1 vol. 2011. (ENG., Illus.). 240p. pap. 19.50 (978-0-462-09960-6(1)) Marshall Cavendish International (Asia) Private Ltd. SGP. Dist: Marshall Cavendish Corp.

—Business Strategy: A Guide to Taking Your Business Forward. 2nd ed. 2009. (Economist Ser.). (ENG., Illus.). 250p. 29.95 (978-1-84568-124-0(3), Bloomberg Pr.) Wiley, John & Sons, Inc.

—100 Great Business Ideas: From Leading Companies Around the World, 1 vol. 2007. (ENG.). 208p. pap. 12.95 (978-1-905736-07-2(X)) Cyan Communications GBR. Dist: Independent Pubs. Group.

Kruger, David & Ramphal, Roy. Operations Management. 2nd ed. 2009. (ENG., Illus.). 424p. pap. 50.00 (978-0-19-598477-4(3)) Oxford Univ. Pr., Inc.

Kurlowicz, Ted, et al. Planning for Business Owners & Professionals. (C). 10th rev. ed. 2009. (ENG.). 500p. 95.00 (978-1-932819-78-6(9)); 11th ed. 2007. 540p. 78.00 (978-1-932819-47-2(9)) American College, The.

Kyne, Frank. GDPS Family: An Introduction to Concepts & Capabilities. (Illus.). 3rd ed. 2007. xii, 162p. (978-0-7384-8888-2(7)) 5th ed. 2009. 218p. pap. (978-0-7384-3347-9(0)) IBM.

Lane, Ken. The Business of Doing Business: A Handbook for Success in Business. 2009. 148p. pap. 14.95 (978-1-4389-3661-1(3)) AuthorHouse.

Lane, Nikala, ed. Strategic Sales & Strategic Marketing. 2011. (ENG.). 152p. (C). 125.00 (978-0-415-61451-1(1)) Routledge.

LaRocco, Lori Ann. Thriving in the New Economy: Lessons from Today's Top Business Minds. 2009. (ENG., Illus.). 304p. 24.95 (978-0-470-55731-0(1), Wiley) Wiley, John & Sons, Inc.

Lawson, Steve. The Guide to Business Bliss: Make Your Small Business More Profitable & More Enjoyable. 2011. 212p. 27.95 (978-1-4269-8866-0(4)); pap. 17.95 (978-1-4269-8865-3(6)) Trafford Publishing.

Lebo, Brad, et al. Exit Planning. 2011. 62p. pap. 9.95 (978-1-257-02479-7(5)) Lulu Enterprises Inc.

Lee, Jennifer. The Right-Brain Business Plan: A Creative, Visual Map for Success. 2011. (ENG., Illus.). 240p. pap. 19.95 (978-1-57731-944-3(3)) New World Library.

Leuser, David. Principles of Management: The Critical Essentials. 2007. (C). ring bd. 50.00 net. incl. cd-rom (978-0-934427-39-5(9)) Ivy Software.

Levinson, Jay Conrad & Neitlich, Andrew. Guerrilla Marketing Job Escape Plan: The Ten Battles You Must Fight to Start Your Own Business, & How to Win Them Decisively. 2011. (Guerilla Marketing Press Ser.). (ENG.). 208p. pap. 19.95 (978-1-61448-014-3(1)) Morgan James Publishing.

Levinson, Jay Conrad & Savage, Steve. Guerrilla Business Secrets: 58 Ways to Start, Build, & Sell Your Business. 2009. (Guerilla Marketing Press Ser.). (ENG.). xv, 284p. pap. 19.95 (978-1-60037-514-9(6)) Morgan James Publishing.

Lieberthal, Kenneth G. Managing the China Challenge: How to Achieve Corporate Success in the People's Republic. 2011. (ENG., Illus.). 149p. 26.95 (978-0-8157-2204-5(4)) Brookings Institution Pr.

Lillehagen, Frank & Krogstie, John. Active Knowledge Modeling of Enterprises. (ENG., Illus.). xx, 436p. 2010. pap. 89.95 (978-3-642-09831-4(2), 3642098312) 2008. 89.95 (978-3-540-79415-8(8), 3540794158) Springer.

Little, Steven S. & Little, Duck & Recover: The Embattled Business Owner's Guide to Survival & Growth. 2009. (ENG., Illus.). 224p. 22.95 (978-0-470-50490-1(0), Wiley) Wiley, John & Sons, Inc.

Liu, Xueyuan, et al. The Agility of Business Process Improvement. 2009. (Illus.). xii, 209p. (978-7-03-024799-5(X)) Science Pr.

Lloyd, David. Business Plans. 2009. (Instant Manager Ser.). (ENG.). 208p. pap. 19.95 (978-0-340-94650-3(4), Hodder & Stoughton) Hodder General Publishing Div. GBR. Dist: Independent Pubs. Group.

Lubiana, VanJa. Start up Cafe Bar: Business Plan. 2010. 84p. pap. (978-3-8383-5422-4(2)) Lambert Academic Publishing.

Lublin, Jill. Get Noticed... Get Referrals: Build Your Client Base & Your Business by Making a Name for Yourself. 2008. (ENG.). 240p. pap. 16.95 (978-0-07-150827-8(9), 0071508279) McGraw-Hill Cos., The.

Lucash, Peter D. Medical Practice Business Plan Workbook. 3rd rev. ed. 2011. (ENG., Illus.). 125p. pap., pap. 79.95 (978-1-4398-5531-7(5)) Productivity Pr.

Lynch, Richard. Strategic Management. 6th rev. ed. 2012. (ENG., Illus.). 880p. pap. 125.00 (978-0-273-75092-5(5)) Pearson Education, Ltd. GBR. Dist: Trans-Atlantic Pubns., Inc.

MacPherson, Duncan & Miller, David. Breakthrough Business Development: A 90-Day Plan to Build Your Client Base & Take Your Business to the Next Level. 2007. (ENG.). 240p. 29.95 (978-0-470-84096-2(X), Wiley) Wiley, John & Sons, Inc.

Magal. Integrated Business Processes with ERP Systems. 2011. (C). pap. 63.95 (978-0-470-92362-7(8), Wiley) Wiley, John & Sons, Inc.

Magal, Simha R. WP Stand Alone Essentials of Business Processes & Information Systems. 2nd ed. 2013. (ENG.). (C). pap. 15.95 (978-1-118-29024-8(0), Wiley) Wiley, John & Sons, Inc.

Magos, Alice H. Business Plans That Work: For Your Small Business. 3rd ed. 2008. (Business Owner's Toolkit Ser.). (ENG.). 244p. pap. 19.95 (978-0-8080-1793-6(4)) Toolkit Media Group.

Mahagaonkar, Prashanth. Money & Ideas: Four Studies on Finance, Innovation & the Business Life Cycle. 2009. (International Studies in Entrepreneurship Ser.). (ENG., Illus.). xvi, 107p. 139.00 (978-1-4419-1227-5(4), 1441912274) Springer.

Maitland, Iain. Successful Business Plans: Learn in a Week, What the Experts Learn in a Lifetime. 2012. (Teach Yourself: General Reference Ser.). (ENG., Illus.). 128p. pap. 12.00 (978-1-4441-5877-9(5), 1444158775) McGraw-Hill Cos., The.

Maltbia, et al. A Leader's Guide to Leveraging Diversity: Strategic Learning Capabilities for Breakthrough Performance. 2011. (ENG., Illus.). 296p. pap. 34.95 (978-0-7506-7892-6(5)) Routledge.

Mangaliso, Mzamo. Strategic Choice under Uncertainty: Multinational Corporations & the Pressure to Disinvest from South Africa. 2010. (Illus.). 212p. E-Book (978-0-7618-5089-2(9)) Univ. Pr. of America, Inc.

Market Entry & Operational Decision Making in East-West Business Relationships. 2007. (ENG.). 306p. 125.00 (978-0-7890-3543-1(X)); (Illus.). per. 69.95 (978-0-7890-3544-8(8)) Routledge.

Martial Arts Business 101: Hooyah - Living the Dream. 2008. 39.99 (978-0-9720884-8-0(2)) Albergo, Allie.

Martin, Reed. The Reel Truth: Everything You Didn't Know You Need to Know about Making an Independent Film. 2009. (ENG., Illus.). 544p. pap. 25.00 (978-0-571-21103-6(8)) Faber & Faber, Inc.

Martinez, Alejandra. Recoupment in Predatory Practices. 2011. 104p. pap. (978-3-8443-0651-4(X)) Lambert Academic Publishing.

Masterfano, Michelle. Effective Business Planning: A Structured Approach - A Guide for Entrepreneurs. rev. ed. 2010. (ENG.). 104p. pap. 44.39 (978-0-7575-7504-4(8)) Kendall Hunt Publishing Co.

Mathur, Shiv S. & Kenyon, Alfred. Creating Valuable Business Strategies. 2007. (ENG., Illus.). 264p. per. 46.95 (978-0-7506-8548-1(4)) Routledge.

Matoka, Chacha. The Process & Management of Organizational Strategic Change. 2011. 220p. pap. (978-3-8443-9176-3(2)) Lambert Academic Publishing.

Matsumoto, Koji. The Rise of the Japanese Corporate System. 2010. (ENG.). 288p. 115.00 (978-0-415-58521-7(X), Routledge) Taylor & Francis Group GBR. Dist: Taylor & Francis Group.

McDermott, Michael. The 2009-2011 Recession Survival Guide: 414 Actions Businesses Can Take to Weather the Storm & Boost Profits. 2009. 144p. pap. 19.95 (978-1-892538-51-2(2)) Oaklea Pr., The.

McGuire, Russell. The Power of Mobility: How Your Business Can Compete & Win in the Next Technology Revolution. 2007. (ENG., Illus.). 256p. 27.95 (978-0-470-17128-8(6), Wiley) Wiley, John & Sons, Inc.

McKaig, C. D. Guides to Achieving Business Strategies. 2010. 136p. pap. 59.75 (978-1-4269-3515-2(3)) Trafford Publishing.

McKay, John. Strategic Foresight in Business. 2010. 288p. 130.00 (978-0-415-46976-0(7)) Routledge.

McKee, Steve. When Growth Stalls: How It Happens, Why You're Stuck, & What to Do about It. 2009. (ENG., Illus.). 240p. 27.95 (978-0-470-39570-7(2), Jossey-Bass) Wiley, John & Sons, Inc.

Mellor, Robert B. Knowledge Management & Information Systems: Strategy for Growing Organizations. 2011. (ENG., Illus.). 208p. pap. 55.00 (978-0-230-28043-4(9)) Palgrave Macmillan.

Meuleman, Louis. Public Management & the Metagovernance of Hierarchies, Networks & Markets: The Feasibility of Designing & Managing Governance Style Combinations. 2010. (Contributions to Management Science Ser.). (ENG., Illus.). xiv, 401p. pap. 169.00 (978-3-7908-2558-9(1), 3790825581) Physica-Verlag DEU. Dist: Springer.

Meyer, Marc H. The Fast Path to Corporate Growth: Leveraging Knowledge & Technologies to New Market Applications. 2007. (ENG., Illus.). 304p. 29.99 (978-0-19-518086-2(0)) Oxford Univ. Pr., Inc.

Meyer, Marc H. & Crane, Frederick G. Entrepreneurship: An Innovator's Guide to Startups & Corporate Ventures. 2010. (Illus.). 472p. (C). pap. 94.00 (978-1-4129-9265-7(6), B55602P) SAGE Pubns., Inc.

Michalewicz, Matthew & Michalewicz, Zbigniew. Winning Credibility. 2007. 272p. per. (978-1-876462-52-9(3)) Hybrid Pubs.

Michaluk, Gerald. The Marketing Director's Role in Business Planning & Corporate Governance. 2008. (ENG., Illus.). 312p. 55.00 (978-0-470-51580-8(5), Wiley) Wiley, John & Sons, Inc.

Mohr, Angie. Finance & Grow Your New Business: Get a Grip on the Money. 2008. (Numbers 101 for Small Business Ser.). (ENG., Illus.). 240p. pap. 18.95 (978-1-55180-820-8(X)) Self-Counsel Pr., Inc. CAN. Dist: Midpoint Trade Bks., Inc.

Moon, Hwy-Chang. Global Business Strategy: Asian Perspective. 2010. 300p. 65.00 (978-981-4273-19-0(8)) World Scientific Publishing Co., Inc.

Moore, Geoffrey A. Escape Velocity: Free Your Company's Future from the Pull of the Past. 2011. (ENG.). 240p. 27.99 (978-0-06-204089-3(8), Collins) HarperCollins Pubs.

Moore, Karl & Hebert, Louis J., eds. Strategy & Globalization, 3 vols. 2008. (Contemporary Issues in Business & Globalization Ser.). (Illus.). 1576p. 995.00 (978-1-4129-3564-7(4), B35644C) SAGE Pubns., Ltd. GBR. Dist: SAGE Pubns., Inc.

Moran, Gwen & Johnson, Sue. Business Plans. 2nd ed. 2009. (Complete Idiot's Guide Ser.). (ENG.). 384p. (gr. 12-18). 19.95 (978-1-59257-973-0(6), Alpha Bks.) Penguin Group (USA) Inc.

—The Complete Idiot's Guide to Business Plans Plus. 2011. (Complete Idiot's Guide Ser.). (ENG.). 432p. (gr. 12). 24.95 (978-1-59257-974-7(4), Alpha Bks.) Penguin Group (USA) Inc.

Morfaw, John N. Project Sustainability: A Comprehensive Guide to Sustaining Projects, Systems & Organizations in A Competitive Marketplace. 2011. 224p. pap. 18.95 (978-1-4620-1271-8(X)) iUniverse, Inc.

Morris, James R. & Daley, John P. Introduction to Financial Models for Management & Planning. 2009. (ENG., Illus.). 754p. (C). 96.95 (978-1-4200-9054-3(2), Chapman & Hall/CRC) CRC Pr. LLC.

Morris, Peter & Pinto, Jeffrey K., eds. The Wiley Guide to Project Organization & Project Management Competencies. 2007. (Wiley Guides to the Management of Projects Ser.: 2). (ENG., Illus.). 360p. pap. 65.00 (978-0-470-22683-4(8), Wiley) Wiley, John & Sons, Inc.

—The Wiley Guide to Project Technology, Supply Chain & Procurement Management. 2007. (Wiley Guides to the Management of Projects Ser.: 4). (ENG., Illus.). 408p. pap. 65.00 (978-0-470-22682-7(X), Wiley) Wiley, John & Sons, Inc.

Morris, Ting, et al. The Wiley Guide to Project Control. 2007. (Wiley Guides to the Management of Projects Ser.: 1). (ENG., Illus.). 240p. pap. 65.00 (978-0-470-22684-1(6), Wiley) Wiley, John & Sons, Inc.

Mourkogiannis, Nikos. Purpose: The Starting Point of Great Companies. 2008. (ENG.). 272p. pap. 16.95 (978-0-230-60530-5(3)) Palgrave Macmillan.

Mroz, Ralph & Gooze, Mitchell. Value Acceleration: The Secrets to Building an Unbeatable Competitive Advantage. 2007. (AFR & ENG., Illus.). 176p. 24.99 (978-1-60194-004-9(1), Elevate) Advantage Media Group.

Muller, Thor, et al. Get Lucky: How to Put Planned Serendipity to Work for You & Your Business. 2012. (ENG.). 288p. 26.95 (978-1-118-24975-8(5), Jossey-Bass) Wiley, John & Sons, Inc.

Mullins, John & Komisar, Randy. Getting to Plan B: Breaking Through to a Better Business Model. 2009. (ENG., Illus.). 272p. 32.95 (978-1-4221-2669-1(2)) Harvard Business Review Pr.

Munene, Gracevasser. Drawing up a Business Plan in Africa Today. 2011. 112p. pap. (978-3-8443-9403-0(6)) Lambert Academic Publishing.

Munro, Allen H. Structures for Strategy: The Business Plan. 2009. (ENG.). 96p. pap. 12.95 (978-1-60037-403-6(4)) Morgan James Publishing.

—Structures for Strategy: The Operations Plan. 2009. (ENG.). 104p. pap. 12.95 (978-1-60037-405-0(0)) Morgan James Publishing.

Murad, Faul. Manhattanizing Las Vegas. 2008. pap. 24.95 (978-0-9769531-3-5(7)) Lotus Pr.

Murcko, Joe. The Missing Principle of Lean: The Art of Alignment. 2008. 88p. pap. 12.95 (978-0-7414-4313-7(9)) Infinity Publishing.

Murg, Stephanie & Terry, Mark, contrib. by. Business Strategies for Molecular Diagnostics in the Lab. 2009. (ENG., Illus.). 262p. pap. 795.00 (978-1-58673-305-6(2)) Institute of Management & Administration, IOMA.

Murg, Stephanie & Terry, Mark, eds. Business Strategies for Anatomic Pathology. 2007. 228p. pap. 895.00 (978-1-58673-242-4(0)) Institute of Management & Administration, IOMA.

—Business Strategies for Molecular Diagnostics in the Lab. 2007. 213p. pap. 995.00 (978-1-58673-163-2(7)) Institute of Management & Administration IOMA.

Murphy, Austin. SIA User's Guide. Bloomquist, Don/Lee, Jr., ed. (C). 2006. 371p. pap. 49.00 net. (978-0-9787344-1-1(6)) 2nd ed. 2007. (ENG.). 359p. pap. 49.00 net. (978-0-9787344-3-5(2)) SIA Publishing, LLC.

Murray, David K. Plan B: How to Hatch a Second Plan That's Always Better Than Your First. 2011. (ENG.). 272p. lib. bdg. 26.00 (978-1-4391-9835-3(7), Free Pr.) Free Pr.

Myers, Kenneth N. Business Continuity Strategies: Protecting Against Unplanned Disasters. 3rd rev. ed. 2006. (ENG., Illus.). 224p. 73.95 (978-0-470-04038-6(6), Wiley) Wiley, John & Sons, Inc.

Nazvanov, Greg. Business Insurance, Estate Planning & Business Succession Planning. 2010. 158p. pap. 24.97 (978-1-4457-1896-5(0)) Lulu Enterprises Inc.

Nemethy, Les. Business Exit Planning: Options, Value Enhancement, & Transaction Management for Business Owners. 2011. (Wiley Finance Ser.: 9). (ENG., Illus.). 187p. 75.00 (978-0-470-90531-9(X), Wiley) Wiley, John & Sons, Inc.

Nesheim, John L. The Power of Unfair Advantage: How to Create It, Build It, & Use It to Maximum. 2010. (ENG.). 368p. pap. 22.99 (978-1-4516-2426-7(3), Free Pr.) Free Pr.

Netherlands Water Partnership. Smart Finance Solutions: Examples of Innovative Financial Mechanisms for Water & Sanitation. 2009. (Smart Solutions Ser.). 72p. pap. 19.95 (978-94-6022-010-4(X)) Royal Tropical Institute Pr. (KIT (Koninklijk Instituut voor de Tropen) NLD. Dist: Stylus Publishing, LLC.

Newman, William D. Understanding SAP BusinessObjects Enterprise Performance Management. 2010. (Illus.). 282p. 69.95 (978-1-59229-348-3(4), SAP PR.) Galileo Pr., Inc.

The Next Big Disaster: Is the Private Sector Prepared?: Hearing Before the Ad Hoc Subcommittee on State, Local, & Private Sector Preparedness & Integration of the Committee on Homeland Security & Governmental Affairs, United States Senate, One Hundred Eleventh Congress, Second Session, March 4, 2010. 2011. (Illus.). iii, 46p. (978-0-16-088636-2(8), 552-070-42805-4) United States Government Printing Office.

Nielsen, Tobias, et al. Penny for your Thoughts: 10 Lessons to Help you Invest in & Grow a Creative Business. 2009. (ENG.). 200p. (C). pap. 30.00 (978-9979-70-562-8(0)) Univ. of Iceland Pr. ISL. Dist: Brown, David Bk. Co., The.

Nilssen, David & Levy, Jeff. Making the Jump into Small Business Ownership. 2011. 152p. pap. 17.95 (978-1-935359-83-8(5)) Book Pubs. Network.

Nirell, Lisa. Energize Growth NOW: The Marketing Guide to a Wealthy Company. 2009. (ENG., Illus.). 212p. 24.95 (978-0-470-41392-0(1), Wiley) Wiley, John & Sons, Inc.

Niven, Paul R. Road Maps & Revelations: Finding the Road to Business Success on Route 101. 2009. (ENG.). 222p. 24.95 (978-0-470-18001-3(3), Wiley) Wiley, John & Sons, Inc.

O'Keeffe, Niamh. Your First 100 Days: How to Make Maximum Impact in Your New Leadership Role. 2011. (Financial Times Ser.). (ENG., Illus.). 176p. pap. 24.99 (978-0-273-75132-8(8)) FT Press.

Okolita, Patricia, ed. Building an Enterprise Business Continuity Program. 2009. (ENG., Illus.). 344p. 82.95 (978-1-4200-8864-9(5)) Auerbach Pubs., Inc.

Olson, Matthew S. & van Bever, Derek. Stall Points: Most Companies Stop Growing — Yours Doesn't Have To. 2009. (ENG., Illus.). 256p. pap. 19.00 (978-0-300-15851-9(3)) Yale Univ. Pr.

Ondieki, Mishael. The Billionaires Guide to Foreclosure: A Step-by-Step Guide to Getting Out of Trouble. 2008. 148p. 24.95 (978-0-595-50908-9(8)) iUniverse, Inc.

O'Rourke, James S. & Boulger, Carolyn Ann. Writing & Presenting a Business Plan. 2nd ed. 2008. (ENG.). 144p. (C). pap. 49.95 (978-0-324-58422-6(9)) Cengage South-Western.

Orr, Stuart. Business Strategy for the Wine Industry. 2009. 252p. pap. (978-3-639-02319-0(6)) VDM Verlag Dr. Mueller e.K.

Orton, Stephen N., et al. Public Health Business Planning: A Practical Guide. 2011. 174p. pap. 84.95 (978-1-4496-4350-8(7)) Jones & Bartlett Learning, LLC.

Orton, Stephen Noyes, et al. Public Health Business Planning: A Practical Guide. 2008. 174p. spiral bd. 87.95 (978-0-7637-4621-6(5)) Jones & Bartlett Learning, LLC.

Padhye, Sameer & Kumar, Ritesh Bansal. Planning Your Long Term Evolution (LTE) Deployment: How to Align Business, Technology & Operational Objectives for a Successful Mobile Network Transformation. rev. ed. 2011. (Networking Technology Ser.). (ENG.). 416p. 89.99 (978-1-58714-282-6(1)) Cisco Pr.

Pantaleo, Daniel & Pal, Nirmal, eds. From Strategy to Execution: Turning Accelerated Global Change into Opportunity. (ENG., Illus.). xvi, 326p. 2010. pap. 79.95 (978-3-642-09095-0(8), 3642090958) 2008. 79.95 (978-3-540-71879-6(6), 3540718796) Springer.

Parker, Glenn. Team Empowerment: 20 Ways to Get There (PTTE) Ptte. 2010. (Illus.). 39p. pap. 9.95 (978-1-59996-201-6(2)) Human Resource Development Pr.

Paul, Mark. The Entrepreneur's Survival Guide: Tips & tricks to help you start & build your Company. 2nd ed. 2007. (Illus.). 226p. per. 25.00 (978-0-9708665-2-3(6)) Cedar Mill Publishing.

Payne, Mark. Make the Numbers, Don't Chase the Numbers. 2007. (Illus.). 120p. per. 34.95 (978-0-9753139-6-1(7)) Penworth Publishing.

Pearce, Lynn. Business Plan Handbook. 14th rev. ed. 2008. (Business Plans Handbook Ser.). (ENG.). 288p. 231.00 (978-0-7876-9503-3(3)) Cengage Gale.

Peng, Mike W. Global Strategy. 2nd ed. 2008. (ENG.). 560p. (C). 195.95 (978-0-324-59099-9(7)) Cengage South-Western.

Peteraf, Margaret A. & Maritan, Catherine A., eds. Competitive Strategy, 2 vols. 2011. (Strategic Management Ser.). (Illus.). 1312p. 720.00 (978-1-84844-232-0(7)) Elgar, Edward Publishing, Inc.

Peterson, Steven D., et al. Business Plans Kit for Dummies, Kit. 3rd ed. 2010. (ENG.). 384p. pap. 34.99 (978-0-470-43854-1(1), For Dummies) Wiley, John & Sons, Inc.

Pillkahn, Ulf. Using Trends & Scenarios as Tools for Strategy Development: Shaping the Future of Your Enterprise. 2008. (ENG., Illus.). 400p. 70.00 (978-3-89578-304-3(8), Wiley) Wiley, John & Sons, Inc.

Pinson, Linda. The Lawyer's Guide to Creating a Business Plan, 2007 Edition: A Step-by-Step Software Package. 2008. cd-rom 179.95 (978-1-59031-938-3(9)) American Bar Assn.

Pinson, Linda J. Anatomy of a Business Plan: The Step-by-Step Guide to Building a Business & Securing Your Company's Future. 7th ed. 2008. (ENG., Illus.). 352p. pap. 22.95 (978-0-944205-37-2(2)) Out of Your Mind & Into the Marketplace.

Pinto, Jeffrey K. & Morris, Peter. The Wiley Guide to Project Program & Portfolio Management. 2007. (Wiley Guides to the Management of Projects Ser.: 3).

B

(ENG., Illus.). 364p. pap. 65.00 *(978-0-470-22685-8(4),* Wiley) Wiley, John & Sons, Inc.

Pitelis, Christos. Green Business Green Values. 2011. (Routledge Studies in Corporate Governance Ser.). (ENG., Illus.). 174p. (C). 125.00 *(978-0-415-88382-5(2))* Routledge.

Plan Pro. Business Plan Pro Software. 2010. (ENG.). (C). cd-rom 20.95 *(978-0-470-88672-4(2),* Wiley) Wiley, John & Sons, Inc.

—Markting Plan Pro Software. 2010. (ENG.). (C). cd-rom 19.95 *(978-0-470-88669-4(2),* Wiley) Wiley, John & Sons, Inc.

Player, W. Hope. Finding the Numbers for Your Business Plan. 2010. 89p. pap. 35.00 *(978-0-578-05544-2(9))* Full Court Pr.

Pledger, Marcia. My Biggest Mistake & How I Fixed It. 2008. 256p. pap. 19.95 *(978-1-933197-50-0(1))* Orange Frazer Pr.

Plunkett, Jack W. The Next Boom: What You Absolutely, Positively Have to Know about the World Between Now And 2025. Plunkett, Jack W., ed. 2011. (ENG.). 274p. 29.99 *(978-1-60879-999-2(9))* Plunkett Research, Ltd.

Port, Michael. Beyond Booked Solid: Your Business, Your Life, Your Way - It's All Inside. 2008. (ENG., Illus.). 240p. 24.95 *(978-0-470-17436-4(6),* Wiley) Wiley, John & Sons, Inc.

Powell, Stephen G. & Batt, Robert J. Modeling for Insight: A Master Class for Business Analysts. 2008. (ENG., Illus.). 466p. pap. 105.00 *(978-0-470-17555-2(9),* Wiley) Wiley, John & Sons, Inc.

Prencipe, Andrew. Strategy, Systems & Scope. (Sage Strategy Ser.). 208p. (C). 2012. pap. 33.95 *(978-0-7619-4038-8(3),* B40375P) 2010. 63.95 *(978-0-7619-4037-1(5),* B40375C) SAGE Pubns., Ltd. GBR. Dist: SAGE Pubns., Inc.

Rad, Parviz. Managing Externally-Funded Projects. 2007. (Illus.). 138p. per. 33.33 *(978-0-9798195-0-6(4))* Project Management Excellence, LLC.

Radmanesh. The Ultimate Keys to Success in Business & Science: The Modern Blueprint for Prosperity. 2008. 464p. 38.99 *(978-1-4343-2618-8(7));* pap. 29.99 *(978-1-4343-2619-5(5))* AuthorHouse.

Rainey, David L. Sustainable Business Development. 2010. (ENG., Illus.). 764p. pap. 45.00 *(978-0-521-14843-6(X))* Cambridge Univ. Pr.

Ramirez, Rafael, et al, eds. Business Planning for Turbulent Times: New Methods for Applying Scenarios. 2nd rev. ed. 2010. (Science in Society Ser.). (ENG., Illus.). 336p. pap. 47.95 *(978-1-84971-061-9(9))* Routledge.

—Business Planning for Turbulent Times: New Methods for Applying Scenarios. 2nd rev. ed. 2010. (Science in Society Ser.). (ENG., Illus.). 336p. 136.00 *(978-1-84971-060-2(0))* Routledge.

—Business Planning in Turbulent Times: New Methods for Applying Scenarios. 2008. (Science in Society Ser.). (Illus.). 240p. 77.95 *(978-1-84407-567-6(2))* Earthscan LLC.

Ramsey, Dan & Windhaus, Stephen. The Everything Business Plan Book with CD: All you need to succeed in a new or growing Business. 2nd ed. 2009. (ENG.). 320p. pap. 19.95 *(978-1-59869-822-0(2))* Adams Media Corp.

Rausch, Erwin. Planning, Common Sense, & Superior Performance. 2008. 216p. (C). *(978-1-59311-879-2(1));* per. *(978-1-59311-878-5(3))* Information Age Publishing, Inc.

Rayment, John & Smith, Jonathan. Misleadership: Holistic Leadership & the Global Fitness Framework. 2010. (Illus.). 240p. 114.95 *(978-0-566-09226-8(3),* Gower Publishing Co., Ltd.) Ashgate Publishing, Ltd. GBR. Dist: Ashgate Publishing Co.

Record, Matthew. Preparing a Winning Business Plan: How to Plan to Succeed & Secure Financial Backing. 5th ed. 2009. (Illus.). 160p. pap. 26.00 *(978-1-84528-302-5(3))* How To Books GBR. Dist: Parkwest Pubns., Inc.

Reeb, William. Securing the Future 1: Succession Planning Basics. 2009. pap. 98.75 *(978-0-87051-854-6(2))* American Institute of Certified Public Accountants.

—Securing the Future 2: Taking Succession to the Next Level. 2009. pap. 98.75 *(978-0-87051-855-3(0))* American Institute of Certified Public Accountants.

Regnell, Bjö, et al, eds. Software Business: Second International Conference, ICSOB 2011, Brussels, Belgium, June 8-10, 2011, Proceedings. 2011. (Lecture Notes in Business Information Processing Ser.). xii, 189p. pap. 72.00 ***(978-3-642-21543-8(2),*** 3642215432) Springer.

Ringland, Gill G., et al. Beyond Crisis: Achieving Renewal in a Turbulent World. 2010. (ENG., Illus.). 346p. 34.95 *(978-0-470-68577-8(8),* Wiley) Wiley, John & Sons, Inc.

Roberts, John. The Modern Firm: Organizational Design for Performance & Growth. 2007. (Clarendon Lectures in Management Studies). (ENG., Illus.). 334p. 35.00 *(978-0-19-829375-0(5))* Oxford Univ. Pr., Inc.

Robertson, Duncan A. & Caldart, Adrián A. The Dynamics of Strategy: Mastering Strategic Landscapes of the Firm. 2009. (ENG., Illus.). 256p. 34.95 *(978-0-19-923416-5(7))* Oxford Univ. Pr., Inc.

Rogers, Steven. Entrepreneurial Finance: Finance & Business Strategies for the Serious Entrepreneur. 2nd ed. 2009. (ENG., Illus.). 372p. 59.95 *(978-0-07-159126-3(5),* 0071591265) McGraw-Hill Cos., The.

Rogoff, Edward G. Bankable Business Plans: Second Edition. 2nd rev. ed. 2007. (ENG., Illus.). 275p. per. 24.95 *(978-0-9791522-0-7(8))* Rowhouse Publishing.

—Bankable Business Plans for Entrepreneurial Ventures: Textbook Edition. 2007. (ENG., Illus.). 380p. (C). per. 95.00 *(978-0-9791522-2-1(4))* Rowhouse Publishing.

Ruehrnoessl, Bjoern. Management Accounting & Controlling. 2008. 96p. pap. *(978-3-639-02228-5(9))* VDM Verlag Dr. Mueller e.K.

Rughase, Olaf G. & Rughase, Schindi. Identity & Strategy: How Individual Visions Enable the Design of a Market Strategy That Works. 2007. (Illus.). 256p. pap. 50.00 *(978-1-84720-656-5(5))* Elgar, Edward Publishing, Inc.

Russo, Michael V. Companies on a Mission: Entrepreneurial Strategies for Growing Sustainably, Responsibly, & Profitably. 2010. (ENG., Illus.). 272p. 27.95 *(978-0-8047-6162-8(0),* Stanford Business Bks.) Stanford Univ. Pr.

Ryan, Eric, et al. The Method Method: Seven Obsessions That Helped Our Scrappy Start-Up Turn an Industry Upside Down. 2011. (ENG., Illus.). 272p. (gr. 12). 26.95 *(978-1-59184-399-3(5),* Portfolio (Hardcover)) Penguin Group (USA) Inc.

Sahlman, William A. How to Write a Great Business Plan. 2008. (Harvard Business Review Classics: Ser.). (ENG., Illus.). 64p. per. 8.95 *(978-1-4221-2142-9(9))* Harvard Business Review Pr.

Saima, Kanwal. Enterprise Resource Planning System: Measuring Employees' Usage Behavior & Its Impact on Performance. 2011. 140p. pap. ***(978-3-639-32913-1(9))*** VDM Verlag Dr. Mueller e.K.

Salina, Pascal & Salina, Jingming Li. Next Generation Networks: Perspectives & Potentials. 2008. (ENG., Illus.). 252p. 110.00 *(978-0-470-51649-2(6),* Wiley) Wiley, John & Sons, Inc.

Sanders, Dane. The Fast Track Photographer Business Plan: Build a Successful Photography Venture from the Ground Up. 2010. (ENG.). 256p. pap. 16.99 *(978-0-8174-0000-2(1),* Amphoto Bks.) Watson-Guptill Pubns., Inc.

Sarkar, Soumodip. Innovation, Market Archetypes & Outcome: An Integrated Framework. 2010. (ENG., Illus.). xii, 202p. pap. 119.00 *(978-3-7908-2534-3(4),* 3790825344) Physica-Verlag DEU. Dist: Springer.

Sato, Masaaki. The Toyota Leaders: An Executive Guide. 2008. (ENG., Illus.). 336p. 19.95 *(978-1-934287-23-1(7))* Vertical, Inc.

Saynac, Xavier. Improving the Performance of Investing Strategies. 2011. 56p. pap. ***(978-3-8454-0483-7(3))*** Lambert Academic Publishing.

Schiffman, Stephan. Selling When No One Is Buying: Growing Prospects, Clients, & Sales in Tough Economic Times. 2009. (ENG.). 176p. pap. 12.95 *(978-1-60550-660-9(5))* Adams Media Corp.

Schmidt, Marty J. Business Case Essentials: A Guide to Structure & Content. 3rd ed. 2009. (ENG., Illus.). 103p. pap. 48.00 *(978-1-929500-02-4(5))* Solution Matrix, Ltd.

Schneider. Intro to Enterprise Res Planng. 2011. (C). 64.95 *(978-0-324-07462-8(X))* Cengage South-Western.

Schulting, M. B. A. M. S. c. Edwin. The Jack-of-all-Trades. 2008. 89p. pap. 26.95 *(978-1-4092-0430-5(8))* Lulu Enterprises Inc.

Schultze, Axel. Channel Excellence. 2007. 308p. pap. 29.95 *(978-0-615-17759-5(X))* Schultze, Axel.

Schumock, Glen T. & Stubbings, JoAnn. How to Develop a Business Plan for Pharmacy Services. 2007. 304p. pap. 49.95 incl. cd-rom *(978-1-932658-57-6(2))* American College of Clinical Pharmacy.

Schwetje, Gerald & Vaseghi, Sam. The Business Plan: How to Win Your Investors' Confidence. 2010. (ENG., Illus.). xii, 181p. pap. 49.95 *(978-3-642-06486-9(8),* 3642064868) Springer.

Scott, Kim & Terry, Mark, eds. Business Strategies for Laboratory Outreach Programs. 2007. 345p. pap. 795.00 *(978-1-58673-182-3(3))* Institute of Management & Administration, IOMA.

Seale, Alan. The Manifestation Wheel: A Practical Process for Creating Miracles. 2008. (ENG., Illus.). 1p. pap. 14.95 *(978-1-57863-414-9(8),* Weiser Bks.) Red Wheel/Weiser.

Seese, Michael. Scrappy Business Contingency Planning: How to Bullet-Proof Your Business & Laugh at Volcanoes, Tornadoes, Locust Plagues, & Hard Drive Crashes. 2010. 170p. pap. 19.95 ***(978-1-60005-150-0(2))*** Happy About.

Seminar Planning Guide - Version 2006. 2006. cd-rom 595.00 *(978-1-932487-31-2(X))* Sleeter Group, Inc., The.

Seminar Planning Guide - Version 2007. 2007. cd-rom 595.00 *(978-1-932487-95-4(6))* Sleeter Group, Inc., The.

Shapiro, Ronald M. & Jordan, Gregory. Dare to Prepare: How to Win Before You Begin. 2009. (ENG.). 304p. pap. 14.95 *(978-0-307-45180-4(1),* Three Rivers Pr.) Crown Publishing Group.

—Dare to Prepare: How to Win Before You Begin. 2008. (ENG.). 304p. 26.00 *(978-0-307-38326-6(1),* Crown Business) Crown Publishing Group.

Sharpe, Bill & Van Der Heijden, Kees, eds. Scenarios for Success: Turning Insights into Action. 2007. (ENG., Illus.). 434p. 75.00 *(978-0-470-51298-2(9),* Wiley) Wiley, John & Sons, Inc.

Shearin, Joyce. Business Ideas to Make A Million Dollars. 2011. 48p. pap. 9.89 ***(978-1-4669-0340-1(6))*** Trafford Publishing.

Sibilia, Mauro Michele. The Impact of Organizational Capability on Competitive Advantage. 2011. 72p. pap. ***(978-3-8454-0502-5(3))*** Lambert Academic Publishing.

Siddiqui, Moid. Who Will Bell the Cat? A Manager's Toolkit for Strategy-Formation & Execution. 2010. (Illus.). 196p. (C). pap. 29.95 *(978-81-321-0461-2(7),* B04612P) SAGE Pubns., Inc.

Sikich, Geary W. Protecting Your Business in a Pandemic: Plans, Tools, & Advice for Maintaining Business Continuity, 1 vol. 2008. (Illus.). 240p. 44.95 *(978-0-313-34602-6(X),* C34602, Praeger Pubs.) Greenwood Publishing Group, Inc.

Silver, David, et al. The Social Network Business Plan: 18 Strategies That Will Create Great Wealth. 2009. (ENG., Illus.). 224p. 24.95 *(978-0-470-41983-0(0),* Wiley) Wiley, John & Sons, Inc.

Simons, Robert. Seven Strategy Questions: A Simple Approach for Better Execution. 2010. (ENG., Illus.). 224p. 26.95 *(978-1-4221-3332-3(X))* Harvard Business Review Pr.

Singh, Balaji. Market Research & Strategic Planning for Global Chemical, Petrochemical, & Plastics Industries. 2012. (ENG.). 400p. 150.00 *(978-0-470-94813-2(2),* Wiley-Scrivener) Wiley, John & Sons, Inc.

Sisodia, Rajendra S., et al. Firms of Endearment: How World-Class Companies Profit from Passion & Purpose. 2007. (ENG., Illus.). 320p. 39.99 *(978-0-13-187372-8(5))* Wharton Schl. Publishing.

Slaunwhite, Steve, et al. The Wealthy Freelancer: 12 Secrets to a Great Income & an Enviable Lifestyle. 2010. (ENG., Illus.). 288p. (gr. 12-18). 16.95 *(978-1-59257-967-9(1),* Alpha Bks.) Penguin Group (USA) Inc.

Snabe, Jim Hagemann, et al. Business Process Management - the SAP Roadmap. 2008. (Illus.). 411p. 69.95 *(978-1-59229-231-8(3),* SAP PR.) Galileo Pr., Inc.

Snedaker, Susan. Business Continuity & Disaster Recovery Planning for IT Professionals. 2007. (ENG., Illus.). 456p. per. 59.95 *(978-1-59749-172-3(1),* Syngress Press) Elsevier Science & Technology Bks.

Sommer. Public Sector Erp Issues in Change Management. 2007. (Illus.). 224p. (C). 119.00 *(978-1-84542-006-2(3))* Elgar, Edward Publishing, Inc.

Sorensen, Hans Eibe. Business Development: A Market-Oriented Perspective. 2012. (ENG., Illus.). 566p. pap. 77.95 ***(978-0-470-68366-8(X),*** Wiley) Wiley, John & Sons, Inc.

Speculand, Robin. Beyond Strategy: The Leader's Role in Successful Implementation. 2009. (ENG., Illus.). 150p. pap. 22.00 *(978-0-470-82498-6(0),* Wiley) Wiley, John & Sons, Inc.

Spedding, Linda S. Due Diligence Handbook: Corporate Governance, Risk Management & Business Planning. 2008. (ENG., Illus.). 752p. 165.00 *(978-0-7506-8621-1(9),* CIMA Publishing) Elsevier Science & Technology Bks.

Squirrell, Gillian. Evaluation in Action: Theory & Practice for Effective Evaluation. 2012. (Illus.). 152p. pap. 34.50 ***(978-1-905541-76-8(7))*** Russell Hse. Publishing Ltd. GBR. Dist: International Specialized Bk. Services.

Srinivasan, Sridhar & Srinivasan, Kumar. SAP BusinessObjects Planning & Consolidation. (Illus.). 2010. 406p. 79.95 *(978-1-59229-239-4(9))* 2nd ed. 2011. 446p. 79.95 *(978-1-59229-397-1(2))* Galileo Pr., Inc. (SAP PR.).

Stanford, Naomi. Guide to Organisation Design: Creating High-Performing & Adaptable Enterprises. 2007. (Economist Ser.). (ENG., Illus.). 343p. 29.95 *(978-1-86197-802-8(2),* Bloomberg Pr.) Wiley, John & Sons, Inc.

Steinberg, Richard M. Governance, Risk Management, & Compliance: It Can't Happen to Us- Avoiding Corporate Disaster While Driving Success. 2011. (Wiley Corporate F&a Ser.: 570). (ENG.). 312p. 49.95 *(978-1-118-02430-0(3),* Wiley) Wiley, John & Sons, Inc.

Stettinius, Wallace, et al. How to Plan & Execute Strategy: 24 Steps to Implement Any Corporate Strategy Successfully. 2006. (Mighty Managers Ser.). (ENG., Illus.). 128p. 12.95 *(978-0-07-148437-4(X),* 007148437X) McGraw-Hill Cos., The.

Stim, Richard & Guerin, Lisa. Running a Side Business: How to Create a Second Income. 2009. (ENG.). 271p. pap. 21.99 *(978-1-4133-1067-2(2))* NOLO.

Stockport, Gary. Practical Strategy. 2011. 280p. pap. 59.95 *(978-0-7346-1112-3(9))* Tilde Publishing AUS. Dist: International Publishers Marketing.

Stowers, James E. Yes, You Can... Reach Your Goals & Achieve Your Dreams. 2008. (ENG.). 19.95 *(978-0-9800457-0-3(3))* Andrews McMeel Publishing.

Strik, Jasper. The Power of Sound in Destination Image Formation. 2011. 120p. pap. ***(978-3-8443-9724-6(8))*** Lambert Academic Publishing.

Studebaker, David. Programming Microsoft Dynamics Nav. 2007. (Illus.). 480p. per. *(978-1-904811-74-9(4))* Packt Publishing, Ltd.

Sturgeon, Ron. Getting to Yes with Your Banker: A Practical Guide for Small Business Owners, 93 Secrets to Getting Your Small Business Funded Plus 76 Tips & 51 Traps. 2011. pap. 19.95 *(978-0-9717031-6-2(7))* French, Mike Publishing.

Stutely, Richard. The Definitive Business Plan: The Fast-Track to Intelligent Business Planning for Executives & Entrepreneurs, 2 vols. 2nd ed. 2007. (Financial Times Ser.). (ENG., Illus.). 336p. pap. 34.99 *(978-0-273-71096-7(6))* FT Press.

Stutely, Richard. The Definitive Business Plan: The Fast Track to Intelligent Planning for Executives & Entrepreneurs. 3rd ed. 2012. (ENG., Illus.). 376p. pap. 39.99 ***(978-0-273-76114-3(5))*** FT Press.

Sukati, Inda & Bakar Abdul Hamid, Abu. A Study of Firm Integration & Supply Chain Orientation. 2011. 184p. pap. ***(978-3-8443-9734-5(5))*** Lambert Academic Publishing.

Susan Degrandpre. Common-Sense Workplace Mentoring: A do-it-yourself system for strengthening your business... one person at a Time. 2010. 124p. pap. 13.95 *(978-1-4502-0780-5(4))* iUniverse, Inc.

Sustainability Planning: How to Create & Implement Sustainability Plans in Any Business or Organization. 2008. (ENG., Illus.). 176p. pap., instr.'s gde. ed. 49.95 *(978-1-84407-616-1(4))* Routledge.

Swartz, Ethné, et al. Business Continuity Management: A Crisis Management Approach. 2nd rev. ed. (Illus.). 272p. 2009. pap. 54.95 *(978-0-415-37109-4(0))* 2007. 155.00 *(978-0-415-37108-7(2))* Routledge.

Syrett, Michel. Successful Strategy Execution: How to Keep Your Business Goals on Target. 2007. (Economist Ser.). (ENG., Illus.). 164p. 29.95 *(978-1-86197-894-3(4),* Bloomberg Pr.) Wiley, John & Sons, Inc.

Tasso, Kim. Growing Your Property Partnership: Plans, Promotion & People. 2009. (ENG., Illus.). 250p. pap. 48.95 *(978-0-7282-0553-6(X))* Estates Gazette, Ltd. GBR. Dist: Taylor & Francis Group.

Tate, Ryan. The 20% Doctrine: How Tinkering, Goofing Off, & Breaking the Rules at Work Drive Success in Business. 2012. (ENG.). 208p. 25.99 *(978-0-06-200323-2(2),* Collins) HarperCollins Pubs.

Taylor, Wayne. The Dark Arts of Business: Elicitation. 2010. 76p. pap. 10.99 *(978-0-557-39994-9(7))* Lulu Enterprises Inc.

Teece, David J. Dynamic Capabilities & Strategic Management: Organizing for Innovation & Growth. 2009. (ENG., Illus.). 304p. 39.95 *(978-0-19-954512-4(X))* Oxford Univ. Pr., Inc.

Teece, David J. Strategy, Innovation & the Theory of the Firm. 2012. 400p. 150.00 ***(978-1-84980-864-4(3))*** Elgar, Edward Publishing, Inc.

Teece, David J. & Augier, Mie, eds. Fundamentals of Business Strategy, 4 vols. 2008. (SAGE Library in Business & Management Ser.). 2296p. 1400.00 *(978-1-4129-0106-2(5),* B01065C) SAGE Pubns., Ltd. GBR. Dist: SAGE Pubns., Inc.

Thammatucharee, Yanyong. Self-Reform Forces: Understanding the Organization Development Concept of Exdysivity. 2010. (Illus.). 244p. pap. 21.49 *(978-1-4520-8483-1(1))* AuthorHouse.

Thompson, Arthur A., Jr. & Strickland, A. J., III. Crafting & Executing Strategy: The Quest for Comptetitive Advantage. 2006. pap. 14.95 *(978-1-4288-1291-8(1))* Cram101 Inc.

Thompson, Arthur A., Jr., et al. Crafting & Executing Strategy. 2006. pap. 14.95 *(978-1-4288-1120-1(6))* Cram101 Inc.

Thorsteinsson, Dr. Gisli, et al. The Design & Marketing of Power Tools. 2011. 68p. pap. ***(978-3-8443-2335-1(X))*** Lambert Academic Publishing.

Tillmann, George. The Business-Oriented CIO: A Guide to Market-Driven Management. 2008. (ENG., Illus.). 256p. 52.95 *(978-0-470-27812-3(9),* Wiley) Wiley, John & Sons, Inc.

Timmons, Jeffry A., et al. Business Plans That Work: A Guide for Small Business. 2nd ed. 2011. (ENG., Illus.). 208p. pap. 20.00 *(978-0-07-174883-4(0),* 0071748830) McGraw-Hill Cos., The.

Tolle, Brian. Shortcut: Getting Through to People. 2011. 100p. pap. 12.95 ***(978-1-4634-2523-4(6))*** AuthorHouse.

Toutenburg, Helge & Knöfel, Philipp. Six Sigma: Methoden und Statistik Fur die Praxis. 2007. (Illus.). 324p. 59.95 *(978-3-540-74210-4(7))* Springer.

—Six Sigma: Methoden und Statistik für die Praxis. 2009. 364p. *(978-3-540-85137-0(2))* Springer Singapore Pte. Ltd.

Tracy, Brian. Flight Plan: The Real Secret of Success. 2009. (ENG.). 168p. pap. 16.95 *(978-1-60509-275-1(4))* Berrett-Koehler Pubs., Inc.

Tsang-Kosma, Winnie. Change Management Strategies in Erp System Adoption. 2011. 296p. pap. ***(978-3-8443-1196-9(3))*** Lambert Academic Publishing.

Turner, James Edward. Introduction to the Golf Driving Range Business: The 48 key questions & answers that you need to know before you build or buy a golf driving Range. 2007. spiral bd. *(978-1-929980-04-8(3))* Forecast Golf Group, Inc.

—Sample Business Plan for a Golf Practice Range: The proven template that shows you how to assemble all the pieces of the puzzle - & secure financing for your golf range Project. 2007. 63p. spiral bd. *(978-1-929980-07-9(8))* Forecast Golf Group, Inc.

Uchino, Kenji. Entrepreneurship for Engineers. 2009. (ENG., Illus.). 366p. 51.95 *(978-1-4398-0063-8(4),* CRC Press) Taylor & Francis Group GBR. Dist: Taylor & Francis Group.

Uphill, Kevin & McMillan, Alex. Buying & Selling a Business for Wealth. 2007. (Illus.). 262p. per. 38.95 *(978-1-85418-394-1(X))* Thorogood GBR. Dist: Stylus Publishing, LLC.

van Putten II, Paul. Five Dollars to Freedom. 2009. 121p. pap. 21.99 *(978-0-557-11686-7(4))* Lulu Enterprises Inc.

Vanwyck, Wayne. The Business Transition Crisis: Plan Your Succession Now to Beat the Biggest Business Selloff in History. 2010. *(978-1-926645-14-8(6))* BPS Bks.

Varley, Philip G. Failure Is Not an Option: The 12-Step Plan to Successful Turnarounds. 2011. 245p. 25.00 ***(978-1-885331-37-3(1))*** Mile High Pr., Ltd.

Vaseghi, Sam, et al. The Business Plan: How to Win Your Investors' Confidence. 2007. (ENG., Illus.). xii, 181p. 49.95 *(978-3-540-25451-5(X),* 354025451X) Springer.

Viguerie, Patrick. Granularity of Growth. 2007. (Illus.). 256p. pap. *(978-0-462-09965-1(2))* Marshall Cavendish.

Vilpola, Inka. User-Centered Design in Erp Implementation Requirements Analysis. 2011. 96p. pap. ***(978-3-8433-7798-0(7))*** Lambert Academic Publishing.

Visible Systems Corp Staff. Visible Systems Standard Edition 2008. 2008. (ENG.). (C). 51.95 *(978-0-470-45765-8(1),* Wiley) Wiley, John & Sons, Inc.

Wagner, Nada, et al. Business Plans for Canadians for Dummies. 2008. (ENG.). 400p. pap. 29.99 *(978-0-470-15420-5(9),* For Dummies) Wiley, John & Sons, Inc.

Wagner, Bret & Monk, Ellen. Concepts in Enterprise Resource Planning. 4th ed. 2012. (ENG.). 272p. pap. 75.95 *(978-1-111-82039-8(2))* Course Technology.

Wagner, Bret J. & Monk, Ellen F. Concepts in Enterprise Resource Planning. 3rd ed. 2008. (ENG., Illus.). 272p. per. 75.95 *(978-1-4239-0179-2(7))* Course Technology.

Warner, Ralph & Laurence, Bethany K. Save Your Small Business: 10 Crucial Strategies to Survive Hard Times or Close down & Move On. 2009. (ENG.). 316p. pap. 29.99 *(978-1-4133-1041-2(9))* NOLO.

Wensveen, J. G. Wheels Up: Airline Business Plan Development. 2nd ed. 2007. *(978-1-57524-293-4(1))* Krieger Publishing Co.

Wenzel, Anne M. The Entrepreneur's Guide to Market Research. 2012. E-Book ***(978-0-313-39606-9(X),*** Praeger Pubs.); 170p. 37.00 ***(978-0-313-39605-2(1),*** A3472C) Greenwood Publishing Group, Inc.

Whaley, Richard. MS-SQL for Dynamics GP Consultants. 2006. 75p. pap. 35.00 *(978-1-931479-06-6(2))* Accolade Pubns., Inc.

Whaley, Richard & Vail, Leslie. Confessions of a Dynamics GP Consultant: For MS Dynamics GP. 2007. (ENG.). 200p. pap. 150.00 *(978-1-931479-07-3(0))* Accolade Pubns., Inc.

White, Andrea. Healthy, Wealthy, & Wise: Planning for yOur Encore Years. 2009. pap. 9.95 (978-1-61623-870-4(4)) Independent Pub.

White, Doug & White, Polly. Let Go to Grow: Why Some Businesses Thrive & Others Fail to Reach Their Potential. 2011. (978-1-928662-60-0(9)) Palari Publishing LLP.

Whittaker, Martyn. An introduction to Internet marketing & Planning. 2009. 224p. pap. 29.95 (978-0-557-03357-7(8)) Lulu Enterprises Inc.

Why Finance Transformation Matters in Global Manufacturing. 2007. (978-1-934025-02-4(X)) Deloitte.

Wiafe Ii, William Nana. The New Competitive Strategy. 2011. 136p. 29.99 **(978-1-4568-6749-2(0))**; pap. 19.99 **(978-1-4568-6748-5(2))** Xlibris Corp.

Wickman, Gino. Traction: Get a Grip on Your Business. 2007. (Illus.). iv, 232p. (978-0-9797990-0-6(7), Eos) HarperCollins Pubs.

Wiersema, M. & Beck, J., eds. Corporate Strategy. 2011. (Illus.). 776p. 415.00 (978-1-84844-405-8(2)) Elgar, Edward Publishing, Inc.

Wiggins, Anne. Worlds Apart. 2010. 524p. pap. (978-3-8383-6837-5(1)) Lambert Academic Publishing.

Wilburn, Kathleen M. Scenarios: Imagining the Future. rev. ed. 2010. (ENG.). 144p. pap. 77.96 (978-0-7575-5208-3(0)) Kendall Hunt Publishing Co.

Williams, Kevan. Brilliant Business Plan: What to Know & Do to Make the Perfect Plan. rev. ed. 2011. (ENG., Illus.). 240p. pap. 42.50 (978-0-273-74252-4(3)) Pearson Education, Ltd. GBR. Dist: Trans-Atlantic Pubns., Inc.

Williams, Paul. The Innovation Manager's Playbook - Distribution Version. 2010. 206p. pap. 19.95 (978-0-557-61145-4(8)) Lulu Enterprises Inc.

Wittmann, Robert & Reuter, Matthias A. Strategic Planning: How to Deliver Maximum Value Through Effective Business Strategy. 2008. (ENG., Illus.). 176p. 29.95 (978-0-7494-5233-9(1)) Kogan Page, Ltd. GBR. Dist: Ingram Pub. Services.

Wood, Ron. Into the Value Zone: Gaining & Sustaining Competitive Advantage. 2008. (ENG., Illus.). 220p. 68.50 (978-0-7618-4019-0(2)); pap. 39.99 (978-0-7618-4020-6(6)) Univ. Pr. of America, Inc.

Wördemann, Wolfram, et al. The Impossible Advantage: Winning the Competitive Game by Changing the Rules. 2009. (ENG.). 220p. 34.95 (978-0-470-71712-7(2), Wiley) Wiley, John & Sons, Inc.

Worsham, C. Bruce. Foundations of Financial Planning: An Overview. 2nd rev. ed. 2009. (ENG.). 500p. (C). 110.00 (978-1-932819-75-5(4)) American College, The.

Worsham, C. Bruce, et al. Foundations of Financial Planning: An Overview. 2007. 400p. (C). 50.00 (978-1-932819-28-1(2)) American College, The.

Wright, Sylvia. Seven Steps to Grow Green Market Share. 2010. 48p. pap. 14.95 (978-0-557-70952-6(0)) Lulu Enterprises Inc.

Wysocki, Robert K. The Business Analyst/Project Manager: A New Partnership for Managing Complexity & Uncertainty. 2010. (ENG., Illus.). 240p. 49.95 (978-0-470-76744-3(8), Wiley) Wiley, John & Sons, Inc.

Zook, Chris & Allen, James. Repeatability: Build Enduring Businesses for a World of Constant Change. 2012. (ENG.). 288p. 30.00 **(978-1-4221-4330-8(9))** Harvard Business Review Pr.

Zurick, Andryce. E-Business Planning & Decision-Making Processes - a Qualitative Study of Strategy. 2008. 256p. pap. (978-3-639-05900-7(X)) VDM Verlag Dr. Mueller e.K.

5 Steps for Strategic Business Planning: A Workbook for the 21st Century Entrepreneur. 2006. 75.95 (978-0-9790863-0-4(2)) English, Paula.

2007 Policies, Procedures & Benefits Survey: Of Architecture, Engineering, Planning & Environmental Consulting Firms. 13th ed. 2007. per. 395.00 (978-1-934150-16-0(9)) ZweigWhite.

BUSINESS PRESENTATION SOFTWARE

see Presentation Graphics Software

BUSINESS PRESENTATIONS

Aarabi, Parham. The Art of Lecturing: A Practical Guide to Successful University Lectures & Business Presentations. 2007. (ENG., Illus.). 170p. per. 27.99 (978-0-521-70352-9(2)) Cambridge Univ. Pr.

Abela, Andrew & Abela, Andrew V. Advanced Presentations by Design: Creating Communication That Drives Action. 2008. (ENG., Illus.). 224p. pap. 50.00 (978-0-7879-9659-8(9), Pfeiffer) Wiley, John & Sons, Inc.

Alred, Gerald J., et al. The Business Writer's Companion. 6th ed. 2010. (ENG.). 480p. (C). spiral bd. 35.95 (978-0-312-63132-1(4)) Bedford/Saint Martin's.

Arnold, Kristin. Boring to Bravo. 2010. 256p. 21.95 (978-1-50832-036-3(7), Greenleaf Book Group Pr.) Greenleaf Book Group.

Artymiak, Jacek. Beginning OpenOffice Calc: From Setting up Simple Spreadsheets to Business Forecasting. 2011. (ENG.). 136p. pap. 39.99 (978-1-4302-3159-2(9)) Apress L. P.

ASTD Staff. 10 Steps to Successful Presentations. 2008. (ENG.). 126p. pap. 19.95 (978-1-56286-514-6(5)) American Society for Training & Development.

Atkinson, Cliff. The Backchannel: How Audiences are Using Twitter & Social Media & Changing Presentations Forever. 2009. (Voices That Matter Ser.). (ENG., Illus.). 240p. pap. 34.99 (978-0-321-65951-4(1)) New Riders Publishing.

—Beyond Bullet Points: Using Microsoft Powerpoint to Create Presentations That Inform, Motivate, & Inspire. 3rd ed. 2011. (ENG., Illus.). 352p. pap. 29.99 (978-0-7356-2735-2(5)) Microsoft Pr.

Atwood, Christee Gabour. Presentation Skills Training. 2007. (ASTD Trainer's Workshop Ser.). (ENG., Illus.). 203p. pap. 49.95 incl. cd-rom (978-1-56286-479-8(3)) American Society for Training & Development.

—Ultimate Basic Business Skills: Training an Effective Workforce. 2009. (ENG., Illus.). 352p. pap. 69.95 incl. cd-rom (978-1-56286-589-4(7)) American Society for Training & Development.

Ball, R. The Small Book of Big Presentation Skill. 2006. (Illus.). 112p. per. (978-1-904995-17-3(9)) Lexden Publishing Ltd.

Barkan, Lawrence. Present & Persuade: Create Talks & Speeches the Capture Hearts & Change Minds. 2008. 156p. per. 16.95 (978-0-9797911-2-3(X)) Alameda Publishing.

Barnes, Mark & Barnes, Mary-Jane. Stand & Deliver: A Master Class in Making Powerful Presentations. 2007. (Illus.). 160p. pap. (978-1-85252-533-0(9)) Management Bks. 2000 Ltd.

Beard, Jane. Speaking for Real. 2011. 116p. pap. 39.95 **(978-1-257-07219-4(6))** Lulu Enterprises Inc.

Bly, Robert. Persuasive Presentations for Business. 2008. (ENG.). 240p. pap. 21.95 (978-1-59918-177-6(0), 1599181770) Entrepreneur Pr. dba Entrepreneur Media, Inc.

Boeheim, Brian J. Stop Presenting! Start Succeeding. 2009. 152p. 24.95 (978-1-4389-4070-0(X)); pap. 16.95 (978-1-4389-4069-4(6)) AuthorHouse.

Booth, David, et al. Own the Room: Business Presentations That Persuade, Engage, & Get Results. 2009. (ENG., Illus.). 288p. pap. 18.95 (978-0-07-162859-4(2), 0071628592) McGraw-Hill Cos., The.

Boross, Paul. The Pitching Bible: The Seven Secrets to a Successful Business Pitch. 2010. (ENG., Illus.). 400p. pap. (978-0-9565358-2-5(8)) CGW Publishing.

Bovee, Courtland & Thill, John V. Business Communication Essentials. 4th ed. 2008. (ENG.). 528p. (C). pap. 146.67 (978-0-13-608441-9(9), Prentice Hall) Prentice Hall PTR.

Bovée, Courtland L. & Thill, John V. Business Communication Essentials. 5th rev. ed. 2010. (ENG.). 528p. (C). pap. 146.67 (978-0-13-253971-5(3), Prentice Hall) Prentice Hall PTR.

Bowman, Lee. High Impact Communications: The Best Way to Communicate Anytime Anywhere. 4th ed. 2007. (ENG.). 232p. pap. 19.95 (978-1-903071-16-8(X)) Bene Factum Publishing, Ltd. GBR. Dist: Independent Pubs. Group.

Boylan, Robert. Brilliant Presentations in 24 Hours or Less: A Crash Course in Creating Presentations That Inspire Action, Generate Buy in, Change Minds, Close Deals. Edelstein, Scott, ed. (Illus.). 130p. per. (978-0-9711022-0-0(1)) Point Pubns.

Butterfield, Jeff. Written Communication, Oral Communication, & Presentation Skills. 2009. (ENG.). (C). 12.95 (978-1-4390-4117-8(2)) Course Technology.

Caplin, James. I Hate Presentations: Transform the Way You Present with a Fresh & Powerful Approach. 2008. (ENG., Illus.). 212p. pap. 19.95 (978-1-84112-809-2(0), Capstone) Wiley, John & Sons, Inc.

Carnegie, Dale. Public Speaking & Influencing Men in Business. 2008. 204p. per. (978-956-291-535-9(2)) Editorial Benei Noaj.

Carroll, Alan. The Broadband Connection: The Art of Delivering a Winning IT Presentation. 2009. (ENG.). 248p. pap. 14.95 (978-1-933771-90-8(9)); (Illus.). xii, 234p. pap. **(978-1-933771-99-1(2))** BenBella Bks.

Civiello, Mary & Matthews, Arlene. Communication Counts: Business Presentations for Busy People. 2008. (ENG., Illus.). 236p. pap. 21.95 (978-0-470-17894-2(9), Wiley) Wiley, John & Sons, Inc.

Coughter, Peter. The Art of the Pitch: Persuasion & Presentations Skills That Win Business. 2012. (ENG., Illus.). 256p. 28.00 (978-0-230-12051-8(2)) Palgrave Macmillan.

Cram101 Textbook Reviews. Outlines & Highlights for Speaking Effectively: Achieving Excellence in Presentations by Kline, ISBN. 2011. 174p. pap. 29.95 **(978-1-61830-044-7(X))** Cram101 Inc.

Cram101 Textbook Reviews & Cram101 Textbook Reviews. Outlines & Highlights for Business Communication Essentials by Courtland L Bovee. 2011. 442p. pap. 36.95 **(978-1-61830-555-8(7))** Cram101 Inc.

Cullen, Maura. 35 Dumb Things Well-Intended People Say. 2008. (ENG.). 141p. pap. 14.95 (978-1-60037-491-3(3)) Morgan James Publishing.

Davies, Graham G. The Presentation Coach: Bare Knuckle Brilliance for Every Presenter. 2010. (ENG., Illus.). 280p. pap. 21.95 (978-0-85708-044-8(X), Capstone) Wiley, John & Sons, Inc.

Dempsey, David. Present Your Way to the Top: Because Every Presentation Can Make or Break Your Career. 2010. (ENG.). 352p. 24.95 (978-0-07-173994-8(7), 0071739947) McGraw-Hill Cos., The.

Denny, Richard. Communicate to Win: Learn the Secrets of Successful Communication & Presentation. 2nd rev. ed. 2009. (ENG.). 144p. pap. 17.95 (978-0-7494-5645-0(0)) Kogan Page, Ltd. GBR. Dist: Ingram Pub. Services.

Diamond, Linda Eve. Perfect Phrases for Sales Presentations: Hundreds of Ready-to-Use Phrases for Delivering Powerful Presentations That Close Every Sale. 2009. (Perfect Phrases Ser.). (ENG.). 208p. pap. 10.95 (978-0-07-163453-3(3), 0071634533) McGraw-Hill Cos., The.

Diamond, Stephanie. Prezi for Dummies. 2010. (ENG., Illus.). 336p. pap 24.99 (978-0-470-62586-6(4), For Dummies) Wiley, John & Sons, Inc.

Duarte, Nancy. Resonate: Present Visual Stories That Transform Audiences. 2010. (ENG., Illus.). 272p. pap. 29.95 (978-0-470-63201-7(1), Wiley) Wiley, John & Sons, Inc.

—Slide-Ology: The Art & Science of Creating Great Presentations. rev. ed. 2008. (ENG., Illus.). 296p. pap. 34.99 (978-0-596-52234-6(7)) O'Reilly Media, Inc.

Earnest & Earnest, Billy. Save Our Slides: Powerpoint Design That Works. 2nd rev. ed. 2011. (ENG.). 88p. spiral bd. 23.15 (978-0-7575-8122-9(6)) Kendall Hunt Publishing Co.

Estep, Tora. Basics of Stand-up Training: Training Basics. 2006. (Infoline Ser.). (ENG., Illus.). 16p. pap. 24.95 (978-1-56286-389-0(4)) American Society for Training & Development.

Etherington, Bob. Presentation Skills for Quivering Wrecks. 2007. (ENG., Illus.). 160p. per. 16.95 (978-1-904879-80-0(2)) Cyan Communications GBR. Dist: Independent Pubs. Group.

Farrell, Yvonne. Impactful Presentations: Best Practice Skills. 2008. (ENG., Illus.). 78p. pap. 14.95 **(978-0-9519738-7-5(8))** Management Briefs Ltd.

Film, Gower. The Floors Is Yours, Now. 2008. 24p. 575.00 (978-0-347-60006-4(9), Gower Publishing Co., Ltd.) Ashgate Publishing, Ltd. GBR. Dist: Ashgate Publishing Co.

Ford, Jeffrey & Ford, Laurie H. The Four Conversations: Daily Communication That Gets Results. 2009. (ENG.). 200p. pap. 20.95 (978-1-57675-920-2(2)) Berrett-Koehler Pubs., Inc.

Ford, Neal, et al. Presentation Patterns: Techniques for Crafting Better Presentations. rev. ed. 2012. (ENG.). 320p. pap. 39.99 **(978-0-321-82080-8(0))** Addison Wesley Professional.

Forsyth, Patrick. How to Craft Successful Business Presentations: And Effective Public Speaking. 2006. (ENG., Illus.). 1p. per. (978-0-572-03218-0(8)) Foulsham, W. Co., Ltd.

—The PowerPoint Detox: Reinvent Your Slides & Add Power to Your Presentation. 2009. (ENG., Illus.). 160p. pap. 24.95 (978-0-7494-5511-8(X)) Kogan Page, Ltd. GBR. Dist: Ingram Pub. Services.

—100 Great Presentation Ideas, 1 vol. 2011. (ENG.). 240p. pap. 19.50 (978-981-4276-91-7(X)) Marshall Cavendish International (Asia) Private Ltd. SGP. Dist: Marshall Cavendish Corp.

Franck, Karen A. & Howard, Teresa Von Sommaruga. Design through Dialogue: A Guide for Architects & Clients. 2010. (ENG., Illus.). 208p. pap. 60.00 (978-0-470-87071-6(0), Wiley) Wiley, John & Sons, Inc.

Gallo, Carmine. The Presentation Secrets of Steve Jobs: How to Be Insanely Great in Front of Any Audience. 2009. (ENG., Illus.). 256p. 21.95 (978-0-07-163608-7(0), 0071636080) McGraw-Hill Cos., The.

Gaulke, Sue. 101 Ways to Captivate a Business Audience. 2007. (ENG.). 176p. (Orig.). per. 16.95 (978-0-8144-0096-8(5)) Amacom.

Gendelman, Joel. Virtual Presentations That Work. 2010. (ENG., Illus.). 288p. pap. 19.95 (978-0-07-173936-8(X), 007173936X) McGraw-Hill Cos., The.

Gillespie, David & Warren, Mark. Teach Yourself the Clinton Factor: Communicating with Charisma. 2008. (Teach Yourself: Business Ser.). (ENG.). 240p. pap. 12.95 (978-0-07-158189-9(8), 0071581898) McGraw-Hill Cos., The.

Goldner, Paul S. Red-Hot Selling: Power Techniques That Win Even the Toughest Sale, 1 vol. 2010. (ENG.). 240p. pap. 17.95 (978-0-8144-7353-5(9)) Amacom.

Greenlaw, Raymond. Technical Writing, Presentational Skills, & Online Communication: Professional Tools & Insights. 2012. (Illus.). xxi, 225p. **(978-1-4666-0239-7(2))** IGI Global.

Greenlaw, Raymond, ed. Technical Writing, Presentational Skills, & Online Communication: Professional Tools & Insights. 2012. (Illus.). 456p. 175.00 **(978-1-4666-0237-3(6)**, Information Science Reference) IGI Global.

Gruhn, Paul. Sell More Through Effective Technical Presentations. 2nd rev ed. 2008. (ENG., Illus.). 126p. pap. 59.00 (978-1-934394-54-0(8)) ISA.

Hager, Peter J., et al. Designing & Delivering Scientific, Technical & Managerial Presentations + Creating More Effective Graphs Set, 2 vols. 2008. (ENG., Illus.). xiv, 345p. pap. 190.00 (978-0-470-38808-2(0), Wiley-Interscience) Wiley, John & Sons, Inc.

Hall, Richard. Brilliant Presentation: What the Best Presenters Know, Do & Say. 3rd rev. ed. 2011. (ENG., Illus.). 248p. pap. 17.99 **(978-0-273-76246-1(X))** FT Press.

—Brilliant Presentation: What the Best Presenters Know, Do & Say. 2nd ed. (Illus.). 2008. 200p. pap. 36.50 (978-0-273-72076-8(7), Prentice Hall) 2009. (ENG., 208p. pap. 33.50 (978-0-273-73067-5(3)) Pearson Education, Ltd. GBR. Dist: Trans-Atlantic Pubns., Inc.

—Brilliant Presentation: What the Best Presenters Know, Say & Do. 2007. (Illus.). 152p. (Orig.). pap. 29.50 (978-0-273-70974-9(7), Financial Times/Prentice Hall) Pearson Education, Ltd. GBR. Dist: Trans-Atlantic Pubns., Inc.

Hanisch, Horst. Rhetoric - Mastering the Art of Persuasion. 2009. 146p. pap. (978-3-8334-8262-5(1)) Books on Demand GmbH.

Harvard Business School Press. Developing a Business Case. 2010. (Pocket Mentor Ser.). (ENG., Illus.). 128p. pap. 9.95 (978-1-4221-2976-0(4)) Harvard Business Review Pr.

Harvard Business School Press Staff, compiled by. Giving Presentations: Expert Solutions to Everyday Challenges. 2007. (Pocket Mentor Ser.). (ENG., Illus.). 96p. per. 9.95 (978-1-4221-1475-9(9)) Harvard Business Review Pr.

Harvey, Bob. Tork & Grunt's Guide to Great Presentations: Arrows Not Bullets. 2008. (Illus.). 80p. pap. 9.95 (978-0-462-09924-8(5)) Marshall Cavendish GBR. Dist: Midpoint Trade Bks., Inc.

Hatton, Angela. The Definitive Business Pitch: How to Make the Best Pitches, Proposals & Presentations, 2 vols. 2006. (ENG., Illus.). 216p. pap. (978-0-273-70826-1(0), Financial Times/Prentice Hall) Pearson Education, Ltd.

Havre, Pierre. Half the World Are Squirrels & the Rest Are Nuts. 2008. 280p. pap. 67.99 (978-1-4389-2753-4(3)) AuthorHouse.

Henderson, Jeanette, et al. There's No Such Thing as Public Speaking: Make Any Presentation or Speech as Persuasive as a One-on-Oneconversation. 2007. (ENG.). 240p. (gr. 12-18). 15.95 (978-0-7352-0415-7(2)) Prentice Hall Pr.

Hendrix, R. Blake. Accounting, Finance & Presentation for Small Business: Commerce Is King. 2007. 204p. per. 18.95 (978-0-595-42734-5(0)) iUniverse, Inc.

Hildinger, Elizabeth, et al. A Practical Guide to Technical Reports & Presentations. 2008. (ENG.). (C). pap. 34.40 (978-0-555-01787-6(7)) Pearson Learning Solutions.

How to Give a Speech: Easy-to-Learn Skills for More Successful & Profitable Presentations, Speeches, Meetings, Sales, & More! 2007. per. 14.95 (978-0-9796314-4-3(0)) Cedar & Maitland Pr., LLC.

Hutchison, David & Hutchison, Michael. Speaking Mastery: The Keys to Delivering High Impact Presentations. 2008. (ENG.). 153p. 24.00 (978-1-60037-221-6(X)); pap. 14.00 (978-1-60037-185-1(X)) Morgan James Publishing.

Jefferys, J. Douglas. And Your Point Is? 2006. (Illus.). 220p. per. 21.95 (978-1-4120-9241-8(8)) Trafford Publishing.

Johnson, Brandt. Presentation Skills for Business Professionals. 2007. viii, 72p. per. (978-0-9785823-0-2(6)) Syntaxis Pr.

Jones, Frances Cole. How to Wow: Proven Strategies for Selling Your [Brilliant] Self in Any Situation. 2009. (ENG.). 224p. pap. 15.00 (978-0-345-50179-0(9), Ballantine Bks.) Random House Publishing Group.

Jones, Roger E. Storytelling Pocketbook. 2011. (ENG., Illus.). n/ap. pap. **(978-1-906610-40-1(1))** Management Pocketbooks GBR. Dist: Ware-Pak, Inc.

Kamille, Stuart J. How to Present Your Idea. 2008. 38p. per. 10.00 (978-0-9774735-3-3(8)) Golden Leaf Press.

Kapterev, Alexei. Presentation Secrets. 2011. (Secrets Ser.: 152). (ENG.). 360p. pap. 34.99 (978-1-118-03496-5(1), Wiley) Wiley, John & Sons, Inc.

Kay, Frances. Smart Skills: Presentations, 1 vol. 2011. (ENG., Illus.). 130p. pap. 14.99 (978-1-908248-08-4(4)) Legend Pr. GBR. Dist: Innovative Logistics.

Khan-Panni, Philip. Making Business Presentations: How to Deliver a Winning Message. rev. ed. 2011. (ENG., Illus.). 184p. pap. 24.99 **(978-0-273-75799-3(7))** FT Press.

Kiriyama, Seiya. Works in Progress: Graphics for Visual Presentations. Yamamoto, Akiko & Sekimoto, Yasuhiro, eds. 2010. (ENG & JPN., Illus.) 168p. 75.00 (978-4-89444-759-2(2), PIE Bks.) Rizzoli International Pubns., Inc.

Klaff, Oren. Pitch Anything: An Innovative Method for Presenting, Persuading, & Winning the Deal. 2011. (ENG., Illus.). 240p. 22.00 (978-0-07-175285-5(4), 0071752854) McGraw-Hill Cos., The.

Knapp, Lesley. An Investigation into Visual Design in the Developement of Educational Web-Based Projects. 2008. 176p. per. (978-3-8364-3527-7(6)) VDM Verlag Dr. Mueller e.K.

Koegel, Tim. The Exceptional Presenter Goes Virtual. 2010. 208p. 21.95 (978-1-60832-046-2(4)) Greenleaf Book Group.

Koegel, Timothy J. The Exceptional Presenter: A Proven Formula to Open up & Own the Room. 2007. (Illus.). 188p. 21.95 (978-1-929774-44-9(3), Greenleaf Book Group Pr.) Greenleaf Book Group.

Kosslyn, Stephen Michael. Better PowerPoint: Quick Fixes Based on How Your Audience Thinks. 2010. (ENG., Illus.). 160p. pap. 14.95 (978-0-19-537675-3(7)) Oxford Univ. Pr., Inc.

Lane, Robert. Relational Presentation: A Visually Interactive Approach. 2007. 394p. pap. 69.99 (978-0-9794156-0-9(8)) Aspire Communications.

Lincwes, Joanne G. The Savvy Presenter: 100 Tips for Mastering Presentations. 2010. (ENG., Illus.). 160p. pap. 19.95 (978-1-86470-361-0(X), Images Publishing Dist Ac) Antique Collectors' Club GBR. Dist: National Bk. Network.

Mablekos, Carole M. Getting It Across: A Guide to Good Presentations. 2006. (ENG., Illus.). 104p. per. 32.00 (978-1-59126-063-9(9), PROPR) Professional Pubns., Inc.

Marathe, Mandar. Successful Speaker 273 Tips for Powerful Presentations. 2007. (Illus.). 145p. pap. 34.95 (978-0-9554873-0-9(7)) Ashwood Hse. Publishing GBR. Dist: Lightning Source UK, Ltd.

Market Your Listings Through Visual Presentation: Real Estate Marketing A Complete Workbook & Guide to Visual Presentation. 2007. 29.95 (978-0-9791119-2-1(7)) Tyree, Stephanie.

Matzka, Kathy. The Medical Staff Meeting Companion: Tools & Techniques for Effective Presentations. 2008. (Illus.). ix, 136p. (978-1-60146-204-6(2)) Opus Communications.

McClain, Gary. Presentations: Proven Techniques for Creating Presentations That Get Results. 2nd ed. 2007. (ENG.). 224p. per. 10.95 (978-1-59869-153-5(8)) Adams Media Corp.

McConnon, Shay. Presenting with Power: Captivate, Motivate, Inspire & Persuade. 3rd rev. ed. 2007. (Illus.). 138p. per. 20.00 (978-1-84528-160-1(8)) How To Books GBR. Dist: Parkwest Pubns., Inc.

Moon, Jon. How to Make an Impact with Presentations. 2012. (Financial Times Ser.). (ENG., Illus.). 272p. pap. 24.99 **(978-0-273-75957-7(4))** FT Press.

Munter, Mary & Paradi, David. Guide to PowerPoint 2007. 2008. (ENG., Illus.). 208p. (C). pap. 36.00 (978-0-13-606871-5(5), Prentice Hall) Prentice Hall PTR.

Munter, Mary & Russell, Lynn. Guide to Presentations. 3rd ed. 2010. (ENG., Illus.). 168p. (C). pap. 36.00 (978-0-13-707508-9(1), Prentice Hall) Prentice Hall PTR.

Nathans-Kelly, Traci & Nicometo, Christine G. Slide Rules: Design, Build, & Archive Presentations in Engineering & Technical Fields. 2013. (IEEE PCS Professional Engineering Communication Ser.). (ENG., Illus.). 250p. pap. 49.95 (978-1-118-00296-4(2), Wiley-IEEE Pr.) Wiley, John & Sons, Inc.

Neumeier, Marty. Marty Neumeier's INNOVATION TOOLKIT. 2009. (Voices That Matter Ser.). (ENG., Illus.). 208p. pap., pap. 49.99 (978-0-321-66048-0(X)) New Riders Publishing.

B

Norma, Sit & Lester, Alison. Present for Success. 2010. 0176p. pap. 15.99 *(978-981-261-674-6(8))* Marshall Cavendish International (Asia) Private Ltd. SGP. Dist: Marshall Cavendish Corp.

Oechsli, Matt. Becoming a Rainmaker: Getting a Downpour of Serious Money. 2007. pap. 29.95 *(978-0-9656765-7-1(9))* Wealth Management Pr.

Oulton, Nicholas B. Killer Presentations. 2nd ed. 2007. (Illus.). 193p. per. 26.00 *(978-1-84528-184-7(5))* Parkwest Pubns., Inc.

Parsons, Heather. You Know What I'm Sayin'? A Handbook on How to Deliver Effective Presentations. 2009. 124p. pap. 10.99 *(978-1-4389-5315-1(1))* AuthorHouse.

Peel, Malcolm & Scott-Brown, David. Presenting in a Week. 2012. (ENG., Illus.). 128p. pap. 12.00 ***(978-1-4441-5970-7(4)***, 1444159704) McGraw-Hill Cos., The.

Peery, Angela. Creating Effective Presentations: Staff Development with Impact. 2011. (ENG.). 110p. 40.00 *(978-1-60709-622-1(6))*; pap. 19.95 *(978-1-60709-623-8(4))* Rowman & Littlefield Education.

Peery, Angela B. Creating Effective Presentations: Staff Development with Impact. 2011. *(978-1-60709-597-2(1))* Rowman & Littlefield Education.

Pike, Betsy Allen, Bob, Bob. Powerful Presentations, Volume 2. 2008. 80p. pap. 24.95 *(978-1-935291-01-5(7))* Creative Training Techniques Pr.

Pike, Bob & Allen, Betsy. Powerful Presentation Techniques, Volume 1: 39 Quick Openers, Puzzlers & Energizers that Spark Interest & Anchor Your Topic. 2007. per. 21.95 *(978-1-56447-038-6(5))* Resources for Organizations, Inc.

Powell, Mark. Dynamic Presentations Student's Book with CDs (2) 2010. (Cambridge Business Skills Ser.). (ENG., Illus.). 96p. pap. 22.50 incl. audio compact disk *(978-0-521-15004-0(3))* Cambridge Univ. Pr.

Provan, Drew. Giving Great Presentations in Easy Steps. 2009. (In Easy Steps Ser.). (ENG.). 192p. pap. 14.99 *(978-1-84078-371-1(0))* Computer Step GBR. Dist: Perseus-PGW.

Reynolds, Garr. The Naked Presenter: Delivering Powerful Presentations with or Without Slides. 2010. (Voices That Matter Ser.). (ENG.). 216p. pap. 24.99 *(978-0-321-70445-0(2))* New Riders Publishing.

—Presentation Zen: Simple Ideas on Presentation Design & Delivery. 2nd rev. ed. 2011. (Voices That Matter Ser.). (ENG.). 312p. pap. 29.99 ***(978-0-321-81198-1(4))*** New Riders Publishing.

—Presentation Zen: The Video. 2009. 12p. 24.99 *(978-0-321-57389-6(7))* New Riders Publishing.

—Presentation Zen Sketchbook. 2010. (Voices That Matter Ser.). (ENG.). 168p. spiral bd. 14.99 *(978-0-321-73479-2(3))* New Riders Publishing.

Rios, Frances. The Glue Factor: Giving Presentations That Make Your Message Stick. 2011. 98p. 24.99 ***(978-1-4568-8328-7(3))***; pap. 15.99 ***(978-1-4568-8327-0(5))*** Xlibris Corp.

Russell, Jane & Whitacker Staff. Give Great Presentations: How to Speak Confidently & Make Your Point. rev. ed. 2010. (Steps to Success Ser.). (ENG.). 96p. pap. 9.95 *(978-1-4081-2802-2(0))* A & C Black GBR. Dist: Macmillan.

Salter, Brian. Effective Presenting. 2009. (Instant Manager Ser.). (ENG., Illus.). 208p. pap. 16.95 *(978-0-340-98518-2(6))*, Hodder & Stoughton) Hodder General Publishing Div. GBR. Dist: Independent Pubs. Group.

Sanow, Arnold J. & Lescault, Henry J. Present with Power, Punch, & Pizzazz! The Ultimate Guide to Delivering Presentations with Poise, Persuasion, & Professionalism. 2011. 260p. 31.95 ***(978-1-4620-2029-4(1))***; pap. 21.95 ***(978-1-4620-2027-0(5))*** iUniverse, Inc.

Scalise, Christina. Presentation Strategies & Dialogue. 2012. (Illus.). 224p. (C). pap. 0.00 *(978-1-60901-144-4(9))* Fairchild Bks.

Schwertly, Scott. How to Be a Presentation God: Build, Design, & Deliver Presentations That Dominate. 2011. (ENG., Illus.). 260p. 22.95 *(978-0-470-91584-4(6)*, Wiley) Wiley, John & Sons, Inc.

Shapiro, Mo. Presenting: Bullet Guides. 2012. (Bullet Guides). (ENG.). 128p. pap. 6.95 ***(978-1-4441-3740-8(9)***, Hodder & Stoughton) Hodder General Publishing Div. GBR. Dist: Independent Pubs. Group.

Siegel, Randy. Powerhouse Presenting. 2007. 124p. pap. 19.96 *(978-0-615-15373-5(9))* Siegel, Randy.

Sklar, Leonard. Great Presentations: How to Keep Your Audiences Awake - All the Time. 2007. 52p. per. 9.95 *(978-0-595-47149-2(8))* iUniverse, Inc.

Smith, Jim & Smith, Jim, Jr. Crash & Learn: 600+ Road-Tested Tips to Keep Audiences Fired up & Engaged! 2007. (ENG.). 224p. per. 19.95 *(978-1-56286-465-1(3))* American Society for Training & Development.

Smith, Scott S. Everything Public Speaking Book: Deliver a Winning Presentation Every Time! 2008. (ENG.). 288p. pap. 14.95 *(978-1-59869-622-6(X))* Adams Media Corp.

Sommerville, Joseph. Rainmaking Presentations: How to Grow Your Business by Leveraging Your Expertise. 2009. (ENG., Illus.). 224p. 24.95 *(978-0-230-60948-8(1))* Palgrave Macmillan.

Soorjoo, Martin. Here's the Pitch: How to Pitch Your Business to Anyone, Get Funded, & Win Clients. 2012. (ENG.). 205p. 24.95 ***(978-1-118-13752-9(3)***, Wiley) Wiley, John & Sons, Inc.

Stanley, Mandi. The No-Panic Plan for Presenters: An A-to-Z Checklist for Speaking Confidently & Compellingly Anywhere, Anytime. 2011. (ENG.). 264p. pap. 16.95 *(978-0-9795187-3-7(3))* Pecan Row Pr.

Steele, William R. Presentation Skills 201: How to Take it to the Next Level as a Confident, Engaging Presenter. 2009. 173p. pap. 14.95 *(978-1-4327-3840-2(2))* Outskirts Pr., Inc.

Step by Step Guide to Preparing Presentations. 2008. (ENG., Illus.). 176p. per. 19.97 *(978-0-9759643-1-6(3))* IT Economics Corp.

Sweetow, Stuart. Corporate Video Production: Beyond the Board Room (and OUT of the Bored Room) 2011. (ENG., Illus.). 336p. pap. 34.95 *(978-0-240-81341-7(3)*, Focal Pr.) Elsevier Science & Technology Bks.

Tarner, Mark. Presentations a to Z: The Presenter's Handbook. 2007. 156p. per. 19.99 *(978-1-58832-150-3(9))* Unlimited Publishing LLC.

Templeton, Melody. Public Speaking & Presentations Demystified. 2009. (Demystified Ser.). (ENG., Illus.). 272p. (C). pap. 19.95 *(978-0-07-160121-4(X)*, 007160121X) McGraw-Hill Cos., The.

Theobald, Theo. Develop Your Presentation Skills. 2011. (Sunday Times Creating Success Ser.). (ENG., Illus.). 176p. pap. 14.95 *(978-0-7494-6278-9(7))* Kogan Page, Ltd. GBR. Dist: Ingram Pub. Services.

Thompson, Jo & Bruno-Magdich, Tom. The Energetics of Charisma. 2008. 172p. pap. 31.50 *(978-1-4092-2573-7(9))* Lulu Enterprises Inc.

Through Visual Presentation of Your Home: Market Real Estate for Sale by Owner. 2007. 25.00 *(978-0-9791119-3-8(5))* Tyree, Stephanie.

Toogood, Granville. The New Articulate Executive: Look, Act & Sound Like a Leader. 2nd ed. 2010. (ENG., Illus.). 240p. 21.95 *(978-0-07-174326-6(X)*, 007174326X) McGraw-Hill Cos., The.

Townsend, John. The Presentations. 2nd ed. 2009. (Illus.). 112p. pap. *(978-1-906610-15-9(0))* Management Pocketbooks.

Turmel, Wayne. 10 Steps to Successful Virtual Presentations. 2011. 176p. pap. 19.95 *(978-1-56286-746-1(6))* American Society for Training & Development.

Ursiny, Tim & DeMoss, Gary. Top Performer's Guide to Speeches & Presentations: Essential Skills That Put You on Top. 2007. (ENG., Illus.). 144p. 9.95 *(978-1-4022-0775-4(1))* Sourcebooks, Inc.

Valentine, Craig & Meyerson, Mitch. World Class Speaking: The Ultimate Guide to Presenting, Marketing & Profiting Like a Champion. 2009. (ENG.). pap. 21.95 *(978-1-60037-473-9(5))* Morgan James Publishing.

Vickers, Amanda & Bavister, Steve. Present with Impact & Confidence: A Teach Yourself Guide. 2011. (ENG.). 256p. pap. 15.00 *(978-0-07-176952-5(8)*, 0071769528) McGraw-Hill Cos., The.

Walker, T. J. How to Give a Pretty Good Presentation: A Speaking Survival Guide for the Rest of Us. 2010. (ENG.). 192p. 19.95 *(978-0-470-59714-9(3)*, Wiley) Wiley, John & Sons, Inc.

Weinschenk, Susan. 100 Things Every Presenter Needs to Know about People. 2012. (ENG.). 272p. pap. 34.99 ***(978-0-321-82124-9(6))*** New Riders Publishing.

Weiss, Alan. MBA V, 5 vols. 2008. (Illus.). 295.00 incl. audio *(978-1-928611-14-1(1))* Summit Consulting Group, Inc.

Weissman, Jerry. Presentations in Action: 80 Memorable Presentation Lessons from the Masters. rev. ed. 2011. (ENG., Illus.). 224p. 24.99 *(978-0-13-248962-1(7))* FT Press.

—Presenting to Win: The Art of Telling Your Story. rev. exp. ed. 2008. (ENG., Illus.). 288p. 26.99 *(978-0-13-714417-4(2))* FT Press.

Whalen, Tim. Winning Oral Presentations: A Management & Sales Approach. 250p. pap. 99.00 *(978-1-56726-035-9(7))* Management Concepts, Inc.

Wilder, Claudyne. Point, Click & Wow! The Techniques & Habits of Successful Presenters. 3rd ed. 2008. (ENG., Illus.). 320p. pap. 39.95 *(978-0-7879-9745-8(5)*, Pfeiffer) Wiley, John & Sons, Inc.

Young, Graham. The A-Z of Effective Business Presentations. 2008. 132p. pap. *(978-1-84923-113-8(3))* YouWriteOn.

Zaremba, Alan Jay. Speaking Professionally: Influence, Power, & Responsibility at the Podium. 2nd ed. 2011. (ENG.). 272p. (C). pap. 68.95 ***(978-0-7656-2974-6(7))*** Sharpe, M.E. Inc.

Zelazny, Gene. The Say It with Charts Complete Toolkit. Roche, Sara & Sakson, Steve, eds. 2006. (ENG., Illus.). 312p. 59.95 *(978-0-07-147470-2(6)*, 0071474706) McGraw-Hill Cos., The.

Zelazny, Gene, et al. The Say It with Charts Complete Toolkit. 2007. (Illus.). ix, 298p. ***(978-0-07-147471-9(4))*** McGraw-Hill Cos., The.

BUSINESS PRESENTATIONS—COMPUTER PROGRAMS

see Presentation Graphics Software

BUSINESS PSYCHOLOGY

see Psychology, Industrial

BUSINESS RECORDS

see also Business—Forms

also specific types of business records, e.g. Financial Statements; Inventories

Adam, Azad. Implementing Electronic Document & Record Management Systems. 2007. (ENG., Illus.). 280p. 99.95 *(978-0-8493-8059-4(6))* Auerbach Pubs., Inc.

Ashton, Helen. The Company Secretary's Handbook: A Guide to Duties & Responsibilities. 4th rev. ed. 2006. (Illus.). 176p. pap. *(978-0-7494-4755-7(9))* Kogan Page, Ltd.

Bantin, Philip C. Understanding Data & Information Systems for Recordkeeping. 2007. (Archivist's & Records Manager's Bookshelf). 75.00 *(978-1-55570-580-0(4))* Neal-Schuman Pubs., Inc.

Bulterman, Dick C. A. DocEng'08: Proceedings of the Eight ACM Symposium on Document Engineering: São Paulo, Brazil, September 16-19, 2008. 2008. (Illus.). xi, 302p. *(978-1-60558-081-4(3))* ACM Pr.

Choksy, Carol E. B. Domesticating Information: Managing Documents Inside the Organization. 2006. (ENG., Illus.). 250p. per. 47.00 *(978-0-8108-5190-0(3))* Scarecrow Pr., Inc.

Cram101 Textbook Reviews & Cram101 Textbook Reviews. Outlines & Highlights for Records Management by Judy Read, Isbn: 9780538731416. 2011. 240p. pap. 31.95 ***(978-1-61461-406-7(7))*** Cram101 Inc.

Davidson, Alan. The Law of Electronic Commerce. 2009. (ENG.). 438p. pap. 60.00 *(978-0-521-67865-0(X))* Cambridge Univ. Pr.

Employee Benefits Institute of America Inc. Form 5500 Workbook for Health & Welfare Plans (2006 Plan Years) Anderson, Brigid Carroll, ed. 2006. ring bd. 185.00 *(978-1-934090-01-5(8))* Employee Benefits Institute of America Inc.

Ginn, Mary Lea & Read, Judith. Study Guide for Read/Ginn's Records Management, 9th. 9th ed. 2010. (ENG.). 128p. (C). pap. 50.95 *(978-0-538-73143-0(5))* Cengage South-Western.

Gutmann, Joanna. Taking Minutes of Meetings. 2nd rev. ed. 2010. (Creating Success Ser.). (ENG.). 160p. pap. 14.95 *(978-0-7494-6029-7(6))* Kogan Page, Ltd. GBR. Dist: Ingram Pub. Services.

Houze, Herbert G. Arming the West: A Fresh Look at the Guns that Were Actually Carried on the Frontier. 2007. (Illus.). 190p. pap. 29.99 *(978-1-931464-34-5(0))* Mowbray, Andrew Inc., Pubs.

Kahn, Randolph, et al. Information Nation: Seven Keys to Information Management Compliance. 2nd ed. 2009. (ENG.). 272p. pap. 50.00 *(978-0-470-45311-7(7)*, Wiley) Wiley, John & Sons, Inc.

King, P. R. & Simske, Steven J. Proceedings of the 2007 ACM Symposium on Document Engineering: August 28-31, 2007, Winnipeg, Manitoba, Canada. 2007. (Illus.). x, 225p. *(978-1-59593-776-6(5))* ACM Pr.

Kinn, Sean. E-Doc-S: Hail the Freelance Renaissance. 2007. 92p. per. 10.95 *(978-0-595-45135-7(7))* iUniverse, Inc.

Mancuso, Anthony. The Corporate Records Handbook: Meetings, Minutes & Resolutions, 2 vols. 5th rev. ed. 2010. (ENG.). 640p. pap. 69.99 *(978-1-4133-1203-4(9))* NOLO.

Matwyshyn, Andrea, ed. Harboring Data: Information Security, Law, & the Corporation. 2009. (ENG., Illus.). 368p. 39.95 *(978-0-8047-6008-9(X))* Stanford Univ. Pr.

Ngoepe, Mpho. Records Management Practices in the South African Public Sector. 2011. 152p. pap. ***(978-3-8454-0105-8(2))*** Lambert Academic Publishing.

Rockley, Ann & Cooper, Charles. Managing Enterprise Content: A Unified Content Strategy. 2nd ed. 2012. (Voices That Matter Ser.). (ENG.). 384p. pap. 39.99 ***(978-0-321-81536-1(X))*** New Riders Publishing.

Wiggins, Bob. Effective Document & Data Management: Unlocking Corporate Content. 3rd rev. ed. 2012. (Illus.). 266p. 134.95 ***(978-1-4094-2328-7(X)***, Gower Publishing Co., Ltd.) Ashgate Publishing, Ltd. GBR. Dist: Ashgate Publishing Co.

Young, Jan. Cycle Count & Physical Inventory Design & Execution. 2010. 77p. pap. 19.95 *(978-0-557-36935-5(5))* Lulu Enterprises Inc.

BUSINESS RELOCATION

Galgóczi, Béla & Watt, Andrew. Jobs on the Move: An Analytical Approach to 'Relocation' & its Impact on Employment. Keune, Maarten, ed. 2008. (Travail & Société - Work & Society Ser.). 243p. pap. 43.95 *(978-90-5201-448-7(5))* PIE - Peter Lang BEL. Dist: Lang, Peter.

Knoben, Joris. Firm Mobility & Organizational Networks: Innovation, Embeddedness & Economic Geography. 2008. (New Horizons in Regional Science Ser.). 192p. (C). 119.00 *(978-1-84720-245-1(4))* Elgar, Edward Publishing, Inc.

Kolko, Jed David, et al. Business Location Decisions & Employment Dynamics in California. 2007. *(978-1-58213-112-2(0))* Public Policy Institute of California.

Masi, Ralph, et al. Supporting the U. S. Army Human Resources Command's Human Capital Strategic Planning. 2009. 218p. pap. 40.00 *(978-0-8330-4728-1(0)*, mg-828) RAND Corp., The.

Stay Connected While Relocating: A Non-Technical Guide through a Technical Communication Nightmare. 2008. Orig. Title: A Field Guide for Small Business Owners. 12.99 *(978-0-9791351-1-8(7))* Stone, Ina.

BUSINESS-REPLY MAIL

see Postal Service

BUSINESS REPORT WRITING

Alamargot, Denis, et al, eds. Written Documents in the Workplace. 2008. (Studies in Writing Ser.: 21). (ENG., Illus.). 336p. 161.00 *(978-0-08-047487-8(X)*, Elsevier Science) Elsevier Science & Technology Bks.

Bischof, Brian. Crystal Reports Encyclopedia Vol. 1: Professional XI Reports. 2007. (ENG., Illus.). 656p. per. 49.95 *(978-0-9749536-0-1(1))* Dotnet Tech, Inc.

—Crystal Reports Encyclopedia Vol. 2: .NET 2005/2008. 2008. (ENG.). 500p. pap. 49.95 *(978-0-9749536-1-8(X))* Dotnet Tech, Inc.

—Crystal Reports Encyclopedia 2008/2011: Professional Reports. 2nd ed. 2012. (ENG.). 650p. pap. 49.95 ***(978-0-9749536-3-2(6))*** Dotnet Tech, Inc.

Bischof, Brian. Crystal Reports Encyclopedia Volume 3: Professional Reports 2008. 2010. (ENG.). 650p. pap. 49.95 *(978-0-9749536-2-5(8))* Dotnet Tech, Inc.

Bowden, John. Writing a Report 8e. 8th ed. 2009. (Illus.). 208p. 20.00 *(978-1-84528-293-6(0))* How To Books GBR. Dist: Parkwest Pubns., Inc.

Campbell, Clark A. The One-Page Project Manager: Communicate & Manage Any Project with a Single Sheet of Paper. 2006. (ENG., Illus.). 160p. per. 19.95 *(978-0-470-05237-2(6)*, Wiley) Wiley, John & Sons, Inc.

—The One-Page Project Manager for IT Projects: Communicate & Manage Any Project with a Single Sheet of Paper. 2008. (ENG., Illus.). 160p. pap. 21.95 *(978-0-470-27588-7(X)*, Wiley) Wiley, John & Sons, Inc.

Campbell, Clark A. & Collins, Mike. The One-Page Project Manager for Execution: Drive Strategy & Solve Problems with a Single Sheet of Paper. 2010. (ENG., Illus.). 182p. pap. 22.95 *(978-0-470-49933-7(8)*, Wiley) Wiley, John & Sons, Inc.

Canavor, Natalie. Business Writing in the Digital Age. 2011. (Illus.). 320p. (C). pap., stu. ed. 30.00 ***(978-1-4129-9250-3(8)***, B92503P) SAGE Pubns., Inc.

Cram101 Textbook Reviews. Outlines & Highlights for Business Communication by Carol Lehman, Isbn: 9780324782189. 2011. 236p. pap. 31.95 ***(978-1-61461-873-7(9))*** Cram101 Inc.

—Outlines & Highlights for Business Communication by Carol M Lehman. 2011. 202p. pap. 30.95 ***(978-1-61906-152-1(X))*** Cram101 Inc.

Cram101 Textbook Reviews & Cram101 Textbook Reviews. Outlines & Highlights for Strategic Writing: Multimedia Writing for Public Relations, Advertising, & More by Charles Marsh. 2011. 122p. pap. 28.95 ***(978-1-61830-182-6(9))*** Cram101 Inc.

Daniel, Carter A. Reader-Friendly Reports: A No-Nonsense Guide to Effective Writing for MBAs, Consultants, & Other Professionals. 2011. (ENG., Illus.). 224p. pap. 20.00 ***(978-0-07-178285-2(0)***, 0071782850) McGraw-Hill Cos., The.

Davis, Kenneth. Business Writing & Communication. 2nd ed. 2010. (McGraw-Hill 36-Hour Courses Ser.). (ENG., Illus.). 256p. pap. 19.95 *(978-0-07-173826-2(6)*, 0071738266) McGraw-Hill Cos., The.

Fitzgerald, Neil. Crystal Reports 2008 Official Guide. 2nd ed. 2008. (Business Objects Press Ser.). (ENG., Illus.). 576p. pap., instr.'s gde. ed. 54.99 *(978-0-672-32989-0(1))* Sams.

Fitzgerald, Neil, et al. Crystal Reports XI Official Guide. 2006. (Business Objects Press Ser.). (ENG., Illus.). 960p. per. 59.99 *(978-0-672-32917-3(4))* Sams.

Forsyth, Patrick. How to Write Reports & Proposals. 2nd rev. ed. 2010. (Creating Success Ser.). (ENG., Illus.). 128p. pap. 14.95 *(978-0-7494-6032-7(6))*; pap. 14.95 *(978-0-7494-5665-8(5))* Kogan Page, Ltd. GBR. Dist: Ingram Pub. Services.

Fugere, Peter. Oracle Hyperion Financial Management Tips & Techniques: Design, Implementation & Support. 2011. (Oracle Press Ser.). (ENG., Illus.). 432p. pap. 70.00 ***(978-0-07-177044-6(5)***, 0071770445) McGraw-Hill Osborne.

Ganz, Carl, Jr. Pro Crystal Enterprise - BusinessObjects XI Programming. 2006. (Expert's Voice in .NET Ser.). (ENG., Illus.). 488p. 79.99 *(978-1-59059-759-0(1))* Apress L. P.

Garrett, Mike. Using SAP Crystal Reports. 2010. (Illus.). 500p. 69.95 *(978-1-59229-327-8(1)*, SAP PR.) Galileo Pr., Inc.

Harty, Kevin J. Strategies for Business & Technical Writing. 7th ed. 2010. (ENG., Illus.). 352p. (C). pap. 72.20 *(978-0-205-74191-5(6))* Longman Publishing Group.

Kuiper, Shirley. Contemporary Business Reports. 4th ed. 2009. (ENG.). 560p. (C). pap. 167.95 *(978-0-324-58742-5(2))* Cengage South-Western.

Kuiper, Shirley & Clippinger, Dorinda. Contemporary Business Reports. 5th ed. 2012. (ENG.). 544p. (C). pap. 167.95 ***(978-1-111-82085-5(6))*** Cengage South-Western.

Laison, Michael D. Oracle CRM on Demand Combined Analyses. 2010. (Oracle Press Ser.). (ENG., Illus.). 192p. pap. 30.00 *(978-0-07-174538-3(6)*, 0071745386) McGraw-Hill Osborne.

—Oracle CRM on Demand Dashboards. 2010. (Oracle Press Ser.). (ENG., Illus.). 208p. pap. 29.99 *(978-0-07-174534-5(3)*, 0071745343) McGraw-Hill Osborne.

—Oracle CRM on Demand Embedded Analytics. 2011. (Oracle Press Ser.). (ENG., Illus.). 192p. pap. 30.00 *(978-0-07-174536-9(X)*, 007174536X) McGraw-Hill Osborne.

Lehman, Carol M. & DuFrene, Debbie D. BCOM. (ENG.). 288p. 3rd ed. 2011. pap. 59.95 *(978-1-111-52777-8(6))* 4th ed. 2012. pap. 64.95 ***(978-1-133-37243-1(0))*** Cengage South-Western.

—Building High-Performance Teams. 16th ed. 2010. (ENG.). 74p. (C). pap. 51.95 *(978-0-324-78219-6(5))* Cengage South-Western.

—Business Communication (Book Only) 16th ed. 2010. (ENG.). 656p. (C). 220.95 *(978-0-324-78218-9(7))* Cengage South-Western.

—Business Communication (with Teams Handbook) 16th ed. 2010. (Business Communication Ser.). (ENG.). 656p. (C). 220.95 *(978-0-324-78217-2(9))* Cengage South-Western.

Lehman, Carol M. & DuFrene, Deborah Daniel. Business Communication. 16th ed. 2011. (Illus.). *(978-0-324-78230-1(6))* Cengage South-Western.

Marsh, Charles, et al. Strategic Writing. 3rd ed. 2011. (ENG., Illus.). 272p. (C). pap. 88.00 *(978-0-205-03197-9(8))* Allyn & Bacon, Inc.

—Strategic Writing: Multimedia Writing for Public Relations, Advertising, & More. 2nd ed. 2008. (ENG., Illus.). 272p. (C). pap. 88.00 *(978-0-205-59162-6(0))* Allyn & Bacon, Inc.

May, Claire B. & May, Gordon S. Effective Writing. 9th ed. 2011. (ENG.). 288p. (C). pap. 60.00 *(978-0-13-256724-4(5)*, Prentice Hall) Prentice Hall PTR.

—Effective Writing: A Handbook for Accountants. 8th ed. 2008. (ENG., Illus.). 288p. (C). pap. 60.00 *(978-0-13-602908-3(6)*, Prentice Hall) Prentice Hall PTR.

Moore, Cynthia. Crystal Reports 2011 for Developers. 2011. (ENG., Illus.). 528p. pap. 49.99 *(978-1-4354-5796-6(X))* Course Technology.

Murray, Jean W. The Complete Guide to Writing Effective & Award Winning Business Proposals: Step-by-Step Instructions. 2008. (ENG.). 288p. per. 24.95 *(978-1-60138-234-4(0))* Atlantic Publishing Co.

Paddock, Rod & Goff, Kevin S. Pro vs 2005 Reporting Using SQL Server & Crystal Reports. 2006. (Expert's Voice In .NET Ser.). (ENG., Illus.). 528p. per. 59.99 *(978-1-59059-688-3(9))* Apress L. P.

Patenaude, Gayle. Business Reports for Busy People. 2009. (ENG.). 1p. 19.99 *(978-1-60163-042-1(5))* Career Pr., Inc.

Peck, George. Crystal Reports 2008. 2008. (Osborne Complete Reference Ser.). (ENG., Illus.). 968p. pap. 59.99 *(978-0-07-159098-3(6)*, 0071590986) McGraw-Hill Osborne.

Peh, Diana, et al. Birt: A Field Guide to Reporting. 3rd rev. ed. 2011. (Eclipse Ser.). (ENG., Illus.). 848p. pap. 54.99 *(978-0-321-73358-0(4))* Addison Wesley Professional.

Powell, Diane L. Written Business Communication: A Learner Centered Approach with Text Addendum. rev. ed. 2009. (ENG.). ring bd. 52.88 *(978-0-7575-6805-3(X))* Kendall Hunt Publishing Co.

Roddick, Ellen. Writing That Means Business: How to Get Your Message Across Simply & Effectively. 2010. 148p. pap. 13.95 *(978-1-4502-2104-7(1))* iUniverse, Inc.

Sanders, Liz & Filkins, Joseph. Effective Reporting, 2nd ed. 2009. (Illus.). 81p. (YA). pap. *(978-1-882393-17-6(1))* Assn. for Institutional Research.

Taylor, Allen G. Crystal Reports 2008 for Dummies. 2008. (ENG., Illus.). 408p. pap. 29.99 *(978-0-470-29077-4(3)*, For Dummies) Wiley, John & Sons, Inc.

Yonce, Coy W. 100 Things You Should Know about Reporting with SAP Crystal Reports. 2011. (ENG., Illus.). 300p. pap. 49.95 *(978-1-59229-390-2(5)*, SAP PR.) Galileo Pr., Inc.

Zapawa, Timothy. Excel 2007 Advanced Report Development, 2 vols. 2007. (ENG., Illus.). 576p. per. 45.00 *(978-0-470-04644-9(9)*, Wiley) Wiley, John & Sons, Inc.

BUSINESS RESEARCH

see Business—Research

BUSINESS SECRETS

see Trade Secrets

BUSINESS SCHOOLS

see also names of business schools, e.g. Harvard University—Graduate School of Business Administration

Adetule, Prince Jide. The Handbook on Management Theories. 2011. 120p. 23.80 ***(978-1-4389-4800-3(X))***; pap. 13.70 ***(978-1-4389-4801-0(8))*** AuthorHouse.

Aspatore Books Staff, creator. Business School Management: Top Educational Leaders on Creating a Strong School Reputation, Offering Competitive Programs, & Thriving in the Educational Marketplace. 2008. (Inside the Minds Ser.). (Illus.). 372p. per. 49.95 *(978-0-314-99001-3(1))* Aspatore Bks.

Augier, Mie & March, James G. The Roots, Rituals, & Rhetorics of Change: North American Business Schools after the Second World War. 2011. (ENG.). 376p. 45.00 *(978-0-8047-7616-5(4)*, Stanford Business Bks.) Stanford Univ. Pr.

Baier, Gundolf & Günther, Gabriele, eds. Aktuelle Herausforderungen der Betriebswirtschaft: Jahrbuch 2008 des Instituts für Betriebswirtschaft der Westsächsischen Hochschule Zwickau. 2008. (Jahrbuch des Instituts für Betriebswirtschaft der Westsächsischen Hochschule Zwickau Ser.). 184p. pap. 52.95 *(978-3-631-57916-9(0))* Lang, Peter GmbH, Europäischer Verlag der Wissenschaften DEU. Dist: Lang, Peter.

Bhandarker, Asha. Shaping Business Leaders: What B-Schools Don't Do. 2008. 240p. (C). pap. 27.50 *(978-81-7829-845-0(7)*, B98450P) SAGE Pubns., Inc.

BIA. Leading Business Schools & Business Libraries. 6th rev. ed. 2006. 350p. (J). pap. 249.00 *(978-1-4187-4390-1(9))* Business Information Agency.

—Leading Business Schools & Business Libraries of the USA. 6th rev. ed. 2006. 350p. (J). pap. 249.00 *(978-1-4187-4439-7(5))* Business Information Agency.

Blackman, Stacy & Brookings, Daniel J. The MBA Application Roadmap: The Essential Guide to Getting into a Top Business School. 2008. 256p. pap. 29.95 *(978-0-912301-89-1(9))* First Bks.

Bodine, Paul. Great Applications for Business School. 2nd ed. 2010. (ENG., Illus.). 256p. (C). pap. 13.00 *(978-0-07-174655-7(2)*, 0071746552) McGraw-Hill Cos., The.

—Perfect Phrases for Business School Acceptance. 2008. (Perfect Phrases Ser.). (ENG.). 272p. (C). pap. 9.95 *(978-0-07-159820-0(0)*, 0071598200) McGraw-Hill Cos., The.

Brc. The Brc Journal of Advances in Education: Vol. 1, No. 2. 2011. 126p. pap. 12.00 ***(978-1-60497-771-4(X))*** Cambria Pr.

Connolly, Arlene. 101 Ways to Score Higher on Your GMAT: What You Need to Know about the Graduate Management Admission Test Explained Simply. 2008. (ENG.). 288p. (C). pap. 21.95 *(978-1-60138-252-8(9))* Atlantic Publishing Co.

Datar, Srikant, et al. Rethinking the MBA: Business Education at a Crossroads. 2010. (ENG., Illus.). 400p. 39.95 *(978-1-4221-3164-0(5))* Harvard Business Review Pr.

Dowhan, Chris, et al. Essays That Will Get You into Business School. 3rd rev. ed. 2009. (Essays That Will Get You intoacirc;€brkbar; Ser.). (ENG.). 192p. pap. 13.99 *(978-0-7641-4228-4(3))* Barron's Educational Series, Inc.

Durand, Thomas & Dameron, Stephanie. The Future of Business Schools: Scenarios & Strategies for 2020. Durand, Thomas & Dameron, Stephanie, eds. 2008. (ENG., Illus.). 240p. 89.00 *(978-0-230-51548-2(7))* Palgrave Macmillan.

Forster, Evan & Thomas, David. The MBA Reality Check: Make the School You Want, Want You. 2010. (ENG.). 336p. (gr. 12-18). 20.00 *(978-0-7352-0448-5(9))* Prentice Hall Pr.

Genetski, Robert. Classical Economic Principles & the Wealth of Nations: Book I. 2011. (ENG.). 120p. 19.99 ***(978-1-60746-389-4(X))*** FastPencil, Inc.

Golosinski, Matt. Wide Awake in the Windy City: Celebrating a Century of Excellence at Northwestern University's Kellogg School of Management, 1908-2008. Honack, Richard P., ed. 2008. (ENG., Illus.). 332p. 34.95 *(978-0-8101-2504-9(8))* Northwestern Univ. Pr.

Gordon, Avi. MBA Admissions Strategy: From profile building to essay Writing. 2nd ed. 2010. (ENG., Illus.). 240p. (C). pap. 30.00 *(978-0-335-24117-0(4)*, 0335241174) McGraw-Hill Education GBR. Dist: McGraw-Hill Cos., The.

Gorman, Tom, MBA. MBA Basics - The Complete Idiot's Guide. 3rd ed. 2011. (Complete Idiot's Guide Ser.). (ENG.). 464p. (gr. 12). 21.95 *(978-1-61564-071-3(1)*, Alpha Bks.) Penguin Group (USA) Inc.

Hightower, et al. School of Business & Industry Superstars: Florida A & M University. 2008. (ENG.). (C). pap. 36.60 *(978-0-555-03657-0(X))* Pearson Learning Solutions.

Iñiguez de Onzoño, Santiago. The Learning Curve: How Business Schools Are Re-inventing Education. 2011. (IE Business Publishing Ser.). (ENG., Illus.). 256p. 42.00 *(978-0-230-28023-6(4))* Palgrave Macmillan.

Isiadinso, Chioma. The Best Business Schools: A Former Harvard Business School Admissions Board Member Reveals the Insider Keys to Getting In. 2008. (ENG.). 336p. pap. 17.95 *(978-1-4022-1213-0(5))* Sourcebooks, Inc.

Lavelle, Louis. The Best B-Schools: Full-Time, Part-Time, & Executive MBA Programs. 2008. (ENG.). 420p. (C). per. 18.95 *(978-0-07-149653-7(X)*, 007149653X) McGraw-Hill Cos., The.

Lorange, Peter. Thought Leadership Meets Business: How Business Schools Can Become More Successful. 2008. (ENG., Illus.). 262p. 48.00 *(978-0-521-89722-8(X))* Cambridge Univ. Pr.

Montauk, Richard, JD. How to Get into the Top MBA Programs. 5th ed. 2010. (ENG.). 640p. (gr. 12). 30.00 *(978-0-7352-0450-8(0))* Prentice Hall Pr.

Montauk, Richard. How to Get into the Top MBA Programs. 6th Edition. 2012. (ENG.). 640p. (gr. 12). 30.00 ***(978-0-7352-0466-9(7))*** Prentice Hall Pr.

Mujtaba, Bahaudin G., et al. The State of Business Schools: Educational & Moral Imperatives for Market Leaders. 2009. 146p. pap. 16.95 *(978-1-936237-00-5(8))* ILEAD Academy, LLC.

Nilsson, Kristina & Bild, Magnus. Teaching & Learning at Business Schools: Transforming Business Education. Mårtensson, Pär, ed. 2008. (Illus.). 330p. 99.95 *(978-0-566-08820-9(7)*, Gower Publishing Co., Ltd.) Ashgate Publishing, Ltd. GBR. Dist: Ashgate Publishing Co.

O'Connor, Ellen. Creating New Knowledge in Management: Appropriating the Field's Lost Foundations. 2011. (ENG.). 264p. 55.00 ***(978-0-8047-7075-0(1)***, Stanford Business Bks.) Stanford Univ. Pr.

Petersam, David. Top MBA Programs. 2009. (ENG.). 512p. pap. 24.95 *(978-1-59357-673-8(0)*, JIST Works) JIST Publishing.

Peterson's. MBA Programs: More Than 4,000 Graduate-Level International Business Programs. Snider, Mark D., ed. 15th ed. 2009. (ENG.). 928p. (YA). 44.95 *(978-0-7689-2704-7(8))* Peterson's.

—Peterson's MBA Programs 2009. DeAngelis, Therese, ed. 14th ed. 2008. (ENG.). 928p. 42.95 *(978-0-7689-2553-1(3))* Peterson's.

Peterson's Guides Staff. MBA Programs 2008. Seghers, Linda, ed. 13th ed. 2007. (ENG.). 962p. 42.00 *(978-0-7689-2411-4(1))* Peterson's.

Peterson's Guides Staff, creator. Peterson's MBA Programs. 12th ed. 2006. (ENG., Illus.). 962p. pap. 42.00 *(978-0-7689-2161-8(9))* Peterson's.

Princeton Review. The Best 294 Business Schools, 2013 Edition. 2012. (Graduate School Admissions Guides). (ENG.). 784p. pap. 22.99 ***(978-0-307-94531-0(6)***, Princeton Review) Random Hse. Information Group.

—Business School Essays That Made a Difference, 5th Edition. 2012. (Graduate School Admissions Guides). (ENG.). 304p. pap. 13.99 ***(978-0-307-94523-5(5)***, Princeton Review) Random Hse. Information Group.

Princeton Review Staff. The Best 294 Business Schools 2012. 2011. (Graduate School Admissions Guides). (ENG.). 784p. pap. 22.99 *(978-0-375-42740-4(6)*, Princeton Review) Random Hse. Information Group.

—Business School Essays That Made a Difference. 4th ed. 2010. (Graduate School Admissions Guides). (ENG.). 304p. pap. 13.99 *(978-0-375-42784-8(8)*, Princeton Review) Random Hse. Information Group.

Richards, David L. One Northwoood: The First Fifty Years. 2009. vii, 168p. *(978-0-578-01389-3(4))* Northwood Univ. Pr.

Royal, Brandon. Secrets to Getting into Business School: 100 Proven Admissions Strategies to Get You Accepted at the MBA Program of Your Dreams. 2010. (ENG.). 308p. *(978-1-897393-80-2(6))* Maven Publishing.

Sauquet Rovira, Alfons & Morsing, Mette. Business Schools & their Contribution to Society. 2011. 280p. (C). 130.00 ***(978-0-85702-386-5(1)***, B23865C); pap. 59.00 ***(978-0-85702-387-2(X)***, B23865P) SAGE Pubns., Ltd. GBR. Dist: SAGE Pubns., Inc.

Shinewald, Jeremy. The Complete Start-to-Finish MBA Admissions Guide. 2010. (ENG.). 256p. pap. 24.00 *(978-1-935707-00-4(0))* Manhattan Prep Publishing.

Starkey, Ken & Tiratsoo, Nick. The Business School & the Bottom Line. 2007. (ENG., Illus.). 252p. 46.99 *(978-0-521-86511-1(5))* Cambridge Univ. Pr.

Sullivan, Lauren & Harbus Staff. 65 Successful Harvard Business School Application Essays: With Analysis by the Staff of the Harbus, the Harvard Business School Newspaper. 2nd ed. 2009. (ENG.). 240p. pap. 14.99 *(978-0-312-55007-3(3)*, St. Martin's Griffin) St. Martin's Pr.

Tanabe & Tanabe, Kelly. Accepted! 50 Successful Business School Admission Essays. 3rd ed. 2010. (ENG.). 224p. pap. 14.95 *(978-1-932662-47-4(2))* SuperCollege LLC.

Williams, Allan P.O., ed. The History of UK Business & Management Education. 2010. (Illus.). 160p. 91.95 *(978-1-84950-780-6(5))* Emerald Group Publishing Ltd. GBR. Dist: Turpin Distribution Services Ltd.

BUSINESS SPANISH

see Spanish Language—Business Spanish

BUSINESS STABILIZATION

see Economic Stabilization

BUSINESS TAX

Here are entered works on a form of tax, largely European, levied on commercial establishments by volume of business, such as the German Gewerbesteuer or the French Patentes.

Bahramsari, Parastu. Zur Persönlichen Zuordnung Von Betriebsausgaben und Werbungskosten Im Einkommensteuerrecht: Drittaufwand und Verwandte Erscheinungen. 2011. (Schriften zum Wirtschafts- und Medienrecht, Steuerrecht und Zivilprozeßrecht Ser.). (GER.). 170p. 57.95 *(978-3-631-61283-5(4))* Lang, Peter GmbH, Europaischer Verlag der Wissenschaften DEU. Dist: Lang, Peter.

Bertram, David, ed. Butterworths Business Tax Service. (Illus.). ring bd. *(978-0-406-99863-7(9)*, BBTSASET, MICHIE) LEXIS Publishing.

Davison, John. VAT & Small Businesses. 2011. 96p. pap. 99.95 *(978-1-904905-59-2(5))* Spiramus Pr. GBR. Dist: International Specialized Bk. Services.

Edwards, Chris & Mitchell, Daniel J. Global Tax Revolution: The Rise of Tax Competition & the Battle to Defend It. 2008. (ENG.). 250p. 21.95 *(978-1-933995-18-2(1))* Cato Institute.

Elisha, Simon. Taxes for Online Sellers: A How-to Guide for Individuals on Federal Tax for Internet Sales. 2007. 168p. per. 19.95 *(978-0-9796328-0-8(3))* Artistic Spaces Publishing Co.

Fishman, Stephen, abr. Home Business Tax Deductions: Keep What You Earn. 8th rev. ed. 2011. (ENG.). 496p. pap. 34.99 *(978-1-4133-1639-1(5))* NOLO.

Gell, Marjorie & Wayne D, Roberts. Practical Guide to the Michigan Business Tax. 2009th ed. 2009. 400p. pap. 99.00 *(978-0-8080-2237-4(7))* Toolkit Media Group.

How Business Tax Reform Can Encourage Job Creation: Hearing Before the Committee on Ways & Means, U.S. House of Representatives, One Hundred Twelfth Congress, First Session, June 2, 2011. 2011. (Illus.). iii, 119p. ***(978-0-16-090151-5(0)***, 552-070-43854-8) United States Government Printing Office.

Johnson, Kevin. Legal Issues in Business. rev. ed. 2008. (ENG.). 394p. pap. 116.47 *(978-0-7575-5515-2(2))* Kendall Hunt Publishing Co.

Jones, Chris. Principles of Business Taxation: Finance Act 2006. 3rd ed. 2007. (CIMA Exam Support Bks.). (ENG.). 640p. (C). per. 89.95 *(978-0-7506-8457-6(7)*, CIMA Publishing) Elsevier Science & Technology Bks.

Kamoroff, C.P.A., Bernard B. 422 Tax Deductions for Businesses & Self Employed Individuals. 7th ed. 2008. (422 Tax Deductions for Businesses & Self-Employed Individuals Ser.). (Illus.). 232p. per. 18.95 *(978-0-917510-26-7(7))* Bell Springs Publishing.

Lessambo, Felix I. Taxation of International Business Transactions. 2009. 360p. pap. 25.95 *(978-0-595-53252-0(7))* iUniverse, Inc.

Marius, Styczen. The Past, Present & the Future for Financial Centers in Belgium: A Comprehensive Case Study of the Tax & Business Environment for Financial Centers in Belgium. 2011. 112p. pap. ***(978-3-639-32483-9(8))*** VDM Verlag Dr. Mueller e.K.

Pace, Ryan. A Conceptual Approach to Business Entity Taxation. 2nd rev. ed. 2011. (ENG.). 376p. pap. 78.00 ***(978-0-7575-9154-9(X))*** Kendall Hunt Publishing Co.

Penn, Ana D. & Arias, Martha L. Global E-Business Law & Taxation. 2009. (ENG., Illus.). 560p. 235.00 *(978-0-19-536721-8(9))* Oxford Univ. Pr., Inc.

Piper, Mike. Surprisingly Simple: Independent Contractor, Sole Proprietor, & LLC Taxes Explained in 100 Pages or Less. 2010. (ENG.). 108p. pap. 11.10 *(978-0-615-15843-3(9))* Simple Subjects, LLC.

—Surprisingly Simple: LLC vs. S-Corp vs. C-Corp Explained in 100 Pages or Less. 2010. (Illus.). 108p. pap. 11.10 *(978-0-9814542-0-7(8))* Simple Subjects, LLC.

Professional Edition SWFT Taxation of Business Entities 2012. 15th ed. 2011. 912p. (C). pap. 234.95 *(978-0-538-47960-8(4))* Cengage South-Western.

Rawal, Radhakishan. The Taxation of Permanent Establishments: An International Perspective. 2006. 551p. (C). pap. 135.00 *(978-1-904905-45-5(5))* Spiramus Pr. GBR. Dist: International Specialized Bk. Services.

Renfeld, Lars. Die Vereinbarkeit des Außensteuergesetzes mit den Grundfreiheiten des EG-Vertrags. 2008. (Bochumer Schriften zum Steuerrecht Ser.). 540p. pap. 124.95 *(978-3-631-58097-4(5))* Lang, Peter GmbH, Europaischer Verlag der Wissenschaften DEU. Dist: Lang, Peter.

Savage, Robert L. Rendering unto Caesar: The Fairest Tax. 2011. pap. 11.99 ***(978-1-61346-314-7(6))*** Tate Publishing & Enterprises, LLC.

Schön, Wolfgang, et al, eds. A Common Consolidated Corporate Tax Base for Europe - Eine Einheitliche Körperschaftsteuerbemessungsgrundlage Für Europa. 2010. (ENG & GER.). xvi, 183p. pap. 129.00 *(978-3-642-09842-0(8)*, 3642098428) Springer.

Smith, James E., et al. South-Western Federal Taxation 2010: Taxation of Business Entities, Professional Version. 13th ed. 2009. (ENG.). 912p. (C). 225.95 *(978-0-324-82860-3(8))* Cengage South-Western.

—South-Western Federal Taxation 2010 Vol. 4: Taxation of Business Entities. 13th ed. 2009. (ENG.). (C). 210.95 *(978-0-324-82858-0(6))* Cengage South-Western.

—South-Western Federal Taxation 2011 Vol. 4: Taxation of Business Entities. 14th ed. 2010. (ENG.). 928p. (C). 234.95 *(978-0-538-78621-8(3))* Cengage South-Western.

Spilker, et al. Loose-leaf taxation of business entities 2012 Edition. 3rd ed. 2011. (ENG., Illus.). (C). ring bd. 181.33 ***(978-0-07-750954-5(4)***, 0077509544, McGraw-Hill/Irwin) McGraw-Hill Higher Education.

Spilker, Brian, et al. Loose-leaf Taxation of Individuals & Business Entities 2011 Edition. 2nd ed. 2010. (ENG.). (C). ring bd. 170.00 *(978-0-07-742064-2(0)*, 0077420640, McGraw-Hill/Irwin) McGraw-Hill Higher Education.

Ssewanyana, Joseph K. Microsimulation Modeling of Ict Policies at Firm Level. 2011. 104p. pap. ***(978-3-8443-2341-2(4))*** Lambert Academic Publishing.

State Taxation: The Role of Congress in Defining Nexus: Hearing Before the Subcommittee on Commercial & Administrative Law of the Committee on the Judiciary, House of Representatives, One Hundred Eleventh Congress, Second Session, February 4, 2010. 2010. iv, 257p. *(978-0-16-085815-4(1)*, 552-070-41032-5) United States Government Printing Office.

Zeus, Alexander. External Intervention in Foreign Exchange Markets. 2008. 80p. pap. *(978-3-639-01176-0(7))* VDM Verlag Dr. Mueller e.K.

Zuschlag, Daniela. Die pauschalierte Gewerbesteueranrechnung nach § 35 EStG. 2009. (Bochumer Schriften zum Steuerrecht Ser.). (GRE.). 370p. pap. 81.95 *(978-3-631-58549-8(7))* Lang, Peter GmbH, Europaischer Verlag der Wissenschaften DEU. Dist: Lang, Peter.

BUSINESS TO BUSINESS ADVERTISING

see Advertising, Industrial

BUSINESS TO BUSINESS MARKETING

see Industrial Marketing

BUSINESS TO BUSINESS SELLING

see Industrial Marketing

BUSINESS TRAVEL

Arrache, Kathleen. The Woman Road Warrior: The Expert's Guide to Domestic & International Business Travel. 2nd ed. 2007. (ENG., Illus.). 210p. per. 14.00 *(978-1-932841-25-1(3))* Agate Publishing, Inc.

Ast, Scott Alan. Managing Security Overseas: Protecting Employees & Assets in Volatile Regions. 2009. (ENG., Illus.). 366p. 87.95 *(978-1-4398-0467-4(2))* Auerbach Pubs., Inc.

Axtell, Roger E. Essential Do's & Taboos: The Complete Guide to International Business & Leisure Travel. 2007. (ENG., Illus.). 308p. pap. 16.95 *(978-0-471-74050-6(0)*, Wiley) Wiley, John & Sons, Inc.

Blacharski, Dan. The Savvy Business Traveler's Guide to Customs & Practices in Other Countries: The Dos & Don'ts to Impress Your Host & Make the Sale. 2008. (ENG., Illus.). 288p. per. 24.95 *(978-1-60138-013-5(5))* Atlantic Publishing Co.

Cannon, James & Richey, Franklin D. Practical Applications in Business Aviation Management. 2011. (ENG.). (C). (gr. 13-17). 320p. 99.00 ***(978-1-60590-763-5(4))***; 384p. pap. 50.00 ***(978-1-60590-770-3(7))*** Government Institutes.

Cannon, James R. & Richey, Franklin D. Practical Applications in Business Aviation Management. 2011. ***(978-1-60590-764-2(2))*** Government Institutes.

Chaddock, David. Qatar: The Business Traveller's Handbook. 2nd ed. 2008. 199p. per. 20.00 *(978-1-56656-697-1(5))* Interlink Publishing Group, Inc.

—Qatar 2008. 3rd ed. 2008. (Illus.). 168p. 63.95 *(978-1-905299-90-4(7)*, Stacey International) Stacey Publishing GBR. Dist: Midpoint Trade Bks., Inc.

Cornello, Luca & De Toni, Alberto F. Journey into Complexity. 2010. 125p. pap. 21.50 *(978-1-4452-6078-5(6))* Lulu Enterprises Inc.

Craighead's Country Reports: 1993 Edition. 95.00 *(978-0-945994-00-8(1))* Craighead, Inc.

DesChamps, Barbara. It's in the Bag: Your Business & Travel Wardrobe. 2008. (Illus.). 128p. pap. 13.95 *(978-0-9710525-2-9(2))* Chateau Publishing.

Duke, William Marshall & Schatz, Rick, compiled by. On the Road: Meditations for Men Who Travel. 2009. (ENG.). 224p. pap. 14.99 *(978-0-8341-2460-8(2)*, 9780834124608) Beacon Hill Pr. of Kansas City.

Enoch, Marcus. Sustainable, Transport, Mobility, Management & Travel Plans. 2012. (Transport & Mobility Ser.). (Illus.). 200p. 99.95 ***(978-0-7546-7939-4(X))*** Ashgate Publishing Co.

Finden, Susan. Casper the Commuting Cat: The True Story of the Cat Who Rode the Bus & Stole our Hearts. 2011. (ENG., Illus.). 232p. pap. 12.95 ***(978-1-84983-175-8(0))*** Simon & Schuster, Ltd. GBR. Dist: Independent Pubs. Group.

Goldstuck, Arthur & Ambrose, Steven. Mobile Office: The Essential Small Business Guide to Office Technology. 2009. 80p. pap. 6.95 *(978-0-7021-7964-8(7))* Double Storey Bks. ZAF. Dist: International Publishers Marketing.

Manzullo, Donald A., ed. The Visa Approval Backlog & its Impact on American Small Business: Congressional Hearing. 2006. (Illus.). 109p. (C). reprint ed. pap. 30.00 *(978-1-4223-0629-1(1))* DIANE Publishing Co.

McCormack, Mark H. Hit the Ground Running: The Insider's Guide to Executive Travel. 268p. pap. 14.00 *(978-1-878843-09-8(5))* International Management Group (International Merchandising Corporation).

Neuhaus, Karsta & Haltem, Margaret, eds. Business Companions: France. 2nd ed. (Illus.). 320p. pap. *(978-0-304-33116-1(3)*, Burns & Oates) Continuum International Publishing Group, Ltd.

—Business Companions: Germany. 2nd ed. (ENG & GER., Illus.). 320p. pap. *(978-0-304-33115-4(5)*, Burns & Oates) Continuum International Publishing Group, Ltd.

Peters, James. The Arab World. 3rd ed. 2009. (ARA & ENG., Illus.). 150p. pap., instr.'s hndbk. ed. 18.95 ***(978-1-906768-03-4(X)***, Stacey International) Stacey Publishing GBR. Dist: Midpoint Trade Bks., Inc.

Quinn, Edward & Smith, John E. Executive Escapes Holiday. 2008. (ENG.). 24.95 *(978-3-8327-9268-8(6))* teNeues Publishing Co.

Shuler, Barry L. Virtual Travel: Embrace or Expire. 2010. 220p. 27.95 *(978-1-4502-4451-0(3))*; (ENG.). pap. 17.95 *(978-1-4502-4452-7(1))* iUniverse, Inc.

Tarolli, John. Road Warriors: Turning Business Travel into Exciting Adventures! 2008. 92p. pap. 34.95 (978-1-4343-4791-6(5)) AuthorHouse.

Teasdale, Malcolm. Travel Diaries of an Atypical Businessman: Conducting Business in Foreign Lands. 2009. 212p. pap. 17.95 (978-0-595-48382-2(8)) iUniverse, Inc.

Tomor, Veronica. L E a N Guide for the Business Traveler: (Living Educated about Nutrition on the GO) 2011. 140p. 29.99 (978-1-4535-9700-2(X)); pap. 19.99 (978-1-4535-9699-9(2)) Xlibris Corp.

Vaidya, Kalyan. Not for $ Anymore. 2010. 143p. pap. (978-81-223-1114-3(8)) Mahal, Pustak Pubs., Booksellers & Order Suppliers.

Wallpaper Magazine Editors. Business, 5 vols., Set. 2008. (ENG., Illus.). pap., instr.'s gde. ed. 49.75 (978-0-7148-5588-2(X)) Phaidon Pr., Inc.

Wilson, Tom. Where's Wilson? 2011. 286p. pap. 16.99 (978-1-932503-97-5(8)) Insight Publishing Group.

Witlox, Frank. International Business Travel in the Global Economy. Derudder, Ben et al, eds. 2010. (Transport & Mobility Ser.). (Illus.). 268p. 124.95 (978-0-7546-7942-4(X)) Ashgate Publishing Co.

BUSINESSOWNERS' INSURANCE

see Business Insurance

BUSINESS TRIPS

see Business Travel

BUSINESS WRITING

see also Business Report Writing; Commercial Correspondence; English Language—Business English; Proposal Writing in Business

Ahern, Tom. How to Write Fundraising Materials that Raise More Money: The Art, the Science, the Secrets. 2007. per. 24.95 (978-1-889102-31-3(8)) Emerson & Church, Pubs.

Alnoor, Alnoor F. The Ambit Technique: An Innovative Approach to Business Writing. 2009. (ENG.). pap. 22.00 (978-1-58982-540-6(3), American Business Pr.) American Bk. Publishing Group.

Alred, Gerald J., et al. The Business Writer's Companion. 6th ed. 2010. (ENG.). 480p. (C). spiral bd. 35.95 (978-0-312-63132-1(4)) Bedford/Saint Martin's.

—The Business Writer's Handbook. (ENG.). (C). 9th ed. 2008. 624p. spiral bd. 46.95 (978-0-312-47709-7(0)) 10th ed. 2011. 656p. spiral bd. 46.95 (978-0-312-67943-9(2)) Bedford/Saint Martin's.

—The Business Writer's Handbook. 10th rev. ed. 2011. (ENG.). 624p. 47.99 (978-1-250-00442-0(X)) St. Martin's Pr.

Alred, Gerald J., et al. The Business Writer's Handbook, Ninth Edition. 9th rev. ed. 2008. (ENG.). 624p. 44.95 (978-0-312-57510-6(6)) St. Martin's Pr.

Andrus, Carol. Fat-Free Writing: Write for the Information Age. 2nd ed. 2011. (ENG.). 106p. pap. 14.95 (978-1-4260-1958-6(0)) Thomson NETg.

Appleman, Jack E. 10 Steps to Successful Business Writing. 2008. (10 Steps Ser.). (ENG.). 150p. per. 19.95 (978-1-56286-481-1(5)) American Society for Training & Development.

Atkinson, Ian. Essential Guide Business Writing: How to Write to Engage, Persuade & Sell. rev. ed. 2011. (ENG., Illus.). 184p. pap. 24.99 (978-0-273-76113-6(7)) FT Press.

Atlantic Publishing Group. How to Write Your Own Effective Employee Handbook in 1 Hour or Less: With Microsoft Word - Compatible Template. 2012. (ENG.). 288p. pap. 29.95 (978-1-60138-630-4(3)) Atlantic Publishing Co.

Bailey, Bill. A Thinker's Guide to Effective Writing. 2007. 160p. 25.00 (978-0-9793626-0-6(1)) Echo Mountain Pr.

Bailey, Edward P. Writing & Speaking at Work. 5th rev. ed. 2010. (ENG., Illus.). 240p. (C). pap. 106.67 (978-0-13-608855-4(4), Prentice Hall) Prentice Hall PTR.

Bailey, Stephen. Academic Writing for International Students of Business. 2010. (ENG., Illus.). 336p. (C). pap. 39.95 (978-0-415-56471-7(9)); 130.00 (978-0-415-56470-0(0)) Routledge.

Barcharts, creator. Learn Intro to Business Technical Writing, Resume Writing, Typing. 2009. (QuickTrain: Computer Based Training Ser.). cd-rom 19.95 (978-1-4232-0128-1(0)) Barcharts, Inc.

Bass, Andrew. The Performance Papers - incisive briefings for busy Leaders. 2011. (ENG.). 230p. (978-1-907498-70-1(2)); pap. (978-1-907498-71-8(0)) Lean Marketing Pr. (Book Shaker).

Benjamin, Susan F. Quick & Painless Business Writing: An Essential Guide to Clear & Powerful Communication. 2006. (ENG.). 1p. per. 14.99 (978-1-56414-900-8(5)) Career Pr., Inc.

Blakesley, David & Hoogeveen, Jeffrey L. The Brief Thomson Handbook. 2007. (Available Titles CengageNOW Ser.). (ENG., Illus.). 624p. (C). pap. 86.95 (978-1-4130-1016-9(4)) Cengage Heinle.

Bly, Robert W. & Kelly, Regina Anne. The Encyclopedia of Business Letters, Faxes, & Emails. rev. ed. 2009. (ENG.). 1p. pap. 19.99 (978-1-60163-029-2(8)) Career Pr., Inc.

Bodine, Paul. Great Applications for Business School. 2nd ed. 2010. (ENG., Illus.). 256p. (C). pap. 13.00 (978-0-07-174655-7(2), 0071746552) McGraw-Hill Cos., The.

Borrowman, Shane. The Cost of Business. 2010. (Longman Topics Ser.). (ENG.). 224p. (C). pap. 23.60 (978-0-205-56294-7(9)) Longman Publishing Group.

Bovee, Courtland & Thill, John V. Business Communication Essentials. 4th ed. 2008. (ENG.). 528p. (C). pap. 146.67 (978-0-13-608441-9(9), Prentice Hall) Prentice Hall PTR.

Bovée, Courtland L. & Thill, John V. Business Communication Essentials. 5th rev. ed. 2010. (ENG.). 528p. (C). pap. 146.67 (978-0-13-253971-5(3), Prentice Hall) Prentice Hall PTR.

Bowser, David W. The Big Picture: A successful business Application. 2008. per. 15.00 (978-1-59872-932-0(2)) Instant Pub.

Brantley & Miller, Toby. Aie Effective Communication for Colleges. 11th ed. 2007. (C). pap. 33.95 (978-0-324-54336-0(0)) Cengage South-Western.

Brantley, Clarice Pennebaker & Miller, Michele Goulet. Effective Communication for Colleges. 11th ed. 2007. (ENG., Illus.). 496p. (C). pap. 174.95 (978-0-324-37476-6(3)) Cengage South-Western.

Brimeyer, James L. Taming the Writing Tiger: A handbook for business Writers. 2nd ed. 2007. pap. 11.50 (978-1-60174-030-4(1), Uncial Pr.) GCT, Inc.

Buckley, Earle A. How to Write Better Business Letters. 2007. (ENG.). 220p. per. (978-1-4067-1051-9(2)) Read Bks.

Butterfield, Jeff. Written Communication, Oral Communication, & Presentation Skills. 2009. (ENG.). (C). 12.95 (978-1-4390-4117-8(2)) Course Technology.

Camp, Lindsay. Can I Change Your Mind? The Craft & Art of Persuasive Writing. 2007. (ENG.). 256p. per. 14.95 (978-0-7136-7849-9(6)) A & C Black GBR. Dist: Macmillan.

Camp, Sue C. & Satterwhite, Marilyn L. College English & Communication. 9th ed. 2007. (Illus.). xvii, 638p. (978-0-07-310651-9(8)) McGraw-Hill Cos., The.

—College English & Communication. 9th ed. 2006. (ENG.). (C). pap. 144.67 (978-0-07-331793-9(4), 0073317934) McGraw-Hill Higher Education.

Canavor, Natalie & Meirowitz, Claire. The Truth about the New Rules of Business Writing. 2009. (Truth About Ser.). (ENG.). 224p. pap. 20.99 (978-0-13-715315-2(5)) FT Press.

Century College English Department Staff. Composition Guide. rev. ed. 2010. 118p. pap. 23.90 (978-0-7575-8142-7(0)) Kendall Hunt Publishing Co.

Clift, Edward M. How Language Is Used to Do Business: Essays on the Rhetoric of Economics. 2008. (Illus.). 476p. 129.95 (978-0-7734-5143-8(9)) Mellen, Edwin Pr., The.

Collins, Stella & Curl, Beth. Writing Skills Pocketbook. 2012. (Illus.). 112p. pap. (978-1-906610-45-6(2)) Management Pocketbooks GBR. Dist: Ware-Pak, Inc.

Cram, Carol M. New Perspectives: Portfolio Projects for Business Communication. 2nd ed. 2009. (New Perspectives Ser.). (ENG.). 304p. pap. 82.95 (978-1-4390-3746-1(9)) Course Technology.

Cram101 Textbook Reviews. Outlines & Highlights for Business Communication: Process & Product by Mary Ellen Guffey. 2011. 352p. pap. 33.95 (978-1-61906-120-0(1)) Cram101 Inc.

—Outlines & Highlights for Business Communication: Process & Product by Mary Guffey, ISBN. 2011. 266p. pap. 31.95 (978-1-61461-862-1(3)) Cram101 Inc.

—Outlines & Highlights for Business Communication by Thomas Means. 2011. 408p. pap. 35.95 (978-1-61906-161-3(9)) Cram101 Inc.

—Outlines & Highlights for Effective Communication for Colleges by Clarice Pennebaker Brantley, Isbn: 9780324374766. 2010. 76p. pap. 27.95 (978-1-61698-003-0(6)) Cram101 Inc.

—Outlines & Highlights for Essentials of Business Communication by Mary Ellen Guffey. 2011. 368p. pap. 34.95 (978-1-61906-082-1(5)) Cram101 Inc.

—Outlines & Highlights for Workplace Communication by Steven M Gerson, Isbn: 0132288087 9780132288088. 2011. 78p. pap. 27.95 (978-1-61812-511-8(7)) Cram101 Inc.

Cram101 Textbook Reviews & Cram101 Textbook Reviews. Outlines & Highlights for Business Communication Essentials by Courtland L Bovee. 2011. 442p. pap. 36.95 (978-1-61830-555-8(7)) Cram101 Inc.

—Outlines & Highlights for Contemporary Business Communications by Scot Ober, Isbn: 0618472525 9780618472529. 2011. 90p. pap. 27.95 (978-1-61461-583-5(7)) Cram101 Inc.

—Outlines & Highlights for Strategic Writing: Multimedia Writing for Public Relations, Advertising, & More by Charles Marsh. 2011. 122p. pap. 28.95 (978-1-61830-182-6(9)) Cram101 Inc.

—Outlines & Highlights for Workplace Communications: Basics by George J. Searles, ISBN. 2011. 70p. pap. 27.95 (978-1-61490-466-3(9)) Cram101 Inc.

Curry, Jane & Young, Diana. Be a Brilliant Business Writer: Write Well, Write Fast, & Whip the Competition. 2010. (ENG., Illus.). 224p. pap. 13.99 (978-1-58008-222-8(X)) Ten Speed Pr.

Davin, Doug & Morris, Diana. Words that Work: Business Writing at Its Best. 2009. 192p. pap. 14.95 (978-1-891019-27-2(9)) New Heights Media, Inc.,.

Davis, Kenneth. Business Writing & Communication. 2nd ed. 2010. (McGraw-Hill 36-Hour Courses Ser.). (ENG., Illus.). 256p. pap. 19.95 (978-0-07-173826-2(6), 0071738266) McGraw-Hill Cos., The.

DeThomas, Arthur R. & Derammelaere, Stephanie A. Writing a Convincing Business Plan. 3rd rev. ed. 2008. (Barron's Business Library Ser.). (ENG.). 272p. pap. 18.99 (978-0-7641-3934-5(7)) Barron's Educational Series, Inc.

Diamond, Harriet & Diamond, Linda Eve. Writing Company Announcements: Hundreds of Ready-to-Use Phrases for Powerful Internal & External Communications. 2010. (Perfect Phrases Ser.). (ENG.). 224p. pap. 10.95 (978-0-07-163452-6(5), 0071634525) McGraw-Hill Cos., The.

Diamond, Linda. Executive Writing American Style. 2007. pap. 16.95 (978-1-933993-17-1(0)) Apocryphile Pr.

Duo, Henri. How to Start a Letter in 100 Different Expressions & 135 Letter Examples. 2011. 160p. pap. 19.99 (978-1-4653-4777-0(1)) Xlibris Corp.

Economist Books Staff. The Economist Style Guide. 10th ed. 2010. (Economist Ser.). (ENG., Illus.). 272p. 26.95 (978-1-84668-175-2(8), Wiley) Wiley, John & Sons, Inc.

Ellison, Pat Taylor. Business English for the 21st Century. 4th ed. 2007. (978-0-13-174291-8(4)) Prentice Hall PTR.

Ettinger, Blanche & Perfetto, Edda L. Business English: Writing in the Workplace. 4th ed. 2006. (ENG.). 416p. per. 99.40 (978-0-13-156570-8(2), Prentice Hall) Prentice Hall PTR.

Fayard, Anne-Laure & Metiu, Anca. Beyond the New Media: The Power of Writing & Organizational Communication. 2012. (Series in Organization & Management Ser.). (ENG., Illus.). 240p. 51.95 (978-0-415-88256-9(7), Routledge) Taylor & Francis Group GBR. Dist: Taylor & Francis Group.

Finch, Brian. How to Write a Business Plan. 3rd rev. ed. 2010. (Creating Success Ser.). (ENG.). 184p. pap. 14.95 (978-0-7494-6030-3(X)); (Illus.). 160p. pap. 14.95 (978-0-7494-5582-8(9)) Kogan Page, Ltd. GBR. Dist: Ingram Pub. Services.

Flood, Timothy. MBA Fundamentals Business Writing. 2008. (Kaplan MBA Fundamentals Ser.). (ENG., Illus.). 224p. pap. 19.95 (978-1-4277-9717-9(X)) Kaplan Publishing.

Forsyth, Patrick. Effective Business Writing. 2009. (Creating Success Ser.). (ENG.). 160p. pap. 17.95 (978-0-7494-5453-1(9)) Kogan Page, Ltd. GBR. Dist: Ingram Pub. Services.

—How to Write Reports & Proposals. 2nd rev. ed. 2010. (Creating Success Ser.). (ENG., Illus.). 128p. pap. 14.95 (978-0-7494-6032-7(6)) Kogan Page, Ltd. GBR. Dist: Ingram Pub. Services.

Foster, Jack. How to Get Ideas. 2nd rev. ed. 2007. (BK Life Ser.). (ENG., Illus.). 214p. pap. 20.95 (978-1-57675-430-6(8)) Berrett-Koehler Pubs., Inc.

Foster, John. Effective Writing Skills for Public Relations. 4th ed. 2008. (PR in Practice Ser.). (ENG., Illus.). 256p. pap. 37.50 (978-0-7494-5109-7(2)) Kogan Page, Ltd. GBR. Dist: Ingram Pub. Services.

Foster, John. Writing Skills for Public Relations: Style & Technique for Mainstream & Social Media. 5th ed. 2012. (PR in Practice Ser.). (ENG.). 272p. pap. 37.50 (978-0-7494-6543-8(3)) Kogan Page, Ltd. GBR. Dist: Ingram Pub. Services.

Frederick, Peter. Persuasive Writing: How to Harness the Power of Words. rev. ed. 2011. (ENG., Illus.). 208p. pap. 39.50 (978-0-273-74613-3(8)) Pearson Education, Ltd. GBR. Dist: Trans-Atlantic Pubns., Inc.

Geffner, Andrea B. Barron's How to Write Better Business Letters. 4th ed. 2007. (ENG., Illus.). 192p. per. 14.99 (978-0-7641-3539-2(2)) Barron's Educational Series, Inc.

—Business English: The Writing Skills You Need for Today's Workplace. 5th rev. ed. 2010. (ENG., Illus.). 384p. pap. 16.99 (978-0-7641-4327-4(1)) Barron's Educational Series, Inc.

Gerson, Sharon J. & Gerson, Steven M. Workplace Communication: Process & Product. 2006. (ENG., Illus.). 352p. per. 77.40 (978-0-13-228808-8(7), Prentice Hall) Prentice Hall PTR.

—Workplace Writing: Planning, Packaging, & Perfecting Communication. 2008. (ENG., Illus.). 640p. (C). pap. 99.80 (978-0-13-159969-7(0), Prentice Hall) Prentice Hall PTR.

Gordon Lewis, Herschell. On the Art of Writing Copy: The Best of Print, Broadcast, Internet, Direct Mail, Social Media. 2011. (Illus.). 402p. pap. 39.95 (978-1-933199-32-0(6)) Racom Communications.

Graham, Daniel, et al. Can Do Writing: The Proven Ten-Step System for Fast & Effective Business Writing. 2009. (ENG., Illus.). 208p. pap. 19.95 (978-0-470-44979-0(9), Wiley) Wiley, John & Sons, Inc.

Greenlaw, Raymond. Technical Writing, Presentational Skills, & Online Communication: Professional Tools & Insights. 2012. (Illus.). xxi, 225p. (978-1-4666-0239-7(2)) IGI Global.

Greenlaw, Raymond, ed. Technical Writing, Presentational Skills, & Online Communication: Professional Tools & Insights. 2012. (Illus.). 456p. 175.00 (978-1-4666-0237-3(6), Information Science Reference) IGI Global.

Guffey, Mary Ellen & Loewy, Dana. Business Communication: Process & Product (Book Only) 7th ed. 2010. (ENG., Illus.). 672p. (C). 206.95 (978-0-538-46626-4(X)) Cengage South-Western.

—Business Communication: Process & Product (with meguffey. com Printed Access Card) 7th ed. 2010. (Business Communication Ser.). (ENG., Illus.). 672p. (C). 206.95 (978-0-538-46625-7(1)) Cengage South-Western.

Guffey, Mary Ellen & Loewy, Dana. Essentials of Business Communication. 9th ed. 2012.Tr. of Infotrac College Edition. (ENG.). 576p. (C). pap. 160.95 (978-1-111-82122-7(4)) Cengage South-Western.

Hamp-Lyons, Liz & Heasley, Ben. Study Writing: A Course in Written English for Academic Purposes. 2nd rev. ed. 2006. (ENG., Illus.). 214p. per. 27.04 (978-0-521-53496-3(8)) Cambridge Univ. Pr.

Hampel, Judith. Business Writing. 2012. (ENG.). 154p. ring bd. 40.00 (978-0-7575-9936-1(2)) Kendall Hunt Publishing Co.

Hamper, Robert J. & Baugh, L. Sue. Handbook for Writing Proposals, Second Edition. 2nd ed. 2010. (ENG., Illus.). 256p. pap. 19.95 (978-0-07-174648-9(X), 007174648X) McGraw-Hill Cos., The.

Hardesty, Ray E. Technical & Business Writing for Working Professionals. 2011. 208p. 29.99 (978-1-4568-1939-2(9)); pap. 19.99 (978-1-4568-1938-5(0)) Xlibris Corp.

Harvard Business School Press Staff, compiled by. Writing for Business: Expert Solutions to Everyday Challenges. 2007. (Pocket Mentor Ser.). (ENG., Illus.). 96p. per. 9.95 (978-1-4221-1472-8(4)) Harvard Business Review Pr.

Hemphill and, McCormick. Business Communication with Writing Impr. 2006. pap. 9.95 (978-1-4288-0543-9(5)) Cram101 Inc.

Hewett, Beth L. & Robidoux, Charlotte, eds. Virtual Collaborative Writing in the Workplace: Computer-Mediated Communication Technologies & Processes. 2010. (Illus.). 350p. 180.00 (978-1-60566-994-6(6)) IGI Global.

Hodges & Hodges, Edward. Keep it Simple: A Guide to Business Writing. 2nd rev. ed. 2012. (ENG.). 122p. pap. 43.00 (978-0-7575-9489-2(1)) Kendall Hunt Publishing Co.

Holtje, Bert. The Complete Idiot's Guide to Writing Business Books. 2009. (Complete Idiot's Guide Ser.). (ENG.). 336p. (gr. 12-18). pap. 20.00 (978-1-59257-879-5(9), Alpha Bks.) Penguin Group (USA) Inc.

Hongqin, Zhao & Wenzhen, Lu. Business Writing in Chinese. 329p. pap. 9.95 (978-7-5619-0270-7(0)) Beijing Language & Culture Univ. Pr., China CHN. Dist: China Bks. & Periodicals, Inc.

Horberry, Roger. Sounds Good on Paper: How to Bring Business Language to Life. 2010. (ENG., Illus.). 256p. pap. 14.95 (978-1-4081-2231-0(6)) A & C Black GBR. Dist: Macmillan.

Houghton, Peggy M., et al. Gregg Reference Manual: The Easy Way! 2009. (978-0-923568-93-1(X)) Baker College Publishing Co.

Jakobs, Eva-Maria & Lehnen, Katrin, eds. Berufliches Schreiben: Ausbildung, Training, Coaching. 2008. (Textproduktion und Medium Ser.). 212p. pap. 52.95 (978-3-631-57717-2(6)) Lang, Peter GmbH, Europaischer Verlag der Wissenschaften DEU. Dist: Lang, Peter.

Janoff, Barbara & Cash-Smith, Ruth. The Graphic Designer's Guide to Better Business Writing. 2007. (ENG., Illus.). 288p. per. 19.95 (978-1-58115-472-6(0), 115472, Allworth Pr.) Skyhorse Publishing Co., Inc.

Jovin, Ellen. E-Mail Etiquette for Business Professionals. 2007. x, 129p. per. (978-0-9785823-3-3(0)) Syntaxis Pr.

—A Writing Guide for Business Professionals. 2007. viii, 96p. per. (978-0-9785823-1-9(4)) Syntaxis Pr.

Jovin, Ellen & Johnson, Brandt. Syntaxis Communication Guides. 2007. per. (978-0-9785823-4-0(9)) Syntaxis Pr.

Kallos, Blogger, Consultant Judith, Author. Business E-mail Etiquette: The Manual. 2008. 144p. pap. 19.50 (978-1-4357-2049-7(0)) Lulu Enterprises Inc.

Kirk, Ken. Writing for Readability. 2010. (ENG.). 16p. pap. 24.95 (978-1-56286-727-0(X)) American Society for Training & Development.

Kolin, Philip C. Successful Writing at Work. 8th ed. 2007. (Illus.). xxiv, 756p. (978-0-618-69396-2(3)) Houghton Mifflin Harcourt Publishing Co.

—Successful Writing at Work: Concise Edition. 3rd ed. 2011. (ENG.). 416p. (C). pap. 89.95 (978-0-495-90194-5(6)) Wadsworth.

Langley, Anne. A Practical Writing Guide for Academic Librarians: Keeping It Short & Sweet. Wallace, Jon, ed. 2010. (Illus.). 172p. pap. 75.00 (978-1-84334-532-9(3), Chandos Publishing) Woodhead Publishing Ltd. GBR. Dist: Neal-Schuman Pubs., Inc.

Lauchman, Richard. Plain Style: Techniques for Simple, Concise, Emphatic Business Writing. 2008. (ENG.). 120p. pap. 12.95 (978-0-8144-1429-3(X)) Amacom.

LearningExpress Staff. Business Writing Clear & Simple. 2007. (ENG., Illus.). 224p. per. 16.95 (978-1-57685-637-6(2)) LearningExpress, LLC.

Levy, Mark. Accidental Genius: Using Writing to Generate Your Best Ideas, Insight, & Content. 2nd ed. 2010. (ENG.). 192p. pap. 16.95 (978-1-60509-525-7(7)) Berrett-Koehler Pubs., Inc.

Lomas, Robert. Mastering Your Business Dissertation. 2011. (ENG., Illus.). 184p. (C). pap. 36.95 (978-0-415-59679-4(3)); 125.00 (978-0-415-59678-7(5)) Routledge.

Lunsford, Andrea A. EasyWriter with 2009 MLA & 2010 APA Updates: A Pocket Reference. 4th ed. 2009. (ENG.). 352p. (C). spiral bd. 26.95 (978-0-312-65031-5(0)) Bedford/Saint Martin's.

Lyle, Linda G. Power Writing. 2011. 84p. pap. 36.99 (978-1-61286-019-0(2)) Avid Readers Publishing Group.

Maclay, K. T. Business Writing, Period: A no-sweat, no-stress guide to getting your ideas on Paper. 2006. pap. 26.95 (978-0-9786435-6-0(9)) Skatekey Productions.

Magrino, William & Goeller, Michael. Effective Business & Professional Writing: From Project to Proposal. rev. ed. 2011. (ENG.). 208p. pap. 36.98 (978-0-7575-6773-5(8)) Kendall Hunt Publishing Co.

Marsen, Sky. Professional Writing: 2nd Edition. 2nd rev. ed. 2007. (Palgrave Study Guides). (ENG., Illus.). 260p. pap. 30.00 (978-0-230-54298-3(0)) Palgrave Macmillan.

Marsh, Charles, et al. Strategic Writing. 3rd ed. 2011. (ENG., Illus.). 272p. (C). pap. 88.00 (978-0-205-03197-9(8)) Allyn & Bacon, Inc.

—Strategic Writing: Multimedia Writing for Public Relations, Advertising, & More. 2nd ed. 2008. (ENG., Illus.). 272p. (C). pap. 88.00 (978-0-205-59162-6(0)) Allyn & Bacon, Inc.

Maslen, Andy. Write to Sell. 2009. 192p. pap. (978-0-462-09975-0(X)) Marshall Cavendish.

—Write to Sell: The Ultimate Guide to Great Copywriting. 2007. (ENG., Illus.). 160p. per. 16.95 (978-1-904879-99-2(3)) Cyan Communications GBR. Dist: Independent Pubs. Group.

Massachi, Dalya F. Writing to Make a Difference: 25 Powerful Techniques to Boost Your Community Impact. 2010. 365p. per. 29.95 (978-0-9788836-0-7(8)) Writing for Community Success.

McIntyre, Catherine. Writing Effective News Releases, 2nd Edition: How to Get Free Publicity for Yourself, Your Business or Your Organization. 2008. (ENG., Illus.). 176p. pap. 20.00 (978-0-941599-00-9(0)) Piccadilly Bks., Ltd.

Means, Thomas. Business Communications. 2nd ed. 2009. (ENG.). 96p. (C). pap., pupil's gde. ed. 38.95 (978-0-538-44959-5(4)) Cengage South-Western.

Means, Thomas L. Business Communication. 2nd ed. 2009. (Introduction to Business Communication Ser.). (ENG.). 672p. (C). 96.95 (978-0-538-44947-2(0)) Cengage South-Western.

—Means' English & Communication for Colleges. 4th ed. 2006. (ENG.). 160p. (C). pap. 50.95 (978-0-538-72994-9(5)) Cengage South-Western.

Means, Thomas L. & Langlois, Elaine. English & Communication for Colleges. 4th rev. ed. 2006. (ENG., Illus.). 640p. (C). 141.95 (978-0-538-73000-6(5)) Cengage South-Western.

Meissner, Joern, et al. Manhattan Review Smart Business Talk. 2008. pap. 19.99 *(978-0-9788435-4-0(1))* Manhattan Review.

Meyer, Carolyn. Communication for Results. 2nd ed. 2010. (ENG., Illus.). 528p. pap., stu. ed. 74.00 *(978-0-19-543164-3(2))* Oxford Univ. Pr., Inc.

Minto, Barbara. The Pyramid Principle: Logical Writing, Thinking & Problem Solving. 3rd rev. ed. (Illus.). 272p. 103.20 *(978-0-273-71051-6(6))* Financial Times/Prentice Hall.

Morgan, Ellis. Writing at Work: A Quick & Easy Guide to Grammar & Effective Business Writing. 2011. (ENG.). 136p. pap. 14.99 ***(978-0-9569466-2-1(3)***, Dormouse Pr.) Guidemark Publishing Limited GBR. Dist: Lightning Source, Inc.

Newsom, Doug & Haynes, Jim. Public Relations Writing: Form & Style. 9th ed. 2010. (ENG.). (C). 448p. pap. 143.95 *(978-1-4390-8272-0(3))*; 160p. pap., wbk. ed. 74.95 *(978-0-495-90498-4(8))* Wadsworth.

Nyheim, Peter D. & Wildes, Vivienne J. Business Writing for Hospitality. 2008. (ENG., Illus.). 128p. (C). pap. 33.00 *(978-0-13-171571-4(2)*, Prentice Hall) Prentice Hall PTR.

Oliu, Walter E., et al. Writing that Works with 2009 MLA & 2010 APA Updates: Communicating Effectively on the Job. 10th ed. 2010. (ENG.). 736p. (C). pap. 84.95 *(978-0-312-69217-9(X))* Bedford/Saint Martin's.

Painter, Mark P. Write Well: 25 Easy Rules to Improve Your Business ans Professional Writing. 2007. per. 14.95 *(978-0-9772720-2-0(8))* Jarndyce & Jarndyce Pr.

Pawar, Badrinarayan Shankar & Monippally, Mathukutty M. Academic Writing: A Guide for Management Students & Researchers. 2010. (Response Bks.). (Illus.). 284p. (C). pap. 33.00 *(978-81-321-0441-4(2)*, B04414P) SAGE Pubns., Inc.

Payne, Mary Ann. Grant Writing DeMYSTiFied. 2010. (Demystified Ser.). (ENG., Illus.). 256p. pap. 22.00 *(978-0-07-173863-7(0)*, 0071738630) McGraw-Hill Cos., The.

Pulley, Mary Lynn & Hilberry, Jane. Get Smart! How E-Mail Can Make or Break Your Career & Your Organization. 2007. (Illus.). 79p. pap. *(978-0-9797420-0-2(5))* Get Smart! Publishing, LLC.

Rhody, et al. Wordsmithing: The Art & Craft of Writing for Public Relations. 2nd ed. 2008. (ENG.). (C). pap. 80.60 *(978-0-558-03093-3(9))* Pearson Learning Solutions.

Rhody, Ron & Hackley, Carol Ann. Wordsmithing: The Art & Craft of Writing for Public Relations. 2nd ed. 2008. (ENG.). (C). pap. 86.20 incl. cd-rom *(978-0-558-05496-0(X))* Pearson Learning Solutions.

Roberts, David D. & Kostelnick, Charles. Designing Visual Language: Strategies for Professional Communicators (Part of the Allyn & Bacon Series in Technical Communication) 2nd ed. 2010. (Technical Communication Ser.). (ENG., Illus.). 432p. (C). pap. 89.00 *(978-0-205-61640-4(2))* Longman Publishing Group.

Roddick, Ellen. Writing That Means Business: How to Get Your Message Across Simply & Effectively. 2010. 148p. pap. 13.95 *(978-1-4502-2104-7(1))* iUniverse, Inc.

Roddick, Hawley. Business Writing Makeovers: Shortcut Solutions to Improve Your Letters, E-Mails, & Faxes. 2011. 288p. pap. 19.95 *(978-1-4502-0884-0(3))* iUniverse, Inc.

Rounds, Mike. Executive Authorship: Write Your Way to Career Advancement. 2009. (Illus.). vi, 114p. pap. *(978-1-891440-57-1(8))* CPM Systems.

Sabin, William. The Gregg Reference: A Manual of Style, Grammar, Usage, & Formatting. 11th ed. 2010. (ENG., Illus.). 784p. (C). spiral bd. 82.67 *(978-0-07-339710-8(5)*, 0073397105) McGraw-Hill Higher Education.

—The Gregg Reference Manual w/ Desktop Edition Access Card. 11th ed. 2011. (ENG.). (C). spiral bd. 76.00 *(978-0-07-751486-0(6)*, 0077514866) McGraw-Hill Higher Education.

Sant, Tom. The Language of Success: Business Writing That Informs, Persuades, & Gets Results, 2. 2008. (ENG., Illus.). 224p. pap. 15.00 *(978-0-8144-7473-0(X))* Amacom.

Schiffrin, Anya & Kircher-Allen, Eamon, eds. Bad News: How America's Business Press Missed the Story of the Century. 2011. (ENG.). 240p. 24.95 *(978-1-59558-549-3(4))* New Pr., The.

Scott, Cynthia & Jaffe, Dennis. The Values Edge Toolkit: Facilitator's Guide. 2011. ***(978-1-58854-715-6(9))*** Organization Design & Development, Inc.

Scott, J. Blake, et al. Critical Power Tools: Technical Communication & Cultural Studies. Scott, J. Blake et al, eds. (SUNY Series, Studies in Scientific & Technical Communication). (Illus.). 293p. 2007. per. 29.95 *(978-0-7914-6776-3(7))* 2006. 80.00 *(978-0-7914-6775-6(9))* State Univ. of New York Pr.

Searles, George J. Workplace Communications: The Basics. 5th ed. 2010. (ENG.). 312p. (C). pap. 70.80 *(978-0-205-82809-8(4))* Longman Publishing Group.

—Workplace Communications: The Basics, Book a la Carte Edition. 5th ed. 2011. (ENG.). (C). ring bd. 46.67 ***(978-0-205-23836-1(X))*** Longman Publishing Group.

—Workplace Communications: The Basics, Books a la Carte Plus MyTechCommLab. 5th ed. 2012. (ENG.). (C). ring bd. 53.33 ***(978-0-321-83853-7(X))*** Addison Wesley.

—Workplace Communications: The Basics, Books a la Carte Plus MyTechCommLab. 5th ed. 2011. (ENG.). (C). ring bd. 53.33 ***(978-0-205-23854-5(8))*** Longman Publishing Group.

Self-Counsel Press Staff. Business Letters Kit. 2010. (ENG.). 11.95 *(978-1-55180-775-1(0))* Self-Counsel Pr., Inc. CAN. Dist: Midpoint Trade Bks., Inc.

Shulman, Myra. In Focus: Strategies for Business Writers. 2006. (ENG., Illus.). 208p. per. 25.95 *(978-0-472-03074-3(4))* Univ. of Michigan Pr.

Shwom, Barbara & Snyder, Lisa Gueldenzoph. Business Communication: Polishing Your Professional Presence. 2011. (ENG.). 600p. (C). pap. 140.00 *(978-0-13-607807-4(9)*, Prentice Hall) Prentice Hall PTR.

Slaunwhite, Steve. The Everything Guide to Writing Copy: From Ads & Press Release to on-Air & Online Promos — All You Need to Create Copy That Sells! 2007. (ENG.). 304p. per. 15.95 *(978-1-59869-251-8(8))* Adams Media Corp.

Sparks FitzGerald, Suzanne. Manager's Guide to Business Writing 2/E. 2nd ed. 2011. (Briefcase Books Ser.). (ENG., Illus.). 192p. pap. 17.00 ***(978-0-07-177226-6(X)***, 007177226X) McGraw-Hill Cos., The.

Starkman, Dean, et al, eds. The Best Business Writing Book 2012. 2012. (Columbia Journalism Review Bks.). (ENG.). 464p. (gr. 17). pap. 18.95 ***(978-0-231-16073-5(9))*** Columbia Univ. Pr.

Stockard, Olivia, ed. The Write Approach. 2nd rev. ed. 2011. (Illus.). 200p. pap. *(978-0-85724-831-2(6))* Emerald Group Publishing Ltd.

Sullivan, Lauren & Harbus Staff. 65 Successful Harvard Business School Application Essays: With Analysis by the Staff of the Harbus, the Harvard Business School Newspaper. 2nd ed. 2009. (ENG.). 240p. pap. 14.99 *(978-0-312-55007-3(3)*, St. Martin's Griffin) St. Martin's Pr.

Talbot, Fiona. Executive Writing Skills for Managers Bk. 3: Master Word Power to Lead Your Teams, Make Strategic Links & Develop Relationships. 2009. (Better Business English Ser.). (ENG., Illus.). 160p. pap. 17.95 *(978-0-7494-5518-7(7))* Kogan Page, Ltd. GBR. Dist: Ingram Pub. Services.

—How to Write Effective Business English Bk. 1: The Essential Toolkit for Composing Powerful Letters, E-Mails & More, for Today's Business Needs. 2009. (Better Business English Ser.). (ENG., Illus.). 160p. pap. 17.95 *(978-0-7494-5520-0(9))* Kogan Page, Ltd. GBR. Dist: Ingram Pub. Services.

—Make an Impact with Your Written English Bk. 2: How to Use Word Power to Impress in Presentations, Reports, PR & Meetings. 2009. (Better Business English Ser.). (ENG., Illus.). 160p. pap. 17.95 *(978-0-7494-5519-4(5))* Kogan Page, Ltd. GBR. Dist: Ingram Pub. Services.

Tatge, Mark W. The New York Times Reader: Business & Economics. rev. ed. 2010. 304p. pap. 28.00 *(978-1-60426-483-8(7))* CQ Pr.

Taylor, Neil. Brilliant Business Writing: How to Inspire, Engage & Persuade Through Words. 2009. 232p. pap. 32.50 *(978-0-273-72079-9(1)*, Prentice Hall) 2nd rev. ed. 2011. (ENG.). 234p. pap. 34.50 *(978-0-273-74458-0(5))* Pearson Education, Ltd. GBR. Dist: Trans-Atlantic Pubns., Inc.

Taylor, Shirley. Email Etiquette: A Fresh Look at Dealing Effectively with e-mail, Developing Great Style, & Writing Clear, Concise Messages. 2010. (Illus.). 178p. pap. *(978-981-261-673-9(X))* Marshall Cavendish.

Taylor, Shirley. Model Business Letters, Emails & Other Business Documents. 7th ed. 2012. (ENG.). 512p. pap. 44.99 ***(978-0-273-75193-9(X))*** FT Press.

VanHuss, Susie H., et al. Keyboarding Course, Lessons 1-25 for Microsoft Word 2007. 17th rev. ed. 2008. (ENG., Illus.). 128p. (C). pap. 80.95 *(978-0-538-73035-8(8))* Cengage South-Western.

Vassallo, Philip. How to Write Fast under Pressure, 1 vol. 2009. (ENG.). 224p. pap. 18.95 *(978-0-8144-1485-9(0))* Amacom.

Watson, Jane. Business Writing Basics. 3rd rev. ed. 2007. (ENG., Illus.). 184p. per. 12.95 *(978-1-55180-769-0(6))* Self-Counsel Pr., Inc. CAN. Dist: Midpoint Trade Bks., Inc.

Wilcox, Dennis L. Public Relations Writing & Media Techniques. 6th ed. 2008 (ENG., Illus.). 576p. (C). pap. 134.00 *(978-0-205-64828-3(2))* Allyn & Bacon, Inc.

Wilson, Kevin & Wauson, Jennifer. The AMA Handbook of Business Documents: Guidelines & Sample Documents That Make Business Writing Easy, 1 vol. 2011. (ENG.). 224p. pap. 19.95 *(978-0-8144-1769-0(8))* Amacom.

—The AMA Handbook of Business Writing: The Ultimate Guide to Style, Grammar, Punctuation, Usage, Construction, & Formatting, 1 vol. 2010. (ENG.). 656p. 34.95 *(978-0-8144-1589-4(X))* Amacom.

Writer's Digest Books Editors & Brewer, Robert, eds. The Craft & Business of Writing: Essential Tools for Writing Success. 2008. (ENG.). 400p. 24.99 *(978-1-58297-487-3(X)*, Writer's Digest Bks.) F&W Media, Inc.

Young, Dona. Foundations of Business English: Developing Skills in Context: Developing Skills in Context. 2007. (ENG., Illus.). 416p. (C). pap. 133.33 *(978-0-07-354542-4(2)*, 0073545422) McGraw-Hill Higher Education.

Young, Dona J. Business English: Writing for the Global Workplace. 2008. (Illus.). x, 398p. *(978-0-07-329194-9(3))* McGraw-Hill Cos., The.

Zappala, Joseph & Carden, Ann R. Public Relations Writing Worktext: A Practical Guide for the Profession. 3rd rev. ed. 2009. (ENG., Illus.). 312p. 126.00 *(978-0-415-99753-9(4))*; pap. 59.95 *(978-0-415-99754-6(2))* Routledge.

BUSINESSMEN

see Businesspeople

BUSINESSOBJECTS (COMPUTER PROGRAM)

Audas, Thierry, et al. Discover SAP BusinessObjects. 2010. (Illus.). 374p. pap. 39.95 *(978-1-59229-315-5(8)*, SAP PR.) Galileo Pr., Inc.

Brogden, Jim, et al. SAP BusinessObjects Web Intelligence. 2010. (Illus.). 583p. 79.95 *(978-1-59229-322-3(0)*, SAP PR.) Galileo Pr., Inc.

Ganz, Carl, Jr. Pro Crystal Enterprise - BusinessObjects XI Programming. 2006. (Expert's Voice in .NET Ser.). (ENG., Illus.). 488p. 79.99 *(978-1-59059-759-0(1))* Apress L. P.

Hilgefort, Ingo. Inside SAP BusinessObjects Advanced Analysis. 2010. (Illus.). 343p. 69.95 *(978-1-59229-371-1(9)*, SAP PR.) Galileo Pr., Inc.

—Inside SAP BusinessObjects Explorer. 2010. (Illus.). 307p. 69.95 *(978-1-59229-340-7(9)*, SAP PR.) Galileo Pr., Inc.

—Integrating SAP BusinessObjects XI 4. X Tools with SAP NetWeaver. 2011. (ENG., Illus.). 325p. 79.95 *(978-1-59229-395-7(6)*, SAP PR.) Galileo Pr., Inc.

—Reporting & Analysis with SAP BusinessObjects. 2nd ed. 2011. (ENG., Illus.). 675p. 79.95 *(978-1-59229-387-2(5)*, SAP PR.) Galileo Pr., Inc.

—Reporting & Analytics with SAP BusinessObjects. 2009. (Illus.). 500p. 79.95 *(978-1-59229-310-0(7)*, SAP PR.) Galileo Pr., Inc.

Howson, Cindi, et al. SAP BusinessObjects BI 4. 0 the Complete Reference 3/E. 3rd ed. 2012. (Complete Reference Ser.). (ENG., Illus.). 752p. pap. 70.00 ***(978-0-07-177312-6(6)***, 0071773126) McGraw-Hill Osborne.

Lai, David & Hacking, Xavier. SAP BusinessObjects Dashboards 4. 0 Cookbook. 2011. 333p. pap. ***(978-1-84968-178-0(3))*** Packt Publishing, Ltd.

Newman, William D. Understanding SAP BusinessObjects Enterprise Performance Management. 2010. (Illus.). 282p. 69.95 *(978-1-59229-348-3(4)*, SAP PR.) Galileo Pr., Inc.

Schmidt, Robert. Web Intelligence XI Vol. 3: Creating Documents with Business Objects. 2010. (Illus.). 420p. pap. 79.99 *(978-0-9828352-0-3(5))* Schmidt Ink, Inc.

Schmidt, Robert D. Creating Documents with Business Objects XI-CBT: Web Intelligence XI. 2007. (Illus.). 234p. pap. 99.99 *(978-0-9722636-4-1(0))* Schmidt Ink, Inc.

Srinivasan, Sridhar & Srinivasan, Kumar. SAP BusinessObjects Planning & Consolidation. (Illus.). 2010. 406p. 79.95 *(978-1-59229-239-4(9))* 2nd ed. 2011. 446p. 79.95 *(978-1-59229-397-1(2))* Galileo Pr., Inc. (SAP PR.).

Torres, Derek, et al. BusinessObjects XI Release 2 for Dummies. 2008. (ENG., Illus.). 344p. pap. 29.99 *(978-0-470-18112-6(5)*, For Dummies) Wiley, John & Sons, Inc.

BUSINESSPEOPLE

see also Businesswomen; Capitalists and Financiers; Industrialists; Merchants

Abbott, Richard H. Cotton & Capital. 2009. 306p. pap. 29.95 *(978-1-55849-745-0(5))* Univ. of Massachusetts Pr.

Abraham, Joe. Entrepreneurial DNA: The Breakthrough Discovery That Aligns Your Business to Your Unique Strengths. 2011. (ENG., Illus.). 256p. 25.00 *(978-0-07-175451-4(2)*, 0071754512) McGraw-Hill Cos., The.

Allmon, Harold. Male Dress & Image: Clothing & Accessories -Things Someone Meant to Tell You When You Bought Your Best-Twenty Percent of Success Is Dress Etiquette on How to Wear It. 2011. (ENG.). 128p. pap. 19.95 *(978-0-917921-81-0(X))* At Ease Pr.

Alpern, Laura Manischewitz. Manischewitz, the Matzo Family: The Making of an American Jewish Icon. 2008. *(978-1-60280-003-8(0))* Ktav Publishing Hse., Inc.

Alwuhaibi, Sami. The Competitive Advantage of Organizations & Nations. 2010. 384p. pap. *(978-3-639-22072-8(2))* VDM Verlag Dr. Mueller e.K.

Arcand, Jean-Philippe. Entering the Ipo Process - Impacts of Replacing the Firm Founder & Ceo. 2008. 120p. per. *(978-3-8364-3676-2(0))* VDM Verlag Dr. Mueller e.K.

Ardener. Professional Identities: Policy & Practice in Business & Bureaucracy. 2007. (Social Identities Ser.). (Illus.). 224p. (C). 90.00 *(978-1-84545-054-0(X))* Berghahn Bks., Inc.

Asbury, Neal. Conscientious Equity: An American Entrepreneur's Solutions to the World's Greatest Problems. 2010. (ENG.). 240p. 27.00 *(978-0-230-10892-9(X))* Palgrave Macmillan.

Austin, Denise. Kingdom-Minded People: Christian Identity & the Contributions of Chinese Business Christians: Christian Identity & the Contributions of Chinese Business Christians. 2011. (Global Pentecostal & Charismatic Studies). (Illus.). 249p. ***(978-90-04-20402-7(4))*** BRILL.

Bailey, Jimmy. Teachers Reaching Out: 25 Dedicated Souls who have changed the lives of young entrepreneurs from YEScarolina. 2011. (ENG.). 104p. pap. 12.99 ***(978-1-59932-262-9(5))*** Advantage Media Group.

Balasubramanian, S. The Art of Business Leadership: Indian Experiences. 2007. (Illus.). 300p. (C). per. 32.95 *(978-0-7619-3587-2(8)*, B35872P) SAGE Pubns., Inc.

Beauchamp, Cari. Joseph P. Kennedy Presents: His Hollywood Years. 2010. (Vintage Ser.). (ENG., Illus.). 528p. pap. 18.95 *(978-0-307-47522-0(0)*, Vintage) Knopf Doubleday Publishing Group.

Benedict, Jeff. The Mormon Way of Doing Business: How Eight Western Boys Reached the Top of Corporate America. 2008. (ENG., Illus.). 256p. pap. 15.99 *(978-0-446-69635-7(8)*, Business Plus) Grand Central Publishing

Bennett-Alexander, Dawn, et al. The Legal, Ethical, & Regulatory Environment of Business in a Diverse Society. 2011. (ENG., Illus.). 544p. (C). 204.00 *(978-0-07-352492-4(1)*, 0073524921, McGraw-Hill/Irwin) McGraw-Hill Higher Education.

Bergére, Marie-Claire. The Golden Age of the Chinese Bourgeoisie, 1911-1937. 2009. (Studies in Modern Capitalism Ser.). (ENG.). 372p. pap. 38.99 *(978-0-521-11071-6(8))* Cambridge Univ. Pr.

Bhattacharya, Jayati. Beyond the Myth: Indian Business Communities in Singapore. 2011. (Illus.). xxv, 371p. ***(978-981-4345-27-9(X))*** Institute of Southeast Asian Studies.

BIC Alliance, prod. Energy Entrepreneurs: Insights & inspiration from self-starters in business & industry. 2007. 205p. 30.00 *(978-0-9768310-1-3(5))* BIC Alliance.

Biradavolu, Monica Rao. Indian Entrepreneurs in Silicon Valley: The Making of a Transnational Techno-Capitalist Class. 2008. (C). 104.95 *(978-1-60497-527-7(X))* Cambria Pr.

Bishop, Matthew & Green, Michael. Philanthrocapitalism: How Giving Can Save the World. 2009. (ENG.). 320p. pap. 18.00 *(978-1-59691-695-1(8))* Bloomsbury Publishing.

Black, Conrad. A Matter of Principle. 2011. (ENG., Illus.). 592p. 35.00 *(978-0-7710-1670-7(0)*, McClelland & Stewart) McClelland & Stewart CAN. Dist: Random Hse., Inc.

Branson, Richard. Screw Business As Usual. 2011. (ENG.). 1p. (gr. 12). 26.95 ***(978-1-59184-434-1(7)***, Portfolio (Hardcover)) Penguin Group (USA) Inc.

Bridge, Rachel. You Can Do It Too: The 20 Essential Things Every Budding Entrepreneur Should Know. 2010. (ENG.). 184p. pap. 19.95 *(978-0-7494-6054-9(7))* Kogan Page, Ltd. GBR. Dist: Ingram Pub. Services.

Brown, H. Les. The Frazzled Entrepreneur's Guide to Having It All: Seven Strategies for Living a Balanced Life. 2007. (Illus.). 259p. cd-rom 15.95 net. *(978-0-9798668-1-4(2))* Life Pilot, LLC.

Buchholz, Todd G. Lasting Lessons from the Corner Office: Essential Wisdom from the Twentieth Century's Greatest Entrepreneurs. 2009. (ENG.). 320p. pap. 16.99 *(978-0-06-119763-5(7)*, Harper Paperbacks) HarperCollins Pubs.

Buchla, Nozer. Why Entrepreneurs Really Fail: The Road to Success ... Always under Construction. 2011. 256p. 30.95 ***(978-1-4502-9938-1(5))***; pap. 20.95 ***(978-1-4502-9937-4(7))*** iUniverse, Inc.

Calonius, Erik. Ten Steps Ahead: What Separates Successful Business Visionaries from the Rest of Us. 2011. (ENG.). 256p. (gr. 12). 25.95 *(978-1-59184-376-4(6)*, Portfolio (Hardcover)) Penguin Group (USA) Inc.

Chen, Jie & Dickson, Bruce J. Allies of the State: China's Private Entrepreneurs & Democratic Change. 2010. (Illus.). 232p. 45.00 *(978-0-674-04996-6(2))* Harvard Univ. Pr.

Ching, Mia Kuang. CFO Guide to Doing Business in China. 2009. (ENG.). 200p. pap. 38.00 *(978-0-470-82373-6(9)*, Wiley) Wiley, John & Sons, Inc.

Chu, Cindy Yik-Yi. Chinese Communists & Hong Kong Capitalists: 1937-1997. 2010. (ENG., Illus.). 208p. 89.00 *(978-0-230-10799-1(0))* Palgrave Macmillan.

Claiborne, Jack. Of Pleasures & Power: The Story of the Charlotte City Club. 2007. (Illus.). vi, 158p. *(978-1-4243-2822-2(5))* Survival in College Pr.

Covert, Jack & Sattersten, Todd. The 100 Best Business Books of All Time: What They Say, Why They Matter, & How They Can Help You. (ENG., Illus.). (gr. 12). 2011. 368p. 16.00 *(978-1-59184-446-4(0)*, Portfolio Trade) 2009. 352p. 25.95 *(978-1-59184-240-8(9)*, Portfolio (Hardcover)) Penguin Group (USA) Inc.

Cram101 Textbook Reviews. Outlines & Highlights for the Legal, Ethical, & Regulatory Environment of Business in a Diverse Society by Dawn Bennett-Alexander, Isbn: 97800735249. 2011. 434p. pap. 35.95 ***(978-1-61812-090-8(5))*** Cram101 Inc.

Cram101 Textbook Reviews & Cram101 Textbook Reviews. Outlines & Highlights for the Legal Environment of Business: A Managerial Approach. 2011. 420p. pap. 35.95 ***(978-1-61461-177-6(7))*** Cram101 Inc.

Davidson, Daniel V. & Forsythe, Lynn M. The Entrepreneur's Legal Companion. 2010. (ENG.). 336p. (C). pap. 60.00 *(978-0-13-607723-7(4)*, Prentice Hall) Prentice Hall PTR.

Dhingra, Pawan. Life Behind the Lobby: Indian American Motel Owners & the American Dream. 2012. (ENG.). 264p. 85.00 ***(978-0-8047-7882-4(5))***; pap. 24.95 ***(978-0-8047-7883-1(3))*** Stanford Univ. Pr.

Double Roads Publishing. The Art of Living a Successful Life. 2007. 78p. per. 14.99 *(978-0-9768164-1-3(6))* Karenzo Media.

Erickson, Charlotte. British Industrialists: Steel & Hosiery, 1850-1950. 2011. (ENG.). 302p. pap. 31.99 *(978-0-521-34948-2(6))* Cambridge Univ. Pr.

Everatt, Lynne. E-Mails from the Edge. 2006. (ENG., Illus.). 224p. per. *(978-1-897178-20-1(4))* Insomniac Pr.

Farmer, Scott. Financial Secrets for the Man of Means. 2008. 175p. spiral bd. 29.95 *(978-1-934449-15-8(6))* Legacy Publishing Services, Inc.

Fetter, Rosemary. The First Hundred Years: Denver Rotary Club 31 Celebrates a Century of Service. 2011. ***(978-1-57864-698-2(7))*** Donning Co. Pubs.

Fortescue, Stephen. Russia's Oil Barons & Metal Magnates: Oligarchs & the State in Transition. 2007. (ENG.). 240p. 100.00 *(978-1-4039-8617-7(7))* Palgrave Macmillan.

Foster, A. & Foster, A. Kristen. Moral Visions & Material Ambit. 2009. (ENG.). 216p. pap. 31.50 *(978-0-7391-3532-7(5))* Lexington Bks.

Fox, Jeffrey J. Rain: What a Paperboy Learned about Business. 2009. (ENG., Illus.). 208p. 18.95 *(978-0-470-40853-7(7)*, Jossey-Bass) Wiley, John & Sons, Inc.

Full Committee Hearing on Heroes of Small Business: Hearing Before the Committee on Small Business, United States House of Representatives, One Hundred Eleventh Congress, Second Session. Hearing Held May 26, 2010. 2010. vi, 121p. *(978-0-16-086217-5(5)*, 552-070-41315-4) United States Government Printing Office.

Garfinkle, Steven J. Entrepreneurs & Enterprise in Early Mesopotamia: A Study of Three Archives from the Third Dynasty of Ur (2112-2004 BC) 2012. ***(978-1-934309-41-4(9)***, CDL Pr.) Univ. Pr. of Maryland.

Garson, Jack. How to Build a Business & Sell It for Millions. 2010. (ENG.). 272p. 25.99 *(978-0-312-38311-4(8))* St. Martin's Pr.

Gerber, Michael E. Awakening the Entrepreneur Within: How Ordinary People Can Create Extraordinary Companies. 2009. (ENG.). 304p. pap. 15.99 *(978-0-06-156815-2(5)*, Collins) HarperCollins Pubs.

Gerson, Richard. The Executive Athlete: How Sports Psychology Helps Business People Become World-Class Performers. 2008. 199p. pap. 19.95 *(978-1-59996-122-4(9))* Human Resource Development Pr.

Gillespie, Alastair W. & Sage, Irene. Made in Canada: A Businessman's Adventures in Politics. 2010. (Illus.). 272p. 37.95 *(978-1-896941-59-2(1))* Brass, Robin Studio, Inc. CAN. Dist: Midpoint Trade Bks., Inc.

Glaser, Evelyne, et al. Intercultural Competence for Professional Mobility. 2008. (Illus.). 54p. pap. incl. cd-rom *(978-92-871-6143-7(7))* Council of Europe.
Goldstein, Gabriel & Greenberg, Elizabeth, eds. A Perfect Fit: The Garment Industry & American Jewry, 1860-1960. 2012. (Costume Society of America Ser.). (ENG., Illus.). 264p. 49.95 ***(978-0-89672-735-9(1))*** Texas Tech Univ. Pr.
Gooley, Lawrence P. Oliver's War: An Adirondack Rebel Battles the Rockefeller Fortune. 2007. (ENG., Illus.). 196p. pap. 22.00 *(978-0-9795741-0-8(2))* Bloated Toe Publishing.
Graham, Norman A. From the Barrack Room to the Boardroom: The Memoirs of A Self-Made Man. 2007. 356p. per. 23.95 *(978-0-595-47715-9(1))* iUniverse, Inc.
Gray, Jim. The Young Leader: Timeless Communication for a New Generation of Achievers. 2013. (ENG.). 232p. pap. 19.99 ***(978-1-4597-0404-6(5))*** Dundurn CAN. Dist: Ingram Pub. Services.
Gruenwald, Hermann. After Auschwitz: One Man's Story. 2007. (ENG., Illus.). 290p. (C). *(978-0-7735-3242-7(0))* McGill-Queen's Univ. Pr.
Guan, Yeoh. Penang & Its Neighbors. 260p. pap. 28.00 *(978-9971-69-423-4(9))* National Univ. of Singapore Pr. SGP. Dist: Univ. of Hawaii Pr.
Gundling & Gundling, Ernest. Working Globesmart: Twelve People Skills for Doing Business Across Borders. 2010. (ENG.). 408p. pap. 34.95 *(978-1-904838-25-8(1))* Ebsco Publishing.
Gunther, Max. The Very, Very Rich & How They Got That Way: The Spectacular Success Stories of 15 Men Who Made It to the Very Top. 2010. (ENG.). 272p. pap. 19.99 *(978-1-906659-99-8(0))* Harriman Hse. Publishing GBR. Dist: Ingram Pub. Services.
Haan, Hans Christiaan. Training for Work in the Informal Micro-Enterprise Sector: Fresh Evidence from Sub-Sahara Africa. 2010. (Technical & Vocational Education & Training: Issues, Concerns & Prospects Ser.). xxxiv, 279p. pap. 189.00 *(978-90-481-6975-7(5)*, 9048169755) Springer.
Haber, Mel. Palm Springs á la Carte: The Colorful World of the Caviar Crowd at Their Favorite Desert Hideaway. 2008. 256p. 23.95 *(978-1-56980-353-0(6))* Barricade Bks., Inc.
Haley, George T., et al. New Asian Emperors: The Business Strategies of the Overseas Chinese. rev. ed. 2009. (ENG., Illus.). 250p. pap. 24.95 *(978-0-470-82334-7(8)*, Wiley) Wiley, John & Sons, Inc.
Harris, Jeffrey A. Transformative Entrepreneurs: How Walt Disney, Steve Jobs, Muhammad Yunus, & Other Innovators Succeeded. 2011. (ENG., Illus.). 224p. 30.00 ***(978-0-230-34026-8(1))*** Palgrave Macmillan.
Harvard Business School Publishing Corporation Staff, creator. Starting a Business. 2007. (Lessons Learned: Ser.). (ENG.). 98p. per. 9.95 *(978-1-4221-2290-7(5))* Harvard Business Review Pr.
Hasegawa, Yozo. Rediscovering Japanese Business Leadership: 15 Japanese Managers & the Companies They're Leading to New Growth. Kimm, Anthony, tr. from JPN. 2010. (ENG.). 256p. pap. 27.95 *(978-0-470-82495-5(6)*, Wiley) Wiley, John & Sons, Inc.
Heberer, Thomas. Doing Business in Rural China: Liangshan's New Ethnic Entrepreneurs. 2007. (Studies on Ethnic Groups in China). (ENG., Illus.). 280p. 50.00 *(978-0-295-98729-3(4))* Univ. of Washington Pr.
Hébert, Robert F. A History of Entrepreneurship. 2009. (Routledge Studies in the History of Economics Ser.). (ENG.). 144p. (C). 110.00 *(978-0-415-77738-4(0))* Routledge.
Heley, Gwendolynn. The Material Culture of the Tradesmen of Newcastle upon Tyne 1545 - 1642: The Durham Probate Record evidence. 2009. (Bar Ser.). (ENG., Illus.). 210p. (C). pap. 102.50 *(978-1-4073-0601-8(4))* British Archaeological Reports Ltd. GBR. Dist: Brown, David Bk. Co., The.
Hill, Napoleon. The Law of Success , Volume Ii & Iii: A. 2006. 108p. per. *(978-956-291-264-8(7))* Editorial Benei Noaj.
—The Law of Success in Sixteen Lessons. 2007. 356p. per. *(978-956-291-592-2(1))* Editorial Benei Noaj.
—The Law of Success in Sixteen Lessons by Napoleon Hill. 2006. 544p. per. *(978-956-291-212-9(4))* Editorial Benei Noaj.
Hirshberg, Meg Cadoux. For Better or for Work: A Survival Guide for Entrepreneurs & Their Families. 2012. (ENG., Illus.). 260p. 23.95 ***(978-0-9839340-0-4(2))*** An Inc. Original.
Hogan, Daniel R. $$$ the Entrepreneur's Guide to Start, Grow, & Manage A Profitable Business. 2011. 352p. 33.00 ***(978-1-4567-6524-8(8))*** AuthorHouse.
Hurwitz, Judith. Smart or Lucky? How Technology Leaders Turn Chance into Success. 2011. (ENG.). 240p. 27.95 *(978-0-470-89142-1(4)*, Jossey-Bass) Wiley, John & Sons, Inc.
ICC. ICC Model Distributorship Contract. 2nd ed. 2009. 65p. pap. *(978-90-411-3185-0(X))* Kluwer Law International.
International Trade Centre. Pionniers à la conquête des Services: Histoires D'entrepreneurs Innovants. 2010. (FRE.). 120p. pap. 70.00 *(978-92-9137-374-1(5))* United Nations Pubns.
International Wealth Success, compiled by. Finder's International Network Directory. 9th ed. 2007. 25.00 *(978-1-56150-874-7(8))* International Wealth Success, Inc.
Ippaso, Robert. The Reasons for the Success or Failure of Entrepreneurs. 2009. 220p. pap. *(978-3-639-16582-1(9))* VDM Verlag Dr. Mueller e.K.
Isaacson, Walter. Profiles in Leadership: Historians on the Elusive Quality of Greatness. 2011. (ENG., Illus.). 331p. pap. 17.95 *(978-0-393-34076-1(7)*, 34076) Norton, W. W. & Co., Inc.
Jacobson, Edmund. Tension Control for Businessmen. 2011. 242p. pap. 13.95 ***(978-1-61427-109-3(7))*** Martino Publishing.
Johnson, Harry A., Jr. Lives of Miraculous Coincidences. 2009. (ENG.). 582p. 26.95 *(978-0-533-16167-6(3))* Vantage Pr., Inc.
Johnson, Michael. Cracking the Boy's Club Code: The Woman's Guide to Being Heard & Valued in the Workplace. 2009. (ENG.). 272p. pap. 16.95 *(978-1-60037-642-9(8))* Morgan James Publishing.
Jordan, Eddie. An Independent Man: The Autobiography. 2007. (ENG., Illus.). 416p. 34.95 *(978-0-7528-7534-7(5))* Orion Publishing Group, Ltd. GBR. Dist: Independent Pubs. Group.
Joyner, Amy. The eBay Billionaires' Club: Exclusive Secrets for Building an Even Bigger & More Profitable Online Business. 2007. (ENG.). 256p. 24.95 *(978-0-470-05574-8(X)*, Wiley) Wiley, John & Sons, Inc.
Kamensky, Jane. The Exchange Artist: A Tale of High-Flying Speculation & America's First Banking Collapse. 2008. (ENG.). 464p. (gr. 12-18). 17.00 *(978-0-14-311490-1(5)*, Penguin (Non-Classics)) Penguin Group (USA) Inc.
Kamuzora, Aurelia. Transaction Costs Affecting Women Businesses. 2010. 84p. pap. *(978-3-8383-0095-5(5))* Lambert Academic Publishing.
Karpik, Lucien & Ruef, Martin. The Entrepreneurial Group: Social Identities, Relations, & Collective Action. 2010. (Kauffman Foundation Series on Innovation & Entrepreneurship Ser.). (ENG., Illus.). 306p. (C). 35.00 *(978-0-691-13809-1(5))* Princeton Univ. Pr.
Kiper, Daniel. The Joslyns of Lynhurst: The True Story of George, Sarah & Their Castle. 2008. 176p. per. 16.95 *(978-1-60008-064-7(2)*, Rooftop Publishing) AuthorHouse.
Kittrell Barksdale, Rosa. The Intuitive Entrepreneur: How I Used Intuition to Start, Grow, & Maintain a Successful Business. 2011. 112p. pap. 11.95 ***(978-1-60844-967-5(X))*** Dog Ear Publishing, LLC.
Kovacs, Andy. Reverse Management: Lessons Learned from Some of the Biggest A#@holes I Have Worked For. 2007. 124p. per. 19.95 *(978-1-4241-9684-5(1))* PublishAmerica, Inc.
Kuhns, John D. China Fortunes: A Tale of Business in the New World. 2011. (ENG.). 592p. 34.95 *(978-0-470-92804-2(2)*, Wiley) Wiley, John & Sons, Inc.
Kurz, Evi. The Kissinger Saga: Walter & Henry Kissinger - Two Brothers from Furth, Germany. 2009. (ENG., Illus.). 240p. 27.95 *(978-0-297-85675-7(8))* Orion Publishing Group, Ltd. GBR. Dist: Independent Pubs. Group.
Lake, Amielle, et al. The Elephant Hunters: Chronicles of the Moneymen. 2008. (ENG., Illus.). 184p. 53.00 *(978-0-230-55369-9(9))* Palgrave Macmillan.
Lancaster, Adelaide & Abrams, Amy. The Big Enough Company: Creating a Business That Works for You. 2011. (ENG.). 288p. (gr. 12). 25.95 *(978-1-59184-421-1(5)*, Portfolio (Hardcover)) Penguin Group (USA) Inc.
Larsen, Jack L. 1894-2007 Hawaiian Pineapple Entrepreneurs. 2009. *(978-1-61623-189-7(0))* Independent Pub.
Levitt, Evan. Honest Business People: Top Advocates, Consultants & Lwayers! 2009. 270p. pap. 16.95 *(978-1-4327-3479-4(2))* Outskirts Pr., Inc.
Lewis, Neil. 100 Rules for Entrepreneurs: Real-life business Lessons. 2010. (ENG.). 176p. pap. 19.99 *(978-0-85719-027-7(X))* Harriman Hse. Publishing GBR. Dist: Ingram Pub. Services.
Lobberecht, Marlene S. & Hammonds Smith, Maxine. Bottom Line Quick Start for Emerging Entrepreneurs. 2008. 124p. per. 10.95 *(978-1-4327-2021-6(X))* Outskirts Pr., Inc.
Lovell, Terry. Bernie Ecclestone: King of Sport. (ENG., Illus.). 2010. 420p. pap. 13.95 *(978-1-84454-826-2(0))* 2008. 288p. 34.95 *(978-1-84454-623-7(3))* Blake, John Publishing, Ltd. GBR. Dist: Independent Pubs. Group.
MacFarlane, Michael. Share & Grow Rich: The Dottie Walters Effect. 2007. (ENG.). 207p. per. 16.99 *(978-1-60194-008-7(4))* Advantage Media Group.
Malkani, Vikas. The Little Manual of Success: 9 Essential Secrets of Self-Made Millionaires. 2009. (ENG., Illus.). 144p. pap. 14.95 *(978-1-84694-228-0(4))* Hunt, John Publishing Ltd. GBR. Dist: National Bk. Network.
Mantle, Jonathan. Companies That Changed the World: From the East India Company to Google. 2009. (ENG., Illus.). 208p. 12.99 *(978-1-84724-241-9(3)*, 1847242413) Quercus GBR. Dist: Book Sales, Inc.
Markovits, Claude. Merchants, Traders, Entrepreneurs: Indian Business in the Colonial ERA. 2008. (ENG.). 320p. 100.00 *(978-0-230-20598-7(4))* Palgrave Macmillan.
Martin, Renee & Martin, Don. The Risk Takers: 16 Top Entrepreneurs Share Their Strategies for Success. 2011. (ENG.). 288p. pap. 15.99 *(978-1-59315-637-4(5))* Vanguard Pr.
—The Risk Takers: 16 Women & Men Who Built Great Businesses Share Their Entrepreneurial Strategies for Success. 2010. (ENG.). 288p. 25.95 *(978-1-59315-587-2(5))* Vanguard Pr.
McDubus, Onyuka Felix. The Positive Side of Negative Enterprise. 2011. 68p. pap. ***(978-3-8454-1001-2(9))*** Lambert Academic Publishing.
McGannon, Juliette & McGannon, Michael. The Business Leader's Health Manual: Tips & Strategies for getting to the top & staying There. 2009. (INSEAD Business Press Ser.). (ENG., Illus.). 256p. 42.00 *(978-0-230-21919-9(5))* Palgrave Macmillan.
McKenzie, Danny & Reed, Jack Raymond. A Time to Speak: Speeches by Jack Reed. 2009. (ENG., Illus.). 192p. 30.00 *(978-1-60473-130-9(3))* Univ. Pr. of Mississippi.
Melvin, Sean. The Legal Environment of Business: A Managerial Approach. 2010. (ENG., Illus.). 800p. (C). 214.00 *(978-0-07-337769-8(4)*, 0073377694, McGraw-Hill/Irwin) McGraw-Hill Higher Education.
Men of Achievement, 4 vol., set. (Men of Achievement Ser.). reprint ed. 500.00 *(978-0-7222-8575-6(2))* Library Reprints, Inc.
Meron, Orly. Beyond the Border: Huguenot Goldsmiths in Northern Europe & North America. Murdoch, Tessa, ed. 2008. (ENG., Illus.). 189p. 89.95 *(978-1-84519-262-4(1))* Sussex Academic Pr. GBR. Dist: International Specialized Bk. Services.
Min, Pyong Gap. Ethnic Solidarity for Economic Survival: Korean Greengrocers in New York City. 2008. (Illus.). 193p. 32.50 *(978-0-87154-577-0(2))* Russell Sage Foundation.
Molloy, Scott. Irish Titan, Irish Toilers: Joseph Banigan & Nineteenth-Century New England Labor. 2008. (Revisiting New England Ser.). (Illus.). 288p. pap. 29.95 *(978-1-58465-691-3(3))* Univ. Pr. of New England.
Moritz, Michael. Return to the Little Kingdom: Steve Jobs & the Creation of Apple. 2010. (ENG.). 352p. (gr. 12). 15.95 *(978-1-59020-401-6(8))* Overlook Pr., The.
Morris, Charles R. The Sages: Warren Buffett, George Soros, Paul Volcker, & the Maelstrom of Markets. 2010. (ENG.). 224p. pap. 14.95 *(978-1-58648-817-8(1))* PublicAffairs.
Muhammad, Cedric. The Entrepreneurial Secret to Startin a Business: Without a Bank Loan, Collateral or Revenue, 3 vols. 2009. *(978-0-578-03794-3(7))*; *(978-0-578-03443-0(3))*; *(978-0-578-03823-0(4))* CM Cap Publishing.
Muller, Jerry Z. Capitalism & the Jews. (ENG.). 2011. 272p. pap. 19.95 ***(978-0-691-15306-3(X))*** 2010. 280p. (C). 24.95 *(978-0-691-14478-8(8))* Princeton Univ. Pr.
Myers, Gustavus. History of the Great American Fortunes. 2009. 422p. 41.99 *(978-1-116-31472-4(X))*; pap. 34.75 *(978-1-116-31475-5(4))* BiblioBazaar.
—History of the Great American Fortunes. 2009. 318p. pap. *(978-0-217-25468-7(3))* Books LLC.
—History of the Great American Fortunes, Vol. I. 296p. 70.00 *(978-0-88286-068-8(2))* Kerr, Charles H. Publishing Co.
Nandan, Raghu. Unleashing Your Entrepreneurial Potential. 2009. (Response Bks.). 380p. (C). pap. 44.95 *(978-81-7829-908-2(9)*, B99082P) SAGE Pubns., Inc.
Nester, William R. From Mountain Man to Millionaire: The Bold & Dashing Life of Robert Campbell, Revised & Expanded Edition. 2nd ed. 2011. (Missouri biography Ser.). (ENG., Illus.). (C). (gr. 8). 360p. 70.00 *(978-0-8262-1926-8(8))*; 324p. pap. 29.95 *(978-0-8262-1929-9(2))* Univ. of Missouri Pr.
Nocera, Joe. Good Guys & Bad Guys: Behind the Scenes with the Saints & Scoundrels of American Business (and Everything in Between) 2011. (ENG.). 304p. (gr. 12). 16.00 *(978-1-59184-439-6(8)*, Portfolio Trade) Penguin Group (USA) Inc.
Oliver, Jamie & Goodwin, Tony. How They Blew It: The CEO's & Entrepreneurs Behind Some of the World's Most Catastrophic Business Failures. 2010. (ENG.). 224p. pap. 19.95 *(978-0-7494-6065-5(2))* Kogan Page, Ltd. GBR. Dist: Ingram Pub. Services.
Osborne, Joseph & Schoenleber, Bill. Tired of Just over Broke - Job - Joy of Business. 2010. 144p. 29.99 *(978-1-4535-1248-7(9))* Xlibris Corp.
Ottavia, Enkhbold Chuluunbaatar. Studying Entrepreneurship Start-up Process: Psychological Perspective Comparative study between Taiwan & Mongolia. 2008. 108p. pap. *(978-3-639-11418-8(3))* VDM Verlag Dr. Mueller e.K.
Özbilgin, Mustafa F. & Malach-Pines, Ayala, eds. Career Choice in Management & Entrepreneurship: A Research Companion. 2009. (Illus.). 616p. pap. 74.00 *(978-1-84844-566-6(0))* Elgar, Edward Publishing, Inc.
Papa, David & Elliott, Lorna. International Trade & the Successful Intermediary. 2009. 280p. 124.95 *(978-0-566-08934-3(3)*, Gower Publishing Co., Ltd.) Ashgate Publishing, Ltd. GBR. Dist: Ashgate Publishing Co.
Pinkney, Andrea Davis & Rosen, Amy. Teen Business Blasts Off! 2010. (Illus.). 139p. ***(978-0-545-21877-1(2))*** Scholastic, Inc.
Piramal, Gita, contrib. by. Business Legends. (Illus.). xx, 654p. *(978-0-670-87898-7(7))* Penguin Group (USA) Inc.
Podruchny, Carolyn. Making the Voyageur World: Travelers & Traders in the North American Fur Trade. 2006. (ENG., Illus.). 347p. pap. *(978-0-8020-9428-5(7))* Univ. of Toronto Pr.
Pota, Vikas. India, Inc. How India's Top Ten Business Leaders Are Winning Globally. 2010. (ENG., Illus.). 240p. 32.95 *(978-1-85788-524-8(4))* Ebsco Publishing.
Rayner, Richard. The Associates: Four Capitalists Who Created California. 2008. (Enterprise Ser.). (ENG., Illus.). 224p. 23.95 *(978-0-393-05913-7(8)*, 5913) Atlas & Co.
Richardson, John. Annual Editions: Business Ethics 11/12. 23rd ed. 2011. (Annual Editions Ser.). (ENG., Illus.). 176p. (C). pap. 44.00 *(978-0-07-352865-6(X)*, 007352865X, McGraw-Hill/Dushkin) McGraw-Hill Higher Education.
Ronson, Gerald & Robinson, Jeffrey. Leading from the Front: My Story. 2009. (ENG., Illus.). 272p. 34.95 *(978-1-84596-509-9(4))* Mainstream Publishing Co., Ltd. GBR. Dist: Independent Pubs. Group.
Sander, Peter. Ultimate Guide to Personal Finance for Entrepreneurs. 2007. 280p. pap. 24.95 *(978-1-59918-059-5(6))* Entrepreneur Pr. dba Entrepreneur Media, Inc.
Scheller, William G. Great Estates: The Lifestyles & Homes of American Magnates. 2011. (Illus.). 240p. 14.98 *(978-0-7893-2250-0(1)*, Rizzoli Universe Promotional Bks.) Rizzoli International Pubns., Inc.
Schmandt, Jurgen. The Idea of Sustainability. 2010. (Illus.). 192p. 32.00 *(978-1-60344-217-6(0))* Texas A&M Univ. Pr.
Schwartz, Brian. 50 Interviews: Thriving in Uncertain Times. 2009. 300p. pap. 24.95 *(978-0-9822907-0-5(5))* Wise Media Group.
Seireeni, Richard & Fields, Scott. The Gort Cloud: The Invisible Force Powering Today's Most Visible Green Brands. 2009. (ENG., Illus.). 240p. pap. 24.95 *(978-1-60358-061-8(1))* Chelsea Green Publishing.
Sixsmith, Martin. Putin's Oil: The Yukos Affair & the Struggle for Russia. 2010. (ENG.). 320p. 24.95 *(978-1-4411-9968-3(3))* Continuum International Publishing Group, Ltd. GBR. Dist: National Bk. Network.
Smith, Keith Cameron. The Top 10 Distinctions Between Entrepreneurs & Employees. 2012. (ENG.). 128p. 15.00 ***(978-0-345-53550-4(2)***, Ballantine Bks.) Random House Publishing Group.
Smith, Roger Dean & Smith, Roger D. Advice Written on the Back of a Business Card: Leaders Share Their Most Valued Words of Guidance. 2009. (Illus.). 299p. ***(978-0-9823040-3-7(X))*** Modelbenders Pr.
Spadaccini, Michael. Ultimate Guide to Forming an LLC in Any State, Second Edition. 2nd ed. 2010. (ENG.). 304p. pap. 29.95 *(978-1-59918-386-2(2)*, 1599183862) Entrepreneur Pr. dba Entrepreneur Media, Inc.
Strom, Claire. Profiting from the Plains: The Great Northern Railway & Corporate Development of the American West. 2007. (ENG., Illus.). 240p. per. 25.00 *(978-0-295-98663-0(8))* Univ. of Washington Pr.
Stromberg, Gary & Merrill, Jane. Second Chances: Top Executives Share Their Stories of Addiction & Recovery. 2009. (ENG.). 256p. pap. 15.95 *(978-0-07-159162-1(1)*, 0071591621) McGraw-Hill Cos., The.
Sugar, Alan. What You See Is What You Get: My Autobiography. 2011. (ENG., Illus.). 640p. pap. 12.95 *(978-0-330-52047-8(4))* Macmillan Pubs., Ltd. GBR. Dist: Independent Pubs. Group.
Takaki, Keiichi. Development & Social Structure: The case of entrepreneurs in Ghana. 2011. 152p. pap. ***(978-3-8454-1445-4(6))*** Lambert Academic Publishing.
The\Planning Shop Staff. Passion to Profits: Business for New Entrepreneurs. Abrams, Rhonda, ed. 2009. (ENG., Illus.). 226p. pap. 29.95 *(978-0-9740801-9-2(5))* Planning Shop, The.
Thomas, Bob. Creating A World Class Company: A Triumph of the Entrepreneurial Spirit: A Triumph of the Entrepreneurial Spirit. 2009. 318p. 29.99 *(978-1-4500-0514-2(4))*; pap. 19.99 *(978-1-4500-0513-5(6))* Xlibris Corp.
Tong, Joy Kooi-Chin. Overseas Chinese Christian Entrepreneurs in Modern China: A Case Study of the Influence of Christian Ethics on Business Life. 2012. (Key Issues in Modern Sociology Ser.). (Illus.). 180p. 99.00 ***(978-0-85728-353-5(7))*** Anthem Pr. GBR. Dist: Books International, Inc.
Tsai, Kellee S. Capitalism Without Democracy: The Private Sector in Contemporary China. 2007. (Illus.). 268p. 63.95 *(978-0-8014-4513-2(2))*; per. 21.95 *(978-0-8014-7326-5(8))* Cornell Univ. Pr.
Tyler, Daniel. WD Farr: Cowboy in the Boardroom. 2011. (ENG., Illus.). 312p. 29.95 *(978-0-8061-4193-0(X))* Univ. of Oklahoma Pr.
Ucbasaran, Deniz, et al. Habitual Entrepreneurs. 2008. (ENG.). 152p. pap. 99.00 net. *(978-1-60198-112-7(0))* Now Pubs.
Valdez, Zulema. The New Entrepreneurs: How Race, Class, & Gender Shape American Enterprise. 2011. (ENG., Illus.). 208p. 65.00 *(978-0-8047-7320-1(3))*; pap. 21.95 *(978-0-8047-7321-8(1))* Stanford Univ. Pr.
Venkler, Cynthia S. Business Beginnings. 2008. 132p. pap. 14.99 *(978-1-60647-592-8(4))* Xulon Pr., Inc.
Vitale, Joe & Perrine, Craig. Inspired Marketing! The Astonishing Fun New Way to Create More Profits for Your Business by Following Your Heart. 2008. (ENG.). 224p. 24.95 *(978-0-470-18364-9(0)*, Wiley) Wiley, John & Sons, Inc.
Wall, Wendy L. Inventing the American Way: The Politics of Consensus from the New Deal to the Civil Rights Movement. 2009. (ENG., Illus.). 400p. pap. 21.95 *(978-0-19-539240-1(X))* Oxford Univ. Pr., Inc.
Wang, Yuan, et al. China Business Culture: Strategies for Success. 2008. 280p. pap. 35.00 *(978-981-04-8704-1(5))* Thorogood GBR. Dist: Stylus Publishing, LLC.
Wayhan, Darel. Corporate Bandits. 2008. pap. 12.00 *(978-0-8059-7919-0(0))* Dorrance Publishing Co., Inc.
Wheatcroft, A. J. M. & Hawatmeh, Christina. A Promise Fulfilled: Elia Costandi Nuqul & His Business Odyssey. 2008. (ENG., Illus.). 240p. 41.00 *(978-1-84511-734-4(4))* I. B. Tauris & Co., Ltd. GBR. Dist: Macmillan.
Wickersheim, Laurel Michele & LeBaron, Rawlene Briar. Colorado on the Eve of Statehood: An Edited Business Directory of the Pioneers Who Built the Centennial State. 2008. (Illus.). iv, 246p. *(978-0-7884-7314-2(X))* Heritage Bks.
Wilburn, Kenneth E. The Life of Statesman & Industrialist Sir James Sivewright of South Africa, 1848-1916: Builder of Railways, Telegraphs, & Waterworks. 2010. (Illus.). xxxii, 567p. 159.95 *(978-0-7734-3673-2(1))* Mellen, Edwin Pr., The.
Wilkinghoff, Steve. Found Money: Simple Strategies for Uncovering the Hidden Profit & Cash Flow in Your Business. 2009. (ENG., Illus.). 224p. 21.95 *(978-0-470-48335-0(0)*, Wiley) Wiley, John & Sons, Inc.
Winters, Larry. Live the Dream: No More Excuses. 2012. (ENG.). 208p. 21.99 ***(978-1-4555-1362-8(8))*** Center St.
Wobick-Segev, Sarah & Reuveni, Gideon, eds. The Economy in Jewish History: New Perspectives on the Interrelationship between Ethnicity & Economic Life. 2010. 252p. 95.00 *(978-1-84545-774-7(9))* Berghahn Bks., Inc.
Young, McGee. Developing Interests: Organizational Change & the Politics of Advocacy. 2010. *(978-0-7006-1703-6(5))*; pap. *(978-0-7006-1704-3(3))* Univ. Pr. of Kansas.
Yu, Shiping. Xin Tai Zi Shang. 2010. (CHI., Illus.). 517p. *(978-962-8744-32-9(1))* Mirror Bks. USA.
Zhao, Litao. Paths to Private Entrepreneurship. 2008. 160p. pap. *(978-3-639-05170-4(X))* VDM Verlag Dr. Mueller e.K.

BUSINESSPEOPLE—BIOGRAPHY

Abdul-Karim, Michael S. Customised down Under. 2010. 214p. pap. 10.99 *(978-1-61667-046-7(0))* Raider Publishing International.

Abebe, Mesfin. The Alleged American. 2009. 412p. 31.50 *(978-1-4389-3092-3(5))*; pap. 22.00 *(978-1-4389-3062-6(3))* AuthorHouse.

Abraham, Horst F. Berlin-Shanghai-Chicago. 2009. 272p. pap. 17.00 *(978-1-4389-7431-6(0))* AuthorHouse.

Abraham, S. Daniel. Everything Is Possible: Life & Business Lessons from a Self-Mad Billionaire & the Founder of Slim-Fast. 2010. (ENG., Illus.). 240p. 24.95 *(978-1-55704-650-9(9))*, Morrow, William & Co.) HarperCollins Pubs.

Acevedo, Ignacio. Corruption & Complicity: Memories of a Franchise & Lawsuits. 2009. 274p. 45.95 *(978-1-60594-379-4(7))*, Llumina Pr.) Aeon Publishing Inc.

Adams, Barney. The Wow Factor: How I Turned One Great Idea & My Unbridled Enthusiasm into a Golf Revolution. 2008. (Illus.). 254p. 24.95 *(978-1-60239-248-9(X))* Skyhorse Publishing Co., Inc.

Adversity Is Temporary. 2008. 192p. 23.95 *(978-0-9766229-3-2(9))* Henry, Norman.

Agno, Randy. God's Hand. 2008. 148p. 11.99 *(978-1-60462-455-7(8))* Tate Publishing & Enterprises, LLC.

Al Barrak, Saad. Dark Horse: Zain & the Art of Leadership. 2012. (ENG.). 272p. 30.00 ***(978-99921-94-67-6(7))*** Bloomsbury Publishing.

Allan, Tony. Making Good: The Inspiring Story of Serial Entrepreneur, Maverick & Restaurateur. 2006. (ENG.). 222p. per. 27.95 *(978-1-84112-631-9(4)*, Capstone) Wiley, John & Sons, Inc.

Allen, Paul. Idea Man: A Memoir by the Co-Founder of Microsoft. 2011. (ENG.). 368p. (gr. 12). 27.95 *(978-1-59184-382-5(0)*, Portfolio (Hardcover)) Penguin Group (USA) Inc.

Allen, Paul, ed. Idea Man: A Memoir by the Co-Founder of Microsoft. 2012. (ENG., Illus.). 368p. (gr. 12). pap. 17.00 ***(978-1-59184-537-9(8)***, Portfolio Trade) Penguin Group (USA) Inc.

Alon, Ilan & Zhang, Wenxian, eds. Biographical Dictionary of New Chinese Entrepreneurs & Business Leaders. 2009. (Elgar Original Reference Ser.). 296p. 182.00 *(978-1-84720-636-7(0))* Elgar, Edward Publishing, Inc.

Alston, James. From Thug to Business Man. 2011. 60p. pap. 15.99 ***(978-1-4500-3946-8(4))*** Xlibris Corp.

Anon, Bach. Dropping Almonds. 2008. 108p. 24.40 *(978-1-4251-6929-9(5))* Trafford Publishing.

Anthony, Michael. Memoirs of a White Man. 2009. 132p. 29.99 *(978-1-4415-8550-9(8))*; pap. 19.99 *(978-1-4415-8549-3(4))* Xlibris Corp.

Armbrester, Margaret. Samuel Ullman & Youth: The Life, the Legacy. 2009. (ENG., Illus.). 166p. pap. 22.50 *(978-0-8173-5589-0(8))* Univ. of Alabama Pr.

Armson, Kenneth A. & McLeod, Marjorie. The Legacy of John Waldie & Sons: A History of the Victoria Harbour Lumber Company. 2007. (ENG., Illus.). 152p. pap. 22.99 *(978-1-55002-758-7(1))* Natural Heritage/Natural History, Inc. CAN. Dist: Ingram Pub. Services.

Aslett, Don. How I Swept My Way to the Top: The Don Aslett Story. Cartaino, Carol, ed. 2008. (Illus.). 570p. pap. 24.99 *(978-0-937750-34-6(4))* Marsh Creek Pr.

Bailey, William H. Looking Up: Finding My Voice in Las Vegas. 2009. 240p. pap. 19.95 *(978-1-935043-04-1(8))* Stephens Pr. LLC.

Baker, Wayne B. Above the Clouds: The Story of an American Entrepreneur. 2008. (Illus.). 288p. pap. 19.95 *(978-0-9741568-3-5(3))* SouthPaw Pubns.

Balch, Michael. Got Coach? A coach's guide for being a top Wholesaler. 2009. 148p. pap. 15.95 *(978-1-4401-5057-9(5))* iUniverse, Inc.

Ballowe, James. A Man of Salt & Trees: The Life of Joy Morton. 2009. (Illus.). 318p. 28.95 *(978-0-87580-398-2(9))* Northern Illinois Univ. Pr.

Bari, Rashidul. Grameen Social Business Model: A Manifesto for Proletariat Revolution. 2011. 220p. pap. 14.03 ***(978-1-4634-0627-1(4))*** AuthorHouse.

Barrold, Bernda & Burden, Charlie. Sir Alan Sugar: The Biography. 2009. (ENG., Illus.). 262p. 29.95 *(978-1-84454-702-9(7))* Blake, John Publishing, Ltd. GBR. Dist: Independent Pubs. Group.

Barry, Ben. Fashioning Reality: A New Generation of Entrepreneurship. rev. ed. 2007. (ENG., Illus.). 256p. 24.95 *(978-1-55263-820-0(0))* Key Porter Bks. CAN. Dist: Perseus-PGW.

Bartholomew, Dave. Before I Forget. 2007. (ENG.). 200p. per. 13.95 *(978-0-7414-3873-7(9))* Infinity Publishing.

Bartlett, Steve. The Grit & the Courage: Stories of Success in an Unforgiving Land. 2008. (Illus.). 150p. pap. *(978-1-897174-29-6(2))* Creative Bk. Publishing.

Battistella, Edwin L. Do You Make These Mistakes in English? The Story of Sherwin Cody's Famous Language School. 2008. (ENG., Illus.). 224p. 29.95 *(978-0-19-536712-6(X))* Oxford Univ. Pr., Inc.

Baum, Stephen H. & Conti, Dave. What Made Jack Welch Jack Welch: How Ordinary People Become Extraordinary Leaders. 2007. (ENG.). 288p. 24.95 *(978-0-307-33720-7(0)*, Crown Business) Crown Publishing Group.

Bélanger, Réal, et al. Canada's Entrepreneurs: From the Fur Trade to the 1929 Stock Market Crash - Portraits from the Dictionary of Canadian Biography. 2011. (Dictionary of Canadian Biography Ser.). (ENG., Illus.). 528p. ***(978-1-4426-4478-6(8))*** Univ. of Toronto Pr.

—Canada's Entrepreneurs: From the Fur Trade to the 1929 Stock Market Crash Portraits from the Dictionary of Canadian Biography. 2011. (Dictionary of Canadian Biography Ser.). (ENG., Illus.). 528p. pap. ***(978-1-4426-1286-0(X))*** Univ. of Toronto Pr.

Benedict, Margaret. An American Entrepreneur - Mr Joyce Clyde Hall - Founder of Hallmark Cards Inc. 2008. 76p. pap. 19.95 *(978-1-4389-0572-3(6))* AuthorHouse.

Benge, Janet & Benge, Geoff. Christian Heroes - Then & Now - David Bussau: Facing the World Head-on. 2008. (ENG.). 206p. per. *(978-1-57658-415-6(1))* YWAM Publishing.

Bennett, Andrew E. 25 Business Stories: A Practical Guide for English Learners. 2008. (ENG.). 144p. (gr. 7). 16.95 *(978-0-87779-683-1(1))* Merriam-Webster, Inc.

Berk, Howard. When My Boss Calls, Get the Name. 2008. 156p. pap. 14.95 *(978-0-595-47355-7(5))* iUniverse, Inc.

Bernhard, Kivi. Leopardology: The Hunt for Profit in A Tough Global Economy. 2009. (ENG.). 236p. 26.95 *(978-1-60037-650-4(9))*; pap. 16.95 *(978-1-60037-649-8(5))* Morgan James Publishing.

Berridge, Charlie. Building a Bill on: The story of John Mccarthy. 2011. (ENG.). 196p. 27.99 *(978-0-85719-117-5(9))* Harriman Hse. Publishing GBR. Dist: Ingram Pub. Services.

Berwanger, Ralph. Summer Of '63. 2007. 296p. per. 12.95 *(978-1-4327-0336-3(6))* Outskirts Pr., Inc.

Bilen, Leif. They Put Me in Charge & Told Me I Didn't Have a Clue: Learning to lead by listening to bosses, co-workers, & Subordinates. 2009. 120p. pap. 11.99 *(978-1-4389-8931-0(8))* AuthorHouse.

Binder, Gordon & Bashe, Philip. Science Lessons: What the Business of Biotech Taught Me about Management. 2008. (ENG., Illus.). 292p. 29.95 *(978-1-59139-861-5(4))* Harvard Business Review Pr.

Binkley, Christina. Winner Takes All: Steve Wynn, Kirk Kerkorian, Gary Loveman, & the Race to Own Las Vegas. (ENG.). 320p. 2009. pap. 15.99 *(978-1-4013-0976-3(3))* 2008. 25.95 *(978-1-4013-0236-8(X))* Hyperion Pr.

Bivona, Michael. Was That Me? Turning Points in My Life by Mike Bivona. 2010. 192p. 24.77 *(978-1-4269-3756-9(3))*; pap. 14.77 *(978-1-4269-3755-2(5))* Trafford Publishing.

Blair, Gwenda. Donald Trump: Master Apprentice. 2007. (ENG.). 320p. pap. 21.95 *(978-1-4165-4654-2(5))* Simon & Schuster.

Blake, S. Prestley & Farnham, Alan. A Friendly Life: The Autobiography of S. Prestley Blake, Co-Founder of the Friendly Ice Cream Corp 2011. (Illus.). 132p. pap. 15.00 *(978-0-9826644-1-4(9)*, Brigantine Media) Raphel Marketing, Inc.

Blanchard, Ken & Covey, Stephen R. Blueprint for Success. 2008. (ENG., Illus.). 214p. pap. 19.95 *(978-1-60013-227-8(8))* Insight Publishing.

Blanchard, Robert & Blanchard, Melinda. Live What You Love: Notes from a Passionate Life. 2010. (ENG., Illus.). 216p. pap. 14.95 *(978-1-4027-7376-1(5))* Sterling Publishing Co., Inc.

Bloch, Thomas M. Many Happy Returns: The Story of Henry Bloch, America's Tax Man. 2010. (ENG., Illus.). 240p. 29.95 *(978-0-470-76777-1(4)*, Wiley) Wiley, John & Sons, Inc.

Bloom, Stephen G. Tears of Mermaids: The Secret Story of Pearls. 2009. (ENG.). 400p. 27.99 *(978-0-312-36326-0(5))* St. Martin's Pr.

Bogle, John C. Don't Count on It! Reflections on Investment Illusions, Capitalism, Mutual Funds, Indexing, Entrepreneurship, Idealism, & Heroes. 2010. (ENG., Illus.). 603p. 29.95 *(978-0-470-64396-9(X)*, Wiley) Wiley, John & Sons, Inc.

Bonami, Francesco & Gingeras, Alison, eds. La Collezione Di Punta Della Dogana: The Catalogue of the Contemporary Art Center in Venice. 2009. (ITA & FRE., Illus.). 300p. 115.00 *(978-88-370-6994-0(4))* Electa ITA. Dist: Trans-Atlantic Pubns., Inc.

Bondy, LeRoy. From manure to Mahogany: Memoirs of a Depression Child. 2007. 124p. pap. 13.95 *(978-1-60145-162-0(8))* Booklocker.com, Inc.

Bongardt, Robert. Where Is Home. 2008. pap. 16.95 *(978-0-7414-4732-6(0))* Infinity Publishing.

Bookman, Bernard K. When You Reach a Fork in the Road, Take It. Folkman Katie, ed. 2009. 112p. 24.95 *(978-0-9773365-7-9(3))* Interview You, LLC.

Bouffard, James Charles. The Entrepreneurial Ben Franklin - Third Edition. 2009. 190p. pap. 15.95 *(978-0-578-01259-9(6))* Paulo, Lynn Foundation.

Bower, Tom. Branson. 2009. (ENG., Illus.). 416p. pap. 16.95 *(978-0-00-726676-0(6))* HarperCollins Pubs. Ltd. GBR. Dist: Independent Pubs. Group.

—Outrageous Fortune: The Rise & Ruin of Conrad & Lady Black. 2006. (Illus.). 448p. 26.95 *(978-0-06-114614-5(5))* HarperCollins Pubs.

Bowling, Jeff. If You Never Quit, You'll Never Fail! Memoir of a Young Entrepreneur. 2007. (Illus.). 584p. pap. 18.50 net. *(978-0-9790237-0-5(X))* Bowling, Jeff.

Bowman, Bertie. Step by Step: A Memoir of Living the American Dream. 2009. (ENG., Illus.). 224p. pap. 15.00 *(978-0-345-50433-3(X)*, One World/Ballantine) Random House Publishing Group.

Boyle, Gert. One Tough Mother: Taking Charge in Life, Business, & Apple Pies. 2006. (ENG., Illus.). 208p. per. 14.95 *(978-0-7867-1914-3(1))* Basic Bks.

Bradley, Ian. Enlightened Entrepreneurs: Business Ethics in Victorian Britain. 2009. (ENG., Illus.). 224p. pap. 19.95 *(978-0-7459-5271-0(2))* Lion Hudson PLC GBR. Dist: Independent Pubs. Group.

Bramble, Linda. Niagara's Wine Visionaries: Profiles of the Pioneering Winemakers. 2009. (ENG., Illus.). 224p. 29.95 *(978-1-55277-429-8(5))* Lorimer, James & Co., Ltd., Pubs. CAN. Dist: Casemate Pubs. & Bk. Distributors, LLC.

Brands, H. W. Masters of Enterprise. 2008. (ENG.). 368p. pap. 23.95 *(978-1-4391-4401-5(X))*, Free Pr.) Free Pr.

Brandt, Richard L. One Click: Jeff Bezos & the Rise of Amazon.Com. 2011. (ENG.). 224p. (gr. 12). 25.95 *(978-1-59184-375-7(8)*, Portfolio (Hardcover)) Penguin Group (USA) Inc.

Branson, Richard. Business Stripped Bare: Adventures of a Global Entrepreneur. 2009. (ENG.). 320p. pap. 14.95 *(978-0-7535-1961-5(5))*; (Illus.). 384p. pap. *(978-0-7535-1503-7(2))* Virgin Bks. Ltd. GBR. Dist: Independent Pubs. Group.

—Losing My Virginity: The Autobiography. 2011. (ENG., Illus.). 624p. pap. 17.00 *(978-0-307-72074-0(8)*, Crown Business) Crown Publishing Group.

—Rebel Billionaire. 2008. (ENG.). 228p. pap. *(978-0-7535-1311-8(0))* Virgin Bks. Ltd. GBR. Dist: Independent Pubs. Group.

Braun, Ralph W. Rise Above: How One Man's Search for Mobility Helped the World Get Moving. 2010. 208p. 24.95 *(978-0-9843380-0-9(4))* Braun Corp., The.

Breen, Howard. A Page from a Ceo's Diary. 2009. 252p. 32.95 *(978-1-4389-3782-3(2))*; pap. 22.95 *(978-1-4389-3781-6(4))* AuthorHouse.

Brenner, Richard A. My Life Seen Through Our Eyes. 2011. 212p. 26.95 ***(978-0-86534-848-6(0))*** Sunstone Pr.

Bridge, Rachel. How I Made It: 40 Successful Entrepreneurs Reveal How They Made Millions. 2nd ed. 2010. (ENG., Illus.). 256p. pap. 19.95 *(978-0-7494-6052-5(0))* Kogan Page, Ltd. GBR. Dist: Ingram Pub. Services.

—My Big Idea: 30 Successful Entrepreneurs Reveal How They Found Inspiration. 2010. (ENG., Illus.). 192p. pap. 19.95 *(978-0-7494-6053-2(9))* Kogan Page, Ltd. GBR. Dist: Ingram Pub. Services.

Bright, Darrell. Growing up with Bob. 2009. 292p. 35.95 *(978-1-60594-051-9(8))*; (ENG.). pap. 17.95 *(978-1-60594-050-2(X))* Aeon Publishing Inc. (Llumina Pr.).

Brody, Leonard & Raffa, David. Everything I Needed to Know about Business... I Learned from a Canadian. 2nd ed. 2009. (ENG., Illus.). 288p. pap. 22.95 *(978-0-470-15975-0(8)*, Wiley) Wiley, John & Sons, Inc.

Bronson, Richard D. The War at the Shore: Steve Wynn, Donald Trump, & the Epic War to Save Atlantic City. 2012. (ENG.). 224p. (gr. 12). 26.00 ***(978-1-4683-0046-8(6))*** Overlook Pr., The.

Bruce, David. On the Level: A Brickies Tale. 2008. 296p. 25.99 *(978-1-4389-1262-2(5))*; pap. 15.49 *(978-1-4389-1255-4(2))* AuthorHouse.

Brumley, Kim. Marland Tragedy: The Turbulent Story of A Forgotten Oklahoma Icon. 2010. pap. 12.99 *(978-1-61566-606-5(0))* Tate Publishing & Enterprises, LLC.

Budd, Edward G. Edward G Budd Father of the Streamliners. 2006. pap. 15.95 *(978-1-4286-5978-0(1))* Kessinger Publishing, LLC.

Budig, Gene A. & Gilman, Sander. Grasping the Ring II: Nine People Who Matter. 2010. (ENG., Illus.). 120p. pap. 14.95 *(978-0-8032-3400-0(7)*, Bison Bks.) Univ. of Nebraska Pr.

Buenger, Victoria & Buenger, Walter L. Texas Merchant: Marvin Leonard & Fort Worth. 2008. (Kenneth E. Montague Series in Oil & Business History Ser.). (ENG.). 264p. pap. 19.95 *(978-1-60344-054-7(2))* Texas A&M Univ. Pr.

Bunch, Jim, et al. Millennial Leaders: Success Stories from Today's Most Brilliant Generation Y Leaders. 2007. 313p. 30.95 *(978-1-60037-351-0(8))* Morgan James Publishing.

Burd, Charlie. Lord Sugar: The Man Who Revolutionised British Business. 2010. (ENG., Illus.). 272p. 27.95 *(978-1-84454-929-0(1))* Blake, John Publishing, Ltd. GBR. Dist: Independent Pubs. Group.

Burd, Charlie. Lord Sugar - the Man Who Revolution. 2011. (ENG., Illus.). 272p. pap. 12.95 ***(978-1-84358-373-8(9))*** Blake, John Publishing, Ltd. GBR. Dist: Independent Pubs. Group.

Burd, Charlie & Newkey-Burden, Chas. Sir Alan Sugar - the Biography. 2010. (ENG., Illus.). 288p. pap. 13.95 *(978-1-84454-891-0(0))* Blake, John Publishing, Ltd. GBR. Dist: Independent Pubs. Group.

Burman, Sanjay. The Art of Persistence: From Building Relationships, to Getting Any Job You Desire... 2007. (ENG.). 120p. per. 10.95 *(978-0-9781380-0-4(7))* Burman Books, Inc. CAN. Dist: Independent Pubs. Group.

Burns, Brian. Lewis Ginter: Richmond's Gilded Age Icon. 2011. 130p. pap. 21.99 ***(978-1-60949-380-6(X))*** History Pr., The.

Burt, David C. & Barry, Craig L. Supplier to the Confederacy: PETER TAIT & CO. LIMERICK. 2011. 136p. pap. ***(978-0-7552-0660-5(6))*** Authors OnLine, Ltd

Cacciotti, Joseph J. Blue Collar Real Estate Mogul: Literary Work. 2006. 129p. per. 10.95 *(978-1-59824-275-1(X))* E-BookTime LLC.

Caesar, Latoy. Damn, If I Had Known. 2011. 88p. 24.99 ***(978-1-4568-7673-9(2))***; pap. 15.99 ***(978-1-4568-7672-2(4))*** Xlibris Corp.

Cain, Herman. This Is Herman Cain! My Journey to the White House. 2011. pap. ***(978-1-4516-6614-4(4))***; (ENG., Illus.). 240p. 25.00 ***(978-1-4516-6613-7(6))*** Threshold Editions. (Threshold Editions).

Callahan, Kevin M. The Profit Pyramid. 2010. 125p. pap. 12.00 *(978-0-557-18470-5(3))* Lulu Enterprises Inc.

Carey, Charles W. American Inventors, Entrepreneurs, & Business Visionaries. 2nd rev. ed. 2010. (American Biographies Ser.). 480p. (C). (gr. 9). 95.00 *(978-0-8160-8146-2(8))* Facts On File, Inc.

Carol, Pine. Follow Me. 2007. 29.95 *(978-0-87839-251-3(3))* North Star Pr. of St. Cloud.

Caswell, Alexis. A Brief Memoir of John Barstow, of Providence, R I by Alexis Caswell. 2011. 18p. pap. 11.99 ***(978-1-4181-9069-9(1))*** MPublishing.

Caswell, Brandon W. Fiddleman. 2009. 312p. pap. 15.49 *(978-1-4490-3779-6(8))* AuthorHouse.

Chouinard, Yvon. Let My People Go Surfing: The Education of a Reluctant Businessman. 2006. (ENG., Illus.). 272p. (gr. 12-18). 18.00 *(978-0-14-303783-5(8)*, Penguin (Non-Classics)) Penguin Group (USA) Inc.

Clark, Francesco. Walking Papers: The Accident That Changed My Life, & the Business That Got Me Back on My Feet. 2010. (ENG.). 240p. 23.99 *(978-1-4013-2343-1(X))* Hyperion Pr.

Clark, Lindie. Finding a Common Interest: The Story of Dick Dusseldorp & Lend Lease. 2007. (ENG., Illus.). 320p. pap. 45.00 *(978-0-521-03994-9(0))* Cambridge Univ. Pr.

Clark, Reg. Across the Shallow Waters the Life and. 2006. 264p. *(978-1-84667-025-1(X))* Derwent Pr., The.

Claudiu Pop Buia. Reaching Home. 2009. (Illus.). 164p. pap. 11.99 *(978-1-4389-5197-3(3))* AuthorHouse.

Clawson, Matthew B. Born in the Barn. 2010. 48p. pap. 15.99 *(978-1-4535-4437-2(2))* Xlibris Corp.

Clinton, Jerry. Accept the Challenge: The Memoirs of Jerry Clinton. 2006. 192p. *(978-1-933370-01-9(7))* Reedy Pr.

Cochran, Mike. Claytie: The Roller-Coaster Life of a Texas Wildcatter. 2007. (ENG., Illus.). 446p. 24.95 *(978-1-58544-634-6(3))* Texas A&M Univ. Pr.

Cohen, Rich. The Fish That Ate the Whale: The Life & Times of America's Banana King. 1 vol. 2012. (ENG., Illus.). 288p. 27.00 ***(978-0-374-29927-9(7))*** Farrar, Straus & Giroux.

Colley, Leroy. Born to Make A Difference. 2010. 124p. 23.99 *(978-1-4490-9293-1(4))*; pap. 13.99 *(978-1-4490-9292-4(6))* AuthorHouse.

Comings, Herbert C. Years of an Old Vermonter: Some Biographical Jottings. 2011. 48p. 35.95 ***(978-1-258-09027-2(9))*** Literary Licensing, LLC.

Conradd, Robert L. Succeed Beyond Adversity Too: Same Day, Different Story. 2010. 232p. pap. 19.95 *(978-1-4327-5612-3(5))* Outskirts Pr., Inc.

Conerd, Geert. Girlfriend in Every City. 2nd ed. 2006. (Illus.). 108p. pap. *(978-1-905823-07-9(X))* Ecademy Pr. Ltd.

Conley, Don. Flying over the Golden Arches. 2010. pap. 14.95 *(978-1-59298-349-0(9))* Beaver's Pond Pr., Inc.

Cooke, Richard William. Make Mine Manhattan: A Memoir. 2007. 280p. per. 19.95 *(978-0-595-47264-2(8))* iUniverse, Inc.

Cooley, Michael G. Rock Bottom: From the Streets to Success. 2011. pap. 16.99 *(978-1-61739-738-7(5))* Tate Publishing & Enterprises, LLC.

Cooper, Havard S. My Story ... His Glory: The Life & Experience of a Bahamian Son: Havard S. Cooper Sr. 2010. 200p. 26.95 *(978-1-4502-5679-7(1))*; pap. 15.95 *(978-1-4502-5678-0(3))* iUniverse, Inc.

Cooper, Richard E. Hickory Bob: the Bob Harmon Story: From Missouri Orphan to the Major Leagues to Louisiana Millionaire, Bob Harmon Touched All the Bases. the True Story of a Dead Ball Era Star. 2007. (Illus.). 60p. 22.95 *(978-1-58597-428-3(5))* Leathers Publishing.

Cooper Sr., Devon D. The Start of an Eternal Legacy. 2011. 18p. pap. 16.95 ***(978-1-4626-1572-8(4))*** PublishAmerica, Inc.

Coppola, Sam. Silent Quarterback. 2010. 176p. pap. 19.95 *(978-0-9766965-9-9(2))* Pull Your Own Weight Sports Marketing.

Coquillette, Robert McTavish. A Family Sag: A record of one man's experiences in the 20th Century. 2009. 180p. pap. 16.95 *(978-1-4401-9194-7(8))* iUniverse Inc.

Cordivari, Bill. A Grander Vision: Becoming God's Leader in the Workplace. 2006. 175p. pap. 14.95 *(978-0-7414-3355-8(9))* Infinity Publishing.

Corey, Alan. A Million Bucks By 30: How to Overcome a Crap Job, Stingy Parents, & a Useless Degree to Become a Millionaire Before (or after) Turning Thirty. 2007. (ENG.). 240p. per. 15.00 *(978-0-345-49972-1(7)*, Ballantine Bks.) Random House Publishing Group.

Courtenay, Arthur. Autobiography & Letters of Arthur Courtenay. 2007. (ENG.). 216p. 39.95 *(978-0-548-15487-8(2))*; pap. 24.95 *(978-1-4304-4915-7(2))* Kessinger Publishing, LLC.

Cowan, George A. Manhattan Project to the Santa Fe Institute: The Memoirs of George A. Cowan. 2010. (ENG., Illus.). 184p. 27.95 *(978-0-8263-4870-8(X))* Univ. of New Mexico Pr.

Crozier, Catherine (Cat). Dancing with the Devil. 2011. 232p. pap. 13.25 ***(978-1-4575-0400-6(6))*** Dog Ear Publishing, LLC.

Dale, Richard. Forever! It's All about Me - Isn't It? 2010. 452p. pap. 20.49 *(978-1-4520-6848-0(8))* AuthorHouse.

Dalglish, Garven & Hillenbrand, John A. Of This Heritage: The Biography of John A. Hillenbrand. 2011. 260p. 47.95 ***(978-1-258-09403-4(7))*** Literary Licensing, LLC.

Dam Foolishness. 2011. 240p. 27.95 *(978-1-885942-22-7(2))* Cune Pr., LLC.

Dando-Collins, Stephen. Tycoon's War: How Cornelius Vanderbilt Invaded a Country to Overthrow America's Most Famous Military Adventurer. 2009. (ENG.). 400p. pap. 17.95 *(978-0-306-81856-1(6))* Da Capo Pr., Inc.

D'Angelo, Frank. Being Frank: the Inspiring Story of Frank D'Angelo, 1 vol. 2011. (ENG.). 168p. pap. 15.95 ***(978-1-927005-03-3(5))*** Burman Books, Inc. CAN. Dist: Innovative Logistics.

Daniel S Fowler. 10 Steps to Energizing Your Business & Your Life: A Commonsense Guide to Stay Successfully Engaged in Your Business & Your Life. 2009. 84p. pap. 10.95 *(978-1-4401-6917-5(9))* iUniverse, Inc.

D'Antonio, Michael. A Full Cup: Sir Thomas Lipton's Extraordinary Life & His Quest for the America's Cup. 2010. (ENG.). 368p. (gr. 12). 26.95 *(978-1-59448-760-6(X)*, Riverhead Bks. (Hardcover)) Penguin Group (USA) Inc.

—Hershey: Milton S. Hershey's Extraordinary Life of Wealth, Empire, & Utopian Dreams. 2007. (ENG., Illus.). 320p. pap. 15.00 *(978-0-7432-6410-5(X))* Simon & Schuster.

de Waal, Edmund. A Hare with Amber Eyes: A Family's Century of Art & Loss. 2010. (ENG., Illus.). 368p. 26.00 *(978-0-374-10597-6(9))* Farrar, Straus & Giroux.

—The Hare with Amber Eyes: A Hidden Inheritance. 2011. (ENG., Illus.). 368p. pap. 16.00 *(978-0-312-56937-2(8))* Picador.

Dearlove, Des. The Unauthorized Guide to Doing Business the Richard Branson Way: 10 Secrets of the World's Greatest Brand Builder. 3rd rev. ed. 2010. (ENG.). 176p. pap. 15.95 *(978-0-85708-061-5(X)*, Capstone) Wiley, John & Sons, Inc.

DeKok, David. The Epidemic: A Collision of Power, Privilege, & Public Health. 2011. (ENG., Illus.). 304p. 22.95 *(978-0-7627-6008-4(7))*, Lyons Pr.) Globe Pequot Pr., The.
Dell, Phil. Living with Me. 2009. 236p. pap. 14.49 *(978-1-4389-3569-0(2))* AuthorHouse.
Derbyshire, Wyn. Six Tycoons: The Lives of John Jacob Astor, Cornelius Vanderbilt, Andrew Carnegie, John D. Rockefeller, Henry Ford & Joseph P. Kennedy. 2009. 251p. pap. 14.95 *(978-1-904905-85-1(4))* Spiramus Pr. GBR. Dist: International Specialized Bk. Services.
Deutsch, Naftali. A Holocaust Survivor: In the Footsteps of His Past. 2007. 320p. per. 22.95 *(978-965-7344-40-8(9))* Mazo Pubs.
Dick, Rudolph C. Nathaniel Griffin of Salem & His Naumk. 2006. pap. 15.95 *(978-1-4286-6065-6(8))* Kessinger Publishing, LLC.
Dietrich, William. Eminent Pittsburghers: Profiles of the City's Founding Industrialists. 2011. (ENG., Illus.). 232p. 24.95 *(978-1-58979-607-2(1))* Taylor Trade Publishing.
Doan, Leland I. Willard Henry Dow President of the Dow C. 2006. pap. 15.95 *(978-1-4286-6066-3(6))* Kessinger Publishing, LLC.
Dobinick, Susan. Mark Zuckerberg & Facebook. 2012. (Internet Biographies Ser.). (ENG.). 128p. (YA). (gr. 7-12). lib. bdg. 34.60 ***(978-1-4488-6909-1(9))*** Rosen Publishing Group, Inc., The.
Doherty, Thomas. The Best Specimen of a Tyrant: The Ambitious Dr. Abraham Van Norstrand & the Wisconsin Insane Hospital. 2007. per. 16.95 *(978-0-9792319-0-2(6))* Spenser-Hoyt.
Dorf, Philip. The Builder: A Biography of Ezra Cornell. 2011. 478p. 58.95 ***(978-1-258-08307-6(8))*** Literary Licensing, LLC.
Doron, Meir & Joseph, Gelman. Confidential: The Life of Secret Agent Turned Hollywood Tycoon - Arnon Milchan. 2011. (Illus.). 400p. pap. 24.95 *(978-0-615-43381-3(2))* Gefen Publishing Hse.
Dorsinville, Jean M. Franklyn V. E. Seales: Life of an Artist. 2011. 264p. pap. 16.95 ***(978-1-4620-3331-7(8))*** iUniverse, Inc.
Douglas, Thompson. Inside the Muslim Brotherhood. 2012. (ENG., Illus.). 288p. 32.95 ***(978-1-85782-687-6(6))*** Blake, John Publishing, Ltd. GBR. Dist: Independent Pubs. Group.
Dream, Inc: Philadelphia Edition. 2008. 271p. pap. 19.95 *(978-0-615-17620-8(8))* Persistent Marketing Inc.
Drexler, Kateri. Icons of Business: An Encyclopedia of Mavericks, Movers, & Shakers, 2 vols., Set. 2006. (Greenwood Icons Ser.). (Illus.). 544p. 175.00 *(978-0-313-33862-5(0)*, GR3862, Greenwood Pr.) Greenwood Publishing Group, Inc.
du Toit, Brian M. Ecusta & the Legacy of Harry H. Straus. 2007. 204p. pap. 24.95 *(978-1-60441-476-9(6))* PublishAmerica, Inc.
Durgin, David L. & Robinson, Sherry. Entrepreneur to Investor the Hard Way. 2009. 204p. pap. 22.95 *(978-0-86534-695-6(X))* Sunstone Pr.
Ebury, Sue. The Many Lives of Kenneth Myer. 2008. (ENG.). 400p. 54.00 *(978-0-522-85546-3(6))* Melbourne Univ. Publishing AUS. Dist: Independent Pubs. Group.
Eckberg, John. The Success Effect: Uncommon Conversations with America's Business Trailblazers. 2008. (ENG.). 300p. pap. 14.95 *(978-0-9779545-8-2(7))* Sterling & Ross Pubs.
Eddins, Rick. Call Me a Countrypolitan. 2008. (ENG.). 160p. pap. 13.99 *(978-1-59932-088-5(6))* Advantage Media Group.
Edmundson, William. The Nitrate King: A Biography of Colonel John Thomas North. 2011. (Studies of the Americas Ser.). (ENG., Illus.). 218p. 85.00 *(978-0-230-11280-3(3))* Palgrave Macmillan.
Edwards, Kasey. 30 Something & over It: What Happens When You Get up & Don't Want to Go to Work... Ever Again. 2009. (ENG.). 224p. pap. 14.95 ***(978-1-84596-446-7(2))*** Mainstream Publishing Co., Ltd. GBR. Dist: Independent Pubs. Group.
Egan, Ferol. Last Bonanza Kings: The Bourns of San Francisco. 2009. (ENG.). 312p. pap. 29.95 *(978-0-87417-786-2(3))* Univ. of Nevada Pr.
Eisenhart, M. Herbert. J J Bausch American Pioneer. 2006. pap. 15.95 *(978-1-4286-6075-5(5))* Kessinger Publishing, LLC.
Elliot, Jay & Simon, William L. The Steve Jobs Way: ILeadership for a New Generation. 2012. (ENG.). 256p. pap. 15.99 ***(978-1-59315-710-4(X))*** Vanguard Pr.
Elliot, Jay, et al. The Steve Jobs Way: Ileadership for a New Generation. 2011. (ENG., Illus.). 256p. 25.99 *(978-1-59315-639-8(1))* Vanguard Pr.
Ellis, Charles D. Joe Wilson & the Creation of Xerox. 2006. (ENG., Illus.). 404p. 27.95 *(978-0-471-99835-8(4)*, Wiley) Wiley, John & Sons, Inc.
Ellsworth, Darrell. Be Someone. 2009. 242p. pap. *(978-1-84923-479-5(5))* YouWriteOn.
Erdle, Jack A. The Wisdom of A & E. Cote, Kate Winters, ed. 2007. (Illus.). 214p. *(978-1-888069-28-0(7))* Biography For Everyone, LLC.
Eriksen, Olof A. Memoirs of an Immigrant. 2008. 560p. 29.95 *(978-1-4327-1014-9(1))* Outskirts Pr., Inc.
Evans, Larry. Stand By! From Fighter Jets to Fine Art hellip; A Life's Journey. 2008. 224p. per. 17.95 *(978-1-60494-009-1(3))* Wheatmark.
Farnham, Sherman. The Hargraves of Wymore: A Family History in Nineteen Chapters, Following the Hargrave Family Through Three Generations from 1850 to 1966. 2007. (Illus.). viii, 137p. *(978-1-60530-599-8(5))* Kan sasana Printer.
Farquhar, A. B. First Million the Hardest an Autobiograp. 2006. pap. 31.95 *(978-1-4286-3728-3(1))* Kessinger Publishing, LLC.
Fasel, Marion & Proddow, Penny. Henry Dunay: A Precious Life. 2007. (ENG., Illus.). 224p. 60.00 *(978-0-8109-9395-2(3))* Abrams.
Fei, Yan. Zhongguo Shi Da Fu Hao Jia Zu. 2011. (CHI., Illus.). 573p. ***(978-1-935981-13-8(7))*** Mirror Bks. USA.
Feigh, Craig T. All My Imperfections, I Inherited from My Mom. 2008. 204p. per. 14.99 *(978-1-60477-791-8(5))* Xulon Pr., Inc.
Fels, Mary. Joseph Fels: His Life-Work. 2007. (ENG.). 284p. 43.95 *(978-0-548-14748-1(5))* 2006. pap. 28.95 *(978-1-4286-6155-4(7))* Kessinger Publishing, LLC.
Fenn, Donna. Alpha Dogs: How Your Small Business Can Become a Leader of the Pack. 2007. (ENG., Illus.). 240p. per. 14.95 *(978-0-06-075868-4(6)*, Collins) HarperCollins Pubs.
Ferendo, Frank J. Spanish Lessons. 2008. pap. 19.95 *(978-0-9795180-1-0(6))* Process Publishing Co.
Fertel, Randy. The Gorilla Man & the Empress of Steak: A New Orleans Family Memoir. 2011. (Willie Morris Books in Memoir & Biography Ser.). (ENG.). 288p. 28.00 ***(978-1-61703-082-6(1))*** Univ. Pr. of Mississippi.
Fields, Bea, et al. Millennial Leaders: Success Stories from Today's Most Brilliant Generation & Leaders. 2nd ed. 2008. (ENG.). 324p. pap. 19.95 *(978-0-9814545-1-8(8))* Writer of the Round Table Pr.
—Millennial Leaders: Success Stories from Today's Most Brilliant Generation Y Leaders. 2nd ed. 2008. 30.95 *(978-0-9814545-0-4(X))* Writer of the Round Table Pr.
Fields, Bea R., et al. Millennial Leaders: Success Stories from Today's Most Brilliant Generation Y Leaders. 2007. (ENG.). 313p. per. 19.95 *(978-1-60037-350-3(X))* Morgan James Publishing.
Fink, Leo Gregory. Memoirs of General Harry Clay Trexler. 2007. (ENG.). 214p. 39.95 *(978-0-548-06383-5(4))* Kessinger Publishing, LLC.
Finnick, Richard J. "Dick". Often Wrong, but Never in Doubt: A look back at a life greatly Blessed. 2009. 252p. 24.99 *(978-1-4490-1379-0(1))*; pap. 14.49 *(978-1-4490-1378-3(3))* AuthorHouse.
Fish, Kevin R. More Than Popcorn: The Life & Times of Orville Clarence (Reddy) Redenbacher-and More. 2008. 95p. pap. 16.95 *(978-1-60703-181-9(7))* PublishAmerica, Inc.
Fisher, Harriet F. The Darlings of Vermont's Northeast Kingdom. 2008. pap. 19.99 *(978-1-59629-380-9(2))* History Pr., The.
Fixman, Ben & Roth, Donald. The Ben Fixman Story: From the Ghetto to the Gold. 2009. *(978-1-61623-248-1(X))* Independent Pub.
Flood, Finbarr. In Full Flood: A Memoir. 2006. (ENG., Illus.). 245p. pap. 25.95 *(978-1-905483-02-0(3))* Liberties Pr. IRL. Dist: Dufour Editions, Inc.
Fong, Gary. The Accidental Millionaire: How to Succeed in Life Without Really Trying. 2009. (ENG.). 272p. pap. 14.95 *(978-1-933771-91-5(7))* BenBella Bks.
Fong, Gary. The Accidental Millionaire: How to Succeed in Life Without Really Trying: A Memoir. 2009. (Illus.). 264p. ***(978-1-933771-96-0(8))*** BenBella Bks.
Fong, William. J. W. McConnell: Financier, Philanthropist, Patriot. 2008. (ENG., Illus.). 752p. (C). *(978-0-7735-3270-0(6))* McGill-Queen's Univ. Pr.
—Sir William C. MacDonald: A Biography. 2007. (ENG., Illus.). 336p. (C). *(978-0-7735-3304-2(4))* McGill-Queen's Univ. Pr.
Ford, David Douglas. Whole Life: Looking Back While Looking Ahead. 2006. kivar 21.95 *(978-0-944435-58-8(0))* Glenbridge Publishing, Ltd.
Ford, Henry. My Life & Work. 2008. 268p. 28.99 *(978-0-554-22394-0(5))*; 25.99 *(978-0-554-31697-0(8))* BiblioBazaar.
—My Life & Work. 2009. 200p. pap. *(978-0-217-25960-6(X))* Books LLC.
—My Life & Work. 2007. 296p. 21.50 *(978-1-60206-935-0(2))* Cosimo, Inc.
—My Life & Work. 2010. 302p. pap. 11.50 *(978-1-57898-916-4(7))* Martino Publishing.
Ford, Henry & Crowther, Samuel. My Life & Work. 2007. (ENG.). 312p. 22.99 *(978-1-59986-693-2(5))* Filiquarian Publishing, LLC.
Foulkes, Nick. Mikimoto. 2008. (ENG., Illus.). 80p. 25.00 *(978-2-7594-0258-8(4))* Assouline FRA. Dist: Perseus Distribution.
Friedricks, William B. In for the Long Haul: The Life of John Ruan. 2010. (Bur Oak Book Ser.). (Illus.). 314p. pap. 20.00 *(978-1-58729-917-9(8))* Univ. of Iowa Pr.
Frost, Joseph W. P. Sir William Pepperrell His Britannic Maj. 2006. (Illus.). pap. 15.95 *(978-1-4286-5982-7(X))* Kessinger Publishing, LLC.
Frusztajer, Boruch B. From Siberia to America: A Story of Survival & Success. 2008. (Illus.). 430p. per. 30.00 *(978-1-58966-155-4(9))* Univ. of Scranton Pr.
Fujii, Jocelyn. Tori Richard the First Fifty Years. 2007. (Illus.). 116p. 49.95 *(978-0-9785466-0-1(1))* Richard, Tori Ltd.
Full Committee Hearing on Heroes of Small Business: Hearing Before the Committee on Small Business, United States House of Representatives, One Hundred Eleventh Congress, First Session, Hearing Held May 20, 2009. 2009. v, 86p. *(978-0-16-083907-8(6)*, 552-070-39596-2) United States Government Printing Office.
Gale, Don. Bags to Riches: The Story of I J Wagner. 2007. (ENG., Illus.). 336p. 25.95 *(978-0-87480-885-8(5))* Univ. of Utah Pr.
Gallner, Melissa. The Missing Thai Silk King. 2009. *(978-1-61623-227-6(7))* Independent Pub.
Gardner, Chris. The Pursuit of Happyness. Lt. ed. 2006. 456p. per. 25.95 *(978-0-06-112067-1(7)*, Morrow, William & Co.) HarperCollins Pubs.
Garner, Paul H. British Lions & Mexican Eagles: Business, Politics, & Empire in the Career of Weetman Pearson in Mexico, 1889-1919. 2011. (ENG.). 336p. 65.00 *(978-0-8047-7445-1(5))* Stanford Univ. Pr.
Gayle, Croswell. Make the First Chance Count, 1 vol. 2009. 64p. pap. 16.95 *(978-1-60672-090-5(2))* PublishAmerica, Inc.
Gergen, Christopher & Vanourek, Gregg. Life Entrepreneurs: Ordinary People Creating Extraordinary Lives. 2008. (J-B Warren Bennis Ser.: 142). (ENG., Illus.). 256p. 24.95 *(978-0-7879-8862-3(6)*, Jossey-Bass) Wiley, John & Sons, Inc.
Goddard, Stephen B. Colonel Albert Pope & His American Dream Machines: The Life & Times of a Bicycle Tycoon Turned Automotive Pioneer. alt. ed. 2008. (ENG.). 263p. pap. 39.95 *(978-0-7864-4089-4(9))* McFarland & Co., Inc. Pubs.
Goffe, Leslie. When Banana Was King. 2007. 332p. *(978-976-8202-50-5(5))* LMH Publishing, Ltd.
Goffe, Leslie Gordon. When Banana Was King: The Life & Times of Jamaican Banana King Alfred Constantine Goffe. 2006. (ENG.). 332p. per. *(978-976-8202-23-9(6))* LMH Publishing, Ltd.
Goldbach, Robert. Faith in an Imperfect World: A Letter to My Grandchildren, 1 vol. 2009. (ENG.). 51p. pap. 16.95 *(978-1-4489-7678-2(2))* PublishAmerica, Inc.
Goldsack, Bob. Behind the Scenes-Eastern States Exposition, West Springfield, Mass: 2nd the Story of New England's Mr Show Business Wayne Mccary. 2006. (Illus.). 88p. pap. 24.00 *(978-1-880545-11-9(X))* Midway Museum Pubns.
Golenbock, Peter. George: The Poor Little Rich Boy Who Built the Yankee Empire. 2010. (ENG., Illus.). 384p. pap. 16.95 *(978-0-470-60204-1(X)*, Wiley) Wiley, John & Sons, Inc.
Golightly, James. Sold in Spite Of: The life, times & confessions of a career estate Agent. 2009. 62p. pap. 10.65 *(978-1-4251-7443-9(4))* Trafford Publishing.
Good, Marcia Russell. A Hidden Vision in Letters. 2006. 332p. 25.00 *(978-0-9669263-1-6(5))* Castle Pr.
Goodridge, Walt F. J. Jamaican in Saipan: The true story of one man's escape from the rat race to live a personal nomadpreneur's dream! (a unique travel guide for the rest of Us) 2007. 150p. per. 14.00 *(978-0-9745313-9-7(1))* Passion Profit Co., The/NicheMarket.
Gordon, Wallace J. Madison Avenue South, 1964- Writing My Way Through the Cola Wars... 2009. 504p. pap. 22.99 *(978-1-4343-9194-0(9))* AuthorHouse.
Gould, Karen Melonie. Supporting Dreams. 2011. 180p. pap. 17.09 ***(978-1-4567-8592-5(3))*** AuthorHouse.
Graham, David. They Ride White Horses: The End of the Search for Significance. 2011. (ENG.). 192p. pap. 14.95 ***(978-1-936417-26-1(X))*** Pilot Communications Group, Inc.
Graham, Norman A. From the Barrack Room to the Boardroom. 2007. 356p. 33.95 *(978-0-595-71375-2(0))* iUniverse, Inc.
Grano, Joseph J. & Levine, Mark. You Can't Predict a Hero: From War to Wall Street, Leading in Times of Crisis. 2009. (ENG., Illus.). 240p. 27.95 *(978-0-470-41167-4(8)*, Jossey-Bass) Wiley, John & Sons, Inc.
Greeley, Bob. Looking Back. 2011. 240p. 29.99 ***(978-1-4628-9697-4(9))***; pap. 19.99 ***(978-1-4628-9696-7(0))*** Xlibris Corp.
Gregory, Benjamin. The Thorough Business Man: Memoirs of Walter Powell, Merchant. 2007. (ENG.). 392p. per. 33.95 *(978-1-4304-4502-9(5))* Kessinger Publishing, LLC.
Griffiths, Tony. Corporate Catalyst: A Chronicle of the (Mis)Management of Canadian Business from a Veteran Insider. 2012. (ENG.). 320p. 36.95 ***(978-1-118-15286-7(7)***, Wiley) Wiley, John & Sons, Inc.
Guerrero, Jose. Bitácora de un Emigrante Gallego. 2011. 428p. 42.95 ***(978-1-61764-932-5(5))***; pap. 27.95 ***(978-1-61764-934-9(1))*** Palibrio.
—Bitacora de un Emigrante Gallego. 2011. (SPA., Illus.). 426p. E-Book ***(978-1-61764-933-2(3))*** AuthorHouse.
Guffey, L. R. Mc Auffe's Arctic. 2009. 176p. pap. 16.25 *(978-1-4269-0341-0(3))* Trafford Publishing.
Guinness, Patrick. Arthur's Round: The Life & Times of Brewing Legend Arthur Guinness. 2007. (ENG., Illus.). 256p. per. 22.95 *(978-0-7206-1296-7(9))* Owen, Peter Ltd. GBR. Dist: Independent Pubs. Group.
Gupta, Fred. The Guptas. 2010. 228p. 24.99 *(978-1-4520-5234-2(4))*; (ENG.). pap. 14.49 *(978-1-4520-5235-9(2))* AuthorHouse.
Hadsall, Guy & Foster, Patrick R. Mister Javelin: Guy Hadsall Jr. at American Motors. 2007. (Illus.). vii, 95p. pap. *(978-0-9662019-2-5(2))* Olde Milford Pr., The.
Hall Freeman. Retail Hell: How I Sold My Soul to the Store. 2010. (ENG.). 288p. pap. 14.95 *(978-1-4405-0577-5(2))* Adams Media Corp.
Hamilton, Dennis. Beyond Tallulah: How Sam Wyly Became America's Boldest Big-Time Entrepreneur. 2011. (ENG.). 336p. 29.95 ***(978-1-59591-069-1(7))*** Melcher Media.
Hammel, Bob. The Bill Cook Story: Ready, Fire, Aim! 2008. (ENG., Illus.). 432p. 29.95 *(978-0-253-35254-5(1)*, 0253352541) Indiana Univ. Pr.
Hammerstein, Oscar Andrew. The Hammersteins: A Musical Theatre Family. 2010. (ENG., Illus.). 232p. 35.00 *(978-1-57912-846-3(7)*, 1579128467) Black Dog & Leventhal Pubs., Inc.
Hampton, Taylor. Gods Gentlemen. 2006. pap. 15.95 *(978-1-4286-6088-5(7))* Kessinger Publishing, LLC.
Harpster, Jack. King of the Slots: William "Si" Redd. 2010. E-Book *(978-0-313-38209-3(3)*, Praeger Pubs.) Greenwood Publishing Group, Inc.
Harpster, John S. & Harpster, Jack. King of the Slots: William Si Redd, 1 vol. 2010. 273p. 44.95 *(978-0-313-38208-6(5)*, A2632C, Praeger Pubs.) Greenwood Publishing Group, Inc.
Hawkins, Harvey. Blue Collar: The Making of a Union Rep. 2009. 284p. pap. 15.49 *(978-1-4389-5501-8(4))* AuthorHouse.
Hayes, Paddy. The First Secret. 2008. 560p. pap. *(978-1-84923-998-1(3))* YouWriteOn.
Heavner, John A. How Bad Can It Get? 2009. 120p. 21.99 *(978-1-4490-3846-5(8))*; pap. 10.99 *(978-1-4490-3845-8(X))* AuthorHouse.
Helps, Arthur. Life & Labours of Mr Brassey 1805-1870 by Sir Arthur Helps, K C B with a Preface to the American Edition, by the Author. 2006. 424p. per. 26.99 *(978-1-4255-4636-6(6))* MPublishing.
Hilgenfeld, Dennis. My Joyous Life as a Hardhat. 2009. 272p. pap. 23.88 *(978-0-557-05282-0(3))* Lulu Enterprises Inc.
Hill, Kirsten Poe, et al. You Buy the Peanut Butter, I'll Get the Bread: The Absolutely True Adventures of Best Friends in Business. 2009. (ENG.). 224p. (gr. 12-18). 15.00 *(978-0-452-29014-3(7)*, Plume) Penguin Group (USA) Inc.
Hill, Z. B. Mark Zuckerberg: From Facebook to Famous. 2012. ***(978-1-4222-2303-1(5))***; pap. ***(978-1-4222-2314-7(0))*** Mason Crest Pubs.
Himelstein, Linda. The King of Vodka: The Story of Pyotr Smirnov & the Upheaval of an Empire. 2010. (P. S. Ser.). (ENG.). 432p. pap. 15.99 *(978-0-06-085591-8(6)*, HarperPerennial) HarperCollins Pubs.
Hoard, Greg. Hannan's Way: An Unlikely Trek Through Life. 2011. *(978-1-933197-80-7(3))* Orange Frazer Pr.
Hof, Dennis & Zmuda, Bob. No Business Like Ho Business. 2006. 224p. 25.95 *(978-0-06-088110-8(0)*, ReganBooks) HarperCollins Pubs.
Hoffman, David. The Oligarchs: Wealth & Power in the New Russia. rev. ed. 2011. (ENG., Illus.). 608p. pap. 21.99 *(978-1-61039-070-5(9))* PublicAffairs.
Hoich, John L. From the Ground Up: It's Not Just Business! 2007. pap. *(978-1-930819-53-5(6))* Tapestry Pr.
Hoich, John Lee. From the Ground Up: It's Not Just Business! 2007. (Illus.). 196p. per. 15.95 *(978-1-930819-52-8(8))* Tapestry Pr.
Hoig, Stan. The Chouteaus: First Family of the Fur Trade. 2008. (ENG., Illus.). 349p. 29.95 *(978-0-8263-4347-5(3))* Univ. of New Mexico Pr.
Holbrook, Stewart. The Age of the Moguls. 2010. (ENG., Illus.). 395p. pap. 32.95 *(978-1-4128-1082-1(5))* Transaction Pubs.
Holechek, James. Henry Perky: The Shredded Wheat King. 2007. 468p. per. 28.95 *(978-0-595-44170-9(X))* iUniverse, Inc.
Hotchkiss, James M., Jr. A Pair of Kings & A Joker. 2009. 225p. pap. 15.95 *(978-0-557-00772-1(0))* Lulu Enterprises Inc.
Howard, Robert. Connecting the Dots: My Life & Inventions, from X-rays to Death Rays. 2009. (ENG.). 288p. 25.00 *(978-1-56649-957-6(7))* Welcome Rain Pubs.
Howe, Ben Ryder. My Korean Deli: Risking It All for a Convenience Store. 2009. 304p. 25.99 *(978-0-06-171033-9(4))* HarperCollins Pubs.
—My Korean Deli: Risking It All for a Convenience Store. 2011. (ENG.). 320p. 25.00 *(978-0-8050-9343-8(5))* Holt, Henry & Co.
—My Korean Deli: Risking It All for a Convenience Store. 2012. (ENG.). 320p. pap. 15.00 ***(978-1-250-00247-1(8))*** Picador.
Hugh Wynn. Joe Havens: Eighty Eventful Years. 2009. 172p. pap. 15.95 *(978-1-4401-8364-5(3))* iUniverse, Inc.
Hughes, Eric. Eric, or Little by Little. 2010. (Illus.). 168p. pap. 13.49 *(978-1-4520-0937-7(6))* AuthorHouse.
Hunt, Bill. Memoirs of a Franchise Gypsy. 2011. 224p. pap. 19.95 ***(978-0-557-76672-7(9))*** Lulu Enterprises Inc.
Hunter, Judith W. Grinnell's Entrepreneurial & Philanthropic Pioneer: A Biography of Claude W. Ahrens. 2009. 182p. pap. 22.95 *(978-0-557-18443-9(6))* Lulu Enterprises Inc.
Imam, Razi. Driven: A How-To Strategy for Unlocking Your Greatest Potential. 2010. (ENG., Illus.). 192p. 24.95 *(978-0-470-59933-4(2)*, Wiley) Wiley, John & Sons, Inc.
In Search of a Better Way: The Lives & Legacies of Gary & Matilda Vermeer. 2008. (Illus.). 308p. pap. 16.95 *(978-0-9800084-1-8(7))* Write Place, The.
Indovino, Shaina C. Michael Dell: From Child Entrepreneur to Computer Magnate. 2012. ***(978-1-4222-2298-0(5))***; pap. ***(978-1-4222-2309-3(4))*** Mason Crest Pubs.
Indovino, Shaina Carmel. Jim Skinner: From Burgers to the Boardroom. 2012. ***(978-1-4222-2313-0(2))***; ***(978-1-4222-2302-4(7))*** Mason Crest Pubs.
Isaacson, Walter. Steve Jobs. 2011. (Vintage Espanol Ser.). (SPA., Illus.). 752p. pap. 17.95 ***(978-0-307-95028-4(X)***, Vintage) Knopf Doubleday Publishing Group.
—Steve Jobs. 2011. (SPA.). pap. ***(978-1-4516-4854-6(5))***; (ENG., Illus.). 656p. 35.00 ***(978-1-4516-4853-9(7))*** Simon & Schuster.
—Steve Jobs. Lt. ed. 2011. (ENG.). 630p. 35.99 ***(978-1-4104-4522-3(4))*** Thorndike Pr.
Jack, Gilley - Aka & Lane, Jack. Rena, My Eternal Love. 2011. 328p. 29.95 ***(978-1-4567-5913-1(2))***; pap. 19.95 ***(978-1-4567-5911-7(6))*** AuthorHouse.
Jackson, John. By Honor & Right: How One Man Boldly Defined the Destiny of a Nation. 2010. (ENG., Illus.). 380p. 28.00 *(978-1-61614-219-3(7))* Prometheus Bks., Pubs.
Jacobs, Harry A. & Taylor, Nick. A Gentleman on Wall Street: My Life in Flying, Skiing, Finance, Love & More. 2010. 195p. 24.95 *(978-1-4327-5343-6(6))*; pap. 13.95 *(978-1-4327-5206-4(5))* Outskirts Pr., Inc.
Jacobson, Ira. A Quest for Excellence: The Incredible Story of the Most Beautiful Store in the World. 2008. 168p. 24.95 *(978-0-9802331-0-0(0))* R & J Pr.
Jacuzzi, Remo. Spirit, Wind & Water: The Unknown History of the Jacuzzi Family. 2007. (ENG., Illus.). 272p. 28.95 *(978-1-56649-145-7(2))* Welcome Rain Pubs.
James M. Knaus, Cfp(R). Why Are You Laughing? 2009. 196p. 25.95 *(978-1-4389-5203-1(1))*; pap. 18.95 *(978-1-4389-5202-4(3))* AuthorHouse.
James, Robert. Tales from a Briefcase. 2007. 308p. per. *(978-0-7552-0299-7(6))* Authors OnLine, Ltd.
James T. White. James T White's Million Dollar Business Bible: One of the World's Youngest Self-Made Millionaires Provides Essential Start-up Business Tips So You Ca. 2009. 116p. 99.99 *(978-1-4389-3888-2(8))*; pap. 89.99 *(978-1-4389-3887-5(X))* AuthorHouse.

Jankovsky, Jason Alan & Trader X. The Art of the Trade: What I Learned (and Lost) Trading the Chicago Futures Markets. 2008. (ENG.). 208p. 29.95 *(978-0-470-13899-1(8)*, Wiley) Wiley, John & Sons, Inc.

John, Martha Tyler & John, Floyd I. Thomas C. Norman, Sr. 2010. 76p. pap. 10.99 *(978-1-60957-816-9(3))* Xulon Pr., Inc.

Johnston, Ian M. Tractors, Kalashnikovs & Green Tea: My Life of Tractors & Travels. 2011. (Illus.). 320p. 39.95 ***(978-1-921719-04-2(4))*** Rosenberg Publishing Pty, Ltd. AUS. Dist: International Specialized Bk. Services.

Johnston, J. P. Twenty Years of Hustling. 2007. (ENG.). 670p. 63.95 *(978-0-548-02641-0(6))* Kessinger Publishing, LLC.

Jordan, Eddie. An Independent Man: The Autobiography. 2008. (ENG., Illus.). 456p. pap. 18.95 *(978-0-7528-9317-4(3))* Orion Publishing Group, Ltd. GBR. Dist: Independent Pubs. Group.

Jordan, Michael. Everyone Says, You Should Write a Book, 1 vol. 2009. 164p. pap. 24.95 *(978-1-4489-8896-9(9))* PublishAmerica, Inc.

Kamoie, Laura Croghan. Irons in the Fire: The Business History of the Tayloe Family & Virginia's Gentry, 1700-1860. 2007. (ENG., Illus.). 256p. (gr. 17). 35.00 *(978-0-8139-2637-7(8))* Univ. Pr. of Virginia.

Kaplan, David A. Mine's Bigger: The Extraordinary Tale of the World's Greatest Sailboat & the Silicon Valley Tycoon Who Built It. 2008. (ENG., Illus.). 288p. pap. 15.95 *(978-0-06-137402-9(4))* HarperCollins Pubs.

Karmin, Craig. Biography of the Dollar: How the Mighty Buck Conquered the World & Why It's under Siege. 2008. (ENG., Illus.). 272p. 25.95 *(978-0-307-33986-7(6)*, Crown Business) Crown Publishing Group.

Katchmark, Richard. You're Invited to More of My World. 2012. pap. 10.95 ***(978-0-7414-6985-4(5))*** Infinity Publishing.

Kelly, Richard E. Growing up in mama's Club: A Childhood Perspective of Jehovah's Witnesses. 2007. 228p. per. 16.95 *(978-0-9795094-1-4(6))* Kelly, Richard.

Kelsey, Kerck. Remarkable Americans: The Washburn Family. 2010. (Illus.). 402p. 25.95 *(978-0-88448-299-4(5))* Tilbury Hse. Pubs.

Kennedy, Dan. My Unfinished Business. 2009. (ENG.). 428p. pap. 18.99 *(978-1-59932-109-7(2))* Advantage Media Group.

Kenneth Suna. It's a Miracle They Ain't Dead Yet: Welcome to the Texas Café. 2009. 144p. 24.95 *(978-1-4401-6336-4(7))*; pap. 14.95 *(978-1-4401-6334-0(0))* iUniverse, Inc.

Kenny, Niedria Dionne. Memoir of My Career: A Reflection of the Last Ten Years, 1 vol. 2009. 87p. pap. 16.95 *(978-1-60749-236-8(9))* PublishAmerica, Inc.

Kesee, Rip. My Life, My Story, My Pain. 2010. 108p. 21.49 *(978-1-4520-3659-5(4))*; pap. 10.99 *(978-1-4520-3658-8(6))* AuthorHouse.

Kiernan, Joseph R. Life as a Guest: Deo Gratias. 2007. 192p. pap. 13.95 *(978-0-7414-4009-9(1))* Infinity Publishing.

King, White Goldfish. Final Series Book of World Famous Television Executive Billionaire Star Celebrity. 2008. 648p. 34.99 *(978-1-4257-7232-1(3))*; pap. 23.99 *(978-1-4257-7226-0(9))* Xlibris Corp.

Kitto, Mark. Chasing China: How I Went to China in Search of a Fortune & Found a Life. 2009. (ENG.). 304p. 22.95 *(978-1-60239-657-9(4)*, 239657) Skyhorse Publishing Co., Inc.

Klein, Emma. Sir Sigmund Sternberg: The Knight with Many Hats. 2012. (Illus.). 264p. 45.00 ***(978-0-85303-835-1(X))*** Vallentine Mitchell Pubs. GBR. Dist: International Specialized Bk. Services.

Kluge, John. John Kluge. 2009. (ENG., Illus.). 192p. (gr. 17). 39.95 *(978-1-884381-26-3(X))* Columbia Univ. Pr.

Knowling, Bob. You Can Get There from Here: My Journey from Struggle to Success. 2011. (ENG.). 288p. (gr. 12). 26.95 ***(978-1-59184-422-8(3)***, Portfolio (Hardcover)) Penguin Group (USA) Inc.

Kriplen, Nancy. The Eccentric Billionaire: John D. MacArthur — Empire Builder, Reluctant Philanthropist, Relentless Adversary. 2008. (ENG., Illus.). 240p. 24.00 *(978-0-8144-0689-6(3))* Amacom.

—Eccentric Billionaire: John D. MacArthur — Empire Builder, Reluctant Philanthropist, Relentless Adversary. 2010. (ENG.). 224p. 24.00 *(978-1-4379-7253-5(5))* DIANE Publishing Co.

Krudop, Jerry. Surviving Financial Corruption: The Attack of a Rogue Bank. 2010. pap. 16.99 *(978-1-61663-463-6(4))* Tate Publishing & Enterprises, LLC.

Krugler, John D. English & Catholic: The Lords Baltimore in the Seventeenth Century. 2008. (Johns Hopkins University Studies in Historical & Political Science Ser.: 122). (ENG., Illus.). 336p. (gr. 17). pap. 27.00 *(978-0-8018-9063-3(7))* Johns Hopkins Univ. Pr.

Kurlansky, Mark. Birdseye: The Adventures of a Curious Man. 2012. (ENG., Illus.). 272p. 25.95 ***(978-0-385-52705-7(5)***, Doubleday) Knopf Doubleday Publishing Group.

Kwan, Stanley S. K. & Kwan, Nicole. The Dragon & the Crown: Hong Kong Memoirs. (Royal Asiatic Society Hong Kong Studies Ser.). (ENG., Illus.). 236p. (gr. 17). 2011. pap. 20.00 *(978-988-8083-17-6(1))* 2008. 45.00 *(978-962-209-955-5(6))* Hong Kong Univ. Pr. HKG. Dist: Columbia Univ. Pr.

Labitan, Bud. The Four Filters Invention of Warren Buffett & Charlie Munger. 2009. 148p. pap. 30.47 *(978-0-615-24129-6(8))* Acalmix.

Ladjevardian, Akbar. The Memoirs of Akbar Ladjevardian. 2008. (PER.). 196p. per. 25.00 *(978-1-58814-061-6(X))* Ibex Pubs., Inc.

Lambert, Lillian Lincoln & Brutico, Rosemary. The Road to Someplace Better: From the Segregated South to Harvard Business School & Beyond. 2010. (ENG., Illus.). 256p. 25.95 *(978-0-470-40166-8(4)*, Wiley) Wiley, John & Sons, Inc.

Lamont, Edward Miner. Ned Miner & His Pioneering Forebears. 2010. (Meliora Press Ser.). 70p. 30.00 *(978-1-58046-384-3(3))* Univ. of Rochester Pr.

Larsen, Andrew, et al. Paul Martin: A Political Biography. 2011. (ENG.). 172p. (C). pap. 24.95 *(978-1-55277-735-0(9))* Lorimer, James & Co., Ltd., Pubs. CAN. Dist: Casemate Pubs. & Bk. Distributors, LLC.

Larson, Frances. An Infinity of Things: How Sir Henry Wellcome Collected the World. 2009. (ENG., Illus.). 320p. 39.95 *(978-0-19-955446-1(3))* Oxford Univ. Pr., Inc.

Lee, J. Edward. John Gary Anderson & His Maverick Motor Company: The Rise & Fall of Henry Ford's Rock Hill Rival. 2007. (Illus.). 126p. pap., per. 19.99 *(978-1-59629-229-1(6))* History Pr., The.

Lehfeldt, Martin. Notes from a Non-Profitable Life. 2008. 132p. pap. 24.96 *(978-0-557-02437-7(4))* Lulu Enterprises Inc.

Lehrer, Morton. The Memoirs of Morton Lehrer. 2007. 132p. per. 14.95 *(978-0-595-45894-3(7))* iUniverse, Inc.

Leitch, Peter Charles & Gifford, Phil. What a Ride, Mate! The Life & Times of the Mad Butcher. 2008. (Illus.). 399p. *(978-1-86950-689-6(8))* HarperCollins Pubs. Australia.

Lempert, Ruth Schafer. Fish, Faith, & Family. 2008. 240p. pap. 24.95 *(978-1-4241-9097-3(5))* PublishAmerica, Inc.

Lentz, Steve. It Was Never about the Ketchup: The Life & Legacy of H. J. Heinz. 2007. (ENG.). per. 13.95 *(978-1-60037-155-4(8))* Morgan James Publishing.

Lessin, Robert H. Lessin's Lessons. 2010. 106p. pap. 100.00 *(978-0-557-12164-9(7))* Lulu Enterprises Inc.

Levy, Gaston. Beyond the Soul: From the Streets of Alexandria to the Halls of Corporate America. 2010. 404p. 35.95 *(978-1-4401-9540-2(4))*; (ENG.). pap. 25.95 *(978-1-4401-9542-6(0))* iUniverse, Inc.

Lewis, Brian. So Clean: Lord Leverhulme, Soap & Civilisation. 2009. (ENG., Illus.). 272p. 84.00 *(978-0-7190-7804-0(0))* Manchester Univ. Pr. GBR. Dist: Macmillan.

Life of a Dropout. 2006. (Illus.). 148p. 19.95 *(978-1-58597-411-5(0))* Leathers Publishing.

The Life of Clement Studebaker. 2009. 195p. pap. 24.95 *(978-0-557-05438-1(9))* Lulu Enterprises Inc.

A Life on the Black River in Arkansas: A Pioneering Banker's Memoir. 2008. 124p. pap. 33.95 *(978-0-9800897-8-3(6))*; 34.95 *(978-1-935106-04-3(X))* Butler Ctr. for Arkansas Studies.

Lincoln, Ed. Life Through the Rearview Mirror. 2011. (Illus.). 328p. ***(978-1-935359-63-0(0))*** Book Pubs. Network.

Lincoln, Ed. Life Through the Rearview Mirror: On the Road with the Creator of the Pink Toe Truck. 2010. (Illus.). 328p. pap. 19.95 *(978-1-935359-54-8(1))* Book Pubs. Network.

Lindberg, Richard C. The Gambler King of Clark Street: Michael C. McDonald & the Rise of Chicago's Democratic Machine. 3rd ed. 2009. (Elmer H Johnson & Carol Holmes Johnson Series in Criminology Ser.). (ENG.). 328p. 29.95 *(978-0-8093-2893-2(3))* Southern Illinois Univ. Pr.

Littmann, Jay. How to Get from There to Here: One Man's Triumph over Addictions, Obesity, & Being down & Out. 2010. pap. 19.95 *(978-1-934572-39-9(X)*, Emerald) Emerald Bk. Co.

Livesay, Harold C. American Made: Shapers of the American Economy. 3rd rev. ed. 2011. (ENG.). 272p. (C). pap. 53.20 ***(978-0-205-20229-4(2)***, Prentice Hall) Prentice Hall PTR.

Lobb, Nancy. 16 Extraordinary American Entrepreneurs. 2nd ed. 2007. (Illus.). 133p. (YA). (gr. 6-12). tchr. ed., per. 25.00 *(978-0-8251-6277-0(7))* Walch Education.

Lobl, Frederick. Don't Pay for Water: Vienna & Cape Cod, A Romance of Business, A Story of Love. 2011. 206p. 44.95 ***(978-1-258-07223-0(3))*** Literary Licensing, LLC.

Locklin, William. A Hobby Out of Control: Ten Life-Based Lessons for Young. 2007. (ENG.). 120p. 30.99 *(978-1-4257-4376-5(5))*; per. 20.99 *(978-1-4257-4375-8(7))* Xlibris Corp.

Lockwood, Brad. Bill Gates: Profile of a Digital Entrepreneur. 2009. (Career Profiles Ser.). 112p. (gr. 9-10). 63.90 *(978-1-61511-792-5(X))* Rosen Publishing Group, Inc., The.

Longo, Sam. Bellmen Don't Get Golden Parachutes. 2010. 200p. 25.99 *(978-1-4490-1273-1(6))*; pap. 15.95 *(978-1-4490-1272-4(8))* AuthorHouse.

Loudermilk, Charlie & Vincent, Coppola. Charlie Just Do Better Next Time: A Memoir of My Mother, Addie Loudermilk. 2012. (Illus.). 160p. 19.95 ***(978-0-9824779-2-2(9))*** Shock Design Bks.

Loveless, Ron. Walmart Inside Out: From Stockboy to Stockholder. 2011. 300p. pap. 16.95 *(978-1-935043-41-6(2))* Stephens Pr. LLC.

Lovell, Terry. Bernie Ecclestone: King of Sport. (ENG., Illus.). 2010. 420p. pap. 13.95 *(978-1-84454-826-2(0))* 2008. 288p. 34.95 *(978-1-84454-623-7(3))* Blake, John Publishing, Ltd. GBR. Dist: Independent Pubs. Group.

Lowe, Janet & Lowe. Google Speaks: Secrets of the World's Greatest Billionaire Entrepreneurs, Sergey Brin & Larry Page. 2009. (ENG.). 315p. 19.95 *(978-0-470-39854-8(X)*, Wiley) Wiley, John & Sons, Inc.

Luchuck, Jaime. From Cubicle Slave to the Next Internet Millionaire. 2007. (ENG.). 265p. 27.95 *(978-1-60037-371-8(2))*; pap. 17.95 *(978-1-60037-372-5(0))* Morgan James Publishing.

Lull, Edward W. Bits & Pieces. 2011. pap. 10.95 ***(978-0-7414-6794-2(1))*** Infinity Publishing.

Luskin, Donald & Greta, Andrew. I Am John Galt: Today's Heroic Innovators Building the World & the Villainous Parasites Destroying It. 2011. (ENG., Illus.). 307p. 27.95 *(978-1-118-01378-6(6)*, Wiley) Wiley, John & Sons, Inc.

Lynch, Frank. Backstage Passes: Memoirs of an American Showman. 2009. 216p. pap. 18.05 *(978-1-4120-2743-4(8))* Trafford Publishing.

Lyons, Bettina. Zeckendorfs & Steinfelds: Merchant Princes of the American Southwest. 2008. *(978-0-910037-49-5(3))* Arizona Historical Society.

Mabie, Christopher. Uncle Louis: The biography of Louis Campau, founder of Saginaw & Grand Rapids. 2007. (ENG.). (YA). per. 14.95 *(978-0-9785815-0-3(4))* Van Naerden Publishing.

Madden, Bill. Steinbrenner: The Last Lion of Baseball. 2011. (ENG.). 512p. pap. 16.99 *(978-0-06-169032-7(5))* 2010. (ENG., Illus.). 480p. 26.99 *(978-0-06-169031-0(7))* 2010. 782p. pap. 26.99 *(978-0-06-197956-9(2)*, HarperLuxe) HarperCollins Pubs.

Magomola, Gaby. Robben Island to Wall Street. 2009. 334p. pap. 33.00 *(978-1-86888-570-1(4))* Unisa Press / Uitgewers GBR. Dist: International Specialized Bk. Services.

Mahafza, Bassem R. Portrait of a CEO: A Guide to Starting & Growing a Small Business. 2010. 168p. pap. 15.49 *(978-1-4520-8459-6(9))* AuthorHouse.

Makura, Moky. Africa's Greatest Entrepreneurs. 2009. (ENG., Illus.). 300p. (gr. 12-18). 25.95 *(978-0-14-302430-9(2)*, Penguin Global) Penguin Group (USA) Inc.

Mallison, Sam T. The Great Wildcatter: The Story of Mike Benedum. 2011. 580p. 63.95 ***(978-1-258-04757-3(8))*** Literary Licensing, LLC.

March, Carlos. Growing Thoughts: A Garden in Andalusia. 2012. (ENG., Illus.). 304p. 65.00 ***(978-0-7112-3378-2(0))*** Lincoln, Frances Ltd. GBR. Dist: Perseus-PGW.

Marden, Orison Swett. Sir Thomas Lipton: the Great Yacht Sportsman Who Took American. 2006. pap. 12.95 *(978-1-4304-1075-1(2))* Kessinger Publishing, LLC.

Margoshes, Dave, et al. Against All Odds: The Story of IPSCO's First Fifty Years, 1 vol. 2007. (ENG., Illus.). 408p. 60.00 *(978-0-9780316-0-2(1))* Coteau Bks. CAN. Dist: Fitzhenry & Whiteside, Ltd.

Marini, Vincent E. Mail Call a Soldier's Worst Nightmare & Recall the Rest of My Story: A Memoir. 2010. 280p. 25.99 *(978-1-4490-9299-3(3))*; pap. 15.49 *(978-1-4490-9298-6(5))* AuthorHouse.

Markowitz, Alan. Topless Prophet. 2009. 24.95 *(978-0-9840855-0-7(5))* AM Enterprises.

Marquis Who's Who Staff. Who's Who in Finance & Business 2008-2009. 36th ed. 2007. 1100p. 349.00 *(978-0-8379-0356-9(4))* Marquis Who's Who, LLC.

Marshall, Walter P. Ezra Cornell His Contributions to Wester. 2006. pap. 15.95 *(978-1-4286-6060-1(7))* Kessinger Publishing, LLC.

Martin, Paul. Hell or High Water: My Life in & out of Politics. 2009. (Illus.). 504p. pap. 18.95 *(978-0-7710-5693-2(1)*, Emblem Edns) McClelland & Stewart CAN. Dist: Random Hse., Inc.

Martinez, Ray. From Darkness to Light: Mai Tran's Journey of Passion. 2009. (ENG., Illus.). 150p. 24.95 *(978-0-9644652-7-5(2))* Chico Publishing.

Martini, Terry. Built like a Battleship: A history of the Ferrograph Company 1920 - 1983. 2008. (Illus.). xiv, 221p. per. *(978-1-4276-2523-6(9))* Aardvark Global Publishing.

Marwood, Maurice E. Professional Nomad. 2009. 274p. pap. 25.00 *(978-1-4251-8035-5(3))* Trafford Publishing.

Marx, Paul. Jim Rouse: Capitalist/Idealist. 2007. (ENG.). 264p. per. 42.99 *(978-0-7618-3944-6(5))* Hamilton Bks.

Mathile, Clayton L. & Garrett, Echo M. Dream No Little Dreams. Crain, Mary Beth, ed. 2007. (Illus.). 336p. 23.95 *(978-1-934282-03-8(0))* DNLD Publishing.

Mayor, Archer H. Southern Timberman: The Legacy of William Buchanan. 2009. (ENG.). 288p. pap. 24.95 *(978-0-8203-3448-5(0))* Univ. of Georgia Pr.

McCann, Peter. Turnarounds: Brains, Guts & Stamina. 2009. 184p. pap. 22.00 *(978-1-4251-9099-6(5))* Trafford Publishing.

McCaskey, Patrick & Sandrolini, Mike. Bear with Me: A Family History of George Halas & the Chicago Bears. 2009. (ENG.). 240p. 24.95 *(978-1-60078-128-5(4))* Triumph Bks.

McCollough, Tom. Commentary & Other Stuff: And even more fragments of Memory. 2011. 188p. pap. 16.95 ***(978-1-4620-1487-3(9))*** iUniverse, Inc.

McCollough, Tom. Vin Yets: Fragments of Memory. 2009. 420p. pap. 26.95 *(978-1-4401-8421-5(6))* iUniverse, Inc.

McCombs, Red. Big Red: Memoirs of a Texas Entrepreneur & Philanthropist. 2010. (ENG., Illus.). 300p. 29.95 *(978-0-9766697-5-3(7))* Briscoe Ctr. for American History.

McConnell, Terry, et al. I'd Trade Him Again: On Gretzky, Politics, & the Pursuit of the Perfect Deal. (ENG., Illus.). 304p. 2011. pap. 21.95 *(978-1-55168-376-8(8))* 2009. 27.95 *(978-1-55168-366-9(0))* Key Porter Bks. CAN. Dist: Perseus-PGW.

McDonald, David R. José Antonio Navarro: In Search of the American Dream in Nineteenth-Century Texas. 2010. (Watson Caufield & Mary Maxwell Arnold Republic of Texas Ser.). (Illus.). 352p. (ENG.). 49.95 *(978-0-87611-243-4(2))*; pap. 24.95 *(978-0-87611-244-1(0))* Texas State Historical Assn.

McEneny, Tim S. Unlocking Your Entrepreneurial Potential: Marketing, Money, & Management Strategies for the Self-Funded Entrepreneur. 2011. 244p. 30.95 ***(978-1-4620-3245-7(1))*** iUniverse, Inc.

McGuire, Donna. Santa's Secret: A Story of Hope: The True Story of America's Secret Santa. 2007. (Illus.). 236p. 19.95 *(978-0-9790248-0-1(3))* World 2 Publishing, LLC.

McLaurine, W. M. James William Cannon His Plants His Peop. 2006. pap. 15.95 *(978-1-4286-5973-5(0))* Kessinger Publishing, LLC.

McMaster, John Bach. Life & Times of Stephen Girard V1 Mari. 2006. pap. 38.95 *(978-1-4286-3753-5(2))* Kessinger Publishing, LLC.

—Life & Times of Stephen Girard V2 Mari. 2006. pap. 38.95 *(978-1-4286-3754-2(0))* Kessinger Publishing, LLC.

McNees, Pat, 1st, ed. Starting Over: The Life of Herman Ernst Sheets. 2007. (Illus.). 400p. per. 24.95 *(978-0-9795885-0-1(2))* Memory Works, LLC, The.

McPherson, Stephanie Sammartino. Sergey Brin & Larry Page: Founders of Google. 2010. (USA TODAY Lifeline Biographies Ser.). (ENG.). 112p. (YA). (gr. 7-12). lib. bdg. 33.26 *(978-0-7613-5221-1(X))* Lerner Publishing Group.

Mee, Benjamin. We Bought a Zoo: The Amazing True Story of a Young Family, a Broken down Zoo, & the 200 Wild Animals That Change Their Lives Forever. 2008. (ENG.). 272p. 24.95 *(978-1-60286-048-3(3)*, Weinstein Bks.) Perseus Bks. Group.

Melnick, Ross. American Showman: Samuel Roxy Rothafel & the Birth of the Entertainment Industry, 1908-1935. 2012. (Film & Culture Ser.). (ENG., Illus.). 576p. (gr. 17). 37.50 ***(978-0-231-15904-3(8))*** Columbia Univ. Pr.

Meredith, Carl. Decline & Fall of the Auto Man Empire. 2009. 95p. pap. 13.95 *(978-0-557-17536-9(4))* Lulu Enterprises Inc.

Mezrich, Ben. The Accidental Billionaires: Sex, Money, Betrayal & the Founding of Facebook. 2010. (CHI., Illus.). 266p. pap. *(978-7-5086-2042-8(9))* CITIC Publishing Hse.

—The Accidental Billionaires: The Founding of Facebook - A Tale of Sex, Money, Genius & Betrayal. movie tie-in ed. 2010. (ENG.). 272p. pap. 15.95 *(978-0-307-74098-4(6))* Knopf Doubleday Publishing Group.

—Rigged: The True Story of an Ivy League Kid Who Changed the World of Oil, from Wall Street to Dubai. 2008. (P. S. Ser.). (ENG.). 320p. pap. 14.95 *(978-0-06-125273-0(5)*, William Morrow Paperbacks) HarperCollins Pubs.

Middendorp, Jan, ed. Creative Characters: Interviews with Font Designers. 2010. (ENG., Illus.). 192p. pap. 32.00 *(978-90-6369-224-7(2))* Bis B.V., Uitgeverij(BIS Publishers) NLD. Dist: Consortium Bk. Sales & Distribution.

Middleton, Earl M. Knowing Who I Am: A Black Entrepreneur's Struggle & Success in the American South. 2008. (Illus.). 183p. 29.95 *(978-1-57003-715-3(9))* Univ. of South Carolina Pr.

Miles, Bill. Scribe among Pharisees. 2008. (Illus.). x, 270p. (J). *(978-0-9818313-1-2(1))* Thompson, Ernestine.

Miller, Larry H. & Robinson, Doug. Driven: An Autobiography. 2012. pap. 18.99 ***(978-1-60908-916-0(2))*** 2010. *(978-1-60641-656-3(1))* Deseret Bk. Co.

Miller, Norman. Beyond the Norm, 0 vols. 2009. 224p. pap. 12.99 *(978-1-59555-331-7(2))* Nelson, Thomas Inc.

Miller, Russell. The House of Getty. 2012. 394p. pap. ***(978-1-4482-0435-9(6)*** 145959, Bloomsbury Reader) Bloomsbury Publishing Plc.

Miller, Steve. The Turnaround Kid: What I Learned Rescuing America's Most Troubled Companies. 2008. (ENG., Illus.). 272p. 25.95 *(978-0-06-125127-6(5)*, Collins) HarperCollins Pubs.

Milligan, Andy. Great Asian Brands: Osim. 2010. 192p. pap. *(978-1-905736-13-3(4))* Marshall Cavendish.

Mills, Anson. My Story. 2008. 416p. 30.99 *(978-0-559-43822-6(2))*; pap. 33.75 *(978-0-559-43820-2(6))* BiblioBazaar.

Mills, Dean. Dollar & A Dream. 2007. pap. 13.00 *(978-0-8059-8563-4(8))* Dorrance Publishing Co., Inc.

Mills, George S., et al. The Little Man in the Long Shadow: The Life & Times of Frederick M. Hubbell. 2011. 294p. 48.95 ***(978-1-258-05064-1(1))*** Literary Licensing, LLC.

Minervino, Joseph. The, Unknown. 2011. (ENG.). 284p. pap. 16.95 ***(978-1-4327-8175-0(8))*** Outskirts Pr., Inc.

Mmaduka, Amala. The Undergraduate Millionaire: From a Poor Frustrated College Student at 19 to a University Millionaire at 21... the Easiest Way to Make Your First Million... 2010. 192p. pap. 18.49 *(978-1-4520-1987-1(8))* AuthorHouse.

Moik, Isador. The Making of an Oilman. 2011. 256p. 47.95 ***(978-1-258-09020-3(1))*** Literary Licensing, LLC.

Molson, Karen. Hartland de Montarville Molson: Man of Honour. 2006. (ENG., Illus.). 328p. pap. 29.95 *(978-1-55407-150-0(X))* Firefly Bks., Ltd.

Monahan, Mike. From the Jungle to the Boardroom. 2011. 148p. 20.00 ***(978-0-9841318-6-0(8))*** Beacon Publishing.

Moos, Rudolf. Journey of Hope & Despair: Volume I. Rise & Fall. 2010. 426p. 34.99 *(978-1-4500-3538-5(8))*; pap. 23.99 *(978-1-4500-3537-8(X))* Xlibris Corp.

Morris, Matt. The Unemployed Millionaire: Escape the Rat Race, Fire Your Boss, & Live Life on Your Terms! 2009. (ENG., Illus.). 272p. 22.95 *(978-0-470-47981-0(7)*, Wiley) Wiley, John & Sons, Inc.

Moulder, Bob. Monday Is a Good Day for Dreamers. 2006. 201p. pap. 24.95 *(978-1-4241-1256-2(7))* PublishAmerica, Inc.

Mounger, William D. Amidst the Fray: My Life in Politics, Culture, & Mississippi. 2006. (Illus.). 480p. 26.95 *(978-1-893062-97-9(X))* Quail Ridge Pr., Inc.

Muir, Andrew Forest. William Marsh Rice & His Institute: The Centennial Edition. Hall, Randal L. & Morris, Sylvia Stallings, eds. 2012. (Illus.). 192p. 25.00 ***(978-1-60344-663-1(X))*** Texas A&M Univ. Pr.

Murphy, Kevin D. Jonathan Fisher of Blue Hill, Maine. 2010. 336p. 49.95 *(978-1-55849-743-6(9))* Univ. of Massachusetts Pr.

Muther, Richard. Reaching: Love Affairs with Industry. 2006. (Illus.). 208p. 19.95 *(978-1-58597-384-2(X))* Leathers Publishing.

Myers, Gene. After Hours, Adventures of an International Businessman. 2009. 172p. 23.75 *(978-1-60860-074-8(2)*, Strategic Bk. Publishing) AEG Literary Publishing Services, Inc.

Myers, Jay. Keep Swinging: An Entrepreneur's Story of Overcoming Adversity & Achieving Small Business Success. 2007. (ENG., Illus.). 157p. pap. 14.00 *(978-1-60037-257-5(0))* Morgan James Publishing.

Myers, Sylvester C. From Coal Fields to Oil Fields: A Life in Pursuit of All I Could Be. 2007. 26.00 *(978-0-8059-8988-5(9))* Dorrance Publishing Co., Inc.

Naimoli, Vince. Business, Baseball & Beyond. 2009. (Illus.). xvii, 132p. ***(978-1-884886-93-5(0))*** StarGroup International.

Nelson, R. L. Paving the Road to Success. 2011. 148p. 24.99 ***(978-1-4634-5007-6(9))***; pap. 14.99 ***(978-1-4634-5008-3(7))*** AuthorHouse.

B

Neu, Irene D. Erastus Corning: Merchant & Financier, 1794-1872. 2010. (Illus.). 224p. pap. 21.00 *(978-0-8014-7645-7(3)*, Fall Creek Bks.) Cornell Univ. Pr.

Nevels, Hezekiah. Raised by a Nine-Year Old King: Vol 1. 2011. 124p. pap. 13.73 ***(978-1-4634-0273-0(2))*** AuthorHouse.

New, Elisa. Jacob's Cane: A Jewish Family's Journey from the Four Lands of Lithuania to the Ports of London & Baltimore - A Memoir in Five Generations. 2011. (ENG.). 336p. (gr. 9). pap. 16.99 *(978-0-465-02254-0(5))* Basic Bks.

Newell, John R. William Stark Newell Shipbuilder of Main. 2006. pap. 15.95 *(978-1-4286-5974-2(9))* Kessinger Publishing, LLC.

Nicholas, C. You Just Don't Know. 2011. 52p. pap. 9.95 ***(978-1-4620-4692-8(4))*** iUniverse, Inc.

Nolte, Michael J. Burned but Not Broken: For What Was I Spared? 2007. (Illus.). 205p. 24.95 *(978-1-934144-16-9(9))* Sphinx Publishing.

Nordstrom, Bruce A. Leave it Better Than You Found It. 2007. (Illus.). 248p. *(978-1-933245-05-8(0))* Documentary Media LLC.

Nui, Chan King. From Poor Migrant to Millionaire: Chan Wing 1873-1947. 2010. (Illus.). 157p. pap. 25.00 *(978-967-978-966-9(7))* Pelanduk Pubns. Malaysia Sdn. Bhd MYS. Dist: Coronet Bks.

Obadan, Damion Levar. The 19 Commandments of the World's Greatest Salesmen. 2011. 48p. pap. 16.95 ***(978-1-4560-5228-7(4))*** PublishAmerica, Inc.

O'Clery, Conor. The Billionaire Who Wasn't: How Chuck Feeney Secretly Made & Gave Away a Fortune. 2008. (ENG., Illus.). 368p. pap. 15.95 *(978-1-58648-642-6(X))* Perseus Bks. Group.

O'Connor, Michael. Ted Turner: A Biography, 1 vol. 2009. (Greenwood Biographies Ser.). (Illus.). 246p. 35.00 *(978-0-313-35042-9(6)*, GR5042) Greenwood Publishing Group, Inc.

O'Dea, Frank. When All You Have Is Hope. 2010. (ENG.). 240p. pap. 17.00 *(978-0-14-305255-5(1)*, Penguin Global) Penguin Group (USA) Inc.

Olson, Robert C. Speck: The Life & Times of Spencer Penrose. 2008. 19.95 *(978-1-932738-50-6(9))* Western Reflections Publishing Co.

—Speck - the Life & Times of Spencer Penrose. 2008. 228p. pap. 15.95 *(978-1-932738-73-5(8))* Western Reflections Publishing Co.

Oltuski, Alicia. Precious Objects: A Story of Diamonds, Family, & a Way of Life. (ENG.). 2012. 384p. pap. 15.00 ***(978-1-4165-4513-2(1))*** 2011. 368p. lib. bdg. 24.00 *(978-1-4165-4512-5(3))* Scribner. (Scribner).

Ooi, Kee Beng. Serving a New Nation: Baey Lian Peck's Singapore Story. 2011. xiv, 141p. ***(978-981-4345-42-2(3))*** Institute of Southeast Asian Studies.

Orberson, Paul, as told by. Something Good's Gonna Happen. 2007. 181p. pap. 16.95 *(978-0-9790286-0-1(4))* Hi- Hope Publishing.

Ouimet, J. -Robert & Semen, Yves. Everything Has Been Loaned to You: The Biography of a Transformational CEO. 2012. ***(978-0-8189-1337-2(1))*** St Pauls.

Pack, Larry J. Service above Self: A History of the Bowling Green Rotary Club & the City that Made It All Possible. 2010. pap. 25.00 *(978-0-615-39632-3(1))* Gerald Printing.

Parrish, Darrell W. Cancer & Me: My Personal Journey. 2010. pap. 11.99 *(978-1-61579-778-3(5))* Xulon Pr., Inc.

Paul, Gerald. My Business Life Cycle: How Innovation, Evolution, & Determination Made Paul Harris Great. 2007. (Illus.). 111p. spiral bd. 29.95 *(978-1-55753-426-2(8))* Purdue Univ. Pr.

Payment, Simone. Donald Trump: Profile of a Real Estate Tycoon. 2007. (Career Profiles Ser.). (Illus.). 112p. (YA). (gr. 7-12). lib. bdg. 31.95 *(978-1-4042-1909-0(9))* Rosen Publishing Group, Inc., The.

—Donald Trump: Profile of a Real-Estate Tycoon. 2009. (Career Profiles Ser.). 112p. (gr. 9-10). 63.90 *(978-1-61511-793-2(8))* Rosen Publishing Group, Inc., The.

Peebles, R. Donahue. The Peebles Principles: Tales & Tactics from an Entrepreneur's Life of Winning Deals, Succeeding in Business, & Creating a Fortune from Scratch. 2007. (ENG., Illus.). 232p. 24.95 *(978-0-470-09930-8(5)*, Wiley) Wiley, John & Sons, Inc.

Pegels, C. Carl. Prominent Dutch American Entrepreneurs: Their Contributions to American Society, Culture, & Economy. 2011. 210p. ***(978-1-61735-500-4(3))***; 210p. pap. ***(978-1-61735-499-1(6))***; E-Book ***(978-1-61735-501-1(1))*** Information Age Publishing, Inc.

Pendrys, ed. Memoirs of a Fast Food Man. 2011. 132p. 23.89 *(978-1-4567-2075-9(9))*; pap. 11.99 *(978-1-4567-2076-6(7))* AuthorHouse.

Pentz, Paul E. Tools for Tomorrow: Memoirs of Paul E. Pentz. 2009. 176p. pap. 11.99 *(978-1-4490-1682-1(0))* AuthorHouse.

Perry, Matthew. The Fourteen Lives of Matt Perry. 2009. 352p. 28.49 *(978-1-4389-4008-3(4))*; pap. 20.09 *(978-1-4389-4007-6(6))* AuthorHouse.

Peterson, Peter G. The Education of an American Dreamer: A Memoir. 2010. (ENG., Illus.). 384p. pap. 16.99 *(978-0-446-55604-0(1)*, Twelve) Grand Central Publishing.

Peverelli, Peter J. & Song, Jiwen. Chinese Entrepreneurship: A Social Capital Approach. 2012. (ENG., Illus.). xiv, 170p. 129.00 ***(978-3-642-28205-8(9)***, 3642282059) Springer.

Pfister, Jude M. Fords of New Jersey. 2010. 170p. pap. 21.99 *(978-1-60949-007-2(X))* History Pr., The.

Pollecoff, Eve A. Pioneer Merchant Trader: The Life & Times of Otto Markus. 2012. (ENG., Illus.). 224p. 55.00 ***(978-1-84885-937-1(6)***, Radcliffe Pr., The) I. B. Tauris & Co., Ltd. GBR. Dist: Macmillan.

Porter, Darwin. Howard Hughes: Hell's Angel. 2nd ed. 2010. (ENG., Illus.). 814p. 32.95 *(978-1-936003-13-6(9))* Blood Moon Productions, Ltd.

Praz, Daniel J. Once upon a Lifetime: How I romanced the woman of my Dreams. 2011. 124p. 29.99 ***(978-1-4628-8977-8(8))***; pap. 19.99 ***(978-1-4628-8976-1(X))*** Xlibris Corp.

Price, Jerry. It Was a Crazy Ride!, 1 vol. 2009. 142p. pap. 24.95 *(978-1-4489-6516-8(0))* PublishAmerica, Inc.

—Let's Go for A Ride. 2007. per. 15.00 *(978-0-9768477-3-1(6))* Windjammer Adventure Publishing.

Price, John. When the White House Calls: From Immigrant Entrepreneur to U. S. Ambassador. 2011. (ENG., Illus.). 712p. (gr. 9). 30.00 *(978-1-60781-143-5(X))* Univ. of Utah Pr.

Prince Revelle, Revelle & Prince Revelle. They Call Him Papa Bud. 2009. 92p. pap. 11.95 *(978-1-4401-8558-8(1))* iUniverse, Inc.

Purnick, Joyce. Mike Bloomberg: Money, Power, Politics. 2010. (ENG., Illus.). 272p. pap. 14.95 *(978-1-58648-899-4(6))* PublicAffairs.

Qingqiuzi. Zhongguo Ren Neng Zuo Dao: Minguo Shi Ye Jia Lu Zuofu. 2010. (CHI.). 315p. *(978-7-80729-647-8(X))* Phoenix Publishing House.

Rabakukk, Marilyn Mackay Ballard. The Mackays of Archieny. 2006. pap. 35.00 *(978-1-59526-471-8(X))* Aeon Publishing Inc.

Rackham, Paul. Paul Rackham: No Time to Waste. 2012. 240p. 28.95 ***(978-1-85418-767-3(8))*** Thorogood GBR. Dist: Stylus Publishing, LLC.

Radez, Robert. On the Fringe of the Real World. 2007. 200p. per. 24.95 *(978-1-4241-7450-8(3))* PublishAmerica, Inc.

Rae, Dwayne. What If: A Lifetime's Reflection on Safety & Leadership. 2011. 196p. 29.99 *(978-1-4567-1798-8(7))*; pap. 17.99 *(978-1-4567-1799-5(5))* AuthorHouse.

Raff, Sam. Random Memories. 2006. (ENG.). 25.50 *(978-1-59330-418-8(8))*; pap. 12.50 *(978-1-59330-416-4(1))* Aventine Pr.

Ramsburg, Jeff. Purgatory, Or? 2011. 104p. 24.99 ***(978-1-4568-8156-6(6))***; pap. 15.99 ***(978-1-4568-8155-9(8))*** Xlibris Corp.

Ramsey, James Gettys McGready. J G M Ramsey: Autobiography & Letters. Hesseltine, William B., ed. 2011. 388p. 53.95 ***(978-1-258-08775-3(8))*** Literary Licensing, LLC.

Ramsey, William E. & Shrier, Betty Dineen. Doorway to Freedom: The Story of David Kaufmann. 2008. (ENG.). 350p. pap. 20.00 *(978-0-88962-887-8(4))* Mosaic Pr.

Rankin, Watson S. James Buchanan Duke A Great Pattern of H. 2006. pap. 15.95 *(978-1-4286-5805-9(X))* Kessinger Publishing, LLC.

Rathbone, John Paul. The Sugar King of Havana: The Rise & Fall of Julio Lobo, Cuba's Last Tycoon. (ENG.). 320p. (gr. 12). 2011. 16.00 *(978-0-14-311933-3(8)*, Penguin (Non-Classics)) 2010. (Illus.). 27.95 *(978-1-59420-258-2(3)*, Penguin Pr. HC, The) Penguin Group (USA) Inc.

Ratner, Gerald. The Rise & Fall... & Rise Again. (ENG., Illus.). 2008. 385p. pap. 16.95 *(978-1-906465-29-2(0))* 2007. 268p. 39.95 *(978-1-84112-786-6(8))* Wiley, John & Sons, Inc. (Capstone).

Redmond, Shirley Raye. Richard Branson: Virgin Mega-brand Mogul. 2011. (Innovators Ser.). 64p. lib. bdg. 28.75 *(978-0-7377-5536-7(9)*, Kidhaven) Cengage Gale.

Reed, Jeremy. The King of Carnaby Street: A Life of John Stephen. 2010. (ENG., Illus.). 352p. 26.00 *(978-1-906598-31-0(2))* Haus Publishing GBR. Dist: Consortium Bk. Sales & Distribution.

Reese, Andrew R. Reese's Peanut Butter Cups: The Untold Story. 2008. (ENG.). 108p. 22.95 *(978-0-595-49107-0(3))*; pap. 12.95 *(978-0-595-48707-3(6))* iUniverse, Inc.

Renehan, Edward J., Jr. Commodore: The Life of Cornelius Vanderbilt. 2009. (ENG.). 400p. pap. 17.50 *(978-0-465-00256-6(0))* Basic Bks.

—Dark Genius of Wall Street: The Misunderstood Life of Jay Gould, King of the Robber Barons. 2007. (Illus.). 352p. reprint ed. 30.00 *(978-1-4223-6837-4(8))* DIANE Publishing Co.

Reser, Al. No Small Potatoes: How a Family Potato Salad Recipe Is Fast Becoming a Billion Dollar Business. 2010. (Illus.). 136p. 19.95 *(978-0-87071-630-0(1))* Oregon State Univ. Pr.

Resnick, Adam B. Bust: How I Gambled & Lost a Fortune, Brought down a Bank — and Lived to Pay for It. 2008. 288p. pap. 14.95 *(978-0-06-137391-6(5))* HarperCollins Pubs.

Reyes, Gerardo. Don Julio Mario: Biografía no Autorizada. 2007. (ENG.). 372p. pap. 19.95 *(978-958-96022-8-7(2))* Ediciones B ESP. Dist: Independent Pubs. Group.

Reynolds, John. One Hell of a Ride: How Craig Dobbin Built the World's Largest Helicopter Company, 1 vol. 2009. (ENG., Illus.). 272p. pap. 17.95 *(978-1-55365-491-9(9))* D&M Pubs. Inc. CAN. Dist: Perseus-PGW.

Rhodes, Joel P. A Missouri Railroad Pioneer: The Life of Louis Houck. 2008. (Missouri biography Ser.). (ENG., Illus.). 312p. (C). 44.95 *(978-0-8262-1798-1(2))* Univ. of Missouri Pr.

Richard, Bako, contrib. by. Who Is Who. 2007. pap. *(978-0-9791826-0-0(3))* Valley Graphics Printing Inc.

Richards, David Adams. Lord Beaverbrook. Saul, John Ralston, ed. 2011. (ENG.). 204p. (gr. 12). 19.95 ***(978-0-670-06614-8(1)***, Penguin Global) Penguin Group (USA) Inc.

Richardson, Willard. The Families of the Green Valley Dairy Farm 1946-1995. 2007. 212p. per. 24.00 *(978-1-4251-2564-6(6))* Trafford Publishing.

Richetti, Sal. Brides Speak: What I Did Right, What I Did Wrong. 2009. 100p. pap. 14.95 *(978-1-4389-5555-1(3))* AuthorHouse.

Rigby, Rhymer. 28 Business Thinkers Who Changed the World: The Management Gurus & Mavericks Who Changed the Way We Think about Business. 2011. (ENG.). 232p. pap. 22.50 *(978-0-7494-6239-0(6))* Kogan Page, Ltd. GBR. Dist: Ingram Pub. Services.

Rijks, Miranda. The Eccentric Entrepreneur: Sir Julien Cahn - Businessman, Philanthropist, Magician & Cricket-Lover. 2011. (ENG., Illus.). 224p. pap. 22.95 ***(978-0-7524-5924-0(4))*** History Pr. Ltd.,The GBR. Dist: Independent Pubs. Group.

Riley, Jim. Oh Really, Riley? The Story of Riley's Trick Shop & the Family behind It. 2010. 192p. 26.95 *(978-1-4502-6549-2(9))*; pap. 16.95 *(978-1-4502-6547-8(2))* iUniverse, Inc.

Ritz, John K. You Did That to Me? 2011. 94p. 24.99 ***(978-1-4628-5910-8(0))***; pap. 15.99 ***(978-1-4628-5909-2(7))*** Xlibris Corp.

Rivella, Ezio. Brunello, Montalcino & I: The Prince of Wines' True Story. 2010. (ENG.). 360p. 26.95 *(978-88-6073-202-6(6))* Baldini Castoldi Dalai Editore ITA. Dist: Independent Pubs. Group.

Rizzo, Michael F. Nine Nine Eight: the Glory Days of Buffalo Shopping. 2007. 168p. pap. 16.95 *(978-1-4303-1386-1(2))* Lulu Enterprises Inc.

Robert, Spector. The Legend of Eddie Bauer. 2nd ed. 2011. (Illus.). 120p. 25.00 *(978-1-933245-22-5(0))* Documentary Media LLC.

Roberts, George A. Distant Force: A Memoir of the Teledyne Corporation & the Man Who Created It. 2007. 39.95 *(978-0-9791303-0-6(X))* Meglin Marketing Communications.

Roberts, Sam. A Kind of Genius: Herb Sturz & Society's Toughest Problems. 2009. (ENG., Illus.). 368p. 27.95 *(978-1-58648-471-2(0))* Perseus Bks. Group.

Robertson, Raymond Glen. Meeting Every Challenge. 2008. pap. 9.95 *(978-0-9798633-7-0(6))* Robertson Publishing.

Roddick, Hawley. Y o u r m e m o i r S: Saving the stories of your life & Work. 2007. 160p. pap. 18.49 *(978-1-4303-1281-9(5))* Lulu Enterprises Inc.

Rogers, Wayne & Young, Josh. Make Your Own Rules: A Renegade Guide to Unconventional Success, 1 vol. 2011. (ENG.). 224p. 23.00 *(978-0-8144-1657-0(8))* Amacom.

Rose, Dave. Saving for the Future: My Life & the Alaska Permanent Fund. 2007. (ENG.), 256p. (gr. 9). per. 17.95 *(978-0-9790470-5-3(6))*; (Illus.). 24.95 *(978-0-9790470-4-6(8))* Epicenter Pr., Inc.

Rose, Jack. Thanks, Jack - in Need of a Miracle: In Need of a Miracle. 2007. per. 19.95 *(978-0-9789546-5-9(3))* Back Channel Pr.

Rosen, Scott D. Wisdom at the Top: Lessons on Leadership & Life from 35 CEOs. 2010. 188p. 29.95 *(978-1-4520-3512-3(1))*; pap. 19.95 *(978-1-4520-3513-0(X))* AuthorHouse.

Rosenbaum, Michael. Six Tires, No Plan: The Impossible Journey of the Most Inspirational Leader That (Almost) NoBody Knows. 2012. (ENG.). 200p. 21.95 ***(978-1-60832-257-2(2)***, Greenleaf Book Group Pr.) Greenleaf Book Group.

Rosenblat, Bruce A. It's a Great Deal, All Three of Me Think So: You Would Be Surprised How Much You Can Sell to Someone with a Multiple Personality Disorder, 1 vol. 2009. 117p. pap. 16.95 *(978-1-4489-8820-4(9))* PublishAmerica, Inc.

Rowbotham, Freddie. From Rags to Riches & Back. 2010. (Illus.). 81p. *(978-1-907629-03-7(3))* ShieldCrest.

Rowland, Peter. Moments of Madness, One Man's Descent into Mental Illness. 2010. (ENG.). 226p. pap. 13.94 *(978-0-557-48692-2(0))* Lulu Enterprises Inc.

Rubino, John "Mariano". Yano: From the Prune Ranch to Skyscrapers. 2007. 204p. (ENG.). 26.95 *(978-0-595-68210-2(3))*; per. 16.95 *(978-0-595-43148-9(8))* iUniverse, Inc.

Russell, William. Romance & Tragedy of A Widely Known Bu. 2006. pap. 14.95 *(978-1-59605-970-2(2)*, Cosimo Classics) Cosimo, Inc.

Russell, William Ingraham. The Romance & Tragedy of a Widely Known Business Man of New York. 2007. (ENG.). 180p. per. *(978-1-4065-8490-5(8))* Dodo Pr.

Ryder, David Warren. Great Citizen: A Biography of William H. Crocker. 2011. 332p. 50.95 ***(978-1-258-08411-0(2))*** Literary Licensing, LLC.

Ryôichi, Sasakawa. Sugamo Diary. Hijino, Ken, tr. from JPN. 2010. (Columbia/Hurst Ser.). (ENG.). 320p. (gr. 17). 40.00 *(978-0-231-70158-7(6))* Columbia Univ. Pr.

Sadagursky, Stephanie. The Road to Happy Days: A Memoir of Life on the Road as an Antique Toy Dealer. 2009. 188p. 26.95 *(978-1-4401-0455-8(7))*; pap. 16.95 *(978-1-4401-0453-4(0))* iUniverse, Inc.

Sage, Connie. Frank Batten: The Untold Story of the Founder of the Weather Channel. 2011. (ENG., Illus.). 216p. 27.95 *(978-0-8139-3155-5(X))* Univ. Pr. of Virginia.

Saito, William Hiroyuki. An Unprogrammed Life: Adventures of an Incurable Entrepreneur. 2012. (ENG.). 320p. pap. 24.95 ***(978-1-118-07703-0(2)***, Wiley) Wiley, John & Sons, Inc.

Salomon, Carlos Manuel. Pío Pico: The Last Governor of Mexican California. (ENG., 2011. Illus.). 248p. pap. 19.95 *(978-0-8061-4237-1(5))* 2010. 256p. (C). 24.95 *(978-0-8061-4090-2(9))* Univ. of Oklahoma Pr.

Sampson, Tony. Miracle Moments: The Ascent of Life. 2009. 152p. pap. 10.95 *(978-1-4327-4362-8(7))* Outskirts Pr., Inc.

Sapet, Kerrily. Google Founders: Larry Page & Sergey Brin. 2012. (Business Leaders Ser.). (Illus.). 112p. (YA). (gr. 7-12). 28.95 ***(978-1-59935-177-3(3))*** Reynolds, Morgan Inc.

Saunders, Alex M. & Saunders, Peter Paul. To Our Credit: Two Autobiographies. 2009. 216p. pap. 18.05 *(978-1-4269-1616-8(7))* Trafford Publishing.

Savoie, Jamie. My Ship Still Sails. 2006. 73p. pap. 16.95 *(978-1-4241-6102-7(9))* PublishAmerica, Inc.

Sawicki, Ludwig. Confessions of an Ex-Gun Dealer. 2010. 318p. pap. 21.95 *(978-1-4327-5839-4(X))* Outskirts Pr., Inc.

Scheller, William G. Great Estates: The Lifestyles & Homes of American Magnates. 2009. (ENG., Illus.). 240p. 35.00 *(978-0-7893-9959-5(8))* Universe Publishing.

Schnakenberg, Heidi. Kid Carolina: Tobacco Fortune, & the Mysterious Death of a Southern Icon. 2010. (ENG., Illus.). 352p. 23.99 *(978-1-59995-103-4(7))* Center St.

Schussler, Steven. It's a Jungle in There: Inspiring Lessons, Hard-Won Insights, & Other Acts of Entrepreneurial Daring. 2010. (ENG.). 256p. 19.95 *(978-1-4027-6289-5(5))* Union Square Pr.

Schuster, Henry D. & Orzes, Caroline A. Abraham's Son: The Making of an American, 1 vol. 2010. 258p. pap. 27.95 *(978-1-4489-5760-6(5))* PublishAmerica, Inc.

Schuster, Randy. Turning Points. 2011. 268p. pap. 14.95 ***(978-1-58570-017-2(7))*** Indaba Pr.

Schwartz, Cipora O. An American Jewish Odyssey: American Religious Freedoms & the Nathan Barnert Memorial Temple. 2007. *(978-0-88125-950-6(0))* Ktav Publishing Hse., Inc.

Scurlock, James D. King Larry: The Life & Ruins of a Billionaire Genius. 2012. (ENG., Illus.). 352p. 26.00 *(978-1-4165-8922-8(8)*, Scribner) Scribner.

Seba, Jaime. Steve Jobs: From Apples to Apps. 2012. ***(978-1-4222-2299-7(3))***; ***(978-1-4222-2310-9(8))*** Mason Crest Pubs.

Semadeni, María Eugenia Vázquez. Doscientos Emprendedores Mexicanos: La Construcción de una Nación, 2 vols. Ludlow, Leonor, ed. 2010. (SPA., Illus.). 753p. 58.00 ***(978-607-7610-17-5(8))*** LID Publishing GBR. Dist: AtlasBooks Distribution.

—200 Emprendedores Mexicanos: La Construcción de una Nación, 2 vols. Ludlow, Leonor, ed. 2010. (SPA., Illus.). 753p. 58.00 ***(978-607-7610-18-2(6))*** LID Publishing GBR. Dist: AtlasBooks Distribution.

Sewell, Homer S. Image in the Mirror: A Man's Personal Life's Journey Whilst Portraying Abe Lincoln. 2010. pap. 23.99 *(978-1-61739-015-9(1))* Tate Publishing & Enterprises, LLC.

Shair, Kamal A. & Shair, Kamal. Out of the Middle East: The Emergence of an Arab Global Business. 2006. (ENG., Illus.). 300p. 68.00 *(978-1-84511-271-4(7))* I. B. Tauris & Co., Ltd. GBR. Dist: Macmillan.

Sharp, Isadore. Four Seasons: The Story of a Business Philosophy. 2009. (ENG., Illus.). 320p. (gr. 12-18). 29.95 *(978-1-59184-244-6(1)*, Portfolio (Hardcover)) Penguin Group (USA) Inc.

Shasho, Ray. Check the Gs: The True Story of an Eclectic American Family & Their Wacky Family Business. 2011. 288p. 30.95 *(978-1-4502-9858-2(3))*; pap. 20.95 *(978-1-4502-9860-5(5))* iUniverse, Inc.

Sheehan, Jack. Forgotten Man: How Circus Circus's Bill Bennett Brought Middle America to Las Vegas. 2010. (Illus.). 244p. 29.95 *(978-1-935043-32-4(3))* Stephens Pr. LLC.

Sheets, Herman Ernst & McNees, Pat. Starting Over: The Life of Herman Ernst Sheets. 2007. (Illus.). x, 383p. *(978-0-9795885-1-8(0))* Memory Works, LLC, The.

Shelp, Ronald, et al. Fallen Giant: The Amazing Story of Hank Greenberg & the History of AIG. 2nd ed. 2009. (ENG., Illus.). 289p. pap. 16.95 *(978-0-470-48002-1(5)*, Wiley) Wiley, John & Sons, Inc.

Shepard, Lucius. With Christmas in Honduras: Men, Myths, & Miscreants in Modern Central America. 2013. (ENG.). 272p. 24.95 *(978-1-56025-679-3(6))* Westview Pr.

Sheppard, Robin. A Solitary Confinement. 2007. 264p. per. *(978-1-905823-25-3(8))* Ecademy Pr. Ltd.

Shifrin, Jason. The First Apprentice. 2011. (ENG., Illus.). 278p. pap. 12.95 ***(978-1-84358-418-6(2))*** Blake, John Publishing, Ltd. GBR. Dist: Independent Pubs. Group.

Shimano, Yoshizo. This Is My Road: The Shimano Story. 2008. (ENG., Illus.). 172p. 22.95 *(978-0-470-82361-3(5)*, Wiley) Wiley, John & Sons, Inc.

Shippen, Katherine B. Milton S. Hershey. 20.95 *(978-0-8488-1164-8(X))* Amereon LTD.

Shute, Jason. Henry Ayers: The Man Who Became a Rock. 2011. (ENG., Illus.). 288p. 45.00 *(978-1-84885-563-2(X))* I. B. Tauris & Co., Ltd. GBR. Dist: Macmillan.

Siegel, Peter A. The First Half of an Average Mans Life: Trust Me I Know What I'm Doing. 2007. 164p. per. 12.95 *(978-1-4327-1442-0(2))* Outskirts Pr., Inc.

Silverman, David. Typo: The Last American Typesetter or How I Made 4 Million Dollars. 2007. (ENG.). 352p. per. 16.95 *(978-1-933368-65-8(9))* Counterpoint LLC.

Silverman, Jeff & Tapley, Drew. Funny Business, 1 vol. 2011. (ENG.). 142p. pap. 14.95 ***(978-1-927005-04-0(3))*** Burman Books, Inc. CAN. Dist: Innovative Logistics.

Simon, Abdallah & Simon, Ed. Abdallah Simon Vintage Years: A Memoir As told to my nephew Edwin Simon. 2009. *(978-1-61623-108-8(4))* Independent Pub.

Simon, Francois. Jean-Paul Hevin: Chocolatier. 2007. (ENG., Illus.). 78p. 25.00 *(978-2-7594-0257-1(6))* Assouline FRA. Dist: Perseus Distribution.

Simons, Suzanne. Master of War: Blackwater USA's Erik Prince & the Business of War. 288p. 2010. (ENG.). pap. 15.99 *(978-0-06-167271-2(8)*, Harper Paperbacks) 2009. 27.99 *(978-0-06-165135-9(4))* HarperCollins Pubs.

Siwisa, S. M. Giant Steps: A Personal Story of Love & Triumph Against Adversity. 2010. (Illus.). 104p. pap. 13.99 *(978-1-4520-0445-7(5))* AuthorHouse.

Skilleter, Paul & Porter, Philip. Sir William Lyons: The Official Biography. 2011. (ENG., Illus.). 384p. pap. 17.95 *(978-0-85733-106-9(X)*, 085733106X) Haynes Publishing PLC GBR. Dist: MBI Distribution Services/Quayside Distribution.

Skorman, Stuart. Confessions of a Serial Entrepreneur: Why I Can't Stop Starting Over. 2007. (ENG., Illus.). 224p. 22.95 *(978-0-7879-8732-9(8)*, Jossey-Bass) Wiley, John & Sons, Inc.

Skrabec, Quentin R. H. J. Heinz: A Biography. 2009. (ENG., Illus.). 291p. pap. 25.00 (978-0-7864-4178-5(X)) McFarland & Co., Inc. Pubs.
—Henry Clay Frick: The Life of the Perfect Capitalist. 2010. (ENG., Illus.). 270p. pap. 45.00 (978-0-7864-4383-3(9)) McFarland & Co. Inc. Pubs.
Skrabec, Quentin R., Jr. Michael Owens & the Glass Industry, 1 vol. 2007. (ENG., Illus.). 320p. 29.95 (978-1-58980-385-5(X)) Pelican Publishing Co., Inc.
Slovinsky, Louis J. Alan Siegel: On Branding & Clear Communications. 2007. Orig. Title: Alan Siegel: on Branding & Clear Communications. (ENG.). 188p. per. (978-0-9790766-4-0(1), Working Biographies) Pinto, Jorge Bks.
Smallwood, Robert B. Sir Thomas Lipton Englands Great Merchan. 2006. pap. 15.95 (978-1-4286-5800-4(9)) Kessinger Publishing, LLC.
Smiles, Samuel. Men of Invention & Industry. 2008. 284p. 28.99 (978-0-554-21530-3(6)) 2008. 284p. 25.99 (978-0-554-30833-3(9)) 2006. (ENG.). 294p. pap. 21.99 (978-1-4264-0314-9(3)) BiblioBazaar.
—Men of Invention & Industry. 2009. 258p. pap. (978-1-150-68497-5(6)) Books LLC.
—Men of Invention & Industry. 2008. (Illus.). 284p. pap. (978-1-4065-7575-0(5)) Dodo Pr.
—Men of Invention & Industry. 2009. (ENG.). 286p. pap. 18.95 (978-1-4385-2353-8(X), Book Jungle) Standard Pubns., Inc.
Smith, Cathy. The Adventures of Henry Dent: Farmer, Poet, Gold Digger, Sawyer. 2010. 92p. pap. 11.49 (978-1-4520-8102-1(6)) AuthorHouse.
Smith, Edward. Dundurn Castle: Sir Allan MacNab & His Hamilton Home. 2007. (ENG., Illus.). 72p. pap. 19.95 (978-1-55028-988-6(8)) Lorimer, James & Co., Ltd., Pubs. CAN. Dist: Casemate Pubs. & Bk. Distributors, LLC.
Somerville Mitchell, David. The Panda & the Prince: Confessions of the 'Panda Diplomat' 2009. 228p. pap. 21.49 (978-1-4389-8749-1(8)) AuthorHouse.
Songor, Amos. Persistence: The Way to Success in America, 1 vol. 2010. 179p. pap. 24.95 (978-1-4489-8327-8(4)) PublishAmerica, Inc.
Spector, Robert. Generations: Kemper Freeman Jr. & the Freeman Family. 2007. (978-1-933245-04-1(2)) Documentary Media LLC.
Spitzig, Norm. How Now, Norm's Tao. 2011. 200p. pap. 25.00 (978-1-4575-0633-8(5)) Dog Ear Publishing, LLC.
Stephenson, J. r. Broken Promises, Betrayals & Barefaced Lies. 2008. 144p. pap. (978-0-9558557-0-2(5)) ShieldCrest.
Stern, David, et al. Crosley: Two Brothers & a Business Empire That Transformed the Nation. 2008. (ENG.). 504p. pap. 15.95 (978-1-57860-322-0(6)) Clerisy Pr.
Steudel, Arthur W. George A Martin Beloved American Incustr. 2006. pap. 15.95 (978-1-4286-5801-1(7)) Kessinger Publishing, LLC.
Stiles, T. J. The First Tycoon: The Epic Life of Cornelius Vanderbilt. (Vintage Ser.). (ENG., Illus.). 736p. 2010. pap. 19.95 (978-1-4000-3174-0(5), Vintage) 2009. 45.00 (978-0-375-41542-5(4), Knopf) Knopf Doubleday Publishing Group.
Stille, Alexander. The Sack of Rome: Media + Money + Celebrity = Power = Silvio Berlusconi. 2007. (ENG.). 400p. (gr. 12-18). 18.00 (978-0-14-311210-5(4), Penguin (Non-Classics)) Penguin Group (USA) Inc.
Stith, Marva Woods. Black Star Girl: A Charter Beneficiary of the Civil Rights Movement Celebrates the Insightful Parenting of Her Father. It's His Story Too. 2010. 252p. 29.95 (978-1-4401-9579-2(X)); pap. 19.95 (978-1-4401-9581-5(1)) iUniverse, Inc.
Stossel, Scott. Sarge: The Life & Times of Sargent Shriver. 2011. (ENG.). 800p. pap. 19.95 (978-1-59051-513-6(7)) Other Pr., LLC.
Stovall, Jim. Este Es el Día (This Is the Day) 2011. (SPA.). 268p. pap. 14.95 (978-1-58802-622-4(1)) Editorial Patmos.
Stowers, James E. The Best Is yet to Be. 2007. (ENG., Illus.). 272p. 29.95 (978-0-9629788-7-6(6)) Andrews McMeel Publishing.
Straube, Win. Enjoying the Ride: Chinese Version. 2007. (CHI., Illus.). mass mkt. (978-0-9777031-2-8(6)) Straube Ctrs. International Corp.
Stuart-Hutcheson, Alan. Destiny of Character. 2006. (Illus.). 218p. pap. 20.63 (978-1-4120-8821-3(6)) Trafford Publishing.
Studwell, Joe. Asian Godfathers: Money & Power in Hong Kong & Southeast Asia. 2008. (ENG., Illus.). 368p. pap. 15.95 (978-0-8021-4391-4(1), Grove Pr.) Grove/Atlantic, Inc.
Sugar, Alan. What You See Is What You Get: My Autobiography. (ENG., Illus.). 2011. 640p. 27.95 (978-0-230-74933-7(X)) 2010. 610p. pap. 22.95 (978-0-230-75056-2(7)) Macmillan Pubs., Ltd. GBR. Dist: Independent Pubs. Group.
Swint, Kerwin. Dark Genius: The Influential Career of Legendary Political Operative & Fox News Founder Roger Ailes. 2008. (ENG., Illus.). 264p. 24.95 (978-1-4027-5445-6(0), Union Square Pr.
Sytin, Ivan D., et al. My Life for the Book: The Memoirs of a Russian Publisher. 2012. (ENG., Illus.). 224p. (C). (978-0-7735-4024-8(5)) McGill-Queen's Univ. Pr.
Talbot, Toby. The New Yorker Theater & Other Scenes from a Life at the Movies. 2009. (ENG., Illus.). 400p. (gr. 17). 24.95 (978-0-231-14566-4(7)) Columbia Univ. Pr.
Tallman, Matthew William. Demos Shakarian, the Life, Legacy, & Vision of a Full Gospel Business Man. 2010. 265p. pap. 18.00 net. (978-1-60947-002-9(8)) Emeth Pr.
Tedlow, Richard S. The Watson Dynasty: The Fiery Reign & Troubled Legacy of IBM's Founding Father & Son. 2006. 340p. reprint ed. pap. 16.00 (978-1-4223-5216-8(1)) DIANE Publishing Co.
Teets, John W. Pursue Your Destiny: Plan, Pray, & Perform Your Way to Lasting Success. 2006. 19.95 (978-0-9769165-0-5(9)) Trout Park Publishing.
The World Famous DJ K-LUV. The Champagne Life: Starts Promoting Parties at Age 15... Networked with Industry's Elite by Age 20... Owns Star-Studded Nightclub by Age 22. 2011. 152p. pap. 14.95 (978-1-4620-1905-2(6)) iUniverse, Inc.
Thomas, Paul Anthony. Winning with Private Equity. 2009. 90p. pap. 19.95 (978-1-4251-8675-3(0)) Trafford Publishing.
Thompson, Eric C. & Walstad, William B. Entrepreneurship in Nebraska: Conditions, Attitudes, & Actions. 2008. (ENG.). 196p. pap. 24.95 (978-1-59562-020-0(6)) Gallup Pr.
Thompson, Robert. Going for the Green: Conversations with Canada's Business & Political Elite. 2009. (ENG.). 296p. pap. 19.95 (978-1-55470-172-8(4)) Key Porter Bks. CAN. Dist: Perseus-PGW.
Tichawangana, Peter Takarasika. If Only I Had My Own Way: A Story to Tell. 2010. (ENG.). 156p. pap. 13.99 (978-1-4490-6542-3(2)) AuthorHouse.
Tobin, William J. Confessions of a Compulsive Entrepreneur & Inventor: How I Secured Fifteen Patents, Started Ten Companies, & Became a Pioneer on the Internet. 2011. 155p. pap. 17.99 (978-1-4520-7781-9(9)) 2010. 164p. 22.49 (978-1-4520-7780-2(0)) AuthorHouse.
Tombs, George. Robber Baron: Lord Black of Crossharbour. 2007. (ENG., Illus.). 350p. 26.95 (978-1-55022-806-9(4)) ECW Pr. CAN. Dist: Independent Pubs. Group.
Tonello, Michael. Bringing Home the Birkin: My Life in Hot Pursuit of the World's Most Coveted Handbag. (Illus.). 272p. 2009. pap. 14.99 (978-0-06-147334-0(0), William Morrow Paperbacks) 2008. (ENG., 25.95 (978-0-06-147333-3(2), Morrow, William & Co.) HarperCollins Pubs.
Toole, Monte. Monte Toole: A Memoir. 2008. 192p. pap. 17.95 (978-0-595-51304-8(2)) iUniverse, Inc.
Topping, Robert W. Just Call Me Orville: The Story of Orville Redenbacher. 2011. (Illus.). 114p. pap. 16.95 (978-1-55753-595-5(7)) Purdue Univ. Pr.
Towe, Kenneth C. William Brown Bell Quaker Lawyer Busines. 2006. pap. 15.95 (978-1-4286-5795-3(9)) Kessinger Publishing, LLC.
Tremain, Alan. Without Reservation, the Ribald Memoirs of Famous Hotelier Alan Tremain. 2010. 246p. 27.95 (978-1-936051-78-6(8)) Peppertree Pr., The.
Troy, Stephen K. Business Biographies: Shaken, Not Stirred ... with a Twist. 2011. 180p. pap. 16.95 (978-1-4502-8325-0(X)) iUniverse, Inc.
Tuccille, Jerome. Dillerland: The Story of Media Mogul Barry Diller. 2009. (ENG.). 296p. 24.95 (978-1-59350-124-2(2)) Alyson Pubns.
Tucker, Barbara M. & Tucker, Kenneth H. Industrializing Antebellum America: The Rise of Manufacturing Entrepreneurs in the Early Republic. 2008. (ENG.). 272p. 95.00 (978-1-4039-8480-7(8)) Palgrave Macmillan.
Turner, Ted & Burke, Bill. Call Me Ted: My Life, My Way. 2009. (ENG., Illus.). 448p. pap. 16.99 (978-0-446-58203-2(4), Business Plus) Grand Central Publishing.
Tyson, Robert. Frontier Life on the Prairie: Life & Times of Jim Tyson 1843-1937. 2011. 296p. 25.99 (978-1-4520-9621-6(X)); pap. 17.49 (978-1-4520-9622-3(8)) AuthorHouse.
Underwood, Larry. Life under the Corporate Microscope: A Maverick's Irreverent Perspective. 2008. 232p. pap. 15.95 (978-1-4327-3393-3(1)) Outskirts Pr., Inc.
Unger, Irwin. The Guggenheims: A Family History. 2009. (ENG.). 550p. pap. 17.00 (978-1-4379-6780-7(9)) DIANE Publishing Co.
Unger, Irwin & Unger, Debi. The Guggenheims: A Family History. 2006. (Illus.). 550p. reprint ed. 30.00 (978-1-4223-5383-7(4)) DIANE Publishing Co.
Van Hasselt, Caroline. High Wire Act: Ted Rogers & the Empire That Debt Built. 2008. (ENG., Illus.). 544p. pap. 26.95 (978-0-470-15756-5(9), Wiley) Wiley, John & Sons, Inc.
Van Hasselt, Caroline & Hasselt, Caroline Van. High Wire Act: Ted Rogers & the Empire That Debt Built. 2007. (ENG., Illus.). 530p. 34.95 (978-0-470-15296-6(6), Wiley) Wiley, John & Sons, Inc.
Van Rensselaer Dey, Frederic. The Magic Story. 2008. 64p. pap. 16.75 (978-0-559-46036-4(8)) BiblioBazaar.
Vaughan, Adrian. Samuel Morton Peto: A Victorian Entrepreneur. 2006. (ENG., Illus.). 192p. 32.95 (978-0-7110-3378-8(1)) Allan, Ian Publishing GBR. Dist: BookMasters Distribution Services (BDS).
Vault Employer Profile: Goldman. pap. (978-1-58131-262-1(8)) Vault.com.
Vault Employer Profile: J. P. Morgan. pap. (978-1-58131-263-8(6)) Vault.com.
Vault Employer Profile: McKinsey & Company. pap. (978-1-58131-261-4(X)) Vault.com.
Villette, Michel & Vuillermot, Catherine. From Predators to Icons: Exposing the Myth of the Business Hero. Holoch, George & Kimberly, John R., trs. from FRE. 2009. (Illus.). 224p. 62.95 (978-0-8014-4700-6(3)); pap. 24.95 (978-0-8014-7566-5(X)) Cornell Univ. Pr.
Virtue, John. The Model American Abroad. 2007. 280p. pap. 19.99 (978-1-59092-405-1(3)) Orchard House Pr.
Wagner, Gerhard. Tears of the Son: An Exposé. 2011. 200p. 26.95 (978-1-4502-9422-5(7)); pap. 16.95 (978-1-4502-9421-8(9)) iUniverse, Inc.
Wahl, Bob. Contending with Horses. 2009. 326p. pap. 19.95 (978-1-4327-3538-8(1)) Outskirts Pr., Inc.
Walby, David. Bond Daddy. 2009. 167p. pap. 14.95 (978-1-4327-4249-2(3)) Outskirts Pr., Inc.
Walker, Johnny. The Price of Second Chances: A True Story of Deceit & Betrayal. 2010. pap. 12.99 (978-1-61663-587-9(8)) Tate Publishing & Enterprises, LLC.
Wang, Yupin. Manchurian American: A Memoir. 2009. (Illus.). vii, 156p. E-Book (978-1-4401-8677-6(4)) iUniverse, Inc.
Watson, Jack. I Was Homer's Child: An Epic Journey from Rags to Riches. 2010. 340p. 33.95 (978-1-4502-5363-5(6)); pap. 23.95 (978-1-4502-5361-1(X)) iUniverse, Inc.
Watson, Kenneth. I Am Bipolar Manic. 2011. 124p. 22.95 (978-1-4502-8190-4(7)); pap. 12.95 (978-1-4502-8189-8(3)) iUniverse, Inc.
Webster, Anthony. The Richest East India Merchant: The Life & Business of John Palmer of Calcutta, 1767-1836. 2007. (Worlds of the East India Company Ser.: Volume 1). (Illus.). 214p. 80.00 (978-1-84383-303-1(4), Boydell Press) Boydell & Brewer, Ltd. GBR. Dist: Boydell & Brewer, Inc.
Weisz, Mischa & Hemsworth, Wade. I Choose to Live: A Self-Made Millionaire Faces Cancer. 2009. (ENG., Illus.). 168p. 35.00 (978-1-55488-718-7(6)) Dundurn CAN. Dist: Ingram Pub. Services.
Wells, George D. & Padberg, Nancy Shonka. The American Dream in A Kilt: CEO Shares Secrets on Leadership, Life & Laughter. 2006. 21.95 (978-1-59594-076-6(6), Wingspan Pr.) WingSpan Publishing.
Werenskiold, Marit, ed. Consul Jonas Lied & Russia: Collector, Diplomat & Industrial Explorer 1910-1931. 2008. (Illus.). 191p. 59.00 (978-82-7477-286-1(5), Oslo Academic Pr.) Unipub forlag NOR. Dist: International Specialized Bk. Services.
West, Michael. What I Learned by Not Killing People. 2009. 96p. pap. 9.95 (978-1-4401-5384-6(1)) iUniverse, Inc.
Whayne, Jeannie. Delta Empire: Lee Wilson & the Transformation of Agriculture in the New South. 2011. (Making the Modern South Ser.). (Illus.). 312p. 45.00 (978-0-8071-3855-7(X)) Louisiana State Univ. Pr.
Whitaker, Sigur E. James Allison: A Biography of the Engine Manufacturer & Indianapolis 500 Cofounder. 2011. (ENG., Illus.). 232p. pap. 35.00 (978-0-7864-6165-3(9)) McFarland & Co., Inc. Pubs.
White, Arthur. The Power & the Glory. 2007. (ENG.). 220p. per. 15.99 (978-1-86024-560-2(9)) Authentic Media.
White, Dedric. My Two Favorite Girls. 2007. 136p. pap. 24.95 (978-1-4241-9192-5(0)) PublishAmerica, Inc.
Whyte, Kenneth. The Uncrowned King: The Sensational Rise of William Randolph Hearst. 2009. (ENG.). 512p. pap. 17.95 (978-1-58243-554-1(5)); (Illus.). 560p. 30.00 (978-1-58243-467-4(0)) Basic Bks. GBR. (Counterpoint Pr.). Dist: Perseus-PGW.
Wiencek, Henry. The Moodys of Galveston & Their Mansion. 2010. (Sara & John Lindsey Series in the Arts & Humanities Ser.). (ENG., Illus.). 136p. pap. 19.95 (978-1-60344-182-7(4)) Texas A&M Univ. Pr.
Wilson, Carol Green. California Yankee: William R. Staats, Business Pioneer. 2007. (ENG.). 238p. 41.95 (978-0-548-05896-1(2)) Kessinger Publishing, LLC.
Wilson, Colin. Food for Thought. 2007. 308p. per. 18.50 (978-1-84426-414-8(9)) Upfront Publishing Ltd. GBR. Dist: Printondemand-worldwide.com.
Wingate, J. Opportunity Is Everywhere: The Story of America's Supermarket Banker. 2007. 180p. 24.95 (978-0-9773365-2-4(2)) Interview You, LLC.
Winston, George Tayloe. A Builder of the New South: Being the Story of the Life Work Of. 2007. (ENG.). 416p. per. 34.95 (978-1-4304-4237-0(9)) Kessinger Publishing, LLC.
Witherell, James L. L. L. Bean: The Man & His Company, 1 vol. 2011. (ENG.). 576p. pap. 20.00 (978-0-88448-329-8(0)) Tilbury Hse. Pubs.
Witt, Lee. The Brickhouse Band: How an Ordinary Mid-Life Couple Created A Business Phenomenon. 2009. (Illus.). 268p. pap. 15.95 (978-1-4327-4986-6(2)) Outskirts Pr., Inc.
Wizelman, Daryl & Dundore, Bruce. Heart Leader: A Personal Journey to the Heart of Business & Life. 2010. 138p. (ENG.). 24.95 (978-0-692-00740-2(7)); pap. 14.95 (978-0-692-00712-9(1)) Heart Leader Bks.
Wohlfelder, Peter. My Missionary Adventure: A True Story. 2009. 100p. pap. 14.00 (978-1-4490-3646-1(5)) AuthorHouse.
Wolcott, Robert W. Woman in Steel Rebecca Lukens. 2006. pap. 15.95 (978-1-4286-6078-6(X)) Kessinger Publishing, LLC.
Wood, John & Wood, John. Leaving Microsoft to Change the World: An Entrepreneur's Odyssey to Educate the World's Children. (ENG., Illus.). 2007. 304p. pap. 16.99 (978-0-06-112108-1(8)) 2006. 272p. 25.95 (978-0-06-112107-4(X)) HarperCollins Pubs. (Collins).
Woodhead, Lindy. Shopping, Seduction & Mr Selfridge. 2007. (Illus.). 310p. 35.00 (978-1-86197-888-2(X)) Profile Bks. Ltd. GBR. Dist: Independent Pubs. Group.
—Shopping, Seduction & Mr Selfridge. 2009. (ENG., Illus.). 320p. pap. 15.95 (978-1-86197-169-2(9)) Profile Bks. Ltd. GBR. Dist: Consortium Bk. Sales & Distribution.
Woods, Lawrence M. Alex Swan & the Swan Companies. 2006. (Western Lands & Waters Ser.: Vol. 22). (ENG., Illus.). 296p. (C). 34.95 (978-0-87062-346-2(X), Clark, Arthur H. Co., The) Univ. of Oklahoma Pr
Woods, Philip H. Bath, Maine's Charlie Morse: Ice King & Wall Street Scoundrel. 2011. 130p. pap. 19.99 (978-1-60949-274-8(9)) History Pr., The.
Wyllie, James. Goering & Goering: Hitler's Henchman & His Anti-Nazi Brother. 2010. (ENG., Illus.). 252p. pap. 16.95 (978-0-7524-5648-5(2)) History Pr. Ltd., The GBR. Dist: Independent Pubs. Group.
Wyly, Sam. 1,000 Dollars & an Idea. 2008. (ENG.). 272p. pap. 15.00 (978-1-55704-825-7(8)) Newmarket Pr.
—1,000 Dollars & an Idea: Entrepreneur to Billionaire. 2008. (ENG.). 272p. 24.95 (978-1-55704-803-5(7)) Newmarket Pr.
—1,000 Dollars & an Idea: Entrepreneur to Billionaire: Expanded Edition. exp. ed. 2009. (ENG.). 304p. pap. 16.95 (978-1-55704-848-6(7)); 26.95 (978-1-55704-864-6(9)) Newmarket Pr.
Wynne, John. Close Calls, Choices & Miracles. 2009. 120p. pap. 10.99 (978-1-4389-8330-1(1)) AuthorHouse.
Zaher, Mahmoud. 40 Years Between Egypt & Us. 2011. 148p. 29.99 (978-1-4568-0161-8(9)); pap. 19.99 (978-1-4568-0160-1(0)) Xlibris Corp.
Zha, Jianying. Tide Players: The Movers & Shakers of a Rising China. 2011. (ENG.). 224p. 24.95 (978-1-59558-620-9(2)) New Pr., The.
Zhang, Wenxian, et al, eds. Entrepreneurial & Business Elites of China: The Chinese Returnees who have Shaped Modern China. 2011. 325p. (978-0-85724-089-7(7)) Emerald Group Publishing Ltd.
Zhang, Wenxian & Alon, Ilan, eds. Biographical Dictionary of New Chinese Entrepreneurs & Business Leaders. 2011. (Elgar Original Reference Ser.). 296p. pap. 49.95 (978-1-84980-130-0(4)) Elgar, Edward Publishing, Inc.
Ziffer, Ronald. Confessions of an Accidental Salesman: How I Survived in Sales Without Really Knowing What I Was Doing. 2008. 132p. pap. 11.95 (978-1-4389-1716-0(3)) AuthorHouse.
2006 Fifty Successful Vietnamese Entrepreneurs in the World. 2006. 20.00 (978-0-9786323-0-4(3)) TransViet IMEX Magazine.

BUSINESSPEOPLE—CORRESPONDENCE

Hack, Richard. Hughes: The Private Diaries, Memos & Letters; the Definitive Biography of the First American Billionaire. 2007. (Illus.). 444p. per. 16.95 (978-1-59777-510-6(X)) Phoenix Bks., Inc.
Warden, Clyde A., Jr. & Chen, Judy F. The Handbook of Quick Business Letters: For Businesspeople in Asia. 4th ed. 2007. pap. 21.80 (978-0-9799042-0-2(X)) QBook International.

BUSINESSPEOPLE—JUVENILE LITERATURE

Byers, Ann. Jeff Bezos: The Founder of Amazon. com. 2006. 116p. (gr. 3-7). pap. 31.95 (978-1-4358-3765-2(7)) Rosen Publishing Group, Inc., The.
Wyckoff, Edwin Brit. The Cornflake King: W. K. Kellogg & His Amazing Cereal. 2010. (Genius at Work! Great Inventor Biographies Ser.). (Illus.). 32p. (J). 22.60 (978-0-7660-3448-6(8), Enslow Elementary) Enslow Pubs., Inc.

BUSINESSPEOPLE—PROFESSIONAL ETHICS

see Business Ethics

BUSINESSPEOPLE—RELIGIOUS LIFE

Addington, Thomas G. & Graves, Stephen R. Behind the Bottom Line: Powering Business Life with Spiritual Wisdom. 2011. (ENG.). 240p. pap. 21.95 (978-1-118-08589-6(2), Jossey-Bass) Wiley, John & Sons, Inc.
Blackaby, Henry, et al. God in the Marketplace: 45 Questions Fortune 500 Executives Ask about Faith, Life, & Business. 2008. (ENG.). 288p. 16.99 (978-0-8054-4688-3(5), B&H Bks.) B&H Publishing Group.
Crawford, Clark. Thank God I Got Caught: From Prisoner to Worshiper. 2009. pap. 9.95 (978-1-934749-51-7(6), CrossHouse Publishing) Hannibal Bks.
Crum, W. Paul "Buddy", Jr. Much More Than a Job: Your 24/7 Mission. 2007. 232p. per. 15.99 (978-0-88270-232-2(7)) Bridge-Logos Foundation.
Day, Frank L. Impact of A Father's Reflection: Seeing God Through My Father, Grandfathers & Spiritual Fathers. 2010. pap. 14.99 (978-1-61579-853-7(6)) Xulon Pr., Inc.
Dragun, Jim. What's Next? 2008-2009: Removing the Economic Viel for God's Children. 2007. 79p. per. 14.95 (978-0-9799340-0-1(1)) Falcon Group.
Finnick, Richard J. "Dick". Often Wrong, but Never in Doubt: A look back at a life greatly Blessed. 2009. 252p. 24.99 (978-1-4490-1379-0(1)); pap. 14.49 (978-1-4490-1378-3(3)) AuthorHouse.
Gallucci, Sam & Arterburn, Stephen. Road Warrior: How to Keep Your Faith, Relationships, & Integrity When Away from Home. 2008. (Every Man Ser.). (ENG.). 192p. per. 16.99 (978-1-4000-7371-9(5)) Doubleday Religious Publishing Group, The.
Heeren, Rick. Marketplace Miracles. 2007. (978-0-8307-4386-5(3), Regal Bks.) Gospel Light Pubns.
—Marketplace Miracles: Extraordinary Stories of Marketplace Turnarounds Transforming Businesses, Schools & Communities. 2008. (ENG.). 240p. 19.99 (978-0-8307-4396-4(0)) Gospel Light Pubns.
Hillman, Os. TGIF: Daily Workplace Inspiration. 2007. (978-0-8307-4513-5(0), Regal Bks.) Gospel Light Pubns.
—TGIF: Today God Is First - Daily Workplace Inspiration. 2007. (ENG.). 384p. 22.99 (978-0-8307-4479-4(7)) Gospel Light Pubns.
Hopkins, Todd. The Janitor: How an Unexpected Friendship Transformed a CEO & His Company, 0 vols. 2009. 160p. pap. 12.99 (978-1-59555-327-0(4)) Nelson, Thomas Inc.
Lambert, Lake, III. Spirituality, Inc: Religion in the American Workplace. 2009. (ENG.). 240p. 25.00 (978-0-8147-5246-3(2)) New York Univ. Pr.
Marr, Steve. Proverbs for Business. 2006. 256p. 5.99 (978-0-8007-8751-6(X)) Revell.
Moulton Reger, Sara J. Lead & Succeed: Lead with Confidence, Compassion, & Courage in an Ever-Changing Business World. 2009. (ENG.). 256p. 21.99 (978-1-59979-527-0(2)) Charisma Media.
Standfield, James L. God You Said: Reminding God of His Word on Your Entrepreneurial Journey. 2009. 164p. pap. 19.99 (978-1-4389-7105-6(2)) AuthorHouse.
Wiman, Carl S., Sr. Thoughts of Everyday Life, by the CEO. 2007. per. (978-1-59916-242-3(3)) Printing Systems.

BUSINESSPEOPLE, AFRICAN AMERICAN

see African Americans in Business

BUSINESSWOMEN

see also Women Executives

Aaltio, Iiris, et al, eds. Women Entrepreneurship & Social Capital: A Dialogue & Construction. 2008. 310p. (C). pap. 52.00 (978-87-630-0210-3(8)) Copenhagen Business Schl. Pr. DNK. Dist: International Specialized Bk. Services.
Abarbanel, Karin & Freeman, Bruce. Birthing the Elephant: The Woman's Go-for-It! Guide to Overcoming the Big Challenges of Launching a Business. 2008. (ENG., Illus.). 224p. pap. 15.99 (978-1-58008-887-9(2)) Ten Speed Pr.

Abbott, Edith. Women in Industry. 2010. 434p. pap. 35.75 (978-1-117-86995-7(4)) BiblioBazaar.

Albert, Erin. Single. Women. Entrepreneurs. 2011. 284p. pap. 24.95 net. (978-1-934922-40-8(4)) IBJ Custom Publishing.

Aldrich, Stephanie. There's No Crying in the Man's World: A Woman's Guide to Succeeding in Business. 2007. 184p. per. 17.95 (978-0-595-43341-4(3)) iUniverse, Inc.

Allen, Robert G. & Nelson Bell, Karen. Nothing down for Women: The Smart Woman's Quick-Start Guide to Real Estate Investing. 2011. (ENG.). 480p. pap. 28.99 (978-0-7432-9785-1(7), Free Pr.) Free Pr.

Allen, Sylvia. A Woman's Guide to Sales Success. 2006. 200p. per. (978-1-59971-144-7(3)) Aardvark Global Publishing.

—A Woman's Guide to Sales Success. 2010. 188p. pap. 35.00 (978-1-4269-3840-5(3)) Trafford Publishing.

Allison, Elaine. The Velvet Hammer: Powherful Leadership Lessons for Women Who Don't Golf. 2006. 151p. per. (978-0-9739065-0-9(2)) Positive Presentations Plus, Incorporated.

Ameche, Kathleen. The Woman Road Warrior: The Expert's Guide to Domestic & International Business Travel. 2nd ed. 2007. (ENG., Illus.). 210p. per. 14.00 (978-1-932841-25-1(3)) Agate Publishing, Inc.

Ann, Cathrine. Beautiful Buttons: A Memoir of Survival & Triumph. 2011. 334p. pap. **(978-1-926645-62-9(6))** BPS Bks.

Assassi, Libby. Gendering of Global Finance: Uncovering the Hidden Agenda. 2009. (ENG.). 224p. 100.00 (978-0-230-51793-6(5)) Palgrave Macmillan.

Awosika, Ibukun. The Girl Entrepreneurs. 2009. 220p. pap. 15.99 (978-1-60791-507-2(3)) Xulon Pr., Inc.

Babcock, Linda & Laschever, Sara. Women Don't Ask: The High Cost of Avoiding Negotiation — and Positive Strategies for Change. 2007. (ENG.). 272p. pap. 15.00 (978-0-553-38387-4(6), Bantam) Random House Publishing Group.

Bagyura, Susan. The Visionary Leader. 2008. 304p. 29.95 (978-1-59930-094-8(X)) LifeSuccess Publishing.

Baker, Susan Rae. The Last Box. 2008. 140p. pap. 16.95 (978-1-4343-6256-8(6)) AuthorHouse.

Balraj, Adalarasu. Functioning & Marketing Strategies of Women Self-Help Group. 2010. 260p. pap. (978-3-8383-9420-6(8)) Lambert Academic Publishing.

Barbara Killmeyer. It's Nobody's Business but Yours: A comprehensive guide for the woman who wants to turn her business idea into a Reality. 2010. 108p. 21.95 (978-1-4269-2187-2(X)); pap. 11.95 (978-1-4269-2186-5(1)) Trafford Publishing.

Bari, Susan Phillips. Yes, I Can Do That! 2007. per. (978-0-9753928-2-9(4)) Women's Business Enterprise National Council.

Barker, Hannah. The Business of Women: Female Enterprise & Urban Development in Northern England 1760-1830. 2006. (ENG., Illus.). 208p. 110.00 (978-0-19-929971-3(4)) Oxford Univ. Pr., Inc.

Barsh, Joanna, et al. How Remarkable Women Lead: The Breakthrough Model for Work & Life. 2009. (ENG., Illus.). 368p. 27.50 (978-0-307-46169-8(6), Crown Business) Crown Publishing Group.

Bartlett, Pam. Women Connected: A Session by Session Coaching Guide for Women's Groups. 2007. per., act. bk. ed. 24.95 (978-0-9776656-0-0(7)) Glenmoore Press.

Benoit, Denise. The Best-Kept Secret: Women Corporate Lobbyists, Policy, & Power in the United States. 2007. (ENG.). 182p. 62.00 (978-0-8135-4065-8(8)); per. 21.95 (978-0-8135-4066-5(6)) Rutgers Univ. Pr.

Bilimoria, Diana & Piderit, Sandy Kristin, eds. Handbook on Women in Business & Management. 2008. (Elgar Original Reference Ser.). 392p. pap. 66.00 (978-1-84844-176-7(2)) Elgar, Edward Publishing, Inc.

Bilimoria, Karan & Piderit. Handbook on Women in Business & Management. 2007. (Elgar Original Reference Ser.). 392p. (C). 215.00 (978-1-84542-432-9(8)) Elgar, Edward Publishing, Inc.

Binaté Fofana, Namizata. Efficacy of micro-financing women's activities in Côte D'Ivoire: Evidence from rural areas & HIV/AIDS-affected Women. 2010. (AWLAE Ser.: 8). 208p. pap. 57.00 (978-90-8686-125-5(3)) Wageningen Academic Publishers NLD. Dist: Enfield Publishing & Distribution Co., Inc.

Blake, Megan K. It Takes a Village. 2008. 140p. pap. (978-3-639-07938-8(8)) VDM Verlag Dr. Mueller e.K.

Bone, Joyce. Millionaire Moms: The Art of Raising a Business & a Family at the Same Time. 2010. (ENG.). 192p. pap. 17.95 (978-1-60037-692-4(4)) Morgan James Publishing.

Boon, Marloes. Women Reaching the Top in the International Luxury Hotel Industry. 2011. 124p. pap. **(978-3-8443-0952-2(7))** Lambert Academic Publishing.

Brown-Glaude, Winnifred. Higglers in Kingston: Women's Informal Work in Jamaica. 2011. (ENG., Illus.). 256p. 55.00 (978-0-8265-1765-4(X)) Vanderbilt Univ. Pr.

Brown, Lisa M. Strong on the Outside, Dying on the Inside. 2011. 122p. 19.99 (978-1-61215-592-0(8)) Xulon Pr., Inc.

Bukari, Shaibu. Challenges of Women Entrepreneurship Development. 2011. 104p. pap. **(978-3-8443-8841-1(9))** Lambert Academic Publishing.

Campbell, Valencia. Advice from the Top: What Minority Women Say about Their Career Success, 1 vol. 2009. (Illus.). 174p. 39.95 (978-0-313-35858-6(3), C35858, Praeger Pubs.) Greenwood Publishing Group, Inc.

Carr, Marilyn & Williams, Mariama, eds. Trading Stories: Experiences with Gender & Trade. 2010. (ENG., Illus.). 300p. pap. 33.00 (978-0-85092-873-0(7)) Commonwealth Secretariat GBR. Dist: Stylus Publishing, LLC.

Chang, Fengbin. Gender Differences. 2007. 164p. per. (978-3-8364-2354-0(5)) VDM Verlag Dr. Mueller e.K.

Chen, Minglü. Tiger Girls: Women & Enterprise in the People's Republic of China. 2011. (Routledge Studies on China in Transition Ser.). (ENG., Illus.). 272p. (C). 140.00 (978-0-415-60013-2(8)) Routledge.

Christensen, Barbara. How I Turned 25 cents into A Quarter ... MILLION DOLLARS! 2009. 93p. pap. 16.72 (978-0-557-09741-8(X)) Lulu Enterprises Inc.

Cloud, Lana. I've Got Your Number! the Insider's Guide: One Woman's Private Secrets to Sales & Sales Management. 2009. 58p. pap. 14.98 (978-0-557-16570-4(9)) Lulu Enterprises Inc.

Cockerham, Ginger & Dixon, Diane. Magnificent Masters in Financial Services: Amazing Women-Sensational Stories. 2007. 176p. per. 16.95 (978-0-595-39674-0(7)) iUniverse, Inc.

Coleman, Susan & Robb, Alicia M. A Rising Tide: Financing Strategies for Women-Owned Firms. 2012. (ENG.). 288p. 85.00 **(978-0-8047-7305-8(X))**; pap. 27.95 **(978-0-8047-7306-5(8))** Stanford Univ. Pr. (Stanford Economics & Finance).

Colligan, Victoria, et al. Ladies Who Launch: An Innovative Program That Will Help You Get Your Dreams off the Ground. 2008. (ENG., Illus.). 240p. pap. 14.95 (978-0-312-35955-3(1), St. Martin's Griffin) St. Martin's Pr.

Cooper, Cary L. & Kossek, Ellen Ernst. Women & Management, 2 vols. Gatrell, Caroline, ed. 2010. (International Library of Critical Writings on Business & Management Ser.). (Illus.). 1136p. 563.00 (978-1-84844-326-6(9)) Elgar, Edward Publishing, Inc.

Cronin, Lynn & Fine, Howard. Damned If She Does, Damned If She Doesn't: Rethinking the Rules of the Game That Keep Women from Succeeding in Business. 2010. (ENG., Illus.). 250p. pap. 19.00 (978-1-61614-174-5(3)) Prometheus Bks., Pubs.

Curry, Elysse. How to Find the Real Deal Without Getting A Raw Deal: A Must Have Guide for Busy Women Who Want to Make Money Working from Home. 2009. 294p. pap. 19.95 (978-1-4327-4618-6(9)) Outskirts Pr., Inc.

Davis-Ali, Susan. How to Become Successful Without Becoming a Man. 2009. 300p. 24.99 (978-1-4363-9215-0(2)); pap. 17.99 (978-1-4363-9214-3(4)) Xlibris Corp.

Davis, Demitri L. A Woman's Worth. 2011. 338p. pap. 29.95 **(978-1-4560-6087-9(2))** PublishAmerica, Inc.

De Bruin, A. Women Entrepreneurs & the Global Environment for Growth: A Research Perspective. Brush, Candida G. et al, eds. 2010. (Illus.). 384p. 149.95 (978-1-84720-914-6(9)) Elgar, Edward Publishing, Inc.

Debroux, Philippe. Female Entrepreneurship in East & South-East Asia: Opportunities & Challenges. 2010. (Chandos Asian Studies). (ENG.). 260p. 120.00 (978-1-84334-398-1(3), Chandos Publishing) Woodhead Publishing Ltd. GBR. Dist: Ingram Pub. Services.

DeVrye, Catherine. Serendipity Road: A Memoir. 2008. (ENG., Illus.). 356p. pap. 24.95 (978-1-55278-645-1(5)) McArthur & Co. CAN. Dist: National Bk. Network.

DiSesa, Nina. Seducing the Boys Club: Uncensored Tactics from a Woman at the Top. 2008. (ENG.). 256p. pap. 16.00 (978-0-345-49699-7(X), Ballantine Bks.) Random House Publishing Group.

Dlamini, Dr. Khetsiwe & Dlamini, Khetsiwe. Promoting Gender Equality & Women's Success in Business. 2010. 104p. pap. (978-3-8383-5478-1(8)) Lambert Academic Publishing.

Dlamini, Khetsiwe & Lize AE Booysen. Recognizing the Role Men Play in the Entrepreneurial Success of Women. 2010. 376p. pap. (978-3-8383-5438-5(9)) Lambert Academic Publishing.

Doe, Helen. Enterprising Women & Shipping in the Nineteenth Century. 2009. (Illus.). 286p. 95.00 (978-1-84383-472-4(3), Boydell Press) Boydell & Brewer, Ltd. GBR. Dist: Boydell & Brewer, Inc.

Doyle, Anne J. Powering Up. 2011. 342p. 29.99 **(978-1-4568-1175-4(4))**; pap. 19.99 **(978-1-4568-1174-7(6))** Xlibris Corp.

Dugan, Ann M., et al. A Woman's Place: The Crucial Roles of Women in Family Business. 2008. 125p. 29.95 (978-1-891652-21-9(4)) Family Enterprise Pubs.

—A Woman's Place: The Crucial Roles of Women in Family Business. 2010. (Family Business Publication). (ENG.). 176p. 48.00 (978-0-230-11122-6(X)) Palgrave Macmillan.

Dutton, Diane. A Woman's Ladder to Success Is Paved with Broken Glass Ceilings. 2007. (Illus.). 172p. per. 19.95 (978-0-9791521-0-8(0)) ESO Pubns.

Dyson, Loraine. Dare to Succeed as a Woman in Real Estate: Discover how your intuition can improve your business & empower your Life. 2006. 136p. per. 14.95 (978-0-9728141-4-0(0)) Small Business Co., The.

Dzisi, Smile. Women Entrepreneurs in Small & Medium Enterprises in Ghan. 2010. 376p. pap. (978-3-8383-1884-4(6)) Lambert Academic Publishing.

Elliott, Carole & Stead, Valerie. Women's Leadership. 2010. (ENG., Illus.). 256p. 100.00 (978-1-4039-9875-0(2)) Palgrave Macmillan.

Ellis, Amanda, et al. Economic Opportunities for Women in the East Asia & Pacific Region: A Regional Overview. 2010. (Directions in Development Ser.). (ENG., Illus.). 118p. pap. 25.00 (978-0-8213-8300-1(0), 9780821383001) World Bank Pubns.

—Gender & Economic Growth in Tanzania: Creating Opportunities for Women. 2007. (Directions in Development Ser.). (ENG.). 132p. pap. 20.00 (978-0-8213-7262-3(9), 9780821372623) World Bank Pubns.

Ellis Eastman, Linda, ed. Overcoming the Super Woman Syndrome. 2007. 19.95 (978-0-9791153-6-3(1)) Professional Woman Publishing.

Endeley, RoseMarie-Rita & Thompson, Rosetta Bola. Management of Credit Schemes for Women Entrepreneurs in Africa. 2007. (Illus.). 407p. pap. 48.95 (978-1-901127-32-4(X)) Studies Forum International GBR. Dist: Stylus Publishing, LLC.

Ettl, Kerstin. Unternehmerinnen und Erfolg aus individueller und kontextueller Perspektive. 2010. (KMU-Forschung Ser.). (GER.). 306p. 79.95 (978-3-631-60420-5(3)) Lang, Peter GmbH, Europaischer Verlag der Wissenschaften DEU. Dist: Lang, Peter.

Expanding Opportunities for Women Entrepreneurs: The Future of Women's Small Business Programs: Hearing Before the Committee on Small Business & Entrepreneurship, United States Senate, One Hundred Tenth Congress, First Session, September 20, 2007. 2008. (Illus.). iv, 142p. (978-0-16-081960-5(1), 552-070-38133-3) United States Government Printing Office.

Faure, Jaxx. Visualize Your Way to Wealth. 2011. 88p. pap. 14.95 **(978-1-60746-051-0(3))** FastPencil, Inc.

Fielden, Sandra L. International Research Handbook on Successful Women Entrepreneurs. Davidson, Marilyn J., ed. 2012. (Elgar Original Reference Ser.). (Illus.). 256p. pap. 45.00 **(978-0-85793-143-6(1))** Elgar, Edward Publishing, Inc.

Fielden, Sandra L. & Davidson, Marilyn J., eds. International Research Handbook on Successful Women Entrepreneurs. 2010. (Elgar Original Reference Ser.). (Illus.). 256p. 182.00 (978-1-84720-918-4(1)) Elgar, Edward Publishing, Inc.

Fitzgerald, Kathie. Country Living Crafting a Business: Make Money Doing What You Love. 2008. (Country Living Ser.). (ENG., Illus.). 192p. 19.95 (978-1-58816-626-5(0)) Hearst Communications, Inc.

—Crafting a Business: Make Money Doing What You Love. 2010. (ENG., Illus.). 216p. pap. 14.95 (978-1-58816-811-5(5)) Hearst Communications, Inc.

Flynn, Jill, et al. Break Your Own Rules: How to Change the Patterns of Thinking That Block Women's Paths to Power. 2011. (ENG., Illus.). 208p. 25.95 (978-1-118-06254-8(X), Jossey-Bass) Wiley, John & Sons, Inc.

Friedman, Caitlin & Yorio, Kimberly. The Girl's Guide to Being a Boss (Without Being a Bitch) Valuable Lessons, Smart Suggestions, & True Stories for Succeeding as the Chick-in-Charge. 2007. (ENG.). 240p. pap. 13.99 (978-0-7679-2285-2(9), Morgan Road Bks.) Broadway Bks.

—The Girl's Guide to Starting Your Own Business: Candid Advice, Frank Talk, & True Stories for the Successful Entrepreneur. rev. ed. 2010. (ENG.). 272p. pap. 15.99 (978-0-06-198924-7(X), Harper Paperbacks) HarperCollins Pubs.

Friedman, Pirjo. Pushing Your Boundaries: The Feminine Principle in Business. 2007. 108p. per. 16.95 (978-1-4241-6334-2(X)) PublishAmerica, Inc.

Full Committee Hearing on SBA's Progress in Implementing the Women's Procurement Program. 2008. v, 127p. (978-0-16-080871-5(5), 552-070-37422-1) United States Government Printing Office.

Full Committee Hearing on the Small Business Administration's Contracting Programs. 2007. v, 94p. (978-0-16-080132-7(X), 552-070-36872-8) United States Government Printing Office.

Gale Editors. National Directory of Woman-owned Business Firms. Business Research Services Staff, ed. 15th ed. 2012. (National Directory of Woman-owned Business Firms Ser.). (ENG.). 1288p. 295.00 (978-0-933527-89-8(6)) Business Research Services, Inc.

Galindo, Miguel-Angel & Ribeiro, Domingo, eds. Women's Entrepreneurship & Economics: New Perspectives, Practices, & Policies. 2011. (International Studies in Entrepreneurship Ser.). (ENG., Illus.). ix, 230p. 139.00 **(978-1-4614-1292-2(7)**, 1461412927) Springer.

Galvano, Mary. Ladies, get a Grip. 2007. 102p. pap. 16.50 (978-0-615-17353-5(5)) Galvano, Mary.

—Ladies Get A Grip: Playing Golf for Business & Pleasure the Feminine Way. 2007. 100p. per. 17.50 (978-0-9800820-0-5(5)) Galvano, Mary.

Ganesamurthy, V., ed. Empowerment of Women in India: Social, Economic & Political. 2008. 321p. 53.50 (978-81-7708-155-8(1)) New Century Publications IND. Dist: International Specialized Bk. Services.

Ganesamurthy, V. S., ed. India: Economic Empowerment of Women. 2007. 270p. (C). 38.50 (978-81-7708-144-2(6)) New Century Publications IND. Dist: International Specialized Bk. Services.

Ganesan, Ramaswamy. Prospects of Women Entrepreneurship Development. 2010. 160p. pap. (978-3-639-24217-1(3)) VDM Verlag Dr. Mueller e.K.

Gilbert, Elena B., ed. Women & Minorities in Business: Demographic Reviews of Business Ownership. 2010. (Women's Issues Ser.). (Illus.). viii, 132p. pap. 47.00 (978-1-60741-276-2(4)) Nova Science Pubs., Inc.

Gill, Tiffany. Beauty Shop Politics: African American Women's Activism in the Beauty Industry. 2010. (Women in American History Ser.). (ENG., Illus.). 208p. pap. 25.00 (978-0-252-07696-1(6)) Univ. of Illinois Pr.

Gimson, Lou & Mitchell, Allison. Making It: Women Entrepreneurs Reveal Their Secrets of Success. 2008. (ENG., Illus.). 214p. pap. 29.95 (978-1-84112-700-2(0), Capstone) Wiley, John & Sons, Inc.

Godwyn, Mary & Stoddard, Donna. Minority Women Entrepreneurs: How Outsider Status Can Lead to Better Business Practices. 2011. (ENG.). 224p. 70.00 (978-0-8047-7477-2(3)); pap. 24.95 (978-0-8047-7478-9(1)) Stanford Univ. Pr. (Stanford Business Bks.).

Graen, George. Jessica's Web: Womens Advantages in the Knowledge Era (PB) 2007. 280p. per. 39.99 (978-1-59311-855-6(4)) Information Age Publishing, Inc.

Greer. Women Athletes & Entrepreneurs: An exploratory, comparative study between women barrel racers & women who own their own Businesses. 2009. 144p. pap. 26.95 (978-1-4389-1274-5(9)) AuthorHouse.

Griffy-Brown, Charla & Jauhari, Vinnie, eds. Women, Technology & Entrepreneurship. 2009. 463p. 68.00 (978-81-8405-042-4(9), Reference Pr.) Ess Ess Pubns. IND. Dist: International Specialized Bk. Services.

Gubbin, Dianne & Ashman, Joann W. Powerladder: Network Your Way to Career Success: A Women's Fast Track Guide. 2008. (ENG.). pap. 13.99 (978-1-59932-054-0(1)) Advantage Media Group.

Guilliano, Mireille. Women, Work & the Art of Savoir Faire: Business Sense & Sensibility. (ENG., Illus.). 272p. 2010. pap. 15.00 (978-1-4165-8920-4(1)) 2009. 24.99 (978-1-4165-8919-8(8)) Atria Bks. (Beyond Words/Atria Bks.).

Gustafsson, Sandra & Sundqvist, Sara. Inter Tional Assignments? 2008. 108p. pap. (978-3-639-07429-1(7)) VDM Verlag Dr. Mueller e.K.

Haigh, Jo. Tales from the Glass Ceiling: A Survival Guide for Women in Business. (ENG.). 256p. 2010. pap. 16.95 (978-0-7499-2957-2(X)) 2008. pap. 19.95 (978-0-7499-2858-2(1)) Piatkus Bks. GBR. Dist: Independent Pubs. Group.

Hale, Stephanie J. Millionaire Women, Millionaire You: The Secret to Getting Rich from Scratch from 12 Ordinary Women Who Did Exactly That. 2010. (Illus.). 272p. pap. (978-1-84876-304-3(2)) Troubadour Publishing Ltd.

Halkias, Daphne, et al. Female Immigrant Entrepreneurs: The Economic & Social Impact of a Global Phenomenon. 2010. (Illus.). 324p. 119.95 (978-0-566-08913-8(0), Gower Publishing Co., Ltd.) Ashgate Publishing, Ltd. GBR. Dist: Ashgate Publishing Co.

Harrison, Terilee. The Business Mom Guide Book: More Life, Less Overwhelm for Mom Entrepreneurs. 2006. 315p. per. (978-1-932279-36-8(9)) Wyatt-MacKenzie Publishing.

Hassink, Jacqueline. Domains of Influence: Arab Women Business Leaders in a New Economy. 2008. (ENG., Illus.). 144p. 58.00 (978-1-84511-659-0(3)) I. B. Tauris & Co., Ltd. GBR. Dist: Macmillan.

Hattab, Hala. External Environment & Female Entrepreneurial Projects. 2011. 160p. pap. **(978-3-8383-2572-9(9))** Lambert Academic Publishing.

Heffernan, Margaret. Women on Top: How Women Entrepreneurs Are Rewriting the Rules of Business Success. 2008. (ENG.). 288p. (gr. 12-18). 15.00 (978-0-14-311280-8(5), Penguin (Non-Classics)) Penguin Group (USA) Inc.

Helm, Karen. A Woman's Agenda 2011, 1 vol. 2010. (ENG.). 192p. spiral bd. 14.95 (978-1-897187-73-9(4)) Second Story Pr. CAN. Dist: Orca Bk. Pubs. USA.

Hewlett, Sylvia Ann & Rashid, Ripa. Winning the War for Talent in Emerging Markets: Why Women Are the Solution. 2011. (ENG.). 288p. 35.00 (978-1-4221-6060-2(2)) Harvard Business Review Pr.

Holmes, Ann M. There's a Business in Every Woman: A 7-Step Guide to Discovering, Starting, & Building the Business of Your Dreams. 2008. (ENG., Illus.). 320p. pap. 15.00 (978-0-8129-7558-1(8), Ballantine Bks.) Random House Publishing Group.

Hone, Annie M. Woman's Enterprise & Genius. reprint ed. 150.00 (978-0-7222-1703-0(X)) Library Reprints, Inc.

Horan, Jim. The One Page Business Plan for Women in Business. 2011. (ENG.). 128p. pap. 34.95 **(978-1-59996-220-7(9))** Human Resource Development Pr.

Hosseinipour, Rosemary. Step into Your Future: A Women's Guide to Business Success. 2007. (ENG.). per. 16.95 (978-1-60037-214-8(7)) Morgan James Publishing.

Huang, Catherine & Rosenberg, Arthur D. Women & the Art of War: Sun Tzu's Strategies for Winning Without Confrontation. 2012. (ENG.). 224p. 17.95 **(978-0-8048-4254-9(X))** Tuttle Publishing.

Hughes, Karen D. & Jennings, Jennifer E. Global Women's Entrepreneurship Research: Diverse Settings, Questions, & Approaches. 2012. 272p. 115.00 **(978-1-84980-462-2(1))** Elgar, Edward Publishing, Inc.

Husain, Zakir, et al. Gender, Employment & the State. 2010. 148p. pap. (978-3-639-27837-8(2)) VDM Verlag Dr. Mueller e.K.

Italian Chamber of Commerce of Toronto, ed. Celebration: 32 Inspiring Canadian Women of Italian Origin/32 Ritratti Di Donne Italo-Canadesi. 2006. (ENG & ITA., Illus.). 160p. per. (978-1-894469-30-2(5)) Mansfield Pr.

Jacob, Zukeka. Motivation & Performance of Women Entrepreneurs in Western Cape: Sa. 2011. 108p. pap. **(978-3-8383-0132-7(3))** Lambert Academic Publishing.

James, Estelle, et al. The Gender Impact of Social Security Reform. 2008. (Illus.). 216p. 35.00 (978-0-226-39200-4(7)) Univ. of Chicago Pr.

Johnson, Thomas D., ed. National Directory of Woman-Owned Business Firms. 14th rev. ed. 2008. 1288p. pap. 295.00 (978-0-933527-86-7(1)) Business Research Services, Inc.

Jones, Nada & Briody, Michelle. 16 Weeks to Your Dream Business: A Weekly Planner for Entrepreneurial Women. 2008. (ENG., Illus.). 272p. spiral bd. 22.00 (978-0-07-158836-2(1), 0071588361) McGraw-Hill Cos., The.

Jones, Rebecca. Business in Red Shoes - the Successful Business Womans Guide. 2011. 220p. pap. **(978-1-907685-96-5(0))** MX Publishing, Ltd.

Kaputa, Catherine. The Female Brand: Using the Female Mindset to Succeed in Business. 2009. (ENG.). 220p. 24.95 (978-0-89106-284-4(X)) Ebsco Publishing.

Kariv, Dafna. Female Entrepreneurship & the New Venture Creation: An International Overview. 2012. (ENG., Illus.). 544p. (C). 150.00 (978-0-415-89686-3(X)); pap. 65.95 (978-0-415-89687-0(8)) Routledge.

Kay, Alison. The Foundations of Female Entrepreneurship. 2012. (ENG., Illus.). 186p. (C). pap. 39.95 **(978-0-415-52268-7(4))** Routledge.

Kay, Alison. The Foundations of Female Entrepreneurship: Women in Business in Mid-Victorian London. 2009. (Routledge International Studies in Business History Ser.). (ENG., Illus.). XVI, 186p. 146.00 (978-0-415-43174-3(3)) Routledge.

Keller, Wendy. Secrets of Successful Negotiating for Women: From Landing a Big Account to Buying the Car of Your Dreams & Everything in Between. 2009.

(ENG.). 224p. 9.99 (978-0-7858-2106-9(6), 0785821066, Castle Bks., Inc.) Book Sales, Inc.

Keveles, Melanie. Scrappy Startups: How 15 Ordinary Women Turned Their Unique Ideas into Profitable Businesses, 1 vol. 2009. 224p. 34.95 (978-0-313-36511-9(3), C36511, Praeger Pubs.) Greenwood Publishing Group, Inc.

Kitakule, Sarah & Snyder, Margaret C. Above the Odds: A Decade of Change for Ugandan Women Entrepreneurs. 2010. (978-1-59221-763-2(X)); 235p. pap. (978-1-59221-764-9(8)) Africa World Pr.

Koja, Marjola & Marjola, Koja. Women Entrepreneurship in Albania: A Study of the Motivations & Barriers Behind the Decision to Start & Run a Business. 2011. 80p. pap. (978-3-639-32426-6(9)) VDM Verlag Dr. Mueller e.K.

Kothari, Tina. Women in Leadership: Five Routes to Success in Business. 2008. (ENG., Illus.). 90p. pap. 20.99 (978-1-906791-13-1(9)) Arena Bks. GBR. Dist: Lightning Source UK, Ltd.

Kurek, Mary. Who's Hiding in Your Address Book? Introducing the Ideal Network for Successful Women. 2007. 150p. per. 12.95 (978-1-931741-87-3(5)) Reed, Robert D. Pubs.

Lahtinen, Sara. The Nadium As Businesswoman. 2011. 116p. pap. (978-3-8443-3292-6(8)) Lambert Academic Publishing.

Larkin, Kathleen. Through These Doors: The Story of a Small Business in the Adirondacks. Gooley, Lawrence P., ed. 2011. (Illus.). 176p. pap. 18.00 (978-0-9795741-8-4(8)) Bloated Toe Publishing.

Laurence, Anne, et al, eds. Women & Their Money, 1700-1950: Essays on Women & Finance. 2008. (Routledge International Studies in Business History Ser.). (ENG., Illus.). 336p. (C). 170.00 (978-0-415-41976-5(X)) Routledge.

Lavanya, T. Women Empowerment through Entrepreneurship. 2010. 230p. 35.50 (978-81-7708-227-2(2)) New Century Publications IND. Dist: International Specialized Bk. Services.

Lavine, Kim & Lavine. The Mommy Manifesto: How to Use Our Power to Think Big, Break Limitations & Achieve Success. 2009. (ENG.). 240p. 24.95 (978-0-470-45545-7(3), Wiley) Wiley, John & Sons, Inc.

Leimon, Averil, et al. Coaching Women to Lead. 2010. (Essential Coaching Skills & Knowledge Ser.). (ENG., Illus.). 248p. (C). 84.95 (978-0-415-49105-1(3)); pap. 30.95 (978-0-415-49106-8(1)) Routledge.

Lewis, Susan Ingalls. Unexceptional Women: Female Proprietors in Mid-Nineteenth-Century Albany, New York, 1830-1885. 2009. (Historical persp bus Enterpris Ser.). (ENG.). 240p. cd-rom 9.95 (978-0-8142-9178-8(3)); (Illus.). 44.95 (978-0-8142-0398-9(1)) Ohio State Univ. Pr.

Lieberman, Nancy. Playbook for Success: A Hall of Famer's Business Tactics for Teamwork & Leadership. 2010. (ENG.). 208p. 24.95 (978-0-470-63552-0(5), Wiley) Wiley, John & Sons, Inc.

Loman, Bart. Unilever's Shakti Project: Empowering Rural Indian Women. 2010. (Illus.). 88p. pap. (978-3-8383-5240-4(8)) Lambert Academic Publishing.

Lynn, Nancy. A Stone Barn. 2010. 280p. 26.00 (978-1-4520-8343-8(6)); pap. 16.00 (978-1-4520-8342-1(8)) AuthorHouse.

Markovic, Mirjana Radovic & Kyaruzi, Imani Silver. Women in Business: Theory, Practice & Flexible Approaches. 2010. 164p. (978-1-906704-44-5(9)); pap. (978-1-906704-69-8(4)) Adonis & Abbey Publishers Ltd.

Martin, Dawn Nicole. MisBehave: Speak Truth to Power. 2011. (ENG.). 196p. 22.95 (978-1-59299-581-3(0)); pap. 14.95 (978-1-59299-582-0(9)) Inkwater Pr.

Martin, Lucy. Make It Your Business. 2008. (Illus.). 288p. pap. (978-1-905862-00-9(8), Spring Hill) How To Books.

Martinello, Marian L. The Search for a Chili Queen: On the Fringes of a Rebozo. 2009. (ENG.). 212p. pap. 17.95 (978-0-87565-386-0(3)) Texas Christian Univ. Pr.

Mayoux, Linda, ed. Sustainable Learning for Women's Empo. 2011. (ENG., Illus.). 352p. 50.00 (978-1-85339-633-5(8)) Intermediate Technology Development Group of North America.

McAdam, Maura. Female Entrepreneurship. 2012. (Routledge ISBE Masters in Entrepreneurship Ser.). (ENG.). 208p. (C). 155.00 (978-0-415-67819-3(6)); pap. 54.95 (978-0-415-67820-9(X)) Routledge.

McDowell, Wilvena. Miss Priss in the Office: First Impressions for Corporate Women. 2010. (ENG.). 92p. pap. 15.49 (978-1-4490-5485-4(4)) AuthorHouse.

Mears, Emira & Bacon, Lauren. The Boss of You: Everything a Woman Needs to Know to Start, Run, & Maintain Her Own Business. 2008. (ENG., Illus.). 312p. pap. 15.95 (978-1-58005-236-8(3)) Seal Pr.

Medina, Mima, told to. Thriving Latina Entrepreneurs in America. 2007. 224p. 24.95 (978-0-8329-5007-0(6), WBusiness Bks.) New Win Publishing.

Meer, Shamim, ed. Women, Land & Authority: Perspectives from South Africa. (ENG.). 160p. pap. 19.15 (978-0-85598-375-8(2)) Oxfam Publishing GBR. Dist: Stylus Publishing, LLC.

Menzies, Jane. Women in International Assignments in Multinational Enterprises. 2009. 308p. pap. (978-3-639-13125-3(8)) VDM Verlag Dr. Mueller e.K.

Meredith, Kim. Work Diva: How to Climb the Corporate Ladder without Selling Your Soul. 2011. 208p. pap. 19.95 (978-1-77020-083-8(5)) Random Hse. Struik (Pty.), Ltd. ZAF. Dist: International Publishers Marketing.

Milazzo, Vickie L. Wicked Success Is Inside Every Woman. 2nd ed. 2011. (ENG., Illus.). 332p. 21.95 (978-1-118-10052-3(2), Wiley) Wiley, John & Sons, Inc.

Minniti, Maria. Gender Issues in Entrepreneurship, Vol. 5. 2009. (Illus.). 136p. pap. 99.00 net. (978-1-60198-302-2(6)) Now Pubs.

Minton, Chrissie. Women at Work in a Man's World. 2007. (Illus.). 88p. per. (978-1-84549-246-5(3)) arima publishing.

Monosoff, Tamara. Secrets of Millionaire Moms: Learn How They Turned Great Ideas into Booming Businesses—And How You Can Too. 2007. (ENG., Illus.). 256p. per. 19.00 (978-0-07-147892-2(2), 0071478922) McGraw-Hill Cos., The.

Moore, Dorothy Perrin. Navigating Barriers: Building Coalitions & a Personal Brand. 2012. (ENG., Illus.). 280p. 100.00 (978-0-415-89684-9(3)); pap. 39.95 (978-0-415-89685-6(1)) Routledge.

Moppert, Kylie. Gendered Entrepreneurship. 2010. 84p. pap. (978-3-8383-1944-5(3)) Lambert Academic Publishing.

Musonera, Etienne. Women Entrepreneurs in Rwanda: Christine's Banana Wine (Coproviba) 2010. (C). pap. 20.00 (978-1-61674-521-9(5)) Davidson, William Institute At The Univ. of Michigan, The.

Naik, Anita. Kitchen Table Tycoon: How to Make It Work As a Mother & an Entrepreneur. 2010. (ENG.). 224p. pap. 14.95 (978-0-7499-2945-9(6)) Piatkus Bks. GBR. Dist: Independent Pubs. Group.

Nasr, Sahar, ed. Egyptian Women Workers & Entrepreneurs: Maximizing Opportunities in the Economic Sphere. 2010. (Directions in Development Ser.). (ENG., Illus.). 120p. pap. 35.00 (978-0-8213-8190-8(3), 9780821381908) World Bank Pubns.

National Directory of Woman Owned Business Firms 13. 13th ed. 2006. 700p. 295.00 (978-0-933527-83-6(7)) Business Research Services, Inc.

Newbold-Coco, Rain L. Lighting the Way for Success: Mentoring Black Professional Women. 2007. 124p. per. 19.95 (978-1-4241-7949-7(1)) PublishAmerica, Inc.

Ojong, Vivian Besem. Transnational Entrepreneurship Through Identity. 2010. 248p. pap. (978-3-8383-4834-6(6)) Lambert Academic Publishing.

Okafor, Chinonye. Motivational Patterns of Women Entrepreneurs. 2010. 364p. pap. (978-3-639-27969-6(7)) VDM Verlag Dr. Mueller e.K.

Ortiz, Brandon R. Women's Business Ownership in the 21st Century. 2011. (Women's Studies). 115.00 (978-1-61209-269-0(1)) Nova Science Pubs., Inc.

Osirim, Mary Johnson. Enterprising Women in Urban Zimbabwe: Gender, Microbusiness, & Globalization. 2009. (ENG., Illus.). 240p. 39.95 (978-0-253-35347-4(5), 0253353475) Indiana Univ. Pr.

Otte, Jean, et al. Women are Changing the Corporate Landscape: Rules for Cultivating Leadership Excellence. 2009. 224p. pap. 15.95 (978-0-9815360-0-2(X)) WOMEN Unlimited, Inc.

Páez, Iliana Gabriunas. Memorias de la Primera Cumbre de Liderazgo Empresarial Femenino. 2007. (SPA., Illus.). 145p. pap. 12.00 (978-958-710-196-6(0)) Universidad Externado de Colombia COL. Dist: Siglo del Hombre.

Page, Brenda & O'Malley, Pauline. Lifestyle Selling for Women: Make the money you deserve & have the time to enjoy Life! 2009. 124p. pap. 25.00 (978-1-4251-4365-7(2)) Trafford Publishing.

Paine, PAINE, Rhiannon. Too Late for the Festival: An American Salary Woman in Japan. 2011. (ENG.). pap. 17.95 (978-0-89733-617-8(8)) Academy Chicago Pubs., Ltd.

Pakroo, Peri H. The Women's Small Business Start-up Kit: A Step-by-Step Legal Guide. 2nd rev. ed. 2012. (ENG.). 536p. pap. 29.99 (978-1-4133-1722-0(7)) NOLO.

Pandya, Pravinaben & Reddy, Krishna. Women & Development. 2010. 92p. pap. (978-3-639-24525-7(3)) VDM Verlag Dr. Mueller e.K.

Partow, Donna. Making Money from Home: How to Run a Successful Home-Based Business. 2010. (ENG.). 272p. pap. 14.99 (978-1-58997-608-5(8)) Tyndale Hse. Pubs.

Pelletier, Tisha Marie. When the Universe Throws a Curve Ball: How a Mom Entrepreneur Went from Disappointment to Living Her Passion. 2010. (Illus.). 151p. pap. 15.95 (978-0-9793301-9-3(X)) Evolving Journeys Publishing Hse.

Pepper, Carol & Webster, Camilla. The Seven Pearls of Financial Wisdom: A Woman's Guide to Enjoying Wealth & Power. 2012. (ENG.). 352p. 25.99 (978-0-312-64166-5(4)) St. Martin's Pr.

Perez-Cerezo, Julia & Pérez-Cerezo, Julia. China's New Leaders: Profiles of Female Entrepreneurs in Modern-Day China. 2011. (ENG., Illus.). 304p. pap. 29.99 (978-1-907794-08-7(5)) LID Publishing GBR. Dist: AtlasBooks Distribution.

Radovic, Mirjana. The Perspective of Women's Entrepreneurship in the Age of Globalization. 2007. (ENG.). 212p. (C). (978-1-59311-770-2(1)); per. (978-1-59311-769-6(8)) Information Age Publishing, Inc.

Rathnam, Dhanalakshmi. Women Entrepreneurship in Small Scale Industries. 2011. 264p. pap. (978-3-8433-9218-1(8)) Lambert Academic Publishing.

Renshaw, Jean R. Korean Women in Management: Shamans, Moneylenders & Company Presidents. 2011. (Routledge Studies in the Growth Economies of Asia Ser.). (ENG., Illus.). 152p. (C). 145.00 (978-0-415-29723-3(0)) Routledge.

Reynolds, Marcia. Wander Woman: How High-Achieving Women Find Contentment & Direction. 2010. (ENG.). 192p. pap. 17.95 (978-1-60509-351-2(3)) Berrett-Koehler Pubs., Inc.

Ribeiro, Michelle Lee. The Mom's Guide to Running a Business: Strategies for Work Success & Family Balance. 2011. (ENG.). 192p. 21.95 (978-1-58816-802-3(6)) Hearst Communications, Inc.

Rivera, Roxanne. There's No Crying in Business: How Women Can Succeed in Male-Dominated Industries. 2009. (ENG.). 188p. 42.00 (978-0-230-61812-1(X)) Palgrave Macmillan.

Ross-Parker, Bonnie & Elsberry, Cindy. 42 Rules for Effective Connections: For Women Who Are Serious about Building A Business Using Successful Networks. 2009. 150p. pap. 19.95 (978-1-60773-046-0(4), Super Star Pr.) Happy About.

Rouda, Kaira Sturdivant. Real You Incorporated: 8 Essentials for Women Entrepreneurs. 2008. (ENG., Illus.). 256p. 24.95 (978-0-470-17658-0(X), Wiley) Wiley, John & Sons, Inc.

Sachayansrisakul, Navarat. Successful Asian Women Entrepreneurs in the Western Context. 2008. 108p. pap. (978-3-639-05391-3(5)) VDM Verlag Dr. Mueller e.K.

Salmansohn, Karen. How to Succeed in Business Without A Penis. 2006. 320p. per. 23.95 (978-0-595-39805-8(7), Authors Choice Pr.) iUniverse, Inc.

Santha, Sunil D. & Vasanthagopal, R. Women Entrepreneurship in India. 2008. 275p. 42.50 (978-81-7708-182-4(9)) New Century Publications IND. Dist: International Specialized Bk. Services.

Scott, Leslie. About Jenga: The Remarkable Business of Creating a Game That Became a Household Name. 2009. 192p. 19.95 (978-1-60832-002-8(2), Greenleaf Book Group Pr.) Greenleaf Book Group.

Scumaci, Dondi. Designed for Success: The 10 Commandments for Women in the Workplace. 2007. (ENG.). 256p. 21.99 (978-1-59979-237-8(0)) Charisma Media.

Sebastian, Liane. Winning at Work for Women. 2009. (Illus.). 224p. pap. 15.95 (978-0-88391-184-6(1)) Fell, Frederick Pubs., Inc.

Seise, Claudia. Women S Micro Businesses in Indonesi. 2008. 60p. pap. (978-3-639-03884-2(3)) VDM Verlag Dr. Mueller e.K.

Selander, Joyce. Joyce, Queen of the Mountain: Female Courage & Hand-to-Hand Combat in the World's Largest Money Pit. 2011. 180p. 26.95 (978-1-4620-4207-4(4)); pap. 16.95 (978-1-4620-4205-0(8)) iUniverse, Inc.

Seligson, Hannah. New Girl on the Job: Advice from the Trenches. 2008. (ENG.). 256p. 14.95 (978-0-8065-2943-1(1), Citadel Pr.) Kensington Publishing Corp.

Seynabou Sakho, Yaye, et al, eds. Gender in Bolivian Production: Reducing Differences in Formality & Productivity of Firms. 2009. (Country Studies). (ENG., Illus.). 80p. pap. 25.00 (978-0-8213-8014-7(1), 9780821380147) World Bank Pubns.

Sheetz-Runkle, Becky. Sun Tzu for Women: The Art of War for Winning in Business. 2011. (ENG.). 224p. pap. 12.95 (978-1-59869-907-4(5)) Adams Media Corp.

Shepard, Molly D., et al. Breaking into the Boys' Club: 8 Ways for Women to Get Ahead in Business. 2009. (ENG.). 240p. pap. 15.95 (978-1-59077-143-3(5)) Evans, M. & Co., Inc.

Sherman, Aliza & Smith, Danielle. Mom, Incorporated: A Guide to Business & Baby. 2011. 192p. pap. 16.95 (978-1-4162-0651-4(5)) Sellers Publishing, Inc.

Siu, Helen F. Merchants' Daughters: Women, Commerce, & Regional Culture in South China. 2010. 388p. (978-988-220-718-9(9)) Hong Kong Univ. Pr.

Siu, Helen F., ed. Merchants' Daughters: Women, Commerce, & Regional Culture in South China. 2010. (ENG.). 388p. (gr. 17). 60.00 (978-962-209-969-2(6)); pap. 25.00 (978-988-8083-48-0(1)) Hong Kong Univ. Pr. HKG. Dist: Columbia Univ. Pr.

Smith-Hunter, A. Women Entrepreneurs in the Global Marketplace. 2012. 224p. 99.95 (978-1-84844-170-5(3)) Elgar, Edward Publishing, Inc.

Solovic, Susan Wilson. The Girls' Guide to Building a Million-Dollar Business. 2007. (ENG.). 240p. pap. 18.95 (978-0-8144-3185-6(2)) Amacom.

Sparks, Edith. Capital Intentions: Female Proprietors in San Francisco, 1850-1920. 2006. (Luther H. Hodges Jr. & Luther H. Hodges Sr. Series on Business, Society, & the State Ser.). (ENG., Illus.). 320p. (C). 69.95 (978-0-8078-3061-1(5)); per. 22.00 (978-0-8078-5775-5(0)) Univ. of North Carolina Pr.

Steele, R. Don. Office Politics: What They Will Never Tell You! 2011. 343p. pap. 25.95 (978-0-9620671-8-1(0)) Steel Balls Pr.

Steelman, Julie. The Effortless Yes: Demystifying the Selling Process & Discover - Your Selling Archetype, Your Natural Asking Style, Your Bankability. 2011. (ENG.). 176p. pap. 14.95 (978-1-936487-02-8(0), 1936487020) Franklin Green Publishing.

Stith, Marva Woods. Black Star Girl: A Charter Beneficiary of the Civil Rights Movement Celebrates the Insightful Parenting of Her Father. It's His Story Too. 2010. 252p. 29.95 (978-1-4401-9579-2(X)); pap. 19.95 (978-1-4401-9581-5(1)) iUniverse, Inc.

Subcommittee Hearing on Federal Government Efforts in Contracting with Women-Owned Businesses. 2007. (Illus.). iii, 86p. (978-0-16-079945-7(7), 552-070-36772-1) United States Government Printing Office.

Subcommittee Hearing on Oversight of the Entrepreneurial Development Programs Implemented by the Small Business Administration & National Veterans Business Development Corporation. 2008. iii, 203p. (978-0-16-080889-0(8), 552-070-37433-7) United States Government Printing Office.

Subcommittee on Rural Development, Entrepreneurship & Trade Markup on Entrepreneurial Development Programs Legislation: Hearing Before the Committee on Small Business, United States House of Representatives, One Hundred Eleventh Congress, First Session, Hearing Held April 30, 2009. 2009. v, 63p. (978-0-16-083686-2(7), 552-070-39392-7) United States Government Printing Office.

Teigen, Mari & Engelstad, Fredrik, eds. Firms, Boards & Gender Quoats: Comparative Perspectives. 2012. (Comparative Social Research Ser.) (Illus.). 288p. (978-1-78052-672-0(5)) Emerald Group Publishing Ltd.

Thomson, Peninah & Lloyd, Tom. Women & the New Business Leadership. 2011. (ENG., Illus.). 256p. 42.00 (978-0-230-27154-8(5)) Palgrave Macmillan.

Ulianova, Galina. Female Entrepreneurs in Nineteenth-Century Russia, 1 vol. 2009. (Perspectives in Economic & Social History Ser.). (ENG.). 272p. 99.00 (978-1-85196-967-8(5)) Pickering & Chatto Pubs., Ltd. GBR. Dist: Ashgate Publishing Co.

Valle, Maya. Entre Mis Sabanas. 2007. (ESP.). 156p. pap. 19.99 (978-0-9774854-8-2(X)) Mosquera, Elsa.

Valterra, Mikelann. How to Set & Raise Your Rates: A Woman's Guide. 2007. spiral bd. (978-0-9794597-0-2(2)) Women's Earning Institute, The.

Villarosa, Clara & Villarosa, Alicia. Down to Business: The First 10 Steps to Entrepreneurship for Women. 2009. (ENG.). 256p. (gr. 12-18). 17.00 (978-1-58333-354-9(1), Avery) Penguin Group (USA) Inc.

Vinnicombe, Susan, et al, eds. Women on Corporate Boards of Directors: International Research & Practice. 2009. (New Horizons in Management Ser.). (Illus.). 272p. 127.00 (978-1-84720-480-6(5)) Elgar, Edward Publishing, Inc.

Wadhera, Kiron & Koreth, George. Rural Women's Road to Empowerment: Micro-Enterprise Through Achievement Motivation. 2011. (Illus.). 252p. (C). pap. 40.00 (978-81-321-0692-0(X), B06920C) SAGE Pubns., Inc.

Wallace, K. L. Stilettopreneurs Rock! Trading in Your Corporate Stilettos for the Ceo Mindset. 2012. 160p. pap. 20.50 (978-0-578-09283-6(2)) Stiletto Woman Media.

Walsh, Laura. Ashamed. 2011. (ENG., Illus.). 240p. pap. 15.95 (978-1-84596-763-5(1)) Mainstream Publishing Co., Ltd. GBR. Dist: Independent Pubs. Group.

Weinstock, Danielle. Can This Elephant Curtsy on Cue? Life Lessons Learned on a Film Set for Women in Business. 2008. (Career Development Ser.). 336p. pap. 17.95 (978-1-57525-568-2(5)) Smith & Kraus Pubs., Inc.

Weisman, Renee. Winning in a Man's World. 2008. 156p. 29.99 (978-1-4363-6423-2(X)) Xlibris Corp.

Wiefling, Kimberly. Scrappy Women in Business: Living Proof that Bending the Rules Isn't Breaking the Law. 2010. 210p. pap. 19.95 (978-1-60005-185-2(5)) Happy About.

Wilen-Daugenti, Tracey. China for Businesswomen: A Strategic Guide to Travel, Negotiating, & Cultural Differences. 2007. (ENG., Illus.). 200p. per. 16.95 (978-1-933330-28-0(7)) Stone Bridge Pr.

Williams, Bethany. Winning Strategies for Women. 2008. (Illus.). 149p. per 16.00 (978-1-929976-44-7(5), TOP) Top Pubns., Ltd.

Williamson, Ella M. For Hurting Women in the Workplace: It's Time to Heal God's Way. 2009. (J). pap. 12.99 (978-1-60799-667-5(7)) Tate Publishing & Enterprises, LLC.

Wills, Leslie P. Which Way Is Up? 2011. 116p. pap. (978-3-8433-8709-5(5)) Lambert Academic Publishing.

Wilmerding, Ginny. Smart Women & Small Business: How to Make the Leap from Corporate Careers to the Right Small Enterprise. 2006. (ENG.). 281p. 22.95 (978-0-471-77868-4(0), Wiley) Wiley, John & Sons, Inc.

Wilson, Marie C. Closing the Leadership Gap: Add Women, Change Everything. rev. ed. 2007. (ENG.). 240p. (gr. 12-18). 15.00 (978-0-14-311403-1(4), Penguin (Non-Classics)) Penguin Group (USA) Inc.

Wingfield, Adia Harvey. Doing Business with Beauty: Black Women, Hair Salons, & the Racial Enclave Economy. 2008. (Perspectives on a Multiracial America Ser.). (ENG.). 176p. 70.00 (978-0-7425-6116-8(X)) Rowman & Littlefield Publishers, Inc.

Wittenberg-Cox, Avivah. How Women Mean Business: A Step by Step Guide to Profiting from Gender Balanced Business. 2010. (ENG., Illus.). 424p. pap., instr.'s gde. ed. 24.95 (978-0-470-68884-7(X), Wiley) Wiley, John & Sons, Inc.

Wittenberg-Cox, Avivah & Maitland, Alison. Why Women Mean Business: Understanding the Emergence of Our Next Economic Revolution. (ENG., Illus.). 2009. 390p. pap. 19.95 (978-0-470-74950-0(4)) 2008. 376p. 34.95 (978-0-470-72508-5(7)) Wiley, John & Sons, Inc. (Jossey-Bass).

Witter, Lisa & Chen, Lisa. The She Spot: Why Women Are the Market for Changing the World - & How to Reach Them. 2008. (Bk Business Ser.). (ENG.). 187p. 24.95 (978-1-57675-472-6(3)) Berrett-Koehler Pubs., Inc.

The Woman's Advantage Workbook. 2007. spiral bd. 35.00 (978-0-9729528-1-1(0)) Cantando & Associates, LLC.

Women's World Banking Staff. The Women's World Banking Atlas of Global Trade, 1989-1990 Edition. 352p. (Orig.). pap. 25.00 (978-0-9624822-0-5(X)) Women's World Banking.

World Bank Staff. Opportunities for Women 2008. rev. ed. 2007. (Doing Business Ser.). (ENG.). 208p. pap. 35.00 (978-0-8213-7231-9(9), 9780821372319) World Bank Pubns.

BUSINESSWOMEN—BIOGRAPHY

Acclaim Press. A Beautiful Journey. 2007. 24.95 (978-0-9798802-4-7(6)) Acclaim Pr., Inc.

Alessio, Jim. The Eternal Flapper. 2009. 376p. 29.50 (978-1-4389-6129-3(4)) AuthorHouse.

—The Eternal Flapper: The Many Lives of Edna Wallace Hopper. 2009. 376p. pap. 19.95 (978-1-4389-6128-6(6)) AuthorHouse.

Ansari, Anousheh & Hickam, Homer. My Dream of Stars: From Daughter of Iran to Space Pioneer. (ENG., Illus.). 256p. 2011. pap. 16.00 (978-0-230-11221-6(8)) 2010. 25.00 (978-0-230-61993-7(2)) Palgrave Macmillan.

Ash, Mary Kay & Pendleton, Yvonne J. The Mary Kay Way: Timeless Principles from America's Greatest Woman Entrepreneur. 2008. (ENG.). 272p. 21.95 (978-0-470-37995-0(2), Wiley) Wiley, John & Sons, Inc.

Bandola, Lia & Dezsi, Tina. The Power of Women United. 2009. 220p. 34.97 (978-0-9819398-1-0(3)) Ultimate Publishing Hse., The.

Barr, Frumi Rachel. Confessions of a Resilient Entrepreneur: Persevering to Success. 2007. (ENG.). 148p. per. (978-1-60005-039-8(5)) Happy About.

Bhargava, Urmila. Sorry, Not for Sale. 2011. 238p. pap. 14.50 (978-1-60976-709-9(8), Eloquent Bks.) AEG Literary Publishing Services, Inc.

Black, Dawn & Petrov, Alexander, eds. Natalia Shelikov: Russian Oligarch of Alaska Commerce. 2010. (University of Alaska Press - Rasmuson Library Historic Translation Ser.). (ENG., Illus.). 250p. pap. 29.95 *(978-1-60223-073-6(0))* Univ. of Alaska Pr.

Blaugrund, Annette. Dispensing Beauty in New York & Beyond: The Triumphs & Tragedies of Harriet Hubbard Ayer. 2011. pap. 21.99 *(978-1-60949-279-3(X))* History Pr., The.

Boswell, Sophie. The Power of Feng Shui. 2008. 240p. 25.95 *(978-1-60693-390-9(6)*, Strategic Bk. Publishing) AEG Literary Publishing Services, Inc.

Brady, Karren. Strong Woman: Ambition, Grit & a Great Pair of Heels. 2012. (ENG., Illus.). 288p. 29.95 **(978-0-00-739592-7(2))** HarperCollins Pubs. Ltd. GBR. Dist: Independent Pubs. Group.

Brown, Gertrude M. Miracles & Memories. 2007. 152p. per. 14.95 *(978-0-595-47056-3(4))* iUniverse, Inc.

Cannings, Mable L. The Heart & Soul of Business: One Woman's Journey. 2008. 248p. pap. 14.99 *(978-1-60647-345-0(X))* Xulon Pr., Inc.

Clarkson, Shirley. Bearly Believable: My Part in the Paddington Bear Story. 2008. (ENG., Illus.). 210p. 29.99 *(978-1-905641-72-7(9))* Harriman Hse. Publishing GBR. Dist: Ingram Pub. Services.

Coffey, Tabatha. It's Not Really about the Hair: The Honest Truth about Life, Love, & the Business of Beauty. 2012. (ENG.). 224p. pap. 14.99 **(978-0-06-210395-6(4))** HarperCollins Pubs.

Cook, Mary J. Straw. Dona Tules: Santa Fe's Courtesan & Gambler. 2007. (ENG., Illus.). 184p. 21.95 *(978-0-8263-4313-0(9))* Univ. of New Mexico Pr.

Cooper, Rebecca B. Beckoning. 2008. 112p. pap. 12.95 *(978-1-4343-6528-6(X))* AuthorHouse.

Cross, Fiona. Spooked! Fear & Loathing on Capitol Hill. 2009. 156p. 25.55 *(978-1-4490-2580-9(3))*; (Illus.). 153p. E-Book *(978-1-4490-2582-3(X))* AuthorHouse.

Davydov, Ilona. Experience of My Life. 2008. (ENG.). 398p. spiral bd. 39.50 *(978-0-9764991-0-7(X))* Express-Method, Inc.

Davydova, Ilona. My Life Experience. 2009. 480p. 39.00 *(978-0-9792424-1-0(X))* Express-Method, Inc.

—My Life Experience Bk. 1: Emigration. 2009. 398p. 24.95 *(978-0-9792424-4-1(4))* Express-Method, Inc.

—My Life Experience (Love in New York) 2009. 410p. 24.95 *(978-0-9675296-8-4(9))* Express-Method, Inc.

Dedeckere, Doris. The Trek of a Retired Flack: (Journey of A Retired Public Relations Person) 2009. 144p. 25.49 *(978-1-4389-5532-2(4))*; pap. 15.49 *(978-1-4389-5531-5(6))* AuthorHouse.

Dilsaver, Donna B. An American Woman's Zest for Living. 2008. (Illus.). 246p. pap. *(978-0-615-26339-7(9))* Dilsaver, D.B. Publishing.

Eckert, J. M. The Cloak of Humility: Success Is Walking Humbly with God. 2009. 184p. 23.95 *(978-1-4401-9591-4(9))*; pap. 13.95 *(978-1-4401-9587-7(0))* iUniverse, Inc.

Edwards, Kasey. 30 Something & over It: What Happens When You Get up & Don't Want to Go to Work... Ever Again. 2009. (ENG.). 224p. pap. 14.95 **(978-1-84596-446-7(2))** Mainstream Publishing Co., Ltd. GBR. Dist: Independent Pubs. Group.

Epstein, Dorothy. A Song of Social Significance: Memoirs of an Activist. 2006. pap. 16.95 *(978-0-9769862-7-0(2))* Yehuda, Ben Pr.

Epstein, Dorothy & Foner, Henry. A Song of Social Signficance: Memoirs of an Activist. 2007. 26.95 *(978-0-9769862-9-4(9))* Yehuda, Ben Pr.

Farrington-Nichols, Isa. Genesis: The Bullet was Meant for Me, D. C. Sniper Story Untold. 2009. 192p. 25.50 *(978-1-934925-48-5(9)*, Eloquent Bks.) AEG Literary Publishing Services, Inc.

Fiorina, Carly. Tough Choices: A Memoir. 2007. (ENG.). 336p. (gr. 12-18). 15.00 *(978-1-59184-181-4(X)*, Portfolio Trade) Penguin Group (USA) Inc.

Fitzpatrick, Shari. Berried in Chocolate: How I Built a Multimillion-Dollar Business by Doing What I Love to Do & How You Can Too, 1 vol. 2010. (ENG., Illus.). 224p. 23.00 *(978-1-58980-881-2(9))* Pelican Publishing Co., Inc.

Fortenberry, Pat. More Than Makeup. 2008. 230p. 19.99 *(978-1-60462-534-9(1))* Tate Publishing & Enterprises, LLC.

—More Than Makeup: A Guide to Finding Strength & Leadership Within You. 2008. (Illus.). 242p. pap. 14.99 *(978-1-60604-155-0(X))* Tate Publishing & Enterprises, LLC.

Gerber, Robin. Barbie & Ruth: The Story of the World's Most Famous Doll & the Woman Who Created Her. 2010. (ENG.). 288p. pap. 14.99 *(978-0-06-134132-8(0)*, Harper Paperbacks) HarperCollins Pubs.

Gorham, Jewel. The Burning Bush 2007. 2007. 108p. (ENG.). 18.99 *(978-1-60266-688-7(1))*; per. 10.99 *(978-1-60266-687-0(3))* Xulon Pr., Inc.

Hand, Edie & Savas, Tina. Women of True Grit: Intimate, Informative, Inspirational. 2010. (Illus.). 244p. 24.95 *(978-0-9825396-0-6(6))* Canterbury Hse. Publishing, Ltd.

Handy, Rose Cathy. Going from Homeless to CEO: The No Excuse. 2011. (ENG.). 128p. pap. 14.95 *(978-1-897404-29-4(8))* Burman Books, Inc. CAN. Dist: Innovative Logistics.

Harper, Katherine, told to. The Longer I Live, the More I Learn: A Memoir. 2007. im. lthr. *(978-0-9742576-9-3(9))* Preserving Memories.

Heineman, Elizabeth D. Before Porn Was Legal: The Erotica Empire of Beate Uhse. 2011. (ENG., Illus.). 240p. 35.00 *(978-0-226-32521-7(0))* Univ. of Chicago Pr.

Hoglund, Patricia. Have I Got a Story for You: A Collection of Life's Lessons. 2008. 48p. pap. 9.95 *(978-0-595-44084-9(3))* iUniverse, Inc.

Hudson, Lynn M. The Making of Mammy Pleasant: A Black Entrepreneur in Nineteenth-Century San Francisco. 2008. (Women in American History Ser.). (ENG., Illus.). 224p. per. 21.00 *(978-0-252-07527-8(7))* Univ. of Illinois Pr.

Hursh, David W. & Goertzen, Chris. Good Medicine & Good Music: A Biography of Mrs. Joe Person, Patent Remedy Entrepreneur & Musician, Including the Complete Text of Her 1903 Autobiography. 2009. (ENG., Illus.). 216p. pap. 39.95 *(978-0-7864-3459-6(7))* McFarland & Co., Inc. Pubs.

Hutchinson, Bobby. Blue Collar B & B. 2009. 172p. pap. 15.95 *(978-1-934938-69-0(6)*, Langdon Street Pr.) Hillcrest Publishing Group, Inc.

Jenner, Kris. Kris Jenner. . .And All Things Kardashian. 2011. (ENG., Illus.). 320p. 26.00 *(978-1-4516-4696-2(8)*, Gallery Books/Karen Hunter Publishing) Gallery Books/Karen Hunter Publishing.

Jenner, Kris. Kris Jenner... & All Things Kardashian. 2012. (ENG., Illus.). 320p. pap. 16.00 **(978-1-4516-4697-9(6)**, Gallery Books/Karen Hunter Publishing) Gallery Books/Karen Hunter Publishing.

Ji, Jeannie. Butterfly: A Life Journey from South Korea to America. 2010. 212p. 27.99 *(978-1-4520-8934-8(5))*; pap. 15.99 *(978-1-4520-8933-1(7))* AuthorHouse.

Jones, Sonia. Daisy & Goliath. 2007. (Illus.). 221p. *(978-0-9781761-2-9(X))* Erser & Pond Pubs., Ltd.

Joynt, Carol Ross. Innocent Spouse: A Memoir. 2011. 288p. 25.00 *(978-0-307-59209-5(X)*, Crown) Crown Publishing Group.

Kalmbach, Sally Sexton. The Jewel of the Gold Coast: Mrs. Potter Palmer's Chicago. 2009. (Illus.). 96p. pap. 17.95 *(978-0-9818126-6-3(X))* Ampersand, Inc.

Langdon, Danny. My Mother Can Beat up Your Father. 2006. 197p. pap. 24.95 *(978-1-4241-4023-7(4))* PublishAmerica, Inc.

Lavine, Kim. Mommy Millionaire: How I Turned My Kitchen Table Idea into a Million Dollars & How You Can, Too! 2008. (ENG., Illus.). 368p. pap. 14.95 *(978-0-312-35471-8(1)*, St. Martin's Griffin) St. Martin's Pr.

Lee, Eunju. Gendered Processes of Korean Small Business Ownership. 2008. 220p. pap. *(978-3-639-09379-7(8))* VDM Verlag Dr. Mueller e.K.

Lee, May. May Lee Live & in Person: It All Begins with Passion. 2009. (ENG., Illus.). 224p. pap. 19.95 *(978-0-470-82458-0(1)*, Wiley) Wiley, John & Sons, Inc.

Lemmon, Gayle Tzemach. The Dressmaker of Khair Khana: Five Sisters, One Remarkable Family, & the Woman Who Risked Everything to Keep Them Safe. (P. S. Ser.). (ENG., Illus.). 2012. 272p. pap. 14.99 *(978-0-06-173247-8(8)*, HarperPerennial) 2011. 288p. 24.99 *(978-0-06-173237-9(0))* HarperCollins Pubs.

—The Dressmaker of Khair Khana: Five Sisters, One Remarkable Family, & the Woman Who Risked Everything to Keep Them Safe. l.t. ed. (ENG.). 287p. 2012. pap. 16.99 **(978-1-59413-575-0(4)**, Large Print Pr.) 2011. 31.99 **(978-1-4104-3965-9(8))** Thorndike Pr.

Levy, Paul. River Queen: The Amazing Story of Tugboat Titan Lucille Johnstone. unabr. ed. 2006. (ENG., Illus.). 272p. 34.95 *(978-1-55017-369-7(3))* Harbour Publishing Co., Ltd. CAN. Dist: Ingram Pub. Services.

Li, Ingrid. Zhang Xin: El Regreso China. 2007. (SPA.). 140p. per. 19.95 *(978-0-9774724-7-5(7))* Pinto, Jorge Bks.

Maher, Laura. Auntie Mom: A Single Woman's Unexpected Adventure into Motherhood. 2011. 256p. pap. 15.95 **(978-1-4620-3401-7(2))** iUniverse, Inc.

Mandelcorn, Susan. A Frog in the Well. 2011. 242p. 25.99 **(978-1-61215-848-8(X))**; pap. 15.99 **(978-1-61215-847-1(1))** Xulon Pr., Inc.

Martin, Don. Belinda: The Political & Private Life of Belinda Stronach. rev. ed. 2007. (ENG., Illus.). 288p. 24.95 *(978-1-55263-814-9(6))* Key Porter Bks. CAN. Dist: Perseus-PGW.

Martin, Lori. The Ex-Slave's Fortune. 2008. 204p. pap. 24.95 *(978-0-557-02715-6(2))* Lulu Enterprises Inc.

Mazzeo, Tilar. The Widow Clicquot: The Story of a Champagne Empire & the Woman Who Ruled It. 2008. (ENG.). 288p. 25.99 *(978-0-06-128856-2(X)*, Collins) HarperCollins Pubs.

McArthur, Annmarie. Recipes from a Life: Essential Ingredients for Your Business Success. 2011. pap. 10.99 *(978-1-61739-710-3(5))* Tate Publishing & Enterprises, LLC.

McDonald, Sharen. LEADERSHIP & GENDER PARITY the Gold & Silver Shield. 2008. 318p. pap. 18.95 *(978-1-4357-4839-2(5))* Lulu Enterprises Inc.

McGarry, Aurea. I Won't Survive I'll Thrive! How I Overcame Domestic Violence, Cancer, & Much More. 2007. 148p. (ENG.). 24.95 *(978-0-595-69709-0(7))*; per. 14.95 *(978-0-595-45369-6(4))* iUniverse, Inc.

McKeough, Sue. A Destiny to Be Reached. 2009. 268p. 27.50 *(978-1-60693-978-9(5)*, Strategic Bk. Publishing) AEG Literary Publishing Services, Inc.

McMichael, Shirley. Politically Betrayed: The Uncovered Truth of the Sydney Dorsey Trial. 2009. 124p. pap. 19.99 *(978-1-4389-2498-4(4))* AuthorHouse.

McMillen, Tedde. Nirvana in a Cup: The Founding of Oregon Chai. 2006. (Illus.). 320p. pap. 12.99 *(978-0-9786475-0-6(5))* Moby Pr.

McNeal, Franne. Off My Chest, but on My Mind: Busting the Barriers of Breast Cancer. 2007. 160p. pap. 21.95 *(978-0-9791643-3-0(8))* Significant Business Results LLC.

Messina, Maggie. Making Maggie: 'Little Miss Tri-County' 2011. 172p. pap. 24.95 **(978-1-4560-6660-4(9))** PublishAmerica, Inc.

Montgomery, Beverly. Imperfect People Managing in an Imperfect World. 2008. 80p. pap. 10.98 *(978-1-4357-1290-4(0))* Lulu Enterprises Inc.

Moriarty-Simmonds, Rosaleen. Four Fingers & Thirteen Toes. 2009. (Illus.). 244p. pap. 14.49 *(978-1-4389-4299-5(0))* AuthorHouse.

Mouille, Patricia F. I Married A Greek. 2009. 140p. pap. 18.95 *(978-1-4251-8680-7(7))* Trafford Publishing.

Nissenson, Marilyn. The Lady Upstairs: Dorothy Schiff & the New York Post. 2008. (ENG., Illus.). 512p. pap. 21.99 *(978-0-312-31311-1(X)*, St. Martin's Paperbacks) St. Martin's Pr.

—Paper Dolly: The Life & Times of Dorothy Schiff. Date not set. mass mkt. *(978-0-312-98909-5(1)*, St. Martin's Paperbacks) St. Martin's Pr.

Novogratz, Jacqueline. The Blue Sweater: Bridging the Gap Between Rich & Poor in an Interconnected World. 2009. (ENG., Illus.). 304p. 24.95 *(978-1-59486-915-0(4))* Rodale Pr., Inc.

O'Mara, Angela. Lipstick Laptops Life: The Rise & Fall, & Rise Again, of A Modern Day Business Woman. 2009. 116p. pap. 19.99 *(978-1-4490-0470-5(9))* AuthorHouse.

O'Neill, Helen. Florence Broadhurst: Her Secret & Extraordinary Lives. 2007. (ENG., Illus.). 248p. 24.95 *(978-0-8118-5937-0(1))* Chronicle Bks. LLC.

Paprocki, Sherry Beck. Martha Stewart: Lifestyle Entrepreneur. 2009. (Women of Achievement Ser.). (Illus.). 136p. (gr. 6-12). 35.00 *(978-1-60413-083-6(0)*, Chelsea Hse.) Facts On File, Inc.

Pollard, Sharon Annette. Loving Myself in Order to Love You. 2011. 124p. pap. 18.00 **(978-1-4634-2875-4(8))** AuthorHouse.

Price, Joann F. Martha Stewart: A Biography, 1 vol. 2007. (Greenwood Biographies Ser.). (Illus.). 168p. 35.00 *(978-0-313-33893-9(0)*, GR3893, Greenwood Pr.) Greenwood Publishing Group, Inc.

Pruett, Alda M. Furnace of Affliction. 2011. 112p. 22.99 **(978-1-4520-8165-6(4))**; pap. 14.50 **(978-1-4520-8164-9(6))** AuthorHouse.

Reed, Veronica L. & Harrill, Vanessa. From Welfare to Wealth: A True Testimony of Faith & the Power of Positive Thinking. 2010. 212p. 24.99 *(978-1-4490-3127-5(7))*; pap. 14.95 *(978-1-4490-3126-8(9))* AuthorHouse.

Roberts, Vm. Memoirs of A Girl from Suffolk. 2010. pap. 14.95 *(978-0-7414-6005-9(X))* Infinity Publishing.

Robinson, P. J. Surviving the Harlem Renaissance. 2011. 158p. pap. 24.95 **(978-1-4560-5159-4(8))** PublishAmerica, Inc.

Rodgers, Ruth E. The Mountaintop. 2010. 264p. 29.99 *(978-1-4500-5713-4(6))*; pap. 19.99 *(978-1-4500-5712-7(8))* Xlibris Corp.

Rooney, David. Ruth Belville: The Greenwich Time Lady. 2008. (ENG., Illus.). 192p. 25.00 *(978-0-948065-97-2(4))* National Maritime Museum GBR. Dist: Independent Pubs. Group.

Salamone, Nancy. Victory over Violence: Nancy's Story & the Business of Me. 2010. 108p. (ENG.). 22.50 *(978-1-4520-2508-7(8))*; pap. 10.99 *(978-1-4520-2507-0(X))* AuthorHouse.

Schroeder, Ok Soon. Journey from the Han River. 2nd rev. ed. 2007. pap. 15.95 *(978-0-9727840-8-5(X))* Mystic Pubs.

Shen, Aisling Juanjuan. A Tiger's Heart: The Story of a Modern Chinese Woman. 2010. (ENG.). 320p. pap. 14.00 *(978-1-56947-648-2(9))* Soho Pr., Inc.

Siebert, Muriel. Changing the Rules: Adventures of a Wall Street Maverick. 2007. (ENG.). 240p. pap. 16.95 *(978-1-4165-7331-9(3)*, Free Pr.) Free Pr.

Simavi, Sevi, et al. Gender Dimensions of Investment Climate Reform: A Guide for Policy Makers & Practitioners. 2010. (ENG.). 184p. pap. 35.00 *(978-0-8213-8095-6(8)*, 9780821380956) World Bank Pubns.

Slesin, Suzanne. Over the Top: Helena Rubinstein, Extraordinary Style, Beauty, Art, Fashion, Design. 2006. (ENG., Illus.). 216p. reprint ed. 95.00 *(978-0-9772661-0-4(3))* Pointed Leaf Pr.

Spencer, Susan. Briefcase Essentials. 2011. 160p. 19.95 *(978-1-60832-080-6(4))* Greenleaf Book Group.

Stafford-Smith, Benita. Man Oman: A Redhead in Arabia. 2010. 132p. pap. 13.95 *(978-1-4502-6213-2(9))* iUniverse, Inc.

Stanfield, Andrea. Phony! How I Faked My Way Through Life. 2008. (ENG.). 240p. 16.98 *(978-1-59102-655-6(5))* Prometheus Bks., Pubs.

States, Quincie. Breakthrough. 2011. 48p. 24.99 **(978-1-4628-5591-9(1))** Xlibris Corp.

Strahan, Jill Blashack. Simply Shine: Stories that Stirred the Fire. 2007. 208p. 24.95 *(978-0-9798098-0-4(0))* Tastefully Simple Inc.

Subotky, Julie. Consider It Done: Accomplish 228 of Life's Trickiest Tasks. 2011. (ENG.). 416p. pap. 15.00 *(978-0-307-59157-9(3))* Broadway Bks.

Taylor, Henrietta. Lavender & Linen. 2008. 336p. *(978-0-7322-8147-2(4)*, Fourth Estate) HarperCollins Pubs. Australia.

Thacker, Tawanna. But I'm Still Here: A Story of Loss, Tragedy, & Triumph. 2009. 100p. pap. 19.95 *(978-1-4327-1198-6(9))* Outskirts Pr., Inc.

The 2008 Top Ten Business Women. The Power of Ten - Extraordinary Stories of Ten Top Business Women. 2008. 200p. pap. 19.95 *(978-1-881276-09-8(0))* Serey/Jones Pubs.

Trump, Ivanka. The Trump Card: Playing to Win in Work & Life. 2010. (ENG.). 256p. pap. 15.00 *(978-1-4391-4015-4(4)*, Touchstone) Touchstone.

Universe Publishing Staff, et al. Amelia: The Motion Picture. 2009. (ENG., Illus.). 144p. 35.00 *(978-0-7893-1840-4(7))* Universe Publishing.

Wilkinson, Neil. Running on Full: The Story of Ruth & Ruby Crawford. 2009. *(978-1-933483-23-8(7))* Kennesaw State Univ. Pr.

Yoast, Sally Robinson. Been There. Done That: Lessons from a Life of Faith. 2011. 208p. 24.59 **(978-1-4634-4186-9(X))**; pap. 14.03 **(978-1-4634-4187-6(8))** AuthorHouse.

BUSINESSWOMEN—JUVENILE LITERATURE

Ward, John. Jews in Business & Their Representation in German Literature, 1827-1934. 2010. (Britische und Irische Studien zur deutschen Sprache und Literatur. British & Irish Studies in German Language & Literature Ser.). 260p. pap. 55.95 *(978-3-0343-0126-8(X))* Lang, Peter AG GBR. Dist: Lang, Peter.

BUSING FOR SCHOOL INTEGRATION

Baugh, Joyce A. The Detroit School Busing Case: Milliken V. Bradley & the Controversy over Desegregation. 2011. 248p. 34.95 *(978-0-7006-1766-1(3))*; pap. 17.95 *(978-0-7006-1767-8(1))* Univ. Pr. of Kansas.

Gaillard, Frye. The Dream Long Deferred: The Landmark Struggle for Desegregation in Charlotte, North Carolina. 3rd ed. 2006. 215p. 34.95 *(978-1-57003-645-3(4))* Univ. of South Carolina Pr.

Masur, Louis P. The Soiling of Old Glory: The Story of a Photograph That Shocked America. 2008. (ENG., Illus.). 240p. pap. 17.00 *(978-1-59691-600-5(1))* Bloomsbury Publishing.

BUSING OF SCHOOL CHILDREN

see Busing for School Integration; School Children—Transportation

BUSONI, FERRUCCIO BENVENUTO, 1866-1924

Crispin, Judith Michelle. The Esoteric Musical Tradition of Ferruccio Busoni & its Reinvigoration in the Music of Larry Sitsky: The Operas Doktor Faust & The Golem. 2007. (Illus.). 296p. (C). 109.95 *(978-0-7734-5407-1(1))* Mellen, Edwin Pr., The.

Glasgow Caledonian University. Manufacturing & the Environment. pap., stu. ed. 50.00 *(978-1-86125-042-1(8))* Institute of Management Consultants.

Kogan, Grigory. Busoni As Pianist. Belsky, Svetlana, tr. from RUS. 2010. (Eastman Studies in Music Ser.: Volume 73). (Illus.). 197p. 75.00 *(978-1-58046-335-5(5))* Univ. of Rochester Pr.

Sitsky, Larry. Busoni & the Piano: The Works, the Writings, & the Recordings. 2nd ed. 2008. *(978-1-57647-158-6(6))* Pendragon Pr.

BUSS ISLAND (LEGENDARY PLACE)

Gosch, C. C. A., ed. Danish Arctic Expeditions, 1605 to 1620 Vol. 2: The Expedition of Captain Jens Munk to Hudson's Bay in Search of a North-West Passage In 1619-20. 2010. (Cambridge Library Collection - Travel & Exploration Ser.). (Illus.). 340p. pap. 29.99 *(978-1-108-01293-5(0))* Cambridge Univ. Pr.

BUSSY D'AMBOISE, 1549?-1579

Chapman, George. Bussy DAmbois & the Revenge of Bussy D. 2006. pap. 34.95 *(978-1-4286-3512-8(2))* Kessinger Publishing, LLC.

BUSY WORK

see Creative Activities and Seat Work

BUTADIYNE

see Acetylene

BUTCHER SHOPS

see Butchers

BUTCHERING

see Slaughtering and Slaughter-Houses

BUTCHERS

see also Meat Cutting

Dielen, Hubert. The Life Story of Hubert Dielen: An Autobiography: 1855-1926. Reininger, Mike, ed. Reininger, Tina, tr. from DUT. 4th rev. ed. 2007. (ENG & DUT., Illus.). 200p. per. 19.95 *(978-0-9772896-1-5(3))* Reininger, Mike.

Leitch, Peter Charles & Gifford, Phil. What a Ride, Mate! The Life & Times of the Mad Butcher. 2008. (Illus.). 399p. *(978-1-86950-689-6(8))* HarperCollins Pubs. Australia.

Lucas, Mary B. Lunchmeat & Life Lessons: Sharing a Butcher's Wisdom. 2006. 96p. pap. 12.00 *(978-0-9791234-0-5(2))* MBL Pr.

Monahan, Sherry A. Taste of Tombstone: A Hearty Helping of History. 2008. (ENG., Illus.). 232p. pap. 9.95 *(978-0-8263-4449-6(6))* Univ. of New Mexico Pr.

Powell, Julie. Cleaving: A Story of Marriage, Meat, & Obsession. (ENG., 2010. Illus.). 336p. pap. 14.99 *(978-0-316-00337-7(9)*, Back Bay Bks.) 2009. 464p. pap. 24.99 *(978-0-316-05382-2(1))* Little Brown & Co.

Whyman, Desmond. Shoulder of Mutton Field. 2011. (ENG., Illus.). 150p. pap. 24.00 *(978-1-907284-73-1(7))* Nottingham Univ. Pr. GBR. Dist: Independent Pubs. Group.

BUTLER, BENJAMIN FRANKLIN, 1818-1893

Butler, Benjamin F. Autobiography & Personal Reminiscences. 2006. pap. 42.95 *(978-1-4286-4840-1(2))* Kessinger Publishing, LLC.

Butler, Benjamin Franklin. An Autobiography & Personal Reminiscences of Major-General Benjamin F. Butler, 2 vol., set. 1154p. reprint ed. 250.00 *(978-0-7222-9273-0(2))* Library Reprints, Inc.

Parton, James. General Butler in New Orleans. 2009. 506p. pap. 34.51 *(978-1-150-66529-5(7))* General Bks. LLC.

—General Butler in New Orleans. reprint ed. 150.00 *(978-0-7222-9274-7(0))* Library Reprints, Inc.

—General Butler in New Orleans History of the Administration of the Department of the Gulf in the Year 1862: With an Account of the Capture of New Orl. 2006. 656p. per. 36.99 *(978-1-4255-6700-2(2))* MPublishing.

Pierrepont, Edwards. A Review by Judge Pierrepont of Gen Butler's Defense, Before the House of Representatives, in Relation to the New Orleans Gold. 2011. 32p. pap. 11.99 **(978-1-4181-9400-0(X))** MPublishing.

Wells, Bruce R. The Bermuda Hundred Campaign: The Creole & the Beast. 2011. 144p. pap. 19.99 **(978-1-60949-314-1(1))** History Pr., The.

Werlich, Robert. Beast Butler: The Incredible Career of Major General Benjamin Franklin Butler. 2011. 176p. 42.95 **(978-1-258-06831-8(1))** Literary Licensing, LLC.

BUTLER, JOSEPH, 1692-1752

Butler, Joseph. Hobart's Analysis of Bishop Butler's Analogy of Religion, Natural & Revealed, to the Constitution & Course of Nature with Notes Also, Craufurd's. 2006. 236p. per. 20.99 *(978-1-4255-2041-0(3))* MPublishing.

Collins, W. Lucas. Butler. 2009. 186p. 26.99 *(978-1-110-41908-1(2))*; 186p. pap. 21.75 *(978-1-110-41907-4(4))*; 188p. 22.99 *(978-1-103-54674-9(0))*; 188p. pap. 16.99 *(978-1-103-54672-5(4))* BiblioBazaar.

—Butler. 2007. 184p. 37.95 *(978-0-548-05888-6(1))* Kessinger Publishing, LLC.

Gillett, E. H. God in Human Thought or, Natural Theology Traced in Literature. 2007. pap. 34.95 *(978-1-4304-5159-4(9))* Kessinger Publishing, LLC.

Penelhum. Butler-arg Philosophers. 2008. (ENG.). 336p. 45.00 *(978-0-415-48786-5(8))* Routledge.

Tennant, Bob. Conscience, Consciousness & Ethics in Joseph Butler's Philosophy & Ministry. 2011. (Studies in Modern British Religious History Ser.: Volume 26). 260p. 99.00 *(978-1-84383-612-4(2)*, Boydell Press) Boydell & Brewer, Ltd. GBR. Dist: Boydell & Brewer, Inc.

BUTLER, SAMUEL, 1612-1680

Butler, Samuel. NoteBooks of Samuel Butler. Lt. ed. 2006. pap. *(978-1-4068-2209-0(4))* Echo Library.

Jones, Henry Festing. Samuel Butler: A Sketch. 2007. 56p. per. *(978-1-4065-3542-6(7))* Dodo Pr.

Parker, Blanford. The Triumph of Augustan Poetics: English Literary Culture from Butler to Johnson. 2006. (Cambridge Studies in Eighteenth-Century English Literature & Thought Ser.). (ENG.). 276p. pap. 53.00 *(978-0-521-02867-7(1))* Cambridge Univ. Pr.

BUTLER, SAMUEL, 1835-1902

Butler, Samuel. The Correspondence of Samuel Butler with His Sister May. Howard, Daniel Francis, ed. 2011. 284p. 48.95 ***(978-1-258-04522-7(2))*** Literary Licensing, LLC.

Butler, Samuel. Note-Books of Samuel Butler. 2008. 472p. 33.99 *(978-0-554-22032-1(6))* 2008. 472p. 31.99 *(978-0-554-31335-1(9))* 2006. 410p. pap. 26.99 *(978-1-4264-1500-5(1))* 2007. (ENG.). 468p. pap. 30.99 *(978-1-4264-1533-3(8))* BiblioBazaar.

Cole, G. D. H. Samuel Butler. 2007. (ENG.). 116p. 34.95 *(978-0-548-06642-3(6))* Kessinger Publishing, LLC.

Harris, John F. Samuel Butler, Author of Erewhon: The Ma. 2006. pap. 28.95 *(978-1-4286-6032-8(1))* Kessinger Publishing, LLC.

—Samuel Butler, Author of Erewhon: The Man & His Work. 2007. (ENG.). 308p. 43.95 *(978-0-548-14673-6(X))* Kessinger Publishing, LLC.

Jones, Henry Festing. Samuel Butler: A Sketch. 2010. 32p. 24.76 *(978-1-169-18460-2(X))*; pap. 12.76 *(978-1-162-68293-8(0))*; 30.95 *(978-1-161-45158-0(7))* Kessinger Publishing, LLC.

Paradis, James G. Samuel Butler, Victorian Against the Grain: A Critical Overview. 2007. (Illus.). 416p. *(978-0-8020-9745-3(6))* Univ. of Toronto Pr.

BUTLER, SMEDLEY DARLINGTON, 1881-1940

Archer, Jules. The Plot to Seize the White House: The Shocking True Story of the Conspiracy to Overthrow FDR. 2007. (ENG., Illus.). 288p. per. 14.95 *(978-1-60239-036-2(3)*, 239036) Skyhorse Publishing Co., Inc.

BUTLER, WALTER, 1752-1781

Cruikshank, Ernest, et al. Butler's Rangers: Three Accounts of the American War of Independence. 2011. 168p. ***(978-0-85706-711-1(7))***; pap. ***(978-0-85706-712-8(5))*** Leonaur Ltd.

BUTLER, WILLIAM FRANCIS, SIR, 1838-1910

Butler, B. F. Butler's Book Set, 2 vols. 1154p. reprint ed. lib. bdg. 250.00 *(978-0-7222-0961-5(4))* Library Reprints, Inc.

BUTTE (MONT.)

Everett, George. Butte Trivia. 2007. (Illus.). 124p. per. 9.95 *(978-1-931832-85-4(4))* Riverbend Publishing.

BUTTE (MONT.)—HISTORY

Jursnich, Edward. Butte's East Side: Gone but Not Forgotten. 2008. 344p. pap. 21.95 *(978-1-4327-2188-6(7))* Outskirts Pr., Inc.

Leskovar, Christy. Finding the Bad Inn: Discovering My Family's. 2010. 25.00 *(978-1-57510-150-7(5))* Pictorial Histories Publishing Co., Inc.

McGlashan, Zena Beth. Buried in Butte. 2010. (Illus.). 460p. pap. 24.95 *(978-1-891057-21-2(9))* Wordz & Ink Publishing.

Vincent, Matt & Okrusch, Chad. Butte. 2011. (Then & Now Ser.). (Illus.). 96p. pap. 21.99 *(978-0-7385-8182-8(8))* Arcadia Publishing.

BUTTER

Pabst, W. R., Jr. Butter & Oleomargarine. (Columbia University, Studies in the Social Sciences: No. 427). reprint ed. 20.00 *(978-0-404-51427-3(8))* AMS Pr., Inc.

Shannon, Angel. Stick of Butter Cookbook. 2007. 125p. spiral bd. 16.99 *(978-1-59955-009-1(1))* Cedar Fort, Inc./CFI Distribution.

BUTTER, ARTIFICIAL

see Margarine

BUTTERFIELD TRAIL

Ormsby, Waterman L. The Butterfield Overland Mail: Only Through Passenger on the First Westbound Stage. Wright, Lyle H. & Bynum, Josephine M., eds. 2007. (Huntington Library Classics Ser.). (Illus.). 179p. per. 19.95 *(978-0-87328-232-1(9))* Huntington Library Pr.

BUTTERFLIES

see also Caterpillars; Monarch Butterfly

American Museum of Natural History & Davies, Hazel. The Exquisite Butterfly Companion: The Science & Beauty of 100 Butterflies. 2011. (ENG., Illus.). 88p. 14.95 *(978-1-4027-7875-9(9)*, Sterling Signature) Sterling Publishing Co., Inc.

Atlas of Neotropical Lepidoptera Series. pap. *(978-0-945417-25-5(X))* Scientific Pubs., Inc.

Bailowitz, Richard A. & Brodkin, Hank. Finding Butterflies in Arizona: A Guide to the Best Sites. 2007. (Illus.). 233p. per. 22.50 *(978-1-55566-352-0(4))* Johnson Bks.

Butterflies. 2007. (Nonfiction Collection). (J). 5.50 *(978-1-60343-021-0(0))* Pioneer Valley Educational Pr., Inc.

Butterflies. cd-rom 11.99 *(978-1-57223-838-1(0)*, 8380) Willow Creek Pr., Inc.

Butterflies of Russia. 139.50 *(978-5-94131-004-3(8))* Tezis, Izdatel'stvo RUS. Dist: Coronet Bks.

Davies, Hazel & Butler, Carol A. Do Butterflies Bite? Fascinating Answers to Questions about Butterflies & Moths. 2008. (Animals Q&A Ser.). (ENG., Illus.). 240p. pap. 19.95 *(978-0-8135-4268-3(5))* Rutgers Univ. Pr.

Delnostro. Only God Can Make a Butterfly. 2011. 252p. pap. 16.99 ***(978-1-61379-502-6(5))*** Xulon Pr., Inc.

Desert. 2009. 108p. pap. *(978-1-4590-7340-1(1))* Books LLC.

Dover, ed. Butterflies. 2007. (Dover Pictura Electronic Clip Art Ser.). (ENG., Illus.). 128p. pap. 39.95 *(978-0-486-99808-4(8))* Dover Pubns., Inc.

Dover, John, et al. eds. Lepidoptera Conservation in a Changing World. 2011. (Illus.). viii, 384p. 239.00 *(978-94-007-1441-0(6)*, 9400714416) Springer.

Fadul, Jose A. The Butterflies that Rizal Chased, Collected & Studied. 2007. 36p. 19.50 *(978-1-4303-2369-3(8))* Lulu Enterprises Inc.

Feinstein, Harold. One Hundred Butterflies. 2009. (ENG., Illus.). 128p. 50.00 *(978-0-316-03363-3(4))* Little Brown & Co.

Gernaat, Hajo. Butterflies of Suriname: A Natural History. 2012. (Illus.). 352p. 69.50 ***(978-94-6022-171-2(8))*** Royal Tropical Institute Pr. (KIT (Koninklijk Instituut voor de Tropen) NLD. Dist: Stylus Publishing, LLC.

Gray, Susan H. Karner Blue Butterfly. 2007. (21st Century Skills Library: Road to Recovery Ser.). (ENG., Illus.). 32p. (gr. 4-8). lib. bdg. 28.50 *(978-1-60279-040-7(X)*, 200083) Cherry Lake Publishing.

Heath, Fred. An Introduction to Southern California Butterflies. (Illus.). 288p. pap. 22.00 *(978-0-87842-475-7(X)*, 339) Mountain Pr. Publishing Co., Inc.

Henderson, Carrol L. Butterflies, Moths, & Other Invertebrates of Costa Rica: A Field Guide. 2010. (ENG., Illus.). 187p. pap. 29.95 *(978-0-292-71966-8(3))* Univ. of Texas Pr.

Hogan, Andréa. The Butterfly. 2010. 28p. 13.99 *(978-1-4520-6717-9(1))* AuthorHouse.

Howell, W. Mike & Charny, Vitaly. Butterflies of Alabama. 2010. (ENG., Illus.). 518p. (C). pap. 35.00 *(978-0-558-55631-0(0))* Pearson Learning Solutions.

Howse, Philip E. Butterflies: Decoding Their Signs & Symbols. 2010. (ENG., Illus.). 192p. 39.95 *(978-1-55407-773-1(7))* Firefly Bks., Ltd.

Kavanagh, James. California Butterflies & Moths: An Introduction to Familiar Species. 2007. (Pocket Naturalist - Waterford Press Ser.). (ENG., Illus.) 1p. 5.95 *(978-1-58355-356-5(8))* Waterford Pr., Inc.

—Florida Butterflies & Moths: An Introduction to Familiar Species. 2007. (Pocket Naturalist - Waterford Press Ser.). (ENG., Illus.). 1p. 5.95 *(978-1-58355-344-2(4))* Waterford Pr., Inc.

—Indiana Wildlife: An Introduction to Familiar Species. 2009. (State Nature Guides). (ENG., Illus.). 1p. 5.95 *(978-1-58355-476-0(9))* Waterford Pr., Inc.

—Kansas Butterflies & Moths: An Introduction to Familiar Species. 2009. (State Nature Guides). (ENG., Illus.). 1p. 5.95 *(978-1-58355-478-4(5))* Waterford Pr., Inc.

—Maine Butterflies & Moths: An Introduction to Familiar Species. 2009. (State Nature Guides). (ENG., Illus.). 1p. 5.95 *(978-1-58355-479-1(3))* Waterford Pr., Inc.

—New Jersey Wildlife: An Introduction to Familiar Species. 2009. (State Nature Guides). (ENG., Illus.). 1p. 5.95 *(978-1-58355-481-4(5))* Waterford Pr., Inc.

—Ohio Wildlife: An Introduction to Familiar Species. 2009. (State Nature Guides). (ENG., Illus.). 1p. 5.95 *(978-1-58355-482-1(3))* Waterford Pr., Inc.

—South Carolina Butterflies & Moths: An Introduction to Familiar Species. 2009. (State Nature Guides). (ENG., Illus.). 1p. 5.95 *(978-1-58355-484-5(X))* Waterford Pr., Inc.

—Southwestern Butterflies: An Introduction to Familiar Species. 2006. (Pocket Naturalist - Waterford Press Ser.). (ENG., Illus.). 1p. 5.95 *(978-1-58355-324-4(X))* Waterford Pr., Inc.

—Texas Butterflies & Moths: An Introduction to Familiar Species. 2007. (Pocket Naturalist - Waterford Press Ser.). (ENG., Illus.). 1p. 5.95 *(978-1-58355-368-8(1))* Waterford Pr., Inc.

—West Virginia Butterflies & Moths: An Introduction to Familiar Species. 2009. (State Nature Guides). (ENG., Illus.). 1p. 5.95 *(978-1-58355-485-2(8))* Waterford Pr., Inc.

Kumar, Sunil. Effects of Spatial Heterogeneity on Species Richness. 2008. 156p. pap. *(978-3-8364-8888-4(4))* VDM Verlag Dr. Mueller e.K.

Lewis, Alcinda, ed. Butterfly Gardens: Luring Nature's Loveliest Pollinators to Your Yard. 2007. (21st-Century Gardening Ser.). (ENG., Illus.). 112p. per. 9.95 *(978-1-889538-32-7(9))* Brooklyn Botanic Garden.

MacDougall, David W. A Field Guide to the Karner Blue Butterfly: Natural History, Indentification & Conservation of a Regional Treasure. 2007. 8.00 *(978-0-9761196-9-2(2))* ECOS: The Environmental Clearinghouse, Inc.

Morgan, Sally. Butterflies & Moths: A Natural History & Identification Guide to the Most Significant Species Including Swallowtails, Whites, Hairstreaks, Yellows, Fritillaries, Blues, Skippers & Tiger Moths. 2012. (ENG., Illus.). 256p. 35.00 *(978-0-7548-1884-7(5))* Anness Publishing GBR. Dist: National Bk. Network.

Neild, A. The Butterflies of Venezuela Vol. 2: Acraeinae, Libytheinae, Nymphalinae, Ithomiinae, Morphinae. 2008. 450p. 220.00 *(978-87-88757-80-4(3))* Apollo Bks. DNK. Dist: International Specialized Bk. Services.

Neild, Andrew F. E. & D'Abrera, Bernard. The Butterflies of Venezuela: Nymphalidae II. 2009. (Illus.). 275p. *(978-0-9527657-1-4(3))* Meridian Pubns.

Neill, William. Butterflies of the Pacific Northwest. 2007. (Illus.). 192p. pap. 18.00 *(978-0-87842-537-2(3))* Mountain Pr. Publishing Co., Inc.

Novotny, Vojtech. Notebooks from New Guinea: Reflections on Life, Nature, & Science from the Depths of the Rainforest. 2011. (ENG., Illus.). 272p. pap. 17.95 *(978-0-19-960964-2(0))* Oxford Univ. Pr., Inc.

Ogard, Paulette Haywood. Butterflies of Alabama: Glimpses into Their Lives. 2010. (Gosse Nature Guides Ser.). (ENG., Illus.). 512p. pap. 34.95 *(978-0-8173-5595-1(2))* Univ. of Alabama Pr.

Overstreet, Leslie K. Botanicals: Butterflies & Insects. 2008. (ENG., Illus.). 300p. 50.00 *(978-2-7594-0269-4(X))* Assouline FRA. Dist: Perseus Distribution.

Preston-Mafham, Ken. 500 Butterflies: From Around the World. 2007. (ENG., Illus.). 528p. 29.95 *(978-1-55407-295-8(6))* Firefly Bks., Ltd.

Publications International Staff, ed. Butterflies. 2010. (Shaped Journals). (Illus.). 14p. (J). bds. 16.98 *(978-1-4127-0019-1(1)*, 3489800) Publications International, Ltd.

Quick Reference Publishing, Inc. Staff. Butterflies of North Texas: A Guide to Common & Notable Species. 2010. 7.95 *(978-0-9826211-8-9(3))* Quick Reference Publishing, Inc.

Schlicht, Dennis W., et al. The Butterflies of Iowa. 2007. (Bur Oak Book Ser.). (Illus.). 252p. 59.95 *(978-1-58729-532-4(6))*; per. 29.95 *(978-1-58729-533-1(4))* Univ. of Iowa Pr.

Shapiro, Arthur M. Butterflies of the San Francisco Bay & Sacramento Valley Regions. 2007. (California Natural History Guides Ser.). (Illus.). 392p. 50.00 *(978-0-520-24469-6(9))* Univ. of California Pr.

—Field Guide to Butterflies of the San Francisco Bay & Sacramento Valley Regions. 2007. (California Natural History Guides Ser.). (Illus.). 345p. pap. 19.95 *(978-0-520-24957-8(7))* Univ. of California Pr.

Speart, Jessica. Winged Obsession: The Pursuit of the World's Most Notorious Butterfly Smuggler. (ENG.). 320p. 2012. pap. 15.99 ***(978-0-06-177244-3(5)***, William Morrow Paperbacks) 2011. 25.99 *(978-0-06-177243-6(7)*, Morrow, William & Co.) HarperCollins Pubs.

Spencer, Lori A. & Simons, Don R. The Diana Fritillary: Arkansas's State Butterfly. 2011. (ENG., Illus.). 24p. pap. 8.95 ***(978-0-912456-26-3(4))*** Ozark Society Foundation.

Tampion, John & Tampion, M. D. Attracting Butterflies to Your Garden. 2011. (ENG., Illus.). 176p. pap. 17.95 *(978-1-86108-856-7(6))* Guild of Master Craftsman Pubns., Ltd. GBR. Dist: Sterling Publishing Co., Inc.

Thompson III, Bill & Toops, Connie. Hummingbirds & Butterflies. 2011. (Peterson Field Guides/Bird Watcher's Digest Backyard Bird Guides). (ENG., Illus.). 304p. pap. 14.95 *(978-0-618-90445-7(X))* Houghton Mifflin Harcourt Trade & Reference Pubs.

Tudor, Guy & Cech, Rick. Butterflies of the East Coast: An Observer's Guide. 2007. (ENG., Illus.). 360p. pap. 32.95 *(978-0-691-09056-6(4))* Princeton Univ. Pr.

Wauer, Roland H. Finding Butterflies in Texas: A Guide to the Best Sites. 2006. (Illus.). 327p. per. 22.50 *(978-1-55566-366-7(4))* Johnson Bks.

Weber, Larry. Butterflies of the North Woods: Minnesota, Wisconsin & Michigan. 2nd rev. ed. 2006. (North Woods Naturalist Guides). (Illus.). 279p. per. 18.95 *(978-0-9673793-5-7(0))* Kollath-Stensaas Pubs.

BUTTERFLIES—ASIA

Gay, Thomas, et al. Butterflies of India. 2nd ed. 2008. (Nature Guides). (ENG., Illus.). 88p. pap. 10.95 *(978-0-19-568801-6(5))* Oxford Univ. Pr., Inc.

Kehimkar, Isaac & Kehimkar, Isaac David. The Book of Indian Butterflies. 2008. (ENG., Illus.). 520p. 74.00 *(978-0-19-569620-2(4))* Oxford Univ. Pr., Inc.

Monastyrskii, A. L. Butterflies of Vietnam Vol. 2: Papilionidae. 2007. 160p. pap. 64.00 *(978-0-9551211-1-1(6))* Apollo Bks. DNK. Dist: International Specialized Bk. Services.

BUTTERFLIES—AUSTRALIA

New, Tim R. Butterfly Conservation in South-Eastern Australia: Progress & Prospects: Progress & Prospects. 2010. (ENG., Illus.). x, 190p. 189.00 *(978-90-481-9925-9(5)*, 9048199255) Springer.

BUTTERFLIES—COSTA RICA

Kavanagh, James. Costa Rica Butterflies & Moths: An Introduction to Familiar Species. 2007. (Pocket Naturalist - Waterford Press Ser.). (ENG., Illus.) 1p. 5.95 *(978-1-58355-340-4(1))* Waterford Pr., Inc.

Miller, Jeffrey C., et al. 100 Butterflies & Moths: Portraits from the Tropical Forests of Costa Rica. 2010. (Illus.). 272p. pap. 26.50 *(978-0-674-03483-9(X)*, Belknap Pr.) Harvard Univ. Pr.

BUTTERFLIES—EUROPE

Kirby, W. F. 600 Butterflies & Moths in Full Color. 2007. (Dover Pictorial Archive Ser.). (ENG., Illus.). 80p. per. 14.95 *(978-0-486-46139-7(4))* Dover Pubns., Inc.

Newland, David, et al. Britain's Butterflies: A Field Guide to the Butterflies of Britain & Ireland. 2nd rev. ed. 2011. (Illus.). 224p. pap. 45.00 *(978-1-903657-30-0(X))* Trans-Atlantic Pubns., Inc.

Settele, Josef, et al, eds. Ecology of Butterflies in Europe. 2009. (ENG., Illus.). 526p. (C). 165.00 *(978-0-521-76697-5(4))*; pap. 77.00 *(978-0-521-74759-2(7))* Cambridge Univ. Pr.

Steiner, Roland, et al. Okologie einer aussterbenden Population des Segelfalters Iphiclides podalirius (Linnaeus, 1758) 2007. (Invertebrate Ecology & Conservation Monographs). (Illus.). 171p. pap. 129.50 *(978-954-642-289-7(4))* Pensoft Pubs. BGR. Dist: Coronet Bks.

Thompson, Robert. The Butterflies & Moths of Northern Ireland. 2007. (ENG., Illus.). 440p. pap. 64.95 *(978-0-900761-47-8(4))* Blackstaff Pr., Ltd. GBR. Dist: Dufour Editions, Inc.

Tolman, Tom & Lewington, Richard. Butterfly Guide: The Most Complete Guide to the Butterflies of Britain & Europe. 2009. (ENG., Illus.). 384p. pap. 34.95 *(978-0-00-727977-7(9))* HarperCollins Pubs. Ltd. GBR. Dist: Independent Pubs. Group.

BUTTERFLIES—GREAT BRITAIN

Dennis, Roger L. H. A Resource-Based Habitat View for Conservation: Butterflies in the British Landscape. 2010. (ENG., Illus.). 420p. 99.95 *(978-1-4051-9945-2(8)*, Wiley-Blackwell) Wiley, John & Sons, Inc.

Dunbar, David. British Butterflies: A History in Books. 2010. (Illus.). 176p. 75.00 *(978-0-7123-5096-9(9))* British Library, The GBR. Dist: Chicago Distribution Ctr.

Newland, D. E. Discover Butterflies in Britain. 2006. (Illus.). 224p. 49.95 *(978-1-903657-12-6(1))* Trans-Atlantic Pubns., Inc.

Oates, Matthew. Butterflies. 2011. (ENG., Illus.). 104p. 12.95 *(978-1-907892-05-9(2))* National Trust, Aylesbury GBR. Dist: Independent Pubs. Group.

Salmon, Michael A., et al. The Aurelian Legacy: British Butterflies & Their Collectors. (Illus.). 432p. 63.00 *(978-0-946589-40-1(2))* Apollo Bks. DNK. Dist: International Specialized Bk. Services.

BUTTERFLIES—NORTH AMERICA

Askew, R. R. & Stafford, P. A. van B. Butterflies of the Cayman Islands. 2008. (Illus.). 169p. 69.50 *(978-87-88757-85-9(4))* Apollo Bks. DNK. Dist: International Specialized Bk. Services.

Bolesta, Murray. Bees, Butterflies & Blossoms of Southern Arizona, 3, Vol. 1. 2007. 72p. per. 19.95 *(978-0-9797842-0-0(4))* CactusHuggers Publishing Co.

Brock, Jim P. Butterflies of the Southwest. 2008. (Natural History Ser.). (Illus.). 96p. pap. 12.95 *(978-1-933855-15-8(0))* Rio Nuevo Pubs.

Brock, Jim P. & Kaufman, Kenn. Kaufman Field Guide to Butterflies of North America: The Easiest Guides for Fast Identification. Kaufman, Kenn, ed. 2006. (Kaufman Field Guides). (ENG., Illus.). 392p. 19.95 *(978-0-618-76826-4(2))* Houghton Mifflin Harcourt Trade & Reference Pubs.

Butterflies of Texas. (Illus.). pap. *(978-0-9672990-3-7(9))* Texas Cooperative Extension.

Cary, Steven J. Butterfly Landscapes of New Mexico. 2009. (ENG., Illus.). 167p. pap. 19.95 *(978-1-934480-03-8(7))* New Mexico Magazine.

Glassberg, Jeffrey. Butterflies of North America. 2011. (ENG., Illus.). 208p. pap. 12.95 *(978-1-4027-8620-4(4))* Sterling Publishing Co., Inc.

James, David G. & Nunnallee, David. Life Histories of Cascadia Butterflies. 2011. (ENG.). 448p. pap. 35.00 ***(978-0-87071-626-3(3))*** Oregon State Univ. Pr.

Kavanagh, James. Alaska Butterflies & Moths: An Introduction to Familiar Species. 2008. (Pocket Naturalist - Waterford Press Ser.). (ENG., Illus.). 1p. 5.95 *(978-1-58355-423-4(8))* Waterford Pr., Inc.

—Arizona Butterflies & Moths: An Introduction to Familiar Species. 2008. (Pocket Naturalist - Waterford Press Ser.). (ENG., Illus.). 1p. 5.95 *(978-1-58355-424-1(6))* Waterford Pr., Inc.

—Colorado Butterflies & Moths: An Introduction to Familiar Species. 2008 (Pocket Naturalist - Waterford Press Ser.). (ENG., Illus.). 1p. 5.95 *(978-1-58355-425-8(4))* Waterford Pr., Inc.

—Great Lakes Butterflies & Moths: An Introduction to Familiar Species. 2008. (Pocket Naturalist - Waterford Press Ser.). (ENG., Illus.). 1p. 5.95 *(978-1-58355-370-1(3))* Waterford Pr., Inc.

—Hawaii Butterflies & Moths: An Introduction to Familiar Species. 2008. (Pocket Naturalist - Waterford Press Ser.). (ENG., Illus.). 1p. 5.95 *(978-1-58355-426-5(2))* Waterford Pr., Inc.

—Illinois Butterflies & Moths: An Introduction to Familiar Species. 2008. (Pocket Naturalist - Waterford Press Ser.). (ENG., Illus.). 1p. 5.95 *(978-1-58355-427-2(0))* Waterford Pr., Inc.

—Massachusetts Butterflies & Moths: An Introduction to Familiar Species. 2008. (Pocket Naturalist - Waterford Press Ser.). (ENG., Illus.). 1p. 5.95 *(978-1-58355-428-9(9))* Waterford Pr., Inc.

—Montana Butterflies & Moths: An Introduction to Familiar Species. 2008. (Pocket Naturalist - Waterford Press Ser.). (ENG., Illus.). 1p. 5.95 *(978-1-58355-429-6(7))* Waterford Pr., Inc.

—New England Butterflies & Moths: An Introduction to Familiar Species. 2008. (Pocket Naturalist - Waterford Press Ser.). (ENG., Illus.). 1p. 5.95 *(978-1-58355-361-9(4))* Waterford Pr., Inc.

—New York State Butterflies & Moths: An Introduction to Familiar Species. 2008. (Pocket Naturalist - Waterford Press Ser.). (ENG., Illus.). 1p. 5.95 *(978-1-58355-430-2(0))* Waterford Pr., Inc.

—North Carolina Butterflies & Moths: An Introduction to Familiar Species. 2007. (Pocket Naturalist - Waterford Press Ser.). (ENG., Illus.). 1p. 5.95 *(978-1-58355-337-4(1))* Waterford Pr., Inc.

—Ohio Butterflies & Moths: An Introduction to Familiar Species. 2008. (Pocket Naturalist - Waterford Press Ser.). (ENG., Illus.). 1p. 5.95 *(978-1-58355-431-9(9))* Waterford Pr., Inc.

—Pacific Northwest Butterflies & Moths: An Introduction to Familiar Species. 2008. (Pocket Naturalist - Waterford Press Ser.). (ENG., Illus.). 1p. 5.95 *(978-1-58355-371-8(1))* Waterford Pr., Inc.

—Rocky Mountain Butterflies & Moths: An Introduction to Familiar Species. 2008. (Pocket Naturalist - Waterford Press Ser.). (ENG., Illus.). 1p. 5.95 *(978-1-58355-366-4(5))* Waterford Pr., Inc.

—Virginia Butterflies & Moths: An Introduction to Familiar Species. 2008. (Pocket Naturalist - Waterford Press Ser.). (ENG., Illus.). 1p. 5.95 *(978-1-58355-419-7(X))* Waterford Pr., Inc.

Laufer, Peter. The Dangerous World of Butterflies: The Startling Subculture of Criminals, Collectors, & Conservationists. 2010. (ENG.). 288p. pap. 16.95 *(978-1-59921-927-1(1),* Lyons Pr.) Globe Pequot Pr., The.

Lynch, Bob & Lynch, Dan. Lake Superior Rocks & Minerals: A Field Guide to the Lake Superior Area. 2008. (Illus.). 208p. pap. 12.95 *(978-1-59193-095-2(2))* Adventure Pubns., Inc.

Pyle, Robert Michael. Mariposa Road: The First Butterfly Big Year. 10th ed. 2010. (ENG., Illus.). 576p. 27.00 *(978-0-618-94539-9(3))* Houghton Mifflin Harcourt Trade & Reference Pubs.

Rick, Cech. Common & Some Exotic Butterflies of Florida. 2009. pap. 7.95 *(978-1-935380-00-9(1))* Lewers, Steven & Assocs.

—Common & Some Exotic Butterflies of New England. 2009. pap. 7.95 *(978-1-935380-03-0(6))* Lewers, Steven & Assocs.

—Common & some exotic Butterflies of the Southeast. 2009. pap. 7.95 *(978-1-935380-01-6(X))* Lewers, Steven & Assocs.

Rick, Chec. Butterflies of the Mid Atlantic & South Central States. 2009. pap. 7.95 *(978-1-935380-02-3(8))* Lewers, Steven & Assocs.

Smart, Paul. The Complete Book of North American Butterflies. Opler, Paul A., ed. 2011. (ENG., Illus.). 192p. pap. 18.95 *(978-1-60710-276-2(5),* Thunder Bay Pr.) Advantage Pubs. Group.

BUTTONS

Barickman, Amy. Button Ware: The art of making creative adornments & Embellishments. 2008. (Illus.). per. 24.99 *(978-0-9754918-4-3(9))* Indygo Junction, Inc.

Beal, Susan. Button It Up: 80 Amazing Vintage Button Projects for Necklaces, Bracelets, Embellishments, Housewares, & More. 2009. (ENG., Illus.). 170p. pap. 21.95 *(978-1-60085-073-8(1))* Taunton Pr., Inc.

Davis, Jane. Bracelets, Buttons & Brooches: 20 Projects Using Innovative Beading Techniques. 2007. (ENG., Illus.). 128p. pap. 22.99 *(978-0-89689-581-2(5))* Krause Pubns.

Davis, Susan. Beautiful Button Jewelry: 60 Easy Heirloom Treasures. 2010. (ENG., Illus.). 144p. pap. 14.95 *(978-1-60059-559-2(6))* Lark Bks.

Edwards, Nina. On the Button: The Significance of an Ordinary Item. 2011. (ENG., Illus.). 272p. 30.00 *(978-1-84885-584-7(2))* I. B. Tauris & Co., Ltd. GBR. Dist: Macmillan.

Gorski, Jill. Busy with Buttons: Save, Stitch, Create & Share. 2009. (ENG., Illus.). 128p. pap. 22.99 *(978-0-89689-732-8(X))* Krause Pubns.

King, Laurence & Lucas, Gavin. Badge - Button - Pin. 2007. (ENG., Illus.). 128p. pap. 19.95 *(978-1-85669-409-4(7))* King, Laurence Publishing GBR. Dist: Hachette Bk. Group.

Kong, Laura West. Fast Fun & Easy Fabric Cover-Button Jewelry: Create Gifts & Glamour in an Afternoon. 2009. (ENG., Illus.). 48p. pap. 14.95 *(978-1-57120-623-7(X))* C & T Publishing.

Literary Licensing. How to Make Buttonholes & Pockets: (A 1960 Literary Licensing Reprint of the Singer Sewing Library) 2011. 34p. 35.95 ***(978-1-258-07567-5(9))*** Literary Licensing, LLC.

Pettit, Juliette. Beads & Buttons. 2008. (Illus.). 96p. pap. 14.95 *(978-1-56906-988-2(3))* Sellers Publishing, Inc.

Pike, Joni. Cute as a Button Quilts: 12 Quick Quilts & Playful Projects to Decorate Your Home. 2006. (ENG., Illus.). 80p. pap. 24.95 *(978-1-57120-345-8(1))* C & T Publishing.

Taylor, Terry. Button! Button! 50 Cute & Crafty Projects. 2008. (ENG., Illus.). 132p. pap. 17.95 *(978-1-60059-145-7(0))* Lark Bks.

BUTTONS—COLLECTORS AND COLLECTING

Hackstein, Stephanie. Buttons. 2008. 128p. 29.95 *(978-3-935129-40-4(8))* Markstein Verlag fur Kultur- und Wirtschaftsgeschichte, Cornelia Fritsch DEU. Dist: National Bk. Network.

Hughes, Elizabeth & Lester, Marion. The Big Book of Buttons: The Encyclopedia of Button History, Design, & Identification. 2nd ed. 2010. (ENG., Illus.). 1100p. 375.00 net. *(978-1-878282-38-5(7))* St. Johann Pr.

Jackson, Sandra. The Scrivener's Button Cabinet: A Twentieth Century Clothing Button Collection. 2009. 172p. pap. 52.00 *(978-1-4343-8194-1(3))* AuthorHouse.

Luscomb, Sally C. The Collector's Encyclopedia of Buttons. 6th ed. 2007. (Schiffer Book for Collectors Ser.). (Illus.). 242p. 24.95 *(978-0-7643-2329-4(6))* Schiffer Publishing, Ltd.

More, Barbara. Collectible Buttons of the Twentieth Century: A New Collector's Treasury. 2007. (Illus.). 75p. 51.99 *(978-1-4257-7304-5(4))* Xlibris Corp.

—Collectible Glass Buttons of the Twentieth Century: A New Collector's Treasury. 2008. (Illus.). 99p. 61.99 *(978-1-4363-4125-7(6))* Xlibris Corp.

Perry, Jane. A collector's guide to peasant silver Buttons. 2007. 188p. pap. 42.50 *(978-1-84799-850-7(X))* Lulu Enterprises Inc.

Skovronsky, Tom. Livery Buttons: Identification, Classification & Heraldry. 2006. (Illus.). 213p. 29.95 *(978-0-9639588-1-5(X))* Gloriosky Art Stuff.

BUYBACKS, DEBT

see Debt Equity Conversion

BUYER BEHAVIOR

see Consumer Behavior

BUYERS' GUIDES

see Consumer Education; Shopping

also subdivision Directories under particular lines of business industry

BUYING

see Purchasing

BUYING, AUTOMOBILE

see Automobiles—Purchasing

BUYING, INDUSTRIAL

see Industrial Procurement

BUZZ BOMB

see V-One Bomb

BY-PRODUCTS

see Waste Products

BYBLOS

Artin, Gassia. La "Necropole Eneolithique" de Byblos. 2009. (FRE & ENG., Illus.). 219p. (C). pap. 100.00 *(978-1-4073-0527-1(1))* British Archaeological Reports Ltd. GBR. Dist: Brown, David Bk. Co., The.

BYLINY

Volkova, Z. N. Russkii Epos: Uchebnoe Posobie Po Analiticheskomu Chteniiu. (RUS., Illus.). 252p. *(978-5-200-00365-5(2),* Nicholson) Russkij jazyk.

BYNG, JOHN, 1704-1757

Ware, Chris. Admiral Byng: His Rise & Execution. 2008. (Illus.). 192p. 45.00 *(978-1-84415-781-5(4))* Pen & Sword Bks. Ltd. GBR. Dist: Casemate Pubs. & Bk. Distributors, LLC.

BYPASS, CARDIOPULMONARY

see Cardiopulmonary Bypass

BYPASS SURGERY, CORONARY

see Coronary Artery Bypass

BYRD, RICHARD EVELYN, 1888-1957

Eggleston, George Cary. Evelyn Byrd. 2009. 196p. pap. *(978-0-217-31741-2(3))* Books LLC.

—Evelyn Byrd. 2009. 196p. pap. 19.99 *(978-0-217-71401-3(3))* General Bks. LLC.

—Evelyn Byrd. 2008. 448p. 51.95 *(978-0-548-99494-8(3))* 2007. (ENG.). 452p. per. 36.95 *(978-0-548-65188-9(4))* Kessinger Publishing, LLC.

Maynard, Jeff. Wings of Ice: The Mystery of the Polar Air Race. 2010. (ENG., Illus.). 304p. 19.95 *(978-1-74166-934-3(0))* Random Hse. Australia AUS. Dist: Independent Pubs. Group.

Rose, Lisle A. Explorer: The Life of Richard E. Byrd. 2008. (ENG., Illus.). 568p. (gr. 9). 34.95 *(978-0-8262-1782-0(6))* Univ. of Missouri Pr.

BYRD, WILLIAM, 1542 OR 3-1623

Brett, Philip. William Byrd & His Contemporaries: Essays & a Monograph. Kerman, Joseph & Moroney, Davitt, eds. 2006. (Illus.). 252p. 45.00 *(978-0-520-24758-1(2))* Univ. of California Pr.

Brown, Alan & Turbet, Richard, eds. Byrd Studies. 2006. (Cambridge Composer Studies). (ENG., Illus.). 296p. pap. 58.00 *(978-0-521-03261-2(X))* Cambridge Univ. Pr.

Harley, John. The World of William Byrd: Musicians, Merchants & Magnates. 2010. (Illus.). 324p. 124.95 *(978-1-4094-0088-2(3))* Ashgate Publishing Co.

McCarthy, Kerry. Liturgy & Contemplation in Byrd's Gradualia. 2007. (Illus.). 239p. 125.00 *(978-0-415-97861-3(0))* Routledge.

Rastall & Rayner. William Byrd: Six Part Fantasies in G Minor. 240p. 67.95 *(978-1-85928-348-6(9))* Ashgate Publishing Co.

Turbet, Richard. William Byrd. 3rd rev. ed. 2012. (Routledge Music Bibliographies Ser.). (ENG., Illus.). 300p. 150.00 ***(978-0-415-87559-2(5))*** Routledge.

BYRD, WILLIAM, 1674-1744

Byrd, William. The Secret Diary of William Byrd of Westover. 49.95 *(978-0-8488-0235-6(7))* Amereon LTD.

—Writings of William Byrd of Westover in Virginia. Bassett, John S., ed. 461p. reprint ed. lib. bdg. 98.00 *(978-0-7222-0993-6(2))* Library Reprints, Inc.

Byrd, William & Wright, Louis B. A Shorthand Diary of William Byrd of Westover: Huntington Library Quarterly V2, No. 4, July 1939. 2011. 12p. pap. 35.95 ***(978-1-258-06916-2(4))*** Literary Licensing, LLC.

BYRD ANTARCTIC EXPEDITIONS

Paine, M L, ed. Footsteps on the Ice: The Antarctic Diaries of Stuart D. Paine, Second Byrd Expedition. 2007. (ENG., Illus.). 400p. (gr. 9). 34.95 *(978-0-8262-1741-7(9))* Univ. of Missouri Pr.

BYRD FAMILY

Byrd Genealogy Extracted from Campbel Genealogy (1927) fac. ed. 146p. pap. 24.00 *(978-0-7404-1354-4(6))* Higginson Bk. Co.

Byrd, William. The Writings of "Colonel William Byrd. 461p. reprint ed. 98.00 *(978-0-7222-6526-0(3))* Library Reprints, Inc.

BYRHTFERTH, B. CA. 970

Lapidge, Michael, ed. Byrhtferth of Ramsey: The Lives of St. Oswald & St. Ecgwine. 2009. (Oxford Medieval Texts). (ENG., Illus.). 450p. 185.00 *(978-0-19-955078-4(6))* Oxford Univ. Pr., Inc.

BYRON, ANNE ISABELLE MILBANKE BYRON, BARONESS, 1792-1860

Graham, William. Last Links with Byron, Shelley, & Keats. 2008. 152p. pap. *(978-1-4097-2994-5(X))* Read Bks.

Markovits, Benjamin. A Quiet Adjustment. 2009. (ENG.). 368p. pap. 14.95 *(978-0-393-33022-9(2),* 33022) Norton, W. W. & Co., Inc.

Stowe, Harriet Beecher. Lady Byron Vindicated. 2008. 336p. 29.99 *(978-0-554-27069-2(2))* 2008. 336p. 28.99 *(978-0-554-36372-1(0))* 2007. (ENG.). 294p. pap. 21.99 *(978-1-4346-2422-2(6))* 2007. (ENG.). 332p. pap. 24.99 *(978-1-4346-2468-0(4))* BiblioBazaar.

—Lady Byron Vindicated. 2006. (ENG.). pap. *(978-1-4065-1073-7(4))* Dodo Pr.

BYRON, GEORGE GORDON BYRON, BARON, 1788-1824

Bancroft, George. History of the Battle of Lake Erie & Miscellaneous Papers. 2007. 266p. reprint ed. pap. 29.95 *(978-1-60105-121-9(2))* Scholar's Bookshelf.

Barton, Anne. Byron. 2008. (Landmarks of World Literature Ser.). (ENG., Illus.). 128p. (C). pap. 29.99 *(978-0-521-33841-7(7))* Cambridge Univ. Pr.

Beatty, Bernard, et al, eds. Liberty & Poetic Licence: New Essays on Byron. 2008. (Liverpool English Texts & Studies). 336p. 85.00 *(978-0-85323-589-7(9))* Liverpool Univ. Pr. GBR. Dist: Chicago Distribution Ctr.

Beatty, Bernard & Howlett, Tony. Liberty & Poetic Licence. 2008. 336p. pap. 85.00 *(978-1-84631-589-3(1))* Reaktion Bks., Ltd. GBR. Dist: Univ. of Chicago Pr.

Bernhard Jackson, Emily A. The Development of Byron's Philosophy of Knowledge: Certain in Uncertainty. 2010. (ENG.). 240p. 84.00 *(978-0-230-23151-1(9))* Palgrave Macmillan.

Bevis, Matthew. The Art of Eloquence: Byron, Dickens, Tennyson, Joyce. 2010. (ENG.). 312p. pap. 50.00 *(978-0-19-959322-4(1))* Oxford Univ. Pr., Inc.

Blessington, Marguerite. Conversations of Lord Byron with the Countess of Blessington. 2011. (Cambridge Library Collection - Literary Studies). (ENG., Illus.). 420p. pap. 31.99 ***(978-1-108-03393-0(8))*** Cambridge Univ. Pr.

Bloom, Harold, ed. George Gordon, Lord Byron. 2009. (Bloom's Classic Critical Views Ser.). 316p. (C). (gr. 9-18). 45.00 *(978-1-60413-438-4(0),* Chelsea Hse.) Facts On File, Inc.

Byron. Childe Harold's Pilgrimage. 2009. 86p. pap. 18.75 *(978-1-110-42364-4(0))* 2008. 280p. 28.99 *(978-0-554-55394-8(5))* 2008. 280p. 25.99 *(978-0-554-55402-0(X))* 2008. 188p. 22.99 *(978-0-554-31223-1(9))* 2008. 188p. 25.99 *(978-0-554-21920-2(4))* 2008. 280p. pap. 26.75 *(978-0-554-55400-6(3))* 2008. 276p. pap. 27.75 *(978-0-554-55397-9(X))* BiblioBazaar.

—Childe Harold's Pilgrimage. 2008. 180p. pap. *(978-1-4099-2685-6(0))* Dodo Pr.

Byron, George Gordon. Byron's Poetry & Prose. Levine, Alice, ed. 2nd ed. 2009. (Norton Critical Edition Ser.). (ENG.). 1088p. (C). (gr. 9-12). pap. 19.53 *(978-0-393-92560-9(9),* 92560) Norton, W. W. & Co., Inc.

—Correspondence of Lord Byron: With a Friend, Including Letters to his Mother. Dallas, R. C., ed. 2011. (Cambridge Library Collection - Literary Studies). (ENG.). 654p. pap. 45.00 ***(978-1-108-03406-7(3))*** Cambridge Univ. Pr.

—The Letters & Journals of Lord Byron. 2007. 360p. per. *(978-1-4068-1229-9(3));* (ENG.). 272p. per. *(978-1-4068-2424-7(0))* Echo Library.

—Lord Byron's Correspondence: Chiefly with Lady Melbourne, Mr. Hobhouse, the Hon. Douglas Kinnaird, & P. B. Shelley. Murray, John, ed. 2011. (Cambridge Library Collection - Literary Studies). (ENG., Illus.). 330p. pap. 28.99 ***(978-1-108-03394-7(6))*** Cambridge Univ. Pr.

—Lord Byron's Correspondence: Volume 2: Chiefly with Lady Melbourne, Mr. Hobhouse, the Hon. Douglas Kinnaird, & P. B. Shelley. Murray, John, ed. 2011. (Cambridge Library Collection - Literary Studies). (ENG., Illus.). 342p. pap. 28.99 ***(978-1-108-03395-4(4))*** Cambridge Univ. Pr.

Byron, George Gordon. Poetical Works. 2009. 282p. 24.99 *(978-1-110-01058-5(3));* 282p. pap. 18.99 *(978-1-110-01056-1(7));* 288p. 24.99 *(978-1-103-96950-0(1));* 288p. pap. 18.99 *(978-1-103-96939-5(0))* BiblioBazaar.

—Poetical Works. 2009. 184p. pap. *(978-0-217-97547-6(X))* Books LLC.

Byron, George Gordon & Moore, Thomas. Works of Lord Byron V1: with His Letters & Journals & His Life. 2007. pap. 33.95 *(978-1-4304-4888-4(1))* Kessinger Publishing, LLC.

Clinton, George. Memoirs of the Life & Writings of Lord Byron. 2009. 604p. pap. 36.65 *(978-1-150-27204-2(X))* General Bks. LLC.

de Loo, Tessa. In Byron's Footsteps. 2011. (Red Bks.). (ENG., Illus.). 220p. 19.95 ***(978-1-906598-77-8(0))*** Haus Publishing GBR. Dist: Consortium Bk. Sales & Distribution.

Dennis, Ian. Lord Byron & the History of Desire. 2009. 266p. 55.00 *(978-0-87413-066-9(2))* Univ. of Delaware Pr.

Dick, William. Byron & His Poetry. 2009. (ENG.). 190p. pap. 21.99 *(978-1-113-96478-6(2));* pap. 23.75 *(978-1-113-96481-6(2))* BiblioBazaar. (BiblioLife).

Edgcumbe, Richard. Byron, the Last Phase. 2010. 442p. pap. 35.75 *(978-1-178-35634-2(5))* BiblioBazaar.

—Byron, the Last Phase. 2010. 228p. pap. 31.08 *(978-1-152-17348-4(0))* General Bks. LLC.

Ehrstine, John W. The Metaphysics of Byron: A Reading of the Plays. (De Proprietatibus Litterarum. Series Practica Ser.). (ENG.). X, 146p. (Orig.). 210.00 ***(978-3-11-177978-2(5))*** De Gruyter, Mouton DEU. Dist: de Gruyter, Walter GmbH & Co. KG.

Ellis, David. Byron in Geneva: That Summer of 1816. 2011. (ENG., Illus.). 189p. 30.00 *(978-1-84631-643-2(X))* Liverpool Univ. Pr. GBR. Dist: Chicago Distribution Ctr.

Fleming, Anne. Byron the Maker & 2, Vol. 1. 2009. (Illus.). 520p. 42.50 *(978-1-84624-339-4(4))* Book Guild, Ltd. GBR. Dist: Trans-Atlantic Pubns., Inc.

Fox, John C. The Byron Mystery. 2010. 260p. 34.36 *(978-1-169-74988-7(7));* 42.95 *(978-1-161-39185-5(1))* Kessinger Publishing, LLC.

Franklin, Caroline. Byron. 2006. (Routledge Guides to Literature Ser.). 160p. (C). 95.00 *(978-0-415-26855-4(9));* 144p. per. 28.95 *(978-0-415-26856-1(7))* Routledge.

—The Female Romantics: Nineteenth-Century Women Novelists & Byronism. 2012. (Routledge Studies in Romanticism Ser.). (ENG., Illus.). 264p. (C). 125.00 *(978-0-415-99541-2(8))* Routledge.

Fuess, Claude Moore. Lord Byron As a Satirist in Verse. 2009. 142p. pap. 19.99 *(978-1-150-27077-2(2))* General Bks. LLC.

Galt, John. The Life of Lord Byron. 2008. 220p. pap. 9.99 *(978-1-60450-300-5(9))* Arc Manor.

—The Life of Lord Byron. 2008. 324p. 28.99 *(978-0-554-32604-7(3))* 2008. 324p. 29.99 *(978-0-554-23301-7(0))* 2007. (ENG.). 320p. pap. 24.99 *(978-1-4264-4157-8(6))* 2006. 288p. pap. 21.99 *(978-1-4264-4142-4(8))* BiblioBazaar.

—The Life of Lord Byron. 2009. 220p. pap. *(978-1-151-12035-9(9))* Books LLC.

—The Life of Lord Byron. 2007. pap. *(978-1-4065-1741-5(0))* Dodo Pr.

—The Life of Lord Byron. 2007. (ENG.). 216p. per. *(978-1-4068-6187-7(1))* Echo Library.

Gamba, Pietro. A Narrative of Lord Byron's Last Journey to Greece. 2009. 72p. pap. *(978-0-217-16053-7(0))* Books LLC.

Gordon, Cosmo. Life & Genius of Lord Byron. 2007. (ENG.). 84p. per. 17.95 *(978-1-4325-3407-3(6))* Kessinger Publishing, LLC.

Gordon, Lord Byron George. Seventeen Letters of George Noel Gordon, Lord Byron, to an Unknown Lady, 1811-1817. Peck, Walter Edwin, ed. 2011. 50p. 35.95 ***(978-1-258-03951-6(6))*** Literary Licensing, LLC.

Graham, William. Last Links with Byron, Shelley & Keats. 2008. 152p. 36.95 *(978-1-4365-0534-5(8))* 2007. (ENG.). 156p. per. 21.95 *(978-0-548-71264-1(6))* Kessinger Publishing, LLC.

Gray, Austin K. Teresa or Her Demon Lover. 2007. (ENG.). 422p. 51.95 *(978-0-548-06768-0(6))* Kessinger Publishing, LLC.

Gray, Duncan. The Life & Work of Lord Byron. 2008. 128p. pap. *(978-1-4097-9217-8(X))* Read Bks.

Green, Matthew J. A. & Pal-Lapinski, Piya, eds. Byron & the Politics of Freedom & Terror. 2011. (ENG., Illus.). 256p. 85.00 *(978-0-230-24646-1(X))* Palgrave Macmillan.

Gribble, Francis. The Love Affairs of Lord Byron. 2009. 408p. pap. 33.75 *(978-1-117-60986-7(3))* BiblioBazaar.

—The Love Affairs of Lord Byron. 2008. 406p. 49.95 *(978-1-4365-9220-8(8))* 2007. (ENG.). 408p. per. 34.95 *(978-0-548-77935-4(X))* Kessinger Publishing, LLC.

Gristwood, Sarah. Poetic Lives: Byron. 2012. (Poetic Lives Ser.). (ENG.). 112p. pap. 12.95 *(978-1-84391-307-8(0))* Hesperus Pr. GBR. Dist: Independent Pubs. Group.

Guiccioli, Teresa. Lord Byron Jugt Par les Ttmoins de Sa Vie My Recollections of Lord Byron; & Those of Eye-Witnesses of His Life. 2006. 676p. per. 36.99 *(978-1-4255-6798-9(3))* MPublishing.

Hay, Daisy. Young Romantics: The Tangled Lives of English Poetry's Greatest Generation, 1 vol. 2011. (ENG., Illus.). 384p. pap. 18.00 *(978-0-374-53293-2(1))* Farrar, Straus & Giroux.

Henderson, Andrea K. Romantic Identities: Varieties of Subjectivity, 1774-1830. 2006. (Cambridge Studies in Romanticism Ser.). (ENG., Illus.). 216p. pap. 50.00 *(978-0-521-02710-6(1))* Cambridge Univ. Pr.

Hobhouse, John Cam. Recollections of a Long Life. Carleton, Charlotte Hobhouse, ed. 2011. (Cambridge Library Collection - Literary Studies). (ENG.). 322p. pap. 24.99 ***(978-1-108-03402-9(0));*** 376p. pap. 29.99 ***(978-1-108-03398-5(9));*** 338p. pap. 28.99 ***(978-1-108-03403-6(9));*** 406p. pap. 31.99 ***(978-1-108-03399-2(7));*** 406p. pap. 31.99 ***(978-1-108-03401-2(2))*** Cambridge Univ. Pr.

Hobhouse, John Cam & Carleton, Charlotte Hobhouse. Recollections of a Long Life. 2011. (Cambridge Library Collection - Literary Studies). (ENG., Illus.). 398p. pap. 31.99 ***(978-1-108-03400-5(4))*** Cambridge Univ. Pr.

Hunt, Leigh. Lord Byron & Some of His Contemporaries. reprint ed. 59.50 *(978-0-404-03419-1(5))* AMS Pr., Inc.

—Lord Byron & Some of His Contemporaries. 2008. 459p. 33.99 *(978-0-554-56527-9(7));* 460p. 31.99 *(978-0-554-56536-1(6));* 460p. pap. 35.75 *(978-0-554-56534-7(X));* 459p. pap. 36.75 *(978-0-554-56530-9(7))* BiblioBazaar.

—Lord Byron & Some of His Contemporaries. 2009. 350p. pap. *(978-0-217-84812-1(5))* Books LLC.

Irving, Washington. The Crayon Miscellany. 2008. 381p. 31.99 *(978-0-559-00049-2(9));* 29.99 *(978-0-559-00059-1(6));* pap. 33.75 *(978-0-559-00050-8(2));* pap. 32.75 *(978-0-559-00055-3(3))* BiblioBazaar.

Jones, Christine Kenyon, ed. Byron: The Image of the Poet. 2008. (Illus.). 129p. 49.50 *(978-0-87413-997-6(X))* Univ. of Delaware Pr.

Lansdown, Richard. The Cambridge Introduction to Byron. 2012. (Cambridge Introductions to Literature Ser.). (ENG., Illus.). 192p. (C). 70.00 ***(978-0-521-11133-1(1));*** pap. 19.99 ***(978-0-521-12873-5(0))*** Cambridge Univ. Pr.

Lutz, Deborah. The Dangerous Lover: Gothic Villains, Byronism, & the Nineteenth-Century Seduction Narrative. 2006. 117p. 44.95 *(978-0-8142-1034-5(1));* xii, 117p. cd-rom 9.95 *(978-0-8142-9111-5(2))* Ohio State Univ. Pr.

Mayne, Ethel Colburn. Byron. 2009. 372p. 26.99 *(978-1-103-99804-3(8));* pap. 20.99 *(978-1-103-99795-4(5))* BiblioBazaar.

Mazzeo, Tilar J. Plagiarism & Literary Property in the Romantic Period. annot. ed. 2006. (Material Texts). 256p. (C). 65.00 *(978-0-8122-3967-6(9))* Univ. of Pennsylvania Pr.

McDayter, Ghislaine. Byromania & the Birth of Celebrity Culture. 2010. (SUNY series, Studies in the Long Nineteenth Century Ser.). (Illus.). 256p. pap. 24.95 *(978-1-4384-2526-9(0), Suny Pr.)* State Univ. of New York Pr.
McDayter, Ghislaine & Mcdayter, G. Byromania & the Birth of Celebrity Culture. 2009. (SUNY series, Studies in the Long Nineteenth Century Ser.). (Illus.). 256p. 75.00 *(978-1-4384-2525-2(2))* State Univ. of New York Pr.
Mole, Tom. Byron's Romantic Celebrity: Industrial Culture & the Hermeneutic of Intimacy. 2007. (Palgrave Studies in the Enlightenment, Romanticism & the Cultures of Print Ser.). (ENG., Illus.). 256p. 95.00 *(978-1-4039-9993-1(7))* Palgrave Macmillan.
Moore, Doris Langley. The Late Lord Byron. 2011. (Neversink Ser.). 544p. pap. 18.95 *(978-1-935554-48-6(4))* Melville Hse. Publishing.
Moore, Thomas. Letters & Journals of Lord Byron V1 Wi. 2006. pap. 38.95 *(978-1-4286-4542-4(X))* Kessinger Publishing, LLC.
—Letters & Journals of Lord Byron V2 Wi. 2006. pap. 43.95 *(978-1-4286-4543-1(8))* Kessinger Publishing, LLC.
—The Life, Letters & Journals of Lord Byron. 735p. reprint ed. lib. bdg. 99.00 *(978-0-7812-0248-0(5))* Reprint Services Co.
—Life of Lord Byron. 2008. 368p. 31.99 *(978-0-554-25130-1(2))*; 29.99 *(978-0-554-34433-1(5))* BiblioBazaar.
Morgan, Monique R. Narrative Means, Lyric Ends: Temporality in the Nineteenth-Century British Long Poem. 2009. 47.95 *(978-0-8142-1111-3(9))*; (ENG.). 280p. cd-rom 14.95 *(978-0-8142-9208-2(9))* Ohio State Univ. Pr.
Nichol, John. Byron. Morley, John, ed. (English Men of Letters Ser.). reprint ed. lib. bdg. 27.50 *(978-0-404-51722-9(6))* AMS Pr., Inc.
—Byron. 2010. 244p. pap. 26.75 *(978-1-178-35434-8(2))* 2010. (ENG.). 232p. pap. 25.75 *(978-1-171-79253-6(0))* 2010. 236p. pap. 26.75 *(978-1-178-16454-1(3))* 2010. 226p. 32.99 *(978-1-140-05845-8(2))* 2010. 240p. pap. 26.75 *(978-1-148-23827-2(1))* 2010. 226p. pap. 25.75 *(978-1-140-05846-5(0))* 2010. 226p. pap. 25.75 *(978-1-148-05627-2(0))* 2010. 688p. pap. 48.75 *(978-1-144-66275-0(3))* 2010. 234p. pap. 25.75 *(978-1-145-89023-7(7))* 2010. 694p. pap. 48.75 *(978-1-144-16237-3(8))* 2009. 230p. 28.99 *(978-1-113-63784-0(6))* 2009. 230p. pap. 24.75 *(978-1-113-63782-6(X))* 2009. 230p. pap. 25.75 *(978-1-113-63783-3(8))* 2009. (ENG.). 228p. pap. 22.99 *(978-1-113-63781-9(1)*, BiblioLife) 2009. (ENG.). 228p. pap. 20.99 *(978-1-113-63780-2(3)*, BiblioLife) 2009. 228p. 23.99 *(978-1-103-10736-0(4))* 2009. 228p. pap. 17.99 *(978-1-103-10734-6(8))* 2008. 204p. 25.99 *(978-0-554-23215-7(4))* 2008. 204p. 22.99 *(978-0-554-32518-7(7))* 2007. (ENG.). 200p. pap. 21.99 *(978-1-4264-3996-4(2))* 2007. 178p. pap. 19.99 *(978-1-4264-3938-4(5))* BiblioBazaar.
—Byron. 2011. (Cambridge Library Collection - English Men of Letters Ser.). (ENG.). 234p. pap. 22.99 ***(978-1-108-03455-5(1))*** Cambridge Univ. Pr.
—Byron. 2007. (ENG.). 160p. per. *(978-1-4065-4040-6(4))* Dodo Pr.
—Byron. 2006. (ENG.). pap. *(978-1-4068-3456-7(4))* Echo Library.
—Byron. 2010. (Illus.). 110p. pap. 20.12 *(978-1-153-59358-8(0))* General Bks. LLC.
—Byron. 2010. 134p. pap. *(978-1-4076-0643-9(3))* HardPr.
Nichol, John & Morley, John. Byron. 2010. 236p. 33.56 *(978-1-169-74243-7(2))*; 41.95 *(978-1-161-37484-1(1))* Kessinger Publishing, LLC.
O'Brien, Edna. Byron in Love. 2009. (Illus.). 248p. *(978-0-297-85553-8(0)*, Weidenfeld & Nicolson) Orion Publishing Group, Ltd.
—Byron in Love: A Short Daring Life. 2009. (ENG., Illus.). 240p. 24.95 *(978-0-393-07011-8(5)*, 7011) Norton, W. W. & Co., Inc.
—Byron in Love: A Short Daring Life. 2010. (ENG., Illus.). 240p. pap. 14.95 *(978-0-393-33847-8(9)*, 33847) Norton, W. W. & Co., Inc.
Origo, Iris. The Last Attachment: The Story of Byron & Teresa Guiccioli. 560p. 2008. 57.95 *(978-1-4367-1608-6(X))* 2007. (ENG.). per. 42.95 *(978-1-4325-9479-4(6))* Kessinger Publishing, LLC.
Parker, Fred. The Devil as Muse: Blake, Byron, & the Adversary. 2011. (Making of the Christian Imagination Ser.). (ENG., Illus.). 215p. 29.95 *(978-1-60258-269-9(6))* Baylor Univ. Pr.
Parry, William. The Last Days of Lord Byron. 2009. (ENG.). 389p. 38.99 *(978-1-117-65868-1(6))* 2009. (ENG.). 389p. pap. 32.75 *(978-1-117-65869-8(4))* 2008. 396p. 29.99 *(978-0-559-57710-9(9))* 2008. 396p. pap. 32.75 *(978-0-559-57706-2(0))* BiblioBazaar.
—The Last Days of Lord Byron: With His Lordship's Opinions on Various Subjects, Particularly on the State & Prospects of Greece. 2007. (ENG.). 272p. 42.95 *(978-0-548-23002-2(1))*; 276p. per. 27.95 *(978-1-4325-5314-2(3))* Kessinger Publishing, LLC.
Payne, Geoff. Dark Imaginings: Ideology & Darkness in the Poetry of Lord Byron. 2008. 278p. pap. 83.95 *(978-3-03911-341-5(0))* Lang, Peter AG GBR. Dist: Lang, Peter.
Powys, John Cowper. Essays on de Gourmont & Byron. 2006. pap. 16.95 *(978-1-4286-4302-4(8))* Kessinger Publishing, LLC.
Pratt, Willis Winslow. Byron at Southwell: The Making of A Poet. 2011. 158p. 41.95 ***(978-1-258-01988-4(4))*** Literary Licensing, LLC.
Rosen, Frederick, ed. Bentham. 2007. (International Library of Essays in the History of Social & Political Thought Ser.). 622p. 350.00 *(978-0-7546-2566-7(4))* Ashgate Publishing Co.
Schmidt, Arnold A. Byron & the Rhetoric of Italian Nationalism. 2010. (Nineteenth-Century Major Lives & Letters Ser.). (ENG.). 220p. 84.00 *(978-0-230-61600-4(3))* Palgrave Macmillan.
Sheila, Spector. Byron & the Jews. 2010. 336p. 59.95 *(978-0-8143-3442-3(3))* Wayne State Univ. Pr.
Stabler, Jane. Byron, Poetics & History. 2009. (Cambridge Studies in Romanticism Ser.). (ENG.). 272p. pap. 38.99 *(978-0-521-11185-0(4))* Cambridge Univ. Pr.
—Palgrave Advances in Byron Studies. 2007. (Palgrave Advances Ser.). (ENG.). 304p. 116.00 *(978-1-4039-4592-1(6))*; pap. 41.00 *(978-1-4039-4593-8(4))* Palgrave Macmillan.
Steffan, Truman Guy. Lord Byron's Cain: Twelve Essays & a Text with Variants & Annotations. 2011. (ENG.). 528p. pap. 42.50 ***(978-0-292-72988-9(X))*** Univ. of Texas Pr.
Stewart, John. Byron & the Websters: The Letters & Entangled Lives of the Poet, Sir James Webster & Lady Frances Webster. 2008. (ENG., Illus.). 224p. pap. 39.95 *(978-0-7864-3240-0(3))* McFarland & Co., Inc. Pubs.
Stock, Paul. The Shelley-Byron Circle & the Idea of Europe. 2010. (Palgrave Studies in Cultural & Intellectual History Ser.). (ENG.). 274p. 84.00 *(978-0-230-61963-0(0))* Palgrave Macmillan.
Stowe, Harriet Beecher. Lady Byron Vindicated. 2008. 336p. 28.99 *(978-0-554-36372-1(0))* 2008. 336p. 29.99 *(978-0-554-27069-2(2))* 2007. (ENG.). 294p. pap. 21.99 *(978-1-4346-2422-2(6))* 2007. (ENG.). 332p. pap. 24.99 *(978-1-4346-2468-0(4))* BiblioBazaar.
—Lady Byron Vindicated. 2006. (ENG.). pap. *(978-1-4065-1073-7(4))* Dodo Pr.
Strathcarron, Ian. Joy Unconfined! Lord Byron's Grand Tour Re-Toured. 2011. (ENG., Illus.). 288p. *(978-1-904955-74-0(6))* Signal Bks.
Thomas Moore. Life of Lord Byron. l.t. ed. 2007. (ENG.). 368p. pap. 26.99 *(978-1-4264-8291-5(4))* BiblioBazaar.
Trelawny, Edward John. Recollections of the Last Days of Shelley & Byron. 2011. (Cambridge Library Collection - Literary Studies). (ENG., Illus.). 322p. pap. 24.99 ***(978-1-108-03405-0(5))*** Cambridge Univ. Pr.
—Records of Shelley, Byron, & the Author. 2010. 250p. pap. 26.75 *(978-1-144-96321-5(4))*; 268p. pap. 27.75 *(978-1-143-08795-0(X))* BiblioBazaar.
—Records of Shelley, Byron, & the Author. 2009. 90p. pap. *(978-1-151-40261-5(3))*; 86p. pap. *(978-1-151-36401-2(0))* Books LLC.
—Records of Shelley, Byron, & the Author. 2009. 92p. pap. 7.30 *(978-1-151-57593-7(3))* General Bks. LLC.
—Records of Shelley, Byron & the Author. 2009. 166p. pap. 8.07 *(978-1-151-03442-7(8))* General Bks. LLC.
Watkins, John. Memoirs of the Life & Writings of the Right Honourable Lord Byron. 2009. 194p. pap. *(978-0-217-86437-4(6))* Books LLC.
Wilson, Cheryl A. Byron: Heritage & Legacy. Wilson, Cheryl A., ed. 2008. (Nineteenth-Century Major Lives & Letters Ser.). (ENG.). 276p. 89.00 *(978-0-230-60029-4(8))* Palgrave Macmillan.
Wood, Clement. Byron & the Women He Loved. 2011. 66p. 36.95 ***(978-1-258-01948-8(5))*** Literary Licensing, LLC.

BYRON, LORD, 1788-1824
see Byron, George Gordon Byron, Baron, 1788-1824

BYRON FAMILY
Nichol, John. Byron. Morley, John, ed. (English Men of Letters Ser.). reprint ed. lib. bdg. 27.50 *(978-0-404-51722-9(6))* AMS Pr., Inc.
—Byron. 2011. (Cambridge Library Collection - English Men of Letters Ser.). (ENG.). 234p. pap. 22.99 ***(978-1-108-03455-5(1))*** Cambridge Univ. Pr.

BYSSINOSIS
see Lungs—Dust Diseases

BYZANTINE ANTIQUITIES
see also Christian Antiquities
Adams, Noel & Entwistle, Chris, eds. Gems of Heaven: Recent Research on Engraved Gemstones in Late Antiquity. 2011. (BMP Research Publication). (ENG., Illus.). 274p. (C). pap. 80.00 *(978-0-86159-177-0(1))* British Museum Pr. GBR. Dist: Brown, David Bk. Co., The.
Carr, Annemarie Weyl. Imprinting the Divine: Byzantine & Russian Icons from the Menil Collection. 2011. (ENG., Illus.). 168p. 50.00 *(978-0-300-16968-3(X))* Yale Univ. Pr.
Cormack, Robin & Vassiliki, Maria. Byzantium, 330-1453. 2008. (ENG., Illus.). 496p. 115.00 *(978-1-905711-26-0(3))* Royal Academy of Arts GBR. Dist: Hachette Bk. Group.
Diehl, Charles. Figures Byzantines. 2009. 352p. 46.95 *(978-1-104-16649-6(6))*; pap. 31.95 *(978-1-104-12726-8(1))* Kessinger Publishing, LLC.
Georganteli, Eurydice S. & Barrie, Cook. Encounters: Travel & Money in the Byzantine World. 2006. (ENG., Illus.). 64p. pap. 11.95 *(978-1-904832-27-0(X))* Giles, D. Ltd. GBR. Dist: Antique Collectors' Club.
Jeffreys, Elizabeth. Proceedings of Hte 21st International Congress of Byzantine Studies London 21-26 August 2006 Vol. 3: Vol 1:Plenary Papers Vol 2: Abstracts of Panel Papers Vol 3:Abstracts of Communications, 3 vols. 2006. (ENG, FRE, ITA & GER., Illus.). 1156p. 400.00 *(978-0-7546-5740-8(X))* Ashgate Publishing Co.
Khroushkova, Liudmila. Les Monuments Chretiens de la Cote Orientale de la Mer Noire: Abkhazie: IVe-XIVe Siecles. 2007. (Bibliothèque de l'Antiquité Tardive Ser.). (Illus.). 340p. pap. 139.00 *(978-2-503-52387-3(0))* Brepols Pubs. BEL. Dist: Brown, David Bk. Co., The.
Papadaki-Oekland, S. Byzantine Illuminated Manuscripts of the Book of Job: A Preliminary Study of the Miniature Illustrations, Its Origin & Development. 2009. (ENG & GEC., Illus.). 478p. (C). 218.00 *(978-2-503-53232-5(2))* Brepols Pubs. BEL. Dist: ISD.
Poulter, Andrew, ed. Nicopolis Ad Istrum 3: A Roman to Early Byzantine Site the Finds & Environmental Evidence. 2007. (Illus.). 280p. 100.00 *(978-1-84217-182-0(8))* Oxbow Bks., Ltd. GBR. Dist: Brown, David Bk. Co., The.
Soustal, Peter, ed. Heilige Berge und Wusten: Byzanz und sein Umfeld. Referate auf dem 21. Internationalen Kongress fur Byzantinistik London, 21. 26. August 2006. 2009. (VERoFFENTLICHUNGEN ZUR BYZANZFORSCHUNG Ser.). (Illus.). 111p. (C). pap. 78.00 *(978-3-7001-6561-3(7))* Austrian Academy of Sciences Press AUT. Dist: Brown, David Bk. Co., The.
Xanthopoulou, M. Les lampes en bronze a l'epoque Paleochretienne. 2010. (Bibliotheque de l'antiquite Tardive Ser.). (FRE., Illus.). 352p. (C). pap. 102.00 *(978-2-503-53369-8(8))* Brepols Pubs. BEL. Dist: Brown, David Bk. Co., The.
Zavagno, Luca. Cities in Transition: Urbanism in Byzantium Between Late Antiquity & the Early Middle Ages (500-900 A. D.) 2009. (Bar S Ser.). (ENG., Illus.). 206p. (C). pap. 100.00 *(978-1-4073-0607-0(3))* British Archaeological Reports Ltd. GBR. Dist: Brown, David Bk. Co., The.

BYZANTINE ARCHITECTURE
see Architecture, Byzantine

BYZANTINE ART
see Art, Byzantine

BYZANTINE CHANTS
Lind, Tore Tvarn. Past Is Always Present: The Revival of the Byzantine Musical Tradition at Mount Athos. 2011. (Europea: Ethnomusicologies & Modernities Ser.). (ENG., Illus.). 262p. (gr. 17). 85.00 ***(978-0-8108-8147-1(0))*** Scarecrow Pr., Inc.
—The Past Is Always Present: The Revival of the Byzantine Musical Tradition at Mount Athos. 2012. (Illus.). xx, 241p. E-Book ***(978-0-8108-8148-8(9))*** Scarecrow Pr., Inc.
Wolfram, Gerda & Wolfram, G., eds. Tradition & Innovation in Late- & Postbyzantine Liturgical Chant: Acta of the Congress Held at Hernen Castle, the Netherlands, in April 2005. 2008. (Eastern Christian Studies). (GER & ENG., Illus.). 381p. (C). pap. 95.00 *(978-90-429-2015-6(7))* Peeters Pubs. & Booksellers BEL. Dist: Brown, David Bk. Co., The.

BYZANTINE EMPIRE
Anastos, Milton Vasil. Studies in Byzantine Intellectual History. 2009. 434p. 68.00 *(978-1-59740-737-3(2))* ACLS Humanities E-Book.
Brubaker, Leslie. Inventing Byzantine Iconoclasm. Wood, Ian, ed. 2012. (Illus.). 160p. pap. 27.95 *(978-1-85399-750-1(1))* Duckworth Publishers GBR. Dist: International Publishers Marketing.
Bryer, Anthony. Manzikert to Lepanto: The Byzantine World & the Turks, 1071-1571 Papers Given at the Nineteenth Spring Symposium of Byzantine Studies, March 1985. 2008. 488p. pap. 52.00 *(978-1-59740-635-3(4))* ACLS Humanities E-Book.
—Peoples & Settlement in Anatolia & the Caucasus, 800-1900. 340p. 2009. 50.00 *(978-1-59740-315-3(6))* 2008. pap. 34.00 *(978-1-59740-634-5(1))* ACLS Humanities E-Book.
Bryer, Anthony & Ursinus, Michael. Manzikert to Lepanto: The Byzantine World & the Turks, 1071-1571 Papers Given at the Nineteenth Spring Symposium of Byzantine Studies, March 1985. 2009. 488p. 70.00 *(978-1-59740-316-0(4))* ACLS Humanities E-Book.
Cutler, Anthony. Image Making in Byzantium, Sasanian Persia & the Early Muslim World: Images & Cultural Relations. 2009. (Variorum Collected Studies). (Illus.). 322p. 170.00 *(978-0-7546-5949-5(6))* Ashgate Publishing Co.
Haldon, John. The Palgrave Atlas of Byzantine History. 2010. (ENG., Illus.). 200p. pap. 30.00 *(978-0-230-24364-4(9))* Palgrave Macmillan.
Haldon, John F. A Social History of Byzantium. Haldon, John F., ed. 2008. (ENG., Illus.). 328p. 116.95 *(978-1-4051-3240-4(X)*, Wiley-Blackwell) Wiley, John & Sons, Inc.
Kennedy, Hugh. The Byzantine & Early Islamic near East. 2006. (Variorum Collected Studies). (Illus.). 288p. 150.00 *(978-0-7546-5909-9(7))* Ashgate Publishing Co.
Kislinger, Ewald, et al, eds. Handelsguter und Verkehrswege: Aspekte der Warenversorgung im ostlichen Mittelmeeraum (4. bis 5. Jahrhundert). Akten des Internationalen Symposions Wien, 19. -22. Oktober 2005. 2010. (VERoFFENTLICHUNGEN ZUR BYZANZFORSCHUNG Ser.). (GER.). 304p. (C). pap. 147.00 *(978-3-7001-6680-1(X))* Austrian Academy of Sciences Press AUT. Dist: Brown, David Bk. Co., The.
Maniatis, George C. Guilds, Price Formation & Market Structures in Byzantium. 2009. (Variorum Collected Studies). (Illus.). 412p. 190.00 *(978-0-7546-5991-4(7))* Ashgate Publishing Co.
Mansel, Philip. Constantinople: City of the World's Desire, 1453-1924. 2006. (ENG., Illus.). 544p. pap. 23.95 *(978-0-7195-6880-0(3))* Murray, John GBR. Dist: Independent Pubs. Group.
Meyer, Mati. An Obscure Portrait: Imaging Women's Reality in Byzantine Art. 2009. (ENG., Illus.). 575p. (C). 300.00 *(978-1-904597-32-2(7))* Pindar Pr. GBR. Dist: Brown, David Bk. Co., The.
Morrisson, Cecile, ed. Trades & Markets in Byzantium. 2012. (Dumbarton Oaks Byzantine Symposia & Colloquia Ser.). (ENG., Illus.). 464p. 85.00 ***(978-0-88402-377-7(X))*** Dumbarton Oaks.
Morrisson, Cecile, et al. Byzantium & the Other: Relations & Exchanges. 2012. (Variorum Collected Studies). 330p. 144.95 ***(978-1-4094-3206-7(8))*** Ashgate Publishing Co.
Papaconstantinou, Arietta, et al, eds. Becoming Byzantine: Children & Childhood in Byzantium. 2009. (Dumbarton Oaks Byzantine Symposia & Colloquia Ser.). (Illus.). 336p. 55.00 *(978-0-88402-356-2(7))* Dumbarton Oaks.
Ferozzo, Serena. Do Corporate Headquarters Add Value? 2011. 116p. pap. ***(978-3-8443-9245-6(9))*** Lambert Academic Publishing.
Peters, Greg. Peter of Damascus: Byzantine Monk & Spiritual Theologian. 2011. (Studies & Texts). (ENG & GEC.). 226p. 75.00 ***(978-0-88844-175-1(4))*** Pontifical Institute of Mediaeval Studies, Dept. of Pubns. CAN. Dist: Univ. of Toronto Pr.
Runciman, Steven. The Last Byzantine Renaissance. 2008. (ENG.). 128p. pap. 31.99 *(978-0-521-09710-9(X))* Cambridge Univ. Pr.
Savvides, A. G. C., et al. Encyclopaedic Prosopographical Lexicon of Byzantine History & Civilization 1. A. 2007. (Encyclopaedic Prosopographical Lexicon of Byzantine History & Civilization Ser.). (ENG & GRE.). 476p. (C). 123.00 *(978-2-503-52303-3(X))* Brepols Pubs. BEL. Dist: ISD.
—Encyclopaedic Prosopographical Lexicon of Byzantine History & Civilization 2 B-E. 2009. (Encyclopaedic Prosopographical Lexicon of Byzantine History & Civilization Ser.). (ENG & GRE.). 458p. (C). 123.00 *(978-2-503-52377-4(3))* Brepols Pubs. BEL. Dist: ISD.
Shepard, Jonathan. Emergent Elites & Byzantium in the Balkans & East-Central Europe. 2011. (Variorum Collected Studies). (Illus.). 434p. 190.00 *(978-1-4094-0364-7(5))* Ashgate Publishing Co.
Skinner, Stephen & Collisson, Marcus. Byzantine Magic: Michael Psellus on the Operation of Daemons. 2010. (ENG.). 96p. 65.00 *(978-0-7387-2354-9(1))* Llewellyn Pubns.

BYZANTINE EMPIRE—CIVILIZATION
Angelov, Dimiter G. Church & Society in Late Byzantium. 2009. 20.00 *(978-1-58044-143-8(2))*; 40.00 *(978-1-58044-142-1(4))* Medieval Institute Pubns.
Billinis, Alex. The Eagle has Two Faces: Journeys through Byzantine Europe. 2011. 160p. pap. 20.36 ***(978-1-4567-7870-5(6))*** AuthorHouse.
Bourbou, Chryssi. Health & Disease in Byzantine Crete. 2010. (Medicine in the Medieval Mediterranean Ser.). (Illus.). 264p. 124.95 *(978-0-7546-6615-8(8))* Ashgate Publishing Co.
Brooks, Sarah T. Byzantium, Faith, & Power (1261-1557) Perspectives on Late Byzantine Art & Culture. 2007. (Metropolitan Museum of Art Symposia Ser.). (Illus.). xi, 201p. 75.00 *(978-1-58839-208-4(2))* Metropolitan Museum of Art, The.
Brubaker, Leslie. Eat, Drink, & Be Merry (Luke 12:19) Food & Wine Byzantium: Papers of the 37th Annual Spring Symposium of Byzantine Studies in Honour of Professor A. A. M. Bryer. Linardou, Kallirroe, ed. 2007. (Publications of the Society for the Promotion of Byzantine Studies). (Illus.). 308p. 134.95 *(978-0-7546-6119-1(9))* Ashgate Publishing Co.
Byron, Robert. The Byzantine Achievement: An Historical Perspective, C.E. 330-1453. 12th ed. 2010. (ENG.). 364p. pap. 12.00 *(978-1-60419-026-7(4))* Axios Pr.
Byron, Robert. The Byzantine Achievement (Routledge Revivals) An historical perspective, A. D. 330-1453. 2012. (Routledge Revivals Ser.). (ENG.). 294p. 140.00 ***(978-0-415-80917-7(7))*** Routledge.
Cartledge, Paul. Ancient Greece: A History in Eleven Cities. 2010. (ENG., Illus.). 266p. 19.95 *(978-0-19-923338-0(1))* Oxford Univ. Pr., Inc.
Dalby, Andrew. Tastes of Byzantium: The Cuisine of a Legendary Empire. 2010. (ENG., Illus.). 272p. pap. 25.00 *(978-1-84885-165-8(0))* I. B. Tauris & Co., Ltd. GBR. Dist: Macmillan.
Evans, Helen C., ed. Byzantium & Islam: Age of Transition. 2012. (ENG., Illus.). 352p. 65.00 ***(978-0-300-17950-7(2))*** Yale Univ. Pr.
Gjuzelev, Vassil & Petkov, Kiril, eds. State & Church: Studies in Medieval Bulgaria & Byzantium. 2011. (ENG., Illus.). 300p. (C). 39.95 ***(978-954-92571-2-0(6))*** American Research Ctr. in Sofia.
Hatzaki, Myrto. Beauty & the Male Body in Byzantium: Perceptions & Representations in Art & Text. 2009. (ENG., Illus.). 240p. 89.00 *(978-0-230-00715-4(5))* Palgrave Macmillan.
Hendrickx, B., et al, eds. Encyclopaedic Prosopographical Lexicon of Byzantine History & Civilization 3: Facundus of Hermiane - Juvenal of Jerusalem. 2011. (Encyclopaedic Prosopographical Lexicon of Byzantine History & Civilization Ser.). (ENG.). 500p. (C). 124.00 *(978-2-503-53243-1(8))* Brepols Pubs. BEL. Dist: Brown, David Bk. Co., The.
Herrin, Judith. Byzantium: The Surprising Life of a Medieval Empire. 2009. (ENG., Illus.). 440p. pap. 19.95 *(978-0-691-14369-9(2))* Princeton Univ. Pr.
Hinterberger, M. & Schabel, C., eds. Greeks, Latins, & Intellectual History 1204-1500. 2011. (Recherches de Theologie et Philosophie Medievales - Bibliotheca Ser.). (ENG.). 463p. (C). pap. 100.00 *(978-90-429-2440-6(3))* Peeters Pubs. & Booksellers BEL. Dist: Brown, David Bk. Co., The.
James, Liz, ed. Art & Text in Byzantine Culture. 2007. (ENG., Illus.). 256p. (C). 105.00 *(978-0-521-83409-4(0))* Cambridge Univ. Pr.
—A Companion to Byzantium. 2010. (Blackwell Companions to the Ancient World Ser.: 37). (ENG., Illus.). 488p. 209.95 *(978-1-4051-2654-0(X)*, Wiley-Blackwell) Wiley, John & Sons, Inc.
Kaldellis, Anthony. Hellenism in Byzantium: The Transformations of Greek Identity & the Reception of the Classical Tradition. 2011. (Greek Culture in the Roman World Ser.). (ENG.). 482p. pap. 60.00 *(978-0-521-29729-5(X))* Cambridge Univ. Pr.
Karampetsos, E. D. Dante & Byzantium. 2009. *(978-1-935244-02-8(7))* Somerset Hall Pr.
Lymberopoulou, Angeliki. Images of the Byzantine World: Visions Messages & Meanings. 2011. (Illus.). 272p. 124.95 *(978-1-4094-0776-8(4))* Ashgate Publishing Co.
Maas, Michael. Readings in Late Antiquity. 2nd rev. ed. 2010. (Routledge Sourcebooks for the Ancient World Ser.). (ENG., Illus.). 528p. (C). 47.95 *(978-0-415-47337-8(3))* Routledge.

B

—Readings in Late Antiquity: A Sourcebook. 2nd rev. ed. 2010. (Routledge Sourcebooks for the Ancient World Ser.). (ENG., Illus.). 528p. (C). 130.00 *(978-0-415-47336-1(5))* Routledge.

Moravcsik, Gyula, et al. Constantine Porphyrogenitus: De Administrando Imperio. Moravcsik, Gyula, ed. Jenkins, Romilly J. H., tr. from GEC. 2nd ed. 2009. (Dumbarton Oaks Texts: 1). (GEC & ENG.). 354p. pap. 19.95 *(978-0-88402-343-2(5))* Dumbarton Oaks.

Morgan, Giles. Byzantium: Capital of an Ancient Empire. 2009. (ENG.). 160p. 8.99 *(978-0-7858-2290-5(9)*, 0785822909, Chartwell) Book Sales, Inc.

Morrisson, Cecile, et al. Women Family & Society in Byzantium. 2011. (Variorum Collected Studies). 292p. 144.95 ***(978-1-4094-3204-3(1))*** Ashgate Publishing Co.

Necipo#287;lu, Nevra. Byzantium between the Ottomans & the Latins: Politics & Society in the Late Empire. 2012. (ENG.). 374p. pap. 40.00 ***(978-1-107-40388-8(X))*** Cambridge Univ. Pr.

Neville, Leonora. Authority in Byzantine Provincial Society, 950-1100. 2009. (ENG., Illus.). 224p. pap. 33.00 *(978-0-521-10117-2(4))* Cambridge Univ. Pr.

Nicol, Donald M. Church & Society in Byzantium. 2008. (ENG.). 176p. pap. 38.99 *(978-0-521-07167-3(4))* Cambridge Univ. Pr.

Potter, David. The Victor's Crown: How the Birth of the Olympics & the Rise of the Roman Games Changed Sport for Ever. 2011. (ENG.). 424p. pap. 24.95 *(978-0-19-984275-9(2))* Oxford Univ. Pr., Inc.

Prosopographie der mittelbyzantinischen Zeit. Prolegomena, Zweite Abteilung. 2009. (GER., Illus.). XXXI, 346p. 137.00 *(978-3-11-016671-2(2))* De Gruyter, Walter Inc.

Rodley, Lyn. Cave Monasteries of Byzantine Cappadocia. 2010. (ENG., Illus.). 286p. pap. 23.99 *(978-0-521-15477-2(4))* Cambridge Univ. Pr.

Stephenson, Paul, ed. The Byzantine World. (Routledge Worlds Ser.). (ENG., Illus.). 640p. 2012. pap. 52.95 ***(978-0-415-52742-2(2))*** 2010. 250.00 *(978-0-415-44010-3(6))* Routledge.

Talbot, A. Dumbarton Oaks Papers 63. 2011. (Dumbarton Oaks Papers: 63). (Illus.). 350p. 125.00 *(978-0-88402-357-9(5))* Dumbarton Oaks.

Talbot, A. M. Dumbarton Oaks Papers, Vol. 62. Talbot, Alice-Mary, ed. 2010. (Dumbarton Oaks Papers). (Illus.). 400p. 125.00 *(978-0-88402-355-5(9))* Dumbarton Oaks.

Talbot, Alice-Mary, ed. Dumbarton Oaks Papers,60. 2007. (Dumbarton Oaks Papers: Vol. 60). (Illus.). 256p. 125.00 *(978-0-88402-316-6(8))* Dumbarton Oaks.

Vryonis, Speros. The Decline of Medieval Hellenism in Asia Minor & the Process of Islamization from the Eleventh Through the Fifteenth Century. 2008. 568p. pap. 56.00 *(978-1-59740-476-1(4))* ACLS Humanities E-Book.

BYZANTINE EMPIRE—DESCRIPTION AND TRAVEL

Patlagean, Evelyne. Structure Sociale, Famille, Chretiente a Byzance, Ive-Xie Siecle. 2008. 352p. pap. 41.00 *(978-1-59740-637-6(6))* ACLS Humanities E-Book.

BYZANTINE EMPIRE—HISTORY

Adams, Noel & Entwistle, Chris, eds. Gems of Heaven: Recent Research on Engraved Gemstones in Late Antiquity. 2011. (BMP Research Publication). (ENG., Illus.). 274p. (C). pap. 80.00 *(978-0-86159-177-0(1))* British Museum Pr. GBR. Dist: Brown, David Bk. Co., The.

Alchermes, et al, eds. Anaohmata Eoptika. 2010. (ENG., Illus.). 346p. (C). 135.00 ***(978-3-8053-4101-1(6))*** Zabern, Philipp von Verlag, GmbH DEU. Dist: Brown, David Bk. Co., The.

Anastos, Milton Vasil. Studies in Byzantine Intellectual History. 2009. 432p. pap. 45.00 *(978-1-59740-759-5(3))* ACLS Humanities E-Book.

Angelov, Dimiter. Imperial Ideology & Political Thought in Byzantium, 1204-1330. (ENG., Illus.). 474p. 2011. pap. 55.00 *(978-0-521-29438-6(X))* 2007. 146.00 *(978-0-521-85703-1(1))* Cambridge Univ. Pr.

Angelov, Dimiter G. Church & Society in Late Byzantium. 2009. 20.00 *(978-1-58044-143-8(2))*; 40.00 *(978-1-58044-142-1(4))* Medieval Institute Pubns.

Ariantzi, Despoina. Kindheit in Byzanz: Emotionale, geistige und materielle Entwicklung im familiären Umfeld vom 6. bis zum 11. Jahrhundert. 2012. (Millennium-Studien / Millennium Studies).Tr. of Childhood in Byzantium. Emotional, Intellectual & Economic Development in Family Structures from the 6th to the 11th Century. (GER.). VIII, 384p. (gr. 17). 154.00 ***(978-3-11-026568-2(0))*** De Gruyter, Walter Inc.

Auge, I. Eglises en Dialogue: Armeniens et Byzantins dans la seconde moitie du XIIe Siecle. 2011. (Corpus Scriptorum Christianorum Orientalium Ser.). (FRE.). 317p. (C). pap. 109.00 *(978-90-429-2357-7(1))* Peeters Pubs. & Booksellers BEL. Dist: Brown, David Bk. Co., The.

Baker, Derek, ed. Relations Between East & West in the Middle Ages. 2009. (ENG.). 167p. pap. 29.95 *(978-0-202-36332-5(5))* Aldine Transaction.

Banaji, Jairus. Agrarian Change in Late Antiquity: Gold, Labour, & Aristocratic Dominance. 2nd rev. ed. 2007. (Oxford Classical Monographs). (ENG., Illus.). 336p. per. 65.00 *(978-0-19-922603-0(2))* Oxford Univ. Pr., Inc.

Barber, Charles E. Contesting the Logic of Painting: Art & Understanding in Eleventh-Century Byzantium. 2007. (Visualising the Middle Ages Ser.). (Illus.). 179p. *(978-90-04-16271-6(2))* BRILL.

Bartusis, Mark. Land & Privilege in Byzantium: The Institution of Pronoia. 2012. (ENG., Illus.). 728p. 170.00 ***(978-1-107-00962-2(6))*** Cambridge Univ. Pr.

Bell, Peter N., ed. Three Political Voices from the Age of Justinian: Agapetus - Advice to the Emperor; Dialogue on Political Science; Paul the Silentiary - Description of Hagia Sophia. 2010. (ENG., Illus.). 256p. pap. 40.00 *(978-1-84631-209-0(4))* Liverpool Univ. Pr. GBR. Dist: Chicago Distribution Ctr.

Benedikz, Benedict. Varangians of Byzantium. 2007. (ICE & ENG.). 260p. pap. 53.00 *(978-0-521-03552-1(X))* Cambridge Univ. Pr.

Bernabò, Massimo. Voci Dell'Oriente: Miniature e Testi Classici Da Bisanzio Alla Biblioteca Medicea Laurenziana. 2011. (ITA., Illus.). 288p. (C). pap. 55.00 ***(978-88-596-0904-9(6))*** Polistampa ITA. Dist: Brown, David Bk. Co., The.

Billinis, Alex. The Eagle has Two Faces: Journeys through Byzantine Europe. 2011. 160p. pap. 20.36 ***(978-1-4567-7870-5(6))*** AuthorHouse.

Blockley, R. C. Fragmentary Classicising Historians of the Later Roman Empire, Volume 1: Eunapius, Olympiodorus, Priscus & Malchus. 2009. (Arca Ser.). (ENG.). 196p. (C). pap. 70.00 *(978-0-905205-51-9(0))* Cairns, Francis Publications, Limited GBR. Dist: Brown, David Bk. Co., The.

—The History of Menander the Guardsman: Introductory Essay, Text, Translation & Historiographical Notes. 2006. (ARCA Classical & Medieval Texts, Papers & Monographs). (ENG., Illus.). 307p. (C). per. 120.00 *(978-0-905205-45-8(6))* Cairns, Francis Publications, Limited GBR. Dist: Brown, David Bk. Co., The.

Bobrick, Benson. The Caliph's Splendor: Islam & the West in the Golden Age of Baghdad. 2012. (ENG., Illus.). 288p. 28.00 ***(978-1-4165-6762-2(3))*** Simon & Schuster.

Brownworth, Lars. Lost to the West: The Forgotten Byzantine Empire That Rescued Western Civilization. 2010. (ENG.). 352p. pap. 15.00 *(978-0-307-40796-2(9)*, Three Rivers Pr.) Crown Publishing Group.

Byron, Robert. The Byzantine Achievement: An Historical Perspective, C.E. 330-1453. 12th ed. 2010. (ENG.). 364p. pap. 12.00 *(978-1-60419-026-7(4))* Axios Pr.

Byron, Robert. The Byzantine Achievement (Routledge Revivals) An historical perspective, A. D. 330-1453. 2012. (Routledge Revivals Ser.). (ENG.). 294p. 140.00 ***(978-0-415-80917-7(7))*** Routledge.

Cabasilas, Nicolaus & Congourdeau, Marie-Hélène. Correspondance de Nicolas Cabasilas. 2010. (FRE & GEC.). 264p. (C). pap. 53.00 ***(978-2-251-74209-0(3))*** Societe d'edition Les Belles lettres FRA. Dist: ISD.

Calligas, E., et al, eds. Scholars, Travels, Archives: Greek History & Culture through the British School at Athens. 2009. (BSA Studies). (ENG & GRE., Illus.). 254p. (C). 110.00 *(978-0-904887-60-0(X))* British Schl. at Athens GBR. Dist: Brown, David Bk. Co., The.

Cameron, Averil. The Byzantines. (Peoples of Europe Ser.: 13). (ENG., Illus.). 296p. 2009. pap. 28.95 *(978-1-4051-9833-2(8))* 2007. 42.95 *(978-0-631-20262-2(5))* Wiley, John & Sons, Inc. (Wiley-Blackwell).

Cheynet, Jean-Claude. The Byzantine Aristocracy & Its Military Functon. 2006. (Variorum Collected Studies). (ENG & FRE.). 380p. 160.00 *(978-0-7546-5902-0(X))* Ashgate Publishing Co.

Colovas, Anthone C. A Quick History of Modern Greece. 2007. 191p. pap. 24.95 *(978-1-60441-079-2(5))* PublishAmerica, Inc.

Dagron, Gilbert. Emperor & Priest: The Imperial Office in Byzantium. Birrell, Jean, tr. from FRE. 2007. (Past & Present Publications). (ENG.). 356p. pap. 45.00 *(978-0-521-03697-9(6))* Cambridge Univ. Pr.

Dal Santo, Matthew, ed. Debating the Saints' Cults in the Age of Gregory the Great. 2012. (Oxford Studies in Byzantium Ser.). (ENG., Illus.). 395p. 150.00 ***(978-0-19-964679-1(1))*** Oxford Univ. Pr., Inc.

Dalby, Andrew. Tastes of Byzantium: The Cuisine of a Legendary Empire. 2010. (ENG., Illus.). 272p. pap. 25.00 *(978-1-84885-165-8(0))* I. B. Tauris & Co., Ltd. GBR. Dist: Macmillan.

Dawson, Timothy. Byzantine Cavalryman C. 900-1204. 2009. (Warrior Ser.). (ENG., Illus.). 64p. pap. 18.95 *(978-1-84603-404-6(3))* Osprey Publishing, Ltd. GBR. Dist: Random Hse., Inc.

—Byzantine Infantryman: Eastern Roman Empire C. 900-1204. 2007. (Warrior Ser.). (ENG., Illus.). 64p. pap. 18.95 *(978-1-84603-105-2(2))* Osprey Publishing, Ltd. GBR. Dist: Random Hse., Inc.

Dennis, George T. Three Byzantine Military Treatises. 2009. (Dumbarton Oaks Texts: 9). (Illus.). 396p. pap. 19.95 *(978-0-88402-339-5(7))* Dumbarton Oaks.

Diehl, Charles. History of the Byzantine Empire. reprint ed. 32.50 *(978-0-404-02129-0(8))* AMS Pr., Inc.

Digeser, Elizabeth Depalma, et al. The Rhetoric of Power in Late Antiquity: Religion & Politics in Byzantium, Europe & the Early Islamic World. 2011. (Library of Classical Studies). (ENG., Illus.). 320p. 99.00 *(978-1-84885-409-3(9)*, Tauris Academic Studies) I. B. Tauris & Co., Ltd. GBR. Dist: Macmillan.

Drake, H. A. Violence in Late Antiquity: Perceptions & Practices. 2006. (Illus.). 418p. 160.00 *(978-0-7546-5498-8(2))* Ashgate Publishing Co.

Errington, R. Malcolm. Roman Imperial Policy from Julian to Theodosius. 2006. (Studies in the History of Greece & Rome). (ENG.). 352p. 49.95 *(978-0-8078-3038-3(0))* Univ. of North Carolina Pr.

Evans, Helen C., ed. Byzantium & Islam: Age of Transition. 2012. (ENG., Illus.). 352p. 65.00 ***(978-0-300-17950-7(2))*** Yale Univ. Pr.

Evans, James. The Power Game in Byzantium: Antonina & the Empress Theodora. 2011. (ENG., Illus.). 288p. 29.95 *(978-1-4411-4078-4(6))* Continuum International Publishing Group, Ltd. GBR. Dist: National Bk. Network.

Faulkner, Neil. Rome: Empire of the Eagles, 753 BC - AD 476. 2008. (ENG., Illus.). 400p. 59.95 *(978-0-582-78495-6(6))* Longman Publishing Group.

Frankopan, Peter. The First Crusade: The Call from the East. 2012. (ENG., Illus.). 268p. 29.95 ***(978-0-674-05994-8(8)***, Belknap Pr.) Harvard Univ. Pr.

Garland, Lynda, ed. Byzantine Women: Varieties of Experience Ad 800-1200. 2006. (Publications of the Centre for Hellenic Studies, King's College London Ser.). (Illus.). 246p. 124.95 *(978-0-7546-5737-8(X))* Ashgate Publishing Co.

Geanakoplos, Deno John. Emperor Michael Palaeologus & the West, 1258-1282: A Study in Byzantine-Latin Relations. 2011. 452p. 57.95 ***(978-1-258-02391-1(1))*** Literary Licensing, LLC.

Gibbon, Edward. The Decline & Fall of the Roman Empire. 2009. 428p. 34.99 *(978-1-113-67895-9(X))*; 41.99 *(978-1-113-67896-6(8))*; pap. 34.75 *(978-1-113-67891-1(7))*; pap. 35.75 *(978-1-113-67893-5(3))* BiblioBazaar.

—The Decline & Fall of the Roman Empire. 2009. 568p. pap. *(978-0-217-11514-8(4))*; 462p. pap. *(978-0-217-89460-9(7))*; 520p. pap. *(978-1-4589-1420-0(8))* Books LLC.

—The Decline & Fall of the Roman Empire. 2009. 472p. pap. 32.56 *(978-1-4589-1417-0(8))* General Bks. LLC.

—The History of the Decline & Fall of the Roman Empire. 2009. 656p. pap. 45.75 *(978-1-115-56388-8(2))* 2009. 656p. pap. 46.75 *(978-1-115-56387-1(4))* 2009. 658p. pap. 34.99 *(978-1-115-69097-3(3))* 2009. 658p. pap. 26.99 *(978-1-115-69098-0(1))* 2008. 572p. 33.99 *(978-0-559-54490-3(1))* 2008. 572p. pap. 42.75 *(978-0-559-54487-3(1))* 2008. 448p. 30.99 *(978-0-554-43596-1(9))* 2008. 448p. 32.99 *(978-0-554-43592-3(6))* 2008. 448p. pap. 36.75 *(978-0-554-43593-0(4))* 2008. 448p. pap. 35.75 *(978-0-554-43595-4(0))* BiblioBazaar.

—The History of the Decline & Fall of the Roman Empire. 2009. 508p. pap. *(978-1-4589-2228-1(6))*; 480p. pap. *(978-1-4589-2233-5(2))*; 276p. pap. *(978-1-4588-8038-3(9))*; 296p. pap. *(978-0-217-59018-1(7))*; 592p. pap. *(978-0-217-59015-0(2))*; 398p. pap. *(978-0-217-59020-4(9))*; 708p. pap. *(978-0-217-59024-2(1))*; 538p. pap. *(978-0-217-80026-6(2))*; 434p. pap. *(978-0-217-80052-5(1))*; 218p. pap. *(978-0-217-80061-7(0))*; 548p. pap. *(978-0-217-80018-1(1))*; 564p. pap. *(978-0-217-80023-5(8))*; 564p. pap. *(978-0-217-80031-0(9))*; 510p. pap. *(978-0-217-80036-5(X))*; 542p. pap. *(978-0-217-80041-9(6))*; 226p. pap. *(978-0-217-80045-7(9))*; 632p. pap. *(978-0-217-80057-0(2))*; 450p. pap. *(978-0-217-38967-9(8))*; 244p. pap. *(978-0-217-11556-8(X))*; 304p. pap. *(978-0-217-11559-9(4))*; 704p. pap. *(978-0-217-11563-6(2))*; 424p. pap. *(978-0-217-11567-4(5))*; 284p. pap. *(978-0-217-11572-8(1))*; 444p. pap. *(978-0-217-08462-8(1))*; 592p. pap. *(978-0-217-08466-6(4))*; 712p. pap. *(978-0-217-08470-3(2))*; 562p. pap. *(978-0-217-08474-1(5))*; 528p. pap. *(978-1-4589-2215-1(4))*; 244p. pap. *(978-1-4589-2217-5(0))*; 390p. pap. *(978-1-4589-2221-2(9))*; 444p. pap. *(978-1-4589-2224-3(3))*; 530p. pap. *(978-0-217-38964-8(3))*; 536p. pap. *(978-0-217-38965-5(1))*; 318p. pap. *(978-0-217-38966-2(X))*; 546p. pap. *(978-0-217-38970-9(8))*; 552p. pap. *(978-0-217-38971-6(6))*; 448p. pap. *(978-0-217-38969-3(4))*; 338p. pap. *(978-0-217-38972-3(4))*; 594p. pap. *(978-0-217-38973-0(2))*; 590p. pap. *(978-0-217-34963-5(3))*; 346p. pap. *(978-0-217-34964-2(1))*; 290p. pap. *(978-0-217-34966-6(8))*; 344p. pap. *(978-0-217-34967-3(6))*; (Illus.). 692p. pap. *(978-0-217-34965-9(X))* Books LLC.

—The History of the Decline & Fall of the Roman Empire. 2009. 580p. pap. 35.07 *(978-1-4589-2230-4(8))*; 284p. pap. 20.77 *(978-1-4589-2235-9(9))*; 438p. pap. 13.87 *(978-1-4588-8032-1(X))*; 542p. pap. 16.39 *(978-1-4588-8035-2(4))*; 194p. pap. 10.21 *(978-1-4589-2226-7(X))* General Bks. LLC.

—History of the Decline & Fall of the Roman Empire. 2009. 704p. 39.99 *(978-0-559-07034-1(9))*; 704p. 35.99 *(978-0-559-07047-1(0))*; 364p. 31.99 *(978-0-559-06741-9(0))*; 364p. 29.99 *(978-0-559-06757-0(7))*; 696p. 39.99 *(978-0-559-06768-6(2))*; 696p. 35.99 *(978-0-559-06782-2(8))*; 584p. 36.99 *(978-0-559-06922-2(7))*; 584p. 33.99 *(978-0-559-06935-2(9))*; 184p. 25.99 *(978-0-559-06944-4(8))*; 184p. 22.99 *(978-0-559-06958-1(8))*; 464p. 33.99 *(978-0-559-06967-3(7))*; 464p. 31.99 *(978-0-559-06983-3(9))*; 732p. 40.99 *(978-0-559-07016-7(0))*; 732p. 36.99 *(978-0-559-07030-3(6))*; 704p. pap. 47.75 *(978-0-559-07043-3(8))*; 364p. pap. 32.75 *(978-0-559-06745-7(3))*; 364p. pap. 31.75 *(978-0-559-06752-5(6))*; 696p. pap. 48.75 *(978-0-559-06773-0(9))*; 696p. pap. 47.75 *(978-0-559-06778-5(X))*; 584p. pap. 43.75 *(978-0-559-06926-0(X))*; 584p. pap. 42.75 *(978-0-559-06932-1(4))*; 704p. pap. 48.75 *(978-0-559-07036-5(5))*; 184p. pap. 22.75 *(978-0-559-06948-2(0))*; 184p. pap. 21.75 *(978-0-559-06955-0(3))*; 464p. pap. 36.75 *(978-0-559-06972-7(3))*; 464p. pap. 35.75 *(978-0-559-06980-2(4))*; 732p. pap. 50.75 *(978-0-559-07021-1(7))*; 732p. pap. 49.75 *(978-0-559-07028-0(4))* BiblioBazaar.

—History of the Decline & Fall of the Roman Empire. 2009. 582p. pap. *(978-0-217-93101-4(4))*; 632p. pap. *(978-0-217-48657-6(6))*; 528p. pap. *(978-0-217-48653-8(3))*; 570p. pap. *(978-0-217-93108-3(1))* Books LLC.

—The History of the Decline & Fall of the Roman Empire, 7 vols., Set. Bury, John B., ed. (Illus.). reprint ed. 495.00 *(978-0-404-02820-6(9))* AMS Pr., Inc.

Gibbon, William Smith. The History of the Decline & Fall of the Roman Empire. 2008. 445p. 30.99 *(978-0-559-03964-5(6))*; 32.99 *(978-0-559-03957-7(3))*; pap. 36.75 *(978-0-559-03958-4(1))*; pap. 35.75 *(978-0-559-03961-4(1))* BiblioBazaar.

Glad, Damien. Origine et Diffusion de L'équipement Défensif Corporel en Méditerranée Orientale (IVe-VIIIe S.) Contribution à L'étude Historique et Archéologique des Armées Antiques et Médiévales. 2009. (Bar S Ser.). (FRE & ENG., Illus.). 164p. (C). pap. 97.50 *(978-1-4073-0246-1(9))* British Archaeological Reports Ltd. GBR. Dist: Brown, David Bk. Co., The.

Graff. The Eurasian Way of War. 2011. (Asian States & Empires Ser.). (ENG.). 208p. (C). 150.00 *(978-0-415-46034-7(4))* Routledge.

Greatrex, Geoffrey. Rome & Persia at War, 502-532. 2006. (ARCA Classical & Medieval Texts, Papers & Monographs). (Illus.). 301p. per. 120.00 *(978-0-905205-48-9(0))* Cairns, Francis Publications, Limited GBR. Dist: Brown, David Bk. Co., The.

Green, Tom. From Rome to Byzantium: Trade & Continuity in the First Millennium AD. 2009. 68p. pap. 14.95 *(978-1-4452-1959-2(X))* Lulu Enterprises Inc.

Gregory, Timothy E. A History of Byzantium. 2nd ed. 2010. (Blackwell History of the Ancient World Ser.: 19). (ENG., Illus.). 480p. pap. 49.95 *(978-1-4051-8471-7(X)*, Wiley-Blackwell) Wiley, John & Sons, Inc.

Grünbart, Michael. Material Culture & Well-Being in Byzantium (400-1453) Proceedings of the International Conference (Cambridge, 8-10 September 2001) 2007. (Veroeffentlichungen zur Byzanzforschung Ser.). (ENG., Illus.). 288p. (C). 117.00 *(978-3-7001-3602-6(1))* Austrian Academy of Sciences Press AUT. Dist: Brown, David Bk. Co., The.

Gwynn, David M., ed. A.H.M. Jones & the Later Roman Empire. 2008. (Brill's Ser. on the Early Middle Ages Ser.). 281p. *(978-90-04-16383-6(2))* BRILL.

Haarer, F K. Anastasius I: Politics & Empire in the Late Roman World. 2006. (ARCA Classical & Medieval Texts, Papers & Monographs). (Illus.). 351p. 130.00 *(978-0-905205-43-4(X))* Cairns, Francis Publications, Limited GBR. Dist: Brown, David Bk. Co., The.

Haldon, John F. The Byzantine Wars. (Illus.). 208p. 35.00 *(978-0-7524-1795-0(9))* History Pr. Ltd.,The GBR. Dist: Trafalgar Square Publishing.

—The Byzantine Wars. 2008. (ENG., Illus.). 240p. pap. 28.95 *(978-0-7524-4565-6(0))* History Pr. Ltd.,The GBR. Dist: Independent Pubs. Group.

—Byzantium in the Iconoclast Era (680-850) A History. 2008. (ENG., Illus.). 976p. 165.00 *(978-0-521-43093-7(3))* Cambridge Univ. Pr.

Haldon, John F., ed. Byzantine Warfare. 2007. (International Library of Essays on Military History). (Illus.). 610p. 350.00 *(978-0-7546-2484-4(6))* Ashgate Publishing Co.

Haldon, John F. & Cormack, Robin. The Oxford Handbook of Byzantine Studies. Jeffreys, Elizabeth, ed. 2009. (Oxford Handbooks Ser.). (ENG., Illus.). 720p. 158.00 *(978-0-19-925246-6(7))* Oxford Univ. Pr., Inc.

Harlow, Mary & Loven, Lena Larsson, eds. Families in the Roman & Late Antique World. 2012. (ENG., Illus.). 288p. 120.00 *(978-1-4411-7468-0(0))* Continuum International Publishing Group, Ltd. GBR. Dist: National Bk. Network.

Harris, Jonathan. Byzantium & the Crusades. 2006. (Crusader Worlds Ser.). (ENG., Illus.). 256p. per. 32.95 *(978-1-85285-501-7(0)*, Hambledon Continuum) Continuum International Publishing Group, Ltd. GBR. Dist: National Bk. Network.

—The End of Byzantium. 2011. (Illus.). 336p. 40.00 ***(978-0-300-11786-8(8))*** Yale Univ. Pr.

Hendrickx, B., et al, eds. Encyclopaedic Prosopographical Lexicon of Byzantine History & Civilization 3: Facundus of Hermiane - Juvenal of Jerusalem. 2011. (Encyclopaedic Prosopographical Lexicon of Byzantine History & Civilization Ser.). (ENG.). 500p. (C). 124.00 *(978-2-503-53243-1(8))* Brepols Pubs. BEL. Dist: Brown, David Bk. Co., The.

Hennessy, Cecily. Images of Children in Byzantium. 2008. (Illus.). 296p. 124.95 *(978-0-7546-5631-9(4))* Ashgate Publishing Co.

Henning, Joachim, ed. Post-Roman Towns, Trade & Settlement in Europe & Byzantium 1: The Heirs of the Roman West. 2007. (Millennium - Studien / Millennium Studies 5/1+2 Ser.: Vol. 5). (ENG., Illus.). XXIII, 568p. 154.00 *(978-3-11-018356-6(0))* De Gruyter, Walter Inc.

Herrin, Judith. Byzantium: The Surprising Life of a Medieval Empire. (Illus.). 2009. (ENG.). 440p. pap. 19.95 *(978-0-691-14369-9(2))* 2008. 391p. 29.95 *(978-0-691-13151-1(1))* Princeton Univ. Pr.

Herrin, Judith & Saint-Guillain, Guillaume. Identities & Allegiances in the Eastern Mediterranean After 1204. 2011. (Illus.). 366p. 124.95 *(978-1-4094-1098-0(6))* Ashgate Publishing Co.

Heslop, Michael, et al. Byzantium & Venice 1204-1453. 2011. (Variorum Collected Studies). (Illus.). 314p. 154.95 *(978-1-4094-2370-6(0))* Ashgate Publishing Co.

Holo, Joshua. Byzantine Jewry in the Mediterranean Economy. 2009. (ENG., Illus.). 298p. 99.00 *(978-0-521-85633-1(7))* Cambridge Univ. Pr.

Howard-Johnston, James. East Rome, Sasanian Persia & the End of Antiquity: Historiographical & Historical Studies. 2006. (Variorum Collected Studies). (Illus.). 336p. 154.95 *(978-0-86078-992-5(6))* Ashgate Publishing Co.

Hughes, Ian. Belisarius: The Last Roman General. 2009. (ENG.). 304p. 26.00 *(978-1-59416-085-1(6))* Westholme Publishing.

Hussey, J. M. The Orthodox Church in the Byzantine Empire. 2010. (ENG., Illus.). 456p. 65.00 *(978-0-19-958276-1(9))* Oxford Univ. Pr., Inc.

Hutton, William Holden. The Church of the Sixth Century: Six Chapters In Ecclesiastical History. 2006. (ENG.). 344p. per. 31.95 *(978-1-4286-4141-9(6))* Kessinger Publishing, LLC.

James, Liz, ed. A Companion to Byzantium. 2010. (Blackwell Companions to the Ancient World Ser.: 37). (ENG., Illus.). 488p. 209.95 *(978-1-4051-2654-0(X)*, Wiley-Blackwell) Wiley, John & Sons, Inc.

Jeffreys, Elizabeth. Proceedings of Hte 21st International Congress of Byzantine Studies London 21-26 August 2006 Vol. 3: Vol 1:Plenary Papers Vol 2: Abstracts of Panel Papers Vol 3:Abstracts of Communications, 3 vols. 2006. (ENG, FRE, ITA & GER., Illus.). 1156p. 400.00 *(978-0-7546-5740-8(X))* Ashgate Publishing Co.

Jeffreys, Elizabeth M., ed. Byzantine Style, Religion & Civilization: In Honour of Sir Steven Runciman. 2006. (ENG., Illus.). 492p. 182.99 *(978-0-521-83445-2(7))* Cambridge Univ. Pr.

Jenkins, R. J. H., ed. Commentary on de Administrando Imperio. 2012. (Dumbarton Oaks Texts: 1A). (ENG., Illus.). 240p. pap. 22.95 ***(978-0-88402-379-1(6))*** Dumbarton Oaks.

John. Chronicle of John, Bishop of Nikiu: Translated from Zotenberg's Ethiopic Text. 2007. *(978-1-889758-87-9(6)*, Evolution Publishing & Manufacturing) Arx Publishing.

Kaegi, Walter E. Heraclius, Emperor of Byzantium. 2007. (ENG., Illus.). 372p. pap. 45.00 *(978-0-521-03698-6(4))* Cambridge Univ. Pr.

—Muslim Expansion & Byzantine Collapse in North Africa. 2010. (ENG., Illus.). 366p. 104.00 *(978-0-521-19677-2(9))* Cambridge Univ. Pr.

Kaegi, Walter Emil. Byzantine Military Unrest, 471-843: An Interpretation. 388p. 2009. 55.00 *(978-1-59740-285-9(0))* 2008. pap. 39.00 *(978-1-59740-632-1(5))* ACLS Humanities E-Book.

—Byzantium & the Decline of Rome. 308p. 2009. 47.00 *(978-1-59740-312-2(1))* 2008. pap. 31.00 *(978-1-59740-633-8(3))* ACLS Humanities E-Book.

Kaldellis, Anthony. Hellenism in Byzantium: The Transformations of Greek Identity & the Reception of the Classical Tradition. (Greek Culture in the Roman World Ser.). (ENG.). 2011. 482p. pap. 60.00 *(978-0-521-29729-5(X))* 2008. 480p. 125.00 *(978-0-521-87688-9(5))* Cambridge Univ. Pr.

Kalligas, H. Monemvasia:Byzantine City Stat. 2006. (Illus.). CCXLp. 123.00 *(978-0-415-24880-8(9))* Routledge.

Komnene, Anna. The Alexiad. Frankopan, Peter, ed. Sewter, E. R. A., tr. from GEC. rev. ed. 2009. (ENG., Illus.). 608p. (gr. 12-18). pap. 18.00 *(978-0-14-045527-4(2)*, Penguin Classics) Penguin Group (USA) Inc.

Kotzabassi, Sofia & Mavromatis, Giannis, eds. Realia Byzantina. 2009. (Byzantinisches Archiv Ser.). (GER & ENG., XIV, 325p. Illus.). 181.00 *(978-3-11-022230-2(2))*; 280.00 ***(978-3-11-174202-1(4))*** De Gruyter, Walter Inc.

Krallis, Dimitris. Michael Attaleiates & the Politics of Imperial Decline in Eleventh-Century Byzantium. 2012. ***(978-0-86698-470-6(4))*** ACMRS.

Kyriakidis, Savvas. Warfare in Late Byzantium, 1204-1453. 2011. (Illus.). 272p. *(978-90-04-20666-3(3))* BRILL.

Laiou, Angeliki E. & Morrisson, Cecile. The Byzantine Economy. 2007. (Cambridge Medieval Textbooks Ser.). (ENG., Illus.). 288p. 90.00 *(978-0-521-84978-4(0))* Cambridge Univ. Pr.

Laiou, Angeliki E. & Morrisson, Cécile. The Byzantine Economy. 2007. (Cambridge Medieval Textbooks Ser.). (Illus.). 288p. (C). per. 38.99 *(978-0-521-61502-0(X))* Cambridge Univ. Pr.

Laiou-Thomadakis, A. E. The Economic History of Byzantium, 3 vols., Set. Laiou, Angeliki E., ed. 2008. (Dumbarton Oaks Studies: 39). (Illus.). 1364p. pap. 125.00 *(978-0-88402-332-6(X))* Dumbarton Oaks.

Lake, S. The Church & the sick in Latin West (4th-8th Centuries). 2011. (Beiträge zur Altertumskunde Ser.). (ENG.). 400p. 117.00 *(978-3-11-019507-1(0))* De Gruyter, Walter Inc.

Lane, Eugene L. & Banchich, Thomas. The History of Zonaras: From Alexander Severus to the Death of Theodosius the Great. 2009. (ENG.). 336p. 120.00 *(978-0-415-29909-1(8))* Routledge.

Lawler, Jennifer. Encyclopedia of the Byzantine Empire. alt. ed. 2011. (ENG., Illus.). 376p. pap. 25.00 *(978-0-7864-6616-0(2))* McFarland & Co., Inc. Pubs.

Leo VI & Dennis, George T. The Taktika of Leo VI. 2010. (Dumbarton Oaks Texts: 12). (GEC & ENG., Illus.). 712p. 60.00 *(978-0-88402-359-3(1))* Dumbarton Oaks.

Luttwak, Edward N. The Grand Strategy of the Byzantine Empire. (Illus.). 512p. 2011. (ENG.). pap. 22.95 *(978-0-674-06207-8(8))* 2009. 35.00 *(978-0-674-03519-5(4))* Harvard Univ. Pr. (Belknap Pr.).

Macrides, Ruth. History as Literature in Byzantium: Papers from the Fortieth Spring Symposium of Byzantine Studies University of Birmingham March 2007. 2010. (Publications of the Society for the Promotion of Byzantine Studies). (Illus.). 350p. 124.95 *(978-1-4094-1206-9(7))* Ashgate Publishing Co.

Maguire, Henry. Byzantine Magic. Maguire, Henry, ed. 2009. (Dumbarton Oaks Other Titles in Byzantine Studies). (Illus.). 224p. pap. 19.95 *(978-0-88402-340-1(0))* Dumbarton Oaks.

Mango, Marlia Mundell, ed. Byzantine Trade, 4th-12th Centuries: The Archaeology of Local, Regional & International Exchange. Papers of the 38th Annual Spring Symposium of Byzantine Studies. 2009. (Publications of the Society for the Promotion of Byzantine Studies). (Illus.). 510p. 144.95 *(978-0-7546-6310-2(8))* Ashgate Publishing Co.

Millar, Fergus. A Greek Roman Empire: Power & Belief under Theodosius II (408-450) 2007. (Sather Classical Lectures). (Illus.). 279p. per. 28.95 *(978-0-520-25391-9(4))* Univ. of California Pr.

Miller, William. The Latins in the Levant: A History of Frankish Greece (1204-1566) 2009. 95.00 *(978-1-57898-779-5(2))* Martino Publishing.

Mitchell, Stephen. A History of the Later Roman Empire, AD 284-641: The Transformation of the Ancient World. 2006. (Blackwell History of the Ancient World Ser.). (ENG., Illus.). 488p. pap. 48.95 *(978-1-4051-0856-0(8)*, Wiley-Blackwell) Wiley, John & Sons, Inc.

Mitchell, Stephen & Mitchell, Stephen. A History of the Later Roman Empire, AD 284-641: The Transformation of the Ancient World. 2006. (Blackwell History of the Ancient World Ser.). (ENG., Illus.). 488p. 136.95 *(978-1-4051-0857-7(6)*, Wiley-Blackwell) Wiley, John & Sons, Inc.

Monferrer-Sala, Juan Pedro, et al, eds. East & West. 2009. 130.00 *(978-1-60724-056-3(4))* Gorgias Pr., LLC.

Morgan, Giles. Byzantium: Capital of an Ancient Empire. 2009. (ENG.). 160p. 8.99 *(978-0-7858-2290-5(9)*, 0785822909, Chartwell) Book Sales, Inc.

Muthesius, Anna. Studies in Byzantine, Islamic & near Eastern Silk Weaving. 2008. (ENG., Illus.). 446p. (C). 300.00 *(978-1-899828-41-8(9))* Pindar Pr. GBR. Dist: Brown, David Bk. Co., The.

Nicol, Donald M. Church & Society in Byzantium. 2008. (ENG.). 176p. pap. 38.99 *(978-0-521-07157-3(4))* Cambridge Univ. Pr.

—The Despotate of Epiros 1267-1479: A Contribution to the History of Greece in the Middle Ages. 2010. (ENG.). 312p. pap. 33.99 *(978-0-521-13089-9(1))* Cambridge Univ. Pr.

Nicolle, David. Cross & Crescent in the Balkans: The Ottoman Conquest of Southeastern Europe (14th - 15th Centuries) 2011. (Illus.). 272p. 39.95 *(978-1-84415-954-3(X))* Pen & Sword Bks. Ltd. GBR. Dist: Casemate Pubs. & Bk. Distributors, LLC.

Obolensky, Dimitri. The Byzantine Commonwealth: Eastern Europe, 500-1453. 2009. 526p. 69.00 *(978-1-59740-735-9(6))* ACLS Humanities E-Book.

O'Donnell, James J. The Ruin of the Roman Empire: A New History. 2009. (ENG.). 448p. pap. 15.99 *(978-0-06-078741-7(4)*, Ecco) HarperCollins Pubs.

Oman, Charles William Chadwick. The Byzantine Empire. 2009. (ENG.). 376p. pap. 15.95 *(978-1-59416-079-0(1))* Westholme Publishing.

Page, Gill. Being Byzantine: Greek Identity Before the Ottomans, 1200-1420. 2008. (ENG., Illus.). 344p. 104.00 *(978-0-521-87181-5(6))* Cambridge Univ. Pr.

Patlagean, Evelyne. Structure Sociale, Famille, Chretiente a Byzance, Ive-Xie Siecle. 2009. 352p. 35.00 *(978-1-59740-778-6(X))* ACLS Humanities E-Book.

Payne Smith, Robert, intro. The Third Part of the Ecclesiastical History of John, Bishop of Ephesus. 2010. 142.64 *(978-1-60724-961-0(8))* Gorgias Pr., LLC.

Pelikan, Jaroslav. Imago Dei: The Byzantine Apologia for Icons. 2011. (Bollingen Series (General) Ser.). (ENG., Illus.). 224p. pap. 35.00 *(978-0-691-14125-1(8))* Princeton Univ. Pr.

Pott, Thomas. Byzantine Liturgical Reform: A Study of Liturgical Change in the Byzantine Tradition. 2010. *(978-0-88141-343-4(7))* St. Vladimir's Seminary Pr.

Procopius. History of the Wars: Books 5-6 (Gothic War) 2007. 464p. per. 18.95 *(978-1-60206-496-6(2))* Cosimo, Inc.

—History of the Wars: The Persian War, Bks. 1-2. l.t. ed. 2007. 264p. pap. 23.99 *(978-1-4346-0624-2(4))* BiblioBazaar.

—History of the Wars: The Vandalic War. 2007. (ENG.). 192p. pap. 19.99 *(978-1-4346-0550-4(7))*;Bks. 3-4. 216p. pap. 22.99 *(978-1-4346-0625-9(2))* BiblioBazaar.

—History of the Wars, Books I & II. 2007. (ENG.). 168p. per. *(978-1-4068-6112-9(X))* Echo Library.

—History of the Wars, Books I & II: The Persian War. 2007. (ENG.). 234p. pap. 20.99 *(978-1-4346-0549-8(3))* BiblioBazaar.

—History of the Wars, Books III & Iv. 2007. (ENG.). 144p. per. *(978-1-4068-6113-6(8))* Echo Library.

—Procopius: History of the Wars Books V & VI. 2007. (ENG.). 186p. pap. 19.99 *(978-1-4346-0130-8(7))*; 200p. pap. 21.99 *(978-1-4346-0132-2(3))* BiblioBazaar.

—The Secret History. 2007. 152p. per. 12.95 *(978-1-60206-538-3(1))* Cosimo, Inc.

—The Secret History. Williamson, G. A. & Sarris, Peter, trs. from GEC. rev. ed. 2007. (ENG., Illus.). 205p. (gr. 12-18). 15.00 *(978-0-14-045528-1(0)*, Penguin Classics) Penguin Group (USA) Inc.

Procopius & Dewing, H. B. History of the Wars: Books 3-4 (Vandalic War) 2007. 500p. per. 18.95 *(978-1-60206-446-1(6))* Cosimo, Inc.

Prokopios. The Secret History: With Related Texts. Kaldellis, Anthony, ed. 2010. (Illus.). (C). 248p. 39.95 *(978-1-60384-181-8(4))*; 276p. pap. 13.95 *(978-1-60384-180-1(6))* Hackett Publishing Co., Inc.

Ramsay, W. M. & Bell, Gertrude L. The Thousand & One Churches. (Illus.). xvi, 580p. reprint ed. lib. bdg. 100.00 *(978-0-89241-121-4(X))* Caratzas, Aristide D. Pub.

Reece, Richard. Later Roman Empire: An Archaeology AD 150-600. 2007. (ENG., Illus.). 208p. pap. 34.95 *(978-0-7524-4205-1(8))* History Pr. Ltd.,The GBR. Dist: Independent Pubs. Group.

Rosen, William. Justinian's Flea: The First Great Plague & the End of the Roman Empire. 2008. (ENG.). 384p. (gr. 12-18). 16.00 *(978-0-14-311381-2(X)*, Penguin (Non-Classics)) Penguin Group (USA) Inc.

Rosser, John H. Historical Dictionary of Byzantium. 2nd ed. 2012. E-Book ***(978-0-8108-7477-0(6))*** 2011. (ENG., Illus.). 642p. 110.00 ***(978-0-8108-7567-8(5))*** Scarecrow Pr., Inc.

Rotman, Youval. Byzantine Slavery & the Mediterranean World. Todd, Jane Marie, tr. from FRE. 2009. (Illus.). 328p. 37.00 *(978-0-674-03611-6(5))* Harvard Univ. Pr.

Rüpke, Jörg. Religion & Law in Classical & Christian Rome. Ando, Clifford, ed. 2006. (Potsdamer Altertumswissenschaftliche Beiträge Ser.: Vol. 15). (ENG.). 176p. (C). 64.00 *(978-3-515-08854-1(7))* Steiner, Franz Verlag Wiesbaden GmbH DEU. Dist: Brown, David Bk. Co., The.

Sarris, Peter. Economy & Society in the Age of Justinian. 2009. (ENG., Illus.). 272p. pap. 41.00 *(978-0-521-11774-6(7))* Cambridge Univ. Pr.

Sarris, Peter. Empires of Faith: The Fall of Rome to the Rise of Islam, 500-700. 2011. (ENG., Illus.). 512p. 65.00 ***(978-0-19-926126-0(1))*** Oxford Univ. Pr., Inc.

Sathas, Constantine. The History of Psellus. 2011. 396p. pap. 32.45 ***(978-1-4460-7759-7(4)***, Kent Pr.) Kent Communications, Ltd.

Sawides, Alexios G. C. & Sawides, A. G. C. Byzantino-Normannica: The Norman Capture of Italy (to A. D. 1081) & the First Two Norman Invasions in Byzantium (A. D. 1081-1085 And 1107-1108) 2007. (Orientalia Lovaniensia Analecta Ser.). (ENG., Illus.). 96p. (C). 80.00 *(978-90-429-1911-2(6))* Peeters Pubs. & Booksellers BEL. Dist: Brown, David Bk. Co., The.

Scott, Richard. Decline & Fall: Byzantium at War. 2008. (Field of GLory Ser.). (ENG., Illus.). 80p. pap. 19.95 *(978-1-84603-402-2(7))* Osprey Publishing, Ltd. GBR. Dist: Random Hse., Inc.

Sevcenko, Ihor, ed. & tr. from GEC. Chronographiae quae Theophanis Continuati nomine fertur Liber V quo Vita Basilii Imperatoris Amplectitur. 2011. (Corpus Fontium Historiae Byzantinae ndash; Series Berolinensis Ser.). (GRE & ENG., Illus.). XII, 570p. 235.00 *(978-3-11-018477-8(X))* De Gruyter, Walter Inc.

Shahid, Irfan & Shahid, I. Byzantium & the Arabs in the Sixth Century, Volume 2, Part 2. 2010. (Dumbarton Oaks Other Titles in Byzantine Studies). (Illus.). 480p. 50.00 *(978-0-88402-347-0(8))* Dumbarton Oaks.

Shepard, Jonathan, ed. The Expansion of Orthodox Europe: Byzantium the Balkans & Russia. 2007. (Expansion of Latin Europe, 1000-1500 Ser.). 588p. 225.00 *(978-0-7546-5920-4(8))* Ashgate Publishing Co.

Siebigs, Gereon. Kaiser Leo I. Das oströmische Reich in den ersten drei Jahren seiner Regierung (457 - 460 n. Chr.) 2010. (Beiträge zur Altertumskunde Ser.). (GER.). XXXII, 1076p. 210.00 *(978-3-11-022584-6(0))* De Gruyter, Walter Inc.

Skylitzes, John & Wortley, John. A Synopsis of Byzantine History, 811-1057: Translation & Notes. 2010. 528p. 135.00 *(978-0-521-76705-7(9))* Cambridge Univ. Pr.

Spaulding, Oliver Lyman. Pen & Sword in Greece & Rome. 2011. 160p. 41.95 ***(978-1-258-03903-5(6))*** Literary Licensing, LLC.

Stephens, W. R. W. Saint Chrysostom His Life & Times. 2007. (ENG.). 488p. 53.95 *(978-0-548-03619-8(5))* Kessinger Publishing, LLC.

Stephenson, Paul. The Legend of Basil the Bulgar-Slayer. 2010. (ENG., Illus.). 190p. pap. 26.99 *(978-0-521-15883-1(4))* Cambridge Univ. Pr.

Stephenson, Paul, ed. The Byzantine World. (Routledge Worlds Ser.). (ENG., Illus.). 640p. 2012. pap. 52.95 ***(978-0-415-52742-2(2))*** 2010. 250.00 *(978-0-415-44010-3(6))* Routledge.

Talbot, Alice-Mary, ed. Dumbarton Oaks Papers, No. 61. 2008. (Dumbarton Oaks Papers). (Illus.). 327p. 125.00 *(978-0-88402-352-4(4))* Dumbarton Oaks.

Thurn, Ioannes, ed. Ioannis Scylitzae, Synopsis Historiarum. (Corpus Fontium Historiae Byzantinae â€" Series Berolinensis Ser.). LVI, 580p. 808.00 ***(978-3-11-177169-4(5))*** De Gruyter, Walter Inc.

Tobias, Norman. Basil I, Founder of the Macedonian Dynasty: A Study of the Political & Military History of the Byzantine Empire in the Ninth Century. 2007. 420p. 129.95 *(978-0-7734-5405-7(5))* Mellen, Edwin Pr., The.

Tougher, Shaun. The Eunuch in Byzantine History & Society. 2010. 244p. pap. 39.95 *(978-0-415-59479-0(0))* 2008. (ENG., Illus.). 256p. 123.00 *(978-0-415-42524-7(7))* 2008. 272p. 41.95 *(978-0-415-42525-4(5))* Routledge.

Tozer, Henry. The Church & the Eastern Empire. 2007. (ENG.). 208p. 39.95 *(978-0-548-05255-6(7))* Kessinger Publishing, LLC.

Treadgold, Warren. The Early Byzantine Historians. (ENG., Illus.). 2010. 456p. pap. 33.00 *(978-0-230-24367-5(3))* 2007. 432p. 110.00 *(978-1-4039-3458-1(4))* Palgrave Macmillan.

Turner, David. Byzantium Student Guide. 2010. (Illus.). 28.95 *(978-0-415-25936-1(3))*; 90.00 *(978-0-415-25935-4(5))* Routledge.

Van Dam, Raymond. Rome & Constantinople: Rewriting Roman History During Late Antiquity. 2010. (ENG., Illus.). 110p. 19.95 *(978-1-60258-201-9(7))* Baylor Univ. Pr.

Varona Codeso, Patricia. Miguel III (842-867) Construcción Histórica y Literaria de un Reinado. 2009. (SPA.). 395p. *(978-84-00-08964-1(2))* Consejo Superior de Investigaciones Cientificas.

Vasiliev, Alexander A. Byzance et les Arabes. 2009. 284p. 60.00 *(978-1-59740-788-5(7))* 2009. 284p. 64.00 *(978-1-59740-787-8(9))* 2008. 280p. pap. 45.00 *(978-1-59740-678-9(3))* 2008. 284p. pap. 26.00 *(978-1-59740-666-6(X))* ACLS Humanities E-Book.

Vryonis, Speros. The Decline of Medieval Hellenism in Asia Minor & the Process of Islamization from the Eleventh Through the Fifteenth Century. 2008. 568p. pap. 56.00 *(978-1-59740-476-1(4))* ACLS Humanities E-Book.

Whitby, Mary, ed. Byzantines & Crusaders in Non-Greek Sources, 1025-1204. 2008. (Proceedings of the British Academy Ser.). (ENG., Illus.). 330p. 135.00 *(978-0-19-726378-5(X))* Oxford Univ. Pr., Inc.

Willoughby, Harold R. Codex 2400 abd Its Miniatures. 2011. 111.25 *(978-1-61143-943-4(4))* Gorgias Pr., LLC.

Wortley, John. Studies on the Cult of Relics in Byzantium up to 1204. 2009. (Variorum Collected Studies). (Illus.). 300p. 144.95 *(978-0-7546-6847-3(9))* Ashgate Publishing Co.

Zachariadou, Elizabeth A. Studies in Pre-Ottoman Turkey & Hte Ottomans. 2007. (Variorum Collected Studies). (FRE & ENG., Illus.). 348p. 165.00 *(978-0-7546-5932-7(1))* Ashgate Publishing Co.

Zavagno, Luca. Cities in Transition: Urbanism in Byzantium Between Late Antiquity & the Early Middle Ages (500-900 A. D.) 2009. (Bar S Ser.). (ENG., Illus.). 206p. (C). pap. 100.00 *(978-1-4073-0607-0(3))* British Archaeological Reports Ltd. GBR. Dist: Brown, David Bk. Co., The.

BYZANTINE EMPIRE—POLITICS AND GOVERNMENT

Alice, Gardner. Theodore of Studium, His Life & Times. 2009. 314p. 32.99 *(978-1-113-47904-4(3))*; pap. 29.75 *(978-1-113-47902-0(7))* BiblioBazaar.

Angelov, Dimiter. Imperial Ideology & Political Thought in Byzantium, 1204-1330. (ENG., Illus.). 474p. 2011. pap. 55.00 *(978-0-521-29438-6(X))* 2007. 146.00 *(978-0-521-85703-1(1))* Cambridge Univ. Pr.

Bury, John B. The Imperial Administrative System in the Ninth Century. 2008. 184p. pap. 18.00 *(978-1-59740-636-9(8))* ACLS Humanities E-Book.

Chekalova, A. A. Senat I Senatorskaia Aristokratiia Konstantinopolia: IV — Pervaia Polovina VII Veka. 2010. (RUS., Illus.). 338p. *(978-5-02-037569-0(3))* Nauka.

Errington, R. Malcolm. Roman Imperial Policy from Julian to Theodosius. 2006. (Studies in the History of Greece & Rome). (ENG.). 352p. 49.95 *(978-0-8078-3038-3(0))* Univ. of North Carolina Pr.

Gardner, Alice. Theodore of Studium: His Life & Times. 2007. 298p. 43.95 *(978-0-548-21169-4(8))*; (ENG.). 300p. per. 28.95 *(978-1-4325-3069-3(0))* Kessinger Publishing, LLC.

Heslop, Michael, et al. Byzantium & Venice 1204-1453. 2011. (Variorum Collected Studies). (Illus.). 314p. 154.95 *(978-1-4094-2370-6(0))* Ashgate Publishing Co.

Jenkins, R. J. H., ed. Commentary on de Administrando Imperio. 2012. (Dumbarton Oaks Texts: 1A). (ENG., Illus.). 240p. pap. 22.95 ***(978-0-88402-379-1(6))*** Dumbarton Oaks.

Kelly, Christopher. Ruling the Later Roman Empire. 2006. (Revealing Antiquity Ser.: 15). (Illus.). 352p. per. 25.00 *(978-0-674-02244-7(0)*, Belknap Pr.) Harvard Univ. Pr.

Koenen, Ulrike & Muller-Wiener, Martina, eds. Grenzgange im ostlichen Mittelmeerraum: Byzanz und die Islamische Welt vom 9. -13. Jahrhundert. 2008. (GER., Illus.). 288p. (C). 99.00 *(978-3-89500-403-2(0))* Reichert, Ludwig Dr. DEU. Dist: Brown, David Bk. Co., The.

Laiou, Angeliki E. & Morrisson, Cecile. The Byzantine Economy. 2007. (Cambridge Medieval Textbooks Ser.). (ENG., Illus.). 288p. 90.00 *(978-0-521-84978-4(0))* Cambridge Univ. Pr.

Laiou, Angeliki E. & Morrisson, Cécile. The Byzantine Economy. 2007. (Cambridge Medieval Textbooks Ser.). (Illus.). 288p. (C). per. 38.99 *(978-0-521-61502-0(X))* Cambridge Univ. Pr.

Luttwak, Edward N. The Grand Strategy of the Byzantine Empire. 2009. (Illus.). 512p. 35.00 *(978-0-674-03519-5(4)*, Belknap Pr.) Harvard Univ. Pr.

Meyendorff, John. Byzantium & the Rise of Russia: A Study of Byzantino-Russian relations in the fourteenth Century. 2010. (ENG., Illus.). 350p. pap. 28.99 *(978-0-521-13533-7(8))* Cambridge Univ. Pr.

Moravcsik, Gyula, et al. Constantine Porphyrogenitus: De Administrando Imperio. Moravcsik, Gyula, ed. Jenkins, Romilly J. H., tr. from GEC. 2nd ed. 2009. (Dumbarton Oaks Texts: 1). (GEC & ENG.). 354p. pap. 19.95 *(978-0-88402-343-2(5))* Dumbarton Oaks.

Necipo#287;lu, Nevra. Byzantium between the Ottomans & the Latins: Politics & Society in the Late Empire. 2012. (ENG.). 374p. pap. 40.00 ***(978-1-107-40388-8(X))*** Cambridge Univ. Pr.

Necipolu, Nevra. Byzantium Between the Ottomans & the Latins: Politics & Society in the Late Empire. 2009. (ENG., Illus.). 372p. 107.00 *(978-0-521-87738-1(5))* Cambridge Univ. Pr.

Ryder, Judith R. The Career & Writings of Demetrius Kydones: A Study of Fourteenth-Century Byzantine Politics, Religion & Society. 296p. *(978-90-04-18565-4(8))* BRILL.

Sophoulis, Panos. Byzantium & Bulgaria, 775-831. 2011. (East Central & Eastern Europe in the Middle Ages Ser.). (Illus.). 480p. ***(978-90-04-20695-3(7))*** BRILL.

Takàcs, Sarolta. The Construction of Authority in Ancient Rome & Byzantium: The Rhetoric of Empire. 2008. (ENG., Illus.). 192p. 80.00 *(978-0-521-87865-4(9))* Cambridge Univ. Pr.

Wood, Philip. 'We have no king but Christ' Christian Political Thought in Greater Syria on the Eve of the Arab Conquest (C. 400-585) 2011. (ENG., Illus.). 350p. 110.00 *(978-0-19-958849-7(X))* Oxford Univ. Pr., Inc.

BYZANTINE EMPIRE—RELIGION

Auge, I. Eglises en Dialogue: Armeniens et Byzantins dans la seconde moitie du XIIe Siecle. 2011. (Corpus Scriptorum Christianorum Orientalium Ser.). (FRE.). 317p. (C). pap. 109.00 *(978-90-429-2357-7(1))* Peeters Pubs. & Booksellers BEL. Dist: Brown, David Bk. Co., The.

Brubaker, Leslie & Cunningham, Mary. The Cult of the Mother of God in Byzantium. 2011. (Birmingham Byzantine & Ottoman Studies). (Illus.). 328p. 124.95 *(978-0-7546-6266-2(7))* Ashgate Publishing Co.

Bumazhnov, D., et al, eds. Bibel, Byzanz und Christlicher Orient: Festschrift fur Stephen Gero zum 65. Geburtstag. 2011. (Orientalia Lovaniensia Analecta Ser.). (ENG & GER., Illus.). 683p. (C). 140.00 *(978-90-429-2177-1(3))* Peeters Pubs. & Booksellers BEL. Dist: Brown, David Bk. Co., The.

Efthymiadis, Stephanos. Hagiography in Byzantium: Literature Social History & Cult. 2011. (Variorum Collected Studies). (Illus.). 374p. 165.00 ***(978-1-4094-3016-2(2))*** Ashgate Publishing Co.

Ermatinger, Cliff. Letters from the Desert: Two Centuries of Prayer in the Byzantine Tradition. 2010. *(978-1-933271-40-8(X))* Circle Pr.

Gastgeber, Christian & Kresten, Otto, eds. Sylloge Diplomatico-Palaeographica I: Studien zu byzantinischen Diplomatik und Palaographie. 2010. (Denkschriften der Phil. -Hist. Klasse Ser.). 294p. (C). pap. 111.00 *(978-3-7001-6492-0(0))* Austrian Academy of Sciences Press AUT. Dist: Brown, David Bk. Co., The.

Gjuzelev, Vassil & Petkov, Kiril, eds. State & Church: Studies in Medieval Bulgaria & Byzantium. 2011. (ENG., Illus.). 300p. (C). 39.95 ***(978-954-92571-2-0(6))*** American Research Ctr. in Sofia.

Jeffreys, Elizabeth M., ed. Byzantine Style, Religion & Civilization: In Honour of Sir Steven Runciman. 2006. (ENG., Illus.). 492p. 182.99 *(978-0-521-83445-2(7))* Cambridge Univ. Pr.

Jones, Lynn. Between Byzantium & Islam: Aght'Amar & the Visual Construction of Medieval Armenian Rulership. 2007. (Illus.). 160p. 114.95 *(978-0-7546-3852-0(9))* Ashgate Publishing Co.

Jordan, R. H. & Morris, Rosemary. The Hypotyposis of the Monastery of the Theotokos Evergetis Constantinople (11th-12th Centuries) Introduction, Translaion & Commentary. 2012. (Illus.). 330p. 124.95 ***(978-1-4094-3687-4(X))*** Ashgate Publishing Co.

Kostash, Myrna. Prodigal Daughter: A Journey to Byzantium. 2010. (Wayfarer Ser.). (Illus.). 352p. pap. 34.95 *(978-0-88864-534-0(1))* Univ. of Alberta Pr. CAN. Dist: Michigan State Univ. Pr.

Kraus, Christof Rudolf. Kleriker im spaten Byzanz: Anagnosten, Hypodiakone, Diakone und Priester 1261-1453. 2007. (Mainzer Veroeffentlichungen zur Byzantinistik Ser.). (GER.). 551p. (C). 132.00 *(978-3-447-05602-1(9))* Harrassowitz, Otto Verlag DEU. Dist: ISD.

Krueger, Derek. Byzantine Christianity. 2010. 320p. (C). pap. 24.00 *(978-0-8006-9721-1(9),* Fortress Pr.) Augsburg Fortress, Pubs.

Magdalino, P. The Old Testament in Byzantium. Nelson, Robert, ed. 2010. (Dumbarton Oaks Byzantine Symposia & Colloquia Ser.). (Illus.). 300p. 35.00 *(978-0-88402-348-7(6))* Dumbarton Oaks.

Raya, Joseph M. Byzantine Church & Culture. De Vinck, Jose M., ed. 72p. pap. *(978-0-911726-55-8(1))* Madonna Hse. Pubns.

—Christmas: Birth of Our Lord God & Saviour, Jesus Christ. 140p. *(978-0-921440-45-1(6))* Madonna Hse. Pubns.

—Transfiguration of Our Lord & Saviour Jesus Christ. 120p. *(978-0-921440-29-1(4))* Madonna Hse. Pubns.

Sherry, Kurt. Kassia the Nun in Context. 2011. 117.25 *(978-1-61143-969-4(8))* Gorgias Pr., LLC.

Soustal, Peter, ed. Heilige Berge und Wusten: Byzanz und sein Umfeld. Referate auf dem 21. Internationalen Kongress fur Byzantinistik London, 21. 26. August 2006. 2009. (VERoFFENTLICHUNGEN ZUR BYZANZFORSCHUNG Ser.). (Illus.). 111p. (C). pap. 78.00 *(978-3-7001-6561-3(7))* Austrian Academy of Sciences Press AUT. Dist: Brown, David Bk. Co., The.

Sullivan, Denis, et al. Byzantine Religious Culture: Studies in Honor of Alice-Mary Talbot. 2011. (Medieval Mediterranean Ser.). (FRE, GER & ENG., Illus.). 592p. ***(978-90-04-21244-2(2))*** BRILL.

BYZANTINE EMPIRE—STUDY AND TEACHING

see also Hellenism

Beck, Hans-G. Byzantinistik Heute. (GER.). 40p. 210.00 ***(978-3-11-178509-7(2))*** De Gruyter, Walter Inc.

Calligas, E., et al, eds. Scholars, Travels, Archives: Greek History & Culture through the British School at Athens. 2009. (BSA Studies). (ENG & GRE., Illus.). 254p. (C). 110.00 *(978-0-904887-60-0(X))* British Schl. at Athens GBR. Dist: Brown, David Bk. Co., The.

BYZANTINE LETTERS

see also Greek Letters

Mullett, Margaret. Letters Literacy & Literature in Byzantium. 2007. (Variorum Collected Studies). 414p. 190.00 *(978-0-7546-5937-2(2))* Ashgate Publishing Co.

BYZANTINE LITERATURE

see also Byzantine Letters; Byzantine Poetry; Greek Literature

Alwis, Anne P. Celibate Marriages in Late Antique & Byzantine Hagiography: The Lives of Saints Julian & Basilissa, Andronikos & Athanasia, & Galaktion & Episteme. 2011. (ENG.). 352p. 120.00 *(978-1-4411-1525-6(0))* Continuum International Publishing Group, Ltd. GBR. Dist: National Bk. Network.

Psellus, Michael. The History of Psellus. (Byzantine Texts: No. 1). reprint ed. 55.00 *(978-0-404-60001-3(8))* AMS Pr., Inc.

Trapp, Erich & Schönauer, Sonja. Lexicologica Byzantina: Beiträge Zum Kolloquium Zur Byzantinischen Lexikographie (Bonn, 13.-15. Juli 2007) 2008. (Super alta perennis. Studien zur Wirkung der Klassischen Antike Ser.). (LAT, FRE, GEC & GER.). 285p. (C). 62.00 *(978-3-89971-484-5(9))* Vandenhoeck & Ruprecht GmbH & Co. KG DEU. Dist: ISD.

Wilson, Nigel G. An Anthology of Byzantine Prose. (Kleine Texte far Vorlesungen Und Acebungen Ser.). (ENG.). VI, 154p. 210.00 ***(978-3-11-177244-8(6))*** De Gruyter, Walter Inc.

BYZANTINE LITERATURE—HISTORY AND CRITICISM

Beaton, Roderick. From Byzantium to Modern Greece: Medieval Texts & Their Modern Reception. 2008. (Variorum Collected Studies). 320p. 154.95 *(978-0-7546-5969-3(0))* Ashgate Publishing Co.

Eideneier, Hans. Spanos: Eine byzantinische Satire als Parodie; Einleitung, kritischer Text, Kommentar und Glossar. (Supplementa Byzantina Ser.). (GER.). XII, 332p. 494.00 ***(978-3-11-175444-4(8))*** De Gruyter, Walter Inc.

George, James. Greek Literature in Late Antiquity: Dynamism Didacticism Classicism. Johnson, Scott Fitzgerald, ed. 2006. (Illus.). 228p. 130.00 *(978-0-7546-5683-8(7))* Ashgate Publishing Co.

Hinterberger, Martin & Schiffer, Elisabeth, eds. Byzantinische Sprachkunst: Studien Zur Byzantinischen Literatur Gewidmet Wolfram Horandner Zum 65. Geburtstag. 2007. (Byzantinisches Archiv Ser.). (Illus.). X, 357p. 196.00 *(978-3-11-019501-9(1))* De Gruyter, Walter Inc.

Hoerandner, Wolfram & Rhoby, Andreas. Die Kulturhistorische Bedeutung byzantinischer Epigramme: Akten des internationalen Workshops (Wien, 1. -2. Dezember 2006) 2008. (VERoFFENTLICHUNGEN ZUR BYZANZFORSCHUNG Ser.). (GER., Illus.). 124p. (C). pap. 63.00 *(978-3-7001-6495-1(5))* Austrian Academy of Sciences Press AUT. Dist: Brown, David Bk. Co., The.

Karla, Grammatiki A. Fiction on the Fringe: Novelistic Writing in the Post-Classical Age. 2009. *(978-90-04-17547-1(4))* BRILL.

Kazhdan, Alexander & Franklin, Simon. Studies on Byzantine Literature of the Eleventh & Twelfth Centuries. 2009. (Past & Present Publications). (ENG.). 316p. pap. 42.00 *(978-0-521-10522-4(6))* Cambridge Univ. Pr.

Kotzabassi, Sofia & Mavromatis, Giannis, eds. Realia Byzantina. 2009. (Byzantinisches Archiv Ser.). (GER & ENG., XIV, 326p. Illus.). 181.00 *(978-3-11-022230-2(2));* 280.00 ***(978-3-11-174202-1(4))*** De Gruyter, Walter Inc.

Macrides, Ruth. History as Literature in Byzantium: Papers from the Fortieth Spring Symposium of Byzantine Studies University of Birmingham March 2007. 2010. (Publications of the Society for the Promotion of Byzantine Studies). (Illus.). 350p. 124.95 *(978-1-4094-1206-9(7))* Ashgate Publishing Co.

Maguire, Henry. Nectar & Illusion: Nature in Byzantine Art & Literature. 2012. (Onassis Series in Hellenic Culture Ser.). (ENG., Illus.). 240p. 55.00 ***(978-0-19-976660-4(6))*** Oxford Univ. Pr., Inc.

Mullett, Margaret. Letters Literacy & Literature in Byzantium. 2007. (Variorum Collected Studies). 414p. 190.00 *(978-0-7546-5937-2(2))* Ashgate Publishing Co.

Rhoby, Andreas & Schiffer, Elisabeth, eds. Imitatio - Aemulatio - Variatio: Akten des internationalen wissenschaftlichen Symposions zur byzantinischen Sprache und Literatur. 2010. (VERoFFENTLICHUNGEN ZUR BYZANZFORSCHUNG Ser.). (Illus.). 286p. (C). pap. 120.00 *(978-3-7001-6825-6(X))* Austrian Academy of Sciences Press AUT. Dist: Brown, David Bk. Co., The.

Wallraff, Martin & Mecella, Laura, eds. Die Kestoi des Julius Africanus und Ihre Äceberlieferung. 2009. (Texte und Untersuchungen zur Geschichte der altchristlichen Literatur Ser.).Tr. of Cesti of Julius Africanus & Its Transmission. (GER, ENG & FRE.). VIII, 395p. 210.00 ***(978-3-11-173289-3(4))*** De Gruyter, Walter Inc.

Wallraff, Martin & Mecella, Laura, eds. Die Kestoi des Julius Africanus und Ihre Überlieferung. 2009. (Texte und Untersuchungen zur Geschichte der altchristlichen Literatur Ser.).Tr. of Cesti of Julius Africanus & Its Transmission. (GER, ENG & FRE.). VIII, 395p. 140.00 *(978-3-11-021958-6(1))* De Gruyter, Walter Inc.

BYZANTINE MUSIC

see Music, Byzantine

BYZANTINE PAINTING

see Painting, Byzantine

BYZANTINE PHILOSOPHY

see Philosophy, Byzantine

BYZANTINE POETRY

see also Hymns, Greek

Rhoby, Andreas. Byzantinische Epigramme auf Fresken und Mosaiken. 2009. (VERoFFENTLICHUNGEN ZUR BYZANZFORSCHUNG Ser.). (GER., Illus.). 503p. (C). pap. 123.00 *(978-3-7001-6106-6(9))* Austrian Academy of Sciences Press AUT. Dist: Brown, David Bk. Co., The.

Van Opstall, Emilie Marlene. Jean Geometre: Poemes en Hexametres et en Distiques Elegiaques. Van Opstall, Emilie Marlene, tr. from GEC. 2008. (Medieval Mediterranean Ser.). (FRE & ENG., Illus.). 606p. *(978-90-04-16444-4(8))* BRILL.

BYZANTINE POETRY—HISTORY AND CRITICISM

Demoen, Kristoffel & Bernard, Floris. Poetry & Its Contexts in 11th-Century Byzantium. 2012. (Illus.). 258p. 124.95 ***(978-1-4094-4071-0(0))*** Ashgate Publishing Co.

Demoen, Kristoffel & Bernard, Floris, eds. Poetry & Its Contexts in 11th-Century Byzantium. 2012. (Illus.). 230p. 124.95 ***(978-1-4094-4072-7(9))*** Ashgate Publishing Co.

Hoerandner, Wolfram & Rhoby, Andreas. Die Kulturhistorische Bedeutung byzantinischer Epigramme: Akten des internationalen Workshops (Wien, 1. -2. Dezember 2006) 2008. (VERoFFENTLICHUNGEN ZUR BYZANZFORSCHUNG Ser.). (GER., Illus.). 124p. (C). pap. 63.00 *(978-3-7001-6495-1(5))* Austrian Academy of Sciences Press AUT. Dist: Brown, David Bk. Co., The.

BYZANTINE STUDIES

see Byzantine Empire—Study and Teaching

BYZANTIUM

see Istanbul (Turkey)

C

C (COMPUTER PROGRAM LANGUAGE)

see also C Plus Plus (Computer Program Language); C Sharp (Computer Program Language)

Ahmed, Anil, et al. Easy C/C++ 2011. 236p. pap. ***(978-3-8443-8433-8(2))*** Lambert Academic Publishing.

Albahari, Ben & Albahari, Joseph. C# 4. 0 Pocket Reference. 3rd ed. 2010. (ENG., Illus.). 218p. pap. 14.99 *(978-1-4493-9401-1(9))* O'Reilly Media, Inc.

Albahari, Joseph & Albahari, Ben. C# 4. 0 in a Nutshell: The Definitive Reference. 4th ed. 2010. (ENG., Illus.). 1060p. pap. 49.99 *(978-0-596-80095-6(9))* O'Reilly Media, Inc.

Alesso, H. Peter & Hillar, Gastón C. Professional Parallel Programming with C# Master Parallel Extensions with .NET 4. 2010. (ENG., Illus.). 576p. pap. 54.99 *(978-0-470-49599-5(5),* Wrox) Wiley, John & Sons, Inc.

Architectural Design Patterns in C# 2011. 69.95 *(978-1-4398-1658-5(1))* Auerbach Pubs., Inc.

Bates, Martin P. Programming 8-Bit PIC Microcontrollers in C: With Interactive Hardware Simulation. 2008. (ENG., Illus.). 304p. pap. 44.95 *(978-0-7506-8960-1(9),* Newnes) Elsevier Science & Technology Bks.

Bell, Douglas & Parr, Mike. C# for Students: Revised Edition. 2009. (ENG., Illus.). 460p. pap. *(978-0-273-72820-7(2),* Addison-Wesley) Pearson Education, Ltd.

Bennett, Gary, et al. Objective-C for Absolute Beginners: iPhone, iPad & Mac Programming Made Easy. 2010. (ENG.). 292p. pap. 39.99 *(978-1-4302-2832-5(6))* Apress L. P.

Blair-Chappell, Stephen & Stokes, Andrew. Parallel Programming with Intel Parallel Studio XE. 2012. (ENG.). 552p. pap. 59.99 *(978-0-470-89165-0(3),* Wrox) Wiley, John & Sons, Inc.

Boehm, Anne & Murach, Joel. Murach's ASP.NET 3.5 Web Programming with C# 2008. 2008. (Illus.). 1000p. pap. 52.50 *(978-1-890774-48-6(0))* Murach, Mike & Assocs., Inc.

Bradley, Aaron R. Programming for Engineers: A Foundational Approach to Learning C & Matlab. 2011. (ENG., Illus.). xiii, 235p. 49.95 ***(978-3-642-23302-9(3),*** 3642233023) Springer.

Bradley, Julia Case & Millspaugh, Anita C. Programming in Visual C# 2008. 3rd ed. 2009. (ENG., Illus.). 704p. (C). pap. 119.67 *(978-0-07-351721-6(6),* 0073517216) McGraw-Hill Higher Education.

Brannan, James A. Objective-C for iPhone Developers, A Beginner's Guide. 2010. (Beginner's Guide Ser.). (ENG., Illus.). 384p. pap. 39.99 *(978-0-07-170328-4(4),* 0071703284) McGraw-Hill Osborne.

Carter, Eric & Lippert, Eric. Visual Studio Tools for Office 2007: VSTO for Excel, Word, & Outlook. 2nd ed. 2009. (Microsoft . NET Development Ser.). (ENG., Illus.). 1120p. pap. 54.99 *(978-0-321-53321-0(6))* Addison Wesley Professional.

Cheeseman, Bill. Cocoa Recipes for Mac OS X. 2nd ed. 2010. (Illus.). 648p. pap. 49.99 *(978-0-321-67041-0(8))* Peachpit Pr.

Chen, Yinong & Tsai, Wei-Tek. Introduction to Programming Languages: Principles, C, C++, Scheme & Prolog. 2nd rev. ed. 2006. (ENG.). 396p. pap. 104.99 *(978-0-7575-2974-0(7))* Kendall Hunt Publishing Co.

Cheng, Harry H. C for Engineers & Scientists: An Interpretive Approach. 2009. *(978-0-07-337605-9(1))* McGraw-Hill Cos., The.

—C for Engineers & Scientists: An Interpretive Approach. 2009. (ENG., Illus.). 928p. (C). pap., pap. 146.67 incl. cd-rom *(978-0-07-729046-7(1),* 0077290461, McGraw-Hill Science, Engineering & Mathematics) McGraw-Hill Higher Education.

Chung, Carlo. Pro Objective-C Design Patterns for IOS. 2011. (ENG.). 392p. pap. 49.99 *(978-1-4302-3330-5(3))* Apress L. P.

Clair, Robert L. Learning Objective-C 2. 0: Objective-C for Mac & iOS Developers. 2010. (Learning Ser.). (ENG., Illus.). 416p. pap. 39.99 *(978-0-321-71138-0(6))* Addison Wesley Professional.

Clark, Dan. Beginning C# Object-Oriented Programming. 2011. (ENG., Illus.). 378p. pap. 49.99 *(978-1-4302-3530-9(6))* Apress L. P.

Comninos, Peter. Mathematical & Computer Programming Techniques for Computer Graphics. 2010. (ENG., Illus.). xx, 547p. pap. 129.00 *(978-1-84996-954-3(X),* 184996954X) Springer.

Cram101 Textbook Reviews. Outlines & Highlights for C How to Program by Paul J Deitel, Isbn: 9780136123569 0136123562. 2011. 424p. pap. 36.95 ***(978-1-61490-427-4(8))*** Cram101 Inc.

—Outlines & Highlights for C Programming: A Modern Approach by K. N. King, ISBN. 2011. 384p. pap. 34.95 ***(978-1-61490-428-1(6))*** Cram101 Inc.

—Outlines & Highlights for Problem Solving & Program Design in C by Elliot B Koffman, Jeri R Hanly, Isbn: 9780321409911. 2010. 182p. pap. 29.95 *(978-1-61698-372-7(8))* Cram101 Inc.

Cram101 Textbook Reviews. Outlines & Highlights for Problem Solving & Program Design in C by Jeri R Hanly. 2011. 254p. pap. 31.95 ***(978-1-61812-438-8(2))*** Cram101 Inc.

Cram101 Textbook Reviews & Cram101 Textbook Reviews. Outlines & Highlights for C# Programming: From Problem Analysis to Program Design by Barbara Doyle. 2011. 268p. pap. 31.95 ***(978-1-61654-722-6(7))*** Cram101 Inc.

Cram101 Textbook Reviews Staff. Outlines & Highlights for Problem Solving & Program Design in C by Elliot B Koffman, Jeri R Hanly, Isbn: 9780321409911. 2009. 162p. pap. 29.95 *(978-1-4288-8601-8(X))* Cram101 Inc.

Dalton, Steve. Financial Applications Using Excel Add-In Development in C/C++ 2nd rev. ed. 2007. (Wiley Finance Ser.: 424). (ENG., Illus.). 584p. 120.00 *(978-0-470-02797-4(5),* Wiley) Wiley, John & Sons, Inc.

Darie, Cristian & Barnett, Wyatt. Build Your Own ASP. NET 4 Web Site Using C# & VB. 4th ed. 2011. (ENG.). 776p. pap. 44.95 ***(978-0-9870908-6-7(0))*** SitePoint Pty, Ltd. AUS. Dist: Ingram Pub. Services.

Davis, Stephen Randy, et al. C# 2008 for Dummies. 2008. (ENG., Illus.). 456p. per. 29.99 *(978-0-470-19109-5(0),* For Dummies) Wiley, John & Sons, Inc.

De Smet, Bart. C# 4. 0 Unleashed. rev. ed. 2011. (Unleashed Ser.). (ENG., Illus.). 1648p. pap. 59.99 *(978-0-672-33079-7(2))* Sams.

Deitel and Associates Staff, et al. C# 2008 Fundamentals, Pts. 1 & 2. 2008. (LiveLessons Ser.). (ENG.). 128p. 99.99 *(978-0-13-713131-0(3),* Prentice Hall) Prentice Hall PTR.

Deitel, Harvey & Deitel, Paul. Visual C# 2010 How to Program. 4th ed. 2010. (ENG.). 992p. (C). pap. 135.00 *(978-0-13-215142-9(1),* Prentice Hall) Prentice Hall PTR.

Deitel, Paul. C - How to Program. 6th ed. 2010. (Illus.). 1008p. pap. *(978-0-13-705966-9(3))* Prentice Hall PTR.

Deitel, Paul & Deitel, Harvey. C How to Program. 7th rev. ed. 2012. (ENG.). 912p. (C). pap. 129.00 ***(978-0-13-299044-8(X),*** Prentice Hall) Prentice Hall PTR.

Deitel, Paul & Deitel, Harvey M. C: How to Program. 6th ed. 2009. (ENG.). 1008p. (C). pap. 135.00 *(978-0-13-612356-9(2),* Prentice Hall) Prentice Hall PTR.

—Online Purchase for C How to Program. 6th ed. 2009. (C). 66.00 *(978-0-13-214097-3(7),* Prentice Hall) Prentice Hall PTR.

Deitel, Paul J. & Deitel, Harvey M. C# 2010 for Programmers. 4th ed. 2010. (Deitel Developer Ser.). (ENG., Illus.). 1296p. pap. 59.99 *(978-0-13-261820-5(6),* Prentice Hall) Prentice Hall PTR.

DelBono, Emanuele, et al. Professional Test Driven Development with C# Developing Real World Applications with TDD. 2011. (ENG., Illus.). 360p. pap. 44.99 *(978-0-470-64320-4(X),* Wrox) Wiley, John & Sons, Inc.

Dey, Pradip & Ghosh, Manas. Programming in C 2/e. 2nd ed. 2012. (ENG., Illus.). 528p. pap. 29.99 ***(978-0-19-806528-9(0))*** Oxford Univ. Pr., Inc.

Dey, Pradip & Manas, Ghosh. Programmin in C. 2009. (Illus.). viii, 779p. pap. 45.00 *(978-0-19-568791-0(4))* Oxford Univ. Pr., Inc.

Di Jasio, Lucio. Programming 16-Bit PIC Microcontrollers in C: Learning to Fly the PIC 24. 2nd ed. 2011. (ENG., Illus.). 416p. pap. 59.95 *(978-1-85617-870-9(6),* Newnes) Elsevier Science & Technology Bks.

—Programming 32-Bit Microcontrollers in C: Exploring the PIC32. 2008. (Embedded Technology Ser.). (ENG., Illus.). 552p. pap. 64.95 *(978-0-7506-8709-6(6),* Newnes) Elsevier Science & Technology Bks.

Dickheiser, Michael J. C++ for Game Programmers. 2nd rev. ed. 2006. (ENG., Illus.). 512p. pap. 49.95 *(978-1-58450-452-8(8))* Charles River Media.

Donahoo, Michael J., et al. TCP/IP Sockets in C: Practical Guide for Programmers. 2nd ed. 2009. (ENG., Illus.). 216p. pap. 30.95 *(978-0-12-374540-8(3),* Morgan Kaufmann) Elsevier Science & Technology Bks.

Douglass, Bruce Powel. Design Patterns for Embedded Systems in C: An Embedded Software Engineering Toolkit. 2010. (ENG.). 472p. pap. 59.95 *(978-1-85617-707-8(6),* Newnes) Elsevier Science & Technology Bks.

Duffy, James E. Collision Repair Fundamentals: Student Workbook & Activity Guide to Accompany. 2007. (ENG.). 384p. (C). pap., wbk. ed., act. bk. ed. 31.95 *(978-1-4180-1337-0(4))* Delmar Cengage Learning.

Etter, Delores M. Engineering Problem Solving with C. 4th rev. ed. 2012. (ENG.). 480p. (C). pap. 119.00 ***(978-0-13-608531-7(8),*** Prentice Hall) Prentice Hall PTR.

Evjen, Bill, et al. Real World .NET, C#, & Silverlight: Indispensible Experiences from 15 MVPs. 2011. (ENG.). 648p. pap. 54.99 *(978-1-118-02196-5(7),* Wrox) Wiley, John & Sons, Inc.

Fairbairn, Christopher, et al. Objective-C Fundamentals. 2011. (ENG.). 368p. pap. 44.99 *(978-1-935182-53-5(6))* Manning Pubns. Co.

Feiler, Jesse. Sams Teach Yourself Objective-C in 24 Hours. 2012. (Sams Teach Yourself — Hours Ser.). (ENG.). 416p. pap. 34.99 ***(978-0-672-33589-1(1))*** Sams.

Freeman, Adam. Pro . NET 4 Parallel Programming in C# 2010. (ENG.). 328p. pap. 59.99 *(978-1-4302-2967-4(5))* Apress L. P.

Friedman, Frank L. & Koffman, Elliot B. Problem Solving, Abstraction, & Design using C++ 6th ed. 2010. (ENG.). 912p. (C). pap. 123.00 *(978-0-13-607947-7(4))* Addison Wesley.

Gaddis, Tony. Starting out with Visual C# 2010. 2nd ed. 2011. (Gaddis Ser.). (ENG.). 792p. (C). pap. 115.00 *(978-0-13-216545-7(7))* Addison Wesley.

Gaddis, Tony, et al. Starting Out with C++ Early Objects. 7th ed. 2010. (ENG.). 1200p. (C). pap. 135.00 *(978-0-13-607774-9(9))* Addison Wesley.

Gaonkar, Ramesh. The PIC Microprocessor with C Language (Book Only) 2010. (ENG.). (C). pap. 84.95 *(978-1-111-32197-0(3))* Delmar Cengage Learning.

Ghenassia, Frank, ed. Transaction-Level Modeling with SystemC: TLM Concepts & Applications for Embedded Systems. 2010. (ENG.). xv, 271p. pap. 169.00 *(978-1-4419-3875-6(3),* 1441938753) Springer.

Gladisch, Christoph. Extending Key for the Verification of C Programs. 2008. 276p. pap. *(978-3-639-00002-3(1))* VDM Verlag Dr. Mueller e.K.

Gmdh-Methodology & Implementation in C (with CD-ROM) 2010. 96.00 *(978-1-84816-610-3(9))* World Scientific Publishing Co., Inc.

Goldstone, Will. Unity 3. x Game Development Essentials. 2nd ed. 2011. (ENG., Illus.). 462p. pap. ***(978-1-84969-144-4(4))*** Packt Publishing, Ltd.

Gookin, Dan. Programmer's Guide to NCurses. 2007. (ENG., Illus.). 556p. per. 54.99 *(978-0-470-10759-1(6),* Wiley) Wiley, John & Sons, Inc.

Grenning, James W. Test-Driven Development for Embedded C: Building High Quality Embedded Software. 2011. (ENG., Illus.). 352p. pap. 34.95 *(978-1-934356-62-3(X),* Pragmatic Bookshelf, The) Pragmatic Programmers, LLC, The.

Griffiths, David & Griffiths, Dawn. Head First C. 2012. (ENG.). 640p. pap. 49.99 ***(978-1-4493-9991-7(6))*** O'Reilly Media, Inc.

Große, Daniel & Drechsler, Rolf. Quality-Driven SystemC Design. 2009. (ENG., Illus.). xix, 170p. 129.00 *(978-90-481-3630-8(X),* 904813630X) Springer.

Hanly, Jeri R. & Koffman, Elliot B. Problem Solving & Program Design in C. (ENG., (C). 6th ed. 2009. Illus.). 936p. pap. 123.00 *(978-0-321-53542-9(1))* 7th rev. ed. 2012. 840p. pap. 103.00 ***(978-0-13-293649-1(6))*** Addison Wesley.

—Problem Solving & Program Design in C: Custom Supplement for Ryerson University. 2007. (Illus.). 148p. *(978-0-536-53212-1(5))* Addison-Wesley Longman, Inc.

Hansen, John C. LEGO Mindstorms NXT Power Programming: Robotics in C. 2009. (ENG.). 560p. pap. 29.95 *(978-0-9738649-7-7(4))* Variant Pr. CAN. Dist: Independent Pubs. Group.

Harbour, Jonathan. Visual C# Game Programming for Teens. 2011. (ENG.). 464p. pap. 34.99 *(978-1-4354-5848-2(6))* Course Technology.

Hearn, Donald D., et al. Computer Graphics with Open GL. 4th ed. 2010. (ENG., Illus.). 888p. (C). 143.00 *(978-0-13-605358-3(0)*, Prentice Hall) Prentice Hall PTR.

Hejlsberg, Anders, et al. The C# Programming Language. 4th annot. ed. 2010. (Microsoft .NET Development Ser.). (ENG., Illus.). 864p. 44.99 *(978-0-321-74176-9(5))* Addison Wesley Professional.

Hillegass, Aaron & Fenoglio, Mark. Objective-C Programming: The Big Nerd Ranch Guide. 2011. (Big Nerd Ranch Guides). (ENG.). 288p. pap. 39.99 *(978-0-321-70628-7(5))* Addison Wesley Professional.

Homer, Alex, et al. Developer's Guide to Microsoft Enterprise Library, No. 5. 2010. (ENG., Illus.). 272p. pap. 34.99 *(978-0-7356-5177-7(9))* Microsoft Pr.

—Developer's Guide to Microsoft Enterprise Library No. 5: Solutions for Enterprise Development. 2010. (ENG., Illus.). 272p. pap. 34.99 *(978-0-7356-4523-3(X))* Microsoft Pr.

Horowitz, Ellis, et al. Fundamentals of Data Structures in C. 2nd ed. 2007. (C). 89.95 *(978-0-929306-40-7(6))* Silicon Pr.

Horton, Ivor. Beginning C. 4th ed. 2006. (ENG., Illus.). 640p. 64.99 *(978-1-59059-735-4(4))* Apress L. P.

Horton, Ivor. Beginning C: From Novice to Professional. 4th ed. 2011. (ENG., Illus.). 540p. pap. 59.99 ***(978-1-4302-4362-5(7))*** Apress L. P.

Ibrahim, Dogan. Advanced PIC Microcontroller Projects in C: From USB to ZIGBEE with the PIC 18F Series, 2 vols. 2008. (ENG., Illus.). 560p. pap. 44.95 *(978-0-7506-8611-2(1)*, Newnes) Elsevier Science & Technology Bks.

Kamat, Rajanish K., et al. Unleash the System on Chip Using FPGAs & Handel C. 2009. (ENG., Illus.). xxiv, 176p. 139.00 *(978-1-4020-9361-6(6)*, 1402093616) Springer.

Kamat, Rajanish K., et al. Unleash the System on Chip using FPGAs & Handel C. 2010. (ENG.). xxiv, 176p. pap. 139.00 ***(978-90-481-8111-7(9)***, 9048181119) Springer.

Kanetkar, Yashavant P. Let Us C. 8th ed. 2008. (ENG., Illus.). 593p. pap. 73.95 *(978-1-934015-25-4(3))* Jones & Bartlett Learning, LLC.

Kanjilal, Joydip. Architectural Design Patterns in C# 2010. 350p. 69.95 *(978-1-4398-1656-1(5))* Auerbach Pubs., Inc.

King, K. N. C Programming: A Modern Approach. 2nd ed. 2008. (ENG., Illus.). 832p. (C). pap. 101.00 net. *(978-0-393-97950-3(4)*, 97950) Norton, W. W. & Co., Inc.

Klima, Robert & Selberherr, Siegfried. Programmieren in C. 2007. (Illus.). XVI, 354p. pap. 59.95 *(978-3-211-40514-7(3)*, 3211405143) Springer.

Kochan, Stephen G. Objective-C LiveLessons (Video-Book Bundle) 2nd rev. ed. 2012. (LiveLessons Ser.). (ENG.). pap. 69.99 ***(978-0-321-82667-1(1))*** Addison Wesley Professional.

Krause, Andrew. Foundations of GTK+ Development. 2007. (Expert's Voice in Open Source Ser.). (ENG., Illus.). 630p. per. 49.99 *(978-1-59059-793-4(1))* Apress L. P.

Lair, Robert. Beginning Silverlight 4 in C# 3rd ed. 2010. (ENG.). 416p. pap. 39.99 *(978-1-4302-2988-9(8))* Apress L. P.

Lecky-Thompson, Guy W. Just Enough C/C++ Programming. 2007. (ENG.). 400p. per. 29.99 *(978-1-59863-468-6(2))* Course Technology.

MacDonald, Matthew. Pro Silverlight 4 in C# 3rd ed. 2010. (ENG.). 912p. pap. 49.99 *(978-1-4302-2979-7(9))* Apress L. P.

—Pro Silverlight 5 in C# 4th ed. 2012. (ENG., Illus.). 700p. pap. 49.99 *(978-1-4302-3479-1(2))* Apress L. P.

Malepati, Hazarathaiah. Digital Media Processing: DSP Algorithms Using C. 2010. (ENG., Illus.). 768p. pap. 72.95 *(978-1-85617-678-1(9)*, Newnes) Elsevier Science & Technology Bks.

Mark, Dave. Learn C on the Mac. 2008. (ENG.). 376p. pap. 39.99 *(978-1-4302-1809-8(6))* Apress L. P.

Marshall, Donis et al & Bruno, John. Solid Code. 2009. (ENG.). 352p. pap. 39.99 *(978-0-7356-2592-1(1))* Microsoft Pr.

Mazidi, Muhammad Ali, et al. AVR Microcontroller & Embedded Systems: Using Assembly & C. 2010. (ENG.). 792p. (C). 133.00 *(978-0-13-800331-9(9)*, Prentice Hall) Prentice Hall PTR.

McClure, Wallace B., et al. iPhone Programming with MonoTouch & .NET/C# 2010. (ENG., Illus.). 384p. pap. 44.99 *(978-0-470-63782-1(X)*, Wrox) Wiley, John & Sons, Inc.

McGrath, Mike. C Programming. 3rd ed. 2009. (In Easy Steps Ser.). (ENG., Illus.). 192p. pap. 14.99 *(978-1-84078-363-6(X))* Computer Step GBR. Dist: Perseus-PGW.

Metsker, Steven John. Design Patterns in C# 2011. (ENG.). 480p. pap. 64.99 *(978-0-321-71893-6(3))* Addison Wesley Professional.

Monk, Simon. Programming Arduino Getting Started with Sketches. 2011. (ENG., Illus.). 176p. pap. 15.00 ***(978-0-07-178422-1(5)***, 0071784225, TAB/Electronics) McGraw-Hill Professional Publishing.

Moore, Andrew. Create Amazing Custom User Interfaces with WPF, C#, & XAML in .NET 3. 0. 2007. (Wrox Briefs Ser.). 39p. 6.99 *(978-0-470-25871-2(3)*, Wrox) Wiley, John & Sons, Inc.

Mselle, Leonard. C for Novice Programmers. 2011. 196p. pap. ***(978-3-8443-1525-7(X))*** Lambert Academic Publishing.

Mungamuru, Nirmala & Aggarwala, Sreedhar. 'C' Programming for Beginners. 2011. 132p. pap. ***(978-3-8443-2612-3(X))*** Lambert Academic Publishing.

Murach, Joel. Murach's C# 2008. 2008. (Murach: Training & Reference Ser.). (Illus.). 796p. pap. 52.50 *(978-1-890774-46-2(4))* Murach, Mike & Assocs., Inc.

Myler, Harley R. & Weeks, Arthur R. The Pocket Handbook of Image Processing Algorithms. 2009. (ENG.). 320p. pap. 50.00 *(978-0-13-703347-8(8))* Prentice Hall PTR.

Nagel, Christian. Microsoft C# 2008 Wrox Box: Professional C# 2008, C# 2008 Programmer's Reference, C# Design & Dev, .NET Domain-Driven Design with C# Problem Design Solution. 2009. (ENG.). 3727p. pap. 169.99 *(978-0-470-47205-7(7)*, Wrox) Wiley, John & Sons, Inc.

Nagel, Christian, et al. Professional C# 4. 0 & . NET 4. 2010. (ENG., Illus.). 1536p. pap. 59.99 *(978-0-470-50225-9(8)*, Wrox) Wiley, John & Sons, Inc.

Nikolaevskaya, Elena, et al. Programming with Multiple Precision. 2012. (Studies in Computational Intelligence Ser.). (ENG., Illus.). xiv, 234p. 129.00 ***(978-3-642-25672-1(4)***, 3642256724) Springer.

Olson, Scott, et al. Professional Cross-Platform Mobile Development in C# 2012. (ENG.). 384p. pap. 44.99 ***(978-1-118-15770-1(2)***, Wrox) Wiley, John & Sons, Inc.

Parab, Jivan, et al. Exploring C for Microcontrollers: A Hands on Approach. 2010. (ENG.). xv, 157p. pap. 139.00 *(978-90-481-7525-3(9)*, 9048175259) Springer.

Parab, Jivan S., et al. Exploring C for Microcontrollers: A Hands on Approach. 2007. (ENG., Illus.). xv, 157p. 139.00 *(978-1-4020-6066-3(1)*, 1402060661) Springer.

Pellikaan, Ruud. The Construction & Decoding of Algebraic Geometry Codes. 2008. 300p. 50.00 *(978-0-521-81711-0(0))* Cambridge Univ. Pr.

Press, William H., et al. Numerical Recipes: The Art of Scientific Computing. 3rd rev. ed. 2007. (ENG., Illus.). 1256p. (C). 159.00 incl. cd-rom *(978-0-521-88407-5(1))* Cambridge Univ. Pr.

Qian, Kai, et al. Embedded Software Development with C. 2009. (ENG., Illus.). xii, 384p. 89.95 *(978-1-4419-0605-2(3)*, 1441906053) Springer.

Qin, Qing-Hua & Wang, Hui. Matlab & C Programming for Trefftz Finite Element Methods. 2008. (ENG., Illus.). 464p. 97.95 *(978-1-4200-7275-4(7)*, Taylor & Francis) Taylor & Francis Group GBR. Dist: Taylor & Francis Group.

Rattz, Joseph C., Jr. & Freeman, Adam. Pro LINQ: Language Integrated Query in C# 2010. 2010. (ENG.). 840p. pap. 44.99 *(978-1-4302-2653-6(6))* Apress L. P.

Reddy, Rama N. & Ziegler, Carol. C Programming for Scientists & Engineers with Applications. 2009. 838p. pap. 134.95 *(978-0-7637-3952-2(9))* Jones & Bartlett Learning, LLC.

Richter, Jeffrey & Nasarre, Christophe. Windows Via C/C++ 5th ed. 2011. (ENG., Illus.). 854p. pap. 64.99 ***(978-0-7356-6377-0(7))*** Microsoft Pr.

Riordan, Rebecca M. Fluent C# rev. ed. 2011. (ENG., Illus.). 888p. pap. 49.99 *(978-0-672-33104-6(7))* Sams.

Russell, David J. Introduction to Embedded Systems: Using Ansi C & the Arduino Development Environment. 2010. (Synthesis Lectures on Digital Circuits & Systems Ser.). 275p. pap. 45.00 *(978-1-60845-498-3(3))* Morgan & Claypool Pubs.

Samek, Miro. Practical UML Statecharts in C/C++ Event-Driven Programming for Embedded Systems. 2nd ed. 2008. (ENG., Illus.). 728p. pap. 51.95 *(978-0-7506-8706-5(1)*, Newnes) Elsevier Science & Technology Bks.

Schildt, Herbert. C# 4. 0 the Complete Reference. 2010. (Complete Reference Ser.). (ENG., Illus.). 976p. pap. 49.99 *(978-0-07-174116-3(X)*, 007174116X) McGraw-Hill Osborne.

Schuller, Daniel. C# Game Programming for Serio. 2010. (ENG., Illus.). 448p. pap. 49.99 *(978-1-4354-5556-6(8))* Course Technology.

Seacord, Robert C. The CERT C Secure Coding Standard. 2008. (SEI Series in Software Engineering Ser.). (ENG., Illus.). 720p. pap. 59.99 *(978-0-321-56321-7(2))* Addison Wesley Professional.

Sedgewick, Robert. Algorithms in C. 2009. (ENG.). 672p. pap. 59.99 *(978-0-7686-8233-5(9))* Addison Wesley Professional.

Sestoft, Peter & Hansen, Henrik I. C# Precisely. 2nd ed. 2011. (ENG., Illus.). 264p. pap. 30.00 ***(978-0-262-51686-0(1))*** MIT Pr.

Sharp, John. Microsoft Visual C# 2010. 2010. (Step by Step Ser.). (ENG., Illus.). 784p. pap. 44.99 *(978-0-7356-2670-6(7))* Microsoft Pr.

Simon, Axel. Value-Range Analysis of C Programs: Towards Proving the Absence of Buffer Overflow Vulnerabilities. (ENG., Illus.). xxii, 300p. 2011. pap. 129.00 *(978-1-84996-702-0(4)*, 1849967024) 2008. 129.00 *(978-1-84800-016-2(2)*, 1848000162) Springer.

Sinclair, Christine. The Zx Spectrum & How to Get the Most from It. 17.95 *(978-0-13-985044-8(9))* Prentice Hall PTR.

Skeet, Jon. C# in Depth. 2nd rev. ed. 2010. (ENG., Illus.). 584p. pap. 49.99 *(978-1-935182-47-4(1))* Manning Pubns. Co.

Solis, Daniel. Illustrated C# 2010. 2010. (ENG.). 744p. pap. 49.99 *(978-1-4302-3282-7(X))* Apress L. P.

Soros, George, et al. Professional Unity & C# Multi-Platform 3D Game Development. 2012. (ENG.). 740p. pap. 44.99 *(978-1-118-06337-8(6)*, Wrox) Wiley, John & Sons, Inc.

Stellman, Andrew & Greene, Jennifer. Head First C# A Learner's Guide to Real-World Programming with Visual C# & .NET. 2nd ed. 2010. (ENG., Illus.). 850p. pap. 49.99 *(978-1-4493-8034-2(4))* O'Reilly Media, Inc.

Stephens, Rod. C# Programming with Visual Studio 2010: 24-Hour Trainer. 2010. (ENG., Illus.). 552p. pap. 44.99 *(978-0-470-59690-6(2)*, Wrox) Wiley, John & Sons, Inc.

—WPF Programmer's Reference: Windows Presentation Foundation with C# 2010 & .NET 4.0. 2010. (ENG., Illus.). 624p. pap. 54.99 *(978-0-470-47722-9(9)*, Wrox) Wiley, John & Sons, Inc.

Sturm, Oliver. Functional Programming in C# Classic Programming Techniques for Modern Projects. 2011. (ENG.). 288p. pap. 34.99 *(978-0-470-74458-1(8)*, Wrox) Wiley, John & Sons, Inc.

Thareja, Reema. Computer Fundamentals & Programming in C. 2012. (ENG., Illus.). 576p. 39.99 ***(978-0-19-807888-3(9))*** Oxford Univ. Pr., Inc.

Thareja, Reema. Data Structures Using C. 2011. (ENG., Illus.). 608p. 29.95 *(978-0-19-806544-9(2))* Oxford Univ. Pr., Inc.

Veerarajan, T. & Ramachandran, T. R. Numerical Methods with Programs in C. 2008. (ENG.). (C). pap. 49.67 *(978-0-07-726374-4(X)*, 007726374X, McGraw-Hill Science, Engineering & Mathematics) McGraw-Hill Higher Education.

Vine, Michael. C Programming for the Absolute Beginner. 2nd ed. 2007. (ENG., Illus.). 336p. per. 29.99 *(978-1-59863-480-8(1))* Course Technology.

Warner, Robert & Privat, Michael. Beginning OS X Lion Apps Development. 2011. (ENG.). 392p. pap. 39.99 *(978-1-4302-3720-4(1))* Apress L. P.

Watson, Karli, et al. Beginning Visual C# 2010. 2010. (ENG., Illus.). 1080p. pap. 44.99 *(978-0-470-50226-6(6)*, Wrox) Wiley, John & Sons, Inc.

Wilcox, Mark. Porting to the Symbian Platform: Open Mobile Development in C/C++ 2009. (Symbian Press Ser.: 31). (ENG., Illus.). 442p. pap. 65.00 *(978-0-470-74419-2(7)*, Wiley) Wiley, John & Sons, Inc.

Wilson, Matthew. Extended STL, Volume 2: Functions, Algorithms, Adaptors, & Allocators. 2009. (C++ In-Depth Ser.). (ENG.). 352p. pap. 44.99 *(978-0-321-48238-9(7))* Addison Wesley Professional.

Yadav, Aditya. Amazon Cloud Computing with C#/. Net. 2009. 256p. pap. 30.00 *(978-0-557-23064-8(0))* Lulu Enterprises Inc.

Yoder, Jon. Learning to Program with Haiku. 2010. 166p. pap. 25.00 *(978-0-557-53969-7(2))* Lulu Enterprises Inc.

C ALGEBRAS

Araki, H. & Kadison, R. V., eds. C*-Algebras & Applications to Physics: Proceedings, Second Japan-USA Seminar, Los Angeles, April 18-22, 1977. 2008. (Lecture Notes in Mathematics Ser.). 204p. pap. 26.00 *(978-3-540-08762-5(1))* Springer.

Østvær, Paul Arne. Homotopy Theory of C*-Algebras. 2010. (Frontiers in Mathematics Ser.). vi, 140p. pap. 59.95 *(978-3-0346-0564-9(1)*, 3034605641) Birkhauser Verlag AG CHE. Dist: Springer.

Blackadar, Bruce. Operator Algebras: Theory of C*-Algebras & von Neumann Algebras. 2010. (Encyclopaedia of Mathematical Sciences Ser.). xx, 517p. pap. 179.00 *(978-3-642-06673-3(9)*, 3642066739) Springer.

Brattell, O. Derivations, Dissipations & Group Actions on C*-algebras. 2008. (Lecture Notes in Mathematics Ser.). pap. 59.95 *(978-3-540-17199-7(1))* Springer.

Brattell, Ola, et al, eds. Operator Algebras: The Abel Symposium 2004. 2010. (Abel Symposia Ser.). (Illus.). x, 279p. pap. 129.00 *(978-3-642-07061-7(2)*, 3642070612) Springer.

Brown, Nathanial P. Invariant Means & Finite Representation Theory of C*-Algebras. 2006. (Memoirs of the American Mathematical Society Ser.: No. 865). 105p. pap. 61.00 *(978-0-8218-3916-4(0))* American Mathematical Society.

Brown, Nathanial P. & Ozawa, Narutaka. C*-Algebras & Finite-Dimensional Approximations. 2008. (Graduate Studies in Mathematics Ser.: Vol. 88). (Illus.). 509p. (C). 81.00 *(978-0-8218-4381-9(8))* American Mathematical Society.

Didenko, Victor. Approximation of Additive Convolution-Like Operators. 2008. (Frontiers in Mathematics Ser.). 400p. spiral bd. 74.95 ***(978-3-7643-8750-1(5)***, 3764387505) Birkhauser Verlag AG CHE. Dist: Springer.

Hofmann, Karl H. The Duality of Compact Semigroups & C*-Bigebras. 2008. (Lecture Notes in Mathematics Ser.). 160p. pap. 26.00 *(978-3-540-04918-0(5)*, 3540049185) Springer.

Itza-Ortiz, Benjamin A. The C*-Algebras of Irrational Time Homeomorphisms of Suspensions. 2008. 80p. pap. *(978-3-639-07385-0(1))* VDM Verlag Dr. Mueller e.K.

Lin, Huaxin. Approximate Homotopy of Homomorphisms from C(X) into a Simple C -Algebra. 2010. (Memoirs of the American Mathematical Society Ser.). 131p. pap. 69.00 *(978-0-8218-5194-4(2))* American Mathematical Society.

Renault, J. A Groupoid Approach to C*-Algebras. 2008. (Lecture Notes in Mathematics Ser.). pap. 39.95 *(978-3-540-09977-2(8))* Springer.

Rordam, M. & Stormer, E. Classification of Nuclear C*-Algebras. Entropy in Operator Algebras. 2010. (Encyclopaedia of Mathematical Sciences Ser.). x, 198p. pap. 169.00 *(978-3-642-07605-3(X)*, 364207605X) Springer.

Rosenberg, Jonathan. Topology, C*-Algebras, & String Duality. 2009. (CBMS Regional Conference Series in Mathematics Ser.). 110p. pap. 33.00 *(978-0-8218-4922-4(0))* American Mathematical Society.

Sakai, Shtichirt. Operator Algebras in Dynamical Systems. 2008. (Encyclopedia of Mathematics & its Applications Ser.). (ENG.). 232p. pap. 53.00 *(978-0-521-06021-9(4))* Cambridge Univ. Pr.

Thomsen, Klaus. C -algebras of Homoclinic & Heteroclinic Structure in Expensive Dynamics. 2010. (Memoirs of the American Mathematical Society Ser.). 122p. pap. 69.00 *(978-0-8218-4692-6(2))* American Mathematical Society.

Vega, Victor. W*-Correspondences, Finite Directed Graphs & Markov Chains. 2009. 116p. pap. *(978-3-639-15524-2(6))* VDM Verlag Dr. Mueller e.K.

Wang, X. On the C*-Algebras of Foliations in the Plane. 2008. (Lecture Notes in Mathematics Ser.). pap. 39.95 *(978-3-540-17903-0(8))* Springer.

Williams, Dana P. Crossed Products of C*-Algebras. 2007. (Mathematical Surveys & Monographs: Vol. 134). 528p. (C). 112.00 *(978-0-8218-4242-3(0))* American Mathematical Society.

C CORPORATIONS

see Corporations

C PLUS PLUS (COMPUTER PROGRAM LANGUAGE)

see also Microsoft Visual C Plus Plus (Computer Program)

Addison-Wesley, Pearson. C++ IDE Supplement. 8th ed. 2010. (ENG.). (C). 4.60 *(978-0-13-257079-4(3))* Addison Wesley.

Ahmed, Anil, et al. Easy C/C++ 2011. 236p. pap. ***(978-3-8443-8433-8(2))*** Lambert Academic Publishing.

Aubert, Michael. Quick Recipes on Symbian OS: Mastering C++ Smartphone Development. 2008. (Symbian Press Ser.). (ENG., Illus.). 382p. pap. 60.00 *(978-0-470-99783-3(4)*, Wiley) Wiley, John & Sons, Inc.

Babin, Steve. Developing Software for Symbian OS: A Beginner's Guide to Creating Symbian OS V9 Smartphone Applications in C++ McNabb, Satu, ed. 2nd rev. ed. 2007. (Symbian Press Ser.). (ENG., Illus.). 460p. per. 65.00 *(978-0-470-72570-2(2)*, Wiley) Wiley, John & Sons, Inc.

BarCharts Inc., Staff, creator. C++ 2006. (ENG.). 4p. instr.'s gde. ed. 4.95 *(978-1-4232-0263-9(5))* Barcharts, Inc.

Becker, Pete. The C++ Standard Library Extensions: A Tutorial & Reference. 2006. 624p. 64.99 *(978-0-321-41299-7(0))* Addison Wesley Professional.

Black, David C., et al. SystemC: From the Ground Up. 2nd ed. 2010. (ENG., Illus.). xxiii, 338p. 139.00 *(978-0-387-69957-8(0)*, 0387699570) Springer.

Blair-Chappell, Stephen & Stokes, Andrew. Parallel Programming with Intel Parallel Studio XE. 2012. (ENG.). 552p. pap. 59.99 *(978-0-470-89165-0(3)*, Wrox) Wiley, John & Sons, Inc.

Blanchette, Jasmin & Summerfield, Mark. C++ GUI Programming with Qt 4. 2nd ed. 2008. (Prentice Hall Open Source Software Development Ser.). (ENG., Illus.). 752p. 69.99 *(978-0-13-235416-5(0))* Prentice Hall PTR.

Boehm, Anne & Murach, Joel. Murach's ASP. NET 4 Web Programming with C# 2010. 4th ed. 2011. (ENG., Illus.). 834p. pap. 54.50 *(978-1-890774-61-5(8))* Murach, Mike & Assocs., Inc.

Bradley, Julia Case & Millspaugh, Anita. Programming in Visual C# 2010. 2010. 704p. pap. 93.13 *(978-0-07-351723-0(2)*, WCB/McGraw-Hill) McGraw-Hill Higher Education.

Brandle, Stefan, et al. C++ Data Structures. 3rd rev. ed. 2008. 173p. pap. 61.95 *(978-0-7637-5564-5(8))* Jones & Bartlett Learning, LLC.

Brands, Gilbert. Das C++ Kompendium: STL, Objektfabriken, Exceptions. 2006. (EXamen. press Ser.). (Illus.). XIV, 711p. pap. 54.95 *(978-3-540-21463-2(1)*, 3540214631) Springer.

Breedlove, Todd W. & Albert, Randal L. C++ An Active Learning Approach. 2008. 653p. pap. 149.95 *(978-0-7637-5723-6(3))* Jones & Bartlett Learning, LLC.

Bronson, Gary J. C++ for Engineers & Scientists. 3rd ed. 2009. (Introduction to Programming Ser.). (ENG.). 848p. pap. 142.95 *(978-0-324-78643-9(3))* Course Technology.

—A First Book of C++, from Here to There. 4th ed. 2011. (Introduction to Programming Ser.). (ENG.). 800p. pap. 123.95 *(978-1-111-53100-3(5))* Course Technology.

Cadenhead, Rogers & Liberty, Jesse. Sams Teach Yourself C++ in 24 Hours. 5th rev. ed. 2011. (Sams Teach Yourself Ser.). (ENG., Illus.). 464p. pap. 34.99 *(978-0-672-33331-6(7))* Sams.

Carrano, Frank M. Data Abstraction & Problem Solving with C++ 5th rev. ed. 2006. (ENG., Illus.). 992p. (C). per. 131.00 *(978-0-321-43332-9(7))* Addison Wesley.

Chen, Yinong & Tsai, Wei-Tek. Introduction to Programming Languages: Principles, C, C++, Scheme & Prolog. 2nd rev. ed. 2006. (ENG.). 396p. pap. 104.99 *(978-0-7575-2974-0(7))* Kendall Hunt Publishing Co.

Childs, Jeffrey C. C++ Classes & Data Structures. 2007. (ENG., Illus.). 416p. (C). pap. 131.00 *(978-0-13-158051-0(5)*, Prentice Hall) Prentice Hall PTR.

Cogswell, Jeffrey M. & Mueller, John Paul. C++ All-in-One Desk Reference for Dummies. 2nd ed. 2009. (ENG., Illus.). 864p. pap. 39.99 *(978-0-470-31735-8(3)*, For Dummies) Wiley, John & Sons, Inc.

A Concise Introduction to Image Processing Using C++ 2011. (C). 83.95 ***(978-1-58488-898-7(9)***, Chapman & Hall/CRC) CRC Pr. LLC.

Cram101 Textbook Reviews. Outlines & Highlights for C for Engineers & Scientists - with Cd by Harry H Cheng, Isbn: 9780077290467. 2010. 64p. pap. 27.95 *(978-1-61698-021-4(4))* Cram101 Inc.

—Outlines & Highlights for C++ Plus Data Structures by Nell B Dale, Isbn: 9780763741587. 2010. 278p. pap. 32.95 *(978-1-61698-368-0(X))* Cram101 Inc.

—Outlines & Highlights for Invitation to Computer Science: C++ Version -Revised by G. Michael Schneider, ISBN. 2010. 432p. pap. 35.95 *(978-1-61698-055-9(9))* Cram101 Inc.

Cram101 Textbook Reviews Staff. Outlines & Highlights for C++ Plus Data Structures by Nell B Dale, Isbn: 9780763741587. 2009. 246p. pap. 31.95 *(978-1-4288-8603-2(6))* Cram101 Inc.

Dale, Nell. C++ Plus Data Structures. 5th ed. 2011. (Illus.). 804p. 162.95 ***(978-1-4496-4675-2(1))*** Jones & Bartlett Learning, LLC.

Dale, Nell & Weems, Chip. Programming & Problem Solving with C++ 5th rev. ed. 2009. 1020p. pap. 146.95 *(978-0-7637-7156-0(2))*; 697p. pap. 134.95 *(978-0-7637-7151-5(1))* Jones & Bartlett Learning, LLC.

Dale, Nell B. C++ Plus Data Structures. 4th rev. ed. 2006. (Illus.). 781p. (C). 162.95 *(978-0-7637-4158-7(2))* Jones & Bartlett Learning, LLC.

—A Laboratory Course in C++ 5th rev. ed. 2009. 450p. pap. 64.95 *(978-0-7637-7882-8(6))* Jones & Bartlett Learning, LLC.

Dalton, Steve. Financial Applications Using Excel Add-In Development in C/C++ 2nd rev. ed. 2007. (Wiley Finance Ser.: 424). (ENG., Illus.). 584p. 120.00 *(978-0-470-02797-4(5)*, Wiley) Wiley, John & Sons, Inc.

Davis, Stephen R. Programming with C++ for Dummies. 2010. (ENG., Illus.). 456p. pap. 29.99 *(978-0-470-61797-7(7)*, For Dummies) Wiley, John & Sons, Inc.

C

Davis, Stephen Randy, et al. C++ for Dummies. 6th ed. 2009. (ENG., Illus.). 432p. pap. 29.99 (978-0-470-31726-6(4), For Dummies) Wiley, John & Sons, Inc.

Dawson, Michael. Beginning C++ Through Game Programming. 3rd ed. 2010. (ENG., Illus.). 432p. pap. 34.99 (978-1-4354-5742-3(0)) Course Technology.

Dawson, Michael & Dawson, Michael. C++ Projects: Programming with Text-Based Games. 2009. (ENG.). 248p. pap. 59.95 (978-1-4239-0227-0(0)) Course Technology.

Dechev, Damian. A Concurrency & Time Centered Framework for Autonomous Space Systems. 2010. 180p. pap. (978-3-8383-7733-9(8)) Lambert Academic Publishing.

Deitel and Associates Staff & Deitel, Paul J. C++ Fundamentals, Nos. 1 & 2. 2010. (LiveLessons Ser.). (ENG.). 1056p. pap. 99.99 (978-0-13-701823-9(1)) Prentice Hall PTR.

Deitel and Deitel Staff, et al. C++ How to Program: International Version. 7th ed. 2010. 1104p. pap. incl. cd-rom (978-0-13-246540-3(X)) Prentice Hall PTR.

Deitel, Harvey M. & Deitel, Paul J. C++ for Programmers. 2009. (Deitel Developer Ser.). (ENG., Illus.). 1056p. pap. 59.99 (978-0-13-700130-9(4)) Prentice Hall PTR.

Deitel, Paul. C - How to Program. 6th ed. 2010. (Illus.). 1008p. pap. (978-0-13-705966-9(3)) Prentice Hall PTR.

Deitel, Paul & Deitel, Harvey. C How to Program. 7th rev. ed. 2012. (ENG.). 912p. (C). pap. 129.00 (978-0-13-299044-8(X), Prentice Hall) Prentice Hall PTR.

Deitel, Paul & Deitel, Harvey. C++ How to Program. 8th ed. 2011. (ENG.). 1104p. (C). pap. 132.00 (978-0-13-266236-9(1), Prentice Hall) Prentice Hall PTR.

Deitel, Paul J. & Deitel, Harvey. C++ How to Program: Late Objects Version. 7th ed. 2010. (ENG.). 960p. (C). pap. 124.00 (978-0-13-216541-9(4), Prentice Hall) Prentice Hall PTR.

Dorman, Scott. Sams Teach Yourself Visual C# 2010 in 24 Hours: Complete Starter Kit. 2010. (Sams Teach Yourself — Hours Ser.). (ENG., Illus.). 560p. pap. 34.99 (978-0-672-33101-5(2)) Sams.

Duffy, Daniel J. Introduction to C++ for Financial Engineers: An Object-Oriented Approach. 2006. (Wiley Finance Ser.: 404). (ENG., Illus.). 438p. 115.00 (978-0-470-01538-4(1), Wiley) Wiley, John & Sons, Inc.

Duffy, Daniel J. & Kienitz, Joerg. Monte Carlo Frameworks: Building Customisable High-performance C++ Applications. 2009. (Wiley Finance Ser.: 406). (ENG., Illus.). 775p. 140.00 (978-0-470-06069-8(7), Wiley) Wiley, John & Sons, Inc.

Etter, Delores M. & Ingber, Jeanine A. Engineering Problem Solving with C++ 3rd rev. ed. 2011. (ENG.). 624p. (C). pap. 121.00 (978-0-13-249265-2(2), Prentice Hall) Prentice Hall PTR.

Eubank, Randall L. Statistical Computing in C++ & R. 2011. (Chapman & Hall/CRC Computer Science & Data Analysis Ser.). (ENG., Illus.). 556p. (C). 89.95 (978-1-4200-6650-0(1), Chapman & Hall/CRC) CRC Pr. LLC.

Ezust, Alan & Ezust, Paul. An Introduction to Design Patterns in C++ with Qt. 2nd rev. ed. 2011. (Prentice Hall Open Source Software Development Ser.). (ENG., Illus.). 768p. 59.99 (978-0-13-282645-7(3), Prentice Hall) Prentice Hall PTR.

Ezust, Paul & Ezust, Alan. An Introduction to Design Patterns in C++ with Qt 4. 2006. (Bruce Perens' Open Source Ser.). (ENG., Illus.). 656p. per. 54.99 (978-0-13-187905-8(7), Prentice Hall) Prentice Hall PTR.

Farrell, Joyce. Object-Oriented Programming Using C++ 4th ed. 2008. (Introduction to Programming Ser.). (ENG., Illus.). 816p. pap. 143.95 (978-1-4239-0257-7(2)) Course Technology.

Fienov, Michael. Hackish C++ Games & Demos. 2006. (ENG., Illus.). 350p. pap. 34.95 (978-1-931769-58-7(3)) A-List, LLC.

Fraser, Stephen R. G. Pro Visual C++/CLI & the . NET 3. 5 Platform. 2008. (ENG.). 1080p. pap. 69.99 (978-1-4302-1053-5(2)) Apress L. P.

Freeman, Adam. Introducing Visual C# 2010. 2010. (ENG.). 1320p. pap. 39.99 (978-1-4302-3171-4(8)) Apress L. P.

Friedman, Frank L. & Koffman, Elliot B. Problem Solving, Abstraction, & Design Using C++ 5th rev. ed. 2006. (ENG., Illus.). 600p. (C). per. 119.00 (978-0-321-45005-0(1)) Addison-Wesley Longman, Inc.

Gaddis & Gaddis, Tony. Starting Out with C++ From Control Structures through Objects & MyProgrammingLab with Pearson eText Student Access Code Card for Starting Out with C++ 7th ed. 2011. (ENG.). (C). pap. 141.67 (978-0-13-277417-8(8)) Addison Wesley.

Gaddis, Tony. Starting Out with C++ From Control Structure to Objects. 7th ed. 2011. (ENG.). 1248p. (C). ring bd. 87.75 (978-0-13-277764-3(9)) Addison Wesley.

—Starting Out with C++ From Control Structures Through Objects. 7th ed. 2011. (ENG.). 1248p. (C). 113.33 (978-0-13-272977-2(6)) Addison Wesley.

—Starting Out with C++ From Control Structures through Objects. 7th rev. ed. 2011. (ENG.). 1248p. (C). pap. 135.00 (978-0-13-257625-3(2)) Addison Wesley.

—Starting Out with C++ From Control Structures Through Objects. 7th rev. ed. 2011. (ENG.). 1032p. (C). pap. 115.00 (978-0-13-277289-1(2)) Pearson Education.

—Starting Out with C++ From Control Structures through Objects, Brief, Student Value Edition. 7th ed. 2011. (ENG.). (C). ring bd. 74.75 (978-0-13-284682-0(9)) Addison Wesley.

Gaddis, Tony. Starting Out with Games & Graphics in C++ 2009. (ENG.). 600p. (C). pap. 119.00 (978-0-321-51291-8(X)) Addison Wesley.

Gaddis, Tony, et al. Starting Out with C++ Early Objects. 6th ed. 2007. (ENG., Illus.). 1152p. (C). pap. 132.40 (978-0-321-51238-3(3)) Addison-Wesley Longman, Inc.

Gan, Guojun. Data Clustering in C++ An Object-Oriented Approach. 2011. (Chapman & Hall/CRC Data Mining & Knowledge Discovery Ser.). (ENG., Illus.). 520p. 89.95 (978-1-4398-6223-0(0), Chapman & Hall/CRC) CRC Pr. LLC.

Ghyam, Massoud. Program Design with C++ From Basics to Objects. rev. ed. 2011. (ENG.). 392p. pap. 108.00 (978-0-7575-7989-9(2)) Kendall Hunt Publishing Co.

Glassborow, Francis. You Can Program in C++ A Programmer's Introduction. 2006. (ENG., Illus.). 388p. pap. 50.00 (978-0-470-01468-4(7), Wiley) Wiley, John & Sons, Inc.

Goodrich. Wp Stand Alone Data Structures & Algorithms in C++ 2E. 2nd ed. 2011. (C). pap. 70.95 (978-1-118-08822-7(0), Wiley) Wiley, John & Sons, Inc.

Goodrich, Michael T. Data Structures & Algorithms in C++ 2006. (Wiley Plus Products Ser.). pap. 51.95 (978-0-470-07561-6(9)); pap. 51.95 (978-0-470-07867-9(7)) Wiley, John & Sons, Inc.

Goodrich, Michael T., et al. Data Structures & Algorithms in C++ 2nd ed. 2011. (ENG., Illus.). 744p. (C). pap. 141.95 (978-0-470-38327-8(5), Wiley) Wiley, John & Sons, Inc.

Gregoire, Marc, et al. Professional C++ 2nd ed. 2011. (ENG., Illus.). 1104p. pap. 44.99 (978-0-470-93244-5(9), Wrox) Wiley, John & Sons, Inc.

Hardnett, Charles. Programming Like a Pro for Teens. 2011. (ENG., Illus.). 480p. pap. 29.99 (978-1-4354-5924-3(5)) Course Technology.

Hardy, Yorick. Computer Algebra with SymbolicC++ 2008. pap. 58.00 (978-981-283-361-7(7)) World Scientific Publishing Co., Inc.

Harrison, Richard & Shackman, Mark, eds. Symbian OS C++ for Mobile Phones, Vol. 3. 2007. (Symbian Press Ser.). (ENG., Illus.). 834p. per. 85.00 (978-0-470-06641-6(5), Wiley) Wiley, John & Sons, Inc.

Hawken, Tony. A C++ notebook: A first course in Programming. 2009. 200p. pap. 29.50 (978-1-4452-4340-5(7)) Lulu Enterprises Inc.

Hogenson, Gordon. C++ - CLI: The Visual C++ Language For . NET. 2006. (Expert's Voice in .NET Ser.). (ENG., Illus.). 448p. 54.99 (978-1-59059-705-7(2)) Apress L. P.

Horowitz, Ellis, et al. Computer Algorithms/C++ 2nd ed. 2008. (C). pap. 89.95 (978-0-929306-42-1(2)) Silicon Pr.

Horstmann. C++ for Everyone 2E Binder Ready Version. 2011. 560p. (C). ring bd. 74.95 (978-0-470-92092-3(0), Wiley) Wiley, John & Sons, Inc.

Horstmann, Cay S. C++ for Everyone. (ENG., Illus.). (C). 2nd ed. 2010. 534p. pap. 124.95 (978-0-470-92713-7(5)) 4th ed. 2008. 528p. pap. 136.95 (978-0-470-38329-2(1)) Wiley, John & Sons, Inc. (Wiley).

Horstmann, Cay S. & Budd, Timothy A. Big C++ 2nd ed. 2008. (ENG., Illus.). 1088p. (C). pap. 141.95 (978-0-470-38328-5(3), Wiley) Wiley, John & Sons, Inc.

Johnston, Barbara. C++ Programming Today. 2nd ed. 2007. (ENG., Illus.). 656p. (C). per. 144.00 (978-0-13-615099-2(3), Prentice Hall) Prentice Hall PTR.

Joshi, M. S. C++ Design Patterns & Derivatives Pricing. 2nd ed. 2008. (Mathematics, Finance & Risk Ser.). (ENG.). 308p. pap. 58.99 (978-0-521-72162-2(8)) Cambridge Univ. Pr.

Josuttis, Nicolai M. The C++ Standard Library: A Tutorial & Reference. 2nd rev. ed. 2012. (ENG.). 1128p. 74.99 (978-0-321-62321-8(5)) Addison Wesley Professional.

Kaiser, Richard. C++ with Borland C++Builder: An Introduction to the ANSI/ISO Standard & Object-Oriented Windows Programming. Biljon, A. V. et al, trs. from GER. 2008. 1000p. 89.95 (978-3-540-01027-2(0), 3540010270) Springer.

—C++ with Microsoft Visual C++ 2005: An Introduction to the C++ Standard & Object Oriented Windows Programming. 2009. 900p. pap. 89.95 (978-3-540-69821-0(3)) Springer.

Kelly, Charles. Programming 2D Games. 2012. (ENG.). 350p. 59.95 (978-1-4665-0868-2(X)) AK Peters, Ltd.

Knowlton, Prentiss. Murach's C++ 2008. 2009. (Illus.). 550p. pap. 52.50 (978-1-890774-54-7(5)) Murach, Mike & Assocs., Inc.

Koffman, Elliot B. & Wolfgang, Paul A. T. Data Structures: Abstraction & Design Using Java. 2nd ed. 2010. (ENG., Illus.). 832p. (C). pap. 141.95 (978-0-470-12870-1(4), Wiley) Wiley, John & Sons, Inc.

Langer, Angelika & Kreft, Klaus. Standard C++ IOStreams & Locales: Advanced Programmer's Guide & Reference. 2008. (ENG.). 672p. pap. 64.99 (978-0-321-58558-5(5)) Addison Wesley Professional.

Langsam, Yedidyah. Workbook for C++ 3rd ed. 2009. (ENG.). (C). pap. 84.20 (978-0-558-34753-6(3)) Pearson Learning Solutions.

Lecky-Thompson, Guy W. Just Enough C/C++ Programming. 2007. (ENG.). 400p. per. 29.99 (978-1-59863-468-6(2)) Course Technology.

Lee, Mark. C++ Programming for the Absolute Beginner. 2nd ed. 2009. (ENG., Illus.). 400p. pap. 29.99 (978-1-59863-875-2(0)) Course Technology.

Lewis, Daniel W. Fundamentals of Embedded Software: Where C & Assembly Meet. 2nd rev. ed. 2012. (ENG., Illus.). 256p. (C). 132.00 (978-0-13-291654-7(1), Prentice Hall) Prentice Hall PTR.

Liang, Y. Daniel. Introduction to Programming with C++ 2nd ed. 2009. (ENG., Illus.). 696p. (C). pap. 135.00 (978-0-13-609720-4(0), Prentice Hall) Prentice Hall PTR.

Liberty, Jesse, et al. Sams Teach Yourself C++ in One Hour a Day. 6th rev. ed. 2008. (Sams Teach Yourself Ser.). (ENG., Illus.). 888p. pap. 49.99 (978-0-672-32941-8(7)) Sams.

Lippman, Stanley B., et al. C++ Primer. 5th ed. 2012. (ENG.). 960p. pap. 59.99 (978-0-321-71411-4(3)) Addison Wesley Professional.

Lischner, Ray. Exploring C++ The Programmer's Introduction to C++ 2008. (ENG.). 725p. pap. 49.99 (978-1-59059-749-1(4)) Apress L. P.

Logan, Syd. Cross-Platform Development in C++ Building Mac OS X, Linux, & Windows Applications. 2007. (ENG., Illus.). 576p. per. 54.99 (978-0-321-24642-4(X)) Addison Wesley Professional.

London, Justin. Modeling Derivatives Applications in Matlab, C++, & Excel. 2006. (ENG., Illus.). 600p. 189.99 (978-0-13-196259-0(0)) FT Press.

Main, Michael & Savitch, Walter. Data Structures & Other Objects Using C++ 4th ed. 2010. (ENG., Illus.). 848p. (C). pap. 131.00 (978-0-13-212948-0(5)) Addison Wesley.

Malik, D. S. C++ Programming: Program Design Including Data Structures. 5th ed. 2010. (Data Structures Ser.). (ENG.). 1616p. (C). pap. 184.95 (978-0-538-79809-9(2)) Course Technology.

—Data Structures Using C++ 2nd ed. 2009. (Data Structures Ser.). (ENG.). 944p. pap. 143.95 (978-0-324-78201-1(2)) Course Technology.

—Introduction to C++ Programming. 2008. (Introduction to Programming Ser.). (ENG.). 736p. pap. 140.95 (978-1-4239-0246-1(7)) Course Technology.

—Lab Manual for Malik's C++ Programming: from Problem Analysis to Program Design. 5th ed. 2010. (ENG.). 504p. pap. 44.95 (978-0-538-79810-5(6)) Course Technology.

Maslanka, John. Introduction to Programming in C++ rev. ed. 2010. (ENG.). 524p. spiral bd. 102.16 (978-0-7575-6536-6(0)) Kendall Hunt Publishing Co.

Maureau, Alex. Reviewing C++ 2009. 467p. pap. 29.00 (978-0-557-03079-8(X)) Lulu Enterprises Inc.

Mcgrath, Mike. C++ Programming in Easy Steps. 2011. (In Easy Steps Ser.). (ENG., Illus.). 192p. pap. 14.99 (978-1-84078-432-9(6)) Computer Step GBR. Dist: Perseus-PGW.

Mehlhorn, Kurt & Näher, Stefan. LEDA Set: A Platform for Combinatorial & Geometric Computing, 2 vols. 2009. (Illus.). 1034p. pap. 95.00 (978-0-521-10941-3(8)) Cambridge Univ. Pr.

Molluzzo, John C. C++ for Business Programmers. 2nd ed. 2006. pap. (978-0-13-234095-3(X)) Pearson Education Canada.

Mompelat, Rodrigue Sabin. The Practical Basics of C++ Programming. 2008. 280p. pap. 50.00 (978-0-87573-097-4(3)) Jain Publishing Company, Inc.

Mueller, John Paul. Start Here! Learn Microsoft Visual C# 2010 Programming. 2011. (ENG., Illus.). 396p. pap. 34.99 (978-0-7356-5772-4(6)) Microsoft Pr.

Müller, Wolfgang, et al, eds. SystemC: Methodologies & Applications. 2010. 350p. pap. 229.00 (978-1-4419-5361-2(2), 1441953612) Springer.

Murach, Joel. Murach's C# 2010. 4th ed. 2010. (Illus.). 812p. pap. 54.50 (978-1-890774-59-2(6)) Murach, Mike & Assocs., Inc.

Musser, David R., et al. STL Tutorial & Reference Guide: C++ Programming with the Standard Template Library. 2nd ed. 2009. (ENG.). 560p. pap. 44.95 (978-0-321-70212-8(3)) Addison Wesley Professional.

Nikolaevskaya, Elena, et al. Programming with Multiple Precision. 2012. (Studies in Computational Intelligence Ser.). (ENG., Illus.). xiv, 234p. 129.00 (978-3-642-25672-1(4), 3642256724) Springer.

Nyhoff, Larry. C++ for Engineers & Scientists. 2012. (ENG., Illus.). 728p. pap. 89.95 (978-1-4398-2534-1(3), CRC Press) Taylor & Francis Group GBR. Dist: Taylor & Francis Group.

Overland, Brian. C++ Without Fear: A Beginner's Guide That Makes You Feel Smart. 2nd rev. ed. 2011. (ENG., Illus.). 624p. pap. 29.99 (978-0-13-267326-6(6), Prentice Hall) Prentice Hall PTR.

Parr, Terence. Language Translation Using PCCTS & C++ A Referenced Guide. Date not set. 34.95 (978-0-9627488-5-1(4)) Automata Publishing Co.

Patil, Varsha H. Data Structures using C++ 2012. (ENG., Illus.). 704p. 39.99 (978-0-19-806623-1(6)) Oxford Univ. Pr., Inc.

Pellikaan, Ruud. The Construction & Decoding of Algebraic Geometry Codes. 2008. 300p. 50.00 (978-0-521-81711-0(0)) Cambridge Univ. Pr.

Pitt-Francis, Joe & Whiteley, Jonathan. Guide to Scientific Computing in C++ 2012. (Undergraduate Topics in Computer Science Ser.). (ENG., Illus.). xii, 250p. pap. 39.95 (978-1-4471-2735-2(8), 1447127358) Springer.

Pozrikidis, Constantine. Introduction to C++ Programming & Graphics. (ENG.). xii, 372p. 2010. pap. 84.95 (978-1-4419-4337-8(4), 1441943374) 2007. (Illus.). 84.95 (978-0-387-68992-0(3), 0387689923) Springer.

Prata, Stephen. C++ Primer Plus. 6th rev. ed. 2011. (Developer's Library). (ENG., Illus.). 1200p. pap. 59.99 (978-0-321-77640-2(2)) Addison Wesley Professional.

Rafiquzzaman, Mohamed. Microcontroller Theory & Applications with the PIC18F. 2011. (ENG., Illus.). 478p. (C). 133.95 (978-0-470-94769-2(1), Wiley) Wiley, John & Sons, Inc.

Raja, M. Chithik, et al. Object Oriented Programming in - C++ 2011. 188p. pap. (978-3-8443-9341-5(2)) Lambert Academic Publishing.

Rao, Siddhartha & Liberty, Jesse. Sams Teach Yourself C++ in One Hour a Day. 7th rev. ed. 2012. (Sams Teach Yourself Ser.). (ENG., Illus.). 768p. pap. 44.99 (978-0-672-33567-9(0)) Sams.

Reddy, Martin. API Design for C++ 2011. (ENG., Illus.). 472p. pap. 59.95 (978-0-12-385003-4(7), Morgan Kaufmann) Elsevier Science & Technology Bks.

Reed, David M. & Zelle, John M. Data Structures & Algorithms Using Python & C++ 2009. (978-1-59028-233-5(7)) Franklin, Beedle & Assocs., Inc.

Reinders, James. Intel Threading Building Blocks: Outfitting C++ for Multi-Core Processor Parallelism. 2007. (ENG., Illus.). 336p. per. 39.99 (978-0-596-51480-8(8)) O'Reilly Media, Inc.

Richter, Jeffrey & Nasarre, Christophe. Windows Via C/C++ 5th ed. 2011. (ENG., Illus.). 854p. pap. 64.99 (978-0-7356-6377-0(7)) Microsoft Pr.

Sahay, Sourav. Object Oriented Programming with C++ 2/e. 2nd ed. 2012. (ENG., Illus.). 512p. pap. 29.99 (978-0-19-806530-2(2)) Oxford Univ. Pr., Inc.

Salov, Valerii. Modeling Maximum Trading Profits with C++ New Trading & Money Management Concepts. 2007. (Wiley Trading Ser.: 298). (ENG., Illus.). 264p. pap. 90.00 (978-0-470-08623-0(8), Wiley) Wiley, John & Sons, Inc.

Samek, Miro. Practical UML Statecharts in C/C++ Event-Driven Programming for Embedded Systems. 2nd ed. 2008. (ENG., Illus.). 728p. pap. 51.95 (978-0-7506-8706-5(1), Newnes) Elsevier Science & Technology Bks.

Savitch, Walter. Absolute C++ 4th ed. 2009. (ENG.). 984p. (C). pap. 135.00 (978-0-13-608381-8(1)) Addison Wesley.

—Student Value Edition for Problem Solving with C++ 8th ed. 2011. (ENG.). (C). ring bd. 74.75 (978-0-13-277334-8(1)) Addison Wesley.

Savitch, Walter & Mock, Kenrick. Absolute C++ 5th rev. ed. 2012. (ENG.). 984p. (C). pap. 135.00 (978-0-13-283071-3(X)) Addison Wesley.

—Absolute C++, Student Value Edition. 5th ed. 2012. (ENG.). 984p. (C). ring bd. 87.75 (978-0-13-284681-3(0)) Addison Wesley.

Savitch, Walter & Mock, Kenrick. Problem Solving with C++ 8th ed. 2011. (ENG.). 1056p. (C). pap. 115.00 (978-0-13-216273-9(3)) Addison Wesley.

Schildt, Herbert. Herb Schildt's C++ Programming Cookbook. 2008. (ENG., Illus.). 509p. pap. 49.99 (978-0-07-148860-0(X), 007148860X) McGraw-Hill Osborne.

Schleiden, Christopher. Exploiting Object Orientation to Parallelize C++ Applications. 2009. 60p. pap. (978-3-639-20667-8(3)) VDM Verlag Dr. Mueller e.K.

Schmalz, Michael. C# Database Basics. 2012. (ENG.). 110p. pap. 19.99 (978-1-4493-0998-5(4)) O'Reilly Media, Inc.

Sengupta, Chandan. Financial Modeling Using C++ 2007. (Wiley Finance Ser.: 348). (ENG.). 565p. pap. 125.00 (978-0-471-78908-6(9), Wiley) Wiley, John & Sons, Inc.

Shapira, Yair. Mathematical Objects in C++ Computational Tools in A Unified Object-Oriented Approach. 2009. (Chapman & Hall/CRC Numerical Analysis & Scientific Computation Ser.). (ENG., Illus.). 609p. 102.95 (978-1-4398-1147-4(4), CRC Press) Taylor & Francis Group GBR. Dist: Taylor & Francis Group.

Shelly, Asaf. Expert one-on-one Visual C++ 2008. 600p. pap. 39.99 (978-0-470-04262-5(1), Wiley-Interscience) Wiley, John & Sons, Inc.

Sivakumar, Nishant. C++/CLI in Action. 2007. (ENG., Illus.). 416p. per. 49.99 (978-1-932394-81-8(8)) Manning Pubns. Co.

Smith, Jo Ann. C++ Programs to Accompany Programming Logic & Design. 2009. (ENG.). 224p. pap. 44.95 (978-0-324-78144-1(X)) Course Technology.

Smith, Richard G. C++ or Engineering & Scientists. 68.00 (978-0-89006-761-1(9)) Artech Hse., Inc.

Stenger, Harvey, text. Introduction to C++, MATLAB & Numerical Methods. 2006. cd-rom 50.00 (978-0-9716051-9-0(X)) New Century Education Services.

Stenger, Harvey & Smith, Charles R. Introduction to C++, Excel Matlab & Basic Engineering Numerical Methods, Vol. 1.1. 2009. (ENG.). (C). 83.00 (978-0-13-612024-7(5), Prentice Hall) Prentice Hall PTR.

Stichbury, Jo. Symbian OS Explained: Effective C++ Programming for Symbian OS V9 Smartphones. 2nd ed. 2009. (Symbian Press Ser.). 432p. pap. 60.00 (978-0-470-99808-3(3)) Wiley, John & Sons, Inc.

Stichbury, Jo, et al. Games on Symbian OS: A Handbook for Mobile Development. 2008. (Symbian Press Ser.: 24). (ENG., Illus.). 400p. pap. 50.00 (978-0-470-99804-5(0), Wiley) Wiley, John & Sons, Inc.

Strobl, Torsten. Modern Concepts Applied to C++ - Object Persistence, Reflection, Events, Garbage Collection & Thread Safety in C++ 2007. 192p. per. (978-3-8364-2138-6(0)) VDM Verlag Dr. Mueller e.K.

Stroustrup, Bjarne. Programming: Principles & Practice Using C++ 2008. (ENG., Illus.). 1272p. pap. 74.99 (978-0-321-54372-1(6)) Addison Wesley Professional.

Summerfield, Mark. Advanced Qt Programming: Creating Great Software with C++ & Qt 4. rev. ed. 2010. (ENG., Illus.). 560p. 49.99 (978-0-321-63590-7(6)) Addison Wesley Professional.

Sutter, Herb & Hyslop, Jim. C++ Conversations. 2011. (ENG.). 256p. pap. 39.99 (978-0-321-44148-5(6)) Addison Wesley Professional.

Thorn, Alan. Introduction to C++ Game Programming. 2007. (Illus.). 367p. per. 44.95 (978-1-59822-032-2(2)) Jones & Bartlett Learning, LLC.

Trevidi, Bhusan. Programming with ANSI C++ A Step-by-Step Approach. 2011. (ENG., Illus.). 716p. pap. 26.95 (978-0-19-806308-7(3)) Oxford Univ. Pr., Inc.

Trivedi, Bhushan. Programming with ANSI C++ 2007. (ENG., Illus.). 544p. 49.95 (978-0-19-569037-8(0)) Oxford Univ. Pr., Inc.

Wagner, Bill. More Effective C# 50 Specific Ways to Improve Your C# 2008. (Effective Software Development Ser.). (ENG., Illus.). 336p. pap. 54.99 (978-0-321-48589-2(0)) Addison Wesley Professional.

Wang, Meiqing & Lai, Choi-Hong. A Concise Introduction to Image Processing using C++ 2008. (Chapman & Hall/CRC Numerical Analy & Scient Comp. Ser.). (ENG., Illus.). 264p. (C). 87.95 (978-1-58488-897-0(0), Chapman & Hall/CRC) CRC Pr. LLC.

Watson, Ben. C# 4. 0 How-to. 2010. (How-to Ser.). (Illus.). 672p. pap. 39.99 (978-0-672-33063-6(6)) Sams.

Weisert, Conrad. Object-Oriented Computation in C++ & Java: A Practical Guide to Design Patterns for Object-Oriented Computing. 2007. pap. 33.95 (978-0-932633-63-7(3)) Dorset Hse. Publishing.

Whitbrook, Amanda. Programming Mobile Robots with Aria & Player: A Guide to C++ Object-Oriented Control. 2009. (ENG., Illus.). xii, 117p. 89.95 (978-1-84882-863-6(2), 1848828632) Springer.

Wilcox, Mark. Porting to the Symbian Platform: Open Mobile Development in C/C++ 2009. (Symbian Press Ser.: 31). (ENG., Illus.). 442p. pap. 65.00 (978-0-470-74419-2(7), Wiley) Wiley, John & Sons, Inc.

Williams, Anthony. C++ Concurrency in Action: Practical Multithreading. 2012. (ENG.). 528p. pap. 69.99 *(978-1-933988-77-1(0))* Manning Pubns. Co.

Wilson, Matthew. Extended STL: Collections & Iterators, Vol. 1. 2007. (ENG.). 624p. pap. 54.99 *(978-0-321-30550-3(7))* Addison Wesley Professional.

Zak, Diane. An Introduction to Programming with C++ 6th ed. 2010. (SAM 2010 Compatible Products Ser.). (ENG., Illus.). 29p. pap. 162.95 *(978-0-538-46652-3(9))* Course Technology.

C SHARP (COMPUTER PROGRAM LANGUAGE)

Abolrous, Sam A. Learn C# Includes the C# 3. 0 Features. 2007. 405p. per. 39.95 *(978-1-59822-035-3(7))* Jones & Bartlett Learning, LLC.

Agarwal, Vidya Vrat, et al. Beginning C# 2008 Databases. 2nd ed. 2008. (Books for Professionals by Professionals). (ENG., Illus.). 482p. pap. 39.99 *(978-1-59059-900-6(4))* Apress L. P.

Allen, K. Programming Windows Workflow Foundation. 2006. pap. *(978-1-904811-21-3(3))* Packt Publishing, Ltd.

Arsenovski, Danijel. Professional Refactoring in C# & ASP. NET. 2009. (ENG., Illus.). 552p. pap. 59.99 *(978-0-470-43452-9(X)*, Wrox) Wiley, John & Sons, Inc.

Bai, Ying. Practical Database Programming with Visual C#. NET. 2010. (ENG., Illus.). 903p. pap. 105.00 *(978-0-470-46727-5(4)*, Wiley-IEEE Pr.) Wiley, John & Sons, Inc.

Baldwin, Kenneth, et al. The Elements of C# Style. 2006. (ENG.). 156p. per. 16.99 *(978-0-521-67159-0(0))* Cambridge Univ. Pr.

Bergin, Joseph, et al. Monty Karel: A Gentle Introduction to the Art of Dynamic Object-Oriented Programming in Python. 2008. (Illus.). 236p. (C). pap. 29.00 net. *(978-0-9705795-2-2(7))* Dreamsongs Pr.

Bernavich, Robert & Somasundaram, Kumar. Professional Visual Studio 2005 Add-ins with C# 2007. 650p. pap. 49.99 *(978-0-470-14093-2(3)*, Wrox) Wiley, John & Sons, Inc.

Bishop, Judith & Bishop, J. M. C# 3.0 Design Patterns. 2007. (ENG., Illus.). 318p. per. 39.99 *(978-0-596-52773-0(X))* O'Reilly Media, Inc.

Bradley, Julia Case & Millspaugh, A. C. Programming in Visual C# 2005. 2008. *(978-0-07-351718-6(6))* McGraw-Hill Cos., The.

Busbice, Timothy. C# Programming for Kids Vs2008. 2011. 146p. pap. 49.49 *(978-0-557-39224-7(1))* Lulu Enterprises Inc.

The Complete Visual C# Programmer's Guide. *(978-0-9716836-0-0(3))* Microgold Software, Inc.

Cornell, Gary & MacDonald, Matthew. Beginning C# Programming: From Novice to Professional. Franklin, John, ed. 2007. 650p. pap. 39.99 *(978-1-59059-415-5(0))* Apress L. P.

Costanich, Bryan. Developing C# Apps for iPhone & iPad using MonoTouch: iOS Apps Development for . NET Developers. 2011. (ENG.). 512p. pap. 49.99 *(978-1-4302-3174-5(2))* Apress L. P.

Darie, Cristian & Brinzarea, Bogdan. Microsoft AJAX C# Essentials: A uniquely practical guide to working with the ASP. NET AJAX Control Toolkit, ASP. NET 2. 0 AJAX Extensions, & the Microsoft AJAX Library: Building Responsive ASP. NET 2. 0 Applications. 2007. (Illus.). 300p. per. *(978-1-84719-098-7(7))* Packt Publishing, Ltd.

Darie, Cristian & Watson, Karli. Beginning ASP. NET E-Commerce in C# 2009. (ENG., Illus.). 736p. pap. 44.99 *(978-1-4302-1074-0(5))* Apress L. P.

Dos Passos Waldemar Staff. Numerical Recipes Algorithms & Tools in C# 2009. (ENG., Illus.). 600p. 102.95 *(978-0-8493-7479-1(0)*, CRC Press) Taylor & Francis Group GBR. Dist: Taylor & Francis Group.

Doyle, Barbara. C# Programming: From Problem Analysis to Program Design. (ENG., Illus.). 2nd rev. ed. 2007. 1032p. per. 150.95 *(978-1-4239-0146-4(0))* 3rd ed. 2010. 1088p. pap. 150.95 *(978-0-538-45302-8(8))* Course Technology.

Farrell, Joyce. Microsoft Visual C# 2008: An Introduction to Object-Oriented Programming. 3rd ed. 2008. (ENG., Illus.). 736p. pap. 140.95 *(978-1-4239-0255-3(5))* Course Technology.

—Microsoft Visual C# 2008 Comprehensive: An Introduction to Object-Oriented Programming. 2009. (ENG., Illus.). 1008p. pap. 144.95 *(978-0-495-80643-1(9))* Course Technology.

—Microsoft Visual C# 2010: An Introduction to Object-Oriented Programming. 4th ed. 2010. (Visual Basic Ser.). (ENG.). 848p. pap. 144.95 *(978-0-538-47951-6(5))* Course Technology.

Ferracchiati, Fabio Claudio. LINQ for Visual C# 2005. 2007. (ENG.). 176p. pap. 24.99 *(978-1-59059-826-9(1))* Apress L. P.

—LINQ for Visual C# 2008. 2008. (ENG.). 200p. pap. 24.99 *(978-1-4302-1580-6(1))* Apress L. P.

Foxall, James. Sams Teach Yourself Visual C# 2008 in 24 Hours: Complete Starter Kit. 2008. (Sams Teach Yourself — Hours Ser.). (ENG., Illus.). 528p. pap. 34.99 *(978-0-672-32990-6(5))* Sams.

Gosselin, Don & Gosselin. ASP. NET Programming with C# & SQL Server. 2009. (Web Technologies Ser.). (ENG., Illus.). 672p. pap. 131.95 *(978-1-4239-0324-6(2))* Course Technology.

Griffiths, Ian, et al. Programming C# 4.0: Building Windows, Web, & Ria Applications for the . NET with C#4.0. 6th ed. 2010. (Animal Guide Ser.). (ENG., Illus.). 858p. pap. 54.99 *(978-0-596-15983-2(8))* O'Reilly Media, Inc.

Gross, Christian. Beginning C# 2008. (Expert's Voice In . Net Ser.). (ENG., 2007, Illus.). 487p. per. 39.99 *(978-1-59059-869-6(5))* 2nd ed. 2008. 550p. pap. 39.99 *(978-1-4302-1033-7(8))* Apress L. P.

Haas, Golo. Auf der Fährte von C++ Einführung und Referenz. 2007. (Xpert. press Ser.). 250p. 19.95 *(978-3-540-27888-7(5)*, 3540278885) Springer.

Hardy, Alexandre & Steeb, Willi-Hans. Mathematical Tools in Computer Graphics with C# Implementations. 2008. (Illus.). 475p. pap. 82.00 *(978-981-279-103-0(5))*; (C). 125.00 *(978-981-279-102-3(7))* World Scientific Publishing Co., Inc.

Hasan, Jeffrey & Duran, Mauricio. Expert Service-Oriented Architecture in C# 2005. 2nd ed. 2006. (ENG., Illus.). 272p. per. 39.99 *(978-1-59059-701-9(X))* Apress L. P.

Heaton, Jeff. HTTP Programming Recipes for C# Bots. 2007. 500p. per. 44.99 *(978-0-9773206-7-7(7))* Heaton Research, Inc.

Hejlsberg, Anders, et al. The C# Programming Language. 3rd annot. ed. 2008. (Microsoft . NET Development Ser.). (ENG.). 784p. pap. 44.99 *(978-0-321-56299-9(2))* Addison Wesley Professional.

Hilyard, Jay & Teilhet, Stephen. C# 3.0 Cookbook. 3rd rev. ed. 2007. (ENG., Illus.). 896p. per. 54.99 *(978-0-596-51610-9(X))* O'Reilly Media, Inc.

Huddleston, James, et al. Beginning C# 2005 Databases: From Novice to Professional. 2006. (ENG., Illus.). 528p. per. 39.99 *(978-1-59059-777-4(X))* Apress L. P.

Jacky, Jonathan, et al. Model-Based Software Testing & Analysis with C. 2007. (ENG., Illus.). 366p. (C). 109.00 *(978-0-521-88655-0(4))*; pap. 49.99 *(978-0-521-68761-4(6))* Cambridge Univ. Pr.

Jagger, Jon, et al. Annotated C# Standard. 2007. (ENG., Illus.). 864p. per. 55.95 *(978-0-12-372511-0(9)*, Morgan Kaufmann) Elsevier Science & Technology Bks.

Jones, Allen, et al. Visual C# 2010 Recipes: A Problem-Solution Approach. 2010. (ENG.). 1016p. pap. 54.99 *(978-1-4302-2525-6(4))* Apress L. P.

—WPF Recipes in C# 2008: A Problem-Solution Approach. 2008. (ENG., Illus.). 700p. pap. 54.99 *(978-1-4302-1084-9(2))* Apress L. P.

Kimmel, Paul. LINQ Unleashed: For C# 2008. (Unleashed Ser.). (ENG., Illus.). 552p. pap. 54.99 *(978-0-672-32983-8(2))* Sams.

Kingsley-Hughes, Adrian & Kingsley-Hughes, Kathie. C# 2005 Programmer's Reference. 2006. (ENG., Illus.). 386p. per. 39.99 *(978-0-470-04641-8(4)*, Wrox) Wiley, John & Sons, Inc.

Kluge, Oliver. Praktische Informationstechnik mit C# (C Sharp) Anwendungen und Grundlagen. 2007. (Xpert. press Ser.). (Illus.). X, 304p. 69.95 *(978-3-540-20812-9(7)*, 3540208127) Springer.

Kumar, Satheesh. Linq Quickly. 2007. 252p. per. *(978-1-84719-254-7(8))* Packt Publishing, Ltd.

Lee, Wei-Meng. C# 2008 Programmer's Reference. 2008. (ENG., Illus.). 840p. pap. 44.99 *(978-0-470-28581-7(8)*, Wrox) Wiley, John & Sons, Inc.

Lhotka, Rockford. Expert C# 2008 Business Objects. 2008. (ENG.). 750p. pap. 59.99 *(978-1-4302-1019-1(2))* Apress L. P.

Liberty, Jesse & MacDonald, Brian. Learning C# 3.0. 3rd rev. ed. 2008. (Learning Ser.). (ENG., Illus.). 696p. pap. 39.99 *(978-0-596-52106-6(5))* O'Reilly Media, Inc.

Liberty, Jesse & Xie, Donald. Programming C# 3. 0. 5th rev. ed. 2007. (ENG., Illus.). 608p. per. 49.99 *(978-0-596-52743-3(8))* O'Reilly Media, Inc.

MacDonald, Matthew. Pro WPF in C# 2010: Windows Presentation Foundation in . NET 4. 3rd ed. 2010. (ENG.). 1216p. pap. 54.99 *(978-1-4302-7205-2(8))* Apress L. P.

MacDonald, Matthew & Szpuszta, Mario. ASP. NET 3. 5 in C# 2008. 2nd ed. 2007. (Expert's Voice In . Net Ser.). (ENG., Illus.). 1498p. per. 59.99 *(978-1-59059-893-1(8))* Apress L. P.

—Pro ASP. NET 3. 5 in C# 2008: Includes Silverlight 2. 3rd ed. 2008. (ENG.). 1520p. pap. 59.99 *(978-1-4302-1567-7(4))* Apress L. P.

—Pro ASP. NET 3. 5 in C# 2008: Includes Silverlight 2 & the ADO. NET Entity Framework, Third Edition. 2008. 1200p. pap. 59.99 *(978-1-4302-1566-0(6))* Apress L. P.

Magennis, Troy. LINQ to Objects Using C# 4.0: Using & Extending LINQ to Objects & Parallel LINQ (PLINQ) 2010. (Addison-Wesley Microsoft Technology Ser.). (ENG., Illus.). 336p. pap. 44.99 *(978-0-321-63700-0(3))* Addison Wesley Professional.

Marguerie, Fabrice, et al. Linq in Action. 2008. (ENG., Illus.). 576p. per. 44.99 *(978-1-933988-16-0(9))* Manning Pubns. Co.

Marshall, Donis. Programming Microsoft Visual C# 2008: The Language. 2008. (ENG., Illus.). 784p. pap. 49.99 *(978-0-7356-2540-2(9))* Microsoft Pr.

Martin, Robert C. & Martin, Micah. Agile Principles, Patterns, & Practices in C# 2006. (Robert C. Martin Ser.). (ENG., Illus.). 768p. 69.99 *(978-0-13-185725-4(8))* Prentice Hall PTR.

Mayo, Joseph. C# 3. 0 Unleashed: With the . NET Framework 3. 5. 2nd ed. 2008. (Unleashed Ser.). (ENG., Illus.). 1056p. pap. 54.99 *(978-0-672-32981-4(6))* Sams.

McCarthy, Tim. . NET Domain-Driven Design with C# Problem - Design - Solution. 2008. (ENG., Illus.). 432p. pap. 39.99 *(978-0-470-14756-6(3)*, Wrox) Wiley, John & Sons, Inc.

McMillan, Michael. Data Structures & Algorithms in C# 2007. (ENG., Illus.). 366p. (C). 119.00 *(978-0-521-87691-9(5))* Cambridge Univ. Pr.

—Data Structures & Algorithms Using C# 2007. (ENG., Illus.). 366p. (C). per. 53.99 *(978-0-521-67015-9(2))* Cambridge Univ. Pr.

Mehta, Vijay P. Pro LINQ Object Relational Mapping in C# 2008. 2008. (Expert's Voice in .NET Ser.). (ENG.). 408p. pap. 49.99 *(978-1-59059-965-5(9))* Apress L. P.

Mellender, Fred. Design Patterns for Searching in C# 2008. 181p. pap. 15.50 *(978-1-4357-2301-6(5))* Lulu Enterprises Inc.

Michaelis, Mark. Essential C# 2. 0. 2006. (Microsoft . NET Development Ser.). (ENG., Illus.). 768p. per. 64.99 *(978-0-321-15077-6(5))* Addison Wesley Professional.

—Essential C# 3. 0: For . NET Framework 3. 5. 2nd ed. 2008. (ENG., Illus.). 880p. pap. 49.99 *(978-0-321-53392-0(5))* Addison Wesley Professional.

—Essential C# 4.0. 3rd ed. 2010. (Microsoft . NET Development Ser.). (ENG., Illus.). 984p. pap. 49.99 *(978-0-321-69469-0(4))* Addison Wesley Professional.

Miller, Rick. C# for Artists: The Art, Philosophy, & Science of Object-Oriented Programming. 2008. (Illus.). per. 79.95 *(978-1-932504-07-1(9))* Pulp Free Pr.

Mueller, John Paul & Mueller. C# Design & Development: Expert One on One. 2009. (ENG., Illus.). 672p. pap. 59.99 *(978-0-470-41596-2(7)*, Wrox) Wiley, John & Sons, Inc.

Nagel, Christian, et al. Professional C# 2005 with .NET 3.0. 2007. (ENG., Illus.). 1800p. per. 59.99 *(978-0-470-12472-7(5)*, Wrox) Wiley, John & Sons, Inc.

—Professional C# 2008. 2008. (ENG., Illus.). 1848p. pap. 59.99 *(978-0-470-19137-8(6)*, Wrox) Wiley, John & Sons, Inc.

Nash, Trey. Accelerated C# 2005. 2006. (ENG., Illus.). 432p. pap. 39.99 *(978-1-59059-717-0(6))* Apress L. P.

—Accelerated C# 2008. 2007. (ENG., Illus.). 510p. per. 39.99 *(978-1-59059-873-3(3))* Apress L. P.

—Accelerated C# 2010. 2010. (ENG., Illus.). 656p. pap. 39.99 *(978-1-4302-2537-9(8))* Apress L. P.

Palmer, Grant & Barker, Jacquie. Beginning C# 2008 Objects: From Concept to Code. 2008. (ENG.). 680p. pap. 49.99 *(978-1-4302-1088-7(5))* Apress L. P.

Pelland, Patrice. Microsoft Visual C# 2008. 2008. (ENG., Illus.). 272p. pap. 19.99 *(978-0-7356-2542-6(5))* Microsoft Pr.

Petricek, Tomas & Skeet, Jon. Real-World Functional Programming: With Examples in F# & C# 2010. (ENG., Illus.). 500p. pap. 49.99 *(978-1-933988-92-4(4))* Manning Pubns. Co.

Purdum, Jack. Beginning C# 3.0: An Introduction to Object Oriented Programming. 2008. (ENG., Illus.). 556p. pap. 39.99 *(978-0-470-26129-3(3)*, Wrox) Wiley, John & Sons, Inc.

Rattz, Joseph C., Jr. Pro LINQ: Language Integrated Query in C# 2008. 2007. (Expert's Voice In . Net Ser.). (ENG., Illus.). 600p. per. 44.99 *(978-1-59059-789-7(3))* Apress L. P.

Richter, Jeffrey. CLR via C# 3rd ed. 2010. (ENG.). 896p. pap. 59.99 *(978-0-7356-2704-8(5))* Microsoft Pr.

Rogers, Ryan. Building Massively Scalable Components with C# Problem Design Solution. 2009. (ENG.). 550p. pap. 59.99 *(978-0-470-42899-3(6)*, Wrox) Wiley, John & Sons, Inc.

Salleh, Shaharuddin, et al. Computing for Numerical Methods Using Visual C++ 2007. (ENG., Illus.). 448p. 136.00 *(978-0-470-12795-7(3)*, Wiley-Interscience) Wiley, John & Sons, Inc.

Sanchez-Clark, Terry. C Programming Interview Questions Answer. 2006. pap. 54.95 *(978-1-933804-55-2(6))* Equity Pr.

Sarknas, Paul. Pro ASP. NET 2. 0 E-Commerce in C# 2005. 2006. (Expert's Voice In . Net Ser.). (ENG., Illus.). 640p. pap. 59.99 *(978-1-59059-724-8(9))* Apress L. P.

Schildt, Herbert. C# 3.0. 2nd ed. 2008. (Beginner's Guide Ser.). (ENG., Illus.). 656p. pap. 39.99 *(978-0-07-158830-0(2)*, 0071588302) McGraw-Hill Osborne.

Sempf, Bill, et al. C# 2010 All-in-One for Dummies. 2010. (ENG., Illus.). 864p. pap. 39.99 *(978-0-470-56348-9(6)*, For Dummies) Wiley, John & Sons, Inc.

Serban, Iulian & Brezoi, Dragos. GDI+ C# Custom Controls. 2006. (ENG.). 276p. per. *(978-1-904811-60-2(4))* Packt Publishing, Ltd.

Sharp, John. Microsoft Visual C# 2008. 2008. (ENG., Illus.). 704p. pap. 39.99 *(978-0-7356-2430-6(5))* Microsoft Pr.

Sharp, John & Miles, Rob. Learn C# Now Toolkit: Visual C#/XNA Game Studio 2. 0. 2008. (ENG.). 880p. pap. 49.99 *(978-0-7356-2598-3(0))* Microsoft Pr.

Sheriff, Paul D. Fundamentals of C# 2008. 208p. pap. 24.95 *(978-0-9793748-9-0(8))* PDSA, Inc.

Solis, Daniel. Illustrated C# 2005. 2006. (Expert's Voice in .NET Ser.). (ENG., Illus.). 592p. per. 39.99 *(978-1-59059-723-1(0))* Apress L. P.

—Illustrated C# 2008. 2008. (Expert's Voice In . Net Ser.). (ENG., Illus.). 728p. per. 44.99 *(978-1-59059-954-9(3))* Apress L. P.

Spaanjaars, Imar. Beginning ASP.NET 3.5: In C# & VB. 2008. (ENG., Illus.). 768p. pap. 44.99 *(978-0-470-18759-3(X)*, Wrox) Wiley, John & Sons, Inc.

Stephens, Rod. C# Graphics Programming. 2008. (Wrox Briefs Ser.). 69p. 6.99 *(978-0-470-34349-4(4)*, Wrox) Wiley, John & Sons, Inc.

Symmonds, Nick. Beginning DotNetNuke 4. 0 Website Creation in VB 2005 with Visual Web Developer 2005 Express. 2006. (Expert's Voice In . Net Ser.). (ENG., Illus.). 448p. per. 39.99 *(978-1-59059-767-5(2))* Apress L. P.

Troelsen, Andrew. C# 2008 & the .NET 3. 5 Platform. 4th ed. 2007. (ENG., Illus.). 1370p. 59.99 *(978-1-59059-884-9(9))* Apress L. P.

—C# With .NET 3.0. 4th ed. 2007. (Expert's Voice In . Net Ser.). (ENG., Illus.). 1250p. 59.99 *(978-1-59059-823-8(7))* Apress L. P.

—Pro C# 2010 & the .NET 4.0 Platform. 5th ed. 2010. (ENG.). 1752p. pap. 59.99 *(978-1-4302-2549-2(1))* Apress L. P.

Verschuuren, Gerard. See Sharper with C# 2008. (Visual Training Ser.). (ENG.). 100p. cd-rom 99.00 *(978-1-932802-34-4(7)*, Holy Macro! Bks.) Tickling Keys, Inc.

Wagner, Bill. Effective C# 50 Specific Ways to Improve Your C# 2nd ed. 2010. (Effective Software Development Ser.). (ENG., Illus.). 352p. pap. 39.99 *(978-0-321-65870-8(1))* Addison Wesley Professional.

Watson, Ben. C# 4. 0 How-to. 2010. (How-to Ser.). (Illus.). 672p. pap. 39.99 *(978-0-672-33063-6(6))* Sams.

Watson, Karli. Beginning C# 2005 Databases. 2006. (ENG., Illus.). 528p. per. 39.99 *(978-0-470-04406-3(3)*, Wrox) Wiley, John & Sons, Inc.

Watson, Karli, et al. Beginning Microsoft Visual C# 2008. 2008. (ENG., Illus.). 1344p. pap. 44.99 *(978-0-470-19135-4(X)*, Wrox) Wiley, John & Sons, Inc.

Wills, Dean C. Pro Visual C++ 2005 for C# Developers. 2006. (ENG., Illus.). 416p. 64.99 *(978-1-59059-608-1(0))* Apress L. P.

Xu, Jack. Practical C# Charts & Graphics: Advanced Chart & Graphics Programming for Real-World . NET Applications. 2007. *(978-0-9793725-0-6(X))* UniCAD, Inc.

CA (INTERPERSONAL COMMUNICATION)

see Conversation Analysis

CAB DRIVERS

see Taxicab Drivers

CABALA

Abulafia, Abraham. Get Ha-Shemot - Divorce of the Names. Din, Talib, ed. Shatil, Sharron, tr. unabr. ed. 2007. (ENG.). 64p. per. *(978-1-897352-03-8(4))* Providence University.

—Ner Elohim - Candle of God. Din, Talib, ed. Shatil, Sharron, tr. unabr. ed. 2007. (ENG.). 180p. per. *(978-1-897352-09-0(3))* Providence University.

—Sefer Ha-Ot - the Book of the Sign. unabr. ed. 2006. (ENG & HEB.). 80p. per. *(978-1-897352-05-2(0))* Providence University.

—Sheva Netivot Ha-Torah - the Seven Paths of Torah. unabr. ed. 2007. (ENG & HEB.). 96p. per. *(978-1-897352-00-7(X))* Providence University.

Achad, Frater. The Natural Basis of Correspondences in the Hebrew Alphabet. 2006. pap. 12.95 *(978-1-4286-6400-5(9))* Kessinger Publishing, LLC.

—The Tarot Trumps & Their Attributions to the Hebrew Alphabet. 2006. pap. 12.95 *(978-1-4286-6406-7(8))* Kessinger Publishing, LLC.

Afilalo, Raphael. Concepts de Kabbalah. 2008. 232p. pap. *(978-2-923241-20-3(7))* Afilalo, Raphael.

—Kabbalah Concepts. 2006. 280p. *(978-2-923241-10-4(X))*; (ENG.). per. *(978-2-923241-11-1(8))* Afilalo, Raphael.

—160 Questions Sur la Kabbalah. 2006. (FRE.). 208p. per. *(978-2-923241-18-0(5))*; *(978-2-923241-19-7(3))* Afilalo, Raphael.

Afilalo, Rav Raphael. Concepts de Kabbalah. 2008. 232p. *(978-2-923241-21-0(5))* Afilalo, Raphael.

Albotini, Yehuda. Sulam Aliyah - Ladder of Ascent. unabr. ed. 2007. (ENG & HEB.). 184p. per. *(978-1-897352-08-3(5))* Providence University.

Amato, Norman. Hidden Angels: An Anthology of Angels. 2008. 108p. pap. 18.00 *(978-1-4251-3853-0(5))* Trafford Publishing.

Anderson, John P. Joyce's Finnegans Wake: The Curse of Kabbalah. 2010. 366p. pap. 29.95 *(978-1-59942-858-1(X))* 2009. 334p. pap. 29.95 *(978-1-59942-901-4(2))* 2008. 460p. pap. 29.95 *(978-1-59942-963-2(2))* Universal Pubs.

Anderson, John P. Joyce's Finnegans Wake: The Curse of Kabbalah Volume 5. 2011. 380p. pap. 29.95 *(978-1-61233-046-4(0))* Universal Pubs.

Andrews, Ted. Secret Doors of the Qabala. 2007. (Illus.). 287p. per. 14.95 *(978-1-888767-49-0(9))* Dragonhawk Publishing.

Aryeh Kaplan & Kaplan, Rabbi. Kabbalah & the Age of the Universe. 2007. 52p. per. *(978-956-291-455-0(0))* Editorial Benei Noaj.

Ashe, Steven. Qabalah - the Complete Golden Dawn Initiate. 2008. 596p. pap. 35.95 *(978-1-4092-3050-2(3))* 2007. 588p. 60.95 *(978-1-84753-780-5(4))* Lulu Enterprises Inc.

—Qabalah of 50 Gates. 2008. 156p. pap. 16.95 *(978-0-9556932-3-6(3))* Glastonbury Bks. GBR. Dist: Lulu Enterprises Inc.

Ashe, Steven, ed. Qabalah -the Book of Enoch - the Book of Watchers. 2008. 120p. 33.95 *(978-0-9556932-0-5(9))* Glastonbury Bks. GBR. Dist: Lulu Enterprises Inc.

Ashlag, Rabbi Baruch. Rabash - The Social Writings. 2011. 440p. 25.00 *(978-1-897448-51-9(1)*, Bnei Baruch) Laitman Kabbalah Pubs. CAN. Dist: National Bk. Network.

Ashlag, Rav Yehuda. And You Shall Choose Life: An Essay on Kabbalah, the Purpose of Life, & Our True Spiritual Work. Berg, Michael, ed. 2011. (ENG.). 384p. 34.95 *(978-1-57189-771-8(2))* Research Centre of Kabbalah.

—The Wisdom of Truth: 12 Essays by the Holy Kabbalist Rav Yehuda Ashlag. Berg, Michael, ed. 2008. (ENG.). 224p. 35.00 *(978-1-57189-605-6(8))* Research Centre of Kabbalah.

Ashlag, Rav Yehuda, et al. Kabbalah for the Student. 2008. (ENG., Illus.). 862p. 40.00 *(978-1-897448-15-1(5)*, Bnei Baruch) Laitman Kabbalah Pubs. CAN. Dist: National Bk. Network.

Ashlag, Yehudah. Shamati: (I Heard) 2008. (ENG.). 408p. pap. 20.00 *(978-1-897448-10-6(4)*, Bnei Baruch) Laitman Kabbalah Pubs. CAN. Dist: National Bk. Network.

Baal-Shem, Salomo. Qabbalistic Magic. 2010. (ENG.). 1p. pap. 24.95 *(978-1-59477-358-7(0)*, Destiny Bks.) Inner Traditions International, Ltd.

Bar Tzadok, Ariel. Walking in the Fire: A manual of classical Torah/Kabbalistic Meditations, Practices & Prayers. 2007. 45.00 *(978-0-9791601-0-3(3))* Kosher Torah Publishing.

Ben-Toviya, Esther. Created in the Image of God: A Foundational Course in the Kabbalah. 2007. (ENG.). 272p. per. 21.95 *(978-1-84694-007-1(9))* O Bks.,John Hunt.

ben Yitzchak of Granada, Avraham. Brit Menucha - Covenant of Rest. unabr. ed. 2006. (ENG & HEB.). 324p. per. *(978-1-897352-01-4(8))* Providence University.

—Brit Menucha - il Patto del Riposo. unabr. ed. 2007. (ITA & HEB.). 320p. per. *(978-1-897352-24-3(7))* Providence University.

C

Benyosef, Simcha H. Living Kabbalah: A Guide to the Sabbath & Festivals in the Teachings of Rabbi Refael Moshe Luria. 2007. 382p. 34.99 *(978-1-58330-893-6(8))* David, Jonathan Pubs., Inc.

Berg, Kabbalist Rav. Nano: Tecnología de la Mente Sobre la Materia. 2009. (SPA & ENG.). 352p. pap. 14.95 *(978-1-57189-631-5(7))* Research Centre of Kabbalah.

Berg, Karen. Dios USA Lapiz Labial. 2006. (SPA & ENG., Illus.). 280p. 17.95 *(978-1-57189-371-0(7))* Research Centre of Kabbalah.

—God Wears Lipstick: Kabbalah for Women. 2007. (ENG.). 288p. per. 14.95 *(978-1-57189-581-3(7))* Research Centre of Kabbalah.

—Simple Light: Wisdom from a Woman's Heart. 2008. (ENG.). 156p. 14.95 *(978-1-57189-593-6(0))* Research Centre of Kabbalah.

—Simplemente Luz: Sabiduría del Corazón de una Mujer. 2009. (ENG & SPA.). 272p. pap. 14.95 *(978-1-57189-628-5(7))* Research Centre of Kabbalah.

Berg, Michael. Days of Connection: A Guide to Kabbalah's Holidays & New Moons. 2008. (ENG.). 184p. per. 15.95 *(978-1-57189-594-3(9))* Research Centre of Kabbalah.

—The Secret: Unlocking the Source of Joy & Fulfillment. 2007. (ENG.). 112p. per. 9.95 *(978-1-57189-588-2(4))* Research Centre of Kabbalah.

—The Secret History of the Zohar. 2008. (ENG.). 144p. 19.95 *(978-1-57189-611-7(2))* Research Centre of Kabbalah.

—Secrets of the Zohar: Stories & Meditations to Awaken the Heart. 2007. (ENG., Illus.). 240p. 24.95 *(978-1-57189-577-6(9))* Research Centre of Kabbalah.

—Well of Life: Kabbalistic Wisdom from a Depth of Knowledge. 2007. (ENG.). 224p. per. 14.95 *(978-1-57189-563-9(9))* Research Centre of Kabbalah.

Berg, Michael, ed. Beloved of My Soul: Letters from Rav Brandwein to Rav Berg. 2010. (ENG.). 464p. 39.95 *(978-1-57189-645-2(7))* Research Centre of Kabbalah.

Berg, Philip S. & Berg, Michael. The Sacred Zohar: The Secrets of the Bible: The Complete Original Aramaic Text. 2007. (HEB & ARC.). xxv, 1800p. *(978-1-57189-554-7(X))* Research Centre of Kabbalah.

Berg, Rav. La Conexion Kabbalista: Como preparar el alma para Pesaj. 2011. (SPA & ENG.). 256p. pap. 14.95 *(978-1-57189-705-3(4))* Research Centre of Kabbalah.

—Educación de un Kabbalista. 2009. (ENG & SPA.). 224p. pap. 14.95 *(978-1-57189-617-9(1))* Research Centre of Kabbalah.

—La Energia de las Letras Hebreas. 2011. (SPA & ENG.). 400p. pap. 14.95 *(978-1-57189-740-4(2))* Research Centre of Kabbalah.

—Immortality: The Inevitability of Eternal Life. 2007. (ENG., Illus.). 228p. per. 14.95 *(978-1-57189-570-7(1))* Research Centre of Kabbalah.

—Navigating the Universe: A roadmap for understanding the cosmic influences that shape our Lives. 2011. (ENG.). 288p. pap. 16.95 *(978-1-57189-739-8(9))* Research Centre of Kabbalah.

—Taming Chaos: Harnessing the Secret Codes of the Universe to Make Sense of Our Lives. 2010. (ENG.). 168p. pap. 12.95 *(978-1-57189-663-6(5))* Research Centre of Kabbalah.

Berg, Rav P. S. The Energy of Hebrew Letters: The Quantum Story of the Original Alphabet. 2010. (ENG.). 400p. pap. 16.95 *(978-1-57189-640-7(6))* Research Centre of Kabbalah.

—Inmortalidad: La Inevitabilidad de le Vida Eterna. 2008. (ENG & SPA.). 240p. pap. 14.95 *(978-1-57189-562-2(0))* Research Centre of Kabbalah.

—The Kabbalah Connection. 2009. (ENG.). 256p. 24.95 *(978-1-57189-634-6(1))* Research Centre of Kabbalah.

—Kabbalistic Astrology: And the Meaning of Our Lives. 2nd ed. 2006. (ENG.). 204p. per. 14.95 *(978-1-57189-556-1(6))* Research Centre of Kabbalah.

Berg, Yehuda. Angel Intelligence. 2007. (ENG.). 256p. 17.95 *(978-1-57189-569-1(8))* Research Centre of Kabbalah.

—Beyond Blame: A Full-Responsibility Approach to Life. 2006. (Technology for the Soul Ser.). (ENG., Illus.). 136p. 9.95 *(978-1-57189-545-5(0))* Research Centre of Kabbalah.

—Deuteronomy. 2010. (Kabbalistic Bible Ser.). (ENG.). 360p. 24.95 *(978-1-57189-627-8(9))* Research Centre of Kabbalah.

—Inteligencia Angelical: Angel Intelligence. 2009. (ENG & SPA.). 176p. pap. 14.95 *(978-1-57189-621-6(X))* Research Centre of Kabbalah.

—Kabbalah: The Power to Change Everything. 2009. (ENG.). 192p. pap. 14.95 *(978-1-57189-633-9(3))* Research Centre of Kabbalah.

—The Kabbalah Book of Sex: And Other Mysteries of the Universe. 2006. (ENG.). 254p. 17.95 *(978-1-57189-544-8(2))* Research Centre of Kabbalah.

—Kabbalah: el Poder de Cambiarlo Todo. 2009. (ENG & SPA.). 384p. pap. 14.95 *(978-1-57189-644-5(9))* Research Centre of Kabbalah.

—The Kabbalah Haggadah: Pesach Decoded. 2009. (ENG & HEB., Illus.). 144p. 19.95 *(978-1-57189-618-6(X))* Research Centre of Kabbalah.

—Kabbalah on Green: Consciousness & the Environment. 2008. (Technology for the Soul Ser.). (ENG.). 140p. 9.95 *(978-1-57189-595-0(7))* Research Centre of Kabbalah.

—Kabbalah on Love. 2006. (Technology for the Soul Ser.). (ENG., Illus.). 136p. 9.95 *(978-1-57189-557-8(4))* Research Centre of Kabbalah.

—Kabbalah on Pain: How to Use It to Lose It. 2007. (Technology for the Soul Ser.). (ENG.). 112p. 9.95 *(978-1-57189-571-4(X))* Research Centre of Kabbalah.

—Kabbalah on Sex: Make Love, Make Light. 2011. (ENG.). 300p. pap. 15.00 *(978-1-57189-738-1(0))* Research Centre of Kabbalah.

—Kabbalah on Sleep. 2009. (Technology for the Soul Ser.). (ENG.). 160p. 9.95 *(978-1-57189-620-9(1))* Research Centre of Kabbalah.

—Kabbalah on the Sabbath. 2008. (Technology for the Soul Ser.). (ENG., Illus.). 144p. 9.95 *(978-1-57189-602-5(3))* Research Centre of Kabbalah.

—Kabbalah y el Amor. 2007. (Technology for the Soul Ser.). (ENG & SPA.). 112p. 9.95 *(978-1-57189-573-8(6))* Research Centre of Kabbalah.

—Kabbalah y Sexo: Y Otros Misterios del Universo. 2007. (ENG & SPA., Illus.). 254p. per. 14.95 *(978-1-57189-574-5(4))* Research Centre of Kabbalah.

—Living Kabbalah: A Practical System for Making the Power Work for You. (ENG.). 2010. 320p. pap. 15.00 *(978-1-57189-660-5(0))* 2007. 256p. 19.95 *(978-1-57189-591-2(4))* Research Centre of Kabbalah.

—Más Allá de la Culpa: Una Vision de la Vida Desde la Total Responsabilidad. 2007. (Technology for the Soul Ser.). (ENG & SPA.). 156p. 9.95 *(978-1-57189-583-7(3))* Research Centre of Kabbalah.

—Meditación de un Kabbalista: The Prayer of the Kabbalist. 2009. (ENG & SPA.). 204p. pap. 14.95 *(978-1-57189-622-3(8))* Research Centre of Kabbalah.

—El Monstruo Es Real! Cómo Enfrentarte a Tus Miedos y Eliminarlos para Siempre. 2007. (Technology for the Soul Ser.). (SPA.). 140p. 9.95 *(978-1-57189-561-5(2))* Research Centre of Kabbalah.

—El Poder de la Kabbalah. rev. ed. 2011.Tr. of Power of Kabbalah. (ENG & SPA.). 272p. pap. 14.95 *(978-1-57189-770-1(4))* Research Centre of Kabbalah.

—The Power of Kabbalah: Thirteen Principles to Overcome Challenges & Achieve Fulfillment. rev. ed. 2011. (ENG.). 272p. pap. 15.00 *(978-1-57189-699-5(6))* Research Centre of Kabbalah.

—The Prayer of the Kabbalist: The 42-Letter Name of God. 2007. (ENG., Illus.). 254p. 19.95 *(978-1-57189-575-2(2))* Research Centre of Kabbalah.

—Rebooting: Defeating Depression with the Power of Kabbalah. 2007. (Technology for the Soul Ser.). (ENG.). 254p. 17.95 *(978-1-57189-560-8(4))* Research Centre of Kabbalah.

—Satan: Una Autobiografia. 2010. (ENG & SPA.). 286p. pap. 14.95 *(978-1-57189-649-0(X))* Research Centre of Kabbalah.

Berg, Yehuda. The Way of the Kabbalist: A User's Guide to Technology for the Soul. (ENG.). 2012. 240p. pap. 14.95 ***(978-1-57189-816-6(6))*** 2008. 224p. 19.95 *(978-1-57189-603-2(1))* Research Centre of Kabbalah.

Berg, Yehuda, ed. Genesis: The Kabbalistic Bible, Volume One. 2008. (ENG & HEB.). 448p. 24.95 *(978-1-57189-606-3(6))* Research Centre of Kabbalah.

—The Kabbalistic Bible - Exodus: Technology for the Soul. 2009. (Kabbalistic Bible Ser.). (ENG & HEB.). 352p. 24.95 *(978-1-57189-614-8(7))* Research Centre of Kabbalah.

—The Kabbalistic Bible - Leviticus: Technology for the Soul. 2010. (Kabbalistic Bible Ser.). (ENG & HEB.). 360p. 24.95 *(978-1-57189-625-4(2))* Research Centre of Kabbalah.

—Numbers. 2010. (Kabbalistic Bible Ser.). (ENG.). 392p. 24.95 *(978-1-57189-626-1(0))* Research Centre of Kabbalah.

Berg, Yehuda, told to. Satan: an Autobiography. 2010. (ENG.). 286p. pap. 15.00 *(978-1-57189-662-9(7))* Research Centre of Kabbalah.

Block, Thomas. Shalom/Salaam: A Story of a Mystical Fraternity. 2010. (ENG.). 248p. pap. 24.95 *(978-1-891785-48-1(6))* Fons Vitae of Kentucky, Inc.

Book Raziel. 12.50 *(978-0-87559-105-6(1))* Shalom, P. Pubns., Inc.

Brennan, Marcia. Flowering Light: Kabbalistic Mysticism & the Art of Elliot R. Wolfson. 2008. *(978-0-89263-008-0(6))*; *(978-0-89263-009-7(4))* Rice Univ. Pr.

Byrd, Alfred D. Kabbalah for Evangelical Christians. 2007. 57p. pap. 15.50 *(978-0-615-16440-3(4))* Byrd, Alfred D.

Case, Jonathan M. Journey to the Soul: Kabbalah's Pathway for Your Present & Future. 2008. 236p. per. 20.95 *(978-1-4327-1957-9(2))* Outskirts Pr., Inc.

Christopher, Lyam Thomas. Kabbalah, Magic & the Great Work of Self-Transformation: A Complete Course. 2006. (ENG., Illus.). 384p. per. 22.95 *(978-0-7387-0893-5(3))* Llewellyn Pubns.

Cohn-Sherbok, Dan. Kabbalah & Jewish Mysticism: An Introductory Anthology. 2nd ed. 2006. (ENG., Illus.). 224p. per. 14.95 *(978-1-85168-454-0(9))* Oneworld Pubns. GBR. Dist: National Bk. Network.

Cohn, Tzvi Meir. Baal Shem Tov Numbers: Mystical Stories of the Legendary Kaballah Master, Vol. 4. 2012. Orig. Title: Faith Love Joy. (ENG.). pap. 14.95 *(978-0-9792865-5-1(7))* BST Publishing.

Cohn, Tzvi Meir, adapted by. Baal Shem Tov Leviticus: Mystical Stories on the Weekly Torah Portion. 2012. Orig. Title: Faith Love Joy. (ENG.). pap. 14.95 *(978-0-9792865-4-4(9))* BST Publishing.

Coleville, W. J. The Secret Tradition in Israel, the Zohar, & the Serpent & Fall Of. 2006. pap. 12.95 *(978-1-4286-7965-8(0))* Kessinger Publishing, LLC.

Conte, Joseph F. Judaeo-Christian Kabbalah: (Part One - not a Subtitle) 2006. 319p. pap. 29.95 *(978-1-4241-0630-1(3))* PublishAmerica, Inc.

—Judaeo-Christian Kabbalah: (Part Two - not a Subtitle) 2006. 605p. pap. 39.95 *(978-1-4241-2897-6(8))* PublishAmerica, Inc.

Cordovero, Moshe. Pardes Rimonim, Orchard of Pomegranates - Vol. 1: Parts 1-4. unabr. ed. 2007. (ENG & HEB.). 340p. per. *(978-1-897352-17-5(4))* Providence University.

Coudert, A. P. Leibniz & the Kabbalah. 2010. (International Archives of the History of Ideas / archives internationales d'histoire des Idées Ser.). 248p. pap. 239.00 *(978-90-481-4465-5(5)*, 9048144655) Springer.

Dan, Joseph. Kabbalah. 2007. (Very Short Introductions Ser.). (ENG., Illus.). 144p. pap. 11.95 *(978-0-19-532705-2(5))* Oxford Univ. Pr., Inc.

Dosick, Wayne D. & Kaufman Dosick, Ellen. 20 Minute Kabbalah: The Daily Personal Spiritual Practice That Brings You to God, Your Soul-Knowing, & Your Heart's Desires. 2008. (ENG., Illus.). 181p. pap. 28.00 *(978-1-933754-50-5(8))* Waterside Publishing.

Drob, Sanford. Kabbalistic Visions: C. G. Jung & Jewish Mysticism. 2009. 313p. pap. 26.95 *(978-1-882670-86-4(8))* Spring Journal.

Drob, Sanford L. Gateway to a New Kabbalah: Jewish Mysticism, Postmodernism, & Contemporary Theology. 2008. (Studies in Judaism Ser.). 83.95 *(978-1-4331-0304-9(4))* Lang, Peter Publishing, Inc.

Dubov, Nissan Dovid. Inward Bound: A Guide to Understanding Kabbalah. 2007. 211p. 21.95 *(978-1-932687-98-9(X)*, Devora Publishing) Simcha Media Group.

Dubuis, Jean. The Experience of Eternity. 2008. 178p. pap. 29.95 *(978-0-615-16107-5(3))* Triad Publishing.

Dunn, James David, ed. Window of the Soul: The Kabbalah of Rabbi Isaac Luria (1534-1572): Selections from Chayyim Vital. Snyder, Nathan, tr. from HEB. 2008. (ENG.). 1p. 22.95 *(978-1-57863-428-6(8)*, Weiser Bks.) Red Wheel/Weiser.

Dureau, Yona. Francesco Giorgio's de Harmonia Mundi. 2011. (Illus.). 704p. 169.95 ***(978-0-7734-1582-9(3))*** Mellen, Edwin Pr., The.

Dureau, Yona Claire. The Christian Cabbalah Movement in Renaissance England & Its Influence on William Shakespeare. 2009. (Illus.). 408p. 119.95 *(978-0-7734-4818-6(7))* Mellen, Edwin Pr., The.

Dweck, Yaacob. The Scandal of Kabbalah: Leon Moden, Jewish Mysticism, Early Modern Venice. 2011. (Jews, Christians, & Muslims from the Ancient to the Modern World Ser.). (ENG., Illus.). 296p. (C). 35.00 *(978-0-691-14508-2(3))* Princeton Univ. Pr.

Dynner, Glenn, ed. Holy Dissent: Jewish & Christian Mystics in Eastern Europe. 2011. 44.95 *(978-0-8143-3517-8(9))* Wayne State Univ. Pr.

Fell Smith, Charlotte. Qabalah - John Dee 1527 - 1608 - the Secret Life of Queen Elizabeth I's Astrologer Royal. 2008. 155p. pap. 16.50 *(978-1-4092-2856-1(8))* Lulu Enterprises Inc.

Fishbane, Eitan. As Light Before Dawn: The Inner World of a Medieval Kabbalist. 2009. (Stanford Studies in Jewish History & C Ser.). (ENG.). 336p. 45.00 *(978-0-8047-5913-7(8))* Stanford Univ. Pr.

Fishbane, Eitan. The Sabbath Soul: Mystical Reflections on the Transformative Power of Holy Time. 2011. (HEB & ENG.). 200p. pap. 18.99 ***(978-1-58023-459-7(3))*** Jewish Lights Publishing.

Flatto, Sharon. The Kabbalistic Culture of Eighteenth-Century Prague: Ezekiel Landau & His Contemporaries. 2010. 282p. 54.50 *(978-1-904113-39-3(7))* Littman Library of Jewish Civilization, The GBR. Dist: International Specialized Bk. Services.

Fondse, Francesca. Angelus: The Face of Love, 2 vols. 2011. (Illus.). 168p. pap. 42.31 ***(978-1-4567-8294-8(0))*** AuthorHouse.

—Angelus: The Gift of Love, 2 vols. 2011. (Illus.). 192p. pap. 46.69 ***(978-1-4567-8293-1(2))*** AuthorHouse.

Frankiel, Tamar. Kabbalah: A Brief Introduction for Christians. 2006. (Illus.). 184p. per. 16.99 *(978-1-58023-303-3(1))* Jewish Lights Publishing.

Garb, Jonathan. The Chosen Will Become Herds: Studies in Twentieth-Century Kabbalah. Berkovits-Murciano, Yaffah, tr. from HEB. 2009. (ENG.). 240p. pap. 50.00 *(978-0-300-12394-4(9))* Yale Univ. Pr.

—Shamanic Trance in Modern Kabbalah. 2011. (ENG.). 288p. 45.00 *(978-0-226-28207-7(4))* Univ. of Chicago Pr.

Gikkatilla, Joseph. Gates of Light: Sha'are Orah. 2010. (Sacred Literature Trust Ser.). (ENG.). 448p. pap. 34.95 *(978-0-300-16513-5(7))* Yale Univ. Pr.

Giller, Pinchas. Kabbalah: A Guide for the Perplexed. 2011. (Guides for the Perplexed Ser.). (ENG., Illus.). 232p. 80.00 *(978-1-4411-1119-7(0))*; pap. 24.95 *(978-1-4411-1032-9(1))* Continuum International Publishing Group, Ltd. GBR. Dist: National Bk. Network.

Ginsburg, Elliot K. The Sabbath in Classical Kabbalah. 2nd rev. ed. 2008. 362p. pap. 29.95 *(978-1-904113-43-0(5))* Littman Library of Jewish Civilization, The GBR. Dist: International Specialized Bk. Services.

—Sod Ha-Shabbat: The Mystery of the Sabbath. 2006. (C). pap. 31.95 *(978-0-7914-7068-8(7))* State Univ. of New York Pr.

Glick, Rabbi Yoel. Seeking the Divine Presence Pt. 1: The Three Pillars of a Jewish Spiritual Life. 2009. 360p. pap. 26.00 *(978-1-4251-9090-3(1))* Trafford Publishing.

Glotzer, Leonard R. The Kabbalistic System of the Ari: The Hidden Meaning, Symbolism & Sexuality of Lurian Mysticism. 2007. 300p. per. 16.95 *(978-1-4327-0876-4(7))* Outskirts Pr., Inc.

Goldwag, Arthur. Cults, Conspiracies, & Secret Societies: The Straight Scoop on Freemasons, the Illuminati, Skull & Bones, Black Helicopters, the New World Order, & Many, Many More. 2009. (Vintage Ser.). (ENG.). 384p. pap. 16.00 *(978-0-307-39067-7(5)*, Vintage) Knopf Doubleday Publishing Group.

Greenspahn, Frederick, ed. Jewish Mysticism & Kabbalah: New Insights & Scholarship. 2011. (ENG., Illus.). 272p. 25.00 ***(978-0-8147-3286-1(0))*** New York Univ. Pr.

Greenspahn, Frederick E. Jewish Mysticism & Kabbalah: New Insights & Scholarship. 2011. (Illus.). xiii, 250p. E-Book ***(978-0-8147-3319-6(0))***; E-Book ***(978-0-8147-3288-5(7))*** New York Univ. Pr.

Greer, John Michael. Paths of Wisdom: A Guide to the Magical Cabala. rev. ed. 2008. 430p. per. 29.95 *(978-1-870450-25-6(6))* Thoth Pubns. GBR. Dist: SCB Distributors.

Guetta, Alessandro. Philosophy & Kabbalah: Elijah Benamozegh & the Reconciliation of Western Thought & Jewish Esotericism. Kahan, Helena, tr. from ITA. 2010. (SUNY series in Contemporary Jewish Thought Ser.). 246p. pap. 24.95 *(978-0-7914-7576-8(X)*, Suny Pr.) State Univ. of New York Pr.

Guetta, Alessandro & Kahan, Helena. Philosophy & Kabbalah: Elijah Benamozegh & the Reconciliation of Western Thought & Jewish Esotericism. Kahan, Helena, tr. from ITA. 2009. 224p. 65.00 *(978-0-7914-7575-1(1))* State Univ. of New York Pr.

Halevi, Z'ev be. Kabbalistic Universe. 2007. 292p. pap. 18.95 *(978-1-56171-822-1(X))* SPI Bks.

—World of Kabbalah. 2007. 292p. pap. 18.95 *(978-1-56171-823-8(8))* SPI Bks.

Halevi, Z'ev ben Shimon. Adam & the Kabbalistic Trees. 2007. (Illus.). 292p. pap. 18.95 *(978-1-56171-218-2(3))* SPI Bks.

Hall, Manly. The Secret Teachings of All Ages. 2007. 640p. (ENG.). 39.99 *(978-1-60459-096-8(3))*; per. 15.99 *(978-1-60459-095-1(5))* Wilder Pubns., Ltd.

Hames, Harvey J. Like Angels on Jacob's Ladder: Abraham Abulafia, the Franciscans, & Joachimism. 2009. 189p. pap. 24.95 *(978-0-7914-7272-9(8))* State Univ. of New York Pr.

—Like Angels on Jacob's Ladder: Abraham Abulafia, the Franciscans & Joachimism. 2008. (Illus.). 171p. 50.00 *(978-0-7914-7271-2(X))* State Univ. of New York Pr.

Harkness, Deborah. John Dee's Conversations with Angels: Cabala, Alchemy, & the End of Nature. 2006. (ENG., Illus.). 268p. pap. 53.00 *(978-0-521-02748-9(9))* Cambridge Univ. Pr.

Haskell, Ellen Davina. Suckling at My Mother's Breasts: The Image of a Nursing God in Jewish Mysticism. 2012. (SUNY Series in Western Esoteric Traditions Ser.). (ENG.). 176p. 75.00 ***(978-1-4384-4381-2(1))*** State Univ. of New York Pr.

Hellner-Eshed, Melila. A River Flows from Eden: The Language of Mystical Experience in the Zohar. (ENG.). 488p. 2011. pap. 29.95 *(978-0-8047-7859-6(0))* 2009. 60.00 *(978-0-8047-5939-7(1))* Stanford Univ. Pr.

Hieronimus, J. Zohara Meyerhoff. Sanctuary of the Divine Presence: Hebraic Teachings on Initiation & Illumination. 2012. E-Book ***(978-1-59477-951-0(1)***, Inner Traditions) Inner Traditions International, Ltd.

Hieronimus, J. Zohara Meyerhoff & Hieronimus, Zohara. Kabbalistic Teachings of the Female Prophets: The Seven Holy Women of Ancient Israel. 2008. (ENG.). 1p. pap. 24.95 *(978-1-59477-227-6(4))* Inner Traditions International, Ltd.

Hoffman, Edward. The Kabbalah Reader. 2010. (ENG.). 272p. pap. 17.95 *(978-1-59030-656-7(2)*, Trumpeter) Shambhala Pubns., Inc.

Hogan, Timothy. The 32 Secret Paths of Solomon: A New Examination of the Qabbalah in Freemasonry. 2009. 100p. pap. 15.00 *(978-0-557-04610-2(6))* Lulu Enterprises Inc.

Idel, Moshe. Kabbalah in Italy, 1280-1510: A Survey. 2011. (ENG.). 512p. 55.00 *(978-0-300-12626-6(3))* Yale Univ. Pr.

—Old Worlds, New Mirrors: On Jewish Mysticism & Twentieth-Century Thought. 2009. (Jewish Culture & Contexts Ser.). 336p. (C). 59.95 *(978-0-8122-4130-3(4))* Univ. of Pennsylvania Pr.

John Littlewood Staff. Way: A Celtic Qabalah. 2009. (ENG., Illus.). 240p. pap. 24.95 *(978-1-84694-136-8(9))* O Bks.,John Hunt.

Kabbal, Jeru. Finding Clarity: A Guide to the Deeper Levels of Your Being. Ritchie, Victoria et al, eds. 2006. (ENG.). 192p. pap. 16.95 *(978-1-55643-620-8(3))* North Atlantic Bks.

Kalet, Zusha. Kabbalah of Yeshua. 2007. 206p. pap. 19.86 *(978-0-615-14776-5(3))* Kabbalah Nation Publishing.

Kalisch, Isidor. Sepher Yezirah: A Book on Creation or the Jewish Metaphysics of Remote Antiquity. 2011. 60p. 36.95 ***(978-1-258-03742-0(4))*** Literary Licensing, LLC.

Kalisch, Isidor & Stenring, Knut, trs. Sepher Yetzirah, the Book of Creation: Two Versions, Explaining Jewish Mystical Philosophy & the Cabala. 2006. (Illus.). 124p. per. 12.95 *(978-1-58509-282-6(7))* Book Tree, The.

Kamenetz, Rodger. Burnt Books: Rabbi Nachman of Bratzlav & Franz Kafka. 2010. 224p. 25.00 *(978-0-8052-4257-7(0)*, Schocken) Knopf Doubleday Publishing Group.

Kantrowitz, Min. Counting the Omer: A Kabbalistic Meditation Guide. 2010. *(978-1-935604-00-6(7))* Gaon Bks.

Karr, Don & Skinner, Stephen. Sepher Raziel: A Sixteenth Century English Grimoire. 2010. (ENG.). 296p. 65.00 *(978-0-7387-2353-2(3))* Llewellyn Pubns.

Kingsford, Anna. The Hermetic Kabbalah of Anna Kingsford. 2007. 231p. pap. 26.50 *(978-1-84753-313-5(2))* Lulu Enterprises Inc.

Klein, Eliahu J. A Mystical Haggadah: Passover Meditations, Teachings, & Tales. 2008. (ENG., Illus.). 200p. pap. 16.95 *(978-1-55643-649-9(1))* North Atlantic Bks.

Knoche, Grace F. Theosophy in the Qabbalah. 2006. (ENG., Illus.). 187p. 21.00 *(978-1-55700-183-2(9))*; pap. 14.00 *(978-1-55700-184-9(7))* Theosophical Univ. Pr.

Koltko-Rivera, Mark E. Learning about the Three Kabbalahs: A Guide to Studying the Jewish Kabbalah, the Christian Cabala, & the Magickal Qabalah, 1 vol., Vol. 1. 2008. (Illus.). 200p. per. 23.95 *(978-0-9801042-1-9(1))* LVX Publishing Co.

Krakovsky, Levi I. Omnipotent Light Revealed the Luminous T. 2006. pap. 19.95 *(978-1-4286-4093-1(2))* Kessinger Publishing, LLC.

Kuhr, Moshe D. Lion Cub of Prague: Thought, Kabbala, Hashkafa from Gur Arye, the Maharal of Prague-Genesis. 2008. 250p. 24.95 *(978-1-934440-12-4(4)*, Devora Publishing) Simcha Media Group.

Kurzweil, Arthur. Kabbalah for Dummies. 2006. (ENG., Illus.). 384p. pap. 19.99 *(978-0-471-91590-4(4)*, For Dummies) Wiley, John & Sons, Inc.

Kushner, Lawrence. I'm God, You're Not: Observations on Organized Religion & Other Disguises of the Ego. 2010. 176p. 21.99 *(978-1-58023-441-2(0))* Jewish Lights Publishing.

Laitman, Michael. From Chaos to Harmony: The Solution to the Global Crisis According to the Wisdom of Kabbalah. 2006. (ENG., Illus.). 208p. pap. 4.95

(978-0-9781590-4-7(7), Bnei Baruch) Laitman Kabbalah Pubs. CAN. Dist: National Bk. Network.

—Gems of Wisdom: Words of the Great Kabbalists from All Generations. 2011. 472p. pap. 10.00 (978-1-897448-49-6(X), Bnei Baruch) Laitman Kabbalah Pubs. CAN. Dist: National Bk. Network.

—Guide to the Hidden Wisdom of Kabbalah. 3rd ed. 2009. (ENG.). 216p. pap., instr.'s gde. ed. 15.00 (978-1-897448-16-8(3), Bnei Baruch) Laitman Kabbalah Pubs. CAN. Dist: National Bk. Network.

—Kabbalah for Beginners. 4th ed. 2007. (ENG., Illus.). 192p. per. 7.00 (978-0-9781590-9-2(8), Bnei Baruch) Laitman Kabbalah Pubs. CAN. Dist: National Bk. Network.

—Kabbalah Revealed: The Ordinary Person's Guide to a More Peaceful Life. 2006. (ENG., Illus.). 1p. pap. 4.95 (978-0-9781590-0-9(4), Bnei Baruch) Laitman Kabbalah Pubs. CAN. Dist: National Bk. Network.

—Kabbalah, Science & the Meaning of Life: Because Your Life Has Meaning. 2006. (ENG., Illus.). 224p. per. 9.95 (978-0-9738268-9-0(4), Bnei Baruch) Laitman Kabbalah Pubs. CAN. Dist: National Bk. Network.

—The Zohar: Annotations to the Ashlag Commentary. 2008. (ENG., Illus.). 520p. 30.00 (978-1-897448-09-0(0), Bnei Baruch) Laitman Kabbalah Pubs. CAN. Dist: National Bk. Network.

Laitman, Rav Michael & Canright, Collin. The Complete Idiot's Guide to Kabbalah. 2007. (Complete Idiot's Guide Ser.). (ENG., Illus.). 320p. (gr. 12-18). 18.95 (978-1-59257-542-8(0), Alpha Bks.) Penguin Group (USA) Inc.

Lancer, Bob. Place It on the Tree: Revealing the Secret Wisdom of the Kabbalah - A Guide for Using Kabbalah Cards. 144p. pap. 10.95 (978-0-9628666-2-3(8)) Tools of the Tree.

Lanza, Fabrizio, ed. Shimmush Tehillim, Tehillim, Psalms 151-155 & Their Kabbalistic Use. unabr. ed. 2007. (ENG.). 356p. per. (978-1-897352-15-1(8)) Providence University.

Latiman, Michael. The Wise Heart: Tales & Allegories of Three Contemporary Sages. 2011. (ENG.). 80p. pap. 15.00 (978-1-897448-47-2(3), Bnei Baruch) Laitman Kabbalah Pubs. CAN. Dist: National Bk. Network.

Lee, Rebecca Carol. The Three Resurrections: Kabballistically Decoding the "Book of Revelations" 168p. pap. (978-0-9670103-0-4(6)) Lee, Rebecca.

Levenda, Peter & Levenda. Stairway to Heaven: Chinese Alchemists, Jewish Kabbalists, & the Art of Spiritual Transformation. 2008. (ENG., Illus.). 272p. pap. 26.95 (978-0-8264-2850-9(9)) Continuum International Publishing Group, Ltd. GBR. Dist: National Bk. Network.

Luzzatto, Moshe Chaim. KLaCh Pischey Chokhmah - 138 Aperture di Saggezza. unabr. ed. 2006. (ITA.). 492p. per. (978-1-897352-23-6(9)) Providence University.

Magid, Shaul. From Metaphysics to Midrash: Myth, History, & the Interpretation of Scripture in Lurianic Kabbala. 2008. (Indiana Studies in Biblical Literature Ser.). (ENG., Illus.). 368p. 39.95 (978-0-253-35088-6(3), 0253350883) Indiana Univ. Pr.

Mancuso, P. Shabbatai Donnolo's Sefer Hakhmoni: Introduction, Critical Text, & Annotated English Translation. 2009. (Studies in Jewish History & Culture Ser.). 432p. (978-90-04-16762-9(5)) BRILL.

Marcus, Cesar Leo. Kabbalah Judeo-Christian the Divine Logic. 2007. 186p. pap. 24.99 (978-1-4303-0826-3(5)) Lulu Enterprises Inc.

Marcus, César Leo. Kabbalah Judeo-Cristiana: El plan Divino. 2006. (SPA.). pap. 19.50 (978-1-59835-016-6(1), CBH Bks.) Cambridge BrickHouse, Inc.

Marcus, Cesar Leo. Kabbalah Judeo Cristiana la Lógica Divina. 2007. 150p. pap. 19.50 (978-1-4303-1043-3(X)) Lulu Enterprises Inc.

Mark, Zvi. The Scroll of Secrets: The Hidden Messianic Vision of R. Nachman of Breslav. 2010. (Reference Library of Jewish Intellectual History Ser.). (ENG.). 320p. 49.00 (978-1-934843-93-2(8)); pap. 25.00 (978-1-934843-94-9(6)) Academic Studies Pr.

Mathers, S. L. MacGregor. The Kabbalah Unveiled. 2009. 416p. 30.99 (978-0-559-12306-1(X)); 32.99 (978-0-559-12291-0(8)); pap. 33.75 (978-0-559-12301-6(9)); pap. 27.99 (978-0-559-12296-5(9)) BiblioBazaar.

—The Kabbalah Unveiled. 2006. (Dover Books on the Occult Ser.). (ENG., Illus.). 384p. per. 14.95 (978-0-486-45137-4(2)) Dover Pubns., Inc.

—The Kabbalah Unveiled. 2007. (ENG.). 380p. 48.95 (978-0-548-28176-5(9)) Kessinger Publishing, LLC.

Matt, Daniel, tr. from ARC. The Zohar. (Zohar: Pritzker Edition Ser.). (ENG., Illus.). Vol. 4. 2007. 592p. 55.00 (978-0-8047-5712-6(7)) Vol. 5. 2009. 656p. 55.00 (978-0-8047-6219-9(8)) Vol. 6. 2011. 472p. 55.00 **(978-0-8047-7663-9(6))** Stanford Univ. Pr.

Michaelson, Jay. God in Your Body: Kabbalah, Mindfulness & Embodied Spiritual Practice. 2006. (Illus.). 247p. per. 16.99 (978-1-58023-304-0(X)) Jewish Lights Publishing.

Morgenstern, Arie & Greenwood, Naftali. The Gaon of Vilna & His Messianic Vision. 2012. **(978-965-229-566-8(3))** Gefen Bks.

Moses ben Shem Tov & Oron, Michal. Sefer Ha-Shem: Ha-Meyuhas Le-R. Moshen de Leon. 2010. (Illus.). 236p. **(978-1-933379-12-8(X))** Cherub Pr.

Mottolese, Maurizio. Analogy in Midrash & Kabbalah: Interpretive Projections of the Sanctuary & Ritual. 2007. 398p. (978-1-933379-07-4(3)) Cherub Pr.

Myers, Jody Elizabeth. Kabbalah & the Spiritual Quest: The Kabbalah Centre in America, 1 vol. 2007. (Religion, Health, & Healing Ser.). (Illus.). 272p. 49.95 (978-0-275-98940-8(2), C8940, Praeger Pubs.) Greenwood Publishing Group, Inc.

Mysticism: Kabbalah. (Mysticism Ser.). 96p. (978-1-4054-8971-3(5)) Parragon, Inc.

Necker, Gerold. Humanistische Kabbala Im Barock: Leben und Werk des Abraham Cohen de Herrera. 2011. (Studia Judaica Ser.). (GER.). XII, 298p. 140.00 **(978-3-11-025220-0(1))** De Gruyter, Walter Inc.

Neissany, Ebrahim. Many Mistakes Many Lives: Kabbalah, Reincarnation, & the Purpose of Life. 2008. 306p. (ENG.). 26.00 (978-0-9801799-1-0(2)); pap. 19.99 (978-0-9801799-0-3(4)) Chesed Avraham Temple.

Nilton Bonder. The Kabbalah of Time: Teachings on the Inexistence of God. 2009. 192p. 19.95 (978-1-4269-2233-6(7)); pap. 9.95 (978-1-4269-2232-9(9)) Trafford Publishing.

Oelberger, Richard. Qualitative Kabbalah. 2008. 144p. per. (978-3-8364-3490-4(3)) VDM Verlag Dr. Mueller e.K.

Paloma, Vanessa. Mystic Siren: Woman's Voice in the Balance of Creation. 2007. 80p. pap. 24.95 (978-0-9777514-5-7(7)) World Arts Pr.

Parfitt, Will. Kabbalah for Life: How to Use the Power & Wisdom of This Ancient Tradition. 2007. (ENG., Illus.). 272p. per. 19.95 (978-1-84604-035-1(3)) Random Hse. GBR. Dist: Independent Pubs. Group.

Patterson, David. Overcoming Alienation: A Kabbalistic Reflection on the Five Levels of the Soul. 2008. 247p. pap. 24.95 (978-1-60441-996-2(2)) PublishAmerica, Inc.

Penczak, Christopher. Temple of High Witchcraft: Ceremonies, Spheres & the Witches' Qabalah. 2007. (Penczak Temple Ser.: 7). (ENG.). 576p. pap. 21.95 (978-0-7387-1165-2(9)) Llewellyn Pubns.

Pick, Bernhard. The Cabala. 2008. (ENG.). 84p. per. 18.75 (978-1-4375-3198-5(9)); 76p. pap. 16.99 (978-1-4346-7882-9(2)); (ENG.). 84p. pap. 18.99 (978-1-4346-7883-6(0)) BiblioBazaar.

Pinson, DovBer. Thirty Two Gates: Awakening Through Kabbalah. 2009. 96p. pap. 9.95 (978-1-934730-24-9(6)) Yehuda, Ben Pr.

Prince Charles, et al. Sophi: Volume 13, No. 2. 2008. 184p. pap. 17.95 (978-0-9798429-1-7(3)) Foundation for Traditional Studies.

Qabalah, Qliphoth & Goetic Magic. 2008. (Illus.). 248p. 35.00 (978-0-9721820-1-0(2)) AJNA.

Regardie, Israel. Foundations of Practical Magic: An Introduction to Qabalistic, Magical & Meditative Techniques. 2nd ed. 2008. (Illus.). 160p. per. 22.95 (978-1-904658-11-5(3)) Aeon Bks. Ltd. GBR. Dist: Stylus Publishing, LLC.

Reiss, Fred. Ancient Secrets of Creation: Sepher Yetzira, the Book That Started Kabbalah, Revealed. 2007. 124p. per. 12.95 (978-0-595-44955-2(7)) iUniverse, Inc.

Richardson, Alan AA. Magical Kabbalah. 2008. (Illus.). 135p. per. 19.95 (978-1-870450-53-9(1)) Thoth Pubns. GBR. Dist: SCB Distributors.

Richter, Joannes. The Celestial God. 2009. 137p. pap. 20.50 (978-1-4092-6632-7(X)) Lulu Enterprises Inc.

Rolls, Derek J. The Web of Wyrd - the Truth Against the World. 2010. 126p. pap. 25.50 (978-1-4461-4034-5(2)); (ENG.). 132p. pap. 62.95 (978-1-4457-8953-8(1)) Lulu Enterprises Inc.

Rosen, Jeremy. Kabbalah Inspirations: Mystic Themes, Texts, & Symbols. 2006. (Illus.). 160p. (978-1-84483-192-0(2)) Duncan Baird Pubs. GBR. Dist: Sterling Publishing Co., Inc.

Ross, Aubrey. The Messiah of Turkey: Discovered! the Sabbateans. the secret Kabbalists of Islam. 2007. (Illus.). 291p. pap. (978-0-9552404-5-4(X)) I2I Publishing.

Rousse-Lacordaire, Jérôme. Une Controverse sur la magie et la kabbale a la Renaissance. 2010. (Travaux d'Humanisme et Renaissance Ser.). (FRE.). 392p. (C). 151.00 (978-2-600-01327-7(X)) Droz, Librairie CHE. Dist: Brown, David Bk. Co., The.

Runes, Dagobert D., frwd. The Wisdom of the Kabbalah: It's Essence & Philosophy. 2011. 184p. 42.95 **(978-1-258-00728-7(2))** Literary Licensing, LLC.

Samuel, Gabriella. Kabbalah Handbook: A Concise Encyclopedia of Terms & Concepts in Jewish Mysticism. 2007. (HEB & ENG.). 480p. (gr. 12-18). 19.95 (978-1-58542-560-0(5), Tarcher) Penguin Group (USA) Inc.

Sasson, Gahl. Cosmic Navigator: Design Your Destiny with Astrology & Kabbalah. 2008. (ENG., Illus.). 1p. pap. 21.95 (978-1-57863-420-0(2), Weiser Bks.) Red Wheel/Weiser.

Schneersohn, Shalom Dov Baer. Tract on Prayer. Danzinger, Y. Eliezer, tr. 2007. (Chasidic Heritage Ser.: Vol. 21). (ENG & HEB.). 178p. 13.95 (978-0-8266-0745-4(4)) Kehot Pubn. Society.

Schneider, Sara. Kabbalistic Writings on the Nature of Feminine & Masculine. 2009. 352p. 27.95 (978-1-934440-17-9(5), Devora Publishing) Simcha Media Group.

Schneider, Stanley & Berke, Joseph H. Centers of Power: The Convergence of Psychoanalysis & Kabbalah. (ENG., Illus.). 2008. 254p. per. 31.50 (978-0-7657-0501-3(X)) 2007. 276p. 89.50 (978-0-7657-0500-6(1)) Rowman & Littlefield Publishers, Inc. (Aronson, Jason).

Schork, Gretchen A. L. MYS 115 Foundations of QBLH. 2008. 248p. pap. 24.99 (978-0-557-00087-6(4)) Lulu Enterprises Inc.

Schusterman, Dale H. Sign Language of the Soul: A Handbook for Healing. 2nd ed. 2008. (Illus.). 219p. pap. 17.95 (978-1-59411-135-8(9)) Writers' Collective, The.

Sefardi, Shem Tov. Shaarei Tzedek - Gates of Righteousness. unabr. ed. 2007. (ENG.). 116p. (C). per. (978-1-897352-07-6(7)) Providence University.

Segol, Maria. Word & Image in Medieval Kabbalah. 2012. (New Middle Ages Ser.). (ENG.). 224p. 85.00 (978-1-4039-6974-3(4)) Palgrave Macmillan.

Shneur Zalman & Gufin, Sheneur Zalman. Shiurim Ba-Hasidut: "Shaar Ha-Yihud Veha-Emunah", Perakim 1-12 Helek Sheni Be-Sefer Ha-Tanya. 2nd ed. 2010. (HEB.). 540p. **(978-965-91675-0-0(4))** Kehot Pubn. Society.

Smith, Howard. Let There Be Light: Modern Cosmology & Kabbalah - A New Conversation Between Science & Religion. 2006. (ENG., Illus.). 286p. per. 15.95 (978-1-57731-548-3(0)) New World Library.

Steinsaltz, Adin. The Thirteen Petalled Rose: A Discourse on the Essence of Jewish Existence & Belief. Hanegbi, Yehuda, tr. from HEB. rev. exp. ed. 2006. (ENG., Illus.). 224p. per. 14.95 (978-0-465-08272-8(6)) Basic Bks.

—Understanding the Tanya: Volume Three in the Definitive Commentary on a Classic Work of Kabbalah by the World's Foremost Authority. Hanegbi, Meir, ed. Shulman, Yaacov David, tr. from HEB. 2007. (ENG.). 384p. 29.95 (978-0-7879-8826-5(X), Jossey-Bass) Wiley, John & Sons, Inc.

Stirling, William, et al. A Kabbalah Reader One: Holmes Esoteric Reader Five. Abel, R. Christopher, ed. 2009. (Esoteric Reader Ser.: 5). pap. 9.95 (978-1-55818-480-0(5)) Holmes Publishing Group, LLC.

Stuckrad, Kocku von. Kabbalah & Modernity: Interpretations, Transformations, Adaptations. Pasi, M., ed. 2010. (Aries Book Ser.). (ENG., Illus.). 442p. (978-90-04-18284-4(5)) BRILL.

Tanhuma, Rabbi. Kabbalistic Bible According to the Zohar. 2006. 108p. per. (978-956-291-326-3(0)) Editorial Benei Noaj.

Ted, Andrews. Pathworking: A Qabala Guide to Empowerment & Initiation. 2nd rev. ed. 2010. 384p. pap. 16.95 (978-1-888767-60-5(X)) Dragonhawk Publishing.

Travis, Yakov. The Foundation of Kabbalah: Rabbi Ezra of Gerona, the Emergence of Jewish Mysticism, & the Mystical Meaning of the Mitzvot. 2006. (ENG & HEB.). 39.95 (978-0-9777202-9-3(2)) Four Worlds Pr.

Trugman, Avraham Arieh. Return Again: The Dynamics of Reincarnation. 2008. 250p. 21.95 (978-1-934440-15-5(9), Devora Publishing) Simcha Media Group.

Twyman, James F. & Gruber, Philip. The Kabbalah Code: A True Adventure. (ENG.). 2012. pap. 15.95 **(978-1-4019-4024-9(2))** 2009. 240p. 22.95 (978-1-4019-2404-1(2)) Hay Hse., Inc.

Unterman, Alan. The Wisdom of the Jewish Mystics. 2009. (ENG.). 97p. pap. 12.00 (978-1-60419-013-7(2)) Axios Pr.

Van Der Naillen, Albert. The Great Message 1925. 2007. (ENG.). 188p. 37.95 (978-0-548-05673-8(0)) Kessinger Publishing, LLC.

Vincent, Samuel K. The English Qabalah. 2009. 280p. pap. (978-0-9809108-0-3(3)) 8th Hse. Publishing.

Vital, Chaim. Ktavim Chadashim - New Writings. unabr. ed. 2006. (ENG & HEB.). 236p. per. (978-1-897352-06-9(9)) Providence University.

—Sefer Ha-Goralot - the Book of Oracles. unabr. ed. 2007. (ENG & HEB.). 164p. per. (978-1-897352-16-8(6)) Providence University.

—Shaarei Kedusha - le Porte della Santità. unabr. ed. 2006. (ITA & HEB.). 220p. per. (978-1-897352-20-5(4)) Providence University.

Vital, Hayyim ben Joseph & Luria, Isaac ben Solomon. The Tree of Life: Chayyim Vital's Introduction to the Kabbalah of Isaac Luria: V. 1, the Palace of Adam Kadmon. 2nd ed. 2008. (Illus.). 452p. (978-0-9795971-0-7(2)) Arizal Pubns., Inc.

Waite, Arthur. The Holy Kabbalah. 2007. 664p. per. 18.85 (978-1-60206-324-2(9)) Cosimo, Inc.

Waton, Harry. Kabbalah & Spinozas Philosophy As A Ba. 2006. pap. 28.95 (978-1-4286-4143-3(2)) Kessinger Publishing, LLC.

Weinstein, R. B. Juvenile Sexuality, Kabbalah, & Catholic Reformation in Italy: Tiferet Bahurim by Pinhas Barukh ben Pelatiyah Monselice. 2009. (Studies in Jewish History & Culture Ser.). 395p. (978-90-04-16757-5(9)) BRILL.

Weisblum, Moshe Pinchas & Visblum, Mosheh. The Hermeneutics of Medieval Jewish Thought: Understanding the Linguistic Codes of Rashi & Nahmanides. 2007. 272p. (978-0-7734-5288-6(5)) Mellen, Edwin Pr., The.

Westcott, W. Wynn. Sepher Yetzirah: The Book of Formation & the 32 Paths of Wisdom. 2010. 44p. 30.95 (978-1-161-57414-2(X)) Kessinger Publishing, LLC.

Whitehouse, Maggy. Kabbalah Made Easy. 2011. (ENG., Illus.). 73p. pap. 12.95 (978-1-84694-544-1(5)) O Bks.,John Hunt.

Wilkinson, Robert J. The Kabbalistic Scholars of the Antwerp Polyglot Bible. 2007. (Studies in the History of Christian Traditions). 141p. (978-90-04-16251-8(8)) BRILL.

—Orientalism, Aramaic & Kabbalah in the Catholic Reformation: The First Printing of the Syriac New Testament. 2007. (Studies in the History of Christian Traditions). 288p. (978-90-04-16250-1(X)) BRILL.

Winkler, Gershon. Daily Kabbalah: Wisdom from the Tree of Life. 2009. (ENG.). 384p. pap. 17.95 (978-1-55643-794-6(3)) North Atlantic Bks.

Wolski, Nathan. A Journey into the Zohar: An Introduction to the Book of Radiance. 2010. 240p. 75.00 (978-1-4384-3053-9(1)); pap. 24.95 (978-1-4384-3054-6(X)) State Univ. of New York Pr.

Worch, J. Hershy. Sefer Yetzira: Chronicles of Desire. 2009. (HEB & ENG., Illus.). 532p. pap. 62.99 (978-0-7618-4974-2(2)) Univ. Pr. of America, Inc.

The Zohar-English Only, 5 vols. 95.00 (978-0-910218-91-7(9)) Bennet, Rebecca Pubns., Inc.

CABALLERO, FERNAN, 1796-1877

Caballero, Fernan & Comellas Aguirrezábal, Mercedes. Obras Escogidas. 2010. (SPA.). lxxvii, 620p. (978-84-96824-67-6(5)) Fundacion Jose Manuel Lara.

CABARETS

see Music-Halls (Variety-Theaters, Cabarets, etc.)

CABEZA DE VACA, ALVAR NUNEZ, 16TH CENT.

see Nunez Cabeza de Vaca, Alvar, 16th cent.

CABBAGE

Allen, Charles. Cabbage, Cauliflower & Allied Vegetables. 2008. (Gardening in America Ser.). (ENG.). 148p. pap. 11.95 (978-1-4290-1301-7(X)) Applewood Bks.

Gregory, James J. H. The Better Days Books Origiganic Guide to Growing Cabbages & Cauliflowers. 2008. 84p. pap. 8.95 (978-1-4357-3319-0(3)) Lulu Enterprises Inc.

CABBALA

see Cabala

CABELL, JAMES BRANCH, 1879-1958

Bregenzer, Don. A Round-Table in Poictesme: A Symposium. 2007. 140p. (ENG.). 24.95 (978-1-4344-9486-3(1)); per. 14.95 (978-1-4344-9485-6(3)) Wildside Pr., LLC.

Brewer, Frances Joan, et al. James Branch Cabell: A Bibliography of His Writings, Biography & Criticism. 2011. 208p. 44.95 **(978-1-258-09030-2(9))** Literary Licensing, LLC.

Cabell, James Branch. Gallantry. 2008. 292p. 28.99 (978-0-554-22827-3(0)); 25.99 (978-0-554-32130-1(0)) BiblioBazaar.

—Gallantry. 2009. 186p. pap. (978-0-217-21826-9(1)); 180p. pap. (978-0-217-72010-6(2)) Books LLC.

—Gallantry. 2008. 268p. pap. (978-1-4065-9733-2(3)) Dodo Pr.

—The Jewel Merchants. 2010. 48p. pap. (978-1-4076-5477-5(2)) HardPr.

Holt, Guy. A Bibliography of the Writings of James Branch Cabell. 2007. (ENG.). 76p. per. 17.95 (978-1-4325-1460-0(1)) Kessinger Publishing, LLC.

Mencken, H. I. James Branch Cabell. 2011. 36p. 35.95 **(978-1-258-02539-7(6))** Literary Licensing, LLC.

Van Doren, Carl. James Branch Cabell. 2007. (ENG.). 108p. 33.95 (978-0-548-02486-7(3)) Kessinger Publishing, LLC.

—James Branch Cabell. 2008. 100p. pap. 19.95 (978-1-4344-6320-3(6)) Wildside Pr., LLC.

Wells, Arvin R. Jesting Moses: A Study in Cabellian Comedy. 2011. 156p. 41.95 **(978-1-258-09068-5(6))** Literary Licensing, LLC.

CABET, ETIENNE, 1788-1856

Shaw, Albert. Icaria: A Chapter in the History of Communism. (Illus.). reprint ed. lib. bdg. 98.00 (978-0-7222-4778-5(8)) Library Reprints, Inc.

—Icaria, a Chapter in the History of Communism. reprint ed. 41.50 (978-0-404-10729-1(X)) AMS Pr., Inc.

CABIN CRUISERS

see Motorboats

CABINDA (AFRICAN PEOPLE)

see Kongo (African People)

CABINET GOVERNMENT

see Cabinet System

CABINET OFFICERS

see also Ministerial Responsibility; Prime Ministers

Albright, Madeleine. Read My Pins: Stories from a Diplomat's Jewel Box. 2009. (ENG., Illus.). 176p. 40.00 (978-0-06-089918-9(2)) HarperCollins Pubs.

Baker, James A., III. Work Hard, Study ... & Keep Out of Politics! 2008. (ENG., Illus.). 496p. pap. 19.95 (978-0-8101-2489-9(0)) Northwestern Univ. Pr.

Barnes, William Horatio. The American Government. 2009. 400p. 41.99 (978-1-116-29917-5(8)); 400p. 30.99 (978-1-116-29918-2(6)); 482p. pap. 37.75 (978-1-116-29914-4(3)); 400p. pap. 34.75 (978-1-116-29919-9(4)); 482p. pap. 38.75 (978-1-116-29913-7(5)); 400p. pap. 33.75 (978-1-116-29920-5(8)) BiblioBazaar.

—The American Government. 2010. 172p. pap. 25.79 (978-1-153-27059-5(5)) General Bks. LLC.

Bell, William Gardner. Secretaries of War & Secretaries of the Army: Portraits & Biographical Sketches. rev. ed. 2011. (Center of Military History Publication). (ENG., Illus.). 204p. 46.00 **(978-0-16-086690-6(1)**, Dept. of the Army) United States Government Printing Office.

Bergen, Ernst & Pellman Good Phyllis. Jumping into Empty Space: A Reluctant Mennonite Businessman Serves in Paraguay's Presidential Cabinet, 1 vol. 2008. (ENG.). 140p. 11.95 (978-1-56148-654-0(X)) Good Bks.

Boulter, Roger Stephen. A Biography of F. C. Erasmus, South African Defence Minister, 1948-1959. 2011. (ENG.). 396p. 129.95 **(978-0-7734-2586-6(1))** Mellen, Edwin Pr., The.

Brown, Mary Beth. Condi, 0 vols. 2009. 336p. pap. 16.99 (978-1-59555-326-3(6)) Nelson, Thomas Inc.

Bryant, C. Stafford Cripps. (Illus.). 534p. pap. 19.95 (978-0-340-69473-2(4)) Headway GBR. Dist: Trafalgar Square Publishing.

Bumiller, Elisabeth. Condoleezza Rice: an American Life: A Biography. 2009. (ENG., Illus.). 464p. pap. 17.00 (978-0-8129-7713-4(0), Random Hse. Trade Paperbacks) Random House Publishing Group.

Cannadine, David. Mellon: An American Life. 2008. (Vintage Ser.). (ENG., Illus.). 832p. pap. 23.00 (978-0-307-38679-3(1), Vintage) Knopf Doubleday Publishing Group.

Carlson, Chris. Cecil Andrus: Idaho's Greatest Governor. 2011. (ENG., Illus.). 298p. pap. 17.95 **(978-0-87004-505-9(9))** Caxton Pr.

Cavazos, Lauro F. A Kineno Remembers: From the King Ranch to the White House. 2008. (Perspectives on South Texas, sponsored by Texas A&M University-Kingsville Ser.). (ENG., Illus.). 300p. per. 19.95 (978-1-60344-044-8(5)) Texas A&M Univ. Pr.

Chace, James. Acheson: The Secretary of State Who Created the American World. 2007. (ENG., Illus.). 512p. pap. 20.00 (978-1-4165-4865-2(3)) Simon & Schuster.

Cheney, Dick. In My Time: A Personal & Political Memoir. (ENG., Illus.). 576p. 2012. pap. 16.00 **(978-1-4391-7622-1(1))** 2011. 35.00 (978-1-4391-7619-1(1)) Threshold Editions. (Threshold Editions).

Cockburn, Andrew. Rumsfeld: His Rise, Fall, & Catastrophic Legacy. 2011. (ENG.). 256p. pap. 17.95 (978-1-4165-3576-8(4), Scribner) Scribner.

C

Cohen, William S. Love in Black & White: A Memoir of Race, Religion, & Romance. 2006. (ENG., Illus.). 304p. 26.95 (978-0-7425-5821-2(5)) Rowman & Littlefield Publishers, Inc.

Connor, John. Anzac & Empire: George Foster Pearce & the Foundations of Australian Defence, 1 vol. 2011. (Australian Army History Ser.). (ENG., Illus.). 248p. 55.00 (978-1-107-00950-9(2)) Cambridge Univ. Pr.

Cook, Robert J. Civil War Senator: William Pitt Fessenden & the Fight to Save the American Republic. 2011. (Conflicting Worlds: New Dimensions of the American Civil War Ser.). 344p. 48.00 (978-0-8071-3707-9(3)) Louisiana State Univ. Pr.

DeSeve, G. Edward. The Presidential Appointee's Handbook. 2008. (ENG., Illus.). 123p. pap. 19.95 (978-0-8157-1833-8(0)) Brookings Institution Pr.

Desker, Barry & Kwa, Chong Guan. Goh Keng Swee: A Public Career Remembered. 2011. 58.00 **(978-981-4291-38-5(2))** World Scientific Publishing Co., Inc.

Desmazières, Erik. A Cabinet of Rarities: Antiquarian Obsessions & the Spell of Death. 2012. (ENG., Illus.). 112p. 45.00 **(978-0-500-51634-8(0)**, 551634) Thames & Hudson.

Downey, Kirstin. The Woman Behind the New Deal: The Life of Frances Perkins, FDR's Secretary of Labor & His Moral Conscience. (ENG.). 2010. 496p. pap. 16.95 (978-1-4000-7856-1(3), Anchor) 2009. (Illus.). 480p. 35.00 (978-0-385-51365-4(8), Talese, Nan A.) Knopf Doubleday Publishing Group.

Dziobek, Linda. Worldwide Government Directory with International Organizations 2010, 01 vols. Dziobek, Linda, ed. rev. ed. 2010. 1984p. pap. 559.00 (978-0-87289-662-8(5)) CQ Pr.

Finch, L. Boyd. Legacies of Camelot: Stewart & Lee Udall, American Culture, & the Arts. 2008. (ENG., Illus.). 208p. 24.95 (978-0-8061-3879-4(3)) Univ. of Oklahoma Pr.

Flippen, J. Brooks. Conservative Conservationist: Russell E. Train & the Emergence of American Environmentalism. 2006. (Illus.). 278p. 29.95 (978-0-8071-3203-6(9)) Louisiana State Univ. Pr.

Foglesong, Richard E. Immigrant Prince: Mel Martinez & the American Dream. 2011. (Florida Government & Politics Ser.). (ENG., Illus.). 320p. 32.00 (978-0-8130-3579-6(1)) Univ. Pr. of Florida.

Goduti, Philip A. Kennedy's Kitchen Cabinet & the Pursuit of Peace: The Shaping of American Foreign Policy, 1961-1963. 2009. (ENG.). 249p. pap. 45.00 (978-0-7864-4020-7(1)) McFarland & Co., Inc. Pubs.

Graham, Bradley. By His Own Rules: The Ambitions, Successes, & Ultimate Failures of Donald Rumsfeld. 2010. (ENG., Illus.). 832p. pap. 18.95 (978-1-58648-710-2(8)) PublicAffairs.

Greene, John Robert. The George W. Bush Years. 2010. (Presidential Profiles Ser.). (Illus.). 432p. (C). (gr. 9). 95.00 (978-0-8160-7765-6(7)) Facts On File, Inc.

Grossman, Mark. Encyclopedia of the United States Cabinet, 2 vols. 2nd rev. ed. 2009. (Illus.). 1600p. 295.00 (978-1-59237-562-2(6)) Grey Hse. Publishing.

Hearn, Chester G. Lincoln, the Cabinet, & the Generals. 2010. 400p. 39.95 (978-0-8071-3637-9(9)) Louisiana State Univ. Pr.

Herspring, Dale R. Rumsfeld's Wars: The Arrogance of Power. 2008. (Modern War Studies). 247p. 34.95 (978-0-7006-1587-2(3)) Univ. Pr. of Kansas.

Horne, Alistair. Kissinger: 1973, the Crucial Year. 2010. (ENG., Illus.). 480p. pap. 17.00 (978-1-4391-9522-2(6)) Simon & Schuster.

Klepak, Hal. Raúl Castro & Cuba: A Military Story. annot. ed. 2012. (Studies of the Americas Ser.). (ENG., Illus.). 192p. 85.00 **(978-0-230-34074-9(1))** Palgrave Macmillan.

Learned, Henry Barrett. The President's Cabinet: Studies in the Origin, Formation & Structure of An American Institution. 471p. reprint ed. 98.00 (978-0-7222-7405-7(X)) Library Reprints, Inc.

Lee, Mordecai. Nixon's Super-Secretaries: The Last Grand Presidential Reorganization Effort. 2010. (Joseph V. Hughes Jr. & Holly O. Hughes Series on the Presidency & Leadership Ser.). (ENG., Illus.). 288p. 55.00 (978-1-60344-179-7(4)) Texas A&M Univ. Pr.

Levy, Herbert. Henry Morgenthau, Jr: The Remarkable Life of FDR's Secretary of the Treasury. 2010. (ENG., Illus.). 576p. 35.00 (978-1-60239-971-6(9), 239971) Skyhorse Publishing Co., Inc.

Macho, Eva. Alexander Freiherr von Bach: Stationen einer umstrittenen Karriere. 2008. (Beiträge zur Neueren Geschichte Österreichs Ser.). (GER., Illus.). 252p. pap. 56.95 (978-3-631-57821-6(0)) Lang, Peter GmbH, Europaischer Verlag der Wissenschaften DEU. Dist: Lang, Peter.

Montgomery, Leslie. The Faith of Condoleezza Rice. 2007. (Illus.). 224p. 19.99 (978-1-58134-799-9(5)) Crossway.

Mubashshiri, Asad Allah & Ladjevardi, Habib. Khatirat-I Asad Allah Mubashshiri. 2007. (PER.). 146p. (978-1-59584-108-7(3)) Ketab Corp.

Nelson, Anna K. & Nelson, Anna Kasten. The Policy Makers: Shaping American Foreign Policy from 1947 to the Present. 2008. (ENG.). 192p. 85.00 (978-0-7425-5041-4(9)); pap. 24.95 (978-0-7425-5042-1(7)) Rowman & Littlefield Publishers, Inc.

Oberle, Frank. Finding Home: A War Child's Journey to Peace, 1 vol. 2010. (ENG., Illus.). 336p. pap. (978-1-894384-76-6(8)) Heritage Hse.

Patterson, Richard S., ed. The Secretaries of State: Portraits & Biographical Sketches. 2011. 134p. 40.95 **(978-1-258-10429-0(6))** Literary Licensing, LLC.

Paulson, Henry M. On the Brink: Inside the Race to Stop the Collapse of the Global Financial System. (ENG., Illus.). 2011. 512p. pap. 16.99 (978-0-446-56194-5(0)) 2010. 496p. 28.99 (978-0-446-56193-8(2)) Grand Central Publishing. (Business Plus).

Penny Colman. A Woman Unafraid: The Achievements of Frances Perkins. 2010. 144p. pap. 12.95 (978-1-4502-0773-7(1)) iUniverse, Inc.

Poore, Benjamin Perley. The Political Register & Congressional Directory. 716p. reprint ed. 148.00 (978-0-7222-7053-0(4)) Library Reprints, Inc.

Pritchett, Wendell E. Robert Clifton Weaver & the American City: The Life & Times of an Urban Reformer. 2008. (ENG., Illus.). 444p. 30.00 (978-0-226-68448-2(2)) Univ. of Chicago Pr.

Puls, Mark. Henry Knox: Visionary General of the American Revolution. 2008. (ENG., Illus.). 288p. 26.95 (978-1-4039-8427-2(1)) Palgrave Macmillan.

Regents of Nations 2nd Ed Vol 5: Index Part 1 Asia & Pacific Oceania. 2nd rev. ed. 2007. (978-3-598-21632-9(7)) Saur, K. G. Verlag GmbH & Co.

Regents of Nations 2nd Ed Vol 5: Index Part 4/1 Western & Southern Europe. 2nd rev. ed. 2007. (978-3-598-21634-3(3)) Saur, K. G. Verlag GmbH & Co.

Regents of Nations 2nd Ed Vol 5: Index Part 4/2 East & Central Europe. 2nd rev. ed. 2007. (978-3-598-21635-0(1)) Saur, K. G. Verlag GmbH & Co.

Regents of Nations 2nd Ed Vol 5: Index Parts 4/1 & 4/2 Europe. 2nd rev. ed. 2007. (978-3-598-21633-6(5)) Saur, K. G. Verlag GmbH & Co.

Rice, Condoleezza. Extraordinary, Ordinary People: A Memoir of Family. (ENG.). 2011. 368p. pap. 15.00 (978-0-307-88847-1(9), Three Rivers Pr.) 2010. (Illus.). 352p. 27.00 (978-0-307-58787-9(8), Crown) Crown Publishing Group.

Rolde, Neil. Continental Liar from the State of Maine: James G. Blaine. 2010. (Illus.). 368p. per. 20.00 (978-0-88448-286-4(3)) Tilbury Hse. Pubs.

Rumsfeld, Donald. Known & Unknown: A Memoir. (ENG., Illus.). 832p. (gr. 12). 2012. 22.00 **(978-1-59523-084-3(X))** 2011. 36.00 (978-1-59523-067-6(X)) Penguin Group (USA) Inc. (Sentinel).

Salazar Nomination: Hearing Before the Committee on Energy & Natural Resources, United States Senate, One Hundred Eleventh Congress, First Session, to Consider the Nomination of Ken Salazar to Be Secretary of the Interior, January 15, 2009. 2009. iii, 76p. (978-0-16-082828-7(7), 552-070-38808-7) United States Government Printing Office.

Sarre, Pablo Latapí. Andante con Brío: Memoria de MIS Interacciones con Los Secretarios de Educación (1963-2006) 2008. (Vida y Pensamiento de México Ser.). (SPA.). 256p. pap. 11.95 (978-968-16-8096-1(0)) Fondo de Cultura Economica USA.

Schmitz, David F. Brent Scowcroft: Internationalism & Post-Vietnam War American Foreign Policy. 2011. (Biographies in American Foreign Policy Ser.). (ENG., Illus.). 232p. 40.00 (978-0-7425-7040-5(1)) Rowman & Littlefield Publishers, Inc.

Scholder, Amy, ed. Dr. Rice in the House. 2007. (ENG., Illus.). 128p. per. 13.95 (978-1-58322-761-9(X)) Seven Stories Pr.

Sun, Tan Siok, et al. Goh Keng Swee: A Portrait. 2010. (ENG.). 228p. pap. 20.00 (978-981-4260-39-8(8), Didier Millet,Csi) Continental Sales, Inc.

Truhart, Peter. Regents of Nations: Antiquity. 2nd ed. 2006. 320p. (978-3-598-21630-5(0)) Saur, K. G. Verlag GmbH & Co.

—Regents of Nations: Index, 5 vols. 2nd ed. 2006. (Regents of Nations Ser.: Vol. 5). 134.00 (978-3-598-21547-6(9)) Saur, K. G. Verlag GmbH & Co. DEU. Dist: Saur, K. G. Verlag GmbH & Co.

Underwood, Rodman L. Stephen Russell Mallory: A Biography of the Confederate Navy Secretary & United States Senator. alt. ed. 2010. (ENG., Illus.). 256p. pap. 35.00 (978-0-7864-4927-9(6)) McFarland & Co., Inc. Pubs.

Van Atta, Dale. With Honor: Melvin Laird in War, Peace, & Politics. 2008. (ENG., Illus.). 648p. 35.00 (978-0-299-22680-0(8)) Univ. of Wisconsin Pr.

Vogel, Lars. Der Weg ins Kabinett - Karrieren von Ministern in Deutschland: Eine empirische Analyse unter besonderer Berücksichtigung der Rekrutierungsfunktion der Parlamente. 2009. (Europäische Hochschulschriften. Reihe 31: Politikwissenschaft Ser.). (GER.). 192p. pap. 43.95 (978-3-631-58846-8(1)) Lang, Peter GmbH, Europaischer Verlag der Wissenschaften DEU. Dist: Lang, Peter.

Wheatley, Henry Benjamin. Samuel Pepys & the World He Lived In. 2010. (Cambridge Library Collection - Printing & Publishing History Ser.). 328p. pap. 24.99 (978-1-108-02152-4(2)) Cambridge Univ. Pr.

Yang, Yun & Fang, Yanhong. Nei Ge Xin San Jiao: Wen Jiabao, Li Keqiang, Wang Qishan Ying Zhan Wei Ji. 2nd ed. 2008. ("Zhongguo Zhang Quan Zhe" Xi Lie Ser.: Vol. 21). (CHI., Illus.). 539p. (978-1-932138-67-2(6)) Mirror Bks. USA.

—Wen Jiabao Bian Ge. 2008. ("Zhongguo Ju Shi" Xi Lie Ser.: Vol. 50). (CHI., Illus.). 341p. (978-1-932138-62-7(5)) Mirror Bks. USA.

CABINET OFFICERS—CANADA

Martin, Don. Belinda: The Political & Private Life of Belinda Stronach. rev. ed. 2007. (ENG., Illus.). 288p. 24.95 (978-1-55263-814-9(6)) Key Porter Bks. CAN. Dist: Perseus-PGW.

Nicole Chénier-Cullen. I Found My Thrill on Parliament Hill: Not Just another Political Memoir. Welcome to the life of Bud Cullen, Trudeau era Cabinet Minister, Member of P. 2009. 400p. 35.95 (978-1-4401-7938-9(7)); pap. 25.95 (978-1-4401-7940-2(9)) iUniverse, Inc.

Tetley, William. The October Crisis 1970: An Insider's View. (ENG.). (C). 2010. 376p. pap. (978-0-7735-3801-6(1)) 2006. 310p. (978-0-7735-3118-5(1)) McGill-Queen's Univ. Pr.

CABINET OFFICERS—GREAT BRITAIN

Berlinski, Samuel, et al. Accounting for Ministers: Scandal & Survival in British Government 1945#x2013;2007. 2012. (ENG., Illus.). 208p. 90.00 **(978-0-521-51972-4(1))** Cambridge Univ. Pr.

Coby, Patrick. Thomas Cromwell: Machiavellian Statecraft & the English Reformation. 2009. (ENG., Illus.). 242p. 73.50 (978-0-7391-3403-0(5)); pap. 31.50 (978-0-7391-3404-7(3)) Lexington Bks.

Crossman, R. H. S. The Diaries of a Cabinet Minister. (Illus.). (978-0-03-020616-0(2)) Holt McDougal.

Hurd, Douglas. Choose Your Weapons: The British Foreign Secretary - 200 Years of Argument, Success & Failure. (ENG., Illus.). 2011. 448p. pap. 23.95 **(978-0-7538-2852-6(9))** 2010. 416p. 44.95 **(978-0-297-85334-3(1))** Orion Publishing Group, Ltd. GBR. (Phoenix). Dist: Independent Pubs. Group.

Jackson, Patrick. Morley of Blackburn. 2012. (ENG., Illus.). 546p. (gr. 17). 105.00 **(978-1-61147-534-0(1))** Fairleigh Dickinson Univ. Pr.

Long, James. Traitor to the Crown: The Untold Story of the Popish Plot & the Consipiracy Against Samuel Pepys. 2009. (ENG.). 336p. (gr. 12). 16.95 (978-1-59020-264-7(3)) Overlook Pr., The.

Pepys, Samuel. The Diary of Samuel Pepys. 2010. 454p. pap. 36.75 (978-1-149-34065-3(7)) BiblioBazaar.

—The Diary of Samuel Pepys. 2010. (Illus.). 280p. pap. 11.46 **(978-1-154-06619-7(3))**; 284p. pap. 12.37 (978-1-154-68262-5(5)); 280p. pap. 13.71 (978-1-154-68260-1(9)); 276p. pap. 19.89 (978-1-154-68266-3(8)); 254p. pap. 10.69 (978-1-154-68267-0(6)); 244p. pap. 10.42 (978-1-153-91574-8(X)); (Illus.). 260p. pap. 10.87 (978-1-154-68265-6(X)); (Illus.). 278p. pap. 16.95 (978-1-154-68263-2(3)); (Illus.). 280p. pap. 11.46 (978-1-153-93397-1(7)); (Illus.). 256p. pap. 10.78 (978-1-154-68264-9(1)); (Illus.). 548p. pap. 60.70 (978-1-153-70006-1(9)); (Illus.). 244p. pap. 12.37 (978-1-154-68261-8(7)) General Bks. LLC.

—The Diary of Samuel Pepys. 2012. 248p. pap. 26.75 **(978-1-276-98303-7(4))** 2012. 422p. pap. 34.75 **(978-1-276-85938-7(4))** 2012. 418p. pap. 34.75 **(978-1-276-60384-3(3))** 2012. 454p. pap. 36.75 **(978-1-277-26336-7(1))** 2012. 42p. pap. 15.75 **(978-1-276-61287-6(7))** 2012. 412p. pap. 34.75 **(978-1-276-78127-5(X))** 2012. 444p. pap. 36.75 **(978-1-276-75243-5(1))** 2012. 546p. pap. 41.75 **(978-1-276-78774-1(X))** 2012. 224p. pap. 25.75 **(978-1-276-52871-9(X))** 2012. 214p. pap. 24.75 **(978-1-276-42654-1(2))** 2012. 430p. pap. 35.75 **(978-1-276-40475-4(1))** 2012. 246p. pap. 26.75 **(978-1-276-04435-6(6))** 2011. 452p. pap. 36.75 **(978-1-179-21470-2(6))** 2011. 396p. pap. 33.75 **(978-1-179-30286-7(9))** 2011. 388p. pap. 33.75 **(978-1-179-31194-4(9))** 2011. 222p. pap. 25.75 **(978-1-179-43249-6(5))** 2011. 418p. pap. 34.75 **(978-1-179-54883-8(3))** 2011. 410p. pap. 34.75 **(978-1-179-49128-8(9))** 2011. 206p. pap. 24.75 **(978-1-179-70784-6(2))** 2011. 450p. pap. 36.75 **(978-1-179-61465-6(8))** 2011. 222p. pap. 24.75 **(978-1-179-93290-3(0))** 2011. 454p. pap. 36.75 **(978-1-179-93393-1(1))** 2011. 208p. pap. 24.75 **(978-1-174-59834-0(4))** 2011. 450p. pap. 36.75 **(978-1-174-99037-3(6))** 2011. 402p. pap. 34.75 **(978-1-174-91442-3(4))** 2011. 418p. pap. 34.75 **(978-1-174-95717-8(4))** 2011. 392p. pap. 33.75 **(978-1-174-91568-0(4))** 2011. 464p. pap. 37.75 **(978-1-174-96578-4(9))** 2011. 454p. pap. 36.75 **(978-1-174-98282-8(9))** 2011. 416p. pap. 34.75 **(978-1-174-92903-8(0))** 2011. 412p. pap. 34.75 **(978-1-175-00969-2(5))** 2011. 332p. pap. 31.75 **(978-1-175-07776-9(3))** 2011. 428p. pap. 35.75 **(978-1-175-92745-3(7))** 2011. 460p. pap. 36.75 **(978-1-175-14964-0(0))** 2011. 454p. pap. 36.75 **(978-1-175-01566-2(0))** 2011. 418p. pap. 34.75 **(978-1-174-96884-6(2))** 2011. 434p. pap. 35.75 **(978-1-175-42679-6(2))** 2011. 550p. pap. 41.75 **(978-1-176-00737-6(8))** 2011. 424p. pap. 35.75 **(978-1-175-43050-2(1))** 2011. 432p. pap. 35.75 **(978-1-175-45412-6(5))** 2011. 430p. pap. 35.75 **(978-1-178-97033-3(7))** 2011. 388p. pap. 33.75 **(978-1-178-88520-0(8))** 2011. 422p. pap. 35.75 **(978-1-178-98457-6(5))** 2011. 390p. pap. 33.75 **(978-1-174-88535-8(1))** 2011. 476p. pap. 37.75 **(978-1-175-07945-9(6))** 2011. 248p. pap. 26.75 **(978-1-179-17167-8(5))** BiblioBazaar.

Pepys, Samuel & Bright, Mynors. The Diary of Samuel Pepys. 2010. 482p. pap. 37.75 (978-1-149-34562-7(4)) BiblioBazaar.

Pepys, Samuel & Bright, Mynors. The Diary of Samuel Pepys. 2012. 204p. pap. 24.75 **(978-1-276-70812-8(2))** 2012. 546p. pap. 41.75 **(978-1-276-49931-6(0))** 2012. 208p. pap. 24.75 **(978-1-276-84915-9(X))** 2012. 450p. pap. 36.75 **(978-1-276-47632-4(9))** 2012. 388p. pap. 33.75 **(978-1-277-02876-8(1))** 2012. 156p. pap. 21.75 **(978-1-276-66344-1(7))** 2012. 188p. pap. 22.75 **(978-1-276-42990-0(8))** 2012. 240p. pap. 26.75 **(978-1-275-98209-3(3))** 2012. 222p. pap. 25.75 **(978-1-275-93788-8(8))** 2012. 212p. pap. 24.75 **(978-1-276-36106-4(8))** 2012. 362p. pap. 32.75 **(978-1-276-30701-7(2))** 2012. 390p. pap. 33.75 **(978-1-276-01973-6(4))** 2011. 416p. pap. 34.75 **(978-1-179-22147-2(8))** 2011. 342p. pap. 31.75 **(978-1-179-74704-0(6))** 2011. 456p. pap. 36.75 **(978-1-174-55682-1(X))** 2011. 424p. pap. 35.75 **(978-1-174-94765-0(9))** 2011. 428p. pap. 35.75 **(978-1-175-23918-1(6))** 2011. 434p. pap. 35.75 **(978-1-175-25629-4(3))** 2011. 484p. pap. 38.75 **(978-1-174-93637-1(1))** 2011. 456p. pap. 36.75 **(978-1-175-01496-2(6))** 2011. 446p. pap. 36.75 **(978-1-175-00380-5(8))** 2011. 426p. pap. 35.75 **(978-1-175-44649-7(1))** 2011. 412p. pap. 34.75 **(978-1-179-02010-5(3))** BiblioBazaar.

Pepys, Samuel, et al. The Diary of Samuel Pepys. 2010. (ENG.). 426p. pap. 35.75 (978-1-171-62507-0(3)); (ENG.). 454p. pap. 36.75 (978-1-171-62495-0(6)); (ENG.). 452p. pap. 36.75 (978-1-171-62400-4(X)); (ENG.). 392p. pap. 33.75 (978-1-171-62442-4(5)); (ENG.). 544p. pap. 41.75 (978-1-176-52334-0(1)); (ENG.). 23p. pap. 14.75 (978-1-176-51407-2(5)); 432p. pap. 35.75 (978-1-175-12242-1(4)); 414p. pap. 34.75 (978-1-149-34560-3(8)); 476p. pap. 37.75 (978-1-149-34561-0(6)) BiblioBazaar.

—Diary of Samuel Pepys. 2010. (ENG.). 832p. pap. 56.75 (978-1-149-77089-4(9)) BiblioBazaar.

Pepys, Samuel, et al. The Diary of Samuel Pepys. 2011. 370p. pap. 32.75 **(978-1-176-01958-4(9))**; 438p. pap. 35.75 **(978-1-176-02438-0(8))**; 414p. pap. 34.75 **(978-1-176-02429-8(9))** BiblioBazaar.

Rhodes, R. A. W. Everyday Life in British Government. 2011. (ENG., Illus.). 320p. 45.00 (978-0-19-960114-1(3)) Oxford Univ. Pr., Inc.

Rice, Geoffrey. The Life of the Fourth Earl of Rochford (1717-1781) Eighteenth-Century Anglo-Dutch Courtier, Diplomat, & Statesman, 2 vols. 2010. (Illus.). xvi, 766p. 169.95 (978-0-7734-1300-9(6)) Mellen, Edwin Pr., The.

Rogal, Samuel J. A Record of Samuel Pepys' Financial Accounts, 1660-1669. 2006. 272p. 109.95 (978-0-7734-5486-6(1)) Mellen, Edwin Pr., The.

Tawney, R. H. Business & Politics under James I: Lionel Cranfield as Merchant & Minister. 2012. (ENG.). 340p. pap. 35.99 **(978-1-107-69843-7(X))** Cambridge Univ. Pr.

Turner, John. Lloyd George's Secretariat. 2009. (Cambridge Studies in the History & Theory of Politics Ser.). (ENG.). 268p. pap. 36.99 (978-0-521-09316-3(3)) Cambridge Univ. Pr.

CABINET SYSTEM

see also Coalition Governments; Ministerial Responsibility

Bergman, Torbjorn & Strom, Kaare. The Madisonian Turn: Political Parties & Parliamentary Democracy in Nordic Europe. 2011. (Illus.). x, 417p. E-Book (978-0-472-02550-3(3)) Univ. of Michigan Pr.

Berlinski, Samuel, et al. Accounting for Ministers: Scandal & Survival in British Government 1945#x2013;2007. 2012. (ENG., Illus.). 208p. 90.00 **(978-0-521-51972-4(1))** Cambridge Univ. Pr.

Blondel, Jean, et al. Governing New European Democracies. 2007. (ENG.). 256p. 105.00 **(978-1-4039-9404-2(8))** Palgrave Macmillan.

Bradshaw, Kenneth & Pring, David. Parliament & Congress. 512p. pap. 9.95 (978-0-7043-3353-6(8)) Quartet Bks., Ltd. GBR. Dist: Charles River Bks.

Buckley, Stephen. The Prime Minister & Cabinet. 2006. (Politics Study Guides). (ENG.). 192p. (gr. 17). pap. 20.00 (978-0-7486-2289-4(6)) Edinburgh Univ. Pr. GBR. Dist: Columbia Univ. Pr.

Cheibub, Jose Antonio. Presidentialism, Parliamentarism, & Democracy. 2006. (Cambridge Studies in Comparative Politics). (ENG., Illus.). 220p. 86.00 (978-0-521-83467-4(8)); 224p. (C). per. 27.99 (978-0-521-54244-9(8)) Cambridge Univ. Pr.

Cross, William P. & Blais, Andre. Politics at the Centre: The Selection & Removal of Party Leaders in the Anglo Parliamentary Democracies. 2012. (ENG.). 280p. 99.00 **(978-0-19-959672-0(7))** Oxford Univ. Pr., Inc.

Ehrman, John. Cabinet Government & War, 1890-1940. 2010. (ENG.). 152p. pap. 20.99 (978-0-521-14122-2(2)) Cambridge Univ. Pr.

Elgie, Robert. Semi-Presidentialism: Sub-Types & Democratic Performance. 2011. (Comparative Politics Ser.). 296p. 99.00 (978-0-19-958598-4(9)) Oxford Univ. Pr., Inc.

Fairclough, Paul. The Prime Minister & the Cabinet. Magee, Eric, ed. 2007. (Illus.). 107p. pap. 34.50 (978-1-84489-448-2(7)) Hodder Education GBR. Dist: Trans-Atlantic Pubns., Inc.

Forsey, Eugene A. How Canadians Govern Themselves. 7th ed. 2010. (Illus.). iv, 52p. (978-1-100-14351-4(3)) Canadian Government Publishing.

Helms, Ludger. Parliamentary Opposition in Old & New Democracies. Helms, Ludger, ed. 2009. (Illus.). 256p. 140.00 (978-0-415-39070-5(2)) Routledge.

Kaarbo, Juliet. Coalition Politics & Cabinet Decision Making: A Comparative Analysis of Foreign Policy Choices. 2012. (ENG.). 352p. (C). 85.00 **(978-0-472-11824-3(2))** Univ. of Michigan Pr.

Kam, Christopher J. Party Discipline & Parliamentary Politics. 2011. (ENG., Illus.). 278p. pap. 55.00 (978-1-107-40269-0(7)) Cambridge Univ. Pr.

Strom, Kaare. Minority Government & Majority Rule. 2008. (Studies in Rationality & Social Change Ser.). (ENG., Illus.). 304p. pap. 42.00 (978-0-521-06472-9(4)) Cambridge Univ. Pr.

Strom, Kaare, et al, eds. Cabinets & Coalition Bargaining: The Democractic Life Cycle in Western Europe. 2010. (ENG., Illus.). 464p. pap. 45.00 (978-0-19-958749-0(3)) Oxford Univ. Pr., Inc.

Vogel, Lars. Der Weg ins Kabinett - Karrieren von Ministern in Deutschland: Eine empirische Analyse unter besonderer Berücksichtigung der Rekrutierungsfunktion der Parlamente. 2009. (Europäische Hochschulschriften. Reihe 31: Politikwissenschaft Ser.). (GER.). 192p. pap. 43.95 (978-3-631-58846-8(1)) Lang, Peter GmbH, Europaischer Verlag der Wissenschaften DEU. Dist: Lang, Peter.

Walpole, Spencer. Essays Political & Biographical. 2009. 346p. pap. 19.99 (978-1-115-71227-9(6)); 344p. 32.99 (978-1-113-70979-0(0)); 344p. 36.99 (978-1-113-70982-0(0)); (ENG.). 342p. pap. 23.99 (978-1-113-70972-1(3), BiblioLife); (ENG.). 342p. pap. 24.99 (978-1-113-70974-5(X), BiblioLife); 344p. pap. 32.75 (978-1-113-70977-6(4)); 344p. pap. 31.75 (978-1-113-70976-9(6)) BiblioBazaar.

—Essays Political & Biographical. 2009. 246p. pap. 19.66 (978-0-217-71543-0(5)) General Bks. LLC.

—Essays Political & Biographical. Holland, Francis, ed. 2008. 348p. 46.95 (978-1-4365-6371-0(2)) 2007. 352p. per. 31.95 (978-0-548-75532-7(9)) Kessinger Publishing, LLC.

—Essays Political & Biographical. 317p. reprint ed. 98.00 (978-0-7222-7995-3(7)) Library Reprints, Inc.

Warwick, Paul. Government Survival in Parliamentary Regimes. 2007. (ENG., Illus.). 200p. pap. 38.99 (978-0-521-03831-7(6)) Cambridge Univ. Pr.

Weller, Patrick. Cabinet Government in Australia, 1901-2006: Practice, Principles, Performance. 2007. (ENG., Illus.). 304p. per. 44.95 (978-0-86840-874-3(3), UNSW Press) NewSouth Publishing AUS. Dist: Independent Pubs. Group.

CABINETMAKERS

Apicella, Mary Ann. Scottish Cabinetmakers in Federal New York. 2008. (Illus.). 200p. 75.00 (978-1-58465-708-8(1)) Univ. Pr. of New England.

Bascom, Mansfield. Wharton Esherick: The Journey of a Creative Mind. 2010. (Illus.). (ENG.). 276p. 80.00 (978-0-8109-9575-8(1),; 275p. **(978-0-8109-9775-2(4))** Abrams.

Bjerkoe, Ethel Hall & Bjerkoe, John Arthur. The Cabinetmakers of Americ: Their Lives & Works. 2011. 302p. 48.95 **(978-1-258-09420-1(7))** Literary Licensing, LLC.

Blankemeyer, Dennis. Craft Furniture: The Legacy of the Human Hand. 2007. (Schiffer Design Book Ser.). (Illus.). 191p. 49.95 (978-0-7643-1787-3(3)) Schiffer Publishing, Ltd.

Cathers, David. Gustav Stickley. 2011. (ENG., Illus.). 240p. pap. 45.00 (978-0-7148-6111-1(1)) Phaidon Pr., Inc.

Connaissance des Arts Editorial Staff. Connaissance des Arts Collection: French Cabinetmakers of the 18th Century. 150.00 (978-0-8288-7388-8(7)) French & European Pubns., Inc.

Griliches, Diane Asseo. An Appalachian Farmer's Story: Portrait of an Extraordinary Common Man. 2007. (Illus.). 144p. 40.00 (978-0-88146-062-9(1)) Mercer Univ. Pr.

NCCER. 27501-07 Cabinetmaking AIG. 2007. (Contren Learning Ser.). pap. (978-0-13-614789-3(5)) Prentice Hall PTR.

Starnes, Lincoln M.. photos by. Mark of the Kite: The Life & Legacy of Ronald W. Starnes, Master Cabinetmaker, 1933-2002. 2008. (Illus.). 152p. 66.99 (978-1-4363-1597-5(2)) Xlibris Corp.

CABINETWORK

see also Furniture; Kitchen Cabinets; Marquetry; Veneers and Veneering

Alciat, Andreas. Emblematum Liber. 2008. (Emblematisches Cabinet Ser.: Vol. X). (GER., Illus.). 88p. reprint ed. 95.00 (978-3-487-06144-3(9)) Olms, Georg Verlag AG DEU. Dist: Lubrecht & Cramer, Ltd.

Better Homes and Gardens Books Staff. Cabinets & Shelves. 2nd rev. ed. 2007. (Do It Yourself Ser.). (ENG.). 128p. pap. 12.95 (978-0-696-23297-8(9), Wiley) Wiley, John & Sons, Inc.

Bouknight, Joanne Kellar. All New Built-Ins Idea Book: Closets*Mudrooms*Cabinets*Pantries. 2012. (Taunton Home Idea Bks.). (ENG., Illus.). 176p. pap. 19.95 **(978-1-60085-388-3(9))** Taunton Pr., Inc.

Coleman, Theresa. Custom Shelves & Built-Ins: Build Custom Add-Ons to Create a One-of-a-Kind Home. 2007. (Black & Decker Complete Guides). (ENG., Illus.). 240p. per. 24.95 (978-1-58923-303-4(4), 1589233034) Quayside.

Creative Homeowner Press Editors, ed. Cabinets & Countertops. 2010. (Smart Guide Ser.). (ENG., Illus.). 112p. (gr. 5). pap. 10.95 **(978-1-58011-501-8(2))** Creative Homeowner.

—Cabinets, Shelves & Home Storage Solutions. 2009. (Home Improvement Ser.). (ENG., Illus.). 224p. (gr. 5). pap. 19.95 (978-1-58011-436-3(9)) Creative Homeowner.

Creative Publishing International Editors. The Complete Guide to Built-Ins: Complete Plans for Custom Cabinets, Shelving, Seating & More. 2nd ed. 2011. (Black & Decker Complete Guide Ser.). (ENG., Illus.). 256p. pap. 24.99 (978-1-58923-602-8(5), 1589236025, Fair Winds Press) Quayside.

Family Handyman Magazine Editors. Organize Your Whole House. 2009. (ENG.). 192p. (gr. 12). 15.95 (978-0-7621-0795-7(2)) Reader's Digest Assn., Inc., The.

Fine Woodworking Magazine Editors & Fine Homebuilding Editors. Shelves, Cabinets & Bookcases. 2008. (ENG., Illus.). 220p. pap. 19.95 (978-1-60085-049-3(9), Taunton) Taunton Pr., Inc.

Fox Chapel Publishing Staff, contrib. by. Cabinet Construction. 2011. (Back to Basics Ser.). (ENG., Illus.). 144p. pap. 19.95 (978-1-56523-529-8(0)) Fox Chapel Publishing Co., Inc.

Haxell, Philip & Haxell, Kate. Quick & Easy Handmade Storage: 23 Step-by-Step Weekend Projects. 2007. (Quick & Easy (Cico Books) Ser.). (ENG., Illus.). 128p. pap. (978-1-904991-78-6(5)) CICO Bks.

Haxton, Jason. The Dibbuk Box. 2011. (ENG., Illus.). 192p. pap. 19.95 (978-1-61248-012-1(8)) Truman State Univ. Pr.

Hylton, Bill. Illustrated Cabinetmaking: How to Design & Construct Furniture That Works. 2008. (ENG., Illus.). 374p. per. 24.95 (978-1-56523-369-0(7)) Fox Chapel Publishing Co., Inc.

Ingham, Robert. Cutting-Edge Cabinetmaking. 2008. (ENG., Illus.). 208p. pap. 24.95 (978-1-86108-518-4(4)) Guild of Master Craftsman Pubns., Ltd. GBR. Dist: Sterling Publishing Co., Inc.

Jacobs, Joe. Build It with Pallets. 2009. (ENG., Illus.). 96p. pap. 12.99 (978-1-904871-43-9(7), 1904871437) Good Life Pr., The GBR. Dist: MBI Distribution Services/Quayside Distribution.

Johnson, Randy, ed. How to Make Kitchen Cabinets: Build, Upgrade, & Install Your Own with the Experts at American Woodworker. 2011. (Best of American Woo Ser.). (ENG.). 256p. pap. 24.95 (978-1-56523-506-9(1)) Fox Chapel Publishing Co., Inc.

—Routers & Router Tables: How to Choose & Use the Most Versatile Power Tool in the Workshop. 2011. (Tool Smarts Ser.). (ENG., Illus.). 240p. pap. 19.95 (978-1-56523-508-3(8)) Fox Chapel Publishing Co., Inc.

Krenov, James. The Fine Art of Cabinetmaking. 2007. (ENG., Illus.). 192p. pap. 21.95 (978-1-933502-09-0(6)) Linden Publishing Co., Inc.

Mundt, Barbara. Der Pommersche Kunstschrank: des Augsburger Unternehmers Hainhofer für den gelehrten Herzog vom Pommern. 2009. (GER., Illus.). 447p. (978-3-7774-8045-9(2)) Hirmer Verlag GmbH.

Piccirillo, Mary Anne. The Countertop Book. 2010. (Illus.). 160p. pap. 29.99 (978-0-7643-3392-7(5)) Schiffer Publishing, Ltd.

Proulx, Danny. Simply Built Cabinets. 2011. (ENG.). 176p. pap. 24.99 (978-1-4403-1305-9(9), Popular Woodworking Bks.) F&W Media, Inc.

Provey, Joseph. Easy Closets: Affordable Storage Solutions for Everyone. 2010. (Home Improvement Ser.). (ENG., Illus.). 160p. (gr. 5). pap. 14.95 (978-1-58011-489-9(X)) Creative Homeowner.

Rae, Andy. Building Doors & Drawers: A Complete Guide to Design & Construction - Dovetailed Drawers, Utility Drawers, Cabinet Doors, Special Doors, Hardware. 2007. (ENG., Illus.). 186p. per. 24.95 (978-1-56158-858-8(7), Taunton) Taunton Pr., Inc.

Ralston, Tom. Cast-in-place Concrete Countertops. 2008. (Illus.). 144p. bds. 29.95 (978-0-7643-2949-4(9)) Schiffer Publishing, Ltd.

Rhodes, Buddy & Anderson, Susan. Making Concrete Countertops with Buddy Rhodes: Advanced Techniques. 2008. (Illus.). 39p. 39.99 (978-0-7643-3014-8(4)) Schiffer Publishing, Ltd.

Robertson, Tim. Quick & Easy Home Storage Projects. 2007. 9.99 (978-0-9789378-5-0(6)) August Home Publishing Co.

Rudman, Jack. Cabinetmaking & Millwork. (Occupational Competency Examination Ser.: Vol. 9). 49.95 (978-0-8373-5759-1(4), Passbooks) National Learning Corp.

Settich, Robert J. Built-Ins. 2009. (Taunton's Build Like a Pro Ser.). (ENG., Illus.). 186p. pap. 19.95 (978-1-56158-873-2(3)) Taunton Pr., Inc.

Simple & Stylish Storage Solutions. 2007. 9.99 (978-0-9789378-6-7(4)) August Home Publishing Co.

Starnes, Lincoln M., photos by. Mark of the Kite: The Life & Legacy of Ronald W. Starnes, Master Cabinetmaker, 1933-2002. 2008. (Illus.). 152p. 66.99 (978-1-4363-1597-5(2)) Xlibris Corp.

Umstattd, William D. & Davis, Charles W. Modern Cabinetmaking: Instructor's Manual. (Illus.). tchr. ed. 16.00 (978-1-56637-505-4(3)) Goodheart-Willcox Pub.

Wells, Percy A. & Hooper, John. Modern Cabinet Work: A Comprehensive Treatise on Making Fine Furniture from the Golden Age of Craftsmanship. 3rd ed. 2006. (ENG., Illus.). 381p. per. 26.95 (978-1-892836-28-1(9)) Fox Chapel Publishing Co., Inc.

Woodworker's Journal Editors. Cabinets & Storage Solutions: 17 Space-Saving Projects from Woodworking's Top Experts. 2007. (Best of Woodworker's Journal Ser.). (ENG., Illus.). 151p. pap. 19.95 (978-1-56523-344-7(1)) Fox Chapel Publishing Co., Inc.

Woodworker's Journal Editors, ed. Desks, Bookcases, & Entertainment Centers: Working Furniture for Your Home. 2008. (Best of Woodworker's Journal Ser.). (ENG., Illus.). 153p. pap. 19.95 (978-1-56523-363-8(8)) Fox Chapel Publishing Co., Inc.

CABINETWORKERS

see Cabinetmakers

CABINS

see Log Cabins

CABLE, GEORGE WASHINGTON, 1844-1925

Richardson, Thomas J. The Grandissimes: Centennial Essays. 2011. 102p. pap. 30.00 **(978-1-61703-032-1(5))** Univ. Pr. of Mississippi.

CABLE, MILDRED, 1878-1952

Cable, Mildred. The Gobi Desert. 2008. pap. (978-1-906393-12-0(5)) Trotamundas Pr., Ltd.

CABLE RAILROADS

see Railroads, Cable

CABLE TELEVISION

Benchmarking Cable Network Financial Statistics. 2007. (978-1-933614-39-7(0)) SNL Kagan.

Brillant, Avigdor. Digital & Analog Fiber Optic Communications for CATV & FTTx Applications. 2008. (Press Monographs). (Illus.). 1090p. 115.00 (978-0-8194-6757-7(X)) SPIE.

Broadcast Cable Credit Association Staff. Understanding Broadcast & Cable Finance: A Primer for Nonfinancial Managers. Batten, Alan & McDowell, Walter, eds. 2nd ed. 2008. (ENG., Illus.). 232p. per. 39.95 (978-0-240-80958-8(0), Focal Pr.) Elsevier Science & Technology Bks.

Browne, Steven E. Getting that Job in Hollywood: The Motion Picture, Cable & Television Industry. 2007. 178p. pap. 12.95 (978-0-7414-4325-0(2)) Infinity Publishing.

Cable Primer. (978-0-940272-04-0(0)) National Cable Television Assn.

Cable TV Advertising Statistics. 2007. (978-1-933614-33-5(1)) SNL Kagan.

Chris, Cynthia & Freitas, Anthony. Cable Visions: Television Beyond Broadcasting. Banet-Weiser, Sarah, ed. 2007. (ENG., Illus.). 384p. per. 26.00 (978-0-8147-9950-5(7)) New York Univ. Pr.

The Comcast/NBC Universal Merger: What Does the Future Hold for Competition & Consumers?: Hearing Before the Subcommittee on Antitrust, Competition Policy, & Consumer Rights of the Committee on the Judiciary, United States Senate, One Hundred Eleventh Congress, Second Session, February 4, 2010. 2011. (Illus.). iv, 195p. **(978-0-16-089015-4(2)**, 552-070-43047-4) United States Government Printing Office.

Copyright Licensing in a Digital Age: Competition, Compensation, & the Need to Update the Cable & Satellite TV Licenses: Hearing Before the Committee on the Judiciary, House of Representatives, One Hundred Eleventh Congress, First Session, February 25, 2009. 2009. iii, 166p. (978-0-16-083380-9(9), 552-070-39195-9) United States Government Printing Office.

Cram101 Textbook Reviews. Outlines & Highlights for Broadcasting, Cable, the Internet & Beyond: Introduction to Electronic Media by Joseph R. Dominick, ISBN. 2010. 176p. pap. 29.95 (978-1-4288-9063-3(7)) Cram101 Inc.

Eastman, Susan Tyler & Ferguson, Douglas A. Media Programming: Strategies & Practices. 8th ed. 2008. (ENG., Illus.). 480p. (C). per. 160.95 (978-0-495-50053-7(4)) Wadsworth.

Exclusive Sports Programming: Examining Competition & Consumer Choice: Hearing Before the Committee on Commerce, Science, & Transportation, United States Senate, One Hundred Tenth Congress, First Session, March 27, 2007. 2010. iii, 63p. (978-0-16-086790-3(8), 552-070-41706-1) United States Government Printing Office.

Fetonni, Daniel J. Broadcast Television in Transition. 2012. (Media & Communications - Technologies, Policies & Challenges Ser.). 96p. pap. 47.00 **(978-1-62100-440-0(6))** Nova Science Pubs., Inc.

Flynn, Robin. Broadband Cable Financial Databook. 2008. spiral bd. (978-1-933614-56-4(0)) SNL Kagan.

Flynn, Robin, ed. Broadband Cable Financial Databook. 2007. (978-1-933614-41-0(2)) SNL Kagan.

Harte, Lawrence. Introduction to Cable Television (CATV) Analog & Digital Television & Modems. 2nd ed. 2007. (ENG., Illus.). 108p. per. 19.99 (978-0-9728053-6-0(2)) Althos.

Introduccion a Cableado de Network Sistemas de Base de Cobre Ver 3. 3 Student Kit. 2006. (C). spiral bd. (978-0-9760193-1-2(0)) C-Tech Assocs., Inc.

Kiuchi, Yuya. Struggles for Equal Voice: The History of African American Media Democracy. 2012. (ENG.). 336p. 85.00 **(978-1-4384-4479-6(6))** State Univ. of New York Pr.

Large, David & Farmer, James. Broadband Cable Access Networks: The HFC Plant. 3rd ed. 2008. (Morgan Kaufmann Series in Networking Ser.). (ENG., Illus.). 432p. 96.95 (978-0-12-374401-2(6), Morgan Kaufmann) Elsevier Science & Technology Bks.

Mullen, Megan. Television in the Multichannel Age: A Brief History of Cable Television. 2008. (ENG., Illus.). 248p. 99.95 (978-1-4051-4969-3(8)); per. 38.95 (978-1-4051-4970-9(1)) Wiley, John & Sons, Inc. (Wiley-Blackwell).

Murray, Glen L. Cable News & Other Stuff. 2008. 104p. pap. 16.95 (978-1-60563-373-2(9)) PublishAmerica, Inc.

National Cable & Telecommunications Association, compiled by. 2007 NCTA Technical Papers. 2007. 225p. per. (978-0-940272-42-2(3)) National Cable & Telecommunications Assn.

Niesen, George, ed. Economics of Basic Cable Networks. 2007. pap. (978-1-933614-40-3(4)) SNL Kagan.

Parsons, Patrick R. Blue Skies: A History of Cable Television. 2008. (ENG.). 816p. 77.00 (978-1-59213-287-4(1)) Temple Univ. Pr.

Producers' Sourcebook: A Guide to Cable TV Program Buyers. 25.00 (978-0-940272-13-2(X)) National Cable Television Assn.

ProQuest Editorial Staff, ed. Broadcasting & Cable Yearbook 2008. 2007. 245.00 (978-1-60030-110-0(X)) CSA Journal Division.

ProQuest LLC Staff, ed. Broadcasting & Cable Year Book 2009. 2008. 275.00 (978-1-60030-121-6(5)) ProQuest LLC.

Public, Educational, & Governmental (PEG) Services in the Digital TV Age: Hearing Before the Subcommittee on Telecommunications & the Internet of the Committee on Energy & Commerce, House of Representatives, One Hundred Tenth Congress, Second Session, January 29, 2008. 2008. (Illus.). v, 190p. (978-0-16-084256-6(5), 552-070-39826-1) United States Government Printing Office.

Rudman, Jack. Cable Television Consumer Services Specialist. (Career Examination Ser.: C-3683). pap. 29.95 (978-0-8373-3683-1(X)) National Learning Corp.

Rutkowski, Katherine, ed. NCTA Technical Papers, 1993. (Illus.). 430p. (Orig.). 50.00 (978-0-940272-21-7(0)) National Cable Television Assn.

Television & Cable Factbook, 4 vols. 75th ed. 2006. 895.00 (978-1-57696-059-2(5), 1) Warren Communications News, Inc.

U. S. Profiles of Cable TV Manufacturers. Date not set. 632p. spiral bd. 995.00 (978-0-7889-0358-8(6), 2841-64) Frost & Sullivan Market Intelligence.

United States, Congress Senate Committee on the Judiciary Staff, contrib. by. Competition in Sports Programming & Distribution: Are Consumers Winning?: Hearing Before the Committee on the Judiciary, United States Senate, One Hundred Ninth Congress, Second Session, November 14, 2006. 2007. iii, 75p. (978-0-16-078112-4(4), 552-070-35514 6) United States Government Printing Office.

—Vertically Integrated Sports Programming: Are Cable Companies Excluding Competition?: Hearing Before the Committee on the Judiciary, United States Senate, One Hundred Ninth Congress, Second Session, December 7, 2006. 2007. iii, 84p. (978-0-16-078186-5(8), 552-070-35576-6) United States Government Printing Office.

Zarkin, Michael J. The FCC & the Politics of Cable TV Regulation, 1952-1980: Organizational Learning & Policy Development. 2010. (978-1-60497-722-6(1)) Cambria Pr.

CABLE TELEVISION—LAW AND LEGISLATION

Carter, Barton & Franklin, Marc. The First Amendment & the Fifth Estate, 6th, 2007 Supplement. 7th rev. ed. 2007. (University Casebook Ser.). 187p. pap. 16.00 (978-1-59941-346-4(9), Foundation Pr.) West.

Goldfarb, Charles B. Local Programming on Broadcast, Cable, & Satellite Television: Statutes & Rules. Wilson, Raymond H., ed. 2008. (Illus.). viii, 94p. pap. 39.00 (978-1-60456-276-7(5)) Nova Science Pubs., Inc.

O'Reilly, Terrance I., ed. Programmer-Distributor Negotiations: Retransmission Consent & Other Federal Rules. 2008. (Illus.). 97p. pap. 39.00 (978-1-60456-279-8(X)) Nova Science Pubs., Inc.

State Video Tax Fairness ACT of 2007: Hearing Before the Subcommittee on Commercial & Administrative Law of the Committee on the Judiciary, House of Representatives, One Hundred Tenth Congress, Second Session, on H.R. 3679, February 14, 2008. 2008. iv, 75p. (978-0-16-082811-9(2), 552-070-38793-5) United States Government Printing Office.

CABLES

American Society of Civil Engineers Staff, contrib. by. Structural Applications of Steel Cables for Buildings. 2010. 46p. pap. 75.00 (978-0-7844-1124-7(7)) American Society of Civil Engineers.

Bender, Amadee & Murawski, Frank. Data & Voice Premises Cabling Systems - U. S. Markets, Competitors & Opportunities: 2000-2005 Analysis & Forecasts. 100p. pap. 4900.00 (978-1-929904-16-7(9)) World Information Technologies, Inc.

—Data & Voice Premises Cabling Systems - U. S. Markets, Competitors & Opportunities: 2001-2005 Analysis & Forecasts. 100p. pap. 4900.00 (978-1-929904-17-4(7)) World Information Technologies, Inc.

Briggs, Charles F. (Charles Frederick). The Story of the Telegraph & a History of the Great Atlantic Cable / by Charles F Briggs & Augustus Maverick. 2006. (Illus.). 268p. per. 23.99 (978-1-4255-2429-6(X)) MPublishing.

Hayes, Jim. Data, Voice, & Video Cabling. 3rd ed. 2008. (ENG.). 112p. (C). pap., lab manual ed. 48.95 (978-1-4283-3473-1(4)) Delmar Cengage Learning.

Mitton, Simon. Dynamic Analysis of Cable Stayed Structures. 2011. 148p. pap. **(978-3-8443-2167-8(5))** Lambert Academic Publishing.

Moutassem, Wael. Ampacity Optimization of Unequally Loaded Power Cables - Procedure for Calculation of Optimal Current Loadings of Dissimilar Underground Cables. 2008. 120p. pap. (978-3-639-06341-7(4)) VDM Verlag Dr. Mueller e.K.

Tsaliovich, Anatoly. Cable Shielding for Electromagnetic Compatibility. 2010. (ENG.). 469p. pap. 179.00 (978-1-4419-4739-0(6), 1441947396) Springer.

Van Rensselaer, Cortlandt. Signals from the Atlantic Cable an Address Delivered at the Telegraphic Celebration, September 1st, 1858, in the City Hall, Burlington, New Jersey B. 2011. 32p. pap. 11.99 **(978-1-4181-9463-5(8))** MPublishing.

CABLES, ELECTRIC

see Cables, Submarine; Electric Cables; Electronic Cables; Telephone Cables

CABLES, SUBMARINE

Blundell, Joseph Wagstaff. The Manual of Submarine Telegraph Companies. 2010. 116p. pap. 26.95 (978-1-4455-5435-8(6)) Harrison House Pubs.

Carter, L. Submarine Cables & the Oceans: Connecting the World. 2012. (ENG., Illus.). pap. 30.00 **(978-0-9563387-2-3(0))** United Nations Pubns.

Cookson, Gillian. The Cable: The Wire That Changed the World. 2007. (ENG.). 160p. 23.00 (978-0-4223-5352-3(4)) DIANE Publishing Co.

—The Cable: The Wire That Changed the World. 2007. (ENG., Illus.). 192p. per. 16.95 (978-0-7524-3903-7(0)) History Pr. Ltd., The GBR. Dist: Independent Pubs. Group.

Field, Henry M. History of the Atlantic Telegraph. 2008. 368p. 48.95 (978-0-548-93474-6(6)) 2007. (ENG.). 372p. per. 33.95 (978-0-548-58930-4(5)) Kessinger Publishing, LLC.

Field, Henry M. (Henry Martyn). History of the Atlantic Telegraph by Henry M Field. 2006. 380p. per. 26.99 (978-1-4255-4017-3(1)); 444p. per. 26.99 (978-1-4255-4915-2(2)) MPublishing.

—History of the Atlantic Telegraph, to the Return of the Expedition Of 1865. 2006. 332p. per. 23.99 (978-1-4255-3309-0(4)) MPublishing.

Finn, Bernard & Yang, Daqing, eds. Communications under the Seas: The Evolving Cable Network & Its Implications. 2009. (Dibner Institute Studies in the History of Science & Technology Ser.). (ENG., Illus.). 312p. (gr. 17). 42.00 (978-0-262-01286-7(3)) MIT Pr.

Gannett, Ezra S. The Atlantic Telegraph: A discourse delivered in the First Church, August 8, 1858. Published by Request. 2011. 22p. pap. 11.99 **(978-1-4181-9162-7(0))** MPublishing.

New York (N.Y.) Common council. Detailed Report of the Proceedings Had in Commemoration of the Successful Laying of the Atlantic Telegraph Cable. 2006. 288p. per. 23.99 (978-1-4255-2630-6(6)) MPublishing.

Russell, William Howard. The Atlantic Telegraph. 2011. (Cambridge Library Collection - Technology Ser.). (ENG., Illus.). 178p. pap. 19.99 (978-1-108-07247-2(X)) Cambridge Univ. Pr.

Worzyk, Thomas. Submarine Power Cables: Design, Installation, Damages & Repair, Environmental Aspects. 2009. (Power Systems Ser.). (ENG., Illus.). xvii, 296p. 179.00 (978-3-642-01269-3(8), 3642012698) Springer.

CABOT, GEORGE, 1752-1823

Lodge, Henry Cabot. Life & Letters of George Cabot. 2009. 472p. pap. (978-0-217-23205-0(1)) Books LLC.

—Life & Letters of George Cabot. 2007. (ENG.). 632p. 60.95 (978-0-548-09037-4(8)) Kessinger Publishing, LLC.

—Life & Letters of George Cabot. 2008. (ENG.). 632p. per. (978-1-4086-7315-7(0)) Read Bks.

—The Life & Letters of George Cabot. 615p. reprint ed. 128.00 (978-0-7222-9020-0(9)) Library Reprints, Inc.

CABOT, JOHN, D. 1498

Columbus, Christopher. Journal of Christopher Columbus (During His First Voyage, 1492-93) And Documents Relating the Voyages of John Cabot & Gaspar Corte Real. 2010. (Cambridge Library Collection - Travel & Exploration Ser.). (ENG., Illus.). 344p. pap. 31.00 (978-1-108-01284-3(1)) Cambridge Univ. Pr.

Hunter, Douglas. The Race to the New World: Christopher Columbus, John Cabot, & a Lost History of Discovery. 2012. (ENG.). 288p. pap. 17.00 **(978-0-230-34165-4(9))** Palgrave Macmillan.

C

Williamson, James A. & Skelton, R. A., eds. The Cabot Voyages & Bristol Discovery under Henry VII. 2010. (Hakluyt Society, Second Ser.). 348p. 69.95 (978-1-4094-1486-5(8)) Hakluyt Society GBR. Dist: Ashgate Publishing Co.

CABOT, SEBASTIAN, 1474-1557

Columbus, Christopher. Journal of Christopher Columbus (During His First Voyage, 1492-93) And Documents Relating the Voyages of John Cabot & Gaspar Corte Real. 2010. (Cambridge Library Collection - Travel & Exploration Ser.). (ENG., Illus.). 344p. pap. 31.00 (978-1-108-01284-3(1)) Cambridge Univ. Pr.

Hakluyt, Richard. Divers Voyages Touching the Discovery of America & the Islands Adjacent: Collected & Published by Richard Hakluyt. Jones, John Winter, ed. 2010. (Cambridge Library Collection - Travel & Exploration Ser.). (ENG., Illus.). 312p. pap. 24.99 (978-1-108-00804-4(6)) Cambridge Univ. Pr.

Williamson, James A. & Skelton, R. A., eds. The Cabot Voyages & Bristol Discovery under Henry VII. 2010. (Hakluyt Society, Second Ser.). 348p. 69.95 (978-1-4094-1486-5(8)) Hakluyt Society GBR. Dist: Ashgate Publishing Co.

CABRAL, PEDRO ALVARES, D. 1520

Bueno, Eduardo. A Viagem Do Descobrimento: A Verdadeira História Da Expedição de Cabral. (POR., Illus.). 137p. (978-85-7302-202-5(7)) Objetiva, Editora Ltda.

Greenlee, William Brooks, ed. The Voyage of Pedro Álvares Cabral to Brazil & India: From Contemporary Documents & Narratives. 2010. (Hakluyt Society, Second Ser.). 298p. 69.95 (978-1-4094-1448-3(5)) Hakluyt Society GBR. Dist: Ashgate Publishing Co.

MacClymont, James Roxburgh, et al. Pedro Cabral. Bridgeman, Keith & Arsham, Tahira, eds. 2009. (Illus.). 233p. pap. 14.60 (978-1-906421-01-4(3)) Viartis GBR. Dist: Ingram Bk. Co.

CABRINI, FRANCES XAVIER, SAINT, 1850-1917

Cicognani, Amleto Giovanni. Travels of Mother Frances Xavier Cabrini: With A Biographical Sketch. 2011. 296p. 48.95 (978-1-258-05719-0(0)) Literary Licensing, LLC.

Di Donato, Pietro & Pizzardo, Joseph. Immigrant Saint: The Life of Mother Cabrini. 2011. 254p. 47.95 (978-1-258-08027-3(3)) Literary Licensing, LLC.

CABS

see Carriages and Carts; Taxicabs

CACAO

Here are entered works on the cacao tree and its culture only. Works dealing with the commercial product are entered under Chocolate and Cocoa.

Laven, Anna. Knowing More about Sustainable Cocoa: The Dutch Knowledge Base. 2011. 144p. pap. 39.95 (978-94-6022-103-3(3)) Royal Tropical Institute Pr. (KIT (Koninklijk Instituut voor de Tropen) NLD. Dist: Stylus Publishing, LLC.

McNeil, Cameron L., ed. Chocolate in Mesoamerica: A Cultural History of Cacao. 2009. (Maya Studies). (ENG., Illus.). 544p. pap. 34.95 (978-0-8130-3382-2(9)) Univ. Pr. of Florida.

Pucciarelli, Deanna. The Medicinal Use of Chocolate: Past, Present & Future (1776-2007) 2008. 388p. pap. (978-3-639-10181-2(2)) VDM Verlag Dr. Mueller e.K.

Rosenblum, Mort. Chocolate: A Bittersweet Saga of Dark & Light. 2006. (ENG., Illus.). 304p. per. 14.00 (978-0-86547-730-8(2), North Point Pr.) Farrar, Straus & Giroux.

—Chocolate: A Bittersweet Saga of Dark & Light. l.t. ed. 29.95 (978-0-7862-7834-3(X), Large Print Pr.) Thorndike Pr.

Young, Allen M. The Chocolate Tree: A Natural History of Cacao. enl. ed. 2007. (ENG., Illus.). 240p. per. 24.95 (978-0-8130-3044-9(7)) Univ. Pr. of Florida.

CACHETS (PHILATELY)

see Postmarks

CACTUS

Anderson, Miles. The Complete Illustrated Guide to Growing Cacti & Succulents. 2012. (ENG., Illus.). 264p. pap. 16.99 (978-1-78019-092-1(1)) Anness Publishing GBR. Dist: National Bk. Network.

Banks, Leo W. All about Saguaros. 2008. 96p. pap. 19.95 (978-1-932082-91-3(3)) Arizona Highways.

Calhoun, Scott. The Gardener's Guide to Cactus: The 100 Best Paddles, Barrels, Columns, & Globes. 2012. (ENG., Illus.). 248p. pap. 24.95 (978-1-60469-200-6(6), 1604692006) Timber Pr., Inc.

Chance, Leo J. Cacti & Succulents for Cold Climates: 274 Outstanding Species for Challenging Conditions. 2012. (ENG., Illus.). 368p. 39.95 (978-1-60469-264-8(2)) Timber Pr., Inc.

Charles, Graham. Cacti & Succulents: An Illustrated Guide to the Plants & Their Cultivation. 2007. (ENG., Illus.). 192p. pap. 35.00 (978-1-86126-872-3(6)) Crowood Pr., Ltd. GBR. Dist: Independent Pubs. Group.

Higgins, Vera. Cactus Growing for Beginners. 2008. 88p. pap. (978-1-4097-2392-9(5)) Read Bks.

Ingram, Stephen. Cacti, Agaves, & Yuccas of California & Nevada. 2008. (Illus.). 256p. (ENG.). 35.95 (978-0-9789971-1-3(5)); pap. 25.95 (978-0-9789971-0-6(7)) Cachuma Pr.

John M. Coulter. A Preliminary Revision of the North American Species of Cactus, Anhalonium, & Lophophora. 2006. (ENG.). 72p. pap. 16.99 (978-1-4264-0040-7(3)); 70p. pap. 12.99 (978-1-4264-0169-5(8)) BiblioBazaar.

King, Robert. Cactus Caprice. 4.95 (978-0-89741-001-4(7)) Gila River Designs.

Loflin, Brian & Loflin, Shirley. Texas Cacti. 2009. (TAM Nature Guides Ser.: No. 42). (ENG.). 312p. pap. 24.00 (978-1-60344-108-7(5)) Texas A&M Univ. Pr.

Manning. What Kinda Cactus Izzat? pap. 6.95 (978-0-918080-95-0(9)) Rio Nuevo Pubs.

Moussa Ayoub, Tamer. Cactus Pear Fruit: A Promising Fruit. 2009. 124p. pap. (978-3-639-13574-9(1)) VDM Verlag Dr. Mueller e.K.

Powell, A. Michael, et al. Cacti of Texas: A Field Guide. 2008. (Grover E. Murray Studies in the American Southwest). 400p. pap. 24.95 (978-0-89672-611-6(8)) Texas Tech Univ. Pr.

Preston-Mafham, Ken. 500 Cacti: Species & Varieties in Cultivation. 2007. (ENG., Illus.). 528p. 29.95 (978-1-55407-261-3(1)) Firefly Bks., Ltd.

Schlegel, Urs. The Composite Structure of Cactus Spines. 2008. 164p. pap. (978-3-639-06809-2(2)) VDM Verlag Dr. Mueller e.K.

Smith, Gideon F. Cacti & Succulents: A Complete Guide to Species, Cultivation & Care. 2007. (ENG., Illus.). 160p. 29.95 (978-1-883052-55-3(6)) Ball Publishing.

Sterman, Nan, et al. Water-Wise Plants for the Southwest. 2010. (Water Gardening Ser.). (ENG.). 256p. pap. 19.95 (978-1-59186-468-4(2), 1591864682) Cool Springs Pr.

Wiersma, Roy. Luther Burbank Spineless Cactus Identification Project. 2008. 92p. pap. 33.95 (978-1-4389-0353-8(7)) AuthorHouse.

Yetman, David. The Great Cacti: Ethnobotany & Biogeography. 2008. (Southwest Center Ser.). (ENG., Illus.). 320p. 59.95 (978-0-8165-2431-0(9)) Univ. of Arizona Pr.

—The Organ Pipe Cactus. 2006. (ENG., Illus.). 80p. pap. 9.95 (978-0-8165-2541-6(2)) Univ. of Arizona Pr.

CAD

see Computer-Aided Design

CAD-CAM SYSTEMS

see also Computer-Aided Design

American Society of Mechanical Engineers, Design Engineering Division Staff & American Society of Mechanical Engineers, Computers and Information in Engineering Division Staff, contrib. by. Proceedings of the ASME Design Engineering Division & the ASME Computers & Information in Engineering Division — 2006: Presented at 2006 ASME International Mechanical Engineering Congress & Exposition, November 5-10, 2006, Chicago, Illinois, USA, 2 vols. 2007. (Illus.). xxv, 1229p. pap. (978-0-7918-4767-1(5)) American Society of Mechanical Engineers, The.

American Society of Mechanical Engineers Staff, ed. Effective CAD/CAM. 170p. 104.00 (978-0-85298-698-1(X)); 372p. 60.00 (978-0-85298-633-2(5)); (Illus.). 158p. 132.00 (978-0-85298-767-4(6)) Professional Engineering Publishing GBR. Dist: SAE Intl.

—Use of CAD/CAM for Fluid Machinery Design & Manufacture. (Illus.). 64p. 32.00 (978-0-85298-665-3(3)) Professional Engineering Publishing GBR. Dist: SAE Intl.

The CAD Connection. 2007. per. 69.95 (978-0-9777812-1-8(6)) Ramacad, Inc.

Chintala, Gopinath. Trends in Cad/Cam. 2011. 208p. pap. (978-3-8443-2537-9(9)) Lambert Academic Publishing.

Fahiem, Muhammad Abuzar & Ali Shah, Abad. 3d Reconstruction from 2d Camera Perspectives. 2011. 72p. pap. (978-3-8443-9243-2(2)) Lambert Academic Publishing.

Garbrah-Aidoo, Yoofi. SolidWorks Ultimate Training. 2011. 808p. pap. 85.00 (978-1-4567-2814-4(8)) AuthorHouse.

Gibson, I., et al. Additive Manufacturing Technologies: Rapid Prototyping to Direct Digital Manufacturing. 2010. (Illus.). xxii, 459p. (978-1-4419-1120-9(0)) Springer.

Gibson, Ian, et al. Additive Manufacturing Technologies: Rapid Prototyping to Direct Digital Manufacturing. 2009. (ENG., Illus.). xxii, 462p. 169.00 (978-1-4419-1119-3(7), 1441911197) Springer.

Green, Robert. Expert CAD Management: The Complete Guide. 2007. (ENG., Illus.). 288p. pap. 49.99 (978-0-470-11653-1(6), Sybex) Wiley, John & Sons, Inc.

Groover, Mikell P. Automation, Production Systems, & Computer-Integrated Manufacturing. 3rd ed. 2007. (ENG., Illus.). 840p. (C). 185.00 (978-0-13-239321-8(2), Prentice Hall) Prentice Hall PTR.

Gu, Ning & Wan, Xiangyu. Computational Design Methods & Technologies: Applications in CAD, CAM, & CAE Education. 2012. (978-1-61350-182-5(X)) 2011. 490p. 175.00 (978-1-61350-180-1(3)) IGI Global.

Han, Jingtao, et al. Advanced Manufacturing Technology: Selected, Peer Reviewed Papers from the 2010 International Conference on Advances in Materials & Manufacturing Processes (ICAMMP 2010), 6-8 November, 2010, Shenzhen, China, 2 vols. 2011. (Illus.). 1814p. pap. (978-0-87849-205-3(4)) Trans Tech Pubns., Ltd.

Huggins, Michael J. Esprit Fundamentals 2007. 2007. spiral bd. 119.95 (978-0-9707464-9-8(0)) Precision Cad/Cam Systems, Inc.

Kuhn, Jerry. The KeyCreator Cookbook: Updated to Include Versions 5 And 6. 2007. spiral bd. (978-0-9777525-0-8(X)) Technology Education Concepts Inc.

Lab-Volt Staff. CNC Lathe: Tech-Design ESeries. 2010. 95p. 9.00 (978-1-60533-164-5(3)); 49p. 5.00 (978-1-60533-273-4(9)); 54p. ring bd. 6.00 (978-1-60533-165-2(1)) Lab-Volt Systems, Inc.

—CNC Mill: Tech-Design ESeries. 2010. 94p. 9.00 (978-1-60533-261-1(5)); 111p. 11.00 (978-1-60533-217-8(8)); 66p. ring bd. 7.00 (978-1-60533-218-5(6)) Lab-Volt Systems, Inc.

Lu, Congda, ed. Digital Design & Manufacturing Technology II: Selected, Peer Reviewed Papers from the 2011 Global Conference on Digital & Manufacturing ... Hangzhou, China. 2011. 411p. pap. (978-3-03785-071-8(X)) Trans Tech Pubns., Ltd.

Makabo, Rita R. Robeil & A. Ismael, Sabah. Evaluation of Zirconia Cores Adaptation Fabricated by Cad/Cam Systems. 2011. 100p. pap. (978-3-8443-8078-1(7)) Lambert Academic Publishing.

Marafon, Priscila & Silva Camara Mattos, Beatriz. Dimensional Stability in Orbital Prothesis. 2010. 64p. pap. (978-3-639-26713-6(3)) VDM Verlag Dr. Mueller e.K.

Orshansky, Michael, et al. Design for Manufacturability & Statistical Design: A Constructive Approach. 2008. (Series on Integrated Circuits & Systems Ser.). (Illus.). 310p. 149.00 (978-0-387-30928-6(4), 0387309284) Springer.

Patrikalakis, Nicholas M. & Maekawa, Takashi. Shape Interrogation for Computer Aided Design & Manufacturing. 2010. (ENG., Illus.). xvi, 408p. pap. 69.95 (978-3-642-04073-3(X), 364204073X) Springer.

Pham, D. T. Innovative Production Machines & Systems: Fourth I*PROMS Virtual International Conference, 1-14 July 2008. Pham, D. T. et al, eds. 2009. (ENG., Illus.). 650p. 289.95 (978-1-4398-0117-8(7)) Whittles Publishing GBR. Dist: Taylor & Francis Group.

Pham, D. T., et al, eds. Innovative Production Machines & Systems: Third I*PROMS Virtual International Conference, 2-13 July 2007. 2008. (Illus.). xxiii, 647p. 94.95 (978-1-4200-7347-8(8)) Whittles Publishing GBR. Dist: Taylor & Francis Group.

Radzevich, Stephen P. CAD/CAM of Sculptured Surfaces on a Multi-Axis NC Machine: The DG/K-Based Approach. 2008. (Synthesis Lectures on Engineering Ser.). 100p. pap. 40.00 (978-1-59829-765-2(1)) Morgan & Claypool Pubs.

Rennels, K. E. & Zecher, J. E. What Every Engineer Should Know about CAD/CAM. 2nd ed. Date not set. (What Every Engineer Should Know Ser.). (978-0-8247-9619-8(5)) Dekker, Marcel Inc.

Scheer, August-Wilhelm & Spath, Dieter, eds. Computer Aided Service Engineering: Informationssysteme in der Dienstleistungsentwicklung. 2010. 332p. (978-3-540-20888-4(7)) Springer Singapore Pte. Ltd.

Tanik, Urcun. Architecting Automated Design Systems. 2008. 408p. pap. (978-3-639-00255-3(5)) VDM Verlag Dr. Mueller e.K.

Technology Research Editors, ed. Rapid Prototyping, 2007 Ed. 2007. pap. 128.50 (978-1-60030-380-7(3), Search-In-Print) CSA Journal Division.

Toriya, Hiroshi. 3D Manufacturing Innovation: Revolutionary Change in Japanese Manufacturing with Digital Data. Ito, Y., tr. 2010. (ENG., Illus.). xviii, 155p. pap. 119.00 (978-1-84996-709-9(1), 1849967091) Springer.

—3D Manufacturing Innovation: Revolutionary Change in Japanese Manufacturing with Digital Data. Ito, Y., tr. from JPN. 2008. (ENG., Illus.). xviii, 155p. 119.00 (978-1-84800-037-7(5), 1848000375) Springer.

Valentino, James & Goldenberg, Joseph. Learning Mastercam X5 Mill 2D Step by Step. 2010. 600p. (C). pap. 74.95 (978-0-8311-3423-5(2)) Industrial Pr., Inc.

Xu, Xun. Integrating Advanced Computer-Aided Design, Manufacturing, & Numerical Control: Principles & Implementations. 2009. 424p. 165.00 (978-1-59904-714-0(4)) IGI Global.

Xu, Xun & Nee, Andrew Y.C., eds. Advanced Design & Manufacturing Based on STEP. 2009. (Springer Series in Advanced Manufacturing Ser.). (ENG., Illus.). xxiv, 481p. 199.00 (978-1-84882-738-7(5), 1848827385) Springer.

Zamani, Nader. CATIA V5 FEA Tutorials Release 16. 2007. 521p. per. 59.95 (978-1-58503-356-0(1), SDC Pubns.) Schroff Development Corp.

CADASTERS

see Cadastres

CADASTRAL MAPS

see Real Property—Maps

CADASTRAL SURVEYS

see Real Property

CADASTRES

Bonnie, Rick. Cadastres, Misconceptions & Northern Gaul. 2009. (ENG.). 160p. (C). pap. 52.00 (978-90-8890-024-2(8)) Sidestone Pr. NLD. Dist: Brown, David Bk. Co., The.

Center of Legal Competence, ed. Land Registration & Cadastre in Selected European Countries: Austria, Bulgaria, Croatia, Hungary, Netherlands, Serbia. 2009. 232p. pap. 59.95 (978-90-5095-944-5(X)) Intersentia Uitgevers N.V. BEL. Dist: International Specialized Bk. Services.

Horner, Daniela & Bataveljic, Dragan. Grundeigentum und Registrierung von Liegenschaften in Serbien: Eigentumsschutz in der Praxis. 2010. (Studien des Instituts für Ostrecht München Ser.). (GER.). 246p. 72.95 (978-3-631-60047-4(X)) Lang, Peter GmbH, Europäischer Verlag der Wissenschaften DEU. Dist: Lang, Peter.

Mapping Science Committee & Land Parcel Databases Committee. National Land Parcel Data: A Vision for the Future. 2007. (ENG., Illus.). 172p. per. 51.00 (978-0-309-11030-3(0)) National Academies Pr.

Olivová, Kveta & Kuba, Bohumil. Byty a Katastr Nemovitostí. 8th ed. 2008. (CZE., Illus.). 542p. (978-80-7201-727-0(6)) Linde Verlag Wien Ges.m.b.H.

Ronsijn, W. De kadasterkaarten van Popp: Een sleutel tot uw lokale geschiedenis: Historische geografie van Aarschot, Asse, Halle en Tienen aan de hand van de kadasterkaarten van Popp. 2007. (Accenten uit de geschiedenis van Vlaams-Brabant Ser.). (ENG.). 148p. (C). pap. 40.00 (978-90-429-2048-4(3)) Peeters Pubs. & Booksellers BEL. Dist: Brown, David Bk. Co., The.

Zenchenko, M. IU. Pistsovye Knigi Verkhnego Zavolzhia. 2010. (RUS.). 447p. (978-5-88451-267-2(8)) Pamjatniki Istoriceskoj Mysli, AO.

CADDISFLIES

Ames, Thomas. Caddisflies: A Field Guide to Eastern Species for Anglers & Other Naturalists. 2008. (ENG., Illus.). 320p. 49.95 (978-0-8117-0456-4(4)) Stackpole Bks.

Crichton, M. I., ed. Proceedings of the Second International Symposium on Trichoptera. 2010. 380p. pap. 245.00 (978-90-481-8516-0(5), 9048185165) Springer.

Graf, W. Distribution & Ecological Preferences of European Freshwater Organisms: Volume 1. Trichoptera. 2008. (Illus.). 388p. pap. 137.50 (978-954-642-441-9(2)) Pensoft Pubs. BGR. Dist: Coronet Bks.

Malicky, Hans. Atlas of European Trichoptera / Atlas der Europäischen Köcherfliegen / Atlas des Trichoptères d' Europe. 2nd ed. 2010. (ENG, GER & FRE.). xxviii, 359p. pap. 289.00 (978-90-481-6755-5(8), 9048167558) Springer.

Pobst, Dick. The Orvis Vest Pocket Guide to Caddisflies: The Illustrated Reference to the Major Species of North America. 2008. (Orvis Guides). (ENG., Illus.). 144p. per. 12.95 (978-1-59228-391-0(8), Lyons Pr.) Globe Pequot Pr., The.

Schwiebert, Ernest G. Nymphs, Volume 2: Stoneflies, Caddisflies, & Other Important Insects Including the Lesser Mayflies. 2007. (ENG., Illus.). 800p. 60.00 (978-1-59921-098-8(3), Lyons Pr.) Globe Pequot Pr., The.

Wagner, R. & Wichard, W. Biology of Trichoptera. 2009. 300p. 112.00 (978-87-88757-75-0(7)) Apollo Bks. DNK. Dist: International Specialized Bk. Services.

CADDO INDIANS

see Indians of North America—Southwest, Old

CADDY, JOHN HERBERT, 1801-1883

Dabell, Norman. How We Won the Ryder Cup: The Caddies' Stories. 2006. (ENG., Illus.). 320p. per. 22.95 (978-1-84596-167-1(6)) Mainstream Publishing Co., Ltd. GBR. Dist: Independent Pubs. Group.

CADILLAC AUTOMOBILE

Cummings, Christopher W. The Cadillac That Followed Me Home: Memoir of a V-16 Dream Realized. 2006. (ENG., Illus.). 243p. per. 25.00 (978-0-7864-2808-3(2)) McFarland & Co., Inc. Pubs.

Haynes, Max. General Motors Cadillac Deville (1994 thru 2005) Cadillac Seville (1992 thru 2004) Cadillac DTS (2006 Thru 2010) 2010. (Haynes Repair Manual Ser.). (ENG., Illus.). 336p. pap. 26.95 (978-1-56392-815-4(9), 1563928159) Haynes Manuals, Inc.

Headrick Jr, Robert J. Cadillac: The Tailfin Years. 2008. (ENG., Illus.). 128p. pap. 34.95 (978-1-58388-212-2(X), 158388212X) Iconografix, Inc.

Henderson, Bob. GM: Cadillac Deville/Seville/DTS, 1999-2005. 2010. (ENG.). 352p. pap. 29.95 (978-1-56392-845-1(0)) Haynes,Chilton.

McPherson, Thomas A. & McCall, Walter. Cadillac Fleetwood Seventy-Five Series Limousines 1937-1987 Photo Archive. 2009. (Photo Archive Ser.). (ENG., Illus.). 128p. pap. 32.95 (978-1-58388-248-1(0), 1583882480) Iconografix, Inc.

Ryan, Mark. General Motors Chevrolet Cavalier & Pontiac Sunfire: 1995 Thru 2005. 2010. (Haynes Repair Manual Ser.). (ENG., Illus.). 176p. pap. 26.95 (978-1-56392-814-7(0), 1563928140) Haynes Manuals, Inc.

CADMIUM

Balart Murria, María José. Management of Hazardous Residues Containing Cd. 2012. (Waste & Waste Management Ser.). (Illus.). 196p. 69.00 (978-1-61209-526-4(7)) Nova Science Pubs., Inc.

Balart Murria, María José, ed. Management of Hazardous Residues Containing Cr(VI) 2011. (Waste & Waste Management Ser.). 388p. pap. 80.00 (978-1-61470-637-3(9)) Nova Science Pubs., Inc.

Hayat, Shamsul & Hayat, Qaiser. Role of Proline & Salicylic Acid in Overcoming the Stress of Cadmium. 2011. 184p. pap. (978-3-8443-1660-5(4)) Lambert Academic Publishing.

Khan, Muhammad Haleem. Influence of Humic Acid on Sorption of Cadmium on Montmorillonite. 2010. 100p. pap. (978-3-639-25015-2(X)) VDM Verlag Dr. Mueller e.K.

Matovi?, Vesna, et al, eds. Zinc, Copper, or Magnesium Supplementation Against Cadmium Toxicity. 2010. (Environmental Science, Engineering & Technology Ser.). xiv, 58p. pap. 43.00 (978-1-61668-332-0(5)) Nova Science Pubs., Inc.

Moreda-Piñeiro, Antonio & Moreda-Piñeiro, Jorge, eds. Analytical Chemistry of Cadmium: Sample Pre-Treatment & Determination Methods. 2010. (Chemistry Research & Applications Ser.). 89.00 (978-1-60876-808-0(2)) Nova Science Pubs., Inc.

Pappas, A. C., et al, eds. Cadmium Toxicity & the Antioxidant System. 2010. (Environmental Health - Physical, Chemical & Biological Factors Ser.). pap. 43.00 (978-1-61668-172-2(1)) Nova Science Pubs., Inc.

Parvau, Reini G., ed. Cadmium in the Environment. 2009. (Environmental Health - Physical, Chemical & Biological Factors Ser.). 195.00 (978-1-60741-934-1(3)) Nova Science Pubs., Inc.

Pattabi, Manjunatha & Sheeja Krishnan. Electron Irradiation Effects in Cadmium Telluride & Silicon Devices. 2010. 120p. pap. (978-3-8383-0714-5(3)) Lambert Academic Publishing.

Seth, C. S. Mechanisms of Cadmium Phtoextraction in Indian Mustard. 2011. 124p. pap. (978-3-8443-2384-9(8)) Lambert Academic Publishing.

Wang, Zaosheng, et al, eds. Mechanisms of Cadmium Toxicity to Various Trophic Saltwater Organisms. 2010. (Environmental Science, Engineering & Technology Ser.). (Illus.). 83p. pap. 43.00 (978-1-60876-646-8(2)) Nova Science Pubs., Inc.

World Health Organization. Evaluation of Certain Food Contaminants: Sixty-Fourth Report of the Joint FAO/WHO Expert Committee on Food Additives. 2006. (Who Technical Report Ser.). (ENG., Illus.). 107p. pap. 48.00 (978-92-4-120930-4(5)) World Health Organization.

CADSES (COMPUTER PROGRAMS)

Cavallucci, Denis, et al, eds. Building Innovation Pipelines through Computer-Aided Innovation: 4th IFIP WG 5. 4 Working Conference, CAI 2011, Strasbourg, France, June 30 - July 1, 2011, Proceedings. 2011. (IFIP Advances in Information & Communication Technology Ser.). (Illus.). x, 193p. 109.00 **(978-3-642-22181-1(5)**, 3642221815) Springer.

Lattanze, Anthony J. Architecting Software Intensive Systems: A Practitioners Guide. 2008. (ENG., Illus.). 416p. 85.95 *(978-1-4200-4569-7(5))* Auerbach Pubs., Inc.

Liu, Haoyang. Applications of Bayesian Classifiers. 2008. 144p. pap. *(978-3-639-03895-3(6))* VDM Verlag Dr. Mueller e.K.

Norman, Peter. Process Modelling & Computer Aided Design in Chemical Engineering. 350p. 100.00 *(978-0-471-93870-5(X))*; pap. 39.95 *(978-0-471-96761-3(0))* Wiley, John & Sons, Inc.

CADWALADER, JOHN, 1742-1786

Cadwalader, John. Cadwalader's Cases: Being Decisions of the Hon. John Cadwalader, 2 vol., set. reprint ed. 250.00 *(978-0-7222-8323-3(7))* Library Reprints, Inc.

CAE

see Computer-Aided Engineering

CAEN, BATTLE OF, CAEN, FRANCE, 1944

Bernage, Georges. Sword, Objectif Caen. 2011. (FRE.). 80p. pap. 14.99 *(978-2-84048-288-8(6))* Editions Heimdal FRA. Dist: Casemate Pubs. & Bk. Distributors, LLC.

Jeanne, édérick. Caen 1944. 2011. (FRE., Illus.). 160p. 39.95 *(978-2-84048-284-0(3))* Editions Heimdal FRA. Dist: Casemate Pubs. & Bk. Distributors, LLC.

McKee, Alexander. Caen: Anvil of Victory. 2nd ed. 2012. (Illus.). 368p. pap. 26.95 **(978-0-285-63559-3(X))** Souvenir Pr. Ltd. GBR. Dist: Independent Pubs. Group.

Thomas, Graham A. Firestorm: Typhoons over Caen 1944. 2006. (ENG., Illus.). 232p. 39.95 *(978-1-86227-345-0(6))* History Pr. Ltd., The GBR. Dist: Independent Pubs. Group.

CAESAR, CAIUS JULIUS

see Caesar, Julius

CAESAR, JULIUS

Abbott, Jacob. History of Julius Caesar. 2008. 196p. 22.99 *(978-0-554-36290-8(2))* 2008. 196p. 25.99 *(978-0-554-26987-0(2))* 2007. (ENG.). 176p. pap. 19.99 *(978-1-4346-2283-9(5))* 2007. (ENG.). 194p. pap. 21.99 *(978-1-4346-2341-6(6))* BiblioBazaar.

—History of Julius Caesar. 2009. 116p. pap. **(978-0-217-00576-0(4))** Books LLC.

Adcock, Frank E. Caesar As Man of Letters. 2011. 124p. 40.95 **(978-1-258-01776-7(8))** Literary Licensing, LLC.

Axelrod, Alan. Julius Caesar, CEO: 6 Principles to Guide &Inspire Modern Leaders. 2012. (CEO Ser.). (ENG.). 248p. 22.95 **(978-1-4027-8484-2(8))** Sterling Publishing Co., Inc.

Billows, Richard A. Julius Caesar. 2011. (ENG.). 336p. pap. 34.95 **(978-0-415-69260-1(1))** Routledge.

Billows, Richard A. Julius Caesar: The Colossus of Rome. 2009. (Roman Imperial Biographies Ser.). (ENG., Illus.). 336p. 130.00 *(978-0-415-33314-6(8))* Routledge.

Bloom, Harold & Locs, Pamela, eds. Julius Caesar. 2008. (Bloom's Shakespeare Through the Ages Ser.). 328p. (C). (gr. 9). per. 18.95 *(978-0-7910-9840-0(0),* Checkmark Bks.) Facts On File, Inc.

Caesar, Julius. Caesar: the Gallic War, Vol. 7. Whiteley, J. L., ed. 2009. (Latin Texts Ser.). (LAT.). pap. 19.95 *(978-1-85399-632-0(7))* Bristol Classical Pr. GBR. Dist: International Publishers Marketing.

—Caesar: the Gallic War. Edwards, H. J., tr. 2007. (ENG.). 644p. per. 45.95 *(978-1-4304-4750-4(8))* Kessinger Publishing, LLC.

—The Gallic War: Commentaries on the Gallic War with an Eighth Commentary. 2009. 136p. pap *(978-0-217-76122-2(4))* Books LLC.

—The Gallic War: Commentaries on the Gallic War with an Eighth Commentary. Edwards, H. J., tr. from LAT. 2006. (Dover Thrift Editions Ser.). (ENG., Illus.). 224p. per. 5.00 *(978-0-486-45107-7(0))* Dover Pubns., Inc.

—The Gallic War: Commentaries on the Gallic War with an Eighth Commentary. Hammond, Carolyn, tr. from LAT. 2008. (Oxford World's Classics Ser.). (ENG., Illus.). 320p. pap. 9.95 *(978-0-19-954026-6(8))* Oxford Univ. Pr., Inc.

Caesar, Julius & Macdevitt, W. A. The Gallic Wars. 2009. 172p. pap. 8.99 *(978-1-60459-762-2(3))* Wilder Pubns., Ltd.

Caesar, Julius & Tatum, W. Jeffrey. A Caesar Reader: Selections from Bellum Gallicum & Bellum Civile, & from Caesar's Letters, Speeches, & Poetry. 2011. (LAT & ENG., Illus.). pap. 19.00 **(978-0-86516-696-7(X))** Bolchazy-Carducci Pubs.

Canfora, Luciano. Julius Caesar: The Life & Times of the People's Dictator. Hill, Marian & Windle, Kevin, trs. from ITA. 2007. 392p. 36.95 *(978-0-520-23502-1(9))* Univ. of California Pr.

Dando-Collins, Stephen. The Ides: Caesar's Murder & the War for Rome. 2010. (ENG., Illus.). 288p. 25.95 *(978-0-470-42523-7(7),* Wiley) Wiley, John & Sons, Inc.

Dodge, Theodore Ayrault. Great Captains. 2009. 110p. pap. *(978-0-217-21814-6(8))* Books LLC.

Fields, Nic. Julius Caesar. 2010. (Command Ser.). (ENG., Illus.). 64p. pap. 18.95 *(978-1-84603-928-7(2))* Osprey Publishing, Ltd. GBR. Dist: Random Hse., Inc.

—Warlords of Republican Rome: Caesar Against Pompey. 2010. (Illus.). 256p. 32.95 *(978-1-935149-06-4(7))* Casemate Pubs. & Bk. Distributors, LLC.

Freeman, Philip. Julius Caesar. 2009. (ENG., Illus.). 416p. pap. 17.00 *(978-0-7432-8954-2(4))* Simon & Schuster.

Froude, James Anthony. Caesar: A Sketch. 2008. 464p. 31.99 *(978-0-554-32048-9(7))* 2006. 410p. pap. 26.99 *(978-1-4264-2937-8(1))* 2008. 464p. 33.99 *(978-0-554-22745-0(2))* 2007. (ENG.). 460p. pap. 30.99 *(978-1-4264-2990-3(8))* BiblioBazaar.

—Caesar: A Sketch. 2008. 432p. pap. *(978-1-4065-7189-9(X))* Dodo Pr.

—Julius Caesar. 2009. 296p. pap. *(978-0-217-49698-8(9))*; 284p. pap. *(978-1-4590-9371-3(2))* Books LLC.

—Julius Caesar. 2007. (ENG.). 504p. 53.95 *(978-0-548-01021-1(8))* Kessinger Publishing, LLC.

Garcea, Alessandro. Caesar's de Analogia: Edition, Translation, & Commentary. 2012. (ENG.). 320p. 150.00 **(978-0-19-960397-8(9))** Oxford Univ. Pr., Inc.

Goldsworthy, Adrian. Caesar: Life of a Colossus. (ENG., Illus.). 608p. 2008. per. 20.00 *(978-0-300-12689-1(1))* 2006. 35.00 *(978-0-300-12048-6(6))* Yale Univ. Pr.

Griffin, Miriam, ed. Companion to Julius Caesar. 2009. (Blackwell Companions to the Ancient World Ser.: 68). (ENG., Illus.). 536p. 209.95 *(978-1-4051-4923-5(X),* Wiley-Blackwell) Wiley, John & Sons, Inc.

Grillo, Luca. The Art of Caesar's Bellum Civile: Literature, Ideology, & Community. 2012. (ENG., Illus.). 234p. 95.00 **(978-1-107-00949-3(9))** Cambridge Univ. Pr.

Hamlyn, Timothy. Pontifex Optimus Maximus. 2011. 132p. pap. **(978-3-8443-0569-2(6))** Lambert Academic Publishing.

Hardy, Ernest George. Some Problems in Roman History: Ten Essays Bearing on the Administrative & Legislative Work of Julius Caesar. 2007. 85.00 *(978-1-58477-753-3(2))* Lawbook Exchange, Ltd., The.

Isenberg, Irwin. The Way of Caesar. 2007. (ENG., Illus.). 160p. pap. 9.95 *(978-1-59687-124-3(5))* IBks., Inc.

Jelusich, Mirko. Caesar. Miall, Bernard, tr. 2007. (ENG.). 438p. 51.95 *(978-0-548-03144-5(4))* Kessinger Publishing, LLC.

Jimenez, Ramon L. Caesar Against the Celts. 2006. (Illus.). 285p. reprint ed. 27.00 *(978-1-4223-5291-5(9))* DIANE Publishing Co.

John, D. A., ed. Caesar: 55 & 54 B. C. Expeditions to Britain. 2010. (Latin Texts Ser.). (LAT.). 112p. pap. 17.95 *(978-0-86292-280-1(1))* Bristol Classical Pr. GBR. Dist: International Publishers Marketing.

Judson, Harry Pratt. Caesar's Army: The Evolution, Composition, Tactics, Equipment & Battles of the Roman Army. 2011. 148p. **(978-0-85706-573-5(4))**; pap. **(978-0-85706-574-2(2))** Leonaur Ltd.

Kamm, Antony. Julius Caesar: A Life. 2006. (Illus.). 172p. 120.00 *(978-0-415-36415-7(9))* Routledge.

Kennedy, Eberhard Christoper, ed. Caesar: Gallic War II. 2009. (Latin Texts Ser.). (LAT.). 145p. pap. 19.95 *(978-0-86292-101-9(5))* Bristol Classical Pr. GBR. Dist: International Publishers Marketing.

Lewin, Thomas. The Invasion of Britain by Julius Caesar. 2007. (ENG.). 148p. 35.95 *(978-0-548-03963-2(1))* Kessinger Publishing, LLC.

Oman, Charles William Chadwick. Seven Roman Statesmen of the Later Republic. 2009. 230p. pap. *(978-0-217-05232-0(0))* Books LLC.

Powell, Anton & Welch, Kathryn, eds. Julius Caesar as Artful Reporter: The War Commentaries as Political Instruments. 2009. (ENG.). 225p. (C). pap. 40.00 *(978-1-905125-28-9(3))* Classical Pr. of Wales, The GBR. Dist: Brown, David Bk. Co., The.

Riggsby, Andrew M. Caesar in Gaul & Rome: War in Words. 2010. (ENG., Illus.). 286p. pap. 25.00 *(978-0-292-72617-8(1))* Univ. of Texas Pr.

Sabben-Clare, James. Caesar & Roman Politics Sixty to Fifty B.C. (LAT.). 222p. reprint ed. pap. 24.95 *(978-0-906515-94-5(7))* Bristol Classical Pr. GBR. Dist: International Publishers Marketing.

Shakespeare, William. Julius Caesar. Raffel, Burton, ed. annot. ed. 2006. (Annotated Shakespeare Ser.). (ENG.). 192p. per. 6.95 *(978-0-300-10809-5(5))* Yale Univ. Pr.

Siehler, E. G. Caesar, Cicero & Ferrero. 2009. pap. 21.52 *(978-1-60724-656-5(2))* Gorgias Pr., LLC.

Southern, Pat. Julius Caesar. (Illus.). 160p. 40.00 *(978-0-7524-1443-0(7))* History Pr. Ltd., The GBR. Dist: Trafalgar Square Publishing.

Tatum, W. Jeffrey. Always I Am Caesar. 2008. (ENG., Illus.). 216p. 87.95 *(978-1-4051-7526-5(5))*; pap. 31.95 *(978-1-4051-7525-8(7))* Wiley, John & Sons, Inc. (Wiley-Blackwell).

Woolf, Greg. Et Tu, Brute? The Murder of Caesar & Political Assassination. 2007. (Profiles in History Ser.). (Illus.). 224p. 19.95 *(978-0-674-02684-1(5))* Harvard Univ. Pr.

Wyke, Maria. Caesar: A Life in Western Culture. 2008. (ENG., Illus.). 288p. 25.00 *(978-0-226-92153-2(0))* Univ. of Chicago Pr.

Wyke, Maria. Caesar in the USA. 2012. (ENG.). 344p. 39.95 **(978-0-520-27391-7(5))** Univ. of California Pr.

Yenne, Bill. Julius Caesar: Lessons in Leadership from the Great Conqueror. 2012. (World Generals Ser.). (ENG., Illus.). 224p. 23.00 **(978-0-230-11231-5(5))** Palgrave Macmillan.

CAESAR, JULIUS—DRAMA

Boas, F. S. Tragedy of Caesars Revenge. 2006. 92p. per. *(978-1-4067-3551-2(5),* Hesperides Pr.) Read Bks.

Kamm, Antony. Julius Caesar: A Life. 2007. (Illus.). 172p. per. 32.95 *(978-0-415-41121-9(1))* Routledge.

Nelson, Richard. Conversations in Tusculum. 2008. (ENG.). 112p. pap. 14.00 *(978-0-86547-992-0(5))* Faber & Faber, Inc.

Shakespeare, William. Julius Caesar. 2009. 256p. 24.99 *(978-1-103-19178-9(0))* 2009. 256p. pap. 18.99 *(978-1-103-19177-2(2))* 2008. 152p. 21.99 *(978-0-554-35684-6(8))* 2008. 152p. 24.99 *(978-0-554-26381-6(5))* 2007 (ENG.). 132p. pap. 18.99 *(978-1-4346-0991-5(X))* 2007. 148p. pap. 19.99 *(978-1-4346-1090-4(X))* BiblioBazaar.

—Julius Caesar. 2009. 80p. pap. 4.95 *(978-1-4209-3283-6(7))* Digireads.com.

—Julius Caesar. 2008. 116p. per. *(978-1-4065-8632-9(3))* Dodo Pr.

—Julius Caesar. 2007. (ENG.). 168p. per. 5.99 *(978-1-59986-775-5(3))* Filiquarian Publishing, LLC.

—Julius Caesar, 1 vol. 2006. (Illustrated Classics Shakespeare Ser.). (ENG., Illus.). 64p. (YA). (gr. 9-12). per. 9.95 *(978-1-59905-145-1(1))* Saddleback Educational Publishing.

—Julius Caesar Thrift Study Edition. 2009. (Dover Thrift Study Edition Ser.). (ENG.). 160p. pap. 4.95 *(978-0-486-47577-6(8))* Dover Pubns., Inc.

—Shakespeare on the Double! Julius Caesar. Snodgrass, Mary Ellen, tr. 2006. (ENG.). 216p. per. 8.99 *(978-0-470-04157-4(9),* Wiley) Wiley, John & Sons, Inc.

—The Tragedy of Julius Caesar. Hatchuel, Sarah & Lake, James H., eds. 2007. (New Kittredge Shakespeare Ser.). (ENG., Illus.). 142p. per. 8.95 *(978-1-58510-260-0(1))* Focus Publishing/R. Pullins Co., Inc.

Shakespeare, William & Hadfield, Andrew. Julius Caesar. 2007. (Barnes & Noble Shakespeare Ser.). 328p. pap. 7.95 *(978-1-4114-0040-5(2),* Barnes & Noble Shakespeare) Barnes & Noble, Inc.

Shakespeare, William & Shakespeare, William. Julius Caesar. 2009. (Graphic Classics Ser.). (ENG., Illus.). 48p. (J). (gr. 3). pap. 8.99 *(978-0-7641-4010-5(8))* Barron's Educational Series, Inc.

Shakespeare, William, et al. Julius Caesar, 1 vol. Saddleback Educational Publishing Staff, ed. 2006. (Shakespeare Made Easy Study Guides). (ENG.). 64p. (gr. 9-12). tchr. ed., per. 18.99 *(978-1-59905-132-1(X))* Saddleback Educational Publishing.

Smith, Robert & Shakespeare, William. Julius Caesar. Shakespeare, William et al, eds. 2nd rev. ed. 2008. (Cambridge School Shakespeare Ser.). (ENG., Illus.). 196p. pap. 10.99 *(978-0-521-70677-3(7))* Cambridge Univ. Pr.

Werstine, Paul. Julius Caesar. Shakespeare, William, ed. pap. 18.00 *(978-0-7434-6657-8(8))* Simon & Schuster, Inc.

CAESAREAN SECTION

see Cesarean Section

CAESARS

see Emperors—Rome

CAESIUM

see Cesium

CAFES

see Coffeehouses; Hotels; Restaurants

CAFETERIAS

see also School Lunchrooms, Cafeterias, etc.

Crump, A. K., photos by. The Cafes of San Francisco: A Guide to the Sights, Sounds, & Tastes of America's Original Cafe Society. 3rd ed. 2009. Orig. Title: The Cafes of San Francisco. (ENG., Illus.). 144p. pap. 15.95 *(978-0-9798640-3-2(8))* TCB-Cafe Publishing.

Dawson, Carol & Johnston, Carol. House of Plenty: The Rise, Fall, & Revival of Luby's Cafeterias. 2006. (ENG., Illus.). 288p. 21.00 *(978-0-292-70656-9(1))* Univ. of Texas Pr.

CAFFEINE

Chambers, Kenneth P. Caffeine & Health Research. 2008. (Illus.). xii, 217p. 110.00 *(978-1-60456-437-2(7))* Nova Science Pubs., Inc.

Smith, Barry D., et al, eds. Caffeine & Activation Theory: Effects on Health & Behavior. 2006. (ENG., Illus.). 400p. 179.95 *(978-0-8493-7102-8(3),* CRC Press) Taylor & Francis Group GBR. Dist: Taylor & Francis Group.

Weinberg, Bennett Alan & Bealer, Bonnie. The Caffeine Advantage: How to Sharpen Your Mind, Improve Your Physical Performance, & Achieve Your Goals - The Healthy Way. 2010. (ENG., Illus.). 272p. pap. 17.99 *(978-0-7432-2897-8(9),* Free Pr.) Free Pr.

CAGE, JOHN, 1912-1992

Addiss, Stephen, et al. John Cage: Zen Ox-Herding Pictures. 2009. (ENG., Illus.). 128p. 34.95 *(978-0-8076-1601-7(X),* 761601) Braziller, George Inc.

Anastasi, William & Levy, Aaron. The Cage Dialogues: A Memoir. 2011. pap. **(978-1-936994-01-4(1))** Slought Foundation.

Bock, Jannika. Concorde in Massachusetts, Discord in the World: The Writings of Henry Thoreau & John Cage. 2008. (American Culture Ser.). (Illus.). 286p. pap. 74.95 *(978-3-631-58413-2(X))* Lang, Peter GmbH, Europaischer Verlag der Wissenschaften DEU. Dist: Lang, Peter.

Brown, Carolyn. Chance & Circumstance: Twenty Years with Cage & Cunningham. 2009. (ENG., Illus.). 656p. pap. 26.95 *(978-0-8101-2513-1(7))* Northwestern Univ. Pr.

Cage, John. The Anarchy of Silence: John Cage & Experimental Art. 2010. (Illus.). 295p. pap. 59.95 *(978-84-92505-14-2(1))* Museu d'Art Contemporani de Barcelona ESP. Dist: Actar Birkhauser Distribution.

—Every Day Is a Good Day: the Visual Art of John Cage. 2010. (ENG., Illus.). 160p. pap. 30.00 *(978-1-85332-283-9(0))* Hayward Gallery Publishing GBR. Dist: D.A.P./Distributed Art Pubs.

—John Cage. Robinson, Julia, ed. 2011. (October Files Ser.). (ENG., Illus.). 232p. (gr. 17). pap. 19.95 *(978-0-262-51630-3(6))* MIT Pr.

—John Cage Book of Days 2011. 2010. (ENG., Illus.). 120p. pap. 25.00 *(978-1-935202-23-3(5))* D.A.P./Distributed Art Pubs.

Cage, John. John Cage Book of Days 2012. Kuhn, Laura, ed. 2011. (ENG., Illus.). 120p. pap. 25.00 **(978-1-935202-64-6(2))** D.A.P./Distributed Art Pubs.

Cage, John & Robinson, Andrew. John Cage. Robinson, Julia, ed. 2011. (October Files Ser.). (ENG., Illus.). 232p. (gr. 17). 35.00 *(978-0-262-01612-4(5))* MIT Pr.

Cancino, Juan Parra, et al. MetaCage: Essays on & around Freeman Etudes, Fontana Mix, Aria. 2010. (Orpheus Research Centre in Music Ser.). (Illus.). 104p. pap. 32.50 *(978-94-90389-01-7(3))* Leuven Univ. Pr. BEL. Dist: Cornell Univ. Pr.

DeLio, Thomas. The Amores of John Cage. 2010. (ENG., Illus.). 176p. pap. 45.00 *(978-1-57647-152-1(9))* Pendragon Pr.

Ekbom, Torsten. En Trädgård Av Ljud: En Bok Om John Cage Och the Cage Age. 2009. (Illus.). 393p. *(978-91-0-012364-2(1))* Bonnier, Albert forlag AB.

Gann, Kyle. No Such Thing as Silence: John Cage's 4'33. 2011. (Icons of America Ser.). (Illus.). 272p. pap. 16.00 *(978-0-300-17129-7(3))* Yale Univ. Pr.

Haskins, Rob. Anarchic Societies of Sounds. 2009. 280p. pap. *(978-3-639-13209-0(2))* VDM Verlag Dr. Mueller e.K.

Haskins, Rob. John Cage. 2012. (Reaktion Books - Critical Lives Ser.). (Illus.). 224p. pap. 16.95 **(978-1-86189-905-7(X))** Reaktion Bks., Ltd. GBR. Dist: Chicago Distribution Ctr.

Jurging, Stefan. Die Tradition des Traditionsbruches: John Cages Amerikanische Asthetik. (Beitrage Aus Anglistik und Amerikanistik Ser.: Vol. 11). (GER.). 201 S.p. 30.95 *(978-3-631-39446-5(2))* Lang, Peter Publishing, Inc.

Kass, Ray. The Sight of Silence: John Cage's Complete Watercolors. 2011. (ENG., Illus.). 144p. 34.95 **(978-0-615-40180-5(5))** Univ. Pr. of Virginia.

Larson, Kay. Where the Heart Beats: John Cage, Zen Buddhism, & the Inner Life of Artists. 2012. (ENG.). 496p. (gr. 12). 29.95 **(978-1-59420-340-4(7)** Penguin Pr. HC, The) Penguin Group (USA) Inc.

Nicholls, David. John Cage. 2007. (American Composers Ser.). (Illus.). 160p. 37.00 *(978-0-252-03215-8(2))* Univ. of Illinois Pr.

Patterson, David. John Cage: Music, Philosophy, & Intention, 1933-1950. 2008. VIII, 280p. 41.95 *(978-0-415-99667-9(8))* Routledge.

Silverman, Kenneth. Begin Again: A Biography of John Cage. 2010. (ENG., Illus.). 496p. 40.00 *(978-1-4000-4437-5(5),* Knopf) Knopf Doubleday Publishing Group.

Weagel, Deborah. Words & Music: Camus, Beckett, Cage, Gould. 2010. (American University Studies XX: Fine Arts Ser.). (Illus.). 176p. (C). 72.95 *(978-1-4331-0836-5(4))* Lang, Peter Publishing, Inc.

CAGE BIRDS

see also names of cage birds, e.g. Canaries

Alderton, David. A Birdkeeper's Guide to Softbills. (Illus.). 118p. 10.95 *(978-3-923880-71-3(5),* 16082) Tetra Pr.

—Caring for Your Pet Bird: A Practical Handbook. 2009. (ENG., Illus.). 96p. pap. 8.99 *(978-1-84476-696-3(9))* Anness Publishing GBR. Dist: National Bk. Network.

Alderton, David. The Ultimate Encyclopedia of Caged & Aviary Birds: Practical family reference guide to keeping pet birds, with expert advice on buying, understanding, breeding & exhibiting Birds. 2011. (ENG., Illus.). 256p. pap. 24.99 **(978-1-78019-048-8(4))** Anness Publishing GBR. Dist: National Bk. Network.

Birmelin, Immanuel & Niemann, Hildegard. Budgerigars. 2nd rev. ed. 2008. (Complete Pet Owner's Manual Ser.). (ENG., Illus.). 64p. pap. 8.99 *(978-0-7641-3897-3(9))* Barron's Educational Series, Inc.

Butler, Arthur G. Foreign Finches in Captivity. 2010. 282p. pap. 49.95 *(978-1-61646-011-2(3))* Coachwhip Pubns.

Demaine, A. F. Roller Canary Its History Breeding Trai. 2006. 92p. per. *(978-1-4067-9595-0(X),* Hesperides Pr.) Read Bks.

Deutsch, Robin. The Healthy Bird Cookbook, 1 vol. 2011. (ENG., Illus.). 192p. pap. 15.95 **(978-0-7938-0716-1(6))** TFH Pubns., Inc.

Greene, W. T. Favourite Foreign Birds for Cages & Av. 2006. pap. *(978-1-4067-9534-9(8))* Read Bks.

—Grey Parrot & How to Manage It. 2006. 84p. per. *(978-1-4067-9597-4(6),* Hesperides Pr.) Read Bks.

HCI, creator. Ultimate Bird Lover: Stories & Advice on Our Feathered Friends at Home & in the Wild. 2010. (Ultimate Ser.). (ENG., Illus.). 328p. pap. 14.95 *(978-0-7573-1438-4(4))* Health Communications, Inc.

Mancini, Julie Rach. Why Does My Bird Do That: A Guide to Parrot Behavior. 2nd rev. ed. 2006. (ENG., Illus.). 256p. pap. 19.99 *(978-0-470-03971-7(X),* Howell Bk. Hse.) Wiley, John & Sons, Inc.

Morrone, Marc & Fernandez, Amy. Ask the Bird Keeper. 2009. (ENG., Illus.). 128p. pap. 14.95 *(978-1-933958-31-6(6))* BowTie Pr.

CAGE INCLUSION COMPOUNDS

see Clathrate Compounds

CAGLIOSTRO, ALESSANDRO, CONTE DI, 1743-1795

Evans, Henry Ridgely. Cagliostro & His Egyptian Rite of Free. 2006. pap. 19.95 *(978-1-4286-4698-5(1))* Kessinger Publishing, LLC.

Faulks, Philippa & Cooper, Robert L. D. The Masonic Magician: The Life & Death of Count Cagliostro & His Egyptian Rite. 2008. (ENG.). 368p. 24.95 *(978-1-905857-82-1(9),* Watkins Publishing) Duncan Baird Pubs. GBR. Dist: Sterling Publishing Co., Inc.

CAGNEY, JAMES, 1899-1986

Nollen, Scott Allen. Warners Wiseguys: All 112 Films That Robinson, Cagney & Bogart Made for the Studio. 2007. (ENG., Illus.). 372p. 55.00 *(978-0-7864-3262-2(4))* McFarland & Co., Inc. Pubs.

C

CAHOKIA (ILL.)

Byers, A. Martin. Cahokia: A World Renewal Cult Heterarchy. (ENG., Illus.). 616p. 2009. pap. 34.95 (978-0-8130-3386-0(1)) 2006. 69.95 (978-0-8130-2958-0(9)) Univ. Pr. of Florida.

Pauketat, Timothy R. Cahokia: Ancient America's Great City on the Mississippi. 2010. (ENG.). 208p. (gr. 12). 14.00 (978-0-14-311747-6(5), Penguin (Non-Classics)) Penguin Group (USA) Inc.

CAI

see Computer-Assisted Instruction

CAIN (BIBLICAL FIGURE)

Byron, John. Cain & Abel in Text & Tradition: Jewish & Christian Interpretations of the First Sibling Rivalry. 2011. 226p. (978-90-04-19252-2(2)) BRILL.

Gessner. The Death of Abel. 2007. (ENG.). 172p. 37.95 (978-0-548-08298-0(7)) Kessinger Publishing, LLC.

LaCocque, Andre. Onslaught Against Innocence: Cain, Abel, & the Yahwist. 2008. 188p. pap. 22.00 (978-1-55635-789-3(3)) Wipf & Stock Pubs.

—Onslaught Against Innocence: Cain, Abel & the Yahwist. 2010. (ENG.). 187p. (C). pap. 39.00 (978-0-227-17319-0(8)) Clarke, James Co., Ltd. GBR. Dist: Brown, David Bk. Co., The.

Whidden, Theodore L. The Bible Plumb Line: Cain's Wife & Other Perspectives. 2006. per. (978-0-9786684-2-6(1)) Heritage Ink Christian Publishing Co., LLC.

CAIN, JAMES MALLAHAN, 1892-1977

Gale, Robert L. Characters & Plots in the Fiction of James M. Cain. 2011. (ENG.). 252p. pap. 75.00 (978-0-7864-5969-8(7)) McFarland & Co., Inc. Pubs.

Madden, David & Mecholsky, Kristopher. James M. Cain: Hard-Boiled Mythmaker. 2011. (ENG.). 240p. 49.00 (978-0-8108-8118-1(7)) Scarecrow Pr., Inc.

Pelizzon, V. Penelope & West, Nancy Martha. Tabloid, Inc: Crimes, Newspapers, Narratives. 2010. (Theory interpretation Narrativ Ser.). (ENG.). 280p. 51.95 (978-0-8142-1117-5(8)); cd-rom 14.95 (978-0-8142-9215-0(1)) Ohio State Univ. Pr.

CAIRN TERRIER

Ash, Edward C. The Cairn Terrier - Care, Management & Exhibition with Leading Owners & Famous Dogs of the Breed. 2008. 172p. (978-1-4437-3289-5(3)) 2007. (Illus.). 168p. per. (978-1-4067-8937-9(2)) Read Bks. (Pomona Pr.).

Coren, Stanley. Born to Bark: My Adventures with an Irrepressible & Unforgettable Dog. (ENG.). 320p. 2011. pap. 16.00 (978-1-4391-8921-4(8)) 2010. (Illus.). 24.00 (978-1-4391-8920-7(X)) Free Pr. (Free Pr.).

Lehman, Patricia F. & Lehman, Patricia. Cairn Terriers. 2nd ed. 2009. (Complete Pet Owner's Manual Ser.). (ENG., Illus.). 96p. pap. 8.99 (978-0-7641-4102-7(3)) Barron's Educational Series, Inc.

Ross, Florence M. The Cairn Terrier. 2007. 116p. per. (978-1-84664-038-4(5)) Read Bks.

CAIRNS

see also Mounds

Cummings, Vicki. From Cairn to Cemetery. 2007. (Bar S Ser.). (Illus.). 188p. (C). pap. 85.00 (978-1-4073-0039-9(3)) British Archaeological Reports Ltd. GBR. Dist: Brown, David Bk. Co., The.

Hallendy, Norman. Tukiliit: The Stone People Who Live in the Wind. 2nd ed. 2009. (ENG, JPN, FRE, GER & SPA., Illus.). 128p. pap. 19.95 (978-1-60223-057-6(9)) Univ. of Alaska Pr.

CAIRO (EGYPT)

Bell, Clark. Medico-Legal Studies. 2010. 282p. pap. 28.75 (978-1-149-01128-7(9)) BiblioBazaar.

Bianca, Stefano & Jodido, Philip. Cairo: Revitalising a Historic Metropolis. Bianca, Stefano, ed. 2006. (ENG., Illus.). 256p. 60.00 (978-88-422-1235-5(0)) Allemandi, Umberto & Co. GBR. Dist: Antique Collectors' Club.

Boghdadi, Magda Sadek. From the Nile to the Hudson: Memoirs of an Immigrant: A Tribute to My Father. 2009. (978-1-890357-24-5(3)) Florida Academic Pr.

Fahmi, Kamal. Beyond the Victim: The Politics & Ethics of Empowering Cairo's Street Children. 2007. (ENG., Illus.). 272p. 29.95 (978-977-416-063-9(0)) American Univ. in Cairo Pr. EGY. Dist: Oxford Univ. Pr., Inc.

Gauldie, Robin. The Best of Cairo & Luxor. 3rd ed. 2009. (Globetrotter Best of Ser.). (ENG., Illus.). 96p. pap. 8.95 (978-1-84773-491-4(X), Globetrotter) New Holland Pubs., Ltd. GBR. Dist: Globe Pequot Pr., The.

Halfon, Saul. The Cairo Consensus: Demographic Surveys, Women's Empowerment, & Regime Change in Population Policy. 2006. (ENG., Illus.). 282p. 62.99 (978-0-7391-1176-5(0)) Lexington Bks.

Ismail, Salwa. Political Life in Cairo's New Quarters: Encountering the Everyday State. 2006. (Illus.). 264p. 67.50 (978-0-8166-4911-2(1)); per. 24.50 (978-0-8166-4912-9(X)) Univ. of Minnesota Pr.

Jodido, Philip. Cairo: Revitalising a Historic Metropolis. Bianca, Stefano, ed. 2007. (ENG., Illus.). 256p. pap. 60.00 (978-88-422-1540-0(6)) Allemandi, Umberto & Co. GBR. Dist: Antique Collectors' Club.

Kaldas, Pauline. Letters from Cairo. 2007. (Illus.). 167p. 19.95 (978-0-8156-0854-7(3)) Syracuse Univ. Pr.

Khuri-Makdisi, Ilham. The Eastern Mediterranean & the Making of Global Radicalism, 1860-1914. 2010. (California World History Library). (ENG., Illus.). 296p. 50.00 (978-0-520-26201-0(8)) Univ. of California Pr.

Lane-Poole, Stanley. The Story of Cairo. 2010. (ENG.). 362p. pap. 32.75 (978-1-172-21030-5(6)); (ENG.). 366p. pap. 32.75 (978-1-177-00000-0(8)); 360p. pap. 32.75 (978-1-145-90609-9(5)); 358p. pap. 32.75 (978-1-142-02214-3(5)); 384p. pap. 33.75 (978-1-142-51068-8(9)) BiblioBazaar.

—The Story of Cairo. 2010. (Illus.). 188p. pap. 16.95 (978-1-150-96061-1(2)) General Bks. LLC.

—The Story of Cairo. (ENG.). 364p. 2007. 46.95 (978-0-548-13856-4(7)) 2006. per. 31.95 (978-1-4286-5028-2(8)) Kessinger Publishing, LLC.

Markus, Tom & Sarver, Linda. The Cairo Diaries: 2004-2006. 2007. 268p. per. 20.95 (978-0-595-45115-9(2)) iUniverse, Inc.

Petry, Carl F. The Civilian Elite of Cairo in the Later Middle Ages. 2008. 508p. pap. 50.00 (978-1-59740-472-3(1)) ACLS Humanities E-Book.

Thomas Cook Publishing Staff. Cairo. 2nd ed. 2010. (Thomas Cook Pocket Guides). (ENG., Illus.). 144p. pap. 9.95 (978-1-84848-304-0(X)) Cook, Thomas Publishing GBR. Dist: Globe Pequot Pr., The.

Warner, Nicholas. The True Description of Cairo: A Sixteenth-Century Venetian View, 3 vols. 2006. (Studies in the Arcadian Library: No. 2). (LAT & ENG., Illus.). 456p. 475.00 (978-0-19-714406-0(3)) Oxford Univ. Pr., Inc.

Wilson, Willow. The Butterfly Mosque: A Young American Woman's Journey to Love & Islam. 2010. (ENG.). 320p. 24.00 (978-0-8021-1887-5(9), Atlantic Monthly Pr.) Grove/Atlantic, Inc.

Wynn, L. L. Pyramids & Nightclubs: A Travel Ethnography of Arab & Western Imaginations of Egypt, from King Tut & a Colony of Atlantis to Rumors of Sex Orgies, Urban Legends about a Marauding Prince, & Blonde Belly Dancers. 2007. (ENG., Illus.). 296p. pap. 24.95 (978-0-292-71702-2(4)) Univ. of Texas Pr.

CAIRO (EGYPT)—DESCRIPTION AND TRAVEL

Behrens-Abouseif, Doris & Warner, Nicholas. Minarets of Cairo. 2010. (ENG., Illus.). 448p. 80.00 (978-1-84885-539-7(7)) I. B. Tauris & Co., Ltd. GBR. Dist: Macmillan.

Betts, Vanessa. Egypt: Cairo & Nile Delta. 2012. (Footprint Focus Ser.). (ENG., Illus.). 160p. pap. 12.95 (978-1-908206-69-5(1)) Footprint Handbooks GBR. Dist: Globe Pequot Pr., The.

Bonechi, Casa. Cairo. (ITA.). 64p. pap. (978-88-7009-231-8(3)) Casa Editrice Bonechi.

Cairo City Map: And complete street Index. 2010. 48p. pap. 19.95 (978-977-416-322-7(2)) American Univ. in Cairo Pr. EGY. Dist: Oxford Univ. Pr., Inc.

Daftary, Farhad, et al, eds. Living in Historic Cairo: Past & Present in an Islamic City. 2010. (Institute of Ismaili Studies). (Illus.). 300p. 60.00 (978-1-898592-28-0(4)) Univ. of Washington Pr.

Francey, Claire E. Cairo the Practical Guide: Maps. rev. ed. 2011. (ENG.). 92p. pap. 12.95 (978-977-416-405-7(9)) American Univ. in Cairo Pr. EGY. Dist: Oxford Univ. Pr., Inc.

Lababidi, Lesley. Cairo: The Practical Guide. 7th rev. ed. 2011. (ENG.). 256p. pap. 19.95 (978-977-416-467-5(9)) American Univ. in Cairo Pr. EGY. Dist: Oxford Univ. Pr., Inc.

Locken, E. Travel Journal Cairo. 2010. 192p. pap. 19.99 (978-0-557-44601-8(5)) Lulu Enterprises Inc.

Nedoroscik, Jeffrey A. Walking in the City of the Dead: A Visitor's Guide. 2010. 144p. pap. 13.14 (978-1-4269-3685-2(0)) Trafford Publishing.

Rough, Guides. The Rough Guide to Cairo & the Pyramids. 2011. (ENG., Illus.). 352p. 19.99 (978-1-84836-531-5(4)) Rough Guides, Ltd. GBR. Dist: Dorling Kindersley Publishing, Inc.

Sims, David. Understanding Cairo: The Logic of a City Out of Control. 2011. (ENG.). 304p. 29.50 (978-977-416-404-0(0)) American Univ. in Cairo Pr. EGY. Dist: Oxford Univ. Pr., Inc.

Wallpaper Magazine Editors. Wallpaper City Guide Cairo. Cook, Richard et al, eds. 2008. (ENG., Illus.). 128p. pap. 8.95 (978-0-7148-4805-1(0)) Phaidon Pr., Inc.

CAIRO (EGYPT)—HISTORY

Ansah, Hassan. Life, Death, & Community in Cairo's City of the Dead. 2010. 108p. pap. 12.95 (978-1-4502-6700-7(9)) iUniverse, Inc.

Assaf, Sherif, et al. Egypt from Repression to Revolution: The Road to Tahrir Square - Front Line Images by Six Young Egyptian Photographers. 2011. (ENG., Illus.). 144p. pap. 24.95 (978-977-416-514-6(4)) American Univ. in Cairo Pr. EGY. Dist: Oxford Univ. Pr., Inc.

Bader, Ali. Cairo Cosmopolitan: Politics, Culture, & Urban Space in the New Globalized Middle East. Singerman, Diane & Amar, Paul, eds. 2009. (ENG., Illus.). 564p. pap. 29.95 (978-977-416-289-3(7)) American Univ. in Cairo Pr. EGY. Dist: Oxford Univ. Pr., Inc.

Daftary, Farhad, et al, eds. Living in Historic Cairo: Past & Present in an Islamic City. 2010. (Institute of Ismaili Studies). (Illus.). 300p. 60.00 (978-1-898592-28-0(4)) Univ. of Washington Pr.

El-Din, Morsi S., et al. Cairo: The Site & the History. (Illus.). 102p. (978-0-905743-55-4(5), Stacey International) Stacey Publishing.

Gottheil, Richard J. H. A Document of the Fifteenth Century concerning Two Synagogues of the Jews in Old Cairo. 2010. (ARA.). pap. 18.76 (978-1-61143-326-5(6)) Gorgias Pr., LLC.

Lagnado, Lucette M. & Lagnado, Lucette. The Man in the White Sharkskin Suit: A Jewish Family's Exodus from Old Cairo to the New World. 2008. (P. S. Ser.). (ENG.). 368p. pap. 14.99 (978-0-06-082218-7(X), HarperPerennial) HarperCollins Pubs.

—The Man in the White Sharkskin Suit: My Family's Exodus from Old Cairo to the New World. 2007. (ENG., Illus.). 352p. 25.95 (978-0-06-082212-5(0), Ecco) HarperCollins Pubs.

Lewicka, Paulina B. Food & Foodways of Medieval Cairenes: Aspects of Life in an Islamic Metropolis of the Eastern Mediterranean. 2011. (Illus.). 760p. (978-90-04-19472-4(X)) BRILL.

MacLeod, Scott, ed. The Cairo Review of Global Affairs: Journal of the AUC School of Global Affairs & Public Policy (Issue #2) 2011. (ENG.). 112p. pap. 14.95 (978-977-416-502-3(0)) American Univ. in Cairo Pr. EGY. Dist: Oxford Univ. Pr., Inc.

Mehrez, Samia. The Literary Life of Cairo: One Hundred Years in the Heart of the City. 2011. 400p. 39.50 (978-977-416-390-6(7)) American Univ. in Cairo Pr. EGY. Dist: Oxford Univ. Pr., Inc.

Peterson, Mark Allen. Connected in Cairo: Growing up Cosmopolitan in the Modern Middle East. 2011. (Public Cultures of the Middle East & North Africa Ser.). (ENG., Illus.). 288p. 70.00 (978-0-253-35628-4(8), 0253356288); pap. 24.95 (978-0-253-22311-1(3), 0253223113) Indiana Univ. Pr.

Singerman, Diane, ed. Cairo Contested: Governance, Urban Space, & Global Modernity. 2nd ed. 2011. (ENG.). 536p. pap. 29.95 (978-977-416-500-9(4)) American Univ. in Cairo Pr. EGY. Dist: Oxford Univ. Pr., Inc.

CAIRO (ILL.)

Lansden, John M. A History of the City of Cairo, Illinois. 2009. (ENG.). 346p. pap. 27.95 (978-0-8093-2936-6(0)) Southern Illinois Univ. Pr.

Lansden, John McMurray. A History of the City of Cairo, Illinois. 2011. 390p. pap. 33.75 (978-1-178-49708-3(9)) 2010. 386p. pap. 33.75 (978-1-146-43369-3(7)) BiblioBazaar.

—A History of the City of Cairo, Illinois. 2009. 274p. pap. (978-1-150-20126-4(6)) Books LLC.

—A History of the City of Cairo, Illinois. 2010. (Illus.). 244p. pap. 32.56 (978-1-154-73090-6(5)) General Bks. LLC.

CAIRO CONFERENCE, 1921

Heiferman, Ronald Ian. The Cairo Conference of 1943: Roosevelt, Churchill, Chiang Kai-Shek & Madame Chiang. 2011. (ENG., Illus.). 207p. pap. 45.00 (978-0-7864-4804-3(0)) McFarland & Co., Inc. Pubs.

CAIRO GENIZAH

Cole, Peter, et al. Sacred Trash: The Lost & Found World of the Cairo Geniza. 2011. (ENG., Illus.). 304p. 26.95 (978-0-8052-4258-4(9), Schocken) Knopf Doubleday Publishing Group.

Glick, Shmuel. Seride Teshuvot: A Descriptive Catalogue of Responsa Fragments from the Jacques Mosseri Collection, Cambridge University Library. 2012. (ENG & HEB.). XXIV, 466p. (978-90-04-22395-0(9)) BRILL.

Glickman, Mark. Sacred Treasure, the Cairo Genizah: The Amazing Discoveries of Forgotten Jewish History in an Egyptian Synagogue Attic. 2010. (Illus.). 300p. 24.99 (978-1-58023-431-3(3)) Jewish Lights Publishing.

Khan, Geoffrey. Arabic Legal & Administrative Documents in the Cambridge Genizah Collections. 2006. (Genizah Ser.). (ENG., Illus.). 567p. (C). per. 60.00 (978-1-905739-04-2(4)) Archaeopress GBR. Dist: Brown, David Bk. Co., The.

Klein, Michael L. Targumic Manuscripts in the Cambridge Genizah Collections. 2006. (Genizah Ser.). 136p. 60.00 (978-1-905739-03-5(6)) Archaeopress GBR. Dist: Brown, David Bk. Co., The.

Lev, Efraim & Amar, Zohar. Practical Materia Medica of the Medieval Eastern Mediterranean According to the Cairo Genizah. 2007. (Sir Henry Wellcome Asian Ser.). (Illus.). 750p. (978-90-04-16120-7(1)) BRILL.

Outhwaite, Ben & Reif, Stefan C. "From a Sacred Source" Genizah Studies in Honor of Stefan C. Reif. Bhayro, Siam, ed. 2010. (Illus.). 411p. (978-90-04-19058-0(9)) BRILL.

Reif, Stefan C., ed. The Cambridge Genizah Collections: Their Contents & Significance. 2011. (Cambridge University Library Genizah Ser.). (ENG.). 276p. pap. 50.00 (978-0-521-15297-6(6)) Cambridge Univ. Pr.

Simonsohn, S. The Jews in Sicily, Volume 16 Notaries of Trapani (end), Erice (Monte San Giuliano), Mazara, Termini Imerese, Corleone & Sciacca, 18 vols. 2009. 11120p. (978-90-04-17384-2(6)) BRILL.

Simonsohn, Shlomo. The Jews in Sicily: Notaries of Trapani (End), Erice (Monte San Giuliano), Mazara, Termini Imerese, Corleone & Sciacca, 18 vols. 2008. xii, 693p. (978-90-04-16760-5(9)) 2006. (ITA & LAT.). xiv, 858p. (978-90-04-15493-3(0)) BRILL.

—The Jews in Sicily: Part Four, 18 vols. 2008. 747p. (978-90-04-16759-9(5)) BRILL.

—The Jews in Sicily, Volume 17 Sciacca (end), Caltabellotta, Agrigento, Syracuse, Noto, Catania, Scicli, Randazzo, Messina, Addenda et Corrigenda, 18 vols. 2010. (Studia Post Biblica Ser.). (978-90-04-18278-3(0)) BRILL.

Wagner, Esther-Miriam. Linguistic Variety of Judaeo-Arabic in Letters from the Cairo Genizah. 2010. (Illus.). viii, 268p. (978-90-04-18776-4(6)) BRILL.

CAISSON-DISEASE

see Decompression Sickness

CAJON PASS (CALIF.)

Walker, Chard. Chard Walker's Cajon: Rail Passage to the Pacific. 2007. (Illus.). 256p. 60.00 (978-1-930013-00-1(0)) Signature Pr.

CAJUN MUSIC

see also Zydeco Music

Ancelet, Barry Jean & Gould, Philip. "One Generation at a Time" Three Decades of the Cajun & Creole Music Festival. 2007. (978-1-887366-80-9(6)) Univ. of Louisiana at Lafayette Pr.

Brasseaux, Ryan André. Cajun Breakdown: The Emergence of an American-Made Music. 2009. (American Musicspheres Ser.). (ENG., Illus.). 336p. 35.00 (978-0-19-534306-9(9)) Oxford Univ. Pr., Inc.

Cook, Alex V. Louisiana Saturday Night: Looking for a Good Time in South Louisiana's Juke Joints, Honky-Tonks, & Dance Halls. 2012. (Illus.). 256p. pap. 24.95 (978-0-8071-4456-5(8)) Louisiana State Univ. Pr.

DeWitt, Mark F. Cajun & Zydeco Dance Music in Northern California: Modern Pleasures in a Postmodern World. (ENG.). 352p. 2011. pap. 25.00 (978-1-61703-049-9(X)) 2008. (Illus.). 50.00 (978-1-60473-090-6(0)) Univ. Pr. of Mississippi.

Yule, Ron. Iry Lejeune: Wailin the Blues Cajun Style. 2007. 25.00 (978-0-9787358-1-4(1)) Fiddle Country Publishing.

Yule, Ron, ed. Cajun French Music Association Hall of Fame, Lake Charles Chapter. 2007. (Illus.). 220p. 30.00 (978-0-9787358-2-1(X)) Fiddle Country Publishing.

CAJUNS

Brasseaux, Carl A. Acadiana: Louisiana's Historic Cajun Country. 2011. (Illus.). 200p. 45.00 (978-0-8071-3723-9(5)) Louisiana State Univ. Pr.

Brasseaux, Ryan André. Cajun Breakdown: The Emergence of an American-Made Music. 2009. (American Musicspheres Ser.). (ENG., Illus.). 336p. 35.00 (978-0-19-534306-9(9)) Oxford Univ. Pr., Inc.

Coen, Cheré Dastugue. Exploring Cajun Country: A Tour of Historic Acadiana. 2011. 160+16p. pap. 19.99 (978-1-59629-995-5(9)) History Pr., The.

Falgoust, Woody. Rise of the Cajun Mariners: The Race for Big Oil. 2007. 283p. 26.95 (978-0-9792920-0-2(X)) Stockard James, LLC.

Henry, Jacques & Le Menestrel, Sara. Working the Field: Accounts from French Louisiana. 2009. (ENG., Illus.). 208p. pap. 25.00 (978-1-60473-223-8(7)) Univ. Pr. of Mississippi.

Hulin, Belinda. Roux Memories: A Cajun-Creole Love Story with Recipes. 2010. (ENG., Illus.). 320p. pap. 19.95 (978-0-7627-5905-7(4), Lyons Pr.) Globe Pequot Pr., The.

Johnson, Rheta Grimsley. Poor Man's Provence: Finding Myself in Cajun Louisiana. 2008. 221p. 23.95 (978-1-58838-218-4(4), NewSouth Bks.) NewSouth, Inc.

Leroy, Fabrice & Ancelet, Barry Jean. Tout Bec Doux: The Complete Cajun Comics of Ken Meaux & Earl Comeaux. 2011. pap. 45.00 (978-1-935754-08-4(4)) Univ. of Louisiana at Lafayette Pr.

Loya, Alex. History of the Cajuns (from Ancient France to Nova Scotia to Louisiana to Colonial Texas) Including the Participation of Louisiana & Texas in the American Revolution. 2007. per. 30.00 (978-1-60458-144-7(1)) Instant Pub.

McNamara, Ed. Cajun Racing: From the Bush Tracks to the Triple Crown. 2008. (ENG.). 224p. 24.95 (978-1-932910-77-3(8)) Daily Racing Form.

McNulty, Ian. Louisiana Rambles: Exploring America's Cajun & Creole Heartland. 2011. (ENG., Illus.). 272p. 55.00 (978-1-60473-945-9(2)); pap. 22.00 (978-1-60473-946-6(0)) Univ. Pr. of Mississippi.

Perrin, Warren A. Une Saga Acadienne, 1755-2003: De Beausoleil Broussard á la Proclamation Royale. 2009. (Illus.). 242p. pap. 22.75 (978-0-9768927-1-7(5)) Andrepont Publishing.

PsychoTherapy for Cajuns. 2006. per. 14.00 (978-0-9624778-0-5(X)) Guirard, Greg.

Robért, Norman A. The Robért Family of South Louisiana: 1772 - 2009. 2011. 340p. pap. 19.52 (978-1-4269-7285-0(7)) Trafford Publishing.

Rodrigue, George. Blue Dog Speaks. 2008. (ENG., Illus.). 512p. 24.95 (978-1-4027-5408-1(6)) Sterling Publishing Co., Inc.

Rundquist, Marie. Cajun by Any Other Name: Recovering the Lost History of A Family- & A People. 2012. pap. 11.95 (978-0-7414-7042-3(X)) Infinity Publishing.

Tassin, Myron. We Are Acadians: Nous Sommes Acadiens, 1 vol. 2nd ed. 2011. (ENG., Illus.). 96p. 14.95 (978-1-4556-1545-2(5)) Pelican Publishing Co., Inc.

Thibodeaux, Ron. Hell or High Water: How Cajun Fortitude Withstood Hurricanes Rita & Ike. 2012. pap. (978-1-935754-11-4(4)) Univ. of Louisiana at Lafayette Pr.

CAJUNS—MUSIC

see Cajun Music

CAKE

see also Cake Decorating; Cheesecake; Cookies; Doughnuts; Gingerbread; Pastry

Allen, Rachel. Bake. 2008. (ENG., Illus.). 224p. 37.95 (978-0-00-725970-0(0)) HarperCollins Pubs. Ltd. GBR. Dist: Independent Pubs. Group.

Amos, Sarah. Sarah's Tea Time, 1 vol. rev. ed. 2009. (ENG., Illus.). 48p. (978-1-894898-76-8(1)) TouchWood Editions.

Amsterdam, Elana. Gluten-Free Cupcakes: 50 Irresistible Recipes Made with Almond & Coconut Flour. 2011. (ENG., Illus.). 112p. pap. 16.99 (978-1-58761-166-7(X), Celestial Arts) Ten Speed Pr.

Anonymous. Cake Bible. 2008. (ENG., Illus.). 132p. (gr. 12-18). 15.00 (978-0-14-300520-9(0), Penguin Global) Penguin Group (USA) Inc.

Arrick, David, et al. The Butch Bakery Cookbook. 2011. (ENG., Illus.). 192p. 19.99 (978-0-470-93088-5(8), Wiley) Wiley, John & Sons, Inc.

Ashcraft, Stephanie. 200 Cake Mix Creations, 1 vol. 2010. (ENG.). 208p. 12.99 (978-1-4236-1705-1(3)) Gibbs Smith, Publisher.

Atkinson, Catherine. The Big Book of Little Cakes. 2011. (ENG., Illus.). 128p. pap. 17.99 (978-1-84476-962-9(3)) Anness Publishing GBR. Dist: National Bk. Network.

—Coffee Cakes & Desserts: 70 Delectable Mousses, Ice Creams, Gateaux, Puddings, Pies, Pastries & Cookies, Shown Step by Step in 300 Gorgeous Photographs. 2008. (ENG., Illus.). 96p. pap. 9.99 (978-1-84476-502-7(4)) Anness Publishing GBR. Dist: National Bk. Network.

Australian Women's Weekly Staff. Christmas Cakes & Puddings. (Illus.). 64p. pap. 5.95 (978-1-86396-204-9(2)) ACP Publishing Pty, Ltd. AUS. Dist: Graphic Arts Ctr. Publishing Co.

Avent, Meg. The Little Book of Cupcakes Tips. 2011. (Little Book Ser.). (ENG.). 112p. pap. 4.95 *(978-1-906650-43-8(8))* Absolute Pr. GBR. Dist: Independent Pubs. Group.

—The Little Book of Macaroon Tips. 2011. (Little Book Ser.). (ENG.). 112p. pap 4.95 *(978-1-906650-46-9(2))* Absolute Pr. GBR. Dist: Independent Pubs. Group.

Bake Me I'm Yours... Christmas: Over 20 Delicious Festive Treats - Cookies, Cupcakes, Brownies & More. 2011. (ENG., Illus.). 128p. 14.99 *(978-1-4463-0060-2(9))* David & Charles Pubs. GBR. Dist: F&W Media, Inc.

Barrett, Valerie. Cakes Galore. 2006. (ENG., Illus.). 192p. pap. 16.95 *(978-1-84601-122-1(1)*, Spruce) Octopus Publishing Group GBR. Dist: Hachette Bk. Group.

Beeton, Isabella. Mrs Beeton's Cakes & Baking. 2006. (ENG., Illus.). 256p. 11.95 *(978-0-304-36829-7(6))* Cassell P L C GBR. Dist: Independent Pubs. Group.

Bent, A. J., et al. Technology of Cakemaking. 6th ed. 2010. (ENG., Illus.). 421p. pap. 249.00 *(978-1-4419-4742-0(6)*, 1441947426) Springer.

Beranbaum, Rose Levy. Rose's Heavenly Cakes. 2009. (ENG., Illus.). 512p. 39.95 *(978-0-471-78173-8(8)*, Wiley) Wiley, John & Sons, Inc.

Berry, Mary. 100 Cakes & Bakes: My Kitchen Table. 2012. (My Kitchen Table Ser.). (ENG., Illus.). 208p. pap. 13.95 ***(978-1-84990-149-9(X))*** BBC Worldwide GBR. Dist: Independent Pubs. Group.

Betty Crocker. Betty Crocker Cupcakes Groc Ed. 2011. 160p. spiral bd. 9.99 ***(978-1-118-12043-9(4))***; spiral bd. 9.99 ***(978-1-118-12183-2(X))*** Wiley, John & Sons, Inc. (Betty Crocker).

Betty Crocker Editors. Betty Crocker Just Cupcakes: 100 Recipes for the Way You Really Cook. 2008. (ENG., Illus.). 160p. 14.95 *(978-0-470-32729-6(4)*, Wiley) Wiley, John & Sons, Inc.

—The Big Book of Cupcakes. 2011. (Betty Crocker Big Book Ser.: 1). (ENG., Illus.). 336p. pap. 19.95 *(978-0-470-90672-9(3)*, Betty Crocker) Wiley, John & Sons, Inc.

Birthday Cakes. 96p. *(978-1-4054-9579-0(0))* Parragon, Inc.

Blair, Bevelyn. Bevelyn Blairs Everyday Cake. 2007. 288p. pap. 16.95 *(978-1-58818-143-5(X))* Hill Street Pr., LLC.

Blake, Susannah. Afternoon Tea. 2006. (ENG., Illus.). 64p. *(978-1-84597-206-6(6))* Ryland Peters & Small.

—Cupcake Heaven. 2008. (ENG., Illus.). 160p. pap. *(978-1-84597-685-9(1))* CICO Bks.

—Cupcakes. 2007. (ENG., Illus.). 64p. *(978-1-84597-379-7(8))* Ryland Peters & Small.

—500 Cakes: The Only Cake Compendium You'll Ever Need. 2009. (Illus.). 288p. 16.95 *(978-1-4162-0534-0(9))* Sellers Publishing, Inc.

Briggs, Janet. Baking Classics. 2008. (Illus.). 416p. *(978-0-89821-612-7(5))* Reiman Pubns., L.P.

Brody, Esther. 1500 Best Bars, Cookies, Muffins, Cakes, & More. 2008. (ENG., Illus.). 624p. pap. 27.95 *(978-0-7788-0194-8(2))* Rose, Robert Inc. CAN. Dist: Firefly Bks., Ltd.

Brown, Debbie. Xtra Naughty Cakes: Step-by-Step Recipes for 19 Cheeky, Fun Cakes. 2007. (ENG., Illus.). 80p. 19.95 *(978-1-84537-586-7(6))* New Holland Pubs., Ltd. GBR. Dist: Sterling Publishing Co., Inc.

Brown, Warren. CakeLove: How to Bake Cakes from Scratch. 2008. (ENG., Illus.). 224p. 27.50 *(978-1-58479-662-6(6))* Stewart, Tabori & Chang.

—United Cakes of America: Recipes Celebrating Every State. 2010. (ENG., Illus.). 224p. 29.95 *(978-1-58479-839-2(4))* Stewart, Tabori & Chang.

Byrn, Anne. The Cake Mix Doctor Returns! With 160 All-New Recipes. 2009. (ENG., Illus.). 502p. pap. 15.95 *(978-0-7611-2961-5(8)*, 0761129618) Workman Publishing Co., Inc.

Case, Greg & Fisher, Keri. One Cake, One Hundred Desserts: Learn One Foolproof Cake Recipe & Make One Hundred Desserts. 2006. (ENG., Illus.). 224p. 29.95 *(978-0-06-076535-4(6)*, Morrow, William Cookbooks) HarperCollins Pubs.

Castella, Krystina. Crazy about Cupcakes. 2006. (Crazy About Ser.). (ENG., Illus.). 256p. pap. 17.95 *(978-1-4027-1994-3(9))* Sterling Publishing Co., Inc.

Castella, Krystina & Stone, Terry Lee. Booze Cakes: Confections Spiked with Spirits, Wine, & Beer. 2010. (ENG., Illus.). 144p. pap. 16.95 *(978-1-59474-423-5(8))* Quirk Bks.

Chattman, Lauren. Cake Keeper Cakes: 100 Simple Recipes for Extraordinary Bundt Cakes, Pound Cakes, Snacking Cakes & Other Good-to-the-Last-Crumb Treats. 2009. (ENG., Illus.). 176p. pap. 17.95 *(978-1-60085-120-9(7))* Taunton Pr., Inc.

—Icebox Cakes: Simply Irresistible No-Bake Desserts. 2007. (ENG., Illus.). 160p. pap. 14.95 *(978-1-55832-345-2(7))*; 29.95 *(978-1-55832-344-5(9))* Harvard Common Pr.

Chovancova, Ilona. Cakes & Loaves: 110 Recipes You Can Make at Home. 2010. (ENG., Illus.). 160p. pap. 24.95 *(978-1-55285-954-4(1))* Whitecap Bks., Ltd. CAN. Dist: Midpoint Trade Bks., Inc.

—Les Petits Plats Francais: Marvellous Mini-Cakes: Marvellous Mini-Cakes. 2011. (Petits Plats Francais Ser.). (ENG., Illus.). 72p. 12.95 *(978-0-85720-107-2(7))* Simon & Schuster, Ltd. GBR. Dist: Independent Pubs. Group.

Clark, Zoe. Chic & Unique Celebration Cakes: 30 Fresh New Designs to Brighten Every Special Occasion. 2011. (ENG., Illus.). 128p. pap. 22.99 *(978-0-7153-3838-4(2))* David & Charles Pubs. GBR. Dist: F&W Media, Inc.

Clee-Cadman, May. Cakes for Romantic Occasions. 2009. (ENG., Illus.). 128p. pap. 24.99 *(978-0-7153-3154-5(X))* David & Charles Pubs. GBR. Dist: F&W Media, Inc.

Coleman, Mary, ed. Celebration Cakes: Easy Style for Every Occasion. (Illus.). 128p. pap. 12.95 *(978-1-86396-183-7(6))* ACP Publishing Pty, Ltd. AUS. Dist: Graphic Arts Ctr. Publishing Co.

Cookbook Resources, ed. Easy Cupcake Recipes. 2010. (ENG.). 176p. *(978-1-59769-045-4(7))* Cookbook Resources, LLC.

CQ Products. Baby Cakes: Good Things Come in Small Packages. 2009. (ENG.). 72p. spiral bd. 10.00 *(978-1-56383-334-2(4))* G & R Publishing.

—Ice Cream Cakes: Simple, Delicious & Impressive Party-Perfect Cakes! 2009. (Illus.). 60p. spiral bd. 12.00 net. *(978-1-56383-338-0(7))*, G & R Publishing.

—Stud Muffins: The Perfect Pick-up! 2009. (ENG.). 72p. spiral bd. 10.00 *(978-1-56383-335-9(2))* G & R Publishing.

Crocker. Betty Crocker Just Cupcakes: 100 Recipes for the Way You Really Cook Bn Edition. 2010. 160p. spiral bd. *(978-1-4351-2483-7(9))* Wiley, John & Sons, Inc.

Cupcakes. (Cooking Ser.). 96p. *(978-1-4075-1489-5(X))*; *(978-1-4054-7138-1(7))* Parragon, Inc.

Cupcakes, Muffins & Baked Goods. 2008. 240p. *(978-1-4075-3960-7(4))* Parragon, Inc.

Dam, Annie. Cake Couture: Modern Sugar-Craft for the Stylish Baker. 2011. (ENG., Illus.). 144p. pap. 19.95 *(978-1-55407-949-0(7))* Firefly Bks., Ltd.

Day, Martha. 101 Best-Ever Cakes: A Card Deck of Delicious Step-by-Step Recipes. 2012. (ENG.). 52p. pap. 14.99 *(978-0-7548-1847-2(0))* Anness Publishing GBR. Dist: National Bk. Network.

Day, Martin. Baking: Breads Muffins Cakes Pies Tarts Cookies & Bars over 400 Step-by-Step Recipes with over 1500 Photographs. 2012. (ENG.). 512p. 29.99 *(978-0-7548-2249-3(4))* Anness Publishing GBR. Dist: National Bk. Network.

Deacon, Carol. Carol Deacon's Party Cakes for Children: Over 20 Fun Cakes. 2007. (ENG., Illus.). 96p. pap. 14.95 *(978-1-84537-750-2(8))* New Holland Pubs., Ltd. GBR. Dist: Sterling Publishing Co., Inc.

—Party Cakes: 45 Fabulous Cakes for All Occasions, with Easy Ideas for Children's Cakes. 2006. (ENG., Illus.). 144p. pap. 14.95 *(978-1-84537-577-5(7))* New Holland Pubs., Ltd. GBR. Dist: Sterling Publishing Co., Inc.

Dodd, Chelsea E. Coffee Mug Cakes Cookbook. 2009. 36p. pap. 19.97 *(978-0-557-16407-3(9))* Lulu Enterprises Inc.

Dorling Kindersley Publishing Staff. Cakes & Cupcakes. 2010. (ENG.). 224p. 20.00 *(978-0-7566-6731-3(3))* Dorling Kindersley Publishing, Inc.

Dorling Kindersley Publishing Staff. Step-by-Step Cakes. 2012. (ENG.). 192p. 18.00 ***(978-0-7566-9267-4(9))*** Dorling Kindersley Publishing, Inc.

Duff, Julie. Cakes: Regional & Traditional. 2008. (Illus.). 288p. pap. *(978-1-904943-19-8(5))* Grub Street.

Duncann, Geraldine. Cake Mix Classics: Sensational Treats Baked the Easy Way. 2007. 96p. *(978-1-933112-28-2(X))* Collectors Pr., Inc.

Esteybar, Nicole. Make Your Dream Wedding Cake: How to Design, Bake, & Decorate Wedding Cakes at Home. 2012. (ENG., Illus.). 144p. pap. 17.95 *(978-1-56975-927-1(8))* Ulysses Pr.

Farrow, Joanna. Creative Christmas Cakes. (Illus.). 80p. 8.95 *(978-1-85391-484-3(3))* Merehurst, Ltd. GBR. Dist: Tuttle Publishing.

—Cupcakes. 2010. (ENG., Illus.). 64p. pap. 12.95 *(978-1-55285-626-0(7))* Whitecap Bks., Ltd. CAN. Dist: Midpoint Trade Bks., Inc.

—Kinky Cupcakes. 2010. (ENG., Illus.). 96p. 12.99 *(978-1-84601-364-5(X)*, Spruce) Octopus Publishing Group GBR. Dist: Hachette Bk. Group.

—200 Cupcakes. 2010. (ENG., Illus.). 240p. pap. 7.99 *(978-0-600-62098-3(0)*, Hamlyn) Octopus Publishing Group GBR. Dist: Hachette Bk. Group.

Farrow, Joanna & Lewis, Sara. Quick & Easy Party Cakes. 2007. (ENG., Illus.). 256p. pap. 17.95 *(978-0-600-61565-1(0)*, Hamlyn) Octopus Publishing Group GBR. Dist: Hachette Bk. Group.

Favish, Melody, tr. from SWE. Swedish Cakes & Cookies. 2008. (ENG.). 192p. 17.95 *(978-1-60239-262-5(5)*, 239262) Skyhorse Publishing Co., Inc.

Favorite Brand Name Recipes Editors. 4 in 1 Cookies, Cakes, Brownies, Cupcakes. 2010. 320p. spiral bd. 14.98 *(978-1-60553-717-7(9))* Publications International, Ltd.

Favorite Brand Name Recipes Editors, ed. 100 Best Cupcake Recipes. 2010. 160p. spiral bd. 10.98 *(978-1-4508-1107-1(8))* Publications International, Ltd.

Fawcett, Abi. Cake Basics: 70 Recipes Illustrated Step by Step. 2011. (My Cooking Class Ser.). (ENG., Illus.). 256p. pap. 24.95 *(978-1-55407-940-7(3))* Firefly Bks., Ltd.

Fiet, Leslie. Mini Cupcakes, 1 vol. 2011. (ENG., Illus.). 96p. 16.99 *(978-1-4236-1808-9(4))* Gibbs Smith, Publisher.

Forster, Felicity. 150 Chocolate Cakes & Cookies. 2011. (ENG., Illus.). 96p. pap. 16.99 *(978-1-84476-964-3(X))* Anness Publishing GBR. Dist: National Bk. Network.

Freeman, Bobby. Welsh Country Cakes & Buns. rev. ed. 2006. (ENG., Illus.). 32p. pap. 4.95 ***(978-0-86243-138-9(7))*** Y Lolfa GBR. Dist: Dufour Editions, Inc.

G & R Publishing Company. Cupcake Cakes: Easy Pull-apart cakes make parties Fun! 2010. (ENG.). 60p. spiral bd. 12.00 *(978-1-56383-363-2(8))* G & R Publishing.

G&R Publishing, compiled by. Take the Cake: Bake, Take & Celebrate. 2007. 128p. spiral bd. 10.00 *(978-1-56383-281-9(X))* G & R Publishing.

Garcia, Michelle & Garcia, Valentin. Who You Callin' Cupcake? 75 In-Your-Face Recipes That Reinvent the Cupcake. 2010. (ENG., Illus.). 144p. pap. 15.95 *(978-1-56975-739-0(9))* Ulysses Pr.

Georgi, William & Gummo, Karen. What Would John Do? Flour Power - Baking Your Way to Happiness. 2010. (ENG., Illus.). 60p. 9.00 ***(978-90-6369-235-3(8))*** Bis B.V., Uitgeverij(BIS Publishers) NLD. Dist: Consortium Bk. Sales & Distribution.

German, Lilach. Cupcakes, Cupcakes & More Cupcakes! 2009. (ENG., Illus.). 144p. 18.95 *(978-0-9822939-8-0(4)*, Imagine Publishing) Charlesbridge Publishing, Inc.

Glander, Amy. Taste of Home Cupcakes! Muffins & More: 130 Scrumptious Delights. 2008. (Illus.). 112p. *(978-0-89821-624-0(9))* Reiman Pubns., L.P.

Goard, Debbie. Twisted Cakes: Deliciously Evil Designs for Every Occasion. 2012. (ENG.). 128p. pap. 19.99 ***(978-0-06-213404-2(3)***, Collins Design) HarperCollins Pubs.

Goble, Karen. Quick & Easy Wedding Cakes. 2006. (Quick & Easy (New Holland) Ser.). (ENG., Illus.). 112p. 24.95 *(978-1-84537-413-6(4))* New Holland Pubs., Ltd. GBR. Dist: Sterling Publishing Co., Inc.

Goldman, Duff & Goldman, Willie. The Ace of Cakes: Inside the World of Charm City Cakes. 2009. (ENG.). 256p. 35.00 *(978-0-06-170301-0(X)*, Morrow, William Cookbooks) HarperCollins Pubs.

Good Food Magazine Staff. Good Food: 201 Perfect Cakes & Bakes. 2011. (ENG., Illus.). 192p. pap. 23.95 ***(978-1-84990-143-7(0))*** BBC Worldwide GBR. Dist: Independent Pubs. Group.

Good Housekeeping Editors, ed. Good Housekeeping the Great Bake Sale Cookbook: 75 Sure-Fire Fund-Raising Favorites. 2009. (ENG., Illus.). 192p. spiral bd. 12.95 *(978-1-58816-787-3(9))* Hearst Communications, Inc.

Goren, Viola. Two-Bite Cupcakes. 2010. (ENG., Illus.). 144p. 18.95 *(978-1-936140-14-5(4)*, 40145, Imagine Publishing) Charlesbridge Publishing, Inc.

Graham, Jennifer. The Crabapple Bakery Cupcake Cookbook. 2008. (ENG., Illus.). 150p. (gr. 12-18). 21.00 *(978-0-14-300494-3(8)*, Penguin Global) Penguin Group (USA) Inc.

Gray, Melissa. All Cakes Considered: A Year's Worth of Weekly Recipes Tested, Tasted, & Approved by the Staff of NPR's All Things Considered. 2009. (ENG., Illus.). 224p. 24.95 *(978-0-8118-6781-8(1))* Chronicle Bks. LLC.

Hakim, Rosette. Roro's MiXeD up Cookbook. 2010. 112p. pap. 39.99 *(978-1-4520-1220-9(2))* AuthorHouse.

Hamlyn. Cupcakes, Kit. 2011. (ENG., Illus.). 64p. pap. 14.99 *(978-0-600-62145-4(6)*, Hamlyn) Octopus Publishing Group GBR. Dist: Hachette Bk. Group.

Hamlyn All Color Staff. 200 Mini Cakes & Bakes: Hamlyn All Color. 2012. (ENG., Illus.). 240p. pap. 7.99 *(978-0-600-62270-3(3)*, Hamlyn) Octopus Publishing Group GBR. Dist: Hachette Bk. Group.

Hamlyn Editors. Wedding Cupcakes. 2012. (ENG., Illus.). 64p. 12.99 *(978-1-84601-393-5(3)*, Spruce) Octopus Publishing Group GBR. Dist: Hachette Bk. Group.

Handy, Amy. War-Time Breads & Cakes. 2007. (Cooking in America Ser.). (ENG., Illus.). 80p. per. 9.95 *(978-1-4290-1014-6(2))* Applewood Bks.

Hannah Miles. Mini Cakes. 2011. (ENG., Illus.). 64p. *(978-1-84975-146-9(3))* Ryland Peters & Small.

Hasson, Julie. 150 Best Cupcake Recipes. 2012. (ENG., Illus.). 192p. pap. 19.95 ***(978-0-7788-0290-7(6))*** Rose, Robert Inc. CAN. Dist: Firefly Bks., Ltd.

Heatter, Maida. Maida Heatter's Cakes. 2011. (ENG.). 368p. pap. 19.99 *(978-1-4494-0114-6(7))* Andrews McMeel Publishing.

Helding, Patricia & Levin, Bryna. Fat Witch Brownies: Brownies, Blondies, & Bars from New York's Legendary Fat Witch Bakery. 2010. (ENG., Illus.). 176p. 22.50 *(978-1-60529-574-9(4))* Rodale Pr., Inc.

h.f.Ullmann, ed. Cakes & Desserts: Handy Recipe Collection to Store or Hang in Your Kitchen, 1 vol. 2011. (ENG.). 72p. 5.99 ***(978-3-8331-6203-9(1))*** h.f.ullmann DEU. Dist: Innovative Logistics.

Hitron, Noga. The Art of Cakes: Colorful Cake Designs for the Creative Baker. 2008. (ENG., Illus.). 112p. 17.95 *(978-1-4027-6124-9(4)*, Sterling/Penn) Sterling Publishing Co., Inc.

—The Art of Cupcakes: More Than 40 Festive Recipes. 2010. (ENG., Illus.). 128p. pap. 17.95 *(978-1-4027-5900-0(2))* Sterling Publishing Co., Inc.

—Mini-Cakes: Tiny Treats to Surprise & Delight. 2010. (ENG., Illus.). 112p. 17.95 *(978-1-4027-3998-9(2))* Sterling Publishing Co., Inc.

Holechek, Kris. Have Your Cake & Vegan Too: 50 Dazzling & Delicious Cake Creations. 2011. (ENG., Illus.). 144p. pap. 17.95 *(978-1-56975-920-2(0))* Ulysses Pr.

Holt, Geraldene. Geraldene Holt's Cakes. 2011. (ENG., Illus.). 304p. (C). pap. 36.00 *(978-1-903018-75-0(7))* Prospect Bks. GBR. Dist: Brown, David Bk. Co., The.

Humble, Nicola. Cake: A Global History. 2010. (Reaktion Books - Edible Ser.). (ENG., Illus.). 144p. 15.95 *(978-1-86189-648-3(4))* Reaktion Bks., Ltd. GBR. Dist: Chicago Distribution Ctr.

Humphries, Carolyn. Gluten-Free Bread & Cakes from Your Breadmaker from Your Breadmaker: With Full Details for Dairy or Lactose Intolerance. 2010. (ENG., Illus.). 160p. pap. 16.95 *(978-0-572-03569-3(1))* Foulsham, W. Co., Ltd. GBR. Dist: APG Sales & Distribution Services.

Izenberg, Max. Who Took My Chocolate Cake? 2011. 210p. pap. 16.95 ***(978-1-936400-93-5(6))*** Mill City Pr., Inc.

Jerome, Helen. Concerning Cake Making. 2008. 268p. *(978-1-4437-3287-1(7))* 2007. 264p. per. *(978-1-4067-8935-5(6))* Read Bks. (Vintage Cockery Bks.).

Kaldunski, Shelly. Cupcakes: Luscious Bakeshop Favorites from Your Home Kitchen. 2008. (ENG., Illus.). 128p. 18.95 *(978-1-4165-8900-6(7)*, Touchstone) Touchstone.

Kay, Ann. 150 Desserts: Pastries, Bakes, Cakes, Tarts & Pies. 2007. (ENG., Illus.). 96p. per. 14.99 *(978-1-84476-382-5(X))* Anness Publishing GBR. Dist: National Bk. Network.

Kay, Ann, et al. 2000 Recipes: Cakes, Cookies & Desserts, 4 vols. 2011. (ENG., Illus.). 264p. pap. 40.00 ***(978-0-7548-2367-4(9))*** Anness Publishing GBR. Dist: National Bk. Network.

Kidwell, Geraldine. Cakes for All Occasions. 2008. (Illus.). 112p. pap. 24.95 *(978-0-7643-2904-3(9))* Schiffer Publishing, Ltd.

Koolish, Lynn. Cupcakes! 30+ Yummy Projects to Sew, Quilt, Knit & Bake. Koolish, Lynn, ed. 2009. (ENG., Illus.). 128p. pap. 16.95 *(978-1-57120-796-8(1))* C & T Publishing.

Koran, Robert E. A Baker's Holiday: Fun Foods to Fit Every Occasion. 2011. 122p. 40.95 ***(978-1-258-07355-8(2))*** Literary Licensing, LLC.

Krasne, Karen & Wright, Tina. Extraordinary Cakes: Recipes for Bold & Sophisticated Desserts. 2011. (ENG., Illus.). 176p. 37.50 *(978-0-8478-5308-8(1))* Rizzoli International Pubns., Inc.

Lane, Rachel. Wild about Cupcakes: Over 130 Recipes. 2009. (ENG.). 288p. 16.99 *(978-0-7641-6277-0(2))* Barron's Educational Series, Inc.

Lanlard, Eric. Cake Boy. 2011. (ENG., Illus.). 224p. 19.99 *(978-1-84533-605-9(4)*, Mitchell Beazley) Octopus Publishing Group GBR. Dist: Hachette Bk. Group.

Lanlard, Eric & Roux, Albert. Glamour Cakes: Exquisite Designs for Every Occasion. 2006. (ENG., Illus.). 160p. 19.95 *(978-0-600-61714-3(9)* Hamlyn) Octopus Publishing Group GBR. Dist: Hachette Bk. Group.

Laskin, Avner. Celebrating Ice Cream & Cake. 2010. (ENG.). 144p. pap. 14.95 *(978-1-60900-011-0(0))* Leisure Arts, Inc.

Legere, Kate. Intoxicated Cupcakes: 41 Tipsy Treats. 2011. (ENG.). 128p. 15.00 *(978-0-7624-3873-0(8))* Running Pr. Bk. Pubs.

Leisure Arts. Celebrating Chocolate: Cakes, Brownies & Bars. 2011. (Celebrating Cookbooks Ser.). (ENG., Illus.). 144p. pap. 14.95 *(978-1-60900-115-5(X))* Leisure Arts, Inc.

Lewis, Sara. 200 Cakes & Bakes: Hamlyn All Color. 2009. (ENG.). 240p. pap. 7.99 *(978-0-600-61871-3(4)*, Hamlyn) Octopus Publishing Group GBR. Dist: Hachette Bk. Group.

Lion House Staff. Lion House Cakes & Cupcakes. 2011. 144p. 19.99 ***(978-1-59038-644-6(2))*** Deseret Bk. Co.

Manning, Anneka. Kids' Party Cakes: 50 Fun, Fabulous & Fast Ideas. 2012. (ENG., Illus.). 168p. pap. 19.95 ***(978-1-77085-135-1(6))*** Firefly Bks., Ltd.

Maréchal, José. Coffee-Time Treats. 2011. (Petits Plats Francais Ser.). (ENG., Illus.). 72p. 12.95 *(978-0-85720-251-2(0))* Simon & Schuster, Ltd. GBR. Dist: Independent Pubs. Group.

—Irresistible Macaroons. 2011. (Petits Plats Francais Ser.). (ENG., Illus.). 72p. 12.95 *(978-0-85720-109-6(3))* Simon & Schuster, Ltd. GBR. Dist: Independent Pubs. Group.

Maritz, Callie & Guy, Mari-Louis. Cakes to Celebrate Love & Life. 2009. (Illus.). 176p. 25.00 *(978-1-77007-783-6(9))* Struik Pubs. ZAF. Dist: International Publishers Marketing.

Martha Stewart Living Magazine Staff. Martha Stewart's Cupcakes: 175 Inspired Ideas for Everyone's Favorite Treat. 2009. (ENG., Illus.). 352p. pap. 24.99 *(978-0-307-46044-8(4)*, Clarkson Potter) Crown Publishing Group.

Matheson, Christie. Cake Simple: Recipes for Bundt-Style Cakes from Classic Dark Chocolate to Luscious Lemon Basil. 2011. (ENG.). 132p. 19.95 *(978-0-8118-7935-1(4))* Chronicle Bks. LLC.

Mcrae, Regina. Taking the Cake: Your Ultimate Cake Guide. 2011. 88p. pap. 14.99 ***(978-1-4634-4845-5(7))*** AuthorHouse.

Mesnier, Roland & Chattman, Lauren. Roland Mesnier's Basic to Beautiful Cakes. 2007. (ENG., Illus.). 304p. 30.00 *(978-0-7432-8789-0(4))* Simon & Schuster.

Mezo, Frances Elizabeth. A Bake-A-Holic's 40 Favorite Recipes. 2010. 83p. pap. 19.95 *(978-0-557-41494-9(6))* Lulu Enterprises Inc.

Miles, Hannah. The Big Book of Cakes & Cookies: 365 Much-Loved Classics & New Favourites. 2009. (ENG., Illus.). 224p. spiral bd. 19.95 *(978-1-84483-848-6(X))* Duncan Baird Pubs. GBR. Dist: Sterling Publishing Co., Inc.

—Cake Pops & Sticks. 2012. (ENG., Illus.). 96p. 17.99 ***(978-0-7548-2171-7(4))*** Anness Publishing GBR. Dist: National Bk. Network.

Miles, Hannah. Whoopie Pies. 2011. (ENG., Illus.). 64p. *(978-1-84975-094-3(7))* Ryland Peters & Small.

Miller, Leslie F. Let Me Eat Cake: A Celebration of Flour, Sugar, Butter, Eggs, Vanilla, Baking Powder, & a Pinch of Salt. 2011. (ENG., Illus.). 352p. pap. 21.99 *(978-1-4165-8874-0(4))* Simon & Schuster.

Milton, Xanthe. Eat Me! The Stupendous, Self-Raising World of Cupcakes & Bakes According to Cookie Girl. 2011. (ENG., Illus.). 160p. 24.95 *(978-0-09-192511-6(8))* Ebury Publishing GBR. Dist: Independent Pubs. Group.

Moon, Jan & Southern Living Magazine Editors. Southern Living Big Book of Cupcakes: 150 Brilliantly Delicious Dreamcakes. 2011. (ENG., Illus.). 256p. pap. 19.95 *(978-0-8487-3437-4(8))* Oxmoor Hse., Inc.

Moore, Kathy & Wyss, Roxanne. 175 Best Babycakes Cake Pops Recipes. 2012. (ENG., Illus.). 240p. pap. 24.95 ***(978-0-7788-0297-6(3))*** Rose, Robert Inc. CAN. Dist: Firefly Bks., Ltd.

Moore, Kathy & Wyss, Roxanne. 175 Best Babycakes Cupcake Maker Recipes: Easy Recipes for Bite-Size Cupcakes, Cheesecakes, Mini Pies & More! 2011. (ENG., Illus.). 216p. pap. 24.95 *(978-0-7788-0283-9(3))* Rose, Robert Inc. CAN. Dist: Firefly Bks., Ltd.

Morov, Alisa. Sensational Cupcakes. 2011. (Petits Plats Francais Ser.). (ENG., Illus.). 72p. 12.95 *(978-0-85720-249-9(9))* Simon & Schuster, Ltd. GBR. Dist: Independent Pubs. Group.

Morphew, Kim. Women's Institute: Celebration Cupcakes. 2011. (ENG., Illus.). 112p. 17.95 ***(978-0-85720-233-8(2))*** Simon & Schuster, Ltd. GBR. Dist: Independent Pubs. Group.

Moses, Michal. Celebrating Cupcakes & Muffins. 2009. (ENG.). 144p. pap. 14.95 *(978-1-57486-032-0(1))* Leisure Arts, Inc.

Moskowitz, Isa Chandra, et al. Vegan Cupcakes Take over the World: 75 Dairy-Free Recipes for Cupcakes that Rule. 2006. (ENG., Illus.). 144p. pap. 15.95 (978-1-56924-273-5(9)) Da Capo Pr., Inc.

Nanette, et al. Sisters Guide to NYC Cupcakes. 2012. **(978-1-57864-738-5(X)**, Orbit Books) Donning Co. Pubs.

Nicol, Ann. The Best-Ever Book of Cakes: 165 Utterly Irresistible & Foolproof Cakes to Bake for Every Kind of Occasion, from Family Tea Parties to Special Celebrations, Shown in 700 Delectable Photographs. 2011. (ENG., Illus.). 256p. 35.00 (978-0-7548-2069-7(6)) Anness Publishing GBR. Dist: National Bk. Network.

Niehaus, Carmen. You, Let's Bake. 2011. 224p. pap. 35.95 (978-0-7981-5125-2(0)) NB Pubs. Ltd. ZAF. Dist: International Publishers Marketing.

Nilsen, Angela, et al. Cakes & Cake Decorating: Two Perfect Books for Bakers: over 600 Recipes for Fabulous Decorated Cakes, with Step-by-Step Techniques & More Than 1250 Photographs, 2 vols. 2012. (ENG., Illus.). 264p. 25.00 **(978-0-7548-2375-9(X))** Anness Publishing GBR. Dist: National Bk. Network.

Noderer, Judy Delgado. Qwik Cakes¬ Gluten Free Recipe & Cookbook: Special diet recipes for multiple food Allergies. 2008. 104p. pap. 11.95 (978-0-595-53069-4(9)) iUniverse, Inc.

Oleson, Jessie. CakeSpy Presents Sweet Treats for a Sugar-Filled Life. 2011. (ENG., Illus.). 160p. pap. 22.95 (978-1-57061-756-0(2)) Sasquatch Bks.

Pappas, Lou Seibert. Coffee Cakes: Simple, Sweet, & Savory. 2006. (ENG., Illus.). 132p. pap. 18.95 (978-0-8118-5507-5(4)) Chronicle Bks. LLC.

Parish, Maisie. Fun & Original Birthday Cakes. 2011. (ENG., Illus.). 128p. pap. 22.99 (978-0-7153-3833-9(1)) David & Charles Pubs. GBR. Dist: F&W Media, Inc.

Pastor, Carol. Cupcakes: Truly Delectable Creations for Every Day, for Special Occasions & for Sharing with Friends, with 100 Ideas Shown Step-by-step & More Than 400 Beautiful Photographs. 2009. (ENG., Illus.). 96p. 19.99 (978-0-7548-1927-1(2)) Anness Publishing GBR. Dist: National Bk. Network.

—Cupcakes & Muffins: Irresistible Creations for Every Occasion - 150 Delicious Recipes Shown in 300 stunning Photographs. 2011. (ENG., Illus.). 224p. 29.99 (978-0-7548-2101-4(3)) Anness Publishing GBR. Dist: National Bk. Network.

Patten, Marguerite. Marguerite Patten's 100 Top Teatime Treats. 2008. (Illus.). 100p. (978-1-904943-29-7(2)) Grub Street.

Pattinson, Dawn. Soul Cake: The Ellen Alice Cake Book. 2009. (Illus.). 64p. pap. 23.49 (978-1-4389-5841-5(2)) AuthorHouse.

Paul, Wendy. 101 Gourmet Cake Bites. 2011. spiral bd. 18.99 (978-1-59955-895-0(5), Front Table Bks.) Cedar Fort, Inc./CFI Distribution.

Pendriegh, Lisa. The Best 100 Cakes. (Illus.). 224p. 27.50 (978-0-09-187831-3(4)) Random Hse. GBR. Dist: Trafalgar Square Publishing.

Pettigrew, Jane. Good Old-Fashioned Cakes. 2010. (ENG., Illus.). 112p. 12.95 (978-1-905400-89-8(6)) National Trust, Aylesbury GBR. Dist: Independent Pubs. Group.

Pickard, Ann. Crafty Cupcakes. 2012. (Cozy Ser.). (ENG., Illus.). 156p. pap. 14.95 **(978-1-86108-853-6(1))** Guild of Master Craftsman Pubns., Ltd. GBR. Dist: Sterling Publishing Co., Inc.

Pillsbury Editors. Best of the Bake-Off 1959. fac. ed. 2009. (ENG., Illus.). 608p. (J). 29.95 (978-0-470-39559-2(1), Betty Crocker) Wiley, John & Sons, Inc.

Pizey, Roger. Small Cakes: From Fondant Fancies to Florentines. 2008. (Small Book of Good Taste Ser.). (ENG., Illus.). 64p. 14.95 (978-1-903221-99-0(4)) Aurum Pr., Ltd. GBR. Dist: Independent Pubs. Group.

Pothitt, C. S. Bonkers for Bundt Cakes. 2007. 68p. pap. 10.96 (978-1-4303-2515-4(1)) Lulu Enterprises Inc.

Ptak, Claire. The Whoopie Pie Book: 60 Irresistible Recipes for Cake Sandwiches Classic & New. 2011. (ENG.). 160p. pap. 15.95 (978-1-61519-039-3(2), 1615190392) Experiment LLC, The.

Publications International Staff, creator. Eagle Brand 3 Books In 1: Cookies & Bars/Cades & Pies/Desserts. 2007. (3 in One Digest Ser.). (Illus.). 288p. 12.98 (978-1-4127-2758-7(8)) Publications International, Ltd.

—100 Best Cupcake Recipes. 2007. (Favorite Brand Name Ser.). (Illus.). 157p. 9.98 (978-1-4127-9315-5(7)) Publications International, Ltd.

Publications International Staff, ed. Cupcakes & Muffins. 2007. spiral bd. 4.98 (978-1-4127-2630-6(1)) Publications International, Ltd.

—Digest 3 in 1 Eagle Brand: Cookies, Cakes & Pies, Desserts. 2007. spiral bd. 14.98 (978-1-4127-2628-3(X)) Publications International, Ltd.

—Rival Crock Pot. 2009. 256p. 14.98 (978-1-4127-7863-3(8), PIL Kids) Publications International, Ltd.

—100 Best Cupcakes. 2008. spiral bd. 12.98 (978-1-4127-2717-4(0)) Publications International, Ltd.

Rhoden, Jodi. Cake Ladies: Celebrating a Southern Tradition. 2011. (ENG., Illus.). 144p. pap. 19.95 (978-1-60059-789-3(0)) Lark Bks.

Richardson, Alan & Tack, Karen. Cupcakes, Cookies & Pie, Oh My! 2012. (ENG., Illus.). 240p. pap. 17.95 (978-0-547-66242-8(4)) Houghton Mifflin Harcourt Trade & Reference Pubs.

Richardson, Julie. Vintage Cakes: Timeless Recipes for Cupcakes, Flips, Rolls, Layer, Angel, Bundt, Chiffon, & Icebox Cakes for Today's Sweet Tooth. 2012. (ENG., Illus.). 176p. 24.00 **(978-1-60774-102-2(4))** Ten Speed Pr.

Rigg, Annie. Birthday Cakes for Kids. 2009. (ENG., Illus.). 128p. (978-1-84597-833-4(1)) Ryland Peters & Small.

Rodgers, Rick. Coffee & Cake: Enjoy the Perfect Cup of Coffee - With Dozens of Delectable Recipes for Café Treats. 2010. (ENG.). 160p. 21.99 (978-0-06-193832-0(7), Morrow, William Cookbooks) HarperCollins Pubs.

Romy Lewis & Victoria Jos. Making Cupcakes with Lola. 2011. (ENG., Illus.). 144p. (978-1-84975-186-5(2)) Ryland Peters & Small.

Rudisill, Marie. Fruitcake: Heirloom Recipes & Memories of Truman Capote & Cousin Sook. 2010. (ENG., Illus.). 80p. pap. 15.00 (978-0-8078-9930-4(5)) Univ. of North Carolina Pr.

Ryland Peters & Small and CICO Books, creator. Easy Cakes & Bakes: Cupcakes, brownies, muffins, loaves & More. 2012. (ENG., Illus.). 240p. **(978-1-84975-212-1(5))** Ryland Peters & Small.

Saetre, Sverre. Norwegian Cakes & Cookies. 2012. (ENG., Illus.). 160p. 19.95 **(978-1-61608-556-8(8)**, 608556) Skyhorse Publishing Co., Inc.

Saulsbury, Camilla V. Enlightened Cakes: More Than 100 Decadently Light Layer Cakes, Bundt Cakes, Cupcakes, Cheesecakes, Tea Cakes, & More, All with Less Fat & Fewer Calories. 2008. (ENG., Illus.). 183p. 22.95 (978-1-58182-626-5(5)) Turner Publishing Co.

—Piece of Cake! One-Bowl, No-Fuss, From-Scratch Cakes. 2011. (Illus.). 288p. spiral bd., spiral bd. 29.95 (978-0-7788-0277-8(9)) Rose, Robert Inc. CAN. Dist: Firefly Bks., Ltd.

Sawyer, Sarah K. The Everything Cake Mix Cookbook. 2009. (ENG.). 304p. pap. 15.95 (978-1-60550-657-9(5)) Adams Media Corp.

Scones, Muffins & Teacakes. (Illus.). 64p. 4.95 (978-0-86411-251-4(3)) Murdoch Bks. Pty Ltd. AUS. Dist: Graphic Arts Ctr. Publishing Co.

Shaffer, Bev. Cakes to Die For!, 1 vol. 2010. (Cookbooks to Die For Ser.). (ENG., Illus.). 288p. 26.95 (978-1-58980-691-7(3)) Pelican Publishing Co., Inc.

Shirazi, Kate. Cake Magic. 2011. (ENG., Illus.). 224p. 22.95 **(978-1-86205-917-7(9))** Chrysalis Children's Bks. GBR. Dist: Independent Pubs. Group.

Short, Susanna. Bundt Cake Bliss: Delicious Desserts from Midwest Kitchens. 2007. (ENG., Illus.). 184p. per. 16.95 (978-0-87351-585-6(4)) Minnesota Historical Society Pr.

Slater, Lisa. The Brownie Lover's Bible: Over 100 Delicious Recipes. 2010. (ENG., Illus.). 192p. pap. 24.95 (978-1-55285-939-1(8)) Whitecap Bks., Ltd. CAN. Dist: Midpoint Trade Bks., Inc.

Smith, Anne. Creative Christening Cakes. (Illus.). 96p. 8.95 (978-1-85391-472-0(X)) Merehurst, Ltd. GBR. Dist: Tuttle Publishing.

Smith, Janet. Cupcakes. 2010. (ENG., Illus.). 160p. pap. 24.95 (978-1-55285-963-6(0)) Whitecap Bks., Ltd. CAN. Dist: Midpoint Trade Bks., Inc.

Smith, Lindy. Bake Me I'm Yours... Cupcake Celebration: Over 25 Excuses to Indulge. 2010. (ENG., Illus.). 128p. 14.99 (978-0-7153-3770-7(X)) David & Charles Pubs. GBR. Dist: F&W Media, Inc.

—Bake Me I'm Yours... Cupcake Love. 2010. (ENG., Illus.). 128p. 14.99 (978-0-7153-3781-3(5)) David & Charles Pubs. GBR. Dist: F&W Media, Inc.

Steege, Gwen. Perfect Chocolate Cake. (Illus.). 87.60 (978-1-58017-399-5(3), 67399) Storey Publishing, LLC.

Steer, Gina. Cakes: Special Occasion Recipes for Parties, Family & Friends. 2011. (ENG.). 144p. 9.99 **(978-0-7858-2864-8(8)**, 0785828648, Chartwell) Book Sales, Inc.

Stewart, Martha & Kromer, Wendy. Martha Stewart's Wedding Cakes. 2007. (ENG., Illus.). 260p. 60.00 (978-0-307-39453-6(0), Clarkson Potter) Crown Publishing Group.

Stinson, Fay. Fay's Finest Cheesecakes. 2010. 76p. pap. 10.49 (978-1-4520-3946-6(1)) AuthorHouse.

Strauss, Elisa & Matheson, Christie. Confetti Cakes for Kids: Delightful Cookies, Cakes, & Cupcakes from New York City's Famed Bakery. 2nd ed. 2008. (ENG., Illus.). 224p. 29.99 (978-0-316-11829-3(X)) Little Brown & Co.

Sweetser, Wendy. Special Cupcakes. 2011. (ENG., Illus.). 144p. 14.95 (978-1-84773-855-4(9)) New Holland Pubs., Ltd. GBR. Dist: Sterling Publishing Co., Inc.

Swift, Martha & Thomas, Lisa. Cupcakes from the Primrose Bakery. 2010. (ENG.). 144p. pap. 18.95 (978-1-906868-08-6(5)) Cathie, Kyle Ltd. GBR. Dist: National Bk. Network.

Tack, Karen & Richardson, Alan. Hello, Cupcake! Irresistibly Playful Creations Anyone Can Make. 2008. (ENG., Illus.). 240p. pap. 15.95 (978-0-618-82925-5(3)) Houghton Mifflin Harcourt Trade & Reference Pubs.

—What's New, Cupcake? Ingeniously Simple Designs for Every Occasion. 2010. (ENG., Illus.). 240p. pap. 16.95 (978-0-547-24181-4(X)) Houghton Mifflin Harcourt Trade & Reference Pubs.

The Chefs of Le Cordon Bleu. Le Cordon Bleu Patisserie & Baking Foundations. 2011. (ENG.). 384p. (C). 64.95 **(978-1-4390-5713-1(3))** Delmar Cengage Learning.

—Le Cordon Bleu Patisserie Foundations Classic Recipes. 2012. (ENG.). 288p. (C). spiral bd. 29.95 **(978-1-4390-5717-9(6))** Delmar Cengage Learning.

Tien, Chi. Introduction to Cake Filtration: Analyses, Experiments & Applications. 2006. (ENG., Illus.). 292p. 255.00 (978-0-444-52156-9(9), Elsevier Science) Elsevier Science & Technology Bks.

Turner, Mich. The Art of the Cake: The Ultimate Step-by-Step Guide to Baking & Decorating Perfection. 2011. (Illus.). 224p. 40.00 (978-0-7893-2215-9(3)) Universe Publishing.

—Wedding Cakes: The Most Exquisite Cake to Celebrate Life's Most Important Day. 2009. (ENG., Illus.). 160p. 37.50 (978-0-7893-1814-5(8)) Universe Publishing.

Valastro, Buddy. Baking with the Cake Boss: 100 of Buddy's Best Recipes & Decorating Secrets. 2011. (ENG.). 272p. 30.00 (978-1-4391-8352-6(X), Free Pr.) Free Pr.

—Cake Boss: Stories & Recipes from Mia Famiglia. (ENG.). 272p. 2012. pap. 16.99 (978-1-4516-1034-5(3)) 2010. (ENG.). 25.99 (978-1-4391-8351-9(1)) Free Pr. (Free Pr.).

Vanilli, Lily. A Zombie Ate My Cupcake: 25 Deliciously Weird Cupcake Recipes. 2011. (Illus.). 64p. 15.95 (978-1-907030-51-2(4)) CICO Bks. GBR. Dist: Ryland Peters & Small.

Walter, Carole. Great Coffee Cakes, Sticky Buns, Muffins & More: 200 Anytime Treats & Special Sweets for Morning to Midnight. 2007. (ENG., Illus.). 416p. 35.00 (978-0-307-23755-2(9), Clarkson Potter) Crown Publishing Group.

Wendy Paul. 101 Gourmet Cupcakes in 10 Minutes. 2009. pap. 16.99 (978-1-59955-259-0(0)) Cedar Fort, Inc./CFI Distribution.

Wendy Paul & Paul, Wendy. 101 Gourmet Cupcakes in 10 Minutes. 2011. spiral bd. 18.99 **(978-1-59955-935-3(8)**, Front Table Bks.) Cedar Fort, Inc./CFI Distribution.

White, Carolyn. Bake Me I'm Yours... Cake Pops: Over 30 Designs for Fun Sweet Treats. 2011. (ENG., Illus.). 128p. 14.99 (978-1-4463-0137-1(0)) David & Charles Pubs. GBR. Dist: F&W Media, Inc.

Whitehead, Jessup. The American Pastry Cook. 2008. 248p. pap. (978-1-4097-7907-0(6)) Read Bks.

Wilson, Dede. Baker's Field Guide to Cupcakes. 2011. (Baker's FG Ser.). (ENG., Illus.). 164p. pap. 14.95 (978-1-55832-752-8(5)) Harvard Common Pr.

—A Baker's Field Guide to Cupcakes: Deliciously Decorated Crowd Pleasers for Parties & Holidays. 2006. (Baker's FG Ser.). (ENG., Illus.). 176p. spiral bd. 18.95 (978-1-55832-323-0(6)) Harvard Common Pr.

—The Birthday Cake Book: 75 Recipes for Candle-Worthy Creations. 2008. (ENG.). 176p. 27.95 (978-1-55832-381-0(3)); (Illus.). pap. 14.95 (978-1-55832-382-7(1)) Harvard Common Pr.

Wilson, Dede. Cake Balls: More Than 60 Delectable & Whimsical Sweet Spheres of Goodness. 2012. (ENG., Illus.). 176p. 16.95 **(978-1-55832-762-7(2))** Harvard Common Pr.

Wilson, Jennifer Lee. Baby Loves Cupcakes. 2009. 28p. pap. 14.95 (978-1-60844-131-0(8)) Dog Ear Publishing, LLC.

Wilson, Joy. Joy the Baker Cookbook: 100 Simple & Comforting Recipes. 2012. (ENG., Illus.). 208p. pap. 19.99 **(978-1-4013-1060-8(5))** Hyperion Pr.

Young, Lucy. The Secrets of the Aga Cakes. 2007. (ENG., Illus.). 160p. 32.95 (978-0-09-192241-2(0)) Ebury Publishing GBR. Dist: Independent Pubs. Group.

CAKE DECORATING

see also Icings, Cake

Australian Women's Weekly Staff, contrib. by. Children's Birthday Cakes: Step-by-Step to the Perfect Birthday Cake. (Illus.). 120p. pap. 12.95 (978-1-86396-281-0(6)) ACP Publishing Pty, Ltd. AUS. Dist: Graphic Arts Ctr. Publishing Co.

Avent, Meg. The Little Book of Cake Decorating Tips. 2008. (Little Book Ser.). (ENG.). 64p. pap. 4.95 (978-1-904573-96-8(7)) Absolute Pr. GBR. Dist: Independent Pubs. Group.

Baird, Heather. SprinkleBakes: 75 Baking Recipes to Inspire Your Inner Artist. 2012. (ENG., Illus.). 288p. pap. 19.95 **(978-1-4027-8636-5(0)**, Sterling Epicure) Sterling Publishing Co., Inc.

Bakes, Molly. Crazy for Cake Pops: 50 All-New Delicious & Adorable Creations. 2011. (ENG., Illus.). 160p. pap. 14.95 **(978-1-61243-044-7(9))** Ulysses Pr.

Bandy, Sallia. Wedding Cakes Aren't Just Desserts. 2011. 144p. 22.23 **(978-1-4567-3529-6(2))**; pap. 11.70 **(978-1-4567-3527-2(6))** AuthorHouse.

Belgrove, Joan & Belgrove, Graham. Bake Me I'm Yours... Cupcake: Over 100 Excuses to Indulge. 2007. (ENG., Illus.). 128p. pap. 14.99 (978-0-7153-2726-5(7)) David & Charles Pubs. GBR. Dist: F&W Media, Inc.

Bowers, Sharon. Candy Construction: How to Build Race Cars, Castles, & Other Cool Stuff out of Store-Bought Candy. 2010. (ENG., Illus.). 144p. pap. 14.95 (978-1-60342-548-3(9), 1603425489) Storey Publishing, LLC.

Brown, Debbie. Easy Party Cakes: 30 Original & Fun Designs for Every Occasion. 2007. (ENG., Illus.). 128p. 24.95 (978-1-84537-618-5(8)) New Holland Pubs., Ltd. GBR. Dist: Sterling Publishing Co., Inc.

—Gorgeous & Gruesome Cakes for Children: 30 Original & Fun Designs for Every Occasion. 2010. (ENG., Illus.). 128p. 19.95 (978-1-84773-646-8(7)) New Holland Pubs., Ltd. GBR. Dist: Sterling Publishing Co., Inc.

—Seriously Naughty Cakes: Step-by-Step Recipes for 38 Cheeky Cakes. 2011. (ENG., Illus.). 144p. pap. 17.95 (978-1-84537-887-5(3)) New Holland Pubs., Ltd. GBR. Dist: Sterling Publishing Co., Inc.

Brown, Rachel. Cake Decorating. 2007. (ENG., Illus.). 160p. 27.95 (978-1-84537-728-1(1)) New Holland Pubs., Ltd. GBR. Dist: Sterling Publishing Co., Inc.

—Cake Decorating Basics: Techniques & Tips for Creating Beautiful Cakes. 2007. (ENG., Illus.). 128p. 19.95 (978-1-84537-518-8(1)) New Holland Pubs., Ltd. GBR. Dist: Sterling Publishing Co., Inc.

Cadman, May Clee. Sweet & Simple Party Cakes. 2008. (ENG., Illus.). 144p. pap. 19.99 (978-0-7153-2687-9(2)) David & Charles Pubs. GBR. Dist: F&W Media, Inc.

Cairns, Fiona. Bake & Decorate: Charming Cakes, Cupcakes & Cookies for Every Occasion. 2010. (ENG., Illus.). 208p. 30.00 (978-1-60529-204-5(4)) Rodale Pr., Inc.

Cake Decorating. 96p. (978-1-4054-5746-0(5)) Parragon, Inc.

Carpenter, Autumn. The Complete Photo Guide to Cake Decorating. 2012. (ENG., Illus.). 328p. pap. 24.99 (978-1-58923-669-1(6), 1589236696) Quayside.

Clark, Zoe. Cake Decorating at Home. 2010. (ENG., Illus.). 128p. pap. 22.99 (978-0-7153-3758-5(0)) David & Charles Pubs. GBR. Dist: F&W Media, Inc.

Clee-Cadman, May. Cakes for Romantic Occasions. 2009. (ENG., Illus.). 128p. pap. 24.99 (978-0-7153-3154-5(X)) David & Charles Pubs. GBR. Dist: F&W Media, Inc.

Clemens, Ruth. The Busy Girls Guide to Cake Decorating: Create impressive cakes & bakes no matter what your time Limit. 2012. (ENG., Illus.). 128p. pap. 23.99 **(978-1-4463-0164-7(8))** David & Charles Pubs. GBR. Dist: F&W Media, Inc.

Coleman, Mary, ed. Fantastic Party Cakes. (Illus.). 120p. pap. (978-1-86396-091-5(0), Australian Women's Weekly) ACP Publishing Pty, Ltd.

Corbin, Pam. Cakes: River Cottage Handbook No. 8. 2011. (ENG., Illus.). 256p. 32.00 **(978-1-4088-0859-7(5))** Bloomsbury Publishing.

Dam, Annie. Cake Couture: Modern Sugar-Craft for the Stylish Baker. 2011. (ENG., Illus.). 144p. pap. 19.95 (978-1-55407-949-0(7)) Firefly Bks., Ltd.

Deacon, Carol. Fabulous Party Cakes & Cupcakes: Matching Cakes & Cupcakes for Every Occasion. 2011. (ENG., Illus.). 80p. 16.95 (978-0-8048-4158-0(6)) Tuttle Publishing.

—Holiday Cakes & Cupcakes: 45 Fondant Designs for Year-Round Celebrations. 2012. (ENG., Illus.). 80p. 16.95 **(978-0-8048-4261-7(2))** Tuttle Publishing.

Deacon, Carol. Perfect Party Cakes Made Easy. 2011. (ENG., Illus.). 192p. pap. 17.95 (978-1-84330-474-6(0)) New Holland Pubs., Ltd. GBR. Dist: Sterling Publishing Co., Inc.

Doell, Sandy & Shonk, Linda. Picture Yourself Decorating Cakes. 2007. (ENG., Illus.). 160p. pap. 24.99 (978-1-59863-440-2(2)) Course Technology.

Dudley, Angie & Bakerella. Cake Pops: Tips, Tricks, & Recipes for More Than 40 Irresistible Mini Treats. 2010. (ENG., Illus.). 160p. 19.95 (978-0-8118-7637-7(3)) Chronicle Bks. LLC.

Dunn, Alan. Alan Dunn's Celebration Cakes. 2010. (ENG., Illus.). 144p. 24.95 (978-1-84773-598-0(3)) New Holland Pubs., Ltd. GBR. Dist: Sterling Publishing Co., Inc.

—Alan Dunn's Christmas Cakes. 2010. (ENG., Illus.). 112p. 19.95 (978-1-84773-771-7(4)) New Holland Pubs., Ltd. GBR. Dist: Sterling Publishing Co., Inc.

—Sugar Flowers for Cake Decorating. 2008. (ENG., Illus.). 144p. 24.95 (978-1-84773-122-7(8)) New Holland Pubs., Ltd. GBR. Dist: Sterling Publishing Co., Inc.

—Tropical & Exotic Flowers for Cakes. 2011. (ENG., Illus.). 144p. 24.95 (978-1-84773-868-4(0)) New Holland Pubs., Ltd. GBR. Dist: Sterling Publishing Co., Inc.

Dunn, Alan & Webb, Claire. Sugarcraft Flowers - 25 Step-by-Step Projects for Simple Garden Flowers. 2010. (ENG., Illus.). 80p. pap. 12.95 (978-1-84773-663-5(7)) New Holland Pubs., Ltd. GBR. Dist: Sterling Publishing Co., Inc.

Elwins, Dannie. How to Be A Cake Decorator & Learn How to Decorate Cakes. 2009. 32p. pap. 16.99 (978-0-557-15551-4(7)) Lulu Enterprises Inc.

Estabrook, Lisa M. My Daughter the Bride Cookbook: Creating Memories in the Way of Food. 2008. 132p. 23.95 (978-0-595-50421-3(3)); pap. 13.95 (978-0-595-51420-5(0)) iUniverse, Inc.

Farrow, Joanna. Creative Christmas Cakes. (Illus.). 80p. 8.95 (978-1-85391-484-3(3)) Merehurst, Ltd. GBR. Dist: Tuttle Publishing.

—Decorating Biscuits. (Illus.). 128p. 14.95 (978-1-85391-809-4(1)) Merehurst, Ltd. GBR. Dist: Whitecap Bks., Ltd.

—Dress Your Cookie: Bake Them! Dress Them! Eat Them! 2012. (ENG., Illus.). 96p. pap. 14.99 (978-1-84601-392-8(5), Spruce) Octopus Publishing Group GBR. Dist: Hachette Bk. Group.

—Dress Your Cupcake: Bake Them! Dress Them! Eat Them! 2011. (ENG., Illus.). 128p. pap. 14.99 (978-1-84601-385-0(2), Spruce) Octopus Publishing Group GBR. Dist: Hachette Bk. Group.

Garcia, Michelle & Garcia, Valentin. Who You Callin' Cupcake? 75 In-Your-Face Recipes That Reinvent the Cupcake. 2010. (ENG., Illus.). 144p. pap. 15.95 (978-1-56975-739-0(9)) Ulysses Pr.

Garrett, Toba M. Professional Cake Decorating. 2nd ed. 2012. (ENG., Illus.). 416p. 65.00 (978-0-470-38009-3(8), Wiley) Wiley, John & Sons, Inc.

—Wedding Cake Art & Design: A Professional Approach. 2010. (ENG., Illus.). 288p. 50.00 (978-0-470-38133-5(7), Wiley) Wiley, John & Sons, Inc.

Goble, Karen. Celebration Cakes: Easy-to-Decorate Cakes for Every Occasion. 2009. (ENG., Illus.). 160p. pap. 17.95 (978-1-84773-226-2(7)) New Holland Pubs., Ltd. GBR. Dist: Sterling Publishing Co., Inc.

Green, Barbara & Kidwell, Geraldine. Sugar Art. 2010. (Illus.). 128p. pap. 24.99 (978-0-7643-3382-8(8)) Schiffer Publishing, Ltd.

Hitron, Noga. The Art of Cakes: Colorful Cake Designs for the Creative Baker. 2008. (ENG., Illus.). 112p. 17.95 (978-1-4027-6124-9(4), Sterling/Penn) Sterling Publishing Co., Inc.

—Fairytale Cakes: 17 Enchanted Creations. 2008. (ENG., Illus.). 132p. pap. 17.95 (978-1-60059-194-5(9)) Lark Bks.

—Mini-Cakes: Tiny Treats to Surprise & Delight. 2010. (ENG., Illus.). 112p. 17.95 (978-1-4027-3998-9(2)) Sterling Publishing Co., Inc.

Hoshino, Akiko. Painted Cookies. 2011. (ENG., Illus.). 88p. pap. 12.95 (978-1-4521-0122-4(1)) Chronicle Bks. LLC.

Ildo And Maureen Nicolello. Chocolate & Sugar Art Inspirations. 2009. 216p. pap. 55.99 (978-1-4389-3895-0(0)) AuthorHouse.

Kidwell, Geraldine. Cakes for All Occasions. 2008. (Illus.). 112p. pap. 24.95 (978-0-7643-2904-3(9)) Schiffer Publishing, Ltd.

Klivans, Elinor & Chronicle Books Staff. Chocolate Cakes: 50 Great Cakes for Every Occasion. 2010. (ENG., Illus.). 144p. 22.95 (978-0-8118-6872-3(9)) Chronicle Bks. LLC.

Lampkin, Sheila. The Cake Decorator's Motif Bible: 150 Fabulous Fondant Designs with Easy-to-Follow Charts & Photographs. 2007. (ENG., Illus.). 256p. spiral bd. 29.95 *(978-1-55407-281-1(6))* Firefly Bks., Ltd.

Lanham, Julie. Party Cakes. 2009. (ENG., Illus.). 252p. (gr. 12). pap. 19.95 *(978-0-14-300814-9(5)*, Penguin Global) Penguin Group (USA) Inc.

Lawrence, Helen & Dunn, Alan. The Wedding Cake Decorator's Bible: A Resource of Mix-and-Match Designs & Embellishments. 2009. (ENG.). 144p. pap. 24.99 *(978-1-60061-168-1(0))* David & Charles Pubs. GBR. Dist: F&W Media, Inc.

LoCicero, Joe. Cake Decorating for Dummies. 2007. (ENG., Illus.). 392p. per. 19.99 *(978-0-470-09911-7(9)*, For Dummies) Wiley, John & Sons, Inc.

MacLeod, Paula. Celebration Cake Pops. 2012. (Twenty to Make Ser.). (ENG., Illus.). 48p. pap. 9.95 ***(978-1-84448-763-9(6))*** Search Pr., Ltd. GBR. Dist: Independent Pubs. Group.

—Twenty to Make: Sugar Sporties. 2012. (Twenty to Make Ser.). (ENG., Illus.). 48p. pap. 9.95 ***(978-1-84448-820-9(9))*** Search Pr., Ltd. GBR. Dist: Independent Pubs. Group.

Mann, Tracey. Cake Decorating Skills: Techniques for Every Cake Maker & Every Kind of Cake. 2011. (ENG., Illus.). 176p. 29.95 *(978-1-55407-907-0(1))* Firefly Bks., Ltd.

Manning, Anneka. Kids' Party Cakes: 50 Fun, Fabulous & Fast Ideas. 2012. (ENG., Illus.). 168p. pap. 19.95 ***(978-1-77085-135-1(6))*** Firefly Bks., Ltd.

McMahon, Sue. Cake Decorating Tricks: Clever Ideas for Creating Fantastic Cakes. 2009. (ENG., Illus.). 128p. 19.95 *(978-1-84773-285-9(2))* New Holland Pubs., Ltd. GBR. Dist: Sterling Publishing Co., Inc.

McNaughton, Frances. Decorated Cup Cakes. 2010. (Twenty to Make Ser.). (ENG., Illus.). 48p. pap. 9.95 *(978-1-84448-519-2(6))* Search Pr., Ltd. GBR. Dist: Independent Pubs. Group.

—Sugar Animals. 2010. (Twenty to Make Ser.). (ENG., Illus.). 48p. pap. 9.95 *(978-1-84448-478-2(5))* Search Pr., Ltd. GBR. Dist: Independent Pubs. Group.

—Sugar Birds. 2011. (Twenty to Make Ser.). (ENG., Illus.). 48p. pap. 9.95 *(978-1-84448-672-4(9))* Search Pr., Ltd. GBR. Dist: Independent Pubs. Group.

McNaughton, Frances & Slatter, Lisa. Cupcakes & Cookies: Decorations for All Occasions. 2011. (ENG., Illus.). 96p. 17.95 *(978-1-84448-663-2(X))* Search Pr., Ltd. GBR. Dist: Independent Pubs. Group.

McNaughton, Frances & Slatter, Lisa. Sweet & Easy Sugar Decorations. 2012. (ENG., Illus.). 96p. 17.95 ***(978-1-84448-752-3(0))*** Search Pr., Ltd. GBR. Dist: Independent Pubs. Group.

Mcrae, Regina. Taking the Cake: Your Ultimate Cake Guide. 2011. 88p. pap. 14.99 ***(978-1-4634-4845-5(7))*** AuthorHouse.

Miller, Marcianne. The Artful Cupcake: Baking & Decorating Delicious Indulgences. 2010. (ENG., Illus.). 144p. pap. 12.95 *(978-1-60059-550-9(2))* Lark Bks.

Mountford, Meaghan. Sugarlicious: 50 Cute & Clever Treats for Every Occasion. 2012. (ENG., Illus.). 240p. pap. ***(978-0-373-89254-9(3))*** Harlequin Enterprises, Ltd.

Murdoch Books Test Kitchen Staff. Cupcakes: More Than 50 Fun Recipes for Creative Cakes. 2012. (ENG., Illus.). 128p. pap. 14.95 ***(978-1-74266-323-4(0))*** Murdoch Bks. Pty Ltd. AUS. Dist: Independent Pubs. Group.

Murfitt, Janice. Cake Decorating: Essential Skills & Techniques. 128p. *(978-1-84038-594-6(4)*, Hermes House) Anness Publishing.

Nilsen, Angela & Maxwell, Sarah. The Cake Decorator's Bible: A complete guide to cake decorating techniques, with over 100 projects, from traditional classics to the latest in contemporary Designs. 2012. (ENG., Illus.). 264p. pap. 12.99 ***(978-1-78019-088-4(3))*** Anness Publishing GBR. Dist: National Bk. Network.

Notter, Ewald, et al. The Art of the Confectioner: Sugarwork & Pastillage. 2012. (ENG., Illus.). 368p. 65.00 ***(978-0-470-39892-0(2)***, Wiley) Wiley, John & Sons, Inc.

Parish, Maisie. Fun & Original Birthday Cakes. 2011. (ENG., Illus.). 128p. pap. 22.99 *(978-0-7153-3833-9(1))* David & Charles Pubs. GBR. Dist: F&W Media, Inc.

Parrish, Maisie. Fun & Original Cakes for Men & Boys. 2012. (ENG., Illus.). 128p. pap. 23.99 ***(978-1-4463-0162-3(1))*** David & Charles Pubs. GBR. Dist: F&W Media, Inc.

—Fun & Original Character Cakes. 2009. (ENG., Illus.). 128p. pap. 22.99 *(978-0-7153-3005-0(5))* David & Charles Pubs. GBR. Dist: F&W Media, Inc.

—Fun & Original Children's Cakes. 2010. (ENG., Illus.). 128p. pap. 22.99 *(978-0-7153-3631-1(2))* David & Charles Pubs. GBR. Dist: F&W Media, Inc.

Penman, Helen. Fondant Modeling for Cake Decorators: 100 Fondant Features to Top off a Special Cake. 2011. (ENG., Illus.). 256p. spiral bd., spiral bd. 29.95 *(978-1-55407-913-1(6))* Firefly Bks., Ltd.

Penman, Helen. 100 Fondant Animal Cake Toppers: Make a Menagerie of Cute Creatures to Sit on Your Cakes. 2012. (ENG., Illus.). 256p. spiral bd. 29.95 ***(978-1-77085-087-3(2))*** Firefly Bks., Ltd.

Peterson, Valerie & Fryer, Janice. Cookie Craft: From Baking to Luster Dust, Designs & Techniques for Creative Cookie Occasions. 2007. (ENG., Illus.). 158p. 18.95 *(978-1-58017-694-1(1)*, 1580176941) Storey Publishing, LLC.

Pickard, Ann. Cake Characters. 2010. (Cozy Ser.). (ENG., Illus.). 156p. pap. 14.95 *(978-1-86108-643-3(1))* Guild of Master Craftsman Pubns., Ltd. GBR. Dist: Sterling Publishing Co., Inc.

—Cakes for Occasions: 25 Special Cakes for Every Celebration. 2011. (ENG., Illus.). 176p. pap. 19.95 *(978-1-86108-826-0(4))* Guild of Master Craftsman Pubns., Ltd. GBR. Dist: Sterling Publishing Co., Inc.

Rawlins, Amanda & Deasy, Caroline. Cool Cake Toppers: Put Anything You Want on A Cake. 2012. (ENG., Illus.). 144p. pap. 19.95 ***(978-1-77085-038-5(4))*** Firefly Bks., Ltd.

Rigg, Annie. Birthday Cakes for Kids. 2009. (ENG., Illus.). 128p. *(978-1-84597-833-4(1))* Ryland Peters & Small.

—Decorating Cupcakes, Cakes, & Cookies: Pretty Cakes, Clever Cookies & Cute Cupcakes. 2010. (ENG., Illus.). 128p. *(978-1-84597-957-7(5))* Ryland Peters & Small.

Rosen, Zilly. Zombie Cupcakes: From the Grave to the Table with 16 Cupcake Corpses. 2011. (ENG.). 80p. pap. 14.99 *(978-1-4494-0112-2(0))* Andrews McMeel Publishing.

Salamony, Sandra & Brown, Gina M. 1000 Ideas for Decorating Cupcakes, Cookies & Cakes. 2010. (1000 Ser.). (ENG., Illus.). 320p. pap. 25.00 *(978-1-59253-651-1(4)*, 1592536514) Quayside.

Shirazi, Kate. Cupcake Magic: Little Cakes with Attitude. 2008. (ENG., Illus.). 112p. 15.95 *(978-1-86205-810-1(5))* Anova Bks. GBR. Dist: Independent Pubs. Group.

Slatter, Lisa. Decorated Cookies. 2010. (Twenty to Make Ser.). (ENG., Illus.). 48p. pap. 9.95 *(978-1-84448-547-5(1))* Search Pr., Ltd. GBR. Dist: Independent Pubs. Group.

Smith, Anne. Creative Christening Cakes. (Illus.). 96p. 8.95 *(978-1-85391-472-0(X))* Merehurst, Ltd. GBR. Dist: Tuttle Publishing.

Smith, Lindy. Cakes to Inspire & Desire. 2007. (ENG., Illus.). 144p. per. 24.99 *(978-0-7153-2497-4(7))* David & Charles Pubs. GBR. Dist: F&W Media, Inc.

—Celebrate with Cupcakes. 2012. (ENG., Illus.). 128p. pap. 22.99 ***(978-1-4463-0054-1(4))*** David & Charles Pubs. GBR. Dist: F&W Media, Inc.

—Celebrate with Mini Cakes. 2010. (ENG., Illus.). 128p. pap. 22.99 *(978-0-7153-3783-7(1))* David & Charles Pubs. GBR. Dist: F&W Media, Inc.

—The Contemporary Cake Decorating Bible: Over 150 Techniques & 80 Stunning Projects. 2011. (ENG.). 160p. pap. 24.99 *(978-0-7153-3837-7(4))* David & Charles Pubs. GBR. Dist: F&W Media, Inc.

Spruce. Cake Pops. 2012. (ENG., Illus.). 64p. 12.99 ***(978-1-84601-402-4(6)***, Spruce) Octopus Publishing Group GBR. Dist: Hachette Bk. Group.

Strauss, Elisa & Matheson, Christie. Confetti Cakes for Kids: Delightful Cookies, Cakes, & Cupcakes from New York City's Famed Bakery. 2nd ed. 2008. (ENG., Illus.). 224p. 29.99 *(978-0-316-11829-3(X))* Little Brown & Co.

Tabor, Laura. Sweet Treats to Make & Decorate. 2011. (Illus.). 128p. 19.95 *(978-1-907563-07-2(5))* CICO Bks. GBR. Dist: Ryland Peters & Small.

Tack, Karen. Hello, Cupcake! What's New? 2011. *(978-0-547-57955-9(1))* Harcourt.

Tack, Karen & Richardson, Alan. Hello, Cupcake! Irresistibly Playful Creations Anyone Can Make. 2008. (ENG., Illus.). 240p. pap. 15.95 *(978-0-618-82925-5(3))* Houghton Mifflin Harcourt Trade & Reference Pubs.

—What's New, Cupcake? Ingeniously Simple Designs for Every Occasion. 2010. (ENG., Illus.). 240p. pap. 16.95 *(978-0-547-24181-4(X))* Houghton Mifflin Harcourt Trade & Reference Pubs.

Turner, Mich. The Art of the Cake: The Ultimate Step-by-Step Guide to Baking & Decorating Perfection. 2011. (Illus.). 224p. 40.00 *(978-0-7893-2215-9(3))* Universe Publishing.

—Party Cakes: Delightful Little Treats for Special Occasions. 2007. (ENG., Illus.). 160p. 19.95 *(978-0-7893-1562-5(9))* Universe Publishing.

—Wedding Cakes: The Most Exquisite Cake to Celebrate Life's Most Important Day. 2009. (ENG., Illus.). 160p. 37.50 *(978-0-7893-1814-5(8))* Universe Publishing.

Valastro, Buddy. Baking with the Cake Boss: 100 of Buddy's Best Recipes & Decorating Secrets. 2011. (ENG.). 272p. 30.00 *(978-1-4391-8352-6(X)*, Free Pr.) Free Pr.

—Cake Boss: Stories & Recipes from Mia Famiglia. (ENG.). 272p. 2012. pap. 16.99 *(978-1-4516-1034-5(3))* 2010. (Illus.). 25.99 *(978-1-4391-8351-9(1))* Free Pr. (Free Pr.).

van Zyl, Katrien. Decorating Cake with Chocolate: Scrumptious Recipes & Original Chocolate Decorations. 2012. (ENG., Illus.). 160p. pap. 29.95 ***(978-1-84448-862-9(4))*** Search Pr., Ltd. GBR. Dist: Independent Pubs. Group.

Various contributors. Make Me I'm Yours... Party: Over 20 Handmade Decorations, Gifts & Treats. 2012. (ENG., Illus.). 128p. pap. 14.99 ***(978-1-4463-0230-9(X))*** David & Charles Pubs. GBR. Dist: F&W Media, Inc.

Webb, Claire. Sugarcraft Flowers: 25 Step-by-Step Projects for Simple Garden Flowers. 2006. (Illus.). 80p. 17.95 *(978-1-84537-282-8(4))* New Holland Pubs., Ltd. GBR. Dist: Sterling Publishing Co., Inc.

Wilkinson, Alison. Fantastic Party Cakes: 20 Fun Cakes to Make & Decorate. 2008. (ENG., Illus.). 80p. pap. 12.95 *(978-1-84773-229-3(1))* New Holland Pubs., Ltd. GBR. Dist: Sterling Publishing Co., Inc.

Yates, Jen. Cake Wrecks: When Professional Cakes Go Hilariously Wrong. 2009. (ENG., Illus.). 208p. 12.99 *(978-0-7407-8537-5(0))* Andrews McMeel Publishing.

CAKE ICINGS

see Icings, Cake

CALABAR (NIGERIA)

Imbua, David Lishilinimle. Intercourse & Crosscurrents in the Atlantic World: Calabar-British Experience, 17th-20th Centuries. 2011. 230p. pap. 30.00 *(978-1-61163-006-0(1))* Carolina Academic Pr.

Waddell, Hope Masterton. Twenty-Nine Years in the West Indies & Central Africa: A Review of Missionary Work & Adventure, 1829-1858. 2010. (Cambridge Library Collection - History Ser.). (Illus.). 708p. pap. 48.00 *(978-1-108-01669-8(3))* Cambridge Univ. Pr.

CALABRIA (ITALY)

Ibbeken, Hillert. Das andere Italien. 2010. (GER & ENG., Illus.). 216p. 75.00 *(978-3-936681-43-7(0))* Edition Axel Menges GmbH DEU. Dist: National Bk. Network.

CALABRIA (ITALY)—DESCRIPTION AND TRAVEL

Douglas, Norman. Old Calabria. 2007. (ENG.). 356p. pap. 25.99 *(978-1-4254-2343-7(8))* BiblioBazaar.

—Old Calabria. 2007. (ENG.). 340p. per. 14.95 *(978-1-60206-376-1(1))* Cosimo, Inc.

—Old Calabria. 2010. (ENG., Illus.). 368p. 20.00 *(978-1-84885-113-9(8)*, Tauris Parke Paperbacks) I. B. Tauris & Co., Ltd. GBR. Dist: Macmillan.

—Old Calabria. Lt. ed. 2007. (ENG.). 386p. pap. 26.99 *(978-1-4264-2391-8(8))* BiblioBazaar.

Thomas Cook Publishing Staff. Traveller Guides Calabria. 2nd ed. 2011. (Travellers - Thomas Cook Ser.). (ENG., Illus.). 176p. pap. 16.95 *(978-1-84848-390-3(2))* Cook, Thomas Publishing GBR. Dist: Globe Pequot Pr., The.

CALAH (EXTINCT CITY)

al-Gailani Werr L., et al, eds. New Light on Nimrud: Proceedings of the Nimrud Conference 11th-13th March 2002. 2008. (ENG., Illus.). 336p. (C). 80.00 *(978-0-903472-24-1(4))* British Schl. of Archaeology in Iraq GBR. Dist: Brown, David Bk. Co., The.

CALAIS (FRANCE)

Rose, Susan. Calais: An English Town in France, 1347-1558. 2008. (Illus.). 198p. 90.00 *(978-1-84383-401-4(4)*, Boydell Press) Boydell & Brewer, Ltd. GBR. Dist: Boydell & Brewer, Inc.

Turpyn, Richard. Chronicle of Calais, in the Reigns of Henry Seventh & Henry Eighth to the Year 1540. Nichols, John G., ed. (Camden Society, London, Publications, First Ser.: No. 35). reprint ed. 50.00 *(978-0-404-50135-8(4))* AMS Pr., Inc.

CALAMITIES

see Disasters

CALAMITY JANE, 1852-1903

McLaird, James D. Wild Bill Hickok & Calamity Jane: Deadwood Legends. 2008. (Illus.). 174p. pap. 12.95 *(978-0-9777955-9-8(4)*, South Dakota State Historical Society Pr.) South Dakota State Historical Society.

Morledge, Phillip J. The 'Real' Wild West. 2009. 438p. pap. 37.95 *(978-0-9559765-0-6(2))* PJM Publishing GBR. Dist: Lulu Enterprises Inc.

CALAS, JEAN, 1698-1762

Chenier, Jean Calas. Cook, Tony, ed. Date not set. (French Texts Ser.: Vol. 64). (FRE., Illus.). 105p. pap. 19.95 *(978-0-85989-268-1(9))* Univ. of Exeter Pr. GBR. Dist: Brown, David Bk. Co., The.

CALCIFICATION

see also Bone; Calcium in the Body

also names of organs of the body, with or without the subdivision Calcification

Bonucci, Ermanno. Biological Calcification: Normal & Pathological Processes in the Early Stages. 2010. (ENG., Illus.). xxii, 592p. pap. 295.00 *(978-3-642-07154-6(6)*, 3642071546) Springer.

Goldberg, H. A., et al, eds. Advances in Chemistry & Biology of Mineralized Tissues: 10th International Conference on the Chemistry & Biology of Mineralized Tissues, Carefree, Ariz., November 2010. Special Topic Issue 'Cells Tissues Organs 2011, Vol. 194, No. 2-4' 2011. (ENG., Illus.). 264p. pap. ***(978-3-8055-9841-5(6))*** Karger, S. AG.

CALCITE

Dobrev, Joana & Markovi?, Petra, eds. Calcite: Formation, Properties & Applications. 2011. (Chemical Engineering Methods & Technology Ser.). 140.00 ***(978-1-61470-782-0(0))*** Nova Science Pubs., Inc.

Travaille, Markus. Soft Interactions, Solid Results. 2009. 224p. pap. *(978-3-639-16306-3(0))* VDM Verlag Dr. Mueller e.K.

CALCIUM

Bootman, Martin D. Calcium Signaling. 2011. 135.00 ***(978-0-87969-903-1(5))*** Cold Spring Harbor Laboratory Pr.

Chung, Mei. Vitamin D & Calcium: A Systematic Review of Health Outcomes. 2009. (Illus.). xvi, 341p. *(978-1-58763-385-0(X))* Agency for Healthcare Research & Quality.

Duncan, C. J., ed. Calcium, Oxygen Radicals & Cellular Damage. 2008. (Society for Experimental Biology Seminar Ser.). (ENG., Illus.). 240p. pap. 53.00 *(978-0-521-05761-5(2))* Cambridge Univ. Pr.

Gussone, Nikolaus, et al, eds. Calcium & Magnesium Stable Isotope Chemistry. 2010. (Advances in Isotope Geochemistry Ser.). (ENG.). 300p. 199.00 *(978-3-540-68948-5(6)*, 3540689486) Springer.

Hu, Jiancheng. Regulation of B Cell Migration & Antigen Receptor Signaling by Lsc. 2010. 136p. pap. *(978-3-639-27472-1(5))* VDM Verlag Dr. Mueller e.K.

Islam, Shahidul, ed. Calcium Signaling. 2012. (Advances in Experimental Medicine & Biology Ser.: 740). (ENG., Illus.). xiii, 1267p. 279.00 ***(978-94-007-2887-5(5)***, 9400728875) Springer.

Lambert, David G., ed. Calcium Signaling Protocols. 2nd ed. 2010. (Methods in Molecular Biology Ser.). (Illus.). 376p. pap. 134.00 *(978-1-61737-573-6(X)*, 161737573X) Humana Pr.

Mun, Hee-Chang. L-Amino Acid Sensing by the Calcium Sensing Receptor. 2009. 196p. pap. *(978-3-639-06192-5(6))* VDM Verlag Dr. Mueller e.K.

Rheaume-Bleue, Kate. Vitamin K2 & the Calcium Paradox: How a Little-Known Vitamin Could Save Your Life. 2011. (ENG., Illus.). 288p. pap. 19.95 ***(978-1-118-06572-3(7)***, Wiley) Wiley, John & Sons, Inc.

Rhoads, Robert E., ed. Signaling Pathways for Translation: Stress, Calcium, & Rapamycin. 2010. (Progress in Molecular & Subcellular Biology Ser.). (Illus.). x, 176p. pap. 149.00 *(978-3-642-07505-6(3)*, 3642075053) Springer.

Verkhratsky, Alexei & Petersen, Ole H., eds. Calcium Measurement Methods. 2009. (Neuromethods Ser.). (ENG., Illus.). xii, 256p. 189.00 *(978-1-60761-475-3(8)*, 1607614758) Humana Pr.

Vitti, Dorinha M. S. S., et al. contrib. by. Phosphorous & Calcium Utilization & Requirements in Farm Animals. 2010. (Illus.). 208p. 160.00 *(978-1-84593-626-6(4))* CABI GBR. Dist: Stylus Publishing, LLC.

Vogel, Hans J., ed. Calcium-Binding Protein Protocols: Volume 1: Reviews & Case Studies. 2010. (Methods in Molecular Biology Ser.). (Illus.). 360p. pap. 119.00 *(978-1-61737-135-6(1)*, 1617371351) Humana Pr.

—Calcium-Binding Protein Protocols: Volume 2: Methods & Techniques. 2010. (Methods in Molecular Biology Ser.). (Illus.). 436p. pap. 119.00 *(978-1-61737-136-3(X)*, 161737136X) Humana Pr.

CALCIUM—METABOLISM

see also Rickets

Carafoli, Ernesto & Brini, Marisa, eds. Calcium Signalling & Disease: Molcular pathology of Calcium. 2007. (Subcellular Biochemistry Ser.). 612p. 319.00 *(978-1-4020-6190-5(0))* Springer.

Falcke, Martin & Malchow, Dieter, eds. Understanding Calcium Dynamics: Experiments & Theory. 2010. (Lecture Notes in Physics Ser.). xii, 300p. pap. 139.00 *(978-3-642-07302-1(6)*, 3642073026) Springer.

Hsu, Chen H., ed. Calcium & Phosphate Metabolism Management in Chronic Renal Disease. (ENG., Illus.). xii, 188p. 2010. pap. 139.00 *(978-1-4419-4122-0(3)*, 1441941223) 2006. 139.00 *(978-0-387-33369-4(X)*, 038733369X) Springer.

Tsaneva-Atanasova, Krasimira. A Mathematical Study of Calcium Oscillations & Waves. 2009. 176p. pap. *(978-3-639-13651-7(9))* VDM Verlag Dr. Mueller e.K.

Weaver, Connie M. & Heaney, Robert P., eds. Calcium in Human Health. 2010. (Nutrition & Health Ser.). (Illus.). 472p. pap. 179.00 *(978-1-61737-579-8(9)*, 1617375799) Humana Pr.

CALCIUM CARBONATE

Peeters, Marloes. Biohybrid Nanocomposites. 2010. 120p. pap. *(978-3-8383-7873-2(3))* Lambert Academic Publishing.

Waly, Tarek Kamal Abdalla. Minimizing the Use of Chemicals to Control Scaling in Sea Water Reverse Osmosis: Improved Prediction of the Scaling Potential of Calcium Carbonate. 2011. (ENG.). 186p. pap. 69.95 *(978-0-415-61578-5(X)*, CRC Press) Taylor & Francis Group GBR. Dist: Taylor & Francis Group.

Whiffin, Victoria. Microbial Caco3 Precipitation. 2008. 168p. pap. *(978-3-639-03872-9(X))* VDM Verlag Dr. Mueller e.K.

CALCIUM IN THE BODY

see also Calcification

Bonnick, Sydney Lou & Lewis, Lori Ann. Bone Densitometry for Technologists. 2010. (Illus.). 344p. pap. 94.50 *(978-1-61737-309-1(5)*, 161737309E) Humana Pr.

Carafoli, Ernesto & Brini, Marisa, eds. Calcium Signalling & Disease: Molcular pathology of Calcium. 2007. (Subcellular Biochemistry Ser.). 612p. 319.00 *(978-1-4020-6190-5(0))* Springer.

—Calcium Signalling & Disease: Molecular pathology of Calcium. 2010. (Subcellular Biochemistry Ser.). xii, 566p. pap. 319.00 *(978-90-481-7560-4(7)*, 9048175607) Springer.

Committee to Review Dietary Reference Intakes for Vitamin D and Calcium & Institute of Medicine. Dietary Reference Intakes for Calcium & Vitamin D. Ross, A. Catharine et al, eds. 2011. (ENG.). 1132p. 69.95 *(978-0-309-16394-1(3))* National Academies Pr.

Czurylo, Edward A. & Kulikova, Natalia. Anatomy & Physiology of Proteins: Caldesmon. 2012. (Series: Protein Biochemistry, Synthesis, Structure & Cellular Functions Ser.). 135p. pap. 47.00 *(978-1-61324-312-1(X))* Nova Science Pubs., Inc.

Krebs, Joachim & Michalak, Marek. Calcium: A Matter of Life or Death. 2007. (New Comprehensive Biochemistry Ser.: 41). (ENG., Illus.). 584p. 205.00 *(978-0-444-52805-6(9)*, Elsevier Science) Elsevier Science & Technology Bks.

Sawyer, Aenor, ed. Bone Densitometry in Growing Patients. 2010. (Current Clinical Practice Ser.). (Illus.). 350p. pap. 149.00 *(978-1-61737-685-6(X)*, 161737685X) Humana Pr.

Weaver, Connie M. & Heaney, Robert P., eds. Calcium in Human Health. 2010. (Nutrition & Health Ser.). (Illus.). 472p. pap. 179.00 *(978-1-61737-579-8(9)*, 1617375799) Humana Pr.

Yamaguchi, Masayoshi. Calcium Signaling. 2012. (Series: Protein Biochemistry, Synthesis, Structure & Cellular Functions Ser.). (Illus.). 245p. 140.00 *(978-1-61324-313-8(8))* Nova Science Pubs., Inc.

CALCIUM METABOLISM

see Calcium—Metabolism

CALCULATING BOARDS, NETWORK

see Electric Network Analyzers

CALCULATING MACHINES

see Calculators

C

CALCULATORS

Here are entered works on present-day calculators as well as on calculators and mechanical computers of pre-1945 vintage. Works on modern electronic computers first developed after 1945 are entered under Computers.

see also Arithmetic; Computers; Graphic Calculators; Programmable Calculators

Babbage, Charles. Babbage's Calculating Engines: Being a Collection of Papers Relating to them; their History & Construction. Babbage, Henry P., ed. 2010. (Cambridge Library Collection - Mathematics Ser.). (ENG.). 388p. pap. 31.99 (978-1-108-00096-3(7)) Cambridge Univ. Pr.

Chinskul, Bunjong. Computational Methods for Assessing Social & Other Types of Subjective Issues. 2011. 169p. pap. 79.95 (978-1-4327-4609-4(X)) Outskirts Pr., Inc.

Duffett-Smith, Peter & Zwart, Jonathan. Practical Astronomy with Your Calculator or Spreadsheet. 4th rev. ed. 2011. (ENG., Illus.). 238p. spiral bd. 40.00 (978-0-521-14654-8(2)) Cambridge Univ. Pr.

Guin, Dominique, et al, eds. The Didactical Challenge of Symbolic Calculators: Turning a Computational Device into a Mathematical Instrument. 2010. (Mathematics Education Library). Orig. Title: Calculations Symboliques. (Illus.). vii, 305p. pap. 199.00 (978-1-4419-3582-3(7), 1441935827) Springer.

Harvard Computation Laboratory Staff. Manual of Operation for Automatic Sequence Controlled Calculator. 2009. (Charles Babbage Institute Reprint Ser.). (ENG.). 607p. pap. 69.00 (978-0-262-51379-1(X)) MIT Pr.

Horsburg, E. M. Modern Instruments & Methods of Calculation. 2010. 254p. pap. (978-1-151-74593-4(6)) Books LLC.

Horsburg, E. M. & Exhibition, Napier Tercentenary. Modern Instruments & Methods of Calculation: A handbook of the Napier Tercentenary Exhibition. 2010. 394p. pap. 33.75 (978-1-177-79569-2(8)) BiblioBazaar.

Horsburgh, E. M. Ed. Modern Instruments & Methods of Calculation, a Handbook of the Napier Tercentenary Exhibition. 2010. (ENG.). 390p. pap. 33.75 (978-1-171-58714-9(7)) BiblioBazaar.

—Modern Instruments & Methods of Calculation, a Handbook of the Napier Tercentenary Exhibition. 2010. 254p. pap. 33.40 (978-1-152-15999-0(2)) General Bks. LLC.

Horsburgh, E. M. Ed & Exhibition, Napier Tercentenary. Modern Instruments & Methods of Calculation; a Handbook of the Napier Tercentenary Exhibition. 2010. 394p. pap. 33.75 (978-1-178-26038-0(0)) BiblioBazaar.

Kamm, James. Essential Equations for the Mechanical PE Exam Using the HP 33s. 2006. (ENG., Illus.). 144p. per. 72.00 (978-1-59126-078-3(7)) Professional Pubns., Inc.

Kelvin, Lord William & Tait, Peter. Treatise on Natural Philosophy: Volume 1. 2007. 528p. per. 27.95 (978-1-60206-268-9(4)) Cosimo, Inc.

—Treatise on Natural Philosophy: Volume 2. 2007. 556p. per. 27.95 (978-1-60206-269-6(2)) Cosimo, Inc.

McKenzie, Jimmy C., et al. Office Machines: With Excel Applications. 7th rev. ed. 2007. 336p. (C). pap. 63.00 (978-0-13-170094-9(4), Prentice Hall) Prentice Hall PTR.

Oldham, Keith B., et al. Equator: A Function Calculator. 2008. (Illus.). cd-rom 24.95 (978-0-387-09773-2(2)) Springer.

Pasewark, William R. Calculators: Printing & Display. 5th ed. 2011. (FBLA - All Ser.). (ENG.). 144p. (C). pap. 44.95 (978-0-8400-6535-3(3)) Cengage South-Western.

Rising, Gerald R. Inside Your Calculator: From Simple Programs to Significant Insights. 2007. (ENG., Illus.). 304p. per. 66.99 (978-0-470-11401-8(0), Wiley-Interscience) Wiley, John & Sons, Inc.

Triola, Mario F. Elementary Statistics: Using the TI-83/84 Plus Calculator. 3rd ed. 2010. (Triola Statistics Ser.). (ENG., Illus.). 896p. (C). 160.00 (978-0-321-64148-9(5)) Addison Wesley.

Wakefield, Dorothy & McLaughlin, Kathleen. TI-83 Plus, TI-84 Plus, & TI-89 Manual. 3rd ed. 2008. (ENG.). 248p. (C). pap. 24.67 (978-0-321-57778-8(7), Prentice Hall) Prentice Hall PTR.

CALCULATORS, PROGRAMMABLE

see Programmable Calculators

CALCULI, BILIARY

see Gallstones

CALCULI, URINARY

see Urinary Organs—Calculi

CALCULUS

see also Curvature; Curves; Differential Equations; Fourier Series; Functions; Harmonic Analysis; Mathematical Analysis; Nonlinear Theories; p-Adic Analysis; Surfaces

Abbott, Paul & Neill, Hugh. Understand Calculus: A Teach Yourself Guide. 3rd ed. 2010. (Teach Yourself: Reference Ser.). (ENG.). 352p. pap. 15.00 (978-0-07-174760-8(5), 0071747605) McGraw-Hill Cos., The.

Adler & Cram101 Textbook Reviews Staff. Modeling the Dynamics of Life: Calculus & Probability for Life Scientists. 2007. 144p. per. 11.95 (978-1-4288-3546-7(6)) Cram101 Inc.

Adrian, Y E O. The Pleasures of Pi, E: And Other Interesting Numbers. 2006. (Illus.). 239p. per. 24.00 (978-981-270-079-7(X)) World Scientific Publishing Co., Inc.

—The Pleasures of Pi, e & Other Interesting Numbers. 2006. 239p. 58.00 (978-981-270-078-0(1)) World Scientific Publishing Co., Inc.

Agrawal, O. P. & Tenreiro Machado, J. A., eds. Advances in Fractional Calculus: Theoretical Developments & Applications in Physics & Engineering. 2007. (ENG., Illus.). xiii, 552p. 219.00 (978-1-4020-6041-0(6), 1402060416) Springer.

Al-Azawi, Saad. Some Results in Fractional Calculus. 2011. 112p. pap. **(978-3-8443-2519-5(0))** Lambert Academic Publishing.

Ambartzumian, R. V. Factorization Calculus & Geometric Probability. 2008. (Encyclopedia of Mathematics & its Applications Ser.). (ENG.). 300p. pap. 58.00 (978-0-521-08978-4(6)) Cambridge Univ. Pr.

Anastassiou, George A. Advances on Fractional Inequalities. 2011. (SpringerBriefs in Mathematics Ser.). (ENG.). x, 122p. pap. 49.95 **(978-1-4614-0702-7(8)**, 1461407028) Springer.

Anton. Calculus Early Transcendentals Single Variable 9E Student Solutions Manual. 9th ed. 2008. (ENG.). 288p. (C). pap. 38.95 (978-0-470-37958-5(8), Wiley) Wiley, John & Sons, Inc.

—Calculus Late Transcendentals Combined. 9th ed. 2008. (C). pap. 83.95 (978-0-470-19432-4(4), Wiley) Wiley, John & Sons, Inc.

Anton & Bivens & Davis & Cram101 Textbook Reviews Staff. Calculus: Early Transcendentals. 2007. 204p. per. 13.95 (978-1-4288-3364-7(1)) Cram101 Inc.

Anton, Bivens & Davis & Cram101 Textbook Reviews Staff. Calculus. 2007. 196p. per. 13.95 (978-1-4288-2692-2(0)) Cram101 Inc.

Anton, Howard. Calclus Early Transcendentals with Student Solutions Manual & Wiley Plus Set. 8th ed. 2007. (Wiley Plus Products Ser.). 179.95 (978-0-470-16347-4(X), Wiley) Wiley, John & Sons, Inc.

—Calculus. 8th rev. ed. 2006. (Wiley Plus Products Ser.). 150.95 (978-0-470-11944-0(6)) Wiley, John & Sons, Inc.

—Calculus: Multivariable. 8th ed. 2006. (Wiley Plus Products Ser.). 113.95 (978-0-470-11503-9(3)) Wiley, John & Sons, Inc.

—Calculus 4th Edition Single Variable Cloth with eGrade Plus Set. 4th rev. ed. 2006. (Wiley Plus Products Ser.). 128.95 (978-0-470-10352-4(3)) Wiley, John & Sons, Inc.

—Calculus 8th Edition Multivariable Edition Desktop Edition. 2007. (Wiley Desktop Editions Ser.). 118.95 (978-0-470-24063-2(6)) Wiley, John & Sons, Inc.

—Calculus Early Transcendentals Combined 8E with Student Solutions Manual SV Student Solutions ManualMV & Wiley Plus Set. 2007. 158.95 (978-0-470-16463-1(8), Wiley) Wiley, John & Sons, Inc.

—Calculus Early Transcendentals Combined 8/E with Student Study Guide SV 8E Student Study Guide MV 8EMaple Stud Ed Rel 10 & Wiley Plus Set. 8th ed. 2007. (Wiley Plus Products Ser.). 167.95 (978-0-470-16365-8(8), Wiley) Wiley, John & Sons, Inc.

—Calculus Early Transcendentals Combined with Wiley Plus Set. 8th ed. 2006. (Wiley Plus Products Ser.). 167.95 (978-0-470-10302-9(7), Sybex) Wiley, John & Sons, Inc.

—Calculus Early Transcendentals Single Variable 8E with Student Solutions Manual & Wiley Plus Set. 8th rev. ed. 2007. 124.95 (978-0-470-16462-4(X), Wiley) Wiley, John & Sons, Inc.

—Calculus Late Transcendentals Combined with Wiley Plus Set. 8th rev. ed. 2006. (Wiley Plus Products Ser.). 167.95 (978-0-470-10303-6(5), Sybex) Wiley, John & Sons, Inc.

—Calculus Late Transcendentals Single Variable with Wiley Plus Set. 8th rev. ed. 2006. (Wiley Plus Products Ser.). 134.95 (978-0-470-10304-3(3), Sybex) Wiley, John & Sons, Inc.

Anton, Howard, et al. Calculus. 9th ed. 2008. (ENG.). 880p. (C). 208.95 (978-0-470-18204-8(0), Wiley) Wiley, John & Sons, Inc.

—Calculus. (ENG.). 1312p. (C). 9th ed. 2009. 228.95 (978-0-470-18349-6(7)) 10th ed. 2012. 212.95 **(978-0-470-64772-1(8))** Wiley, John & Sons, Inc. (Wiley).

—Calculus: Early Transcendentals. (ENG.). 1312p. (C). 9th ed. 2008. 228.95 (978-0-470-18345-8(4)) 10th ed. 2011. (Illus.). 212.95 **(978-0-470-64769-1(8))** Wiley, John & Sons, Inc. (Wiley).

—Calculus: Multivariable. 9th ed. (C). 2008. pap., pupil's gde. ed. 38.95 (978-0-470-37965-3(0)) 2009. (ENG.). 120p. pap. 57.95 (978-0-470-37964-6(2), Wiley) Wiley, John & Sons, Inc.

—Calculus: Single Variable. 9th ed. (C). 2009. (ENG., Illus.). 880p. 206.95 (978-0-470-18347-2(0), Wiley) 2008. pap., pupil's gde. ed. 38.95 (978-0-470-37963-9(4)) 2008. pap., pupil's gde. ed. 38.95 (978-0-470-37959-2(6), Wiley) 2009. (ENG.). 288p. pap. 57.95 (978-0-470-37962-2(6), Wiley) Wiley, John & Sons, Inc.

—Calculus Early Transcendentals Single Variable. 10th ed. 2011. (ENG.). 880p. (C). 194.95 **(978-0-470-64768-4(X)**, Wiley) Wiley, John & Sons, Inc.

—Calculus Early Transcendentals/Single Variable. 8th rev. ed. 2006. (Wiley Plus Products Ser.). (Illus.). 134.95 (978-0-470-11962-4(4)) Wiley, John & Sons, Inc.

—Calculus Multivariable. (ENG., (C). 9th ed. 2009. Illus.). 448p. 187.95 (978-0-470-18346-5(2)) 10th ed. 2012. 144p. pap. 57.95 **(978-1-118-17383-1(X))** Wiley, John & Sons, Inc. (Wiley).

—Calculus Single Variable. 10th ed. 2012. (ENG.). 880p. (C). 194.95 **(978-0-470-64770-7(1)**, Wiley) Wiley, John & Sons, Inc.

Anton, Howard, et al. Calculus, Textbook & Student Study Guide & Student Solutions Manual: Early Transcendentals Single Variable. 8th ed. 2008. (ENG.). (C). 259.95 (978-0-470-40857-5(X), Wiley) Wiley, John & Sons, Inc.

Armstrong. Applied Calculus. 2011. 144.95 (978-0-7637-9330-2(2)) Jones & Bartlett Learning, LLC.

—Brief Calculus for Business, Social & Life Sciences 3E. 3rd rev. ed. 2011. 141.95 (978-0-7637-9328-9(0)) Jones & Bartlett Learning, LLC.

—College Mathematics: Problem Solv in Finite & Calculus. 2011. 179.95 (978-0-7637-9332-6(9)) Jones & Bartlett Learning, LLC.

Augustus De Morgan. Elementary Illustrations of the Differential & Integral Calculus. 2008. 152p. pap. 9.95 (978-1-60386-148-9(3), Merchant Bks.) Rough Draft Printing.

Baleanu, Dumitru. Fractional Calculus: Models & Numerical Methods. 2012. 450p. 130.00 **(978-981-4355-20-9(8))** World Scientific Publishing Co., Inc.

Baleanu, Dumitru, et al, eds. New Trends in Nanotechnology & Fractional Calculus Applications. 2009. (ENG., Illus.). xi, 531p. 169.00 (978-90-481-3292-8(4), 9048132924) Springer.

Banner, Adrian. The Calculus Lifesaver: All the Tools You Need to Excel at Calculus. 2007. (Princeton Lifesaver Study Guides). (Illus.). 728p. 60.00 (978-0-691-13153-5(8)); (ENG., 752p. pap. 24.95 (978-0-691-13088-0(4)) Princeton Univ. Pr.

BarCharts Inc., Staff. Calculus. 2007. (Quickstudy Bks.). (ENG., Illus.). 144p. pap. 6.95 (978-1-4232-0268-4(6)) Barcharts, Inc.

Barnett. Calculus F/Bus., Econ, Lifescience plus Acc. 12th ed. 2010. (ENG.). (C). pap. 167.33 (978-0-321-70901-1(2)) Addison Wesley.

Barnett & Ziegler & Byleen & Cram101 Textbook Reviews Staff. Calculus for Business, Economics, Life Sciences, & Social Sciences. 2007. 124p. per. 11.95 (978-1-4288-3354-8(4)) Cram101 Inc.

Barnett, Raymond A., et al. Additional Calculus Topics for Calculus for Business, Economics, Life Sciences & Social Sciences. 12th ed. 2010. (ENG.). 384p. (C). pap. 32.00 (978-0-321-65509-7(5), Prentice Hall) Prentice Hall PTR.

—Calculus for Business, Economics, Life Sciences & Social Sciences. 11th ed. 2008. (Illus.). 704p. pap. (978-0-13-206974-8(1)) 12th ed. 2010. (ENG.). 704p. (C). 157.33 (978-0-321-61399-8(6), Prentice Hall) 12th ed. 2010. (ENG.). 576p. (C). pap. 36.67 (978-0-321-65498-4(6), Prentice Hall) Prentice Hall PTR.

—Calculus for Business, Economics, Life Sciences & Social Sciences, Books a la Carte Edition. 12th ed. 2010. (ENG.). (C). ring bd. 94.40 (978-0-321-69245-0(4)) Addison Wesley.

—Calculus for Business, Economics, Life Sciences & Social Sciences Value Package (includes MyMathLab/MyStatLab Student Access) 11th ed. 2010. (ENG.). (C). pap. 160.67 (978-0-321-75193-5(0)) Pearson Education.

—Student Worksheets for Calculus for Business, Economics, Life Sciences, & Social Sciences. 12th ed. 2010. 288p. (C). pap. 26.67 (978-0-321-65398-7(X)) Addison-Wesley Longman, Inc.

Barnett, Ziegler & Cram101 Textbook Reviews Staff. Applied Calculus for Business, Economics, Life Sciences, & Social Sciences. 2007. 148p. per. 12.95 (978-1-4288-3634-1(9)) Cram101 Inc.

Bass, Richard F., et al. Moderate Deviations for the Range of Planar Random Walks. 2009. (Memoirs of the American Mathematical Society Ser.). 82p. pap. 62.00 (978-0-8218-4287-4(0)) American Mathematical Society.

Bauer, Wolfgang W. & Westfall, Gary Duane. University Physics (Standard Version, Chapters 1-35) 2010. (ENG., Illus.). 1024p. (C). 236.33 (978-0-07-735470-1(2), 0077354702, McGraw-Hill Science, Engineering & Mathematics) McGraw-Hill Higher Education.

—University Physics Volume 1 (Chapters 1-20), 2 vols. 2010. (ENG., Illus.). 608p. (C). 146.67 (978-0-07-735483-1(4), 0077354834, McGraw-Hill Science, Engineering & Mathematics) McGraw-Hill Higher Education.

—University Physics Volume 2 (Chapters 21-40) 2010. (ENG., Illus.). 672p. (C). 146.67 (978-0-07-735479-4(6), 0077354796, McGraw-Hill Science, Engineering & Mathematics) McGraw-Hill Higher Education.

—University Physics with Modern Physics (Chapters 1-40) 2010. (ENG., Illus.). 1408p. (C). 250.00 (978-0-07-735478-7(8), 0077354788, McGraw-Hill Science, Engineering & Mathematics) McGraw-Hill Higher Education.

Baxandall, Peter R. & Liebeck, Hans. Vector Calculus. 2008. (Dover Books on Mathematics Ser.). (ENG., Illus.). 560p. pap. 27.95 (978-0-486-46620-0(5)) Dover Pubns., Inc.

Bell, John L. A Primer of Infinitesimal Analysis. 2nd ed. 2008. (ENG., Illus.). 140p. 59.00 (978-0-521-88718-2(6)) Cambridge Univ. Pr.

Bengtson, Jesper. Formalising Process Calculi. 2010. (Uppsala Dissertations from the Faculty of Science & Technology Ser.). (Illus.). 498p. pap. 115.00 (978-91-554-7801-8(8)) Uppsala Universitet/Acta Universitatis Upsaliensis SWE. Dist: Coronet Bks.

Berg, M. Douglas. The Foundations of Business Analysis: An Introduction to Derivative Calculus & Statistics. 2011. (ENG.). 152p. pap. 48.95 (978-0-7575-8163-2(3)) Kendall Hunt Publishing Co.

Berresford, Geoffrey C. Applied Calculus. 4th ed. 2006. (ENG.). 384p. (C). pap. 76.95 (978-0-618-60637-5(8), 304402) Brooks/Cole.

Berresford, Rockett & Cram101 Textbook Reviews Staff. Brief Applied Calculus. 2007. 120p. per. 11.95 (978-1-4288-3618-1(7)) Cram101 Inc.

Beyer, Horst R. Calculus & Analysis: A Combined Approach. 2010. (ENG., Illus.). 671p. 139.00 (978-0-470-61795-3(0), Wiley) Wiley, John & Sons, Inc.

Bittinger & Cram101 Textbook Reviews Staff. Calculus & Its Applications. 2007. 108p. per. 10.95 (978-1-4288-3484-2(2)) Cram101 Inc.

Bittinger, Marvin L. Introductory Algebra. 11th ed. 2010. (Bittinger Worktext Ser.). (ENG., Illus.). 816p. (C). pap. 162.00 (978-0-321-59921-6(7)) Addison Wesley.

—Introductory Algebra. 11th ed. 2010. tchr. ed. (978-0-321-62897-8(7)) Pearson Education.

Bittinger, Marvin L. & Ellenbogen, David J. Calculus & Its Applications. 9th ed. 2007. (ENG.). (C). 408p. pap. 36.67 (978-0-321-45056-2(6)); (Illus.). 704p. 154.67 (978-0-321-39534-4(4)) Addison Wesley.

—Calculus & Its Applications plus MyMathLab Student Starter Kit. 9th ed. 2007. (ENG.). 648p. (C). pap. 164.67 (978-0-321-45413-3(8)) Addison Wesley.

Bittinger, Marvin L., et al. Calculus & Its Applications. 10th rev. ed. 2011. (ENG.). 696p. (C). 154.67 (978-0-321-69433-1(3)) Addison Wesley.

—Calculus & Its Applications, Books a la Carte Edition. 10th ed. 2011. (ENG.). (C). ring bd. 92.80 (978-0-321-73823-3(3)) Addison Wesley.

—Graphing Calculator Manual for Calculus & Its Applications. 10th rev. ed. 2011. 96p. (C). pap. 24.67 (978-0-321-74496-8(9)) Pearson Education.

—Student Solutions Manual for Calculus & Its Applications. 10th ed. 2011. 256p. (C). pap. 36.67 (978-0-321-74495-1(0)) Pearson Education.

Blank, Brian E. Calculus: Single Variable 2nd Edition (Chs 1-8) & WileyPLUS Combo Set. 2nd ed. 2011. (C). 199.95 **(978-1-118-13577-8(6))** Wiley, John & Sons, Inc.

Blank, Brian E. & Krantz, Steven G. Calculus. 2nd ed. 2011. (ENG., Illus.). 504p. (C). 181.95 (978-0-470-45359-9(1), Wiley) Wiley, John & Sons, Inc.

—Calculus: Single Variable. (ENG.). (C). 2008. 771p. pap. 136.95 (978-0-470-41277-0(1)) 2nd ed. 2011. (Illus.). 832p. 206.95 (978-0-470-60198-3(1)) Wiley, John & Sons, Inc. (Wiley).

—Calculus: Single Variable, Student Study & Solutions Companion. 2nd ed. 2011. (ENG.). 432p. (C). pap. 53.95 (978-0-470-45815-0(1), Wiley) Wiley, John & Sons, Inc.

—Calculus, Multivariable. 2008. (ENG., Illus.). 466p. (C). pap. 39.95 (978-0-470-41278-7(X), Wiley) Wiley, John & Sons, Inc.

—Calculus Multivariable. 2nd ed. 2008. (ENG.). 439p. (C). pap. 104.95 (978-0-470-41271-8(2), Wiley) Wiley, John & Sons, Inc.

—Calculus, Student Study & Solutions Companion: Single Variable. 2008. (ENG.). 816p. (C). pap., stu. ed. 41.95 (978-0-470-41282-4(8), Wiley) Wiley, John & Sons, Inc.

Blitzer & Blitzer, Robert F. Precalculus Essentials plus MyMathLab/MyStatLab Student Code Card. 3rd ed. 2010. (ENG.). (C). pap. 158.00 (978-0-321-74452-4(7)) Addison Wesley.

Boer, R. De & Schroeder, J. Tensor Calculus for Engineers: Analytical & Computational Aspects. 2008. 600p. pap. 79.95 (978-3-540-24224-6(4), 3540242244) Springer.

Bona, Miklos. Concepts in Calculus II Beta Version. 2011. (ENG.). 200p. (C). pap. 25.00 **(978-1-61610-156-5(3))** Orange Grove Bks.

Bona, Miklos & Shabanov, Sergei. Concepts in Calculus I. 2011. (ENG.). 188p. (C). pap. 25.00 **(978-1-61610-160-2(1))** Orange Grove Bks.

Bowman, Frank & Gerard, F. A. Higher Calculus. 2009. (ENG.). 436p. pap. 55.00 (978-0-521-09335-4(X)) Cambridge Univ. Pr.

Bradley, Robert E. & Sandifer, C. Edward. Cauchy's Cours d'analyse: An Annotated Translation. 2009. (Sources & Studies in the History of Mathematics & Physical Sciences Ser.). (Illus.). xx, 412p. 159.00 (978-1-4419-0548-2(0), 1441905480) Springer.

Briggs, et al. Calculus: Early Transcendentals, Books a la Carte Plus MyMathLab/MyStatLab Student Access Kit. 2010. (ENG.). (C). ring bd. 128.80 (978-0-321-72176-1(4)) Addison Wesley.

Briggs, Bill, et al. Calculus Alternate Late Transcendentals plus MyMathLab Student Access Kit. 2012. (ENG.). (C). pap. 208.00 **(978-0-321-83209-2(4))** Addison Wesley.

—Calculus for Scientists & Engineers Early Transcendentals, Books a la Carte Edition plus MyMathLab. 2012. (ENG.). (C). ring bd. 128.80 **(978-0-321-83215-3(9))** Addison Wesley.

—Calculus for Scientists & Engineers Multivariable plus MyMathLab Student Access Kit. 2012. (ENG.). (C). 208.00 **(978-0-321-83772-1(X))** Addison Wesley.

Briggs, William, et al. Calculus for Scientists & Engineers: Early Transcendentals, Books a la Carte Edition. 2012. (ENG.). 1344p. (C). ring bd. 118.80 **(978-0-321-78546-6(0))** Addison Wesley.

—Calculus for Scientists & Engineers: Early Transcendentals, Single Variable. 2012. (ENG.). 864p. (C). pap. 101.33 **(978-0-321-78550-3(9))** Addison Wesley.

—Calculus for Scientists & Engineers, Books a la Carte Edition. 2012. (ENG.). 1344p. (C). ring bd. 128.80 **(978-0-321-82672-5(8))** Addison Wesley.

—Calculus for Scientists & Engineers, Multivariable. 2012. (ENG.). 672p. (C). pap. 101.33 **(978-0-321-78551-0(7))** Addison Wesley.

—Student Solutions Manual for Calculus for Scientists & Engineers: Early Transcendentals, Multivariable. 2012. (ENG.). 400p. (C). pap. 36.67 **(978-0-321-78545-9(2))** Addison Wesley.

Briggs, William L. & Cochran, Lyle. Calculus. 2010. (Briggs/Cochran Calculus Ser.). (ENG.). 1264p. (C). 198.00 (978-0-321-33611-8(9)); ring bd. 118.80 (978-0-321-69353-2(1)) Addison Wesley.

—Calculus: Early Transcendentals. 2010. (Briggs/Cochran Calculus Ser.). (ENG., Illus.). 1216p. (C). 198.00 (978-0-321-57056-7(1)) Addison Wesley.

—Multivariable for Calculus & Calculus Pt. 2: Early Transcendentals. 2010. (ENG.). 288p. (C). pap. 36.67 (978-0-321-66411-2(6)) Addison Wesley.

—Single Variable Calculus, Pt. 1. 2010. (Briggs/Cochran Calculus Ser.). (ENG.). 650p. (C). pap. 101.33 (978-0-321-66407-5(8)) Addison Wesley.

—Single Variable for Calculus Pt. 1: Early Transcendentals. 2010. (ENG.). 384p. (C). pap. 36.67 (978-0-321-66410-5(8)) Addison Wesley.

Briggs, William L., et al. Calculus. 2010. (ENG.). (C). 850p. ring bd. 60.80 (978-0-321-69295-5(0));Pt. 2. 656p. pap. 101.33 (978-0-321-66415-0(9)) Addison Wesley.

—Calculus: Early Transcendentals. 2010. (ENG.). 1170p. (C). ring bd. 118.80 (978-0-321-69294-8(2)) Addison Wesley.

—Calculus for Scientists & Engineers. 2012. (ENG.). 1344p. (C). 198.00 **(978-0-321-82669-5(8))** Addison Wesley.

—Calculus for Scientists & Engineers, Single Variable. 2012. (ENG.). 650p. (C). pap. 101.33 **(978-0-321-82671-8(X))** Addison Wesley.

—Multivariable Calculus, Books a la Carte Edition. 2010. (ENG.). 500p. (C). ring bd. 60.80 *(978-0-321-69297-9(7))* Addison Wesley.
—Multivariable Calculus, Books a la Carte Plus MyMathLab/MyStatLab Student Access Kit. 2010. (ENG.). (C). ring bd. 104.67 *(978-0-321-73696-3(6))* Addison Wesley.
—Single Variable Calculus: Early Transcendentals. 2010. (Briggs/Cochran Calculus Ser.). (ENG.). 816p. (C). pap. 101.33 *(978-0-321-66414-3(0))* Addison Wesley.
—Single Variable Calculus: Early Transcendentals, Books a la Carte Plus MyMathLab/MyStatLab Student Access Kit. 2010. (ENG.). (C). ring bd. 104.67 *(978-0-321-71517-3(9))* Addison Wesley.
—Single Variable Calculus, Books a la Carte Edition. 2010. (ENG.). 650p. (C). ring bd. 60.80 *(978-0-321-69421-8(X))* Addison Wesley.
Brown, Jason I. Calculus Workbook. 2008. 250p. pap. 26.67 *(978-0-13-186714-7(8)*, Prentice Hall) Prentice Hall PTR.
Burgin, Mark, ed. Neoclassical Analysis: Calculus Closer to the Real World. 2008. 396p. (C). 79.00 *(978-1-60021-946-7(2))* Nova Science Pubs., Inc.
Byleen, Karl E., et al. Calculus: For Business, Economics, Life Sciences, & Social Sciences. 11th ed. 2007. (ENG., Illus.). 704p. (C). 153.33 *(978-0-13-232818-0(6)*, Prentice Hall) Prentice Hall PTR.
Cajori, Florian. A History of the Conceptions of Limits & Fluxions in Great Britain from Newton to Woodhouse. 2008. 310p. 45.95 *(978-1-4366-4580-5(8))*; 312p. pap. 30.95 *(978-0-548-89138-4(9))* Kessinger Publishing, LLC.
—A History of the Conceptions of Limits & Fluxions in Great Britain from Newton to Woodhouse. 2007. 310p. 65.00 *(978-1-57898-598-2(6))* Martino Publishing.
—A History of the Conceptions of Limits & Fluxions in Great Britain, from Newton to Woodhouse. (Illus.). reprint ed. lib. bdg. *(978-0-7222-3039-8(7))* Library Reprints, Inc.
Calculus: For Science & Engineering Students. 2011. 88.00 *(978-981-4291-48-4(X))*; pap. 48.00 *(978-981-4291-49-1(8))* World Scientific Publishing Co., Inc.
Callahan, James. Calculus in Context. tchr. ed., instr.'s hndbk. ed. 24.00 *(978-0-7167-2683-8(1))* Freeman, W. H. & Co.
Callahan, James J. Advanced Calculus: A Geometric View. 2010. (Undergraduate Texts in Mathematics Ser.). (Illus.). xvi, 526p. 84.95 *(978-1-4419-7331-3(1)*, 1441973311) Springer.
Calter, Michael A. Technical Mathematics with Calculus 6th Edition with Student Solutions Manua Math 6th Edition & Tech Math 6th Edition Set. 6th ed. 2011. (C). 209.95 ***(978-1-118-11834-4(0))*** Wiley, John & Sons, Inc.
Calter, Michael A. & Calter, Paul A. Technical Mathematics with Calculus, Fifth Edition & Technical Mathematics, Fifth Edition Student Solutions Manual. 5th ed. 2007. (ENG., Illus.). 379p. (C). pap. 66.95 *(978-0-471-69596-7(3)*, Wiley) Wiley, John & Sons, Inc.
Calter, P. A. Technical Mathematics. 5th ed. 2006. 94.00 net. *(978-0-470-14445-9(9))* Wiley, John & Sons, Inc.
Calter, Paul A. & Calter, Michael A. Technical Mathematics with Calculus, Test Bank. 5th ed. 2008. 812p. pap. 0.01 *(978-0-470-05285-3(6))* Wiley, John & Sons, Inc.
—Technical Mathematics with Calculus, Textbook & Student Solutions Manual. 2006. (ENG.). (C). 1388p. 232.95 *(978-0-470-14066-6(6))*; 224.95 *(978-0-470-14067-3(4))* Wiley, John & Sons, Inc. (Wiley).
Campbell & Dierker. Calculus. 2nd ed. Date not set. (Mathematics Ser.). tchr. ed. 7.75 net. *(978-0-87150-579-8(7))*; suppl. ed. 7.75 net. *(978-0-87150-264-3(X))* Brooks/Cole. (Brooks/Cole).
Carlen, Eric & Loss, Michael. Calculus for a Scientific Curriculum. 2014. (ENG.). 504p. (C). 93.95 *(978-0-7167-4892-2(4))* Freeman, W. H. & Co.
—Multivariable Calculus. 2014. (ENG.). 504p. (C). 87.95 *(978-0-7167-4890-8(8))* Freeman, W. H. & Co.
—Multivariable Calculus for a Scientific Curriculum. 2008. (ENG.). 504p. (C). 80.95 *(978-0-7167-8591-0(9))* Freeman, W. H. & Co.
Carroll, R. W. Calculus Revisited. 2010. (Mathematics & Its Applications Ser.). 528p. pap. 269.00 *(978-1-4419-5237-0(3)*, 1441952373) Springer.
Cates, Dennis M. A Guide to Cauchy's Calculus: A Translation & Analysis of Calcul Infinitesimal. 2011. (ENG., Illus.). 616p. 139.00 ***(978-0-9838837-0-8(X))*** Fairview Academic Pr.
Church, Albert E. (Albert Ensign). Elements of the Differential & Integral Calculus. 2006. 396p. per. 26.99 *(978-1-4255-4197-2(6))* MPublishing.
—Elements of the Differential & Integral Calculus Arranged by Albert E Church. 2006. 360p. per. 26.99 *(978-1-4255-3701-2(4))* MPublishing.
Clark, James Gregory. Elements of the Infinitesimal Calculus, with Numerous Examples & Applications to Analysis & Geometry by James G Clark. 2006. 448p. per. 26.99 *(978-1-4255-4935-0(7))* MPublishing.
Coburn, John. Precalculus. 2nd ed. 2009. (ENG.). 1216p. (C). 185.67 *(978-0-07-727650-8(7)*, 0077276507, McGraw-Hill Science, Engineering & Mathematics) McGraw-Hill Higher Education.
Cochran, Lyle, et al. Calculus for Scientists & Engineers: Early Transcendentals. 2012. (ENG.). 1344p. (C). 198.00 ***(978-0-321-78537-4(1))*** Addison Wesley.
Cohen, David, et al. Precalculus. 7th ed. 2011. (Precalculus Ser.). (ENG.). 1184p. (C). 234.95 ***(978-0-8400-6942-9(1))*** Brooks/Cole.
Colley & Cram101 Textbook Reviews Staff. Vector Calculus. 2007. 144p. per. 11.95 ***(978-1-4288-3684-6(5))*** Cram101 Inc.
Connally, Eric. Functions Modeling Change: A Preparation for Calculus 3rd Edition with Functions Modling Change 3rd Edition Desktop Edition Set. 2008. 240.85 *(978-0-470-39862-3(0))* Wiley, John & Sons, Inc.
—Functions Modeling Change: A Preparation for Calculus 3rd Edition with WebAssign 1 Semester Set. 2008. (ENG.). (C). pap. 182.95 *(978-0-470-40396-9(9)*, Wiley) Wiley, John & Sons, Inc.
—Functions Modeling Change, Textbook & Student Solutions Manual: A Preparation for Calculus. 3rd ed. 2006. (ENG.). 808p. (C). pap. 186.95 *(978-0-470-14064-2(X)*, Wiley) Wiley, John & Sons, Inc.
Connally, Eric & Hughes-Hallett, Deborah. Functions Modeling Change: A Preparation for Calculus. 3rd ed. 2007. (Wiley Plus Products Ser.). pap. 68.95 *(978-0-470-10243-5(8))* Wiley, John & Sons, Inc.
Connally, Eric, et al. Functions Modeling Change: A Preparation for Calculus. 3rd rev. ed. 2006. (ENG., Illus.). 624p. (C). 204.95 *(978-0-471-79302-1(7)*, Wiley) Wiley, John & Sons, Inc.
Consumer Dummies Staff. Calculus for Dummies Education Bundle. 2008. pap. 29.99 *(978-0-470-43101-6(6)*, For Dummies) Wiley, John & Sons, Inc.
Cooper, Daryl. Calculus & Mathematical Reasoning for Social & Life Sciences. rev. ed. 2010. (ENG.). 330p. pap. 34.81 *(978-0-7872-8698-9(2))* Kendall Hunt Publishing Co.
Courant, Richard. Differential & Integral Calculus, Vol. 2. McShane, Edward James, tr. from GER. 2010. (Illus.). 692p. (C). pap. 39.95 *(978-4-87187-835-7(X))* Ishi Pr. International.
—Differential & Integral Calculus, Vol. One. McShane, Edward James, tr. from GER. 2010. (ENG., Illus.). 668p. (C). pap. *(978-4-87187-838-8(4))* Ishi Pr. International.
Courtenay, Edward Henry. A Treatise on the Differential & Integral Calculus, & on the Calculus of Variations by Edward H Courtenay. 2006. 512p. per. 29.99 *(978-1-4255-5741-6(4))*; (ENG.). per. 29.99 *(978-1-4255-5742-3(2))* MPublishing.
Cram101 Textbook Reviews. Outlines & Highlights for Advanced Calculus: A Transition to Analysis by Thomas P. Dence. 2011. 150p. pap. 29.95 ***(978-1-61905-107-2(9))*** Cram101 Inc.
—Outlines & Highlights for Advanced Calculus: An Introduction to Linear Analysis by Leonard F. Richardson. 2011. 166p. pap. 29.95 ***(978-1-61905-157-7(5))*** Cram101 Inc.
—Outlines & Highlights for Applied Calculus for the Life & Social Sciences by Ron Larson, Isbn: 9780618962594. 2010. 182p. pap. 29.95 *(978-1-61698-034-4(6))* Cram101 Inc.
—Outlines & Highlights for Calculus: Early Transcendental Functions. 2011. 462p. pap. 36.95 ***(978-1-61830-976-1(5))*** Cram101 Inc.
—Outlines & Highlights for Calculus: Early Transcendentals by Jon Rogawski, ISBN. 2010. 554p. pap. 38.95 *(978-1-61698-010-8(9))* Cram101 Inc.
—Outlines & Highlights for Calculus: Early Transcendentals by William L. Briggs. 2011. 638p. pap. 40.95 ***(978-1-61905-049-5(8))*** Cram101 Inc.
—Outlines & Highlights for Calculus: Single & Multivariable by Brian E. Blank. 2011. 422p. pap. 35.95 ***(978-1-61830-977-8(3))*** Cram101 Inc.
—Outlines & Highlights for Calculus: Single & Multivariable by Deborah Hughes-Hallett, ISBN. 2010. 246p. pap. 31.95 *(978-1-61698-839-5(8))* Cram101 Inc.
—Outlines & Highlights for Calculus: Single Variable by Brian E. Blank. 2011. 386p. pap. 34.95 ***(978-1-61830-980-8(3))*** Cram101 Inc.
—Outlines & Highlights for Calculus, 1st Edition by Soo T Tan. 2011. 488p. pap. 37.95 ***(978-1-61905-048-8(X))*** Cram101 Inc.
—Outlines & Highlights for Calculus & Its Applications by Marvin L Bittinger. 2011. 200p. pap. 30.95 ***(978-1-61905-043-3(9))*** Cram101 Inc.
—Outlines & Highlights for Calculus by James Stewart. 2011. 372p. pap. 34.95 ***(978-1-61905-042-6(0))*** Cram101 Inc.
—Outlines & Highlights for Calculus by William L Briggs. 2011. 584p. pap. 39.95 ***(978-1-61905-030-3(7))*** Cram101 Inc.
—Outlines & Highlights for Calculus Concepts: An Informal Approach to the Mathematics of Change by Donald R. Latorre. 2011. 178p. pap. 29.95 ***(978-1-61905-031-0(5))*** Cram101 Inc.
—Outlines & Highlights for Calculus I by Ron Larson. 2011. 284p. pap. 32.95 ***(978-1-61905-044-0(7))*** Cram101 Inc.
—Outlines & Highlights for Calculus Multivariable by Brian E Blank. 2011. 202p. pap. 30.95 ***(978-1-61905-016-7(1))*** Cram101 Inc.
—Outlines & Highlights for Calculus of a Single Variable: Early Transcendental Functions by Ron Larson. 2011. 350p. pap. 33.95 ***(978-1-61905-047-1(1))*** Cram101 Inc.
—Outlines & Highlights for Essential Calculus: Early Transcendental Functions by Ron Larson, ISBN. 2010. 298p. pap. 32.95 *(978-1-4288-4340-0(X))* Cram101 Inc.
—Outlines & Highlights for Multivariable Calculus by James Stewart. 2011. 292p. pap. 32.95 ***(978-1-4672-4131-1(8))*** Cram101 Inc.
—Outlines & Highlights for Professional Calculus, Single Variable by Carl V Lutzer. 2011. 226p. pap. 30.95 ***(978-1-4672-4661-3(1))*** Cram101 Inc.
—Outlines & Highlights for Single Variable Calculus: Early Transcendentals by James Stewart. 2011. 402p. pap. 35.95 ***(978-1-4672-5185-3(2))*** Cram101 Inc.
—Outlines & Highlights for Single Variable Calculus: Early Transcendentals by William L. Briggs. 2011. 514p. pap. 37.95 ***(978-1-4672-0575-7(3))*** Cram101 Inc.
—Outlines & Highlights for Single Variable Calculus, Volume 1 by James Stewart. 2011. 180p. pap. 29.95 ***(978-1-4672-4669-9(7))*** Cram101 Inc.
—Outlines & Highlights for Single Variable Calculus, Volume 2 by James Stewart. 2011. 248p. pap. 31.95 ***(978-1-4672-4731-3(6))*** Cram101 Inc.
—Outlines & Highlights for Thomas Calculus by George B Thomas. 2011. 518p. pap. 37.95 ***(978-1-4672-1860-3(X))*** Cram101 Inc.
—Outlines & Highlights for University Calculus, Early Transcendentals, Multivariable by Joel Hass. 2011. 264p. pap. 31.95 ***(978-1-4672-1896-2(0))*** Cram101 Inc.
Cram101 Textbook Reviews & Cram101 Textbook Reviews. Outlines & Highlights for Applied Calculus for the Managerial, Life, & Social Sciences: A Brief Approach by Soo Tan, ISBN. 2011. 120p. pap. 28.95 ***(978-1-61461-306-0(0))*** Cram101 Inc.
Cram101 Textbook Reviews Staff. Outlines & Highlights for Applied Calculus by Berresford, Rockett, Isbn: 9780547169781. 2009. 132p. pap. 28.95 *(978-1-4288-2861-2(3))* Cram101 Inc.
—Outlines & Highlights for Applied Calculus by Frank C Wilson, Scott Adamson, Isbn: 9780618611041. 2009. 158p. pap. 29.95 *(978-1-4288-2673-1(4))* Cram101 Inc.
—Outlines & Highlights for Applied Calculus by Hughes-Hallett / Lock / Gleason / Flath / Gordon / Lomen / Lovelock, Isbn: 9780471681212. 2009. 96p. pap. 27.95 *(978-1-4288-3633-4(0))* Cram101 Inc.
—Outlines & Highlights for Applied Calculus by Tan, Isbn: 053446503x. 2009. 58p. pap. 26.95 *(978-1-4288-3927-4(5))* Cram101 Inc.
—Outlines & Highlights for Applied Calculus, Enhanced Review Edition by Stefan Waner, Steven Costenoble, Isbn: 9780495384281. 2009. 82p. pap. 27.95 *(978-1-4288-3685-3(3))* Cram101 Inc.
—Outlines & Highlights for Applied Calculus for Business, Economics, & the Social & Life Sciences, Expanded Edition by Hoffmann, Bradley, Isbn: 978. 2009. 56p. pap. 26.95 *(978-1-4288-2871-1(0))*; 174p. pap. 29.95 *(978-1-4288-7591-3(3))* Cram101 Inc.
—Outlines & Highlights for Applied Calculus for the Life & Social Sciences, Enhanced Edition by Larson, Isbn: 9781439047835. 2009. 124p. pap. 28.95 *(978-1-4288-2809-4(5))*; 154p. pap. 29.95 *(978-1-4288-7620-0(0))* Cram101 Inc.
—Outlines & Highlights for Applied Calculus for the Managerial, Life, & Social Sciences by Soo T Tan, Isbn: 9780495015826. 2009. 98p. pap. 27.95 *(978-1-4288-3627-3(6))* Cram101 Inc.
—Outlines & Highlights for Applied Calculus for the Managerial, Life, & Social Sciences by Soo T Tan, Isbn: 9780495387541. 2009. 62p. pap. 27.95 *(978-1-4288-3647-1(0))* Cram101 Inc.
—Outlines & Highlights for Brief Applied Calculus by Berresford & Rockett, Isbn: 9780547169774. 2009. 86p. pap. 27.95 *(978-1-4288-2827-8(3))*; 58p. pap. 26.95 *(978-1-4288-7610-1(3))* Cram101 Inc.
—Outlines & Highlights for Brief Calculus: An Applied Approach 8e by Ron Larson, ISBN. 2009. 106p. pap. 28.95 *(978-1-4288-3635-8(7))* Cram101 Inc.
—Outlines & Highlights for Brief Calculus: An Applied Approach by Ron Larson, Bruce H. Edwards, ISBN. 2009. 60p. pap. 26.95 *(978-1-4288-3708-9(6))* Cram101 Inc.
—Outlines & Highlights for Brief Calculus: An Applied Approach, Enhanced Edition by Larson & Edwards, ISBN. 2009. 104p. pap. 28.95 *(978-1-4288-2795-0(1))*; 116p. pap. 28.95 *(978-1-4288-8471-7(8))* Cram101 Inc.
—Outlines & Highlights for Brief Calculus & Its Application by Larry J Goldstein, David I Schneider, Asmar, David I, Isbn: 9780131919655. 2009. 70p. pap. 27.95 *(978-1-4288-3707-2(8))* Cram101 Inc.
—Outlines & Highlights for Brief Calculus & Its Applications by Larry J Goldstein, David I Schneider, David C Lay, Nakhle H Asmar, Isbn: 9780321568. 2009. 88p. pap. 27.95 *(978-1-4288-3659-4(4))* Cram101 Inc.
—Outlines & Highlights for Calculus: An Applied Approach by Ron Larson, Robert P. Hostetler, David C. Falvo, ISBN. 2009. 100p. pap. 27.95 *(978-1-4288-3693-8(4))* Cram101 Inc.
—Outlines & Highlights for Calculus: An Applied Approach, Enhanced Edition by Larson, ISBN. 2009. 160p. pap. 29.95 *(978-1-4288-8653-7(2))* Cram101 Inc.
—Outlines & Highlights for Calculus: Applied Approach by Ron Larson, ISBN. 2009. 138p. pap. 28.95 *(978-1-4288-2753-0(6))*; 226p. pap. 29.95 *(978-1-4288-8677-3(X))* Cram101 Inc.
—Outlines & Highlights for Calculus: Concepts & Contexts - Enhanced - with 2 CDs by James Stewart, ISBN. 2009. 250p. pap. 31.95 *(978-1-4288-1999-3(1))* Cram101 Inc.
—Outlines & Highlights for Calculus: Concepts & Contexts by James Stewart, ISBN. 2009. 310p. pap. 32.95 *(978-1-4288-8732-9(6))* Cram101 Inc.
—Outlines & Highlights for Calculus: Concepts & Contexts by Stewart, ISBN. 2009. 184p. pap. 29.95 *(978-1-4288-3934-2(8))* Cram101 Inc.
—Outlines & Highlights for Calculus: Concepts & Contexts, Enhanced Review Edition by James Stewart, ISBN. 2009. 208p. pap. 30.95 *(978-1-4288-1977-1(0))* Cram101 Inc.
—Outlines & Highlights for Calculus: Early Transcendental Function by Robert T. Smith, ISBN. 2009. 302p. pap. 32.95 *(978-1-4288-2769-1(2))*; 454p. pap. 32.95 *(978-1-4288-8667-4(2))* Cram101 Inc.
—Outlines & Highlights for Calculus: Early Transcendental Functions by Ron Larson, Bruce H. Edwards, Robert P. Hostetler, ISBN. 2009. 258p. pap. 31.95 *(978-1-4288-3641-9(1))* Cram101 Inc.
—Outlines & Highlights for Calculus: Early Transcendental Functions, Enhanced Edition by Larson, Hostetler, & Edwards, ISBN. 2009. 244p. pap. 31.95 *(978-1-4288-2813-1(3))* Cram101 Inc.
—Outlines & Highlights for Calculus: Early Transcendentals Single Variable by Howard Anton, ISBN. 2009. 174p. pap. 29.95 *(978-1-4288-2257-3(7))* Cram101 Inc.
—Outlines & Highlights for Calculus: Late Transcendentals Single & Multivariable by Howard Anton, ISBN. 2009. 258p. pap. 31.95 *(978-1-4288-1983-2(5))* Cram101 Inc.
—Outlines & Highlights for Calculus: Multivariable by Howard Anton, Stephen Davis, Irl C. Bivens, ISBN. 2009. 228p. pap. 31.95 *(978-1-4288-3665-5(9))* Cram101 Inc.
—Outlines & Highlights for Calculus: Multivariable by Lock, ISBN. 2009. 90p. pap. 27.95 *(978-1-4288-2911-4(3))*; 128p. pap. 28.95 *(978-1-4288-7810-5(6))* Cram101 Inc.
—Outlines & Highlights for Calculus: Multivariable Early Transcendental Functions by Smith, ISBN. 2009. 100p. pap. 27.95 *(978-1-4288-2003-6(5))* Cram101 Inc.
—Outlines & Highlights for Calculus: One Variable by Saturnino L. Salas, ISBN. 2009. 124p. pap. 28.95 *(978-1-4288-1951-1(7))* Cram101 Inc.
—Outlines & Highlights for Calculus: Single & Multivariable by Deborah Hughes-Hallett, ISBN. 2009. 124p. pap. 28.95 *(978-1-4288-2375-4(1))* Cram101 Inc.
—Outlines & Highlights for Calculus: Single Variable by Hughes-Hallett, Deborah, ISBN. 2009. 134p. pap. 28.95 *(978-1-4288-3609-9(8))* Cram101 Inc.
—Outlines & Highlights for Calculus: Single Variable by Smith, ISBN. 2009. 220p. pap. 30.95 *(978-1-4288-1985-6(1))* Cram101 Inc.
—Outlines & Highlights for Calculus & Its Applications by Larry J Goldstein, David I Schneider, David C Lay, Nakhle H Asmar, Isbn: 9780321571304. 2009. 112p. pap. 28.95 *(978-1-4288-2661-8(0))*; 120p. pap. 28.95 *(978-1-4288-7836-5(X))* Cram101 Inc.
—Outlines & Highlights for Calculus by Houghton Mifflin, Isbn: 9780618634088. 2009. 252p. pap. 31.95 *(978-1-4288-2055-5(8))* Cram101 Inc.
—Outlines & Highlights for Calculus by James Stewart, Isbn: 9780495011606. 2009. 156p. pap. 29.95 *(978-1-4288-3653-2(5))* Cram101 Inc.
—Outlines & Highlights for Calculus by Minton, Roland B & Smith, Robert T, Isbn: 9780073312705. 2009. 326p. pap. 33.95 *(978-1-4288-8708-4(3))* Cram101 Inc.
—Outlines & Highlights for Calculus by Ron Larson, Isbn: 9780547167022. 2009. 266p. pap. 31.95 *(978-1-4288-2283-2(6))*; 122p. pap. 28.95 *(978-1-4288-9952-0(9))* Cram101 Inc.
—Outlines & Highlights for Calculus by Smith & Minton, Isbn: 007283093x. 2009. 244p. pap. 31.95 *(978-1-4288-3945-8(3))* Cram101 Inc.
—Outlines & Highlights for Calculus, Classic Edition by Earl W Swokowski, Isbn: 9780534435387. 2009. 150p. pap. 29.95 *(978-1-4288-1987-0(8))* Cram101 Inc.
—Outlines & Highlights for Calculus, Early Transcendentals, Single Variable, Volume 1 by James Stewart, Isbn: 9780495384250. 2009. 106p. pap. 28.95 *(978-1-4288-3623-5(3))* Cram101 Inc.
—Outlines & Highlights for Calculus, Early Vectors by James Stewart, Isbn: 9780534493486. 2009. 238p. pap. 31.95 *(978-1-4288-2005-0(1))* Cram101 Inc.
—Outlines & Highlights for Calculus for Business, Economics, & the Social & Life Sciences, Brief by Laurence Hoffmann, Isbn: 9780077292737. 2009. 100p. pap. 27.95 *(978-1-4288-2501-7(0))*; 108p. pap. 28.95 *(978-1-4288-8958-3(2))* Cram101 Inc.
—Outlines & Highlights for Calculus for Life Sciences by Marvin L Bittinger, Isbn: 9780321279354. 2009. 88p. pap. 27.95 *(978-1-4288-3683-9(7))* Cram101 Inc.
—Outlines & Highlights for Calculus for the Managerial, Life, & Social Sciences by Soo T Tan, Isbn: 9780534419868. 2009. 66p. pap. 27.95 *(978-1-4288-1981-8(9))* Cram101 Inc.
—Outlines & Highlights for Calculus Late Transcendentals Combined by Davis, Isbn: 9780470183496. 2009. 62p. pap. 27.95 *(978-1-4288-2803-2(6))*; 308p. pap. 32.95 *(978-1-4288-7642-2(1))* Cram101 Inc.
—Outlines & Highlights for Calculus Late Transcendentals Single Variable by Davis, Isbn: 9780470183472. 2009. 164p. pap. 29.95 *(978-1-4288-2903-9(2))*; 212p. pap. 30.95 *(978-1-4288-7814-3(9))* Cram101 Inc.
—Outlines & Highlights for Calculus Multivariable by Davis, Isbn: 9780470183465. 2009. 90p. pap. 27.95 *(978-1-4288-2905-3(9))*; 106p. pap. 28.95 *(978-1-4288-7813-6(0))* Cram101 Inc.
—Outlines & Highlights for Calculus Multivariable by Larson & Edwards, Isbn: 9780547209975. 2009. 110p. pap. 28.95 *(978-1-4288-2907-7(5))*; 120p. pap. 28.95 *(978-1-4288-7812-9(2))* Cram101 Inc.
—Outlines & Highlights for Calculus, Multivariable Calculus: Early Transcendentals by James Stewart, ISBN. 2009. 154p. pap. 29.95 *(978-1-4288-2731-8(5))* Cram101 Inc.
—Outlines & Highlights for Calculus of a Single Variable: Early Transcendental Functions by Ron Larson, Bruce H. Edwards, Robert P. Hostetler, ISBN. 2009. 156p. pap. 29.95 *(978-1-4288-3700-3(0))* Cram101 Inc.
—Outlines & Highlights for Calculus of a Single Variable by Larson & Edwards, Isbn: 9780547209982. 2009. 86p. pap. 27.95 *(978-1-4288-2909-1(1))*; 216p. pap. 30.95 *(978-1-4288-7811-2(4))* Cram101 Inc.
—Outlines & Highlights for Calculus of a Single Variable by Ron Larson, Isbn: 9780618503032. 2009. 166p. pap. 29.95 *(978-1-4288-2285-6(2))*; 80p. pap. 27.95 *(978-1-4288-9951-3(0))* Cram101 Inc.
—Outlines & Highlights for Calculus, Single Variable: Late Transcendental Functions by Minton, Roland B. & Smith, Robert T., ISBN. 2009. 194p. pap. 30.95 *(978-1-4288-2755-4(2))*; 208p. pap. 30.95 *(978-1-4288-8676-6(1))* Cram101 Inc.
—Outlines & Highlights for Calculus with Applications: Brief Edition by Lial & Greenwell & Ritchey, ISBN. 2009. 82p. pap. 27.95 *(978-1-4288-3943-4(7))* Cram101 Inc.

C

—Outlines & Highlights for Calculus with Applications by Lial, Margaret L , Isbn: 9780321421326. 2009. 128p. pap. 28.95 *(978-1-4288-3681-5(0))* Cram101 Inc.
—Outlines & Highlights for Calculus with Applications by Margaret L Lial, Raymond N Greenwell, Nathan P Ritchey, Isbn: 9780321422743. 2009. 76p. pap. 27.95 *(978-1-4288-3710-2(8))* Cram101 Inc.
—Outlines & Highlights for College Algebra & Calculus: An Applied Approach by Larson, ISBN. 2009. 238p. pap. 31.95 *(978-1-4288-7807-5(6))* Cram101 Inc.
—Outlines & Highlights for Companion to Calculus by Dennis C Ebersole, Isbn: 9780495011248. 2009. 80p. pap. 27.95 *(978-1-4288-3982-3(8))* Cram101 Inc.
—Outlines & Highlights for Concepts of Calculus with Applications, Updated by Martha Goshaw, Isbn: 9780321577443. 2009. 126p. pap. 28.95 *(978-1-4288-1949-8(5))* Cram101 Inc.
—Outlines & Highlights for Essential Calculus: Early Transcendentals by Stewart, James, ISBN. 2009. 234p. pap. 31.95 *(978-1-4288-3669-3(1))* Cram101 Inc.
—Outlines & Highlights for Essential Calculus by D Franklin Wright, Isbn: 9780918091956. 2009. 84p. pap. 27.95 *(978-1-4288-3273-2(4))* Cram101 Inc.
—Outlines & Highlights for Essential Calculus by James Stewart, Isbn: 9780495014423. 2009. 224p. pap. 30.95 *(978-1-4288-3661-7(6))* Cram101 Inc.
—Outlines & Highlights for Finite Mathematics & Calculus with Applications by Margaret L Lial, Raymond N Greenwell, Nathan P Ritchey, Isbn: 978032. 2009. 272p. pap. 32.95 *(978-1-4288-3485-9(0))* Cram101 Inc.
—Outlines & Highlights for Multivariable Calculus: Early Transcendentals by Jon Rogawski, ISBN. 2009. 192p. pap. 30.95 *(978-1-4288-2113-2(9))* Cram101 Inc.
—Outlines & Highlights for Multivariable Calculus by James Stewart, Isbn: 9780495011637. 2009. 164p. pap. 29.95 *(978-1-4288-8991-0(4))* Cram101 Inc.
—Outlines & Highlights for Multivariable Calculus by Ron Larson, Isbn: 9780618503025. 2009. 90p. pap. 27.95 *(978-1-4288-2725-7(0))*; 88p. pap. 27.95 *(978-1-4288-8706-0(7))* Cram101 Inc.
—Outlines & Highlights for Single Variable Calculus: Chapters 5-12 by James Stewart, ISBN. 2009. 106p. pap. 28.95 *(978-1-4288-3671-6(3))* Cram101 Inc.
—Outlines & Highlights for Single Variable Calculus: Concepts & Contexts by James Stewart, ISBN. 2009. 174p. pap. 29.95 *(978-1-4288-3649-5(7))*; 234p. pap. 31.95 *(978-1-4288-7667-5(7))* Cram101 Inc.
—Outlines & Highlights for Single Variable Calculus: Early Transcendentals by Jon Rogawski, ISBN. 2009. 252p. pap. 31.95 *(978-1-4288-2179-8(1))* Cram101 Inc.
—Outlines & Highlights for Single Variable Calculus: Early Transcendentals by Stewart, ISBN. 2009. 256p. pap. 31.95 *(978-1-4288-6741-3(4))* Cram101 Inc.
—Outlines & Highlights for Single Variable Calculus: Early Transcendentals, Volume 2 by James Stewart, ISBN. 2009. 98p. pap. 27.95 *(978-1-4288-3637-2(3))*; 124p. pap. 28.95 *(978-1-4288-7666-8(9))* Cram101 Inc.
—Outlines & Highlights for Single Variable Calculus by James Stewart, Isbn: 9780495011613. 2009. 206p. pap. 30.95 *(978-1-4288-3615-0(2))* Cram101 Inc.
—Outlines & Highlights for Single Variable Essential Calculus: Early Transcendentals by James Stewart, ISBN. 2009. 152p. pap. 29.95 *(978-1-4288-2323-5(9))*; 82p. pap. 27.95 *(978-1-4288-9854-7(9))* Cram101 Inc.
—Outlines & Highlights for Thomas Calculus by George B Thomas, Isbn: 9780321489876. 2009. 224p. pap. 30.95 *(978-1-4288-2371-6(9))*; 102p. pap. 27.95 *(978-1-4288-9763-2(1))* Cram101 Inc.
—Outlines & Highlights for Thomas Calculus Early Transcendentals by Weir, Maurice D , Isbn: 9780321495754. 2009. 196p. pap. 30.95 *(978-1-4288-3651-8(9))* Cram101 Inc.
—Outlines & Highlights for Thomascalculus, Pt 1 by George B Thomas, Isbn: 9780321498755. 2009. 164p. pap. 29.95 *(978-1-4288-2061-6(2))* Cram101 Inc.
—Outlines & Highlights for University Calculus: Elements with Early Transcendentals by Joel Hass, George B. Thomas, Maurice D. Weir, ISBN. 2009. 114p. pap. 28.95 *(978-1-4288-3655-6(1))* Cram101 Inc.
—Outlines & Highlights for University Calculus by Joel Hass, Isbn: 9780321350145. 2009. 250p. pap. 31.95 *(978-1-4288-2687-8(4))*; 238p. pap. 31.95 *(978-1-4288-9049-7(1))* Cram101 Inc.
Curien, Pierre-Louis. Typed Lambada Calculi & Applications: 9th International Conference, TLCA 2009, Brasilia, Brazil, July 1-3, 2009, Proceedings. 2009. (Lecture Notes in Computer Science / Theoretical Computer Science & General Issues Ser.). xiii, 417p. pap. 89.95 *(978-3-642-02272-2(3)*, 3642022723) Springer.
Damiano. Multivariable Calculus. rev. ed. 2011. 544p. 145.95 *(978-0-7637-8247-4(5))* Jones & Bartlett Learning, LLC.
Daniels, Mark. The Effect of Implementing a University Content-Methods Calculus I Course. 2008. 124p. pap. *(978-3-639-01611-6(4))* VDM Verlag Dr. Mueller e.K.
Das, Shantanu. Functional Fractional Calculus. 2nd ed. 2011. (Illus.). xxviii, 616p. 229.00 *(978-3-642-20544-6(5)*, 3642205445) Springer.
—Functional Fractional Calculus for System Identification & Controls. 2010. (ENG., Illus.). xviii, 240p. pap. 159.00 *(978-3-642-09178-0(4)*, 3642091784) Springer.
Davies, Charles. Elements of the Differential & Integral Calculus by Charles Davies. 2006. 288p. per. 23.99 *(978-1-4255-2676-4(4))* MPublishing.
De Morgan, Augustus. Differential & Integral Calculus. 2006. 156p. per. *(978-1-4067-3675-5(9)*, Hesperides Pr.) Read Bks.
Dence, Joseph B. & Dence, Thomas P. Advanced Calculus: A Transition to Analysis. 2009. (ENG., Illus.). 392p. (C). 110.00 *(978-0-12-374955-0(7)*, Academic Pr.) Elsevier Science & Technology Bks.
Diefenderfer, Caren & Nelsen, Roger B., eds. The Calculus Collection: A Resource for AP* & Beyond. 2009. (ENG.). 528p. 49.95 net. *(978-0-88385-761-8(8))* Mathematical Assn. of America.
Diethelm, Kai. The Analysis of Fractional Differential Equations: An Application-Oriented Exposition Using Differential Operators of Caputo Type. 2010. (Lecture Notes in Mathematics Ser.). (Illus.). viii, 247p. pap. 59.95 *(978-3-642-14573-5(6)*, 3642145736) Springer.
Downing, Douglas. E-Z Calculus. 5th rev. ed. 2010. (Barron's E-Z Ser.). (ENG.). 504p. pap. 16.99 *(978-0-7641-4461-5(8))* Barron's Educational Series, Inc.
Dugopolski, Mark. Fundamentals of Precalculus. 2nd ed. 2008. (Dugopolski Precalculus Ser.). (ENG., Illus.). 528p. (C). 148.00 *(978-0-321-50697-9(9))* Addison Wesley.
—Fundamentals of Precalculus. 2007. tchr. ed. *(978-0-321-53675-4(4))* Pearson Education.
Edwards & Penney & Cram101 Textbook Reviews Staff. Calculus: Early Transcendentals Version. 2007. 220p. per. 13.95 *(978-1-4288-3550-4(4))* Cram101 Inc.
Edwards, Bruce H. Larson Essential Calculus Student Solution Guide Volume One. 2007. (ENG., Illus.). 384p. (C). per. 68.95 *(978-0-618-87919-9(6)*, 332151) Brooks/Cole.
Edwards, Bruce H. & Larson, Ron. Essential Calculus: Early Transcendental Functions. 2007. (ENG., Illus.). 208p. (C). per. 68.95 *(978-0-618-87920-5(X)*, 332152) Brooks/Cole.
Edwards, Bruce H., et al. Calculus: Early Transcendental Functions. 2007. 220p. per. 13.95 *(978-1-4288-3452-1(4))* Cram101 Inc.
Eriksson, Kenneth, et al. Applied Mathematics: Body & Soul: Volume 1: Derivatives & Geometry in IR3. 2010. (ENG., Illus.). xliv, 426p. pap. 69.95 *(978-3-642-05659-8(8)*, 3642056598) Springer.
—Applied Mathematics: Body & Soul: Volume 3: Calculus in Several Dimensions. 2010. (ENG., Illus.). xliv, 428p. pap. 69.95 *(978-3-642-05660-4(1)*, 3642056601) Springer.
Etgen, Garret J., et al. Calculus: One & Several Variables. 10th rev. ed. 2006. (ENG., Illus.). 1168p. (C). 259.95 *(978-0-471-69804-3(0)*, Wiley) Wiley, John & Sons, Inc.
Eunice Kolitsoe, Moru. Epistemological Obstacles in Understanding the Idea of Limit. 2010. 248p. pap. *(978-3-8383-1681-9(9))* Lambert Academic Publishing.
Faires, Defranza & Cram101 Textbook Reviews Staff. Precalculus. 2007. (ENG.). 100p. per. 10.95 *(978-1-4288-3652-5(7))* Cram101 Inc.
Finney, Ross L. Calculus: Graphical, Numerical, Algebraic. 4th ed. 2011. *(978-0-13-317857-9(9))* Addison-Wesley Longman, Inc.
—Calculus: Graphical, Numerical, Algebraic. 3rd ed. 2009. *(978-0-13-368840-5(2))*; *(978-0-13-368839-9(9))* Prentice Hall PTR.
Fisher, Irving. A Brief Introduction to the Infinitesimal Calculus. 2007. (ENG.). 108p. 33.95 *(978-0-548-15870-8(3))*; 96p. per. 18.95 *(978-1-4304-5381-9(8))* Kessinger Publishing, LLC.
—A Brief Introduction to the Infinitesimal Calculus. 2007. 100p. per. 12.95 *(978-1-933998-68-8(7)*, Merchant Bks.) Rough Draft Printing.
—A Brief Introduction to the Infinitesimal Calculus. 2011. 97p. pap. 9.95 ***(978-1-4585-0131-8(0))*** Univ. of Michigan Library.
Fitzpatrick, Patrick M. Advanced Calculus. 2nd rev. ed. 2009. (Pure & Applied Undergraduate Texts Ser.). (Illus.). 590p. 82.00 *(978-0-8218-4791-6(0))* American Mathematical Society.
Flath, Daniel E., et al. Applied Calculus. 4th ed. 2009. (ENG.). 560p. (C). pap. 165.95 *(978-0-470-17052-6(2)*, Wiley) Wiley, John & Sons, Inc.
Flynt, John P. & Meltreger, Boris. Beginning Math Concepts for Game Developers. 2006. (Applied Mathematics Ser.). (ENG., Illus.). 336p. pap. 29.99 *(978-1-59863-290-3(6))* Course Technology.
Folland & Cram101 Textbook Reviews Staff. Advanced Calculus. 2007. 120p. per. 11.95 *(978-1-4288-3384-5(6))* Cram101 Inc.
Friedman, Avner. Advanced Calculus. 2007. (Dover Books on Mathematics Ser.). (ENG., Illus.). 432p. per. 23.95 *(978-0-486-45795-6(8))* Dover Pubns., Inc.
Friedman, Menahem & Kandel, Abraham. Calculus Light. 2011. (Intelligent Systems Reference Library). (Illus.). xii, 300p. 129.00 *(978-3-642-17847-4(2)*, 3642178472) Springer.
Fuchs, Dirk, ed. Cooperation in Heterogeneous Theorem Prover Networks. 36.00 *(978-1-58603-124-4(4))* IOS Pr., Inc.
FURNARI, Sig. Giuseppe. Calculus without Limits. 2010. 104p. pap. 16.95 *(978-1-4452-2198-4(5))* Lulu Enterprises Inc.
G. H. Hardy. A Course of Pure Mathematics. 2007. 448p. per. 15.95 *(978-1-60386-049-9(5))* Rough Draft Printing.
Ganter, Susan L. Calculus Renewal: Issues for Undergraduate Mathematics Education in the Next Decade. 2010. (ENG.). 176p. pap. 129.00 *(978-1-4419-3334-8(4)*, 1441933344) Springer.
Gay, Daniel & Gambelin, Jacques. Structural Modelling & Calculus: An Introduction. 2007. 640p. 270.00 *(978-1-905209-19-4(3))* ISTE/Hermes Science Publishing GBR. Dist: Independent Pubs. Group.
Gervasi. Ssg- Calculus: Early Transcendentals 4E Student Resc Manual. 4th rev. ed. 2010. 422p. pap. 61.95 *(978-0-7637-7353-3(0))* Jones & Bartlett Learning, LLC.
—Ssg- Multivariable Calculus 4E Student Resource Manual. 4th rev. ed. 2010. 422p. pap. 49.95 *(978-0-7637-9141-4(5))* Jones & Bartlett Learning, LLC.
—Ssg- Single Variable Calculus 4E Student Resource Manual. 4th rev. ed. 2010. 294p. pap. 55.95 *(978-0-7637-9139-1(3))* Jones & Bartlett Learning, LLC.
Ghorpade, Sudhir R. & Limaye, Balmohan V. A Course in Calculus & Real Analysis. 2010. (Undergraduate Texts in Mathematics Ser.). (Illus.). x, 432p. pap. 69.95 *(978-1-4419-2145-1(1)*, 1441921451) Springer.
Gibilisco, Stan. Calculus: Beginner to Advanced, & Everything in Between. 2008. (ENG., Illus.). 806p. (C). pap. 29.95 *(978-0-07-154931-8(5)*, 0071549315, TAB/Electronics) McGraw-Hill Professional Publishing.
—Pre-Calculus Know-It-ALL. 2009. (ENG., Illus.). 608p. pap. 24.95 *(978-0-07-162702-3(2)*, 0071627022, TAB/Electronics) McGraw-Hill Professional Publishing.
Goldstein & Lay & Schneider & Cram101 Textbook Reviews Staff. Brief Calculus & Its Applications. 2007. 124p. per. 11.95 *(978-1-4288-3406-4(0))* Cram101 Inc.
Goldstein, Larry. Precalculus & Its Applications. Date not set. 656p. (C). stu. ed. 44.50 *(978-1-891304-10-1(0))*; (Illus.). 704p. tchr. ed. *(978-1-891304-11-8(9))* Mobius Communications, Ltd.
—Precalculus & Its Applications: Instructor's Solutions Manual. Date not set. 458p. pap., tchr. ed. *(978-1-891304-14-9(3))* Mobius Communications, Ltd.
Goldstein, Larry J., et al. Brief Calculus & Its Applications. 12th ed. 2009. (ENG., Illus.). 512p. (C). pap. 157.33 *(978-0-321-56856-4(7)*, Prentice Hall) Prentice Hall PTR.
—Brief Calculus & Its Applications Plus MyMathLab/MyStatLab Student Access Code Card. 12th ed. 2010. (ENG.). (C). pap., pap. 167.33 *(978-0-321-74446-3(2))* Addison Wesley.
—Calculus & Its Applications. 12th ed. 2009. (ENG., (C). Illus.). 656p. 157.33 *(978-0-321-57130-4(4))*; 200p. pap. 36.67 *(978-0-321-59901-8(2))* Prentice Hall PTR. (Prentice Hall).
Goldstein, Larry Joel, et al. Calculus & Its Applications Pkg. 11th ed. 2007. (Illus.). *(978-0-13-174625-1(1))* Pearson Education Canada.
Gong, Sheng & Gong, Youhong, eds. Concise Complex Analysis. 2007. (Illus.). 237p. 82.00 *(978-981-270-693-5(3))* World Scientific Publishing Co., Inc.
Gonick, Larry. The Cartoon Guide to Calculus. 2011. (ENG., Illus.). 256p. pap. 18.99 ***(978-0-06-168909-3(2)***, William Morrow Paperbacks) HarperCollins Pubs.
Goshaw, Martha. Concepts of Calculus with Applications, Updated Edition. 2008. (ENG.). 688p. (C). 154.67 *(978-0-321-57744-3(2))* Addison Wesley.
Goursat, Edouard. A Course in Mathematical Analysis - Volume I - Derivatives & Differentials - Definite Integrals - Expansion in Series - Applications to Geometry. Hedrick, Earle, tr. 2006. 564p. 44.95 *(978-1-933998-45-9(8)*, Merchant Bks.) Rough Draft Printing.
Grabe, Michael. Generalized Gaussian Error Calculus. 2010. (ENG., Illus.). xiii, 301p. 159.00 *(978-3-642-03304-9(0)*, 3642033040) Springer.
Grady, Leo J. & Polimeni, Jonathan R. Discrete Calculus: Applied Analysis on Graphs for Computational Science. 2010. (ENG., Illus.). xvi, 366p. 129.00 *(978-1-84996-289-6(8)*, 1849962898) Springer.
Gregersen, Erik, ed. The Britannica Guide to Analysis & Calculus. 2010. (Math Explained Ser.). (Illus.). 296p. (YA). 90.00 *(978-1-61530-223-9(9))* Rosen Publishing Group, Inc., The.
Haase, Markus. The Functional Calculus for Sectorial Operators. 2006. (Operator Theory, Advances & Applications Ser.: Vol. 169). (Illus.). xiv, 392p. 129.00 *(978-3-7643-7697-0(X)*, 376437697X) Birkhauser Boston.
—The Functional Calculus for Sectorial Operators. 2006. (Operator Theory, Advances & Applications Ser.: Vol. 169). (Illus.). xiv, 392p. *(978-0-8176-7697-1(X))* Birkhauser Verlag AG.
Hands, Krista. The Business Calculus Gmt. 2008. 192p. pap. *(978-3-639-07443-7(2))* VDM Verlag Dr. Mueller e.K.
Hardy, G. A Course of Pure Mathematics - Illustrated. 2006. (Illus.). 452p. 29.95 *(978-1-933998-46-6(6)*, Merchant Bks.) Rough Draft Printing.
Hass, Joel, et al. Student's Solutions Manual for University Calculus, Early Transcendentals, Multivariable. 2nd ed. 2011. (ENG.). 216p. (C). pap. 36.67 *(978-0-321-69454-6(6))* Pearson Education.
—Student's Solutions Manual for University Calculus, Early Transcendentals, Single Variable. 2nd rev. ed. 2011. (ENG.). 440p. (C). pap. 36.67 *(978-0-321-69462-1(7))* Pearson Education.
—University Calculus: Elements with Early Transcendentals. 2008. (University Calculus Ser.). (ENG., (C). Illus.). 791p. 126.67 *(978-0-321-53348-7(8))*; 108p. pap. 36.67 *(978-0-321-55917-3(7))* Addison Wesley.
—University Calculus: Part One Single Variable, Pt. 1. alt. ed. 2007. (University Calculus Ser.). (ENG., Illus.). 720p. (C). per. 101.33 *(978-0-321-47519-0(4))* Addison Wesley.
—University Calculus Pt. 1: Elements with Early Transcendentals. 2008. 200p. (C). pap. 36.67 *(978-0-321-53608-2(8))* Addison Wesley Higher Education.
—University Calculus, Early Transcendentals. 2nd rev. ed. 2011. (ENG.). 1080p. (C). 140.00 *(978-0-321-71739-9(2))* Addison Wesley.
—University Calculus, Early Transcendentals, Books a la Carte Edition. 2nd ed. 2011. (ENG.). 900p. (C). ring bd. 84.00 *(978-0-321-69461-4(9))* Addison Wesley.
—University Calculus, Early Transcendentals, Multivariable. 2nd rev. ed. 2011. (ENG.). 576p. (C). pap. 101.33 *(978-0-321-69460-7(0))* Addison Wesley.
—University Calculus, Early Transcendentals, Single Variable. 2nd rev. ed. 2011. (ENG.). 744p. (C). pap. 101.33 *(978-0-321-69459-1(7))* Addison Wesley.
Hass, Joel, et al. University Calculus, Early Transcendentals, Single Variable plus MyMathLab (ad hoc for Valuepacks) 2nd ed. 2011. (ENG.). (C). pap. 111.33 ***(978-0-321-79069-9(3))*** Addison Wesley.
Heinonen, Juha, et al. Nonlinear Potential Theory of Degenerate Elliptic Equations. 2006. (Dover Books on Mathematics Ser.). (ENG., Illus.). 416p. per. 19.95 *(978-0-486-45050-6(3))* Dover Pubns., Inc.
Hennessy, Matthew. A Distributed Pi-Calculus. 2007. (ENG., Illus.). 278p. 71.00 *(978-0-521-87330-7(4))* Cambridge Univ. Pr.
Herrmann, Richard. Fractional Calculus: An Introduction for Physicists. 2011. (Illus.). 276p. 85.00 *(978-981-4340-24-3(3))* World Scientific Publishing Co., Inc.
Hijab, Omar. Introduction to Calculus & Classical Analysis. (Undergraduate Texts in Mathematics Ser.). (Illus.). 2nd ed. 2010. x, 342p. pap. 69.95 *(978-1-4419-2409-4(4)*, 1441924094) 3rd ed. 2011. xii, 364p. 74.95 *(978-1-4419-9487-5(4)*, 1441994874) Springer.
Hill, Greg. The Everything Guide to Calculus 1 Vol. 1: A Step-by-Step Guide to the Basics of Calculus - In Plain English! 2011. (ENG.). 320p. pap. 16.95 *(978-1-4405-0629-1(9))* Adams Media Corp.
Hille, Einar, et al. Calculus: Several Variables. 10th rev. ed. 2007. (ENG., Illus.). 240p. (C). per. 57.95 *(978-0-470-12729-2(5)*, Wiley) Wiley, John & Sons, Inc.
Himonas & Howard & Cram101 Textbook Reviews Staff. Calculus Ideas & Applications. 2007. 212p. per. 13.95 *(978-1-4288-3526-9(1))* Cram101 Inc.
Himonas, Alex. Calculus: Ideas & Applications, Brief Edition with Student Solutions Manual Set. 2007. (ENG.). 928p. (C). 213.95 *(978-0-470-17691-7(1)*, Wiley) Wiley, John & Sons, Inc.
—Calculus: Ideas & Applications 1st Edition with Student Solutions Manual & Maple Student Edition Release 10 Set. 2006. 1p. 199.95 *(978-0-470-10116-2(4))* Wiley, John & Sons, Inc.
Hindley, J. Roger & Seldin, Jonathan P. Lambda-Calculus & Combinators: An Introduction. 2nd ed. 2008. (ENG., Illus.). 360p. 72.00 *(978-0-521-89885-0(4))* Cambridge Univ. Pr.
Hoag, John. Calculus & Techniques of Optimization. . 2007. (C). 73.00 *(978-981-277-493-4(9))* World Scientific Publishing Co., Inc.
Hoffmann & Bradley & Cram101 Textbook Reviews Staff. Calculus. 2007. 140p. per. 11.95 *(978-1-4288-3430-9(3))* Cram101 Inc.
Hoffmann, Laurence & Bradley, Gerald. Calculus: For Business, Economics, & the Social & Life Sciences. 10th ed. 2010. (ENG.). (C). ring bd. 127.00 *(978-0-07-745215-5(1)*, 0077452151, McGraw-Hill Science, Engineering & Mathematics) McGraw-Hill Higher Education.
Hoffmann, Laurence & Bradley, Gerald. Student's Solution Manual for Calculus for Business, Economics, & the Social & Life Sciences. 11th ed. 2012. (ENG.). 416p. (C). pap. 86.33 ***(978-0-07-742738-2(6)***, 0077427386, McGraw-Hill Science, Engineering & Mathematics) McGraw-Hill Higher Education.
Hoffmann, Laurence, et al. Applied Calculus for Business, Economics & the Social & Life Sciences, Expanded Edition. 11th ed. 2012. (ENG., Illus.). 1088p. (C). 193.67 ***(978-0-07-353237-0(1)***, 0073532371) McGraw-Hill Cos., The.
Hoffmann, Laurence D. Calculus for Business, Economics, & the Social & Life Sciences. 11th ed. 2012. (ENG., Illus.). 800p. (C). 181.00 ***(978-0-07-353238-7(X)***, 007353238X) McGraw-Hill Cos., The.
Hoffmann, Laurence D. & Bradley, Gerald. Applied Calculus for Business, Economics, & the Social & Life Sciences, Expanded Edition. 10th ed. 2009. (ENG.). 1056p. (C). 193.67 *(978-0-07-729788-6(1)*, 0077297881, McGraw-Hill Science, Engineering & Mathematics) McGraw-Hill Higher Education.
Hoffmann, Laurence D. & Bradley, Gerald L. Applied Calculus for Business, Economics, & the Social & Life Sciences. 10th ed. 2009. *(978-0-07-353233-2(9))* McGraw-Hill Cos., The.
—Applied Calculus for Business, Economics, & the Social & Life Sciences. 9th ed. 2007. (Illus.). 1011p. 157.81 *(978-0-07-330926-2(5)*, 9780073309262, McGraw-Hill Science, Engineering & Mathematics) McGraw-Hill Higher Education.
—Calculus Brief Edition: For Business, Economics, & the Social & Life Sciences. 9th rev. ed. 2006. (Illus.). 758p. 145.94 *(978-0-07-330927-9(3)*, 9780073309279, McGraw-Hill Science, Engineering & Mathematics) McGraw-Hill Higher Education.
—Calculus for Business, Economics, & the Social & Life Sciences. 10th ed. 2009. *(978-0-07-353231-8(2))* McGraw-Hill Cos., The.
Hoffmann, Laurence D., et al. Calculus: For Business, Economics, & the Social & Life Sciences. 10th ed. 2009. (ENG.). (C). 181.00 *(978-0-07-729273-7(1)*, 0077292731, McGraw-Hill Science, Engineering & Mathematics) McGraw-Hill Higher Education.
Hubbard, John H. & Hubbard, Barbara Burke. Vector Calculus, Linear Algebra, & Differential Forms: A Unified Approach. 4th ed. 2009. *(978-0-9715766-5-0(3))* Matrix Editions.
Hubbard, John Hamal & Hubbard, Barbara Burke. Student Solution Manual 2nd Edition: To accompapny 3rd edition of Vector Calculus, Linear Algebra, & Differential Forms: A Unified Approach. 2nd rev. ed. 2007. (Illus.). 268p. (C). per. 33.00 *(978-0-9715766-4-3(5))* Matrix Editions.
—Vector Calculus, Linear Algebra, & Differential Forms: A Unified Approach, 1. 3rd ed. 2007. (Illus.). 802p. (C). 78.00 *(978-0-9715766-3-6(7))* Matrix Editions.
Hughes-Hallett & Gleason & McCallum, Et & Cram101 Textbook Reviews Staff. Calculus: Single & Multivariable. 2007. 176p. per. 12.95 *(978-1-4288-3458-3(3))* Cram101 Inc.
Hughes-Hallett, Deborah. Applied Calculus with Wiley Plus Blackboard Chalk Set, Set. 2006. (Wiley Plus Products Ser.). pap. 122.95 *(978-0-470-11530-5(0)*, Wiley) Wiley, John & Sons, Inc.

—Applied Calculus with Wiley Plus WebCT Powerpack Set. 3rd ed. 2006. (Wiley Plus Products Ser.). pap. 122.95 *(978-0-470-11535-0(1),* Wiley) Wiley, John & Sons, Inc.

—Calc 4th Edition SV Cloth eGP/Bb Set Calculus 4th Edition Single Variable Cloth with eGrade Plus/Blackboard Set. 4th rev. ed. 2006. (Wiley Plus Products Ser.). 128.95 *(978-0-470-10351-7(5))* Wiley, John & Sons, Inc.

—Calculus: Single & Multivariable 5th Edition Binder Ready Version with 2 Binder & WP SA 5. 0 Set. 5th ed. 2011. (C). ring bd. 161.95 ***(978-1-118-13933-2(X))*** Wiley, John & Sons, Inc.

—Calculus: Single & Multivariable Combo with WP SA Online Combo Set. 5th ed 2011. (C). 231.95 ***(978-1-118-14036-9(2))*** Wiley, John & Sons, Inc.

—Calculus: Single Variable + WileyPlus Registration Card. 4th rev. ed. 2006. (Wiley Plus Products Ser.). pap. 123.95 *(978-0-470-10354-8(X))* Wiley, John & Sons, Inc.

—Calculus: Single Variable 4th Edition Paper with iClicker Radio Frequency Student Clicker & Wiley Plus Set. 4th rev. ed. 2006. (Wiley Plus Products Ser.). pap. 131.95 *(978-0-470-11349-3(9))* Wiley, John & Sons, Inc.

—Calculus: Single Variable 4th Edition with Maple Student Editon Release 10 & Wiley Plus Set. 2007. (Wiley Plus Products Ser.). 127.95 *(978-0-470-17574-3(5))* Wiley, John & Sons, Inc.

—Calculus: Single Variable 4th Edition with WebAssign 2 Semester Set. 2008. (ENG.). (C). pap. 167.95 *(978-0-470-40050-0(1),* Wiley) Wiley, John & Sons, Inc.

—Calculus: Single Variable 5th Edition Binder Ready Version with 2 Binder & Online Print Text SV Set. 5th ed. 2011. (C). ring bd. 133.95 ***(978-1-118-13934-9(8))*** Wiley, John & Sons, Inc.

—Calculus: Single Variable 5th Edition with Online Print Text SV Set. 5th ed. 2011. (C). 192.95 ***(978-1-118-13948-6(8))*** Wiley, John & Sons, Inc.

—Calculus: Single Variable Paper with Student Study Guide & WileyPLUS Set. 4th ed. 2007. (Wiley Plus Products Ser.). pap. 123.95 *(978-0-470-16471-6(9),* Wiley) Wiley, John & Sons, Inc.

—Calculus 4th Edition Combo with Student Solutions Manual & eGrade Plus Set. 4th rev. ed. 2006. (Wiley Plus Products Ser.). 179.95 *(978-0-470-10353-1(1))* Wiley, John & Sons, Inc.

—Calculus 4th Edition Single Variable & Student Solutions Manual with eGrade Plus Set. 4th rev. ed. 2006. (Wiley Plus Products Ser.). pap. 137.95 *(978-0-470-10350-0(7))* Wiley, John & Sons, Inc.

—Calculus: Single & Multivariable 4E with StudentSolutions Manual & Wiley Plus Set. 2007. 156.95 *(978-0-470-16465-5(4),* Wiley) Wiley, John & Sons, Inc.

—Calculus: Single Variable 4E Cloth with Student Solutions Manual & Wiley Plus Set. 2007. 129.95 *(978-0-470-16464-8(6),* Wiley) Wiley, John & Sons, Inc.

—Calculus: Single Variable 5th Edition with Calculus Online Print Text SV Set. 5th ed. 2011. (C). pap. 186.95 ***(978-1-118-13681-2(0))*** Wiley, John & Sons, Inc.

Hughes-Hallett, Deborah. (WCS)Calculus Single & Multivariable 4th Edition Flex Format. 2006. 1104p. pap. 100.95 *(978-0-471-75234-9(7),* Wiley) Wiley, John & Sons, Inc.

Hughes-Hallett, Deborah & Hallett, Deborah Hughes. Calculus: Single & Multivariable. 5th ed. 2008. (ENG.). 1168p. (C). 235.95 *(978-0-470-08914-9(8),* Wiley) Wiley, John & Sons, Inc.

Hughes-Hallett, Deborah, et al. Calculus: Single Variable. 5th ed. 2008. (ENG.). 736p. (C). 200.95 *(978-0-470-13159-6(4),* Wiley) Wiley, John & Sons, Inc.

—Calculus: Single Variable. 5th ed. 2008. (ENG., Illus.). 736p. (C). pap. 194.95 *(978-0-470-08915-6(6),* Wiley) Wiley, John & Sons, Inc.

—Calculus, Textbook & Student Study Guide: Single Variable. 4th ed. 2007. (ENG.). 1036p. (C). pap. 208.95 *(978-0-470-19026-5(4),* Wiley) Wiley, John & Sons, Inc.

—Calculus WileyPLUS Learning Kit. 2011. 464p. (C). pap. 103.99 *(978-0-470-57367-4(X),* Wiley) Wiley, John & Sons, Inc.

—Multivariable Calculus Fifth Edition Binder Ready Version. 2008. (ENG.). 480p. (C). ring bd. 104.95 *(978-0-470-45556-2(X),* Wiley) Wiley, John & Sons, Inc.

—(WCCS) Custom for Queen's University, Selected Chapters from Hughes-Hallet: Calculus: Single & Multivariable. 4th ed. 2009. (C). pap. 28.95 *(978-0-470-16122-7(1))* Wiley, John & Sons, Inc.

Hughes-Hallett, Et Al. & Cram101 Textbook Reviews Staff. Applied Calculus. 2007. 124p. per. 11.95 *(978-1-4288-3664-8(0))* Cram101 Inc.

Hughes-Hallett, Gleason & Cram101 Textbook Reviews Staff. Calculus Single Variable. 2007. 160p. per. 12.95 *(978-1-4288-3610-5(1))* Cram101 Inc.

Inagaki, Y., et al, eds. Algorithms & Computation: Third International Symposium, ISAAC '92, Nagoya, Japan, December 16-18, 1992. Proceedings, 3rd:International Sy. 2007. (Lecture Notes in Computer Science Ser.). 536p. per. 89.95 *(978-3-540-56279-5(6))* Springer.

Jiang, Yuming & Liu, Yong. Stochastic Network Calculus. 2008. (Computer Communications & Networks Ser.). (ENG., Illus.). xix, 232p. 109.00 *(978-1-84800-126-8(6),* 1848001266) Springer.

Kaplan Publishing Staff & Cram101 Textbook Reviews Staff. Advanced Calculus. 2007. 156p. per. 12.95 *(978-1-4288-3412-5(5))* Cram101 Inc.

Kaplan, Wilfred & Lewis, Donald. Calculus & Linear Algebra: Vectors in the Plane & One-Variable Calculus, Vol. 1. 2007. (ENG., Illus.). 712p. (C). per. 24.95 *(978-1-4255-8913-4(6))* MPublishing.

Keisler, H. Jerome. Elementary Calculus: An Infinitesimal Approach. 3rd ed. 2012. (Dover Books on Mathematics Ser.). (ENG., Illus.). 1008p. pap. 39.95 ***(978-0-486-48452-5(1))*** Dover Pubns., Inc.

Kirillov, A. A., ed. Representation Theory & Noncommutative Harmonic Analysis II: Homogeneous Spaces, Representations & Special Functions. Dijk, G. van et al, trs. 2010. (Encyclopaedia of Mathematical Sciences Ser.). (Illus.). vii, 266p. pap. 169.00 *(978-3-642-08126-2(6),* 3642081266) Springer.

Klafter, Joseph, et al. Fractional Dynamics: Recent Advances. 2011. 160.00 ***(978-981-4340-58-8(8))*** World Scientific Publishing Co., Inc.

Klebaner, Fima C. Introduction to Stochastic Calculus with Applications. 3rd ed. 2011. 470p. 98.00 ***(978-1-84816-831-2(4))***; pap. 58.00 ***(978-1-84816-832-9(2))*** Imperial College Pr. GBR. Dist: World Scientific Publishing Co., Inc.

Kleine Buning, Hans. Theory & Applications of Satisfiability Testing - Sat 2008. 2008. (Lecture Notes in Computer Science / Theoretical Computer Science & General Issues Ser.). spiral bd. 79.95 *(978-3-540-79718-0(1),* 3540797181) Springer.

Kochman, Stanley O. Single Variable Calculus: Concepts, Applications, & Theory. 4th ed. (Illus.). xiii, 821p. ***(978-1-256-29759-8(3))*** Pearson Bks.

Kojima, Hiroyuki, et al. The Manga Guide to Calculus. 2009. (Manga Guide to Science Ser.). (ENG., Illus.). 256p. pap. 19.95 *(978-1-59327-194-7(8))* No Starch Pr., Inc.

Kosek, Wojciech K. Calculus for the Forgetful: How to understand more & memorize Less. 2007. pap. 19.95 *(978-0-9795199-0-1(X))* Magimath.

Krantz & Cram101 Textbook Reviews Staff. Calculus Demystified. 2007. 64p. per. 9.95 *(978-1-4288-3680-8(2))* Cram101 Inc.

Krantz, Steven G. & Blank, Brian E. Calculus: Single & Multivariable. 2nd ed. 2011. (ENG., Illus.). 1304p. (C). 235.95 *(978-0-470-45360-5(5),* Wiley) Wiley, John & Sons, Inc.

Krupka, Demeter & Saunders, David, eds. Handbook of Global Analysis. 2007. (ENG., Illus.). 1244p. 275.00 *(978-0-444-52833-9(4),* Elsevier Science) Elsevier Science & Technology Bks.

Kuttler, Kenneth. Calculus - Theory & Applications, 2 vols. 2011. 424p. 92.00 *(978-981-4324-27-4(2))* 2011. 424p. pap. 45.00 *(978-981-4329-70-5(3))* 2010. 500p. pap. 42.00 *(978-981-4329-69-9(X))* Vol. 1. 2010. 500p. 89.00 *(978-981-4324-26-7(4))* Vol. 2. 2011. 424p. 156.00 *(978-981-4335-71-3(1))* Vol. 2. 2011. 424p. pap. 76.00 *(978-981-4335-72-0(X))* World Scientific Publishing Co., Inc.

Lamb, Horace. An Elementary Course of Infinitesimal Calculus. 2009. (Cambridge Library Collection - Mathematics Ser.). (ENG.). 552p. pap. 39.99 *(978-1-108-00534-0(9))* Cambridge Univ. Pr.

Larson, Ron. Applied Calculus for the Life & Social Sciences. 2008. (ENG.). 864p. (C). 207.95 *(978-0-618-96259-4(X))* CENGAGE Learning.

—Applied Calculus for the Life & Social Sciences, Enhanced Edition (with Enhanced WebAssign 1-Semester Printed Access Card) 2009. (Available 2010 Titles Enhanced Web Assign Ser.). (ENG.). 896p. (C). 184.95 *(978-1-4390-4783-5(9))* Brooks/Cole.

—Calculus. 8th ed. 2007. (ENG.). (C). wbk. ed. 44.95 *(978-0-547-00830-1(9),* 1030040) CENGAGE Learning.

—Calculus. 8th ed. 2008. (ENG.). 448p. (C). pap. 65.95 *(978-0-618-96265-5(4),* 1021658) Brooks/Cole.

—Calculus, Vol. 2. 9th ed. 2009. (ENG.). 272p. (C). pap. 66.95 *(978-0-547-21310-1(7))* Brooks/Cole.

—Calculus: An Applied Approach, Enhanced Edition (with Enhanced WebAssign 1-Semester Printed Access Card) 8th ed. 2009. (Available 2010 Titles Enhanced Web Assign Ser.). (ENG.). 960p. (C). 195.95 *(978-1-4390-4778-1(2))* Brooks/Cole.

—Calculus: Vectors & Value Functions, 6 vols. 6th ed. Date not set. (C). pap. 11.96 *(978-0-395-89554-2(5))* CENGAGE Learning.

Larson, Ron. College Algebra & Calculus: An Applied Approach. 2nd ed. 2012. (Textbooks Available with Cengage YouBook Ser.). (ENG.). 1200p. (C). pap. 204.95 ***(978-1-133-10506-0(8))*** Brooks/Cole.

Larson, Ron & Edwards, Bruce. Calculus, International Edition. 9th ed. 2010. 1328p. pap. ***(978-1-4390-3033-2(2))*** Brooks/Cole.

Larson, Ron & Edwards, Bruce H. Brief Calculus: An Applied Approach, Enhanced Edition (with Enhanced WebAssign 1-Semester Printed Access Card) 8th ed. 2009. (Available 2010 Titles Enhanced Web Assign Ser.). (ENG.). 736p. (C). 177.95 *(978-1-4390-4780-4(4))* Brooks/Cole.

—Calculus. 9th ed. 2009. (ENG.). 320p. (C). pap., instr.'s gde. ed. 52.95 *(978-0-547-21308-8(5))* Brooks/Cole.

—Calculus: Early Transcendental Functions. 5th ed. 2010. (Textbooks Available with Cengage YouBook Ser.). (ENG.). (C). 1360p. 217.95 *(978-0-538-73550-6(3))*; 312p. pap., instr.'s gde. ed. 43.95 *(978-0-538-73671-8(2))* Brooks/Cole.

—Calculus: Early Transcendental Functions, Hybrid (with Enhanced WebAssign Homework & eBook LOE Printed Access Card for Multi Term Math & Science) 5th ed. 2011. (Cengage Learningrsquo;s New Hybrid Editions! Ser.). (ENG.). (C). 928p. pap. 154.95 *(978-1-133-10382-0(0))*; 640p. pap. 133.95 *(978-1-133-10379-0(0))* Brooks/Cole.

—Calculus Vol. 1: Early Transcendental Functions. 5th ed. 2010. (ENG.). 640p. (C). pap. 59.95 *(978-0-538-73920-7(7))* Brooks/Cole.

—Calculus of a Single Variable. 9th ed. 2008. (Available 2010 Titles Enhanced Web Assign Ser.). (ENG.). 912p. (C). 210.95 *(978-0-547-20998-2(3))* Brooks/Cole.

Larson, Ron, et al. Brief Calculus: An Applied Approach. 2007. 148p. per. 11.95 *(978-1-4288-3528-3(8))* Cram101 Inc.

—Calculus. 2007. 224p. per. 13.95 *(978-1-4288-3470-5(2))* Cram101 Inc.

—Calculus. 9th ed. 2009. (Textbooks Available with Cengage YouBook Ser.). (ENG.). 1328p. (C). 216.95 *(978-0-547-16702-2(4))* Brooks/Cole.

—Calculus AP ED. 9th ed. 2010. ***(978-0-547-21289-0(5))*** Brooks/Cole.

—Calculus I with Precalculus. 3rd ed. 2011. (Textbooks Available with Cengage YouBook Ser.). (ENG.). 1056p. (C). 238.95 *(978-0-8400-6833-0(6))* Brooks/Cole.

—Calculus Multivariable. 9th ed. 2009. (Available 2010 Titles Enhanced Web Assign Ser.). (ENG.). 512p. (C). 190.95 *(978-0-547-20997-5(5))* Brooks/Cole.

—Essential Calculus: Early Transcendental Functions. 2007. (Available 2010 Titles Enhanced Web Assign Ser.). (ENG., Illus.). 1008p. (C). 191.95 *(978-0-618-87918-2(8),* 332150) CENGAGE Learning.

LaTorre, D. R. Calculus Concepts: An Applied Approach to the Mathematics of Change. 4th ed. 2008. (Illus.). xx, 667p. *(978-0-618-78983-2(9))* Houghton Mifflin Harcourt Publishing Co.

LaTorre, Donald R., et al. Calculus Concepts: An Applied Approach to the Mathematics of Change. 4th ed. 2007. (ENG.). 240p. (C). pap. 65.95 *(978-0-618-78986-3(3),* 332210) Brooks/Cole.

—Calculus Concepts: An Applied Approach to the Mathematics of Change. 4th ed. 2007. (ENG., Illus.). 544p. (C). pap. 185.95 *(978-0-618-78982-5(0),* 332206) CENGAGE Learning.

—Calculus Concepts: An Informal Approach to the Mathematics of Change. 5th ed. 2011. (Textbooks Available with Cengage YouBook Ser.). (ENG.). 744p. (C). 198.95 *(978-1-4390-4957-0(2))* Brooks/Cole.

—Calculus Student Solutions Manual. 5th ed. 2011. (ENG.). 336p. (C). pap. 65.95 *(978-0-538-73541-4(4))* Brooks/Cole.

Lawrence, David P. Calculus Using the TI-80. Date not set. (Skill & Practice Masters Ser.). ring bd. 14.95 *(978-1-881641-96-4(1))* Pencil Point Pr., Inc.

Lial, et al. Finite Mathematics & Calculus Plus Applications, Books a la Carte Plus MyMathLab/MyStatLab Student Access Kit. 8th ed. 2010. (ENG.). (C). ring bd. 116.67 *(978-0-321-72018-4(0))* Addison Wesley.

Lial & Greenwell & Ritchey & Cram101 Textbook Reviews Staff. Calculus with Applications: Brief Edition. 2007. 152p. per. 12.95 *(978-1-4288-3472-9(9))* Cram101 Inc.

Lial, Greenwell & Cram101 Textbook Reviews Staff. Calculus with Applications. 2007. 184p. per. 12.95 *(978-1-4288-3584-9(9))* Cram101 Inc.

Lial, Margaret, et al. Books a la Carte Edition, Calculus with Applications, Brief Version. 10th ed. 2011. (ENG.). 696p. (C). ring bd. 92.80 ***(978-0-321-75794-4(7))*** Addison Wesley.

—Books a la Carte Edition for Calculus with Applications. 10th ed. 2011. (ENG.). 816p. (C). ring bd. 94.40 ***(978-0-321-75787-6(4))*** Addison Wesley.

—Finite Mathematics & Calculus with Applications, Books a la Carte Edition. 9th ed. 2011. (ENG.). 1136p. (C). ring bd. 104.80 ***(978-0-321-74660-3(0))*** Addison Wesley.

—Graphing Calculator & Excel Spreadsheet Manual for Finite Mathematics & Calculus with Applications Series. 10th rev. ed. 2011. (ENG.). 120p. (C). pap. 24.67 ***(978-0-321-70966-0(7))*** Addison Wesley.

Lial, Margaret L., et al. Calculus with Applications. (ENG.). (C). 9th ed. 2009. ring bd. 92.80 *(978-0-321-65522-6(2))* 9th ed. 2007. (Illus.). 948p. 157.33 *(978-0-321-42132-6(9))* 9th ed. 2007. (Illus.). 720p. 154.67 *(978-0-321-42274-3(0))* 10th rev. ed. 2011. 640p. 154.67 *(978-0-321-74857-7(3))* Addison Wesley.

—Calculus with Applications. 10th rev. ed. 2011. (ENG.). 832p. (C). 157.33 ***(978-0-321-74900-0(6))*** Addison Wesley.

—Calculus with Applications, Brief, plus MyMathLab Student Starter Kit. 9th ed. 2008. (ENG.). 624p. (C). pap. 164.67 *(978-0-321-45396-9(4))* Addison Wesley.

—Calculus with Applications plus MyMathLab Student Starter Kit. 9th ed. 2008. (ENG.). 816p. (C). pap. 167.33 *(978-0-321-44873-6(1))* Addison Wesley.

—Finite Mathematics & Calculus with Applications. (ENG., (C). 8th ed. 2007. Illus.). 1328p. 174.67 *(978-0-321-42651-2(7))* 9th rev. ed. 2011. 1136p. 174.67 ***(978-0-321-74908-6(1))*** Addison Wesley.

—Finite Mathematics & Mathematics with Applications. 10th ed. 2010. (ENG.). 504p. (C). pap. 36.67 *(978-0-321-64582-1(0))* Addison-Wesley Longman, Inc.

Ligozat, Gérard. Qualitative Spatial & Temporal Reasoning. 2011. (Iste Ser.: 524). (ENG., Illus.). 544p. 195.00 *(978-1-84821-252-7(6),* Wiley-ISTE) Wiley, John & Sons, Inc.

Lin. Free Calculus. 2008. 37.00 *(978-981-270-458-0(2))* World Scientific Publishing Co., Inc.

Lin Zhengyan & Lu Zhuarong. Strong Limit Theorems. 2010. (Mathematics & its Applications Ser.). 212p. pap. 289.00 *(978-90-481-4167-8(2),* 9048141672) Springer.

Love, Clyde E. Differential & Integral Calculus. 2009. 368p. 26.99 *(978-1-103-15878-2(3))*; pap. 20.99 *(978-1-103-15877-5(5))* BiblioBazaar.

Lovric, Miroslav. Vector Calculus. 2007. (ENG., Illus.). 640p. (C). 172.95 *(978-0-471-72569-5(2),* Wiley) Wiley, John & Sons, Inc.

—Vector Calculus, Student Solutions Manual. 2006. (ENG.). 255p. (C). pap. stu. ed. 57.95 *(978-0-471-72571-8(4),* Wiley) Wiley, John & Sons, Inc.

Lutzer, Carl V. Professional Calculus. 2012. (ENG.). (C). pap. 38.95 *(978-0-470-94766-1(7),* Wiley) Wiley, John & Sons, Inc.

Lutzer, Carl V. & Goodwill, H. T. Calculus, Single Variable. 2010. (ENG.). 939p. (C). pap. 87.95 *(978-0-470-17930-7(9),* Wiley) Wiley, John & Sons, Inc.

—Professional Calculus Single Variable Preliminaryedition Student Solutions Manual. 2011. 300p. (C). pap. 38.95 *(978-0-470-94764-7(0),* Wiley) Wiley, John & Sons, Inc.

Mainardi, Francesco. Fractional Calculus & Waves in Linear Viscoelasticity: An Introduction to Mathematical Models. 2010. (Illus.). 368p. 70.00 *(978-1-84816-329-4(0))* Imperial College Pr. GBR. Dist: World Scientific Publishing Co., Inc.

Marek, Victor W. & Marek, V. W. Introduction to Mathematics of Satisfiability. 2009. (Chapman & Hall/CRC Studies in Informatics Ser.). (ENG., Illus.). 364p. 89.95 *(978-1-4398-0167-3(3),* Chapman & Hall/CRC) CRC Pr. LLC.

Margulies, Timothy S. Mathematics & Science Applications & Frontiers. 2009. 412p. 34.99 *(978-1-4415-0449-4(4))*; pap. 23.99 *(978-1-4415-0448-7(6))* Xlibris Corp.

Marsden & Tromba & Cram101 Textbook Reviews Staff. Vector Calculus. 2007. 152p. per. 12.95 *(978-1-4288-3468-2(0))* Cram101 Inc.

Marsden, Jerrold E. Vector Calculus Instructor's Manual. 5th ed. instr.'s gde. ed. 24.50 *(978-0-7167-0646-5(6))* Freeman, W. H. & Co.

Marsden, Jerrold E. & Tromba, Anthony. Vector Calculus. 6th ed. 2011. (ENG.). 752p. (C). 155.95 ***(978-1-4292-1508-4(9))*** Freeman, W. H. & Co.

Math 1400 College Math with Calculus: Class Notes & Workbook. 2007. (C). per. *(978-0-9774658-5-9(3))* Univ. of North Texas Copy Ctr.

Mathai, A. M. Special Functions for Applied Scientists. 2008. (ENG., Illus.). xxvi, 470p. 109.00 *(978-0-387-75893-0(3),* 0387758933) Springer.

Maxwell, E. A. An Analytical Calculus: Volume 1: For School & University, 4 vols. 2008. (ENG., Illus.). 180p. pap. 31.99 *(978-0-521-09035-3(0))* Cambridge Univ. Pr.

—An Analytical Calculus: Volume 2: For School & University, 4 vols. 2008. (ENG., Illus.). 284p. pap. 38.99 *(978-0-521-09036-0(9))* Cambridge Univ. Pr.

—An Analytical Calculus: Volume 3: For School & University, 4 vols. 2008. (ENG., Illus.). 204p. pap. 32.99 *(978-0-521-09037-7(7))* Cambridge Univ. Pr.

—An Analytical Calculus: Volume 4: For School & University, 4 vols. 2008. (ENG., Illus.). 304p. pap. 42.00 *(978-0-521-09041-4(5))* Cambridge Univ. Pr.

McCallum, et al. Calculus: Multivariable. 4th ed. 2006. pap. 156.95 *(978-0-470-14883-9(7),* Wiley) Wiley, John & Sons, Inc.

McCallum, William G. Calculus: Multivariable + Wileyplus/Blackboard Access Card. 4th rev. ed. 2006. (Wiley Plus Products Ser.). pap. 97.95 *(978-0-470-11549-7(1),* Wiley) Wiley, John & Sons, Inc.

—Calculus: Multivariable 4th Edition with Mpale Student Edition Release 10 & Wiley Plus Set. 4th rev. ed. 2007. (Wiley Plus Products Ser.). pap. 115.95 *(978-0-470-17573-6(7),* Wiley) Wiley, John & Sons, Inc.

—Calculus: Multivariable 4th Edition with WebAssign 1 Semester Set. 2008. (C). pap. 118.95 *(978-0-470-40395-2(0))* Wiley, John & Sons, Inc.

—Calculus: Multivariable 5th Edition with WP SA 5. 0 Online Combo Set. 5th ed. 2011. (C). pap. 167.95 ***(978-1-118-13689-8(6))*** Wiley, John & Sons, Inc.

—Calculus: Multivariable Wiley Plus Set. 4th rev. ed. 2006. (Wiley Plus Products Ser.). pap. 102.95 *(978-0-470-12024-8(X),* Wiley) Wiley, John & Sons, Inc.

McCallum, William G. Multivariable Calculus 5th Edition Binder Ready Version with 2 Binder & WP SA Online Combo Set. 5th ed. 2011. (C). ring bd. 123.95 ***(978-1-118-13935-6(6))*** Wiley, John & Sons, Inc.

Meadows, Yelena. Is This Cylinder Left or Right? 2009. 232p. pap. *(978-3-639-13469-8(9),* VDM Verlag Dr. Mueller e.K.

Meerschaert, Mark M. & Sikorskii, Alla. Stochastic Models for Fractional Calculus. (De Gruyter Studies in Mathematics Ser.). (ENG.). X, 291p. 2012. (gr. 17). E-Book 210.00 ***(978-3-11-220472-6(7))*** 2011. (Illus.). 140.00 ***(978-3-11-025869-1(2))*** De Gruyter, Walter Inc.

Mendelson, Elliott. Schaum's Outline of Beginning Calculus, Third Edition. 3rd ed. 2009. (Schaum's Outline Ser.). (ENG., Illus.). 416p. (C). pap. 20.00 *(978-0-07-163535-6(1),* 0071635351) McGraw-Hill Cos., The.

Menger, Karl. Calculus: A Modern Approach. 2007. (Dover Books on Mathematics Ser.). (ENG., Illus.). 384p. per. 19.95 *(978-0-486-45771-0(0))* Dover Pubns., Inc.

Michaelson, Greg. An Introduction to Functional Programming Through Lambda Calculus. 2011. (Dover Books on Mathematics Ser.). (ENG.). 336p. pap. 24.95 *(978-0-486-47883-8(1))* Dover Pubns., Inc.

Miller, Robert. Bob Miller's High School Calc for the Clueless: Honors & AP Calculus AB & BC. 2007. (Bob Miller's Clueless Ser.). (ENG., Illus.). 246p. per. 12.95 *(978-0-07-148845-7(6),* 0071488456) McGraw-Hill Cos., The.

Monje, Concepción A., et al. Fractional-order Systems & Controls: Fundamentals & Applications. 2010. (Advances in Industrial Control Ser.). (Illus.). xxvi, 415p. 209.00 *(978-1-84996-334-3(7),* 1849963347) Springer.

Munem-Foulis. Calculus. 2nd rev. ed. 2011. (ENG.). 1120p. pap. 120.00 ***(978-0-7575-9485-4(9))*** Kendall Hunt Publishing Co.

Nickerson, H. K., et al. Advanced Calculus. 2011. (Dover Books on Mathematics Ser.). (ENG.). 560p. pap. 24.95 *(978-0-486-48090-9(9))* Dover Pubns., Inc.

Nourdin, Ivan & Peccati, Giovanni. Normal Approximations with Malliavin Calculus: From Stein's Method to Universality. 2012. (Cambridge Tracts in Mathematics Ser.: 192). (ENG., Illus.). 256p. 80.00 ***(978-1-107-01777-1(7))*** Cambridge Univ. Pr.

Nunno, Giulia Di. Malliavin Calculus for Levy Processes with Applications to Finance. 2008. (Universitext Ser.). 350p. spiral bd. 59.95 *(978-3-540-78571-2(X),* Springer.

Olney, Edward. A General Geometry & Calculus Including Book I of the General Geometry, Treating of Loci in a Plane; & an Elementary Course in the Differential. 2006. 388p. per. 26.99 *(978-1-4255-7197-9(2))* MPublishing.

Opamica, Ljubica. Generalized Functions in Mechanical Models. 2009. 144p. pap. *(978-3-639-20612-8(6))* VDM Verlag Dr. Mueller e.K.

Ortigueira, Manuel Duarte. Fractional Calculus for Scientists & Engineers. 2011. (Lecture Notes in Electrical Engineering Ser.). (ENG., Illus.). xiv, 152p. 129.00 *(978-94-007-0746-7(0),* 9400707460) Springer.

Osserman, Robert. Two-Dimensional Calculus. 2011. (Dover Books on Mathematics Ser.). (ENG., Illus.). 480p. pap. 22.95 *(978-0-486-48163-0(8))* Dover Pubns., Inc.

Pasquale, Andrew, et al. Calculus: Multivariable. 5th ed. 2008. (ENG., Illus.). 480p. (C). pap. 165.95 *(978-0-470-13158-9(6),* Wiley) Wiley, John & Sons, Inc.

Peck, William G. (William Guy). Practical Treatise on the Differential & Integral Calculus, with Some of Its Applications to Mechanics & Astronomy by William G Peck. 2006. 244p. per. 20.99 *(978-1-4255-2077-9(4))* MPublishing.

Physics with Calculus: Electricity & Magnetism. 49.95 *(978-0-8373-6557-2(0)*, DANTES-57) National Learning Corp.

Physics with Calculus: Mechanics. 49.95 *(978-0-8373-6556-5(2)*, DANTES-56) National Learning Corp.

Poggiolesi, Francesca. Gentzen Calculi for Modal Propositional Logic. 2010. (Trends in Logic Ser.). (Illus.). xi, 222p. 139.00 *(978-90-481-9669-2(8)*, 9048196698) Springer.

Ponge, Raphael S. Heisenberg Calculus & Spectral Theory of Hypoelliptic Operators on Heisenberg Manifolds. 2008. (Memoirs of the American Mathematical Society Ser.: No. 906). 134p. pap. 69.00 *(978-0-8218-4148-8(3))* American Mathematical Society.

Prasolov, Victor V. Polynomials. Leites, D., tr. from SLA. 2009. (Algorithms & Computation in Mathematics Ser.). Orig. Title: Mnogochleny. (ENG., Illus.). xiii, 301p. pap. 69.95 *(978-3-642-03979-9(0)*, 3642039790) Springer.

Pyrros, Georgia B. Oh Calculus: A Workbook for Math 221. 3rd rev. ed. 2010. (ENG.). 194p. pap. 40.83 *(978-0-7575-4437-8(1))* Kendall Hunt Publishing Co.

Pyrros, Georgia B. Oh Calculus: A Workbook for Math 221. 4th rev. ed. 2012. (ENG.). 210p. pap. 43.00 ***(978-0-7575-9339-0(9))*** Kendall Hunt Publishing Co.

Qian, Maijian. Business Calculus. 2010. (ENG.). pap. 115.00 *(978-0-7575-5331-8(1))* Kendall Hunt Publishing Co.

Quant Systems, compiled by. Essential Calculus 2nd AIE. 2007. (C). 0.00 net. *(978-1-932628-39-5(8))* Hawkes Learning Systems.

Rabinowitz, Avi. Warped Spacetime, the Einstein Equations, & the Expanding Universe: A Calculus-Based Introduction to General Relativity. 2010. (Illus.). 400p. 69.00 *(978-0-387-20847-3(X))* Springer.

Raffoul, Raed. Functional Calculus & Coadjoint Orbits. 2009. 96p. pap. *(978-3-639-15578-5(5))* VDM Verlag Dr. Mueller e.K.

Richardson, Leonard F. Advanced Calculus: An Introduction to Linear Analysis. 2008. (ENG., Illus.). 416p. 133.00 *(978-0-470-23288-0(9)*, Wiley-Interscience) Wiley, John & Sons, Inc.

Rigdon, Steve. Calculus. 9th ed. 2006. (ENG.). 496p. (C). pap. 36.67 *(978-0-13-146966-2(5))* Addison Wesley.

Rock, Nathaniel Max. Ap Ab Calculus Exam Test Prep First Edition. 2008. 260p. per. 39.99 *(978-1-59980-025-7(X))* Nathaniel Max Rock.

—Standards Driven Math: Combo Book. 2007. 688p. pap. 99.99 *(978-1-59980-033-2(0))* Nathaniel Max Rock.

Rogawski & Rogawski, Jon. Student Solutions Manual for Late Transcendentals Single Variable. 2nd ed. 2011. (ENG.). 805p. (C). pap. 37.95 ***(978-1-4292-4290-5(6))*** Freeman, W. H. & Co.

Rogawski, Jon. Calculus. (ENG., 1050p. (C). 2007. Illus.). 130.95 *(978-1-4292-1066-9(4))* 2007. (Illus.). per. 105.95 *(978-1-4292-1072-0(9))* 2nd ed. 2011. 130.95 *(978-1-4292-0839-0(2))* Freeman, W. H. & Co.

—Calculus: Early Transcendentals. (ENG., 1050p. (C). 2007. Illus.). 130.95 *(978-1-4292-1073-7(7))* 2007. (Illus.). per. 118.95 *(978-1-4292-1074-4(5))* 2nd ed. 2011. ring bd. 85.95 ***(978-1-4292-6016-9(5))*** Freeman, W. H. & Co.

—Calculus: Multivariable. 2nd ed. 2011. (ENG.). 600p. (C). 99.95 *(978-1-4292-3187-9(4))* Freeman, W. H. & Co.

—Calculus: Single Variable. 2nd ed. 2011. (ENG.). 800p. (C). 105.95 *(978-1-4292-3183-1(1))*; pap. 99.95 *(978-1-4292-3182-4(3))* Freeman, W. H. & Co.

—Calculus Combo, Early Transcendentals. 2nd ed. 2011. (ENG.). 1050p. (C). pap. 118.95 *(978-1-4292-3184-8(X))* Freeman, W. H. & Co.

—Calculus: Early Transcendentals. 2nd ed. 2011. (ENG.). 1050p. (C). 130.95 *(978-1-4292-0838-3(4))* Freeman, W. H. & Co.

—Calculus: Early Transcendentals Single Variable (Loose Leaf) 2nd ed. 2011. (ENG.). 800p. (C). 69.95 ***(978-1-4292-9891-9(X))*** Freeman, W. H. & Co.

—Calculus Late Transcendentals (Loose Leaf) 2nd ed. 2011. (ENG.). 1050p. (C). 85.95 ***(978-1-4292-9490-4(6))*** Freeman, W. H. & Co.

—Calculus, Late Transcendentals (Paper) 2nd ed. 2011. (ENG.). 1050p. (C). pap. 118.95 *(978-1-4292-3191-6(2))* Freeman, W. H. & Co.

—Multivariable Calculus. (ENG., (C). 2007. Illus.). 600p. per. 93.95 *(978-1-4292-1069-0(9))* 2007. 512p. pap. 37.95 *(978-0-7167-9880-4(8))* 2nd ed. 2011. 600p. 99.95 *(978-1-4292-3193-0(9))* Freeman, W. H. & Co.

—Multivariable Calculus: Early Transcendentals. 2007. (ENG., Illus.). 600p. (C). per. 93.95 *(978-1-4292-1079-9(6))* Freeman, W. H. & Co.

—Single Variable Calculus. (ENG., (C). 2007. Illus.). 800p. 93.95 *(978-1-4292-1071-3(0))* 2007. (Illus.). 800p. per. 99.95 *(978-1-4292-1070-6(2))* 2007. (Illus.). 800p. per. 99.95 *(978-1-4292-1076-8(1))* 2007. 512p. pap. 37.95 *(978-0-7167-9594-0(9))* 2nd ed. 2011. 800p. 105.95 *(978-1-4292-3190-9(4))* 2nd ed. 2011. 800p. pap. 99.95 *(978-1-4292-3189-3(0))* Vol. 1. 2007. (Illus.). 500p. per. 62.95 *(978-1-4292-1077-5(X))* Vol. 2. 2007. (Illus.). 600p. per. 49.95 *(978-1-4292-1067-6(2))* Freeman, W. H. & Co.

—Single Variable Calculus: Early Transcendentals. 2007. (ENG., Illus.). 800p. (C). 105.95 *(978-1-4292-1075-1(3))* Freeman, W. H. & Co.

—Single Variable Calculus, Early Transcendentals Student's Solutions Manual. 2nd ed. 2011. (ENG.). 512p. (C). pap. 37.95 *(978-1-4292-5500-4(5))* Freeman, W. H. & Co.

—Single Variable Calculus: Early Transcendentals, Volume 2. 2007. (ENG., Illus.). 600p. (C). per. 55.95 *(978-1-4292-1078-2(8))* Freeman, W. H. & Co.

—Single Variable Calculus, Volume 1. 2007. (ENG., Illus.). 500p. (C). per. 55.95 *(978-1-4292-1068-3(0))* Freeman, W. H. & Co.

Ronchi Della Rocca, Simona. Typed Lambda Calculi & Applications: 8th International Conference, TLCA 2007, Paris, France, June 26-28, 2007, Proceedings. 2007. (Lecture Notes in Computer Science / Theoretical Computer Science & General Issues Ser.). x, 397p. pap. 89.95 *(978-3-540-73227-3(6))* Springer.

Ronchi Della Rocca, Simona & Paolini, Luca. The Parametric Lambda Calculus: A Metamodel for Computation. 2010. (Texts in Theoretical Computer Science. an EATCS Ser.). x, 252p. pap. 109.00 *(978-3-642-05746-5(2)*, 3642057462) Springer.

Rosenbaum, R. A. & Johnson, G. P. Calculus: Basic Concepts & Applications. 2009. (ENG.). 440p. pap. 55.00 *(978-0-521-09590-7(5))* Cambridge Univ. Pr.

Ross, Debra Anne & Ross, Debra. Calculus. 2nd ed. 2009. (ENG.). 344p. pap. 18.99 *(978-1-59863-986-5(2))* Course Technology.

Ross, Kenneth A. Elementary Analysis: The Theory of Calculus. 2010. (Undergraduate Texts in Mathematics Ser.). (Illus.). x, 368p. pap. 54.95 *(978-1-4419-2811-5(1)*, 1441928111) Springer.

Rudman, Jack. Physics with Calculus: Mechanics. (Dantes Subject Standardized Tests Ser.: Vol. DANTES-56). (C). pap. 29.95 *(978-0-8373-6656-2(9)*, Passbooks) National Learning Corp.

Ryan, Mark. Calculus Essentials for Dummies. 2010. (ENG., Illus.). 192p. pap. 9.99 *(978-0-470-61835-6(3)*, For Dummies) Wiley, John & Sons, Inc.

Sabatier, J., et al, eds. Advances in Fractional Calculus: Theoretical Developments & Applications in Physics & Engineering. 2010. (ENG.). xiii, 552p. pap. 219.00 *(978-90-481-7513-0(5)*, 9048175135) Springer.

Sakallah, Karem A. & Simon, Laurent, eds. Theory & Application of Satisfiability Testing: 14th International Conference, SAT 2011, Ann Arbor, MI, USA, June 19-22, 2011, Proceedings. 2011. (Lecture Notes in Computer Science / Theoretical Computer Science & General Issues Ser.). (Illus.). xiii, 371p. pap. 83.00 ***(978-3-642-21580-3(7)***, 3642215807) Springer.

Salas, Hille & Hetgen & Cram101 Textbook Reviews Staff. One & Several Variables: Calculus. 2007. 192p. per. 13.95 *(978-1-4288-3450-7(8))* Cram101 Inc.

Salas, Satunino L. Calculus: One & Several Variables. 10th ed. 2007. (Wiley Plus Products Ser.). (Illus.). 167.95 *(978-0-470-13655-3(3))* Wiley, John & Sons, Inc.

—Calculus: One & Several Variables 9th Edition with WIE Elementary Linear Algebra w/Applications Set. 2006. 179.95 *(978-0-470-11696-8(X))* Wiley, John & Sons, Inc.

—Calculus: One Variable. 10th rev. ed. 2007. (Wiley Plus Products Ser.). (Illus.). 134.95 *(978-0-470-14771-9(7))* Wiley, John & Sons, Inc.

—Calculus Combo. 10th ed. 2007. (Wiley Plus Products Ser.). pap. 86.95 *(978-0-470-10233-6(0))* Wiley, John & Sons, Inc.

—Calculus One & Several Variable 9th Edition with Student Solutions Manual & Cliff Trig Set. 2006. 256.95 *(978-0-470-11896-2(2))* Wiley, John & Sons, Inc.

—Calculus: One Variable 9th Edition with Calculus: Several Variables 9th Edition Set. 2006. 1328p. 188.95 *(978-0-470-11654-8(4))* Wiley, John & Sons, Inc.

—Wiley Plus/Blackboard Stand-alone to accompany Calculus Combo. 10th ed. 2006. (Wiley Plus Products Ser.). pap., pap. 86.95 *(978-0-470-10239-8(X))* Wiley, John & Sons, Inc.

—Wiley Plus/WebCT Stand-alone to accompany Calculus Combo, Vol. 10. 10th ed. 2007. (Wiley Plus Products Ser.). pap. 86.95 *(978-0-470-10245-9(4))* Wiley, John & Sons, Inc.

Salas, Satunino L., et al. Calculus: One & Several Variables. 10th ed. 2007. (Wiley Plus Products Ser.). 167.95 *(978-0-470-13220-3(5))* Wiley, John & Sons, Inc.

—Calculus: One Variable. 10th ed. 2007. (Wiley Plus Products Ser.). pap. 69.95 *(978-0-470-10507-8(0)*, For Dummies) Wiley, John & Sons, Inc.

—Calculus, Textbook & Student Solutions Manual: One & Several Variables. 10th ed. 2007. (ENG.). (C). 267.95 *(978-0-470-14062-8(3)*, Wiley) Wiley, John & Sons, Inc.

Salas, Saturnino L. (WCS)Calc: Several Variables 10th Edition Vol II. 2007. 456p. pap. 44.95 *(978-0-470-13940-0(4)*, Wiley) Wiley, John & Sons, Inc.

—(WCS)Calculus: One Variable 10th Edition Volume 1. 2007. 626p. pap. 77.95 *(978-0-470-13941-7(2)*, Wiley) Wiley, John & Sons, Inc.

Salas, Saturnino L., et al. Calculus: One Variable. 10th ed. 2007. (ENG., Illus.). 384p. (C). pap. 48.95 *(978-0-470-10553-5(4)*, Wiley) Wiley, John & Sons, Inc.

—Calculus: One Variable. 10th rev. ed. 2006. (ENG., Illus.). 736p. (C). 223.95 *(978-0-470-07333-9(0)*, Wiley) Wiley, John & Sons, Inc.

Saxon, John H., Jr. & Wang, Frank Y. Homeschool Testing Book for Calculus. 2nd ed. 2006. (Saxon Calculus Ser.). (gr. 9-12). per. 12.50 *(978-1-60032-015-6(5))* Houghton Mifflin Harcourt Supplemental Pubs.

Schaaf, William L. & Mathematics Centre Staff. The Calculus Primer. 2011. (Dover Books on Mathematics Ser.). (ENG.). 432p. pap. 19.95 ***(978-0-486-48579-9(X))*** Dover Pubns., Inc.

Schikhof, W. H. Ultrametric Calculus: An Introduction to p-Adic Analysis. 2007. (Cambridge Studies in Advanced Mathematics). (ENG.). 320p. pap. 61.00 *(978-0-521-03287-2(3))* Cambridge Univ. Pr.

Schreiber. Calculus for the Life Sciences. rev. ed. 2011. 205.95 *(978-0-7637-8939-8(9))* Jones & Bartlett Learning, LLC.

Shen, Jie, et al. Spectral Methods: Algorithms, Analysis & Applications. 2011. (Springer Series in Computational Mathematics Ser.). (ENG., Illus.). 500p. 124.00 *(978-3-540-71040-0(X)*, 354071040X) Springer.

Sheng, Hu, et al. Fractional Processes & Fractional-Order Signal Processing: Techniques & Applications. 2011. (Signals & Communication Technology Ser.). (ENG., Illus.). xxvi, 295p. 179.00 ***(978-1-4471-2232-6(1)***, 1447122321) Springer.

Simpson, Stephen G. Subsystems of Second Order Arithmetic. 2nd ed. 2009. (Perspectives in Logic Ser.). (ENG., Illus.). 464p. 95.00 *(978-0-521-88439-6(X))* Cambridge Univ. Pr.

Smirnov, Vladimir. Feynman Integral Calculus. 2006. (ENG., Illus.). x, 287p. 109.00 *(978-3-540-30610-8(2)*, 3540306102) Springer.

Smith & Minton & Cram101 Textbook Reviews Staff. Calculus. 2007. 216p. per. 13.95 *(978-1-4288-3460-6(5))* Cram101 Inc.

Smith, Minton & Cram101 Textbook Reviews Staff. Calculus Concepts & Connections. 2007. 236p. per. 14.95 *(978-1-4288-3692-1(6))* Cram101 Inc.

Smith, Robert. Student Solutions Manual for Calculus. 4th ed. 2011. (ENG.). 512p. (C). pap. 68.67 *(978-0-07-725696-8(4)*, 0077256964, McGraw-Hill Science, Engineering & Mathematics) McGraw-Hill Higher Education.

—Student Solutions Manual for Calculus: Early Transcendental Functions. 4th ed. 2011. (ENG.). 512p. (C). pap. 68.67 *(978-0-07-723590-1(8)*, 0077235908, McGraw-Hill Science, Engineering & Mathematics) McGraw-Hill Higher Education.

Smith, Robert & Minton, Roland. Calculus: Early Transcendental Functions. 4th ed. 2011. (ENG.). (C). 165.67 *(978-0-07-747573-4(9)*, 0077475739, McGraw-Hill Science, Engineering & Mathematics) McGraw-Hill Higher Education.

—Calculus: LTF w/ Connect Plus Access Card. 4th ed. 2011. (ENG.). (C). 165.67 *(978-0-07-750941-5(2)*, 0077509412, McGraw-Hill Science, Engineering & Mathematics) McGraw-Hill Higher Education.

—Loose Leaf Version for Calculus. 4th ed. 2011. (ENG.). (C). ring bd. 110.67 *(978-0-07-743140-2(5)*, 0077431405, McGraw-Hill Science, Engineering & Mathematics) McGraw-Hill Higher Education.

—Loose Leaf Version for Calculus Early Transcendental Functions. 4th ed. 2011. (ENG.). (C). ring bd. 110.67 *(978-0-07-743139-6(1)*, 0077431391, McGraw-Hill Science, Engineering & Mathematics) McGraw-Hill Higher Education.

Smith, Robert T. & Minton, Roland B. Calculus. 3rd ed. 2007. *(978-0-07-326847-7(X))* 2006. (Illus.). xxxii, 1253p. *(978-0-07-340606-0(6))* 2006. (Illus.). 864p. *(978-0-07-326846-0(1))* McGraw-Hill Cos., The.

—Calculus. 4th ed. 2011. (ENG., Illus.). 1376p. (C). 158.00 *(978-0-07-338311-8(2)*, 0073383112, McGraw-Hill Science, Engineering & Mathematics) McGraw-Hill Higher Education.

—Calculus: Early Transcendental Functions. (ENG., Illus.). (C). 3rd ed. 2007. 1376p. 158.00 *(978-0-07-330944-6(3)*, 0073309443) 4th ed. 2011. 1248p. 158.00 *(978-0-07-353232-5(0)*, 0073532320) McGraw-Hill Higher Education. (McGraw-Hill Science, Engineering & Mathematics).

—Calculus: Late Transcendental Functions with MathZone. 3rd rev. ed. 2007. (ENG.). 1392p. (C). 158.00 *(978-0-07-331270-5(3)*, 0073312703, McGraw-Hill Science, Engineering & Mathematics) McGraw-Hill Higher Education.

—Calculus, Multivariable: Early Transcendental Functions. 3rd ed. 2006. (ENG., Illus.). 560p. (C). 166.67 *(978-0-07-330937-8(0)*, 0073309370, McGraw-Hill Science, Engineering & Mathematics) McGraw-Hill Higher Education.

—Calculus, Single Variable: Early Transcendental Functions. 3rd rev. ed. 2006. (ENG., Illus.). 952p. (C). 185.00 *(978-0-07-330943-9(5)*, 0073309435, McGraw-Hill Science, Engineering & Mathematics) McGraw-Hill Higher Education.

—Calculus, Single Variable: Late Transcendental Functions. 3rd rev. ed. 2007. (ENG.). 880p. (C). 185.00 *(978-0-07-331419-8(6)*, 0073314196, McGraw-Hill Science, Engineering & Mathematics) McGraw-Hill Higher Education.

Smyth, William. Elements of the Differential & Integral Calculus, by William Smyth. 2006. 244p. per. 20.99 *(978-1-4255-2079-3(0))* MPublishing.

Steeb. Problems & Solutions in Introductory. . 2006. (Illus.). x, 239p. 86.00 *(978-981-256-916-5(2))* World Scientific Publishing Co., Inc.

Steeb, Willi-Hans. Problems & Solutions in Introductory & Advanced Matrix Calculus. 2006. 239p. pap. 43.00 *(978-981-270-202-9(4))* World Scientific Publishing Co., Inc.

Steland, A. Financial Statistics & Mathematical Finance: Methods, Models & Applications. 2012. (ENG.). 400p. 90.00 ***(978-0-470-71058-6(6)***, Wiley) Wiley, John & Sons, Inc.

Stewart & Cram101 Textbook Reviews Staff. Calculus. 2007. 228p. per. 13.95 *(978-1-4288-3648-8(9))* Cram101 Inc.

—Calculus: Concepts & Contexts. 2007. 204p. per. 13.95 *(978-1-4288-3556-6(3))* Cram101 Inc.

—Calculus Early Transcendentals. 2007. 88p. per. 10.95 *(978-1-4288-3624-2(1))* Cram101 Inc.

—Early Transcendental Single Variable Calculus. 2007. 196p. per. 13.95 *(978-1-4288-3510-8(5))* Cram101 Inc.

Stewart, James. Ap Calculus. 5th ed. 2006. (C). 126.95 *(978-0-495-11340-9(9))* Brooks/Cole.

—Calclabs with Mathematica Single Variable Calculus. 6th ed. 2007. (ENG.). 272p. (C). pap. 68.95 *(978-0-495-38245-4(0))* Brooks/Cole.

—Calculus. (C). 6th ed. 2007. ring bd. 125.95 *(978-0-495-55378-6(6))* 6th ed. 2007. (ENG., Illus.). 1344p. 235.95 *(978-0-495-01160-6(6))* 7th ed. 2011. (ENG.). 1368p. 224.95 *(978-0-538-49781-7(5))* Brooks/Cole.

—Calculus: Concepts & Contexts. (Available 2010 Titles Enhanced Web Assign Ser.). (ENG., (C). 3rd ed. 2006. Illus.). 1168p. pap. 259.95 *(978-0-495-38491-5(7))* 4th ed. 2009. 1152p. 228.95 *(978-0-495-55742-5(0))* 4th alt. ed. 2009. 1184p. pap. 185.95 *(978-0-538-73365-6(9))* Brooks/Cole.

—Calculus: Early Transcendentals. 2006. (ENG.). 480p. (C). per. 61.95 *(978-0-495-01429-4(X))* Brooks/Cole.

—Calculus: Early Transcendentals. (Available 2010 Titles Enhanced Web Assign Ser.). (ENG., (C). 6th ed. 2007. Illus.). 1336p. 224.95 *(978-0-495-01166-8(5))* 7th ed. 2010. 1344p. 224.95 *(978-0-538-49790-9(4))* Brooks/Cole.

—Calculus: Early Transcendentals, Hybrid Edition (with Enhanced WebAssign with eBook Printed Access Card for Multi Term Math & Science) 7th ed. 2011. (Cengage Learningrsquo;s New Hybrid Editions! Ser.). (ENG.). 1056p. (C). pap. 154.95 *(978-1-111-42668-2(6))* Brooks/Cole.

—Essential Calculus. (ENG., (C). 2006. Illus.). 480p. per. 61.95 *(978-0-495-01444-7(3))* 2nd ed. 2012. 904p. 174.95 ***(978-1-133-11229-7(3))*** Brooks/Cole.

—Essential Calculus: Early Transcendentals. 2nd ed. 2012. (ENG.). 912p. (C). 174.95 ***(978-1-133-11228-0(5))*** Brooks/Cole.

—Essential Calculus: Early Transcendentals, Enhanced Edition (with Enhanced WebAssign with eBook Printed Access Card for Multi Term Math & Science) 2010. (Available Titles CourseMate Ser.). (ENG.). 944p. (C). 162.95 *(978-0-538-49739-8(4))* Brooks/Cole.

—Fast Track to a Five for Stewart's Calculus. 6th ed. 2009. (ENG.). 352p. (C). pap. 33.95 *(978-1-4390-4969-3(6))* Brooks/Cole.

—Metric Edition - Multivariable Calculus: Concepts & Contexts, International Edition. 4th ed. 2010. (Illus.). 496p. *(978-1-4390-4692-0(1))* Brooks/Cole.

—Multivariable Calculus. (Available 2010 Titles Enhanced Web Assign Ser.). (ENG., (C). 6th ed. 2007. Illus.). 596p. 189.95 *(978-0-495-01163-7(0))* 7th ed. 2011. 480p. pap., pupil's gde. ed. 73.95 *(978-0-8400-5410-4(6))* 7th ed. 2011. 600p. 187.95 *(978-0-538-49787-9(4))* Brooks/Cole.

—Multivariable Calculus: Concepts & Contexts. 4th ed. 2009. (Available 2010 Titles Enhanced Web Assign Ser.). (ENG., Illus.). 512p. (C). 186.95 *(978-0-495-56054-8(5))* Brooks/Cole.

—Multivariable Calculus: Early Transcendentals. 6th ed. 2007. (Available 2010 Titles Enhanced Web Assign Ser.). (ENG., Illus.). 600p. (C). 187.95 *(978-0-495-01172-9(X))* Brooks/Cole.

—Single Variable Calculus. 7th ed. 2011. (ENG.). (C). 608p. pap., pupil's gde. ed. 73.95 *(978-0-8400-5409-8(2))*; 960p. 200.95 *(978-0-538-49783-1(1))*; 720p. pap. 133.95 *(978-1-111-42670-5(8))* Brooks/Cole.

—Single Variable Calculus: Concepts & Contexts. (Available 2010 Titles Enhanced Web Assign Ser.). (C). 4th ed. 2009. (ENG.). 784p. 214.95 *(978-0-495-55972-6(5))* 6th ed. 2007. 130.95 *(978-0-495-38244-7(2))* 6th ed. 2007. (ENG., Illus.). 948p. 210.95 *(978-0-495-01161-3(4))* Brooks/Cole.

—Single Variable Calculus: Concepts & Contexts. 3rd ed. 69.20 net. *(978-0-534-32788-0(5))* 3rd ed. 71.20 net. *(978-0-534-32787-3(7))* 6th ed. 2007. 144.95 *(978-0-495-42426-0(9))* CENGAGE Learning.

—Single Variable Calculus: Early Transcendentals. (Available 2010 Titles Enhanced Web Assign Ser.). (ENG., (C). 6th ed. 2007. Illus.). 912p. 200.95 *(978-0-495-01169-9(X))* 7th ed. 2011. 936p. 200.95 *(978-0-538-49867-8(6))* 7th ed. 2011. 576p. pap. 77.95 *(978-0-8400-4934-6(X))* Brooks/Cole.

—Single Variable Calculus: Early Transcendentals Student Guide. 7th ed. 2011. (ENG.). 512p. (C). pap. 70.95 *(978-0-8400-5420-3(3))* Brooks/Cole.

—Single Variable Calculus Student Solutions Manua. 7th ed. 2011. (ENG.). 592p. (C). pap. 85.95 *(978-0-8400-4949-0(8))* Brooks/Cole.

—Study Guide for Stewart's Multivariable Calculus: Concepts & Contexts, 4th. 4th ed. 2010. (ENG.). 352p. (C). pap. 52.95 *(978-0-495-56057-9(X))* Brooks/Cole.

—Study Guide for Stewart's Single Variable Calculus: Concepts & Contexts, 4th. 4th ed. 2009. (ENG.). 448p. (C). pap. 89.95 *(978-0-495-56064-7(2))* Brooks/Cole.

—Transcendentals. 6th ed. 2009. (ENG.). 352p. (C). pap. 33.95 *(978-1-4390-4970-9(X))* Brooks/Cole.

Stewart, James & Clegg, Daniel. Applied Calculus. 2012. (ENG.). 700p. (C). pap. 33.95 *(978-0-534-42387-2(6))* Brooks/Cole.

Stewart, James, et al. Precalculus: Mathematics for Calculus. 6th ed. 2011. (ENG.). 452p. (C). pap. 78.95 *(978-0-8400-6879-8(4))* Brooks/Cole.

—Study Guide for Stewart/Redlin/Watson's Precalculus: Mathematics for Calculus, 6th. 6th ed. 2011. (ENG.). 368p. (C). pap. 74.95 *(978-0-8400-6917-7(0))* Brooks/Cole.

Stewart, James (James Stewart). Calculus, Hybrid Edition (with Enhanced WebAssign with eBook for Multi Term Math & Science) 7th ed. 2011. (Cengage Learningrsquo;s New Hybrid Editions! Ser.). (ENG.). 1080p. (C). pap. 154.95 *(978-1-133-11271-6(4))* Brooks/Cole.

—Single Variable Calculus, Hybrid Reprint. 7th ed. 2011. (Cengage Learningrsquo;s New Hybrid Editions! Ser.). (ENG.). 744p. (C). pap. 133.95 *(978-1-133-11211-2(0))* Brooks/Cole.

Stewart, Scott. Calculus. 6th alt. ed. 2007. (C). 111.95 *(978-0-495-55377-9(8))* Brooks/Cole.

—Calculus: Early Transcendentals Alternate Edition. 6th ed. 2007. (C). pap. 111.95 *(978-0-495-55379-3(4))* Brooks/Cole.

—Calculus: Early Transcendentals Looseleaf. 6th ed. 2007. (C). ring bd. 125.95 *(978-0-495-55380-9(8))* Brooks/Cole.

Stewart, Scott & Stewart. Complete Solutions Manual for Stewart's Single Variable Calculus: Early Transcendentals. 6th ed. 2008. 1056p. pap. 38.95 *(978-0-495-01255-9(6))* Brooks/Cole.

Strang & Strang, Gilbert. Calculus. 2nd ed. (ENG., Illus.). 600p. *(978-0-9802327-4-5(0))* Wellesley-Cambridge Pr.

Strogatz, Steven. The Calculus of Friendship - What a Teacher & a Student Learned about Life while Corresponding about Math. 2011. (ENG., Illus.). 184p. pap. 14.95 *(978-0-691-15038-3(9))* Princeton Univ. Pr.

Strogatz, Steven H. & Joffray, Don. The Calculus of Friendship: What a Teacher & a Student Learned about Life While Corresponding about Math. 2009. (ENG., Illus.). 184p. (C). 19.95 *(978-0-691-13493-2(6))* Princeton Univ. Pr.

Sullivan & Cram101 Textbook Reviews Staff. Precalculus. 2007. (ENG.). 60p. per. 27.95 *(978-1-4288-3488-0(5))* Cram101 Inc.

Swinyard, Craig. Students' Reasoning about Limit. 2009. 304p. pap. *(978-3-639-16464-0(4))* VDM Verlag Dr. Mueller e.K.

Swokowski, Earl William. Calculus with Analytic Geometry in Spanish. 2nd ed. (SPA.). pap. *(978-968-7270-43-2(8))* CENGAGE Learning.

Szecsei, Denise. Calculus. 2006. (Homework Helpers Ser.). (ENG., Illus.). 288p. pap. 14.99 *(978-1-56414-914-5(5))* Career Pr., Inc.

Tahan, Malba. Hoem que Calculava. pap. 25.95 *(978-85-01-06196-6(4))* Edioura Publicacoes SA BRA. Dist: Distribooks, Inc.

Tan. Interactive Video Skillbuilder CD-ROM for Tan's Calculus. 2010. (ENG.). (C). 15.95 *(978-0-534-49438-4(2))* Brooks/Cole.

—Itext Access Card for Tan's Calculus: Early Transcendentals. 2008. (C). 19.95 *(978-0-534-46563-6(3))* Brooks/Cole.

—Itext for Tan's Calculus. 2008. (C). 19.95 *(978-0-534-49444-5(7))* Brooks/Cole.

Tan & Cram101 Textbook Reviews Staff. Applied Calculus. 2007. 164p. per. 12.95 *(978-1-4288-3596-2(2))* Cram101 Inc.

—Calculus. 2007. 60p. per. 9.95 *(978-1-4288-3494-1(X))* Cram101 Inc.

Tan, Soo T. Applied Calculus for the Managerial, Life, & Social Sciences. (ENG.). 896p. (C). 7th ed. 2006. 235.95 *(978-0-495-38312-3(0))* 8th ed. 2010. 226.95 *(978-0-495-55969-6(5))* Brooks/Cole.

—Calculus. 2009. (Textbooks Available with Cengage YouBook Ser.). (ENG.). 1456p. (C). 144.95 *(978-0-534-46579-7(X))* Brooks/Cole.

—Calculus for the Managerial, Life, & Social Sciences. 7th ed. 2007. (ENG., Illus.). 1p. (C). pap. 217.95 *(978-0-495-39018-3(6))* Brooks/Cole.

—Finite Mathematics for the Managerial Life, & Social Sciences. 9th ed. 2008. (Available 2010 Titles Enhanced Web Assign Ser.). (ENG., Illus.). 640p. (C). 195.95 *(978-0-495-38753-4(3))* Brooks/Cole.

—Interactive Video Skillbuilder CD-ROM for Tan's Calculus: Early Transcendentals. 2010. (ENG.). (C). 15.95 *(978-0-534-46562-9(5))* Brooks/Cole.

—Single Variable Calculus. 2009. (Available 2011 Titles Enhanced Web Assign Ser.). (ENG.). 1008p. (C). 137.95 *(978-0-534-46566-7(8))* Brooks/Cole.

—Single Variable Calculus: Early Transcendentals. 2010. (Available 2011 Titles Enhanced Web Assign Ser.). (ENG.). 1008p. (C). 137.95 *(978-0-534-46570-4(6))* Brooks/Cole.

—Student Solutions Manual for Tan's Multivariable Calculus. 2010. (ENG.). 256p. (C). pap. 41.95 *(978-0-534-46577-3(3))* Brooks/Cole.

—Student Solutions Manual for Tan's Single Variable Calculus. 2010. (ENG.). 416p. (C). pap. 48.95 *(978-0-534-46568-1(4))* Brooks/Cole.

—Student Solutions Manual for Tan's Single Variable Calculus: Early Transcendentals. 2010. (ENG.). 400p. (C). pap. 41.95 *(978-0-534-46573-5(0))* Brooks/Cole.

Tan, Soo Tang. Applied Calculus for the Managerial, Life, & Social Sciences. 7th ed. 2007. (Illus.). xx, 868p. *(978-0-495-39235-4(9))* Brooks/Cole.

Taraporevala, Amavaz, et al. Visualizing calculus by way of maple: an emphasis on problem Solving. 2011. (ENG.). 592p. (C). pap. 43.33 ***(978-0-07-803598-2(8)***, 0078035988, McGraw-Hill Science, Engineering & Mathematics) McGraw-Hill Higher Education.

Tarasov, Vasily E. Fractional Dynamics: Applications of Fractional Calculus to Dynamics of Particles, Fields & Media. 2011. (Nonlinear Physical Science Ser.). (ENG.). 450p. 169.00 *(978-3-642-14002-0(5)*, 3642140025) Springer.

Terefe Weldegebriel, Araniyos. Fundamental Concepts in Calculus. 2011. 168p. pap. ***(978-3-8443-8912-8(1))*** Lambert Academic Publishing.

Theory & Applications of Satisfiability Testing - SAT 2007: 10th International Conference, Lisbon, Portugal, May 28-31, 2007 Proceedings. 2007. (Lecture Notes in Computer Science Ser.). (Illus.). 384p. pap. 79.95 *(978-3-540-72787-3(6))* Springer.

Thielscher, Michael. Reasoning Robots: The Art & Science of Programming Robotic Agents. 2010. (Applied Logic Ser.). xiii, 327p. pap. 249.00 *(978-90-481-6783-3(3)*, 9048167833) Springer.

Thomas, et al. Thomas' Calculus, Early Transcendentals, Books a la Carte Plus MyMathLab/MyStatLab Student Access Kit. 12th ed. 2010. (ENG.). (C). ring bd. 128.80 *(978-0-321-73529-4(3))* Addison Wesley.

Thomas & Finney & Cram101 Textbook Reviews Staff. Thomas' Calculus. 2007. 220p. per. 13.95 *(978-1-4288-3480-4(X))* Cram101 Inc.

Thomas, Christopher & LearningExpress Staff. Calculus Success in 20 Minutes a Day. 2007. (Skill Builders (Learningexpress) Ser.). (ENG., Illus.). 208p. per. 16.00 *(978-1-57685-536-2(8))* LearningExpress, LLC.

Thomas, George B., et al. Thomas' Calculus. 12th ed. 2009. (Thomas Calculus 12th Edition Ser.). (ENG.). 1236p. (C). 198.00 *(978-0-321-58799-2(5))* Addison Wesley.

Thomas, George B., Jr., et al. Thomas' Calculus: Early Transcendentals. 12th ed. 2010. (ENG.). 700p. (C). ring bd. 118.80 *(978-0-321-73078-7(X))* Addison Wesley.

Thomas, George B., et al. Thomas' Calculus: Single Variable. 12th ed. 2009. (Thomas' Calculus 12th Edition Ser.). (ENG., Illus.). 936p. (C). pap. 101.33 *(978-0-321-63742-0(9))* Addison Wesley.

—Thomas' Calculus 11th Media Upgrade Part One plus MyMathLab. 11th ed. 2007. (ENG.). (C). pap., pap. 111.33 *(978-0-321-51338-0(X))* Addison Wesley.

—Thomas' Calculus 11th Media Upgrade Part Two Plus MyMathLab. 11th ed. 2007. (ENG.). (C). pap., pap. 111.33 *(978-0-321-51340-3(1))* Addison Wesley.

—Thomas' Calculus, Books a la Carte Edition. 12th ed. 2010. (ENG.). 1080p. (C). ring bd. 118.80 *(978-0-321-73067-1(4))* Addison Wesley.

—Thomas' Calculus, Early Transcendentals, Single Variable, Books a la Carte Edition. 12th ed. 2010. (ENG.). (C). ring bd. 118.80 *(978-0-321-73079-4(8))* Addison Wesley.

—Thomas' Calculus Early Transcendentals. 12th ed. 2009. (Thomas Calculus 12th Edition Ser.). (ENG.). 1160p. (C). 198.00 *(978-0-321-58876-0(2))* Addison Wesley.

—Thomas' Calculus Early Transcendentals, Single Variable. 12th ed. 2009. (Thomas Calculus 12th Edition Ser.). (ENG.). 816p. (C). pap. 101.33 *(978-0-321-62883-1(7))* Addison Wesley.

—Thomas' Calculus, Single Variable, Books a la Carte Edition, Thomas' Calculus. 12th ed. 2010. (ENG.). 750p. (C). ring bd. 60.80 *(978-0-321-73068-8(2))* Addison Wesley.

Thomas, George Brinton. Thomas' Calculus Early Transcendentals: Part One: Media Upgrade. 11th ed. 2007. (Thomas Ser.). (ENG., Illus.). 864p. (C). per. 101.33 *(978-0-321-49874-8(7))* Addison Wesley.

—Thomas' Calculus Part One Media Upgrade. 11th ed. 2007. (Thomas Ser.). (ENG., Illus.). 864p. (C). per. 101.33 *(978-0-321-49875-5(5))* Addison Wesley.

—Thomas' Calculus Part Two Media Upgrade. 11th ed. 2007. (Thomas Ser.). (ENG., Illus.). (C). per. 101.33 *(978-0-321-50103-5(9))* Addison Wesley.

Thomas, George Brinton, et al. Thomas' Calculus Early Transcendentals. 11th rev. ed. 2007. (Thomas 11e Ser.). (ENG., Illus.). 1212p. (C). 198.00 *(978-0-321-49575-4(6))* Addison Wesley.

—Thomas' Calculus Media. 11th rev. ed. 2007. (Thomas 11e Ser.). (ENG., Illus.). 1228p. (C). 198.00 *(978-0-321-48987-6(X))* Addison Wesley.

Thompson, J. E. Calculus for the Practical Man. 2007. 360p. per. *(978-1-4067-5672-2(5))* Read Bks.

Thompson, Silvanus P. Calculus Made Easy. 2008. 316p. pap. *(978-1-4097-2467-4(0))* Read Bks.

Toeplitz, Otto. The Calculus: A Genetic Approach. 2007. (Illus.). 201p. per. 30.00 *(978-0-226-80668-6(5))* Univ. of Chicago Pr.

Ungar, Abraham Albert. Barycentric Calculus in Euclidean & Hyperbolic Geometry: A Comparative Introduction. 2010. (Illus.). 360p. 97.00 *(978-981-4304-93-1(X))* World Scientific Publishing Co., Inc.

Uribe, Alejandro. Vector Calculus. 2014. (ENG.). 608p. (C). 83.95 *(978-0-7167-1756-0(5))* Freeman, W. H. & Co.

Vaniwaarde. College Outline: Precalculus. Date not set. (C). pap. *(978-0-15-502065-6(4))* Harcourt College Pubs.

Varberg, Dale, et al. Student Study Pack for Calculus. 9th ed. 2006. (ENG.). (C). pap., pap. 36.67 *(978-0-13-220323-4(5)*, Prentice Hall) Prentice Hall PTR.

Waner, Stefan & Costenoble, Steven. Applied Calculus. 5th ed. 2010. (Available 2011 Titles Enhanced Web Assign Ser.). (ENG.). 752p. (C). 228.95 *(978-1-4390-4923-5(8))* Brooks/Cole.

—Finite Math & Applied Calculus. 5th ed. 2010. (Available 2011 Titles Enhanced Web Assign Ser.). (ENG.). 1296p. (C). 230.95 *(978-1-4390-4925-9(4))* Brooks/Cole.

Waner, Stefan & Costenoble, Steven R. S. S. M. Applied Calculus. 4th ed. 2006. (ENG., Illus.). 304p. (C). per. 50.95 *(978-0-495-01699-1(3))* Brooks/Cole.

Washington, Allyn J. Basic Technical Mathematics with Calculus. 9th ed. 2008. (ENG.). 1152p. (C). 193.80 *(978-0-13-814226-1(2)*, Prentice Hall) Prentice Hall PTR.

—Student Solution's Manual for Basic Technical Mathematics with Calculus, SI Version. 9th ed. 2009. (ENG.). 416p. (C). pap. 53.40 *(978-0-13-506443-6(0))* Addison Wesley.

Weir, Maurice D., et al. Thomas' Calculus with Second Order Differential Equations. 11th ed. 2006. (ENG., Illus.). 1228p. (C). 149.33 *(978-0-321-49069-8(X))* Addison Wesley.

—Thomas' Calculus with Second-Order Differential Equations, Books a la Carte Edition. 2010. (ENG.). 1200p. (C). ring bd. 89.60 *(978-0-321-73827-1(6))* Addison Wesley.

West, Bruce, et al. Physics of Fractal Operators. 2011. (Institute for Nonlinear Science Ser.). (ENG., Illus.). ix, 354p. pap. 134.00 *(978-1-4419-3054-5(X)*, 144193054X) Springer.

Wiersema, Ubbo F. Brownian Motion Calculus. 2008. (ENG., Illus.). 330p. pap. 55.00 *(978-0-470-02170-5(5)*, Wiley) Wiley, John & Sons, Inc.

Wiley, creator. Applied Calculus. 3rd rev. ed. 2006. (Wiley Plus Products Ser.). pap. 122.95 *(978-0-470-11912-9(8))* Wiley, John & Sons, Inc.

Wiley and Sons, Inc. Staff. Calculus As a Second Language. 2006. pap. 38.95 *(978-0-471-72728-6(8))* Wiley, John & Sons, Inc.

Willard. Calculus & Its Applications. Date not set. (Mathematics Ser.). tchr. ed. 5.75 net. *(978-0-87150-565-1(7)*, Brooks/Cole) Brooks/Cole.

Wilson, Frank. Applied Calc. 2011. (Textbooks Available with Cengage YouBook Ser.). (ENG.). 256p. pap. 83.95 *(978-0-8400-6563-6(9))* Brooks/Cole.

Wilson, Frank C. Brief Applied Calculus. 2007. (ENG., Illus.). 576p. (C). 204.95 *(978-0-618-61105-8(3)*, 360081) CENGAGE Learning.

—Finite Mathematics & Applied Calculus. 2006. (ENG.). 528p. (C). pap., stu. ed. 92.95 *(978-0-618-33300-4(2)*, 360472) Brooks/Cole.

—Finite Mathematics & Applied Calculus. 2007. (Illus.). xi, 964p. *(978-0-618-73265-4(9))* Houghton Mifflin Harcourt Publishing Co.

Wilson, Frank C. & Adamson, Scott. Applied Calculus. 2008. (Available 2010 Titles Enhanced Web Assign Ser.). (ENG., Illus.). 944p. (C). 217.95 *(978-0-618-61104-1(5))* CENGAGE Learning.

Winter, Michael. Goguen Categories: A Categorical Approach to L-fuzzy Relations. (Trends in Logic Ser.). (Illus.). 2010. xii, 208p. pap. 169.00 *(978-90-481-7554-3(2)*, 9048175542) 2007. 224p. (C). 169.00 *(978-1-4020-6163-9(3))* Springer.

Woolhouse, Wesley Stoker. Elements of the Differential Calculus. 2011. 170p. pap. 27.95 ***(978-1-4460-6404-7(2))*** Barclay Pr., Inc.

Wrede, Robert & Spiegel, Murray. Schaum's Outline of Advanced Calculus, Third Edition. 3rd ed. 2010. (Schaum's Outline Ser.). (ENG., Illus.). 456p. (C). pap. 18.95 *(978-0-07-162366-7(3)*, 0071623663) McGraw-Hill Cos., The.

Yi-Zhong & Cheng, Sui Sun. Dual Sets of Envelopes & Characteristic Regions of Quasi-Polynomials. 2009. 230p. 81.00 *(978-981-4277-27-3(4))* World Scientific Publishing Co., Inc.

Zegarelli, Mark. Calculus II for Dummies. 2nd ed. 2012. (ENG.). 384p. pap. 19.99 ***(978-1-118-16170-8(X)***, For Dummies) Wiley, John & Sons, Inc.

Zhivetin, Vladimir B. Advanced Calculus: Lectures. Zubchenko, Natalia, tr. from RUS. 2007. (Illus.). 544p. 215.00 *(978-5-98664-012-9(8))* Institut problem riska RUS. Dist: Coronet Bks.

Zill. Calculus 4E: Early Transcendentals International Version. 4th rev. ed. 2009. (Illus.). pap. 149.95 *(978-0-7637-8652-6(7))* Jones & Bartlett Learning, LLC.

Zill & Wright, Tony. Calculus with Analytic Geometry, No. II. pap., stu. ed., suppl. ed. 14.25 net. *(978-0-87150-435-7(9))* CENGAGE Learning.

Zill, Dennis G. Basic Math for Calculus. Date not set. (Math). stu. ed. 8.25 net. *(978-0-534-01894-8(7))* Brooks/Cole.

Zill, Dennis G. & Wright, Scott. Calculus: Early Transcendentals. 4th rev. ed. 2009. 994p. 168.95 *(978-0-7637-5995-7(3))* Jones & Bartlett Learning, LLC.

Zill, Dennis G. & Wright, Warren S. Calculus of a Single Variable: Early Transcendentals. 4th rev. ed. 2009. 673p. 140.95 *(978-0-7637-4965-1(6))* Jones & Bartlett Learning, LLC.

—Multivariable Calculus, Vol. 2. 4th rev. ed. 2009. (Illus.). 469p. 135.95 *(978-0-7637-4966-8(4))* Jones & Bartlett Learning, LLC.

ölicher, A. & Bucher, W. Calculus in Vector Spaces Without Norm. 2007. (Lecture Notes in Mathematics Ser.). 160p. per. 26.00 *(978-3-540-03612-8(1))* Springer.

CALCULUS—DATA PROCESSING

Briggs, et al. Calculus, Books a la Carte Plus MyMathLab/MyStatLab Student Access Kit. 2010. (ENG.). (C). ring bd. 128.80 *(978-0-321-73882-0(9))* Addison Wesley.

Gerber, Leon. Algebra & Calculus with Excel for Business & Economics. 2007. (C). per. *(978-0-9792926-0-6(3))* Gerber, Leon.

—Finite Math, Statistics, & Calculus with Excel for Science. 2007. (C). per. *(978-0-9792926-1-3(1))* Gerber, Leon.

Goldstein, Larry J., et al. Calculus & Its Applications Plus MyMathLab/MyStatLab Student Access Code Card. 12th ed. 2010. (ENG.). (C). pap. 167.33 *(978-0-321-74463-0(2))* Addison Wesley.

Hollis, Selwyn. CalcLabs with Mathematica for Single Variable Calculus. 5th ed. 2011. (ENG.). (C). pap. 85.95 ***(978-0-8400-5814-0(4))*** Brooks/Cole.

—Multivariable Calculus: Concepts & Contexts. 4th ed. 2009. (ENG.). 288p. (C). pap. 46.95 *(978-0-495-82722-1(3))* Brooks/Cole.

Hollis, Selwyn. Multivariable Calculus Calclabs W/Mathematica. 5th ed. 2011. (ENG.). (C). pap. 51.95 ***(978-0-8400-5813-3(6))*** Brooks/Cole.

Jay, Barry. Pattern Calculus: Computing with Functions & Structures. 2009. (ENG., Illus.). xvii, 213p. 129.00 *(978-3-540-89184-0(6)*, 3540891846) Springer.

Larson, Ron & Edwards, Bruce H. Calculus - Early Transcendental Functions. 5th ed. 2010. (ENG.). 368p. (C). pap. 37.95 *(978-0-538-75711-9(6))* Brooks/Cole.

Stewart, James. Multivariable Calculus. 6th ed. 2007. (ENG.). 272p. (C). pap. 54.95 *(978-0-495-01231-3(9))* Brooks/Cole.

—Multivariable Calculus. 6th ed. 2007. (ENG.). 288p. (C). pap. 59.95 *(978-0-495-11890-9(7))* Brooks/Cole.

—Single Variable Calculus. 6th ed. 2007. (ENG.). 272p. (C). pap. 71.95 *(978-0-495-01235-1(1))* Brooks/Cole.

Stewart, James, et al. Single Variable Calculus. 4th ed. 2009. (ENG.). 272p. (C). pap. 82.95 *(978-0-495-56062-3(6))* Brooks/Cole.

Waner, Stefan & Costenoble, Steven. Applied Calculus. 5th ed. 2010. (ENG.). 176p. (C). pap., lab manual ed. 52.95 *(978-0-538-73320-5(9))* Brooks/Cole.

CALCULUS—EXAMINATIONS, QUESTIONS, ETC.

Anaxos Inc. Staff, et al. Shortcut Calculus: A Quick & Easy Way to Increase Your Calculus Knowledge & Test Scores. 2nd ed. 2007. (ENG., Illus.). 272p. pap. 12.00 *(978-1-4195-5289-2(9))* Kaplan Publishing.

Asher, Randy J., et al. 5 Steps to a 5 500 AP Calculus AB/BC Questions to Know by Test Day. 2012. (5 Steps to a 5 on the Advanced Placement Examinations Ser.). (ENG., Illus.). 288p. (C). pap. 14.00 *(978-0-07-175370-8(2)*, 0071753702) McGraw-Hill Cos., The.

Cade, Sharon, et al. Preparing for the AP Calculus AB & Calculus BC Examinations. 2012. (ENG.). 342p. pap. 18.99 ***(978-1-4354-6128-4(2))*** Course Technology.

Clark, William & McCune, Sandra. Practice Makes Perfect Calculus. 2010. (Practice Makes Perfect Ser.). (ENG.). 208p. (C). pap. 12.95 *(978-0-07-163815-9(6)*, 0071638156) McGraw-Hill Cos., The.

Digital Actuarial Resources. Headway Test Prep for AP Calculus AB. 2008. 154p. (YA). pap. 19.99 *(978-0-9798071-9-0(0))* Digital Actuarial Resources, LLC.

Guisse, Amadou, et al. CLEP Precalculus. 2008. (CLEP Test Preparation Ser.). (ENG.). 272p. (C). (gr. 13-14). pap. 27.95 *(978-0-7386-0174-8(8))* pap. 34.95 *(978-0-7386-0175-5(6))* Research & Education Assn.

Hill, Gregory. CLEP Calculus. 2008. (CLEP Test Preparation Ser.). (ENG., Illus.). 336p. (C). (gr. 12-13). pap. 34.95 *(978-0-7386-0305-6(8))*; pap. 27.95 *(978-0-7386-0304-9(X))* Research & Education Assn.

Howell, Mark & Montgomery, Martha. Be Prepared for the AP Calculus Exam. Litvin, Gary, ed. 2nd ed. 2011. 448p. (YA). pap. 19.95 ***(978-0-9824775-5-7(4))*** Skylight Publishing.

Kelley, W. Michael, et al. Master AP Calculus AB & BC. 2nd ed. 2007. (ENG., Illus.). 720p. pap. 19.00 *(978-0-7689-2470-1(7))* Peterson's.

Larson, Ron & Edwards, Bruce H. Calculus AP Fast Track To 5. 9th ed. 2009. (ENG.). 352p. (C). pap. 30.95 *(978-0-547-21307-1(7))* Brooks/Cole.

Lederman, David & Wood, Ethel. Multiple-Choice & Free-Response Questions in Preparation for the AP Calculus AB Examination. 2011. pap. 24.14 net. ***(978-1-934780-08-4(1))*** D & S Marketing Systems, Inc.

Levy, Norman. AP Calculus AB & BC. 2nd ed. 2009. (Advanced Placement (AP) Test Preparation Ser.). (ENG.). 544p. (gr. 9-12). pap. 24.95 *(978-0-7386-0628-6(6))* Research & Education Assn.

Ma, William. AP Calculus AB & BC, 2012-2013. 4th ed. 2011. (5 Steps to a 5 on the Advanced Placement Examinations Ser.). (ENG., Illus.). 480p. (C). pap. 18.95 *(978-0-07-175172-8(6)*, 0071751726) McGraw-Hill Cos., The.

Mendelson, Elliott. McGraw-Hill's 500 College Calculus Questions to Know by Test Day. 2012. (ENG., Illus.). 192p. (C). pap. 16.00 ***(978-0-07-178963-9(4)***, 0071789634) McGraw-Hill Cos., The.

Newman, Donald & Boxer, Robert J. Calculus I Exam File. 2nd ed. 2007. (ENG.). 170p. pap. 17.95 *(978-1-4195-1806-5(2))* Kaplan Publishing.

Princeton Review. Cracking the AP Calculus AB & BC Exams, 2013 Edition. 2012. (College Test Preparation Ser.). (ENG.). 896p. pap. 19.99 ***(978-0-307-94486-3(7)***, Princeton Review) Random Hse. Information Group.

Princeton Review Staff. Cracking the AP Calculus AB & BC Exams, 2012 Edition. 2011. (College Test Preparation Ser.). (ENG.). 896p. pap. 19.99 *(978-0-375-42720-6(1)*, Princeton Review) Random Hse. Information Group.

REA Staff, et al. AP Calculus AB & BC Crash Course. 2011. (Advanced Placement (AP) Crash Course Ser.). (ENG.). 224p. (gr. 11-12). pap. 11.95 *(978-0-7386-0887-7(4))* Research & Education Assn.

Rogawski, Jonathan D. Single Variable Calculus Student Solutions Manual. 2007. (ENG.). 512p. (C). pap. 37.95 *(978-0-7167-9866-8(2))* Freeman, W. H. & Co.

Ruby, Tamara Lefcourt, et al. Kaplan AP Calculus AB & BC 2012. 2011. (Kaplan AP Ser.). (ENG.). 624p. pap. 18.99 *(978-1-60714-961-3(3))* Kaplan Publishing.

Wheater, Carolyn. My Max Score AP Calculus AB/BC: Maximize Your Score in Less Time. 2011. (ENG.). 352p. pap. 14.99 *(978-1-4022-4313-4(8))* Sourcebooks, Inc.

CALCULUS—HISTORY

Bardi, Jason Socrates. The Calculus Wars: Newton, Leibniz, & the Greatest Mathematical Clash of All Time. 2007. (ENG., Illus.). 304p. per. 16.95 *(978-1-56025-992-3(2))* Basic Bks.

Caramalho Domingues, Joao. Lacroix & the Calculus. 2008. (Science Networks. Historical Studies). 169.00 *(978-3-7643-8637-5(1)*, 3764386371) Birkhauser Verlag AG CHE. Dist: Springer.

Dunham, William. The Calculus Gallery: Masterpieces from Newton to Lebesgue. 2008. (ENG., Illus.). 256p. (C). pap. 21.95 *(978-0-691-13626-4(2))* Princeton Univ. Pr.

Grier, David Alan. When Computers Were Human. 2007. (ENG., Illus.). 424p. (C). per. 31.95 *(978-0-691-13382-9(4))* Princeton Univ. Pr.

Izmirli, Ilhan. Study of Instantaneous Rate of Change in a Historical Context. 2010. 612p. pap. *(978-3-639-09358-2(5))* VDM Verlag Dr. Mueller e.K.

Otero, Daniel E. Calculus from an Historical Perspective. 234p. *(978-1-58692-039-5(1))* Courier Custom Publishing, Inc.

Schubring, Gert. Conflicts Between Generalization, Rigor, & Intuition: Number Concepts Underlying the Development of Analysis in 17th-19th Century France & Germany. 2010. (Sources & Studies in the History of Mathematics & Physical Sciences Ser.). (Illus.). xiv, 680p. pap. 189.00 *(978-1-4419-1987-8(2)*, 1441919872) Springer.

Simmons, George F. Calculus Gems: Brief Lives & Memorable Mathematics. 2007. (MAA-Spectrum Ser.). (ENG., Illus.). 372p. 48.95 *(978-0-88385-561-4(5))* Mathematical Assn. of America.

CALCULUS—PROBLEMS, EXERCISES, ETC.

Anton, Howard, et al. Calculus Multivariable, Textbook & Student Solutions Manual. 9th ed. 2010. (ENG.). (C). 201.95 *(978-0-470-92428-0(4))* Wiley, John & Sons, Inc.

Arterburn, D. R. Calculus II Exam File. 2007. (ENG.). 170p. pap. 17.95 *(978-1-4277-6627-4(4))* Kaplan Publishing.

Axler, Sheldon. Precalculus: A Prelude to Calculus. 2008. (ENG., Illus.). 624p. (C). 152.95 *(978-0-470-41674-7(2)*, Wiley) Wiley, John & Sons, Inc.

Axler, Sheldon J. Precalculus: A Prelude to Calculus. 2008. (ENG., Illus.). 624p. (C). pap. 118.95 *(978-0-470-18072-3(2)*, Wiley) Wiley, John & Sons, Inc.

Ayres, Frank & Mendelson, Elliott. Calculus. 5th ed. 2008. (Schaum's Outline Ser.). (ENG., Illus.). 552p. (C). pap. 20.00 *(978-0-07-150861-2(9)*, 0071508619) McGraw-Hill Cos., The.

BarCharts Inc., Staff. Calculus Equations & Answers. 2009. (ENG.). 6p. 5.95 *(978-1-4232-0856-3(0))* Barcharts, Inc.

Blank, Brian E. & Krantz, Steven G. Calculus, Multivariable Student Study & Solutions Companion. 2nd ed. 2011. (ENG.). 296p. (C). pap. 47.95 *(978-0-470-64724-0(8)*, Wiley) Wiley, John & Sons, Inc.

Briggs, William, et al. Student Solutions Manual Part for Calculus for Scientists & Engineers: Early Transcendentals, Single Variable. 2012. (ENG.). 400p. (C). pap. 36.67 ***(978-0-321-78544-2(4))*** Addison Wesley.

Briggs, William L. & Cochran, Lyle. Calculus, Kit. 2010. (ENG.). (C). pap., pap. 111.33 *(978-0-321-66524-9(4))* Addison Wesley.

—Student Solutions Manual, Single Variable for Calculus, Pt. 1. 2010. (ENG.). 416p. (C). pap. 36.67 *(978-0-321-66521-8(X))* Addison Wesley.

Calter, Paul A. Technical Mathematics with Calculus. 6th ed. 2011. (ENG.). 424p. (C). pap. 68.95 *(978-0-470-53494-6(X)*, Wiley) Wiley, John & Sons, Inc.

C

Clark, William & McCune, Sandra. Practice Makes Perfect Calculus. 2010. (Practice Makes Perfect Ser.). (ENG.). 208p. (C). pap. 12.95 (978-0-07-163815-9(6), 0071638156) McGraw-Hill Cos., The.
Cochran, Lyle, et al. Student's Solutions Manual foir Calculus for Scientists & Engineers. 2012. (ENG.). 350p. (C). pap. 36.67 **(978-0-321-82676-3(0))** Addison Wesley.
Edwards, C. Henry & Penney, David E. Calculus Early Transcendentals. 7th ed. 2007. (ENG., Illus.). 1344p. (C). 198.00 (978-0-13-156989-8(9), Prentice Hall) Prentice Hall PTR.
Ghorpade, Sudhir & Limaye, Balmohan Vishnu. A Course in Multivariable Calculus & Analysis. 2010. (Illus.). xii, 475p. **(978-1-4419-1621-1(0))** Springer.
Ghorpade, Sudhir R. & Limaye, Balmohan V. A Course in Multivariate Calculus & Analysis. 2009. (Undergraduate Texts in Mathematics Ser.). (ENG., Illus.). xii, 475p. 69.95 (978-1-4419-1620-4(2), 1441916202) Springer.
Goberstein, Faina. From Developmental Mathematics to Calculus: A Road to Success: A Student Handbook. 2nd rev. ed. 2010. (ENG.). 248p. pap. 52.24 (978-0-7575-8143-4(9)) Kendall Hunt Publishing Co.
Hughes-Hallett, Deborah. Applied Calculus. 4th ed. 2010. (ENG.). 168p. (C). pap. 61.95 (978-0-470-17053-3(0), Wiley) Wiley, John & Sons, Inc.
Hughes-Hallett, Deborah, et al. Calculus Combo: Single & Multivariable. 4th ed. 2008. (ENG.). 456p. (C). pap. 62.95 (978-0-470-41414-9(6), Wiley) Wiley, John & Sons, Inc.
—Student Solutions Manual to Accompany Calculus. 5th ed. 2008. (ENG.). 288p. (C). pap. 57.95 (978-0-470-41412-5(X), Wiley) Wiley, John & Sons, Inc.
Kelley, W. Michael. The Humongous Book of Calculus Problems: For People Who Don't Speak Math. 2007. (ENG., Illus.). 576p. (gr. 12-18). 19.95 (978-1-59257-512-1(9), Alpha Bks.) Penguin Group (USA) Inc.
Kly & Mason, John H. Using Counter-Examples in Calculus. 2009. (Illus.). 120p. 65.00 (978-1-84816-359-1(2)) Imperial College Pr. GBR. Dist: World Scientific Publishing Co., Inc.
Krantz, Steven G. Calculus DeMYSTiFieD. 2nd rev. ed. 2010. (Demystified Ser.). (ENG., Illus.). 416p. pap. 20.00 (978-0-07-174363-1(4), 0071743634) McGraw-Hill Professional Publishing.
Kuang, Yang & Gilman, Michelle Rose. Pre-Calculus Workbook for Dummies. 2nd ed. 2011. (ENG., Illus.). 360p. pap., wbk. ed. 16.99 (978-0-470-92322-1(9), For Dummies) Wiley, John & Sons, Inc.
Larson, Ron & Edwards, Bruce H. Calculus of a Single Variable: Early Transcendental Functions. 5th ed. 2010. (Available 2011 Titles Enhanced Web Assign Ser.). (ENG.). 944p. (C). 209.95 (978-0-538-73552-0(X)) Brooks/Cole.
LearningExpress Editors. Calculus Success in 20 Minutes a Day. 2nd rev. ed. 2012. (ENG.). 208p. pap. 18.00 **(978-1-57685-889-9(8))** LearningExpress, LLC.
Mason, John H. Using Counter-Examples in Calculus. 2009. 120p. pap. 32.00 (978-1-84816-360-7(6)) Imperial College Pr. GBR. Dist: World Scientific Publishing Co., Inc.
McCallum, William G., et al. Calculus: Multivariable. 4th ed. 2008. (ENG.). 192p. (C). pap. 51.95 (978-0-470-41413-2(8), Wiley) Wiley, John & Sons, Inc.
McKibben, Mark. 501 Calculus Questions. 2012. (ENG.). 384p. pap. 19.95 (978-1-57685-765-6(4)) LearningExpress, LLC.
Mendelson, Elliott. Schaum's 3,000 Solved Problems in Calculus. 2009. (Schaum's 3000 Ser.). (ENG., Illus.). 480p. (C). pap. 29.00 (978-0-07-163534-9(3), 0071635343) McGraw-Hill Cos., The.
Mendelson, Elliott & Ayres, Frank. Calculus. 2nd ed. 2010. (Schaum's Easy Outlines Ser.). (ENG., Illus.). 144p. (C). pap. 11.00 (978-0-07-174582-6(3), 0071745823) McGraw-Hill Cos., The.
Mishra, Bimal Kumar. Lecture Notes in Calculus. 2010. 272p. (C). pap. (978-93-80578-28-6(8)) I.K. International Publishing House Pvt. Ltd.
Nitecki, Zbigniew H. Calculus Deconstructed: A Second Course in First-Year Calculus. 2009. 508p. **(978-0-88385-756-4(1))** Mathematical Assn. of America.
Ouellette, Jennifer. The Calculus Diaries: How Math Can Help You Lose Weight, Win in Vegas, & Survive a Zombie Apocalypse. 2010. (ENG.). 336p. (gr. 12). 15.00 (978-0-14-311737-7(8), Penguin (Non-Classics)) Penguin Group (USA) Inc.
Patrick, David. Calculus. 2010. (Illus.). 336p. pap. 44.00 (978-1-934124-18-5(4)) AoPS Inc.
Patrick, David & Copeland, Jeremy. Calculus Solutions Manual. 2010. 128p. pap. 10.00 (978-1-934124-19-2(2)) AoPS Inc.
Shahriari, Shahriar. Approximately Calculus. 2006. (Illus.). 292p. (C). 50.00 (978-0-8218-3750-4(8)) American Mathematical Society.
Stewart, James. Multivariable Calculus Student Solutions Manual. 7th ed. 2011. (ENG.). 384p. (C). pap. 73.95 (978-0-8400-4945-2(5)) Brooks/Cole.
—Single Variable Calculus Vol. 1: Early Transcendentals. 7th ed. (ENG.). (C). 2011. 504p. 136.95 (978-0-538-49784-8(X)) 2010. 600p. 128.95 (978-0-538-49869-2(2)) Brooks/Cole.
—Single Variable Calculus Vol. 2: Early Transcendentals. 7th ed. (ENG.). (C). 2011. 648p. 136.95 (978-0-538-49785-5(8)) 2010. 552p. 128.95 (978-0-538-49870-8(6)) Brooks/Cole.
—Student Solutions Manual for Stewart's Single Variable Calculus: Concepts & Contexts, 4th. 4th ed. 2009. (ENG.). 432p. (C). pap. 105.95 (978-0-495-56061-6(8)) Brooks/Cole.
Stewart, James & Clegg, Dan. Applied Calculus. 2011. (Textbooks Available with Cengage YouBook Ser.). (ENG.). 700p. (C). 144.95 (978-0-534-42382-7(5)) Brooks/Cole.
Stewart, Scott & Stewart. Complete Solutions Manual for Stewart's Single Variable Calculus. 6th ed. 2008. 1,104p. pap. 38.95 (978-0-495-01232-0(7)) Brooks/Cole.
Student Solutions Manual for Stewart's Calculus: Early Vectors, 2nd. 2nd ed. 2009. (C). pap. 42.95 (978-0-534-39350-2(0)) Brooks/Cole.
Sullivan, Michael, III, et al. Student Solutions Manual for Precalculus: Enhanced with Graphing Utilities. 5th ed. 2008. (ENG.). 760p. (C). pap. 36.67 (978-0-13-235622-0(8), Prentice Hall) Prentice Hall PTR.
Tan, Soo T. Applied Calculus for the Managerial, Life, & Social Sciences: A Brief Approach. 9th ed. 2011. (Textbooks Available with Cengage YouBook Ser.). (ENG.). 688p. (C). 194.95 (978-0-538-49890-6(0)) Brooks/Cole.
—Calculus: Early Transcendentals. 2010. (Textbooks Available with Cengage YouBook Ser.). (ENG.). 1464p. (C). 144.95 (978-0-534-46554-4(4)) Brooks/Cole.
—Multivariable Calculus. 2009. (Available 2011 Titles Enhanced Web Assign Ser.). (ENG.). 568p. (C). 120.95 (978-0-534-46575-9(7)) Brooks/Cole.
—Student Solutions Manual for Tan's Applied Calculus for the Managerial, Life, & Social Sciences: A Brief Approach, 9th. 9th ed. 2011. (ENG.). 256p. (C). pap. 65.95 (978-0-8400-6847-7(6)) Brooks/Cole.
Thomas, George B., et al. Calculus. 12th ed. 2009. (Thomas' Calculus 12th Edition Ser.). (ENG.). 584p. (C). pap. 101.33 (978-0-321-64369-8(0)) Addison Wesley.
—Calculus. 12th ed. 2009. (ENG.). 250p. (C). pap. 36.67 (978-0-321-60070-7(3)) Addison-Wesley Longman, Inc.
—Early Transcendentals. 12th ed. 2010. (ENG.). 384p. (C). pap. 36.67 (978-0-321-65692-6(X)) Addison-Wesley Longman, Inc.
—Multivariable for Thomas' Calculus. 12th ed. 2010. (ENG.). 216p. (C). pap. 36.67 (978-0-321-60071-4(1)) Addison-Wesley Longman, Inc.
—Study Guide Part One for Thomas' Calculus. 12th ed. 2009. (ENG.). 400p. (C). pap. 33.33 (978-0-321-60810-9(0)) Addison-Wesley Longman, Inc.
—Study Guide Part Two for Thomas' Calculus. 12th ed. 2009. 400p. (C). pap. 33.33 (978-0-321-60073-8(8)) Addison-Wesley Longman, Inc.
Thomas, Kenneth W., et al. Addison-Wesley's Calculus Review. 2nd ed. 2006. (ENG.). (C). 4.00 (978-0-321-39841-3(6)) Prentice Hall PTR.
—Addison-Wesley's Calculus Review 2. 2nd ed. 2006. (ENG.). (C). 4.00 (978-0-321-39840-6(8)) Prentice Hall PTR.
Waner, Stefan & Costenoble, Steven. Applied Calculus SSM. 5th ed. 2010. (ENG.). 288p. (C). pap. 52.95 (978-1-4390-4990-7(4)) Brooks/Cole.
—Finite Math & Applied Calculus. 5th ed. 2010. (ENG.). 588p. (C). pap. 47.95 (978-0-538-73482-0(5)) Brooks/Cole.

CALCULUS, ABSOLUTE DIFFERENTIAL

see Calculus of Tensors

CALCULUS, DIFFERENTIAL

Alfred Lodge. Differential Calculus for Beginners. 2007. 304p. per. 14.95 (978-1-60386-079-6(7), Merchant Bks.) Rough Draft Printing.
Bischof, Christian. Advances in Automatic Differentiation. Utke, Jean et al, eds. 2008. (Lecture Notes in Computational Science & Engineering Ser.). (Illus.). xviii, 370p. pap. 159.00 (978-3-540-68935-5(4), 3540689354) Springer.
De Morgan, Augustus. Differential & Integral Calculus. 2007. 156p. per. 18.95 (978-1-60206-379-2(6)) Cosimo, Inc.
—Differential & Integral Calculus. 2008. 160p. (978-1-4437-2578-1(1), Hesperides Pr.) Read Bks.
—Elementary Illustrations of the Differential & Integral Calculus. 2010. 74p. pap. (978-1-152-89577-5(X)) Books LLC.
Delfour, Michel C. Introduction to Optimization & Semidifferential Calculus. 2012. (ENG.). **(978-1-61197-214-6(0))** Society for Industrial and Applied Mathematics.
Demyanov, Vladimir F. & Rubinov, Alexander M., eds. Quasidifferentiability & Related Topics. 2010. (Nonconvex Optimization & Its Applications Ser.). 400p. pap. 289.00 (978-1-4419-4830-4(9), 1441948309) Springer.
Edwards, Joseph. Differential Calculus - with Applications & Numerous Examples. 2007. (Illus.). 464p. 29.95 (978-1-933998-66-4(0), Merchant Bks.) Rough Draft Printing.
—Differential Calculus with Applications & Numerous Examples; an Elementary Treatise. 2006. 544p. per. 32.99 (978-1-4181-8532-9(9)) MPublishing.
Flett, T. M. Differential Analysis: Differentiation, Differential Equations & Differential Inequalities. 2008. (ENG., Illus.). 368p. pap. 48.00 (978-0-521-09030-8(X)) Cambridge Univ. Pr.
Hass, Joel, et al. University Calculus. alt. ed. 2007. (University Calculus Ser.). (ENG., Illus.). 1056p. (C). 140.00 (978-0-321-47196-3(2)) Addison Wesley.
Keller, H. H. Differential Calculus in Locally Convex Spaces. 2008. (Lecture Notes in Mathematics Ser.). 152p. pap. 39.95 (978-3-540-06962-1(3)) Springer.
MacCallum, Malcolm A. H. & Mikhailov, Alexander V., eds. Algebraic Theory of Differential Equations. 2008. (London Mathematical Society Lecture Note Ser.). (ENG., Illus.). 248p. pap. 74.00 (978-0-521-72008-3(7)) Cambridge Univ. Pr.
Meghea, Constantin & Meghea, Irina. Treatise of Differential Calculus: Volume 1. 2011. pap. 120.00 **(978-1-933153-16-2(4)**, OCP Science) Old City Publishing, Inc.
Paris, Alessandro De & Vinogradov, Alexandre M. Fat Manifolds & Linear Connections. 2008. 250p. 97.00 (978-981-281-904-8(5)) World Scientific Publishing Co., Inc.
Rall, L. B. Automatic Differentiation: Techniques & Applications. 2007. (Lecture Notes in Computer Science Ser.). 180p. per. 39.95 (978-3-540-10861-0(0)) Springer.
Rohde, Ulrich L., et al. Introduction to Differential Calculus: Systematic Studies with Engineering Applications for Beginners. 2012. (ENG., Illus.). 784p. 140.00 **(978-1-118-11775-0(1)**, Wiley) Wiley, John & Sons, Inc.
Spare, John. The Differential Calculus: With Unusual & Particular Analysis of Its Elementary Principles, & Copious Illustrations of Its Practical Application. 2006. 272p. per. 23.99 (978-1-4255-2462-3(1)) MPublishing.
Wauquiez, Christian. Shape Optimization of Low Speed Airfoils. 2009. 68p. pap. (978-3-639-11623-6(2)) VDM Verlag Dr. Mueller e.K.
Wilson, Edwin Bidwell. Advanced Calculus: A Text upon Select Parts of Differential Calculus, Differential Equations, Intergral Calculus, Theory of Functions, with Numerous Exercises. 566p. reprint ed. lib. bdg. (978-0-7222-3040-4(0)) Library Reprints, Inc.

CALCULUS, INTEGRAL

see also Integrals; Integrals, Generalized

De Morgan, Augustus. Differential & Integral Calculus. 2007. 156p. per. 18.95 (978-1-60206-379-2(6)) Cosimo, Inc.
—Differential & Integral Calculus. 2008. 160p. (978-1-4437-2578-1(1), Hesperides Pr.) Read Bks.
—Elementary Illustrations of the Differential & Integral Calculus. 2010. 74p. pap. (978-1-152-89577-5(X)) Books LLC.
Denneberg, D. Non-Additive Measure & Integral. 2010. (Theory & Decision Library B Ser.). 196p. pap. 279.00 (978-90-481-4404-4(3), 9048144043) Springer.
FURNARI, Sig. Giuseppe. Calculus without Limits. 2009. 104p. pap. 16.95 (978-1-4092-8821-3(8)) Lulu Enterprises Inc.
Godement, Roger. Analyse mathematique IV. 2008. pap. 59.95 (978-3-540-43841-0(6)) Springer.
—Analyse Mathtmatique II. 2nd ed. 2007. (FRE., Illus.). VIII, 490p. pap. 59.95 (978-3-540-00655-8(9), 3540006559) Springer.
Hardy, G. H. Integration of Functions. 2nd rev. ed. 2011. (ENG.). 76p. pap. 19.99 (978-0-521-17222-6(5)) Cambridge Univ. Pr.
Holtz, Markus. Sparse Grid Quadrature in High Dimensions with Applications in Finance & Insurance. 2010. (Lecture Notes in Computational Science & Engineering Ser.). (Illus.). viii, 182p. 74.95 (978-3-642-16003-5(4), 3642160034) Springer.
Misra, Ram Bilas. Advanced Integral Calculus. 2011. 108p. pap. **(978-3-8443-1916-3(6))** Lambert Academic Publishing.
Rohde, Ulrich L., et al. Introduction to Integral Calculus: Systematic Studies with Engineering Applications for Beginners. 2012. (ENG., Illus.). 432p. 115.00 **(978-1-118-11776-7(X)**, Wiley) Wiley, John & Sons, Inc.
Si. Introduction to Hida Distributions. 2011. 65.00 (978-981-283-688-5(8)) World Scientific Publishing Co., Inc.
Smirnov, Vladimir A. Feynman Integral Calculus. 2010. (ENG., Illus.). x, 287p. pap. 109.00 (978-3-642-06789-1(1), 3642067891) Springer.
Todhunter, Isaac. A Treatise on the Integral Calculus & Its Applications. 2009. 278p. 30.99 (978-1-110-06890-6(5)); pap. 26.75 (978-1-110-06887-6(5)) BiblioBazaar.

CALCULUS, OPERATIONAL

see also Laplace Transformation

Busbridge, I. W. The Mathematics of Radiative Transfer. 2008. (ENG.). 156p. pap. 38.99 (978-0-521-09066-7(0)) Cambridge Univ. Pr.
Davies, E. Brian. Linear Operators & Their Spectra. 2007. (Cambridge Studies in Advanced Mathematics). (ENG., Illus.). 464p. 88.99 (978-0-521-86629-3(4)) Cambridge Univ. Pr.
Franz, U. & Schott, René. Stochastic Processes & Operator Calculus on Quantum Groups. 2010. (Mathematics & Its Applications Ser.). (Illus.). 236p. pap. 125.00 (978-90-481-5290-2(9), 9048152909) Springer.
Glaeske, Hans-Jurgen & Prudnikov, A. P. Operational Calculus & Related Topics. 2006. (Analytical Methods & Special Functions Ser.: Vol. 10). (ENG., Illus.). 424p. 102.95 (978-1-58488-649-5(8), C6498, Chapman & Hall/CRC) CRC Pr. LLC.
Govindaraju. Moment Analysis for Subsurface Hydrologi. 2007. (Water Science & Technology Library). (Illus.). x, 292p. 139.00 (978-1-4020-5751-9(2)) Springer.
Govindaraju, Rao S. & Das, Bhabani S. Moment Analysis for Subsurface Hydrologic Applications. 2010. (Water Science & Technology Library). (Illus.). x, 292p. pap. 139.00 (978-90-481-7438-6(4), 9048174384) Springer.
Marshall, Murray. Positive Polynomials & Sums of Squares. 2008. (Mathematical Surveys & Monographs Ser.). (Illus.). 187p. 67.00 (978-0-8218-4402-1(4)) American Mathematical Society.
McLachlan, M. W. Complex Variable Theory & Transform Calculus: With Technical Applications. 2nd rev. ed. 2010. (ENG.). 400p. pap. 23.99 (978-0-521-15415-4(4)) Cambridge Univ. Pr.
Pol, Balth van der & Bremmer, H. Operational Calculus: Based on the Two-Sided Laplace Integral. 2008. (ENG.). 432p. pap. 79.00 (978-0-521-09180-0(2)) Cambridge Univ. Pr.
Schott, Rene & Staples, G. Stacey. Operator Calculus on Graphs: Theory & Applications in Computer Science. 2012. 420p. 134.00 **(978-1-84816-876-3(4))** Imperial College Pr. GBR. Dist: World Scientific Publishing Co., Inc.

CALCULUS OF DIFFERENCES

see Difference Equations

CALCULUS OF SPINORS

see Spinor Analysis

CALCULUS OF TENSORS

see also Generalized Spaces; Spinor Analysis

Ahsan, Z. A. F. A. R. Tensor analysis with Applications. 2008. (Illus.). 260p. 70.00 (978-1-905740-86-4(7)) Anshan GBR. Dist: Publishers Storage & Shipping.
Alkhalil, Faysal. Introductory Tensorial Algorithms in Structural Mechanics. 2011. (Illus.). 500p. pap. 34.01 **(978-1-4567-8165-1(0))** AuthorHouse.
Ammari, Habib & Kang, Hyeonbae. Polarization & Moment Tensors: With Applications to Inverse Problems & Effective Medium Theory. (Applied Mathematical Sciences Ser.). (Illus.). x, 316p. 2010. pap. 99.00 (978-1-4419-2449-0(3), 1441924493) 2007. 99.00 (978-0-387-71565-0(7)) Springer.
Bowen, Ray M. & Wang, C. -C. Introduction to Vectors & Tensors, 2 vols. in 1. 2nd ed. 2009. (Dover Books on Mathematics Ser.). (ENG.). 560p. pap. 24.95 (978-0-486-46914-0(X)) Dover Pubns., Inc.
Das, Anadijiban. Tensors: The Mathematics of Relativity Theory & Continuum Mechanics. 2007. (ENG., Illus.). xii, 292p. 139.00 (978-0-387-69468-9(4), 0387694684) Springer.
Dimitrienko, Yuriy I. Tensor Analysis & Nonlinear Tensor Functions. 2010. 684p. pap. 235.00 (978-90-481-6169-0(X), 904816169X) Springer.
Dolotin, V. & Morozov, A. Introduction to Non-Linear Algebra. 2008. (Illus.). 269p. 69.00 (978-981-270-800-7(6)) World Scientific Publishing Co., Inc.
Erven, J. & Falkowski, B. J. Low Order Cohomology & Applications. 2008. (Lecture Notes in Mathematics Ser.). 136p. pap. 39.95 (978-3-540-10864-1(5)) Springer.
Itskov, Mikhail. Tensor Algebra & Tensor Analysis for Engineers: With Applications to Continuum Mechanics. 2007. XII, 244p. (C). 59.95 (978-3-540-36046-9(8), 3540360468) Springer.
Itskov, Mikhail. Tensor Algebra & Tensor Analysis for Engineers: With Applications to Continuum Mechanics. 2nd ed. (ENG., Illus.). xiii, 247p. 2010. pap. 69.95 **(978-3-642-10103-8(8)**, 3642101038) 2009. 69.95 (978-3-540-93906-1(7), 3540939067) Springer.
Jeevanjee, Nadir. An Introduction to Tensors & Group Theory for Physicists. 2011. (ENG., Illus.). xvi, 242p. 59.95 **(978-0-8176-4714-8(7)**, 0817647147) Birkhauser Verlag AG CHE. Dist: Springer.
Kay, David. Tensor Calculus. 2011. (Schaum's Outline Ser.). (ENG.). 240p. (C). pap. 20.00 (978-0-07-175603-7(5), 0071756035) McGraw-Hill Cos., The.
Krogdahl, Wasley S. Tensor Analysis: Fundamentals & Applications. 2006. 424p. (C). per. 149.95 (978-1-4184-3066-5(8), 4338) Mountain Valley Publishing, LLC.
Laidlaw, David & Weickert, Joachim. Visualization & Processing of Tensor Fields. 2009. (Mathematics & Visualization Ser.). (Illus.). 464p. 149.00 (978-3-540-88377-7(0)) Springer.
Landsberg, J. M. Tensors: Geometry & Applications. 2011. (Graduate Studies in Mathematics Ser.). (Illus.). 439p. 74.00 **(978-0-8218-6907-9(8))** American Mathematical Society.
Lebedev, Leonid P. Tensor Analysis with Applications in Mechanics. 2010. 380p. 107.00 (978-981-4313-12-4(2)) World Scientific Publishing Co., Inc.
Lichnerowicz, A. Magnetohydrodynamics: Waves & Shock Waves in Curved Space-Time: Waves & Shock Waves in Curved Space-Time. 2010. (Mathematical Physics Studies). 292p. pap. 249.00 (978-90-481-4390-0(X), 904814390X) Springer.
Liebscher, Volkmar. Random Sets & Invariants for (Type II) Continuous Tensor Product Systems of Hilbert Spaces. 2009. (Memoirs of the American Mathematical Society Ser.). 101p. pap. 66.00 (978-0-8218-4318-5(4)) American Mathematical Society.
Light, W. & Cheney, E. Approximation Theory in Tensor Product Spaces. 2008. (Lecture Notes in Mathematics Ser.). pap. 39.95 (978-3-540-16057-1(4)) Springer.
Michal, Aristotle D. Matrix & Tensor Calculus: With Applications to Mechanics, Elasticity & Aeronautics. 2008. (Dover Books on Engineering Ser.). (ENG.). 144p. pap. 10.95 (978-0-486-46246-2(3)) Dover Pubns., Inc.
Parthasarathy, K. R. & Schmidt, K. Positive Definite Kernels, Continuous Tensor Products, & Central Limit Theorems of Probability Theory. 2008. (Lecture Notes in Mathematics Ser.). 120p. pap. 39.95 (978-3-540-05908-0(3)) Springer.
Schade, Heinz. Tensoranalysis. 2006.Tr. of Tensoranalysis. (GER.). xv, 398p. 49.90 (978-3-11-018943-8(7)) de Gruyter, Walter GmbH & Co. KG DEU. Dist: De Gruyter, Walter Inc.
Schade, Heinz & Neemann, Klaus. Tensoranalysis. 3rd ed. 2009. (De Gruyter Lehrbuch Ser.).Tr. of Tensoranalysis. (GER.). XVIII, 444p. (C). pap. 52.00 (978-3-11-020696-8(X)) De Gruyter, Walter Inc.
Schouten, Jan Arnoldus. Ricci-Calculus: An Introduction to Tensor Analysis & its Geometrical Applications. 2012. (Grundlehren der mathematischen Wissenschaften Ser.). (ENG.). 540p. pap. 49.95 (978-3-642-05692-5(X), 364205692X) Springer.
Talpaert, Y. R. Tensor Analysis & Continuum Mechanics. 2010. 612p. pap. 149.00 (978-90-481-6190-4(8), 9048161908) Springer.
Tinder. Tensor Properties of Solids. 2008. (Synthesis Lectures on Engineering Ser.). 100p. pap. 50.00 (978-1-59829-348-7(6)) Morgan & Claypool Pubs.
Tsamparlis, Michael. Special Relativity. 2010. (ENG., Illus.). xvii, 586p. 119.00 (978-3-642-03836-5(0), 3642038360) Springer.
Wasserman, Robert H. Tensors & Manifolds: With Applications to Physics. 2nd ed. 2009. (ENG., Illus.). 464p. pap. 65.00 (978-0-19-956482-8(5)) Oxford Univ. Pr., Inc.
Weatherburn, C. E. An Introduction to Riemannian Geometry & the Tensor Calculus. 2008. (ENG.). 204p. pap. 32.99 (978-0-521-09188-6(8)) Cambridge Univ. Pr.

CALCULUS OF VARIATIONS

see also Convex Domains; Functional Analysis

Agranovsky, Mark, et al, eds. Complex Analysis & Dynamical Systems IV Pt. 2: General Relativity, Geometry, & Pde. 2011. (Contemporary Mathematics Ser.). 284p. pap. 99.00 *(978-0-8218-5197-5(7))* American Mathematical Society.

Agrawal, S. K. & Fabien, B. C. Optimization of Dynamic Systems. 2010. (Solid Mechanics & Its Applications Ser.). (Illus.). 240p. pap. 189.00 *(978-90-481-5205-6(4),* 9048152054) Springer.

Alama, Stanley, et al, eds. Singularities in Pde & the Calculus of Variations. 2008. (CRM Proceedings & Lecture Notes Ser.). 267p. (C). pap. 102.00 *(978-0-8218-4350-5(8))* American Mathematical Society.

Ambrosio, Luigi, et al. Calculus of Variations & Nonlinear Partial Differential Equations: Lectures Given at the C. I. M. E. Summer School Held in Cetraro, Italy, June 27-July 2 2005. Dacorogna, Bernard, ed. 2008. (Lecture Notes in Mathematics / Fondazione C. I. M. E. , Firenze Ser.). (Illus.). 196p. pap. 69.95 *(978-3-540-75913-3(1))* Springer.

Arutyunov, A. V. Optimality Conditions: Abnormal & Degenerate Problems: Abnormal & Degenerate Problems. 2010. (Mathematics & Its Applications Ser.). 312p. pap. 146.00 *(978-90-481-5596-5(7),* 9048155967) Springer.

Aubert, Gilles & Kornprobst, Pierre. Mathematical Problems in Image Processing: Partial Differential Equations & the Calculus of Variations. 2nd ed. 2010. (Applied Mathematical Sciences Ser.). (Illus.). xxxii, 377p. pap. 89.95 *(978-1-4419-2182-6(6),* 1441921826) Springer.

Bardi, Martino & Capuzzo-Dolcetta, Italo. Optimal Control & Viscosity Solutions of Hamilton-Jacobi-Bellman Equations. 2008. (Modern Birkhäuser Classics Ser.). (Illus.). 570p. pap. 49.95 *(978-0-8176-4754-4(5))* Birkhauser Verlag AG CHE. Dist: Springer.

Basdevant, Jean-Louis. Variational Principles in Physics. 2010. (ENG., Illus.). x, 184p. pap. 74.95 *(978-1-4419-2279-3(2),* 1441922792) Springer.

Berdichevskii, V. L. Variational Principles of Continuum Mechanics, 2 vols. 2009. (Interaction of Mechanics & Mathematics Ser.). (Illus.). 159.00 *(978-3-540-88465-1(3),* 3540884653) Springer.

Berdichevsky, Victor. Variational Principles of Continuum Mechanics, 2 vols. 2009. (Interaction of Mechanics & Mathematics Ser.). (Illus.). 426p. pap. 99.00 *(978-3-540-88468-2(8))* Springer.

Bolza, Oskar. Lectures on the Calculus of Variations. 3rd ed. 14.95 *(978-0-8284-0145-6(4),* Chelsea Publishing Co., Inc.) American Mathematical Society.

—Lectures on the Calculus of Variations - Illustrated. 2007. (Illus.). 288p. 29.95 *(978-1-933998-58-9(X),* Merchant Bks.) Rough Draft Printing.

Borwein, Jonathan M. & Zhu, Qiji. Techniques of Variational Analysis. 2010. (CMS Books in Mathematics Ser.). (Illus.). vi, 366p. pap. 99.00 *(978-1-4419-2026-3(9),* 1441920269) Springer.

Botelho, Fabio. Variational Convex Analysis. 2010. 264p. pap. *(978-3-8383-7274-7(3))* Lambert Academic Publishing.

Bourdin, Blaise, et al. The Variational Approach to Fracture. 2010. (ENG.). x, 164p. pap. 99.00 *(978-90-481-7624-3(7),* 9048176247) Springer.

Brunt, Bruce van. The Calculus of Variations. 2010. (Universitext Ser.). (Illus.). xii, 302p. pap. 79.95 *(978-1-4419-2316-5(0),* 1441923150) Springer.

Bulirsch, R., et al, eds. Optimization & Optimal Control. 2008. (Lecture Notes in Mathematics Ser.). 308p. pap. 59.95 *(978-3-540-07393-2(0))* Springer.

Burachik, Regina S. & Yao, Jen-Chih, eds. Variational Analysis & Generalized Differentiation in Optimization & Control: In Honor of Boris S. Mordukhovich. 2010. (Springer Optimization & Its Applications Ser.). (Illus.). x, 232p. 124.00 *(978-1-4419-0436-2(0),* 1441904360) Springer.

Calculus of Variations & Partial Differential Equations: Proceedings of a Conference, held in Trento, Italy, June 16-21, 1986. 2008. (Lecture Notes in Mathematics Ser.). pap. 46.00 *(978-3-540-50119-0(3))* Springer.

Capogna. Introduction to the Heisenberg Group & T. 2007. (Progress in Mathematics Ser.). xvi, 223p. 79.95 *(978-3-7643-8132-5(9),* 3764381329) Birkhauser Verlag AG CHE. Dist: Springer.

Capriz, Gianfranco. New Variational Techniques in Mathematical Physics: Lectures given at the Centro Internazionale Matematico Estivo (C. I. M. E.) held in Bressanone (Bolzano), Italy, June 17-26 1973. 2010. (CIME Summer Schools Ser.). 420p. pap. 69.95 *(978-3-642-10958-4(6),* 3642109586) Springer.

Cecconi, J. P. & Zolezzi, T., eds. Mathematical Theories of Optimization: Proceedings of the International Conference Held in S. Margherita Ligure (Genova), November 30 - December 4, 1981. 2008. (Lecture Notes in Mathematics Ser.). pap. 59.95 *(978-3-540-11999-9(X))* Springer.

Chang, Mou-Hsiung. Stochastic Control of Hereditary Systems & Applications. 2010. (Stochastic Modelling & Applied Probability Ser.). xviii, 406p. pap. 109.00 *(978-1-4419-2605-0(4),* 1441926054) Springer.

Colding, Tobias H. & Minicozzi, William P. A Course in Minimal Surfaces. 2011. (Graduate Studies in Mathematics Ser.). (Illus.). 313p. 63.00 *(978-0-8218-5323-8(6))* American Mathematical Society.

Combet, E. Integrales Exponentielles: Developpements Asymptotiques, Proprietes Lagrangiennes. 2008. (Lecture Notes in Mathematics Ser.). 128p. pap. 26.00 *(978-3-540-11566-3(8))* Springer.

Conti, Roberto. Calculus of variations, Classical & Modern: Lectures given at the Centro Internazionale Matematico Estivo (C. I. M. E.) held in Bressanone (Bolzano), Italy, June 10-18 1966. 2010. (CIME Summer Schools Ser.). 369p. pap. 49.95 *(978-3-642-11041-2(X),* 364211041X) Springer.

Dacorogna, Bernard. Direct Methods in the Calculus of Variations. 2nd ed. (Applied Mathematical Sciences Ser.). 2010. xii, 622p. pap. 89.95 *(978-1-4419-2259-5(8),* 1441922598) 2007. (Illus.). 619p. 89.95 *(978-0-387-35779-9(3),* 0387357793) Springer.

—Introduction to the Calculus of Variations. 2nd ed. 2008. 300p. 88.00 *(978-1-84816-333-1(9))*; (Illus.). pap. 54.00 *(978-1-84816-334-8(7))* World Scientific Publishing Co., Inc.

David, Guy & Toro, Tatiana. Reifenberg Parameterizations for Sets with Holes. 2012. (Memoirs of the American Mathematical Society Ser.). 102p. pap. 71.00 *(978-0-8218-5310-8(4))* American Mathematical Society.

De Lellis, Camillo & Spadaro, Emanuele Nunzio. Q-Valued Functions Revisited. 2011. (Memoirs of the American Mathematical Society Ser.). 79p. pap. 66.00 *(978-0-8218-4914-9(X))* American Mathematical Society.

Ding, Yanheng. Variational Methods for Strongly Indefinite Problems. 2007. (Interdisciplinary Mathematical Sciences Ser.). 168p. 86.00 *(978-981-270-962-2(2))* World Scientific Publishing Co., Inc.

Elsgolc, Lev D. Calculus of Variations. 2007. (Dover Books on Mathematics Ser.). (ENG., Illus.). 192p. per. 11.95 *(978-0-486-45799-4(0))* Dover Pubns., Inc.

Facchinei, Francisco & Pang, Jong-Shi. Finite-Dimensional Variational Inequalities & Complementarity Problems: Volume I. 2012. (Springer Series in Operations Research & Financial Engineering Ser.). (ENG., Illus.). xxxii, 728p. pap. 109.00 *(978-1-4419-3063-7(9),* 1441930639) Springer.

Fattorini, Hector O. Infinite Dimensional Optimization & Control Theory. 2010. (Encyclopedia of Mathematics & its Applications Ser.). (ENG., Illus.). 816p. pap. 140.00 *(978-0-521-15454-3(5))* Cambridge Univ. Pr.

Ferronsky, V. I. & Ferronsky, S. V. Dynamics of the Earth: Theory of Planet Motion Based on Dynamic Equilibrium. 2010. (ENG., Illus.). xv, 299p. 129.00 *(978-90-481-8722-5(2),* 9048187222) Springer.

Fisher, S. W. & Jerome, J. W. Minimum Norm Extremals in Function Spaces. 2008. (Lecture Notes in Mathematics Ser.). 224p. pap. 59.95 *(978-3-540-07394-9(5))* Springer.

Fonseca, Irene & Leoni, Giovanni. Modern Methods in the Calculus of Variations: LP Spaces. 2007. (Springer Monographs in Mathematics Ser.). (Illus.). 599p. 74.95 *(978-0-387-35784-3(X),* 038735784X) Springer.

—Modern Methods in the Calculus of Variations: L^p Spaces. 2010. (Springer Monographs in Mathematics Ser.). xiv, 600p. pap. 74.95 *(978-1-4419-2260-1(1),* 1441922601) Springer.

Garay, Oscar J. Curvature & Variational Modeling in Physics & Biophysics: Santiago de Compostela, Spain, 17-28 September 2007. 2008. (A P Conference Proceedings Ser.). (Illus.). 266p. 152.00 *(978-0-7354-0521-9(2))* American Institute of Physics.

Ghoussoub, Nassif. Self-Dual Partial Differential Systems & Their Variational Principles. 2008. (Springer Monographs in Mathematics Ser.). xiv, 354p. 69.95 *(978-0-387-84896-9(7))* Springer.

—Self-dual Partial Differential Systems & Their Variational Principles. 2010. (Springer Monographs in Mathematics Ser.). (ENG.). xiv, 354p. pap. 69.95 *(978-1-4419-2744-6(1),* 1441927441) Springer.

Giaquinta, M. Topics in Calculus of Variations: Lectures given at the 2nd 1987 Session of the Centro Internazionale Matematico Estivo (C.I.M.E.) held at Montecatini Terme, Italy, July 20-28, 1987. 2008. (Lecture Notes in Mathematics Ser.). pap. 34.00 *(978-3-540-50727-7(2))* Springer.

Giaquinta, Mariano & Hildebrandt, Stefan. Calculus of Variations I: The Lagrangian Formalism. 2010. (Grundlehren der mathematischen Wissenschaften Ser.). (Illus.). xxix, 474p. pap. 195.00 *(978-3-642-08074-6(X),* 364208074X) Springer.

Giaquinta, Mariano & Mucci, Domenico. Maps into Manifolds & Currents: Area & W1,2-, W1/2-, BV-Energies. 2006. (Publications of the Scuola Normale Superiore / CRM Ser.). xxii, 391p. 34.95 *(978-88-7642-200-3(5),* 8876422005) Scuola Normale Superiore ITA. Dist: Springer.

Giaquinta, Mariano, et al. Cartesian Currents in the Calculus of Variations I: Cartesian Currents. 2010. (Ergebnisse der Mathematik und ihrer Grenzgebiete. 3. Folge A Series of Modern Surveys in Mathematics Ser.). (Illus.). xxiv, 714p. pap. 299.00 *(978-3-642-08374-7(9),* 3642083749) Springer.

—Cartesian Currents in the Calculus of Variations II: Variational Integrals. 2010. (Ergebnisse der Mathematik und ihrer Grenzgebiete. 3. Folge A Series of Modern Surveys in Mathematics Ser.). (Illus.). xxiv, 697p. pap. 299.00 *(978-3-642-08375-4(7),* 3642083757) Springer.

Gossez, J. P., et al, eds. Nonlinear Operators & the Calculus of Variations: Summer School Held in Bruxelles, 8- 9 September 1975. 2008. (Lecture Notes in Mathematics Ser.). 244p. pap. 46.00 *(978-3-540-07867-8(3))* Springer.

Harper, L. H. Global Methods for Combinatorial Isoperimetric Problems. 2010. (Cambridge Studies in Advanced Mathematics Ser.). (ENG.). 250p. pap. 39.99 *(978-0-521-18383-3(9))* Cambridge Univ. Pr.

Haslinger, J., et al. Finite Element Method for Hemivariational Inequalities: Theory, Methods & Applications. 2010. (Nonconvex Optimization & Its Applications Ser.). 288p. pap. 179.00 *(978-1-4419-4815-1(5),* 1441948155) Springer.

Ignat, Radu. Singularities in Some Variational Problems. 2010. 260p. pap. *(978-3-639-17515-8(8))* VDM Verlag Dr. Mueller e.K.

Jost, Jürgen & Li-Jost, Xianqing. Calculus of Variations. 2008. (Cambridge Studies in Advanced Mathematics). (ENG.). 340p. pap. 70.00 *(978-0-521-05712-7(4))* Cambridge Univ. Pr.

Kichoon Yang. Exterior Differential Systems & Equivalence Problems. 2010. (Mathematics & Its Applications Ser.). 208p. pap. 209.00 *(978-90-481-4118-0(4),* 9048141184) Springer.

Komzsik, Louis. Applied Calculus of Variations for Engineers. 2008. (ENG., Illus.). 175p. 64.95 *(978-1-4200-8662-1(6),* CRC Press) Taylor & Francis Group GBR. Dist: Taylor & Francis Group.

Kosmann-Schwarzbach, Yvette. The Noether Theorems: Invariance & Conservation Laws in the Twentieth Century. 2011. (Illus.). xiii, 205p. E-Book *(978-0-387-87868-3(8))* Springer.

Krantz, Steven G. & Parks, Harold. Geometric Integration Theory. 2008. (Cornerstones Ser.). (Illus.). 382p. 69.95 *(978-0-8176-4676-9(0))* Birkhauser Boston.

Krupkova, Olga & Saunders, D. J. Variations, Geometry & Physics. 2008. 89.00 *(978-1-60456-920-9(4))* Nova Science Pubs., Inc.

Leipholz, U. Direct Variational Methods & Eigenvalue Problems in Engineering. 2010. (Mechanics of Elastic Stability Ser.). 260p. pap. 359.00 *(978-90-481-8466-8(5),* 9048184665) Springer.

Liberzon, Daniel. Calculus of Variations & Optimal Control Theory: A Concise Introduction. 2011. (ENG., Illus.). 256p. (C). 75.00 *(978-0-691-15187-8(3))* Princeton Univ. Pr.

Lindenstrauss, Joram. Fréchet Differentiability of Lipschitz Functions & Porous Sets in Banach Spaces. 2012. (Annals of Mathematics Studies). (ENG.). 424p. (C). 165.00 *(978-0-691-15355-1(8))* Princeton Univ. Pr.

Lindenstrauss, Joram, et al. Fréchet Differentiability of Lipschitz Functions & Porous Sets in Banach Spaces. 2012. (Annals of Mathematics Studies). (ENG.). 424p. (C). pap. 75.00 *(978-0-691-15356-8(6))* Princeton Univ. Pr.

Lucchetti, Roberto & Revalski, Julian, eds. Recent Developments in Well-Posed Variational Problems. 2010. (Mathematics & Its Applications Ser.). 276p. pap. 229.00 *(978-90-481-4578-2(3),* 9048145783) Springer.

Mesterton-Gibbons, Mike. A Primer on the Calculus of Variations & Optimal Control Theory. 2009. (Student Mathematical Library). (Illus.). 252p. pap. 45.00 *(978-0-8218-4772-5(4))* American Mathematical Society.

Mielke, A. Hamiltonian & Lagrangian Flows on Center Manifolds: with Applications to Elliptic Variational Problems. 2008. (Lecture Notes in Mathematics Ser.). 150p. pap. 26.00 *(978-3-540-54710-5(X))* Springer.

Mordukhovich, Boris S. Variational Analysis & Generalized Differentiation I: Basic Theory. 2010. (Grundlehren der mathematischen Wissenschaften Ser.). xxii, 582p. pap. 119.00 *(978-3-642-06482-1(5),* 3642064825) Springer.

—Variational Analysis & Generalized Differentiation II: Applications. 2010. (Grundlehren der mathematischen Wissenschaften Ser.). xxii, 612p. pap. 119.00 *(978-3-642-06483-8(3),* 3642064833) Springer.

Morrey, Charles Bradfield. Multiple Integrals in the Calculus of Variations 2008. (Classics in Mathematics Ser.). (ENG.). xvi, 506p. pap. 69.95 *(978-3-540-69915-6(5),* 3540699155) Springer.

Morse, Marston. Variational Analysis: Critical Extremals & Sturmian Extensions. 2007. (Dover Books on Mathematics Ser.). (ENG., Illus.). 272p. per. 14.95 *(978-0-486-45787-1(7))* Dover Pubns., Inc.

Motreanu, Dumitru & Radulescu, Vicentiu D. Variational & Non-Variational Methods in Nonlinear Analysis & Boundary Value Problems. 2010. (Nonconvex Optimization & Its Applications Ser.). 388p. pap. 219.00 *(978-1-4419-5248-6(9),* 1441952489) Springer.

Nicolaescu, Liviu I. An Invitation to Morse Theory. 2007. (Universitext Ser.). (Illus.). xiv, 241p. 49.95 *(978-0-387-49510-1(X))* Springer.

Nualart, David. Malliavin Calculus & Its Applications. 2009. (CBMS Regional Conference Ser. in Mathematics Ser.). 85p. pap. 29.00 *(978-0-8218-4779-4(1))* American Mathematical Society.

Pajitnov, Andrei V. Circle-Valued Morse Theory. 2006. (De Gruyter Studies in Mathematics Ser.). (ENG., Illus.). IX, 454p. 154.00 *(978-3-11-015807-6(8))* De Gruyter, Walter Inc.

Pardalos, Panos M., et al, eds. Nonlinear Analysis & Variational Problems: In Honor of George Isac. 2009. (Springer Optimization & Its Applications Ser.). (ENG., Illus.). xxvii, 490p. 199.00 *(978-1-4419-0157-6(4),* 1441901574) Springer.

Fars, L. A. An Introduction to the Calculus of Variations. 2010. (Dover Books on Mathematics Ser.). (ENG.). 368p. pap. 15.95 *(978-0-486-47420-5(8))* Dover Pubns., Inc.

Patriksson, Michael. Nonlinear Programming & Variational Inequality Problems: A Unified Approach. 2010. (Applied Optimization Ser.). 352p. pap. 259.00 *(978-1-4419-4806-9(6),* 1441948066) Springer.

Rockafellar, R. Tyrrell & Wets, Roger J. -B. Variational Analysis. 2010. (Grundlehren der mathematischen Wissenschaften Ser.). (Illus.). xiii, 734p. pap. 175.00 *(978-3-642-08304-4(8),* 3642083048) Springer.

Salinetti, G., ed. Multifunctions & Integrands: Stochastic Analysis, Approximation, & Optimization. Proceedings of a Conference held in Catania, Italy, June 1983. 2008. (Lecture Notes in Mathematics Ser.). pap. 46.00 *(978-3-540-13882-2(X))* Springer.

Santambrogio, Filippo. Variational Problems in Transport Theory with Mass Concentration. 2008. (Tesi (Edizioni Della Normale) Ser.). (Illus.). 98p. pap. 24.95 *(978-88-7642-312-3(5))* Scuola Normale Superiore ITA. Dist: Springer.

Sobolev, S. L. Some Applications of Functional Analysis in Mathematical Physics. 3rd rev. ed. 2008. (Translations of Mathematical Monographs Ser.). 286p. pap. 99.00 *(978-0-8218-1937-1(2))* American Mathematical Society.

Sofonea, Mircea & Matei, Andaluzia. Variational Inequalities with Applications: A Study of Antiplane Frictional Contact Problems. (Advances in Mechanics & Mathematics Ser.). (ENG., Illus.). xix, 230p. 2010. pap. 89.95 *(978-1-4419-2765-1(4),* 1441927654) 2009. 89.95 *(978-0-387-87459-3(3))* Springer.

Song, Zhen, et al. Optimal Observation for Cyber-physical Systems: A Fisher-information-matrix-based Approach. 2009. (ENG., Illus.). xviii, 174p. 159.00 *(978-1-84882-655-7(9),* 1848826559) Springer.

Struwe, Michael. Variational Methods: Applications to Nonlinear Partial Differential Equations & Hamiltonian Systems. 4th ed. 2010. (Ergebnisse der Mathematik und Ihrer Grenzgebiete. 3. Folge a Series of Modern Surveys in Mathematics Ser.). xx, 302p. pap. 179.00 *(978-3-642-09329-6(9),* 3642093299) Springer.

Suttmeier, Franz-Theo. Numerical Solution of Variational Inequalities by Adaptive Finite Elements. 2008. (Advances in Numerical Mathematics Ser.). (ENG., Illus.). x, 161p. pap. 79.95 *(978-3-8348-0664-2(1),* 3834806641) Vieweg Verlag, Friedr, & Sohn Verlagsgesellschaft mbH DEU. Dist: Springer.

Tromba, Anthony J. A Theory of Branched Minimal Surfaces. 2012. (Springer Monographs in Mathematics Ser.). (ENG., Illus.). ix, 191p. 99.00 *(978-3-642-25619-6(8),* 3642256198) Springer.

Walsh, Mark P. Metrics of Positive Scalar Curvature & Generalised Morse Functions, Pt. 1. 2011. (Memoirs of the American Mathematical Society Ser.). 80p. pap. 69.00 *(978-0-8218-5304-7(X))* American Mathematical Society.

William E. Byerly. Introduction to the Calculus of Variations - Mathematical Tracts for Physicists. 2007. 56p. per. 9.95 *(978-1-60386-003-1(7),* Merchant Bks.) Rough Draft Printing.

Wood, John C. Harmonic Maps & Differential Geometry. Loubeau, E & Montaldo, S., eds. 2011. (Contemporary Mathematics Ser.). (Illus.). 284p. pap. 99.00 *(978-0-8218-4987-3(5))* American Mathematical Society.

Zaslavski, Alexander J. Turnpike Properties in the Calculus of Variations & Optimal Control. 2010. (Nonconvex Optimization & Its Applications Ser.). xxii, 395p. pap. 99.00 *(978-1-4419-3924-1(5),* 1441939245) Springer.

CALCUTTA (INDIA)

Betts, Vanessa. Kolkata & West Bengal Footprint Focus. 2011. (Footprint Focus Ser.). (ENG., Illus.). 88p. pap. 8.95 *(978-1-908206-40-4(3))* Footprint Handbooks GBR. Dist: Globe Pequot Pr., The.

Blechynden, Richard & Robb, Peter. Sentiment & Self: Richard Blechynden's Calcutta Diaries, 1791-1822. 2011. (ENG.). 312p. 55.00 *(978-0-19-807512-7(X))* Oxford Univ. Pr., Inc.

—Sex & Sensibility: Richard Blechynden's Calcutta Diaries, 1791-1822. 2011. (ENG.). 328p. 55.00 *(978-0-19-807511-0(1))* Oxford Univ. Pr., Inc.

Gingras, Sandy. At the Beach House: A Guest Book. (ENG.). 64p. 18.95 *(978-1-59322-006-8(5))* Down The Shore Publishing.

Gupta, Sudakshina. Passenger Transport Subsidy in West Bengal: Use or Misuse? 2007. x, 268p. *(978-81-7827-167-5(2))* Manak Pubns. Pvt., Ltd.

Kipling, Rudyard. The City of Dreadful Night & Other Places. reprint ed. lib. bdg. 98.00 *(978-0-7426-2826-7(4))* Classic Bks.

Massey, Montague. Recollections of Calcutta for over Half a Century. 2009. 156p. 22.99 *(978-0-559-05933-9(7))*; 25.99 *(978-0-559-05920-9(5))*; pap. 21.75 *(978-0-559-05923-0(X))*; pap. 20.75 *(978-0-559-05930-8(2))* BiblioBazaar.

—Recollections of Calcutta for over Half a Century. 2008. 112p. pap. 10.99 *(978-1-59547-664-7(4))* NuVision Pubns., LLC.

—Recollections of Calcutta for over Half a Century. 2008. 248p. *(978-1-4437-2435-7(1),* Hesperides Pr.) Read Bks.

Osborne, Lawrence. Naked Tourist: In Search of Adventure & Beauty in the Age of the Airport Mall. 2007. (ENG.). 288p. pap. 20.00 *(978-0-86547-741-4(8),* North Point Pr.) Farrar, Straus & Giroux.

Watts, Greg. Mother Teresa: Faith in the Darkness. 2010. (History Makers Ser.). (ENG., Illus.). 192p. pap. 16.95 *(978-0-7459-5283-3(6))* Lion Hudson PLC GBR. Dist: Independent Pubs. Group.

CALDECOTT, RANDOLPH, 1846-1886

Blackburn, Henry. Randolph Caldecott: A Personal Memoir of his Early Art Career. 2010. (Cambridge Library Collection - Printing & Publishing History Ser.). (ENG., Illus.). 240p. pap. 22.99 *(978-1-108-01230-0(2))* Cambridge Univ. Pr.

CALDECOTT MEDAL

American Library Association Staff, ed. The Newbery & Caldecott Awards: A Guide to the Medal Honor Books, 2008. 2008. 192p. pap. 19.00 *(978-0-8389-3574-3(5))* American Library Assn.

Association for Library Service to Children, compiled by. In the Words of the Winners: The Newbery & Caldecott Medals, 2001-2010. 2010. pap. *(978-0-8389-3586-6(9))* American Library Assn.

Association for Library Service to Children (ALSC). The Newbery & Caldecott Awards: A Guide to the Medal & Honor Books. 2007. (Newbery & Caldecott Awards Ser.). 186p. per. 19.00 *(978-0-8389-3567-5(2))* American Library Assn.

Association for Library Service to Children (ALSC), creator. The Newbery & Caldecott Awards: A Guide to the Medal & Honor Books. 2011. 172p. 28.00 *(978-0-8389-8569-4(6))* American Library Assn.

Association for Library Service to Children Staff. The Newbery & Caldecott Awards: A Guide to the Medal Honor Books. 2009. 168p. pap. 25.00 *(978-0-8389-3585-9(0))* American Library Assn.

Lewis, Marguerite. Hooked on the Caldecott Winners! 60 Crossword Puzzles Based on the Caldecott Gold Medal Books. 2007. (Illus.). 98p. (J). reprint ed. pap. 15.00 *(978-1-4223-6639-4(1))* DIANE Publishing Co.

Provensen, Alice & Provensen, Martin. The Glorious Flight: Across the Channel with Louis Bleriot. 2009. (JPN., Illus.). 40p. (J). *(978-4-7764-0353-1(6))* BL Publishing Co., Ltd.

CALDER, ALEXANDER, 1898-1976

Argan, Giulio Carlo. Alexander Calder: Sculptures. 2008. (ENG., Illus.). 64p. pap. *(978-88-89854-21-1(9),* Officina Libraria (Acc)) Antique Collectors' Club.

Calder, Alexander, et al. Calder Jewelry. 2007. *(978-0-300-13674-6(9))*; pap. *(978-0-9797956-0-2(5))* Yale Univ. Pr.

Davidson, Susan, text. Yves Tanguy & Alexander Calder: Between Surrealism & Abstraction. 2010. (ENG., Illus.). 180p. 75.00 *(978-0-9790942-8-6(3))* L & M Arts.

C

Gimenez, Carmen & Rower, Alexander S. C. Calder: Gravity & Grace. 2009. (ENG., Illus.). 268p. pap. 49.95 *(978-0-7148-4634-7(1))* Phaidon Pr., Inc.
Rower, Alexander. Alexander Calder. 2010. (ENG., Illus.). 260p. 75.00 *(978-88-6413-008-8(X),* Ore Cultura Srl (Acc)) Antique Collectors' Club GBR. Dist: National Bk. Network.
Rower, Alexander S. C., et al. Calder: Storm King Art Center. 2008. (Illus.). 56p. 34.95 *(978-0-9606270-3-5(0),* 9780960627035) Storm King Art Ctr.
Warren, Lynne, ed. Alexander Calder & Contemporary Art: Form - Balance - Joy. 2010. (ENG., Illus.). 176p. 45.00 *(978-0-500-51523-5(9),* 551523) Thames & Hudson.
—Alexander Calder & Contemporary Art: Form · Balance · Joy. 2010. (Illus.). 168p. pap. *(978-0-933856-89-9(X))* Museum of Contemporary Art, Chicago.
Watkins, Nicholas. Behind the Mirror: Miro, Giacometti, Calder, Braque. 2008. (ENG., Illus.). 160p. 65.00 *(978-1-905711-38-3(7))* Royal Academy of Arts GBR. Dist: Hachette Bk. Group.
Zabel, Barbara Beth & Calder, Alexander. Calder's Portraits: A New Language. 2011. (ENG.). 176p. 65.00 *(978-0-9788460-9-1(5))* Smithsonian Institution Scholarly Pr.

CALDERON DE LA BARCA, PEDRO, 1600-1681

Carreño-Rodriguez, Antonio. Alegorías del Poder: Crisis imperial y comedia Nueva, 1598-1659. 2009. (Monografías A Ser.: Volume 274). (SPA., Illus.). 280p. 95.00 *(978-1-85566-186-8(1),* Tamesis Bks.) Boydell & Brewer, Ltd. GBR. Dist: Boydell & Brewer, Inc.
Carrión, Gabriela. Staging Marriage in Early Modern Spain: Conjugal Doctrine in Lope, Cervantes, & Calderón. 2011. (ENG.). 166p. 60.00 *(978-1-61148-052-8(3))* Bucknell Univ. Pr.
Cruickshank, Don W. Don Pedro Calderòn. 2009. (ENG., Illus.). 494p. 102.00 *(978-0-521-76515-2(3))* Cambridge Univ. Pr.
Flasche, Hans & Coloquio Anglogermano , Wolfenbüttel, 1975, Wolfenbüttel, eds. Hacia Calderon: Cuarto Coloquio Anglogermano, Wolfenbüttel 1975. (Hamburger Romanistische Studien / Reihe A Ser.). (SPA., Illus.). VIII, 132p. 135.00 ***(978-3-11-006849-8(4))*** De Gruyter, Walter Inc.
Howard, Anita. The King Within: Reformations of Power in Shakespeare & Calderón. 2010. 199p. pap. 51.95 *(978-3-03911-530-3(8))* Lang, Peter AG GBR. Dist: Lang, Peter.
Kidd, Michael, tr. from SPA. & intro. Pedro Calderon de la Barca: Life's a Dream. 2011. (Hispanic Classics Ser.). (ENG & SPA.). 266p. (C). 80.00 *(978-0-85668-896-6(7));* pap. 30.00 *(978-0-85668-895-9(9))* Aris & Phillips GBR. Dist: Brown, David Bk. Co., The.
López-Peláez Casellas, Jesús. Honourable Murderers: El Concepto Del Honor en Othello de Shakespeare, y en Los Dramas de Honor de Calderón. 2009. (Hispanic Studies: Culture & Ideas Ser.). (SPA.). 321p. 67.95 *(978-3-03911-825-0(0))* Lang, Peter AG GBR. Dist: Lang, Peter.
McGarry, M. Frances. Allegorical & Metaphorical Language in the Autos Sacramentales of Calderon. (Catholic University of America, Studies in Romance Languages & Literatures: No. 16). reprint ed. 37.50 *(978-0-404-50316-1(0))* AMS Pr., Inc.
Parker, Alexander Augustine. The Mind & Art of Calderòn: Essays on the Comedias. Kong, Deborah, ed. 2009. (Major European Authors Ser.). (ENG.). 432p. pap. 42.00 *(978-0-521-12117-0(5))* Cambridge Univ. Pr.
Schaeffer, Adolf. Geschichte Des Spanischen Nationaldramas, Volume 1. 2009. 332p. 32.99 *(978-1-113-02477-0(1));* pap. 30.75 *(978-1-113-02474-9(7))* BiblioBazaar.
Sullivan, Henry W. Calderòn in the German Lands & the Low Countries: His Reception & Influence, 1654-1980. 2009. (Cambridge Iberian & Latin American Studies). 540p. pap. 58.00 *(978-0-521-12160-6(4))* Cambridge Univ. Pr.

CALDWELL, ERSKINE, 1903-1987

Allred, Jeff. American Modernism & Depression Documentary. 2009. (ENG., Illus.). 288p. 65.00 *(978-0-19-533568-2(6))* Oxford Univ. Pr., Inc.
Rieger, Christopher. Clear-Cutting Eden: Ecology & the Pastoral in Southern Literature. 2009. (ENG.). 264p. 39.75 *(978-0-8173-1641-9(8))* Univ. of Alabama Pr.
Van Vechten, Carl. Firecrackers. 2011. 196p. pap. 17.45 ***(978-1-59569-224-5(X))*** Mondial.

CALEDONIA NUEVA, 1698-1700

see Darien Scots' Colony, 1698-1700

CALENDAR

see also Aztec Calendar; Chronology; Church Calendar; Days; Jewish Calendar; Maya Calendar; Months; Time

Angler's Fly Fishing. cd-rom 11.99 *(978-1-57223-849-7(6),* 8496) Willow Creek Pr., Inc.
Archer, Peter. The Christian Calendar & the Gregorian Reform. 2011. 136p. 40.95 ***(978-1-258-04548-7(6))*** Literary Licensing, LLC.
Barrett, Mark J., contrib. by. Horse Feathers. cd-rom 11.99 *(978-1-57223-883-1(6),* 8836) Willow Creek Pr., Inc.
—Romancing the Horse. cd-rom 11.99 *(978-1-57223-882-4(8),* 8828) Willow Creek Pr., Inc.
Ben-Dov, Jonathan, et al. Living the Lunar Calendar. 2012. (ENG., Illus.). 350p. (C). pap. 60.00 ***(978-1-84217-481-4(9))*** Oxbow Bks., Ltd. GBR. Dist: Brown, David Bk. Co., The.
Booth, Janet. Janet's Plan-its 2007 Celestial Planner: Easy-to-Use Astrology Calendar. 2006. 60p. 12.95 *(978-0-9711903-5-1(6))* Astrology Booth, LLC.
Bryan, Denver, photos by. Hunting Labs. (Illus.). cd-rom 11.99 *(978-1-57223-812-1(7),* 8127) Willow Creek Pr., Inc.
Censorinus & Censorinus. The Birthday Book. Parker, Holt N., tr. from LAT. 2007. (Illus.). 120p. 30.00 *(978-0-226-09974-3(1))* Univ. of Chicago Pr.
Chambers, Robert. The Book of Days: A Miscellany of Popular Antiquities in Connection with the Calendar. 2008. (Gorgias Reference Classics Ser.: 1). (ENG.). 322.00 *(978-1-59333-793-3(0));* Vol. 1. (ENG.). 161.00 *(978-1-59333-794-0(9));* Vol. 2. 161.00 *(978-1-59333-795-7(7))* Gorgias Pr., LLC.
Colts & Fillies. cd-rom 11.99 *(978-1-57223-879-4(8),* 8798) Willow Creek Pr., Inc.
Cram101 Textbook Reviews & Cram101 Textbook Reviews. Outlines & Highlights for Calendar & Time Diary Methods in Life Course Research by Robert F Belli, Isbn: 9781412940634. 2011. 68p. pap. 27.95 ***(978-1-61461-643-6(4))*** Cram101 Inc.
Davis, Hilarie. Building a Culture of Literacy Month-By-Month. 2007. (ENG.). 211p. pap. 34.95 *(978-1-59667-067-9(3))* Eye On Education, Inc.
A Desert View. cd-rom *(978-1-57223-861-9(5),* 8615) Willow Creek Pr., Inc.
Design Collective. Count down Calendars: 24 Stitched Projects to Celebrate Any Date. 2011. (ENG., Illus.). 112p. pap. 15.95 *(978-1-60705-174-9(5))* C & T Publishing.
Diacu, Florin. The Lost Millennium: History's Timetables under Siege. 2nd ed. 2011. (ENG., Illus.). 248p. (gr. 17). 60.00 ***(978-1-4214-0287-1(4));*** pap. 25.00 ***(978-1-4214-0288-8(2))*** Johns Hopkins Univ. Pr.
Eagles. cd-rom 11.99 *(978-1-57223-829-9(1),* 8291) Willow Creek Pr., Inc.
Earle, David. The Open Daybook. 2010. (ENG., Illus.). 384p. 45.00 *(978-1-935613-07-7(3))* Batty, Mark Pub., LLC.
Fairies 2004 Calendar. 14.99 *(978-1-932431-36-0(5))* Angel Gate Publishing.
Fielder, John. Colorado Scenic Wall Calendar. 12.95 *(978-1-56579-503-7(2),* A20105) Westcliffe Pubs.
—Colorado Weekly Engagement Calendar. (Illus.). 13.95 *(978-1-56579-504-4(0),* A20205) Westcliffe Pubs.
Freeman, Gordon R. Canada's Stonehenge: Astounding Archaeological Discoveries in Canada, England, & Wales. 2008. (ENG.). 312p. 29.95 *(978-0-9784526-1-2(5))* Kingsley Publishing Services CAN. Dist: Ingram Pub. Services.
Garden Birds. cd-rom 11.99 *(978-1-57223-839-8(9),* 8399) Willow Creek Pr., Inc.
Georgeon, François & Hitzel, édéric, eds. Les Ottomans et le Temps. 2011. (Ottoman Empire & Its Heritage Ser.). (FRE & ENG., Illus.). ***(978-90-04-21132-2(2))*** BRILL.
Germann, Nadja. De Temporum Ratione: Quadrivium und Gotteserkenntnis Am Beispiel Abbos Von Fleury und Hermanns Von Reichenau. 2006. (Studien und Texte Zur Geistesgeschichte des Mittelalters Ser.). (Illus.). 384p. *(978-90-04-15395-0(0))* BRILL.
Golden Rules. cd-rom 11.99 *(978-1-57223-807-7(0),* 8070) Willow Creek Pr., Inc.
Gould, Stephen Jay. Questioning the Millennium: A Rationalist's Guide to a Precisely Arbitrary Countdown. rev. ed. 2011. (ENG., Illus.). 224p. pap. 16.95 *(978-0-674-06164-4(0),* Belknap Pr.) Harvard Univ. Pr.
Greene, Candace S. & Thornton, Russell, eds. The Year the Stars Fell: Lakota Winter Counts at the Smithsonian. 2007. (ENG., Illus.). 377p. 45.00 *(978-0-8032-2211-3(4))* Univ. of Nebraska Pr.
Grizzly Bears. cd-rom 11.99 *(978-1-57223-840-4(2),* 8402) Willow Creek Pr., Inc.
Henning, Edward & Lin, Justin Yifu. Kalacakra & the Tibetan Calendar. 2007. (Treasury of the Buddhist Sciences Ser.). (ENG., Illus.). 408p. (gr. 17). 49.00 *(978-0-9753734-9-1(8))* American Institute of Buddhist Studies.
Hooley, Susanna. Daily Planner - 2012. 2011. 184p. spiral bd. 13.99 *(978-1-932676-19-8(8))* Vision Pubs., LLC.
Jackson, W. H. & Fielder, John. Colorado Then & Now. 12.95 *(978-1-56579-507-5(5),* A21205) Westcliffe Pubs.
Jones, Donald M., photos by. Bull Elk. (Illus.). cd-rom 11.99 *(978-1-57223-837-4(2),* 8372) Willow Creek Pr., Inc.
Just Basset Hounds. cd-rom 11.99 *(978-1-57223-791-9(0),* 7910) Willow Creek Pr., Inc.
Just Beagles. cd-rom 11.99 *(978-1-57223-792-6(9),* 7929) Willow Creek Pr., Inc.
Just Bichon Frise. cd-rom 11.99 *(978-1-57223-793-3(7),* 7937) Willow Creek Pr., Inc.
Just Black Labs. cd-rom 11.99 *(978-1-57223-813-8(5),* 8135) Willow Creek Pr., Inc.
Just Border Collies. cd-rom 11.99 *(978-1-57223-795-7(3),* 7953) Willow Creek Pr., Inc.
Just Boston Terriers. cd-rom 11.99 *(978-1-57223-794-0(5),* 7945) Willow Creek Pr., Inc.
Just Boxers. cd-rom 11.99 *(978-1-57223-796-4(1),* 7961) Willow Creek Pr., Inc.
Just Bulldogs. cd-rom 11.99 *(978-1-57223-797-1(X),* 797X) Willow Creek Pr., Inc.
Just Cats. cd-rom 11.99 *(978-1-57223-784-1(8),* 7848) Willow Creek Pr., Inc.
Just Cavalier King Charles Spaniels. cd-rom 11.99 *(978-1-57223-798-8(8),* 7988) Willow Creek Pr., Inc.
Just Chesapeake Bay Retrievers. cd-rom 11.99 *(978-1-57223-799-5(6),* 7996) Willow Creek Pr., Inc.
Just Chihuahuas. cd-rom 11.99 *(978-1-57223-800-8(3),* 8003) Willow Creek Pr., Inc.
Just Chocolate Labs. cd-rom 11.99 *(978-1-57223-814-5(3),* 8143) Willow Creek Pr., Inc.
Just Cocker Spaniels. cd-rom 11.99 *(978-1-57223-801-5(1),* 8011) Willow Creek Pr., Inc.
Just Corgis. cd-rom 11.99 *(978-1-57223-802-2(X),* 802X) Willow Creek Pr., Inc.
Just Cows. cd-rom 11.99 *(978-1-57223-867-1(4),* 8674) Willow Creek Pr., Inc.
Just Dachshunds. cd-rom 11.99 *(978-1-57223-803-9(8),* 8038) Willow Creek Pr., Inc.
Just Doberman Pinschers. cd-rom 11.99 *(978-1-57223-872-5(0),* 8720) Willow Creek Pr., Inc.
Just English Springer Spaniels. cd-rom 11.99 *(978-1-57223-804-6(6),* 8046) Willow Creek Pr., Inc.
Just German Shepherds. cd-rom 11.99 *(978-1-57223-805-3(4),* 8054) Willow Creek Pr., Inc.
Just German Shorthairs. cd-rom 11.99 *(978-1-57223-874-9(7),* 8747) Willow Creek Pr., Inc.
Just Golden Puppies. cd-rom 11.99 *(978-1-57223-870-1(4),* 8704) Willow Creek Pr., Inc.
Just Goldens. cd-rom 11.99 *(978-1-57223-806-0(2),* 8062) Willow Creek Pr., Inc.
Just Horses. cd-rom 11.99 *(978-1-57223-830-5(5),* 8305) Willow Creek Pr., Inc.
Just Kitties. cd-rom 11.99 *(978-1-57223-785-8(6),* 7856) Willow Creek Pr., Inc.
Just Lab Puppies. cd-rom 11.99 *(978-1-57223-871-8(2),* 8712) Willow Creek Pr., Inc.
Just Labs. cd-rom 11.99 *(978-1-57223-810-7(0),* 8100) Willow Creek Pr., Inc.
Just Maltese. cd-rom 11.99 *(978-1-57223-816-9(X),* 816X) Willow Creek Pr., Inc.
Just Moms. cd-rom 11.99 *(978-1-57223-846-6(1),* 8461) Willow Creek Pr., Inc.
Just Mutts. cd-rom 11.99 *(978-1-57223-817-6(8),* 8178) Willow Creek Pr., Inc.
Just Papillons. cd-rom 11.99 *(978-1-57223-818-3(6),* 8186) Willow Creek Pr., Inc.
Just Pitbulls. cd-rom 11.99 *(978-1-57223-873-2(9),* 8739) Willow Creek Pr., Inc.
Just Poodles. cd-rom 11.99 *(978-1-57223-864-0(X),* 864X) Willow Creek Pr., Inc.
Just Pugs. cd-rom 11.99 *(978-1-57223-819-0(4),* 8194) Willow Creek Pr., Inc.
Just Puppies. cd-rom 11.99 *(978-1-57223-820-6(8),* 8208) Willow Creek Pr., Inc.
Just Rottweilers. cd-rom 11.99 *(978-1-57223-821-3(6),* 8216) Willow Creek Pr., Inc.
Just Schnauzers. cd-rom 11.99 *(978-1-57223-822-0(4),* 8224) Willow Creek Pr., Inc.
Just Shelties. cd-rom 11.99 *(978-1-57223-823-7(2),* 8232) Willow Creek Pr., Inc.
Just Shih Tzus. cd-rom 11.99 *(978-1-57223-824-4(0),* 8240) Willow Creek Pr., Inc.
Just Siamese Cats. cd-rom 11.99 *(978-1-57223-786-5(4),* 7864) Willow Creek Pr., Inc.
Just Siberian Huskies. cd-rom 11.99 *(978-1-57223-825-1(9),* 8259) Willow Creek Pr., Inc.
Just Us Chickens. cd-rom 11.99 *(978-1-57223-868-8(2),* 8682) Willow Creek Pr., Inc.
Just Westies. cd-rom 11.99 *(978-1-57223-827-5(5),* 8275) Willow Creek Pr., Inc.
Just Yellow Labs. cd-rom 11.99 *(978-1-57223-815-2(1),* 8151) Willow Creek Pr., Inc.
Just Yorkies. cd-rom 11.99 *(978-1-57223-828-2(3),* 8283) Willow Creek Pr., Inc.
Kayaking. cd-rom 11.99 *(978-1-57223-852-7(6),* 8526) Willow Creek Pr., Inc.
Krischan, Donna & Krischan, Tom, photos by. Orchids. (Illus.). cd-rom 11.99 *(978-1-57223-866-4(6),* 8666) Willow Creek Pr., Inc.
Lab Rules. cd-rom *(978-1-57223-811-4(9),* 8119) Willow Creek Pr., Inc.
Langrish, Bob, photos by. Arabians. (Illus.). cd-rom 11.99 *(978-1-57223-833-6(X),* 833X) Willow Creek Pr., Inc.
Lawrence, Amy N. 50 Special Event Ideas. 2010. 72p. pap. 12.95 *(978-0-9796170-8-9(1))* ATR Publishing.
Loons. cd-rom 11.99 *(978-1-57223-834-3(8),* 8348) Willow Creek Pr., Inc.
Moose. cd-rom 11.99 *(978-1-57223-835-0(6),* 8356) Willow Creek Pr., Inc.
A Mountain View. cd-rom 11.99 *(978-1-57223-859-6(3),* 8593) Willow Creek Pr., Inc.
Mountaineering. cd-rom 11.99 *(978-1-57223-853-4(4),* 8534) Willow Creek Pr., Inc.
Nuttall, Zelia. Fundamental Principles of Old & New World Civilization. (HU PMP Ser.: Vol. 2). 65.00 *(978-0-527-01190-1(8))* Periodicals Service Co.
An Ocean View. cd-rom 11.99 *(978-1-57223-858-9(5),* 8585) Willow Creek Pr., Inc.
O'Dell, Dale, illus. UFOs. cd-rom 11.99 *(978-1-57223-863-3(1),* 8631) Willow Creek Pr., Inc.
Orcas. cd-rom 11.99 *(978-1-57223-841-1(0),* 8410) Willow Creek Pr., Inc.
Outdoor Photographer Magazine Calendar. 11.95 *(978-1-56579-510-5(5),* X20105) Westcliffe Pubs.
Passmore, Nancy, ed. The Lunar Calendar: Dedicated to the Goddess in Her Many Guises. Date not set. 32p. 20.00 *(978-1-877920-10-3(X))* Luna Pr.
Philip, Alexander. The Calendar: Its History, Structure & Improvement. 2012. (ENG.). 118p. pap. 34.00 ***(978-1-107-64021-4(0))*** Cambridge Univ. Pr.
A Prairie View. cd-rom *(978-1-57223-860-2(7),* 8607) Willow Creek Pr., Inc.
Pruitt, Kathleen. Cloud School: Learn the Days of the Week & the Months of the Year. 2011. 40p. pap. 24.95 ***(978-1-4560-4020-8(0))*** PublishAmerica, Inc.
Publications International Staff, ed. 365 Household Hints & Tips Perpetual Calendar. 2011. 384p. spiral bd. 5.98 *(978-1-4508-1277-1(5))* Publications International, Ltd.
Quarter Horses. cd-rom 11.99 *(978-1-57223-875-6(5),* 8755) Willow Creek Pr., Inc.
Reingold, Edward M. & Dershowitz, Nachum. Calendrical Calculations. 3rd rev. ed. 2007. (ENG., Illus.). 512p. per. 32.99 *(978-0-521-70238-6(0));* 105.00 *(978-0-521-88540-9(X))* Cambridge Univ. Pr.
Rock Climbing. (Illus.). cd-rom 11.99 *(978-1-57223-854-1(2),* 8542) Willow Creek Pr., Inc.
Rodeo. cd-rom *(978-1-57223-877-0(1),* 8771) Willow Creek Pr., Inc.
Seasons of the Whitetail. cd-rom *(978-1-57223-844-2(5),* 8445) Willow Creek Pr., Inc.
Shattil, Wendy & Rozinski, Bob. Colorado Wildlife. 10.95 *(978-1-56579-508-2(3),* A20605) Westcliffe Pubs.
Shaw, Matthew. Time & the French Revolution: The Republican Calendar, 1789-Year XIV. 2011. (Royal Historical Society Studies in History New Ser.: Volume 78). (Illus.). 204p. 90.00 *(978-0-86193-311-2(7))* Royal Historical Society GBR. Dist: Boydell & Brewer, Inc.
Smetana, Dusan, photos by. Bass. (Illus.). cd-rom 11.99 *(978-1-57223-850-3(X),* 850X) Willow Creek Pr., Inc.
—Just Jack Russells. (Illus.). cd-rom 11.99 *(978-1-57223-809-1(7),* 8097) Willow Creek Pr., Inc.
Society for the Preservation of Old Mills, The & Davis, Allen, photos by. The Old Mill. (Illus.). cd-rom *(978-1-57223-886-2(0),* 8860) Willow Creek Pr., Inc.
Sporting Dogs. cd-rom 11.99 *(978-1-57223-826-8(7),* 8267) Willow Creek Pr., Inc.
Stern, Sacha. Calendars in Antiquity: Empires, States, & Societies. 2012. (ENG., Illus.). 512p. 185.00 ***(978-0-19-958944-9(5))*** Oxford Univ. Pr., Inc.
Ten Hoeve, Jaap. The Big Calender Book 1900 - 2100. 2011. 214p. pap. 20.95 ***(978-1-4475-3105-0(1))*** Lulu Enterprises Inc.
UltiMutt. cd-rom 11.99 *(978-1-57223-876-3(3),* 8763) Willow Creek Pr., Inc.
A View from the Porch. cd-rom 11.99 *(978-1-57223-856-5(9),* 8569) Willow Creek Pr., Inc.
A View of the Garden. cd-rom 11.99 *(978-1-57223-862-6(3),* 8623) Willow Creek Pr., Inc.
Wading Birds. cd-rom 11.99 *(978-1-57223-881-7(X),* 881X) Willow Creek Pr., Inc.
Warntjes, Immo. The Munich Computus - Text & Translation: Irish computistics between Isidore of Seville & the Venerable Bede & its reception in Carolingian Times. 2010. (Sudhoffs Archiv - Beihefte Ser.). (LAT & ENG., Illus.). 402p. (C). 134.00 *(978-3-515-09701-7(5))* Steiner, Franz Verlag Wiesbaden GmbH DEU. Dist: Brown, David Bk. Co., The.
What Cats Teach Us. cd-rom 11.99 *(978-1-57223-788-9(0),* 7880) Willow Creek Pr., Inc.
What Cats Teach Us Notecards. tchr. ed. 14.95 *(978-1-57223-505-2(5),* 5055) Willow Creek Pr., Inc.
What Dogs Teach Us. cd-rom 11.99 *(978-1-57223-790-2(2),* 7902) Willow Creek Pr., Inc.
What Horses Teach Us. cd-rom 11.99 *(978-1-57223-832-9(1),* 8321) Willow Creek Pr., Inc.
Whitetail Monarchs. cd-rom 11.99 *(978-1-57223-845-9(3),* 8453) Willow Creek Pr., Inc.
Why Cats Do That. cd-rom 11.99 *(978-1-57223-789-6(9),* 7899) Willow Creek Pr., Inc.
The Wilderness Society. 11.95 *(978-1-56579-509-9(1),* U20105) Westcliffe Pubs.
Willow Creek Press, creator. What Dogs Teach Us Notecards. (ENG.). 24p. tchr. ed. 14.95 *(978-1-57223-506-9(3),* 5063) Willow Creek Pr., Inc.
Yogananda, Paramhansa. Inner Reflections Engagement Calendar 2012. 2011. 132p. 13.95 *(978-0-87612-201-3(2))* Self-Realization Fellowship Pubs.
Zavaroni, Adolfo. On the Structure & Terminology of the Gaulish Calendar. 2007. (BAR International Ser.: Vol. 1609). (Illus.). 98p. 65.00 *(978-1-4073-0026-9(1))* Archaeopress GBR. Dist: Brown, David Bk. Co., The.
12 Uses for a Golden. cd-rom 11.99 *(978-1-57223-808-4(9),* 8089) Willow Creek Pr., Inc.

CALENDAR—REFORM

see Calendar Reform

CALENDAR, ARAB

see Islamic Calendar

CALENDAR, AZTEC

see Aztec Calendar

CALENDAR, CHINESE

Bredon, Juliet & Mitrophanow, Igor. The Moon Year - a Record of Chinese Customs & Festivals. 2009. 576p. pap. *(978-0-9812717-7-4(4))* Soul Care Publishing.
Gong, Duqing. Chinese Rabbit New Year. 2011. 60p. pap. 15.66 ***(978-1-4567-7979-5(6))*** AuthorHouse.

CALENDAR, ECCLESIASTICAL

see Church Calendar

CALENDAR, EGYPTIAN

Bennett, C. Alexandria & the Moon: An Investigation into the Lunar Macedonian Calendar of Ptolemaic Egypt. 2011. (Studia Hellenistica Ser.). (ENG.). 276p. (C). pap. 99.00 ***(978-90-429-2505-2(1))*** Peeters Pubs. & Booksellers BEL. Dist: Brown, David Bk. Co., The.
Bomhard, Anne-Sophie von. The Naos of the Decades: Underwater Archaeology in the Canopic region in Egypt. 2008. (OCMA Monograph Ser.). (ENG., Illus.). 300p. (C). 90.00 *(978-1-905905-04-1(1))* Oxford Univ. Schl. of Archaeology GBR. Dist: Brown, David Bk. Co., The.

CALENDAR, GREEK

Bennett, C. Alexandria & the Moon: An Investigation into the Lunar Macedonian Calendar of Ptolemaic Egypt. 2011. (Studia Hellenistica Ser.). (ENG.). 276p. (C). pap. 99.00 ***(978-90-429-2505-2(1))*** Peeters Pubs. & Booksellers BEL. Dist: Brown, David Bk. Co., The.
Graninger, Denver. Cult & Koinon in Hellenistic Thessaly. 2011. XII, 212p. ***(978-90-04-20710-3(4))*** BRILL.
Lehoux, Daryn. Astronomy, Weather, & Calendars in the Ancient World: Parapegmata & Related Texts in Classical & near-Eastern Societies. 2007. (ENG., Illus.). 580p. 140.00 *(978-0-521-85181-7(5))* Cambridge Univ. Pr.
Turfa, Jean MacIntosh. Divining the Etruscan World: The Brontoscopic Calendar & Religious Practice. 2012. (ENG., Illus.). 400p. 99.00 ***(978-1-107-00907-3(3))*** Cambridge Univ. Pr.

CALENDAR, HEBREW

see Jewish Calendar

CALENDAR, ISLAMIC
see Islamic Calendar
CALENDAR, JEWISH
see Jewish Calendar
CALENDAR, MAYA
see Maya Calendar
CALENDAR, MUSLIM
see Islamic Calendar
CALENDAR, ROMAN
Feeney, D. C. Caesar's Calendar: Ancient Time & the Beginnings of History. 2007. (Sather Classical Lectures). (Illus.). 372p. 45.00 *(978-0-520-25119-9(9))* Univ. of California Pr.
Feeney, Denis. Caesar's Calendar: Ancient Time & the Beginnings of History. 2008. (Sather Classical Lectures). (ENG., Illus.). 392p. pap. 21.95 *(978-0-520-25801-3(0))* Univ. of California Pr.
Forsythe, Gary. Time in Roman Religion. 2012. (Routledge Studies in Ancient History Ser.). (ENG., Illus.). 222p. (C). 125.00 ***(978-0-415-52217-5(X))*** Routledge.
Johnson, Van L. The Roman Origins of Our Calendar. 80p. 5.25 *(978-0-939507-11-5(0, B406)* American Classical League, The.
Lehoux, Daryn. Astronomy, Weather, & Calendars in the Ancient World: Parapegmata & Related Texts in Classical & near-Eastern Societies. 2007. (ENG., Illus.). 580p. 140.00 *(978-0-521-85181-7(5))* Cambridge Univ. Pr.
Rupke, J. Revolutionizing Time - the History of the Roman Calendar. 2011. 240p. 149.95 *(978-1-4443-9653-9(6))*, Wiley-Blackwell) Wiley, John & Sons, Inc.
Rupke, Jorg. The Roman Calendar from Numa to Constantine: Time, History, & the Fasti. Richardson, David M. B., tr. from GER. 2011. (ENG., Illus.). 240p. 149.95 *(978-0-470-65508-5(9)*, Wiley-Blackwell) Wiley, John & Sons, Inc.
CALENDAR REFORM
Wu, Dezhi. Temporal Structures in Individual Time Management: Practices to Enhance Calendar Tool Design. Wu, Dezhi, ed. 2009. 306p. 180.00 *(978-1-60566-776-8(5)*, Business Science Reference) IGI Global.
CALENDAR STONE OF MEXICO
see Aztec Calendar
CALENDARS
see also Almanacs; Birthday Books; Devotional Calendars
Alwin, Duane Francis, et al. Calendar & Time Diary Methods in Life Course Research. Alwin, Duane Francis et al, eds. 2008. 360p. (C). pap. 52.00 *(978-1-4129-4063-4(X)*, B4063XP) SAGE Pubns., Inc.
Barta, Miroslav & Vymazalova, Hana, eds. Chronology & Archaeology in Ancient Egypt: The Third Millennium BC. 2008. (ENG.). 319p. (C). 100.00 *(978-80-7308-245-1(4))* Czech Institute of Egyptology CZE. Dist: Brown, David Bk. Co., The.
Basheer Graphic Group. Creative Calendar Collection. 2011. (ENG.). 251p. 57.00 *(978-84-15123-37-8(X))* Links International (Leading International Key Services Barcelona, S.A.) ESP. Dist: National Bk. Network.
Beardsley, Laura. The Philadelphia Citizen's Almanac. 2010. (ENG.). 428p. 29.95 *(978-1-59652-546-7(0))* Turner Publishing Co.
Benedict XVI, pseud. Roman Martyrology Published by Order of. 2006. pap. 38.95 *(978-1-4286-4475-5(X))* Kessinger Publishing, LLC.
Booth, Janet. 2008 Janet's Plan-its Celestial Planner: Easy-to-Use Astrology Calendar. Wolf, Ilene, ed. 2007. 64p. 14.95 *(978-0-9711903-6-8(4))* Astrology Booth, LLC.
Calendar Procedures Key: California Civil Litigation. 2009. spiral bd. *(978-0-9777010-3-2(4))* Thomasbooks LLC.
Capstone Press Staff. Illinois. 2006. (Real Readers en español Ser.). (ENG.). 32p. (gr. 4-8). pap. 10.60 *(978-1-4042-7576-8(2)*, Rosen Classroom Bks. & Materials) Rosen Publishing Group, Inc., The.
Cardinals. cd-rom 11.99 *(978-1-57223-878-7(X)*, 878X) Willow Creek Pr., Inc.
Channing, William Ellery & Chapiro, José. Channing Day by Day: Thoughts for Each Day Selected from the Writings of William Ellery Channing. 2011. 472p. 57.95 ***(978-1-258-01801-6(2))*** Literary Licensing, LLC.
Chase, William Henry. Day by Day: A Compilation from the Writings of Ancient & Modern Friends. 2007. (ENG.). 434p. 51.95 *(978-0-548-03808-6(2))* Kessinger Publishing, LLC.
Colorado. (Proseries Wall Map Ser.). 229.00 *(978-0-528-85857-4(2))* Rand McNally.
Derwentwater, Laura F. Rainbow Men 2001. Date not set. (Illus.). 24p. pap. *(978-1-894619-00-4(5))* Calendar Buzz, Inc.
Flavia Gift Book: Birthday. 56p. 5.95 *(978-0-7683-2695-6(9))* CEDCO Publishing.
Georgia. (Rand Mcnally Wall Maps Ser.). 229.00 *(978-0-528-86135-2(2))* Rand McNally.
Gimenez, Marc. 365 Days of Design: Creative Calendar Solutions. Minguet, Josep Maria & Gimenez, Marc, eds. 2011. (ENG & SPA., Illus.). 192p. pap. 62.50 ***(978-84-15223-10-8(2))*** Instituto Monsa de Ediciones, S.A. ESP. Dist: Trans-Atlantic Pubns., Inc.
Gregoriades, P. & Gregoriades, P. D. The Creation of Prototypes: World Civilization & Human Progress: the Minoan Calendar Today. 2010. (History of Mechanism & Machine Science Ser.). (Illus.). iv, 196p. 139.00 *(978-90-481-9721-7(X)*, 904819721X) Springer.
Harrison, Kenneth. The Framework of Anglo-Saxon History: To A. D. 900. 2010. (ENG.). 184p. pap. 19.99 *(978-0-521-14392-9(6))* Cambridge Univ. Pr.
Hay, Louise L. You Can Heal Your Life Calendar. 2011. 13.99 ***(978-1-60237-502-4(X))*** Amber Lotus Publishing.
Idaho. (Rand Mcnally Wall Maps Ser.). 229.00 *(978-0-528-86149-9(2))* Rand McNally.
Illinois. (Rand Mcnally Wall Maps Ser.). 229.00 *(978-0-528-86136-9(0))* Rand McNally.
Jay, William. Evening Exercises for the Closet: For Every Day in the Year. by William Jay ... 2006. 704p. per. 38.99 *(978-1-4255-6569-6(6))* MPublishing.
Kjos, Lee Thomas, photos by. Lab Rules Notecards. (ENG., Illus.). 24p. tchr. ed. 14.95 *(978-1-57223-507-6(1)*, 5071) Willow Creek Pr., Inc.
Layton, Marcia L. Calendar Kids: Handprint Quilts Through the Year. 2007. (ENG., Illus.). 80p. per. 24.95 *(978-1-56477-702-7(2))* Martingale & Co.
Lebovics, Dania. Baby Chronicles Pregnancy Planner: A Portable Planner for the Mom to Be. 2nd rev. ed. 2009. (ENG., Illus.). 56p. spiral bd. 9.95 *(978-0-9733994-5-5(7))* Kiddy Chronicles Publishing CAN. Dist: Firefly Bks., Ltd.
Mannering, Rosslyn. The Gardener's Weekly Guide. 2006. 100p. per. *(978-1-4067-9606-3(9)*, Hesperides Pr.) Read Bks.
Martignette, Charles G. & Meisel, Louis K. Elvgren, Pin Ups: 25 Jahre TASCHEN. 25th ed. 2008. (FRE, GER & ENG., Illus.). 271p. 14.99 *(978-3-8365-0305-1(0))* TASCHEN DEU. Dist: Ingram Pub. Services.
Michael. The Book of Michael of Rhodes Vol. 2: A Fifteenth-Century Maritime Manuscript. Stahl, Alan M. et al, eds. Rossi, Franco, tr. from ITA. 2009. (ITA & ENG., Illus.). 732p. (gr. 17). 75.00 *(978-0-262-19590-4(9))* MIT Pr.
—The Book of Michael of Rhodes Vol. 3: A Fifteenth-Century Maritime Manuscript. Stahl, Alan M. et al, eds. 2009. (ITA & ENG., Illus.). 384p. (gr. 17). 45.00 *(978-0-262-12308-2(8))* MIT Pr.
Michael, et al. The Book of Michael of Rhodes Vol. 1: A Fifteenth-Century Maritime Manuscript. McGee, David et al, eds. Stahl, Alan M., tr. fac. ed. 2009. (ITA & ENG., Illus.). 534p. (gr. 17). 65.00 *(978-0-262-13503-0(5))* MIT Pr.
Michigan. (Rand Mcnally Wall Maps Ser.). 229.00 *(978-0-528-86139-0(5))* Rand McNally.
Minnesota. (Proseries Wall Map Ser.). 229.00 *(978-0-528-85861-1(0))* Rand McNally.
Montana. (Rand Mcnally Wall Maps Ser.). 229.00 *(978-0-528-86153-6(0))* Rand McNally.
Mystic Design Inc. Another Day of Living. 2009. pap. 22.95 *(978-1-61623-755-4(4))* Independent Pub.
Nabarz, Payam & Taqizadeh, S. H. The Persian 'Mar Nameh' The Zoroastrian 'Book of the Snake' Omens & Calendar & the Old Persian Calendar. 2006. (PER & ENG., Illus.). 132p. per. *(978-1-905524-25-9(0))* Twin Serpents, Ltd.
New Mexico. (Rand Mcnally Wall Maps Ser.). 229.00 *(978-0-528-86152-9(2))* Rand McNally.
Oregon. (Rand Mcnally Wall Maps Ser.). 229.00 *(978-0-528-86143-7(3))* Rand McNally.
Robson, Mark. Aurora. 2011. (Dragon Orb Ser.). (ENG., Illus.). 352p. (J). (gr. 4-7). pap. 8.99 *(978-1-84738-448-5(X))* Simon & Schuster, Ltd. GBR. Dist: Independent Pubs. Group.
Senn, Bryan. A Year of Fear: A Day-by-Day Guide to 366 Horror Films. 2007. (ENG., Illus.). 560p. per. 35.00 *(978-0-7864-3196-0(2))* McFarland & Co., Inc. Pubs.
Shaddick, Stan. Skywatchers 2011: A Sky-Guide Calendar by Stan Shadick, 1 vol. 2010. (ENG.). 24p. *(978-1-926613-63-5(5))* Heritage Hse.
Spiegel, Ted. New York in Bloom 2012: Public Gardens & Parks of New York State. 2011. (ENG.). 24p. pap. 12.99 ***(978-1-4384-3925-9(3)***, Suny Pr.) State Univ. of New York Pr.
Steele, John M. Calendars & Years: Astronomy & Time in the Ancient near East. 2010. (ENG., Illus.). 176p. (C). per. 50.00 *(978-1-84217-302-2(2))* Oxbow Bks., Ltd. GBR. Dist: Brown, David Bk. Co., The.
Virginia. (Rand Mcnally Wall Maps Ser.). 229.00 *(978-0-528-86147-5(6))* Rand McNally.
Visionaire, compiled by. Visionaire No. 57: 2010. 2010. (ENG., Illus.). 295.00 *(978-1-888645-79-8(2))* Visionaire Publishing.
CALENDARS—JUVENILE LITERATURE
Steffora, Tracey. Relojes y Calendarios. 2011. (Medir el Tiempo Ser.). (SPA.). 24p. (gr. -1-1). 21.99 *(978-1-4329-5628-8(0)*, Bellota) Heinemann-Raintree.
CALF
see Calves
CALGARY (ALTA.)
Corbett, Bill. Day Trips from Calgary: Best of Alberta. 3rd rev. ed. 2010. (Illus.). 304p. pap. 19.95 *(978-1-55285-766-3(2))* Whitecap Bks., Ltd. CAN. Dist: Midpoint Trade Bks., Inc.
Formac Publishing Company Limited Staff. The Canadian Rockies. Inigo-Jones, Terry, ed. 4th rev. ed. 2010. (Colourguide Travel Ser.). (ENG., Illus.). 208p. pap. 19.95 *(978-0-88780-897-5(2))* Formac Publishing Co., Ltd. CAN. Dist: Casemate Pubs. & Bk. Distributors, LLC.
Hempstead, Andrew. Moon Spotlight Calgary. 2010. (Moon Spotlight Ser.). (ENG.). 78p. pap. 7.95 *(978-1-59880-554-3(1))* Avalon Travel Publishing.
Joubert, Christine. Christine's Found & Shared Country Home Cooking Recipes. 2009. 148p. pap. 41.75 *(978-1-4251-8510-7(X))* Trafford Publishing.
MacEwan, Grant. Eye Opener Bob: The Story of Bob Edwards, 1 vol. Martin, James, ed. annot. ed. (ENG., Illus.). 224p. pap. 16.95 *(978-0-9732431-6-6(5))* Brindle & Glass Publishing CAN. Dist: Literary Pr. Group of Canada.
Moore, Joyce. A Guide to Alberta Outdoors. 2009. (ENG., Illus.). 96p. 9.95 *(978-1-897411-11-7(1))* Bayeux Arts, Inc. CAN. Dist: Chicago Distribution Ctr.
Walls, Martha & McDonald, Roberta. Calgary Book of Everything: Everything You Wanted to Know about Calgary & Were Going to Ask Anyway. 2007. (Book of Everything Ser.). (ENG.). 192p. pap. 14.95 *(978-0-9738063-5-9(4))* MacIntyre & Purcell Publishing CAN. Dist: Independent Pubs. Group.
Webber, George. Last Call, 1 vol. 2010. (ENG., Illus.). 128p. *(978-1-926855-08-0(6))*; *(978-1-926855-02-8(7))* Rocky Mountain Bks.
CALHOUN, JOHN C. (JOHN CALDWELL), 1782-1850
Bancroft, Frederic. Calhoun & the South Carolina Nullification Movement. 208p. 2010. pap. 19.96 *(978-1-163-19479-9(4))* 2008. 39.95 *(978-1-4366-8251-0(7))* 2007. (ENG.). per. 24.95 *(978-1-4325-9760-3(4))* Kessinger Publishing, LLC.
Calhoun, John Caldwell. The Works of John C. Calhoun, 6 vol., set. reprint ed. 750.00 *(978-0-7222-9021-7(7))* Library Reprints, Inc.
Capers, Gerald M. John C Calhoun, Opportunist: A Reappraisal. 2011. 232p. 48.95 ***(978-1-258-04026-0(3))*** Literary Licensing, LLC.
Dodd, William Edward. Statesmen of the Old South: From Radicalism to Conservative Revolt. 242p. reprint ed. 98.00 *(978-0-7222-8387-5(3)*, Library Reprints, Inc.
Holst, Hermann Edouard von. John C. Calhoun. (American Statesmen Ser.). 356p. reprint ed. 98.00 *(978-0-7222-8486-5(1))*; 98.00 *(978-0-7222-9022-4(5))* Library Reprints, Inc.
Hunt, Gaillard. John C. Calhoun. (American Crisis Biographies Ser.). 335p. reprint ed. 98.00 *(978-0-7222-8441-4(1))*; 98.00 *(978-0-7222-9023-1(3))* Library Reprints, Inc.
Jenkins, John S. Life of John Caldwell Calhoun. 2006. pap. 37.95 *(978-1-4286-3656-9(0))* Kessinger Publishing, LLC.
Life of John C Calhoun Presenting A Cond. 2006. pap. 17.95 *(978-1-4286-6049-6(6))* Kessinger Publishing, LLC.
Meigs, William Montegomery. The Life of John Caldwell Calhoun, 2 vol., set. reprint ed. 250.00 *(978-0-7222-9024-8(1))* Library Reprints, Inc.
Niven, John. John C. Calhoun & the Price of Union: A Biography. Date not set. (Southern Biography Ser.). (Illus.). xvi, 392p. (C). pap. 23.95 *(978-0-8071-1858-0(3))* Louisiana State Univ. Pr.
Pinckney, Gustavus M. The Life of John C. Calhoun. 251p. reprint ed. 98.00 *(978-0-7222-9025-5(X))* Library Reprints, Inc.
Read, James H. Majority Rule Versus Consensus: The Political Thought of John C. Calhoun. 2009. xi, 276p. 34.95 *(978-0-7006-1635-0(7))* Univ. Pr. of Kansas.
Trent, William Peterfield. Southern Statesmen of the Old Regime: Washington, Jefferson, Randolph, Calhoun, Stephens, Toombs,and Jefferson Davis. (Library of Economics & Politics). 293p. reprint ed. 98.00 *(978-0-7222-8408-7(X))* Library Reprints, Inc.
Von Holst, Hermann E. John C. Calhoun. 356p. reprint ed. 98.00 *(978-0-7222-8514-5(0))* Library Reprints, Inc.
CALIBAN (FICTITIOUS CHARACTER)
Morales-Diaz, Enrique. Reinaldo Arenas, Caliban, & Postcolonial Counter-Discourse. 2009. 208p. 104.99 *(978-1-60497-617-5(9))* Cambria Pr.
Sarwoto, Paulus. The Figuration of Caliban in the Constellation of Postcolonial Theory. 2009. 64p. pap. *(978-3-639-15537-2(8))* VDM Verlag Dr. Mueller e.K.
CALIFORNIA
Cool Springs Press Publications Staff, creator. I Didnt Know That Almanac 2008. 2007. (I Didn't Know That Almanac Ser.). (ENG.). 176p. pap. 12.95 *(978-1-59186-372-4(4))* Cool Springs Pr.
Crawford, Dorothy Lamb. A Windfall of Musicians: Hitler's Emigres & Exiles in Southern California. 2011. (ENG., Illus.). 336p. pap. 23.00 *(978-0-300-17123-5(4))* Yale Univ. Pr.
Habberton, John. Romance of California Life. 2008. 476p. 33.99 *(978-0-554-30469-4(4))*; 476p. 31.99 *(978-0-554-39772-6(2))*; (ENG.). 428p. pap. 34.75 *(978-1-4375-0346-3(2))*; (ENG.). 472p. pap. 37.75 *(978-1-4375-0347-0(0))* BiblioBazaar.
—Romance of California Life. 2009. 326p. pap. *(978-0-217-27973-4(2))* Books LLC.
—Romance of California Life. 2007. (ENG., Illus.). 512p. per. *(978-1-4065-1554-1(X))* Dodo Pr.
—Romance of California Life. 2006. (ENG.). pap. *(978-1-84702-504-3(8))* Echo Library.
—Romance of California Life. 2009. 510p. 55.95 *(978-1-120-64479-8(7))*; pap. 40.95 *(978-1-120-69507-9(4))* Kessinger Publishing, LLC.
Markham, Edwin. California the Wonderful. 2009. 284p. pap. *(978-1-4590-3987-2(4))*; 272p. pap. *(978-1-4590-3988-9(2))*; 288p. pap. *(978-1-4590-3986-5(6))* Books LLC.
Portman, Janet & Brown, David. California Tenants' Rights. 18th rev. ed. 2010. (ENG., Illus.). 394p. pap. 29.99 *(978-1-4133-0936-2(4))* NOLO.
Price, Steven D., intro. 1001 Greatest Things Ever Said about California. 2007. (1001 Ser.). (ENG.). 384p. per. 12.95 *(978-1-59921-095-7(9)*, Lyons Pr.) Globe Pequot Pr., The.
CALIFORNIA—ANTIQUITIES
Arnold, Jeanne E. & Walsh, Michael R. California's Ancient Past: From the Pacific to the Range of Light. 2010. *(978-0-932839-40-4(1))* Society for American Archaeology.
Barnatt, John. The Archaeology of a Great Estate: Chatsworth & Beyond. 2009. (ENG., Illus.). 232p. pap. 40.00 *(978-1-905119-27-1(5))* Windgather Pr. GBR. Dist: Brown, David Bk. Co., The.
Breschini, Gary S. Models of Population Movements in Central California Prehistory. fac. ed. 25p. reprint ed. pap. 23.75 *(978-1-55567-923-1(4))* Coyote Pr.
Chapman, Charles E. Expedition on the Sacremento & San Joaquin Rivers in 1817 Vol. 2:5: Diary of Fray Narciss Duran. fac. ed. (University of California, Publications of the Academy of Pacific Coast History Ser.). 23p. reprint ed. pap. 2.81 *(978-1-55567-945-3(5))* Coyote Pr.
Ciolek-Torrello, Richard. A Passage in Time. 2006. (ENG.). 312p. pap. 30.00 *(978-1-879442-89-4(2))* Statistical Res.
Curtis, Freddie. Arroyo Sequit, Archaeological Investigations in Les Carillo Beach State Park, Los Angeles County, California, Vol. 9. fac. ed. (State of California, Dept. of Parks & Recreation, Division of Beaches & Parks Ser.). (Illus.). 144p. reprint ed. pap. 15.63 *(978-1-55567-917-0(X))* Coyote Pr.
Daniel, et al. Archaeological Research of the Southern Santa Clara Valley Project: Data Recovery from Sites CA-SCL-54, 163, 178, 237 & 241. fac. ed. (Illus.). 578p. reprint ed. pap. 59.38 *(978-1-55567-957-6(9))* Coyote Pr.
de Cessac, Leon, et al. Papers on California Archaeology, 13-16, Vol. 12. fac. ed. (University of California Archaeology Survey, Department of Anthropology Berkeley, CA Ser.). (Illus.). 44p. reprint ed. pap. 5.00 *(978-1-55567-924-8(2))* Coyote Pr.
Delgado, James P. Gold Rush Port: The Maritime Archaeology of San Francisco's Waterfront. 2009. (ENG., Illus.). 256p. 45.00 *(978-0-520-25580-7(1))* Univ. of California Pr.
Erlandson, Jon M. Early Hunter-Gatherers of the California Coast. 2010. (Interdisciplinary Contributions to Archaeology Ser.). 350p. pap. 159.00 *(978-1-4419-3231-0(3)*, 1441932313) Springer.
Fagan, Brian M., et al. Life on the Dunes. 2007. (ENG.). 200p. pap. 30.00 *(978-1-879442-96-2(5))* Statistical Res.
Final Report of the New Melones Archeological Project, California, 9 vols., Set. Incl. Vol. 1. Natural History. Goldberg, Susan K. & Moratto Michael J. 160p. 1988. pap. 24.95 *(978-1-55567-001-6(6))*; Vol. 5. Data Recovery from Historical Sites. Greenwood, Roberta S. (Illus.). xvi, 346p. 1990. pap. 37.45 *(978-1-55567-005-4(9))*; Vol. 7. Review & Synthesis of Research at Historical Sites. Greenwood, Roberta S. & Shoup, Laurence H. (Illus.). xviii, 474p. 1987. pap. 37.45 *(978-1-55567-007-8(5))*; (Illus.). (Orig.). pap. *(978-1-55567-000-9(8))* Coyote Pr.
Garfinkle, Alan P. A Cultural Resource Management Plan for the Fossil Falls/Little Lake Locality. fac. ed. (Illus.). 98p. reprint ed. pap. 10.94 *(978-1-55567-896-8(3))* Coyote Pr.
Glassow, Michael A. Exploring Methods of Faunal Analysis: Insights from California Archaeology. Joslin, Terry L., ed. 2012. (ENG.). 276p. (C). pap. 34.95 ***(978-1-931745-87-1(0))*** Cotsen Institute of Archaeology at UCLA.
Goddard, P. E. Life & Culture of the Hupa. Putnam, Frederic W., ed. fac. ed. (University of California Publications in American Archaeology & Ethnology: Vol. 1: 1). (Illus.). 150p. (C). reprint ed. pap. 16.25 *(978-1-55567-159-7(6))* Coyote Pr.
Greengo, Robert E. Molluscan Species in California Shell Middens, Vol. 13. fac. ed. (University of California Archaeological Survey, Department of Anthropology, Berkeley CA Ser.). 33p. reprint ed. pap. 3.75 *(978-1-55567-895-1(5))* Coyote Pr.
Henshaw, Henry W. Perforated Stones from California. 2007. (ENG.). 48p. per. 15.95 *(978-0-548-59738-5(3))* Kessinger Publishing, LLC.
Jones, Terry L. California Prehistory: Colonization, Culture, & Complexity. Klar, Kathryn A., ed. 2010. (ENG.). 408p. pap. 44.95 *(978-0-7591-1960-4(0))* AltaMira Pr.
Jones, Terry L. & Klar, Kathryn. California Prehistory: Colonization, Culture, & Complexity. 2007. *(978-0-7591-0870-7(6))* AltaMira Pr.
Jones, Terry L. & Perry, Jennifer E. Contemporary Issues in California Archaeology. 2012. E-Book ***(978-1-61132-093-0(3))*** Left Coast Pr., Inc.
Jones, Terry L. & Perry, Jennifer E., eds. Contemporary Issues in California Archaeology. 2012. (ENG.). 400p. pap. 39.95 ***(978-1-61132-092-3(5))***; (Illus.). 396p. 94.00 ***(978-1-61132-091-6(7))*** Left Coast Pr., Inc.
Jones, Terry L., et al. Archaeological Test Excavations for the State Highway 1 Widening Project Near Castroville, Monterey County, California. fac. ed. (Illus.). 390p. reprint ed. pap. 40.63 *(978-1-55567-893-7(9))* Coyote Pr.
Jones/Klar. California Prehistory: Colonization, Culture, & Complexity. 2007. (ENG.). 408p. 99.95 *(978-0-7591-0872-1(2))* AltaMira Pr.
McGuire, Kelly R. & Garfinkle, Alan P. Archaeological Investigations in the Southern Sierra Nevada: The Bear Mountain Segment of the Pacific Crest Trail. fac. ed. (Bureau of Land Management Ser.). (Illus.). 340p. reprint ed. pap. 35.63 *(978-1-55567-905-7(6))* Coyote Pr.
McKusick, M. B. & Warren, C. N. Introduction to San Clemente Island Archaeology, Vol. 1. fac. ed. (University of California, Archaeological Survey Reports: Vol. 1959). (Illus.). 103p. reprint ed. pap. 11.56 *(978-1-55567-958-3(7))* Coyote Pr.
Meighan, C. W. & Euler, Robert C. Archaeological Resources of Borrego State Park: Annual Report 1958-1959. fac. ed. (University of California, Los Angeles, Dept. of Anthropology-Sociology, Article Ser.). (Illus.). 28p. reprint ed. pap. 3.13 *(978-1-55567-931-6(5))* Coyote Pr.
Merriam, C. Hart. The Classification & Distribution of the Pit River Indian Tribes of California, Vol. 78:3. fac. ed. (Smithsonian Institution, Miscellaneous Collections). (Illus.). 85p. reprint ed. pap. 9.69 *(978-1-55567-941-5(2))* Coyote Pr.
Raab, L. Mark, et al. California Maritime Archaeology: A San Clemente Island Perspective. 2009. (ENG.). 290p. 75.00 *(978-0-7591-1316-9(5))* AltaMira Pr.
Reinman, Fred M. & Townsend, Sam-Joe. Six Burial Sites on San Nicolas Island, Vol. 2. fac. ed. (University of California, Anthropological Records Ser.: Vol. 1960). (Illus.). 134p. reprint ed. pap. 15.00 *(978-1-55567-959-0(5))* Coyote Pr.

C

Rick, Torben. The Archaeology & Historical Ecology of Late Holocene San Miguel Island. 2007. (Perspectives in California Archaeology Ser.: 8). (ENG.). 192p. (C). 72.00 *(978-1-931745-37-6(4))* Cotsen Institute of Archaeology at UCLA.

Rick, Torben C. The Archaeology & Historical Ecology of Late Holocene San Miguel Island. 2007. (Perspectives in California Archaeology Ser.: 8). (ENG., Illus.). 192p. (C). per. 42.00 *(978-1-931745-36-9(6))* Cotsen Institute of Archaeology at UCLA.

Scott, S. G., et al. Journal of California & Great Basin Anthropology, Vol. 8:1. fac. ed. (Malki Museum, Inc. Ser.). (Illus.). 143p. reprint ed. 15.63 *(978-1-55567-938-5(2))* Coyote Pr.

Silliman, Stephen W. Lost Laborers in Colonial California: Native Americans & the Archaeology of Rancho Petaluma, Silliman, Stephen W. 2008. (ENG., Illus.). 250p. pap. 24.95 *(978-0-8165-2804-2(7))* Univ. of Arizona Pr.

Taylor, Jennifer Brandt. Vintage L. A. Eats, Boutiques, Décor, Landmarks, Markets & More. 2008. (ENG., Illus.). 240p. 34.95 *(978-0-06-112278-1(5)*, Morrow, William & Co.) HarperCollins Pubs.

Townsend, Joan B. Two Rock Shelters & a Village Site Borrego State Park: Annual Report 1959-1960. fac. ed. (University of California, Los Angeles, Dept. of Anthropology-Sociology, Article Ser.). (Illus.). 30p. reprint ed. pap. 3.44 *(978-1-55567-932-3(3))* Coyote Pr.

Warren, Elizabeth V. & Roske, Ralph J. Cultural Resources of the California Desert, 1776-1980: Historic Trails & Wagon Roads. fac. ed. (Bureau of Land Management Ser.). 208p. reprint ed. pap. 21.88 *(978-1-55567-903-3(X))* Coyote Pr.

Zogg, Marueen G. Archaeological Avifauna of the San Francisco Bay Area. 300p. (C). pap. 31.88 *(978-1-55567-832-6(7))* Coyote Pr.

CALIFORNIA—BIBLIOGRAPHY

Bancroft, Hubert Howe. California Pastoral. 2007. (ENG.). 816p. per. 55.95 *(978-0-548-50158-0(0))* Kessinger Publishing, LLC.

Frankel, Art. Flew by the Seat of My Pants. 2010. 172p. 25.95 *(978-1-4502-6929-2(X))* iUniverse, Inc.

Historical Society Of South. California. Annual Publication of the Historical Society of Southern California 1927. 2011. 68p. 36.95 ***(978-1-258-09369-3(3))*** Literary Licensing, LLC.

Hudson, D. T., et al. The Journal of California Anthropology. fac. ed. (Malki Museum, Journal of California Anthropology Ser.: Vol. 3:2). 116p. (C). reprint ed. pap. 13.13 *(978-1-55567-767-1(3))* Coyote Pr.

CALIFORNIA—BIOGRAPHY

Abe, Hitoshi & Pollock, Naomi. Hitoshi Abe. 2009. (ENG., Illus.). 208p. 79.95 *(978-0-7148-4665-1(1))* Phaidon Pr., Inc.

Abrahamson, Jennifer. Sweet Relief. 2013. (ENG.). 272p. pap. 18.99 *(978-1-4391-6523-2(8))* Gallery Pr., The IRL. Dist: Simon & Schuster, Inc.

Adamson, Jeremy. The Furniture of Sam Maloof. 2006. (ENG., Illus.). 272p. pap. 39.95 *(978-0-393-73214-6(2)*, 73214) Norton, W. W. & Co., Inc.

Adamson, Ted. Up from Down: A True Story of Recovery from Addiction. 2011. 136p. 28.95 ***(978-1-4497-2502-0(3))***; pap. 11.95 ***(978-1-4497-2501-3(5))*** Author Solutions, Inc. (WestBow Pr.).

Akbar, Said Hyder & Burton, Susan. Come Back to Afghanistan: Trying to Rebuild a Country with My Father, My Brother, My One-Eyed Uncle, Bearded Tribesmen, & PR. 2006. (ENG.). 352p. per. 16.00 *(978-1-59691-068-3(2))* Bloomsbury Publishing.

Alexzander, Rene. Branded Too Much Trouble: One Man's True Story, Every Child's Nightmare. 2011. 132p. 21.23 ***(978-1-4634-1626-3(1))***; pap. 14.99 ***(978-1-4634-1625-6(3))*** AuthorHouse.

Algubllan, Hamad. Citizen of the Global Village. 2007. 176p. pap. 12.95 *(978-0-9776232-9-7(7))* PathBinder Publishing, LLC.

Anderson, Eric G. Summer Of '57: Sabin, Salk, Mantle & Me, 1 vol. 2010. 210p. pap. 24.95 *(978-1-4512-1441-3(3))* PublishAmerica, Inc.

Arellano, Gustavo. Orange County: A Personal History. 2010. (ENG.). 288p. pap. 18.99 *(978-1-4165-4005-2(9)*, Scribner) Scribner.

Armato, Sam. I'm Afraid That Won't Do. 2011. 128p. pap. 19.99 ***(978-1-4568-5718-9(5))*** Xlibris Corp.

Armitage, Merle & Whitsett, William Paul. Success in No Accident: The Biography of William Paul Whitsett. 2011. 358p. 51.95 ***(978-1-258-09352-5(9))*** Literary Licensing, LLC.

Arneson, Erik. Mickey Thompson: The Fast Life & Tragic Death of a Racing Legend. 2011. (ENG., Illus.). 304p. pap. 17.99 *(978-0-7603-4015-8(3)*, 0760340153, Motorbooks) MBI Publishing Co. LLC.

Arnold, Daniel. Early Days in the Range of Light: Encounters with Legendary Mountaineers. 2009. (ENG., Illus.). 432p. 29.95 *(978-1-58243-519-0(7)*, Counterpoint Pr.) Basic Bks. GBR. Dist: Perseus-PGW.

—Early Days in the Range of Light: Encounters with Legendary Mountaineers. 2011. (ENG., Illus.). 432p. pap. 24.95 *(978-1-58243-616-6(9)*, Counterpoint) Counterpoint LLC.

Atkinson, Richard C. The Pursuit of Knowledge: Speeches & Papers of Richard C. Atkinson. 2007. (Illus.). 210p. per. 24.95 *(978-0-520-25199-1(7))* Univ. of California Pr.

Babiuk, Andy. The Story of Paul Bigsby: The Father of the Modern Electric Solid Body Guitar. 2009. (ENG., Illus.). 200p. 50.00 incl. audio compact disk *(978-0-615-24304-7(5)*, 0615243045) FG Publishing.

Bair, Richard "Yogi". Still Wandering Aimlessly, 1 vol. 2010. 160p. pap. 24.95 *(978-1-60836-996-6(X))* PublishAmerica, Inc.

Baker, William J. Billy Don't. 2011. 328p. 28.99 ***(978-1-4670-7011-9(4))***; pap. 19.95 ***(978-1-4670-7012-6(2))*** AuthorHouse.

Baker Young, J. Nothing but Love: A Katrina Volunteer Finds Inspiration in the Aftermath. 2008. 255p. pap. 21.95 *(978-0-615-25539-2(6))* Baker Young Publishing.

Bakker, Dona & Ingols, Ralph. St. Helena High School - Circa 1940-1972 - the Golden Years: An Age of Maturity & Achievement. 2008. (Illus.). 118p. pap. 13.95 *(978-0-9760276-3-8(1))* Pastime Pubns.

Ball, John. Living Well, Running Hard: Lessons Learned from Living with Parkinson's Disease. 2011. 208p. 27.95 ***(978-1-4620-1432-3(1))***; pap. 17.95 ***(978-1-4620-1430-9(5))*** iUniverse, Inc.

Ball, William B. Tales from a Grandfather. 2008. 256p. per. 16.50 *(978-1-59858-537-7(1))* Dog Ear Publishing, LLC.

Barker, Scott. Yokohl: A History of Its People & Their Culture. 2009. (Illus.). 266p. pap. *(978-0-615-29677-7(7))* Print Projects.

Barry, Angela. The Form, Function & Distribution of High Rising Intonation: A Comparative Study of HRT in Southern Californian & Southern British English. 2008. 304p. pap. *(978-3-639-10994-8(5))* VDM Verlag Dr. Mueller e.K.

Barton, Jorane King. El Monte. 2006. (Images of America Ser.). (ENG., Illus.). 128p. per. 21.99 *(978-0-7385-4652-0(6))* Arcadia Publishing.

Baszile, Jennifer Lynn. The Black Girl Next Door: A Memoir. 2009. (ENG., Illus.). 320p. pap. 15.00 *(978-1-4165-4328-2(7)*, Touchstone) Touchstone.

Baugh, Tim. Spirit of Hunter. 2010. 208p. 39.95 *(978-0-944197-87-5(6))* Companion Pr.

Baumann-Parkhurst, Marion. Searching Survivor & the Answer I Found. EDGE, Tracey, ed. 2007. 196p. pap. 14.95 *(978-0-9777251-5-1(4))* GenieHoldings.com, Inc.

Baumgart, Nomi & Gallucci, Chris. Elephant Man. 2008. (ENG., Illus.). 160p. 39.95 *(978-1-55407-422-8(3))* Firefly Bks., Ltd.

Beates, M. A. C. S(S. W.) Chet. Son of a Gun - the Life & Times of a Lifer Brat. 2007. 218p. pap. 29.95 *(978-1-4303-2588-8(7))* Lulu Enterprises Inc.

Becker, Judi. Beyond the Edge: All the Kings Horses... 2006. 284p. per. 19.95 *(978-0-9776975-0-2(9))* Sapphire Ridge Publishers.

Beebe, Rose Marie & Senkewicz, Robert M. Testimonios: Early California Through the Eyes of Women, 1815-1848. 2006. (Illus.). 470p. per. 18.95 *(978-1-59714-033-1(3))* Heyday.

Benziger, Jeff. Waterford. 2011. (Images of America Ser.). (Illus.). 128p. pap. 21.99 *(978-0-7385-7452-3(X))* Arcadia Publishing.

Berlanga, Richard Sotelo. Our Final Hour: A Vision of the Future. 2008. 76p. pap. 15.00 *(978-1-4327-3111-3(4))* Outskirts Pr., Inc.

Black, Dale & Gire, Ken. Flight to Heaven: A Plane Crash... A Lone Survivor... A Journey to Heaven — and Back. 2010. (Illus.). 192p. pap. 14.99 *(978-0-7642-0794-5(6))* Bethany Hse. Pubs.

Black, Tess. Portraits of Pescadero: A memory album of five families & Friends. 2006. per. 22.95 *(978-0-9788514-0-8(4))* Music By Piano & Birds Pr.

Blatchford, Chris. The Black Hand: The Bloody Rise & Redemption of Boxer Enriquez, a Mexican Mob Killer. 2009. (ENG., Illus.). 368p. pap. 14.99 *(978-0-06-194418-5(1)*, William Morrow Paperbacks) HarperCollins Pubs.

—The Black Hand: The Story of Rene Boxer Enriquez & His Life in the Mexican Mafia. 2009. (ENG.). 432p. mass mkt. 7.99 *(978-0-06-125730-8(3))* HarperCollins Pubs.

Blotnick, Elihu. Seedlings: The Canyon Kids. 2009. (ENG., Illus.). 84p. (YA). pap. 14.50 *(978-0-915090-16-7(3))* Firefall Editions.

Boessenecker, John. Bandido: The Life & Times of Tiburcio Vasquez. 2010. (ENG., Illus.). 496p. (C). 34.95 *(978-0-8061-4127-5(1))* Univ. of Oklahoma Pr.

Bongardt, Robert. Where Is Home. 2008. pap. 16.95 *(978-0-7414-4732-6(0))* Infinity Publishing.

Bonilla, German Y. Gloria. Esperanza Despues Del Dolor: Porque Todas Las Cosas Ayudan para Bien. 2010. 116p. pap. 12.95 *(978-1-4502-2351-5(6))* iUniverse, Inc.

Botts, Joseph. Hungry Flats: East of Lucia. 2010. 338p. 27.95 *(978-1-4327-5798-4(9))*; (ENG., Illus.). pap. 17.95 *(978-1-4327-4868-5(8))* Outskirts Pr., Inc.

Brantley, Julia. A Score of Intervals: Sharps & Flats on Brusca. 2009. 424p. pap. 20.99 *(978-1-4490-0062-2(2))* AuthorHouse.

Bridge, Andrew. Hope's Boy. 2009. (ENG.). 336p. pap. 14.99 *(978-1-4013-0974-9(7))* Hyperion Pr.

Brock, Sherwood H. My Life Adventure: (Volume One) an Autobiography. 2009. 646p. pap. 42.99 *(978-1-4251-1746-7(5))* Trafford Publishing.

Brower, Martin Aaron. Orange County Jew: A Memoir. 2010. 176p. 25.95 *(978-1-4490-7348-0(4))*; (ENG.). 176p. pap. 17.95 *(978-1-4490-7349-7(2))*; xi, 160p. E-Book *(978-1-4490-7350-3(6))* AuthorHouse.

Brown, Allan. California Split. 2010. 500p. pap. 25.99 *(978-0-578-05542-8(2))* ABCOM.

Brown, Rachel Manija. All the Fishes Come Home to Roost: An American Misfit in India. 2006. (ENG.). 352p. pap. 18.95 *(978-1-59486-526-8(4))* Rodale Pr., Inc.

Bruno, Peter A. & Bruno, Angela R. Dying to Fight: The Tony Bruno Story. 2008. 218p. 24.95 *(978-1-4327-2572-3(6))*; pap. 18.95 *(978-1-4327-2501-3(7))* Outskirts Pr., Inc.

Bryan, Pg. The Fish & Rice Chronicles: My Extraordinary Adventures in Palau & Micronesia. 2011. 334p. 29.99 ***(978-1-4628-9097-2(0))***; pap. 19.99 ***(978-1-4628-9096-5(2))*** Xlibris Corp.

Bryant, Dominance. Mr Dominance: Truthfully the Way I Feel. 2011. 138p. pap. 24.95 ***(978-1-4560-8492-9(5))*** PublishAmerica, Inc.

Bucklin, Linda Hale. Beyond His Control: Memories of a Disobedient Daughter. 2007. (ENG., Illus.). 181p. per. 18.95 *(978-1-932717-12-9(9))* Hope Publishing Hse.

Burchett, Author Walter, BA. An abused man's battles, trying to protect his Boys. 2007. 65p. pap. 14.95 *(978-0-615-15191-5(4))* Crossover Ministries.

Burdick, John G. A Sphinx: The Memories of a Reluctant Spy in Vietnam. 2008. 452p. 37.95 *(978-0-595-50430-5(2))*; pap. 27.95 *(978-0-595-51159-4(7))* iUniverse, Inc.

Burdsal, Bill. Memoirs of a Human Being. 2008. 552p. pap. 28.12 *(978-1-4357-1916-3(6))* Lulu Enterprises Inc.

Burns, Richard. Live or Die: A Stroke of Good Luck. 2010. 160p. pap. 14.95 *(978-0-615-23590-5(5))* D & N Bks.

Burns, Richard L. Live or Die - A Stroke of Good Luck. 2012. (ENG.). 165p. pap. 14.95 ***(978-0-615-52036-0(7))*** D & N Bks.

Busch, Colleen Morton. Fire Monks: Zen Mind Meets Wildfire. 2012. (ENG., Illus.). 272p. (gr. 12). pap. 16.00 ***(978-0-14-312137-4(5)***, Penguin (Non-Classics)) Penguin Group (USA) Inc.

Busch, Colleen Morton. Fire Monks: Zen Mind Meets Wildfire at the Gates of Tassajara. 2011. (ENG.). 272p. (gr. 12). 25.95 *(978-1-59420-291-9(5)*, Penguin Pr. HC, The) Penguin Group (USA) Inc.

Byrnes, Isabel Stenzel & Stenzel, Anabel. The Power of Two: A Twin Triumph over Cystic Fibrosis. 2007. (ENG., Illus.). 312p. (gr. 9). 29.95 *(978-0-8262-1754-7(0))* Univ. of Missouri Pr.

Caesar, Latroy. Damn, If I Had Known. 2011. 88p. 24.99 ***(978-1-4568-7673-9(2))***; pap. 15.99 ***(978-1-4568-7672-2(4))*** Xlibris Corp.

Cage, John. John Cage Book of Days 2012. Kuhn, Laura, ed. 2011. (ENG., Illus.). 120p. pap. 25.00 ***(978-1-935202-64-6(2))*** D.A.P./Distributed Art Pubs.

Campbell, Sara. Collector without Walls: Norton Simon & His Hunt for the Best. 2010. (Illus.). 260p. 65.00 *(978-0-9726681-8-7(7))* Norton Simon Museum.

Carr, Alan B. The Forgotten Physicist: Robert F. Bacher, 1905-2004. 2008. *(978-0-941232-36-4(0))* Los Alamos Historical Society.

Carrico, Richard L. Ramona. 2011. (Images of America Ser.). (ENG., Illus.). 128p. pap. 21.99 *(978-0-7385-8162-0(3))* Arcadia Publishing.

Cass, Maxine. Speaking Ill of the Dead: Jerks in California History. 2012. (Speaking Ill of the Dead: Jerks in Histo Ser.). (ENG., Illus.). 232p. pap. 16.95 *(978-0-7627-7240-7(9))* Globe Pequot Pr., The.

Chick, Stevie. Spray Paint the Walls: The Story of Black Flag. 2011. (ENG.). 432p. pap. 19.95 *(978-1-60486-418-2(4))* PM Pr.

Chiles, Frederic Caire. Justinian Caire & Santa Cruz Island: The Rise & Fall of a California Dynasty. 2011. (ENG., Illus.). 240p. 34.95 *(978-0-87062-400-1(8)*, Clark, Arthur H. Co., The) Univ. of Oklahoma Pr.

Chinese Historical and Cultural Project, et al. Chinese in San Jose & the Santa Clara Valley. 2007. (Images of America Ser.). (ENG., Illus.). 128p. per. 19.99 *(978-0-7385-4777-0(8))* Arcadia Publishing.

Christensen, Ken. Up North with Uncle Bob. 2009. 248p. pap. 22.97 *(978-0-557-09457-8(7))* Lulu Enterprises Inc.

Chukwu, Raymond L. My American Dream: From an Orphan to an American Success Story. 2007. 96p. per. 11.95 *(978-0-595-44991-0(3))* iUniverse, Inc.

Chung, Arthur W. Bitter Roots. 2007. (Illus.). 157p. 18.00 *(978-1-928753-25-4(6))* Pacific Heritage Bks.

Cipriani, Hugo. Va Fa Sa. 2008. (ENG.). 191p. pap. 10.95 *(978-0-533-15846-1(X))* Vantage Pr., Inc.

Clarke, Michael A. It All Began in Fresno. 2011. 156p. pap. 14.95 ***(978-1-61434-240-3(7))*** Booklocker.com, Inc.

Colorful Men Women & Tales of the Mother Lode. 2006. (Illus.). 275p. pap. 16.95 *(978-0-9653428-3-4(2))* Irene, Jan Pubns.

Cook, Tommy. Fourth & Long. 2010. pap. 15.99 *(978-1-61663-264-9(X))* Tate Publishing & Enterprises, LLC.

Cornu, Jean. I Missed My Basque Mother's Love. 2008. 156p. pap. 16.00 *(978-0-8059-7865-0(8))* Dorrance Publishing Co., Inc.

Cornwall, Harry. Back to California. 2010. 271p. pap. 22.95 *(978-1-4327-4296-6(5))* Outskirts Pr., Inc.

—Down from Arcturus: A Survivor. 2008. 212p. pap. 18.95 *(978-1-4327-3382-7(6))* Outskirts Pr., Inc.

Costello, Shelley. Holiday Road. 2011. 224p. 29.99 ***(978-1-4568-7399-8(7))***; pap. 19.99 ***(978-1-4568-7398-1(9))*** Xlibris Corp.

Cox, Mitch. Fathead Goes to Chico. 2007. 160p. per. 14.95 *(978-0-595-46565-1(X))* iUniverse, Inc.

Crivello, James. Love's Message & Journey. 2007. 176p. per. 24.95 *(978-1-4241-8684-6(6))* PublishAmerica, Inc.

Cruz, David & Anthony, David. Town Boy: Memoir of a Santa Cruz Street Kid. 2011. 204p. pap. 15.95 ***(978-1-61434-442-1(6))*** Booklocker.com, Inc.

Dailey, Richard. Sailing on Edge! or Jump, Jump on the High Side! 2011. 154p. pap. 19.99 ***(978-1-4568-6997-7(3))*** Xlibris Corp.

Dalberg, Lana. A Dream Journey: The Incredible Story of the Founding of Eastside College Preparatory School. 2008. 62p. *(978-0-9770735-1-1(3))* Univ. of Dreams.

Day, Aaron L. & Kaletucker, Indira. The Heritage of African-Americans in Long Beach: Over 100 Years. 2007. 308p. pap. 24.95 *(978-0-7414-3514-9(4))* Infinity Publishing.

De Borges, Dianna Maria. Sleigh Rides in Lake Tahoe: Memoirs of Sam Borges. 2009. 140p. pap. 15.99 *(978-1-4389-9496-3(6))* AuthorHouse.

de Kehoe, Joe. The Silence & the Sun: An historical account of people, places & events on old Route 66 & railroad communities in the Eastern Mojave Desert, California. 2007. (Illus.). 282p. pap. 29.95 *(978-0-9793827-0-3(X))* Trails End Publishing Co.

Debrino, Preacher Frank. The Way Maker (A Street Called Straight) The Premier Guide to Deliverance from Addictions. 2008. 96p. pap. 9.99 *(978-1-60647-536-2(3))* Xulon Pr., Inc.

Del Mar, Walter. For the Love of Belle. 2010. 176p. pap. *(978-1-55452-455-6(5)*, Epic Pr.) Essence Publishing.

Delgado, Manuel Ruben. The Last Chicano: A Mexican American Experience. 2009. 308p. 31.99 *(978-1-4490-1415-5(1))*; pap. 21.49 *(978-1-4490-1414-8(3))* AuthorHouse.

Dennis Charles Sacco Staff. The Jiggy Joggers. 2009. 152p. pap. 14.95 *(978-1-4343-9785-0(8))* AuthorHouse.

Denton, Robert W. Stories of a Country Doctor. 2009. 212p. pap. 18.99 *(978-1-58930-239-6(7))* Selah Publishing Group, LLC.

Desmond, Jim. From down Canyon to the Mountaintop. 2011. 300p. pap. 22.95 ***(978-1-4497-2556-3(2)***, WestBow Pr.) Author Solutions, Inc.

Diehl, Darlyne & Diehl, Philip. Triumph: Traveling Towards Death: Preparing for a New Life. 2007. 144p. per. 15.95 *(978-0-9727721-9-8(7))* Robertson Publishing.

Dillow, Ben. So Far: Reflections on the Journey. 2011. 416p. 36.95 *(978-1-4502-8260-4(1))*; pap. 26.95 *(978-1-4502-8234-5(2))* iUniverse, Inc.

Discovering Bodie. 2010. (Illus.). 80p. pap. 21.99 *(978-0-9843634-0-7(8))* Gariaeff, Nick.

Doerr, Harold L. A Square of Daffodils, Capitalism, & Why Children Don't Learn: The Story of Building a Wonderful, Loving Family. 2011. 256p. 29.95 ***(978-1-4502-9342-6(5))***; pap. 19.95 ***(978-1-4502-9340-2(9))*** iUniverse, Inc.

Dominguez, Lalo. The Book of Lalo. 2009. 228p. pap. 18.95 *(978-1-4401-6913-7(6))* iUniverse, Inc.

Douglas, Pamela. Back to Life: A Journey of Transformation through Back Surgery. 2011. (ENG., Illus.). 200p. pap. 16.95 *(978-1-61125-002-2(1))* Divine Arts.

Doupont, Ann. God Can Heal Anything. 2006. pap. 11.50 *(978-1-59330-432-4(3))* Aventine Pr.

Dove, Angela. No Room for Doubt. 2009. (ENG.). 384p. (gr. 12-18). 15.00 *(978-0-425-22588-2(7)*, Berkley Trade) Penguin Group (USA) Inc.

Dugard, Jaycee. A Stolen Life: A Memoir. (ENG.). 288p. 2012. pap. 15.00 ***(978-1-4516-2919-4(2))*** 2011. 24.99 ***(978-1-4516-2918-7(4))*** Simon & Schuster.

—A Stolen Life: A Memoir. 2011. (ENG.). 288p. pap. 20.00 ***(978-1-4516-6494-2(X))*** Simon & Schuster Children's Publishing.

Dully, Howard & Fleming, Charles. My Lobotomy: A Memoir. (ENG.). 2008. 304p. pap. 13.95 *(978-0-307-38127-9(7)*, Three Rivers Pr.) 2007. (Illus.). 288p. 24.95 *(978-0-307-38126-2(9)*, Crown) Crown Publishing Group.

Dumas, Firoozeh. Funny in Farsi. 2011. 14.05 *(978-0-7848-3409-1(1)*, Everbind) Marco Bk. Co.

Dupee, C. R. Opera Thoughts: A Synopsis of My Synapses. 2008. 147p. pap. 11.95 *(978-0-7414-4623-7(5))* Infinity Publishing.

Duran Chad Duran, Alfredo. Prop 8 Overturn. 2011. 52p. pap. 9.95 *(978-1-4620-0393-8(1))* iUniverse, Inc.

Eben, Jeffrey. How Many Wins Have YOU Had Today? 2006. 204p. 20.00 *(978-0-9777666-1-1(6))* Garden of Eben Publishing.

Edmond, John G. Union Cemetery, Redwood City, California: The People, Their Lives, Their Communities: Including the Towns of Searsville, Summit Springs, & West Union. 2nd ed. 2009. *(978-0-89863-310-8(9))* Star Publishing Co.

Ellis, Ella. Dune Child. 2011. 150p. pap. 20.00 ***(978-0-9795285-9-0(3))*** El Leon Literary Arts.

Elmore, Lavinia. Tides of Life. 2010. 136p. pap. 11.95 *(978-1-60844-374-1(4))* Dog Ear Publishing, LLC.

Emery, William. Edges of Bounty: Adventures in the Edible Valley. 2008. 224p. pap. 20.00 *(978-1-59714-108-6(9))* Heyday.

Engelhardt, Zephyrin. The Franciscans in California. 2009. 392p. pap. *(978-0-217-75980-9(7))* Books LLC.

Enrique "Blyhe" Horta. Confessions & Memoirs of an Airline Pilot. 2009. 300p. 25.99 *(978-1-4389-2814-2(9))*; pap. 15.49 *(978-1-4389-2815-9(7))* AuthorHouse.

Enss, Chris. Outlaw Tales of California: True Stories of the Golden State's Most Infamous Crooks, Culprits, & Cutthroats. 2008. (Outlaw Tales Ser.). (Illus.). 128p. per. 12.95 *(978-0-7627-3852-6(9)*, TwoDot) Globe Pequot Pr., The.

Espinoza, Yolanda. El Caracol - the Story of Alfonso: Labor Camp Child. 2010. (ENG.). 176p. pap. 14.95 *(978-1-936400-58-4(8))* Mill City Pr., Inc.

Esquevin, Christian. Adrian: Silver Screen to Custom Label. 2008. (ENG., Illus.). 224p. (gr. 12). 50.00 *(978-1-58093-193-9(6))* Monacelli Pr., Inc.

Evans, Stacy. Pen Pals: Letters from the Heart. 2007. 200p. per. 16.95 *(978-0-595-42197-8(0))* iUniverse, Inc.

Faessel, Stephen J. Anaheim 1940-2007. 2007. (Images of America Ser.). (ENG., Illus.). 128p. per. 19.99 *(978-0-7385-4743-5(3))* Arcadia Publishing.

Fante, Dan. Fante: A Family's Legacy of Writing, Drinking & Surviving. 2011. (P. S. Ser.). (ENG.). 288p. pap. 14.99 *(978-0-06-202709-2(3)*, HarperPerennial) HarperCollins Pubs.

Farnbach, Rebecca & Barnett, Loretta. Fallbrook. 2007. (Images of America Ser.). (ENG., Illus.). 128p. per. 19.99 *(978-0-7385-4747-3(6))* Arcadia Publishing.

Fella, Angelo. Hippie: the Evolution. 2010. 177p. pap. 11.99 *(978-0-557-27057-6(X))* Lulu Enterprises Inc.

Fenske, Doug Dane. Holding on- I Sued the Mafia & Lived to Tell about It the Story of Sundance Dane & Kerri James. 2011. 290p. pap. 17.50 ***(978-1-60911-328-5(4)***, Strategic Bk. Publishing) AEG Literary Publishing Services, Inc.

Fernandez, Rick. An Uncharted Desert Isle. 2009. 260p. 24.99 *(978-1-4343-6032-8(6))*; pap. 19.95 *(978-1-4343-3738-2(3))* AuthorHouse.

Ferry, David. For the Love of A Deer. 2008. pap. 12.00 *(978-0-8059-8497-2(6))* Dorrance Publishing Co., Inc.

Fiala, Marie Lawson. Letters from a Distant Shore. 2010. (LaurelBooks Ser.). (ENG.). 338p. pap. 21.00 (978-1-933880-19-8(8)) Cavankerry Pr., Ltd.
Field, Maria Antonia. Where Castilian Roses Bloom: Memoirs of Maria Antonia Field. 2011. 200p. 44.95 (978-1-258-10453-5(9)) Literary Licensing, LLC.
Fielding, Timmy. Untold Stories: How I Survived A Child Fom Ring. 2011. 232p. 28.95 (978-1-4620-4715-4(7)); pap. 18.95 (978-1-4620-4714-7(9)) iUniverse, Inc.
Fieldy, et al. Got the Life: My Journey of Addiction, Faith, Recovery, & Korn. 2009. (Illus.). 288p. 26.99 (978-0-06-166249-2(6), Morrow, William & Co.) HarperCollins Pubs.
Fisher, Derek. Character Driven: Life, Lessons, & Basketball. 2012. (ENG., Illus.). 272p. pap. 14.99 (978-1-4516-7207-7(1), Howard Bks.) Howard Books.
Fisher, Patrick. Experiences with Earth First! 2009. 185p. pap. 20.55 (978-0-557-05265-3(3)) Lulu Enterprises Inc.
Fitzgerald, Kevin Patrick. My Ex-Wife, My Savior: The Awakening of an Egoholic. 2008. 192p. pap. 16.95 (978-1-4401-0635-4(5)) iUniverse, Inc.
Fitzgerald, Timothy. The Wawona Brotherhood, the San Jose State Campus Revolt. 2009. 328p. 33.85 (978-1-60860-077-9(7), Strategic Bk. Publishing) AEG Literary Publishing Services, Inc.
Fitzpatrick, Linda & Conkle, James M. Needles. 2010. (Images of America Ser.). (Illus.). 128p. pap. 21.99 (978-0-7385-8064-7(3)) Arcadia Publishing.
Fogelson, Hillary. Pale Girl Speaks: A Year Uncovered. 2012. (ENG.). 256p. pap. 16.00 (978-1-58005-444-7(7)) Seal Pr.
Foust, Traci. Nowhere near Normal: A Memoir of OCD. 2011. (ENG.). 384p. 24.00 (978-1-4391-9250-4(2)) Gallery Pr., The IRL. Dist: Simon & Schuster, Inc.
Fraley, Michal. Skating the Starlight Express. 2011. 366p. pap. 22.95 (978-1-4583-7432-5(7)) Lulu Enterprises Inc.
Frank, Matthew Gavin. Pot Farm. 2012. (ENG.). 232p. pap. 16.95 (978-0-8032-3784-1(7)) Univ. of Nebraska Pr.
Frankie, Chris. Nailed. 2010. 256p. 24.95 (978-1-60078-433-0(X)) Triumph Bks.
Franklin "Dub", W. A. Dining with Dub. 2009. 92p. pap. 11.95 (978-1-4401-2220-0(2)) iUniverse, Inc.
Freed, Charlie. Vet Tails: Small Stories from a Small Town, Small Animal Veterinarian. 2008. pap. 14.99 (978-1-60604-504-6(0)) Tate Publishing & Enterprises, LLC.
Frimtzis, Robert. From Tajikistan to the Moon: A Story of Tragedy, Survival & Triumph of the Human Spirit. 2009. 360p. 26.95 (978-0-615-19903-0(8)) Ecliptic Publishing.
Fujino, Diane C. Samurai among Panthers: Richard Aoki on Race, Resistance, & a Paradoxical Life. 2012. (Critical American Studies). 496p. 75.00 (978-0-8166-7786-3(7)); pap. 24.95 (978-0-8166-7787-0(5)) Univ. of Minnesota Pr.
Gale, Kate & De Turenne, Veronique. The Devil's Punchbowl: A Cultural & Geographic Map of California Today. 2010. (ENG.). 208p. pap. 25.95 (978-1-59709-164-0(2)) Red Hen Pr.
Gallo, Kenny & Rancazzo, Matthew. Breakshot: A Life in the 21st Century American Mafia. 2010. (ENG., Illus.). 512p. mass mkt. 7.99 (978-1-4391-9583-3(8), Pocket Star) Pocket Star.
Gallo, Kenny & Rancazzo, Matthew, V. Breakshot: A Life in the 21st Century American Mafia. 2009. 350p. 24.95 (978-1-59777-615-8(7)) Phoenix Bks., Inc.
Galván, Elías Huerta Melgoza. Un Recuerdo: A Fond Remembrance. 2007. (ENG & SPA., Illus.). 65p. 20.00 (978-1-4257-1739-1(X)) Xlibris Corp.
Gavin, Camille. A Bakersfield Childhood. 2011. 92p. pap. 19.95 (978-1-4560-1932-7(5)) PublishAmerica, Inc.
George, Steven. Stream of Unconsciousness: From Addiction to Redemption in the City of Angels. Hunt, Marie, ed. 2007. 176p. per. 15.95 (978-0-9769689-4-8(0)) Free Educational Publications International, Inc.
Gibson, Dewan. The Imperfect Enjoyment: A Bachelor's Memoir. 2008. (C). pap. 10.95 (978-0-615-22568-3(8)) Irc Bks.
Glabb, Scott. A Saint in the City: Coaching at-Risk Kids to Be Champions. 2010. pap. 18.99 (978-1-933290-61-4(7)) Tate Publishing & Enterprises, LLC.
Glatt, John. Lost & Found: The True Story of Jaycee Lee Dugard & the Abduction That Shocked the World. 2010. (ENG., Illus.). 352p. 7.99 (978-0-312-38827-0(6), St. Martin's True Crime) St. Martin's Pr.
Goffings, J. P. The Hedonist: The Remake. 2009. 304p. pap. 23.00 (978-1-4251-9156-6(6)) Trafford Publishing.
Gonen, Eitan. From Jerusalem to Beverly Hills: Memoir of a Palestinian Jew. 2010. 352p. 28.28 (978-1-4520-9293-5(1)); pap. 17.75 (978-1-4520-9294-2(X)) AuthorHouse.
Gonsalez, Marti Hope, et al, eds. The Scientist & Humanist. 2010. (Modern Pioneers in Psychological Science: an APS-Psychology Press Ser.). (ENG.). 400p. 84.95 (978-1-84872-867-7(0), Psychology Press) Taylor & Francis Group GBR. Dist: Taylor & Francis Group.
Gonzales, Frank "Pancho" Chronicles of a Fisherman. 2009. 78p. pap. 15.99 (978-1-4415-7399-5(2)) Xlibris Corp.
Gorman, Thomas. To Believe or Not Believe, That Is the Question. 2007. 296p. per. 15.99 (978-1-60034-988-1(9)) Xulon Pr., Inc.
Gosling, Geo. Tbi Hell A Traumatic Brain Injury Reall. 2006. 164p. pap. 14.95 (978-1-59800-722-0(X)) Outskirts Pr., Inc.
Granger, Orman. The Triumph of Persistence, Determination & Preparation: If I could do it, you can Too. 2011. 158p. 29.99 (978-1-4653-6151-6(0)); pap. 19.99 (978-1-4653-6150-9(2)) Xlibris Corp.
Graysmith, Robert. The Girl in Alfred Hitchcock's Shower: A Murder that Became a Real-Life Mystery, A Mystery that Became an Obsession. l.t. ed. 2010. 492p. 30.95 (978-1-4104-2672-7(6)) Thorndike Pr.
Green, Reg. Il Dono Di Nicholas: Una Testimonianza Sul Potere Dell'Amore. 2011. (ITA.). 284p. pap. 14.50 (978-1-4670-4374-8(5)) AuthorHouse.
Greenfield, Robert. A Day in the Life: One Family, the Beautiful People, & the End of the Sixties. 2009. (ENG., Illus.). 368p. 24.95 (978-0-306-81622-2(9)) Perseus Bks. Group.
Grijalva, Edward. Glasspar Boat Builder: Circa 1952-1962. 2008. 48p. pap. 16.95 (978-1-60610-882-6(4)) PublishAmerica, Inc.
Guinn, J. M. History & Biographical Record of Monterey & San Benito, CA, Vol. II. fac. ed. (Illus.). 453p. reprint ed. pap. 46.88 (978-1-55567-753-4(3)) Coyote Pr.
—History & Biographical Record of Monterey & San Benito Counties & History of the State of California . (Illus.). 334p. (C). pap. 35.00 (978-1-55567-752-7(5)) Coyote Pr.
Guittard, E. V., ed. California Masonry. 2011. 340p. 51.95 (978-1-258-00169-8(1)) Literary Licensing, LLC.
Gwilliam, J. Gary. Getting a Winning Verdict in My Personal Life: A Trial Lawyer Finds His Soul. 2007. (978-1-4243-4283-9(X)) Pavior Publishing.
Haas, Kurt. Why America? 2009. 144p. pap. 14.95 (978-1-4401-2237-8(7)) iUniverse, Inc.
Haber, Mel. Palm Springs à la Carte: The Colorful World of the Caviar Crowd at Their Favorite Desert Hideaway. 2008. 256p. 23.95 (978-1-56980-353-0(6)) Barricade Bks., Inc.
Hadley, Peter E. Wings of the Tern: A Flyers Odyssey. 2010. (Illus.). 599p. pap. 22.95 (978-1-4327-5093-0(3)) Outskirts Pr., Inc.
Haight Cattani, Dana & Haight, Angela B. A P Giannini: The Man with the Midas Touch. 2009. 148p. 22.95 (978-1-4389-5493-6(X)); pap. 11.99 (978-1-4389-5492-9(1)) AuthorHouse.
Halberstadt, April Hope, et al. John Brown's Family in California: A Journey by Funeral Train, Covered Wagon, Through Archives, to the Valley of Heart's Delight. Libby, Jean, ed. enl. ed. 2006. 15.00 (978-0-9773638-2-7(1)) Allies for Freedom Pubs.
Hall, Douglas Scott. From Fantasy Football to Fatherhood: A Comedic & Spiritual Look at a Man's Year of Transformation. 2007. pap. 11.00 (978-0-8059-8695-2(2)) Dorrance Publishing Co., Inc.
Hall Freeman. Retail Hell: How I Sold My Soul to the Store. 2010. (ENG.). 288p. pap. 14.95 (978-1-4405-0577-5(2)) Adams Media Corp.
Halperin, Ian. The Governator: From Muscle Beach to His Quest for the White House - The Improbable Rise of Arnold Schwarzenegger. 2010. (ENG., Illus.). 288p. 25.99 (978-0-06-199004-5(3), Morrow, William & Co.) HarperCollins Pubs.
—The Governator: From Muscle Beach to New Camelot the Untold Story of Arnold Schwarzenegger. l.t. ed. 2010. (ENG.). 408p. pap. 25.99 (978-0-06-200223-5(6), HarperLuxe) HarperCollins Pubs.
Hanson, Victor Davis. Mexifornia: A State of Becoming. 2nd ed. 2007. (ENG.). 150p. per. 17.95 (978-1-59403-217-2(3)) Encounter Bks.
Harris, Quinn. The Quinn Harris Story: From Funky Blues to Good News. 2011. 272p. pap. 15.19 (978-1-4567-6960-4(X)) AuthorHouse.
Hart, Herbert Hoover. Triumph Beyond Silence. 2009. 262p. 31.99 (978-1-4257-6788-4(5)); pap. 21.99 (978-1-4257-6780-8(X)) Xlibris Corp.
Hart, Melissa. Gringa: A Contradictory Girlhood. 2009. (ENG.). 288p. pap. 16.95 (978-1-58005-294-8(0)) Seal Pr.
Hartman, Kent. The Wrecking Crew: The Inside Story of Rock & Roll's Best-Kept Secret. 2012. (ENG., Illus.). 304p. 25.99 (978-0-312-61974-9(X), Dunne, Thomas Bks.) St. Martin's Pr.
Harvey, James E. Cops, Crooks, & Clergy: A Long Journey to Inside the Catholic Church. 2007. 244p. per. 11.95 (978-1-4327-1264-8(0)) Outskirts Pr., Inc.
Harwood, Craig S. & Fogel, Gary. Quest for Flight: John J. Montgomery & the Dawn of Aviation in the West. 2012. (978-0-8061-4264-7(2)) Univ. of Oklahoma Pr.
Heagen, Paul. The Groove Project: Two Unlikely Friends, an Unlucky Car, & A Lifetime They Never Imagined. 2010. 212p. 27.95 (978-1-4502-4375-9(4)); pap. 17.95 (978-1-4502-4373-5(8)) iUniverse, Inc.
Heimoff, Steve. New Classic Winemakers of California: Conversations with Steve Heimoff. 2010. (ENG., Illus.). 292p. pap. 19.95 (978-0-520-26791-6(5)) Univ. of California Pr.
Henshaw, Betty. Children of the Dust: An Okie Family Story. Scofield, Sandra, ed. 2006. (Plains Histories Ser.). (Illus.). 264p. 29.95 (978-0-89672-585-0(5)) Texas Tech Univ. Pr.
Henshaw, Betty Grant. Children of the Dust: An Okie Family Story. 2008. (Plains Histories Ser.). (Illus.). 272p. pap. 22.95 (978-0-89672-631-4(2)) Texas Tech Univ. Pr.
Herzberger, Leslie. Something Happened in Paradise: Thermidor in America. 2009. 192p. pap. 19.99 (978-1-4415-6917-2(0)) Xlibris Corp.
Hicks, Louise. A Hill to Climb: A Teenager's Battle with Cancer, Depression, & Drug Addiction. 2010. pap. 14.99 (978-1-61566-252-4(9)) Tate Publishing & Enterprises, LLC.
Higham, John. 360 Degrees Longitude: One Family's Journey Around the World-A Memoir. 2009. (ENG., Illus.). 336p. pap. 17.95 (978-1-59350-108-2(0)) Alyson Pubns.
Hill, Herman. Baja's Hidden Gold: Treasure along the Mission Trail. 2008. 188p. pap. 16.95 (978-1-934248-72-0(X)) Mill City Pr., Inc.
Hines, Pamela. America's Basso. 2009. 282p. pap. 15.95 (978-1-60693-662-7(X), Eloquent Bks.) AEG Literary Publishing Services, Inc.
Hobbs, David. Out of the Fire. 2nd ed. 2007. (Illus.). 382p. per. 15.00 (978-1-59971-661-9(5)) Aardvark Global Publishing.
Hopple, Edwards R. Wise in the Road. 2009. 212p. 31.99 (978-1-4415-0358-9(7)); pap. 21.99 (978-1-4415-0357-2(9)) Xlibris Corp.
Horton, Jane. The 60 / 70 Sparkling - A Palo Alto Dreamer. 2010. 386p. pap. 26.50 (978-0-557-19084-3(3)) Lulu Enterprises Inc.
Hotchkiss, James M., Jr. A Pair of Kings & A Joker. 2009. 225p. pap. 15.95 (978-0-557-00772-1(0)) Lulu Enterprises Inc.
Howland, Bill. A California Bonesetter's Autobiography, 1 vol. 2009. 205p. pap. 29.95 (978-1-61546-222-3(8)); pap. 24.95 (978-1-60563-745-7(9)) PublishAmerica, Inc.
Hoyt, Scott R. Two Years of Eternity. 2011. 312p. pap. 15.95 (978-0-533-16357-1(9)) Vantage Pr., Inc.
Hubbard Crawford, Leslie. Coronado. 2011. (Images of America Ser.). (ENG., Illus.). 128p. pap. 21.99 (978-0-7385-8130-9(5)) Arcadia Publishing.
Hubbert, Bob. Only When I Talk. pap. 11.95 (978-1-4327-0066-9(9)) Outskirts Pr., Inc.
Hulstrum, Bill. Perris: A Place to Remember. 2007. (978-1-57864-409-4(7)) Donning Co. Pubs.
Hunter, Russell. Heir Conditioning at Open Country. 2011. 232p. pap. 15.95 (978-1-4502-9105-7(8)) iUniverse, Inc.
Industan, Edmund Melig. Kollawan. 2007. 156p. per. 13.99 (978-1-60477-163-3(1)) Xulon Pr., Inc.
Jacobs, J. Bruce. What a Ride: Recount of Extraordinary Life Passages. 2008. 260p. pap. 19.99 (978-1-4363-8536-7(9)) Xlibris Corp.
Jamero, Peter. Growing up Brown: Memoirs of a Filipino American. 2006. (Scott & Laurie Oki Series in Asian American Studies). (ENG., Illus.). 348p. per. 24.95 (978-0-295-98642-5(5)) Univ. of Washington Pr.
Jasinski, Frank. From an Oak Tree. 2010. 203p. 29.99 (978-1-4500-7671-5(8)); pap. 19.99 (978-1-4500-7670-8(X)) Xlibris Corp.
Jean Anne Turner. A Year on the Brink. 2009. 540p. 33.99 (978-1-4389-5611-4(8)); pap. 23.49 (978-1-4389-5612-1(6)) AuthorHouse.
Jenkins, Susan Elaine. Scandalon: Running from Shame & Finding God's Scandalous Love. 2009. 288p. pap. 13.99 (978-0-9818929-0-0(6)) CLADACH Publishing.
Jennings, Ross. My Year in Africa & How One Thing Led to Another. 2010. 275p. pap. 16.00 (978-0-557-41844-2(5)) Lulu Enterprises Inc.
Jiménez, Francisco. Mas alla de mi Reaching Out Spanish Edition. 2009. (ENG.). 224p. (YA). (gr. 7). pap. 6.99 (978-0-547-25031-1(2), Graphia) Houghton Mifflin Harcourt Trade & Reference Pubs.
Joe Novak. Something to Do with Wings: A Memoir. 2010. 360p. pap. 23.95 (978-1-4401-9778-9(4)) iUniverse, Inc.
Johnson, Darren. The Parolee. 2009. 48p. pap. 10.49 (978-1-4490-4328-5(3)) AuthorHouse.
Johnson, Dave, et al. Teddy Bear: Stolen Innocence. 2011. 15.95 net. (978-1-61156-163-0(9)) Dr. Due Bks.
Jones, Ed D. From Out House to Outer Space. 2009. 118p. 48.99 (978-1-4257-8643-4(X)) Xlibris Corp.
Jones, Ned. Life with a Thoroughbred Named Evander. 2008. 78p. pap. 16.95 (978-1-4241-9033-1(9)) PublishAmerica, Inc.
Jones, Ray. Yosemite National Park: Remarkable Events That Shaped History. 2010. (It Happened in Ser.). (ENG., Illus.). 160p. pap. 14.95 (978-0-7627-5060-3(X)) Globe Pequot Pr., The.
Kaeser, Sophia. Memoirs of Our Cabin in Yosemite; & Our Backyard Wilderness. 2009. 108p. 22.95 (978-1-4401-4082-2(0)); pap. 12.95 (978-1-4401-4080-8(4)) iUniverse, Inc.
Kaiser, David. How the Hippies Saved Physics: Science, Counterculture, & the Quantum Revival. 2011. (ENG., Illus.). 372p. 26.95 (978-0-393-07636-3(9), 7636) Norton, W. W. & Co., Inc.
Kamei, Midori Kitazono. Granddaughter of a Samurai: Memoirs of Midori Kamei. 2008. pap. 13.99 (978-1-60477-359-0(6)) Xulon Pr., Inc.
Kando, Thomas. A Tale of Survival: From War Ravaged Europe to the Promise of America. 2008. 400p. pap. 17.95 net. (978-0-615-21932-5(2)) European American Publishing.
Kang, Grace S., et al. Eric Elsesser. 2010. (978-1-932884-47-0(5)) Earthquake Engineering Research Institute.
Keibel, John A. Behind the Barbed Wire: History of Naval Weapons Station Concord. 2009. (Illus.). 352p. pap. 28.95 (978-0-615-27907-7(4)) Keibel, John A. Documentary Photography.
KickStart. Memoirs of a Biker, 1 vol. 2009. 380p. pap. 29.95 (978-1-60749-069-2(2)) PublishAmerica, Inc.
Knott, Stephen F. & Chidester, Jeffrey L. At Reagan's Side: Insiders' Recollections from Sacramento to the White House. 2009. (ENG.). 264p. 49.95 (978-0-7425-6625-5(0)) Rowman & Littlefield Publishers, Inc.
Knox, Reggie. Growing up Hood, 1 vol. 2010. 49p. pap. 16.95 (978-1-4489-9085-6(8)) PublishAmerica, Inc.
Koch, Rod. When the Green Flag Drops. 2011. 498p. 34.99 (978-1-4568-5863-6(7)); pap. 23.99 (978-1-4568-5862-9(9)) Xlibris Corp.
Koestenbaum, Robert, et al, texts. Lari Pittman. 2011. (Illus.). 276p. 75.00 (978-0-8478-3576-8(6), Skira) Rizzoli International Pubns., Inc.
Kogan, Milt M. D. Second Act: Returning to College at Age 71. 2010. 88p. pap. 30.49 (978-1-4520-0344-3(0)) AuthorHouse.
Koning, Ben & Matz, Anneke. Sunnyvale. 2011. (Images of America Ser.). (ENG., Illus.). 128p. pap. 21.99 (978-0-7385-7435-6(X)) Arcadia Publishing.
Kopelman, Jay. From Baghdad to America: Life Lessons from a Dog Named Lava. (ENG., Illus.). 208p. 2010. pap. 14.95 (978-1-60239-743-9(0), 239743) 2008. 23.95 (978-1-60239-264-9(1), 239264) Skyhorse Publishing Co., Inc.
Korby, Carol. Rescue in Mt Shasta Forest. 2011. 78p. 24.99 (978-1-4628-8731-6(7)); pap. 15.99 (978-1-4628-8730-9(9)) Xlibris Corp.
Kramer, Carol A. & Calaveras Big Trees Association. Calaveras Big Trees. 2010. (Images of America Ser.). (Illus.). 128p. pap. 21.99 (978-0-7385-8118-7(6)) Arcadia Publishing.
Lardner, W. B. & Brock, M. J. History of Placer & Nevada Counties, California, V1. 2011. 438p. 56.95 (978-1-258-08287-1(X)) Literary Licensing, LLC.
—History of Placer & Nevada Counties, California, V2: Biographical Review, Pioneers, Past & Present. 2011. 812p. 74.95 (978-1-258-08320-5(5)) Literary Licensing, LLC.
Leaf, Norman. Are Those Real? True Tales of Plastic Surgery from Beverly Hills. 2010. 172p. (ENG.). 25.95 (978-1-4502-1842-9(3)); pap. 15.95 (978-1-4502-1840-5(7)) iUniverse, Inc.
Lee, Hector. 20 Tales of California, 2nd Edition: A Rare Collection of Western Stories. 2nd ed. 2008. (Illus.). 192p. pap. 12.95 (978-1-877810-72-5(X)) Rayve Productions, Inc.
Legacy. 2007. per. 14.95 (978-0-9795554-0-4(X)) SoHo Services.
Leonard, Nick. Roller Skaters & Wine Makers. 2010. 128p. pap. 21.50 (978-1-4457-4670-8(0)) Lulu Enterprises Inc.
Leung, L. P. Portraits of Pride II - Chinese-American Legacies - First 160 Years in America. 2011. (Illus.). 288p. 40.00 (978-0-930377-01-4(X)) Chinese Historical Society of Southern California, Inc.
Levitch, Edward L. Once from the Enemies & Once from the Perils of Life. Date not set. pap. (978-0-9655974-1-8(5)) Mad Dog Publishing.
Lewis, Louise. No Experts Needed: The Meaning of Life According to You! 2007. 236p. per. 18.95 (978-0-595-42971-4(8)) iUniverse, Inc.
Lick, Sue Fagalde. Stories Grandma Never Told: Portuguese Women in California. 2007. (Illus.). 265p. per. 18.95 (978-1-892076-35-9(7)) Dancing Moon Pr.
Liechty, Delbert. Personal Testament. 2011. 204p. pap. 24.95 (978-1-4560-3500-6(2)) PublishAmerica, Inc.
Lindgren-Kurtz, Pat. Picking Willows: Daisy & Lilly Baker, Maidu Basket Makers of Lake Almanor. 2011. 136p. pap. 13.95 (978-1-4620-5551-7(6)) iUniverse, Inc.
Linick, Anthony. The Lives of Ingolf Dahl. 2008. 652p. 36.49 (978-1-4389-1401-5(6)); pap. 25.99 (978-1-4343-8003-6(3)) AuthorHouse.
Littleton, C. Scott. 2500 Strand: Growing up in Hermosa Beach, California, during World War II. 2007. 272p. pap. (978-1-897244-32-6(0)) Red Pill Pr.
Lockwood, Craig. Peanuts: Exploring Legend, Myth & Archetype in California's Surfing Subculture: an Oral Biography. 2009. (ENG., Illus.). 160p. 35.00 (978-0-9704228-3-5(0)) Croul Family Foundation.
Lorenc, Cameron. ADD - Is It Me? A Personal Account. 2007. (Illus.). 246p. per. 19.95 (978-0-9774319-2-2(4)) Slight Edge.
Lorier, April. God's Battered Child. 2007. 159p. pap. 15.95 (978-0-7414-3896-6(8)) Infinity Publishing.
Lowry, Chag. The Original Patriots: Northern California Indian Veterans of World War Two. 2007. (Illus.). 270p. pap. (978-0-9791709-0-4(7)) Lowry, Chag.
Luther, Arch. Many Threads: the Saga of an Electronics Engineer. 2008. 312p. pap. 25.96 (978-0-557-02199-4(5)) Lulu Enterprises Inc.
Lutton, Brookelea. Old Man of the Mountains: The Story of Peter Voiss, California's Most Notorious, Eccentric Gold Prospector of the 20th Century. 2008. 120p. pap. 15.95 (978-0-9815913-0-8(2)) Gold Dust Publishing.
Ly. No Dream Beyond My Reach: One woman's remarkable journey from Cambodian refugee to American MD. 2009. 132p. pap. 15.99 (978-1-4389-3456-8(1)) AuthorHouse.
Machado, Angie. Through My Eyes All about Me. 2010. (ENG.). 56p. pap. 13.95 (978-1-4505-9882-9(4)) CreateSpace.
Mahaffey, A. L. Skip. Adventures with My Father: Childhood Recollections of Divorce, Dysfunction & the Summer of Love. 2009. 230p. pap. 19.95 (978-1-4327-4392-5(9)) Outskirts Pr., Inc.
Mahlendorf, Ursula. The Shame of Survival: Working Through a Nazi Childhood. 2010. (Illus.). 344p. pap. 21.95 (978-0-271-03448-5(3)) Pennsylvania State Univ. Pr.
Mahlendorf, Ursula R. & Mahlendorf, Ursula. The Shame of Survival: Working Through a Nazi Childhood. 2009. (ENG., Illus.). 344p. 29.95 (978-0-271-03447-8(5)) Pennsylvania State Univ. Pr.
Mangelos, John F. Ripon. 2011. (Images of America Ser.). (Illus.). 128p. pap. 21.99 (978-0-7385-8166-8(6)) Arcadia Publishing.
Manly, William Lewis. Death Valley in '49: An Important Chapter of California Pioneer History. 2007. (ENG.). 566p. 58.95 (978-0-548-01544-5(9)) Kessinger Publishing, LLC.
Maradas, Tadaram. A Pictorial Memoir: 23 Years in the Making. 2010. 244p. pap. 78.49 (978-1-4520-0167-8(7)) AuthorHouse.
Maran, Meredith. My Lie: A True Story of False Memory. 2010. (ENG.). 272p. 24.95 (978-0-470-50214-3(2), Jossey-Bass) Wiley, John & Sons, Inc.
Marin, Rosario. Leading Between Two Worlds: Lessons from the First Mexican-Born Treasurer of the United States. 2007. (ENG., Illus.). 288p. pap. 18.99 (978-0-7432-8645-9(6), Beyond Words/Atria Bks.) Atria Bks.
Marrazzo, Frederick W. Italians in the Santa Clara Valley. 2007. (Images of America Ser.). (ENG., Illus.). 128p. pap. 21.99 (978-0-7385-5562-1(2)) Arcadia Publishing.
Mas Masumoto, David. Wisdom of the Last Farmer: Harvesting Legacies from the Land. 2010. (ENG.). 272p. pap. 14.00 (978-1-4391-8242-0(6), Free Pr.) Free Pr.
Masumoto, David Mas. Heirlooms: Letters from a Peach Farmer. 2007. 202p. 21.95 (978-1-59714-064-5(3)) Heyday.
Matthews, Stephen. Too True for Lies: A Child's Story. 2009. 130p. pap. 20.70 (978-0-557-09427-1(5)) Lulu Enterprises Inc.
Maulhardt, Jeffrey Wayne. Oxnard. 2009. (Postcard History Ser.). (Illus.). 128p. pap. 21.99 (978-0-7385-6937-6(2)) Arcadia Publishing.

C

Mauritzen, T. G. Printers Ink on a Shoestring: A Rebel Who Wouldn't Stay Put. 2011. 68p. 36.95 (978-1-258-09988-6(8)) Literary Licensing, LLC.
McArdle, Barry. I Sold the Moon! A True Story. 2007. (Illus.). 264p. per. 14.95 (978-0-9793673-9-7(5)) Silver Street Publishing.
McBride, Brian. Drummers Bk. 1: Rites of Passage on the Parade Route. 2008. 235p. pap. 24.95 (978-1-60672-451-4(7)) PublishAmerica, Inc.
McClelland, Gordon T. & Last, Jay T. California Watercolors (1850-1970) An Illustrated History & Biographical Dictionary. 132p. 49.00 (978-0-914589-10-5(5)) Hillcrest Pr.
McClure, Samuel L. Compare 50 Years Ago with the Present & Let's Share the Blame. 2011. 156p. pap. 13.99 (978-1-4269-5456-6(5)) Trafford Publishing.
McCollough, Tom. Commentary & Other Stuff: And even more fragments of Memory. 2011. 188p. pap. 16.95 (978-1-4620-1487-3(9)) iUniverse, Inc.
McCollough, Tom. Vin Yets: Fragments of Memory. 2009. 420p. pap. 26.95 (978-1-4401-8421-5(6)) iUniverse, Inc.
McCovey, Mavis & Salter, John Frederick. Medicine Trails: A Life in Many Worlds. 2009. pap. (978-1-59714-117-8(8)) Heyday.
McCune, Sara Miller. Being Sage: Memories of the First 45 Years. 2010. (978-1-4129-8909-1(4)) SAGE Pubns., Inc.
McDonnell, Jeanne Farr. Juana Briones of Nineteenth-Century California. 2008. (ENG., Illus.). 288p. (C). 50.00 (978-0-8165-2586-7(2)); pap. 22.95 (978-0-8165-2587-4(0)) Univ. of Arizona Pr.
McGroarty, John Steven. California of the South V1: A History. 2011. 568p. 63.95 (978-1-258-07243-8(2)) Literary Licensing, LLC.
—California of the South V2: A History, Biographical. 2011. 504p. 58.95 (978-1-258-07245-2(9)) Literary Licensing, LLC.
—California of the South V3: A History, Biographical. 2011. 502p. 58.95 (978-1-258-07246-9(7)) Literary Licensing, LLC.
—California of the South V4: A History, Biographical. 2011. 826p. 75.95 (978-1-258-07247-6(5)) Literary Licensing, LLC.
—California of the South V5: A History, Biographies. 2011. 828p. 75.95 (978-1-258-07248-3(3)) Literary Licensing, LLC.
McIlhany, Edward. Recollections of A '49er. 2010. 214p. pap. 14.95 (978-1-4290-4543-8(4)) Applewood Bks.
McManus, Rick. Letters from Bum Bum. 2011. 208p. pap. 14.95 (978-1-4620-2309-7(6)) iUniverse, Inc.
Mellon, Don. The First Wave of Stories. 2010. (ENG.). 190p. pap. 15.00 (978-1-4528-8666-4(0)) CreateSpace.
Meredith, Don. Varieties of Darkness Cb. 2011. (ENG.). 240p. (gr. 17). 70.00 (978-0-7618-5722-8(2)) Hamilton Bks.
—Varieties of Darkness Pb. 2011. (ENG.). 240p. (gr. 17). pap. 29.99 (978-0-7618-5723-5(0)) Hamilton Bks.
Mey, Savann T. Life in Americ. 2011. 206p. 29.99 (978-1-4363-4187-5(6)); pap. 19.99 (978-1-4363-4186-8(8)) Xlibris Corp.
Miller, Chris Ann & Roberts, Jerry. Hermosa Beach. 2007. (Postcard History Ser.). (ENG., Illus.). 128p. per. 21.99 (978-0-7385-4709-1(3)) Arcadia Publishing.
Miller, Thos. Kent. Baby James: A Legacy of Love & Family Courage. 2007. 216p. (ENG.). 24.95 (978-1-4344-9239-5(7)); per. 14.95 (978-1-4344-9145-9(5)) Wildside Pr., LLC. (Borgo Pr.).
Mirandé, Alfredo. Rascuache Lawyer: Toward a Theory of Ordinary Litigation. 2011. (ENG.). 272p. pap. 29.95 (978-0-8165-2983-4(3)) Univ. of Arizona Pr.
Mitchell, Chris. Cast Member Confidential: A Disneyfied Memoir. 2010. (ENG.). 320p. pap. 15.95 (978-0-8065-3128-1(2), Citadel Pr.) Kensington Publishing Corp.
Mitchell, Janet. Taking a Stand. 2006. 396p. per. 12.99 (978-1-60098-001-5(5)) Green Key Bks.
Molander, Robert P. Extra! Extra! 2008. 232p. 28.95 (978-1-4251-3889-9(6)) Trafford Publishing.
Monaghan, Gerri & Monaghan, Brian. When a Loved One Falls Ill: How to Be an Effective Patient Advocate. 2011. (ENG.). 252p. pap. 14.95 (978-0-7611-6507-1(X), 076116507X) Workman Publishing Co., Inc.
Mooney, Vert. The Unguarded Moment. 2006. pap. 13.95 (978-0-533-15584-2(3)) Vantage Pr., Inc.
Moore, Dorothy Lord. Adventures of a California Woman in the Twentieth Century. McKnew, Janet Moore, ed. 2nd ed. 2011. 478p. per. 39.95 (978-1-932252-49-1(5)) Creative Continuum, Inc.
Moore, Rick. The Mindset: One God, One Race, One Love, One Faith. 2009. pap. 14.99 (978-1-61566-107-7(7)) Tate Publishing & Enterprises, LLC.
Moore, Schuyler M. Advice from Dad. 2011. 184p. pap. 14.95 (978-1-935098-64-5(0), Bascom Hill Publishing Group, Ltd.) Hillcrest Publishing Group, Inc.
Moore, Terry N. A Tigers Tale. 2008. 92p. pap. 10.99 (978-1-60647-861-5(3)) Xulon Pr., Inc.
Mora, Henry. The House on Granada Street: A Spiritual Journey. 2011. 226p. pap. 24.95 (978-1-4560-6124-1(0)) PublishAmerica, Inc.
Morrell, Margot. Reagan's Journey: Lessons from a Remarkable Career. 2011. (ENG., Illus.). 320p. 25.00 (978-1-4516-2085-6(3), Threshold Editions) Threshold Editions.
Mulford, Prentice. Prentice Mulford's Story: Life by Land & Sea. 2007. 252p. per. 14.95 (978-1-60206-168-2(8)) Cosimo, Inc.
—Prentice Mulford's Story: Life by Land & Sea. 2007. 196p. per. 15.95 (978-1-4344-0103-8(0)) Wildside Pr., LLC.
Murphy, Frank. Sister + Brother = TROUBLE (A Memoir) 2010. 87p. pap. 14.98 (978-0-557-28404-7(X)) Lulu Enterprises Inc.
Nakai, T. Roy. Elephant À la Mode: An Epicurean Guide to Life. 2009. 233p. pap. 14.95 (978-1-4327-4577-6(8)) Outskirts Pr., Inc.
Neuman, Gareth Bill. You Can Do It!, in a Job or Your Own Business, Make Your Life a Success. 2009. 112p. 23.50 (978-1-60693-664-1(6), Eloquent Bks.) AEG Literary Publishing Services, Inc.
Niall Flynn. 36 & Counting Kerry's Football Story To 2009. 2009. 408p. 25.70 (978-1-4269-2069-1(5)); pap. 15.70 (978-1-4269-2070-7(9)) Trafford Publishing.
Noble, Tim. From Ship to Shore - the Transition. 2009. 260p. pap. 14.49 (978-1-4389-2639-1(1)) AuthorHouse.
Noirot, Kitty. Noirot's Call of the Moose: The Biography of Clark Noirot. 2010. 272p. 30.95 (978-1-4502-6733-5(5)) iUniverse, Inc.
North, Michael. At the Apron: A Night at the Fights. 2011. 124p. 23.95 (978-1-4620-3669-1(4)); pap. 13.95 (978-1-4620-3670-7(8)) iUniverse, Inc.
Nourmand, Myra. From Homemaker to Breadwinner: How to Make It Big in Real Estate Sales. 2007. 151p. per. 19.95 (978-0-9797730-1-3(6)); (Illus.). 19.95 (978-0-9797730-0-6(8)) Nourmand & Assocs.
O'Brien, Stacey. Wesley the Owl: The Remarkable Love Story of an Owl & His Girl. l.t. ed. 2009. 337p. 30.95 (978-1-4104-1310-9(1)) Thorndike Pr.
O'Connell, Jay. Train Robber's Daughter: The Melodramatic Life of Eva Evans, 187601970. 2008. (Illus.). 320p. pap. 18.95 (978-0-9673370-2-9(X)) Raven River Pr.
o'connell, william. Homeless in Paradise: Communicating with the Bohemian Venice Beach Subculture. 2009. (Illus.). 310p. pap. 25.46 (978-0-557-03501-4(5)) Lulu Enterprises Inc.
O'Donnell, Barbara. Bram. 2009. 120p. pap. 12.95 (978-1-4401-7309-7(5)) iUniverse, Inc.
Oldfield, John. El Obispo del Barrio: Una Biografico del Obispo Alphonso Gallegos, OAR. Alvarez, Beatriz O., tr. from ENG. 2007. (SPA., Illus.). 101p. per. 12.95 (978-0-8091-4431-0(X), 4431-x) Paulist Pr.
Ollestad, Norman. Crazy for the Storm: A Memoir of Survival. l.t. ed. 2009. 360p. pap. 25.99 (978-0-06-178208-4(4), HarperLuxe) HarperCollins Pubs.
Onika Pointer. Humble Bastard: A Memoir. 2010. 376p. 34.95 (978-1-4502-1272-4(7)) iUniverse, Inc.
O'Roark, Bobby. They Call Me Bubbins: Reflections in Time. 2011. 212p. 27.95 (978-1-4620-3408-6(X)); pap. 17.95 (978-1-4620-3407-9(1)) iUniverse, Inc.
Otis, Carre & Schwyzer, Hugo. Beauty, Disrupted: A Memoir. 2011. (ENG.). 256p. 25.99 (978-0-06-202445-9(0)) HarperCollins Pubs.
Owen Valley High Project Ignition, compiled by. Shifting Gears: Alert today, alive Tomorrow. 2007. 96p. per. 15.95 (978-0-9800429-1-7(7)) Pen & Publish Inc.
Pace, Joseph D. Happy Landing: Memoirs of a Soldier. 2009. 104p. pap. 11.95 (978-1-4401-4373-1(0)) iUniverse, Inc.
Padilla, Lucio. Memorias de un Lechuguero. 2009. 220p. pap. 14.99 (978-1-4389-4188-2(9)) AuthorHouse.
Pannell, Ted. Vietnam Stories - Dreams to Nightmares: Vietnam 1967. 2010. pap. 12.99 (978-1-61663-820-7(6)) Tate Publishing & Enterprises, LLC.
Pardey, Lin. Bull Canyon: A Boatbuilder, a Writer & other Wildlife. 2011. (Illus.). 320p. 24.95 (978-1-929214-67-9(7)) Pardey Bks.
Parks, Larry Everett. Sandbox Memories of Larry Everett Parks. 2006. (Illus.). 328p. per. 22.50 (978-1-4251-0404-7(5)) Trafford Publishing.
Parsons, Bret & Colcord, Gerard Rae. Colcord: Home. 2008. (978-1-883318-88-8(2)) Angel City Pr.
Paskowitz, Richard. Soldier joker the 1849 Surveys. 2008. 89p. pap. 18.50 (978-1-4357-2504-1(2)) Lulu Enterprises Inc.
Patrick, Curtis. Reagan: What Was He Really Like? 2011. (ENG.). 336p. pap. 24.95 (978-1-60037-909-3(5)) Morgan James Publishing.
Patterson, Bruce. Turned Round in My Boots: A Memoir. 2010. pap. (978-1-59714-144-4(5)) Heyday.
—Walking Tractor: And Other Country Tales. 2008. 218p. pap. 14.95 (978-1-59714-082-9(1)) Heyday.
Pavlik, Robert C. Norman Clyde: Legendary Mountaineer of California's Sierra Nevada. 2008. pap. (978-1-59714-110-9(0)) Heyday.
Peck, Willys I. & Halberstadt, April. Willys Peck's Saratoga. 2010. (978-0-935089-30-1(6)) California History Ctr.
Pelto, Vonda L. Without Remorse: The Story of the Woman Who Kept Los Angeles' Serial Killers Alive. 2007. (Illus.). 354p. per. 18.95 (978-0-9795852-8-9(7)) Seven Locks Pr.
Peterson, Neil. Embracing the Edge: Stories of Tenacity & Personal Power. 2008. (ENG., Illus.). 195p. pap. 15.95 (978-1-887542-95-1(7)) Book Pubs. Network.
Petroff, Serge P. Life Journey: A Family Memoir. 2008. 288p. 30.95 (978-0-595-51165-5(1)); pap. 20.95 (978-0-595-51115-0(5)) iUniverse, Inc.
Pettibon, Raymond. Raymond Pettibon. Rugoff, Ralph, ed. 2012. (ENG., Illus.). 384p. 135.00 (978-0-8478-3500-3(6)) Rizzoli International Pubns., Inc.
Phelps, Carissa. Runaway Girl: Escaping Life on the Streets, One Helping Hand at a Time. 2012. (ENG.). 320p. (gr. 12). 26.95 (978-0-670-02372-1(8), Viking Adult) Penguin Group (USA) Inc.
Phelps, John & Phelps, Ruth. Memories of This Octogenarian. Date not set. (Illus.). 210p. pap. (978-0-9667166-0-3(4)); 2nd ed. (978-0-9667166-1-0(2)) Phelps, Ruth M.
Phillips, John Renning. The Good Intent: The Story & Heritage of a Fresno Family. 2007. (Illus.). 512p. 34.95 (978-0-9797867-0-9(3)); (ENG., pap. 19.95 (978-0-9797867-1-6(1)) Magnolia Group Pr.
Pineda, Albino R. Entre Los Repatriados: Autobiografia de un Mexico Americano. 2011. 202p. 29.99 (978-1-4628-8951-8(4)); pap. 19.99 (978-1-4628-8952-5(2)) Xlibris Corp.
Pochman, Owen. I'm Just A Kicker. 2007. 273p. per. (978-1-934379-14-1(X)) Printmedia Bks.
Ponce Jr., Ernest F. In Too Deep. 2011. 24p. pap. 8.99 (978-1-61215-624-8(X)) Xulon Pr., Inc.
Pool-Goodrich, Nona. 90 Years... Still Counting. 2008. 56p. (YA). pap. 14.99 (978-0-9655792-9-2(8)) Don Paul Publishing, LLC.
Prainito, Bill T. A Prophet's Ministry: Testimony Teaching Guide. 2008. 172p. pap. 13.99 (978-1-60647-506-5(1)) Xulon Pr., Inc.
Presley, Todd & Harrison, Romana. Mr. Determination. 2009. 208p. 29.99 (978-1-4500-0958-4(1)) Xlibris Corp.
Price, Ryan Lee. Stories of Old Glendora. 2012. 128p. pap. 19.99 (978-1-60949-533-6(0)) History Pr., The.
Purves, Rodrick. Crosswalk: One Nation under God. 2008. 316p. per. 15.95 (978-1-4327-1473-4(2)) Outskirts Pr., Inc.
Quang, Bright. Animosity & Love. 2008. 468p. pap. 20.49 (978-1-4389-2617-9(0)) AuthorHouse.
Raffaele, Beverly J. Tsunami in Crescent City California ~ March 27 1964. 2009. 55p. pap. 8.50 (978-0-557-04411-5(1)) Lulu Enterprises Inc.
Rambeau, Sheryl. Georgetown. 2010. (Images of America Ser.). (Illus.). 128p. pap. 21.99 (978-0-7385-8113-2(5)) Arcadia Publishing.
Raskin, Jonah. Field Days: A Year of Farming, Eating, & Drinking Wine in California. 2009. (Illus.). 344p. 40.00 (978-0-520-25902-7(5)) Univ. of California Pr.
Raskin, Jonah & Green, Paige. Field Days: A Year of Farming, Eating, & Drinking Wine in California. 2010. (ENG., Illus.). 344p. pap. 19.95 (978-0-520-26803-6(2)) Univ. of California Pr.
Rathi, Veena. A Fijian at Heart: A Story of an Amazing Journey with the beauty of Diversity Fiji & Beyond. 2011. 124p. 23.95 (978-1-4567-1590-8(9)); pap. 19.95 (978-1-4567-1588-5(7)) AuthorHouse.
Razo, Max. Born under a Bad Sign. 2009. 220p. pap. 19.99 (978-1-4415-4046-1(6)) Xlibris Corp.
Rendon, Adam. The Vallie: Not A Diary, the Truth. 2011. 120p. pap. 11.00 (978-1-4634-1925-7(2)) AuthorHouse.
Rice, Jim. A View of God from My Rearview Mirror: Seeing God's Presence in Everyday Life. 2010. pap. 16.99 (978-1-61579-902-2(8)) Xulon Pr., Inc.
Rice, William C. Noogie Circles. 2010. 386p. (ENG.). 35.95 (978-1-4327-5218-7(9)); pap. 20.95 (978-1-4327-4907-1(2)) Outskirts Pr., Inc.
Richards, Dick. Workin' Mime to Five: The Hidden Secrets of Cruise Ship Pantomimery; Revealed! 2011. (ENG.). 120p. pap. 17.00 (978-1-935904-03-8(5)) Write Bloody Publishing.
Roach, Freddie. It May End up Killing You: Hard Fought Lessons from a Life in the Ring. 2012. (ENG., Illus.). 320p. 24.95 (978-1-61608-030-3(2), 608030) Skyhorse Publishing Co., Inc.
Robert Anderson. The Back Door to Medicine: An Embedded Anthropologist Tells All. 2009. 276p. pap. 20.95 (978-1-4401-7289-2(7)) iUniverse, Inc.
Roberts, Isaac Phillips. Autobiography of a Farm Boy. 2009. 158p. pap. (978-0-217-68663-1(X)) Books LLC.
—Autobiography of a Farm Boy. 2009. (Illus.). 228p. pap. 22.95 (978-0-8014-7549-8(X), Fall Creek Bks.) Cornell Univ. Pr.
—Autobiography of a Farm Boy. 2007. 348p. 46.95 (978-0-548-54812-7(9)); (ENG.). per. 31.95 (978-0-548-49127-0(5)) Kessinger Publishing, LLC.
Roberts, Monty. The Man Who Listens to Horses: The Story of a Real-Life Horse Whisperer. 2008. (ENG.). 288p. pap. 16.00 (978-0-345-51045-7(3), Ballantine Bks.) Random House Publishing Group.
Robertson, Edith Coffin. Stopwatch Teacher. 2007. 130p. per. 12.95 (978-0-9727721-3-6(8)) Robertson Publishing.
Rock, Francis John. J Ross Browne: A Biography. 2011. 92p. 38.95 (978-1-258-08497-4(X)) Literary Licensing, LLC.
Rodriguez, Art. East Side Dreams. 2010. (ENG.). 266p. pap. 13.95 (978-0-9671555-6-2(8)) Dream House Pr.
Rohde, Chuck. A Taste for Fear. 2011. 166p. pap. 24.95 (978-1-4560-0199-5(X)) PublishAmerica, Inc.
Rovina, Nesta. Tree Barking: A Memoir. 2008. 196p. pap. 14.95 (978-1-59714-081-2(3)) Heyday.
Royce, Sarah. Across the Plains: Sarah Royce's Western Narrative. Jennifer Dawes, Adkison, ed. 2009. (Western Women's Voices Ser.). (ENG., Illus.). 136p. pap. 19.95 (978-0-8165-2726-7(1)) Univ. of Arizona Pr.
Rubino, John "Mariano". Yano: From the Prune Ranch to Skyscrapers. 2007. 204p. (ENG.). 26.95 (978-0-595-68210-2(3)); per. 16.95 (978-0-595-43148-9(8)) iUniverse, Inc.
Ruether, Rosemary Radford & Ruether, David. Many Forms of Madness: A Family's Struggle with Mental Illness & the Mental Health System. 2009. (Illus.). 208p. pap. 22.00 (978-0-8006-9651-1(4), Fortress Pr.) Augsburg Fortress, Pubs.
Runways in the Sand: The History of Blythe Army Air Base in World War II. 2008. (Illus.). 128p. 21.95 (978-0-615-21889-2(X)) Wilson, Art.
Rushton, Jack L. It's Good to Be Alive: Observations from a Wheelchair. 2010. 19.99 (978-1-59955-408-2(9)) Cedar Fort, Inc./CFI Distribution.
Ryan, Joan. The Water Giver: The Story of a Mother, a Son, & Their Second Chance. 2009. (ENG., Illus.). 272p. 24.00 (978-1-4165-7652-5(5)) Simon & Schuster.
Saks, Elyn R. The Center Cannot Hold: My Journey Through Madness. 2008. (ENG.). 368p. pap. 15.99 (978-1-4013-0944-2(5)) Hyperion Pr.
Salcido, Carmina & Jackson, Steve. Not Lost Forever: My Story of Survival. 2011. (ENG., Illus.). 368p. mass mkt. 7.99 (978-0-06-204494-5(X)) HarperCollins Pubs.
Salomon, Carlos Manuel. Pio Pico: The Last Governor of Mexican California. 2011. (ENG., Illus.). 248p. pap. 19.95 (978-0-8061-4237-1(5)) Univ. of Oklahoma Pr.
Sanner, A. E. & Goodwin, John W. John W Goodwin: A Biography. 2011. 162p. 41.95 (978-1-258-09614-4(5)) Literary Licensing, LLC.
Saucedo, Marcelino. Dream Makers & Dream Catchers: The Story of the Mexican Heritage on Catalina Island. 2008. (978-1-57864-474-2(7)) Donning Co. Pubs.
Saunders, Dave. Arnold: Schwarzenegger & the Movies. 2009. (ENG., Illus.). 256p. pap. 18.95 (978-1-84511-948-5(7)) I. B. Tauris & Co., Ltd. GBR. Dist: Macmillan.
Schaffner, Susan. Scruffy Speaks. 2010. 176p. pap. 11.99 (978-1-4490-9706-6(5)) AuthorHouse.
Schoenkopf, Rebecca. Commie Girl in the OC. 2008. (ENG., Illus.). 224p. pap. 16.95 (978-1-84467-258-5(1), 844258) Verso Bks. GBR. Dist: Norton, W. W. & Co., Inc.
Secrest, William B. Showdown! Lionhearted Lawmen of Old California. 2010. (ENG., Illus.). 312p. pap. 15.95 (978-1-884995-65-1(9)) Linden Publishing Co., Inc.
See, Lisa. Bai Nian Jin Shan: Wo de Mei Ji Hua Ren Jia Zu Fen Dou Shi = On Gold Mountain: The One-Hundred-Year Odyssey of My Chinese-American Family. 2010. (CHI., Illus.). (978-7-5633-9087-8(1)) Guangxi Teachers Univ. Pr.
See, Lisa. On Gold Mountain. 2012. (Vintage Ser.). (ENG., Illus.). 464p. pap. 15.95 (978-0-307-95039-0(5), Vintage) Knopf Doubleday Publishing Group.
Seidenberg Jr., Daniel. Vietnam Ambush, 1 vol. 2010. 97p. pap. 16.95 (978-1-4489-7447-4(X)) PublishAmerica, Inc.
Shatner, William. Shatner Rules: Your Key to Understanding the Shatnerverse & the World at Large. 2011. (ENG.). 208p. (gr. 12). 21.95 (978-0-525-95251-0(9), Dutton Adult) Penguin Group (USA) Inc.
Sheila Gale Kandlbinder. Saved by Dolphins: The Todd Endris Story. 2009. 44p. pap. 18.99 (978-1-4389-5755-5(6)) AuthorHouse.
Shillinglaw, Susan. A Journey into Steinbeck's California. 2nd ed. 2011. (ArtPlace Ser.). (ENG.). 230p. pap. 24.95 (978-0-9846239-1-4(4)); (978-0-9846254-7-5(X)) Roaring Forties Pr.
Silvers, Cathy. Happy Days Healthy Living: From Sit-Com Teen to the Health-Food Scene. 2007. (ENG., Illus.). 336p. 30.00 (978-1-55643-734-2(X)); pap. 18.95 (978-1-55643-714-4(5)) North Atlantic Bks.
Simon, Neil. Here I Am Again: The Complete Memoirs. 2011. (ENG., Illus.). 700p. 35.00 (978-1-4516-4027-4(7)) Simon & Schuster.
Simone M. Bahou. Me vs. You. 2010. 180p. (ENG.). 26.95 (978-1-4502-1167-3(4)); pap. 16.95 (978-1-4502-1163-5(1)) iUniverse, Inc.
Sinclair, David William. The Great Life I'Ve Had! 2008. 250p. pap. 19.95 (978-0-615-23583-7(2)) Sinclair Family Trust.
Sitton, Tom. Grand Ventures: The Banning Family & the Shaping of Southern California. 2010. (ENG., Illus.). 376p. 34.95 (978-0-87328-243-7(4)) Huntington Library Pr.
Skiffer, La Tanya. How Black Female Offenders Explain Their Crime & Describe Their Hopes: A Case Study of Inmates in a California Prison. 2008. iii, 144p. (978-0-7734-4916-9(7)) Mellen, Edwin Pr., The.
Smith, David Walter. Street Music & Other Love Stories: (... in a Van down by the Ocean; A Homeless Memoir Part Two) 2011. 416p. pap. 29.95 (978-1-4560-2326-3(8)) PublishAmerica, Inc.
Smith, Jim & Smith, Vicki. Friends Forever. 2006. pap. 14.99 (978-1-60034-789-4(4)) Xulon Pr., Inc.
Snell, Jim. At the Precipice: My Three-Year Journey from Stroke to Good Health with Type 2 Diabetes. 2011. 92p. pap. 9.95 (978-1-4620-3456-7(X)) iUniverse, Inc.
Sparzo, Anthony & Cossette, Michael. From Judas to Me. 2010. 260p. (ENG.). 29.95 (978-1-4502-4057-4(7)); pap. 19.95 (978-1-4502-4056-7(9)) iUniverse, Inc.
Stanley, Damon Booth. Mirrors, Monuments Memories. 2010. (Illus.). 392p. 35.95 (978-1-60594-454-8(8), Llumina Pr.) Aeon Publishing Inc.
Starrett, Richard. Warrior from Adelaide. 2011. pap. 21.99 (978-1-61777-240-5(2)) Tate Publishing & Enterprises, LLC.
Statton, Charles. Charles D. Statton: An Autobiography. 2007. 116p. (ENG.). 22.95 (978-0-595-68168-6(9)); per. 12.95 (978-0-595-42603-4(4)) iUniverse, Inc.
Statton, Charles D. The Statton Family Adventure. 2007. 112p. (ENG.). 22.95 (978-0-595-70839-0(0)); per. 12.95 (978-0-595-47108-9(0)) iUniverse, Inc.
Sterling, Robert E. I Made it Through the Rain: A Story about Overcoming Panic Disorder. 2011. 228p. pap. 15.95 (978-1-4620-5599-9(0)) iUniverse, Inc.
Stern, Michael Z. I Had a Ball: My Friendship with Lucille Ball. 2011. 228p. 28.95 (978-1-4502-8730-2(1)); pap. 18.95 (978-1-4502-8731-9(X)) iUniverse, Inc.
Stevens, Dave. Brush with Passion: The Art & Life of Dave Stevens. Fenner, Arnie & Fenner, Cathy, eds. 2008. (ENG., Illus.). 288p. 39.95 (978-1-59929-010-2(3)) Underwood Books.
Stevens, Janice, compiled by. Stories of Service, Volume 2: Valley Veterans Remember World War II, Korea, Vietnam & the Cold War. 2011. (ENG., Illus.). 244p. 24.95 (978-1-61035-005-1(7)) Linden Publishing Co., Inc.
The Story of My Life. 2009. 372p. pap. (978-1-150-59850-0(6)) Books LLC.
Stott, Greg. Notes from Beyond the Fringe. 2009. 676p. 46.95 (978-1-4401-3584-2(3)); pap. 36.95 (978-1-4401-3582-8(7)) iUniverse, Inc.
Street, Wayne J. Game, Set, Life: My Match with Crohn's & Cancer. 2010. pap. 14.99 (978-1-61566-260-9(X)) Tate Publishing & Enterprises, LLC.
Stuart, Reginald R., et al. Tully Knoles of Pacific: Horseman, Teacher, Minister, College President, Traveler, & Public Speaker. 2011. 192p. 42.95 (978-1-258-10192-3(0)) Literary Licensing, LLC.

Sullivan, Julie. Voices of Lafayette: A Collection of Oral Histories. 2009. 292p. pap. 19.95 (978-0-9745540-3-7(0)) Big Hat Pr.

Swain, Robert. An American Life: Autobiography of Robert Swain. 2009. 15.95 (978-0-9799495-3-1(X), Rio Norte Pr.) River's Bend Pr.

Tamini, Dofini. Coming to USA, 1 vol. 2010. 128p. pap. 19.95 (978-1-4489-5221-2(2)) PublishAmerica, Inc.

Tash, Joe. Dear Guests, Beware of Wild Monkeys: Tips & Tales from a Family World Odyssey. 2010. 400p. pap. 18.99 (978-1-4520-4446-0(5)) AuthorHouse.

Tayag, Elnora Kelly. Filipinos in Ventura County. 2011. (Images of America Ser.). (Illus.). 128p. pap. 21.99 (978-0-7385-7473-8(2)) Arcadia Publishing.

Taylor, Jack. Prophetic Dreams. 2007. 320p. per. 16.95 (978-1-59858-318-2(2)) Dog Ear Publishing, LLC.

Taylor, Patrick A. Memories of Pinecrest. 2006. per. 17.95 (978-0-9789240-0-3(2)) Taylor Pr.

Taylor, William, et al. Lessons of Infinite Advantage: William Taylor's California Experiences. 2010. (Pietist & Wesleyan Studies). 326p. pap. 53.00 (978-0-8108-6059-9(7)) Scarecrow Pr., Inc.

Terlato, Anthony. Taste: A Life in Wine. 2009. (ENG.). 267p. pap. 16.00 (978-1-57284-106-2(0)) Surrey Bks.

Tetro, Joe. Lost in Americ: Memoirs of a Maverick. 2008. 704p. pap. 25.99 (978-1-4389-2454-0(2)) AuthorHouse.

Thomas, Donna. I'm Sorry I Lied to You: , the Confession of Scott Peterson. 2nd ed. 2007. (Illus.). 220p. reprint ed. per. 26.95 (978-0-9802093-1-0(5)) Digi-Tall Media.

Thomas, Gene. Tree House to Palm Trees: My Life from Childhood to Grandchildren. 2011. 184p. 23.95 **(978-1-4620-6289-8(X))**; pap. 13.95 **(978-1-4620-6287-4(3))** iUniverse, Inc.

Thomas, Jr. & Menefee, David. Otay! - the Billy Buckwheat Thomas Story. 2010. 100p. pap. 14.95 (978-1-59393-519-1(6)) BearManor Media.

Thomas, Jr. & Menefee, David W. Otay! - the Billy Buckwheat Thomas Story. 2010. 160p. 24.95 (978-1-59393-207-7(3)) BearManor Media.

Thompkins, E. W., Jr. 101 Road Patrol Tales: Memoirs of a Chippie of the California Highway Patrol. 2011. (ENG.). 240p. pap. 16.95 (978-1-61035-000-6(6)) Linden Publishing Co., Inc.

Tolin, Ernie. Chasing Dreams. 2010. 168p. pap. 12.50 (978-1-4490-8379-3(X)) AuthorHouse.

Tompkins, Walker. Santa Barbara History Makers. 2011. (Illus.). 423p. pap. 25.00 **(978-0-9768008-8-0(8))** BoehmGroup, Inc.

Treser, David. That Reminds Me: As I Remember It. 2009. 188p. 24.99 (978-1-4389-4090-8(4)); pap. 14.49 (978-1-4389-4091-5(2)) AuthorHouse.

Trevenon, Stacy. Kings Mountain. 2008. (Images of America Ser.). (ENG., Illus.). 128p. pap. 19.99 (978-0-7385-5829-5(X)) Arcadia Publishing.

Trippon, George W. Ode to Jimmie. 2007. 64p. per. 9.95 (978-0-595-45177-7(2)) iUniverse, Inc.

Tuggle, Jeremy M. A Journey Through Time: Ono & the Bald Hills. 2008. (Illus.). 96p. pap. 10.00 (978-0-9742578-8-6(0)) Preserving Memories.

Tweedie, Donald. Reminiscence: The Progress of a Christian Pilgrim. 2009. 332p. pap. 18.99 (978-1-61579-417-1(4)) Xulon Pr., Inc.

Uddin, Qazi Nasir. The Other Side. 2011. 272p. pap. 14.03 (978-1-4520-7951-6(X)) AuthorHouse.

Ulloa, Edward. Intricate Journey: Autobiography of Edward Ulloa. 2011. 100p. pap. 19.95 **(978-1-4512-7728-9(8))** PublishAmerica, Inc.

Ulloa, Edward. 27: A Football Coach's Memoirs. 2008. 104p. pap. 16.95 (978-1-60672-003-5(1)) PublishAmerica, Inc.

Ulrich, Isolde. The Romance of Kilimanjaro: The Anatomy of a Midlife Crisis Series. 2011. pap. 19.99 **(978-1-61346-496-0(7))** Tate Publishing & Enterprises, LLC.

Union City Historical Museum Oral History Book: By Myria Raymundo, MBA. 2010.Tr. of 02/01/2010. (Illus.). 214p. pap. 20.00 net. (978-0-9715211-6-2(6)) FolgerGraphics, Inc.

Valentino, Gino. Cowboy: The Legend. 2011. 164p. 33.49 **(978-1-4567-4885-2(8))**; pap. 13.49 **(978-1-4567-4886-9(6))** AuthorHouse.

Varmus, Harold E., et al. The Art & Politics of Science. 2009. (ENG., Illus.). 256p. 24.95 (978-0-393-06128-4(0), 6128) Norton, W. W. & Co., Inc.

Vaughan, Ruben V. Print of My Remembrance an Autobiography. 2006. pap. 22.95 (978-1-4286-5790-8(8)) Kessinger Publishing, LLC.

Vergote, Suzanne. Wake up, America! We're Headed in the Wrong Direction. 2010. 120p. pap. 12.95 (978-1-4502-4900-3(0)) iUniverse, Inc.

Villasenor, Victor. Beyond Rain of Gold. (ENG.). 2012. 416p. pap. 17.95 **(978-1-4019-3123-0(5))** 2011. 256p. 27.95 (978-1-4019-3122-3(7)) Hay Hse., Inc.

Villaseñor, Victor. Beyond Rain of Gold. 2011. (978-1-4019-3124-7(3)) Hay Hse., Inc.

Villasenor, Victor. Burro Genio. 2006. (SPA & ENG., Illus.). 336p. per. 13.95 (978-0-06-056683-8(3), Rayo) HarperCollins Pubs.

—Crazy Loco Love: A Memoir. 2010. (ENG., Illus.). 416p. pap. 16.00 (978-1-58270-272-8(1), Beyond Words/Atria Bks.) Atria Bks.

Villaseñor, Victor. Crazy Loco Love: A Memoir. 2010. E-Book (978-1-4391-9382-2(7)) Beyond Words Publishing, Inc.

—Wild Steps of Heaven: A Memoir. 2006. 304p. pap. 13.95 (978-0-06-113903-1(3), Rayo) HarperCollins Pubs.

Virginia, Kate. The Brown Rabbit: Let the Truth Be Told. 2007. 392p. 35.95 (978-0-595-90991-9(4)); per. 25.95 (978-0-595-42215-9(2)) iUniverse, Inc.

Von Bulow, Jack. Molar Jockey Memoirs: Making Dentistry Fun. 2007. 200p. pap. 22.50 (978-0-9746950-9-9(2)) Von Bulow, Jack.

Wagenknecht, Louise. Light on the Devils: Coming of Age on the Klamath. 2011. (ENG.). 232p. pap. 19.95 **(978-0-87071-611-9(5))** Oregon State Univ. Pr.

Wainwright, Mary-Jo. Pleasanton. 2007. (Images of America Ser.). (ENG., Illus.). 128p. pap. 21.99 (978-0-7385-4761-9(1)) Arcadia Publishing.

Walker, Alice. The Chicken Chronicles: Sitting with the Angels Who Have Returned with My Memories - Glorious, Rufus, Gertrude Stein, Splendor, Hortensia, Agnes of God, the Gladyses, & Babe - A Memoir. 2011. (ENG.). 208p. 21.95 (978-1-59558-645-2(8)) New Pr., The.

Warren, Spring. Quarter-Acre Farm: How I Kept the Patio, Lost the Lawn, & Fed My Family for a Year. 2011. (ENG., Illus.). 336p. pap. 17.95 (978-1-58005-340-2(8)) Seal Pr.

Waters, John, Jr. Calistoga. 2008. (Illus.). 127p. pap. (978-0-7835-5594-2(6)) Arcadia Publishing.

Waters, Lou. Have I Got a Song for You! 2009. 166p. pap. 21.95 (978-0-7414-5616-8(8)) Infinity Publishing.

Waxman, Henry. The Waxman Report: How Congress Really Works. 2010. (ENG.). 272p. pap. 14.99 (978-0-446-51926-7(X), Twelve) Grand Central Publishing.

Weber, Francis J. Catholic Heroes of Southern California. 2007. (Illus.). 192p. 29.95 (978-2-7468-1290-1(8)) Editions du Signe FRA. Dist: Gem Guides Bk. Co.

Webster, Henry. The Cosmic Seed Trilogy Companion. 2008. pap. 19.95 (978-0-9700430-4-7(X)) Fulco Enterprises.

Weeks, Donna Tessandori. The Italians of Kern County. 2011. 552p. 34.99 **(978-1-4535-7252-8(X))**; pap. 23.99 **(978-1-4535-7251-1(1))** Xlibris Corp.

Weintraub, Daniel. Party of One: Arnold Schwarzenegger & the Rise of the Independent Voter. 2008. (ENG.). 237p. 19.95 (978-0-9794822-2-9(4)) PoliPointPress, LLC.

Weisbrod, Marie Webster. Jasper Newton Field, DD: Founder & First President of the University of California, 1. 2006. (Illus.). 136p. per. 20.00 (978-1-891030-46-8(9)) Paragon Agency, The.

Welch, Brian. Washed by Blood: Lessons from My Time with Korn & My Journey to Christ. 2008. (ENG.). 224p. pap. 13.95 (978-0-06-155580-0(0), HarperOne) HarperCollins Pubs.

Westwood & Rohrbacher. Yesteryear's Child: Golden Days & Summer Nights. 2010. 148p. pap. 18.95 (978-1-4269-3374-5(6)) Trafford Publishing.

White, Dana. Perfect Chaos Spring Break in San Quentin. 2008. 112p. pap. 19.99 (978-1-4363-3761-8(5)) Xlibris Corp.

Whitener, Gary Lee. Gary Lee Whitener: My Life & Times. 2010. 112p. 22.95 (978-1-4502-3188-6(8)) iUniverse, Inc.

Willets, George. That's Easy for You to Say: Memoirs of a smoker, laryngectomee & public Speaker. 2010. 92p. pap. 11.95 (978-1-4502-3037-7(7)) iUniverse, Inc.

Wilson, Rebecca. A House with No Roof: After My Father's Assassination, a Memoir. 2011. (ENG., Illus.). 256p. pap. 16.95 (978-1-58243-754-5(8), Counterpoint) Counterpoint LLC.

Wilson, Richard L. The Journal of A Modern Mad Man. 2011. 128p. pap. 12.95 **(978-1-4670-3485-2(1))** AuthorHouse.

Wilson, Warren Barrios. Dark, Light, Almost White: Memoir of a Creole Son. 254p. 2009. (Illus.). pap. 10.95 (978-0-9706849-2-9(4)) 2007. 21.98 (978-0-9706849-3-6(2)) Barrios Trust, The.

Without Risk There's No Reward. 2008. 23.95 (978-0-9801270-9-6(2)) Seven Locks Pr.

Wood, Walter. Thanks Mom & Dad. 2006. 120p. pap. 10.95 (978-0-7414-3570-5(5)) Infinity Publishing.

Wyss, Jakob Otto, et al. Postmaster in Klau: Letters from California. 2007. (Illus.). xix, 315p. (978-0-89725-819-7(3)) Picton Pr.

Yamagawa, Hana & Hibbett, Akiko Yamagawa. From Okinawa to the Americas: Hana Yamagawa & Her Reminiscences of a Century. 2011. (Illus.). xviii, 210p. (978-0-8248-3400-5(3)); pap. (978-0-8248-3551-4(4)) Univ. of Hawaii Pr.

Yeadon, Virbie Kathleen Mabry. Virbie. 2008. 172p. pap. 14.99 (978-1-60647-777-9(3)) Xulon Pr., Inc.

Yee, Kevin. Mouse Trap: Memoir of a Disneyland Cast Member. 2008. (Illus.). 202p. per. 17.99 (978-0-9773758-1-3(1)) Ultimate Orlando Pr.

CALIFORNIA—CENSUS

California Census Index, 1870 San Francisco County F.C.I. (Includes City of San Francisco) (Illus.). lib. bdg. 145.00 (978-0-89593-229-7(6), Accelerated Indexing Systems International (AISI)) Genealogical Services.

California Census Index, 1880 Los Angeles County Federal C.I. (Illus.). lib. bdg. (978-0-89593-231-0(8), Accelerated Indexing Systems International (AISI)) Genealogical Services.

California Census Index, 1880 San Francisco County Federal C.I. (Illus.). lib. bdg. (978-0-89593-232-7(6), Accelerated Indexing Systems International (AISI)) Genealogical Services.

California Federal Census Index, 1870, Includes San Francisco County, 2 vols., Set. (Illus.). lib. bdg. 275.00 (978-0-89593-228-0(8), Accelerated Indexing Systems International (AISI)) Genealogical Services.

California North Federal Census Index, 1880 (Excludes San Francisco) (Illus.). lib. bdg. (978-0-89593-230-3(X), Accelerated Indexing Systems International (AISI)) Genealogical Services.

Jackson, Ronald V. California Early 1834 Census (San Barbara 1834), Vol. 2. (Illus.). lib. bdg. 34.00 (978-0-89593-275-4(X), Accelerated Indexing Systems International (AISI)) Genealogical Services.

—Connecticut Early Census, Vol. 1. (Illus.). lib. bdg. 35.00 (978-0-89593-720-9(4), Accelerated Indexing Systems International (AISI)) Genealogical Services.

CALIFORNIA—CLIMATE

Baur, John E. The Health Seekers of Southern California, 1870-1900. 2008. (Huntington Library Classics Ser.). 224p. pap. 24.95 (978-0-87328-225-3(6)) Huntington Library Pr.

Bedsworth, Louise & Hanak, Ellen. Preparing California for a Changing Climate. 2008. (978-1-58213-132-0(5)) Public Policy Institute of California.

Garooglan, David, ed. Profiles of California 2010. 2nd rev. ed. 2010. pap. 149.00 (978-1-59237-559-2(6)) Grey Hse. Publishing.

Holland, V. L. & Keil, David J. California Vegetation. rev. ed. 2010. (ENG.). 528p. pap. 72.78 (978-0-7872-2685-5(8)) Kendall Hunt Publishing Co.

Stuckless, John S. & Levich, Robert A. The Geology & Climatology of Yucca Mountain & Vicinity, Southern Nevada & California. 2007. 65.00 (978-0-8137-1199-7(1)) Geological Society of America, Inc.

CALIFORNIA—DESCRIPTION AND TRAVEL

Adams, Carole & Bogacki, John. Point Piedras Blancas. 2008. 128p. pap. 19.99 (978-0-7385-5819-6(2)) Arcadia Publishing.

Aguirre, David. Waterman's Eye - Emil Sigler - Surfing San Diego to San Onofre 1928-1940. 2007. (Illus.). 35.00 (978-0-9785978-1-8(8)) Tabler, Joseph Bks.

Albino, Joseph. Death Valley National Park & Ash Meadows National Wildlife Refuge. 2009. 52p. pap. 31.99 (978-1-4363-4760-0(2)) Xlibris Corp.

Alexander, Pat & Napa Valley Museum. Yountville. 2009. (Images of America Ser.). (ENG., Illus.). 128p. pap. 21.99 (978-0-7385-6965-9(8)) Arcadia Publishing.

Anderson, Karl. The Salton Sea. 2011. (Postcard History Ser.). (ENG., Illus.). 128p. pap. 21.99 (978-0-7385-7455-4(4)) Arcadia Publishing.

Antilla, Shelley. Photographers' Vintage Treasures & the People Who Wore Them: (Including Vintage Clothing Price Guide) Early Photography & Memoirs from Mendocino Cou. 2009. 112p. pap. 35.49 (978-1-4490-2663-7(4)) AuthorHouse.

Arax, Mark. West of the West: Dreamers, Believers, Builders & Killers in the Golden State. 2009. (ENG., Illus.). 368p. 26.95 (978-1-58648-390-6(0)) Perseus Bks. Group.

—West of the West: Dreamers, Believers, Builders, & Killers in the Golden State. 2011. (ENG., Illus.). 368p. pap. 15.99 (978-1-58648-983-0(6)) PublicAffairs.

Arcata Eye Staff & Arcata Union Staff. On This Day in Arcata. 2008. (On this Day Ser.). (Illus.). 128p. pap. 19.99 (978-0-7385-5682-6(3)) Arcadia Publishing.

Armand, Dione F. Trinidad. 2010. (Images of America Ser.). (ENG., Illus.). 128p. pap. 21.99 (978-0-7385-7161-4(X)) Arcadia Publishing.

Arnold, Mary Ellicott & Reed, Mabel. In the Land of the Grasshopper Song: Two Women in the Klamath River Indian Country in 1908-09, Second Edition. 2nd ed. 2011. (ENG., Illus.). 352p. pap. 19.95 **(978-0-8032-3637-0(9)**, Bison Bks.) Univ. of Nebraska Pr.

Austin, Linda & Hammond, Norm. Oceano. 2010. (Images of America Ser.) (Illus.). 128p. pap. 21.99 (978-0-7385-8087-6(2)) Arcadia Publishing.

Austin, Mary Hunter. The Land of Little Rain. 2009. 304p. 24.99 (978-1-103-12063-5(8)) 2009. 304p. pap. 18.99 (978-1-103-12060-4(3)) 2008. 112p. 21.99 (978-0-554-32053-3(3)) 2008. 112p. 24.99 (978-0-554-22750-4(9)) 2007. 100p. pap. 16.99 (978-1-4264-8631-9(6)) BiblioBazaar.

—Land of Little Rain. 2006. pap. (978-1-4068-0678-6(1)) Echo Library.

—The Land of Little Rain. Lt. ed. 2007. (ENG.). 110p. pap. 19.99 (978-1-4264-2995-8(9)) BiblioBazaar.

—The Land of Little Rain: Facsimile of Original 1904 Edition. 2007. (ENG.). 320p. per. 26.95 (978-0-86534-540-9(6)) Sunstone Pr.

Bachand, Thomas. Lake Tahoe: A Fragile Beauty. 2008. (ENG., Illus.). 176p. 35.00 (978-0-8118-6309-4(3)) Chronicle Bks. LLC.

—Lake Tahoe: A Fragile Beauty. 2008. (ENG.). 176p. 35.00 (978-0-8118-8960-5(2)) Chronicle Bks. LLC.

Baggese, Carl P. Modesto. 2011. (Postcard History Ser.). (ENG., Illus.). 128p. pap. 21.99 **(978-0-7385-7579-7(8))** Arcadia Publishing.

Baggese, Carl P. & McHenry Museum. Modesto. 2009. (Images of America Ser.). (ENG., Illus.). 128p. pap. 21.99 (978-0-7385-7150-8(4)) Arcadia Publishing.

Bailey, Brad. Palomar Mountain. 2009. (Images of America Ser.). (ENG., Illus.). 128p. pap. 21.99 (978-0-7385-7001-3(X)) Arcadia Publishing.

Ball, Guy & Tustin Area Historical Society. Tustin. 2011. (Images of America Ser.). (Illus.). 128p. pap. 21.99 (978-0-7385-7037-2(0)) Arcadia Publishing.

Baltz, Lewis. Candlestick Point. 2011. (ENG., Illus.). 128p. 72.00 (978-3-86930-109-9(0)) Steidl, Gerhard Druckerei und Verlag DEU. Dist: Innovative Logistics.

—Lewis Baltz: The new Industrial Parks near Irvine, California. 2010. (ENG., Illus.). 112p. 50.00 (978-3-86521-764-6(8)) Steidl, Gerhard Druckerei und Verlag DEU. Dist: D.A.P./Distributed Art Pubs.

Bancroft, Hubert Howe. California Pastoral. 2007. (ENG.). 816p. per. 55.95 (978-0-548-50158-0(0)) Kessinger Publishing, LLC.

Bartlett, Serena. Oakland. 2007. 201p. pap. 16.95 (978-0-9791462-0-6(8)) GrassRoutes Travel.

Barratt, Elizabeth & Carmel Valley Historical Society. Carmel Valley. 2009. (Images of America Ser.). (ENG., Illus.). 128p. pap. 21.99 (978-0-7385-7162-1(8)) Arcadia Publishing.

Bash, Kevin & Jouxtel, Brigitte. The Navy in Norco. 2011. (Images of America Ser.). (Illus.). 128p. pap. 21.99 **(978-0-7385-7526-1(7))** Arcadia Publishing.

Bates, D. B. Incidents on Land & Water, or Four Years on the Pacific Coast Being a Narrative of the Burning of the Ships Nonantum, Humayoon & Fanchon, Togethe. 2006. 348p. per. 23.99 (978-1-4255-3504-9(6)) MPublishing.

Bauer, Gene. Botanical Serigraphs: The Gene Bauer Collector. 2010. (ENG.). 264p. 40.00 (978-1-58948-253-1(0), ESRI Pr.) ESRI, Inc.

Baxter, R. Scott & Wooten, Kimberly. Shenandoah Valley & Amador Wine Country. 2008. (Images of America Ser.). (Illus.). 127p. per. 19.99 (978-0-7385-5603-1(3)) Arcadia Publishing.

Baxter, R. Scott & Wooten, Kimberly J. Breweries of the Gold Country. 2012. (Images of America Ser.). (ENG., Illus.). 128p. pap. 21.99 **(978-0-7385-7621-3(2))** Arcadia Publishing.

Beasley, Thomas Dykes. A Tramp Through the Bret Harte Country. 2009. 72p. pap. (978-0-217-80851-4(4)) Books LLC.

—A Tramp Through the Bret Harte Country. 2007. (ENG.). 60p. per. (978-1-4065-3697-3(0)) Dodo Pr.

Beaver, Christopher. After the Storm: Bob Walker & the East Bay Regional Park District. 2007. (ENG., Illus.). 192p. pap. 25.00 (978-0-89997-453-8(8)) Wilderness Pr.

Bebek, Diana. California: A Visual Journey. 2010. (ENG., Illus.). 192p. 39.95 (978-1-55285-851-6(0)) Whitecap Bks., Ltd. CAN. Dist: Midpoint Trade Bks., Inc.

Bell, Ellen Baker & the Irvine Historical Society. Irvine. 2011. (Images of America Ser.). (ENG., Illus.). 128p. pap. 21.99 **(978-0-7385-7575-9(5))** Arcadia Publishing.

Benbow, Bob, et al. Baldwin Park. 2011. (Images of America Ser.). (Illus.). 128p. pap. 21.99 (978-0-7385-7484-4(8)) Arcadia Publishing.

Benziger, Jeff. Ceres. 2010. (Images of America Ser.). (ENG., Illus.). 128p. pap. 21.99 (978-0-7385-8101-9(1)) Arcadia Publishing.

—Waterford. 2011. (Images of America Ser.). (Illus.). 128p. pap. 21.99 (978-0-7385-7452-3(X)) Arcadia Publishing.

Beren, Peter, ed. California the Beautiful. 2009. (ENG., Illus.). 160p. 19.95 (978-1-59962-074-9(X), Welcome Bks.) Welcome Enterprises, Inc.

—Hidden Napa Valley, Revised & Expanded Edition. 2010. (ENG., Illus.). 172p. 19.95 (978-1-59962-080-0(4), Welcome Bks.) Welcome Enterprises, Inc.

Bergere, Darline. Ukiah. 2009. (Images of America Ser.). (ENG., Illus.). 128p. pap. 21.99 (978-0-7385-7040-2(0)) Arcadia Publishing.

Berk, Lucy Jones & Covey, Stephen A. Escondido Grape Day Festivals. 2010. (Postcards of America Ser.). 7.99 (978-0-7385-8137-8(2)) Arcadia Publishing.

Best, Jennifer. Best Family Adventures: San Luis Obispo County (Second Edition) Peterson, Lynn & Cabreros, Julia, eds. 2011. (Illus.). 272p. pap. 18.95 **(978-0-9769050-3-5(5))** Pen & Pad Publishing.

Bezzubov, Sasha. Wildfire. 2009. (Illus.). 66p. (978-1-59005-247-1(1)) Nazraeli Pr.

Blackwell, Laird R. Wildflowers of California: A Month-by-Month Guide. 2012. (ENG., Illus.). 570p. 70.00 **(978-0-520-27205-7(6))**; pap. 29.95 **(978-0-520-27206-4(4))** Univ. of California Pr.

Blair, Richard & Goodwin, Kathleen. California Trip. 2007. 300p. 49.95 (978-0-9671527-3-8(9)) Color & Light.

Boghosian, Paula & Cox, Don. Sacramento's Boulevard Park. 2006. (Images of America Ser.). (ENG., Illus.). 128p. per. 19.99 (978-0-7385-2955-4(9)) Arcadia Publishing.

Bomford et al, David. Seeing the Getty Center Set: Collections, Building, & Gardens, 3 vols. 2009. (ENG., Illus.). 192p. pap. 24.95 (978-0-89236-975-1(2)) Oxford Univ. Pr., Inc.

Boster, Mark. Four Seasons of Yosemite: A Photographer's Journey. 2011. (ENG.). 128p. 34.95 **(978-0-9823242-3-3(5))** Time Capsule Pr., LLC.

Bradley, Donna. Native Americans of San Diego County. 2009. (Images of America Ser.). (ENG., Illus.). 128p. pap. 21.99 (978-0-7385-5984-1(9)) Arcadia Publishing.

Brewer, William H. Up & down California in 1860-1864: The Journal of William H. Brewer. Farquhar, Francis P., ed. 2011. 628p. 65.95 **(978-1-258-08386-1(8))** Literary Licensing, LLC.

Brewster, Tom. Portrait of Palm Springs. 2007. 120p. 24.95 (978-1-56037-470-1(5)) Farcountry Pr.

Brigandi, Phil. Orange. 2008. (Images of America Ser.). (ENG., Illus.). 128p. pap. 21.99 (978-0-7385-5905-6(9)) Arcadia Publishing.

Brown, Ann Marie. Monterey & Carmel: Including Santa Cruz & Big Sur. 3rd ed. 2009. (Moon Handbooks Ser.). (ENG., Illus.). 250p. pap. 16.95 (978-1-56691-995-1(9)) Westview Pr.

Brown, Jim. Folsom Prison. 2008. (Images of America Ser.). (Illus.). 128p. pap. 21.99 (978-0-7385-5921-6(0)) Arcadia Publishing.

Bryant, Edwin. What I Saw in California. 2008. 228p. 27.99 (978-0-554-24465-5(9)) 2007. 204p. pap. 20.99 (978-1-4264-6558-1(0)) 2006. (ENG.). 226p. pap. 22.99 (978-1-4264-6617-5(X)) BiblioBazaar.

—What I Saw in California. 2009. 382p. pap. (978-0-217-14575-6(2)); 380p. pap. (978-0-217-55526-2(2)) Books LLC.

—What I Saw in California. 2008. 204p. pap. (978-1-4099-3244-4(3)) Dodo Pr.

—What I Saw in California. 2008. (ENG.). 188p. pap. 13.95 (978-1-4385-1024-8(1), Book Jungle) Standard Pubns., Inc.

Buck, Michael. Camp Mather. 2008. (Images of America Ser.). (ENG., Illus.). 128p. pap. 19.99 (978-0-7385-5847-9(8)) Arcadia Publishing.

Building the Benicia-Martinez Bridge. 2007. 29.95 (978-0-9744124-4-3(9)); pap. 19.95 (978-0-9744124-5-0(7)) Carquinez Pr.

Bunyan, Bob & Foundation, The Aliso Viejo Community. Aliso Viejo. 2011. (Images of America Ser.). (ENG., Illus.). 128p. pap. 21.99 **(978-0-7385-7424-0(4))** Arcadia Publishing.

Burg, William. Sacramento. 2008. (Then & Now Ser.). (ENG., Illus.). 96p. pap. 21.99 (978-0-7385-5900-1(8)) Arcadia Publishing.

—Sacramento's Southside Park. 2007. (Images of America Ser.). (Illus.). 127p. per. 19.99 (978-0-7385-4796-1(4)) Arcadia Publishing.

C

Burnett, Claudine. Haunted Long Beach 2: The Odd & Unusual in & Around Long Beach, California. 2010. (Illus.). xiii, 200p. ***(978-1-4520-5446-9(0))*** AuthorHouse.

Butler, William J. March Air Force Base. 2009. (Images of America Ser.). (ENG., Illus.). 128p. pap. 21.99 *(978-0-7385-7159-1(8))* Arcadia Publishing.

California. (Rand McNally Wall Maps Ser.). 229.00 *(978-0-528-86134-5(4))* Rand McNally.

California State Automobile Assn. Staff. Palo Alto/Mountain View, CA. *(978-1-57835-120-6(0))* California State Automobile Assn.

Carlberg, Marvin & Epting, Chris. Huntington Beach. 2009. (Postcard History Ser.). (ENG., Illus.). 128p. pap. 21.99 *(978-0-7385-6983-3(6))* Arcadia Publishing.

Carle, David & Banta, Don. Mono Lake Basin. 2008. (Images of America Ser.). (ENG., Illus.). 128p. pap. 21.99 *(978-0-7385-5909-4(1))* Arcadia Publishing.

Carmel, Elizabeth. Brilliant Waters: Portraits of Lake Tahoe, Yosemite, & the High Sierra. 2006. (Illus.). 94p. 49.95 *(978-0-9776877-0-1(8))* Hawks Peak Publishing.

CARMONA. Fuckramento. 2009. 93p. pap. 9.50 *(978-0-557-06260-7(8))* Lulu Enterprises Inc.

Carnes, Marilyn & Nye, Matthew. Early National City. 2008. (Images of America Ser.). (ENG., Illus.). 128p. pap. 19.99 *(978-0-7385-5910-0(5))* Arcadia Publishing.

Cashman, Robert. Wildomar. 2010. (Images of America Ser.). (ENG., Illus.). 128p. pap. 21.99 *(978-0-7385-7082-2(6))* Arcadia Publishing.

Castle, Roger, et al. Morro Bay. 2010. (Then & Now Ser.). (ENG., Illus.). 96p. pap. 21.99 *(978-0-7385-8129-3(1))* Arcadia Publishing.

Castro-Bran, Rose. Lighthouses of the Ventura Coast. 2011. (Images of America Ser.). (Illus.). 128p. pap. 21.99 *(978-0-7385-8186-6(0))* Arcadia Publishing.

Chandler, Carol L. A Walk Through Nature at the University's Arboretum in Davis, California. 2007. 52p. pap. 25.95 *(978-1-4357-0078-9(3))* Lulu Enterprises Inc.

Chester Smith Lyman. Around the Horn to the Sandwich Islands & California, 1845-1850: Teggart, Frederick J., ed. 2006. (ENG.). 384p. per. 33.95 *(978-1-4286-5502-7(6))* Kessinger Publishing, LLC.

Chinese Historical and Cultural Project, et al. Chinese in San Jose & the Santa Clara Valley. 2007. (Images of America Ser.). (ENG., Illus.). 128p. per. 19.99 *(978-0-7385-4777-0(8))* Arcadia Publishing.

Christian, Victoria. Sunol. 2007. (Images of America Ser.). (Illus.). 128p. per. 19.99 *(978-0-7385-5554-6(1))* Arcadia Publishing.

Churchill, Marlowe J. The Riverside National Cemetery Story: A Field of Warriors. 2009. *(978-1-57864-588-6(3))* Donning Co. Pubs.

City of Walnut & Walnut Historical Society. Walnut. 2012. (Images of America Ser.). (ENG., Illus.). 128p. pap. 21.99 ***(978-0-7385-9547-4(0))*** Arcadia Publishing.

Clark, Galen. Indians of the Yosemite Alley & Vicinity. 2008. pap. *(978-1-84830-915-9(5))*, Wildhern Pr.) Echo Library.

Clark, Ralph A. Lodi. 2009. (Images of America Ser.). (ENG., Illus.). 128p. pap. 21.99 *(978-0-7385-6924-6(0))* Arcadia Publishing.

Clark, Ralph A. & Lodi Historical Society. Lodi: 1945-2005. 2011. (Images of America Ser.). (Illus.). 128p. pap. 21.99 *(978-0-7385-7548-3(8))* Arcadia Publishing.

Clark, Susan M. The Sea Ranch. 2009. (Images of America Ser.). (Illus.). 128p. pap. 21.99 *(978-0-7385-5990-2(3))* Arcadia Publishing.

Clark, Susie. Round Trip from the Hub to the Golden Gate. 2007. (Travel in America Ser.). (ENG.). 204p. 49.95 *(978-1-4290-0490-9(8))*; per. 24.95 *(978-1-4290-0491-6(6))* Applewood Bks.

Clovis Centennial Committee. Clovis. 2011. (Images of America Ser.). (Illus.). 128p. pap. 21.99 ***(978-0-7385-7613-8(1))*** Arcadia Publishing.

Clucas, Donald Laine, et al. Upland. 2009. (Images of America Ser.). (ENG., Illus.). 128p. pap. 21.99 *(978-0-7385-6984-0(4))* Arcadia Publishing.

Coachella Valley above All. 2006th ed. 2006. *(978-0-9726856-3-4(4))* Soltys, Richard J. Productions.

Coddington, Chris. California in the Beginning: In the Beginning. 2008. (ENG., Illus.). 160p. 75.00 *(978-0-9762197-9-8(4))* Oakana Hse.

Colton, Walter. Deck & Port; or, Incidents of a Cruise in the United States Frigate Congress to California with Sketches of Rio Janeiro, Valparaiso, Lima, Honolulu. 2006. 444p. per. 26.99 *(978-1-4255-4867-4(9))* MPublishing.

—Three Years in California by Rev Walter Colton. 2006. 484p. per. 29.99 *(978-1-4255-5304-3(4))* MPublishing.

Cook, Deborah Coleen. Ione & the Jackson Valley. 2008. (Images of America Ser.). (ENG., Illus.). 128p. pap. 19.99 *(978-0-7385-5602-4(5))* Arcadia Publishing.

Cooper, Ed. Soul of Yosemite: Portraits of Light & Stone. 2011. (ENG., Illus.). 160p. pap. 19.95 *(978-0-7627-6995-7(5)*, Falcon Guides) Globe Pequot Pr., The.

Cornell, Daniell. Backyard Oasis: The Swimming Pool in Southern California Photography, 1945-1982. 2012. (Illus.). 256p. 60.00 ***(978-3-7913-5176-6(1))*** Prestel Publishing.

Cosmic Debris Etc., Inc. Staff, et al. Hooked on Hiking - 50 Hiking Adventures: Southern California. 2009. (ENG., Illus.). 50p. 16.95 *(978-0-8118-6637-8(8))* Chronicle Bks. LLC.

Costigan, Lucy. Travels in California. 2007. 73p. pap. 32.95 *(978-1-84799-779-1(1))* Lulu Enterprises Inc.

Covey, Stephen A. Early Escondido: The Louis A. Havens Collection. 2008. (Images of America Ser.). (ENG., Illus.). 128p. per. 21.99 *(978-0-7385-5595-9(9))* Arcadia Publishing.

Cowan, Ernie. Anza-Borrego: A Photographic Journey. 2008. (Adventures in the Natural History & Cultural Heritage of the Californias Ser.). (Illus.). 80p. 19.95 *(978-0-932653-88-8(X))* Sunbelt Pubns., Inc.

Cox, Lynne. Grayson. 2008. (ENG., Illus.). 176p. pap. 13.00 *(978-0-15-603467-8(0)*, Mariner Bks.) Houghton Mifflin Harcourt Trade & Reference Pubs.

—Grayson. Magnet, Alberto, tr. from ENG. 2007. (Vintage Espanol Ser.). (SPA & ENG.). 160p. pap. 9.95 *(978-0-307-27947-7(2)*, Vintage) Knopf Doubleday Publishing Group.

—Grayson. 2006. (ENG.). 160p. 16.95 *(978-0-307-26454-1(8)*, Knopf) Knopf Doubleday Publishing Group.

Crabb, Guy. San Luis Obispo: 100 Years of Downtown Businesses: Higuera Street. 2007. (Illus.). 108p. pap. *(978-0-9790616-0-8(1))* Crabb, Guy.

Crabbe, Gary. Greetings from California: Legends, Landmarks & Lore of the Golden State. 2011. (ENG., Illus.). 160p. 25.00 *(978-0-7603-3728-8(4)*, 0760337284, Voyageur Pr) MBI Publishing Co. LLC.

Cragg, Curt. Solvang. 2008. (Postcard History Ser.). (Illus.). 128p. pap. 19.99 *(978-0-7385-5935-3(0))* Arcadia Publishing.

Criddle, Robert & Criddle, Ruth. Hammonton & Marigold. 2007. (Images of America Ser.). (ENG., Illus.). 128p. per. 19.99 *(978-0-7385-4760-2(3))* Arcadia Publishing.

Crimmen, Dave & Kopp, Foreword by Quentin. Broadmoor Village. 2010. (Images of America Ser.). (Illus.). 128p. pap. 21.99 *(978-0-7385-8092-0(9))* Arcadia Publishing.

Cueva-Fernandez, Olivia. Mexican Americans in Wilmington. 2011. (Images of America Ser.). (ENG., Illus.). 128p. pap. 21.99 *(978-0-7385-8174-3(7))* Arcadia Publishing.

Cunningham. Best East Day Hiking Guide & Trail Map Bundle: Joshua Tree National Park. 2010. (Best Easy Day Hikes Ser.). (ENG.). pap. 19.95 *(978-0-7627-7135-6(6)*, Falcon Guides) Globe Pequot Pr., The.

Cunningham, Bill & Cunningham, Polly. Death Valley National Park. 2nd ed. 2010. (Best Easy Day Hikes Ser.). (ENG., Illus.). 112p. pap. 9.95 *(978-0-7627-6052-7(4)*, Falcon Guides) Globe Pequot Pr., The.

Daily, Marla & Santa Cruz Island Foundation. The California Channel Islands. 2012. (Images of America Ser.). (ENG., Illus.). 128p. 21.99 ***(978-0-7385-9508-5(X))*** Arcadia Publishing.

Dana, Richard Henry. A Yankee in Mexican California, 1834-1836. 2010. pap. *(978-1-59714-119-2(4))* Heyday.

Datel, Robin, et al. Woodland. 2012. (Images of America Ser.). (ENG., Illus.). 128p. pap. 21.99 ***(978-0-7385-8900-8(4))*** Arcadia Publishing.

Davis, Harold. The Photographer's Guide to Yosemite & the High Sierra: Where to Find Perfect Shots & How to Take Them. 2008. (ENG., Illus.). 96p. per. 14.95 *(978-0-88150-762-1(8))* Countryman Pr.

De Long, David G., ed. Sunnylands: Art & Architecture of the Annenberg Estate in Rancho Mirage, California. 2009. (Illus.). 200p. 34.95 *(978-0-8122-4161-7(4))* Univ. of Pennsylvania Pr.

de Martino, Thomas, et al. Chino. 2011. (Images of America Ser.). (Illus.). 128p. pap. 21.99 *(978-0-7385-8142-2(9))* Arcadia Publishing.

Deering, Susan. Silverado Canyon. 2008. (Images of America Ser.). (Illus.). 128p. pap. 21.99 *(978-0-7385-5962-9(8))* Arcadia Publishing.

Delaney, Jeff. Newport Beach. 2011. (Then & Now Ser.). (Illus.). 96p. pap. 21.99 *(978-0-7385-8202-3(6))* Arcadia Publishing.

—Newport Beach's Balboa & Balboa Island. 2007. (Images of America Ser.). (ENG., Illus.). 128p. per. 19.99 *(978-0-7385-5575-1(4))* Arcadia Publishing.

DeRooy, Carola & Livingston, Dewey. Point Reyes Peninsula. 2008. (Images of America Ser.). (ENG., Illus.). 128p. pap. 19.99 *(978-0-7385-5848-6(6))* Arcadia Publishing.

Desolation Wilderness South. 2007. per. *(978-0-9626124-3-5(X))* Taote Publishing.

Dever, Kathleen & Whitson, Judy. Lake Mathews & Gavilan Hills. 2007. (Images of America Ser.). (ENG., Illus.). 128p. per. 19.99 *(978-0-7385-4779-4(4))* Arcadia Publishing.

Dirksen, Diane & Dirksen, Jake. Recreation Lakes of California 15th Ed. 2009. 256p. pap. 19.95 *(978-0-943798-23-3(X))* Recreation Sales Publishing.

Doisneau, Robert. Palm Springs 1960. 2010. (ENG., Illus.). 156p. 34.95 *(978-2-08-030129-1(2))* Flammarion et Cie FRA. Dist: Random Hse., Inc.

Donovan, Christine. Coronado California: Hometown, Homeport, Home Away from Home. 2010. 105p. pap. 29.95 *(978-0-9828438-0-2(1))* Island Bound Pr.

Doppenberg, Jean Saylor. California's Wine Country: A Guide to Napa & Sonoma Counties. 8th ed. 2009. (Insiders' Guide Ser.). (ENG., Illus.). 304p. pap. 18.95 *(978-0-7627-4915-7(6)*, Insiders' Guide) Globe Pequot Pr., The.

Dorling Kindersley Publishing Staff. Back Roads California. 2012. (Eyewitness travel back Roads Ser.). (ENG.). 264p. 25.00 *(978-0-7566-7494-6(8))* Dorling Kindersley Publishing, Inc.

Dougal, William. Off for Californi: Letters, Log & Sketches of William Dougal, Gold Rush Artist. Stanger, Frank M., ed. 2011. 76p. 36.95 ***(978-1-258-03263-0(5))*** Literary Licensing, LLC.

Drylie, Gary "Old Town Griz". Hesperia. 2010. (Images of America Ser.). (Illus.). 128p. pap. 21.99 *(978-0-7385-8107-1(0))* Arcadia Publishing.

Dutcher, Greta, et al. Alameda. 2008. (Images of America Ser.). (ENG., Illus.). 128p. pap. 21.99 *(978-0-7385-5953-7(9))* Arcadia Publishing.

Duvall, Marius. A Navy Surgeon in California, 1846-1847: The Journal of Marius Duvall. Rogers, Fred Blackburn, ed. 2011. 136p. 40.95 ***(978-1-258-01231-1(6))*** Literary Licensing, LLC.

Dwyer, Jeff. Ghost Hunter's Guide to California's Wine Country, 1 vol. 2008. (Ghost Hunter's Guide Ser.). (ENG., Illus.). 240p. pap. 15.95 *(978-1-58980-604-7(2))* Pelican Publishing Co., Inc.

Edwards, Philip Leget. The Diary of Philip Leget Edwards: The Great Cattle Drive from California to Oregon In 1837. 2011. 54p. 36.95 ***(978-1-258-00458-3(5))*** Literary Licensing, LLC.

Ehlers, Chad. A Bug & a Nikon on the West Coast. 2010. 76p. pap. 27.49 *(978-1-4490-5712-1(8))* AuthorHouse.

Ehrenreich, V. K. North Sacramento. 2010. (Images of America Ser.). (ENG., Illus.). 128p. pap. 21.99 *(978-0-7385-8003-6(1))* Arcadia Publishing.

Eldredge, Ward. Kings Canyon National Park. 2009. (Images of America Ser.). (ENG., Illus.). 128p. pap. 21.99 *(978-0-7385-5996-4(2))* Arcadia Publishing.

Eldridge, Ward. Sequoia NATL Park. 2008. (Images of America Ser.). (ENG., Illus.). 128p. pap. 21.99 *(978-0-7385-5940-7(7))* Arcadia Publishing.

Emick, Paula. Rancho Cucamonga. 2011. (Images of America Ser.). (ENG., Illus.). 128p. pap. 21.99 ***(978-0-7385-7500-1(3))*** Arcadia Publishing.

Epting, Chris. Baseball in Orange County. 2012. (Images of America Ser.). (ENG., Illus.). 128p. pap. 21.99 ***(978-0-7385-9328-9(1))*** Arcadia Publishing.

—Huntington Beach. 2008. (Then & Now Ser.). (ENG., Illus.). 96p. pap. 19.99 *(978-0-7385-5828-8(1))* Arcadia Publishing.

—Orange County. 2011. (Then & Now Ser.). (Illus.). 96p. pap. 21.99 *(978-0-7385-8115-6(1))* Arcadia Publishing.

—Vanishing Orange County. 2008. (Images of America Ser.). (Illus.). 128p. pap. 21.99 *(978-0-7385-5974-2(1))* Arcadia Publishing.

Erlandson, Jon M., et al. A Canyon through Time: Archaeology, History, & Ecology of the Tecolote Canyon Area, Santa Barbara County, California. 2008. (ENG., Illus.). 216p. pap. 35.00 *(978-0-87480-879-7(0))* Univ. of Utah Pr.

Espinoza, Arturo. Photography by Arturo Espinoza Jr. 2010. 104p. pap. 11.95 *(978-1-4502-5698-8(8))* iUniverse, Inc.

Faessel, Stephen J. Anaheim 1940-2007. 2007. (Images of America Ser.). (ENG., Illus.). 128p. per. 19.99 *(978-0-7385-4743-5(3))* Arcadia Publishing.

Faessel, Stephen J., text. Historic Photos of Anaheim. 2007. (Historic Photos Ser.). (ENG., Illus.). 204p. 39.95 *(978-1-59652-333-3(6))* Turner Publishing Co.

Faibyshev, Dolly. Palm Springs Mid-Century Modern. 2nd ed. 2010. (Illus.). 128p. 29.99 *(978-0-7643-3461-0(1))* Schiffer Publishing, Ltd.

Fanning, Branwell. Marin County. 2007. (Images of America Ser.). (ENG., Illus.). 128p. per. 21.99 *(978-0-7385-5571-3(1))* Arcadia Publishing.

—Maritime Marin. 2008. (Images of America Ser.). (ENG., Illus.). 128p. pap. 19.99 *(978-0-7385-5904-9(0))* Arcadia Publishing.

Farnbach, Rebecca & Barnett, Loretta. Fallbrook. 2007. (Images of America Ser.). (ENG., Illus.). 128p. per. 19.99 *(978-0-7385-4747-3(6))* Arcadia Publishing.

Farnbach, Rebecca, et al. Murrieta Hot Springs. 2008. (Images of America Ser.). (ENG., Illus.). 128p. pap. 21.99 *(978-0-7385-5956-8(3))* Arcadia Publishing.

—Temecula Wine Country. 2009. 15p. pap. 7.99 *(978-0-7385-7015-0(X))* Arcadia Publishing.

Farnham, Thomas Jefferson. The Early Days of California. 2006. 356p. per. 26.99 *(978-1-4255-3677-0(8))* MPublishing.

Federal Writers' Project, Florida. Seeing Fernandina: A Guide to the City & Its Industries. (American Guide Ser.). reprint ed. 20.00 *(978-0-404-57908-1(6))* AMS Pr., Inc.

Felzmann, Lukas. Waters in Between. 2008. (Illus.). 320p. 74.95 *(978-3-03778-138-8(6)*, 3037781386) Springer.

Figler, Jeff. Poway. 2007. (Images of America Ser.). (ENG., Illus.). 128p. per. 21.99 *(978-0-7385-5597-3(5))* Arcadia Publishing.

Fiorelli, Lalo. Secret Splendors of the Desert: Anza Borrego Desert State Park. 2008. (Illus.). 100p. pap. 23.95 *(978-0-9717228-4-2(6))* Splendors Publishing.

Fitzgerald, O. P. California Sketches, Second Series. 2006. (ENG.). 176p. pap. 19.99 *(978-1-4264-6180-4(1))*; 190p. pap. 21.99 *(978-1-4264-6235-1(2))* BiblioBazaar.

Fitzpatrick, Linda & Conkle, James M. Needles. 2010. (Images of America Ser.). (Illus.). 128p. pap. 21.99 *(978-0-7385-8064-7(3))* Arcadia Publishing.

Flaherty, Dennis. Day in Ancient Bristlecone Pine. 2008. 64p. pap. 19.95 *(978-0-944197-85-1(X))* Companion Pr.

Fliedner, Colleen. Quick Escapes from Orange County: The Best Weekend Getaways. 2010. (Quick Escapes From Ser.). (ENG., Illus.). 296p. pap. 14.95 *(978-0-7627-6043-5(5))* Globe Pequot Pr., The.

Fortuna Depot Museum. Fortuna & the Eel River Valley. 2011. (Images of America Ser.). (Illus.). 128p. pap. 21.99 *(978-0-7385-7522-3(4))* Arcadia Publishing.

Fradkin, Philip L. The Left Coast: California on the Edge. 2011. (ENG., Illus.). 126p. pap. 29.95 *(978-0-520-25509-8(7))* Univ. of California Pr.

Frank, Dana. Local Girl Makes History: Exploring Northern California's Kitsch Monuments. 2007. (ENG., Illus.). 278p. per. 16.95 *(978-1-931404-09-9(7))* City Lights Foundation.

Frank, Phil. Houseboats of Sausalito. 2008. (Images of America Ser.). (ENG., Illus.). 128p. pap. 19.99 *(978-0-7385-5552-2(5))* Arcadia Publishing.

Freeman, Glenn Edward. Riverside. 2009. (Then & Now Ser.). (ENG., Illus.). 128p. pap. 21.99 *(978-0-7385-7079-2(6))* Arcadia Publishing.

Fregulia, Carolyn. Logging in the Central Sierra. 2008. (Images of America Ser.). (ENG., Illus.). 128p. pap. 21.99 *(978-0-7385-5816-5(8))* Arcadia Publishing.

Gabriel, Louise B. & Santa Monica Historical Society. Santa Monica: 1950-2010. 2011. (Images of America Ser.). (ENG., Illus.). 128p. pap. 21.99 *(978-0-7385-8143-9(7))* Arcadia Publishing.

Gahagan, Michael. Sonora. 2007. (Images of America Ser.). (ENG., Illus.). 128p. per. 21.99 *(978-0-7385-4783-1(2))* Arcadia Publishing.

Gale, Kate & De Turenne, Veronique. The Devil's Punchbowl: A Cultural & Geographic Map of California Today. 2010. (ENG.). 208p. pap. 25.95 *(978-1-59709-164-0(2))* Red Hen Pr.

Gallivan, Mickey & Historical Society of Pomona Valley. Early Pomona. 2007. (Images of America Ser.). (ENG., Illus.). 128p. per. 19.99 *(978-0-7385-4776-3(X))* Arcadia Publishing.

Garcia, Mary. Santa Ana's Logan Barrio; Its History, Stories, & Families. 2007. (Illus.). 88p. spiral bd. 17.95 *(978-0-9797619-0-4(5))* Santa Ana Historical Preservation Society.

Gardner, Theodore Roosevelt, 2nd. Hermitage Santa Barbara at Twenty. 2010. (Illus.). 168p. 75.00 *(978-1-888310-30-6(8))* Knoll, Allen A. Pubs.

Garey, Jennifer A. & San Clemente Historical Society. San Clemente. 2010. (Images of America Ser.). (ENG., Illus.). 128p. pap. 21.99 *(978-0-7385-8051-7(1))* Arcadia Publishing.

Garnett Clark, Ginger. Rancho Palos Verdes. 2009. (Images of America Ser.). (ENG., Illus.). 128p. pap. 21.99 *(978-0-7385-6920-8(8))* Arcadia Publishing.

Gatto, Mariann. Los Angeles's Little Italy. 2009. (Images of America Ser.). 128p. pap. 21.99 *(978-0-7385-7188-1(1))* Arcadia Publishing.

Gay, Ronald K. & Oakland County Pioneer and Historical Society. Pontiac. 2010. (Images of America Ser.). (Illus.). 128p. pap. 21.99 *(978-0-7385-7814-9(2))* Arcadia Publishing.

Gerber, Judith. Farming in Torrance & the South Bay. 2008. (Images of America Ser.). (ENG., Illus.). 128p. pap. 21.99 *(978-0-7385-5930-8(X))* Arcadia Publishing.

Gibb, Daniel Aaron. Fountain Valley. 2007. (Images of America Ser.). (ENG., Illus.). 128p. per. 19.99 *(978-0-7385-4745-9(X))* Arcadia Publishing.

Gibbs Smith Publisher Staff, ed. Dream Homes San Diego & Orange County. 2007. lib. bdg. 34.95 *(978-1-933415-39-0(8))* Panache Partners, LLC.

Gibson, Dorothy E. Marin Headlands. 2009. (Images of America Ser.). (ENG., Illus.). 128p. pap. 21.99 *(978-0-7385-7024-2(9))* Arcadia Publishing.

Gibson, Jack. Mount Tamalpais & the Marin Municipal Water District. 2012. (Images of America Ser.). (ENG., Illus.). 128p. pap. 21.99 ***(978-0-7385-9317-3(6))*** Arcadia Publishing.

Gillespie, Bunny & Crimmen, Dave. Daly City. 2011. (Then & Now Ser.). (Illus.). 96p. pap. 21.99 *(978-0-7385-7523-0(2))* Arcadia Publishing.

Gillmore, Inez Haynes. The Californiacs & the Native Son. 2007. 48p. per. *(978-1-4065-4466-4(3))* Dodo Pr.

Goin, Peter. Lake Tahoe: A Maritime History. 2012. (Images of America Ser.). (ENG., Illus.). 128p. pap. 21.99 ***(978-0-7385-8912-1(8))*** Arcadia Publishing.

Goin, Peter. South Lake Tahoe. 2010. (Then & Now Ser.). (Illus.). 96p. pap. 21.99 *(978-0-7385-8018-0(X))* Arcadia Publishing.

Goldstein, Steve. LA's Graveside Companion: Where the V. I. P.'s, R. I. P. 2009. 192p. pap. 19.99 *(978-0-7643-3154-1(X))* Schiffer Publishing, Ltd.

Gomez, Dolores & Thilmany, Christy. Brisbane. 2009. 128p. pap. 21.99 *(978-0-7385-7048-8(6))* Arcadia Publishing.

Gonzales, Anne. Stockton: Renewed, Revitalized, Redefined. 2008. 59.50 *(978-1-882933-09-9(5))* Cherbo Publishing Group, Inc.

Gossard, Gloria Hine. Tehachapi. 2008. (Images of America Ser.). (ENG., Illus.). 128p. per. 21.99 *(978-0-7385-5560-7(6))* Arcadia Publishing.

Gottesman, Nancy, et al. Hometown Santa Monica: The Bay Cities Book. Bates, Colleen D. et al, eds. 2007. (Illus.). 256p. pap. 24.95 *(978-0-9753939-2-5(8))* Prospect Park Bks., LLC.

Graffy, Neal. Historic Santa Barbara: An Illustrated History. 2010. (Illus.). 208p. ***(978-1-935377-14-6(0))*** Historical Publishing Network.

Le Grand History: Memories of le Grand History Club. 2007. (Illus.). 99p. (C). pap. 9.95 *(978-0-9729318-5-4(6))* Merced County Historical Society.

Granger, Lewis. Letters of Lewis Granger. 2011. 56p. 36.95 ***(978-1-258-02897-8(2))*** Literary Licensing, LLC.

Griggs, Gary. Beaches & Coast. 2010. (California Natural History Guides). (ENG., Illus.). 328p. 50.00 *(978-0-520-26289-8(1))* Univ. of California Pr.

Griggs, Gary & Ross, Deepika Shrestha. Santa Cruz Coast. 2006. (Then & Now Ser.). (ENG., Illus.). 96p. per. 21.99 *(978-0-7385-4666-7(6))* Arcadia Publishing.

Gross, Victoria. Ghosts of Orange County. 2009. 192p. pap. 14.99 *(978-0-7643-3171-8(X))* Schiffer Publishing, Ltd.

Guild, Novato Historical & Vela, Ron. Novato. 2009. 96p. pap. 21.99 *(978-0-7385-7194-2(6))* Arcadia Publishing.

Gurba, Norma H. & West, Nicholas J. Palmdale. 2010. (Images of America Ser.). (Illus.). 128p. pap. 21.99 *(978-0-7385-8122-4(4))* Arcadia Publishing.

Halberstadt, April, et al. Saratoga. 2009. (Images of America Ser.). (Illus.). 128p. pap. 21.99 *(978-0-7385-6963-5(1))*; pap. 7.99 *(978-0-7385-6964-2(X))* Arcadia Publishing.

Hall, Barbara-Ann & Covina Valley Historical Society. Covina. 2007. (Images of America Ser.). (ENG., Illus.). 128p. per. 21.99 *(978-0-7385-5555-3(X))* Arcadia Publishing.

Hall, Marian. Malibu, California's Most Famous Sea Side Community. 2009. 40.00 *(978-1-61623-396-9(6))* Independent Pub.

Hallowell, Joell, et al. Take Me to the River: Fishing, Swimming, & Dreaming on the San Joaquin. 2010. (Illus.). xii, 145p. pap. *(978-1-59714-143-7(7))* Heyday.

Hamlin, David & Arena, Brett. Los Angeles's Original Farmers Market. 2009. (Images of America Ser.). (ENG., Illus.). 128p. pap. 21.99 *(978-0-7385-7005-1(2))* Arcadia Publishing.

Hanley, Ken. Fly Fishing California: A No Nonsense Guide to Top Waters. 2nd ed. 2007. (No Nonsense Fly Fishing Guidebooks). (ENG., Illus.). 168p. pap. 28.95 *(978-1-892469-10-6(3))* No Nonsense Guides.

Hanson, Joyce A. & Suzie Earp, and Erin Shanks. Community Hospital of San Bernardino. 2009. 128p. pap. 21.99 *(978-0-7385-7022-8(2))* Arcadia Publishing.

Harris, C. Nelson. Norfolk & Western Railway Stations & Depots. 2009. (Images of Rail Ser.). (ENG., Illus.). 128p. pap. 21.99 (978-0-7385-6669-6(1)) Arcadia Publishing.

Harris, Joel A. Concord. 2009. (Images of America Ser.). (ENG., Illus.). 128p. pap. 21.99 (978-0-7385-6913-0(5)) Arcadia Publishing.

Harton, Deborah & McCloud, Ron. Dunsmuir. 2010. (Images of America Ser.). (ENG., Illus.). 128p. pap. 21.99 (978-0-7385-8056-2(2)) Arcadia Publishing.

Hastings, Lansford. The Emigrants' Guide to Oregon & Californ. 2007. 156p. per. 10.95 (978-1-60206-729-5(5)) Cosimo, Inc.

Hastings, Lansford W. The Emigrants Guide to Oregon & Califo. 2006. 156p. per. (978-1-4067-9579-0(8), Pierides Pr.) Read Bks.

Hauf, Tim. Channel Islands National Park & National Marine Sanctuary. 2008. (Illus.). 159p. **(978-0-9788219-2-0(0))**; pap. **(978-0-9788219-3-7(9))** Hauf, Tim Photography.

Hauf, Tim. Ventura County: Land of Everlasting Summers. 2009. (Illus.). 141p. (978-0-9788219-4-4(7)) Hauf, Tim Photography.

Hawk, Diane. Touring the Old Redwood Highway: Humboldt County: 2ed Printing Revised. 2007. (Illus.). 199p. per. 23.95 (978-0-9672162-8-7(1)) Hawk Mountaintop Publishing.

Hayes, Benjamin. Pioneer Notes from the Diaries of Judge Benjamin Hayes, 1849-1875. Wolcott, Marjorie Tisdale, ed. 2011. 332p. 50.95 **(978-1-258-10022-3(3))** Literary Licensing, LLC.

Hecteman, Kevin W. Sacramento Southern Railroad. 2009. (Images of Rail Ser.). (ENG., Illus.). 128p. pap. 21.99 (978-0-7385-6986-4(0)) Arcadia Publishing.

—Sacramento's Southern Pacific Shops. 2010. (Images of Rail Ser.). (Illus.). 128p. pap. 21.99 (978-0-7385-8052-4(X)) Arcadia Publishing.

Hedley, Bungy. View from the Top of the Mast. 2008. 336p. 31.99 (978-1-4343-7223-9(5)) AuthorHouse.

Hee-Chorley, Lorraine. Chinese in Mendocino County. 2009. (Images of America Ser.). (ENG., Illus.). 128p. pap. 21.99 (978-0-7385-5913-1(X)) Arcadia Publishing.

Helper, Hinton Rowan. The Land of Gold Reality Versus Fiction. 2006. 304p. per. 23.99 (978-1-4255-2827-0(9)) MPublishing.

Hemet Area Museum Association. Hemet. 2008. (Images of America Ser.). (ENG., Illus.). 128p. pap. 19.99 (978-0-7385-5846-2(X)) Arcadia Publishing.

Henderson, Moya & Palm Springs Historical Society. Palm Springs. 2009. (Images of America Ser.). (ENG., Illus.). 128p. pap. 21.99 (978-0-7385-5982-7(2)) Arcadia Publishing.

Hendricks, Carson. California State Fair. 2010. (Images of America Ser.). (ENG., Illus.). 128p. pap. 21.99 (978-0-7385-8089-0(9)) Arcadia Publishing.

Hendrickson, Nancy. Historic Photos of Old California. 2009. (Historic Photos Ser.). (ENG.). 205p. 39.95 (978-1-59652-524-5(X)) Turner Publishing Co.

—Remembering Old California. 2011. (Remembering Ser.). (ENG.). 134p. pap. 16.95 (978-1-59652-796-6(X)) Turner Publishing Co.

Hennessey, Beverly. Hetch Hetchy. 2012. (Images of America Ser.). (ENG., Illus.). 128p. pap. 21.99 **(978-0-7385-9322-7(2))** Arcadia Publishing.

Hickenbottom, Thomas, et al. Surfing in Santa Cruz. 2009. (Images of America Ser.). (ENG., Illus.). 128p. pap. 21.99 (978-0-7385-7076-1(1)) Arcadia Publishing.

Hier, Jim. Granada Hills. 2007. (Images of America Ser.). (ENG., Illus.). 128p. per. 21.99 (978-0-7385-4771-8(9)) Arcadia Publishing.

Hill, Suki. Mill Valley. 2007. (Then & Now Ser.). (ENG., Illus.). 96p. per. 21.99 (978-0-7385-5574-4(6), Arcadia Publishing.

Hilton, Eveylena. California Here We Come. 2011. 60p. pap. 11.95 **(978-1-4670-6732-4(6))** AuthorHouse.

Hinkle, George Henry & Hinkle, Bliss McGlashan. Sierra-Nevada Lakes: The American Lakes Series. Quaife, Milo M., ed. 2011. 400p. 54.95 **(978-1-258-07700-6(0))** Literary Licensing, LLC.

Historical Society of Palm Desert & Historical Society of Palm Desert. Palm Desert. 2009. (Images of America Ser.). (ENG., Illus.). 128p. pap. 21.99 (978-0-7385-5964-3(4)) Arcadia Publishing.

Hoberg, Donna. Resorts of Lake County. 2007. (Images of America Ser.). (Illus.). 127p. per. 21.99 (978-0-7385-4798-5(0)) Arcadia Publishing.

Holtzclaw, Kenneth M. & Chong, Tom. Cherry Valley. 2008. (Images of America Ser.). (ENG., Illus.). 128p. pap. 19.99 (978-0-7385-5952-0(0)) Arcadia Publishing.

Holtzclaw, Kenneth M. & Christian, Peggy. San Timoteo Canyon. 2007. (Images of America Ser.). (Illus.). 127p. per. 19.99 (978-0-7385-4744-2(1)) Arcadia Publishing.

Holtzclaw, Kenneth M. & Moreno Valley Historical Society. Moreno Valley. 2007. (Images of America Ser.). (ENG., Illus.). 128p. per. 19.99 (978-0-7385-5569-0(X)) Arcadia Publishing.

Hoye, Richard, et al. Ojai. (Postcard History Ser.). (ENG., Illus.). 128p. 2010. pap. 21.99 (978-0-7385-8108-8(9)) 2007. per. 21.99 (978-0-7385-5577-5(0)) Arcadia Publishing.

Hubbard Crawford, Leslie. Coronado. 2011. (Images of America Ser.). (ENG., Illus.). 128p. pap. 21.99 (978-0-7385-8130-9(5)) Arcadia Publishing.

Hubbard, Jean & Hoving, Gary. Arroyo Grande. 2009. 15p. pap. 7.99 (978-0-7385-6945-1(3)) Arcadia Publishing.

Hubbard, Jean, et al. Arroyo Grande. 2009. (Images of America Ser.). (ENG., Illus.). 128p. pap. 21.99 (978-0-7385-6944-4(5)) Arcadia Publishing.

Hubbartt, Michael Don. The Sutter Buttes. 2010. (Images of America Ser.). (ENG., Illus.). 128p. pap. 21.99 (978-0-7385-8013-5(9)) Arcadia Publishing.

Humphrey, Joanne. The Best Road Trip Ever: Highway One-Sausalito to Montana de Oro. 2008. (Illus.). 126p. spiral bd. 15.95 (978-0-9768477-7-9(9)) Windjammer Adventure Publishing.

Ibbeken, Hillert. California: Impressions from the American West / Impressionen aus dem amerikanischen Westen. 2007. (GER & ENG., Illus.). 120p. 49.00 (978-3-936681-11-6(2)) Edition Axel Menges GmbH DEU. Dist: National Bk. Network.

Irwin, Inez Haynes. The Californiacs. 2009. 74p. pap. 16.75 (978-1-110-41959-3(7)) BiblioBazaar.

Jackson, Glenda J. Ventura. 2009. (Then & Now Ser.). (ENG., Illus.). 96p. pap. 21.99 (978-0-7385-7155-3(5)) Arcadia Publishing.

Jacoby, Kam & Ward, Cynthia Carbone. Layers: Composite Photographs from the Lompoc Valley. 2009. pap. (978-1-61623-775-8(5)) Independent Pub.

Jaffe, Matthew. The Santa Monica Mountains: Range on the Edge. 2006. (978-1-883318-51-2(3)) Angel City Pr.

James, Don, photos by. Surfing San Onofre to Point Dume, 1936-1942: Photographs by Don James, 1 vol. 2008. (ENG., Illus.). 144p. 29.95 (978-1-933045-81-8(7)) D.A.P./Distributed Art Pubs.

Jasmin, Paul. California Dreaming, 1 vol. 2011. (ENG., Illus.). 160p. 65.00 (978-3-86930-030-6(2)) Steidl, Gerhard Druckerei und Verlag DEU. Dist: Innovative Logistics.

Jauregui, Jannette. Ventura County Veterans: World War II to Vietnam. 2011. (Images of America Ser.). (Illus.). 128p. pap. 21.99 (978-0-7385-7491-2(0)) Arcadia Publishing.

Jennings, Jay. Knott's Berry Farm: The Early Years. 2009. (Images of America Ser.). (ENG., Illus.). 128p. pap. 21.99 (978-0-7385-6921-5(6)) Arcadia Publishing.

—Knott's Berry Farm: The Early Years. 2009. 15p. pap. 7.99 (978-0-7385-6922-2(4)) Arcadia Publishing.

Jennings, Sherry E. Truckee. 2011. (Images of America Ser.). (Illus.). 128p. pap. 21.99 (978-0-7385-7495-0(3)) Arcadia Publishing.

Jensen, Carol A. The California Delta. 2007. (Images of America Ser.). (ENG., Illus.). 128p. per. 21.99 (978-0-7385-4787-9(5)) Arcadia Publishing.

Jensen, Carol A. & East Contra Costa Historical Society. East Contra Costa County. 2007. (Postcard History Ser.). (ENG., Illus.). 128p. per. 19.99 (978-0-7385-4774-9(3)) Arcadia Publishing.

Jensen, Carol A. & The North Lake Tahoe Historical Society. Lake Tahoe's West Shore. 2012. (Images of America Ser.). (ENG., Illus.). 128p. pap. 21.99 **(978-0-7385-8891-9(1))** Arcadia Publishing.

John Muir. The Mountains of Californ. 2009. 228p. pap. 6.95 (978-1-60386-261-5(7), Merchant Bks.) Rough Draft Printing.

Johnson and Chris Diaz, The City of Lynwood with Ilu & Diaz, Chris. Lynwood. 2012. (Images of America Ser.). (ENG., Illus.). 128p. pap. 21.99 **(978-0-7385-8889-6(X))** Arcadia Publishing.

Johnson, Robert Lee. Compton. 2012. (Images of America Ser.). (ENG., Illus.). 128p. pap. 21.99 **(978-0-7385-9539-9(X))** Arcadia Publishing.

Johnson, Theodore. Sights in the Gold Region. 2011. 292p. pap. 18.95 (978-1-4290-4610-7(4)) Applewood Bks.

Jones Berk, Lucy & Covey, Stephen A. Escondido Grape Day Festivals. 2010. (Images of America Ser.). (ENG., Illus.). 128p. pap. 21.99 (978-0-7385-5949-0(0)) Arcadia Publishing.

Judah, Paula Amen & Coodley, Lauren. Napa Valley Farming. 2011. (Images of America Ser.). (Illus.). 128p. pap. 21.99 **(978-0-7385-7524-7(0))** Arcadia Publishing.

Kasser, Daniel & Zimmerman, Amanda. Stockton. 2012. (Then & Now Ser.). (ENG., Illus.). 96p. pap. 21.99 **(978-0-7385-8888-9(1))** Arcadia Publishing.

Keller, Russell L. Big Bear. 2008. (Postcard History Ser.). (ENG., Illus.). 128p. pap. 19.99 (978-0-7385-5912-4(1)) Arcadia Publishing.

Kennedy, Rick. Jesus, History & Mount Darwin: An Academic Excursion. 2008. (ENG.). 112p. pap. 33.00 (978-0-7188-9189-3(9)) Lutherworth Pr., The GBR. Dist: Brown, David Bk. Co., The.

Kidder, Lyn & Brunell, Herb. Ruidoso & Ruidoso Downs. 2009. (Images of America Ser.). (ENG., Illus.). 128p. pap. 21.99 (978-0-7385-7069-3(9)) Arcadia Publishing.

Kinsey, James. Huntington Park. 2007. (Images of America Ser.). (ENG., Illus.). 128p. per. 19.99 (978-0-7385-4711-4(5)) Arcadia Publishing.

Kip, Leonard. California Sketches with Recollections of the Gold Mines. 2010. 59p. pap. 9.95 (978-1-4290-4541-4(8)) Applewood Bks.

Kirby, Joe. The Lockheed Plant. 2011. (Images of America Ser.). (ENG., Illus.). 128p. pap. 21.99 **(978-0-7385-8796-7(6))** Arcadia Publishing.

Klett, Mark, et al. Yosemite in Time: Ice Ages, Tree Clocks, Ghost Rivers. 2008. (ENG., Illus.). 144p. per. 29.95 (978-1-59534-042-9(4)) Trinity Univ. Pr.

Klippert, Zoë, ed. An Englishwoman in California: The Letters of Catherine Hubback, 1871-76. 2010. (Illus.). 240p. 40.00 (978-1-85124-344-0(5)) Bodleian Library GBR. Dist: Chicago Distribution Ctr.

Kneeland, Samuel. The Wonders of the Yosemite Valley, & of California. 2011. 100p. pap. 14.99 **(978-1-4255-0555-4(4))** MPublishing.

Knower, Daniel. The Adventures of a Forty-Niner. 2007. (Illus.). 104p. per. (978-1-4065-2929-6(X)) Dodo Pr.

Koehler, Cheryl Angelina. Touring the Sierra Nevada. 2007. (ENG., Illus.). 432p. per. 24.95 (978-0-87417-700-8(6)) Univ. of Nevada Pr.

Koning, Ben & Metz, Anneke. Sunnyvale. 2011. (Images of America Ser.). (ENG., Illus.). 128p. pap. 21.99 (978-0-7385-7435-6(X)) Arcadia Publishing.

Kramer, Carol A. & Calaveras Big Trees Association. Calaveras Big Trees. 2010. (Images of America Ser.). (Illus.). 128p. pap. 21.99 (978-0-7385-8118-7(6)) Arcadia Publishing.

Krintz, Jennifer. Redondo Beach Pier. 2011. (Images of America Ser.). (Illus.). 128p. pap. 21.99 (978-0-7385-7502-5(X)) Arcadia Publishing.

Kurtz, Patricia. Mountain Maidu & Pioneers: A History of Indian Valley, Plumas County, California, 1850 - 1920. 2010. 96p. pap. 16.95 (978-1-4502-6175-3(2)) iUniverse, Inc.

Kushman, Rick & Beal, Hank. A Moveable Thirst: Tales & Tastes from a Season in Napa Wine Country. 2007. (ENG.). 336p. pap. 18.95 (978-0-471-79386-1(8), Wiley) Wiley, John & Sons, Inc.

Lally, Bart, concept. Northern California Experience. 2008. 45.00 (978-0-615-18274-2(7)) MARCOA Publishing, Inc.

Landau, Nathan. Car-Free Los Angeles & Southern California. 2011. (ENG., Illus.). 416p. pap. 18.95 (978-0-89997-656-3(5)) Wilderness Pr.

Lane, Beverly, et al. Vintage Danville: 150 Years of Memories. 2008. (978-1-57864-492-6(5)) Donning Co. Pubs.

Langley, Christopher & Prather, Michael. Mount Whitney. 2012. (Images of America Ser.). (ENG., Illus.). 128p. pap. 21.99 **(978-0-7385-9536-8(5))** Arcadia Publishing.

Larkins, William T. & Alameda Naval Air Museum. Alameda Naval Air Station. 2010. (Images of America Ser.). (ENG., Illus.). 128p. pap. 21.99 (978-0-7385-8040-1(6)) Arcadia Publishing.

Latimer, Larry & Downey Historical Society. Downey. 2010. (Images of America Ser.). (ENG., Illus.). 128p. pap. 21.99 (978-0-7385-7164-5(4)) Arcadia Publishing.

Lavoie, Steven. Historic Photos of Oakland. 2009. (Historic Photos Ser.). (ENG.). 206p. 39.95 (978-1-59652-529-0(0)) Turner Publishing Co.

—Remembering Oakland. 2011. (Remembering Ser.). (ENG.). 144p. pap. 16.95 (978-1-59652-795-9(1)) Turner Publishing Co.

Lee, Rodi & Lynch, Michael G. American River Canyon. 2012. (Images of America Ser.). (ENG., Illus.). 128p. pap. 21.99 **(978-0-7385-9319-7(2))** Arcadia Publishing.

Leicester, Marti & Nopel, David. The Humboldt Wagon Road. 2012. (Images of America Ser.). (ENG., Illus.). 128p. pap. 21.99 **(978-0-7385-7643-5(3))** Arcadia Publishing.

Library, Special Collections of the Sacramento Public. Mather Field. 2012. (Images of America Ser.). (ENG., Illus.). 128p. pap. 21.99 **(978-0-7385-8877-3(6))** Arcadia Publishing.

Liebman, Daniel & Campbell, Nora. California. Liebman, Daniel, ed. 2009. (America the Beautiful Ser.). (ENG., Illus.). 96p. 18.95 (978-1-55407-545-4(9)) Firefly Bks., Ltd.

Light, Melanie & Light, Ken, photos by. Valley of Shadows & Dreams. 2012. **(978-1-59714-172-7(0))** Heyday.

Lippard, Lucy R., et al. The Great Picture: The Making of the World's Largest Photograph. 2012. (ENG., Illus.). 196p. 75.00 **(978-1-55595-373-7(5))** Hudson Hills Pr. LLC.

Loomis Basin Historical Society. Loomis. 2009. (Images of America Ser.). (ENG., Illus.). 128p. pap. 21.99 (978-0-7385-7019-8(2)) Arcadia Publishing.

Loomis, Jan. Pacific Palisades. 2009. 15p. pap. 7.99 (978-0-7385-6949-9(6)) Arcadia Publishing.

Lost Hotels on California's Historic Ridge Route. 2008. (Illus.). 120p. pap. 21.95 (978-0-9800144-0-2(9)) Harrison Irving, Scott.

Loviot, Fanny. A Lady's Captivity among Chinese Pirates. 2008. (ENG.). 144p. 17.00 (978-1-906367-00-8(0)) National Maritime Museum GBR. Dist: Independent Pubs. Group.

Loviot, Fanny. A Lady's Captivity among Chinese Pirates: The Adventures of a Lady Traveller During The 1850s. 2011. 112p. **(978-0-85706-655-8(2))**; pap. **(978-0-85706-656-5(0))** Leonaur Ltd.

Lowell, Waverly B. & Baer, Morley. Living Modern: A Biography of Greenwood Common. 2009. (Illus.). 173p. (978-0-9795508-6-7(6)) Stout, William Pubs.

Lugo Cerra, Julie & Wanamaker, Marc. Movie Studios of Culver City. 2011. (Images of America Ser.). (ENG., Illus.). 128p. pap. 21.99 (978-0-7385-8200-9(X)) Arcadia Publishing.

Luong, Quang-Tuan, photos by. Spectacular Yosemite. 2011. (Illus.). 144p. 45.00 (978-0-7893-2224-1(2)) Universe Publishing.

Lynch, Michael G. California State Park Rangers. 2009. (Images of America Ser.). (ENG., Illus.). 128p. pap. 21.99 (978-0-7385-5993-3(8)) Arcadia Publishing.

Lynch, Mike. Dublin. 2007. (Images of America Ser.). (ENG., Illus.). 128p. per. 19.99 (978-0-7385-4766-4(2)) Arcadia Publishing.

MacIver, Ron & MacIver, Elfriede. La Palma. 2008. (Images of America Ser.). (ENG., Illus.). 128p. pap. 21.99 (978-0-7385-5957-5(1)) Arcadia Publishing.

Magan, Manchan. Angels & Rabies: A Journey Through the Americas. 2007. (ENG., Illus.). 278p. per. 22.95 (978-0-86322-349-5(4)) Brandon/Mount Eagle Pubns., Ltd. IRL. Dist: Dufour Editions, Inc.

Maggia, Filippo & Basilico, Gabriele. Gabriele Basilico -Silicon Valley. Maggia, Filippo & Phillips, Sandra, eds. 2008. (ENG., Illus.). 162p. 19.99 (978-88-6130-300-3(5)) Skira Editore ITA. Dist: Random Hse., Inc.

Malaspina, Rick. Italian Oakland. 2011. (Images of America Ser.). (Illus.). 128p. pap. 21.99 (978-0-7385-8170-5(4)) Arcadia Publishing.

Mallea-Olaetxe, Joxe. The Basques of Reno & the Northeastern Sierra. 2009. (Images of America Ser.). (ENG., Illus.). 128p. pap. 21.99 (978-0-7385-6961-1(5)) Arcadia Publishing.

Mallette, Leo A. Rancho Mirage. 2011. (Images of America Ser.). (Illus.). 128p. pap. 21.99 (978-0-7385-7501-8(1)) Arcadia Publishing.

Mangelos, John P. Ripon. 2011. (Images of America Ser.). (Illus.). 128p. pap. 21.99 (978-0-7385-8166-8(6)) Arcadia Publishing.

Manning, Kathleen & Crow, Jerry. Pacifica. 2010. (Then & Now Ser.). (Illus.). 96p. pap. 21.99 (978-0-7385-8042-5(2)) Arcadia Publishing.

Marcus, Ben & Wanamaker, Marc. Malibu. 2011. (Images of America Ser.). (ENG., Illus.). 128p. pap. 21.99 **(978-0-7385-7614-5(X))** Arcadia Publishing.

Margiloff, Irwin & Earle, Neil. Duarte. 2009. 15p. pap. 7.99 (978-0-7385-6912-3(7)) Arcadia Publishing.

Margiloff, Irwin, et al. Duarte. 2009. (Images of America Ser.). (ENG., Illus.). 128p. pap. 21.99 (978-0-7385-6911-6(9)) Arcadia Publishing.

Marin History Museum. Modern San Rafael: 1940-2000. 2012. (Images of America Ser.). (ENG., Illus.). 128p. pap. 21.99 **(978-0-7385-9307-4(9))** Arcadia Publishing.

Marin History Museum Staff. Early San Rafael. 2008. (Images of America Ser.). (ENG., Illus.). 128p. pap. 19.99 (978-0-7385-5941-4(5)) Arcadia Publishing.

Marquez, Ernest. Santa Monica Beach: A Collector's Pictorial History. 2011. (Illus.). 207p. pap. 29.95 **(978-1-883318-95-6(5))** Angel City Pr.

Marryat, Frank & Grau, Scott R. Mountains & Molehills, or, Recollections of a Burnt Journal. 2009. pap. (978-1-59714-100-0(3)) Heyday.

Marshall, Amelia Sue & Tobey, Terry L. Oakland's Equestrian Heritage. 2008. (Images of America Ser.). (ENG., Illus.). 128p. pap. 19.99 (978-0-7385-5810-3(9)) Arcadia Publishing.

Martin, Ernest O. The Beauty of Holiness: Story of the Wayfarers Chapel. 2007. (Illus.). 96p. (978-1-57864-404-9(6)) Donning Co. Pubs.

Martin, S. W. Atascadero. 2012. (Images of America Ser.). (ENG., Illus.). 128p. pap. 21.99 **(978-0-7385-8916-9(0))** Arcadia Publishing.

Martinez, Roberta H. Latinos in Pasadena. 2009. (Images of America Ser.). (ENG., Illus.). 128p. pap. 21.99 (978-0-7385-6955-0(0)) Arcadia Publishing.

Marvin, Judith & Brejla, Terry. Jamestown & Western Tuolumne County. 2011. (Images of America Ser.). (Illus.). 128p. pap. 21.99 (978-0-7385-8171-2(2)) Arcadia Publishing.

Marvin, Judith, et al. Angels Camp & Copperopolis. 2009. (Images of America Ser.). (ENG., Illus.). 128p. pap. 21.99 (978-0-7385-5981-0(4)) Arcadia Publishing.

Marx, Jennifer. PassPorter's Treasure Hunts at Disneyland. 2012. (PassPorter Ser.). (ENG., Illus.). 192p. pap. 17.95 (978-1-58771-077-3(3), PassPorter Travel Pr.) MediaMarx, Inc.

Mathes, Wayne A. & McHenry Museum. Modesto. 2011. (Then & Now Ser.). (Illus.). 96p. pap. 21.99 (978-0-7385-7485-1(6)) Arcadia Publishing.

Maulhardt, Jeffrey Wayne. Conejo Valley. 2010. (Images of America Ser.). (ENG., Illus.). 128p. pap. 21.99 (978-0-7385-8039-5(2)) Arcadia Publishing.

—Oxnard. 2009. (Postcard History Ser.). (Illus.). 128p. pap. 21.99 (978-0-7385-6937-6(2)) Arcadia Publishing.

May, Vonn Marie & Rancho Santa Fe Historical Society. Rancho Santa Fe. 2010. (Images of America Ser.). (ENG., Illus.). 128p. pap. 21.99 (978-0-7385-7185-0(7)) Arcadia Publishing.

Maya, Anita. Orange County: Portrait of a Place. 2007. (Portrait of a Place Ser.). (ENG., Illus.). 111p. 14.95 (978-0-88240-663-3(9)) Graphic Arts Ctr. Publishing Co.

Mazariegos, Darla Greb. Mount Shasta. 2007. (Images of America Ser.). (ENG., Illus.). 128p. per. 21.99 (978-0-7385-5572-0(X)) Arcadia Publishing.

McClure, R. A. Mill Creek Road. 2010. 113p. pap. 20.00 (978-0-557-46303-9(3)) Lulu Enterprises Inc.

McColl, Michael W. The Frugal Romantic: Affordable Romantic Getaways in Northern California. Date not set. (Illus.). 250p. (Orig.). pap. 12.95 (978-0-9633512-2-7(2)) Insider Pubns.

McCulloh, Douglas. Dream Street. 2009. 176p. pap. 22.50 (978-1-59714-103-1(8)) Heyday.

McDonald, Don & Los Altos History Museum. Early Los Altos & Los Altos Hills. 2010. (Images of America Ser.). (ENG., Illus.). 128p. pap. 21.99 (978-0-7385-8010-4(4)) Arcadia Publishing.

McGovern, Janet. Caltrain & the Peninsula Commute Service. 2012. (Images of Rail Ser.). (ENG., Illus.). 128p. pap. 21.99 **(978-0-7385-7622-0(0))** Arcadia Publishing.

McGovern, Reg, et al. Redwood City. 2008. (Images of America Ser.). (ENG., Illus.). 128p. pap. 21.99 (978-0-7385-5924-7(5)) Arcadia Publishing.

McGregor, Sheri. Anza-Borrego Desert State Park. 2007. (Day & Overnight Hikes Ser.). (ENG., Illus.). 192p. per. 12.95 (978-0-89732-971-2(6)) Menasha Ridge Pr., Inc.

McLeod, Dean L. Port Chicago. 2007. (Images of America Ser.). (Illus.). 127p. per. 19.99 (978-0-7385-5551-5(7)) Arcadia Publishing.

McNassor, Cathy. Los Angeles's la Brea Tar Pits & Hancock Park. 2011. (Images of America Ser.). (Illus.). 128p. pap. 21.99 **(978-0-7385-7611-4(5))** Arcadia Publishing.

Merritt, Christopher & Lynxwiler, J. Eric. Knott's Preserved: From Boysenberry to Theme Park: The History of Knott's Berry Farm. 2010. (978-1-883318-77-2(7)); (978-1-883318-97-0(1)) Angel City Pr.

Miesse, William C. & Peterson, Robyn G. Sudden & Solitary: Mount Shasta & Its Artistic Legacy, 1841-2008. 2008. (Illus.). 227p. pap. 35.00 (978-1-59714-088-1(0)) Heyday.

Millard, Catherine. CALIFORNIA: America's First New England. 2010. (Illus.). 170p. **(978-0-692-01131-7(5))** Christian Heritage Ministries.

Millbrae Historical Society. Millbrae. 2007. (Images of America Ser.). (ENG., Illus.). 128p. per. 19.99 (978-0-7385-4790-9(5)) Arcadia Publishing.

Miller, Joaquin. Joaquin Miller, His California Diary: Beginning in 1855, Ending In 1857. Richards, John Stewart, ed. 2011. 104p. 39.95 **(978-1-258-08788-3(X))** Literary Licensing, LLC.

Mitchell, Ann, photos by. Austin Val Verde: Impressions of a Montecito Masterpiece. 2007. (ENG., Illus.). 144p. 50.00 (978-1-890449-31-5(6)) Balcony Pr.

Moir, Michael & Brisick, Jamie. The Eighties at Echo Beach. 2011. (ENG.). 156p. 35.00 *(978-1-4521-0489-8(1))* Chronicle Bks. LLC.

Monsma, Bradley John. The Sespe Wild: Southern California's Last Free River. 2007. (Environmental Arts & Humanities Ser.). (ENG.). 176p. per. 18.95 *(978-0-87417-704-6(9))* Univ. of Nevada Pr.

Montoya, Carina Monica & Santa Maria Valley Historical Society. Santa Maria Valley. 2011. (Images of America Ser.). (ENG., Illus.). 128p. pap. 21.99 ***(978-0-7385-8880-3(6))*** Arcadia Publishing.

Moodian, Michael A. Rancho Santa Margarita. 2010. (Images of America Ser.). (Illus.). 128p. pap. 21.99 *(978-0-7385-8004-3(X))* Arcadia Publishing.

Moon, Avia Belle. Spiritland: Ghosts of California's Central Coast. 2011. (Illus.). 192p. pap. 19.99 ***(978-0-7643-3901-1(X)***, Schiffer Publishing Ltd) Schiffer Publishing, Ltd.

Moon, Handbks & Brown, Ann Marie. Moon California Waterfalls: More Than 200 Falls You Can Reach by Foot, Car, or Bike. 4th ed. 2011. (Moon Outdoors Ser.). (ENG.). 512p. pap. 19.99 *(978-1-59880-376-1(X))* Avalon Travel Publishing.

Morin, Edgar. California Journal. 2008. (ENG.). 161p. pap. 32.50 *(978-1-84519-275-4(3))* Sussex Academic Pr. GBR. Dist: International Specialized Bk. Services.

Morning, Robin. Tracks of Passion: Eastern Sierra Skiing, Dave McCoy, & Mammoth Mountain: A Photo Essay. 2008. (Illus.). 367p. *(978-1-60461-869-3(8))* Independent Pub.

Morrall, June. Moss Beach. 2010. (Images of America Ser.). (ENG., Illus.). 128p. pap. 21.99 *(978-0-7385-8075-3(9))* Arcadia Publishing.

—Princeton-by-the-Sea. 2007. (Images of America Ser.). (Illus.). 127p. per. 19.99 *(978-0-7385-5583-6(5))* Arcadia Publishing.

Morris, Kathryn, et al. Fullerton. 2007. (Postcard History Ser.). (ENG., Illus.). 128p. per. 19.99 *(978-0-7385-4788-6(3))* Arcadia Publishing.

Moss, Wayne. The Trinity Alps Companion: Hiking Trails & Angling Tales in the California Wilderness. 2nd rev. ed. 2009. 320p. pap. 21.95 *(978-1-893272-12-5(5)*, Ecopress) Finney Co., Inc.

Mount Diablo Interpretive Association. Trees & Shrubs of Mount Diablo. 2008. 89p. pap. 5.00 *(978-0-9748925-4-2(8))* Mount Diablo Interpretive Assoc.

Muckenthaler Cultural Center Foundation. Muckenthaler Cultural Center. 2011. (Images of America Ser.). (Illus.). 128p. pap. 21.99 *(978-0-7385-7551-3(8))* Arcadia Publishing.

Muir, John. The Mountains of California. 2008. 296p. 28.99 *(978-0-554-23177-8(8))* BiblioBazaar.

—The Mountains of California. 2008. (ENG.). pap. 10.99 *(978-1-4209-3103-7(2))* Digireads.com.

—The Mountains of California. 2007. (ENG.). 220p. per. *(978-1-4065-8278-9(6))* Dodo Pr.

—The Mountains of California. 2007. (Large Print Ser.). lib. bdg. 26.00 *(978-1-58287-938-3(9))* North Bks.

—The Mountains of California. Hoagland, Edward, ed. & intro. by. rev. ed. 2008. (ENG., Illus.). 304p. (gr. 12-18). 13.00 *(978-0-14-310525-1(6)*, Penguin Classics) Penguin Group (USA) Inc.

—Stickeen: The Story of a Dog. 2008. 108p. pap. 14.95 *(978-1-4344-7153-6(5))* Wildside Pr., LLC.

—A Thousand-Mile Walk to the Gulf. 2009. 270p. 30.99 *(978-1-110-62183-5(3))*; 270p. pap. 26.75 *(978-1-110-62180-4(9))*; (ENG.). 269p. pap. 21.99 *(978-1-110-62177-4(9)*, BiblioLife); (ENG.). 269p. pap. 23.99 *(978-1-110-62178-1(7)*, BiblioLife) BiblioBazaar.

—A Thousand-Mile Walk to the Gulf. 2009. 104p. pap. *(978-0-217-31253-0(5))* Books LLC.

—A Thousand-Mile Walk to the Gulf. Bade, William Frederic, ed. 2008. (Illus.). 124p. pap. *(978-1-4099-4179-8(5))* Dodo Pr.

—A Thousand-Mile Walk to the Gulf. Bade, William Frederic, ed. 2008. 274p. 42.95 *(978-0-548-98154-2(X))* 2007. (ENG.). 276p. per. 27.95 *(978-0-548-66593-0(1))* Kessinger Publishing, LLC.

—A Thousand Mile Walk to the Gulf. 2007. (Twelve-Point Ser.). lib. bdg. 25.00 *(978-1-58287-454-8(9))*; lib. bdg. 26.00 *(978-1-58287-939-0(7))* North Bks.

—A Thousand-Mile Walk to the Gulf. 219p. reprint ed. lib. bdg. 98.00 *(978-0-7222-0164-0(8))* Library Reprints, Inc.

Muir, John & Allen, Francis H. Stickeen: The Story of a Dog. 2010. 116p. pap. 19.75 *(978-1-149-08431-1(6))*; pap. 19.75 *(978-1-149-16645-1(2))* BiblioBazaar.

Mulford, Prentice. Prentice Mulford's Story: Life by Land & Sea. 2007. 252p. per. 14.95 *(978-1-60206-168-2(8))* Cosimo, Inc.

—Prentice Mulford's Story: Life by Land & Sea. 2007. 196p. per. 15.95 *(978-1-4344-0103-8(0))* Wildside Pr., LLC.

Museum Society of Willows, et al. Willows. 2010. (Images of America Ser.). (Illus.). 128p. pap. 21.99 *(978-0-7385-8060-9(0))* Arcadia Publishing.

Myers, Tom. Sacramento. 2010. (Postcard History Ser.). (ENG., Illus.). 128p. pap. 21.99 *(978-0-7385-7152-2(0))* Arcadia Publishing.

Myers, Tom, et al, photos by. Sacramento Impressions. 2007. (Impressions (Farcountry Press) Ser.). (Illus.). 80p. pap. 9.95 *(978-1-56037-464-0(0))* Farcountry Pr.

Nahmias, Rick. The Migrant Project: Contemporary California Farm Workers. 2008. (ENG., Illus.). 168p. pap. 27.95 *(978-0-8263-4407-6(0))* Univ. of New Mexico Pr.

Nancy McEnery with the Napa County Historical Society. The Napa River. 2012. (Images of America Ser.). (ENG., Illus.). 128p. pap. 21.99 ***(978-0-7385-9504-7(7))*** Arcadia Publishing.

Neumann, Phyllis L. Pescadero: A California Coastal Town. 2007. (ENG., Illus.). 64p. pap. 22.95 *(978-0-9769376-2-3(X))* Penngrove Pubns.

Newcombe, Robert, et al. The Crescenta Valley. 2010. (Then & Now Ser.). (ENG., Illus.). 96p. pap. 21.99 *(978-0-7385-8079-1(1))* Arcadia Publishing.

Newell Christenson, Lynne & Sweet, Ellen L. Ranchos of San Diego County. 2008. (Images of America Ser.). (Illus.). 128p. pap. 21.99 *(978-0-7385-5965-0(2))* Arcadia Publishing.

Nichols, Gina. The Navy at Point Mugu. 2011. (Images of America Ser.). (Illus.). 128p. pap. 21.99 *(978-0-7385-7532-2(1))* Arcadia Publishing.

Nichols, Richard. Sebastopol Walks: A Guide to Exploring Sebastopol on Foot. 2007. per. 7.00 *(978-1-59872-976-4(4))* Instant Pub.

Nihipali, Elizabeth "Nani", et al. Hawaiians in Los Angeles. 2012. (Images of America Ser.). (ENG., Illus.). 128p. pap. 21.99 ***(978-0-7385-9320-3(6))*** Arcadia Publishing.

Nilsen, Adam P. Pleasant Hill. 2007. (Images of America Ser.). (ENG., Illus.). 128p. per. 21.99 *(978-0-7385-5565-2(7))* Arcadia Publishing.

Nordhoff, Charles. Northern California Oregon & the Sandw. 2006. pap. *(978-1-4068-3541-0(2))* Echo Library.

—Northern California, Oregon & the Sandwich Islands. 2008. 260p. 42.95 *(978-0-548-98038-5(1))* 2007. (ENG.). 264p. per. 27.95 *(978-0-548-66700-2(4))* Kessinger Publishing, LLC.

Norris, Jim. Los Olivos. 2008. (Images of America Ser.). (ENG., Illus.). 128p. per. 19.99 *(978-0-7385-5619-2(X))* Arcadia Publishing.

Noske, Carole, et al. Vacaville. 2007. (Then & Now Ser.). (Illus.). 96p. per. 19.99 *(978-0-7385-5563-8(0))* Arcadia Publishing.

Nottingham, Marvin A., ed. Victor & Connections to Pacific Spiny Lobster: Tales of Land & Sea. 2011. 108p. 22.95 *(978-1-4502-9273-3(9))*; pap. 12.95 *(978-1-4502-9274-0(7))* iUniverse, Inc.

Novato Historical Guild Staff. Hamilton Field. 2008. (Images of America Ser.). (ENG., Illus.). 128p. pap. 21.99 *(978-0-7385-5908-7(3))* Arcadia Publishing.

Noy, Gary & Heide, Rick. The Illuminated Landscape: A Sierra Nevada Anthology. 2010. 352p. pap. 19.95 *(978-1-59714-128-4(3))* Heyday.

Oates, Bridget. Sam's Castle. 2011. (Images of America Ser.). (Illus.). 128p. pap. 21.99 *(978-0-7385-7486-8(4))* Arcadia Publishing.

Ofield, Helen M., et al. Lemon Grove. 2010. (Images of America Ser.). (ENG., Illus.). 128p. pap. 21.99 *(978-0-7385-7193-5(8))* Arcadia Publishing.

O'Hara, Susan J. P. & Stockton, Dave. Humboldt Redwoods State Park. 2012. (Images of America Ser.). (ENG., Illus.). 128p. pap. 21.99 ***(978-0-7385-9513-9(6))*** Arcadia Publishing.

Olson, Arleen, photos by. Humboldt Wild. 2008. 168p. pap. 29.99 *(978-0-9798196-0-5(1))* Pratt Mountain Pr.

—Humboldt Wild: Mountains, Forests & Rivers. 2008. pap. 11.99 *(978-0-9798196-2-9(8))* Pratt Mountain Pr.

Olten, Carol, et al. La Jolla. 2008. (Images of America Ser.). (ENG., Illus.). 128p. pap. 19.99 *(978-0-7385-5803-5(6))* Arcadia Publishing.

O'Neil, Dorothy M. Winters. 2009. 128p. pap. 21.99 *(978-0-7385-6914-7(3))* Arcadia Publishing.

Orcutt Henderson, Mary Alice. Santa Paula: 1930-1960. 2009. (Images of America Ser.). (Illus.). 128p. pap. 21.99 *(978-0-7385-7165-2(2))* Arcadia Publishing.

Orozco, Amy Marie. Solvang: A Guide to the Danish Capital of America. 2011. (Tourist Town Guides). 168p. pap. 13.95 *(978-1-935455-21-9(4))* Channel Lake, Inc.

Orozco, Michael Anthony. Alhambra. 2012. (Images of America Ser.). (ENG., Illus.). 128p. pap. 21.99 ***(978-0-7385-7607-7(7))*** Arcadia Publishing.

Osbaldeston, Peter. The Palm Springs Diner's Bible: A Restaurant Guide for Palm Springs, Cathedral City, Rancho Mirage, Palm Desert, Indian Wells, la Quinta, Bermuda Dunes, Indio, & Desert Hot Springs, 1 vol. 2nd ed. 2010. (ENG.). 352p. pap. 19.95 *(978-1-58980-750-1(2))* Pelican Publishing Co., Inc.

Otto, Ken. Azusa Pacific University. 2008. (Campus History Ser.). (ENG., Illus.). 128p. pap. 19.99 *(978-0-7385-5926-1(1))* Arcadia Publishing.

Page, David T. Yosemite & the Southern Sierra Nevada - An Explorer's Guide: Includes Mammoth Lakes, Sequoia, Kings Canyon & Death Valley - A Great Destination. 2nd ed. 2011. (Explorer's Guides). (ENG., Illus.). 424p. pap. 21.95 *(978-1-58157-140-0(2)*, 157140) Countryman Pr.

Palazzo, Robert P. Death Valley. 2008. (Images of America Ser.). (ENG., Illus.). 128p. pap. 21.99 *(978-0-7385-5824-0(9))* Arcadia Publishing.

Palazzo, Robert P. Railroads of Death Valley. 2011. (Images of Rail Ser.). (Illus.). 128p. pap. 21.99 ***(978-0-7385-7479-0(1))*** Arcadia Publishing.

Palmer, Tim, text. Rivers of California: Natural Lifelines of the Golden State. 2010. 208p. 39.95 *(978-1-59714-129-1(1))* Heyday.

Panache Partners LLC Staff, ed. Dream Homes Coastal California: An Exclusive Showcase of the Finest Architects, Designers & Builders of California's Central Coast Including Santa Barbara, San Luis Obispo & Monterey Counties. 2008. (Dream Homes Ser.). (ENG., Illus.). 224p. 34.95 *(978-1-933415-50-5(9))* Panache Partners, LLC.

Panache Partners Staff. California's Central Coast: A Captivating Tour of Established, Estate & Boutique Wineries. 2010. (Spectacular Wineries Ser.). (ENG., Illus.). 300p. 40.00 *(978-1-933415-64-2(9))* Panache Partners, LLC.

Parent, Traci & Terhune, Karen. Black Diamond Mines Regional Preserve. 2009. (Images of America Ser.). (ENG., Illus.). 128p. pap. 21.99 *(978-0-7385-6995-6(X))* Arcadia Publishing.

Patacsil, Judy, et al. Filipinos in San Diego. 2010. (Images of America Ser.). (ENG., Illus.). 128p. pap. 21.99 *(978-0-7385-8001-2(5))* Arcadia Publishing.

Patrick, K. C. The Pomo of Lake County. 2008. (Images of America Ser.). (Illus.). 128p. pap. 19.99 *(978-0-7385-5604-8(1))* Arcadia Publishing.

Patris, Michael A. & Mount Lowe Preservation Society. Mount Lowe. 2010. (Postcard History Ser.). (Illus.). 128p. pap. 21.99 *(978-0-7385-8123-1(2))* Arcadia Publishing.

Patris, Michael A., et al. Mount Lowe Railway. 2012. (Then & Now Ser.). (ENG., Illus.). 96p. pap. 21.99 ***(978-0-7385-8879-7(2))*** Arcadia Publishing.

Pattie, James Ohio & Flint, Thomas. Pattie's Personal Narrative of a Voyage to the Pacific & in Mexico, June 20, 1824-August 30 1830. 2007. (Travel in America Ser.). (ENG.). 368p. 49.95 *(978-1-4290-0142-7(9))*; per. 24.95 *(978-1-4290-0143-4(7))* Applewood Bks.

Pauley, Kenneth E. & Dominguez Rancho Adobe Museum. The 1910 Los Angeles International Air Meet. 2009. (Images of Aviation Ser.). (ENG., Illus.). 128p. pap. 21.99 *(978-0-7385-7190-4(3))* Arcadia Publishing.

Peck, Willys I. & Halberstadt, April. Willys Peck's Saratoga. 2010. *(978-0-935089-30-1(6))* California History Ctr.

Pepe, William J. & Pepe, Elaine A. Quincy. 2008. (Postcard History Ser.). (ENG., Illus.). 128p. per. 21.99 *(978-0-7385-5539-3(8))* Arcadia Publishing.

Perkins, Maggi. Newhall. 2010. (Images of America Ser.). (ENG., Illus.). 128p. pap. 21.99 *(978-0-7385-8025-8(2))* Arcadia Publishing.

Peyton, Paige M. Calico. 2012. (Images of America Ser.). (ENG., Illus.). 128p. pap. 21.99 ***(978-0-7385-8905-3(5))*** Arcadia Publishing.

Phillips, Bob. Growing up in California. 2008. 220p. pap. 15.95 *(978-0-557-01495-8(6))* Lulu Enterprises Inc.

Phillips, Cedar Imboden & The Pasadena Museum of History. Early Pasadena. 2008. (Images of America Ser.). (ENG., Illus.). 128p. pap. 19.99 *(978-0-7385-5837-0(0))* Arcadia Publishing.

Phillips, John. Palos Verdes Estates. 2010. (Images of America Ser.). (ENG., Illus.). 128p. pap. 21.99 *(978-0-7385-8144-6(5))* Arcadia Publishing.

Pike, Gale. Laguna Beach & its Restaurants: The Way it Used to Be. 2011. 48p. pap. 12.99 *(978-1-4567-2531-0(9))* AuthorHouse.

Place, Chuck. The Beautiful Santa Ynez Valley, 1 vol, Vol.1. 2007. (Illus.). 68p. (ENG.). 29.95 *(978-0-9799008-1-5(6))*; pap. 19.95 *(978-0-9799008-0-8(8))* Lomita Publishing.

Pluth, Lisa Ann. The Del Mar Picture Book. Pluth, Lisa Ann, ed. 2006. (Illus.). 200p. kivar 39.95 *(978-0-9746821-2-9(8))* Del Mar Media Group.

Posedel, Jennifer & Lawton, Stephen. Hercules. 2011. (Images of America Ser.). (Illus.). 128p. pap. 21.99 *(978-0-7385-7440-0(6))* Arcadia Publishing.

Poster, Shellye. Death Valley: Where to Find Perfect Shots & How to Take Them. 2009. (Photographer's Guide Ser.). (ENG.). 96p. pap. 14.95 *(978-0-88150-789-8(X)*, 150789) Countryman Pr.

Powers, Stephen. Muskingum Legends, with Other Sketches & Papers Descriptive of the Young Men of Germany & the Old Boys of America by Stephen Powers. 2006. 364p. per. 26.99 *(978-1-4255-3760-9(X))* MPublishing.

Preston, Debbi. Dog-Friendly Trails for All Seasons in California's Foothills & the Sierra Nevad. 2011. 220p. pap. 16.00 ***(978-1-4520-8288-2(X))*** AuthorHouse.

Price, Ryan Lee. Glendora. 2008. (Postcard History Ser.). (ENG., Illus.). 128p. pap. 19.99 *(978-0-7385-5800-4(1))* Arcadia Publishing.

Pyron, Jennifer. Lathrop. 2010. (Images of America Ser.). (ENG., Illus.). 128p. pap. 21.99 *(978-0-7385-8017-3(1))* Arcadia Publishing.

Racina, Amy. Angels in the Wilderness: The True Story of One Woman's Survival Against All Odds. 2009. 280p. pap. 15.95 *(978-1-60070-066-8(7)*, Elite Bks.) Author's Publishing Cooperative.

Radanovich, Leroy. Yosemite Valley Railroad. 2010. (Images of Rail Ser.). (ENG., Illus.). 128p. pap. 21.99 *(978-0-7385-8111-8(9))* Arcadia Publishing.

Rand McNally, creator. Rand Mcnally Santa Barbara, San Luis Obispo & Ventura Counties Easy-to-Read Street Guide. 2nd ed. 2008. (Thomas Guide Santa Barbara/San Luis Obispo/Ventura Counties Street Guide & Directory Ser.). (Illus.). 656p. pap. 32.95 *(978-0-528-87049-1(1))* Rand McNally.

—The Thomas Guide Alameda County Streetguide. 57th ed. 2008. (Thomas Guide Alameda County Street Guide & Directory Ser.). (Illus.). pap. 19.95 *(978-0-528-87383-6(0))* Rand McNally.

—The Thomas Guide Bay Area Metro Streetguide. 23rd ed. 2008. (Thomas Guide Bay Area Metro Street Guide Ser.). (Illus.). pap. 39.95 *(978-0-528-87389-8(X))* Rand McNally.

—The Thomas Guide Contra Costa County Streetguide. 39th ed. 2008. (Thomas Guide Contra Costa County Street Guide & Directory Ser.). (Illus.). pap. 19.95 *(978-0-528-87384-3(9))* Rand McNally.

—The Thomas Guide Easy-to-Read Santa Barbara & San Luis Obispo Counties Streetguide. 2nd ed. 2008. (Thomas Guide Santa Barbara/San Luis Obispo Counties Street Guide & Directory Ser.). pap. 19.95 *(978-0-528-87364-5(4))* Rand McNally.

—The Thomas Guide Monterey Bay Metro Street Guide. 15th ed. 2008. (Thomas Guide Monterey Bay Metro Street Guide Ser.). (Illus.). pap. 29.95 *(978-0-528-86078-2(X))* Rand McNally.

—The Thomas Guide Sacramento & Solano Counties Streetguide. 40th ed. 2008. (Thomas Guide Sacramento/Solano Counties Ser.). (Illus.). pap. 29.95 *(978-0-528-87434-5(9))* Rand McNally.

—The Thomas Guide Sacramento County Streetguide. 40th ed. 2008. (Thomas Guide Sacramento County: Including Portions of Placer & el Dorado Counties Ser.). (Illus.). pap. 24.95 *(978-0-528-87433-8(0))* Rand McNally.

—The Thomas Guide Santa Clara & San Mateo Counties Streetguide. 38th ed. 2008. (Thomas Guide Santa Clara/San Mateo Counties Street Guide & Directory Ser.). (Illus.). pap. 29.95 *(978-0-528-87388-1(1))* Rand McNally.

Rand McNally and Company Staff, creator. Santa Clara County Street Guide. 38th ed. 2008. (Thomas Guide Santa Clara County Street Guide & Directory Ser.). (Illus.). 54p. pap. 19.95 *(978-0-528-87382-9(2))* Rand McNally.

Reed, Roberta A. & The Santa Ana Historical Preservation Society Staff. Santa Ana: 1940-2007. 2008. (Illus.). 128p. pap. 19.99 *(978-0-7385-5834-9(6))* Arcadia Publishing.

Reiser, Ronald J. California Passport. 2007. 36p. pap. *(978-0-9625515-3-6(8))* Reiser, R. J. & Co.

Reuther, Ronald T. & Larkins, William T. Oakland Aviation. 2008. (Images of Aviation Ser.). (ENG., Illus.). 128p. pap. 21.99 *(978-0-7385-5600-0(9))* Arcadia Publishing.

Rice, Walter, et al. San Francisco's California Street Cable Cars. 2008. (Images of Rail Ser.). (Illus.). 128p. pap. 19.99 *(978-0-7385-5963-6(6))* Arcadia Publishing.

Richardson, Rob. Railroads & Depots of Orange County. 2010. (Images of Rail Ser.). (Illus.). 128p. pap. 21.99 *(978-0-7385-8011-1(2))* Arcadia Publishing.

Rippens, Paul & San Dimas Historical Society. San Dimas. 2008. (Images of America Ser.). (Illus.). 128p. pap. 19.99 *(978-0-7385-5934-6(2))* Arcadia Publishing.

Roach, John P. California, the First 100 Years: Padre Serra to Statehood & the Golden Spike. 2010. 216p. 29.95 *(978-1-4520-1177-6(X))*; pap. 24.95 *(978-1-4520-1176-9(1))* AuthorHouse.

Robinson, Lisa. The San Lorenzo Valley. 2012. (Images of America Ser.). (ENG., Illus.). 128p. pap. 21.99 ***(978-0-7385-9229-9(3))*** Arcadia Publishing.

Rodriquez, JoAnn. Legallay Driving the 50 States of the USA — CA: All the information you need to make your California car trip safe & hassle Free! 2007. 2p. (YA). pap. 9.95 *(978-0-9800246-0-9(9))* Lucre Publishing.

Rogers, Steve R. Hanford. 2012. (Then & Now Ser.). (ENG., Illus.). 96p. pap. 21.99 ***(978-0-7385-9311-1(7))*** Arcadia Publishing.

Rogerson, Bruce & Point Cabrillo Lightkeepers Association Staff. Point Cabrillo Light Station. 2008. (Images of America Ser.). (Illus.). 128p. pap. 19.99 *(978-0-7385-5950-6(4))* Arcadia Publishing.

Ron, Dial, prod. Dinuba 100: A Place of New Beginnings. 2007. (Illus.). 136p. 33.00 *(978-0-9793650-0-3(7))* Dial, Ron Photography.

Rose, Gene. Yosemite's Tioga Country. 2006. pap. 24.95 *(978-1-892622-28-0(9))* Bear State Bks.

Roseman, Frank M. & Watry, Peter J. Chula Vista. 2010. (Then & Now Ser.). (ENG., Illus.). 96p. pap. 21.99 *(978-0-7385-8016-6(3))* Arcadia Publishing.

Roseman, Frank M., et al. Chula Vista. 2008. (Images of America Ser.). (ENG., Illus.). 128p. pap. 19.99 *(978-0-7385-5616-1(5))* Arcadia Publishing.

Roseville Historical Society. Roseville. 2010. (Images of America Ser.). (ENG., Illus.). 128p. pap. 21.99 *(978-0-7385-7029-7(X))* Arcadia Publishing.

Roseville Historical Society Staff. Roseville. 2010. (Postcards of America Ser.). 15p. 7.99 *(978-0-7385-7030-3(3))* Arcadia Publishing.

Ross Matthews, Stephanie, et al. Los Gatos. 2009. (Postcard History Ser.). (ENG., Illus.). 128p. pap. 21.99 *(978-0-7385-6962-8(3))* Arcadia Publishing.

Rubin, Saul. You Know You're in California When... 101 Quintessential Places, People, Events, Customs, Lingo, & Eats of the Golden State. 2007. (You Know You're in Ser.). (ENG., Illus.). 112p. per. 9.95 *(978-0-7627-3745-1(X)*, 1269734) Globe Pequot Pr., The.

Russell, Gene H. The Land of Orland. 2008. (Images of America Ser.). (ENG., Illus.). 128p. per. 19.99 *(978-0-7385-5617-8(3))* Arcadia Publishing.

Sacramento Archives and Museum Collection Center. Sacramento's Elmhurst, Tahoe Park & Colonial Heights. 2008. (Images of America Ser.). (Illus.). 127p. per. 19.99 *(978-0-7385-5590-4(8))* Arcadia Publishing.

Sanborn, Kate. A Truthful Woman in Southern California. 2008. 249p. 25.99 *(978-0-554-86830-1(X))*; 200p. 25.99 *(978-0-554-58347-1(X))*; 190p. 25.99 *(978-0-554-83721-5(8))*; 190p. pap. 24.75 *(978-0-554-83723-9(4))*; 273p. pap. 24.75 *(978-0-554-86832-5(6))*; 200p. pap. 23.75 *(978-0-554-58350-1(X))* BiblioBazaar.

—A Truthful Woman in Southern California. 2007. 96p. per. *(978-1-4065-4300-1(4))* Dodo Pr.

—A Truthful Woman in Southern California. 2008. 208p. 39.95 *(978-1-4369-2348-4(4))*; pap. 24.95 *(978-1-4367-5678-5(2))* Kessinger Publishing, LLC.

Sanders, Ian. Views of Morgan Hill: Postcards & Images of Morgan Hill, California. 2010. (Illus.). 156p. 19.99 *(978-0-615-38051-3(4))* Bks.mart Enterprises Inc.

Santa Barbara Conservancy. Stone Architecture in Santa Barbara. 2009. (Images of America Ser.). (ENG., Illus.). 128p. pap. 21.99 *(978-0-7385-6968-0(2))* Arcadia Publishing.

Santa Fe Springs Historical Committee. Santa Fe Springs. 2012. (Images of America Ser.). (ENG., Illus.). 128p. pap. 21.99 ***(978-0-7385-7576-6(3))*** Arcadia Publishing.

Santos, Kristen. Turlock: A Pictorial History, 1950-2005. 2007. *(978-1-57864-425-4(9))* Donning Co. Pubs.

Schaadt, Mike, et al. Cabrillo Beach Coastal Park. 2009. (Images of America Ser.). (ENG., Illus.). 128p. pap. 21.99 *(978-0-7385-7189-8(X))* Arcadia Publishing.

—San Pedro's Cabrillo Beach. 2008. (Images of America Ser.). (Illus.). 128p. pap. 21.99 *(978-0-7385-5997-1(0))* Arcadia Publishing.

Schipske, Gerrie. Early Long Beach. 2011. (Images of America Ser.). (ENG., Illus.). 128p. pap. 21.99 ***(978-0-7385-7577-3(1))*** Arcadia Publishing.

Schipske, Gerrie. Rosie the Riveter in Long Beach. 2008. (Images of America Ser.). (Illus.). 128p. pap. 19.99 *(978-0-7385-5814-1(1))* Arcadia Publishing.

Schlenz, Mark A. Exploring Mammoth Lakes: Four Seasons of Eastern Sierra Adventure. 2006. (Illus.). 80p. per. 19.95 *(978-0-944197-78-3(7))* Companion Pr.

Schmale, John & Schmale, Katrina. Petaluma & Santa Rosa Railway. 2009. (Images of Rail Ser.). (Illus.). 128p. pap. 21.99 *(978-0-7385-5959-9(8))* Arcadia Publishing.

Schoenherr, Steven, et al. Bonita. 2009. 128p. pap. 21.99 *(978-0-7385-7000-6(1))* Arcadia Publishing.
Schubert, John C. & Munthe, Valerie A. Russian River. 2011. (Then & Now Ser.). (Illus.). 96p. pap. 21.99 *(978-0-7385-8195-8(X))* Arcadia Publishing.
Scott, James & Tolley, Tom, texts. Historic Photos of Sacramento. 2007. (Historic Photos Ser.). (ENG., Illus.). 204p. 39.95 *(978-1-59652-308-1(5))* Turner Publishing Co.
Secrest, William B. Greetings from Fresno California: Vintage Postcards from California's Heartland. 2007. (ENG., Illus.). 64p. 26.95 *(978-1-933502-12-0(6))* Linden Publishing Co., Inc.
Sederquist, Betty. Coloma. 2012. (Images of America Ser.). (ENG., Illus.). 128p. pap. 21.99 ***(978-0-7385-9549-8(7))*** Arcadia Publishing.
Selters, Andy. Inyo National Forest. 2012. (Images of America Ser.). (ENG., Illus.). 128p. pap. 21.99 ***(978-0-7385-9305-0(2))*** Arcadia Publishing.
Sempervirens Fund Staff. Castle Rock. 30p. 9.95 *(978-0-9701178-4-7(1))*; pap. 5.95 *(978-0-9701178-3-0(3))* Sempervirens Fund.
Shaw, Steven. San Bernardino. 2008. (Postcard History Ser.). (Illus.). 127p. per. 19.99 *(978-0-7385-5581-2(9))* Arcadia Publishing.
Shower, Anita. Grover Beach. 2008. (Images of America Ser.). (ENG., Illus.). 128p. per. 19.99 *(978-0-7385-5596-6(7))* Arcadia Publishing.
Sinclair, Mick & Globetrotter Staff. California. 2nd ed. 2008. (Globetrotter Travel Packs Ser.). (ENG., Illus.). 128p. pap. 14.95 *(978-1-84537-959-9(4))* New Holland Pubs., Ltd. GBR. Dist: Globe Pequot Pr., The.
Singleton, Jill M. & Holmes, Philip. Centerville, Fremont. 2011. (Images of America Ser.). (Illus.). 128p. pap. 21.99 *(978-0-7385-8177-4(1))* Arcadia Publishing.
Slater, Tom. California Road Trip. 2009. 456p. pap. 49.95 *(978-0-9824988-0-4(2))* Partners Bk. Distributing, Inc.
Smith, Robert B. & Idyllwild Area Historical Society. Idyllwild & the High San Jacintos. 2009. (Images of America Ser.). (ENG., Illus.). 128p. pap. 21.99 *(978-0-7385-5985-8(7))* Arcadia Publishing.
Sommers, Arthur. Donner Summit. 2011. (Images of America Ser.). (Illus.). 128p. pap. 21.99 *(978-0-7385-7477-6(5))* Arcadia Publishing.
—Placer County. 2010. (Images of America Ser.). (ENG., Illus.). 128p. pap. 21.99 *(978-0-7385-7153-9(9))* Arcadia Publishing.
Soquel Pioneer and Historical Association. Soquel. 2011. (Images of America Ser.). (Illus.). 128p. pap. 21.99 *(978-0-7385-7081-5(8))* Arcadia Publishing.
Special Collections of the Sacramento Public Library. Sacramento's Alkali Flat. 2009. (Images of America Ser.). (Illus.). 128p. pap. 21.99 *(978-0-7385-7151-5(2))* Arcadia Publishing.
Sperbeck Drsquo;Arcy, Roberta. Browns Valley. 2012. (Images of America Ser.). (ENG., Illus.). 128p. pap. 21.99 ***(978-0-7385-8896-4(2))*** Arcadia Publishing.
Sprung, Stu, et al. Oceanside Fire Department. 2010. (Images of America Ser.). (Illus.). 128p. pap. 21.99 *(978-0-7385-8105-7(4))* Arcadia Publishing.
Stamolis, Tony, photos by. Frezno. 2008. (ENG.). 132p. 29.95 *(978-1-934170-04-5(6))* Process Packaging.
Stanley, Eric. Santa Rosa. 2008. (Then & Now Ser.). (Illus.). 96p. pap. 21.99 *(978-0-7385-5979-7(2))* Arcadia Publishing.
Stansfield, Charles A., Jr. & Stansfield, Charles. Haunted Northern California: Ghosts & Strange Phenomena of the Golden State. 2009. (Haunted Ser.). (ENG., Illus.). 144p. pap. 10.95 *(978-0-8117-3586-5(9))* Stackpole Bks.
Stark, Julie. Yuba City, Our Home Town. 2008. *(978-1-57864-498-8(4))* Donning Co. Pubs.
Stark, Michael L. & Skipper Ret., John. Redondo Beach Police Department. 2011. (Images of America Ser.). (Illus.). 128p. pap. 21.99 *(978-0-7385-8164-4(X))* Arcadia Publishing.
Stephens, E. J. & Wanamaker, Marc. Early Warner Bros. Studios. 2010. (Images of America Ser.). (ENG., Illus.). 128p. pap. 21.99 *(978-0-7385-8091-3(0))* Arcadia Publishing.
Stephens, E. J. & Wanamaker, Marc. Griffith Park. 2011. (Images of America Ser.). (ENG., Illus.). 128p. pap. 21.99 ***(978-0-7385-8883-4(0))*** Arcadia Publishing.
Stern, Ralph & Huber, Nicole, texts. Urbanizing the Mojave Desert: Las Vegas. 2008. (GER & ENG., Illus.). 192p. 35.00 *(978-3-939633-50-1(X))* Jovis Verlag GmbH DEU. Dist: D.A.P./Distributed Art Pubs.
Stevens, Janice & Hunter, Pat. Fresno's Architectural Past, Vol. 2. 2007. (ENG., Illus.). 76p. 26.95 *(978-1-933502-13-7(4))* Linden Publishing Co., Inc.
—Fresno's Architectural Past Box Set. 2007. (ENG.). 164p. 49.95 *(978-1-933502-14-4(2))* Linden Publishing Co., Inc.
Stevenson, Robert. The Silverado Squatters. 2007. (Travel in America Ser.). (ENG.). 124p. 49.95 *(978-1-4290-0510-4(6))*; per. 24.95 *(978-1-4290-0511-1(4))* Applewood Bks.
Stevenson, Robert Louis. The Silverado Squatters. 2009. 220p. 23.99 *(978-1-103-07110-4(6))* 2009. 220p. pap. 17.99 *(978-1-103-07108-1(4))* 2007. (ENG.). 92p. pap. 16.99 *(978-1-4346-3858-8(8))* 2007. (ENG.). 100p. pap. 18.99 *(978-1-4346-3859-5(6))* BiblioBazaar.
—The Silverado Squatters. 2007. (ENG.). 84p. per. *(978-1-4065-8222-2(0))* Dodo Pr.
—The Silverado Squatters. 2008. (ENG.). 84p. pap. 8.45 *(978-1-4385-0263-2(X))*; pap. 8.95 *(978-1-4385-1007-1(1))* Standard Pubns., Inc. (Book Jungle).
Stienstra, Tom & Brown, Ann Marie. California Deserts Camping & Hiking: Including Death Valley, Mojave, Joshua Tree, & Anza-Borrego. 2009. (Moon Spotlight Ser.). (ENG.). 125p. pap. 8.95 *(978-1-59880-279-5(8))* Avalon Travel Publishing.
Stoddard, Charles Warren. In the Footprints of the Padres. 2009. 354p. 38.99 *(978-1-115-59745-6(0))*; 354p. pap. 31.75 *(978-1-115-59748-7(5))*; 236p. 27.99 *(978-0-559-11290-4(4))*; 236p. 24.99 *(978-0-559-11307-9(2))*; 236p. pap. 25.75 *(978-0-559-11294-2(7))*; 236p. pap. 24.75 *(978-0-559-11301-7(3))* BiblioBazaar.
—In the Footprints of the Padres. 2008. (Illus.). 212p. pap. *(978-1-4065-7550-7(X))* Dodo Pr.
Stone, Leslie. Historic Photos of Orange County. 2008. (Historic Photos Ser.). (ENG.). 216p. 39.95 *(978-1-59652-487-3(1))* Turner Publishing Co.
Sweet, Ellen L. & Newell, Lynne. Historic Stage Routes of San Diego County. 2011. (Images of America Ser.). (Illus.). 128p. pap. 21.99 ***(978-0-7385-7468-4(6))*** Arcadia Publishing.
Swenson, Timothy. Union City. 2008. (Images of America Ser.). (Illus.). 128p. per. 19.99 *(978-0-7385-5809-7(5))* Arcadia Publishing.
Tahja, Katy M. Early Mendocino Coast. 2008. (Images of America Ser.). (ENG., Illus.). 128p. pap. 21.99 *(978-0-7385-5946-9(6))* Arcadia Publishing.
Tanner, Lesa & Graton Community Club. Graton. 2009. (Images of America Ser.). (ENG., Illus.). 128p. pap. 21.99 *(978-0-7385-6989-5(5))* Arcadia Publishing.
Tapper, Joan. The Most Beautiful Villages & Towns of California. 2007. (ENG., Illus.). 208p. 40.00 *(978-0-500-51368-2(6))* Thames & Hudson.
Tarbell Cooper, Suzanne, et al. RMS Queen Mary. 2010. (Images of America Ser.). (Illus.). 128p. pap. 21.99 *(978-0-7385-8067-8(8))* Arcadia Publishing.
Tayag, Elnora Kelly. Filipinos in Ventura County. 2011. (Images of America Ser.). (Illus.). 128p. pap. 21.99 *(978-0-7385-7473-8(2))* Arcadia Publishing.
Taylor, Bayard. Eldorado; or, Adventures in the Path of Empire: Comprising A Voyage to California, Via Panama; Life in San Francisco & Monterey; Pictures of the Gol. 2006. 460p. per. 29.99 *(978-1-4255-5132-2(7))*; 468p. per. 29.99 *(978-1-4255-5174-2(2))* MPublishing.
Taylor, Benjamin F. Between the Gates. 2007. (ENG.). 296p. 43.95 *(978-0-548-01133-1(8))* Kessinger Publishing, LLC.
Taylor, Joseph E., III. Pilgrims of the Vertical: Yosemite Rock Climbers & Nature at Risk. 2010. (Illus.). 384p. 29.95 *(978-0-674-05287-1(0))* Harvard Univ. Pr.
Taylor, William. California Life Illustrated by William Taylor Sixteen Engravings. 2006. (Illus.). 352p. per. 23.99 *(978-1-4255-3555-1(0))* MPublishing.
Teurlay, Frank. Riverside's Camp Anza & Arlanza. 2008. (Images of America Ser.). (Illus.). 128p. pap. 19.99 *(978-0-7385-5918-6(0))* Arcadia Publishing.
Thomas, Daniel Paul. 100 Miles. 2007. 124p. per. 9.95 *(978-0-9766269-6-1(9))* Stansbury Publishing.
Thomas, Jan. The Colors of California. 2011. 48p. pap. 17.99 *(978-1-4567-4259-1(0))* AuthorHouse.
Thomas, Rick. South Pasadena's Raymond Hotel. 2008. (Images of America Ser.). (Illus.). 128p. pap. 21.99 *(978-0-7385-5919-3(9))* Arcadia Publishing.
Thomas, Rick R. South Pasadena's Ostrich Farm. 2007. (Images of America Ser.). (Illus.). 127p. *(978-0-7385-5578-2(9))* Arcadia Publishing.
Thomas, Tim & League, the Monterey Japanese American Citizens. The Japanese on the Monterey Peninsula. 2011. (Images of America Ser.). (ENG., Illus.). 128p. pap. 21.99 ***(978-0-7385-7497-4(X))*** Arcadia Publishing.
Thwaites, Reuben Gold. Early Western Travels, 1748-1846: Pattie's Personal Narrative, 1824-1830; Willard's Inland Trade with New Mexico, 1825, & Downfall of the Fredonian Republic; & Malte-Brun's Account of Mexico, Vol. XVIII. 2007. cd-rom 15.95 *(978-0-7884-4420-3(4))* Heritage Bks.
Tom, Brian, et al. Marysville's Chinatown. 2008. (Images of America Ser.). (ENG., Illus.). 128p. pap. 19.99 *(978-0-7385-5976-6(8))* Arcadia Publishing.
Torliatt, Lee. Historic Photos of Sonoma County. 2008. (Historic Photos Ser.). (ENG., Illus.). 205p. 39.95 *(978-1-59652-409-5(X))* Turner Publishing Co.
Torrey, Bradford. Field Days in California. 2009. 268p. 42.95 *(978-1-120-23725-5(4))*; pap. 27.95 *(978-1-120-19597-5(7))* Kessinger Publishing, LLC.
—Field-Days in California. 2008. (Illus.). 148p. pap. *(978-1-4099-1075-3(8))* Dodo Pr.
—Field-Days in California. reprint ed. lib. bdg. *(978-0-7222-3072-5(9))* Library Reprints, Inc.
Trahan, Kendra. Disney's California Adventure Detective: An Independent Guide to Exploring the Trivia, Secrets & Magic of the Park Dedicated to California. 2008. (ENG.). 224p. pap. 14.95 *(978-0-9717464-5-9(1))* PermaGrin Publishing.
Trela, Christopher. Newport Beach Centennial: Celebrating a Century. 2006. pap. 23.20 *(978-0-615-13688-2(5))* City of Newport Beach.
Tress, Arthur, photos by. Wheels on Waves: California Skate Parks. 2007. 112p. 45.00 *(978-0-9794727-1-8(7))* Five Ties Publishing.
Trimble, Paul C. Riverboats of Northern California. 2011. (Images of America Ser.). (Illus.). 128p. pap. 21.99 ***(978-0-7385-7496-7(1))*** Arcadia Publishing.
Tucker, Wehtahnah & Bujkovsky, Gus. Cardiff-by-the-Sea. 2009. (Images of America Ser.). (ENG., Illus.). 128p. pap. 21.99 *(978-0-7385-6951-2(8))* Arcadia Publishing.
Turner, Michelle L. & Pasadena Museum of History. The Rose Bowl. 2010. (Images of America Ser.). (Illus.). 128p. pap. 21.99 *(978-0-7385-8058-6(9))* Arcadia Publishing.
Tyson, James. Diary of a Physician in California. 2010. 94p. pap. 9.95 *(978-1-4290-4557-5(4))* Applewood Bks.
Unzelman, Gail & Wine Library Associates of Sonoma County. Sonoma County Wineries. 2006. (Postcard History Ser.). (Illus.). 128p. per. 19.99 *(978-0-7385-4667-4(4))* Arcadia Publishing.
Van Maren, James. Citrus Heights. 2011. (Images of America Ser.). (Illus.). 128p. pap. 21.99 *(978-0-7385-7459-2(7))* Arcadia Publishing.
Vargo, Cecile Page & Vargo, Roger W. Cerro Gordo. 2012. (Images of America Ser.). (ENG., Illus.). 128p. pap. 21.99 ***(978-0-7385-9520-7(9))*** Arcadia Publishing.
Vaughan, Pam & Vaughan, Brenden. Bishop. 2011. (Images of America Ser.). (ENG., Illus.). 128p. pap. 21.99 *(978-0-7385-8183-5(6))* Arcadia Publishing.
Veronico, Betty S. Lighthouses of the Bay Area. 2008. (Images of America Ser.). (ENG., Illus.). 128p. pap. 19.99 *(978-0-7385-5943-8(1))* Arcadia Publishing.
Veronico, Nicholas A. & Veronico, Betty S. San Carlos. 2007. (Images of America Ser.). (Illus.). 127p. per. 19.99 *(978-0-7385-4793-0(X))* Arcadia Publishing.
Veterans Equity Center Staff. Filipino WW II Soldiers: America's Second-Class Veterans. Date not set. (Illus.). 83p. pap. *(978-0-615-22506-7(3))* Veterans Equity Ctr.
Vizgirdas, Ray S. & Rey-Vizgirdas, Edna M. Wild Plants of the Sierra Nevada. 2009. (ENG.). 384p. pap. 29.95 *(978-0-87417-789-3(8))* Univ. of Nevada Pr.
Vogel, Claire Marie. Laguna Beach. 2009. (Images of America Ser.). (ENG., Illus.). 128p. pap. 21.99 *(978-0-7385-6997-0(6))* Arcadia Publishing.
Vollmann, William T., photos by. Imperial. 2009. (ENG.). 224p. 55.00 *(978-1-57687-489-9(3)*, powerHouse Bks.) powerHouse Cultural Entertainment, Inc.
Vrilakas Simons, Cynthia. San Leandro. 2008. (Images of America Ser.). (Illus.). 128p. pap. 19.99 *(978-0-7385-5937-7(7))* Arcadia Publishing.
Waddell, James Albert. Cal North Outdoor Scenic Byway Tour: Northern California Wild Lands volume, 6 Vols., Vol. 6. Waddell, James Albert, ed. 2006. (Cal North Outdoor Scenic Byway Tour Ser.: Vol. 6). 93p. pap. 20.00 *(978-0-9761434-6-8(1))* Waddell, James Albert.
—Cal North Outdoor Scenic Byway Tour: Paperback Book of Northern California Wilderness Areas. Waddell, James Albert, ed. 2006. (California North Outdoor Scenic Byway Tour Ser.: 3). (Illus.). 68p. pap. 20.00 *(978-0-9761434-3-7(7))* Waddell, James Albert.
—Cal North Outdoor Scenic Byway Tour: Siskiyou Notes of History, Vol. 5. Waddell, James Albert, ed. 2006. (Cal North Outdoor Scenic Byway Tour Ser.: Vol. 5). 69p. pap. 20.00 *(978-0-9761434-5-1(3))* Waddell, James Albert.
—Cal North Outdoor Scenic Byway Tour - Siskiyou Names: Siskiyou County Names of History. Waddell, James Albert, ed. 2006. (Cal North Outdoor Scenic Byway Tour Ser.: Vol. 4). 72p. pap. 20.00 *(978-0-9761434-4-4(5))* Waddell, James Albert.
—California North Outdoor Scenic Byway Main Tour Book: Outdoor Photo Book of Main Tour from Compact Disk. Waddell, James Albert, ed. 2006. (California North Outdoor Scenic Byway Tour Ser.: Vol. 2). 47p. pap. 40.00 *(978-0-9761434-1-3(0))* Waddell, James Albert.
—Uncle Lee: Mule-Packer: Northern California Mountains in History. Waddell, James Albert, ed. 2007. (Illus.). 120p. pap. 46.50 *(978-0-9761434-9-9(6))* Waddell, James Albert.
Wagele, Joan, et al. Cloverdale. 2008. (Images of America Ser.). (ENG., Illus.). 128p. pap. 19.99 *(978-0-7385-5914-8(8))* Arcadia Publishing.
Walker, Doris I. Orange County: A Natural HIST. 2009. 128p. pap. 21.99 *(978-0-7385-6908-6(9))* Arcadia Publishing.
—Orange County Then & Now. 2006. (Then & Now Thunder Bay Ser.). (ENG., Illus.). 144p. 19.95 *(978-1-59223-599-5(9)*, Thunder Bay Pr.) Advantage Pubs. Group.
Wallace, David Rains. Chuckwalla Land: The Riddle of California's Desert. 2011. (ENG.). 272p. 27.50 *(978-0-520-25616-3(6))* Univ. of California Pr.
Wanamaker, Marc. San Fernando Valley. 2011. (Images of America Ser.). (ENG., Illus.). 128p. pap. 21.99 *(978-0-7385-7157-7(1))* Arcadia Publishing.
Warneke, Jack, et al. San Jacinto. 2008. (Images of America Ser.). (Illus.). 128p. pap. 19.99 *(978-0-7385-5842-4(7))* Arcadia Publishing.
Warner, Charles Dudley. On Horseback. 2008. 84p. pap. *(978-1-4099-4670-0(3))* Dodo Pr.
—Our Italy. 2009. 184p. pap. *(978-0-217-24409-1(2))* Books LLC.
—Our Italy. 2009. (Illus.). 172p. pap. *(978-1-4099-7839-8(7))* Dodo Pr.
Warren, Eric H. Eagle Rock. 2009. (Images of America Ser.). (ENG., Illus.). 128p. pap. 21.99 *(978-0-7385-6996-3(8))* Arcadia Publishing.
Waters, John. Calistoga. 2008. (Images of America Ser.). (ENG., Illus.). 128p. pap. 19.99 *(978-0-7385-5594-2(0))* Arcadia Publishing.
Waters, John, Jr. Calistoga. 2008. (Illus.). 127p. pap. *(978-0-7835-5594-2(6))* Arcadia Publishing.
Weeks, John Howard. Inland Empire. 2008. (Postcard History Ser.). (ENG., Illus.). 128p. pap. 19.99 *(978-0-7385-5907-0(5))* Arcadia Publishing.
Weeks, John Howard. Mojave Desert. 2012. (Postcard History Ser.). (ENG., Illus.). 128p. pap. 21.99 ***(978-0-7385-8887-2(3))*** Arcadia Publishing.
Wehrey, Jane. Manzanar. 2008. (Images of America Ser.). (ENG., Illus.). 128p. pap. 21.99 *(978-0-7385-5808-0(7))* Arcadia Publishing.
Weimer, C. Buck. The Darien Jungle Shakedown Cruise. 2008. 255p. pap. 15.95 *(978-0-615-25185-1(4))* Weimer, C. Buck.
Welch, Diane Y. & Welch, B. Paul. Del Mar Fairgrounds. 2008. (Postcards of America Ser.). (ENG., Illus.). 15p. pap. 7.99 *(978-0-7385-2531-0(6))*; 128p. pap. 19.99 *(978-0-7385-5822-6(2))* Arcadia Publishing.
Wellman, Gregory L. A History of Alcatraz Island: 1853-2008. 2008. (Images of America Ser.). (ENG., Illus.). 128p. pap. 21.99 *(978-0-7385-5815-8(X))* Arcadia Publishing.
Westerbeck, Colin & Westwell, Ian. The Unseen Ansel Adams. 2010. (ENG.). 180p. 39.95 *(978-1-60710-013-3(4)*, Thunder Bay Pr.) Advantage Pubs. Group.
Western Sonoma County Historical Society. Sebastopol's Gravenstein Apple Industry. 2011. (Images of America Ser.). (Illus.). 128p. pap. 21.99 *(978-0-7385-8173-6(9))* Arcadia Publishing.
Wheatland Historical Society. Wheatland. 2009. (Images of America Ser.). (ENG., Illus.). 128p. pap. 21.99 *(978-0-7385-6977-2(1))* Arcadia Publishing.
White, Michael D. Port of Long Beach. 2009. (Images of America Ser.). (ENG., Illus.). 128p. pap. 21.99 *(978-0-7385-6985-7(2))* Arcadia Publishing.
White, Mike. Afoot & Afield - Reno-Tahoe: A Comprehensive Hiking Guide. 2006. (Afoot & Afield Ser.). (ENG., Illus.). 384p. per. 19.95 *(978-0-89997-333-3(7))* Wilderness Pr.
Whitehead III, Jerry. Tuolumne City. 2012. (Images of America Ser.). (ENG., Illus.). 128p. pap. 21.99 ***(978-0-7385-8918-3(7))*** Arcadia Publishing.
Wicken, Ingrid P. Skiing in Southern California. 2007. (Images of America Ser.). (Illus.). 127p. per. 19.99 *(978-0-7385-5558-3(1))* Arcadia Publishing.
Wilentz, Amy. I Feel Earthquakes More Often Than They Happen: Coming to California in the Age of Schwarzenegger. 2007. (ENG.). 352p. pap. 21.99 *(978-0-7432-6440-2(1))* Simon & Schuster.
Wilkerson, Lyn. Slow Travels-California & Nevada. 2010. 327p. pap. 24.99 *(978-0-557-60764-8(7))* Lulu Enterprises Inc.
Willard, Steve & LaValle, Ed. San Diego Police: Case Files. 2012. (Images of America Ser.). (ENG., Illus.). 128p. pap. 21.99 ***(978-0-7385-9548-1(9))*** Arcadia Publishing.
Williams, Gregory L. California State University, Dominguez Hills. 2010. (Campus History Ser.). (ENG., Illus.). 128p. pap. 21.99 *(978-0-7385-8005-0(8))* Arcadia Publishing.
Willis, Barbara & The Escalon Historical Society. Escalon. 2008. (Images of America Ser.). (ENG., Illus.). 128p. pap. 21.99 *(978-0-7385-5903-2(2))* Arcadia Publishing.
Wilson, David Stark, photos by. Above All: Mount Whitney & California's Highest Peaks. 2008. 144p. 35.00 *(978-1-59714-107-9(0))* Heyday.
Winn, Mary Bryner. Corona. (Then & Now Ser.). (ENG., Illus.). 2012. 96p. pap. 21.99 ***(978-0-7385-9313-5(3))*** 2006. 128p. per. 21.99 *(978-0-7385-4672-8(0))* Arcadia Publishing.
Wood III, Thomas N. Saratoga. 2010. (Postcard History Ser.). (Illus.). 128p. pap. 21.99 *(978-0-7385-7327-4(2))* Arcadia Publishing.
Woods, Daniel B. Sixteen Months at the Gold Diggings. 2010. 228p. pap. 25.75 *(978-1-145-22492-6(X))* BiblioBazaar.
—Sixteen Months at the Gold Diggings. 2009. 138p. pap. *(978-0-217-79232-5(4))* Books LLC.
—Sixteen Months at the Gold Diggings. 210p. 2010. pap. 19.96 *(978-1-166-97227-1(5))* 2009. 39.95 *(978-1-120-79681-3(4))* 2009. pap. 24.95 *(978-1-120-70852-6(4))* Kessinger Publishing, LLC.
Woods, Samuel D. Lights & Shadows of Life on the Pacific Coast. 2009. 240p. pap. *(978-1-151-27648-3(0))* Books LLC.
—Lights & Shadows of Life on the Pacific Coast. 2007. (ENG.). 482p. 53.95 *(978-0-548-01829-3(4))* Kessinger Publishing, LLC.
Wright, Cynthia J. & Cox-Finney, Judy. Lemoore. 2010. (Images of America Ser.). (Illus.). 128p. pap. 21.99 *(978-0-7385-8154-5(2))* Arcadia Publishing.
Yasuda, Anita. Coastal Ghosts of Southern California. 2009. 176p. pap. 14.99 *(978-0-7643-3150-3(7))* Schiffer Publishing, Ltd.
—Haunted Monterey Peninsula. 2009. 160p. pap. 14.99 *(978-0-7643-3151-0(5))* Schiffer Publishing, Ltd.
Yogi, Stan, et al. Highway 99: A Literary Journey Through California's Great Central Valley. 2007. (Illus.). 545p. per. *(978-1-59714-067-6(8)*, Great Valley Bks.) Heyday.
Young, Alison. Orange Crate Labels of Orange County, California. Ball, Guy, ed. 2008. (Illus.). 48p. 14.00 *(978-0-9797619-1-1(3))* Santa Ana Historical Preservation Society.
Yucaipa Valley Historical Society. Yucaipa: 1940s-1980s. 2009. (Images of America Ser.). (Illus.). 128p. pap. 21.99 *(978-0-7385-7080-8(X))* Arcadia Publishing.
Zaverukha, Lydia B. & Bogdan, Nina. Russian San Francisco. 2009. (Images of America Ser.). (Illus.). 128p. pap. 21.99 *(978-0-7385-7167-6(9))* Arcadia Publishing.

CALIFORNIA—DIRECTORIES

Dershem, Larry D. California Legal Research Handbook. 2nd ed. 2008. pap. *(978-0-8377-1531-5(8))* Hein, William S. & Co., Inc.
Fleming, E. J., compiled by. The Movieland Directory: Nearly 30,000 Addresses of Celebrity Homes, Film Locations & Historical Sites in the Los Angeles Area, 1900-Present. alt. ed. 2010. (ENG., Illus.). 528p. pap. 95.00 *(978-0-7864-4337-6(5))* McFarland & Co., Inc. Pubs.
Gorman, Brian, compiled by. Gorman's 2007 Northern California Publicity Guide. 2007. 120p. 59.95 *(978-0-9794959-0-8(3))* Gormans Guides.
Harris InfoSource Staff. Directory of California Wholesalers & Service Companies. annuals Carlsen, Frances L., ed. rev. ed. 179.00 *(978-1-55600-708-8(6))* Harris InfoSource.
—Southern California Business Directory & Buyers Guide. annuals Carlsen, Frances L., ed. rev. ed. 179.00 *(978-1-55600-714-9(0))* Harris InfoSource.
Hollywood Creative Directory Staff. Hollywood Creative Directory. 64th ed. 2008. 475p. pap. 64.95 *(978-1-928936-66-4(0))* Hollywood Creative Directory.
Hollywood Creative Directory Staff, creator. Blu-Book Production Directory. rev. ed. 2007. (Hollywood Reporter Blu-Book Production Directory Ser.). (Illus.). 480p. per. 74.95 *(978-1-928936-55-8(5))* Hollywood Creative Directory.
—Hollywood Representation Directory. 35th ed. 2008. (Hollywood Representation Directory Ser.). Orig. Title: Hollywood Agents & Manager's Directory. (Illus.). 440p. pap. 64.95 *(978-1-928936-65-7(2))* Hollywood Creative Directory.
Hollywood Creative Directory Staff, ed. Hollywood Creative Directory. 63rd ed. 2008. (Hollywood Creative Directory Ser.). (Illus.). 472p. pap. 64.95 *(978-1-928936-64-0(4))* Hollywood Creative Directory.
—Hollywood Distribution Directory. 19th ed. 2008. 450p. 64.95 *(978-1-928936-67-1(9))* Hollywood Creative Directory.
MDR School Directories, 2006-07: California, 51 vols. 29th ed. 2006. 766p. 102.00 *(978-1-57953-489-9(9))* Market Data Retrieval.

Rainbow Resource Directory - Riverside & San Bernardino Counties. 2007. pap. (978-1-58012-120-0(9)) James Publishing, Inc.

Rich's Everyday Sales Prospecting Directory to San Mateo County: 2007 Edition. 2006. ring bd. 179.00 (978-0-914189-98-5(0)) Rich's Business Directories.

Rich's Everyday Sales Prospecting Directory to Santa Clara County: 2007 Edition. 2006. ring bd. 195.00 (978-1-934228-01-2(X)) Rich's Business Directories.

Rich's High Tech Business Guide to Southern California: 2009-07 Edition. 2006. ring bd. 350.00 (978-1-934228-03-6(6)) Rich's Business Directories.

Taliaferro, Lisa. Bargain Beaters: The Handbook for Saving Money in North County & San Diego. (Illus.). 120p. (Orig.). per. 9.95 (978-0-9633958-0-1(7)) Bargain Beaters.

Thornton, Meg Malpaya, ed. Asian American & Pacific Islander Community Directory: For Los Angeles & Orange Counties 2008. 10th ed. 2008. (ENG.). 360p. pap. 20.00 (978-0-934052-44-3(1)) Univ. of California, Los Angeles, Asian American Studies Ctr.

2007 Directory of California Manufacturers. 2007. per. 208.00 (978-1-58202-440-0(5)) Manufacturers' News, Inc.

2008/2009 Directory Justice Agencies CA, HI, NV. 2008. 490p. pap. 24.99 (978-1-56325-124-5(8)) Lawtech Publishing Co., Ltd.

CALIFORNIA—ECONOMIC CONDITIONS

Bauman, Robert. Race & the War on Poverty: From Watts to East L. A. 2008. (Race & Culture in the American West Ser.). (ENG., Illus.). 192p. (C). 34.95 (978-0-8061-3965-4(X)) Univ. of Oklahoma Pr.

Bohn, Sarah & Schiff, Eric. The Great Recession & Distribution of Income in California. 2011. **(978-1-58213-148-1(1))** Public Policy Institute of California.

Cleland, Robert Glass & Hardy, Osgood. March of Industry: California. 2007. (ENG.). 332p. 45.95 (978-0-548-01535-3(X)) Kessinger Publishing, LLC.

Dixon, Lloyd & Sorensen, Paul. Balancing Environment & Development Amid Rapid Urban Growth: Costs, Revenues, & Benefits of the Western Riverside County Multiple Species Habitat Conservation Plan. 2008. 270p. pap. 37.00 (978-0-8330-4609-3(8), mg-816) RAND Corp., The.

Elkind, Sarah S. How Local Politics Shape Federal Policy: Business, Power, & the Environment in Twentieth-Century Los Angeles. 2011. (Luther H. Hodges Jr. & Luther H. Hodges Sr. Series on Business, Society, & the State Ser.). (ENG., Illus.). 280p. 45.00 (978-0-8078-3489-3(0)) Univ. of North Carolina Pr.

Ferris, John Alexander. The Financial Economy of the United States Illustrated. 2009. (Illus.). 294p. pap. (978-1-4588-7659-1(4)) Books LLC.

—The Financial Economy of the United States Illustrated. 2006. (Illus.). 436p. per. 26.99 (978-1-4255-4734-9(6)) MPublishing.

Field, Mona & Kennedy, Brian. The People & Promise of California. 2007. (Longman Topics Ser.). (ENG.). 288p. (C). per. 23.60 (978-0-321-43489-0(7)) Longman Publishing Group.

Flanigan, James. Smile Southern California, You're the Center of the Universe: The Economy & People of a Global Region. 2009. (ENG., Illus.). 216p. 27.95 (978-0-8047-5625-9(2), Stanford General Bks.) Stanford Univ. Pr.

Garoogian, David, ed. Profiles of California 2010. 2nd rev. ed. 2010. pap. 149.00 (978-1-59237-559-2(6)) Grey Hse. Publishing.

Gilmore, Ruth Wilson. Golden Gulag: Prisons, Surplus, Crisis, & Opposition in Globalizing California. 2006. (American Crossroads Ser.: Vol. 21). (Illus.). 388p. 55.00 (978-0-520-22256-4(3)); per. 24.95 (978-0-520-24201-2(7)) Univ. of California Pr.

Gonzales, Anne. Stockton: Renewed, Revitalized, Redefined. 2008. 59.50 (978-1-882933-09-9(5)) Cherbo Publishing Group, Inc.

González, Ignacio, comment. California Real Estate Economics. 2010. (ENG.). 564p. pap. 37.35 (978-1-4277-9214-3(3)) Kaplan Publishing.

Heyday Books, creator. Our Valley, Our Choice: Building a Livable Future for the San Joaquin. 2007. (Great Valley Ser.). (Illus.). 112p. per. 17.95 (978-1-59714-058-4(9)) Heyday.

Hittell, John Shertzer. The Resources of California, Comprising Agriculture, Mining, Geography, Climate, Commerce, etc etc & the Past & Future Development of the State. 2006. 484p. per. 29.99 (978-1-4255-5303-6(6)) MPublishing.

Icon Group International, Inc. Staff, compiled by. The 2006 Economic & Product Market Databook for Long Beach, United States. 2006. 618p. ring bd. 95.00 (978-0-497-80879-2(X)) Icon Group International, Inc.

—The 2006 Economic & Product Market Databook for Los Angeles , United States. 2006. 618p. ring bd. 95.00 (978-0-497-80880-8(3)) Icon Group International, Inc.

—The 2006 Economic & Product Market Databook for San Diego , United States. 2006. 618p. ring bd. 95.00 (978-0-497-81417-5(X)) Icon Group International, Inc.

—The 2006 Economic & Product Market Databook for San Jose, United States. 2006. 618p. ring bd. 95.00 (978-0-497-81422-9(6)) Icon Group International, Inc.

Johnson, Hans P., et al. The Inland Empire in 2015. 2008. (Illus.). xviii, 121p. (978-1-58213-128-3(7)) Public Policy Institute of California.

Light, Melanie & Light, Ken, photos by. Valley of Shadows & Dreams. 2012. **(978-1-59714-172-7(0))** Heyday.

Lowenthal, Abraham F. Global California: Rising to the Cosmopolitan Challenge. 2009. (ENG., Illus.). 240p. 60.00 (978-0-8047-6226-7(0)) Stanford Univ. Pr.

McCormick, Thomas P. Loma Prieta Earthquake: Collapse of the Bay Bridge & the Cypress Viaduct. 2007. (Illus.). 36p. (C). reprint ed. pap. 15.00 (978-1-4223-1589-7(4)) DIANE Publishing Co.

Moffat, Amy. 2020: Visions for the Central Valley. 2010. pap. 12.95 (978-1-59714-133-8(X)) Heyday.

Sackman, Douglas Cazaux. Orange Empire: California & the Fruits of Eden. 2007. (Illus.). 386p. per. 27.95 (978-0-520-25167-0(9)) Univ. of California Pr.

Santos, Kristen. Turlock: A Pictorial History, 1950-2005. 2007. (978-1-57864-425-4(9)) Donning Co. Pubs.

Schrag, Peter. California: America's High-Stakes Experiment. 2007. 328p. per. 21.95 (978-0-520-25405-3(8)) Univ. of California Pr.

Seabury, Seth A. & McLaren, Christopher F. The Frequency, Severity, & Economic: Consequences of Musculoskeletal Injuries to Firefighters in California. 2010. (ENG.). 96p. pap. 27.00 (978-0-8330-5002-1(8), mg-1018) RAND Corp., The.

Silverman, Victor & Glover, Laurie. California: On-the-Road Histories. 2011. (ENG., Illus.). 320p. pap. 22.00 (978-1-56656-809-8(9), Interlink Bks.) Interlink Publishing Group, Inc.

Sprague-Bentley, Jeannie. Carlsbad. 2009. (Images of America Ser.). (ENG., Illus.). 128p. pap. 21.99 (978-0-7385-6992-5(5)) Arcadia Publishing.

Stapleton. California Real Estate Principles 7E Update. 2010. (ENG.). 576p. pap. 49.18 (978-1-4277-2642-1(6)) Kaplan Publishing.

Stark, Julie. Yuba City, Our Home Town. 2008. (978-1-57864-498-8(4)) Donning Co. Pubs.

Starr, Kevin. Golden Dreams: California in an Age of Abundance, 1950-1963, 1 vol. (Americans & the California Dream Ser.). (ENG., Illus.). 576p. 2011. pap. 24.95 (978-0-19-983249-1(8)) 2009. 34.95 (978-0-19-515377-4(4)) Oxford Univ. Pr., Inc.

Thaler, John H. The Decline & Fall of California... & the Rise of Social Liberalism. 2007. 360p. pap. 24.95 (978-0-7414-4211-6(6)) Infinity Publishing.

Verge, Arthur. Paradise Transformed: Los Angeles During the Second World War. rev. ed. 2009. (ENG.). 190p. pap. 52.25 (978-0-7872-0531-7(1)) Kendall Hunt Publishing Co.

Westwick, Peter J. & Deverell, William, eds. Blue Sky Metropolis: The Aerospace Century in Southern California. 2012. (Western Histories Ser.). (ENG., Illus.). 278p. 44.95 **(978-0-87328-249-9(3))** Huntington Library Pr.

Winn, Ira. Small Town / Big Town: Growing Pains on California's Central Coast. 2010. 208p. pap. 16.95 (978-1-4502-0944-1(0)) iUniverse, Inc.

Zimmerman, Tom. Paradise Promoted: The Booster Campaign That Created Los Angeles, 1870-1930. 2008. (Illus.). 207p. 35.00 (978-1-883318-64-2(5)) Angel City Pr.

CALIFORNIA—GENEALOGY

California Genealogical Society Staff, contrib. by. The Ancestry of Theodore Timothy Judge & Ellen Sheehy Judge: Including the Families of Boland, Roussel, Harman, McMurphy, Kelley, Bohane, Chapin, Freiermuth, Taylor, Moore & Fameman. 2010. (Illus.). xx, 204p. **(978-0-9785694-9-5(0))** California Genealogical Society.

Chavez, Christina. Five Generations of a Mexican American Family in Los Angeles. 2007. (ENG., Illus.). 198p. 84.00 (978-0-7425-3881-8(8)); per. 28.95 (978-0-7425-3882-5(6)) Rowman & Littlefield Publishers, Inc.

Close, Barbara Ross & Deubler, Vernon A., compiled by. San Francisco Deaths,1865-1905: Abstracts from Surviving Civil Records, 4 vols. 2010. **(978-0-9785694-3-3(1)); (978-0-9785694-2-6(3)); (978-0-9785694-4-0(X)); (978-0-9785694-1-9(5))** California Genealogical Society.

Collins, Joyce L. & Herman, Audrey. Index & Abstracts of Wills, Sonoma County, California, 1850-1900. 2007. 215p. pap. 32.50 (978-0-7884-4492-0(1)) Heritage Bks.

Deubler, Vernon A., compiled by. San Francisco Probate 1906-1942: Register of Actions, 2. 2010. 2. (ENG.). 480p. pap. 38.00 (978-0-9785694-8-8(2)) Vol. I. 487p. pap. 38.00 (978-0-9785694-7-1(4)) California Genealogical Society.

Fetzer, Leland. The Cuyamacas: The Story of San Diego's High Country, 1772-2003. 2008. (978-0-932653-94-9(4)) Sunbelt Pubns., Inc.

Keister, Douglas, photos by. Forever L. A. A Field Guide to Los Angeles Area Cemeteries & Their Residents. 2010. (ENG., Illus.). 256p. pap. 19.99 (978-1-4236-0522-5(5)) Gibbs Smith, Publisher.

Lacy, Hermagene P. The Descendants of Frederick & Caroline Palenske of Wabaunsee County, Kansas. (Illus.). vii, 225p. 20.00 (978-0-938717-50-8(2)) Shumway Family History Services.

Lee, Bill & Lee, LaVonne, compiled by. OSWALD & OSWALT in parts of California. 2009. 64p. 16.95 (978-0-9818048-7-3(X)) Lee, Bill.

—ZUMWALT in parts of California & Texas. 2008. 78p. 18.95 (978-0-9818048-4-2(5)) Lee, Bill.

Moore, Dorothy Lord. Adventures of a California Woman in the Twentieth Century. McKnew, Janet Moore, ed. 2nd ed. 2011. 478p. per. 39.95 (978-1-932252-49-1(5)) Creative Continuum, Inc.

Mulholland, Catherine. Calabasas Girls: An Intimate History 1885-1912. 2008. 192p. pap. 16.95 (978-0-9700481-6-5(5)) Many Moons Pr.

Nelson, Robert L. Remembering Our Own: The Santa Cruz County Military Roll of Honor 1861-2010. 2010. (978-0-940283-21-3(2)) Museum of Art & History.

Ngai, Mae. The Lucky Ones: One Family & the Extraordinary Invention of Chinese America. 2010. (ENG., Illus.). 304p. 26.00 (978-0-618-65116-0(0)) Houghton Mifflin Harcourt Trade & Reference Pubs.

Nichols, Jeremy D. Potter's Field: The Chanate Historical Cemetery in Santa Rosa, California. 2009. 174p. pap. 26.00 (978-0-7884-5010-5(7)) Heritage Bks.

Nichols, Jeremy Dwight. Potter's Field: The Chanate Historic Cemetery in Santa Rosa, California: A History of the Old Sonoma County Cemetery: Plus a Biographical Record of Burials, 1881-1944. 2009. (Illus.). xxxiv, 139p. (978-0-7884-8202-1(5)) Heritage Bks.

Peterson, Nancy Simons. Raking the Ashes: Genealogical Strategies for Pre-1906 San Francisco Research. 2nd ed. 2011. (Illus.). xvi, 224p. pap. 25.00 **(978-0-9785694-5-7(8))** California Genealogical Society.

Pubols, Louise. The Father of All: The de la Guerra Family, Power, & Patriarchy in Mexican California. 2009. (Western Histories Ser.). (ENG., Illus.). 304p. 44.95 (978-0-87328-240-6(X)) Huntington Library Pr.

Rasmussen, Louis J. San Francisco Ship Passenger Lists. 2010. 292p. 45.00 (978-0-8063-5469-9(0)) Clearfield Co.

Santa Rosa Rural Cemetery Preservation Committee Staff, contrib. by. Santa Rosa Rural Cemetery, 1854-2007: A Listing of Burials in Fulkerson, Moke, Rural, & Stanley Cemeteries, Now Known Collectively As Santa Rosa Rural Cemetery. 2007. (Illus.). 224p. pap. 43.50 (978-0-7884-4181-3(7)) Heritage Bks.

Sonoma County Genealogical Society. Index to Vital Data in Local Newspapers of Sonoma County, California, Volume V: 1891-1899. 2007. pap. 50.00 (978-0-7884-4287-2(2)) Heritage Bks.

—Index to Vital Data in Local Newspapers of Sonoma County, California, Volume VI: 1900-1903. 2007. pap. 49.50 (978-0-7884-4358-9(5)) Heritage Bks.

—Index to Vital Data in Local Newspapers of Sonoma County, California, Volume VII: 1904-1906. 2008. pap. 46.50 (978-0-7884-4512-5(X)) Heritage Bks.

—Index to Vital Data in Local Newspapers of Sonoma County, California, Volume VIII: 1907-1909. 2009. pap. 49.50 (978-0-7884-4940-6(0)) Heritage Bks.

Weeks, Donna Tessandori. The Italians of Kern County. 2011. 552p. 34.99 **(978-1-4535-7252-8(X))**; pap. 23.99 **(978-1-4535-7251-1(1))** Xlibris Corp.

CALIFORNIA—GOLD DISCOVERIES

Badella, Robert. Gold Rush of Californi. 2009. 80p. pap. 15.95 (978-1-4490-0961-8(1)) AuthorHouse.

Bates, D. B. Incidents on Land & Water, or Four Years on the Pacific Coast Being a Narrative of the Burning of the Ships Nonantum, Humayoon & Fanchon, Togethe. 2006. 348p. per. 23.99 (978-1-4255-3504-9(6)) MPublishing.

Bidlack, Russell E. Letters Home: The Story of Ann Arbor's Forty-Niners. 2011. 66p. 36.95 **(978-1-258-03345-3(3))** Literary Licensing, LLC.

Bonsal, Stephen. Edward Fitzgerald Beale. 2009. 364p. 38.99 (978-1-117-27198-9(6)); (ENG.). 363p. pap. 31.75 (978-1-117-27199-6(4)) BiblioBazaar.

—Edward Fitzgerald Beale. 312p. reprint ed. 98.00 (978-0-7222-8987-7(1)) Library Reprints, Inc.

Buss, R. L. Spread Out Across the Lowering Sky. Buss, R. L., ed. 2006. 13.95 (978-0-9713360-3-2(2)) Sun Wolf Pr.

Chamberlain, Newell D. & Trabucco, J. J. The Call of Gold: True Tales on the Gold Road to Yosemite. 2011. 258p. 47.95 **(978-1-258-06746-5(3))** Literary Licensing, LLC.

Chambers, Ruth. The Weight of Gold: 1849 Gold Rush, California. 2009. 264p. pap. 14.49 (978-1-4389-9725-4(6)) AuthorHouse.

Chandonnet, Ann. Gold Rush Grub: From Turpentine Stew to Hoochinoo. 2006. (Illus.). 248p. pap. 24.95 (978-1-889963-95-2(X)) Univ. of Alaska Pr.

Church, Andrew. Memoirs of Andrew Smith Church: The Society of California Pioneers, V3, No. 4. 2011. 54p. 36.95 **(978-1-258-08905-4(X))** Literary Licensing, LLC.

Colorful Men Women & Tales of the Mother Lode. 2006. (Illus.). 275p. pap. 16.95 (978-0-9653428-3-4(2)) Irene, Jan Pubns.

Colton, Walter. Three Years in California by Rev Walter Colton. 2011. 472p. pap. 29.99 **(978-1-4255-8953-0(7))** MPublishing.

Cook, Elliott Wilkinson. Land Ho! the Original Diary of a Forty-Niner. Cook, Jane James, ed. 2011. 42p. 35.95 **(978-1-258-09134-7(8))** Literary Licensing, LLC.

Corbett, Christopher. The Poker Bride: The First Chinese in the Wild West. (ENG.). 240p. 2011. pap. 14.95 (978-0-8021-4527-7(2), Grove Pr.) 2010. 24.00 (978-0-8021-1909-4(3), Atlantic Monthly Pr.) Grove/Atlantic, Inc.

Coy, Owen Cochran. The Great Trek. McCarthy, John Russell, ed. 2007. (ENG.). 364p. per. 31.95 (978-0-548-45398-8(5)) Kessinger Publishing, LLC.

—The Great Trek. 2007. 368p. 39.95 (978-1-4344-9053-7(X)); (ENG.). per. 24.95 (978-1-4344-9054-4(8)) Wildside Pr., LLC. (Borgo Pr.).

Davies, J. Kenneth & Hansen, Lorin K. Mormon Gold: Mormons in the California Gold Rush, Contributing to the Development of California & the Monetary Solvency of Early Utah. 2nd ed. 2010. (ENG., Illus.). 460p. 59.95 (978-0-9830832-0-7(7)) Granite Mountain Publishing Co.

Delano, Alonzo. Life on the Plains & among the Diggings. 2009. (Native American Ser.). (ENG.). 398p. pap. 24.95 (978-1-4290-2241-5(8)) Applewood Bks.

—Life on the Plains & among the Diggings. 2009. 228p. pap. 19.66 (978-1-150-56847-3(X)) General Bks. LLC.

Evans, George. Mexican Gold Trail: The Journey of a Forty-Niner. Dumke, Glenn S., ed. 2006. (Huntington Library Classics Ser.). (Illus.). 340p. per. 24.95 (978-0-87328-222-2(1)) Huntington Library Pr.

Fracchia, Charles A. When the Water Came up to Montgomery Street: San Francisco During the Gold Rush. 2009. (978-1-57864-586-2(7)) Donning Co. Pubs.

Gillis, William R. Gold Rush Days with Mark Twain. (Illus.). reprint ed. 34.50 (978-0-404-02774-2(1)) AMS Pr., Inc.

Grunsky, Charles E. From Europe to California: Extracts from Letters of Charles Grunsky & His Wife Clotilde, 1844-1853. Grunsky, Clotilde, ed. Grunsky, C. E., tr. 2011. 42p. 35.95 **(978-1-258-03612-6(6))** Literary Licensing, LLC.

Gudde, Erwin G. California Gold Camps: A Geographical & Historical Dictionary of Camps, Towns, & Localities Where Gold Was Found & Mined; Wayside Stations & Trading Centers. Gudde, Elisabeth K., ed. 2009. pap. 39.95 (978-0-520-26144-0(5)) Univ. of California Pr.

Hambleton, Chalkley J. A Gold Hunter's Experience. 2009. 120p. 24.99 (978-1-113-74059-5(0)); pap. 19.75 (978-1-113-74053-3(1)); pap. 19.75 (978-1-113-74055-7(8)) BiblioBazaar.

—A Gold Hunter's Experience. 2009. 50p. pap. (978-1-4099-9016-1(8)) Dodo Pr.

Helper, Hinton Rowan. The Land of Gold Reality Versus Fiction. 2006. 304p. per. 23.99 (978-1-4255-2827-0(9)) MPublishing.

Johnson, Theodore. Sights in the Gold Region. 2011. 292p. pap. 18.95 (978-1-4290-4610-7(4)) Applewood Bks.

Klein, Robert F. Dubuque During the California Gold Rush: When the Midwest Went West. 2011. 160p. pap. 19.99 **(978-1-60949-491-9(1))** History Pr., The.

Knower, Daniel. The Adventures of a Forty Niner. 2007. (ENG.). 120p. 34.95 (978-0-548-00727-3(6)) Kessinger Publishing, LLC.

—The Adventures of a Forty-Niner. 2007. (Illus.). 104p. per. (978-1-4065-2929-6(X)) Dodo Pr.

Kull, Irving Stoddard. Gold Rush: Jerseymen in California. 2006. Orig. Title: New Brunswick Adventurers Of '49. 24p. 3.95 (978-1-58057-523-2(4), B25A3) Digital Antiquaria, Inc.

Leete, Harley M. Sketches of the Gold Country. 2006. (Illus.). pap. 15.95 (978-1-4286-5919-3(6)) Kessinger Publishing, LLC.

[Letts, John M.]. California Illustrated; Including a Description of the Panama & Nicaragua Routes by a Returned Californian. 2006. (Illus.). 324p. per. 23.99 (978-1-4255-3129-4(6)) MPublishing.

Manly, William Lewis. Death Valley In '49. 2008. 436p. 30.99 (978-0-554-33485-1(2)) 2008. 436p. 32.99 (978-0-554-24182-1(X)) 2007. 390p. pap. 25.99 (978-1-4264-5908-5(4)) 2007. (ENG.). 432p. pap. 28.99 (978-1-4264-5976-4(9)) BiblioBazaar.

—Death Valley In '49. 2009. 268p. pap. (978-1-4590-6638-0(3)) Books LLC.

—Death Valley In '49. 2009. (Illus.). 406p. pap. (978-1-4099-8788-8(4)) Dodo Pr.

—Death Valley In '49: An Important Chapter of California Pioneer History. 2007. (ENG.). 566p. 58.95 (978-0-548-01544-5(9)) Kessinger Publishing, LLC.

McKeeby, Lemuel Clarke. The Memoirs of Lemuel Clarke Mckeeby. 2011. 78p. 37.95 **(978-1-258-08904-7(1))** Literary Licensing, LLC.

Michalski, Henry, et al. Napa Valley's Jewish Heritage. 2012. (Images of America Ser.). (ENG., Illus.). 128p. pap. 21.99 **(978-0-7385-8898-8(9))** Arcadia Publishing.

Mulford, Prentice. Prentice Mulford's Story: Life by Land & Sea. 2007. 252p. per. 14.95 (978-1-60206-168-2(8)) Cosimo, Inc.

—Prentice Mulford's Story: Life by Land & Sea. 2007. 196p. per. 15.95 (978-1-4344-0103-8(0)) Wildside Pr., LLC.

Richards, Leonard L. The California Gold Rush & the Coming of the Civil War. 2008. (Vintage Civil War Library). (ENG., Illus.). 304p. pap. 14.95 (978-0-307-27757-2(7), Vintage) Knopf Doubleday Publishing Group.

Richards, Rand. Mud, Blood, & Gold: San Francisco In 1849. 2011. (Illus.). 288p. pap. 19.95 **(978-1-879367-07-4(6))** Heritage Hse. Pubs.

Rix, Alfred, et al. New England to Gold Rush California: The Journal of Alfred & Chastina W. Rix, 1849-1854. 2011. (ENG.). 356p. (C). 45.00 (978-0-87062-392-9(3), Clark, Arthur H. Co., The) Univ. of Oklahoma Pr.

Rosen, Fred. Gold! The Story of the 1848 Gold Rush & How It Shaped a Nation. 2006. (ENG., Illus.). 352p. per. 15.95 (978-1-56025-961-9(2)) Running Pr. Bk. Pubs.

Ross, Delmer G. The Bagdad Chase Mine & Its Ludlow & Southern Railway: The Quest for Gold in California's Mojave Desert. 2009. (Illus.). 204p. 109.95 (978-0-7734-4863-6(2)) Mellen, Edwin Pr., The.

Royce, Sarah. Across the Plains: Sarah Royce's Western Narrative. Jennifer Dawes, Adkison, ed. 2009. (Western Women's Voices Ser.). (ENG., Illus.). 136p. pap. 19.95 (978-0-8165-2726-7(1)) Univ. of Arizona Pr.

Stillson, Richard. Spreading the Word: A History of Information in the California Gold Rush. 2008. (ENG.). 284p. pap. 24.95 (978-0-8032-1827-7(3)) Univ. of Nebraska Pr.

Stone, Ted. Great Tales of the Gold Rush. (ENG.). 208p. pap. 16.95 (978-1-55105-242-7(3)) Lone Pine Publishing USA.

Sutter, John Augustus & Marshall, James W. The Sutter-Marshall Lease with the Yalesumney Indians for Monopoly of the Gold-Bearing Lands. 2011. 12p. pap. 35.95 **(978-1-258-09797-4(4))** Literary Licensing, LLC.

Taylor, Bayard. Eldorado; or, Adventures in the Path of Empire: Comprising A Voyage to California, Via Panama; Life in San Francisco & Monterey; Pictures of the Gol. 2006. 468p. per. 29.99 (978-1-4255-5174-2(2)); 460p. per. 29.99 (978-1-4255-5132-2(7)) MPublishing.

Taylor, Henry. From Lead Mines to Gold Fields: Memories of an Incredibly Long Life. Parman, Donald L., ed. 2006. (ENG., Illus.). 230p. pap. 24.95 (978-0-8032-9461-5(1)) Univ. of Nebraska Pr.

Taylor, R. R. Seeing the Elephant: Letters of R. R. Taylor, Forty-Niner. Caughey, John Walton, ed. 2011. 122p. 40.95 **(978-1-258-00944-1(7))** Literary Licensing, LLC.

Vail, Robert W. G., ed. California Letters of the Gold Rush Period: Proceedings of the American Antiquarian Society V47, No. 1. 2011. 42p. 35.95 **(978-1-258-06939-1(3))** Literary Licensing, LLC.

White, Stewart Edward. The Forty-Niners: A Chronicle of the California Trail & el Dorado. 2008. 280p. 25.99 (978-0-559-79181-9(X)) 2008. 280p. pap. 26.75 (978-0-559-79178-9(X)) 2007. 154p. pap. 19.99 (978-1-4346-6078-7(8)) 2007. (ENG.). 164p. pap. 21.99 (978-1-4346-6079-4(6)) BiblioBazaar.

—The Forty-Niners: A Chronicle of the California Trail & el Dorado. 2007. 140p. per. (978-1-4065-6625-3(X)) Dodo Pr.

—The Forty-Niners: A Chronicle of the California Trail & El Dorado. (Chronicles of America Ser.). 273p. reprint ed. 98.00 (978-0-7222-7141-4(7)) Library Reprints, Inc.

Woods, Daniel B. Sixteen Months at the Gold Diggings. 2010. 228p. pap. 25.75 (978-1-145-22492-6(X)) BiblioBazaar.

—Sixteen Months at the Gold Diggings. 2009. 138p. pap. *(978-0-217-79232-5(4))* Books LLC.

—Sixteen Months at the Gold Diggings. 210p. 2010. pap. 19.96 *(978-1-166-97227-1(5))* 2009. 39.95 *(978-1-120-79681-3(4))* 2009. pap. 24.95 *(978-1-120-70852-6(4))* Kessinger Publishing, LLC.

CALIFORNIA—GUIDEBOOKS

Arnold, Jim & Lamis, Ingrid. Wine Clubs of Sonoma County: A Guide to the Pleasures & Perks of Belonging, 1 vol. 2007. (ENG., Illus.). 232p. pap. 22.95 *(978-1-58980-432-6(5))* Pelican Publishing Co., Inc.

Badger, K. Reka & Crabtree, Cheryl. California Directory of Fine Wineries: Central Coast. 2009. (California Directory of Fine Wineries Ser.). (ENG., Illus.). 144p. 19.95 *(978-0-9724993-0-9(X))* Wine Hse. Pr.

Badger, K. Reka & Olmstead, Marty. The California Directory of Fine Wineries: Napa, Sonoma, Mendocino. 2011. (California Directory of Fine Wineries Ser.). (ENG., Illus.). 160p. 19.95 *(978-0-9724993-5-4(0))* Wine Hse. Pr.

Baker, Christopher P. Palm Springs & Desert Resorts. 2008. (Great Destinations Ser.). (ENG.). 288p. pap. 18.95 *(978-1-58157-048-9(1)*, 157048) Countryman Pr.

Bakus, Gerald J. Natural History of California. 2011. 331p. pap. 94.95 ***(978-1-4327-7639-8(8))*** Outskirts Pr., Inc.

Barrett, Steven. Disneyland's Hidden Mickeys: A Field Guide to the Disneyland Resort's Best-Kept Secrets. 3rd rev. ed. 2011. (ENG.). 129p. pap. 9.95 *(978-1-887140-93-5(X))* Intrepid Traveler, The.

Bartlett, Serena. Northern California Wine Country: Green Road Trips. 2009. (GrassRoutes Travel Ser.). (ENG., Illus.). 288p. pap. 16.95 *(978-1-57061-607-5(8))* Sasquatch Bks.

Bates, Colleen Dunn, et al. The Unofficial Guide to California with Kids. 7th ed. 2010. (Unofficial Guides: 265). (ENG., Illus.). 448p. pap. 19.99 *(978-0-470-62107-3(9)*, Frommers) Wiley, John & Sons, Inc.

Bauer, Linda & Bauer, Steve. Recipes from Historic California: A Restaurant Guide & Cookbook. 2008. (Illus.). x, 318p. 24.95 *(978-1-58979-400-9(1)*, 1288743) Taylor Trade Publishing.

Baylor, Katherine. California Rocks. 2010. 0128p. pap. 16.00 *(978-0-87842-565-5(9))* Mountain Pr. Publishing Co., Inc.

Benson, Sam. Coastal California, 70 vols. 4th rev. ed. 2012. (Regional Guide Ser.). (ENG., Illus.). 536p. pap. 19.99 ***(978-1-74179-981-1(3))*** Lonely Planet Pubns.

Benson, Sara. California, 101 vols. 6th rev. ed. 2012. (Regional Guide Ser.). (ENG., Illus.). 792p. pap. 23.99 ***(978-1-74179-695-7(4))*** Lonely Planet Pubns.

—California. 2006. (Real Readers en español Ser.). (ENG.). 32p. (gr. 4-8). pap. 10.60 *(978-1-4042-7574-4(6)*, Rosen Classroom Bks. & Materials) Rosen Publishing Group, Inc., The.

Benti, Wynne. Favorite Dog Hikes: Death Valley to Yosemite. 2006. (Illus.). 288p. pap. 15.95 *(978-1-893343-13-9(8))* Spotted Dog Pr., Inc.

Best, Jennifer. Best Family Adventures: Santa Barbara County. 2010. (Illus.). pap. 18.95 *(978-0-9769050-2-8(7))* Pen & Pad Publishing.

Bigley, Michele. Northern California. 2009. (Explorer's Complete Ser.). (ENG., Illus.). 560p. pap. 21.95 *(978-0-88150-832-1(2)*, 150832) Countryman Pr.

Binshtock, Avital. Napa & Sonoma. 2nd ed. 2010. (Frommer's Day by Day - Pocket Ser.: 108). (ENG., Illus.). 228p. pap. 13.99 *(978-0-470-50379-9(3)*, Frommers) Wiley, John & Sons, Inc.

Birnbaum Travel Guides Staff. Birnbaum's Disneyland Resort 2011. 2010. (ENG.). 144p. pap. 14.95 *(978-1-4231-2377-4(8)*, Disney Editions) Disney Pr.

Bisbort, Alan & Puterbaugh, Parke. California Beaches: The Best Places to Swim, Play, Eat, & Stay. 2009. (Moon Handbooks Ser.). (ENG., Illus.). 576p. pap. 21.95 *(978-1-56691-614-1(3))* Westview Pr.

—Ventura & Santa Barbara Beaches. 2009. (Moon Spotlight Ser.). (ENG., Illus.). 70p. pap. 6.95 *(978-1-59880-333-4(6))* Avalon Travel Publishing.

Bishop, Greg, et al. California: Your Travel Guide to California's Local Legends & Best Kept Secrets. 2009. (Weird Ser.). (ENG., Illus.). 304p. pap. 14.95 *(978-1-4027-6683-1(1))* Sterling Publishing Co., Inc.

Bliss, Christopher, photos by. California. 2008. (ENG., Illus.). 144p. 15.00 *(978-3-8327-9241-1(4))* teNeues Publishing Co.

Bob, Lorentzen. Hikers Hip Pkt GT Mendo 4th. 2007. 240p. pap. 17.00 *(978-0-939431-33-5(5))* Bored Feet Pr.

Bondurant, Julie & Thompson, Laura. Trail Planning for California Communities. 2009. (ENG., Illus.). 430p. pap. 95.00 net. *(978-0-923956-81-3(6))* Solano Pr. Bks.

Borsting, Elizabeth. Open Road's Best of Northern California: Your Passport to the Perfect Trip! - Includes One-Day, Weekend, One-Week & Two-Week Trips. 2008. (ENG., Illus.). 224p. pap. 14.95 *(978-1-59360-102-7(6))* Open Road Publishing.

—Open Road's Best of Southern California. 2007. (ENG., Illus.). 288p. pap. 14.95 *(978-1-59360-094-5(1))* Open Road Publishing.

—Orange County. 2010. (Insiders' Guide Ser.). (ENG., Illus.). 200p. pap. 18.95 *(978-0-7627-5961-3(5)*, Insiders' Guide) Globe Pequot Pr., The.

Brady, Patrick. Bicycling Los Angeles County: A Guide to Great Road Bike Rides. 2007. (Bicycling Ser.). (ENG., Illus.). 240p. per. 15.95 *(978-0-89732-950-7(3))* Menasha Ridge Pr., Inc.

Brenner, Jan & Harrington, Jolene Rae. Here Comes the Guide Southern California: Wedding Locations & Services. 2011. (ENG., Illus.). 700p. pap. 23.95 ***(978-1-885355-19-5(X))*** Hopscotch Pr.

Brenner, Jan, et al. Here Comes the Guide, Northern California: Wedding Locations & Services. 2011. (ENG., Illus.). 800p. pap. 23.95 *(978-1-885355-17-1(3))* Hopscotch Pr.

Brenner, Maria & Siegel, Kathy Lynn. Veg Out! Vegetarian Guide to Southern California. 2nd ed. 2008. (ENG., Illus.). 192p. pap. *(978-1-4236-0272-9(2))* Gibbs Smith, Publisher.

British Auto Association & Holmes, Robert. Frommer's 25 Great Drives in California. 8th ed. 2011. (Best Loved Driving Tours Ser.). (ENG.). 208p. pap. 19.99 *(978-0-470-90446-6(1)*, Frommers) Wiley, John & Sons, Inc.

Brooks, Patricia & Brooks, Jonathan. Laid to Rest in California: A Guide to the Cemeteries & Grave Sites of the Rich & Famous. 2006. (Insiders' Guide Ser.). (ENG., Illus.). 352p. per. 15.95 *(978-0-7627-4101-4(5))* Globe Pequot Pr., The.

Brown, Ann Marie. The Creaky Knees Guide Northern California: The 80 Best Easy Hikes. 2011. (ENG., Illus.). 320p. pap. 18.95 *(978-1-57061-741-6(4))* Sasquatch Bks.

—Moon Northern California Waterfalls. 2011. (Moon Outdoors Ser.). (ENG.). 384p. pap. 16.99 *(978-1-59880-547-5(9))* Avalon Travel Publishing.

—Moon Yosemite. 2011. (Moon Handbooks Ser.). (ENG., Illus.). 296p. pap. 17.99 *(978-1-59880-749-3(8))* Avalon Travel Publishing.

Brown, Ann Marie & Scott, Liz Hamill. Coastal California. 3rd ed. 2009. (Moon Handbooks Ser.). (ENG.). 528p. pap. 19.95 *(978-1-56691-997-5(5))* Westview Pr.

Brown, June Eveleigh. Karen Brown's California 2010: Exceptional Places to Stay & Itineraries. 2010. (ENG.). 272p. pap. 19.95 *(978-1-933810-69-0(6))* Karen Brown's Guides.

Browning, Peter. Exploring the Back Roads: 28 Day Trips in the Greater Bay Area. 2006. (Illus.). 125p. per. 12.95 *(978-0-944220-21-4(5))* Great West Bks.

Bruce, Kevin. Large Art in Small Places: Discovering the California Mural Towns. 2009. (ENG., Illus.). 192p. pap. 24.95 *(978-1-58008-880-0(5))* Ten Speed Pr.

Brundige, Don & Brundige, Sharron. Cycling Orange County: 58 Rides with Detailed Maps & Elevation Contours. 3rd ed. 2006. (Illus.). 205p. per. 14.95 *(978-0-932653-80-2(4))* Sunbelt Pubns., Inc.

Bryan, T. Scott & Tucker-Bryan, Betty. Death Valley National Park. 2nd ed. 2009. (ENG., Illus.). 496p. pap. 23.95 *(978-0-87081-962-9(3))* Univ. Pr. of Colorado.

Buchholz, Sue & Woolridge, Edna. Destination Disneyland Resort with Disabilities: A Guidebook & Planner for Families & Folks with Disabilities traveling to Disneyland Resort Park & Disney California Adventure Park. 2011. (ENG.). 152p. pap. 14.95 ***(978-1-60037-934-5(6))*** Morgan James Publishing.

Caldwell, Peter & Caldwell, Donald. Desolation Wilderness, North: A Photographic Tour. 2008. (Illus.). 94p. pap. *(978-0-9626124-4-2(8))* Taote Publishing.

California Coastal Commission. Beaches & Parks from Monterey to Ventura: Experience the California Coast. 2007. (Experience the California Coast Ser.). (Illus.). 318p. pap. 26.95 *(978-0-520-24949-3(6))* Univ. of California Pr.

California Coastal Commission Staff. Beaches & Parks in Southern California: Counties Included - Los Angeles, Orange, San Diego. 2009. (Experience the California Coast Ser.). (ENG., Illus.). 352p. pap. 26.95 *(978-0-520-25852-5(5))* Univ. of California Pr.

California Native Plant Society, contrib. by. Wildflowers of Nevada & Placer Counties, California. 2007. (Illus.). 480p. pap. 29.95 *(978-0-943460-48-2(4))* California Native Plant Society.

Cavalieri, Nate. Northern California, 68 vols. 2012. (Regional Guide Ser.). (ENG., Illus.). 584p. (Orig.). pap. 19.99 ***(978-1-74220-590-8(9))*** Lonely Planet Pubns.

Cervin, Michael. Moon Santa Barbara & the Central Coast. 2010. (Moon Handbooks Ser.). (ENG., Illus.). 356p. pap. 16.95 *(978-1-59880-648-9(3))* Avalon Travel Publishing.

—Moon Spotlight Cambria & San Simeon: Including Hearst Castle & Morro Bay. 2011. (Moon Spotlight Ser.). (ENG.). 73p. pap. 7.99 *(978-1-59880-926-8(1))* Avalon Travel Publishing.

Chalmers, Claudine & Grass Valley Downtown Association. Grass Valley. 2006. (Images of America Ser.). (ENG., Illus.). 128p. per. 21.99 *(978-0-7385-4697-1(6))* Arcadia Publishing.

Chase, J. Smeaton. California Coast Trails. 2010. 386p. pap. 33.75 *(978-1-175-05117-2(9))* 2009. 380p. 38.99 *(978-1-116-31562-2(9))* 2009. 380p. pap. 32.75 *(978-1-116-31565-3(3))* 2009. (ENG.). 378p. pap. 26.99 *(978-1-116-31566-0(1)*, BiblioLife) BiblioBazaar.

—California Desert Trails. 2009. (ENG.). 469p. 42.99 *(978-1-116-99622-7(7))*; (ENG.). 469p. 35.99 *(978-1-116-99623-4(5))*; (ENG.). 469p. pap. 28.99 *(978-1-116-99627-2(8)*, BiblioLife); (ENG.). 469p. pap. 30.99 *(978-1-116-99626-5(X)*, BiblioLife); (ENG.). 469p. pap. 36.75 *(978-1-116-99625-8(1))*; 470p. pap. 37.75 *(978-1-116-99624-1(3))* BiblioBazaar.

—California Desert Trails. 2008. 477p. 53.95 *(978-1-4365-7011-4(5))* 2007. (ENG.). 480p. per. 38.95 *(978-0-548-76366-7(6))* Kessinger Publishing, LLC.

Chase, J Smeaton & Chase, J. Smeaton. California Desert Trails. 2010. 476p. pap. 37.75 *(978-1-149-31207-0(6))* BiblioBazaar.

Coloma, Cindy. Northern California. 4th ed. 2008. (Best in Tent Camping Ser.). (ENG., Illus.). 204p. pap. 14.95 *(978-0-89732-674-2(1))* Menasha Ridge Pr., Inc.

Copp, Nelson. Cycling Palm Springs Region. 2008. 160p. pap. 17.95 *(978-0-932653-93-2(6))* Sunbelt Pubns., Inc.

Cosmic Debris Etc., Inc. Staff, et al. Hooked on Hiking: Northern California - 50 Hiking Adventures. 2009. (ENG.). 50p. (Orig.). 16.95 *(978-0-8118-6636-1(X))* Chronicle Bks. LLC.

Costello, Mike. Fly Fishing the California Delta. 2009. (No Nonsense Fly Fishing Guidebooks Ser.). (ENG., Illus.). 192p. 49.95 *(978-1-892469-23-6(5))* No Nonsense Guides.

Courtney, Tom. Walkabout Northern California: Hiking Inn to Inn. 2011. (ENG., Illus.). 224p. pap. 16.95 *(978-0-89997-658-7(1))* Wilderness Pr.

Critser, Greg. National Geographic Traveler: California. 3rd rev. ed. 2008. (ENG., Illus.). 400p. 27.95 *(978-1-4262-0324-4(1)*, National Geographic) National Geographic Society.

Crooks, Pamela. Discover Balboa Park: A Complete Guide to America's Greatest Urban Park. 2nd ed. 2007. pap. 14.95 *(978-0-9706219-5-5(7))* Ridgway Park Publishing.

Cunningham, Bill & Cunningham, Polly. Best Easy Day Hikes Joshua Tree National Park. 2nd ed. 2010. (Best Easy Day Hikes Ser.). (ENG., Illus.). 96p. pap. 9.95 *(978-0-7627-6053-4(2)*, Falcon Guides) Globe Pequot Pr., The.

—Hiking Anza-Borrego Desert State Park: 25 Day & Overnight Hikes. 2007. (Hiking Ser.). (ENG., Illus.). 96p. per. 12.95 *(978-0-7627-4462-6(6)*, Falcon Guides) Globe Pequot Pr., The.

—Hiking California's Desert Parks: A Guide to the Greatest Hiking Adventures in Anza-Borrego, Joshua Tree, Mojave, & Death Valley. 2nd ed. 2006. (Regional Hiking Ser.). (ENG., Illus.). 416p. per. 19.95 *(978-0-7627-3545-7(7)*, Falcon Guides) Globe Pequot Pr., The.

—Hiking Death Valley National Park: 36 Day & Overnight Hikes. 2007. (Falcon Guides Hiking Ser.). (ENG., Illus.). 144p. per. 12.95 *(978-0-7627-4463-3(4)*, Falcon Guides) Globe Pequot Pr., The.

—Hiking Joshua Tree National Park: 38 Day & Overnight Hikes. 2007. (Where to Hike Ser.). (ENG., Illus.). 144p. per. 12.95 *(978-0-7627-4464-0(2)*, Falcon Guides) Globe Pequot Pr., The.

—Hiking Mojave National Preserve: 15 Day & Overnight Hikes. 2007. (Where to Hike Ser.). (ENG., Illus.). 96p. per. 12.95 *(978-0-7627-4465-7(0)*, Falcon Guides) Globe Pequot Pr., The.

Dawson, Doug. Northern California's Best 100 Public Golf Courses. 2009. pap. *(978-1-61623-281-8(1))* Independent Pub.

Del Rosso, Laura. Northern California. 2008. (Great Escapes Ser.). (ENG., Illus.). 192p. pap. 16.95 *(978-0-88150-783-6(0)*, 150783) Countryman Pr.

DeLorme, creator. California Atlas & Gazetteer. 2008. (Delorme Atlas & Gazetteer Ser.). 160p. 24.95 *(978-0-89933-383-0(4))* DeLorme.

DeMund, Tom. Feather River Country Adventure Trails. 2nd ed. 330p. pap. 19.95 *(978-0-9679740-1-9(1))* Know DeFeet Publishing Co.

—Feather River Country Adventure Trails: 101 Fun Hikes Within the Region of the Feather River Upper Middle Fork, the Lakes Basin, & the North Yuba River. 4th ed. 2008. (Illus.). 320p. pap. 19.95 *(978-0-9679740-3-3(8))* Know DeFeet Publishing Co.

Denton, Bradley & Denton, Kristine. Outdoor Guide to Palos Verdes Peninsula. 2nd ed. 2007. 224p. pap. 19.95 *(978-0-932653-86-4(3))* Sunbelt Pubns., Inc.

Deutsch, Rick. One Best Hike: Yosemite's Half Dome. 2nd ed. 2012. (One Best Hike Ser.). (ENG., Illus.). 176p. pap. 14.95 ***(978-0-89997-674-7(3))*** Wilderness Pr.

Dickey, Jeff & Rough Guides Staff. The Rough Guide to Los Angeles & Southern California. 2nd ed. 2011. (ENG., Illus.). 384p. 19.99 *(978-1-84836-583-4(7))* Rough Guides, Ltd. GBR. Dist: Dorling Kindersley Publishing, Inc.

Digonnet, Michel. Hiking Western Death Valley National Park: Panamint, Saline, & Eureka Valleys. 2009. (Illus.). 568p. (C). pap. 19.95 *(978-0-9659178-1-0(9))* Digonnet, Michel.

Dodge, Kathleen. John Muir Trail. 2007. (Day & Section Hikes Ser.). (ENG., Illus.). 160p. per. 13.95 *(978-0-89732-963-7(5))* Menasha Ridge Pr., Inc.

Dorling Kindersley Publishing Staff. Top 10: California Wine Country: California Wine Country. 2012. (Eyewitness Top 10 Travel Guide Ser.). (ENG.). 128p. 14.00 ***(978-0-7566-8897-4(3))*** Dorling Kindersley Publishing, Inc.

A Driving Tour of the Palos Verdes Peninsula. 2nd ed. (Illus.). 152p. pap. 9.95 *(978-0-9634861-0-3(1))* Bilkidy Pr.

Dwyer, Jeff. Ghost Hunter's Guide to California's Gold Rush Country, 1 vol. 2009. (Ghost Hunter's Guide Ser.). (ENG., Illus.). 216p. pap. 14.95 *(978-1-58980-687-0(5))* Pelican Publishing Co., Inc.

—Ghost Hunter's Guide to Monterey & California's Central Coast, 1 vol. 2010. (ENG., Illus.). 240p. pap. 14.95 *(978-1-58980-809-6(6))* Pelican Publishing Co., Inc.

Dye, Barbara & Richardson, Mary E. Best Hikes on the Palos Verdes Peninsula. 2007. (Illus.). 72p. per. 15.00 *(978-0-9794487-0-6(0))* Palos Verdes Peninsula Land Conservatory.

Eargle, Dolan H., Jr. Native California Guide: Introduction to the Original Peoples from Earliest Times to the Present. Dodsworth, Fred, ed. 2007. (ENG., Illus.). 330p. pap. 25.00 *(978-0-937401-10-1(2))* Trees Co. Pr.

Elbroch, Mark, et al. Field Guide to Animal Tracks & Scat of California. 2012. (California Natural History Guides). (ENG.). 398p. 75.00 ***(978-0-520-25378-0(7))***; pap. 34.95 ***(978-0-520-27109-8(2))*** Univ. of California Pr.

Eng, John & Biondo, Adriene. Southern California Eats. 2009. (Illus.). 144p. pap. 24.99 *(978-0-7643-3332-3(1))* Schiffer Publishing, Ltd.

—Southern California Eats 2. 2010. (Illus.). 144p. 24.99 *(978-0-7643-3639-3(8))* Schiffer Publishing, Ltd.

Entertainment Publications, Inc. Staff, compiled by. Bakersfield 2009 Entertainment Book. 2008. pap. 25.00 *(978-1-59878-691-0(1))* Entertainment Pubns., Inc.

—East Bay 2009 Entertainment Book. 2008. pap. 30.00 *(978-1-59878-647-7(4))* Entertainment Pubns., Inc.

—Fresno 2009 Entertainment Book. 2008. pap. 30.00 *(978-1-59878-675-0(X))* Entertainment Pubns., Inc.

—Orange County 2009 Entertainment Book. 2008. pap. 40.00 *(978-1-59878-608-8(3))* Entertainment Pubns., Inc.

—Orange County 2009 Values Book. 2008. pap. 20.00 *(978-1-59878-762-7(4))* Entertainment Pubns., Inc.

—Sacramento 2009 Entertainment Book. 2008. pap. 45.00 *(978-1-59878-634-7(2))* Entertainment Pubns., Inc.

—Sacramento 2009 Gold C Book. 2008. pap. 12.00 *(978-1-59878-757-3(8))* Entertainment Pubns., Inc.

—San Fernando 2009 Entertainment Book. 2008. pap. 25.00 *(978-1-59878-606-4(7))* Entertainment Pubns., Inc.

—San Gabriel 2009 Entertainment Book. 2008. pap. 25.00 *(978-1-59878-686-6(5))* Entertainment Pubns., Inc.

—San Jose/Santa Clara 2009 Entertainment Book. 2008. pap. 30.00 *(978-1-59878-604-0(0))* Entertainment Pubns., Inc.

—Santa Barbara/Ventura 2009 Entertainment Book. 2008. pap. 25.00 *(978-1-59878-677-4(6))* Entertainment Pubns., Inc.

—Sonoma/Marin 2009 Entertainment Book. 2008. pap. 30.00 *(978-1-59878-710-8(1))* Entertainment Pubns., Inc.

—Stockton/Modesto 2009 Entertainment Book. 2008. pap. 25.00 *(978-1-59878-690-3(3))* Entertainment Pubns., Inc.

Evans, Steven L. Top Trails Sacramento: Exploring Valley, Foothills, & Mountains in the Sacramento Region. 2007. (Top Trails: Must-Do Hikes Ser.). (ENG., Illus.). 320p. per. 16.95 *(978-0-89997-381-4(7))* Wilderness Pr.

Ferranti, Philip. 140 Great Hikes in & near Palm Springs. rev. ed. 2009. (ENG., Illus.). pap. 22.95 *(978-1-56579-639-3(X))* Westcliffe Pubs.

Fish, Peter, et al. California Wine Country. rev. ed. 2007. (Sunset Field Guide Ser.). (ENG., Illus.). 160p. pap. 19.95 *(978-0-376-06947-4(3)*, Sunset Bks./Sunset Publishing Corp.) Oxmoor Hse., Inc.

Fish, Tim & Melnik, Peg. Napa & Sonom - An Explorer's Guide: A Great Destination. 9th ed. 2011. (Explorer's Guides). (ENG., Illus.). 256p. pap. 19.95 *(978-1-58157-136-3(4)*, 157136) Countryman Pr.

Fleming, Charles. Secret Stairs: East Bay: A Walking Guide to the Historic Staircases of Berkeley & Oakland. 2011. (ENG.). 240p. pap. 16.95 *(978-1-59580-063-3(8))* Santa Monica Pr.

Fodor's. Fodor's California 2013. 2012. (Full-color Travel Guide Ser.). (ENG.). 968p. pap. 22.99 ***(978-0-307-92948-8(5)***, Fodor's) Fodor's Travel Pubns.

Fodor's Travel Publications, Inc. Staff. Compass American Guides: California Wine Country, 6th Edition. 6th ed. 2010. (Compass American Guides) (ENG., Illus.). 384p. pap. 21.99 *(978-1-4000-0492-8(6)*, Compass America Guides) Fodor's Travel Pubns.

—Compass American Guides: Yosemite & Sequoia/Kings Canyon National Parks, 2nd Edition. 2012. (Compass American Guides). (ENG.). 384p. pap. 19.99 ***(978-0-307-92848-1(9)***, Fodor's) Fodor's Travel Pubns.

—Disneyland & Southern California. 10th ed. 2010. (Special-Interest Titles Ser.). (ENG., Illus.). 464p. pap. 16.99 *(978-1-4000-0427-0(6)*, Fodor's) Fodor's Travel Pubns.

—Fodor's California 2012. 2011. (Full-Color Gold Guides). (ENG., Illus.). 964p. pap. 22.99 *(978-0-679-00951-1(5)*, Fodor's) Fodor's Travel Pubns.

—Fodor's Exploring California. 6th ed. 2009. (Exploring Guides). 288p. pap. 22.00 *(978-1-4000-0763-9(1)*, Fodor's) Fodor's Travel Pubns.

—Fodor's in Focus Napa & Sonoma, 1st Edition. 2010. (In Focus-Color Ser.). (ENG., Illus.). 240p. pap. 11.99 *(978-1-4000-0493-5(4)*, Fodor's) Fodor's Travel Pubns.

—Fodor's Northern California 2012: With Napa, Sonoma, Yosemite, San Francisco & Lake Tahoe. 2011. (Full-Color Gold Guides). (ENG., Illus.). 600p. pap. 19.99 *(978-0-679-00961-0(2)*, Fodor's) Fodor's Travel Pubns.

—Fodor's Southern California 2012: With Central Coast, Yosemite, Los Angeles, & San Diego. 2011. (Full-Color Gold Guides). (ENG., Illus.). 576p. pap. 19.99 *(978-0-679-00962-7(0)*, Fodor's) Fodor's Travel Pubns.

—Yosemite, Sequoia & Kings Canyon. 2009. (In Focus Ser.). (ENG.). 224p. 10.99 *(978-1-4000-0374-7(1)*, Fodor's) Fodor's Travel Pubns.

Frank Amato Publications, creator. Northern California River Maps & Fishing Guide. 2006. (Illus.). 47p. pap. 29.95 *(978-1-57188-392-6(4)*, NCAM) Amato, Frank Pubns., Inc.

Frank, Susan & Frank, Phil. The Ranger's Guide to Yosemite: Insider Advice from Park Ranger Dick. 2008. (ENG., Illus.). 180p. pap. 16.95 *(978-1-59880-129-3(5))* Westview Pr.

Freeze, Dennis. Mendocino Outdoors. 2008. (ENG., Illus.). 64p. spiral bd. 16.95 *(978-0-9722769-5-5(5))* Monolith Pr.

Gaines, Bob. Best Climbs Joshua Tree National Park: The Best Sport & Trad Routes in the Park. 2011. (Best Climbs Ser.). (ENG., Illus.). 192p. pap. 18.95 *(978-0-7627-7019-9(8)*, Falcon Guides) Globe Pequot Pr., The.

Gillis, Sandy & Ganon, Jill. Hometown Pasadena 2009-2010: The San Gabriel Valley Book. Bates, Colleen Dunn, ed. 2nd rev. ed. 2008. (ENG.). 280p. pap. 24.95 *(978-0-9753939-4-9(4))* Prospect Park Bks., LLC.

Goldsmith, Philip. Moon Napa & Sonoma. 2010. (Moon Handbooks Ser.). (ENG., Illus.). 332p. pap. 16.95 *(978-1-59880-596-3(7))* Avalon Travel Publishing.

—Moon Napa Valley. 2009. (Moon Spotlight Ser.). (ENG.). 100p. pap. 9.99 *(978-1-59880-262-7(3))* Avalon Travel Publishing.

—Moon Sonoma Valley. 2009. (Moon Spotlight Ser.). (ENG.). 125p. pap. 8.95 *(978-1-59880-263-4(1))* Avalon Travel Publishing.

Goldsmith, Philip & Cervin, Michael. Moon California Wine Country. 2011. (Moon Handbooks Ser.). (ENG., Illus.). 648p. pap. 21.99 *(978-1-59880-595-6(9))* Avalon Travel Publishing.

Goodavage, Maria. The Dog Lover's Companion to California: The Inside Scoop on Where to Take Your Dog. 2011. (Dog Lover's Companion Guides). (ENG., Illus.). 1008p. pap. 24.99 *(978-1-59880-743-1(9))* Avalon Travel Publishing.

C

Green, Michelin. Michelin California. 7th rev. ed. 2010. (Green Guide Ser.). (ENG., Illus.). 384p. pap. 21.99 (978-1-906261-74-0(1)) Michelin Travel & Lifestyle.
Grubbs, Bruce. Best Easy Day Hikes Palm Springs & Coachella Valley. 2010. (Best Easy Day Hikes Ser.). (ENG., Illus.). 104p. pap. 9.95 (978-0-7627-5261-4(0), Falcon Guides) Globe Pequot Pr., The.
—Explore! Shasta Country. 2006. (Falcon Guide Ser.). (ENG., Illus.). 160p. per. 15.95 (978-0-7627-3412-2(4), Falcon Guides) Globe Pequot Pr., The.
—Joshua Tree National Park Pocket Guide. 2009. (Falcon Pocket Guides Ser.). (ENG., Illus.). 96p. 9.95 (978-0-7627-5136-5(3), Falcon Guides) Globe Pequot Pr., The.
Halm, Meesha & Gollin, Randi, eds. Zagat California Wine Country Restaurants. 2007. (ENG.). 80p. per. 5.95 (978-1-57006-890-4(9)) Zagat Survey.
Hamilton, Patricia, et al. California Healthy: The Adventurer's Guide to Local Delicacies, Fine Wine, Great Walks & the Good Life. 2007. (ENG., Illus.). 384p. pap. 19.95 (978-1-877809-43-9(8), CAH-SC-2007) Park Place Pubns.
—California Healthy: Central California: A Green Guide to Eat Well, Have Fun & Stay Fit at Home & on the Road. 2008. (ENG.). 288p. pap. 17.95 (978-1-877809-41-5(1)) Park Place Pubns.
Hansen, Douglas, et al. California: An Illustrated Guide to Building a Safe House. 2009. (Code Check Ser.). (ENG., Illus.). 32p. pap. 18.95 (978-1-60085-084-4(7), Taunton) Taunton Pr., Inc.
Hardin, Debbie K. Southern California. 2011. (Explorer's Guides). (ENG., Illus.). 384p. pap. 21.95 (978-0-88150-893-2(4), 150893) Countryman Pr.
Hauserman, Tim. Cross-Country Skiing in the Sierra Nevada: The Best Resorts & Touring Centers in California & Nevada. 2007. (ENG., Illus.). 96p. per. 11.95 (978-0-88150-740-9(7)) Countryman Pr.
—Tahoe Rim Trail: The Official Guide for Hiker's, Mountain Biker's, & Equestrians. 2nd ed. 2008. (ENG., Illus.). 232p. pap. 17.95 (978-0-89997-472-9(4)) Wilderness Pr.
Heid, Matt. 101 Hikes in Northern California: Exploring Mountains, Valley, & Seashore. 2nd ed. 2008. (101 Hikes Ser.). (ENG.). 328p. pap. 17.95 (978-0-89997-474-3(0)) Wilderness Pr.
Hill, Kathleen Thompson & Hill, Gerald. Santa Barbara & the Central Coast, 4th: California's Riviera. 4th ed. 2008. (Hill Guides). (ENG., Illus.). 304p. pap. 14.95 (978-0-7627-4559-3(2)) Globe Pequot Pr., The.
Hiss, Mark & Mueller, Garth. Frommer's California Day by Day. 2011. (Frommer's Day by Day - Full Size Ser.: 113). (ENG., Illus.). 720p. pap. 29.99 (978-0-470-57115-6(2), Frommers) Wiley, John & Sons, Inc.
Hodges, Montana. Best Easy Day Hikes Redding, California. 2010. (Best Easy Day Hikes Ser.). (ENG., Illus.). 96p. pap. 9.95 (978-0-7627-5254-6(8), Falcon Guides) Globe Pequot Pr., The.
Holt, JoBea. Baby's Day Out in Southern California: Fun Places to Go with Babies & Toddlers. 2nd ed. 2006. (Illus.). 336p. pap. 16.95 (978-1-889786-36-0(5)) Gem Guides Bk. Co.
Huegel, Tony. California Desert Byways: 68 of California's Best Backcountry Drives. 3rd rev. ed. 2006. (ENG.). 200p. pap. 18.95 (978-0-89997-413-2(9)) Wilderness Pr.
—Sierra Nevada Byways: 51 of the Sierra Nevada's Best Backcountry Drives. 3rd ed. 2008. (ENG., Illus.). 184p. pap. 18.95 (978-0-89997-473-6(2)) Wilderness Pr.
Hughes, Rees & Lewis, Corey, eds. Pacific Crest Trailside Reader: California. 2011. (ENG.). 320p. pap. **(978-1-59485-508-5(0))** Mountaineers Bks., The.
Hughes, Rees & Lewis, Corey Lee. The Pacific Crest Trailside Reader, California: Adventure, History, & Legend on the Long-Distance Trail. 2011. E-Book **(978-1-59485-510-8(2))** Mountaineers Bks., The.
Hurt, Jeanette. The Cheeses of California: A Culinary Travel Guide. 2009. (ENG., Illus.). 208p. pap. 19.95 (978-0-88150-812-3(8), 150812) Countryman Pr.
Infusino, Divina. Day Trips from Orange County, CA: Getaway Ideas for the Local Traveler. 2010. (Day Trips Ser.). (ENG.). 256p. pap. 14.95 (978-0-7627-5957-6(7)) Globe Pequot Pr., The.
Jensen, Carol A., et al. Byron Hot Springs. 2006. (Images of America Ser.). (ENG., Illus.). 128p. pr. 19.99 (978-0-7385-4700-8(X)) Arcadia Publishing.
Jones, Ray & Virga, Vincent. California: Mapping the Golden State Through History - Rare & Unusual Maps from the Library of Congress. 2009. (Mapping the States through History Ser.). (ENG., Illus.). 128p. 24.95 (978-0-7627-4530-2(4)) Globe Pequot Pr., The.
Kaiser, James. Yosemite - The Complete Guide: Yosemite National Park. 2nd ed. 2011. (ENG., Illus.). 304p. pap. 22.95 (978-0-9825172-2-2(X)) Destination Pr.
Kath, Laura & Price, Pamela Joy. Fun with the Family Southern California: Hundreds of Ideas for Day Trips with the Kids. 8th ed. 2011. (Fun with the Family Ser.). (ENG.). 272p. pap. 14.95 (978-0-7627-5723-7(X)) Globe Pequot Pr., The.
Katz, Lena, et al, eds. Zagat Los Angeles So. California Restaurants Leather. 2007. (ENG., Illus.). 400p. lthr. 25.95 (978-1-57006-894-2(1)) Zagat Survey.
Kavanagh, James. Yosemite Wildlife: An Introduction to Familiar Species of the Yosemite Area. 2007. (Pocket Naturalist - Waterford Press Ser.). (ENG., Illus.). 1p. 5.95 (978-1-58355-369-5(X)) Waterford Pr., Inc.
Kavin, Kim. The Everything Family Guide to Northern California & Lake Tahoe: A Complete Guide to San Francisco, Yosemite, Monterey, & Lake Tahoe- And All the Beautiful Spots in Between. 2008. (ENG.). 416p. pap. 14.95 (978-1-59869-714-8(5)) Adams Media Corp.
Ken, Stanton. Great Day Hikes Napa 3rd. 2007. 192p. pap. 16.00 (978-0-939431-35-9(1)) Bored Feet Pr.
Klein, Karin. Orange County. 2010. (50 Hikes Ser.). (ENG.). 256p. pap. 18.95 (978-0-88150-872-7(1), 150872) Countryman Pr.
Koehler, Cheryl. California Sierra Nevada. (Illus.). 356p. pap. 24.95 (978-962-217-719-2(0)) Airphoto International/Odyssey HKG. Dist: Norton, W. W. & Co., Inc.
Kohn, Beth. Discover California, 50 vols. 2nd rev. ed. 2012. (Regional Guide Ser.). (ENG., Illus.). 416p. pap. 24.99 **(978-1-74220-561-8(5))** Lonely Planet Pubns.
Kohn, Beth & Benson, Sara. Yosemite, Sequoia & Kings Canyon National Parks, 45 vols. 3rd rev. ed. 2012. (National Parks Ser.). (ENG., Illus.). 256p. pap. 19.99 (978-1-74179-406-9(4)) Lonely Planet Pubns.
Langenscheidt Editorial Staff. Mobil Travel Guide Northern California. 50th anniv. ed. 2008. (Mobil Travel Guide: Northern California Ser.). (Illus.). 224p. 17.95 (978-0-8416-0314-1(6)) Langenscheidt Publishing Group.
—Mobil Travel Guide Southern California & Hawaii. 50th anniv. ed. 2008. (Mobil Travel Guide: Southern California Ser.). (Illus.). 264p. 17.95 (978-0-8416-0318-9(9)) Langenscheidt Publishing Group.
Lewis, Leland. The Baja Sea Guide. Date not set. (Sea Guide Ser.). (Illus.). 368p. reprint ed. 37.50 (978-0-688-04314-8(3)) Hearst Marine Bks.
Livingston, Jill. That Ribbon of Highway II: Highway 99 from Sacramento to the Mexican Border. 2nd ed. 2009. (978-0-9768321-2-6(7)) Living Gold Pr.
Locken, E. Travel Journal Disneyland. 2010. 192p. pap. 19.99 (978-0-557-41578-6(0)) Lulu Enterprises Inc.
—Travel Journal Disneyworld. 2010. 192p. pap. 19.99 (978-0-557-41584-7(5)) Lulu Enterprises Inc.
Lonely Planet Staff, et al. Discover California. 2011. (Full Color Regional Guides). (ENG., Illus.). 400p. pap. 24.99 (978-1-74220-260-0(8)) Lonely Planet Pubns.
Lovell, Jacquie & Mathews, Tom. Wine Bar Reveries - 2006: Wine Bars, Restaurants & Wine Shops in Ventura, Camarillo & Oxnard. 2006. (Illus.). 108p. pap. 14.95 (978-1-59800-450-2(6)) Outskirts Pr., Inc.
Mall, Jeff & Silvers, Josh. Down Home: Downtown: Seasonal Recipes from Two Sonoma Wine Country Restaurants. 2009. (Illus.). 144p. 24.95 (978-0-615-28546-7(5)) Rodney trong Vineyards.
Mangin, Daniel & Norton, Clark. AAA Spiral California. 5th ed. 2011. (ENG.). 208p. spiral bd. 17.95 (978-1-59508-425-5(8)) AAA.
Marco Polo. California Marco Polo Guide. 2012. (Marco Polo Guides Ser.). (ENG., Illus.). 140p. pap. 9.99 **(978-3-8297-0683-4(9))** Marco Polo Travel Publishing GBR. Dist: Innovative Logistics.
Marrazzo, Frederick W. Italians in the Santa Clara Valley. 2007. (Images of America Ser.). (ENG., Illus.). 128p. pap. 21.99 (978-0-7385-5562-1(2)) Arcadia Publishing.
Marx, Jennifer & Marx, Dave. Disneyland Resort & Southern California 2009: The Unique Travel Guide, Planner, Organizer, Journal, & Keepsake! 2nd deluxe ed. 2013. (PassPorter Ser.). (ENG., Illus.). 296p. ring bd. 42.95 (978-1-58771-043-8(9), PassPorter Travel Pr.) MediaMarx, Inc.
—Disneyland Resort & Southern California Attractions 2007: The Unique Travel Guide, Planner, Organizer, Journal, & Keepsake! 2nd ed. 2013. (PassPorter Ser.). (ENG., Illus.). 296p. spiral bd. 23.95 (978-1-58771-042-1(0), PassPorter Travel Pr.) MediaMarx, Inc.
Massey, Peter. Backcountry Adventures Southern California. 2008. 44.95 (978-1-930193-33-8(5)) Adler Publishing Co.
Massey, Peter & Wilson, Jeanne. California Trails Northern Sierra Region. 2006. (Illus.). 359p. per. 19.95 (978-1-930193-23-9(8)) Adler Publishing Co.
Massey, Peter, et al. California Trails Central Mountains Region. 2006. (Illus.). 305p. per. 19.95 (978-1-930193-19-2(X)) Adler Publishing Co.
—California Trails Desert Region. 2006. (Illus.). 337p. per. 19.95 (978-1-930193-20-8(3)) Adler Publishing Co.
—California Trails High Sierra Region. 2006. (Illus.). 249p. per. 19.95 (978-1-930193-21-5(1)) Adler Publishing Co.
—California Trails North Coast Region. 2006. (Illus.). 247p. per. 19.95 (978-1-930193-22-2(X)) Adler Publishing Co.
—California Trails South Coast Region. 2006. (Illus.). 254p. per. 19.95 (978-1-930193-24-6(6)) Adler Publishing Co.
Mazzeo, Tilar. Back Lane Wineries of Napa. 2010. (ENG., Illus.). 272p. pap. 19.95 (978-1-892145-83-3(9)) Little Bookroom.
Mazzeo, Tilar J. Back Lane Wineries of Sonoma. 2009. (ENG., Illus.). 256p. pap. 19.95 (978-1-892145-69-7(3)) Little Bookroom.
McCloskey, Erin. Northern California Nature Guide. 2008. (ENG., Illus.). 224p. pap. (978-976-8200-44-0(8)) Lone Pine Publishing International Inc.
—Southern California Nature Guide. 2009. (ENG.). 224p. pap. 19.95 (978-976-8200-55-6(3)) Lone Pine Publishing USA.
McKinney, John. Orange County Day Hiker's Guide. 2006. pap. 16.95 (978-0-9786575-1-2(9)) Trailmaster, Inc., The.
—Southern California Day Hiker's Guide. 4th ed. 2006. (Illus.). pap. 16.95 (978-0-9786575-2-9(7)) Trailmaster, Inc., The.
McKinney, John, et al. Frommer's Best Hiking Trips in Northern California. 2009. (Frommer's Best Hiking Trips Ser.: 10). (ENG., Illus.). 272p. pap. 19.99 (978-0-470-15991-0(X), Frommers) Wiley, John & Sons, Inc.
McKowen, Ken. California Coast. (Highroad Guides Ser.). 352p. pap. 18.95 (978-0-89997-342-5(6)) Wilderness Pr.
McKowen, Ken & McKowen, Dahlynn. Best of California's Missions, Mansions, & Museums: A Behind-the-Scenes Guide to the Golden State's Historic & Cultural Treasures. 2006. (ENG., Illus.). 248p. per. 21.95 (978-0-89997-398-2(1)) Wilderness Pr.
Medley, Stephen P. The Complete Guidebook to Yosemite National Park. 6th ed. 2008. (Illus.). 120p. pap. 12.95 (978-1-59714-087-4(2)) Heyday.
Meyer, Laurie & Howard, M. J. The Way We Were California: Nostalgic Images of the Golden State. 2009. (Way We Were Ser.). (ENG., Illus.). 128p. 19.95 (978-0-7627-5452-6(4)) Globe Pequot Pr., The.
Millhouse, Autumn. Romantic Napa Valley: An Insider's Guide for Couples. 2008. 168p. (978-0-9815881-0-0(7)) Romantic Travel Publishing.
Milne, Brian. Top Trails California Central Coast: Must-Do Hikes for Everyone. 2008. (Top Trails Ser.). (ENG., Illus.). 316p. pap. 18.95 (978-0-89997-437-8(6)) Wilderness Pr.
Mingori, Dan & Greenberg, Nate. Backcountry Skiing California's Eastern Sierra: 166 Ski & Snowboard Descents in the Range of Light Between Tioga Pass & Bishop Creek. 2009. (Illus.). 240p. pap. 29.00 (978-0-9792644-6-7(4)) Wolverine Publishing, LLC.
Miramontes, Robert. Joshua Tree: A Color Guide to the 2600 Best Rock Climbs & Boulder Problems. (Illus.). 460p. **(978-0-9826154-4-7(2))** Wolverine Publishing, LLC.
Misuraca, Karen. Backroads of the California Coast: Your Guide to Scenic Getaways & Adventures. 2009. (ENG., Illus.). 256p. pap. 21.99 (978-0-7603-3343-3(2), 0760333432, Voyageur Pr) MBI Publishing Co. LLC.
—Fun with the Family Northern California, 8th: Hundreds of Ideas for Day Trips with the Kids. 2011. (Fun with the Family Ser.). (ENG., Illus.). 304p. pap. 14.95 (978-0-7627-5719-0(1)) Globe Pequot Pr., The.
Mitchell, Patrick. Santa Ana River Guide: From Crest to Coast - 110 Miles along Southern California's Largest River System. 2006. (ENG., Illus.). 168p. per. 15.95 (978-0-89997-411-8(2)) Wilderness Pr.
Mitchell, Roger & Mitchell, Loris. Southern CA SUV Trails, Vol. 2. 2007. 360p. pap. 21.95 (978-0-9789978-0-9(8)) Track & Trail Pubns.
Mobil Regional Gd. Northern California 2010. 3rd rev. ed. 2009. (Regional Guide Ser.). 224p. pap. 17.99 (978-0-8416-1421-5(0)) Langenscheidt Publishing Group.
—Southern California 2010. 3rd rev. ed. 2009. (Regional Guide Ser.). 224p. pap. 17.99 (978-0-8416-1425-3(3)) Langenscheidt Publishing Group.
Mobil Travel Gd, ed. Northern California 2009. 2009. (Mobil Travel Guide Ser.). 328p. 18.95 (978-0-8416-0855-9(5)) Langenscheidt Publishing Group.
—Southern California & Hawaii. 2009. (Mobil Travel Guide Ser.). 208p. 17.95 (978-0-8416-0859-7(8)) Langenscheidt Publishing Group.
Molloy, Johnny. Best Easy Day Hikes Greensboro & Winston-Salem. 2nd ed. 2010. (Best Easy Day Hikes Ser.). (ENG., Illus.). 112p. pap. 9.95 (978-0-7627-5462-5(1), Falcon Guides) Globe Pequot Pr., The.
Moore, Jim. Lake Tahoe & Reno: Includes California Gold Country & the Northern Sierra Nevada. 2008. (Great Destinations Ser.). (ENG.). 320p. pap. 18.95 (978-1-58157-082-3(1), 157082) Countryman Pr.
Morey, Kathy. Hot Showers, Soft Beds, & Dayhikes in the Sierra: Walks & Strolls near Lodgings. 3rd ed. 2008. (ENG., Illus.). 338p. pap. 18.95 (978-0-89997-435-4(X)) Wilderness Pr.
Mullally, Linda & Mullally, David. Best Hikes with Dogs: Central California. 2008. (Best Hikes with Dogs Ser.). (ENG., Illus.). 240p. pap. 16.95 (978-1-59485-049-3(6)) Mountaineers Bks., The.
Neider, Susan M. Golden Country: Touring Scenic California. 2007. (ENG., Illus.). 128p. pap. 19.95 (978-0-7627-4303-2(4), Falcon Guides) Globe Pequot Pr., The.
Nevada County Historical Landmarks Commission. Exploring Nevada County: An Illustrated Guide to Local Landmarks & Historic Sites. rev. ed. 2010. (ENG., Illus.). 160p. pap. 16.50 (978-0-933994-30-0(3)) Comstock Bonanza Pr.
O'Brien, Chip. California's Best Fly Fishing: Premier Streams & Rivers from Northern California to the Eastern Sierra. 2010. (ENG., Illus.). 240p. pap. 29.95 (978-1-934753-03-3(3)) Headwater Bks.
O'Brien, Sean & Riedel, Allen. San Diego. 2nd ed. 2009. (Best Easy Day Hikes Ser.). (ENG., Illus.). 104p. pap. 9.95 (978-0-7627-5113-6(4), Falcon Guides) Globe Pequot Pr., The.
Ochterbeck, Cynthia Clayton, ed. California. 6th rev. ed. 2007. (Michelin Green Guide California Ser.). (Illus.). 384p. 21.95 (978-1-906261-03-0(2)) Michelin.
Olken, Charles E. & Furstenthal, Joseph. The New Connoisseurs' Guidebook to California Wine & Wineries. 2010. (Illus.). 480p. pap. 27.50 (978-0-520-25313-1(2)) Univ. of California Pr.
Olmstead, Marty. California Directory of Fine Wineries. 3rd rev. ed. 2006. (Illus.). 144p. 19.95 (978-0-9724993-3-0(4)) Wine Hse. Pr.
Olmstead, Marty & Riegert, Ray. Hidden Wine Country: Including Napa, Sonoma, & Mendocino. 4th ed. 2007. (Hidden Travel Ser.). (ENG., Illus.). 224p. pap. 14.95 (978-1-56975-598-3(1)) Ulysses Pr.
Orr, J. Michael. A Day or Two in the Napa Valley. 2007. per. 19.95 (978-0-9786044-0-0(7)) Napa Valley Art Studio.
Palethorpe, Jillian, illus. Birding the Santa Monica Mountains. 2008. 159p. pap. 12.95 (978-0-9627530-3-9(3)) Hillside Pr.
Palmer, Tim. Field Guide to California Rivers. 2012. (California Natural History Guides). (ENG., Illus.). 416p. 70.00 **(978-0-520-26643-8(9))**; pap. 27.95 **(978-0-520-26644-5(7))** Univ. of California Pr.
Panache Partners LLC Staff. Sonoma County. 2009. (Spectacular Wineries Ser.). (ENG., Illus.). 300p. 40.00 (978-1-933415-66-6(5)) Panache Partners, LLC.
Panache Partners LLC., Staff, ed. Spectacular Wineries of the Napa Valley: A Captivating Tour of Established, Estate & Boutique Wineries. 2007. (Spectacular Wineries Ser.). (ENG., Illus.). 400p. 34.95 (978-1-933415-40-6(1)) Panache Partners, LLC.
Patten, Carolyn & Van Vechten, Ken. Insiders Guide to Palm Springs E02. 2nd ed. 2010. (Insiders' Guide Ser.). (ENG., Illus.). 208p. pap. 18.95 (978-0-7627-5733-6(7), Insiders' Guide) Globe Pequot Pr., The.
Patterson, Charles. Southern California. 4th ed. 2008. (Best in Tent Camping Ser.). (ENG., Illus.). 180p. pap. 14.95 (978-0-89732-675-9(X)) Menasha Ridge Pr., Inc.
Patterson, Charles Falk. Mountain Bike! Los Angeles County: A Wide-Grin Ride Guide. 2007. (Mountain Bike! Ser.). (ENG., Illus.). 224p. per. 16.95 (978-0-89732-646-9(6)) Menasha Ridge Pr., Inc.
Peterson, Eric. Frommer's Yosemite & Sequoia & Kings Canyon National Parks. 8th ed. 2012. (Park Guides: 50). (ENG., Illus.). 192p. pap. 12.99 **(978-1-118-07474-9(2)**, Frommers) Wiley, John & Sons, Inc.
Peterson, Eric. Yosemite & Sequoia & Kings Canyon National Parks. 7th ed. 2010. (Park Guides). (ENG., Illus.). 192p. pap. 12.99 (978-0-470-53773-2(6), Frommers) Wiley, John & Sons, Inc.
Poole, Matthew R. Frommer's California 2012. 7th ed. 2011. (Frommer's Colour Complete Ser.). (ENG.). 896p. pap. 23.99 **(978-1-118-01731-9(5)**, Frommers) Wiley, John & Sons, Inc.
Poole, Matthew Richard & Luna, Kristin, eds. Best Places Northern California. 6th ed. 2009. (Best Places Ser.). (ENG., Illus.). 576p. pap. 21.95 (978-1-57061-601-3(9)) Sasquatch Bks.
Poultney, John & Amador County Archives. Amador County. 2006. (Images of America Ser.). (ENG., Illus.). 128p. per. 21.99 (978-0-7385-4701-5(8)) Arcadia Publishing.
Preston, Thomas & Preston, Elizabeth. The Double Eagle Guide to Western State Parks: Volume 3 Far West, 3 of 6. 4th ed. 2007. (Double Eagle Guides Ser.: 3). 21.95 (978-1-932417-17-3(6), Double Eagle Guides) Discovery Publishing.
Rails-to-Trails Conservancy Staff. Rail-Trails West: California, Arizona, & Nevada - The Official Rails-to-Trails Conservancy Guidebook. 2009. (Rail-Trails Ser.). (ENG.). 264p. pap. 16.95 (978-0-89997-489-7(9)) Wilderness Pr.
Reid, Don. Yosemite Free Climbs. 3rd ed. 2007. (Illus.). 440p. pap. 30.00 (978-0-7627-2317-1(3), Falcon Guides) Globe Pequot Pr., The.
Rhodes, Bob & Rhodes, Cindy. The Grape Escapes: Temecula Wineries & Tasting Rooms. 2008. 292p. pap. 19.95 (978-1-59858-573-5(8)) Dog Ear Publishing, LLC.
Richins, Paul, Jr. Mount Whitney: The Complete Trailhead to Summit Guide. 2nd rev. ed. 2008. (ENG., Illus.). 256p. pap. 18.95 (978-1-59485-042-4(9)) Mountaineers Bks., The.
Ridge, Menasha, et al. The Unofficial Guide to Disneyland 2011. 6th ed. 2010. (Unofficial Guides). (ENG., Illus.). 384p. pap. 17.99 (978-0-470-61532-4(X), Wiley) Wiley, John & Sons, Inc.
Riedel, Allen. Best Easy Day Hikes Conejo Valley. 2011. (Best Easy Day Hikes Ser.). (ENG., Illus.). 112p. pap. 9.95 (978-0-7627-5292-8(0), Falcon Guides) Globe Pequot Pr., The.
—Best Easy Day Hikes San Bernardino. 2009. (Best Easy Day Hikes Ser.). (ENG., Illus.). 96p. pap. 9.95 (978-0-7627-5256-0(4), Falcon Guides) Globe Pequot Pr., The.
—Riverside. 2009. (Best Easy Day Hikes Ser.). (ENG., Illus.). 96p. pap. 9.95 (978-0-7627-5255-3(6), Falcon Guides) Globe Pequot Pr., The.
Riedel, Allen & Reynolds, Kirsten. Southern California. 2006. (Best Hikes with Dogs Ser.). (ENG., Illus.). 269p. pap. 17.95 (978-0-89886-691-9(X)) Mountaineers Bks., The.
Riedel, Allen & Riedel, Monique. Best Hikes near Los Angeles. 2011. (Best Hikes near Ser.). (ENG., Illus.). 256p. pap. 18.95 (978-0-7627-4641-5(6), Falcon Guides) Globe Pequot Pr., The.
Riedel, Monique. Best Easy Day Hikes Ventura. 2009. (Best Easy Day Hikes Ser.). (ENG., Illus.). 96p. pap. 9.95 (978-0-7627-5121-1(5), Falcon Guides) Globe Pequot Pr., The.
Riegert, Ray. Hidden Coast of California: Including San Diego, Los Angeles, Santa Barbara, Monterey, San Francisco, & Mendocino. 11th rev. ed. 2007. (Hidden Travel Ser.). (ENG.). 576p. pap. 19.95 (978-1-56975-595-2(7)) Ulysses Pr.
—Hidden San Francisco & Northern California: Including Napa, Sonoma, Mendocino, Santa Cruz, Monterey, Yosemite, & Lake Tahoe. 13th ed. 2009. (Hidden Travel Ser.). (ENG., Illus.). 592p. pap. 19.95 (978-1-56975-695-9(3)) Ulysses Pr.
—Hidden Southern California: Including Los Angeles, Hollywood, San Diego, Santa Barbara & Palm Springs. 10th ed. 2006. (Hidden Travel Ser.). (ENG., Illus.). 616p. per. 19.95 (978-1-56975-539-6(6)) Ulysses Pr.
Roshell, Starshine & Crabtree, Cheryl. Hometown Santa Barbara: The Central Coast Book. Ransohoff, Nancy Roberts, ed. 2008. (ENG.). 256p. pap. 24.95 (978-0-9753939-5-6(2)) Prospect Park Bks., LLC.
Roth, Anna. West Coast Road Eats: The Best Road Food from San Diego to the Canadian Border. 2011. (ENG., Illus.). 368p. pap. 22.95 (978-1-57061-690-7(6)) Sasquatch Bks.
Rough, Guide. The Rough Guide to California. 10th ed. 2011. (ENG., Illus.). 768p. 23.99 (978-1-84836-862-0(3)) Rough Guides, Ltd. GBR. Dist: Dorling Kindersley Publishing, Inc.
Rusmore, Jean. Bay Area Ridge Trail: The Official Guide for Hikers, Moutain Bikers, & Equestrians. 3rd ed. 2008. (ENG., Illus.). 314p. pap. 18.95 (978-0-89997-469-9(4)) Wilderness Pr.
Salcedo-Chourre, Tracy. Best Easy Day Hikes Fresno. 2011. (Best Easy Day Hikes Ser.). (ENG., Illus.). 112p. pap. 9.95 (978-0-7627-7280-3(8), Falcon Guides) Globe Pequot Pr., The.
—Best Easy Day Hikes Lake Tahoe. 2nd ed. 2010. (Best Easy Day Hikes Ser.). (ENG., Illus.). 112p. pap. 9.95 (978-0-7627-5253-9(X), Falcon Guides) Globe Pequot Pr., The.
—Best Easy Day Hikes Sacramento. 2009. (Best Easy Day Hikes Ser.). (ENG., Illus.). 112p. pap. 9.95 (978-0-7627-5111-2(8), Falcon Guides) Globe Pequot Pr., The.
—Best Easy Day Hikes San Jose. 2009. (Best Easy Day Hikes Ser.). (ENG., Illus.). 112p. pap. 9.95 (978-0-7627-5115-0(0), Falcon Guides) Globe Pequot Pr., The.

—Best Rail Trails California: More Than 70 Rail Trails Throughout the State. 2008. (Best Rail Trails Ser.). (ENG., Illus.). 320p. pap. 15.95 *(978-0-7627-4677-4(7),* Falcon Guides) Globe Pequot Pr., The.

—Lake Tahoe. 2010. (Best Easy Day Hikes Ser.). (ENG.). 112p. pap. 19.95 *(978-0-7627-5973-6(9),* Falcon Guides) Globe Pequot Pr., The.

San Diego. (Rand Mcnally Wall Maps Ser.). 229.00 *(978-0-528-86114-7(X));* 229.00 *(978-0-528-86161-1(1))* Rand McNally.

Sandler, Corey. Econoguide Disneyland Resort, Universal Studios Hollywood: And Other Major Southern California Attractions Including Disney's California Adventure. 5th ed. 2007. (Econoguide Ser.). (ENG., Illus.). 384p. per. 17.95 *(978-0-7627-4167-0(8))* Globe Pequot Pr., The.

Santa Barbara Fun: For Ages 1 To 100. 2008. (Illus.). 384p. per. 20.95 *(978-0-9791465-0-3(X))* AAAKQ Pr.

Schaffer, Jeffrey P. Top Trails: Yosemite: Must-Do Hikes for Everyone. 2007. (Top Trails: Must-Do Hikes Ser.). (ENG., Illus.). 386p. per. 16.95 *(978-0-89997-425-5(2))* Wilderness Pr.

Scheidt, Laurel. Best Easy Day Hikes Sequoia & Kings Canyon National Parks. 2nd ed. 2011. (Best Easy Day Hikes Ser.). (ENG., Illus.). 112p. pap. 9.95 *(978-0-7627-6054-1(0),* Falcon Guides) Globe Pequot Pr., The.

—Hiking Sequoia & Kings Canyon, 2nd. 2nd ed. 2011. (Regional Hiking Ser.). (ENG., Illus.). 336p. pap. 18.95 *(978-0-7627-6104-3(0)* Falcon Guides) Globe Pequot Pr., The.

Scholl, Steve. Beaches & Parks from San Francisco to Monterey: Counties Included - Marin, San Francisco, San Mateo, Santa Cruz, Monterey. 2012. (Experience the California Coast Ser.). (ENG.). 320p. pap. 29.95 ***(978-0-520-27157-9(2))*** Univ. of California Pr.

Scott, Liz Hamill. Moon Northern California. 2009. (Moon Handbooks). (ENG., Illus.). 536p. pap. 19.95 *(978-1-59880-252-8(6))* Avalon Travel Publishing.

—Moon Southern California. 2009. (Moon Handbooks). (ENG., Illus.). 372p. pap. 18.95 *(978-1-59880-251-1(8))* Avalon Travel Publishing.

—Palm Springs: Including Joshua Tree & Death Valley National Parks. 2009. (Moon Spotlight Ser.). (ENG.). 80p. pap. 6.95 *(978-1-59880-356-3(5))* Avalon Travel Publishing.

Secor, R. J. High Sierra: Peaks, Passes, & Trails. 3rd ed. 2008. (ENG.). pap. 29.95 *(978-0-89886-971-2(4))* Mountaineers Bks., The.

Sehlinger, Bob, et al. The Unofficial Guide to Disneyland 2012. 7th ed. 2011. (Unofficial Guides: 279). (ENG., Illus.). 384p. pap. 17.99 *(978-1-118-01228-4(3),* Wiley) Wiley, John & Sons, Inc.

Shabram, Patrick L. Shabram's Guide to California's Professional Ballparks. 2007. 11.95 *(978-0-9795107-0-0(8))* BAEB Publishing.

Simpson, Ann & Simpson, Rob. Yosemite National Park Pocket Guide. 2009. (Falcon Pocket Guides Ser.). (ENG., Illus.). 96p. 9.95 *(978-0-7627-4811-2(7),* Falcon Guides) Globe Pequot Pr., The.

Simpson, Rob & Simpson, Ann. Sequoia & Kings Canyon National Parks Pocket Guide. 2010. (Falcon Pocket Guides Ser.). (ENG., Illus.). 96p. 9.95 *(978-0-7627-5139-6(8),* Falcon Guides) Globe Pequot Pr., The.

Smith, Bridget. The Unauthorized Legoland Guidebook. 2009. 122p. pap. 17.95 *(978-0-615-25501-9(9))* Family Adventure Guidebook.

Smith, Fay. California. 4th ed. (Illus.). 272p. pap. 14.95 *(978-1-86315-119-1(2))* Little Hills Pr. AUS. Dist: CPG Publishing, Inc.

Smith, Julie. 50 Hikes in the Sierra Nevada: Hikes & Backpacks from Lake Tahoe to Sequoia National Park. 2009. (50 Hikes Ser.). (ENG., Illus.). 288p. pap. 18.95 *(978-0-88150-810-9(1),* 150810) Countryman Pr.

Soares, John R. California's Lassen Park & Mount Shasta Regions. 2006. (100 Hikes Ser.). (ENG., Illus.). 240p. pap. 15.95 *(978-0-89886-466-3(6))* Mountaineers Bks., The.

Soares, John R. & Soares, Mark. 100 Classic Hikes in Northern California. 3rd ed. 2007. (ENG.). 240p. pap. *(978-1-59485-062-2(3))* Mountaineers Bks., The.

Solomon, Brian. Railroads of California: The Complete Guide to Historic Trains & Railway Sites. 2009. (ENG., Illus.). 160p. 30.00 *(978-0-7603-3333-4(5),* 0760333335, Voyageur Pr) MBI Publishing Co. LLC.

Sorensen, AnneLise. California. 2010. (Eyewitness Travel Guides). (ENG.). 660p. pap. 30.00 *(978-0-7566-6180-9(3))* Dorling Kindersley Publishing, Inc.

Sorensen, AnneLise. DK Eyewitness Travel Guide: California: California. 2012. (Eyewitness Travel Guide Ser.). (ENG.). 424p. pap. 30.00 ***(978-0-7566-8560-7(5))*** Dorling Kindersley Publishing, Inc.

Sorensen, AnneLise & Dorling Kindersley Publishing Staff. San Francisco & Northern California. 2011. (Eyewitness Travel Guide Ser.). (ENG.). 336p. 25.00 *(978-0-7566-6974-4(X))* Dorling Kindersley Publishing, Inc.

Starr, Kevin & Roper, Steve, contrib. by. Yosemite in the Sixties, 1 vol. 2007. (ENG., Illus.). 144p. 60.00 *(978-0-9790659-0-3(9))* Adler, T.

Steakley, Douglas. Photographing Big Sur: Where to Find Perfect Shots & How to Take Them. 2011. (Photographer's Guide Ser.). (ENG., Illus.). 96p. pap. 15.95 *(978-0-88150-928-1(0),* 150928) Countryman Pr.

Stienstra, Stephani, et al. Yosemite & Mammoth Lakes Camping & Hiking. 2009. (Moon Spotlight Ser.). (ENG.). 130p. pap. 8.95 *(978-1-59880-277-1(1))* Avalon Travel Publishing.

Stienstra, Tom. California Recreational Lakes & Rivers: The Complete Guide to Boating, Fishing, & Water Sports. 4th ed. 2008. (Moon Handbooks Ser.). (ENG., Illus.). 560p. pap. 21.95 *(978-1-59880-018-0(3))* Westview Pr.

—Moon California Camping: The Complete Guide to More Than 1,400 Tent & RV Campgrounds. 2011. (Moon Outdoors Ser.). (ENG., Illus.). 936p. pap. 24.99 *(978-1-59880-752-3(8))* Avalon Travel Publishing.

—Moon California Fishing: The Complete Guide to Fishing on Lakes, Streams, Rivers, & the Coast. 8th ed. 2008. (Moon Handbooks Ser.). (ENG., Illus.). 720p. per. 24.95 *(978-1-56691-840-4(5))* Westview Pr.

—Moon Northern California Camping: The Complete Guide to Tent & RV Camping. 2011. (Moon Outdoors Ser.). (ENG., Illus.). 736p. pap. 19.99 *(978-1-59880-753-0(6))* Avalon Travel Publishing.

—Shasta & Lassen Camping & Hiking. 2009. (Moon Spotlight Ser.). (ENG.). 235p. pap. 11.95 *(978-1-59880-276-4(3))* Avalon Travel Publishing.

—Tahoe Camping & Hiking. 2009. (Moon Spotlight Ser.). (ENG.). 180p. pap. 9.95 *(978-1-59880-275-7(5))* Avalon Travel Publishing.

—West Coast RV Camping: The Complete Guide to More Than 1,800 RV Parks & Campgrounds in California, Oregon, & Washington. 2010. (Moon Outdoors Ser.). (ENG., Illus.). 1272p. pap. 24.95 *(978-1-59880-162-0(7,)* Avalon Travel Publishing.

Stienstra, Tom & Brown, Ann Marie. Sequoia & Kings Canyon Camping & Hiking. 2009. (Moon Spotlight Ser.). (ENG.). 165p. pap. 9.95 *(978-1-59880-278-8(X))* Avalon Travel Publishing.

Stillson, Richard. Spreading the Word: A History of Information in the California Gold Rush. 2008. (ENG.). 284p. pap. 24.95 *(978-0-8032-1827-7(3))* Univ. of Nebraska Pr.

Stone, Robert. Day Hikes Around Santa Barbara, 3rd. 2010. (ENG., Illus.). 320p. pap. 17.95 *(978-1-57342-060-0(3))* Day Hike Bks.

—Day Hikes Around Ventura County, 3rd. 2011. (ENG., Illus.). 320p. pap. 17.95 *(978-1-57342-062-4(X))* Day Hike Bks.

—Day Hikes in Yosemite National Park, 3rd. 2009. (ENG., Illus.). 208p. pap. 13.95 *(978-1-57342-059-4(X))* Day Hike Bks.

—Day Hikes on the California Central Coast, 2nd. 2nd ed. 2008. (ENG., Illus.). 320p. pap. 17.95 *(978-1-57342-058-7(1))* Day Hike Bks.

—Napa Valley: 88 Great Hikes. 2008. (Day Hikes Ser.). (ENG., Illus.). 288p. per. 16.95 *(978-1-57342-057-0(3))* Day Hike Bks.

Stone, Robert & Stone, Robert. Day Hikes Around Sonoma County: 95 Great Hikes. 2007. (Day Hikes Ser.). (ENG., Illus.). 272p. per. 16.95 *(978-1-57342-053-2(0))* Day Hike Bks.

Strong, Kathy. Southern California off the Beaten Path: A Guide to Unique Places. 8th ed. 2011. (Off the Beaten Path Ser.). (ENG., Illus.). 256p. pap. 14.95 *(978-0-7627-6484-6(8))* Globe Pequot Pr., The.

Summers, Jordan. Easy Hikes Close to Home: Sacramento. 2009. (Easy Hikes Close to Home Ser.). (ENG., Illus.). 96p. pap. 8.95 *(978-0-89732-698-8(9))* Menasha Ridge Pr., Inc.

—Most Beautiful Hikes. 2009. (Day & Overnight Hikes Ser.). (ENG., Illus.). 170p. pap., instr.'s gde. ed. 15.95 *(978-0-89732-959-0(7))* Menasha Ridge Pr., Inc.

—Sacramento: Including Davis, Roseville, & Auburn. 2008. (60 Hikes within 60 Miles Ser.). (ENG., Illus.). 352p. per. 17.95 *(978-0-89732-556-1(7))* Menasha Ridge Pr., Inc.

Summerson, John. The Complete Guide to Climbing (by Bike) in California: A Guide to Cycling Climbing & the Most Difficult Hill Climbs in California. 2010. (Illus.). 295p. pap. 18.95 *(978-0-9792571-2-4(3))* Extreme Pr.

Swedo, Suzanne. Hiking Yosemite National Park: A Guide to 64 of the Park's Greatest Hiking Adventures. 3rd ed. 2011. (Regional Hiking Ser.). (ENG., Illus.). 320p. pap. 18.95 *(978-0-7627-6109-8(1),* Falcon Guides) Globe Pequot Pr., The.

—Yosemite National Park. 2010. (Best Easy Day Hikes Ser.). (ENG.). 96p. pap. 19.95 *(978-0-7627-5974-3(7));* 3rd ed. (Illus.). 112p. pap. 9.95 *(978-0-7627-5528-8(8))* Globe Pequot Pr., The. (Falcon Guides).

Thomas Cook Publishing. Traveller Guides California, 4th: Popular, compact guides for discovering the very best of country, regional & city Destinations. 4th ed. 2011. (Travellers - Thomas Cook Ser.). (ENG., Illus.). 192p. pap. 16.95 *(978-1-84848-444-3(5))* Cook, Thomas Publishing GBR. Dist: Globe Pequot Pr., The.

Thomas Cook Publishing Staff. California Driving Guide. 4th ed. 2010. (Drive Around - Thomas Cook Ser.). (ENG., Illus.). 288p. pap. 26.95 *(978-1-84848-329-3(5))* Cook, Thomas Publishing GBR. Dist: Globe Pequot Pr., The.

Travel Guide, Forbes. Forbes Travel Guide 2011 Northern California. 2011. (Forbes Travel Guide Regional Guide Ser.). (ENG.). 224p. pap. 18.95 *(978-1-936010-89-9(5))* Five Star Travel Corp., The.

—Forbes Travel Guide 2011 Southern California. 2011. (Forbes Travel Guide Regional Guide Ser.). (ENG.). 224p. pap. 18.95 *(978-1-936010-93-6(3))* Five Star Travel Corp., The.

Tway, Linda E. Tidepools: Southern California: A Guide to 92 Locations from Point Conception to Mexico. 2011. (ENG., Illus.). 200p. spiral bd. 18.95 *(978-0-89997-633-4(6))* Wilderness Pr.

Van Voorst, Joy. Tawanda's Bed & Breakfast. 2006. (ENG.). 180p. per. 16.95 *(978-1-59800-749-7(1))* Outskirts Pr., Inc.

Vance, Ashlee. Geek Silicon Valley: A Circuitry of Places & People — And the Stories That Created Today's High-Tech Lifestyle. 2007. (ENG., Illus.). 264p. pap. 15.95 *(978-0-7627-4239-4(9))* Globe Pequot Pr., The.

Varney, Philip. Ghost Towns of California: Your Guide to the Hidden History & Old West Haunts of California. 2012. (ENG., Illus.). 240p. pap. 24.99 ***(978-0-7603-4082-0(X),*** 076034082X, Voyageur Pr) MBI Publishing Co. LLC.

Ver Berkmoes, Ryan, et al. Lonely Planet California Trips. 2009. (Regional Guide Ser.). (ENG., Illus.). 416p. pap. 19.99 *(978-1-74179-727-5(6))* Lonely Planet Pubns.

Villani, John. Art Towns California: A Guide to Galleries, Museums, Festivals, Lodging & Dining. 2008. (ENG.). 272p. pap. 18.95 *(978-0-88150-696-9(6),* 150696) Countryman Pr.

Vogel, Randy & Gaines, Bob. Orange County. 2nd ed. 2009. (Best Easy Day Hikes Ser.). (ENG., Illus.). 112p. pap. 9.95 *(978-0-7627-5107-5(X),* Falcon Guides) Globe Pequot Pr., The.

Wares, Donna. Southern California. 2008. (Great Escapes Ser.). (ENG., Illus.). 192p. pap. 16.95 *(978-0-88150-779-9(2),* 150779) Countryman Pr.

Weir, Kim & Scott, Liz. California. 2nd ed. 2009. (Moon Handbooks Ser.). (ENG.). 650p. pap. 21.95 *(978-1-56691-649-3(6))* Westview Pr.

Wenk, Elizabeth. One Best Hike: Mt. Whitney. 2008. (One Best Hike Ser.). (ENG., Illus.). 142p. pap. 12.95 *(978-0-89997-464-4(3))* Wilderness Pr.

Wenk, Elizabeth. 50 Best Short Hikes: Yosemite National Park & Vicinity. 2012. (ENG., Illus.). 256p. pap. 16.95 ***(978-0-89997-631-0(X))*** Wilderness Pr.

White, Greg & Riedel, Allen. Best Easy Day Hikes San Gabriel Valley. 2009. (Best Easy Day Hikes Ser.). (ENG., Illus.). 96p. pap. 9.95 *(978-0-7627-5258-4(0),* Falcon Guides) Globe Pequot Pr., The.

White, Mike. Lassen Volcanic National Park: A Complete Hiker's Guide. 4th ed. 2008. (ENG., Illus.). 290p. pap. 17.95 *(978-0-89997-470-5(8))* Wilderness Pr.

—Top Trails Sequoia & Kings Canyon: Must-Do Hikes for Everyone. 2009. (Top Trails Ser.). (ENG.). 372p. pap. 17.95 *(978-0-89997-486-6(4))* Wilderness Pr.

White, Mike, photos by. Trinity Alps & Vicinity: Including Whiskeytown, Russian Wilderness, & Castle Crags Areas. 5th ed. 2010. (ENG., Illus.). 336p. pap. 19.95 *(978-0-89997-501-6(1))* Wilderness Pr.

Whitfield, Paul & Rough Guides Staff. Yosemite, Sequoia & Kings Canyon - Rough Guide. 4th ed. 2011. (ENG., Illus.). 256p. pap. 19.99 *(978-1-84836-899-6(2))* Rough Guides, Ltd. GBR. Dist: Dorling Kindersley Publishing, Inc.

Wilcer, Matt. Yosemite Valley Bouldering. 2007. (Illus.). 159p. pap. 27.95 *(978-0-9765235-2-9(3))* SuperTopo.

Wilderness Press. Backpacking California: Mountain, Foothill, Coastal & Desert Adventures in the Golden State. 2nd ed. 2008. (Backpacking Ser.). (ENG., Illus.). 490p. pap. 24.95 *(978-0-89997-446-0(5))* Wilderness Pr.

Wilkerson, Lyn. Slow Travels — California. 2009. 270p. pap. 19.94 *(978-0-557-08807-2(0))* Lulu Enterprises Inc.

Williams, Deke. Best Easy Day Hikes San Fernando Valley. 2009. (Best Easy Day Hikes Ser.). (ENG., Illus.). 96p. pap. 9.95 *(978-0-7627-5257-7(2),* Falcon Guides) Globe Pequot Pr., The.

Williams, Mark R. & Cass, Maxine. Northern California off the Beaten Path: A Guide to Unique Places. 8th ed. 2009. (Off the Beaten Path Ser.). (ENG., Illus.). 224p. pap. 14.95 *(978-0-7627-5050-4(2))* Globe Pequot Pr., The.

Wilmer, Thomas C. The Wine Seeker's Guide to Livermore Valley. 2010. (ENG.). 232p. pap. 18.95 *(978-0-9793840-2-8(8),* Riverwood Bks.) Caveat Pr., Inc.

Wilson, Alex & Pitterle, Bryn Fox. Best Easy Day Hikes Santa Barbara. 2009. (Best Easy Day Hikes Ser.). (ENG., Illus.). 104p. pap. 9.95 *(978-0-7627-5117-4(7),* Falcon Guides) Globe Pequot Pr., The.

Wilson, Alex & Riedel, Allen. Best Easy Day Hikes San Luis Obispo. 2011. (Best Easy Day Hikes Ser.). (ENG., Illus.). 112p. pap. 9.95 *(978-0-7627-5116-7(9),* Falcon Guides) Globe Pequot Pr., The.

Winter, Mick. The Napa Valley Book: Everything You Need to Know about California's Premium Wine Country. 3rd ed. 2007. (Illus.). 252p. per. 16.95 *(978-0-9659000-7-2(X))* Westsong Publishing.

Womack, David. Mountain Bike! Orange County: A Wide-Grin Ride Guide. 2007. (Mountain Bike! Ser.). (ENG., Illus.). 208p. per. 16.95 *(978-0-89732-980-4(5))* Menasha Ridge Pr., Inc.

Wurman, Richard Saul & Wurman, Richard S. Access California Wine Country. 8th ed. 2007. (Access California Wine Country Ser.). (ENG., Illus.). 240p. pap. 21.95 *(978-0-06-126062-9(2))* HarperCollins Pubs.

Yasuda, Anita. Snapshots of San Diego: Sun, Surf & Sand. 2008. (Illus.). 128p. pap. 24.95 *(978-0-7643-2804-6(2))* Schiffer Publishing, Ltd.

Yesavage, Jerome. Lake Tahoe's Desolation Wilderness Fishing Guide. 2008. 48p. pap. 25.00 *(978-0-615-25034-2(3))* Talmont Trout Pubns.

Young, Brad. A Climber's Guide to Pinnacles National Monument. 2007. 408p. 35.00 *(978-0-9797421-0-1(2))* Young, Brad.

Young, Wills & Ryan, Mick. Bishop Bouldering. (Illus.). 2007. 350p. per. 36.00 *(978-0-9721609-9-5(X))* 2nd ed. 2010. 428p. pap. *(978-0-9826154-1-6(8))* Wolverine Publishing, LLC.

Zagat Survey Staff. Disneyland Insider's Guide 2010. 2009. (ENG.). 144p. pap. 14.95 *(978-1-60478-196-0(3))* Zagat Survey.

—Sacramento Restaurants 2010. 2009. (ENG.). 96p. pap. 6.95 *(978-1-60478-194-6(7))* Zagat Survey.

Zagat Survey Staff, creator. Zagat California Wine Country Restaurants. rev. ed. 2006. (Zagat Survey: California Wine Country Restaurants Ser.). (ENG.). 64p. per. 5.95 *(978-1-57006-809-6(7))* Zagat Survey.

Zagat Survey Staff, ed. Sacramento Restaurants. 2008. (ENG.). 80p. pap., instr.'s gde. ed. 5.95 *(978-1-60478-071-0(1))* Zagat Survey.

—2009 California Wine Country Restaurants. 2008. (ENG.). 80p. pap. 5.95 *(978-1-57006-999-4(9))* Zagat Survey.

—2009 Orange County Restaurants. 2008. (ENG.). 80p. pap. 5.95 *(978-1-60478-024-6(X))* Zagat Survey.

CALIFORNIA—HISTORY

see also Bear Flag Revolt, 1846; Kearny Expedition, 1845; Portola's Expedition, Calif., 1769-1770

Alexander, Jack. The California Combined Harvester. 2010. 265p. pap. 27.51 *(978-0-557-32412-5(2))* Lulu Enterprises Inc.

Andersen, Arthur R. & Whitsell, Leon O. California's First Century of Scottish Rite Masonry. 2011. 368p. 53.95 ***(978-1-258-00266-4(3))*** Literary Licensing, LLC.

Anderson, Karl. The Salton Sea. 2011. (Postcard History Ser.). (ENG., Illus.). 128p. pap. 21.99 *(978-0-7385-7455-4(4))* Arcadia Publishing.

Arax, Mark. West of the West: Dreamers, Believers, Builders & Killers in the Golden State. 2009. (ENG., Illus.). 368p. pap. 26.95 *(978-1-58648-390-6(0))* Perseus Bks. Group.

—West of the West: Dreamers, Believers, Builders, & Killers in the Golden State. 2011. (ENG., Illus.). 368p. pap. 15.99 *(978-1-58648-983-0(6))* PublicAffairs.

Arcadia Historical Society. Arcadia. 2008. (Images of America Ser.). (ENG., Illus.). 128p. pap. 19.99 *(978-0-7385-5806-6(0))* Arcadia Publishing.

Arcata Eye Staff & Arcata Union Staff. On This Day in Arcata. 2008. (On this Day Ser.). (Illus.). 128p. pap. 19.99 *(978-0-7385-5682-6(3))* Arcadia Publishing.

Arnold, Daniel. Early Days in the Range of Light: Encounters with Legendary Mountaineers. 2009. (ENG., Illus.). 432p. 29.95 *(978-1-58243-519-0(7),* Counterpoint Pr.) Basic Bks. GBR. Dist: Perseus-PGW.

Asmus, Peter. Introduction to Energy in California. 2009. (California Natural History Guides Ser.). (ENG., Illus.). 444p. 50.00 *(978-0-520-25752-8(9));* pap. 19.95 *(978-0-520-25751-1(0))* Univ. of California Pr.

Atherton, Gertrude Franklin Horn. California: An Intimate History. 2007. (ENG.). 344p. per. 31.95 *(978-1-4326-3760-6(6))* Kessinger Publishing, LLC.

Austin, Mary Hunter. The Flock. 2010. 286p. pap. 28.75 *(978-1-178-30515-9(5));* 286p. pap. 28.75 *(978-1-141-02373-8(3));* 282p. pap. 28.75 *(978-1-141-49107-0(9))* BiblioBazaar.

—The Flock. 2009. 94p. pap. *(978-0-217-29454-6(5))* Books LLC.

Babcock, Elizabeth. Magnificent Mavericks: History of the Navy at China Lake, California, Volume 3. 2007. (Illus.). 648p. pap. *(978-0-9676977-1-0(9))* China Lake Museum Foundation.

—Magnificent Mavericks: Transition of the Naval Ordnance Test Station from Rocket Station to Research, Development, Test, & Evaluation Center, 1948-58. 2008. (ENG., Illus.). 646p. 64.00 *(978-0-945274-56-8(4),* Dept. of the Navy) United States Government Printing Office.

Badella, Robert. Gold Rush of Californi. 2009. 80p. pap. 15.95 *(978-1-4490-0961-8(1))* AuthorHouse.

Baggese, Carl P. Modesto. 2011. (Postcard History Ser.). (ENG., Illus.). 128p. pap. 21.99 ***(978-0-7385-7579-7(8))*** Arcadia Publishing.

Baggese, Carl P. & McHenry Museum. Modesto. 2009. (Images of America Ser.). (ENG., Illus.). 128p. pap. 21.99 *(978-0-7385-7150-8(4))* Arcadia Publishing.

Bailey, Brad. Palomar Mountain. 2009. (Images of America Ser.). (ENG., Illus.). 128p. pap. 21.99 *(978-0-7385-7001-3(X))* Arcadia Publishing.

Baker, Patricia Laflin. Indio. 2008. (Images of America Ser.). (ENG., Illus.). 128p. per. 19.99 *(978-0-7385-5618-5(1))* Arcadia Publishing.

Bakker, Dona. Run of the Mill: A True Life, Napa Valley Adventure. 2008. (Illus.). pap. 13.95 *(978-0-9760276-4-5(X))* Pastime Pubns.

Bakus, Gerald J. Natural History of Santa Catalina Island. 2011. (ENG.). 403p. pap. 99.95 ***(978-1-4327-7552-0(9));*** 388p. pap. 28.95 ***(978-1-4327-7550-6(2))*** Outskirts Pr., Inc.

Ball, Guy & Tustin Area Historical Society. Tustin. 2011. (Images of America Ser.). (Illus.). 128p. pap. 21.99 *(978-0-7385-7037-2(0))* Arcadia Publishing.

Bancroft, Hubert Howe. California Pastoral. 2007. (ENG.). 816p. per. 55.95 *(978-0-548-50158-0(0))* Kessinger Publishing, LLC.

—History of California. 2009. 630p. pap. *(978-0-217-48763-4(7));* 680p. pap. *(978-0-217-48781-8(5));* 630p. pap. *(978-0-217-00490-9(3));* 628p. pap. *(978-0-217-48774-0(2))* Books LLC.

—History of California. 2009. 606p. pap. 43.06 *(978-1-150-44629-0(3))* General Bks. LLC.

Bancroft, Sarah C. Two Schools of Cool. 2012. (Illus.). 112p. pap. 29.95 ***(978-3-7913-5188-9(5))*** Prestel Publishing.

Bandini, Helen Elliott. History of California. 2008. 220p. 27.99 *(978-0-554-22684-2(7))* BiblioBazaar.

Bandini, Henry Elliot. History of California. 2007. (ENG.). 192p. pap. 19.99 *(978-1-4264-2857-9(X));* 216p. pap. 22.99 *(978-1-4264-2894-4(4))* BiblioBazaar.

Barker, Scott. Yokohl: A History of Its People & Their Culture. 2009. (Illus.). 266p. pap. *(978-0-615-29677-7(7))* Print Projects.

Barratt, Elizabeth & Carmel Valley Historical Society. Carmel Valley. 2009. (Images of America Ser.). (ENG., Illus.). 128p. pap. 21.99 *(978-0-7385-7162-1(8))* Arcadia Publishing.

Barrett, Samuel Alfred & Gifford, Edward Winslow. Miwok Material Culture: Indian Life of the Yosemite Region. 2011. 260p. 47.95 ***(978-1-258-02232-7(X))*** Literary Licensing, LLC.

Barry, Patricia A. In Search of Captain Warner. 1849. rev. ed. (Riders of the Western Great Basin Ser.: Vol. 1). (Illus.). 72p. pap. 10.00 *(978-0-9645403-0-9(4))* Barry, Patricia.

Barton, Jorane King. El Monte. 2006. (Images of America Ser.). (ENG., Illus.). 128p. per. 21.99 *(978-0-7385-4652-0(6))* Arcadia Publishing.

Bash, Kevin & Jouxtel, Brigitte. The Navy in Norco. 2011. (Images of America Ser.). (Illus.). 128p. pap. 21.99 ***(978-0-7385-7526-1(7))*** Arcadia Publishing.

Bash, Kevin & Jouxtel, Brigitte. The Norconian Resort. 2007. (Images of America Ser.). (ENG., Illus.). 128p. per. 21.99 *(978-0-7385-5559-1(2))* Arcadia Publishing.

Baumgardner, Frank H. Yanks in the Redwoods: Carving Out a Life in Northern California. 2010. *(978-0-87586-801-1(0));* 300p. pap. 31.95 *(978-0-87586-802-8(9))* Algora Publishing.

Baxter, R. Scott & Wooten, Kimberly J. Breweries of the Gold Country. 2012. (Images of America Ser.). (ENG., Illus.). 128p. pap. 21.99 ***(978-0-7385-7621-3(2))*** Arcadia Publishing.

Bayard, Samuel, abr. A Sketch of the Life of Com. Robert F. Stockton. 2009. (Military History Ser.). (ENG.). 348p. pap. 21.95 *(978-1-4290-2121-0(7))* Applewood Bks.

[Bayard, Samuel John]. A Sketch of the Life of Com Robert F Stockton; with an Appendix, Comprising His Correspondence with the Navy Department Respecting His Conquest of C. 2006. 348p. per. 23.99 *(978-1-4255-3526-1(7))* MPublishing.

Beals, Herbert K., et al, eds. Four Travel Journals: The Americas, Antarctica & Africa, 1775-1874. 2008. (Hakluyt Society, Third Series: 18 Ser.). (Illus.). 414p. 99.95 *(978-0-904180-90-9(5))* Hakluyt Society GBR. Dist: Ashgate Publishing Co.

Bear, John. Mendocino. 2011. (Illus.). 96p. 39.95 ***(978-0-9838172-0-8(0))*** Flying Bear Pr.

Bear-Step, Richard Shatka. The Ahwahnee Legend Kos-Soo-Kah & Tee Hee Neh: Lost Arrow of the Yosemite. 2011. 28p. 35.95 ***(978-1-258-02672-1(4))*** Literary Licensing, LLC.

Beebe, Rose Marie & Senkewicz, Robert M. Testimonios: Early California Through the Eyes of Women, 1815-1848. 2006. (Illus.). 470p. per. 18.95 *(978-1-59714-033-1(3))* Heyday.

Beebe, Rose Marie & Senkewicz, Robert M., eds. To Toil in that Vineyard of the Lord: Contemporary Scholarship on Junípero Serra. 2010. (Illus.). pap. 12.00 net. *(978-0-88382-312-5(8))* Academy of American Franciscan History.

Benbow, Bob, et al. Baldwin Park. 2011. (Images of America Ser.). (Illus.). 128p. pap. 21.99 *(978-0-7385-7484-4(8))* Arcadia Publishing.

Benelli, James. Ski Tales: The History of China Peak & Sierra Summit. 2009. (ENG.). 166p. pap. 10.95 *(978-1-884995-66-8(7))* Linden Publishing Co., Inc.

Benziger, Jeff. Waterford. 2011. (Images of America Ser.). (Illus.). 128p. pap. 21.99 *(978-0-7385-7452-3(X))* Arcadia Publishing.

Bergere, Darline. Ukiah. 2009. (Images of America Ser.). (ENG., Illus.). 128p. pap. 21.99 *(978-0-7385-7040-2(0))* Arcadia Publishing.

Berk, Lucy Jones & Covey, Stephen A. Escondido Grape Day Festivals. 2010. (Postcards of America Ser.). 7.99 *(978-0-7385-8137-8(2))* Arcadia Publishing.

Bishop, Greg, et al. California: Your Travel Guide to California's Local Legends & Best Kept Secrets. 2009. (Weird Ser.). (ENG., Illus.). 304p. pap. 14.95 *(978-1-4027-6683-1(1))* Sterling Publishing Co., Inc.

Blaschek-Miller, Travis, ed. California Cures: Translating Opportunity into California¿s Success. 2008. (Illus.). cd-rom *(978-0-9789300-2-8(9))* BayBio.

Boschetti, Edie. Oakdale Golf & Country Club: The First Fifty Years. 2011. ***(978-1-57864-691-3(X))*** Donning Co. Pubs.

Botts, Joseph. The Pleyto Hills. 2010. 186p. 23.95 *(978-1-4327-5766-3(0))*; (Illus.). pap. 14.95 *(978-1-4327-5760-1(1))* Outskirts Pr., Inc.

Boyd, William Harland. Kern County's Desert Country: An Historical Overview. (Illus.). 128p. 16.95 *(978-0-943500-16-4(8))* Kern County Historical Society.

Brigandi, Phil. A Brief History of Orange, California: The Plaza City. 2011. 160p. pap. 19.99 ***(978-1-60949-287-8(0))*** History Pr., The.

Brigandi, Phil. Orange. 2008. (Images of America Ser.). (ENG., Illus.). 128p. pap. 21.99 *(978-0-7385-5905-6(9))* Arcadia Publishing.

Broggie, Michael. The History of Irwindale: How the Rock Capital of Southern California Is Reinventing Itself. 2009. *(978-1-57864-548-0(4))* Donning Co. Pubs.

Bryant, Edwin. What I Saw in California. 2008. 228p. 27.99 *(978-0-554-24465-5(9))* 2007. 204p. pap. 20.99 *(978-1-4264-6558-1(0))* 2006. (ENG.). 226p. pap. 22.99 *(978-1-4264-6617-5(X))* BiblioBazaar.

—What I Saw in California. 2009. 382p. pap. *(978-0-217-14575-6(2))*; 380p. pap. *(978-0-217-65526-2(2))* Books LLC.

—What I Saw in California. 2008. 204p. pap. *(978-1-4099-3244-4(3))* Dodo Pr.

—What I Saw in California. 2008. (ENG.). 188p. pap. 13.95 *(978-1-4385-1024-8(1)*, Book Jungle) Standard Pubns., Inc.

Bullard, Edward F. History of Saratog: An Address. 2011. 26p. pap. 11.99 ***(978-1-4181-9274-7(0))*** MPublishing.

Burg, William. Sacramento. 2008. (Then & Now Ser.). (ENG., Illus.). 96p. pap. 21.99 *(978-0-7385-5900-1(8))* Arcadia Publishing.

Burnett, Claudine. Haunted Long Beach 2: The Odd & Unusual in & Around Long Beach, California. 2010. 220p. pap. 19.99 *(978-1-4520-5448-3(7))* AuthorHouse.

—Murderous Intent? Long Beach, CA. 2009. 176p. pap. 17.99 *(978-1-4389-4044-1(0))* AuthorHouse.

Butler, William J. March Air Force Base. 2009. (Images of America Ser.). (ENG., Illus.). 128p. pap. 21.99 *(978-0-7385-7159-1(8))* Arcadia Publishing.

California, Pa. , 1849-1881: A History of a Boat Building Town. 2009. (Illus.). 466p. pap. 20.00 *(978-0-9630513-5-6(0))* Yohogania Pr.

California State Automobile Assn. Staff. Palo Alto/Mountain View, CA. *(978-1-57835-120-6(0))* California State Automobile Assn.

Campbell, J. Howard. From Cinnabar to Quicksilver. 2009. 86p. pap. 14.68 *(978-0-578-01486-9(6))* New Almaden Quicksilver County Park Assn.

Carberg, David. Bolsa Chica: Its History from Prehistoric Times to the Present. 2009. 251p. pap. 17.95 *(978-1-934379-92-9(1))* Printmedia Bks.

Carle, David & Banta, Don. Mono Lake Basin. 2008. (Images of America Ser.). (ENG., Illus.). 128p. pap. 21.99 *(978-0-7385-5909-4(1))* Arcadia Publishing.

Carpenter, Neva Calvert. Harem Scarem in El Cerrito: The Life of a Little Girl Growing up in El Cerrito, California. 2006. 124p. mass mkt. 13.75 *(978-0-9789320-0-8(5))* Carpenter, Neva.

Carrico, Richard L. Ramona. 2011. (Images of America Ser.). (ENG., Illus.). 128p. pap. 21.99 *(978-0-7385-8162-0(3))* Arcadia Publishing.

Cass, Maxine. Speaking Ill of the Dead: Jerks in California History. 2012. (Speaking Ill of the Dead: Jerks in Histo Ser.). (ENG., Illus.). 232p. pap. 16.95 *(978-0-7627-7240-7(9))* Globe Pequot Pr., The.

Cavalier, Lois Vaughan. Vista. 2008. (Images of America Ser.). (ENG., Illus.). 128p. pap. 21.99 *(978-0-7385-5939-1(3))* Arcadia Publishing.

Cenotto, Lawrence A. Logan's Alley: Amador County Yesterdays in Picture & Prose, Five. 2006. 39.95 *(978-0-938121-16-9(2))* Cenotto Pubns.

Chalquist, Craig. Deep Californi: Images & Ironies of Cross & Sword on el Camino Real. 2008. 736p. pap. 38.95 *(978-0-595-51462-5(6))* iUniverse, Inc.

Chambers, Ruth. The Weight of Gold: 1849 Gold Rush, California. 2009. 264p. pap. 14.49 *(978-1-4389-9725-4(6))* AuthorHouse.

Champion, Jerry Lewis. The Fading Voices of Alcatraz. 2011. 192p. 24.60 *(978-1-4567-1487-1(2))*; pap. 15.00 *(978-1-4567-1488-8(0))* AuthorHouse.

Chester Smith Lyman. Around the Horn to the Sandwich Islands & California, 1845-1850. Teggart, Frederick J., ed. 2006. (ENG.). 384p. per. 33.95 *(978-1-4286-5502-7(6))* Kessinger Publishing, LLC.

Chiang, Connie Y. Shaping the Shoreline: Fisheries & Tourism on the Monterey Coast. (ENG., Illus.). 320p. (C). 2011. pap. 25.00 *(978-0-295-99139-9(9))* 2008. 35.00 *(978-0-295-98831-3(2))* Univ. of Washington Pr.

Chiles, Frederic Caire. Justinian Caire & Santa Cruz Island: The Rise & Fall of a California Dynasty. 2011. (ENG., Illus.). 240p. 34.95 *(978-0-87062-400-1(8)*, Clark, Arthur H., Co., The) Univ. of Oklahoma Pr.

Chinese Historical and Cultural Project, et al. Chinese in San Jose & the Santa Clara Valley. 2007. (Images of America Ser.). (ENG., Illus.). 128p. per. 19.99 *(978-0-7385-4777-0(8))* Arcadia Publishing.

Christian, Victoria. Sunol. 2007. (Images of America Ser.). (Illus.). 128p. per. 19.99 *(978-0-7385-5554-6(1))* Arcadia Publishing.

Chung, Arthur W. Bitter Roots. 2007. (Illus.). 157p. 18.00 *(978-1-928753-25-4(6))* Pacific Heritage Bks.

Churchill, Marlowe J. The Riverside National Cemetery Story: A Field of Warriors. 2009. *(978-1-57864-588-6(3))* Donning Co. Pubs.

City of Walnut & Walnut Historical Society. Walnut. 2012. (Images of America Ser.). (ENG., Illus.). 128p. pap. 21.99 ***(978-0-7385-9547-4(0))*** Arcadia Publishing.

Clark, Ralph A. & Lodi Historical Society. Lodi: 1945-2005. 2011. (Images of America Ser.). (Illus.). 128p. pap. 21.99 *(978-0-7385-7548-3(8))* Arcadia Publishing.

Clark, Susan M. The Sea Ranch. 2009. (Images of America Ser.). (Illus.). 128p. pap. 21.99 *(978-0-7385-5990-2(3))* Arcadia Publishing.

Clovis Centennial Committee. Clovis. 2011. (Images of America Ser.). (Illus.). 128p. pap. 21.99 ***(978-0-7385-7613-8(1))*** Arcadia Publishing.

Clucas, Donald Laine. Century of Community: Upland California-the First 100 Years. 2011. 256p. 34.95 *(978-0-944933-16-9(5))* Stephens Pr. LLC.

Clucas, Donald Laine, et al. Upland. 2009. (Images of America Ser.). (ENG., Illus.). 128p. pap. 21.99 *(978-0-7385-6984-0(4))* Arcadia Publishing.

Colorful Men Women & Tales of the Mother Lode. 2006. (Illus.). 275p. pap. 16.95 *(978-0-9653428-3-4(2))* Irene, Jan Pubns.

Colton, Walter. Three Years in California by Rev Walter Colton. 2011. 472p. pap. 29.99 ***(978-1-4255-8953-0(7))*** MPublishing.

Comstock, David Allan, anno. News & Advertising in the Early Gold Camps of Nevada County 1850-1852. 2008. 228p. spiral bd. 30.00 *(978-0-933994-36-2(2))* Comstock Bonanza Pr.

—News & Advertising in the Early Gold Camps of Nevada County 1853, 9 vols., Vol. 2. 2008. 178p. spiral bd. 25.00 *(978-0-933994-37-9(0))* Comstock Bonanza Pr.

—News & Advertising in the Early Gold Camps of Nevada County 1854. 2008. 195p. spiral bd. 25.00 *(978-0-933994-38-6(9))* Comstock Bonanza Pr.

—News & Advertising in the Early Gold Camps of Nevada County 1855. 2007. 169p. spiral bd. 25.00 *(978-0-933994-39-3(7))* Comstock Bonanza Pr.

—News & Advertising in the Early Gold Camps of Nevada County 1856. 2007. 260p. spiral bd. 30.00 *(978-0-933994-40-9(0))* Comstock Bonanza Pr.

—News & Advertising in the Early Gold Camps of Nevada County 1857. 2007. 282p. spiral bd. 30.00 *(978-0-933994-41-6(9))* Comstock Bonanza Pr.

—News & Advertising in the Early Gold Camps of Nevada County 1858, 9 vols., Vol. 7. 2007. 279p. spiral bd. 30.00 *(978-0-933994-42-3(7))* Comstock Bonanza Pr.

—News & Advertising in the Early Gold Camps of Nevada County 1859, 9 vols., Vol. 8. 2007. 243p. spiral bd. 30.00 *(978-0-933994-43-0(5))* Comstock Bonanza Pr.

Comstock, David Allan, compiled by & anno. News & Advertising in the Early Gold Camps of Nevada County 1860. 2008. 330p. spiral bd. 35.00 *(978-0-933994-44-7(3))* Comstock Bonanza Pr.

Conaway, Peggy. Los Gatos Generations. 2007. (Images of America Ser.). (ENG., Illus.). 128p. pap. 19.99 *(978-0-7385-5561-4(4))* Arcadia Publishing.

Conmy, Peter Thomas. Philip Augustine Roach, 1820-1889: California Pioneer. 2011. 32p. pap. 35.95 ***(978-1-258-08708-1(1))*** Literary Licensing, LLC.

Convis, Charles. California in Old West. 2008. pap. 11.95 *(978-1-892156-25-9(3))* Pioneer Pr.

Conyers, Patrick, et al. Pasadena: 1940-2008. 2009. (Images of America Ser.). (Illus.). 128p. pap. 21.99 *(978-0-7385-6907-9(0))* Arcadia Publishing.

—Pasadena: A Business History. 2007. (Images of America Ser.). (Illus.). 127p. per. 19.99 *(978-0-7385-4778-7(6))* Arcadia Publishing.

Coodley, Lauren. California: A Multicultural Documentary History. 2008. (ENG., Illus.). 384p. (C). per. 45.60 *(978-0-13-188410-6(7)*, Prentice Hall) Prentice Hall PTR.

—Napa: The Transformation of an American Town. 2007. (ENG., Illus.). 192p. per. 24.99 *(978-0-7385-2502-0(2))* Arcadia Publishing.

Cooke, Philip, abr. The Conquest of New Mexico & California. 2009. (Military History Ser.). (ENG.). 315p. pap. 20.95 *(978-1-4290-2090-9(3))* Applewood Bks.

Cooper, Martin M. North of Mulholland: Essays from the San Fernando Valley Business Journal. 2010. 260p. 28.95 *(978-1-4490-8211-6(4))*; pap. 18.95 *(978-1-4490-8212-3(2))* AuthorHouse.

Covey, Stephen A. Early Escondido: The Louis A. Havens Collection. 2008. (Images of America Ser.). (ENG., Illus.). 128p. per. 21.99 *(978-0-7385-5595-9(9))* Arcadia Publishing.

Cragg, Curt. Solvang. 2008. (Postcard History Ser.). (Illus.). 128p. pap. 19.99 *(978-0-7385-5935-3(0))* Arcadia Publishing.

Cram101 Textbook Reviews. Outlines & Highlights for Elusive Eden: A New History of California by Richard Rice. 2011. 416p. pap. 35.95 ***(978-1-61906-023-4(X))*** Cram101 Inc.

Cueva-Fernandez, Olivia. Mexican Americans in Wilmington. 2011. (Images of America Ser.). (ENG., Illus.). 128p. pap. 21.99 *(978-0-7385-8174-3(7))* Arcadia Publishing.

Cushing, Lincoln. All of Us or None: Social Justice Posters of the San Francisco Bay Area. 2012. pap. ***(978-1-59714-185-7(2))*** Heyday.

Cutts, James, abr. The Conquest of California & New Mexico. 2009. (Military History Ser.). (ENG.). 268p. pap. 17.95 *(978-1-4290-2089-3(X))* Applewood Bks.

Dace, Catherine Egbert. Early San Fernando, Memoirs of Mrs Catherine Dace: Southern California Quarterly, V44, No. 3, September 1962. Dixon, Elizabeth I., ed. 2011. 52p. 36.95 ***(978-1-258-07089-2(8))*** Literary Licensing, LLC.

Daily, Marla & Santa Cruz Island Foundation. The California Channel Islands. 2012. (Images of America Ser.). (ENG., Illus.). 128p. 21.99 ***(978-0-7385-9508-5(X))*** Arcadia Publishing.

Dalberg, Lana. A Dream Journey: The Incredible Story of the Founding of Eastside College Preparatory School. 2008. 62p. *(978-0-9770735-1-1(3))* Univ. of Dreams.

Dan Colchico: The Port Chicago Defense. 2007. pap. *(978-1-933846-08-8(9))* Media Man! Productions.

Dana, Richard Henry. A Yankee in Mexican California, 1834-1836. 2010. pap. *(978-1-59714-119-2(4))* Heyday.

Datel, Robin, et al. Woodland. 2012. (Images of America Ser.). (ENG., Illus.). 128p. pap. 21.99 ***(978-0-7385-8900-8(4))*** Arcadia Publishing.

Davies, J. Kenneth & Hansen, Lorin K. Mormon Gold: Mormons in the California Gold Rush, Contributing to the Development of California & the Monetary Solvency of Early Utah. 2nd ed. 2010. (ENG., Illus.). 460p. 59.95 *(978-0-9830832-0-7(7))* Granite Mountain Publishing Co.

Davis, John F. California Romantic & Resourceful. 2009. 48p. pap. *(978-1-4099-0470-0(9))* Dodo Pr.

Day, Aaron L. & Kaletucker, Indira. The Heritage of African-Americans in Long Beach: Over 100 Years. 2007. 308p. pap. 24.95 *(978-0-7414-3514-9(4))* Infinity Publishing.

de Kehoe, Joe. The Silence & the Sun: An historical account of people, places & events on old Route 66 & railroad communities in the Eastern Mojave Desert, California. 2007. (Illus.). 282p. pap. 29.95 *(978-0-9793827-0-3(X))* Trails End Publishing Co.

de Martino, Thomas, et al. Chino. 2011. (Images of America Ser.). (Illus.). 128p. pap. 21.99 *(978-0-7385-8142-2(9))* Arcadia Publishing.

Deering, Susan. Silverado Canyon. 2008. (Images of America Ser.). (Illus.). 128p. pap. 21.99 *(978-0-7385-5962-9(8))* Arcadia Publishing.

Delamere, Henry & Hopkins, Tammy L. Marysville. 2007. (Images of America Ser.). (ENG., Illus.). 128p. per. 21.99 *(978-0-7385-4737-4(9))* Arcadia Publishing.

Delaney, Jeff. Newport Beach. 2011. (Then & Now Ser.). (Illus.). 96p. pap. 21.99 *(978-0-7385-8202-3(6))* Arcadia Publishing.

Dellenbaugh, Frederick S. Fremont & 49 the Story of A Remarkable. 2006. pap. 50.95 *(978-1-4286-5184-5(5))* Kessinger Publishing, LLC.

Devaul, Gary & Thallander, Mark. Champions Plus. 2007. 232p. per. 14.95 *(978-1-59330-501-7(X))* Aventine Pr.

Dever, Kathleen & Whitson, Judy. Lake Mathews & Gavilan Hills. 2007. (Images of America Ser.). (ENG., Illus.). 128p. per. 19.99 *(978-0-7385-4779-4(4))* Arcadia Publishing.

Discovering Bodie. 2010. (Illus.). 80p. pap. 21.99 *(978-0-9843634-0-7(8))* Gariaeff, Nick.

Draney, Daniel W. When Streams Diverge: John Murdoch Macinnis & the Origins of Protestant Fundamentalism in Los Angeles. 2008. (Studies in Evangelical History & Thought Ser.). (Illus.). 292p. pap. 34.00 *(978-1-60608-015-3(6))* Wipf & Stock Pubs.

Drew, Kjysten W. Peacekeepers: A concise History of Ferndale, Washington & the Men Who Upheld the Law(One Hundred Years 1907-2007. 2009. pap. *(978-1-61623-841-4(0))* Independent Pub.

Drylie, Gary "Old Town Griz". Hesperia. 2010. (Images of America Ser.). (Illus.). 128p. pap. 21.99 *(978-0-7385-8107-1(0))* Arcadia Publishing.

Dunn, Joe. Pocket of Paradise: The Story of Beach Road. 2008. (Illus.). 108p. pap. 30.00 *(978-0-9753939-7-0(9))* Prospect Park Bks., LLC.

Dunne, John Gregory. Delano: The Story of the California Grape Strike. 2007. (Illus.). 202p. per. 24.95 *(978-0-520-25433-6(3))* Univ. of California Pr.

Dutcher, Greta, et al. Alameda. 2008. (Images of America Ser.). (ENG., Illus.). 128p. pap. 21.99 *(978-0-7385-5953-7(9))* Arcadia Publishing.

Eargle, Dolan H. Native California Guide. 2008. 333p. pap. 25.00 *(978-0-937401-11-8(0))* Trees Co. Pr.

Eargle, Dolan H., Jr. Native California Guide: Introduction to the Original Peoples from Earliest Times to the Present. Dodsworth, Fred, ed. 2007. (ENG., Illus.). 330p. pap. 25.00 *(978-0-937401-10-1(2))* Trees Co. Pr.

East, Claudia A., et al. Yreka. 2007. (Images of America Ser.). (Illus.). 128p. per. 19.99 *(978-0-7385-4735-0(2))* Arcadia Publishing.

Eastis, Annette L. Making Room: A California Christmas Gift. 2010. pap. 7.99 *(978-1-61663-176-5(7))* Tate Publishing & Enterprises, LLC.

Edmonds, John G. The Civil War: Northern California's Unrecognized Valor. 2010. *(978-0-89863-326-9(5))* Star Publishing Co.

Eldredge, Ward. Kings Canyon National Park. 2009. (Images of America Ser.). (ENG., Illus.). 128p. pap. 21.99 *(978-0-7385-5996-4(2))* Arcadia Publishing.

Eldredge, Zoeth S. The March of Portola & the Discovery of the Bay of San Francisco. Molera, E. J., tr. 2007. 72p. per. *(978-1-4065-1790-3(9))* Dodo Pr.

—The March of Portola & the Discovery of the Bay of San Francisco. 2007. (ENG.). 72p. per. *(978-1-4068-6299-7(1))* Echo Library.

Eldridge, Ward. Sequoia NATL Park. 2008. (Images of America Ser.). (ENG., Illus.). 128p. pap. 21.99 *(978-0-7385-5940-7(7))* Arcadia Publishing.

Elliott, Onnolee. Twelve Flags over California: California's History Makers 1542-1850, 1. 2006. (Illus.). 230p. 30.00 *(978-1-891030-52-9(3))* Paragon Agency, The.

Emick, Paula. Rancho Cucamonga. 2011. (Images of America Ser.). (ENG., Illus.). 128p. pap. 21.99 ***(978-0-7385-7500-1(3))*** Arcadia Publishing.

Epting, Chris. Baseball in Orange County. 2012. (Images of America Ser.). (ENG., Illus.). 128p. pap. 21.99 ***(978-0-7385-9328-9(1))*** Arcadia Publishing.

—Orange County. 2011. (Then & Now Ser.). (Illus.). 96p. pap. 21.99 *(978-0-7385-8115-6(1))* Arcadia Publishing.

—Vanishing Orange County. 2008. (Images of America Ser.). (Illus.). 128p. pap. 21.99 *(978-0-7385-5974-2(1))* Arcadia Publishing.

F. H. Oberding Usaf (Ret.). Hamilton Field Diary: The Country Club Airbase. 2011. 386p. 29.99 ***(978-1-4628-9604-2(9))***; pap. 19.99 ***(978-1-4628-9603-5(0))*** Xlibris Corp.

Faessel, Stephen J. Anaheim 1940-2007. 2007. (Images of America Ser.). (ENG., Illus.). 128p. per. 19.99 *(978-0-7385-4743-5(3))* Arcadia Publishing.

Faessel, Stephen J., text. Historic Photos of Anaheim. 2007. (Historic Photos Ser.). (ENG., Illus.). 204p. 39.95 *(978-1-59652-333-3(6))* Turner Publishing Co.

Fages, Pedro & Serra, Junipero. Letters of Captain Don Pedro Fages & President Junipero Serra at San Diego, California in October 1772. 2011. 16p. pap. 35.95 ***(978-1-258-02669-1(4))*** Literary Licensing, LLC.

Falany, Henry. God, Gold & Glory! The California Contribution. 2009. (Illus.). 268p. pap. 26.95 *(978-1-4327-5209-5(X))* Outskirts Pr., Inc.

Fanning, Branwell. Marin County. 2007. (Images of America Ser.). (ENG., Illus.). 128p. per. 21.99 *(978-0-7385-5571-3(1))* Arcadia Publishing.

—Maritime Marin. 2008. (Images of America Ser.). (ENG., Illus.). 128p. pap. 19.99 *(978-0-7385-5904-9(0))* Arcadia Publishing.

—Tiburon & Belvedere. 2010. (Then & Now Ser.). (Illus.). 96p. pap. 21.99 *(978-0-7385-8188-0(7))* Arcadia Publishing.

Fanning, Branwell & Wong, William. Angel Island. 2007. (Images of America Ser.). (ENG., Illus.). 128p. per. 21.99 *(978-0-7385-4719-0(0))* Arcadia Publishing.

Farnbach, Rebecca, et al. Murrieta Hot Springs. 2008. (Images of America Ser.). (ENG., Illus.). 128p. pap. 21.99 *(978-0-7385-5958-8(3))* Arcadia Publishing.

—Temecula Wine Country. 2009. 15p. pap. 7.99 *(978-0-7385-7015-0(X))* Arcadia Publishing.

Farnham, Thomas Jefferson. The Early Days of California. 2006. 356p. per. 26.99 *(978-1-4255-3677-0(8))* MPublishing.

Fetzer, Leland. The Cuyamacas: The Story of San Diego's High Country, 1772-2003. 2008. *(978-0-932653-94-9(4))* Sunbelt Pubns., Inc.

Filipelli, Deborah L. Before Smokey Bear There Was Woodbridge Metcalf. 2008. 304p. pap. *(978-3-639-08286-9(9))* VDM Verlag Dr. Mueller e.K.

Fitzpatrick, Linda & Conkle, James M. Needles. 2010. (Images of America Ser.). (Illus.). 128p. pap. 21.99 *(978-0-7385-8064-7(3))* Arcadia Publishing.

Fortunate Eagle, Adam & Findley, Tim. Heart of the Rock: The Indian Invasion of Alcatraz. 2008. (ENG., Illus.). 232p. pap. 19.95 *(978-0-8061-3989-0(7))* Univ. of Oklahoma Pr.

Fradkin, Philip L. The Left Coast: California on the Edge. 2011. (ENG., Illus.). 126p. pap. 29.95 *(978-0-520-25509-8(7))* Univ. of California Pr.

Frank, Phil. Houseboats of Sausalito. 2008. (Images of America Ser.). (ENG., Illus.). 128p. pap. 19.99 *(978-0-7385-5552-2(5))* Arcadia Publishing.

Freeman, Glenn Edward. Riverside. 2009. (Then & Now Ser.). (ENG., Illus.). 128p. pap. 21.99 *(978-0-7385-7079-2(6))* Arcadia Publishing.

Gabriel, Louise B. & Santa Monica Historical Society. Santa Monica: 1950-2010. 2011. (Images of America Ser.). (ENG., Illus.). 128p. pap. 21.99 *(978-0-7385-8143-9(7))* Arcadia Publishing.

Gamble, Lynn H. Chumash World at European Contact: Power, Trade, & Feasting among Complex Hunter-Gatherers. 2008. (Illus.). 376p. 55.00 *(978-0-520-25441-1(4))* Univ. of California Pr.

—The Chumash World at European Contact: Power, Trade, & Feasting among Complex Hunter-Gatherers. 2011. (ENG.). 376p. pap. 29.95 *(978-0-520-27124-1(6))* Univ. of California Pr.

Ganster, Paul. Loreto: Future of First Capital of California. 2008. 704p. pap. *(978-0-925613-52-3(5))* San Diego State Univ., Institute for Regional Studies of the Californias.

Garate, Donald T. Termo to Madeline: Northern California's Last Frontier. Date not set. (Illus.). 436p. 14.95 *(978-0-938373-18-6(8))* Lahontan Images.

Gardner, Jeanette & De Graaf, Lawrence. Early Placentia. 2007. (Images of America Ser.). (ENG., Illus.). 128p. per. 21.99 *(978-0-7385-4728-2(X))* Arcadia Publishing.

Garnett Clark, Ginger. Rancho Palos Verdes. 2009. (Images of America Ser.). (ENG., Illus.). 128p. pap. 21.99 *(978-0-7385-6920-8(8))* Arcadia Publishing.

Geissinger, Terri Lynn. Bodie: 1859-1962. 2009. (Images of America Ser.). (ENG., Illus.). 128p. pap. 21.99 *(978-0-7385-5986-5(5))* Arcadia Publishing.

Gerber, Judith. Farming in Torrance & the South Bay. 2008. (Images of America Ser.). (ENG., Illus.). 128p. pap. 21.99 *(978-0-7385-5930-8(X))* Arcadia Publishing.

Gerston, Larry N. Not so Golden after All: The Rise & Fall of California. 2012. (ENG., Illus.). 342p. 59.95 ***(978-1-4398-8012-8(3)***, CRC Press) Taylor & Francis Group GBR. Dist: Taylor & Francis Group.

Gibson, Dorothy E. Marin Headlands. 2009. (Images of America Ser.). (ENG., Illus.). 128p. pap. 21.99 *(978-0-7385-7024-2(9))* Arcadia Publishing.

Gibson, Jack. Mount Tamalpais & the Marin Municipal Water District. 2012. (Images of America Ser.). (ENG., Illus.). 128p. pap. 21.99 ***(978-0-7385-9317-3(6))*** Arcadia Publishing.

Gillespie, Bunny & Crimmen, Dave. Daly City. 2011. (Then & Now Ser.). (Illus.). 96p. pap. 21.99 *(978-0-7385-7523-0(2))* Arcadia Publishing.

Gillingham, Harry J. Pioneer Masonry of the Golden State & Other Historical Sketches. 2011. 126p. 40.95 ***(978-1-258-03488-7(3))*** Literary Licensing, LLC.

Godfrey, Donal. Gays & Grays: The Story of the Inclusion of the Gay Community at Most Holy Redeemer Catholic Parish in San Francisco. 2008. (ENG.). 208p. pap. 26.50 *(978-0-7391-1938-9(9))* Lexington Bks.

Goin, Peter. Lake Tahoe: A Maritime History. 2012. (Images of America Ser.). (ENG., Illus.). 128p. pap. 21.99 ***(978-0-7385-8912-1(8))*** Arcadia Publishing.

Gomez, Dolores & Thilmany, Christy. Brisbane. 2009. 128p. pap. 21.99 *(978-0-7385-7048-8(6))* Arcadia Publishing.

Goodwin, Frederick. The Ranger Badge: Book Two of the Parsons Family Trilogy. 2008. 320p. pap. 19.99 *(978-1-4259-3499-6(4))* AuthorHouse.

Gordon, Maggie. Historical Casitas of la Quinta Cove. 2007. 98p. pap. 12.95 *(978-0-7414-3937-6(9))* Infinity Publishing.

Gossard, Gloria Hine. Tehachapi. 2008. (Images of America Ser.). (ENG., Illus.). 128p. per. 21.99 *(978-0-7385-5560-7(6))* Arcadia Publishing.

Graffy, Neal. Historic Santa Barbara: An Illustrated History. 2010. (Illus.). 208p. ***(978-1-935377-14-6(0))*** Historical Publishing Network.

Graham, Seana & Wojna, Lisa. Bathroom Book of Southern California. 2007. (Bathroom Book Of... Ser.). (ENG., Illus.). 224p. per. *(978-1-897278-29-1(2))* Lone Pine Publishing USA.

Le Grand History: Memories of le Grand History Club. 2007. (Illus.). 99p. (C). pap. 9.95 *(978-0-9729318-5-4(6))* Merced County Historical Society.

Guild, Novato Historical & Vela, Ron. Novato. 2009. 96p. pap. 21.99 *(978-0-7385-7194-2(6))* Arcadia Publishing.

Guinn, J. M. History & Biographical Record of Monterey & San Benito, CA, Vol. II. fac. ed. (Illus.). 453p. reprint ed. pap. 46.88 *(978-1-55567-753-4(3))* Coyote Pr.

—History & Biographical Record of Monterey & San Benito Counties & History of the State of California I. (Illus.). 334p. (C). pap. 35.00 *(978-1-55567-752-7(5))* Coyote Pr.

Gunther, Vanessa. Ambiguous Justice: Native Americans & the Law in Southern California, 1848-1890. annot. ed. 2006. (Native American Ser.). (ENG.). 191p. per. 29.95 *(978-0-87013-779-2(4))* Michigan State Univ. Pr.

Hackel, Steven W., ed. Alta California: Peoples in Motion, Identities in Formation. 2009. (Western Histories Ser.). (ENG., Illus.). 304p. 55.00 *(978-0-87328-242-0(6))* Huntington Library Pr.

Halberstadt, April, et al. Saratoga. 2009. (Postcards of America Ser.). (Illus.). 128p. pap. 7.99 *(978-0-7385-6964-2(X))*; pap. 21.99 *(978-0-7385-6963-5(1))* Arcadia Publishing.

Hall, Barbara-Ann. Covina Valley Citrus Industry. 2011. (Images of America Ser.). (Illus.). 128p. pap. 21.99 *(978-0-7385-7442-4(2))* Arcadia Publishing.

Hall, Barbara-Ann & Covina Valley Historical Society. Covina. 2007. (Images of America Ser.). (ENG., Illus.). 128p. per. 21.99 *(978-0-7385-5555-3(X))* Arcadia Publishing.

Hall, Marian. Malibu, California's Most Famous Sea Side Community. 2009. 40.00 *(978-1-61623-396-9(6))* Independent Pub.

Hall, Roger. The West of the West: Perspectives on California State History. 2nd rev. ed. 2010. (ENG.). 268p. pap. 54.26 *(978-0-7575-6521-2(2))* Kendall Hunt Publishing Co.

Hansen, Debra Gold & Valdez, Lisa. A Pioneering & Independent Spirit: The History of San José State University's School of Library & Information Science. 2010. 164p. 35.00 *(978-1-4269-2108-7(X))*; pap. 25.00 *(978-1-4269-2109-4(8))* Trafford Publishing.

Hanson, Joyce A. & Suzie Earp, and Erin Shanks. Community Hospital of San Bernardino. 2009. 128p. pap. 21.99 *(978-0-7385-7022-8(2))* Arcadia Publishing.

Harris, Jim. Santa Monica Pier: A Century of the Last Great Pleasure Pier. 2009. (Illus.). 128p. *(978-1-883318-82-6(3))* Angel City Pr.

Harris, Joel A. Concord. 2009. (Images of America Ser.). (ENG., Illus.). 128p. pap. 21.99 *(978-0-7385-6913-0(5))* Arcadia Publishing.

Hastings, Lansford. The Emigrants' Guide to Oregon & Californi. 2007. 156p. per. 10.95 *(978-1-60206-729-5(5))* Cosimo, Inc.

Hastings, Lansford W. The Emigrants Guide to Oregon & Califo. 2006. 156p. per. *(978-1-4067-9579-0(8))*, Pierides Pr.) Read Bks.

Hayes-Bautista, David E. El Cinco de Mayo: An American Tradition. 2012. (ENG., Illus.). 303p. 65.00 ***(978-0-520-27212-5(9))***; pap. 26.95 ***(978-0-520-27213-2(7))*** Univ. of California Pr.

Hecteman, Kevin W. Sacramento Southern Railroad. 2009. (Images of Rail Ser.). (ENG., Illus.). 128p. pap. 21.99 *(978-0-7385-6986-4(0))* Arcadia Publishing.

Hee-Chorley, Lorraine. Chinese in Mendocino County. 2009. (Images of America Ser.). (ENG., Illus.). 128p. pap. 21.99 *(978-0-7385-5913-1(X))* Arcadia Publishing.

Heidenreich, Linda. This Land Was Mexican Once: Histories of Resistance from Northern California. 2007. (Chicana Matters Ser.). (ENG., Illus.). 272p. pap. 25.00 *(978-0-292-71634-6(6))* Univ. of Texas Pr.

Heinle and Heinle Staff. Heinle & Heinle California Brochure. 0.95 *(978-0-8384-7668-0(6))* Cengage Heinle.

Hemet Area Museum Association. Hemet. 2008. (Images of America Ser.). (ENG., Illus.). 128p. pap. 19.99 *(978-0-7385-5846-2(X))* Arcadia Publishing.

Henderson, Moya & Palm Springs Historical Society. Palm Springs. 2009. (Images of America Ser.). (ENG., Illus.). 128p. pap. 21.99 *(978-0-7385-5982-7(2))* Arcadia Publishing.

Hendrickson, Nancy. Historic Photos of Old California. 2009. (Historic Photos Ser.). (ENG.). 205p. 39.95 *(978-1-59652-524-5(X))* Turner Publishing Co.

—Remembering Old California. 2011. (Remembering Ser.). (ENG.). 134p. pap. 16.95 *(978-1-59652-796-6(2))* Turner Publishing Co.

Hennessey, Beverly. Hetch Hetchy. 2012. (Images of America Ser.). (ENG., Illus.). 128p. pap. 21.99 ***(978-0-7385-9322-7(2))*** Arcadia Publishing.

Hill, Suki. Mill Valley. 2007. (Then & Now Ser.). (ENG., Illus.). 96p. per. 21.99 *(978-0-7385-5574-4(5))* Arcadia Publishing.

Historical Society of Palm Desert & Historical Society of Palm Desert. Palm Desert. 2009. (Images of America Ser.). (ENG., Illus.). 128p. pap. 21.99 *(978-0-7385-5964-3(4))* Arcadia Publishing.

History of Mesa Consolidated Water District: 1960/2010 Celebrating Fifty Years of Water Service to Our Community. 2010. *(978-1-57864-651-7(0))* Donning Co. Pubs.

Hoberg, Donna. Resorts of Lake County. 2007. (Images of America Ser.). (Illus.). 127p. per. 21.99 *(978-0-7385-4798-5(0))* Arcadia Publishing.

Hollenbeck, J. M. The Golden Star: An Illustrated History of the Badges, Patches, & Insignia of the Orange County, California Sheriff's Department. 2007. (Illus.). lib. bdg. 45.00 *(978-1-932439-80-9(3))* M.T. Publishing Co., Inc.

Holtzclaw, Kenneth M. & Chong, Tom. Cherry Valley. 2008. (Images of America Ser.). (ENG., Illus.). 128p. pap. 19.99 *(978-0-7385-5952-0(0))* Arcadia Publishing.

Homan, Anne Marshall. Historic Livermore, California: Illustrated, A-Z. 2007. (Illus.). 583p. pap. *(978-0-9678989-7-1(8))* Hardscratch Pr.

Homor, Jody E., compiled by. The Golden Hub, Sacramento: 19th Century Sacramento County. 2008. (Illus.). 312p. pap. 24.95 *(978-0-9766976-8-8(8))*, Nineteenth Century Bks.) Electric Canvas.

—4 Book Set with Hub: Golden Corridor, Golden Hub & Golden Highway 49 Vol 1 And 2. 2008. (Illus.). 1080p. pap. 99.95 *(978-0-9766976-2-6(9))*, Nineteenth Century Bks.) Electric Canvas.

Homor, Ric, photos by. The Golden Highway Highway 49 Volume I: El Dorado, Placer, Nevada, Sierra Counties, 2 vols., Vol. 1. 2006. (ENG., Illus.). 266p. per. 22.95 *(978-0-9766976-6-4(1))*, Nineteenth Century Bks.) Electric Canvas.

—The Golden Highway Highway 49 Volume II: Amador, Calveras, Tuolumne, Mariposa & Madera Counties. 2007. (ENG., Illus.). 296p. per. 22.95 *(978-0-9766976-7-1(X))*, Nineteenth Century Bks.) Electric Canvas.

Horton, Jane. The 60 / 70 Sparkling - A Palo Alto Dreamer. 2010. 386p. pap. 26.50 *(978-0-557-19084-3(3))* Lulu Enterprises Inc.

Hubbard Crawford, Leslie. Coronado. 2011. (Images of America Ser.). (ENG., Illus.). 128p. pap. 21.99 *(978-0-7385-8130-9(5))* Arcadia Publishing.

Hubbard, Jean & Hoving, Gary. Arroyo Grande. 2009. 15p. pap. 7.99 *(978-0-7385-6945-1(3))* Arcadia Publishing.

Hubbard, Jean, et al. Arroyo Grande. 2009. (Images of America Ser.). (ENG., Illus.). 128p. pap. 21.99 *(978-0-7385-6944-4(5))* Arcadia Publishing.

Hubbard, Steve. Powerhouses of the Sierra Nevada. 2007. (Images of America Ser.). (Illus.). 128p. per. 19.99 *(978-0-7385-4757-2(3))* Arcadia Publishing.

Hubbartt, Michael Don. The Sutter Buttes. 2010. (Images of America Ser.). (ENG., Illus.). 128p. pap. 21.99 *(978-0-7385-8013-5(9))* Arcadia Publishing.

Hughes, John, abr. Doniphan's Expedition. 2009. (Military History Ser.). (ENG.). 148p. pap. 11.95 *(978-1-4290-2088-6(1))* Applewood Bks.

Hulstrum, Bill. Perris: A Place to Remember. 2007. *(978-1-57864-409-4(7))* Donning Co. Pubs.

Huntley, Jennifer. Making of Yosemite. 2011. 248p. 34.95 ***(978-0-7006-1805-7(8))*** Univ. Pr. of Kansas.

Hurtado, Albert L. John Sutter: A Life on the North American Frontier. (ENG.). 412p. 2008. pap. 24.95 *(978-0-8061-3929-6(3))* 2006. (Illus.). 34.95 *(978-0-8061-3772-8(X))* Univ. of Oklahoma Pr.

Hyslop, Richard S., et al. California Eclectic: A Topical Geography. rev ed. 2010. (ENG.). 260p. pap. 79.91 *(978-0-7575-7060-5(7))* Kendall Hunt Publishing Co.

Hyslop, Stephen G. Contest for California: From Spanish Colonization to the American Conquest. 2012. (Before Gold: California under Spain & Mexico Ser.). (ENG., Illus.). 408p. 39.95 ***(978-0-87062-411-7(3)***, Clark, Arthur H. Co., The) Univ. of Oklahoma Pr.

Ide, Simeon. The Conquest of Californi: A Biography of William B. Ide. 2011. 206p. 44.95 ***(978-1-258-09528-4(9))*** Literary Licensing, LLC.

Igler, David & Deverell, William, eds. A Companion to California History. 2008. (Blackwell Companions to American History Ser.: 35). (ENG., Illus.). 544p. 229.95 *(978-1-4051-6183-1(3)*, Wiley-Blackwell) Wiley, John & Sons, Inc.

Irwin, Catherine. Twice Orphaned: Voices from the Children's Village of Manzanar. 2008. pap. *(978-0-930046-24-8(2))* California State Univ. Fullerton, Ctr. for Oral & Public History.

Isenberg, Andrew C. Mining California: An Ecological History. 2006. (ENG., Illus.). 256p. pap. 17.00 *(978-0-8090-6932-3(6)*, Hill & Wang) Farrar, Straus & Giroux.

Jacknis, Ira, ed. Food in California Indian Culture. 2007. (Classics in California Anthropology Ser.). (ENG., Illus.). 490p. per. 35.00 *(978-0-936127-08-8(2))* Hearst, P. A. Museum of Anthropology.

Jacoby, Kam & Ward, Cynthia Carbone. Layers: Composite Photographs from the Lompoc Valley. 2009. pap. *(978-1-61623-715-8(5))* Independent Pub.

Jan, Lyle. Old Chinatown- Revisited. 2010. pap. 13.95 *(978-0-7414-6031-8(9))* Infinity Publishing.

Jenkins, Gordon. The Golden Anniversary of Bermuda Dunes Country Club 1959-2009. 2008. *(978-1-57864-521-3(2))* Donning Co. Pubs.

Jennings, Jay. Knott's Berry Farm: The Early Years. 2009. 15p. pap. 7.99 *(978-0-7385-6922-2(4))* Arcadia Publishing.

Jennings, Sherry E. Truckee. 2011. (Images of America Ser.). (Illus.). 128p. pap. 21.99 *(978-0-7385-7495-0(3))* Arcadia Publishing.

Jensen, Carol A. The California Delta. 2007. (Images of America Ser.). (ENG., Illus.). 128p. per. 21.99 *(978-0-7385-4787-9(5))* Arcadia Publishing.

Jensen, Carol A. & East Contra Costa Historical Society. East Contra Costa County. 2007. (Postcard History Ser.). (ENG., Illus.). 128p. per. 19.99 *(978-0-7385-4774-9(3))* Arcadia Publishing.

Jensen, Carol A. & The North Lake Tahoe Historical Society. Lake Tahoe's West Shore. 2012. (Images of America Ser.). (ENG., Illus.). 128p. pap. 21.99 ***(978-0-7385-8891-9(1))*** Arcadia Publishing.

Johnson and Chris Diaz, The City of Lynwood with Ilu & Diaz, Chris. Lynwood. 2012. (Images of America Ser.). (ENG., Illus.). 128p. pap. 21.99 ***(978-0-7385-8889-6(X))*** Arcadia Publishing.

Johnson, Kim Jarrell. Rubidoux. 2007. (Images of America Ser.). (Illus.). 127p. per. 19.99 *(978-0-7385-4764-0(6))* Arcadia Publishing.

Johnson, Robert Lee. Compton. 2012. (Images of America Ser.). (ENG., Illus.). 128p. pap. 21.99 ***(978-0-7385-9539-9(X))*** Arcadia Publishing.

Jones, Ray. Myths & Mysteries of California: True Stories of the Unsolved & Unexplained. 2011. (Myths & Mysteries Ser.). (ENG., Illus.). 168p. pap. 14.95 *(978-0-7627-6369-6(8))* Globe Pequot Pr., The.

—Yosemite National Park: Remarkable Events That Shaped History. 2010. (It Happened in Ser.). (ENG., Illus.). 160p. pap. 14.95 *(978-0-7627-5060-3(X))* Globe Pequot Pr., The.

Jorae, Wendy Rouse. The Children of Chinatown: Growing up Chinese American in San Francisco, 1850-1920. 2009. (ENG., Illus.). 304p. 62.95 *(978-0-8078-3313-1(4))*; pap. 24.95 *(978-0-8078-5973-5(7))* Univ. of North Carolina Pr.

Jordan, David Starr. The Call of the Twentieth Century, & California & the Californians. 2007. 48p. per. *(978-1-4065-4657-6(7))* Dodo Pr.

Judah, Paula Amen & Coodley, Lauren. Napa Valley Farming. 2011. (Images of America Ser.). (Illus.). 128p. pap. 21.99 ***(978-0-7385-7524-7(0))*** Arcadia Publishing.

Jurmain, Claudia K., et al. Rancho Los Alamitos: Ever Changing, Always the Same. 2011. (Illus.). xx, 227p. ***(978-1-59714-149-9(6))***; pap. 35.00 ***(978-1-59714-148-2(8))*** Heyday.

Kasser, Daniel & Zimmerman, Amanda. Stockton. 2012. (Then & Now Ser.). (ENG., Illus.). 96p. pap. 21.99 ***(978-0-7385-8888-9(1))*** Arcadia Publishing.

Keibel, John A. Behind the Barbed Wire: History of Naval Weapons Station Concord. 2009. (Illus.). 352p. pap. 28.95 *(978-0-615-27907-7(4))* Keibel, John A. Documentary Photography.

Keller, Russell L. Big Bear. 2008. (Postcard History Ser.). (ENG., Illus.). 128p. pap. 19.99 *(978-0-7385-5912-4(1))* Arcadia Publishing.

Kelley, Kevin E. Imperial Irrigation District: A Century of Service. 2011. ***(978-1-57864-693-7(6))*** Donning Co. Pubs.

Kennedy, Elijah Robinson. The Contest for California in 1861: How Colonel E.d. Baker Saved the Pacific States in the Union. 361p. reprint ed. 98.00 *(978-0-7222-8044-7(0))* Library Reprints, Inc.

Kidder, Lyn & Brunell, Herb. Ruidoso & Ruidoso Downs. 2009. (Images of America Ser.). (ENG., Illus.). 128p. pap. 21.99 *(978-0-7385-7069-3(9))* Arcadia Publishing.

King, T. Butler. T Butler King's Report on California Message from the President of the United States, Transmitting the Report of T Butler King, Esq, Heretofore Ap. 2011. 34p. pap. 11.99 ***(978-1-4181-9394-2(1))*** MPublishing.

Kinsey, James. Huntington Park. 2007. (Images of America Ser.). (ENG., Illus.). 128p. per. 19.99 *(978-0-7385-4711-4(5))* Arcadia Publishing.

Kirby, Joe. The Lockheed Plant. 2011. (Images of America Ser.). (ENG., Illus.). 128p. pap. 21.99 ***(978-0-7385-8796-7(6))*** Arcadia Publishing.

Koning, Ben & Metz, Anneke. Sunnyvale. 2011. (Images of America Ser.). (ENG., Illus.). 128p. pap. 21.99 *(978-0-7385-7435-6(X))* Arcadia Publishing.

Kramer, Carol A. & Calaveras Big Trees Association. Calaveras Big Trees. 2010. (Images of America Ser.). (Illus.). 128p. pap. 21.99 *(978-0-7385-8118-7(6))* Arcadia Publishing.

Krintz, Jennifer. Redondo Beach Pier. 2011. (Images of America Ser.). (Illus.). 128p. pap. 21.99 *(978-0-7385-7502-5(X))* Arcadia Publishing.

Kulczyk, David. California Justice: Shootouts, Lynchings & Assassinations in the Golden State. 2007. (ENG., Illus.). 180p. pap. 15.95 *(978-1-884995-54-5(3))* Quill Driver Bks.

—Death in California: The Bizarre, Freakish, & Just Curious Ways People Die in the Golden State. 2009. (ENG., Illus.). 169p. pap. 15.95 *(978-1-884995-57-6(8))* Linden Publishing Co., Inc.

Kurtz, Patricia. Mountain Maidu & Pioneers: A History of Indian Valley, Plumas County, California, 1850 - 1920. 2010. 96p. pap. 16.95 *(978-1-4502-6175-3(2))* iUniverse, Inc.

Kurtz, Skip. Pop n Me or Tales of the Duncan Ranch. 2007. 288p. pap. 27.95 *(978-1-4241-6295-6(5))* PublishAmerica, Inc.

Lake Elsinore Historical Society & Lake Elsinore Historical Society. Lake Elsinore. 2008. (Postcard History Ser.). (ENG., Illus.). 128p. per. 19.99 *(978-0-7385-5588-1(6))* Arcadia Publishing.

Lamont, Deane. America's Healthiest City. 2010. 332p. pap. *(978-3-639-23120-5(1))* VDM Verlag Dr. Mueller e.K.

Lane, Beverly, et al. Vintage Danville: 150 Years of Memories. 2008. *(978-1-57864-492-6(5))* Donning Co. Pubs.

Langley, Christopher & Prather, Michael. Mount Whitney. 2012. (Images of America Ser.). (ENG., Illus.). 128p. pap. 21.99 ***(978-0-7385-9536-8(5))*** Arcadia Publishing.

Lardner, W. B. & Brock, M. J. History of Placer & Nevada Counties, California, V1. 2011. 438p. 56.95 ***(978-1-258-08287-1(X))*** Literary Licensing, LLC.

—History of Placer & Nevada Counties, California, V2: Biographical Review, Pioneers, Past & Present. 2011. 812p. 74.95 ***(978-1-258-08320-5(5))*** Literary Licensing, LLC.

Larkins, William T. & Alameda Naval Air Museum. Alameda Naval Air Station. 2010. (Images of America Ser.). (ENG., Illus.). 128p. pap. 21.99 *(978-0-7385-8040-1(6))* Arcadia Publishing.

Laufer, Peter. Calexico: True Lives of the Borderlands. 2011. (ENG., Illus.). 248p. pap. 19.95 *(978-0-8165-2951-3(5))* Univ. of Arizona Pr.

Lavoie, Steven. Historic Photos of Oakland. 2009. (Historic Photos Ser.). (ENG.). 206p. 39.95 *(978-1-59652-529-0(0))* Turner Publishing Co.

Lawson, Scott J. & Elliott, Daniel R. Logging in Plumas County. 2008. (Images of America Ser.). (ENG., Illus.). 128p. pap. 19.99 *(978-0-7385-5929-2(6))* Arcadia Publishing.

Lécuyer, Christophe. Making Silicon Valley: Innovation & the Growth of High Tech, 1930-1970. 2007. (Inside Technology Ser.). (ENG., Illus.). 408p. (gr. 17). per. 25.00 *(978-0-262-62211-0(4))* MIT Pr.

Lee, Erika & Yung, Judy. Angel Island: Immigrant Gateway to America. 1 vol. (ENG., Illus.). 2012. 432p. pap. 21.95 ***(978-0-19-989615-8(1))*** 2010. 400p. 27.95 *(978-0-19-973408-5(9))* Oxford Univ. Pr., Inc.

Lee, Hector. 20 Tales of California, 2nd Edition: A Rare Collection of Western Stories. 2nd ed. 2008. (Illus.). 192p. pap. 12.95 *(978-1-877810-72-5(X))* Rayve Productions, Inc.

Lee, Rodi & Lynch, Michael G. American River Canyon. 2012. (Images of America Ser.). (ENG., Illus.). 128p. pap. 21.99 ***(978-0-7385-9319-7(2))*** Arcadia Publishing.

Leete, Harley M. Sketches of the Gold Country. 2006. (Illus.). pap. 15.95 *(978-1-4286-5919-3(6))* Kessinger Publishing, LLC.

Leicester, Marti & Nopel, David. The Humboldt Wagon Road. 2012. (Images of America Ser.). (ENG., Illus.). 128p. pap. 21.99 ***(978-0-7385-7643-5(3))*** Arcadia Publishing.

Library, Special Collections of the Sacramento Public. Mather Field. 2012. (Images of America Ser.). (ENG., Illus.). 128p. pap. 21.99 ***(978-0-7385-8877-3(6))*** Arcadia Publishing.

Lindquist, Heather C., ed. Children of Manzanar. 2012. (Illus.). xi, 145p. pap. 17.95 ***(978-1-59714-160-4(7))*** Heyday.

Lindsay, Brendan C. Murder State: California's Native American Genocide, 1846-1873. 2012. (ENG., Illus.). 456p. 70.00 ***(978-0-8032-2480-3(X))*** Univ. of Nebraska Pr.

Loomis, Jan. Pacific Palisades. 2009. 15p. pap. 7.99 *(978-0-7385-6949-9(6))* Arcadia Publishing.

Lost Hotels on California's Historic Ridge Route. 2008. (Illus.). 120p. pap. 21.95 *(978-0-9800144-0-2(9))* Harrison Irving, Scott.

Lovret, Juanita. Tustin as it Once Was. 2011. (Illus.). 144p. pap. 19.99 ***(978-1-60949-461-2(X))*** History Pr., The.

Lugo Cerra, Julie & Wanamaker, Marc. Movie Studios of Culver City. 2011. (Images of America Ser.). (ENG., Illus.). 128p. pap. 21.99 *(978-0-7385-8200-9(X))* Arcadia Publishing.

Lynch, Michael G. California State Park Rangers. 2009. (Images of America Ser.). (ENG., Illus.). 128p. pap. 21.99 *(978-0-7385-5993-3(8))* Arcadia Publishing.

MacDonald, Donald & Nadel, Ira. Alcatraz: History & Design of a Landmark. 2012. (ENG., Illus.). 144p. 16.95 ***(978-1-4521-0153-8(1))*** Chronicle Bks. LLC.

MacIver, Ron & MacIver, Elfriede. La Palma. 2008. (Images of America Ser.). (ENG., Illus.). 128p. pap. 21.99 *(978-0-7385-5957-5(1))* Arcadia Publishing.

Makley, Michael J. A Short History of Lake Tahoe. 2011. (ENG., Illus.). 192p. pap. 21.95 ***(978-0-87417-850-0(9))*** Univ. of Nevada Pr.

Mallea-Olaetxe, Joxe. The Basques of Reno & the Northeastern Sierra. 2009. (Images of America Ser.). (ENG., Illus.). 128p. pap. 21.99 *(978-0-7385-6961-1(5))* Arcadia Publishing.

Mallette, Leo A. Rancho Mirage. 2011. (Images of America Ser.). (Illus.). 128p. pap. 21.99 *(978-0-7385-7501-8(1))* Arcadia Publishing.

Mangelos, John P. Ripon. 2011. (Images of America Ser.). (Illus.). 128p. pap. 21.99 *(978-0-7385-8166-8(6))* Arcadia Publishing.

Marcus, Ben & Wanamaker, Marc. Malibu. 2011. (Images of America Ser.). (ENG., Illus.). 128p. pap. 21.99 ***(978-0-7385-7614-5(X))*** Arcadia Publishing.

Margiloff, Irwin & Earle, Neil. Duarte. 2009. 15p. pap. 7.99 *(978-0-7385-6912-3(7))* Arcadia Publishing.

Margiloff, Irwin, et al. Duarte. 2009. (Images of America Ser.). (ENG., Illus.). 128p. pap. 21.99 *(978-0-7385-6911-6(9))* Arcadia Publishing.

Margolin, Malcolm. Following the Game: Hunting Traditions of Native California. Date not set. 27.95 *(978-1-890771-06-5(6))* Heyday.

Marin History Museum. Modern San Rafael: 1940-2000. 2012. (Images of America Ser.). (ENG., Illus.). 128p. pap. 21.99 ***(978-0-7385-9307-4(9))*** Arcadia Publishing.

Marin History Museum Staff. Early San Rafael. 2008. (Images of America Ser.). (ENG., Illus.). 128p. pap. 19.99 *(978-0-7385-5941-4(5))* Arcadia Publishing.

C

Mariotti, Joseph, et al. Pinole. 2009. (Images of America Ser.). (ENG., Illus.). 128p. pap. 21.99 (978-0-7385-7042-6(7)) Arcadia Publishing.

Marquez, Ernest. Santa Monica Beach: A Collector's Pictorial History. 2011. (Illus.). 207p. pap. 29.95 (978-1-883318-95-6(5)) Angel City Pr.

Marshall, Amelia Sue & Tobey, Terry L. Oakland's Equestrian Heritage. 2008. (Images of America Ser.). (ENG., Illus.). 128p. pap. 19.99 (978-0-7385-5810-3(9)) Arcadia Publishing.

Martin, Elinor. Canyon Lake. 2007. (Images of America Ser.). (ENG., Illus.). 128p. per. 19.99 (978-0-7385-4712-1(3)) Arcadia Publishing.

Martin, Joan Gilbert & McInerney-Meagher, Colleen. Pogonip: Jewel of Santa Cruz. 2007. (Illus.). viii, 192p. (978-1-890625-08-5(6)) Otter B Bks.

Martin, Mary L. & Hufford, Kim. Greetings from Pasadena. 2008. (Illus.). 128p. pap. 24.95 (978-0-7643-2852-7(2)) Schiffer Publishing, Ltd.

Martin, Mike. The History of Cerro Gordo & Oakley: Mens Fastpitch Softball. 2010. 224p. 24.99 (978-1-4520-3810-0(4)); pap. 14.49 (978-1-4520-3809-4(0)) AuthorHouse.

Martin, S. W. Atascadero. 2012. (Images of America Ser.). (ENG., Illus.). 128p. pap. 21.99 (978-0-7385-8916-9(0)) Arcadia Publishing.

Martini, John & Haller, Stephen. The Last Missile Site: An Operational & Physical History of Nike Site SF-88, Fort Barry, California. 2010. (ENG., Illus.). 158p. mass mkt. 19.95 (978-0-9761494-1-5(9)) Hole in the Head Pr.

Marvin, Judith, et al. Angels Camp & Copperopolis. 2009. (Images of America Ser.). (ENG., Illus.). 128p. pap. 21.99 (978-0-7385-5981-0(4)) Arcadia Publishing.

Masich, Andrew E. The Civil War in Arizona: The Story of the California Volunteers, 1861-1865. 2008. (ENG., Illus.). 384p. (C). pap. 26.95 (978-0-8061-3900-5(5)) Univ. of Oklahoma Pr.

Maston, Wendy & Kessell, Robin. Antioch. 2007. (Images of America Ser.). (ENG., Illus.). 128p. per. 19.99 (978-0-7385-5065-7(5)) Arcadia Publishing.

Mathes, Wayne A. & McHenry Museum. Modesto. 2011. (Then & Now Ser.). (Illus.). 96p. pap. 21.99 (978-0-7385-7485-1(6)) Arcadia Publishing.

Maulhardt, Jeffrey Wayne. Oxnard. 2009. (Postcard History Ser.). (Illus.). 128p. pap. 21.99 (978-0-7385-6937-6(2)) Arcadia Publishing.

May, Vonn Marie & Rancho Santa Fe Historical Society. Rancho Santa Fe. 2010. (Images of America Ser.). (ENG., Illus.). 128p. pap. 21.99 (978-0-7385-7185-0(7)) Arcadia Publishing.

Mazariegos, Darla Greb. Mount Shasta. 2007. (Images of America Ser.). (ENG., Illus.). 128p. per. 21.99 (978-0-7385-5572-0(X)) Arcadia Publishing.

Mcafee, Ward M. Never an Island: A History of California. 2007. 216p. per. 19.95 (978-0-89370-909-9(3), Borgo Pr.) Wildside Pr., LLC.

McClelland, Gordon T. & Last, Jay T. California Watercolors (1850-1970) An Illustrated History & Biographical Dictionary. 132p. 49.00 (978-0-914589-10-5(5)) Hillcrest Pr.

McCutchen, Steve D. We Were Free for a While. 2008. 232p. pap. 24.95 (978-1-60441-675-6(0)) PublishAmerica, Inc.

McCutcheon, Richard. Indian Valley. 2008. (Images of America Ser.). (ENG., Illus.). 128p. pap. 19.99 (978-0-7385-5836-3(2)) Arcadia Publishing.

McGovern, Janet. Caltrain & the Peninsula Commute Service. 2012. (Images of Rail Ser.). (ENG., Illus.). 128p. pap. 21.99 (978-0-7385-7622-0(0)) Arcadia Publishing.

McGovern, Reg, et al. Redwood City. 2008. (Images of America Ser.). (ENG., Illus.). 128p. pap. 21.99 (978-0-7385-5924-7(5)) Arcadia Publishing.

McGroarty, John Steven. California of the South V1: A History. 2011. 568p. 63.95 (978-1-258-07243-8(2)) Literary Licensing, LLC.

—California of the South V2: A History, Biographical. 2011. 504p. 58.95 (978-1-258-07245-2(9)) Literary Licensing, LLC.

—California of the South V3: A History, Biographical. 2011. 502p. 58.95 (978-1-258-07246-9(7)) Literary Licensing, LLC.

—California of the South V4: A History, Biographical. 2011. 826p. 75.95 (978-1-258-07247-6(5)) Literary Licensing, LLC.

—California of the South V5: A History, Biographies. 2011. 828p. 75.95 (978-1-258-07248-3(3)) Literary Licensing, LLC.

McGuinness, Aims. Path of Empire: Panama & the California Gold Rush. (United States in the World Ser.). (Illus.). 2009. 264p. pap. 19.95 (978-0-8014-7538-2(4)) 2007. 249p. 60.95 (978-0-8014-4521-7(3)) Cornell Univ. Pr.

McKibben, Carol. Racial Beachhead: Diversity & Democracy in a Military Town. 2011. (ENG.). 352p. 80.00 (978-0-8047-7698-1(9)) Stanford Univ. Pr.

McKinney, Gage. The 1930s: No Depression Here. 2009. (Illus.). 632p. pap. 30.00 (978-0-933994-47-8(8)) Comstock Bonanza Pr.

McLeod, Dean L. Port Chicago. 2007. (Images of America Ser.). (Illus.). 127p. per. 19.99 (978-0-7385-5551-5(7)) Arcadia Publishing.

McMahon, Joseph & Hendershot, Carla. San Juan Bautista. 2007. (Images of America Ser.). (Illus.). 127p. per. 19.99 (978-0-7385-4773-2(5)) Arcadia Publishing.

McNassor, Cathy. Los Angeles's la Brea Tar Pits & Hancock Park. 2011. (Images of America Ser.). (Illus.). 128p. pap. 21.99 (978-0-7385-7611-4(5)) Arcadia Publishing.

Meg Rogers with support from the Portuguese Historical Museum. The Portuguese in San Jose. 2007. (Images of America Ser.). (ENG., Illus.). 128p. pap. 21.99 (978-0-7385-4781-7(6)) Arcadia Publishing.

Merian, Dee. Southern California Stories. 2009. 80p. pap. 10.95 (978-1-4401-2441-9(8)) iUniverse, Inc.

Merideth, Lee. California. 2009. 240p. pap. 16.95 (978-1-932714-74-6(X)) Savas Beatie.

Meyer, Amy. New Guardians for the Golden Gate: How America Got a Great National Park. 2006. (Illus.). 338p. 35.00 (978-0-520-23534-2(7)) Univ. of California Pr.

Meyer, Laurie & Howard, M. J. The Way We Were California: Nostalgic Images of the Golden State. 2009. (Way We Were Ser.). (ENG., Illus.). 128p. 19.95 (978-0-7627-5452-6(4)) Globe Pequot Pr., The.

Millard, Catherine. CALIFORNIA: America's First New England. 2010. (Illus.). 170p. (978-0-692-01131-7(5)) Christian Heritage Ministries.

Millbrae Historical Society. Millbrae. 2007. (Images of America Ser.). (ENG., Illus.). 128p. per. 19.99 (978-0-7385-4790-9(5)) Arcadia Publishing.

Miller, Chris Ann & Roberts, Jerry. Hermosa Beach. 2007. (Postcard History Ser.). (ENG., Illus.). 128p. per. 21.99 (978-0-7385-4709-1(3)) Arcadia Publishing.

Mitchell, Bruce M. California's First Maritimers. 2008. 92p. pap. 16.95 (978-1-60563-553-8(7)) PublishAmerica, Inc.

Molander, Robert P. Extra! Extra! 2008. 232p. 28.95 (978-1-4251-3889-9(6)) Trafford Publishing.

Monsma, Bradley John. The Sespe Wild: Southern California's Last Free River. 2007. (Environmental Arts & Humanities Ser.). (ENG.). 176p. per. 18.95 (978-0-87417-704-6(9)) Univ. of Nevada Pr.

Montoya, Carina Monica & Santa Maria Valley Historical Society. Santa Maria Valley. 2011. (Images of America Ser.). (ENG., Illus.). 128p. pap. 21.99 (978-0-7385-8880-3(6)) Arcadia Publishing.

Moore, Annette. The University of Southern California: 1880 To 2005. 2007. 39.95 (978-1-932800-19-7(0)) Figueroa Pr.

Morris, Kathryn, et al. Fullerton. 2007. (Postcard History Ser.). (ENG., Illus.). 128p. per. 19.99 (978-0-7385-4788-6(3)) Arcadia Publishing.

Moruzzi, Peter. Palm Springs Holiday, 1 vol. 2009. (ENG., Illus.). 176p. 30.00 (978-1-4236-0476-1(8)) Gibbs Smith, Publisher.

Moses, Mary J. Morro Bay Remembered: Interviews recalling the '40s, '50s And '60s. 2007. 84p. per. 10.95 (978-0-595-44570-7(5), Authors Choice Pr.) iUniverse, Inc.

Most, Stephen. River of Renewal: Myth & History in the Klamath Basin. 2006. (ENG., Illus.). 288p. per. 22.50 (978-0-295-98622-7(0)) Univ. of Washington Pr.

Muckenthaler Cultural Center Foundation. Muckenthaler Cultural Center. 2011. (Images of America Ser.). (Illus.). 128p. pap. 21.99 (978-0-7385-7551-3(8)) Arcadia Publishing.

Mulholland, Catherine. Calabasas Girls: An Intimate History 1885-1912. 2008. 192p. pap. 16.95 (978-0-9700481-6-5(5)) Many Moons Pr.

Myers, Tom. Sacramento. 2010. (Postcard History Ser.). (ENG., Illus.). 128p. pap. 21.99 (978-0-7385-7152-2(0)) Arcadia Publishing.

Nancy McEnery with the Napa County Historical Society. The Napa River. 2012. (Images of America Ser.). (ENG., Illus.). 128p. pap. 21.99 (978-0-7385-9504-7(7)) Arcadia Publishing.

National Park Service (U.S.), Cultural Landscape Program Staff, prod. Manzanar National Historic Site Cultural Landscape Report. 2006. (ENG.). 340p. pap. 53.50 (978-0-16-077094-4(7)) National Park Service Div. of Pubns.

Nelson, Lawrence Emerson. Redlands: Biography of A College. 2011. 320p. 50.95 (978-1-258-08351-9(5)) Literary Licensing, LLC.

Nevada County Historical Landmarks Commission. Exploring Nevada County: An Illustrated Guide to Local Landmarks & Historic Sites. rev. ed. 2010. (ENG., Illus.). 160p. pap. 16.50 (978-0-933994-30-0(3)) Comstock Bonanza Pr.

Newell Christenson, Lynne & Sweet, Ellen L. Ranchos of San Diego County. 2008. (Images of America Ser.). (Illus.). 128p. pap. 21.99 (978-0-7385-5965-0(2)) Arcadia Publishing.

Newland, James D. Cleveland NATL Forest. 2008. (Images of America Ser.). (ENG., Illus.). 128p. pap. 21.99 (978-0-7385-5804-2(4)) Arcadia Publishing.

Nichols, Gina. The Navy at Point Mugu. 2011. (Images of America Ser.). (Illus.). 128p. pap. 21.99 (978-0-7385-7532-2(1)) Arcadia Publishing.

Nihipali, Elizabeth "Nani", et al. Hawaiians in Los Angeles. 2012. (Images of America Ser.). (ENG., Illus.). 128p. pap. 21.99 (978-0-7385-9320-3(6)) Arcadia Publishing.

Norton, Edwin Clarence Norton. The Dean Speaks Again. Hinckley, Edith Parker & Benner, Katharine Norton, eds. 2011. 142p. 40.95 (978-1-258-09201-6(8)) Literary Licensing, LLC.

Noske, Carole, et al. Vacaville. 2007. (Then & Now Ser.). (Illus.). 96p. per. 19.99 (978-0-7385-5563-8(0)) Arcadia Publishing.

Novato Historical Guild Staff. Hamilton Field. 2008. (Images of America Ser.). (ENG., Illus.). 128p. pap. 21.99 (978-0-7385-5908-7(3)) Arcadia Publishing.

Noy, Gary & Heide, Rick. The Illuminated Landscape: A Sierra Nevada Anthology. 2010. 352p. pap. 19.95 (978-1-59714-128-4(3)) Heyday.

Nusbaum, Mark H. One Hundred Years of Freemasonry, 1857-1957: Fidelity Lodge No. 120, San Francisco, California. 2011. 28p. 35.95 (978-1-258-03155-8(8)) Literary Licensing, LLC.

Oates, Bridget. Sam's Castle. 2011. (Images of America Ser.). (Illus.). 128p. pap. 21.99 (978-0-7385-7486-8(4)) Arcadia Publishing.

Ochoa, Maria & The Hayward Area Historical Society. Russell City. 2009. (Images of America Ser.). (ENG., Illus.). 128p. pap. 21.99 (978-0-7385-7004-4(4)) Arcadia Publishing.

Ofield, Helen M., et al. Lemon Grove. 2010. (Images of America Ser.). (ENG., Illus.). 128p. pap. 21.99 (978-0-7385-7193-5(8)) Arcadia Publishing.

O'Hara, Susan J. P. & Stockton, Dave. Humboldt Redwoods State Park. 2012. (Images of America Ser.). (ENG., Illus.). 128p. pap. 21.99 (978-0-7385-9513-9(6)) Arcadia Publishing.

O'Hara, Thomas Q. The Marines at Twentynine Palms. 2007. (Images of America Ser.). (ENG., Illus.). 128p. pap. 19.99 (978-0-7385-4772-5(7)) Arcadia Publishing.

The Old Salt Point Township: Sonoma County, California, 1841-1941. 2009. (Illus.). 218p. pap. (978-0-9712160-1-3(0)) Hay Pr., The.

Olten, Carol, et al. La Jolla. 2008. (Images of America Ser.). (ENG., Illus.). 128p. pap. 19.99 (978-0-7385-5803-5(6)) Arcadia Publishing.

O'Meara, Brendan. Six Weeks in Saratoga: How Three-Year-Old Filly Rachel Alexandra Beat the the Boys & Became Horse of the Year. 2011. (Excelsior Editions Ser.). 206p. 24.95 (978-1-4384-3941-9(5)) State Univ. of New York Pr.

O'Neil, Dorothy M. Winters. 2009. 128p. pap. 21.99 (978-0-7385-6914-7(3)) Arcadia Publishing.

Orcutt Henderson, Mary Alice. Santa Paula: 1930-1960. 2009. (Images of America Ser.). (Illus.). 128p. pap. 21.99 (978-0-7385-7165-2(2)) Arcadia Publishing.

Orozco, Michael Anthony. Alhambra. 2012. (Images of America Ser.). (ENG., Illus.). 128p. pap. 21.99 (978-0-7385-7607-7(7)) Arcadia Publishing.

Otto, Ken. Azusa Pacific University. 2008. (Campus History Ser.). (ENG., Illus.). 128p. pap. 19.99 (978-0-7385-5926-1(1)) Arcadia Publishing.

Palazzo, Robert P. Death Valley. 2008. (Images of America Ser.). (ENG., Illus.). 128p. pap. 21.99 (978-0-7385-5824-0(9)) Arcadia Publishing.

Palazzo, Robert P. Railroads of Death Valley. 2011. (Images of Rail Ser.). (Illus.). 128p. pap. 21.99 (978-0-7385-7479-0(1)) Arcadia Publishing.

Palm, Carl. This Day in California History. 2008. 443p. pap. 19.95 (978-0-9754832-2-0(6)) Northcross Bks.

Palou, Francis. Life of Padre Junipero Serra. 2006. pap. 21.95 (978-1-4286-4281-2(1)) Kessinger Publishing, LLC.

Palou, Francisco. Historical Memoirs of New California, V1. Bolton, Herbert Eugene, ed. 2011. 442p. 56.95 (978-1-258-08073-0(7)) Literary Licensing, LLC.

—Historical Memoirs of New California, V2. Bolton, Herbert Eugene, ed. 2011. 424p. 56.95 (978-1-258-08113-3(X)) Literary Licensing, LLC.

—Historical Memoirs of New California, V3. Bolton, Herbert Eugene, ed. 2011. 422p. 56.95 (978-1-258-08114-0(8)) Literary Licensing, LLC.

—Historical Memoirs of New California, V4. Bolton, Herbert Eugene, ed. 2011. 484p. 58.95 (978-1-258-08115-7(6)) Literary Licensing, LLC.

Palou, Fray Francisco. The Expedition into California of the Venerable Padre Fray Junipero Serra & His Companions in the Year 1769. 2011. 146p. 40.95 (978-1-258-04479-4(X)) Literary Licensing, LLC.

Papina, Anne M. Nicasio. 2008. (Images of America Ser.). (ENG., Illus.). 128p. pap. 19.99 (978-0-7385-5802-8(8)) Arcadia Publishing.

Parent, Traci & Terhune, Karen. Black Diamond Mines Regional Preserve. 2009. (Images of America Ser.). (ENG., Illus.). 128p. pap. 21.99 (978-0-7385-6995-6(X)) Arcadia Publishing.

Parkman, Francis. The Oregon Trail. l.t. ed. 2006. (ENG.). 316p. pap. 24.99 (978-1-4264-0185-5(X)) BiblioBazaar.

Parson, Thomas E. Bear Flag & Bay State in the Civil War: The Californians of the Second Massachusetts Cavalry. alt. ed. 2007. (ENG., Illus.). 228p. pap. 39.95 (978-0-7864-3257-8(8)) McFarland & Co., Inc. Pubs.

Paskowitz, Richard A. Soldier joker the Legacy. 2008. 120p. pap. 18.50 (978-1-4357-2474-7(7)) Lulu Enterprises Inc.

Paskowitz, Richard. Soldier joker the 1849 Surveys. 2008. 89p. pap. 18.50 (978-1-4357-2504-1(2)) Lulu Enterprises Inc.

Patris, Michael A., et al. Mount Lowe Railway. 2012. (Then & Now Ser.). (ENG., Illus.). 96p. pap. 21.99 (978-0-7385-8879-7(2)) Arcadia Publishing.

Patton, Mishael & Patton, W. Craig. Love Heals Hearts: Transform Your Relationship. 2010. 132p. 21.99 (978-1-4490-1548-0(4)) AuthorHouse.

Pauley, Kenneth E. & Dominguez Rancho Adobe Museum. The 1910 Los Angeles International Air Meet. 2009. (Images of Aviation Ser.). (ENG., Illus.). 128p. pap. 21.99 (978-0-7385-7190-4(3)) Arcadia Publishing.

Peck, Willys I. & Halberstadt, April. Willys Peck's Saratoga. 2010. (978-0-935089-30-1(6)) California History Ctr.

Pepe, William J. & Pepe, Elaine A. Quincy. 2008. (Postcard History Ser.). (ENG., Illus.). 128p. per. 21.99 (978-0-7385-5539-3(8)) Arcadia Publishing.

Perry, Frank. Notes from Santa Cruz: The County's Music History: Emphasizing the Period from the 1870s to 1970s. 2011. (978-0-940283-22-0(0)) Museum of Art & History.

Peyton, Paige M. Calico. 2012. (Images of America Ser.). (ENG., Illus.). 128p. pap. 21.99 (978-0-7385-8905-3(5)) Arcadia Publishing.

Phillips, Bob. Growing up in California. 2008. 220p. pap. 15.95 (978-0-557-01495-8(6)) Lulu Enterprises Inc.

Posedel, Jennifer & Lawton, Stephen. Hercules. 2011. (Images of America Ser.). (Illus.). 128p. pap. 21.99 (978-0-7385-7440-0(6)) Arcadia Publishing.

Postel, Mitchell. The History of the Peninsula Golf & Country Club. 2011. (978-1-57864-724-8(X)) Donning Co. Pubs.

Postel, Mitchell. San Mateo County: A Sesquicentennial History. 2007. (978-0-89863-285-9(4)) Star Publishing Co.

Pratt, Barbara J. & Twenty Mule Team Museum. Around Boron. 2009. (Images of America Ser.). (ENG., Illus.). 128p. pap. 21.99 (978-0-7385-6943-7(7)) Arcadia Publishing.

Price, Ryan Lee. Glendora. 2008. (Postcard History Ser.). (ENG., Illus.). 128p. pap. 19.99 (978-0-7385-5800-4(1)) Arcadia Publishing.

Price, Ryan Lee. Stories of Old Glendora. 2012. 128p. pap. 19.99 (978-1-60949-533-6(0)) History Pr., The.

Pryor, Alton. More Little Known Tales in California History. 2007. 178p. pap. 11.95 (978-0-9660053-0-1(9)) Stagecoach Publishing.

Pyron, Jennifer. Lathrop. 2010. (Images of America Ser.). (ENG., Illus.). 128p. pap. 21.99 (978-0-7385-8017-3(1)) Arcadia Publishing.

Rarick, Ethan. California Votes: The 2006 Governor's Race. 2007. (978-0-87772-425-4(3)) Univ. of California, Institute of Governmental Studies.

Rawls & Bean & Cram101 Textbook Reviews Staff. Californi: An Interpretive History. 2007. 140p. per. 11.95 (978-1-4288-2816-2(8)) Cram101 Inc.

Rawls, James J. & Bean, Walton. California: An Interpretive History. (Illus.). 9th ed. 2008. xvii, 553p. pap. (978-0-07-353464-0(1)) 9th ed. 2006. (ENG., 576p. (C). pap., pap. 106.88 (978-0-07-331326-9(2), 0073313262) 10th ed. 2011. (ENG., 576p. (C). pap. 117.67 (978-0-07-340696-1(1), 0073406961) McGraw-Hill Cos., The.

Redwood City Public Library, Archives Committee Staff, contrib. by. Redwood City: A Hometown History. 2007. (978-0-89863-297-2(8)) Star Publishing Co.

Reece, Colleen L. Veiled Joy. l.t. ed. 2010. 233p. 29.99 (978-1-4104-3186-8(X)) Thorndike Pr.

Reed, Roberta A. & The Santa Ana Historical Preservation Society Staff. Santa Ana: 1940-2007. 2008. (Illus.). 128p. pap. 19.99 (978-0-7385-5834-9(6)) Arcadia Publishing.

Reiser, Ronald J. California Passport. 2007. 36p. pap. (978-0-9625515-3-6(8)) Reiser, R. J. & Co.

Reuther, Ronald T. & Larkins, William T. Oakland Aviation. 2008. (Images of Aviation Ser.). (ENG., Illus.). 128p. pap. 21.99 (978-0-7385-5600-0(9)) Arcadia Publishing.

Revere, Joseph, abr. Keel & Saddle. 2009. (Military History Ser.). (ENG.). 374p. pap. 23.95 (978-1-4290-2160-9(8)) Applewood Bks.

Reyes, Bárbara O. Private Women, Public Lives: Gender & the Missions of the Californias. 2010. (ENG., Illus.). 245p. pap. 25.00 (978-0-292-72347-4(4)) Univ. of Texas Pr.

Rice, Richard, et al. The Elusive Eden: A New History of California. 4th ed. 2011. (ENG., Illus.). 736p. (C). pap. 117.67 (978-0-07-338556-3(5), 0073385565) McGraw-Hill Cos., The.

Rice, Walter & Echeverria, Emiliano. Rails of California's Central Coast. 2008. (Images of Rail Ser.). (ENG., Illus.). 128p. per. 21.99 (978-0-7385-5591-1(6)) Arcadia Publishing.

Rice, Walter, et al. San Francisco's California Street Cable Cars. 2008. (Images of Rail Ser.). (Illus.). 128p. pap. 19.99 (978-0-7385-5963-6(6)) Arcadia Publishing.

Richman, Irving B. From Discovery Through Kino: California under Spain & Mexico, 1535-1847. 75p. reprint ed. pap. 10.00 (978-1-877959-00-4(6)) Henson, Dave Bks.

Ries, Ed, text. Tales of the Golden Years of California Ocean Fishing 1900-1950. 2nd rev. ed. 2007. (Illus.). 148p. per. 19.95 (978-0-9679247-1-7(5)) Monterey Pubns.

Rimmington, Pat. The Adobes of Twentynine Palms. 2nd ed. 2009. (Illus.). xii, 164p. (Orig.). pap. (978-0-9842373-0-2(5), Orbit Books) Desert Spirit Pr.

Rippens, Paul & San Dimas Historical Society. San Dimas. 2008. (Images of America Ser.). (Illus.). 128p. pap. 19.99 (978-0-7385-5934-6(2)) Arcadia Publishing.

Roach, John P. California, the First 100 Years: Padre Serra to Statehood & the Golden Spike. 2010. 216p. 29.95 (978-1-4520-1177-6(X)); pap. 24.95 (978-1-4520-1176-9(1)) AuthorHouse.

Roberts, Sylvia Alden. Mining for Freedom: Black History Meets the California Gold Rush. 2008. 160p. pap. 14.95 (978-0-595-52492-1(3)) iUniverse, Inc.

Robinson, Lisa. The San Lorenzo Valley. 2012. (Images of America Ser.). (ENG., Illus.). 128p. pap. 21.99 (978-0-7385-9229-9(3)) Arcadia Publishing.

Roe, Kenn Sherwood. Cross Current. 2008. 236p. 24.99 (978-1-4343-5943-8(3)); pap. 14.49 (978-1-4343-5942-1(5)) AuthorHouse.

Rogers, Steve R. Hanford. 2012. (Then & Now Ser.). (ENG., Illus.). 96p. pap. 21.99 (978-0-7385-9311-1(7)) Arcadia Publishing.

Rogerson, Bruce & Point Cabrillo Lightkeepers Association Staff. Point Cabrillo Light Station. 2008. (Images of America Ser.). (Illus.). 128p. pap. 19.99 (978-0-7385-5950-6(4)) Arcadia Publishing.

Rolle, Andrew & Verge, Arthur. California: A History. 7th ed. 2008. (Illus.). 450p. pap. (978-0-88295-256-7(0)) Davidson, Harlan Inc.

Ron, Dial, prod. Dinuba 100: A Place of New Beginnings. 2007. (Illus.). 136p. 33.00 (978-0-9793650-0-3(7)) Dial, Ron Photography.

Roque-Ramirez, Horacio N. Queer Latino San Francisco: An Oral History, 1960s-1990s. 2012. (Palgrave Studies in Oral History Ser.). (ENG.). 240p. 95.00 (978-0-230-11129-5(7)); pap. 30.00 (978-0-230-11130-1(0)) Palgrave Macmillan.

Rose, Gene. Kings Canyon: America¿s Premier Wilderness National Park, A History. 2011. (ENG., Illus.). 140p. (978-1-878441-27-0(2)) Sequoia Natural History Assn.

Roseman, Frank M., et al. Chula Vista. 2008. (Images of America Ser.). (ENG., Illus.). 128p. pap. 19.99 (978-0-7385-5616-1(5)) Arcadia Publishing.

Ross, Blake. The Golden Crucible: An Introduction to the History of American California 1850 To 1905. 2007. (ENG.). 122p. 35.95 (978-0-548-02392-1(1)) Kessinger Publishing, LLC.

Round, Phillip H. The Impossible Land: Story & Place in California's Imperial Valley. 2008. (ENG., Illus.). 204p. pap. 24.95 (978-0-8263-4323-9(6)) Univ. of New Mexico Pr.

Royce, Josiah. California from the Conquest in 1846 to the Second Vigilance Committee in San Francisco. 2008. 528p. 32.99 (978-0-559-66376-5(5)); pap. 39.75 (978-0-559-66373-4(0)) BiblioBazaar.

—California from the Conquest in 1846 to the Second Vigilance Committee in San Francisco: A Study of American Character (1886) 2008. 540p. 57.95

(978-1-4365-4716-1(4)) 2007. 544p. per. 42.95 *(978-0-548-70386-1(8))* Kessinger Publishing, LLC.

Runner, Fred. Mount Tamalpais Scenic Railway. 2008. (Images of Rail Ser.). (ENG., Illus.). 128p. pap. 21.99 *(978-0-7385-5942-1(3))* Arcadia Publishing.

Ruwedel, Mark, photos by. Westward the Course of Empire. 2008. (ENG., Illus.). 180p. 65.00 *(978-0-300-14134-4(3))* Yale Univ. Art Gallery.

Ryder, David Warren. Memoirs of the Mendocino Coast. 2011. 136p. 40.95 ***(978-1-258-09008-1(2))*** Literary Licensing, LLC.

Sackman, Douglas Cazaux. Orange Empire: California & the Fruits of Eden. 2007. (Illus.). 386p. per. 27.95 *(978-0-520-25167-0(9))* Univ. of California Pr.

Sanchez, George J. Beyond Alliances: The Jewish Role in Reshaping the Racial Landscape of Southern California. 2011. (Jewish Role in American Life Ser.). (ENG., Illus.). 146p. 25.00 ***(978-1-55753-623-5(6))*** Purdue Univ. Pr.

Sanders, Ian. Views of Morgan Hill: Postcards & Images of Morgan Hill, California. 2010. (Illus.). 156p. 19.99 *(978-0-615-38051-3(4))* Bks.mart Enterprises Inc.

Sandos, James A. Converting California: Indians & Franciscans in the Missions. 2008. (ENG., Illus.). 272p. per. 20.00 *(978-0-300-13643-2(9))* Yale Univ. Pr.

Sands, Monty. Murder in Metheny: The April Holley Story 2008. (Illus.). 159p. per. 15.95 *(978-1-892622-25-9(4))* Bear State Bks.

Santa Barbara Conservancy. Stone Architecture in Santa Barbara. 2009. (Images of America Ser.). (ENG., Illus.). 128p. pap. 21.99 *(978-0-7385-6968-0(2))* Arcadia Publishing.

Santa Cruz Seaside Company. The Santa Cruz Beach Boardwalk: A Century by the Sea. 2007. (ENG., Illus.). 176p. 28.95 *(978-1-58008-815-2(5))*; pap. 19.95 *(978-1-58008-814-5(7))* Ten Speed Pr.

Santa Fe Springs Historical Committee. Santa Fe Springs. 2012. (Images of America Ser.). (ENG., Illus.). 128p. pap. 21.99 ***(978-0-7385-7576-6(3))*** Arcadia Publishing.

Santillan, Richard A., et al. Mexican American Baseball in the Inland Empire. 2012. (Images of Baseball Ser.). (ENG., Illus.). 128p. pap. 21.99 ***(978-0-7385-9316-6(8))*** Arcadia Publishing.

Santos, Kristen. Turlock: A Pictorial History, 1950-2005. 2007. *(978-1-57864-425-4(9))* Donning Co. Pubs.

Sappers, Vernon R. Key System Streetcars: Transit, Real Estate, & the Growth of the East Bay. 2007. (Illus.). 480p. 70.00 *(978-1-930013-07-0(8))* Signature Pr.

Saucedo, Marcelino. Dream Makers & Dream Catchers: The Story of the Mexican Heritage on Catalina Island. 2008. *(978-1-57864-474-2(7))* Donning Co. Pubs.

Saunders, Charles Francis. Capistrano Nights. 2007. 228p. (ENG.). 35.00 *(978-1-4344-8973-9(6))*; per. 19.95 *(978-1-4344-8972-2(8))* Wildside Pr., LLC.

Sawyer, John O. Northwest California: A Natural History. 2006. (Illus.). 247p. 75.00 *(978-0-520-23286-0(0))* Univ. of California Pr.

Schaadt, Mike, et al. Cabrillo Beach Coastal Park. 2009. (Images of America Ser.). (ENG., Illus.). 128p. pap. 21.99 *(978-0-7385-7189-8(X))* Arcadia Publishing.

—San Pedro's Cabrillo Beach. 2008. (Images of America Ser.). (Illus.). 128p. pap. 21.99 *(978-0-7385-5997-1(0))* Arcadia Publishing.

Scheuring, Ann Foley. Valley Empires: Hugh Glenn & Henry Miller in the Shaping of California. 2010. (Illus.). 320p. pap. 29.95 *(978-0-615-34123-1(3))* Gold Oak Pr.

Schipske, Gerrie. Rosie the Riveter in Long Beach. 2008. (Images of America Ser.). (Illus.). 128p. pap. 19.99 *(978-0-7385-5814-1(1))* Arcadia Publishing.

Schmale, John & Schmale, Katrina. Petaluma & Santa Rosa Railway. 2009. (Images of Rail Ser.). (Illus.). 128p. pap. 21.99 *(978-0-7385-5959-9(8))* Arcadia Publishing.

Schoenherr, Steven, et al. Bonita. 2009. 128p. pap. 21.99 *(978-0-7385-7000-6(1))* Arcadia Publishing.

Schubert, John C. & Munthe, Valerie A. Russian River. 2011. (Then & Now Ser.). (Illus.). 96p. pap. 21.99 *(978-0-7385-8195-8(X))* Arcadia Publishing.

Scott, James & Tolley, Tom, texts. Historic Photos of Sacramento. 2007. (Historic Photos Ser.). (ENG., Illus.). 204p. 39.95 *(978-1-59652-308-1(5))* Turner Publishing Co.

Secrest, William B. Showdown! Lionhearted Lawmen of Old California. 2010. (ENG., Illus.). 312p. pap. 15.95 *(978-1-884995-65-1(9))* Linden Publishing Co., Inc.

Sederquist, Betty. Coloma. 2012. (Images of America Ser.). (ENG., Illus.). 128p. pap. 21.99 ***(978-0-7385-9549-8(7))*** Arcadia Publishing.

Selters, Andy. Inyo National Forest. 2012. (Images of America Ser.). (ENG., Illus.). 128p. pap. 21.99 ***(978-0-7385-9305-0(2))*** Arcadia Publishing.

Semones, JoAnn. Hard Luck Coast: The Perilous Reefs of Point Montara. 2010. (Illus.). 26.95 *(978-1-889901-51-0(2))* Glencannon Pr.

—Sea of Troubles: The Lost Ships of Point Sur. 2012. 256p. 27.95 ***(978-1-889901-55-8(5))*** Glencannon Pr.

Semones, JoAnn. Shipwrecks, Scalawags, & Scavengers: The Storied Waters of Pigeon Point. 2007. (Illus.). 160p. 24.95 *(978-1-889901-42-8(3))* Glencannon Pr.

Shaffer, Kathy. Houseboats: Aquatic Architecture of Sausalito. 2007. (Illus.). 192p. pap. 39.95 *(978-0-7643-2722-3(4))* Schiffer Publishing, Ltd.

Shanks, Ralph C. California Indian Baskets: San Diego to Santa Barbara & Beyond to the San Joaquin Valley, Mountains & Deserts. Shanks, Lisa Woo, ed. 2010. (Indian Baskets of California & Oregon, vol. II Ser.). (ENG., Illus.). 168p. 39.95 *(978-0-930268-20-6(2))* Costano Bks.

Sharon McGriff-Payne. John Grider's Century: African Americans in Solano, Napa, & Sonoma Counties from 1845 To 1925. 2009. 184p. 26.95 *(978-1-4401-6093-6(7))*; pap. 16.95 *(978-1-4401-6091-2(0))* iUniverse, Inc.

Sherer, Caroline Shaw. How Much He Remembered: The Life of John Calvin Sherer, 1852-1949. 2011. 92p. 38.95 ***(978-1-258-02632-5(5))*** Literary Licensing, LLC.

Shoup, Laurence H. Rulers & Rebels: A People's History of Early California, 1769-1901. 2010. 568p. 42.95 *(978-1-4502-5592-9(2))*; pap. 32.95 *(978-1-4502-5590-5(6))* iUniverse, Inc.

Shower, Anita. Grover Beach. 2008. (Images of America Ser.). (ENG., Illus.). 128p. per. 19.99 *(978-0-7385-5596-6(7))* Arcadia Publishing.

Shulman, Todd L. Napa County. 2009. 15p. pap. 7.99 *(978-0-7385-7043-3(5))*; 128p. pap. 21.99 *(978-0-7385-7039-6(7))* Arcadia Publishing.

Silverman, Victor & Glover, Laurie. California: On-the-Road Histories. 2011. (ENG., Illus.). 320p. pap. 22.00 *(978-1-56656-809-8(9))*, Interlink Bks.) Interlink Publishing Group, Inc.

Simonds, William Day. Starr King in California. 2008. 60p. pap. *(978-1-4099-4282-5(1))* Dodo Pr.

Singleton, Jill M. & Holmes, Philip. Centerville, Fremont. 2011. (Images of America Ser.). (Illus.). 128p. pap. 21.99 *(978-0-7385-8177-4(1))* Arcadia Publishing.

Sitton, Tom. Grand Ventures: The Banning Family & the Shaping of Southern California. 2010. (ENG., Illus.). 376p. 34.95 *(978-0-87328-243-7(4))* Huntington Library Pr.

Smith, James R. San Francisco's Playland at the Beach: The Early Years. 2010. (Illus.). 152p. pap. 21.95 *(978-1-884995-67-5(5))* Linden Publishing Co., Inc.

Smith, Ross. History of the Danville Grange: Patrons of Husbandry. 2008. (Illus.). 119p. 23.00 net. *(978-0-938260-03-5(0))* Ashford Pubns.

Smith, Terry, et al. Celebrating Petaluma. Smith, Terry, ed. 2007. (Illus.). 224p. 34.95 *(978-0-9801716-0-0(1))* Petaluma Visitor's Program.

Smookler, Michael. Colma. 2007. (Images of America Ser.). (ENG., Illus.). 128p. per. 19.99 *(978-0-7385-4727-5(1))* Arcadia Publishing.

Society for American Baseball Research (SABR). The National Pastime, Endless Seasons 2011: Baseball in Southern California. 2011. (ENG.). pap. 14.95 ***(978-1-933599-20-5(0))*** Society for American Baseball Research.

Solana Beach Civic, prod. La Colonia & Solana Beach: Spring up from Colonel Ed Fletcher's Running Water. 2010. (Illus.). 100p. pap. 20.00 *(978-0-615-33122-5(X))* Solana Beach Civic & Historical Society.

Soltys, Richard. Coachella Valley: Yesterday, Today. 2006. 194p. 49.95 *(978-0-9726856-0-3(X))* Soltys, Richard J. Productions.

Sommers, Arthur. Placer County. 2010. (Images of America Ser.). (ENG., Illus.). 128p. pap. 21.99 *(978-0-7385-7153-9(9))* Arcadia Publishing.

Soquel Pioneer and Historical Association. Soquel. 2011. (Images of America Ser.). (Illus.). 128p. pap. 21.99 *(978-0-7385-7081-5(8))* Arcadia Publishing.

Sosnowski, Vivienne. When the Rivers Ran Red: An Amazing Story of Courage & Triumph in America's Wine Country. (ENG., Illus.). 256p. 2010. pap. 16.00 *(978-0-230-10337-5(5))* 2009. 26.95 *(978-0-230-60574-9(5))* Palgrave Macmillan.

Soule, Frank & Gihon, John H. The Annals of San Francisco. 592p. 2010. 47.96 *(978-1-163-32029-7(3))* 2010. pap. 35.96 *(978-1-162-79223-1(X))* 2007. (ENG.). 59.95 *(978-0-548-00804-1(3))* Kessinger Publishing, LLC.

Sparks, Edith. Capital Intentions: Female Proprietors in San Francisco, 1850-1920. 2006. (Luther H. Hodges Jr. & Luther H. Hodges Sr. Series on Business, Society, & the State Ser.). (ENG., Illus.). 320p. (C). 69.95 *(978-0-8078-3061-1(5))* Univ. of North Carolina Pr.

Special Collections of the Sacramento Public Library. Sacramento's Alkali Flat. 2009. (Images of America Ser.). (Illus.). 128p. pap. 21.99 *(978-0-7385-7151-5(2))* Arcadia Publishing.

Sperbeck Drsquo;Arcy, Roberta. Browns Valley. 2012. (Images of America Ser.). (ENG., Illus.). 128p. pap. 21.99 ***(978-0-7385-8896-4(2))*** Arcadia Publishing.

Sprague-Bentley, Jeannie. Carlsbad. 2009. (Images of America Ser.). (ENG., Illus.). 128p. pap. 21.99 *(978-0-7385-6952-5(X))* Arcadia Publishing.

St. Clements, compiled by. Saint Clement's Episcopal Church: The First 100 Years 1908-2008. 2010. (Illus.). 86p. 25.00 *(978-0-9819945-5-0(5))* Synthesis Group, Inc.

Stanley, Eric. Santa Rosa. 2008. (Then & Now Ser.). (Illus.). 96p. pap. 21.99 *(978-0-7385-5979-7(2))* Arcadia Publishing.

Stark, Julie. Yuba City, Our Home Town. 2008. *(978-1-57864-498-8(4))* Donning Co. Pubs.

Stark, Michael L. & Skipper Ret., John. Redondo Beach Police Department. 2011. (Images of America Ser.). (Illus.). 128p. pap. 21.99 *(978-0-7385-8164-4(X))* Arcadia Publishing.

Starr, Kevin. California: A History. 2007. (Modern Library Chronicles Ser.). (ENG., Illus.). 400p. pap. 14.95 *(978-0-8129-7753-0(X)*, Modern Library) Random House Publishing Group.

—Golden Dreams: California in an Age of Abundance, 1950-1963, 1 vol. (Americans & the California Dream Ser.). (ENG., Illus.). 576p. 2011. pap. 24.95 *(978-0-19-983249-1(8))* 2009. 34.95 *(978-0-19-515377-4(4))* Oxford Univ. Pr., Inc.

Stephens, E. J. & Wanamaker, Marc. Griffith Park. 2011. (Images of America Ser.). (ENG., Illus.). 128p. pap. 21.99 ***(978-0-7385-8883-4(0))*** Arcadia Publishing.

Stringfellow, Kim. Greetings from the Salton Sea: Folly & Intervention in the Southern California Landscape, 1905-2005. 2nd ed. 2011. (Center for American Places - Center Books on American Places Ser.). (Illus.). 152p. pap. 25.00 *(978-1-935195-32-0(8))* Ctr. for American Places, Inc.

Sullivan, Julie. Voices of Lafayette: A Collection of Oral Histories. 2009. 292p. pap. 19.95 *(978-0-9745540-3-7(0))* Big Hat Pr.

Sullivan, Noelle. Southern California: Thirty Remarkable Events That Shaped History. 2nd ed. 2009. (It Happened in Ser.). (ENG., Illus.). 144p. pap. 14.95 *(978-0-7627-5423-6(0))* Globe Pequot Pr., The.

Sunnyside Country Club (Fresno, Calif.), Centennial Committee Staff, contrib. by. Sunnyside Country Club: Centennial Celebration/By the Centennial Committee. 2011. ***(978-1-57864-694-4(4))*** Donning Co. Pubs.

Sweet, Ellen L. & Newell, Lynne. Historic Stage Routes of San Diego County. 2011. (Images of America Ser.). (Illus.). 128p. pap. 21.99 ***(978-0-7385-7468-4(6))*** Arcadia Publishing.

Syvret, Marguerite, et al. Balleine's History of Jersey. 2011. (ENG., Illus.). 336p. pap. 45.00 ***(978-1-86077-650-2(7))*** History Pr. Ltd.,The GBR. Dist: Independent Pubs. Group.

Tahja, Katy M. Early Mendocino Coast. 2008. (Images of America Ser.). (ENG., Illus.). 128p. pap. 21.99 *(978-0-7385-5946-9(6))* Arcadia Publishing.

Tatam, Robert D. & Myers, Loicy. Old Times in Stanislaus County: A Journey to the Past. Tatam, Robert D., ed. (Illus.). 182p. (Orig.). pap. 14.99 *(978-0-9637954-2-7(2))* Highland Pubs.

Tavares, Dennis. How Mendocino County Went to Pot: Memories of Life in Mendocino Redwood Country in the Last Half of the 1900s. 2011. 352p. pap. 19.92 ***(978-1-4269-8886-8(9))*** Trafford Publishing.

Taylor, Alexander S. A Historical Summary of Lower California. 200p. 18.95 *(978-0-87026-044-5(8))* Westernlore Pubns.

Taylor, Patrick A. Memories of Pinecrest. 2006. per. 17.95 *(978-0-9789240-0-3(2))* Taylor Pr.'.

Teurlay, Frank. Riverside's Camp Anza & Arlanza. 2008. (Images of America Ser.). (Illus.). 128p. pap. 19.99 *(978-0-7385-5918-6(0))* Arcadia Publishing.

Thomas, Bill. San Clemente: Hither, Thither & Yon. 2009. 528p. pap. 23.95 *(978-1-4327-3562-3(4))* Outskirts Pr., Inc.

Thomas, Rick. South Pasadena. 2007. (Images of America Ser.). (ENG., Illus.). 128p. per. 21.99 *(978-0-7385-4748-0(4))* Arcadia Publishing.

—South Pasadena's Raymond Hotel. 2008. (Images of America Ser.). (Illus.). 128p. pap. 21.99 *(978-0-7385-5919-3(9))* Arcadia Publishing.

Thomas, Rick R. South Pasadena's Ostrich Farm. 2007. (Images of America Ser.). (Illus.). 127p. *(978-0-7385-5578-2(9))* Arcadia Publishing.

Thomas, Tim & League, the Monterey Japanese American Citizens. The Japanese on the Monterey Peninsula. 2011. (Images of America Ser.). (ENG., Illus.). 128p. pap. 21.99 ***(978-0-7385-7497-4(X))*** Arcadia Publishing.

Thomson, Thomas. Historical Atlas Map Tulare Co. 2006. 147p. 149.95 *(978-1-892622-29-7(7))* Bear State Bks.

Thurnher, Oskar R. A History of Ambulance Service in Santa Clara County. 2008. 84p. per. *(978-0-9801675-0-4(7))* Robertson Publishing.

Tilchen, Mark. Floods of the Kaweah. 2010. (Illus.). 49p. pap. *(978-1-878441-25-6(6))* Sequoia Natural History Assn.

Tom, Brian, et al. Marysville's Chinatown. 2008. (Images of America Ser.). (ENG., Illus.). 128p. pap. 19.99 *(978-0-7385-5976-6(8))* Arcadia Publishing.

Tracy Callis And Chuck Johnston. Boxing in the Los Angeles Are: 1880-2005. 2009. 168p. pap. 24.95 *(978-1-4269-1686-5(4))* Trafford Publishing.

Tramble, Thomas & Tramble, Wilma. The Pullman Porters & West Oakland. 2007. (Images of America Ser.). (Illus.). 127p. per. 19.99 *(978-0-7385-4789-3(1))* Arcadia Publishing.

Trimble, Paul C. Riverboats of Northern California. 2011. (Images of America Ser.). (Illus.). 128p. pap. 21.99 ***(978-0-7385-7496-7(1))*** Arcadia Publishing.

Tucker, Wehtahnah & Bujkovsky, Gus. Cardiff-by-the-Sea. 2009. (Images of America Ser.). (ENG., Illus.). 128p. pap. 21.99 *(978-0-7385-6951-2(8))* Arcadia Publishing.

Tuggle, Jeremy M. A Journey Through Time: Ono & the Bald Hills. 2008. (Illus.). 96p. pap. 10.00 *(978-0-9742576-8-6(0))* Preserving Memories.

Tuthill, Franklin. The History of California. 2010. (Historiography Ser.). 676p. pap. 38.95 *(978-1-4290-2234-7(5))* Applewood Bks.

Ungermann-Marshall, Yana. Flintridge. 2008. (Images of America Ser.). (ENG., Illus.). 128p. per. 19.99 *(978-0-7385-5585-0(1))* Arcadia Publishing.

Union City Historical Museum Oral History Book: By Myrla Raymundo, MBA. 2010.Tr. of 02/01/2010. (Illus.). 214p. pap. 20.00 net. *(978-0-9715211-6-2(6))* FolgerGraphics, Inc.

Van Maren, James. Citrus Heights. 2011. (Images of America Ser.). (Illus.). 128p. pap. 21.99 *(978-0-7385-7459-2(7))* Arcadia Publishing.

Van Raaphorst, Donna L. Alcatraz - the History of an Island Prison: From the Development to an American Myth. 2011. (Illus.). 560p. 159.95 ***(978-0-7734-1596-6(3))*** Mellen, Edwin Pr., The.

Van Sicklen, Helen Putnam, ed. The Quarterly of the Society of California Pioneers, V10 1933. 2011. 118p. 39.95 ***(978-1-258-03676-8(2))*** Literary Licensing, LLC.

Van Winkle, H. L. Quarterly of the Society of California Pioneers, V6, No 2, June 1929. Van Sicklen, Helen Putnam, ed. 2011. 58p. 36.95 ***(978-1-258-08123-2(7))*** Literary Licensing, LLC.

Vargo, Cecile Page & Vargo, Roger W. Cerro Gordo. 2012. (Images of America Ser.). (ENG., Illus.). 128p. pap. 21.99 ***(978-0-7385-9520-7(9))*** Arcadia Publishing.

Vasquez, Antonio Gonzalez & Carpio, Genevieve. Mexican Americans in Redlands. 2012. (Images of America Ser.). (ENG., Illus.). 128p. pap. 21.99 ***(978-0-7385-9522-1(5))*** Arcadia Publishing.

Vaughan, Pam & Vaughan, Brenden. Bishop. 2011. (Images of America Ser.). (ENG., Illus.). 128p. pap. 21.99 *(978-0-7385-8183-5(6))* Arcadia Publishing.

Vaught, David. After the Gold Rush: Tarnished Dreams in the Sacramento Valley. 2007. (ENG., Illus.). 328p. (gr. 17). 60.00 *(978-0-8018-8497-9(7))* Johns Hopkins Univ. Pr.

Vaught, David & Vaught, D. After the Gold Rush: Tarnished Dreams in the Sacramento Valley. 2009. (ENG., Illus.). 328p. (gr. 17). pap. 32.00 *(978-0-8018-9257-8(0))* Johns Hopkins Univ. Pr.

Veldhuis, Debbie. Glendale. 2010. (Then & Now Ser.). (ENG., Illus.). 96p. pap. 21.99 *(978-0-7385-7895-8(9))* Arcadia Publishing.

Ventimiglia, Mike. Monterey Fire Department. 2012. (Images of America Ser.). (ENG., Illus.). 128p. pap. 21.99 ***(978-0-7385-7623-7(9))*** Arcadia Publishing.

Veronico, Betty S. Lighthouses of the Bay Area. 2008. (Images of America Ser.). (ENG., Illus.). 128p. pap. 19.99 *(978-0-7385-5943-8(1))* Arcadia Publishing.

Vogel, Claire Marie. Laguna Beach. 2009. (Images of America Ser.). (ENG., Illus.). 128p. pap. 21.99 *(978-0-7385-6997-0(6))* Arcadia Publishing.

Vollmann, William T. Imperial. 2009. (ENG., Illus.). 1344p. (gr. 12-18). 55.00 *(978-0-670-02061-4(3)*, Viking Adult) Penguin Group (USA) Inc.

Vrilakas Simons, Cynthia. San Leandro. 2008. (Images of America Ser.). (Illus.). 128p. pap. 19.99 *(978-0-7385-5937-7(7))* Arcadia Publishing.

Waddell, James Albert. Cal North Outdoor Scenic Byway Tour: Siskiyou Notes of History, Vol. 5. Waddell, James Albert, ed. 2006. (Cal North Outdoor Scenic Byway Tour Ser.: Vol. 5). 69p. pap. 20.00 *(978-0-9761434-5-1(3))* Waddell, James Albert.

—Cal North Outdoor Scenic Byway Tour - Siskiyou County Names of History. Waddell, James Albert, ed. 2006. (Cal North Outdoor Scenic Byway Tour Ser.: Vol. 4). 72p. pap. 20.00 *(978-0-9761434-4-4(5))* Waddell, James Albert.

Wagenknecht, Louise. Light on the Devils: Coming of Age on the Klamath. 2011. (ENG.). 232p. pap. 19.95 ***(978-0-87071-611-9(5))*** Oregon State Univ. Pr.

Wainwright, Mary-Jo. Pleasanton. 2007. (Images of America Ser.). (ENG., Illus.). 128p. pap. 21.99 *(978-0-7385-4761-9(1))* Arcadia Publishing.

Walker, Ardis Manly. Death Valley & Manly: Symbols of Destiny. 2011. 42p. 35.95 ***(978-1-258-06974-2(1))*** Literary Licensing, LLC.

Walker, Chard. Chard Walker's Cajon: Rail Passage to the Pacific. 2007. (Illus.). 256p. 60.00 *(978-1-930013-00-1(0))* Signature Pr.

Walker, Doris I. Orange County: A Natural HIST. 2009. 128p. pap. 21.99 *(978-0-7385-6908-6(9))* Arcadia Publishing.

—Orange County Then & Now. 2006. (Then & Now Thunder Bay Ser.). (ENG., Illus.). 144p. 19.95 *(978-1-59223-599-5(9)*, Thunder Bay Pr.) Advantage Pubs. Group.

Wanamaker, Marc. San Fernando Valley. 2011. (Images of America Ser.). (ENG., Illus.). 128p. pap. 21.99 *(978-0-7385-7157-7(1))* Arcadia Publishing.

Ward, David A., et al. Alcatraz: The Gangster Years. 2009. (ENG., Illus.). 576p. 40.00 *(978-0-520-25607-1(7))* Univ. of California Pr.

Warren, Eric H. Eagle Rock. 2009. (Images of America Ser.). (ENG., Illus.). 128p. pap. 21.99 *(978-0-7385-6996-3(8))* Arcadia Publishing.

Waters, John. Calistoga. 2008. (Images of America Ser.). (ENG., Illus.). 128p. pap. 19.99 *(978-0-7385-5594-2(0))* Arcadia Publishing.

Waters, John, Jr. Calistoga. 2008. (Illus.). 127p. pap. *(978-0-7835-5594-2(6))* Arcadia Publishing.

Weber, Lin. Queen of the Valley, 50 Years. 2007. (Illus.). 133p. *(978-0-9667014-6-3(1))* Wine Ventures Publishing.

Weekes, Don & Banks, Kerry. Hockey's Top 100: The Game's Greatest Records, 1 vol. 2008. (ENG., Illus.). 168p. pap. 15.95 *(978-1-55365-274-8(5)*, Greystone Bks.) D&M Pubs. Inc. CAN. Dist: Perseus-PGW.

Weeks, John Howard. Inland Empire. 2008. (Postcard History Ser.). (ENG., Illus.). 128p. pap. 19.99 *(978-0-7385-5907-0(5))* Arcadia Publishing.

Weeks, John Howard. Mojave Desert. 2012. (Postcard History Ser.). (ENG., Illus.). 128p. pap. 21.99 ***(978-0-7385-8887-2(3))*** Arcadia Publishing.

Wehrey, Jane. Manzanar. 2008. (Images of America Ser.). (ENG., Illus.). 128p. pap. 21.99 *(978-0-7385-5808-0(7))* Arcadia Publishing.

Weisser, Kai. Huntington Beach Lifeguards. 2008. (Images of America Ser.). (ENG., Illus.). 128p. pap. 19.99 *(978-0-7385-5605-5(X))* Arcadia Publishing.

Wellman, Gregory L. A History of Alcatraz Island: 1853-2008. 2008. (Images of America Ser.). (ENG., Illus.). 128p. pap. 21.99 *(978-0-7385-5815-8(X))* Arcadia Publishing.

Wendler, John. Brewers & Bottlers of California 1860 To 1919. 2007. 208p. per. 39.95 *(978-1-4327-0733-0(7))* Outskirts Pr., Inc.

Wesch, Hank. Del Mar: Where the Turf Meets the Surf. 2011. (Illus.). 150p. pap. 19.99 ***(978-1-60949-310-3(9))*** History Pr., The.

Western Sonoma County Historical Society. Sebastopol's Gravenstein Apple Industry. 2011. (Images of America Ser.). (Illus.). 128p. pap. 21.99 *(978-0-7385-8173-6(9))* Arcadia Publishing.

Westwick, Peter J. & Deverell, William, eds. Blue Sky Metropolis: The Aerospace Century in Southern California. 2012. (Western Histories Ser.). (ENG., Illus.). 278p. 44.95 ***(978-0-87328-249-9(3))*** Huntington Library Pr.

Wheatland Historical Society. Wheatland. 2009. (Images of America Ser.). (ENG., Illus.). 128p. pap. 21.99 *(978-0-7385-6977-2(1))* Arcadia Publishing.

Wheeler, Wally. La Quinta Legend in the Making. 2007. (ENG., Illus.). 92p. per. 14.95 *(978-0-9727572-4-9(4))* Desert Springs Publishing.

White, C. Todd, ed. San Dieguito & la Jolla: Collected Papers of Claude Warren & Colleagues. 2007. (Ethnographics Monographs: 15). (ENG., Illus.). 181p. (C). pap. 50.00 *(978-1-878986-15-3(5))* Ethnographics Pr.

White, Michael D. Port of Long Beach. 2009. (Images of America Ser.). (ENG., Illus.). 128p. pap. 21.99 *(978-0-7385-6985-7(2))* Arcadia Publishing.

White, Stewart Edward. The Forty-Niners: A Chronicle of the California Trail & el Dorado. 2008. 280p. 25.99 *(978-0-559-79181-9(X))* 2008. 280p. pap. 26.75 *(978-0-559-79178-9(X))* 2007. 154p. pap. 19.99 *(978-1-4346-6078-7(8))* 2007. (ENG.). 164p. pap. 21.99 *(978-1-4346-6079-4(6))* BiblioBazaar.

—The Forty-Niners: A Chronicle of the California Trail & el Dorado. 2007. 140p. per. *(978-1-4065-6625-3(X))* Dodo Pr.

Whitehead III, Jerry. Tuolumne City. 2012. (Images of America Ser.). (ENG., Illus.). 128p. pap. 21.99 ***(978-0-7385-8918-3(7))*** Arcadia Publishing.

C

Whitsell, Leon O. One Hundred Years of Freemasonry in California V1. 2011. 476p. 57.95 **(978-1-258-02975-3(8))** Literary Licensing, LLC.

—One Hundred Years of Freemasonry in California V2. 2011. 454p. 57.95 **(978-1-258-02981-4(2))** Literary Licensing, LLC.

—One Hundred Years of Freemasonry in California V3. 2011. 714p. 70.95 **(978-1-258-02982-1(0))** Literary Licensing, LLC.

Wickson, Gladys C. California Historical Society Quarterly, V29, No 2, June 1950. 2011. 112p. 39.95 **(978-1-258-07027-4(8))** Literary Licensing, LLC.

Willard, Steve & LaValle, Ed. San Diego Police: Case Files. 2012. (Images of America Ser.). (ENG., Illus.). 128p. pap. 21.99 **(978-0-7385-9548-1(9))** Arcadia Publishing.

Willis, Barbara & The Escalon Historical Society. Escalon. 2008. (Images of America Ser.). (ENG., Illus.). 128p. pap. 21.99 *(978-0-7385-5903-2(2))* Arcadia Publishing.

Wilson, Carol Green. California Yankee: William R. Staats, Business Pioneer. 2007. (ENG.). 238p. 41.95 *(978-0-548-05896-1(2))* Kessinger Publishing, LLC.

Wilson, Karen. Reclamation District 1000: 100 Years in the Natomas Basin. 2011. **(978-1-57864-717-0(7))** Donning Co. Pubs.

Wilson, Lori Lee. The Joaquín Band: The History Behind the Legend. 2011. (ENG., Illus.). 336p. 29.95 *(978-0-8032-3461-1(9))* Univ. of Nebraska Pr.

Winn, Mary Bryner. Corona. 2012. (Then & Now Ser.). (ENG., Illus.). 96p. pap. 21.99 **(978-0-7385-9313-5(3))** Arcadia Publishing.

Winthrop, R. C. Admission of California: Speech of the Honorable R. C. Winthrop of Massachusetts. 28p. pap. 10.00 *(978-0-8466-0154-8(0),* S-154) Shorey's Bookstore.

Woelfel, Monica & Wojna, Lisa. Bathroom Book of Northern California Trivia. 2007. (Bathroom Book Of... Ser.). (ENG., Illus.). 248p. per. *(978-1-897278-23-9(3))* Lone Pine Publishing USA.

Wood III, Thomas N. Saratoga. 2010. (Postcard History Ser.). (Illus.). 128p. pap. 21.99 *(978-0-7385-7327-4(2))* Arcadia Publishing.

Worthen, James. Governor James Rolph & the Great Depression in California. 2006. (ENG., Illus.). 235p. per. 39.95 *(978-0-7864-2574-7(1))* McFarland & Co., Inc. Pubs.

Wright, Cynthia J. & Cox-Finney, Judy. Lemoore. 2010. (Images of America Ser.). (Illus.). 128p. pap. 21.99 *(978-0-7385-8154-5(2))* Arcadia Publishing.

Wyman, Nona Mock. Bamboo Women: Stories from Ming Quong, a Chinese Orphanage in California. 2012. (ENG., Illus.). 225p. pap. 19.95 **(978-0-8351-0006-9(5))** Long River Pr.

Young, Alison. Orange Crate Labels of Orange County, California. Ball, Guy, ed. 2008. (Illus.). 48p. 14.00 *(978-0-9797619-1-1(3))* Santa Ana Historical Preservation Society.

Yucaipa Valley Historical Society. Yucaipa. 2007. (Images of America Ser.). (Illus.). 127p. per. 19.99 *(978-0-7385-4733-6(6))* Arcadia Publishing.

—Yucaipa: 1940s-1960s. 2009. (Images of America Ser.). (Illus.). 128p. pap. 21.99 *(978-0-7385-7080-8(X))* Arcadia Publishing.

Yusada, Anita & Beuster, Kirsten. Historic Monterey. 2008. (Illus.). 112p. pap. 19.95 *(978-0-7643-2871-8(9))* Schiffer Publishing, Ltd.

Zaverukha, Lydia B. & Bogdan, Nina. Russian San Francisco. 2009. (Images of America Ser.). (Illus.). 128p. pap. 21.99 *(978-0-7385-7167-6(9))* Arcadia Publishing.

CALIFORNIA—HISTORY—SOURCES

Colton, Walter. Three Years in California by Rev Walter Colton. 2006. 484p. per. 29.99 *(978-1-4255-5304-3(4))* MPublishing.

Duvall, Marius. A Navy Surgeon in California, 1846-1847: The Journal of Marius Duvall. Rogers, Fred Blackburn, ed. 2011. 136p. 40.95 **(978-1-258-01231-1(6))** Literary Licensing, LLC.

Haas, Christopher. A Documentary History of California. 2008. pap. *(978-0-312-26026-2(1))* St. Martin's Pr.

CALIFORNIA—HISTORY, LOCAL

Adams, Carole & Bogacki, John. Point Piedras Blancas. 2008. 128p. pap. 19.99 *(978-0-7385-5819-6(2))* Arcadia Publishing.

Alexander, Pat & Napa Valley Museum. Yountville. 2009. (Images of America Ser.). (ENG., Illus.). 128p. pap. 21.99 *(978-0-7385-6965-9(8))* Arcadia Publishing.

Allen, Annalee. Selections from the Oakland Tribune Archives. 2006. (Images of America Ser.). (Illus.). 128p. per. 19.99 *(978-0-7385-4678-0(X))* Arcadia Publishing.

Areyan, Alex Moreno. Mexican Americans in Redondo Beach & Hermosa Beach. 2007. (Images of America Ser.). (ENG., Illus.). 128p. per. 19.99 *(978-0-7385-4699-5(2))* Arcadia Publishing.

Arias, Priscila R. Treasures of the Sierras. 2009. (ENG.). 224p. pap. 24.95 *(978-1-60813-602-5(7))* PublishAmerica, Inc.

Armand, Dione F. Trinidad. 2010. (Images of America Ser.). (ENG., Illus.). 128p. pap. 21.99 *(978-0-7385-7161-4(X))* Arcadia Publishing.

Austin, Mary Hunter. The Land of Little Rain. 2007. 100p. pap. 16.99 *(978-1-4264-8631-9(6))* BiblioBazaar.

Barnett, Loretta, et al. Murrieta. 2006. (Images of America Ser.). (ENG., Illus.). 128p. per. 19.99 *(978-0-7385-4669-8(0))* Arcadia Publishing.

Baxter, R. Scott & Wooten, Kimberly. Shenandoah Valley & Amador Wine Country. 2008. (Images of America Ser.). (Illus.). 127p. per. 19.99 *(978-0-7385-5603-1(3))* Arcadia Publishing.

Bell, Ellen Baker & the Irvine Historical Society. Irvine. 2011. (Images of America Ser.). (ENG., Illus.). 128p. pap. 21.99 **(978-0-7385-7575-9(5))** Arcadia Publishing.

Bellamy, Stanley E. Running Springs. 2007. (Images of America Ser.). (Illus.). 127p. per. 19.99 *(978-0-7385-4679-7(8))* Arcadia Publishing.

Benziger, Jeff. Ceres. 2010. (Images of America Ser.). (ENG., Illus.). 128p. pap. 21.99 *(978-0-7385-8101-9(1))* Arcadia Publishing.

Black, Tess. Portraits of Pescadero: A memory album of five families & Friends. 2006. per. 22.95 *(978-0-9788514-0-8(4))* Music By Piano & Birds Pr.

Breschini, Gary, et al. Spreckels. 2006. (Images of America Ser.). (Illus.). 128p. per. 19.99 *(978-0-7385-4684-1(4))* Arcadia Publishing.

Brewer, William H. Up & down California in 1860-1864: The Journal of William H. Brewer. Farquhar, Francis P., ed. 2011. 628p. 65.95 **(978-1-258-08386-1(8))** Literary Licensing, LLC.

Briggs, Randy & Edwards, Fred. Redlands. 2006. (Postcard History Ser.). (Illus.). 128p. pap. 19.99 *(978-0-7385-4680-3(1))* Arcadia Publishing.

Brower, Maria E. Gold Rush Towns of Nevada County. 2006. (Images of America Ser.). (ENG., Illus.). 128p. per. 21.99 *(978-0-7385-4692-6(5))* Arcadia Publishing.

Bunyan, Bob & Foundation, The Aliso Viejo Community. Aliso Viejo. 2011. (Images of America Ser.). (ENG., Illus.). 128p. pap. 21.99 **(978-0-7385-7424-0(4))** Arcadia Publishing.

Burg, William. Sacramento's Streetcars. 2006. (Images of America Ser.). (ENG., Illus.). 128p. per. 21.99 *(978-0-7385-3147-2(2))* Arcadia Publishing.

Burnett, Claudine. Soaring Skyward: A History of Aviation in & Around Long Beach, California. 2011. 308p. pap. 29.95 **(978-1-4670-3361-9(8))** AuthorHouse.

Burrill, Robert & Rogers, Lynn. Alviso, San Jose. 2006. (Images of America Ser.). (ENG., Illus.). 128p. per. 19.99 *(978-0-7385-3140-3(5))* Arcadia Publishing.

Cairns, Kathleen A. Hard Time at Tehachapi: California's First Women's Prison. 2009. (ENG., Illus.). 215p. (C). 29.95 *(978-0-8263-4572-1(7))* Univ. of New Mexico Pr.

Campos, Jim & Bonnie Kelm, Dave Moore, Tom Moore, and the Carpinteria Valley Museum of History. Greater Carpinteria: Summerland & la Conchita. 2009. (Images of America Ser.). (ENG., Illus.). 128p. pap. 21.99 *(978-0-7385-7098-3(2))* Arcadia Publishing.

Campos, Jim, et al. Carpinteria. 2007. (Images of America Ser.). (ENG., Illus.). 128p. per. 19.99 *(978-0-7385-4758-9(1))* Arcadia Publishing.

Carlberg, Marvin & Epting, Chris. Huntington Beach. 2009. (Postcard History Ser.). (ENG., Illus.). 128p. pap. 21.99 *(978-0-7385-6983-3(6))* Arcadia Publishing.

Carnes, Marilyn & Nye, Matthew. Early National City. 2008. (Images of America Ser.). (ENG., Illus.). 128p. pap. 19.99 *(978-0-7385-5910-0(5))* Arcadia Publishing.

Cashman, Robert. Wildomar. 2010. (Images of America Ser.). (ENG., Illus.). 128p. pap. 21.99 *(978-0-7385-7082-2(6))* Arcadia Publishing.

Clough, Charles, ed. Calaveras County Illustrated & Described, 1885. (Illus.). 112p. reprint ed. 13.45 *(978-0-944194-28-7(1));* pap. 8.95 *(978-0-944194-27-0(3))* Linrose Publishing Co.

Clovis, Margaret. Monterey County's North Coast & Coastal Valleys. 2006. (Images of America Ser.). (ENG., Illus.). 128p. per. 21.99 *(978-0-7385-4677-3(1))* Arcadia Publishing.

Cook, Deborah Coleen. Ione & the Jackson Valley. 2008. (Images of America Ser.). (ENG., Illus.). 128p. pap. 19.99 *(978-0-7385-5602-4(5))* Arcadia Publishing.

Cornejo, Jeffrey Lawrence & Cornejo, Jeffrey Lawrence, Jr. Azusa. 2007. (Images of America Ser.). (ENG., Illus.). 128p. per. 19.99 *(978-0-7385-4710-7(7))* Arcadia Publishing.

Cresson, David V. Turning Points: A History of Half Moon Bay & the Coastside As It Has Unfolded near the House That Zaballa Built. 2009. *(978-0-89863-300-9(1))* Star Publishing Co.

Crimmen, Dave & Kopp, Foreword by Quentin. Broadmoor Village. 2010. (Images of America Ser.). (Illus.). 128p. pap. 21.99 *(978-0-7385-8092-0(9))* Arcadia Publishing.

Culver, Lawrence. The Frontier of Leisure: Southern California & the Shaping of Modern America, 1 vol. (ENG., Illus.). 336p. 2012. pap. 21.95 **(978-0-19-989192-4(3))** 2010. 29.95 *(978-0-19-538263-1(3))* Oxford Univ. Pr., Inc.

Dean, Edward. The Wine Thief. 2009. 380p. 28.95 *(978-1-60693-325-1(6),* Eloquent Bks.) AEG Literary Publishing Services, Inc.

DeRooy, Carola & Livingston, Dewey. Point Reyes Peninsula. 2008. (Images of America Ser.). (ENG., Illus.). 128p. pap. 19.99 *(978-0-7385-5848-6(6))* Arcadia Publishing.

Desoucy, M. David. San Bernardino County Sheriff's Department. 2006. (Images of America Ser.). (ENG., Illus.). 128p. per. 19.99 *(978-0-7385-4663-6(1))* Arcadia Publishing.

Dougherty, Bob. La Honda. 2007. (Images of America Ser.). (ENG., Illus.). 128p. per. 19.99 *(978-0-7385-4738-1(7))* Arcadia Publishing.

Dwyer, Jeff. Ghost Hunter's Guide to Monterey & California's Central Coast, 1 vol. 2010. (ENG., Illus.). 240p. pap. 14.95 *(978-1-58980-809-6(6))* Pelican Publishing Co., Inc.

Edmond, John G. Union Cemetery, Redwood City, California: The People, Their Lives, Their Communities: Including the Towns of Searsville, Summit Springs, & West Union. 2nd ed. 2009. *(978-0-89863-310-8(9))* Star Publishing Co.

Ehrenreich, V. K. North Sacramento. 2010. (Images of America Ser.). (ENG., Illus.). 128p. pap. 21.99 *(978-0-7385-8003-6(1))* Arcadia Publishing.

Epting, Chris. Huntington Beach. 2008. (Then & Now Ser.). (ENG., Illus.). 96p. pap. 19.99 *(978-0-7385-5828-8(1))* Arcadia Publishing.

Erlandson, Jon M., et al. A Canyon through Time: Archaeology, History, & Ecology of the Tecolote Canyon Area, Santa Barbara County, California. 2008. (ENG., Illus.). 216p. pap. 35.00 *(978-0-87480-879-7(0))* Univ. of Utah Pr.

Farley, Adriana & Holman, Jan. Durham. 2008. (Images of America Ser.). (ENG., Illus.). 128p. pap. 19.99 *(978-0-7385-5817-2(6))* Arcadia Publishing.

Figler, Jeff. Poway. 2007. (Images of America Ser.). (ENG., Illus.). 128p. per. 21.99 *(978-0-7385-5597-3(5))* Arcadia Publishing.

Fortuna Depot Museum. Fortuna & the Eel River Valley. 2011. (Images of America Ser.). (Illus.). 128p. pap. 21.99 *(978-0-7385-7522-3(4))* Arcadia Publishing.

Gahagan, Michael. Sonora. 2007. (Images of America Ser.). (ENG., Illus.). 128p. per. 21.99 *(978-0-7385-4783-1(2))* Arcadia Publishing.

Gallivan, Mickey & Historical Society of Pomona Valley. Early Pomona. 2007. (Images of America Ser.). (ENG., Illus.). 128p. per. 19.99 *(978-0-7385-4776-3(X))* Arcadia Publishing.

Gardena Heritage Committee. Gardena. 2006. (Images of America Ser.). (ENG., Illus.). 128p. per. 21.99 *(978-0-7385-4676-6(3))* Arcadia Publishing.

Garey, Jennifer A. & San Clemente Historical Society. San Clemente. 2010. (Images of America Ser.). (ENG., Illus.). 128p. pap. 21.99 *(978-0-7385-8051-7(1))* Arcadia Publishing.

Gay, Ronald K. & Oakland County Pioneer and Historical Society. Pontiac. 2010. (Images of America Ser.). (Illus.). 128p. pap. 21.99 *(978-0-7385-7814-9(2))* Arcadia Publishing.

Gildersleeve, Matthew. San Lucas: The History of a California Cattle Town. (Illus.). viii, 100p. (C). reprint ed. pap. 11.88 *(978-1-55567-587-5(5))* Coyote Pr.

Goerke, Betty. Chief Marin: Leader, Rebel, & Legend. 2007. (Illus.). 292p. per. *(978-1-59714-053-9(8))* Heyday.

Goin, Peter. South Lake Tahoe. 2010. (Then & Now Ser.). (Illus.). 96p. pap. 21.99 *(978-0-7385-8018-0(X))* Arcadia Publishing.

Gurba, Norma H. & West, Nicholas J. Palmdale. 2010. (Images of America Ser.). (Illus.). 128p. pap. 21.99 *(978-0-7385-8122-4(4))* Arcadia Publishing.

Hamlin, David & Arena, Brett. Los Angeles's Original Farmers Market. 2009. (Images of America Ser.). (ENG., Illus.). 128p. pap. 21.99 *(978-0-7385-7005-1(2))* Arcadia Publishing.

Harris, Richard. Early Amusement Parks of Orange County. 2008. (Images of America Ser.). (ENG., Illus.). 128p. pap. 21.99 *(978-0-7385-5947-6(4))* Arcadia Publishing.

Hart, Bill. East Orange. 2006. (Images of America Ser.). (ENG., Illus.). 128p. per. 19.99 *(978-0-7385-4549-3(X))* Arcadia Publishing.

Harton, Deborah & McCloud, Ron. Dunsmuir. 2010. (Images of America Ser.). (ENG., Illus.). 128p. pap. 21.99 *(978-0-7385-8056-2(2))* Arcadia Publishing.

Hatheway, Roger G. & Keller, Russell L. Lake Arrowhead. 2007. (Postcard History Ser.). (ENG., Illus.). 128p. per. 19.99 *(978-0-7385-4702-2(6))* Arcadia Publishing.

Hecteman, Kevin W. Sacramento's Southern Pacific Shops. 2010. (Images of Rail Ser.). (Illus.). 128p. pap. 21.99 *(978-0-7385-8052-4(X))* Arcadia Publishing.

Hickenbottom, Thomas, et al. Surfing in Santa Cruz. 2009. (Images of America Ser.). (ENG., Illus.). 128p. pap. 21.99 *(978-0-7385-7076-1(1))* Arcadia Publishing.

Hobbs, Andrea H., et al. Paso Robles. 2007. (Images of America Ser.). (ENG., Illus.). 128p. per. 21.99 *(978-0-7385-4721-3(2))* Arcadia Publishing.

Holtzclaw, Kenneth M. & Moreno Valley Historical Society. Moreno Valley. 2007. (Images of America Ser.). (ENG., Illus.). 128p. per. 19.99 *(978-0-7385-5569-0(X))* Arcadia Publishing.

Hoye, Richard, et al. Ojai. (Postcard History Ser.). (ENG., Illus.). 128p. 2010. pap. 21.99 *(978-0-7385-8108-8(9))* 2007. per. 21.99 *(978-0-7385-5577-5(0))* Arcadia Publishing.

Jaenke, Margaret Wellman & Hamilton Museum. Around Anza Valley. 2008. (Images of America Ser.). (ENG., Illus.). 128p. per. 19.99 *(978-0-7385-5592-8(4))* Arcadia Publishing.

Jensen, Carol A., et al. Brentwood. 2008. (Images of America Ser.). (ENG., Illus.). 128p. pap. 19.99 *(978-0-7385-5825-7(7))* Arcadia Publishing.

Johnson, Robert A. & Riggins, Charlene. A Different Shade of Orange: Voices of Orange County, California, Black Pioneers. 2009. pap. *(978-0-930046-25-5(0))* California State Univ., San Bernardino, Robert V. Fullerton Art Museum.

Jones Berk, Lucy & Covey, Stephen A. Escondido Grape Day Festivals. 2010. (Images of America Ser.). (ENG., Illus.). 128p. pap. 21.99 *(978-0-7385-5949-0(0))* Arcadia Publishing.

Karlberg, Virginia. Who Lived in This House? The Story of the Byer / Nail House & the History of California Farming in the East Contra Costa County & San Joaquin Val. 2009. 44p. pap. 17.99 *(978-1-4389-6643-4(1))* AuthorHouse.

King, William F. La Puente: Where the Past Meets the Future. 2006. (Illus.). 80p. *(978-1-57864-372-1(4))* Donning Co. Pubs.

Land, R. A. Americas First Commercial Airfield. 2006. 73p. pap. 10.00 *(978-1-4257-0295-3(3))* Xlibris Corp.

Latimer, Larry & Downey Historical Society. Downey. 2010. (Images of America Ser.). (ENG., Illus.). 128p. pap. 21.99 *(978-0-7385-7164-5(4))* Arcadia Publishing.

Lech, Steve. Riverside, 1870-1940. 2007. (Images of America Ser.). (Illus.). 127p. per. 19.99 *(978-0-7385-4716-9(6))* Arcadia Publishing.

Lehmann, Bob & Blanck, Bob. San Gorgonio Search & Rescue Team. 2008. (Images of America Ser.). (Illus.). 128p. pap. 19.99 *(978-0-7385-5576-8(2))* Arcadia Publishing.

Livermore Heritage Guild. Early Livermore. 2006. (Images of America Ser.). (ENG., Illus.). 128p. per. 21.99 *(978-0-7385-3099-4(9))* Arcadia Publishing.

Lovato, Michelle. Apple Valley. 2007. (Images of America Ser.). (ENG., Illus.). 128p. per. 19.99 *(978-0-7385-4749-7(2))* Arcadia Publishing.

Lyon, Mary Lou. Early Cupertino. 2006. (Images of America Ser.). (ENG., Illus.). 128p. per. 19.99 *(978-0-7385-3141-0(3))* Arcadia Publishing.

Mabalon, Dawn B., et al. Filipinos in Stockton. 2008. (Images of America Ser.). (ENG., Illus.). 128p. per. 19.99 *(978-0-7385-5624-6(6))* Arcadia Publishing.

Manning, Kathleen & Crow, Jerry. Pacifica. 2010. (Then & Now Ser.). (Illus.). 96p. pap. 21.99 *(978-0-7385-8042-5(2))* Arcadia Publishing.

Martinez, Roberta H. Latinos in Pasadena. 2009. (Images of America Ser.). (ENG., Illus.). 128p. pap. 21.99 *(978-0-7385-6955-0(0))* Arcadia Publishing.

Marvin, Judith & Brejla, Terry. Jamestown & Western Tuolumne County. 2011. (Images of America Ser.). (Illus.). 128p. pap. 21.99 *(978-0-7385-8171-2(2))* Arcadia Publishing.

Marvin, Judith, et al. Northern Calaveras County. 2007. (Images of America Ser.). (ENG., Illus.). 128p. per. 21.99 *(978-0-7385-4782-4(4))* Arcadia Publishing.

Maulhardt, Jeffrey Wayne. Camarillo. 2006. (Images of America Ser.). (ENG., Illus.). 128p. per. 21.99 *(978-0-7385-4658-2(5))* Arcadia Publishing.

—Conejo Valley. 2010. (Images of America Ser.). (ENG., Illus.). 128p. pap. 21.99 *(978-0-7385-8039-5(2))* Arcadia Publishing.

McArdle, Phil. Oakland Police Department. 2007. (Images of America Ser.). (ENG., Illus.). 128p. pap. 19.99 *(978-0-7385-4726-8(3))* Arcadia Publishing.

McBurney, William J. & Milholland, Mary Rice. Greater French Valley. 2009. (Images of America Ser.). (ENG., Illus.). 128p. pap. 21.99 *(978-0-7385-6918-5(6))* Arcadia Publishing.

McCosker, Mary & Solon, Mary. Lafayette. 2007. (Images of America Ser.). (ENG., Illus.). 128p. pap. 21.99 *(978-0-7385-4755-8(7))* Arcadia Publishing.

McDonald, Don & Los Altos History Museum. Early Los Altos & Los Altos Hills. 2010. (Images of America Ser.). (ENG., Illus.). 128p. pap. 21.99 *(978-0-7385-8010-4(4))* Arcadia Publishing.

McKinzie, Joe. San Pedro. 2007. (Postcard History Ser.). (ENG., Illus.). 128p. per. 21.99 *(978-0-7385-4707-7(7))* Arcadia Publishing.

Meigs, Tom. Baseball in Long Beach. 2008. (Images of Baseball Ser.). (ENG., Illus.). 128p. pap. 19.99 *(978-0-7385-5823-3(0))* Arcadia Publishing.

Melikian, Robert A. Hotel San Carlos. 2009. (Images of America Ser.). (ENG., Illus.). 128p. pap. 21.99 *(978-0-7385-7141-6(5))* Arcadia Publishing.

Milliken, Randall. Native Americans of Mission San Jose. 2008. (Ballena Press Anthropological Papers: No. 49). (ENG.). pap. *(978-0-87919-148-1(1))* Malki-Ballena Pr.

Moodian, Michael A. Rancho Santa Margarita. 2010. (Images of America Ser.). (Illus.). 128p. pap. 21.99 *(978-0-7385-8004-3(X))* Arcadia Publishing.

Mornin, Edward & Mornin, Lorna. Saints of California: A Guide to Places & Their Patrons. 2009. (ENG., Illus.). 192p. pap. 19.95 *(978-0-89236-984-3(1))* Oxford Univ. Pr., Inc.

Morrall, June. Moss Beach. 2010. (Images of America Ser.). (ENG., Illus.). 128p. pap. 21.99 *(978-0-7385-8075-3(9))* Arcadia Publishing.

—Princeton-by-the-Sea. 2007. (Images of America Ser.). (Illus.). 127p. per. 19.99 *(978-0-7385-5583-6(5))* Arcadia Publishing.

Museum Society of Willows, et al. Willows. 2010. (Images of America Ser.). (Illus.). 128p. pap. 21.99 *(978-0-7385-8060-9(0))* Arcadia Publishing.

Newcombe, Robert, et al. The Crescenta Valley. 2010. (Then & Now Ser.). (ENG., Illus.). 96p. pap. 21.99 *(978-0-7385-8079-1(1))* Arcadia Publishing.

Nilsen, Adam P. Pleasant Hill. 2007. (Images of America Ser.). (ENG., Illus.). 128p. per. 21.99 *(978-0-7385-5565-2(7))* Arcadia Publishing.

Noble, Butch & Sports Car Racing Association of the Monterey Peninsula. Mazda Raceway Laguna Seca. 2009. (Images of Sports Ser.). (ENG., Illus.). 128p. pap. 21.99 *(978-0-7385-6925-3(9))* Arcadia Publishing.

Norris, Jim. Los Olivos. 2008. (Images of America Ser.). (ENG., Illus.). 128p. per. 19.99 *(978-0-7385-5619-2(X))* Arcadia Publishing.

Novak, Michael J. Newport Beach Fire Department. 2008. (Images of America (Arcadia Publishing) Ser.). (ENG., Illus.). 128p. per. 19.99 *(978-0-7385-5593-5(2))* Arcadia Publishing.

Osborne, James. Missions of Southern California. 2007. (Postcard History Ser.). (ENG., Illus.). 128p. per. 19.99 *(978-0-7385-4740-4(9))* Arcadia Publishing.

Patacsil, Judy, et al. Filipinos in San Diego. 2010. (Images of America Ser.). (ENG., Illus.). 128p. pap. 21.99 *(978-0-7385-8001-2(5))* Arcadia Publishing.

Patrick, K. C. The Pomo of Lake County. 2008. (Images of America Ser.). (Illus.). 128p. pap. 19.99 *(978-0-7385-5604-8(1))* Arcadia Publishing.

Perkins, Maggi. Newhall. 2010. (Images of America Ser.). (ENG., Illus.). 128p. pap. 21.99 *(978-0-7385-8025-8(2))* Arcadia Publishing.

Pfaelzer, Jean. Driven Out: The Forgotten War against Chinese Americans. 2008. (Illus.). 432p. pap. 24.95 *(978-0-520-25694-1(8))* Univ. of California Pr.

Phillips, Cedar Imboden & The Pasadena Museum of History. Early Pasadena. 2008. (Images of America Ser.). (ENG., Illus.). 128p. pap. 19.99 *(978-0-7385-5837-0(0))* Arcadia Publishing.

Pinkerton, Elizabeth. Elk Grove. 2007. (Images of America Ser.). (ENG., Illus.). 128p. per. 19.99 *(978-0-7385-3128-1(6))* Arcadia Publishing.

Pluth, Lisa Ann. The Del Mar Picture Book. Pluth, Lisa Ann, ed. 2006. (Illus.). 200p. kivar 39.95 *(978-0-9746821-2-9(8))* Del Mar Media Group.

Radanovich, Leroy. Yosemite Valley Railroad. 2010. (Images of Rail Ser.). (ENG., Illus.). 128p. pap. 21.99 *(978-0-7385-8111-8(9))* Arcadia Publishing.

Reel Index to the Microform Edition of California County & Regional Histories. 14p. 35.00 *(978-0-89235-048-3(2),* Primary Source Microfilm) Cengage Gale.

Rice, Harvey. Letters from the Pacific Slope. 2011. 143p. pap. 11.95 *(978-1-4290-4579-7(5))* Applewood Bks.

Richardson, Rob. Railroads & Depots of Orange County. 2010. (Images of Rail Ser.). (Illus.). 128p. pap. 21.99 *(978-0-7385-8011-1(2))* Arcadia Publishing.

Richvale Writing Group. Richvale: A Legacy of Courage, Dedication, & Perseverance. Ward, Teresa, ed. 2006. (Illus.). 320p. 65.00 *(978-0-9787251-0-5(7))* Community Foundation of Richvale, The.

Roberts, Robin Michael. Hanford: 1900-2000. 2007. (Images of America Ser.). (ENG., Illus.). 128p. per. 21.99 *(978-0-7385-4768-8(9))* Arcadia Publishing.
Robinson, John V. & Crane, Veronica. Port Costa. 2007. (Images of America Ser.). (Illus.). 127p. per. 19.99 *(978-0-7385-4654-4(2))* Arcadia Publishing.
Roseman, Frank M. & Wetry, Peter J. Chula Vista. 2010. (Then & Now Ser.). (ENG., Illus.). 96p. pap. 21.99 *(978-0-7385-8016-6(3))* Arcadia Publishing.
Roseville Historical Society. Roseville. 2010. (Images of America Ser.). (ENG., Illus.). 128p. pap. 21.99 *(978-0-7385-7029-7(X))* Arcadia Publishing.
Roseville Historical Society Staff. Roseville. 2010. (Postcards of America Ser.). 15p. 7.99 *(978-0-7385-7030-3(3))* Arcadia Publishing.
Ross Matthews, Stephanie, et al. Los Gatos. 2009. (Postcard History Ser.). (ENG., Illus.). 128p. pap. 21.99 *(978-0-7385-6962-8(3))* Arcadia Publishing.
Russell, Gene H. The Land of Orland. 2008. (Images of America Ser.). (ENG., Illus.). 128p. per. 19.99 *(978-0-7385-5617-8(3))* Arcadia Publishing.
Sacramento Archives, et al, creators. Sacramento's Midtown. 2006. (Images of America Ser.). (ENG., Illus.). 128p. per. 21.99 *(978-0-7385-4656-8(9))* Arcadia Publishing.
Sacramento Archives and Museum Collection Center. Sacramento's Elmhurst, Tahoe Park & Colonial Heights. 2008. (Images of America Ser.). (Illus.). 127p. per. 19.99 *(978-0-7385-5590-4(8))* Arcadia Publishing.
Saga of Rancho el Tejon. 2006. pap. 24.95 *(978-1-892622-30-3(0))* Bear State Bks.
Sanders, J. R. Oak Glen & Los Rios Rancho. 2006. (Then & Now Ser.). (ENG., Illus.). 128p. per. 19.99 *(978-0-7385-4653-7(4))* Arcadia Publishing.
Sandul, Paul J. P. & Swim, Tory D. Orangevale. 2006. (Images of America Ser.). (Illus.). 128p. per. 19.99 *(978-0-7385-4696-4(8))* Arcadia Publishing.
Shelton, William. Red Bluff. 2006. (Images of America Ser.). (Illus.). 127p. per. 19.99 *(978-0-7385-3148-9(0))* Arcadia Publishing.
—Towns of Mount Lassen. 2007. (Images of America Ser.). (Illus.). 127p. per. 19.99 *(978-0-7385-4720-6(4))* Arcadia Publishing.
Shulman, Todd. Napa County Police. 2007. (Images of America Ser.). (ENG., Illus.). 128p. per. 19.99 *(978-0-7385-4752-7(2))* Arcadia Publishing.
Slotte, Ferol M. School Bell Memories: Horse & Buggy to Space Age. (Illus.). 55p. reprint ed. pap. 8.00 *(978-0-9617960-0-6(6))* Del Monte Pr.
Smith, Jeffrey A. & Trafzer, Clifford. Native Americans of Riverside County. 2006. (Images of America Ser.). (ENG., Illus.). 128p. per. 19.99 *(978-0-7385-4685-8(2))* Arcadia Publishing.
Smith, Paul F., et al. Twentynine Palms. 2007. (Images of America Ser.). (Illus.). 127p. per. 19.99 *(978-0-7385-3149-6(9))* Arcadia Publishing.
Smith, Robert B. & Idyllwild Area Historical Society. Idyllwild & the High San Jacintos. 2009. (Images of America Ser.). (ENG., Illus.). 128p. pap. 21.99 *(978-0-7385-5985-8(7))* Arcadia Publishing.
Sommers, Arthur. Auburn. 2008. (Images of America Ser.). (ENG., Illus.). 128p. pap. 21.99 *(978-0-7385-5944-5(X))* Arcadia Publishing.
Stephens, E. J. & Wanamaker, Marc. Early Warner Bros. Studios. 2010. (Images of America Ser.). (ENG., Illus.). 128p. pap. 21.99 *(978-0-7385-8091-3(0))* Arcadia Publishing.
Stevens, Janice. Remembering the California Missions. 2010. (ENG., Illus.). 130p. 26.95 *(978-1-884995-64-4(0))* Linden Publishing Co., Inc.
Swenson, Timothy. Union City. 2008. (Images of America Ser.). (Illus.). 128p. per. 19.99 *(978-0-7385-5809-7(5))* Arcadia Publishing.
Tac, Pablo. Pablo Tac, Indigenous Scholar: Writing on Luiseño Language & Colonial History, C.1840. Haas, Lisbeth, ed. 2011. (ENG & LUI., Illus.). 288p. 49.95 *(978-0-520-26189-1(5))* Univ. of California Pr.
Tanner, Lesa & Graton Community Club. Graton. 2009. (Images of America Ser.). (ENG., Illus.). 128p. pap. 21.99 *(978-0-7385-6989-5(5))* Arcadia Publishing.
Tarbell Cooper, Suzanne, et al. RMS Queen Mary. 2010. (Images of America Ser.). (Illus.). 128p. pap. 21.99 *(978-0-7385-8067-8(8))* Arcadia Publishing.
Thomas, Daniel Paul. 100 Miles. 2007. 124p. per. 9.95 *(978-0-9766269-6-1(9))* Stansbury Publishing.
Thomas, John W., et al. Long Beach Art Deco. 2006. (Images of America Ser.). (ENG., Illus.). 128p. per. 21.99 *(978-0-7385-4670-4(4))* Arcadia Publishing.
Thompson, Jerry & Deterville, Duane. Black Artists in Oakland. 2007. (Images of America Ser.). (ENG., Illus.). 128p. per. 19.99 *(978-0-7385-4725-1(5))* Arcadia Publishing.
Titus, Roger L. Destinations. 2008. 96p. pap. 16.95 *(978-0-9778152-0-3(X))* Los Angeles Railroad Heritage Foundation.
Trevenon, Stacy. Kings Mountain. 2008. (Images of America Ser.). (ENG., Illus.). 128p. pap. 19.99 *(978-0-7385-5829-5(X))* Arcadia Publishing.
Tuholski, Robert. Around Orange. 2006. (Images of America Ser.). (ENG., Illus.). 128p. per. 19.99 *(978-0-7385-4920-0(7))* Arcadia Publishing.
Varney, Philip. Ghost Towns of California: Your Guide to the Hidden History & Old West Haunts of California. 2012. (ENG., Illus.). 240p. pap. 24.99 ***(978-0-7603-4082-0(X)***, 076034082X, Voyageur Pr) MBI Publishing Co. LLC.
Velm, Greg. True Gold: History & Adventure in Sacramento & the Gold Country. 2006. (Illus.). 184p. pap. 18.49 *(978-0-9774819-0-3(5))* Cabin in the Sky.
Verge, Arthur C. Santa Monica Lifeguards. 2007. (Images of America Ser.). (Illus.). 127p. per. 19.99 *(978-0-7385-4698-8(4))* Arcadia Publishing.
Veronico, Nicholas A. & Veronico, Betty S. San Carlos. 2007. (Images of America Ser.). (Illus.). 127p. per. 19.99 *(978-0-7385-4793-0(X))* Arcadia Publishing.
Walker, Doris I. Dana Point. 2007. (Images of America Ser.). (ENG., Illus.). 128p. per. 21.99 *(978-0-7385-4732-9(8))* Arcadia Publishing.
Wanamaker, Marc. Beverly Hills: 1930-2005. 2006. (Images of America Ser.). (ENG., Illus.). 128p. per. 21.99 *(978-0-7385-4659-9(3))* Arcadia Publishing.
Warneke, Jack, et al. San Jacinto. 2008. (Images of America Ser.). (Illus.). 128p. pap. 19.99 *(978-0-7385-5842-4(7))* Arcadia Publishing.
Welch, Diane & Holtzclaw, Kenneth M. Encinitas. 2006. (Images of America Ser.). (ENG., Illus.). 128p. per. 21.99 *(978-0-7385-4665-0(8))* Arcadia Publishing.
West Sacramento Historical Society. Port of Sacramento. 2007. (Images of America Ser.). (ENG., Illus.). 128p. per. 19.99 *(978-0-7385-4736-7(0))* Arcadia Publishing.
Williams, Gregory L. California State University, Dominguez Hills. 2010. (Campus History Ser.). (ENG., Illus.). 128p. pap. 21.99 *(978-0-7385-8005-0(8))* Arcadia Publishing.
Wooten, Kimberly & Baxter, R. Scott. Sutter Creek. 2006. (Images of America Ser.). (ENG., Illus.). 128p. per. 21.99 *(978-0-7385-4686-5(0))* Arcadia Publishing.

CALIFORNIA—IMPRINTS

Chaney, Robert Galen. Reincarnation: The Cycle of Opportunity. 2011. 24p. pap. 35.95 ***(978-1-258-03915-8(X))*** Literary Licensing, LLC.
Clymer, R. Swinburne. The Power of Thought: Teachings of the Rose Cross College - 2006. pap. 9.95 *(978-1-4286-7886-6(7))* Kessinger Publishing, LLC.
—Success & Failure: Teachings of the Rose Cross College - 2006. pap. 9.95 *(978-1-4286-7884-2(0))* Kessinger Publishing, LLC.
De Purucker, G. The Story of Jesus. 2011. 68p. 36.95 ***(978-1-258-05181-5(8))*** Literary Licensing, LLC.
Flowers, Sarah. Metaphysical Thesaurus of Positive & N. 2006. pap. 8.95 *(978-1-59605-385-4(2)*, Cosimo Classics) Cosimo, Inc.
George, Llewellyn. How to Succeed in the Study & Practice of Astrology. 2011. 48p. 35.95 ***(978-1-258-02418-5(7))*** Literary Licensing, LLC.
Hall, Franklin. Formula for Raising the Dead & the Baptism of Fire. 2011. 54p. 36.95 ***(978-1-258-02179-5(X))*** Literary Licensing, LLC.
Haven, Girard. Notes from a Conscious Teaching. Date not set. 164p. 10.00 *(978-0-9645782-1-0(2))* Ulysses Bks.
Hopkins, Marian Stinchfield & Hopkins, Lambert Arundel. The Divine Compass. 2011. 178p. 42.95 ***(978-1-258-04796-2(9))*** Literary Licensing, LLC.
Hotema, Hilton. We Do Not Die. 2011. 40p. 35.95 ***(978-1-258-05659-9(3))*** Literary Licensing, LLC.
Howard, Dana. The Keys to the Citadel of Space. 2011. 204p. 44.95 ***(978-1-258-05001-6(3))*** Literary Licensing, LLC.
Krishna, Bala. Essence of Yoga for Everlasting Youth. Cushman, Betty J., ed. 2011. 50p. 35.95 ***(978-1-258-00404-0(6))*** Literary Licensing, LLC.
Kriyananda, Swami. Religion in the New Age: And Other Essays for the Spiritual Seeker. 2009. (ENG.). 428p. pap. 15.95 *(978-1-56589-236-1(4))* Crystal Clarity Pubs.
Lee, Gloria. Why We Are Here? 2007. (ENG.). 180p. 37.95 *(978-0-548-08469-4(6))* Kessinger Publishing, LLC.
Moen, Orrin. The Mirror of Your Mind. 2011. 150p. 40.95 ***(978-1-258-06058-9(2))*** Literary Licensing, LLC.
Moglen, Helene & Chen, Nancy N., eds. Bodies in the Making: Transgressions & Transformations. 2007. (ENG., Illus.). 216p. pap. 12.00 *(978-0-9712546-3-3(X))* North Atlantic Bks.
Murphy, Joseph. Magic of Faith. 2011. 62p. pap. 7.99 ***(978-1-61720-239-1(8))*** Wilder Pubns., Ltd.
Rexford, Orcella. Your Name & You: Numerology Made Easy. 2011. 98p. 38.95 ***(978-1-258-06436-5(7))*** Literary Licensing, LLC.
Wallis, Jean. Divine Pattern for Living. 2011. 96p. 38.95 ***(978-1-258-01742-2(3))*** Literary Licensing, LLC.
Warn, Charles Lathrup. Today, As in the Days of Noah. 2011. 66p. 36.95 ***(978-1-258-05429-8(9))*** Literary Licensing, LLC.
Weston, Joseph Harry. Mormons Are Different! 2011. 228p. 46.95 ***(978-1-258-07836-2(8))*** Literary Licensing, LLC.
Zain, C. C. & Benjamine, Elbert. Chart Your Future. 2011. 66p. 36.95 ***(978-1-258-00172-8(1))*** Literary Licensing, LLC.

CALIFORNIA—JUVENILE LITERATURE

Jeffrey, Gary. The Gold Rush. 2012. (Graphic History of the American West Ser.). (ENG., Illus.). 24p. (J). (gr. 4-7). lib. bdg. 23.95 ***(978-1-4339-6739-9(1))*** Stevens, Gareth Publishing LLLP.

CALIFORNIA—MAPS

American Map Corp, creator. Los Angeles County California Street Atlas. 2007. (American Map Ser.). (Illus.). 328p. 19.95 *(978-0-8416-2685-0(5))* American Map Corp.
—Los Angeles/Orange Counties California Street Atlas. 2007. (American Map Ser.). (Illus.). 480p. 34.95 *(978-0-8416-2683-6(9))* American Map Corp.
—Orange Counties California Street Atlas. 2007. (American Map Ser.). (Illus.). 152p. 19.95 *(978-0-8416-2684-3(7))* American Map Corp.
—San Diego, California Street Atlas. 2007. (American Map Ser.). (Illus.). 228p. 21.95 *(978-0-8416-2686-7(3))* American Map Corp.
American Map Staff. City Streets San Diego. 2010. 7.99 *(978-0-8416-8817-9(6))* American Map Corp.
Baselt, David. Big Basin Redwoods State Park: Annotated Trail Map. 2006. 6.95 *(978-1-934127-00-1(0))* Redwood Hikes Pr.
—San Lorenzo Valley: Henry Cowell Redwoods State Park/Fall Creek State Park/Pogonip/Bonny Doon Ecological Reserve/Quail Hollow Ranch County Park / Annotated Trail Map. 2006. 6.95 *(978-1-934127-02-5(7))* Redwood Hikes Pr.
California Road & Recreation Atlas. 6th ed. 2009. (ENG.). 144p. 24.95 *(978-0-929591-49-0(6))* Map Link.
Chitwood, Danielle, et al. Not for Tourists Guide to Los Angeles. 2007. (Not for Tourists Guide to Los Angeles Ser.). (Illus.). 415p. 21.95 *(978-0-9793945-6-0(2))* Not for Tourists, Inc.
DeLorme, creator. California Atlas & Gazetteer. 2008. (Delorme Atlas & Gazetteer Ser.). 160p. 24.95 *(978-0-89933-383-0(4))* DeLorme.
Frank Amato Publications, creator. Northern California River Maps & Fishing Guide. 2006. (Illus.). 47p. pap. 29.95 *(978-1-57188-392-6(4)*, NCAM) Amato, Frank Pubns., Inc.
Goldsmith, Philip. Moon Napa Valley. 2009. (Moon Spotlight Ser.). (ENG.). 100p. pap. 9.99 *(978-1-59880-262-7(3))* Avalon Travel Publishing.
—Moon Sonoma Valley. 2009. (Moon Spotlight Ser.). (ENG.). 125p. pap. 8.95 *(978-1-59880-263-4(1))* Avalon Travel Publishing.
Hayes, Derek. Historical Atlas of California. 2007. (Illus.). 256p. 45.00 *(978-0-520-25258-5(6))* Univ. of California Pr.
Heinle and Heinle Staff. California Components Chart. 1.00 *(978-0-8384-7669-7(4))* Cengage Heinle.
Jones, Ray & Virga, Vincent. California: Mapping the Golden State Through History - Rare & Unusual Maps from the Library of Congress. 2009. (Mapping the States through History Ser.). (ENG., Illus.). 128p. 24.95 *(978-0-7627-4530-2(4))* Globe Pequot Pr., The.
Mission Trails Regional Park Map. pap. 4.95 *(978-0-932653-33-8(2))* Sunbelt Pubns., Inc.
Not For Tourists Staff. Not for Tourists Guide to San Francisco 2012. 2011. (ENG., Illus.). 384p. pap. 16.95 ***(978-1-61608-531-5(2)***, 608531, Not For Tourist) Skyhorse Publishing Co., Inc.
Not for Tourists Staff, creator. Not for Tourists Guide to San Francisco. 2008. (Not for Tourists Guide to San Francisco Ser.). (Illus.). 338p. 15.95 *(978-0-9793945-7-7(0))* Not for Tourists, Inc.
Pirone, Jane & Not for Tourists Staff. Los Angeles 2009. 8th rev. ed. 2008. (ENG., Illus.). 512p. 24.95 *(978-0-9814887-6-9(5))* Not for Tourists, Inc.
Preston, Ralph N. & Preston, Monte L. California Gold & Gem Maps - Northern. (Illus.). pap. 11.00 *(978-0-9657558-9-4(4))* Pioneer Pr.
Rand McNally. San Bernardino County Street Guide. 2007. (Thomas Guide San Bernardino County Street Guide & Directory Ser.). 5862p. spiral bd. 79.95 *(978-0-528-86964-8(7))* Rand McNally.
Rand McNally, creator. The Thomas Guide Alameda & Contra Costa Counties Street Guide. 2007. (Thomas Guide Alameda & Contra Costa Counties Street Guide & Directory Ser.). pap. 29.95 *(978-0-528-86065-2(8))* Rand McNally.
—The Thomas Guide Alameda County Street Guide. 2007. (Thomas Guide Alameda County Street Guide & Directory Ser.). pap. 19.95 *(978-0-528-86063-8(1))* Rand McNally.
—The Thomas Guide Bay Area Metro Street Guide. 2007. (Thomas Guide Metropolitan Bay Area Street Guide & Directory Ser.). pap. 45.95 *(978-0-528-86071-3(2))* Rand McNally.
—The Thomas Guide Central San Joaquin Valley Street Guide. 19th ed. 2007. (Thomas Guide Central San Joaquin Valley Ser.). (Illus.). pap. 19.95 *(978-0-528-86602-9(8))* Rand McNally.
—The Thomas Guide Contra Costa County Street Guide. 2007. (Thomas Guide Contra Costa County Street Guide & Directory Ser.). pap. 19.95 *(978-0-528-86064-5(X))* Rand McNally.
—Thomas Guide Easy-to-Read Riverside County Street Guide. 2007. (Thomas Guide Easy-to-Read Riverside County Street Guide Ser.). (Illus.). pap. 19.95 *(978-0-528-86848-1(9))* Rand McNally.
—The Thomas Guide Easy-to-Read San Bernardino County Street Guide. 2007. (Thomas Guide Easy-to-Read San Bernardino County Street Guide Ser.). (Illus.). pap. 19.95 *(978-0-528-86847-4(0))* Rand McNally.
—The Thomas Guide Kern County Street Guide. 17th ed. 2007. (Thomas Guide Kern County Ser.). (Illus.). pap. 14.95 *(978-0-528-86601-2(X))* Rand McNally.
—The Thomas Guide Los Angeles & San Bernardino Counties Street Guide. 2007. (Thomas Guide Los Angeles & San Bernardino Counties Street Guide Ser.). spiral bd. 34.95 *(978-0-528-86720-0(2))* Rand McNally.
—The Thomas Guide Los Angeles & Ventura County Street Guide. 2007. (Thomas Guide Los Angeles/Ventura Counties Street Guide & Directory Ser.). (Illus.). pap. 34.95 *(978-0-528-86716-3(4))* Rand McNally.
—The Thomas Guide Pro Series Los Angeles & Orange Counties Street Guide. 2007. pap. 79.95 *(978-0-528-86963-1(9))* Rand McNally.
—The Thomas Guide Riverside & Orange Counties Street Guide. 2007. (Thomas Guide Riverside/Orange Counties Street Guide & Directory Ser.). (Illus.). pap. 29.95 *(978-0-528-86719-4(9))* Rand McNally.
—The Thomas Guide Riverside County Street Guide. 2007. (Thomas Guide Riverside/San Diego Counties Street Guide & Directory Ser.). (Illus.). pap. 29.95 *(978-0-528-86694-4(X))* Rand McNally.
—The Thomas Guide Sacramento & Solano Counties Street Guide: Including Portions of Placer, el Dorado, & Yolo Counties. 2008. (Thomas Guide Sacramento/Solano Counties Ser.). (Illus.). 574p. pap. 29.95 *(978-0-528-86647-0(8))* Rand McNally.
—Thomas Guide Sacramento County Street Guide. 2006. (Thomas Guide Sacramento County: Including Portions of Placer & el Dorado Counties Ser.). (Illus.). pap. 24.95 *(978-0-528-85977-9(3))* Rand McNally.
—The Thomas Guide San Bernardino County Street Guide. 2007. (Thomas Guide San Bernardino County Street Guide & Directory Ser.). (Illus.). pap. 19.95 *(978-0-528-86678-4(8))* Rand McNally.
—The Thomas Guide San Francisco & Marin Counties Street Guide. 2007. (Thomas Guide San Francisco & Marin Counties Street Guide Ser.). pap. 24.95 *(978-0-528-86066-9(6))* Rand McNally.
—The Thomas Guide San Francisco & San Mateo Counties Street Guide. 2007. (Thomas Guide San Francisco/San Mateo Counties Street Guide & Directory Ser.). pap. 29.95 *(978-0-528-86067-6(4))* Rand McNally.
—The Thomas Guide San Joaquin County Street Guide. 7th ed. 2007. (Thomas Guide Northern San Joaquin Valley Ser.). 1127p. pap. 19.95 *(978-0-528-86603-6(6))* Rand McNally.
—The Thomas Guide Santa Barbara & San Luis Obispo Counties Street Guide: Easy-to-Read. 2007. (Thomas Guide Santa Barbara/San Luis Obispo Counties Street Guide & Directory Ser.). (Illus.). pap. 19.95 *(978-0-528-86852-8(7))*; spiral bd. 32.95 *(978-0-528-86717-0(2))* Rand McNally.
—The Thomas Guide Santa Clara & San Mateo Counties Street Guide. 2007. (Thomas Guide Santa Clara/San Mateo Counties Street Guide & Directory Ser.). pap. 29.95 *(978-0-528-86068-3(2))* Rand McNally.
—The Thomas Guide Santa Clara County Street Guide. 2007. (Thomas Guide Santa Clara County Street Guide & Directory Ser.). pap. 19.95 *(978-0-528-86060-7(7))* Rand McNally.
—The Thomas Guide Ventura County Street Guide: Easy-to-Read. 2007. (Illus.). pap. 19.95 *(978-0-528-86851-1(9))* Rand McNally.
—Ventura County Street Guide. 2006. (Thomas Guide Ventura County Street Guide & Directory Ser.). (Illus.). spiral bd. 19.95 *(978-0-528-99357-2(7))* Rand McNally.
Rand McNally and Company Staff, creator. Santa Clara County Street Guide. 38th ed. 2008. (Thomas Guide Santa Clara County Street Guide & Directory Ser.). (Illus.). 54p. pap. 19.95 *(978-0-528-87382-9(2))* Rand McNally.
Rand McNally Staff. California State & US/World. 2008. 4.95 *(978-0-528-94241-9(7))* Rand McNally.
Sempervirens Fund Staff. Big Basin. 50p. pap. 5.95 *(978-0-9701178-1-6(7))* Sempervirens Fund.
Sinclair, Mick. San Francisco. 3rd ed. 2008. (The Globetrotter Travel Ser.). (ENG., Illus.). 128p. 14.95 *(978-1-84773-037-4(X))* New Holland Pubs., Ltd. GBR. Dist: Globe Pequot Pr., The.
Solnit, Rebecca. Infinite City: A San Francisco Atlas. 2010. (Illus.). 144p. 49.95 *(978-0-520-26249-2(2))*; pap. 24.95 *(978-0-520-26250-8(6))* Univ. of California Pr.
Stienstra, Stephani, et al. Yosemite & Mammoth Lakes Camping & Hiking. 2009. (Moon Spotlight Ser.). (ENG.). 130p. pap. 8.95 *(978-1-59880-277-1(1))* Avalon Travel Publishing.
Stienstra, Tom. Shasta & Lassen Camping & Hiking. 2009. (Moon Spotlight Ser.). (ENG.). 235p. pap. 11.95 *(978-1-59880-276-4(3))* Avalon Travel Publishing.
Stienstra, Tom & Brown, Ann Marie. Sequoia & Kings Canyon Camping & Hiking. 2009. (Moon Spotlight Ser.). (ENG.). 165p. pap. 9.95 *(978-1-59880-278-8(X))* Avalon Travel Publishing.
Streetwise Maps Inc., des. & rev. Streetwise Los Angeles Map - Laminated City Street Map of Los Angeles, California: Folding pocket size travel map with integrated metro system featuring red line tracks & Stations. 2011. (ENG.). 7.95 *(978-1-931257-16-9(7))* Streetwise Maps, Inc.
Thomas Brothers Maps Staff, creator. The Thomas Guide San Diego County: Street Guide. 2007. (Thomas Guide San Diego County Including Imperial County Street Guide & Directory Ser.). (Illus.). pap. 24.95 *(978-0-528-86691-3(5))* Rand McNally.
Thomas Guide Staff, contrib. by. California Road Atlas. 2008. pap. 19.95 *(978-0-528-86820-7(9))* Rand McNally.
Thomson, Thomas. Historical Atlas Map Tulare Co. 2006. 147p. 149.95 *(978-1-892622-29-7(7))* Bear State Bks.
Vogel, Randy & Gaines, Bob. Orange County. 2nd ed. 2009. (Best Easy Day Hikes Ser.). (ENG., Illus.). 112p. pap. 9.95 *(978-0-7627-5107-5(X)*, Falcon Guides) Globe Pequot Pr., The.
Weekes, Don & Banks, Kerry. Hockey's Top 100: The Game's Greatest Records, 1 vol. 2008. (ENG., Illus.). 168p. pap. 15.95 *(978-1-55365-274-8(6)*, Greystone Bks.) D&M Pubs. Inc. CAN. Dist: Perseus-PGW.
Wilderness Adventures Press, creator. California's Best Fishing Waters: 182 Detailed Maps of 31 of the Best Rivers & Streams. 2007. (Best Fishing Waters Ser.). (Illus.). 182p. pap. 29.95 *(978-1-932098-49-5(6))* Wilderness Adventures Pr., Inc.
Williams, Larry. California Atlas. 2007. 32p. pap. 8.95 *(978-0-9793569-0-2(3))* California Geographic Assocs.
Zagat Survey Staff, creator. Zagat San Francisco Book & Map Pack. 2007. (Zagat Survey: San Francisco Bay Area Restaurants Ser.). (ENG.). pap. 18.90 *(978-1-57006-921-5(2))* Zagat Survey.

CALIFORNIA—POLITICS AND GOVERNMENT

Adams, Brian E. Citizen Lobbyists: Local Efforts to Influence Public Policy. 2007. (Illus.). 248p. 75.50 *(978-1-59213-569-1(2))*; per. 27.95 *(978-1-59213-570-7(6))* Temple Univ. Pr.
Anagnoson, J. Theodore, et al. Governing California in the Twenty-First Century. 3rd ed. 2011. (ENG.). 234p. (C). pap. 24.00 net. *(978-0-393-91202-9(7)*, 91202) Norton, W. W. & Co., Inc.
Bagley, William T. California's Golden Years: When Government Worked & Why. 2009. *(978-0-87772-434-6(2))* Univ. of California, Institute of Governmental Studies.
Baker, Maureen. Outrageous Hero: The Story of B. T. Collins. 2008. 300p. 25.00 net. *(978-0-9798697-3-0(0))* Bryce Hill Publishing.
Baldassare, Mark & Katz, Cheryl. The Coming Age of Direct Democracy: California's Recall & Beyond. 2007. (ENG.). 260p. 77.00 *(978-0-7425-3871-9(0))*; per. 25.95 *(978-0-7425-3872-6(9))* Rowman & Littlefield Publishers, Inc.

Baxter, Ken. California State & Local Government: An Overview, Perspectives, & Politics. 2009. (ENG.). (C). pap. 29.40 (978-0-558-19988-3(7)) Pearson Learning Solutions.

Bell, Jonathan. California Crucible: The Forging of Modern American Liberalism. 2012. (Politics & Culture in Modern America Ser.). 352p. (C). 47.50 (978-0-8122-4387-1(0)) Univ. of Pennsylvania Pr.

Beltrami, Albert P. A Primer for California County Managers. 2007. (Illus.). xiv, 38p. (978-0-9748934-6-4(3)) Mendocino County Museum Grassroots History Pubns.

Blaschek-Miller, Travis, ed. California Cures: Translating Opportunity into California¿s Success. 2008. (Illus.). cd-rom (978-0-9789300-2-8(9)) BayBio.

Bonsal, Stephen. Edward Fitzgerald Beale. 2009. 364p. 38.99 (978-1-117-27198-9(6)); (ENG.). 363p. pap. 31.75 (978-1-117-27199-6(4)) BiblioBazaar.

—Edward Fitzgerald Beale. 312p. reprint ed. 98.00 (978-0-7222-8987-7(1)) Library Reprints, Inc.

Boyarsky, Bill. Big Daddy: Jesse Unruh & the Art of Power Politics. 2007. (Illus.). 265p. 37.95 (978-0-520-21967-0(8)) Univ. of California Pr.

Bradley, Omar. The King of Compton! The Assassination of a Dream. 2007. 481p. per. 15.95 (978-0-9799308-8-1(X)) Milligan Bks.

Brown, Willie L., Jr. Basic Brown: My Life & Our Times. 2011. (ENG., Illus.). 368p. pap. 22.99 (978-0-7432-9082-1(8)) Simon & Schuster.

C. Ji, Chang-Ho & Ji, Chang-Ho C. Invisible Partisanship: Partisan Bias in Nonpartisan Elections & Its Impact on Local Policy Representation in California Reform Cities. 2008. (ENG., Illus.). 430p. pap. 57.99 (978-0-7618-4139-5(3)) Univ. Pr. of America, Inc.

California Journal Staff & State Net Staff, eds. California State Government Directory. (Illus.). 170p. ring bd. 125.00 (978-0-930302-75-7(3)) California Journal Pr.

Cherny, Robert W., et al, eds. California Women & Politics: From the Gold Rush to the Great Depression. 2011. (ENG., Illus.). 424p. pap. 40.00 (978-0-8032-3503-8(8)) Univ. of Nebraska Pr.

Christman, Henry M., ed. The Public Papers of Chief Justice Earl Warren. 2011. 250p. 46.95 (978-1-258-05563-9(5)) Literary Licensing, LLC.

Clayton Jay Collins And Donella Williams. Politics, Crime, Money & Lies. 2009. 324p. 29.99 (978-1-4415-2339-6(1)); pap. 19.99 (978-1-4415-2338-9(3)) Xlibris Corp.

Connerly, Ward. Creating Equal: My Fight Against Race Preferences. 2007. (ENG.). 298p. 24.95 (978-1-59403-218-9(1)) Encounter Bks.

Covin, David. Black Politics after the Civil Rights Movement: Activity & Beliefs in Sacramento, 1970-2000. 2009. (ENG., Illus.). 236p. pap. 49.95 (978-0-7864-4258-4(1)) McFarland & Co., Inc. Pubs.

Cram101 Textbook Reviews & Cram101 Textbook Reviews. Outlines & Highlights for Coming Age of Direct Democracy by Mark Baldassare, Isbn: 9780742538719. 2011. 118p. pap. 28.95 (978-1-61461-460-9(1)) Cram101 Inc.

—Outlines & Highlights for Supplement: Living Democracy, Brief California Edition by Daniel Shea, ISBN. 2011. 516p. pap. 37.95 (978-1-61461-630-6(2)) Cram101 Inc.

Cressman, Derek. The Recall's Broken Promise: How Big Money Still Runs California Politics. 2007. 368p. per. 14.95 (978-0-9786405-0-7(0), Poplar Leaf Pr.) Poplar Institute, The.

Cummings, Stephen D. California after Arnold. 2009. 224p. pap. 23.95 (978-0-87586-738-0(3)) Algora Publishing.

Cummings, Stephen D. & Reddy, Patrick B. California after Arnold. 2009. 33.95 (978-0-87586-739-7(1)) Algora Publishing.

DeBow, Ken & Syer, John C. Power & Politics in California. 9th ed. 2008. (ENG., Illus.). 272p. (C). per. 91.00 (978-0-205-62219-1(4)) Longman Publishing Group.

Dimmitt, Michael. Ninety Years of Health Insurance Reform Efforts in California. 2007. (Illus.). ii, 61p. pap. (978-1-58703-230-1(9)) California Research Bureau.

Dochuk, Darren. From Bible Belt to Sunbelt: Plain-Folk Religion, Grassroots Politics, & the Rise of Evangelical Conservatism. (ENG.). 2012. 560p. pap. 18.95 (978-0-393-33904-8(1), 33904) 2010. (Illus.). 520p. 35.00 (978-0-393-06682-1(7), 6682) Norton, W. W. & Co., Inc.

Domhoff, G. William & Gendron, Richard. The Leftmost City: Power & Progressive Politics in Santa Cruz. 2008. (ENG.). 256p. pap. 29.00 (978-0-8133-4438-6(7)) Westview Pr.

Dressler, Albert, ed. Letters to a Pioneer Senator. 2011. 36p. 35.95 (978-1-258-08765-4(0)) Literary Licensing, LLC.

Elkind, Sarah S. How Local Politics Shape Federal Policy: Business, Power, & the Environment in Twentieth-Century Los Angeles. 2011. (Luther H. Hodges Jr. & Luther H. Hodges Sr. Series on Business, Society, & the State Ser.). (ENG., Illus.). 280p. 45.00 (978-0-8078-3489-3(0)) Univ. of North Carolina Pr.

Erie, Steven, et al. Paradise Plundered: Fiscal Crisis & Governance Failures in San Diego. 2011. (ENG.). 360p. 75.00 (978-0-8047-5602-0(3)); pap. 24.95 (978-0-8047-5603-7(1)) Stanford Univ. Pr.

Field, Mona. California Government & Politics Today. 11th ed. 2006. (Illus.). 148p. per. 42.00 (978-0-321-43654-2(7)) Longman Publishing.

—California Government & Politics Today. 13th ed. 2010. (ENG.). 160p. (C). pap. 58.00 (978-0-205-79146-0(8)) Longman Publishing Group.

—California Government & Politics Today. 14th rev. ed. 2012. (ENG.). 160p. (C). pap. 58.00 (978-0-205-25178-0(1), Prentice Hall) Prentice Hall PTR.

Field, Mona. California Government & Politics Today Election Update. 11th ed. 2006. (Illus.). 148p. per. 46.00 (978-0-205-52115-9(0)) Longman Publishing.

Field, Mona & Kennedy, Brian. The People & Promise of California. 2007. (Longman Topics Ser.). (ENG.). 288p. (C). per. 23.60 (978-0-321-43489-0(7)) Longman Publishing Group.

Gerston & Christensen & Cram101 Textbook Reviews Staff. Californi: Politics & Government. 2007. 108p. per. 10.95 (978-1-4288-2310-5(7)) Cram101 Inc.

Gerston, Larry N. Not so Golden after All: The Rise & Fall of California. 2012. (ENG., Illus.). 342p. 59.95 (978-1-4398-8012-8(3), CRC Press) Taylor & Francis Group GBR. Dist: Taylor & Francis Group.

Gerston, Larry N. & Christensen, Terry. California Politics & Government: A Practical Approach. 11th ed. 2011. (ENG.). 192p. (C). pap. 64.95 (978-0-495-91345-0(6)) Wadsworth.

Giventer, Lawrence L. Governing California. 2nd ed. 2007. (ENG., Illus.). 224p. (C). pap. 53.67 (978-0-07-352633-1(9), 0073526339) McGraw-Hill Cos., The.

Grant, James. Mr. Speaker! The Life & Times of Thomas B. Reed - The Man Who Broke the Filibuster. 2012. (ENG., Illus.). 448p. pap. 16.00 (978-1-4165-4494-4(1)) Simon & Schuster.

Grant, James. Mr. Speaker! The Life & Times of Thomas B. Reed the Man Who Broke the Filibuster. 2011. (ENG., Illus.). 448p. 28.00 (978-1-4165-4493-7(3)) Simon & Schuster.

Gruber, Frank. Urban Worrier: Making Politics Personal. 2009. 340p. pap. 16.95 (978-0-615-27122-4(7)) City Image Pr.

Hanak, Ellen. Managing California's Water: From Conflict to Reconciliation. 2011. (978-1-58213-141-2(4)) Public Policy Institute of California.

Hichborn, Franklin. Story of the Session of the California Legislature Of 1909. 2009. 304p. 28.99 (978-0-559-08073-9(5)); 25.99 (978-0-559-08088-3(3)); pap. 23.99 (978-0-559-08077-7(8)); pap. 18.99 (978-0-559-08084-5(0)) BiblioBazaar.

HoSang, Daniel. Racial Propositions: Ballot Initiatives & the Making of Postwar California. 2010. (American Crossroads Ser.). (ENG., Illus.). 392p. 60.00 (978-0-520-26664-3(1)); pap. 24.95 (978-0-520-26666-7(8)) Univ. of California Pr.

Igler, David & Deverell, William, eds. A Companion to California History. 2008. (Blackwell Companions to American History Ser.: 35). (ENG., Illus.). 544p. 229.95 (978-1-4051-6183-1(3), Wiley-Blackwell) Wiley, John & Sons, Inc.

Jacobson, Robin Dale. The New Nativism: Proposition 187 & the Debate over Immigration. 2008. (Illus.). 224p. 60.00 (978-0-8166-5027-9(6)); pap. 19.95 (978-0-8166-5028-6(4)) Univ. of Minnesota Pr.

Janiskee/Masugi. Democracy in California: Politics & Government in the Golden State. (ENG.). 2nd ed. 2007. 144p. (C). (gr. 13-17). 70.00 (978-0-7425-4835-0(X)) 2nd rev. ed. 2007. 144p. (C). (gr. 13-17). pap. 24.95 (978-0-7425-4836-7(8)) 3rd ed. 2011. 172p. pap. 26.95 (978-1-4422-0338-9(2)) Rowman & Littlefield Publishers, Inc.

Kaskla, Edgar. California Politics: The Fault Lines of Power, Wealth, & Diversity. rev. ed. 2007. 147p. (C). pap. 39.00 (978-0-87289-276-7(X)) CQ Pr.

Kennedy, Elijah Robinson. The Contest for California in 1861: How Colonel E.d. Baker Saved the Pacific States in the Union. 361p. reprint ed. 98.00 (978-0-7222-8044-7(0)) Library Reprints, Inc.

Korey, John L. California Government. 5th ed. 2008. (ENG.). 168p. (C). pap. 62.95 (978-0-547-04193-3(4)) Wadsworth.

Lowenthal, Abraham F. Global California: Rising to the Cosmopolitan Challenge. 2009. (ENG., Illus.). 240p. 60.00 (978-0-8047-6226-7(0)) Stanford Univ. Pr.

Lowenthal, Abraham F. & Lowenthal, Abraham. Global California: Rising to the Cosmopolitan Challenge. 2009. (ENG., Illus.). 240p. pap. 21.95 (978-0-8047-6227-4(9)) Stanford Univ. Pr.

Lubenow, Gerald C., ed. California Political Almanac. 2007. (Illus.). 562p. per. 59.95 (978-0-87289-504-1(1)) CQ Pr.

Lund, Jay R. Comparing Futures for the Sacramento-San Joaquin Delta. 2008. (978-1-58213-130-6(9)) Public Policy Institute of California.

Lustig, R. Jeffrey. Remaking California: Reclaiming the Public Good. 2010. pap. (978-1-59714-134-5(8)) Heyday.

Marxen, Christopher J. Security & Privacy Recommendations for Government-Issued Identity Documents Using Radio Frequency Identification Tags or Other Technologies. 2008. iii, 100p. pap. (978-1-58703-238-7(4)) California Research Bureau.

Masket, Seth. No Middle Ground: How Informal Party Organizations Control Nominations & Polarize Legislatures. 2011. (Illus.). 240p. pap. 27.95 (978-0-472-03467-3(7)) Univ. of Michigan Pr.

Masry, Feriel & Chenard, Susan. Running for All the Right Reasons: A Saudi-born Woman's Pursuit of Democracy. 2009. (Illus.). 232p. 24.95 (978-0-8156-0911-7(6)) Syracuse Univ. Pr.

Mathews, Joe & Paul, Mark. California Crackup: How Reform Broke the Golden State & How We Can Fix It. 2010. (ENG., Illus.). 240p. 50.00 (978-0-520-26852-4(0)); pap. 21.95 (978-0-520-26656-8(0)) Univ. of California Pr.

Matsumura, Kenneth. Arnold Remade: How the Fear of His Own Recall Transformed Him & Reshaped California. 2006. per. 12.95 (978-0-9606924-4-6(4)) Alin Foundation Pr.

Matthews, Glenna. The Golden State in the Civil War: Thomas Starr King, the Republican Party, & the Birth of Modern California. 2012. (ENG., Illus.). 272p. 95.00 (978-0-521-19400-6(8)); pap. 25.99 (978-1-107-63921-8(2)) Cambridge Univ. Pr.

McCarthy, Kevin F. & Archibald, Rae W. Facing the Challenge of Implementing Proposition F in San Diego. 2007. 60p. pap. 18.00 (978-0-8330-3828-9(1), MG-411) RAND Corp., The.

McGhee, Eric. Redistricting & Legislative Partisanship. 2008. xvii, 79p. (978-1-58213-131-3(7)) Public Policy Institute of California.

Mitchell, Greg. The Campaign of the Century: Upton Sinclair's Race for Governor of California & the Birth of Media Politics. 2nd ed. 2010. (ENG.). 686p. pap. 24.95 (978-1-936227-08-2(8)) PoliPointPress, LLC.

Pearson Learning Solutions. California Politics (Longman State Politics Series) 8th ed. 2011. (ENG., Illus.). 120p. (C). pap. 21.60 (978-0-205-06669-8(0)) Longman Publishing Group.

Provost, David H. Bernard L. Hyink's Politics & Government in California. 17th ed. 2006. (ENG., Illus.). 272p. (C). per. 91.00 (978-0-321-43608-5(3)) Longman Publishing Group.

Rarick, Ethan. California Votes: The 2006 Governor's Race. 2007. (978-0-87772-425-4(3)) Univ. of California, Institute of Governmental Studies.

Rarick, Ethan. California Votes: The 2010 Governor's Race. 2012. (978-0-87772-440-7(7)) Univ. of California, Institute of Governmental Studies.

Rhomberg, Chris. No There There: Race, Class, & Political Community in Oakland. 2007. (Illus.). 315p. per. 28.95 (978-0-520-25166-3(0)) Univ. of California Pr.

Richards, Leonard L. The California Gold Rush & the Coming of the Civil War. 2008. (Vintage Civil War Library). (ENG., Illus.). 304p. pap. 14.95 (978-0-307-27757-2(7), Vintage) Knopf Doubleday Publishing Group.

Schockman, H. Eric, et al. Rethinking California. 2nd ed. 2009. (ENG., Illus.). 256p. (C). pap. 55.40 (978-0-13-184292-2(7), Prentice Hall) Prentice Hall PTR.

Schrag, Peter. California: America's High-Stakes Experiment. 2007. 328p. per. 21.95 (978-0-520-25405-3(8)) Univ. of California Pr.

Shea, Daniel M., et al. Living Democracy. 3rd ed. 2010. (ENG.). 864p. (C). pap. 119.00 (978-0-205-82766-4(7)) Longman Publishing Group.

—Living Democracy, 2010 Update, Brief California Edition, Books a la Carte Edition. 2nd ed. 2010. (ENG.). 896p. (C). ring bd. 86.80 (978-0-205-83483-9(3)) Longman Publishing Group.

—Living Democracy, 2010 Update, Brief California Edition, Books a la Carte Plus MyPoliSciLab. 2nd ed. 2010. (ENG.). (C). ring bd. 93.47 (978-0-205-83491-4(4)) Longman Publishing Group.

—Living Democracy, 2010 Update Edition, California Edition. 2nd ed. 2010. (ENG.). 992p. (C). pap. 168.00 (978-0-205-79994-7(9)) Longman Publishing Group.

—Living Democracy Brief California, Books a la Carte Edition. 3rd ed. 2010. (ENG.). 832p. (C). ring bd. 77.80 (978-0-205-83499-0(X)) Longman Publishing Group.

—Living Democracy Brief California, Books a la Carte Plus MyPoliSciLab. 3rd ed. 2010. (ENG.). (C). ring bd. 84.47 (978-0-205-83500-3(7)) Longman Publishing Group.

—Living Democracy, California Edition. 2nd ed. 2009. (ENG.). 992p. (C). pap. 168.00 (978-0-13-602797-3(0), Prentice Hall) Prentice Hall PTR.

Thaler, John H. The Decline & Fall of California... & the Rise of Social Liberalism. 2007. 360p. pap. 24.95 (978-0-7414-4211-6(6)) Infinity Publishing.

Ting. California Government in National Perspective. 7th rev. ed. 2011. (ENG.). 194p. pap. 35.89 (978-0-7575-9152-5(3)) Kendall Hunt Publishing Co.

Toyota, Tritia. Envisioning America: New Chinese Americans & the Politics of Belonging. 2009. (Asian America Ser.). (ENG.). 256p. 65.00 (978-0-8047-6241-0(4)) Stanford Univ. Pr.

Van Vechten, Renée. California Politics: A Primer. 2nd rev. ed. 2011. 168p. pap. 23.00 (978-1-4522-0306-5(7)) CQ Pr.

Weintraub, Daniel. Party of One: Arnold Schwarzenegger & the Rise of the Independent Voter. 2008. (ENG.). 237p. 19.95 (978-0-9794822-2-9(4)) PoliPointPress, LLC.

Wilkinson, M. James. Who Rules Santa Rosa & Why It Matters. 2010. 192p. pap. 16.95 (978-1-4502-2532-8(2)) iUniverse, Inc.

CALIFORNIA—POPULATION

Breschini, Gary S. Models of Population Movements in Central California Prehistory. fac. ed. 225p. reprint ed. pap. 23.75 (978-1-55567-923-1(4)) Coyote Pr.

Cook, S. F. Population Trends among the California Mission Indians, Vol. 17. fac. ed. (Ibero-Americana Ser.). (Illus.). 56p. reprint ed. pap. 6.88 (978-1-55567-907-1(2)) Coyote Pr.

Fredrickson, Vera-Mae & Peri, David. Mihilakawna & Makahmo Pamo: People of Lake Sonoma. fac. ed. (U. S. Army Corps of Engineers Ser.). (Illus.). 76p. reprint ed. pap. 8.75 (978-1-55567-894-4(7)) Coyote Pr.

Garoogian, David, ed. Profiles of California 2010. 2nd rev. ed. 2010. pap. 149.00 (978-1-59237-559-2(6)) Grey Hse. Publishing.

Holmes, William H. Review of the Evidence Relating to Auriferous Gravel Man in California. fac. ed. (Smithsonian Institution, Smithsonian Reports for 1899 Ser.). (Illus.). 74p. reprint ed. pap. 8.75 (978-1-55567-899-9(8)) Coyote Pr.

Information Publications, creator. California Cities, Towns, & Counties. 2008. (State & Municipal Profiles Ser.). (Illus.). 697p. pap. 165.50 (978-0-911273-42-7(5)) Information Pubns., Inc.

Information Publications, ed. California Cities, Towns & Counties 2008. 2008. 720p. cd-rom 119.00 (978-0-911273-43-4(3)) Information Pubns., Inc.

Merriam, C. Hart. The Indian Population of California, Vol. 7:4. fac. ed. (American Anthropological Reprints Ser.). 18p. reprint ed. pap. 2.19 (978-1-55567-901-9(3)) Coyote Pr.

—Totemism in California, Vol. 10:4. fac. ed. (American Anthropological Reprints Ser.). 7p. reprint ed. pap. 1.25 (978-1-55567-900-2(5)) Coyote Pr.

CALIFORNIA—SOCIAL CONDITIONS

Almaguer, Tomás. Racial Fault Lines: The Historical Origins of White Supremacy in California. 2nd ed. 2008. (ENG.). 304p. pap. 24.95 (978-0-520-25786-3(3)) Univ. of California Pr.

Alpert, Michael E. Solving California's Corrections Crisis: Time Is Running Out. 2007. (Illus.). 86p. (C). pap. 20.00 (978-1-4223-1585-9(1)) DIANE Publishing Co.

Anjejo, Dixon. Risk Behaviors of African Born Adolescents in United States of Americ. 2010. 148p. pap. (978-3-8383-4959-6(8)) Lambert Academic Publishing.

Axelrod, J. B. C. Inventing Autopia: Dreams & Visions of the Modern Metropolis in Jazz Age Los Angeles. 2009. (ENG., Illus.). 427p. pap. 25.95 (978-0-520-25285-1(3)) Univ. of California Pr.

Axelrod, Jeremiah B. C. & Axelrod, J. B. C. Inventing Autopia: Dreams & Visions of the Modern Metropolis in Jazz Age Los Angeles. 2009. (ENG., Illus.). 427p. 65.00 (978-0-520-25284-4(5)) Univ. of California Pr.

Bathina, Dr Jyothi. Among the Groves: Lindsay Lives. Bathina, Jyothi, ed. 2011. 228p. pap. 15.95 (978-1-61434-250-2(4)) Booklocker.com, Inc.

Beland, Nancy. A Pathway to Senior Care in San Diego: Resource Guide for Adult Children & Caregivers to Seniors. 2010. 168p. (ENG.). 25.95 (978-1-4502-1277-9(8)); pap. 15.95 (978-1-4502-1275-5(1)) iUniverse, Inc.

Boal, Iain, et al, eds. West of Eden: Communes & Utopia in Northern California. 2012. (ENG., Illus.). 304p. pap. 24.95 (978-1-60486-427-4(3)) PM Pr.

Brilliant, Mark. The Color of America Has Changed: How Racial Diversity Shaped Civil Rights Reform in California, 1941-1978, 1 vol. 2010. (ENG., Illus.). 384p. 34.95 (978-0-19-516050-5(9)) Oxford Univ. Pr., Inc.

Brown, Cupcake. A Piece of Cake: A Memoir. 2007. (ENG.). 480p. pap. 15.00 (978-1-4000-5229-5(7), Three Rivers Pr.) Crown Publishing Group.

Buss, R. L. Spread Out Across the Lowering Sky. Buss, R. L., ed. 2006. 13.95 (978-0-9713360-3-2(2)) Sun Wolf Pr.

Casas, Maria Raquel. Married to a Daughter of the Land: Spanish-Mexican Women & Interethnic Marriage in Calif. , 1820-1880. 2009. (ENG., Illus.). 280p. pap. 24.95 (978-0-87417-778-7(2)) Univ. of Nevada Pr.

—Married to a Daughter of the Land: Spanish-Mexican Women & Interethnic Marriage in California, 1820-1880. 2007. (ENG., Illus.). 272p. 34.95 (978-0-87417-697-1(2)) Univ. of Nevada Pr.

Cashill, Jack. What's the Matter with California? Cultural Rumbles from the Golden State & Why the Rest of Us Should Be Shaking. 2008. (ENG.). 368p. pap. 14.00 (978-1-4165-3103-6(3), Threshold Editions) Threshold Editions.

Chavez-Garcia, Miroslava. Negotiating Conquest: Gender & Power in California, 1770s to 1880s. 2006. (ENG., Illus.). 241p. pap. 22.95 (978-0-8165-2600-0(1)) Univ. of Arizona Pr.

CQ Press, ed. California Crime in Perspective 2010 Edition, 00 vols. rev. ed. 2010. 24p. pap. 32.00 (978-1-60871-444-5(6)) CQ Pr.

—California Edication in Perspective 2010-11 Edition, 00 vols. rev. ed. 2010. 24p. pap. 32.00 (978-1-60871-445-2(4)) CQ Pr.

—California Health Care in Perspective 2010 Editon, 00 vols. rev. ed. 2010. 24p. pap. 32.00 (978-1-60871-446-9(2)) CQ Pr.

—California in Perspective 2010 Edition, 00 vols. rev. ed. 2010. 24p. pap. 32.00 (978-1-60871-447-6(0)) CQ Pr.

Crowley, Kent. Surf Beat: Rock 'n' Roll's Forgotten Revolution. 2011. (ENG., Illus.). 256p. pap. 19.99 (978-1-61713-007-6(9), 1617130079, Backbeat Books) Leonard, Hal Corp.

Davidson, Elsa. The Burdens of Aspiration: Schools, Youth, & Success in the Divided Social Worlds of Silicon Valley. 2011. 272p. E-Book (978-0-8147-2089-9(7)) New York Univ. Pr.

Davidson, Elsa. The Burdens of Aspiration: Schools, Youth, & Success in the Divided Social Worlds of Silicon Valley. 2011. (ENG.). 264p. 75.00 (978-0-8147-2087-5(0)); pap. 24.00 (978-0-8147-2088-2(9)) New York Univ. Pr.

Davis, Lois M., et al. Reparable Harm: Assessing & Addressing Disparities Faced by Boys & Men of Color in California. 2009. (Illus.). 146p. pap. 55.00 (978-0-8330-4561-4(X)); 24p. pap. 29.00 (978-0-8330-4563-8(6)) RAND Corp., The.

de Jesús Acosta, Frank. The History of Barrios Unidos: Healing Community Violence. Ramos, Henry A. J., ed. 2007. (Hispanic Civil Rights Ser.). 253p. per. 16.95 (978-1-55885-483-3(5)) Arte Publico Pr.

Doe, Tanis, et al. How it Works: At Narratives from California. Doe, Tanis, ed. 2007.Tr. of Cómo Funciona: Narrativas de TA de California. (SPA.). per. (978-0-9727905-1-2(9)) California Foundation for Independent Living Ctrs.

Du Bry, Travis. Immigrants, Settlers, & Laborers: The Socioeconomic Transformation of a Farming Community. 2006. (Illus.). (C). (978-1-59332-157-4(0)) LFB Scholarly Publishing LLC.

Earthquake Monitoring, Research, & Preparation: Field Hearing Before the Subcommittee on Disaster Prevention & Prediction of the Committee on Commerce, Science, & Transportation, United States Senate, One Hundred Ninth Congress, Second Session, April 18, 2006. 2011. (Illus.). iii, 74p. (978-0-16-088143-5(9), 552-070-42560-8) United States Government Printing Office.

Education-Sac, Ca Dept Of & Ong, Faye. Physical Education Framework for California Public Schools, Kindergarten Through Grade Twelve. 2009. (Illus.). xi, 330p. (978-0-8011-1696-4(1), Branch Line Video) California Dept. of Education.

Elinson, Elaine & Yogi, Stan. Wherever There's a Fight: How Runaway Slaves, Suffragists, Immigrants, Strikers, & Poets Shaped Civil Liberties in California. 2009. 512p. pap. 24.95 (978-1-59714-114-7(3)) Heyday.

Elliott, Lisa Ruth. Ten Years That Shook the City: San Francisco 1968-1978: A Reclaiming San Francisco Book. Carlsson, Chris, ed. 2011. (ENG.). 344p. pap. 18.95 (978-1-931404-12-9(7)) City Lights Bks.

Espinoza, Yolanda. El Caraco - the Story of Alfonso: Labor Camp Child. 2010. (ENG.). 176p. pap. 14.95 *(978-1-936400-58-4(8))* Mill City Pr., Inc.

Field, Mona & Kennedy, Brian. The People & Promise of California. 2007. (Longman Topics Ser.). (ENG.). 288p. (C). per. 23.60 *(978-0-321-43489-0(7))* Longman Publishing Group.

Gershon, Ilana. Making Differences Cultural. 2012. (Expertise: Cultures & Technologies of Knowledge Ser.). (ENG.). 208p. 69.95 ***(978-0-8014-5078-5(0))*** Cornell Univ. Pr.

—No Family Is an Island: Cultural Expertise among Samoans in Diaspora. 2012. (Expertise: Cultures & Technologies of Knowledge Ser.). (ENG.). 208p. pap. 22.95 ***(978-0-8014-7805-5(7))*** Cornell Univ. Pr.

Le Grand History: Memories of le Grand History Club. 2007. (Illus.). 99p. (C). pap. 9.95 *(978-0-9729318-5-4(6))* Merced County Historical Society.

Guevarra, Rudy P., Jr. Becoming Mexipino: Multiethnic Identities & Communities in San Diego. 2012. (Latinidad: Transnational Cultures in the United States Ser.). (ENG.). 256p. 72.00 ***(978-0-8135-5283-5(4))*** Rutgers Univ. Pr.

—Becoming Mexipino: Multiethnic Identities & Communities in San Diego. 2012. (Latinidad: Transnational Cultures in the United States Ser.). (ENG., Illus.). 256p. (C). pap. 25.95 ***(978-0-8135-5284-2(2))*** Rutgers Univ. Pr.

Hackel, Steven W., ed. Alta California: Peoples in Motion, Identities in Formation. 2009. (Western Histories Ser.). (ENG., Illus.). 304p. 55.00 *(978-0-87328-242-0(6))* Huntington Library Pr.

Hanson, Victor Davis. Mexifornia: A State of Becoming. 2nd ed. 2007. (ENG.). 150p. per. 17.95 *(978-1-59403-217-2(3))* Encounter Bks.

Heyday Books, creator. Our Valley, Our Choice: Building a Livable Future for the San Joaquin. 2007. (Great Valley Ser.). (Illus.). 112p. per. 17.95 *(978-1-59714-058-4(9))* Heyday.

Hingst, Amanda Jane. The Written World: Past & Place in the Work of Orderic Vitalis. 2009. (ENG., Illus.). 312p. pap. 40.00 *(978-0-268-03086-5(3))* Univ. of Notre Dame Pr.

H.R. 4384, to Establish Utah Navajo Trust Fund Commission; H.R. 5023, "Requirements, Expectations, & Standard Procedures for Executive Consultation with Tribes Act"; & H.R. 5468, "Bridgeport Indian Colony Land Trust, Health, & Economic Development ACT of 2010" Legislative Hearing Before the Committee on Natural Resources, U.S. House of Representatives, One Hundred Eleventh Congress, Second Session, Wednesday, July 28, 2010. 2010. (Illus.). iii, 62p. *(978-0-16-086626-5(X)*, 552-070-41604-8) United States Government Printing Office.

Igler, David & Deverell, William, eds. A Companion to California History. 2008. (Blackwell Companions to American History Ser.: 35). (ENG., Illus.). 544p. 229.95 *(978-1-4051-6183-1(3)*, Wiley-Blackwell) Wiley, John & Sons, Inc.

Information Publications, creator. California Cities, Towns, & Counties. 2008. (State & Municipal Profiles Ser.). (Illus.). 697p. pap. 165.50 *(978-0-911273-42-7(5))* Information Pubns., Inc.

Information Publications, ed. California Cities, Towns & Counties 2008. 2008. 720p. cd-rom 119.00 *(978-0-911273-43-4(3))* Information Pubns., Inc.

Jendian, Matthew A. Becoming American, Remaining Ethnic: The Case of Armenian-Americans in Central California. 2008. (Law & Society Ser.). 226p. 80.00 *(978-1-59332-261-8(5))* LFB Scholarly Publishing LLC.

Jones, Kevin & Johnson, Christina. Fabulous! Ten Years of FIDM Museum Acquisitions, 2000-2010. 2011. (ENG.). 85.00 ***(978-0-615-48860-8(9))***; pap. 65.00 ***(978-0-615-48627-9(3))*** FIDM Museum & Library, Inc.

Keune, Kathrin. A Ritual Journey Towards Change. 2010. 108p. pap. *(978-3-639-27322-9(2))* VDM Verlag Dr. Mueller e.K.

Kisslinger, C. & Rikitake, Tsuneji, eds. Practical Approaches to Earthquake Prediction & Warning. 2010. 500p. pap. 375.00 *(978-90-481-8421-7(5)*, 9048184215) Springer.

Klein, Norman. A History of Forgetting: Los Angeles & the Erasure of Memory, New & Fully Updated Edition. 2nd rev. ed. 2008. (ENG.). 352p. 110.00 *(978-1-84467-241-7(7)*, 844241) Verso Bks. GBR. Dist: Norton, W. W. & Co., Inc.

Kropp, Phoebe S. California Vieja: Culture & Memory in a Modern American Place. 2008. (Illus.). 384p. pap. 26.95 *(978-0-520-25804-4(5))* Univ. of California Pr.

Lally, et al. Infant/Toddler Caregiving. 2nd ed. 2009. (Illus.). x, 85p. *(978-0-8011-1701-5(1))* California Dept. of Education.

Lanuza, Fredrick. Racial Isolation, Educational Equity, & the Right to Equal Access. 2008. 416p. pap. *(978-3-639-07329-4(0))* VDM Verlag Dr. Mueller e.K.

Laufer, Peter. Calexico: True Lives of the Borderlands. 2011. (ENG., Illus.). 248p. pap. 19.95 *(978-0-8165-2951-3(5))* Univ. of Arizona Pr.

Laufer, Peter & Kounalakis, Markos. Calexico: Hope & Hysteria in the California Borderlands. 2009. (ENG.). 260p. 21.95 *(978-0-9815769-3-0(1))* PoliPointPress, LLC.

Lowney, Jeremiah. Stoned, Drunk, or Sober? Understanding Alcohol & Drug Use Through Qualitative, Quantitative, & Longitudinal Research. 2008. (Studies in the History of Judaism Ser.). (ENG.). 200p. pap. 36.99 *(978-0-7618-4103-5(8))* Univ. Pr. of America, Inc.

McCormick, Thomas P. Loma Prieta Earthquake: Collapse of the Bay Bridge & the Cypress Viaduct. 2007. (Illus.). 36p. (C). reprint ed. pap. 15.00 *(978-1-4223-1589-7(4))* DIANE Publishing Co.

McKanna, Clare V., Jr. Race & Homicide in Nineteenth-Century California. 2007. (Wilbur S. Shepperson Series in History & Humanities). (ENG., Illus.). 166p. per. 17.95 *(978-0-87417-728-2(6))* Univ. of Nevada Pr.

Millner, Steven M., et al. California's Changing Majority: Historic & Contemporary Dynamics. rev. ed. 2008. (ENG.). 354p. pap. 62.12 *(978-0-7575-1446-3(4))* Kendall Hunt Publishing Co.

Moffat, Amy. 2020: Visions for the Central Valley. 2010. pap. 12.95 *(978-1-59714-133-8(X))* Heyday.

Morgan, Scott, ed. California in Perspective 2011, 00 vols. rev. ed. 2011. 24p. pap. 32.00 *(978-1-4522-0019-4(X))* CQ Pr.

Morin, Edgar. California Journal. 2008. (ENG.). 161p. pap. 32.50 *(978-1-84519-275-4(3))* Sussex Academic Pr. GBR. Dist: International Specialized Bk. Services.

Paik, Leslie. Discretionary Justice: Looking Inside a Juvenile Drug Court. 2011. (Critical Issues in Crime & Society Ser.). (ENG., Illus.). 272p. (C). 72.00 *(978-0-8135-5006-0(8))*; pap. 25.95 *(978-0-8135-5007-7(6))* Rutgers Univ. Pr.

Perez, Rossana & Ramos, Henry A. J., eds. Flight to Freedom: The Story of Central American Refugees in California. Villarroel, Carolina, tr. from SPA. 2007. (Hispanic Civil Rights Ser.). (Illus.). 193p. per. 16.95 *(978-1-55885-329-4(4))* Arte Publico Pr.

Rhomberg, Chris. No There There: Race, Class, & Political Community in Oakland. 2007. (Illus.). 315p. per. 28.95 *(978-0-520-25166-3(0))* Univ. of California Pr.

Rios, Victor. Punished: Policing the Lives of Black & Latino Boys. 2011. (ENG.). 237p. 70.00 *(978-0-8147-7637-7(X))*; pap. 20.00 *(978-0-8147-7638-4(8))* New York Univ. Pr.

Roque-Ramirez, Horacio N. Queer Latino San Francisco: An Oral History, 1960s-1990s. 2012. (Palgrave Studies in Oral History Ser.). (ENG.). 240p. 95.00 *(978-0-230-11129-5(7))*; pap. 30.00 *(978-0-230-11130-1(0))* Palgrave Macmillan.

Rosser, Kevin. Study of the Planetary Boundary Layer. 2010. 128p. pap. *(978-3-8383-1879-0(X))* Lambert Academic Publishing.

Ryan, Joan. The Water Giver: The Story of a Mother, a Son, & Their Second Chance. 2010. (ENG.). 272p. pap. 15.00 *(978-1-4165-7653-2(3))* Simon & Schuster.

S. 2956, the Pechanga Band of Luiseño Mission Indians Water Rights Settlement ACT, & S. 3290, the Blackfeet Water Rights Settlement ACT of 2010: Hearing Before the Committee on Indian Affairs, United States Senate, One Hundred Eleventh Congress, Second Session, July 22, 2010. 2011. (Illus.). iii, 135p. ***(978-0-16-088317-0(2)**, 552-070-42622-1)* United States Government Printing Office.

Santos, Kristen. Turlock: A Pictorial History, 1950-2005. 2007. *(978-1-57864-425-4(9))* Donning Co. Pubs.

Schou, Nicholas. Orange Sunshine: The Brotherhood of Eternal Love & Its Quest to Spread Peace, Love, & Acid to the World. 2010. (ENG., Illus.). 304p. 24.99 *(978-0-312-55183-4(5)*, Dunne, Thomas Bks.) St. Martin's Pr.

Schrag, Peter. California: America's High-Stakes Experiment. 2007. 328p. per. 21.95 *(978-0-520-25405-3(8))* Univ. of California Pr.

Secrest, William B. Showdown! Lionhearted Lawmen of Old California. 2010. (ENG., Illus.). 312p. pap. 15.95 *(978-1-884995-65-1(9))* Linden Publishing Co., Inc.

Shankar, Shalini. Desi Land: Teen Culture, Class, & Success in Silicon Valley. 2008. (ENG.). 264p. (C). 84.95 *(978-0-8223-4300-4(2))*; pap. 23.95 *(978-0-8223-4315-8(0))* Duke Univ. Pr.

Sheff, David. Mi hijo Precioso: El viaje de un padre a través de la adicción de su Hijo. 2009. (Vintage Espanol Ser.). (SPA.). 400p. pap. 14.95 *(978-0-307-45568-0(8)*, Vintage) Knopf Doubleday Publishing Group.

Silverman, Victor & Glover, Laurie. California: On-the-Road Histories. 2011. (ENG., Illus.). 320p. pap. 22.00 *(978-1-56656-809-8(9)*, Interlink Bks.) Interlink Publishing Group, Inc.

Slow Food Nation, et al. Come to the Table: The Slow Food Way of Living. Heron, Katrina, ed. 2008. (ENG., Illus.). 176p. 29.95 *(978-1-60529-895-5(6)*, Modern Times) Rodale Pr., Inc.

Sosnowski, Vivienne. When the Rivers Ran Red: An Amazing Story of Courage & Triumph in America's Wine Country. 2010. (ENG., Illus.). 256p. pap. 16.00 *(978-0-230-10337-5(5))* Palgrave Macmillan.

Stamolis, Tony, photos by. Frezno. 2008. (ENG.). 132p. 29.95 *(978-1-934170-04-5(6))* Process Packaging.

Starr, Kevin. Golden Dreams: California in an Age of Abundance, 1950-1963, 1 vol. (Americans & the California Dream Ser.). (ENG., Illus.). 576p. 2011. pap. 24.95 *(978-0-19-983249-1(8))* 2009. 34.95 *(978-0-19-515377-4(4))* Oxford Univ. Pr., Inc.

Thaler, John H. The Decline & Fall of California... & the Rise of Social Liberalism. 2007. 360p. pap. 24.95 *(978-0-7414-4211-6(6))* Infinity Publishing.

Tripp, Terry L. Here, Our Open Hearts: A Student Anthology. 2010. 84p. pap. 10.95 *(978-1-4502-2974-6(3))* iUniverse, Inc.

Van Ecke, Yolanda. Attachment & Immigrants: Emotional security among Dutch & Belgian immigrants in California, U. S. A. 2007. (UvA Proefschriften Ser.). 124p. per. *(978-90-5629-480-9(6)*, Leiden Univ. Pr.) Amsterdam Univ. Pr.

Varzally, Allison. Making a Non-White America: Californians Coloring outside Ethnic Lines, 1925-1955. 2008. (Illus.). 320p. 60.00 *(978-0-520-25344-5(2))* Univ. of California Pr.

Vasquez, Antonio Gonzalez & Carpio, Genevieve. Mexican Americans in Redlands. 2012. (Images of America Ser.). (ENG., Illus.). 128p. pap. 21.99 ***(978-0-7385-9522-1(5))*** Arcadia Publishing.

Vergara, Benito. Pinoy Capital: The Filipino Nation in Daly City. 2008. (Asian American History & Culture Ser.). (ENG., Illus.). 232p. 78.50 *(978-1-59213-664-3(8))*; pap. 27.95 *(978-1-59213-665-0(6))* Temple Univ. Pr.

Vollmann, William T. Imperial. 2009. (ENG., Illus.). 1344p. (gr. 12-18). 55.00 *(978-0-670-02061-4(3)*, Viking Adult) Penguin Group (USA) Inc.

Westwick, Peter J. & Deverell, William, eds. Blue Sky Metropolis: The Aerospace Century in Southern California. 2012. (Western Histories Ser.). (ENG., Illus.). 278p. 44.95 ***(978-0-87328-249-9(3))*** Huntington Library Pr.

Wilkinson, M. James. Who Rules Santa Rosa & Why It Matters. 2010. 192p. pap. 16.95 *(978-1-4502-2532-8(2))* iUniverse, Inc.

Winn, Ira. Small Town / Big Town: Growing Pains on California's Central Coast. 2010. 208p. pap. 16.95 *(978-1-4502-0944-1(0))* iUniverse, Inc.

Wollenberg, Charles. Berkeley: A City in History. 2007. (Illus.). 224p. pap. 21.95 *(978-0-520-25307-0(8))* Univ. of California Pr.

Wynne, Sharon. CTEL California Teacher of English Learners. 2010. (Xam Cset Ser.). (ENG.). 280p. pap. 64.95 *(978-1-60787-025-8(8))* XAMonline, Inc.

Zilberg, Elana. Space of Detention: The Making of a Transnational Gang Crisis between Los Angeles & San Salvador. 2011. (ENG.). 360p. 89.95 *(978-0-8223-4713-2(X))* Duke Univ. Pr.

—Space of Detention: The Making of a Transnational Gang Crisis Between Los Angeles & San Salvador. 2011. (ENG.). 360p. pap. 24.95 *(978-0-8223-4730-9(X))* Duke Univ. Pr.

CALIFORNIA—SOCIAL LIFE AND CUSTOMS

Adams, Carole & Bogacki, John. Point Piedras Blancas. 2008. 128p. pap. 19.99 *(978-0-7385-5819-6(2))* Arcadia Publishing.

Adema, Pauline. Garlic Capital of the World: Gilroy, Garlic, & the Making of a Festive Foodscape. 2009. (ENG., Illus.). 192p. 55.00 *(978-1-60473-120-0(6))*; pap. 30.00 *(978-1-60473-121-7(4))* Univ. Pr. of Mississippi.

Anderson, Karl. The Salton Sea. 2011. (Postcard History Ser.). (ENG., Illus.). 128p. pap. 21.99 *(978-0-7385-7455-4(4))* Arcadia Publishing.

Arellano, Gustavo. Orange County: A Personal History. 2010. (ENG.). 288p. pap. 18.99 *(978-1-4165-4005-2(9)*, Scribner) Scribner.

Arnold, Mary Ellicott & Reed, Mabel. In the Land of the Grasshopper Song: Two Women in the Klamath River Indian Country in 1908-09, Second Edition. 2nd ed. 2011. (ENG., Illus.). 352p. pap. 19.95 ***(978-0-8032-3637-0(9)**,* Bison Bks.) Univ. of Nebraska Pr.

Austin, Linda & Hammond, Norm. Oceano. 2010. (Images of America Ser.). (Illus.). 128p. pap. 21.99 *(978-0-7385-8087-6(2))* Arcadia Publishing.

Austin, Mary Hunter. The Land of Little Rain: Facsimile of Original 1904 Edition. 2007. (ENG.). 320p. per. 26.95 *(978-0-86534-540-9(6))* Sunstone Pr.

Baggese, Carl P. Modesto. 2011. (Postcard History Ser.). (ENG., Illus.). 128p. pap. 21.99 ***(978-0-7385-7579-7(8))*** Arcadia Publishing.

Ball, Guy & Tustin Area Historical Society. Tustin. 2011. (Images of America Ser.). (Illus.). 128p. pap. 21.99 *(978-0-7385-7037-2(0))* Arcadia Publishing.

Barton, Jorane King. El Monte. 2006. (Images of America Ser.). (ENG., Illus.). 128p. per. 21.99 *(978-0-7385-4652-0(6))* Arcadia Publishing.

Benziger, Jeff. Waterford. 2011. (Images of America Ser.). (Illus.). 128p. pap. 21.99 *(978-0-7385-7452-3(X))* Arcadia Publishing.

Browne, J. Ross (John Ross). Crusoe's Island: A Ramble in the Footsteps of Alexander Selkirk, with Sketches of Adventure in California & Washoe. by J. Ross Browne. 2006. 448p. per. 26.99 *(978-1-4255-4863-6(6))* MPublishing.

Buckley, Aileen M. From the Driver's Seat. 2006. 139p. pap. 11.95 *(978-0-7414-3366-4(4))* Infinity Publishing.

Burrill, Robert & Rogers, Lynn. Alviso, San Jose. 2006. (Images of America Ser.). (ENG., Illus.). 128p. per. 19.99 *(978-0-7385-3140-3(5))* Arcadia Publishing.

California, Pa. , 1849-1881: A History of a Boat Building Town. 2009. (Illus.). 466p. pap. 20.00 *(978-0-9630513-5-6(0))* Yohogania Pr.

Carkeet, David. Campus Sexpot: A Memoir. 2007. (Association of Writers & Writing Programs Award for Creative Nonfiction Ser.). (ENG.). 152p. per. 17.95 *(978-0-8203-3013-6(2))* Univ. of Georgia Pr.

Carrico, Richard L. Ramona. 2011. (Images of America Ser.). (ENG., Illus.). 128p. pap. 21.99 *(978-0-7385-8162-0(3))* Arcadia Publishing.

Chalquist, Craig. Deep Californi: Images & Ironies of Cross & Sword on el Camino Real. 2008. 736p. pap. 38.95 *(978-0-595-51462-5(6))* iUniverse, Inc.

Clark, Ralph A. & Lodi Historical Society. Lodi: 1945-2005. 2011. (Images of America Ser.). (Illus.). 128p. pap. 21.99 *(978-0-7385-7548-3(8))* Arcadia Publishing.

Clovis Centennial Committee. Clovis. 2011. (Images of America Ser.). (Illus.). 128p. pap. 21.99 ***(978-0-7385-7613-8(1))*** Arcadia Publishing.

Convis, Charles. California in Old West. 2008. pap. 11.95 *(978-1-892156-25-9(3))* Pioneer Pr.

Crawford, Richard. The Way We Were in San Diego. 2011. 160p. pap. 19.99 ***(978-1-60949-441-4(5))*** History Pr., The.

Cueva-Fernandez, Olivia. Mexican Americans in Wilmington. 2011. (Images of America Ser.). (ENG., Illus.). 128p. pap. 21.99 *(978-0-7385-8174-3(7))* Arcadia Publishing.

Culver, Lawrence. The Frontier of Leisure: Southern California & the Shaping of Modern America, 1 vol. (ENG., Illus.). 336p. 2012. pap. 21.95 ***(978-0-19-989192-4(3))*** 2010. 29.95 *(978-0-19-538263-1(3))* Oxford Univ. Pr., Inc.

Danisi, Tim & Rohnert Park Historical Society. Rohnert Park. 2012. (Images of America Ser.). (ENG., Illus.). 128p. pap. 21.99 ***(978-0-7385-8924-4(1))*** Arcadia Publishing.

de Martino, Thomas, et al. Chino. 2011. (Images of America Ser.). (Illus.). 128p. pap. 21.99 *(978-0-7385-8142-2(9))* Arcadia Publishing.

Delamere, Henry & Hopkins, Tammy L. Marysville. 2007. (Images of America Ser.). (ENG., Illus.). 128p. per. 21.99 *(978-0-7385-4737-4(9))* Arcadia Publishing.

Dochuk, Darren. From Bible Belt to Sunbelt: Plain-Folk Religion, Grassroots Politics, & the Rise of Evangelical Conservatism. (ENG.). 2012. 560p. pap. 18.95 ***(978-0-393-33904-8(1)**,* 33904) 2010. (Illus.). 520p. 35.00 *(978-0-393-06682-1(7)*, 6682) Norton, W. W. & Co., Inc.

Doisneau, Robert. Palm Springs 1960. 2010. (ENG., Illus.). 156p. 34.95 *(978-2-08-030129-1(2))* Flammarion et Cie FRA. Dist: Random Hse., Inc.

Drylie, Gary "Old Town Griz". Hesperia. 2010. (Images of America Ser.). (Illus.). 128p. pap. 21.99 *(978-0-7385-8107-1(0))* Arcadia Publishing.

Du Bois, Cora. The 1870 Ghost Dance: Anthropological Records V3, No. 1. 2011. 160p. 41.95 ***(978-1-258-04241-7(X))*** Literary Licensing, LLC.

Dubin, Margaret & Hogeland, Kim, eds. Spring Salmon, Hurry to Me! The Seasons of Native California. 2008. (California Legacy Ser.). (Illus.). 115p. pap. 16.95 *(978-1-59714-079-9(1))* Heyday.

Dunn, Joe. Pocket of Paradise: The Story of Beach Road. 2008. (Illus.). 108p. pap. 30.00 *(978-0-9753939-7-0(9))* Prospect Park Bks., LLC.

Epting, Chris. Huntington Beach. 2008. (Then & Now Ser.). (ENG., Illus.). 96p. pap. 19.99 *(978-0-7385-5828-8(1))* Arcadia Publishing.

Fitzgerald, O. P. California Sketches, Second Series. 2006. (ENG.). 176p. pap. 19.99 *(978-1-4264-6180-4(1))*; 190p. pap. 21.99 *(978-1-4254-6235-1(2))* BiblioBazaar.

Fitzpatrick, Linda & Conkle, James M. Needles. 2010. (Images of America Ser.). (Illus.). 128p. pap. 21.99 *(978-0-7385-8064-7(3))* Arcadia Publishing.

Gabriel, Louise B. & Santa Monica Historical Society. Santa Monica: 1950-2010. 2011. (Images of America Ser.). (ENG., Illus.). 128p. pap. 21.99 *(978-0-7385-8143-9(7))* Arcadia Publishing.

Gale, Kate & De Turenne, Veronique. The Devil's Punchbowl: A Cultural & Geographic Map of California Today. 2010. (ENG.). 208p. pap. 25.95 *(978-1-59709-164-0(2))* Red Hen Pr.

Garcia, Mary. Santa Ana's Logan Barrio; Its History, Stories, & Families. 2007. (Illus.). 88p. spiral bd. 17.95 *(978-0-9797619-0-4(5))* Santa Ana Historical Preservation Society.

Gruber, Frank. Urban Worrier: Making Politics Personal. 2009. 340p. pap. 16.95 *(978-0-615-27122-4(7))* City Image Pr.

Haber, Mel. Palm Springs à la Carte: The Colorful World of the Caviar Crowd at Their Favorite Desert Hideaway. 2008. 256p. 23.95 *(978-1-56980-353-0(6))* Barricade Bks., Inc.

Harris, Jim. Santa Monica Pier: A Century of the Last Great Pleasure Pier. 2009. (Illus.). 128p. *(978-1-883318-82-6(3))* Angel City Pr.

Hendrickson, Nancy. Remembering Old California. 2011. (Remembering Ser.). (ENG.). 134p. pap. 16.95 *(978-1-59652-796-6(X))* Turner Publishing Co.

Heyday Books, creator. Our Valley, Our Choice: Building a Livable Future for the San Joaquin. 2007. (Great Valley Ser.). (Illus.). 112p. per. 17.95 *(978-1-59714-058-4(9))* Heyday.

Holtzclaw, Kenneth M. & Moreno Valley Historical Society. Moreno Valley. 2007. (Images of America Ser.). (ENG., Illus.). 128p. per. 19.99 *(978-0-7385-5569-0(X))* Arcadia Publishing.

Hopkins, Nancy & Hopkins, Heidi. These Are My Flowers: Raising a Family on the Big Sur Coast. 2007. (Illus.). 160p. *(978-0-9702294-3-4(7))* Glyph Publishing Arts.

Hoye, Richard, et al. Ojai. 2010. (Postcard History Ser.). (ENG., Illus.). 128p. pap. 21.99 *(978-0-7385-8108-8(9))* Arcadia Publishing.

Hubbard Crawford, Leslie. Coronado. 2011. (Images of America Ser.). (ENG., Illus.). 128p. pap. 21.99 *(978-0-7385-8130-9(5))* Arcadia Publishing.

Isaac, Frederick. Jews of Oakland & Berkeley. 2009. (Images of America Ser.). (ENG., Illus.). 128p. pap. 21.99 *(978-0-7385-7033-4(8))* Arcadia Publishing.

Jamero, Peter. Growing up Brown: Memoirs of a Filipino American. 2006. (Scott & Laurie Oki Series in Asian American Studies). (ENG., Illus.). 348p. per. 24.95 *(978-0-295-98642-5(5))* Univ. of Washington Pr.

Jauregui, Jannette. Ventura County Veterans: World War II to Vietnam. 2011. (Images of America Ser.). (Illus.). 128p. pap. 21.99 *(978-0-7385-7491-2(0))* Arcadia Publishing.

Jennings, Sherry E. Truckee. 2011. (Images of America Ser.). (Illus.). 128p. pap. 21.99 *(978-0-7385-7495-0(3))* Arcadia Publishing.

Jordan, David Starr. The Call of the Twentieth Century, & California & the Californians. 2007. 48p. per. *(978-1-4065-4657-6(7))* Dodo Pr.

Jurmain, Claudia K., et al. Rancho Los Alamitos: Ever Changing, Always the Same. 2011. (Illus.). xx, 227p. ***(978-1-59714-149-9(6))***; pap. 35.00 ***(978-1-59714-148-2(8))*** Heyday.

Keller, Russell L. Big Bear. 2008. (Postcard History Ser.). (ENG., Illus.). 128p. pap. 19.99 *(978-0-7385-5912-4(1))* Arcadia Publishing.

Kirby, Joe. The Lockheed Plant. 2011. (Images of America Ser.). (ENG., Illus.). 128p. pap. 21.99 ***(978-0-7385-8796-7(6))*** Arcadia Publishing.

Klippert, Zoë, ed. An Englishwoman in California: The Letters of Catherine Hubback, 1871-76. 2010. (Illus.). 240p. 40.00 *(978-1-85124-344-0(5))* Bodleian Library GBR. Dist: Chicago Distribution Ctr.

Koning, Ben & Metz, Anneke. Sunnyvale. 2011. (Images of America Ser.). (ENG., Illus.). 128p. pap. 21.99 *(978-0-7385-7435-6(X))* Arcadia Publishing.

Kramer, Carol A. & Calaveras Big Trees Association. Calaveras Big Trees. 2010. (Images of America Ser.). (Illus.). 128p. pap. 21.99 *(978-0-7385-8118-7(6))* Arcadia Publishing.

Krintz, Jennifer. Redondo Beach Pier. 2011. (Images of America Ser.). (Illus.). 128p. pap. 21.99 *(978-0-7385-7502-5(X))* Arcadia Publishing.

Lavoie, Steven. Historic Photos of Oakland. 2009. (Historic Photos Ser.). (ENG.). 206p. 39.95 *(978-1-59652-529-0(0))* Turner Publishing Co.

[Letts, John M.]. California Illustrated; Including a Description of the Panama & Nicaragua Routes by a Returned Californian. 2006. (Illus.). 324p. per. 23.99 *(978-1-4255-3129-4(6))* MPublishing.

Lick, Sue Fagalde. Stories Grandma Never Told: Portuguese Women in California. 2007. (Illus.). 265p. per. 18.95 *(978-1-892076-35-9(7))* Dancing Moon Pr.

Lopez, Gloria. An american Paella: Becoming american while staying spanish: a century of memories in winters, California. 2007. 204p. *(978-0-9799348-0-3(X))* Lopez, Autry Production Co.

Lovret, Juanita. Tustin as it Once Was. 2011. (Illus.). 144p. pap. 19.99 ***(978-1-60949-461-2(X))*** History Pr., The.

Macías, Anthony. Mexican American Mojo: Popular Music, Dance, & Urban Culture in Los Angeles, 1935-1968. 2008. (Refiguring American Music Ser.). (ENG., Illus.). 408p. pap. 26.95 *(978-0-8223-4322-6(3))* Duke Univ. Pr.

Malaspina, Rick. Italian Oakland. 2011. (Images of America Ser.). (Illus.). 128p. pap. 21.99 *(978-0-7385-8170-5(4))* Arcadia Publishing.

Mallea-Olaetxe, J. Speaking Through the Aspens: Basque Tree Carvings in Nevada & California. 2008. (Basque Ser.). (ENG., Illus.). 256p. pap. 29.95 *(978-0-87417-762-6(6))* Univ. of Nevada Pr.

Mangelos, John P. Ripon. 2011. (Images of America Ser.). (Illus.). 128p. pap. 21.99 *(978-0-7385-8166-8(6))* Arcadia Publishing.

Marin History Museum. Modern San Rafael: 1940-2000. 2012. (Images of America Ser.). (ENG., Illus.). 128p. pap. 21.99 ***(978-0-7385-9307-4(9))*** Arcadia Publishing.

Markels, Bobby. Being Here. Date not set. (Mendocino Malady Ser.). (Illus.). 68p. reprint ed. pap. 6.50 *(978-1-880991-04-6(7))* Stone Publishing Co.

Marrazzo, Frederick W. Italians in the Santa Clara Valley. 2007. (Images of America Ser.). (ENG., Illus.). 128p. pap. 21.99 *(978-0-7385-5562-1(2))* Arcadia Publishing.

Martin, Joan Gilbert & McInerney-Meagher, Colleen. Pogonip: Jewel of Santa Cruz. 2007. (Illus.). viii, 192p. *(978-1-890625-08-5(6))* Otter B Bks.

Marvin, Judith & Brejla, Terry. Jamestown & Western Tuolumne County. 2011. (Images of America Ser.). (Illus.). 128p. pap. 21.99 *(978-0-7385-8171-2(2))* Arcadia Publishing.

Maxson, Michael J. If the Souls Could Speak. 2011. 134p. pap. 14.99 *(978-1-60957-862-6(7))* Xulon Pr., Inc.

McGovern, Reg, et al. Redwood City. 2008. (Images of America Ser.). (ENG., Illus.). 128p. pap. 21.99 *(978-0-7385-5924-7(5))* Arcadia Publishing.

Miller, Chris Ann & Roberts, Jerry. Hermosa Beach. 2007. (Postcard History Ser.). (ENG., Illus.). 128p. per. 21.99 *(978-0-7385-4709-1(3))* Arcadia Publishing.

Moodian, Michael A. Rancho Santa Margarita. 2010. (Images of America Ser.). (Illus.). 128p. pap. 21.99 *(978-0-7385-8004-3(X))* Arcadia Publishing.

Morin, Edgar. California Journal. 2008. (ENG.). 161p. pap. 32.50 *(978-1-84519-275-4(3))* Sussex Academic Pr. GBR. Dist: International Specialized Bk. Services.

Moruzzi, Peter. Palm Springs Holiday, 1 vol. 2009. (ENG., Illus.). 176p. 30.00 *(978-1-4236-0476-1(8))* Gibbs Smith, Publisher.

Museum Society of Willows, et al. Willows. 2010. (Images of America Ser.). (Illus.). 128p. pap. 21.99 *(978-0-7385-8060-9(0))* Arcadia Publishing.

Nahmias, Rick. Golden States of Grace: Prayers of the Disinherited. 2010. (ENG., Illus.). 232p. pap. 45.00 *(978-0-8263-4677-3(4))* Univ. of New Mexico Pr.

Nelson, Kevin. Wheels of Change from Zero to 600 M.P.H: The Amazing Story of California & the Automobile. 2009. pap. 24.95 *(978-1-59714-113-0(5))* Heyday.

Nichols, Gina. The Navy at Point Mugu. 2011. (Images of America Ser.). (Illus.). 128p. pap. 21.99 *(978-0-7385-7532-2(1))* Arcadia Publishing.

o'connell, william. Homeless in Paradise: Communicating with the Bohemian Venice Beach Subculture. 2009. (Illus.). 310p. pap. 25.46 *(978-0-557-03501-4(5))* Lulu Enterprises Inc.

Orcutt Henderson, Mary Alice. Santa Paula: 1930-1960. 2009. (Images of America Ser.). (Illus.). 128p. pap. 21.99 *(978-0-7385-7165-2(2))* Arcadia Publishing.

Peck, Willys I. & Halberstadt, April. Willys Peck's Saratoga. 2010. *(978-0-935089-30-1(6))* California History Ctr.

Perkins, Maggi. Newhall. 2010. (Images of America Ser.). (ENG., Illus.). 128p. pap. 21.99 *(978-0-7385-8025-8(2))* Arcadia Publishing.

Phillips, Donald M. & Phillips, Paul Gary. Magic Lantern Stories: The Memoirs of Donald M. Phhillips. 2010. (Illus.). 150p. lthr. *(978-0-9772337-8-6(2))* Modern Memoirs Publishing.

Posedel, Jennifer & Lawton, Stephen. Hercules. 2011. (Images of America Ser.). (Illus.). 128p. pap. 21.99 *(978-0-7385-7440-0(6))* Arcadia Publishing.

Pugh, Allison J. & Pugh, A. J. Longing & Belonging: Parents, Children, & Consumer Culture. 2009. (ENG.). 320p. pap. 24.95 *(978-0-520-25844-0(4))* Univ. of California Pr.

Pyron, Jennifer. Lathrop. 2010. (Images of America Ser.). (ENG., Illus.). 128p. pap. 21.99 *(978-0-7385-8017-3(1))* Arcadia Publishing.

Rambeau, Sheryl. Georgetown. 2010. (Images of America Ser.). (Illus.). 128p. pap. 21.99 *(978-0-7385-8113-2(5))* Arcadia Publishing.

Rodriguez-Valls, Fernando. L a Barriohoods: Vernacular Voices & Conversations of Transculturation. 2008. 104p. pap. *(978-3-639-07494-9(7))* VDM Verlag Dr. Mueller e.K.

Roseman, Frank M. & Watry, Peter J. Chula Vista. 2010. (Then & Now Ser.). (ENG., Illus.). 96p. pap. 21.99 *(978-0-7385-8016-6(3))* Arcadia Publishing.

Rossi, Vincent Nicholas. From Field to Town: Chronicles of North County History. 2008. (Illus.). 102p. pap. 11.95 *(978-0-9822671-0-3(X))* StorySeekers.

Sanders, Ian. Views of Morgan Hill: Postcards & Images of Morgan Hill, California. 2010. (Illus.). 156p. 19.99 *(978-0-615-38051-3(4))* Bks.mart Enterprises Inc.

Saucedo, Marcelino. Dream Makers & Dream Catchers: The Story of the Mexican Heritage on Catalina Island. 2008. *(978-1-57864-474-2(7))* Donning Co. Pubs.

Schou, Nicholas. Orange Sunshine: The Brotherhood of Eternal Love & Its Quest to Spread Peace, Love, & Acid to the World. 2011. (ENG., Illus.). 320p. pap. 15.99 *(978-0-312-60717-3(2),* St. Martin's Griffin) St. Martin's Pr.

Scott, James & Tolley, Tom, texts. Historic Photos of Sacramento. 2007. (Historic Photos Ser.). (ENG., Illus.). 204p. 39.95 *(978-1-59652-308-1(5))* Turner Publishing Co.

Sewell, Jessica Ellen. Women & the Everyday City: Public Space in San Francisco, 1890-1915. 2011. (Architecture, Landscape & Amer Culture Ser.). (ENG., Illus.). 280p. 75.00 *(978-0-8166-6973-8(2));* pap. 25.00 *(978-0-8166-6974-5(0))* Univ. of Minnesota Pr.

Singleton, Jill M. & Holmes, Philip. Centerville, Fremont. 2011. (Images of America Ser.). (Illus.). 128p. pap. 21.99 *(978-0-7385-8177-4(1))* Arcadia Publishing.

Smith, Evelyn Eileen. Boardinghouse Stew: A Novel. 2011. (Illus.). 200p. 24.95 ***(978-0-9835615-1-4(6))*** Phoenix International, Inc.

Soquel Pioneer and Historical Association. Soquel. 2011. (Images of America Ser.). (Illus.). 128p. pap. 21.99 *(978-0-7385-7081-5(8))* Arcadia Publishing.

Stark, Julie. Yuba City, Our Home Town. 2008. *(978-1-57864-498-8(4))* Donning Co. Pubs.

Stern, Jean & Siple, Molly. California Light: A Century of Landscapes - Paintings of the California Art Club. 2011. (ENG., Illus.). 276p. 50.00 *(978-0-8478-3625-3(8),* Skira) Rizzoli International Pubns., Inc.

Stevens, Pam. Mira Mesa. 2011. (Images of America Ser.). (Illus.). 128p. pap. 21.99 *(978-0-7385-8203-0(4))* Arcadia Publishing.

Stevenson, Robert Louis. The Silverado Squatters: A Sojourn in Napa County, California, in the Summer Of 1880. 2010. (ENG.). 184p. pap. 16.95 *(978-1-84511-990-4(8),* Tauris Parke Paperbacks) I. B. Tauris & Co., Ltd. GBR. Dist: Macmillan.

Sullivan, Julie. Voices of Lafayette: A Collection of Oral Histories. 2009. 292p. pap. 19.95 *(978-0-9745540-3-7(0))* Big Hat Pr.

Templeton, Ed, frwd. Deanna Templeton: cratch My Name on Your Arm. 2011. (ENG., Illus.). 132p. 50.00 *(978-94-90624-06-4(3))* Schunck NLD. Dist: D.A.P./Distributed Art Pubs.

Thomas, Tim & League, the Monterey Japanese American Citizens. The Japanese on the Monterey Peninsula. 2011. (Images of America Ser.). (ENG., Illus.). 128p. pap. 21.99 ***(978-0-7385-7497-4(X))*** Arcadia Publishing.

Timbrook, Jan. Chumash Ethnobotany: Plant Knowledge among the Chumash People of Southern California. 2007. (Santa Barbara Museum of Natural History Monographs). (Illus.). 271p. pap. *(978-1-59714-048-5(1))* Heyday.

Trevenon, Stacy. Kings Mountain. 2008. (Images of America Ser.). (ENG., Illus.). 128p. pap. 19.99 *(978-0-7385-5829-5(X))* Arcadia Publishing.

Turner, Michelle L. & Pasadena Museum of History. The Rose Bowl. 2010. (Images of America Ser.). (Illus.). 128p. pap. 21.99 *(978-0-7385-8058-6(9))* Arcadia Publishing.

Valdés, Guadalupe, et al. Developing Minority Language Resources: The Case of Spanish in California. 2006. (Bilingual Education & Bilingualism Ser.: Vol. 58). (ENG., Illus.). 344p. 119.95 *(978-1-85359-898-2(4));* pap. 49.95 *(978-1-85359-897-5(6))* Multilingual Matters GBR. Dist: Univ. of Toronto Pr.

Vasquez, Olga A., et al. Pushing Boundaries: Language & Culture in a Mexicano Community. 2007. (ENG., Illus.). 240p. pap. 51.00 *(978-0-521-04857-6(5))* Cambridge Univ. Pr.

Wainwright, Mary-Jo. Pleasanton. 2007. (Images of America Ser.). (ENG., Illus.). 128p. pap. 21.99 *(978-0-7385-4761-9(1))* Arcadia Publishing.

Waters, John, Jr. Calistoga. 2008. (Illus.). 127p. pap. *(978-0-7835-5594-2(6))* Arcadia Publishing.

Western Sonoma County Historical Society. Sebastopol's Gravenstein Apple Industry. 2011. (Images of America Ser.). (Illus.). 128p. pap. 21.99 *(978-0-7385-8173-6(9))* Arcadia Publishing.

Whiteside, Anne. 'We Are the Explorers' Transnational Yucatec Maya-speakers NegotiatingMultilingual California. 2008. 204p. pap. *(978-3-639-04616-8(1))* VDM Verlag Dr. Mueller e.K.

Wilentz, Amy. I Feel Earthquakes More Often Than They Happen: Coming to California in the Age of Schwarzenegger. 2007. (ENG.). 352p. pap. 21.99 *(978-0-7432-6440-2(1))* Simon & Schuster.

Willard, Steve & LaValle, Ed. San Diego Police: Case Files. 2012. (Images of America Ser.). (ENG., Illus.). 128p. pap. 21.99 ***(978-0-7385-9548-1(9))*** Arcadia Publishing.

Williams, Jack. The Shosone of California. 2009. (Library of Native Americans Ser.). 64p. (gr. 4-4). 58.50 *(978-1-60853-763-1(3),* PowerKids Pr.) Rosen Publishing Group, Inc., The.

Yasuda, Anita. Snapshots of San Diego: Sun, Surf & Sand. 2008. (Illus.). 128p. pap. 24.95 *(978-0-7643-2804-6(2))* Schiffer Publishing, Ltd.

CALIFORNIA, GULF OF (MEXICO)

Aitchison, Stewart W. The Desert Islands of Mexico's Sea of Cortez. 2010. (ENG., Illus.). 120p. pap. 15.95 *(978-0-8165-2774-8(1))* Univ. of Arizona Pr.

Brusca, Richard C. The Gulf of California: Biodiversity & Conservation. 2010. (ENG., Illus.). 400p. 75.00 *(978-0-8165-2739-7(3))* Univ. of Arizona Pr.

Hupp, Betty & Malone, Marilyn. The Edge of the Sea of Cortez: Tidewalker's Guide to the Upper Gulf of California. 2009. (ENG., Illus.). 96p. pap. 27.95 *(978-0-615-24828-8(4))* Operculum, LLC.

Kelsey, Elin. Watching Giants: The Secret Lives of Whales. 2008. (Illus.). 216p. 40.00 *(978-0-520-24976-9(3))* Univ. of California Pr.

Steinbeck, John & Ricketts, Edward F. Sea of Cortez: A Leisurely Journal of Travel & Research. 2009. (ENG.). 656p. (gr. 12-18). 25.00 *(978-0-14-311721-6(1),* Penguin (Non-Classics)) Penguin Group (USA) Inc.

United States. Army. Corps Of Engineers. Report of the Secretary of War, Communicating a Reconnoissance of the Gulf of California & the Colorado River by Lieutenant Derby. 2011. 30p. pap. 11.99 ***(978-1-4181-9300-3(3))*** MPublishing.

CALIFORNIA, UNIVERSITY OF

see University of California (System)

CALIFORNIA, UNIVERSITY OF, BERKELEY

see University of California, Berkeley

CALIFORNIA, UNIVERSITY OF, LOS ANGELES

see University of California, Los Angeles

CALIFORNIA ANGELS (BASEBALL TEAM)

see Los Angeles Angels of Anaheim (Baseball Team)

CALIFORNIA CAVALRY BATALLION (1862-1865)

Parson, Thomas E. Bear Flag & Bay State in the Civil War: The Californians of the Second Massachusetts Cavalry. alt. ed. 2007. (ENG., Illus.). 228p. per. 39.95 *(978-0-7864-3257-8(8))* McFarland & Co., Inc. Pubs.

CALIFORNIA CONDOR

Mee, Allan & Hall, Linnea S., eds. California Condors in the 21st Century: Series in Ornithology, No. 2. 2007. 280p. 40.00 *(978-0-943610-77-1(X));* per. 20.00 *(978-0-943610-74-0(5))* American Ornithologists Union.

Mesta, Robert. Condor: Spirit of the Canyon. 2007. (ENG., Illus.). 32p. (gr. -1). pap. 9.95 *(978-0-938216-97-1(X))* Grand Canyon Assn.

Osborn, Sophie A. H. Condors in Canyon Country: The Return of the California Condor to the Grand Canyon Region. 2007. (ENG., Illus.). 160p. 29.95 *(978-0-938216-87-2(2));* pap. 18.95 *(978-0-938216-98-8(8))* Grand Canyon Assn.

CALIFORNIA GOLD RUSH, 1848-1852

see California—Gold Discoveries

CALIFORNIA INSTITUTE OF TECHNOLOGY

Carr, Alan B. The Forgotten Physicist: Robert F. Bacher, 1905-2004. 2008. *(978-0-941232-36-4(0))* Los Alamos Historical Society.

Goodstein, Judith. Millikan's School: A History of the California Institute of Technology. 2006. 352p. per. 23.95 *(978-0-393-32998-8(4))* Norton, W. W. & Co., Inc.

Johnson, Katherine, ed. The Sherman Fairchild Library: A Celebration of Ten Years. 2nd rev. ed. 2007. (Illus.). 110p. lib. bdg. 37.95 *(978-1-60049-002-6(6))* California Institute of Technology.

CALIFORNIA STATE PRISON AT SAN QUENTIN

Comfort, Megan. Doing Time Together: Love & Family in the Shadow of the Prison. 2008. (Illus.). 256p. 55.00 *(978-0-226-11462-0(7));* pap. 22.00 *(978-0-226-11463-7(5))* Univ. of Chicago Pr.

Dallas, Bill. Lessons from San Quentin: Everything I Needed to Know about Life I Learned in Prison. 2010. (ENG.). 240p. pap. 14.99 *(978-1-4143-2657-3(2))* Tyndale Hse. Pubs.

Davidson, Ted. Danger & Trust: San Quentin, the Mexican Mafia & the Chicano Movement. 2010. 148p. pap. 14.95 *(978-1-4502-0447-7(3))* iUniverse, Inc.

Martin, Buzzy. Don't Shoot! I'm the Guitar Man. Black, Faith, ed. 2010. (ENG.). 224p. (gr. 12). 15.00 *(978-0-425-24005-2(3),* Berkley Trade) Penguin Group (USA) Inc.

CALIFORNIA STATE UNIVERSITY

De Graaf, Lawrence Brooks. The Fullerton Way: 50 Years of Memories at California State University, Fullerton. 2009. *(978-0-930046-26-2(9));* pap. *(978-0-930046-28-6(5))* California State Univ., San Bernardino, Robert V. Fullerton Art Museum.

Gerth, Donald R. The People's University: A History of the California State University. 2010. *(978-0-87772-435-3(0))* Univ. of California, Institute of Governmental Studies.

Monica, Masino. Instructional Television in Distance Learning: An Evaluation of an Introduction to Computer Course Given Via Television. 2011. 48p. pap. ***(978-3-639-33910-9(X))*** VDM Verlag Dr. Mueller e.K.

Williams, Gregory L. California State University, Dominguez Hills. 2010. (Campus History Ser.). (ENG., Illus.). 128p. pap. 21.99 *(978-0-7385-8005-0(8))* Arcadia Publishing.

CALIFORNIA TRAIL

Fender, Stephen. Plotting the Golden West: American Literature & the Rhetoric of the California Trail. 2010. (ENG., Illus.). 256p. pap. 27.99 *(978-0-521-13571-9(0))* Cambridge Univ. Pr.

CALIFS

see Caliphs

CALIGULA, EMPEROR OF ROME, 12-41

Adams, Geoff W. The Roman Emperor Gaius "Caligula" & His Hellenistic Aspirations. 2007. (ENG.). 308p. per. 25.95 *(978-1-59942-423-1(1),* Brown Walker Pr.) Universal Pubs.

Barber, Stephen & Reed, Jeremy. Caligula: Divine Carnage: Atrocities of the Roman Emperors. 2006. 153p. per. 14.95 *(978-0-9714578-1-2(6))* Solar Bks.

Lindsay, H., ed. Suetonius: Caligula. 2008. (Latin Texts Ser.). (LAT.). 240p. pap. 19.95 *(978-1-85399-375-6(1))* Bristol Classical Pr. GBR. Dist: International Publishers Marketing.

van Deman, Esther. The House of Caligula. 2009. pap. 20.08 *(978-1-60724-456-1(X))* Gorgias Pr., LLC.

Winterling, Aloys. Caligula: A Biography. Schneider, Deborah Lucas, tr. from GER. 2009. (Illus.). 240p. 34.95 *(978-0-520-24895-3(3))* Univ. of California Pr.

Yo, Caligula. (Memorias Coleccion). (SPA., Illus.). 120p. pap. 18.95 *(978-84-207-3822-2(0),* ANY220) Grupo Anaya, S.A. ESP. Dist: Continental Bk. Co., Inc.

CALIMERA

Maraspini, A. L. The study of an Italian Village. (ENG.). 270p. 210.00 ***(978-3-11-206991-2(9));*** 135.00 ***(978-3-11-117506-5(5))*** De Gruyter, Mouton DEU. Dist: de Gruyter, Walter GmbH & Co. KG.

CALIPHATE

see also Caliphs

Ali, Souad Tagelsir. A Religion, Not a State: Ali Abd Al-Raziq's Islamic Justification of Political Secularism. 2009. (Utah Series in Turkish & Islamic Stud Ser.). (ENG.). 180p. (gr. 13). pap. 25.00 *(978-0-87480-951-0(7))* Univ. of Utah Pr.

Ardic, Nurullah. Islam & the Politics of Secularism: The Caliphate & Middle Eastern Modernization in the Early 20th Century. 2012. (SOAS/Routledge Studies on the Middle East Ser.). (ENG., Illus.). 408p. (C). 145.00 *(978-0-415-67166-8(3))* Routledge.

El-Hibri, Tayeb. Parable & Politics in Early Islamic History: The Rashidun Caliphs. 2010. (ENG & MUL., Illus.). 488p. (gr. 17). 60.00 *(978-0-231-15082-8(2));* 512p. E-Book 47.99 *(978-0-231-52165-9(0))* Columbia Univ. Pr.

Faruqi, Imam Muhammad Masoom & Nizamani, Abdul Rahim. Maktubat Masoomiya: Excerpts from the Letters of Imam Muhammad Masoom Faruqi. 2010. 121p. pap. 17.90 *(978-1-4461-6473-0(X))* Lulu Enterprises Inc.

Hanne, Eric J. Putting the Caliph in His Place: Power, Authority, & the Late Abbasid Caliphate. 2007. (Illus.). 280p. (C). 54.50 *(978-0-8386-4113-2(X))* Fairleigh Dickinson Univ. Pr.

Hazleton, Lesley. After the Prophet: The Epic Story of the Shia-Sunni Split in Islam. 2010. (ENG., Illus.). 256p. pap. 16.00 *(978-0-385-52394-3(7),* Anchor) Knopf Doubleday Publishing Group.

Lappin, Yaakov. Virtual Caliphate: Exposing the Islamist State on the Internet. 2010. 212p. 26.95 *(978-1-59797-511-7(7))* Potomac Bks., Inc.

Marsham, Andrew. Rituals of Islamic Monarchy: Accession & Succession in the First Muslim Empire. 2009. (ENG., Illus.). 320p. (gr. 17). 120.00 *(978-0-7486-2512-3(7))* Edinburgh Univ. Pr. GBR. Dist: Columbia Univ. Pr.

Oliver-Dee, Sean. Caliphate Question: The British Government & Islamic Governance. 2009. (ENG.). 216p. 73.50 *(978-0-7391-3601-0(1))* Lexington Bks.

CALIPHS

see also Caliphate; Fatimites

Bennison, Amira K. The Great Caliphs: The Golden Age of the 'Abbasid Empire. (Illus.). 256p. 2010. pap. 22.00 *(978-0-300-16798-6(9))* 2009. (ENG., 30.00 *(978-0-300-15227-2(2))* Yale Univ. Pr.

Borrut, Antoine. Entre mémoire et Pouvoir: L'espace syrien sous les derniers Omeyyades et les premiers Abbassides (V. 72-193/692-809) 2010. (Islamic History & Civilization Ser.). (FRE., Illus.). 484p. *(978-90-04-18561-6(5))* BRILL.

Collins, Roger. Caliphs & Kings, 798-1033. 2012. (History of Spain Ser.). (ENG., Illus.). 328p. 74.95 ***(978-0-631-18184-2(9),*** Wiley-Blackwell) Wiley, John & Sons, Inc.

El-Hibri, Tayeb. Parable & Politics in Early Islamic History: The Rashidun Caliphs. 2010. (ENG & MUL., Illus.). 488p. (gr. 17). 60.00 *(978-0-231-15082-8(2));* 512p. E-Book 47.99 *(978-0-231-52165-9(0))* Columbia Univ. Pr.

Fierro, Maria Isabel. Abderraman III y el califato Omeya de Cordoba. 2011. (SPA.). 250p. pap. 45.95 *(978-84-96431-85-0(1))* Nerea Editorial ESP. Dist: Independent Pubs. Group.

Hanne, Eric J. Putting the Caliph in His Place: Power, Authority, & the Late Abbasid Caliphate. 2007. (Illus.). 280p. (C). 54.50 *(978-0-8386-4113-2(X))* Fairleigh Dickinson Univ. Pr.

Hoyland, Robert, tr. Theophilus of Edessa's Chronicle: And The Circulation of Historical Knowledge in Late Antiquity & Early Islam. 2011. (Liverpool University Press - Translated Texts for Historians Ser.). (ENG., Illus.). 368p. 95.00 *(978-1-84631-697-5(9))* Liverpool Univ. Pr. GBR. Dist: Chicago Distribution Ctr.

—Theophilus of Edessa's Chronicle: The Circulation of Historical Knowledge in Late Antiquity & Early Islam. 2011. (Liverpool University Press - Translated Texts for Historians Ser.). (ENG., Illus.). 224p. pap. 34.95 *(978-1-84631-698-2(7))* Liverpool Univ. Pr. GBR. Dist: Chicago Distribution Ctr.

Humphreys, R. Stephen. Mu'awiya Ibn Abi Sufyan: From Arabia to Empire. 2006. (Makers of the Muslim World Ser.). (ENG.). 160p. 40.00 *(978-1-85168-402-1(6))* Oneworld Pubns. GBR. Dist: National Bk. Network.

Keshk, Khaled. The Historians' Muʿawiya: The Depiction of Muʿawiya in the Early Islamic Sources. 2008. 204p. pap. *(978-3-639-09945-4(1))* VDM Verlag Dr. Mueller e.K.

Ockley, Simon. The History of the Saracens: Comprising. 2006. pap. 42.95 *(978-1-4286-3483-1(5))* Kessinger Publishing, LLC.

Robinson, Chase F. Abd Al-Malik. 2007. (Makers of the Muslim World Ser.). (ENG., Illus.). 160p. pap. 19.95 *(978-1-85168-507-3(3))* Oneworld Pubns. GBR. Dist: National Bk. Network.

Tholib, Udjang. The Reign of the 'Abbasid Caliph Al-Qadir Billah. 2009. 340p. pap. *(978-3-639-21748-3(9))* VDM Verlag Dr. Mueller e.K.

Tritton, A. S. Caliphs & their Non-Muslim Subjects: A Critical Study of the Covenant of 'Umar. 2007. (ENG., Illus.). 256p. (C). 175.00 *(978-0-415-44095-0(5))* Routledge.

CALISTHENICS

see also Gymnastics; Physical Education and Training

Lewis, Dio. The New Gymnastics for Men, Women & Children. 2006. 280p. per. 23.99 *(978-1-4255-2489-0(3))* MPublishing.

—A the New Gymnastics for Men, Women & Children: With. 2007. pap. 27.95 *(978-1-4304-5126-6(2))* Kessinger Publishing, LLC.

—The Weak Lungs & How to Make Them Strong or, Diseases Of. 2007. (ENG.). 364p. per. 31.95 *(978-1-4304-5048-1(7))* Kessinger Publishing, LLC.

Sears, Al. PACE: Rediscover Your Native Fitness. 2007. 143p. pap. 37.95 *(978-0-9794703-0-1(7))* Wellness Research & Consulting, Inc.

CALIXARENES

Asfari, M. -Z., et al, eds. Calixarenes 2001. 2010. (Illus.). 700p. pap. 277.00 *(978-90-481-5700-6(5)*, 9048157005) Springer.

Deska, M. & Sliwa, W. Covalently & Noncovalently Bound Assemblies of Calixarenes. 2011. (Chemistry Research & Applications Ser.). pap. 43.00 *(978-1-61761-780-5(6)*, Nova Novinka) Nova Science Pubs., Inc.

Sliwa, Wanda & Kozlowski, Cezary. Calixarenes & Resorcinarenes: Synthesis, Properties & Applications. 2009. (ENG., Illus.). 324p. 205.00 *(978-3-527-32263-3(9)*, Wiley-VCH) Wiley, John & Sons, Inc.

Surov, O. V., et al, eds. Calixarene Complexes with Solvent Molecules. 2010. (Chemistry Research & Applications Ser.). (Illus.). 63p. pap. 38.70 *(978-1-61568-755-7(X))* Nova Science Pubs., Inc.

Vicens, Jacques & Harrowfield, Jack, eds. Calixarenes in the Nanoworld. 2006. (ENG.). ix, 395p. 219.00 *(978-1-4020-5021-3(6)*, 1402050216) Springer.

—Calixarenes in the Nanoworld. 2010. (ENG.). ix, 395p. pap. 219.00 *(978-90-481-7258-0(6)*, 9048172586) Springer.

CALL CENTERS

Here are entered works on service units devoted to handling inbound and/or outbound telephone transactions with customers.

Askun Çelik, Duysal. Call Centers' Quality of Working Life. 2011. 136p. pap. ***(978-3-8443-8295-2(X)***, Lambert Academic Publishing.

Basi, J. K. Tina. Women, Identity & India's Call Centre Industry. 2012. (ENG., Illus.). 232p. (C). pap. 42.95 ***(978-0-415-62741-2(9))*** Routledge.

Basi, J. K. Tina. Women, Identity & India's Call Centre Industry: Close Calls & Hang Ups. 2009. (Routledge Research on Gender in Asia Ser.). (ENG., Illus.). 16p. 150.00 *(978-0-415-48228-8(3))* Routledge.

Berg, Josée G. M. L. Omarming van uw Bereikbaarheid. 2010. (DUT.). 116p. pap. 21.95 *(978-1-4116-6183-7(4))* Lulu Enterprises Inc.

Bergevin, Real, et al. Call Centers for Dummies. 2nd ed. 2010. (ENG., Illus.). 408p. pap. 24.99 *(978-0-470-67743-8(0)*, For Dummies) Wiley, John & Sons, Inc.

Best, Geoffrey A. 42 Rules for Outsourcing Your Call Center: Best Practices for Outsourcing Call Center Planning, Operations & Management. Lowell, Laura, ed. 2011. pap. 19.95 ***(978-1-60773-068-2(5)***, Super Star Pr.) Happy About.

Blokdijk, Gerard. Call Center 100 success Secrets. 2007. 172p. per. *(978-0-9804599-2-0(3))* Emereo Pty Ltd.

Blokdijk, Gerard & Menken, Ivanka. Delivering Unforgettable Customer Service: The Guide for Implementing Perfect Service in Your Organization. 2009. 144p. pap. *(978-1-921644-19-1(2))* Emereo Pty Ltd.

Brown, Judith A. Turn Calls into Customers: Maximize Customer Experience with Your Call Center. 2008. (Illus.). 116p. pap. 129.00 *(978-1-60146-190-2(9))* Opus Communications.

Connell, Julia & Burgess, John, eds. Developments in the Call Centre Industry: Analysis, Changes & Challenges. 2012. (Routledge Studies in Business Organizations & Networks Ser.). (ENG., Illus.). 208p. (C). pap. 42.95 ***(978-0-415-51148-3(8))*** Routledge.

De Carvalho, Luiz Augusto & Alves, Olavo. Telecom Management for Call Centers: A Practical Guide. 2011. 220p. 25.95 ***(978-1-4620-5683-5(0))***; pap. 15.95 ***(978-1-4620-5682-8(2))*** iUniverse, Inc.

Doellgast, Virginia Lee. Disintegrating Democracy at Work. 2012. (ENG., Illus.). 272p. 65.00 ***(978-0-8014-5047-1(0))*** Cornell Univ. Pr.

Economic & Security Concerns in Tourism & Commerce: H.R. 3232 & H.R. 1776: Hearing Before the Subcommittee on Commerce, Trade, & Consumer Protection of the Committee on Energy & Commerce, House of Representatives, One Hundred Tenth Congress, Second Session, September 11, 2008. 2010. (Illus.). vi, 181p. ***(978-0-16-088154-1(4)***, 552-070-42571-3) United States Government Printing Office.

Farrell, Dennis, et al. Operations & Management Principles for Contact Centres. Molefi, Kgosietsile Simon & Cant, Michael, eds. 2008. (ENG., Illus.). 448p. spiral bd. 62.00 *(978-0-7021-7704-0(0))* Juta Academic ZAF. Dist: Independent Pubs. Group.

Garber, Peter R. Learning Points. 2007. (Illus.). vii, 120p. pap. *(978-0-87425-388-7(8))* Human Resource Development Pr.

Green, Ken. Call Centers Technology & Techniques. 2006. pap. 8.95 *(978-1-4288-0569-9(9))* Cram101 Inc.

Green, Rue. Cisco Unified Customer Voice Portal: Building Unified Contact Centers. 2011. (Networking Technology: IP Communications Ser.). (ENG., Illus.). 600p. pap. 64.99 ***(978-1-58714-290-1(2))*** Cisco Pr.

Güngör, Hüseyin. Emotional Satisfaction of Customer Contacts. 2007. (UvA Proefschriften Ser.). pap. *(978-90-5629-466-3(0)*, Leiden Univ. Pr.) Amsterdam Univ. Pr.

Hart, Phil. Screamer on Line Two - Telephone Complaint Handling Made Very Simple. 2010. (Illus.). 108p. pap. *(978-1-907211-85-0(3))* Grosvenor Hse. Publishing Ltd.

Hechanova, Ma Regina M. 1-800-Philippines: Understanding & Managing the Filipino Call Center Worker. 2011. (Illus.). xiv, 124p. 28.00 ***(978-971-8610-59-6(6))*** Ateneo de Manila Univ. Pr. PHL. Dist: Univ. of Hawaii Pr.

Henken, Kirsten. Dynamic Contact Centers with Impatien: Customers & Retrials. 2008. 268p. pap. *(978-3-8364-9633-9(X))* VDM Verlag Dr. Mueller e.K.

Krafft, Christine. Standard American English & South African English in a Call Centre Environment. 2011. 148p. pap. ***(978-3-8433-8898-6(9))*** Lambert Academic Publishing.

Motseke, Keke. Call Centre Agents & Class Identity. 2010. 92p. pap. *(978-3-8383-5926-7(7))* Lambert Academic Publishing.

National Learning Corporation, creator. Call Center Representative. 2011. (Career Examination Passbooks Ser.). (Illus.). spiral bd. 34.95 ***(978-0-8373-4114-9(0))*** National Learning Corp.

Noronha, Ernesto & D'Cruz, Premilla. Employee Identity in Indian Call Centres: The Notion of Professionalism. 2009. (Response Bks.). 204p. (C). pap. 19.95 *(978-81-321-0079-9(4)*, B00799P) SAGE Pubns., Inc.

Patel, Reena. Working the Night Shift: Women in India's Call Center Industry. 2010. (ENG.). 208p. 60.00 *(978-0-8047-6913-6(3))*; (Illus.). pap. 21.95 *(978-0-8047-6914-3(1))* Stanford Univ. Pr.

Prahalad, C. K., et al. 24/7 Customer: Beyond Call Center Operations. 2010. (C). pap. 20.00 *(978-1-61674-004-7(3))*; pap. 20.00 *(978-1-61674-002-3(7))* Davidson, William Institute At The Univ. of Michigan, The.

Russell, Bob. Smiling down the Line: Info-Service Work in the Global Economy. 2009. (Studies in Comparative Political Economy & Public Policy Ser.). (Illus.). 352p. pap. *(978-1-4426-0981-5(8))*; (ENG., *(978-1-4426-3994-2(6))* Univ. of Toronto Pr.

Russell, Bob & Thite, Mohan, eds. The Next Available Operator: Managing Human Resources in Indian Business Process Outsourcing Industry. 2009. (Illus.). 340p. (C). pap. 29.95 *(978-81-7829-932-7(1)*, B99327P) SAGE Pubns., Inc.

Wilson, John P. The Call Centre Training Handbook: A Complete Guide to Learning & Development in Contact Centres. 2009. (ENG., Illus.). 336p. instr.'s hndbk. ed. 49.95 *(978-0-7494-5088-5(6))* Kogan Page, Ltd. GBR. Dist: Ingram Pub. Services.

CALL GIRLS

see Prostitutes

CALL OPTIONS

see Options (Finance)

CALLAGHAN, JAMES, 1912-2005

Conroy, Harry. Callaghan. 2006. (British Prime Ministers of the 20th Century Ser.). (ENG., Illus.). 169p. pap. 16.95 *(978-1-904950-70-7(1))* Haus Publishing GBR. Dist: Consortium Bk. Sales & Distribution.

Deveney, Paul J. Callaghan's Journey to Downing Street. 2010. (ENG.). 240p. 89.00 *(978-0-230-57958-3(2))* Palgrave Macmillan.

CALLAGHAN, MORLEY, 1903-1990

Callaghan, Morley. Essays, Reviews, Meditations & Talks, 1928-1990. 2008. (ENG.). 332p. 34.95 *(978-1-55096-099-0(7))* Exile Editions, Ltd. CAN. Dist: Independent Pubs. Group.

—That Summer in Paris. 2007. (Exile Classics Ser.). (ENG., Illus.). 232p. pap. 16.95 *(978-1-55096-688-6(X))* Exile Editions, Ltd. CAN. Dist: Independent Pubs. Group.

CALLAS, MARIA, 1923-1977

Buraya, Luis Carlos. Maria Callas. 2007. (Mujeres en la historia Ser.). (ENG., Illus.). 192p. 8.95 *(978-84-9764-734-2(3))* Edimat Libros, S. A. ESP. Dist: Independent Pubs. Group.

Callas, Maria. The Young Maria Callas. Tosi, Bruno, ed. 2010. (Essay Ser.). (ENG., Illus.). 208p. 23.00 *(978-1-55071-327-5(2))* Guernica Editions, Inc. CAN. Dist: Univ. of Toronto Pr.

edel Entertainment. Maria Callas: La Diva - La Musica. 2008. (ITA, GER & ENG., Illus.). 120p. (Orig.). 60.00 *(978-3-940004-36-9(7)*, Earbooks) edel classics GmbH DEU. Dist: AtlasBooks Distribution.

Heritage, Anne, tr. Callas: Images of a Legend. 2007. (Illus.). 261p. 49.95 *(978-3-8296-0314-0(2))* Schirmer/Mosel Verlag GmbH DEU. Dist: Prestel Publishing.

Jarman-Ivens, Freya. Queer Voices: Technologies, Vocalities, & the Musical Flaw. 2011. (Critical Studies in Gender, Sexuality, & Culture Ser.). (ENG., Illus.). 208p. 80.00 *(978-0-230-10590-4(4))* Palgrave Macmillan.

Levine, Robert. Maria Callas Pack: A Musical Biography. 2010. (ENG., Illus.). 240p. pap. 24.99 incl. audio compact disk *(978-1-57467-183-4(9)*, 1574671839, Amadeus Press) Leonard, Hal Corp.

Morbio, Vittoria Crespi. Maria Callas: The Scala Years. 2008. (ENG., Illus.). 160p. 70.00 *(978-88-422-1560-8(0))* Allemandi, Umberto & Co. GBR. Dist: Antique Collectors' Club.

Sutherland. Maria Callas. (Illus.). xi, 292p. 35.00 *(978-0-09-478790-2(5))* Random Hse. GBR. Dist: Trafalgar Square Publishing.

CALLIGRAPHERS

Holliday, Peter. Edward Johnston: Master Calligrapher. 2007. (Illus.). 412p. 49.95 *(978-1-58456-198-9(X))* Oak Knoll Pr.

Pronenko, L. I. Russian Calligraphy: One Teacher, 222 Students. 2007. *(978-1-934227-04-6(8))*; pap. *(978-1-934227-05-3(6))* Operina LLC.

Shui, Laiyou. Mi Fu Shu Fa Shi Liao Ji. 2009. (CHI., Illus.). *(978-7-80725-192-7(1))* Shanghai Calligraphy and Painting Publishing Hse.

Zoby, Brenda Casey, compiled by. The Uncommon Numbers Trilogy: Source Books for Calligraphers & Graphic Artists. 2010. (ENG., Illus.). 64p. pap. 39.95 *(978-0-9651382-4-6(0))* PenUltimates.

CALLIGRAPHIC PAINTINGS

see Letter-Pictures

CALLIGRAPHY

see also Islamic Calligraphy

Balchin, Judy. Celtic Alphabets. 2010. (ENG., Illus.). 176p. spiral bd. 21.95 *(978-1-84448-457-7(2))* Search Pr., Ltd. GBR. Dist: Independent Pubs. Group.

Baldwin, Karol. Uncial Calligraphy Workbook & How to Uncial Calligraphy DVD. 2006. pap. 24.00 incl. DVD *(978-1-884107-04-7(4))* Baldwin, Karol Lee.

Barker, Nicolas. The Glory of the Art of Writing: The Complete Calligraphic Work of Francesco Alunno of Ferrara, 2 vols. 2009. (Illus.). 141p. *(978-0-9745168-3-7(X))* Cotsen Occasional Pr.

Bennett, Jim. Calligraphy for Dummies. 2007. (ENG., Illus.). 340p. per. 19.99 *(978-0-470-11771-2(0)*, For Dummies) Wiley, John & Sons, Inc.

Booth, Ruth. Celebration Calligraphy: Complete Instructions & Templates for Special-Occasion Alphabets, Borders, & Motifs. 2008. (ENG., Illus.). 128p. pap. 21.99 *(978-0-7641-3948-2(7))* Barron's Educational Series, Inc.

Calderhead, Christopher. Calligraphy Studio: The Ultimate Introduction to the Art of Hand Lettering. 2012. (ENG., Illus.). 208p. pap. 22.95 *(978-1-4027-3369-7(0))* Sterling Publishing Co., Inc.

Calderhead, Christopher & Cohen, Holly, eds. The World Encyclopedia of Calligraphy: The Ultimate Compendium on the Art of Fine Writing-History, Craft, Technique. 2011. (ENG., Illus.). 320p. 35.00 *(978-1-4027-3368-0(2))* Sterling Publishing Co., Inc.

Callery, Emma. The Calligraphy Handbook: Simple Techniques & Step-by-Step Projects. 2007. (Artist's Bibles Ser.). (ENG., Illus.). 192p. spiral bd. 14.99 *(978-0-7858-2300-1(X)*, 078582300X, Chartwell) Book Sales, Inc.

Callery, Emma & Grebenstein, Maryanne. Calligraphy Bible: A Complete Guide to More Than 100 Essential Projects & Techniques. 2012. (ENG., Illus.). 256p. pap. 24.99 ***(978-0-8230-9934-4(2))*** Watson-Guptill Pubns., Inc.

Cusick, Rick. What Our Lettering Needs: The Contribution of Hermann Zapf to Calligraphy & Type Design at Hallmark Cards. 2011. (ENG., Illus.). 136p. pap. 24.95 ***(978-1-933360-55-3(0)***, RIT Cary Graphic Arts Pr.) Rochester Institute of Technology, Cary Graphic Arts Pr.

Davis, Courtney, et al. Compendium of Celtic Crafts. 2009. (ENG., Illus.). 192p. pap. 19.95 *(978-1-84448-355-6(X))* Search Pr., Ltd. GBR. Dist: Independent Pubs. Group.

Delamotte, F. Examples of Modern Alphabets Plain & Ornamental. 2007. *(978-1-934227-16-9(1))*; pap. *(978-1-934227-17-6(X))* Operina LLC.

Diagram Group Staff. Lettering & Calligraphy Workbook. 2006. (ENG., Illus.). 288p. per. 12.95 *(978-1-4027-4101-2(4))* Sterling Publishing Co., Inc.

Elliot, Sanje. How to Write Tibetan Calligraphy: The Alphabet & Beyond. 2012. (ENG.). 96p. pap. 14.95 ***(978-0-86171-699-9(X))*** Wisdom Pubns.

Engelbrecht, Lisa. Modern Calligraphy & Hand Lettering: A Mark-Making Workbook for Crafters, Cardmakers, & Journal Artists. 2010. (ENG., Illus.). 160p. pap. 17.99 *(978-1-59253-644-3(1)*, 1592536441) Quayside.

—Modern Mark Making: From Classic Calligraphy to Hip Hand-Lettering. 2008. (ENG., Illus.). 160p. 24.99 *(978-1-59253-419-7(8)*, 1592534198, Quarry Books) Quayside.

Ferraro, Cari. Calligraphy & Illumination: Learn the Art of Beautiful Writing. 2007. (How to Draw & Paint Ser.). (ENG., Illus.). 32p. pap. 8.95 *(978-1-60058-047-5(5)*, 1600580475) Foster, Walter Publishing, Inc.

Ferraro, Cari, et al. The Art of Calligraphy & Lettering: Master techniques for traditional & contemporary handwritten Fonts. 2011. (Collector's Ser.). (ENG., Illus.). 144p. pap. 19.95 *(978-1-60058-200-4(1)*, 1600582001) Foster, Walter Publishing, Inc.

Fox, Tanya, ed. CardMaker's Hand-Lettering Workbook. 2011. (ENG., Illus.). 64p. pap. 8.95 ***(978-1-59635-378-7(3)***, Annie's Attic, LLC) Annie's Publishing, LLC.

Gauthier, Jeaneen. Calligraphy: Master Basic Skills & Techniques Easily Through Step-by-Step Instruction. 2010. (101 Ser.). (ENG., Illus.). 240p. spiral bd. 24.99 *(978-1-58923-503-8(7)*, 1589235037) Quayside.

Gibbs, Jon. Caligrafia. (SPA.). 240p. *(978-84-7927-360-6(7))* Robinbk., Ediciones S.L. ESP. Dist: Lectorum Pubns., Inc.

Gourdie, Tom & A & C Black Publishers Ltd Staff. Calligraphy for Beginners. 2008. (ENG., Illus.). 64p. pap. 12.95 *(978-0-7136-6715-8(X))* A & C Black GBR. Dist: Macmillan.

Graham-Flynn, Fiona. The Simple Art of Celtic Calligraphy. 2008. (ENG., Illus.). 128p. pap. 19.95 *(978-1-906094-91-1(8))* CICO Bks. GBR. Dist: Ryland Peters & Small.

Graham-Flynn, Fiona, et al. The Complete Guide to Calligraphy: Master Scripts of the West & East, Step-by-Step with 45 Projects. Cleminson, Ralph, ed. 2006. (ENG., Illus.). 224p. spiral bd. 35.00 *(978-1-55407-179-1(8))* Firefly Bks., Ltd.

Grebenstein, Maryanne & Grebenstein, Mayanne. Calligraphy: A Course in Hand Lettering. 2006. (ENG., Illus.). 144p. spiral bd. 19.95 *(978-0-8230-0553-6(4))* Watson-Guptill Pubns., Inc.

Hayes, James F. Notes on Calligraphy. 2011. 12p. pap. 35.95 ***(978-1-258-03150-3(7))*** Literary Licensing, LLC.

Hazeldine, Gillian. Contemporary Calligraphy: How to Use Formal Scripts Today. 2011. (Illus.). 184p. 38.95 ***(978-0-7090-8745-8(4))*** Hale, Robert Ltd. GBR. Dist: Independent Pubs. Group.

Horrigan, Terry. Whispers. 2009. 8p. pap. 155.00 *(978-0-9762829-3-8(3))* Protean Pr.

Horrigan, Terry, creator. Aeolian Island. 2007. 178.00 *(978-0-9762829-1-4(7))* Protean Pr.

Kespersaks, Veiko. Calligraphy in 24 Hours. 2011. (ENG.). 160p. pap. 21.99 *(978-0-7641-4506-3(1))* Barron's Educational Series, Inc.

Mao Mao Packaging. 2007. 45.00 *(978-0-06-114997-9(7)*, Collins Design) HarperCollins Pubs.

Mehigan, Janet. Mastering the Art of Calligraphy. 2012. (ENG., Illus.). 264p. 19.99 *(978-0-7548-2178-6(1))* Anness Publishing GBR. Dist: National Bk. Network.

Mehigan, Janet & Noble, Mary. Beginner's Guide to Calligraphy. 96p. 9.99 *(978-0-7858-1934-9(7))* Book Sales, Inc.

Meulman, Niels & Euwens, Adam. Calligraffiti: The Graphic Art of Niels 'Shoe' Meulman. 2010. (Illus.). 144p. 29.95 *(978-3-937946-21-4(7))* From Here To Fame GmbH DEU. Dist: SCB Distributors.

Newton, Lee. The Classic Art of Calligraphy. 2008. (ENG.). 88p. pap. 8.95 *(978-0-7624-3191-5(1))* Perseus Bks. Group.

Noble, Mary & Mehigan, Janet. Calligraphy Alphabets for Beginners: The Easy Way to Learn Lettering & Illumination Techniques. 2008. (ENG., Illus.). 256p. 21.99 *(978-0-7641-6115-5(6))* Barron's Educational Series, Inc.

Parramon's Editorial Team Staff. Calligraphy: An Indispensable Manual for Artists & Hobbyists. 2010. (All about Techniques Ser.). (ENG., Illus.). 144p. 29.99 *(978-0-7641-6388-3(4))* Barron's Educational Series, Inc.

Pronenko, L. I. Russian Calligraphy: One Teacher, 222 Students. 2007. *(978-1-934227-04-6(8))*; pap. *(978-1-934227-05-3(6))* Operina LLC.

Ravenal, John B., et al. Xu Bing: Tobacco Project, Duke/Shanghai/Virginia, 1999-2011. Tomii, Reiko, ed. 2011. (ENG., Illus.). 144p. (C). (gr. 13-17). pap. 35.00 *(978-0-917046-96-4(X))* Univ. Pr. of Virginia.

Sassoon, Rosemary. Lettering - From Formal to Informal: A Journey with Pen & Brush. 2010. (ENG., Illus.). 112p. pap. 19.95 *(978-1-4081-1267-0(1))* A & C Black GBR. Dist: Macmillan.

Schmitz, Barbara. From Lahore: Essays on Painting & Calligraphy. 2010. 160p. 65.00 *(978-81-85026-97-8(1))* Marg Pubns. IND. Dist: National Bk. Network.

Shepherd, Margaret. Learn World Calligraphy: Discover African, Arabic, Chinese, Ethiopic, Greek, Hebrew, Indian, Japanese, Korean, Mongolian, Russian, Thai, Tibetan Calligraphy, & Beyond. 2011. (ENG., Illus.). 192p. pap. 24.99 *(978-0-8230-3346-1(5))* Watson-Guptill Pubns., Inc.

Sidaway, Ian, et al. A Practical Masterclass & Manual of Drawing & Pastels, Pencil Skills, Penmanship & Calligraphy. 2010. (ENG., Illus.). 512p. pap. 24.99 *(978-1-84476-927-8(5))* Anness Publishing GBR. Dist: National Bk. Network.

Sullivan, Maureen. Start Calligraphy: All the Techniques & Tips You Need to Get You Started. 2011. (Illus.). 96p. pap. 13.95 *(978-1-84448-638-0(9))* Search Pr., Ltd. GBR. Dist: Independent Pubs. Group.

Taylor, Peter E. Calligraphy for Greeting Cards & Scrapbooking. 2012. (ENG., Illus.). 176p. pap. 19.95 ***(978-1-86108-882-6(5))*** Guild of Master Craftsman Pubns., Ltd. GBR. Dist: Sterling Publishing Co., Inc.

Vaughan, Nel. Calligraphy. (Mini Lifestyle Kits Ser.). (ENG., Illus.). 32p. *(978-1-84510-597-6(4))* Top That! Publishing PLC.

Weller, Alan. Photoshop Brushes & Creative Tools: Calligraphic & Abstract Designs. 2010. (Electronic Clip Art Photoshop Brushes Ser.). (ENG.). 48p. pap. 19.95 *(978-0-486-99101-6(6))* Dover Pubns., Inc.

Weller, Alan & Clip Art Staff. Calligraphic Vector Motifs. 2012. (Dover Electronic Clip Art Ser.). (ENG., Illus.). 48p. pap. 19.95 ***(978-0-486-99201-3(2))*** Dover Pubns., Inc.

Wilson, Diana Hardy. Encyclopedia of Calligraphy Techniques. 2012. (ENG., Illus.). 192p. pap. 19.95 ***(978-1-84448-810-0(1))*** Search Pr., Ltd. GBR. Dist: Independent Pubs. Group.

Wright, Elaine Julia. Muraqqa' Imperial Mughal Albums from the Chester Beatty Library. 2008. (Illus.). 528p. 79.95 *(978-0-88397-154-3(2))* Art Services International.

Wright, Elaine Julia, et al. Muraqqa' Imperial Mughal Albums from the Chester Beatty Library, Dublin. 2008. (Illus.). xxvii, 500p. pap. *(978-0-88397-153-6(4))* Art Services International.

Zoby, Brenda Casey, ed. A Passion for the Pen: The Art of Georgina Artigas. 2006. (ENG., Illus.). 64p. pap. 10.95 *(978-0-9651382-2-2(4))* PenUltimates.

Zoby, Brenda Casey, ed. & compiled by. Uncommon Numbers II: A Source Book for Calligraphers & Graphic Artists. 2010. (ENG., Illus.). 64p. pap. 14.95 *(978-0-9651382-3-9(2))* PenUltimates.

CALLIGRAPHY—COPY-BOOKS

see Copybooks

CALLIGRAPHY, ARABIC

Boutros, Mourad. Talking about Arabic. 2009. (ENG., Illus.). 80p. pap. 16.95 *(978-0-9795546-6-7(7))* Batty, Mark Pub., LLC.

Fraser, Marcus & Kwiatkowski, Will. Ink & Gold: Islamic Calligraphy. 2006. (Sam Fogg Ser.). (ENG., Illus.). 96p. pap. 40.00 *(978-0-9549014-8-6(7))* Sam, Fogg Rare Books GBR. Dist: Univ. of Washington Pr.

Mahfouz, Tarek. Learn Arabic Calligraphy. 2010. 160p. pap. 49.50 *(978-0-557-07371-9(5))* Lulu Enterprises Inc.

Massoudy, Hassan. The Calligrapher's Garden. 2010. (ARA & ENG., Illus.). 160p. 24.95 *(978-0-86356-619-6(7))* Saqi Bks. GBR. Dist: Consortium Bk. Sales & Distribution.

Zoghbi, Pascal & Zaza, Con M. Arabic Graffiti. 2nd ed. 2011. (ENG., Illus.). 200p. 34.95 *(978-3-937946-26-9(8))* From Here To Fame GmbH DEU. Dist: SCB Distributors.

CALLIGRAPHY, CHINESE

Chang, Willow Weilan Hai, et al. The Last Emperor's Collection: Painting & Calligraphy from Liaoning. Barrett, J. May Lee, ed. 2008. lib. bdg. *(978-0-9774054-3-5(5))* China Institute Gallery, China Institute in America.

Chen, Tingyou. Chinese Calligraphy. 3rd ed. 2011. (Introductions to Chinese Culture Ser.). (CHI & ENG., Illus.). 134p. pap. 19.99 *(978-0-521-18645-2(5))* Cambridge Univ. Pr.

C

Driscoll, Lucy & Toda, Kenji. Chinese Calligraphy. 2007. 84p. per. 17.95 *(978-1-4325-5917-5(6))* Kessinger Publishing, LLC.

Ellsworth, Robert H. Later Chinese Painting & Calligraphy, 1800-1950, 3 vols., Set. (Illus.). 295.00 *(978-0-394-55463-1(9))* Art Media Resources, Inc.

Fan, Di'an. Le Pavillon des Orchidées: L'art de L'écriture en Chine. 2009. (FRE., Illus.). 238p. *(978-90-6153-890-5(4)); (978-90-6153-889-9(0))* Mercatorfonds N. V.

Fong, Wen C., et al. Chinese Calligraphy. 2008. (Culture & Civilization of China Ser.). (ENG., Illus.). 520p. 75.00 *(978-0-300-12107-0(5))* Yale Univ. Pr.

Gill, John & Tidwell, Susan, eds. After Many Autumns: A Collection of Chinese Buddhist Literature. Balcom, John, tr. from CHI. 2011. (CHI & ENG.). 383p. pap. 15.95 *(978-1-932293-49-4(3))* Buddha's Light Publishing.

Greenbaum, Jamie. Chen Jiru (1558-1639) The Development & Subsequent Uses of Literary Personae. 2007. (Sinica Leidensia Ser.). 350p. *(978-90-04-16358-4(1))* BRILL.

Ho, Yat-Ming Cathy. The Chinese Calligraphy Bible: The Essential Illustrated Guide to over 300 Beautiful Characters. 2007. (ENG., Illus.). 256p. 24.99 *(978-0-7641-5922-0(4))* Barron's Educational Series, Inc.

Kexi, Zhou & Yawtsong, Lee. The Art of Chinese Calligraphy. 2010. (ENG., Illus.). 224p. pap. 26.95 *(978-1-60220-117-0(X))* BetterLink Pr., Inc.

Kuo, Jason C. Perspectives on Connoisseurship of Chinese Painting. 2008. 236p. 34.00 *(978-0-9800814-7-3(5))* New Academia Publishing, LLC.

Lei, Qu Lei. The Complete Guide to Chinese Calligraphy: Discover the Five Major Scripts to Create Classic Characters & Beautiful Projects. 2007. (ENG., Illus.). 144p. pap. *(978-1-904991-87-8(4))* Ryland Peters & Small.

Li, Wendan. Chinese Writing & Calligraphy. 2010. (C). pap. 25.00 *(978-0-8248-3364-0(3))* Univ. of Hawaii Pr.

Little, Stephen. New Songs on Ancient Tunes: 19th-20th Century Chinese Paintings & Calligraphy from the Richard Fabian Collection. Barrett, J. May Lee, ed. 2007. (ENG., Illus.). 536p. 75.00 *(978-0-937426-79-1(2))* Honolulu Academy of the Arts.

Little, Stephen, et al. New Songs on Ancient Tunes: 19th-20th Century Chinese Paintings & Calligraphy from the Richard Fabian Collection. 2007. pap. *(978-0-937426-80-7(6))* Honolulu Academy of the Arts.

Liu, Shi-Yee & Hearn, Maxwell K. Straddling East & West: Lin Yutang, a Modern Literatus: The Lin Yutang Family Collection of Chinese Painting & Calligraphy. 2007. 24.95 *(978-1-58839-270-1(8))* Metropolitan Museum of Art, The.

Liu, Yang. The Poetic Mandarin: Chinese Calligraphy from the James Hayes Collection.Tr. of Huan hai mo yun: Zhan Mu Si Cang. (Illus.). 144p. 40.00 *(978-0-7347-6380-8(8))* Art Media Resources, Inc.

McCausland, Shane. Zhao Mengfu: Calligraphy & Painting for Khubilai's China. 2011. (ENG., Illus.). 448p. (gr. 17). 55.00 *(978-988-8028-57-3(X))* Hong Kong Univ. Pr. HKG. Dist: Columbia Univ. Pr.

Meier, Scott & Meier, Oliver. Playful Letters: the Fun of Calligraphy. 2007. 49p. pap. 25.25 *(978-1-4303-1141-6(X))* Lulu Enterprises Inc.

O, Se-Ch'ang. Kunmuk, 5 vols. 2009. (KOR., Illus.). *(978-89-7986-797-8(2)); (978-89-7986-798-5(0))* Sungkyunkwan Univ.Pr. (Spotlight Poets).

Peiqi, Xie. The Dao of Writing: Chinese Calligraphy. Nugent-Head, Andrew, tr. 44p. pap. 12.00 *(978-1-888179-53-8(8))* Assn. for Traditional Studies.

Tobing, Anne Lumban. Schriftkunst in Rot und Weiss: Kunstlersiegel der Ming- und Ch'ing-Zeit, unter besonderer Berucksichtigung der Siegel des Chao Chih-ch'ien (1829-1884) 2010. (Studien zur Ostasiatischen Schriftkunst Ser.). (GER., Illus.). 216p. (C). pap. 90.00 *(978-3-515-08376-8(6))* Steiner, Franz Verlag Wiesbaden GmbH DEU. Dist: Brown, David Bk. Co., The.

Traités Chinois de Peinture et de Calligraphie. 2010. (FRE., Illus.). 1240p. (C). pap. 98.00 ***(978-2-252-03574-0(9))*** Klincksieck, Editions FRA. Dist: ISD.

Wen, Gonglie. Wei Jin Nan Bei Chao Shu Fa Mei Xue Yan Jiu: WeiJinnanbeichao Shufameixue Yanjiu. 2009. (CHI., Illus.). *(978-7-5633-9183-7(5))* Guangxi Teachers Univ. Pr.

Wen wu chu ban she Staff & Xi'an bei lin bo wu guan Staff, contrib. by. Di Qi Jie Zhongguo Shu Fa Shi Lun Guo Ji Yan Tao Hui Lun Wen Ji. 2009. (CHI., Illus.). *(978-7-5010-2852-8(4))* Cultural Relics Publishing Hse.

Wile, Douglas, tr. & compiled by. Zheng Manqing's Uncollected Writings on Taijiquan, Qigong, & Health, with New Biographical Notes. 2007. (ENG.). 140p. pap. *(978-0-912059-05-1(2))* Sweet Ch'I Pr.

Wong, Chung Kin & Mui, King Chau. Shu Fa Chu Yu: Four Specimens of Chinese Calligraphy. 2011. 76p. 36.95 ***(978-1-258-03779-6(3))*** Literary Licensing, LLC.

Yu, Jianhua & Yu, Jin. Dan Qing Yi Hen Mi Zu Zhen. 2009. (Illus.). 328p. *(978-7-80730-913-0(X))* Xuelin Publishing Hse.

Yu, Le. Zhongguo Shu Fa. 2008. (CHI., Illus.). 148p. *(978-7-80170-733-8(8))* Contemporary China Publishing Hse.

Yuan, Yi & Mingxiang, Xiong. The Beginner's Guide to Chinese Calligraphy: An Introduction to Kaishu. Yajun, Jiang & Xiang, Chen, trs. 2010. (ENG., Illus.). 80p. pap. 12.95 *(978-1-60220-113-2(7))* BetterLink Pr., Inc.

Zhou, Kexi. Chinese Calligraphy. 2010. (Discovering China Ser.). (ENG., Illus.). 120p. 14.95 *(978-1-60652-154-0(3))* Reader's Digest Assn., Inc., The.

Zuzao, Lin, et al, eds. History & Cultural Heritage of Chinese Calligraphy, Printing, & Library Work. 2010. (IFLA Publications). (ENG., Illus.). 251p. *(978-3-598-22046-3(4))* Saur, K. G. Verlag GmbH & Co.

CALLIGRAPHY, ISLAMIC

see Islamic Calligraphy

CALLIGRAPHY, JAPANESE

Heinrich, Amy V., ed. Seasons of Sacred Celebration: Flowers & Poetry from an Imperial Convent. 2006. (ENG., Illus.). 114p. per. 19.95 *(978-1-891640-35-3(6))* Floating World Editions.

Nagoya, Akira. Nihon Shodoshi: Ketteiban. 2009. (JPN., Illus.). xvi, 190p. *(978-4-87586-166-9(4))* Geijutsu Shinbun-Sha.

Takesaki, Kunii. An Introduction to Japanese Kanji Calligraphy. 2007. (Illus.). 128p. per. 24.95 *(978-4-88024-335-1(3))* Archipelago Pr IDN. Dist: Tuttle Publishing.

Takezaki, Kunii & Godin, Bob. An Introduction to Japanese Kanji Calligraphy. 2008. (ENG., Illus.). 128p. per. 24.95 *(978-4-8053-0925-4(3))* Tuttle Publishing.

Van Ghelue, Nadja. The Heart Sutra in Calligraphy: A Visual Appreciation of the Perfection of Wisdom. 2008. (CHI & ENG., Illus.). 120p. pap. 19.95 *(978-1-933330-79-2(1))* Stone Bridge Pr.

CALLIMACHUS

Acosta-Hughes, Benjamin & Stephens, Susan A. Callimachus in Context: From Plato to the Augustan Poets. 2012. (ENG., Illus.). 344p. 99.00 *(978-1-107-00857-1(3))* Cambridge Univ. Pr.

Acosta-Hughes, Benjamin, et al. Brill's Companion to Callimachus. 2010. 450p. *(978-90-04-15673-9(9))* BRILL.

Bing, Peter. The Well-Read Muse: Present & Past in Callimachus & the Hellenistic Poets. 2008. (ENG.). 163p. (C). 35.00 *(978-0-9799713-0-3(6))* Michigan Classical Pr.

Blum, Rudolf. Kallimachos: The Alexandrian Library & the Origins of Bibliography. Wellisch, Hans H., tr. from GER. 2011. (Wisconsin Studies in Classics Ser.). 288p. pap. 35.00 *(978-0-299-13174-6(2))* Univ. of Wisconsin Pr.

Callimachus & Durbec, Yannick. Fragments Poétiques: Origines, Iambes, Hécalè, Fragments de Poèmes épiques et élégiaques, Fragments de Place Incertaine. 2006. (FRE & GEC.). 310p. (C). pap. 50.00 ***(978-2-251-74204-5(2))*** Societe d'edition Les Belles lettres FRA. Dist: ISD.

Epaphroditus. The Grammarian Epaphroditus: Testimonia & Fragments. (Illus.). 454p. pap. 61.95 *(978-3-03911-450-4(6))* Lang, Peter CHE. Dist: Lang, Peter Publishing, Inc.

Slavkova Petrovic, Ivana. Von den Toren des Hades zu den Hallen des Olymp. Artemiskult bei Theokrit und Kallimachos. 2006. 256p. *(978-90-04-15154-3(0))* BRILL.

CALLING

see Vocation

CALLISTHENICS

see Calisthenics

CALLS (FINANCE)

see Options (Finance)

CALLUS

Mansour, Ahmed. Genetic Inheritance of Callus Induction in Plants. 2008. 100p. pap. *(978-3-639-06362-2(7))* VDM Verlag Dr. Mueller e.K.

CALOOSAHATCHEE RIVER

McCarthy, Kevin M. Caloosahatchee River Guidebook. 2012. (ENG.). 256p. pap. 14.95 ***(978-1-56164-507-7(9))*** Pineapple Pr., Inc.

Williams, Amy Bennett. Along the Caloosahatchee River. 2011. (Images of America Ser.). (Illus.). 128p. pap. 21.99 ***(978-0-7385-8747-9(8))*** Arcadia Publishing.

CALORIE CONTENT OF FOOD

see Food—Caloric Content

CALORIMETERS

Höhne, Ganther, et al. Differential Scanning Calorimetry. 2nd ed. 2010. (ENG., Illus.). xii, 298p. pap. 249.00 *(978-3-642-05593-5(1),* 3642055931) Springer.

CALORIMETERS AND CALORIMETRY

see Calorimeters; Calorimetry

CALORIMETRY

Auroux, Aline, ed. Calorimetry & Thermal Methods in Catalysis. 2010. (Springer Series in Materials Science Ser.). (Illus.). 300p. 189.00 *(978-3-642-11953-8(0),* 3642119530) Springer.

Brown, Michael E. & Gallagher, Patrick K. Handbook of Thermal Analysis & Calorimetry: Recent Advances, Techniques & Applications. 2007. (Handbook of Thermal Analysis & Calorimetry Ser.: 5). (ENG., Illus.). 780p. 320.00 *(978-0-444-53123-0(8),* Elsevier Science) Elsevier Science & Technology Bks.

Enss, Christian, ed. Cryogenic Particle Detection. 2010. (Topics in Applied Physics Ser.). (Illus.). xvi, 507p. pap. 349.00 *(978-3-642-05758-8(6),* 3642057586) Springer.

Gaisford, Simon & O'Neill, Michael A. A. Pharmaceutical Isothermal Calorimetry. 2006. (ENG., Illus.). 363p. 230.00 *(978-0-8493-3155-8(2))* CRC Pr. LLC.

Höhne, Ganther, et al. Differential Scanning Calorimetry. 2nd ed. 2010. (ENG., Illus.). xii, 298p. pap. 249.00 *(978-3-642-05593-5(1),* 3642055931) Springer.

Kaletunç, Gönül, ed. Calorimetry in Food Processing: Analysis & Design of Food Systems. 2009. (Institute of Food Technologists Ser.). (ENG., Illus.). 412p. 219.95 *(978-0-8138-1483-4(9),* Wiley-Blackwell) Wiley, John & Sons, Inc.

Kraftmakher, Yaakov. Modulation Calorimetry: Theory & Applications. 2010. (ENG., Illus.). xii, 283p. pap. 195.00 *(978-3-642-05922-3(8),* 3642059228) Springer.

Lörinczy, Dénes, ed. The Nature of Biological Systems as Revealed by Thermal Methods. 2010. (Hot Topics in Thermal Analysis & Calorimetry Ser.). (Illus.). ix, 353p. pap. 289.00 *(978-90-481-6616-9(0),* 9048166160) Springer.

Magill, Stephen R. & Yoshida, Rik, eds. Calorimetry in High Energy Physics: XII International Conference, Chicago, Illinois, 5-9 June 2006. 2006. (AIP Conference Proceedings Ser.). (Illus.). 616p. 229.00 *(978-0-7354-0364-2(3))* American Institute of Physics.

McLean, J. A. & Tobin, G. Animal & Human Calorimetry. 2007. (Illus.). 356p. pap. 74.00 *(978-0-521-04885-9(0))* Cambridge Univ. Pr.

Parrish, W. R. & Lewis, E. A. Handbook of Calorimetry. Date not set. *(978-0-8247-9529-0(6))* Dekker, Marcel Inc.

Reading, Mike & Hourston, Douglas J., eds. Modulated Temperature Differential Scanning Calorimetry: Theoretical & Practical Applications in Polymer Characterisation. 2010. (Hot Topics in Thermal Analysis & Calorimetry Ser.). xiii, 329p. pap. 249.00 *(978-90-481-6952-8(6),* 9048169526) Springer.

Zielenkiewicz, W. & Margas, E. Theory of Calorimetry. 2010. (Hot Topics in Thermal Analysis & Calorimetry Ser.). (Illus.). 200p. pap. 269.00 *(978-90-481-6092-1(8),* 9048160928) Springer.

CALOTYPE

Taylor, Roger. Impressed by Light: British Photographs from Paper Negatives, 1840-1860. 2007. (ENG., Illus.). 452p. 75.00 *(978-0-300-12405-7(8))* Yale Univ. Pr.

Taylor, Roger & Schaaf, Larry J. Impressed by Light: British Photographs from Paper Negatives, 1840-1860. 2007. 75.00 *(978-1-58839-225-1(2))* Metropolitan Museum of Art, The.

CALUMNY

see Libel and Slander

CALVERT FAMILY

Krugler, John D. English & Catholic: The Lords Baltimore in the Seventeenth Century. 2008. (Johns Hopkins University Studies in Historical & Political Science Ser.: 122). (ENG., Illus.). 336p. (gr. 17). pap. 27.00 *(978-0-8018-9083-3(7))* Johns Hopkins Univ. Pr.

Morris, John Gottlieb. The Lords Baltimore. (Maryland Historical Society Fund Ser.). 61p. reprint ed. 88.00 *(978-0-7222-9028-6(4))* Library Reprints, Inc.

CALVES

Lunsford, Terry. Characteristics of Beef Cattle That Determine the Price Difference Between Traditional & Cph Sales. 2008. (Illus.). 68p. pap. *(978-3-8364-9366-6(7))* VDM Verlag Dr. Mueller e.K.

Marta, Terre. Enhanced-Growth Feeding Programs for Dairy Calves - Nutrition, Management. 2008. 156p. pap. *(978-3-8364-7777-2(7))* VDM Verlag Dr. Mueller e.K.

CALVIN, JEAN, 1509-1564

Balserak, Jon. Divinity Compromised: A Study of Divine Accommodation in the Thought of John Calvin. 2010. (Studies in Early Modern Religious Reforms Ser.). x, 214p. pap. 199.00 *(978-90-481-7268-9(3),* 9048172683) Springer.

—Establishing the Remnant Church in France: Calvin's Lectures on the Minor Prophets, 1556-1559. 2011. XIV, 226p. *(978-90-04-19144-0(5))* BRILL.

Banks, Charles W. The Life & Times of John Calvin: With an Earnest Appeal for the Adoption of Open-Air Preaching. reprint ed. 42.50 *(978-0-404-19867-1(8))* AMS Pr., Inc.

Barth, Karl. The Faith of the Church: A Commentary on the Apostles' Creed According to Calvin's Catechism. Leuba, Jean-Louis, ed. Vahanian, Gabriel, tr. 2006. 188p. pap. 22.00 *(978-1-59752-800-9(5),* Wipf and Stock) Wipf & Stock Pubs.

Beach, J. Piety's Wisdom: A Summary of Calvin's Institutes with Study Questions. 2010. pap. *(978-1-60178-082-9(6))* Reformation Heritage Bks.

Beeke, Joel R., ed. Calvin for Today. 2010. *(978-1-60178-084-3(2))* Reformation Heritage Bks.

Beeke, Joel R., ed. The Soul of Life: The Piety of John Calvin. 2009. (Illus.). pap. 10.00 *(978-1-60178-057-7(5))* Reformation Heritage Bks.

Beeke, Joel R., selected by. 365 Days with Calvin: A Unique Collection of 365 Readings from the Writings of John Calvin. 2008. (356 Days With Ser.). 397p. *(978-1-84625-114-6(1))* DayOne Pubns.

Beeke, Joel R. & Williams, Garry, eds. Calvin, Theologian & Reformer. 2010. 176p. pap. *(978-1-60178-091-1(5))* Reformation Heritage Bks.

Benedict, Philip. Calvin & His Influence: 1509-2009, 1 vol. Backus, Irena, ed. 2011. (ENG., Illus.). 368p. pap. 39.95 ***(978-0-19-975185-3(4))*** Oxford Univ. Pr., Inc.

Billings, J. Todd & Hesselink, I. John, eds. Calvin's Theology & Its Reception: Disputes, Developments, & New Possibilities. 2012. (ENG.). 224p. pap. 30.00 ***(978-0-664-23423-2(2))*** Westminster John Knox Pr.

Blackburn, William Maxwell. Young Calvin in Paris, & the Little Flock That He Fed by the Rev Wm M Blackburn. 2006. 168p. per. 18.99 *(978-1-4255-1335-1(2))* MPublishing.

Blackburn, William W. Young Calvin in Paris: or The Scholar & the Cripple. reprint ed. 40.00 *(978-0-404-19869-5(4))* AMS Pr., Inc.

Blacketer, Raymond A. The School of God: Pedagogy & Rhetoric in Calvin's Interpretation of Deuteronomy. 2010. (Studies in Early Modern Religious Reforms Ser.). xvii, 300p. pap. 189.00 *(978-90-481-6995-5(X),* 904816995X) Springer.

Blanchard, Kathryn D. The Protestant Ethic or the Spirit of Capitalism: Christians, Freedom, & Free Markets. 2010. 262p. pap. 29.00 *(978-1-60608-659-9(6),* Cascade Bks.) Wipf & Stock Pubs.

Boer, Roland. Political Grace: The Revolutionary Theology of John Calvin. 2009. (ENG.). 176p. pap. 25.00 *(978-0-664-23393-8(7))* Westminster John Knox Pr.

Bonnet, Jules. Letters of John Calvin V1. 2007. (ENG.). 504p. 53.95 *(978-0-548-13870-0(2))* 2006. pap. 38.95 *(978-1-4286-5042-8(3))* Kessinger Publishing, LLC.

—Letters of John Calvin V2. 2007. (ENG.). 452p. 52.95 *(978-0-548-13871-7(0))* 2006. pap. 37.95 *(978-1-4286-5043-5(1))* Kessinger Publishing, LLC.

Boulton, Matthew Myer. Life in God: John Calvin, Practical Formation, & the Future of Protestant Theology. 2011. 264p. pap. 28.00 ***(978-0-8028-6564-9(X))*** Eerdmans, William B. Publishing Co.

Bratt, John H. The Life & Teachings of John Calvin: A Study Manual. 2011. 74p. 36.95 ***(978-1-258-05020-7(X))*** Literary Licensing, LLC.

Breukelman, Frans H. The Structure of Sacred Doctrine in Calvin's Theology. Reeling Brouwer, Rinse H., ed. Kessler, Martin, tr. from DUT. 2007. (Illus.). 272p. pap. 35.00 *(978-0-8028-2459-2(5))* Eerdmans, William B. Publishing Co.

Burnett, Amy Nelson, ed. John Calvin, Myth & Reality: Images & Impact of GenevaÕs Reformer. Papers of the 2009 Calvin Studies Society Colloquium. 2011. 272p. pap. 30.00 ***(978-1-60899-693-3(X),*** Cascade Bks.) Wipf & Stock Pubs.

Calvin, Jean. Institutes of the Christian Religion. 2009. 560p. pap. *(978-0-217-49072-6(7))* Books LLC.

Calvin, Jean & Allen, John. Institutes of the Christian Religion. 2009. 692p. pap. 47.75 *(978-1-115-59866-8(X))* BiblioBazaar.

Calvin, John. Calvin, CD-ROM Edition (Institution) Institutes of the Christian Religion. 2008. cd-rom 249.95 *(978-0-664-23171-2(3))* Westminster John Knox Pr.

—Calvin, Individual Use License: Institutes of the Christian Religion. 2008. (Library of Christian Classics Ser.). (ENG.). cd-rom 80.00 *(978-0-664-23170-5(5))* Westminster John Knox Pr.

—Calvin's Commentaries, 1 vol. 500th ed. 2009. 250.00 *(978-0-8010-1331-7(3))* Baker Bks.

—Institutes of the Christian Religion. 2008. 692p. 35.99 *(978-0-559-87608-0(4));* pap. 47.75 *(978-0-559-87606-6(8))* BiblioBazaar.

—Joannis Calvini Opera Selecta, vol. I: Scripta Calvini ab anno 1533 usque ad annum 1541 Continens. Barth, Petrus & Niesel, Guilelmus, eds. 2011. 542p. pap. 46.00 *(978-1-61097-173-7(6),* Wipf and Stock) Wipf & Stock Pubs.

—Joannis Calvini Opera Selecta, vol. II: Tractus Theologicos minores ab anno 1542 usque ad annum 1564 editos Continens. Barth, Petrus & Niesel, Guilelmus, eds. 2011. 424p. pap. 36.00 *(978-1-61097-174-4(4),* Wipf and Stock) Wipf & Stock Pubs.

—John Calvin on the Christian Faith. McNeill, John T., ed. 2011. 252p. 46.95 ***(978-1-258-02797-1(6))*** Literary Licensing, LLC.

Calvin, John. Letters of John Calvin. 2007. 1898p. pap. 150.00 *(978-1-55635-246-1(8),* Wipf and Stock) Wipf & Stock Pubs.

Calvin, John & Allen, John. Institutes of the Christian Religion. 2009. 702p. 47.99 *(978-1-117-68184-9(X));* (ENG.). 701p. pap. 48.75 *(978-1-117-68185-6(8))* BiblioBazaar.

Calvin, John & Calvin, Jean. Institutes of the Christian Religion. Beveridge, Henry, tr. from LAT. 2008. 1059p. (gr. 13). 29.95 *(978-1-59856-168-5(5))* Hendrickson Pubs. Marketing, LLC.

Canlis, Julie. Calvin's Ladder: A Spiritual Theology of Ascent & Ascension. 2010. 336p. pap. 32.00 *(978-0-8028-6449-9(X))* Eerdmans, William B. Publishing Co.

Chen, David S. Calvin's Passion for the Church & the Holy Spirit. 2008. 372p. pap. 20.99 *(978-1-60647-346-7(8))* Xulon Pr., Inc.

Chung, Paul S. Christian Spirituality & Ethical Life. 2010. (Illus.). 178p. pap. 20.00 *(978-1-55635-790-9(7),* Pickwick Pubns.) Wipf & Stock Pubs.

Chung, Sung Wook, ed. John Calvin & Evangelical Theology: Legacy & Prospect. 2009. (ENG.). 256p. pap. 40.00 *(978-0-664-23346-4(5))* Westminster John Knox Pr.

Currid, John D. Calvin & the Biblical Languages. 2007. (ENG.). 128p. per. 16.99 *(978-1-84550-212-6(4))* Christian Focus Pubns. GBR. Dist: STL Distribution North America.

Cuthbertson, David. A Tragedy of the Reformation: Being the Authentic Narrative of the History & Burning of the "Christianismi Restitutio", 1553, with a Succinct Account of the Theological Controversy Between Michael Servetus, Its Author, & the Reformer, John Calvin. reprint ed. 37.50 *(978-0-404-19826-8(0))* AMS Pr., Inc.

Davies, Alfred T. John Calvin: Many Sided Genius. reprint ed. 37.50 *(978-0-404-19827-5(9))* AMS Pr., Inc.

—John Calvin: Many Sided Genius. 2011. 96p. 38.95 ***(978-1-258-02635-6(X))*** Literary Licensing, LLC.

Davies, Rupert E. The Problem of Authority in the Continental Reformers: A Study in Luther, Zwingli, & Calvin. 2009. 158p. pap. 18.00 *(978-1-60608-728-2(2),* Wipf and Stock) Wipf & Stock Pubs.

Doerksen, Daniel W. Picturing Religious Experience: George Herbert, Calvin, & the Scriptures. 2011. (ENG.). 256p. 75.00 ***(978-1-61149-356-6(0))*** Univ. of Delaware Pr.

Dommen, Edward & Bratt, James D., eds. John Calvin Rediscovered: The Impact of His Social & Economic Thought. 2007. (Princeton Theological Seminary Studies in Reformed Theology & History Ser.). (ENG.). 161p. per. 30.00 *(978-0-664-23227-6(2))* Westminster John Knox Pr.

Ellis, Brannon. Calvin, Classical Trinitarianism, & the Aseity of the Son. 2012. (ENG.). 256p. 135.00 ***(978-0-19-965240-2(6))*** Oxford Univ. Pr., Inc.

Engelsma, David J. The Reformed Faith of John Calvin: The Institutes in Summary. 2009. 472p. 34.95 *(978-1-936054-00-8(0))* Reformed Free Publishing Assn.

Garcia, Mark A. Life in Christ: Union with Christ & Twofold Grace in Calvin's Theology. 2008. (Studies in Christian History & Thought Ser.). (ENG.). 380p. 49.99 *(978-1-84227-572-6(0),* Paternoster) Authentic Media.

—Life in Christ: Union with Christ & Twofold Grace in Calvin's Theology. 2008. (Studies in Christian History & Thought Ser.). 388p. pap. 46.00 *(978-1-55635-865-4(2))* Wipf & Stock Pubs.

Godfrey, W. Robert. John Calvin: Pilgrim & Pastor. 2009. 208p. pap. 15.99 *(978-1-4335-0132-6(5))* Crossway.

Gordon, Bruce. Calvin. 2011. (ENG., Illus.). 416p. pap. 23.00 *(978-0-300-17084-9(X))* Yale Univ. Pr.

Greef, Wulfert de. The Writings of John Calvin, Expanded Edition: An Introductory Guide. Bierma, Lyle D., tr. from DUT. 2008. (ENG., Illus.). 296p. 40.00 *(978-0-664-23230-5(2))* Westminster John Knox Pr.

Hall, David W. Calvin in the Public Square: Liberal Democracies, Rights, & Civil Liberties. 2009. pap. *(978-1-59638-099-8(3))* P & R Publishing.

—A Heart Promptly Offered: The Revolutionary Leadership of John Calvin. annot. ed. 2006. (Leaders in Action Ser.). (ENG.). 360p. 16.95 *(978-1-58182-505-3(6))* Turner Publishing Co.

—The Legacy of John Calvin: His Influence on the Modern World. 2008. 112p. pap. *(978-1-59638-085-1(3))* P & R Publishing.

—Tributes to John Calvin: A Celebration of His Quincentenary. 2010. *(978-1-59638-096-7(9))* P & R Publishing.

Hall, David W. & Burton, Mathew D. Calvin & Commerce: The Transforming Power of Calvinism in Market Economies. 2009. pap. *(978-1-59638-095-0(0))* P & R Publishing.

Hall, David W. & Lillback, Peter A., eds. A Theological Guide to Calvin's Institutes: Essays & Analysis. 2008. (Calvin 500 Ser.). 506p. 35.99 *(978-1-59638-091-2(8))* P & R Publishing.

Hall, David W. & Padgett, Marvin. Calvin & Culture: Exploring a Worldview. 2010. pap. *(978-1-59638-098-1(5))* P & R Publishing.

Harkness, Georgia E. John Calvin: The Man & His Ethics. reprint ed. 32.50 *(978-0-404-19830-5(9))* AMS Pr., Inc.

Harms, Frederik Av. In God's Custody: The Church, a History of Divine Protection: A Study of John Calvin's Ecclesiology based on his Commentary on the Minor Prophets. 2010. (Reformed Historical Theology Ser.). (GER & ENG.). 248p. (C). 108.00 *(978-3-525-56922-1(X))* Vandenhoeck & Ruprecht GmbH & Co. KG DEU. Dist: ISD.

Helm, Calvin. 2008. (Guides for the Perplexed Ser.). (ENG.). 192p. 24.95 *(978-0-567-03202-7(7))* 110.00 *(978-0-567-03201-0(9))* Continuum International Publishing Group, Ltd. GBR. (T&T Clark Int'l). Dist: National Bk. Network.

Henry, Paul E. The Life & Times of John Calvin, 2 vols., Set. Stebbing, Henry, tr. from GER. reprint ed. 95.00 *(978-0-404-19831-2(7))* AMS Pr., Inc.

Hirzel, Martin Ernst & Sallmann, Martin, eds. John Calvin's Impact on Church & Society, 1509-2009. 2009. 256p. pap. 30.00 *(978-0-8028-6474-1(0))* Eerdmans, William B. Publishing Co.

Hoogstra, Jacob T., ed. John Calvin, Contemporary Prophet: A Symposium. 2011. 256p. 47.95 ***(978-1-258-02704-9(6))*** Literary Licensing, LLC.

Hoogstra, Jacobo. Juan Calvino Profeta Contemporaneo: John Calvin: Contemporary. (SPA.). 264p. *(978-84-7228-099-1(3),* 220518) Clie, Editorial.

Huijgen, Arnold. Divine Accommodation in John Calvin's Theology: Analysis & Assessment. 2011. (Reformed Historical Theology Ser.). (ENG.). 416p. (C). 122.00 ***(978-3-525-56944-3(0))*** Vandenhoeck & Ruprecht GmbH & Co. KG DEU. Dist: ISD.

Hunt, Robert N. Calvin. reprint ed. 37.50 *(978-0-404-19835-0(X))* AMS Pr., Inc.

Hunter, Adam M. The Teaching of Calvin: A Modern Interpretation. reprint ed. 37.50 *(978-0-404-19836-7(8))* AMS Pr., Inc.

Irwin, Clarke H. John Calvin: The Man & His Work. (Illus.). reprint ed. 32.50 *(978-0-404-19837-4(6))* AMS Pr., Inc.

Istafanous, Abd-el-Masih. Calvin's Doctrine of Biblical Authority. 2010. 240p. pap. 27.00 *(978-1-60899-644-5(1),* Wipf and Stock) Wipf & Stock Pubs.

Joby, Christopher Richard & Joby, C. R. Calvinism in the Arts: A Re-Assessment. 2007. (Studies in Philosophical Theology Ser.). (ENG., Illus.). 240p. (C). pap. 63.00 *(978-90-429-1923-5(X))* Peeters Pubs. & Booksellers BEL. Dist: Brown, David Bk. Co., The.

John Calvin: For a New Reformation. 2010. 576p. 39.99 *(978-1-4335-1281-0(5))* Crossway.

Johnson, Robert Clyde, et al. Johnson Speaks to Us: Professor Robert Clyde Johnson's Lecture Notes on Martin Luther, John Calvin, Soren Kierkegaard, & Karl Barth. 2007. (C). *(978-1-57506-802-2(8))* Eisenbrauns, Inc.

Johnson, Thomas C. John Calvin & the Genevan Reformation: A Sketch. reprint ed. 27.50 *(978-0-404-13838-1(4))* AMS Pr., Inc.

Johnson, William Stacy. John Calvin, Reformer for the 21st Century. 2009. (ENG.). 144p. pap. 15.00 *(978-0-664-23408-9(9))* Westminster John Knox Pr.

Lane, Anthony N. S. A Reader's Guide to Calvin's Institutes. 2009. 174p. (C). pap. 15.00 *(978-0-8010-3731-3(X))* Baker Academic.

Lane, Anthony N. S., ed. Jean Calvin: Defensio sanae et orthodoxae doctrinae de servitute et liberatione humani arbitrii. Series IV. Scripta didactica et Polemica. 2008. (Ioannis Calvini Opera Omnia Ser.). (FRE & LAT.). 465p. (C). 220.00 *(978-2-600-01144-0(7))* Droz, Librairie CHE. Dist: Brown, David Bk. Co., The.

Larson, Mark J. Calvin's Doctrine of the State: A Reformed Doctrine & Its American Trajectory, the Revolutionary War, & the Founding of the Republic. 2009. 148p. pap. 18.00 *(978-1-60608-073-3(3))* Wipf & Stock Pubs.

Lawson, Steven J. The Expository Genius of John Calvin. 2007. (Long Line of Godly Men Profile Ser.). 142p. *(978-1-56769-085-9(8))* Reformation Pubs.

Lee, Daniel Y. K. The Holy Spirit As Bond in Calvin's Thought. 2011. 296p. pap. 65.95 *(978-3-0343-0219-7(3))* Lang, Peter AG GBR. Dist: Lang, Peter.

Leith, John H. John Calvin's Doctrine of the Christian Life. 2010. 230p. pap. 25.00 *(978-1-60899-440-3(6))* Wipf & Stock Pubs.

Light in the Labyrinth. 2007. per. 12.95 *(978-0-9773389-1-7(6))* Contra Mundum Productions.

Mackenzie, Catherine. John Calvin: After Darkness Light. 2009. (Trailblazer Ser.). (ENG.). 160p. mass mkt. 8.99 *(978-1-84550-084-9(9))* Christian Focus Pubns. GBR. Dist: STL Distribution North America.

Mackinnon, James. Calvin & the Reformation. reprint ed. 37.50 *(978-0-404-19841-1(4))* AMS Pr., Inc.

Mannion, Gerard & Borght, Eddy van der, eds. John Calvin's Ecclesiology: Ecumenical Perspectives. 2011. (Ecclesiological Investigations Ser.). (ENG.). 254p. 120.00 *(978-0-567-08102-5(8),* T&T Clark Int'l) Continuum International Publishing Group, Ltd. GBR. Dist: National Bk. Network.

McCrie, Thomas. The Early Years of John Calvin: A Fragment, 1509-1536. reprint ed. 32.50 *(978-0-404-19840-4(6))* AMS Pr., Inc.

Meehan, Christopher H. Pursued by God: The Amazing Life & Lasting Influence of John Calvin. 2009. *(978-1-59255-503-1(9))* Faith Alive Christian Resources.

Methuen, Charlotte. Luther & Calvin - Religious Revolutionaries. 2012. (ENG.). 192p. pap. 16.95 *(978-0-7459-5340-3(9))* Lion Hudson PLC GBR. Dist: Independent Pubs. Group.

Miles, Robert W. That Frenchman, John Calvin. reprint ed. 29.00 *(978-0-404-19843-5(0))* AMS Pr., Inc.

Miles, Robert Whitfield. That Frenchman, John Calvin. 2011. 220p. 44.95 ***(978-1-258-04277-6(0))*** Literary Licensing, LLC.

Moon, Byung-Ho. Christ the Mediator of the Law: Calvin's Christological Understanding of the Law as the Rule of Living & Life-Giving. 2006. (Studies in Christian History & Thought Ser.). 336p. pap. 32.00 *(978-1-59752-782-8(3),* Wipf and Stock) Wipf & Stock Pubs.

Mouw, Richard J. The Challenges of Cultural Discipleship: Essays in the Line of Abraham Kuyper. 2011. pap. 20.00 ***(978-0-8028-6696-1(0))*** Eerdmans, William B. Publishing Co.

Mullett, Michael. Calvin. 2011. (Routledge Historical Biographies Ser.). (ENG., Illus.). 312p. 100.00 *(978-0-415-47698-0(4));* pap. 27.95 *(978-0-415-47699-7(2))* Routledge.

Murphy, Joseph P. The Fountain of Life in John Calvin & the Devotio Moderna: Metaphorical Theology of the Trinity in Word & Sacrament. 2010. 264p. lib. bdg. *(978-1-933146-95-9(8))* Academica Pr., LLC.

Murray, John. Calvin on Scripture & Divine Sovereignty. 2009. 84p. pap. 12.00 *(978-1-59925-203-2(1))* Solid Ground Christian Bks.

Neuser, Wilhelm H. Johann Calvin - Leben und Werk in seiner Frühzeit 1509-1541. 2009. (Reformed Historical Theology Ser.). (GER.). 352p. (C). 111.00 *(978-3-525-56915-3(7))* Vandenhoeck & Ruprecht GmbH & Co. KG DEU. Dist: ISD.

Nixon, LeRoy. John Calvin's Teachings on Human Reason & Their Implications for Theory of Reformed Protestant Christian Education. 2011. 292p. 48.95 ***(978-1-258-02505-2(1))*** Literary Licensing, LLC.

Oberman, Heiko. Jean Calvin & the Reformation of the Refugees. 2009. (Travaux d'Humanisme et Renaissance Ser.). 232p. (C). 126.00 *(978-2-600-00687-3(7))* Droz, Librairie CHE. Dist: Brown, David Bk. Co., The.

Olson, Bessie G. John Calvin: A Great Statesman. 2011. 50p. 35.95 ***(978-1-258-02455-0(1))*** Literary Licensing, LLC.

Opitz, Peter. Leben und Werk Johannes Calvins. 2009. (GER.). 176p. (C). 23.00 *(978-3-525-55000-7(6))* Vandenhoeck & Ruprecht GmbH & Co. KG DEU. Dist: ISD.

Paddison, Angus. Theological Hermeneutics & 1 Thessalonians. 2008. (Society for New Testament Studies Monograph Ser.). (ENG.). 248p. pap. 36.00 *(978-0-521-09005-6(9))* Cambridge Univ. Pr.

Pak, G. Sujin. The Judaizing Calvin: Sixteenth-Century Debates over the Messianic Psalms. 2009. (History Theology Ser.). (ENG.). 240p. 65.00 *(978-0-19-537192-5(5))* Oxford Univ. Pr., Inc.

Parker, T. H. L. John Calvin: A Biography. 2007. (ENG.). 224p. per. 20.00 *(978-0-664-23181-1(0))* Westminster John Knox Pr.

Parsons, Burk. John Calvin: A Heart for Devotion, Doctrine, & Doxology. 2008. *(978-1-56769-106-1(4))* Ligonier Ministries.

Partee, Charles. The Theology of John Calvin. 2008. (ENG.). 376p. 40.00 *(978-0-664-23119-4(5))* Westminster John Knox Pr.

Pattison, Bonnie L. Poverty in the Theology of John Calvin. 2006. (Princeton Theological Monographs). 392p. pap. 37.00 *(978-1-59752-691-3(6),* Pickwick Pubns.) Wipf & Stock Pubs.

Paul, Herman & Wallet, Bart. Sober, Strict, & Scriptural: Collective Memories of John Calvin, 1800-2000. de Niet, Johan, ed. 2009. 408p. *(978-90-04-17424-5(9))* BRILL.

Penning, L. Genius of Genev: A Popular Account of the Life & Times of John Calvin. Berrington, B. S., tr. 2011. 422p. 54.95 ***(978-1-258-02181-8(1))*** Literary Licensing, LLC.

Piper, John. John Calvin & His Passion for the Majesty of God. 2008. 64p. pap. 7.99 *(978-1-4335-0182-1(1))* Crossway.

—The Legacy of Sovereign Joy: God's Triumphant Grace in the Lives of Augustine, Luther, & Calvin. 2nd ed. 2006. (Swans Are Not Silent Ser.: Vol. 1). 160p. pap. 15.99 *(978-1-58134-813-2(4))* Crossway.

Quistorp, H. Calvin's Doctrine of the Last Things. 2009. 200p. pap. 23.00 *(978-1-60608-762-6(2),* Wipf and Stock) Wipf & Stock Pubs.

Quistorp, Heinrich. Calvin's Doctrine of the Last Things. Knight, Harold, tr. reprint ed. 37.50 *(978-0-404-19846-6(5))* AMS Pr., Inc.

Reinhardt, Volker. Die Tyrannei der Tugend: Calvin und die Reformation in Genf. 2009. (GER., Illus.). 271p. *(978-3-406-57556-3(0))* C. H. Beck'sch Verlagsbuchhandlung.

Reyburn, Hugh Y. John Calvin: His Life, Letters & Work. reprint ed. 45.00 *(978-0-404-19847-3(3))* AMS Pr., Inc.

Riggs, John W. Baptism in the Reformed Tradition: A Historical & Practical Theology. 2009. pap. *(978-0-664-23682-3(0))* Westminster John Knox Pr.

Rilliet, Albert. Calvin & Servetus: The Reformer's Share in the Trial of Michael Servetus Historically Ascertained. Tweedie, W. K., tr. from FRE. reprint ed. 31.50 *(978-0-404-19848-0(1))* AMS Pr., Inc.

Rorem, Paul. Calvin & Bullinger on the Lord's Supper. 2009. 88.00 *(978-1-60724-367-0(9))* Gorgias Pr., LLC.

Santrac, Aleksandar S. A Comparison of John Calvin & Alvin Plantinga's Concept of Sensus Divinitatis: Phenomenology of the Sense of Divinity: with Interview & Comments by Alvin Plantinga. 2011. 108p. 99.95 ***(978-0-7734-3926-9(9))*** Mellen, Edwin Pr., The.

Selderhuis, H. J. The Calvin Handbook. Guder, Judith J. & Baron, Henry J., trs. from DUT. 2009. 600p. pap. 35.00 *(978-0-8028-6230-3(6))* Eerdmans, William B. Publishing Co.

Selderhuis, Herman J. John Calvin: A Pilgrim's Life. 2009. (ENG.). 287p. pap. 25.00 *(978-0-8308-2921-7(0),* IVP Acad.) InterVarsity Pr.

Selderhuis, Herman J., ed. Calvin - Saint or Sinner? 2010. (GER., Illus.). 326p. 177.50 *(978-3-16-150339-9(2))* Mohr Siebeck GmbH & Co. KG DEU. Dist: Coronet Bks.

Selderhuis, Herman J. & Selderhuis, H. J. Calvinus sacrarum literarum interpres: Papers of the International Congress on Calvin Research. 2008. (Reformed Historical Theology Ser.). (ENG.). 302p. (C). 114.00 *(978-3-525-56914-6(9))* Vandenhoeck & Ruprecht GmbH & Co. KG DEU. Dist: ISD.

Servetus, Michael & Hoffman, Christopher A. Thirty Letters to Calvin, Preacher to the Genevans: And Sixty Signs of the Kingdom of the Antichrist & His Revelation Which Is Now at Hand: (From the Restoration of Christianity, 1553) 2010. lxxxvi, 175p. 109.95 *(978-0-7734-1316-0(2))* Mellen, Edwin Pr., The.

Shepherd, Victor A. A Ministry Dearer Than Life: The Pastoral Legacy of John Calvin. 2009. 84p. pap. 9.95 *(978-1-894667-95-1(6))* Clements Publishing.

Smyth, Thomas. Calvin & His Enemies: A Memoir of the Life, Character & Principles of Calvin. enl. rev. ed. reprint ed. 39.50 *(978-0-404-19849-7(X))* AMS Pr., Inc.

Spijker, Willem van 't. Calvin: A Brief Guide to His Life & Thought. 2009. (ENG.). 200p. pap. 25.00 *(978-0-664-23225-2(6))* Westminster John Knox Pr.

Stauffer, Richard. The Humanness of John Calvin: The Reformer as a Husband, Father, Pastor & Friend. Shriver, George, tr. 2008. 100p. pap. 13.00 *(978-1-59925-155-4(8))* Solid Ground Christian Bks.

Steinmetz, David Curtis. Calvin in Context. 2nd ed. 2010. (ENG.). 328p. pap. 29.95 *(978-0-19-973638-6(3))* Oxford Univ. Pr., Inc.

Stroup, George W. Calvin. 2009. (Abingdon Pillars of Theology Ser.). 85p. pap. 12.00 *(978-0-687-65913-5(2))* Abingdon Pr.

Topping, Richard R. & Vissers, John A., eds. Calvin@500: Theology, History, & Practice. 2011. 198p. pap. 23.00 ***(978-1-61097-131-7(0),*** Pickwick Pubns.) Wipf & Stock Pubs.

Tulloch, John. The Leaders of the Reformation: Luther, Calvin, Latimer, Knox. 2007. pap. 28.95 *(978-1-4304-5310-9(9))* Kessinger Publishing, LLC.

Van Den Belt, Henk. The Authority of Scripture in Reformed Theology: Truth & Trust. 2008. (Studies in Reformed Theology Ser.). 384p. *(978-90-04-16307-2(7))* BRILL.

van den Berg, Michiel A. Friends of Calvin. Bruinsma, Reinder, tr. from DUT. 2009. (Illus.). 286p. pap. 20.00 *(978-0-8028-6227-3(6))* Eerdmans, William B. Publishing Co.

Van Halsema, Thea B. This Was John Calvin. 2010. (J). pap. *(978-1-894666-90-9(9))* Inheritance Pubns.

Venema, Cornelis P. Accepted & Renewed in Christ: The Twofold Grace of God & the Interpretation of Calvin's Theology. 2007. (Reformed Historical Theology Ser.). (ENG.). 296p. (C). 77.00 *(978-3-525-56910-8(6))* Vandenhoeck & Ruprecht GmbH & Co. KG DEU. Dist: ISD.

Vliet, Jason van. Children of God: The Imago Dei in John Calvin & His Context. 2009. (Reformed Historical Theology Ser.). (ENG.). 285p. (C). 125.00 *(978-3-525-56918-4(1))* Vandenhoeck & Ruprecht GmbH & Co. KG DEU. Dist: ISD.

Vollmer, Philip. John Calvin: Man of the Millennium. Strackbein, Wesley, ed. 2008. (Illus.). 341p. 20.00 *(978-1-934554-35-7(9))* Vision Forum, Inc., The.

Walchenbach, John R. John Calvin as Biblical Commentator. 2010. (Illus.). 218p. pap. 24.00 *(978-1-60899-328-4(0),* Wipf and Stock) Wipf & Stock Pubs.

Warfield, Benjamin, et al, contrib. by. Calvin Memorial Addresses: The 400th Anniversary of Calvin's Birth. 2007. 300p. per. 25.00 *(978-1-59925-122-6(1))* Solid Ground Christian Bks.

Warfield, Benjamin Breckenridge. Calvin & Augustine. Craig, Samuel G., ed. 2011. 518p. 60.95 ***(978-1-258-01604-3(4))*** Literary Licensing, LLC.

Weig, Staffan Z. Erasmus the Right to Heresy. 2006. 404p. per. *(978-1-4067-3260-3(5),* Hesperides Pr.) Read Bks.

Wilson, Douglas. A Study Guide to Calvin's Institutes. 2011. pap. ***(978-1-59128-086-6(9))*** Canon Pr.

Young, Davis A. John Calvin & the Natural World. 2007. (ENG.). 260p. 73.50 *(978-0-7618-3712-1(4));* pap. 41.99 *(978-0-7618-3713-8(2))* Univ. Pr. of America, Inc.

Zachman, Randall C. Reconsidering John Calvin. 2011. (Current Issues in Theology Ser.). (ENG.). 220p. 80.00 ***(978-1-107-01575-3(8));*** pap. 28.99 ***(978-1-107-60177-2(0))*** Cambridge Univ. Pr.

Zachman, Randall C., ed. John Calvin & Roman Catholicism: Critique & Engagement, Then & Now. 2008. 224p. (C). pap. 27.00 *(978-0-8010-3597-5(X))* Baker Academic.

CALVIN, JOHN, 1509-1564

see Calvin, Jean, 1509-1564

CALVINISM

see also Antinomianism; Arminianism; Congregationalism; Mercersburg Theology; New England Theology; Perseverance (Theology); Predestination; Presbyterianism; Puritans

Allen, David L. & Lemke, Steve W., eds. Whosoever Will: A Biblical-Theological Critique of Five-Point Calvinism. 2010. (ENG.). 320p. pap. 24.99 *(978-0-8054-6416-0(6),* B&H Academic) B&H Publishing Group.

Beckley, Daniel F. The Balancing Act Arminianism V. Calvinism. 2007. per. 16.95 *(978-0-9771809-5-0(6))* Painted WORD Studios.

Beeke, Joel R., ed. Calvin for Today. 2010. *(978-1-60178-084-3(2))* Reformation Heritage Bks.

Beeke, Joel R., ed. The Soul of Life: The Piety of John Calvin. 2009. (Illus.). pap. 10.00 *(978-1-60178-057-7(5))* Reformation Heritage Bks.

Beeke, Joel R. & Ferguson, Sinclair B. Living for God's Glory: An Introduction to Calvinism. 2008. xvi, 416p. *(978-1-56769-105-4(6))* Ligonier Ministries.

Berridge, John. The Christian World Unmasked with Life of the Author, by the Rev Thomas Guthrie. 2006. 212p. per. 20.99 *(978-1-4255-1754-0(4))* MPublishing.

Boettner, Loraine. The Reformed Doctrine of Predestination. 2011. 450p. 56.95 ***(978-1-258-05745-9(X))*** Literary Licensing, LLC.

—The Reformed Doctrine of the Atonement. 2011. 138p. pap. 13.00 ***(978-1-59925-254-4(6))*** Solid Ground Christian Bks.

Boice, James Montgomery & Ryken, Philip Graham. The Doctrines of Grace: Rediscovering the Evangelical Gospel. 2009. 240p. pap. 17.99 *(978-1-4335-1128-8(2))* Crossway.

Bonney, Richard & Trim, D. J. B., eds. Persecution & Pluralism: Calvinists & Religious Minorities in Early Modern Europe 1550-1700, Vol. 2. 2006. (Studies in the History of Religious & Political Pluralism Ser.). 326p. (C). pap. 63.95 *(978-3-03910-570-0(1))* International Academic Pubs.

—Persecution & Pluralism: Calvinists & Religious Minorities in Early Modern Europe 1550-1700, Vol. 2. 2006. (Studies in the History of Religious & Political Pluralism Ser.). 326p. (C). pap. *(978-0-8204-7597-4(1))* Lang, Peter AG.

Boulton, Matthew Myer. Life in God: John Calvin, Practical Formation, & the Future of Protestant Theology. 2011. 264p. pap. 28.00 ***(978-0-8028-6564-9(X))*** Eerdmans, William B. Publishing Co.

Breed, Geoffrey R. Calvinism & Communion in Victorian England: Studies in Nineteenth-Century Strict-Communion Baptist Ecclesiology: Comprising the Minutes of the London Association of Strict Baptist Ministers & Churches, 1846-1855 & the Ramsgate Chapel Case, 1862. 2008. (Illus.). xii, 646p. *(978-1-888514-29-2(9))* Particular Baptist Pr.

Brown, Craig R. The Five Dilemmas of Calvinism. 2007. (Illus.). 127p. per. *(978-1-56769-086-6(6))* Ligonier Ministries.

Bruening, Michael W. Calvinism's First Battleground: Conflict & Reform in the Pays de Vaud, 1528-1559. 2010. (Studies in Early Modern Religious Reforms Ser.). xvi, 286p. pap. 219.00 *(978-90-481-7066-1(4),* 9048170664) Springer.

Calvin, Jean. Institutes of the Christian Religion. 2009. 560p. pap. *(978-0-217-49072-6(7))* Books LLC.

Calvin, Jean & Allen, John. Institutes of the Christian Religion. 2009. 692p. pap. 47.75 *(978-1-115-59866-8(X))* BiblioBazaar.

Calvin, John. Institutes of the Christian Religion. 2008. 692p. 35.99 *(978-0-559-87608-0(4));* pap. 47.75 *(978-0-559-87606-6(8))* BiblioBazaar.

—Sumario: Instit. de la Rel. Cristiana: Summary of Calvin's Institutes. (SPA.). *(978-84-7645-491-6(0),* 223439) Clie, Editorial.

Calvin, John & Allen, John. Institutes of the Christian Religion. 2009. 702p. 47.99 *(978-1-117-68184-9(X));* (ENG.). 701p. pap. 48.75 *(978-1-117-68185-6(8),* BiblioBazaar.

Calvin, John & Calvin, Jean. Institutes of the Christian Religion. Beveridge, Henry, tr. from LAT. 2008. 1059p. (gr. 13). 29.95 *(978-1-59856-168-5(5))* Hendrickson Pubs. Marketing, LLC.

Calvinistic Action Committee. God-Centered Living or Calvinism in Action: A Symposium. 2011. 270p. 47.95 ***(978-1-258-09832-2(6))*** Literary Licensing, LLC.

Coffey, John & Lim, Paul C. H., eds. The Cambridge Companion to Puritanism. 2008. (Cambridge Companions to Religion Ser.). (ENG.). 400p. (C). pap. 30.99 *(978-0-521-67800-1(5))* Cambridge Univ. Pr.

Coffey, John & Lim, Paul Chang-Ha. The Cambridge Companion to Puritanism. Coffey, John & Lim, Paul C. H., eds. 2008. (Cambridge Companions to Religion Ser.). (ENG.). 400p. (C). 89.00 *(978-0-521-86088-8(1))* Cambridge Univ. Pr.

Connell, John S. The Tulip in the Garden: Pruning the Petals of Calvinism. 2010. 120p. pap. 12.99 *(978-1-61507-130-2(X))* Cross Bks. Publishing.

Cooney, Jonathan. The Lord Is My Shepherd, Etc. 2008. 360p. per. *(978-3-8364-3476-8(8))* VDM Verlag Dr. Mueller e.K.

Crawford, Raymond I. E. Out of Love: A Computer Nerd. 2009. pap. 18.99 *(978-1-60791-812-7(9))* Xulon Pr., Inc.

Cremeans, Charles D. The Reception of Calvinistic Thought in England. reprint ed. 41.50 *(978-0-404-19896-1(1))* AMS Pr., Inc.

Crew, Phyllis Mack. Calvinist Preaching & Iconoclasm in the Netherlands, 1544-1569. 2008. (Cambridge Studies in Early Modern History Ser.). (ENG.). 236p. pap. 31.99 *(978-0-521-08883-1(6))* Cambridge Univ. Pr.

Crisp, Oliver D. & Sweeney, Douglas A., eds. After Jonathan Edwards: The Courses of the New England Theology. 2012. (ENG.). 352p. pap. 29.95

(978-0-19-975630-8(9)); 2nd ed. (Illus.). 99.00 ***(978-0-19-975629-2(5))*** Oxford Univ. Pr., Inc.

Dabney, Robert. The five points of Calvinism. 2007. (ENG.). 88p. per. 10.99 *(978-1-59925-096-0(9))* Solid Ground Christian Bks.

Dakin, A. Calvinism. 2007. 252p. per. *(978-1-4067-8900-3(3)*, Pomona Pr.) Read Bks.

Davis, Thomas J. John Calvin's American Legacy, 1 vol. 2010. (ENG.). 304p. 99.00 *(978-0-19-539097-1(0))*; pap. 29.95 *(978-0-19-539098-8(9))* Oxford Univ. Pr., Inc.

Dickinson, Jonathan. The True Scripture Doctrine Concerning Some Important Points of Christian Faith. 2009. (Amer Philosophy, Religion Ser.). (ENG.). 256p. pap. 17.95 *(978-1-4290-1769-5(4))* Applewood Bks.

Dooyeweerd, Herman, et al. The Struggle for a Christian Politics: An Essay in Grounding the Calvinistic Worldview in Its Law-Idea. 2009. xiii, 316p. *(978-0-7734-4895-7(0))* Mellen, Edwin Pr., The.

Ely, Ezra. Contrast Between Calvinism & Hopkinsia. 2009. (Amer Philosophy, Religion Ser.). (ENG.). 288p. pap. 19.95 *(978-1-4290-1605-6(1))* Applewood Bks.

Engammare, Max & Maag, Karin. On Time, Punctuality, & Discipline in Early Modern Calvinism. 2009. (ENG., Illus.). 286p. 93.00 *(978-0-521-76997-6(3))* Cambridge Univ. Pr. GBR. Dist: Cambridge Univ. Pr.

Fehler, Brian M. Calvinist Rhetoric in Nineteenth-Century America: The Bartlet Professors of Sacred Rhetoric of Andover Seminary. 2007. 208p. *(978-0-7734-5430-9(6))* Mellen, Edwin Pr., The.

Foster, Randolph Sinks. Objections to Calvinism As It Is, in a Series of Letters Addressed to Rev N L Rice by R S Foster, with an Appendix, Containing Replies & Rejoin. 2006. 312p. per. 23.99 *(978-1-4255-2962-8(3))* MPublishing.

Garcia, Mark A. Life in Christ: Union with Christ & Twofold Grace in Calvin's Theology. 2008. (Studies in Christian History & Thought Ser.). (ENG.). 380p. 49.99 *(978-1-84227-572-6(0)*, Paternoster) Authentic Media.

Gill, John. The Cause of God & Truth. 2009. 168p. pap. *(978-1-150-75681-8(0))* Books LLC.

Gordon, Bruce. Calvin. 2011. (ENG., Illus.). 416p. pap. 23.00 *(978-0-300-17084-9(X))* Yale Univ. Pr.

Greek Grammar & Syntax Versus Calvinism: The Five Points of Calvinism Refuted. 2007. pap. 29.95 *(978-0-9747216-3-7(8))* Crisis Pubns., Inc.

Grell, Ole Peter. Brethren in Christ: A Calvinist Network in Reformation Europe. 2011. (ENG., Illus.). 338p. 99.00 ***(978-1-107-00881-6(6))*** Cambridge Univ. Pr.

Hancock, Ralph C. Calvin & the Foundations of Modern Politics. 2011. 240p. (C). pap. 24.00 *(978-1-58731-102-4(X))* St. Augustine's Pr., Inc.

Hansen, Collin. Young, Restless, Reformed: A Journalist's Journey with the New Calvinists. 2008. 160p. pap. 15.99 *(978-1-58134-940-5(8))* Crossway.

Hart, Hendrik, et al, eds. Rationality in the Calvinian Tradition. 2011. 420p. (Orig.). pap. 58.00 ***(978-1-61097-610-7(X)***, Wipf and Stock) Wipf & Stock Pubs.

Haykin, Michael. A Cloud of Witnesses: Calvinistic Baptists in the 18th Century. 2006. (Et Perspectives Ser.). (Illus.). 96p. per. *(978-0-9500129-3-3(9))* Evangelical Times.

Hiagbe, Komi Ahiatroga. Reconciled to Reconcile: An African View of John Calvin's Doctrine of Salvation. 2008. (Europäische Hochschulschriften. Reihe 23: Theologie Ser.). 230p. pap. 61.95 *(978-3-631-57166-8(6))* Lang, Peter GmbH, Europaischer Verlag der Wissenschaften DEU. Dist: Lang, Peter.

Hirzel, Martin Ernst & Sallmann, Martin, eds. John Calvin's Impact on Church & Society, 1509-2009. 2009. 256p. pap. 30.00 *(978-0-8028-6474-1(0))* Eerdmans, William B. Publishing Co.

Hitchcock, Steven L. Recanting Calvinism. 2011. 672p. pap. 29.99 ***(978-1-61379-202-5(6))*** Xulon Pr., Inc.

Holt, Mack P. & Armstrong, Brian G. Adaptations of Calvinism in Reformation Europe: Essays in Honour of Brian G. Armstrong. Holt, Mack P., ed. 2007. (St Andrews Studies in Reformation History Ser.). (Illus.). 266p. 124.95 *(978-0-7546-5149-9(5))* Ashgate Publishing Co.

Hoogstra, Jacob, ed. The Sovereignty of God: Proceedings of the First American Calvinistic Conference In 1939. 2008. 224p. pap. 18.00 *(978-1-59925-191-2(4))* Solid Ground Christian Bks.

Hunt, Dave. What Love Is This? Calvinism's Misrepresentation of God. 590p. 2007. (ENG.). 27.99 *(978-1-928660-12-5(6))* 2006. 27.99 *(978-1-928660-47-7(9))* Berean Call, The.

Hunt, David. A Calvinist's Honest Doubts Resolved: By Reason & God's Amazing Grace. 2007. (ENG.). 104p. per. 7.99 *(978-1-928660-34-7(7))* Berean Call, The.

Hunter, Adam M. The Teaching of Calvin: A Modern Interpretation. reprint ed. 37.50 *(978-0-404-19836-7(8))* AMS Pr., Inc.

Joby, Christopher Richard & Joby, C. R. Calvinism in the Arts: A Re-Assessment. 2007. (Studies in Philosophical Theology Ser.). (ENG., Illus.). 240p. (C). pap. 63.00 *(978-90-429-1923-5(X))* Peeters Pubs. & Booksellers BEL. Dist: Brown, David Bk. Co., The.

Keane, Webb. Christian Moderns: Freedom & Fetish in the Mission Encounter. 2007. (Anthropology of Christianity Ser.: Vol. 1). (Illus.). 323p. 55.00 *(978-0-520-24651-5(9))* Univ. of California Pr.

Kranendonk, David H. Teaching Predestination: Elnathan Parr & Pastoral Ministry in Early Stuart England. 2011. pap. ***(978-1-60178-148-2(2))*** Reformation Heritage Bks.

Kuyper, Abraham. Lectures on Calvinism. 2007. (ENG.). 200p. per. 11.75 *(978-1-60206-840-7(2))* Cosimo, Inc.

—Lectures on Calvinism: The Stone Lectures Of 1898. 2008. (Hendrickson Christian Classics Ser.). 227p. (C). 12.95 *(978-1-59856-298-9(3))* Hendrickson Pubs. Marketing, LLC.

Lawson, Steven J. Foundations of Grace: 1400 BC - Ad 100. 2006. (Long Line of Godly Men Ser.). 577p. *(978-1-56769-077-4(7)*, Jacqui Small) Ligonier Ministries.

Mason, John F. Calvinism: A Road to Nowhere. 2010. 464p. pap. 24.99 *(978-1-60957-792-6(2))* Xulon Pr., Inc.

Mouw, Richard J. The Challenges of Cultural Discipleship: Essays in the Line of Abraham Kuyper. 2011. pap. 20.00 ***(978-0-8028-6698-1(0))*** Eerdmans, William B. Publishing Co.

Murrell, Adam. Predestined to Believe. 2009. 136p. pap. 17.00 *(978-1-60608-853-1(X)*, Resource Pubns.) Wipf & Stock Pubs.

—The Young Baptist's Catechism: A Beginner's Guide to the Baptist Confession of Faith Of 1689. 2007. 52p. pap. 7.00 *(978-1-55635-261-4(1)*, Resource Pubns.) Wipf & Stock Pubs.

Naylor, Peter. Calvinism, Communion & the Baptists: A Study of English Calvinistic Baptists from the Late 1600s to the Early 1800s. 2007. (Studies in Baptist History & Thought Ser.). 306p. pap. 31.00 *(978-1-59752-740-8(8)*, Wipf and Stock) Wipf & Stock Pubs.

Oberman, Heiko. Jean Calvin & the Reformation of the Refugees. 2009. (Travaux d'Humanisme et Renaissance Ser.). 232p. (C). 126.00 *(978-2-600-00687-3(7))* Droz, Librairie CHE. Dist: Brown, David Bk. Co., The.

Palm, Franklin C. Calvinism & the Religious Wars. reprint ed. 32.50 *(978-0-404-19880-0(5))* AMS Pr., Inc.

Palmer, Edwin H. The Five Points of Calvinism: A Study Guide, 1 vol. 3rd ed. 2010. (ENG.). 144p. pap. 13.99 *(978-0-8010-7244-4(1))* Baker Bks.

Parker, Charles H. Faith on the Margins: Catholics & Catholicism in the Dutch Golden Age. 2008. (Illus.). 346p. 57.50 *(978-0-674-02662-9(4))* Harvard Univ. Pr.

Picken, Stuart. Historical Dictionary of Calvinism. 2011. (Historical Dictionaries of Religions, Philosophies, & Movements Ser.). (ENG.). 290p. 80.00 ***(978-0-8108-7224-0(2))*** Scarecrow Pr., Inc.

Picken, Stuart D. B. Historical Dictionary of Calvinism. 2012. E-Book ***(978-0-8108-7471-8(7))*** Scarecrow Pr., Inc.

Piper, John. TULIP: The Pursuit of God's Glory in Salvation. 2009. (John Piper Small Group Ser.). 216p. pap. 12.99 *(978-1-4335-0763-2(3))* Crossway.

Punt, Neal. A Theology of Inclusivism. 2008. pap. *(978-0-945315-46-9(5))* Northland Bks.

Rear Admiral Joseph H. Miller. Calvin, the Psychopath. 2009. 572p. 38.49 *(978-1-4389-5980-1(X))*; pap. 26.49 *(978-1-4389-5979-5(6))* AuthorHouse.

Robinson, Marilynne. When I Was a Child I Read Books: Essays. 2012. (Platinum Nonfiction Ser.). (ENG.). 500p. 33.95 ***(978-1-61173-428-7(2))*** Ctr. Point Large Print.

—When I Was a Child I Read Books: Essays. 2012. (ENG., Illus.). 224p. 24.00 ***(978-0-374-29878-4(5))*** Farrar, Straus & Giroux.

Schirrmacher, Thomas, ed. Calvin & World Mission. 2009. 206p. pap. *(978-3-941750-20-3(8))* VTR Verlag fur Theologie und Religionswissenschaft.

Schonberg, David. Is Calvinism Good News. 2010. 182p. pap. 14.99 *(978-1-61579-772-1(6))* Xulon Pr., Inc.

Shearer, Douglas R. Calvin on the Ropes: A Verse by Verse Exposition of Romans That Puts Calvin on the Ropes. 2009. 212p. pap. 17.99 *(978-1-60647-979-7(2))* Xulon Pr., Inc.

Skolny, Chad. Diary of a Calvinist. 2009. 86p. pap. 15.99 *(978-1-4415-5327-0(4))* Xlibris Corp.

Smelley, Hutson. Deconstructing Calvinism: A Biblical Analysis & Refutation. 2009. pap. 15.99 *(978-1-60791-679-6(7))* Xulon Pr., Inc.

Spurgeon, Charles H. The Doctrines of Grace. 2008. 244p. pap. 17.76 *(978-0-557-02143-7(X))* Lulu Enterprises Inc.

Steinmetz, David Curtis. Calvin in Context. 2nd ed. 2010. (ENG.). 328p. pap. 29.95 *(978-0-19-973638-6(3))* Oxford Univ. Pr., Inc.

Stewart, Kenneth J. Ten Myths about Calvinism: Recovering the Breadth of the Reformed Tradition. 2011. (ENG., Illus.). 301p. pap. 24.00 *(978-0-8308-3898-1(8)*, IVP Acad.) InterVarsity Pr.

Storms, Sam. Chosen for Life: The Case for Divine Election. 2007. 240p. pap. 17.99 *(978-1-58134-843-9(6))* Crossway.

Stroup, George W. Calvin. 2009. (Abingdon Pillars of Theology Ser.). 85p. pap. 12.00 *(978-0-687-65913-5(2))* Abingdon Pr.

Sturley, John. Help! I Don't Understand What Is Happening to My Church: A Layman's Field Guide to Calvinist Controversy. 2008. 404p. pap. 24.99 *(978-1-60647-073-2(6))* Xulon Pr., Inc.

Sweetman, Robert. In the Phrygian Mode: Neo-Calvinism, Antiquity, & the Lamentations of Reformational Philosophy. (ENG.). 336p. 2012. 69.95 *(978-0-7618-3020-7(0))* 2007. per. 47.50 *(978-0-7618-3021-4(9))* Univ. Pr. of America, Inc.

Tausch, Arno. Muslim Calvinism: Internal Security & the Lisbon Process in Europe. 2008. 248p. pap. 44.00 *(978-90-5170-995-7(1))* Purdue Univ. Pr.

Todd, Margo, ed. The Perth Kirk Session Book, 1577-1590. 2012. (Scottish History Society 6th Ser.: Volume 2). (Illus.). 584p. 70.00 ***(978-0-906245-31-6(1))*** Scottish History Society GBR. Dist: Boydell & Brewer, Inc.

Toon, Peter. The Emergence of Hyper-Calvinism in English Nonconformity 1689Ð1765. 2011. 172p. pap. 20.00 *(978-1-60899-688-9(3)*, Wipf and Stock) Wipf & Stock Pubs.

Turner, Allan. The Christian & Calvinism. 2007. 204p. pap. 18.95 *(978-0-9777350-3-7(6))* Allanita Pr.

Waggoner, Brad J. & Clendenen, E. Ray. Calvinism: A Southern Baptist Dialogue. 2008. (ENG.). 304p. pap. 19.99 *(978-0-8054-4835-1(7)*, B&H Academic) B&H Publishing Group.

Wallace, Dewey D. Shapers of English Calvinism, 1660-1714: Variety, Persistence, & Transformation, 1 vol. 2011. (Oxford Studies in Historical Theology Ser.). (ENG.). 368p. 74.00 *(978-0-19-974483-1(1))* Oxford Univ. Pr., Inc.

Wallace, Ronald S. Calvin: Geneva & the Reformation. 320p. *(978-0-7073-0512-7(8)*, Burns & Oates) Continuum International Publishing Group, Ltd.

Ward, Dudley. Programmed by God or Free to Choose? Five-Point Calvinism under the Searchlight. 2008. 142p. pap. 18.00 *(978-1-55635-391-8(X)*, Resource Pubns.) Wipf & Stock Pubs.

Washburn, Owen Redington. John Calvin in New England, 1620-1943. 2011. 112p. 39.95 ***(978-1-258-02456-7(X))*** Literary Licensing, LLC.

Whytock, Jack C. Continental Calvinian Influences on the Scottish Reformation: The First Book of Discipline (1560) 2009. (Illus.). 160p. 99.95 *(978-0-7734-4751-6(2))* Mellen, Edwin Pr., The.

Williamson, John. L of the Tulip: A Case for Particular Redemption, 1 vol. 2009. 98p. pap. 16.95 *(978-1-60813-293-5(5))* PublishAmerica, Inc.

Yeager, Jonathan. Enlightened Evangelicalism: The Life & Thought of John Erskine, 1 vol. 2011. (ENG., Illus.). 336p. 74.00 *(978-0-19-977255-1(X))* Oxford Univ. Pr., Inc.

Zafirovski, Milan. Destiny of Modern Societies: The Calvinist Predestination of a New Society. 2011. (Studies in Critical Social Sciences Ser.). (ENG.). 622p. pap. 36.00 ***(978-1-60846-125-7(4))*** Haymarket Bks.

Zafirovski, Milan & Zafirovski. The 'Destiny' of Modern Societies: The Calvinist 'Predestination' of a New Society. 2009. 624p. *(978-90-04-17629-4(2))* BRILL.

CALVINO, ITALO, 1923-1985

Anderson, Douglas. Pictures of Ascent in the Fiction of Edgar Allan Poe. 2009. (ENG., Illus.). 216p. 89.00 *(978-0-230-61943-2(6))* Palgrave Macmillan.

Calvino, Italo, et al. Italo Calvino en México. 2006. (SPA., Illus.). 56p. pap. 13.95 ***(978-968-6445-61-9(7))*** Petra Ediciones, S.A. de C.V. MEX. Dist: Independent Pubs. Group.

Cavallaro, Dani. The Mind of Italo Calvino: A Critical Exploration of His Thought & Writings. 2010. (ENG., Illus.). 210p. pap. 35.00 *(978-0-7864-4766-4(4))* McFarland & Co., Inc. Pubs.

Federici, Federico. Translation as Stylistic Evolution: Italo Calvino Creative Translator of Raymond Queneau. 2009. (Illus.). 320p. pap. 83.00 *(978-90-420-2569-1(7))* Rodopi.

Ferrara, Enrica. Calvino e il Teatro: Storia Di una Passione Rimossa. 2011. (ITA.). *(978-3-0343-0176-3(6))* Lang, Peter Publishing, Inc.

Grundtvig, Birgitte, et al, eds. Image, Eye & Art in Calvino: Writing Visibility. 2006. (Legenda Main Ser.). (ENG., Illus.). 2p. (C). 69.00 *(978-1-904350-59-0(3))* European Humanities Research Ctr. GBR. Dist: Brown, David Bk. Co., The.

Modena, Letizia. Italo Calvino's Architecture of Lightness. 2011. (Routledge Studies in Twentieth-Century Literature Ser.). (ENG., Illus.). 284p. (C). 125.00 *(978-0-415-88038-1(6))* Routledge.

Nannicini Streitberger, Chiara. La revanche de la Discontinuité: Bouleversements du Récit chez Bachmann, Valvino et Perec. 2008. (Nouvelle poétique comparatiste - New Comparative Poetics Ser.). (FRE., Illus.). 322p. pap. 50.95 *(978-90-5201-530-9(9))* PIE - Peter Lang BEL. Dist: Lang, Peter.

Zaccaro, Vanna. Andar per Tracce: Percorsi Di Lettura Su Italo Calvino. 2010. 168p. *(978-88-8232-740-8(X))* Pensa Multimedia.

CALYPSO (MUSIC)

Guilbault, Jocelyne. Governing Sound: Cultural Politics of Trinidad's Carnival Musics. 2007. (Chicago Studies in Ethnomusicology Ser.). (Illus.). 352p. 67.50 *(978-0-226-31059-6(0))* Univ. of Chicago Pr.

—Governing Sound: The Cultural Politics of Trinidad's Carnival Musics. 2007. (Chicago Studies in Ethnomusicology Ser.). (ENG., Illus.). 352p. 30.00 *(978-0-226-31060-2(4))* Univ. of Chicago Pr.

Laplume, Tony. The Cloak of Shrouded Men: Escapades of the Eidolon, Cotton Colinaude. 2007. 348p. per. 19.95 *(978-0-595-45252-1(3))* iUniverse, Inc.

Regis, Louis. Black Stalin: Kaisonian. 2007. (Illus.). 156p. pap. *(978-976-8189-51-6(7))* Arawak Pubns.

CAMALDOLESE

Camaldolese Spirituality. 2007. pap. 17.00 *(978-0-9728132-5-9(X))* Holy Family Hermitage.

CAMARGUE (FRANCE)

Daraux, Jean-Loup. And Dreams of Home. 2011. (Illus.). 272p. 95.00 ***(978-1-905216-22-2(X))*** Verbavolantedizioni ITA. Dist: Ingram Pub. Services.

CAMARO AUTOMOBILE

Banacki, Walter J. Camaro Z28 Is Back! 2009. 60p. pap. 15.49 *(978-1-4389-4364-0(4))* AuthorHouse.

Edsall, Larry. Camaro: A Legend Reborn. 2009. (ENG., Illus.). 144p. 30.00 *(978-0-7603-2819-4(6)*, 0760328196, Motorbooks) MBI Publishing Co. LLC.

Holmstrom, Darwin. Camaro: Five Generations of Performance. 2011. (ENG., Illus.). 348p. pap. 29.99 *(978-0-7603-4018-9(8)*, 0760340188, Motorbooks) MBI Publishing Co. LLC.

Newhardt, David. The Complete Book of Camaro: Every Model Since 1967. 2012. (ENG., Illus.). 288p. 50.00 *(978-0-7603-3961-9(9)*, 0760339619, Motorbooks) MBI Publishing Co. LLC.

Newhardt, David, photos by. Camaro. 2009. (First Gear Ser.). (ENG., Illus.). 256p. pap. 19.99 *(978-0-7603-3588-8(5)*, 0760335885, Motorbooks) MBI Publishing Co. LLC.

Old Cars Weekly Staff. Camaro & Firebird: GM's Power Twins. 2010. (ENG., Illus.). 208p. pap. 16.99 *(978-1-4402-1550-6(2))* F&W Media, Inc.

Potak, Joseph. 1993-2002 Camaro & Firebird Performance Handbook. 2010. (Motorbooks Workshop Ser.). (ENG., Illus.). 160p. pap. 24.99 *(978-0-7603-3709-7(8)*, 0760337098, Motorbooks) MBI Publishing Co. LLC.

Publications International Staff & Witzenburg, Gary. Camaro: An American Icon. 2009. 160p. 13.98 *(978-1-4127-1667-3(5))* Publications International, Ltd.

Schild, Jim. Chevrolet Camaro: 1970-1981. 2008. (Collector's Originality Guide Ser.). (ENG., Illus.). 144p. 37.95 *(978-0-7603-3134-7(0)*, 0760331340, Motorbooks) MBI Publishing Co. LLC.

Scott, Jason. Restorer's Reference Camaro 1967-1969. 2012. (Restorer's Reference Ser.). (ENG., Illus.). 128p. pap. 27.99 ***(978-0-7603-4299-2(7)***, 0760342997, Motorbooks) MBI Publishing Co. LLC.

Sessions, Ron. Classic Camaro HP1564: Repair, Restoration & Upgrades. 2011. 176p. 21.95 *(978-1-55788-564-7(8)*, HP Trade) Penguin Group (USA) Inc.

Tony, Huntimer. How to Restore Your Camaro 1967-1969. 2010. 160p. pap. 29.95 *(978-1-934709-10-8(7)*, S-A Design) CarTech, Inc.

Young, Anthony. Camaro. (Illus.). 156p. pap. *(978-0-681-20005-0(7)*, Lowe & B. Hould Pubs.) Borders Pr.

CAMBISTRY

see Foreign Exchange

CAMBODIA

Chatterjee, Bijan R. Indian Cultural Influences in Cambodia. reprint ed. 28.00 *(978-0-404-16799-8(3))* AMS Pr., Inc.

Poree, Guy. Moeurs et Coutumes des Khmers. (Illus.). reprint ed. 42.50 *(978-0-404-16850-6(7))* AMS Pr., Inc.

CAMBODIA—ANTIQUITIES

see also Angkor (Extinct City)

Briggs, Lawrence Palmer. The Ancient Khmer Empire: Transactions of the American Philosophical Society, V41, Part 1, February 1951. 2011. 300p. 48.95 ***(978-1-258-10377-4(X))*** Literary Licensing, LLC.

Sobol, Richard. The Mysteries of Angkor Wat. 2011. (Traveling Photographer Ser.). (ENG., Illus.). 48p. (J). (gr. 1-5). 17.99 *(978-0-7636-4166-5(9))* Candlewick Pr.

CAMBODIA—BIOGRAPHY

Am, Pheara (Peter). Blessing over Darkness: A Real Life Journey from Darkness to Blessing. 2009. 184p. pap. 16.95 *(978-1-4401-2407-5(8))* iUniverse, Inc.

Ashe, Var Hong. From Phnom Penh to Paradise. (Illus.). 222p. pap. *(978-0-340-41590-0(8)*, Hodder & Stoughton) Hodder General Publishing Div.

Bohlender, Heather & Blake, Chris. Honestly, I'm Struggling: Living Beyond the Student Missionary Cliche. 2010. (Illus.). 204p. *(978-0-280-24495-0(9))* Review & Herald Publishing Assn.

—Honestly, I'm Struggling: Stretched, Challenged, & Charged: Blogs from a Student Missionary. 2010. 204p. pap. 14.99 *(978-0-8280-2449-5(9))* Review & Herald Publishing Assn.

Boulom, Jeudi. Enhancing Your Life Now: Four Basic Principles to Achieving Wellness. 2010. 234p. pap. *(978-1-935586-13-5(0))* Aviva Publishing.

Grossman, Kari Grady. Bones That Float: A Story of Adopting Cambodia. 2007. (Illus.). 256p. 24.95 *(978-0-9792493-0-3(9)*, BTF-HC) Wild Heaven Pr.

Heinzl, Richard. Cambodia Calling: A Memoir from the Frontlines of Humanitarian Aid. 2008. (ENG., Illus.). 272p. 26.95 *(978-0-470-15325-3(3)*, Wiley) Wiley, John & Sons, Inc.

Hen, Siphallen. The Hidden Identity. 2007. 284p. per. 13.95 *(978-1-4327-1371-3(X))* Outskirts Pr., Inc.

Himm, Sokreaksa S. After the Heavy Rain: The Khmer Rouge Killed His Family - He Tracked Them Down — But Not for Revenge ..., 1 vol. 2007. (Illus.). 192p. pap. 11.99 *(978-0-8254-6181-1(2)*, Monarch Bks.) Lion Hudson PLC GBR. Dist: Kregel Pubns.

Lach, Mony. The Chapters of My Life. 2008. 461p. pap. 29.95 *(978-1-60563-711-2(4))* PublishAmerica, Inc.

Lim, Kieng Sieu. Red Undertow. 2010. 622p. pap. 27.88 *(978-0-557-55476-8(4))* Lulu Enterprises Inc.

Pa, Chileng & Mortland, Carol A. Escaping the Khmer Rouge: A Cambodian Memoir. 2008. (ENG., Illus.). 240p. per. 29.95 *(978-0-7864-3672-9(7))* McFarland & Co., Inc. Pubs.

Penner, Barbara. To a Third Country. 2011. 322p. pap. ***(978-1-77069-204-6(5))*** Word Alive Pr.

Tonya K. Brown. Just How Much You Can Bear. 2007. 84p. per. 12.95 *(978-1-4327-0798-9(1))* Outskirts Pr., Inc.

Ung, Loung. Lucky Child. 2007. *(978-0-7322-8348-3(5)*, HarperPerennial) HarperCollins Pubs. Australia.

Ung, Loung. Lulu in the Sky: A Daughter of Cambodia Finds Love, Healing, & Double Happiness. 2012. (P. S. Ser.). (ENG.). 368p. pap. 15.99 ***(978-0-06-209191-8(3)***, HarperPerennial) HarperCollins Pubs.

Wright, O. B. Whiskey Oscar Seven Bravo... /WO7B, A Tale of Cambodia 1993. 2009. 188p. pap. 12.94 *(978-1-4357-3026-7(7))* Lulu Enterprises Inc.

Yimsut, Ronnie. Facing the Khmer Rouge: A Cambodian Journey. 2011. (Genocide, Political Violence, Human Rights Ser.). (ENG.). 288p. 72.00 *(978-0-8135-5151-7(X))*; (Illus.). 270p. (C). pap. 26.95 *(978-0-8135-5152-4(8))* Rutgers Univ. Pr.

CAMBODIA—DESCRIPTION AND TRAVEL

Ashe, Var Hong. From Phnom Penh to Paradise. (Illus.). 222p. pap. *(978-0-340-41590-0(8)*, Hodder & Stoughton) Hodder General Publishing Div.

Boobbyer, Claire & Spooner, Andrew. Vietnam, Cambodia & Laos Handbook. 3rd ed. 2011. (Footprint - Handbooks Ser.). (ENG., Illus.). 506p. 25.95

(978-1-907263-16-3(0)) Footprint Handbooks GBR. Dist: Globe Pequot Pr., The.

Brukoff, Barry & Jassup, Helen Ibbitson. The Temples of Cambodia: The Heart of Angkor. 2011. (ENG., Illus.). 256p. 65.00 *(978-0-86565-262-0(7))* Vendome Pr., The.

Candee, Helen Churchill. Angkor the Magnificent: The Wonder City of Ancient Cambodia. Davis, Kent, ed. 2008. (ENG., Illus.). 376p. 49.00 *(978-1-934431-00-9(1))* DatASIA.

Chavanat, Damien, et al. Cambodia & Angkor: A Travel Sketchbook. 2007. (ENG., Illus.). 190p. 35.00 *(978-981-4068-72-7(1)*, Didier Millet,Csi) Continental Sales, Inc.

Collard, Paul M. Cambodge et Cambodgiens: Metamorphose du Royaume Khmer par une Methode Francaise de Protectorat. reprint ed. 37.50 *(978-0-404-16806-3(X))* AMS Pr., Inc.

Dorling Kindersley Publishing Staff. Eyewitness Travel Guide - Cambodia & Laos. 2011. (Eyewitness Travel Guides). (ENG.). 304p. pap. 25.00 *(978-0-7566-6977-5(4))* Dorling Kindersley Publishing, Inc.

DuBasky, Valentina. The Cambodian Journal: Drawings 1994-1998. 2009. (Illus.). 68p. pap. 25.00 *(978-0-9823480-1-7(0)*, Abingdon Square) Abingdon Square Publishing, Ltd.

El-Sawy, Twefic. To Cambodia with Love. Brouwer, Andy, ed. 2010. (To Asia with Love Ser.). (ENG.). 240p. pap. 21.95 *(978-1-934159-08-8(5))* ThingsAsian Pr.

Graceffo, Antonio. Rediscovering the Khmers. 2008. 200p. pap. *(978-1-932966-56-5(0))* Gom Publishing, LLC.

Gray, Spalding. Swimming to Cambodia. 2008. (ENG.). 48p. pap. 8.50 *(978-1-58342-571-8(3))* Dramatic Publishing Co.

Kemp, Hans & Wall, Conor. Carrying Cambodia. 2010. (Illus.). 144p. pap. 22.95 *(978-962-85637-8-4(5))* Visionary World, Ltd. HKG. Dist: AtlasBooks Distribution.

Krantz, Jim, photos by. Surviving Cambodia. 2006. per. 20.00 *(978-0-9707278-6-2(0))* Paper Mirror Pr.

Leclere, Adhemard. Cambodge: Fetes Civiles et Religieuses. reprint ed. 47.50 *(978-0-404-16832-2(9))* AMS Pr., Inc.

Locken, E. Travel Journal Cambodia. 2009. 192p. pap. 20.95 *(978-0-557-08028-1(2))* Lulu Enterprises Inc.

Lonely Planet Staff, et al. Cambodia. 7th ed. 2010. (Country Guide Ser.). (ENG., Illus.). 376p. pap. 22.99 *(978-1-74179-457-1(9))* Lonely Planet Pubns.

Loti, Pierre. Siam. 2006. (ENG.). 220p. per. *(978-1-4067-3375-4(X)*, Hesperides Pr.) Read Bks.

North, Peter. Cambodia. 1 vol. 2008. (CultureShock! Ser.). (ENG., Illus.). 280p. pap. 15.95 *(978-0-7614-5477-9(2))* Marshall Cavendish Corp.

—CultureShock! Cambodia. 2007. (Illus.). 280p. pap. 15.95 *(978-981-232-901-1(3))* Marshall Cavendish International (Asia) Private Ltd. SGP. Dist: Marshall Cavendish Corp.

Palmer, Beverley & Rough Guides Staff. The Rough Guide to Cambodia. 4th ed. 2011. (ENG., Illus.). 360p. 21.99 *(978-1-84836-889-7(5))* Rough Guides, Ltd. GBR. Dist: Dorling Kindersley Publishing, Inc.

Passage to Angkor. 3rd ed. 2008. (Illus.). 144p. 59.95 *(978-0-9653574-3-2(0))* Friends Without a Border.

Ranges, Trevor. National Geographic Traveler: Cambodia. 2010. (National Geographic Traveler Ser.). (ENG., Illus.). 320p. pap. 25.95 *(978-1-4262-0520-0(1)*, National Geographic) National Geographic Society.

Ray, Nick. Cambodia. 8th rev. ed. 2012. (Country Guide Ser.). (ENG., Illus.). 384p. pap. 23.99 ***(978-1-74179-965-1(1))*** Lonely Planet Pubns.

Ray, Nick. Vietnam, Cambodia, Laos & Northern Thailand, 85 vols. 3rd rev. ed. 2012. (Multi Country Guide Ser.). (ENG., Illus.). 544p. pap. 24.99 *(978-1-74179-823-4(X))* Lonely Planet Pubns.

Ripa, Giuseppe, photos by & suppl. Giuseppe Ripa: Stone Memories, 1 vol. 2007. (ITA & ENG., Illus.). 104p. pap. 39.95 *(978-88-8158-629-2(7))* Charta ITA. Dist: D.A.P./Distributed Art Pubs.

Rooney, Dawn. Angkor: Cambodia's Wondrous Khmer Temples. 6th ed. 2011. (Odyssey Illustrated Guides). (ENG., Illus.). 496p. pap. 27.95 *(978-962-217-802-1(2)*, 217802) Airphoto International/Odyssey HKG. Dist: Norton, W. W. & Co., Inc.

Rooney, Dawn F. Angkor Observed: A Travel Anthology of 'Those There Before' 2006. (Orchid Guides Ser.). (ENG., Illus.). pap. 23.00 *(978-974-8304-79-3(5))* Orchid Pr. THA. Dist: National Bk. Network.

Sok, Channthy & Liao, Chun-Hsiung. Tourist's Satisfaction - Measuring Tourist's Satisfaction on Destination Loyalty: A Case of Angkor Tourism Sites. 2008. 92p. pap. *(978-3-8364-8118-2(9))* VDM Verlag Dr. Mueller e.K.

Spooner, Andrew. Angkor Wat Footprint Focus. 2011. (Footprint Focus Ser.). (ENG., Illus.). 88p. pap. 8.95 *(978-1-908206-14-5(4))* Footprint Handbooks GBR. Dist: Globe Pequot Pr., The.

—Travel Guide to Cambodia. 6th ed. 2011. (Footprint - Handbooks Ser.). (ENG., Illus.). 296p. 24.95 *(978-1-907263-20-0(9))* Footprint Handbooks GBR. Dist: Globe Pequot Pr., The.

Stanford, David. Angkor. 2009. (ENG., Illus.). 112p. 29.95 *(978-0-7112-3044-6(7))* Lincoln, Frances Ltd. GBR. Dist: Perseus-PGW.

Sterling, Richard & Dorling Kindersley Publishing Staff. Vietnam & Angkor Wat. 2011. (Eyewitness Travel Guides). (ENG.). 312p. pap. 25.00 *(978-0-7566-7031-3(4))* Dorling Kindersley Publishing, Inc.

Thomas Cook Publishing Staff. Cambodia. 2nd ed. 2010. (Travellers - Thomas Cook Ser.). (ENG., Illus.). 176p. pap. 16.95 *(978-1-84848-238-8(8))* Cook, Thomas Publishing GBR. Dist: Globe Pequot Pr., The.

Travis, Tim & Travis, Cindie. Down the Road in Thailand, Cambodia & Vietnam: A Bicycle Tour Through War, Genocide & Forgiveness. 2010. (Illus.). 228p. pap. ***(978-0-9754427-6-0(7))*** Down The Road Publishing.

Vater, Tom. Moon Cambodia. 2009. (Moon Handbooks). (ENG., Illus.). 344p. pap. 19.95 *(978-1-59880-214-6(3))* Avalon Travel Publishing.

—Moon Spotlight Angkor Wat. 2010. (Moon Spotlight Ser.). (ENG.). 72p. pap. 7.95 *(978-1-59880-561-1(4))* Avalon Travel Publishing.

CAMBODIA—ECONOMIC CONDITIONS

Ear, Sophal. Aid Dependence in Cambodia: How Financial Assistance Undermines Democracy. 2012. (ENG., Illus.). 240p. (gr. 17). 50.00 ***(978-0-231-16112-1(3))*** Columbia Univ. Pr.

Hughes, Caroline & Kiernan, Ben, eds. Conflict Change in Cambodia. 2006. 160p. 160.00 *(978-0-415-36592-3(X))* Routledge.

Hughes, Caroline, et al. Dependent Communities: Aid & Politics in Cambodia & East Timor. 2009. (Illus.). 275p. 46.95 *(978-0-87727-778-1(8))*; pap. 23.95 *(978-0-87727-748-4(6))* Cornell Univ. Pr.

Icon Group International, Inc. Staff, compiled by. The 2006 Economic & Product Market Databook for Bhnom Penh, Cambodia. 2006. 618p. ring bd. 95.00 *(978-0-497-80195-3(7))* Icon Group International, Inc.

—The 2006 Economic & Product Market Databook for Kompong Cham, Cambodia. 2006. 618p. ring bd. 95.00 *(978-0-497-82008-4(0))* Icon Group International, Inc.

Kerbo, Harold R. The Persistence of Cambodian Poverty: From the Killing Fields to Today. 2011. (ENG., Illus.). 228p. pap. 45.00 *(978-0-7864-6408-1(9))* McFarland & Co., Inc. Pubs.

Ollier, Leakthina Chan-Pech, ed. Expressions of Cambodia: The Politics of Tradition, Identity, & Change. 2006. (Routledge Contemporary Southeast Asia Ser.: Vol. 12). (ENG., Illus.). 248p. (C). 160.00 *(978-0-415-38554-1(7))* Routledge.

An Overview of Cambodia & the Need for Debt Recycling: How Can the U.S. Be of Assistance?: Hearing Before the Subcommittee on Asia, the Pacific, & the Global Environment of the Committee on Foreign Affairs, House of Representatives, One Hundred Tenth Congress, First [i.e. Second] Session, February 14, 2008. 2008. (Illus.). iii, 52p. *(978-0-16-081511-9(8)*, 552-070-37867-7) United States Government Printing Office.

Roberts, Wade C. Landmines in Cambodia: Past, Present, & Future. 2011. *(978-1-60497-761-5(2))* Cambria Pr.

Seng, Youraden. Sustainability of Commercial Microfinance. 2010. 132p. pap. *(978-3-8383-8077-3(0))* Lambert Academic Publishing.

Sokphea, Young & Pongquan, Soparth. Governance of Decentralized Commune Development Planning. 2010. 236p. pap. *(978-3-8383-7915-9(2))* Lambert Academic Publishing.

Torres, Juliana. Community Based Ecotourism & Conservation. 2010. 134p. pap. *(978-3-8383-9331-5(7))* Lambert Academic Publishing.

CAMBODIA—FOREIGN RELATIONS

Bull, Carolyn. No Entry Without Strategy: Building the Rule of Law under un Transitional Administration. 2008. (ENG., Illus.). 360p. pap. 35.00 *(978-92-808-1151-3(7))* United Nations Pubns.

Cambodia's Small Debt: When Will the U.S. Forgive?: Hearing Before the Subcommittee on Asia, the Pacific, & the Global Environment of the Committee on Foreign Affairs, House of Representatives, One Hundred Eleventh Congress, Second Session, September 30, 2010. 2010. ii, 44p. ***(978-0-16-087569-4(2)***, 552-070-42199-8) United States Government Printing Office.

Clymer, Kenton J. Troubled Relations: The United States & Cambodia since 1870. 2007. (Illus.). 266p. pap. 25.00 *(978-0-87580-615-0(5))* Northern Illinois Univ. Pr.

Fielding, Leslie. Before the Killing Fields: Witness to Cambodia & the Vietnam War. 2007. (ENG., Illus.). 288p. 58.00 *(978-1-84511-493-0(0))* I. B. Tauris & Co., Ltd. GBR. Dist: Macmillan.

Hallsey, Joshua. Us Foreign Policy in Cambodia, 1945-1993. 2009. 120p. pap. *(978-3-639-17036-8(9))* VDM Verlag Dr. Mueller e.K.

Mahoney, Robert J. The Mayaguez Incident: Testing America's Resolve in the Post-Vietnam Era. 2011. (Modern Southeast Asia Ser.). (Illus.). 320p. 39.95 *(978-0-89672-719-9(X))* Texas Tech Univ. Pr.

An Overview of Cambodia & the Need for Debt Recycling: How Can the U.S. Be of Assistance?: Hearing Before the Subcommittee on Asia, the Pacific, & the Global Environment of the Committee on Foreign Affairs, House of Representatives, One Hundred Tenth Congress, First [i.e. Second] Session, February 14, 2008. 2008. (Illus.). iii, 52p. *(978-0-16-081511-9(8)*, 552-070-37867-7) United States Government Printing Office.

Peou, Sorpong. International Democracy Assistance for Peacebuilding: Cambodia & Beyond. 2007. (Rethinking Peace & Conflict Studies). (ENG.). 240p. 100.00 *(978-0-230-52137-7(1))* Palgrave Macmillan.

Richardson, Sophie. China, Cambodia, & the Five Principles of Peaceful Coexistence. 2009. (ENG.). 344p. (gr. 17). 50.00 *(978-0-231-14336-8(9))* Columbia Univ. Pr.

Rogers, Lisa Waller. The Great Storm: The Hurricane Diary of J. T. King, Galveston, Texas 1900. 2010. (Lone Star Journals). (Illus.). 160p. (J). pap. 14.95 *(978-0-89672-720-5(3))* Texas Tech Univ. Pr.

Van der Kraan, Alfons & Van der Cruysse, Alfons. Murder & Mayhem in Seventeenth-Century Cambodia: Anthony Van Diemen vs. King Ramadhipati I. 2009. (Illus.). 80p. (C). pap. 22.00 ***(978-974-9511-62-6(X))*** Silkworm Bks. THA. Dist: Univ. of Washington Pr.

CAMBODIA—HISTORY

Am, Pheara (Peter). Blessing over Darkness: A Real Life Journey from Darkness to Blessing. 2009. 184p. pap. 16.95 *(978-1-4401-2407-5(8))* iUniverse, Inc.

Au, Sokhieng. Mixed Medicines: Health & Culture in French Colonial Cambodia. 2011. (ENG., Illus.). 280p. 95.00 *(978-0-226-03163-7(2))*; pap. 35.00 *(978-0-226-03164-4(0))* Univ. of Chicago Pr.

Bizot, Francois & Andouard, Antoine. Facing the Torturer: Inside the Mind of a War Criminal. West, Joseph & Mandell, Charlotte, trs. from FRE. 2012. (ENG.). 224p. 25.00 ***(978-0-307-27350-5(4)***, Knopf) Knopf Doubleday Publishing Group.

Bracken, Gregory Byrne. Angkor: Sketches of an Ancient City, 1 vol. 2010. (ENG.). 120p. pap. 24.50 *(978-981-261-875-7(9))* Marshall Cavendish Corp.

Briggs, Lawrence Palmer. The Ancient Khmer Empire: Transactions of the American Philosophical Society, V41, Part 1, February 1951. 2011. 300p. 48.95 ***(978-1-258-10377-4(X))*** Literary Licensing, LLC.

Brinkley, Joel. Cambodia's Curse: The Modern History of a Troubled Land. 2011. (ENG., Illus.). 416p. 27.99 *(978-1-58648-787-4(6))* PublicAffairs.

Chandler, David. A History of Cambodia. 4th ed. 2007. (ENG., Illus.). 384p. pap. 38.00 *(978-0-8133-4363-1(1))* Westview Pr.

Chon, Gina & Thet, Sambath. Behind the Killing Fields: A Khmer Rouge Leader & One of His Victims. 2010. (Pennsylvania Studies in Human Rights Ser.). (Illus.). 212p. (C). 49.95 *(978-0-8122-4245-4(9))* Univ. of Pennsylvania Pr.

Conboy, Ken. Fank: A History of the Cambodian Armed Forces 1970-1975. 2011. 286p. pap. ***(978-979-3780-86-3(X))*** Equinox Publishing Ltd.

Conrad, Penne D. Out of the Killing Fields, into the Light. 2011. pap. 9.99 *(978-1-59955-525-6(5))* Cedar Fort, Inc./CFI Distribution.

Corfield, Justin. The History of Cambodia, 1 vol. 2009. (Greenwood Histories of the Modern Nations Ser.). (Illus.). 165p. 49.95 *(978-0-313-35722-0(6)*, GR5722) Greenwood Publishing Group, Inc.

Cormack, Don. Killing Fields Living Fields. 2009. (ENG., Illus.). 464p. 13.99 *(978-1-84550-511-0(5))* Christian Focus Pubns. GBR. Dist: STL Distribution North America.

Cummins, Nick. The 1997 Coup in Cambodia: The Prince, the Comrade & the Revolutionary. 2007. 34p. (C). pap. 9.95 *(978-1-876924-51-5(9)*, Monash Univ. Pr.) Monash Univ. Publishing AUS. Dist: International Specialized Bk. Services.

Fielding, Leslie. Before the Killing Fields: Witness to Cambodia & the Vietnam War. 2007. (ENG., Illus.). 288p. 58.00 *(978-1-84511-493-0(0))* I. B. Tauris & Co., Ltd. GBR. Dist: Macmillan.

Guilmartin, John F., Jr. A Very Short War: The Mayaguez & the Battle of Koh Tang. 46th ed. 2011. (Williams-Ford Texas A&M University Military History Ser.). (ENG.). 268p. pap. 23.95 *(978-1-60344-196-4(4))* Texas A&M Univ. Pr.

Hansen, Anne Ruth & Ledgerwood, Judy, eds. At the Edge of the Forest: Essays on Cambodia, History, & Narrative in Honor of David Chandler. 2009. 251p. 46.95 *(978-0-87727-776-7(1))*; pap. 23.95 *(978-0-87727-746-0(X))* Cornell Univ., Southeast Asia Program Pubns.

Heckman, Charles W. The Phnom Penh Airlift: Confessions of a Pig Pilot in the Early 1970s. alt. ed. 2012. (ENG., Illus.). 240p. pap. 25.00 ***(978-0-7864-6763-1(0))*** McFarland & Co., Inc. Pubs.

Hel, Christopher A. The Adventures of Kid Combat: A Secret Lost, Vol 1. 2007. (Kid Combat Ser.). (ENG.). 156p. (YA). per. 13.95 *(978-1-58736-815-8(3))* Wheatmark.

Herschensohn, Bruce. An American Amnesia: How the U.S. Congress Forced the Surrenders of South Vietnam & Cambodia. 2010. 192p. 22.00 *(978-0-8253-0632-7(9))* Beaufort Bks., Inc.

Himm, Sokreaksa S. After the Heavy Rain: The Khmer Rouge Killed His Family - He Tracked Them Down — But Not for Revenge ..., 1 vol. 2007. (Illus.). 192p. pap. 11.99 *(978-0-8254-6181-1(2)*, Monarch Bks.) Lion Hudson PLC GBR. Dist: Kregel Pubns.

Jacq-Hergoualc'h, Michel. The Armies of Angkor: Military Structure & Weaponry of the Khmers. Smithies, Michael, tr. from FRE. 2007. (ENG., Illus.). 200p. 40.00 *(978-974-524-096-4(6))* Orchid Pr. THA. Dist: National Bk. Network.

Jacques, Claude & Freeman, Michael. Ancient Angkor. 2009. (ENG., Illus.). 240p. pap. 25.00 *(978-974-9863-81-7(X)*, River Bks. Pr. Dist A C) Antique Collectors' Club GBR. Dist: National Bk. Network.

Jacques, Claude & LaFond, Philippe. The Khmer Empire: Cities & Sactuaries from the 5th to the 13th Century. White, Tom, tr. 2007. (ENG., Illus.). 280p. *(978-974-9863-30-5(5)*, River Bks. Pr. Dist A C) Antique Collectors' Club.

Kem, Chanthou. The Land I Lost, 1 vol. 2009. 207p. pap. 19.95 *(978-1-61582-692-6(0))* PublishAmerica, Inc.

Kiernan, Ben. Genocide & Resistance in Southeast Asia: Documentation, Denial, & Justice in Cambodia & East Timor. 2007. (ENG., Illus.). 363p. (gr. 11). 49.95 *(978-1-4128-0668-8(2))*; pap. 29.95 *(978-1-4128-0669-5(0))* Transaction Pubs.

Levine, Peg. Love & Dread in Cambodia. 2010. (Illus.). 260p. pap. 28.00 *(978-9971-69-472-2(7))* National Univ. of Singapore Pr. SGP. Dist: Univ. of Hawaii Pr.

Marston, John, ed. Anthropology & Community in Cambodia: Reflections on the Work of May Ebihara. 2011. 258p. pap. 29.95 *(978-1-876924-74-4(6)*, Monash Univ. Pr.) Monash Univ. Publishing AUS. Dist: International Specialized Bk. Services.

Muller, Gregor. Colonial Cambodia's 'Bad Frenchmen' The rise of French rule & the life of Thomas Caraman, 1840-87. 2009. 294p. pap. 39.95 *(978-0-415-54553-2(6))* Routledge.

Osborne, Milton. Phnom Penh: A Cultural History. 2008. (CityScapes Ser.). (ENG., Illus.). 256p. 60.00 *(978-0-19-534247-5(X))*; pap. 16.95 *(978-0-19-534248-2(8))* Oxford Univ. Pr., Inc.

Reminick, Gerald. An ACT of Piracy: The Seizure of the American-Flag Merchant Ship Mayagüez In 1975. 2009. 22.95 *(978-1-889901-47-3(4))* Glencannon Pr.

Roberts, Wade C. Landmines in Cambodia: Past, Present, & Future. 2011. *(978-1-60497-761-5(2))* Cambria Pr.

Roveda, Vittorio. Buddhist Painting in Cambodia. 2009. (ENG., Illus.). 200p. *(978-974-9863-52-7(6)*, River Bks. Pr. Dist A C) Antique Collectors' Club.

Roveda, Vittorio & Clark, Joyce. Bayon Reconsidered. 2007. (Illus.). 256p. 85.00 *(978-974-9863-05-3(4))* River Bks. THA. Dist: Antique Collectors' Club.

Smithies, Michael, tr. from FRE. Angkor & Cambodia in the Sixteenth Century: According to Portuguese & Spanish Sources. 2006. (ENG., Illus.). 208p. 35.00 *(978-974-524-053-7(2))* Orchid Pr. THA. Dist: National Bk. Network.

Snellgrove, David L. Khmer Civilization & Angkor. 2006. (Orchid Guides Ser.). (ENG., Illus.). pap. 19.00 *(978-974-8304-95-3(7))* Orchid Pr. THA. Dist: National Bk. Network.

Sok, Channthy & Liao, Chun-Hsiung. Tourist's Satisfaction - Measuring Tourist's Satisfaction on Destination Loyalty: A Case of Angkor Tourism Sites. 2008. 92p. pap. *(978-3-8364-8118-2(9))* VDM Verlag Dr. Mueller e.K.

Stuart-Fox, Martin & Ung, Bunheang. The Murderous Revolution: Life & Death in Pol Pot's Kampuchea. 2006. (Asian Portraits Ser.). (ENG., Illus.). pap. 23.00 *(978-974-8299-14-3(7))* Orchid Pr. THA. Dist: National Bk. Network.

Touch, Van. Behind the Cambodian Killing Fields. 2007. (C). pap. *(978-0-9796878-1-5(0))*; pap. *(978-0-9796878-2-2(9))*; pap. *(978-0-9796878-0-8(2))* Touch, Van.

Tyner, James A. The Killing of Cambodia: Geopolitics, Genocide & the Unmaking of Space. 2008. (Illus.). 228p. 114.95 *(978-0-7546-7096-4(1))* Ashgate Publishing Co.

Van der Kraan, Alfons & Van der Cruysse, Alfons. Murder & Mayhem in Seventeenth-Century Cambodia: Anthony Van Diemen vs. King Ramadhipati I. 2009. (Illus.). 80p. (C). pap. 22.00 ***(978-974-9511-62-6(X))*** Silkworm Bks. THA. Dist: Univ. of Washington Pr.

Vecchia, Stefano. The Khmers. 2008. (ENG., Illus.). 208p. 35.00 *(978-88-544-0311-6(3))* White Star ITA. Dist: Random Hse., Inc.

Waring, Rob. Cambodia Animal Rescue. 2008. (ENG.). 24p. (C). pap. 10.95 *(978-1-4240-4432-0(4))* Cengage Heinle.

Weltig, Matthew Scott. Pol Pot's Cambodia. 2008. (Dictatorships Ser.). (YA). (gr. 7-12). lib. bdg. 38.60 *(978-0-8225-8668-5(1))* Twenty First Century Bks.

Winter, Tim. Post-Conflict Heritage Postcolonial Tourism. 2011. (ENG.). 200p. pap. 42.95 ***(978-0-415-68958-8(9))*** Routledge.

Wise, James & Baron, Scott. 14 Hour War. 2011. (Illus.). 256p. 34.95 *(978-1-59114-974-3(6))* Naval Institute Pr.

Witcher, Russ. The Debate in the U.S. Senate about the War in South Vietnam & Cambodia, 1973-1975: Chronicling the Struggle for Power Between the Congress & the Presidency. 2008. 120p. 99.95 *(978-0-7734-4961-9(2))* Mellen, Edwin Pr., The.

Wood, Richard. Call Sign Rustic: The Secret Air War over Cambodia, 1970-1973. 2010. (ENG., Illus.). 208p. pap. 19.95 *(978-1-58834-284-3(0))* Smithsonian Institution Pr.

Yimsut, Ronnie. Facing the Khmer Rouge: A Cambodian Journey. 2011. (Genocide, Political Violence, Human Rights Ser.). (ENG.). 288p. 72.00 *(978-0-8135-5151-7(X))*; (Illus.). 270p. (C). pap. 26.95 *(978-0-8135-5152-4(8))* Rutgers Univ. Pr.

CAMBODIA—POLITICS AND GOVERNMENT

Affonço, Denise. To the End of Hell: One Woman's Struggle to Survive Cambodia's Khmer Rouge. 2009. (ENG.). 232p. pap. *(978-1-906702-07-6(1))* Reportage Pr.

Ali, Pervaiz. The Depletion of Forests in Cambodi. 2011. 56p. pap. ***(978-3-8443-0708-5(7))*** Lambert Academic Publishing.

Bergin, Sean. The Khmer Rouge & the Cambodian Genocide. (Genocide in Modern Times Ser.). 64p. 2009. (gr. 6-6). 58.50 *(978-1-61512-675-0(9))* 2008. (Illus.). (YA). (gr. 9-12). lib. bdg. 29.25 *(978-1-4042-1822-2(X))* Rosen Publishing Group, Inc., The.

Brinkley, Joel. Cambodia's Curse: The Modern History of a Troubled Land. 2011. (ENG., Illus.). 416p. 27.99 *(978-1-58648-787-4(6))* PublicAffairs.

Bull, Carolyn. No Entry Without Strategy: Building the Rule of Law under un Transitional Administration. 2008. (ENG., Illus.). 360p. pap. 35.00 *(978-92-808-1151-3(7))* United Nations Pubns.

Chhalith Ou R. Z. Halleson. Spare Them? No Profit Remove Them? No Loss: The True Story of a Young Teenager in Pol Pot's Cambodia. 2010. 204p. pap. 17.95 *(978-1-4502-0623-5(9))* iUniverse, Inc.

Chon, Gina & Thet, Sambath. Behind the Killing Fields: A Khmer Rouge Leader & One of His Victims. 2010. (Pennsylvania Studies in Human Rights Ser.). (Illus.). 212p. (C). 49.95 *(978-0-8122-4245-4(9))* Univ. of Pennsylvania Pr.

Chum, Samnang. Ngo Coordination & Cambodia's Aid Effectiveness. 2010. 224p. pap. *(978-3-8383-4604-5(1))* Lambert Academic Publishing.

Cummins, Nick. The 1997 Coup in Cambodia: The Prince, the Comrade & the Revolutionary. 2007. 34p. (C). pap. 9.95 *(978-1-876924-51-5(9)*, Monash Univ. Pr.) Monash Univ. Publishing AUS. Dist: International Specialized Bk. Services.

Ear, Sophal. Aid Dependence in Cambodia: How Financial Assistance Undermines Democracy. 2012. (ENG., Illus.). 240p. (gr. 17). 50.00 ***(978-0-231-16112-1(3))*** Columbia Univ. Pr.

Gilfillan, Beth. Coercion & Resistance. 2010. 232p. pap. *(978-3-639-25258-3(6))* VDM Verlag Dr. Mueller e.K.

Halleson, R. Z. & Ou, Chhalith. Spare Them? No Profit Remove Them? No Loss: The True Story of a Young Teenager in Pol Pot's Cambodia. 2010. 204p. 27.95 *(978-1-4502-0621-1(2))* iUniverse, Inc.

Hansen, Anne Ruth & Ledgerwood, Judy, eds. At the Edge of the Forest: Essays on Cambodia, History, & Narrative in Honor of David Chandler. 2009. 251p. 46.95 *(978-0-87727-776-7(1))*; pap. 23.95 *(978-0-87727-746-0(X))* Cornell Univ., Southeast Asia Program Pubns.

Harris, Ian. Cambodian Buddhism: History & Practice. 2008. (Illus.). 352p. pap. 27.00 *(978-0-8248-3298-8(1))* Univ. of Hawaii Pr.

Hughes, Caroline & Kiernan, Ben, eds. Conflict Change in Cambodia. 2006. 160p. 160.00 *(978-0-415-38592-3(X))* Routledge.

Hughes, Caroline, et al. Dependent Communities: Aid & Politics in Cambodia & East Timor. 2009. (Illus.). 275p. 46.95 *(978-0-87727-778-1(8))*; pap. 23.95 *(978-0-87727-748-4(6))* Cornell Univ. Pr.

Kiernan, Ben. Genocide & Resistance in Southeast Asia: Documentation, Denial, & Justice in Cambodia & East Timor. 2007. (ENG., Illus.). 363p. (gr. 11). 49.95 *(978-1-4128-0668-8(2))*; pap. 29.95 *(978-1-4128-0669-5(0))* Transaction Pubs.

—The Pol Pot Regime: Race, Power, & Genocide in Cambodia under the Khmer Rouge, 1975-79, Third Edition. 3rd ed. 2008. (ENG., Illus.). 544p. (C). pap. 25.00 *(978-0-300-14434-5(2))* Yale Univ. Pr.

Lilja, Mona. Power, Resistance & Women Politicians in Cambodia: Discourses of Emancipation. 2008. (Nias Monographs). (Illus.). 214p. *(978-87-91114-71-7(3))* Nordic Institute of Asian Studies.

Maeda, Mitsuko. Power Relations in Development Cooperation: Patterns, Concepts, & Approaches in a Japanese-assisted Education Project. 2008. 200p. pap. *(978-3-639-08450-4(0))* VDM Verlag Dr. Mueller e.K.

Mongo, Achiri. The State of Rural Roads in Cameroon: How Conscious Neglect of Infrastructure Has Perpetuated Economic Stagnation. 2010. 222p. pap. 23.95 *(978-1-4327-4411-3(9))* Outskirts Pr., Inc.

Nasseh, Nicole. Cultivating Ripeness Through Third Party Intervention. 2009. 112p. pap. *(978-3-639-14700-1(6))* VDM Verlag Dr. Mueller e.K.

Ollier, Leakthina Chan-Pech, ed. Expressions of Cambodia: The Politics of Tradition, Identity, & Change. 2006. (Routledge Contemporary Southeast Asia Ser.: Vol. 12). (ENG., Illus.). 248p. (C). 160.00 *(978-0-415-38554-1(7))* Routledge.

Pa, Chileng & Mortland, Carol A. Escaping the Khmer Rouge: A Cambodian Memoir. 2008. (ENG., Illus.). 240p. per. 29.95 *(978-0-7864-3672-9(7))* McFarland & Co., Inc. Pubs.

Sao, Bounchoeum, et al. Bending with the Wind: Memoir of a Cambodian Couple's Escape to America. 2012. (ENG., Illus.). 228p. pap. 35.00 ***(978-0-7864-6377-0(5))*** McFarland & Co., Inc. Pubs.

Serra, Hl. Oops! a War Story for Children. 2009. 20p. pap. 12.95 *(978-1-4490-0636-5(1))* AuthorHouse.

Sokphea, Young & Pongquan, Soparth. Governance of Decentralized Commune Development Planning. 2010. 236p. pap. *(978-3-8383-7915-9(2))* Lambert Academic Publishing.

Springer, Simon. Cambodia's Neoliberal Order: Violence, Authoritarianism, & the Contestation of Public Space. 2012. (ENG., Illus.). 224p. (C). pap. 42.95 ***(978-0-415-62753-5(2))*** Routledge.

—Cambodia's Neoliberal Order: Violence, Authoritarianism, & the Contestation of Public Space. 2010. (Routledge Pacific Rim Geographies Ser.). (ENG., Illus.). 224p. (C). 130.00 *(978-0-415-56819-7(6)*, Routledge) Taylor & Francis Group GBR. Dist: Taylor & Francis Group.

Touch, Van. Behind the Cambodian Killing Fields. 2007. (C). pap. *(978-0-9796878-1-5(0))*; pap. *(978-0-9796878-0-8(2))*; pap. *(978-0-9796878-2-2(9))* Touch, Van.

Ty, Makararavy. Concepts of Decentralization Reforms at National & Local Levels. 2011. 128p. pap. ***(978-3-8433-8994-5(2))*** Lambert Academic Publishing.

Ung, Loung. First They Killed My Father: A Daughter of Cambodia Remembers. 2011. 13.76 *(978-0-7848-3434-3(2)*, Everbind) Marco Bk. Co.

Widyono, Benny. Dancing in Shadows: Sihanouk, the Khmer Rouge, & the United Nations in Cambodia. 2007. (Asian Voices Ser.). (ENG., Illus.). 356p. 90.00 *(978-0-7425-5552-5(6))*; per. 32.95 *(978-0-7425-5553-2(4))* Rowman & Littlefield Publishers, Inc.

Yimsut, Ronnie. Facing the Khmer Rouge: A Cambodian Journey. 2011. (Genocide, Political Violence, Human Rights Ser.). (ENG.). 288p. 72.00 *(978-0-8135-5151-7(X))*; (Illus.). 270p. (C). pap. 26.95 *(978-0-8135-5152-4(8))* Rutgers Univ. Pr.

CAMBODIA—SOCIAL CONDITIONS

Chum, Samnang. Ngo Coordination & Cambodia's Aid Effectiveness. 2010. 224p. pap. *(978-3-8383-4604-5(1))* Lambert Academic Publishing.

De Lopez, Thanakvaro. Where the Stone Flowers - the People of Angkor. 2007. (Illus.). 218p. 55.00 *(978-0-9795620-0-6(7))* Blue Reamker.

Eng, Davuth & Charles S. Johnston. Tourism Impacts. 2011. 176p. pap. ***(978-3-8433-9387-4(7))*** Lambert Academic Publishing.

Fennell, S., et al, eds. The Extraordinary Chambers in the Courts of Cambodia Collection: Volume 1: Basic Documents on the Court. 2010. 352p. pap. 80.00 *(978-90-5887-914-1(3))* International Courts Assn. NLD. Dist: International Specialized Bk. Services.

—The Extraordinary Chambers in the Courts of Cambodia Collection: Volume 2: The Case of Kaing Guek EAV - 1. 2010. 404p. pap. 80.00 *(978-90-5887-915-8(1))* International Courts Assn. NLD. Dist: International Specialized Bk. Services.

Gartrell, Alexandra. Flying on Hope. 2010. 376p. pap. *(978-3-639-24645-2(4))* VDM Verlag Dr. Mueller e.K.

Greenfield, Craig. The Urban Halo: A Story of Hope for Orphans of the Poor. 2007. (ENG.). 224p. per. 14.99 *(978-1-85078-727-3(1))* Authentic Media.

Heywood, Denise. Cambodian Dance: Celebration of the Gods. 2009. (ENG., Illus.). 192p. 29.95 *(978-974-9863-40-4(2)*, River Bks. Pr. Dist A C) Antique Collectors' Club.

Hughes, Caroline & Kiernan, Ben, eds. Conflict Change in Cambodia. 2006. 160p. 160.00 *(978-0-415-38592-3(X))* Routledge.

Imam, Zeba. Fighting Gender-Based Violence in Cambodi. 2010. 148p. pap. *(978-3-8383-8218-0(8))* Lambert Academic Publishing.

Kattenburg, David. Foxy Lady: Truth, Memory & the Death of Western Yachtsmen in Democratic Kampuchea. 2010. 280p. pap. 27.99 *(978-1-926780-03-0(5))* Key Publishing Hse., Inc., The CAN. Dist: AtlasBooks Distribution.

Kumar, Sanjay. Quantitative Analysis of Effect. 2010. 60p. pap. *(978-3-639-26839-3(3))* VDM Verlag Dr. Mueller e.K.

Lambray, Maureen, photos by. War Remnants of the Khmer Rouge. 2011. (ENG., Illus.). 136p. 60.00 ***(978-1-884167-31-7(4))*** Umbrage Editions.

Mam, Somaly. The Road of Lost Innocence: The True Story of a Cambodian Heroine. 2009. (ENG.). 224p. pap. 15.00 *(978-0-385-52622-7(9))* Spiegel & Grau.

Ollier, Leakthina Chan-Pech, ed. Expressions of Cambodia: The Politics of Tradition, Identity, & Change. 2006. (Routledge Contemporary Southeast Asia Ser.: Vol. 12). (ENG., Illus.). 248p. (C). 160.00 *(978-0-415-38554-1(7))* Routledge.

Parolo, Martin. Marketing Challenges & Social Marketing for Pous in Emerging Markets. 2009. 180p. pap. *(978-3-639-20279-3(1))* VDM Verlag Dr. Mueller e.K.

Roy, Norman Jean & Pearl, Mariane. Traffik. 2008. (ENG.). 224p. 50.00 *(978-1-57687-474-5(5))* powerHouse Cultural Entertainment, Inc.

Siv, Sichan. Golden Bones: An Extraordinary Journey from Hell in Cambodia to a New Life in America. 2008. (Illus.). 336p. 25.95 *(978-0-06-134068-0(5))* HarperCollins Pubs.

Sok, Serey, et al. Basic Education for Rural Children in Cambodi. 2010. 64p. pap. *(978-3-8383-9352-0(X))* Lambert Academic Publishing.

Springer, Simon. Cambodia's Neoliberal Order: Violence, Authoritarianism, & the Contestation of Public Space. 2012. (ENG., Illus.). 224p. (C). pap. 42.95 ***(978-0-415-62753-5(2))*** Routledge.

—Cambodia's Neoliberal Order: Violence, Authoritarianism, & the Contestation of Public Space. 2010. (Routledge Pacific Rim Geographies Ser.). (ENG., Illus.). 224p. (C). 130.00 *(978-0-415-56819-7(6)*, Routledge) Taylor & Francis Group GBR. Dist: Taylor & Francis Group.

Vong, Sreytouch. Female Education & Family Planning. 2011. 112p. pap. ***(978-3-8443-3028-1(3))*** Lambert Academic Publishing.

CAMBODIAN LANGUAGE

see Khmer Language

CAMBODIANS

see also Khmers

Liev, Man Hau. Adaptation of Cambodians in New Zealand. 2009. 436p. pap. *(978-3-639-11606-9(2))* VDM Verlag Dr. Mueller e.K.

Nou, Ker & Nou, Nhieuk. Book of Khmer Marriage: Cambodian Weddings Rules & Traditions. 2009. pap. *(978-1-61623-480-5(6))* Independent Pub.

CAMBODIANS—FOREIGN COUNTRIES

McLellan, Janet. Cambodian Refugees in Ontario: Resettlement, Religion, & Identity. 2009. (ENG.). 272p. *(978-0-8020-9962-4(9))* Univ. of Toronto Pr.

CAMBRAI, BATTLE OF, CAMBRAI, FRANCE, 1917

Hammond, Bryn. Cambrai 1917: The Myth of the First Great Tank Battle. (ENG., Illus.). 2010. 416p. pap. 17.95 *(978-0-7538-2605-8(4)*, Phoenix) 2008. 500p. 34.95 *(978-0-297-84553-9(5)*, Weidenfeld & Nicolson) Orion Publishing Group, Ltd. GBR. Dist: Sterling Publishing Co., Inc.

McNab, Chris. Battle Story Cambrai 1917. 2012. (Battle Story Ser.). (ENG., Illus.). 160p. 17.95 ***(978-0-7524-7977-4(6))*** History Pr. Ltd.,The GBR. Dist: Independent Pubs. Group.

Sanders, Ian J. The Battle of Cambrai 1917 - from German Trench Maps. 2007. 26p. 26.50 *(978-1-84753-402-6(3))* Lulu Enterprises Inc.

Sheldon, Jack. German Army at Cambrai. 2009. (Illus.). 352p. 50.00 *(978-1-84415-944-4(2))* Pen & Sword Bks. Ltd. GBR. Dist: Casemate Pubs. & Bk. Distributors, LLC.

Turner, Alexander. Cambrai 1917: The Birth of Armoured Warfare. 2007. (Campaign Ser.). (ENG., Illus.). 96p. pap. 19.95 *(978-1-84603-147-2(8))* Osprey Publishing, Ltd. GBR. Dist: Random Hse., Inc.

CAMBRIAN PERIOD

see Geology, Stratigraphic—Cambrian

CAMBRIAN RAILWAYS COMPANY

Gasquoine, C. P. The Story of the Cambrian: A Biography of a Railway. 2007. (Illus.). 164p. per. *(978-1-4065-2811-4(0))* Dodo Pr.

CAMBRIDGE, CATHERINE, DUCHESS OF, 1982-

Andersen, Christopher. William & Kate: A Royal Love Story. 2010. (ENG., Illus.). 320p. 26.00 *(978-1-4516-2145-7(0))* Gallery Pr., The IRL. Dist: Simon & Schuster, Inc.

Andersen, Christopher P. William & Kate: A Royal Love Story. 2011. (ENG., Illus.). 336p. pap. 16.00 *(978-1-4516-2146-4(9))* Gallery Pr., The IRL. Dist: Simon & Schuster, Inc.

Bullen, Annie. William & Catherine: A Royal Wedding Souvenir. 2011. (ENG., Illus.). 64p. 14.99 *(978-1-4597-0114-4(3))* Dundurn CAN. Dist: Ingram Pub. Services.

—William & Kate: A Royal Souvenir. 2011. (ENG., Illus.). 64p. pap. 14.95 *(978-1-84165-353-2(5))* History Pr. Ltd.,The GBR. Dist: Independent Pubs. Group.

Clench, James. William & Kate: A Royal Love Story. 2010. (ENG., Illus.). 192p. 19.95 *(978-1-4027-8784-3(7))* Sterling Publishing Co., Inc.

Cywinski, Sara. Kate Style Princess: The Fashion & Beauty Secrets of Britain's Most Glamorous Royal. 2011. (ENG., Illus.). 226p. 29.95 *(978-1-84358-393-6(3))* Blake, John Publishing, Ltd. GBR. Dist: Independent Pubs. Group.

Debrett's, Debrett's. Debrett's - A Modern Royal Marriage: A Modern Royal Marriage. 2011. (ENG., Illus.). 176p. 45.00 ***(978-0-85720-685-5(0))*** Simon & Schuster, Ltd. GBR. Dist: Independent Pubs. Group.

Ewart, Tim & Lloyd, Ian. Invitation to the Royal Wedding. 2011. (ENG., Illus.). 192p. 32.95 ***(978-1-84732-823-6(7))*** Carlton Bks., Ltd. GBR. Dist: Independent Pubs. Group.

Jobson, Robert. William & Kate: The Love Story - A Celebration of the Wedding of the Century. 2011. (ENG., Illus.). 262p. 27.95 *(978-1-84454-736-4(1))* Blake, John Publishing, Ltd. GBR. Dist: Independent Pubs. Group.

Joseph, Claudia. Kate: Kate Middleton: Princess in Waiting. 2010. 272p. pap. 13.99 *(978-0-06-195171-8(4)*, William Morrow Paperbacks) HarperCollins Pubs.

—Kate: the Making of a Princess. 2011. 272p. pap. 13.99 *(978-0-06-208229-9(9)*, William Morrow Paperbacks) HarperCollins Pubs.

Knight, Julian. The Royal Wedding for Dummies. 2011. (ENG., Illus.). 216p. pap. 9.99 *(978-1-119-97030-9(X)*, For Dummies) Wiley, John & Sons, Inc.

Life Magazine Editors. The Royal Wedding of Prince William & Kate Middleton. exp. ed. 2011. (ENG.). 128p. 19.95 *(978-1-60320-216-9(1))* Time Home Entertainment, Inc.

Morton, Andrew. William & Catherine: Their Story. 2011. (ENG., Illus.). 224p. 29.99 *(978-0-312-64340-9(3))* St. Martin's Pr.

Nicholl, Katie. The Making of a Royal Romance: William, Kate, & Harry — A Look Behind the Palace Walls. rev. exp. ed. 2011. (ENG., Illus.). 384p. pap. 15.00 *(978-1-60286-153-4(6))* Perseus Bks. Group.

Nunn, Robin. William & Kate: Celebrating a Royal Engagement. 2011. (ENG., Illus.). 144p. 24.95 *(978-1-86205-843-9(1))* Chrysalis Children's Bks. GBR. Dist: Independent Pubs. Group.

Taylor, John A. How the Internet Exposed the Private Lives of the Royal Family: The Marriage of Prince William & Kate Middleton. 2011. 184p. 109.95 *(978-0-7734-1507-2(6))* Mellen, Edwin Pr., The.

Whitman Publishing, creator. William & Kate: A Royal Love Story. 2011. (Illus.). 96p. pap. 9.95 *(978-0-7948-3391-6(8))* Whitman Publishing LLC.

Wilkinson, James. The Royal Wedding: The Official Westminster Abbey Souvenir. 2011. (ENG., Illus.). 40p. pap. 8.00 *(978-1-85759-724-0(9))* Scala, Editions FRA. Dist: National Bk. Network.

CAMBRIDGE, GEORGE WILLIAM FREDERICK CHARLES, DUKE OF, 1819-1904

Verner, William Willoughby Cole. The Military Life of H R H George. 2009. 424p. pap. *(978-1-4588-8991-1(2))* Books LLC.

Verner, Willoughby & Parker, Erasmus Darwin. The Military Life of H R H George Duke of Cambridge V1: 1819-1871. 2007. 562p. 58.95 *(978-0-548-15128-0(8))*; 564p. per. 43.95 *(978-1-4304-4473-2(8))* Kessinger Publishing, LLC.

Willoughby Cole Verner, Erasmus Darwin P. The Military Life of H R H George, Duke of Cambridge. 2009. 496p. 35.99 *(978-1-113-26521-0(3))*; pap. 37.75 *(978-1-113-26519-7(1))* BiblioBazaar.

CAMBRIDGE, WILLIAM, PRINCE, DUKE OF, 1982-

Andersen, Christopher. William & Kate: A Royal Love Story. 2010. (ENG., Illus.). 320p. 26.00 *(978-1-4516-2145-7(0))* Gallery Pr., The IRL. Dist: Simon & Schuster, Inc.

Andersen, Christopher P. William & Kate: A Royal Love Story. 2011. (ENG., Illus.). 336p. pap. 16.00 *(978-1-4516-2146-4(9))* Gallery Pr., The IRL. Dist: Simon & Schuster, Inc.

Blizzard, Christina. Young Royals on Tour: William & Catherine in Canada. 2011. (ENG., Illus.). 64p. pap. 14.99 *(978-1-4597-0186-1(0))* Dundurn CAN. Dist: Ingram Pub. Services.

Bullen, Annie. William & Catherine: A Royal Wedding Souvenir. 2011. (ENG., Illus.). 64p. 14.99 *(978-1-4597-0114-4(3))* Dundurn CAN. Dist: Ingram Pub. Services.

—William & Kate: A Royal Souvenir. 2011. (ENG., Illus.). 64p. pap. 14.95 *(978-1-84165-353-2(5))* History Pr. Ltd.,The GBR. Dist: Independent Pubs. Group.

Clench, James. William & Kate: A Royal Love Story. 2010. (ENG., Illus.). 192p. 19.95 *(978-1-4027-8784-3(7))* Sterling Publishing Co., Inc.

Cohen, David Elliot. Prince William & Her Royal Highness Catherine: Their Life & Wedding in Photographs. 2011. (ENG., Illus.). 224p. 24.95 *(978-1-4027-8816-1(9))* Sterling Publishing Co., Inc.

Debrett's, Debrett's. Debrett's - A Modern Royal Marriage: A Modern Royal Marriage. 2011. (ENG., Illus.). 176p. 45.00 ***(978-0-85720-685-5(0))*** Simon & Schuster, Ltd. GBR. Dist: Independent Pubs. Group.

Ewart, Tim & Lloyd, Ian. Invitation to the Royal Wedding. 2011. (ENG., Illus.). 192p. 32.95 ***(978-1-84732-823-6(7))*** Carlton Bks., Ltd. GBR. Dist: Independent Pubs. Group.

Jobson, Robert. William & Kate: The Love Story - A Celebration of the Wedding of the Century. 2011. (ENG., Illus.). 262p. 27.95 *(978-1-84454-736-4(1))* Blake, John Publishing, Ltd. GBR. Dist: Independent Pubs. Group.

Joseph, Claudia. Kate: the Making of a Princess. 2011. 272p. pap. 13.99 *(978-0-06-208229-9(9)*, William Morrow Paperbacks) HarperCollins Pubs.

Knight, Julian. The Royal Wedding for Dummies. 2011. (ENG., Illus.). 216p. pap. 9.99 *(978-1-119-97030-9(X)*, For Dummies) Wiley, John & Sons, Inc.

Life Magazine Editors. The Royal Wedding of Prince William & Kate Middleton. exp. ed. 2011. (ENG.). 128p. 19.95 *(978-1-60320-216-9(1))* Time Home Entertainment, Inc.

Morton, Andrew. William & Catherine: Their Story. 2011. (ENG., Illus.). 224p. 29.99 *(978-0-312-64340-9(3))* St. Martin's Pr.

Nicholl, Katie. The Making of a Royal Romance: William, Kate, & Harry — A Look Behind the Palace Walls. rev. exp. ed. 2011. (ENG., Illus.). 384p. pap. 15.00 *(978-1-60286-153-4(6))* Perseus Bks. Group.

—William & Harry: Behind the Palace Walls. 2010. (ENG., Illus.). 352p. 24.95 *(978-1-60286-140-4(4))* Perseus Bks. Group.

Nunn, Robin. William & Kate: Celebrating a Royal Engagement. 2011. (ENG., Illus.). 144p. 24.95 *(978-1-86205-843-9(1))* Chrysalis Children's Bks. GBR. Dist: Independent Pubs. Group.

Price, Joann F. Prince William: A Biography, 1 vol. 2011. (Greenwood Biographies Ser.). (Illus.). 175p. 35.00 *(978-0-313-39285-6(4)*, A3300C); E-Book *(978-0-313-39286-3(2)*, Greenwood Pr.) Greenwood Publishing Group, Inc.

Seward, Ingrid. William & Harry: The People's Princes. 2009. (ENG., Illus.). 192p. 35.00 *(978-1-84732-123-7(2))* Carlton Bks., Ltd. GBR. Dist: Sterling Publishing Co., Inc.

Taylor, John A. How the Internet Exposed the Private Lives of the Royal Family: The Marriage of Prince William & Kate Middleton. 2011. 184p. 109.95 *(978-0-7734-1507-2(6))* Mellen, Edwin Pr., The.

Whitman Publishing, creator. William & Kate: A Royal Love Story. 2011. (Illus.). 96p. pap. 9.95 *(978-0-7948-3391-6(8))* Whitman Publishing LLC.

Wilkinson, James. The Royal Wedding: The Official Westminster Abbey Souvenir. 2011. (ENG., Illus.). 40p. pap. 8.00 *(978-1-85759-724-0(9))* Scala, Editions FRA. Dist: National Bk. Network.

CAMBRIDGE (ENGLAND)

Goldschmidt, E. P. The First Cambridge Press in its European Setting. 2010. (ENG.). 116p. pap. 19.99 *(978-0-521-14332-5(2))* Cambridge Univ. Pr.

Harvard Student Agencies Inc. Staff & Avalon Travel Publishing Staff. Let's Go London, Oxford, Cambridge & Edinburgh: The Student Travel Guide. 2010. (Let's Go Ser.). (ENG., Illus.). 232p. pap. 14.95 *(978-1-59880-711-0(0)*, Let's Go) Avalon Travel Publishing.

Le Vay, Benedict. Eccentric Cambridge: The Bradt City Guide. 2007. (Bradt Mini Guide Ser.). (ENG., Illus.). 192p. pap. 13.95 *(978-1-84162-172-2(2))* Bradt Travel Guides GBR. Dist: Globe Pequot Pr., The.

Lubenow, W. C. The Cambridge Apostles, 1820-1914: Liberalism, Imagination, & Friendship in British Intellectual & Professional Life. 2007. (ENG., Illus.). 476p. pap. 58.00 *(978-0-521-03728-0(X))* Cambridge Univ. Pr.

Marr, John Edward & Shipley, Arthur Everett. Handbook to the Natural History of Cambridgeshire. 2010. (Cambridge Library Collection - Cambridge Ser.). (Illus.). 280p. pap. 23.99 *(978-1-108-00766-5(X))* Cambridge Univ. Pr.

Saturley, Galen, photos by. Cambridge: Portrait of a Restaurant. 2007. (Illus.). 128p. 30.00 *(978-0-9792014-1-7(1))* Blue Tree, LLC.

Sayle, Charles E. Fitzwilliam Museum McClean Bequest: Catalogue of the Early Printed Books Bequeathed to the Museum. 2010. (ENG., Illus.). 212p. pap. 22.99 *(978-1-108-00783-2(X))* Cambridge Univ. Pr.

CAMBRIDGE (ENGLAND)—HISTORY

Bartholomew, A. T., ed. Catalogue of the Books & Papers for the Most Part Relating to the University, Town, & County of Cambridge Bequeathed to the University by John Willis Clark, M. A. 2010. (Cambridge Library Collection - Cambridge Ser.). (Illus.). 306p. pap. 24.99 *(978-1-108-01592-9(1))* Cambridge Univ. Pr.

A Concise & Accurate Description of the University, Town & County of Cambridge: Containing a Particular History of the Colleges & Public Buildings. 2009. (Cambridge Library Collection - Cambridge Ser.). (ENG.). 212p. pap. 12.99 *(978-1-108-00065-9(7))* Cambridge Univ. Pr.

Cooper, Charles Henry. Annals of Cambridge. 2009. 408p. pap. *(978-0-217-67833-9(5))*; 476p. pap. *(978-0-217-77904-3(2))*; 404p. pap. *(978-0-217-17137-3(0))* Books LLC.

—Annals of Cambridge. 2009. (Cambridge Library Collection - Cambridge Ser.). (ENG.). 652p. pap. 45.00 *(978-1-108-00031-4(2))*; 684p. pap. 48.00 *(978-1-108-00032-1(0))*; 752p. pap. 48.00 *(978-1-108-00033-8(9))*; 676p. pap. 45.00 *(978-1-108-00034-5(7))*; 492p. pap. 35.99 *(978-1-108-00030-7(4))* Cambridge Univ. Pr.

—Annals of Cambridge. 2009. 398p. pap. 39.71 *(978-0-217-67837-7(8))* General Bks. LLC.

Dong-Won Kim. Leadership & Creativity: A History of the Cavendish Laboratory, 1871-1919. 2010. (Archimedes Ser.). 248p. pap. 139.00 *(978-90-481-5956-7(3)*, 9048159563) Springer.

Forshaw, Alec. Growing up in Cambridge. 2010. (ENG., Illus.). 128p. pap. 24.95 *(978-0-7524-5004-9(2))* History Pr. Ltd.,The GBR. Dist: Independent Pubs. Group.

Gunning, Henry. Reminiscences of Cambridge: A Selection Chosen by D. A. Winstanley. 2012. (ENG.). 174p. pap. 24.00 ***(978-1-107-62829-8(6))*** Cambridge Univ. Pr.

Keynes, Florence Ada. By-Ways of Cambridge History. 2009. (Cambridge Library Collection - Cambridge Ser.). (ENG., Illus.). 208p. pap. 22.99 *(978-1-108-00233-2(1))* Cambridge Univ. Pr.

Kirk, Kate. The Cambridge Phenomenon. 2012. (ENG.). 208p. 80.00 *(978-1-906507-52-7(X))* Third Millenium Publishing GBR. Dist: National Bk. Network.

Nelson, Alan H. Early Cambridge Theatres: College, University & Town Stages, 1464-1720. 2007. (ENG., Illus.). 212p. (C). pap. 50.00 (978-0-521-03597-2(X)) Cambridge Univ. Pr.

Pottinger, David T., ed. Cambridge Historical Society, Publications 16, Proceedings for the Year 1922. 2011. 154p. 41.95 (978-1-258-06572-0(X)) Literary Licensing, LLC.

Zanders, Rosemary. The Cambridge Book of Days. 2011. (ENG.). 368p. 16.95 (978-0-7524-5953-0(8)) History Pr. Ltd.,The GBR. Dist: Independent Pubs. Group.

CAMBRIDGE (MASS.)

Alexander, Philip N. A Widening Sphere: Evolving Cultures at MIT. 2011. (ENG., Illus.). 520p. (gr. 17). 29.95 (978-0-262-01563-9(3)) MIT Pr.

Gilman, Arthur. Theatrum Majorum the Cambridge Of 1776: Where-in Is Set Forth an Account of the town, & of the Events It Witnessed. 2006. 140p. per. 16.99 (978-1-4255-1011-4(6)) MPublishing.

Lotman, Mo. Harvard Square: An Illustrated History since 1950. 2009. (ENG., Illus.). 240p. 50.00 (978-1-58479-747-0(9)) Stewart, Tabori & Chang.

Nisbet, Peter. Birthday Presents: Acquisitions for the 100th Anniversary of the Busch-Reisinger Museum, Harvard University. 2006. (Paperback Ser.). (ENG., Illus.). 56p. pap. 15.00 (978-1-891771-37-8(X), Harvard Art Museum (Acc)) Antique Collectors' Club GBR. Dist: National Bk. Network.

Rooney, E. Ashley & Ashley, Rooney E. Cambridge, Massachusetts: Ghosts, Legends, Lore. 2009. (Illus.). 160p. pap. 14.99 (978-0-7643-3255-5(4)) Schiffer Publishing, Ltd.

Stearns, Frank Preston. Cambridge Sketches. 2009. 388p. 33.99 (978-1-115-49281-2(0)); pap. 32.75 (978-1-115-49283-6(7)); pap. 33.75 (978-1-115-49282-9(9)) BiblioBazaar.

—Cambridge Sketches. 2008. (ENG.). 212p. per. (978-1-4065-7520-0(8)) Dodo Pr.

—Cambridge Sketches. 2006. (ENG.). 212p. pap. (978-1-4068-3013-2(5)) Echo Library.

Vetter, Herbert F. The Harvard Square Book. 2007. 110p. pap. 13.95 (978-0-615-16082-5(4)) Harvard Square Library.

CAMBRIDGE PLATONISTS

Colie. Light & Enlightenment. 2009. (ENG.). 180p. pap. 31.99 (978-0-521-10823-2(3)) Cambridge Univ. Pr.

Crocker, R. Henry More, 1614-1687: A Biography of the Cambridge Platonist. 2010. (International Archives of the History of Ideas / archives internationales d'histoire des Idées Ser.). 292p. pap. 189.00 (978-90-481-6373-1(0), 9048163730) Springer.

Howard, Claud. Coleridge's Idealism: A Study of Its Relationship to Kant & to the Cambridge Platonists. 2011. 108p. 39.95 (978-1-258-01719-4(9)) Literary Licensing, LLC.

Kroll, Richard, et al, eds. Philosophy, Science, & Religion in England 1640-1700. 2008. (ENG.). 304p. (C). pap. 42.00 (978-0-521-07585-5(8)) Cambridge Univ. Pr.

Panichas, George A. The Greek Spirit & the Mysticism of Henry More. 2011. 24p. 35.95 (978-1-258-04848-8(5)) Literary Licensing, LLC.

Powicke, Frederick J. The Cambridge Platonists: A Study. 2007. 239p. 45.00 (978-1-57898-563-0(3)) Martino Publishing.

Rogers, G. A., et al, eds. The Cambridge Platonists in Philosophical Context: Politics, Metaphysics & Religion. 2010. (International Archives of the History of Ideas / archives internationales d'histoire des Idées Ser.). 272p. pap. 279.00 (978-90-481-4844-8(8), 9048148448) Springer.

CAMBRIDGE SCHOOL OF ECONOMICS

see Neoclassical School of Economics

CAMBRIDGE-SOMERVILLE YOUTH STUDY

Farrington, David P., intro. Crime & Family: Selected Essays of Joan Mccord. 2007. (Illus.). 320p. 79.50 (978-1-59213-557-8(9)) Temple Univ. Pr.

McCord, Joan. Crime & Family: Selected Essays of Joan Mccord. 2007. (Illus.). 320p. per. 29.95 (978-1-59213-558-5(7)) Temple Univ. Pr.

CAMBRIDGE UNIVERSITY

see University of Cambridge

CAMBRIDGE UNIVERSITY PRESS

Barnes, G. R. A List of Books Printed in Cambridge at the Cambridge University Press, 1521-1800. 2010. (ENG.). 58p. pap. 19.99 (978-0-521-15541-0(X)) Cambridge Univ. Pr.

Goldschmidt, E. P. The First Cambridge Press in its European Setting. 2010. (ENG.). 116p. pap. 19.99 (978-0-521-14332-5(2)) Cambridge Univ. Pr.

McKenzie, Donald Francis. Cambridge University Press, 1696-1712: A Bibliographical Study. 2010. (ENG.). 396p. pap. 31.99 (978-1-108-00775-7(9)); (Illus.). 484p. pap. 35.99 (978-1-108-00774-0(0)) Cambridge Univ. Pr.

—Cambridge University Press 1696-1712 2 Volume Set: A Bibliographical Study, 2 vols. 2010. (Cambridge Library Collection - Printing & Publishing History Ser.). (ENG.). 871p. pap. 65.00 (978-1-108-00776-4(7)) Cambridge Univ. Pr.

Roberts, S. C. Adventures with Authors. 2010. 288p. pap. 30.99 (978-0-521-13641-9(5)) Cambridge Univ. Pr.

Roberts, Sydney Castle. A History of the Cambridge University Press, 1521-1921. 2009. (Cambridge Library Collection - Cambridge Ser.). (ENG., Illus.). 232p. pap. 22.99 (978-1-108-00251-6(X)) Cambridge Univ. Pr.

War Record of the Cambridge University Press, 1914-1919. 2009. (Cambridge Library Collection - Cambridge Ser.). (ENG.). 88p. pap. 19.99 (978-1-108-00294-3(3)) Cambridge Univ. Pr.

CAMBRIDGESHIRE (ENGLAND)

Clark, John Willis. The Observances in Use at the Augustinian Priory of S. Giles & S. Andrew at Barnwell, Cambridgeshire. 2011. (Cambridge Library Collection - History Ser.). (ENG., Illus.). 368p. pap. 29.99 (978-1-108-03000-7(9)) Cambridge Univ. Pr.

Cyril, Fox. The Archaeology of the Cambridge Region: A Topographical Study of the Bronze, Early Iron, Roman & Anglo-Saxon Ages, with an Introductory Note on the Neolithic Age. 2010. (Cambridge Library Collection - Cambridge Ser.). (Illus.). 492p. pap. 39.99 (978-1-108-01169-3(1)) Cambridge Univ. Pr.

Farrer, William. Feudal Cambridgeshire. 2009. (Cambridge Library Collection - Cambridge Ser.). 372p. pap. 29.99 (978-1-108-00238-7(2)) Cambridge Univ. Pr.

Wittering, Shirley. Ecology of Enclosure: The Effect of Enclosure on Society, Farming & the Environment in South Cambridgeshire, 1798-1850. 2012. (ENG., Illus.). 192p. pap. 70.00 (978-1-905119-44-8(5)) Windgather Pr. GBR. Dist: Brown, David Bk. Co., The.

CAMBRIDGESHIRE (ENGLAND)—DESCRIPTION AND TRAVEL

Long, Peter, ed. The Hidden Places of Cambridgeshire & Lincolnshire. 5th ed. (Hidden Places Ser.). (Illus.). 200p. pap. 14.95 (978-1-902007-28-1(X)) Travel Publishing, Ltd. GBR. Dist: Casemate Pubs. & Bk. Distributors, LLC.

Souden, David. Wimpole Hall. 2006. (National Trust Guidebooks Ser.). (ENG., Illus.). 96p. pap. 13.95 (978-1-84359-034-7(4)) History Pr. Ltd.,The GBR. Dist: Independent Pubs. Group.

CAMBRIDGESHIRE (ENGLAND)—HISTORY

Cunningham, W. The Story of Cambridgeshire. 2009. (Cambridge Library Collection - Cambridge Ser.). (ENG.). 76p. pap. 12.99 (978-1-108-00341-4(9)) Cambridge Univ. Pr.

Gunnning, Henry. Reminiscences of Cambridge: A Selection Chosen by D. A. Winstanley. 2012. (ENG.). 174p. pap. 24.00 (978-1-107-62829-8(5)) Cambridge Univ. Pr.

Kelly, Paul W. R. Found in a Foot Locker: The Forgotten Sacrifice of Robert L. Todd. 2009. (Illus.). 220p. pap. 14.49 (978-1-4389-4253-7(2)) AuthorHouse.

Lovell, John. Boyhood Memories of Village Life & Its People in Nineteen Forties Great Stukeley. 2011. (Illus.). 166p. pap. (978-0-7552-1308-5(4)) Authors OnLine, Ltd.

Storey, Neil. A Grim Almanac of Cambridgeshire. 2010. (ENG., Illus.). 192p. pap. 28.95 (978-0-7524-5010-0(7)) History Pr. Ltd.,The GBR. Dist: Independent Pubs. Group.

CAMCORDERS

Bass, Warren. Professional Results with Canon Vixia Camcorders: A Field Guide to Canon G10 & XA10. 2012. (ENG.). 256p. pap. 39.99 (978-1-133-70259-7(7)) Course Technology.

Breen, Christopher & Breen, Christopher. The Flip Mino Pocket Guide. 2009. (Pocket Guide Ser.). (ENG., Illus.). 192p. pap. 14.99 (978-0-321-63753-6(4)) Peachpit Pr.

Goodman, Robert M. Goodman's Guide to the Grass Valley Viper. 2007. (Illus.). 220p. (978-0-9753430-3-6(3)) AMGMedia Pubs.

—Goodman's Guide to the Panasonic HDX900. 2007. (Illus.). viii, 252p. (978-0-9753430-4-3(1)) AMGMedia Pubs.

—Goodman's Guide to the Panasonic P2 System. 2008. (Illus.). viii, 232p. (978-0-9753430-5-0(X)) AMGMedia Pubs.

Hutsko, Joe & Davidson, Drew. Flip Video for Dummies. 2010. (ENG., Illus.). 240p. pap. 24.99 (978-0-470-87916-0(5), For Dummies) Wiley, John & Sons, Inc.

Mullen, Steve. Field Guide to the Sony NEX-VG10. 2012. (ENG., Illus.). 224p. pap. 39.99 (978-1-4354-5903-8(2)) Course Technology.

Musburger,, Robert B. Single-Camera Video Production. 5th ed. 2010. (ENG., Illus.). 316p. pap. 25.95 (978-0-240-81264-9(6), Focal Pr.) Elsevier Science & Technology Bks.

Rapp, Holger. Investigation of Correlating TOF-Camera Systems: TOF for Dummies: Why you are getting bad data from your camera & what to do about it 2008. 92p. pap. (978-3-8364-7955-4(9)) VDM Verlag Dr. Mueller e.K.

Watson, Lonzell & Watson. Canon VIXIA HD Camcorder Digital Field Guide. 2009. (Digital Field Guide Ser.: 196). (ENG., Illus.). 272p. pap. 19.99 (978-0-470-39236-2(3), Wiley) Wiley, John & Sons, Inc.

CAMDEN SOCIETY (GREAT BRITAIN)

Camden Society, London Staff. Camden Society Publications, 1838 to 1872, 105 vols. reprint ed. 5780.00 (978-0-404-50100-6(1)) AMS Pr., Inc.

Milne, A. R. Centenary Guide to RHS. 260p. 9.00 (978-0-901050-00-7(8)) Brown, David Bk. Co., The.

Nichols, John G., ed. Descriptive Catalogue of the Works of the Camden Society. (Camden Society, London, Publications, First Ser.: No. 80B). reprint ed. 25.00 (978-0-404-50208-9(3)) AMS Pr., Inc.

CAMELLIA

Ackerman, William L. Beyond the Camellia Belt: Breeding, Propagating, & Growing Cold-Hardy Camellias. 2007. (ENG., Illus.). 240p. 39.95 (978-1-883052-52-2(1)) Ball Publishing.

Halliday, Robert. Practical Camellia Culture. 2009. (Gardening in America Ser.). (ENG., Illus.). 156p. pap. 12.95 (978-1-4290-1398-7(2)) Applewood Bks.

Trehane, Jennifer. Camellias: The Gardener's Encyclopedia. 2007. (ENG., Illus.). 380p. 59.95 (978-0-88192-848-8(8), 0881928488) Timber Pr., Inc.

CAMELOT (LEGENDARY PLACE)

Coppens, Philip. Land of the Gods: How a Scottish Landscape Was Sanctified to Become Arthur's Camelot. 2007. (Illus.). 238p. pap. 17.95 (978-1-931882-69-9(X)) Adventures Unlimited Pr.

Gidlow, Christopher. Revealing King Arthur: Swords, Stones & Digging for Camelot. 2010. (ENG., Illus.). 256p. 29.95 (978-0-7524-5507-5(3)) History Pr. Ltd.,The GBR. Dist: Independent Pubs. Group.

Reiser, Oliver Leslie. This Holyest Erthe, the Glastonbury Zodiac & King Arthur's Camelot. 2007. pap. (978-1-59731-201-1(0)) Perennis, Sophia.

Wood-Langford, Eve. Looking for Camelot: (A New Hypothesis) 2007. (Illus.). 124p. per. (978-1-906210-17-5(9)) Grosvenor Hse. Publishing Ltd.

CAMELS

Appleton, David B. Camels in Heraldry. 2007. (Illus.). 58p. pap. 30.00 (978-0-9801366-3-0(6)) Appleton Studios.

DesCôteaux, Luc, et al, eds. Practical Atlas of Ruminant & Camelid Reproductive Ultrasonography. 2010. (ENG., Illus.). 244p. 194.99 (978-0-8138-1551-0(7), Wiley-Blackwell) Wiley, John & Sons, Inc.

El Behiry, Ayman. Clinical & Laboratory Studies on Some Camel Affections. 2009. 112p. pap. (978-3-639-15996-7(9)) VDM Verlag Dr. Mueller e.K.

Field, Henry. Camel Brands & Graffiti from Iraq, Syria, Jordan, Iran & Arabi. 2011. 82p. 37.95 (978-1-258-01401-8(7)) Literary Licensing, LLC.

Irwin, Robert. Camel. 2010. (Reaktion Books - Animal Ser.). (ENG., Illus.). 224p. pap. 19.95 (978-1-86189-649-0(2)) Reaktion Bks., Ltd. GBR. Dist: Chicago Distribution Ctr.

Ishag, Ibrahim. Camels of Sudan. 2011. 108p. pap. (978-3-8433-8933-4(0)) Lambert Academic Publishing.

Johnson, Forrest Bryant. The Last Camel Charge: The Untold Story of America's Desert Military Experiment. 2012. (ENG.). 384p. (gr. 12). 25.95 (978-0-425-24569-9(1), Berkley Hardcover) Penguin Group (USA) Inc.

MacMichael, H. A. Brands Used by the Chief Camel-owning Tribes of Kordofán: A Supplement to the Tribes of Northern & Central Kordofán. 2012. (ENG., Illus.). 133p. pap. 34.00 (978-1-107-65862-2(4)) Cambridge Univ. Pr.

Mirzaei Dehaghi, Mohammad & Fathi, Saeid. Occurrence of Hydatidosis in Camels in Kerman Area, Southeast of Iran. 2011. 56p. pap. (978-3-8443-9291-3(2)) Lambert Academic Publishing.

Nori, Michele. Milking Drylands. 2011. 320p. pap. (978-3-8433-5313-7(1)) Lambert Academic Publishing.

Pietruschka, Ute & Streck, Michael P., eds. Symbolische Repräsentation und Wirklichkeit nomadischen Lebens. 2010. (Nomaden & Sesshafte Ser.). (GER & ENG., Illus.). 216p. (C). 115.00 (978-3-89500-657-9(2)) Reichert, Ludwig Dr. DEU. Dist: Brown, David Bk. Co., The.

Steel, John. A Manual of the Diseases of the Camel & of His Management & Uses - Indian Veterinary Manuals III. 2010. 258p. pap. 29.95 (978-1-4460-2249-8(8)) Research Pr.

Yahaya Abdullahi, Umar. Common Parasites Infesting Camels in Nigeri. 2011. 272p. pap. (978-3-8443-9575-4(X)) Lambert Academic Publishing.

Zeb, Muhammad Tariq, et al. Udder Health of Camels under Pastoralist Management Conditions. 2011. 88p. pap. (978-3-8443-1662-9(0)) Lambert Academic Publishing.

CAMEOS

see also Gems

Belozerskaya, Marina. Medusa's Gaze: The Extraordinary Journey of the Tazza Farnese, 1 vol. 2012. (Emblems of Antiquity Ser.). (ENG., Illus.). 296p. 24.95 (978-0-19-973931-8(5)) Oxford Univ. Pr., Inc.

Clements, Monica Lynn & Clements, Patricia Rosser. Cameos. 3rd enl. ed. 2011. (Illus.). 160p. (978-0-7643-3807-6(2), Schiffer Publishing Ltd) Schiffer Publishing, Ltd.

—Cameos: Classical to Costume. 2nd exp. rev. ed. 2008. (Illus.). 224p. bds. 59.99 (978-0-7643-2994-4(4)) Schiffer Publishing, Ltd.

Davenport, Cyril. Cameos. 2010. 154p. pap. 21.75 (978-1-143-04974-3(8)) BiblioBazaar.

—Cameos. 2010. 138p. 28.76 (978-1-169-71111-2(1)) 2010. 138p. 35.95 (978-1-161-77166-4(2)) 2008. 140p. pap. 20.95 (978-1-4367-9530-9(X)) Kessinger Publishing, LLC.

Draper, James David. Cameo Appearances. 2008. 19.95 (978-1-58839-282-4(1)) Metropolitan Museum of Art, The.

Miller, Anna M. Cameos Old & New. 4th ed. 2008. (ENG., Illus.). 382p. pap. 19.99 (978-0-943763-60-6(6)) GemStone Pr.

Wagner, Claudia & Boardman, John. Gem Mounts & the Classical Tradition. 2009. (ENG., Illus.). 120p. (C). pap. 87.50 (978-1-4073-0434-2(8)) British Archaeological Reports Ltd. GBR. Dist: Brown, David Bk. Co., The.

Zwierlein-Diehl, Erika. Antike Gemmen und Ihr Nachleben. 2007. (GER., Illus.). XV, 567p. 391.00 (978-3-11-019450-0(3)) De Gruyter, Walter Inc.

CAMERA LENSES

see Photographic Lenses

CAMERALISM

see Mercantile System

CAMERAS

see also Canon Camera; Digital Cameras; Hasselblad Camera; Leica Camera; Medium Format Cameras; Miniature Cameras; Minolta Camera; Motion Picture Cameras; Nikon Camera; Olympus Camera; Pentax Cameras; Photographic Lenses; Rollei Camera; Single-Lens Reflex Cameras; View Cameras; Zeiss Cameras

Ayers, Joyce. My Views As Seen Thru This Camer. 2009. 64p. pap. 38.49 (978-1-4389-8627-2(0)) AuthorHouse.

Bates, Michelle. Plastic Cameras: Toying with Creativity. 2nd ed. 2010. (ENG., Illus.). 288p. pap. 29.95 (978-0-240-81421-6(5), Focal Pr.) Elsevier Science & Technology Bks.

Belbachir, Ahmed Nabil, ed. Smart Cameras. 2009. (ENG., Illus.). xx, 404p. 129.00 (978-1-4419-0952-7(4), 1441909524) Springer.

Cecchi, Danilo. Asahi Pentax & Pentax SLR 35mm Cameras, 1952-89. 2006. (Hove Collector's Guide Ser.). (ENG., Illus.). 192p. 34.95 (978-0-906447-62-8(3), 0906447623) Hove Bks. GBR. Dist: MBI Distribution Services/Quayside Distribution.

Chen, Mark. Unleashing the Raw Power of Adobe Camera Raw: Master Techniques for Professional Digital Photographers. 2010. (ENG., Illus.). 128p. pap. 34.95 (978-1-60895-238-0(X)) Amherst Media, Inc.

Daniilidis, Kostas & Klette, Reinhard, eds. Imaging Beyond the Pinhole Camera. 2010. (Computational Imaging & Vision Ser.). xii, 368p. pap. 129.00 (978-90-481-7220-7(9), 9048172209) Springer.

Dudley-Dance, C. "Flash" the Traffic Camer. 2011. 28p. pap. 15.99 (978-1-4628-7110-0(0)) Xlibris Corp.

Fauer, Jon. Arriflex 16SR3 the Camera System: The Book & Film Series, 3 cass.; set. 78.00 incl. audio, VHS (978-0-936763-04-0(3)) Arriflex Corp.

Gruen, Armin & Huang, Thomas S., eds. Calibration & Orientation of Cameras in Computer Vision. 2010. (Springer Series in Information Sciences Ser.). (Illus.). xii, 235p. pap. 219.00 (978-3-642-08463-8(X), 364208463X) Springer.

Grycewicz, Thomas J., et al. Focal Plane Arrays for Space Telescopes III: 27-28 August 2007, San Diego, California, USA. 2007. (Proceedings of SPIE Ser.). (Illus.). 258p. pap. 70.00 (978-0-8194-6838-3(X)) SPIE.

Gustavson, Todd & House, George Eastman. 500 Cameras: 170 Years of Photographic Innovation. 2011. (ENG., Illus.). 480p. pap. 26.95 (978-1-4027-8086-8(9), Sterling Signature) Sterling Publishing Co., Inc.

Haigh-Hutchinson, Mark. Real Time Cameras: A Guide for Game Designers & Developers. 2009. (Morgan Kaufmann Series in Interactive 3D Technology Ser.). (ENG., Illus.). 544p. 61.95 (978-0-12-311634-5(1), Morgan Kaufmann) Elsevier Science & Technology Bks.

Hansen, Bill & Dierdorff, Michael. Japanese 35mm SLR Cameras: A Comprehensive Data Guide. 2006. (ENG., Illus.). 256p. pap. 29.95 (978-1-874707-29-5(4), 1874707294) Hove Bks. GBR. Dist: MBI Distribution Services/Quayside Distribution.

Harding, Colin. Classic Cameras. 2009. (ENG., Illus.). 192p. 35.00 (978-1-86108-529-0(X)) Sterling Publishing Co., Inc.

Hockney, David & Hockney, David. Secret Knowledge: Rediscovering the Lost Techniques of the Old Masters. exp. ed. 2006. (ENG., Illus.). 336p. (gr. 12-18). pap. 45.00 (978-0-14-200512-5(6), Studio) Penguin Group (USA) Inc.

Long, Brian. Canon: A Celebration. 2008. (ENG., Illus.). 224p. 65.00 (978-1-84797-021-3(4)) Crowood Pr., Ltd. GBR. Dist: Independent Pubs. Group.

—35mm Cameras. 2007. (Crowood Collectors' Ser.). (ENG., Illus.). 176p. 49.95 (978-1-86126-948-5(X)) Crowood Pr., Ltd. GBR. Dist: Independent Pubs. Group.

Meredith, Kevin. Fantastic Plastic Cameras: Tips & Tricks for 40 Toy Cameras. 2011. (ENG.). 176p. pap. 16.95 (978-0-8118-7753-4(1)) Chronicle Bks. LLC.

Montanaro, Marco. Hybrid Products & Blurred Categories. 2011. 88p. pap. (978-3-8443-9373-6(0)) Lambert Academic Publishing.

Nekourouh, Ali. Microcontroller Camer: A Robotics Application in Fuzzy Logic. 2010. 104p. pap. (978-3-8383-4197-2(X)) Lambert Academic Publishing.

Pardubický, Ludvík. The X-Slits Stereo. 2010. 136p. pap. (978-3-8383-7270-9(0)) Lambert Academic Publishing.

Quinnell, Justin. Build Fun Paper Cameras: Take Eye-Catching Pinhole Photos. 2009. (Lark Photography Book Ser.). (ENG., Illus.). 96p. 19.95 (978-1-60059-528-8(6)) Lark Bks.

Scorzafava, Dick. Spies in the Deer Woods: How to Hunt with a Scouting Camera. 2008. (ENG., Illus.). 184p. pap. 21.95 (978-0-8117-3512-4(5)) Stackpole Bks.

Smith, Graham StJohn. Painting with the Camer. 2008. 120p. pap. 36.99 (978-1-4343-9285-5(6)) AuthorHouse.

Song, Dezhen. Sharing a Vision. 2009. (Springer Tracts in Advanced Robotics Ser.). (ENG., Illus.). xx, 186p. 129.00 (978-3-540-88064-6(X)) Springer.

Wade, John. Cameras in Disguise. 2008. (Shire Library). (ENG., Illus.). 48p. per. 12.95 (978-0-7478-0637-0(3)) Shire Pubns., Ltd. GBR. Dist: Random Hse., Inc.

—Cine Cameras. 2008. (Shire Library). (ENG., Illus.). 48p. pap. 12.95 (978-0-7478-0592-2(X)) Shire Pubns., Ltd. GBR. Dist: Random Hse., Inc.

CAMERAS—MAINTENANCE AND REPAIR

Kuzyk, Hrad. 35mm for the Proletariat. 2007. 80p. pap. 8.00 (978-0-615-14488-7(8)) Kuzyk, Hrad.

CAMERON, JAMES, 1954-

Dunham, Brent, ed. James Cameron: Interviews. 2011. (Conversations with Filmmakers Ser.). (ENG.). 240p. 65.00 (978-1-61703-131-1(3)); pap. 25.00 (978-1-61703-132-8(1)) Univ. Pr. of Mississippi.

Etingoff, Kim. James Cameron: From Truck Driver to Director. 2012. (978-1-4222-2481-6(3)); pap. (978-1-4222-2484-7(8)) Mason Crest Pubs.

Keegan, Rebecca. The Futurist: The Life & Films of James Cameron. 2010. (ENG.). 304p. pap. 15.00 (978-0-307-46032-5(0), Three Rivers Pr.) Crown Publishing Group.

Keller, Alexandra. James Cameron. 2006. (Routledge Film Guidebooks Ser.). (Illus.). 208p. 110.00 (978-0-415-28851-4(7), RU24962); 193p. per. 29.95 (978-0-415-28852-1(5), RU24963) Routledge.

CAMEROON

Here are entered works about the United Republic of Cameroon, as well as works on the same territory when known by other names such as Cameroons or the German protectorate Kamerun.

Amin, Aloysius Aloysius & Dubois, Jean-Luc. Croissance et Dtveloppement Au Cameroun: D'une Croissance EquilibrTe a un DTveloppement Equitable. 2008. (FRE.). 440p. pap. *(978-9956-558-87-2(7))* Langaa Research & Publishing Common Initiative Group CMR. Dist: Michigan State Univ. Pr.

Charlier, Florence, et al. Sustaining Reforms for Inclusive Growth in Cameroon: A Development Policy Review. 2009. (ENG., Illus.). 312p. pap. 35.00 *(978-0-8213-7403-0(6)*, 9780821374030) World Bank Pubns.

Endeley, Joyce B. Mbongo & Sikod, Fondo. The Social Impact of the Chad-Cameroon Oil Pipeline: How Industrial Development Affects Gender Relations, Land Tenure, & Local Culture. 2006. (Illus.). 236p. 109.95 *(978-0-7734-5485-9(3))* Mellen, Edwin Pr., The.

Fardon. Lela in Bali: History Through a Ceremony in Cameroon. 2006. (Cameroon Studies: Vol. 7). (Illus.). 176p. (C). 90.00 *(978-1-84545-215-5(1))* Berghahn Bks., Inc.

Fokwang, Jude. Mediating Legitimacy: Chieftaincy & Democratisation in Two African Chiefdoms. 2009. 140p. pap. *(978-9956-558-64-3(8))* Langaa Research & Publishing Common Initiative Group CMR. Dist: Michigan State Univ. Pr.

Fokwang, Jude & Langmia, Kehbuma, eds. Society & Change in Bali Nyonga: Critical Perspectives. 2011. 196p. pap. ***(978-9956-579-39-6(4))*** Langaa Research & Publishing Common Initiative Group.

Icon Group International, Inc. Staff, compiled by. The 2006 Economic & Product Market Databook for Foumban, Cameroon. 2006. 618p. ring bd. 95.00 *(978-0-497-80549-4(9))* Icon Group International, Inc.

Mbah, Emmanuel M. Land/Boundary Conflict in Africa: The Case of Former British Colonial Bamenda, Present-Day North-West Province of the Republic of Cameroon, 1916-1996. 2008. 312p. 119.95 *(978-0-7734-5053-0(X))* Mellen, Edwin Pr., The.

Robinson, Clinton D. Language Use in Rural Development: An African Perspective. (Contributions to the Sociology of Language [CSL] Ser.). (ENG.). IX, 327p. 225.00 ***(978-3-11-187389-3(7))*** De Gruyter, Mouton DEU. Dist: de Gruyter, Walter GmbH & Co. KG.

Rupp, Stephanie. Forests of Belonging: Identities, Ethnicities, & Stereotypes in the Congo River Basin. 2011. (ENG., Illus.). 304p. (C). 70.00 *(978-0-295-99105-4(4))*; pap. 30.00 *(978-0-295-99106-1(2))* Univ. of Washington Pr.

Schilder. Quest for Self-Esteem: State, Islam, & Mundang Ethnicity in Northern Cameroon. (Illus.). xiv, 283p. *(978-90-5448-021-1(1))* Afrika-Studiecentrum.

Taku, Michael Fontem. Fontem Defang: Reminiscences of Leadership in a Post Colonial African Kingdom. 2008. (Illus.). 387p. pap. *(978-0-9755261-5-6(4))* Nkemnji Global Tech.

Tande, Dibussi. Scribbles from the Den Essays on Politics & Collective Memory in Cameroon. 2009. 232p. pap. *(978-9956-558-91-9(5))* Langaa Research & Publishing Common Initiative Group CMR. Dist: Michigan State Univ. Pr.

CAMEROON—DESCRIPTION AND TRAVEL

Colored People. 100th ltd. ed. 2008. (Illus.). 50p. *(978-0-9792486-2-7(0))* C & C Pr.

Locken, E. Travel Journal Cameroon. 2010. 192p. pap. 19.99 *(978-0-557-43454-1(8))* Lulu Enterprises Inc.

CAMEROON—HISTORY

Anyangwe, Carlson. Betrayal of Too Trusting a People the un, the Uk & the Trust Territory of the Southern Cameroons. 2009. 260p. pap. *(978-9956-558-81-0(8))* Langaa Research & Publishing Common Initiative Group CMR. Dist: Michigan State Univ. Pr.

—Imperialistic Politics in Cameroun: Resistance & the Inception of the Restoration of the Statehood of Southern Cameroons. 2008. 172p. pap. *(978-9956-558-50-6(8))* Langaa Research & Publishing Common Initiative Group CMR. Dist: Michigan State Univ. Pr.

Argenti, Nicolas. The Intestines of the State: Youth, Violence, & Belated Histories in the Cameroon Grassfields. 2007. (Illus.). 352p. 75.00 *(978-0-226-02611-4(6))*; per. 30.00 *(978-0-226-02612-1(4))* Univ. of Chicago Pr.

Atanga, Mufor. The Anglophone Cameroon Predicament. 2011. 266p. pap. ***(978-9956-717-11-8(8))*** Langaa Research & Publishing Common Initiative Group.

Atangana, Martin. The End of French Rule in Cameroon. 2010. (ENG.). 160p. pap. 25.50 *(978-0-7618-5278-0(6))* Univ. Pr. of America, Inc.

Barley, Nigel. Symbolic Structures: An Exploration of the Culture of the Dowayos. 2009. (ENG.). 136p. pap. 31.99 *(978-0-521-10534-7(X))* Cambridge Univ. Pr.

Berns, Marla C., et al, eds. Central Nigeria Unmasked: Arts of the Benue River Valley. 2011. (ENG., Illus.). 608p. 100.00 ***(978-0-9778344-6-4(8))*** Univ. of California, Los Angeles, Fowler Museum of Cultural History.

—Central Nigeria Unmasked: Arts of the Benue River Valley, 1 vol. 2011. (ENG., Illus.). 608p. pap. 75.00 ***(978-0-9778344-5-7(X))*** Univ. of California, Los Angeles, Fowler Museum of Cultural History.

Chem-Langhee, B. & Fanso, V.G., eds. Nso' & Its Neighbours Readings in the Social History of the Western Grassfields of Cameroon. 2011. 522p. pap. ***(978-9956-717-53-8(3))*** Langaa Research & Publishing Common Initiative Group.

Colince, Nguelo. Biofuel Impacts on Food Crisis. 2010. 116p. pap. *(978-3-8383-6247-2(0))* Lambert Academic Publishing.

Cottes, A. La Mission Cottes au Sud-Cameroun (1905-1908) (B. E. Ser.: No. 145). (FRE.). 30.00 *(978-0-8115-3066-8(3))* Periodicals Service Co.

Cowell, John. Elephant Grass. 2009. (ENG.). 260p. pap. 15.95 *(978-1-84454-711-1(6))* Blake, John Publishing, Ltd. GBR. Dist: Independent Pubs. Group.

David, Nicholas. Metals in Mandara Mountains' Society & Culture. 2012. ***(978-1-59221-889-9(X))***; pap. ***(978-1-59221-890-5(3))*** Africa World Pr.

DeLancey, Mark D. & Mbuh, Rebecca A. Historical Dictionary of the Republic of Cameroon. 4th ed. 2010. (Historical Dictionaries of Africa Ser.). (ENG.). 530p. 121.00 *(978-0-8108-5824-4(X))* Scarecrow Pr., Inc.

Doh, Emmanuel Fru. Africa's Political Wastelands: The Bastardization of Cameroon. 2008. 200p. pap. *(978-9956-558-62-9(1))* Langaa Research & Publishing Common Initiative Group CMR. Dist: Michigan State Univ. Pr.

Enga Awaseh, Stanley. Microfinance & Community Development in Cameroon. 2010. 84p. pap. *(978-3-8383-5860-4(0))* Lambert Academic Publishing.

Gam Nkwi, Walter. Voicing the Voiceless: Contributions to Closing Gaps in Cameroon History, 1958-2009. 2010. 200p. pap. *(978-9956-616-40-4(0))* Langaa Research & Publishing Common Initiative Group CMR. Dist: Michigan State Univ. Pr.

Koloss, Hans-Joachim. World-View & Society in Oku (Cameroon) 2009. (ENG.). 484p. pap. 128.00 *(978-3-496-02682-2(0)*, Art Stock Bks. Ltd/Csi) Continental Sales, Inc.

Manyong, Peterkins. God the Politician. 2008. 200p. *(978-9956-558-96-4(6))* Langaa Research & Publishing Common Initiative Group CMR. Dist: Michigan State Univ. Pr.

Mbeseha, Timothy & Nkemnji, John. Bellah Ngeh Development Insight. 2008. (Illus.). 144p. *(978-0-9755261-6-3(2))* Nkemnji Global Tech.

Mokosso, Henry Efesoa. American Evangelical Enterprise in Africa: The Case of the United Presbyterian Mission in Cameroon, 1879-1957. 2007. (Illus.). (C). 70.95 *(978-0-8204-8684-0(1))* Lang, Peter Publishing, Inc.

Nana, Genevoix. Language Related Issues in Primary Schooling in Cameroon. 2010. 144p. pap. *(978-3-639-22609-6(7))* VDM Verlag Dr. Mueller e.K.

Ntsou, Bakwowi Jeshma. The Role of Agriculture to Reduce Poverty in Sub Sahara Afric. 2011. 88p. pap. ***(978-3-8454-0352-6(7))*** Lambert Academic Publishing.

Nug Bissohong, Thomas Théophile. L'hymne National du Cameroun: Un Poème-Chant à Décolonialiser et à Réécrire: Relectures Critiques et Perspectives. 2009. (FRE.). 94p. *(978-9956-0-9148-5(0))* Cle, Editions.

Nyamndi, G. D. Whether Losing, Whether Winning Essays in Political Realism. 2008. 120p. pap. *(978-9956-558-52-0(4))* Langaa Research & Publishing Common Initiative Group CMR. Dist: Michigan State Univ. Pr.

Ottih, Mazi Ngozi. Reflections of a Glorious Life: Patrick Nwakamma Ottih. 2008. (Illus.). 51p. pap. 15.99 *(978-1-4363-5762-3(4))* Xlibris Corp.

Percival, John. The 1961 Cameroon Plebiscite: Choice or Betrayal. 2008. 160p. *(978-9956-558-49-0(4))* Langaa Research & Publishing Common Initiative Group CMR. Dist: Michigan State Univ. Pr.

Schler, Lynn. The Strangers of New Bell: Immigration, Public Space & Community in Colonial Douala, Cameroon, 1914-1960. 2008. 168p. pap. *(978-1-86888-489-6(9))* Unisa Press / Uitgewers GBR. Dist: Michigan State Univ. Pr.

Tangwa, Godfrey B. I Spit on Their Graves: Testimony Relevant to the Democratization Struggle in Cameroon. 2010. 222p. pap. *(978-9956-616-26-8(5))* Langaa Research & Publishing Common Initiative Group CMR. Dist: Michigan State Univ. Pr.

Torrent, Melanie. Diplomacy & Nation-Building in Africa: Franco-British relations & Cameroon at the End of Empire. 2012. (International Library of African Studies). (ENG.). 304p. 96.00 ***(978-1-84885-777-3(2))*** I. B. Tauris & Co., Ltd. GBR. Dist: Macmillan.

CAMEROONS

see Cameroon

CAMILLA, DUCHESS OF CORNWALL, 1947-

Andersen, Christopher. After Diana: William, Harry, Charles, & the Royal House of Windsor. (ENG., 352p. 2008. Illus.). mass mkt. 7.99 *(978-0-7868-9124-5(6))* 2007. 25.95 *(978-1-4013-0360-0(9))* Hyperion Pr.

Brandreth, Gyles Daubeney & Brandreth, Gyles. Charles & Camilla: Portrait of a Love Affair. 2007. (ENG., Illus.). 368p. pap. 14.95 *(978-0-09-949087-6(0)*, Arrow Bks., Ltd.) Random Hse. GBR. Dist: Independent Pubs. Group.

CAMISARDS

Randall, Catharine. From a Far Country: Camisards & Huguenots in the Atlantic World. (ENG.). 186p. 2011. pap. 24.95 *(978-0-8203-3820-0(6))* 2009. 44.95 *(978-0-8203-3390-8(5))* Univ. of Georgia Pr.

CAMOES, LUIZ DE, 1524?-1580

Gil, Fernando & Macedo, Helder. The Traveling Eye: Retrospection, Vision, & Prophecy in the Portuguese Renaissance. 2009. (Adamastor Ser.). (Illus.). 440p. pap. 29.95 *(978-1-933227-29-0(X))* Tagus Pr.

Meihuizen, Nicholas. Ordering Empire: The Poetry of Camoes, Pringle & Campbell. 283p. pap. 69.95 *(978-3-03911-023-0(3))* Lang, Peter CHE. Dist: Lang, Peter Publishing, Inc.

CAMORRA

see Mafia

CAMOUFLAGE (BIOLOGY)

Forbes, Peter. Dazzled & Deceived: Mimicry & Camouflage. (Illus.). 304p. 2011. pap. 17.00 *(978-0-300-17896-8(4))* 2009. (ENG., 27.50 *(978-0-300-12539-9(9))* Yale Univ. Pr.

Howse, Philip E. Butterflies: Decoding Their Signs & Symbols. 2010. (ENG., Illus.). 192p. 39.95 *(978-1-55407-773-1(7))* Firefly Bks., Ltd.

Jennings, Terry. Camouflage. 2008. (Listen Read Think Science Ser.). (Illus.). 24p. (J). (gr. 2-5). pap. 5.49 *(978-1-4206-8146-8(X))* Teacher Created Resources, Inc.

Najafi, Sina, ed. Cabinet 33: Deception. 2009. (ENG., Illus.). 112p. pap. 12.00 *(978-1-932698-31-2(0))* Cabinet.

Newark, Tim. Camouflage. 2007. (ENG., Illus.). 208p. 45.00 *(978-0-500-51347-7(3)*, 551347) Thames & Hudson.

Shell, Hanna Rose. Hide & Seek: Camouflage, Photography, & the Media of Reconnaissance. 2012. (ENG., Illus.). 256p. (gr. 17). 32.95 ***(978-1-935408-22-2(4))*** Zone Bks.

Stevens, Martin & Merilaita, Sami, eds. Animal Camouflage: Mechanisms & Function. 2011. (ENG., Illus.). 376p. 125.00 *(978-0-521-19911-7(5))*; pap. 65.00 *(978-0-521-15257-0(7))* Cambridge Univ. Pr.

CAMOUFLAGE (MILITARY SCIENCE)

Brayley, Martin J. Camouflage Uniforms: International Combat Dress 1940-2010, 1 vol. 2010. (ENG., Illus.). 96p. 34.95 *(978-1-84797-137-1(7)*, 1847971377) Crowood Pr., Ltd. GBR. Dist: MBI Distribution Services/Quayside Distribution.

Goodden, Henrietta. Camouflage & Art: Design for Deception in World War 2. 2007. (ENG., Illus.). 192p. 55.00 *(978-0-906290-87-3(2))* Unicorn Pr., London GBR. Dist: National Bk. Network.

Green, Brett, et al. Luftwaffe Camouflage & Markings, 1933-1945 - Photo Archive 1, Vol. 1. 2010. (ENG., Illus.). 144p. 44.95 *(978-1-85780-275-7(6))* Allan, Ian Publishing GBR. Dist: BookMasters Distribution Services (BDS).

Hartcup, Guy. Camouflage: The History of Concealment & Deception in War. 2008. (Illus.). 160p. 39.95 *(978-1-84415-769-3(5))* Pen & Sword Bks. Ltd. GBR. Dist: Casemate Pubs. & Bk. Distributors, LLC.

Newark, Tim. Camouflage. 2007. (ENG., Illus.). 208p. 45.00 *(978-0-500-51347-7(3)*, 551347) Thames & Hudson.

United States Army Staff. Army Field Manual FM 20-3 (Camouflage, Concealment, & Decoys) 2007. per. 19.99 *(978-1-4209-2834-1(1))* Digireads.com.

U.S. Army. Camouflage of Fixed Installations. 2006. pap. 25.00 *(978-1-4101-0914-9(3))* Fredonia Bks.

Wessels, Nelmarie. Supply Chain Management. 2011. 160p. pap. ***(978-3-8443-0883-9(0))*** Lambert Academic Publishing.

Williams, David L. Naval Camouflage, 1914-1945: A Complete Visual Reference. (Illus.). 256p. 65.00 *(978-1-55750-496-8(2))* Naval Institute Pr.

Zaloga, Steven J. U. S. Armour Camouflage & Markings, 1917-45. (Vanguard Ser.: No. 39). (Illus.). 48p. pap. 10.95 *(978-0-85045-515-1(4)*, 9328) Osprey Publishing, Ltd. GBR. Dist: Stackpole Bks.

CAMP COOKING

see Outdoor Cooking

CAMP COUNSELORS

Coutellier, Connie. Camp Is for the Camper: A Counselor's Guide to Youth Development. 2nd ed. 2007. (Illus.). 69p. per. 9.95 *(978-1-58518-041-7(6)*, Healthy Learning) Coaches Choice.

Fergeson, Nancy. Training Staff to Be Spiritual Leaders: Activities & Resources for Christian Camps. 2008. (Illus.). 123p. pap. 19.95 *(978-1-58518-665-5(1)*, Healthy Learning) Coaches Choice.

CAMP DAVID AGREEMENTS (1978)

The U.S.-Israel-Egypt Trilateral Relationship: Shoring up the Foundation of Regional Peace: Hearing Before the Subcommittee on the Middle East & South Asia of the Committee on Foreign Affairs, House of Representatives, One Hundred Tenth Congress, Second Session, May 21, 2008. 2008. iii, 35p. *(978-0-16-081330-6(1)*, 552-070-37710-7) United States Government Printing Office.

CAMP MAINTENANCE

see Camp Sites, Facilities, etc.

CAMP MANAGEMENT

see Camps—Management

CAMP MEETINGS

see also Church Camps

David, Jonathan. Together Let Us Sweetly Live: The Singing & Praying Bands. 2007. (Music in American Life Ser.). (Illus.). 264p. 83.00 *(978-0-252-03170-0(9))*; pap. 28.00 *(978-0-252-07419-6(X))* Univ. of Illinois Pr.

Doerr, Mary Jane. Bay View: An American Idea: an American Idea. 2011. (Illus.). 208p. 29.95 *(978-1-886167-31-5(1))* Priscilla Pr.

Johnson, Donna M. Holy Ghost Girl: A Memoir. 2011. (ENG.). 288p. (gr. 12). 26.00 *(978-1-59240-630-2(0)*, Gotham) Penguin Group (USA) Inc.

Lehman, James O. Mennonite Tent Revivals: Howard Hammer & Myron Augsburger, 1952-1963. (Illus.). xxii, 318p. 29.25 *(978-1-894710-22-0(3))* Pandora Pr. CAN. Dist: Herald Pr.

Robertson, James. Hedding among the Pines. 2008. (Illus.). 400p. per. 34.95 *(978-1-933002-65-1(4))* PublishingWorks.

CAMP SITES, FACILITIES, ETC.

Here are entered works on places in the country that offer temporary lodging to individuals in an outdoor atmosphere, as well as works on the facilities provided in these places. Works on places in the country that offer simple, temporary group accommodations in an outdoor atmosphere together with an organized program of recreational or instructional activities are entered under Camps. Works on the technique of setting up and living in camps are entered under Camping.

see also Tourist Camps, Hostels, etc.

AA Publishing & AA Publishing Staff. Caravan & Camping France 2011. 8th ed. 2011. (ENG., Illus.). 256p. pap. 19.95 *(978-0-7495-6790-3(2))* Automobile Assn. GBR. Dist: Independent Pubs. Group.

AA Publishing, A. A. Publishing. Caravan & Camping Europe 2011. 21st ed. 2011. (ENG., Illus.). 400p. pap. 19.95 ***(978-0-7495-6834-4(8))*** Automobile Assn. GBR. Dist: Independent Pubs. Group.

Automobile Association Staff, contrib. by. Caravan & Camping in Europe 2004. rev. ed. (Illus.). 400p. pap. 19.99 *(978-0-7495-3929-0(1))* Automobile Assn. GBR. Dist: Trafalgar Square Publishing.

Automobile Club of Michigan Staff. Michigan State Parks: Location, Features, Facilities. (Illus.). reprint ed. lib. bdg. 125.00 *(978-0-7222-0132-9(X))* Library Reprints, Inc.

Balkan, Evan L. Maryland: A Guide for Car Campers Who Hate RVs, Concrete Slabs, & Loud Portable Stereos. 2008. (Best in Tent Camping Ser.). (ENG., Illus.). 192p. pap. 14.95 *(978-0-89732-977-4(5))* Menasha Ridge Pr., Inc.

Basch, Harry & Slater, Shirley. Exploring America by RV. 7th ed. 2012. (Frommer's Complete Guides). (ENG., Illus.). 448p. pap. 19.99 ***(978-1-118-08602-5(3)***, Frommers) Wiley, John & Sons, Inc.

Camping France 2007. 51st rev. ed. (FRE., Illus.). 610p. pap. 16.00 *(978-2-06-712251-2(7))* Michelin.

Church, Mike & Church, Terri. Pacific Northwest Camping Destinations: RV & Car Camping Destinations in Oregon, Washington, & British Columbia. (Camping Destinations Ser.). (ENG., Illus.). 2nd ed. 2008. 512p. pap. 19.95 *(978-0-9749471-7-4(2))* 3rd ed. 2012. 608p. pap. 21.95 ***(978-0-9823101-2-0(9))*** Rolling Homes Pr.

—Southwest Camping Destinations: RV & Car Camping Destinations in Arizona, New Mexico, & Utah. 2nd ed. 2008. (Camping Destinations Ser.). (ENG., Illus.). 544p. pap. 19.95 *(978-0-9749471-9-8(9))* Rolling Homes Pr.

—Traveler's Guide to Mexican Camping: Explore Mexico, Guatemala, & Belize with Your RV or Tent. 2009. (Traveler's Guide Ser.). (ENG.). 544p. pap. 21.95 *(978-0-9823101-0-6(2))* Rolling Homes Pr.

Clancy, Michael T. & Clancy, Anna. A User's Guide to Saskatchewan Parks. 2006. (Discover Saskatchewan Ser.). (ENG., Illus.). 443p. pap. 24.95 *(978-0-88977-198-7(7))* Canadian Plains Research Ctr. CAN. Dist: Univ. of Toronto Pr.

Coloma, Cindy. Northern California. 4th ed. 2008. (Best in Tent Camping Ser.). (ENG., Illus.). 204p. pap. 14.95 *(978-0-89732-674-2(1))* Menasha Ridge Pr., Inc.

Davis, Holly & Davis, Burt. Dwelling Portably 1990-1999. 2009. (Illus.). 168p. pap. 8.00 *(978-1-934620-20-5(3))* Microcosm Publishing.

de Vos, Robert C. A. & Brice, Tracy A., eds. The RVer's Friend: North American Diesel/Parking Directory. 2007. 368p. per. 14.95 *(978-1-890141-32-5(1))* TR Information Pubs.

Dirksen, Diane & Dirksen, Jake. Recreation Lakes of California 15th Ed. 2009. 256p. pap. 19.95 *(978-0-943798-23-3(X))* Recreation Sales Publishing.

DuFresne, Jim. Michigan's Best Campgrounds: A Guide to the Best 150 Public Campgrounds in the Great Lakes State. 4th ed. 2011. Orig. Title: Camping Michigan: Lower Michigan's 75 Best Campgrounds. (ENG., Illus.). 384p. pap. 17.95 *(978-1-933272-27-6(9))* Thunder Bay Pr.

Expanding Access to Federal Lands for People with Disabilities: Oversight Hearing Before the Subcommittee on National Parks, Forests, & Public Lands of the Committee on Natural Resources, U.S. House of Representatives, One Hundred Tenth Congress, Second Session, Thursday, July 24, 2008. 2009. iii, 55p. *(978-0-16-082725-9(6)*, 552-070-38735-8) United States Government Printing Office.

Folsom, Gil. Colorado Campgrounds: The 100 Best & All the Rest. 4th rev. ed. 2008. (ENG.). 302p. pap. 24.95 *(978-1-56579-618-8(7))* Westcliffe Pubs.

Forster, Matt. Best Tent Camping - Michigan. 2011. (Best in Tent Camping Ser.). (ENG., Illus.). 192p. pap. 15.95 *(978-0-89732-642-1(3))* Menasha Ridge Pr., Inc.

Hailey, Charlie. Camps: A Guide to 21st Century Space. 2009. pap. *(978-0-262-08370-6(1))* MIT Pr.

—Camps: A Guide to 21st-Century Space. 2009. (ENG., Illus.). 560p. (gr. 17). pap. 32.95 *(978-0-262-51287-9(4))* MIT Pr.

—Campsite: Architectures of Duration & Place. 2008. (Illus.). 339p. 39.95 *(978-0-8071-3323-1(X))* Louisiana State Univ. Pr.

Judd, Ron. Camping Washington: The Best Public Campgrounds for Tents & RVS. 2009. (ENG.). 320p. pap. 18.95 *(978-1-59485-092-9(5))* Mountaineers Bks., The.

Lomax, Becky. Montana, Wyoming & Idaho Camping: Including Yellowstone, Grand Teton, & Glacier National Parks. 2010. (Moon Outdoors Ser.). (ENG., Illus.). 512p. pap. 19.95 *(978-1-59880-373-0(5))* Avalon Travel Publishing.

—Moon Spotlight Idaho Panhandle Camping. 2011. (Moon Spotlight Ser.). (ENG.). 95p. pap. 8.99 *(978-1-59880-928-2(8))* Avalon Travel Publishing.

Lowe, Harriet, ed. Site & Facilities Matters: By the Experts. 2007. (ACA's by the Experts Ser.). 94p. per. 19.95 *(978-1-58518-035-6(1))* Coaches Choice.

Meltzer, Jack and Julee. Camping & RVing with Dogs: The Complete Reference for Dog-Loving Campers & RVers. 2009. (ENG.). 226p. pap. 21.95 *(978-0-7627-5461-8(3))* Woodall Publishing Co.

Mickelsen, Carol. Camping Europe: Includes Scandinavia, Central & Eastern Europe. 3rd ed. 2008. (Camping Europe: Includes Scandinavia, Central & Eastern Ser.). (ENG., Illus.). 950p. per. 24.95 *(978-0-917120-20-6(5))* Carousel Pr.

CAMPANIA (ITALY)—DESCRIPTION AND TRAVEL

Attini, Antonio, photos by. Naples: In Flight over the City & Campania. 2009. (ENG., Illus.). 224p. 29.95 *(978-88-544-0369-7(5))* White Star ITA. Dist: Random Hse., Inc.

Campania. 128p. pap. *(978-88-476-0066-9(9))* Casa Editrice Bonechi.

CAMPANOLOGY

see Bells

CAMPBELL, ALEXANDER, 1788-1866

Cherok, Richard J., et al. Debating for God: Alexander Campbell's Challenge to Skepticism in Antebellum America. 2008. (Illus.). 224p. *(978-0-89112-530-3(2))*; pap. *(978-0-89112-531-0(0))* Abilene Christian Univ. Pr.

Maxey, Robert T. Alexander Campbell & the Peculiar Institution. 332p. pap. 12.99 *(978-0-89900-291-0(9))* College Pr. Publishing Co., Inc.

Morrison, John L. Alexander Campbell: Educating the Moral Person. 238p. pap. 9.99 *(978-0-89900-584-3(5))* College Pr. Publishing Co., Inc.

Thomas, Cecil K. Alexander Campbell & His New Version. 2011. 224p. pap. 19.00 ***(978-1-61097-563-6(4)***, Wipf and Stock) Wipf & Stock Pubs.

Wrather, Eva Jean. Alexander Campbell Vol. 1: Adventurer in Freedom - A Literary Biography. Cummins, D. Duane, ed. 2009. (ENG., Illus.). 290p. pap. 17.95 *(978-0-87565-369-3(3))* Texas Christian Univ. Pr.

—Alexander Campbell Vol. 3: Adventurer in Freedom. Cummins, D. Duane, ed. 3rd ed. 2009. (ENG., Illus.). 308p. 25.00 *(978-0-87565-400-3(2))* Texas Christian Univ. Pr.

—Alexander Campbell, Volume 2: Adventurer in Freedom A Literary Biography. Cummins, D. Duane, ed. 2007. (Illus.). 412p. 25.00 *(978-0-87565-343-3(X))* Texas Christian Univ. Pr.

CAMPBELL, BEATRICE STELLA, 1865-1940

see Campbell, Patrick, Mrs., 1865-1940

CAMPBELL, DONALD, 1921-1967

Bem-Campbell, Tonia. Donald Campbell: My Life with a Hero. rev. ed. 2007. (ENG., Illus.). 283p. per. 16.95 *(978-0-7509-4533-2(8))* Sutton Publishing.

Sheppard, Neil. This Rather Stony Path: Donald Campbell's Last Record Attempt. 2011. (ENG., Illus.). 256p. 49.95 ***(978-0-7524-5973-8(2))*** History Pr. Ltd., The GBR. Dist: Independent Pubs. Group.

Stevens, Donald. Bluebird CN7: The Inside Story of Donald Campbell's Last Land Speed Record Car. 2010. (ENG., Illus.). 128p. 49.95 *(978-1-84584-280-2(4)*, 1845842804) Veloce Publishing Ltd. GBR. Dist: MBI Distribution Services/Quayside Distribution.

CAMPBELL, IAN JAMES, 1931-1963

Wambaugh, Joseph. The Onion Field. 2007. (ENG.). 512p. pap. 15.00 *(978-0-385-34159-2(8)*, Delta) Random House Publishing Group.

CAMPBELL, JOHN ARCHIBALD, 1811-1889

Connor, Henry G. John Archibald Campbell: Associate Justice of the United States Supreme Court, 1853-1861. 2007. 324p. 45.95 *(978-0-548-54452-5(2))*; (ENG.). per. 30.95 *(978-0-548-50066-8(5))* Kessinger Publishing, LLC.

CAMPBELL, JOSEPH, 1904-1987

Kesti, Tutta. Heroes of Middle-Earth. 2010. 92p. pap. *(978-3-8383-3478-3(7))* Lambert Academic Publishing.

Rauch, Stephen. Neil Gaiman's the Sandman & Joseph Campbell: In Search of the Modern Myth: In Search of the Modern Myth. 2007. 224p. pap. 12.95 *(978-0-8095-7168-0(4))* Wildside Pr., LLC.

Rensma, Ritske. The Innateness of Myth: A New Interpretation of Joseph Campbell's Reception of C. G. Jung. 2011. (ENG.). 238p. pap. 44.95 ***(978-1-4411-7567-0(9))*** Continuum International Publishing Group, Ltd. GBR. Dist: National Bk. Network.

Rensma, Ritske & Rensma. The Innateness of Myth: A New Interpretation of Joseph Campbell's Reception of C. G. Jung. 2010. (Continuum Advances in Religious Studies). (ENG.). 240p. 120.00 *(978-1-4411-5112-4(5))* Continuum International Publishing Group, Ltd. GBR. Dist: National Bk. Network.

CAMPBELL, PATRICK, MRS., 1865-1940

Campbell, Patrick. My Life & Some Letters. 2009. (ENG.). 510p. 43.99 *(978-1-117-24133-3(5))*; pap. 38.75 *(978-1-117-24134-0(3))* BiblioBazaar.

—My Life & Some Letters. 2009. 240p. pap. *(978-0-217-23955-4(2))* Books LLC.

—My Life & Some Letters. 2007. (ENG.). 510p. 55.95 *(978-0-548-01344-1(6))* Kessinger Publishing, LLC.

CAMPBELL, ROBERT, 1769-1846

Huss, Stephen F. Irish Mountain Man. 12.95 *(978-1-893937-02-4(X))* Independent Publishing Corp.

CAMPBELL, ROY, 1901-1957

Meihuizen, Nicholas. Ordering Empire: The Poetry of Camoes, Pringle & Campbel. 283p. pap. 69.95 *(978-3-03911-023-0(3))* Lang, Peter CHE. Dist: Lang, Peter Publishing, Inc.

CAMPBELL, THOMAS, 1763-1854

Beattie, William. Life & Letters of Thomas Campbell. 2009. 558p. 44.99 *(978-1-115-29225-2(0))*; 37.99 *(978-1-115-29224-5(2))*; pap. 42.75 *(978-1-115-29223-8(4))* BiblioBazaar.

—Life & Letters of Thomas Campbell. 2009. 402p. pap. *(978-1-150-67669-7(8))*; 310p. pap. *(978-0-217-50299-3(7))* Books LLC.

—Life & Letters of Thomas Campbell. 2009. 302p. pap. 23.37 *(978-1-150-35682-7(0))* General Bks. LLC.

Hanna, William Herbert. Thomas Campbell: Seceder & Christian Union Advocate. 2007. (Illus.). 222p. pap. 24.00 *(978-1-55635-414-4(2)*, Wipf and Stock) Wipf & Stock Pubs.

CAMPBELL-BANNERMAN, HENRY, SIR, 1836-1908

Hattersley, Roy. Campbell-Bannermann. 2006. (British Prime Ministers of the 20th Century Ser.). (ENG., Illus.). 161p. pap. 16.95 *(978-1-904950-56-1(6))* Haus Publishing GBR. Dist: Consortium Bk. Sales & Distribution.

CAMPBELL FAMILY

Burgess, Mary W. The Campbell Chronicles: Samuel Campbell of Lancaster County, Pennsylvania, & His Descendants. Date not set. (Borgo Family Histories Ser.: No. 3). (Illus.). 128p. pap. *(978-0-89370-478-0(4)*, Millefleurs) Wildside Pr., LLC.

Byrd Genealogy Extracted from Campbel Genealogy (1927) fac. ed. 146p. pap. 24.00 *(978-0-7404-1354-4(6))* Higginson Bk. Co.

Campbell, James A. Home Forgotten: The Campbells of the North River. 2007. (Illus.). 284p. 49.95 *(978-0-9789766-4-4(9))* Northbooks.

Campbell, L. L. Campbell Clan in Virginia. fac. ed. 154p. reprint ed. pap. 27.00 *(978-0-7404-1356-2(9))* Higginson Bk. Co.

Campbell, Liza. A Charmed Life: Growing up in Macbeth's Castle. 2008. (ENG., Illus.). 352p. pap. 14.95 *(978-0-312-38496-8(3)*, St. Martin's Griffin) St. Martin's Pr.

Davis, Thulani. My Confederate Kinfolk: A Twenty-First Century Freedwoman Discovers Her Roots. 2007. (ENG., Illus.). 352p. per. 15.00 *(978-0-465-01574-0(3)*, Basic Civitas Bks.) Basic Bks.

Innes, Cosmo N. Black Book of Taymouth. (Bannatyne Club, Edinburgh Publications: No. 100). reprint ed. 105.00 *(978-0-404-52848-5(1))* AMS Pr., Inc.

MacCulloch, Patrick C. The Campbell Quest: A Saga of Family & Fortune. 2009. (ENG., Illus.). 352p. (gr. 9). 27.95 *(978-1-883982-67-6(7))* Missouri Historical Society Pr.

Meyer, Craig A., ed. Confederate Girlhoods: A Women's History of Early Springfield, Missouri. 2010. (ENG., Illus.). 360p. pap. 24.95 *(978-0-913785-10-2(5)*, Moon City Pr.) Department of English.

CAMPBELLITES

see Disciples of Christ

CAMPER TRAILERS

see Camping Trailers

CAMPERS AND COACHES, TRUCK

see Truck Campers

CAMPIN, ROBERT

Frinta, Mojmír Svatopluk. The genius of Robert Campin. (ENG.). 123p. 210.00 ***(978-3-11-205252-5(8))***; 135.00 ***(978-3-11-118882-9(5))*** De Gruyter, Mouton DEU. Dist: de Gruyter, Walter GmbH & Co. KG.

CAMPING

Here are entered works on the techniques of setting up and living in camps. Works on places in the country that offer simple, temporary group accommodations in an outdoor atmosphere together with an organized program of recreational or instructional activities are entered under Camps. Works on places in the country that offer temporary lodging to individuals in an outdoor atmosphere, as well as works on the facilities provided in these places are entered under Camp Sites, Facilities, etc.

see also Backpacking; Bicycle Touring; Camp Sites, Facilities, etc.; Camps; Outdoor Life; Tourist Camps, Hostels, etc.

Ahrendt, Sue, ed. Becoming a Boundary Waters Family: Woods Wisdom Shared by the Outfitters of the Gunflint Trail. 2009. (Illus.). 76p. spiral bd. 15.99 *(978-1-60743-855-7(0))* Independent Pub.

Ainsworth, Jim H. Biscuits Across the Brazos: A Recollection of a Memorable Horseback & Wagon Journey. 2010. 100p. pap. 14.95 *(978-0-86534-754-0(9))* Sunstone Pr.

Allee, Mellody R. L. Camping in a Pop-up Camper Is Paradise: A carry-along guide for novice & experienced camping enthusiasts interested in tent-trailer Camping. 2010. 232p. pap. 18.95 *(978-1-60844-540-0(2))* Dog Ear Publishing, LLC.

Bean, Leon Leonwood. Hunting, Fishing, & Camping: 100th Anniversary Edition. 100th ed. 2012. (ENG., Illus.). 112p. 19.95 ***(978-1-60893-012-8(2))*** Down East Bks.

Beard, Adelia Belle & Beard, Lina. On the Trail: An Outdoor Book for Girls. 2007. (Illus.). 228p. per. *(978-1-4065-3693-5(8))* Dodo Pr.

Beard, D. C. Shelters Shacks & Shanties: And How to Build Them. 2nd ed. 2008. 243p. pap. 14.95 *(978-1-59921-333-0(8)*, Lyons Pr.) Globe Pequot Pr., The.

Beard, Daniel & Beard, Daniel Carter. The Field & Forest Handy Book. 2007. (Dover Children's Activity Bks.). (ENG., Illus.). 448p. per. 12.95 *(978-0-486-46191-5(2))* Dover Pubns., Inc.

Beard, Daniel Carter & Beard, Daniel C. The Book of Camp-Lore & Woodcraft. 2008. (ENG., Illus.). 288p. (gr. 4-18). pap. 12.95 *(978-1-56792-352-0(6)*, Non Pareil Bks.) Godine, David R. Pub.

Beard, Lina & Beard, Adelia Belle. On the Trail: An Outdoor Book for Girls. 2007. (ENG.). 216p. pap. 20.99 *(978-1-4264-9347-8(9))*; 244p. pap. 22.99 *(978-1-4264-9728-5(8))* BiblioBazaar.

Beattie, Rob. The Boating Companion: All You Need to Know for Life on the Water. 2008. (ENG., Illus.). 144p. pap. 19.95 *(978-0-7624-3186-1(5))* Running Pr. Bk. Pubs.

Behrens, Tom. Texas: A Comprehensive Guide to More Than 200 Campgrounds. 2009. (Regional Camping Ser.). (ENG., Illus.). 192p. pap. 16.95 *(978-0-7627-4605-7(X)*, Falcon Guides) Globe Pequot Pr., The.

Black, David. Survival Retreats: A Practical Guide to Creating a Sustainable, Defendable Refuge. 2011. (ENG., Illus.). 320p. pap. 14.95 *(978-1-61608-417-2(0)*, 608417) Skyhorse Publishing Co., Inc.

Brennan, Virginia. Gasoline Gypsies: David & Virginia's Life on the Road. 2009. 132p. pap. 14.95 *(978-1-4327-0391-2(9))* Outskirts Pr., Inc.

Bridge, Raymond. Bike Touring: The Sierra Club Guide to Travel on Two Wheels. 2nd ed. 2009. (Sierra Club Outdoor Adventure Guide Ser.). (ENG., Illus.). 448p. pap. 18.95 *(978-1-57805-142-7(8))* Sierra Club Bks.

Burnham, Bill & Burnham, Mary. Car Camping: A Step-by-Step Guide to Planning Your Outdoor Adventure. 2009. (Knack: Make It Easy Ser.). (ENG., Illus.). 256p. pap. 19.95 *(978-1-59921-505-1(5)*, Knack) Globe Pequot Pr., The.

Callan, Kevin. Wilderness Pleasures: A Practical Guide to Camping Bliss. 2008. (ENG., Illus.). 240p. pap. 24.95 *(978-1-55046-497-9(3))* Boston Mills Pr. CAN. Dist: Firefly Bks., Ltd.

Canoe Camping. 2007. (Essential Guides (Heliconia Press) Ser.). (Illus.). 123p. per. *(978-1-896980-22-5(8))* Heliconia Pr., Inc.

Cavanagh, James A. Tall Tales from the Road. 2010. 89p. pap. 16.50 *(978-0-557-53696-2(0))* Lulu Enterprises Inc.

Church, Mike & Church, Terri. Southwest Camping Destinations: RV & Car Camping Destinations in Arizona, New Mexico, & Utah. 2nd ed. 2008. (Camping Destinations Ser.). (ENG., Illus.). 544p. pap. 19.95 *(978-0-9749471-9-8(9))* Rolling Homes Pr.

Clip Art. The Great Outdoors CD-ROM & Book: Vintage Illustrations of Camping, Hiking & Fishing. Menges, Jeff A., ed. 2013. (Dover Electronic Clip Art Ser.). (ENG.). 48p. pap. 19.95 ***(978-0-486-99212-9(8))*** Dover Pubns., Inc.

Coz, Steven. Where Memories Dream: Campfire Stories from the Boundary Waters. 2011. (Illus.). 216p. pap. 14.95 *(978-1-886028-92-0(3))* Savage Pr.

Creekmore. Dirt-Cheap Survival Retreat: One Man's Solution. 2011. 88p. pap. 12.00 ***(978-1-58160-747-5(4))*** Paladin Pr.

Daney, Dave. Packing with Burros. 2010. *(978-0-87961-280-1(0))*; (Illus.). xii, 142p. pap. *(978-978-087-961-7(7))* Naturegraph Pubs., Inc.

Davis, Holly & Davis, Burt. Dwelling Portably 1990-1999. 2009. (Illus.). 168p. pap. 8.00 *(978-1-934620-20-5(3))* Microcosm Publishing.

Davis, Todd. Handy Dad in the Great Outdoors: More Than 30 Super-Cool Projects & Activities for Dads & Kids. 2012. (ENG., Illus.). 160p. pap. 24.95 ***(978-1-4521-0213-9(9))*** Chronicle Bks. LLC.

Department of the Army Staff, ed. Survival Handbook: The Official U. S. Army Guide. 2008. (ENG., Illus.). 288p. pap. 9.95 *(978-0-486-46184-7(X))* Dover Pubns., Inc.

Dorling Kindersley Publishing Staff. The Survival Handbook: Essential Skills for Outdoor Adventure. 2012. (ENG.). 320p. pap. 17.95 ***(978-0-7566-9038-0(2))*** Dorling Kindersley Publishing, Inc.

Dorrance, Ward A. Three Ozark Streams: Log of the Mocassin & the Wilma. (Illus.). 58p. reprint ed. lib. bdg. 88.00 *(978-0-7222-0581-5(3))* Library Reprints, Inc.

Douglass, Frazier. Lightweight Camping for Motorcycle Travel. 2008. 268p. pap. 20.95 *(978-0-595-49650-1(4))*; 30.95 *(978-0-595-49394-4(7))* iUniverse, Inc.

—Lightweight Camping for Motorcycle Travel: Revised Edition. 2009. 348p. 33.95 *(978-1-4401-7647-0(7))*; pap. 23.95 *(978-1-4401-7645-6(0))* iUniverse, Inc.

Durham, Wil. Bisky Dog: Children's camping cookbook for Adults. 2009. 108p. 24.99 *(978-1-4500-0491-6(1))*; pap. 15.99 *(978-1-4500-0490-9(3))* Xlibris Corp.

Elwins, Dannie. Family Camping 101: How the Family Can Have Fun Together Camping. 2009. 48p. pap. 16.99 *(978-0-557-15554-5(1))* Lulu Enterprises Inc.

Eskow, Philip G. Camping for Beginners. 2008. 104p. pap. 15.99 *(978-1-4257-8984-8(6))* Xlibris Corp.

Fearing, Jerry. Campfire Tales. 2009. pap. 14.95 *(978-1-932472-91-2(6))* Nodin Pr.

Ferguson, Nancy. S'More Time with God. 2011. 128p. 12.99 *(978-0-8170-1663-0(5))* Judson Pr.

Foerster, Victor. Naked in the Stream: Isle Royale Stories. 2010. (Illus.). pap. 18.95 *(978-1-933926-22-3(8))* Arbutus Pr.

Forster, Matt. Best Tent Camping - Michigan. 2011. (Best in Tent Camping Ser.). (ENG., Illus.). 192p. pap. 15.95 *(978-0-89732-642-1(3))* Menasha Ridge Pr., Inc.

Freund, John. The Camping Trip. 2011. 28p. pap. ***(978-1-4269-8848-6(6))*** Trafford Publishing (UK) Ltd.

Gibson, H. W. Camping for Boys. 2007. (Illus.). 264p. per. *(978-1-4065-2840-4(4))* Dodo Pr.

Gibson, Henry William. Camping for Boys. 2008. 276p. 25.99 *(978-0-554-34418-8(1))* 2008. 276p. 28.99 *(978-0-554-25115-8(9))* 2007 (ENG.). 238p. pap. 20.99 *(978-1-4264-8168-0(3))* 2007. 274p. pap. 23.99 *(978-1-4264-8240-3(X))* BiblioBazaar.

—Camping for Boys. 2009. 152p. pap. *(978-0-217-45435-3(6))* Books LLC.

—Camping for Boys. 2008. 304p. 43.95 *(978-1-4369-5894-3(6))*; pap. 28.95 *(978-1-4367-9664-4(4))* Kessinger Publishing, LLC.

Gibson, W. Hamilton. Camp Life in the Woods: And the Tricks of Trapping & Trap Making. 2nd ed. 2009. (ENG., Illus.). 312p. 14.95 *(978-1-59921-803-8(8)*, Lyons Pr.) Globe Pequot Pr., The.

—Camp Life in the Woods & the Tricks of Trapping & Trap Making. 2007. (Illus.). 328p. per. *(978-1-4065-2842-8(0))* Dodo Pr.

—Camp Life in the Woods & the Tricks of Trapping & Trap Making. 2009. (Illus.). 292p. pap. *(978-1-4068-2809-2(2))* Echo Library.

Gorman, Stephen. The Winter Camping Handbook: Wilderness Travel & Adventure in the Cold-Weather Months. rev. ed. 2007. (ENG., Illus.). 224p. per. 16.95 *(978-0-88150-782-9(2))* Countryman Pr.

Gould, John M. How to Camp Out. 2008. (Illus.). 92p. pap. *(978-1-4099-5819-2(1))* Dodo Pr.

—How to Camp Out. 2007. (ENG.). 84p. per. *(978-1-4068-6240-9(1))* Echo Library.

—How to Camp Out: Advice from a Civil War Veteran. Watson, William J., ed 2007. 144p. per. 15.95 *(978-0-9774892-4-4(8))* Broken Lance Enterprises.

Hacking, Vickie. Girls Camp Made Easy. 2008. 107p. (YA). pap. 12.99 *(978-1-59955-121-0(7))* Cedar Fort, Inc./CFI Distribution.

Hailey, Charlie. Camps: A Guide to 21st Century Space. 2009. pap. *(978-0-262-08370-6(1))* MIT Pr.

Hanson, Jennifer A. Hiking the Continental Divide Trail: One Woman's Journey. 2011. (ENG., Illus.). 275p. pap. 16.95 *(978-1-56825-120-2(3))* Rainbow Bks., Inc.

Hatley, George. Horse Camping. rev. ed. 2009. (ENG., Illus.). 152p. (Orig.). pap. 24.95 *(978-0-87422-303-3(2))* Washington State Univ. Pr.

Hauserman, Tim. Monsters in the Woods: Backpacking with Children. 2007. (ENG., Illus.). 152p. per. 15.95 *(978-0-87417-711-4(1))* Univ. of Nevada Pr.

Hemphill, Kendal. The Buck Never Got Here. 2010. pap. 14.99 *(978-1-61663-123-9(6))* Tate Publishing & Enterprises, LLC.

Jacobson, Cliff. Basic Illustrated Camping. 2008. (Basic Essentials Ser.). (ENG., Illus.). 96p. pap. 9.95 *(978-0-7627-4849-5(4)*, Falcon Guides) Globe Pequot Pr., The.

—Canoeing & Camping Beyond the Basics. 3rd ed. 2007. (How to Paddle Ser.). (ENG., Illus.). 224p. pap. 16.95 *(978-0-7627-4018-5(3)*, Falcon Guides) Globe Pequot Pr., The.

James, Laura. The Girl's Guide to Camping: Outdoor Living in Serious Style. 2010. (ENG., Illus.). 128p. pap. 14.95 *(978-1-60239-964-8(6)*, 239964) Skyhorse Publishing Co., Inc.

Kavanagh, James. Camping 101: An Introduction to Everything a Novice Needs to Know. 2010. (Duraguide Ser.). 2p. 7.95 *(978-1-58355-552-1(8))* Waterford Pr., Inc.

Kessler, Cassandra. Cooking & Camping with Cass. 2007. 114p. pap. 19.95 *(978-1-60441-663-3(7))* PublishAmerica, Inc.

Knight, Jared R. 101 Age-Appropriate Camp Activities. 2008. (Illus.). 142p. pap. 19.95 *(978-1-58518-099-8(8))* Coaches Choice.

Koller, Larry. Complete Book of Camping & the Outdoors. 2011. 130p. 40.95 ***(978-1-258-06908-7(3))*** Literary Licensing, LLC.

Kreps, E. Camp & Trail Methods. (Illus.). 273p. pap. 4.00 *(978-0-936622-01-6(6))* Harding, A.R. Publishing Co.

Lewis, William Victor. Pass & Fail: Letting you know what works & doesn't while Camping. 2009. pap. *(978-1-61623-595-6(0))* Independent Pub.

Lindstrom, Larry. The Circle of Friends. 2010. 64p. pap. 10.95 *(978-1-4269-3033-1(X))* Trafford Publishing.

Little, Mike, et al. Biologischer Tabakanbau in Amerika. 2009. 208p. pap. 22.95 *(978-0-86534-740-3(9))* Sunstone Pr.

Lomax, Becky. Moon Spotlight Idaho Panhandle Camping. 2011. (Moon Spotlight Ser.). (ENG.). 95p. pap. 8.99 *(978-1-59880-928-2(8))* Avalon Travel Publishing.

—Yellowstone & Grand Teton Camping. 2010. (Moon Spotlight Ser.). (ENG.). 166p. pap. 11.95 *(978-1-59880-577-2(0))* Avalon Travel Publishing.

Low, Lafe. New England: A Guide for Car Campers Who Hate RVs, Concrete Slabs, & Loud Portable Stereos. 3rd ed. 2008. (Best in Tent Camping Ser.). (ENG., Illus.). 228p. pap. 15.95 *(978-0-89732-666-7(0))* Menasha Ridge Pr., Inc.

Macfarlan, Allan A. Living Like Indians: 1,001 Projects, Games, Activities, & Crafts. 2011. (ENG., Illus.). 320p. pap. 14.95 *(978-1-60239-983-9(2)*, 239983) Skyhorse Publishing Co., Inc.

Masterson, Elizabeth S. Round the Campfire: A Family Guide to Successful Camping. 2011. 128p. pap. 19.95 ***(978-1-4626-1297-0(0))*** PublishAmerica, Inc.

Mathews, Franklin K., ed. Hitting the Trail. 2011. 194p. 42.95 ***(978-1-258-08272-7(1))*** Literary Licensing, LLC.

Matson, Mike. Utah Camping: The Complete Guide to Tent & RV Camping. 2nd ed. 2009. (Foghorn Outdoors Ser.). (ENG.). 352p. pap. 17.95 *(978-1-59880-195-8(3))* Avalon Travel Publishing.

Meltzer, Jack and Julee. Camping & RVing with Dogs: The Complete Reference for Dog-Loving Campers & RVers. 2009. (ENG.). 226p. pap. 21.95 *(978-0-7627-5461-8(3))* Woodall Publishing Co.

Menicucci, Heather. Let's Get Primitive: The Urban Girl's Guide to Camping. 2007. (ENG., Illus.). 236p. pap. 14.95 *(978-1-58008-788-9(4))* Ten Speed Pr.

Miller, George Oxford. Lone Star Travel Guide to Texas Parks & Campgrounds. Fifth Edition. 5th ed. 2009. (ENG.). 344p. pap. 19.95 *(978-1-58979-397-2(8))* Taylor Trade Publishing.

Moeller, Bill & Moeller, Jan. The Complete Book of Boondock RVing: Camping off the Beaten Path. 2007. (ENG., Illus.). 176p. per. 16.95 *(978-0-07-149065-8(5)*, 0071490655, International Marine/Ragged Mountain Pr.) McGraw-Hill Professional Publishing.

Molloy, Johnny. Beach & Coastal Camping in the Southeast. 2006. (ENG., Illus.). 208p. per. 18.95 *(978-0-8130-3000-5(5))* Univ. Pr. of Florida.

—The Best in Tent Camping: the Carolinas: A Guide for Car Campers Who Hate RVs, Concrete Slabs, & Loud Portable Stereos. 3rd ed. 2010. (Best in Tent Camping Ser.). (ENG., Illus.). 192p. pap. 15.95 *(978-0-89732-798-5(5))* Menasha Ridge Pr., Inc.

C

—Georgia: A Guide for Car Campers Who Hate RVs, Concrete Slabs, & Loud Portable Stereos. 2nd ed. 2007. (Best in Tent Camping Ser.). (ENG., Illus.). 178p. per. 14.95 (978-0-89732-724-4(1)) Menasha Ridge Pr., Inc.
—Kentucky: A Guide for Car Campers Who Hate RVs, Concrete Slabs, & Loud Portable Steros. 2006. (Best in Tent Camping Ser.). (ENG., Illus.). 192p. per. 14.95 (978-0-89732-609-4(1)) Menasha Ridge Pr., Inc.
—The Southern Appalachian & Smoky Mountains: A Guide for Car Campers Who Hate RVs, Concrete Slabs, & Loud Portable Stereos. 4th ed. 2007. (Best in Tent Camping Ser.). (ENG., Illus.). 192p. per. 14.95 (978-0-89732-960-6(0)) Menasha Ridge Pr., Inc.
Molloy, Johnny & Lipker, Kim. Colorado: A Guide for Car Campers Who Hate RVs, Concrete Slabs, & Loud Portable Stereos. 4th ed. 2007. (Best in Tent Camping Ser.). (ENG., Illus.). 200p. per. 14.95 (978-0-89732-646-2(8)) Menasha Ridge Pr., Inc.
Molloy, Johnny & Revolinski, Kevin. The Best in Tent Camping: A Guide for Car Campers Who Hate Rvs, Concrete Slabs, & Loud Portable Stereos. 2nd ed. 2007. (Best in Tent Camping Ser.). (ENG., Illus.). 192p. per. 14.95 (978-0-89732-616-2(4)) Menasha Ridge Pr., Inc.
Motavalli, Jim. Naked in the Woods: Joseph Knowles & the Legacy of Frontier Fakery. 2008. (ENG., Illus.). 368p. 26.95 (978-0-7867-2008-8(5)) Da Capo Pr., Inc.
Olmon, Kirstin & Phillips, Kelly. Arizona. 2008. (Best in Tent Camping Ser.). (ENG., Illus.). 176p. pap. 14.95 (978-0-89732-648-3(2)) Menasha Ridge Pr., Inc.
Olsson, Helen. The down & Dirty Guide to Camping with Kids: How to Plan Memorable Family Adventures & Connect Kids to Nature. 2012. (ENG., Illus.). 256p. pap. 17.95 **(978-1-59030-955-1(3)**, Roost Books) Shambhala Pubns., Inc.
Peck, Steven. 101 Fun, Creative, & Interactive Games for Kids. 2007. (Illus.). 144p. pap. 19.95 (978-1-58518-038-7(6)) Coaches Choice.
—101 Teambuilding Games. 2008. (Illus.). 169p. pap. 19.95 (978-1-58518-662-4(7)) Coaches Choice.
Pitt, Michael D. Beyond the End of the Road: A Winter of Contentment North of the Arctic Circle. 2009. (ENG., Illus.). 338p. pap. 19.95 (978-1-897435-36-6(3)) Agio Publishing Hse. CAN. Dist: Lightning Source, Inc.
Popular Mechanics Press Editors. The Boy Camper: 160 Outdoor Projects & Activities. 2008. (Popular Mechanics Ser.). (ENG., Illus.). 256p. 9.95 (978-1-58816-703-3(8)) Hearst Communications, Inc.
Rinehart, Mary Roberts. Tenting To-Night. 2007. (ENG.). 124p. per. (978-1-4065-6280-4(7)) Dodo Pr.
—Tenting To-Night. 2007. (ENG.). 100p. per. (978-1-4068-3924-1(8)) Echo Library.
Rooker, Steve, et al. The Original VW Camper Cookbook: 80 Tasty Recipes Specially Composed for Cooking in a Camper. 2009. (Illus.). 162p. (978-91-631-9684-3(0)) Samlingsnummer for enstaka enskilt utgivna arbeten.
Schirle, John. Illinois: A Guide for Car Campers Who Hate Rvs, Concrete Slabs, & Loud Portable Stereos. 2009. (Best in Tent Camping Ser.). (ENG., Illus.). 208p. pap. 15.95 (978-0-89732-643-8(1)) Menasha Ridge Pr., Inc.
Scriver, Mark. Canoe Camping: An Essential Guide. 2011. (ENG., Illus.). 112p. pap. 16.95 (978-1-56523-646-2(7)) Fox Chapel Publishing Co., Inc.
Seton, Ernest Thompson. Woodcraft & Indian Lore: A Classic Guide from a Founding Father of the Boy Scouts of America. 2007. (ENG., Illus.). 624p. per. 14.95 (978-1-60239-058-4(4), 239058) Skyhorse Publishing Co., Inc.
Sherrey & Andy Newman. Coyote's Thunder Revenge. 2009. 260p. pap. 19.99 (978-1-4257-8752-3(5)) Xlibris Corp.
Shillington, Ben & Sandiford, Rebecca. Winter Backpacking: Your Guide to Safe & Warm Winter Camping & Day Trips. 2011. (ENG., Illus.). 160p. pap. 19.95 (978-1-56523-636-3(X)) Fox Chapel Publishing Co., Inc.
Slade, Andrew. Camping the North Shore: A Guide to the 23 Best Campgrounds in Minnesota's Spectacular Lake Superior Region. 2008. (There & Back Guides). (Illus.). 131p. pap. 14.95 (978-0-9794675-1-6(9)) There & Back Bks.
Smith, Patrick. Camping, Simple & Cheap. 2010. 96p. pap. 11.95 (978-1-4502-2071-2(1)) iUniverse, Inc.
Snyder, Adeline. Camping. 2012. (Great Outdoors Ser.). 24p. (gr. 2-5). pap. 8.15 **(978-1-4339-7088-7(0))**; lib. bdg. 22.60 **(978-1-4339-7087-0(2))** Stevens, Gareth Publishing LLLP.
Soles, Clyde. Backpacker magazine's Backpacking Basics: Planning, Preparing, & Packing. 2011. (Backpacker Magazine Ser.). (ENG., Illus.). 96p. pap. 12.95 (978-0-7627-5549-3(0), Falcon Guides) Globe Pequot Pr., The.
Stanhope, Sally. Liberation of the Southern Lady. 2010. 164p. pap. (978-3-639-27283-8(3)) VDM Verlag Dr. Mueller e.K.
Stattler, Gary L. A short history of the winnebago council, boy scouts of america, & it's Camps. 2007. per. 20.00 (978-1-888461-12-1(8)) Islewest Publishing.
Steadman, Jeffrey. Utah: Car Campers Who Hate Rvs, Concrete Slabs, & Loud Portable Stereos. 2007. (Best in Tent Camping Ser.). (ENG., Illus.). 224p. per. 14.95 (978-0-89732-647-6(4)) Menasha Ridge Pr., Inc.
Tawrell, Paul. Wilderness Camping & Hiking: The Ultimate Outdoors Book. 2008. (ENG., Illus.). 224p. 25.00 (978-0-9740820-3-5(1)) Globe Pequot Pr., The.
Tawrell, Paul Leonard. Camping & Survival: The Ultimate Outdoors Book. 2011. (ENG., Illus.). 624p. pap. 30.00 (978-0-9740820-5-9(8)) Globe Pequot Pr., The.
Townsend, Chris. The Backpacker's Handbook. 4th ed. 2011. (ENG., Illus.). 480p. pap. 21.00 **(978-0-07-175489-7(X)**, 007175489X, International Marine/Ragged Mountain Pr.) McGraw-Hill Professional Publishing.
Van Hees, Thomas. You Might Be an Rver If. 2011. 240p. pap. 24.95 **(978-1-4626-2565-9(7))** PublishAmerica, Inc.
Villaire, Ted. Camping Illinois: A Comprehensive Guide to the State's Best Campgrounds. 2010. (State Camping Ser.). (ENG., Illus.). 168p. pap. 16.95 (978-0-7627-4690-3(4), Falcon Guides) Globe Pequot Pr., The.
Vorenberg, Mike. Faithful & True: 100 Years of Keewaydin on Like Dunmore. 2009. (978-1-61623-796-7(1)) Independent Pub.
Waitzman, Michelle. Sex in a Tent: A Wild Couple's Guide to Getting Naughty in Nature. 2007. (ENG., Illus.). 176p. pap. 14.95 (978-0-89997-432-3(5)) Wilderness Pr.
Watson, Mark. The Next Exit. 2009. (Next Exit: the Most Complete Interstate Highway Guide Ever Printed Ser.). (Illus.). 552p. pap. 14.95 (978-0-9714073-8-1(X)) Next Exit, Inc.
Weisenbarger, David. Tatyana Goes Nude Backpacking Through Ukraine. 2010. 200p. pap. 89.95 (978-0-557-48798-1(6)) Lulu Enterprises Inc.
Wells, Catharine, et al. New York State: A Guide for Car Campers Who Hate RVs, Concrete Slabs, & Loud Portable Stereos. 2007. (Best in Tent Camping Ser.). (ENG., Illus.). 204p. per. 14.95 (978-0-89732-641-4(5)) Menasha Ridge Pr., Inc.
White, Stewart Edward. Camp & Trail. 2008. 248p. 41.95 (978-1-4369-3777-1(9)); pap. 26.95 (978-1-4367-9641-5(5)) Kessinger Publishing, LLC.
—Camp & Trail. 2008. 236p. pap. (978-1-4086-7828-2(4)) Read Bks.
Withrow, Wendel. Texas: A Guide for Car Campers Who Hate RVs, Concrete Slabs, & Loud Portable Stereos. 2009. (Best in Tent Camping Ser.). (ENG., Illus.). 208p. pap. 15.95 (978-0-89732-684-1(9)) Menasha Ridge Pr., Inc.
Woofter, Bob. Motorcycle Camping Made Easy. 2nd ed. 2010. (ENG., Illus.). 200p. pap. 19.95 (978-1-884313-83-7(3), 1884313833) Whitehorse Pr.
Wright, Micah. Camping with the Corps of Engineers: The complete guide to campgrounds built & operated by the U. S. Army Corps of Engineers. 2011. 368p. pap. 17.95 **(978-0-937877-51-7(4))** Cottage Pubns., Inc.
Young, David & Young, Cheryl. Camping: The Lifetime Adventure. 2010. (Illus.). 208p. 19.95 (978-0-9776703-3-8(3)) Perigee Learning, LLC.
—Gourmet Camp Cooking. 2010. 98p. 19.95 (978-0-9824419-4-7(0)) Perigee Learning, LLC.
Zamek, Scott. New Jersey State Parks Camping & Recreation Guide. 2008. (ENG., Illus.). 288p. per. 19.95 (978-0-8117-3473-8(0)) Stackpole Bks.

CAMPING—EQUIPMENT AND SUPPLIES

Adsmond, Lou. The Appalachian Trail Food Planner: Recipes & Menus for a 2,000-Mile Hike. 2nd rev. ed. 2009. 134p. spiral bd. 18.95 (978-1-889386-61-4(8)) Appalachian Trail Conservancy.
Beard, Daniel Carter. The Book of Camp-Lore & Woodcraft. 2008. (ENG.). 288p. 19.95 (978-1-56792-357-5(7)) Godine, David R. Pub.
Beard, Daniel Carter & Beard, Daniel C. The Book of Camp-Lore & Woodcraft. 2008. (ENG., Illus.). 288p. (gr. 4-18). pap. 12.95 (978-1-56792-352-0(6), Non Pareil Bks.) Godine, David R. Pub.
Dorling Kindersley Publishing Staff. The Camping Book: Stay Dry, Sleep Well & Eat Great Food. 2009. (Illus.). 192p. pap. (978-1-4053-4120-2(3)) Dorling Kindersley Publishing, Inc.
Drake, Peter G. Practical Camping Handbook: How to Make the Outdoor Vacations - Everything from Planning Your Trip to Setting up Camp & Cooking Outside, with 300 Practical Step-by-Step Photographs. 2009. (ENG., Illus.). 96p. pap., instr.'s hndbk. ed. 8.99 (978-1-84476-723-6(X)) Anness Publishing GBR. Dist: National Bk. Network.
Faverman, Mike & Mac, Pat. Ultimate Camp Cooking. 2011. (ENG.). 216p. pap. 14.99 (978-1-4494-0159-7(7)) Andrews McMeel Publishing.
Gilpatrick, Gil. Building Outdoor Gear, 2nd Edition, Revised & Expanded: Easy-to-Make Projects for Camping, Fishing, Hunting & Canoeing (Canoe Paddle, Pack Frame, Reflector Oven, Trip Boxes, Bucksaw, Other Trail-Tested Projects) 2nd rev. ed. 2012. (ENG., Illus.). 120p. pap. 19.95 **(978-1-56523-484-0(7))** Fox Chapel Publishing Co., Inc.
Gorman, Leon. L. L. Bean: The Making of an American Icon. 2006. (ENG., Illus.). 304p. 26.95 (978-1-57851-183-9(6)) Harvard Business Review Pr.
Haney, Lynn. Camping in Comfort: A Guide to Roughing It with Ease & Style. 2007. (ENG., Illus.). 192p. per. 16.95 (978-0-07-145421-6(7), 0071454217, International Marine/Ragged Mountain Pr.) McGraw-Hill Professional Publishing.
Masumoto, David Mas. Letters to the Valley: A Harvest of Memories. 2006. (Great Valley Book Ser.). (Illus.). 134p. pap. (978-1-59714-038-6(4)) Heyday.
McCann, John D. Stay Alive! 2011. (ENG.). 256p. pap. 22.99 (978-1-4402-1830-9(7)) Krause Pubns.
Robert, Spector. The Legend of Eddie Bauer. 2nd ed. 2011. (Illus.). 120p. 25.00 (978-1-933245-22-5(0)) Documentary Media LLC.
Shillington, Ben. Winter Backpacking: Your Guide to Safe & Warm Winter Camping & Day Trips. Sandiford, Rebecca, ed. 2009. 160p. pap. (978-1-896980-41-6(4)) Heliconia Pr., Inc.
Snyder, Susan. Past Tents: The Way We Camped. 2006. (Illus.). 145p. per. 17.95 (978-1-59714-039-3(2)) Heyday.
St. Clair, Lucas & Maurer, Yemaya. AMC Guide to Winter Hiking & Camping: Everything You Need to Know to Plan Your Next Cold-Weather Adventure. 2008. (ENG., Illus.). 244p. pap. 16.95 (978-1-934028-12-4(6)) Appalachian Mountain Club Bks.
Videen, Leif. Bunkhouse Built: A Guide to Making Your Own Cowboy Gear. 2009. (Illus.). 129p. pap. 15.00 (978-0-87842-554-9(3)) Mountain Pr. Publishing Co., Inc.

CAMPING—ALASKA

Church, Mike & Church, Terri. Traveler's Guide to Alaskan Camping: Alaska & Yukon Camping with RV or Tent. 5th ed. 2010. (Traveler's Guide Ser.). (ENG., Illus.). 480p. pap. 21.95 (978-0-9823101-3-0(0)) Rolling Homes Pr.

CAMPING—CALIFORNIA

Coloma, Cindy. Northern California. 4th ed. 2008. (Best in Tent Camping Ser.). (ENG., Illus.). 204p. pap. 14.95 (978-0-89732-674-2(1)) Menasha Ridge Pr., Inc.
Patterson, Charles. Southern California. 4th ed. 2008. (Best in Tent Camping Ser.). (ENG., Illus.). 180p. pap. 14.95 (978-0-89732-675-9(X)) Menasha Ridge Pr., Inc.
Stienstra, Stephani, et al. Yosemite & Mammoth Lakes Camping & Hiking. 2009. (Moon Spotlight Ser.). (ENG.). 130p. pap. 8.95 (978-1-59880-277-1(1)) Avalon Travel Publishing.
Stienstra, Tom. Moon Northern California Camping: The Complete Guide to Tent & RV Camping. 2011. (Moon Outdoors Ser.). (ENG., Illus.). 736p. pap. 19.99 (978-1-59880-753-0(6)) Avalon Travel Publishing.
—Shasta & Lassen Camping & Hiking. 2009. (Moon Spotlight Ser.). (ENG.). 235p. pap. 11.95 (978-1-59880-276-4(3)) Avalon Travel Publishing.
—Tahoe Camping & Hiking. 2009. (Moon Spotlight Ser.). (ENG.). 180p. pap. 9.95 (978-1-59880-275-7(5)) Avalon Travel Publishing.
Stienstra, Tom & Brown, Ann Marie. California Deserts Camping & Hiking: Including Death Valley, Mojave, Joshua Tree, & Anza-Borrego. 2009. (Moon Spotlight Ser.). (ENG.). 125p. pap. 8.95 (978-1-59880-279-5(8)) Avalon Travel Publishing.

CAMPING—CANADA

Dzieciol, Patrick. The Camp Tripper: The Secrets of Successful Family Camping in Ontario. 2010. 172p. (ENG.). 25.95 (978-1-4502-2627-1(2)); pap. 15.95 (978-1-4502-2625-7(6)) iUniverse, Inc.
Wilcox, Walter. The Rockies of Canada: A Revised & Enlarged Edition of Camping in the Canadian Rockies, 1 vol. rev. ed. 2009. (Mountain Classics Collection). (ENG., Illus.). 216p. pap. (978-1-897522-14-1(2)) Rocky Mountain Bks.
Wilson, Hap. Trails & Tribulations: Confessions of a Wilderness Pathfinder. 2009. (ENG., Illus.). 216p. pap. 26.99 (978-1-55488-397-4(0)) Dundurn CAN. Dist: Ingram Pub. Services.

CAMPING—EUROPE

Mickelsen, Carol. Camping Europe: Includes Scandinavia, Central & Eastern Europe. 3rd ed. 2008. (Camping Europe: Includes Scandinavia, Central & Eastern Ser.). (ENG., Illus.). 950p. per. 24.95 (978-0-917120-20-6(5)) Carousel Pr.

CAMPING—FLORIDA

Hailey, Charlie. Campsite: Architectures of Duration & Place. 2008. (Illus.). 339p. 39.95 (978-0-8071-3323-1(X)) Louisiana State Univ. Pr.
Molloy, Johnny. Beach & Coastal Camping in Florida. 2nd ed. 2008. (ENG., Illus.). 208p. per. 16.95 (978-0-8130-3223-8(7)) Univ. Pr. of Florida.
—Florida: A Guide for Car Campers Who Hate Rvs, Concrete Slabs, & Loud Portable Stereos. 4th ed. 2009. (Best in Tent Camping Ser.). (ENG., Illus.). 192p. pap. 15.95 (978-0-89732-721-3(7)) Menasha Ridge Pr., Inc.
Moore, Marilyn A. Florida RV Camping. 2006. (Moon Outdoors Ser.). (ENG., Illus.). 490p. per. 22.95 (978-1-56691-988-3(6)) Avalon Travel Publishing.
Sapp, Rick. Camping Florida: A Comprehensive Guide to Hundreds of Campgrounds. 2009. (State Camping Ser.). (ENG., Illus.). 224p. pap. 16.95 (978-0-7627-4447-3(2), Falcon Guides) Globe Pequot Pr., The.

CAMPING—GREAT BRITAIN

Bird, Brad. Footloose! Newlyweds Go Walking in England & Germany. 2011. 216p. pap. 12.95 **(978-1-4269-0502-5(5))** Trafford Publishing.
Coast & Country Holidays in Britain: The Original Farm Holiday Guide. 2007. (Illus.). 320p. pap. 13.95 (978-1-85055-401-1(3)) Graphic Arts Ctr. Publishing Co.
Philpott, Don. Britain Goes Camping: Camping, Cooking & Exploring the Great Outdoors. 2011. (ENG., Illus.). 208p. 29.95 (978-1-907892-07-3(9)) National Trust, Aylesbury GBR. Dist: Independent Pubs. Group.

CAMPING—MEXICO

Church, Mike & Church, Terri. Traveler's Guide to Mexican Camping: Explore Mexico, Guatemala, & Belize with Your RV or Tent. 2009. (Traveler's Guide Ser.). (ENG.). 544p. pap. 21.95 (978-0-9823101-0-6(2)) Rolling Homes Pr.

CAMPING—NORTH AMERICA

Balkan, Evan L. Maryland: A Guide for Car Campers Who Hate RVs, Concrete Slabs, & Loud Portable Stereos. 2008. (Best in Tent Camping Ser.). (ENG., Illus.). 192p. pap. 14.95 (978-0-89732-977-4(5)) Menasha Ridge Pr., Inc.
"Mountain" (Aka W. Clifford Dean). The Reflecting Pool: Reflections of a mountain Man. 2009. 212p. 24.99 (978-1-4389-4974-1(X)); pap. 15.95 (978-1-4389-4973-4(1)) AuthorHouse.
Parr, Monte R. New Mexico: A Guide for Car Campers Who Hate Rvs, Concrete Slabs, & Loud Portable Stereos. 2008. (Best in Tent Camping Ser.). (ENG., Illus.). 208p. pap. 14.95 (978-0-89732-602-5(4)) Menasha Ridge Pr., Inc.
Reed, Tom & Gookin, John. Bear Essentials: Hiking & Camping in Bear Country. 2009. (Nols Ser.). (ENG., Illus.). 112p. pap. 9.95 (978-0-8117-3549-0(4)) Stackpole Bks.
Sportsman Connection, ed. Mich North All Outdoor Atlas. 2008. 176p. pap. 29.95 (978-1-885010-73-5(7)) Sportsman's Connection.
—Mich South All Outdoor Atlas. 2008. 176p. pap. 29.95 (978-1-885010-74-2(5)) Sportsman's Connection.
Valerio, Maurizio. Top Rated Outdoor Family Adventures: Vacationing in the Outdoors with Your Children. Date not set. (Top Rated Outdoor Ser.). (Illus.). 200p. (Orig.). pap. 18.95 (978-1-889807-09-6(5)) Picked-By-You Guides.

CAMPING—OREGON

Gerald, Paul, et al. Best in Tent Camping - Oregon: A Guide for Car Campers Who Hate RVs, Concrete Slabs, & Loud Portable Stereos. 2nd ed. 2009. (Best in Tent Camping Ser.). (ENG., Illus.). 208p. pap. 15.95 (978-0-89732-706-0(3)) Menasha Ridge Pr., Inc.
Hill, Sean Patrick, et al. Oregon Coast Camping & Hiking. 2010. (Moon Spotlight Ser.). (ENG.). 210p. pap. 11.95 (978-1-59880-573-4(8)) Avalon Travel Publishing.
Stienstra, Tom. Oregon Camping: Tent & RV Camping. 3rd ed. 2010. (Moon Outdoors Ser.). (ENG., Illus.). 448p. pap. 19.95 (978-1-56691-841-1(3)) Westview Pr.
—Pacific Northwest Camping: Tent & RV Camping in Washington & Oregon. 2010. (Moon Outdoors Ser.). (ENG., Illus.). 800p. pap. 24.95 (978-1-56691-842-8(1)) Westview Pr.

CAMPING—WASHINGTON (STATE)

Judd, Ron. Camping Washington: The Best Public Campgrounds for Tents & RVS. 2009. (ENG.). 320p. pap. 18.95 (978-1-59485-092-9(5)) Mountaineers Bks., The.
Pyle, Jeanne. Washington: A Guide for Car Campers Who Hate RVs, Concrete Slabs, & Loud Portable Stereos. 2nd ed. 2009. (Best in Tent Camping Ser.). (ENG., Illus.). 208p. pap. 15.95 (978-0-89732-696-4(2)) Menasha Ridge Pr., Inc.
Stienstra, Tom. Pacific Northwest Camping: Tent & RV Camping in Washington & Oregon. 2010. (Moon Outdoors Ser.). (ENG., Illus.). 800p. pap. 24.95 (978-1-56691-842-8(1)) Westview Pr.

CAMPING TRAILERS

Archer, Len. The Essential Handbook of Caravanning & Trailer Tenting. (Illus.). 192p. pap. (978-1-901295-96-2(6)) Veloce Publishing Ltd. GBR. Dist: MBI Distribution Services/Quayside Distribution.
Banham, Russ, ed. Wanderlust: Airstream at 75. 2007. (Illus.). 192p. 38.95 (978-0-615-13807-7(1)) Airstream, Inc.
Brunkowski, John & Closen, Michael. RV & Camper Toys: The History of RVing in Miniature. 2008. (ENG., Illus.). 128p. pap. 19.95 (978-1-58388-207-8(3), 1583882073) Iconografix, Inc.
Victor, Jim. Pulling Your Tail. 2008. 101p. pap. 17.95 (978-0-557-01720-1(3)) Lulu Enterprises Inc.

CAMPION, THOMAS, 1567-1620

MacDonagh, Thomas. Thomas Campion & the Art of English Poetry. 2009. 142p. 24.99 (978-1-116-20742-2(7)); 28.99 (978-1-116-20741-5(9)); pap. 20.75 (978-1-116-20743-9(5)); pap. 19.75 (978-1-116-20744-6(3)) BiblioBazaar.
—Thomas Campion & the Art of English Poetry. 2010. 60p. pap. (978-1-152-06601-4(3)) Books LLC.

CAMPMEETINGS

see Camp Meetings

CAMPS

Here are entered works on places in the country that offer simple, temporary group accommodations in an outdoor atmosphere together with an organized program of recreational or instructional activities. Works on places in the country that offer temporary lodging to individuals in an outdoor atmosphere, as well as works on the facilities provided in these places are entered under Camp Sites, Facilities, etc. Works on the techniques of setting up and living in camps are entered under Camping.

see also Camp Sites, Facilities, etc.; Camping; Church Camps; Labor Camps

Adler, Bill. Letters from Camp. 2011. 122p. 39.95 **(978-1-258-08688-6(3))** Literary Licensing, LLC.
Adventures at Wohelo Camp: Summer Of 1928. 2011. 208p. pap. 17.95 **(978-1-4620-2503-9(X))** iUniverse, Inc.
Ahern, Jack. Bound for Munsungun: Family Heirloom Edition. 2009. (Illus.). 278p. (978-0-9749291-9-4(0), Pear Tree Publishing) Obert, Christopher Publishing.
Bond, Hallie E., et al. A Paradise for Boys & Girls: Children's Camps in the Adirondacks. 2006. (Illus.). 146p. 39.95 (978-0-8156-0822-6(5)) Syracuse Univ. Pr.
Bragg, Don. Kamp Olympik. 2008. (ENG.). 272p. pap. 20.00 (978-0-9818939-3-8(7)); (Illus.). 304p. 25.00 (978-0-9799537-9-8(0)) Africana Homestead Legacy Pubs., Inc.
Brereton, Derek. Campsteading (paperback Direct) Family, Place, & Experience at Squam Lake, New Hampshire. 2010. (ENG., Illus.). 336p. (C). pap. 29.95 (978-0-415-59200-0(3)) Routledge.
Brereton, Derek Pomeroy. Campsteading: Family, Place, & Experience at Squam Lake, New Hampshire. 2009. (ENG., Illus.). XXVIII, 292p. 140.00 (978-0-415-56296-6(1)) Routledge.
Burch, Monte. The Hunting & Fishing Camp Builder's Guide: A Complete Guide to Building Your Own Outdoor Lodge. 2012. (ENG., Illus.). 224p. pap. 19.95 **(978-1-61608-466-0(9)**, 608466) Skyhorse Publishing Co., Inc.
Church, William & VanValkenburg, Jill. Chippewa Ranch. 2007. 134p. 24.95 (978-1-58909-358-4(5)) Bookstand Publishing.
Farfaglia, Jim. Camp Hollis. 2008. 128p. pap. 19.99 (978-1-59629-582-7(1)) History Pr., The.
Fersen, Paul. Great Fishing Lodges of North America: Fly Fishing's Finest Destinations. 2010. (ENG., Illus.). 240p. 50.00 (978-0-8478-3424-2(7)) Rizzoli International Pubns., Inc.
Fitzgerald, F-Stop. Adirondack Style: Great Camps & Rustic Lodges. 2011. (ENG., Illus.). 224p. 50.00 (978-0-7893-2266-1(8)) Universe Publishing.
Gish, Sarah. The Summer Book. 2011. 156p. pap. 12.95 (978-0-9728507-8-0(3)) Gish Creative.

Hackett, Allen & Hackett, Frank Sutliff. Quickened Spirit: A Biography of Frank Sutliff Hackett. 2011. 250p. 46.95 ***(978-1-258-09407-2(X))*** Literary Licensing, LLC.

Halley, Charlie. Camps: A Guide to 21st Century Space. 2009. pap. *(978-0-262-08370-6(1))* MIT Pr.

—Camps: A Guide to 21st-Century Space. 2009. (ENG., Illus.). 560p. (gr. 17). pap. 32.95 *(978-0-262-51287-9(4))* MIT Pr.

Hardy, Dennis & Ward, C. Goodnight Campers! The history of the British holiday Camp. 2011. (ENG.). 192p. pap. 42.95 ***(978-0-415-51510-8(6))*** Routledge.

Lowe, Harriet, ed. Health Matters: By the Experts. 2007. 88p. pap. 19.95 *(978-1-58518-031-8(9))* Coaches Choice.

MacNutt, Barry. Noble Life: Memories of a Summer Camp in Maine. 2007. 148p. per. 14.95 *(978-0-595-45791-5(6))* iUniverse, Inc.

Mamminga, Marnie O. Return to Wake Robin: One Cabin in the Heyday of Northwoods Resorts. 2012. (ENG., Illus.). 200p. 22.95 ***(978-0-87020-491-3(2))*** Wisconsin Historical Society.

Moffitt, Jill. Day Camp Programming & Administration: Core Skills & Practices. 2011. (ENG., Illus.). 184p. 32.00 *(978-0-7360-7517-6(8))* Human Kinetics Pubs.

Murphy, Dervla. Tibetan Foothold. 2012. (ENG., Illus.). 240p. pap. 29.95 ***(978-1-906011-64-2(8))*** Eland Bks. GBR. Dist: Dufour Editions, Inc.

Paris, Leslie. Children's Nature: The Rise of the American Summer Camp. (ENG.). 368p. 2010. pap. 23.00 *(978-0-8147-6782-5(5))* 2008. (Illus.). 60.00 *(978-0-8147-6707-8(9))* New York Univ. Pr.

Schneider, Mindy. Not a Happy Camper: A Memoir. 2008. (ENG., Illus.). 256p. (gr. 8). pap. 14.00 *(978-0-8021-4369-3(5)*, Grove Pr.) Grove/Atlantic, Inc.

Schoon, Kenneth J. & Urtel, Mark G. Brosius Bred: The IL Family Camp in Wisconsin. 2008. *(978-1-57864-489-6(5))* Donning Co. Pubs.

Shelton, Michael. Multiculturalism in Camps & Youth Programs: How Us & Them Became Just Us. 2008. (Illus.). 127p. pap. 19.95 *(978-1-58518-667-9(8)*, Healthy Learning) Coaches Choice.

Shipman, Jack. Yellow Footprints: 1969 Marine Corps Boot Camp. 2011. 580p. 39.95 ***(978-1-4502-8374-8(8))***; pap. 29.95 ***(978-1-4502-8373-1(X))*** iUniverse, Inc.

Shoemaker, Bo. A History of Camp Cory. 2011. ***(978-1-60949-361-5(3))*** History Pr., The

Van Slyck, Abigail A. A Manufactured Wilderness: Summer Camps & the Shaping of American Youth, 1890-1960. 2006. (Architecture, Landscape, & American Culture Ser.). (Illus.). 296p. 34.95 *(978-0-8166-4876-4(X))* Univ. of Minnesota Pr.

Van Slyck, Abigail Ayres. A Manufactured Wilderness: Summer Camps & the Shaping of American Youth, 1890-1960. 2010. (Architecture, Landscape, & American Culture Ser.). (ENG., Illus.). 296p. pap. 27.50 *(978-0-8166-4877-1(8))* Univ. of Minnesota Pr.

Varney, Philip. Ghost Towns of California: Your Guide to the Hidden History & Old West Haunts of California. 2012. (ENG., Illus.). 240p. pap. 24.99 ***(978-0-7603-4082-0(X)***, 076034082X, Voyageur Pr) MBI Publishing Co. LLC.

Wall, Sharon. The Nurture of Nature: Childhood, Antimodernism, & Ontario Summer Camps, 1920-55. 2010. (ENG., Illus.). 392p. pap. 32.95 *(978-0-7748-1640-3(6))* Univ. of Washington Pr.

Wolk, Josh. Cabin Pressure: One Man's Desperate Attempt to Recapture His Youth as a Camp Counselor. 2007. (ENG., Illus.). 288p. 22.95 *(978-1-4013-0260-3(2))* Hyperion Pr.

CAMPS—ADMINISTRATION
see Camps—Management

CAMPS—COUNSELORS
see Camp Counselors

CAMPS—DIRECTORIES

Camps 2007: A Directory of Camps & Summer Programs for Children & Youth with Disabilities & Special Needs in the Metro New York Area. 23rd ed. 2007. (SPA & ENG.). per. 25.00 *(978-0-9755116-4-0(5))* Resources for Children with Special Needs, Inc.

Peterson's Guides Staff. Make Summer Count 2008: Programs & Camps for Teens & Kids. Oram, Fern, ed. 2nd ed. 2007. (ENG.). 480p. pap. 17.00 *(978-0-7689-2518-0(5))* Peterson's.

—Summer Programs for Kids & Teenagers: Explore Summer Camps, Arts Programs, Sports Clinics, Academic Courses, Travel Tours, & Wilderness Adventures. Oram, Fern A., ed. 24th ed. 2006. (ENG., Illus.). 888p. per. 30.00 *(978-0-7689-2173-1(2))* Peterson's.

—Summer Programs for Kids & Teenagers 2008. Oram, Fern, ed. 25th ed. 2007. (ENG., Illus.). 888p. pap. 39.95 *(978-0-7689-2422-0(7))* Peterson's.

Porter Sargent Handbooks Staff, ed. Guide to Summer Camps & Summer Schools: An Objective, Comparative Reference Source for Residential Summer Programs. 2010. (Illus.). 896p. 45.00 *(978-0-87558-169-9(2))*; (ENG., pap. 27.00 *(978-0-87558-170-5(6))* Porter Sargent Handbooks.

Porter Sargent Publishers, creator. Guide to Summer Camps & Summer Schools: An Objective Comparative Reference Source for Residential Summer Programs. 31st ed. 2007. (Guide to Summer Camps & Summer Schools Ser.). (Illus.). 862p. pap. 33.75 *(978-0-87558-164-4(1))* Porter Sargent Handbooks.

—Guide to Summer Camps & Summer Schools: An Objective, Comparative Reference Source for Residential Summer Programs. 31st ed. 2007. (Guide to Summer Camps & Summer Schools Ser.). (Illus.). 862p. 56.25 *(978-0-87558-163-7(3))* Porter Sargent Handbooks.

Resources for Children with Special Needs, creator. Camps 2008: A Directory of Camps & Summer Programs for Children & Youth with Disabilities & Special Needs in the Metro New York Area. 2008. (ENG & SPA.). 400p. per. 25.00 *(978-0-9755116-5-7(3))* Resources for Children with Special Needs, Inc.

Thomas, Charlotte & Peterson's Guides Staff. Make Summer Count: Programs & Camps for Teens & Kids. 2006. (ENG., Illus.). 480p. per. 19.00 *(978-0-7689-2445-9(5))* Peterson's.

CAMPS—FOOD SERVICE

Spain, Vikki. 101 Camp Cooking Tips. 2008. (Illus.). 87p. pap. 19.95 *(978-1-58518-668-6(5)*, Healthy Learning) Coaches Choice.

CAMPS—MANAGEMENT

American Camp Association, creator. Designing Quality Youth Programs: Strategic Changes Across Structures, Policies, & Activities. 2008. (Illus.). 110p. pap. 29.95 incl. cd-rom *(978-1-58518-663-1(5)*, Healthy Learning) Coaches Choice.

American Camping Association Staff, contrib. by. American Camp Association's Accreditation Process Guide. 2007. 316p. *(978-1-58518-996-0(0))* American Camping Assn.

—American Camp Association's Accreditation Process Guide. 2007. (Illus.). 316p. *(978-1-58518-997-7(9)*, Healthy Learning) Coaches Choice.

—American Camp Association's Accreditation Process Guide Organizer. 2007. 474p. *(978-1-58518-028-8(9)*, Healthy Learning) Coaches Choice.

Coutellier, Connie. Risk & Crisis Management: A Workbook for Organization & Program Administrators. 3rd ed. 2008. (Illus.). 491p. pap. 49.95 incl. cd-rom *(978-1-58518-097-4(1)*, Healthy Learning) Coaches Choice.

Jodi, Rudick. 101 Marketing Essentials Every Camp Needs to Know. 2007. (Illus.). 201p. pap. 24.95 *(978-1-58518-039-4(4))* Coaches Choice.

Knight, Jared R. 101 Creative Programs for Children. 2007. (Illus.). 244p. per. 22.95 *(978-1-58518-010-3(6))* Coaches Choice.

Lowe, Harriet, ed. Mangement Matters: By the Experts. 2007. (Illus.). 119p. pap. 19.95 *(978-1-58518-034-9(3))* Coaches Choice.

Ripley, G. Sherman & Boy Scouts Of America. Fun Around the Campfire. 2011. 116p. 39.95 ***(978-1-258-06051-0(5))*** Literary Licensing, LLC.

SofterWare, Inc. EZ-CAMP2 Version 7 User Manual. 2010. 394p. pap. 31.00 *(978-0-557-47805-7(7))* Lulu Enterprises Inc.

CAMPS—WATER PROGRAMS
see Aquatic Sports

CAMPS (CHURCH)
see Church Camps

CAMPUS CRUSADE FOR CHRIST

Hayes, Dan. Developing Campus Prayer Movement: Leader's Handbook. Date not set. 26p. (C). pap. 5.99 *(978-1-57902-031-6(3))* Integrated Resources.

Turner, John G. Bill Bright & Campus Crusade for Christ: The Renewal of Evangelicalism in Postwar America. 2008. (ENG., Illus.). 304p. 66.50 *(978-0-8078-3185-4(9))*; per. 22.00 *(978-0-8078-5873-8(0))* Univ. of North Carolina Pr.

CAMPUS CULTURES
see Educational Anthropology

CAMPUS DISORDERS
see Student Movements; Student Strikes

CAMPUS PLANNING

Bardaglio, Peter Winthrop & Putman, Andrea. Boldly Sustainable: Hope & Opportunity for Higher Education in the Age of Climate Change. 2009. *(978-1-56972-046-2(0))* National Assn. of College & Univ. Business Officers.

Brown, Tim. Change by Design: How Design Thinking Transforms Organizations & Inspires Innovation. 2009. (ENG., Illus.). 288p. 27.99 *(978-0-06-176608-4(9)*, Collins) HarperCollins Pubs.

Coulson, Jonathan, et al. University Planning & Architecture: The Search for Perfection. 2010. (ENG., Illus.). 272p. 125.00 *(978-0-415-57110-4(3))* Routledge.

Dubey, Jai Prakash. University Extension Services. 2010. 180p. pap. *(978-3-8383-4546-8(0))* Lambert Academic Publishing.

Gyure, Dale Allen. Frank Lloyd Wright's Florida Southern College. 2010. (Florida History & Culture Ser.). (ENG., Illus.). 240p. 39.95 *(978-0-8130-3523-9(6))* Univ. Pr. of Florida.

Haar, Sharon. The City as Campus: Urbanism & Higher Education in Chicago. 2011. (ENG., Illus.). 264p. 82.50 *(978-0-8166-6564-8(8))*; pap. 27.50 *(978-0-8166-6565-5(6))* Univ. of Minnesota Pr.

Kolac, Enver. University Campus Design. 2010. 116p. pap. *(978-3-8383-7321-8(9))* Lambert Academic Publishing.

May, Vonn Marie, et al. Celebrating the Cultural Landscape Heritage of Mills College: Using the Past to Inform Campus Planning & Design. 2008. (Illus.). 159p. per. 18.00 *(978-0-9648938-6-3(X))* Mills College, Ctr. for the Bk.

Mitchell, William J. Imagining MIT: Designing a Campus for the Twenty-First Century. (ENG., Illus.). 152p. (gr. 17). 2011. pap. 14.95 *(978-0-262-51611-2(X))* 2007. 26.95 *(978-0-262-13479-8(9))* MIT Pr.

National Intramural-Recreational Sports Association (U.S.) Staff. Campus Recreational Sport Facilities: Planning, Design, & Construction Guidelines. 2009. (ENG., Illus.). 296p. (gr. 13-16). 52.00 *(978-0-7360-6383-8(8))* Human Kinetics Pubs.

—Space Planning Guidelines for Campus Recreational Sport Facilities. 2008. (ENG., Illus.). 136p. (gr. 13-16). pap. 25.00 *(978-0-7360-7487-2(2))* Human Kinetics Pubs.

Tolles, Bryant F. Jr. Architecture & Academe: College Buildings in New England Before 1860. 2011. (Illus.). 260p. 50.00 *(978-1-58465-891-7(6))* Univ. Pr. of New England.

CAMPUS STORES
see College Stores

CAMPYLOBACTER PYLORI
see Helicobacter Pylori

CAMPYLOBACTER PYLORI INFECTIONS
see Helicobacter Pylori Infections

CAMS

American Society of Mechanical Engineers Staff, ed. Cams for Industry. (Illus.). 364p. 138.00 *(978-0-85298-960-9(1))* Professional Engineering Publishing GBR. Dist: SAE Intl.

Bonk, Aaron. High-Performance Sport Compact Heads & Cams. 2007. (ENG., Illus.). 128p. pap. 24.95 *(978-1-932494-35-8(9)*, S-A Design) CarTech, Inc.

Norton. Cam Design & Manufacturing Handbook. 2nd ed. 2009. 640p. (C). 99.95 *(978-0-8311-3367-2(8))* Industrial Pr., Inc.

Rouillion, Louis, et al. Advanced Design & Cutting of Cams. 2006. 112p. 36.95 *(978-1-4276-1407-0(5))* Wexford College Pr.

CAMUS, ALBERT, 1913-1960

Bastien, Sophie, et al, eds. La Passion du Théâtre: Camus à la Scène. 2011. (FRE., Illus.). 238p. pap. 7100.00 ***(978-90-420-3420-4(3))*** Rodopi.

Bloom, Harold, ed. The Stranger. 2008. (Bloom's Guides). 96p. (C). (gr. 9). 30.00 *(978-0-7910-9829-5(X)*, Chelsea Hse.) Facts On File, Inc.

—The Stranger - Albert Camus. 2nd rev. ed. 2011. (Bloom's Modern Critical Interpretations Ser.). 174p. (C). (gr. 9-18). 45.00 *(978-1-60413-580-0(8)*, Chelsea Hse.) Facts On File, Inc.

Eronner, Stephen Eric. Camus: Portrait of a Moralist. 2009. (ENG.). 200p. pap. 18.00 *(978-0-226-07567-9(2))* Univ. of Chicago Pr.

Camus, Albert. Camus at Combat: Writing 1944-1947. Levi-Valensi, Jacqueline, ed. Goldhammer, Arthur, tr. from FRE. 2007. (ENG.). 384p. (C). per. 24.95 *(978-0-691-13376-8(X))* Princeton Univ. Pr.

—Notebooks, 1935-1942. 2010. (ENG.). 236p. pap. 16.95 *(978-1-56663-872-2(0))* Dee, Ivan R. Pub.

—Notebooks 1942-1951, Vol. 2. 2010. (ENG.). 288p. pap. 18.95 *(978-1-56663-873-9(9))* Dee, Ivan R. Pub.

—Notebooks 1951-1959, Vol. 3. 2010. (ENG.). 288p. pap. 18.95 *(978-1-56663-850-0(X))* Dee, Ivan R. Pub.

—Notebooks 1951-1959, Vol. 3. Bloom, Ryan, tr. from FRE. 2008. (ENG.). 288p. 27.50 *(978-1-56663-775-6(9))* Dee, Ivan R. Pub.

Carroll, David. Albert Camus the Algerian: Colonialism, Terrorism, Justice. (ENG.). 256p. (gr. 17). 2008. pap. 24.00 *(978-0-231-14087-4(8))* 2007. (Illus.). 75.00 *(978-0-231-14086-7(X))* Columbia Univ. Pr.

Chaulet-Achour, Christiane. Albert Camus, Alger: L'étranger et Autres Récits. (FRE.). 217p. *(978-2-84394-089-7(3))* Atlantica editions.

Foley, John. Albert Camus: From the Absurd to Revolt. 2008. (ENG.). 288p. (C). pap. *(978-0-7735-3467-4(9))* McGill-Queen's Univ. Pr.

—Albert Camus: From the Absurd to Revolt. 2008. (ENG.). 288p. (C). 95.00 *(978-0-7735-3466-7(0))* Queen's Univ., Schl. of Policy Studies CAN. Dist: McGill-Queen's Univ. Pr.

Foxlee, Neil. Albert Camus's "The New Mediterranean Culture" A Text & Its Contexts. 2010. 349p. 68.95 *(978-3-0343-0207-4(X))* Lang, Peter Publishing, Inc.

Hawes, Elizabeth. Camus, a Romance. 2010. (ENG.). 336p. pap. 14.00 *(978-0-8021-4488-1(8)*, Grove Pr.) Grove/Atlantic, Inc.

Henry, Patrick. We Only Know Men: The Rescue of Jews in France During the Holocaust. 2007. (Illus.). 192p. 59.95 *(978-0-8132-1493-1(9))* Catholic Univ. of America Pr.

Hughes, Edward J., ed. The Cambridge Companion to Camus. 2007. (Cambridge Companions to Literature Ser.). (ENG.). 252p. (C). per. 31.99 *(978-0-521-54978-3(7))*; 248p. 105.00 *(978-0-521-84048-4(1))* Cambridge Univ. Pr.

Judt, Tony. The Burden of Responsibility: Blum, Camus, Aron, & the French Twentieth Century. 2007. (ENG., Illus.). 204p. per. 17.50 *(978-0-226-41419-5(1))* Univ. of Chicago Pr.

Kellman, Steven G. Albert Camus. 2011. ***(978-1-58765-825-9(9))*** Salem Pr., Inc.

King, Adele. Camus. 2010. (Life&Times Ser.). (ENG., Illus.). 192p. pap. 14.95 *(978-1-906598-40-2(1))* Haus Publishing GBR. Dist: Consortium Bk. Sales & Distribution.

Levi-Valensi. Les Critiques de Notre Temps et Camus. (FRE.). 13.95 *(978-0-7859-0036-8(5)*, F91100) French & European Pubns., Inc.

Longstaffe, Moya. The Fiction of Albert Camus: A Complex Simplicity. 2007. 300p. 62.95 *(978-3-03910-304-1(0))*; pap. 68.95 *(978-0-8204-7229-4(8))* Lang, Peter Publishing, Inc.

Mairowitz, David Zane & Korkos, Alain. Introducing Camus. 2012. (Introducing Ser.). (ENG., Illus.). 126p. 9.95 ***(978-1-84831-345-3(4))*** Totem Bks. GBR. Dist: Consortium Bk. Sales & Distribution.

Margerrison, Christine. ¿Ces forces obscures de L¿âme¿. Women, race & origins in the writings of Albert Camus. 2008. 360p. pap. 72.00 *(978-90-420-2379-6(1))* Rodopi.

Margerrison, Christine, et al, eds. Albert Camus in the 21st Century: A Reassessment of his Thinking at the Dawn of the New Millennium. 2008. (ENG & FRE.). 296p. per. 90.00 *(978-90-420-2358-1(9))* Rodopi.

Maze, John Robert. Albert Camus: Plague & Terror, Priest & Atheist. 2010. 201p. pap. 56.95 *(978-3-0343-0006-3(9))* Lang, Peter GmbH, Europaischer Verlag der Wissenschaften DEU. Dist: Lang, Peter.

Novello, Samantha. Albert Camus as Political Thinker: Nihilisms & the Politics of Contempt. 2010. (ENG.). 256p. 89.00 *(978-0-230-24098-8(4))* Palgrave Macmillan.

Orme, Mark. The Development of Albert Camus's Concern for Social & Political Justice: "Justice Pour un Juste" 2007. 352p. 65.00 *(978-0-8386-4110-1(5))* Fairleigh Dickinson Univ. Pr.

Peyre, Henri. Albert Camus Moraliste: The First Kathleen Morris Scruggs Memorial Lecture. 2011. 30p. 35.95 ***(978-1-258-00967-0(6))*** Literary Licensing, LLC.

Sartre, Jean-Paul. Existentialism Is a Humanism. Kulka, John, ed. Macomber, Carol, tr. from FRE. annot. ed. 2007. (ENG., Illus.). 128p. per. 9.95 *(978-0-300-11546-8(6))* Yale Univ. Pr.

Sessler, Tal. Levinas & Camus: Humanism for the Twenty-First Century. 2008. (Continuum Studies in Continental Philosophy Ser.). (ENG.). 128p. 90.00 *(978-0-8264-9832-8(9))* Continuum International Publishing Group, Ltd. GBR. Dist: National Bk. Network.

Sherman, David. Camus. 2008. (Blackwell Great Minds Ser.: 15). (ENG.). 232p. 99.95 *(978-1-4051-5930-2(8))*; pap. 33.95 *(978-1-4051-5931-9(6))* Wiley, John & Sons, Inc. (Wiley-Blackwell).

Sleasman, Brent C. Albert Camus's Philosophy of Communication: Making Sense in an Age of Absurdity. 2011. 194p. ***(978-1-60497-791-2(4))*** Cambria Pr.

Solomon, Robert C. Dark Feelings, Grim Thoughts: Experience & Reflection in Camus & Sartre. 2006. (ENG.). 256p. 50.00 *(978-0-19-518157-9(3))* Oxford Univ. Pr., Inc.

Srigley, Ronald D. Albert Camus' Critique of Modernity. 2011. (ENG., Illus.). 202p. (C). (gr. 13). 60.00 *(978-0-8262-1924-4(1))* Univ. of Missouri Pr.

Todd, Oliver. Albert Camus une Vie. pap. 31.95 *(978-2-07-041062-0(5))* Gallimard, Editions FRA. Dist: Distribooks, Inc.

Todd, Olivier. Albert Camus Una Vida. (SPA.). 386p. *(978-84-8310-022-6(3)*, 6020) Tusquets Editores.

Toumi, Alek Baylee. Albert Camus Aujourd'hui: De L'Etranger Au Premier Homme. 2012. xvii, 165p. ***(978-1-4331-1849-4(1))*** Lang, Peter Publishing, Inc.

Vanborre, Emmanuelle. Lectures Blanchotiennes de Malraux et Camus. 2010. (Currents in Comparative Romance Languages & Literatures Ser.). 186p. (C). 76.95 *(978-1-4331-1056-6(3))* Lang, Peter Publishing, Inc.

Weagel, Deborah. Words & Music: Camus, Beckett, Cage, Gould. 2010. (American University Studies XX: Fine Arts Ser.). (Illus.). 176p. (C). 72.95 *(978-1-4331-0836-5(4))* Lang, Peter Publishing, Inc.

Wittmann, Heiner. Albert Camus: Kunst und Moral. (Literatur und Kultur Italiens und Frankreichs Ser.: Vol. 6). (GER.). 114p. 17.95 *(978-3-631-39525-7(6))* Lang, Peter Publishing, Inc.

Zaretsky, Robert. Albert Camus - Elements of a Life. 2010. (Illus.). 200p. 24.95 *(978-0-8014-4805-8(0))* Cornell Univ. Pr.

CANAAN VALLEY (W. VA.)

Kennedy, Philip Pendleton. The Blackwater Chronicle: A Narrative of an Expedition into the Land of Canaan. 2007. (ENG.). 226p. 41.95 *(978-0-548-18701-2(0))*; 228p. per. 26.95 *(978-1-4304-9059-3(4))* Kessinger Publishing, LLC.

[Kennedy, Philip Pendleton]. The Blackwater Chronicle, a Narrative of an Expedition into the Land of Canaan, in Randolph County, Virginia by the Clerke of Oxenforde with Il. 2006. 244p. per. 20.99 *(978-1-4255-2046-5(4))* MPublishing.

CANAANITE LANGUAGE

Rainey, Anson F. Canaanite in the Amarna Tablets: A Linguistic Analysis of the Mixed Dialect Used by Scribes from Canaan. 2010. (SEM & ENG.). 230p. pap. 29.95 *(978-1-58983-471-2(2))*; 208p. pap. 27.95 *(978-1-58983-474-3(7))*; 296p. pap. 38.95 *(978-1-58983-473-6(9))*; 436p. pap. 56.95 *(978-1-58983-472-9(0))* Society of Biblical Literature.

CANAANITE MYTHOLOGY
see Mythology, Canaanite

CANAANITES

Bar, Shay, et al, eds. Egypt, Canaan & Israel: History, Imperialism, Ideology & Literature: Proceedings of a Conference at the University of Haifa, 3-7 May 2009. 2011. (Illus.). X, 370p. ***(978-90-04-19493-9(2))*** BRILL.

Chalmers, R. Scott. The Struggle of Yahweh & El for Hosea's Israel. 2008. (HEB & ENG.). 288p. *(978-1-905048-40-3(8))* Sheffield Phoenix Pr.

Dawson, Tess. Whisper of Stone: Natib Qadish: Modern Canaanite Religion. 2009. (ENG., Illus.). 448p. pap. 39.95 *(978-1-84694-190-0(3))* Hunt, John Publishing Ltd. GBR. Dist: National Bk. Network.

Golden, Jonathan M. Ancient Canaan & Israel: An Introduction. 2009. (ENG., Illus.). 432p. pap. 24.95 *(978-0-19-537985-3(3))* Oxford Univ. Pr., Inc.

Katz, Jill & Katz, Jill Citron. The Archaeology of Cult in Middle Bronze Age Canaan: The Sacred Area at Tel Haror, Israel. 2009. (Illus.). xiii, 251p. *(978-1-59333-791-9(4))* Gorgias Pr., LLC.

Kuzar, Ron. Hebrew & Zionism: A Discourse Analytic Cultural Study. (Language, Power & Social Process [LPSP] Ser.). (ENG.). XII, 324p. 196.00 ***(978-3-11-187068-7(5))***; 84.00 ***(978-3-11-181137-6(9))*** De Gruyter, Mouton DEU. Dist: de Gruyter, Walter GmbH & Co. KG.

Levine, Baruch A. & Gross, Andrew. In Pursuit of Meaning: Collected Studies of Baruch A. Levine. 2011. 109.50 *(978-1-57506-206-8(2))*; *(978-1-57506-208-2(9))*; *(978-1-57506-207-5(0))* Eisenbrauns, Inc.

C

CANADA

Du Roi, August Wilhelm. Journal of Du Roi the Elder: The Lieutenant & Adjutant, in the Service of the Duke of Brunswick, 1776-1778. (Americana Germanica Ser.). 189p. reprint ed. 88.00 *(978-0-7222-7670-9(2))* Library Reprints, Inc.

MacNaughton, Sara B. My Canadian Memories. reprint ed. 150.00 *(978-0-7222-6951-0(X))* Library Reprints, Inc.

Sjogren, Gwen. Cross-Canada Crosswords 3. unabr. ed. 2007. (ENG., Illus.). 64p. pap. *(978-1-55017-405-2(3))* Harbour Publishing Co., Ltd.

Warburton, George. Hochelaga. Warburton, Eliot, ed. 2007. (Travel in America Ser.). (ENG.). 404p. 49.95 *(978-1-4290-0252-3(2))* Applewood Bks.

—Hochelaga: Or, England in the New World. Warburton, Eliot, ed. 2007. (Travel in America Ser.). (ENG.). 404p. per. 24.95 *(978-1-4290-0253-0(0))* Applewood Bks.

CANADA—ANTIQUITIES

Birket-Smith, Kaj. The Caribou Eskimos. (Thule Expedition Ser.: Vol. 5). reprint ed. 137.50 *(978-0-404-58316-3(4))* AMS Pr., Inc.

Carr-Locke, Sarah. Sharing the Past. 2008. 100p. pap. *(978-3-639-04487-4(8))* VDM Verlag Dr. Mueller e.K.

Clark, Brenda, et al, eds. Victoria Underfoot: Excavating a City's Secrets. unabr. ed. 2009. (ENG., Illus.). 144p. pap. 24.95 *(978-1-55017-419-9(3))* Harbour Publishing Co., Ltd. CAN. Dist: Ingram Pub. Services.

Deller, D. Brian & Ellis, Christopher J. Crowfield (Afhj-31) A Unique Paleoindian Fluted Point Site from Southwestern Ontario. 2011. (ENG., Illus.). 224p. ***(978-0-915703-76-0(9))*** Univ. of Michigan, Museum of Anthropology, Pubns. Dept.

Dempsey, L. James. Blackfoot War Art: Pictographs of the Reservation Period, 1880-2000. 2007. (ENG., Illus.). 488p. (C). 45.00 *(978-0-8061-3804-6(1))* Univ. of Oklahoma Pr.

Ferris, Neal. The Archaeology of Native-Lived Colonialism: Challenging History in the Great Lakes. (Archaeology of Colonialism in Native North America Ser.). (ENG.). 240p. 2011. pap. 24.95 *(978-0-8165-0238-7(2))* 2009. (Illus.). 50.00 *(978-0-8165-2705-2(9))* Univ. of Arizona Pr.

Freeman, Gordon R. Hidden Stonehenge: An Ancient Temple in North America Reveals the Key to Ancient Wonders. 2012. (ENG., Illus.). 294p. pap. 19.95 ***(978-1-78028-095-0(5)***, Watkins Publishing) Duncan Baird Pubs. GBR. Dist: Sterling Publishing Co., Inc.

Gronnow, Bjarne, ed. On the Track of the Thule Culture from Bering Strait to East Greenland: Proceedings of the SILA Conference the Thule Culture - New Perspectives in Inuit Prehistory. Papers in honour of Hans Christian Gullov. 2010. (Studies in archaeology & History Ser.). (ENG., Illus.). 263p. (C). 60.00 *(978-87-7602-106-1(8))* Aarhus Universitetsforlag DNK. Dist: ISD.

Haycock, Maurice. On Site with Maurice Haycock: Artist of the Arctic: Paintings & Drawings of Historical Sites in the Canadian Arctic, 1 vol. 2007. (ENG., Illus.). 112p. 50.00 *(978-0-88866-655-0(1))* Dundurn CAN. Dist: Univ. of Toronto Pr.

Keenlyside, David E. & Pilon, Jean-Luc. Painting the Past with a Broad Brush: Papers in Honour of James Valliere Wright. 2010. (Illus.). 765p. pap. 39.95 *(978-0-660-19912-2(2))* Univ. of Washington Pr.

Kerber, Jordan E., ed. Archaeology of the Iroquois: Selected Readings & Research Sources. 2007. (Iroquois & Their Neighbors Ser.). (Illus.). 557p. per. 45.00 *(978-0-8156-3139-2(1))* Syracuse Univ. Pr.

MacNutt, James W. Les Édifices de la Démocratie: L'Histoire et l'Architecture des Édifices des Assemblées Législatives de la Nouvelle-Écosse, de l'Île-du-Prince-Édouard et du Nouveau-Brunswick. 2010. (FRE., Illus.). 128p. pap. 24.95 *(978-0-88780-941-5(3))* Formac Publishing Co., Ltd. CAN. Dist: Casemate Pubs. & Bk. Distributors, LLC.

Magne, Martin P. R. & Matson, R. G. Athapaskan Migrations: The Archaeology of Eagle Lake, British Columbia. 2007. (ENG., Illus.). 224p. 65.00 *(978-0-8165-2489-1(0))* Univ. of Arizona Pr.

Morrissey, Greg. Tools & Change. 2011. 212p. pap. ***(978-3-8383-9164-9(0))*** Lambert Academic Publishing.

Olsen, Brad. Sacred Places North America: 108 Destinations. 2nd ed. 2008. (Sacred Places: 108 Destinations Ser.). (ENG., Illus.). 408p. pap. 19.95 *(978-1-888729-13-9(9))* Consortium of Collective Consciousness.

Orchard, Trevor J. Otters & Urchins: Continuity & Change in Haida Economy during the Late Holocene & Maritime Fur Trade Periods. 2009. (Illus.). 232p. (C). pap. 107.50 *(978-1-4073-0604-9(9))* British Archaeological Reports Ltd. GBR. Dist: Brown, David Bk. Co., The.

Peck, Trevor R. Light from Ancient Campfires: Archaeological Evidence for Native Lifeways on the Northern Plains. 2011. (ENG., Illus.). 336p. pap. 44.95 *(978-1-897425-96-1(1))* UBC Pr. CAN. Dist: Univ. of Washington Pr.

Saunders, Della. Palaeoethnobotany of Princess Point, Lower Great Lakes Region, Southern Ontario, Canada. 2008. (Bar S Ser.). (ENG., Illus.). 110p. (C). pap. 67.50 *(978-1-4073-0278-2(7))* British Archaeological Reports Ltd. GBR. Dist: Brown, David Bk. Co., The.

Spude, Catherine Holder, et al, eds. Eldorado! The Archaeology of Gold Mining in the Far North. 2011. (Historical Archaeology of the American West Ser.). (ENG., Illus.). 376p. pap. 55.00 *(978-0-8032-1099-8(X))* Univ. of Nebraska Pr.

Storck, Peter L. Journey to the Ice Age: Discovering an Ancient World. 2006. (ENG., Illus.). 376p. pap. 29.95 *(978-0-7748-1029-6(7))* UBC Pr. CAN. Dist: Univ. of Washington Pr.

Tuck, Jim, et al. From the Arctic to Avalon: Papers in Honour of Jim Tuck. 2006. (BAR International Ser.: Vol. 1507). (ENG., Illus.). 174p. (C). pap. 102.50 *(978-1-84171-743-2(6))* British Archaeological Reports Ltd. GBR. Dist: Brown, David Bk. Co., The.

Wagner, Frances J. Fossils of Ontario Pt. 2: Macroinvertebrates & Vertebrates of the Champlain Sea with a Listing of Nonmarine Species. (Illus.). 198p. pap. *(978-0-88854-295-3(X))* BRILL.

Walls, Matthew. Caribou Inuit Traders of the Kivalliq Nunavut, Canada. 2009. (Bar S Ser.). (Illus.). 73p. (C). 62.50 *(978-1-4073-0377-2(5))* British Archaeological Reports Ltd. GBR. Dist: Brown, David Bk. Co., The.

Watts, Christopher M. Pot/Potter Entanglements & Networks of Agency in Late Woodland Period (C. AD 900-1300) Southwestern Ontario, Canada. 2008. (Bar S Ser.). (Illus.). x, 223p. (C). pap. 107.50 *(978-1-4073-0227-0(2))* British Archaeological Reports Ltd. GBR. Dist: Brown, David Bk. Co., The.

Wright, J. V. A History of the Native People of Canada, Volume I: 10,000-1,000 BC. 2007. (Mercury Ser.). (Illus.). 506p. per. *(978-0-660-19642-8(5))* Canadian Museum of Civilization/Musee Canadien des Civilisations.

CANADA—ARMED FORCES

see Canada—Canadian Armed Forces

CANADA—ARMY

see Canada—Canadian Army

CANADA—BIBLIOGRAPHY

Gagnon, Phileas. Essai de Bibliographie Canadienne, 2 vols. (French-Canadian Civilization Ser.). (FRE.). reprint ed. lib. bdg. 93.00 *(978-0-89197-751-3(1))*;1. lib. bdg. 48.00 *(978-0-697-00004-0(4))*;2. lib. bdg. 48.00 *(978-0-697-00005-7(2))* Irvington Pubs.

Lyons, Terri L. & Rumney, Thomas A. Canadian Geography: A Scholarly Bibliography, 2 vols. 2009. (ENG.). 896p. (gr. 17). 250.00 *(978-0-8108-6717-8(6))* Scarecrow Pr., Inc.

Peters, Diane E. International Students & Academic Libraries: A Survey of Issues & Annotated Bibliography. 2010. (ENG.). 218p. (gr. 17). pap. 60.00 *(978-0-8108-7429-9(6))* Scarecrow Pr., Inc.

CANADA—BIOGRAPHY

Ackles, Bob & Mulgrew, Ian. The Water Boy: From the Sidelines to the Owner's Box - Inside the CFL, the XFL, & the NFL. 2008. (ENG., Illus.). 304p. pap. 21.95 *(978-0-470-15591-2(4)*, Wiley) Wiley, John & Sons, Inc.

Agger, Helen. Following Nimishoomis: The Oral History Dediaayaanimanook Sarah Keesick Olsen, 1 vol. 2008. (ENG., Illus.). 220p. pap. 22.95 *(978-1-894778-60-2(X))* Theytus Bks., Ltd. CAN. Dist: Univ. of Toronto Pr.

Ahmed, Syed Habib. From South Asia to North America: An Autobiography 1915 - 2000. 2009. 432p. pap. 19.22 *(978-1-4269-0991-7(8))* Trafford Publishing.

Aimée, Rose. A Road Without A Map. 2011. 120p. 22.95 ***(978-1-4620-5611-8(3))***; pap. 12.95 ***(978-1-4620-5610-1(5))*** iUniverse, Inc.

Albani, Emma. Forty Years of Song. 2011. 178p. ***(978-1-84902-532-4(0))*** Benediction Classics.

Alexander, Lincoln. Go to School, You're a Little Black Boy: The Honourable Lincoln M. Alexander - A Memoir. 2010. (ENG., Illus.). 256p. pap. 26.99 *(978-1-55488-733-0(X))* Dundurn CAN. Dist: Ingram Pub. Services.

Allen, Jimmy. Extreme Heat: A Firefighter's Life. 2009. 16.95 *(978-0-9781070-7-9(1))* Manor Hse. Publishing, Inc. CAN. Dist: APG Sales & Distribution Services.

Allison, Leslie Mintum. Mildred Mintum: A Biography. (Illus.). 192p. pap. *(978-0-9698752-3-9(1))* Shoreline.

Amanda Wolfe. Beneath the Silver Lining Trilogy. 2010. 382p. 29.99 *(978-1-4535-2746-7(X))* Xlibris Corp.

Ambridge, D. W. Frank Harris Anson Pioneer in the North. 2006. pap. 15.95 *(978-1-4286-5983-4(8))* Kessinger Publishing, LLC.

Andra-Warner, Elle. David Thompson: A Life of Adventure & Discovery, 1 vol. 2010. (Amazing Stories Ser.). (ENG., Illus.). 144p. pap. *(978-1-926613-32-1(5))* Heritage Hse.

Andrew, Caroline, et al, eds. Gilles Paquet: Homo Hereticus. 2009. (Governance Ser.). (FRE & ENG., Illus.). 402p. (gr. 10-12). pap. *(978-0-7766-0692-7(1))* Univ. of Ottawa Pr./Presses de l'Universite d'Ottawa.

Angus, Colin. Beyond the Horizon: The First Human-Powered Expedition to Circle the Globe. 2008. (ENG.). 384p. 24.95 *(978-0-89732-685-8(7))* Menasha Ridge Pr., Inc.

Angus, Julie. Rowboat in a Hurricane: My Amazing Journey Across a Changing Atlantic Ocean, 1 vol. 2009. (ENG., Illus.). 272p. pap. 17.95 *(978-1-55365-337-0(8)*, Greystone Bks.) D&M Pubs. Inc. CAN. Dist: Perseus-PGW.

Ann, Cathrine. Beautiful Buttons: A Memoir of Survival & Triumph. 2011. 334p. pap. ***(978-1-926645-62-9(6))*** BPS Bks.

Anthony, Leslie. Snakebit: Confessions of a Herpetologist, 1 vol. (ENG.). 2011. 304p. pap. 18.95 *(978-1-55365-527-5(3))* 2009. 288p. 27.95 *(978-1-55365-236-6(3))* D&M Pubs. Inc. CAN. (Greystone Bks.). Dist: Perseus-PGW.

Antonson, Rick, et al. Slumach's Gold: In Search of a Legend, 1 vol. 2007. (ENG., Illus.). 160p. pap. *(978-1-894974-35-6(2))* Heritage Hse.

Aoki, Jodi, ed. Revisiting Our Forest Home: The Immigrant Letters of Frances Stewart. 2011. (ENG., Illus.). 288p. 35.00 *(978-1-55488-776-7(3))* Natural Heritage/Natural History, Inc. CAN. Dist: Ingram Pub. Services.

Appleby, Timothy. A New Kind of Monster: The Secret Life & Shocking True Crimes of an Officer ... & a Murderer. 2011. 304p. pap. 15.00 *(978-0-307-88872-3(X))* Broadway Bks.

Arbour, Linda Marie. Tales Out of School: A Challenge to Catholic Educators. 2011. 260p. pap. 19.95 ***(978-1-4502-8909-2(6))*** iUniverse, Inc.

Arch, Douglas E. The Life of a Screw: Life on the Inside, Everbody has a desire to learn what life is really like on the Inside of a Correctional Facility, the life of a Screw given the reader a 10 year span of one Mans true events while serving with the Department of Corrections. 2010. 88p. pap. 10.95 *(978-1-4502-7064-9(6))* iUniverse, Inc.

Archambeau, Gerald A. A Struggle to Walk with Dignity: The True Story of a Jamaican-Born Canadian. 2008. (ENG., Illus.). 277p. pap. 19.95 *(978-0-9784982-0-7(8))* Dundurn CAN. Dist: Ingram Pub. Services.

Arden, Jann. Falling Backwards: A Memoir. 2011. (ENG., Illus.). 288p. 29.95 *(978-0-307-39984-7(2)*, Knopf Canada) Knopf Canada CAN. Dist: Random Hse., Inc.

—Falling Backwards: A Memoir. 2012. (ENG.). 288p. pap. 18.00 ***(978-0-307-39985-4(0)***, Vintage Canada) Random Hse. of Canada, Ltd. CAN. Dist: Random Hse., Inc.

Armson, Kenneth A. & McLeod, Marjorie. The Legacy of John Waldie & Sons: A History of the Victoria Harbour Lumber Company. 2007. (ENG., Illus.). 152p. pap. 22.99 *(978-1-55002-758-7(1))* Natural Heritage/Natural History, Inc. CAN. Dist: Ingram Pub. Services.

Armstrong, Mary K. Confessions of a Trauma Therapist: A Memoir of Healing & Transformation. 2010. *(978-1-926645-19-3(7))* BPS Bks.

Arnold, Gladys. One Woman's War: A Canadian Reporter with the Free French. 2011. (ENG.). 238p. (C). pap. 24.95 ***(978-1-55277-958-3(0))*** Lorimer, James & Co., Ltd., Pubs. CAN. Dist: Casemate Pubs. & Bk. Distributors, LLC.

Arquette, Dorothy Baxter & Brassard, Judy Arquette. Beyond Trail's End. 2011. 164p. 25.95 ***(978-1-4620-1628-0(6))***; pap. 15.95 ***(978-1-4620-1627-3(8))*** iUniverse, Inc.

Auger, Dale. Medicine Paint: The Art of Dale Auger, 1 vol. 2009. (ENG., Illus.). 176p. *(978-1-894974-75-2(1))* Heritage Hse.

Avery, Martin & Avery, Phyllis. Big Phyl's Ashes. 2008. 349p. pap. 19.96 *(978-0-557-01888-6(9))* Lulu Enterprises Inc.

Bacher, John. Two Billion Trees & Counting: The Legacy of Edmund Zavitz. 2011. (ENG., Illus.). 280p. pap. 26.99 *(978-1-4597-0111-3(9))* Dundurn CAN. Dist: Ingram Pub. Services.

Baergen, John & Baergen, Lorraine. Unwritten. 2011. ***(978-1-77069-253-4(3))*** Word Alive Pr.

Bahari, Maziar & Molloy, Aimee. Then They Came for Me: A Family's Story of Love, Captivity, & Survival. 2011. 384p. 27.00 *(978-1-4000-6946-0(7)*, Random House) Random House Publishing Group.

Bailey, Fred. Sins of the Fathers. 2011. 244p. pap. ***(978-1-84991-461-1(3))*** Chipmunkapublishing.

Bailey, Peter. Justin Morneau: All-Star Ball Star. 2008. (ENG., Illus.). 128p. (J). pap. 12.95 *(978-1-55168-326-3(1))* Key Porter Bks. CAN. Dist: Perseus-PGW.

Baillie, Laureen, compiled by. American Biographical Index, 10 vols. 3rd enl. ed. 2007.Tr. of Amerikanischer Biographischer Index. CCLXXX, 6660p. *(978-3-598-34837-2(1))* Saur, K. G. Verlag GmbH & Co.

Bamford, Don & Carroll, Paul. Four Years on the Great Lakes, 1813-1816: The Journal of Lieutenant David Wingfield, Royal Navy. 2009. (ENG., Illus.). 280p. pap. 28.99 *(978-1-55488-393-6(8))* Dundurn CAN. Dist: Ingram Pub. Services.

Bann, Stephen. Paul Delaroche: History Painted. 2008. (ENG., Illus.). 304p. 95.00 *(978-1-86189-007-8(9))* Reaktion Bks., Ltd. GBR. Dist: Chicago Distribution Ctr.

Barbe, Léo. Slaying the Dragon. 2010. 184p. pap. 22.99 *(978-0-9811606-8-9(9))* Key Publishing Hse., Inc., The CAN. Dist: AtlasBooks Distribution.

Barbeau, Jacques & Hughes, E. J. A Journey with E.J. Hughes. 2nd collector's ed. (Illus.). 50.00 *(978-1-55365-153-6(7))* D&M Pubs. Inc. CAN. Dist: Perseus-PGW.

Barber, Bruce, ed. & intro. Condé & Beveridge: Class Works. 2009. (ENG., Illus.). 160p. pap. 45.00 *(978-0-919616-48-6(8))* Press of the Nova Scotia College of Art & Design CAN. Dist: D.A.P./Distributed Art Pubs.

Barnes, Mike. The Lily Pond: A Memoir of Madness, Memory, Myth & Metamorphosis. 2008. (ENG., Illus.). 220p. pap. 18.95 *(978-1-897231-48-7(2))* Biblioasis CAN. Dist: Chicago Distribution Ctr.

Barnholden, Michael. Circumstances Alter Photographs: Captin James Peters' Reports from the War of 1885. 2009. (ENG., Illus.). 144p. 35.00 *(978-0-88922-621-0(0))* Talonbooks, Ltd. CAN. Dist: Consortium Bk. Sales & Distribution.

Barnholden, Michael & Dumont, Gabriel. Gabriel Dumont Speaks. 2nd rev. ed. 2009. (ENG.). 96p. pap. 16.95 *(978-0-88922-625-8(3))* Talonbooks, Ltd. CAN. Dist: Consortium Bk. Sales & Distribution.

Barry, Ben. Fashioning Reality: A New Generation of Entrepreneurship. rev. ed. 2007. (ENG., Illus.). 256p. 24.95 *(978-1-55263-820-0(0))* Key Porter Bks. CAN. Dist: Perseus-PGW.

Bartleman, James K. Raisin Wine: A Boyhood in a Different Muskoka. 2008. (OJI & ENG.). 272p. pap. 14.95 *(978-0-7710-1264-8(0)*, Gibson, Douglas Bks.) McClelland & Stewart CAN. Dist: Random Hse., Inc.

Bates, Paul & Emid, Al. What I've Learned So Far... & How It Can Help You: Clues for Succeeding in Crisis from 50 Graduates of the School of Hard Knocks. 2010. 150p. pap. 24.95 *(978-1-897526-52-1(0))* Knowledge Bureau Ltd. CAN. Dist: Univ. of Toronto Pr.

Bates, Wesley. In Black & White: A Wood Engraver's Odyssey. 2008. (ENG., Illus.). 148p. *(978-1-55447-058-7(7))* Gaspereau Pr.

Baxter, Edward. Canada's Prime Ministers: Macdonald to Trudeau - Portraits from the Dictionary of Canadian Biography. Cook, Ramsay & Bélanger, Réal, eds. 2007. (Dictionary of Canadian Biography Ser.). (ENG., Illus.). 384p. pap. *(978-0-8020-9174-1(1))* Univ. of Toronto Pr.

Beaulieu, Hubert. Out of the Shadows. 2009. 78p. pap. 16.50 *(978-0-557-20520-2(4))* Lulu Enterprises Inc.

Bedford, Terri-Jean. Dominatrix on Trial: Bedford vs. Canada. 2011. 276p. 28.95 ***(978-1-4620-2677-7(X))***; pap. 18.95 ***(978-1-4620-2676-0(1))*** iUniverse, Inc.

Begg, Carolyn. Secluded Rendezvous. 2008. (ENG.). 200p. pap. 17.50 *(978-1-935125-04-4(4))* Robertson Publishing.

Bélanger, Réal, et al. Canada's Entrepreneurs: From the Fur Trade to the 1929 Stock Market Crash - Portraits from the Dictionary of Canadian Biography. 2011. (Dictionary of Canadian Biography Ser.). (ENG., Illus.). 528p. ***(978-1-4426-4478-6(8))*** Univ. of Toronto Pr.

—Canada's Entrepreneurs: From the Fur Trade to the 1929 Stock Market Crash Portraits from the Dictionary of Canadian Biography. 2011. (Dictionary of Canadian Biography Ser.). (ENG., Illus.). 528p. pap. ***(978-1-4426-1286-0(X))*** Univ. of Toronto Pr.

Belcourt, Herb. Walking in the Woods: A Métis Journey, 1 vol. 2006. (ENG., Illus.). 124p. per. *(978-1-897142-17-2(X))* Brindle & Glass Publishing.

Ben, David. Dai Vernon: Artist, Magician, Muse, 1894-1941. 2006. (Illus.). 368p. 39.95 *(978-0-9744681-5-0(0))* Squash Publishing.

Bennett, Alan. Captain Roy Brown: The Definitive Biography, Including His Encounter with the Red Baron, Manfred Von Richthofen. 2011. (ENG., Illus.). 350p. 29.95 *(978-1-883283-56-8(6))* IBks., Inc.

Bentley, Peter. One Family's Journey: Canfor & the Transformation of British Columbia's Forest Industry, 1 vol. 2012. (ENG., Illus.). 336p. 35.00 ***(978-1-55365-868-9(X))*** D&M Pubs. Inc. CAN. Dist: Perseus-PGW.

Berens, William. Memories, Myths, & Dreams of an Ojibwe Leader. Hallowell, A. Irving & Gray, Susan Elaine, eds. 2009. (Rupert's Land Record Society Ser.). (ENG., Illus.). 288p. (C). *(978-0-7735-3586-2(1))* McGill-Queen's Univ. Pr.

Berman, Tzeporah & Leiren-Young, Mark. This Crazy Time: Living Our Environmental Challenge. 2011. (ENG., Illus.). 384p. 32.00 ***(978-0-307-39978-6(8))*** Knopf Canada CAN. Dist: Random Hse., Inc.

—This Crazy Time: Living Our Environmental Challenge. 2012. (ENG., Illus.). 384p. pap. 18.00 ***(978-0-307-39979-3(6)***, Vintage Canada) Random Hse. of Canada, Ltd. CAN. Dist: Random Hse., Inc.

Bertin, Johanna. Don Messer: The Man Behind the Music. 2009. (ENG., Illus.). 280p. pap. 16.95 *(978-0-86492-531-2(X))* Goose Lane Editions CAN. Dist: Univ. of Toronto Pr.

Bethune, George W. (George Washington). Memoirs of Mrs Joanna Bethune, by Her Son, the Rev George W Bethune, D D with an Appendix, Containing Extracts from the Writings of Mrs Bethune. 2006. 268p. per. 23.99 *(978-1-4255-2450-0(8))* MPublishing.

Bidini, Dave. Writing Gordon Lightfoot: The Man, the Music, & the World in 1972. 2011. (ENG., Illus.). 288p. 27.95 *(978-0-7710-1262-4(4)*, McClelland & Stewart) McClelland & Stewart CAN. Dist: Random Hse., Inc.

Bidini, Dave. Writing Gordon Lightfoot: The Man, the Music, & the World In 1972. 2012. (ENG.). 288p. pap. 18.99 ***(978-0-7710-1263-1(2)***, McClelland & Stewart) McClelland & Stewart CAN. Dist: Random Hse., Inc.

Biography & Genealogy. 2011. 611.00 *(978-1-4144-4564-9(4))* Cengage Gale.

Bittermann, Rusty & McCallum, Margaret. Lady Landlords of Prince Edward Island: Imperial Dreams & the Defence of Property. 2008. (ENG., Illus.). 224p. (C). *(978-0-7735-3389-9(3))* McGill-Queen's Univ. Pr.

Black, Conrad. A Matter of Principle. 2011. (ENG., Illus.). 592p. 35.00 *(978-0-7710-1670-7(0)*, McClelland & Stewart) McClelland & Stewart CAN. Dist: Random Hse., Inc.

Black, Jack. You Can't Win, Complete & Unabridged by Jack Black. 2010. 256p. pap. 9.49 *(978-1-61720-024-3(7))* Wilder Pubns., Ltd.

Black, Michael. Leonardo, Romancia & R: Art History. 2009. (Illus.). 128p. pap. *(978-1-84991-004-0(9))* Chipmunkapublishing.

Black, Robert & Maguire, Marnie. Picture Perfect: The Story of Black's Photography. 2009. (ENG.). 210p. 29.95 *(978-0-86492-541-1(7))* Goose Lane Editions CAN. Dist: Univ. of Toronto Pr.

Blair, Margaret. Gudao, Lone Islet: The War Years in Shanghai: A Childhood Memoir. 2008. (Illus.). 220p. pap. 19.05 *(978-1-4251-1142-7(4))* Trafford Publishing.

Blatchford, Christie. Fifteen Days: Stories of Bravery, Friendship, Life & Death from Inside the New Canadian Army. 2008. (ENG., Illus.). 416p. pap. 19.00 *(978-0-385-66467-7(2)*, Anchor Can) Doubleday Canada, Ltd. CAN. Dist: Random Hse., Inc.

Bliss, Michael. Writing History: A Professor's Life. 2011. (ENG., Illus.). 432p. 40.00 *(978-1-55488-953-2(7)*, Dundurn Pr.) Dundurn CAN. Dist: Ingram Pub. Services.

Bogaard, Paul A. Profiles of Science & Society in the Maritimes Prior to 1914. 283p. pap. 12.95 *(978-0-919107-27-4(3))* Acadiensis Pr. CAN. Dist: Goose Lane Editions.

Boldt, Peter. Back to the Jungle. 2009. 176p. pap. *(978-1-55452-398-6(2))* Essence Publishing.

Bombay, Cal. A Man Worth Knowing. 2007. *(978-1-897213-43-8(3))* Castle Quay Bks. Canada.

Bondrup-Nielsen, Soren. A Sound Like Water Dripping: In Search of the Boreal Owl. 2009. (ENG.). 240p. pap. *(978-1-55447-074-7(9))* Gaspereau Pr.

BOURASSA, Rollie, ed. One Family's War: The Wartime Letters of Clarence Bourassa(1940-1944) 2010. (Trade Books Based in Scholarship(TBS) Ser.). (ENG.). 596p. pap. 29.95 *(978-0-88977-221-2(5))* Canadian Plains Research Ctr. CAN. Dist: Univ. of Toronto Pr.

Bower, Johnny & Duff, Bob. The China Wall: The Timeless Legend of Johnny Bower. 2008. (ENG., Illus.). 224p. *(978-1-55168-350-8(4))* Fenn, H. B. & Co., Ltd.

—The China Wall: The Timeless Legend of Johnny Bower. 2009. (ENG., Illus.). 224p. pap. 17.95 *(978-1-55168-360-7(1))* Key Porter Bks. CAN. Dist: Perseus-PGW.

Bowering, George. Pinboy: A Memoir. 2011. (ENG.). 320p. 32.00 *(978-1-897151-93-8(4))* Cormorant Bks. Inc. CAN. Dist: Univ. of Toronto Pr.

Bowes, Jennifer & Lyon. Wallis Simpson - My Life with David. Date not set. (Illus.). 240p. *(978-1-85685-124-4(9))* Robert Smith Literary Agency.

Boyanowsky, Ehor. Savage Gods, Silver Ghosts: In the Wild with Ted Hughes, 1 vol. 2010. (ENG., Illus.). 208p. 24.95 *(978-1-55365-323-3(8))* D&M Pubs. Inc. CAN. Dist: Perseus-PGW.

Boyden, Joseph. Louis Riel & Gabriel Dumont. 2011. (ENG.). 208p. (gr. 12). 19.95 ***(978-0-670-06671-1(0)***, Penguin Global) Penguin Group (USA) Inc.

Boyer, J. Patrick. A Passion for Justice: How 'Vinegar Jim' McRuer Became Canada's Greatest Law Reformer. 2008. (ENG., Illus.). 439p. pap. 28.95 *(978-0-9781600-0-5(2))* Dundurn CAN. Dist: Ingram Pub. Services.

Boyer, Patricia M. The March of Days: Optimistic Realism Through the Seasons of Life. 2009. (ENG.). 226p. pap. 22.95 *(978-0-9784982-1-4(6))* Dundurn CAN. Dist: Ingram Pub. Services.

Boyer, Patrick, et al. Solitary Courage: Mona Winberg & the Triumph over Disability. 2010. (ENG.). 383p. pap. 22.95 ***(978-0-9781600-5-0(3))*** Dundurn CAN. Dist: Ingram Pub. Services.

Bradburn, Morris. Growing up North. 2011. 180p. 26.95 ***(978-1-4620-1895-6(5))***; pap. 16.95 ***(978-1-4620-1894-9(7))*** iUniverse, Inc.

Brawn, Dale. Every Stone a Story II: Manitoba's Buried History. 2009. (Every Stone a Story Ser.). (ENG.). 152p. 29.95 *(978-1-894283-96-0(1))* Great Plains Pubns. CAN. Dist: Univ. of Toronto Pr.

Brennan, Brian. The Good Steward: Ernest C. Manning Story, 1 vol. 2009. (ENG., Illus.). 240p. 24.95 *(978-1-897252-16-1(1))* Fitzhenry & Whiteside, Ltd. CAN. Dist: Ingram Pub. Services.

Bridge, Kathryn. A Passion for Mountains: The Lives of Don & Phyllis Munday, 1 vol. 2010. (ENG., Illus.). 240p. per. *(978-1-894765-69-5(9))* Rocky Mountain Bks.

Bridle, Augustus. Sons of Canada. reprint ed. 150.00 *(978-0-7222-6881-0(5))* Library Reprints, Inc.

Brink, Nicky L. & Bown, Stephen R. Forgotten Highways: Wilderness Journeys down the Historic Trails of the Canadian Rockies, 1 vol. 2007. (ENG., Illus.). 240p. per. *(978-1-897142-24-0(2))* Brindle & Glass Publishing.

Broda, Brian. The Family of Semen Gurba 1772-1927. 2008. 259p. pap. 19.95 *(978-0-557-01255-8(4))* Lulu Enterprises Inc.

Brody, Leonard & Raffa, David. Everything I Needed to Know about Business... I Learned from a Canadian. 2nd ed. 2009. (ENG., Illus.). 288p. pap. 22.95 *(978-0-470-15975-0(8)*, Wiley) Wiley, John & Sons, Inc.

Brooke, Margaret. My Life in Sarawak. 2010. 178p. pap. 26.44 *(978-1-152-19241-6(8))* General Bks. LLC.

Brooks, Kim, ed. Justice Bertha Wilson: One Woman's Difference. 2010. (ENG., Illus.). 344p. (C). pap. 35.95 *(978-0-7748-1733-2(X))* UBC Pr. CAN. Dist: Univ. of Washington Pr.

Broughton, Ralph. All in a Lifetime. 2006. (ENG., Illus.). 164p. per. 19.57 *(978-1-4120-9720-8(7))* Trafford Publishing.

Brown, Bern Will. Free Spirits: Portraits from the North. 2007. (Illus.). 146p. per. *(978-2-89507-900-2(5))* Novalis Publishing.

Brown, Ian. The Boy in the Moon: A Father's Journey to Understand His Extraordinary Son. (ENG.). 304p. 2012. pap. 14.99 ***(978-0-312-67541-7(0)***, St. Martin's Griffin) 2011. 24.99 *(978-0-312-67183-9(0))* St. Martin's Pr.

Brown, Patrick. Butterfly Mind: Revolution, Recovery, & One Reporter's Road to Understanding China, 1 vol. 2009. (ENG.). 264p. pap. 15.95 *(978-0-88784-830-8(3))* House of Anansi Pr. CAN. Dist: Perseus-PGW.

Bublé, Michael. Onstage, Offstage. 2011. (ENG., Illus.). 304p. 27.00 ***(978-1-4516-7471-2(6))*** Gallery Pr., The IRL. Dist: Simon & Schuster, Inc.

Budgell, Leonard. Arctic Twilight: Leonard Budgell & Canada's Changing North. 2009. (ENG., Illus.). 469p. 39.95 *(978-0-9781600-1-2(0))* Dundurn CAN. Dist: Univ. of Toronto Pr.

Bueschke, Edgar. Traces of Heimweh: Family Memoirs. 2009. 552p. 33.99 *(978-1-4389-2697-1(9))* AuthorHouse.

Buhler, R. A. Letters Home, 2 vols. 2006. (ENG., Illus.). 240p. per. 19.09 *(978-1-4120-9280-7(9))*; per. 19.09 *(978-1-4120-9279-1(5))* Trafford Publishing.

Buist, Ron. Tales from under the Rim: The Marketing of Tim Hortons. 2011. (ENG., Illus.). 218p. pap. 19.95 *(978-0-86492-660-9(X))* Goose Lane Editions CAN. Dist: Univ. of Toronto Pr.

Bumsted, J. M. A History of the Canadian Peoples. 4th ed. 2011. (ENG., Illus.). 616p. (Orig.). pap. 85.00 *(978-0-19-543931-1(7))* Oxford Univ. Pr., Inc.

Burgess, John H. Doctor to the North: Thirty Years Treating Heart Disease among the Inuit. 2008. (Footprints Ser.). (ENG., Illus.). 178p. (C). *(978-0-7735-3431-5(8))* McGill-Queen's Univ. Pr.

Burgess, Steve. Who Killed Mom? A Delinquent Son's Meditation on Family, Mortality, & Very Tacky Candles, 1 vol. 2012. (ENG.). 264p. pap. 18.95 ***(978-1-55365-833-7(7)***, Greystone Bks.) D&M Pubs. Inc. CAN. Dist: Perseus-PGW.

Burke, Terry "Stoney". Cold War Soldier: Life on the Front Lines of the Cold War. 2011. (ENG., Illus.). 182p. pap. 22.99 *(978-1-55488-959-4(6)*, Dundurn Pr.) Dundurn CAN. Dist: Ingram Pub. Services.

Burles, Mary-Jo. Millionenschwere Kirchenmäuse: Eine kanadische Erfolgsgeschichte der etwas anderen Art. Braun, Klaus, tr. from ENG. 2011.Tr. of First & Second Kings, Maurice & Harold. (GER., Illus.). 184p. pap. *(978-0-9783192-4-3(9))* HBLS.

Burzek, Michael C. Blood on My Shirt: Memoirs of a BC Paramedic. 2011. 240p. 26.26 *(978-1-4269-5680-5(0))*; pap. 16.26 *(978-1-4269-5681-2(9))* Trafford Publishing.

Butlin, Susan. The Practice of Her Profession: Florence Carlyle, Canadian Painter in the Age of Impressionism. 2009. (McGill-Queen's/Beaverbrook Canadian Foundation Studies in Art History Ser.). (ENG., Illus.). 352p. (C). *(978-0-7735-3509-1(8))* McGill-Queen's Univ. Pr.

Buttuls, Peter I. From Country to Country. 2006. (Illus.). 229p. per. 21.15 *(978-1-4120-8923-4(9))* Trafford Publishing.

Bye, Chris. Crash Test. 2007. pap. *(978-0-9784402-6-8(9))* BPS Bks.

Calce, Michael & Silverman, Craig. Mafiaboy: A Portrait of the Hacker as a Young Man. 2011. 272p. 22.95 *(978-0-7627-7055-7(4)*, Lyons Pr.) Globe Pequot Pr., The.

Cameron, Elspeth. And Beauty Answers: The Life of Frances Loring & Florence Wyle. 2007. (ENG., Illus.). 504p. 36.95 *(978-1-897151-13-6(6))* Cormorant Bks. Inc. CAN. Dist: Univ. of Toronto Pr.

Cameron, Stevie. On the Farm: Robert William Pickton & the Tragic Story of Vancouver's Missing Women. (ENG., Illus.). 768p. 2011. pap. 19.95 *(978-0-676-97585-7(2)*, Vintage Canada) 2010. 31.00 ***(978-0-676-97584-0(4))*** Knopf Canada CAN. Dist: Random Hse., Inc.

Campbell, John Douglas Sutherland. Memories of Canada & Scotland: Speeches & Verses. 2007. (ENG.). 278p. pap. 21.99 *(978-1-4264-2186-0(9))*; 302p. pap. 24.99 *(978-1-4264-2254-6(7))* BiblioBazaar.

—Memories of Canada & Scotland: Speeches & Verses. 2007. 204p. per. *(978-1-4068-4183-1(8))* Echo Library.

Campbell, Peter. Rose Henderson: A Woman for the People. 2010. (ENG., Illus.). 400p. (C). *(978-0-7735-3764-4(3))* McGill-Queen's Univ. Pr.

Campbell, T. J. Pioneer Laymen of North America V1. (ENG.). 340p. 2007. 46.95 *(978-0-548-14371-1(4))* 2006. per. 31.95 *(978-1-4286-5623-9(5))* Kessinger Publishing, LLC.

—Pioneer Laymen of North America V2. 2007. (ENG.). 368p. 48.95 *(978-0-548-14372-8(2))* 2006. pap. 33.95 *(978-1-4286-5624-6(3))* Kessinger Publishing, LLC.

—Pioneer Priests of North America: Among the Hurons 1642 to 1710, Vol. 2. 2007. 474p. 52.95 *(978-0-548-01533-9(3))* Kessinger Publishing, LLC.

Canada Communication Group Staff. 125 Portraits: Companions of the Order of Canada. (FRE., Illus.). 159p. pap. *(978-0-660-57322-9(9))* Canadian Government Publishing.

Canadian Heroes: Heritage. (Canadian Heroes Ser.). reprint ed. 125.00 *(978-0-7222-6888-9(2))* Library Reprints, Inc.

Canadian Who's Who & Why. reprint ed. 150.00 *(978-0-7222-6890-2(4))* Library Reprints, Inc.

Caplette, Jim. Haywire. unabr. ed. (ENG.). 224p. (Orig.). pap. *(978-1-55017-084-9(8))* Harbour Publishing Co., Ltd.

Cariou, Heather Summerhayes. Sixtyfive Roses: A Sister's Memoir. (ENG., Illus.). 2008. 436p. 29.95 *(978-1-55278-611-6(0))* 2007. 386p. pap. 16.95 *(978-1-55278-678-9(1))* McArthur & Co. CAN. Dist: National Bk. Network.

Carpenter, David. A Hunter's Confession, 1 vol. 2011. (ENG.). 256p. pap. 17.95 *(978-1-55365-825-2(6)*, Greystone Bks.) D&M Pubs. Inc. CAN. Dist: Perseus-PGW.

Carr, Deborah. Sanctuary: The Story of Naturalist Mary Majka. 2010. (ENG., Illus.). 248p. pap. 19.95 *(978-0-86492-624-1(3))* Goose Lane Editions CAN. Dist: Univ. of Toronto Pr.

Carr, E. Hundreds & Thousands. mass mkt. 5.99 *(978-0-7725-1617-6(0))* Irwin Publishing CAN. Dist: Fitzhenry & Whiteside, Ltd.

Carr, Emily. Opposite Contraries: The Unknown Journals of Emily Carr & Other Writings. Crean, Susan, ed. 2006. (ENG., Illus.). 256p. pap. 19.95 *(978-1-55365-110-9(3))* D&M Pubs. Inc. CAN. Dist: Perseus-PGW.

Carson, Ann Elizabeth. My Grandmother's Hair, 1 vol. 2006. (ENG., Illus.). 238p. per. 32.99 *(978-0-88866-654-3(3))* Dundurn CAN. Dist: Ingram Pub. Services.

Carter, Doug. Cool Fool: Blues Rockin' in the Hammer. 2010. (ENG., Illus.). 171p. pap. 22.95 *(978-0-9808879-8-3(4))* Seraphim Editions CAN. Dist: Univ. of Toronto Pr.

Carter, Joyce L. My Long Life. 2010. 84p. pap. 10.49 *(978-1-4490-7955-0(5))* AuthorHouse.

Casey, Stephen. The Greater Glory: Thirty-Seven Years with the Jesuits. 2007. (Footprints Ser.). (ENG., Illus.). 264p. (C). *(978-0-7735-3243-4(9))* McGill-Queen's Univ. Pr.

Cashman, Tony. When Edmonton Was Young. 2009. (ENG., Illus.). 172p. pap. 19.95 *(978-0-88864-511-1(2))* Univ. of Alberta Pr. CAN. Dist: Michigan State Univ. Pr.

Cassata, Mary Anne. The Essential Jim Carrey. 2010. 144p. pap. 19.95 *(978-1-59393-517-7(X))* BearManor Media.

Celis, Peter. One Who Almost Made It Back: The Remarkable Story of One of World War Two's Unsung Heroes, Sqn Ldr Edward Teddy Blenkinsop, DFC, CdeG (Belge), RCAF. 2008. (Illus.). 224p. 42.95 *(978-1-906502-16-4(1))* Grub Street GBR. Dist: Casemate Pubs. & Bk. Distributors, LLC.

Cellucci, Paul. Unquiet Diplomacy. rev. ed. 2007. (ENG., Illus.). 256p. pap. 16.95 *(978-1-55263-875-0(8))* Key Porter Bks. CAN. Dist: Perseus-PGW.

Chakrabarty, Moushumi. Champions of Women's Rights: Leading Canadian women & their battles for social Justice. 2011. (Amazing Stories Ser.). (ENG.). 160p. pap. 9.95 *(978-1-55277-727-5(8))* Lorimer, James & Co., Ltd., Pubs. CAN. Dist: Casemate Pubs. & Bk. Distributors, LLC.

Chan, Arlene. The Chinese in Toronto From 1878: From Outside to Inside the Circle. 2011. (ENG., Illus.). 241p. pap. 35.00 *(978-1-55488-979-2(0))* Dundurn CAN. Dist: Ingram Pub. Services.

Chapnick, Adam. Canada's Voice: The Public Life of John Wendell Holmes. 2010. (ENG.). 384p. pap. 35.95 *(978-0-7748-1672-4(4))* Univ. of Washington Pr.

Chatto, James. The Man Who Ate Toronto. 2010. (ENG.). 352p. 29.95 *(978-1-897330-64-7(2))* Madison Pr. Bks. CAN. Dist: Independent Pubs. Group.

Chatto, James & Darling, Michael. Mordecai Richler Was Here. 2010. (ENG.). 211p. pap. 24.95 *(978-1-897330-33-3(2))* Madison Pr. Bks. CAN. Dist: Independent Pubs. Group.

Chernia, Ruth. The Best of the Branches: A Selected Collection of Articles from Recent OGS Branch Newsletters. 2008. (Illus.). ***(978-0-7779-3425-8(6))*** Ontario Genealogical Society.

Cherry, Don. Don Cherry's Hockey Stories & Stuff. 2009. (ENG.). 304p. pap. 15.95 *(978-0-7710-1956-2(4)*, McClelland & Stewart) McClelland & Stewart CAN. Dist: Random Hse., Inc.

Christian, William. Parkin: Canada's Most Famous Forgotten Man. 2008. (ENG., Illus.). 349p. pap. 26.95 *(978-0-9781600-3-6(7))* Dundurn CAN. Dist: Ingram Pub. Services.

Christopher, Bruce. "Superstroke" 2008. 168p. per. *(978-1-55452-269-9(2))* Essence Publishing.

—Superstroke Bruce Christopher My Winning Secrets. 2008. per. *(978-1-55452-268-2(4)*, Epic Pr.) Essence Publishing.

Clarke, Kenneth. Confessions of a Banjo Picker. 2011. 218p. 29.99 ***(978-1-4568-3742-6(7))***; pap. 19.99 ***(978-1-4568-3741-9(9))*** Xlibris Corp.

Clarkson, Adrienne. Norman Bethune. 2011. (ENG.). 204p. (gr. 12). 19.95 ***(978-0-670-06731-2(8)***, Penguin Global) Penguin Group (USA) Inc.

Clarkson, Michael. The Secret Life of Glenn Gould: A Genius in Love. 2010. (ENG., Illus.). 300p. 24.95 *(978-1-55022-919-6(2))* ECW Pr. CAN. Dist: Independent Pubs. Group.

Clelland, Ian James. The Road Leading Home: Small-town Stories of Family, Friends, Trials, & Triumphs. 2007. 156p. per. 14.95 *(978-0-595-43736-8(2))* iUniverse, Inc.

Coady, Mary Frances. Georges & Pauline Vanier: Portrait of a Couple. 2011. (Footprints Ser.). (Illus.). 296p. (C). ***(978-0-7735-3883-2(6))*** McGill-Queen's Univ. Pr.

Cohen, Andrew. Lester B. Pearson. Ralston, Saul, ed. 2012. (ENG.). 224p. (gr. 12). 19.95 ***(978-0-670-06738-1(5)***, Penguin Global) Penguin Group (USA) Inc.

Cojocaru, Steven. Glamour, Interrupted: How I Became the Best-Dressed Patient in Hollywood. 2009. 176p. pap. 14.99 *(978-0-06-079138-4(1))* HarperCollins Pubs.

Colapinto, John. As Nature Made Him: The Boy Who Was Raised as a Girl. 2006. (P. S. Ser.). (ENG., Illus.). 336p. pap. 14.99 *(978-0-06-112056-5(1)*, HarperPerennial) HarperCollins Pubs.

Cole, Gale Caniff. When You Stand Alone, Stand Tall. 2010. 22.95 *(978-1-55452-534-8(9))* Epic Pr.

Cole, Jean Murray, ed. Sir Sandford Fleming: His Early Diaries, 1845-1853. 2009. (ENG., Illus.). 328p. 30.00 *(978-1-55488-450-6(0))* Dundurn CAN. Dist: Ingram Pub. Services.

Coleman, A. P. The Canadian Rockies: New & Old Trails. 2009. (Mountain Classics Collection #1 Ser.). (ENG.). 232p. pap. *(978-1-897522-50-9(9))* Rocky Mountain Bks.

Collier, Eric. Three Against the Wilderness, 1 vol. 2007. (Classics West Collection Ser.). (ENG., Illus.). 320p. pap. *(978-1-894898-54-6(0))* TouchWood Editions.

Collins, Joseph Edmund. The Story of Louis Riel: The Rebel Chief. 2008. 188p. 22.99 *(978-0-554-32599-6(3))* 2008. 188p. 25.99 *(978-0-554-23296-6(0))* 2007. (ENG.). 166p. pap. 19.99 *(978-1-4264-4078-6(2))* 2007. (ENG.). 168p. pap. 21.99 *(978-1-4264-4137-0(1))* BiblioBazaar.

Connelly, Brent. Holy Old Whistlin' Yarns about Algonquin Park Loggers. (Illus.). viii, 139p. *(978-1-897113-34-9(X))* General Store Publishing Hse.

Cook, Ramsay & Bélanger, Réal, eds. Canada's Prime Ministers: MacDonald to Trudeau - Portraits from the Dictionary of Canadian Biography. 2007. (Dictionary of Canadian Biography Ser.). (ENG., Illus.). 384p. *(978-0-8020-9173-4(3))* Univ. of Toronto Pr.

Cooper, Dave. Bent. 2010. (ENG., Illus.). 80p. 22.99 *(978-1-60699-378-1(X)*, 699378) Fantagraphics Bks.

Cooper, R. F. Memories of Another Time. 2008. 84p. pap. 16.95 *(978-1-60610-541-2(8))* PublishAmerica, Inc.

Coulter, Myrl. The House with the Broken Two: A Birthmother Remembers. 2011. (ENG., Illus.). 160p. pap. 18.00 *(978-1-897535-72-1(4))* Anvil Pr. CAN. Dist: Univ. of Toronto Pr.

Crane, Sonia Gwen. Rise up My Beloved. 2008. 220p. pap. 15.99 *(978-1-60647-002-2(7))* Xulon Pr., Inc.

Currell, Harvey. Byways & Bylines. 2009. 380p. pap. 26.00 *(978-1-4269-1047-0(9))* Trafford Publishing.

Currelly, Charles Trick. I Brought the Ages Home. 90th ed. 2008. (ENG.). 314p. 39.95 *(978-0-88854-445-2(6))* Royal Ontario Museum CAN. Dist: Univ. of Toronto Pr.

Curtis, Wayne. Wild Apples: Field Notes from a River Farm. 2006. (ENG.). 166p. pap. 16.95 *(978-0-86492-485-8(2))* Goose Lane Editions CAN. Dist: Univ. of Toronto Pr.

Czajkowski, Chris. Wildfire in the Wilderness. unabr. ed. 2007. (ENG., Illus.). 224p. pap. 19.95 *(978-1-55017-375-8(8))* Harbour Publishing Co., Ltd. CAN. Dist: Ingram Pub. Services.

Dale-Burnett, Lisa Lynne. Saskatchewan Agriculture: Lives Past & Present. 2006. (Trade Books based in Scholorship(TBS) Ser.). (ENG., Illus.). 205p. pap. 19.95 *(978-0-88977-169-7(3))* Canadian Plains Research Ctr. CAN. Dist: Univ. of Toronto Pr.

Dallaire, Deny. Many Shades of Green: Running Toward the Finish Line, One Cancer at a Time. 2010. (ENG.). 200p. pap. 18.95 *(978-0-9865408-0-6(3))* DreamCatcher Publishing CAN. Dist: Univ. of Toronto Pr.

Dalton, Anthony. Arctic Naturalist: The Life of J. Dewey Soper. 2010. (ENG., Illus.). 392p. pap. 29.99 *(978-1-55488-746-0(1))* Dundurn CAN. Dist: Ingram Pub. Services.

D'Angelo, Frank. Being Frank: the Inspiring Story of Frank D'Angelo, 1 vol. 2011. (ENG.). 168p. pap. 15.95 ***(978-1-927005-03-3(5))*** Burman Books, Inc. CAN. Dist: Innovative Logistics.

Dasi, Visakha. Harmony & the Bhagavad-Gita: Lessons from a Life-Changing Move to the Wilderness. 2011. (Illus.). 188p. pap. 14.95 *(978-0-9817273-5-6(2))* Torchlight Publishing.

David Newton. Kipling's Canadian: Colonel Fraser Hunter, MPP, maverick soldier-mapmaker in the Great Game . 2010. 212p. pap. 17.95 *(978-1-4502-1086-7(4))* iUniverse, Inc.

Davis, Ann, ed. Cover & Uncover: Eric Cameron. 2011. (ENG., Illus.). 132p. pap. 59.95 ***(978-1-55238-534-0(5))*** Univ. of Calgary Pr. CAN. Dist: Chicago Distribution Ctr.

Davis, William B. Where There's Smoke... Musings of a Cigarette Smoking Man, a Memoir. 2011. (ENG., Illus.). 290p. pap. 19.95 *(978-1-77041-052-7(X))* ECW Pr. CAN. Dist: Independent Pubs. Group.

de Couto, John. Interesting Faces: My Encounters with Patients. 2008. pap. 13.00 *(978-0-8059-7958-9(1))* Dorrance Publishing Co., Inc.

De Rango-Adem, Adebe & Thompson, Andrea, eds. Other Tongues: Mixed-Race Women Speak Out. 2010. (ENG., Illus.). 302p. pap. 24.95 ***(978-1-926708-14-0(8))*** Inanna Pubns. & Education, Inc. CAN. Dist: SPD-Small Pr. Distribution.

Debogorski, Alex. King of the Road: True Tales from a Legendary Ice Road Trucker. (ENG., Illus.). 2011. 240p. pap. 14.95 ***(978-1-118-14828-0(2))*** 2010. 248p. 24.95 *(978-0-470-64368-6(4))* Wiley, John & Sons, Inc. (Wiley).

Decter, Michael. Tales from the Back Room: Memories of a Political Insider. 2010. 224p. pap. 24.95 *(978-1-926531-06-9(X))* Great Plains Pubns. CAN. Dist: Univ. of Toronto Pr.

Deitch, Patricia. Living in the Presence of His Absence. 2008. 184p. pap. *(978-3-639-06404-9(6))* VDM Verlag Dr. Mueller e.K.

Delisle, Guy. Burma Chronicles. 2010. (ENG., Illus.). 240p. pap. 16.95 *(978-1-77046-025-6(X))* Drawn & Quarterly Pubns. CAN. Dist: Macmillan.

Dempsey, Hugh A. Always an Adventure: An Autobiography. 2011. (West Ser.). (ENG., Illus.). 414p. pap. 34.95 ***(978-1-55238-522-7(1))*** Univ. of Calgary Pr. CAN. Dist: Chicago Distribution Ctr.

Dempsey, Hugh A. Maskepetoon: Leader, Warrior, Peacemaker, 1 vol. 2010. (ENG., Illus.). 240p. pap. *(978-1-926613-68-0(6))* Heritage Hse.

Dempsey, Hugh Aylmer. Tom Three Persons: Legend of an Indian Cowboy. 2006. (Illus.). 160p. *(978-1-895830-08-8(7))* Purich Publishing.

Denault, Todd. Jacques Plante: The Man Who Changed the Face of Hockey. 2010. (ENG., Illus.). 336p. pap. 18.95 *(978-0-7710-2627-0(7)*, McClelland & Stewart) McClelland & Stewart CAN. Dist: Random Hse., Inc.

Dennis, Lloyd. Marching Orders: A Memoir. 2010. (ENG.). 276p. pap. 25.00 *(978-1-55005-066-0(4))* Fitzhenry & Whiteside, Ltd. CAN. Dist: Ingram Pub. Services.

Dent, John Charles. Canadian Notabilities. 2008. 140p. 24.99 *(978-0-554-23138-9(7))* 2008. 140p. 21.99 *(978-0-554-32441-8(5))* Vol. 1. 2007. (ENG.). 286p. pap. 23.99 *(978-1-4264-3859-2(1))* BiblioBazaar.

—Canadian Notabilities. 2009. 122p. pap. *(978-1-4099-6772-9(7))* Dodo Pr.

—Canadian Notabilities, Volume 1. l.t. ed. 2007. (ENG.). 126p. pap. 18.99 *(978-1-4264-3789-2(7))* BiblioBazaar.

DeSoto, Lewis. Emily Carr. Saul, John Ralston, ed. 2011. (ENG.). 204p. (gr. 12). 19.95 ***(978-0-670-06670-4(2)***, Penguin Global) Penguin Group (USA) Inc.

DeVrye, Catherine. Serendipity Road: A Memoir. 2008. (ENG., Illus.). 356p. pap. 24.95 *(978-1-55278-645-1(5))* McArthur & Co. CAN. Dist: National Bk. Network.

Diamond, A. J. Sketches: From Here & There, 1 vol. 2011. (ENG., Illus.). 144p. 45.00 *(978-1-55365-591-6(5))* D&M Pubs. Inc. CAN. Dist: Perseus-PGW.

Diehl, Charlene. Out of Grief, Singing. 2010. 176p. pap. 15.95 *(978-1-897109-44-1(X))* Signature Editions CAN. Dist: Univ. of Toronto Pr.

Dietrich, Don, et al. No Guarantees. 2008. (Illus.). 201p. 20.87 *(978-1-4251-3072-5(0))* Trafford Publishing.

Dillon, Marie Suzanne. Two Weeks in Vieques: A Lifetime of Memories. 2010. 164p. (ENG.). 25.95 *(978-1-4502-4439-8(4))*; pap. 15.95 *(978-1-4502-4440-4(8))* iUniverse, Inc.

DiManno, Rosie. Coach: Pat Burns Story. 2012. (ENG.). 288p. 27.95 *(978-0-385-67636-6(0)*, Doubleday Can) Doubleday Canada, Ltd. CAN. Dist: Random Hse., Inc.

Djwa, Sandra, ed. Giving Canada a Literary History: A Memoir. 266p. *(978-0-88629-162-4(3))* McGill-Queen's Univ. Pr.

Domino & Bridle, Augustus. The Masques of Ottawa. 2008. 282p. 43.95 *(978-1-4366-4125-8(X))*; 284p. pap. 28.95 *(978-0-548-85508-9(0))* Kessinger Publishing, LLC.

Dorje, Tulku Hung Kar, frwd. A Path Strewn with Flowers & Bones: A Memoir with the Reflections of Tulku Sherdor. 2009. (Illus.). 305p. pap. 19.95 *(978-0-9801730-2-4(7))* Blazing Wisdom.

Dorricott, Keith. I Want to Live: The Story of My Battle with Leukemia, My Journey of Discovery, & the Many who Helped in my Healing. 2010. 256p. pap. 19.95 *(978-1-4502-1654-8(4))* iUniverse, Inc.

Doucet, Julie. 365 Days. 2008. (ENG., Illus.). 360p. 29.95 *(978-1-897299-15-9(X))* Drawn & Quarterly Pubns. CAN. Dist: Macmillan.

C

Doucette, Fred. Empty Casing: A Soldier's Memoir of Sarajevo under Siege, 1 vol. (ENG., Illus.). 256p. 2009. pap. 18.95 (978-1-55365-449-0(8)) 2008. 29.95 (978-1-55365-291-5(6)) D&M Pubs. Inc. CAN. Dist: Perseus-PGW.

Douglas, Jeremiah. A Life Not Worth Taking. 2006. i, 201p. (ENG.). 28.00 (978-1-4122-0167-4(5)); pap. 18.70 (978-1-4120-9243-2(4)) Trafford Publishing.

Douglas, Tom. To Wawa with Love. 2012. (ENG.). 156p. pap. 19.95 (978-1-4594-0044-3(5)) Lorimer, James & Co., Ltd., Pubs. CAN. Dist: Casemate Pubs. & Bk. Distributors, LLC.

Doulis, Alex. Lost on Bay Street: I Came, I Saw, I Almost Conquered. 2007. (ENG.). 224p. pap. 24.95 (978-0-9782221-3-0(X)) ECW Pr. CAN. Dist: Independent Pubs. Group.

Dreger, Derek. Clare Drake the Coaches' Coach: Hockey's Quite Revolutionary. 2007. (978-0-919035-32-4(9)) E.S.P. Marketing & Communications, Ltd. CAN. Dist: Lone Pine Publishing.

Drew, Benjamin. The Refugee: Narratives of Fugitive Slaves in Canada. 2008. (ENG.). 384p. pap. 29.99 (978-1-55002-801-0(4), Dundurn Pr.) Dundurn CAN. Dist: Ingram Pub. Services.

Drummond, Thane. The Old Days. 2010. 108p. 21.95 (978-1-4269-2921-2(8)); pap. 11.95 (978-1-4269-2920-5(X)) Trafford Publishing.

Dubbin, Bruce. The Bruce Dubbin Memoirs. 2011. 142p. 29.99 (978-1-4628-9634-9(0)); pap. 19.99 (978-1-4628-9633-2(2)) Xlibris Corp.

Durrett, Deanne. Unsung Heroes of World War II: The Story of the Navajo Code Talkers. 2009. (ENG., Illus.). 144p. pap. 14.95 (978-0-8032-2456-8(7), Bison Bks.) Univ. of Nebraska Pr.

Durschmied, Erik. Shooting Wars. 3.99 (978-5-553-40843-5(1)) World Pr., Ltd.

Dykes, Mervyn. Remember Me: The Charles Morgan Blessing Story. 2010. (Illus.). 104p. pap. 11.95 (978-0-88839-627-3(9)) Hancock Hse. Pubs.

Egoyan, Atom. Atom Egoyan: Interviews. Morris, T. J., ed. 2010. (Conversations with Filmmakers Ser.). (ENG.). 224p. 50.00 (978-1-60473-486-7(8)); pap. 22.00 (978-1-60473-487-4(6)) Univ. Pr. of Mississippi.

Eichhorn, Virginia M. & Harris, Adam Duncan. George McLean: The Living Landscape. 2010. (Illus.). 60.00 (978-0-86492-625-8(1)) Goose Lane Editions CAN. Dist: Univ. of Toronto Pr.

Einarson, John. Four Strong Winds: Ian & Sylvia. 2012. (ENG., Illus.). 336p. pap. 19.99 (978-0-7710-3039-0(8), Emblem Edns) McClelland & Stewart CAN. Dist: Random Hse., Inc.

Einarson, John. Four Strong Winds: Ian & Sylvia - Their Story. 2011. (Illus.). 336p. 29.95 (978-0-7710-3038-3(X), McClelland & Stewart) McClelland & Stewart CAN. Dist: Random Hse., Inc.

Elliott, David R. Adventures in the West: Henry Halpin, Fur Trader & Indian Agent. 2008. (ENG., Illus.). 240p. pap. 26.99 (978-1-55002-803-4(0)) Dundurn CAN. Dist: Ingram Pub. Services.

Elliott, Jayne, et al, eds. Place & Practice in Canadian Nursing History. 2009. (ENG.). 224p. pap. 29.95 (978-0-7748-1558-1(2)) UBC Pr. CAN. Dist: Univ. of Washington Pr.

Elson, Bryan. First to Die: The First Canadian Navy Casualties in the First World War. 2010. (ENG., Illus.). 96p. pap. 24.95 (978-0-88780-913-2(8)) Formac Publishing Co., Ltd. CAN. Dist: Casemate Pubs. & Bk. Distributors, LLC.

Endrenyi, John. Old Times, Evil Times: Memoirs. 2010. 144p. 24.95 (978-1-4502-0161-2(X)); (ENG.). pap. 14.95 (978-1-4502-0159-9(8)) iUniverse, Inc.

English, John. Just Watch Me Vol. 2: The Life of Pierre Elliott Trudeau, 1968-2000. 2010. (ENG., Illus.). 832p. pap. 21.95 (978-0-676-97524-6(0), Vintage Canada) Random Hse. of Canada, Ltd. CAN. Dist: Random Hse., Inc.

Englishman, Michael. 163256: A Memoir of Resistance. 2007. (Life Writing Ser.). (ENG., Illus.). 128p. pap. 24.95 (978-1-55458-009-5(9)) Wilfrid Laurier Univ. Pr. CAN. Dist: Univ. of Toronto Pr.

Ennamorato, Judith. Astrals, Auras & Apparitions: A Compendi. 2006. xxi, 188p. 27.99 (978-1-4122-0171-1(3)) Trafford Publishing.

Eryaman, Mustafa Yumus. Peter McLaren, Education & the Struggle for Liberation. 2008. (978-1-57273-757-0(3)); (978-1-57273-756-3(5)) Hampton Pr., Inc.

Evans, Harvey. From Fox Moths to Jet Rangers: A Bush Pilot's Life. 2009. (ENG., Illus.). 272p. pap. 26.95 (978-1-55017-463-2(0)) Harbour Publishing Co., Ltd. CAN. Dist: Ingram Pub. Services.

Eversole, Linda. Stella: Unrepentant Madam, 1 vol. 2010. (ENG., Illus.). 208p. per. (978-1-894898-31-7(1)) TouchWood Editions.

Falkenhagen, Rose Hertel & Hertel-Falkenhagen, Rose. Wilderness Beginnings. unabr. ed. (ENG.). 352p. pap. (978-0-920576-67-0(2)) Caitlin Pr., Inc.

Fantino, Julian & Amernic, Jerry. Duty: The Life of a Cop. rev. ed. 2007. (ENG., Illus.). 304p. 26.95 (978-1-55263-874-3(X)) Key Porter Bks. CAN. Dist: Perseus-PGW.

Farquharson, Vanessa. Sleeping Naked Is Green: How an Eco-Cynic Unplugged Her Fridge, Sold Her Car, & Found Love in 366 Days. 2009. (ENG.). 288p. pap. 12.25 (978-0-470-15510-3(8)) Wiley, John & Sons, Inc.

Farringtonmedia. Eight Miles North the Smilin Johnnie Sto. 2006. (Illus.). 240p. 30.00 (978-1-4122-0195-7(0)) Trafford Publishing.

Faryon, Cynthia. Unsung Heroes of the Canadian Army: Incredible Tales of Courage & Daring During World War II. 2006. (ENG., Illus.). 112p. pap. 9.95 (978-1-55439-009-0(5)) Lorimer, James & Co., Ltd., Pubs. CAN. Dist: Casemate Pubs. & Bk. Distributors, LLC.

Faulder, Liane. The Long Walk Home: Paul Franklin's Journey from Afghanistan - A Soldier's Story, 1 vol. 2007. (ENG., Illus.). 224p. per. (978-1-897142-25-7(0)) Brindle & Glass Publishing.

Faust, Reg. My Father Is a Twiner. 2008. 76p. pap. 15.49 (978-1-4343-9756-0(4)) AuthorHouse.

Fawcett, Brian. A Blue Spruce Christmas. 2010. (ENG., Illus.). 120p. 24.00 (978-1-897151-94-5(2)) Cormorant Bks. Inc. CAN. Dist: Univ. of Toronto Pr.

Feindel, Andrew, et al. Kickstart: How Successful Canadians Got Started. 2008. (ENG., Illus.). 240p. (gr. 6). pap. 26.99 (978-1-55002-783-9(2)) Dundurn CAN. Dist: Ingram Pub. Services.

Ferguson, Bonnie. The Streets of Kingston. 2012. (978-1-55452-775-5(9)) Essence Publishing.

Ferguson, Will. Why I Hate Canadians. pap. 22.95 (978-1-55054-600-2(7)); 10th ed. 2007. (ENG.). 336p. pap. 15.95 (978-1-55365-279-3(7)) D&M Pubs. Inc. CAN. Dist: Perseus-PGW.

Ferrabee, James & Harrison, Michael St B. Staying Connected: How MacDougall Family Traditions Built a Business over 160 Years. 2009. (ENG., Illus.). 256p. (C). (978-0-7735-3661-6(2)) McGill-Queen's Univ. Pr.

Finch, David. R. M. Patterson: A Life of Great Adventure, 1 vol. 2010. (ENG., Illus.). 312p. pap. (978-1-894898-95-9(8)) TouchWood Editions.

Finkelstein, Bernie. True North: A Life Inside the Music Business. 2012. (ENG., Illus.). 304p. 32.99 (978-0-7710-4793-0(2), McClelland & Stewart) McClelland & Stewart CAN. Dist: Random Hse., Inc.

Fisette, Paul. What? Is! the Meaning of Life. 2008. 363p. pap. 25.00 (978-0-557-02922-8(8)) Lulu Enterprises Inc.

FitzGerald, James. What Disturbs Our Blood: A Son's Quest to Redeem the Past. (Illus.). 512p. 2012. (ENG.). pap. 19.50 (978-0-679-31316-8(8), Vintage Canada) 2010. 28.95 (978-0-679-31315-1(X), Random Hse CAN) Random Hse. of Canada, Ltd. CAN. Dist: Random Hse., Inc.

Fleischmann, Arthur. Carly's Voice: Breaking Through Autism. 2012. (ENG.). 400p. 24.00 (978-1-4391-9414-0(9), Touchstone) Touchstone.

Fleischmann, Arthur & Fleischmann, Carly. Carly's Voice: Breaking Through Autism. 2012. pap. (978-1-4391-9415-7(7)) Simon & Schuster.

Fleming, R. B., ed. The Wartime Letters of Leslie & Cecil Frost, 1915-1919. 2007. (Life Writing Ser.). (ENG., Illus.). 420p. 45.95 (978-1-55458-000-2(5)) Wilfrid Laurier Univ. Pr. CAN. Dist: Univ. of Toronto Pr.

Fleury, Theo & Day, Kirstie Mclellan. Playing with Fire. 2011. (ENG.). 336p. pap. 14.95 (978-1-60078-637-2(5)) Triumph Bks.

Fleury, Theo & McLellan Day, Kirstie. Playing with Fire. 2009. (ENG.). 322p. 24.95 (978-1-60078-199-5(3)) Triumph Bks.

Flyers Novice AE Team (Hockey Team) Staff, contrib. by. Thanks to My Hockey Dad. 2010. (ENG., Illus.). 64p. 7.99 (978-1-55470-283-1(6)) Key Porter Bks. CAN. Dist: Perseus-PGW.

Fong, William. J. W. McConnell: Financier, Philanthropist, Patriot. 2008. (ENG., Illus.). 752p. (C). (978-0-7735-3270-0(6)) McGill-Queen's Univ. Pr.

Footman, Tim. Leonard Cohen: Hallelujah: A New Biography. 2009. (ENG., Illus.). 300p. pap. 19.95 (978-1-84240-472-0(5)) Chrome Dreams GBR. Dist: Independent Pubs. Group.

Foran, Charles. Maurice Richard. 2011. (ENG.). 208p. (gr. 12). 19.95 (978-0-670-06412-0(2), Penguin Global) Penguin Group (USA) Inc.

Forsberg, Tor. North of Iskut: Grizzlies, Bannock & Adventure. unabr. ed. 2010. (ENG., Illus.). 224p. pap. 24.95 (978-1-894759-42-7(7)) Caitlin Pr., Inc. CAN. Dist: Partners Pubs. Group, Inc.

Forsey, Helen. Eugene Forsey: Canada's Maverick Sage. 2012. (ENG., Illus.). 488p. 35.00 (978-1-926577-15-9(9)) Dundurn CAN. Dist: Ingram Pub. Services.

Forster, Merna. 100 More Canadian Heroines: Famous & Forgotten Faces. 2011. (Canadian Heroines Ser.). (ENG., Illus.). 408p. pap. 24.99 (978-1-55488-970-9(7)) Dundurn CAN. Dist: Ingram Pub. Services.

Fostaty, Gerry. As You Were: The Tragedy at Valcartier. 2011. 198p. pap. 19.95 (978-0-86492-648-7(0)) Goose Lane Editions CAN. Dist: Univ. of Toronto Pr.

Foster, Emily. The Banquet: My Grandma's Memories of China. 2008. 152p. pap. 14.95 (978-0-595-52957-5(9)) iUniverse, Inc.

Foster, Sheilagh. Everett Monroe, the Legend & the Life. 2009. 328p. pap. 20.95 (978-1-60693-093-9(1), Eloquent Bks.) AEG Literary Publishing Services, Inc.

Foster, Susan & Brewer, Carl. The Power of Two: Winning the Battle With the Powerbrokers of Hockey. 2006. (ENG., Illus.). 341p. (978-1-55168-289-1(3)) Fenn, H. B. & Co., Ltd.

Fournier, Allan. Prison Memoirs. 2009. 144p. pap. 11.99 (978-1-4490-4437-4(9)) AuthorHouse.

Frampton, Kenneth. Five North American Architects: An Anthology. 2012. (ENG., Illus.). 240p. pap. 55.00 (978-3-03778-256-9(0)) Lars Muller Pubs. CHE. Dist: Prestel Publishing.

Francis, Daniel, ed. Imagining British Columbia: Land, Memory, & Place. 2008. (ENG., Illus.). 256p. pap. 18.00 (978-1-895636-90-1(6)) Anvil Pr. CAN. Dist: Univ. of Toronto Pr.

Fraser, Eric R. Living with Shadows. 2011. 60p. pap. 12.00 (978-1-4269-3764-4(4)) Trafford Publishing.

Fraser, Marian Botsford. Requiem for My Brother, 1 vol. 2008. (ENG., Illus.). 248p. pap. 19.95 (978-1-55365-378-3(5), Greystone Bks.) D&M Pubs. Inc. CAN. Dist: Perseus-PGW.

Fraser, Susan. The Road Home. 2012. 64p. pap. (978-1-55452-859-2(3)) Essence Publishing.

Fromhold, Joachim. The Western Cree (Pakisimotan Wi Iniwak) - Donald Whitford C1840-1927. 2010. 178p. pap. 22.95 (978-0-557-54943-6(4)) Lulu Enterprises Inc.

Frost, Karolyn Smardz. I've Got a Home in Glory Land: A Lost Tale of the Underground Railroad. 2008. (ENG., Illus.). 480p. pap. 18.00 (978-0-374-53125-6(0)) Farrar, Straus & Giroux.

Fry, Alan. The Ranch on the Cariboo. 2009. 290p. 43.95 (978-1-104-84893-4(7)) 2007. (ENG.). 288p. per. 28.95 (978-0-548-45144-1(3)) Kessinger Publishing, LLC.

—The Ranch on the Cariboo, 1 vol. 2010. (ENG.). 288p. pap. (978-1-926741-00-0(5)) TouchWood Editions.

Frye, Northrop. Northrop Frye: Selected Letters, 1934-1991. Denham, Robert D., ed. 2009. (ENG., Illus.). 346p. pap. 49.95 (978-0-7864-4362-8(6)) McFarland & Co., Inc. Pubs.

Fukawa, Masako, ed. Nikkei Fishermen on the BC Coast: Their Biographies & Photographs. unabr. ed. 2007. (ENG., Illus.). 208p. 39.95 (978-1-55017-436-6(3)) Harbour Publishing Co., Ltd. CAN. Dist: Ingram Pub. Services.

Gagliardi, Rosino. Rosie: The Biography of A Canadian Soldier. 2011. 88p. pap. 10.95 (978-1-4620-2289-2(8)) iUniverse, Inc.

Gale Editor, ed. Biography & Genealogy Master Index Supplement 2012. 2012th ed. 2011. lib. bdg. 611.00 (978-1-4144-5808-3(8)) Cengage Gale.

Gardfre, Mtlissa. The Wind of Destiny: It may take you where you never Expected. 2008. 252p. pap. 18.00 (978-1-4389-2239-3(6)) AuthorHouse.

Gardiner, T. M. 'Scotty'. In the Mind of a Mountie. 2010. 772p. (978-1-897435-39-7(8)); 680p. pap. (978-1-897435-37-3(1)) Agio Publishing Hse.

Garfinkel, Jonathan. Ambivalence: Adventures in Israel & Palestine. 2008. (ENG.). 368p. 25.95 (978-0-393-06674-6(6), 6674) Norton, W. W. & Co., Inc.

Gayton, Don. Man Facing West, 1 vol. 2011. (Illus.). 170p. pap. 18.95 (978-1-897235-79-9(8)) Thistledown Pr., Ltd. CAN. Dist: Univ. of Toronto Pr.

Gervais, Marty. Afternoons with the Devil: Growing up Catholic in a Border Town. 2010. (ENG., Illus.). 150p. pap. 15.00 (978-0-88962-919-6(6)) Mosaic Pr.

Getty, George L. Wages of S I N. 2011. 88p. pap. 15.99 (978-1-4568-5350-1(3)) Xlibris Corp.

Gibb, David A. The Camouflaged Killer: The Shocking Double Life of Canadian Air Force Colonel Russell Williams. 2011. (ENG.). 384p. (gr. 12). 15.00 (978-0-425-24439-5(3), Berkley Trade) Penguin Group (USA) Inc.

Gibb, David A. Camouflaged Killer: The Shocking Double Life of Canadian Air Force Colonel Russell Williams. 2012. (ENG.). 592p. (gr. 12). pap. 9.99 (978-0-425-25919-1(6), Berkley) Penguin Group (USA) Inc.

Gibbins, Ralph. My Spirit Moose. 2008. 176p. pap. 29.99 (978-1-4363-2086-3(0)) Xlibris Corp.

Gidluck, Lynn. Visionaries, Crusaders, & Firebrands: The Idealistic Canadians Who Built the NDP. 2012. (ENG., Illus.). 248p. pap. 24.95 (978-1-4594-0053-5(4)) Lorimer, James & Co., Ltd., Pubs. CAN. Dist: Casemate Pubs. & Bk. Distributors, LLC.

Gillespie, Alastair W. & Sage, Irene. Made in Canada: A Businessman's Adventures in Politics. 2010. (Illus.). 272p. 37.95 (978-1-896941-59-2(1)) Brass, Robin Studio, Inc. CAN. Dist: Midpoint Trade Bks., Inc.

Gilmore, Jon Barnard. On Retirements: Playing Seriously with the Work of Getting Old. 2010. (978-1-926645-26-1(X)) BPS Bks.

Glendinning, Victoria, ed. Love's Civil War: Elizabeth Bowen & Charles Ritchie. 2009. (ENG., Illus.). 496p. pap. 19.95 (978-0-7710-3568-5(3), Emblem Edns) McClelland & Stewart CAN. Dist: Random Hse., Inc.

Golden, Namiko. A Crystal Seal. 2009. 316p. pap. 16.95 (978-1-60844-005-4(2)) Dog Ear Publishing, LLC.

Goldenberg, Eddie. The Way It Works: Inside Ottawa. 2007. (ENG.). 408p. pap. 17.95 (978-0-7710-3562-3(4), Gibson, Douglas Bks.) McClelland & Stewart CAN. Dist: Random Hse., Inc.

Goodbrand, Grant. Therafields: The Rise & Fall of Lea Hindley-Smith's Pyschoanalytic Commune. 2010. (ENG., Illus.). 300p. 32.95 (978-1-55022-976-9(1)) ECW Pr. CAN. Dist: Independent Pubs. Group.

Goodnough, Rev. Larry James. Prodigal Son: One Man's Spiritual Journey. 2011. 136p. pap. 19.99 (978-1-4628-9168-9(3)) Xlibris Corp.

Goodridge, Gary & Dorsey, Mark. Gatekeeper: The Fighting Life of Gary Big Daddy Goodridge. 2011. (ENG., Illus.). 208p. pap. 18.95 (978-1-55022-993-6(1)) ECW Pr. CAN. Dist: Independent Pubs. Group.

Goodwin, Debi. Citizens of Nowhere: From Refugee Camp to Canadian Campus. 2010. (ENG., Illus.). 336p. 27.95 (978-0-385-66722-7(1)) Doubleday Canada, Ltd. CAN. Dist: Random Hse., Inc.

Gordon, Charles W. The Life of James Robertson. (ENG.). 448p. 2007. 51.95 (978-0-548-14301-8(3)) 2006. per. 36.95 (978-1-4286-5535-5(2)) Kessinger Publishing, LLC.

Gourluck, Russ. Mosaic Village: A History of Winnipeg's North End. 2010. (ENG., Illus.). 272p. pap. 29.95 (978-1-894283-86-1(4), Great Plains Teen Fiction) Great Plains Pubns. CAN. Dist: Univ. of Toronto Pr.

—Picturing Manitoba: Legacies of the Winnipeg Tribune. 2008. (ENG., Illus.). 272p. pap. 29.95 (978-1-894283-76-2(7)) Great Plains Pubns. CAN. Dist: Univ. of Toronto Pr.

Graham, Norman A. From the Barrack Room to the Boardroom. 2007. 356p. 33.95 (978-0-595-71375-2(0)) iUniverse, Inc.

—From the Barrack Room to the Boardroom: The Memoirs of A Self-Made Man. 2007. 356p. per. 23.95 (978-0-595-47715-9(1)) iUniverse, Inc.

Grain, John, photos by. Flylines & Fishtales: The Story of Glimpse Lake Lodge. 2008. 160p. pap. 17.95 (978-1-891759-26-0(4)) Ingram Pub. Services.

Gray, Charlotte. Gold Diggers: Striking It Rich in the Klondike. (ENG., 432p. 2011. Illus.). pap. 18.95 (978-1-58243-765-1(3)) 2010. 29.95 (978-1-58243-611-1(8)) Counterpoint LLC. (Counterpoint).

Gray, Charlotte. Nellie McClung. Saul, John Ralston, ed. 2011. (ENG.). 204p. (gr. 12). 19.95 (978-0-670-06674-2(5), Penguin Global) Penguin Group (USA) Inc.

Green, Bob. Eavesdroppings: Stories from Small Towns When Sin Was Fun. 2006. (ENG.). 200p. pap. 22.99 (978-1-55002-629-0(1), Dundurn Pr.) Dundurn CAN. Dist: Ingram Pub. Services.

Green, Deneace. My Thoughts, My Life: Institutionalized Racism in Canada. 2011. 376p. (978-1-77067-157-7(9)); pap. (978-1-77067-158-4(7)) FriesenPress.

Griffiths, Margaret. Morning Light: Triumph at Sea & Tragedy on Everest, 1 vol. rev. ed. 2009. (ENG., Illus.). 312p. (978-1-897522-08-0(8)) Rocky Mountain Bks.

Griffiths, Naomi E. S. The Golden Age of Liberalism: A Portrait of Roméo Leblanc. 2011. (ENG., Illus.). 376p. 35.00 (978-1-55277-896-8(7)) Lorimer, James & Co., Ltd., Pubs. CAN. Dist: Casemate Pubs. & Bk. Distributors, LLC.

Griffiths, Tony. Corporate Catalyst: A Chronicle of the (Mis)Management of Canadian Business from a Veteran Insider. 2012. (ENG.). 320p. 36.95 (978-1-118-15286-7(7), Wiley) Wiley, John & Sons, Inc.

Gutkin, Harry. The Worst of Times the Best of Times: Growing up in Winnipeg's North End. 2010. (ENG.). 288p. pap. 25.00 (978-1-55005-210-7(1)) Fitzhenry & Whiteside, Ltd. CAN. Dist: Ingram Pub. Services.

Guttman, Frank Myron. The Devil from Saint-Hyacinthe: Senator TTlesphore-Damien Bouchard. 2007. 428p. per. 25.95 (978-0-595-40302-8(6)) iUniverse, Inc.

Gwyn, Richard. John A: The Man Who Made Us, 2 vols. 2008. (ENG., Illus.). 560p. pap. 19.50 (978-0-679-31476-9(8), Vintage Canada) Random Hse. of Canada, Ltd. CAN. Dist: Random Hse., Inc.

Gwyn, Richard J. Nation Maker: Sir John A. MacDonald - His Life, Our Times, 2 vols. 2012. (ENG., Illus.). 688p. pap. 23.00 (978-0-307-35645-1(0), Vintage Canada) Random Hse. of Canada, Ltd. CAN. Dist: Random Hse., Inc.

Hagen, Darrin. The Edmonton Queen: The Final Voyage, 1 vol. 2007. (ENG., Illus.). 256p. per. (978-1-897142-20-2(X)) Brindle & Glass Publishing.

Haigh, Jerry. Of Moose & Men: A Wildlife Vet's Pursuit of the World's Largest Deer. 2012. (ENG., Illus.). 240p. pap. 22.95 (978-1-77041-091-6(0)) ECW Pr. CAN. Dist: Independent Pubs. Group.

Hall, M. Ann. Immodest & Sensational: 150 Years of Canadian Women in Sport. 2008. (ENG., Illus.). 96p. pap. 19.95 (978-1-55277-021-4(4)) Lorimer, James & Co., Ltd., Pubs. CAN. Dist: Casemate Pubs. & Bk. Distributors, LLC.

Halperin, Ian. Guy Laliberté: The Fabulous Story of The Creator of Cirque Du Soleil. 2nd ed. 2009. (ENG., Illus.). 226p. 25.00 (978-1-926745-15-2(9)) Transit Publishing (Transit Editeur Inc.) CAN. Dist: Midpoint Trade Bks., Inc.

Hamblin, Jennifer & Finch, David. The Diva & the Rancher: The Story of Norma Piper & George Pocaterra, 1 vol. 2010. (ENG., Illus.). 320p. pap. (978-1-894765-70-1(2)) Rocky Mountain Bks.

Hamilton, Matt. Through Travel & Error: Confessions of an Asylum-Seeking Canadian. 2009. 292p. pap. 20.95 (978-1-935278-53-5(3), iUniverse Star) iUniverse, Inc.

Hammer, Dave. From Out of the Flames. 2011. (978-1-77069-337-1(8)) Word Alive Pr.

Hammond, Melvin Ormond. Canadian Confederation & Its Leaders. 2009. 144p. pap. 19.99 (978-1-150-77069-2(4)) General Bks. LLC.

—Canadian Confederation & Its Leaders. 333p. reprint ed. 98.00 (978-0-7222-6883-4(1)) Library Reprints, Inc.

Hannant, Larry & Whyte, Bert. Champagne & Meatballs: Adventures of a Canadian Communist. 2011. (ENG., Illus.). 348p. (C). pap. 32.95 (978-1-926836-08-9(1)) Univ. of British Columbia Pr. CAN. Dist: Univ. of Washington Pr.

Harbord, Heather. Desolation Sound: A History. unabr. ed. 2007. (ENG., Illus.). 256p. pap. 24.95 (978-1-55017-407-6(X)) Harbour Publishing Co., Ltd. CAN. Dist: Ingram Pub. Services.

Harder, Lois & Patten, Steve. The Chretien Legacy: Politics & Public Policy in Canada. 2006. (ENG.). 366p. (C). per. (978-0-7735-3107-9(6)) McGill-Queen's Univ. Pr.

Harder, Lois & Patten, Steven C. The Chrétien Legacy: Politics & Public Policy in Canada. 2006. (ENG.). 366p. (C). (978-0-7735-3095-9(9)) McGill-Queen's Univ. Pr.

Hare, Jan & Barman, Jean. Good Intentions Gone Awry: Emma Crosby & the Methodist Mission on the Northwest Coast. 2007. (ENG., Illus.). 344p. 29.95 (978-0-7748-1271-9(0)) UBC Pr. CAN. Dist: Univ. of Washington Pr.

Harper, Janis, ed. Body Breakdowns: Tales of Illness & Recovery. 2007. (ENG., Illus.). 168p. per. 15.00 (978-1-895636-86-4(8)) Anvil Pr. CAN. Dist: Univ. of Toronto Pr.

Hart, Bret. Hitman: My Real Life in the Cartoon World of Wrestling. 2009. (ENG., Illus.). 592p. pap. 16.99 (978-0-446-54528-0(7)) Grand Central Publishing.

Hart, E. J. Jimmy Simpson: Legend of the Rockies, 1 vol. 2009. (ENG., Illus.). 224p. pap. (978-1-897522-25-7(8)) Rocky Mountain Bks.

Harvey, Edward B. The Lansdowne ERA: Victoria College, 1946-1963. 2008. (ENG., Illus.). 216p. (C). (978-0-7735-3436-0(9)) McGill-Queen's Univ. Pr.

Hayes, Adrian. Pegahmagabow: Life-Long Warrior. 2009. (ENG.). 165p. pap. 19.95 (978-0-9784982-9-0(1)) Dundurn CAN. Dist: Ingram Pub. Services.

Heath, Terrence. Joe Fafard, 1 vol. 2008. (ENG., Illus.). 232p. 45.00 (978-1-55365-221-2(5)) D&M Pubs. Inc. CAN. Dist: Perseus-PGW.

Heatley, Michael. At This Moment: The Michael Buble Story. 2011. (ENG., Illus.). 288p. 29.95 (978-1-84938-978-5(0)) Omnibus Pr.

Heintzman, Ralph, ed. Tom Symons: A Canadian Life. 2011. (ENG., Illus.). 488p. (978-0-7766-3043-4(1)) Univ. of Ottawa Pr./Presses de l'Universite d'Ottawa.

Hellyer, Josh. Give Life a Squeeze: Juicy Observations from My Life's First Quarter. 2007. 128p. (ENG.). 23.95 (978-0-595-70090-5(X)); per. 13.95 (978-0-595-46213-1(8)) iUniverse, Inc.

Henderson, J. L., ed. John Strachan: Documents & Opinions, No. 44. 290p. pap. 18.95 (978-0-7710-9744-7(1)) McClelland & Stewart CAN. Dist: Random Hse. of Canada, Ltd.

Henderson, Paula Laureen. Lost Angels: Encounters with First Nations. 2011. (ENG & FRE.). 223p. pap. (978-0-9783141-1-8(5)) Gumdrop Enterprise.

Henighan, Tom. Vilhjalmur Stefansson: Arctic Adventurer. 2009. (Quest Biography Ser.). (ENG., Illus.). 216p. pap. 19.99 (978-1-55002-874-4(X)) Dundurn CAN. Dist: Ingram Pub. Services.

Hennessey, Catherine. CatherineHennessey. com. 2009. 348p. pap. 26.97 (978-0-557-06413-7(9)) Lulu Enterprises Inc.

Heritage House Group Staff, compiled by. Outlaws & Lawman of Western Canada, * vol., Vol. 2. 2007. (ENG., Illus.). 128p. reprint ed. pap. (978-0-919214-54-5(1)) Heritage Hse.

Herzog, Fred. Fred Herzog: Photographs, 1 vol. 2011. (ENG., Illus.). 204p. 55.00 (978-1-55365-555-9(3)) D&M Pubs. Inc. CAN. Dist: Perseus-PGW.

Hesler, Harold. War Interlude 1916 -1919. 2011. 124p. 23.95 (978-1-4620-0353-2(2)); pap. 13.95 (978-1-4620-0352-5(4)) iUniverse, Inc.

Hesler, William. Muleskinner: The European War of a Niagara Artilleryman. 2010. 152p. 24.95 (978-1-4502-7158-5(8)); pap. 14.95 (978-1-4502-7157-8(X)) iUniverse, Inc.

Hildebrandt, Sherri. More Than Enough. 2011. (978-1-77069-220-6(7)) Word Alive Pr.

Hill, K. Little Cavey: View of Reality. 2007. 268p. per. (978-1-84747-431-5(4)) Chipmunkapublishing.

Hillen, Ernest & MacGregor, Roy. A Weekend Memoir. 2009. (ENG.). 320p. 16.95 (978-0-19-542992-3(3)) Oxford Univ. Pr., Inc.

Hillier, Rick. A Soldier First. 2010. 552p. pap. 18.99 (978-0-06-202667-5(4)) HarperCollins Pubs.

Hincks, Francis. Baldwin. reprint ed. 150.00 (978-0-7222-6933-6(1)) Library Reprints, Inc.

Hodgins, Bruce W. & Hodgins, Carol. Paddling Partners: Fifty Years of Northern Canoe Travel. 2008. (ENG., Illus.). 176p. pap. 24.99 (978-1-55002-761-7(1)) Natural Heritage/Natural History, Inc. CAN. Dist: Ingram Pub. Services.

Holmes, Jessica. I Love Your Laugh: Finding the Light in My Screwball Life. (ENG., Illus.). 256p. 2011. pap. 17.95 (978-0-7710-4135-8(7)) 2010. 27.99 (978-0-7710-4134-1(9)) McClelland & Stewart CAN. (McClelland & Stewart). Dist: Random Hse., Inc.

Horn, Bernd. ed. Les guerriers Intrepides: Perspectives sur les chefs militaires Canadiens. 2007. (FRE & ENG., Illus.). 328p. pap. 39.95 (978-1-55002-721-1(2), Dundurn Pr.) Dundurn CAN. Dist: Ingram Pub. Services.

—Intrepid Warriors: Perspectives on Canadian Military Leaders. 2007. (ENG., Illus.). 272p. pap. 39.95 (978-1-55002-711-2(5), Dundurn Pr.) Dundurn CAN. Dist: Ingram Pub. Services.

Horton, Nancy. Hope in the Midst of Darkness: A Breast Cancer Survivor's Journey. 2011. 400p. pap. (978-1-77069-194-0(4)) Word Alive Pr.

Hoshowsky, Robert J. The Last to Die: Ronald Turpin, Arthur Lucas, & the End of Capital Punishment in Canada. 2007. (ENG., Illus.). 224p. pap. 24.99 (978-1-55002-672-6(0), Hounslow Pr.) Dundurn CAN. Dist: Ingram Pub. Services.

Hoyle, Gwyneth. The Northern Horizons of Guy Blanchet: Intrepid Surveyor, 1884-1966. 2007. (ENG., Illus.). 224p. pap. 24.99 (978-1-55002-759-4(X)) Natural Heritage/Natural History, Inc. CAN. Dist: Ingram Pub. Services.

Huber, Ron. Facing the World Without Love, How the Welfare & Foster Care System Has Destroyed Our Society's Throwaway Children. 2009. 148p. 22.50 (978-1-60860-096-0(3), Eloquent Bks.) AEG Literary Publishing Services, Inc.

Hudon, Alfred J. Memoirs of A Magman: P. I. & Crooked Cops. 2010. 248p. pap. 19.95 (978-1-4502-5321-5(0)) iUniverse, Inc.

Hueglin, Thomas O. We All Giggled: A Bourgeois Family Memoir. 2010. (Life Writing Ser.). (Illus.). 246p. (C). pap. 24.95 (978-1-55458-262-4(8)) Wilfrid Laurier Univ. Pr. CAN. Dist: Univ. of Toronto Pr.

Hughes, Mary E. Frank Welsman Canadian Conductor. 2006. (ENG., Illus.). 252p. pap. 23.43 (978-1-4120-8856-5(9)) Trafford Publishing.

Hughes, Roy. Canada's Bridge Warriors: Eric Murray & Sami Kehela. 2007. (Illus.) 336p. per. (978-1-897106-21-1(1)) Master Point Pr.

Hunter, Avalyn. The Kingmaker: How Northern Dancer Founded a Racing Dynasty. 2009. (ENG., Illus.). 254p. pap. 16.95 (978-1-58150-203-9(6), Eclipse Pr.) Blood-Horse, Inc., The.

Hunter, Martin. Young Hunting: A Memoir. 2008. (ENG.). 208p. pap. 19.95 (978-1-55022-852-6(8)) ECW Pr. CAN. Dist: Independent Pubs. Group.

Hutchison, Bruce & Palmer, Vaughn. The Incredible Canadian: A Candid Portrait of Mackenzie King. 2011. (ENG.). 464p. pap. 21.95 (978-0-19-543890-1(6)) Oxford Univ. Pr., Inc.

Iglauer, Edith. Fishing with John. 3rd ed. (ENG., Illus.). 305p. reprint ed. pap. 24.95 (978-1-55017-048-1(1)) Harbour Publishing Co., Ltd. CAN. Dist: Ingram Pub. Services.

—The Strangers Next Door. unabr. ed. (ENG.). 304p. 32.95 (978-1-55017-054-2(6)) Harbour Publishing Co., Ltd. CAN. Dist: Ingram Pub. Services.

Iredale, Kathryn & Martineau, Sheila. Finding a Good Fit: The Life & Work of Architect Rand Iredale. 2007. (ENG., Illus.). 400p. pap. 39.95 (978-1-894965-90-3(6)) Simply Read Bks. CAN. Dist: Perseus-PGW.

Irvine, Holli. Bittersweet Mayfair Memories. 2011. 160p. pap. 14.95 (978-1-4620-2146-8(8)) iUniverse, Inc.

Irving, Joe. Life of an Ironworker: The Collected Works of Joseph Red Irving. 2011. 220p. pap. 13.66 (978-1-4269-9380-0(3)) Trafford Publishing.

Ishaya, Arianne. New Lamps for Old. 2009. pap. 48.00 (978-1-60724-585-8(X)) Gorgias Pr., LLC.

Italian Chamber of Commerce of Toronto, ed. Celebration: 32 Inspiring Canadian Women of Italian Origin/32 Ritratti Di Donne Italo-Canadesi. 2006. (ENG & ITA., Illus.). 160p. per. (978-1-894469-30-2(5)) Mansfield Pr.

Ivantchev, Sergei. The Journey: The Dream of a 6th Grader. 2011. 112p. 23.99 (978-1-4567-1221-1(7)); pap. 13.99 (978-1-4567-1220-4(9)) AuthorHouse.

Ivison, Pam. In the Palm of His Hand. 2008. 224p. pap. (978-1-55452-271-2(4)) Essence Publishing.

Jackson, Kate. Mean & Lowly Things: Snakes, Science, & Survival in the Congo. (Illus.). 336p. 2010. pap. 17.95 (978-0-674-04842-3(3)) 2008. 27.95 (978-0-674-02974-3(7)) Harvard Univ. Pr.

Jackson, Mary Percy. Suitable for the Wilds: Letters from Northern Alberta, 1929-31. Dickin, Janice, ed. 2nd ed. 2006. (Legacies Shared Ser.). (ENG., Illus.). 336p. pap. 24.95 (978-1-55238-169-4(2)) Univ. of Calgary Pr. CAN. Dist: Chicago Distribution Ctr.

Jackson, Stewart. Writings of George Godwin: A Twentieth Century Romantic. 2011. 144p. pap. 14.90 (978-1-4269-4990-6(1)) Trafford Publishing.

Jacques, David. Lanscape Modernism Renounced: The Career of Christopher Tunnard (1910-1979) 2009. (ENG., Illus.). 288p. 155.00 (978-0-415-49720-6(5)) Routledge.

—Lanscape Modernism Renounced: The Career of Christopher Tunnard, 1910-1979. 2009. (ENG., Illus.). 288p. pap. 62.95 (978-0-415-49722-0(1)) Routledge.

James, Russell. Maud Allan Affair. 2008. (Illus.). 480p. 50.00 (978-1-84468-041-2(X)) Pen & Sword Bks. Ltd. GBR. Dist: Casemate Pubs. & Bk. Distributors, LLC.

Jenish, D'Arcy. Epic Wanderer: David Thompson & the Mapping of the Canadian West. 2009. (ENG., Illus.). 320p. pap. 18.95 (978-0-8032-2452-0(4), Bison Bks.) Univ. of Nebraska Pr.

Jenkins, Phil. Beneath My Feet: The Memoirs of George Mercer Dawson. 2008. (ENG., Illus.). 368p. pap. 21.00 (978-0-7710-4333-8(3), Emblem Edns) McClelland & Stewart CAN. Dist: Random Hse., Inc.

Jericho, Chris. A Lion's Tale: Around the World in Spandex. 2008. (ENG.). 544p. mass mkt. 7.99 (978-0-446-69861-0(X)) Grand Central Publishing.

—Undisputed: How to Become the World Champion in 1,372 Easy Steps. (ENG., Illus.). 2012. 528p. mass mkt. 7.99 (978-0-446-53816-9(7)) 2011. 448p. 27.99 (978-0-446-53815-2(9)) Grand Central Publishing.

Joan Woodley. One Woman's Scrapbook. 2009. 124p. pap. 19.95 (978-1-4251-3843-1(8)) Trafford Publishing.

Jodoin, Mark. Shadow Soldiers of the American Revolution: Loyalist Tales from New York to Canada. 2009. (Regional Histories Ser.). 160p. pap. 21.99 (978-1-59629-726-5(3)) History Pr., The.

Johnson, Jordy. The Willpower to Live. 2011. 206p. 29.99 (978-1-4628-6402-7(3)); pap. 19.99 (978-1-4628-6401-0(5)) Xlibris Corp.

Johnson, Ron. Hooked on a Drumbeat. Currie, Daryl, ed. 2008. 228p. pap. 19.00 (978-1-4251-7917-5(7)) Trafford Publishing.

Johnston, Faith. A Great Restlessness: The Life & Times of Dorise Nielsen. 2006. (ENG., Illus.). 392p. pap. 28.95 (978-0-88755-690-6(6)) Univ. of Manitoba Pr. CAN. Dist: Chicago Distribution Ctr.

Johnston, William Victor. Before the Age of Miracles: Memoirs of a Country Doctor. 2010. (ENG.). 226p. pap. 20.00 (978-1-55005-188-9(1)) Fitzhenry & Whiteside, Ltd. CAN. Dist: Ingram Pub. Services.

Johnstone, Bill. Coal Dust in My Blood: The Autobiography of a Coal Miner, 1 vol. 2nd ed. 2010. (ENG., Illus.). 192p. pap. (978-0-7726-4689-7(9)) Royal British Columbia Museum.

Jokinen, Tom. Curtains: Adventures of an Undertaker-in-Training. 2010. (ENG.). 288p. pap. 15.95 (978-0-306-81891-2(4)) Da Capo Pr., Inc.

—Curtains: Adventures of an Undertaker-in-Training. 2010. (ENG.). 288p. (978-0-307-35568-3(3), Random Hse CAN) Random Hse. of Canada, Ltd. CAN. Dist: Random Hse., Inc.

Jones, Paul. Pembina Country. unabr. ed. (ENG., Illus.). 240p. pap. (978-0-920576-73-1(7)) Caitlin Pr., Inc.

Jones, Paul H. Shaheen. 2007. (Illus.). 160p. 34.95 (978-0-88839-638-9(4)) Hancock Hse. Pubs.

Jones, Terry. The Ferbey Four: The Kings of Canadian Curling. 2007. (ENG.). 240p. (978-1-896124-12-4(7)) Dragon Hill Publishing CAN. Dist: Lone Pine Publishing.

Joseph Weinstein. The White Ojibway Medicine Man & Other Stories. 2009. 192p. 26.95 (978-0-595-71431-5(5)); pap. 16.95 (978-0-595-46622-1(2)) iUniverse, Inc.

Juma, Florence Akumu. All Things Work Together for Good. 2010. (978-1-926676-97-5(1)) Word Alive Pr.

June D. Swadron. Re-Write Your Life: A Transformational Guide to Writing & Healing the Stories of Our Lives. 2009. 272p. 31.50 (978-1-4269-2064-6(4)); pap. 21.50 (978-1-4251-0294-4(8)) Trafford Publishing.

Just Love Her: A Mother's Journey of Healing Through Her Daughter's Drug Addiction. 2007. per. 13.95 (978-0-9793515-0-1(2)) Lifeguide House.

Kain, Conrad. Where the Clouds Can Go, 1 vol. 2009. (ENG., Illus.). 560p. pap. (978-1-897522-45-5(2)) Rocky Mountain Bks.

Karram, Kerry. Four Degrees Celsius: A Story of Arctic Peril. 2012. (ENG., Illus.). 224p. pap. 22.99 (978-1-4597-0051-2(1)) Natural Heritage/Natural History, Inc. CAN. Dist: Ingram Pub. Services.

Kawatski, Deanna. Wilderness Mother: The Chronicles of a Modern Pioneer. (Illus.). 208p. 14.95 (978-1-55110-168-2(8)) Whitecap Bks., Ltd. CAN. Dist: Graphic Arts Ctr. Publishing Co.

Kay, Linda. The Sweet Sixteen: The Journey That Inspired the Canadian Women's Press Club. 2012. (ENG., Illus.). 224p. (C). (978-0-7735-3967-9(0)) McGill-Queen's Univ. Pr.

Kearney, Mark & Ray, Randy. Whatever Happened To ... ? Catching up with Canadian Icons. 2006. (ENG., Illus.). 264p. pap. 21.99 (978-1-55002-654-2(2), Hounslow Pr.) Dundurn CAN. Dist: Ingram Pub. Services.

Keegan, Rebecca. The Futurist: The Life & Films of James Cameron. 2010. (ENG.). 304p. pap. 15.00 (978-0-307-46032-5(0), Three Rivers Pr.) Crown Publishing Group.

Keeling, Frank D. Nobody's Son. 2007. (Illus.). 321p. 24.98 (978-1-4251-1710-8(4)) Trafford Publishing.

Keithley, Joe. Talk - Action = Zero: An Illustrated History of D. O. A. 2011. (ENG., Illus.). 224p. pap. 27.95 (978-1-55152-396-5(5)) Arsenal Pulp Pr. CAN. Dist: Consortium Bk. Sales & Distribution.

Keller, Keith. Zella's Story. 2010. 304p. (978-1-926582-52-8(7)); pap. (978-1-926582-51-1(9)) Insomniac Pr.

Kelly, Deirdre. Paris Times Eight: Finding Myself in the City of Dreams, 1 vol. 2009. (ENG.). 320p. pap. 16.95 (978-1-55365-268-7(1), Greystone Bks.) D&M Pubs. Inc. CAN. Dist: Perseus-PGW.

Kelly, John Joseph. A Taste for Speed: The Biography of Will Braden: Canada's Top Raceboat Driver 1915-1958. 2010. 188p. pap. 22.95 (978-1-4502-4789-4(X)) iUniverse, Inc.

Kennedy, Des. An Ecology of Enchantment: A Year in the Life of a Garden, 1 vol. 10th ed. 2008. (ENG.). 336p. pap. 18.95 (978-1-55365-370-7(X), Greystone Bks.) D&M Pubs. Inc. CAN. Dist: Perseus-PGW.

—The Way of a Gardener: A Life's Journey, 1 vol. 2010. (ENG.). 272p. pap. 17.95 (978-1-55365-417-9(X), Greystone Bks.) D&M Pubs. Inc. CAN. Dist: Perseus-PGW.

Kennedy, Sheldon. Why I Didn't Say Anything: The Sheldon Kennedy Story. 2006. (ENG., Illus.). 240p. (978-1-897178-07-2(7)) Insomniac Pr.

Kennedy, Stephen J. A Search for There. 2011. 116p. 22.95 (978-1-4502-9378-5(6)); pap. 12.95 (978-1-4502-9376-1(X)) iUniverse, Inc.

Kenney, Sue. Confessions of a Pilgrim. 2007. 256p. per. 18.95 (978-0-595-42790-1(1)) iUniverse, Inc.

Kerans, Marion Douglas. A Legacy of Love: Remembering Muriel Duckworth, Her Later Years 1996-2009. 2011. (ENG.). 96p. pap. 14.95 (978-1-55266-381-3(7)) Fernwood Publishing Co., Ltd. CAN. Dist: Independent Pubs. Group.

Kerenyi, Norbert. Stories of a Survivor. 2011. 434p. 34.99 (978-1-4535-9759-0(X)); pap. 23.99 (978-1-4535-9758-3(1)) Xlibris Corp.

Khan, Farheen. Behind the Veil: A Hijabi's Journey to Happiness. 2010. (ENG.). 153p. pap. 15.95 (978-1-897404-23-2(9)) Burman Books, Inc. CAN. Dist: Innovative Logistics.

Kielley, Kim. Rex Goudie Idolized. 2006. (Illus.). 84p. per. (978-1-897174-13-5(6)) Creative Bk. Publishing.

Kilrea, Brian & Duthie, James. They Call Me Killer: Tales from Junior Hockey's Legendary Hall-of-Fame Coach. 2010. (ENG., Illus.). 288p. 29.95 (978-0-470-67742-1(2), Wiley) Wiley, John & Sons, Inc.

King, Olivia. Michael Buble: Crazy Life. 2012. (ENG., Illus.). 144p. 17.95 (978-1-4091-4033-7(4)) Orion Bks. Ltd. GBR. Dist: Sterling Publishing Co., Inc.

Kirby, Mary-Ann. I Am Hutterite: The Fascinating Story of a Young Woman's Journey to Reclaim Her Heritage. l.t. ed. 2011. 448p. pap. 17.99 (978-1-59415-390-7(6)) Cengage Gale.

Kiriloff, Nikita. Voice Over: Memoir of an Interpreter. 2011. (ENG., Illus.). 256p. pap. (978-0-7766-0758-0(8)) Univ. of Ottawa Pr./Presses de l'Universite d'Ottawa.

Kirkpatrick, David. In Praise of Strong Women: A Psychiatrist's Memoir. 2009. (ENG.). 320p. pap. (978-1-894694-70-4(8)) Granville Island Publishing.

Klassen, Mari. Another Hannah. 2011. (978-1-77069-268-8(1)) Word Alive Pr.

Knowles, Valerie. From Telegrapher to Titan: The Life of William C. Van Horne. 2010. (Railroads Past & Present Ser.). (ENG., Illus.). 504p. pap. 29.95 (978-0-253-22250-3(8), 0253222508) Indiana Univ. Pr.

Kopas, Cliff. No Path but My Own: Horseback Adventures in the Chilcotin & the Rockies. unabr. ed. (ENG., Illus.). 224p. 26.95 (978-1-55017-151-8(8)) Harbour Publishing Co., Ltd. CAN. Dist: Ingram Pub. Services

Kostash, Myrna, et al. Her Own Woman. (ENG.). 212p. pap. (978-0-88780-128-0(5), Goodreads) Formac Publishing Co., Ltd.

Kotliar, Leonid. Eleven Months. 2010. 96p. pap. 10.49 (978-1-4490-6071-8(4)) AuthorHouse.

Kramer, Reinhold & Mitchell, Tom. When the State Trembled: How A. J. Andrews & the Citizens Broke the Winnipeg General Strike. 2010. (Canadian Social History Ser.). (ENG., Illus.). 464p. (978-1-4426-4219-5(X)); pap. (978-1-4426-1116-0(2)) Univ. of Toronto Pr.

Krause, Pat. Acts of Love: A Memoir. 2008. (ENG.). 256p. per. (978-1-55050-368-5(5)) Coteau Bks.

Kroll, Bob. Rogues & Rascals: Stories of Maritimes Lives & Legends, 1 vol. 2012. (ENG.). 213p. pap. 17.95 (978-1-55109-864-7(4)) Down East Bks.

Kuich, Brad. Hag'Em: Memoirs of a Police Dog Handler. 2008. 304p. pap. 15.49 (978-1-4389-0599-0(8)) AuthorHouse.

Kumar, Parvez. The Cry of the Eagle: The Life & Times of an Aerospace Engineer. 2008. (Illus.). xvi, 533p. 35.00 (978-1-4251-3978-0(7)) Trafford Publishing.

Laarhuis, Joseph & Majeau, Mary. The Eventful Life of a Dutch Farmer's Son: From Prisoner of War #47211 to Canadian Farmer. 2011. 148p. pap. 22.99 (978-1-4251-2792-3(4)) Trafford Publishing.

Lade, Kurt. Born into Fascism & WW II, 1 vol. 2009. 201p. pap. 24.95 (978-1-60749-861-2(8)) PublishAmerica, Inc.

Ladha, Mansoor. A Portrait in Pluralism: The Aga Khan's Shia Ismailis. 2007. (Illus.). 238p. 27.95 (978-1-55059-353-2(6)) Detselig Enterprises, Ltd. CAN. Dist: Temeron Bks., Inc.

Lajoie, Roger & Henderson, Paul. The Goal of My Life: A Memoir. 2012. (ENG.). 304p. 29.99 (978-0-7710-4650-6(2), McClelland & Stewart) McClelland & Stewart CAN. Dist: Random Hse., Inc.

Lakusta, Ernie. The Intrepid Explorer: James Hector's Explorations in the Canadian Rockies, 1 vol. 2007. (ENG., Illus.). 240p. pap. 17.99 (978-1-894856-82-9(1)) Fifth Hse. Pubs. CAN. Dist: Ingram Pub. Services.

Lam, Vincent. Tommy Douglas. 2011. (ENG.). 204p. (gr. 12). 19.95 (978-0-670-06851-7(9), Penguin Global) Penguin Group (USA) Inc.

Lambert, Barbara Ann. Old-Time Stories: Billy-Goat Smith, a Powell River Co. Xmas, Mr. Dipple, & Others. 2006. (Illus.). 244p. per. 21.74 (978-1-4251-0039-1(2)) Trafford Publishing.

Lampard, Louise. A Year in My Shoes: A Cancer Survivor's Story. 2007. 148p. (ENG.). 24.95 (978-0-595-70586-3(3)); per. 14.95 (978-0-595-46081-6(X)) iUniverse, Inc.

Lang, Michale. Bears: Tracks Through Time, 1 vol. 2010. (ENG., Illus.). 128p. pap. (978-1-897522-82-0(7)) Rocky Mountain Bks.

Langton, Jerry. Fighter: The Unauthorized Biography of Georges St-Pierre, UFC Champion. 2011. (ENG.). 240p. 26.95 (978-1-118-00803-4(0), Wiley) Wiley, John & Sons, Inc.

Lanois, Daniel. Soul Mining: A Musical Life, 1 vol. (ENG., Illus.). 240p. 2011. pap. 15.00 (978-0-86547-859-6(7)) 2010. 26.00 (978-0-86547-934-5(4)) Faber & Faber, Inc.

Lanteigne, Florent. The Fisherman's Wife. 2012. (ENG.). 125p. pap. 14.95 (978-0-9865278-9-0(0)) DreamCatcher Publishing CAN. Dist: Univ. of Toronto Pr.

Larocque, Peter J. & Buckland, Peter. Portraits: New Brunswick Painters = Peintres du Nouveau-Brunswick. 2009. (FRE & ENG., Illus.). 160p. pap. 30.00 (978-0-919326-62-0(5)) New Brunswick Museum CAN. Dist: Univ. of Toronto Pr.

Larsen, Andrew, et al. Paul Martin: A Political Biography. 2011. (ENG.). 172p. (C). pap. 24.95 (978-1-55277-735-0(9)) Lorimer, James & Co., Ltd., Pubs. CAN. Dist: Casemate Pubs. & Bk. Distributors, LLC.

Larsen, Wayne. Tom Thomson: Artist of the North. 2011. (Quest Biography Ser.). (ENG., Illus.). 189p. pap. 19.99 (978-1-55488-772-9(0)) Dundurn CAN. Dist: Ingram Pub. Services.

Lasley, Mike. Through the Eyes of an Orphan. 2007. 158p. pap. (978-0-9679032-4-8(6)) Miami Graphics Services, Inc.

Lavis, Rose. Rose's World. 2007. 292p. (ENG.). 31.95 (978-0-595-71195-6(2)); per. 21.95 (978-0-595-47559-9(0)) iUniverse, Inc.

Lawrence Foort. Child of the Storm: The adventures of a west coast Kid. 2010. 364p. pap. 24.73 (978-1-4269-1555-0(1)) Trafford Publishing.

Lawrence, Mary. My People, Myself. unabr. ed. (ENG., Illus.). 254p. pap. (978-0-920576-59-5(1)) Caitlin Pr., Inc.

Lazier, Mary R. I'd Rather Be A Mermaid. 2008. 254p. pap. 29 50 (978-1-4357-0557-9(2)) Lulu Enterprises Inc.

Leavey, Peggy Dymond. Laura Secord: Heroine of the War of 1812. 2012. (Quest Biography Ser.). (ENG., Illus.). 224p. pap. 19.99 (978-1-4597-0366-7(9)) Dundurn CAN. Dist: Ingram Pub. Services.

Leddy, Mary Jo. Our Friendly Local Terrorist. 2010. 207p. pap. 24.95 (978-1-897071-60-1(4)) Between the Lines CAN. Dist: Univ. of Toronto Pr.

Lee, J. J. The Measure of a Man: The Story of a Father, a Son, & a Suit. (ENG.). 304p. 2012. pap. 19.99 (978-0-7710-4648-3(0), Emblem Edns) 2011. (Illus.). 29.99 (978-0-7710-4647-6(2), McClelland & Stewart) McClelland & Stewart CAN. Dist: Random Hse., Inc.

Lee, John B. Left Hand Horses. 2007. (ENG., Illus.). 96p. pap. 16.00 (978-0-88753-441-6(4)) Black Moss Pr. CAN. Dist: LitDistCo.

Lemke, Helmut. A Life Fully Lived: Loving Hildegard. 2010. 428p. pap. 22.20 (978-1-4520-3719-6(1)) AuthorHouse.

Lennox, Doug. Now You Know Canada's Heroes. 2009. (Now You Know Ser.). (ENG.). 192p. pap. 19.99 (978-1-55488-444-5(6)) Dundurn CAN. Dist: Ingram Pub. Services.

Lennox, Muriel. The Horse & the Tiger. 2010. (978-0-9699025-5-3(7)) Beach Hse. Bks.

Leochko, Larry. The Moose House: The Devil in the Closet. 2007. 132p. per. 13.95 (978-0-595-45855-4(6)) iUniverse, Inc.

Lescheid, Helen Grace. Lead Kindly Light: A mother's escape from Communist Russia during World War II. 2009. 284p. pap. 15.99 (978-1-4141-1356-2(0)) Pleasant Word.

Levine, Allan. King: William Lyon Mackenzie King: A Life Guided by the Hand of Destiny, 1 vol. 2012. (ENG., Illus.). 552p. 36.95 (978-1-55365-560-2(5)) D&M Pubs. Inc. CAN. Dist: Perseus-PGW.

Levy, Paul. River Queen: The Amazing Story of Tugboat Titan Lucille Johnstone. unabr. ed. 2006. (ENG., Illus.). 272p. 34.95 (978-1-55017-369-7(3)) Harbour Publishing Co., Ltd. CAN. Dist: Ingram Pub. Services.

Levy, Robyn Michele. Most of Me: Surviving My Medical Meltdown, 1 vol. 2012. (ENG.). 256p. pap. 16.95 (978-1-55365-632-6(6), Greystone Bks.) D&M Pubs. Inc. CAN. Dist: Perseus-PGW.

Lewis, Laurie. Little Comrades. 2011. (ENG., Illus.). 216p. pap. 22.95 (978-0-88984-342-4(2)) Porcupine's Quill, Inc. CAN. Dist: Univ. of Toronto Pr.

Lewry, David. Channel of the Broken Gun. 2010. 280p. pap. 21.95 (978-0-557-32763-8(6)) Lulu Enterprises Inc.

C

Li, Ling. Constructing Teacher's Professional Identity in China & Canada: Life Stories in Context. 2008. 280p. pap. (978-3-639-09503-6(0)) VDM Verlag Dr. Mueller e.K.

Lillebuen, Steve. The Devil's Cinema: The Untold Story Behind Mark Twitchell's Kill Room. 2012. (ENG., Illus.). 352p. 27.95 (978-0-7710-5033-6(X), McClelland & Stewart) McClelland & Stewart CAN. Dist: Random Hse., Inc.

Lin, Paul. In the Eye of the China Storm: A Life Between East & West. 2011. (Illus.). 256p. (C). (978-0-7735-3857-3(7)) McGill-Queen's Univ. Pr.

Lind, Jane, ed. Joyce Wieland: Writings & Drawings, 1952-1971. 2009. (ENG., Illus.). 224p. pap. 27.95 (978-0-88984-321-9(X)) Porcupine's Quill, Inc. CAN. Dist: Univ. of Toronto Pr.

Lister, Kenneth R., text. Paul Kane, the Artist: Wilderness to Studio. 2010. (ENG.). 416p. 75.00 (978-0-88854-480-3(4)) Royal Ontario Museum CAN. Dist: Univ. of Toronto Pr.

Livesque, Andrie. Red Travellers: Jeanne Corbin & Her Comrades. Klein, Yvonne M., tr. from FRE. 2006. (Footprints Ser.). (ENG., Illus.). 248p. (C). (978-0-7735-3125-3(4)) McGill-Queen's Univ. Pr.

Loiselle, Micheline. Life Lessons & Deep Thoughts: How True Life Can Be!! 2010. 52p. pap. 10.49 (978-1-4490-1456-8(9)) AuthorHouse.

Loney, James. Captivity: 118 Days in Iraq & the Struggle for a World Without War. 2011. (ENG.). 432p. 27.95 (978-0-307-39927-4(3)) Knopf Canada CAN. Dist: Random Hse., Inc.

—Captivity: 118 Days in Iraq & the Struggle for a World Without War. 2012. (ENG.). 432p. pap. 18.00 (978-0-307-39928-1(1), Vintage Canada) Random Hse. of Canada, Ltd. CAN. Dist: Random Hse., Inc.

Loranger, Patricia L. Child of Woe, Child of Sorrow. 2011. (978-1-77069-258-9(4)) Word Alive Pr.

Louis, Shirley. Q'Sapi: A History of Okanagan People As Told by Okanagan Families, 1 vol. 2nd ed. 2008. (ENG., Illus.). 262p. pap. 24.95 (978-1-894778-64-0(2)) Theytus Bks., Ltd. CAN. Dist: Univ. of Toronto Pr.

Lual, Chagai Chol. How Childhood Hardship Prepared Me for Life. 2009. 172p. pap. 25.98 (978-1-4269-0147-8(X)) Trafford Publishing.

Lukasiewicz, Julius. Rue Lukasiewicz: Glimpses of a Life. 2011. (ENG., Illus.). 392p. 40.00 (978-1-894908-08-5(2)) Golden Dog Pr. CAN. Dist: Univ. of Toronto Pr.

Lumley, Elizabeth. Canadian Who's Who 2009. 2009. (Canadian Who's Who on CD-ROM Ser.). (ENG.). cd-rom (978-0-8020-4093-0(4)) Univ. of Toronto Pr.

Lyall, Ernie. An Arctic Man: The Classic Account of Sixty-Five Years in Canada's North. 3rd rev. ed. 2011. (ENG., Illus.). 222p. pap. 19.95 (978-0-88780-945-3(6)) Formac Publishing Co., Ltd. CAN. Dist: Casemate Pubs. & Bk. Distributors, LLC.

Lybbert, Lyle R. The Night of the Cougar: Memories I Could Do Without. 2010. 136p. 26.95 (978-1-4269-0054-9(6)); pap. 16.95 (978-1-4269-0053-2(8)) Trafford Publishing.

Ma, Yuan. Yuan M: Childhood Memories. 2011. 88p. pap. 51.99 (978-1-4628-9635-6(9)) Xlibris Corp.

MacDonald, Cheryl. Isaac Brock: Canada's Hero in the War of 1812. 2012. (Amazing Stories Ser.). (ENG.). 128p. pap. 9.95 (978-1-4594-0059-7(3)) Lorimer, James & Co., Ltd., Pubs. CAN. Dist: Casemate Pubs. & Bk. Distributors, LLC.

MacDonald, Kyle. One Red Paperclip: Or How an Ordinary Man Achieved His Dream with the Help of a Simple Office Supply. 2007. (ENG., Illus.). 320p. pap. 13.95 (978-0-307-35316-0(8), Three Rivers Pr.) Crown Publishing Group.

MacEwan, Grant. Eye Opener Bob: The Story of Bob Edwards, 1 vol. Martin, James, ed. annot. ed. (ENG., Illus.). 224p. pap. 16.95 (978-0-9732481-6-6(5)) Brindle & Glass Publishing CAN. Dist: Literary Pr. Group of Canada.

MacGregor, Roy. Northern Light. 2011. (ENG., Illus.). 400p. pap. 19.50 (978-0-307-35740-3(6), Vintage Canada) Random Hse. of Canada, Ltd. CAN. Dist: Random Hse., Inc.

—Wayne Gretzky's Ghost: And Other Tales from a Lifetime in Hockey. 2012. (ENG.). 368p. pap. 17.95 (978-0-307-35742-7(2), Vintage Canada) Random Hse. of Canada, Ltd. CAN. Dist: Random Hse., Inc.

—Wayne Gretzky's Ghost: And Other Tales from a Lifetime in Hockey. 2011. (ENG., Illus.). 400p. 25.99 (978-0-307-35741-0(4), Random Hse CAN) Random Hse. of Canada, Ltd. CAN. Dist: Random Hse., Inc.

Mack, Clayton. Bella Coola Man: More Stories of Clayton Mack. Thommasen, Harvey, ed. unabr. ed. (ENG., Illus.). 240p. 28.95 (978-1-55017-104-4(6)) Harbour Publishing Co., Ltd. CAN. Dist: Ingram Pub. Services.

MacKay, Donald. Safe Passage: Travels Through the Twentieth Century. 2010. 232p. pap. 27.95 (978-1-896941-61-5(3)) Brass, Robin Studio, Inc. CAN. Dist: Midpoint Trade Bks., Inc.

MacKay, Sandra Yuen. My Schizophrenic Life: The Road to Recovery. 2010. 206p. pap. (978-0-9810037-9-5(6)) Bridgeross Communications Inc.

Mackintosh, Joe. Andy de Jarlis: The Life & Music of an Old-Time Fiddler. 2010. (ENG.). 168p. pap. 24.95 (978-1-926531-05-2(1)) Great Plains Pubns. CAN. Dist: Univ. of Toronto Pr.

MacLaren, Roy D. The Fundamental Things Apply: A Memoir. 2011. (ENG., Illus.). 296p. (C). (978-0-7735-3843-6(7)) McGill-Queen's Univ. Pr.

Maclennan, Roderick Ward & Goss, Chris. The Ideals & Training of a Flying Officer. 2009. (Illus.). 104p. pap. 12.95 (978-0-85979-130-4(0)) Crecy Publishing GBR. Dist: Crecy Publishing.

MacQuarrie, Patricia. Deadly Canadian Women: The Stories Behind the Crimes of Canada's Most Notorious Women. 2008. (ENG., Illus.). 256p. pap. (978-0-9783409-2-6(2)) Quagmire Pr., Ltd. CAN. Dist: Lone Pine Publishing.

Maddigan, Debbie. A Little Girl Called Squeaks: A Story of Hope. 2011. 344p. 35.00 (978-1-4567-5406-8(8)); pap. 26.58 (978-1-4567-5405-1(X)) AuthorHouse.

Mahler, Ron. My Fanatical, Regrettable Tour of Ministry. 2011. 296p. pap. (978-1-77069-305-0(X)) Word Alive Pr.

The Makers of Canada, 21 vol., set. (Makers of Canada Ser.). reprint ed. 2625.00 (978-0-7222-6892-6(0)) Library Reprints, Inc.

Makkannaw, Rita. I Am White: Eagle Woman Flies with Raven. 2011. 340p. 29.52 (978-1-4269-5152-7(3)); pap. 19.52 (978-1-4269-5151-0(5)) Trafford Publishing.

Malanchuk, Terry. Blakeburn-British Columbia's Forgotten Ghost Town-Revised Second Edition. 2008. 228p. pap. 24.95 (978-0-557-03095-8(1)) Lulu Enterprises Inc.

—It was a good Blakeburn. 2008. 167p. pap. 22.51 (978-0-557-03094-1(3)) Lulu Enterprises Inc.

Maloney, Sean. Fighting for Afghanistan. 2011. (Illus.). 352p. 36.95 (978-1-59114-509-7(0)) Naval Institute Pr.

The Man from Grizzly Creek. 2008. per. 17.95 (978-0-9779953-1-8(3)) Man from Grizzly Creek, The.

Manion, Gene. Flying on the Edge. 2011. 384p. pap. 19.99 (978-1-4568-4057-0(6)) Xlibris Corp.

Mansbridge, Peter. Peter Mansbridge One on One: Favourite Conversations & the Stories Behind Them. 2010. (ENG., Illus.). 352p. pap. 19.50 (978-0-307-35785-4(6), Vintage Canada) Random Hse. of Canada, Ltd. CAN. Dist: Random Hse., Inc.

Maraj, Frank. Snapshots II: Navigating the University Years. 2011. 464p. 33.99 (978-1-4269-5321-7(6)); pap. 23.99 (978-1-4269-5322-4(4)) Trafford Publishing.

Marcone, Massimo. Acquired Tastes: On the Trail of the World's Most Sought-after Delicacies. 2010. (ENG., Illus.). 256p. pap. 16.95 (978-1-55470-279-4(8)) Key Porter Bks. CAN. Dist: Perseus-PGW.

Marcone, Massimo Francesco. In Bad Taste: The Adventures & Science Behind Food Delicacies. 2010. (ENG., Illus.). 198p. pap. 16.95 (978-1-55470-288-6(7)) Key Porter Bks. CAN. Dist: Perseus-PGW.

Marks, Don. They Call Me Chief: Warriors on Ice. 2008. (ENG., Illus.). 280p. pap. 27.95 (978-1-897289-34-1(0)) Shillingford, J. Gordon Publishing CAN. Dist: Univ. of Toronto Pr.

Maron, Doris. Untamed Spirit II: Living a Dream. 2010. 272p. pap. 20.95 (978-1-4502-3277-7(9)) iUniverse, Inc.

Marshall, Debbie. Give Your Other Vote to the Sister: A Woman's Journey into the Great War. 2007. (Legacies Shared Ser.). (ENG., Illus.). 338p. per. 29.95 (978-1-55238-228-8(1)) Univ. of Calgary Pr. CAN. Dist: Chicago Distribution Ctr.

Martin, Bernice Medbury & Stevenson, Jane. The Railroader's Wife: Letters from the Grand Trunk Pacific Railway. unabr. ed. 2010. (ENG., Illus.). 196p. pap. 24.95 (978-1-894759-43-4(5)) Caitlin Pr., Inc. CAN. Dist: Partners Pubs. Group, Inc.

Martin, Nora. Little Person, Long Journey: Theresa's Story. 2011. 80p. 24.99 (978-1-4568-9004-9(2)); pap. 15.99 (978-1-4568-9003-2(4)) Xlibris Corp.

Martin, Paul. Hell or High Water: My Life in & out of Politics. 2009. (Illus.). 504p. pap. 18.95 (978-0-7710-5693-2(1), Emblem Edns) McClelland & Stewart CAN. Dist: Random Hse., Inc.

Martz, Fraidie. A Fiery Soul: The Life & Theatrical Times of John Hirsch. 2012. (ENG., Illus.). 328p. pap. 22.00 (978-1-55065-319-9(9)) Vehicule Pr. CAN. Dist: Independent Pubs. Group.

Masetti, Jorge. In the Pirate's Den: My Life as a Secret Agent for Castro. 2006. (Illus.). 164p. reprint ed. 25.00 (978-1-4223-5885-6(2)) DIANE Publishing Co.

Matthias, Otto. When the Fire goes Out: A Journey to the Spirit World. 2010. 108p. (ENG.). 22.50 (978-1-4269-3191-8(3)); pap. 12.50 (978-1-4269-3190-1(5)) Trafford Publishing.

Maturié, Pierre. Man Proposes, God Disposes: Recollections of a French Pioneer. Bosley, Vivian, tr. from FRE. 2011. (Our Lives: Diary, Memoir, & Letters Ser.). (ENG.). 260p. (C). pap. 32.95 (978-1-926836-55-3(3)) Athabasca University Pr. CAN. Dist: Univ. of Washington Pr.

Mayse, Arthur. My Father, My Friend. unabr. ed. (ENG.). 168p. pap. (978-1-55017-086-3(4)) Harbour Publishing Co., Ltd.

Mayse, Susan. Ginger: The Life & Death of Albert Goodwin. unabr. ed. (ENG., Illus.). 236p. (978-1-55017-018-4(X)) Harbour Publishing Co., Ltd.

McBride, Herbert W. A Rifleman Went to War. 2011. 416p. pap. 13.95 (978-1-61427-167-3(4)); pap. 14.65 (978-1-61427-063-8(5)) Martino Publishing.

McBurney, Margaret, ed. It's All about Kindness: Remembering June Callwood. 2010. (ENG.). 256p. 20.00 (978-1-897151-79-2(9)) Cormorant Bks. Inc. CAN. Dist: Univ. of Toronto Pr.

McCarthy, Gerald J. & Partridge, David. A Man of Substances: The Misdeeds & Growing Pains of a Pot Pioneer. 2010. 256p. 29.95 (978-1-4502-2469-7(5)); pap. 19.95 (978-1-4502-2468-0(7)) iUniverse, Inc.

Mccaw, Stewart. Galloping to Space. 2011. (Illus.). 104p. pap. 15.66 (978-1-4567-9363-0(2)) AuthorHouse.

McClinchey, Gregory W. Stickin' to His Guns. 2007. 204p. per. 16.95 (978-0-595-43836-5(9)) iUniverse, Inc.

—Stickin' to His Guns: A Through-the-Keyhole Look at Mr. Paul Daniel Steckle. 2007. 204p. 26.95 (978-0-595-68351-2(7)) iUniverse, Inc.

McConnell, Terry, et al. I'd Trade Him Again: On Gretzky, Politics, & the Pursuit of the Perfect Deal. 2009. (ENG., Illus.). 304p. 27.95 (978-1-55168-366-9(0)) Key Porter Bks. CAN. Dist: Perseus-PGW.

McCoy, Heath. Pain & Passion: The History of Stampede Wrestling. 2007. (ENG., Illus.). 336p. pap. 19.95 (978-1-55022-787-1(4)) ECW Pr. CAN. Dist: Independent Pubs. Group.

McCrorie, James N. The Guy in the Green Truck: John St. Amand - A Biography. 2010. (ENG., Illus.). 176p. pap. 22.95 (978-1-55266-324-0(8)) Fernwood Publishing Co., Ltd. CAN. Dist: Independent Pubs. Group.

McCutcheon, Malcolm. Babies & Soldiers for the King. 2009. (ENG.). 163p. pap. 14.95 (978-0-9810721-8-0(6)) DreamCatcher Publishing CAN. Dist: Univ. of Toronto Pr.

McDiarmid, Joy S. Clickety Clack: My Bipolar Express. 2010. (ENG., Illus.). 189p. pap. 19.95 (978-1-926577-02-9(7)) Dundurn CAN. Dist: Ingram Pub. Services.

McDonald, Sharen. A Gentleman & a Scholar. (Illus.). 192p. pap. (978-1-896754-02-4(3)) Shoreline.

McFarlane, Brian. From the Broadcast Booth: A Career in the World of Network Hockey. 2009. (ENG., Illus.). 256p. 27.95 (978-1-55168-327-0(X)) Key Porter Bks. CAN. Dist: Perseus-PGW.

McIntyre, Mike. Devil among Us: How Canada Failed to Stop a Pedophile. 2008. (ENG.). 320p. mass mkt. 11.95 (978-1-894283-80-9(5)) Great Plains Pubns. CAN. Dist: Univ. of Toronto Pr.

McKenty, Neil. The Inside Story: A Former Jesuit Priest's Story of Self-Discovery. 160p. pap. (978-1-896754-01-7(5)) Shoreline.

McKenzie, Bob. Hockey Dad: True Confessions from a (Crazy) Hockey Parent. 2009. (ENG., Illus.). 288p. 24.95 (978-0-470-15939-2(1), Wiley) Wiley, John & Sons, Inc.

Mckillop, Brian. Pierre Berton: A Biography. 2010. (ENG., Illus.). 808p. pap. 21.00 (978-0-7710-5756-4(3), Emblem Edns) McClelland & Stewart CAN. Dist: Random Hse., Inc.

McKirdy, Margaret. The Colour of Gold. unabr. ed. (ENG., Illus.). 208p. pap. (978-0-920576-66-3(4)) Caitlin Pr., Inc.

McMaster, Susan. The Gargoyle Ears. 2007. (ENG., Illus.). 112p. pap. 17.00 (978-0-88753-443-0(0)) Black Moss Pr. CAN. Dist: LitDistCo.

McMurren, Irving. The Abernathy Chronicles, Part One. 2008. 296p. pap. 17.50 (978-1-4357-1388-8(5)) Lulu Enterprises Inc.

McNamara, Eugene. Irving's Coat: Windsor's Literary Renaissance. 2006. (ENG., Illus.). 80p. per. 15.00 (978-0-88753-421-8(X)) Black Moss Pr. CAN. Dist: LitDistCo.

McQuiston, James A. Captain Jack: Father of the Yukon. 2007. 268p. per. 22.95 (978-1-4327-1458-1(9)) Outskirts Pr., Inc.

Meadow, Charles. The Number One Dog in Victori. 2010. 232p. pap. 19.95 (978-1-4251-7500-9(7)) Trafford Publishing.

Meindl, Maria. Outside the Box: The Life & Legacy of Writer Mona Gould, the Grandmother I Thought I Knew. 2011. (ENG., Illus.). 304p. (C). (978-0-7735-3911-2(5)) McGill-Queen's Univ. Pr.

Mellanby, Ralph. Walking with Legends: The Real Stories of Hockey Night in Canada. 2007. (ENG., Illus.). 304p. 24.95 (978-1-55168-305-8(9)) Key Porter Bks. CAN. Dist: Perseus-PGW.

Mellanby, Ralph & Brophy, Mike. Walking with Legends: The Real Stories of Hockey Night in Canada. 2008. (ENG., Illus.). 304p. pap. 19.95 (978-1-55168-336-2(9)) Key Porter Bks. CAN. Dist: Perseus-PGW.

Melnick, Henry. By My Mother's Hand. 2011. 212p. pap. 18.00 (978-0-557-52253-8(6)) Lulu Enterprises Inc.

Mercredi, Morningstar. Morningstar: A Warrior's Spirit. 2006. (ENG.). 181p. per. 17.95 (978-1-55050-346-3(4)) Coteau Bks. CAN. Dist: Fitzhenry & Whiteside, Ltd.

Mesaros, M.D., Helen. Bravo Fortissimo Glenn Gould: The Mind of a Canadian Virtuoso. 2008. (Illus.). 471p. 34.95 (978-1-56167-985-0(2)) American Literary Pr.

Meyntz, Nelly. A Walk in My Wooden Shoes. 2007. 196p. per. 16.95 (978-0-595-47282-6(6)) iUniverse, Inc.

Mikkelsen, Glen. Checkered Courage: Chuckwagon Racing's Glass Family. (Illus.). 208p. pap. 19.95 (978-0-921835-62-2(0)) Johnson Gorman Bk. Pubs. CAN. Dist: Fitzhenry & Whiteside, Ltd.

Miller, Carman. A Knight in Politics: A Biography of Sir Frederick Borden. 2010. (ENG., Illus.). 416p. (C). (978-0-7735-3730-9(9)) McGill-Queen's Univ. Pr.

Milne, Carly. Sexography: One Woman's Journey from Ignorance to Bliss. 2007. 449p. 24.95 (978-1-59777-543-4(6)) Phoenix Bks., Inc.

Milnes, John E. Making a Difference: My First Forty Years as an Immigrant. 2011. 264p. 29.95 (978-1-4620-1311-1(2)); pap. 19.95 (978-1-4620-1309-8(0)) iUniverse, Inc.

Moggridge, Donald E. Harry Johnson: A Life in Economics. 2008. (Historical Perspectives on Modern Economics Ser.). (ENG., Illus.). 500p. 100.00 (978-0-521-87482-3(3)) Cambridge Univ. Pr.

Moodie, Susanna. Roughing it in the Bush: Or, Life in Canada. 2011. (Cambridge Library Collection - Women's Writing Ser.). (ENG.). 320p. pap. 24.99 (978-1-108-03361-9(X)); 304p. pap. 24.99 (978-1-108-03362-6(8)) Cambridge Univ. Pr.

—Roughing It in the Bush, or, Life in Canada. 2010. 314p. pap. 29.75 (978-1-143-14693-0(X)) 2008. 320p. 28.99 (978-0-559-30435-4(8)) 2008. 320p. pap. 29.75 (978-0-559-30434-7(X)) BiblioBazaar.

—Roughing It in the Bush, or, Life in Canada. 2009. 170p. pap. 19.99 (978-1-151-09566-4(4)) General Bks. LLC.

—Roughing It in the Bush; or, Life in Canada by Susanna Moodie + Part. 2006. 228p. per. 20.99 (978-1-4255-1925-4(3)) MPublishing.

—Roughing It in the Bush; or, Life in Canada by Susanna Moodie ++ Part1. 2006. 224p. per. 20.99 (978-1-4255-1855-4(9)) MPublishing.

Morgan, Henry James. The Canadian Men & Women of the Time, 2 vol., set. 1117p. reprint ed. 250.00 (978-0-7222-6891-9(2)) Library Reprints, Inc.

Morimoto, Tom. Breaking Trail: From Canada's Northern Frontier to the Oil Fields of Dubai, 1 vol. 2007. (ENG., Illus.). 296p. per. 18.99 (978-1-897252-17-8(X)) Fifth Hse. Pubs. CAN. Dist: Ingram Pub. Services.

Morneau, Hilda. Hilda Morneau: My Incredible Journey. 2011. (978-0-8280-2498-3(7)) Review & Herald Publishing Assn.

Morton, William Lewis, ed. Monck, Letters & Journals, 1863-1868: Canada from Government House at Confederation, No. 52. 395p. pap. 19.95 (978-0-7710-9752-2(2)) McClelland & Stewart CAN. Dist: Random Hse. of Canada, Ltd.

Mowat, Farley. Bay of Spirits: A Love Story. 2007. (ENG., Illus.). 320p. 25.95 (978-0-7867-1994-5(X)) Da Capo Pr., Inc.

—Bay of Spirits: A Love Story. 2007. (ENG., Illus.). 376p. pap. 18.95 (978-0-7710-6505-7(1), McClelland & Stewart) McClelland & Stewart CAN. Dist: Random Hse., Inc.

Muchnick, Irvin. Chris & Nancy: The True Story of the Benoit Murder-Suicide & Pro Wrestling's Cocktail of Death. 2009. (ENG., Illus.). 240p. pap. 19.95 (978-1-55022-902-8(8)) ECW Pr. CAN. Dist: Independent Pubs. Group.

Mullen, J. Ken. Saskatchewan Homestead: Book Four. 2007. (Illus.). 162p. pap. 15.85 (978-1-4251-2152-5(7)) Trafford Publishing.

Mulroney, Brian. Memoirs. 2008. (ENG., Illus.). 1152p. pap. 24.99 (978-0-7710-6485-2(3), Emblem Edns) McClelland & Stewart CAN. Dist: Random Hse., Inc.

Munro, Angus. A Full House-but Empty. 2007. 272p. per. 20.95 (978-0-595-43719-1(2)) iUniverse, Inc.

Munro, Sheila. Lives of Mothers & Daughters: Growing up with Alice Munro. 2008. (ENG., Illus.). 288p. per. 12.95 (978-1-4027-5763-1(8)) Union Square Pr.

Munro, Vera Gauley. The September Years. (Illus.). 170p. pap. (978-0-9695160-6-8(4)) Shoreline.

Murphy, Emily F. Janey Canuck in the West. 2008. (Illus.). 228p. pap. (978-1-4099-2370-1(3)) Dodo Pr.

Murray, Anne & Posner, Michael. All of Me. 2010. (ENG., Illus.). 352p. pap. 19.50 (978-0-307-39845-1(5), Vintage Canada) Random Hse. of Canada, Ltd. CAN. Dist: Random Hse., Inc.

Nadel, Ira Bruce. Various Positions: A Life of Leonard Cohen. 2007. (Jewish History, Life, & Culture Ser.). (ENG., Illus.). 360p. pap. 24.95 (978-0-292-71732-9(6)) Univ. of Texas Pr.

Nakamoto, Jack. Jack's Japonic. 2011. 272p. 29.99 (978-1-4568-5509-3(3)) Xlibris Corp.

Nash, Mike. The Mountain Knows No Expert: George Evanoff, Outdoorsman & Contemporary Hero. 2009. (ENG., Illus.). 320p. pap. 28.99 (978-1-55002-868-3(5)) Dundurn CAN. Dist: Ingram Pub. Services.

Naugle, George R. The Luckiest Hunter Still Alive. 2008. 252p. 23.95 (978-1-60594-021-2(6), Llumina Pr.) Aeon Publishing Inc.

Nemeth, Jason D. Edge, 1 vol. 2009. (Stars of Pro Wrestling Ser.). (ENG.). 32p. (gr. 3-4). lib. bdg. 27.32 (978-1-4296-3346-8(8), Edge Bks.) Capstone Pr., Inc.

Nemni, Max & Nemni, Monique. Trudeau Transformed: The Shaping of a Statesman 1944-1965. (ENG.). 2012. 352p. pap. 24.99 (978-0-7710-5127-2(1)) 2011. 544p. 32.99 (978-0-7710-5125-8(5)) McClelland & Stewart CAN. (McClelland & Stewart). Dist: Random Hse., Inc.

Newkey-Burden, Chas. Justin Bieber: The Unauthorized Biography. 2010. (ENG., Illus.). 224p. (YA). (gr. 3-7). 17.95 (978-1-84317-523-0(1)) O'Mara, Michael Bks., Ltd. GBR. Dist: Independent Pubs. Group.

Newman, Nancy & Barnholden, Michael. Street Stories: 100 Years of Homelessness in Vancouver. 2007. (ENG., Illus.). 144p. per. 16.00 (978-1-895636-85-7(X)) Anvil Pr. CAN. Dist: Univ. of Toronto Pr.

Newton, David. Kipling's Canadian. 2009. 300p. pap. 21.95 (978-1-4251-9141-2(X)) Trafford Publishing.

Nicolas, Ron. Living on the Edge: Coming of Age During Difficult Times. 2009. 96p. pap. 10.49 (978-1-4389-7824-6(3)) AuthorHouse.

Nielsen, Flemming. On Course for Adventure: The exciting life of a young Danish Immigrant. 2011. 548p. pap. 31.95 (978-1-4620-0016-6(9)) iUniverse, Inc.

Nilsen, George. A Syttende Mai Son. 2008. 209p. pap. 24.95 (978-1-60563-755-6(6)) PublishAmerica, Inc.

Nimegeers, Matthew T. Squatters & Friends of the Souris Valley. 2011. 162p. pap. 24.95 (978-1-4560-0491-0(3)) PublishAmerica, Inc.

Norquay, Margaret. Broad Is the Way: Stories from Mayerthorpe. 2008. (Life Writing Ser.). (ENG., Illus.). 120p. pap. 24.95 (978-1-55458-020-0(X)) Wilfrid Laurier Univ. Pr. CAN. Dist: Univ. of Toronto Pr.

Norris, Marjorie Barron, ed. Medicine & Duty: The World War I Memoir of Captain Harold W. Mcgill, Medical Officer, 31st Batallion C. E. F. 2007. (Legacies Shared Ser.). (ENG., Illus.). 406p. per. 39.95 (978-1-55238-193-9(5)) Univ. of Calgary Pr. CAN. Dist: Chicago Distribution Ctr.

Novak, Walter A. The Narrow Way. 2009. 200p. pap. 17.33 (978-1-4269-1575-8(6)) Trafford Publishing.

Nunn, Darrell & Russett, Donna. Faces of China: From Mao to Now. 2007. 308p. per. 21.95 (978-0-595-44456-4(3)) iUniverse, Inc.

Oakland, Roger. Let There Be Light: From Evolutionist to Creationist How One Man Left His Canadian Farm to Spread the Gospel Throughout the World. 2011. pap. (978-0-9846366-9-3(2)) Lighthouse Trails Publishing Co.

O'Connor, Mary Elizabeth & Tweedie, Katherine. Seduced by Modernity: The Photography of Margaret Watkins. 2007. (ENG., Illus.). 352p. (C). (978-0-7735-3119-2(X)) McGill-Queen's Univ. Pr.

O'Dea, Frank. When All You Have Is Hope. 2010. (ENG.). 240p. pap. 17.00 (978-0-14-305255-5(1), Penguin Global) Penguin Group (USA) Inc.

O'Flaherty, William. Tomcats & House Calls: Memoirs of a Country Doctor. 2012. (ENG.). 192p. pap. (978-1-927099-10-0(2), Boulder Pubns.

O'Keefe, Derrick. Michael Ignatieff: The Lesser Evil? 2011. (Counterblasts Ser.). (ENG.). 192p. pap. 16.95 (978-1-84467-615-6(3), 844615) Verso Bks. GBR. Dist: Norton, W. W. & Co., Inc.

Olafsen, Jake. Wearing the Green Beret: A Canadian with the Royal Marine Commandos. 2012. (ENG., Illus.). 304p. pap. 19.95 (978-0-7710-6857-7(3), McClelland & Stewart) McClelland & Stewart CAN. Dist: Random Hse., Inc.

Ollivier, Bert. Travel's My Game: Ollivier's My Name. 2008. (Illus.). vii, 185p. 23.95 (978-1-4251-2044-3(X)) Trafford Publishing.

Olszewski, Gary. Marjorie White: Her Life & Work. 2011. 118p. pap. 19.95 (978-1-59393-625-9(7)) BearManor Media.

Omasta, Michael, et al. John Cook: Viennese by Choice, Filmemacher Von Beruf. Omasta, Michae & Moller, Olaf, eds. 2007. (Austrian Film Museum Bks.). (GER & ENG., Illus.). 256p. (gr. 17). pap. 27.50 (978-3-901644-17-7(2)) Synema Gesellschaft fur Film u. Medien AUT. Dist: Columbia Univ. Pr.

Ore, Florence Bell. The Road Between. 2011. (ENG., Illus.). pap. 12.00 (978-0-9827377-6-7(9)) Raven Publishing Inc. of Montana.

O'Riordan, Dave. Bipolar Shoes: People Do Matter. 2009. 158p. pap. 20.99 (978-1-4389-2317-8(1)) AuthorHouse.

Ostryzniuk, Natalie. Blossoming of a Ukrainian Canadian: Savella Stechishin. 2009. 236p. pap. 19.95 (978-1-4269-0394-6(4)) Trafford Publishing.

Outlaws & Lawmen of Western Canada, 3 vols., Vol. 3. 2010. (Illus.). 160p. reprint ed. pap. (978-0-919214-88-0(6)) Heritage Hse.

Packard, Debbie. A Published Author At 58: Dreams Really Do Come True! 2011. 30p. pap. 16.95 (978-1-4560-0392-0(5)) PublishAmerica, Inc.

Padulo, Rick. I Can Get It for You Retail: Down & Dirty Tales from a Canadian Ad Man. 2012. (ENG., Illus.). 224p. 29.99 (978-1-4597-0500-5(9)) Dundurn CAN. Dist: Ingram Pub. Services.

Palmer, Mary. Jedediah Days: One Woman's Island Paradise. unabr. ed. 2007. (ENG., Illus.). 224p. pap. (978-1-55017-452-6(5)) Harbour Publishing Co., Ltd.

—Jedediah Days: One Woman's Island Paradise. unabr. ed. (ENG., Illus.). 224p. 26.95 (978-1-55017-184-6(4)) Harbour Publishing Co., Ltd. CAN. Dist: Ingram Pub. Services.

Palmer, Ron. A Hole in The Ocean. 2006. 184p. per. 17.39 (978-1-4251-0105-3(4)) Trafford Publishing.

Panofsky, Ruth. The Literary Legacy of the Macmillan Company of Canada: Making Books & Mapping Culture. 2012. (Studies in Book & Print Culture Ser.). (ENG.). 352p. (978-0-8020-9877-1(0)) Univ. of Toronto Pr.

Paquin, Ethel. Johana Harris: A Biography. 2011. (ENG.). 288p. (gr. 17). 65.00 (978-0-8108-7759-7(7)); E-Book (978-0-8108-7760-3(0)) Scarecrow Pr., Inc.

Parsons, Tony. A Life in the News. 2009. (ENG., Illus.). 288p. 32.95 (978-1-55017-461-8(4)) Harbour Publishing Co., Ltd. CAN. Dist: Ingram Pub. Services.

Parvis, Sarah. Justin Bieber. 2010. (ENG., Illus.). 80p. 5.99 (978-1-4494-0151-8(3)) Andrews McMeel Publishing.

Patterson, R. M. Trail to the Interior, 1 vol. 2007. (RM Patterson Collection Ser.). (ENG., Illus.). 288p. pap. (978-1-894898-50-8(8)) TouchWood Editions.

Pawley, Howard. Keep True: A Life in Politics. 2011. (ENG., Illus.). 304p. pap. 31.95 (978-0-88755-724-8(4)) Univ. of Manitoba Pr. CAN. Dist: Chicago Distribution Ctr.

Pearson, Patricia. A Brief History of Anxiety (Yours & Mine) 2009. (ENG.). 208p. pap. (978-0-679-31499-8(7), Vintage Canada) Random Hse. of Canada, Ltd. CAN. Dist: Random Hse., Inc.

Peart, Neil. Far & Away: A Prize Every Time. 2011. (ENG., Illus.). 312p. 29.95 (978-1-77041-058-9(9)) ECW Pr. CAN. Dist: Independent Pubs. Group.

Peel, Juliet. Michael Bublé: The Biography. 2009. (ENG., Illus.). 288p. 24.95 (978-0-7499-4158-3(3)) Piatkus Bks. GBR. Dist: Independent Pubs. Group.

Pegg, Ron. Giant among Giants. 2010. 156p. pap. (978-1-926676-82-1(3)) Word Alive Pr.

Penner, Barbara. To a Third Country. 2011. 322p. pap. (978-1-77069-204-6(5)) Word Alive Pr.

Penner, Roland. A Glowing Dream: A Memoir. 2007. (ENG., Illus.). 306p. pap. 24.95 (978-1-897289-19-8(7)) Shillingford, J. Gordon Publishing CAN. Dist: Univ. of Toronto Pr.

Perry, Aubrey. A Child's World, 1 vol. 2009. 124p. pap. 19.95 (978-1-60836-699-6(5)) PublishAmerica, Inc.

Pete Knight: The Cowboy King. 2007. pap. 18.95 (978-0-9771610-2-7(1)) Wild Horse Pr.

Peter Rowlands. Man on the Move: The Pete Friesen Story. 2009. 336p. 32.95 (978-1-4401-5957-2(2)); pap. 22.95 (978-1-4401-5955-8(6)) iUniverse, Inc.

Peterman, Michael A., ed. The Backwoods of Canada: Catharine Parr Traill, No. 11. 408p. (978-0-88629-311-6(1)) McGill-Queen's Univ. Pr.

Peters, Jason. Aboriginal Sport Heroes: Atlantic Canada. 2011. (ENG.). 125p. pap. 14.95 (978-0-9865278-7-6(4)) DreamCatcher Publishing CAN. Dist: Univ. of Toronto Pr.

Peters, Russell. Call Me Russell: My Family, My Friends, My Life. 2012. (ENG.). 256p. 24.95 (978-1-118-27067-7(3), Wiley) Wiley, John & Sons, Inc.

Phillips, Ray. The Little Green Valley: The Kleindale Story. 2010. (ENG., Illus.). 288p. pap. (978-1-55017-483-0(5)) Harbour Publishing Co., Ltd.

Pinsent, Gordon & Anthony, George. So Far So Good. 2012. (ENG., Illus.). 352p. 32.99 (978-0-7710-7137-9(X), McClelland & Stewart) McClelland & Stewart CAN. Dist: Random Hse., Inc.

Piro, Robert Vincent. When God Called on My Cellphone. 2011. 134p. 29.99 (978-1-4628-7208-4(5)); pap. 19.99 (978-1-4628-7207-7(7)) Xlibris Corp.

Pitman, Walter. Elmer Iseler: Choral Visionary. 2008. (ENG., Illus.). 352p. 40.00 (978-1-55002-815-7(4), Dundurn Pr.) Dundurn CAN. Dist: Ingram Pub. Services.

—Victor Feldbrill: Canadian Conductor Extraordinaire. 2010. (ENG., Illus.). 384p. 40.00 (978-1-55488-768-2(2)) Dundurn CAN. Dist: Ingram Pub. Services.

Pitt, Michael D. Beyond the End of the Road: A Winter of Contentment North of the Arctic Circle. 2009. (ENG., Illus.). 338p. pap. 19.95 (978-1-897435-35-6(3)) Agio Publishing Hse. CAN. Dist: Lightning Source, Inc.

Plaut, Jonathan V. The Jews of Windsor, 1790-1990: A Historical Chronicle. 2007. (ENG., Illus.). 320p. pap. 30.00 (978-1-55002-706-8(9), Dundurn Pr.) Dundurn CAN. Dist: Ingram Pub. Services.

Plourde, Joseph C. Rising from the Dark Side of Life: One Man's Spiritual Journey from Fear to Enlightenment. 2011. 168p. 25.95 (978-1-4502-1037-9(6)); pap. 15.95 (978-1-4502-1039-3(2)) iUniverse, Inc.

Plummer, Christopher. In Spite of Myself. 2012. (Vintage Ser.). (ENG., Illus.). 656p. pap. 17.95 (978-0-345-60322-1(1), Vintage) Knopf Doubleday Publishing Group.

Pocock, Geoffrey A. Outrider of Empire: The Life & Adventures of Roger Pocock. 2008. (ENG., Illus.). 400p. pap. 34.95 (978-0-88864-443-0(5)) Univ. of Alberta Pr. CAN. Dist: Michigan State Univ. Pr.

Podnieks, Andrew. Sid vs. Ovi: Crosby & Ovechkin - Natural Born Rivals. 2011. (ENG., Illus.). 320p. pap. 19.95 (978-0-7710-7116-4(7), McClelland & Stewart) McClelland & Stewart CAN. Dist: Random Hse., Inc.

Pohl, Herb. The Lure of Faraway Places: Reflections on Wilderness & Solitude. Raffan, James, ed. 2007. (ENG., Illus.). 232p. pap. 23.95 (978-1-897045-24-4(7)) Natural Heritage/Natural History, Inc. CAN. Dist: Ingram Pub. Services.

Poirier, Thelma, et al, eds. A Voice of Her Own. 2006. (Legacies Shared Ser.). (Illus.). 489p. per. 34.95 (978-1-55238-180-9(3)) Univ. of Calgary Pr. CAN. Dist: Michigan State Univ. Pr.

Poitras, Jacques. Beaverbrook: A Shattered Legacy. (ENG., 318p. 2007. Illus.). 30.00 (978-0-86492-497-1(6)) 2nd ed. 2008. pap. 19.95 (978-0-86492-522-0(0)) Goose Lane Editions CAN. Dist: Univ. of Toronto Pr.

Poling, Jim. Waking Nanabijou: Uncovering a Secret Past. 2007. (ENG., Illus.). 288p. pap. 26.99 (978-1-55002-757-0(3)) Natural Heritage/Natural History, Inc. CAN. Dist: Ingram Pub. Services.

Poliquin, Daniel. René Levesque. 2011. (ENG.). 204p. (gr. 12). 19.95 (978-0-670-06919-4(1), Penguin Global) Penguin Group (USA) Inc.

Pond, Marilyn. Never Say Whoa in a Bad Place. 2010. (Illus.). 226p. pap. 19.95 (978-1-57258-649-9(4)) TEACH Services, Inc.

Poplak, Richard, et al. Kenk: A Graphic Portrait. 2010. (Illus.). 304p. pap. 25.95 (978-0-9864884-0-5(2)) Pop Sandbox, Inc. CAN. Dist: Diamond Bk. Distributors.

Pound, Richard W. Unlucky to the End: The Story of Janise Marie Gamble. 2007. (ENG., Illus.). 272p. (978-0-7735-3300-4(1)) McGill-Queen's Univ. Pr.

Prakash, A. K. Independent Spirit: Early Canadian Women Artists. 2008. (ENG., Illus.). 408p. 75.00 (978-1-55407-417-4(7)) Firefly Bks., Ltd.

Pratte, Andre. Wilfrid Laurier. 2011. (ENG.). 204p. (gr. 12). 19.95 (978-0-670-06918-7(3), Penguin Global) Penguin Group (USA) Inc.

Press, Karen. Types of Canadian Women, Volume II. 2006. (ENG., Illus.). 128p. lthr. (978-1-55447-023-5(4)) Gaspereau Pr.

Price, Lily Hoy. I Am Full Moon: Stories of a Ninth Daughter, 1 vol. 2009. (ENG., Illus.). 192p. pap. (978-1-897142-38-7(2)) Brindle & Glass Publishing.

Primeau, Liz. My Natural History: The Evolution of a Gardener, 1 vol. 2008. (ENG.). 240p. 27.00 (978-1-55365-376-9(9), Greystone Bks.) D&M Pubs. Inc. CAN. Dist: Perseus-PGW.

Prückl, Erna Maria. A Journey Beyond: A Chronicle of Pioneer Life in Canada. 2010. 188p. pap. 20.55 (978-1-4251-8702-6(1)) Trafford Publishing.

Pyves, Richard. Night Madness: A Rear Gunners Tale of Courage, Adversity & Hope in WWII, 1 vol. 2012. (ENG.). 288p. 24.95 (978-0-88995-464-9(X)) Red Deer Pr. CAN. Dist: Ingram Pub. Services.

Quinn, Shawna. Agnes Warner & the Nursing Sisters of the Great War. 2010. (New Brunswick Military Heritage Ser.). (ENG., Illus.). 174p. pap. 16.95 (978-0-86492-633-3(2)) Goose Lane Editions CAN. Dist: Univ. of Toronto Pr.

Raffan, James. Emperor of the North. 2010. 496p. pap. 18.99 (978-0-06-202665-1(8)) HarperCollins Pubs.

Ramandt, Dianne. Death's Doorstep Prayer & a Miracle. 2011. (978-1-77069-232-9(0)) Word Alive Pr.

Rasky, Harry. The Song of Leonard Cohen: Portrait of a Poet, a Friendship & a Film. 2nd ed. 2010. (ENG., Illus.). 170p. pap. 20.00 (978-0-88962-915-8(3)) Mosaic Pr.

Ratcliffe, Peter. Eye of the Storm. 352p. 29.95 (978-1-930983-01-4(8), 042920) Lewis International, Inc.

Rauhala, Ann, ed. The Lucky Ones: Our Stories of Adopting Children from China. 2008. (ENG., Illus.). 350p. per. 19.95 (978-1-55022-823-6(4)) ECW Pr. CAN. Dist: Independent Pubs. Group.

Reed, Fred A. Then We Were One. 2012. (ENG.). 304p. pap. 19.95 (978-0-88922-667-8(9)) Talonbooks, Ltd. CAN. Dist: Consortium Bk. Sales & Distribution.

Rees, Tony. Arc of the Medicine Line: Mapping the World's Largest Undefended Border Across the Western Plains. 2007. (Illus.). 384p. (978-1-55365-278-6(9)) D&M Pubs. Inc.

Reid, Iain. One Bird's Choice: A Year in the Life of an Overeducated, Underemployed Twenty-Something Who Moves Back Home, 1 vol. 2011. (ENG.). 264p. 24.95 (978-0-88784-243-6(7)) House of Anansi Pr. CAN. Dist: Perseus-PGW.

Reimer, Chad. Writing British Columbia History, 1784-1958. 2010. (ENG.). 216p. pap. 32.95 (978-0-7748-1645-8(7)) UBC Pr. CAN. Dist: Univ. of Washington Pr.

Remus, Harold. I Remember Laurier: Reflections by Retirees on Life at WLU. Blackmore, Rose & McDonald, Boyd, eds. 2011. 240p. (C). pap. 24.95 (978-1-55458-383-6(7)) Wilfrid Laurier Univ. Pr. CAN. Dist: Univ. of Toronto Pr.

Reynolds, John. One Hell of a Ride: How Craig Dobbin Built the World's Largest Helicopter Company, 1 vol. 2009. (ENG., Illus.). 272p. pap. 17.95 (978-1-55365-491-9(9)) D&M Pubs. Inc. CAN. Dist: Perseus-PGW.

Ricci, Nino. Pierre Elliott Trudeau. Ralston, Saul, ed. 2011. (ENG.). 204p. (gr. 12). 19.95 (978-0-670-06660-5(5), Penguin Global) Penguin Group (USA) Inc.

Richens, Marvin Gene. Dreams of Reality. 2008. 56p. pap. 15.49 (978-1-4389-0470-2(3)) AuthorHouse.

Rickard, J. N. Politics of Command: Lieutenant-General A. G. L. McNaughton & the Canadian Army, 1939-1943. 2010. (Illus.). 416p. (978-1-4426-4002-3(2)) Univ. of Toronto Pr.

Riehm, Elaine McKinnon & Hoffman, Frances. Turbulent Times in Mathematics: The Life of J. C. Fields & the History of the Fields Medal. 2011. (Illus.). 258p. pap. 45.00 (978-0-8218-6914-7(0)) American Mathematical Society.

Rieti, Barbara. Making Witches: Newfoundland Traditions of Spells & Counterspells. 2008. (ENG.). 208p. (C). (978-0-7735-3360-8(5)) McGill-Queen's Univ. Pr.

Riley, Jonathon. A Matter of Honour: The Life, Campaigns & Generalship of Isaac Brock. 2011. 352p. pap. 27.95 (978-1-896941-65-3(6)) Brass, Robin Studio, Inc. CAN. Dist: Midpoint Trade Bks., Inc.

Rimmer, Jim. Pie Tree Press: Memories from the Composing Room Floor. 2008. (ENG., Illus.). 128p. (978-1-55447-062-4(5)) Gaspereau Pr.

Rivett, Bess Burrows. Looking Back. (Illus.). 96p. pap. (978-0-9698752-8-4(2)) Shoreline.

Roberts Creek Historical Committee. Remembering Roberts Creek: 1889 - 1955. unabr. ed. 2008. (ENG., Illus.). 190p. pap. 24.95 (978-1-55017-457-1(6)) Harbour Publishing Co., Ltd. CAN. Dist: Ingram Pub. Services.

Roberts, Joan. Joan & Goodridge: My Life with Goodridge Roberts. 2010. (ENG., Illus.). 160p. pap. 19.95 (978-1-55065-262-8(1)) Vehicule Pr. CAN. Dist: Independent Pubs. Group.

Robertson, Ray. Why Not? Fifteen Reasons to Live. 2011. (ENG.). 175p. pap. 16.95 (978-1-926845-27-2(7)) Biblioasis CAN. Dist: Consortium Bk. Sales & Distribution.

Robichaud, Stella & Robichaud, Hélène. La Corneille et le Goéland. 2009. (FRE., Illus.). 162p. (978-2-89627-177-1(5)) Editions de la Francophonie.

Rodin, Renee. Subject to Change. 2010. (ENG.). 160p. pap. 18.95 (978-0-88922-644-9(X)) Talonbooks, Ltd. CAN. Dist: Consortium Bk. Sales & Distribution.

Rodney, William. Kootenai Brown: The Unknown Frontiersman, 1 vol. 2010. (ENG., Illus.). 256p. pap. (978-1-926613-65-9(1)) Heritage Hse.

Rogatnick, Abraham J., et al. B.C. Binning. (Illus.). 192p. 50.00 (978-1-55365-171-0(5)) D&M Pubs. Inc. CAN. Dist: Perseus-PGW.

Roozeboom, Willem Bakhuys. Through My Viewfinder. 2011. 352p. pap. 83.99 (978-1-4567-1327-0(2)) AuthorHouse.

Rose, Geo Maclean. A Cyclopaedia of Canadian Biography, 2 vol., set. (National Biography Ser.). reprint ed. 250.00 (978-0-7222-6915-2(3)) Library Reprints, Inc.

Rowles Scott, Beth. Pinch Me: A Memoir. 2009. (ENG., Illus.). 224p. pap. (978-1-894694-74-2(0)) Granville Island Publishing.

Roy Goostrey. Bugle Boy: Memories. 2009. 144p. 24.80 (978-1-4269-1677-9(9)); pap. 14.80 (978-1-4269-1676-2(0)) Trafford Publishing.

Rubenstein, Lorne. Moe & Me: Encounters with Moe Norman, Golf's Mysterious Genius. 2012. (ENG., Illus.). 200p. pap. 19.95 (978-1-77041-053-4(8)) ECW Pr. CAN. Dist: Independent Pubs. Group.

Rubinstein, Robert Eli. An Italian Renaissance: Choosing Life in Canada. 2010. (Illus.). 178p. 24.95 (978-965-524-044-3(4)) Urim Pubns. ISR. Dist: Coronet Bks.

Russo, Rose Aline. Just a Farm-Raised Canuck. 2008. 95p. pap. 16.95 (978-1-60703-834-4(X)) PublishAmerica, Inc.

Rutledge-Mathison, Dutchie. Wild Roses: Memories of a Homesteader's Daughter. 2007. (Illus.). 72p. pap. 17.95 (978-0-88839-625-9(2)) Hancock Hse. Pubs.

Ruud, Charles A. The Constant Diplomat: Robert Ford in Moscow. 2009. (ENG., Illus.). 344p. (C). (978-0-7735-3585-5(3)) McGill-Queen's Univ. Pr.

Safarik, Norman & Safarik, Allan. Bluebacks & Silver Brights: A Lifetime in the BC Fish Industry from Bounty to Plunder. 2012. (ENG.). 280p. pap. 22.95 (978-1-77041-041-1(4)) ECW Pr. CAN. Dist: Independent Pubs. Group.

Sahapoglu, Erato. With Love As Guide. 2009. 232p. pap. 18.77 (978-1-4251-7980-9(0)) Trafford Publishing.

Saltzman, Devyani. Shooting Water: A Memoir of Second Chances, Family, & Filmmaking. 2007. (ENG., Illus.). 304p. per. 14.95 (978-1-55704-785-4(5), William Morrow Paperbacks) HarperCollins Pubs.

Sargeant, Stanley F. Blackfish in the Chuck: A Tale of Adventures & God's Love for a Prodigal. 2008. 196p. pap. 24.95 (978-1-60672-803-1(2)) PublishAmerica, Inc.

Saunders, Alex M. & Saunders, Peter Paul. To Our Credit: Two Autobiographies. 2009. 216p. pap. 18.05 (978-1-4269-1616-8(7)) Trafford Publishing.

Sauvage, Claude. Laurent Coderre: Artiste Peintre, L'uvre D'une Vie. 2010. (FRE., Illus.). 156p. (978-2-923715-38-4(1)) Broquet, Inc.

Saywell, John T. Someone to Teach Them: York & the Great University Explosion, 1960-1973. 2008. (ENG., Illus.). 320p. (978-0-8020-9827-6(4)) Univ. of Toronto Pr.

Scantlebury, Michael. Called to Be an Apostle: The Life & Ministry of Michael Scantlebury. 2011. (978-1-77069-240-4(1)) Word Alive Pr.

Schneiderman, Simon. Preoccupied with My Father. 2007. (ENG., Illus.). 84p. 19.95 (978-1-55022-810-6(2)) ECW Pr. CAN. Dist: Independent Pubs. Group.

Schnerch, Patrick J. & Baldwin, Marc D. The Peaceful Warrior: The Memoirs of a Damaged Mind & Soul. 2006. (ENG.). 212p. per. 17.39 (978-1-4120-9508-2(5)) Trafford Publishing.

Schwartz, Ellen & Trapunski, Ed. Lessons from Jacob: A Disabled Son Teaches His Mother about Courage, Hope & the Joy of Living Each Day to the Fullest. 2007. (ENG., Illus.). 144p. 16.95 (978-1-55263-850-7(2)) Key Porter Bks. CAN. Dist: Perseus-PGW.

Scott, Andrew. Encyclopedia of Raincoast Place Names: A Complete Reference to Coastal British Columbia. unabr. ed. 2009. (ENG., Illus.). 664p. 49.95 (978-1-55017-484-7(3)) Harbour Publishing Co., Ltd. CAN. Dist: Ingram Pub. Services.

Secord, Rev. Thomas A. From Rebel to Reverend: The Journey of a Lifetime. 2011. 188p. pap. 24.95 (978-1-4512-7900-9(0)) PublishAmerica, Inc.

See, Bill. 33 Days: Touring in A Van, Sleeping on Floors, Chasing A Dream. 2011. 278p. pap. 14.99 (978-0-557-75881-4(5)) Lulu Enterprises Inc.

Sellar, Gordon. Narrative of Gordon Sellar Who Emigrate. 2006. pap. (978-1-4068-0451-5(7)) Echo Library.

Sellers, C. A. & Gillam, Earnest O. Soapy. Soapy: An Authorized Biography of Earnest O. Soapy Gillam. 2011. 166p. 41.95 (978-1-258-01375-2(4)) Literary Licensing, LLC.

Senia, Parco. Blessed with Evil: A Story of the Hell's Angels & the Evil Spirits Motorcycle Clubs. 2007. 120p. per. 12.95 (978-0-595-45969-8(2)) iUniverse, Inc.

Shadbolt, Doris. Bill Reid, 1 vol. rev. ed. (ENG., Illus.). 216p. pap. 45.00 (978-1-55054-915-7(4)) D&M Pubs. Inc. CAN. Dist: Perseus-PGW.

Shalof, Tilda. The Making of a Nurse. 2008. (ENG.). 328p. pap. 16.95 (978-0-7710-7983-2(4), McClelland & Stewart) McClelland & Stewart CAN. Dist: Random Hse., Inc.

Shalof, Tilda. Opening My Heart: A Journey from Nurse to Patient & Back Again. (ENG.). 328p. 2012. pap. 18.99 (978-0-7710-7989-4(3), Emblem Edns) 2011. 27.95 (978-0-7710-7988-7(5), McClelland & Stewart) McClelland & Stewart CAN. Dist: Random Hse., Inc.

Shapiro, Marc. Justin Bieber: The Fever! 2010. (ENG., Illus.). 224p. (YA). pap. 9.99 (978-0-312-67878-4(9), St. Martin's Griffin) St. Martin's Pr.

Shapiro, Marc & Cooke, C. W. Fame: Drake. 2012. (ENG., Illus.). 32p. (YA). pap. 3.99 (978-1-4507-8960-8(9)) Bluewater Productions, Inc.

Sharp, Rosalie Wise. Rifke: An Improbable Life. 2007. (ENG., Illus.). 220p. 34.95 (978-1-55022-775-8(0)) ECW Pr. CAN. Dist: Independent Pubs. Group.

Sharpe, Rosalie. Rifke: An Improbable Life. 2009. (ENG., Illus.). 256p. pap. 18.00 (978-0-14-317148-5(8), Penguin Global) Penguin Group (USA) Inc.

Shatner, William. Up till Now: The Autobiography. l.t. ed. 2008. 581p. (YA). 31.95 (978-1-4104-0869-3(8)) Thorndike Pr.

Shatner, William & Fisher, David. Up till Now: The Autobiography. 2009. (ENG., Illus.). 368p. pap. 15.95 (978-0-312-56163-5(6), St. Martin's Griffin) St. Martin's Pr.

Shea, Kevin. Barilko: Without a Trace. 2010. (ENG.). 312p. pap. 19.95 (978-1-55168-378-2(4)) Key Porter Bks. CAN. Dist: Perseus-PGW.

Shea, Kevin & Wilson, John Jason. Lord Stanley: The Man Behind the Cup. 2010. (ENG.). 457p. pap. (978-1-55168-311-9(3)) Fenn, H. B. & Co., Ltd.

Shearer, Alan. Alan Shearer's Story So Far. (Illus.). xii, 211p. 35.00 (978-0-340-69603-3(6), Hodder & Stoughton) Hodder General Publishing Div. GBR. Dist: Trafalgar Square Publishing.

Sheikh, Nazneen. Moon over Marrakech: A Memoir of Loving Too Deeply in a Foreign Land. 2010. (ENG.). 288p. 22.00 (978-1-897151-71-6(3)) Cormorant Bks. Inc. CAN. Dist: Univ. of Toronto Pr.

Sheppard, David. Leonard Cohen. 2006. 136p. reprint ed. pap. 14.00 (978-1-4223-5805-4(4)) DIANE Publishing Co.

Sherk, Bill. Keep up If You Can: Confessions of a High School Teacher. 2012. (ENG., Illus.). 216p. pap. 24.99 (978-1-4597-0357-5(X)) Dundurn CAN. Dist: Ingram Pub. Services.

Sherwood, Surveying Central British Columbia: A Photojournal of Frank Swannell, 1920-1928, 1 vol. Sherwood, Jay, ed. 2010. (ENG., Illus.). 192p. pap. (978-0-7726-5742-8(4)) Royal British Columbia Museum.

Shilliday, Jim. Canada's Wheat King: The Life & Times of Seager Wheeler. 2007. (Trade Books based in Scholorship(TBS) Ser.). (ENG., Illus.). 177p. pap. 19.95 (978-0-88977-187-1(1)) Canadian Plains Research Ctr. CAN. Dist: Univ. of Toronto Pr.

Shipman, Linda. What I Didn't Tell My Husband: The Tigeress. 2007. 236p. 27.95 (978-0-9789770-2-3(5)) R&T Enterprise, Inc.

Shirriff, Charles W. It's Not Where You're Going: It's how you get There. 2009. 216p. pap. 17.95 (978-1-4401-1491-5(9)) iUniverse, Inc.

Shulman, Morton. Coroner. 2010. (ENG.). 166p. pap. 18.00 (978-1-55005-167-4(9)) Fitzhenry & Whiteside, Ltd. CAN. Dist: Ingram Pub. Services.

—Member of the Legislature. 2010. (ENG.). 226p. pap. 18.00 (978-1-55005-169-8(5)) Fitzhenry & Whiteside, Ltd. CAN. Dist: Ingram Pub. Services.

C

Sikakane, Ebenezer M. Wrestling with Apartheid: An Autobiography. 2010. *(978-1-77069-009-7(3))* Word Alive Pr.

Simmons, Sylvie. I'm Your Man: The Life of Leonard Cohen. 2012. (ENG.). 576p. 27.99 *(978-0-06-199498-2(7)*, Ecco) HarperCollins Pubs.

Singleton, Margaret. The Box in the Closet: My Journey to Claim Who I Am. 2011. 292p. 27.89 ***(978-1-4269-9001-4(4))***; pap. 17.89 ***(978-1-4269-9000-7(6))*** Trafford Publishing.

Sleigh, Daphne. The Man Who Saved Vancouver: Major James Skitt Matthews, 1 vol. 2008. (ENG., Illus.). 240p. pap. *(978-1-894974-39-4(5))* Heritage Hse.

Smilin' Johnnie. The Smilin' Johnnie Story Featuring Eleanor Dahl: Eight Miles North — And One Mile East of Wroxton. 2006. (ENG., Illus.). 244p. per. 21.74 *(978-1-4120-8912-8(3))* Trafford Publishing.

Smith, Denis. Ignatieff's World: Iggy Goes to Ottawa. rev. ed. 2009. (ENG.). 248p. pap. *(978-1-55277-406-9(6))* Lorimer, James & Co., Ltd., Pubs. CAN. Dist: Casemate Pubs. & Bk. Distributors, LLC.

Smith, Donald B. Honore Jaxon: Prairie Visionary. 2008. (ENG., Illus.). 294p. per. *(978-1-55050-367-8(7))* Coteau Bks.

Smith, Hilary. Welcome to the Jungle: Everything You Ever Wanted to Know about Bipolar but Were Too Freaked Out to Ask. 2010. (ENG.). 208p. pap. 16.95 *(978-1-57324-472-5(4)*, Conari Pr.) Red Wheel/Weiser.

Smith, Margaret M. A Spiritual Journey: An Autobiography. 2009. 172p. pap. 17.50 *(978-1-4389-6603-8(2))* AuthorHouse.

Smith, Ron. Kid Dynamite: The Gerry James Story. 2011. (ENG.). 320p. 30.00 ***(978-0-88982-276-4(X))*** Oolichan Bks. CAN. Dist: Univ. of Toronto Pr.

Smoke in the Cockpit: The Flying Adventures of Don Smokey Patry. 2006. (Illus.). 118p. per. *(978-1-897126-07-3(7))* NeWest Pubs., Ltd.

Sonmor, Glen. Old Time Hockey: Memories & Musings of a Lifetime on Ice... 2007. (Illus.). 136p. per. 19.95 *(978-0-9787809-1-3(4))* Bernstein Enterprises.

Sornberger, J. F. Dreams & Due Diligence: Till & Mcculloch's Stem Cell Discovery & Legacy. 2011. (ENG., Illus.). 144p. ***(978-1-4426-4485-4(0))*** Univ. of Toronto Pr.

Sparling, Fred & Sparling, Joyce. North to Nunavut: An Arctic Love Affair. 2011. (Illus.). 246p. pap. 24.95 ***(978-1-59715-080-4(0))*** Chapel Hill Pr.

Spring, Joyce. The Sky's the Limit: Canadian Women Bush Pilots. 2006. (ENG., Illus.). 200p. pap. 24.95 *(978-1-897045-16-9(6))* Natural Heritage/Natural History, Inc. CAN. Dist: Ingram Pub. Services.

Stafford-Smith, Benita. Man Oman: A Redhead in Arabia. 2010. 132p. pap. 13.95 *(978-1-4502-6213-2(9))* iUniverse, Inc.

Starr, David. From Bombs to Books: Refugee children, their families, & an exceptional Canadian School. 2011. (ENG., Illus.). 192p. pap. 22.95 ***(978-1-55277-860-9(6))*** Lorimer, James & Co., Ltd., Pubs. CAN. Dist: Casemate Pubs. & Bk. Distributors, LLC.

Stefanowicz, Dawn. Out from Under: The Impact of Homosexual Parenting. 2007. 245p. per. 14.95 *(978-1-59977-011-6(3))* Annotation Pr.

Steinberg, David. The Book of David. 2007. (ENG.). 208p. 23.00 *(978-0-7432-7232-2(3))* Simon & Schuster.

Steinhilper, Ulrich & Osborne, Peter. Full Circle: The Long Way Home from Canada. Geiger, Eugen, tr. from GER. (Illus.). 408p. 34.95 *(978-1-872836-02-7(X))* Independent Bks. Keston GBR. Dist: Crecy Publishing.

—Ten Minutes to Buffalo: The Story of Germany's Great Escaper. Coombs, L.F.E. & Osborne, Carol, eds. (Illus.). 431p. 26.95 *(978-1-872836-01-0(1))* Independent Bks. Keston GBR. Dist: Crecy Publishing.

Stellick, Gord. Stellicktricity: Stories, Highlights, & Other Hockey Juice from a Life Plugged into the Game. 2011. (ENG.). 288p. 24.95 ***(978-1-118-07610-1(9)***, Wiley) Wiley, John & Sons, Inc.

Stevenson, Richard. Riding on a Magpie Riff. 2006. (ENG., Illus.). 82p. per. 17.00 *(978-0-88753-423-2(6))* Black Moss Pr. CAN. Dist: LitDistCo.

Stewart, Sharon & Stewart, Roderick. Phoenix: The Life of Norman Bethune. 2011. (Illus.). 488p. (C). *(978-0-7735-3819-1(4))* McGill-Queen's Univ. Pr.

Stewart, W. Brian. The Ermatingers: A 19th-Century Ojibwa-Canadian Family. 2007. (ENG., Illus.). 224p. *(978-0-7748-1233-7(8))* Univ. of British Columbia Pr.

Stinson, Bill. Meals & Memories: A Celebration of Food on the Trail. Shirreff, Shannon, ed. 2009. 88p. pap. 26.86 *(978-1-4251-2992-7(7))* Trafford Publishing.

Stirling, David. Birds, Beasts & a Bike under the Southern Cross: Two Canadian Naturalists Camping Rough in New Zealand & Australia in The 1950s. 2008. 192p. pap. *(978-1-897435-19-9(3))* Agio Publishing Hse.

Stonechild, Blair. Buffy Sainte-Marie: It's My Way, 1 vol. 2012. (ENG., Illus.). 256p. 24.95 *(978-1-897252-78-9(1))* Fifth Hse. Pubs. CAN. Dist: Ingram Pub. Services.

Stonier-Newman, Lynne. Peter O' Reilly: The Rise of a Reluctant Immigrant, 1 vol. 2010. (ENG., Illus.). 288p. pap. *(978-1-926741-04-8(8))* TouchWood Editions.

Storck, Peter L. Journey to the Ice Age: Discovering an Ancient World. 2006. (ENG., Illus.). 376p. pap. 29.95 *(978-0-7748-1029-6(7))* UBC Pr. CAN. Dist: Univ. of Washington Pr.

Strachan, Bruce. Hazardous Pursuit. unabr. ed. (ENG., Illus.). 232p. pap. *(978-0-920576-55-7(9))* Caitlin Pr., Inc.

Stratton, Sharon. Between Forest & Sky: A Fire-Tower Journal, 1 vol. 2010. (ENG., Illus.). 224p. pap. *(978-1-894974-16-5(6))* Heritage Hse.

Summers, Sophia. Asperger's-If You Only Knew: A Family's Struggle with Asperger's Syndrome. 2007. 152p. per. 14.95 *(978-0-595-44932-3(8))* iUniverse, Inc.

Sunshine, Sandy. The One. 2008. 376p. pap. 20.99 *(978-1-60647-800-4(1))* Xulon Pr., Inc.

Surik, Nechama. The Will to Live. 2009. 192p. 24.99 *(978-1-4389-0947-9(0))*; pap. 14.49 *(978-1-4389-0946-2(2))* AuthorHouse.

Sutherland, Diane. Bloodstains: Canada's Multiple Murderers. 2007. (Illus.). 182p. pap. 26.95 *(978-1-55059-322-8(6))* Detselig Enterprises, Ltd. CAN. Dist: Temeron Bks., Inc.

Suzuki, David. David Suzuki: The Autobiography, 1 vol. (ENG., Illus.). 2007. 416p. pap. 18.95 *(978-1-55365-281-6(9))* 2006. 400p. 29.95 *(978-1-55365-156-7(1))* D&M Pubs. Inc. CAN. (Greystone Bks.). Dist: Perseus-PGW.

Swinton, Marion. A Duffle Bag, Close Friends, & a Lot of Memories: The Photo Diary of Marion Swinton, W. R. C. N. S. Fowler, Michelle, ed. 2009. (ENG., Illus.). 72p. (C). pap. 12.95 *(978-0-9783441-8-4(9))* Wilfrid Laurier Univ. Pr. CAN. Dist: Univ. of Toronto Pr.

Szalados, Imre. The Price of Freedom. 2007. 224p. per. 17.95 *(978-0-595-46782-2(2))* iUniverse, Inc.

Szollosi, Nick. Escape: One Refugee's Journey. 2009. (Illus.). v, 78p. E-Book *(978-1-4389-7359-3(4))* AuthorHouse.

Talbot, Robert J. Negotiating the Numbered Treaties: An Intellectual & Political Biography of Alexander Morris. 2009. (Illus.). 224p. pap. *(978-1-895830-36-1(2))* Purich Publishing.

Taylor, Jeanette. The Quadra Story: A History of Quadra Island. 2009. (ENG., Illus.). 272p. 32.95 *(978-1-55017-488-5(6))* Harbour Publishing Co., Ltd. CAN. Dist: Ingram Pub. Services.

—Tidal Passages: A History of the Discovery Islands. unabr. ed. 2009. (ENG., Illus.). 316p. pap. 24.95 *(978-1-55017-460-1(6))* Harbour Publishing Co., Ltd. CAN. Dist: Ingram Pub. Services.

Taylor, Robert. Beyond the Music. 2011. 132p. pap. 12.60 *(978-1-4269-6108-3(1))* Trafford Publishing.

Taylor, Scott. Unembedded: Two Decades of Maverick War Reporting, 1 vol. 2009. (ENG., Illus.). 400p. 27.95 *(978-1-55365-292-2(4))* D&M Pubs. Inc. CAN. Dist: Perseus-PGW.

Teed, Valerie, ed. Uncle Cy's War: The First World War Letters of Major Cyrus F. Inches. 2009. (New Brunswick Military Heritage Ser.). (ENG., Illus.). 304p. pap. 18.95 *(978-0-86492-542-8(5))* Goose Lane Editions CAN. Dist: Univ. of Toronto Pr.

Terry Julian. An Ordinary Miracle: John A Macdonald. 2010. 104p. pap. 19.95 *(978-1-4269-1584-0(5))* Trafford Publishing.

Thatcher, Colin. Final Appeal: Anatomy of a Frame. 2009. (ENG.). 440p. 34.95 *(978-1-55022-879-3(X))* ECW Pr. CAN. Dist: Independent Pubs. Group.

Therrien, Stéphane. The Refining Journey of a Warrior. 2011. (Illus.). viii, 118p. pap. ***(978-1-77069-304-3(1))*** Word Alive Pr.

Thiessen, Abe. A Media Pioneer: The Abe Thiessen Story. 2011. 386p. pap. 29.41 ***(978-1-4120-5150-7(9))*** Trafford Publishing.

Thomas, Peter & Tracy, Nicholas. Master & Madman: The Surprising Rise & Disastrous Fall of the Hon. Anthony Lockwood RN. 2012. (ANG & ENG., Illus.). 274p. 35.00 ***(978-0-86492-667-8(7))*** Goose Lane Editions CAN. Dist: Univ. of Toronto Pr.

Thomas, Shane Silky. Unstoppable: No Matter How Strong or Smart My Enemies are, they're Still Unable to Create my Downfall. 2011. 196p. pap. 17.00 ***(978-1-4269-7384-0(5))*** Trafford Publishing.

Thompson, Jack. Where the Hell Is John O'Groats? 2009. (Illus.). 354p. pap. *(978-0-9813593-1-1(0))* Cybercom Publishing, Inc.

Thompson, John K. Estate in the Valley. 2010. pap. 16.95 *(978-0-7414-5995-4(7))* Infinity Publishing.

Thompson, Robert. Going for the Green: Conversations with Canada's Business & Political Elite. 2009. (ENG.). 296p. pap. 19.95 *(978-1-55470-172-8(4))* Key Porter Bks. CAN. Dist: Perseus-PGW.

Thomson, Colin A. The Romance of Manitoba Settlements. 2008. (Illus.). 200p. *(978-1-55059-350-1(1))* Detselig Enterprises, Ltd. CAN. Dist: Temeron Bks., Inc.

Thomson, Donna. The Four Walls of My Freedom. 2010. (ENG., Illus.). 200p. 29.95 *(978-1-55278-890-5(3))* McArthur & Co. CAN. Dist: National Bk. Network.

Thornton, Martin. Sir Robert Borden? Canada. 2011. (Makers of the Modern World Ser.). (ENG., Illus.). 220p. 19.95 *(978-1-905791-84-2(4))* Haus Publishing GBR. Dist: Consortium Bk. Sales & Distribution.

Tibbs, Brian. They Did Not Return: Honouring St. Catharines' War Dead: WWII 1939-1945 Korea 1950-1953 Afghanistan 2009. 2010. (Illus.). 185p. *(978-0-9739629-3-2(3))* Mayholme Foundation.

Tippett, Maria. The Life of Yousuf Karsh: Portrait in Light & Shadow. 2008. (ENG., Illus.). 448p. 35.00 *(978-0-300-13650-0(1))* Yale Univ. Pr.

Todd, Jack. Desertion in the Time of Vietnam: A Memoir. 2012. (ENG.). 312p. pap. 18.95 ***(978-0-8032-3981-4(5))*** Univ. of Nebraska Pr.

Tombs, George. Robber Baron: Lord Black of Crossharbour. 2007. (ENG., Illus.). 350p. 26.95 *(978-1-55022-806-9(4))* ECW Pr. CAN. Dist: Independent Pubs. Group.

Toole, Monte. Monte Toole: A Memoir. 2008. 192p. pap. 17.95 *(978-0-595-51304-8(2))* iUniverse, Inc.

Topp, Brian. How We Almost Gave the Tories the Boot: The Inside Story Behind the Coalition. 2010. (ENG.). 192p. pap. 24.95 ***(978-1-55277-502-8(X))*** Lorimer, James & Co., Ltd., Pubs. CAN. Dist: Casemate Pubs. & Bk. Distributors, LLC.

Totten, Mark. Nasty, Brutish, & Short: The lives of gang members in Canada. 2012. (ENG., Illus.). 296p. pap. 24.95 ***(978-1-4594-0038-2(0))*** Lorimer, James & Co., Ltd., Pubs. CAN. Dist: Casemate Pubs. & Bk. Distributors, LLC.

Tougas, Luke. Meet My Shadow. 2010. 224p. (ENG.). 28.95 *(978-1-4502-1280-9(8))*; pap. 18.95 *(978-1-4502-1278-6(6))* iUniverse, Inc.

Traill, Catharine Parr. The Backwoods of Canada. 2008. 280p. 28.99 *(978-0-554-27040-1(4))* 2007. (ENG.). 248p. pap. 20.99 *(978-1-4346-2392-8(0))* 2007. (ENG.). 276p. pap. 23.99 *(978-1-4346-2438-3(2))* BiblioBazaar.

—The Backwoods of Canada. 2009. 240p. pap. *(978-1-4099-3621-3(X))* Dodo Pr.

—The Backwoods of Canada. 2010. (ENG., Illus.). 336p. pap. 17.95 *(978-0-7710-9448-4(5)*, New Can Library) McClelland & Stewart CAN. Dist: Random Hse., Inc.

Travis, David, ed. Karsh: Beyond the Camera. 2012. pap. 24.95 ***(978-1-56792-438-1(7))*** Godine, David R. Pub.

Tremblay, Michel & Killick, Rachel. Michel Tremblay - Les Belles-Soeurs. 2011. (Modern Language Ser.). (FRE & ENG., Illus.). 134p. pap. 19.95 *(978-1-85399-550-7(9))* Bristol Classical Pr. GBR. Dist: International Publishers Marketing.

Trepanier, Claire. A Woman of Valour: The Biography of Marie-Louise Bouchard Labelle. 2010. 240p. pap. 24.95 *(978-1-897425-84-8(8))* Univ. of Washington Pr.

Triesman, Gerard. Man Ah Bush. 2008. 208p. pap. 24.95 *(978-1-60672-347-0(2))* PublishAmerica, Inc.

Trkulja, Vlad. Great Canadian Mortgage Plan. 2008. (ENG., Illus.). 324p. *(978-1-897178-45-4(X))* Insomniac Pr.

—Great Canadian Mortgage Plan. 2009. (ENG., Illus.). 224p. pap. 2.99 *(978-1-897415-25-2(7))* Insomniac Pr. CAN. Dist: Sony Electronics.

Trudeau, Margaret. Changing My Mind. 2010. 352p. 27.99 *(978-0-06-206487-5(8))* HarperCollins Pubs.

Trueman, Howard. The Chignecto Isthmus & Its First Sett. 2006. pap. *(978-1-4068-1127-8(0))* Echo Library.

Trueman, Jonathan. One for the Ditch. 2009. 80p. pap. 11.49 *(978-1-4490-1719-4(3))* AuthorHouse.

Truscott, Gerald. Free Spirit: Stories of You, Me & BC, 1 vol. 2010. (ENG.). 180p. pap. *(978-0-7726-5870-8(6))* Royal British Columbia Museum.

Tulloch, Judith. La Famille Bell à Baddeck: Alexander Graham Bell et Mabel Bell au Cap-Breton. Cantin, Monique, tr. from ENG. 2009. (FRE., Illus.). 96p. pap. *(978-0-88780-868-5(9))* Formac Publishing Co., Ltd.

Tupper, Ferdinand Br. The Life & Correspondence of Sir Isaac. 2006. pap. *(978-1-4068-3365-2(7))* Echo Library.

Tupper, Ferdinand Brock. The Life & Correspondence of Sir Isaac Brock. 2007. (ENG.). 352p. pap. 25.99 *(978-1-4346-2481-9(1))* BiblioBazaar.

Turnbull, Frank. Operating on the Frontier. 2nd unabr. ed. (ENG., Illus.). 312p. reprint ed. pap. *(978-1-55017-137-2(2))* Harbour Publishing Co., Ltd.

Turner, Wesley B. The Astonishing General: The Life & Legacy of Sir Isaac Brock. 2011. (ENG., Illus.). 376p. 35.00 *(978-1-55488-777-4(1)*, Dundurn Pr.) Dundurn CAN. Dist: Ingram Pub. Services.

Tyson, Ian. The Long Trail: My Life in the West. (ENG., Illus.). 208p. 2011. pap. 18.50 *(978-0-307-35936-0(0)*, Vintage Canada) 2010. 25.95 *(978-0-307-35935-3(2)*, Random Hse CAN) Random Hse. of Canada, Ltd. CAN. Dist: Random Hse., Inc.

University of Toronto Press. Canadian Who's Who (Bk Only) 2010. 2010. (Canadian Who's Who Ser.). 1449p. *(978-1-4426-4155-6(X))* Univ. of Toronto Pr.

UNIVERSITY OF TORONTO PRESS. Canadian Who's Who (Network Licence) 2011. ***(978-1-4426-4173-0(8))*** Univ. of Toronto Pr.

Urbaniak, Tom. Her Worship: Hazel McCallion & the Development of Mississauga. 2009. (ENG., Illus.). 336p. *(978-0-8020-9902-0(5))*; pap. *(978-0-8020-9602-9(6))* Univ. of Toronto Pr.

Urquhart, Jane, frwd. Painting, Vol. 2. 2008. (ENG., Illus.). 328p. 75.00 *(978-0-9739739-5-2(1))* Magenta Publishing for the Arts CAN. Dist: Consortium Bk. Sales & Distribution.

Uwacu, Louise. The Nightmare of a Positivision: Yes We are Dying. but we are still Breathing. 2009. 240p. 25.95 *(978-1-4389-3444-0(0))*; pap. 15.95 *(978-1-4389-3443-3(2))* AuthorHouse.

van den Hoonaard, Deborah. By Himself: The Older Man's Experience of Widowhood. 2010. 176p. *(978-1-4426-4109-9(6))* Univ. of Toronto Pr.

Van Doorn, Margreet Jansen. Row, Row, Row My Boat! A Woman's Incredible Journey with Breast Cancer. 2007. (ENG.). 188p. pap. 20.83 *(978-1-4120-7993-8(4))* Trafford Publishing.

Van Hasselt, Caroline. High Wire Act: Ted Rogers & the Empire That Debt Built. 2008. (ENG., Illus.). 544p. pap. 26.95 *(978-0-470-15756-5(9)*, Wiley) Wiley, John & Sons, Inc.

Van Hasselt, Caroline & Hasselt, Caroline Van. High Wire Act: Ted Rogers & the Empire That Debt Built. 2007. (ENG., Illus.). 530p. 34.95 *(978-0-470-15296-6(6)*, Wiley) Wiley, John & Sons, Inc.

Van Luven, Lynne & Gillespie, Bruce. Nobody's Father: Life Without Kids, 1 vol. rev. ed. 2009. (ENG.). 256p. pap. *(978-1-894898-74-4(5))* TouchWood Editions.

Vassilopoulos, Peter. John M. Horton: Mariner Artist, 1 vol. 2007. (ENG., Illus.). 176p. *(978-1-894974-34-9(4))* Heritage Hse.

Vaughan, Walter. The Life & Work of Sir William Van Horne. 2009. 250p. pap. *(978-0-217-35449-3(1))* Books LLC.

—The Life & Work of Sir William Van Horne. 2008. 418p. 49.95 *(978-0-548-93856-0(3))* 2007. (ENG.). 420p. per. 34.95 *(978-0-548-60352-9(9))* Kessinger Publishing, LLC.

Verbisky, Nicholas. Embarras Portage: Before, & After. 2010. 356p. pap. 24.37 *(978-1-4269-0748-7(6))* Trafford Publishing.

Virk, Manjit. Reena: A Father's Story, 1 vol. rev. ed. 2009. (ENG., Illus.). 192p. *(978-1-894974-51-6(4))* Heritage Hse.

Virtue, John. Fred Taylor: Brother in the Shadows. 2008. (ENG., Illus.). 320p. (C). *(978-0-7735-3359-2(1))* McGill-Queen's Univ. Pr.

Virtue, Tessa & Moir, Scott. Tessa & Scott: Our Journey from Childhood Dream to Gold, 1 vol. 2011. (ENG., Illus.). 192p. pap. 19.95 ***(978-0-88784-297-9(6))*** House of Anansi Pr. CAN. Dist: Perseus-PGW.

Vogler, Stephen. Only in Whistler: Tales of a Mountain Town. unabr. ed. 2009. (ENG., Illus.). 240p. pap. 24.95 *(978-1-55017-504-2(1))* Harbour Publishing Co., Ltd. CAN. Dist: Ingram Pub. Services.

Wahl, Ryan. Legacy in Wood: The Wahl Family Boat Builders. 2009. (ENG., Illus.). 240p. 32.95 *(978-1-55017-433-5(9))* Harbour Publishing Co., Ltd. CAN. Dist: Ingram Pub. Services.

Wainwright, A. Memoirs of a Fellwanderer. 2008. (Illus.). 210p. pap. 25.00 *(978-0-7112-2239-7(8))* Lincoln, Frances Ltd. GBR. Dist: Perseus-PGW.

Waiser, Bill & Houston, C. S. Tommy's Team: The Men & Women Behind the Douglas Years, 1 vol. 2010. (ENG., Illus.). 208p. pap. 19.95 *(978-1-897252-75-8(7))* Fifth Hse. Pubs. CAN. Dist: Ingram Pub. Services.

Waite, P. B. In Search of R. B. Bennett. 2012. (ENG., Illus.). 344p. (C). ***(978-0-7735-3908-2(5))*** McGill-Queen's Univ. Pr.

Walker, George A. The Mysterious Death of Tom Thomson. 2012. (Graphic Novels Ser.). (ENG., Illus.). 224p. pap. 22.95 ***(978-0-88984-348-6(1))*** Porcupine's Quill, Inc. CAN. Dist: Univ. of Toronto Pr.

Walker, George A., illus. Images from the Neocerebellum. 2007. (ENG.). 168p. pap. 21.95 *(978-0-88984-291-5(4))* Porcupine's Quill, Inc. CAN. Dist: Univ. of Toronto Pr.

Wanders, Ted. The Law & the Truck Driver. 2010. 800p. pap. 36.49 *(978-1-4520-5767-5(2))* AuthorHouse.

Wardhaugh, Robert A. Behind the Scenes: The Life & Work of William Clifford Clard. 2010. (IPAC Series in Public Management & Governance Ser.). (Illus.). 560p. (ENG.). *(978-1-4426-4126-6(6))*; pap. *(978-1-4426-1052-1(2))* Univ. of Toronto Pr.

Warren, Donald. The House on the Hill: Recollections of a Rideau Canal Lockmaster's Son. 2008. 212p. pap. 17.00 *(978-1-4251-6019-7(0))* Trafford Publishing.

Warren, Jim. An Elderly Eclectic Gentleman. 2011. 384p. ***(978-1-77067-463-9(2))***; pap. ***(978-1-77067-464-6(0))*** FriesenPress.

Warren, William Robinson. The Life & Labors of Archibald Mclean. (ENG.). 436p. 2007. 51.95 *(978-0-548-14330-8(7))* 2006. per. 36.95 *(978-1-4286-5567-6(0))* Kessinger Publishing, LLC.

Watson, Alexander John. Marginal Man: The Dark Vision of Harold Innis. 2007. (ENG., Illus.). 480p. pap. *(978-0-8020-9478-0(3))* Univ. of Toronto Pr.

Watson, Daniel J. Hitchhike to Heaven. 2010. ***(978-1-77069-089-9(1))*** Word Alive Pr.

Watson, Paul. Where War Lives: A Journey into the Heart of War. 2008. 18.50 *(978-1-60529-789-7(5))* Rodale Pr., Inc.

Webb, Peter. Rainbows End. 2008. 228p. pap. 16.95 *(978-1-4327-2483-2(5))* Outskirts Pr., Inc.

Weekes, Mary. Trader King: The Thrilling Story of Forty Years' Service in the North-West Territories, 1 vol. 2008. (Western Canadian Classics Ser.). (ENG., Illus.). 176p. per. 17.95 *(978-1-897252-15-4(3))* Fifth Hse. Pubs. CAN. Dist: Ingram Pub. Services.

Wegenast, Franklin Wellington. Liberty Is Dead: A Canadian in Germany 1938. Derry, Margaret E., ed. 2012. (WCGS German Studies). (ENG.). 190p. (C). pap. 32.95 ***(978-1-55458-053-8(6))*** Wilfrid Laurier Univ. Pr. CAN. Dist: Univ. of Toronto Pr.

Weisz, Mischa & Hemsworth, Wade. I Choose to Live: A Self-Made Millionaire Faces Cancer. 2009. (ENG., Illus.). 168p. 35.00 *(978-1-55488-718-7(6))* Dundurn CAN. Dist: Ingram Pub. Services.

Wells, Jon. Heat: A Firefighter's Story. 2006. (ENG., Illus.). 256p. pap. *(978-1-55028-928-2(4))* Lorimer, James & Co., Ltd., Pubs. CAN. Dist: Casemate Pubs. & Bk. Distributors, LLC.

Wells, Robert P. Mile Post 104 & Beyond: We Have Walked Together in the Shadow of the Rainbow. 2011. 152p. 23.42 *(978-1-4269-5797-0(1))*; pap. 13.42 *(978-1-4269-5796-3(3))* Trafford Publishing.

Weston, Hartley A. Shadows on the Wind. 2010. 468p. pap. 24.99 *(978-1-4269-0189-8(5))* Trafford Publishing.

Wilkie, George, et al, eds. The Bench & Bar of Ontario. 2011. 445p. 89.00 ***(978-1-60449-117-3(5))*** Gaunt, Inc.

Willems Snopek, Roxanne. More Great Cat Stories: Incredible Tales about Exceptional Cats, 1 vol. 2008. (Amazing Stories Ser.). (ENG., Illus.). 128p. pap. *(978-1-894974-55-4(7))* Heritage Hse.

Williams, Georgina. Beyond the Walls. 2006. (ENG.). 288p. per. 22.95 *(978-1-59800-815-9(3))* Outskirts Pr., Inc.

—Rehearsals in Madness. 2007. 272p. per. 22.95 *(978-1-4327-1685-1(9))* Outskirts Pr., Inc.

—Whispering Wild Fire. 2009. 276p. pap. 28.95 *(978-1-4327-4319-2(8))* Outskirts Pr., Inc.

Williams, Lorraine O'Donnell. Memories of the Beach: Reflections on a Toronto Childhood. 2010. (ENG., Illus.). 248p. pap. 26.99 *(978-1-55488-389-9(X))* Dundurn CAN. Dist: Ingram Pub. Services.

Williams, Lynn. One Day Longer: A Memoir. 2011. 340p. 39.95 ***(978-0-8014-5067-9(5))***, ILR Pr.) Cornell Univ. Pr.

Williamson, Mary F. & Sharp, Tom. Just a Larger Family: Letters of Marie Williamson from the Canadian Home Front,1940-1944. 2011. (Life Writing

Ser.). (Illus.). 395p. (C). pap. 29.95 *(978-1-55458-323-2(3))* Wilfrid Laurier Univ. Pr. CAN. Dist: Univ. of Toronto Pr.
Williamson, Ronald F. & Bisson, Michael S. The Archaeology of Bruce Trigger: Theoretical Empiricism. 2006. (ENG., Illus.). 320p. (C). per. *(978-0-7735-3161-1(0))* McGill-Queen's Univ. Pr.
Willsher, Graham. For the Life of Me... Anecdotes from A Career in Hospitality. 2011. 168p. pap. 15.95 *(978-1-4620-5874-7(4))* iUniverse, Inc.
Wilson, David A. Thomas D'Arcy McGee: The Extreme Moderate, 1857-1868. 2011. (Illus.). 528p. (C). *(978-0-7735-3903-7(4))* McGill-Queen's Univ. Pr.
—Thomas D'Arcy Mcgee, Volume 1: Passion, Reason, & Politics, 1825-1857. 2012. (ENG., Illus.). 448p. (C). pap. *(978-0-7735-4023-1(7))* McGill-Queen's Univ. Pr.
Wise, Leonard & Gould, Allan. Toronto Street Names: An Illustrated Guide to Their Origins. 2nd enl. ed. 2011. (ENG., Illus.). 272p. pap. 24.95 *(978-1-55407-968-1(3))* Firefly Bks., Ltd.
Wise, S. F., ed. Sir Francis Bond Head: A Narrative. 261p. pap. 19.95 *(978-0-7710-9743-0(3))* McClelland & Stewart CAN. Dist: Random Hse. of Canada, Ltd.
Wiss, Ray H. FOB Doc: A Doctor on the Front Lines in Afghanistan - A War Diary, 1 vol. 2010. (ENG., Illus.). 224p. 26.95 *(978-1-55365-472-8(2))* D&M Pubs. Inc. CAN. Dist: Perseus-PGW.
Witt, David L. & Seton, Ernest Thompson. Ernest Thompson Seton: The Life & Legacy of an Artist & Conservationist, 1 vol. 2010. (ENG., Illus.). 192p. 40.00 *(978-1-4236-0391-7(5))* Gibbs Smith, Publisher.
Wolf, Jim & Owen, Patricia. Yi Fao: Speaking Through Memory - A History of New Westminster's Chinese Community,1858-1980, 1 vol. rev. ed. 2008. (ENG., Illus.). 144p. pap. *(978-1-894974-40-0(9))* Heritage Hse.
Woman's Who's Who of America. 961p. reprint ed. 248.00 *(978-0-7222-8418-6(7))* Library Reprints, Inc.
Wood, June. Nechako Country: In the Footsteps of Bert Irvine, 1 vol. 2007. (ENG., Illus.). 192p. pap. *(978-1-894974-27-1(1))* Heritage Hse.
Woodcock, George. Beyond the Blue Mountain: An Autobiography. 2010. (ENG.). 300p. pap. 25.00 *(978-1-55005-184-1(9))* Fitzhenry & Whiteside, Ltd. CAN. Dist: Ingram Pub. Services.
—Letter to the Past: An Autobiography. 2010. (ENG.). 331p. pap. 30.00 *(978-1-55005-192-6(X))* Fitzhenry & Whiteside, Ltd. CAN. Dist: Ingram Pub. Services.
Wright, Juiwanna Leah. This World Is My Home. 2011. 88p. pap. 19.95 *(978-1-4626-0915-4(5))* PublishAmerica, Inc.
Wyse, Robert. Bamboo Cage: The POW Diary of Flight Lieutenant Robert Wyse, 1942-1943. Vance, Jonathan F., ed. 2009. (New Brunswick Military Heritage Ser.). (ENG.). 146p. pap. 14.95 *(978-0-86492-529-9(8))* Goose Lane Editions CAN. Dist: Univ. of Toronto Pr.
Yamagishi, N. Rochelle. Japanese Canadian Journey: The Nakagama Story. 2010. 112p. pap. 12.95 *(978-1-4269-2937-3(4))* Trafford Publishing.
Yardley, Joyce. Yukon Tears & Laughter. 2007. 176p. pap. 13.95 *(978-0-88839-594-8(9))* Hancock Hse. Pubs.
Yelin, Shulamis. Shulamis: Stories from a Montreal Childhood. (Illus.). 170p. pap. *(978-0-9695160-7-5(2))* Shoreline.
Young, Astrid. Being Young: Scott, Neil & Me. 2010. (ENG., Illus.). 320p. pap. *(978-1-897178-88-1(3))* Insomniac Pr.
Zechlin-Jones, Inge. As I Saw It: One Woman's Canadian Experience. 2007. 320p. per. 23.06 *(978-1-4251-1348-3(6))* Trafford Publishing.
Ziedenberg, Gerald. Inspiration through Adversity. 2010. 288p. (ENG.). 29.95 *(978-1-4520-3130-9(4))*; pap. 24.95 *(978-1-4520-3129-3(0))* AuthorHouse.
Zieroth, David. How I Joined Humanity at Last. unabr. ed. (ENG.). 112p. pap. *(978-1-55017-182-2(8))* Harbour Publishing Co., Ltd.
Zoltvany, Yves. Philippe de Rigaud de Vaudreuil, Governor of New France, 1703-1725. 242p. pap. 19.95 *(978-0-7710-9780-5(8))* McClelland & Stewart CAN. Dist: Random Hse. of Canada, Ltd.
Zuk, Bill. True-Life Adventures of Canada's Bush Pilots. 2009. (ENG.). 136p. (gr. 6-12). pap. 9.95 *(978-1-55277-409-0(0))* Lorimer, James & Co., Ltd., Pubs. CAN. Dist: Casemate Pubs. & Bk. Distributors, LLC.
Zytaruk, Tom. Like a Rock: The Chuck Cadman Story. unabr. ed. 2008. (ENG., Illus.). 304p. pap. 26.95 *(978-1-55017-427-4(4))* Harbour Publishing Co., Ltd CAN. Dist: Ingram Pub. Services.

CANADA—BIOGRAPHY—BIBLIOGRAPHY

Hopkins, John Castell. Canadian Annual Review of Public Affairs, 1901-08. reprint ed. 150.00 *(978-0-7222-6841-4(6))* Library Reprints, Inc.

CANADA—BIOGRAPHY—DICTIONARIES

Lumley, Elizabeth. Canadian Who's Who 2007, 2 vols. 2007. (Canadian Who's Who Ser.). (ENG.). 1450p. bds. *(978-0-8020-4062-6(4))* Univ. of Toronto Pr.
—Canadian Who's Who 2009. (ENG.). 2010. *(978-0-8020-9966-2(1))* 2009. 1449p. *(978-0-8020-9965-5(3))* 2009. 1449p. *(978-0-8020-4092-3(6))* Univ. of Toronto Pr.
Lumley, Elizabeth, ed. Canadian Who's Who 2007. 2007. (Canadian Who's Who Ser.). (ENG.). 1450p. cd-rom *(978-0-8020-4063-3(2))*; Vol. 42. *(978-0-8020-4061-9(6))* Univ. of Toronto Pr.
—Canadian Who's Who 2008. 2008. (Canadian Who's Who Ser.). (ENG.). 1450p. *(978-0-8020-4073-2(X))*; 1450p. *(978-0-8020-4071-8(3))*; cd-rom *(978-0-8020-4072-5(1))* Univ. of Toronto Pr.
Lumley, Elizabeth & University of Toronto Press Staff. The Canadian Who's Who 1910. 2010. (Canadian Who's Who Ser.). 278p. pap. *(978-1-4426-1111-5(1))* Univ. of Toronto Pr.

CANADA—BOUNDARIES

Alper, Donald K. & Loucky, James. Canada-US Border Securitization: Implications for Binational Cooperation. 2007. 44p. *(978-1-882582-61-7(6))* Canadian-American Ctr.
Behiels, Michael & Stuart, Reginald C. Transnationalism: Canada-United States History into the Twenty-first Century. 2010. (Illus.). 320p. *(978-0-7735-3762-0(7))*; pap. *(978-0-7735-3763-7(5))* McGill-Queen's Univ. Pr.
Byers, Michael. Who Owns the Arctic? Understanding Sovereignty Disputes in the North, 1 vol. 2010. (ENG., Illus.). 192p. pap. 17.95 *(978-1-55365-499-5(4))* D&M Pubs. Inc. CAN. Dist: Perseus-PGW.
Cavell, Janice & Noakes, Jeff. Acts of Occupation: Canada & Arctic Sovereignty, 1918-25. 2011. (ENG., Illus.). 348p. pap. 37.95 *(978-0-7748-1868-1(9))* UBC Pr. CAN. Dist: Univ. of Washington Pr.
Challenges Facing First Responders in Border Communities: Hearing Before the Subcommittee on Emergency Communications, Preparedness & Response of the Committee on Homeland Security, House of Representatives, One Hundred Tenth Congress, First Session, July 12, 2007. 2009. iii, 58p. *(978-0-16-083895-8(9))*, 552-070-39584-9) United States Government Printing Office.
Coleman, E. C. The Pig War: The Most Perfect War in History. 2010. (ENG., Illus.). 240p. 27.95 *(978-0-7524-5227-2(4))* History Pr. Ltd.,The GBR. Dist: Independent Pubs. Group.
Hutchison, Bruce & Palmer, Vaughn. The Struggle for the Border. 2012. (ENG., Illus.). 520p. pap. 24.95 *(978-0-19-544792-7(1))* Oxford Univ. Pr., Inc.
Johnson, Benjamin & Graybill, Andrew R., eds. Bridging National Borders in North America: Transnational & Comparative Histories. 2010. (American Encounters/Global Interactions Ser.). (ENG., Illus.). 384p. 94.95 *(978-0-8223-4688-3(5))*; pap. 26.95 *(978-0-8223-4699-9(0))* Duke Univ. Pr.
Konrad, Victor, et al. Beyond Walls: Re-Inventing the Canada-United States Borderlands. 2008. (Border Regions Ser.). (Illus.). 368p. 124.95 *(978-0-7546-7202-9(6))* Ashgate Publishing Co.
Lundy, Derek. Borderlands: Riding the Edge of America. 2011. (Illus.). 432p. pap. 17.95 *(978-0-307-39863-5(3)*, Vintage Canada) Knopf Canada CAN. Dist: Random Hse., Inc.
McDorman, Ted L. Salt Water Neighbors: International Ocean Law Relations Between the United States & Canada. 2009. (ENG., Illus.). 304p. 99.00 *(978-0-19-538360-7(5))* Oxford Univ. Pr., Inc.
Poitras, Jacques. Imaginary Line: Life on an Unfinished Border. 2011. (ENG., Illus.). 342p. pap. 19.95 *(978-0-86492-650-0(2))* Goose Lane Editions CAN. Dist: Univ. of Toronto Pr.
United States. Congress. House. Committe. Views on the Free Navigation of the St Lawrence, Reported by Mr Buel, to Accompany Joint Resolution on the Same Subject from the Committee on Foreig. 2011. 26p. pap. 11.99 *(978-1-4181-9220-4(1))* MPublishing.
The Western Hemisphere Travel Initiative: Perspectives of a Community on the U.S.-Canada Border: Full Field Hearing Before the Committee on Homeland Security, House of Representatives, One Hundred Tenth Congress, First Session, July 20, 2007. 2009. iv, 77p. *(978-0-16-084087-6(2)*, 552-070-39703-5) United States Government Printing Office.

CANADA—CANADIAN ARMED FORCES

see also Canada—Canadian Army; Canada—Royal Canadian Air Force; Canada—Royal Canadian Navy

Appleby, Timothy. A New Kind of Monster: The Secret Life & Shocking True Crimes of an Officer ... & a Murderer. 2011. 304p. pap. 15.00 *(978-0-307-88872-3(X))* Broadway Bks.
Arsenault, Chris. Blowback: A Canadian History of Agent Orange & the War at Home. 2009. (ENG., Illus.). 96p. pap. 15.95 *(978-1-55266-296-0(9))* Fernwood Publishing Co., Ltd. CAN. Dist: Independent Pubs. Group.
Bagley, Fred. They Answered the Call: Nine Canadians Go to War. 2007. 29.95 *(978-1-55059-343-3(9))* Detselig Enterprises, Ltd. CAN. Dist: Temeron Bks., Inc.
Bland, Douglas L. & Queen's University Staff. Canada's National Defence Vol. 1: Defence Policy. pap. *(978-0-88911-792-1(6))* McGill-Queen's Univ. Pr.
Blatchford, Christie. Fifteen Days: Stories of Bravery, Friendship, Life & Death from Inside the New Canadian Army. 2008. (ENG., Illus.). 416p. pap. 19.00 *(978-0-385-66467-7(2)*, Anchor Can) Doubleday Canada, Ltd. CAN. Dist: Random Hse., Inc.
Blaxland, John C. Strategic Cousins: Australian & Canadian Expeditionary Forces & the British & American Empires. 2006. (ENG., Illus.). 432p. (C). *(978-0-7735-3035-5(5))* McGill-Queen's Univ. Pr.
Brewster, Murray. The Savage War: The Untold Battles of Afghanistan. 8th ed. 2011. (ENG., Illus.). 384p. 34.95 *(978-1-118-11593-0(7)*, Wiley) Wiley, John & Sons, Inc.
Commission of Inquiry into the Deployment of Canad. Dishonoured Legacy: The Lessons of the Somalia Affair - Executive Summary. 82p. pap. *(978-0-660-60271-4(7))* Canadian Government Publishing.
Conrad, John. Ce que dit le Tonnerre: Reflexions d'un officier canadien a Kandahar. 2009. (FRE., Illus.). 280p. pap. 29.95 *(978-1-55488-419-3(5)*, Dundurn Pr.) Dundurn CAN. Dist: Ingram Pub. Services.
—Scarce Heard amid the Guns: An Inside Look at Canadian Peacekeeping. 2011. (ENG., Illus.). 328p. pap. 26.99 *(978-1-55488-981-5(2)*, Dundurn Pr.) Dundurn CAN. Dist: Ingram Pub. Services.
Coombs, Howard G., ed. Les Insubordonnes et les Insurges: Des Exemples Canadiens de Mutinerie et de Desobeissance, de 1920 a Nos Jours. 2008. (FRE & ENG., Illus.). 472p. pap. 49.95 *(978-1-55002-765-5(4)*, Dundurn Pr.) Dundurn CAN. Dist: Ingram Pub. Services.
Corbett, Ron. First Soldiers Down: Canada's Friendly Fire Deaths in Afghanistan. 2012. (ENG., Illus.). 240p. pap. 28.99 *(978-1-4597-0327-8(8))* Dundurn CAN. Dist: Ingram Pub. Services.
Currie, J. A. The Red Watch: With the First Canadian Division in Flanders During the Great War. 2011. 260p. *(978-0-85706-649-7(8))*; pap. *(978-0-85706-650-3(1))* Leonaur Ltd.
Dawson, Grant. Here Is Hell: Canada's Engagement in Somalia. 2007. (ENG., Illus.). 240p. pap. *(978-0-7748-1298-6(2))* Univ. of British Columbia Pr.
English, Allan, et al. Networked Operations & Transformation: Context & Canadian Contributions. 2007. (ENG.). 200p. per. *(978-0-7735-3339-4(7))* McGill-Queen's Univ. Pr.
English, Allan D., et al. Networked Operations & Transformation: Context & Canadian Contributions. 2007. (ENG., Illus.). 200p. (C). *(978-0-7735-3285-4(4))* McGill-Queen's Univ. Pr.
Frisconalti, Michael. Friendly Fire: The Untold Story of the U. S. Bombing That Killed Four Canadian Soldiers in Afghanistan. 2006. (ENG.). 608p. pap. 24.95 *(978-0-470-83918-8(X)*, Wiley) Wiley, John & Sons, Inc.
Gaudet, Al. Cyprus 1974: This Ain't No Picnic, It's War - The Combat Diary of Al Gaudet, Canadian Peacekeeper. Kielstra, David A., ed. 2010. (Laurier Military History Ser.). (ENG., Illus.). 88p. (C). pap. 14.95 *(978-1-926804-03-3(1))* Wilfrid Laurier Univ. Pr. CAN. Dist: Univ. of Toronto Pr.
Gibb, David A. The Camouflaged Killer: The Shocking Double Life of Canadian Air Force Colonel Russell Williams. 2011. (ENG.). 384p. (gr. 12). 15.00 *(978-0-425-24439-5(3)*, Berkley Trade) Penguin Group (USA) Inc.
Gibb, David A. Camouflaged Killer: The Shocking Double Life of Canadian Air Force Colonel Russell Williams. 2012. (ENG.). 592p. (gr. 12). pap. 9.99 *(978-0-425-25919-1(6)*, Berkley) Penguin Group (USA) Inc.
Gimblett, Richard H., ed. The Naval Service of Canada, 1910-2010: The Centennial Story. 2009. (ENG., Illus.). 230p. 39.95 *(978-1-55488-470-4(5))* Dundurn CAN. Dist: Univ. of Toronto Pr.
Goddard, Lance. Hell & High Water: Canada & the Italian Campaign. 2007. (ENG., Illus.). 288p. pap. 29.99 *(978-1-55002-728-0(X)*, Dundurn Pr.) Dundurn CAN. Dist: Ingram Pub. Services.
Granatstein, J. L. Canada's Army. 2nd ed. 2011. (Illus.). xiv, 573p. pap. *(978-1-4426-1178-8(2))* Univ. of Toronto Pr.
Harold A. Skaarup. Canadian Warplanes. 2009. 640p. pap. 49.95 *(978-1-4401-6758-4(3))* iUniverse, Inc.
Hillier, Rick. A Soldier First. 2010. 552p. pap. 18.99 *(978-0-06-202667-5(4))* HarperCollins Pubs.
Horn, Bernd. No Lack of Courage: Operation Medusa, Afghanistan. 2010. (ENG., Illus.). 184p. pap. 30.00 *(978-1-55488-766-8(6))* Dundurn CAN. Dist: Ingram Pub. Services.
Horn, Bernd, ed. Fortune Favours the Brave: Tales of Courage & Tenacity in Canadian Military History. 2009. (ENG., Illus.). 446p. pap. 35.00 *(978-1-55002-841-6(3))* Dundurn CAN. Dist: Ingram Pub. Services.
—Les guerriers Intrepides: Perspectives sur les chefs militaires Canadiens. 2007. (FRE & ENG., Illus.). 328p. pap. 39.95 *(978-1-55002-721-1(2)*, Dundurn Pr.) Dundurn CAN. Dist: Ingram Pub. Services.
—Intrepid Warriors: Perspectives on Canadian Military Leaders. 2007. (ENG., Illus.). 272p. pap. 39.95 *(978-1-55002-711-2(5)*, Dundurn Pr.) Dundurn CAN. Dist: Ingram Pub. Services.
Horn, Bernd & Balasevicius, Tony, eds. Casting Light on the Shadows: Canadian Perspectives on Special Operations Forces. 2007. (ENG.). 328p. pap. 39.95 *(978-1-55002-694-8(1)*, Dundurn Pr.) Dundurn CAN. Dist: Ingram Pub. Services.
—Lumières Sur les Forces de l'Ombre: Une Perspective Canadienne Sur les Forces d'Opérations Spéciales. 2007. (FRE & ENG.). 344p. pap. 39.95 *(978-1-55002-696-2(8)*, Dundurn Pr.) Dundurn CAN. Dist: Ingram Pub. Services.
Horn, Bernd & Legault, Roch, eds. Loyal Service: Perspectives on French-Canadian Military Leaders. 2007. (ENG., Illus.). 336p. pap. 39.95 *(978-1-55002-693-1(3)*, Dundurn Pr.) Dundurn CAN. Dist: Ingram Pub. Services.
Jackson, Paul. One of the Boys: Homosexuality in the Military during World War II. 2nd ed. 2010. (ENG., Illus.). 376p. pap. *(978-0-7735-3714-9(7))* McGill-Queen's Univ. Pr.
Keery, Paul. Canada at War: A Graphic History of World War Two, 1 vol. 2012. (ENG., Illus.). 176p. (gr. 8). pap. 24.95 *(978-1-55365-596-1(6))* D&M Pubs. Inc. CAN. Dist: Perseus-PGW.
Laxer, James. Mission of Folly: Canada & Afghanistan. 2008. 168p. pap. 22.95 *(978-1-897071-37-3(X))* Between the Lines CAN. Dist: Univ. of Toronto Pr.
Legault, Roch & Horn, Bernd, eds. Le Leadership Militaire Canadien Français: Continuité, Efficacité et Loyauté. 2007. (FRE & ENG., Illus.). 368p. pap. 39.95 *(978-1-55002-695-5(X)*, Dundurn Pr.) Dundurn CAN. Dist: Ingram Pub. Services.
Maloney, Sean. Fighting for Afghanistan. 2011. (Illus.). 352p. 36.95 *(978-1-59114-509-7(0))* Naval Institute Pr.
Mantle, Craig L., ed. The Apathetic & the Defiant: Case Studies of Canadian Mutiny & Disobedience, 1812-1919. 2007. (ENG., Illus.). 496p. pap. 49.95 *(978-1-55002-710-5(7)*, Dundurn Pr.) Dundurn CAN. Dist: Ingram Pub. Services.
Mantle, Craig Leslie & Mantle, Craig L. Les Apathiques et les Rebelles: Des Exemples Canadiens de Mutinerie et de Desobeissance, 1812 A 1919. 2007. (FRE., Illus.). 392p. pap. 49.95 *(978-1-55002-720-4(4)*, Dundurn Pr.) Dundurn CAN. Dist: Ingram Pub. Services.
Montague, Art. Canadian Forces: An Historical Salute to Those on the Front Line. 2011. (ENG., Illus.). 208p. pap. 19.95 *(978-1-926916-09-5(3))* MacIntyre & Purcell Publishing CAN. Dist: Independent Pubs. Group.
National Defence Act. pap. *(978-0-660-16791-6(3))* Canadian Government Publishing.
Pierrebourg, Fabrice de. Martyrs D'une Guerre Perdue D'avance: Le Canada en Afghanistan. 2010. (FRE., Illus.). 270p. *(978-2-7604-1073-2(0))* Editions Internationales Alain Stanke, Limitee.
Pigott, Peter. Canada in Afghanistan: The War So Far. 2007. (ENG., Illus.). 240p. 35.00 *(978-1-55002-674-0(7)*, Dundurn Pr.) Dundurn CAN. Dist: Ingram Pub. Services.
—From Far & Wide: A Complete History of Canada's Arctic Sovereignty. 2011. (ENG., Illus.). 312p. 35.00 *(978-1-55488-987-7(1))* Dundurn CAN. Dist: Ingram Pub. Services.
Plamondon, Aaron. The Politics of Procurement: Military Acquisitions in Canada & the Sea King Helicopter. 2010. (ENG., Illus.). 288p. (C). pap. 35.95 *(978-0-7748-1715-8(1))* UBC Pr. CAN. Dist: Univ. of Washington Pr.
Pupetz, Ron. In the Line of Duty: Canadian Joint Forces Somalia, 1992-1993. (Illus.). 291p. pap. 11.95 *(978-1-55068-110-9(9))* Vanwell Publishing, Ltd CAN. Dist: Howell Pr.
Reid, Brian A. Named by the Enemy: A History of the Royal Winnipeg Rifles. 2010. 300p. 75.00 *(978-1-896941-60-8(5))* Brass, Robin Studio, Inc. CAN. Dist: Midpoint Trade Bks., Inc.
Rennick, Joanne. Religion in the Ranks: Belief & Religious Experience in the Canadian Forces. 2011. (Illus.). 224p. *(978-1-4426-4287-4(4))* Univ. of Toronto Pr.
Sroka, Mike. Snowbirds: Behind the Scenes with Canada's Air Demonstration Team, 1 vol. 2006. (ENG., Illus.). 160p. 14.95 *(978-1-894856-86-7(4))* Fifth Hse. Pubs. CAN. Dist: Ingram Pub. Services.
Stewart, Lyle, ed. Afghanistan & Canada: Is There an Alternative to the War? 2009. (ENG.). 224p. 44.99 *(978-1-55164-329-8(4))*; pap. 24.99 *(978-1-55164-328-1(6))* Black Rose Bks. CAN. Dist: Consortium Bk. Sales & Distribution.
Thompson, Roy. Cap Badges & Insignia of the Canadian Army, 1953-1973. rev. ed. (Military Reference Ser.). (Illus.). 220p. reprint ed. pap. 13.00 *(978-1-878973-05-4(3))* House of History.
Wakelam, Randall, et al, eds. The Report of the Officer Development Board: Maj-Gen Roger Rowley & the Education of the Canadian Forces. 2010. (ENG.). 370p. (C). pap. 49.95 *(978-0-9783441-9-1(7))* Wilfrid Laurier Univ. Pr. CAN. Dist: Univ. of Toronto Pr.
Whelan, Dianne. This Vanishing Land: A Woman's Journey to the Canadian Arctic. 2009. (ENG., Illus.). 160p. pap. 28.95 *(978-1-894759-38-0(9))* Caitlin Pr., Inc. CAN. Dist: Ingram Pub. Services.
Whitlock, Flint. If Chaos Reigns: The Near-Disaster & Ultimate Triumph of the Allied Airborne Forces on D-Day, June 6 1944. 2011. (Illus.). 352p. 29.95 *(978-1-61200-000-8(2))* Casemate Pubs. & Bk. Distributors, LLC.
Williams, Alan S. Reinventing Canadian Defence Procurement: A View from the Inside. 2007. (Illus.). 168p. per. *(978-0-9781693-0-5(1))* Breakout Educational Network.
Windsor, Lee A., et al. Kandahar Tour: The Turning Point in Canada's Afghan Mission. 2010. (ENG., Illus.). 256p. 36.95 *(978-0-470-15761-9(5)*, Wiley) Wiley, John & Sons, Inc.
Winegard, Timothy C. For King & Kanata: Canadian Indians & the First World War. 2012. (ENG., Illus.). 240p. pap. 28.95 *(978-0-88755-728-6(7))* Univ. of Manitoba Pr. CAN. Dist: Chicago Distribution Ctr.
Winslow, Donna & Commission of Inquiry into the Deployment of Canadian Forces to Somalia. A Socio-Cultural Inquiry into the Activities of the Canadian Airborne Regiment in Somalia. pap. *(978-0-660-16944-6(4))* Canadian Government Publishing.
Wiss, Ray. A Line in the Sand: Canadians at War in Kandahar, 1 vol. 2011. (ENG., Illus.). 424p. pap. 18.95 *(978-1-55365-926-6(0))*; 29.95 *(978-1-55365-592-3(3))* D&M Pubs. Inc. CAN. Dist: Perseus-PGW.
Wiss, Ray H. FOB Doc: A Doctor on the Front Lines in Afghanistan - A War Diary, 1 vol. 2010. (ENG., Illus.). 224p. 26.95 *(978-1-55365-472-8(2))* D&M Pubs. Inc. CAN. Dist: Perseus-PGW.

CANADA—CANADIAN ARMY

Balzer, Timothy. The Information Front: The Canadian Army & News Management during the Second World War. 2011. (Studies in Canadian Military History Series Published in Association with the Canadian War Museum Ser.). (ENG., Illus.). 272p. pap. 35.95 *(978-0-7748-1900-8(6))* UBC Pr. CAN. Dist: Univ. of Washington Pr.
Barnholden, Michael. Circumstances Alter Photographs: Captin James Peters' Reports from the War of 1885. 2009. (ENG., Illus.). 144p. 35.00 *(978-0-88922-621-0(0))* Talonbooks, Ltd. CAN. Dist: Consortium Bk. Sales & Distribution.
Barris, Ted. Victory at Vimy: Canada Comes of Age, April 9-12, 1917. 2007. (ENG., Illus.). 368p. *(978-0-88762-253-3(4))* Allen, Thomas Pubs.
Bennett, Y. A., ed. Kiss the Kids for Dad, Don't Forget to Write: The Wartime Letters of George Timmins, 1916-18. 2010. (ENG.). 224p. pap. 32.95 *(978-0-7748-1609-0(0))* Univ. of Washington Pr.
Bick, Arthur Hardie & Bick, Peter Hardie. The Diary of an Artillery Officer: The First Canadian Divisional Artillery on the Western Front. 2011. (ENG., Illus.). 224p. 28.99 *(978-1-4597-0040-6(6))* Dundurn CAN. Dist: Ingram Pub. Services.

C

Bjarnason, Dan. Triumph at Kapyong: Canada's Pivotal Battle in Korea. 2011. (ENG., Illus.). 200p. pap. 22.99 *(978-1-55488-872-6(7)*, Dundurn Pr.) Dundurn CAN. Dist: Ingram Pub. Services.

Blaxland, John C. Strategic Cousins: Australian & Canadian Expeditionary Forces & the British & American Empires. 2006. (ENG., Illus.). 432p. (C). per. *(978-0-7735-3064-5(9))* McGill-Queen's Univ. Pr.

Boileau, John. Canada's Soldiers in South Africa: Tales from the Boer War, 1899-1902. 2011. (Amazing Stories Ser.). (ENG., Illus.). 144p. pap. 9.95 *(978-1-55277-725-1(1))* Lorimer, James & Co., Ltd., Pubs. CAN. Dist: Casemate Pubs. & Bk. Distributors, LLC.

BOURASSA, Rollie, ed. One Family's War: The Wartime Letters of Clarence Bourassa(1940-1944) 2010. (Trade Books Based in Scholarship(TBS) Ser.). (ENG.). 596p. pap. 29.95 *(978-0-88977-221-2(5))* Canadian Plains Research Ctr. CAN. Dist: Univ. of Toronto Pr.

Cassar, George H. Hell in Flanders Fields: Canadians at the Second Battle of Ypres. 2010. (ENG., Illus.). 424p. 36.00 *(978-1-55488-728-6(3))* Dundurn CAN. Dist: Ingram Pub. Services.

Chartrand, Rene. The Canadian Corps in World War I. 2007. (Men-at-Arms (Osprey) Ser.). (ENG., Illus.). 48p. pap. 17.95 *(978-1-84603-186-1(9))* Osprey Publishing, Ltd. GBR. Dist: Random Hse., Inc.

Conrad, John. What the Thunder Said: Reflections of a Canadian Officer in Kandahar. 2009. (ENG., Illus.). 240p. pap. 29.95 *(978-1-55488-408-7(X)*, Dundurn Pr.) Dundurn CAN. Dist: Ingram Pub. Services.

Copp, Terry. The Brigade: The Fifth Canadian Infantry Brigade in World War II. 2007. (Stackpole Military History Ser.). (ENG., Illus.). 208p. per. 16.95 *(978-0-8117-3422-6(6))* Stackpole Bks.

—Canadian Battlefields 1915-18: A Visitor's Guide. 2011. (ENG.). 130p. (C). pap. 32.99 ***(978-1-926804-11-8(2))*** Wilfrid Laurier Univ. Pr. CAN. Dist: Univ. of Toronto Pr.

—Cinderella Army: The Canadians in Northwest Europe, 1944-1945. 2007. (ENG., Illus.). 392p. pap. *(978-0-8020-9522-0(4))* Univ. of Toronto Pr.

—Cinderella Army: The Canadians in Northwest Europe 1944-1945. 2006. (ENG., Illus.). 392p. *(978-0-8020-3925-5(1))* Univ. of Toronto Pr.

—1st Canadian Radar Battery 1944-45. 2010. (Laurier Military History Ser.). (ENG., Illus.). 48p. (C). pap. 14.95 *(978-1-926804-05-7(8))* Wilfrid Laurier Univ. Pr. CAN. Dist: Univ. of Toronto Pr.

Desquesnes, Rémy. The Canadians in Europe's Rescue. 2011. (ENG & FRE., Illus.). 112p. pap. 49.90 *(978-2-8151-0029-8(0))* OREP Edition & Communication FRA. Dist: Casemate Pubs. & Bk. Distributors, LLC.

Dickson, Paul Douglas. A Thoroughly Canadian General: A Biography of General H. D. G. Crerar. 2007. (ENG., Illus.). 528p. *(978-0-8020-0802-2(X))* Univ. of Toronto Pr.

Engen, Robert. Canadians under Fire: Infantry Effectiveness in the Second World War. 2009. (ENG., Illus.). 240p. (C). *(978-0-7735-3626-5(4))* McGill-Queen's Univ. Pr.

English, John A. & English, John. The Canadian Army & the Normandy Campaign. 2009. (Military History Ser.). (ENG., Illus.). 352p. pap. 21.95 *(978-0-8117-3576-6(1))* Stackpole Bks.

Falconer, Simon. Canada's Black Watch: An Illustrated History of the Regular Force Battalions 1951-1970. 2008. (ENG., Illus.). 168p. 35.00 *(978-0-86492-521-3(2))* Goose Lane Editions CAN. Dist: Univ. of Toronto Pr.

Faryon, Cynthia. Unsung Heroes of the Canadian Army: Incredible Tales of Courage & Daring During World War II. 2006. (ENG., Illus.). 112p. pap. 9.95 *(978-1-55439-009-0(5))* Lorimer, James & Co., Ltd., Pubs. CAN. Dist: Casemate Pubs. & Bk. Distributors, LLC.

Fleming, R. B., ed. The Wartime Letters of Leslie & Cecil Frost, 1915-1919. 2007. (Life Writing Ser.). (ENG., Illus.). 420p. 45.95 *(978-1-55458-000-2(5))* Wilfrid Laurier Univ. Pr. CAN. Dist: Univ. of Toronto Pr.

Hayes, Adrian. Pegahmagabow: Life-Long Warrior. 2009. (ENG.). 165p. pap. 19.95 *(978-0-9784982-9-0(1))* Dundurn CAN. Dist: Ingram Pub. Services.

Hayes, Geoffrey. The Lincs: A History of the Lincoln & Welland Regiment at War. 2nd ed. 2007. (ENG., Illus.). 129p. (C). pap. 24.95 *(978-0-9783441-1-5(1))* Wilfrid Laurier Univ. Pr. CAN. Dist: Univ. of Toronto Pr.

Hesler, William. Muleskinner: The European War of a Niagara Artilleryman. 2010. 152p. 24.95 *(978-1-4502-7158-5(8))*; pap. 14.95 *(978-1-4502-7157-8(X))* iUniverse, Inc.

Horn, Bernd. Establishing a Legacy: The History of the Royal Canadian Regiment, 1883-1953. 2008. (ENG., Illus.). 408p. pap. 39.95 *(978-1-55002-817-1(0)*, Dundurn Pr.) Dundurn CAN. Dist: Ingram Pub. Services.

—From Cold War to New Millennium: The History of the Royal Canadian Regiment, 1953-2008. 2011. (Illus.). 424p. pap. 39.95 ***(978-1-55488-898-6(0))***; (ENG., 49.95 *(978-1-55488-896-2(4)*, Dundurn Pr.); (ENG., pap. 39.95 *(978-1-55488-895-5(6)*, Dundurn Pr.); (ENG., lthr. 80.00 *(978-1-55488-897-9(2)*, Dundurn Pr.) Dundurn CAN. Dist: Univ. of Toronto Pr., Ingram Pub. Services.

Iarocci, Andrew. Shoestring Soldiers: The 1st Canadian Division at War, 1914-1915. 2008. (Illus.). 384p. *(978-0-8020-9822-1(3))* Univ. of Toronto Pr.

Isitt, Benjamin. From Victoria to Vladivostok: Canada's Siberian Expedition, 1917-19. 2010. (ENG., Illus.). 352p. (C). pap. 32.95 *(978-0-7748-1802-5(6))* Univ. of British Columbia Pr. CAN. Dist: Univ. of Washington Pr.

Jarymowycz, Roman. Tank Tactics: From Normandy to Lorraine, 1 vol. 2008. (Military History Ser.). (ENG., Illus.). 384p. pap. 21.95 *(978-0-8117-3559-9(1))* Stackpole Bks.

Jeanne, édérick. Caen 1944. 2011. (FRE., Illus.). 160p. 39.95 *(978-2-84048-284-0(3))* Editions Heimdal FRA. Dist: Casemate Pubs. & Bk. Distributors, LLC.

Johnson, Charles Monroe. Action with the Seaforths. 2011. 348p. 51.95 ***(978-1-258-06466-2(9))*** Literary Licensing, LLC.

Johnson, David E. & Gordon, John, IV. Observations on Recent Trends in Armored Forces. 2010. 14p. pap. 20.00 *(978-0-8330-4927-8(5))* RAND Corp., The.

Lackenbauer, P. Whitney & Kikkert, Peter. The Canadian Forces & Arctic Sovereignty: Debating Roles, Interests, & Requirements, 1968-1974. 2010. (ENG., Illus.). 398p. (C). pap. 34.95 *(978-1-926804-00-2(7))* Wilfrid Laurier Univ. Pr. CAN. Dist: Univ. of Toronto Pr.

MacFarlane, John. Triquet's Cross: A Study of Military Heroism. 2009. (ENG., Illus.). 232p. (C). *(978-0-7735-3577-0(2))* McGill-Queen's Univ. Pr.

Marquis, T. G. Canada's Sons on Kopje & Veldta Hstorical Account of the Canadian Contingents. 2009. 514p. pap. *(978-1-84734-952-1(8))* Naval & Military Pr., The.

McBride, Herbert W. A Rifleman Went to War. 2011. 416p. pap. 13.95 ***(978-1-61427-167-3(4))***; pap. 14.65 ***(978-1-61427-063-8(5))*** Martino Publishing.

McGeer, Eric & Symes, Matt. The Canadian Battlefields in Italy: Ortona & the Liri Valley. 2007. (ENG.). 112p. (C). pap. 32.95 *(978-0-9783441-0-8(3))* Wilfrid Laurier Univ. Pr. CAN. Dist: Univ. of Toronto Pr.

—The Canadian Battlefields in Italy: Sicily & Southern Italy. 2008. (ENG., Illus.). 85p. (C). pap. 32.95 *(978-0-9783441-5-3(4))* Wilfrid Laurier Univ. Pr. CAN. Dist: Univ. of Toronto Pr.

—The Canadian Battlefields in Italy: The Gothic Line & the Battle of the Rivers. 2010. (ENG.). 140p. (C). pap. 34.95 *(978-1-926804-07-1(4))* Wilfrid Laurier Univ. Pr. CAN. Dist: Univ. of Toronto Pr.

Nickerson, Janice. York's Sacrifice: Militia Casualties of the War of 1812. 2012. (ENG., Illus.). 224p. pap. 19.99 ***(978-1-4597-0595-1(5))*** Dundurn CAN. Dist: Ingram Pub. Services.

Norris, Marjorie Barron, ed. Medicine & Duty: The World War I Memoir of Captain Harold W. Mcgill, Medical Officer, 31st Batallion C. E. F. 2007. (Legacies Shared Ser.). (ENG., Illus.). 406p. per. 39.95 *(978-1-55238-193-9(5))* Univ. of Calgary Pr. CAN. Dist: Chicago Distribution Ctr.

Rickard, J. N. Politics of Command: Lieutenant-General A. G. L. McNaughton & the Canadian Army, 1939-1943. 2010. (Illus.). 416p. *(978-1-4426-4002-3(2))* Univ. of Toronto Pr.

Rickard, John Nelson. Politics of Command: Lieutenant-General Andrew Mcnaughton & the Canadian Army, 1939-1943. 2008. (Illus.). 224p. 34.95 *(978-1-55125-132-5(9))* Vanwell Publishing, Ltd. CAN. Dist: Casemate Pubs. & Bk. Distributors, LLC.

Saunders, Tim. Operation Varsity: Rhine Crossing: The British & Canadian Airborne Assault. 2007. (Illus.). 192p. pap. 24.95 *(978-1-84415-601-6(X))* Pen & Sword Bks. Ltd. GBR. Dist: Casemate Pubs. & Bk. Distributors, LLC.

Sendzikas, Aldona. Stanley Barracks: Toronto's Military Legacy. 2011. (ENG., Illus.). 212p. pap. 29.99 *(978-1-55488-788-0(7))* Dundurn CAN. Dist: Ingram Pub. Services.

Shaw, Susan Evans. Canadians at War: A Guide to the Battlefields of World War I. 2011. (Illus.). 352p. pap. 24.95 *(978-0-86492-654-8(5))* Goose Lane Editions CAN. Dist: Univ. of Toronto Pr.

Singer, Horace C. History of the 31st Canadian Infantry Battalion C. E. F. Knight, Darrell, ed. 2006. (Illus.). 523p. 64.95 *(978-1-55059-316-7(1))* Detselig Enterprises, Ltd. CAN. Dist: Temeron Bks., Inc.

Sliz, John. Storm Boat Kings: The 23Rd R. C. E. at Arnhem 1944. 2009. (Illus.). 128p. 24.95 *(978-1-55125-103-5(5))* Vanwell Publishing, Ltd. CAN. Dist: Casemate Pubs. & Bk. Distributors, LLC.

Teed, Valerie, ed. Uncle Cy's War: The First World War Letters of Major Cyrus F. Inches. 2009. (New Brunswick Military Heritage Ser.). (ENG., Illus.). 304p. pap. 18.95 *(978-0-86492-542-8(5))* Goose Lane Editions CAN. Dist: Univ. of Toronto Pr.

Theobald, Andrew. The Bitter Harvest of War: New Brunswick & the Conscription Crisis of 1917. 2008. (New Brunswick Military Heritage Ser.). (ENG., Illus.). 124p. pap. 16.95 *(978-0-86492-511-4(5))* Goose Lane Editions CAN. Dist: Univ. of Toronto Pr.

Thomas, Yann. Juno Beach: The Canadian Assault. 2011. (Illus.). 32p. pap. 10.95 *(978-2-8151-0038-0(X))* OREP Edition & Communication FRA. Dist: Casemate Pubs. & Bk. Distributors, LLC.

Toman, Cynthia. An Officer & a Lady: Canadian Military Nursing & the Second World War. 2007. (Studies in Canadian Military History Ser.). (ENG., Illus.). 272p. *(978-0-7748-1447-8(0))* Univ. of British Columbia Pr.

Watson, Brent Byron. Far Eastern Tour: The Canadian Infantry in Korea, 1950-1953. 2007. (ENG.). 260p. (C). per. *(978-0-7735-3258-8(7))* McGill-Queen's Univ. Pr.

Wattie, Chris. Contact Charlie: The Canadian Army, the Taliban & the Battle That Saved Afghanistan. 2009. (ENG., Illus.). 304p. 28.95 *(978-1-55470-084-4(1))* Key Porter Bks. CAN. Dist: Perseus-PGW.

—Contact Charlie: The Canadian Army, the Taliban, & the Battle That Saved Afghanistan. 2010. (ENG., Illus.). 304p. pap. 16.95 *(978-1-55470-276-3(3))* Key Porter Bks. CAN. Dist: Perseus-PGW.

Windsor, Lee A. Steel Cavalry: The 8th (New Brunswick) Hussars & the Second World War. 2011. 120p. pap. 16.95 ***(978-0-86492-657-9(X))*** Goose Lane Editions CAN. Dist: Univ. of Toronto Pr.

Zuehlke, Mark. Assault on Juno, 1 vol. 2012. (Rapid Reads Ser.). (ENG.). 160p. pap. 9.95 ***(978-1-4598-0036-6(2)***, Raven Bks.) Literations.

—Brave Battalion: The Remarkable Saga of the 16th Battalion (Canadian Scottish) in the First World War. 2008. (ENG.). 272p. 36.95 *(978-0-470-15416-8(0)*, Wiley) Wiley, John & Sons, Inc.

—Breakout from Juno: First Canadian Army & the Normandy Campaign, July 4-August 21 1944, 1 vol. 2012. (ENG., Illus.). 544p. 36.95 ***(978-1-55365-325-7(4))*** D&M Pubs. Inc. CAN. Dist: Perseus-PGW.

—The Gothic Line: Canada's Month of Hell in World War II Italy, 1 vol. 2006. (ENG., Illus.). 592p. pap. 24.95 *(978-1-55365-068-3(9))* D&M Pubs. Inc. CAN. Dist: Perseus-PGW.

—On to Victory: The Canadian Liberation of the Netherlands, March 23-May 5 1945, 1 vol. (ENG., Illus.). 552p. 2011. pap. 27.95 *(978-1-55365-813-9(2))* 2010. 35.00 *(978-1-55365-430-8(7))* D&M Pubs. Inc. CAN. Dist: Perseus-PGW.

—Operation Husky: The Canadian Invasion of Sicily, July 10-August 7, 1943, 1 vol. 2009. (ENG., Illus.). 520p. 35.00 *(978-1-55365-324-0(6))* D&M Pubs. Inc. CAN. Dist: Perseus-PGW.

—Operation Husky: The Canadian Invasion of Sicily, July 10-August 7 1943, 1 vol. 2010. (ENG., Illus.). 520p. pap. 24.95 *(978-1-55365-539-8(7))* D&M Pubs. Inc. CAN. Dist: Perseus-PGW.

—Ortona Street Fight, 1 vol. 2011. (Rapid Reads Ser.). (ENG., Illus.). 144p. pap. 9.95 ***(978-1-55469-398-6(5)***, Raven Bks.) Literations.

Zuehlke, Mark. Terrible Victory: First Canadian Army & the Scheldt Estuary Campaign, September 13-November 6 1944, 1 vol. 2007. (ENG., Illus.). 560p. 30.00 *(978-1-55365-227-4(4))* D&M Pubs. Inc. CAN. Dist: Perseus-PGW.

CANADA—CENSUS

Canada 1770-1777 Census Index Nova Scotia. (Illus.). lib. bdg. 33.00 *(978-0-89593-233-4(4)*, Accelerated Indexing Systems International (AISI)) Genealogical Services.

Canada 1848-1850 Census Index Upper Canada. (Illus.). lib. bdg. 80.00 *(978-0-89593-237-2(7)*, Accelerated Indexing Systems International (AISI)) Genealogical Services.

Canada 1881 Census Index New Brunswick. (Illus.). lib. bdg. *(978-0-89593-242-6(3)*, Accelerated Indexing Systems International (AISI)) Genealogical Services.

Canada 1881 Census Index Northwest Territory (Includes Alberta, Sasawatchen, & Yukon Territory) (Illus.). lib. bdg. 120.00 *(978-0-89593-240-2(7)*, Accelerated Indexing Systems International (AISI)) Genealogical Services.

James, June. 1891 Ontario Census: Bexley Township, Victoria County. 2007. ii, 34p. pap. ***(978-0-7779-3352-7(7))*** Ontario Genealogical Society.

Kanen-Smith, Shirley. 1861 Census: Town of St. Catharines: Part 3, St. George's Ward, District 7 & St. Thomas Ward, District 8, Grantham Township, Lincoln County. 2008. 46p. pap. ***(978-0-7779-3833-1(2))*** Ontario Genealogical Society.

Thompson, Phyllis. 1861 Census for Goderich Township, Huron County: Transcribed from Microfilm, Fully Indexed. 2007. (Illus.). 74p. pap. ***(978-0-7779-1777-0(7))*** Ontario Genealogical Society.

CANADA—CHURCH HISTORY

Attridge, Michael, et al, eds. Vatican II: Experiences Canadiennes - Canadian Experiences. 2011. (Religion & Beliefs Ser.). (ENG & FRE.). 580p. pap. *(978-2-7603-0763-6(8))* Univ. of Ottawa Pr./Presses de l'Universite d'Ottawa.

Bigart, Robert J., ed. Crossroad of Cultures: Sacramental Records at St. John the Baptist Catholic Church, Frenchtown, Montana, 1866-1899. Scott, Anita O. & Scott, James M., trs. from LAT. 2009. (Illus.). 240p. pap. 12.95 *(978-1-934594-05-6(9))* Salish Kootenia College Pr.

Cahill, Barry, et al. The Blue Banner: The Presbyterian Church of Saint David & Presbyterian Witness in Halifax. 2008. (ENG., Illus.). 352p. (C). *(978-0-7735-3358-5(3))* McGill-Queen's Univ. Pr.

Christie/Gauvreau, Nancy/Michael. Religion, Peoples & the Making Of. 2010. (Themes in Canadian History Ser.). x, 232p. *(978-0-8020-8949-6(6))* Univ. of Toronto Pr.

—Religion,Peoples & the Making Of. 2010. x, 232p. pap. *(978-0-8020-8632-7(2))* Univ. of Toronto Pr.

Gauvreau, Michael & Hubert, Ollivier. The Churches & Social Order in Nineteenth- & Twentieth-Century Canada. 2006. (McGill-Queen's Studies in the History of Religion Ser.). (ENG., Illus.). 328p. (C). per. *(978-0-7735-3098-0(3))* McGill-Queen's Univ. Pr.

Gottlieb, Laurence. The Catholic Church & Economic Growth in Quebec from 1919 to 1929. 2007. (Illus.). 147p. *(978-0-7734-5321-0(0))* Mellen, Edwin Pr., The.

Healey, Robynne. From Quaker to Upper Canadian: Faith & Community among Yonge Street Friends, 1801-1850. 2006. (McGill-Queen's Studies in the History of Religion Ser.). (ENG., Illus.). 320p. (C). *(978-0-7735-3136-9(X))* McGill-Queen's Univ. Pr.

Heath, Gordon L. A War with a Silver Lining: Canadian Protestant Churches & the South African War, 1899-1902. 2009. (McGill-Queen's Studies in the History of Religion Ser.). (ENG., Illus.). 240p. (C). *(978-0-7735-3480-3(6))* McGill-Queen's Univ. Pr.

Héroux, Florent J. La Ferveur Continue: Notre-Dame-Du-Sacré-Cur, North Cobalt, Ontario. 2010. (FRE & ENG., Illus.). 140p. *(978-0-9680298-8-6(4))* Heroux, Florent J.

Hollett, Calvin. Shouting, Embracing, & Dancing with Ecstasy: The Growth of Methodism in Newfoundland, 1774-1874. 2010. (McGill-Queen's Studies in the History of Religion Ser.). (ENG., Illus.). 368p. (C). *(978-0-7735-3671-5(X))* McGill-Queen's Univ. Pr.

Hubert, Ollivier. The Churches & Social Order in Nineteenth- & Twentieth-Century Canada. Gauvreau, Michael, ed. 2006. (McGill-Queen's Studies in the History of Religion). (ENG., Illus.). 328p. (C). *(978-0-7735-3057-7(6))* McGill-Queen's Univ. Pr.

Jones, Gordon F. A Month of Sundays. 2011. ***(978-0-9865683-5-0(X))*** Erser & Pond Pubs., Ltd.

Jones, Preston. A Highly Favored Nation: The Bible & Canadian Meaning, 1860-1900. 2007. (ENG.). 132p. per. 28.50 *(978-0-7618-3903-3(8))* Univ. Pr. of America, Inc.

Letourneau, David, et al. Bent but Not Broken: Today's Canadian Church. 176p. pap. *(978-0-9695180-1-3(3))* Shoreline.

MacKenzie, R. Sheldon. The Master Teacher: Sermons from Mark. 2007. 170p. *(978-0-7880-2189-3(3)*, Fairway Pr.) CSS Publishing Co.

Noll, Mark A. What Ever Happened to Christian Canada. 2007. (ENG.). 60p. per. *(978-1-57383-405-6(X)*, Regent College Publishing) Regent College Publishing.

Pacey, Elizabeth & Fitch, Sheree. Kisses Kisses, Baby-O! 2008. (Illus.). 10p. (J). bds. 6.50 *(978-1-55109-464-9(9))* Nimbus Publishing, Ltd. CAN. Dist: Orca Bk. Pubs. USA.

Pratt, Ron. Declarari. 2006. 376p. per. 24.35 *(978-1-4120-8974-6(3))* Trafford Publishing.

Renfree, Harry A. Heritage & Horizon: The Baptist Story in Canada. 2007. (Illus.). 408p. pap. 46.00 *(978-1-55635-138-9(0)*, Wipf and Stock) Wipf & Stock Pubs.

Vissers, John. The Neo-Orthodox Theology of W. W. Bryden. 2011. (ENG.). 296p. pap. 40.00 *(978-0-227-17370-1(8))* Clarke, James Co., Ltd. GBR. Dist: Brown, David Bk. Co., The.

Wilkinson, Michael. Canadian Pentecostalism: Transition & Transformation. 2009. (McGill-Queen's Studies in the History of Religion). (ENG.). 328p. (C). *(978-0-7735-3457-5(1))* McGill-Queen's Univ. Pr.

Wilkinson, Michael & Althouse, Peter. Winds from the North: Canadian Contributions to the Pentecostal Movement. 2010. (Religion in the Americas Ser.). 281p. *(978-90-04-18574-6(7))* BRILL.

Zuidema, Jason, ed. The History of French-Speaking Protestantism in Quebec. 2011. (Religion in the Americas Ser.). (Illus.). 310p. ***(978-90-04-21176-6(4))*** BRILL.

CANADA—CIVILIZATION

Bennett, John W. & Bennett, John. Northern Plainsmen: Adaptive Strategy & Agrarian Life. 2007. (ENG., Illus.). 368p. pap. 34.95 *(978-0-202-30964-4(9))* Transaction Pubs.

Berland, Jody. North of Empire: Essays on the Cultural Technologies of Space. 2009. (ENG., Illus.). 408p. 94.95 *(978-0-8223-4288-5(X))*; pap. 26.95 *(978-0-8223-4306-6(1))* Duke Univ. Pr.

Bibby, Reginald W. The Boomer Factor: What Canada's Most Famous Generation Is Leaving Behind. 2006. (ENG.). 192p. pap. *(978-0-9780554-4-8(6))* ECW Pr. CAN. Dist: Independent Pubs. Group.

Caplan, Ron, ed. Magnificent Obsessions: They Wrote about Cape Breton They Wrote about Cape Breton, 1 vol. 2010. (Illus.). 168p. pap. *(978-1-895415-96-4(9))* Breton Bks.

Cheadle, Norman & Pelletier, Lucien, eds. Canadian Cultural Exchange (Échanges Culturels au Canada) Translation & Transculturation (Traduction et Transculturation) 2007. (Cultural Studies Ser.). (FRE & ENG.). 432p. 85.00 *(978-0-88920-519-2(1))* Wilfrid Laurier Univ. Pr. CAN. Dist: Univ. of Toronto Pr.

Christie, Nancy, ed. Transatlantic Subjects: Ideas, Institutions, & Social Experience in Post-Revolutionary British North America. 2008. (ENG., Illus.). 496p. (C). *(978-0-7735-3334-9(6))*; pap. *(978-0-7735-3388-2(5))* McGill-Queen's Univ. Pr.

Cowan, Paul. How the Scots Created Canada. 2007. (ENG., Illus.). 240p. pap. *(978-1-896124-10-0(0))* Dragon Hill Publishing CAN. Dist: Lone Pine Publishing.

Davies, Gwendolyn, ed. Myth & Milieu: Atlantic Literature & Culture, 1918-1939. 225p. pap. 14.95 *(978-0-919107-39-7(7))* Acadiensis Pr. CAN. Dist: Goose Lane Editions.

den Otter, A. A. Civilizing the Wilderness: Culture & Nature in Pre-Confederation Canada & Rupertis Land. 2012. (ENG., Illus.). 472p. pap. 49.95 *(978-0-88864-546-3(5))* Univ. of Alberta Pr. CAN. Dist: Michigan State Univ. Pr.

Di Sciascio-Andrews, Josie. How the Italians Created Canada: From Giovanni Caboto to the Cultural Renaissance. 2008. (ENG., Illus.). 240p. pap. *(978-1-896124-14-8(3))* Dragon Hill Publishing CAN. Dist: Lone Pine Publishing.

Dummitt, Christopher. The Manly Modern: Masculinity in Postwar Canada. 2007. (ENG., Illus.). 232p. 85.00 *(978-0-7748-1274-0(5))* UBC Pr. CAN. Dist: Univ. of Washington Pr.

Dyck, Ian, et al. A World Inside: A 150-Year History of the Canadian Museum of Civilization. 2007. (Illus.). 103p. per. 29.95 *(978-0-660-19558-2(5))* Canadian Museum of Civilization/Musee Canadien des Civilisations CAN. Dist: Univ. of Washington Pr.

Henderson, Paul & Prime, Jim. How Hockey Explains Canada: The Sport That Defines a Country. 2011. (ENG.). 208p. 32.95 ***(978-1-60078-575-7(1))*** Triumph Bks.

Hillmer, Norman & Chapnick, Adam. Canadas of the Mind: The Making & Unmaking of Canadian Nationalisms in the Twentieth Century. 2007. (ENG., Illus.). 336p. *(978-0-7735-3272-4(2))*; per. *(978-0-7735-3273-1(0))* McGill-Queen's Univ. Pr.

Hoerder, Dirk. To Know Our Many Selves: Changing Across Time & Space. 2010. (AU Press Ser.). (ENG.). 360p. (C). pap. 37.95 *(978-1-897425-72-5(4))* UBC Pr. CAN. Dist: Univ. of Washington Pr.

Ikas, Karin, ed. Global Realignments & the Canadian Nation in the Third Millennium. 2009. (Kultur- und sozialwissenschaftliche Studien /Studies in Cultural & Social Sciences Ser.). (ENG.). 242p. (C). 87.00 *(978-3-447-06134-6(0))* Harrassowitz, Otto Verlag DEU. Dist: ISD.

James, Patrick & Kasoff, Mark, eds. Canadian Studies in the New Millennium. 2007. (ENG., Illus.). 496p. pap. *(978-0-8020-9468-1(6))* Univ. of Toronto Pr.

Lewis, Thomas Tandy. The Forties in America, 3 vols., Set. 2010. 1296p. 364.00 *(978-1-58765-659-0(0))* Salem Pr., Inc.

Lewis, Thomas Tandy & Lewis, Thomas T. The Forties in America. 2010. *(978-1-58765-662-0(0))*; *(978-1-58765-661-3(2))*; *(978-1-58765-660-6(4))* Salem Pr., Inc.

Mookerjea, Sourayan, et al, eds. Canadian Cultural Studies: A Reader. 2009. (ENG.). 608p. 104.95 *(978-0-8223-4398-1(3))*; pap. 32.95 *(978-0-8223-4416-2(5))* Duke Univ. Pr.

Newhouse, David, et al. Hidden in Plain Sight - Vol. 2: Contributions of Aboriginal Peoples to Canadian Identity & Culture. 2009. (Illus.). (ENG.). *(978-1-4426-4074-0(X))*; pap. *(978-1-4426-1012-5(3))* Univ. of Toronto Pr.

Opp, James & Walsh, John C., eds. Placing Memory & Remembering Place in Canada. 2011. (ENG., Illus.). 352p. pap. 35.95 *(978-0-7748-1841-4(7))* UBC Pr. CAN. Dist: Univ. of Washington Pr.

Timpson, Annis May, ed. First Nations, First Thoughts: The Impact of Indigenous Thought in Canada. 2010. (ENG., Illus.). 336p. pap. 35.95 *(978-0-7748-1552-9(3))* Univ. of Washington Pr.

Tovias, Blanca. Colonialism on the Prairies: Blackfoot Settlement & Cultural Transformation, 1870-1920. 2011. (ENG., Illus.). 324p. 74.95 *(978-1-84519-307-2(5))* Sussex Academic Pr. GBR. Dist: International Specialized Bk. Services.

Vance, Jonathan F. A History of Canadian Culture. 2011. (ENG., Illus.). 512p. 24.95 *(978-0-19-544422-3(1))* Oxford Univ. Pr., Inc.

Vance, Jonathan F. Maple Leaf Empire: Canada, Britain, & Two World Wars. 2012. (ENG., Illus.). 272p. 35.00 ***(978-0-19-544809-2(X))*** Oxford Univ. Pr., Inc.

CANADA—CLIMATE

Danielson, Bill. Cape Breton Weather Watching: For the Naturally Curious. 2007. (Illus.). 280p. pap. *(978-1-897009-13-0(5))* Cape Breton Univ. Pr.

Hume, Bill. Weather of Alberta. 2008. (ENG., Illus.). 240p. pap. *(978-1-55105-602-9(X))* Lone Pine Publishing.

Paehlke, Robert C. & Paehlke, Robert. Some Like It Cold: The Politics of Climate Change in Canada. 2008. 168p. pap. 22.95 *(978-1-897071-39-7(6))* Between the Lines CAN. Dist: Univ. of Toronto Pr.

Philips, David. The Climates of Canada. 176p. pap. *(978-0-660-13459-8(4))* Canadian Government Publishing.

St. Clair, Chris. Canada's Weather: The Climate That Shapes a Nation. 2009. (ENG., Illus.). 232p. 29.95 *(978-1-55407-338-2(3))* Firefly Bks., Ltd.

Woo, Ming-ko, ed. Cold Region Atmospheric & Hydrologic Studies: The Mackenzie GEWEX Experience, Volumes 1-2, 2 vols. 2009. 1000p. 329.00 *(978-3-540-75135-9(1)*, 3540751351) Springer.

CANADA—COMMERCE

Barry, Patrick. The Theory & Practice of the International Trade of the United States & England, & of the Trade of the United States & Canada by P Barry. 2006. 180p. per. 18.99 *(978-1-4255-1418-1(9))* MPublishing.

Belisle, Donica. Retail Nation: Department Stores & the Making of Modern Canada. 2011. (ENG., Illus.). 320p. pap. 35.95 *(978-0-7748-1948-0(0))* UBC Pr. CAN. Dist: Univ. of Washington Pr.

Belyea, Barbara. Dark Storm Moving West. 2007. (ENG., Illus.). 205p. (C). pap. 49.95 *(978-1-55238-182-3(X))* Univ. of Calgary Pr. CAN. Dist: Chicago Distribution Ctr.

BIA. Essential Canadian Manufacturers: Food, Textile, Clothing, & Chemical Companies. 6th rev. ed. 2006. 400p. (J). pap. 249.00 *(978-1-4187-4236-2(8))* Business Information Agency.

Bratt, Duane. The Politics of Candu Exports. 2006. (Institute of Public Administration of Canada Series in Public Management & Governance Ser.). (ENG., Illus.). 336p. *(978-0-8020-9091-1(5))* Univ. of Toronto Pr.

Canada: Business Financing Handbook. (Illus.). 70p. (Orig.). pap. 295.00 *(978-0-7605-1184-8(5))* Rector Pr., Ltd.

Carlos, Ann M. & Lewis, Frank D. Commerce by a Frozen Sea: Native Americans & the European Fur Trade. 2010. (Illus.). 264p. (C). 49.95 *(978-0-8122-4231-7(9))* Univ. of Pennsylvania Pr.

Cushing, Caleb. The Treaty of Washington: Its Negotiation, Execution, & the Discussions Relating Thereto. 2009. 284p. 24.99 *(978-1-103-61375-5(8))*; pap. 18.99 *(978-1-103-61372-4(3))* BiblioBazaar.

Donaghy, Greg & Carroll, Michael, eds. In the National Interest: Canadian Foreign Policy & the Department of Foreign Affairs & International Trade, 1909-2009. 2011. (Beyond Boundaries: Canadian Defense And Ser.). (ENG.). 284p. pap. 41.95 ***(978-1-55238-538-8(8))*** Univ. of Calgary Pr. CAN. Dist: Chicago Distribution Ctr.

Elleboudt, Adrien S. The Limits of Consociationalism. 2008. 64p. pap. *(978-3-639-02271-1(8))* VDM Verlag Dr. Mueller e.K.

Environment Canada Staff. Men & Ships in the Canada Trade, 1660-1760: A Biographical Dictionary. pap. *(978-0-660-14449-8(2))* Canadian Government Publishing.

Finch, David. Hell's Half Acre: Early Years in the Great Alberta Oil Patch, 1 vol. 2009. (ENG., Illus.). 208p. pap. *(978-1-894384-82-7(2))* Heritage Hse.

Gordon, John S. Exporting to Canada: Documentation & Procedures. 2007. (ENG.). 284p. spiral bd. 69.00 *(978-1-891249-25-9(8))* Global Training Ctr.

Hübner, Kurt, ed. Europe, Canada & the Comprehensive Economic Partnership Agreement: Taming Globalization? 2011. (Routledge Studies in Governance & Change in the Global Era Ser.). (ENG., Illus.). 344p. (C). 140.00 *(978-0-415-60028-6(6))* Routledge.

Jollimore, Troy. Doing Business in Canada. Date not set. (Doing Business in Regions & Countries Around the World Ser.). 80p. *(978-1-882390-54-0(7))* Training Management Corp.

McGrath, James & Milnes, Arthur. Age of the Offered Hand: The Cross-Border Partnership Between President George H. W. Bush & Prime Minister Brian Mulroney, A Documentary History. 2009. (Library of Political Leadership Ser.). (ENG., Illus.). 144p. (C). pap. *(978-1-55339-232-3(9))* McGill-Queen's Univ. Pr.

McGrath, James & Milnes, Arthur, eds. Age of the Offered Hand: The Cross-Border Partnership Between President George H. W. Bush & Prime Minister Brian Mulroney, A Documentary History. 2009. (Library of Political Leadership Ser.). (ENG., Illus.). 144p. (C). *(978-1-55339-233-0(7))* McGill-Queen's Univ. Pr.

Ng, Alex. Performance of Stock Market Driven Acquisitions. 2009. 68p. pap. *(978-3-639-13685-2(3))* VDM Verlag Dr. Mueller e.K.

Paisey, Alan & Li, Jian. Transfer Pricing: A Diagrammatic & Case Study Introduction, with Special Reference to China. 2012. pap. ***(978-1-61233-549-0(7)*** Brown Walker Pr.) Universal Pubs.

Regular, Keith. Neighbours & Networks: The Blood Tribe in the Southern Alberta Economy, 1884-1939. 2008. (Northern Lights Ser.). (Illus.). 240p. pap. 34.95 *(978-1-55238-243-1(5))* Univ. of Calgary Pr. CAN. Dist: Michigan State Univ. Pr.

Urban Land Institute. Dollars & Cents of Shopping Centers/the SCORE: 2008. 2008. (ENG.). 576p. pap. 299.95 *(978-0-87420-094-2(6))* Urban Land Institute.

Wagner, Henry R. Peter Pond: Fur Trader & Explorer. 2011. 120p. 39.95 *(978-1-258-08443-1(0))* Literary Licensing, LLC.

Walls, Matthew. Caribou Inuit Traders of the Kivalliq Nunavut, Canada. 2009. (Bar S Ser.). (Illus.). 73p. (C). 62.50 *(978-1-4073-0377-2(5))* British Archaeological Reports Ltd. GBR. Dist: Brown, David Bk. Co., The.

Winroth, Anders. The Conversion of Scandinavia: Vikings, Merchants, & Missionaries in the Remaking of Northern Europe. 2012. (ENG., Illus.). 256p. 38.00 *(978-0-300-17026-9(2))* Yale Univ. Pr.

CANADA—CONSTITUTIONAL HISTORY

see Constitutional History—Canada

CANADA—CONSTITUTIONAL LAW

see Constitutional Law—Canada

CANADA—DEFENSES

Hillier, Rick. A Soldier First. 2010. 552p. pap. 18.99 *(978-0-06-202667-5(4))* HarperCollins Pubs.

Lackenbauer, P. Whitney & Kikkert, Peter. The Canadian Forces & Arctic Sovereignty: Debating Roles, Interests, & Requirements, 1968-1974. 2010. (ENG., Illus.). 398p. (C). pap. 34.95 *(978-1-926804-00-2(7))* Wilfrid Laurier Univ. Pr. CAN. Dist: Univ. of Toronto Pr.

Robinson, Charles Walker. Canada & Canadian Defence: The Defensive Policy of the Dominion in Relation to the Character of Her Frontier, the Events of the War of 1812-14 & Her Position To-Day. 186p. reprint ed. 88.00 *(978-0-7222-7846-8(2))* Library Reprints, Inc.

Sloan, Elinor C. Security & Defence in the Terrorist Era: Canada & the United States Homeland. 2nd ed. 2010. 216p. pap. *(978-0-7735-3694-4(9))* McGill-Queen's Univ. Pr.

—Security & Defence in the Terrorist Era - Canada & the United States Homeland. 2nd ed. 2010. (ENG.). 216p. (C). *(978-0-7735-3679-1(5))* McGill-Queen's Univ. Pr.

Tabuteau, Éric. "A Safe & Secure Canada" Politique et Enjeux Sécuritaires Au Canada Depuis le 11 Septembre 2001. Tolazzi, Sandrine, ed. 2011. (Études Canadiennes - Canadian Studies). (FRE.). 187p. pap. 45.95 ***(978-90-5201-715-0(8))*** PIE - Peter Lang BEL. Dist: Lang, Peter.

Wilson, Gordon. Defending North America from Bears. 2011. (Illus.). 208p. pap. 30.00 ***(978-1-4456-0263-9(6))*** Amberley Publishing GBR. Dist: Casemate Pubs. & Bk. Distributors, LLC.

CANADA—DESCRIPTION AND TRAVEL

Anburey, Thomas. Travels through the Interior Parts of America Set, 2 vols. (Illus.). reprint ed. lib. bdg. 250.00 *(978-0-7222-0906-6(1))* Library Reprints, Inc.

Anderson, Scott. Distant Fires: Duluth to Hudson Bay. 2008. (Illus.). 176p. pap. 15.95 *(978-0-8166-5503-8(0))* Univ. of Minnesota Pr.

Anonymous. Diary in America, Series One. 2009. 437p. pap. 26.99 *(978-1-117-50512-1(X)*, BiblioLife) BiblioBazaar.

Antor, Heinz, et al, eds. Refractions of Canada in European Literature & Culture. (ENG., Illus.). VIII, 301p. 255.00 ***(978-3-11-182056-9(4))*** De Gruyter, Walter Inc.

Arbizzani, Ron. Living Aboard a Boat Named Farfetched: A Couple Tells Their Story of Eight Years Living & Traveling Aboard Their Boat. 2008. 224p. pap. 15.95 *(978-0-595-52973-5(9))* iUniverse, Inc.

Armstrong, Bruce. Sable Island. 2nd rev. ed. 2010. (ENG., Illus.). 192p. pap. 29.95 *(978-0-88780-911-8(1))* Formac Publishing Co., Ltd. CAN. Dist: Casemate Pubs. & Bk. Distributors, LLC.

Arnott, Kim, et al. Hamilton Book of Everything: Everything You Wanted to Know about Hamilton & Were Going to Ask Anyway. 2008. (Book of Everything Ser.). (ENG.). 208p. pap. 14.95 *(978-0-9784784-6-9(0))* MacIntyre & Purcell Publishing CAN. Dist: Independent Pubs. Group.

Aubertin, J. A Fight with Distances: The States, the Hawaiian Islands, Canada, British Columbia, Cuba, the Bahamas. 2007. (Travel in America Ser.). (ENG.). 436p. 49.95 *(978-1-4290-0484-8(3))*; per. 24.95 *(978-1-4290-0485-5(1))* Applewood Bks.

Ballantyne, Robert Michael. Hudson Bay. 2008. 260p. 28.99 *(978-0-554-27683-0(6))* 2008. 260p. 25.99 *(978-0-554-36986-0(9))* 2007. (ENG.). 230p. pap. 20.99 *(978-1-4346-3757-4(3))* 2007. (ENG.). 256p. pap. 23.99 *(978-1-4346-3771-0(9))* BiblioBazaar.

Bates, E. A Year in the Great Republic. 2007. (Travel in America Ser.). (ENG.). Vol. 1. 316p. 49.95 *(978-1-4290-0476-3(2))* Vol. 1. 316p. per. 24.95 *(978-1-4290-0477-0(0))* Vol. 2. 332p. 49.95 *(978-1-4290-0474-9(6))* Applewood Bks.

Bird, Isabella L. The Englishwoman in America. 2009. (Cambridge Library Collection - History Ser.). 476p. pap. 35.99 *(978-1-108-00384-1(2))* Cambridge Univ. Pr.

—The Englishwoman in America. 2008. (ENG.). 312p. per. *(978-1-4065-9204-7(8))* Dodo Pr.

Bird, Isabella Lucy. The Englishwoman in America. 2007. (Travel in America Ser.). (ENG.). 480p. 49.95 *(978-1-4290-0336-0(7))*; per. 24.95 *(978-1-4290-0337-7(5))* Applewood Bks.

—The Englishwoman in America. 2008. 360p. 31.99 *(978-0-554-22526-5(3))* 2007. (ENG.). 332p. pap. 23.99 *(978-1-4264-2529-5(5))* 2007. (ENG.). 358p. pap. 26.99 *(978-1-4264-2552-3(X))* BiblioBazaar.

Bishop, Nathaniel Holmes. Voyage of the Paper Canoe: A geographical journey of 2500 miles from Quebec. 2007. (ENG.). 226p. pap. 20.99 *(978-1-4346-1441-4(7))* BiblioBazaar.

—Voyage of the Paper Canoe: A Geographical Journey of 2500 Miles from Quebec. I.t. ed. 2007. (ENG.). 246p. pap. 22.99 *(978-1-4346-1535-0(9))* BiblioBazaar.

Bishop, Ted. Riding with Rilke. 2007. (ENG.). 272p. pap. 14.95 *(978-0-393-33074-8(5)*, 33074) Norton, W. W. & Co., Inc.

—Riding with Rilke: Reflections on Motorcycles & Books. 2006. (Illus.). 261p. 23.95 *(978-0-393-06261-8(9))* Norton, W. W. & Co., Inc.

Blane, William. Excursion. 2007. (Travel in America Ser.). (ENG.). 528p. 49.95 *(978-1-4290-0098-7(8))* Applewood Bks.

—An Excursion: Through the United States & Canada During the Years, 1822-23. 2007. (Travel in America Ser.). (ENG.). 528p. per. 24.95 *(978-1-4290-0099-4(6))* Applewood Bks.

Boardman, James. America, & the Americans. 2010. (ENG.). 454p. pap. 36.75 *(978-1-176-17795-6(8))* 2010. 458p. pap. 36.75 *(978-1-143-06299-5(X))* 2008. 446p. 32.99 *(978-0-559-04515-8(8))* 2008. 446p. 30.99 *(978-0-559-04523-3(9))* 2008. 446p. pap. 36.75 *(978-0-559-04516-5(6))* 2008. 446p. pap. 35.75 *(978-0-559-04521-9(2))* BiblioBazaar.

—America, & the Americans. 2010. 152p. pap. 18.01 *(978-1-151-87522-8(8))* 2009. 184p. pap. 18.01 *(978-1-150-33252-4(2))* General Bks. LLC.

—America, & the Americans. 2008. 444p. 51.95 *(978-1-4370-0093-1(2))*; pap. 36.95 *(978-1-4367-6514-5(5))* Kessinger Publishing, LLC.

Boardman, James & Collier, Price. America, & the Americans. 2007. (Travel in America Ser.). (ENG.). 49.95 *(978-1-4290-0148-9(8))*; per. 24.95 *(978-1-4290-0149-6(6))* Applewood Bks.

Bonnycastle, Richard Henry. Canada & the Canadians- Volume I. 2007. (ENG.). 150p. pap. 18.99 *(978-1-4346-3534-1(1))*; 170p. pap. 21.99 *(978-1-4346-3535-8(X))* BiblioBazaar.

Boorman, Charley. Extreme Frontiers: Racing Across Canada from Newfoundland to the Rockies. 2012. (ENG., Illus.). 224p. 32.95 ***(978-1-84744-559-9(4))*** Little, Brown Bk. Group Ltd. GBR. Dist: Independent Pubs. Group.

Bothwell, Robert. Canada. 2010. (Traveller's History Ser.). (ENG., Illus.). 256p. pap. 14.95 *(978-1-56656-386-4(0))* Interlink Publishing Group, Inc.

Bouchette, Joseph. British Dominions in North America, 2 vols., Set. reprint ed. 295.00 *(978-0-404-00936-6(0))* AMS Pr., Inc.

Bousfield, Arthur & Toffoli, Garry. Royal Tours 1786-2010: Home to Canada. 2010. (ENG., Illus.). 160p. pap. 24.99 *(978-1-55488-800-9(X))* Dundurn CAN. Dist: Ingram Pub. Services.

Bradley, Arthur Granville. Canada in the Twentieth Century. 2009. 352p. pap. *(978-0-217-82079-0(4))*; 368p. pap. *(978-0-217-45469-8(0))* Books LLC.

—Canada in the Twentieth Century. 2009. 544p. 57.95 *(978-1-104-07495-9(0))*; pap. 42.95 *(978-1-104-04496-1(X))* Kessinger Publishing, LLC.

—Canada in the Twentieth Century. 428p. reprint ed. 98.00 *(978-0-7222-6758-5(4))* Library Reprints, Inc.

Braithwaite, Bob. Smitten by Canada! Another %!@^! Travel Memoir. 2010. 184p. pap. 16.95 *(978-1-4502-5495-3(0))* iUniverse, Inc.

Brooke, Rupert. Letters from America. 2008. 128p. 24.99 *(978-0-554-28683-3(4))* BiblioBazaar.

—Letters from America. 2008. 104p. pap. *(978-1-4099-1824-0(6))* Dodo Pr.

—Letters from America: Travels in the USA & Canada. 2007. (Modern Voices Ser.). (ENG.). 124p. pap. 15.95 *(978-1-84391-433-4(6))* Hesperus Pr. GBR. Dist: Independent Pubs. Group.

Brooke, Rupert & James, Henry. Letters from America. 2007. (ENG.). 112p. pap. 18.99 *(978-1-4346-6470-9(8))*; 124p. pap. 19.99 *(978-1-4346-6471-6(6))* BiblioBazaar.

Burpee, Lawrence Johnstone. Index & Dictionary of Canadian History. (Makers of Canada Ser.). 446p. reprint ed. 98.00 *(978-0-7222-6914-5(5))*; 98.00 *(978-0-7222-6896-4(3))* Library Reprints, Inc.

Campbell, John. A Short American Tramp: On the Fall of 1864. 2007. (Travel in America Ser.). (ENG.). 448p. 49.95 *(978-1-4290-0394-0(4))*; per. 24.95 *(978-1-4290-0395-7(2))* Applewood Bks.

Casey, Allan. Lakeland: Journeys into the Soul of Canada. 2009. (ENG., Illus.). 360p. 25.00 *(978-1-55365-308-0(4)*, Greystone Bks.) D&M Pubs. Inc. CAN. Dist: Perseus-PGW.

Cavell, Janice & Noakes, Jeff. Acts of Occupation: Canada & Arctic Sovereignty, 1918-25. 2011. (ENG., Illus.). 348p. pap. 37.95 *(978-0-7748-1868-1(9))* UBC Pr. CAN. Dist: Univ. of Washington Pr.

Chambers, William. Things as They Are in America. 2007. (Travel in America Ser.). (ENG.). 372p. 49.95 *(978-1-4290-0312-4(X))*; per. 24.95 *(978-1-4290-0313-1(8))* Applewood Bks.

Cheadle, Walter. Cheadle's Journal of Trip Across Canada:Of Trip Across Canada, 1862-1863, 1 vol. 2010. (ENG., Illus.). 312p. pap. *(978-1-926741-07-9(2))* TouchWood Editions.

Chesters, Graeme & Jennings, Sally. Culture Wise Canada: The Essential Guide to Culture, Customs & Business Etiquette. 2008. (Culture Wise Ser.). (ENG., Illus.). 224p. pap. 17.95 *(978-1-905303-21-2(1))* Survival Bks., Ltd.

Christmas, Henry & Rose, A. W. H. The Emigrant Churchman in Canada. 2007. (Travel in America Ser.). (ENG.). 400p. per. 24.95 *(978-1-4290-0275-2(1))* Applewood Bks.

Cloutier, Eugène & Marshall, Joyce. No Passport: A Discovery of Canada. rev. ed. 2011. (ENG., Illus.). 304p. 16.95 *(978-0-19-543458-3(7))* Oxford Univ. Pr., Inc.

Cockburn, James Seaton. Canada for Gentlemen. 2007. pap. *(978-1-4065-1333-2(4))* Dodo Pr.

Coffin, Stewart. Black Spruce Journals: Tales of Canoe-Tripping in the Maine Woods, the Boreal Spruce Forests of Northern Canada, & the Barren Grounds. 2007. (Illus.). 183p. pap. 24.95 *(978-1-933937-40-3(8))* Heron Dance.

Coke, E. A Subaltern's Furlough. 2007. (Travel in America Ser.). (ENG.). 428p. 49.95 *(978-1-4290-0146-5(1))* Applewood Bks.

—A Subaltern's Furlough: Descriptive of Scenes in Various Parts of the United States, Upper & Lower Canada, New-Brunswick, & Nova Scotia, During the Summer & Autumn of 1832. 2007. (Travel in America Ser.). (ENG.). 428p. per. 24.95 *(978-1-4290-0147-2(X))* Applewood Bks.

Cornwallis, Kinahan. Royalty in the New World. 2009. (Cambridge Library Collection - History Ser.). 308p. pap. 24.99 *(978-1-108-00298-1(6))* Cambridge Univ. Pr.

—Royalty in the New World; or, the Prince of Wales in America by Kinahan Cornwallis. 2006. 308p. per. 23.99 *(978-1-4255-2893-5(7))* MPublishing.

Cram101 Textbook Reviews. Outlines & Highlights for Regional Landscapes of U S & Canada by Eugene Palka, Isbn: 9780470098264 0470098260. 2011. 288p. pap. 32.95 ***(978-1-61490-657-5(2))*** Cram101 Inc.

de Figueiredo, Dan. Canadian Top Ten Lists. 2007. (ENG., Illus.). 216p. pap. *(978-1-897278-20-8(9))* Blue Bike Bks. CAN. Dist: Lone Pine Publishing.

De Roos, Fred. Personal Narrative of Travels: In the United States & Canada in 1826 ... with Remarks on the Present State of the American Navy. 2007. (Travel in America Ser.). (ENG.). 244p. 49.95 *(978-1-4290-0116-3(X))*; per. 24.95 *(978-1-4290-0117-5(8))* Applewood Bks.

Dixon, James. Dixon's Personal Narrative of a Tour: Through a Part of the United States & Canada: with Notices of the History & Institutions of Methodism in America:With Notices of the History & Institutions of Methodism in America. 2007. (Travel in America Ser.). (ENG.). 440p. 49.95 *(978-1-4290-0268-4(9))*; per. 24.95 *(978-1-4290-0269-1(7))* Applewood Bks.

Douglas, George Mellis. Lands Forlorn: A Story of an Expedition to Hearne's Coppermine River. Hildebrand, Robert S., ed. & frwd. by. 2008. (Illus.). 452p. 39.00 *(978-0-615-19529-2(6))* Zancudo Pr.

Duthie, Peter, et al. Canada: The Far Northern Frontier. 2006. (Exploring Countries of the WOR Ser.). (ENG., Illus.). 128p. 9.95 *(978-88-544-0113-6(7)*, White Star) Rizzoli International Pubns., Inc.

Egbert, Barbara. Zero Days: The Real Life Adventure of Captain Bligh, Nellie Bly, & 10-Year-Old Scrambler on the Pacific Crest Trail. 2007. (ENG., Illus.). 224p. 21.95 *(978-0-89997-458-3(9))*; pap. 15.95 *(978-0-89997-438-5(4))* Wilderness Pr.

Engleheart, Gardner. Journal of the Progress of H. R. H. The Prince of Wales Through British North America. 2007. (Travel in America Ser.). (ENG.). 140p. 49.95 *(978-1-4290-0356-8(1))*; per. 24.95 *(978-1-4290-0357-5(X))* Applewood Bks.

Erickson, George. Back to the Barrens: On the Wing with Da Vinci & Friends. 2007. (ENG.). 352p. pap. 17.95 *(978-0-88839-642-6(2))* Hancock Hse. Pubs.

Everest, Robert. Everest's Journey Through the United States & Part of Canada. 2007. (Travel in America Ser.). (ENG.). 196p. per. 24.95 *(978-1-4290-0317-9(0))*; 49.95 *(978-1-4290-0316-2(2))* Applewood Bks.

Falk, Alfred. Falk's Trans-Pacific Sketches: A Tour Through the United States & Canada. 2007. (Travel in America Ser.). (ENG.). 336p. 49.95 *(978-1-4290-0436-7(3))* Applewood Bks.

—Falk's Trans-Pacific Sketches a Tour Through the United States & Canada. 2007. (Travel in America Ser.). (ENG.). 336p. per. 24.95 *(978-1-4290-0437-4(1))* Applewood Bks.

Faust, Reg. My Father Is a Twiner. 2008. 76p. pap. 15.49 *(978-1-4343-9756-0(4))* AuthorHouse.

Ferguson, Steven H, et al, eds. A Little Less Arctic: Top Predators in the World's Largest Northern Inland Sea, Hudson Bay. 2010. (ENG., Illus.). x, 288p. 129.00 *(978-90-481-9120-8(3)*, 9048191203) Springer.

Fergusson, James. 'the Personal Observations of a Man of Intelligence' Notes of a Tour in North America In 1861. 2009. Orig. Title: Notes of a Tour in North America In 1861. 176p. lib. bdg. 45.00 *(978-0-9791116-3-1(3))* True Bill Pr., The.

C

Flowers, Pam. Alone Across the Arctic: One Woman's Epic Journey by Dog Team. rev. ed. 2011. (ENG., Illus.). 120p. pap. 12.95 *(978-0-88240-836-1(4),* Alaska Northwest Bks.) Graphic Arts Ctr. Publishing Co.

Foran, Charles. Join the Revolution, Comrade: Journeys & Essays. 2008. (ENG., Illus.). 192p. pap. 19.95 *(978-1-897231-41-8(5))* Biblioasis CAN. Dist: Chicago Distribution Ctr.

Franklin, John. The Journey to the Polar Sea. 2008. 508p. 35.99 *(978-0-554-24676-5(7))* 2006. (ENG.). 452p. pap. 28.99 *(978-1-4264-7069-1(X))* 2007. 504p. pap. 31.99 *(978-1-4264-7145-2(9))* BiblioBazaar.

Glazier, Willard. Peculiarities of American Cities. 2007. (Travel in America Ser.). (ENG.). 608p. 49.95 *(978-1-4290-0452-7(5));* per. 24.95 *(978-1-4290-0453-4(3))* Applewood Bks.

—Peculiarities of American Cities. 2008. (ENG.). 575p. pap. 20.75 *(978-1-4375-4031-4(7));* pap. 25.75 *(978-1-4375-4039-0(2))* BiblioBazaar.

—Peculiarities of American Cities. 2008. 618p. 60.95 *(978-0-548-94500-1(4))* 2007. (ENG.). 620p. per. 45.95 *(978-0-548-59461-2(9))* Kessinger Publishing, LLC.

Gourluck, Russ. Picturing Manitoba: Legacies of the Winnipeg Tribune. 2008. (ENG., Illus.). 272p. pap. 29.95 *(978-1-894283-76-2(7))* Great Plains Pubns. CAN. Dist: Univ. of Toronto Pr.

Grant, Peter. Victoria: A History in Photographs, 1 vol. 2010. (ENG., Illus.). 112p. pap. *(978-1-926613-33-8(3))* Heritage Hse.

Greenwood, Simon & Greenwood, Fiona. Greenwood Guides to Australia & New Zealand, Canada, & South Africa: The Greenwood Guide to Canada-Special Hand-Picked Accommodation. (Illus.). 136p. pap. 15.95 *(978-0-9537980-3-2(8))* Greenwood Guides GBR. Dist: CPG Publishing, Inc.

Grey, F. Seeking Fortune in America. 2007. (Travel in America Ser.). (ENG.). 336p. 49.95 *(978-1-4290-0558-6(0));* per. 24.95 *(978-1-4290-0559-3(9))* Applewood Bks.

Grinnell, George James. Death on the Barrens: A True Story of Courage & Tragedy in the Canadian Arctic. 2010. (ENG., Illus.). 296p. pap. 17.95 *(978-1-55643-882-0(6))* North Atlantic Bks.

Gurney, Joseph John. A Journey in North America, Described in Familiar Letters to Amelia Opie. 2007. (Travel in America Ser.). (ENG.). 172p. 49.95 *(978-1-4290-0220-2(4));* per. 24.95 *(978-1-4290-0221-9(2))* Applewood Bks.

Hall, Francis. Hall's Travels in Canada. 2007. (Travel in America Ser.). (ENG.). 556p. 49.95 *(978-1-4290-0052-9(X))* Applewood Bks.

—Hall's Travels in Canada 1818: and the United States, in 1816 & 1817. 2007. (Travel in America Ser.). (ENG.). 556p. per. 24.95 *(978-1-4290-0053-6(8))* Applewood Bks.

Hamilton, Thomas. Men & Manners in America. 2007. (Travel in America Ser.). (ENG.). 404p. 49.95 *(978-1-4290-0170-0(4));* 408p. 49.95 *(978-1-4290-0168-7(2));* 404p. per. 24.95 *(978-1-4290-0171-7(2))* Applewood Bks.

—Men & Manners in America, 2 vols. 2009. (Cambridge Library Collection - History Ser.). (ENG.). 416p. Vol. 1. pap. 31.99 *(978-1-108-00275-2(7))* Vol. 2. pap. 31.99 *(978-1-108-00278-3(1))* Cambridge Univ. Pr.

—Men & Manners in America V1. 2007. (ENG.). 436p. 51.95 *(978-0-548-13382-8(4))* 2006. pap. 36.95 *(978-1-4286-4483-0(0))* Kessinger Publishing, LLC.

—Men & Manners in America V2. 2007. (ENG.). 412p. 49.95 *(978-0-548-13383-5(2))* 2006. pap. 34.95 *(978-1-4286-4484-7(9))* Kessinger Publishing, LLC.

Hanlon, Christine, et al. Manitoba Book of Everything: Everything You Wanted to Know about Manitoba & Were Going to Ask Anyway. 2008. (Book of Everything Ser.). (ENG.). 208p. pap. 14.95 *(978-0-9784784-5-2(2))* MacIntyre & Purcell Publishing CAN. Dist: Independent Pubs. Group.

Hanna, Jonathan, et al. Portraits of Canada: Photographic Treasures of the CPR, 1 vol. 2006. (ENG., Illus.). 216p. 39.95 *(978-1-894856-77-5(5))* Fifth Hse. Pubs. CAN. Dist: Ingram Pub. Services.

Hanus, Chris & Shaske, John. Canada by Train: The Complete Via Rail Travel Guide. 2009. (Illus.). 320p. (C). 26.95 *(978-0-9730897-5-2(X))* Way Of The Rail Publishing CAN. Dist: AtlasBooks Distribution.

Haycock, Maurice. On Site with Maurice Haycock: Artist of the Arctic: Paintings & Drawings of Historical Sites in the Canadian Arctic, 1 vol. 2007. (ENG., Illus.). 112p. 50.00 *(978-0-88866-655-0(1))* Dundurn CAN. Dist: Univ. of Toronto Pr.

Heller, Carolyn. Living Abroad in Canada. 2008. (Living Abroad Ser.). (ENG.). 350p. pap. 19.95 *(978-1-59880-046-3(9))* Westview Pr.

Hempstead, Andrew. Moon Atlantic Canada: Nova Scotia, New Brunswick, Prince Edward Island, Newfoundland, & Labrador. 5th ed. 2009. (Moon Handbooks). (ENG.). 488p. pap. 19.95 *(978-1-59880-153-8(8))* Avalon Travel Publishing.

Henry, Alexander. Travels & Adventures: In Canada & the Indian Territories. 2009. (Native American Ser.). (ENG.). 399p. pap. 25.95 *(978-1-4290-2244-6(2))* Applewood Bks.

—Travels & Adventures in Canada & the Indian Territories Between the Years 1760 & 1776. 2007. *(978-0-9625144-6-3(2))* Bliss Publishing Co., Inc.

Henry, Lori. Dancing Through History: In Search of the Stories that Define Canada. 2012. (ENG., Illus.). 208p. pap. ***(978-0-9876897-6-4(2),*** Dancing Traveller Publishing) Dancing Traveller Media.

Heriot, George. Travels Through the Canadas. 2010. 284p. pap. 28.75 *(978-1-147-16891-4(1))* BiblioBazaar.

—Travels Through the Canadas. 2009. 122p. pap. *(978-0-217-41132-5(0))* Books LLC.

Hodgson, Adam. Letters from North America Vol. 1: Written During a Tour in the United States & Canada. 2007. (Travel in America Ser.). (ENG.). 436p. 49.95 *(978-1-4290-0102-1(X));* 452p. 49.95 *(978-1-4290-0100-7(3));* 436p. per. 24.95 *(978-1-4290-0103-8(8))* Applewood Bks.

Holyoake, George. Travels in Search. 2007. (Travel in America Ser.). (ENG.). 164p. 49.95 *(978-1-4290-0462-6(2))* Applewood Bks.

—Travels in Search of a Settler's Guide-book of America & Canada. 2007. (Travel in America Ser.). (ENG.). 164p. per. 24.95 *(978-1-4290-0463-3(0))* Applewood Bks.

Howard of Glossop, Winefred. Howard of Glossop's Journal of a Tour. 2007. (Travel in America Ser.). (ENG.). 440p. per. 24.95 *(978-1-4290-0517-3(3))* Applewood Bks.

—Howard of Glossop's Journal of a Tour in the United States, Canada & Mexico. 2007. (Travel in America Ser.). (ENG.). 440p. 49.95 *(978-1-4290-0516-6(5))* Applewood Bks.

Hoyle, Gwyneth. The Northern Horizons of Guy Blanchet: Intrepid Surveyor, 1884-1966. 2007. (ENG., Illus.). 224p. pap. 24.99 *(978-1-55002-759-4(X))* Natural Heritage/Natural History, Inc. CAN. Dist: Ingram Pub. Services.

Hudson, T. A Scamper Through America. 2007. (Travel in America Ser.). (ENG.). 352p. 49.95 *(978-1-4290-0444-2(4))* Applewood Bks.

—A Scamper Through America - Or, Fifteen Thousand Miles of Ocean & Continent in Sixty Days. 2007. (Travel in America Ser.). (ENG.). 352p. per. 24.95 *(978-1-4290-0445-9(2))* Applewood Bks.

Hutchison, Bruce. The Unknown Country: Canada & Her People. 2009. 422p. 49.95 *(978-1-104-84982-5(8))* 2007. (ENG.). 420p. per. 34.95 *(978-0-548-45331-5(4))* Kessinger Publishing, LLC.

Hutchison, Bruce & Palmer, Vaughn. The Unknown Country: Canada & Her People. 2010. (ENG.). 416p. pap. 22.50 *(978-0-19-543891-8(4))* Oxford Univ. Pr., Inc.

Ireland, Barbara, ed. The New York Times 36 Hours: 150 Weekends in the United States & Canada. 2011. (ENG., Illus.). 700p. 39.99 ***(978-3-8365-2639-5(5))*** TASCHEN DEU. Dist: Ingram Pub. Services.

J, C. & A, C. The United States & Canada. 2007. (Travel in America Ser.). (ENG.). 152p. per. 24.95 *(978-1-4290-0375-9(8))* Applewood Bks.

J., C. & C.A., Gold. The United States & Canada. 2007. (Travel in America Ser.). (ENG.). 152p. 49.95 *(978-1-4290-0374-2(X))* Applewood Bks.

Johnston, Jas. F. W. (James Finlay Weir). Notes on North America, Agricultural, Economical, & Social. 2006. 436p. pap. 26.99 *(978-1-4255-4719-6(2));* 528p. per. 29.99 *(978-1-4255-5806-2(2))* MPublishing.

Josefine, Claire. Following Raven, Finding Ground: A Road Trip in Search of Home. 2007. 112p. pap. 12.95 *(978-0-9747372-1-8(6))* Winter's Daughter Pr.

Kalm, Peter. The America of 1750 Set: Peter Kalm's Travels in North America, 2 vols. (Illus.). reprint ed. lib. bdg. 250.00 *(978-0-7222-0226-5(1))* Library Reprints, Inc.

Keddie, Mario. Canada Past Present & Future: A Series of Books about Canada. 2011. 56p. pap. 16.46 ***(978-1-4269-6132-8(4));*** 28p. pap. 13.54 ***(978-1-4269-6131-1(6));*** 68p. pap. 23.29 ***(978-1-4269-6133-5(2));*** 40p. pap. 16.46 ***(978-1-4269-6129-8(4))*** Trafford Publishing.

Kelland, Philip. Transatlantic Sketches. 2007. (Travel in America Ser.). (ENG.). 96p. 49.95 *(978-1-4290-0346-9(4));* per. 24.95 *(978-1-4290-0347-6(2))* Applewood Bks.

Kent, Timothy J. A Modern-Day Voyageur Family: Paddling the 3,000 Mile Fur Trade Canoe Route Across the U. S. & Canada. 2009. (Illus.). 760p. 59.95 *(978-0-9657230-6-0(2))* Silver Fox Enterprises.

Kesselheim, Alan S. Let Them Paddle: Coming of Age on the Water. 2012. (ENG., Illus.). 256p. pap. 19.95 ***(978-1-55591-351-9(2))*** Fulcrum Publishing.

Kingsford, William, abr. The Canadian Canals. 2009. (Transportation Ser.). (ENG.). 200p. pap. 14.95 *(978-1-4290-2002-2(4))* Applewood Bks.

Kipling, Rudyard. Letters to the Family. reprint ed. lib. bdg. 98.00 *(978-0-7426-2854-0(X))* Classic Bks.

Knight, David B., ed. Our Geographic Mosaic: Research Essays in Honour of G. C. Merrill. 217p. pap. *(978-0-88629-034-4(1))* McGill-Queen's Univ. Pr.

Kobalenko, Jerry. Arctic Eden: Journeys Through the Changing High Arctic, 1 vol. 2010. (ENG., Illus.). 200p. 40.00 *(978-1-55365-442-1(0),* Greystone Bks.) D&M Pubs. Inc. CAN. Dist: Perseus-PGW.

Kreuzer, Terese Loeb & Bennett, Carol. How to Move to Canada: A Primer for Americans. 2006. (ENG., Illus.). 256p. pap. 15.99 *(978-0-312-34986-8(6),* St. Martin's Griffin) St. Martin's Pr.

La Rochefoucauld, Francois de. Travels Through the United States of North America, the Country of the Iroquois, & Upper Canada, in the Years 1795, 1796, & 1797: With an Authentic Account of Lower Canada, 4 vols. (Illus.). reprint ed. lib. bdg. 500.00 *(978-0-7222-0907-3(X))* Library Reprints, Inc.

Lahontan, Louis Armand de Lom d'Arce. New Voyages to North-America, by the Baron De Lahontan. reprint ed. 250.00 *(978-0-7222-6734-9(7))* Library Reprints, Inc.

Latham, Henry. Black & White: A Journal of a Three Months' Tour in the United States. 2007. (Travel in America Ser.). (ENG.). 324p. 49.95 *(978-1-4290-0406-0(1));* per. 24.95 *(978-1-4290-0407-7(X))* Applewood Bks.

Leighton, Douglas, photos by. The Canadian Rockies (English Mt. Assiniboine Paperback) 2007. 112p. pap. *(978-1-55153-255-4(7))* Altitude Publishing Canada Ltd.

—The Canadian Rockies (French Mt. Assiniboine Paperback) 2007. 112p. pap. *(978-1-55153-257-8(3))* Altitude Publishing Canada Ltd.

Levinge, R. G. A. Echoes from the Backwoods: Or, Sketches of Transatlantic Life. 2011. (Cambridge Library Collection - Travel & Exploration Ser.). (ENG.). 276p. pap. 23.99 ***(978-1-108-03352-7(0));*** (Illus.). 324p. pap. 24.99 ***(978-1-108-03351-0(2))*** Cambridge Univ. Pr.

Lewis, George. Impressions of America & the American Churches. 2009. 268p. pap. *(978-1-4590-8383-7(0))* Books LLC.

Locken, E. Travel Journal Canada. 2010. 192p. pap. 19.99 *(978-0-557-43453-4(X))* Lulu Enterprises Inc.

Logan, James. Logan's Notes of a Journey: Through Canada, the United States of Americ. 2007. (Travel in America Ser.). (ENG.). 280p. 49.95 *(978-1-4290-0196-0(8))* Applewood Bks.

—Logan's Notes of a Journey: Through Canada, the United States of America, & the West Indies. 2007. (Travel in America Ser.). (ENG.). 280p. per. 24.95 *(978-1-4290-0197-7(6))* Applewood Bks.

Luca, Frederic William. Appendiculae Historicae. 216p. reprint ed. 98.00 *(978-0-7222-6739-4(8))* Library Reprints, Inc.

Lyell, Charles. Lyell's Travels in North America. 2007. (Travel in America Ser.). (ENG.). 340p. 49.95 *(978-1-4290-0326-1(X));* 292p. 49.95 *(978-1-4290-0324-7(3))* Applewood Bks.

—Lyell's Travels in North America. 2007. 180p. per. 11.95 *(978-1-59462-813-9(0),* Book Jungle) Standard Pubns., Inc.

—Lyell's Travels in North America, Canada, & Nova Scotia with Geological Observations. 2007. (Travel in America Ser.). (ENG.). 340p. per. 24.95 *(978-1-4290-0327-8(8))* Applewood Bks.

—Travels in North America: With Geological Observations on the United States, Canada, & Nova Scotia. 2010. (Cambridge Library Collection - Physical Sciences Ser.). (ENG.). 304p. pap. 24.99 *(978-1-108-02021-3(6));* (Illus.). 356p. pap. 29.99 *(978-1-108-02020-6(8))* Cambridge Univ. Pr.

Lysons, Daniel. Early Reminiscences. 2009. 118p. pap. 14.14 *(978-1-150-74444-0(8))* General Bks. LLC.

—Early Reminiscences. 2009. 260p. 42.95 *(978-1-104-06848-6(6));* pap. 27.95 *(978-1-104-05108-2(7))* Kessinger Publishing, LLC.

—Early Reminiscences. 246p. reprint ed. 98.00 *(978-0-7222-6941-1(2))* Library Reprints, Inc.

MacGregor, John. Our Brothers & Cousins: A Summer Tour in Canada & the States. 2007. (Travel in America Ser.). (ENG.). 184p. 49.95 *(978-1-4290-0352-0(9));* per. 24.95 *(978-1-4290-0353-7(7))* Applewood Bks.

Mackay, Charles. Life & Liberty in America; or, Sketches of a Tour in the United States & Canada, in 1857-8 by Charles MacKay. 2006. 420p. per. 26.99 *(978-1-4255-4486-7(X))* MPublishing.

MacKenzie, William. Sketches of Canada & the United States. 2007. (Travel in America Ser.). (ENG.). 532p. 49.95 *(978-1-4290-0154-0(2));* per. 24.95 *(978-1-4290-0155-7(0))* Applewood Bks.

Malaurie, Jean. Hummocks: Journeys & Inquiries among the Canadian Inuit. 2007. (ENG., Illus.). 424p. (C). *(978-0-7735-3200-7(5))* McGill-Queen's Univ. Pr.

Marryat. Diary in America, Series. 2008. (ENG.). 400p. 0.99 *(978-1-4378-0153-8(6));* 396p. 99.99 *(978-1-4378-0155-2(2));* (ENG.). 396p. per. 93.99 *(978-1-4378-0157-6(9));* (ENG.). 400p. per. 93.99 *(978-1-4378-0156-9(0))* IndyPublish.com.

—Diary in America with Remarks on Its Institutions. 2010. 136p. pap. 19.99 *(978-1-154-05066-0(1))* General Bks. LLC.

Marryat, Frederick. A Diary in America. 2009. 272p. pap. *(978-0-217-42544-5(5))* Books LLC.

—A Diary in America: With Remarks on its Institutions. 2011. (Cambridge Library Collection - Travel & Exploration Ser.). (ENG.). 312p. pap. 24.99 ***(978-1-108-03244-5(3));*** 370p. pap. 29.99 ***(978-1-108-03246-9(X));*** 320p. pap. 24.99 ***(978-1-108-03243-8(5));*** 328p. pap. 28.99 ***(978-1-108-03242-1(7));*** (Illus.). 322p. pap. 24.99 ***(978-1-108-03245-2(1))*** Cambridge Univ. Pr.

—Diary in America - Series II. 2008. 416p. pap. *(978-1-4099-3586-5(8))* Dodo Pr.

—Diary in America, Series. 2009. 504p. 35.99 *(978-0-559-08119-4(7))* 2009. 504p. 32.99 *(978-0-559-08131-6(6))* 2009. 504p. pap. 23.99 *(978-0-559-08129-3(4))* 2009. 504p. pap. 39.75 *(978-0-559-08122-4(7))* 2008. 482p. per. 38.75 *(978-1-4375-2220-4(3))* 2008. (ENG.). 436p. per. 34.75 *(978-1-4375-2045-3(6))* BiblioBazaar.

—Diary in America, Series. 2010. (Illus.). 264p. pap. 34.33 *(978-1-153-77459-8(3))* General Bks. LLC.

—Diary in America, Series One. 2008. 436p. pap. 34.75 *(978-1-4375-0478-1(7));* 482p. pap. 38.75 *(978-1-4375-0479-8(5))* BiblioBazaar.

—Diary in America V1. 2010. 126p. 28.76 *(978-1-169-25251-6(6));* pap. 16.76 *(978-1-162-65979-4(3));* 35.95 *(978-1-161-42844-5(5))* Kessinger Publishing, LLC.

—Diary in America V2. 2010. 266p. 34.36 *(978-1-169-30663-9(2));* pap. 22.36 *(978-1-162-65980-0(7));* 42.95 *(978-1-161-42845-2(3))* Kessinger Publishing, LLC.

—A Diary in America V2: With Remarks on Its Institutions. 232p. 2010. pap. 21.56 *(978-1-163-77318-5(2))* 2010. 33.56 ***(978-1-163-84435-9(7))*** 2007. 41.95 *(978-0-548-53226-3(5))* 2007. per. 26.95 *(978-0-548-50204-4(8))* Kessinger Publishing, LLC.

—A Diary in America V3: With Remarks on Its Institutions, Part Second (1839) 2010. 366p. 37.56 ***(978-1-164-37850-1(3))*** 2010. 366p. pap. 25.56 ***(978-1-164-19098-1(9))*** 2008. 364p. 46.95 *(978-1-4366-5537-8(4))* 2008. 364p. pap. 31.95 *(978-0-548-88078-4(6))* Kessinger Publishing, LLC.

—A Diary in America, with Remarks on Its Institutions. 2010. (ENG.). 236p. pap. 26.75 *(978-1-177-42163-8(1))* 2009. 328p. 25.99 *(978-1-103-07809-7(7))* 2009. 328p. pap. 19.99 *(978-1-103-07806-6(2))* BiblioBazaar.

—A Diary in America, with Remarks on Its Institutions. 2010. 138p. pap. 22.63 *(978-1-152-63741-2(X))* General Bks. LLC.

—Diary in America with Remarks on Its Institutions. 2010. 974p. pap. 63.75 *(978-1-174-31097-3(9))* BiblioBazaar.

—Diary in America with Remarks on Its Institutions. 2009. 284p. pap. *(978-1-151-10937-8(1))* Books LLC.

—A Diary in America; with Remarks on Its Institutions. 2010. 86p. pap. 14.14 *(978-1-154-35611-3(6));* (Illus.). 92p. pap. 19.99 *(978-1-154-37268-7(5));* (Illus.). 88p. pap. 12.98 ***(978-1-154-11922-0(X));*** (Illus.). 94p. pap. 19.99 ***(978-1-154-11924-4(6));*** 136p. pap. 22.44 *(978-1-152-63743-6(6));* 136p. pap. 22.44 *(978-1-152-63745-0(2))* General Bks. LLC.

—A Diary in America: with Remarks on Its Institutions. 2009. 231p. pap. 22.99 *(978-1-115-45809-2(4));* (ENG.). pap. 20.99 *(978-1-115-45810-8(8))* BiblioBazaar. (BiblioLife).

—A Diary in America with Remarks on Its Institutions. 2010. 146p. pap. 19.99 *(978-1-150-89412-1(1))* General Bks. LLC.

—A Diary in America: with Remarks on Its Institutions: In 3 Vol. 2010. 96p. pap. 19.99 *(978-1-154-07361-4(0))* General Bks. LLC.

—A Diary in America, with Remarks on Its Institutions Part. 2010. (ENG.). 374p. pap. 33.75 *(978-1-177-51553-5(9))* BiblioBazaar.

—A Diary in America, with Remarks on Its Institutions Part. 2010. 114p. pap. *(978-1-152-02667-4(4))* Books LLC.

—A Diary in America, with Remarks on Its Institutions Part. 2009. 152p. pap. 19.99 *(978-0-217-66439-4(3))* General Bks. LLC.

—A Diary in America, with Remarks on Its Institutions, Volume II. 2009. 324p. pap. 24.99 *(978-1-110-05224-0(3));* (ENG.). pap. 23.99 *(978-1-110-05223-3(5))* BiblioBazaar. (BiblioLife).

—Second Series of a Diary in America, with Remarks on Its Institutions. 2007. (Travel in America Ser.). (ENG.). 308p. 49.95 *(978-1-4290-0218-9(2))* Applewood Bks.

—Second Series of a Diary in America, with Remarks on Its Institutions. 2007. (Travel in America Ser.). (ENG.). 308p. per. 24.95 *(978-1-4290-0219-6(0))* Applewood Bks.

Mathiassen, Therkel. Contributions to the Geography of Baffin Land & Melville Peninsula. (Thule Expedition, 5th, 1921-1924 Ser.: Vol. 1, No. 3). reprint ed. 39.50 *(978-0-404-58303-3(2))* AMS Pr., Inc.

—Contributions to the Physiography of Southampton Island. (Thule Expedition, 5th, 1921-1924 Ser.: Vol. 1, No. 2). reprint ed. 32.50 *(978-0-404-58302-6(4))* AMS Pr., Inc.

Maurice, Edward Beauclerk. The Last Gentleman Adventurer: Coming of Age in the Arctic. 2006. (ENG., Illus.). 392p. per. 14.95 *(978-0-618-77358-9(4),* Mariner Bks.) Houghton Mifflin Harcourt Trade & Reference Pubs.

Mears, Ray. Northern Wilderness: Bushcraft of the Far North. 2010. (ENG., Illus.). 224p. 29.95 *(978-0-340-98082-8(6),* Hodder & Stoughton) Hodder General Publishing Div. GBR. Dist: Independent Pubs. Group.

Melin, Margaret. Modern Pioneering in Alask. 2011. 98p. 38.95 ***(978-1-258-09282-5(4))*** Literary Licensing, LLC.

Moore, George. Journal of a Voyage Across the Atlantic: With Notes on Canada & the United States, & Return to Great Britain In 1844. 2007. (Travel in America Ser.). (ENG.). 112p. 49.95 *(978-1-4290-0250-9(6));* per. 24.95 *(978-1-4290-0251-6(4))* Applewood Bks.

Murray, Amelia Matilda. Letters from the United States, Cuba & Canada by the Hon Amelia M Murray. 2006. 412p. per. 26.99 *(978-1-4255-4400-3(2))* MPublishing.

Murray, Henry. Lands of the Slave & the Free: Or, Cuba, the United States, & Canada. (Civil War Ser.). (ENG.). 2008. 500p. pap. 29.95 *(978-1-4290-1630-8(2))* 2007. 532p. 49.95 *(978-1-4290-0340-7(5))* 2007. 532p. per. 24.95 *(978-1-4290-0341-4(3))* Applewood Bks.

Oliphant, Laurence. Minnesota & the Far West. 2011. (Cambridge Library Collection - Travel & Exploration Ser.). (ENG., Illus.). 340p. pap. 28.99 ***(978-1-108-03334-3(2))*** Cambridge Univ. Pr.

Owl, Grey. The Men of the Last Frontier. 2011. (ENG., Illus.). 289p. pap. 26.99 *(978-1-55488-804-7(2))* Dundurn CAN. Dist: Ingram Pub. Services.

Palka, Eugene, et al. Regional Landscapes of the United States & Canada. 7th ed. 2008. (ENG., Illus.). 416p. (C). 115.95 *(978-0-470-09826-4(0),* Wiley) Wiley, John & Sons, Inc.

Patten, Edmund. A Glimpse at the United States. 2007. (Travel in America Ser.). (ENG.). 132p. 49.95 *(978-1-4290-0300-1(6))* Applewood Bks.

—A Glimpse at the United States & the Northern States of America, with the Canadas, Comprising Their Rivers, Lakes, & Falls During the Autumn of 1852. 2007. (Travel in America Ser.). (ENG.). 132p. per. 24.95 *(978-1-4290-0301-8(4))* Applewood Bks.

Patterson, R. M. Those Earlier Hills Reminiscences,1928-1961, 1 vol. rev. ed. 2008. (ENG., Illus.). 176p. *(978-1-894898-67-6(2))* TouchWood Editions.

Pelly, David F. The Old Way North: Following the Oberholtzer-Magee Expedition. 2008. (ENG., Illus.). 224p. 27.95 *(978-0-87351-616-7(8),* Borealis Bk.) Minnesota Historical Society Pr.

Pitt, Michael D. Beyond the End of the Road: A Winter of Contentment North of the Arctic Circle. 2009. (ENG., Illus.). 338p. pap. 19.95 *(978-1-897435-36-6(3))* Agio Publishing Hse. CAN. Dist: Lightning Source, Inc.

Pouchot, M. Memoir upon the Late War in North America, Between the French & English, 1755-60. Hough, Franklin Benjamin, tr. 2007. 276p. per. 27.95 *(978-0-548-63206-2(5))* Kessinger Publishing, LLC.

Power, Tyrone, Jr. Impressions of America. 2007. (Travel in America Ser.). (ENG.). Vol. 1. 456p. 49.95 *(978-1-4290-0178-6(X))* Vol. 2. 420p. 49.95 *(978-1-4290-0176-2(3))* Applewood Bks.

—Impressions of America During the Years 1833, 1834, & 1835, Vol. 1. 2007. (Travel in America Ser.). (ENG.). 456p. per. 24.95 *(978-1-4290-0179-3(8))* Applewood Bks.
Rayleigh, Clara. The British Association's Visit to Montreal 1884: Letters. 2008. 128p. 21.99 *(978-0-554-38136-7(2))* 2007. (ENG.). 112p. pap. 18.99 *(978-1-4346-6370-2(1))* 2007. (ENG.). 124p. pap. 19.99 *(978-1-4346-6371-9(X))* BiblioBazaar.
—The British Association's Visit to Montreal 1884: Letters. 2007. 84p. per. *(978-1-4068-3756-8(3))* Echo Library.
Reynolds, John & Swink, Wade. Out-of-the-Way Places: Green Peas Don't Make Good Soup! 2008. 144p. 24.95 *(978-1-4401-1202-7(9))*; pap. 14.95 *(978-1-4401-0752-8(1))* iUniverse, Inc.
Rhys, Horton. A Theatrical Trip for a Wager. 2007. (Travel in America Ser.). (ENG.). 88p. 49.95 *(978-1-4290-0358-2(8))*; per. 24.95 *(978-1-4290-0359-9(6))* Applewood Bks.
Robinson, Guy. Canada. 2008. (ENG.). 48p. pap. 5.99 *(978-1-4022-1739-5(0))* Sourcebooks, Inc.
Rogers, Barbara Radcliffe & Rogers, Stillman. Travel Adventures Canada's Atlantic Provinces. 4th ed. 2009. 672p. pap. 25.99 *(978-1-58843-691-7(8))* Hunter Publishing, Inc.
Rose, A. & Christmas, Henry. The Emigrant Churchman in Canada. 2007. (Travel in America Ser.). (ENG.). 400p. 49.95 *(978-1-4290-0274-5(3))* Applewood Bks.
Rose, A. W. H. & Christmas, Henry. The Emigrant Churchman in Canada, Vol. 2. 2007. (Travel in America Ser.). (ENG.). 348p. 49.95 *(978-1-4290-0272-1(7))* Applewood Bks.
Rowan, John. The Emigrant & Sportsman in Canada. 2007. (Applewood Canadiana Ser.). (ENG.). 452p. per. 24.95 *(978-1-55709-973-0(1))* Applewood Bks.
Runtz, Michael. Algonquin Souvenir. 2007. (ENG., Illus.). 96p. 19.95 *(978-1-55046-494-8(9))* Boston Mills Pr. CAN. Dist: Firefly Bks., Ltd.
Russell, Frank. Explorations in the Far North. 2009. 344p. 25.99 *(978-0-559-99905-5(4))*; pap. 19.99 *(978-0-559-99903-1(8))* BiblioBazaar.
—Explorations in the Far North. 2009. 226p. pap. *(978-0-217-71648-2(2))* Books LLC.
Santosuosso, John. Canada: an Introduction for Americans. 2007. (ENG.). 224p. per. 24.95 *(978-1-4241-6505-6(9))* PublishAmerica, Inc.
Schmidt, Dennis & Schmidt, Esther. Wildlife of Western Canada. 96p. *(978-1-55153-814-3(8))* Altitude Publishing Canada Ltd.
Seavey, Elaine. Canadian Summers. 2006. 194p. pap. 13.95 *(978-0-7414-3297-1(8))* Infinity Publishing.
Seton, Ernest Thompson. The Arctic Prairies. 2008. 220p. 24.99 *(978-0-554-33082-2(2))*; 27.99 *(978-0-554-23779-4(2))* BiblioBazaar.
—The Arctic Prairies. 2008. (ENG.). 196p. per. *(978-1-4065-9174-3(2))* Dodo Pr.
—The Arctic Prairies. 2006. pap. *(978-1-84702-461-9(0))* Echo Library.
Shirreff, Patrick. Shirreff's Tour Through North America. 2007. (Travel in America Ser.). (ENG.). 492p. 49.95 *(978-1-4290-0174-8(7))* Applewood Bks.
—Shirreff's Tour Through North America: Together with a Comprehensive View of the Canadas & United States, as Adapted for Agricultural Emigration. 2007. (Travel in America Ser.). (ENG.). 492p. per. 24.95 *(978-1-4290-0175-5(5))* Applewood Bks.
Slaney, Robert. Short Journal of a Visit to Canada & the States of America, in 1860. 2007. (Travel in America Ser.). (ENG.). 88p. per. 24.95 *(978-1-4290-0367-4(7))* Applewood Bks.
—Slaney's Short Journal. 2007. (Travel in America Ser.). (ENG.). 88p. 49.95 *(978-1-4290-0366-7(9))* Applewood Bks.
Spence, Thomas. The Settler's Guide: In the United States & British North American Provinces. 2007. (Travel in America Ser.). (ENG.). 568p. 49.95 *(978-1-4290-0372-8(3))*; per. 24.95 *(978-1-4290-0373-5(1))* Applewood Bks.
Stewart, Barry D. Across the Land a Canadian Journey of Discovery. 2009. 276p. 31.00 *(978-1-4269-1500-0(4))* Trafford Publishing.
Stewart, George. Canada Under the Administration of the Earl of Dufferin. 696p. reprint ed. 128.00 *(978-0-7222-6829-2(7))* Library Reprints, Inc.
Stinson, Bill. Meals & Memories: A Celebration of Food on the Trail. Shirreff, Shannon, ed. 2009. 88p. pap. 26.86 *(978-1-4251-2992-7(7))* Trafford Publishing.
Stoddard, John L. John L. Stoddard's Lectures, 10. l.t. ed. 2007. (ENG.). 268p. pap. 23.99 *(978-1-4264-8740-8(1))* BiblioBazaar.
—John L. Stoddard's Lectures Volume 10. 2007. (ENG.). 228p. pap. 20.99 *(978-1-4264-8685-2(5))* BiblioBazaar.
Tappan, Adney. The Travel Journals of Tappan Adney: 1887-1890. Behne, Ted, ed. 2010. (ENG., Illus.). 160p. pap. 16.95 *(978-0-86492-628-9(6))* Goose Lane Editions CAN. Dist: Univ. of Toronto Pr.
Thompson, F. M. "Punk". Living a Dream. 2007. 176p. per. 24.95 *(978-1-4241-8971-7(3))* PublishAmerica, Inc.
Todd, Henry. Todd's Notes upon Canada: And the United States - From 1832 to 1840. 2007. (Travel in America Ser.). (ENG.). 288p. per. 24.95 *(978-1-4290-0217-2(4))* Applewood Bks.
—Todd's Notes upon Canada & the United States from 1832 to 1840. 2007. (Travel in America Ser.). (ENG.). 288p. 49.95 *(978-1-4290-0216-5(6))* Applewood Bks.
Traill, Catharine Parr. The Backwoods of Canada. 2008. 280p. 28.99 *(978-0-554-27040-1(4))* 2007. (ENG.). 248p. pap. 20.99 *(978-1-4346-2392-8(0))* 2007. (ENG.). 276p. pap. 23.99 *(978-1-4346-2438-3(2))* BiblioBazaar.
—The Backwoods of Canada. 2009. 240p. pap. *(978-1-4099-3621-3(X))* Dodo Pr.
—The Backwoods of Canada. 2010. (ENG., Illus.). 336p. pap. 17.95 *(978-0-7710-9448-4(5)*, New Can Library) McClelland & Stewart CAN. Dist: Random Hse., Inc.
Trollope, Anthony. North America. 2011. (Cambridge Library Collection - Travel & Exploration Ser.). (ENG.). 508p. pap. 37.99 ***(978-1-108-04126-3(4))***; (Illus.). 484p. pap. 34.99 ***(978-1-108-04125-6(6))*** Cambridge Univ. Pr.
—North America, 2. reprint ed. lib. bdg. 196.00 *(978-0-7426-2445-0(5))* Classic Bks.
—North America - Volume 1. 2006. pap. *(978-1-4068-1077-6(0))* Echo Library.
—North America by Anthony Trollope. 2006. 672p. per. 36.99 *(978-1-4255-6768-2(1))* MPublishing.
—North America (Volume 1) l.t. ed. 2006. (Large Print Ser.). lib. bdg. 26.00 *(978-1-58287-897-3(8))* North Bks.
—North America (Volume 2) l.t. ed. 2006. (Large Print Ser.). lib. bdg. 26.00 *(978-1-58287-898-0(6))* North Bks.
Trotter, Isabella Strange. First Impressions of the New World: On Two Travellers from the Old in the Autumn Of 18. 2007. (ENG.). 180p. pap. 19.99 *(978-1-4264-9386-7(X))*; 198p. pap. 21.99 *(978-1-4264-9767-4(9))* BiblioBazaar.
Tuck, John R. Adventures in Living. 2011. 126p. 40.95 ***(978-1-258-06757-1(9))*** Literary Licensing, LLC.
Vigne, Godfrey. Six Months in America. 2007. (Travel in America Ser.). (ENG.). 216p. 49.95 *(978-1-4290-0152-6(6))*; per. 24.95 *(978-1-4290-0153-3(4))* Applewood Bks.
Walter, John. First Impressions of America. 2007. (Travel in America Ser.). (ENG.). 140p. 49.95 *(978-1-4290-0408-4(8))*; per. 24.95 *(978-1-4290-0409-1(6))* Applewood Bks.
Warburton, George. The Conquest of Canada by the Author of Hochelaga. 2006. 360p. per. 26.99 *(978-1-4255-3686-2(7))*; (ENG.). 376p. per. 26.99 *(978-1-4255-3934-4(3))* MPublishing.
Warkentin, John. So Vast & Various: Interpreting Canada's Regions in the Nineteenth & Twentieth Centuries. 2010. (Carleton Library Ser.). (ENG.). 520p. (C). *(978-0-7735-3719-4(8))*; pap. *(978-0-7735-3738-5(4))* McGill-Queen's Univ. Pr.
Watson, Adam. A Zoologist on Baffin Island 1953. 2011. 242p. pap. ***(978-1-907611-70-4(3))*** Paragon Publishing, Rothersthorpe.
Weider, George. Blue Mountain. (Illus.). 160p. *(978-1-55046-009-4(9))* Boston Mills Pr.
Weisberg, Ellen & Yaffe, Mike. All Across Canad. 2008. 40p. pap. *(978-1-84747-726-2(7))* Chipmunkapublishing.
Weld, Charles. A Vacation Tour in the United States & Canada. 2007. (Travel in America Ser.). (ENG.). 440p. 49.95 *(978-1-4290-0318-6(9))* Applewood Bks.
—Vacation Tour in the United States & Canada. 2007. (Travel in America Ser.). (ENG.). 440p. per. 24.95 *(978-1-4290-0319-3(7))* Applewood Bks.
Weld, Isaac. Weld's Travels: And the Provinces of Upper & Lower Canada During the Years 1795, 1796, & 1797. 2007. (Travel in America Ser.). (ENG.). 468p. 49.95 *(978-1-4290-0032-1(5))* Applewood Bks.
—Weld's Travels: Through the States of North America - And the Provinces of Upper & Lower Canada During the Years 1795, 1796 & 1797. 2007. (Travel in America Ser.). (ENG.). 468p. per. 24.95 *(978-1-4290-0033-8(3))* Applewood Bks.
—Weld's Travels: Through the States of North America, & the Provinces of Upper & Lower Canada During the Years 1795, 1796, & 1797. 2007. (Travel in America Ser.). (ENG.). 396p. 49.95 *(978-1-4290-0030-7(9))* Applewood Bks.
Wilson, Hap. Trails & Tribulations: Confessions of a Wilderness Pathfinder. 2009. (ENG., Illus.). 216p. pap. 26.99 *(978-1-55488-397-4(0))* Dundurn CAN. Dist: Ingram Pub. Services.
Woods, John, Jr. The Prince of Wales. 2007. (Travel in America Ser.). (ENG.). 456p. 49.95 *(978-1-4290-0370-4(7))* Applewood Bks.
Woods, John. The Prince of Wales in Canada & the United States. 2007. (Travel in America Ser.). (ENG.). 456p. per. 24.95 *(978-1-4290-0371-1(5))* Applewood Bks.

CANADA—DIPLOMATIC AND CONSULAR SERVICE

Canadian Representatives Abroad: December 1993. (FRE.). 16p. pap. *(978-0-660-59104-9(9))* Canadian Government Publishing.

CANADA—DIRECTORIES

American Correctional Association Staff, contrib. by. 2006 Directory: Adult & Juvenile Correctional Departments, Institutions, Agencies, & Probation & Parole Authorities. 67th ed. 2006. 959p. pap. 100.00 *(978-1-56991-238-6(6))* American Correctional Assn.
American Psychological Association Staff. Graduate Study in Psychology. 2010. (C). 28.95 *(978-1-4338-0902-6(8))* American Psychological Assn.
Anderson, Jon P., ed. 2007 Random Lengths' Buyers' & Sellers' Guide: A Directory of the Forest Products Industry. 2007. per. 239.95 *(978-1-884311-24-6(5))* Random Lengths Pubns., Inc.
Assistantships & Graduate Fellowships in the Mathematical Sciences 2010. 2010. 94p. pap. 23.00 *(978-0-8218-5236-1(1))* American Mathematical Society.
Bobcat. Bond's Franchise Guide 2009. Bond, Robert E. & Yang, Michelle, eds. 20th ed. 2009. (ENG., Illus.). 488p. pap. 34.95 *(978-1-887137-65-2(3))* Source Bk. Pubns.
Bond, Robert E. Bond's Franchise Guide 2008. 19th ed. 2008. (ENG., Illus.). 528p. pap. 34.95 *(978-1-887137-59-1(9))* Source Bk. Pubns.
Brewers Publications. 2009-2010 North American Brewers' Resource Directory. 2009. (ENG.). 224p. pap. 99.00 *(978-0-937381-94-6(2))* Brewers Pubns.
Browne, Lynn. Ontario Legal Directory 2011 (Cd) 2011. (Ontario Legal Directory Ser.). ***(978-1-4426-9660-0(5))*** Univ. of Toronto Pr.
—Ontario Legal Directory 2011 Net Licence. 2011. ***(978-1-4426-9661-7(3))*** Univ. of Toronto Pr.
de Vos, Robert C. A. & Brice, Tracy A., eds. Fuel Finder: The Professional Driver's Guide to North American Diesel Locations, 13. 13th rev. ed. 2007. 368p. per. 14.95 *(978-1-890141-33-2(X))* TR Information Pubs.
Dept. Human Resources Development Canada Staff. Directory of Labour Organizations in Canada 1997. 287p. pap. *(978-0-660-60281-3(4))* Canadian Government Publishing.
Fodor's Travel Publications, Inc. Staff. Fodor's Golf Digest's Best Places to Play. 8th ed. 2008. (Special-Interest Titles Ser.). 864p. pap. 22.00 *(978-1-4000-0743-1(7)*, Fodor's) Fodor's Travel Pubns.
Ford, Steve, ed. The ARRL Repeater Directory. 37th ed. 2008. (ARRL Repeater Directory Ser.). (Illus.). 750p. pap. 10.95 *(978-0-87259-127-1(1))* American Radio Relay League, Inc.
Grey House Publishing, creator. Food & Beverage Market Place, Volume 1: Food & Beverage Manufacturers, Product Categories, Company Profiles. 7th ed. 2007. (Thomas Food & Beverage Market Place: V. 1 Food & Beverage Manufacturers Ser.). (Illus.). 1610p. per. 437.50 *(978-1-59237-199-0(X))* Grey Hse. Publishing.
—Food & Beverage Market Place, Volume 2: Equipment, Supplies & Services Product Categories, Company Profiles. 7th ed. 2007. (Thomas Food & Beverage Market Place: V. 2 Equipment & Supply Companies, Transportation, Ser.). (Illus.). 1086p. per. 312.50 *(978-1-59237-200-3(7))* Grey Hse. Publishing.
Grey House Publishing Staff, creator. Financial Services Canada 2007/2008. 10th ed. 2007. (ENG & FRE.). 1100p. pap. 325.00 *(978-1-59237-221-8(X))* Grey Hse. Publishing.
Headquarters USA 2010. 32nd rev. ed. 2009. 216.00 *(978-0-7808-1095-2(3))* Omnigraphics, Inc.
Ibp, Usa. Canada Industrial & Business Directory. 2006. (Illus.). pap. 99.95 *(978-0-7397-9709-9(3))* International Business Pubns., USA.
ISA, creator. ISA Directory of Automation: Products & Services. 2008. (ISA Directory of Automation Ser.). (Illus.). 287p. pap. 163.25 *(978-1-934394-71-7(8))* ISA.
Lang, Robert. Canadian Parliamentary Guide 2008. 2008. 1000p. pap. 184.00 *(978-1-59237-310-9(0))* Grey Hse. Publishing.
Lang, Robert, ed. Canadian Almanac & Directory. 2011. 350.00 *(978-1-59237-769-5(6))* 2011th rev. ed. 2010. 350.00 *(978-1-59237-589-9(8))* Grey Hse. Publishing.
—Canadian Parliamentary Directory. 2011. 1000p. 224.00 *(978-1-59237-765-7(3))* Grey Hse. Publishing.
Lindner, Eileen, ed. Yearbook of AMER & Canadia. 2009. 464p. pap. 55.00 *(978-0-687-65880-0(2))* Abingdon Pr.
—Yearbook of American & Canadian Churches 2010. 2010. pap. 55.00 *(978-0-687-46686-3(5))* Abingdon Pr.
Lindner, Eileen W., ed. Yearbook of American & Canadian Churches. 75th ed. 2007. (Yearbook of American & Canadian Churches Ser.). 439p. per. 50.00 *(978-0-687-33569-5(8))* Abingdon Pr.
Mars, Laura. Associations Canada 2010. Lang, Robert, ed. 2010. 365.00 *(978-1-59237-570-7(7))* Grey Hse. Publishing.
—Canadian Environmental Directory 2010. Lang, Robert, ed. 2010. pap. 350.00 *(978-1-59237-569-1(3))* Grey Hse. Publishing.
—Financial Services Canada 2010. Lang, Robert, ed. 2010. pap. 350.00 *(978-1-59237-571-4(5))* Grey Hse. Publishing.
Mars, Laura, ed. Directory of Healthcare Group Purchasing Organizations 2010. 17th rev. ed. 2010. pap. 325.00 *(978-1-59237-541-7(3))* Grey Hse. Publishing.
—Food & Beverage Market Place, 3 vols., Set. 10th rev. ed. 2010. pap. 595.00 *(978-1-59237-577-6(4))* Grey Hse. Publishing.
—Food & Beverage Market Place: Volume 2 - Suppliers, 3 vols. 10th rev. ed. 2010. pap. 250.00 *(978-1-59237-579-0(0))* Grey Hse. Publishing.
Mars-Proietti, Laura. Associations Canada. 29th ed. 2008. 1600p. 315.00 *(978-1-59237-277-5(5))* Grey Hse. Publishing.
Mars-Proietti, Laura, ed. Associations Canada: 2007. 2007. 1600p. 315.00 *(978-1-59237-219-5(8))* Grey Hse. Publishing.
—Associations Canada: 2009. 2009. 1600p. 325.00 *(978-1-59237-401-4(8))* Grey Hse. Publishing.
—Canadian Almanac & Directory: 2009. 2008. 1600p. 325.00 *(978-1-59237-370-3(4))* Grey Hse. Publishing.
—Canadian Almanac & Directory: Repertoire et Almanach Canadien. 161st ed. 2007. (Canadian Almanac & Directory Ser.). (Illus.). 1732p. 315.00 *(978-1-59237-220-1(1))* Grey Hse. Publishing.
—Canadian Almanac & Directory 2010. 2009. 1600p. 325.00 *(978-1-59237-439-7(5))* Grey Hse. Publishing.
—Canadian Environmental Directory: 2008. 2007. 900p. pap. 315.00 *(978-1-59237-224-9(4))* Grey Hse. Publishing.
—Canadian Environmental Directory 2009. 2009. 900p. pap. 325.00 *(978-1-59237-374-1(7))* Grey Hse. Publishing.
—Canadian Government Directory. 2007. 900p. 315.00 *(978-1-59237-217-1(1))* Grey Hse. Publishing.
—Canadian Parliamentary Directory: 2009. 2009. 1600p. 184.00 *(978-1-59237-417-5(4))* Grey Hse. Publishing.
—Directory of Healthcare Group Purchasing Organizations: 2008. 16th rev. ed. 2008. 600p. pap. 325.00 *(978-1-59237-287-4(2))* Grey Hse. Publishing.
—Directory of Libraries in Canada: 2006. 2007. 850p. 315.00 *(978-1-59237-222-5(8))* Grey Hse. Publishing.
—The Grey House Safety & Security Directory: 2008. 6th rev. ed. 2007. 1600p. pap. 165.00 *(978-1-59237-205-8(8))* Grey Hse. Publishing.
—The Grey House Safety & Security Directory: 2009. 7th rev. ed. 2008. 1600p. pap. 165.00 *(978-1-59237-375-8(5))* Grey Hse. Publishing.
—The Grey House Safety & Security Directory 2010. 8th rev. ed. 2009. 1600p. pap. 165.00 *(978-1-59237-447-2(6))* Grey Hse. Publishing.
—Sports Market Place Directory: 2009. 7th rev. ed. 2009. 1800p. pap. 225.00 *(978-1-59237-418-2(2))* Grey Hse. Publishing.
Nelson, Robert E., ed. Directory of American Toolmakers. 2007. 1170p. cd-rom *(978-0-943196-05-3(1))* Early American Industries Assn., Inc.
Omnigraphics, creator. City Profiles USA: A Traveler's Guide to Major U. S. & Canadian Cities. 9th ed. 2008. (City Profiles USA: A Traveler's Guide to Major U. S. Cities Ser.). (Illus.). 1074p. 193.00 *(978-0-7808-1025-9(2))* Omnigraphics, Inc.
Peroni, Gwen. Canadian Insurance Claims Directory 2007. 75th ed. 2007. (Illus.). 300p. pap. *(978-0-8020-4065-7(9))* Univ. of Toronto Pr.
—Canadian Insurance Claims Directory 2009 - Listings. 2009. (ENG.). pap. *(978-0-8020-9676-0(X))* Univ. of Toronto Pr.
Peterson's. Graduate Programs in the Physical Science, Mathematics, Agricultural Sciences, the Environment & Natural Resources 2011: More Than 2,700 Graduate Programs in 59 Disciplines. 45th ed. 2010. (ENG.). 476p. (YA). 54.95 *(978-0-7689-2855-6(9))* Peterson's.
—Nursing Programs 2011. Snider, Mark, ed. 16th ed. 2010. (ENG.). 614p. (YA). pap. 28.95 *(978-0-7689-2836-5(2))* Peterson's.
—Private Secondary Schools 2010-2011: More Than 1,400 Schools in the United States & Abroad. Schwartz, Jill, ed. 31st ed. 2010. (ENG.). 1272p. (YA). pap. 39.95 *(978-0-7689-2824-2(9))* Peterson's.
Peterson's Guides Staff. MBA Programs 2008. Seghers, Linda, ed. 13th ed. 2007. (ENG.). 962p. 42.00 *(978-0-7689-2411-4(1))* Peterson's.
—Private Secondary Schools 2007-2008. Oram, Fern A., ed. 28th ed. 2007. (ENG., Illus.). 1488p. per. 30.00 *(978-0-7689-2399-5(9))* Peterson's.
Peterson's Magazine Staff. Nursing Programs 2009. 14th ed. 2008. (ENG.). 672p. pap. 28.00 *(978-0-7689-2554-8(1))* Peterson's.
Planetizen 2007 Guide to Graduate Urban Planning Programs. 2006. per. 44.95 *(978-0-9789329-0-9(0))* Urban Insight Inc.
Planetizen Press, ed. Planetizen Guide to Graduate Urban Planning Programs, 2009 Edition. 2008. 305p. pap. 49.95 *(978-0-9789329-1-6(9))* Urban Insight Inc.
Sporting News Staff. Hockey Guide & Register 2007-2008 Edition: Every Player Every Stat. 2007. (ENG.). 600p. pap. 22.95 *(978-0-89204-876-2(X))* Sporting News Publishing Co.
SRI Consulting Staff, compiled by. 2008 Directory of Chemical Producers: Canada. 2008. 1840.00 *(978-0-9795259-5-7(0))* SRI Consulting.
Trailer Life Books Publishing Staff. Trailer Life RV Parks, Campgrounds, & Services Directory 2011. TL Enterprises Staff, ed. 2011. (ENG., Illus.). 1728p. pap. 24.95 *(978-0-9824894-3-7(9)*, Trailer Life Bks.) TL Enterprises, Inc.
Trailer Life Enterprises. Trailer Life Directory RV Road Atlas. 2013. (Trailer Life Ser.). (ENG., Illus.). 176p. spiral bd. 29.95 *(978-0-9824894-0-6(4))* Trailer Life Directory & Bks.
University Aviation Association, prod. Collegiate Aviation Guide: Reference of Collegiate Aviation Programs. 5th ed. 2008. (YA). mass mkt *(978-0-9678602-2-0(9))* Univ. Aviation Assn.
Wagman, Tracie. Help! . We've Got Kids. 18th ed. 2011. (Help!.. We've Got Kids Ser.). (ENG., Illus.). 278p. pap. ***(978-1-896208-27-5(4))*** Help...We've Got Kids.
2007 Directory of Chemical Producers - Canada. 2007. 880.00 *(978-0-9778175-6-6(3))* SRI Consulting.

CANADA—ECONOMIC CONDITIONS

Abbott, Michael, et al. Retirement Policy Issues in Canada. 2008. (John Deutsch Institute Ser.). (ENG., Illus.). 550p. (C). pap. *(978-1-55339-152-3(4))* McGill-Queen's Univ. Pr.
Beach, Charles M. & Boadway, Robin W. Retirement Policy Issues in Canada. Abbott, Michael, ed. 2008. (John Deutsch Institute Ser.). (ENG.). 550p. (C). pap. *(978-1-55339-161-6(6))* McGill-Queen's Univ. Pr.
Beavon, Daniel J. K., et al. Aboriginal Well-Being: Canada's Continuing Challenge. 2008. (ENG.). 246p. pap. 35.95 *(978-1-55077-177-0(9))* Thompson Educational Publishing CAN. Dist: Univ. of Toronto Pr.
BIA. Essential Canadian Manufacturers: Food, Textile, Clothing, & Chemical Companies. 6th rev. ed. 2006. 400p. (J). pap. 249.00 *(978-1-4187-4236-2(8))* Business Information Agency.
Bone, Robert M. The Canadian North: Issues & Challenges, Fourth Edition. 4th ed. 2012. (ENG., Illus.). 344p. pap. 75.00 ***(978-0-19-544503-9(1))*** Oxford Univ. Pr., Inc.
Brzustowski, Tom. The Way Ahead: Meeting Canada's Productivity Challenge. 2008. (Governance Ser.). (ENG., Illus.). 192p. pap. *(978-0-7766-0669-9(7))* Univ. of Ottawa Pr./Presses de l'Universite d'Ottawa.
Campbell, Don R. 51 Success Stories from Canadian Real Estate Investors. 2008. (ENG., Illus.). 288p. pap. 26.95 *(978-0-470-83916-4(3)*, Wiley) Wiley John & Sons, Inc.
Choudhry, Sujit, et al, eds. Dilemmas of Solidarity: Rethinking Distribution in the Canadian Federation. 2006. (ENG., Illus.). 224p. *(978-0-8020-9126-0(1))* Univ. of Toronto Pr.

C

—Dilemmas of Solidarity: Rethinking Redistribution in the Canadian Federation. 2006. (ENG., Illus.). 224p. pap. *(978-0-8020-9407-0(4))* Univ. of Toronto Pr.

Choudry, Aziz, et al. Fight Back: Workplace Justice for Immigrants. 2009. (ENG.). 128p. pap. 17.95 *(978-1-55266-297-7(7))* Fernwood Publishing Co., Ltd. CAN. Dist: Independent Pubs. Group.

Cram101 Textbook Reviews. Outlines & Highlights for Regional Landscapes of U S & Canada by Eugene Palka, Isbn: 9780470098264 0470098260. 2011. 288p. pap. 32.95 ***(978-1-61490-657-5(2))*** Cram101 Inc.

Cunningham, W. H. (Hank). In Your Best Interest: The Ultimate Guide to the Canadian Bond Market. 3rd ed. 2012. Orig. Title: English. (ENG., Illus.). 224p. pap. 28.99 *(978-1-55488-889-4(1))* Dundurn CAN. Dist: Ingram Pub. Services.

Deimert, Elroy. Pubs, Pulpits & Prairie Fires. 2010. (ENG., Illus.). 304p. pap. 24.95 *(978-1-55266-320-2(5))* Fernwood Publishing Co., Ltd. CAN. Dist: Independent Pubs. Group.

Egeni, Camilius Chike. Suicide Case Study, Theories, Application & Solutions: Socioeconomic & Environmental Effects on Public Behavior: the Case of Inuit Suicide. 2011. 256p. 80.00 *(978-1-4567-0174-1(6))*; pap. 50.50 *(978-1-4567-0175-8(4))* AuthorHouse.

Epp, Roger. We Are All Treaty People: Prairie Essays. 2008. (ENG.). 248p. pap. 26.95 *(978-0-88864-506-7(6))* Univ. of Alberta Pr. CAN. Dist: Michigan State Univ. Pr.

Europa Publications, ed. USA & Canada 2009. 11th rev. ed. 2008. (ENG., Illus.). 644p. 760.00 *(978-1-85743-478-1(1))* Routledge.

Europa Publications, ed. The Usa & Canada 2012. 14th rev. ed. 2011. (ENG.). 676p. 880.00 ***(978-1-85743-629-7(6))*** Routledge.

Europa Publications Staff, ed. USA & Canada 2010. 12th rev. ed. 2009. (ENG., Illus.). 648p. 810.00 *(978-1-85743-536-8(2))* Routledge.

Fahmi, Magda & Rutherdale, Robert, eds. Creating Postwar Canada: Community, Diversity, & Dissent, 1945-75. 2008. (ENG., Illus.). 360p. *(978-0-7748-1384-6(9))* Univ. of British Columbia Pr.

Finkel, Alvin. Working People in Alberta: A History. 2011. (Working Canadians: Books from the CCLH Ser.). (ENG., Illus.). 360p. (C). pap. 45.95 ***(978-1-926836-58-4(8))*** Athabasca University Pr. CAN. Dist: Univ. of Washington Pr.

Globerman, Steven & Storer, Paul. The Impacts of 9/11 on Canada-U. S. Trade. 2008. (ENG., Illus.). 176p. *(978-0-8020-9786-6(3))* Univ. of Toronto Pr.

Godwin, Grieve, et al. Columbia, or the Future of Canada Albyn or Scotland & the Future Achates or Canada ... the Future of Ireland, 25 vols. 2008. (Illus.). IV, 476p. 245.00 *(978-0-415-46348-5(3))* Routledge.

Gogia, Nupur & Slade, Bonnie. About Canada: Immigration. 2011. (About Canada Ser.). (ENG.). 144p. pap. 17.95 ***(978-1-55266-407-0(4))*** Fernwood Publishing Co., Ltd. CAN. Dist: Independent Pubs. Group.

Goyder, John. Prestige Squeeze: Occupational Prestige in Canada since 1965. 2009. (ENG., Illus.). 236p. pap. *(978-0-7735-3611-1(6))* McGill-Queen's Univ. Pr.

Gray, Douglas. Making Money in Real Estate: The Canadian Guide to Profitable Investing in Residential Property. 3rd ed. 2012. (ENG., Illus.). 424p. 39.95 ***(978-1-118-11594-7(5)***, Wiley) Wiley, John & Sons, Inc.

Gray, James Henry & Gray, James H. The Roar of the Twenties, 1 vol. 2006. (Western Canadian Classics Ser.). (ENG., Illus.). 400p. pap. 14.95 *(978-1-897252-10-9(2))* Fitzhenry & Whiteside, Ltd. CAN. Dist: Ingram Pub. Services.

Griffiths, Rudyard. Who We Are: A Citizen's Manifesto, 1 vol. 2009. (ENG.). 224p. 26.95 *(978-1-55365-124-6(3))* D&M Pubs. Inc. CAN. Dist: Perseus-PGW.

Hejazi, Jamal. Three Essays on Inflation Targeting. 2009. 140p. pap. *(978-3-639-17278-2(7))* VDM Verlag Dr. Mueller e.K.

Hiller, Harry H. Second Promised Land: Migration to Alberta & the Transformation of Canadian Society. 2009. (ENG., Illus.). 568p. (C). *(978-0-7735-3517-6(9))*; pap. *(978-0-7735-3526-8(8))* McGill-Queen's Univ. Pr.

Hurtig, Mel. The Truth about Canada: Some Important, Some Astonishing, & Some Truly Appalling Things All Canadians Should Know about Our Country. 2009. (ENG.). 408p. pap. 18.95 *(978-0-7710-4166-2(7)*, Emblem Edns) McClelland & Stewart CAN. Dist: Random Hse., Inc.

Icon Group International, Inc. Staff, compiled by. The 2006 Economic & Product Market Databook for Calgary, Canada. 2006. 618p. ring bd. 95.00 *(978-0-497-80287-5(2))* Icon Group International, Inc.

—The 2006 Economic & Product Market Databook for Edmonton, Canada. 2006. 618p. ring bd. 95.00 *(978-0-497-80502-9(2))* Icon Group International, Inc.

—The 2006 Economic & Product Market Databook for Halifax, Canada. 2006. 618p. ring bd. 95.00 *(978-0-497-81875-3(2))* Icon Group International, Inc.

—The 2006 Economic & Product Market Databook for Hamilton, Canada. 2006. 618p. ring bd. 95.00 *(978-0-497-81881-4(7))* Icon Group International, Inc.

—The 2006 Economic & Product Market Databook for Niagara Falls, Canada. 2006. 618p. ring bd. 95.00 *(978-0-497-81122-8(7))* Icon Group International, Inc.

—The 2006 Economic & Product Market Databook for Quebec, Canada. 2006. 618p. ring bd. 95.00 *(978-0-497-81317-8(3))* Icon Group International, Inc.

—The 2006 Economic & Product Market Databook for Regina, Canada. 2006. 618p. ring bd. 95.00 *(978-0-497-81338-3(6))* Icon Group International, Inc.

—The 2006 Economic & Product Market Databook for Saint John's, Canada. 2006. 618p. ring bd. 95.00 *(978-0-497-81227-0(4))* Icon Group International, Inc.

—The 2006 Economic & Product Market Databook for Thunder Bay, Canada. 2006. 618p. ring bd. 95.00 *(978-0-497-81676-6(8))* Icon Group International, Inc.

—The 2006 Economic & Product Market Databook for Vancouver, Canada. 2006. 618p. ring bd. 95.00 *(978-0-497-81776-3(4))* Icon Group International, Inc.

—The 2006 Economic & Product Market Databook for Victoria, Canada. 2006. 618p. ring bd. 95.00 *(978-0-497-81786-2(1))* Icon Group International, Inc.

—The 2006 Economic & Product Market Databook for Winnipeg, Canada. 2006. 618p. ring bd. 95.00 *(978-0-497-81826-5(4))* Icon Group International, Inc.

International Monetary Fund Staff. Northern Star. Bayoumi, Tamim et al, eds. 2007. (Illus.). 147p. pap. *(978-1-58906-614-4(6))* International Monetary Fund.

Inwood, Kris, ed. Farm, Factory & Fortune: New Studies in the Economic History of the Maritime Provinces. 288p. pap. 16.95 *(978-0-919107-38-0(9))* Acadiensis Pr. CAN. Dist: Goose Lane Editions.

Kranc & Roman. Living & Working in Canada 3e. 3rd ed. 2008. (Illus.). 224p. 22.00 *(978-1-84528-142-7(X))* How To Books GBR. Dist: Parkwest Pubns., Inc.

Laut, Agnes C. The Canadian Commonwealth. 2008. 232p. 24.99 *(978-0-554-36598-5(7))* 2008. 232p. 27.99 *(978-0-554-27295-5(4))* 2007. (ENG.). 206p. per. 20.99 *(978-1-4346-2920-3(1))* 2007. (ENG.). 230p. per. 22.99 *(978-1-4346-2944-9(9))* BiblioBazaar.

—The Canadian Commonwealth. 2009. 168p. pap. *(978-0-217-88932-2(8))* Books LLC.

—The Canadian Commonwealth. 2007. 200p. per. *(978-1-4065-3588-4(5))* Dodo Pr.

—The Canadian Commonwealth. 2007. (ENG.). 350p. 46.95 *(978-0-548-17750-1(3))*; 352p. per. 31.95 *(978-1-4304-7738-9(5))* Kessinger Publishing, LLC.

Laxer, James. Beyond the Bubble - Imagining a New Canadian Economy: The New World Economy, & Canada's Place in It. 2009. 264p. pap. 20.95 *(978-1-897071-55-7(8))* Between the Lines CAN. Dist: Univ. of Toronto Pr.

Layton, Jack. Speaking Out: Ideas That Work for Canadians. 2nd rev. ed. 2006. (ENG.). 448p. pap. 19.95 *(978-1-55263-688-6(7))* Key Porter Bks. CAN. Dist: Perseus-PGW.

Litsios, Ioannis. Neoclassical & Keynesian Dynamics for a Small Open Economy. 2011. 220p. pap. ***(978-3-8433-7980-9(7))*** Lambert Academic Publishing.

Loxley, John & Loxley, Salim. Public Service, Private Profits: The Political Economy of Public - Private Partnerships in Canada. 2010. (ENG.). 208p. pap. 24.95 *(978-1-55266-338-7(8))* Fernwood Publishing Co., Ltd. CAN. Dist: Independent Pubs. Group.

Mackintosh, W. A. The Economic Background of Dominion-Provincial Relations. 191p. pap. 19.95 *(978-0-7705-1842-4(7))* Nelson Education Ltd. CAN. Dist: McGill-Queen's Univ. Pr.

Mansiz, Umit. Net Foreign Assets & Consumption in Canad. 2009. 72p. pap. *(978-3-639-20177-2(9))* VDM Verlag Dr. Mueller e.K.

Marchak, M. Patricia. Ideological Perspectives on Canada. 2011. 146p. (C). pap. *(978-0-7735-3868-9(2))* McGill-Queen's Univ. Pr.

Marchildon, Gregory, ed. Business & Industry: History of the Prairie West #4. 2012. (Hpws Ser.). (ENG.). 440p. 59.95 ***(978-0-88977-238-0(X))*** Canadian Plains Research Ctr. CAN. Dist: Univ. of Toronto Pr.

Marsden, William. Stupid to the Last Drop: How Alberta Is Bringing Environmental Armageddon to Canada (and Doesn't Seem to Care) 2008. (ENG., Illus.). 256p. pap. 16.95 *(978-0-676-97914-5(9)*, Vintage Canada) Random Hse. of Canada, Ltd. CAN. Dist: Random Hse., Inc.

Marshall, Herbert, et al. Canadian-American Industry. 360p. pap. 19.95 *(978-0-7710-9793-5(X))* McClelland & Stewart CAN. Dist: Random Hse. of Canada, Ltd.

Marshall, Joan. Tides of Change on Grand Manan Island: Culture & Belonging in a Fishing Community. 2008. (ENG., Illus.). 416p. pap. *(978-0-7735-3476-6(8))*; (C). *(978-0-7735-3475-9(X))* McGill-Queen's Univ. Pr.

McBride, Stephen, et al. Private Affluence, Public Austerity: Economic Crisis & Democratic Malaise in Canada. 2011. (ENG.). 192p. pap. 24.95 ***(978-1-55266-403-2(1))*** Fernwood Publishing Co., Ltd. CAN. Dist: Independent Pubs. Group.

McDonald, Ted, et al. Canadian Immigration: Economic Evidence for a Dynamic Policy Environment. 2010. (ENG.). 344p. (C). pap. *(978-1-55339-281-1(7))* McGill-Queen's Univ. Pr.

McDowall, Duncan. The Sum of the Satisfactions: Canada in the Age of National Accounting. 2008. (ENG.). 328p. (C). *(978-0-7735-3288-5(9))* McGill-Queen's Univ. Pr.

McManus, Curtis R. Happyland: A History of the Dirty Thirties in Saskatchewan, 1914-1937. 2011. (West Ser.). (ENG., Illus.). 275p. pap. 41.95 *(978-1-55238-524-1(8))* Univ. of Calgary Pr. CAN. Dist: Chicago Distribution Ctr.

Murray, Kristine. Creating an Identity. 2008. 184p. pap. *(978-3-8364-3606-9(X))* VDM Verlag Dr. Mueller e.K.

Mutimer, David. Canadian Annual Review of Politics & Public Affairs 2003. 2009. (Canadian Annual Review of Politics & Public Affairs Ser.). (ENG.). 304p. *(978-0-8020-9985-3(8))* Univ. of Toronto Pr.

Mutimer, David, ed. Canadian Annual Review of Politics & Public Affairs 2001. 2007. (Canadian Annual Review of Politics & Public Affairs Ser.). (ENG.). 304p. *(978-0-8020-9235-9(7))* Univ. of Toronto Pr.

—Canadian Annual Review of Politics & Public Affairs 2002. 2008. (ENG., Illus.). 304p. *(978-0-8020-9819-1(3))* Univ. of Toronto Pr.

Myers, Gustavus. History of Canadian Wealth. 2009. 352p. 32.99 *(978-1-113-09533-6(4))*; pap. 31.75 *(978-1-113-09530-5(X))* BiblioBazaar.

Naylor, R. T. Canada in the European Age, 1453-1919. 2nd ed. 2006. (ENG.). 648p. (C). *(978-0-7735-3090-4(8))*; per. *(978-0-7735-3091-1(6))* McGill-Queen's Univ. Pr.

Nellist, John G. Aircraft Production During World War Ii: Boeing Aircraft of Canada. 2010. 68p. pap. 27.68 *(978-1-4269-3820-7(9))* Trafford Publishing.

Organisation for Economic Co-operation and Development Staff. Oecd Economic Surveys: Canada - Volume 2006 Issue 10. 2006. (Illus.). 148p. per. 52.00 *(978-92-64-02525-7(1))* Organization for Economic Cooperation & Development.

—OECD Economic Surveys: Canada 2008. 2008. 164p. pap. 63.00 *(978-92-64-04393-0(4))* Organization for Economic Cooperation & Development.

Parkin, Michael. Microeconomics. 8th ed. 2007. (Illus.). 552p. pap. *(978-0-321-41661-2(9))* Pearson Bks.

—Microeconomics. 9th ed. 2009. (ENG.). 552p. (C). pap. 186.67 *(978-0-321-59287-3(5)*, Prentice Hall) Prentice Hall PTR.

Penfold, Steven & Penfold, Steve. The Donut: A Canadian History. 2008. (ENG., Illus.). 256p. *(978-0-8020-9797-2(9))* Univ. of Toronto Pr.

Peterson. Wake up, Canada! Reflections on Vital National Issues. 2010. 160p. pap. 24.67 *(978-1-152-10851-6(4))* General Bks. LLC.

Peterson, C. W. 1868-1944. Wake up, Canada! Reflections on Vital National Issues. 2010. 390p. pap. 33.75 *(978-1-177-82341-8(1))*; (ENG.). 388p. pap. 33.75 *(978-1-177-27175-2(3))* BiblioBazaar.

Pupo, Norene & Thomas, Mark, eds. Interrogating the New Economy: Restructuring Work in the 21st Century. 2009. (ENG., Illus.). 250p. *(978-1-4426-0057-7(8))*; xxii, 292p. pap. *(978-1-4426-0055-3(1))* Univ. of Toronto Pr.

Quarter, Jack, et al. Understanding the Social Economy: A Canadian Perspective. 2009. (ENG., Illus.). 344p. *(978-0-8020-9695-1(6))*; xvii, 387p. pap. *(978-0-8020-9645-6(X))* Univ. of Toronto Pr.

Raphael, Dennis. Poverty & Policy in Canada: Implications for Health & Quality of Life. 2007. (ENG., Illus.). 440p. pap. 47.95 *(978-1-55130-323-9(X))* Canadian Scholars' Pr., Inc. CAN. Dist: Ingram Pub. Services.

Regular, Keith. Neighbours & Networks: The Blood Tribe in the Southern Alberta Economy, 1884-1939. 2008. (Northern Lights: Ser.). (Illus.). 240p. pap. 34.95 *(978-1-55238-243-1(5))* Univ. of Calgary Pr. CAN. Dist: Michigan State Univ. Pr.

Safarian, A. E. The Canadian Economy in the Great Depression. 3rd ed. 2009. (Carleton Library Ser.). (Illus.). 288p. *(978-0-7735-3702-6(3))* McGill-Queen's Univ. Pr.

—'the Canadian Economy in the Great Depression: Third Edition. 3rd ed. 2009. (Carleton Library Ser.). (Illus.). 288p. pap. *(978-0-7735-3713-2(9))* McGill-Queen's Univ. Pr.

Saunders, S. A. The Economic History of the Maritime Provinces. 139p. pap. 9.95 *(978-0-919107-03-8(6))* Acadiensis Pr. CAN. Dist: Goose Lane Editions.

Siam, John. Hedging Canadian Short-Term Interest Rates: The bax Market. 2010. 152p. pap. *(978-3-8383-0204-1(4))* Lambert Academic Publishing.

Slowey, Gabrielle. Navigating Neoliberalism: Self-Determination & the Mikisew Cree First Nation. 2008. (ENG., Illus.). 128p. *(978-0-7748-1405-8(5))* Univ. of British Columbia Pr.

SoubliêRe, Marion. Getting Work with the Federal Government: A Guide to Figuring Out the Procurement Puzzle. 2010. 100p. pap. 26.95 *(978-1-4502-4505-0(6))* iUniverse, Inc.

Swartz, Mark. Get Wired, You're Hired! The Canadian Internet Job Search Guide. 4th ed. 2008. *(978-1-896324-31-9(2))* Student Employment Network.

Sweeny, Alastair. Black Bonanza: Canada's Oil Sands & the Race to Secure North America's Energy Future. 2010. (ENG.). 272p. 32.00 *(978-0-470-16138-8(8)*, Wiley) Wiley, John & Sons, Inc.

Teixeira, Carlos, et al, eds. Immigrant Geographies of North American Cities. 2012. (ENG., Illus.). 392p. 75.00 ***(978-0-19-543782-9(9))*** Oxford Univ. Pr., Inc.

Thomas, David M. & Torrey, Barbara Boyle, eds. Canada & the United States, third Edition: Differences that Count. 3rd ed. 2007. (Illus.). 400p. pap. ***(978-1-55111-712-6(6))*** Univ. of Toronto Pr.

Thraves, Bernard D., et al, eds. Saskatchewan: Geographic Perspectives. 2007. (ENG., Illus.). 486p. pap. 75.00 *(978-0-88977-189-5(8))* Canadian Plains Research Ctr. CAN. Dist: Univ. of Toronto Pr.

Toner, Glen, ed. Sustainable Production: Building Canadian Capacity. 2007. (ENG., Illus.). 272p. pap. 29.95 *(978-0-7748-1252-8(4))* UBC Pr. CAN. Dist: Univ. of Washington Pr.

Turner, John N., et al. Politics of Purpose: The Right Honourable John N. Turner, 17th Prime Minister of Canada. 40th anniv. ed. 2008. (Library of Political Leadership Ser.). (ENG., Illus.). 144p. (C). pap. *(978-1-55339-227-9(2))* McGill-Queen's Univ. Pr.

The Usa & Canada 2007. 9th rev. ed. 2006. (ENG., Illus.). 624p. 615.00 *(978-1-85743-396-8(3))* Routledge.

The Usa & Canada 2011. 13th rev. ed. 2011. (ENG.). 664p. 835.00 *(978-1-85743-574-0(5))* Routledge.

Watkins, Melville Henry. Staples & Beyond: Selected Writings of Mel Watkins. Grant, Hugh & Wolfe, David, eds. 2006. (Carleton Library: Vol. 210). (ENG.). 304p. per. *(978-0-7735-3145-1(9))* McGill-Queen's Univ. Pr.

Wilson, Bruce G. The Enterprises of Robert Hamilton: A Study of Wealth & Influence in Early Upper Canada, 1776-1812. 243p. *(978-0-88629-010-8(4))* McGill-Queen's Univ. Pr.

CANADA—ECONOMIC POLICY

Beach, Charles M. & Boadway, Robin W. Retirement Policy Issues in Canada. Abbott, Michael, ed. 2008. (John Deutsch Institute Ser.). (ENG.). 550p. (C). pap. *(978-1-55339-161-6(6))* McGill-Queen's Univ. Pr.

Bernard, Prosper. External Pressure, National Response: Industrial Adjustment in Canada since the 1970s. 2009. (ENG.). 170p. pap. 28.50 *(978-0-7618-4578-2(X))* Univ. Pr. of America, Inc.

Canada Northern Social Concerns: Companies-Products-Services. (Orig.). 435p. pap. 195.00 *(978-0-7605-1865-6(3))*; 160p. pap. 195.00 *(978-0-7605-1862-5(9))* Rector Pr., Ltd.

Doern, G. Bruce, et al. Public Budgeting in Canada: Politics, Economics & Management, No. 147. 256p. pap. *(978-0-88629-069-6(4))* McGill-Queen's Univ. Pr.

Finkel, Alvin. Working People in Alberta: A History. 2011. (Working Canadians: Books from the CCLH Ser.). (ENG., Illus.). 360p. (C). pap. 45.95 ***(978-1-926836-58-4(8))*** Athabasca University Pr. CAN. Dist: Univ. of Washington Pr.

Francois, Joseph F. & Shiells, Clinton R., eds. Modeling Trade Policy: Applied General Equilibrium Assessments of North American Free Trade. 2008. (ENG., Illus.). 372p. pap. 48.00 *(978-0-521-08756-8(2))* Cambridge Univ. Pr.

Gillespie, W. Irwin. Tax, Borrow & Spend: Financing Federal Spending in Canada, 1867-1990, No. 170. (Illus.). 357p. pap. *(978-0-88629-153-2(4))* McGill-Queen's Univ. Pr.

Grinspun, Ricardo & Shamsie, Yasmine, eds. Whose Canada? Continental Integration, Fortress North America, & the Corporate Agenda. 2007. (ENG., Illus.). 592p. (C). *(978-0-7735-3191-8(2))*; per. *(978-0-7735-3192-5(0))* McGill-Queen's Univ. Pr.

Grossman, Perry. Globalization & the Linkage of Trade & Environmental Issues. 2009. 240p. pap. *(978-3-639-17481-6(X))* VDM Verlag Dr. Mueller e.K.

Howard-Hassmann, Rhoda E. & Welch, Claude E., eds. Economic Rights in Canada & the United States. 2009. (Pennsylvania Studies in Human Rights Ser.). 288p. (C). pap. 24.95 *(978-0-8122-2093-3(5))* Univ. of Pennsylvania Pr.

International Monetary Fund Staff. Northern Star. Bayoumi, Tamim et al, eds. 2007. (Illus.). 147p. pap. *(978-1-58906-614-4(6))* International Monetary Fund.

Johnson, Harry G. The Canadian Quandary: Economic Problems & Policies, No. 106. 368p. pap. 19.95 *(978-0-7710-9811-6(1))* McClelland & Stewart CAN. Dist: Random Hse. of Canada, Ltd.

Joseph, Thomas W. 8 Days of Crisis on the Hill; Political Blip or Stephen Harper's Revolution Derailed? 2009. 264p. pap. 19.95 *(978-1-4401-4135-5(5))* iUniverse, Inc.

Leeson, Robert, ed. Canadian Policy Debates & Case Studies in Honour of David Laidler. 2010. (ENG., Illus.). 272p. 105.00 *(978-0-230-23734-6(7))* Palgrave Macmillan.

Marchak, M. Patricia. Ideological Perspectives on Canada. 2011. 146p. (C). pap. *(978-0-7735-3868-9(2))* McGill-Queen's Univ. Pr.

Martin, Roger & Milway, James. Canada: What It Is, What It Can Be. 2012. (ENG., Illus.). 232p. ***(978-1-4426-4465-6(6))*** Univ. of Toronto Pr.

Maslove, Allan M., ed. How Ottawa Spends, 2009-2010: Economic Upheaval & Political Dysfunction. 2009. (ENG.). 312p. pap. *(978-0-7735-3612-8(4))* McGill-Queen's Univ. Pr.

McBride, Stephen, et al. Private Affluence, Public Austerity: Economic Crisis & Democratic Malaise in Canada. 2011. (ENG.). 192p. pap. 24.95 ***(978-1-55266-403-2(1))*** Fernwood Publishing Co., Ltd. CAN. Dist: Independent Pubs. Group.

Organisation for Economic Co-operation and Development Staff. Oecd Economic Surveys: Canada - Volume 2006 Issue 10. 2006. (Illus.). 148p. per. 52.00 *(978-92-64-02525-7(1))* Organization for Economic Cooperation & Development.

—OECD Economic Surveys: Canada 2008. 2008. 164p. pap. 63.00 *(978-92-64-04393-0(4))* Organization for Economic Cooperation & Development.

Rymes, Thomas K. Welfare, Property Rights & Economic Policy: Essays & Tributes in Honour of H. Scott Gordon. 190p. *(978-0-88629-143-3(7))* McGill-Queen's Univ. Pr.

Shefner, Jon & Fernandez-Kelly, Patricia, eds. NAFTA & Beyond: Alternative Perspectives in the Study of Global Trade & Development. 2007. (ANNALS of the American Academy of Political & Social Science Ser.: 610). (Illus.). 287p. (C). 47.00 *(978-1-4129-5753-3(2)*, 295610C) SAGE Pubns., Inc.

Summers, Valerie. Regime Change in a Resource Economy: The Politicies of Underdevelopment in Newfoundland since 1825. (ENG.). 80p. pap. *(978-1-55081-093-6(6))* Breakwater Bks., Ltd.

Wardhaugh, Robert A. Behind the Scenes: The Life & Work of William Clifford Clard. 2010. (IPAC Series in Public Management & Governance Ser.). (Illus.). 560p. (ENG.). *(978-1-4426-4126-6(6))*; pap. *(978-1-4426-1052-1(2))* Univ. of Toronto Pr.

Watkins, M. H. & Wolfe, David. Staples & Beyond: Selected Writings of Mel Watkins. Grant, Hugh M. K., ed. 2006. (Carleton Library: Vol. 210). (ENG.). 304p. (C). *(978-0-7735-3144-4(0))* McGill-Queen's Univ. Pr.

CANADA—EMIGRATION AND IMMIGRATION

Abu-Laban, Yasmeen & Gabriel, Christina. Selling Diversity: Immigration, Multiculturalism, Employment Equity, & Globalization. 2008. (ENG.). 202p. pap. *(978-1-4426-0072-0(1))* Univ. of Toronto Pr.

Andrew, Caroline, et al. Immigration, Integration, & Inclusion in Ontario Cities. 2012. (ENG.). 250p. (C). pap. *(978-1-55339-292-7(2))* McGill-Queen's Univ. Pr.

Ayukawa, Michiko Midge. Hiroshima Immigrants in Canada, 1891-1941. 2008. (ENG., Illus.). 208p. *(978-0-7748-1431-7(4))* Univ. of British Columbia Pr.

Babaskina, Tatiana. The Effect of Immigration on Labour Market Outcomes in Norway. 2009. 68p. pap. *(978-3-639-13046-1(4))* VDM Verlag Dr. Mueller e.K.

Barbu, Cornel. Electrican's book electrician in north America. 2009. 96p. pap. 19.34 *(978-0-557-09379-3(1))* Lulu Enterprises Inc.

Beatson, Peter. Wheels, Waves, Wings & Drums: My Twentieth Century Journey. 2010. 180p. 30.00 *(978-1-4269-4168-9(4))*; pap. 20.00 *(978-1-4269-4167-2(6))* Trafford Publishing.

Beaugrand, Honore. Jeanne la Fileuse: Pisode de l'Émigration Franco-Canadienne Aux États. 2007. 190p. pap. 19.99 *(978-1-4346-3484-9(1))*; (FRE.). 210p. pap. 22.99 *(978-1-4346-3485-6(X))* BiblioBazaar.

Biemond-Boer, Betsy. Die Hollanders Zijn Gek! Identiteit en Integratie Van Bevindelijk Gereformeerden in Canada. 2012. (DUT., Illus.). 169p. 28.75 ***(978-90-5260-279-0(4))*** Aksant Academic Pubs. NLD. Dist: Amsterdam Univ. Pr.

Biles, John, et al. Integration & Inclusion of Newcomers & Minorities across Canada. 2011. (ENG.). 250p. (C). pap. *(978-1-55339-290-3(6))* McGill-Queen's Univ. Pr.

Bjarnadottir, Birna & Gudmundsson, Finnbogi, eds. My Parents: Memoirs of New World Icelanders. 2007. (ENG., Illus.). 144p. pap. 26.95 *(978-0-88755-699-9(X))* Univ. of Manitoba Pr. CAN. Dist: Chicago Distribution Ctr.

Bray, Martin. Immigration to Canada. 2008. pap. 29.99 *(978-0-9814695-0-8(7))* Rapid Publishing LLC.

Breton, Raymond. Different Gods: Integrating Non-Christian Minorities into a Primarily Christian Society. 2012. (ENG.). 232p. (C). ***(978-0-7735-3968-6(9))***; pap. ***(978-0-7735-3993-8(X))*** McGill-Queen's Univ. Pr.

Brochmann, Grete & Hagelund, Anniken. Immigration Policy & the Scandinavian Welfare State 1945-2010. 2012. (ENG., Illus.). 312p. 90.00 ***(978-0-230-30238-9(6))*** Palgrave Macmillan.

Buckingham, James Silk. Canada, Nova Scotia, New Brunswick, & the Other British Provinces in North America: With a Plan of National Colonization. 2011. (Cambridge Library Collection - Travel & Exploration Ser.). (ENG., Illus.). 580p. pap. 43.00 ***(978-1-108-03337-4(7))*** Cambridge Univ. Pr.

Caccia, Ivana. Managing the Canadian Mosaic in Wartime: Shaping Citizenship Policy, 1939-1945. 2010. (McGill-Queen's Studies in Ethnic History Ser.). (Illus.). 384p. *(978-0-7735-3658-6(2))* McGill-Queen's Univ. Pr.

Campey, Lucille H. Planters, Paupers, & Pioneers: English Settlers in Atlantic Canada. 2010. (ENG., Illus.). 384p. pap. 35.00 *(978-1-55488-748-4(8))* Dundurn CAN. Dist: Ingram Pub. Services.

Campey, Lucille H. Seeking a Better Future: The English Pioneers of Ontario & Quebec. 2012. (English in Canada Ser.). (ENG., Illus.). 472p. pap. 35.00 ***(978-1-4597-0351-3(0))*** Dundurn CAN. Dist: Ingram Pub. Services.

Cancian, Sonia. Families, Lovers, & Their Letters: Italian Postwar Migration to Canada. 2010. (Studies in Immigration & Culture Ser.). (ENG.). 192p. pap. 34.95 *(978-0-88755-715-6(5))* Univ. of Manitoba Pr. CAN. Dist: Chicago Distribution Ctr.

Cancian, Sonia & Mclennan, Rob. Families, Lovers, & Their Letters: Italian Postwar Migration to Canada. 2010. (ENG.). 192p. 55.00 *(978-0-88755-187-1(4))* Univ. of Manitoba Pr. CAN. Dist: Michigan State Univ. Pr.

Chilton, Lisa. Agents of Empire: British Female Migration to Canada & Australia, 1860s-1930. 2007. (Studies in Gender & History Ser.). (ENG., Illus.). 272p. *(978-0-8020-9274-8(8))*; pap. *(978-0-8020-9474-2(0))* Univ. of Toronto Pr.

Clark, Tom. Singh to Suresh: Non-Citizens, the Canadian Courts & Human Rights Obligations. 2006. 256p. pap. 19.09 *(978-1-4251-0429-0(0))* Trafford Publishing.

Cockburn, James Seaton. Canada for Gentlemen. 2007. pap. *(978-1-4065-1333-2(4))* Dodo Pr.

Creese, Gillian Laura. The New African Diaspora in Vancouver: Migration, Exclusion, & Belonging. 2011. (ENG.). 288p. ***(978-1-4426-4295-9(5))***; pap. ***(978-1-4426-1159-7(6))*** Univ. of Toronto Pr.

Dachyshyn, Darcey. Refugee Families with Preschool Children. 2008. 200p. pap. *(978-3-639-00271-3(7))* VDM Verlag Dr. Mueller e.K.

Di Sciascio-Andrews, Josie. How the Italians Created Canada: From Giovanni Caboto to the Cultural Renaissance. 2008. (ENG., Illus.). 240p. pap. *(978-1-896124-14-8(3))* Dragon Hill Publishing CAN. Dist: Lone Pine Publishing.

Ding, Yueya. Negotiating Individual Space. 2010. 252p. pap. *(978-3-639-27523-0(3))* VDM Verlag Dr. Mueller e.K.

Errington, Elizabeth Jane. Emigrant Worlds & Transatlantic Communities: Migration to Upper Canada in the First Half of the Nineteenth Century. 2007. (McGill-Queen's Studies in Ethnic History Ser.). (ENG., Illus.). 256p. (C). *(978-0-7735-3265-6(X))*; per. *(978-0-7735-3266-3(8))* McGill-Queen's Univ. Pr.

Ertler, Klaus-Dieter & Löschnigg, Martin, eds. Cultural Constructions of Migration in Canada / Constructions Culturelles de la Migration Au Canada. 2011. (Canadiana. Literaturen/Kulturen, Literatures/Cultures, Littératures/Cultures Ser.). (ENG & FRE.). 270p. 56.95 *(978-3-631-61454-9(3))* Lang, Peter GmbH, Europaischer Verlag der Wissenschaften DEU. Dist: Lang, Peter.

Falge, Christiane, et al. Migrants & Health: Political & Institutional Responses to Cultural Diversity in Health Systems. 2012. (Global Health Ser.). 170p. 99.95 ***(978-0-7546-7915-8(2))*** Ashgate Publishing Co.

Fekete, Orsolya. Canadian-Romanian Theatres: A Case Study of CanadianMulticulturalism: The Canadian Mosaic & the Ethnic Theatres Within. 2008. 72p. pap. *(978-3-639-09548-7(0))* VDM Verlag Dr. Mueller e.K.

Fleming, Douglas. Becoming Canadian - Racialized Citizenship, Esl Learners, National Second Language Policy, & the Canadian Language Benchmark. 2008. 244p. pap. *(978-3-639-00346-8(2))* VDM Verlag Dr. Mueller e.K.

Flint, Cameron D. 'to Secure to Themselves & Their Countrymen an Agreeable & Happy Retreat.' - the Continuity of Scottish Highland Mercena. 2008. 84p. pap. *(978-3-639-00953-8(3))* VDM Verlag Dr. Mueller e.K.

Geiger, Andrea. Refracting Difference: Japanese Immigrant Negotiations of Race, Caste, & Borders, 1885-1928. 2011. (Lamar Series in Western History Ser.). (ENG., Illus.). 304p. 45.00 *(978-0-300-16963-8(9))* Yale Univ. Pr.

Gerber, David. Authors of Their Lives: The Personal Correspondence of British Immigrants to North America in the Nineteenth Century. 2008. (ENG.). 432p. pap. 26.00 *(978-0-8147-3200-7(3))* New York Univ. Pr.

Godwin, Grieve, et al. Columbia, or the Future of Canada Albyn or Scotland & the Future Act ates or Canada ... the Future of Ireland, 25 vols. 2008. (Illus.). IV, 476p. 245.00 *(978-0-415-46348-5(3))* Routledge.

Gogia, Nupur & Slade, Bonnie. About Canada: Immigration. 2011. (About Canada Ser.). (ENG.). 144p. pap. 17.95 ***(978-1-55266-407-0(4))*** Fernwood Publishing Co., Ltd. CAN. Dist: Independent Pubs. Group.

Goutor, David. Guarding the Gates: The Canadian Labour Movement & Immigration, 1872-1934. 2007. (ENG., Illus.). 288p. 85.00 *(978-0-7748-1364-3(4))* UBC Pr. CAN. Dist: Univ. of Washington Pr.

Hachey, Jean M. The Canadian Guide to Working & Living Overseas: 1995 Edition. 2nd ed. 500p. *(978-0-9696001-1-4(9))* Intercultural Systems/Systemes Interculturel (ISSI).

Harney, Robert F. & Harney, Nicholas De Maria. From the Shores of Hardship: Italians in Canada: Essays. (Illus.). xii, 216p. *(978-0-921831-34-1(X))* Soleil Publishing, Inc.

Ighodaro, MacDonald E. Living the Experience: Migration, Exclusion, & Anti-Racist Practice. 2007. (ENG.). 192p. pap. 24.95 *(978-1-55266-210-6(1))* Fernwood Publishing Co., Ltd. CAN. Dist: Independent Pubs. Group.

Imbric, Dragana. Michael Ondaatje's in the Skin of a Lion & Multiculturalism. 2010. 96p. pap. *(978-3-639-27449-3(0))* VDM Verlag Dr. Mueller e.K.

Isaksen, Lise Widding, ed. Global Care Work: Gender & Migration in Nordic Societies. 2011. (ENG., Illus.). 240p. pap. 49.95 *(978-91-85509-48-5(5))* Nordic Academic Pr., Sweden SWE. Dist: Independent Pubs. Group.

Jaenen, Cornelius J. Promoters, Planters & Pioneers: The Course & Context of Belgian Settlement in Western Canada. 2011. (West Ser.). (ENG., Illus.). 348p. pap. 41.95 ***(978-1-55238-258-5(3))*** Univ. of Calgary Pr. CAN. Dist: Chicago Distribution Ctr.

Jarratt, Melynda. Captured Hearts: New Brunswick's War Brides. 2008. (New Brunswick Military Heritage Ser.). (ENG., Illus.). 148p. pap. 16.95 *(978-0-86492-519-0(0))* Goose Lane Editions CAN. Dist: Univ. of Toronto Pr.

—War Brides: The Stories of the Women Who Left Everything Behind to Follow the Men They Loved. 2009. (ENG., Illus.). 288p. pap. 28.00 *(978-1-55488-386-8(5))*, Dundurn Pr.) Dundurn CAN. Dist: Ingram Pub. Services.

John J. S. Roders. Monkey Bottom: A Memoir. 2010. 200p. pap. 19.95 *(978-1-4269-2146-9(2))* Trafford Publishing.

Johnson, Stanley Currie. A History of Emigration from the United Kingdom to North America, 1763-1912. (Studies in Economics & Political Science Ser.). 387p. reprint ed. 98.00 *(978-0-7222-6454-6(2))* Library Reprints, Inc.

Jones, Terry-Ann. Jamaican Immigrants in the United States & Canada: Race, Transnationalism, & Social Capital. 2007. (New Americans). 198p. lib. bdg. 62.00 *(978-1-59332-237-3(2))* LFB Scholarly Publishing LLC.

Kazimi, Ali. Undesirables: White Canada & the Komagata Maru - An Illustrated History, 1 vol. 2012. (ENG., Illus.). 176p. 39.95 ***(978-1-55365-973-0(2))*** D&M Pubs. Inc. CAN. Dist: Perseus-PGW.

Kelley, Ninette & Trebilcock, Michael J. The Making of the Mosaic: A History of Canadian Immigration Policy. 2nd ed. 2010. pap. ***(978-0-8020-9536-7(4))*** Univ. of Toronto Pr.

Kershaw, Roger & Sacks, Janet. New Lives for Old: The Story of Britain's Child Migrants. 2007. (Illus.). 240p. 34.95 *(978-1-905615-17-9(5))* National Archives (PRO), The GBR. Dist: International Publishers Marketing.

Knowles, Valerie. Strangers at Our Gates: Canadian Immigration & Immigration Policy, 1540-2006. 2nd rev. ed. 2007. (ENG., Illus.). 312p. pap. 26.99 *(978-1-55002-698-6(4)*, Dundurn Pr.) Dundurn CAN. Dist: Ingram Pub. Services.

Kranc & Roman. Living & Working in Canada 3e. 3rd ed. 2008. (Illus.). 224p. 22.00 *(978-1-84528-142-7(X))* How To Books GBR. Dist: Parkwest Pubns., Inc.

Kukushkin, Vadim. From Peasants to Labourers: Ukrainian & Belarusan Immigration from the Russian Empire to Canada. 2007. (McGill-Queen's Studies in Ethnic History Ser.). (ENG., Illus.). 304p. (C). *(978-0-7735-3267-0(6))* McGill-Queen's Univ. Pr.

Ley, David. Millionaire Migrants: Trans-Pacific Life Lines. 2010. (RGS-IBG Book Ser.: 38). (ENG., Illus.). 328p. pap. 39.95 *(978-1-4051-9292-7(5))*; 94.95 *(978-1-4051-9291-0(7))* Wiley, John & Sons, Inc. (Wiley-Blackwell).

Lyster, Coral. Most Excellent Citizens: Canada's War Brides of World War II. 2010. 276p. pap. 20.76 *(978-1-4269-0250-5(6))* Trafford Publishing.

Magnusson, Anna. The Quarriers Story: One Man's Vision That Gave 7,000 Children a New Life in Canada. 2006. (ENG., Illus.). 208p. pap. 24.99 *(978-1-55002-655-9(0)*, Dundurn Pr.) Dundurn CAN. Dist: Ingram Pub. Services.

Mar, Lisa Rose. Brokering Belonging: Chinese in Canada's Exclusion ERA, 1885-1945. 2010. (ENG., Illus.). 256p. 99.00 *(978-0-19-973313-2(9))*; pap 24.95 *(978-0-19-973314-9(7))* Oxford Univ. Pr., Inc.

Marchildon, Gregory P. Immigration & Settlement, 1870-1939. 2009. (History of the Prairie West Ser.). (ENG.). 608p. 39.95 *(978-0-88977-230-4(4))* Canadian Plains Research Ctr. CAN. Dist: Univ. of Toronto Pr.

McDonald, Ted, et al. Canadian Immigration: Economic Evidence for a Dynamic Policy Environment. 2010. (ENG.). 344p. (C). pap. *(978-1-55339-281-1(7))*, McGill-Queen's Univ. Pr.

McGrath, M. Eleanor, ed. A Story to Be Told: Personal Reflections on the Irish Immigrant Experience in Canada. 2009. (ENG., Illus.). 215p. 64.95 *(978-1-905785-46-9(1))* Liffey Pr., The IRL. Dist: Dufour Editions, Inc.

Nandasena, Hirantha. Success in Toronto: A Guide for New Immigrants. 2011. 156p. pap. 19.47 *(978-1-4567-5877-6(2))* AuthorHouse.

Noh, Samuel, et al. Korean Immigrants in Canada. 2011. (ENG.). *(978-1-4426-4218-8(1))*; pap. *(978-1-4426-1115-3(4))* Univ. of Toronto Pr.

Parker, Roy. Uprooted: The shipment of poor children. 2008. 416p. 110.00 *(978-1-84742-014-5(1))* Policy Pr. GBR. Dist: International Specialized Bk. Services.

—Uprooted: The Shipment of Poor Children to Canada, 1867-1917. 2010. (Illus.). 376p. pap. 34.95 *(978-1-84742-668-0(9))* Policy Pr. GBR. Dist: Chicago Distribution Ctr.

Perin, Roberto, et al, eds. Arrangiarsi: The Italian Immigration Experience in Canada. 3rd ed. 2006. (Picas Ser.). (ENG., Illus.). 256p. 15.00 *(978-1-55071-255-1(1))* Guernica Editions, Inc. CAN. Dist: Univ. of Toronto Pr.

Rodriguez-Garcia, Dan. Managing Immigration & Diversity in Canada: A Transatlantic Dialogue in the New Age of Migration. 2012. (ENG.). 250p. (C). pap. *(978-1-55339-289-7(2))* McGill-Queen's Univ. Pr.

Romvary, Susan. Zsuzsa Not Zsazsa: Balance with a Smile. (Illus.). 140p. pap. *(978-0-9695180-4-4(8))* Shoreline.

Rowan, John. The Emigrant & Sportsman in Canada. 2007. (Applewood Canadiana Ser.). (ENG.). 452p. per. 24.95 *(978-1-55709-973-0(1))* Applewood Bks.

Sandercock, Leonie & Attili, Giovanni. Where Strangers Become Neighbours: Integrating Immigrants in Vancouver, Canada. 2009. (Urban & Landscape Perspectives Ser.). (Illus.). 304p. 159.00 *(978-1-4020-9034-9(X)*, 140209034X) Springer.

Swyripa, Frances. Storied Landscapes: Ethno-Religious Identity & the Canadian Prairies. 2010. (Studies in Immigration & Culture Ser.). (ENG.). 312p. pap. 30.95 *(978-0-88755-720-0(1))*; (Illus.). 296p. 55.00 *(978-0-88755-191-8(2))* Univ. of Manitoba Pr. CAN. Dist: Chicago Distribution Ctr., Michigan State Univ. Pr.

Taylor, Lynne. Polish Orphans of Tengeru: The Dramatic Story of Their Long Journey to Canada ,1941-1949. 2009. (ENG., Illus.). 280p. pap. 28.00 *(978-1-55488-004-1(1)*, Dundurn Pr.) Dundurn CAN. Dist: Ingram Pub. Services.

Tullius, Nick. My journey from the Banat to Canada. 2011. 204p. 24.59 ***(978-1-4634-1835-9(3))***; pap. 14.03 ***(978-1-4634-1836-6(1))*** AuthorHouse.

Vincent. Immigration: Phénomène Souhaitable et Inévitable. (FRE., Illus.). 267p. *(978-2-89037-726-4(1))* Quebec Amerique.

Vineberg, Robert. Responding to Immigrants' Settlement Needs: the Canadian Experience: The Canadian Experience. 2011. (SpringerBriefs in Population Studies). (ENG., Illus.). xiv, 91p. pap. 49.95 ***(978-94-007-2687-1(2)***, 9400726872) Springer.

Wagner, Jonathan. A History of Migration from Germany to Canada, 1850-1939. 2006. (ENG.). 352p. pap. *(978-0-7748-1216-0(8))* Univ. of British Columbia Pr.

Watson, Scott D. The Securitization of Humanitarian Migration: Digging moats & sinking Boats. 2009. (Routledge Advances in International Relations & Global Politics Ser.). (Illus.). 12p. 128.00 *(978-0-415-49690-2(X))* Routledge.

Wilson, David A. Irish Nationalism in Canada. 2009. (McGill-Queen's Studies in Ethnic History Ser.). (ENG.). 244p. (C). *(978-0-7735-3635-7(3))*; pap *(978-0-7735-3636-4(1))* McGill-Queen's Univ. Pr.

Woolford, Daniel, compiled by. Research Projects Supported by the Canadian Ethnic Studies Program, 1973-1992. (FRE & ENG.). v, 90p *(978-0-662-60102-9(5))* Bow Historical Bks.

Yakimov, Radka. Caft the Blue Danube. 2008. 180p. 26.95 *(978-0-595-71410-0(2))*; pap. 16.95 *(978-0-595-47672-5(4))* iUniverse, Inc.

Young, Robert & Tolley, Erin. Immigrant Settlement Policy in Canadian Municipalities. 2011. (ENG.). 344p. (C). ***(978-0-7735-3877-1(1))***; pap. ***(978-0-7735-3888-7(7))*** McGill-Queen's Univ. Pr.

Zapata-Barrero, Ricard, ed. Immigration & Self-Government of Minority Nations. 2009. 177p. pap. 43.95 *(978-90-5201-547-7(3))* PIE - Peter Lang BEL. Dist: Lang, Peter.

CANADA—ENGLISH-FRENCH RELATIONS

see also Quebec (Province)—History—Autonomy and Independence Movements

Heller, Monica. Crosswords: Language, Education & Ethnicity in French Ontario. (Contributions to the Sociology of Language [CSL] Ser.). (ENG.). X, 252p. 210.00 ***(978-3-11-178418-2(5))*** De Gruyter, Mouton DEU. Dist: de Gruyter, Walter GmbH & Co. KG.

Jedwab, Jack & Landry, Rodrigue. Life after Forty: Official Languages Policy in Canada. 2011. (ENG.). 250p. (C). *(978-1-55339-280-4(9))*; pap. *(978-1-55339-279-8(5))* McGill-Queen's Univ. Pr.

Jones, Richard. Community in Crisis: French-Canadian Nationalism in Perspective, No. 59. 215p. pap. 19.95 *(978-0-7710-9759-1(X))* McClelland & Stewart CAN. Dist: Random Hse. of Canada, Ltd.

CANADA—ENVIRONMENTAL CONDITIONS

Amofah, Kwaku & Kusi-Appiah, Twumasi A. Measuring Household Access to Environmental & Health Education. 2011. 76p. pap. ***(978-3-8454-2063-9(4))*** Lambert Academic Publishing.

Armstrong, Christopher, et al. The River Returns: An Environmental History of the Bow. (Illus.). 2011. (ENG.). 506p. pap. *(978-0-7735-3870-2(4))* 2009. 488p. *(978-0-7735-3584-8(5))* McGill-Queen's Univ. Pr.

Caquard, Sébastien, et al, eds. Mapping Environmental Issues in the City: Arts & Cartography Cross Perspectives. 2011. (Lecture Notes in Geoinformation & Cartography Ser.). (ENG., Illus.). xiv, 273p. 129.00 ***(978-3-642-22440-9(7)*** 3642224407) Springer.

Culver, Keith & Castle, David, eds. Aquaculture, Innovation & Social Transformation. 2008. (International Library of Environmental, Agricultural & Food Ethics Ser.). (ENG., Illus.). xii, 348p. 229.00 *(978-1-4020-8834-6(5)*, 1402088345) Springer.

Doern, G. Bruce & Kinder, Jeffrey S. Strategic Science in the Public Interest: Canada's Government Laboratories & Science-Based Agencies. 2007. (ENG., Illus.). 224p. *(978-0-8020-8853-6(8))* Univ. of Toronto Pr.

Dube, Peter. Stolen Treasure: The horrendous environmental & ecological scandals that are destroying the natural heritage of Eastern Canada & the United States. 2009. 144p. pap. 19.95 *(978-1-4389-6564-2(8))* AuthorHouse.

Durant, Darrin & Johnson, Genevieve Fuji, eds. Nuclear Waste Management in Canada: Critical Issues, Critical Perspectives. 2010. (ENG., Illus.). 208p. (C). pap. 35.95 *(978-0-7748-1709-7(7))* UBC Pr. CAN. Dist: Univ. of Washington Pr.

Etkin, David, et al, eds. An Assessment of Natural Hazards & Disasters in Canada. 2010. 392p. pap. 146.00 *(978-90-481-6246-8(7)*, 9048162467) Springer.

Evenden, Matthew D. Fish versus Power: An Environmental History of the Fraser River. 2007. (Studies in Environment & History). (ENG., Illus.). 328p. (C). pap. 42.00 *(978-0-521-04103-4(1))* Cambridge Univ. Pr.

Fisheries and Oceans Canada Staff. Marine Environmental Assessment of the Estuary & the Gulf of St. Lawrence (Evaluation du Milieu Marin de l'Estuaire et du Golfe du St.-Laurent) 2nd ed. 52p. pap. *(978-0-660-16852-4(9))* Canadian Government Publishing.

Forbes, Gerry J. Reducing Litter on Roadsides. 2009. (Illus.). 68p. pap. *(978-0-309-09840-3(8))* Transportation Research Board.

Forkey, Neil. Tapestry of Life & Place. 2010. (Themes in Canadian History Ser.). (ENG.). *(978-0-8020-9022-5(2))*; pap. *(978-0-8020-4896-7(X))* Univ. of Toronto Pr.

Gale. Worldmark Encyclopedia of U. S. & Canadian Environmental Issues. 6th ed. 2012. (Worldmark Encyclopedia of US & Canada Ser.). (ENG., Illus.). 600p. (J). lib. bdg. 160.00 ***(978-1-4144-9088-5(7))*** Cengage Gale.

Gall, Susan B., et al. Worldmark Encyclopedia of U.S. & Canadian Environmental Issues. 2012. E-Book ***(978-1-4144-9089-2(5))*** Cengage Gale.

Gauthier, Pierre, et al, eds. Montreal at the Crossroads: Super Highways, Turcot & Environment. 2010. (ENG., Illus.). 200p. 34.99 *(978-1-55164-343-4(X))* Black Rose Bks. CAN. Dist: Consortium Bk. Sales & Distribution.

Giesbrecht, Kelly. Community Control in Resource Management. 2009. 120p. pap. *(978-3-639-18005-3(4))* VDM Verlag Dr. Mueller e.K.

Haerens, Margaret. Canada. 2011. (Opposing Viewpoints Ser.). 240p. pap. 26.50 *(978-0-7377-5212-0(2))*; lib. bdg. 39.70 *(978-0-7377-5211-3(4))* Cengage Gale. (Greenhaven Pr., Inc.).

Hall, Britt. Methylmercury Cycling in Boreal Forest Uplands. 2009. 160p. pap. *(978-3-639-14499-4(6))* VDM Verlag Dr. Mueller e.K.

Hammond, Herb. Maintaining Whole Systems on Earth's Crown: Ecosystem-Based Conservation Planning for the Boreal Forest. 2009. (ENG.). 410p. pap. 49.95 *(978-0-9734779-0-0(3)*, 9780973477900) Silva Forest Foundation CAN. Dist: Consortium Bk. Sales & Distribution.

Hele, Karl S., ed. The Nature of Empires & the Empires of Nature: Indigenous Peoples & the Great Lakes Environment. 2011. (Indigenous Studies). (ENG., Illus.). 288p. (C). 95.00 *(978-1-55458-328-7(4))* Wilfrid Laurier Univ. Pr. CAN. Dist: Univ. of Toronto Pr.

Jaccard, Mark, et al. Hot Air: Meeting Canada's Climate Change Challenge. 2008. (ENG., Illus.). 288p. pap. 18.99 *(978-0-7710-8097-5(2)*, Emblem Edns) McClelland & Stewart CAN. Dist: Random Hse., Inc.

Jorgensen, Finn Arne. Making a Green Machine: The Infrastructure of Beverage Container Recycling. 2011. (Studies in Modern Science, Technology, & the Environment Ser.). (ENG., Illus.). 208p. (C). 44.95 *(978-0-8135-5054-1(8))* Rutgers Univ. Pr.

Lang, Robert, ed. Canadian Environmental Resource Guide. 2011. pap. 350.00 *(978-1-59237-768-8(8))* Grey Hse. Publishing.

Locher, Peter. A Time of Change. 2010. 168p. pap. *(978-3-8383-4372-3(7))* Lambert Academic Publishing.

Lowther, Christine & Sinner, Anita, eds. Writing the West Coast: In Love with Place. 2008. (ENG., Illus.). 240p. pap. *(978-1-55380-055-2(9))* Ronsdale Pr.

Marchildon, Gregory P. A Dry Oasis: Institutional Adaptation to Climate on the Canadian Plains. 2009. (University of Regina Publications(UR) Ser.). (ENG.). 312p. pap. 34.95 *(978-0-88977-217-5(7))* Canadian Plains Research Ctr. CAN. Dist: Univ. of Toronto Pr.

Maris, Lauren. Live Green, Calgary! Local Programs, Products & Services to Green Your Life & Save You Money, 1 vol. 2010. (ENG., Illus.). 112p. pap. *(978-1-897522-57-8(6))* Rocky Mountain Bks.

Mars-Proietti, Laura, ed. Canadian Environmental Directory: 2008. 2007. 900p. pap. 315.00 *(978-1-59237-224-9(4))* Grey Hse. Publishing.

C

—Canadian Environmental Directory 2009. 2009. 900p. pap. 325.00 (978-1-59237-374-1(7)) Grey Hse. Publishing.

Mears, Ray. Northern Wilderness: Bushcraft of the Far North. 2010. (ENG., Illus.). 224p. 29.95 (978-0-340-98082-8(6), Hodder & Stoughton) Hodder General Publishing Div. GBR. Dist: Independent Pubs. Group.

Merem, Edmund C. Environmental Accounting for Oil & Natural Gas: A North American Case Study of Canada & the Southeast of the United States. 2010. (Illus.). 380p. 119.95 (978-0-7734-1379-5(0)) Mellen, Edwin Pr., The.

Moldovan, Brett J. & Henry, M. Jim. Fate & Transport of Arsenic in Uranium Mine Tailings. 2008. 200p. pap. (978-3-639-00524-0(4)) VDM Verlag Dr. Mueller e.K.

Moss, Stephen. Volcanology of the A154n Kimberlite at Diavik. 2010. 236p. pap. (978-3-8383-4023-4(X)) Lambert Academic Publishing.

Murphy, Raymond. Leadership in Disaster: Learning for a Future with Global Climate Change. 2011. 424p. pap. (978-0-7735-3872-6(0)) 2009. (ENG., Illus.). 480p. (C). (978-0-7735-3524-4(1)) McGill-Queen's Univ. Pr.

Murray, Laurel. Laying Tracks. 2010. 60p. pap. (978-3-639-22321-7(7)) VDM Verlag Dr. Mueller e.K.

Paehlke, Robert C. & Paehlke, Robert. Some Like It Cold: The Politics of Climate Change in Canada. 2008. 168p. pap. 22.95 (978-1-897071-39-7(6)) Between the Lines CAN. Dist: Univ. of Toronto Pr.

Parr, Joy. Sensing Changes: Technologies, Environments, & the Everyday, 1953-2003. 2010. (ENG., Illus.). 304p. (C). pap. 35.95 (978-0-7748-1724-0(0)) Univ. of Washington Pr.

Piper, Liza. The Industrial Transformation of Subarctic Canada. 2010. 424p. pap. 35.95 (978-0-7748-1533-8(7)) Univ. of Washington Pr.

—Industrial Transformation of Subarctic Canada: Nature/ History/ Society. 2009. (ENG., Illus.). 368p. (978-0-7748-1532-1(9)) Univ. of British Columbia Pr.

Poulter, Gillian. Green Party. 2011. 32p. (gr. 5-8). pap. **(978-1-77071-701-5(3))** Weigl Educational Pubs. Ltd.

Richardson, Boyce. Strangers Devour the Land. 2008. (ENG., Illus.). 376p. (Orig.). pap. 25.00 (978-1-60358-004-5(2)) Chelsea Green Publishing.

Ross, Stephanie. Fanning the Flames. 2008. 184p. pap. (978-3-639-07084-2(4)) VDM Verlag Dr. Mueller e.K.

Sandford, Robert W. Ecology & Wonder: In the Canadian Rocky Mountain Parks World Heritage Site. 2009. (ENG., Illus.). 400p. pap. 48.95 (978-1-897425-57-2(0)) UBC Pr. CAN. Dist: Univ. of Washington Pr.

Sauchyn, David, et al, eds. The New Normal: The Canadian Prairies in a Changing Climate. 2010. (Ur Ser.). 450p. 75.00 (978-0-88977-231-1(2)) Canadian Plains Research Ctr. CAN. Dist: Univ. of Toronto Pr.

Sweeny, Alastair. Black Bonanza: Canada's Oil Sands & the Race to Secure North America's Energy Future. 2010. (ENG.). 272p. 32.00 (978-0-470-16138-8(8), Wiley) Wiley, John & Sons, Inc.

Wadewitz, Lissa K. The Nature of Borders: Salmon, Boundaries, & Bandits on the Salish Sea, 1 vol. 2012. (ENG., Illus.). 384p. pap. 24.95 **(978-0-295-99182-5(8))** Univ. of Washington Pr.

White, Rodney. Climate Change in Canada. 2010. (ENG.). 184p. 19.95 (978-0-19-543060-8(3)) Oxford Univ. Pr., Inc.

Williston, Byron. Environmental Ethics for Canadians. 2011. (ENG., Illus.). 448p. pap. 85.00 **(978-0-19-543363-0(7))** Oxford Univ. Pr., Inc.

Wulff, Ricardo. The Reclamation & Re-Occupation of the Burloak Employment Lands. 2011. 136p. pap. **(978-3-8454-2280-0(7))** Lambert Academic Publishing.

Wynn, Graeme. Canada & Arctic North America: An Environmental History. Stoll, Mark R., ed. 2006. (Nature & Human Societies Ser.). (Illus.). 503p. 85.00 (978-1-85109-437-0(7)) ABC-CLIO, LLC.

Zalatan, Rebecca. Climate Change & Caribou. 2008. 128p. pap. (978-3-639-03755-5(3)) VDM Verlag Dr. Mueller e.K.

CANADA—ETHNIC RELATIONS

Abu-Laban, Yasmeen & Gabriel, Christina. Selling Diversity: Immigration, Multiculturalism, Employment Equity, & Globalization. 2008. (ENG.). 202p. pap. (978-1-4426-0072-0(1)) Univ. of Toronto Pr.

Bouchard, Chantal. Obsessed with Language: A Sociolinguistic History of Quebec. Von Flotow, Luise, tr. from FRE. 2008. (Essay Ser.). (ENG.). 291p. 27.00 (978-1-55071-293-3(4)) Guernica Editions, Inc. CAN. Dist: Univ. of Toronto Pr.

Bramadat, Paul & Seljak, David, eds. Christianity & Ethnicity in Canada, Vol. 2. 2008. 448p. (978-0-8020-9875-7(4)); (Illus.). pap. (978-0-8020-9584-8(4)) Univ. of Toronto Pr.

Dahab, F. Elizabeth. Voices of Exile in Contemporary Canadian Francophone Literature. 2010. (After the Empire: the Francophone World & Postcolonial France Ser.). (ENG.). 246p. pap. 29.95 (978-0-7391-1879-5(X)) Lexington Bks.

Encyclopaedia Britannica, Inc., compiled by. Canada: True North, 4 vols. 2008. 49.95 (978-1-59339-636-7(8)) Encyclopaedia Britannica, Inc.

—Canada: True North: Relationship. 2008. 49.95 (978-1-59339-637-4(6)) Encyclopaedia Britannica, Inc.

—Canada: True North: the Immigrants. 2008. 49.95 (978-1-59339-640-4(6)) Encyclopaedia Britannica, Inc.

—Canada: True North: Where Is Here. 2008. 49.95 (978-1-59339-638-1(4)) Encyclopaedia Britannica, Inc.

Fekete, Orsolya. Canadian-Romanian Theatres: A Case Study of CanadianMulticulturalism: The Canadian Mosaic & the Ethnic Theatres Within. 2008. 72p. pap. (978-3-639-09548-7(0)) VDM Verlag Dr. Mueller e.K.

Fong, Eric, et al, eds. Immigrant Adaptation in Multiethnic Societies. 2012. (Routledge Advances in Sociology Ser.: 78). (ENG., Illus.). 256p. (C). 125.00 **(978-0-415-62854-9(7))** Routledge.

Haenens, L. d'. New Citizens, New Policies? Developments in Diversity Policy in Canada & Flanders. Gezduci, Hasibe et al, eds. 2006. 230p. pap. 30.00 (978-90-382-1021-6(3)) Academia Pr. BEL. Dist: Univ. Pr. of New England.

Hamdon, Evelyn Leslie. Islamophobia & the Question of Muslim Identity: The Politics of Difference & Solidarity. 2010. (Fernwood Basics Ser.). (ENG.). 112p. pap. 17.95 (978-1-55266-339-4(6)) Fernwood Publishing Co., Ltd. CAN. Dist: Independent Pubs. Group.

Helin, Calvin. Dances with Dependency: Indigenous Success Through Self-Reliance. 2010. (ENG., Illus.). 240p. 22.95 (978-1-932824-08-7(1)) Cubbie Blue Publishing.

Hier, Sean P. & Bolaria, B. Singh, eds. Identity & Belonging: Rethinking Race & Ethnicity in Canadian Society. 2006. (ENG., Illus.). 278p. per. 34.95 (978-1-55130-312-3(4)) Canadian Scholars' Pr., Inc. CAN. Dist: Ingram Pub. Services.

Kazemipur, Abdolmohammad. Social Capital & Diversity: Some Lessons from Canada. 2008. (Illus.). 245p. pap. (978-3-03911-710-9(6)) Lang, Peter.

Kostov, Chris. Contested Ethnic Identity: The Case of Macedonian Immigrants in Toronto, 1900-1996. 2010. (ENG.). 318p. pap. 68.95 (978-3-0343-0196-1(0)) Lang, Peter AG GBR. Dist: Lang, Peter.

Kramer, Jennifer. Switchbacks: Art, Ownership, & Nuxalk National Identity, 1 vol. 2007. (ENG., Illus.). 264p. pap. 29.95 (978-0-7748-1228-3(1)) UBC Pr. CAN. Dist: Univ. of Washington Pr.

Krouse, Susan Applegate & Howard, Heather, eds. Keeping the Campfires Going: Native Women's Activism in Urban Communities. 2009. (ENG.). 232p. pap. 30.00 (978-0-8032-2050-8(2)) Univ. of Nebraska Pr.

Li, Xiaoping. Voices Rising: Asian Canadian Cultural Activism. 2007. (ENG., Illus.). 320p. pap. (978-0-7748-1222-1(2)) Univ. of British Columbia Pr.

Reitz, Jeffrey G., et al. Multiculturalism & Social Cohesion: Potentials & Challenges of Diversity. (ENG.). viii, 196p. 2010. pap. 139.00 **(978-90-481-8228-2(X)**, 904818228X) 2009. (Illus.). 139.00 (978-1-4020-9957-1(6), 1402099576) Springer.

Roskies, David. Yiddishlands: A Memoir. 2008. (Illus.). 240p. 27.95 (978-0-8143-3397-6(4)) Wayne State Univ. Pr.

Russell, Daniel & Russell, Dan. People's Dream: Aboriginal Self-Government in Canada. (ENG., Illus.). 296p. pap. (978-0-7748-0799-9(7)) Univ. of British Columbia Pr.

Simpson, Leanne, ed. Lighting the Eighth Fire: The Liberation, Resurgence, & Protection of Indigenous Nations. 2008. (ENG., Illus.). 232p. pap. 21.95 (978-1-894037-33-4(2)) Arbeiter Ring Publishing CAN. Dist: AK Pr. Distribution.

Strachan, Bruce. Hazardous Pursuit. unabr. ed. (ENG., Illus.). 232p. pap. (978-0-920576-55-7(9)) Caitlin Pr., Inc.

Taylor, Alan. The Divided Ground: Indians, Settlers, & the Northern Borderland of the American Revolution. 2007. (Vintage Ser.). (ENG.). 560p. pap. 18.00 (978-1-4000-7707-6(9), Vintage) Knopf Doubleday Publishing Group.

Tettey, Wisdom J., ed. The African Diaspora in Canada: Negotiating Identity & Belonging. 2006. (Africa Ser.). (ENG., Illus.). 248p. per. 39.95 (978-1-55238-175-5(7)) Univ. of Calgary Pr. CAN. Dist: Chicago Distribution Ctr.

Winland, Daphne N. We Are Now a Nation: Croats Between 'Home' & 'Homeland' 2007. (Anthropological Horizons Ser.). (ENG., Illus.). 264p. (978-0-8020-9346-2(9)) Univ. of Toronto Pr.

CANADA—EXPLORING EXPEDITIONS

Hubbard, Leonidas. A Woman's Way Through Unknown Labrador. 2010. 182p. 30.36 (978-1-169-27805-9(1)); pap. 18.36 (978-1-162-65107-1(5)) Kessinger Publishing, LLC.

Hubbard, Mina Benson. Woman's Way Through Unknown Labrador. 2010. (Illus.). 134p. pap. 22.26 (978-1-153-73404-2(4)) General Bks. LLC.

—A Woman's Way Through Unknown Labrador. 2010. 384p. pap. 33.75 (978-1-142-18612-8(1)) 2008. 200p. 22.99 (978-0-554-31302-3(2)) 2008. 200p. 25.99 (978-0-554-21999-8(9)) 2006. (ENG.). 210p. pap. 20.99 (978-1-4264-1393-3(9)) BiblioBazaar.

—A Woman's Way Through Unknown Labrador. 2009. 148p. pap. (978-1-151-11194-4(5)) Books LLC.

—A Woman's Way Through Unknown Labrador. 2007. 148p. per. (978-1-4068-1347-0(8)) Echo Library.

—A Woman's Way Through Unknown Labrador. Grace, Sherrill E., ed. 2008. (ENG., Illus.). 346p. pap. (978-0-7735-2740-9(0)) McGill-Queen's Univ. Pr.

Hubbard, Mrs Leonidas & Hubbard, Leonidas. A Woman's Way Through Unknown Labrador. 2010. 182p. 37.95 (978-1-161-41972-6(1)) Kessinger Publishing, LLC.

Neill, Edward D. Sieur de la Verendrye & His Sons, the Discoverers of the Rocky Mountains, by Way of Lakes Superior & Winnepeg, & Rivers Assineboin & Missouri. 2011. 18p. pap. 11.99 **(978-1-4181-8945-7(6))** MPublishing.

Peterman, Michael A., ed. The Backwoods of Canada: Catharine Parr Traill, No. 11. 408p. (978-0-88629-311-6(1)) McGill-Queen's Univ. Pr.

Traill, Catharine Parr. The Backwoods of Canada. 2008. 280p. 28.99 (978-0-554-27040-1(4)) 2007. (ENG.). 248p. pap. 20.99 (978-1-4346-2392-8(0)) 2007. (ENG.). 276p. pap. 23.99 (978-1-4346-2438-3(2)) BiblioBazaar.

—The Backwoods of Canada. 2009. 240p. pap. (978-1-4099-3621-3(X)) Dodo Pr.

—The Backwoods of Canada. 2010. (ENG., Illus.). 336p. pap. 17.95 (978-0-7710-9448-4(5), New Can Library) McClelland & Stewart CAN. Dist: Random Hse., Inc.

Warkentin, Germaine, ed. Canadian Exploration Literature: An Anthology. 2nd ed. 2007. (ENG., Illus.). 600p. pap. 29.99 (978-1-55002-661-0(5), Dundurn Pr.) Dundurn CAN. Dist: Ingram Pub. Services.

CANADA—FOREIGN ECONOMIC RELATIONS

Donaghy, Greg & Nossal, Kim Richard, eds. Architects & Innovators: Building the Department of Foreign & International Trade, 1909-2009. 2009. (ENG & FRE.). 280p. pap. 39.95 (978-1-55339-269-9(8)) Queen's Univ., Schl. of Policy Studies CAN. Dist: McGill-Queen's Univ. Pr.

—Architects & Innovators/Architectes et Innovateurs: Building the Department of Foreign & International Trade, 1909-2009/Le Développement du Ministère des Affaires Étrangères et du Commerce International, 1909-2009. 2009. (ENG & FRE.). 280p. (C). 95.00 (978-1-55339-270-5(1)) Queen's Univ., Schl. of Policy Studies CAN. Dist: McGill-Queen's Univ. Pr.

Gagnon, Liam A. Canada: Background & U. S. Relations. 2011. (Global Political Studies). (Illus.). ix, 218p. 115.00 (978-1-61761-557-3(9)) Nova Science Pubs., Inc.

Gordon, Todd. Imperialist Canada. 2010. (ENG., Illus.). 432p. 24.95 (978-1-894037-45-7(6)) Arbeiter Ring Publishing CAN. Dist: AK Pr. Distribution.

Hübner, Kurt, ed. Europe, Canada & the Comprehensive Economic Partnership Agreement: Taming Globalization? 2011. (Routledge Studies in Governance & Change in the Global Era Ser.). (ENG., Illus.). 344p. (C). 140.00 (978-0-415-60028-6(6)) Routledge.

Morales, Daniel S. & Medina, Luis A. U. S. Economic & Trade Relations with Canada & Mexico. 2011. (America in the 21st Century: Political & Economic Issues Ser.). 129.00 (978-1-61209-447-2(3)) Nova Science Pubs., Inc.

Naylor, R. T. Canada in the European Age, 1453-1919. 2nd ed. 2006. (ENG.). 648p. (C). (978-0-7735-3090-4(8)); per. (978-0-7735-3091-1(6)) McGill-Queen's Univ. Pr.

Nelson, James K. & Reynolds, Mathew B., eds. Canadian Imports & Trade Issues. 2008. (Illus.). 191p. (C). 69.00 (978-1-60456-261-3(7)) Nova Science Pubs., Inc.

Rugman, Andrew & Anderson, Andrew D. M. Administered Protection in America (Routledge Revivals) 2011. (Routledge Revivals Ser.). (ENG.). 162p. 110.00 **(978-0-415-69988-4(6))** Routledge.

The Softwood Lumber War: Politics, Economics, & the Long U.S.-Canada Trade Dispute. 2007. (ENG., Illus.). 320p. 100.00 (978-1-933115-55-9(6)); per. 39.95 (978-1-933115-56-6(4)) Routledge.

CANADA—FOREIGN RELATIONS

Akuffo, Edward Ansah. Canadian Foreign Policy in Africa: Regional Approaches to Peace Security & Development. 2012. (Global Security in a Changing World Ser.). 251p. 99.95 **(978-1-4094-3452-8(4))** Ashgate Publishing Co.

Beier, J. Marshall & Wylie, Lana. Canadian Foreign Policy in Critical Perspective. 2010. (ENG., Illus.). 260p. 50.00 (978-0-19-542888-9(9)) Oxford Univ. Pr., Inc.

Bell, John. Rebels on the Great Lakes: Confederate Naval Commando Operations Launched from Canada, 1863-1864. 2011. (ENG., Illus.). 256p. pap. 27.99 (978-1-55488-986-0(3)) Dundurn CAN. Dist: Ingram Pub. Services.

Bernstein, Steven, et al, eds. A Globally Integrated Climate Policy for Canada. 2007. (Illus.). 352p. pap. (978-0-8020-9596-1(8)) Univ. of Toronto Pr.

Bland, Douglas L. & Queen's University Staff. Canada's National Defence Vol. 1: Defence Policy. pap. (978-0-88911-792-1(6)) McGill-Queen's Univ. Pr.

Blaxland, John C. Strategic Cousins: Australian & Canadian Expeditionary Forces & the British & American Empires. 2006. (ENG., Illus.). 432p. (C). (978-0-7735-3035-5(5)) McGill-Queen's Univ. Pr.

Bothwell, Robert. Alliance & Illusion: Canada & the World, 1945-1984. 2007. (ENG.). 480p. (978-0-7748-1368-6(7)) Univ. of British Columbia Pr.

—Alliance & Illusion: Canada & the World, 1945-1984. 2008. (ENG.). 480p. pap. 38.95 (978-0-7748-1369-3(5)) Univ. of Washington Pr.

Bothwell, Robert & Daudelin, Jean, eds. Canada among Nations 2008: 100 Years of Canadian Foreign Policy. 2009. (ENG.). 336p. (C). (978-0-7735-3434-6(2)); pap. (978-0-7735-3438-4(5)) McGill-Queen's Univ. Pr.

Bow, Brian J. & Lennox, Patrick. An Independent Foreign Policy for Canada? Challenges & Choices for the Future. 2008. 224p. (978-0-8020-9690-6(5)); (ENG.). pap. (978-0-8020-9634-0(4)) Univ. of Toronto Pr.

Bratt, Duane & Kukucha, Christopher J., eds. Altered Landscapes: Readings in Canadian Foreign. 2006. (ENG., Illus.). 416p. 85.00 (978-0-19-542369-3(0)) Oxford Univ. Pr., Inc.

Brewster, Murray. The Savage War: The Untold Battles of Afghanistan. 8th ed. 2011. (ENG., Illus.). 384p. 34.95 **(978-1-118-11593-0(7)**, Wiley) Wiley, John & Sons, Inc.

Canada - U. S. A. Trade Disputes. pap. (978-0-660-15253-0(3)) Canadian Government Publishing.

Canadian - United States Steel Trade 1993. pap. (978-0-660-15233-2(9)) Canadian Government Publishing.

Canadian Representatives Abroad: December 1993. (FRE.). 16p. pap. (978-0-660-59104-9(9)) Canadian Government Publishing.

Canadian/American Relations. pap. (978-0-660-14846-5(3)) Canadian Government Publishing.

Cao, Huhua & Poy, Vivienne, eds. The China Challenge: Sino-Canadian Relations in the 21st Century. 2011. (ENG.). 310p. pap. (978-0-7766-0764-1(2)) Univ. of Ottawa Pr./Presses de l'Universite d'Ottawa.

Carroll, Michael K. Pearson's Peacekeepers: Canada & the United Nations Emergency Force, 1956-67. 2010. (ENG., Illus.). 254p. pap. 32.95 (978-0-7748-1582-6(5)) Univ. of Washington Pr.

Cavell, Janice. Affaires étrangères et Commerce International Canada: Une Histoire en Documents, 1909-2009. 2009. (FRE & ENG., Illus.). xiii, 338p. (978-0-660-64534-6(3)) Canadian Government Publishing.

Cavell, Janice & Noakes, Jeff. Acts of Occupation: Canada & Arctic Sovereignty, 1918-25. 2011. (ENG., Illus.). 348p. pap. 37.95 (978-0-7748-1868-1(9)) UBC Pr. CAN. Dist: Univ. of Washington Pr.

Cellucci, Paul. Unquiet Diplomacy. rev. ed. 2007. (ENG., Illus.). 256p. pap. 16.95 (978-1-55263-875-0(8)) Key Porter Bks. CAN. Dist: Perseus-PGW.

Champion, C. P. The Strange Demise of British Canada: The Liberals & Canadian Nationalism, 1964-68. 2010. (FRE & ENG.). 336p. (C). pap. (978-0-7735-3691-3(4)) McGill-Queen's Univ. Pr.

Chapnick, Adam. Canada's Voice: The Public Life of John Wendell Holmes. 2010. (ENG.). 384p. pap. 35.95 (978-0-7748-1672-4(4)) Univ. of Washington Pr.

Clark, Joe. A Bridge to the World, a Passport to Our Future. 2012. (ENG., Illus.). 304p. 32.00 (978-0-307-35907-0(7), Random Hse CAN) Random Hse. of Canada, Ltd. CAN. Dist: Random Hse., Inc.

Clarkson, Stephen, ed. An Independent Foreign Policy for Canada? 304p. pap. 14.95 (978-0-7710-9901-4(0)) McClelland & Stewart CAN. Dist: Random Hse. of Canada, Ltd.

Commission of Inquiry into the Deployment of Canad. Dishonoured Legacy: The Lessons of the Somalia Affair - Executive Summary. 82p. pap. (978-0-660-60271-4(7)) Canadian Government Publishing.

Cyr, Hugo. Canadian Federalism & Treaty Powers: Existential Communities, Functional Regimes & the Organic Constitution. 2009. (Illus.). 305p. 41.95 (978-90-5201-453-1(1)) PIE - Peter Lang BEL. Dist: Lang, Peter.

Dafoe, John W. Canada: An American Nation. reprint ed. 20.00 (978-0-404-00616-7(7)) AMS Pr., Inc.

Daudelin, Jean & Schwanen, Daniel. Canada among Nations 2007: What Room to Manoeuvre? 2008. (ENG., Illus.). 344p. (C). (978-0-7735-3396-7(6)) McGill-Queen's Univ. Pr.

Daudelin, Jean & Schwanen, Daniel, eds. Canada among Nations 2007: What Room to Manoeuvre? 2008. (ENG., Illus.). 344p. (C). pap. (978-0-7735-3397-4(4)) McGill-Queen's Univ. Pr.

Dept. Foreign Affairs and International Trade Staff. Documents on Canadian External Relations Vol. 15: 1949. 1870p. pap. (978-0-660-59785-0(3)) Canadian Government Publishing.

Donaghy, Greg & Carroll, Michael, eds. In the National Interest: Canadian Foreign Policy & the Department of Foreign Affairs & International Trade, 1909-2009. 2011. (Beyond Boundaries: Canadian Defense And Ser.). (ENG.). 284p. pap. 41.95 **(978-1-55238-538-8(8))** Univ. of Calgary Pr. CAN. Dist: Chicago Distribution Ctr.

Donaghy, Greg & Nossal, Kim Richard, eds. Architects & Innovators: Building the Department of Foreign & International Trade, 1909-2009. 2009. (ENG & FRE.). 280p. pap. 39.95 (978-1-55339-269-9(8)) Queen's Univ., Schl. of Policy Studies CAN. Dist: McGill-Queen's Univ. Pr.

—Architects & Innovators/Architectes et Innovateurs: Building the Department of Foreign & International Trade, 1909-2009/Le Développement du Ministère des Affaires Étrangères et du Commerce International, 1909-2009. 2009. (ENG & FRE.). 280p. (C). 95.00 (978-1-55339-270-5(1)) Queen's Univ., Schl. of Policy Studies CAN. Dist: McGill-Queen's Univ. Pr.

Drache, Daniel, ed. Big Picture Realities: Canada & Mexico at the Crossroads. 2008. (ENG.). 312p. pap. 42.95 (978-1-55458-045-3(5)) Wilfrid Laurier Univ. Pr. CAN. Dist: Univ. of Toronto Pr.

Engler, Yves. The Black Book of Canadian Foreign Policy. 2010. (ENG.). 288p. pap. 24.95 (978-1-55266-314-1(0)) Fernwood Publishing Co., Ltd. CAN. Dist: Independent Pubs. Group.

—Canada & Israel: Building Apartheid. 2010. (ENG.). 240p. pap. 19.95 (978-1-55266-355-4(8)) Fernwood Publishing Co., Ltd. CAN. Dist: Independent Pubs. Group.

G Le Prestre, Philippe & Stoett, Peter. Continental Ecopolitics: Continuity & Change in Canadian- American Environemental Relations. 2006. (Global Environmental Governance Ser.). (Illus.). 306p. 140.00 (978-0-7546-4177-3(5)) Ashgate Publishing Co.

Gordon, Todd. Imperialist Canada. 2010. (ENG., Illus.). 432p. 24.95 (978-1-894037-45-7(6)) Arbeiter Ring Publishing CAN. Dist: AK Pr. Distribution.

Great Britain, the Empire & America, 2 Vols, Set. 2008. 986p. 440.00 (978-0-415-46353-9(X)) Routledge.

Haerens, Margaret. Canada. 2011. (Opposing Viewpoints Ser.). 240p. pap. 26.50 (978-0-7377-5212-0(2)); lib. bdg. 39.70 (978-0-7377-5211-3(4)) Cengage Gale. (Greenhaven Pr., Inc.).

Hampson, Fen & Heinbecker, Paul, eds. Canada among Nations 2009-2010: As Others See Us. 2009. (ENG.). 336p. (C). (978-0-7735-3627-2(2)); pap. (978-0-7735-3628-9(0)) McGill-Queen's Univ. Pr.

Hampson, Fen O. & Maule, Christopher J., eds. Canada among Nations, 1992-93: A New World Order? 301p. pap. (978-0-88629-167-9(4)) McGill-Queen's Univ. Pr.

Hannaford, Elizabeth Elsie. Vision of Canada 2020: Save Canadian Medicare & Money. 2011. 136p. 25.95 (978-1-4502-8053-2(6)); pap. 15.95 (978-1-4502-8052-5(8)) iUniverse, Inc.

Hayes, Geoffrey & Sedra, Mark, eds. Afghanistan: Transition under Threat. 2008. (Studies in International Governance Ser.). (ENG., Illus.). 348p. pap. 42.95 (978-1-55458-011-8(0)) Wilfrid Laurier Univ. Pr. CAN. Dist: Univ. of Toronto Pr.

Heinbecker, Paul & Dundurn Press Staff. Getting Back in the Game: A Foreign Policy Handbook for Canada. 2011. (ENG.). 312p. pap. 24.99 (978-1-4597-0165-6(8)) Dundurn CAN. Dist: Ingram Pub. Services.

Heinbecker, Paul & Momani, Bessma, eds. Canada & the Middle East: In Theory & Practice. 2007. (Studies in International Governance Ser.). (ENG.). 246p. pap. 42.95 *(978-1-55458-024-8(2))* Wilfrid Laurier Univ. Pr. CAN. Dist: Univ. of Toronto Pr.

Holloway, Steven Kendall. Canadian Foreign Policy: Defining the National Interest. 2006. (ENG.). 288p. pap. *(978-1-55111-816-1(5))* Univ. of Toronto Pr.

Holmes, John W. Canada: A Middle-Aged Power, No 98. 301p. pap. 19.95 *(978-0-7710-9798-0(0))* McClelland & Stewart CAN. Dist: Random Hse. of Canada, Ltd.

Horn, Bernd. No Lack of Courage: Operation Medusa, Afghanistan. 2010. (ENG., Illus.). 184p. pap. 30.00 *(978-1-55488-766-8(6))* Dundurn CAN. Dist: Ingram Pub. Services.

Hornsby, Stephen J., et al, eds. The Northeastern Borderlands: Four Centuries of Interaction. 160p. pap. 8.95 *(978-0-919107-17-5(6))* Acadiensis Pr. CAN. Dist: Goose Lane Editions.

Hutchison, Bruce. The Struggle for the Border. 2009. 518p. 55.95 *(978-1-104-84957-3(7))* 2007. (ENG.). 516p. per. 40.95 *(978-0-548-44595-9(6))* Kessinger Publishing, LLC.

Hynek, Nik & Bosold, David, eds. Canada's Foreign & Security Policy: Soft & Hard Strategies of a Middle Power. 2010. (ENG., Illus.). 328p. 60.00 *(978-0-19-543169-8(3))* Oxford Univ. Pr., Inc.

Isitt, Benjamin. From Victoria to Vladivostok: Canada's Siberian Expedition, 1917-19. 2010. (ENG., Illus.). 352p. (C). pap. 32.95 *(978-0-7748-1802-5(6))* Univ. of British Columbia Pr. CAN. Dist: Univ. of Washington Pr.

Jones, David T. & Kilcour, David. Uneasy Neighbors: Canada, the USA & the Dynamics of State, Industry & Culture. 2007. (ENG.). 320p. 33.95 *(978-0-470-15306-2(7), Wiley)* Wiley, John & Sons, Inc.

Jutta, Brunnée. Globally Integrated Climate Policy for Canada. Bernstein, Steven et al, eds. 2007. (ENG.). 352p. *(978-0-8020-9878-8(9))* Univ. of Toronto Pr.

Kay, Zachariah. The Diplomacy of Impartiality: Canada & Israel, 1958-1968. 2010. (ENG.). 138p. (C). 85.00 *(978-1-55458-187-0(7))* Wilfrid Laurier Univ. Pr. CAN. Dist: Univ. of Toronto Pr.

Kukucha, Christopher J. & Bratt, Duane, eds. Readings in Canadian Foreign Policy: Classic Debates & New Ideas. 2nd ed. 2011. (ENG., Illus.). 544p. pap. 74.95 ***(978-0-19-543781-2(0))*** Oxford Univ. Pr., Inc.

Lin, Paul. In the Eye of the China Storm: A Life Between East & West. 2011. (Illus.). 256p. (C). *(978-0-7735-3857-3(7))* McGill-Queen's Univ. Pr.

Lui, Andrew. Why Canada Cares: Human Rights & Foreign Policy in Theory & Practice. 2012. (ENG.). 304p. (C). ***(978-0-7735-3996-9(4))*** McGill-Queen's Univ. Pr.

MacLaren, Roy. Commissions High: Canada in London, 1870-1971. 2006. (ENG. Illus.). 584p. (C). *(978-0-7735-3036-2(3))* McGill-Queen's Univ. Pr.

Melady, John. Korea: Canada's Forgotten War. 2nd ed. 2012. (ENG., Illus.). 328p. pap. 27.99 *(978-1-4597-0132-8(1))* Dundurn CAN. Dist: Ingram Pub. Services.

Molot, Maureen A. & Hampson, Fen O., eds. Canada among Nations 1989: The Challenge of Change, Vol. 2. 243p. pap. *(978-0-88629-106-8(2))* McGill-Queen's Univ. Pr.

Morales, Isidro. National Solutions to Trans-Border Problems? The Governance of Security & Risk in a Post-Nafta North America. 2011. (International Political Economy of New Regionalisms Ser.). (Illus.). 278p. 99.95 *(978-1-4094-0918-2(X))* Ashgate Publishing Co.

Muirhead, Bruce. Dancing Around the Elephant: Creating a Prosperous Canada in an Era of American Dominance, 1957-1973. 2007. (ENG., Illus.). 360p. *(978-0-8020-9016-4(8))* Univ. of Toronto Pr.

Mutimer, David. Canadian Annual Review of Politics & Public Affairs 2003. 2009. (Canadian Annual Review of Politics & Public Affairs Ser.). (ENG.). 304p. *(978-0-8020-9965-3(8))* Univ. of Toronto Pr.

Mutimer, David, ed. Canadian Annual Review of Politics & Public Affairs 2001. 2007. (Canadian Annual Review of Politics & Public Affairs Ser.). (ENG.). 304p. *(978-0-8020-9235-9(7))* Univ. of Toronto Pr.

—Canadian Annual Review of Politics & Public Affairs 2002. 2008. (ENG., Illus.). 304p. *(978-0-8020-9819-1(3))* Univ. of Toronto Pr.

Nurse, Andrew & Blake, Raymond. Beyond National Dreams: Essays on Canadian Citizenship & Nationalism, 1 vol. 2009. (ENG.). 432p. pap. 35.00 *(978-1-55041-969-6(2))* Fitzhenry & Whiteside, Ltd. CAN. Dist: Ingram Pub. Services.

Potter, Evan H. & Potter, Evan. Branding Canada: Projecting Canada's Soft Power Through Public Diplomacy. 2008. (Illus.). 464p. *(978-0-7735-3435-3(0))* McGill-Queen's Univ. Pr.

Raj, Christopher S. & Abdul Nafey. Canada's Global Engagements & Relations with India. 2007. xiv, 354p. *(978-81-7827-168-2(0))* Manak Pubns. Pvt., Ltd.

Ritchie, Charles. Undiplomatic Diaries: 1937-1971. 2008. (ENG.). 608p. pap. 24.99 *(978-0-7710-7538-4(3), Emblem Edns)* McClelland & Stewart CAN. Dist: Random Hse., Inc.

Rowlands, Dane. Canada among Nations 2006: Minorities & Priorities. Cooper, Andrew ed. 2006. (ENG.). 384p. (C). pap. *(978-0-7735-3170-3(X))* McGill-Queen's Univ. Pr.

Rowlands, Dane & Cooper, Andrew F. Canada among Nations 2006: Minorities & Priorities. 2006. (Canada among Nations Ser.). (ENG., Illus.). 384p. *(978-0-7735-3164-2(5))* McGill-Queen's Univ. Pr.

Ruud, Charles A. The Constant Diplomat: Robert Ford in Moscow. 2009. (ENG., Illus.). 344p. (C). *(978-0-7735-3585-5(3))* McGill-Queen's Univ. Pr.

Sasikumar, Karthika & Huntley, Wade. Canadian Policy on Nuclear Cooperation with India: Confronting New Dilemmas. 2007. 171p. pap. 9.84 *(978-1-4303-0811-9(7))* Lulu Enterprises Inc.

Stewart, Lyle, ed. Afghanistan & Canada: Is There an Alternative to the War? 2009. (ENG.). 224p. 44.99 *(978-1-55164-329-8(4))*; pap. 24.99 *(978-1-55164-328-1(6))* Black Rose Bks. CAN. Dist: Consortium Bk. Sales & Distribution.

Thompson, John H. & Randall, Stephen J. Canada & the United States: Ambivalent Allies. 2nd ed. (ENG.). 352p. pap. *(978-0-7735-2138-4(0))* McGill-Queen's Univ. Pr.

University of Toronto Press. Perceptions of Cuba: Canadian & American Policies in Comparative Perspective. 2010. 176p. (ENG.). *(978-1-4426-4061-0(8))*; pap. *(978-1-4426-1007-1(7))* Univ. of Toronto Pr.

Wigley, Philip G. Canada & the Transition to Commonwealth: British-Canadian Relations 1917-1926. 2009. (Cambridge Commonwealth Ser.). (ENG.). 308p. pap. 42.00 *(978-0-521-09319-4(8))* Cambridge Univ. Pr.

Wilkshire, Michael, ed. & tr. from FRE. A Gentleman in the Outports: Gobineau & Newfoundland, No. 177. 299p. pap. *(978-0-88629-215-7(8))* McGill-Queen's Univ. Pr.

Winslow, Donna & Commission of Inquiry into the Deployment of Canadian Forces to Somalia. A Socio-Cultural Inquiry into the Activities of the Canadian Airborne Regiment in Somalia. pap. *(978-0-660-16944-6(4))* Canadian Government Publishing.

Wright, Robert. Our Place in the Sun: Canada & Cuba in the Castro Era. Wylie, Lana, ed. 2009. (Illus.). 320p. pap. *(978-0-8020-9666-1(2))* Univ. of Toronto Pr.

Wright, Robert A. Our Place in the Sun: Canada & Cuba in the Castro Era. Wylie, Lana, ed. 2009. (Illus.). 320p. *(978-0-8020-9970-9(X))* Univ. of Toronto Pr.

CANADA—FOREIGN RELATIONS—UNITED STATES

Anderson, Greg & Sands, Christopher. Forgotten Partnership Redux: Canada-U.S. Relations in the 21st Century. 2011. ***(978-1-60497-762-2(0))*** Cambria Pr.

Bow, Brian. The Politics of Linkage: Power, Interdependence, & Ideas in Canada-US Relations. 2010. (ENG.). 232p. (C). pap. 35.95 *(978-0-7748-1696-0(1))* UBC Pr. CAN. Dist: Univ. of Washington Pr.

Bow, Brian J. The Politics of Linkage: Power, Interdependence, & Ideas in Canada-US Relations. 2009. 256p. ***(978-0-7748-1695-3(3))*** Univ. of British Columbia Pr.

Canadian Centre for Policy Alternatives Staff. Living with Uncle: Canada-US Relations in an Age of Empire. Campbell, Bruce & Finn, Ed, eds. 2006. (Canadian Centre for Policy Alternatives Ser.). (ENG., Illus.). 280p. pap. 24.95 *(978-1-55028-960-2(8))* Lorimer, James & Co., Ltd., Pubs. CAN. Dist: Casemate Pubs. & Bk. Distributors, LLC.

Dyment, David. Doing the Continental: A New Canadian-American Relationship. 2010. (ENG.). 171p. pap. 19.99 *(978-1-55488-758-3(5))* Dundurn CAN. Dist: Ingram Pub. Services.

Encyclopaedia Britannica, Inc., compiled by. Canada: True North: A Song for Quebec. 2008. 49.95 *(978-1-59339-639-8(2))* Encyclopaedia Britannica, Inc.

Europa Publications Staff. USA & Canada 2008. 10th rev. ed. 2007. (Illus.). 624p. 700.00 *(978-1-85743-434-7(X))* Routledge.

Evans, Sterling, ed. The Borderlands of the American & Canadian Wests: Essays on Regional History of the Forty-ninth Parallel. 2008. (ENG.). 424p. pap. 29.95 *(978-0-8032-1794-2(3))* Univ. of Nebraska Pr.

Gotlieb, Allan. The Washington Diaries: 1981-1989. 2007. (ENG., Illus.). 656p. pap. 19.95 *(978-0-7710-3563-0(2), McClelland & Stewart)* McClelland & Stewart CAN. Dist: Random Hse., Inc.

Haerens, Margaret. Canada. 2011. (Opposing Viewpoints Ser.). 240p. pap. 26.50 *(978-0-7377-5212-0(2))*; lib. bdg. 39.70 *(978-0-7377-5211-3(4))* Cengage Gale. (Greenhaven Pr., Inc.).

Hale, Geoffrey. Managing Alternate Realities: 'autonomy' vs. 'relevance'?: Engaging US Foreign & Security Policies. 2007. 52p. *(978-1-882582-60-0(8))* Canadian-American Ctr.

Jung, Karsten. Of Peace & Power: Promoting Canadian Interests through Peacekeeping. 2009. (Europäische Hochschulschriften. Reihe 31: Politikwissenschaft Ser.). 138p. pap. 35.95 *(978-3-631-59255-7(8))* Lang, Peter GmbH, Europaischer Verlag der Wissenschaften DEU. Dist: Lang, Peter.

Lennox, Patrick. At Home & Abroad: The Canada-US Relationship & Canada's Place in the World. 2010. (ENG.). 192p. (C). pap. 35.95 *(978-0-7748-1706-6(2))* UBC Pr. CAN. Dist: Univ. of Washington Pr.

—At Home & Abroad: The Canada-US Relationship & Canada's Place in the World. 2009. 224p. ***(978-0-7748-1705-9(4))*** Univ. of British Columbia Pr.

McKenna, Peter. Canada Looks South: In Search of an American Policy. 2010. (ENG.). *(978-1-4426-4206-5(8))* Univ. of Toronto Pr.

McMahon, Patricia I. Essence of Indecision: Diefenbaker's Nuclear Policy, 1957-1963. 2009. (ENG.). 264p. (C). *(978-0-7735-3498-8(9))* McGill-Queen's Univ. Pr.

Milnes, Arthur. In Roosevelt's Bright Shadow: A Collection in Honour of the 70th Anniversary of FDR's 1938 Speech at Queen's University & Marking Canada's Special Relationship with America's Presidents 1938 to Present Day. 2009. (Library of Political Leadership Ser.). (ENG.). 234p. (C). *(978-1-55339-231-6(0))*; pap. *(978-1-55339-230-9(2))* McGill-Queen's Univ. Pr.

Milnes, Arthur, ed. Jimmy & Rosalynn Carter: A Canadian Tribute. 2011. (Library of Political Leadership Ser.). (ENG.). 232p. (C). *(978-1-55339-301-6(5))*; pap. *(978-1-55339-300-9(7))* McGill-Queen's Univ. Pr.

Samuels, H. Raymond, 2nd, ed. Canada-Piracy: CanWest Global & other attempts to destroy Canada's national political Consciousness. 2006. per. *(978-1-897318-40-9(5), Canadian National Newspaper, The)* Agora Publishing Consortium.

Stuart, Reginald C. Dispersed Relations: Americans & Canadians in Upper North America. 2007. (ENG.). 424p. (gr. 17). 60.00 *(978-0-8018-8785-7(2))* Johns Hopkins Univ. Pr.

University of Toronto Press. Prejudice & Pride: Canadian Intellectuals Confront the United States, 1891-1945. 2010. 320p. *(978-1-4426-4045-0(6))* Univ. of Toronto Pr.

Warner, Donald F. The Idea of Continental Union: Agitation for the Annexation of Canada to the United States, 1849-1893. 2008. 296p. pap. 29.00 *(978-1-59740-419-8(5))* ACLS Humanities E-Book.

CANADA—FRENCH-ENGLISH RELATIONS

see Canada—English-French Relations

CANADA—GENEALOGY

Ainlay, Margaret McNickle & Ainlay, John Albert. Ainlay Genealogy & a History of the Ainlay Family. 2011. 142p. 40.95 ***(978-1-258-07799-0(X))*** Literary Licensing, LLC.

Belcourt, Herb. Walking in the Woods: A Métis Journey, 1 vol. 2006. (ENG., Illus.). 224p. per. *(978-1-897142-17-2(X))* Brindle & Glass Publishing.

Biography & Genealogy. 2011. 611.00 *(978-1-4144-4564-9(4))* Cengage Gale.

Bunnell, Paul J. French & Native North American Marriages & Other Sources: Volume 3. 2009. pap. 20.00 *(978-1-59712-341-9(2))* Catawba Publishing Co.

Campey, Lucille H. Planters, Paupers, & Pioneers: English Settlers in Atlantic Canada. 2010. (ENG., Illus.). 384p. pap. 35.00 *(978-1-55488-748-4(8))* Dundurn CAN. Dist: Ingram Pub. Services.

Clift, G. Glenn. Loyalists in the American Revolution. cd-rom 19.99 *(978-0-8063-9711-5(X))* Genealogical Publishing Co., Inc.

Coldham, Peter Wilson, compiled by. North American Wills Registered in London, 1611-1857. 2007. 156p. 28.50 *(978-0-8063-1773-1(6))* Genealogical Publishing Co., Inc.

Cox, Ken. Call to the Colours: Tracing Your Canadian Military Ancestors. 2011. (Genealogist's Refere Ser.). (ENG., Illus.). 344p. pap. 26.99 *(978-1-55488-864-1(6))* Dundurn CAN. Dist: Ingram Pub. Services.

Dixon, J. D. History of Charles Dixon, One of the Early English Settlers of Sackville, N. B. fac. ed. 204p. reprint ed. pap. 30.50 *(978-0-7404-1434-3(8))*; pap. 19.50 *(978-0-7404-1435-0(6))* Higginson Bk. Co.

Dobson, David. Scots in the USA & Canada, 1825-1875, Part V. 2007. pap. 21.50 *(978-0-8063-5364-7(3))* Clearfield Co.

Dobson, David. Ships from Scotland to America, 1628-1828. 2010. 124p. pap. 20.00 ***(978-0-8063-5511-5(5))*** Clearfield Co.

Doherty, Constantine. Family History. 2011. 254p. ***(978-1-907611-93-3(2))*** Paragon Publishing, Rothersthorpe.

Gale Editor, ed. Biography & Genealogy Master Index Supplement 2012. 2012th ed. 2011. lib. bdg. 611.00 *(978-1-4144-5808-3(8))* Cengage Gale.

Graupner, John. The Gallant Graham's Graham of Canada. (Illus.). 680p. 90.00 *(978-0-8187-0133-7(1))* Harlo Pr.

Harrison, Keith. The Missionary, the Violinist & the Aunt Whose Head was Squeezed. 2010. (ENG.). 264p. pap. 18.95 *(978-0-88982-265-8(4))* Oolichan Bks. CAN. Dist: Univ. of Toronto Pr.

Horne, Adrienne. Genealogy Mania. 2008. 140p. pap. *(978-3-639-01336-8(0))* VDM Verlag Dr. Mueller e.K.

Irvine, Sherry & Obee, Dave. Finding Your Canadian Ancestors: A Beginner's Guide. 2007. (ENG., Illus.). 269p. per. 18.95 *(978-1-59331-316-6(0))* Turner Publishing Co.

James, June. 1891 Ontario Census: Bexley Township, Victoria County. 2007. ii, 34p. pap. ***(978-0-7779-3352-7(7))*** Ontario Genealogical Society.

Jetté, René. Dictionnaire Genealogique des Familles du Quebec: Des Origines a 1730. (FRE.). 1177p. *(978-2-7606-0646-3(5))* Bow Historical Bks.

Landry, Peter. The Lion & the Lily. 2007. 644p. pap. 40.00 *(978-1-4251-5450-9(6))* Trafford Publishing.

Layden, Zella Robichaud. As-Tu du Leblanc? Ginialogie de la Famille Leblanc (Leurs Ancitres et Leurs Descendants) 2007. (FRE.). 432p. per. 45.95 *(978-1-4251-0706-2(0))* Trafford Publishing.

Louis, Shirley. Q'Sapi: A History of Okanagan People As Told by Okanagan Families, 1 vol. 2nd ed. 2008. (ENG., Illus.). 262p. pap. 24.95 *(978-1-894778-64-0(2))* Theytus Bks., Ltd. CAN. Dist: Univ. of Toronto Pr.

Morin, Gail & Rozyk, Rosemary. St. Francois Xavier, Manitoba 1834-1870 Baptisms, Marriages & Burials. 2007. 260p. 30.95 *(978-1-886560-34-5(X))* Quintin Pubns.

Passager & Immigration Lists Cumulative Index, 2006-20010, 3 vols., Set. 110th rev. ed. 2010. (ENG.). 943.00 *(978-1-4144-4763-6(9))* Cengage Gale.

Passager & Immigration Lists Index 2011, Vol. 1. 2011th ed. 2010. (ENG.). 436.00 *(978-1-4144-4184-9(3))* Cengage Gale.

Poitras, Jean-Guy. Répertoire des Naissances et des Décès, Rivière-Verte (Sacré-Cur), Comté de Madawaska, Nouveau-Brunswick, 1923-2010: Birth & Death Records, Rivière-Verte (Sacré-Cur), Madawaska County, New Brunswick, 1923-2010. 2010. (FRE & ENG., Illus.). 152p. *(978-0-9810055-5-3(1))* Poitras, Jean-Guy.

Punch, Terrence M. Erin's Sons. 2009. 200p. pap. 30.00 *(978-0-8063-1789-2(2))* Genealogical Publishing Co., Inc.

—Erin's Sons: Irish Arrivals in Atlantic Canada, 1751-1858. Volume III. 2009. 200p. pap. 30.00 *(978-0-8063-1805-9(8))* Genealogical Publishing Co., Inc.

—Erin's Sons: Irish Arrivals in Atlantic Canada, 1761-1853. 2008. 200p. pap. 30.00 *(978-0-8063-1782-3(5))* Genealogical Publishing Co., Inc.

Roberts, John A. Discover Your Metis Ancestry: A Beginner's Guide. 2008. ***(978-0-7779-3421-0(3))*** Ontario Genealogical Society.

Robichaud, Stella & Robichaud, Hélène. La Corneille et le Goéland. 2009. (FRE., Illus.). 162p. *(978-2-89627-177-1(5))* Editions de la Francophonie.

Tanguay, Cyprien. Dictionnaire Genealogique des Familles Canadiennes, Set. (FRE.). reprint ed. lib. bdg. 225.00 *(978-0-404-06340-5(3), AMS Pr., Inc.*

Thomas, Laverne. LeDoux: A Pioneer Franco-American Family with Detailed Sketches of Allied Families. 2008. (Illus.). xix, 895p. *(978-0-9817282-0-9(0), Gateway Pr.)* White-Bowden Assocs.

Trueman, Howard. The Chignecto Isthmus & Its First Sett. 2006. pap. *(978-1-4068-1127-8(0))* Echo Library.

Tupper, Franklin Whitt. Thomas Tupper & His Descendants. 2006. pap. 17.95 *(978-1-4286-5621-5(9))* Kessinger Publishing, LLC.

Wilkinson, Margaret Ann. Genealogy & the Law in Canada. 2010. (Genealogist's Reference Shelf Ser.). (ENG., Illus.). 128p. pap. 19.99 *(978-1-55488-452-0(7), Dundurn Pr.)* Dundurn CAN. Dist: Ingram Pub. Services.

Wynn Savoy, Jo. A Wynn Family History. 2009. 280p. pap. 29.99 *(978-1-4389-8886-3(9))* AuthorHouse.

CANADA—GEOGRAPHY

Bone, Robert. The Regional Geography of Canada. 5th ed. 2010. (ENG., Illus.). 552p. 85.00 *(978-0-19-543373-9(4))* Oxford Univ. Pr., Inc.

Bone, Robert M. The Canadian North: Issues & Challenges, Fourth Edition. 4th ed. 2012. (ENG., Illus.). 344p. pap. 75.00 ***(978-0-19-544503-9(1))*** Oxford Univ. Pr., Inc.

Cram101 Textbook Reviews. Outlines & Highlights for Regional Geography of the United States & Canada by Tom L Mcknight, Isbn: 9780131014732. 2010. 314p. pap. 33.95 *(978-1-61698-645-2(X))* Cram101 Inc.

Cram101 Textbook Reviews Staff. Outlines & Highlights for Regional Geography of the United States & Canada by Tom L Mcknight, Isbn: 9780131014732. 2009. 138p. pap. 28.95 *(978-1-4288-8128-0(X))* Cram101 Inc.

Getis & Getis & Quastler & Cram101 Textbook Reviews Staff. The United States & Canad: The Land of the People. 2007. 60p. per. 27.95 *(978-1-4288-2288-7(7))* Cram101 Inc.

Harvey, Al. Wild Beauty: A Visual Exploration of BC, 1 vol. 2010. (ENG., Illus.). 128p. pap. *(978-1-894974-93-6(X))* Heritage Hse.

Lyons, Terri L. & Rumney, Thomas A. Canadian Geography: A Scholarly Bibliography, 2 vols. 2009. (ENG.). 896p. (gr. 17). 250.00 *(978-0-8108-6717-8(6))* Scarecrow Pr., Inc.

McGillivray, Brett. Geography of British Columbia: People & Landscapes in Transition. 3rd ed. 2011. (Illus.). xii, 307p. E-Book *(978-0-7748-2079-0(4))* Univ. of British Columbia Pr.

—Geography of British Columbia: People & Landscapes in Transition. 3rd ed. 2011. (ENG., Illus.). 320p. (C). pap. 60.00 *(978-0-7748-2078-3(0))* Univ. of British Columbia Pr. CAN. Dist: Univ. of Washington Pr.

Nelson, Gordon. Beyond the Global City: Understanding & Planning for the Diversity of Ontario. 2012. (ENG.). 504p. (C). pap. ***(978-0-7735-3986-0(7))***; (Illus.). ***(978-0-7735-3985-3(9))*** McGill-Queen's Univ. Pr.

Thraves, Bernard D., et al, eds. Saskatchewan: Geographic Perspectives. 2007. (ENG., Illus.). 486p. pap. 75.00 *(978-0-88977-189-5(8))* Canadian Plains Research Ctr. CAN. Dist: Univ. of Toronto Pr.

CANADA—GUIDEBOOKS

Access Press Staff, creator. Access Montreal & Quebec City. 5th ed. 2007. (Access Montreal & Quebec City Ser.). (ENG., Illus.). 176p. pap. 21.95 *(978-0-06-114586-5(6))* HarperCollins Pubs.

Aiken, Kenneth & Gillis, Rannis. Motorcycle Journeys Through Atlantic Canada. 2011. (Motorcycle Journeys Ser.). (ENG., Illus.). 375p. pap. 29.95 *(978-1-884313-84-4(1), 1884313841)* Whitehorse Pr.

Atlantic Coast & Bay of Fundy. (FRE., Illus.). 86p. pap. *(978-0-660-58863-6(3))* Canadian Government Publishing.

Avery, Martin. Zen Forest Meditations. 2010. 111p. pap. 18.00 *(978-0-557-73414-6(2))* Lulu Enterprises Inc.

Bartosik, John. Whistler & Blackcomb Country. 3rd unabr. ed. (ENG., Illus.). 48p. reprint ed. pap. 9.95 *(978-1-55017-176-1(3))* Harbour Publishing Co., Ltd. CAN. Dist: Ingram Pub. Services.

Bell, Brian, ed. Canada. 7th rev. ed. 2007. (Insight Guides). (ENG., Illus.). 400p. pap. 23.95 *(978-981-258-599-8(0))* APA Publications Services SGP. Dist: Ingram Pub. Services.

Berger, Jonathan & Terry, Thomas. Canoe Atlas of the Little North. 2007. (ENG., Illus.). 144p. 95.00 *(978-1-55046-496-2(5))* Boston Mills Pr. CAN. Dist: Firefly Bks., Ltd.

Betzman, Harvey. Finger Lakes Bicyclist's Tour Guide. 2nd rev. ed. 2011. (Illus.). 288p. pap. 26.95 *(978-1-889602-33-2(7))* Cyclotour Guide Bks.

Brown, Tricia. The World-Famous Alaska Highway: A Guide to the Alcan & Other Wilderness Roads of the North. 4th ed. 2011. (ENG.). 288p. pap. 22.95 *(978-1-55591-749-4(6))* Fulcrum Publishing.

Callan, Kevin. A Paddler's Guide to Quetico & Beyond. 2007. (Paddler's Guide Ser.). (ENG., Illus.). 192p. pap. 24.95 *(978-1-55046-500-6(7))* Boston Mills Pr. CAN. Dist: Firefly Bks., Ltd.

Church, Mike & Church, Terri. Traveler's Guide to Alaskan Camping: Alaska & Yukon Camping with RV or Tent. 5th ed. 2010. (Traveler's Guide Ser.). (ENG., Illus.). 480p. pap. 21.95 *(978-0-9823101-1-3(0))* Rolling Homes Pr.

C

Collective & Ulysses Travel Guide Staff. Fabulous Canada: Discover Canada's Wide Open Spaces. 2009. 288p. pap. 29.95 (978-2-89464-869-8(3)) Ulysses Travel Guides CAN. Dist: Hunter Publishing, Inc.

Corbett, Bill. The 11,000ers of the Canadian Rockies, 1 vol. rev. ed. 2009. (ENG., Illus.). 224p. pap. (978-1-897522-40-0(1)) Rocky Mountain Bks.

Cousins, Jean & Cousins, Norman. Easy Cycling Around Vancouver: Fun Day Trips for All Ages, 1 vol. 2nd ed. 2011. (ENG., Illus.). 192p. pap. 19.95 (978-1-55365-582-4(6), Greystone Books.) D&M Pubs. Inc. CAN. Dist: Perseus-PGW.

Daffern, Tony. Popular Day Hikes 2: Canadian Rockies, 1 vol. rev. ed. 2008. (Popular Day Hikes Ser.). (ENG., Illus.). 144p. pap. (978-1-897522-01-1(0)) Rocky Mountain Bks.

Davis, James Luther. The Northwest Nature Guide: Where to Go & What to See Month by Month in Oregon, Washington, & British Columbia. 2009. (ENG., Illus.). 448p. pap. 24.95 (978-0-88192-867-9(4), 0881928674) Timber Pr., Inc.

Deichmann, Hank. Out & about in New Brunswick. 2008. (ENG., Illus.). 165p. pap. 15.00 (978-1-894372-33-6(6)) DreamCatcher Publishing CAN. Dist: Univ. of Toronto Pr.

Domm, Jeffrey C. Nova Scotia Birds - Formac Field Guide. 3rd ed. 2012. (ENG., Illus.). 224p. pap. 24.95 **(978-1-4595-0049-5(0))** Formac Publishing Co., Ltd. CAN. Dist: Casemate Pubs. & Bk. Distributors, LLC.

Domm, Jeffrey C., illus. Formac Pocketguide to Canada's Atlantic Seashore. 2nd ed. 2012. (ENG.). 96p. (J). pap. 9.95 **(978-1-4595-0064-8(4))** Formac Publishing Co., Ltd. CAN. Dist: Casemate Pubs. & Bk. Distributors, LLC.

Dorling Kindersley Publishing Staff. DK Eyewitness Travel Guide: Canada: Canada. 2012. (Eyewitness Travel Guides). (ENG.). 448p. pap. 25.00 (978-0-7566-8415-0(3)) Dorling Kindersley Publishing, Inc.

Dun-Map Inc. & Waterfront Regeneration Trust. Waterfront Trail & Greenway Mapbook. Ian Dunlop, ed. 2009. 188p. pap. (978-1-894955-24-9(2)) Dun-Map, Inc.

Eaton, Diane & Eaton, Allison. Exploring the BC Coast by Car. 2nd unabr. rev. ed. 2008. (ENG., Illus.). 400p. pap. 24.95 (978-1-55017-415-1(0)) Harbour Publishing Co., Ltd. CAN. Dist: Ingram Pub. Services.

Ehringer, Gavin. 100 Best Ranch Vacations in North America: The Top Guest & Resort Ranches with Activities for All Ages. 2nd ed. 2007. (100 Best Ser.). (ENG., Illus.). 224p. per. 17.95 (978-0-7627-4391-9(3)) Globe Pequot Pr., The.

Elliot, Elaine & Lee, Virginia. Maritime Flavours: Guidebook & Cookbook. 7th rev. ed. 2008. (ENG., Illus.). 176p. pap. (978-0-88780-768-8(2)) Formac Publishing Co., Ltd.

Entertainment Publications, Inc. Staff, compiled by. Calgary 2009 Entertainment Book. 2008. pap. 45.00 (978-1-59878-656-9(3)) Entertainment Pubns., Inc.

—Okanagan 2009 Entertainment Book. 2008. pap. 35.00 (978-1-59878-689-7(X)) Entertainment Pubns., Inc.

—Ottawa/Outaouais 2009 Entertainment Book. 2008. pap. 40.00 (978-1-59878-658-3(X)) Entertainment Pubns., Inc.

FamilyTravelForum.com Staff & McCarthy, Kyle. The Complete Idiot's Guide to the Best Family Destinations. 2011. (Complete Idiot's Guide Ser.). (ENG.). 416p. (gr. 12). 18.95 (978-1-61564-047-8(9), Alpha Bks.) Penguin Group (USA) Inc.

Fischer, George & Hudson, Noel. Unforgettable Canada: 100 Destinations. 2nd ed. 2007. (ENG., Illus.). 288p. pap. 29.95 (978-1-55046-461-0(2)) Boston Mills Pr. CAN. Dist: Firefly Bks., Ltd.

Fischer, George & Hudson, Noel. Unforgettable Canada: 115 Destinations. 3rd rev. ed. 2012. (ENG., Illus.). 320p. pap. 29.95 **(978-1-77085-020-0(1))** Boston Mills Pr. CAN. Dist: Firefly Bks., Ltd.

Fodor's Travel Publications, Inc. Staff. Canada. Cantor, Joanna et al, eds. 29th ed. 2008. (Fodor's Gold Guides). (ENG., Illus.). 896p. pap. 22.95 (978-1-4000-0734-9(8), Fodor's) Fodor's Travel Pubns.

Gardner, Matthew. Western Canada Handbook. 4th ed. 2011. (Footprint - Handbooks Ser.). (ENG., Illus.). 448p. 24.95 (978-1-907263-25-5(X)) Footprint Handbooks GBR. Dist: Globe Pequot Pr., The.

Green, Michelin. Michelin Green Gd Canada. 12th rev. ed. 2010. (Green Guide Ser.). (ENG., Illus.). 480p. pap. 21.99 (978-1-906261-75-7(X)) Michelin Travel & Lifestyle.

Greenwood, Simon & Greenwood, Fiona. Greenwood Guides to Australia & New Zealand, Canada, & South Africa: The Greenwood Guide to Australia & New Zealand-Special Hand-Picked Accommodation. (Illus.). 264p. pap. 19.95 (978-0-9537980-1-8(1)) Greenwood Guides GBR. Dist: CPG Publishing, Inc.

—Greenwood Guides to Australia & New Zealand, Canada, & South Africa: The Greenwood Guide to Canada-Special Hand-Picked Accommodation. (Illus.). 136p. pap. 15.95 (978-0-9537980-3-2(8)) Greenwood Guides GBR. Dist: CPG Publishing, Inc.

—Greenwood Guides to Australia & New Zealand, Canada, & South Africa: The Greenwood Guide to South Africa-Special Hand-Picked Accommodation. 2nd ed. (Illus.). 224p. pap. 19.95 (978-0-9537980-2-5(X)) Greenwood Guides GBR. Dist: CPG Publishing, Inc.

Hampshire, David & Jennings, Sally. Canada. 4th rev. ed. 2009. (ENG., Illus.). 352p. pap., instr.'s hndbk. ed. 25.95 (978-1-905303-64-9(5)) Survival Bks., Ltd.

Hempstead, Andrew. Moon Alberta: Including Banff, Jasper & the Canadian Rockies. 2010. (Moon Handbooks). (ENG., Illus.). 544p. pap. 19.95 (978-1-59880-371-6(9)) Avalon Travel Publishing.

—Moon Western Canada. 2010. (Moon Handbooks). (ENG., Illus.). 640p. pap. 23.95 (978-1-59880-370-9(0)) Avalon Travel Publishing.

Hempstead, Andrew, et al. Frommer's Canada. 16th ed. 2011. (Frommer's Complete Guides). (ENG.). 864p. pap. 24.99 (978-0-470-93653-5(3), Frommers) Wiley, John & Sons, Inc.

Hempstead, Andrew, et al. Frommer's Far & Wide: A Weekly Guide to Canada's Best Travel Experiences. 2011. (ENG., Illus.). 320p. pap. 29.95 **(978-1-118-09168-5(X)**, Frommers) Wiley, John & Sons, Inc.

Insight Guides. Canada. 8th ed. 2011. (Insight Guides). (ENG., Illus.). 416p. pap. 22.99 (978-981-282-161-4(9)) APA Publications Services SGP. Dist: Ingram Pub. Services.

Isherwood, Judith. Randonnee a Pied de Sainte-Anne-de-Bellevue. Arnaud, Bridger and Associates Staff, tr.Tr. of Historical Walking Tour of Sainte-Anne-de-Bellevue. (ENG & FRE., Illus.). 28p. (Orig.). pap. (978-0-9695180-3-7(X)) Shoreline.

Ivory, Michael. Canada. 2nd ed. 2006. (National Geographic Traveler Ser.). (ENG., Illus.). 400p. pap. 27.95 (978-0-7922-6201-5(8), National Geographic) National Geographic Society.

Jepson, Tim, et al. Canada. 7th ed. 2010. (ENG., Illus.). 996p. 26.99 (978-1-84836-503-2(9)) Rough Guides, Ltd. GBR. Dist: Dorling Kindersley Publishing, Inc.

Kagume, Krista. Ontario Nature Guide. 2008. (ENG., Illus.). 224p. pap. (978-1-55105-564-0(3)) Lone Pine Publishing.

Kain, Tara & Kain, Len. DogFriendly. com's East Coast Dog Travel Guide: Premier Edition 6,000+ Dog-Friendly Places! 2008. (Illus.). 677p. pap. 21.95 (978-0-9795551-2-1(4)) DogFriendly.com, Inc.

Karr, Paul. Nova Scotia, New Brunswick & Prince Edward Island. 8th ed. 2010. (Frommer's Complete Guides: 770). (ENG., Illus.). 352p. pap. 16.99 (978-0-470-58250-3(2), Frommers) Wiley, John & Sons, Inc.

Kilgore, Gene. Gene Kilgore's Ranch Vacations. 8th ed. 2011. (Gene Kilgore's Ranch Vacations Ser.). (Illus.). 200p. pap. 22.95 **(978-0-692-01290-1(7))** Ranch Web.

Kives, Bartley. A Daytripper's Guide to Manitoba: Exploring Canada's Undiscovered Province. 2nd ed. 2010. (ENG.). 234p. pap. 24.95 (978-1-926531-01-4(9)) Great Plains Pubns. CAN. Dist: Univ. of Toronto Pr.

Kranc, Benjamin A. & Roman, Karina. Live & Work in Canada: Comprehensive, Up-to-Date, Practical Information about Everyday Life. 4th ed. 2010. (ENG., Illus.). 180p. pap. 22.00 (978-1-84528-338-4(4)) How To Books GBR. Dist: Parkwest Pubns., Inc.

Langenscheidt Editorial Staff. Mobil Travel Guide Canada. 2008. (Mobil Travel Guide: Canada Ser.). (Illus.). 232p. 17.95 (978-0-8416-0307-3(3)) Langenscheidt Publishing Group.

—On the Road with Your Pet. 3rd rev. ed. 2008. (Mobil Travel Guide: on the Road with Your Pet Ser.). (Illus.). 224p. 18.95 (978-0-8416-0322-6(7)) Langenscheidt Publishing Group.

Langenscheidt Publishers Staff. Canada. Ochterbeck, Cynthia Clayton, ed. 11th rev. ed. 2008. (Michelin Travel Guide Canada Ser.). (Illus.). 480p. 21.95 (978-1-906261-24-5(5)) Michelin.

Lee, John. British Columbia & the Canadian Rockies. 5th rev. ed. 2011. (Regional Travel Guide Ser.). (ENG., Illus.). 296p. pap. 20.99 (978-1-74179-804-3(3)) Lonely Planet Pubns.

Lemieux, Diane. Canada: A Quick Guide to Customs & Etiquette. 2008. (Culture Smart! Ser.). (ENG., Illus.). 168p. pap. 9.95 (978-1-85733-454-8(X)) Kuperard Pubs. GBR. Dist: Random Hse., Inc.

Lemon, Frances & Penrith, Deborah. Canada: The Most Accurate, Practical & Comprehensive Guide to Living & Working in Canada. 5th ed. 2009. (ENG., Illus.). 352p. pap. 24.95 (978-1-85458-427-4(8)) Crimson Publishing, Ltd. GBR. Dist: National Bk. Network.

Leocha, Charles A. Ski Snowboard America. Giordano, Steve et al, eds. 20th rev. ed. 2007. (Illus.). 560p. per. 24.95 (978-0-915009-87-9(0)) World Leisure Corp.

Leocha, Charlie. Leocha's Ski Snowboard America (2009) Top Winter Resorts in USA & Canada. 21st rev. ed. 2008. 560p. pap. 24.95 (978-0-915009-88-6(9)) World Leisure Corp.

—Ski Snowboard America 2007: Top Winter Resorts in USA & Canada. Giordano, Steve & Kaplan, Mitch, eds. 19th ed. 2010. (Illus.). 560p. per. 24.95 (978-0-915009-85-5(4)) World Leisure Corp.

Lonely Planet Staff & Zimmerman, Karla. Canada. 2011. (Full Color Country Guide Ser.). (ENG., Illus.). 400p. pap. 24.99 (978-1-74220-284-6(5)) Lonely Planet Pubns.

Loomis, Jim. All Aboard: The Complete North American Train Travel Guide. 3rd ed. 2011. (ENG., Illus.). 368p. pap. 18.95 (978-1-56976-309-4(7)) Chicago Review Pr., Inc.

Milepost Editors. The Milepost: Legendary Alaska Trip Planner & Alaska Travel Guide to the Highways, Roads, Ferries, Lodgings, Recreation, Sightseeing Attractions & Services along the Alaska Highway to & Within Alaska, Including Alberta, British Columbia, Northwest Territories & the Yukon. 63rd ed. 2011. 784p. pap. 29.95 (978-1-892154-28-6(5)) Milepost, The.

Mobil Regional Gd. Mobil Regional Guide Canada 2010. 3rd rev. ed. 2009. (Regional Guide Ser.). 224p. pap. 17.99 (978-0-8416-1414-7(8)) Langenscheidt Publishing Group.

Mobil Travel Gd, ed. Canada 2009. 2009. (Mobil Travel Guide Ser.). 220p. 17.95 (978-0-8416-0856-6(3)) Langenscheidt Publishing Group.

Mobil Travel Guide. Vineyards & Wineries. 2008. (ENG.). 176p. pap. 17.95 (978-1-936010-11-0(9)) Five Star Travel Corp., The.

Mobil Travel Guide Canada 2009. 2009. (MOBIL TRAVEL GUIDE Ser.). 220p. 17.95 (978-0-8416-0766-8(4)) Langenscheidt Publishing Group.

Monaco Books, ed. Dream Routes of USA & Canada, 1 vol. 2010. (ENG., Illus.). 256p. 29.95 (978-3-89944-576-3(7), Monaco Bks.) Verlag Wolfgang Kunth GmbH & Co. KG DEU. Dist: Innovative Logistics.

National Geographic Society Staff. National Geographic Guide des parcs nationaux du Canada . 2011. (ENG., Illus.). 352p. pap. 26.00 (978-1-4262-0875-1(8), National Geographic) National Geographic Society.

—National Geographic Guide to the National Parks of Canada. 2011. (ENG., Illus.). 352p. pap. 26.00 (978-1-4262-0805-8(7), National Geographic) National Geographic Society.

Nature Vancouver Staff. Parks & Nature Places Around Vancouver. Parkinson, Alison, ed. unabr. ed. 2009. (ENG., Illus.). 272p. pap. 24.95 (978-1-55017-464-9(9)) Harbour Publishing Co., Ltd. CAN. Dist: Ingram Pub. Services.

Olsen, Brad. Sacred Places North America: 108 Destinations. 2nd ed. 2008. (Sacred Places: 108 Destinations Ser.). (ENG., Illus.). 408p. pap. 19.95 (978-1-888729-13-9(9)) Consortium of Collective Consciousness.

Olson, Donald, et al. Frommer's Canada. 15th ed. 2008. (Frommer's Complete Guides: 575). (ENG., Illus.). 864p. pap. 24.99 (978-0-470-25706-7(7), Frommers) Wiley, John & Sons, Inc.

Omnigraphics, creator. City Profiles USA: A Traveler's Guide to Major U. S. & Canadian Cities. 9th ed. 2008. (City Profiles USA: A Traveler's Guide to Major U. S. Cities Ser.). (Illus.). 1074p. 193.00 (978-0-7808-1025-9(2)) Omnigraphics, Inc.

Pang, Guek-Cheng & Barlas, Robert. Canada: A Survival Guide to Customs & Etiquette. 2009. 312p. pap. 15.95 (978-0-7614-5661-2(9)) Marshall Cavendish Corp.

Perich, Shawn & Ellis, Gord. 1997 Northern Ontario Outdoor Guide Book. Date not set. 160p. (Orig.). pap. 8.95 (978-0-9649257-3-1(7)) Outdoor News, Inc.

Phenix, Penny. Canada Spiral Guide. 2nd ed. 2008. (ENG.). 232p. spiral bd. 17.95 (978-1-59508-233-6(6)) AAA.

Pitt, John. USA by Rail. 8th rev. ed. 2012. (ENG., Illus.). 336p. 24.99 **(978-1-84162-389-4(X))** Bradt Travel Guides GBR. Dist: Globe Pequot Pr., The.

Pole, Graeme. Hiking in the Canadian Rockies Recommended. 2007. (Canada Recommended Ser.). (Illus.). 272p. pap. (978-1-55153-648-4(X)) Altitude Publishing Canada Ltd.

Poole, Stephen. Halifax: Discovering Its Heritage. 2nd ed. 2012. (ENG., Illus.). 72p. pap. 19.95 **(978-1-4595-0052-5(0))** Formac Publishing Co., Ltd. CAN. Dist: Casemate Pubs. & Bk. Distributors, LLC.

Prieur, Benoit. Atlantic Canada. 4th ed. (Illus.). 304p. 17.95 (978-2-89464-427-0(2)) Ulysses Travel Guides CAN. Dist: Hunter Publishing, Inc.

Publications International Staff. Amazing Places to Take Your Kids in NA. 2007. (Illus.). 320p. 15.98 (978-1-4127-1320-7(X), PIL Kids) Publications International, Ltd.

Publications International Staff & Speck, Gary B. Yesterday & Today Ghost Towns. 2010. 192p. 24.95 (978-1-60553-424-4(2)) Publications International, Ltd.

Remillard, Francois. Quebec. 7th rev. ed. (Illus.). 544p. pap. 22.95 (978-2-89464-595-6(3)) Ulysses Travel Guides CAN. Dist: Hunter Publishing, Inc.

Ross, Jane & Kyba, Daniel. The David Thompson Highway: A Hiking Guide, 1 vol. 2009. (ENG., Illus.). 256p. (Orig.). pap. (978-1-897522-48-6(7)) Rocky Mountain Bks.

Sanford, Emerson & Beck, Janice Sanford. Historic Hikes Around Mount Robson & the Snake Indian River. 2012. (Life of the Trail Ser.: Vol. 7). (ENG., Illus.). 200p. pap. **(978-0-9879270-0-2(0))** Alpine Vista Pubs. CAN. Dist: Alpine Bk. Peddlers.

Schultz, Patricia. 1,000 Places to See in the U. S. & Canada Before You Die. 2011. (ENG., Illus.). 1200p. pap. 19.95 (978-0-7611-6336-7(0), 0761163360) Workman Publishing Co., Inc.

—1,000 Places to See in the USA & Canada Before You Die. 2007. (ENG., Illus.). 1200p. 27.95 (978-0-7611-4738-1(1), 0761147381) Workman Publishing Co., Inc.

Seagrave, Jayne. Camping British Columbia: A Complete Guide to Provincial & National Park Campgrounds, 1 vol. 6th ed. 2009. (ENG., Illus.). 256p. pap. (978-1-894974-60-8(3)) Heritage Hse.

Shea, Gerry. The Aspiring Hiker's Guide 1: Mountain Treks in Alberta, 1 vol. 2010. (ENG., Illus.). 224p. pap. (978-1-897522-79-0(7)) Rocky Mountain Bks.

Stone, Kas. Paddling & Hiking the Georgian Bay Coast. 2008. (ENG., Illus.). 224p. pap. 29.95 (978-1-55046-477-1(9)) Boston Mills Pr. CAN. Dist: Firefly Bks., Ltd.

Thomas Cook Publishing. Drive Around Canadian Rockies, 3rd: Your guide to great drives. Top 25 Tours. 2009. (Drive Around - Thomas Cook Ser.). (ENG., Illus.). 288p. pap. 26.95 (978-1-84848-202-9(7)) Cook, Thomas Publishing GBR. Dist: Globe Pequot Pr., The.

Tice, Janet & Wilford, Jane. 100 Best Family Resorts in North America: 100 Quality Resorts with Leisure Activities for Children & Adults. 9th ed. 2008. (100 Best Ser.). (ENG., Illus.). 304p. per. 17.95 (978-0-7627-4529-6(0)) Globe Pequot Pr., The.

Trains Magazine Staff, compiled by. Tourist Trains Guidebook. 2011. (ENG., Illus.). 344p. pap. 19.95 (978-0-87116-430-8(2)) Kalmbach Publishing Co., Bks. Div.

Valencia, Kris. The Milepost. 59th ed. 2007. (Milepost Ser.). (Illus.). 800p. per. 27.95 (978-1-892154-21-7(8)) Morris Communications Co., LLC.

Walters, Heather M. Take Your Pet Too! Fun Things to Do - Great U. S. Vacations. Date not set. (Pet Travel Ser.). 300p. pap. 16.95 (978-0-9648913-1-9(X)) MCE Pr.

Zimmerman, Karla. Canada. 11th rev. ed. 2011. (Country Guide Ser.). (ENG., Illus.). 902p. pap. 26.99 (978-1-74179-234-8(7)) Lonely Planet Pubns.

CANADA—HISTORICAL GEOGRAPHY

Clarke, John. The Ordinary People of Essex: Environment, Culture, & Economy on the Frontier of Upper Canada. 2010. (Carleton Library Ser.). (ENG.). 776p. (C). (978-0-7735-3674-6(4)) McGill-Queen's Univ. Pr.

Hayes, Derek. Historical Atlas of British Columbia & the Pacific Northwest: Maps of Exploration-British Columbia, Washington, Oregon, Alaska & Yukon. 55.00 (978-1-55289-900-7(4)) D&M Pubs. Inc. CAN. Dist: Perseus-PGW.

—Historical Atlas of Toronto, 1 vol. 2009. (ENG.). 192p. pap. 29.95 (978-1-55365-497-1(8)) D&M Pubs. Inc. CAN. Dist: Perseus-PGW.

McGillivray, Brett. Canada: A Nation of Regions. 2nd ed. 2009. (ENG., Illus.). 448p. 65.00 (978-0-19-542990-9(7)) Oxford Univ. Pr., Inc.

Warkentin, John. So Vast & Various: Interpreting Canada's Regions in the Nineteenth & Twentieth Centuries. 2010. (Carleton Library Ser.). (ENG.). 520p. (C). (978-0-7735-3719-4(8)); pap. (978-0-7735-3738-5(4)) McGill-Queen's Univ. Pr.

CANADA—HISTORIOGRAPHY

Burnett, Kristin & Read, Geoff, eds. Aboriginal History: A Reader. 2012. (ENG., Illus.). 512p. pap. 85.00 **(978-0-19-543235-0(5))** Oxford Univ. Pr., Inc.

Gordon, Alan. The Hero & the Historians: Historiography & the Uses of Jacques Cartier. 2010. (ENG., Illus.). 248p. (C). pap. 32.95 (978-0-7748-1742-4(9)) UBC Pr. CAN. Dist: Univ. of Washington Pr.

LaRocque, Emma. When the Other Is Me: Native Resistance Discourse, 1850-1990. 2010. (ENG.). 218p. pap. 31.95 (978-0-88755-703-3(1)) Univ. of Manitoba Pr. CAN. Dist: Chicago Distribution Ctr.

McKay, Ian & Bates, Robin. In the Province of History: The Making of the Public Past in Twentieth-Century Nova Scotia. 2010. (ENG., Illus.). 481p. (978-0-7735-3703-3(1)); (C). pap. (978-0-7735-3704-0(X)) McGill-Queen's Univ. Pr.

Mohamed, Feisal & Nyquist, Mary. Milton & Questions of History: Essays by Canadians Past & Present. 2012. (ENG.). 424p. **(978-1-4426-4392-5(7))** Univ. of Toronto Pr.

Reimer, Chad. Writing British Columbia History, 1784-1958. 2010. (ENG.). 216p. pap. 32.95 (978-0-7748-1645-8(7)) UBC Pr. CAN. Dist: Univ. of Washington Pr.

CANADA—HISTORY

Anderson, William James. A Canadian History & Biography, & Passages in the Lives Of. 2007. (ENG.). 56p. per. 16.95 (978-1-4304-4260-8(3)) Kessinger Publishing, LLC.

Antor, Heinz, et al, eds. Refractions of Canada in European Literature & Culture. (ENG., Illus.). VIII, 301p. 255.00 **(978-3-11-182056-9(4))** De Gruyter, Walter Inc.

Armstrong, Alexander. A Personal Narrative of the Discovery of the North-West Passage: While in Search of the Expedition under Sir John Franklin. 2011. (Cambridge Library Collection - Travel & Exploration Ser.). (ENG., Illus.). 654p. pap. 45.00 **(978-1-108-03335-0(0))** Cambridge Univ. Pr.

Armstrong-Reid, Susan & Murray, David. Armies of Peace: Canada & the UNRRA Years. 2008. 448p. (978-0-8020-9321-9(3)) Univ. of Toronto Pr.

Audet, Francois J. Canadian Historical Dates & Events, 1492-1915. 239p. reprint ed. 98.00 (978-0-7222-6842-1(4)) Library Reprints, Inc.

Awards, Honors & Prizes: United States & Canada, 2.0. 32nd ed. 2011. pap. 454.00 (978-1-4144-5806-9(1)) Cengage Gale.

Ayukawa, Michiko Midge. Hiroshima Immigrants in Canada, 1891-1941. 2008. (ENG., Illus.). 208p. (978-0-7748-1431-7(4)) Univ. of British Columbia Pr.

Bailey, Alfred G. Culture & Nationality, No. 58. 225p. pap. 14.95 (978-0-7710-9758-4(1)) McClelland & Stewart CAN. Dist: Random Hse. of Canada, Ltd.

Bain, Colin. GED Canadian Social Studies. 2007. (GED & TABE Test Preparation Ser.). (ENG.). 240p. (gr. 12). pap. 16.95 (978-0-7386-0309-4(0)) Research & Education Assn.

Bain, Colin M., et al. Canadian History. 2007. (Super Reviews Ser.). (ENG., Illus.). 368p. per. 9.95 (978-0-7386-0308-7(2)) Research & Education Assn.

Balcom, Karen. The Traffic in Babies. 2011. (Studies in Gender & History Ser.). pap. **(978-0-8020-9613-5(1))** Univ. of Toronto Pr.

—The Traffic in Babies: Cross-Border Adoption & Baby-Selling between the United States & Canada, 1930-1972. 2011. (Illus.). 448p. **(978-0-8020-9918-1(1))** Univ. of Toronto Pr.

Beattie, Christopher. The Last Forty Year, No. 62. 224p. pap. 18.95 (978-0-7710-9762-1(X)) McClelland & Stewart CAN. Dist: Random Hse. of Canada, Ltd.

Bennett, Paul W. The Grammar School: Striving for Excellence for 50 Years in a Public School World. 2009. (ENG., Illus.). 96p. pap. (978-0-88780-839-5(5)) Formac Publishing Co., Ltd.

Bernage, Georges. Buron la Sanglante: Mourir pour l'Abbaye D'Ardenne. (FRE., Illus.). 64p. 16.95 (978-2-84048-005-1(0)) Editions Heimdal FRA. Dist: Casemate Pubs. & Bk. Distributors, LLC.

Blake, Raymond. From Rights to Needs: A History of Family Allowances in Canada, 1929-92. 2009. (ENG.). 384p. pap. 34.95 (978-0-7748-1573-4(6)) UBC Pr. CAN. Dist: Univ. of Washington Pr.

Borneman, Walter R. The French & Indian War: Deciding the Fate of North America. (P. S. Ser.). (Illus.). 2007. (ENG.). 416p. pap. 15.99 (978-0-06-076185-1(7), HarperPerennial) 2006. 384p. 27.95 (978-0-06-076184-4(9)) HarperCollins Pubs.

Bothwell, Bob. Penguin History of Canada. 2008. (ENG., Illus.). 432p. (gr. 12-18). 20.00 (978-0-14-305032-2(X), Penguin Global) Penguin Group (USA) Inc.

Bothwell, Robert. Canada. 2010. (Traveller's History Ser.). (ENG., Illus.). 256p. pap. 14.95 (978-1-56656-386-4(0)) Interlink Publishing Group, Inc.

Bourdeau, Jean Ovide. AMBROSIA: Impromptu Reflections. 2010. 148p. pap. 14.50 *(978-0-557-58047-7(1))* Lulu Enterprises Inc.
Bourinot, John George. Canada. 2009. 344p. pap. *(978-1-4099-8347-7(1))* Dodo Pr.
—Canada. (Story of the Nations Ser.). 463p. reprint ed. 98.00 *(978-0-7222-6753-0(3))* Library Reprints, Inc.
—Canada under British Rule, 1760-1900. 2009. 206p. pap. *(978-1-151-11283-5(6))* Books LLC.
—Canada under British Rule, 1760-1900. (Cambridge Historical Ser.). 346p. reprint ed. 98.00 *(978-0-7222-6847-6(5))*; 98.00 *(978-0-7222-6754-7(1))* Library Reprints, Inc.
—Canada under British Rule 17601900. 2006. 372p. per. *(978-1-4067-3736-3(4))*, Hesperides Pr.) Read Bks.
—The Story of Canada. 2008. 500p. 53.95 *(978-1-4374-1864-4(3))*; pap. 38.95 *(978-1-4373-3257-5(9))* Kessinger Publishing, LLC.
Boyd, John. Sir George Etienne Cartier, His Life & Times: A Political History of Canada from 1814 until 1873. 439p. reprint ed. 98.00 *(978-0-7222-6921-3(8))* Library Reprints, Inc.
Bradley, Arthur Granville. Britain Across the Seas: America. 454p. reprint ed. 98.00 *(978-0-7222-6452-2(6))* Library Reprints, Inc.
—Canada. 256p. reprint ed. 98.00 *(978-0-7222-6757-8(6))* Library Reprints, Inc.
—The Fight with France for North America. (First American Frontier Ser.). 391p. reprint ed. 98.00 *(978-0-7222-6755-4(X))* Library Reprints, Inc.
—The Making of Canada. 396p. reprint ed. 98.00 *(978-0-7222-6756-1(8))* Library Reprints, Inc.
Brown, Craig. The Illustrated History of Canada. 2011. 622p. (C). pap. ***(978-0-7735-3969-3(7))*** McGill-Queen's Univ. Pr.
Brown, Craig, ed. The Illustrated History of Canada. 5th rev. ed. 2007. (ENG., Illus.). 648p. pap. 32.95 *(978-1-55263-920-7(7))* Key Porter Bks. CAN. Dist: Perseus-PGW.
Browne, G. P. Documents on the Confederation of British North America. 2009. (Carleton Library Ser.). (ENG.). 440p. pap. *(978-0-7735-3609-8(4))* McGill-Queen's Univ. Pr.
Brumwell, Stephen. Paths of Glory: The Life & Death of General James Wolfe. 2007. (ENG., Illus.). 430p. (C). per. *(978-0-7735-3370-7(2))* McGill-Queen's Univ. Pr.
Brune, Nick. The Story of Canada: The Epic Story of the True North Strong & Free. 2011. (ENG., Illus.). 62p. 39.95 *(978-1-86200-707-9(1))* Carlton Bks., Ltd. GBR. Dist: Sterling Publishing Co., Inc.
Brunelle, J. Robert. An American Story: The Tellier & Brunelle Families 1665 - 2009. 2010. 223p. pap. 15.95 *(978-1-4327-5615-4(X))* Outskirts Pr., Inc.
Bryce, George. A Short History of the Canadian People. 2009. 494p. pap. *(978-0-217-31053-6(2))* Books LLC.
—A Short History of the Canadian People. 621p. reprint ed. 128.00 *(978-0-7222-6759-2(2))* Library Reprints, Inc.
Buckner, Phillip & Reid, John G. 1759 Revisited: The Conquest of Canada in Historical Perspective. 2011. (ENG.). (C). 288p. ***(978-1-4426-4407-6(9))***; pap. ***(978-1-4426-1242-6(8))*** Univ. of Toronto Pr.
Buma, Michael. Refereeing Identity: The Cultural Work of Canadian Hockey Novels. 2012. (ENG.). 328p. (C). ***(978-0-7735-3987-7(5))***; pap. ***(978-0-7735-3988-4(3))*** McGill-Queen's Univ. Pr.
Bumsted, et al, eds. Interpreting Canada's Past: A Post-Confederation Reader. 4th ed. 2012. (ENG., Illus.). 512p. pap. 75.00 ***(978-0-19-542780-6(7))*** Oxford Univ. Pr., Inc.
Bumsted, J. The Peoples of Canada: A Pre-Confederation History. 3rd ed. 2008. (ENG., Illus.). 648p. (C). 64.95 *(978-0-19-542340-2(2))* Oxford Univ. Pr., Inc.
Bumsted, J. M. A History of the Canadian Peoples. 4th ed. 2011. (ENG., Illus.). 616p. (Orig.). pap. 85.00 *(978-0-19-543931-1(7))* Oxford Univ. Pr., Inc.
Burt, Alfred Leroy. A Short History of Canada for Americans. 2009. (ENG.). 325p. pap. 60.00 *(978-0-8166-5947-0(8))* Univ. of Minnesota Pr.
Butterley, Keith & Macpherson, Ken. River Class Destroyers. 2nd ed. 2008. (Illus.). 112p. pap. 29.95 *(978-1-55125-093-9(4))* Vanwell Publishing, Ltd. CAN. Dist: Casemate Pubs. & Bk. Distributors, LLC.
Calkin, J. B. History of the Dominion of Canada. 464p. reprint ed. 98.00 *(978-0-7222-6794-3(0))* Library Reprints, Inc.
Campbell, Claire, ed. A Century of Parks Canada, 1911-2011. 2011. (Energy, Ecology & the Environment Ser.). (ENG., Illus.). 250p. pap. 41.95 *(978-1-55238-526-5(4))* Univ. of Calgary Pr. CAN. Dist: Chicago Distribution Ctr.
Campbell, John Douglas S. Memories of Canada & Scotland Speeches. 2007. pap. *(978-1-4065-1251-9(6))* Dodo Pr.
Campbell, John Douglas Sutherland. Memories of Canada & Scotland. 2008. 304p. 29.99 *(978-0-554-22393-3(7))*; 28.99 *(978-0-554-31696-3(X))* BiblioBazaar.
—Memories of Canada & Scotland: Speeches & Verses. 2007. 204p. per. *(978-1-4068-4133-1(8))* Echo Library.
Campbell, T. J. Pioneer Priests of North America: Among the Hurons 1642 to 1710, Vol. 2. 2007. 474p. 52.95 *(978-0-548-01533-9(3))* Kessinger Publishing, LLC.
Canadian Archives Pubns. Staff. State Papers, 20 vol., set. reprint ed. 2500.00 *(978-0-7222-6722-6(3))* Library Reprints, Inc.
Canadian Heritage Staff. Symbols of Canada. (Illus.). 60p. pap. *(978-0-660-16169-3(9))* Canadian Government Publishing.
Canadian Heroes: Heritage. (Canadian Heroes Ser.). reprint ed. 125.00 *(978-0-7222-6888-9(2))* Library Reprints, Inc.
Canadian Who's Who & Why. reprint ed. 150.00 *(978-0-7222-6890-2(4))* Library Reprints, Inc.
Careless, J. M. S. Canada: A Story of Challenge. 2nd rev. ed. 2011. (ENG.). 492p. pap. 34.99 *(978-1-107-67581-0(2))* Cambridge Univ. Pr.
Champlain, Samuel de. Samuel de Champlain: Founder of New France: A Brief History with Documents. Brunelle, Gayle, ed. 2012. (ENG.). 160p. (C). pap. 15.95 ***(978-0-312-59263-9(9))*** Bedford/Saint Martin's.
Charlebois, E. Struggles for Canadian Nationhood. 2010. 538p. pap. 27.95 *(978-1-4327-5379-5(7))* Outskirts Pr., Inc.
Chronicles of Canada Series, 33 vol., set. reprint ed. 4125.00 *(978-0-7222-6760-8(6))* Library Reprints, Inc.
Clark, Doug. The Roaring Game: A Sweeping Saga of Curling. 2008. (ENG., Illus.). 288p. pap. 19.95 *(978-1-55470-118-6(X))* Key Porter Bks. CAN. Dist: Perseus-PGW.
Clement, Dominique, et al. Debating Dissent: Canada & the Sixties. 2010. (Canadian Social History Ser.). pap. *(978-1-4426-1078-1(6))* Univ. of Toronto Pr.
Cockburn, Alexander Peter. Political Annals of Canada. 574p. reprint ed. 98.00 *(978-0-7222-6853-7(X))* Library Reprints, Inc.
Coffin, Victor. Province of Quebec & the Early America. 2006. pap. 30.95 *(978-1-4286-4279-9(X))* Kessinger Publishing, LLC.
Cole, Catherine C. GWG: Piece by Piece. 2012. (ENG., Illus.). 214p. pap. 29.95 ***(978-0-86492-641-8(3))*** Goose Lane Editions CAN. Dist: Univ. of Toronto Pr.
Colombo, John Robert. Fascinating Canada: A Book of Questions & Answers. 2011. (ENG.). 240p. pap. 19.99 *(978-1-55488-923-5(5)*, Dundurn Pr.) Dundurn CAN. Dist: Ingram Pub. Services.
Colquhoun, Arthur Hugh Urquhart. The Fathers of Confederation: A Chronicle of the Birth of the Dominion. (Chronicles of Canada Ser.). 200p. reprint ed. 98.00 *(978-0-7222-6765-3(7))* Library Reprints, Inc.
Conlin, Dan. Pirates of the Atlantic: Robbery, Murder & Mayhem off the Canadian East Coast. 2009. (ENG., Illus.). 96p. pap. 19.95 *(978-0-88780-741-1(0))* Formac Publishing Co., Ltd. CAN. Dist: Casemate Pubs. & Bk. Distributors, LLC.
Conrad, Margaret. A Concise History of Canada. 2012. (Cambridge Concise Histories Ser.). (ENG., Illus.). 344p. (C). 99.00 ***(978-0-521-76193-2(X))***; pap. 26.99 ***(978-0-521-74443-0(1))*** Cambridge Univ. Pr.
Corcoran, Frank & Rabinovitch, Victor. Treasures from the Canadian Museum of Civilization & the Canadian War Museum. 2011. (ENG., Illus.). 200p. (C). pap. 49.95 *(978-0-660-19915-3(7))* Canadian Museum of Civilization/Musee Canadien des Civilisations CAN. Dist: Univ. of Washington Pr.
Craig, Béatrice & Dagenais, Maxime. The Land in Between: The Upper Saint John Valley, Prehistory to World War I, 1 vol. 2010. (ENG., Illus.). 464p. pap. 30.00 *(978-0-88448-319-9(3))* Tilbury Hse. Pubs.
Cran, Gregory J. Negotiating Buck Naked: Doukhobors, Public Policy, & Conflict Resolution, 1 vol. 2007. (ENG., Illus.). 192p. per. 29.95 *(978-0-7748-1259-7(1))* UBC Pr. CAN. Dist: Univ. of Washington Pr.
Dalton, Anthony. Baychimo: Arctic Ghost Ship, 1 vol. 2010. (ENG., Illus.). 256p. per. *(978-1-894974-14-1(X))* Heritage Hse.
de Figueiredo, Dan. What Is Canada? The Ultimate Canadian Quiz Book. 2008. (ENG., Illus.). 392p. (YA). pap. *(978-1-897278-50-5(0))* Blue Bike Bks. CAN. Dist: Lone Pine Publishing.
Dent, John Charles. The Last Forty Years, 2 vol., set. reprint ed. 250.00 *(978-0-7222-6796-7(7))* Library Reprints, Inc.
Dewdney, Christopher & de Kergommeaux, Davin. Canadian Whisky: The Portable Expert. 2012. (ENG., Illus.). 352p. 22.00 ***(978-0-7710-2743-7(5)***, McClelland & Stewart) McClelland & Stewart CAN. Dist: Random Hse., Inc.
Dix, Edwin Asa. Champlain: The Founder of New France. (Appleton's Historic Lives Ser.). 246p. reprint ed. 98.00 *(978-0-7222-6434-8(8))* Library Reprints, Inc.
Dixon, Joan & Read, Tracey. Celebrating the Calgary Exhibition & Stampede: The Story of the Greatest Outdoor Show on Earth, 1 vol. 2007. (ENG.). 160p. *(978-1-55153-723-8(0))* Heritage Hse.
Doughty, Arthur George. The Cradle of New France. 314p. reprint ed. 98.00 *(978-0-7222-6798-1(3))* Library Reprints, Inc.
Dryden, Ken. Becoming Canada: Our Story, Our Politics, Our Future. 2010. 248p. 26.95 *(978-0-7710-2945-5(4)*, McClelland & Stewart) McClelland & Stewart CAN. Dist: Random Hse., Inc.
Ducharme, Michel. Liberalism & Hegemony: Debating the Canadian Liberal Revolution. Constant, Jean-François, ed. 2009. (ENG.). 464p. *(978-0-8020-9882-5(7))*; pap. *(978-0-8020-9589-3(5))* Univ. of Toronto Pr.
Dummitt, Christopher & Dawson, Michael, eds. Contesting Clio's Craft: New Directions & Debates in Canadian History. 2009. (ENG.). 200p. pap. 29.95 *(978-1-900039-88-8(5))* Institute of Latin American Studies GBR. Dist: Brookings Institution Pr.
Duncan, Dorothy. Canadians at Table: Food, Fellowship, & Folklore: A Culinary History of Canada. 2nd ed. 2011. (ENG., Illus.). 248p. pap. 24.99 *(978-1-4597-0038-3(4))* Dundurn CAN. Dist: Ingram Pub. Services.
Durham, John George Lambton. A Report on British North America. reprint ed. 150.00 *(978-0-7222-6729-5(0))* Library Reprints, Inc.
Elections Canada Staff. A History of the Vote in Canada (L'Histoire du Vote au Canada) 2nd ed. 110p. pap. *(978-0-660-16172-3(9))* Canadian Government Publishing.
Environment Canada Staff. Men & Ships in the Canada Trade, 1660-1760: A Biographical Dictionary. pap. *(978-0-660-14449-8(2))* Canadian Government Publishing.
Errington, Elizabeth Jane. The Lion, the Eagle, & Upper Canada: A Developing Colonial Ideology. 2nd ed. 2012. (ENG.). 272p. (C). pap. ***(978-0-7735-4026-2(1))*** McGill-Queen's Univ. Pr.
Ertler, Klaus-Dieter & Gill, Stewart, eds. Canadian Studies: the State of the Art / ÉTudes Canadiennes: Questions de Recherché: 1981-2011: International Council for Canadian Studies (Iccs) / 1981-2011: Conseil International D'éTudes Canadiennes (Ciec) 2011. (Canadiana. Literaturen/Kulturen, Literatures/Cultures, Littératures/Cultures Ser.). 544p. 86.95 ***(978-3-631-61599-7(X))*** Lang, Peter GmbH, Europaischer Verlag der Wissenschaften DEU. Dist: Lang, Peter.
Evans, Brian L. The Other Side of Gold Mountain: Glimpses of Early Chinese Pioneer Life on the Prairies from the Wallace B. Chung & Madeline H. Chung Collection. 2010. (CHI & ENG., Illus.). 63p. pap. 25.00 *(978-1-55195-189-8(4))* Univ. of Alberta Pr. CAN. Dist: Michigan State Univ. Pr., Chicago Distribution Ctr.
Fahmi, Magda & Rutherdale, Robert, eds. Creating Postwar Canada: Community, Diversity, & Dissent, 1945-75. 2008. (ENG., Illus.). 360p. *(978-0-7748-1384-6(9))* Univ. of British Columbia Pr.
Ferguson, Will. Bastards & Boneheads: Our Glorious Leaders, Past & Present, 1 vol. (ENG., Illus.). 336p. pap. 24.95 *(978-1-55054-737-5(2))* D&M Pubs. Inc. CAN. Dist: Perseus-PGW.
Fraser, Douglas. The History of the Supreme Council of the Ancient & Accepted Scottish Rite in Canada, 1868-1960. 2011. 126p. 40.95 ***(978-1-258-02188-7(9))*** Literary Licensing, LLC.
Fromhold, Joachim. Western Canadian People in the Past 1600-1900 D-G. 2010. 178p. pap. 22.50 *(978-0-557-54940-5(X))* Lulu Enterprises Inc.
—Western Canadian People in the Past 1600-1900 H-L. 2010. 193p. pap. 22.95 *(978-0-557-56322-7(4))* Lulu Enterprises Inc.
Gairdner, William D. Oh, Oh, Canada! A Voice from the Conservative Resistance. 2008. 208p. per. *(978-0-9784402-9-9(3))* BPS Bks.
Garneau, Francois-Xavier. History of Canada: From the Time of Its Discovery Till the Union Year 1840-41, 2 vol.,set. reprint ed. 250.00 *(978-0-7222-6801-8(7))* Library Reprints, Inc.
Gidney, R. D. & Millar, W. P. J. How Schools Worked: Public Education in English Canada, 1900-1940. 2012. (Carleton Library Ser.). (ENG., Illus.). 616p. (C). ***(978-0-7735-3953-2(0))*** McGill-Queen's Univ. Pr.
Gimblett, Richard H. & Hadley, Michael L., eds. Citizen Sailors: Chronicles of Canada's Naval Reserve, 1910-2010. 2010. (ENG., Illus.). 248p. 39.95 *(978-1-55488-867-2(0))* Dundurn CAN. Dist: Ingram Pub. Services.
—Le Marin-Citoyen: Chroniques de la Réserve Navale du Canada, 1910-2010. 2010. (FRE & ENG., Illus.). 246p. 39.95 *(978-1-55488-876-4(X))* Dundurn CAN. Dist: Ingram Pub. Services.
Glasner, Joyce. Pirates & Privateers: Swashbuckling Stories from the East Coast. 2nd ed. 2011. (Amazing Stories Ser.). (ENG.). 144p. pap. 9.95 ***(978-1-55277-963-7(7))*** Lorimer, James & Co., Ltd., Pubs. CAN. Dist: Casemate Pubs. & Bk. Distributors, LLC.
Gough, Barry M. Historical Dictionary of Canada. 2nd ed. (Illus.). 2011. l, 487p. E-Book *(978-0-8108-7504-3(7))* 2010. (ENG., 548p. 99.00 *(978-0-8108-5496-3(1))* Scarecrow Pr., Inc.
Gourlay, Robert. Statistical Account of Upper Canada. 2010. 278p. pap. *(978-1-151-82437-0(2))* Books LLC.
Greenhill, Pauline. Make the Night Hideous: Four Canadian Charivaris 1881-1940. 2010. (Canadian Social History Ser.). (Illus.). 272p. *(978-1-4426-4077-1(4))* Univ. of Toronto Pr.
—Make the Night Hideous: Four English-Canadian Charivaris, 1881-1940. 2010. (Canadian Social History Ser.). (Illus.). 272p. *(978-1-4426-1015-6(8))* Univ. of Toronto Pr.
Greswell, William Henry Parr. History of the Dominion of Canada. 339p. reprint ed. 98.00 *(978-0-7222-6802-5(5))* Library Reprints, Inc.
Guildford, Janet & Morton, Suzanne, eds. Separate Spheres: Women's Worlds in the 19th Century Maritimes. 253p. pap. 17.95 *(978-0-919107-41-0(9))* Acadiensis Pr. CAN. Dist: Goose Lane Editions.
Haight, Canniff. Life in Canada Fifty Years Ago. 2007. (ENG.). 160p. per. *(978-1-4065-1561-9(2))* Dodo Pr.
—Life in Canada Fifty Years Ago. 2006. (ENG.). pap. *(978-1-4068-1084-4(3))* Echo Library.
Hampson, Fen O. & Maule, Christopher J., eds. Canada among Nations, 1992-93: A New World Order? 301p. pap. *(978-0-88629-167-9(4))* McGill-Queen's Univ. Pr.
Harris, R. Cole & Warkentin, John. Canada Before Confederation: A Study in Historical Geography, No. 166. 362p. pap. *(978-0-88629-137-2(2))* Bow Historical Bks.
Harris-Zsovan, Jane. Eugenics & the Firewall: Why Alberta's UFA/Social Credit Legacy Matters to 21st Century Canadians. 2010. (ENG.). 208p. pap. 24.95 *(978-1-897289-51-8(0))* Shillingford, J. Gordon Publishing CAN. Dist: Univ. of Toronto Pr.
Harrison, Julia & Darnell, Regna, eds. Historicizing Canadian Anthropology. 2007. (ENG.). 352p. pap. *(978-0-7748-1273-3(7))* Univ. of British Columbia Pr.
Haycock, Maurice. On Site with Maurice Haycock: Artist of the Arctic: Paintings & Drawings of Historical Sites in the Canadian Arctic, 1 vol. 2007. (ENG., Illus.). 112p. 50.00 *(978-0-88866-655-0(1))* Dundurn CAN. Dist: Univ. of Toronto Pr.
Heidenreich, Conrad. Samuel de Champlain Before 1604: Des Sauvages & other Documents Related to the Period. Ritch, K. Janet, ed. 2010. (FRE & ENG.). 526p. (C). *(978-0-7735-3757-6(0))* McGill-Queen's Univ. Pr.
Henderson, Paul & Prime, Jim. How Hockey Explains Canada: The Sport That Defines a Country. 2011. (ENG.). 208p. 32.95 ***(978-1-60078-575-7(1))*** Triumph Bks.
Henry, Alexander. New Light on the Early History of the Greater Northwest. 2009. 356p. pap. *(978-0-217-73179-9(1))* Books LLC.
Heritage House Group Staff, compiled by. Outlaws & Lawmen of Western Canada, 1 vol., Vol. 2. 2007. (ENG., Illus.). 128p. reprint ed. pap. *(978-0-919214-54-5(1))* Heritage Hse.
Hesler, Harold. War Interlude 1916-1919. 2011. 124p. 23.95 *(978-1-4620-0353-2(2))*; pap. 13.95 *(978-1-4620-0352-5(4))* iUniverse, Inc.
Hildebrandt, Walter. Views from Fort Battleford: Constructed Visions of an Anglo-Canadian West. 2008. (ENG., Illus.). 140p. pap. 30.00 *(978-0-88977-220-5(7))* Athabasca University Pr. CAN. Dist: Univ. of Toronto Pr.
Hildebrandt, Walter & Hubner, Brian. The Cypress Hills: An Island by Itself. Orig. Title: The Cypress Hills: the Land & its People. (Illus.). 184p. pap. *(978-1-895830-30-9(3))* Purich Publishing.
—The Cypress Hills: The Land & Its People. 2006. (Purich's Aboriginal Issues Ser.). (Illus.). 136p. *(978-1-895830-02-6(8))* Purich Publishing.
Hillen, Ernest & MacGregor, Roy. A Weekend Memoir. 2009. (ENG.). 320p. 16.95 *(978-0-19-542992-3(3))* Oxford Univ. Pr., Inc.
Hillmer, Norman & Chapnick, Adam. Canadas of the Mind: The Making & Unmaking of Canadian Nationalisms in the Twentieth Century. 2007. (ENG., Illus.). 336p. *(978-0-7735-3272-4(2))*; per. *(978-0-7735-3273-1(0))* McGill-Queen's Univ. Pr.

C

Hobson, Archie, ed. The Cambridge Gazetteer of the USA & Canada: A Dictionary of Places. 2011. (ENG., Illus.). 786p. pap. 50.00 *(978-1-107-40257-7(3))* Cambridge Univ. Pr.
Hodson, Christopher. The Acadian Diaspora: An Eighteenth-Century History. 2012. (ENG., Illus.). 272p. 34.95 ***(978-0-19-973977-6(3))*** Oxford Univ. Pr., Inc.
Holm, Elisabeth. It Feels Like a Healing Process. 2010. 108p. pap. *(978-3-8383-7852-7(0))* Lambert Academic Publishing.
Hopkins, John C. Canada. 188p. reprint ed. 88.00 *(978-0-7222-6840-7(8))* Library Reprints, Inc.
Hopkins, John Castell. Canada, 6 vol., set. reprint ed. 750.00 *(978-0-7222-6807-0(6))* Library Reprints, Inc.
—The Story of the Dominion, Four Hundred Years in the Annals of Half a Continent: A History of Canada from Its Early Discovery & Settlement to the Present Time. 644p. reprint ed. 128.00 *(978-0-7222-6805-6(X))* Library Reprints, Inc.
Horwood, Harold. Plunder & Pillage: Atlantic Canada's Brutal & Bloodthirsty Pirates & Privateers. 2011. (ENG., Illus.). 216p. pap. 19.95 *(978-0-88780-949-1(9))* Formac Publishing Co., Ltd. CAN. Dist: Casemate Pubs. & Bk. Distributors, LLC.
Huneault, Kristina & Anderson, Janice. Rethinking Professionalism: Women & Art in Canada, 1850-1970. 2012. (McGill-Queen's/Beaverbrook Canadian Foundation Studies in Art History Ser.). (ENG., Illus.). 472p. (C). ***(978-0-7735-3966-2(2))*** McGill-Queen's Univ. Pr.
Hurtig, Mel. The Truth about Canada: Some Important, Some Astonishing, & Some Truly Appalling Things All Canadians Should Know about Our Country. 2009. (ENG.). 408p. pap. 18.95 *(978-0-7710-4166-2(7)*, Emblem Edns) McClelland & Stewart CAN. Dist: Random Hse., Inc.
Hutchison, Bruce & Palmer, Vaughn. The Struggle for the Border. 2012. (ENG., Illus.). 520p. pap. 24.95 ***(978-0-19-544792-7(1))*** Oxford Univ. Pr., Inc.
Ignatieff, Michael. Untitled Ignatieff 1/1 On Exploration Of Canada. Date not set. 26.00 *(978-0-8050-7045-3(1)*, Metropolitan Bks.) Holt, Henry & Co.
Inwood, Kris, ed. Farm, Factory & Fortune: New Studies in the Economic History of the Maritime Provinces. 288p. pap. 16.95 *(978-0-919107-38-0(9))* Acadiensis Pr. CAN. Dist: Goose Lane Editions.
Janigan, Mary. Let the Eastern Bastards Freeze in the Dark. 2012. (ENG., Illus.). 352p. 27.50 ***(978-0-307-40062-8(X))*** Knopf Canada CAN. Dist: Random Hse., Inc.
Johnson, E. Pauline. Canadian Born. 2008. 80p. pap. 26.45 *(978-1-4086-7833-6(0))* Audubon Pr. & Christian Bk. Service.
—Canadian Born. 2009. 48p. pap. *(978-1-4099-3143-0(9))* Dodo Pr.
—Canadian Born. 2007. (ENG.). 76p. per. 17.95 *(978-0-548-77683-4(0))* Kessinger Publishing, LLC.
Johnston, Harry Hamilton. Pioneers in Canada. 2008. (Illus.). 320p. 29.99 *(978-0-554-24466-2(7))* 2006. (ENG.). 284p. pap. 21.99 *(978-1-4264-6559-8(9))* 2007. 316p. pap. 24.99 *(978-1-4264-6618-2(8))* BiblioBazaar.
Johnston, William, et al. Du Littoral à la Mer Vol. 1: Histoire Officielle de la Marine Royale du Canada, 1867-1939. 2011. (ENG & FRE., Illus.). 1130p. 70.00 *(978-1-55488-909-9(X))* Dundurn CAN. Dist: Ingram Pub. Services.
—The Seabound Coast Vol. 1: The Official History of the Royal Canadian Navy, 1867-1939. 2011. (ENG., Illus.). 1014p. 70.00 *(978-1-55488-907-5(3)*, Dundurn Pr.) Dundurn CAN. Dist: Ingram Pub. Services.
Karram, Kerry. Four Degrees Celsius: A Story of Arctic Peril. 2012. (ENG., Illus.). 224p. pap. 22.99 ***(978-1-4597-0051-2(1))*** Natural Heritage/Natural History, Inc. CAN. Dist: Ingram Pub. Services.
Kay, Linda. The Sweet Sixteen: The Journey That Inspired the Canadian Women's Press Club. 2012. (ENG., Illus.). 224p. (C). ***(978-0-7735-3967-9(0))*** McGill-Queen's Univ. Pr.
Kearney, Mark & Ray, Randy. The Big Book of Canadian Trivia. 2009. (ENG., Illus.). 504p. pap. 29.99 *(978-1-55488-417-9(9)*, Dundurn Pr.) Dundurn CAN. Dist: Ingram Pub. Services.
—Whatever Happened To ... ? Catching up with Canadian Icons. 2006. (ENG., Illus.). 264p. pap. 21.99 *(978-1-55002-654-2(2)*, Hounslow Pr.) Dundurn CAN. Dist: Ingram Pub. Services.

Keddie, Marlo. Canada Past Present & Future: A Series of Books about Canada. 2011. 56p. pap. 16.46 ***(978-1-4269-6132-8(4))***; 28p. pap. 13.54 ***(978-1-4269-6131-1(6))***; 40p. pap. 16.46 ***(978-1-4269-6129-8(4))***; 68p. pap. 23.29 ***(978-1-4269-6133-5(2))*** Trafford Publishing.

Kingsford, William. The History of Canada. 2010. 292p. pap. *(978-1-152-83279-4(4))* 2010. 406p. pap. *(978-1-152-83285-5(9))* 2010. 476p. pap. *(978-1-152-83287-9(5))* 2009. 478p. pap. *(978-0-217-38807-8(8))* 2009. 590p. pap. *(978-0-217-11909-2(3))* 2009. 564p. pap. *(978-1-4589-1957-1(9))* Books LLC.

—The History of Canada. 2009. 496p. pap. 26.25 *(978-1-4589-1960-1(9))*; 560p. pap. 29.04 *(978-1-4589-1962-5(5))* General Bks. LLC.

—The History of Canada, 10 vol., set. reprint ed. 1250.00 *(978-0-7222-6809-4(2))* Library Reprints, Inc.

—History of Canada, Sixteen Hundred Eight-Eighteen Forty-One, 10 vols., Set. reprint ed. 900.00 *(978-0-404-03720-8(8))* AMS Pr., Inc.

Knegt, Peter. About Canada: Queer Rights. 2012. 128p. pap. 17.95 ***(978-1-55266-437-7(6))*** Fernwood Publishing Co., Ltd. CAN. Dist: Independent Pubs. Group.

Knight, David B. Choosing Canada's Capital: Conflict Resolution in a Parliamentary System, No. 168. 2nd ed. 416p. pap. *(978-0-88629-136-5(4))* McGill-Queen's Univ. Pr.

Kroll, Bob. Rogues & Rascals: Stories of Maritimes Lives & Legends, 1 vol. 2012. (ENG.). 213p. pap. 17.95 ***(978-1-55109-864-7(4))*** Down East Bks.

Ladha, Mansoor. A Portrait in Pluralism: The Aga Khan's Shia Ismailis. 2007. (Illus.). 238p. 27.95 *(978-1-55059-353-2(6))* Detselig Enterprises, Ltd. CAN. Dist: Temeron Bks., Inc.

Lafferty, Renee. Canadian Studies: An Introductory Reader. rev. ed. 2010. (ENG.). 572p. pap. 91.83 *(978-0-7575-3308-2(6))* Kendall Hunt Publishing Co.

Lakusta, Ernie. Banff & Lake Louise History Explorer. 2007. 160p. pap. *(978-1-55153-643-9(9))* Altitude Publishing Canada Ltd.

Landry, Peter. The Lion & the Lily. 2007. 644p. pap. 40.00 *(978-1-4251-5450-9(6))* Trafford Publishing.

Laut, Agnes C. Canada: The Empire of the North. 2007. (Illus.). 492p. per. *(978-1-4065-3587-7(7))* Dodo Pr.

—Canada, the Empire of the North: The Romantic Story of the New Dominion's Growth from Colony to Kingdom. 446p. reprint ed. 98.00 *(978-0-7222-6811-7(4))* Library Reprints, Inc.

Lavoie, Michel. Le Domaine du Roi, 1652-1859: Souveraineté, Contrôle, Mainmise, Propriété, Possession, Exploitation. 2010. (Illus.). 271p. *(978-2-89448-624-5(3))* Editions du Septentrion.

Leddy, Mary Jo. The Other Face of God: When the Stranger Calls Us Home. 2011. 160p. pap. 20.00 *(978-1-57075-910-9(3))* Orbis Bks.

Lee, David. Great Forests & Mighty Men: Early Years in Canada's Vast Woodlands. 2007. (ENG., Illus.). 96p. pap. 24.95 *(978-1-55028-984-8(5))* Lorimer, James & Co., Ltd., Pubs. CAN. Dist: Casemate Pubs. & Bk. Distributors, LLC.

Litwiller, Roger. Warships of the Bay of Quinte. 2011. (ENG., Illus.). 197p. pap. 28.00 *(978-1-55488-929-7(4)*, Dundurn Pr.) Dundurn CAN. Dist: Ingram Pub. Services.

Lloyd, John Arthur Thomas. The Real Canadian. 249p. reprint ed. 98.00 *(978-0-7222-6812-4(2))* Library Reprints, Inc.

Lockett, Jerry. Captain James Cook in Atlantic Canada: The Adventurer & Map Maker's Formative Years. 2010. (ENG., Illus.). 200p. 29.95 *(978-0-88780-920-0(0))* Formac Publishing Co., Ltd. CAN. Dist: Casemate Pubs. & Bk. Distributors, LLC.

Lownsbrough, John. The History of Canada Series:the Best Place to Be. 2012. (ENG.). 368p. (gr. 12). 30.00 ***(978-0-670-06862-3(4)***, Penguin Global) Penguin Group (USA) Inc.

Macdonald, A. John. Troublous Times in Canada. 2007. 252p. (ENG.). 43.99 *(978-1-4280-7478-1(3))*; per. 37.99 *(978-1-4280-7472-9(4))* IndyPublish.com.

MacDonald, A. John. Troublous Times in Canada: A History of the Fenian Raids of 1866 And 1870. 2007. (ENG.). 272p. pap. 21.99 *(978-1-4346-3260-9(1))* BiblioBazaar.

—Troublous Times in Canada: A History of the Fenian Raids of 1866 & 1870. l.t. ed. 2007. 306p. pap. 24.99 *(978-1-4346-3261-6(X))* BiblioBazaar.

MacDonald, John A. Troublous Times in Canada, a History of the Fenian Raids of 1866 And 1870. 2007. 260p. per. *(978-1-4065-2970-8(2))* Dodo Pr.

MacEwan, Grant. A Century of Grant MacEwan: Collected Writings. 256p. pap. *(978-1-894739-00-9(0))* Blue Couch Bks.

Maclaren, Eli. Dominion & Agency: Copyright & the Structuring of the Canadian Book Trade, 1867-1918. 2011. (Studies in Book & Print Culture Ser.). (Illus.). 224p. ***(978-1-4426-4321-5(8))*** Univ. of Toronto Pr.

MacLeod, D. Peter & Canadian War Museum Staff. The Canadian Iroquois & the Seven Years' War. 2012. (ENG., Illus.). 248p. pap. 29.99 *(978-1-55488-977-8(4))* Dundurn CAN. Dist: Ingram Pub. Services.

Macleod, Dave & Olson, Barbara. O Canada Crosswords - 75 Themed Daily Sized Crosswords, Bk. 9. (ENG., Illus.). 115p. pap. 9.95 *(978-0-88971-225-6(5))* Nightwood Editions CAN. Dist: Graphic Arts Ctr. Publishing Co.

MacMechan, Archibald McKellar. The Winning of Popular Government. (Chronicles of Canada Ser.). 172p. reprint ed. 88.00 *(978-0-7222-6775-2(4))* Library Reprints, Inc.

MacMullen, John. The History of Canada. 613p. reprint ed. 128.00 *(978-0-7222-6816-2(5))* Library Reprints, Inc.

Macpherson, Ian. Each for All: A History of the Co-Operative Movement in English Canada, 1900-1945. 270p. pap. 19.95 *(978-0-7705-1771-7(4))* Nelson Education Ltd. CAN. Dist: McGill-Queen's Univ. Pr.

Maeder, Pascal. Forging a New Heimat: Expellees in Post-War West Germany & Canada. 2011. (Transkulturelle Perspektiven Ser.). (ENG., Illus.). 296p. (C). pap. 49.00 ***(978-3-89971-805-8(4))*** Vandenhoeck & Ruprecht GmbH & Co. KG DEU. Dist: ISD.

Mahon, Reginald Henry. Life of General the Hon. James Murray: A Builder of Canada. 457p. reprint ed. 98.00 *(978-0-7222-6954-1(4))* Library Reprints, Inc.

Mair, Rafe. Rants, Raves & Recollections. (ENG.). 224p. pap. 19.95 *(978-1-55285-145-6(1))* Whitecap Bks., Ltd. CAN. Dist: Graphic Arts Ctr. Publishing Co.

The Makers of Canada, 21 vol., set. (Makers of Canada Ser.). reprint ed. 2625.00 *(978-0-7222-6892-6(0))* Library Reprints, Inc.

Marshall, Dianne. Heroes of the Acadian Resistance: The Story of Joseph Beausoleil Broussard & Pierre II Surette, 1702-1765. 2011. (ENG., Illus.). 208p. pap. 22.95 ***(978-0-88780-978-1(2))*** Formac Publishing Co., Ltd. CAN. Dist: Casemate Pubs. & Bk. Distributors, LLC.

Maseres, Francis. The Maseres Letters, 1766-1768. 135p. reprint ed. 88.00 *(978-0-7222-6741-7(X))* Library Reprints, Inc.

McCord, F. A. Handbook of Canadian Dates. reprint ed. 150.00 *(978-0-7222-6843-8(2))* Library Reprints, Inc.

McCreery, Christopher. On Her Majesty's Service: Royal Honours & Recognitions in Canada. 2008. (ENG., Illus.). 176p. 30.00 *(978-1-55002-742-6(5)*, Dundurn Pr.) Dundurn CAN. Dist: Ingram Pub. Services.

McCulloch, Ian MacPherson. A Bard of Wolfe's Army HC: James Thompson, Gentleman Volunteer, 1733-1830. Chapman, Earl John, ed. 2010. (Illus.). 388p. 67.50 *(978-1-896941-63-9(X))* Brass, Robin Studio, Inc. CAN. Dist: Midpoint Trade Bks., Inc.

McCulloch, Ian MacPherson & Charles, H. W. A Bard of Wolfe's Army: James Thompson, Gentleman Volunteer, 1733-1830. Chapman, Earl John, ed. 2010. (Illus.). 388p. pap. 37.95 *(978-1-896941-62-2(1))* Brass, Robin Studio, Inc. CAN. Dist: Midpoint Trade Bks., Inc.

McGhee, Robert. The Thousand Year Path: The Canada Hall at the Canadian Museum of Civilization. 2009. (ENG., Illus.). 132p. pap. 29.95 *(978-1-100-10786-8(X))* Canadian Museum of Civilization/Musee Canadien des Civilisations CAN. Dist: Univ. of Washington Pr.

Mcllwraith, Jean Newton. Canada. reprint ed. 150.00 *(978-0-7222-6815-5(7))* Library Reprints, Inc.

McKay, Ian. Warrior Nation: Rebranding Canada in a Fearful Agee. 2011. 300p. pap. 24.95 ***(978-1-926662-77-0(6))*** Between the Lines CAN. Dist: Univ. of Toronto Pr.

McKinnon-Wrong, George. The Fall of Canada: The History of the Seven Years' War. 272p. reprint ed. 98.00 *(978-0-7222-6838-4(6))* Library Reprints, Inc.

Mestern, Pat Mattaini. Fergus: A Scottish Town by Birthright. 2008. (ENG.). 128p. pap. 19.99 *(978-1-55002-884-3(7))* Dundurn CAN. Dist: Ingram Pub. Services.

Millard, James P. Lake Passages: The Lake Champlain, Lake George, & Richelieu River Timelines 1609-1909, 2 vols., Vol. 1. 2007. (Illus.). 350p. pap. *(978-0-9749854-3-5(0))* America's Historic Lakes.

Miller, J. R. Compact, Contract, Covenant: Aboriginal Treaty-Making in Canada. 2009. (Illus.). 448p. (ENG.). *(978-0-8020-9741-5(3))*; pap. *(978-0-8020-9515-2(1))* Univ. of Toronto Pr.

Miller, Lawrence. The Avro Arrow: A Picture History. 2011. (Amazing Stories Ser.). (ENG., Illus.). 128p. mass mkt. 9.95 ***(978-1-55277-895-1(9))*** Lorimer, James & Co., Ltd., Pubs. CAN. Dist: Casemate Pubs. & Bk. Distributors, LLC.

Milton, Robert A. Straight from the Top: The Truth about Air Canada. annot. ed. 2006. (ENG.). 280p. pap. 18.95 *(978-1-55365-127-7(8)*, Greystone Bks.) D&M Pubs. Inc. CAN. Dist: Perseus-PGW.

Mitchell, James. Canada (1535-2001) (Bell's English History Source Bks.). 120p. reprint ed. 88.00 *(978-0-7222-6752-3(5))* Library Reprints, Inc.

Moffett, Samuel Erasmus. The Americanization of Canada. 2008. 291p. 24.99 *(978-0-554-86643-7(9))*; 190p. pap. 20.75 *(978-0-554-86646-8(3))* BiblioBazaar.

Molot, Maureen A. & Hampson, Fen O., eds. Canada among Nations 1989: The Challenge of Change, Vol. 2. 243p. pap. *(978-0-88629-106-8(2))* McGill-Queen's Univ. Pr.

Morassutti, William. Imagining Canada: A Century of Photographs from the New York Times. 2012. (ENG.). 256p. 40.00 ***(978-0-385-67709-7(X))*** Doubleday Canada, Ltd. CAN. Dist: Random Hse., Inc.

Morck, Randall, ed. Re-Creating Canada: Essays in Honour of Paul Weiler. 2011. (ENG.). 248p. (C). pap. 39.95 *(978-1-55339-273-6(6))* Queen's Univ., Schl. of Policy Studies CAN. Dist: McGill-Queen's Univ. Pr.

Morris, Charles. The Nation's Navy. 333p. reprint ed. 98.00 *(978-0-7222-7506-1(4))* Library Reprints, Inc.

Morton, William Lewis. Contexts of Canada's Past. McKillop, A. B., ed. 289p. pap. 19.95 *(978-0-7705-1847-9(8))* Nelson Education Ltd. CAN. Dist: McGill-Queen's Univ. Pr.

Munro, William Bennett. Canada & British North America. (History of North America Ser.). 487p. reprint ed. 98.00 *(978-0-7222-6820-9(3))* Library Reprints, Inc.

National Library of Canada Staff. Class FC: A Classification for Canadian History. 129p. pap. *(978-0-660-15428-2(5))* Canadian Government Publishing.

Nelles, H. V. A Little History of Canada. 2nd ed. 2011. (ENG., Illus.). 248p. 65.00 ***(978-0-19-544562-6(7))*** Oxford Univ. Pr., Inc.

Nemni, Max & Nemni, Monique. Trudeau Transformed: The Shaping of a Statesman 1944-1965. (ENG.). 2012. 352p. pap. 24.99 ***(978-0-7710-5127-2(1))*** 2011. 544p. 32.99 *(978-0-7710-5125-8(5))* McClelland & Stewart CAN. (McClelland & Stewart). Dist: Random Hse., Inc.

Neufeld, James. Passion to Dance: The National Ballet of Canada. 2011. (ENG., Illus.). 480p. 50.00 *(978-1-4597-0121-2(6))* Dundurn CAN. Dist: Ingram Pub. Services.

Newell, Peter E. The Impossibilists: A Brief Profile of the Socialist Party of Canada. 2008. (Illus.). 440p. pap. *(978-1-84748-323-2(2))* Athena Pr.

No Time to Lose: Challenge. pap. *(978-0-660-56245-2(6))* Canadian Government Publishing.

Nurse, Andrew & Blake, Raymond. Beyond National Dreams: Essays on Canadian Citizenship & Nationalism, 1 vol. 2009. (ENG.). 432p. pap. 35.00 *(978-1-55041-969-6(2))* Fitzhenry & Whiteside, Ltd. CAN. Dist: Ingram Pub. Services.

Nursey, Walter R. The Story of Isaac Brock, Hero, Defender & Saviour of Upper Canada, 1812. 2007. 160p. pap. 19.99 *(978-1-4264-5086-0(9))*; (ENG.). 178p. pap. 21.99 *(978-1-4264-5387-8(6))* BiblioBazaar.

—The Story of Isaac Brock, Hero, Defender & Saviour of Upper Canada, 1812. 2007. 176p. per. *(978-1-4065-4048-2(X))* Dodo Pr.

—The Story of Isaac Brock, Hero, Defender & Saviour of Upper Canada, 1812. 2006. pap. *(978-1-4068-3567-0(6))* Echo Library.

Obracht-Prondzynski, Cezary & Wicherkiewicz, Tomasz. The Kashubs: Past & Present. 2011. (Nationalisms across the Globe Ser.). (ENG., Illus.). 299p. pap. 64.95 ***(978-3-03911-975-2(3))*** Lang, Peter AG GBR. Dist: Lang, Peter.

Opp, James. The Lord for the Body: Religion, Medicine, & Protestant Faith Healing in Canada, 1880-1930. 2007. (McGill-Queen's Studies in the History of Religion Ser.). (ENG., Illus.). 288p. (C). per. *(978-0-7735-2906-9(3))* McGill-Queen's Univ. Pr.

Outlaws & Lawmen of Western Canada, 3 vols., Vol. 3. 2010. (Illus.). 160p. reprint ed. pap. *(978-0-919214-88-0(6))* Heritage Hse.

Palaeologu, M. Athena, ed. The Sixties in Canada: A Turbulent & Creative Decade. (ENG., Illus.). 2010. 224p. 39.99 *(978-1-55164-331-1(6))* 2009. 384p. pap. 24.99 *(978-1-55164-330-4(8))* Black Rose Bks. CAN. Dist: Consortium Bk. Sales & Distribution.

Pammett, Jon H. & Doman, Christopher, eds. The Canadian Federal Election Of 2011. 2011. (ENG., Illus.). 368p. pap. 36.99 *(978-1-4597-0180-9(1))* Dundurn CAN. Dist: Ingram Pub. Services.

Parkman, Francis. A Half-Century of Conflict, 2 vol., set. (France & England in North America Ser.: Pt. 6). reprint ed. 250.00 *(978-0-7222-6573-4(5))* Library Reprints, Inc.

Perrone, Julie. How the French Created Canada. 2009. (ENG.). 248p. pap. *(978-1-896124-18-6(6))* Dragon Hill Publishing CAN. Dist: Lone Pine Publishing.

Pigott, Peter. From Far & Wide: A Complete History of Canada's Arctic Sovereignty. 2011. (ENG., Illus.). 312p. 35.00 *(978-1-55488-987-7(1))* Dundurn CAN. Dist: Ingram Pub. Services.

—Wingwalkers: The Rise & Fall of Canada's Other Airline. 2nd rev. unabr. ed. (ENG., Illus.). 448p. pap. 26.95 *(978-1-55017-292-8(1))* Harbour Publishing Co., Ltd. CAN. Dist: Ingram Pub. Services.

Pike, Corinna & McCreery, Christopher. Canadian Symbols of Authority: Maces, Chains, & Rods of Office. 2011. (ENG., Illus.). 288p. 60.00 *(978-1-55488-901-3(4)*, Dundurn Pr.) Dundurn CAN. Dist: Ingram Pub. Services.

Poverty in Canada 1993. pap. *(978-0-660-15459-6(5))* Canadian Government Publishing.

Ramirez, Bruno. The Canadian Duce: Il Duce Canadese. 2006. (Drama Ser.). (ENG.). 148p. 15.00 *(978-1-55071-257-5(8))* Guernica Editions, Inc. CAN. Dist: Univ. of Toronto Pr.

Ray, Arthur J. An Illustrated History of Canada's Native People: I Have Lived Here since the World Began. 2010. (ENG., Illus.). 488p. pap. 34.95 *(978-1-55470-270-1(4))* Key Porter Bks. CAN. Dist: Perseus-PGW.

Roberts, Charles G. D. A History of Canada. 2007. (ENG.). 504p. 53.95 *(978-0-548-33320-4(3))*; per. 38.95 *(978-1-4326-9212-4(7))* Kessinger Publishing, LLC.

—A History of Canada. 493p. reprint ed. 98.00 *(978-0-7222-6825-4(4))* Library Reprints, Inc.

Royle, Stephen A. Company, Crown & Colony: The Hudson's Bay Company & Territorial Endeavour in Western Canada. 2011. (ENG., Illus.). 256p. 92.00 *(978-1-84885-132-0(4))* I. B. Tauris & Co., Ltd. GBR. Dist: Macmillan.

Rudin, Ronald. Remembering & Forgetting in Acadie: A Historian's Journey Through Public Memory. 2009. (ENG.). 384p. *(978-0-8020-9950-1(5))*; pap. *(978-0-8020-9657-9(3))* Univ. of Toronto Pr.

Samson, Daniel, ed. Contested Countryside: Rural Workers & Modern Society in Atlantic Canada, 1800-1950, Vol. 4. (Illus.). 280p. pap. 16.95 *(978-0-919107-40-3(0))* Acadiensis Pr. CAN. Dist: Goose Lane Editions.

Sandwell, Ruth, ed. To the Past: History Education, Public Memory, & Citizenship in Canada. 2006. (ENG.). 120p. *(978-0-8020-3891-3(3))*; pap. *(978-0-8020-3814-2(X))* Univ. of Toronto Pr.

Sangster, Joan. Through Feminist Eyes: Essays on Canadian Women's History. 2011. (ENG.). 440p. (C). pap. 37.95 ***(978-1-926836-18-8(9))*** UBC Pr. CAN. Dist: Univ. of Washington Pr.

Santosuosso, John. Canada: an Introduction for Americans. 2007. (ENG.). 224p. per. 24.95 *(978-1-4241-6505-6(9))* PublishAmerica, Inc.

Schrauwers, Albert. 'Union Is Strength' W. L. Mackenzie, the Children of Peace, & the Emergence of Joint Stock Democracy in Upper Canada. 2009. (ENG., Illus.). 384p. *(978-0-8020-9927-3(0))* Univ. of Toronto Pr.

See, Scott, ed. History of Canada. 2nd rev. ed. 2010. (Illus.). 421p. 165.00 *(978-1-59237-610-0(X))* Grey Hse. Publishing.

Segrave, Kerry. Women & Capital Punishment in America, 1840-1899: Death Sentences & Executions in the United States & Canada. 2008. (ENG.). 218p. pap. 39.95 *(978-0-7864-3823-5(1))* McFarland & Co., Inc. Pubs.

Sharpe, Robert J. & McMahon, Patricia. The Persons Case: The Origins & Legacy of the Fight for Legal Personhood. 2008. (Osgoode Society for Canadian Legal History Ser.). (ENG.). 272p. pap. *(978-0-8020-9628-9(X))* Univ. of Toronto Pr.

Shaw, Amy J. Crisis of Conscience: Conscientious Objection in Canada during the First World War. 2009. (ENG.). 240p. pap. 32.95 *(978-0-7748-1594-9(9))* UBC Pr. CAN. Dist: Univ. of Washington Pr.

Shortt, Adam. Canada & Its Provinces: A History of the Canadian People & Their Institutions, 23 vol., set. reprint ed. 2875.00 *(978-0-7222-6746-2(0))* Library Reprints, Inc.

Shortt, Adam & Doughty, Arthur G., eds. Canada & Its Provinces: A History of the Canadian People & Their Institutions, 23 vols. reprint ed. 2875.00 *(978-0-7222-2562-2(8))* Library Reprints, Inc.

Simmons, Deidre. Keepers of the Record: The History of the Hudson's Bay Company Archives. (ENG., Illus.). 384p. (C). 2009. pap. *(978-0-7735-3620-3(5))* 2007. *(978-0-7735-3291-5(9))* McGill-Queen's Univ. Pr.

Sir John George Bourinot. Canada under British Rule: 1760-1900. l.t. ed. 2007. (ENG.). 328p. pap. 24.99 *(978-1-4264-6442-3(8))* BiblioBazaar.

Skelton, Oscar D. The Canadian Dominion: A Chronicle of Our Northern Neighbor. 2008. 144p. pap. *(978-1-4099-4577-2(4))* Dodo Pr.

—The Canadian Dominion: A Chronicle of Our Northern Neighbor. (Chronicles of America Ser.). 296p. reprint ed. 98.00 *(978-0-7222-6826-1(2))*; 98.00 *(978-0-7222-7131-5(X))* Library Reprints, Inc.

Skelton, Oscar Douglas. The Canadian Dominion: A Chronicle of Our Northern Neighbor. l.t. ed. 2007. (ENG.). 172p. pap. 21.99 *(978-1-4346-2685-1(7))* BiblioBazaar.

Smith, Andrew. British Businessmen & Canadian Confederation: Constitution Making in an Era of Anglo-Globalization. 2008. (ENG.). 240p. (C). *(978-0-7735-3405-6(9))* McGill-Queen's Univ. Pr.

Smith, Joshua M. Battle for the Bay: The Naval War of 1812. 2011. (New Brunswick Military Heritage Ser.). 16.95 ***(978-0-86492-644-9(8))*** Goose Lane Editions CAN. Dist: Univ. of Toronto Pr.

Smith, Justin Harvey. Our Struggle for the Fourteenth Colony, 2 vols. reprint ed. 250.00 *(978-0-7222-6827-8(0))*; 250.00 *(978-0-7222-7686-0(9))* Library Reprints, Inc.

Stagg, Ronald. The Golden Dream: A History of the St. Lawrence Seaway. 2010. (ENG., Illus.). 296p. 35.00 *(978-1-55002-887-4(1)*, Dundurn Pr.) Dundurn CAN. Dist: Ingram Pub. Services.

Steckley, John. White Lies about the Inuit. 2007. (Teaching Culture: UTP Ethnographies for the Classroom Ser.). (ENG.). 168p. pap. *(978-1-55111-875-8(0))* Univ. of Toronto Pr.

Sterling, Sharon. Changing Your World: Investigating Empowerment. (ENG., Illus.). 300p. spiral bd. *(978-0-19-542046-3(2))* Oxford Univ. Pr., Inc.

Stewart, Barry D. Across the Land a Canadian Journey of Discovery. 2009. 276p. 31.00 *(978-1-4269-1500-0(4))* Trafford Publishing.

Stortz, Paul & Panayotidis, E. Lisa, eds. Historical Identities: The Professoriate in Canada. 2006. (ENG., Illus.). 450p. *(978-0-8020-9000-3(1))* Univ. of Toronto Pr.

Taylor, Greg. The Law of the Land: The Advent of the Torrens System in Canada. 2008. (Osgoode Society for Canadian Legal History Ser.). (ENG.). 256p. *(978-0-8020-9913-6(0))* Univ. of Toronto Pr.

Teigrob, Robert. Warming up to the Cold War: Canada & the United States' Coalition of the Willing, from Hiroshima to Korea. 2009. (ENG.). 312p. *(978-0-8020-9923-5(8))*; pap. *(978-0-8020-9615-9(8))* Univ. of Toronto Pr.

Theobald, Andrew. The Bitter Harvest of War: New Brunswick & the Conscription Crisis of 1917. 2008. (New Brunswick Military Heritage Ser.). (ENG., Illus.). 124p. pap. 16.95 *(978-0-86492-511-4(5))* Goose Lane Editions CAN. Dist: Univ. of Toronto Pr.

Thomas, Mary. Canadians with Custer. 2012. (ENG., Illus.). 224p. pap. 24.99 ***(978-1-4597-0407-7(X))*** Dundurn CAN. Dist: Ingram Pub. Services.

Thompson, Wayne C. Canada. 24th ed. 2008. (Canada (Stryker-Post) Ser.). (Illus.). 201p. pap. 15.50 *(978-1-887985-91-8(3))* Stryker-Post Pubns.

Thwaites, Reuben Gold. France in America, 1497-1763. 2009. 372p. 38.99 *(978-1-117-11656-3(5))*; pap. 31.75 *(978-1-117-11657-0(3))* BiblioBazaar.

—France in America, 1497-1763. 2009. 198p. pap. 19.99 *(978-1-150-77212-2(3))* General Bks. LLC.

—France in America, 1497-1763. (American Nation Ser.). 320p. reprint ed. 98.00 *(978-0-7222-6831-5(9))*; 98.00 *(978-0-7222-7196-4(4))* Library Reprints, Inc.

Touchie, Rodger D. Bear Child: The Life & Times of Jerry Potts, 1 vol. 2010. (ENG., Illus.). 336p. pap. *(978-1-894384-63-6(6))* Heritage Hse.

Tracy, Frank B. The Tercentenary History of Canada, from Champlain to Laurier, 3 Vols. reprint ed. 375.00 *(978-0-7222-6832-2(7))* Library Reprints, Inc.

Trueman, Howard. The Chignecto Isthmus & Its First Sett. 2006. pap. *(978-1-4068-1127-8(0))* Echo Library.

Tuck, John R. Adventures in Living. 2011. 126p. 40.95 ***(978-1-258-06757-1(9))*** Literary Licensing, LLC.

Tucker, Gilbert N. The Canadian Commercial Revolution, 1845-1851. Aitkin, Hugh G., ed. 189p. pap. 6.95 *(978-0-7710-9719-5(0))* McClelland & Stewart CAN. Dist: Random Hse. of Canada, Ltd.

Tupper, Charles. Recollections of Sixty Years in Canada. 2008. 454p. 52.95 *(978-1-4365-9472-1(3))* 2007. (ENG.). 456p. per. 37.95 *(978-0-548-79335-0(2))* Kessinger Publishing, LLC.
—Recollections of Sixty Years in Canada. 414p. reprint ed. 98.00 *(978-0-7222-6972-5(2))* Library Reprints, Inc.
Tuttle, Charles Richard. Short History of the Dominion of Canada, from 1500 To 1878: The Contemporaneous History of England & the United States, Together with a Brief Account of the Turko Russian War of 1877. 666p. reprint ed. 128.00 *(978-0-7222-6833-9(5))* Library Reprints, Inc.
Vallières, Nicole & Cooper, Cynthia. 90 Treasures, 90 Stories, 90 Years. 2012. (Illus.). 268p. (C). pap. ***(978-1-895615-16-6(X))*** McGill-Queen's Univ. Pr.
Valverde, Mariana. The Age of Light, Soap, & Water: Moral Reform in English Canada, 1885-1925. 2008. (Canadian Social History Ser.). 208p. pap. *(978-0-8020-9595-4(X))* Univ. of Toronto Pr.
Vance, Jonathan F. A History of Canadian Culture. 2011. (ENG., Illus.). 512p. 24.95 *(978-0-19-544422-3(1))* Oxford Univ. Pr., Inc.
Vronsky, Peter. Ridgeway: The American Fenian Invasion & the 1866 Battle That Made Canada. 2012. (ENG., Illus.). 368p. (gr. 12). 30.00 ***(978-0-670-06803-6(9)***, Penguin Global) Penguin Group (USA) Inc.
Wallace, William Stewart. The Family Compact: A Chronicle of the Rebellion in Upper Canada. (Chronicles of Canada Ser.). 172p. reprint ed. 88.00 *(978-0-7222-6783-7(5))* Library Reprints, Inc.
War Criminals Deschenes. pap. *(978-0-660-16759-6(X))* Canadian Government Publishing.
Weisberg, Ellen & Yaffe, Mike. All Across Canad. 2008. 40p. pap. *(978-1-54747-725-2(7))* Chipmunkapublishing.
Willson, Gordon B. Canada. (Romance of Empire Ser.). 304p. reprint ed. 98.00 *(978-0-7222-6834-6(3))* Library Reprints, Inc.
Wilson, Bruce G. The Enterprises of Robert Hamilton: A Study of Wealth & Influence in Early Upper Canada, 1776-1812. 243p. *(978-0-88629-010-8(4))*; pap. *(978-0-88629-009-2(0))* McGill-Queen's Univ. Pr.
Wilson, Diana. Triumph & Tragedy in the Crowsnest Pass. 1 vol. 2nd ed. 2010. (ENG., Ilus.). 168p. per. *(978-1-894384-16-2(4))* Heritage Hse.
Wilson, Gordon A. A. NORAD & the Soviet Nuclear Threat: Canada's Secret Electronic Air War. 2012. (ENG., Illus.). 288p. pap. 28.99 ***(978-1-4597-0410-7(X))*** Dundurn CAN. Dist: Ingram Pub. Services.
Wise, S. F., ed. Sir Francis Bond Head: A Narrative. 261p. pap. 19.95 *(978-0-7710-9743-0(3))* McClelland & Stewart CAN. Dist: Random Hse. of Canada Ltd.
Withrow, William H. History of Canada. reprint ed. 150.00 *(978-0-7222-6835-3(1))* Library Reprints, Inc.
Wojna, Lisa. Canadian Firsts: Inventions, Sports, Medicine, Space, Women's Rights, Explorers, Science, Research, Arts, World Affairs. 2008. (ENG., Illus.). 264p. pap. *(978-1-894864-75-6(1))* Folklore Publishing CAN. Dist: Lone Pine Publishing.
Wood, J. David. Places of Last Resort: The Expansion of the Farm Frontier into the Boreal Forest in Canada C., 1910-1940. 2006. (ENG., Illus.). 264p. (C). *(978-0-7735-3059-3(6))* McGill-Queen's Univ. Pr.
Wood, William. In the Heart of Old Canada. reprint ed. 150.00 *(978-0-7222-6837-7(8))* Library Reprints, Inc.
Wood, William C. H. The Fight for Canada: A Naval & Military Sketch from the History of the Great Imperial War. 363p. reprint ed. 98.00 *(978-0-7222-6836-0(X))* Library Reprints, Inc.
Wood, William Charles Henry. The Father of British Canada: A Chronicle of Carleton. 239p. reprint ed. 98.00 *(978-0-7222-6788-2(6))* Library Reprints, Inc.
—The Logs of the Conquest of Canada. (Publications of the Champlain Society). 335p. reprint ed. 98.00 *(978-0-7222-6751-6(7))* Library Reprints, Inc.
—The Passing of New France: A Chronicle of Montcalm. 149p. reprint ed. 88.00 *(978-0-7222-6790-5(8))* Library Reprints, Inc.
Wright, J. V. A History of the Native People of Canada, Volume I: 10,000-1,000 BC. 2007. (Mercury Ser.). (Illus.). 506p. per. *(978-0-660-19642-8(5))* Canadian Museum of Civilization/Musee Canadien des Civilisations.
Wrong, George M. & Langton, H. H. Chronicles of Canada Series, 32 vols. reprint ed. 4000.00 *(978-0-7222-2561-5(X))* Library Reprints, Inc.
Yakimov, Radka. Caft the Blue Danube. 2008. 180p. 26.95 *(978-0-595-71410-0(2))*; pap. 16.95 *(978-0-595-47672-5(4))* iUniverse, Inc.
Zuehlke, Mark. On to Victory: The Canadian Liberation of the Netherlands, March 23-May 5 1945, 1 vol. 2011. (ENG., Illus.). 552p. pap. 27.95 *(978-1-55365-813-9(2))* D&M Pubs. Inc. CAN. Dist: Perseus-PGW.

CANADA—HISTORY—BIBLIOGRAPHY

Aubin, Paul & Cote, Louis-Marie. Bibliographie de l'Histoire du Quebec et du Canada, 1946-1965 (Bibliography of the History of Quebec & Canada), 2 vols. (ENG & FRE.). 1316p. *(978-2-89224-098-6(0))* Bow Historical Bks.
Griffin, Appleton Prentiss Clark. Bibliography of the Historical Societies of the United States, 3 vol., set. 1890p. reprint ed. 375.00 *(978-0-7222-7000-4(3))* Library Reprints, Inc.

CANADA—HISTORY—HUMOR, CARICATURES, ETC.

Bengough, John Wilson. A Caricature History of Canadian Politics, 2 vol., set. reprint ed. 250.00 *(978-0-7222-6844-5(0))* Library Reprints, Inc.
Martin, Ian Alexander. Canada for Foreigners. 2008. (Illus.). 160p. *(978-1-905532-25-4(3))* Humdrumming, Ltd.
Shatner, William & Regan, Chris. Shatner Rules: Your Guide to Understanding the Shatnerverse & the World at Large. 2012. (ENG.). 272p. (gr. 12). pap. 15.00 ***(978-0-451-23648-7(3)***, N A L Trade) Penguin Group (USA) Inc.
—Shatner Rules: Your Key to Understanding the Shatnerverse & the World at Large. Lt. ed. 2011. 31.99 ***(978-1-4104-4304-5(3))*** Thorndike Pr.

CANADA—HISTORY—JUVENILE LITERATURE

Goyette, Linda. Kidmonton: True Stories of River City Kids, 1 vol. (ENG., Illus.). 128p. pap. 6.95 *(978-0-9732481-7-3(3))* Brindle & Glass Publishing CAN. Dist: Literary Pr. Group of Canada.
Samuels, Barbara. Multiculturalism in Early Canada: Multiculturalism in Canada. 2011. 32p. (gr. 5-8). pap. ***(978-1-77071-707-7(2))*** Weigl Educational Pubs. Ltd.

CANADA—HISTORY—SOURCES

Browne, G. P. Documents on the Confederation of British North America. 2009. (Carleton Library Ser.). (ENG.). 440p. (C). *(978-0-7735-3602-9(7))* McGill-Queen's Univ. Pr.
Bumsted, J. M., et al. Interpreting Canada's Past: A Pre-Confederation Reader. 4th ed. 2011. (ENG., Illus.). 496p. pap. 75.00 *(978-0-19-542779-0(3))* Oxford Univ. Pr., Inc.
Burpee, Lawrence Johnstone. Index & Dictionary of Canadian History. (Makers of Canada Ser.). 446p. reprint ed. 98.00 *(978-0-7222-6896-4(3))*; 98.00 *(978-0-7222-6914-5(5))* Library Reprints, Inc.
Cavell, Janice. Affaires étrangères et Commerce International Canada: Une Histoire en Documents, 1909-2009. 2009. (FRE & ENG., Illus.). xiii, 338p. *(978-0-660-64534-6(3))* Canadian Government Publishing.
Dyck, Ian & Smith, Charles, eds. William E. Logan's 1845 Survey of the Upper Ottawa Valley. 2007. (Mercury Ser.). (ENG., Illus.). 256p. pap. *(978-0-660-19662-6(X))* Canadian Museum of Civilization/Musee Canadien des Civilisations.
Earl. Speeches on Canadian Affairs. reprint ed. 150.00 *(978-0-7222-6851-3(3))* Library Reprints, Inc.
The Jesuit Relations & Allied Documents. 527p. reprint ed. 98.00 *(978-0-7222-6731-8(2))* Library Reprints, Inc.
Public Archives Canada Staff. Documents Relating to the Constitutional History of Canada, 1819-1828. (Public Archives). 538p. reprint ed. 98.00 *(978-0-7222-6747-9(9))*; 98.00 *(978-0-7222-5727-1(4))* Library Reprints, Inc.
Thorner, Thomas. Country Nourished on Self Doubt: Documents in Post-Confederation Canadian History. 3rd ed. 2010. 600p. pap. *(978-1-4426-0019-5(5))* Univ. of Toronto Pr.

CANADA—HISTORY—TO 1763 (NEW FRANCE)

see also Quebec Campaign, 1759

A. Religious of the Ursuline Community. The Life of the Venerable Mother Mary of the Incarnation. 2007. (ENG.). 270p. pap. 21.99 *(978-1-4264-4937-6(2))* 2006. 294p. pap. 23.99 *(978-1-4264-5238-3(1))* BiblioBazaar.
Alston, Sandra & Evans, Karen. A Bibliography of Canadiana. (Illus.). *(978-0-88773-029-0(9))* Bow Historical Bks.
Bibaud, M. (Michel), creator. Histoire du Canada Sous la Domination Française. 2010. 430p. pap. 35.75 ***(978-1-172-62362-4(7))*** BiblioBazaar.
Bibaud, Michel. Histoire du Canada, Sous la Domination Française. 2012. 380p. pap. 33.75 ***(978-1-276-31069-7(2))*** BiblioBazaar.
Brumath, Adrien Leblond de. The Makers of Canada: Bishop Laval. 2007. (ENG.). 164p. pap. 19.99 *(978-1-4346-0731-7(3))*; 184p. pap. 21.99 *(978-1-4346-0791-1(7))* BiblioBazaar.
Brunelle, J. Robert. An American Story: The Tellier & Brunelle Families 1665 - 2009. 2010. 223p. pap. 15.95 *(978-1-4327-5615-4(X))* Outskirts Pr., Inc.
Bumsted, J. M. The Peoples of Canada: A Pre-Confederation History. 2nd enl. ed. 2009. (Illus.). 624p. (Orig.). pap. 65.00 *(978-0-19-543101-8(4))* Oxford Univ. Pr., Inc.
Cahall, Raymond Du Bois. The Sovereign Council of New France. 2009. 206p. pap. 19.99 *(978-0-217-79840-2(3))* General Bks. LLC.
—The Sovereign Council of New France: A Study in Canadian Constitutional History. (Columbia University, Studies in the Social Sciences: No. 156). reprint ed. 36.50 *(978-0-404-51156-2(2))* AMS Pr., Inc.
Campbell, T. J. Pioneer Laymen of North America V1. (ENG.). 340p. 2007. 46.95 *(978-0-548-14371-1(4))* 2006. per. 31.95 *(978-1-4286-5623-9(5))* Kessinger Publishing, LLC.
—Pioneer Laymen of North America V2. 2007. (ENG.). 368p. 48.95 *(978-0-548-14372-8(2))* 2006. pap. 33.95 *(978-1-4286-5624-6(3))* Kessinger Publishing, LLC.
Casgrain, Henri Raymond. Wolfe & Montcalm. 2009. (ENG.). 325p. 36.99 *(978-1-116-98489-7(X))* BiblioBazaar.
—Wolfe & Montcalm. 2009. 136p. pap. 19.99 *(978-1-151-28189-0(1))* General Bks. LLC.
—Wolfe & Montcalm. (Makers of Canada Ser.). 296p. reprint ed. 98.00 *(978-0-7222-6979-4(X))*; 98.00 *(978-0-7222-6898-8(X))* Library Reprints, Inc.
Chapais, Thomas. The Great Intendant: A Chronicle of Jean Talon in Canada, 1665-1672. (Chronicles of Canada Ser.). 139p. reprint ed. 88.00 *(978-0-7222-6762-2(2))* Library Reprints, Inc.
Charlevoix, Pierre Francois Xavier de. History & General Description of New France, 6 vol., set. reprint ed. 750.00 *(978-0-7222-6724-0(X))* Library Reprints, Inc.
Chartrand, Rene. The Forts of New France in Northeast America 1600-1763. 2008. (Fortress Ser.). (ENG., Illus.). 64p. pap. 18.95 *(978-1-84603-255-4(5))* Osprey Publishing, Ltd. GBR. Dist: Random Hse., Inc.
Colby, Charles W. The Fighting Governor. 2007. (ENG.). 96p. per. *(978-1-4068-4666-9(X))* Echo Library.
Colby, Charles Willia. Fighting Governor A Chronicle of Fronten. 2007. pap. *(978-1-4065-1349-3(0))* Dodo Pr.
—Founder of New France A Chronicle of Cha. 2007. pap. *(978-1-4065-1350-9(4))* Dodo Pr.
Colby, Charles William. Canadian Types of the Old Regime, 1608-1698. 366p. reprint ed. 98.00 *(978-0-7222-6882-7(3))* Library Reprints, Inc.
—The Fighting Governor: A Chronicle of Frontenac. (Chronicles of Canada Ser.). 167p. reprint ed. 88.00 *(978-0-7222-6706-6(1))*; 88.00 *(978-0-7222-6763-9(0))* Library Reprints, Inc.
—The Founder of New France: A Chronicle of Champlain. (Chronicles of Canada Ser.). 158p. reprint ed. 88.00 *(978-0-7222-6764-6(9))*; 88.00 *(978-0-7222-6432-4(1))* Library Reprints, Inc.
Dionne, Narcisse-Eutrope. Champlain. 2009. 315p. 36.99 *(978-1-115-24085-7(4))*; 32.99 *(978-1-115-24084-0(6))*; pap. 30.75 *(978-1-115-24082-6(X))* BiblioBazaar.
—Champlain. 2009. 198p. pap. *(978-0-217-45641-8(3))* Books LLC.
—Champlain. 299p. reprint ed. 98.00 *(978-0-7222-6901-5(3))*; 98.00 *(978-0-7222-6433-1(X))* Library Reprints, Inc.
Dix, Edwin Asa. Champlain the Founder of New France. 2009. 272p. 34.99 *(978-1-113-64779-5(5))*; 30.99 *(978-1-113-64777-1(9))*; pap. 26.75 *(978-1-113-64774-0(4))*; pap. 27.75 *(978-1-113-64776-4(0))* BiblioBazaar.
—Champlain the Founder of New France. 2007. (ENG.). 268p. 42.95 *(978-0-548-02176-7(7))* Kessinger Publishing, LLC.
Douglas-Hamilton, James. New England & New France: Contrasts & Parallels in Colonial History. 560p. reprint ed. 98.00 *(978-0-7222-6668-7(5))* Library Reprints, Inc.
—Old France in the New World: Quebec in the Seventeenth Century. 597p. reprint ed. 98.00 *(978-0-7222-6799-8(1))* Library Reprints, Inc.
Finley, John. The French in the Heart of America. 2008. 348p. 29.99 *(978-0-554-22363-6(5))* 2007. (ENG.). 320p. pap. 23.99 *(978-1-4264-2157-0(5))* 2007. (ENG.). 414p. pap. 28.99 *(978-1-4264-2225-6(3))* BiblioBazaar.
—The French in the Heart of America. 2007. (ENG.). 296p. per. *(978-1-4065-3149-7(9))* Dodo Pr.
Finley, John Huston. The French in the Heart of America. 431p. reprint ed. 98.00 *(978-0-7222-6800-1(9))* Library Reprints, Inc.
Fischer, David Hackett. Champlain's Dream. 2009. (ENG., Illus.). 848p. pap. 18.99 *(978-1-4165-9333-1(0))* Simon & Schuster.
Fiske, John. New France & New England. 2008. (Illus.). 428p. reprint ed. pap. 33.00 *(978-0-7884-0650-8(7), F374)* Heritage Bks.
—New France & New England. 2007. (ENG.). 424p. 51.95 *(978-0-548-06451-1(2))* Kessinger Publishing, LLC.
—New France & New England. 378p. reprint ed. 98.00 *(978-0-7222-6674-8(X))* Library Reprints, Inc.
Gordon, Alan. The Hero & the Historians: Historiography & the Uses of Jacques Cartier. 2010. (ENG., Illus.). 248p. (C). pap. 32.95 *(978-0-7748-1742-4(9))* UBC Pr. CAN. Dist: Univ. of Washington Pr.
Harrisse, Henry. Notes Pour Servir a L'histoire, a la Bibliographie et a la Cartographie De la Nouvelle-France et Des pays adjacents, 1545-1700. (French-Canadian Civilization Ser.). (FRE.). reprint ed. lib. bdg. 50.00 *(978-0-697-00006-4(0))* Irvington Pubs.
Kirke, Henry. The First English Conquest of Canada: With Some Account of the Earliestsettlements in Nova Scotia & Newfoundland. 227p. reprint ed. 98.00 *(978-0-7222-6810-0(6))* Library Reprints, Inc.
Lahontan, Louis Armand de Lom d'Arce. New Voyages to North-America, by the Baron De Lahontan. reprint ed. 250.00 *(978-0-7222-6734-9(7))* Library Reprints, Inc.
Larson, Denise. Companions of Champlain: Founding Families of Quebec, 1608-1635. 2008. pap. 22.95 *(978-0-8063-5367-8(8))* Clearfield Co.
Le Clercq, Chretien. First Establishment of the Faith in New France, 2 vols., Set. reprint ed. 87.50 *(978-0-404-03914-1(6))* AMS Pr., Inc.
—First Establishment of the Faith in New France. 2010. 130p. pap. 21.98 *(978-1-152-46061-4(7))* General Bks. LLC.
Le Sueur, William D. Count Frontenac. (ENG.). 2007. 398p. 49.95 *(978-0-548-14893-8(7))* 2006. pap. 34.95 *(978-1-4304-4183-0(6))* Kessinger Publishing, LLC.
Le Sueur, William Dawson. Count Frontenac. 2009. 392p. 33.99 *(978-1-116-83644-8(0))*; 38.99 *(978-1-116-83643-1(2))*; pap. 33.75 *(978-1-116-83645-5(9))*; pap. 32.75 *(978-1-116-83646-2(7))* BiblioBazaar.
—Count Frontenac. (Makers of Canada Ser.). 382p. reprint ed. 98.00 *(978-0-7222-6904-6(8))* Library Reprints, Inc.
Leblond de Brumath, A. Bishop Laval. 2007. 172p. per. *(978-1-4065-3648-5(2))* Dodo Pr.
Leblond de Brumath, Adrien. Bishop Laval. (Makers of Canada Ser.). 284p. reprint ed. 98.00 *(978-0-7222-6713-4(4))*; 98.00 *(978-0-7222-6906-0(4))* Library Reprints, Inc.
Lutie, Nancy Oestreich & Jung, Patrick J. The Nicolet Corrigenda: New France Revisited. 2009. (Illus.). 168p. (C). pap. 16.50 *(978-1-57766-606-6(2))* Waveland Pr., Inc.
Munro, William Bennet. Crusaders of New France. 2006. 244p. per. *(978-1-4067-3365-5(2)*, Hesperides Pr.) Read Bks.
Munro, William Bennett. Crusaders of New France: A Chronicle of the Fleur-de-Lis- in the Wilderness. (Chronicles of America Ser.). 237p. reprint ed. 98.00 *(978-0-7222-6821-6(1))* Library Reprints, Inc.
—Crusaders of New France: A Chronicle of the Fleur-de-Lis in the Wilderness. (Chronicles of America Ser.). 237p. reprint ed. 98.00 *(978-0-7222-7119-3(0))* Library Reprints, Inc.
Nicholls, Andrew. A Fleeting Empire: Early Stuart Britain & the Merchant Adventurers to Canada. 2010. (ENG., Illus.). 256p. (C). *(978-0-7735-3778-1(3))* McGill-Queen's Univ. Pr.
Parkman, Francis. Count Frontenac & New France under Louis XIV. 2011. 560p. pap. 42.75 ***(978-1-172-79146-0(5))*** 2011. 492p. pap. 38.75 ***(978-1-241-54892-6(7)***, British Library, Historical Print Editions) 2010. (ENG.). 490p. pap. 38.75 *(978-1-171-69777-0(5))* 2010. 562p. pap. 42.75 *(978-1-177-14845-0(5))* 2010. (ENG.). 500p. pap. 38.75 *(978-1-177-42247-5(6))* 2010. 488p. pap. 38.75 *(978-1-178-09791-7(9))* 2010. (France & England in North America Ser.: Pt. 5). 486p. pap. 38.75 *(978-1-145-89321-4(X))* 2010. (France & England in North America Ser.: Pt. 5). 488p. pap. 38.75 *(978-1-144-89171-6(X))* 2007. (France & England in North America Ser.: Pt. 5). 144p. pap. 19.99 *(978-1-4264-5336-6(1))* 2010. (France & England in North America Ser.: Pt. 5). 486p. reprint ed. pap. 38.75 *(978-1-146-20011-0(0))* 2010. (France & England in North America Ser.: Pt. 5). 546p. reprint ed. pap. 41.75 *(978-1-146-08437-6(4))* 2010. (France & England in North America Ser.: Pt. 5). 458p. reprint ed. pap. 36.75 *(978-1-142-47642-7(1))* 2009. (France & England in North America Ser.: Pt. 5). 540p. reprint ed. 43.99 *(978-1-117-38039-1(4))* 2009. (France & England in North America Ser.: Pt. 5). 482p. reprint ed. 42.99 *(978-1-117-35664-8(7))* 2009. (France & England in North America Ser.: Pt. 5). 480p. reprint ed. pap. 36.75 *(978-1-117-35665-5(5))* 2009. (France & England in North America Ser.: Pt. 5). 540p. reprint ed. pap. 39.75 *(978-1-117-38040-7(8))* 2009. (France & England in North America Ser.: Pt. 5). 540p. reprint ed. pap. 30.99 *(978-1-117-38041-4(6)*, BiblioLife) 2009. (France & England in North America Ser.: Pt. 5). 480p. reprint ed. pap. 28.99 *(978-1-117-35666-2(3)*, BiblioLife) 2007. (France & England in North America Ser.: Pt. 5). 328p. reprint ed. pap. 23.99 *(978-1-4264-5035-8(4))* BiblioBazaar.
—Count Frontenac & New France under Louis XIV. 2009. (France & England in North America: Pt. 5). reprint ed. 284p. pap. *(978-0-217-92569-3(3))*; 284p. pap. *(978-0-217-70135-8(3))*; 266p. pap. *(978-0-217-70138-9(8))* Books LLC.
—Count Frontenac & New France under Louis XIV. 2007. (France & England in North America Ser.: Pt. 5). 304p. per. *(978-1-4065-4078-9(1))* Dodo Pr.
—Count Frontenac & New France under Louis XIV. 2010. 214p. pap. 29.69 *(978-1-153-59777-7(2))*; (France & England in North America Ser.: Pt. 5). 254p. reprint ed. pap. 29.69 *(978-1-152-00836-6(6))*; (France & England in North America Ser.: Pt. 5). 114p. reprint ed. pap. 17.85 *(978-1-153-33514-0(X))*; (France & England in North America Ser.: Pt. 5). 148p. reprint ed. pap. 29.69 *(978-1-153-33516-4(6))* General Bks. LLC.
—Count Frontenac & New France under Louis XIV. 2011. 480p. 53.95 ***(978-1-169-84329-5(8))*** 2010. 480p. 43.16 *(978-1-163-33641-0(6))* 2010. 480p. pap. 31.16 *(978-1-162-71901-6(X))* 2007. (France & England in North America Ser.: Pt. 5). 556p. 57.95 *(978-0-548-10297-8(X))* 2007. (France & England in North America Ser.: Pt. 5). 478p. reprint ed. 53.95 *(978-0-548-02473-7(1))* Kessinger Publishing, LLC.
—Count Frontenac & New France under Louis XIV, 2 vol., set. (France & England in North America Ser.: Pt. 5). reprint ed. 250.00 *(978-0-7222-6571-0(9))*; 463p. 98.00 *(978-0-7222-6708-0(8))* Library Reprints, Inc.
—Count Frontenac & New France under Louis XIV. 2006. (France & England in North America Ser.: Pt. 5). 484p. reprint ed. pap. 29.99 *(978-1-4255-5433-0(4))* MPublishing.
—Count Frontenac & New France under Louis XIV (Webster's French Thesaurus Edition) 2008. (France & England in North America Ser.). (FRE.). 382p. pap. 28.95 *(978-0-497-96610-2(7))* Icon Group International, Inc.
—Count Frontenac & New France under Louis XIV (Webster's Spanish Thesaurus Edition) 2008. (France & England in North America Ser.: Pt. 5). (SPA.). 393p. pap. 28.95 *(978-0-497-99855-4(6))* Icon Group International, Inc.
—France & England in North America. 2008. 348p. 29.99 *(978-0-554-23172-3(7))* BiblioBazaar.
—France & England in North America. 2009. 284p. pap. *(978-0-217-21577-0(7))*; 344p. pap. *(978-0-217-72075-5(7))* Books LLC.
—France & England in North America: A Series of Historical Narratives - Part 3. Lt. ed. 2007. (ENG.). 302p. pap. 23.99 *(978-1-4264-3827-1(3))* BiblioBazaar.
—France & England in North America: Pioneers of France in the New World, the Jesuits in North America in the Seventeenth Century, la Salle & the Discovery of the Great West, the Old Régime in Canada, 9 vol., set. (American Classics Ser.). reprint ed. 1125.00 *(978-0-7222-6822-3(X))* Library Reprints, Inc.
—France & England in North America Pt. 3: A Series of Historical Narratives. Lt. ed. 2006. 346p. pap. 23.99 *(978-1-4264-3895-0(8))* BiblioBazaar.
—Frontenac: Works, 16 vol.,set. reprint ed. 2000.00 *(978-0-7222-6562-8(X))* Library Reprints, Inc.
—A Half-Century of Conflict. 2011. 446p. pap. 36.75 ***(978-1-176-00709-3(2))*** 2010. (ENG.). 420p. pap. 34.75 *(978-1-171-71555-9(2))* 2010. (ENG.). 352p. pap. 32.75 *(978-1-176-64618-6(4))* 2010. (ENG.). 450p. pap. 36.75 *(978-1-177-31036-9(8))* 2010. (ENG.). 392p. pap. 33.75 *(978-1-177-48864-8(7))* 2010. 450p. pap. 36.75 *(978-1-178-17008-5(X))* 2010. 398p. pap. 33.75 *(978-1-177-94357-4(3))* 2010. 352p. pap. 32.75 *(978-1-147-00609-4(1))* 2010. (France & England in North America Ser.: Pt. 6). 452p. pap. 36.75 *(978-1-146-63852-4(3))* 2010. 396p. pap. 33.75 *(978-1-145-38091-2(3))* 2010. (France & England in North America Ser.: Pt. 6). 438p. pap. 35.75 *(978-1-145-97150-9(4))* 2009. (France & England in North America Ser.: Pt. 6). 416p. 34.99 *(978-1-116-53437-5(1))* 2009. (France & England in North America Ser.: Pt. 6). 416p. pap. 34.75 *(978-1-116-53438-2(X))* 2009. (France & England in North America Ser.: Pt. 6). 450p. 41.99 *(978-1-115-82008-0(7))* 2009. (France & England in North America Ser.: Pt. 6). 415p. pap. 28.99 *(978-1-116-53440-5(1)*, BiblioLife)

C

2009. (France & England in North America Ser.: Pt. 6). 415p. pap. 26.99 *(978-1-116-53441-2(X)*, BiblioLife) 2009. (France & England in North America Ser.: Pt. 6). 449p. pap. 26.99 *(978-1-115-82013-4(3)*, BiblioLife) 2009. (France & England in North America Ser.: Pt. 6). 416p. 27.99 *(978-1-103-00828-5(5))* 2008. (France & England in North America Ser.: Pt. 6). 436p. 30.99 *(978-0-559-31362-2(4))* 2008. (France & England in North America Ser.: Pt. 6). 196p. 22.99 *(978-0-554-31646-8(3))* 2008. (France & England in North America Ser.: Pt. 6). 196p. 25.99 *(978-0-554-22343-8(0))* BiblioBazaar.

—A Half-Century of Conflict. 2009. (France & England in North America: Pt. 6). 292p. pap. *(978-0-217-76716-3(8))*; 164p. pap. *(978-0-217-33564-5(0))* Books LLC.

—A Half-Century of Conflict. 2010. (France & England in North America Ser.: Pt. 6). 166p. pap. 15.85 *(978-1-154-07386-7(6))* 2010. (France & England in North America Ser.: Pt. 6). 264p. pap. 15.85 *(978-1-154-08030-8(7))* 2010. (France & England in North America Ser.: Pt. 6). 166p. pap. 19.40 *(978-1-154-02672-6(8))* 2010. (France & England in North America Ser.: Pt. 6). 224p. pap. 23.82 *(978-1-152-47423-9(5))* 2010. (France & England in North America Ser.: Pt. 6). 164p. pap. 23.82 *(978-1-152-47417-8(0))* 2010. (France & England in North America Ser.: Pt. 6). 154p. pap. 15.85 *(978-1-152-47497-0(9))* 2009. 198p. pap. 15.85 *(978-1-151-01663-8(2))* 2009. (France & England in North America Ser.: Pt. 6). 264p. pap. 15.37 *(978-1-151-08467-5(0))* General Bks. LLC.

—A Half-Century of Conflict. 2006. (France & England in North America Ser.: Pt. 6). 420p. per. 26.99 *(978-1-4255-4593-2(9))* MPublishing.

—A Half Century of Conflict. 2010. 234p. 33.56 *(978-1-169-29688-6(2))*; pap. 21.56 *(978-1-162-64868-2(6))*; 41.95 *(978-1-161-41733-3(8))* Kessinger Publishing, LLC.

—A Half-Century of Conflict. 2011. 352p. pap. 32.75 ***(978-1-179-87095-3(6))***; 350p. pap. 32.75 ***(978-1-179-87139-4(1))***; 422p. pap. 34.75 ***(978-1-179-13455-0(9))*** BiblioBazaar.

—A Half Century of Conflict. 2011. 356p. pap. 32.75 ***(978-1-179-29367-7(3))*** BiblioBazaar.

—A Half-Century of Conflict. (France & England in North America Ser.: Pt. 6). 2010. 354p. reprint ed. pap. 32.75 *(978-1-142-38943-7(X))* 2009. 416p. reprint ed. pap. 33.75 *(978-1-116-53439-9(8))* 2009. 450p. reprint ed. 34.99 *(978-1-115-82009-7(5))* 2009. 450p. reprint ed. pap. 35.75 *(978-1-115-82011-0(7))* 2009. 449p. reprint ed. pap. 28.99 *(978-1-115-82012-7(5)*, BiblioLife) 2009. 416p. reprint ed. pap. 21.99 *(978-1-103-00825-4(0))* 2008. 436p. reprint ed. pap. 34.75 *(978-0-559-31361-5(6))* Vol. 1. 2010. 392p. pap. 33.75 *(978-1-144-82332-8(3))* Vol. 1. 2010. 386p. pap. 33.75 *(978-1-144-93811-4(2))* Vol. 2. 2006. 204p. pap. 20.99 *(978-1-4264-2135-8(4))* Vol. 2. 2007. 194p. pap. 21.99 *(978-1-4264-2203-4(2))* Vol. 2. 2010. 406p. reprint ed. pap. 34.75 *(978-1-145-53406-3(6))* BiblioBazaar.

—A Half-Century of Conflict. 2010. (France & England in North America: Pt. 6). 166p. reprint ed. pap. *(978-1-152-92858-9(9))* Books LLC.

—A Half-Century of Conflict. 2009. (France & England in North America Ser.: Pt. 6). 458p. reprint ed. pap. *(978-1-4099-4826-1(9))* Dodo Pr.

—A Half-Century of Conflict. 2010. (France & England in North America Ser.: Pt. 6). reprint ed. (Illus.). 130p. pap. 21.98 *(978-1-153-58329-9(1))*; 226p. pap. 15.85 *(978-1-152-47516-8(9))*; 226p. pap. 30.89 *(978-1-152-47512-0(6))* General Bks. LLC.

—A Half-Century of Conflict. 2010. (France & England in North America Ser.: Pt. 6). 152p. reprint ed. pap. *(978-1-4076-4168-3(9))* HardPr.

—A Half-Century of Conflict. 2007. (France & England in North America Ser.: Pt. 6). 416p. reprint ed. per. 34.95 *(978-1-4326-3838-2(6))*; Vol. 1. 392p. 48.95 *(978-0-548-10302-9(X))*; Vol. 1. 412p. reprint ed. 49.95 *(978-0-548-23724-3(7))*; Vol. 2. 444p. 51.95 *(978-0-548-10301-2(1))* Kessinger Publishing, LLC.

—The Jesuits in North America in the Seventeenth Century. 2010. (France & England in North America Ser.: Pt. 2). reprint ed. 568p. pap. 43.75 *(978-1-142-56467-4(3))*; 562p. pap. 42.75 *(978-1-142-65726-0(4))*; 568p. pap. 43.75 *(978-1-142-06548-5(0))* BiblioBazaar.

—The Jesuits in North America in the Seventeenth Century. 2008. (France & England in North America Ser.: Pt. 2). 292p. reprint ed. pap. *(978-1-4068-6537-0(0))* Echo Library.

—The Jesuits in North America in the Seventeenth Century. 2007. (France & England in North America Ser.: Pt. 2). 624p. reprint ed. 60.95 *(978-0-548-10299-2(6))* Kessinger Publishing, LLC.

—The Jesuits in North America in the Seventeenth Century. 2006. (France & England in North America Ser.: Pt. 2). 560p. reprint ed. per. 32.99 *(978-1-4255-6179-6(9))* MPublishing.

—The Jesuits in North America in the Seventeenth Century. 2008. (France & England in North America Ser.: Pt. 2). 312p. reprint ed. pap. *(978-1-4437-0065-8(7))* Read Bks.

—Montcalm & Wolfe. (France & England in North America Ser.: Pt. 7). 2010. 558p. pap. 42.75 *(978-1-146-62565-4(0))* 2010. 552p. pap. 41.75 *(978-1-146-60903-6(5))* 2010. 532p. pap. 40.75 *(978-1-144-75698-5(7))* 2010. 532p. pap. 40.75 *(978-1-144-75212-3(4))* 2010. 582p. pap. 43.75 *(978-1-145-20529-1(1))* 2010. 572p. pap. 43.75 *(978-1-144-13210-9(X))* 2010. 562p. pap. 42.75 *(978-1-142-78154-5(2))* 2009. 390p. pap. 25.99 *(978-1-117-79136-4(X*, BiblioLife) 2009. 586p. 33.99 *(978-1-113-83322-8(X))* 2009. 585p. pap. 30.99 *(978-1-113-83321-1(1)*, BiblioLife) 2008. 448p. pap. 35.75 *(978-0-559-36078-7(9))* Vol. 1. 2008. 572p. 33.99 *(978-0-559-48966-2(8))* Vol. 1. 2008. 572p. pap. 42.75 *(978-0-559-48963-1(3))* Vol. 2. 2009. 585p. pap. 30.99 *(978-1-113-83314-3(9)*, BiblioLife) BiblioBazaar.

—Montcalm & Wolfe. 2009. (France & England in North America: Pt. 7). 268p. pap. *(978-1-150-66377-2(4))* Books LLC.

—Montcalm & Wolfe. (France & England in North America Ser.: Pt. 7). 2010. (Illus.). 458p. pap. 52.34 *(978-1-153-64261-3(1))* 2010. 148p. pap. 52.34 *(978-1-153-04863-7(9))* 2010. 232p. pap. 31.36 *(978-1-153-04372-4(6))* 2010. 298p. pap. 22.72 *(978-1-153-04373-1(4))* 2010. 164p. pap. 19.22 *(978-1-153-04861-3(2))* 2010. 292p. pap. 19.22 *(978-1-152-47441-3(3))* 2010. 220p. pap. 52.34 *(978-1-153-04865-1(5))* 2010. 232p. pap. 52.34 *(978-1-152-47429-1(4))* 2009. 262p. pap. 52.34 *(978-1-150-08205-4(4))* 2009. 318p. pap. 52.34 *(978-1-150-27530-2(8))* General Bks. LLC.

—Montcalm & Wolfe, Vol. 1. 2008. (France & England in North America Ser.: Pt. 7). 566p. 58.95 *(978-1-4365-7243-9(6))* Kessinger Publishing, LLC.

—The Old Régime in Canada. 2010. 590p. pap. 44.75 *(978-1-145-38576-4(1))* 2009. (ENG.). 310p. pap. 28.75 *(978-1-117-46216-5(1)*, BiblioLife) 2009. 316p. 36.99 *(978-1-117-18715-0(2))* 2009. 316p. pap. 23.99 *(978-1-117-18717-4(9)*, BiblioLife) 2010. (France & England in North America Ser.: Pt. 4). 598p. reprint ed. pap. 44.75 *(978-1-144-78111-6(6))* 2010. (France & England in North America Ser.: Pt. 4). 468p. reprint ed. pap. 37.75 *(978-1-146-21016-4(7))* 2010. (France & England in North America Ser.: Pt. 4). 464p. reprint ed. pap. 36.75 *(978-1-144-65641-4(9))* 2010. (France & England in North America Ser.: Pt. 4). 320p. reprint ed. pap. 30.75 *(978-1-143-00779-8(4))* 2010. (France & England in North America Ser.: Pt. 4). 480p. reprint ed. pap. 37.75 *(978-1-142-00049-3(4))* 2009. (France & England in North America Ser.: Pt. 4). 310p. reprint ed. 36.99 *(978-1-117-46215-8(3))* 2009. (France & England in North America Ser.: Pt. 4). 310p. reprint ed. pap. 23.99 *(978-1-117-46217-2(X)*, BiblioLife) 2009. (France & England in North America Ser.: Pt. 4). 318p. reprint ed. pap. 29.75 *(978-1-117-18716-7(0))* 2010. (France & England in North America Ser.: Pt. 4). 536p. pap. 40.75 *(978-1-146-48576-0(X))* BiblioBazaar.

—The Old Régime in Canada. 2009. 272p. pap. *(978-1-150-18893-0(6))* 2009. (France & England in North America: Pt. 4). 330p. pap. *(978-1-4589-3123-8(4))* 2010. (France & England in North America). 154p. reprint ed. pap. *(978-1-153-06758-4(7))* 2010. (France & England in North America: Pt. 4). 120p. reprint ed. pap. *(978-1-151-76395-2(0))* Books LLC.

—The Old Régime in Canada. 2010. (Illus.). 120p. pap. 19.90 *(978-1-154-39756-7(4))* 2009. (France & England in North America Ser.: Pt. 4). 232p. reprint ed. pap. 20.40 *(978-1-151-20106-5(5))* 2009. (France & England in North America Ser.: Pt. 4). 136p. reprint ed. pap. 15.37 *(978-1-151-10504-2(X))* General Bks. LLC.

—The Old Régime in Canada. (France & England in North America Ser.: Vol. 4). 2010. 600p. 47.96 *(978-1-163-41063-9(2))* 2007. 600p. 59.95 *(978-0-548-10295-4(3))* 2007. 528p. reprint ed. 55.95 *(978-0-548-00761-7(6))* Kessinger Publishing, LLC.

—The Old Régime in Canada. 2010. (France & England in North America Ser.: Pt. 4). 448p. reprint ed. 98.00 *(978-0-7222-6570-3(0))* Library Reprints, Inc.

—The Old Régime in Canada. 2006. (France & England in North America Ser.: Pt. 4). 468p. reprint ed. pap. 29.99 *(978-1-4255-5175-9(0))* MPublishing.

—Pioneers of France in the New World. (France & England in North America Ser.: Pt. 1). 2010. 520p. pap. 39.75 *(978-1-146-36349-5(4))* 2010. 512p. reprint ed. pap. 39.75 *(978-1-146-70038-2(5))* 2010. 516p. reprint ed. pap. 39.75 *(978-1-145-39682-1(8))* 2010. 518p. reprint ed. pap. 39.75 *(978-1-143-10500-5(1))* 2010. 516p. reprint ed. pap. 39.75 *(978-1-142-64233-4(X))* 2010. 508p. reprint ed. pap. 39.75 *(978-1-142-79714-0(7))* 2010. 472p. reprint ed. pap. 37.75 *(978-1-142-39877-4(3))* 2010. 470p. reprint ed. pap. 37.75 *(978-1-142-25680-7(4))* 2010. 532p. reprint ed. pap. 40.75 *(978-1-141-97657-7(9))* 2010. 466p. reprint ed. pap. 37.75 *(978-1-142-42483-1(9))* 2009. 504p. reprint ed. pap. 43.99 *(978-1-115-61653-9(6))* 2009. 504p. reprint ed. pap. 38.75 *(978-1-115-61654-6(4))* 2009. 502p. reprint ed. pap. 30.99 *(978-1-115-61655-3(2)*, BiblioLife) 2009. 502p. reprint ed. pap. 30.99 *(978-1-116-49361-0(6)*, BiblioLife) 2009. 502p. reprint ed. pap. 31.99 *(978-1-116-49360-3(8)*, BiblioLife) BiblioBazaar.

—Pioneers of France in the New World. 2010. (France & England in North America: Pt. 1). 240p. reprint ed. pap. *(978-1-151-78292-2(0))* Books LLC.

—Pioneers of France in the New World. 2008. (France & England in North America Ser.: Pt. 1). 200p. reprint ed. pap. *(978-1-4068-6539-4(7))* Echo Library.

—Pioneers of France in the New World. (France & England in North America Ser.: Pt. 1). reprint ed. 2010. (Illus.). 176p. pap. 26.16 *(978-1-153-67771-4(7))* 2010. 158p. pap. 26.16 *(978-1-153-08880-0(0))* 2010. 116p. pap. 26.16 *(978-1-153-08877-0(0))* 2009. 254p. pap. 33.49 *(978-1-151-09344-8(0))* General Bks. LLC.

—Pioneers of France in the New World. (France & England in North America Ser.: Pt. 1). reprint ed. 2009. 460p. pap. 37.95 *(978-1-120-33674-3(0))* 2007. 536p. 57.95 *(978-0-548-10298-5(8))* Kessinger Publishing, LLC.

—Pioneers of France in the New World (Webster's French Thesaurus Edition) 2008. (France & England in North America Ser.: Pt. 1). 349p. pap. 28.95 *(978-0-497-96611-9(5))* Icon Group International, Inc.

—Pioneers of France in the New World (Webster's Korean Thesaurus Edition) 2008. (France & England in North America Ser.: Pt. 1). (KOR & ENG.). 351p. pap. 28.95 *(978-0-546-54072-7(4))* Icon Group International, Inc.

—Pioneers of France in the New World (Webster's Spanish Thesaurus Edition) 2008. (France & England in North America Ser.: Pt. 1). (SPA & ENG.). 354p. pap. 28.95 *(978-0-497-99856-1(4))* Icon Group International, Inc.

—The Struggle for a Continent. 2009. 316p. pap. 24.02 *(978-1-150-52316-8(6))* General Bks. LLC.

—The Struggle for a Continent. Edgar, Pelham, ed. 2009. 584p. 58.95 *(978-1-104-45549-1(8))*; pap. 43.95 *(978-1-104-40116-0(9))* Kessinger Publishing, LLC.

—The Struggle for a Continent. 542p. reprint ed. 98.00 *(978-0-7222-6564-2(6))* Library Reprints, Inc.

—Works, 20 vols. (Illus.). reprint ed. 1395.00 *(978-0-404-04920-1(6))* AMS Pr., Inc.

Peyser, Joseph L. & Brandão, José António, eds. Edge of Empire: Documents of Michilimackinac, 1671 1716. Peyser, Joseph L., tr. from FRE. 2008. (ENG., Illus.). 192p. 39.95 *(978-0-87013-820-1(0))* Michigan State Univ. Pr.

Poussin, Guillaume Tell. The United States; Its Power & Progress by Guillaume Tell Poussin. 2006. 484p. per. 29.99 *(978-1-4255-5309-8(5))* MPublishing.

Pritchard, James. Anatomy of a Naval Disaster: The 1746 French Expedition to North America. 2011. (ENG., Illus.). 352p. (C). pap. *(978-0-7735-3874-0(7))* McGill-Queen's Univ. Pr.

Salone, Emile. La Colonisation de la Nouvelle-France: Etude sur les Origines de la Nation Canadienne-Francaise. 3rd ed. (French-Canadian Civilization Ser.). reprint ed. lib. bdg. 47.00 *(978-0-697-00056-9(7))* Irvington Pubs.

Slafter, Edmund F., ed. Sir William Alexander & American Colonization: Including Three Royal Charters. 2007. (ENG.). 290p. 43.95 *(978-0-548-21515-9(4))*; 292p. per. 28.95 *(978-1-4325-3488-2(2))* Kessinger Publishing, LLC.

Slafter, Edmund Farwell. Sir William Alexander & American Colonization. 2009. 300p. 24.99 *(978-1-103-52040-4(7))*; pap. 18.99 *(978-1-103-52036-7(9))* BiblioBazaar.

—Sir William Alexander & American Colonization. 2009. 182p. pap. 19.99 *(978-0-217-79134-2(4))* General Bks. LLC.

Slafter, Edmund Farwell, et al. Sir William Alexander & American Colonization: Including Three Royal Charters; a Tract on Colonization; a Patent of the County of Canada & of Lo. 2010. 314p. pap. 29.75 *(978-1-146-57596-6(3))* BiblioBazaar.

Thorner, Thomas & Frohn-Nielson, Thor, eds. A Few Acres of Snow: Documents in Pre-Confederation Canadian History. 3rd ed. 2009. 260p. pap. *(978-1-4426-0029-4(2))* Univ. of Toronto Pr.

Warburton, George. The Conquest of Canada by the Author of Hochelaga. 2006. (ENG.). 376p. per. 26.99 *(978-1-4255-3934-4(3))*; 360p. per. 26.99 *(978-1-4255-3686-2(7))* MPublishing.

Watts, Edward. In This Remote Country: French Colonial Culture in the Anglo-American Imagination, 1780-1860. annot. ed. 2006. (ENG.). 288p. per. 22.00 *(978-0-8078-5762-5(9))* Univ. of North Carolina Pr.

William Bennett Munro. Crusaders of New France Volume 4: A Chronicle of the Fleur-de-Lis in the Wilderness. 2007. (ENG.). 130p. pap. 18.99 *(978-1-4346-3896-0(0))*; 142p. pap. 19.99 *(978-1-4346-3897-7(9))* BiblioBazaar.

Wrong, George M. The Conquest of New France. (ENG.). 254p. 2010. pap. 26.75 *(978-1-171-05122-0(0))* 2009. 34.99 *(978-1-117-58919-0(6))* 2009. pap. 25.75 *(978-1-117-58920-6(X))* 2009. pap. 21.99 *(978-1-117-58921-3(8)*, BiblioLife) BiblioBazaar.

—The Conquest of New France: A Chronicle of the Colonial Wars. 2008. 120p. pap. *(978-1-4099-1026-8(1))* Dodo Pr.

Wrong, George McKinnon. The Conquest of New France. (Chronicles of America Ser.). 246p. reprint ed. 98.00 *(978-0-7222-6839-1(4))*; 98.00 *(978-0-7222-7144-5(1))* Library Reprints, Inc.

CANADA—HISTORY—1763-1791

Brumwell, Stephen. Paths of Glory: The Life & Death of General James Wolfe. 2006. (ENG., Illus.). 430p. (C). *(978-0-7735-3261-8(7))* McGill-Queen's Univ. Pr.

Buckner, Phillip, ed. Canada & the British Empire. (Illus.). 2010. (ENG.). 312p. pap. 37.95 *(978-0-19-956374-6(8))* 2008. 320p. 75.00 *(978-0-19-927164-1(X))* Oxford Univ. Pr., Inc.

Bumsted, J. M. The Peoples of Canada: A Pre-Confederation History. 2nd enl. ed. 2009. (Illus.). 624p. (Orig.). pap. 65.00 *(978-0-19-543101-8(4))* Oxford Univ. Pr., Inc.

Burt, Alfred Leroy. Old Province of Quebec. 2009. (ENG.). 569p. pap. 60.00 *(978-0-8166-6042-1(5))* Univ. of Minnesota Pr.

Christie, Nancy, ed. Transatlantic Subjects: Ideas, Institutions, & Social Experience in Post-Revolutionary British North America. 2008. (ENG., Illus.). 496p. (C). *(978-0-7735-3334-9(6))* McGill-Queen's Univ. Pr.

John Wolfe, Lydekker. The Faithful Mohawks. 2010. (Cambridge Library Collection - History Ser.). (Illus.). 264p. pap. 23.99 *(978-1-108-01068-9(7))* Cambridge Univ. Pr.

Lanctot, Gustave. Canada & the American Revolution, 1774-1783. 2008. 356p. pap. 35.00 *(978-1-59740-412-9(8))* ACLS Humanities E-Book.

Lucas, Charles Prestwood. A History of Canada, 1763-1812. 2010. 238p. pap. *(978-1-152-95101-3(7))* Books LLC.

—A History of Canada, 1763-1812. 360p. reprint ed. 98.00 *(978-0-7222-6813-1(0))* Library Reprints, Inc.

Skelton, Oscar Douglas. The Canadian Dominion: A Chronicle of Our Northern Neighbor. 2007. (ENG.). 156p. pap. 19.99 *(978-1-4346-2607-3(5))* BiblioBazaar.

Stone, Edwin Martin. The Invasion of Canada In 1775. 2007. (Illus.). 144p. reprint ed. pap. 29.95 *(978-1-60105-137-0(9)*, 6D7M) Scholar's Bookshelf.

Watt, Gavin K. A Dirty, Trifling Piece of Business Vol. 1: The Revolutionary War as Waged from Canada in 1781. 2009. (ENG., Illus.). 504p. pap. 35.00 *(978-1-55488-420-9(9))* Dundurn CAN. Dist: Ingram Pub. Services.

—I Am Heartily Ashamed Vol. 2: The Revolutionary War's Final Campaign As Waged from Canada in 1782. 2010. (ENG., Illus.). 464p. pap. 30.00 *(978-1-55488-715-6(1))* Dundurn CAN. Dist: Ingram Pub. Services.

Wood, William. The Father of British Canada: A Chronicle of Carleton. 2007. (ENG.). 126p. pap. 18.99 *(978-1-4346-4421-3(9))*; 138p. pap. 19.99 *(978-1-4346-4422-0(7))* BiblioBazaar.

CANADA—HISTORY—1763-1867

Christie, Nancy, ed. Transatlantic Subjects: Ideas, Institutions, & Social Experience in Post-Revolutionary British North America. 2008. (ENG., Illus.). 496p. (C). pap. *(978-0-7735-3388-2(5))* McGill-Queen's Univ. Pr.

Feltoe, Richard. The Flames of War: The Fight for Upper Canada, July-December 1813. 2013. (Upper Canada Preserv Ser.: 3). (ENG., Illus.). 176p. pap. 19.99 ***(978-1-4597-0702-3(8))*** Dundurn CAN. Dist: Ingram Pub. Services.

—The Pendulum of War: The Fight for Upper Canada, January-August 1813. 2013. (Upper Canada Preserv Ser.: 2). (ENG., Illus.). 176p. pap. 19.99 ***(978-1-4597-0699-6(4))*** Dundurn CAN. Dist: Ingram Pub. Services.

Grant, John & Jones, Ray. The War of 1812: A Guide to Battlefields & Historic Sites. 2011. (ENG.). 192p. pap. 24.95 ***(978-1-59652-830-7(3))*** Turner Publishing Co.

Nursey, Walter R. The Story of Isaac Brock, Hero, Defender & Saviour of Upper Canada, 1812. 2012. 244p. pap. 26.75 ***(978-1-278-73707-2(3))*** 2010. (ENG.). 236p. pap. 26.75 *(978-1-177-53158-0(5))* 2008. 180p. 25.99 *(978-0-554-23852-4(7))* 2010. (ENG.). 252p. reprint ed. pap. 26.75 *(978-1-177-46423-9(3))* 2010. 244p. reprint ed. pap. 26.75 *(978-1-149-55700-6(1))* 2008. 180p. reprint ed. 22.99 *(978-0-554-33155-3(1))* BiblioBazaar.

—The Story of Isaac Brock, Hero, Defender & Saviour of Upper Canada, 1812. 2009. 112p. reprint ed. pap. *(978-1-150-63156-6(2))* Books LLC.

—The Story of Isaac Brock, Hero, Defender & Saviour of Upper Canada, 1812. 2010. (Illus.). 88p. pap. 7.75 *(978-1-77045-066-0(1))*; 90p. reprint ed. pap. 7.75 *(978-1-152-48510-5(5))* General Bks. LLC.

—The Story of Isaac Brock, Hero, Defender & Saviour of Upper Canada, 1812. 2010. 230p. pap. 21.56 *(978-1-163-97056-0(5))* 2010. 230p. 33.56 ***(978-1-164-28057-6(0))*** 2008. 228p. 41.95 *(978-0-548-97788-0(7))* 2007. (ENG.). 232p. reprint ed. per. 26.95 *(978-0-548-66989-1(9))* Kessinger Publishing, LLC.

Nursey, Walter R., creator. The Story of Isaac Brock, Hero, Defender & Saviour of Upper Canada, 1812. 2010. 252p. reprint ed. pap. 26.75 *(978-1-175-83227-6(8))* BiblioBazaar.

Richardson, John. War of 1812 First Series. 2010. 186p. pap. 22.75 ***(978-1-149-58918-2(3))*** BiblioBazaar.

Thorner, Thomas & Frohn-Nielson, Thor, eds. A Few Acres of Snow: Documents in Pre-Confederation Canadian History. 3rd ed. 2009. 260p. pap. *(978-1-4426-0029-4(2))* Univ. of Toronto Pr.

CANADA—HISTORY—1791-1841

Bamford, Don & Carroll, Paul. Four Years on the Great Lakes, 1813-1816: The Journal of Lieutenant David Wingfield, Royal Navy. 2009. (ENG., Illus.). 280p. pap. 28.99 *(978-1-55488-393-6(8))* Dundurn CAN. Dist: Ingram Pub. Services.

Blane, William. Excursion. 2007. (Travel in America Ser.). (ENG.). 528p. 49.95 *(978-1-4290-0098-7(8))* Applewood Bks.

—An Excursion: Through the United States & Canada During the Years, 1822-23. 2007. (Travel in America Ser.). (ENG.). 528p. per. 24.95 *(978-1-4290-0099-4(6))* Applewood Bks.

Buckner, Phillip, ed. Canada & the British Empire. (Illus.). 2010. (ENG.). 312p. pap. 37.95 *(978-0-19-956374-6(8))* 2008. 320p. 75.00 *(978-0-19-927164-1(X))* Oxford Univ. Pr., Inc.

Bumsted, J. M. The Peoples of Canada: A Pre-Confederation History. 2nd enl. ed. 2009. (Illus.). 624p. (Orig.). pap. 65.00 *(978-0-19-543101-8(4))* Oxford Univ. Pr., Inc.

Christie, Nancy, ed. Transatlantic Subjects: Ideas, Institutions, & Social Experience in Post-Revolutionary British North America. 2008. (ENG., Illus.). 496p. (C). *(978-0-7735-3334-9(6))* McGill-Queen's Univ. Pr.

Gurney, Joseph John. A Journey in North America, Described in Familiar Letters to Amelia Opie. 2007. (Travel in America Ser.). (ENG.). 172p. 49.95 *(978-1-4290-0220-2(4))*; per. 24.95 *(978-1-4290-0221-9(2))* Applewood Bks.

Malcomson, Robert. Lords of the Lake: The Naval War on Lake Ontario, 1812-1814. 2009. (Illus.). 430p. pap. 27.95 *(978-1-896941-24-0(9))* Brass, Robin Studio, Inc. CAN. Dist: Midpoint Trade Bks., Inc.

Martin, Ged. The Durham Report & British Policy: A Critical Essay. 2008. (Cambridge Commonwealth Ser.). (ENG.). 136p. pap. 33.99 *(978-0-521-08282-2(X))* Cambridge Univ. Pr.

Richardson, John. War of 1812 First Series. 2010. 144p. pap. 23.19 *(978-1-153-20262-6(X))* General Bks. LLC.

Turner, Wesley B. The Astonishing General: The Life & Legacy of Sir Isaac Brock. 2011. (ENG., Illus.). 376p. 35.00 *(978-1-55488-777-4(1)*, Dundurn Pr.) Dundurn CAN. Dist: Ingram Pub. Services.

CANADA—HISTORY—19TH CENTURY

see also Fenians

Boychuk, Gerard William. National Health Insurance in the United States & Canada: Race, Territory, & the Roots of Difference. 2008. (American

Governance & Public Policy Ser.). (ENG., Illus.). 256p. pap. 26.95 *(978-1-58901-206-6(2))* Georgetown Univ. Pr.
Chambers, William. Things as They Are in America. 2007. (Travel in America Ser.). (ENG.). 372p. 49.95 *(978-1-4290-0312-4(X))*; per. 24.95 *(978-1-4290-0313-1(8))* Applewood Bks.
Chartrand, René. Forts of the War of 1812. 2012. (Fortress Ser.). (ENG., Illus.). 64p. pap. 18.95 ***(978-1-84908-576-2(5))*** Osprey Publishing, Ltd. GBR. Dist: Random Hse., Inc.
Collins, Joseph Edmund. Canada's Patriot Statesman: The Life & Career of the Right Honourable Sir John A. Macdonald, Based on the Work of Edmund Collins. rev. ed. 613p. 128.00 *(978-0-7222-6944-2(7))* Library Reprints, Inc.
—Life & Times of the Right Honourable Sir John A. Macdonald: Premier of the Dominion of Canada. 642p. reprint ed. 128.00 *(978-0-7222-6946-6(3))* Library Reprints, Inc.
Errington, Elizabeth Jane. Emigrant Worlds & Transatlantic Communities: Migration to Upper Canada in the First Half of the Nineteenth Century. 2007. (McGill-Queen's Studies in Ethnic History Ser.). (ENG., Illus.). 256p. (C). *(978-0-7735-3265-6(X))*; per. *(978-0-7735-3266-3(8))* McGill-Queen's Univ. Pr.
Filewod, Alan. Committing Theatre: Theatre Radicalism & Political Intervention in Canada. 2011. 350p. pap. 29.95 ***(978-1-926662-76-3(8))*** Between the Lines CAN. Dist: Univ. of Toronto Pr.
Gwyn, Richard J. Nation Maker: Sir John A. MacDonald - His Life, Our Times, 2 vols. 2011. (ENG., Illus.). 688p. 37.00 *(978-0-307-35644-4(2)*, Random Hse CAN) Random Hse. of Canada, Ltd. CAN. Dist: Random Hse., Inc.
Henry, Natasha L. Emancipation Day: Celebrating Freedom in Canada. 2010. (ENG., Illus.). 288p. pap. 28.99 *(978-1-55488-717-0(8))* Dundurn CAN. Dist: Ingram Pub. Services.
Hopkins, John Castell. Progress of Canada in the Century. 2009. (Illus.). 276p. pap. 22.07 *(978-1-150-37177-6(3))* General Bks. LLC.
—Progress of Canada in the Century. (Nineteenth Century Ser.). 538p. reprint ed. 98.00 *(978-0-7222-6804-9(1))* Library Reprints, Inc.
Jenish, D'Arcy. Epic Wanderer: David Thompson & the Mapping of the Canadian West. 2009. (ENG., Illus.). 320p. pap. 18.95 *(978-0-8032-2452-0(4)*, Bison Bks.) Univ. of Nebraska Pr.
Parkin, George Robert. Sir John A. Macdonald. (Makers of Canada Ser.). 372p. reprint ed. 98.00 *(978-0-7222-6947-3(1))*; 98.00 *(978-0-7222-6911-4(0))* Library Reprints, Inc.
Podruchny, Carolyn. Making the Voyageur World: Travelers & Traders in the North American Fur Trade. 2006. (ENG., Illus.). 347p. pap. *(978-0-8020-9428-5(7))* Univ. of Toronto Pr.
Prince, Bryan. One More River to Cross. 2012. (ENG., Illus.). 192p. pap. 24.99 *(978-1-4597-0153-3(4))* Dundurn CAN. Dist: Ingram Pub. Services.
Raible, Chris. The Power of the Press: The Lasting Impressions Made by Canada's Early Printers. 2007. (ENG & GER., Illus.). 96p. pap. *(978-1-55028-982-4(9))* Lorimer, James & Co., Ltd., Pubs. CAN. Dist: Casemate Pubs. & Bk. Distributors, LLC.
Thomas, Peter & Tracy, Nicholas. Master & Madman: The Surprising Rise & Disastrous Fall of the Hon. Anthony Lockwood RN. 2012. (ANG & ENG., Illus.). 274p. 35.00 ***(978-0-86492-667-8(7))*** Goose Lane Editions CAN. Dist: Univ. of Toronto Pr.
Wagner, Jonathan. A History of Migration from Germany to Canada, 1850-1939. 2006. (ENG.). 352p. pap. *(978-0-7748-1216-0(8))* Univ. of British Columbia Pr.
Warkentin, John. So Vast & Various: Interpreting Canada's Regions in the Nineteenth & Twentieth Centuries. 2010. (Carleton Library Ser.). (ENG.). 520p. (C). *(978-0-7735-3719-4(8))*; pap. *(978-0-7735-3738-5(4))* McGill-Queen's Univ. Pr.

CANADA—HISTORY—WAR OF 1812

see United States—History—War of 1812

CANADA—HISTORY—REBELLION, 1837-1838

Ajzenstat, Janet, et al. Lord Durham's Report: An Abridgement. 2006. (Carleton Library Ser.). (ENG.). 262p. *(978-0-7735-3000-3(2))* McGill-Queen's Univ. Pr.
—Lord Durham's Report: An Abridgement. 2006. (Carleton Library). (ENG.). 262p. per. *(978-0-7735-3001-0(0))* McGill-Queen's Univ. Pr.
Da Silva, Maria & Hind, Andrew. Rebels Against Tories in Upper Canada 1837. 2010. (ENG., Illus.). 128p. (gr. 6-12). pap. 9.95 *(978-1-55277-491-5(0))* Lorimer, James & Co., Ltd., Pubs. CAN. Dist: Casemate Pubs. & Bk. Distributors, LLC.
De Celles, Alfred Duclos. The 'Patriotes' of '37: A Chronicle of the Lower Canadian Rebellion. (Chronicles of Canada Ser.). 140p. reprint ed. 88.00 *(978-0-7222-6766-0(5))* Library Reprints, Inc.
Dent, John Charles. The Story of the Upper Canadian Rebellion: Largely Derived from Original Sources & Documents, 2 vol., set. reprint ed. 250.00 *(978-0-7222-6797-4(5))* Library Reprints, Inc.
Durham, John George Lambton. Lord Durham's Report on the Affairs of British North America, 3 vol.,set. reprint ed. 375.00 *(978-0-7222-6728-8(2))* Library Reprints, Inc.
Kilbourn, William. The Firebrand: William Lyon Mackenzie & the Rebellion in Upper Canada. 2008. (ENG.). 288p. pap. 24.99 *(978-1-55002-800-3(6)*, Dundurn Pr.) Dundurn CAN. Dist: Ingram Pub. Services.
Lindsey, Charles. William Lyon Mackenzie. 542p. reprint ed. 98.00 *(978-0-7222-6908-4(0))* Library Reprints, Inc.
Little, J. I. Loyalties in Conflict: A Canadian Borderland in War & Rebellion, 1812-1840. 2008. (Canadian Social History Ser.). (ENG., Illus.). 192p. *(978-0-8020-9773-6(1))* Univ. of Toronto Pr.
Little, John. Loyalties in Conflict: A Canadian Borderland in War & Rebellion, 1812-1840. 2008. (ENG., Illus.). 192p. pap. *(978-0-8020-9525-1(9))* Univ. of Toronto Pr.
McLaughlin, Shaun J. The Patriot War along the New York/Canada Border: Raiders & Rebels. 2012. 160p. pap. 19.99 ***(978-1-60949-465-0(2))*** History Pr., The.
Wallace, William Stewart. The Family Compact: A Chronicle of the Rebellion in Upper Canada. (Chronicles of Canada Ser.). 172p. reprint ed. 88.00 *(978-0-7222-6783-7(5))* Library Reprints, Inc.

CANADA—HISTORY—1841-1867

Bell, John. Rebels on the Great Lakes: Confederate Naval Commando Operations Launched from Canada, 1863-1864. 2011. (ENG., Illus.). 256p. pap. 27.99 *(978-1-55488-986-0(3))* Dundurn CAN. Dist: Ingram Pub. Services.
Creighton, Donald. The Road to Confederation: The Emergence of Canada, 1863-1867. 2012. (ENG., Illus.). 544p. pap. 24.95 ***(978-0-19-544921-1(5))*** Oxford Univ. Pr., Inc.
den Otter, A. A. Civilizing the Wilderness: Culture & Nature in Pre-Confederation Canada & Rupert's Land. 2012. (ENG., Illus.). 472p. pap. 49.95 *(978-0-88864-546-3(5))* Univ. of Alberta Pr. CAN. Dist: Michigan State Univ. Pr.

CANADA—HISTORY—1867-

Ajzenstat, Janet. The Canadian Founding: John Locke & Parliament. 2007. (McGill-Queen's Studies in the History of Religion Ser.). (ENG.). 216p. *(978-0-7735-3152-9(1))*; (C). per. *(978-0-7735-3224-3(2))* McGill-Queen's Univ. Pr.
Bumsted, J. M. The Peoples of Canada: A Post-Confederation History. 3rd ed. 2011. (ENG., Illus.). 704p. 55.00 *(978-0-19-542341-9(0))* Oxford Univ. Pr., Inc.
Comacchio, Cynthia. The Dominion of Youth: Adolescence & the Making of Modern Canada, 1920 To 1950. 2008. (Studies in Childhood & Family in Canada Ser.). (ENG.). 312p. pap. 42.95 *(978-1-55458-151-1(6))* Wilfrid Laurier Univ. Pr. CAN. Dist: Univ. of Toronto Pr.
Conrad, Margaret & Finkel, Alvin. Nation & Society: Readings in Post-Confederation Canadian History, Vol. 2. 2nd ed. 2007. (ENG.). 544p. (C). pap. *(978-0-321-49416-0(4))* Pearson Education Canada.
Creighton, Donald. Canada's First Century. 2012. (ENG., Illus.). 416p. 22.95 ***(978-0-19-544922-8(3))*** Oxford Univ. Pr., Inc.
The Federation of Canada, 1867-1917: Four Lectures Delivered in the University of toronto in March, 1917, to Commemorate the Fiftieth Anniversary of the Federation. 144p. reprint ed. 88.00 *(978-0-7222-6871-1(8))* Library Reprints, Inc.
Hanna, Jonathan, et al. Portraits of Canada: Photographic Treasures of the CFR, 1 vol. 2006. (ENG., Illus.). 216p. 39.95 *(978-1-894856-77-5(5))* Fifth Hse. Pubs. CAN. Dist: Ingram Pub. Services.
Rayner, William. The Canadian Journey: Provocative Glimpses into Canada's Past. 2006. 256p. pap. 26.95 *(978-1-55059-313-6(7))* Detselig Enterprises, Ltd. CAN. Dist: Temeron Bks., Inc.
Thorner, Thomas. Country Nourished on Self Doubt: Documents in Post-Confederation Canadian History. 3rd ed. 2010. 600p. pap. *(978-1-4426-0019-5(5))* Univ. of Toronto Pr.

CANADA—HISTORY—1867-1914

Denison, George T. The Struggle for Imperial Unity: Recollections & Experiences. 2007. pap. 36.95 *(978-1-4304-9359-4(3))* Kessinger Publishing, LLC.
Denison, George Taylor. The Struggle for Imperial Unity. 422p. reprint ed. 98.00 *(978-0-7222-6795-0(9))* Library Reprints, Inc.
MacKenzie, David & Dutil, Patrice. Canada 1911: The Decisive Election That Shaped the Country. 2011. (ENG., Illus.). 378p. pap. 29.99 *(978-1-55488-947-1(2)*, Dundurn Pr.) Dundurn CAN. Dist: Ingram Pub. Services.
Pennington, Christopher. The Destiny of Canada: MacDonald, Laurier, & the Election of 1891. 2012. (ENG., Illus.). 368p. (gr. 12). 30.00 ***(978-0-670-06621-6(4)***, Penguin Global) Penguin Group (USA) Inc.
Tovias, Blanca. Colonialism on the Prairies: Blackfoot Settlement & Cultural Transformation, 1870-1920. 2011. (ENG., Illus.). 324p. 74.95 *(978-1-84519-307-2(5))* Sussex Academic Pr. GBR. Dist: International Specialized Bk. Services.

CANADA—HISTORY—REBELLION, 1869-1870

see Red River Rebellion, 1869-1870

CANADA—HISTORY—REBELLION, 1885

see Riel Rebellion, 1885

CANADA—HISTORY—1914-1945

Currie, Arthur. The Selected Papers of Sir Arthur Currie: Diaries, Letters, & Report to the Ministry, 1917-33. Humphries, Mark Osborne, ed. 2008. (ENG.). 408p. (C). pap. 34.95 *(978-0-9783441-2-2(X))* Wilfrid Laurier Univ. Pr. CAN. Dist: Univ. of Toronto Pr.
Francis, Daniel. Seeing Reds: The Red Scare of 1918-1919, Canada's First War on Terror. 2011. (ENG., Illus.). 220p. 26.95 *(978-1-55152-373-6(6))* Arsenal Pulp Pr. CAN. Dist: Consortium Bk. Sales & Distribution.
Keshen, Jeffrey A. Saints, Sinners, & Soldiers: Canada's Second World War. 2007. (Studies in Canadian Military History Ser.). (ENG., Illus.). 416p. pap. 30.95 *(978-0-7748-0924-5(8))* Univ. of Washington Pr.
Lewis, Thomas Tandy. The Forties in America, 3 vols., Set. 2010. 1296p. 364.00 *(978-1-58765-659-0(0))* Salem Pr., Inc.
Lewis, Thomas Tandy & Lewis, Thomas T. The Forties in America. 2010. *(978-1-58765-660-6(4))*; *(978-1-58765-662-0(0))*; *(978-1-58765-661-3(2))* Salem Pr., Inc.
McLaughlin, Robert. Irish Canadian Conflict & the Struggle for Irish Independence, 1912-1925. 2010. *(978-1-4426-4186-0(X))*; pap. *(978-1-4426-1097-2(2))* Univ. of Toronto Pr.
Paige, Christopher Robin. Canada & Chemical Warfare 1939-1945. 2011. 116p. pap. ***(978-1-926635-56-9(6))*** Adlibbed, Ltd.
Paull, Dorothy S. Scarlet Fever: A Story of Early Years in Banff & My Life As a Royal Canadian Mounted Policeman's Wife, 1914-1956. Chvojka, Laural, ed. (Illus.). 122p. 14.95 *(978-0-9697242-0-9(9))* Hancock Hse. Pubs.
Rayner, William. Canada on the Doorstep: 1939. 2011. (ENG., Illus.). 248p. pap. 24.99 *(978-1-55488-992-1(8))* Dundurn CAN. Dist: Ingram Pub. Services.
Tovias, Blanca. Colonialism on the Prairies: Blackfoot Settlement & Cultural Transformation, 1870-1920. 2011. (ENG., Illus.). 324p. 74.95 *(978-1-84519-307-2(5))* Sussex Academic Pr. GBR. Dist: International Specialized Bk. Services.
Waterston, Elizabeth Hillman. Blitzkrieg & Jitterbugs: College Life in Wartime, 1939-1942. 2012. (Footprints Ser.). (ENG., Illus.). 288p. (C). ***(978-0-7735-3976-1(X))*** McGill-Queen's Univ. Pr.

CANADA—HISTORY—1945-

Blake, Raymond B. Transforming the Nation: Canada & Brian Mulroney. 2007. (ENG., Illus.). 480p. (C). pap. *(978-0-7735-3215-1(3))* McGill-Queen's Univ. Pr.
Blake, Raymond B., ed. Transforming the Nation: Canada & Brian Mulroney. 2007. (ENG., Illus.). 480p. (C). *(978-0-7735-3214-4(5))* McGill-Queen's Univ. Pr.
Bothwell, Robert. Alliance & Illusion: Canada & the World, 1945-1984. 2008. (ENG.). 480p. pap. 38.95 *(978-0-7748-1369-3(5))* Univ. of Washington Pr.
Champion, C. P. The Strange Demise of British Canada: The Liberals & Canadian Nationalism, 1964-68. 2010. (ENG & FRE.). 336p. (C). *(978-0-7735-3690-6(6))* McGill-Queen's Univ. Pr.
Chenier, Elise. Strangers in Our Midst: Sexual Deviancy in Post-War Ontario. 2008. (Studies in Gender & History Ser.). (Illus.). 384p. *(978-0-8020-9226-7(8))*; pap. *(978-0-8020-9453-7(8))* Univ. of Toronto Pr.
The High Arctic Relocation: A Report on the 1953-55 Relocation. 190p. pap. *(978-0-660-15544-9(3))* Canadian Government Publishing.
James Lorimer & Company Ltd., Publishers & Finkel, Alvin. Our Lives: Canada After 1945. 2nd ed. 2012. (ENG.). 448p. (C). pap. 29.95 ***(978-1-4594-0050-4(X))*** Lorimer, James & Co., Ltd., Pubs. CAN. Dist: Casemate Pubs. & Bk. Distributors, LLC.
Keshen, Jeffrey A. Saints, Sinners, & Soldiers: Canada's Second World War. 2007. (Studies in Canadian Military History Ser.). (ENG., Illus.). 416p. pap. 30.95 *(978-0-7748-0924-5(8))* Univ. of Washington Pr.
Palmer, Bryan D. Canada's 1960s: The Ironies of Identity in a Rebellious Era. 2008. (Illus.). 480p. *(978-0-8020-9954-9(8))*; (ENG., pap. *(978-0-8020-9659-3(X))* Univ. of Toronto Pr.
Paull, Dorothy S. Scarlet Fever: A Story of Early Years in Banff & My Life As a Royal Canadian Mounted Policeman's Wife, 1914-1956. Chvojka, Laural, ed. (Illus.). 122p. 14.95 *(978-0-9697242-0-9(9))* Hancock Hse. Pubs.

CANADA—HISTORY, LOCAL

Boles, Glen W., et al. Canadian Mountain Place Names: The Rockies & Columbia Mountains, 1 vol. 2nd ed. 2010. (ENG., Illus.). 288p. per. *(978-1-894765-79-4(6))* Rocky Mountain Bks.
Ford, Catherine. Against the Grain: An Irreverent View of Alberta. 2006. (ENG.). 272p. per. 16.50 *(978-0-7710-4778-7(9)*, McClelland & Stewart) McClelland & Stewart CAN. Dist: Random Hse., Inc.
Gordon, Tammy. Private History in Public: Exhibition & the Settings of Everyday Life. 2010. (American Association for State & Local History Ser.). (ENG., Illus.). 170p. 80.00 *(978-0-7591-1934-5(1))* AltaMira Pr.
Gordon, Tammy S. Private History in Public: Exhibition & the Settings of Everyday Life. 2010. (American Association for State & Local History Ser.). (ENG., Illus.). 170p. pap. 29.95 *(978-0-7591-1935-2(X))* AltaMira Pr.
Howard Trueman. The Chignecto Isthmus & Its First Settlers. I.t. ed. 2006. (ENG.). 190p. pap. 21.99 *(978-1-4264-0161-9(2))* BiblioBazaar.
McKirdy, Margaret. The Colour of Gold. unabr. ed. (ENG., Illus.). 208p. pap. *(978-0-920576-66-3(4))* Caitlin Pr., Inc.
Ring, Dan, et al. Qu'Appelle: Tales of Two Valleys. (Illus.). 160p. 25.95 *(978-1-896359-32-8(9))* Mendel Art Gallery CAN. Dist: Coteau Bks.

CANADA—HISTORY, MILITARY

Berton, Pierre. The American Invasion of Canada: The War of 1812's First Year. 2012. (ENG., Illus.). 368p. pap. 16.95 ***(978-1-61608-335-9(2)***, 608335) Skyhorse Publishing Co., Inc.
Blaxland, John C. Strategic Cousins: Australian & Canadian Expeditionary Forces & the British & American Empires. 2006. (ENG., Illus.). 432p. (C). per. *(978-0-7735-3064-5(9))* McGill-Queen's Univ. Pr.
Bothwell, Robert. Alliance & Illusion: Canada & the World, 1945-1984. 2007. (ENG.). 480p. *(978-0-7748-1368-6(7))* Univ. of British Columbia Pr.
Brandon, Laura & Ogden, Glenn. A Brush with War: Military Art From Korea to Afghanistan. 2009. (ENG., Illus.). 72p. pap. 19.95 *(978-0-660-19854-5(1))* Canadian Museum of Civilization/Musee Canadien des Civilisations CAN. Dist: Univ. of Washington Pr.
Coombs, Howard, ed. The Insubordinate & the Noncompliant: Case Studies of Canadian Mutiny & Disobedience, 1920 to Present. 2008. (ENG., Illus.). 448p. pap. 49.95 *(978-1-55002-764-8(6)*, Dundurn Pr.) Dundurn CAN. Dist: Ingram Pub. Services.
Coombs, Howard G., ed. Les Insubordonnes et les Insurges: Des Exemples Canadiens de Mutinerie et de Desobeissance, de 1920 a Nos Jours. 2008. (FRE & ENG., Illus.). 472p. pap. 49.95 *(978-1-55002-765-5(4)*, Dundurn Pr.) Dundurn CAN. Dist: Ingram Pub. Services.
Copp, Terry. Cinderella Army: The Canadians in Northwest Europe, 1944-1945. 2007. (ENG., Illus.). 392p. pap. *(978-0-8020-9522-0(4))* Univ. of Toronto Pr.
—Cinderella Army: The Canadians in Northwest Europe 1944-1945. 2006. (ENG., Illus.). 392p. *(978-0-8020-3925-5(1))* Univ. of Toronto Pr.
Currie, Arthur. The Selected Papers of Sir Arthur Currie: Diaries, Letters & Report to the Ministry, 1917-33. Humphries, Mark Osborne, ed. 2008. (ENG.). 408p. (C). pap. 34.95 *(978-0-9783441-2-2(X))* Wilfrid Laurier Univ. Pr. CAN. Dist: Univ. of Toronto Pr.
Curry, Frederic C. & Keene, Louis. The 1st Canadians at War: Two Accounts of the First Canadian Division in the Great War. 2010. 232p. *(978-1-84677-982-4(0))*; pap. *(978-1-84677-981-7(2))* Leonaur Ltd.
Dallison, Robert L. A Neighbourly War: New Brunswick & the War of 1812. 2012. (New Brunswick Military Heritage Ser.: 19). (ENG., Illus.). 160p. pap. 17.95 ***(978-0-86492-653-1(7))*** Goose Lane Editions CAN. Dist: Univ. of Toronto Pr.
Dawson, Grant. Here Is Hell: Canada's Engagement in Somalia. 2007. (ENG., Illus.). 240p. pap. *(978-0-7748-1298-6(2))* Univ. of British Columbia Pr.
Ducharme, Michel. Concept de Liberté au Canada À l'Époque des Révolutions Atlantiques (1776-1838) 2010. (Studies on the History of Quebec/Études d'histoire du Quebec Ser.). (FRE & ENG.). 360p. (C). pap. *(978-0-7735-3624-1(8))* McGill-Queen's Univ. Pr.
Feltoe, Richard. The Flames of War: The Fight for Upper Canada, July-December 1813. 2013. (Upper Canada Preserv Ser.: 3). (ENG., Illus.). 176p. pap. 19.99 ***(978-1-4597-0702-3(8))*** Dundurn CAN. Dist: Ingram Pub. Services.
—The Pendulum of War: The Fight for Upper Canada, January-August 1813. 2013. (Upper Canada Preserv Ser.: 2). (ENG., Illus.). 176p. pap. 19.99 ***(978-1-4597-0699-6(4))*** Dundurn CAN. Dist: Ingram Pub. Services.
Frisconalti, Michael. Friendly Fire: The Untold Story of the U. S. Bombing That Killed Four Canadian Soldiers in Afghanistan. 2006. (ENG.). 608p. pap. 24.95 *(978-0-470-83918-8(X)*, Wiley) Wiley, John & Sons, Inc.
Gimblett, Richard H., ed. The Naval Service of Canada, 1910-2010: The Centennial Story. 2009. (ENG., Illus.). 230p. 39.95 *(978-1-55488-470-4(5))* Dundurn CAN. Dist: Univ. of Toronto Pr.
Goddard, Lance. Hell & High Water: Canada & the Italian Campaign. 2007. (ENG., Illus.). 288p. pap. 29.99 *(978-1-55002-728-0(X)*, Dundurn Pr.) Dundurn CAN. Dist: Ingram Pub. Services.
Granatstein, J. L. Canada's Army. 2nd ed. 2011. (Illus.). xiv, 573p. pap. ***(978-1-4426-1178-8(2))*** Univ. of Toronto Pr.
Granatstein, J. L. & Oliver, Dean Frederick. The Oxford Companion to Canadian Military History. 2011. (ENG., Illus.). 528p. 74.00 *(978-0-19-543088-2(3))* Oxford Univ. Pr., Inc.
High, Steven, ed. Occupied St John's: A Social History of a City at War, 1939-1945. 2010. (ENG., Illus.). 416p. (C). *(978-0-7735-3750-7(3))* McGill-Queen's Univ. Pr.
Horn, Bernd. Show No Fear: Daring Actions in Canadian Military History. 2008 (ENG., Illus.). 384p. pap. 35.00 *(978-1-55002-816-4(2)*, Dundurn Pr.) Dundurn CAN. Dist: Ingram Pub. Services.
Horn, Bernd, ed. Fortune Favours the Brave: Tales of Courage & Tenacity in Canadian Military History. 2009. (ENG., Illus.). 446p. pap. 35.00 *(978-1-55002-841-6(3))* Dundurn CAN. Dist: Ingram Pub. Services.
Horn, Bernd & Balasevicius, Tony, eds. Casting Light on the Shadows: Canadian Perspectives on Special Operations Forces. 2007. (ENG.). 328p. pap. 39.95 *(978-1-55002-694-8(1)*, Dundurn Pr.) Dundurn CAN. Dist: Ingram Pub. Services.
—Lumières Sur les Forces de l'Ombre: Une Perspective Canadienne Sur les Forces d'Opérations Spéciales. 2007. (FRE & ENG.). 344p. pap. 39.95 *(978-1-55002-696-2(8)*, Dundurn Pr.) Dundurn CAN. Dist: Ingram Pub. Services.
Horn, Bernd & Legault, Roch, eds. Loyal Service: Perspectives on French-Canadian Military Leaders. 2007. (ENG., Illus.). 336p. pap. 39.95 *(978-1-55002-693-1(3)*, Dundurn Pr.) Dundurn CAN. Dist: Ingram Pub. Services.
Horn, Bernd & Wyczynski, Michel. Canadian Airborne Forces Since 1942. 2006. (Elite Ser.). (ENG., Illus.). 64p. pap. 18.95 *(978-1-84176-985-1(1))* Osprey Publishing, Ltd. GBR. Dist: Random Hse., Inc.
Hunt, C. W. Dancing in the Sky: The Royal Flying Corps in Canada. 2009. (ENG., Illus.). 360p. pap. 28.99 *(978-1-55002-864-5(2))* Dundurn CAN. Dist: Ingram Pub. Services.
Irving, L. Homfray. Canadian Military Institute Officers of the British Forces in Canada During the War Of 1812-15. 2009. 324p. pap. 29.95 *(978-1-4446-0597-6(6))* Thorndike Pr.
Joyce, Ken. Snow Plough & the Jupiter Deception: The True Story of the 1st Special Service Force. 2006. (Illus.). 320p. 41.95 *(978-1-55125-094-6(2))* Vanwell Publishing, Ltd. CAN. Dist: Casemate Pubs. & Bk. Distributors, LLC.
Lackenbauer, P. Whitney & Kikkert, Peter. The Canadian Forces & Arctic Sovereignty: Debating Roles, Interests, & Requirements, 1968-1974. 2010. (ENG., Illus.). 398p. (C). pap. 34.95 *(978-1-926804-00-2(7))*, Wilfrid Laurier Univ. Pr. CAN. Dist: Univ. of Toronto Pr.
Langford, Martha & Langford, John W. A Cold War Tourist & His Camera. 2011. (Illus.). 208p. pap. *(978-0-7735-3821-4(6))* McGill-Queen's Univ. Pr.
Le Couteur, John & Graves, Donald E. Merry Hearts Make Light Days: The War of 1812 Journal of Lieutenant John le Couteur, 104th Foot. 2nd rev. ed. 2012.

C

306p. pap. 27.95 **(978-1-896941-66-0(4))** Brass, Robin Studio, Inc. CAN. Dist: Midpoint Trade Bks., Inc.

Legault, Roch & Horn, Bernd, eds. Le Leadership Militaire Canadien Français: Continuité, Efficacité et Loyauté. 2007. (FRE & ENG., Illus.). 368p. pap. 39.95 (978-1-55002-695-5(X), Dundurn Pr.) Dundurn CAN. Dist: Ingram Pub. Services.

Leversedge, T. F. J. Canadian Combat & Support Aircraft: A Military Compendium. 2007. (Illus.). 348p. 50.00 (978-1-55125-116-5(7)) Vanwell Publishing, Ltd. CAN. Dist: Casemate Pubs. & Bk. Distributors, LLC.

Lucas, Charles Prestwood. The Canadian War of 1812. 269p. reprint ed. 98.00 (978-0-7222-7839-0(X)) Library Reprints, Inc.

Maloney, Sean M. Confronting Chaos: A Rogue Military Historian Returns to Afghanistan. 2009. (Illus.). 384p. 34.95 (978-1-59114-508-0(2)) Naval Institute Pr.

—Learning to Love the Bomb: Canada's Nuclear Weapons During the Cold War. 2007. (Illus.). 400p. 29.95 (978-1-57488-616-0(9)) Potomac Bks., Inc.

Mantle, Craig L., ed. The Apathetic & the Defiant: Case Studies of Canadian Mutiny & Disobedience, 1812-1919. 2007. (ENG., Illus.). 496p. pap. 49.95 (978-1-55002-710-5(7), Dundurn Pr.) Dundurn CAN. Dist: Ingram Pub. Services.

Mantle, Craig Leslie & Mantle, Craig L. Les Apathiques et les Rebelles: Des Exemples Canadiens de Mutinerie et de Desobeissance, 1812 A 1919. 2007. (FRE., Illus.). 392p. pap. 49.95 (978-1-55002-720-4(4), Dundurn Pr.) Dundurn CAN. Dist: Ingram Pub. Services.

Milner, Marc & Leonard, Glenn. New Brunswick & the Navy: Four Hundred Years. 2010. (New Brunswick Military Heritage Ser.). (ENG., Illus.). 156p. pap. 16.95 (978-0-86492-632-6(4)) Goose Lane Editions CAN. Dist: Univ. of Toronto Pr.

Montague, Art. Canadian Forces: An Historical Salute to Those on the Front Line. 2011. (ENG., Illus.). 208p. pap. 19.95 (978-1-926916-09-5(3)) MacIntyre & Purcell Publishing CAN. Dist: Independent Pubs. Group.

Morton, Desmond. A Military History of Canada. 5th ed. 2007. (ENG.). 432p. pap. 24.99 (978-0-7710-6481-4(0), McClelland & Stewart) McClelland & Stewart CAN. Dist: Random Hse., Inc.

Nursey, Walter R. The Story of Isaac Brock, Hero, Defender & Saviour of Upper Canada, 1812. 2012. 242p. pap. **(978-1-290-14802-3(3))** HardPr.

Pearson, George. Battle, Capture & Escape: The Experiences of a Canadian Light Infantryman During the Great War. 2008. 152p. (978-1-84677-600-7(7)); pap. (978-1-84677-599-4(X)) Leonaur Ltd.

Reid, Brian A. & Reid, Brian. No Holding Back: Operation Totalize, Normandy, August 1944. 2009. (Military History Ser.). (ENG., Illus.). 528p. pap. 21.95 (978-0-8117-0584-4(6)) Stackpole Bks.

Sharpe, Robert J. The Last Day, the Last Hour: The Currie Libel Trial. 2009. (Illus.). 320p. (978-0-8020-9619-7(0)) Univ. of Toronto Pr.

Smith, A. Britton. Legend of the Lake, New Discovery Edition: The 22-Gun Brig-Sloop Ontario 1780. 2009. 176p. 39.95 (978-1-894997-17-1(4)) Quarry Heritage Bks. CAN. Dist: SCB Distributors.

Sweeny, Alastair. Fire along the Frontier: Great Battles of the War of 1812. 2012. (ENG., Illus.). 224p. pap. 24.99 **(978-1-4597-0433-6(9))** Dundurn CAN. Dist: Ingram Pub. Services.

Tupper, Ferdinand Br. The Life & Correspondence of Sir Isaac. 2006. pap. (978-1-4068-3365-2(7)) Echo Library.

Winslow, Donna & Commission of Inquiry into the Deployment of Canadian Forces to Somalia. A Socio-Cultural Inquiry into the Activities of the Canadian Airborne Regiment in Somalia. pap. (978-0-660-16944-6(4)) Canadian Government Publishing.

Zuehlke, Mark D. & Daniel, C. Stuart. Canadian Military Atlas: Four Centuries of Conflict from New France to Kosovo, 1 vol. 2006. (ENG., Illus.). 240p. pap. 40.00 (978-1-55365-209-0(6)) D&M Pubs. Inc. CAN. Dist: Perseus-PGW.

CANADA—IMPRINTS

Brisebois, Michel & National Library of Canada Staff. Impressions: 250 Years of Printing in the Lives of Canadians, 1 vol. (ENG.). 210p. pap. (978-1-55041-408-0(9)) Bow Historical Bks.

DeBeyer, Michael & Kennedy, Kate. Gaspereau Gloriatur Book of the Blessed Tenth Year Vol. 3: Annotated Bibliography, 3 vols. Steeves, Andrew & Stevens, Joe, eds. 2010. (ENG., Illus.). 192p. pap. (978-1-55447-040-2(4)) Gaspereau Pr.

DeBeyer, Michael & Stevens, Joe. Gaspereau Gloriatur: Liber Beati Anni Decimi: Three Volumes Celebrating the Decadian Accomplishments of Gaspereau Press, 3 vols. Steeves, Andrew et al, eds. 2007. (ENG.). 288p. pap. (978-1-55447-039-6(0)) Gaspereau Pr.

Steeves, Andrew, et al, eds. Gaspereau Gloriatur: Book of the Blessed Tenth Year, 3 vols. 2007. (ENG.). 192p. pap. (978-1-55447-038-9(2)) Gaspereau Pr.

CANADA—INTELLECTUAL LIFE

Anctil, Pierre, et al, eds. New Readings of Yiddish Montreal - Traduire le Montreal Yiddish. 2007. (International Canadian Studies Ser.). (ENG, FRE & YID., Illus.). 136p. pap. (978-2-7603-0631-8(3)) Univ. of Ottawa Pr./Presses de l'Universite d'Ottawa.

Brydon, Diana & Dvorfk, Marta, eds. Crosstalk: Canadian & Global Imaginaries in Dialogue. 2010. (ENG.). 286p. (C). 85.00 (978-1-55458-264-8(4)) Wilfrid Laurier Univ. Pr. CAN. Dist: Univ. of Toronto Pr.

Compton, Wayde. After Canaan: Essays on Race, Writing, & Region. 2011. (ENG., Illus.). 176p. pap. 18.95 (978-1-55152-374-3(4)) Arsenal Pulp Pr. CAN. Dist: Consortium Bk. Sales & Distribution.

Friesen, Gerald & Owram, Doug. Thinkers & Dreamers. 2010. (978-1-4426-4195-2(9)) Univ. of Toronto Pr.

Helmes-Hayes, Rick. Measuring the Mosaic: An Intellectual Biography of John Porter. 2010. 592p. (978-0-8020-9703-3(0)) Univ. of Toronto Pr.

Kenner, Hugh & Glasheen, Adaline. A Passion for Joyce: The Letters of Hugh Kenner & Adaline Glasheen. Burns, Edward, ed. 2008. (ENG.). 471p. 159.95 (978-1-904558-96-5(8)) Univ. College Dublin Pr. IRL. Dist: Dufour Editions, Inc.

Mendelson, Alan. Exiles from Nowhere: The Jews & the Canadian Elite. 2008. 432p. pap. 34.95 (978-1-896941-55-4(9)) Brass, Robin Studio, Inc. CAN. Dist: Midpoint Trade Bks., Inc.

Snider, Norman. The Roaring Eighties & Other Good Times. 2008. (ENG.). 290p. 26.95 (978-1-55096-093-8(8)) Exile Editions, Ltd. CAN. Dist: Independent Pubs. Group.

Steiner, Rudolf. Christmas: An Introductory Reader. 2007. (Pocket Library of Spiritual Wisdom Ser.). 160p. per. (978-1-85584-189-5(4)) Steiner, Rudolf Pr.

Timpson, Annis May, ed. First Nations, First Thoughts: The Impact of Indigenous Thought in Canada. 2010. (ENG., Illus.). 336p. pap. 35.95 (978-0-7748-1552-9(3)) Univ. of Washington Pr.

Ty, Eleanor Rose. Unfastened: Globality & Asian North American Narratives. 2010. (Illus.). 216p. 67.50 (978-0-8166-6507-5(9)); (ENG., pap. 22.50 (978-0-8166-6508-2(7)) Univ. of Minnesota Pr.

Wyman, Max. The Defiant Imagination: Why Culture Matters. pap. 22.95 (978-1-55365-007-2(7)) D&M Pubs. Inc. CAN. Dist: Perseus-PGW.

CANADA—JUVENILE LITERATURE

McDonnell, Kathleen. Emily Included, 1 vol. 2012. (ENG., Illus.). 126p. (J). (gr. 3-7). mass mkt. 8.95 **(978-1-926920-33-7(3))** Second Story Pr. CAN. Dist: Orca Bk. Pubs. USA.

Wearing, Judy. Roberta Bondar: Canada's First Woman in Space. 2010. (Crabtree Groundbreaker Biographies Ser.). (ENG., Illus.). 112p. (J). pap. (978-0-7787-2549-7(9)) Crabtree Publishing Co.

CANADA—LANGUAGES

see also American Sign Language; Inuit Language

Cameron, David R. & Simeon, Richard, eds. Language Matters: How Canadian Voluntary Associations Manage French & English. 2010. (ENG.). 232p. pap. 32.95 (978-0-7748-1504-8(3)) Univ. of Washington Pr.

Edwards, John, ed. Language in Canada. 2010. (ENG., Illus.). 524p. pap. 65.00 (978-0-521-56528-8(6)) Cambridge Univ. Pr.

Foster, Graham. Working Together to Improve Literacy: How to Set Goals, Implement, & Assess School-Wide Reading & Writing Initiatives. 2008. (ENG.). 112p. (C). (gr. k-12). pap. 21.00 (978-1-55138-224-1(5)) Stenhouse Pubs.

Joy, Richard. Languages in Conflict: The Canadian Experience, No. 61. 162p. pap. 5.95 (978-0-7710-9761-4(1)) McClelland & Stewart CAN. Dist: Random Hse. of Canada, Ltd.

Muller, Janet. Language & Conflict in Northern Ireland & Canada: A Silent War. 2010. (Palgrave Studies in Minority Languages & Communities Ser.). (ENG., Illus.). 340p. 89.00 (978-0-230-23065-1(2)) Palgrave Macmillan.

Neuhaus, Mareike. That's Raven Talk: Holophrastic Readings of Contemporary Indigenous Literatures. 2011. (Cps Ser.). 320p. 34.95 (978-0-88977-233-5(9)) Canadian Plains Research Ctr. CAN. Dist: Univ. of Toronto Pr.

Official Languages Act: Consolidation by the Office of the Commissioner of Official Languages: Revised Statutes of Canada, 1985, C. (FRE & ENG.). 66p. (978-0-662-64317-3(8)) Canadian Government Publishing.

Quinby, Rohan. Time & the Suburbs: The Politics of Built Environments & the Future of Dissent. 2012. (Semaphore Ser.). (ENG & OJI., Illus.). 150p. pap. 19.95 **(978-1-894037-52-5(9))** Arbeiter Ring Publishing CAN. Dist: AK Pr. Distribution.

School District 70. ¿uklaamah: Quuquuaca. 2011. 16p. pap. 10.96 **(978-1-4251-8787-3(0))** Trafford Publishing.

Simpson, Leanne. Dancing on Our Turtle's Back: Stories of Nishnaabeg Re-Creation, Resurgence, & a New Emergence. 2011. (ENG., Illus.). 166p. pap. 19.95 (978-1-894037-50-1(2)) Arbeiter Ring Publishing CAN. Dist: AK Pr. Distribution.

Wilhelm, Andrea. Telicity & Durativity: A Study of Aspect in Dene Suline (Chipewyan) & German. 2007. (Outstanding Dissertations in Linguistics Ser.). (Illus.). 339p. 126.00 (978-0-415-97645-9(6)) Routledge.

Yalden, Maxwell. Transforming Rights: Reflections from the Front Lines. 2009. 256p. (978-1-4426-4007-8(3)) Univ. of Toronto Pr.

CANADA—MAPS

AAA CAA North American Road Atlas. 2008. pap. (978-1-59508-209-1(3)) AAA.

AAA Publishing. AAA Easy Reading Road Atlas 2012. 2011. (ENG.). 104p. pap. 9.95 (978-1-59508-441-5(X)) AAA.

—AAA Road Atlas 2012. 2011. (ENG.). 144p. pap. 12.95 (978-1-59508-440-8(1)) AAA.

American Map, creator. 2009 Pocket Road Atlas: United States, Canada, Mexico. 2008. (American Map Ser.). (Illus.). 64p. 3.95 (978-0-8416-2845-8(9)) Langenscheidt Publishing Group.

American Map Corporation, creator. Pocket Road Atlas. 2006. (US ROAD Ser.). 64p. 3.95 (978-0-8416-2339-2(2)) American Map Corp.

British Columbia & Alberta Map. 2009. 5.95 (978-1-55368-305-6(6)) Map Art Publishing Corp CAN. Dist: Rand McNally.

CAA North American Road Atlas French. 2006. pap. (978-1-59508-085-1(6)) AAA.

Cadman, Michael D. Atlas of the Breeding Birds of Ontario, 2001-2005. 2009. (ENG., Illus.). 728p. 92.50 (978-1-896059-15-0(5)) Federation of Ontario Naturalists CAN. Dist: Firefly Bks., Ltd.

Canada Tide Current Atlas 1995. pap. (978-0-660-59637-2(7)) Canadian Government Publishing.

Canadian Atlas 1996. pap. (978-0-660-59848-2(5)) Canadian Government Publishing.

COMPASS MAPS, LTD. & Compass Maps Staff. Vancouver Popoutmap. 2010. (Illus.). 2p. pap. 6.95 (978-1-84587-767-5(5)) Compass Maps Ltd. GBR. Dist: Rand McNally.

Dun-Map Inc. & Waterfront Regeneration Trust. Waterfront Trail & Greenway Mapbook. Ian Dunlop, ed. 2009. 188p. pap. (978-1-894955-24-9(2)) Dun-Map, Inc.

Edwards, Melissa. The Geist Atlas of Canada: Meat Maps & Other Strange Cartographies. 2006. (ENG., Illus.). 128p. pap. (978-1-55152-216-6(0)) Arsenal Pulp Pr. CAN. Dist: Consortium Bk. Sales & Distribution.

Hamilton, Jennifer & Hamilton, James. Cruising the Secret Coast: Unexplored Anchorages on British Columbia's Inside Passage, 1 vol. 2008. (ENG., Illus.). 272p. pap. 44.95 (978-0-935727-29-6(9)) Weatherly Pr.

Hayes, Derek. Historical Atlas of Canada: A Thousand Years of Canada's History in Maps. (Illus.). 60.00 (978-1-55054-918-8(9)) D&M Pubs. Inc. CAN. Dist: Perseus-PGW.

—Historical Atlas of Toronto, 1 vol. 2009. (ENG.). 192p. pap. 29.95 (978-1-55365-497-1(8)) D&M Pubs. Inc. CAN. Dist: Perseus-PGW.

Hempstead, Andrew. Moon Nova Scotia. 2009. (Moon Handbooks). (ENG.). 250p. pap. 17.95 (978-1-59880-157-6(0)) Avalon Travel Publishing.

Johnson, Linda. The Kandik Map. 2011. (ENG.). 232p. pap. 19.95 (978-1-60223-042-2(0)) Univ. of Alaska Pr.

Kimantas, John. A Kayaking, Hiking & Recreation Guide for North & West Vancouver Island Vol. 1: The Wild Coast. 2nd ed. 2012. (Kayaking & Small Boat Atlas Series #1 Ser.). (Illus.). 64p. spiral bd. 29.95 (978-1-77050-057-0(X)) Whitecap Bks., Ltd. CAN. Dist: Midpoint Trade Bks., Inc.

Mapart Publishing Staff. Queen Charlotte Islands/Inside Passage. 2009. 3.95 (978-1-55198-109-3(2)) Map Art Publishing Corp CAN. Dist: Rand McNally.

MapArt Staff. Atlas Canada Road. 2008. 12.95 (978-1-55368-647-7(0)) Map Art Publishing Corp CAN. Dist: Langenscheidt Publishing Group.

MAPSCO Staff, creator. Mapsco Road Atlas: United States, Canada, Mexico. 2008. (Illus.). 144p. pap. 13.95 (978-1-56966-462-9(5)); 96p. pap. 9.95 (978-1-56966-463-6(3)) Mapsco, Inc.

Marleau, Jason. Eastern Ontario Fishing Mapbook: Ontario Lakes & Rivers Guide. 2nd ed. 2007. (Backroad Mapbooks Ser.). (Illus.). 103p. spiral bd. (978-1-897225-17-2(2)) Mussio Ventures, Ltd.

McKnight, Tom L. Regional Geography of the United States & Canada. 5th ed. 2011. (ENG.). 550p. (C). pap. 111.80 (978-0-321-64376-6(3), Prentice Hall) Prentice Hall PTR.

Minutillo, Carmine & Marleau, Jason. Eastern Ontario. Mussio, Russell & Mussio, Wesley, eds. 2nd ed. 2007. (Backroad Mapbooks Ser.). (Illus.). 119p. spiral bd. (978-1-897225-15-8(6)) Mussio Ventures, Ltd.

Morrow, Robert. Pearson School Atlas. (Illus.). (978-0-13-122506-0(5)) Prentice Hall Higher Education.

Mussio, Russell & Ernst, Trent. Southwestern BC Fishing Mapbook: Region 2 - Lower Mainland, Region 3 - Thompson Nicola, 1 vol. 2nd ed. 2008. (Backroad Mapbooks Ser.). (ENG., Illus.). 208p. spiral bd., spiral bd. 27.95 (978-1-897225-00-4(8)) Backroads.

New Brunswick Map. 2009. (Illus.). 4.95 (978-1-55368-249-3(1)) Map Art Publishing Corp CAN. Dist: Rand McNally.

Oliver, Edmund Henry. The Canadian North-West, Its Early Development & Legislative Records: Minutes of the Councils of the Red River Colony & the Northern Department of Rupert's Land, 2 vol., set. (Publications of the Canadian Archives: 9). reprint ed. 250.00 (978-0-7222-6743-1(6)) Library Reprints, Inc.

Rand McNally, compiled by. Rand Mcnally Road Atlas: United States, Canada, Mexico. 2011. (Rand Mcnally Road Atlas: United States/Canada/Mexico Ser.). (Illus.). 140p. pap. 16.95 **(978-0-528-00339-4(9))** Rand McNally.

Rand McNally, creator. Deluxe Midsize Road Atlas. deluxe ed. 2007. (Rand Mcnally Mid-Size Road Atlas: Deluxe Ser.). 192p. pap. 9.95 (978-0-528-93968-6(8)) Rand McNally.

—Harley Davidson Ride Atlas of North America. 2nd ed. 2007. (Illus.). 336p. pap. 34.95 (978-0-528-93955-6(6)) Rand McNally.

—Pocket Size Road Atlas. 2007. (Rand Mcnally Road Atlas Ser.). 64p. per. 3.95 (978-0-528-93969-3(6)) Rand McNally.

—Rand Mcnally Midsize Road Atlas. 2008. (Rand Mcnally Road Atlas Ser.). (Illus.). 90p. pap. 7.95 (978-0-528-94206-8(9)) Rand McNally.

—Rand Mcnally Road Atlas: United States/Canada/Mexico. 2008. (Rand Mcnally Road Atlas Ser.). (Illus.). 140p. pap. 16.95 (978-0-528-94205-1(0)); pap. 13.95 (978-0-528-94201-3(8)) Rand McNally.

—Rand Mcnally the Road Atlas. 2007. 140p. pap. 16.95 (978-0-528-93966-2(1)) Rand McNally.

Reader's Digest & Canadian Geographic. The Canadian Atlas: Our Nation, Environment & People, 1 vol. (ENG., Illus.). 192p. 69.95 (978-1-55365-082-9(4)) D&M Pubs. Inc. CAN. Dist: Perseus-PGW.

Road Atlas 2008. 6th rev. ed. 2007. (Michelin Atlases Ser.). (Illus.). 288p. 18.95 (978-2-06-712980-1(5)) Michelin.

Ruggles, Richard I. A Country So Interesting: The Hudson's Bay Company & Two Centuries of Mapping, 1670-1870. 2011. (Rupert's Land Record Society Ser.). (ENG., Illus.). 320p. (C). pap. **(978-0-7735-3885-6(2))** McGill-Queen's Univ. Pr.

Saskatchewan Map. 2009. (Illus.). 4.95 (978-1-55368-241-7(6)) Map Art Publishing Corp CAN. Dist: Rand McNally.

Vancouver Island Map. 2009. (Illus.). 4.95 (978-1-55368-218-9(1)) Map Art Publishing Corp CAN. Dist: Rand McNally.

Western Canada Map. 2009. (Illus.). 5.95 (978-1-55368-248-6(3)) Map Art Publishing Corp CAN. Dist: Rand McNally.

CANADA—NATIONAL SECURITY

see National Security—Canada

CANADA—PICTORIAL WORKS

Bathgate, Andy, et al, frwds. Official Guide to the Players of the Hockey Hall of Fame. 2010. (ENG., Illus.). 544p. pap. 19.95 (978-1-55407-662-8(5)) Firefly Bks., Ltd.

Benson, Daryl. Canada. 2008. (FRE & ENG., Illus.). 176p. 49.95 (978-0-9684576-4-1(9)) Lone Pine Publishing USA.

Brown, Craig, ed. The Illustrated History of Canada. 5th rev. ed. 2007. (ENG., Illus.). 648p. pap. 32.95 (978-1-55263-920-7(7)) Key Porter Bks. CAN. Dist: Perseus-PGW.

Collective & Ulysses Travel Guide Staff. Fabulous Canada: Discover Canada's Wide Open Spaces. 2009. 288p. pap. 29.95 (978-2-89464-869-8(3)) Ulysses Travel Guides CAN. Dist: Hunter Publishing, Inc.

Falconer, Simon. Canada's Black Watch: An Illustrated History of the Regular Force Battalions 1951-1970. 2008. (ENG., Illus.). 168p. 35.00 (978-0-86492-521-3(2)) Goose Lane Editions CAN. Dist: Univ. of Toronto Pr.

Fischer, George & Hudson, Noel. Unforgettable Canada: 115 Destinations. 3rd rev. ed. 2012. (ENG., Illus.). 320p. pap. 29.95 **(978-1-77085-020-0(1))** Boston Mills Pr. CAN. Dist: Firefly Bks., Ltd.

Grandmaison, Mike. Canada. 2009. (ENG., Illus.). 240p. pap. 25.00 (978-1-55470-219-0(4)) Key Porter Bks. CAN. Dist: Perseus-PGW.

Hall, Gerald Bryan. Spectacular Canada. 2009. (ENG., Illus.). 132p. 25.00 (978-0-7893-2059-9(2)) Universe Publishing.

—Spectacular Canada French Edition. 2009. (FRE., Illus.). 132p. 25.00 (978-0-7893-2063-6(0)) Universe Publishing.

Hanna, Jonathan, et al. Portraits of Canada: Photographic Treasures of the CPR, 1 vol. 2006. (ENG., Illus.). 216p. 39.95 (978-1-894856-77-5(5)) Fifth Hse. Pubs. CAN. Dist: Ingram Pub. Services.

Herzog, Fred. Fred Herzog: Photographs, 1 vol. 2011. (ENG., Illus.). 204p. 55.00 (978-1-55365-558-9(3)) D&M Pubs. Inc. CAN. Dist: Perseus-PGW.

Irwin, Jane. Old Canadian Cemeteries: Places of Memory. 2007. (ENG., Illus.). 320p. 75.00 (978-1-55407-146-3(1)) Firefly Bks., Ltd.

Joubert, Christine. Christine's Country of Many Quotes: Open Randomly for Fun & Guidance. 2011. 224p. 35.00 **(978-1-4269-5518-1(9))**; pap. 25.00 **(978-1-4269-5519-8(7))** Trafford Publishing.

Kopelow, Gerry. All Our Changes: Images from the Sixties Generation. 2009. (ENG., Illus.). 158p. pap. 39.95 **(978-0-88755-714-9(7))** Univ. of Manitoba Pr. CAN. Dist: Chicago Distribution Ctr.

Kraulis, J. A., photos by & text. The Canadian Landscape / le Paysage Canadien. 2007. (ENG & FRE., Illus.). 176p. pap. 24.95 (978-1-55297-989-1(X)) Firefly Bks., Ltd.

Kyi, Tanya Lloyd & Kyi, Tanya Lloyd. Canada: A Visual Journey. 2nd rev. ed. 2010. (ENG., Illus.). 256p. 39.95 (978-1-55285-759-5(X)) Whitecap Bks., Ltd. CAN. Dist: Midpoint Trade Bks., Inc.

Lambert, Barbara Ann. Powell River 100: The Largest Single Site Newsprint Manufacturer in the World. 2009. 364p. pap. 25.00 (978-1-4269-0547-6(5)) Trafford Publishing.

Langford, Martha & Langford, John. Scissors, Paper, Stone: Expressions of Memory in Contemporary Photographic Art. 2007. (ENG., Illus.). 368p. (C). (978-0-7735-3211-3(0)) McGill-Queen's Univ. Pr.

Lee, Alastair. Baffin Island. 2011. (ENG., Illus.). 128p. 40.00 **(978-0-7112-3221-1(0))** Lincoln, Frances Ltd. GBR. Dist: Perseus-PGW.

Marcolin, Lorenzo. A Great Lakes Treasury of Old Postcards: Canadian Harbour Scenes 1894-1960. 2010. (ENG., Illus.). 176p. pap. 24.99 (978-1-55488-743-9(7)) Dundurn CAN. Dist: Ingram Pub. Services.

Menke, Kathleen M. K. Alaska/Yukon/Arctic Light: Gifts of the Wild. 2007. per. 29.00 (978-0-9764261-1-0(0)) Crystal Images.

Miller, Lawrence. The Avro Arrow: A Picture History. 2011. (Amazing Stories Ser.). (ENG., Illus.). 128p. mass mkt. 9.95 **(978-1-55277-895-1(9))** Lorimer, James & Co., Ltd., Pubs. CAN. Dist: Casemate Pubs. & Bk. Distributors, LLC.

Montague, Kenneth, intro. Position As Desired: Exploring African Canadian Identity: Photographs from the Wedge Collection. 2011. (ENG., Illus.). 80p. pap. 25.00 (978-0-9783370-1-8(8)) Wedge Curatorial Projects CAN. Dist: D.A.P./Distributed Art Pubs.

Morassutti, William. Imagining Canada: A Century of Photographs from the New York Times. 2012. (ENG.). 256p. 40.00 **(978-0-385-67709-7(X))** Doubleday Canada, Ltd. CAN. Dist: Random Hse., Inc.

Naftel, William D. Wartime Halifax: The Photo History of a Canadian City at War, 1939-1945. 2009. (ENG., Illus.). 128p. pap. (978-0-88780-835-7(2)) Formac Publishing Co., Ltd.

Nicholson, Sandy, photos by. 2nd: The Face of Defeat. 2008. (ENG., Illus.). 128p. 40.00 (978-0-9739739-4-5(3)) Magenta Publishing for the Arts CAN. Dist: Consortium Bk. Sales & Distribution.

Philipson, Claire Leila. The Little Gift Book of Canada. 2008. (Little Gift Book of Ser.). (ENG., Illus.). 96p. 14.95 (978-1-55285-944-5(4)) Whitecap Bks., Ltd. CAN. Dist: Midpoint Trade Bks., Inc.

PhotoSensitive. Cancer Connections: Images of Hope & Courage Across Canada. 2011. (ENG., Illus.). 192p. 36.95 (978-0-470-96449-1(9), Wiley) Wiley, John & Sons, Inc.

Pietropaolo, Vincenzo. Harvest Pilgrims: Mexican & Caribbean Migrant Farm Workers in Canada. 2009. (Illus.). 144p. pap. 35.00 *(978-1-897071-54-0(X))* Between the Lines CAN. Dist: Univ. of Toronto Pr.

Pyle, Don. Trouble in the Camera Club: A Photographic Narrative of Toronto's Punk History, 1976 - 1980. 2011. (ENG., Illus.). 304p. pap. 29.95 *(978-1-55022-966-0(4))* ECW Pr. CAN. Dist: Independent Pubs. Group.

Remillard, Francois & Prieur, Benoit. Fabulous Quebec. 2008. (Illus.). 256p. pap. 22.95 *(978-2-89464-716-5(6))* Ulysses Travel Guides CAN. Dist: Hunter Publishing, Inc.

Ruwedel, Mark. Westward the Course of Empire. 2008. (Illus.). *(978-0-89467-970-4(8))* Yale Univ. Art Gallery.

Savard, David. Images from the Likeness House, 1 vol. 2010. (ENG., Illus.). 224p. pap. *(978-0-7726-6150-0(2))* Royal British Columbia Museum.

Schacter, Mark. Roads, 1 vol. 2011. (ENG., Illus.). 192p. 39.95 *(978-1-897252-60-4(9))* Fifth Hse. Pubs. CAN. Dist: Ingram Pub. Services.

Scobbie, James. From a Canoe. 2007. 176p. pap. 59.50 *(978-1-4303-2282-5(9))* Lulu Enterprises Inc.

Svin'in, Pavel. A Russian Paints America: The Travels of Pavel P. Svinin, 1811-1813. Swoboda, Marina & Whisenhunt, William Benton, eds. 2008. (ENG., Illus.). 230p. (C). *(978-0-7735-3414-8(8))* McGill-Queen's Univ. Pr.

Western Canada: Screen Saver. cd-rom *(978-1-55153-177-9(1))* Altitude Publishing Canada Ltd.

CANADA—POLITICS AND GOVERNMENT

Abele, Frances, et al, eds. The Northern Exposure: Peoples, Powers & Prospects in Canada's North. 4th ed. 2009. (Art of the State Ser.). (ENG., Illus.). 500p. (C). pap. *(978-0-88645-205-6(8))* McGill-Queen's Univ. Pr.

Aboriginal Self-Government. pap. *(978-0-660-14636-2(3))* Canadian Government Publishing.

Adams, Christopher. Politics in Manitoba: Parties, Leaders, & Voters. 2008. (ENG.). 200p. pap. 28.95 *(978-0-88755-704-0(X))* Univ. of Manitoba Pr. CAN. Dist: Chicago Distribution Ctr.

Ajzenstat, Janet. The Canadian Founding: John Locke & Parliament. 2007. (McGill-Queen's Studies in the History of Religion Ser.). (ENG.). 216p. *(978-0-7735-3152-9(1))*; (C). per. *(978-0-7735-3224-3(2))* McGill-Queen's Univ. Pr.

Ajzenstat, Janet, et al. Lord Durham's Report: An Abridgement. 2006. (Carleton Library Ser.). (ENG.). 262p. *(978-0-7735-3000-3(2))* McGill-Queen's Univ. Pr.

—Lord Durham's Report: An Abridgement. 2006. (Carleton Library). (ENG.). 262p. per. *(978-0-7735-3001-0(0))* McGill-Queen's Univ. Pr.

Åkerman, Sune & Granatstein, J. L. Welfare States in Trouble: Historical Perspectives on Canada & Sweden. (Illus.). viii, 184p. *(978-91-7191-039-4(5))* Umea universitet.

Alfredson, Lisa S. Creating Human Rights: How Noncitizens Made Sex Persecution Matter to the World. 2008. (Pennsylvania Studies in Human Rights). (Illus.). 328p. (C). 69.95 *(978-0-8122-4125-9(8))* Univ. of Pennsylvania Pr.

Allan, John R., et al. Transitions 2006-2007: Fiscal & Political Federalism in an Era of Change. 2008. (ENG.). 390p. (C). *(978-1-55339-191-3(8))*; pap. *(978-1-55339-189-0(6))* McGill-Queen's Univ. Pr.

Anastakis, Dimitry. Framing Canadian Federalism. Bryden, P. E., ed. 2009. (ENG.). 304p. pap. *(978-0-8020-9436-0(8))* Univ. of Toronto Pr.

Anastakis, Dimitry & Bryden, Penny. Framing Canadian Federalism. 2009. (ENG.). 304p. *(978-0-8020-9193-2(8))* Univ. of Toronto Pr.

Angus, Ian H. Identity & Justice. 2008. (ENG.). 120p. *(978-0-8020-9881-8(9))* Univ. of Toronto Pr.

Appadurai, Samy. Canad: The meat of the world Sandwich. 2009. 216p. 24.99 *(978-1-4389-7927-4(4))*; pap. 14.49 *(978-1-4389-7926-7(6))* AuthorHouse.

Bakvis, Herman & Skogstad, Grace, eds. Canadian Federalism: 3rd ed. 2012. (ENG., Illus.). 416p. pap. 70.50 ***(978-0-19-543979-3(1))*** Oxford Univ. Pr., Inc.

Bakvis, Herman, et al. Contested Federalism: Certainty & Ambiguity in the Canadian Federation. 2009. (ENG., Illus.). 320p. pap. 50.00 *(978-0-19-542529-1(4))* Oxford Univ. Pr., Inc.

Baldwin, Doug. Conservatives: Canada's Political Parties. 2011. 32p. (gr. 5-8). ***(978-1-77071-695-7(5))*** Weigl Educational Pubs. Ltd.

—Liberal: Canada's Political Parties. 2011. 32p. (gr. 5-8). ***(978-1-77071-697-1(1))*** Weigl Educational Pubs. Ltd.

Baldwin, Douglas & Baldwin, Patricia. Bloc Québécois. 2011. 32p. (gr. 5-8). pap. ***(978-1-77071-699-5(8))*** Weigl Educational Pubs. Ltd.

Banting, Keith G. & Brock, Kathy Lenore, eds. The Nonprofit Sector & Government in a New Century. 256p. *(978-0-88911-905-5(8))* McGill-Queen's Univ. Pr.

Bashevkin, Sylvia. Women, Power, Politics: The Hidden Story of Canada's Unfinished Democracy. 2009. (ENG.). 136p. pap. 24.95 *(978-0-19-543170-4(7))* Oxford Univ. Pr., Inc.

Battram, Robert A. Canada in Crisis... An Agenda to Unify the Nation. 2010. 408p. pap. 16.10 *(978-1-4269-1897-1(6))* Trafford Publishing.

—Canada in Crisis... An Agenda to Unify the Nation. 2010. 408p. 26.10 *(978-1-4269-1898-8(4))* Trafford Publishing.

—Canada in Crisis (2) An Agenda for Survival of the Nation. 2010. 492p. (ENG.). 34.95 *(978-1-4269-3392-9(4))*; pap. 24.95 *(978-1-4269-3391-2(6))* Trafford Publishing.

Beach, Charles M. & Wilson, Thomas A. The 2006 Federal Budget: Rethinking Fiscal Priorities. Smart, Michael, ed. 2007. (John Deutsch Institute Ser.). (ENG., Illus.). 234p. (C). per. 34.95 *(978-1-55339-125-8(X))* Queen's Univ., Schl. of Policy Studies CAN. Dist: McGill-Queen's Univ. Pr.

Beach, Charles M., et al. The 2006 Federal Budget: Rethinking Fiscal Priorities. 2007. (John Deutsch Institute Ser.). (ENG., Illus.). 234p. (C). 95.00 *(978-1-55339-126-5(8))* Queen's Univ., Schl. of Policy Studies CAN. Dist: McGill-Queen's Univ. Pr.

—The 2009 Federal Budget: Challenge, Response & Retrospect. 2010. (John Deutsch Institute Ser.). (ENG.). 366p. (C). *(978-1-55339-166-1(7))*; pap. *(978-1-55339-165-4(9))* McGill-Queen's Univ. Pr.

Beisel, Vivienne. Ödo Not Take Them from Myself & My Children Foreverö - Aboriginal Water Rights in Treaty 7 Territories & the Duty to Consult. 2008. 164p. pap. *(978-3-639-02779-2(5))* VDM Verlag Dr. Mueller e.K.

Bejermi, John. Canadian Parliamentary Handbook/Ripertoire Parlementaire Canadien. 18th ed. *(978-0-88887-833-5(8))* Borealis Pr.

Bengough, John Wilson. A Caricature History of Canadian Politics, 2 vol., set. reprint ed. 250.00 *(978-0-7222-6844-5(0))* Library Reprints, Inc.

Bickerton, James. Canadian Politics. Gagnon, Alain-G, ed. 5th ed. 2009. (ENG., Illus.). 415p. (C). pap. *(978-1-4426-0121-5(3))* Univ. of Toronto Pr.

Biggar, Charles R. Sir Oliver Mowat: A Biographical Sketch, 2 vols., Set. (BCL Ser. I). reprint ed. 105.00 *(978-0-404-00858-1(5))* AMS Pr., Inc.

Biggar, Charles Robert Webster. Sir Oliver Mowat: A Biographical Sketch, 2 vol., set. reprint ed. 250.00 *(978-0-7222-6953-4(6))* Library Reprints, Inc.

Biggar, Emerson Bristol. Anecdotal Life of Sir John Macdonald. 332p. reprint ed. 98.00 *(978-0-7222-6945-9(5))* Library Reprints, Inc.

Blais, A. Governments, Parties & Public Sector Employees: Canada, United States, Britain & France. (ENG.). 220p. *(978-0-7735-1695-3(6))*; pap. *(978-0-7735-1696-0(4))* McGill-Queen's Univ. Pr.

Blake, Raymond E. Transforming the Nation: Canada & Brian Mulroney. 2007. (ENG., Illus.). 480p. (C). pap. *(978-0-7735-3215-1(3))* McGill-Queen's Univ. Pr.

Blake, Raymond B., ed. Transforming the Nation: Canada & Brian Mulroney. 2007. (ENG., Illus.). 480p. (C). *(978-0-7735-3214-4(5))* McGill-Queen's Univ. Pr.

Blakeney, Allan. An Honourable Calling: Political Memoirs. 2008. (ENG., Illus.) 256p. *(978-0-8020-9891-7(6))* Univ. of Toronto Pr.

Boatright, Robert G. Interest Groups & Campaign Finance Reform in the United States & Canada. 2011. (ENG.). 276p. 85.00 *(978-0-472-07144-9(0))*; (Illus.). pap. 35.00 *(978-0-472-05144-1(X))* Univ. of Michigan Pr.

Boisvert, Yves. L'institutionnalisation de L'éthique Gouvernementale: Quelle Place Pour L'éthique? 2011. (FRE.). ix, 205p. *(978-2-7605-2631-0(3))* Presses de l'Universite du Quebec.

Borden, Robert Laird. Canadian Constitutional Studies. 2010. 76p. pap. *(978-1-151-94820-5(9))* Books LLC.

—Canadian Constitutional Studies. rev. ed. 163p. 88.00 *(978-0-7222-6845-2(9))* Library Reprints, Inc.

Borovoy, A. Alan. Categorically Incorrect: Ethical Fallacies in Canada's War on Terror. annot. ed. 2008. (ENG.). 220p. pap. 24.99 *(978-1-55002-628-3(3))* Dundurn Pr.) Dundurn CAN. Dist: Ingram Pub. Services.

—The New Anti-Liberals. (ENG.). 193p. pap. 18.95 *(978-1-55130-137-2(7))* Canadian Scholars' Pr., Inc. CAN. Dist: Ingram Pub. Services.

Bosch, Nuria & Durán, José M., eds. Fiscal Federalism & Political Decentralization: Lessons from Spain, Germany & Canada. 2008. (Studies in Fiscal Federalism & Statendash;local Finance Ser.). 288p. (C). 135.00 *(978-1-84720-467-7(8))* Elgar, Edward Publishing, Inc.

Bothwell, Robert. Alliance & Illusion: Canada & the World, 1945-1984. 2007. (ENG.). 480p. *(978-0-7748-1368-6(7))* Univ. of British Columbia Pr.

—Alliance & Illusion: Canada & the World, 1945-1984. 2008. (ENG.). 480p. pap. 38.95 *(978-0-7748-1369-3(5))* Univ. of Washington Pr.

Bourgeois, Daniel. Canadian Bilingual Districts: From Cornerstone to Tombstone. 2007. (ENG.). 344p. (C). pap. *(978-0-7735-3102-4(5))* McGill-Queen's Univ. Pr.

Bourinot, John George. Federal Government in Canada. 2010. 362p. pap. 24.95 *(978-1-152-65580-5(9))* General Bks. LLC.

—Parliamentary Procedure & Practice in the Dominion of Canada. Flint, Thomas Barnard, ed. 4th ed. 2008. 713p. 125.00 *(978-1-58477-881-3(4))* Lawbook Exchange, Ltd., The.

Bouthillier, Guy & Cloutier, Édouard, eds. Trudeau's Darkest Hour: War Measures in Time of Peace: October 1970. 2010. (ENG., Illus.). 190p. 19.95 *(978-1-926824-04-8(0))* Baraka Bks. CAN. Dist: Independent Pubs. Group.

Boyce, William, et al. Adolescent Health: Policy, Science, & Human Rights. 2009. (ENG., Illus.). 304p. (C). 95.00 *(978-0-7735-3511-4(X))* Queen's Univ., Schl. of Policy Studies CAN. Dist: McGill-Queen's Univ. Pr.

Boychuk, Gerard William. National Health Insurance in the United States & Canada: Race, Territory, & the Roots of Difference. 2008. (American Governance & Public Policy Ser.). (ENG., Illus.). 256p. pap. 26.95 *(978-1-58901-206-6(2))* Georgetown Univ. Pr.

Boyko, John. Into the Hurricane: Attacking Socialism & the CCF. 2006. (ENG.). 224p. pap. 19.95 *(978-1-897289-09-9(X))* Shillingford, J. Gordon Publishing CAN. Dist: Univ. of Toronto Pr.

Bradshaw, Frederick. Self-Government in Canada: How It Was Achieved. 414p. reprint ed. 98.00 *(978-0-7222-6848-3(3))* Library Reprints, Inc.

Bratt, Duane & Kukucha, Christopher J., eds. Altered Landscapes: Readings in Canadian Foreign. 2006. (ENG., Illus.). 416p. 85.00 *(978-0-19-542369-3(0))* Oxford Univ. Pr., Inc.

Bravo, Michael & Triscott, Nicola, eds. Arctic Perspective Cahier No. 2: Geopolitics & Autonomy. 2011. (ENG., Illus.). 116p. 30.00 *(978-3-7757-2681-8(0))* Hatje Cantz Verlag GmbH & Co KG DEU. Dist: D.A.P./Distributed Art Pubs.

Brock, Deborah R. Making Work, Making Trouble: Prostitution as a Social Problem, 2nd ed. 2009. (ENG.). 256p. pap. *(978-0-8020-9828-3(2))* Univ. of Toronto Pr.

—Making Work, Making Trouble: The Social Regulation of Sexual Labour. 2nd ed. 2009. 256p. pap. *(978-0-8020-9557-2(7))* Univ. of Toronto Pr.

Brodie, Janine & Jenson, Jane. Crisis, Challenge & Change: Party & Class in Canada Revisited, No. 148. 341p. pap. *(978-0-88629-074-0(0))* McGill-Queen's Univ. Pr.

Brooke, Jeffrey. Divided Loyalties: The Liberal Party of Canada, 1984-2008. 2009. (Illus.). 689p. pap. *(978-1-4426-1065-1(4))* Univ. of Toronto Pr.

Brooks, Stephen. Canadian Democracy. 7th ed. 2011. (ENG., Illus.). 624p. (Orig.). pap. 90.00 ***(978-0-19-544155-0(9))*** Oxford Univ. Pr., Inc.

Browne, G. P. Documents on the Confederation of British North America. 2009. (Carleton Library Ser.). (ENG.). 440p. pap. *(978-0-7735-3609-8(4))* (C) *(978-0-7735-3602-9(7))* McGill-Queen's Univ. Pr.

Brunelle, Dorval. From World Order to Global Disorder: States, Markets, & Dissent. Howard, Richard, tr. from FRE. 2007. (ENG.). 224p. 75.00 *(978-0-7748-1360-0(1))* UBC Pr. CAN. Dist: Univ. of Washington Pr.

—From World Order to Global Disorder: States, Markets, & Dissent. Howard, Richard, tr. 2008. (ENG.). 224p. pap. 32.95 *(978-0-7748-1361-7(X))* Univ. of Washington Pr.

Byers, Michael. Who Owns the Arctic? Understanding Sovereignty Disputes in the North, 1 vol. 2010. (ENG., Illus.). 192p. pap. 17.95 *(978-1-55365-499-5(4))* D&M Pubs. Inc. CAN. Dist: Perseus-PGW.

Callihoo, Christine. Participation Equality in the Public Policy Process. 2010. 216p. pap. *(978-3-8383-2307-7(6))* Lambert Academic Publishing.

Cameron, Alex M. Power Without Law: The Supreme Court of Canada, the Marshall Decisions & the Failure of Judicial Activism. 2009. 176p. pap. *(978-0-7735-3610-4(8))* McGill-Queen's Univ. Pr.

Canada, Department of Foreign Affairs and International Trade Staff. Canadian Representatives Abroad 1999. pap. *(978-0-662-64200-8(7))* Canadian Government Publishing.

—Canadian Representatives Abroad January 2001. 358p. pap. *(978-0-660-61587-5(8))* Canadian Government Publishing.

Canadian Archives Pubns. Staff. State Papers, 20 vol., set. reprint ed. 2500.00 *(978-0-7222-6722-6(3))* Library Reprints, Inc.

Canadian Parliamentary Guide. 99th ed. Date not set. 60.00 *(978-0-7876-3559-6(6))* Cengage Gale.

Carment, David. The World in Canada: Diaspora, Demography, & Domestic Politics. Bercuson, David, ed. 2008. (ENG., Illus.). 272p. (C). *(978-0-7735-3296-0(X))* McGill-Queen's Univ. Pr.

Carment, David & Bercuson, David, eds. The World in Canada: Diaspora, Demography, & Domestic Politics. 2008. (ENG., Illus.). 272p. (C). pap. *(978-0-7735-3297-7(8))* McGill-Queen's Univ. Pr.

Chalk, Frank, et al. Mobilizing the Will to Intervene: Leadership to Prevent Mass Atrocities. 2010. (ENG.). 200p. (C). pap. *(978-0-7735-3804-7(6))* McGill-Queen's Univ. Pr.

Champion, C. P. The Strange Demise of British Canada: The Liberals & Canadian Nationalism, 1964-68. 2010. 336p. (C). (ENG & FRE.). *(978-0-7735-3690-6(6))*; (FRE & ENG.). pap. *(978-0-7735-3691-3(4))* McGill-Queen's Univ. Pr.

Chapnick, Adam. The Middle Power Project: Canada & the Founding of the United Nations. 2006. (ENG.). 240p. pap. *(978-0-7748-1246-1(6))* Univ. of British Columbia Pr.

Chrétien, Jean. My Years as Prime Minister. 2008. (ENG., Illus.). 448p. pap. 19.00 *(978-0-676-97901-5(7))*, Vintage Canada) Random Hse. of Canada, Ltd. CAN. Dist: Random Hse., Inc.

Clarke, Harold D., et al. Making Political Choices: Canada & the United States. 2008. (ENG., Illus.). 270p. *(978-1-4426-0136-9(1))*; pap. *(978-0-8020-9674-6(3))* Univ. of Toronto Pr.

Clearwater, John. Just Dummies: Cruise Missile Testing in Canada. 2006. (ENG., Illus.). 302p. per. 39.95 *(978-1-55238-211-0(7))* Univ. of Calgary Pr. CAN. Dist: Chicago Distribution Ctr.

Clement, Dominique, et al. Debating Dissent: Canada & the Sixties. 2010. (Canadian Social History Ser.). pap. *(978-1-4426-1078-1(6))* Univ. of Toronto Pr.

—Debating Dissent: Canada & the Sixties Debating Dissent. 2010. (Canadian Social History Ser.). *(978-1-4426-4164-8(9))* Univ. of Toronto Pr.

Clippingdale, Richard. The Power of the Pen: The Politics, Nationalism, & Influence of Sir John Willison. 2012. (ENG., Illus.). 392p. pap. 30.00 ***(978-1-4597-0372-8(3))*** Dundurn CAN. Dist: Ingram Pub. Services.

Cockburn, Alexander Peter. Political Annals of Canada. 574p. reprint ed. 98.00 *(978-0-7222-6853-7(X))* Library Reprints, Inc.

Coffin, Victor. Province of Quebec & the Early America. 2006. pap. 30.95 *(978-1-4286-4279-9(X))* Kessinger Publishing, LLC.

Cohen, Andrew. Lester B. Pearson. Ralston, Saul, ed. 2012. (ENG.). 224p. (gr. 12). 19.95 ***(978-0-670-06738-1(5))***, Penguin Global) Penguin Group (USA) Inc.

Cole, Taylor. Canadian Bureaucracy & Federalism, Nineteen Forty-Seven to Sixty-Five. (Monograph Series in World Affairs: Vol. 3, 1965-66, Bk. 3). (Orig.). pap. 3.95 *(978-0-87940-009-5(9))* Univ. of Denver, Graduate Schl. of International Studies, Monograph Series in World Affairs.

Courtney, John & Smith, David, eds. The Oxford Handbook of Canadian Politics, 1 vol. 2010. (Oxford Handbooks Ser.). (ENG., Illus.). 576p. 150.00 *(978-0-19-533535-4(X))* Oxford Univ. Pr., Inc.

Cram101 Textbook Reviews. Outlines & Highlights for Party Discipline & Parliamentary Politics by Christopher J Kam. 2011. 88p. pap. 27.95 ***(978-1-61905-026-6(9))*** Cram101 Inc.

Creighton, Donald. The Road to Confederation: The Emergence of Canada, 1863-1867. 2012. (ENG., Illus.). 544p. pap. 24.95 ***(978-0-19-544921-1(5))*** Oxford Univ. Pr., Inc.

Cross, William, ed. Auditing Canadian Democracy. 2011. (Canadian Democratic Audit Ser.). (ENG., Illus.). 272p. pap. 35.95 *(978-0-7748-1920-6(0))* UBC Pr. CAN. Dist: Univ. of Washington Pr.

Cullen, Roy. Beyond Question Period: Or What Really Goes on in Ottawa. 2011. 196p. 24.99 ***(978-1-4269-6947-8(3))***; pap. 14.99 ***(978-1-4269-6946-1(5))*** Trafford Publishing.

Cullis, Suzuki E. Notes from Canada's Young Activists: A Generation Stands up for Change, 1 vol. Cullis-Suzuki, Severn et al, eds. 2007. (ENG., Illus.). 240p. pap. 17.95 *(978-1-55365-237-3(1))*, Greystone Bks.) D&M Pubs. Inc. CAN. Dist: Perseus-PGW.

Culver, Keith & Castle, David, eds. Aquaculture, Innovation & Social Transformation. 2008. (International Library of Environmental, Agricultural & Food Ethics Ser.). (ENG., Illus.). xii, 348p. 229.00 *(978-1-4020-8834-6(5))*, 1402088345) Springer.

Curtis, Bruce. Governing through Education: Politics,Schooling & Insurrection in Colonial Canada. 2009. (ENG.). *(978-1-4426-4118-1(5))*; pap. *(978-1-4426-1049-1(2))* Univ. of Toronto Pr.

Dafoe, John W. Canada: An American Nation. reprint ed. 20.00 *(978-0-404-00616-7(7))* AMS Pr., Inc.

Daudelin, Jean & Schwanen, Daniel. Canada among Nations 2007: What Room to Manoeuvre? 2008. (ENG., Illus.). 344p. (C). *(978-0-7735-3396-7(6))* McGill-Queen's Univ. Pr.

Dawson, Grant. Here Is Hell: Canada's Engagement in Somalia. 2007. (ENG., Illus.). 240p. pap. *(978-0-7748-1298-6(2))* Univ. of British Columbia Pr.

Day, Kathleen M. & Winer, Stanley. Interregional Migration & Public Policy in Canada: An Empirical Study. 2012. (Carleton Library Ser.). (ENG., Illus.). (C). 480p. ***(978-0-7735-3744-6(9))***; 432p. pap. ***(978-0-7735-3745-3(7))*** McGill-Queen's Univ. Pr.

DeBardeleben, Joan & Pammett, Jon H. Activating the Citizen: Dilemmas of Participation in Europe & Canada. DeBardeleben, Joan et al, eds. 2009. (ENG., Illus.). 288p. 95.00 *(978-0-230-57594-3(3))* Palgrave Macmillan.

Decter, Michael. Tales from the Back Room: Memories of a Political Insider. 2010. 224p. pap. 24.95 *(978-1-926531-06-9(X))* Great Plains Pubns. CAN. Dist: Univ. of Toronto Pr.

Deneault, Alain, et al. Imperial Canada Inc. Legal Haven of Choice for the World's Mining Industries. Reed, Fred A. & Philpot, Robin, trs. from FRE. 2010. (ENG.). 320p. pap. 29.95 *(978-0-88922-635-7(0))* Talonbooks, Ltd. CAN. Dist: Consortium Bk. Sales & Distribution.

Dept. Statutes Staff. A Consolidation of the Constitution Acts, 1867-1982. (Illus.). 80p. pap. *(978-0-660-59988-5(0))* Canadian Government Publishing.

—The Constitution Act of 1982, Amended by Constitution Amendment Proclamation, 1983 (SI/84-102); Constitution Amendment, 1993 (New Brunswick) (SI/93-54) 27p. pap. *(978-0-660-59989-2(9))* Canadian Government Publishing.

Dhamoon, Rita. Identity, Difference Politics: How Difference Is Produced, & Why It Matters. 2010. (ENG.). 208p. pap. 29.95 *(978-0-7748-1591-8(4))* Univ. of Washington Pr.

Diab, Robert. Guantanamo North: Terrorism & the Administration of Justice in Canada. 2009. (ENG.). 128p. pap. 15.95 *(978-1-55266-279-3(9))* Fernwood Publishing Co., Ltd. CAN. Dist: Independent Pubs. Group.

Dimitrios, et al. Les Politiques Publiques Au Canada: Pouvoir, Conflits et Idéologies. (FRE.). xii, 392p. *(978-2-7637-8752-7(5))* Les Presses de l'Universite Laval.

Dobrowolsky, Alexandra, ed. Women & Public Policy in Canada: Neoliberalism & After? 2009. (ENG., Illus.). 240p. pap. 45.00 *(978-0-19-543061-5(1))* Oxford Univ. Pr., Inc.

Dobuzinskis, Laurent & Howlett, Michael. Policy Analysis in Canada: The State of the Art. Dobuzinskis, Laurent & Howlett, Michael, eds. Laycock, David, ed. 2007. (Institute of Public Administration of Canada Series in Public Management & Governance). (Illus.). 592p. pap. *(978-0-8020-3787-9(9))* Univ. of Toronto Pr.

Dobuzinskis, Laurent, et al. Policy Analysis in Canada: The State of the Art. Dobuzinskis, Laurent et al, eds. 2007. (Institute of Public Administration of Canada Series in Public Management & Governance Ser.). (ENG., Illus.). 592p. *(978-0-8020-8004-2(9))* Univ. of Toronto Pr.

Doern, G. Bruce. How Ottawa Spends, 2007-2008: The Harper Conservatives - Climate of Change. 2007. (How Ottawa Spends Ser.). (ENG., Illus.). 336p. (C). per. *(978-0-7735-3283-0(8))* McGill-Queen's Univ. Pr.

—The Road to Better Public Services: Progress & Constraints in Five Canadian Federal Agencies. 107p. *(978-0-88645-168-4(X))* Institute for Research on Public Policy/Institut de Recherche en Politiques Publiques.

Doern, G. Bruce & Johnson, Robert, eds. Rules, Rules, Rules, Rules: Multilevel Regulatory Governance. 2006. (Studies in Comparative Political Economy & Public Policy). (ENG., Illus.). 368p. *(978-0-8020-3858-6(1))* Univ. of Toronto Pr.

Doern, G. Bruce & Stoney, Christopher, eds. How Ottawa Spends, 2010-2011: Recession, Realignment, & the New Deficit Era. 2010. (ENG., Illus.). 307p. (C). pap. *(978-0-7735-3728-6(7))* McGill-Queen's Univ. Pr.

Domino & Bridle, Augustus. The Masques of Ottawa. 2008. 232p. 43.95 *(978-1-4366-4125-8(X))*; 284p. pap. 28.95 *(978-0-548-85508-9(0))* Kessinger Publishing, LLC.

C

Doman, Christopher & Pammett, Jon H., eds. The Canadian Federal Election Of 2006. 2006. (ENG., Illus.). 288p. pap. 34.99 *(978-1-55002-650-4(X)*, Dundurn Pr.) Dundurn CAN. Dist: Ingram Pub. Services.

Doughty, Howard A. & Tuzi, Marino, eds. Discourse & Community: Multidisciplinary Studies of Canadian Culture. 2006. (Essay Ser.). (ENG.). 80p. 18.00 *(978-1-55071-256-8(X))* Guernica Editions, Inc. CAN. Dist: Univ. of Toronto Pr.

Dryden, Ken. Becoming Canada: Our Story, Our Politics, Our Future. 2010. 248p. 26.95 *(978-0-7710-2945-5(4)*, McClelland & Stewart) McClelland & Stewart CAN. Dist: Random Hse., Inc.

Dube, Jacques. Lexique Analogique. (FRE.). pap. *(978-0-660-60255-4(5))* Canadian Government Publishing.

Ducharme, Michel. Concept de Liberté au Canada À l'Époque des Révolutions Atlantiques (1776-1838) 2010. (Studies on the History of Quebec/Études d'histoire du Quebec Ser.). (FRE & ENG.). 360p. (C). pap. *(978-0-7735-3624-1(8))* McGill-Queen's Univ. Pr.

—Liberalism & Hegemony: Debating the Canadian Liberal Revolution. Constant, Jean-François, ed. 2009. (ENG.). 464p. *(978-0-8020-9882-5(7))*; pap. *(978-0-8020-9589-3(5))* Univ. of Toronto Pr.

Dunn, Christopher, ed. Canadian Public Administration. 2nd ed. 2010. (ENG., Illus.). 568p. instr.'s hndbk. ed. 95.00 *(978-0-19-542983-1(4))* Oxford Univ. Pr., Inc.

—Provinces: Canadian Provincial Politics. 3rd ed. 2006. (ENG.). 544p. pap. *(978-1-4426-0068-3(3))* Univ. of Toronto Pr.

Dunn, Christopher & Brownsey, Keith, eds. Canadian Provinces (Set) 2009. (ENG.). *(978-1-55402-587-9(7))* Univ. of Toronto Pr.

Durham, John George Lambton. Lord Durham's Report on the Affairs of British North America, 3 vol.,set. reprint ed. 375.00 *(978-0-7222-6728-8(2))* Library Reprints, Inc.

Dutil, Patrice, et al. The Service State: Rhetoric, Reality & Promise. 2010. (Governance Ser.). (ENG.). 224p. pap. *(978-0-7766-0743-6(X))* Univ. of Ottawa Pr./Presses de l'Universite d'Ottawa.

Dwivedi, O. P., et al, eds. The Evolving Physiology of Government: Canadian Public Administration in Transition. 2009. (Governance Ser.). (ENG.). 450p. (gr. 10-12). pap. *(978-0-7766-0706-1(5))* Univ. of Ottawa Pr./Presses de l'Universite d'Ottawa.

Dyment, David. Doing the Continental: A New Canadian-American Relationship. 2010. (ENG.). 171p. pap. 19.99 *(978-1-55488-758-3(5))* Dundurn CAN. Dist: Ingram Pub. Services.

Edwardson, Ryan. Canadian Content: Culture & the Quest for Nationhood. 2008. (ENG.). 288p. *(978-0-8020-9759-0(6))*; (Illus.). pap. *(978-0-8020-9519-0(4))* Univ. of Toronto Pr.

Egerton, Hugh Edward. Canadian Constitutional Development: Selected Speeches & Despatches. 472p. reprint ed. 98.00 *(978-0-7222-6854-4(8))* Library Reprints, Inc.

Emberley, Julia. Defamiliarizing the Aboriginal: Cultural Practices & Decolonization in Canada. 2009. (Illus.). 228p. pap. *(978-1-4426-1025-5(5))* Univ. of Toronto Pr.

English, John. Citizen of the World Vol. 1: The Life of Pierre Elliott Trudeau, 1919-1968. 2007. (ENG., Illus.). 624p. pap. 20.95 *(978-0-676-97522-2(4)*, Vintage Canada) Knopf Canada CAN. Dist: Random Hse., Inc.

—Just Watch Me Vol. 2: The Life of Pierre Elliott Trudeau, 1968-2000. 2010. (ENG., Illus.). 832p. pap. 21.95 *(978-0-676-97524-6(0)*, Vintage Canada) Random Hse. of Canada, Ltd. CAN. Dist: Random Hse., Inc.

Ertler, Klaus-Dieter & Gill, Stewart, eds. Canadian Studies: the State of the Art / ÉTudes Canadiennes: Questions de Recherché: 1981-2011: International Council for Canadian Studies (Iccs) / 1981-2011: Conseil International D'éTudes Canadiennes (Ciec) 2011. (Canadiana. Literaturen/Kulturen, Literatures/Cultures, Littératures/Cultures Ser.). 544p. 86.95 ***(978-3-631-61599-7(X))*** Lang, Peter GmbH, Europaischer Verlag der Wissenschaften DEU. Dist: Lang, Peter.

Europa Publications, ed. USA & Canada 2009. 11th rev. ed. 2008. (ENG., Illus.). 644p. 760.00 *(978-1-85743-478-1(1))* Routledge.

The Federation of Canada, 1867-1917: Four Lectures Delivered in the University of toronto in March, 1917, to Commemorate the Fiftieth Anniversary of the Federation. 144p. reprint ed. 88.00 *(978-0-7222-6871-1(8))* Library Reprints, Inc.

Fergusson, James G. Canada & Ballistic Missile Defence, 1954-2009: Déjà Vu All over Again. 2010. (ENG., Illus.). 352p. (C). pap. 37.95 *(978-0-7748-1751-6(8))* Univ. of British Columbia Pr. CAN. Dist: Univ. of Washington Pr.

Fernando, Shanti. Race & the City: Chinese Canadian & Chinese American Political Mobilization. 2007. (ENG.). 192p. pap. 29.95 *(978-0-7748-1346-4(6))* UBC Pr. CAN. Dist: Univ. of Washington Pr.

Fingard, Judith & Rutherford, John. Protect, Befriend, Respect: Nova Scotia's Mental Health Movement, 1908-2008. 2009. (ENG.). 144p. pap. 17.95 *(978-1-55266-275-5(6))* Fernwood Publishing Co., Ltd. CAN. Dist: Independent Pubs. Group.

Fisher, Pete. Highway of Heroes: True Patriot Love. 2011. (ENG., Illus.). 184p. pap. 24.99 *(978-1-55488-971-6(5))* Dundurn CAN. Dist: Ingram Pub. Services.

Flanagan, Tom. Harper's Team: Behind the Scenes in the Conservative Rise to Power. 2nd ed. 2009. (ENG.). 360p. (C). pap. *(978-0-7735-3545-9(4))* McGill-Queen's Univ. Pr.

—Waiting for the Wave: The Reform Party & the Conservative Movement. 2009. (ENG.). 272p. pap. *(978-0-7735-3568-8(3))*; (C). *(978-0-7735-3546-6(2))* McGill-Queen's Univ. Pr.

Flanagan, Tom & Flanagan, Thomas. Harper's Team: Behind the Scenes in the Conservative Rise to Power. 2007. (ENG., Illus.). 336p. *(978-0-7735-3298-4(6))* McGill-Queen's Univ. Pr.

Fleming, Douglas. Becoming Canadian - Racialized Citizenship, Esl Learners, National Second Language Policy, & the Canadian Language Benchmark. 2008. 244p. pap. *(978-3-639-00346-8(2))* VDM Verlag Dr. Mueller e.K.

Ford, Catherine. Against the Grain: An Irreverent View of Alberta. 2006. (ENG.). 272p. per. 16.50 *(978-0-7710-4778-7(9)*, McClelland & Stewart) McClelland & Stewart CAN. Dist: Random Hse., Inc.

Forsey, Eugene, ed. Freedom & Order: Collected Essays, No. 73. 350p. pap. 19.95 *(978-0-7710-9773-7(5))* McClelland & Stewart CAN. Dist: Random Hse. of Canada, Ltd.

Forsey, Eugene A. How Canadians Govern Themselves. 7th ed. 2010. (Illus.). iv, 52p. *(978-1-100-14351-4(3))* Canadian Government Publishing.

Forsey, Helen. Eugene Forsey: Canada's Maverick Sage. 2012. (ENG., Illus.). 488p. 35.00 ***(978-1-926577-15-9(9))*** Dundurn CAN. Dist: Ingram Pub. Services.

Friedland, Martin L. A Place Apart: Judicial Independence & Accountability in Canada. 424p. pap. *(978-0-660-16166-2(4))* Canadian Government Publishing.

Froese, Marc D. Canada at the WTO: Trade Litigation & the Future of Public Policy. 2010. (Illus.). 175p. (C). *(978-1-4426-0152-9(3))*; pap. *(978-1-4426-0138-3(8))* Univ. of Toronto Pr.

G Le Prestre, Philippe & Stoett, Peter. Continental Ecopolitics: Continuity & Change in Canadan- American Environemental Relations. 2006. (Global Environmental Governance Ser.). (Illus.). 306p. 140.00 *(978-0-7546-4177-3(5))* Ashgate Publishing Co.

Gagnon, Alain-G & Iacovino, Raffaele. Federalism, Citizenship, & Quebec: Debating Multinationalism. 2006. (ENG.). 228p. *(978-0-8020-9216-8(0))* Univ. of Toronto Pr.

Gairdner, William. The Trouble with Canad: A Citizen Speaks Out. 2007. 500p. per. *(978-0-9784402-2-0(6))* BPS Bks.

Gairdner, William D. Oh, Oh, Canada! A Voice from the Conservative Resistance. 2008. 208p. per. *(978-0-9784402-9-9(3))* BPS Bks.

—The Trouble with Canada — Still! A Citizen Speaks Out. 2011. 546p. pap. ***(978-1-926645-67-4(7))*** BPS Bks.

Gairdner, William D. The Trouble with Canada ... Still: A Citizen Speaks Out. 2011. (ENG.). 448p. pap. 24.95 *(978-1-55470-247-3(X))* Key Porter Bks. CAN. Dist: Perseus-PGW.

Gidengil, Elisabeth, et al. Dominance & Decline: Making Sense of Recent Canadian Elections. 2012. (ENG.). 240p. pap. ***(978-1-4426-0389-9(5))*** Univ. of Toronto Pr.

Gidluck, Lynn. Visionaries, Crusaders, & Firebrands: The Idealistic Canadians Who Built the NDP. 2012. (ENG., Illus.). 248p. pap. 24.95 ***(978-1-4594-0053-5(4))*** Lorimer, James & Co., Ltd., Pubs. CAN. Dist: Casemate Pubs. & Bk. Distributors, LLC.

Gillespie, Alastair W. & Sage, Irene. Made in Canada: A Businessman's Adventures in Politics. 2010. (Illus.). 272p. 37.95 *(978-1-896941-59-2(1))* Brass, Robin Studio, Inc. CAN. Dist: Midpoint Trade Bks., Inc.

Goff, Patricia M. Limits to Liberalization: Local Culture in a Global Marketplace. 2006. (Cornell Studies in Political Economy). 197p. 38.95 *(978-0-8014-4458-6(6))* Cornell Univ. Pr.

Goldenberg, Eddie. The Way It Works: Inside Ottawa. 2007. (ENG.). 408p. pap. 17.95 *(978-0-7710-3562-3(4)*, Gibson, Douglas Bks.) McClelland & Stewart CAN. Dist: Random Hse., Inc.

Graham, Ron. The Last Act: Pierre Trudeau, the Gang of Eight, & the Fight for Canada. 2012. (ENG., Illus.). 368p. (gr. 12). 30.00 ***(978-0-670-06662-9(1)***, Penguin Global) Penguin Group (USA) Inc.

Grant, George. Lament for a Nation: The Defeat of Canadian Nationalism, No. 50. 106p. pap. *(978-0-88629-257-7(3))* McGill-Queen's Univ. Pr.

Grant, George, et al. Collected Works of George Grant, 1970-1988, 4 vols., Vol. 4. Roper, Henry, ed. 2009. (Collected Works of George Grant Ser.). (ENG., Illus.). 1104p. *(978-0-8020-9930-3(0))* Univ. of Toronto Pr.

Griffiths, Naomi E. S. The Golden Age of Liberalism: A Portrait of Roméo Leblanc. 2011. (ENG., Illus.). 376p. 35.00 ***(978-1-55277-896-8(7))*** Lorimer, James & Co., Ltd., Pubs. CAN. Dist: Casemate Pubs. & Bk. Distributors, LLC.

Griffiths, Rudyard. Who We Are: A Citizen's Manifesto, 1 vol. 2009. (ENG.). 224p. 26.95 *(978-1-55365-124-6(3))* D&M Pubs. Inc. CAN. Dist: Perseus-PGW.

Gwyn, Richard. John A: The Man Who Made Us, 2 vols. 2008. (ENG., Illus.). 560p. pap. 19.50 *(978-0-679-31476-9(8)*, Vintage Canada) Random Hse. of Canada, Ltd. CAN. Dist: Random Hse., Inc.

Gwyn, Richard J. Nation Maker: Sir John A. MacDonald - His Life, Our Times, 2 vols. (ENG., Illus.). 688p. 2012. pap. 23.00 ***(978-0-307-35645-1(0)***, Vintage Canada) 2011. 37.00 *(978-0-307-35644-4(2)*, Random Hse CAN) Random Hse. of Canada, Ltd. CAN. Dist: Random Hse., Inc.

Haas, R. Nelson. Existential Liberalism & the Republic of Canada: A Manifesto of Moderation. 2011. 464p. 38.95 ***(978-1-4620-5664-4(4))***; pap. 28.95 ***(978-1-4620-5662-0(8))*** iUniverse, Inc.

Haerens, Margaret. Canada. 2011. (Opposing Viewpoints Ser.). 240p. pap. 26.50 *(978-0-7377-5212-0(2))*; lib. bdg. 39.70 *(978-0-7377-5211-3(4))* Cengage Gale. (Greenhaven Pr., Inc.).

Hammond, Melvin Ormond. Canadian Confederation & Its Leaders. 2009. 144p. pap. 19.99 *(978-1-150-77069-2(4))* General Bks. LLC.

—Canadian Confederation & Its Leaders. 333p. reprint ed. 98.00 *(978-0-7222-6883-4(1))* Library Reprints, Inc.

Hampson, Fen & Heinbecker, Paul, eds. Canada among Nations 2009-2010: As Others See Us. 2009. (ENG.). 336p. (C). *(978-0-7735-3627-2(2))*; pap. *(978-0-7735-3628-9(0))* McGill-Queen's Univ. Pr.

Hampson, Fen, et al. Canada's International Relations: Agendas, Alternatives, & Politics. 2011. (ENG.). 400p. pap. 42.50 *(978-0-19-542109-5(4))* Oxford Univ. Pr., Inc.

Hannay, James. Sir Leonard Tilley. (Makers of Canada Ser.). 156p. reprint ed. 88.00 *(978-0-7222-6977-0(3))* Library Reprints, Inc.

—Sir Leonard Tilley. 2008. 164p. pap. *(978-1-4086-7215-0(4))* Read Bks.

—Wilmot & Tilley. 2008. 312p. 28.99 *(978-0-559-62768-2(8))*; pap. 28.75 *(978-0-559-62764-4(5))* BiblioBazaar.

—Wilmot & Tilley. 2009. 146p. pap. *(978-1-151-29731-0(3))* Books LLC.

—Wilmot & Tilley. 2009. 192p. pap. *(978-1-4099-3156-0(0))* Dodo Pr.

—Wilmot & Tilley. 301p. reprint ed. 98.00 *(978-0-7222-6903-9(X))*; 98.00 *(978-0-7222-6970-1(6))* Library Reprints, Inc.

Harder, Lois & Patten, Steve. The Chretien Legacy: Politics & Public Policy in Canada. 2006. (ENG.). 366p. (C). per. *(978-0-7735-3107-9(6))* McGill-Queen's Univ. Pr.

Harder, Lois & Patten, Steven C. The Chrétien Legacy: Politics & Public Policy in Canada. 2006. (ENG.). 366p. (C). *(978-0-7735-3095-9(9))* McGill-Queen's Univ. Pr.

Harland Prechel Staff. Politics & Public Policy. 2008. (Illus.). xviii, 206p. 110.99 *(978-1-84855-178-7(9))* Emerald Group Publishing Ltd. GBR. Dist: Turpin Distribution Services Ltd.

Harrison, Kathryn, ed. Racing to the Bottom? Provincial Interdependence in the Canadian Federation. 2006. (Illus.). 305p. per. *(978-0-7748-1226-9(5))* Univ. of British Columbia Pr.

Hassard, Albert Richard. Canadian Constitutional History & Law. 2009. 104p. pap. *(978-0-217-45484-1(4))* Books LLC.

—Canadian Constitutional History & Law. reprint ed. 150.00 *(978-0-7222-6855-1(6))* Library Reprints, Inc.

Headley, Glyden. Elements of Accounting & Financial Management in the Government of Canada. 2010. 392p. pap. 50.00 *(978-1-4251-6267-2(3))* Trafford Publishing.

Heath, Jamey. Dead Centre: Hope, Possibility & Unity for Canadian Progressives. 2007. (ENG.). 272p. per. 26.95 *(978-0-470-84073-3(0)*, Wiley) Wiley, John & Sons, Inc.

Helleiner, Eric. Towards North American Monetary Union? The Politics & History of Canada's Exchange Rate Regime. 2007. (ENG., Illus.). 352p. per. *(978-0-7735-3178-9(5))* McGill-Queen's Univ. Pr.

Hier, Sean P. Panoptic Dreams: Streetscape Video Surveillance in Canada. 2011. (ENG., Illus.). 328p. pap. 35.95 *(978-0-7748-1872-8(7))* UBC Pr. CAN. Dist: Univ. of Washington Pr.

Hier, Sean P. & Greenberg, Josh, eds. Surveillance: Power, Problems, & Politics. 2010. (ENG., Illus.). 296p. pap. 35.95 *(978-0-7748-1612-0(0))* Univ. of Washington Pr.

Hilton, D. Craig. Shaping Commitment: Resolving Canada's Strategic Gap in Afghanistan & Beyond. 2007. (Carlisle Papers Ser.). *(978-1-58487-299-3(3))* Strategic Studies Institute, U.S. Army War College Commandant (AWCC-DSI/Pubns.).

Hopkins, John Castell. Life & Work of Sir John Thompson Prime. 2006. pap. 20.95 *(978-1-4286-4394-9(X))* Kessinger Publishing, LLC.

Houston, William. Documents Illustrative of the Canadian Constitution. 2010. 364p. pap. 32.75 *(978-1-144-00285-3(0))* BiblioBazaar.

—Documents Illustrative of the Canadian Constitution. 2009. 314p. pap. 34.18 *(978-1-150-91965-7(5))* General Bks. LLC.

Houston, William, ed. Documents Illustrative of the Canadian Constitution. 2008. 368p. 46.95 *(978-1-4369-8372-3(X))*; pap. 31.95 *(978-1-4368-2432-3(X))* Kessinger Publishing, LLC.

Howland, O. A. The New Empire. reprint ed. 150.00 *(978-0-7222-6856-8(4))* Library Reprints, Inc.

Hubbard, Ruth & Paquet, Gilles. The Black Hole of Public Administration. 2010. (Governance Ser.). (ENG., Illus.). 544p. pap. *(978-0-7766-0742-9(1))* Univ. of Ottawa Pr./Presses de l'Universite d'Ottawa.

—Gomery's Blinders & Canadian Federalism. 2007. (Governance Ser.). (ENG., Illus.). 137p. pap. *(978-0-7766-0641-5(7))* Univ. of Ottawa Pr./Presses de l'Universite d'Ottawa.

Hurtig, Mel. The Truth about Canada: Some Important, Some Astonishing, & Some Truly Appalling Things All Canadians Should Know about Our Country. 2009. (ENG.). 408p. pap. 18.95 *(978-0-7710-4166-2(7)*, Emblem Edns) McClelland & Stewart CAN. Dist: Random Hse., Inc.

Hutchison, Bruce & Palmer, Vaughn. The Incredible Canadian: A Candid Portrait of Mackenzie King. 2011. (ENG.). 464p. pap. 21.95 *(978-0-19-543890-1(6))* Oxford Univ. Pr., Inc.

Hylton, John H., ed. Aboriginal Self-Government in Canada: Current Trends & Issues. 2nd rev. ed. 2006. 480p. pap. *(978-1-895830-14-9(1))* Purich Publishing.

Hyson, Stewart, ed. Provincial & Territorial Ombudsman Offices in Canada. 2009. (IPAC Series in Public Management & Governance Ser.). (ENG., Illus.). 304p. *(978-1-4426-4067-2(7))* Univ. of Toronto Pr.

Iacovino, Raffaele & Gagnon, Alain G. Federalism, Citizenship, & Quebec: Debating Multinationalism. 2006. (ENG.). 228p. pap. *(978-0-8020-9448-3(1))* Univ. of Toronto Pr.

Ibbitson, John. Open & Shut: Why America Has Barack Obama, & Canada Has Stephen Harper. 2009. (ENG.). 176p. pap. 14.95 *(978-0-7710-4318-5(X)*, McClelland & Stewart) McClelland & Stewart CAN. Dist: Random Hse., Inc.

—The Polite Revolution: Perfecting the Canadian Dream. 2006. (ENG.). 288p. pap. 16.50 *(978-0-7710-4317-8(1)*, McClelland & Stewart) McClelland & Stewart CAN. Dist: Random Hse., Inc.

Irlbacher-Fox, Stephanie. Finding Dahshaa: Self-Government, Social Suffering, & Aboriginal Policy in Canada. 2010. (ENG., Illus.). 216p. pap. 35.95 *(978-0-7748-1625-0(2))* Univ. of Washington Pr.

Irvine, William. The Farmers in Politics. 2009. 94p. pap. 20.00 *(978-0-217-51669-3(6))* General Bks. LLC.

—The Farmers in Politics. 2009. 256p. 42.95 *(978-1-120-85590-9(X))*; pap. 27.95 *(978-1-120-75898-9(X))* Kessinger Publishing, LLC.

Jansson, Maija, ed. Realities of Representation: State Building in Early Modern Europe & European America. 2007. (ENG., Illus.). 252p. 89.00 *(978-1-4039-7534-8(5))* Palgrave Macmillan.

Johnson, David. Thinking Government: Public Administration & Politics in Canada. 3rd rev. ed. 2011. (ENG., Illus.). 528p. pap. ***(978-1-4426-0396-7(8))*** Univ. of Toronto Pr.

Johnson, William. Stephen Harper & the Future of Canada. 2006. (ENG.). 512p. per. 18.95 *(978-0-7710-9554-2(6)*, Gibson, Douglas Bks.) McClelland & Stewart CAN. Dist: Random Hse., Inc.

Jones, Esyllt & Perry, Adele, eds. A People's Citizenship Guide: A Response to Conservative Canada. 2012. (ENG., Illus.). 100p. pap. 14.95 ***(978-1-894037-56-3(1))*** Arbeiter Ring Publishing CAN. Dist: AK Pr. Distribution.

Jones, Richard. Community in Crisis: French-Canadian Nationalism in Perspective, No. 59. 215p. pap. 19.95 *(978-0-7710-9759-1(X))* McClelland & Stewart CAN. Dist: Random Hse. of Canada, Ltd.

Joseph, Thomas W. 8 Days of Crisis on the Hill; Political Blip or Stephen Harper's Revolution Derailed? 2009. 264p. pap. 19.95 *(978-1-4401-4135-5(5))* iUniverse, Inc.

Juillet, Luc & Rasmussen, Ken. Defending a Contested Ideal: Merit & the Public Service Commission, 1908-2008. 2008. (Governance Ser.). (ENG.). 264p. (gr. 10-12). pap. *(978-0-7766-0684-2(0))* Univ. of Ottawa Pr./Presses de l'Universite d'Ottawa.

Kaplan, William. A Secret Trial: Brian Mulroney & the Public Trust. 2008. (ENG., Illus.). 272p. (C). pap. *(978-0-7735-3460-5(1))* McGill-Queen's Univ. Pr.

Keil, Roger & Mahon, Rianne, eds. Leviathan Undone? Towards a Political Economy of Scale. 2010. (ENG.). 380p. pap. 37.95 *(978-0-7748-1631-1(7))* Univ. of Washington Pr.

Kelly, James B. Governing with the Charter: Legislative & Judicial Activism & Framers' Intent. 2006. (Law & Society Ser.). (ENG., Illus.). 336p. pap. *(978-0-7748-1212-2(5))* Univ. of British Columbia Pr.

Kelly, James B. & Manfredi, Christopher P., eds. Contested Constitutionalism: Reflections on the Canadian Charter of Rights & Freedoms. 2010. (ENG.). 336p. pap. 32.95 *(978-0-7748-1675-5(9))* Univ. of Washington Pr.

Kennedy, William Paul McClure. Documents of the Canadian Constitution. 707p. reprint ed. 148.00 *(978-0-7222-6857-5(2))*; 148.00 *(978-0-7222-6732-5(0))* Library Reprints, Inc.

Kinsella, Warren. Fight the Right. 2012. (ENG.). 256p. pap. 22.95 ***(978-0-307-36165-3(9)***, Random Hse CAN) Random Hse. of Canada, Ltd. CAN. Dist: Random Hse., Inc.

Kitchin, Heather A. Research Ethics & the Internet: Negotiating Canada's Tri-Council Policy Statement. 2008. (ENG.). 128p. pap. 17.95 *(978-1-55266-234-2(9))* Fernwood Publishing Co., Ltd. CAN. Dist: Independent Pubs. Group.

Klein, L. Ruth. Nazi Germany, Canadian Responses: Confronting Antisemitism in the Shadow of War. 2012. (ENG.). 336p. (C). ***(978-0-7735-4017-0(2))*** McGill-Queen's Univ. Pr.

Knight, David B. Choosing Canada's Capital: Conflict Resolution in a Parliamentary System, No. 168. 2nd ed. 416p. pap. *(978-0-88629-136-5(4))* McGill-Queen's Univ. Pr.

Kornberg, Allan & Clarke, Harold D. Citizens & Community: Political Support in a Representative Democracy. 2011. (Cambridge Studies in Comparative Politics Ser.). (ENG.). 304p. pap. 39.99 *(978-0-521-20832-1(7))* Cambridge Univ. Pr.

Kroeger, Arthur. Retiring the Crow Rate: A Narrative of Political Management. 2009. (ENG., Illus.). 280p. pap. 34.95 *(978-0-88864-513-5(9))* Univ. of Alberta Pr. CAN. Dist: Michigan State Univ. Pr.

Kulchyski, Peter Keith & Tester, Frank J. Kiumajut (Talking Back) Game Management & Inuit Rights, 1900-70. 2008. (ENG., Illus.). 336p. pap. *(978-0-7748-1242-9(7))* Univ. of British Columbia Pr.

Laforest, Rachel, ed. The New Federal Policy Agenda & the Voluntary Sector: On the Cutting Edge. 2009. (School of Policy Studies). (ENG.). 184p. (C). pap. 34.95 *(978-1-55339-132-6(2))* Queen's Univ., Schl. of Policy Studies CAN. Dist: McGill-Queen's Univ. Pr.

Lam, Vincent. Tommy Douglas. 2011. (ENG.). 204p. (gr. 12). 19.95 ***(978-0-670-06851-7(9)***, Penguin Global) Penguin Group (USA) Inc.

Larsen, Andrew, et al. Paul Martin: A Political Biography. 2011. (ENG.). 172p. (C). pap. 24.95 *(978-1-55277-735-0(9))* Lorimer, James & Co., Ltd., Pubs. CAN. Dist: Casemate Pubs. & Bk. Distributors, LLC.

Layton, Jack. Speaking Out: Ideas That Work for Canadians. 2nd rev. ed. 2006. (ENG.). 448p. pap. 19.95 *(978-1-55263-688-6(7))* Key Porter Bks. CAN. Dist: Perseus-PGW.

LeDuc, Lawrence, et al. Dynasties & Interludes: Past & Present in Canadian Electoral Politics. 2010. (ENG., Illus.). 496p. 80.00 *(978-1-55488-886-3(7))*;

pap. 35.00 *(978-1-55488-796-5(8))* Dundurn CAN. Dist: Ingram Pub. Services.

Leeson, Howard A. Saskatchewan Politics: Crowding the Centre. 2009. (University of Regina Publications(UR) Ser.). (ENG.). 494p. pap. 32.95 *(978-0-88977-234-2(7))* Canadian Plains Research Ctr. CAN. Dist: Univ. of Toronto Pr.

Lefroy, A. H. F. Canada's Federal System Being aTreatise on Canadian Constitutional Law under the British North America Act. 898p. reprint ed. 198.00 *(978-0-7222-6858-2(0))* Library Reprints, Inc.

—A Short Treatise on Canadian Constitutional Law. 322p. reprint ed. 98.00 *(978-0-7222-6859-9(9))* Library Reprints, Inc.

—A Short Treatise on Canadian Constitutional Law: With an Historical Introduction by W. P. M. Kennedy. 2007. 369p. 95.00 *(978-1-58477-777-9(X))* Lawbook Exchange, Ltd., The.

Levant, Ezra. The Enemy Within: Terror, Lies, & the Whitewashing of Omar Khadr. 2012. (ENG.). 264p. 27.99 ***(978-0-7710-4600-1(6)***, McClelland & Stewart) McClelland & Stewart CAN. Dist: Random Hse., Inc.

Levine, Allan. King: William Lyon Mackenzie King: A Life Guided by the Hand of Destiny. 1 vol. 2012. (ENG., Illus.). 552p. 36.95 ***(978-1-55365-560-2(5))*** D&M Pubs. Inc. CAN. Dist: Perseus-PGW.

Levy, David. Stalin's Man in Canada: Fred Rose & Soviet Espionage. 2011. (ENG., Illus.). 320p. 24.00 ***(978-1-936274-27-7(2))*** Enigma Bks.

Little, Bruce. Fixing the Future: How Canada's Usually Fractious Governments Worked Together to Rescue the Canada Pension Plan. 2008. (ENG., Illus.). 224p. *(978-0-8020-9874-0(6))*; pap. *(978-0-8020-9583-1(6))* Univ. of Toronto Pr.

Long, John. Treaty No. 9: Making the Agreement to Share the Land in Far Northern Ontario in 1905. 2010. (Rupert's Land Record Society Ser.). (ENG., Illus.). 624p. (C). *(978-0-7735-3760-6(0))* McGill-Queen's Univ. Pr.

Longley, James Wilberforce. Sir Charles Tupper. (Makers of Canada Ser.). 304p. reprint ed. 98.00 *(978-0-7222-6973-2(0))* Library Reprints, Inc.

Loukacheva, Natalia. The Arctic Promise: Legal & Political Autonomy of Greenland & Nunavut. 2007. (ENG., Illus.). 272p. *(978-0-8020-9295-3(0))*; pap. *(978-0-8020-9486-5(4))* Univ. of Toronto Pr.

MacDonald, L. Ian. Politics, People, & Potpourri. 2010. (ENG.). 344p. (C). *(978-0-7735-3685-2(X))* McGill-Queen's Univ. Pr.

MacFarlane, John. Triquet's Cross: A Study of Military Heroism. 2009. (ENG., Illus.). 232p. (C). *(978-0-7735-3577-0(2))* McGill-Queen's Univ. Pr.

MacKay, R. A. The Unreformed Senate of Canada. 216p. pap. 17.95 *(978-0-7710-9706-5(9))* McClelland & Stewart CAN. Dist: Random Hse. of Canada, Ltd.

MacKenzie, David & Dutil, Patrice. Canada 1911: The Decisive Election That Shaped the Country. 2011. (ENG., Illus.). 378p. pap. 29.99 *(978-1-55488-947-1(2)*, Dundurn Pr.) Dundurn CAN. Dist: Ingram Pub. Services.

Mackey, Lloyd. The Pilgrimage of Stephen Harper. 2006. (ENG., Illus.). 240p. pap. 19.95 *(978-1-55022-752-9(1))* ECW Pr. CAN. Dist: Independent Pubs. Group.

MacLaren, Roy D. The Fundamental Things Apply: A Memoir. 2011. (ENG., Illus.). 296p. (C). *(978-0-7735-3843-6(7))* McGill-Queen's Univ. Pr.

Mair, Rafe. Over the Mountains: More Thoughts on Things That Matter. 2006. (ENG.). 304p. pap. *(978-1-55017-371-0(5))* Harbour Publishing Co., Ltd.

Malcolmson, Patrick & Myers, Richard. The Canadian Regime: An Introduction to Parliamentary Government in Canada. 4th ed. 2009. (Illus.). 270p. pap. *(978-1-4426-0047-8(0))* Univ. of Toronto Pr.

Mallea, Paula. Fearmonger: Stephen Harper's Tough-on-Crime Agenda. 2011. (ENG., Illus.). 232p. pap. 24.95 ***(978-1-55277-898-2(3))*** Lorimer, James & Co., Ltd., Pubs. CAN. Dist: Casemate Pubs. & Bk. Distributors, LLC.

Malleson, Tom. Whose Streets? The Toronto G20 & the Challenges of Summit Protest. 2011. 224p. pap. 24.95 ***(978-1-926662-79-4(2))*** Between the Lines CAN. Dist: Univ. of Toronto Pr.

Manley-Casimir, Michael & Manley-Casimir, Kristen, eds. The Courts, the Charter, & the Schools: The Impact of the Charter of Rights & Freedoms on Educational Policy & Practice, 1982-2007. 2009. (ENG.). 384p. pap. *(978-0-8020-9440-7(6))* Univ. of Toronto Pr.

Marlies, Panciera. Canada's Multiculturalism Policy: Theory & Practice of an Innovative Approach to Integration. 2011. 132p. pap. ***(978-3-639-33201-8(6))*** VDM Verlag Dr. Mueller e.K.

Mars-Proietti, Laura, ed. Canadian Government Directory. 2007. 900p. 315.00 *(978-1-59237-217-1(1))* Grey Hse. Publishing.

Marsden, William. Stupid to the Last Drop: How Alberta Is Bringing Environmental Armageddon to Canada (and Doesn't Seem to Care) 2007. (ENG., Illus.). 256p. 23.95 *(978-0-676-97913-8(0)*, Knopf Canada) Knopf Canada CAN. Dist: Random Hse., Inc.

Martin, Don. Belinda: The Political & Private Life of Belinda Stronach. rev. ed. 2007. (ENG., Illus.). 288p. 24.95 *(978-1-55263-814-9(6))* Key Porter Bks. CAN. Dist: Perseus-PGW.

Maslove, Allan M., ed. How Ottawa Spends, 2009-2010: Economic Upheaval & Political Dysfunction. 2009. (ENG.). 312p. pap. *(978-0-7735-3612-8(4))* McGill-Queen's Univ. Pr.

May, Elizabeth. Losing Confidence: Power, Politics, & the Crisis in Canadian Democracy. 2009. (ENG.). 280p. pap. 16.95 *(978-0-7710-5760-1(1)*, McClelland & Stewart) McClelland & Stewart CAN. Dist: Random Hse., Inc.

Mcarthur, Shanley. Arrested Development? Critical Perspectives on the Merging of Security & Development in Canadian & Western Foreign Policy. 2008. 132p. pap. *(978-3-639-03213-0(6))* VDM Verlag Dr. Mueller e.K.

McBride, Stephen, et al. Private Affluence, Public Austerity: Economic Crisis & Democratic Malaise in Canada. 2011. (ENG.). 192p. pap. 24.95 ***(978-1-55266-403-2(1))*** Fernwood Publishing Co., Ltd. CAN. Dist: Independent Pubs. Group.

McCall, Christina. My Life as a Dame: The Personal & Political Writings of Christina McCall. Clarkson, Stephen, ed. 2009. (ENG.). 376p. pap. 15.95 *(978-0-88784-820-9(6))* House of Anansi Pr. CAN. Dist: Perseus-PGW.

McDonald, Marci. The Armageddon Factor: The Rise of Christian Nationalism in Canada. 2011. (ENG.). 464p. pap. 19.50 *(978-0-307-35647-5(7)*, Vintage Canada) Random Hse. of Canada, Ltd. CAN. Dist: Random Hse., Inc.

McDonald, Ted, et al. Canadian Immigration: Economic Evidence for a Dynamic Policy Environment. 2010. (ENG.). 344p. (C). pap. *(978-1-55339-281-1(7))* McGill-Queen's Univ. Pr.

McGrane, David. New Directions in Saskatchewan Public Policy. 2011. (Cpp Ser.). (Illus.). vi, 266p. 39.95 ***(978-0-88977-256-4(8))*** Canadian Plains Research Ctr. CAN. Dist: Univ. of Toronto Pr.

McKay, Ian. Reasoning Otherwise: Leftists & the People's Enlightenment in Canada, 1890-1920. 2008. (Illus.). 656p. pap. 49.95 *(978-1-897071-49-6(3))* Between the Lines CAN. Dist: Univ. of Toronto Pr.

McLaughlin, Robert. Irish Canadian Conflict & the Struggle for Irish Independence, 1912-1925. 2010. *(978-1-4426-4186-0(X))*; pap. *(978-1-4426-1097-2(2))* Univ. of Toronto Pr.

McMahon, Patricia I. Essence of Indecision: Diefenbaker's Nuclear Policy, 1957-1963. 2009. (ENG.). 264p. (C). *(978-0-7735-3498-8(9))* McGill-Queen's Univ. Pr.

Meighen, Arthur & Milnes, Arthur. Unrevised & Unrepented II: Debating Speeches & Others by the Right. 2011. (Queen's Policy Studies Ser.). (ENG.). 336p. (C). *(978-1-55339-297-2(3))* McGill-Queen's Univ. Pr.

Meighen, Arthur & Milnes, Arthur, eds. Unrevised & Unrepented II: Debating Speeches & Others by the Right. 2011. (Queen's Policy Studies Ser.). (ENG.). 336p. (C). pap. *(978-1-55339-296-5(5))* McGill-Queen's Univ. Pr.

Messamore, Barbara. Canada's Governors General, 1847-1878: Biography & Constitutional Evolution. 2006. (ENG., Illus.). 300p. *(978-0-8020-9061-4(3))* Univ. of Toronto Pr.

Messamore, Barbara J. & Messamore, Barbara. Canada's Governors General, 1847-1878: Biography & Constitutional Evolution. 2006. (ENG., Illus.) 300p. pap. *(978-0-8020-9385-1(X))* Univ. of Toronto Pr.

Miljan, Lydia. Public Policy in Canada: An Introduction. 6th ed. 2012. (ENG., Illus.). 368p. pap. 75.00 ***(978-0-19-544277-9(6))*** Oxford Univ. Pr., Inc.

Miller, Carman. A Knight in Politics: A Biography of Sir Frederick Borden. 2010. (ENG., Illus.). 416p. (C). *(978-0-7735-3730-9(9))* McGill-Queen's Univ. Pr.

Miller, J. R. Compact, Contract, Covenant: Aboriginal Treaty-Making in Canada. 2009. (Illus.). 448p. (ENG.). *(978-0-8020-9741-5(3))*; pap. *(978-0-8020-9515-2(1))* Univ. of Toronto Pr.

Miller, John Ormsby. The New Era in Canada: Essays Dealing with the Upbuilding of the Canadian Commonwealth. 421p. reprint ed. 98.00 *(978-0-7222-6818-6(1))* Library Reprints, Inc.

Molson, Karen. Hartland de Montarville Molson: Man of Honour. 2006. (ENG., Illus.). 328p. pap. 29.95 *(978-1-55407-150-0(X))* Firefly Bks., Ltd.

Morck, Randall, ed. Re-Creating Canada: Essays in Honour of Paul Weiler. 2011. (ENG.). 248p. (C). pap. 39.95 *(978-1-55339-273-6(6))* Queen's Univ., Schl. of Policy Studies CAN. Dist: McGill-Queen's Univ. Pr.

Morison, John Lyle. British Supremacy & Canadian Self-Government, 1839-1854. 2009. 386p. 33.99 *(978-1-115-22923-4(0))*; 386p. 38.99 *(978-1-115-22925-8(7))*; 386p. pap. 33.75 *(978-1-115-22921-0(4))*; (ENG.). 384p. pap. 26.99 *(978-1-115-22917-3(6)*, BiblioLife); (ENG.). 384p. pap. 25.99 *(978-1-115-22915-9(X)*, BiblioLife) BiblioBazaar.

—British Supremacy & Canadian Self-Government, 1839-1854. 369p. reprint ed. 98.00 *(978-0-7222-6819-3(X))* Library Reprints, Inc.

Mulroney, Brian. Memoirs. 2008. (ENG., Illus.). 1152p. pap. 24.99 *(978-0-7710-6485-2(3)*, Emblem Edns) McClelland & Stewart CAN. Dist: Random Hse., Inc.

Murphy, Isaac. In Season, Out of Season. 2009. 144p. pap. *(978-3-639-17317-8(1))* VDM Verlag Dr. Mueller e.K.

Murphy, Michael. Quebec & Canada in the New Century - New Dynamics, New Opportunities. Salée, Daniel, ed. 2007. (Canada: the State of the Federation Ser.). (ENG.). 304p. (C). 95.00 *(978-1-55339-017-6(2))* Queens Univ., Institute of Intergovernmental Relations CAN. Dist: McGill-Queen's Univ. Pr.

Murphy, Michael & Salée, Daniel, eds. Quebec & Canada in the New Century - New Dynamics, New Opportunities. 2007. (Canada: the State of the Federation Ser.). (ENG.). 304p. (C). pap. 34.95 *(978-1-55339-018-3(0))* Queen's Univ., Schl. of Policy Studies CAN. Dist: McGill-Queen's Univ. Pr.

Mutimer, David. Canadian Annual Review of Politics & Public Affairs 2003. 2009. (Canadian Annual Review of Politics & Public Affairs Ser.). (ENG.). 304p. *(978-0-8020-9985-3(8))* Univ. of Toronto Pr.

Mutimer, David. Canadian Annual Review of Politics & Public Affairs 2005. 2012. (Canadian Annual Review of Politics & Public Affairs Ser.). (ENG.). 352p. ***(978-1-4426-4385-7(4))*** Univ. of Toronto Pr.

Mutimer, David, ed. Canadian Annual Review of Politics & Public Affairs 2001. 2007. (Canadian Annual Review of Politics & Public Affairs Ser.). (ENG.). 304p. *(978-0-8020-9235-9(7))* Univ. of Toronto Pr.

—Canadian Annual Review of Politics & Public Affairs 2002. 2008. (ENG., Illus.). 304p. *(978-0-8020-9819-1(3))* Univ. of Toronto Pr.

Nadeau, Christian. Rogue in Power: Why Stephen Harper Is Remaking Canada by Stealth. Chodos, Robert et al, trs. from FRE. 2011. (ENG.). 160p. pap. 22.95 *(978-1-55277-730-5(8))* Lorimer, James & Co., Ltd., Pubs. CAN. Dist: Casemate Pubs. & Bk. Distributors, LLC.

Nathoo, Tasnim & Ostry, Aleck. The One Best Way? Breastfeeding History, Politics, & Policy in Canada. 2009. (Studies in Childhood & Family in Canada Ser.). (ENG., Illus.). 282p. pap. 29.95 *(978-1-55458-147-4(8))* Wilfrid Laurier Univ. Pr. CAN. Dist: Univ. of Toronto Pr.

Nemni, Max & Nemni, Monique. Trudeau Transformed: The Shaping of a Statesman 1944-1965. (ENG.). 2012. 352p. pap. 24.99 ***(978-0-7710-5127-2(1))*** 2011. 544p. 32.99 *(978-0-7710-5125-8(5))* McClelland & Stewart CAN. (McClelland & Stewart). Dist: Random Hse., Inc.

Newman, Peter C. The Secret Mulroney Tapes: Unguarded Confessions of a Prime Minister. 2006. (ENG., Illus.). 480p. pap. 20.95 *(978-0-679-31352-6(4)*, Vintage Canada) Random Hse. of Canada, Ltd. CAN. Dist: Random Hse., Inc.

Niezen, Ronald. The Rediscovered Self: Indigenous Identity & Cultural Justice. 2009. (McGill-Queen's Native & Northern Ser.). (ENG.). 240p. (C). *(978-0-7735-3529-9(2))*; (Illus.). pap. *(978-0-7735-3530-5(6))* McGill-Queen's Univ. Pr.

Noh, Samuel, et al. Korean Immigrants in Canada. 2011. (ENG.). *(978-1-4426-4218-8(1))*; pap. *(978-1-4426-1115-3(4))* Univ. of Toronto Pr.

Orsini, Michael & Smith, Miriam, eds. Critical Policy Studies. 2007. (ENG.). 400p. pap. 33.95 *(978-0-7748-1318-1(0))* Univ. of British Columbia Pr. CAN. Dist: Univ. of Toronto Pr.

O'Sullivan, D. A. Government in Canada: The Principles & Institutions of Our Federal & Provincial Constitutions. the B. N. A. ACT, 1867, Compared with the United States Constitution, with a Sketch of the Constitutional History of Canada. 2nd ed. 2007. 363p. 95.00 *(978-1-58477-850-9(4))* Lawbook Exchange, Ltd., The.

O'Sullivan, Dennis Ambrose. A Manual of Government in Canada: The Principles & Institutions of Our Federal & Provincial Constitutions. 246p. reprint ed. 98.00 *(978-0-7222-6863-6(7))* Library Reprints, Inc.

Palley, Howard A. Community-Based Programs & Policies: Contributions to Social Policy Development. 2008. (Illus.). (ENG.). 170p. 150.00 *(978-0-7890-3832-6(3))*; 200p. pap. 45.95 *(978-0-7890-3833-3(1))* Routledge.

Pammett, Jon H. & Dornan, Christopher. The Canadian Federal Election of 2008. 2009. (ENG., Illus.). 352p. pap. 36.99 *(978-1-55488-407-0(1)*, Dundurn Pr.) Dundurn CAN. Dist: Ingram Pub. Services.

Pammett, Jon H. & Dornan, Christopher, eds. The Canadian Federal Election Of 2011. 2011. (ENG., Illus.). 368p. pap. 36.99 *(978-1-4597-0180-9(1))* Dundurn CAN. Dist: Ingram Pub. Services.

Paquette, Jerald & Fallon, Gérald. First Nation Educational Policy in Canada: Policy of Gridlock? 2009. *(978-1-4426-4153-2(3))* Univ. of Toronto Pr.

Parkin, George Robert. Sir John A. Macdonald. (Makers of Canada Ser.). 372p. reprint ed. 98.00 *(978-0-7222-6911-4(0))*; 98.00 *(978-0-7222-6947-3(1))* Library Reprints, Inc.

Pawley, Howard. Keep True: A Life in Politics. 2011. (ENG., Illus.). 304p. pap. 31.95 *(978-0-88755-724-8(4))* Univ. of Manitoba Pr. CAN. Dist: Chicago Distribution Ctr.

Peach, Ian, ed. Constructing Tomorrow's Federalism: New Perspectives on Canadian Governance. 2007. (ENG., Illus.). 220p. pap. 31.95 *(978-0-88755-697-5(3))* Univ. of Manitoba Pr. CAN. Dist: Chicago Distribution Ctr.

Pegg, Ron. Giant among Giants. 2010. 156p. pap. *(978-1-926676-82-1(3))* Word Alive Pr.

Pennington, Christopher. The Destiny of Canada: MacDonald, Laurier, & the Election of 1891. 2012. (ENG., Illus.). 368p. (gr. 12). 30.00 ***(978-0-670-06621-6(4)***, Penguin Global) Penguin Group (USA) Inc.

Pepall, John. Against Reform. 2010. (U of T Centre for Public Management Series on Public Policy & Administration Ser.). x, 164p. ***(978-0-7727-8624-1(0))***; pap. ***(978-0-7727-8623-4(2))*** Univ. of Toronto Pr.

Peterson. Wake up, Canada! Reflections on Vital National Issues. 2010. 160p. pap. 24.67 *(978-1-152-10851-6(4))* General Bks. LLC.

Peterson, C. W. 1868-1944. Wake up, Canada! Reflections on Vital National Issues. 2010. (ENG.). 388p. pap. 33.75 *(978-1-177-27175-2(3))*; 390p. pap. 33.75 *(978-1-177-82341-8(1))* BiblioBazaar.

Peterson-Hunt, William S. Canadian Essays & Addresses. 373p. reprint ed. 98.00 *(978-0-7222-6823-0(8))*; 98.00 *(978-0-7222-6864-3(5))* Library Reprints, Inc.

Pigott, Peter. Canada in Afghanistan: The War So Far. 2007. (ENG., Illus.). 240p. 35.00 *(978-1-55002-674-0(7)*, Dundurn Pr.) Dundurn CAN. Dist: Ingram Pub. Services.

Pope, Joseph. Memoirs of the Right Honorable Sir John Alexander Macdonald, 2 vols. reprint ed. 115.00 *(978-0-404-05085-6(9))* AMS Pr., Inc.

—Memoirs of the Right Honourable Sir John Alexander Macdonald: First Prime Minister of the Dominion of Canada, 2 vol., set. reprint ed. 250.00 *(978-0-7222-6942-8(0))* Library Reprints, Inc.

Porritt, Edward. Evolution of the Dominion of Canada: Its Government & Its Politics. (Government Handbooks Ser.). 540p. reprint ed. 98.00 *(978-0-7222-6865-0(3))* Library Reprints, Inc.

Poulter, Gillian. Green: Canada's Political Parties. 2011. 32p. (gr. 5-8). ***(978-1-77071-696-4(3))*** Weigl Educational Pubs. Ltd.

Pratte, Andre. Wilfred Laurier. 2011. (ENG.). 204p. (gr. 12). 19.95 ***(978-0-670-06918-7(3)***, Penguin Global) Penguin Group (USA) Inc.

Presthus, Robert. Elite Accommodation in Canadian Politics. 2010. (ENG.). 388p. pap. 42.00 *(978-0-521-13105-6(7))* Cambridge Univ. Pr.

Preston, William Thomas Rochester. Strathcona & the Making of Canada. 2009. 326p. 45.95 *(978-1-120-82240-6(8))*; pap. 30.95 *(978-1-120-71556-2(3))* Kessinger Publishing, LLC.

—Strathcona & the Making of Canada. 324p. reprint ed. 98.00 *(978-0-7222-6964-0(1))* Library Reprints, Inc.

Prince, Michael John. Absent Citizens: Disability Politics & Policy in Canada. 2009. (ENG.). 240p. *(978-0-8020-9939-6(4))* Univ. of Toronto Pr.

Pross, Catherine A. & Pross, A. Paul. A Guide to the Identification & Acquisition of Canadian Provincial Government Publications. pap. *(978-0-7703-0153-8(3))* Bow Historical Bks.

Quinby, Rohan. Time & the Suburbs: The Politics of Built Environments & the Future of Dissent. 2012. (Semaphore Ser.). (ENG & OJI., Illus.). 150p. pap. 19.95 ***(978-1-894037-52-5(9))*** Arbeiter Ring Publishing CAN. Dist: AK Pr. Distribution.

Rabe, Barry G. The Absence of Governance: Climate Change in Canada & the United States. 2008. 44p. *(978-1-882582-62-4(4))* Canadian-American Ctr.

Ragan, Christopher & Leonard, Jeremy, eds. A Canadian Priorities Agenda: Policy Choices to Improve Economic & Social Well-Being. 2008. (ENG., Illus.). 588p. pap. *(978-0-88645-203-2(1))* McGill-Queen's Univ. Pr.

Ramos, John P. Space Policy & its Ramifications. 2011. (Space Science, Exploration & Policies Ser.). 129.00 *(978-1-61761-555-9(2))* Nova Science Pubs., Inc.

Reese, Laura A. & Rosenfeld, Raymond A. Comparative Civic Culture: The Role of Local Culture in Urban Policy-Making. 2012. (Illus.). 434p. 119.95 ***(978-1-4094-3654-6(3))*** Ashgate Publishing Co.

Rhodes, R. A. W., et al. Comparing Westminster. 2011. (ENG.). 288p. pap. 40.00 *(978-0-19-969558-4(X))* Oxford Univ. Pr., Inc.

Ricci, Nino. Pierre Elliott Trudeau. Ralston, Saul, ed. 2011. (ENG.). 204p. (gr. 12). 19.95 ***(978-0-670-06660-5(5)***, Penguin Global) Penguin Group (USA) Inc.

Riddell, William Renwick. The Canadian Constitution in Form & in Fact. 2010. 87p. *(978-1-58477-962-9(4))* Lawbook Exchange, Ltd., The.

Ritchie, Charles. Undiplomatic Diaries: 1937-1971. 2008. (ENG.). 608p. pap. 24.99 *(978-0-7710-7538-4(3)*, Emblem Edns) McClelland & Stewart CAN. Dist: Random Hse., Inc.

Rossiter, Juanita. Ndp: Canada's Political Parties. 2011. 32p. (gr. 5-8). ***(978-1-77071-698-8(X))*** Weigl Educational Pubs. Ltd.

Roy, Jeffrey. Business & Government in Canada. 2007. (Governance Ser.). (ENG., Illus.). 208p. pap. *(978-0-7766-0658-3(1))* Univ. of Ottawa Pr./Presses de l'Universite d'Ottawa.

Royal Commission on Aboriginal People, ed. Summaries of Reports by Federal Bodies & Aboriginal Organizations, Vol. 2. 374p. pap. *(978-0-660-15413-8(7))* Canadian Government Publishing.

—Summaries of Reports by Provincial & Territorial Bodies & Other Organizations, Vol. 3. 341p. pap. *(978-0-660-15414-5(5))* Canadian Government Publishing.

Rozovsky, Lorne Elkin. Canadian Healthcare Forms & Policies. 2007. (Illus.). 247p. *(978-0-433-44770-2(2))* Butterworths Canada, Ltd.

Russell, Peter H. & Sossin, Lorne, eds. Parliamentary Democracy in Crisis: The Dilemmas, Choices & Future of Parliamentary Government in Canada. 2009. (ENG.). 224p. *(978-1-4426-4076-4(6))* Univ. of Toronto Pr.

—Parliamentary Democracy in Crisis: The Dilemmas,Choices & Future of Parliamentary Govt in Canada. 2009. 224p. pap. *(978-1-4426-1014-9(X))* Univ. of Toronto Pr.

Samuels, H. Raymond, 2nd, ed. Traitors among Us: The Betrayers of Canada. 2007. pap. *(978-1-897036-07-5(6)*, Canadian National Newspaper, The) Agora Publishing Consortium.

Santosuosso, John. Canada: an Introduction for Americans. 2007. (ENG.). 224p. per. 24.95 *(978-1-4241-6505-6(9))* PublishAmerica, Inc.

Savoie, Donald J. Power: Where Is It? 2010. (ENG.). 302p. (C). *(978-0-7735-3726-2(0))*; pap. *(978-0-7735-3758-3(9))* McGill-Queen's Univ. Pr.

Sawchuk, Joe. The Dynamics of Native Politics: The Alberta Metis Experience. 2006. 192p. pap. *(978-1-895830-09-5(5))* Purich Publishing.

Schrauwers, Albert. 'Union Is Strength' W. L. Mackenzie, the Children of Peace, & the Emergence of Joint Stock Democracy in Upper Canada. 2009. (ENG., Illus.). 384p. *(978-0-8020-9927-3(0))* Univ. of Toronto Pr.

Scott, Walter Samuel. The Canadian Constitution Historically Explained by Annotated Statutes: Original Documents & Leading Cases. 289p. reprint ed. 98.00 *(978-0-7222-6867-4(X))* Library Reprints, Inc.

Segal, Hugh W. Right Balance: Canada's Conservative Tradition. 1 vol. 2011. (ENG.). 264p. 32.95 *(978-1-55365-549-7(4))* D&M Pubs. Inc. CAN. Dist: Perseus-PGW.

Shortt, Adam. Lord Sydenham. 2009. 380p. 33.99 *(978-1-116-64969-7(1))*; 33.99 *(978-1-116-64968-0(3))*; pap. 32.75 *(978-1-116-64971-0(3))*; pap. 33.75 *(978-1-116-64970-3(5))* BiblioBazaar.

—Lord Sydenham. (Makers of Canada Ser.). 367p. reprint ed. 98.00 *(978-0-7222-6913-8(7))*; 98.00 *(978-0-7222-6913-8(7))* Library Reprints, Inc.

—Lord Sydenham. 2008. 380p. pap. *(978-1-4086-8520-4(5))* Read Bks.

Siddiqui, Zafar. The Z-Book on Scientific Research & Experimental Development: Deserving Is Not Enough. 2011. 144p. pap. 21.95 ***(978-1-4502-9896-4(6))*** iUniverse, Inc.

Simpson, Leanne. Dancing on Our Turtle's Back: Stories of Nishnaabeg Re-Creation, Resurgence, & a New Emergence. 2011. (ENG., Illus.). 166p. pap. 19.95 *(978-1-894037-50-1(2))* Arbeiter Ring Publishing CAN. Dist: AK Pr. Distribution.

Simpson, Leanne, ed. Lighting the Eighth Fire: The Liberation, Resurgence, & Protection of Indigenous Nations. 2008. (ENG., Illus.). 232p. pap. 21.95 *(978-1-894037-33-4(2))* Arbeiter Ring Publishing CAN. Dist: AK Pr. Distribution.

C

Sinno, Abdulkader H., ed. Muslims in Western Politics. 2008. (ENG., Illus.). 320p. pap. 24.95 (978-0-253-22024-0(6), 0253220246) Indiana Univ. Pr.
Skogstad, Grace. Policy Paradigms, Transnationalism, & Domestic Politics. 2011. (Studies in Comparative Political Economy & Public Policy Ser.). (ENG.). 288p. pap. **(978-1-4426-1220-4(7))** Univ. of Toronto Pr.
Slowey, Gabrielle. Navigating Neoliberalism: Self-Determination & the Mikisew Cree First Nation. 2008. (ENG., Illus.). 128p. (978-0-7748-1405-8(5)) Univ. of British Columbia Pr.
Smith, David E. The Canadian Senate in Bicameral Perspective. 2006. (ENG.). 272p. pap. (978-0-8020-9464-3(3)) Univ. of Toronto Pr.
—Federalism & the Constitution Canada. 2010. xiii, 225p. **(978-1-4426-4270-6(X))**; pap. **(978-1-4426-1151-1(0))** Univ. of Toronto Pr.
—Lipset's Agrarian Socialism: A Re-Examination. 2007. (Saskatchewan Institute of Public Policy(SIPP) Ser.). (ENG.). 92p. pap. 10.00 (978-0-88977-205-2(3)) Canadian Plains Research Ctr. CAN. Dist: Univ. of Toronto Pr.
—The People's House of Commons: Theories of Democracy in Contention. 2007. (ENG.). 192p. (978-0-8020-9255-7(1)); pap. (978-0-8020-9465-0(1)) Univ. of Toronto Pr.
Smith, Denis. Ignatieff's World: Iggy Goes to Ottawa. rev. ed. 2009. (ENG.). 248p. pap. (978-1-55277-406-9(6)) Lorimer, James & Co., Ltd., Pubs. CAN. Dist: Casemate Pubs. & Bk. Distributors, LLC.
Smith, Goldwin. Canada & the Canadian Question. 340p. 2009. 25.99 (978-1-103-75083-2(6)) 2009. pap. 19.99 (978-1-103-75075-7(5)) 2008. 28.99 (978-0-559-80684-1(1)) 2008. pap. 30.75 (978-0-559-80682-7(5)) BiblioBazaar.
—Canada & the Canadian Question. 2009. 198p. pap. (978-0-217-45463-6(1)); pap. (978-0-217-82074-5(3)) Books LLC.
—Canada & the Canadian Question. 2008. 336p. 45.95 (978-1-4369-7336-6(8)); pap. 30.95 (978-1-4367-9675-0(X)) Kessinger Publishing, LLC.
—Canada & the Canadian Question. 325p. reprint ed. 98.00 (978-0-7222-6868-1(8)) Library Reprints, Inc.
Smith, Jennifer & Jackson, D. Michael. The Evolving Canadian Crown. 2012. (ENG., Illus.). 450p. (C). pap. **(978-1-55339-202-6(7))** McGill-Queen's Univ. Pr.
Smith, Miriam, ed. Group Politics & Social Movements in Canada. 2007. (ENG.). 378p. pap. (978-1-55111-771-3(1)) Univ. of Toronto Pr.
—Social Movements in Canada (Set) 2009. (ENG.). 378p. pap. (978-1-55402-779-8(9)) Univ. of Toronto Pr.
Smith, Miriam & Orsini, Michael, eds. Critical Policy Studies. 2006. (ENG., Illus.). 320p. (978-0-7748-1317-4(2)) Univ. of British Columbia Pr.
Spencer, Dick. Singing the Blues: The Conservatives in Saskatchewan. 2007. (Canadian Plains Studies(CPS) Ser.). (ENG., Illus.). 259p. pap. 24.95 (978-0-88977-206-9(1)) Canadian Plains Research Ctr. CAN. Dist: Univ. of Toronto Pr.
Srebrnik, Henry F. Jerusalem on the Amur: Birobidzhan & the Canadian Jewish Communist Movement, 1924-1951. 2008. (McGill-Queen's Studies in Ethnic History Ser.). (Illus.). 360p. (C). (978-0-7735-3428-5(8)) McGill-Queen's Univ. Pr.
Srebrnik, Henry Felix. Creating the Chupah: The Zionist Movement & the Drive for Jewish Communal Unity in Canada, 1898-1921. 2011. (Jews in Space & Time Ser.). (ENG., Illus.). 225p. 69.00 **(978-1-936235-71-1(4))** Academic Studies Pr.
Staples, Steven. Missile Defence: Round One. 2006. (ENG., Illus.). 248p. pap. (978-1-55028-929-9(2)) Lorimer, James & Co., Ltd., Pubs. CAN. Dist: Casemate Pubs. & Bk. Distributors, LLC.
Statutes of the Province of Canada: Passed in the Twenty -Fourth Year of the Reign of Her Majesty Queen Victoria & in the Fourth Session of the Sixth Parliament of Canada. 2010. 392p. 85.00 (978-1-60449-047-3(0)) Gaunt, Inc.
Stewart, David & Archer, Keith. Quasi-Democracy? Parties & Leadership Selection in Alberta. (ENG.). 208p. pap. (978-0-7748-0791-3(1)) Univ. of British Columbia Pr.
Stewart, George. Canada Under the Administration of the Earl of Dufferin. 696p. reprint ed. 128.00 (978-0-7222-6829-2(7)) Library Reprints, Inc.
Stewart, Ian. Just One Vote: From Jim Walding's Nomination to Constitutional Defeat. 2009. (ENG., Illus.). 264p. pap. 26.95 (978-0-88755-711-8(2)) Univ. of Manitoba Pr. CAN. Dist: Michigan State Univ. Pr.
Stewart, Ian & Stewart, David K. Conventional Choices: Maritime Leadership Politics. 2007. (ENG.). 320p. (C). 85.00 (978-0-7748-1341-9(5)) UBC Pr. CAN. Dist: Univ. of Washington Pr.
Stewart, Ian, et al. Conventional Choices: Maritime Leadership Politics. 2008. (ENG., Illus.). 320p. pap. 36.95 (978-0-7748-1342-6(3)) Univ. of Washington Pr.
Stewart, Lyle, ed. Afghanistan & Canada: Is There an Alternative to the War? 2009. (ENG.). 224p. 44.99 (978-1-55164-329-8(4)); pap. 24.99 (978-1-55164-328-1(6)) Black Rose Bks. CAN. Dist: Consortium Bk. Sales & Distribution.
Stokes, John, ed. Do Extra-Terrestrials Exist? A compilation of articles from the Canadian National Newspaper. 2007. per. incl. DVD (978-1-897318-09-6(X), Canadian National Newspaper, The) Agora Publishing Consortium.
Story, Donald C., et al, eds. Political Leadership & Representation in Canada: Essays in Honour of John C. Courtney. 2007. (ENG., Illus.). 240p. (978-0-8020-9187-1(3)) Univ. of Toronto Pr.
Summers, Valerie. Regime Change in a Resource Economy: The Politicies of Underdevelopment in Newfoundland since 1825. (ENG.). 80p. pap. (978-1-55081-093-6(6)) Breakwater Bks., Ltd.
Supply And Services Canada Canada Staff. Organization of the Government of Canada. 418p. pap. (978-0-660-13642-4(2)) Canadian Government Publishing.
Swain, Harry. Oka: A Political Crisis & Its Legacy, 1 vol. 2011. (ENG., Illus.). 280p. 34.95 (978-1-55365-429-2(3)) D&M Pubs. Inc. CAN. Dist: Perseus-PGW.
Taylor, Malcolm G. & Maslove, Allan. Health Insurance & Canadian Public Policy: The Seven Decisions That Created the Health Insurance System & Their Outcomes. 2nd ed. 2009. (Carleton Library Ser.). (ENG.). 592p. (978-0-7735-3566-4(7)); (C). pap. (978-0-7735-3569-5(1)) McGill-Queen's Univ. Pr.
Thomas, Paul & Brown, Curtis, eds. Manitoba Politics & Government: Issues, Institutions, Traditions. 2010. (ENG., Illus.). 462p. pap. 34.95 (978-0-88755-719-4(8)) Univ. of Manitoba Pr. CAN. Dist: Chicago Distribution Ctr.
Thompson, Wayne C. Canada. 24th ed. 2008. (Canada (Stryker-Post) Ser.). (Illus.). 201p. pap. 15.50 (978-1-887985-91-8(3)) Stryker-Post Pubns.
Thornton, Martin. Sir Robert Borden? Canada. 2011. (Makers of the Modern World Ser.). (ENG., Illus.). 220p. 19.95 (978-1-905791-84-2(4)) Haus Publishing GBR. Dist: Consortium Bk. Sales & Distribution.
Tidridge, Nathan. Canada's Constitutional Monarchy. 2011. (ENG., Illus.). 285p. pap. 26.99 (978-1-55488-980-8(4)) Dundurn CAN. Dist: Ingram Pub. Services.
Toner, Glen, et al, eds. Policy: From Ideas to Implementation. 2010. (ENG., Illus.). 290p. (C). pap. (978-0-7735-3715-6(5)) McGill-Queen's Univ. Pr.
Topp, Brian. How We Almost Gave the Tories the Boot: The Inside Story Behind the Coalition. 2010. (ENG.). 192p. pap. 24.95 **(978-1-55277-502-8(X))** Lorimer, James & Co., Ltd., Pubs. CAN. Dist: Casemate Pubs. & Bk. Distributors, LLC.
Triadafilopoulos, Triadafilos, ed. Wanted & Welcome? Policies for Highly Skilled Immigrants in Comparative Perspective. 2012. (Immigrants & Minorities, Politics & Policy Ser.). (ENG.). 10p. 139.00 (978-1-4614-0081-3(3), 1461400813) Springer.
Trost, Christine & Gash, Alison. Conflict of Interest & Public Life: Cross-National Perspectives. 2008. (ENG., Illus.). 276p. 80.00 (978-0-521-88142-5(0)) Cambridge Univ. Pr.
Trudeau, Pierre Elliott & Owen, Ivon. Approaches to Politics. 2010. (ENG., Illus.). 104p. 16.95 (978-0-19-543893-2(0)) Oxford Univ. Pr., Inc.
Tufts, Bill & Fairbanks, Lee. Pension Ponzi: How Public Sector Unions Are Bankrupting Canada's Health Care, Education & Your Retirement. 2011. (ENG.). 256p. pap. 26.95 **(978-1-118-09873-8(0)**, Wiley) Wiley, John & Sons, Inc.
Tupper, Charles. The Life & Letters of the Rt. Hon. Sir Charles Tupper, 2 vol., set. reprint ed. 250.00 (978-0-7222-6974-9(9)) Library Reprints, Inc.
—Political Reminiscences of the Right Honorable Sir Charles Tupper. 302p. reprint ed. 98.00 (978-0-7222-6971-8(4)) Library Reprints, Inc.
Turner, John N., et al. Politics of Purpose: The Right Honourable John N. Turner, 17th Prime Minister of Canada. 40th anniv. ed. 2008. (Library of Political Leadership Ser.). (ENG., Illus.). 144p. (C). pap. (978-1-55339-227-9(2)) McGill-Queen's Univ. Pr.
Turner, Royalty Patrenia. Royalty Patrenia Turner Writes the Unofficial Pledge to the Flag of Canada North America. 2007. (Illus.). 13p. (978-0-9793803-5-8(9)) Turner, Royalty Patrenia.
University of Toronto Press. Health Care in Canada: Policy & Politics. 2009. (ENG.). (978-1-4426-4003-0(0)); pap. (978-1-4426-0983-9(4)) Univ. of Toronto Pr.
—Re-Imagining Ukrainian-Canadians: History, Politics, & Identity. 2010. (Canadian Social History Ser.). 448p. (ENG.). (978-1-4426-4134-1(7)); pap. (978-1-4426-1062-0(X)) Univ. of Toronto Pr.
van Dam, Kim. A Place Called Nunavut: Multiple Identities for a New Region. 2008. (Circumpolar Studies). (ENG., Illus.). 336p. (C). pap. 30.00 **(978-90-77922-45-3(8))** Barkhuis Publishing NLD. Dist: Brown, David Bk. Co., The.
Visart de Bocarmé, Pascale & Petit, Pierre, eds. Le Canada Inuit/Inuit Canada: Pour une approche réflexive de la recherche anthropologique autochtone/Reflexive Approaches to Native Anthropological Research. 2008. (Études Canadiennes - Canadian Studies). (FRE & ENG., Illus.). 195p. pap. 43.95 (978-90-5201-427-2(2)) PIE - Peter Lang BEL. Dist: Lang, Peter.
Waiser, Bill & Houston, C. S. Tommy's Team: The Men & Women Behind the Douglas Years, 1 vol. 2010. (ENG., Illus.). 208p. pap. 19.95 (978-1-897252-75-8(7)) Fifth Hse. Pubs. CAN. Dist: Ingram Pub. Services.
Waite, P. B. In Search of R. B. Bennett. 2012. (ENG., Illus.). 344p. (C). **(978-0-7735-3908-2(5))** McGill-Queen's Univ. Pr.
Warner, Tom & Between the Lines Staff. Losing Control: Canada's Social Conservatives in the Age of Rights. 2010. 300p. pap. 29.95 (978-1-897071-41-0(8)) Between the Lines CAN. Dist: Univ. of Toronto Pr.
Watkins, Melville Henry. Staples & Beyond: Selected Writings of Mel Watkins. Grant, Hugh & Wolfe, David, eds. 2006. (Carleton Library: Vol. 210). (ENG.). 304p. per. (978-0-7735-3145-1(9)) McGill-Queen's Univ. Pr.
Weinstein, John. Quiet Revolution West: The Rebirth of Metis Nationalism, 1 vol. 2008. (ENG., Illus.). 256p. per. 23.95 (978-1-897252-21-5(8)) Fifth Hse. Pubs. CAN. Dist: Ingram Pub. Services.
Welsh, Jennifer & Woods, Ngaire, eds. Exporting Good Governance: Temptations & Challenges in Canada's Aid Program. 2007. (Studies in International Governance Ser.). (ENG.). 336p. pap. 42.95 (978-1-55458-029-3(3)) Wilfrid Laurier Univ. Pr. CAN. Dist: Univ. of Toronto Pr.
White, Jerry P. Aboriginal Policy Research, 9 vols. 2010. (ENG., Illus.). 244p. pap. 34.95 (978-1-55077-196-1(5)) Thompson Educational Publishing CAN. Dist: Univ. of Toronto Pr.
White, Rodney. Climate Change in Canada. 2010. (ENG.). 184p. 19.95 (978-0-19-543060-8(3)) Oxford Univ. Pr., Inc.
Wiles, Anne. Strategically Natural. 2010. 324p. pap. (978-3-8383-1978-0(8)) Lambert Academic Publishing.
Williams, Colin H., ed. Language & Governance. 2007. (University of Wales Press - Politics & Society in Wales Ser.). (Illus.). 320p. per. 35.00 (978-0-7083-2112-6(7)) Univ. of Wales Pr. GBR. Dist: Chicago Distribution Ctr.
Willison, John Stephen. Reminiscences, Political & Personal. 351p. reprint ed. 98.00 (978-0-7222-6976-3(5)) Library Reprints, Inc.
—Sir Wilfrid Laurier & the Liberal Party: A Political History, 2 vol., set. reprint ed. 250.00 (978-0-7222-6940-4(4)) Library Reprints, Inc.
Willson, Beckles. The Life of Lord Strathcona & Mount Royal. 2009. (ENG.). 558p. 44.99 (978-1-117-21218-0(1)); pap. 41.75 (978-1-117-21219-7(X)) BiblioBazaar.
—The Life of Lord Strathcona & Mount Royal, 2 Vols. reprint ed. 250.00 (978-0-7222-6965-7(X)) Library Reprints, Inc.
Wilson, David A. Thomas D'Arcy McGee: The Extreme Moderate, 1857-1868. 2011. (Illus.). 528p. (C). **(978-0-7735-3903-7(4))** McGill-Queen's Univ. Pr.
—Thomas D'Arcy McGee Vol. 1: Passion, Reason, & Politics, 1825-1857. 2008. (ENG., Illus.). 448p. (978-0-7735-3357-8(5)) McGill-Queen's Univ. Pr.
Wilson, David A. Thomas D'Arcy Mcgee, Volume 1: Passion, Reason, & Politics, 1825-1857. 2012. (ENG., Illus.). 448p. (C). pap. **(978-0-7735-4023-1(7))** McGill-Queen's Univ. Pr.
Wilson, Everett A. The Intellectual & Political Communication. 2010. 164p. pap. (978-3-8383-4415-7(4)) Lambert Academic Publishing.
Wilson, Gordon. Defending North America from Bears. 2011. (Illus.). 208p. pap. 30.00 **(978-1-4456-0263-9(6))** Amberley Publishing GBR. Dist: Casemate Pubs. & Bk. Distributors, LLC.
Winland, Daphne N. We Are Now a Nation: Croats Between 'Home' & 'Homeland' 2007. (Anthropological Horizons Ser.). (ENG., Illus.). 264p. (978-0-8020-9346-2(9)) Univ. of Toronto Pr.
Wiseman, Nelson. In Search of Canadian Political Culture. 2007. (ENG.). 288p. (C). 85.00 (978-0-7748-1388-4(1)) UBC Pr. CAN. Dist: Univ. of Washington Pr.
Wright, Barry. Canadian State Trials Vol. 3: Political Trials & Security Measures, 1840-1914. Binnie, Susan, ed. 2009. (Osgoode Society for Canadian Legal History Ser.). (Illus.). 656p. (978-1-4426-4015-3(4)) Univ. of Toronto Pr.
Yakimov, Radka. Caft the Blue Danube. 2008. 180p. 26.95 (978-0-595-71410-0(2)); pap. 16.95 (978-0-595-47672-5(4)) iUniverse, Inc.
Young, James. Public Men & Public Life in Canada. 2008. 445p. 32.99 (978-0-554-63139-4(3)); 117p. pap. 35.75 (978-0-554-63141-7(5)) BiblioBazaar.
—Public Men & Public Life in Canada. 2009. 274p. pap. (978-0-217-74787-5(6)) Books LLC.
—Public Men & Public Life in Canada. 406p. reprint ed. 98.00 (978-0-7222-6887-2(4)) Library Reprints, Inc.
Young, Lisa & Jansen, Harold J., eds. Money, Politics, & Democracy: Canada's Party Finance Reforms. 2011. (ENG., Illus.). 236p. pap. 35.95 **(978-0-7748-1892-6(1))** Univ. of British Columbia Pr. CAN. Dist: Univ. of Washington Pr.
Zureik, Elia & Pike, Robert M., eds. Socialization & Values in Canadian Society: Political Socialization. 294p. pap. 19.95 (978-0-7705-1758-8(7)) Nelson Education Ltd. CAN. Dist: McGill-Queen's Univ. Pr.
Zytaruk, Tom. Like a Rock: The Chuck Cadman Story. unabr. ed. 2008. (ENG., Illus.). 304p. pap. 26.95 (978-1-55017-427-4(4)) Harbour Publishing Co., Ltd. CAN. Dist: Ingram Pub. Services.

CANADA—POPULATION

Cheung, Edward. Baby Boomers, Generation X & Social Cycles: North American Long-Waves, Vol. 1. 2007th exp. ed. 2007. Orig. Title: Baby-Boomers, Generation-X & Social Cycles. (Illus.). 320p. (978-1-896330-00-6(2)) Longwave Pr.
Fong, Eric. The Changing Canadian Population. Edmonston, Barry, ed. 2011. (ENG., Illus.). 384p. (C). (978-0-7735-3793-4(7)); pap. (978-0-7735-3794-1(5)) McGill-Queen's Univ. Pr.
Howard, Heather A. & Proulx, Craig, eds. Aboriginal Peoples in Canadian Cities: Transformation & Continuities. 2010. (Indigenous Studies). (Illus.). 268p. (C). pap. 38.95 (978-1-55458-260-0(1)) Wilfrid Laurier Univ. Pr. CAN. Dist: Univ. of Toronto Pr.
Kerr, Don & Beaujot, Roderic, eds. The Changing Face of Canada: Essential Readings in Population. 2007. (ENG., Illus.). 392p. per. 44.95 (978-1-55130-322-2(1)) Canadian Scholars' Pr., Inc. CAN. Dist: Ingram Pub. Services.

CANADA—RACE RELATIONS

Agard, Rawle. Strange Fruit - Race, Racial Profiling, & the Myth of Official Multiculturalism in the Canadian Imaginary. 2008. 176p. pap. (978-3-639-04402-7(9)) VDM Verlag Dr. Mueller e.K.
Agnew, Vijay, ed. Racialized Migrant Women in Canada: Essays on Health, Violence & Equity. 2009. (ENG., Illus.). 320p. (978-0-8020-9904-4(1)); pap. (978-0-8020-9605-0(0)) Univ. of Toronto Pr.
Bolaria, B. Singh & Hier, Sean P., eds. Race & Racism in 21st Century Canada: Continuity, Complexity, & Change. 2007. (ENG., Illus.). 354p. pap. (978-1-55111-794-2(0)) Univ. of Toronto Pr.
Cannon, Martin J. & Sunseri, Lina, eds. Racism, Colonialism, & Indigeneity in Canada: A Reader. 2011. (ENG.). 352p. pap. 71.95 (978-0-19-543231-2(2)) Oxford Univ. Pr., Inc.
Carr, P. & Lund, D. E., eds. The Great White North? Exploring Whiteness, Privilege & Identity in Education. 2007. 264p. per. (978-90-8790-142-4(9)) Sense Pubs.
Carr, Paul R. & Lund, Darren E., eds. The Great White North? Exploring Whiteness, Privilge & Identity in Education. 2008. 264p. (978-90-8790-143-1(7)) Sense Pubs.
Coleman, Daniel. White Civility: The Literary Project of English Canada. 2008. (ENG.). 320p. pap. (978-0-8020-9642-5(5)) Univ. of Toronto Pr.
Enomoto, Randy & Johnson, Genevieve Fuji, eds. Race, Racialization & Antiracism in Canada & Beyond. 2007. (ENG., Illus.). 384p. pap. (978-0-8020-9504-6(6)) Univ. of Toronto Pr.
Fernando, Shanti. Race & the City: Chinese Canadian & Chinese American Political Mobilization. 2007. (ENG.). 192p. pap. 29.95 (978-0-7748-1346-4(6)) UBC Pr. CAN. Dist: Univ. of Washington Pr.
Haenens, L. d'. New Citizens, New Policies? Developments in Diversity Policy in Canada & Flanders. Gezduci, Hasibe et al, eds. 2006. 230p. pap. 30.00 (978-90-382-1021-6(3)) Academia Pr. BEL. Dist: Univ. Pr. of New England.
Hier, Sean P. & Bolaria, B. Singh, eds. Identity & Belonging: Rethinking Race & Ethnicity in Canadian Society. 2006. (ENG., Illus.). 278p. per. 34.95 (978-1-55130-312-3(4)) Canadian Scholars' Pr., Inc. CAN. Dist: Ingram Pub. Services.
Madden, Paula C. African Nova Scotian: Mi'Kmaw Relations. 2010. (Fernwood Basics Ser.). (ENG.). 128p. pap. 15.95 (978-1-55266-323-3(X)) Fernwood Publishing Co., Ltd. CAN. Dist: Independent Pubs. Group.
Mascarenhas, Michael. Where the Waters Divide: Neoliberalism, White Privilege, & Environmental Racism in Canada. 2012. (ENG., Illus.). 188p. (gr. 17). 60.00 **(978-0-7391-6827-1(4))** Lexington Bks.
Mawani, Renisa. Colonial Proximities: Crossracial Encounters & Juridical Truths in British Columbia, 1871-1921. 2010. (ENG.). 288p. pap. 35.95 (978-0-7748-1634-2(1)) Univ. of Washington Pr.
McGrath, Melanie. The Long Exile: A Tale of Inuit Betrayal & Survival in the High Arctic. 2008. (Vintage Ser.). (ENG., Illus.). 288p. pap. 13.95 (978-1-4000-3288-4(1)) Knopf, Alfred A. Inc.
Nelson, Jennifer J. Razing Africville: A Geography of Racism. 2008. (ENG.). 192p. (978-0-8020-9252-6(7)) Univ. of Toronto Pr.
Patrias, Carmela. Jobs & Justice. 2012. (ENG., Illus.). 256p. **(978-1-4426-4236-2(X))** Univ. of Toronto Pr.
Ray, Shumona Michelle. Where Are You from Miss? 2008. 332p. pap. (978-3-639-03146-1(6)) VDM Verlag Dr. Mueller e.K.
Sandercock, Leonie & Attili, Giovanni. Where Strangers Become Neighbours: Integrating Immigrants in Vancouver, Canada. 2009. (Urban & Landscape Perspectives Ser.). (Illus.). 304p. 159.00 (978-1-4020-9034-9(X), 140209034X) Springer.
Satzewich, Vic. Racism in Canada. 2011. (ENG.). 152p. 24.95 (978-0-19-543066-0(2)) Oxford Univ. Pr., Inc.
Sawchuk, Joe. The Dynamics of Native Politics: The Alberta Metis Experience. 2006. 192p. pap. (978-1-895830-09-5(5)) Purich Publishing.
Schick, Carol & McNinch, James. "I Thought Pocahontas Was a Movie" Perspectives on Race/Culture Binaries in Education & Service Professions. 2009. (University of Regina Publications(UR) Ser.). (ENG.). 240p. pap. 29.95 (978-0-88977-211-3(8)) Canadian Plains Research Ctr. CAN. Dist: Univ. of Toronto Pr.
Stanley, Timothy J. Contesting White Supremacy: School Segregation, Anti-Racism, & the Making of Chinese Canadians. 2011. (ENG., Illus.). 344p. pap. 37.95 **(978-0-7748-1932-9(4))** Univ. of British Columbia Pr. CAN. Dist: Univ. of Washington Pr.
Strachan, Bruce. Hazardous Pursuit. unabr. ed. (ENG., Illus.). 232p. pap. (978-0-920576-55-7(9)) Caitlin Pr., Inc.
Strouthes, Daniel P. Settlement, Nesting Territories & Conflicting Legal Systems in a Micmac Community, Vol. 89. 2010. (Yale University Publications in Anthropology Ser.). (ENG., Illus.). 496p. pap. 69.95 (978-0-913516-25-6(2)) Yale Univ. Pubns. in Anthropology.
Thobani, Sunera. Exalted Subjects: Studies in the Making of Race & Nation in Canada. 2007. (ENG.). 384p. (978-0-8020-9227-4(6)); pap. (978-0-8020-9454-4(6)) Univ. of Toronto Pr.
Turkel, William J. The Archive of Place: Unearthing the Pasts of the Chilcotin Plateau. 2007. (Nature/History/Society Ser.). (ENG., Illus.). 352p. 85.00 (978-0-7748-1376-1(8)) UBC Pr. CAN. Dist: Univ. of Washington Pr.
Vickers, Jill & Isaac, Annette. The Politics of Race: Canada, the United States, & Australia. 2nd ed. 2012. (ENG., Illus.). 304p. pap. **(978-1-4426-1131-3(6))** Univ. of Toronto Pr.
Zellen, Barry Scott. On Thin Ice: The Inuit, the State, & the Challenge of Arctic Sovereignty. 2009. (ENG.). 270p. 73.50 (978-0-7391-3278-4(4)) Lexington Bks.

CANADA—RELATIONS—FOREIGN COUNTRIES

Alba, Francisco, et al. Integración en América Del Norte: Diálogo, Cooperación Política e Instituciones. 2007. (Estudios Internacionales Ser.). (Illus.). 284p. pap. 59.99 (978-968-12-1314-5(9)) El Colegio de México, A.C., Biblioteca Miguel Cosío Villegas MEX. Dist: Fondo de Cultura Economica USA.
Allan, Chantal Nikkel. Bomb Canada: The Case for War & Other Unkind Remarks in the American Media. 2009. (ENG., Illus.). 160p. pap. 26.95 (978-1-897425-49-7(X)) UBC Pr. CAN. Dist: Univ. of Washington Pr.
Assessment of Risks at the Northern Border & the Infrastructure Necessary to Address Those Risks: Joint Hearing Before the Subcommittee on Economic Security, Infrastructure Protection, & Cybersecurity Joint with the

Subcommittee on Emergency Preparedness, Science, & Technology of the Committee on Homeland Security, House of Representatives, One Hundred Ninth Congress, Second Session, August 8, 2006. 2007. iv, 86p. *(978-0-16-079844-3(2)*, 552-070-36738-1) United States Government Printing Office.

Berland, Jody. North of Empire: Essays on the Cultural Technologies of Space. 2009. (ENG., Illus.). 408p. 94.95 *(978-0-8223-4288-5(X))*; pap. 26.95 *(978-0-8223-4306-6(1))* Duke Univ. Pr.

Carl Ek, Blas Nunez-Neto et al., Ian FFergusson. Canada-U. S. Relations in Focus. 2008. 104p. (C). 69.00 *(978-1-60456-252-1(8))* Nova Science Pubs., Inc.

Champion, C. P. The Strange Demise of British Canada: The Liberals & Canadian Nationalism, 1964-68. 2010. (ENG & FRE.). 336p. (C). *(978-0-7735-3690-6(6))* McGill-Queen's Univ. Pr.

Christie, Nancy, ed. Transatlantic Subjects: Ideas, Institutions, & Social Experience in Post-Revolutionary British North America. 2008. (ENG., Illus.). 496p. (C). pap. *(978-0-7735-3388-2(5))* McGill-Queen's Univ. Pr.

Clarkson, Stephen & Mildenberger, Matto. Dependent America? How Canada & Mexico Construct US Power. 2011. (ENG., Illus.). 352p. ***(978-1-4426-4463-2(X))*** Univ. of Toronto Pr.

Dafoe, John W. Canada: An American Nation. reprint ed. 20.00 *(978-0-404-00615-7(7))* AMS Pr., Inc.

Dept. Foreign Affairs and International Trade Staff. Canadian Representatives Abroad, December 1994. 16p. pap. *(978-0-660-59797-3(7))* Canadian Government Publishing.

Dept. of External Affairs Staff. Documents on Canadian External Relations. Vol. 18. 1625p. *(978-0-660-55848-6(3))* Vol. 19. *(978-0-660-56478-4(5))* Canadian Government Publishing.

Gilbert, Paula Ruth & Santoro, Milena. Transatlantic Passages: Literary & Cultural Relations Between Quebec & Francophone Europe. 2010. (ENG., Illus.). 344p. pap. *(978-0-7735-3790-3(2))* McGill-Queen's Univ. Pr.

Grinspun, Ricardo & Shamsie, Yasmine, eds. Whose Canada? Continental Integration, Fortress North America, & the Corporate Agenda. 2007. (ENG., Illus.). 592p. (C). *(978-0-7735-3191-8(2))*; per. *(978-0-7735-3192-5(0))* McGill-Queen's Univ. Pr.

Hale, Geoffrey & Gattinger, Monica, eds. Borders & Bridges: Canada's Policy Relations in North America. 2010. (ENG., Illus.). 400p. 60.00 *(978-0-19-543200-8(2))* Oxford Univ. Pr., Inc.

Heinbecker, Paul & Momani, Bessma, eds. Canada & the Middle East: In Theory & Practice. 2007. (Studies in International Governance Ser.). (ENG.). 246p. pap. 42.95 *(978-1-55458-024-8(2))* Wilfrid Laurier Univ. Pr. CAN. Dist: Univ. of Toronto Pr.

Hutchison, Bruce & Palmer, Vaughn. The Struggle for the Border. 2012. (ENG., Illus.). 520p. pap. 24.95 ***(978-0-19-544792-7(1))*** Oxford Univ. Pr., Inc.

Jones, David T. & Kilgour, David. Uneasy Neighbors: Canada, the USA & the Dynamics of State, Industry & Culture. 2007. (ENG.). 320p. 33.95 *(978-0-470-15306-2(7)*, Wiley) Wiley, John & Sons, Inc.

Poitras, Jacques. Imaginary Line: Life on an Unfinished Border. 2011. (ENG., Illus.). 342p. pap. 19.95 ***(978-0-86492-650-0(2))*** Goose Lane Editions CAN. Dist: Univ. of Toronto Pr.

Potter, Evan H. Branding Canada: Projecting Canada's Soft Power Through Public Diplomacy. 2010. (Illus.). 464p. pap. *(978-0-7735-3452-0(0))* McGill-Queen's Univ. Pr.

Potter, Evan H. & Potter, Evan. Branding Canada: Projecting Canada's Soft Power Through Public Diplomacy. 2008. (Illus.). 464p. *(978-0-7735-3435-3(0))* McGill-Queen's Univ. Pr.

Raj, Christopher S. & Abdul Nafey. Canada's Global Engagements & Relations with India. 2007. xiv, 354p. *(978-81-7827-168-2(0))* Manak Pubns. Pvt., Ltd.

Santoro, Miléna. Transatlantic Passages: Literary & Cultural Relations Between Quebec & Francophone Europe. Gilbert, Paula Ruth, ed. 2010. (ENG., Illus.). 360p. (C). *(978-0-7735-3787-3(2))* McGill-Queen's Univ. Pr.

Sharp, Paul F. Whoop-Up Country: The Canadian-American West, 1865-1885. 2009. 266p. pap. 50.00 *(978-0-8166-6012-4(3))* Univ. of Minnesota Pr.

Wright, Robert. Our Place in the Sun: Canada & Cuba in the Castro Era. Wylie, Lana, ed. 2009. (Illus.). 320p. pap. *(978-0-8020-9666-1(2))* Univ. of Toronto Pr.

Wright, Robert A. Our Place in the Sun: Canada & Cuba in the Castro Era. Wylie, Lana, ed. 2009. (Illus.). 320p. *(978-0-8020-9970-9(X))* Univ. of Toronto Pr.

CANADA—RELIGION

Aleshire, Daniel O. Earthen Vessels: Hopeful Reflections on the Work & Future of Theological Schools. 2008. 192p. pap. 20.00 *(978-0-8028-6361-4(2))* Eerdmans, William B. Publishing Co.

Beaman, L. & Beyer, P., eds. Religion & Diversity in Canada. 2008. (Religion & the Social Order Ser.). (Illus.). 236p. *(978-90-04-17015-5(4))* BRILL.

Bramadat, Paul & Seljak, David, eds. Christianity & Ethnicity in Canada, Vol. 2. 2008. 448p. *(978-0-8020-9875-7(4))*; (Illus.). pap. *(978-0-8020-9584-8(4))* Univ. of Toronto Pr.

—Religion & Ethnicity in Canada. 2009. (Illus.). 264p. pap. *(978-1-4426-1018-7(2))* Univ. of Toronto Pr.

Brewster, Joy. Diminishment: A Memoir. 2011. 19.95 ***(978-1-894667-88-3(3))*** Clements Publishing.

Bruno-Jofré, Rosa del Carmen & Tétreault, Dora. Les Missionaires Oblates: Vision et Mission. 2008. (McGill-Queen's Studies in the History of Religion Ser.). (FRE & ENG., Illus.). 248p. (C). pap. *(978-0-7735-3418-6(0))* McGill-Queen's Univ. Pr.

Carell, Paulette E. A Basket Full of Miracles. 2010. ***(978-1-77069-134-6(0))*** Word Alive Pr.

Christie/Gauvreau, Nancy/Michael. Religion, Peoples & the Making Of. 2010. (Themes in Canadian History Ser.). x, 232p. *(978-0-8020-8949-6(6))* Univ. of Toronto Pr.

—Religion,Peoples & the Making Of. 2010. x, 232p. pap. *(978-0-8020-8632-7(2))* Univ. of Toronto Pr.

Colombo, John Robert. Jeepers Creepers: Canadian Accounts of Weird Events & Experiences. 2011. (ENG.). 216p. pap. 19.99 *(978-1-55488-976-1(6)*, Dundurn Pr.) Dundurn CAN. Dist: Ingram Pub. Services.

Dinham, Adam. Faith, Public Policy & Civil Society: Problems, Policies, Controversies. 2009. (ENG., Illus.). 304p. 95.00 *(978-0-230-57330-7(4))* Palgrave Macmillan.

Echevarria, Lynn. Life Histories of Bahá'í Women in Canada: Constructing Religious Identity in the Twentieth Century. 2011. ix, 229p. (C). 78.95 ***(978-1-4331-1457-1(7))*** Lang, Peter Publishing, Inc.

Egerton, George, ed. Anglican Essentials: Reclaiming Faith in the Anglican Church of Canada. 320p. 9.95 *(978-1-55126-095-2(6))* Forward Movement Pubns.

Fox, Leo. Education Is Our Buffalo: A Teachers' Resource for First Nations, Métis & Inuit Education in Alberta. (Illus.). xi, 62p. pap. *(978-1-897196-10-6(5))* Alberta Teachers' Assn.

Gilchrist, Francine. From Darkness to Light: From the Street to Ministry. 2010. ***(978-1-77069-131-5(6))*** Word Alive Pr.

Gray, Colleen. The Congrégation de Notre-Dame, Superiors, & the Paradox of Power, 1693-1796. 2008. (McGill-Queen's Studies in the History of Religion Ser.). (ENG., Illus.). 272p. (C). pap. *(978-0-7735-3284-7(6))* McGill-Queen's Univ. Pr.

Harding, John S., et al, eds. Wild Geese: Buddhism in Canada. 2010. (Illus.). 416p. (C). pap. *(978-0-7735-3667-8(1))* McGill-Queen's Univ. Pr.

Hughes, Albert. The Whole Armour of God. 2011. 142p. 40.95 ***(978-1-258-05958-3(4))*** Literary Licensing, LLC.

James, William Closson. God's Plenty: Religious Diversity in Kingston. 2011. (ENG., Illus.). 472p. (C). ***(978-0-7735-3889-4(5))*** McGill-Queen's Univ. Pr.

Laugrand, Frederic & Oosten, Jarich G. Inuit Shamanism & Christianity: Transitions & Transformations in the Twentieth Century. 2010. (McGill-Queen's Native & Northern Ser.). (Illus.). 467p. (C). *(978-0-7735-3589-3(6))*; (ENG., pap. *(978-0-7735-3590-9(X))* McGill-Queen's Univ. Pr.

McCann, Gillian. Vanguard of the New Age: The Toronto Theosophical Society, 1891-1945. 2012. (McGill-Queen's Studies in the History of Religion Ser.). (ENG.). 232p. (C). ***(978-0-7735-3998-3(0))*** McGill-Queen's Univ. Pr.

Radhananda, Swami. Carried by A Promise: A Life Transformed Through Yoga. 2011. 264p. pap. 19.95 *(978-1-932018-36-3(0))* Timeless Bks.

Rennick, Joanne. Religion in the Ranks: Belief & Religious Experience in the Canadian Forces. 2011. (Illus.). 224p. ***(978-1-4426-4287-4(4))*** Univ. of Toronto Pr.

Scott, Jamie S., ed. The Religions of Canadians. 2012. (ENG., Illus.). 480p. pap. ***(978-1-4426-0516-9(2))*** Univ. of Toronto Pr.

Simpson, Patricia. Marguerite Bourgeoys et la Congrégation de Notre Dame, 1665-1700. Beaudry, Albert, tr. from ENG. 2007. (FRE & ENG., Illus.). 328p. (C). per. *(978-0-7735-3274-8(9))* McGill-Queen's Univ. Pr.

Soucy, Alexander Duncan, et al, eds. Wild Geese: Buddhism in Canada. 2010. (Illus.). 416p. (C). *(978-0-7735-3666-1(3))* McGill-Queen's Univ. Pr.

Thiessen, Janis Lee. Manufacturing Mennonites: Work & Religion in Post War Manitoba. 2010. (ENG.). *(978-1-4426-4213-3(0))*; pap. *(978-1-4426-1113-9(8))* Univ. of Toronto Pr.

Wilkinson, Michael. Canadian Pentecostalism: Transition & Transformation. 2010. (McGill-Queen's Studies in the History of Religion Ser.). 328p. pap. *(978-0-7735-3733-0(3))* McGill-Queen's Univ. Pr.

Yee, Russell. Worship on the Way: Exploring Asian North American Christian Experience. 2012. (ENG.). 256p. pap. 17.99 ***(978-0-8170-1707-1(0))***, Judson Pr.

CANADA—ROYAL CANADIAN AIR FORCE

Bennett, Alan. Captain Roy Brown: The Definitive Biography, Including His Encounter with the Red Baron, Manfred Von Richthofen. 2011. (ENG., Illus.). 350p. 29.95 *(978-1-883283-56-8(6))* IBks., Inc.

Bollam, Owen J. Not Bloody Likely! 2007. 88p. per. *(978-1-84748-013-2(5))* Athena Pr.

Carswell, Andrew. Over the Wire: A Canadian Pilot's Memoir of War & Survival as a POW. 2011. (ENG., Illus.). 288p. pap. 22.95 *(978-1-118-10969-4(4))*; 27.95 ***(978-1-118-10968-7(6))*** Wiley, John & Sons, Inc. (Wiley).

Chapman, Dick. The Story of a Canadian in Aviation: From 1934 To 2009. 2010. 268p. pap. 17.95 *(978-1-4269-2702-7(9))* Trafford Publishing.

Darling, Ian. Amazing Airmen: Canadian Flyers in the Second World War. 2009. (ENG., Illus.). 264p. pap. 24.99 *(978-1-55488-424-7(1))* Dundurn CAN. Dist: Ingram Pub. Services.

Duddridge, Lew. The Flying Duddridges of Hanley. 2011. 320p. 29.11 ***(978-1-4269-6654-5(7))***; pap. 19.11 ***(978-1-4269-6653-8(9))*** Trafford Publishing.

Durrett, Deanne. Unsung Heroes of World War II: The Story of the Navajo Code Talkers. 2009. (ENG., Illus.). 144p. pap. 14.95 *(978-0-8032-2456-8(7)*, Bison Bks.) Univ. of Nebraska Pr.

Fostaty, Gerry. As You Were: The Tragedy at Valcartier. 2011. 198p. pap. 19.95 *(978-0-86492-648-7(0))* Goose Lane Editions CAN. Dist: Univ. of Toronto Pr.

Knight, Darrell. Artillery Flyers at War. 2010. 484p. (ENG.). 49.50 *(978-0-557-32964-9(7))*; pap. 32.50 *(978-0-557-32963-2(9))* Lulu Enterprises Inc.

Nijboer, Donald. No 126 Wing RCAF. 2010. (Aviation Elite Units Ser.). (ENG., Illus.). 128p. pap. 25.95 *(978-1-84603-483-1(3))* Osprey Publishing, Ltd. GBR. Dist: Random Hse., Inc.

Smith, David S. Lifting the Silence: A World War II RCAF Bomber Pilot Reunites with His Past. 2010. (ENG., Illus.). 248p. pap. 27.99 *(978-1-55488-774-3(7))* Dundurn CAN. Dist: Ingram Pub. Services.

Wilson, Brent & Gill, Barbara J., eds. Hurricane Pilot: The Wartime Letters of W. O. Harry L. Gill, D. F. M., 1940-1943. 2007. (New Brunswick Military Heritage Ser.). (ENG., Illus.). 146p. pap. 16.95 *(978-0-86492-499-5(2))* Goose Lane Editions CAN. Dist: Univ. of Toronto Pr.

CANADA—ROYAL CANADIAN MOUNTED POLICE

see Royal Canadian Mounted Police

CANADA—ROYAL CANADIAN NAVY

Burnett, David. The Best of Lives: Air Commodore Wilf Burnett. 2010. 236p. 29.99 *(978-1-4520-6480-2(6))*; pap. 19.99 *(978-1-4520-6481-9(4))* AuthorHouse.

Butterley, Keith & Macpherson, Ken. River Class Destroyers. 2nd ed. 2008. (Illus.). 112p. pap. 29.95 *(978-1-55125-093-9(4))* Vanwell Publishing, Ltd. CAN. Dist: Casemate Pubs. & Bk. Distributors, LLC.

Elson, Bryan. First to Die: The First Canadian Navy Casualties in the First World War. 2010. (ENG., Illus.). 96p. pap. 24.95 *(978-0-88780-913-2(8))* Formac Publishing Co., Ltd. CAN. Dist: Casemate Pubs. & Bk. Distributors, LLC.

Elworthy, Terence. Spindrift. 2011. 264p. pap. 17.08 ***(978-1-4269-0106-5(2))*** Trafford Publishing.

Gimblett, Richard H., ed. The Naval Service of Canada, 1910-2010: The Centennial Story. 2009. (ENG., Illus.). 230p. 39.95 *(978-1-55488-470-4(5))* Dundurn CAN. Dist: Univ. of Toronto Pr.

Goodwin, James. Our Gallant Doctor: Enigma & Tragedy - Surgeon Lieutenant George Hendry & HMCS Ottawa 1942. 2007. (ENG., Illus.). 280p. 35.00 *(978-1-55002-687-0(9)*, Dundurn Pr.) Dundurn CAN. Dist: Ingram Pub. Services.

Henderson, T. Stephen. Angus L. MacDonald: A Provincial Liberal. 2007. (Illus.). 368p. (ENG.). *(978-0-8020-9231-1(4))*; pap. *(978-0-8020-9459-9(7))* Univ. of Toronto Pr.

Johnston, Mac. Corvettes Canada: Convoy Veterans of WWII Tell Their True Stories. 2008. (ENG., Illus.). 272p. 39.95 *(978-0-470-15429-8(2)*, Wiley) Wiley, John & Sons, Inc.

Johnston, William, et al. Du Littoral à la Mer Vol. 1: Histoire Officielle de la Marine Royale du Canada, 1867-1939. 2011. (ENG & FRE., Illus.). 1130p. 70.00 *(978-1-55488-909-9(X))* Dundurn CAN. Dist: Ingram Pub. Services.

—The Seabound Coast Vol. 1: The Official History of the Royal Canadian Navy, 1867-1939. 2011. (ENG., Illus.). 1014p. 70.00 *(978-1-55488-907-5(3)*, Dundurn Pr.) Dundurn CAN. Dist: Ingram Pub. Services.

Litwiller, Roger. Warships of the Bay of Quinte. 2011. (ENG., Illus.). 197p. pap. 28.00 *(978-1-55488-929-7(4)*, Dundurn Pr.) Dundurn CAN. Dist: Ingram Pub. Services.

Marshall, Debbie. Give Your Other Vote to the Sister: A Woman's Journey into the Great War. 2007. (Legacies Shared Ser.). (ENG., Illus.). 338p. per. 29.95 *(978-1-55238-228-8(1))* Univ. of Calgary Pr. CAN. Dist: Chicago Distribution Ctr.

Mayne, Richard O. Betrayed: Scandal, Politics, & Canadian Naval Leadership. 2007. (Studies in Canadian Military History Ser.). (ENG., Illus.). 296p. pap. *(978-0-7748-1296-2(6))* Univ. of British Columbia Pr.

Mayne, Richard O. & Mayne, Richard. Betrayed: Scandal, Politics, & Canadian Naval Leadership. 2006. (Studies in Canadian Military History). (ENG., Illus.). 296p. *(978-0-7748-1295-5(8))* Univ. of British Columbia Pr.

Milner, Marc. Canada's Navy: The First Century. 2nd ed. 2010. (ENG., Illus.). 504p. pap. *(978-0-8020-9604-3(2))* Univ. of Toronto Pr.

Morris, Charles. The Nation's Navy. 333p. reprint ed. 98.00 *(978-0-7222-7506-1(4))* Library Reprints, Inc.

Sales-Jones, Frank. Joining the Grey Funnel Line: The Story of a Canadian Boy Who Entered the Royal Navy in World War II at the Age of Fifteen. 2009. 392p. pap. 25.99 *(978-1-4269-0255-0(7))* Trafford Publishing.

Swinton, Marion. A Duffle Bag, Close Friends, & a Lot of Memories: The Photo Diary of Marion Swinton, W. R. C. N. S. Fowler, Michelle, ed. 2009. (ENG., Illus.). 72p. (C). pap. 12.95 *(978-0-9783441-8-4(9))* Wilfrid Laurier Univ. Pr. CAN. Dist: Univ. of Toronto Pr.

CANADA—RURAL CONDITIONS

Calbert, Louise. Rural Women's Leadership in Atlantic Canada: First-Hand Perspectives on Local Public Life & Participation in Electoral Politics. 2006. (ENG., Illus.). 176p. *(978-0-8020-9125-3(3))* Univ. of Toronto Pr.

Epp, Roger. We Are All Treaty People: Prairie Essays. 2008. (ENG.). 248p. pap. 26.95 *(978-0-88864-506-7(6))* Univ. of Alberta Pr. CAN. Dist: Michigan State Univ. Pr.

George, E. Wanda, et al. Rural Tourism Development: Localism & Cultural Change. 2009. (Tourism & Cultural Change Ser.). (ENG., Illus.). 240p. 49.95 *(978-1-84541-099-5(8))*; 149.95 *(978-1-84541-100-8(5))* Channel View Pubns., Ltd. GBR. Dist: Univ. of Toronto Pr.

McManus, Curtis R. Happyland: A History of the Dirty Thirties in Saskatchewan, 1914-1937. 2011. (West Ser.). (ENG., Illus.). 275p. pap. 41.95 *(978-1-55238-524-1(8))* Univ. of Calgary Pr. CAN. Dist: Chicago Distribution Ctr.

Peterman, Michael A., ed. The Backwoods of Canada: Catharine Parr Traill, No. 11. 408p. *(978-0-88629-311-6(1))* McGill-Queen's Univ. Pr.

Samson, Daniel, ed. Contested Countryside: Rural Workers & Modern Society in Atlantic Canada, 1800-1950, Vol. 4. (Illus.). 280p. pap. 16.95 *(978-0-919107-40-3(0))* Acadiensis Pr. CAN. Dist: Goose Lane Editions.

Widdis, Randy William. Voices from Next Year Country: An Oral History of Rural Saskatchewan. 2006. (Canadian Plains Reports(CPR) Ser.). (ENG.). 104p. pap. 10.00 *(978-0-88977-202-1(9))* Canadian Plains Research Ctr. CAN. Dist: Univ. of Toronto Pr.

CANADA—SOCIAL CONDITIONS

Agard, Rawle. Strange Fruit - Race, Racial Profiling, & the Myth of Official Multiculturalism in the Canadian Imaginary. 2008. 176p. pap. *(978-3-639-04402-7(9))* VDM Verlag Dr. Mueller e.K.

Agnew, Vijay, ed. Racialized Migrant Women in Canada: Essays on Health, Violence & Equity. 2009. (ENG., Illus.). 320p. *(978-0-8020-9904-4(1))*; pap. *(978-0-8020-9605-0(0))* Univ. of Toronto Pr.

Åkerman, Sune & Granatstein, J. L. Welfare States in Trouble: Historical Perspectives on Canada & Sweden. (Illus.). viii, 184p. *(978-91-7191-039-4(5))* Umea universitet.

Anctil, Pierre & Bernd, Zila, eds. Canada from the Outside in le Canada Vu D'Ailleurs: New Trends in Canadian Studies Nouvelles Tendances en Etudes Canadiennes, Vol. 7. 2006. (Canadian Studies - Etudes Canadiennes Ser.). (ENG & FRE.). 294p. pap. 41.95 *(978-0-8204-6686-6(7))* Lang, Peter Publishing, Inc.

Anderson, Kim. Life Stages & Native Women: Memory, Teachings, & Story Medicine. 2011. (ENG.). 223p. pap. 31.95 ***(978-0-88755-726-2(0))*** Univ. of Manitoba Pr. CAN. Dist: Chicago Distribution Ctr.

Andres/Wyn. Making of a Generation. 2010. *(978-0-8020-9258-8(6))*; (ENG.). pap. *(978-0-8020-9467-4(8))* Univ. of Toronto Pr.

Appadurai, Samy. Canad: The meat of the world Sandwich. 2009. 216p. 24.99 *(978-1-4389-7927-4(4))*; pap. 14.49 *(978-1-4389-7926-7(6))* AuthorHouse.

Bain, Colin. GED Canadian Social Studies. 2007. (GED & TABE Test Preparation Ser.). (ENG.). 240p. (gr. 12). pap. 16.95 *(978-0-7386-0309-4(0))* Research & Education Assn.

Bakht, Natasha. Belonging & Banishment: Being Muslim in Canada. 2008. 240p. pap. 25.95 *(978-1-894770-48-4(X))* TSAR Pubns. CAN. Dist: Univ. of Toronto Pr.

Beattie, Christopher. The Last Forty Year, No. 62. 224p. pap. 18.95 *(978-0-7710-9762-1(X))* McClelland & Stewart CAN. Dist: Random Hse. of Canada, Ltd.

Beavon, Daniel J. K., et al. Aboriginal Well-Being: Canada's Continuing Challenge. 2008. (ENG.). 246p. pap. 36.95 *(978-1-55077-177-0(9))* Thompson Educational Publishing CAN. Dist: Univ. of Toronto Pr.

Beisel, Vivienne. Ödo Not Take Them from Myself & My Children Foreverö - Aboriginal Water Rights in Treaty 7 Territories & the Duty to Consult. 2008. 164p. pap. *(978-3-639-02779-2(5))* VDM Verlag Dr. Mueller e.K.

Bell, Stacy L., et al. Firefighter Exam for Dummies. 2011. (ENG.). 432p. pap. 17.99 *(978-0-470-76946-1(7)*, For Dummies) Wiley, John & Sons, Inc.

Berland, Jody. North of Empire: Essays on the Cultural Technologies of Space. 2009. (ENG., Illus.). 408p. 94.95 *(978-0-8223-4288-5(X))*; pap. 26.95 *(978-0-8223-4306-6(1))* Duke Univ. Pr.

Berland, Jody & Fitzpatrick, Blake. Cultures of Militarization. 2010. (Illus.). 468p. *(978-1-897009-56-7(9))* Cape Breton Univ. Pr.

Biles, John, et al. Integration & Inclusion of Newcomers & Minorities across Canada. 2011. (ENG.). 250p. (C). pap. *(978-1-55339-290-3(6))* McGill-Queen's Univ. Pr.

Bilson, Janet Mancini & Mancini, Kyra. Inuit Women: Their Powerful Spirit in a Century of Change. 2007. (ENG., Illus.). 496p. 94.00 *(978-0-7425-3596-1(7))*; per. 44.95 *(978-0-7425-3597-8(5))* Rowman & Littlefield Publishers, Inc.

Blanie-Clark, Georgina. Wheat & Woman. 2010. 184p. pap. 8.61 *(978-1-152-11403-6(4))* General Bks. LLC.

—Wheat & Woman. 2006. (Illus.). 384p. pap. *(978-0-8020-3813-5(1))* Univ. of Toronto Pr.

Bolaria, B. Singh & Hier, Sean P., eds. Race & Racism in 21st Century Canada: Continuity, Complexity, & Change. 2007. (ENG., Illus.). 354p. pap. *(978-1-55111-794-2(0))* Univ. of Toronto Pr.

Boyd, M., et al. Ascription & Achievement: Studies in Mobility & Status Attainment in Canada, No. 133. 539p. pap. *(978-0-88629-023-8(6))* McGill-Queen's Univ. Pr.

Boyd, Michelle Hebert. Enriched by Catastrophe: Social Work & Social Conflict after the Halifax Explosion. 2007. (ENG., Illus.). 144p. pap. 17.95 *(978-1-55266-227-4(6))* Fernwood Publishing Co., Ltd. CAN. Dist: Independent Pubs. Group.

Breton, Raymond. Different Gods: Integrating Non-Christian Minorities into a Primarily Christian Society. 2012. (ENG.). 232p. (C). ***(978-0-7735-3968-6(9))***; pap. ***(978-0-7735-3993-8(X))*** McGill-Queen's Univ. Pr.

Buckner, Phillip, ed. Canada & the British Empire. (Illus.). 2010. (ENG.). 312p. pap. 37.95 *(978-0-19-956374-6(8))* 2008. 320p. 75.00 *(978-0-19-927164-1(X))* Oxford Univ. Pr., Inc.

Camfield, David. Canadian Labour in Crisis: Reinventing the Workers Movement. 2011. 160p. pap. 19.95 ***(978-1-55266-416-2(3))*** Fernwood Publishing Co., Ltd. CAN. Dist: Independent Pubs. Group.

Canfield, Jack, et al. Chicken Soup for the Soul: O Canada: 101 Heartwarming & Inspiring Stories by & for Canadians. 2011. (ENG.). 448p. pap. 14.95 *(978-1-935096-75-7(3))* Chicken Soup for the Soul Publishing, LLC.

Cannon, Martin J. & Sunseri, Lina, eds. Racism, Colonialism, & Indigeneity in Canada: A Reader. 2011. (ENG.). 352p. pap. 71.95 *(978-0-19-543231-2(2))* Oxford Univ. Pr., Inc.

C

Cardinal, Linda & Brown, Nicholas, eds. Managing Diversity: Practices of Citizenship. 2007. (Governance Ser.). (ENG.). 232p. pap. *(978-0-7766-0654-5(9))* Univ. of Ottawa Pr./Presses de l'Universite d'Ottawa.

Carr, P. & Lund, D. E., eds. The Great White North? Exploring Whiteness, Privilege & Identity in Education. 2007. 264p. per. *(978-90-8790-142-4(9))* Sense Pubs.

Carr, Paul R. & Lund, Darren E., eds. The Great White North? Exploring Whiteness, Privilge & Identity in Education. 2008. 264p. *(978-90-8790-143-1(7))* Sense Pubs.

Chang, Kornel. Pacific Connections: The Making of the US-Canadian Borderlands. 2012. (American Crossroads Ser.). (ENG.). 264p. 65.00 ***(978-0-520-27168-5(8))***; pap. 29.95 ***(978-0-520-27169-2(6))*** Univ. of California Pr.

Cho, Lily. Eating Chinese. 2010. (Cultural Spaces Ser.). (Illus.). 224p. ***(978-1-4426-4105-1(3))***; pap. ***(978-1-4426-1040-8(9))*** Univ. of Toronto Pr.

Choudry, Aziz, et al. Fight Back: Workplace Justice for Immigrants. 2009. (ENG.). 128p. pap. 17.95 *(978-1-55266-297-7(7))* Fernwood Publishing Co., Ltd. CAN. Dist: Independent Pubs. Group.

Christie, Nancy, ed. Transatlantic Subjects: Ideas, Institutions, & Social Experience in Post-Revolutionary British North America. 2008. (ENG., Illus.). 496p. (C). pap. *(978-0-7735-3388-2(5))* McGill-Queen's Univ. Pr.

Connell, Mary Anne & Cummings, Harry. Impacts of School Construction Projects by Canadian Ngos in Nicaragu. 2010. 248p. pap. *(978-3-8383-8521-1(7))* Lambert Academic Publishing.

Cooper, Sherry. The New Retirement: How It Will Change Our Future. 2008. (ENG.). 256p. (gr. 12-18). 23.50 *(978-0-670-06688-9(5)*, Penguin Global) Penguin Group (USA) Inc.

Courchene, Thomas J., et al, eds. Belonging? Diversity, Recognition & Shared Citizenship in Canada. 2007. (Institute for Research on Public Policy Ser.). (ENG., Illus.). 708p. (C). per. *(978-0-88645-201-8(5))* McGill-Queen's Univ. Pr.

Crooks, et al. Engaging & Empowering Aboriginal Youth: A Toolkit for Service Providers. 2010. 164p. pap. 54.99 *(978-1-4269-4267-9(2))* Trafford Publishing.

Crowe, Cathy. Dying for a Home: Homeless Activists Speak Out. 2007. (ENG., Illus.). 1p. per. 26.95 *(978-1-897071-22-9(1))* Between the Lines CAN. Dist: Univ. of Toronto Pr.

Curtis, James E. & Tepperman, Lorne, eds. Principles of Sociology: Canadian Perspectives. 2nd ed. 2009. (ENG., Illus.). 464p. pap. 74.00 *(978-0-19-542982-4(6))* Oxford Univ. Pr., Inc.

Dorais, Michel & Corriveau, Patrice. Gangs & Girls: Understanding Juvenile Prostitution. 2009. (ENG., Illus.). 192p. (C). pap. *(978-0-7735-3442-1(3))* McGill-Queen's Univ. Pr.

Dueck, Cameron. The New Northwest Passage: A Voyage to the Front Line of Climate Change. 2012. (ENG., Illus.). 256p. pap. 24.95 ***(978-1-926531-36-6(1))*** Great Plains Pubns. CAN. Dist: Univ. of Toronto Pr.

Durflinger, Serge Marc. Veterans with a Vision: Canada's War Blinded in Peace & War. 2010. (ENG., Illus.). 484p. (C). pap. 29.95 *(978-0-7748-1856-8(5))* UBC Pr. CAN. Dist: Univ. of Washington Pr.

Egeni, Camilius Chike. Suicide Case Study, Theories, Application & Solutions: Socioeconomic & Environmental Effects on Public Behavior: the Case of Inuit Suicide. 2011. 256p. 80.00 *(978-1-4567-0174-1(6))*; pap. 50.50 *(978-1-4567-0175-8(4))* AuthorHouse.

Emberley, Julia. Defamiliarizing the Aboriginal: Cultural Practices & Decolonization in Canada. 2009. (Illus.). 228p. pap. *(978-1-4426-1025-5(5))* Univ. of Toronto Pr.

Endicott, Stephen. Raising the Workers' Flag: The Workers''Unity League of Canada, 1930-1936. 2011. (ENG.). (C). 432p. ***(978-1-4426-4373-4(0))***; pap. ***(978-1-4426-1226-6(6))*** Univ. of Toronto Pr.

Enomoto, Randy & Johnson, Genevieve Fuji, eds. Race, Racialization, & Antiracism in Canada & Beyond. 2007. (ENG., Illus.). 384p. *(978-0-8020-8014-1(6))* Univ. of Toronto Pr.

Ertler, Klaus-Dieter & Gill, Stewart, eds. Canadian Studies: the State of the Art / ÉTudes Canadiennes: Questions de Recherché: 1981-2011: International Council for Canadian Studies (Iccs) / 1981-2011: Conseil International D'éTudes Canadiennes (Ciec) 2011. (Canadiana. Literaturen/Kulturen, Literatures/Cultures, Littératures/Cultures Ser.). 544p. 86.95 ***(978-3-631-61599-7(X))*** Lang, Peter GmbH, Europaischer Verlag der Wissenschaften DEU. Dist: Lang, Peter.

Europa Publications, ed. The Usa & Canada 2012. 14th rev. ed. 2011. (ENG.). 676p. 880.00 ***(978-1-85743-629-7(6))*** Routledge.

Evans, Sterling, ed. The Borderlands of the American & Canadian Wests: Essays on Regional History of the Forty-ninth Parallel. 2008. (ENG.). 424p. pap. 29.95 *(978-0-8032-1794-2(3))* Univ. of Nebraska Pr.

Fahmi, Magda & Rutherdale, Robert, eds. Creating Postwar Canada: Community, Diversity, & Dissent, 1945-75. 2008. (ENG., Illus.). 360p. *(978-0-7748-1384-6(9))* Univ. of British Columbia Pr.

Faust, Reg. My Father Is a Twiner. 2008. 76p. pap. 15.49 *(978-1-4343-9756-0(4))* AuthorHouse.

Ferry, Darren. Uniting in Measures of Common Good: The Construction of Liberal Identities in Central Canada, 1830-1900. 2008. (ENG., Illus.). 448p. (C). *(978-0-7735-3423-0(7))* McGill-Queen's Univ. Pr.

Finch, David. Hell's Half Acre: Early Years in the Great Alberta Oil Patch, 1 vol. 2009. (ENG., Illus.). 208p. pap. *(978-1-894384-82-7(2))* Heritage Hse.

Frazier, John W., et al, eds. The African Diaspora in the United State & Canada at the Dawn of the 21st Century. 2010. (Global Academic Publishing Ser.). (Illus.). 383p. pap. 49.00 *(978-1-4384-3684-5(X)*, Suny Pr.) State Univ. of New York Pr.

Frideres, James S., et al, eds. Immigration & Integration in Canada in the Twenty-First Century. 2008. (ENG., Illus.). 304p. (C). *(978-1-55339-217-0(5))*; pap. *(978-1-55339-216-3(7))* McGill-Queen's Univ. Pr.

Friesen, Gerald & Jones, Esyllt Wynne, eds. Prairie Metropolis: New Essays on Winnipeg Social History. 2009. (ENG.). 264p. pap. 34.95 *(978-0-88755-713-2(9))* Univ. of Manitoba Pr. CAN. Dist: Chicago Distribution Ctr.

Gairdner, William. The Trouble with Canad: A Citizen Speaks Out. 2007. 500p. per. *(978-0-9784402-2-0(6))* BPS Bks.

—The War Against the Family: A Parent Speaks Out on the Political, Economic, & Social Policies That Threaten Us All. 2007. 672p. per. *(978-0-9784402-1-3(8))* BPS Bks.

Gairdner, William D. The Trouble with Canada — Still! A Citizen Speaks Out. 2011. 546p. pap. ***(978-1-926645-67-4(7))*** BPS Bks.

Gairdner, William D. The Trouble with Canada ... Still: A Citizen Speaks Out. 2011. (ENG.). 448p. pap. 24.95 *(978-1-55470-247-3(X))* Key Porter Bks. CAN. Dist: Perseus-PGW.

Gauvreau, Michael & Hubert, Ollivier. The Churches & Social Order in Nineteenth- & Twentieth-Century Canada. 2006. (McGill-Queen's Studies in the History of Religion Ser.). (ENG., Illus.). 328p. (C). per. *(978-0-7735-3098-0(3))* McGill-Queen's Univ. Pr.

Gleason, Mona, et al, eds. Lost Kids: Vulnerable Children & Youth in Twentieth-Century Canada & the United States. 2010. (ENG., Illus.). 272p. (C). pap. 37.95 *(978-0-7748-1687-8(2))* UBC Pr. CAN. Dist: Univ. of Washington Pr.

Goyder, John. Prestige Squeeze: Occupational Prestige in Canada since 1965. 2009. (ENG., Illus.). 236p. pap. *(978-0-7735-3611-1(6))* McGill-Queen's Univ. Pr.

Grabb, Edward G. & Curtis, James E. Regions Apart: The Four Societies of Canada & the United States. 2010. (ENG., Illus.). 344p. pap. 27.95 *(978-0-19-543830-7(2))* Oxford Univ. Pr., Inc.

grammer, caroline & Grammer, Caroline. It's Not Quite Like Home. 2010. 184p. pap. *(978-3-8383-4052-4(3))* Lambert Academic Publishing.

Gray, James Henry & Gray, James H. The Roar of the Twenties, 1 vol. 2006. (Western Canadian Classics Ser.). (ENG., Illus.). 400p. pap. 14.95 *(978-1-897252-10-9(2))* Fitzhenry & Whiteside, Ltd. CAN. Dist: Ingram Pub. Services.

Griffiths, Rudyard. Who We Are: A Citizen's Manifesto, 1 vol. 2009. (ENG.). 224p. 26.95 *(978-1-55365-124-6(3))* D&M Pubs. Inc. CAN. Dist: Perseus-PGW.

Haerens, Margaret. Canada. 2011. (Opposing Viewpoints Ser.). 240p. pap. 26.50 *(978-0-7377-5212-0(2))*; lib. bdg. 39.70 *(978-0-7377-5211-3(4))* Cengage Gale. (Greenhaven Pr., Inc.).

Hamilton, Dwight & Rimsa, Kostas. Terror Threat: International & Homegrown Terrorists & Their Threat to Canada. 2007. (ENG., Illus.). 248p. 35.00 *(978-1-55002-736-5(0*, Dundurn Pr.) Dundurn CAN. Dist: Ingram Pub. Services.

Hammond-Callaghan, Marie & Hayday, Matthew, eds. Mobilizations, Protests & Engagements: Canadian Perspectives on Social Movements. 2008. (ENG., Illus.). 256p. pap. 27.95 *(978-1-55266-263-2(2))* Fernwood Publishing Co., Ltd. CAN. Dist: Independent Pubs. Group.

Hanrahan, Maura, ed. Through a Mirror Dimly. 290p. *(978-1-55081-065-1(5))* Breakwater Bks., Ltd.

Haque, Eve. Multiculturalism Within a Bilingual Framework: Language & the Racial Ordering of Difference & Belonging in Canada. 2009. (ENG.). *(978-1-4426-4078-8(2))*; pap. *(978-1-4426-1016-3(6))* Univ. of Toronto Pr.

Hassan, Shereen. Rice Alcohol: A Policy Impact Analysis. 2008. 188p. pap. *(978-3-639-04957-2(8))* VDM Verlag Dr. Mueller e.K.

Herie, Marilyn & Skinner, Wayne. Substance Abuse in Canada. 2010. (ENG., Illus.). 272p. 24.95 *(978-0-19-543387-6(4))* Oxford Univ. Pr., Inc.

Hiller, Harry. Urban Canada. 2nd ed. 2009. (ENG., Illus.). 392p. pap. 60.00 *(978-0-19-543011-0(5))* Oxford Univ. Pr., Inc.

Hiller, Harry H. Second Promised Land: Migration to Alberta & the Transformation of Canadian Society. 2009. (ENG., Illus.). 568p. (C). *(978-0-7735-3517-6(9))*; pap. *(978-0-7735-3526-8(8))* McGill-Queen's Univ. Pr.

Hird, Myra & Pavlich, George, eds. Questioning Sociology: Canadian Perspectives. 2nd ed. 2012. (ENG., Illus.). 384p. pap. 62.95 ***(978-0-19-544031-7(5))*** Oxford Univ. Pr., Inc.

Hirji, Faiza. Dreaming in Canadian: South Asian Youth, Bollywood, & Belonging. 2011. (ENG.). 264p. pap. 35.95 *(978-0-7748-1799-8(2))* UBC Pr. CAN. Dist: Univ. of Washington Pr.

Howard, Heather A. & Proulx, Craig, eds. Aboriginal Peoples in Canadian Cities: Transformation & Continuities. 2010. (Indigenous Studies). (Illus.). 268p. (C). pap. 38.95 *(978-1-55458-260-0(1))* Wilfrid Laurier Univ. Pr. CAN. Dist: Univ. of Toronto Pr.

Howard, Irene. Gold Dust on His Shirt: The True Story of an Immigrant Mining Family. 2008. 266p. pap. 26.95 *(978-1-897071-45-8(0))* Between the Lines CAN. Dist: Univ. of Toronto Pr.

Hubert, Ollivier. The Churches & Social Order in Nineteenth- & Twentieth-Century Canada. Gauvreau, Michael, ed. 2006. (McGill-Queen's Studies in the History of Religion). (ENG., Illus.). 328p. (C). *(978-0-7735-3057-7(6))* McGill-Queen's Univ. Pr.

Hurtig, Mel. The Truth about Canada: Some Important, Some Astonishing, & Some Truly Appalling Things All Canadians Should Know about Our Country. 2009. (ENG.). 408p. pap. 18.95 *(978-0-7710-4166-2(7*, Emblem Edns) McClelland & Stewart CAN. Dist: Random Hse., Inc.

Ignatieff, Michael. The Rights Revolution, 1 vol. 2nd ed. 2007. (CBC Massey Lecture Ser.). (ENG.). 192p. pap. 16.95 *(978-0-88784-762-2(5))* House of Anansi Pr. CAN. Dist: Perseus-PGW.

James Lorimer and Company Ltd., Publishers Staff, et al. Family Violence: A Canadian Introduction. 2nd rev. ed. 2011. (ENG.). 288p. pap. 24.95 ***(978-1-55277-902-6(5))*** Lorimer, James & Co., Ltd., Pubs. CAN. Dist: Casemate Pubs. & Bk. Distributors, LLC.

Janigan, Mary. Let the Eastern Bastards Freeze in the Dark. 2012. (ENG., Illus.). 352p. 27.50 ***(978-0-307-40062-8(X))*** Knopf Canada CAN. Dist: Random Hse., Inc.

Jeffrey, Leslie Ann. Sex Workers in the Maritimes Talk Back. 2007. (ENG.). 288p. per. *(978-0-7748-1332-7(6))* Univ. of British Columbia Pr.

Jones, Esyllt W. Influenza 1918: Disease, Death, & Struggle in Winnipeg. 2007. (Studies in Gender & History Ser.). (ENG.). 240p. *(978-0-8020-9197-0(0))*; (Illus.). pap. *(978-0-8020-9439-1(2))* Univ. of Toronto Pr.

Joy, Richard. Languages in Conflict: The Canadian Experience, No. 61. 162p. pap. 5.95 *(978-0-7710-9761-4(1))* McClelland & Stewart CAN. Dist: Random Hse. of Canada, Ltd.

Karlis, George. Leisure & Recreation in Canadian Society: An Introduction. 2nd ed. 2010. (Illus.). 246p. pap. 64.95 *(978-1-55077-167-1(1))* Thompson Educational Publishing CAN. Dist: Univ. of Toronto Pr.

Kazemipur, Abdolmohammad. Social Capital & Diversity: Some Lessons from Canada. 2008. (Illus.). 245p. pap. *(978-3-03911-710-9(6))* Lang, Peter.

Kerr-Ritchie, Jeffrey R. Rites of August First: Emancipation Day in the Black Atlantic World. 2011. (Antislavery, Abolition, & the Atlantic World Ser.). 312p. pap. 23.00 ***(978-0-8071-4364-3(2))*** Louisiana State Univ. Pr.

Keshen, Jeffrey A. Saints, Sinners, & Soldiers: Canada's Second World War. 2007. (Studies in Canadian Military History Ser.). (ENG., Illus.). 416p. pap. 30.95 *(978-0-7748-0924-5(8))* Univ. of Washington Pr.

Kesselman, Jonathan & Green, David A., eds. Dimensions of Inequality in Canada, 1 vol. 2007. (Equality, Security, Community Ser.). (ENG., Illus.). 480p. pap. 34.95 *(978-0-7748-1208-5(7))* UBC Pr. CAN. Dist: Univ. of Washington Pr.

Knegt, Peter. About Canada: Queer Rights. 2012. 128p. pap. 17.95 ***(978-1-55266-437-7(6))*** Fernwood Publishing Co., Ltd. CAN. Dist: Independent Pubs. Group.

Kranc & Roman. Living & Working in Canada 3e. 3rd ed. 2008. (Illus.). 224p. 22.00 *(978-1-84528-142-7(X))* How To Books GBR. Dist: Parkwest Pubns., Inc.

Ksenych, Ed, ed. Exploring Deviance in Canada: A Reader. 2011. (ENG., Illus.). 440p. 85.00 ***(978-0-19-543990-8(2))*** Oxford Univ. Pr., Inc.

Kwok, Siu-ming & Kwok, Siu-Ming. Coping with a Spoiled Self. 2009. 148p. pap. *(978-3-639-14645-5(X))* VDM Verlag Dr. Mueller e.K.

Langton, Jerry. Gangland: The Rise of the Mexican Drug Cartels from El Paso to Vancouver. 2011. (ENG., Illus.). 288p. pap. 22.95 ***(978-1-118-00805-8(7)***, Wiley) Wiley, John & Sons, Inc.

Layton, Jack. Speaking Out: Ideas That Work for Canadians. 2nd rev. ed. 2006. (ENG.). 448p. pap. 19.95 *(978-1-55263-688-6(7))* Key Porter Bks. CAN. Dist: Perseus-PGW.

Leiper, Jean McKenzie. Bar Codes: Women in the Legal Profession. 2007. (ENG.). 256p. pap. *(978-0-7748-1320-4(2))* Univ. of British Columbia Pr.

Lucas, Rex A. & Tepperman, Lorne. Minetown, Milltown, Railtown: Life in Canadian Communities of Single Industry. 2009. (ENG., Illus.). 448p. 26.95 *(978-0-19-542887-2(0))* Oxford Univ. Pr., Inc.

Luce, Jacquelyne Marie. Beyond Expectation: Lesbian - Bi - Queer Women & Assisted Conception. 2010. 304p. pap. *(978-1-4426-1008-8(5))* Univ. of Toronto Pr.

—Beyond Expectation: Lesbian/Bi/Queer Women & Assisted Conception. 2010. 304p. *(978-1-4426-4063-4(4))* Univ. of Toronto Pr.

Maidment, MaDonna R. Doing Time on the Outside: Deconstructing the Benevolent Community. 2006. (ENG.). 192p. *(978-0-8020-9080-5(X))*; pap. *(978-0-8020-9389-9(2))* Univ. of Toronto Pr.

Mair, Rafe. Over the Mountains: More Thoughts on Things That Matter. 2006. (ENG.). 304p. pap. *(978-1-55017-371-0(5))* Harbour Publishing Co., Ltd.

Malleson, Tom. Whose Streets? The Toronto G20 & the Challenges of Summit Protest. 2011. 224p. pap. 24.95 ***(978-1-926662-79-4(2))*** Between the Lines CAN. Dist: Univ. of Toronto Pr.

Marchak, M. Patricia. Ideological Perspectives on Canada. 2011. 146p. (C). pap. *(978-0-7735-3868-9(2))* McGill-Queen's Univ. Pr.

Marshall, Joan. Tides of Change on Grand Manan Island: Culture & Belonging in a Fishing Community. 2008. (ENG., Illus.). 416p. pap. *(978-0-7735-3476-6(8))*; (C). *(978-0-7735-3475-9(X))* McGill-Queen's Univ. Pr.

McCall, Christina. My Life as a Dame: The Personal & Political Writings of Christina McCall. Clarkson, Stephen, ed. 2009. (ENG.). 376p. pap. 15.95 *(978-0-88784-820-9(6))* House of Anansi Pr. CAN. Dist: Perseus-PGW.

McCann, Larry, ed. People & Place, No. 6. 263p. pap. 12.95 *(978-0-919107-09-0(5))* Acadiensis Pr. CAN. Dist: Goose Lane Editions.

McCauley, Timothy, ed. Canadian Society: Global Perspectives. 2010. 293p. pap. 61.95 *(978-1-897160-30-5(5))*; 300p. 66.95 *(978-1-897160-31-2(3))* de Sitter Pubns. CAN. Dist: International Specialized Bk. Services.

McCreery, Christopher. The Beginner's Guide to Canadian Honours. 2008. (ENG., Illus.). 96p. pap. 19.99 *(978-1-55002-748-8(4))* Dundurn CAN. Dist: Ingram Pub. Services.

McDonald, Ted, et al. Canadian Immigration: Economic Evidence for a Dynamic Policy Environment. 2010. (ENG.). 344p. (C). pap. *(978-1-55339-281-1(7))* McGill-Queen's Univ. Pr.

McLaughlin, Darrell. Differing Developments of Organic Agriculture in Canada & Sweden: The Experiences of the Farmers Themselves. 2008. 292p. *(978-0-7734-5437-8(3))* Mellen, Edwin Pr., The.

Miller, Mary Jane. Outside Looking In: Viewing First Nations Peoples in Canadian Dramatic Television Series. 2008. (McGill-Queen's Native & Northern Ser.). (ENG., Illus.). 504p. *(978-0-7735-3366-0(4))*; (C). pap. *(978-0-7735-3367-7(2))* McGill-Queen's Univ. Pr.

Montague, Kenneth, intro. Position As Desired: Exploring African Canadian Identity: Photographs from the Wedge Collection. 2011. (ENG., Illus.). 80p. pap. 25.00 *(978-0-9783370-1-8(6))* Wedge Curatorial Projects CAN. Dist: D.A.P./Distributed Art Pubs.

Mooney, Linda A. & Knox, David. Understanding Social Problems. 3rd ed. 2006. pap. 11.95 *(978-1-4288-1648-0(8))* Cram101 Inc.

Mowat, Farley. People of the Deer. 25.95 *(978-0-89190-818-0(8))* Amereon LTD.

Nathoo, Tasnim & Ostry, Aleck. The One Best Way? Breastfeeding History, Politics, & Policy in Canada. 2009. (Studies in Childhood & Family in Canada Ser.). (ENG., Illus.). 282p. pap. 29.95 *(978-1-55458-147-4(8))* Wilfrid Laurier Univ. Pr. CAN. Dist: Univ. of Toronto Pr.

Naugler, Diane, ed. Canadian Perspectives in Sexualities Studies: 2012. (ENG., Illus.). 560p. pap. 78.95 ***(978-0-19-543973-1(2))*** Oxford Univ. Pr., Inc.

Nine, Cara. Global Justice & Territory. 2012. (ENG.). 232p. 85.00 ***(978-0-19-958021-7(9))*** Oxford Univ. Pr., Inc.

Ninoslav, Mladenovic. The Legacy of Cuerrier: Issues Unresolved, Questions Unanswered. 2011. 76p. pap. ***(978-3-639-33549-1(X))*** VDM Verlag Dr. Mueller e.K.

Oecd Publishing. Oecd Rural Policy Reviews Oecd Rural Policy Reviews: Québec, Canada 2010. 2010. 304p. pap. 63.00 *(978-92-64-08214-4(X))* Organization for Economic Cooperation & Development.

Palmer, Bryan D. Canada's 1960s: The Ironies of Identity in a Rebellious Era. 2008. (Illus.). 480p. *(978-0-8020-9954-9(8))*; (ENG., pap. *(978-0-8020-9659-3(X))* Univ. of Toronto Pr.

Paquet, Gilles. Crippling Epistemologies & Governance Failures: A Plea for Experimentalism. 2009. (Governance Ser.). (ENG.). 298p. (gr. 10-12). pap. *(978-0-7766-0703-0(0))* Univ. of Ottawa Pr./Presses de l'Universite d'Ottawa.

Parrouty, Josiane. Burnout among French Immersion Teachers in British Columbia, Canad. 2010. 164p. pap. *(978-3-639-27512-4(8))* VDM Verlag Dr. Mueller e.K.

Penfold, Steven & Penfold, Steve. The Donut: A Canadian History. 2008. (ENG., Illus.). 256p. pap. *(978-0-8020-9545-9(3))* Univ. of Toronto Pr.

—The Donut: A Canadian History. 2008. (ENG., Illus.). 256p. *(978-0-8020-9797-2(9))* Univ. of Toronto Pr.

Perry, Barbara J. Diversity, Crime, & Justice in Canada. 2011. (ENG., Illus.). 400p. 80.00 ***(978-0-19-543233-6(9))*** Oxford Univ. Pr., Inc.

Podruchny, Carolyn. Making the Voyageur World: Travelers & Traders in the North American Fur Trade. 2006. (ENG., Illus.). 347p. pap. *(978-0-8020-9428-5(7))* Univ. of Toronto Pr.

Porter, John. The Measure of Canadian Society: Education, Equality & Opportunity. 359p. pap. *(978-0-88629-065-8(1))* McGill-Queen's Univ. Pr.

Prince, Michael John. Absent Citizens: Disability Politics & Policy in Canada. 2009. 240p. pap. *(978-0-8020-9630-2(1))* Univ. of Toronto Pr.

Quarter, Jack, et al. Understanding the Social Economy: A Canadian Perspective. 2009. (ENG., Illus.). 344p. *(978-0-8020-9695-1(6))*; xvii, 387p. pap. *(978-0-8020-9645-6(X))* Univ. of Toronto Pr.

Rajala, Richard A. & Rajala. Up-Coast: Forests & Industry on British Columbia's North Coast, 1870-2005, 1 vol. 2010. (ENG., Illus.). 304p. *(978-0-7726-5460-1(3))* Royal British Columbia Museum.

Ramsay, Christine, ed. Making It Like a Man: Canadian Masculinities in Practice. 2011. (Cultural Studies). (ENG., Illus.). 430p. pap. 42.95 *(978-1-55458-327-0(6))* Wilfrid Laurier Univ. Pr. CAN. Dist: Univ. of Toronto Pr.

Raphael, Dennis. Poverty & Policy in Canada: Implications for Health & Quality of Life. 2007. (ENG., Illus.). 440p. pap. 47.95 *(978-1-55130-323-9(X))* Canadian Scholars' Pr., Inc. CAN. Dist: Ingram Pub. Services.

Redekop, Bill. Made in Manitoba: Best of the Open Road Stories. 2011. (ENG.). 224p. pap. 19.95 *(978-1-926916-11-8(5))* MacIntyre & Purcell Publishing CAN. Dist: Independent Pubs. Group.

Rees, Diana. Grace Helen Mowat & the Making of Cottage Craft. 2009. (ENG., Illus.). 220p. pap. 16.95 *(978-0-86492-532-9(8))* Goose Lane Editions CAN. Dist: Univ. of Toronto Pr.

Roach, Kent. The 9/11 Effect: Comparative Counter-Terrorism. 2011. (ENG.). 448p. 99.00 *(978-1-107-00616-4(3))*; pap. 32.99 *(978-0-521-18505-9(X))* Cambridge Univ. Pr.

Roberts, Gillian. Prizing Literature. 2011. (Cultural Spaces Ser.). ***(978-1-4426-4271-3(8))*** Univ. of Toronto Pr.

Robidoux, Michael A. Stickhandling Through the Margins: First Nations Hockey in Canada. 2012. (ENG.). 176p. ***(978-1-4426-4523-3(7))***; pap. ***(978-1-4426-1338-6(6))*** Univ. of Toronto Pr.

Rompkey, Ronald. Grenfell of Labrador: A Biography. 2009. (ENG., Illus.). 368p. (C). pap. *(978-0-7735-3531-2(4))* McGill-Queen's Univ. Pr.

Ross, Colin. Northern Canada: Collected Essays Volume I. 2008. (ENG.). 134p. pap. *(978-0-9765508-6-0(5))* Manitou Communications, Inc.

Ruddel, David-Thiery & Tremblay, Robert. By Hammer & Hand, All Acts Do Stand: Blacksmithing in Canada Before 1950. 2010. (Illus.). xx, 82p. *(978-0-660-19960-3(2))* Canadian Government Publishing.

Russell, H. G. Adjacent Precast Concrete Box Beam Bridges: Connection Details. 2009. (Illus.). 75p. pap. *(978-0-309-09830-4(0))* Transportation Research Board.

Rutherdale, Myra, ed. Caregiving on the Periphery: Historical Perspectives on Nursing & Midwifery in Canada. 2010. (McGill-Queen's/Associated Medical Services Studies in the History of Medicine, H Ser.). (ENG., Illus.). 376p. (C). *(978-0-7735-3675-3(2))* McGill-Queen's Univ. Pr.

Salverson, Julie, ed. Community Engaged Theatre Vol. 19: Critical Perspectives on Canadian Theatre in English. 2011. (Critical Perspectives on Canadian Theatre in English Ser.). (ENG.). 208p. pap. 25.00 ***(978-0-88754-932-8(2))*** Playwrights Canada Pr. CAN. Dist: Consortium Bk. Sales & Distribution.

Samson, Daniel, ed. Contested Countryside: Rural Workers & Modern Society in Atlantic Canada, 1800-1950, Vol. 4. (Illus.). 280p. pap. 16.95 *(978-0-919107-40-3(0))* Acadiensis Pr. CAN. Dist: Goose Lane Editions.

Samuelson, Les & Antony, Wayne, eds. Power & Resistance: Critical Thinking about Canadian Social Issues. 4th ed. 2007. (ENG., Illus.). 448p. pap. 44.95 *(978-1-55266-224-3(1))* Fernwood Publishing Co., Ltd. CAN. Dist: Independent Pubs. Group.

Saunders, Janice. Cricket's Child, 1945-1955: How I Never Learned to Love the Bomb. 2008. (ENG.). 120p. pap. 26.50 *(978-0-7618-3994-1(1))* Hamilton Bks.

Schissel, Bernard. About Canada - Youth & Children. 2011. (About Canada Ser.). (ENG.). 144p. pap. 17.95 ***(978-1-55266-412-4(0))*** Fernwood Publishing Co., Ltd. CAN. Dist: Independent Pubs. Group.

Schlick, Mary Dodds. Coming to Stay: A Columbia River Journey. 2007. (ENG., Illus.). 208p. per. *(978-0-295-98670-8(0))* Oregon Historical Society Pr.

Schmitt, Irina. wir sind halt alle anders: Eine gesellschaftspolitische Analyse deutscher und kanadischer Jugendlicher zu Zugehörigkeit, Gender und Vielkulturalität. 2008. (Transkulturelle Perspektiven Ser.). (GER., Illus.). 320p. (C). pap. 53.00 *(978-3-89971-452-4(0))* Vandenhoeck & Ruprecht GmbH & Co. KG DEU. Dist: ISD.

Seyyed Najafi, Aref. Bubble-Solid Surface Interactions. 2010. 156p. pap. *(978-3-639-24004-7(9))* VDM Verlag Dr. Mueller e.K.

Silver, Jim, ed. In Their Own Voices: Building Urban Aboriginal Communities. 2006. (ENG.). 160p. pap. 19.95 *(978-1-55266-191-8(1))* Fernwood Publishing Co., Ltd. CAN. Dist: Independent Pubs. Group.

Spitzer, Denise L. Engendering Migrant Health: Canadian Perspectives. 2011. (ENG., Illus.). 312p. (C). pap. ***(978-0-8020-9562-6(3))*** Univ. of Toronto Pr.

—Engendering Migrant Health: Canadian Perspectives. 2011. (ENG., Illus.). 312p. ***(978-0-8020-9836-8(3))*** Univ. of Toronto Pr.

Steckley, John & Letts, Guy Kirby. Elements of Sociology: A Critical Canadian Introduction. 2nd ed. 2010. (ENG., Illus.). 456p. 65.00 *(978-0-19-543166-7(9))* Oxford Univ. Pr., Inc.

Stewart, Jan. Between Two Worlds: Supporting Refugee Children & Youth. 2011. (Illus.). xxiv, 348p. pap. *(978-1-4426-0030-0(6))* Univ. of Toronto Pr.

Stewart, W. Brian. The Ermatingers: A 19th-Century Ojibwa-Canadian Family. 2007. (ENG., Illus.). 224p. *(978-0-7748-1233-7(8))* Univ. of British Columbia Pr.

Sykes, Heather. Queer Bodies: Sexualities, Genders, & Fatness in Physical Education. 2010. (Complicated Conversation: A Book Ser. of Curriculum Studies). 176p. (C). pap. 32.95 *(978-1-4331-1161-7(6))*; 99.95 *(978-1-4331-1162-4(4))* Lang, Peter Publishing, Inc.

Teixeira, Carlos, et al, eds. Immigrant Geographies of North American Cities. 2012. (ENG., Illus.). 392p. 75.00 ***(978-0-19-543782-9(9))*** Oxford Univ. Pr., Inc.

Tepperman, Lorne, et al, eds. Sociology: A Canadian Perspective. 3rd ed. 2012. (ENG., Illus.). 744p. 99.00 ***(978-0-19-544380-6(2))*** Oxford Univ. Pr., Inc.

Tepperman, Lorne & Curtis, Josh. Social Problems: A Canadian Perspective. 3rd ed. 2011. (ENG., Illus.). 528p. pap. 99.00 ***(978-0-19-543239-8(8))*** Oxford Univ. Pr., Inc.

Tepperman, Lorne & Dickinson, Harley D. Reading Sociology: Canadian Perspectives. Tepperman, Lorne & Dickinson, Harley, eds. 2007. (ENG., Illus.). 355p. 45.00 *(978-0-19-542292-4(9))* Oxford Univ. Pr., Inc.

Tepperman, Lorne & Kalyta, Angela, eds. Reading Sociology: Canadian Perspectives. 2nd ed. 2011. (ENG., Illus.). 368p. pap. 65.00 ***(978-0-19-544129-1(X))*** Oxford Univ. Pr., Inc.

Tepperman, Lorne, et al. Sociology: A Canadian Perspective. 2nd ed. 2010. (ENG., Illus.). 778p. 95.00 *(978-0-19-543360-9(2))* Oxford Univ. Pr., Inc.

Tettey, Wisdom J., ed. The African Diaspora in Canada: Negotiating Identity & Belonging. 2006. (Africa Ser.). (ENG., Illus.). 248p. per. 39.95 *(978-1-55238-175-5(7))* Univ. of Calgary Pr. CAN. Dist: Chicago Distribution Ctr.

Thobani, Sunera. Exalted Subjects: Studies in the Making of Race & Nation in Canada. 2007. (ENG.). 384p. *(978-0-8020-9227-4(6))*; pap. *(978-0-8020-9454-4(6))* Univ. of Toronto Pr.

Thomas, Paul & Brown, Curtis, eds. Manitoba Politics & Government: Issues, Institutions, Traditions. 2010. (ENG., Illus.). 462p. pap. 34.95 *(978-0-88755-719-4(8))* Univ. of Manitoba Pr. CAN. Dist: Chicago Distribution Ctr.

Thong Tri, Thay Thich & Avery, Martin. Wake up Here & Now: How to Recover Your Life Before It Is Over. 2010. 60p. pap. 15.00 *(978-0-557-73123-7(2))* Lulu Enterprises Inc.

Turner, John N., et al. Politics of Purpose: The Right Honourable John N. Turner, 17th Prime Minister of Canada. 40th anniv. ed. 2008. (Library of Political Leadership Ser.). (ENG., Illus.). 144p. (C). pap. *(978-1-55339-227-9(2))* McGill-Queen's Univ. Pr.

University of Toronto Press. Disability & Questions of Access. 2010. (ENG.). pap. *(978-1-4426-1000-2(X))* Univ. of Toronto Pr.

The Usa & Canada 2007. 9th rev. ed. 2006. (ENG., Illus.). 624p. 615.00 *(978-1-85743-396-8(3))* Routledge.

van den Hoonaard, Deborah. By Himself: The Older Man's Experience of Widowhood. 2010. 176p. *(978-1-4426-4109-9(6))* Univ. of Toronto Pr.

Viers, Kenneth G. Discourses of Assisted Dying. 2010. 220p. pap. *(978-3-8383-8354-5(0))* Lambert Academic Publishing.

Wallace, Schuyler T. Tin Lizard Tales: Reflections from A Train. 2007. 348p. per. 15.95 *(978-1-4327-1254-9(3))* Outskirts Pr., Inc.

Walsh, John C. & Opp, James. Home, Work, & Play: Situating Canadian Social History, 1840-1980. 2nd ed. 2010. (ENG., Illus.). 408p. pap. 145.00 *(978-0-19-543124-7(3))* Oxford Univ. Pr., Inc.

Wang, Yina. Understanding of Career & Attitudes Toward Career Counselling. 2010. 120p. pap. *(978-3-639-23776-4(5))* VDM Verlag Dr. Mueller e.K.

Waugh, Thomas, et al. Challenge for Change: Activist Documentary at the National Film Board of Canada. 2010. (Illus.). 574p. (C). *(978-0-7735-3662-3(0))* McGill-Queen's Univ. Pr.

Webb, Jeff A. The Voice of Newfoundland: A Social History of the Broadcasting Corporation of Newfoundland, 1939-1949. 2008. (ENG., Illus.). 288p. *(978-0-8020-9820-7(7))*; pap. *(978-0-8020-9553-4(4))* Univ. of Toronto Pr.

White, Jerry P. Aboriginal Policy Research, 9 vols. 2010. (ENG., Illus.). 244p. pap. 34.95 *(978-1-55077-196-1(5))* Thompson Educational Publishing CAN. Dist: Univ. of Toronto Pr.

Whitmore, Elizabeth, et al, eds. Activism That Works. 2011. 160p. pap. 19.95 *(978-1-55266-411-7(2))* Fernwood Publishing Co., Ltd. CAN. Dist: Independent Pubs. Group.

Widdowson, Frances & Howard, Albert. Disrobing the Aboriginal Industry: The Deception Behind Indigenous Cultural Preservation. 2008. (ENG., Illus.). 336p. (C). pap. *(978-0-7735-3421-6(0))* McGill-Queen's Univ. Pr.

Wilson, Christopher. Radically Changed: 37 Real Life Inspirational Stories. 2010. 352p. pap. 17.99 *(978-1-4490-8146-1(0))* AuthorHouse.

Wojna, Lisa. Missing: The Disappeared, Lost or Abducted in Canada. 2007. (ENG., Illus.). 264p. pap. *(978-0-9783409-0-2(6))* Quagmire Pr., Ltd. CAN. Dist: Lone Pine Publishing.

Wong, John Chi-Kit, ed. Coast to Coast: Hockey in Canada to the Second World War. 2009. (Illus.). 256p. *(978-0-8020-9778-1(2))*; pap. *(978-0-8020-9532-9(1))* Univ. of Toronto Pr.

Yousif, Ahmad F. Muslims in Canada: A Question of Identity. 2nd ed. 2008. (Illus.). *(978-1-894508-99-5(8))* LEGAS.

Zawilski, Valerie, ed. Inequality in Canada: A Reader on the Intersections of Gender, Race, & Class. 2nd ed. 2009. (ENG., Illus.). 480p. 60.00 *(978-0-19-543012-7(3))* Oxford Univ. Pr., Inc.

Zzz & McAdam, Sylvia. Cultural Teachings: First Nations Protocols & Methodologies. (CRE, DAK & ENG., Illus.). xii, 57p. pap. *(978-1-55165-528-4(4))* Saskatchewan Indian Cultural Ctr.

CANADA—SOCIAL LIFE AND CUSTOMS

Adler, Ronald B., et al. Understanding Human Communication, 1 vol. 11th ed. 2011. 512p. (C). pap. 89.95 *(978-0-19-974733-2(5))* Oxford Univ. Pr., Inc.

Alia, Valerie. Names & Nunavut: Culture & Identity in the Inuit Homeland. 2006. (Illus.). 208p. (C). 90.00 *(978-1-84545-165-3(1))* Berghahn Bks., Inc.

Amos, Dorian. The Good Life Gets Better: Panning for Gold. 2006. (ENG., Illus.). 200p. pap. 15.95 *(978-1-903070-48-2(1))* Eye Bks. GBR. Dist: Independent Pubs. Group.

Anderson, Kim. Life Stages & Native Women: Memory, Teachings, & Story Medicine. 2011. (ENG.). 223p. pap. 31.95 ***(978-0-88755-726-2(0))*** Univ. of Manitoba Pr. CAN. Dist: Chicago Distribution Ctr.

Azoulay, Dan. Hearts & Minds: Canadian Romance at the Dawn of the Modern Era, 1900-1930. 2011. (West Ser.). (ENG., Illus.). 300p. pap. 41.95 *(978-1-55238-520-3(5))* Univ. of Calgary Pr. CAN. Dist: Chicago Distribution Ctr.

Beavan, F. Sketches & Tales Illustrative of Life in the Backwoods of New Brunswick, North America. 2008. 124p. 24.99 *(978-0-554-24361-0(X))* BiblioBazaar.

—Sketches & Tales Illustrative of Life in the Backwoods of New Brunswick, North America. 2007. 96p. per. *(978-1-4065-3701-7(2))* Dodo Pr.

—Sketches & Tales Illustrative of Life in the Backwoods of New Brunswick, North America: Gleaned from Actual Observation & Experience Dur. 2007. 110p. pap. 18.99 *(978-1-4264-6378-5(2))* 2006. (ENG.). 122p. pap. 19.99 *(978-1-4264-6452-2(5))* BiblioBazaar.

Belcourt, Herb. Walking in the Woods: A Métis Journey, 1 vol. 2006. (ENG., Illus.). 224p. per. *(978-1-897142-17-2(X))* Brindle & Glass Publishing.

Bennett, John & Rowley, Susan, eds. Uqalurait: An Oral History of Nunavut. 2008. (McGill-Queen's Native & Northern Ser.). (ENG., Illus.). 520p. pap. *(978-0-7735-2341-8(3))* McGill-Queen's Univ. Pr.

Billson, Janet Mancini & Mancini, Kyra. Inuit Women: Their Powerful Spirit in a Century of Change. 2007. (ENG., Illus.). 496p. 94.00 *(978-0-7425-3596-1(7))* Rowman & Littlefield Publishers, Inc.

Bird, Isabella Lucy. The Englishwoman in America. 2007. (Travel in America Ser.). (ENG.). 480p. 49.95 *(978-1-4290-0336-0(7))*; per. 24.95 *(978-1-4290-0337-7(5))* Applewood Bks.

—The Englishwoman in America. 2008. 360p. 31.99 *(978-0-554-22526-5(3))* 2007. (ENG.). 332p. pap. 23.99 *(978-1-4264-2529-5(5))* 2007. (ENG.). 358p. pap. 26.99 *(978-1-4264-2552-3(X))* BiblioBazaar.

Boas, Franz. Eskimo Story (Written for My Children) My Arctic Expedition 1883-1884. Boas, Norman F., ed. 2007. (Illus.). 56p. (YA). (gr. 1-12). pap. 6.00 *(978-0-9672626-3-5(1))* Boas & Meyer, Pubs.

Bravo, Michael & Triscott, Nicola, eds. Arctic Perspective Cahier No. 2: Geopolitics & Autonomy. 2011. (ENG., Illus.). 116p. 30.00 *(978-3-7757-2681-8(0))* Hatje Cantz Verlag GmbH & Co KG DEU. Dist: D.A.P./Distributed Art Pubs.

Brun, Josette. Vie et Mort du Couple en Nouvelle-France: Québec et Louisbourg au XVIIIe Siècle. 2006. (Studies on the History of Quebec/Etudes d?histoire du Quebec Ser.). (FRE & ENG.). 200p. (C). *(978-0-7735-3067-6(3))*; pap. *(978-0-7735-3068-3(1))* McGill-Queen's Univ. Pr.

Chesters, Graeme & Jennings, Sally. Culture Wise Canada: The Essential Guide to Culture, Customs & Business Etiquette. 2008. (Culture Wise Ser.). (ENG., Illus.). 224p. pap. 17.95 *(978-1-905303-21-2(1))* Survival Bks., Ltd.

ChGteauclair, Wilfrid. The Young Seigneur or, Nation-Making. 2007. 132p. per. *(978-1-4068-4524-2(8))* Echo Library.

Christie/Gauvreau, Nancy/Michael. Religion, Peoples & the Making Of. 2010. (Themes in Canadian History Ser.). x, 232p. *(978-0-8020-8949-6(6))* Univ. of Toronto Pr.

—Religion,Peoples & the Making Of. 2010. x, 232p. pap. *(978-0-8020-8632-7(2))* Univ. of Toronto Pr.

Comacchio, Cynthia. The Dominion of Youth: Adolescence & the Making of Modern Canada, 1920 To 1950. 2008. (Studies in Childhood & Family in Canada Ser.). (ENG.). 312p. pap. 42.95 *(978-1-55458-151-1(6))* Wilfrid Laurier Univ. Pr. CAN. Dist: Univ. of Toronto Pr.

Cooke, Nathalie. What's to Eat? Entrées in Canadian Food History. 2009. (ENG., Illus.). 320p. (C). pap. *(978-0-7735-3571-8(3))* McGill-Queen's Univ. Pr.

Cooke, Nathalie, ed. What's to Eat? Entrées in Canadian Food History. 2009. (ENG., Illus.). 320p. (C). *(978-0-7735-3570-1(5))* McGill-Queen's Univ. Pr.

Demeter, Emil. Will There Be Another Day. 2006. 57p. pap. 17.95 *(978-0-7414-3722-8(8))* Infinity Publishing.

Dennis, Richard, et al, eds. The Contemporary Canadian Metropolis. 2012. (ENG.). 200p. pap. 29.95 *(978-1-900039-90-1(7))* Institute of Latin American Studies GBR. Dist: Brookings Institution Pr.

Doughty, Howard A. & Tuzi, Marino, eds. Discourse & Community: Multidisciplinary Studies of Canadian Culture. 2006. (Essay Ser.). (ENG.). 80p. 18.00 *(978-1-55071-256-8(X))* Guernica Editions, Inc. CAN. Dist: Univ. of Toronto Pr.

Duncan, Dorothy. Feasting & Fasting: Canada's Heritage Celebrations. 2010. (ENG., Illus.). 256p. 26.99 *(978-1-55488-757-6(7))* Dundurn CAN. Dist: Ingram Pub. Services.

Ertler, Klaus-Dieter & Löschnigg, Martin, eds. Inventing Canada - Inventer le Canada. 2008. (Canadiana. Literaturen/Kulturen, Literatures/Cultures Littératures/Cultures Ser.). 308p. pap. 74.95 *(978-3-631-57852-0(0))* Lang, Peter GmbH, Europaischer Verlag der Wissenschaften DEU. Dist: Lang, Peter.

Ferguson, Will. Why I Hate Canadians. pap. 22.95 *(978-1-55054-600-2(7))*; 10th ed. 2007. (ENG.). 336p. pap. 15.95 *(978-1-55365-279-3(7))* D&M Pubs. Inc. CAN. Dist: Perseus-PGW.

Ford, Catherine. Against the Grain: An Irreverent View of Alberta. 2006. (ENG.). 272p. per. 16.50 *(978-0-7710-4778-7(9), McClelland & Stewart)* McClelland & Stewart CAN. Dist: Random Hse., Inc.

Fox, Leo. Education Is Our Buffalo: A Teachers' Resource for First Nations, Métis & Inuit Education in Alberta. (Illus.). xi, 62p. pap. *(978-1-897196-10-6(5))* Alberta Teachers' Assn.

Fraser, Graham. Sorry, I Don't Speak French: Confronting the Canadian Crisis That Won't Go Away. 2007. (ENG.). 352p. per. 16.50 *(978-0-7710-4767-1(3), Gibson, Douglas Bks.)* McClelland & Stewart CAN. Dist: Random Hse., Inc.

Gill, Rupinder. On the Outside Looking Indian: How My Second Childhood Changed My Life. 2012. (ENG.). 288p. (gr. 12). 15.00 ***(978-1-59448-577-0(1)***, Riverhead Trade (Paperbacks)) Penguin Group (USA) Inc.

Gieseking, Bernd & Müller-Wile, Ludger. Inuit & Whalers on Baffin Islands Through German Eyes: Wilhelm Wieke's Arctic Journal & Letters (1883-1884) 2011. (ENG., Illus.). 270p. 29.95 ***(978-1-926824-11-6(3))*** Baraka Bks. CAN. Dist: Independent Pubs. Group.

Goyder, John. Prestige Squeeze: Occupational Prestige in Canada since 1965. 2009. (ENG., Illus.). 236p. (C). *(978-0-7735-3582-4(9))* McGill-Queen's Univ. Pr.

Green, Bob. Eavesdroppings: Stories from Small Towns When Sin Was Fun. 2006. (ENG.). 200p. pap. 22.99 *(978-1-55002-629-0(1), Dundurn Pr.)* Dundurn CAN. Dist: Ingram Pub. Services.

Greenhill, Pauline. Make the Night Hideous: Four Canadian Charivaris, 1881-1940. 2010. (Canadian Social History Ser.). (Illus.). 272p. *(978-1-4426-4077-1(4))* Univ. of Toronto Pr.

—Make the Night Hideous: Four English-Canadian Charivaris, 1881-1940. 2010. (Canadian Social History Ser.). (Illus.). 272p. *(978-1-4426-1015-6(8))* Univ. of Toronto Pr.

Hannaford, Elizabeth Elsie. Vision of Canada 2020: Save Canadian Medicare & Money. 2011. 136p. 25.95 *(978-1-4502-8053-2(6))*; pap. 15.95 *(978-1-4502-8052-5(8))* iUniverse, Inc.

Heer, Jeet, et al. Too Asian? Racism & Post-Secondary Education in Canada. 2011. 224p. pap. 26.95 ***(978-1-926662-78-7(4))*** Between the Lines CAN. Dist: Univ. of Toronto Pr.

Henderson, Paula Laureen. Lost Angels: Encounters with First Nations. 2011. (ENG & FRE.). 223p. pap. *(978-0-9783141-1-8(5))* Gumdrop Enterprise.

Hoagland, Edward. Early in the Season: A British Columbia Journal, 1 vol. 2009. (ENG., Illus.). 176p. 22.95 *(978-1-55365-428-5(5))* D&M Pubs. Inc. CAN. Dist: Perseus-PGW.

Hoffman, Frances & Taylor, Ryan. Much to Be Done: Private Life in Ontario from Victorian Diaries. 2nd ed. 2007. (ENG., Illus.). 288p. pap. 21.99 *(978-1-55002-772-3(7))* Natural Heritage/Natural History, Inc. CAN. Dist: Ingram Pub. Services.

Holt, Faye Reineberg. Alberta: A History in Photographs, 1 vol. 2009. (History in Photographs Ser.). (ENG., Illus.). 112p. pap. *(978-1-894974-87-5(5))* Heritage Hse.

Howse, Jennifer. Boxing Day: Canadian Celebrations. 2010. (Illus.). 24p. pap. *(978-1-77071-638-4(6))* Weigl Educational Pubs. Ltd.

Julian & Wright, Wilmer Cave. The Works of the Emperor Julian: Letters, Epigrams, Against the Galileans, Fragments. 2011. 516p. 60.95 ***(978-1-258-09081-4(3))*** Literary Licensing, LLC.

Keleher, Terry R. J. & Collins, Donald P. Saint John in the Golden Age of Postcards: 1900-1915. 2009. (Historic Canada Ser.). (Illus.). 128p. pap. 21.99 *(978-0-7385-7286-4(1))* Arcadia Publishing.

Kirby, Mary-Ann. I Am Hutterite: The Fascinating Story of a Young Woman's Journey to Reclaim Her Heritage. l.t. ed. 2011. 448p. pap. 17.99 *(978-1-59415-390-7(6))* Cengage Gale.

Kopelow, Gerry. All Our Changes: Images from the Sixties Generation. 2009. (ENG., Illus.). 158p. pap. 39.95 ***(978-0-88755-714-9(7))*** Univ. of Manitoba Pr. CAN. Dist: Chicago Distribution Ctr.

Kranc, Benjamin A. & Roman, Karina. Live & Work in Canada: Comprehensive, Up-to-Date, Practical Information about Everyday Life. 4th ed. 2010. (ENG., Illus.). 180p. pap. 22.00 *(978-1-84528-338-4(4))* How To Books GBR. Dist: Parkwest Pubns., Inc.

Kuyek, Joan. Community Organizing: A Holistic Approach. 2012. 176p. pap. 24.95 ***(978-1-55266-444-5(9))*** Fernwood Publishing Co., Ltd. CAN. Dist: Independent Pubs. Group.

Leenders, Gordon J. H. To Be Continued..., Vol. 3. 2007. (To Be Continued ... Ser.). (ENG.). 234p. pap. 17.95 *(978-1-55022-767-3(X))* ECW Pr. CAN. Dist: Independent Pubs. Group.

Lemieux, Diane. Canada: A Quick Guide to Customs & Etiquette. 2008. (Culture Smart! Ser.). (ENG., Illus.). 168p. pap. 9.95 *(978-1-85733-454-8(X))* Kuperard Pubs. GBR. Dist: Random Hse., Inc.

Li, Xiaoping. Voices Rising: Asian Canadian Cultural Activism. 2007. (ENG., Illus.). 320p. pap. *(978-0-7748-1222-1(2))* Univ. of British Columbia Pr.

Liu, Zhaobin. Peaking of Holiday Traffic. 2008. 164p. pap. *(978-3-639-04303-7(0))* VDM Verlag Dr. Mueller e.K.

Maraj, Frank. Snapshots II: Navigating the University Years. 2011. 464p. 33.99 *(978-1-4269-5321-7(6))*; pap. 23.99 *(978-1-4269-5322-4(4))* Trafford Publishing.

Marshall, Joan. Tides of Change on Grand Manan Island: Culture & Belonging in a Fishing Community. 2008. (ENG., Illus.). 416p. pap. *(978-0-7735-3476-6(8))*; (C). *(978-0-7735-3475-9(X))* McGill-Queen's Univ. Pr.

Maurice, Edward Beauclerk. The Last Gentleman Adventurer: Coming of Age in the Arctic. 2006. (ENG., Illus.). 392p. per. 14.95 *(978-0-618-77358-9(4), Mariner Bks.)* Houghton Mifflin Harcourt Trade & Reference Pubs.

McCann, Larry, ed. People & Place, No. 6. 263p. pap. 12.95 *(978-0-919107-09-0(5))* Acadiensis Pr. CAN. Dist: Goose Lane Editions.

McCormack, Derek. Christmas Days: From Fake Snow to Santalands - The Things That Make Christmas Christmas. 2010. (ENG., Illus.). 320p. pap. 12.95 *(978-0-88784-839-1(7))* House of Anansi Pr. CAN. Dist: Perseus-PGW.

McKay, Ian. Warrior Nation: Rebranding Canada in a Fearful Agee. 2011. 300p. pap. 24.95 ***(978-1-926662-77-0(6))*** Between the Lines CAN. Dist: Univ. of Toronto Pr.

Mears, Ray. Northern Wilderness: Bushcraft of the Far North. 2010. (ENG., Illus.). 224p. 29.95 *(978-0-340-98082-8(6), Hodder & Stoughton)* Hodder General Publishing Div. GBR. Dist: Independent Pubs. Group.

Mellin, Robert. Tilting: House Launching, Slide Hauling, Potato Trenching, & Other Tales from a Newfoundland Fishing Village. 2008. (ENG., Illus.). 253p. pap. 24.95 *(978-1-56898-807-8(9))* Princeton Architectural Pr.

Mookerjea, Sourayan, et al, eds. Canadian Cultural Studies: A Reader. 2009. (ENG.). 608p. 104.95 *(978-0-8223-4398-1(3))*; pap. 32.95 *(978-0-8223-4416-2(5))* Duke Univ. Pr.

Mowat, Farley. People of the Deer. 25.95 *(978-0-89190-818-0(8))* Amereon LTD.

Olson, Sherry & Thornton, Patricia. Peopling the North American City: Montreal, 1840-1900. 2011. (Carleton Library Ser.). (ENG., Illus.). 544p. (C). pap. *(978-0-7735-3831-3(3))* McGill-Queen's Univ. Pr.

Pang, Guek-Cheng & Barlas, Robert. Canada: A Survival Guide to Customs & Etiquette. 2009. 312p. pap. 15.95 *(978-0-7614-5661-2(9))* Marshall Cavendish Corp.

Pang, Guek Cheng, et al. Cultureshock! Canada, 1 vol. 2007. (Cultureshock Canada: A Survival Guide to Customs & Etiquette Ser.). (ENG., Illus.). 32p. pap. 15.95 *(978-0-7614-2491-8(1))* Marshall Cavendish Corp.

Paquet, Gilles. Deep Cultural Diversity: A Governance Challenge. 2008 (Governance Ser.). (ENG.). 248p. (gr. 10-12). pap. *(978-0-7766-0673-6(5))* Univ. of Ottawa Pr./Presses de l'Universite d'Ottawa.

Perley, Bernard C. Defying Maliseet Language Death: Emergent Vitalities of Language, Culture, & Identity in Eastern Canada. 2011. (ENG., Illus.). 256p. 50.00 *(978-0-8032-2529-9(6))* Univ. of Nebraska Pr.

Redekop, Bill. Made in Manitoba: Best of the Open Road Stories. 2011. (ENG.). 224p. pap. 19.95 *(978-1-926916-11-8(5))* MacIntyre & Purcell Publishing CAN. Dist: Independent Pubs. Group.

Sanosuosso, John. Canada: an Introduction for Americans. 2007. (ENG.). 224p. per. 24.95 *(978-1-4241-6505-6(9))* PublishAmerica, Inc.

Saunders, Janice. Cricket's Child, 1945-1955: How I Never Learned to Love the Bomb. 2008. (ENG.). 120p. pap. 26.50 *(978-0-7618-3994-1(1))* Hamilton Bks.

Siltanen, Janet & Doucet, Andrea. Gender Relations: Intersectionality & Beyond. 2008. (ENG.). 204p. pap. 55.00 *(978-0-19-542320-4(8))* Oxford Univ. Pr., Inc.

Sjogren, Gwen. Cross-Canada Crosswords 6: 50 Themed Puzzles for Canadian Crossword Connoisseurs. unabr. ed. 2010. (ENG.). 128p. pap. *(978-1-55017-469-4(X))* Harbour Publishing Co., Ltd.

Sparling, Fred & Sparling, Joyce. North to Nunavut: An Arctic Love Affair. 2011. (Illus.). 246p. pap. 24.95 ***(978-1-59715-080-4(0))*** Chapel Hill Pr.

Szekely, Eva. Hungarian - Canadian Cultural Identities. 2009. 64p. pap. *(978-3-639-20757-6(2))* VDM Verlag Dr. Mueller e.K.

Tempelman-Kluit, Anne, ed. Sleds, Sleighs & Snow: A Canadian Christmas Carol. 2007. (ENG., Illus.). 292p. pap. 19.95 *(978-1-55285-905-6(3))* Whitecap Bks., Ltd. CAN. Dist: Midpoint Trade Bks., Inc.

Tepperman, Lorne. Sense & Sociability: The Forces That Push Us Apart & Pull Us Back Together. 2010. (ENG., Illus.). 416p. 35.00 *(978-0-19-543929-8(5))* Oxford Univ. Pr., Inc.

Thompson, A. K. Black Bloc, White Riot: Antiglobalization & the Geneaology of Dissent. 2010. (ENG., Illus.). 192p. pap. 17.95 *(978-1-84935-014-3(0))* AK Pr. GBR. Dist: Consortium Bk. Sales & Distribution.

Tuzi, Marino. Culture & Difference: Essays on Canadian Society. Doughty, Howard, ed. 2011. (Essay Ser.). (ENG.). 210p. 18.00 *(978-1-55071-287-2(X))* Guernica Editions, Inc. CAN. Dist: Univ. of Toronto Pr.

University of Toronto Press. Re-Imagining Ukrainian-Canadians: History, Politics, & Identity. 2010. (Canadian Social History Ser.). 448p. (ENG.). *(978-1-4426-4134-1(7))*; pap. *(978-1-4426-1062-0(X))* Univ. of Toronto Pr.

van Dam, Kim. A Place Called Nunavut: Multiple Identities for a New Region. 2008. (Circumpolar Studies). (ENG., Illus.). 336p. (C). pap. 30.00 ***(978-90-77922-45-3(8))*** Barkhuis Publishing NLD. Dist: Brown, David Bk. Co., The.

Vance, Jonathan F. A History of Canadian Culture. 2011. (ENG., Illus.). 512p. 24.95 *(978-0-19-544422-3(1))* Oxford Univ. Pr., Inc.

Visart de Bocarmé, Pascale & Petit, Pierre, eds. Le Canada Inuit/Inuit Canada: Pour une approche réflexive de la recherche anthropologique autochtone/Reflexive Approchaes to Native Anthropological Research. 2008. (Études Canadiennes - Canadian Studies). (FRE & ENG., Illus.). 195p. pap. 43.95 *(978-90-5201-427-2(2))* PIE - Peter Lang BEL. Dist: Lang, Peter.

Wilkins, Charles. In the Land of Long Fingernails: A Gravedigger in the Age of Aquarius. 2009. (ENG.). 240p. 24.95 *(978-1-60239-709-5(0)*, 239709) Skyhorse Publishing Co., Inc.

Woods, Anna. Healing Waters. (Mayan Ser.). (Illus.). 64p. pap. *(978-0-9698752-4-6(X))* Shoreline.

CANADA—SOCIAL POLICY

Abu-Laban, Yasmeen & Gabriel, Christina. Selling Diversity: Immigration, Multiculturalism, Employment Equity, & Globalization. 2008. (ENG.). 202p. pap. *(978-1-4426-0072-0(1))* Univ. of Toronto Pr.

Béland, Daniel & Lecours, André. Nationalism & Social Policy: The Politics of Territorial Solidarity. 2010. (ENG.). 240p. pap. 35.00 *(978-0-19-954685-5(1))* Oxford Univ. Pr., Inc.

Bloemraad, Irene. Becoming a Citizen: Incorporating Immigrants & Refugees in the United States & Canada. 2006. (Illus.). 369p. per. 25.95 *(978-0-520-24899-1(6))*; 60.00 *(978-0-520-24898-4(8))* Univ. of California Pr.

Cohen, Marjorie Griffin & Pulkingham, Jane. Public Policy for Women: The State, Income Security & Labour Market Issues. Cohen, Marjorie Griffin & Pulkingham, Jane, eds. 2009. (Studies in Comparative Political Economy & Public Policy Ser.). (ENG., Illus.). 384p. 75.00 *(978-0-8020-9500-8(3))* Univ. of Toronto Pr.

Cohen, Marjorie Griffin & Pulkingham, Jane, eds. Public Policy for Women: The State, Income Security, & Labour Market Issues. 2009. (Studies in Comparative Political Economy & Public Policy Ser.). (ENG., Illus.). 384p. *(978-0-8020-9332-5(9))* Univ. of Toronto Pr.

Cosgrave, James F. & Klassen, Thomas. Casino State: Legalized Gambling in Canada. Klassen, Thomas R., ed. 2009. (ENG., Illus.). 256p. *(978-0-8020-9688-3(3))* Univ. of Toronto Pr.

Fossum, John Erik, et al. The Ties That Bind: Accommodating Complex Diversity in Canada & the European Union. 2009. (Illus.). 364p. 54.95 *(978-90-5201-475-3(2))* PIE - Peter Lang BEL. Dist: Lang, Peter.

Gairdner, William. The War Against the Family: A Parent Speaks Out on the Political, Economic, & Social Policies That Threaten Us All. 2007. 672p. per. *(978-0-9784402-1-3(8))* BPS Bks.

Johnston, Richard & Kay, Fiona. Social Capital, Diversity, & the Welfare State. 2007. (Equality, Security, Community Ser.). (ENG.). 368p. *(978-0-7748-1309-9(1))* Univ. of British Columbia Pr.

Kay, Fiona M. & Johnston, Richard, eds. Social Capital, Diversity, & the Welfare State. 2007. (ENG., Illus.). 368p. per. *(978-0-7748-1310-5(5))* Univ. of British Columbia Pr.

Laforest, Rachel, ed. The New Federal Policy Agenda & the Voluntary Sector: On the Cutting Edge. 2009. (School of Policy Studies). (ENG.). 184p. (C). pap. 34.95 *(978-1-55339-132-6(2))* Queen's Univ., Schl. of Policy Studies CAN. Dist: McGill-Queen's Univ. Pr.

Lecours, André & Béland, Daniel. Nationalism & Social Policy: The Politics of Territorial Solidarity. Oxford University Press Staff, ed. 2008. (ENG.). 248p. 99.00 *(978-0-19-954684-8(3))* Oxford Univ. Pr., Inc.

Morris, Michael A., ed. Canadian Language Policies in Comparative Perspective. 2010. (ENG., Illus.). 536p. (C). *(978-0-7735-3705-7(8))*; pap. *(978-0-7735-3706-4(6))* McGill-Queen's Univ. Pr.

New Reproductive Technologies & the Science, Industry, Education & Social Welfare Systems in Canada, Vol. 5. 493p. pap. *(978-0-662-21379-6(3))* Canadian Government Publishing.

Paquette, Jerald & Fallon, Gérald. First Nation Educational Policy in Canada: Policy of Gridlock? 2009. *(978-1-4426-4153-2(3))*; pap. *(978-1-4426-1072-9(7))* Univ. of Toronto Pr.

Peach, Ian & Warriner, William. Canadian Social Policy Renewal, 1994-2000. 2008. (ENG.). 208p. pap. 24.95 *(978-1-55266-253-3(5))* Fernwood Publishing Co., Ltd. CAN. Dist: Independent Pubs. Group.

Raphael, Dennis. Poverty & Policy in Canada: Implications for Health & Quality of Life. 2007. (ENG., Illus.). 440p. pap. 47.95 *(978-1-55130-323-9(X))* Canadian Scholars' Pr., Inc. CAN. Dist: Ingram Pub. Services.

Regan, Vera, et al, eds. Multiculturalism & Integration: Canadian & Irish Experiences. 2010. (ENG.). 290p. pap. *(978-0-7766-0722-1(7))* Univ. of Ottawa Pr./Presses de l'Universite d'Ottawa.

Ryan, Phil. Multicultiphobia. 2010. 256p. (ENG.). *(978-1-4426-4146-4(0))*; pap. *(978-1-4426-1068-2(9))* Univ. of Toronto Pr.

University of Toronto Press. Prejudice & Pride: Canadian Intellectuals Confront the United States, 1891-1945. 2010. 320p. *(978-1-4426-4045-0(6))* Univ. of Toronto Pr.

Westhues, Anne, ed. Canadian Social Policy: Issues & Perspectives, 4th Edition. 4th ed. 2006. (ENG.). 412p. (C). pap. 44.95 *(978-0-88920-504-8(3))* Wilfrid Laurier Univ. Pr. CAN. Dist: Univ. of Toronto Pr.

Westhues, Anne & Wharf, Brian, eds. Canadian Social Policy: Issues & Perspectives, 5th Edition. 5th ed. 2012. (ENG.). 494p. (C). pap. 52.95 ***(978-1-55458-359-1(4))*** Wilfrid Laurier Univ. Pr. CAN. Dist: Univ. of Toronto Pr.

CANADA—STATISTICS

Bouchette, Joseph. British Dominions in North America, 2 vols., Set. reprint ed. 295.00 *(978-0-404-00936-6(0))* AMS Pr., Inc.

Vanier Institute of the Family Staff, contrib. by. Profiling Canada's Families. (Illus.). xii, 148p. *(978-0-919520-55-4(3))* Institut Vanier de la Famille.

CANADA, WESTERN

Here are entered works dealing collectively with British Columbia, Alberta, Saskatchewan and Manitoba.

see also Northwest, Canadian; Prairie Provinces

Prentiss, William C. & Kuijt, Ian, eds. Complex Hunter-Gatherers: Evolution & Organization of Prehistoric Communities on the Plateau of Northwestern North America. 2007. (Anthropology of Pacific North America Ser.). (Illus.). 219p. per. 45.00 *(978-0-87480-924-4(X))* Univ. of Utah Pr.

CANADA, WESTERN—DESCRIPTION AND TRAVEL

Devine, Bob. Lands of the Setting Sun: Discovering Alaska & Western Canada. 2006. (Illus.). 191p. *(978-0-7922-5551-2(8))* National Geographic Society.

Flanagan, Darris. Indian Trails of the Northern Rockies. (Illus.). 192p. pap. 14.95 *(978-1-931291-10-1(1))* Stoneydale Pr. Publishing Co.

Mobil Travel Gd, ed. Northwest 2009. 2009. (Mobil Travel Guide Ser.). 328p. 18.95 *(978-0-8416-0865-8(2))* Langenscheidt Publishing Group.

Monaco Books, ed. Western Canada, 1 vol. 2010. (ENG., Illus.). 224p. pap. 19.95 *(978-3-89944-590-9(2)*, Monaco Bks.) Verlag Wolfgang Kunth GmbH & Co. KG DEU. Dist: Innovative Logistics.

Owl, Grey. Tales of an Empty Cabin. 380p. 2008. 48.95 *(978-1-4366-9458-2(2))* 2007. (ENG.). per. 33.95 *(978-1-4325-7987-6(8))* Kessinger Publishing, LLC.

Pole, Graeme. Canadian Rockies Recommended. 2007. (Canada Recommended Ser.). (Illus.). 256p. pap. *(978-1-55153-646-0(3))* Altitude Publishing Canada Ltd.

Ulysses. Fabulous Western Canada: Capture the Excitement of the Great West. Ulysses Travel Guide Staff, ed. 2008. (Illus.). 288p. pap. 29.95 *(978-2-89464-875-9(8))* Ulysses Travel Guides CAN. Dist: Hunter Publishing, Inc.

CANADA, WESTERN—HISTORY

Belcourt, Herb. Walking in the Woods: A Métis Journey, 1 vol. 2006. (ENG., Illus.). 224p. per. *(978-1-897142-17-2(X))* Brindle & Glass Publishing.

Finkel, Alvin, et al. The West & Beyond: New Perspectives on an Imagined Region. 2010. 226p. pap. 29.95 *(978-1-897425-80-0(5))* Univ. of Washington Pr.

Graybill, Andrew R. & Graybill, Andrew. Policing the Great Plains: Rangers, Mounties, & the North American Frontier, 1875-1910. 2007. (ENG., Illus.). 293p. pap. 24.95 *(978-0-8032-6002-3(4))* Univ. of Nebraska Pr.

MacBeth, Roderick George. The Making of the Canadian West. 279p. reprint ed. 98.00 *(978-0-7222-6814-8(9))* Library Reprints, Inc.

Weinstein, John. Quiet Revolution West: The Rebirth of Metis Nationalism, 1 vol. 2008. (ENG., Illus.). 256p. per. 23.95 *(978-1-897252-21-5(8))* Fifth Hse. Pubs. CAN. Dist: Ingram Pub. Services.

CANADA GOOSE

Plum, Sydney Landon. Solitary Goose. 2009. (ENG.). 152p. pap. 18.95 *(978-0-8203-3432-5(4))* Univ. of Georgia Pr.

—Solitary Goose. 2007. (ENG.). 152p. 24.95 *(978-0-8203-2966-6(5))* Univ. of Georgia Pr.

CANADIAN ARCHITECTURE

see Architecture—Canada

CANADIAN ARCTIC EXPEDITION, 1913-1918

Jenness, Stuart E. Stefansson, Dr. Anderson & the Canadian Arctic Expedition, 1913-1918: A Story of Exploration, Science & Sovereignty. 2011. (ENG., Illus.). 400p. (C). pap. 39.95 *(978-0-660-19971-9(8))* Canadian Museum of Civilization/Musee Canadien des Civilisations CAN. Dist: Univ. of Washington Pr.

CANADIAN AUTHORS

see Authors, Canadian

CANADIAN BALLADS AND SONGS

see Folk Songs, Canadian; Songs, Canadian

CANADIAN COOKING

see Cooking, Canadian

CANADIAN DRAMA

Aquino, Nina Lee, ed. Love & Relasianships One: Contemporary Asian-Canadian Drams. 2010. (ENG.). 300p. pap. 29.95 *(978-0-88754-777-5(X))* Playwrights Canada Pr. CAN. Dist: Consortium Bk. Sales & Distribution.

—Love & Relasianships Two: Contemporary Asian-Canadian Drama. 2010. (ENG.). 300p. pap. 29.95 *(978-0-88754-779-9(6))* Playwrights Canada Pr. CAN. Dist: Consortium Bk. Sales & Distribution.

Barker, Roberta & Solga, Kim, eds. New Canadian Realisms: Eight Plays. 2012. (ENG.). 400p. pap. 29.95 ***(978-1-77091-073-7(5))*** Playwrights Canada Pr. CAN. Dist: Consortium Bk. Sales & Distribution.

Bose, Neilesh, ed. Beyond Bollywood & Broadway: Plays from the South Asian Diaspora. 2009. (ENG.). 520p. 75.00 *(978-0-253-35300-9(9)*, 0253353009); pap. 29.95 *(978-0-253-22068-4(8)*, 0253220688) Indiana Univ. Pr.

Brennan, Kit, ed. Out on a Limb: Short Plays by New Playwrights. 2011. (ENG.). 196p. pap. 22.95 ***(978-1-897109-55-7(5))*** Signature Editions CAN. Dist: Univ. of Toronto Pr.

Brennan, Kit, ed. Things That Go Bump: Volume 2, Plays for Young Audiences. 2009. 312p. pap. 22.95 *(978-1-897109-41-0(5))* Signature Editions CAN. Dist: Univ. of Toronto Pr.

Fairhead, Wayne & Gardner, Jane. Festival Voices: Plays Written by Students & Teachers for the Sears Ontario Drama Festival. 2010. (ENG., Illus.). 304p. (gr. 8-12). pap. 25.00 ***(978-0-88754-905-2(5))*** Playwrights Canada Pr. CAN. Dist: Consortium Bk. Sales & Distribution.

Forsyth, Louise. Anthology of Québec Women's Plays in English Translation. 2010. (ENG.). 304p. pap. 29.95 ***(978-0-88754-785-0(0))*** Playwrights Canada Pr. CAN. Dist: Consortium Bk. Sales & Distribution.

—Anthology of Québec Women's Plays in English Translation. 2007. (ENG.). 300p. pap. 55.00 *(978-0-88754-868-0(7))* Theatre Communications Group, Inc.

Hengen, Shannon Eileen & Osawabine, Joe. Stories from the Bush: The Woodland Plays of De-Ba-Jeh-Mu-Jig Theatre Group. 2009. (OJI & ENG.). 208p. pap. 19.95 *(978-0-88754-815-4(6))* Playwrights Canada Pr. CAN. Dist: Consortium Bk. Sales & Distribution.

Huston-Findley, Shirley Annette & Howard, Rebecca, eds. Footpaths & Bridges: Voices from the Native American Women Playwrights Archive. 2008. (CRE & ENG.). 304p. 90.00 *(978-0-472-11613-3(4))* Univ. of Michigan Pr.

Kerr, Rosalind, ed. Lesbian Plays: Coming of Age in Canada. 2007. (ENG., Illus.). 300p. per. 46.00 *(978-0-88754-864-2(4))* Theatre Communications Group, Inc.

Knowles, Richard & Mojica, Monique. Staging Coyote's Dream, Volume 2: An Anthology of First Nations Drama in English, Volume 2. 2009. (ENG.). 380p. pap. 29.95 *(978-0-88754-735-5(4))* Playwrights Canada Pr. CAN. Dist: Consortium Bk. Sales & Distribution.

Louise, Forsyth, ed. Anthology of Québec Women's Plays in English Translation,I. 2008. (ENG.). 250p. pap. 50.00 *(978-0-88754-719-5(2))* Theatre Communications Group, Inc.

Martini, Clem, ed. Four by Four by Four, 1 vol. 2007. (ENG.). 128p. pap. 9.95 *(978-0-88995-366-6(X))* Red Deer Pr. CAN. Dist: Ingram Pub. Services.

Moore, Cairn A., ed. Generation NeXXt. 2010. (ENG., Illus.). 132p. pap. 16.95 *(978-1-897289-59-4(6)*, Scirocco Drama) Shillingford, J. Gordon Publishing CAN. Dist: Univ. of Toronto Pr.

Moses, Daniel David & Callaghan, Barry, eds. The Exile Book of Native Canadian Fiction & Drama. 2011. (Exile Book Of Ser.). (ENG.). 394p. pap. 22.95 *(978-1-55096-145-4(4))* Exile Editions, Ltd. CAN. Dist: Independent Pubs. Group.

Playwrights Canada Press Staff & Theatre Direct Canada Staff, contrib. by. Acting Out: Monologues & Scenes from Theatre Direct (Canada's Plays ForYoung People) 2007. (ENG., Illus.). 176p. pap. 19.95 *(978-0-88754-882-6(2))* Theatre Communications Group, Inc.

Renders, Kim, et al, eds. Canadian Theatre Review. 148th ed. 2011. (Fall 2011 Ser.). (ENG.). 112p. pap. ***(978-1-4426-1188-7(X))*** Univ. of Toronto Pr.

Sears, Djanet, et al. Afrika, Solo: Three AfriCanadian Plays. 2011. (ENG.). 304p. pap. 25.00 ***(978-0-88754-839-0(3))*** Playwrights Canada Pr. CAN. Dist: Consortium Bk. Sales & Distribution.

Sokoloski, Robin. Uth Ink: Word from the Street. 2009. (ENG., Illus.). 116p. (J). pap. 19.95 *(978-0-88754-837-6(7))* Playwrights Canada Pr. CAN. Dist: Consortium Bk. Sales & Distribution.

Solga, Kim, ed. Canadian Theatre Review. 2011. (Summer 2011 Ser.). (ENG.). 112p. pap. ***(978-1-4426-1230-3(4))*** Univ. of Toronto Pr.

St Bernard, Donna-Michelle, et al. Refractions: Solo. 2012. (ENG.). 256p. pap. 19.95 ***(978-0-88754-920-5(9))*** Playwrights Canada Pr. CAN. Dist: Consortium Bk. Sales & Distribution.

Theatre Ontario Staff, contrib. by. Ontario Playwrights: Eight Short Plays. 2009. (ENG.). 294p. pap. 29.95 *(978-0-88754-821-5(0))* Playwrights Canada Pr. CAN. Dist: Consortium Bk. Sales & Distribution.

Yee, David. Lady in the Red Dress. 2010. (ENG.). 96p. pap. 16.95 ***(978-0-88754-907-6(1))*** Playwrights Canada Pr. CAN. Dist: Consortium Bk. Sales & Distribution.

CANADIAN DRAMA—HISTORY AND CRITICISM

Aquino, Nina Lee & Knowles, Ric. Asian Canadian Theatre. 2011. (ENG.). 240p. pap. 25.00 ***(978-0-88754-986-1(1))*** Playwrights Canada Pr. CAN. Dist: Consortium Bk. Sales & Distribution.

Barton, Bruce. Collective Creation, Collaboration & Devising. 2009. (Critical Perspectives on Canadian Theatre in English Ser.). (ENG.). 312p. pap. 30.00 *(978-0-88754-755-3(9))* Playwrights Canada Pr. CAN. Dist: Consortium Bk. Sales & Distribution.

Bennett, Susan. Feminist Theatre & Performance. 2009. (Critical Perspectives on Canadian Theatre in English Ser.). (ENG & FRE.). 161p. pap. 25.00 *(978-0-88754-798-0(2))* Playwrights Canada Pr. CAN. Dist: Consortium Bk. Sales & Distribution.

Brennan, Kit, ed. Three on the Boards. 2007. (ENG., Illus.). 312p. pap. 19.95 *(978-1-897109-19-9(9))* Signature Editions CAN. Dist: Univ. of Toronto Pr.

Burnett, Linda Avril. Theatre in Atlantic Canada. 2010. (Critical Perspectives on Canadian Theatre in English Ser.). (ENG.). 208p. pap. 25.00 ***(978-0-88754-890-1(3))*** Playwrights Canada Pr. CAN. Dist: Consortium Bk. Sales & Distribution.

Day, Moira, ed. West-Words: Celebrating Western Canadian Theatre & Playwriting. 2011. (Cpp Ser.). 336p. pap. 39.95 ***(978-0-88977-235-9(5))*** Canadian Plains Research Ctr. CAN. Dist: Univ. of Toronto Pr.

Gallagher, Kathleen. The Theatre of Urban: Youth & Schooling in Dangerous Times. 2007. (ENG., Illus.). 192p. pap. *(978-0-8020-9483-4(X))* Univ. of Toronto Pr.

Grace, Sherrill E. & La Flamme, Michelle. Sharon Pollock. 2009. (Critical Perspectives on Canadian Theatre in English Ser.). (ENG.). 208p. pap. 25.00 *(978-0-88754-751-5(6))* Playwrights Canada Pr. CAN. Dist: Consortium Bk. Sales & Distribution.

Hadfield, D. A. Re: Producing Women's Dramatic History: The Politics of Playing in Toronto. Davey, Frank, ed. 2007. (ENG.). 288p. pap. 24.95 *(978-0-88922-563-3(X))* Talonbooks, Ltd. CAN. Dist: Consortium Bk. Sales & Distribution.

Houston, Andrew, ed. Environmental & Site-Specific Theatre. 2007. (Critical Perspectives on Canadian Theatre in English Ser.). (ENG.). 224p. per. 25.00 *(978-0-88754-806-2(7))* Playwrights Canada Pr. CAN. Dist: Consortium Bk. Sales & Distribution.

Kerr, Rosalind. Queer Theatre in Canada. 2008. (Critical Perspectives on Canadian Theatre in English Ser.). (ENG.). 224p. per. 30.00 *(978-0-88754-804-8(0))* Playwrights Canada Pr. CAN. Dist: Consortium Bk. Sales & Distribution.

Knowles, Ric. The Masks of Judith Thompson. 2009. (ENG.). 149p. pap. 25.00 *(978-0-88754-900-7(4))* Playwrights Canada Pr. CAN. Dist: Consortium Bk. Sales & Distribution.

Lane, Harry. George F. Walker. 2009. (Critical Perspectives on Canadian Theatre in English Ser.). (ENG.). 232p. pap. 25.00 *(978-0-88754-800-0(8))* Playwrights Canada Pr. CAN. Dist: Consortium Bk. Sales & Distribution.

Maufort, Marc & De Wagter, Caroline, eds. Signatures of the Past: Cultural Memory in Contemporary Anglophone North American Drama. 2008. (Illus.). 312p. pap. 54.95 *(978-90-5201-454-8(X))* PIE - Peter Lang BEL. Dist: Lang, Peter.

McKinnie, Michael, ed. Space & the Geographies of Theatre. 2007. (Critical Perspectives on Canadian Theatre in English Ser.). (ENG.). 224p. per. 25.00 *(978-0-88754-808-6(3))* Playwrights Canada Pr. CAN. Dist: Consortium Bk. Sales & Distribution.

Moses, Daniel David & Moses, Daniel D. Pursued by a Bear: Talks, Monologues & Tales. 2007. (ENG.). 183p. pap. 19.95 *(978-1-55096-646-6(4))* Exile Editions, Ltd. CAN. Dist: Independent Pubs. Group.

Nothof, Anne. Theatre in Alberta. 2009. (Critical Perspectives on Canadian Theatre in English Ser.). (ENG.). 200p. pap. 25.00 *(978-0-88754-753-9(2))* Playwrights Canada Pr. CAN. Dist: Consortium Bk. Sales & Distribution.

Ratsoy, Ginny. Theatre in British Columbia. 2009. (Critical Perspectives on Canadian Theatre in English Ser.: Vol. 6). (ENG.). 228p. pap. 25.00 *(978-0-88754-802-4(4))* Playwrights Canada Pr. CAN. Dist: Consortium Bk. Sales & Distribution.

Salverson, Julie. Popular Political Theatre & Performance. 2010. (Critical Perspectives on Canadian Theatre in English Ser.). (ENG.). 208p. pap. 25.00 ***(978-0-88754-891-8(1))*** Playwrights Canada Pr. CAN. Dist: Consortium Bk. Sales & Distribution.

Salverson, Julie, ed. Community Engaged Theatre Vol. 19: Critical Perspectives on Canadian Theatre in English. 2011. (Critical Perspectives on Canadian Theatre in English Ser.). (ENG.). 208p. pap. 25.00 ***(978-0-88754-932-8(2))*** Playwrights Canada Pr. CAN. Dist: Consortium Bk. Sales & Distribution.

Scott, Shelley. The Violent Woman as a New Theatrical Character Type: Cases from Canadian Drama. 2007. (Illus.). 136p. *(978-0-7734-5445-3(4))* Mellen, Edwin Pr., The.

Stephenson, Jenn. Solo Performance. 2011. (Critical Perspectives on Canadian Theatre in English Ser.). (ENG.). 208p. pap. 25.00 ***(978-0-88754-933-5(0))*** Playwrights Canada Pr. CAN. Dist: Consortium Bk. Sales & Distribution.

Turcott, Iris & Turnbull, Keith. Canada on Stage: Scenes & Monologues: A Survey of Canadian Theatre. 2007. (ENG.). 250p. per. 27.00 *(978-0-88754-888-8(1))* Theatre Communications Group, Inc.

Wilmer, S. E. Native American Performance & Representation. 2011. (ENG.). 296p. pap. 29.95 *(978-0-8165-0240-0(4))* Univ. of Arizona Pr.

Wilmer, S. E., ed. Native American Performance & Representation. 2009. (ENG., Illus.). 298p. (C). 49.95 *(978-0-8165-2646-8(X))* Univ. of Arizona Pr.

CANADIAN ESSAYS

Bland, Jared. Finding the Words: Writers on Inspiration, Desire, War, Celebrity, Exile, & Breaking the Rules. 2011. 328p. pap. 24.99 *(978-0-7710-1369-0(8)*, McClelland & Stewart) McClelland & Stewart CAN. Dist: Random Hse., Inc.

Brownlow, Timothy. Hiding Places. 2008. (ENG.). 228p. pap. 18.95 *(978-0-83982-251-1(4))* Oolichan Bks. CAN. Dist: Univ. of Toronto Pr.

Carolan, Trevor, ed. Making Waves: Reading B. C. & Pacific Northwest Literature. 2010. (Illus.). 272p. 20.00 *(978-1-897535-29-5(5))* Anvil Pr. CAN. Dist: Univ. of Toronto Pr.

Huynh, Kim. Pro Production. 2010. (ENG & SPA., Illus.). 132p. pap. 21.95 *(978-1-897411-30-8(8))* Bayeux Arts, Inc. CAN. Dist: Chicago Distribution Ctr.

CANADIAN FICTION

see also Short Stories, Canadian

Akerman, Beverly. The Meaning of Children. 2012. (ENG.). 230p. pap. 17.95 *(978-1-55096-148-5(9))* Exile Editions, Ltd. CAN. Dist: Independent Pubs. Group.

Colombo, John Robert & Savory, Brett Alexander. Strange Canadian Stories, 1 vol. 2010. (ENG.). 344p. pap. 17.95 ***(978-1-894063-37-1(6))*** Edge Science Fiction & Fantasy Publishing CAN. Dist: Ingram Pub. Services.

Distad, Linda & Meier, Jr., John H. The John H. Meier, Jr. Governor General's Literary Award for Fiction Collection, 1936-2009. 2010. (ENG.). 88p. pap. *(978-1-55195-264-2(5))* Univ. of Alberta Pr. CAN. Dist: Michigan State Univ. Pr.

Flanagan, Mary & Booth, Austin, eds. Re - Skin. 2009. (ENG., Illus.). 376p. (gr. 17). pap. 21.00 *(978-0-262-51249-7(1))* MIT Pr.

Gibb, Camilla, et al, eds. The Journey Prize Stories 21: The Best of Canada's New Writers. 2009. (ENG.). 272p. pap. 17.99 *(978-0-7710-3427-5(X)*, McClelland & Stewart) McClelland & Stewart CAN. Dist: Random Hse., Inc.

Hill, Lawrence, et al, contrib. by. Tok, 3-Book Set: Writing the New Toronto. 2008. (ENG., Illus.). 600p. pap. 35.00 *(978-0-9734112-7-0(9)*, Zephyr Pr.) Chicago Review Pr., Inc.

Lake, Steve. More Sci-Fi from the Rock: A Collection of Short Stories. 2011. ***(978-1-926903-03-3(X))*** Engen Bks.

Leroux, Coralee & Cunningham, Troy, eds. Writing Without Direction: Ten & a Half Short Stories by Canadian Authors under Thirty. 2010. 200p. pap. *(978-0-9784892-2-9(5))* Clark-Nova Bks.

Malla, Pasha, et al, selected by. The Journey Prize Stories 22: The Best of Canada's New Writers. 2010. 240p. pap. 17.99 *(978-0-7710-4344-4(9)*, McClelland & Stewart) McClelland & Stewart CAN. Dist: Random Hse., Inc.

Moses, Daniel David & Callaghan, Barry, eds. The Exile Book of Native Canadian Fiction & Drama. 2011. (Exile Book Of Ser.). (ENG.). 394p. pap. 22.95 *(978-1-55096-145-4(4))* Exile Editions, Ltd. CAN. Dist: Independent Pubs. Group.

Sawyer, Robert J., ed. Distant Early Warnings: Canada's Best Science Fiction, 1 vol. 2009. (ENG.). 308p. pap. 22.95 *(978-0-88995-438-0(0))* Red Deer Pr. CAN. Dist: Ingram Pub. Services.

Tregebov, Rhea, ed. Arguing with the Storm: Stories by Yiddish Women Writers. 2007. (ENG., Illus.). 190p. pap. *(978-1-894549-63-9(5)*, Sumach Pr.) Canadian Scholars' Pr., Inc.

CANADIAN FICTION—HISTORY AND CRITICISM

Antje, Schumacher. Brian Moore's Black Robe: Novel, Screenplay(s) & Film. 2010. (Europäische Hochschulschriften. Reihe 14: Angelsächsische Sprache und Literatur Ser.). 164p. pap. 50.95 *(978-3-631-60321-5(5))* Lang, Peter GmbH, Europaischer Verlag der Wissenschaften DEU. Dist: Lang, Peter.

Bloom, Harold, ed. Alice Munro. 2009. (Bloom's Modern Critical Views Ser.). 218p. (C). (gr. 9-18). 45.00 *(978-1-60413-587-9(5)*, Chelsea Hse.) Facts On File, Inc.

Bowen, Deborah C. Stories of the Middle Space: Reading the Ethics in Postmodern Realisms. 2010. (ENG.). 304p. (C). *(978-0-7735-3689-0(2))* McGill-Queen's Univ. Pr.

Cabajsky, Andrea, et al, eds. National Plots: Historical Fiction & Changing Ideas of Canada. 2010. (ENG.). 276p. pap. 42.95 *(978-1-55458-061-3(7))* Wilfrid Laurier Univ. Pr. CAN. Dist: Univ. of Toronto Pr.

Chapman, Rosemary. Between Languages & Cultures: Colonial & Postcolonial Readings of Gabrielle Roy. 2009. (ENG., Illus.). 320p. (C). *(978-0-7735-3456-4(2))* McGill-Queen's Univ. Pr.

Cuder-Dominguez, Pilar, et al, eds. Transnational Poetics: Asian Canadian Women's Fiction of The 1990s. 2011. (ENG.). 200p. pap. 28.95 *(978-1-894770-68-2(4))* TSAR Pubns. CAN. Dist: Univ. of Toronto Pr.

De Young, James B. Burning down 'the Shack' How the 'Christian' bestseller Is deceiving Millions. 2010. 288p. pap. 15.95 ***(978-1-935071-84-6(X))*** WND Bks, Inc.

Dupuis, Gilles & Ertler, Klaus-Dieter. À la Carte: Le Roman Québécois (2000-2005) (FRE.). 493p. pap. 59.95 *(978-3-631-55340-4(4))* Lang, Peter GmbH, Europaischer Verlag der Wissenschaften DEU. Dist: Lang, Peter Publishing, Inc.

Dvorak, Marta & New, W. H., eds. Tropes & Territories: Short Fiction, Postcolonial Readings, Canadian Writing in Context. 2007. (ENG.). 384p. (C). *(978-0-7735-3269-2(7))* McGill-Queen's Univ. Pr.

Frederic, Madeleine. Polyptyque Quebecois: Decouvrir le Roman Contemporain (1945-2001) (SPA & FRE.). 176p. 21.95 *(978-90-5201-096-0(X))* Lang, Peter Publishing, Inc.

Gammel, Irene & Lefebvre, Benjamin. Anne's World: A New Century of 'Anne of Green Gables' 2010. (Illus.). 304p. (ENG.). *(978-1-4426-4202-7(5))*; pap. *(978-1-4426-1106-1(5))* Univ. of Toronto Pr.

Genetsch, Martin. The Texture of Identity: The Fiction of MG Vassanji, Neil Bissoondath & Rohinton Mistry. 2007. (Illus.). 256p. pap. 25.95 *(978-1-894770-41-5(2))* TSAR Pubns. CAN. Dist: Univ. of Toronto Pr.

Hamilton, Ian. The Water Rat of Wanchai. 2011. 424p. pap. ***(978-0-88787-251-8(4))*** House of Anansi Pr.

Heller, Deborah. DAUGHTERS & MOTHERS in Alice Munro's Later Stories. 2009. (ENG.). 50p. pap. 12.00 *(978-0-9820073-3-4(7))* Workwomans Pr.

Hodgins, Jack. Jack Hodgins: Essays on His Works. Hannan, Annika, ed. 2009. (Writers Ser.). (ENG.). 250p. 18.00 *(978-1-55071-300-8(0))* Guernica Editions, Inc. CAN. Dist: Univ. of Toronto Pr.

Hooper, Brad. The Fiction of Alice Munro: An Appreciation, 1 vol. 2008. (Illus.). 184p. 44.95 *(978-0-275-99121-0(0)*, C9121, Praeger Pubs.) Greenwood Publishing Group, Inc.

Johansen, K. V. Beyond Window Dressing? Canadian Children's Fantasy at the Millennium. 2007. 147p. pap. 20.00 *(978-0-9688024-5-8(1))* Sybertooth Inc. CAN. Dist: Lightning Source, Inc.

Keith, W. J. God's Plenty: Study of Hugh Hood's Short Fiction. 2010. (ENG., Illus.). 300p. pap. 24.95 *(978-1-897231-99-9(7))* Biblioasis CAN. Dist: Chicago Distribution Ctr.

Koustas, Jane. Les Belles Étrangères: Canadians in Paris. 2008. (Perspectives on Translation Ser.). (ENG.). 192p. pap. *(978-0-7766-0671-2(9))* Univ. of Ottawa Pr./Presses de l'Universite d'Ottawa.

Lams, Victor J. Robertson Davies's Cornish Trilogy: A Reader's Guide. 2008. (Illus.). 228p. (C). 70.95 *(978-1-4331-0228-8(5))* Lang, Peter Publishing, Inc.

Langer, Jessica. Postcolonialism & Science Fiction. 2012. (ENG., Illus.). 200p. 80.00 ***(978-0-230-32144-1(5))*** Palgrave Macmillan.

McPherson, Karen. Archaeologies of an Uncertain Future: Recent Generations of Canadian Women Writing. 2006. (ENG.). 330p. (C). *(978-0-7735-3135-2(1))* McGill-Queen's Univ. Pr.

Meier, John H., Jr. The John H. Meier, Jr. Governor General's Literary Award for Fiction Collection, 1936-2009. 2010. 88p. *(978-1-55195-265-9(3))* Univ. of Alberta Pr. CAN. Dist: Michigan State Univ. Pr.

Nischik, Reingard M., ed. The Canadian Short Story: Interpretations. 2007. (European Studies in North American Literature & Culture Ser.). 436p. 75.00 *(978-1-57113-127-0(2))* Camden Hse.

Perrakis, Phyllis Sternberg. Adventures of the Spirit: The Older Woman in the Works of Doris Lessing, Margaret Atwood, & Other Contemporary Women Writers. 2007. (ENG.). 321p. 49.95 *(978-0-8142-1064-2(3))* 2006. cd-rom 9.95 *(978-0-8142-9142-9(2))* Ohio State Univ. Pr.

Rosenthal, Caroline. New York & Toronto Novels after Postmodernism: Explorations of the Urban Symbolic Urban Spaces. 2011. (European Studies in North American Literature & Culture Ser.). 322p. 80.00 *(978-1-57113-489-9(1))* Camden Hse.

Sanders, Joe Sutliff. Disciplining Girls: Understanding the Origins of the Classic Orphan Girl Story. 2011. (ENG.). 240p. (gr. 17). 60.00 *(978-1-4214-0318-2(8))* Johns Hopkins Univ. Pr.

Stovel, Nora Foster. Divining Margaret Laurence: A Study of Her Complete Writings. 2008. (ENG.). 432p. *(978-0-7735-3376-9(1))*; pap. *(978-0-7735-3437-7(7))* McGill-Queen's Univ. Pr.

Turcotte, Gerry. Peripheral Fear: Transformations of the Gothic in Canadian & Australian Fiction. 2009. (Nouvelle poétique comparatiste - New Comparative Poetics Ser.). 258p. pap. 49.95 *(978-90-5201-488-3(4))* PIE - Peter Lang BEL. Dist: Lang, Peter.

University of Toronto Press. Modern Realism in English-Canadian Fiction. 2009. *(978-1-4426-4056-6(1))* Univ. of Toronto Pr.

Zinöcker, Agnes. The Politics of Storytelling. 2010. 148p. pap. *(978-3-639-25341-2(8))* VDM Verlag Dr. Mueller e.K.

CANADIAN FOLK SONGS

see Folk Songs, Canadian

CANADIAN FOOTBALL

Ackles, Bob & Mulgrew, Ian. The Water Boy: From the Sidelines to the Owner's Box: Inside the CFL, the XFL, & the NFL. 2007. (ENG., Illus.). 304p. 29.95 *(978-0-470-15345-1(8)*, Wiley) Wiley, John & Sons, Inc.

Brunt, Stephen & Canadian Football League. Canada's Own: A Celebration of 100 Grey Cups. 2012. (ENG., Illus.). 256p. 45.00 ***(978-0-7710-1744-5(8)***, McClelland & Stewart) McClelland & Stewart CAN. Dist: Random Hse., Inc.

Dunigan, Matt & Taylor, Jim. Goin' Deep: The Life & Times of a CFL Quarterback. unabr. ed. 2007. (ENG., Illus.). 304p. 32.95 *(978-1-55017-448-9(7))* Harbour Publishing Co., Ltd. CAN. Dist: Ingram Pub. Services.

Januska, Michael. Grey Cup Century. 2012. (ENG., Illus.). 224p. pap. 14.99 ***(978-1-4597-0448-0(7))*** Dundurn CAN. Dist: Ingram Pub. Services.

Proudfoot, Tony & Wall, Ted. First & Goal: The CFL & the Pursuit of Excellence. 2006. (ENG., Illus.). 192p. *(978-1-55168-316-4(4))* Fenn, H. B. & Co., Ltd.

CANADIAN INVASION, 1775-1776

Codman, John. Arnold's Expedition to Quebec. 2009. 376p. 33.99 *(978-1-110-17687-8(2))*; pap. 32.75 *(978-1-110-17683-0(X))* BiblioBazaar.

—Arnold's Expedition to Quebec. 2009. 198p. pap. *(978-0-217-17554-8(6))* Books LLC.

—Arnold's Expedition to Quebec. 2008. 368p. 46.95 *(978-1-4369-8358-7(4))*; pap. 31.95 *(978-1-4367-8126-8(4))* Kessinger Publishing, LLC.

—Arnold's Expedition to Quebec. Abbatt, William, ed. 2007. (ENG.). 464p. per. 37.95 *(978-0-548-65120-9(5))* Kessinger Publishing, LLC.

—Arnold's Expedition to Quebec. 340p. reprint ed. 98.00 *(978-0-7222-9264-8(3))* Library Reprints, Inc.

—Arnold's Expedition to Quebec. 2007. (ENG.). 368p. per. *(978-1-4067-5273-1(8))* Read Bks.

Cubbison, Douglas R. The American Northern Theater Army in 1776: The Ruin & Reconstruction of the Continental Force. 2010. (ENG., Illus.). 326p. pap. 45.00 *(978-0-7864-4564-6(5))* McFarland & Co., Inc. Pubs.

Darley, Stephen. Voices from A Wilderness Expedition: The Journals & Men of Benedict Arnold's Expedition to Quebec in 1775. 2011. 324p. 36.95 ***(978-1-4567-6108-0(0))***; pap. 24.95 ***(978-1-4567-6106-6(4))*** AuthorHouse.

Desjardin, Thomas A. Through a Howling Wilderness: Benedict Arnold's March to Quebec 1775. 2007. (ENG., Illus.). 256p. pap. 16.99 *(978-0-312-33905-0(4)*, St. Martin's Griffin) St. Martin's Pr.

Drake, Samuel Adams. Burgoyne's Invasion Of 1777. 2010. 156p. pap. 27.45 *(978-1-4455-3717-7(6))* Thorndike Pr.

Henry, John Joseph. Account of Arnold's Campaign Against Quebec & of the Hardships & Sufferings of That Band Of Heroes Who Traversed the Wilderness of Maine from Cambridge to the St. Lawrence, in the Autumn of 1775. 198p. reprint ed. 88.00 *(978-0-7222-9265-5(1))* Library Reprints, Inc.

Jones, Charles Henry. History of the Campaign for the Conquest of Canada in 1776: From the Death of Montgomery to the Retreat of the British Army under Sir Guy Carleton. 234p. reprint ed. 98.00 *(978-0-7222-6808-7(4))* Library Reprints, Inc.

Lefkowitz, Arthur S. Benedict Arnold's Army: The 1775 American Invasion of Canada During the Revolutionary War. 2008. (Illus.). 380p. 32.95 *(978-1-932714-03-6(0))* Savas Beatie.

Mason, Richard A. The Quiet Patriot, Colonel Return Jonathan Meigs: With Meigs's 1775 Journal of the Quebec Expedition. 2010. pap. 33.00 *(978-0-7884-5185-0(5))* Heritage Bks.

Mason, Richard A. & Meigs, Return Jonathan. The Quiet Patriot: Colonel Return Jonathan Meigs: With Meig's 1775 Journal of the Quebec Expedition. 2010. (Illus.). xii, 369p. ***(978-0-7884-8404-9(4))*** Heritage Bks.

Melvin, James. The Journal of James Melvin, Private Solider in Arnold's Expedition Against Quebec in the Year 1775. 90p. reprint ed. 88.00 *(978-0-7222-9267-9(8))* Library Reprints, Inc.

Morison, George Abbot. An Interesting Journal of Occurrences: The Expedition to Quebec Conducted by the Celebrated Arnold at the Commencement of the American Revolution. (Magazine of History with Notes & Queries Ser.). 44p. reprint ed. 88.00 *(978-0-7222-7727-0(X))* Library Reprints, Inc.

Smith, Justin Harvey. Arnold's March from Cambridge to Quebec: A Critical Study. 498p. reprint ed. 98.00 *(978-0-7222-9268-6(6))* Library Reprints, Inc.

—Arnold's March from Cambridge to Quebec: A Critical Study, Together with a Reprint of Arnold's Journal. 498p. reprint ed. 98.00 *(978-0-7222-7685-3(0))* Library Reprints, Inc.

—Our Struggle for the Fourteenth Colony, 2 vols. reprint ed. 250.00 *(978-0-7222-6827-8(0))*; 250.00 *(978-0-7222-7686-0(9))* Library Reprints, Inc.

Thayer, Simeon. The Invasion of Canada in 1775. 102p. reprint ed. 88.00 *(978-0-7222-7729-4(6))* Library Reprints, Inc.

Wurtele, Frederick Christian. Blockade of Quebec in 1775-1776: The American Revolutionists (Les Bastonnais), 2 vol., set. reprint ed. 250.00 *(978-0-7222-6880-3(7))* Library Reprints, Inc.

York, Mark A. Patriot on the Kennebec: Major Reuben Colburn, Benedict Arnold & the March to Quebec 1775. 2012. 128p. pap. 19.99 ***(978-1-60949-500-8(4))*** History Pr., The.

CANADIAN LITERATURE

see also Canadian Drama; Canadian Essays; Canadian Fiction; Canadian Poetry; Canadian Wit and Humor; French-Canadian Literature

Anctil, Pierre & Loiselle, Andre, eds. Canada Exposed/le Canada à Découvert. 2009. (Études Canadiennes - Canadian Studies). (ENG & FRE.). 368p. pap. 64.95 *(978-90-820154-8-5(X))* PIE - Peter Lang BEL. Dist: Lang, Peter.

Asfour, John Mikhail & Gardiner, Elee Kraljii, eds. V6a: Writing from Vancouver's Downtown Eastside. 2012. (ENG.). 150p. pap. 19.95 ***(978-1-55152-462-7(7))*** Arsenal Pulp Pr. CAN. Dist: Consortium Bk. Sales & Distribution.

Bennett, Donna & Brown, Russell. An Anthology of Canadian Literature in English. 3rd ed. 2010. (ENG., Illus.). 1264p. pap. 75.00 *(978-0-19-542781-3(5))* Oxford Univ. Pr., Inc.

Berg, William J. Literature & Painting in Quebec: From Imagery to Identity. 2012. (ENG., Illus.). 416p. ***(978-1-4426-4398-7(6))*** Univ. of Toronto Pr.

Bitney, Katherine & Taskans, Andris, eds. A/Cross Sections: New Manitoba Writing. 2007. (ENG.). 400p. pap. 28.95 ***(978-0-9692525-6-6(0))*** Manitoba Writer's Guild, Inc. CAN. Dist: Univ. of Toronto Pr.

Coady, Lynn, ed. The Anansi Reader: Forty Years of Very Good Books, 1 vol. 2008. (ENG.). 328p. pap. 15.95 *(978-0-88784-775-2(7))* House of Anansi Pr. CAN. Dist: Perseus-PGW.

Crawford, Allison, et al, eds. Body & Soul: Narratives of Healing from Ars Medica. 2011. (ENG., Illus.). 336p. pap. ***(978-1-4426-1290-7(8))*** Univ. of Toronto Pr.

Davies, Gwendolyn, ed. Myth & Milieu: Atlantic Literature & Culture, 1918-1939. 225p. pap. 14.95 *(978-0-919107-39-7(7))* Acadiensis Pr. CAN. Dist: Goose Lane Editions.

DiGiovanni, Caroline, ed. Italian Canadian Voices: A Literary Anthology, 1946-2005. 2010. (ENG.). 244p. per. 18.00 *(978-0-88962-858-8(0))* Mosaic Pr.

Dumont, Marilyn, ed. Initiations: A Selection of Young Native Writings. 2007. (ENG., Illus.). 168p. pap. 16.95 *(978-1-894778-47-3(2))* Theytus Bks., Ltd. CAN. Dist: Univ. of Toronto Pr.

ECW Press Staff. The Mind's Eye: CBC Literary Awards Winners, 2001 - 2006. 2008. (ENG.). 256p. pap. 19.95 *(978-1-55022-832-8(3))* ECW Pr. CAN. Dist: Independent Pubs. Group.

Edwards, Robert F. River of Life. 2011. 380p. pap. 25.45 *(978-1-4269-5675-1(4))* Trafford Publishing.

Elton, Sarah, ed. City of Words: Toronto Through Her Writers' Eyes. 2009. (ENG., Illus.). 360p. 49.00 *(978-1-897151-49-5(7))* Cormorant Bks. Inc. CAN. Dist: Univ. of Toronto Pr.

Fazio, Venera & De Santis, Delia. Sweet Lemons 2: International Writings with a Sicilian Accent. 2010. pap. *(978-1-881901-76-1(9))* LEGAS.

Graydon, Shari. I Feel Great about My Hands: And Other Unexpected Joys of Aging, 1 vol. 2011. (ENG., Illus.). 264p. pap. 17.95 *(978-1-55365-786-6(1))* D&M Pubs. Inc. CAN. Dist: Perseus-PGW.

Grenville, Bruce & Steedman, Scott, eds. Visions of British Columbia: A Landscape Manual, 1 vol. 2010. (ENG., Illus.). 256p. pap. 35.00 *(978-1-55365-500-8(1))* D&M Pubs. Inc. CAN. Dist: Perseus-PGW.

Howe, Joseph. Poems & Essays. 2009. (Illus.). 250p. pap. *(978-0-217-78441-2(0))* Books LLC.

Kasturi, Sandra & Villegas, Halli. Imaginarium 2011: The Best Canadian Speculative Writing. 2011. (Illus.). 250p. pap. 15.95 *(978-1-926851-15-0(3))* ChiZine Pubns. CAN. Dist: Diamond Bk. Distributors.

Koop, Doug. Northern Lights: An Anthology of Contemporary Christian Writing in Canada. Rempel-Burkholder, Byron & Dueck, Dora, eds. 2008. (ENG.). 256p. pap. 24.95 *(978-0-470-15526-4(4)*, Wiley) Wiley, John & Sons, Inc.

Long, Mark C. & Waage, Frederick O. Teaching North American Environmental Literature. Christensen, Laird, ed. 2008. (ENG.). 40.00 *(978-0-87352-809-2(3))*; pap. 22.00 *(978-0-87352-810-8(7))* Modern Language Assn. of America.

McCulloch, Thomas. The Mephibosheth Stepsure Letters. Davies, Gwendolyn, ed. (Illus.). 508p. *(978-0-88629-042-9(2))* McGill-Queen's Univ. Pr.

Moscovitch, Hannah, et al. The Mill. 2012. (ENG.). 304p. pap. 24.95 ***(978-1-77091-009-6(3))*** Playwrights Canada Pr. CAN. Dist: Consortium Bk. Sales & Distribution.

Mount, Nick. When Canadian Literature Moved to New York. 2006. (Studies in Book & Print Culture Ser.). (ENG., Illus.). 210p. pap. *(978-0-8020-9485-8(6))* Univ. of Toronto Pr.

Neufeld, Elsie, et al, eds. Half in the Sun: Anthology of Mennonite Writing. 2006. (ENG., Illus.). 254p. per. *(978-1-55380-038-5(9))* Ronsdale Pr.

Newhouse, Miriam & Messaline, Peter. The Actor's Survival Kit. 4th ed. 2007. (ENG.). 264p. pap. 24.99 *(978-1-55002-678-8(X)*, Simon & Pierre) Dundurn CAN. Dist: Ingram Pub. Services.

Nischik, Reingard M., ed. History of Literature in Canada: English-Canadian & French-Canadian. 2010. (European Studies in North American Literature & Culture Ser.). 618p. 45.00 *(978-1-57113-359-5(3))* Camden Hse.

Pugh, Terry & McLaughlin, Darrell, eds. Our Board Our Business: Why Farmers Support the Canadian Wheat Board. 2007. (ENG., Illus.). 100p. pap. 14.95 *(978-1-55266-237-3(3))* Fernwood Publishing Co., Ltd. CAN. Dist: Independent Pubs. Group.

Purdy, Al. The Al Purdy A Frame Anthology. Vermeersch, Paul, ed. 2009. (ENG., Illus.). 160p. pap. 26.95 *(978-1-55017-502-8(5))* Harbour Publishing Co., Ltd. CAN. Dist: Ingram Pub. Services.

Renaud, Normand. Le Salut de L'arrière-Pays: Figures Légendaires, Récits Imaginaires et Humour Crucifère du Nord de L'Ontario. 2010. (FRE.). 299p. *(978-2-89423-246-0(2))* Prise de Parole, Inc.

Reznowski, Gabriella. Literary Research & Canadian Literature: Strategies & Sources. 2011. (Literary Research: Strategies & Sources Ser.). (ENG., Illus.). 224p. pap. 39.95 *(978-0-8108-7768-9(6))* Scarecrow Pr., Inc.

Reznowski, Gabriella Natasha. Literary Research & Canadian Literature: Strategies & Sources. 2011. E-Book *(978-0-8108-7769-6(4))* Scarecrow Pr., Inc.

Richardson, John. Wacousta, or, the Prophecy; a Tale of the Canadas. 2009. (Illus.). 114p. pap. *(978-1-150-76453-0(8))* Books LLC.

—Wacousta, or, the Prophecy; a Tale of the Canadas. 2009. 120p. pap. 20.00 *(978-1-150-41516-6(9))* General Bks. LLC.

Routley, Andrea, ed. Walk Myself Home: An Anthology to End Violence Against Women. unabr. ed. 2010. (ENG.). 184p. pap. *(978-1-894759-51-9(6))* Caitlin Pr., Inc.

Sadowski-Smith, Claudia. Border Fictions: Globalization, Empire, & Writing at the Boundaries of the United States. 2008. (New World Studies). (ENG.). 208p. (C). (gr. 13-17). per. 22.50 *(978-0-8139-2678-0(5))* Univ. Pr. of Virginia.

Steeves, Andrew, et al, eds. Gaspereau Gloriatur: Book of the Blessed Tenth Year, 3 vols. 2007. (ENG.). 192p. pap. *(978-1-55447-038-9(2))* Gaspereau Pr.

Swan, Alison, ed. Fresh Water: Women Writing on the Great Lakes. 2006. (ENG.). 256p. per. 26.95 *(978-0-87013-789-1(1))* Michigan State Univ. Pr.

Vipond, Douglas & Hunt, Russell A., eds. The STU Reader. 2010. (ENG.). 246p. pap. 17.95 *(978-0-86492-613-5(8))* Goose Lane Editions CAN. Dist: Univ. of Toronto Pr.

Warwick, Samantha. The Story That Brought Me Here: To Alberta from Everywhere, 1 vol. Goyette, Linda, ed. 2009. (ENG., Illus.). 240p. pap. *(978-1-897142-34-9(X))* Brindle & Glass Publishing.

CANADIAN LITERATURE—BIBLIOGRAPHY

Kandiuk, Mary. Caribbean & South Asian Writers in Canada: A Bibliography of Their Works & of English-Language Criticism. 2007. (ENG.). 244p. per. 55.00 *(978-0-8108-5883-1(5))* Scarecrow Pr., Inc.

C

Koustas, Jane. Les Belles Étrangères: Canadians in Paris. 2008. (Perspectives on Translation Ser.). (ENG.). 192p. pap. *(978-0-7766-0671-2(9))* Univ. of Ottawa Pr./Presses de l'Universite d'Ottawa.

Lecker, Robert & David, Jack. The Annotated Bibliography of Canada's Major Authors, 8 Vols. *(978-0-920802-08-3(7))* Bow Historical Bks.

Mazur, Carol. Alice Munro: An Annotated Bibliography of Works & Criticism. Moulder, Cathy, ed. annot. ed. 2007. (ENG.). 472p. 95.00 *(978-0-8108-5924-1(6))* Scarecrow Pr., Inc.

Oh, Seiwoong. Encyclopedia of Asian American Literature. 2007. (Encyclopedia of American Ethnic Literature Ser.). 400p. (C). (gr. 9). 75.00 *(978-0-8160-6086-3(X))* Facts On File, Inc.

Rankin, Sharon, ed. The Moravian Beginnings of Canadian Inuit Literature. 2010. (FRE & ENG., Illus.). 112p. pap. 15.00 *(978-0-9821703-6-6(X))* International Polar Institute Pr.

Rigelhof, T. F. Hooked on Canadian Books: The Good, the Better, & the Best Canadian Novels since 1984. 2010. (ENG.). 336p. 32.00 *(978-1-897151-75-4(6))* Cormorant Bks. Inc. CAN. Dist: Univ. of Toronto Pr.

Toye, William. The Concise Oxford Companion to Canadian Literature. 2nd ed. (ENG.). 704p. 2012. 39.95 ***(978-0-19-544529-9(5))*** 2011. 75.00 *(978-0-19-542885-8(4))* Oxford Univ. Pr., Inc.

CANADIAN LITERATURE—HISTORY AND CRITICISM

Anselmi, William & ANSELMI, William, eds. Mary Melfi: Essays on Her Works. 2006. (Writers Ser.). (ENG.). 194p. 15.00 *(978-1-55071-251-3(9))* Guernica Editions, Inc. CAN. Dist: Univ. of Toronto Pr.

Armstrong, Luanne & Landale, Zoë, eds. Slice Me Some Truth: An Anthology of Canadian Creative Non-fiction. 2011. (ENG.). 400p. pap. 29.00 ***(978-1-894987-60-8(8))*** Wolsak & Wynn Pubs., Ltd. CAN. Dist: Univ. of Toronto Pr.

Atwood, Margaret. Second Words: Selected Critical Prose 1960-1982. 2011. (ENG.). 448p. pap. 29.95 ***(978-1-77089-010-7(6))*** House of Anansi Pr. CAN. Dist: Perseus-PGW.

Beard, Laura J. Acts of Narrative Resistance: Women's Autobiographical Writings in the Americas. 2009. (New World Studies). (ENG., Illus.). 216p. (C). (gr. 13-17). pap. 21.50 *(978-0-8139-2863-0(X))*; (gr. 17). 55.00 *(978-0-8139-2862-3(1))* Univ. Pr. of Virginia.

Beckford, Sharon Morgan. Naturally Woman: The Search for Self in Black Canadian Women's Literature. 2011. (ENG., Illus.). 278p. pap. 29.95 ***(978-1-926708-12-6(1))*** Inanna Pubns. & Education, Inc. CAN. Dist: SPD-Small Pr. Distribution.

Bednarski, Betty & Ellenwood, Ray. Jacques Ferron Hors Québec. 2010. (FRE & ENG., Illus.). xii, 314p. *(978-1-897018-46-0(0))* Editions du GREF.

Bennett, Donna & Brown, Russell. An Anthology of Canadian Literature in English. 3rd ed. 2010. (ENG., Illus.). 1264p. pap. 75.00 *(978-0-19-542781-3(5))* Oxford Univ. Pr., Inc.

Benson, Mark. La quête érotique d'Yves Thériault. 2008. (FRE.). 234p. pap. *(978-3-03911-663-8(0))* Lang, Peter.

Boss, Allan. Identifying Mavor Moore: A Historical & Literary Study. 2011. (ENG.). 416p. pap. 24.95 ***(978-0-88754-919-9(5))*** Playwrights Canada Pr. CAN. Dist: Consortium Bk. Sales & Distribution.

Bouson, J. Brooks. Embodied Shame: Uncovering Female Shame in Contemporary Women's Writings. 2010. 236p. pap. 24.95 *(978-1-4384-2728-7(X)*, Suny Pr.) 2009. 256p. 70.00 *(978-1-4384-2727-0(1))* State Univ. of New York Pr.

—Margaret Atwood: The Robber Bride, the Blind Assassin, Oryx & Crake. 2011. (Continuum Studies in Contemporary North American Fiction Ser.). (ENG.). 224p. 29.95 *(978-0-8264-3062-5(7))*; 100.00 *(978-0-8264-2437-2(6))* Continuum International Publishing Group, Ltd. GBR. Dist: National Bk. Network.

Chen, John Z. Ming. The Influence of Daoism on Asian-Canadian Writers. 2009. (CHI & ENG.). 300p. 109.95 *(978-0-7734-4810-0(1))* Mellen, Edwin Pr., The.

Clarke, George Elliot. Odysseys Home 2. 2010. *(978-0-8020-9153-6(9))*; (ENG.). pap. *(978-0-8020-9425-4(2))* Univ. of Toronto Pr.

Coates, Donna & Melnyk, George, eds. Wild Words: Essays on Alberta Literature. 2009. (ENG.). 224p. pap. 37.95 *(978-1-897425-30-5(9))* UBC Pr. CAN. Dist: Univ. of Washington Pr.

Coleman, Daniel. White Civility: The Literary Project of English Canada. 2008. (ENG.). 320p. pap. *(978-0-8020-9642-5(5))* Univ. of Toronto Pr.

Concilio, Carmen & Lane, Richard J., eds. Image Technologies in Canadian Literature: Narrative, Film, & Photography. 2009. (Études Canadiennes - Canadian Studies). 164p. pap. 42.95 *(978-90-5201-474-6(4))* PIE - Peter Lang BEL. Dist: Lang, Peter.

Darias-Beautell, Eva. Unruly Penelopes & the Ghosts: Narratives of English Canada. 2012. (ENG.). 254p. (C). 85.00 ***(978-1-55458-363-8(2))*** Wilfrid Laurier Univ. Pr. CAN. Dist: Univ. of Toronto Pr.

Denham, Robert D. The Northrop Frye Handbook: A Biographical & Bibliographic Guide. 2012. (ENG.). 334p. pap. 95.00 ***(978-0-7864-6370-1(8))*** McFarland & Co., Inc. Pubs.

Dickinson, Mark & Goulet, Clare, eds. Lyric Ecology: Essays in Honour of Jan Zwicky. 2010. (ENG.). 304p. 30.00 *(978-1-897151-77-8(2))* Cormorant Bks. Inc. CAN. Dist: Univ. of Toronto Pr.

Dickinson, Peter. Screening Gender, Framing Genre: Canadian Literature into Film. 2007. (ENG., Illus.). 304p. *(978-0-8020-4475-4(1))* Univ. of Toronto Pr.

Djwa, Sandra, ed. Giving Canada a Literary History: A Memoir. 266p. *(978-0-88629-162-4(3))* McGill-Queen's Univ. Pr.

Dobson, Kit. Transnational Canadas: Anglo-Canadian Literature & Globalization. 2009. (TransCanada Ser.). (ENG.). 258p. pap. 42.95 *(978-1-55458-063-7(3))* Wilfrid Laurier Univ. Pr. CAN. Dist: Univ. of Toronto Pr.

Duncan, Isla. Alice Munro's Narrative Art. 2011. (ENG., Illus.). 194p. 80.00 ***(978-0-230-33857-9(7))*** Palgrave Macmillan.

Dvorak, Marta & Jones, Manina, eds. Carol Shields & the Extra-Ordinary. 2007. (ENG., Illus.). 288p. (C). *(978-0-7735-3220-5(X))* McGill-Queen's Univ. Pr.

Easton, Lee & Harrison, Richard. The Secret Identity Reader: Superheroes, Graphic Tales & Us. 2008. (ENG., Illus.). 120p. pap. 19.00 *(978-0-88753-437-9(6))* Black Moss Pr. CAN. Dist: LitDistCo.

Ertler, Klaus-Dieter & Lutz, Hartmut, eds. Canada in Grainau / le Canada à Grainau: A Multidisciplinary Survey of Canadian Studies after 30 Years Tour d'horizon multidisciplinaire d'Études canadiennes, 30 ans Après. 2009. (Canadiana. Literaturen/Kulturen, Literatures/Cultures, Littératures/Cultures Ser.). 344p. 79.95 *(978-3-631-58942-7(5))* Lang, Peter GmbH, Europaischer Verlag der Wissenschaften DEU. Dist: Lang, Peter.

Fiamengo, Janice, ed. Other Selves: Animals in the Canadian Literary Imagination. 2007. (Reappraisals: Canadian Writers Ser.). (ENG., Illus.). 366p. (gr. 14). pap. *(978-0-7766-0645-3(X))* Univ. of Ottawa Pr./Presses de l'Universite d'Ottawa.

Friskney, Janet B. New Canadian Library: The Ross-McClelland Years, 1952-1978. 2007. (Studies in Book & Print Culture Ser.). (ENG., Illus.). 256p. *(978-0-8020-9746-0(4))* Univ. of Toronto Pr.

Gault, Cinda. National & Female Identity in Canadian Literature, 1965-1980: The Fiction of Margaret Laurence, margaret Atwood, & Marian Engel. 2012. 320p. 149.95 ***(978-0-7734-2622-1(1))*** Mellen, Edwin Pr., The.

Geddes, Gary. Gary Geddes: Essays on His Works. May, Robert G., ed. 2009. (Writers Ser.). (ENG.). 250p. 18.00 *(978-1-55071-299-5(3))* Guernica Editions, Inc. CAN. Dist: Univ. of Toronto Pr.

Gelfant, Blanche H. Cross-Cultural Reckonings: A Triptych of Russian, American & Canadian Texts. 2009. (Cambridge Studies in American Literature & Culture Ser.). (ENG.). 208p. pap. 31.99 *(978-0-521-10675-7(3))* Cambridge Univ. Pr.

Gilbert, Paula Ruth & Santoro, Milena. Transatlantic Passages: Literary & Cultural Relations Between Quebec & Francophone Europe. 2010. (ENG., Illus.). 344p. pap. *(978-0-7735-3790-3(2))* McGill-Queen's Univ. Pr.

Goldman, Marlene. DisPossession: Haunting in Canadian Fiction. 2012. (ENG.). 384p. (C). ***(978-0-7735-3950-1(6))*** McGill-Queen's Univ. Pr.

Goldsby, Jacqueline. A Spectacular Secret: Lynching in American Life & Literature. 2006. (Illus.). 384p. 72.50 *(978-0-226-30137-2(0))*; per. 30.00 *(978-0-226-30138-9(9))* Univ. of Chicago Pr.

Gorjup, Branko, ed. Margaret Atwood: Essays on Her Works. 2007. (Writers Ser.). (ENG.). 300p. 18.00 *(978-1-55071-267-4(5))* Guernica Editions, Inc. CAN. Dist: Univ. of Toronto Pr.

—Northrop Frye's Canadian Literary Criticism & Its Influence. 2009. (Frye Studies). (ENG.). 368p. *(978-0-8020-9938-9(6))* Univ. of Toronto Pr.

Hammill, Faye. Canadian Literature. 2007. (Edinburgh Critical Guides to Literature Ser.). (ENG.). 172p. (gr. 17). 120.00 *(978-0-7486-2161-3(X))*; pap. 32.00 *(978-0-7486-2162-0(8))* Edinburgh Univ. Pr. GBR. Dist: Columbia Univ. Pr.

Hazelton, Hugh. Latinocanada: A Critical Study of Ten Latin American Writers of Canada. 2007. (ENG.). 320p. (C). *(978-0-7735-3207-6(2))* McGill-Queen's Univ. Pr.

Hebert, Anne L. Anne Hébert: Essays on Her Works. Skallerup, Lee, ed. 2010. (Writers Ser.). (ENG.). 184p. 18.00 *(978-1-55071-278-0(0))* Guernica Editions, Inc. CAN. Dist: Univ. of Toronto Pr.

Howells, Coral Ann & Kröller, Eva-Marie, eds. The Cambridge History of Canadian Literature. 2009. (Illus.). 802p. 175.00 *(978-0-521-86876-1(9))* Cambridge Univ. Pr.

Huck, Sybille. Frauenrollen in Margaret Laurences Romanen: Weibliche Identitätsentwicklung in The Stone Angel, A Bird in the House und The Diviners. 2008. (GER & ENG.). 106p. ***(978-3-8366-6144-7(6))*** Diplomica GmbH.

Kamboureli, Smaro. Scandalous Bodies: Diasporic Literature in English Canada. 2009. (TransCanada Ser.). (ENG.). 288p. pap. 42.95 *(978-1-55458-064-4(1))* Wilfrid Laurier Univ. Pr. CAN. Dist: Univ. of Toronto Pr.

Kamboureli, Smaro & Miki, Roy, eds. Trans. Can. Lit: Resituating the Study of Canadian Literature. 2007. (TransCanada Ser.). (ENG., Illus.). 252p. pap. 38.95 *(978-0-88920-513-0(2))* Wilfrid Laurier Univ. Pr. CAN. Dist: Univ. of Toronto Pr.

Kamboureli, Smaro & Zacharias, Robert, eds. Shifting the Ground of Canadian Literary Studies: Nation-State, Indigeneity, Culture. 2012. (TransCanada Ser.). (ENG.). 310p. (C). pap. 42.95 ***(978-1-55458-365-2(9))*** Wilfrid Laurier Univ. Pr. CAN. Dist: Univ. of Toronto Pr.

Kandiuk, Mary. Caribbean & South Asian Writers in Canada: A Bibliography of Their Works & of English-Language Criticism. 2007. (ENG.). 244p. per. 55.00 *(978-0-8108-5883-1(5))* Scarecrow Pr., Inc.

Keith, W. J. Canadian Literature in English, 2 vols. (ENG.). (C). Vol. 1. 2006. 224p. pap. 24.95 *(978-0-88984-283-0(3))* Vol. 2. 2007. 208p. pap. 24.95 *(978-0-88984-285-4(X))* Porcupine's Quill, Inc. CAN. Dist: Univ. of Toronto Pr.

Kim, Christine, et al, eds. Cultural Grammars of Nation, Diaspora, & Indigeneity in Canada. 2012. (TransCanada Ser.). (ENG., Illus.). 284p. (C). pap. 49.95 *(978-1-55458-336-2(5))* Wilfrid Laurier Univ. Pr. CAN. Dist: Univ. of Toronto Pr.

Král, Françoise. Critical Identities in Contemporary Anglophone Diasporic Literature. 2009. (ENG., Illus.). 240p. 84.00 *(978-0-230-22041-6(X))* Palgrave Macmillan.

Kramer, Reinhold. Mordecai Richler: Leaving St Urbain. 2010. (Art of Living Ser.). (ENG., Illus.). 498p. (C). pap. *(978-0-7735-3742-2(2))* McGill-Queen's Univ. Pr.

Laferrière, Dany. Un Art de Vivre Par Temps de Catastrophe. 2006. (Henry Kreisel Memorial Lecture Ser.).Tr. of Art of Living in Catastrophic Times. (ENG & FRE.). 68p. pap. 10.95 *(978-0-88864-553-1(8))* Univ. of Alberta Pr. CAN. Dist: Michigan State Univ. Pr., Chicago Distribution Ctr.

Lane, Richard J. Concise History of Canadian Literature. 2011. (Routledge Concise Histories of Literature Ser.). (ENG., Illus.). 272p. (C). 110.00 *(978-0-415-47045-2(5))*; pap. 28.95 *(978-0-415-47046-9(3))* Routledge.

LaRocque, Emma. When the Other Is Me: Native Resistance Discourse, 1850-1990. 2010. (ENG.). 218p. pap. 31.95 *(978-0-88755-703-3(1))* Univ. of Manitoba Pr. CAN. Dist: Chicago Distribution Ctr.

Lecker, Robert. Dr. Delicious: Memoirs of a Life in Canlit. 2006. (ENG., Illus.). 300p. per. 15.95 *(978-1-55065-210-9(9))* Vehicule Pr. CAN. Dist: Independent Pubs. Group.

Leith, Linda. Writing in the Time of Nationalism: From Two Solitudes to Blue Metropolis. 2010. 176p. pap. 15.95 *(978-1-897109-48-9(2))* Signature Editions CAN. Dist: Univ. of Toronto Pr.

Macpherson, Heidi Slettedahl. The Cambridge Introduction to Margaret Atwood. 2010. (Cambridge Introductions to Literature Ser.). (ENG.). 156p. (C). 69.00 *(978-0-521-87298-0(7))*; pap. 19.99 *(978-0-521-69463-6(9))* Cambridge Univ. Pr.

—Courting Failure: Women & the Law in Twentieth-Century Literature. 2007. (Series on Law, Politics, & Society). 292p. 52.95 *(978-1-931968-47-8(0))*; pap. 24.95 *(978-1-931968-48-5(9))* Univ. of Akron Pr., The.

McKegney, Sam. Magic Weapons: Aboriginal Writers Remaking Community after Residential Schools. 2007. (ENG.). 241p. pap. 32.95 *(978-0-88755-702-6(3))* Univ. of Manitoba Pr. CAN. Dist: Chicago Distribution Ctr.

McKenzie, Stephanie. Before the Country: Native Renaissance, Canadian Mythology. 2007. (ENG.). 224p. *(978-0-8020-9208-3(X))*; pap. *(978-0-8020-9446-9(5))* Univ. of Toronto Pr.

McLean, Scott A. & Vance, Michael E., eds. William Wye Smith: Recollections of a Nineteenth Century Scottish Canadian. 2008. (ENG., Illus.). 424p. pap. 25.99 *(978-1-55002-804-1(9)*, Dundurn Pr.) Dundurn CAN. Dist: Ingram Pub. Services.

McMaster, Lindsey. Working Girls in the West: Representations of Wage-Earning Women. 2008. (ENG.). 224p. pap. *(978-0-7748-1456-0(X))* Univ. of British Columbia Pr.

Mcwilliams, Ellen. Margaret Atwood & the Female Bildungsroman. 2009. 184p. 99.95 *(978-0-7546-6027-9(3))* Ashgate Publishing Co.

Metcalf, John. Shut up He Explained: A Literary Memoir. 2007. (ENG., Illus.). 402p. 34.95 ***(978-1-897231-32-6(6))*** Biblioasis CAN. Dist: Chicago Distribution Ctr.

Naves, Elaine Kalman. Robert Weaver: Godfather of Canadian Literature. 2008. (ENG., Illus.). 178p. pap. 17.95 *(978-1-55065-233-8(8))* Vehicule Pr. CAN. Dist: Independent Pubs. Group.

Neuhaus, Mareike. That's Raven Talk: Holophrastic Readings of Contemporary Indigenous Literatures. 2011. (Cps Ser.). 320p. 34.95 *(978-0-88977-233-5(9))* Canadian Plains Research Ctr. CAN. Dist: Univ. of Toronto Pr.

Nischik, Reingard M. Engendering Genre: The Works of Margaret Atwood. 2010. (ENG., Illus.). 328p. pap. *(978-0-7766-0724-5(3))* Univ. of Ottawa Pr./Presses de l'Universite d'Ottawa.

Nischik, Reingard M., ed. History of Literature in Canada: English-Canadian & French-Canadian. 2010. (European Studies in North American Literature & Culture Ser.). 618p. 45.00 *(978-1-57113-359-5(3))* Camden Hse.

Nischik, Reingard M. & von Flotow, Luise, eds. Translating Canada. 2007. (Perspectives on Translation Ser.). (ENG., Illus.). 352p. pap. *(978-0-7766-0661-3(1))* Univ. of Ottawa Pr./Presses de l'Universite d'Ottawa.

Nunn, Robert, ed. Drew Hayden Taylor: Essays on His Works. 2007. (Writers Ser.). (ENG.). 200p. 18.00 *(978-1-55071-268-1(3))* Guernica Editions, Inc. CAN. Dist: Univ. of Toronto Pr.

Obracht-Prondzynski, Cezary & Wicherkiewicz, Tomasz. The Kashubs: Past & Present. 2011. (Nationalisms across the Globe Ser.). (ENG., Illus.). 299p. pap. 64.95 ***(978-3-03911-975-2(3))*** Lang, Peter AG GBR. Dist: Lang, Peter.

Olinder, Britta, ed. Literary Environments: Canada & the Old World. 246p. pap. 32.95 *(978-90-5201-296-4(2))* Lang, Peter Publishing, Inc.

Oliva, Juan Ignacio. The Painful Chrysalis: Essays on Contemporary Cultural & Literary Identity. 2011. (Spanish Perspectives on English & American Literature, Communication & Culture Ser.). (ENG.). 276p. pap. ***(978-3-0343-0666-9(0))*** Lang, Peter.

Omhovere, Claire. Sensing Space: The Poetics of Geography in Contemporary English-Canadian Writing. 2007. (Canadian Studies Ser.: Vol. 11). 186p. pap. *(978-90-5201-053-3(6))* Lang, Peter AG.

Panofsky, Ruth. At Odds in the World: Essays on Jewish Canadian Women Writers. 2009. (ENG., Illus.). 117p. pap. 25.95 *(978-0-9808822-4-7(9))* Inanna Pubns. & Education, Inc. CAN. Dist: SPD-Small Pr. Distribution.

Panofsky, Ruth. The Literary Legacy of the Macmillan Company of Canada: Making Books & Mapping Culture. 2012. (Studies in Book & Print Culture Ser.). (ENG.). 352p. ***(978-0-8020-9877-1(0))*** Univ. of Toronto Pr.

Pawliez, Myreille. Une etude semantico-narratologique de Dis-moi que je vis (1964) et du Portique (1967)de Michele Mailhot: Colimacon et oscillation dans les soliloques de Josee. 2010. (FRE.). x, 356p. *(978-0-7734-1322-1(7))* Mellen, Edwin Pr., The.

Pivato, Joseph & PIVATO, Joseph, eds. Mary Di Michele: Essays on Her Works. 2006. (Writers Ser.). (ENG.). 214p. 15.00 *(978-1-55071-249-0(7))* Guernica Editions, Inc. CAN. Dist: Univ. of Toronto Pr.

Rae, Ian. From Cohen to Carson: The Poet's Novel in Canada. 2008. (ENG.). 400p. (C). *(978-0-7735-3276-2(5))* McGill-Queen's Univ. Pr.

Reid, Verna. Women Between: Construction of Self in the Work of Sharon Butala, Aganetha Dyck, Mary Meigs, & Mary Pratt. 2008. (Illus.). 327p. pap. 39.95 *(978-1-55238-242-4(7))* Univ. of Calgary Pr. CAN. Dist: Michigan State Univ. Pr.

Reimer, Mavis. Home Words: Discourses of Children's Literature in Canada. Reimer, Mavis, ed. 2008. (Studies in Childhood & Family in Canada Ser.). (ENG., Illus.). 308p. 85.00 *(978-1-55458-016-3(1))* Wilfrid Laurier Univ. Pr. CAN. Dist: Univ. of Toronto Pr.

Rhenisch, Harold. The Wolves at Evelyn: Journeys Through a Dark Century, 1 vol. 2006. (ENG., Illus.). 320p. per. *(978-1-897142-10-3(2))* Brindle & Glass Publishing.

Ridington, Robin & Ridington, Jillian. When You Sing It Now, Just Like New: First Nations Poetics, Voices, & Representations. 2006. (ENG., Illus.). 346p. pap. 24.95 *(978-0-8032-9009-9(8))* Univ. of Nebraska Pr.

Rifkind, Candida. Comrades & Critics: Women, Literature, & the Left in 1930s Canada. 2009. (ENG.). 256p. *(978-0-8020-9267-0(5))* Univ. of Toronto Pr.

Roberts, Gillian. Prizing Literature. 2011. (Cultural Spaces Ser.). ***(978-1-4426-4271-3(8))*** Univ. of Toronto Pr.

Runte, Hans R., et al. Entre Textes et Images: Constructions Identitaires en Acadie et Au Québec. 2010. (FRE., Illus.). 392p. *(978-0-9810041-5-0(6))* Institut d'études acadiennes.

Rymhs, Deena. From the Iron House: Imprisonment in First Nations Writing. 2008. (Aboriginal Studies). (ENG.). 162p. 65.00 *(978-1-55458-021-7(8))* Wilfrid Laurier Univ. Pr. CAN. Dist: Univ. of Toronto Pr.

Saul, Joanne. Writing the Roaming Subject: The Biotext in Canadian Literature. 2006. (ENG.). 200p. *(978-0-8020-9012-6(5))* Univ. of Toronto Pr.

Sheckels, Theodore F. The Political in Margaret Atwood's Fiction: The Writing on the Wall of the Tent. 2012. 200p. 99.95 ***(978-1-4094-3379-8(X))*** Ashgate Publishing Co.

Siemerling, Winfried & Casteel, Sarah Phillips. Canada & Its Americas: Transnational Navigations. 2010. 360p. (ENG & FRE.). *(978-0-7735-3657-9(4))*; pap. *(978-0-7735-3684-5(1))* McGill-Queen's Univ. Pr.

Simmins, Geoffrey. Spirit Matters: Ron (Gyo-zo) Spickett, Artist, Poet, Priest. 2009. (Art in Profile Ser.). (ENG., Illus.). 296p. pap. 45.95 *(978-1-55238-255-4(9))* Univ. of Calgary Pr. CAN. Dist: Chicago Distribution Ctr.

Stacey, Robert David, ed. RE: Reading the Postmodern: Canadian Literature & Criticism after Modernism. 2010. (Reappraisals: Canadian Writers Ser.). (ENG., Illus.). 440p. pap. *(978-0-7766-0739-9(1))* Univ. of Ottawa Pr./Presses de l'Universite d'Ottawa.

Sugars, Cynthia & Turcotte, Gerry, eds. Unsettled Remains: Canadian Literature & the Postcolonial Gothic. 2009. (ENG.). 324p. pap. 42.95 *(978-1-55458-054-5(4))* Wilfrid Laurier Univ. Pr. CAN. Dist: Univ. of Toronto Pr.

Suhonen, Katri. Canada: Images of a Post/National Society. Florby, Gunilla & Shackleton, Mark, eds. 2009. (Études Canadiennes - Canadian Studies). 386p. pap. 62.95 *(978-90-5201-485-2(X))* PIE - Peter Lang BEL. Dist: Lang, Peter.

Thacker, Robert. Alice Munro: Writing Her Lives. 2011. (Illus.). 664p. pap. 22.99 *(978-0-7710-8510-9(9)*, Emblem Edns) McClelland & Stewart CAN. Dist: Random Hse., Inc.

Thúy, Kim. Ru. Fischman, Sheila, tr. from FRE. 2012. (ENG.). 160p. 22.00 *(978-0-307-35970-4(0)*, Random Hse CAN) Random Hse. of Canada, Ltd. CAN. Dist: Random Hse., Inc.

Ty, Eleanor & Verduyn, Christl, eds. Asian Canadian Writing Beyond Autoethnography. 2008. (ENG., Illus.). 342p. pap. 42.95 *(978-1-55458-023-1(4))* Wilfrid Laurier Univ. Pr. CAN. Dist: Univ. of Toronto Pr.

Ty, Eleanor Rose. Unfastened: Globality & Asian North American Narratives. 2010. (Illus.). 216p. 67.50 *(978-0-8166-6507-5(9))*; (ENG.). pap. 22.50 *(978-0-8166-6508-2(7))* Univ. of Minnesota Pr.

Uma Parameswaran. Writing the Diaspora: Essays on Cul[t]ure & Identity. 2007. 392p. 42.00 *(978-81-316-0073-3(4))* Rawat Pubns. IND. Dist: International Specialized Bk. Services.

Ventura, Héliane & Dvorak, Marta. Resurgence in Jane Urquhart's Oeuvre. 2010. (FRE & ENG.). 228p. 51.95 *(978-90-5201-634-4(8))* Lang, Peter Publishing, Inc.

Walsh, Helen, ed. Tok, Book 2: Diaspora Dialogues. 2007. (ENG., Illus.). 200p. pap. 19.95 *(978-0-9734112-4-9(4)*, Zephyr Pr.) Chicago Review Pr., Inc.

Williams, Emily Allen. Beyond the Canebrakes: Caribbean Women Writers in Canada. 2008. *(978-1-59221-552-2(1))*; 358p. pap. *(978-1-59221-553-9(X))* Africa World Pr.

Wilson, Sheena, ed. Joy Kogawa: Essays on Her Works. 2011. (Writers Ser.). (ENG.). 200p. pap. 18.00 *(978-1-55071-311-4(6))* Guernica Editions, Inc. CAN. Dist: Univ. of Toronto Pr.

Wisker, Gina. Atwood's the Handmaid's Tale. 2010. (Reader's Guides). (ENG.). 160p. 19.95 *(978-0-8264-2601-7(8))*; 90.00 *(978-0-8264-6362-3(2))* Continuum International Publishing Group, Ltd. GBR. Dist: National Bk. Network.

Wyile, Herb. Anne of Tim Hortons: Globalization & the Reshaping of Atlantic-Canadian Literature. 2011. (Illus.). 294p. (C). pap. 42.95 *(978-1-55458-326-3(8))* Wilfrid Laurier Univ. Pr. CAN. Dist: Univ. of Toronto Pr.

Wynne-Davies, Marion. Margaret Atwood. 2010. (Writers & Their Work Ser.). (ENG.). 119p. (C). pap. 26.00 *(978-0-7463-0943-8(0))* Northcote Hse. Publishers, Ltd. GBR. Dist: Brown, David Bk. Co., The.

CANADIAN LITERATURE—INDIAN AUTHORS

Kim, Christine, et al, eds. Cultural Grammars of Nation, Diaspora, & Indigeneity in Canada. 2012. (TransCanada Ser.). (ENG., Illus.). 284p. (C). pap. 49.95 *(978-1-55458-336-2(5))* Wilfrid Laurier Univ. Pr. CAN. Dist: Univ. of Toronto Pr.

McKegney, Sam. Magic Weapons: Aboriginal Writers Remaking Community after Residential Schools. 2007. (ENG.). 241p. pap. 32.95 *(978-0-88755-702-6(3))* Univ. of Manitoba Pr. CAN. Dist: Chicago Distribution Ctr.

Neuhaus, Mareike. That's Raven Talk: Holophrastic Readings of Contemporary Indigenous Literatures. 2011. (Cps Ser.). 320p. 34.95 *(978-0-88977-233-5(9))* Canadian Plains Research Ctr. CAN. Dist: Univ. of Toronto Pr.

Rymhs, Deena. From the Iron House: Imprisonment in First Nations Writing. 2008. (Aboriginal Studies). (ENG.). 162p. 65.00 *(978-1-55458-021-7(8))* Wilfrid Laurier Univ. Pr. CAN. Dist: Univ. of Toronto Pr.

CANADIAN LITERATURE—WOMEN AUTHORS

Beckford, Sharon Morgan. Naturally Woman: The Search for Self in Black Canadian Women's Literature. 2011. (ENG., Illus.). 276p. pap. 29.95 ***(978-1-926708-12-6(1))*** Inanna Pubns. & Education, Inc. CAN. Dist: SPD-Small Pr. Distribution.

Bouson, J. Brooks. Embodied Shame: Uncovering Female Shame in Contemporary Women's Writings. 2010. 236p. pap. 24.95 *(978-1-4384-2728-7(X),* Suny Pr.) 2009. 256p. 70.00 *(978-1-4384-2727-0(1))* State Univ. of New York Pr.

De Rango-Adem, Adebe & Thompson, Andrea, eds. Other Tongues: Mixed-Race Women Speak Out. 2010. (ENG., Illus.). 302p. pap. 24.95 ***(978-1-926708-14-0(8))*** Inanna Pubns. & Education, Inc. CAN. Dist: SPD-Small Pr. Distribution.

Kelm, Mary-Ellen, ed. The Letters of Margaret Butcher: Missionary-Imperialism on the North Pacific Coast. 2006. (Legacies Shared Ser.). (ENG., Illus.). 312p. per. 29.95 *(978-1-55238-166-3(8))* Univ. of Calgary Pr. CAN. Dist: Chicago Distribution Ctr.

Nischik, Reingard M. Engendering Genre: The Works of Margaret Atwood. 2010. (ENG., Illus.). 328p. pap. *(978-0-7766-0724-5(3))* Univ. of Ottawa Pr./Presses de l'Universite d'Ottawa.

Reid, Verna. Women Between: Construction of Self in the Work of Sharon Butala, Aganetha Dyck, Mary Meigs, & Mary Pratt. 2008. (Illus.). 327p. pap. 39.95 *(978-1-55238-242-4(7))* Univ. of Calgary Pr. CAN. Dist: Michigan State Univ. Pr.

Rifkind, Candida. Comrades & Critics: Women, Literature, & the Left in 1930s Canada. 2009. (ENG.). 256p. *(978-0-8020-9267-0(5))* Univ. of Toronto Pr.

The Korean Canadian Women's Anthology Editorial Collective, ed. Han Kut: Radical Art & Writing by Korean Canadian Women. 2007. (KOR & ENG., Illus.). 248p. per. 29.95 *(978-0-9736709-8-1(3))* Inanna Pubns. & Education, Inc. CAN. Dist: SPD-Small Pr. Distribution.

Williams, Emily Allen. Beyond the Canebrakes: Caribbean Women Writers in Canada. 2008. *(978-1-59221-552-2(1))*; 358p. pap. *(978-1-59221-553-9(X))* Africa World Pr.

CANADIAN LITERATURE (FRENCH)

see French-Canadian Literature

CANADIAN MARITIMES

see Maritime Provinces

CANADIAN MUSIC

see Music, Canadian

CANADIAN NATIONAL CHARACTERISTICS

see National Characteristics, Canadian

CANADIAN NEWSPAPERS

Gale Directory of Publications & Broadcast Media. 147th ed. 2011. 1297.00 *(978-1-4144-4715-5(9))* Cengage Gale.

Gregory, Winifred. Union List of Newspapers. 791p. reprint ed. lib. bdg. 148.00 *(978-0-7222-0330-9(6))* Library Reprints, Inc.

CANADIAN NORTHWEST

see Northwest, Canadian

CANADIAN PACIFIC RAILWAY COMPANY

Hanna, Jonathan, et al. Portraits of Canada: Photographic Treasures of the CPR, 1 vol. 2006. (ENG., Illus.). 216p. 39.95 *(978-1-894856-77-5(5))* Fifth Hse. Pubs. CAN. Dist: Ingram Pub. Services.

Jones, David Laurence. Famous Name Trains: Travelling in Style with the CPR. 2006. (ENG., Illus.). 178p. 29.95 *(978-1-894856-51-5(1))* Fifth Hse. Pubs. CAN. Dist: Ingram Pub. Services.

Knowles, Valerie. From Telegrapher to Titan: The Life of William C. Van Horne. 2010. (Railroads Past & Present Ser.). (ENG., Illus.). 504p. pap. 29.95 *(978-0-253-22250-3(8),* 0253222508) Indiana Univ. Pr.

—William C. Van Horne: Railway Titan. 2010. (Quest Biography Ser.). (ENG., Illus.). 216p. pap. 19.99 *(978-1-55488-702-6(X))* Dundurn CAN. Dist: Ingram Pub. Services.

Lavallee, Omer. Van Horne's Road: The Building of the Canadian Pacific Railway. 2nd ed. 2007. (Railfare Books (Fifth House) Ser.). (ENG., Illus.). 336p. 60.00 *(978-1-897252-35-9(6))* Fifth Hse. Pubs. CAN. Dist: Ingram Pub. Services.

McDonnell, Greg. Canadian Pacific: Stand Fast, Craigellachie! 2006. (ENG., Illus.). 240p. pap. 35.00 *(978-1-55046-490-0(6))* Boston Mills Pr. CAN. Dist: Firefly Bks., Ltd.

Murray, Tom. Rails Across Canada: The History of Canadian Pacific & Canadian National Railways. 2011. (ENG., Illus.). 320p. pap. 30.00 *(978-0-7603-4008-0(0),* 0760340080, Voyageur Pr) MBI Publishing Co. LLC.

Pole, Graeme. Gravity, Steam & Steel: An Illustrated Railway History of Rogue Pass, 1 vol. 2012. (ENG., Illus.). 128p. pap. 16.95 ***(978-1-897252-46-8(3))*** Fifth Hse. Pubs. CAN. Dist: Ingram Pub. Services.

Pole, Graeme. The Spiral Tunnels & the Big Hill (New Edition) A Canadian Railway Adventure. 2007. (Illus.). 80p. pap. *(978-1-55153-717-7(6))* Altitude Publishing Canada Ltd.

Willson, Beckles. The Life of Lord Strathcona & Mount Royal. 2009. (ENG.). 558p. 44.99 *(978-1-117-21218-0(1))*; pap. 41.75 *(978-1-117-21219-7(X))* BiblioBazaar.

—The Life of Lord Strathcona & Mount Royal, 2 Vols. reprint ed. 250.00 *(978-0-7222-6965-7(X))* Library Reprints, Inc.

CANADIAN PAINTING

see Painting, Canadian

CANADIAN PERIODICALS

Anuik, Jonathan. First in Canada: An Aboriginal Book of Days. 2011. (Tbs Ser.). (ENG.). 200p. 24.95 *(978-0-88977-240-3(1))* Canadian Plains Research Ctr. CAN. Dist: Univ. of Toronto Pr.

Gale Directory of Publications & Broadcast Media. 147th ed. 2011. 1297.00 *(978-1-4144-4715-5(9))* Cengage Gale.

Karaplis, Joanna, ed. The Canadian Writer's Market, 18th Edition. 2010. (ENG.). 464p. pap. 23.95 *(978-0-7710-9585-6(6),* McClelland & Stewart) McClelland & Stewart CAN. Dist: Random Hse., Inc.

Tooze, Sandra. The Canadian Writer's Market. 17th ed. 2007. (ENG.). 472p. pap. 21.00 *(978-0-7710-8528-4(1),* McClelland & Stewart) McClelland & Stewart CAN. Dist: Random Hse., Inc.

CANADIAN PHILOSOPHY

see Philosophy, Canadian

CANADIAN POETRY

see also French-Canadian Poetry

Amabile, George & Dales, Kim, eds. No Feather, No Ink: After Riel. (ENG.). 192p. 2008. pap. 25.00 *(978-0-920633-02-1(1))* 2006. pap. 12.00 *(978-0-920633-03-8(X))* Thistledown Pr., Ltd. CAN. Dist: Univ. of Toronto Pr.

Bachinsky, Elizabeth. Curio: Grotesques & Satires from the Electronic Age. 2nd ed. 2009. (ENG., Illus.). 111p. pap. 20.00 *(978-1-897388-40-2(3))* BookThug CAN. Dist: SPD-Small Pr. Distribution.

Crozier, Lorna. Small Beneath the Sky: A Prairie Memoir, 1 vol. 2011. (ENG.). 208p. pap. 16.95 *(978-1-55365-577-0(X),* Greystone Bks.) D&M Pubs. Inc. CAN. Dist: Perseus-PGW.

Davies, Gwendolyn & Gerson, Carole, eds. Canadian Poetry from the Beginnings Through the First World War. 2010. (ENG.). 464p. pap. 17.95 *(978-0-7710-9364-7(0),* New Can Library) McClelland & Stewart CAN. Dist: Random Hse., Inc.

Deahl, James, ed. Poetry Markets for Canadians. 6th ed. 240p. pap. 15.95 *(978-1-55128-030-1(2))* Mercury Bks. CAN. Dist: LPC/InBook.

Drover, Devin. [Word]: A Journal of Canadian Poetry. 2009. 72p. pap., pap. 13.95 *(978-0-9813933-0-8(6))* Undertow Pr. CAN. Dist: Lulu Enterprises Inc.

Hannan, Jack. Some Frames: Poems. 2011. 108p. pap. 18.00 *(978-1-77086-005-6(3))* Cormorant Bks. Inc. CAN. Dist: Univ. of Toronto Pr.

Hill, Lawrence, et al, contrib. by. Tok, 3-Book Set: Writing the New Toronto. 2008. (ENG., Illus.). 600p. pap. 35.00 *(978-0-9734112-7-0(9),* Zephyr Pr.) Chicago Review Pr., Inc.

House of Anansi Press Editors & House. The 2008 Griffin Poetry Prize Anthology: A Selection of the Shortlist. Bowering, George, ed. 2008. (Griffin Poetry Prize Anthology Ser.). (ENG.). 104p. pap. 12.95 *(978-0-88784-789-9(7))* House of Anansi Pr. CAN. Dist: Perseus-PGW.

Kizuk, R. Alexander. A Critical Anthology of English-Canadian Verse in the Times of Sir Wilfred Laurier & William Lyon Mackenzie King (1896-1911 And 1921-1947) The Sunny Way. 2010. 377p. 119.95 *(978-0-7734-1415-0(0))* Mellen, Edwin Pr., The.

Lynes, Jeanette. The New Blue Distance. 2009. 88p. pap. 17.00 *(978-1-894987-31-8(4))* Wolsak & Wynn Pubs., Ltd. CAN. Dist: Univ. of Toronto Pr.

Macdonald, Hugh & MacLaine, Brent. Landmarks: An Anthology of New Atlantic Canadian Poetry of the Land. (Illus.). 160p. pap. 14.95 *(978-0-9698606-9-3(2))* Acorn Pr., The CAN. Dist: Goose Lane Editions.

Mancini, Donato. Aethel. 2007. (ENG., Illus.). 96p. pap. 18.00 *(978-1-55420-030-6(X))* New Star Bks., Ltd. CAN. Dist: SPD-Small Pr. Distribution.

Purdy, Al. The Al Purdy A Frame Anthology. Vermeersch, Paul, ed. 2009. (ENG., Illus.). 160p. pap. 26.95 *(978-1-55017-502-8(5))* Harbour Publishing Co., Ltd. CAN. Dist: Ingram Pub. Services.

Swift, Todd & Jones, Evan, eds. Modern Canadian Poets. 2010. (ENG.). 220p. pap. 29.95 *(978-1-85754-938-6(4))* Carcanet Pr., Ltd. GBR. Dist: Independent Pubs. Group.

Taylor, Bruce. No End in Strangeness: New & Selected Poems. 2011. 119p. pap. 18.00 *(978-1-77086-008-7(8))* Cormorant Bks. Inc. CAN. Dist: Univ. of Toronto Pr.

Taylor, Rob. The Other Side of Ourselves: Poems. 2011. 63p. pap. 18.00 *(978-1-77086-009-4(6))* Cormorant Bks. Inc. CAN. Dist: Univ. of Toronto Pr.

Trehearne, Brian, selected by. Canadian Poetry, 1920 to 1960. 2010. (ENG.). 488p. 32.95 *(978-0-7710-8631-1(8))*; pap. 24.95 *(978-0-7710-8634-2(2))* McClelland & Stewart CAN. (New Can Library). Dist: Random Hse., Inc.

CANADIAN POETRY—HISTORY AND CRITICISM

Bartlett, Brian & BARTLETT, Brian, eds. Don Mckay: Essays on His Works. 2006. (Writers Ser.). (ENG.). 200p. 15.00 *(978-1-55071-252-0(7))* Guernica Editions, Inc. CAN. Dist: Univ. of Toronto Pr.

Brandt, Di & Godard, Barbara, eds. Wider Boundaries of Daring: The Modernist Impulse in Canadian Women's Poetry. 2009. (ENG.). 424p. (C). pap. 42.95 *(978-1-55458-032-3(3))* Wilfrid Laurier Univ. Pr. CAN. Dist: Univ. of Toronto Pr.

Burnham, Clint. The Only Poetry That Matters: Reading the Kootenay School of Writing. 2012. (ENG.). 296p. pap. 23.95 ***(978-1-55152-429-0(5))*** Arsenal Pulp Pr. CAN. Dist: Consortium Bk. Sales & Distribution.

Camlot, Jason. Language Acts: Anglo-Qubec Poetry, 1976 to the 21st Century. Swift, Todd, ed. 2007. (ENG., Illus.). 276p. pap. 17.95 *(978-1-55065-225-3(7))* Vehicule Pr. CAN. Dist: Independent Pubs. Group.

Collis, Stephen. Phyllis Webb & the Common Good: Poetry / Anarchy / Abstraction. 2007. (ENG.). 224p. pap. 24.95 *(978-0-88922-559-6(1))* Talonbooks, Ltd. CAN. Dist: Consortium Bk. Sales & Distribution.

Compton, Anne. Meetings with Maritime Poets: Interviews, 1 vol. 2007. (ENG.). 397p. per. 27.95 *(978-1-55041-996-2(X))* Fitzhenry & Whiteside, Ltd. CAN. Dist: Ingram Pub. Services.

COOK, Gregory M. Alden Nowlan: Essays on His Works. Cook, Gregory M., ed. 2006. (Writers Ser.). (ENG.). 144p. 13.00 *(978-1-55071-254-4(3))* Guernica Editions, Inc. CAN. Dist: Univ. of Toronto Pr.

Davey, Frank. When Tish Happens: The Unlikely Story of Canada's Most Influential Literary Magazine. 2011. (ENG., Illus.). 342p. pap. 19.95 *(978-1-55022-958-5(3))* ECW Pr. CAN. Dist: Independent Pubs. Group.

Finley, Robert, et al. A Ragged Pen: Essays on Poetry & Memory. 2006. (ENG., Illus.). 96p. pap. *(978-1-55447-030-3(7))* Gaspereau Pr.

Goldstein, Mark. Tracelanguage: A Shared Breath. 2010. (ENG., Illus.). 112p. pap. 19.95 *(978-1-897388-55-6(1))* BookThug CAN. Dist: SPD-Small Pr. Distribution.

Hogg, Robert, ed. An English Canadian Poetics Vol. 1: The Confederation Poets. 2009. (ENG.). 320p. pap. 29.95 *(978-0-88922-613-5(X))* Talonbooks, Ltd. CAN. Dist: Consortium Bk. Sales & Distribution.

Hunter, Jeffrey W. Cont Lit Crit. 2011. 461p. 328.00 *(978-1-4144-4612-7(9))* Cengage Gale.

Hutchman, Laurence. Writers' Words: Conversations with Eight Canadian Poets. 2011. (Duologue Ser.). (ENG.). 188p. 18.00 *(978-1-55071-309-1(4))* Guernica Editions, Inc. CAN. Dist: Univ. of Toronto Pr.

Jodha, Avinash. Michael Ondaatje's Fiction: Poetics of Exile. 2011. 208p. 40.00 ***(978-81-316-0452-6(7))*** Rawat Pubns. IND. Dist: International Specialized Bk. Services.

Loriggio, Francesco, ed. The Last Effort of Dreams: Essays on the Poetry of Pier Giorgio Di Cicco. 2007. (ENG., Illus.). 228p. 35.00 *(978-1-55458-019-4(6))* Wilfrid Laurier Univ. Pr. CAN. Dist: Univ. of Toronto Pr.

MacDonald, Tanis. The Daughter's Way: Canadian Women's Paternal Elegies. 2012. (ENG.). 270p. (C). 85.00 ***(978-1-55458-362-1(4))*** Wilfrid Laurier Univ. Pr. CAN. Dist: Univ. of Toronto Pr.

Mayne, Seymour, et al, eds. Pluriel: An Anthology of Diverse Voices - Une Anthologie des Voix. 2008. (FRE & ENG.). 304p. pap. *(978-0-7766-0611-8(5))* Univ. of Ottawa Pr./Presses de l'Universite d'Ottawa.

McLennan, Rob. Subverting the Lyric. 2008. (ENG., Illus.). 240p. pap. 19.95 *(978-1-55022-801-4(3))* ECW Pr. CAN. Dist: Independent Pubs. Group.

Nicosia, James F. & Nicosia, James. Reading Mark Strand: His Collected Works, Career, & the Poetics of the Privative. annot. ed. 2007. (ENG.). 232p. 89.00 *(978-1-4039-7670-3(8))* Palgrave Macmillan.

Peters, Carl. Textual Vishyuns: Image & text in the workof bill Bissett. 2011. (ENG.). 224p. pap. 24.95 *(978-0-88922-661-6(X))* Talonbooks, Ltd. CAN. Dist: Consortium Bk. Sales & Distribution.

Ruthig, Ingrid, ed. Richard Outram: Essays on His Works. 2011. (Writers Ser.). (ENG., Illus.). 220p. pap. 18.00 *(978-1-55071-280-3(2))* Guernica Editions, Inc. CAN. Dist: Univ. of Toronto Pr.

Sanger, Peter. Through Darkling Air: The Poetry of Richard Outram. 2010. (ENG.). 312p. *(978-1-55447-061-7(7))* Gaspereau Pr.

Sarah, Robyn. Little Eurekas: A Decade's Thoughts on Poetry. 2008. (ENG., Illus.). 276p. per. 22.95 *(978-1-897231-29-5(6))* Biblioasis CAN. Dist: Chicago Distribution Ctr.

Simon, Sherry. Failure's Opposite: Listening to A. M. Klein. Ravvin, Norman, ed. 2011. (FRE, YID & ENG., Illus.). 287p. (C). *(978-0-7735-3832-0(1))* McGill-Queen's Univ. Pr.

Smith, A. J. M. Selected Writings. Gnarowski, Michael, ed. 2006. (ENG.). 200p. pap. 15.00 *(978-1-55002-665-8(8),* Dundurn Pr.) Dundurn CAN. Dist: Ingram Pub. Services.

Tolley, A. T. My Proper Ground: A Study of the Work of Philip Larkin & Its Development. 239p. pap. *(978-0-88629-138-9(0))* McGill-Queen's Univ. Pr.

Uppal, Priscila. We Are What We Mourn: The Contemporary English-Canadian Elegy. 2008. (ENG.). 318p. (C). *(978-0-7735-3456-8(3))* McGill-Queen's Univ. Pr.

Wolf, Elana. Implicate Me. 2010. (Essay Ser.). (ENG.). 152p. 18.00 *(978-1-55071-323-7(X))* Guernica Editions, Inc. CAN. Dist: Univ. of Toronto Pr.

Zhang, Benzi. Asian Diaspora Poetry in North America. 2007. (Literary Criticism & Cultural Theory Ser.). (ENG.). 194p. 125.00 *(978-0-415-95717-5(6))* Routledge.

CANADIAN POETRY—WOMEN AUTHORS

Brandt, Di & Godard, Barbara, eds. Wider Boundaries of Daring: The Modernist Impulse in Canadian Women's Poetry. 2009. (ENG.). 424p. (C). pap. 42.95 *(978-1-55458-032-3(3))* Wilfrid Laurier Univ. Pr. CAN. Dist: Univ. of Toronto Pr.

Downie, Mary Alice & Robertson, Barbara, eds. Early Voices: Portraits of Canada by Women Writers, 1639-1914. 2010. (ENG., Illus.). 316p. pap. 28.99 *(978-1-55488-769-9(0))* Dundurn CAN. Dist: Ingram Pub. Services.

MacDonald, Tanis. The Daughter's Way: Canadian Women's Paternal Elegies. 2012. (ENG.). 270p. (C). 85.00 ***(978-1-55458-362-1(4))*** Wilfrid Laurier Univ. Pr. CAN. Dist: Univ. of Toronto Pr.

Szumigalski, Anne. The Word, the Voice, the Text: The Life of a Writer. 160p. pap. 14.95 *(978-0-920079-65-2(2))* Fifth Hse. Pubs. CAN. Dist: Fitzhenry & Whiteside, Ltd.

CANADIAN POTTERY

see Pottery, Canadian

CANADIAN ROCKIES (B.C. AND ALTA.)

Beck, Janice Sanford. No Ordinary Woman: The Story of Mary Schaffer Warren, 1 vol. 2006. (ENG., Illus.). 224p. pap. *(978-0-921102-82-3(8))* Rocky Mountain Bks.

Benn, Carl. Canadian Rockies. (Illus.). 128p. *(978-88-8029-793-2(7))* Casa Editrice Bonechi.

Boles, Glen. My Mountain Album: Art & Photography of the Canadian Rockies & Columbia Mountains, 1 vol. 2006. (ENG., Illus.). 168p. *(978-1-894765-78-7(8))* Rocky Mountain Bks.

Bridge, Kathryn. A Passion for Mountains: The Lives of Don & Phyllis Munday, 1 vol. 2010. (ENG., Illus.). 240p. per. *(978-1-894765-69-5(9))* Rocky Mountain Bks.

Calvert, Kathy & Portman, Dale. Guardians of the Peaks: Mountain Rescue in the Canadian Rockies & Columbia Mountains, 1 vol. 2010. (ENG., Illus.). 328p. per. *(978-1-894765-80-0(X))* Rocky Mountain Bks.

Canadian Rockies: Screen Saver. cd-rom *(978-1-55153-117-5(8))* Altitude Publishing Canada Ltd.

Cannings, Richard. Birds of Interior BC & the Rockies, 1 vol. 2009. (ENG., Illus.). 448p. pap. *(978-1-894974-59-2(X))* Heritage Hse.

Coleman, A. P. The Canadian Rockies: New & Old Trails. 2009. (Mountain Classics Collection #1 Ser.). (ENG.). 232p. pap. *(978-1-897522-50-9(9))* Rocky Mountain Bks.

Copeland, Kathy & Copeland, Craig. Don't Waste Your Time in the Canadian Rockies: The Opinionated Hiking Guide. 6th ed. 2009. (Illus.). 544p. *(978-0-9783427-5-3(5))* hikingcamping.com, Inc.

Corbett, Bill. The 11,000ers of the Canadian Rockies, 1 vol. rev. ed. 2009. (ENG., Illus.). 224p. pap. *(978-1-897522-40-0(1))* Rocky Mountain Bks.

Daffern, Tony. Popular Day Hikes 2: Canadian Rockies, 1 vol. rev. ed. 2008. (Popular Day Hikes Ser.). (ENG., Illus.). 144p. pap. *(978-1-897522-01-1(0))* Rocky Mountain Bks.

Dettling, Peter. The Will of the Land, 1 vol. 2010. (ENG., Illus.). 176p. *(978-1-926855-00-4(0))* Rocky Mountain Bks.

Dodd, John & Helgason, Gail. Canadian Rockies Access Guide. Craig, Lee, ed. 3rd ed. 2009. (ENG., Illus.). 384p. pap. *(978-1-55105-560-2(0))* Lone Pine Publishing.

Doyle, Pam. Canmore, Kananaskis, & the Canadian Rockies, 1 vol. 2007. (ENG., Illus.). 96p. *(978-1-894765-88-6(5))*; pap. *(978-1-894765-87-9(7))* Rocky Mountain Bks.

Ernst, Trent. Kootenay Rockies BC, 1 vol. 4th ed. 2008. (Backroad Mapbook Ser.). (ENG., Illus.). 133p. spiral bd. *(978-1-897225-28-8(8))* Mussio Ventures, Ltd.

Fay, Samuel Prescott. The Forgotten Explorer: Samuel Prescott Fay's 1914 Expedition to the Northern Rockies, 1 vol. Helm, Charles & Murtha, Mike, eds. (ENG., Illus.). 320p. 2010. pap. *(978-1-897522-55-4(X))* 2009. *(978-1-897522-56-1(8))* Rocky Mountain Bks.

Flagler, Stephen. Canadian Rockies Panorama, 1 vol. 2009. (Illus.). 64p. (ENG.). pap. *(978-1-897522-22-6(3))*; (JPN., pap. *(978-1-55153-099-4(6))* Rocky Mountain Bks.

Formac Publishing Company Limited Staff. The Canadian Rockies. Inigo-Jones, Terry, ed. 4th rev. ed. 2010. (Colourguide Travel Ser.). (ENG., Illus.). 208p. pap. 19.95 *(978-0-88780-897-5(2))* Formac Publishing Co., Ltd. CAN. Dist: Casemate Pubs. & Bk. Distributors, LLC.

Freeman, Lewis R. & Sanford, Emerson. On the Roof of the Rockies: The Great Columbia Icefield of the Canadian Rockies, 1 vol. 2009. (Mountain Classics Collection #6 Ser.). (ENG., Illus.). 176p. pap. *(978-1-897522-46-2(0))* Rocky Mountain Bks.

Grandmaison, Mike. The Canadian Rockies. rev. ed. 2007. (ENG., Illus.). 240p. 40.00 *(978-1-55263-836-1(7))* Key Porter Bks. CAN. Dist: Perseus-PGW.

Grobler, Sabrina. The Canadian Rockies. 64p. pap. *(978-1-55153-835-8(0))* Altitude Publishing Canada Ltd.

Grobler, Sabrina, photos by. The Canadian Rockies: A Complete Photographic Portrait, 1 vol. 2009. (KOR.). 64p. pap. *(978-1-55153-250-9(6))* Rocky Mountain Bks.

Hempstead, Andrew. Moon Alberta: Including Banff, Jasper & the Canadian Rockies. 2010. (Moon Handbooks). (ENG., Illus.). 544p. pap. 19.95 *(978-1-59880-371-6(9))* Avalon Travel Publishing.

—Moon Canadian Rockies: Including Banff & Jasper National Parks. 2010. (Moon Handbooks). (ENG., Illus.). 352p. pap. 17.95 *(978-1-59880-372-3(7))* Avalon Travel Publishing.

—Moon Spotlight Banff National Park. 2010. (Moon Spotlight Ser.). (ENG.). 80p. pap. 7.95 *(978-1-59880-556-7(8))* Avalon Travel Publishing.

Hornaday, William T. Campfires in the Canadian Rockies. 2007. (ENG.). 492p. 53.95 *(978-0-548-11707-1(1))* Kessinger Publishing, LLC.

Lakusta, Ernie. The Intrepid Explorer: James Hector's Explorations in the Canadian Rockies, 1 vol. 2007. (ENG., Illus.). 240p. pap. 17.99 *(978-1-894856-82-9(1))* Fifth Hse. Pubs. CAN. Dist: Ingram Pub. Services.

C

Lee, John. British Columbia & the Canadian Rockies. 5th rev. ed. 2011. (Regional Travel Guide Ser.). (ENG., Illus.). 296p. pap. 20.99 *(978-1-74179-804-3(3))* Lonely Planet Pubns.

Leighton, Douglas. The Canadian Rockies, 1 vol. rev. ed. 2009. (ENG., Illus.). 112p. *(978-1-897522-35-6(5))* Rocky Mountain Bks.

Leighton, Douglas, photos by. The Canadian Rockies, 1 vol. rev. ed. 2009. (ENG., Illus.). 112p. *(978-1-897522-34-9(7))* Rocky Mountain Bks.

—The Canadian Rockies (English Mt. Assiniboine Paperback) 2007. 112p. pap. *(978-1-55153-255-4(7))* Altitude Publishing Canada Ltd.

—The Canadian Rockies (French Mt. Assiniboine Paperback) 2007. 112p. pap. *(978-1-55153-257-8(3))* Altitude Publishing Canada Ltd.

—The Canadian Rockies (Japanese Mt. Assiniboine Paperback) 2007. 112p. pap. *(978-1-55153-256-1(5))* Altitude Publishing Canada Ltd.

Lynx, Dustin. Hiking Canada's Great Divide Trail, 1 vol. 2nd rev. ed. 2007. (ENG., Illus.). 256p. per. *(978-1-894765-89-3(3))* Rocky Mountain Bks.

Marriott, John, photos by. Banff & Lake Louise: Images of Banff National Park. 2007. (Illus.). 80p. *(978-1-894768-01-6(9))* JEM Photography & Consulting.

Martin, John & Jones, Jon. Sport Climbs in the Canadian Rockies, 1 vol. 6th rev. ed. 2009. (ENG., Illus.). 384p. pap. *(978-1-897522-39-4(8))* Rocky Mountain Bks.

McRae, Bill & Olson, Donald. Frommer's British Columbia & the Canadian Rockies. 6th ed. 2010. (Frommer's Complete Guides: 774). (ENG., Illus.). 448p. pap. 20.99 *(978-0-470-59153-6(6)*, Frommers) Wiley, John & Sons, Inc.

Michelin Travel Publications Staff. British Columbia & the Rockies. 2009. (Green Guide Ser.). (ENG., Illus.). 288p. pap. 19.95 *(978-1-906261-54-2(7))* Michelin Travel & Lifestyle.

Nugara, Andrew W. More Scrambles in the Canadian Rockies, 1 vol. 2007. (ENG., Illus.). 264p. pap. *(978-1-894765-86-2(9))* Rocky Mountain Bks.

Outram, James. In the Heart of the Canadian Rockies. 2009. 488p. 53.95 *(978-1-104-21783-9(X))*; pap. 38.95 *(978-1-104-18283-0(1))* Kessinger Publishing, LLC.

—In the Heart of the Canadian Rockies, 1 vol. 2007. (Mountain Classics Collection). (ENG.). 312p. per. *(978-1-894765-96-1(6))* Rocky Mountain Bks.

Pashby, Christie. Frommer's Banff & the Canadian Rockies Day by Day. 2010. (Frommer's Day by Day - Pocket Ser.: 177). (ENG., Illus.). 184p. pap. 12.99 *(978-0-470-73628-9(3)*, Frommers) Wiley, John & Sons, Inc.

Perry, Lorne. Drawing from the Mountain: An Illustrated Journey, 1 vol. 2010. (ENG., Illus.). 144p. *(978-1-894765-81-7(8))* Rocky Mountain Bks.

Pole, Graeme. Canadian Rockies Recommended. 2007. (Canada Recommended Ser.). (Illus.). 256p. pap. *(978-1-55153-646-0(3))* Altitude Publishing Canada Ltd.

—Hiking in the Canadian Rockies Recommended. 2007. (Canada Recommended Ser.). (Illus.). 272p. pap. *(978-1-55153-648-4(X))* Altitude Publishing Canada Ltd.

Reineberg Holt, Faye. Canada's Rocky Mountains: A History in Photographs, 1 vol. 2010. (ENG., Illus.). 112p. pap. *(978-1-894974-99-8(9))* Heritage Hse.

Sandford, Robert W. Ecology & Wonder: In the Canadian Rocky Mountain Parks World Heritage Site. 2009. (ENG., Illus.). 400p. pap. 48.95 *(978-1-897425-57-2(0))* UBC Pr. CAN. Dist: Univ. of Washington Pr.

Sanford, Emerson & Beck, Janice Sanford. Life of the Trail 3: The Historic Route from Old Bow Fort to Jasper, 1 vol. 2009. (ENG., Illus.). 224p. pap. *(978-1-897522-41-7(X))* Rocky Mountain Bks.

Schäffer, Mary T. S. Old Indian Trails of the Canadian Rockies, 1 vol. 2nd rev. ed. 2011. (Mountain Classics Collection). (ENG.). 200p. pap. *(978-1-897522-49-3(5))* Rocky Mountain Bks.

Stutfield, Hugh E. M. & Collie, J. Norman. Climbs & Exploration in the Canadian Rockies, 1 vol. rev. ed. 2008. (Mountain Classics Collection). (ENG.). 208p. pap. *(978-1-897522-06-6(1))* Rocky Mountain Bks.

Thomas Cook Publishing. Drive Around Canadian Rockies, 3rd: Your guide to great drives. Top 25 Tours. 2009. (Drive Around - Thomas Cook Ser.). (ENG., Illus.). 288p. pap. 26.95 *(978-1-84848-202-9(7))* Cook, Thomas Publishing GBR. Dist: Globe Pequot Pr., The.

Wilson, Elizabeth. Canadian Rockies Photo Album, 1 vol. 2009. (ENG., Illus.). 96p. pap. *(978-1-897522-23-3(1))* Rocky Mountain Bks.

—Portrait of the Canadian Rockies, 1 vol. 2009. (ENG., Illus.). 96p. *(978-1-897522-19-6(3))*; pap. *(978-1-897522-18-9(5))* Rocky Mountain Bks.

CANADIAN SONGS

see Songs, Canadian

CANADIAN WIT AND HUMOR

Baratgin, Louis, illus. Cartoon Review of the War: Louis Baratgin's World War II Album. 2010. (ENG.). 65p. pap. 21.95 *(978-1-55065-288-8(5))* Vehicule Pr. CAN. Dist: Independent Pubs. Group.

Bengough, John Wilson. A Caricature History of Canadian Politics, 2 vol., set. reprint ed. 250.00 *(978-0-7222-6844-5(0))* Library Reprints, Inc.

Burke, J. C. A Treasury of Newfoundland Humour & Wit. (ENG., Illus.). 128p. pap. *(978-0-919519-97-8(0))* Breakwater Bks., Ltd.

Chackowicz, Howard. Howie Action Comix. 2008. (Bdang Ser.). (ENG., Illus.). 80p. pap. *(978-1-894994-30-9(2))* Conundrum Pr.

De Figueiredo, Dan. Fakin' Eh! How to Pretend to Be Canadian. 2007. (ENG., Illus.). 224p. per. *(978-0-9739116-3-3(8))* Folklore Publishing.

Ferguson, Will. Why I Hate Canadians. pap. 22.95 *(978-1-55054-600-2(7))*; 10th ed. 2007. (ENG.). 336p. pap. 15.95 *(978-1-55365-279-3(7))* D&M Pubs. Inc. CAN. Dist: Perseus-PGW.

Ferguson, Will, et al. How to Be A Canadian, 1 vol. 2nd ed. 2008. (ENG.). 368p. pap. 18.95 *(978-1-55365-311-0(4))* D&M Pubs. Inc. CAN. Dist: Perseus-PGW.

Green, Bob. Eavesdroppings: Stories from Small Towns When Sin Was Fun. 2006. (ENG.). 200p. pap. 22.99 *(978-1-55002-629-0(1)*, Dundurn Pr.) Dundurn CAN. Dist: Ingram Pub. Services.

Griffiths, Bus. Now You're Logging! 2nd unabr. ed. (ENG., Illus.). 120p. (Orig.). pap. 24.95 *(978-1-55017-033-7(3))* Harbour Publishing Co., Ltd. CAN. Dist: Ingram Pub. Services.

Henry, Tom. The Ideal Dog: And Other Delusions. unabr. ed. (ENG., Illus.). 192p. *(978-1-55017-150-1(X))* Harbour Publishing Co., Ltd.

Hunt, Stephen. The White Guy, 1 vol. 2009. (ENG.). 288p. pap., instr.'s gde. ed. 16.95 *(978-1-55365-302-8(5))* D&M Pubs. Inc. CAN. Dist: Perseus-PGW.

Hyland, Gary, et al, eds. 200% Cracked Wheat. (Illus.). 416p. mass mkt. *(978-1-55050-038-7(4))* Coteau Bks.

Leacock, Stephen. Model Memoirs & Other Sketches Form Simple to Serious. 2011. 324p. 50.95 ***(978-1-258-09623-6(4))*** Literary Licensing, LLC.

McCulloch, Thomas. The Mephibosheth Stepsure Letters. Davies, Gwendolyn, ed. (Illus.). 508p. *(978-0-88629-042-9(2))* McGill-Queen's Univ. Pr.

Snider, Norman. The Roaring Eighties & Other Good Times. 2008. (ENG.). 290p. 26.95 *(978-1-55096-093-8(8))* Exile Editions, Ltd. CAN. Dist: Independent Pubs. Group.

Wright, Doug. The Collected Doug Wright Vol. 1: Canada's Master Cartoonist. Mackay, Seth & Mackay, Brad, eds. 2009. (ENG., Illus.). 240p. 39.95 *(978-1-897299-52-4(4))* Drawn & Quarterly Pubns. CAN. Dist: Macmillan.

CANADIANISMS

Here are entered works on the usage of words and idiomatic expressions peculiar to Canada.

Barber, Katherine. Only in Canada, You Say: A Treasury of Canadian Language. 2008. (ENG.). 288p. 12.95 *(978-0-19-542984-8(2))* Oxford Univ. Pr., Inc.

Fee, Margery & McAlpine, Janice. Guide to Canadian English Usage. 2nd rev. ed. 2008. (ENG.). 680p. 29.95 *(978-0-19-542602-1(9))* Oxford Univ. Pr., Inc.

Fee, Margery & McAlpine, Janice. Guide to Canadian English Usage: Reissue. 2nd ed. 2011. (ENG., Illus.). 676p. 50.00 ***(978-0-19-544593-0(7))*** Oxford Univ. Pr., Inc.

Harvey, C. Munro. Fitzhenry & Whiteside Canadian Thesaurus: The Word You Want, Where & When You Want It, 1 vol. Ballantyne, Elizabeth et al, eds. (ENG.). 1135p. pap. *(978-1-55041-198-0(5))* Fitzhenry & Whiteside, Ltd.

CANADIANS

see also French-Canadians

Chisholm, Clive Scott. Following the Wrong God Home: Footloose in an American Dream. 2009. (Outdoor Lives Ser.). (ENG., Illus.). 424p. pap. 19.95 *(978-0-8032-2431-5(1)*, Bison Bks.) Univ. of Nebraska Pr.

Heron, Barbara. Desire for Development: Whiteness, Gender, & the Helping Imperative. 2007. (ENG.). 204p. pap. 42.95 *(978-1-55458-001-9(3))* Wilfrid Laurier Univ. Pr. CAN. Dist: Univ. of Toronto Pr.

Morgan, Cecilia. A Happy Holiday: English-Canadians & Transatlantic Tourism, 1870-1930. 2008. 416p. (ENG.). *(978-0-8020-9758-3(8))*; pap. *(978-0-8020-9518-3(6))* Univ. of Toronto Pr.

Tapp-McDougall, Caroline. The Complete Canadian Eldercare Guide: Expert Solutions to Help You Make the Best Decisions for Your Loved Ones. 2nd ed. 2008. (ENG.). 320p. pap. 26.95 *(978-0-470-83449-7(8)*, Wiley) Wiley, John & Sons, Inc.

VanWart, Helen. Letters from Helen: A Canadian Student in Germany on the Eve of the Great War. Lochhead, Douglas, ed. 2010. pap. 20.00 *(978-0-9810244-9-3(1))* Sybertooth Inc. CAN. Dist: Lightning Source, Inc.

Vincent, Francois & Gagnon, Cécile. Contes Traditionnels du Québec. (FRE., Illus.). 166p. *(978-2-84113-647-6(7))* Editions Milan.

Wallace, Jim. Knowing No Fear: The Canadian Scouts in South Africa 1900 - 1902. 2008. 256p. 35.00 *(978-1-4251-4392-3(X))* Trafford Publishing.

Williamson, Janice. Omar Khadr, Oh Canada. 2012. (ENG., Illus.). 400p. (C). pap. ***(978-0-7735-4022-4(9))*** McGill-Queen's Univ. Pr.

CANADIANS—UNITED STATES

Brault, Gerard J. The French-Canadian Heritage in New England. (Illus.). 288p. *(978-0-7735-0536-0(9))*; pap. *(978-0-7735-0537-7(7))* McGill-Queen's Univ. Pr.

Gray, Douglas A. The Canadian Snowbird Guide: Everything You Need to Know about Living Part-Time in the USA & Mexico. 4th ed. 2009. (ENG.). 352p. pap. 26.95 *(978-0-470-15375-8(X)*, Wiley) Wiley, John & Sons, Inc.

Lake, Kirk. There Will Be Rainbows: A Biography of Rufus Wainwright. 2010. (Illus.). 320p. pap. 14.99 *(978-0-06-198846-2(4))* HarperCollins Pubs.

Ritchie, Terry F. & Wruk, Brian D. The American in Canada: Real-Life Tax & Financial Insights into Moving & Living in Canada. 2008. (ENG., Illus.). 240p. pap. 24.95 *(978-1-55022-790-1(4))* ECW Pr. CAN. Dist: Independent Pubs. Group.

Shephard, Michelle. Guantanamo's Child: The Untold Story of Omar Khadr. 2008. (ENG., Illus.). 320p. 27.95 *(978-0-470-84117-4(6)*, Wiley) Wiley, John & Sons, Inc.

University of Toronto Press. Prejudice & Pride: Canadian Intellectuals Confront the United States, 1891-1945. 2010. 320p. *(978-1-4426-4045-0(6))* Univ. of Toronto Pr.

Walters, Dale. Taxation of Canadians in America. 2012. (ENG.). 176p. pap. 22.95 incl. cd-rom ***(978-1-77040-133-4(4))*** Self-Counsel Pr., Inc. CAN. Dist: National Bk. Network.

Wruk, Brian D. The Canadian in America: Real-Life Tax & Financial Insights into Moving & Living in the U. S. 2007. (ENG., Illus.). 240p. pap. 24.95 *(978-1-55022-757-4(2))* ECW Pr. CAN. Dist: Independent Pubs. Group.

CANAL, ANTONIO, CALLED CANALETTO, 1697-1768

see Canaletto, 1697-1768

CANAL-BOATS

see also Barges

Aitken, Hugh G. J. The Welland Canal Company. 3.50 *(978-0-674-94921-8(8))* Harvard Univ. Pr.

Corble, Nick & O'Driscoll, Patricia. Britain's Canals: A Handbook. 2010. (ENG., Illus.). 96p. pap. 24.95 *(978-1-4456-0025-3(0))* Amberley Publishing GBR. Dist: Casemate Pubs. & Bk. Distributors, LLC.

Darlington, Terry. Narrow Dog to Carcassonne. 2008. (ENG.). 336p. pap. 15.00 *(978-0-385-34208-7(X)*, Delta) Random House Publishing Group.

—Narrow Dog to Indian River. 2009. (ENG., Illus.). 352p. pap. 15.00 *(978-0-385-34209-4(8)*, Delta) Random House Publishing Group.

Gantz, Carroll. The Resurrection of the St. Helena: Nineteenth-Century Ohio Canal Boat. 2012. ***(978-1-60635-122-2(2))*** Kent State Univ. Pr.

Haywood, Steve. Narrowboat Dreams: A Journey North by England Northways. 2008. (ENG., Illus.). 320p. pap. 14.95 ***(978-1-84024-670-4(7))*** Summerdale Pubs. GBR. Dist: Independent Pubs. Group.

McKay, Hugh. Steam on the Canals; Report Made to Hon Peter Cooper. 2011. 18p. pap. 11.99 ***(978-1-4181-8983-9(9))*** MPublishing.

Rolt, Sonia. Canal People: The Photographs of Robert Longden. 2009. (ENG., Illus.). 160p. pap. 32.95 *(978-0-7524-5110-7(3))* History Pr. Ltd.,The GBR. Dist: Independent Pubs. Group.

Yorke, Trevor. Narrowboats Explained. 2009. (England's Living History Ser.). (ENG., Illus.). 96p. (C). pap. 21.95 *(978-1-84674-146-3(7))* Countryside Bks. GBR. Dist: Brown, David Bk. Co., The.

CANAL ZONE

Aguirre, Robert. The Panama Canal. 2010. (International Straits of the World Ser.). 223p. *(978-90-04-17728-4(0))* BRILL.

Engdahl, Sylvia, ed. Building the Panama Canal. 2012. (Perspectives on Modern World History Ser.). (ENG., Illus.). 224p. (gr. 10-12). lib. bdg. 41.70 ***(978-0-7377-6364-5(7)***, Greenhaven Pr., Inc.) Cengage Gale.

CANALETTO, 1697-1768

Beddington, Charles. Venice: Canaletto & His Rivals. 2010. (ENG., Illus.). 192p. 50.00 *(978-1-85709-418-3(2))* Yale Univ. Pr.

Libby, Alexandra & Stanton, Thomas. Venice in the Age of Canaletto. 2009. (Illus.). 224p. 60.00 *(978-3-7913-8000-1(1))* Prestel Publishing.

Uzanne, Octave. Canaletto. 2008. (Temporis Ser.). (ENG., Illus.). 255p. 39.95 *(978-1-85995-683-0(1))* Parkstone International GBR. Dist: Ingram Pub. Services.

CANALS

see also Intracoastal Waterways

also names of canals, e.g. Erie Canal

Aguirre, Robert. The Panama Canal. 2010. (International Straits of the World Ser.). 223p. *(978-90-04-17728-4(0))* BRILL.

Bartholomew, Ann, compiled by. Delaware & Lehigh Canals: A Pictorial History of the Delaware & Lehigh Canals National Heritage Corridor in Pennsylvania. 2nd ed. 2006. (Illus.). 165p. per. 24.95 *(978-0-930973-38-4(0)*, Canal History & Technology Pr.) Moore, Hugh Historical Park & Museums, Inc.

Blair, John, ed. Waterways & Canal-Building in Medieval England. 2008. (Medieval History & Archaeology Ser.). (ENG., Illus.). 314p. 110.00 *(978-0-19-921715-1(7))* Oxford Univ. Pr., Inc.

Burton, Anthony. Canal 250: The Story of Britain's Canals. 2011. (ENG., Illus.). 192p. 32.95 ***(978-0-7524-5952-3(X))*** History Pr. Ltd.,The GBR. Dist: Independent Pubs. Group.

Burton, Anthony & Pratt, Derek. Anatomy of Canals: The Mania Years. (ENG., Illus.). 176p. pap. 35.00 *(978-0-7524-2385-2(1))* History Pr. Ltd.,The GBR. Dist: Trafalgar Square Publishing.

Collins, Paul. Black Country Canals. 2011. (ENG., Illus.). 128p. pap. 23.95 ***(978-0-7509-2031-5(9))*** History Pr. Ltd.,The GBR. Dist: Independent Pubs. Group.

Conway, J. North. The Cape Cod Canal: Breaking Through the Bared & Bended Arm. 2008. (Illus.). 157p. pap. 19.99 *(978-1-59629-374-8(8))* History Pr., The.

Corble, Nick & O'Driscoll, Patricia. Britain's Canals: A Handbook. 2010. (ENG., Illus.). 96p. pap. 24.95 *(978-1-4456-0025-3(0))* Amberley Publishing GBR. Dist: Casemate Pubs. & Bk. Distributors, LLC.

Covington, Jonathan. Augusta Georgia, the Canal. 2008. 232p. pap. 24.78 *(978-0-557-03508-3(2))* Lulu Enterprises Inc.

Doolittle, William E. Canal Irrigation in Prehistoric Mexico: The Sequence of Technological Change. 2011. (ENG., Illus.). 219p. pap. 25.00 *(978-0-292-72953-7(7))* Univ. of Texas Pr.

Duess, Marie Murphy. The Delaware Canal: From Stone Coal Highway to Historic Landmark. 2008. pap. 19.99 *(978-1-59629-487-5(6))* History Pr., The.

Engdahl, Sylvia, ed. Building the Panama Canal. 2012. (Perspectives on Modern World History Ser.). (ENG., Illus.). 224p. (gr. 10-12). lib. bdg. 41.70 ***(978-0-7377-6364-5(7)***, Greenhaven Pr., Inc.) Cengage Gale.

Gallatin, Albert. Report of the Secretary of the Treasury on the Subject of Public Roads & Canals. 2008. 124p. pap. *(978-1-4099-5240-4(1))* Dodo Pr.

Gantz, Carroll. The Resurrection of the St. Helena: Nineteenth-Century Ohio Canal Boat. 2012. ***(978-1-60635-122-2(2))*** Kent State Univ. Pr.

Giannuzzi, Maria. Windsor Locks Canal. 2007. (Images of America Ser.). (Illus.). 127p. per. 19.99 *(978-0-7385-4966-8(5))* Arcadia Publishing.

Gollasch, Stephan, et al, eds. Bridging Divides: Maritime Canals as Invasion Corridors. 2010. (Monographiae Biologicae Ser.). (Illus.). xiii, 315p. pap. 219.00 *(978-90-481-7265-8(9)*, 9048172659) Springer.

Goussard, Jean-Jacques. Automation of Canal Irrigation Systems, 1993. (Illus.). 116p. 28.00 *(978-81-85068-44-2(5))* U. S. Committee on Irrigation & Drainage.

Haywood, Steve. Narrowboat Dreams: A Journey North by England Northways. 2008. (ENG., Illus.). 320p. pap. 14.95 ***(978-1-84024-670-4(7))*** Summerdale Pubs. GBR. Dist: Independent Pubs. Group.

—Too Narrow to Swing A Cat. 2011. (ENG., Illus.). 320p. pap. 13.95 ***(978-1-84953-065-1(3))*** Summerdale Pubs. GBR. Dist: Independent Pubs. Group.

Hoffman, Jon T. The Panama Canal: an Army's Enterprise: An Army's Enterprise. Center of Military History Staff, ed. 2009. (ENG., Illus.). 103p. pap. 12.00 *(978-0-16-084098-2(8)*, Dept. of the Army) United States Government Printing Office.

Homer, Damian & Homer, Siobhan. For Better for Worse. 2010. (ENG., Illus.). 304p. 14.95 *(978-0-7538-2322-4(5)*, Phoenix) Orion Publishing Group, Ltd. GBR. Dist: Independent Pubs. Group.

Jefferson, David. Through the French Canals. 11th ed. 2006. (ENG., Illus.) 320p. pap. 29.95 *(978-1-57409-233-2(2))* Sheridan Hse., Inc.

Kapsch, Robert J. Historic Canals & Waterways of South Carolina. 2010. 296p. 44.95 *(978-1-57003-867-9(8))* Univ. of South Carolina Pr.

Kennish, William. The Practicability & Importance of a Ship Canal to Connect the Atlantic & Pacific Oceans with a History of the Enterprise from Its First Inception. 2011. 78p. pap. 14.99 ***(978-1-4255-0302-4(0))*** MPublishing.

Kingsford, William, abr. The Canadian Canals. 2009. (Transportation Ser.). (ENG.). 200p. pap. 14.95 *(978-1-4290-2002-2(4))* Applewood Bks.

Latif, Muhammad & Mahmood, Sajid. Energy Generation: Layout plan for hydro-electric power Project. 2010. 76p. pap. *(978-3-639-25051-0(6))* VDM Verlag Dr. Mueller e.K.

Lewis, Christopher. The Canal Pioneers: Brindley's School of Engineers. 2012. (ENG., Illus.). 160p. pap. 26.95 ***(978-0-7524-6166-3(4))*** History Pr. Ltd.,The GBR. Dist: Independent Pubs. Group.

Mabry, Jonathan B. Las Capas: Early Irrigation & Sedentism in a Southwestern Floodplain. 2008. (Illus.). xxii, 457p. pap. ***(978-1-886398-62-7(3))*** Ctr. for Desert Archaeology.

Mahmood, Sajid & Manzoor Ahmed, Saqib. Crop Water Allocation Model - Cwam. 2010. 80p. pap. *(978-3-639-25798-4(7))* VDM Verlag Dr. Mueller e.K.

McKay, Hugh. Steam on the Canals; Report Made to Hon Peter Cooper. 2011. 18p. pap. 11.99 ***(978-1-4181-8983-9(9))*** MPublishing.

Mendez V, Nestor, ed. A New Approach of Sediment Transport in the Design & Operation of Irrigation Canals. 2006. (Ihe Lecture Note Ser.). (ENG., Illus.). 240p. 113.95 *(978-0-415-42693-0(6)*, Taylor & Francis) Taylor & Francis Group GBR. Dist: Taylor & Francis Group.

Missal, Alexander. Seaway to the Future: American Social Visions & the Construction of the Panama Canal. 2008. (Studies in American Thought & Culture Ser.). (ENG., Illus.). 280p. 34.95 *(978-0-299-22940-5(8))* Univ. of Wisconsin Pr.

Munir, Sarfraz. Role of Sediment Transport in Operation & Maintenance of Supply & Demand Based Irrigation Canals: Application to Machai-Maira Branch Canals. 2011. (ENG.). 286p. pap. 79.95 *(978-0-415-66947-4(2)*, CRC Press) Taylor & Francis Group GBR. Dist: Taylor & Francis Group.

Noll, Steven & Tegeder, David. Ditch of Dreams: The Cross Florida Barge Canal & the Struggle for Florida's Future. 2009. (Florida History & Culture Ser.). (ENG., Illus.). 352p. 29.95 *(978-0-8130-3406-5(X))* Univ. Pr. of Florida.

Pratt, Derek. The Architecture of Canals. 2008. (Shire Library). (ENG., Illus.). 56p. per. 12.95 *(978-0-7478-0632-5(2))* Shire Pubns., Ltd. GBR. Dist: Random Hse., Inc.

—London's Canals. 4th ed. 2008. (Shire Library). (ENG., Illus.). 56p. pap. 12.95 *(978-0-7478-0601-1(2))* Shire Pubns., Ltd. GBR. Dist: Random Hse., Inc.

Proceedings of the National Ship-Canal Convention, Held at the City of Chicago, June 2 And 3 1863. 2006. 252p. per. 20.99 *(978-1-4255-2135-6(5))* MPublishing.

Putnam, James William. The Illinois & Michigan Canal: A Study in Economic History. (Illus.). reprint ed. lib. bdg. 125.00 *(978-0-7222-0061-2(7))* Library Reprints, Inc.

Resini, Daniele. Venice: The Grand Canal. 2006. (ENG.). 144p. 120.00 incl. lp *(978-88-7200-224-7(9))* Vianello Libri ITA. Dist: National Bk. Network.

Rolt, L. T. C. Narrow Boat: Take a Trip down the Waterways of England During Their Hey-Day. 2009. (ENG., Illus.). 224p. pap. 29.95 *(978-0-7524-5109-1(X))* History Pr. Ltd.,The GBR. Dist: Independent Pubs. Group.

Rolt, Sonia. Canal People: The Photographs of Robert Longden. 2009. (ENG., Illus.). 160p. pap. 32.95 *(978-0-7524-5110-7(3))* History Pr. Ltd.,The GBR. Dist: Independent Pubs. Group.

Rudman, Jack. Canal Section Superintendent. (Career Examination Ser.: C-3661). pap. 34.95 *(978-0-8373-3661-9(9))* National Learning Corp.

Sampson, Marmaduke B. Central America & the Transit Between the Oceans by Marmaduke B Sampson Reprinted from the Westminster Review, for April 1850. 2011. 34p. pap. 11.99 ***(978-1-4181-9489-5(1))*** MPublishing.

Scott-Davies, Allan. Death on the Waterways. 2011. (ENG., Illus.). 160p. pap. 23.95 ***(978-0-7524-5966-0(X))*** History Pr. Ltd.,The GBR. Dist: Independent Pubs. Group.

Seymour. The Isthmian Routes a Brief Description of Each Projected Route, & of Those Now Existing, Showing the Capacity of Their Harbors, the Comparative Ad. 2011. 28p. pap. 11.99 ***(978-1-4181-9352-2(6))*** MPublishing.

Shill, Ray. Silent Highways: The Forgotten Heritage of the Midlands Canals. 2011. (ENG., Illus.). 192p. pap. 29.95 *(978-0-7524-5842-7(6))* History Pr. Ltd.,The GBR. Dist: Independent Pubs. Group.

Stoker, Simon. The Adventures of the Hebe. 2011. (Illus.). 192p. pap. 24.95 ***(978-1-4456-0221-9(0))*** Amberley Publishing GBR. Dist: Casemate Pubs. & Bk. Distributors, LLC.

Vine, Paul. Portsmouth & Arundel Navigation. 2008. (ENG.). 128p. pap. 30.95 *(978-0-7524-4518-2(9))* History Pr. Ltd.,The GBR. Dist: Independent Pubs. Group.

Way, Peter. Common Labour: Workers & the Digging of North American Canals 1780-1860. 2009. (ENG., Illus.). 328p. pap. 42.00 *(978-0-521-10265-0(0))* Cambridge Univ. Pr.

Wood, Cyril J. Duke's Cut: Bridgewater Canal. 2009. (ENG., Illus.). 128p. pap. 24.95 *(978-0-7524-5111-4(1))* History Pr. Ltd.,The GBR. Dist: Independent Pubs. Group.

Woods, Terry K., compiled by. The Ohio & Erie Canal: A Glossary of Terms. 2nd ed. 56p. (Orig.). pap. 15.00 *(978-1-60635-106-2(0))* Kent State Univ. Pr.

CANAPES

see Appetizers

CANARESE LANGUAGE

see Kannada Language

CANARIES

Demaine, A. F. Roller Canary Its History Breeding Trai. 2006. 92p. per. *(978-1-4067-9595-0(X),* Hesperides Pr.) Read Bks.

Haupt, Thomas. Canaries. 2010. (Complete Pet Owner's Manuals Ser.). (ENG., Illus.). 64p. pap. 8.99 *(978-0-7641-4430-1(8))* Barron's Educational Series, Inc.

House, C. A. Canaries A Complete & Practical Guide. 2006. pap. *(978-1-4067-9600-1(X))* Read Bks.

Keenan, Brian. Keeping Canaries. 2012. (ENG., Illus.). 160p. pap. 29.95 ***(978-1-84797-299-6(3))*** Crowood Pr., Ltd. GBR. Dist: Independent Pubs. Group.

Mannering, Rosslyn. Mules & Hybrids - Production, Manageme. 2006. 120p. per. *(978-1-4067-9569-1(0),* Hesperides Pr.) Read Bks.

Moustaki, Nikki. Canaries, 1 vol. 2008. (Animal Planet Pet Care Library). (ENG., Illus.). 112p. 11.95 *(978-0-7938-3795-3(2))* TFH Pubns., Inc.

Rogers, Cyril H. Different Varieties of Canaries - Notes on the Appearance & Habits of the Different Canaries with Tips on Preparing Them to Show. 2011. 26p. pap. 8.45 ***(978-1-4474-1515-2(9),*** Kent Pr.) Kent Communications, Ltd.

Shackleton. Shackleton's Yorkshire Canary - Its Bree. 2006. (Illus.). 112p. per. *(978-1-4067-9589-9(5),* Hesperides Pr.) Read Bks.

Stroud, Robert. Diseases of Canaries. 2008. 256p. *(978-1-4437-3505-6(1),* Home Farm Bks.) Read Bks.

CANARIS, WILHELM, 1887-1945

Bassett, Richard. Hitler's Spy Chief. 2007. (Cassell Military Paperbacks Ser.). (ENG., Illus.). 336p. per. 12.95 *(978-0-304-36718-4(4))* Cassell Guides GBR. Dist: Sterling Publishing Co., Inc.

Mueller, Michael. Canaris: The Life & Death of Hitler's Spymaster. Brooks, Geoffrey, tr. from GER. 2007. (Illus.). 368p. 34.95 *(978-1-59114-101-3(X))* Naval Institute Pr.

CANARY, MARTHA, 1852-1903

see Calamity Jane, 1852-1903

CANARY ISLANDS

Markham, Clements, ed. The Guanches of Tenerife the Holy Image of Our Lady of Candelaria An. 2010. (Hakluyt Society, Second Ser.). 248p. 69.95 *(978-1-4094-1388-2(8))* Hakluyt Society GBR. Dist: Ashgate Publishing Co.

Pacheco-Dias, Agstin. 2,050 km de palabras/ 2,050 km of Words. 2007. (SPA.). 334p. pap. *(978-84-96687-70-7(8))* Balle del Sol, Ediciones S. L.

Schmincke, Hans-Ulrich. Volcanic Evolution of the Canary Islands. 2012. (Geoparks of the World Ser.). (ENG., Illus.). 250p. 139.00 ***(978-3-642-23104-9(7),*** 3642231047) Springer.

CANARY ISLANDS—DESCRIPTION AND TRAVEL

Dillon, Paddy. Walking on la Gomera & el Hierro. 2011. (Illus.). 240p. pap. 21.95 *(978-1-85284-601-5(1))* Cicerone Pr. GBR. Dist: Midpoint Trade Bks., Inc.

—Walking on la Palma: The World's Steepest Island. 2nd rev. ed. 2011. (Illus.). 240p. pap. 21.95 *(978-1-85284-604-6(6))* Cicerone Pr. GBR. Dist: Midpoint Trade Bks., Inc.

Dillon, Paddy. Walking on Tenerife. 2nd ed. 2012. (ENG., Illus.). 250p. pap. 24.95 ***(978-1-85284-599-5(6))*** Cicerone Pr. GBR. Dist: Midpoint Trade Bks., Inc.

Dorling Kindersley Publishing Staff. Canary Islands. 2010. (Eyewitness Travel Guides). (ENG.). 216p. pap. 25.00 *(978-0-7566-6134-2(X))* Dorling Kindersley Publishing, Inc.

Flowers of the Canary Islands. *(978-88-8029-638-6(8))* Casa Editrice Bonechi.

Grand Canaria. 96p. pap. *(978-88-7009-800-6(1))* Casa Editrice Bonechi.

Gravette, Andy. Canary Islands. 5th ed. 2009. (Globetrotter Travel Packs Ser.). (ENG., Illus.). 128p. 14.95 *(978-1-84773-306-1(9),* Globetrotter) New Holland Pubs., Ltd. GBR. Dist: Globe Pequot Pr., The.

—Globetrotters: Canary Islands. 3rd ed. (Illus.). 128p. pap. 14.95 *(978-1-84330-813-3(4))* New Holland Pubs., Ltd. GBR. Dist: Globe Pequot Pr., The.

Locken, E. Travel Journal Puerto de Mogan. 2010. 192p. pap. 19.99 *(978-0-557-42214-2(0))* Lulu Enterprises Inc.

—Travel Journal Puerto Rico, Gran Canaria. 2010. 192p. pap. 19.99 *(978-0-557-42217-3(5))* Lulu Enterprises Inc.

Mead, Rowland. Gran Canaria Travel Pack. 3rd ed. 2009. (Globetrotter Travel Packs Ser.). (ENG., Illus.). 128p. 14.95 *(978-1-84773-040-4(X))* New Holland Pubs., Ltd. GBR. Dist: Globe Pequot Pr., The.

—Lanzarote. (Illus.). 128p. 2nd ed. pap. 14.95 *(978-1-84330-943-7(2))* 4th ed. 2010. (ENG., 14.95 *(978-1-84773-736-6(6),* Globetrotter) New Holland Pubs., Ltd. GBR. Dist: Globe Pequot Pr., The.

Pomares Rodríguez, Pilar. La Escuelita. 2008. (Collection Tigotán). (SPA.). 88p. *(978-84-96407-70-1(5))* Idea, Ediciones.

Quintero, Josephine & Butler, Stuart. Canary Islands, 47 vols. 5th rev. ed. 2012. (Regional Guide Ser.). (ENG., Illus.). 284p. pap. 19.99 *(978-1-74179-164-8(2))* Lonely Planet Pubns.

Rochford, Noel. Fuerteventura. 3rd ed. (Illus.). 128p. pap. 14.99 *(978-1-85691-248-8(5))* Sunflower Bks. (UK) GBR. Dist: Hunter Publishing, Inc.

—Landscapes of Gran Canaria: A Countryside Guide. 4th ed. (Illus.). 136p. pap. 14.99 *(978-1-85691-230-3(2))* Hunter Publishing, Inc.

—Landscapes of la Palma & el Hierro: A Countryside Guide. 4th rev. ed. 2007. (Sunflower Guides la Palma & el Hierro Ser.). (Illus.). 136p. per. 17.99 *(978-1-85691-300-3(7))* Hunter Publishing, Inc.

—Landscapes of la Palma & el Hierro: A Countryside Guide. 3rd ed. (Illus.). 136p. pap. 14.95 *(978-1-85691-214-3(0))* Sunflower Bks. (UK) GBR. Dist: Hunter Publishing, Inc.

—Landscapes of Southern Tenerife & la Gomera: A Countryside Guide. 4th ed. (Illus.). 136p. pap. 14.95 *(978-1-85691-218-1(3))* Hunter Publishing, Inc.

—Landscapes of Tenerife: A Countryside Guide. 6th rev. ed. 2007. (Sunflower Guides Tenerife Ser.). (Illus.). 144p. pap. 15.99 *(978-1-85691-270-9(1))* Hunter Publishing, Inc.

—Landscapes of Tenerife: A Countryside Guide. 5th ed. (Illus.). 152p. pap. 14.95 *(978-1-85691-176-4(4))* Sunflower Bks. (UK) GBR. Dist: Hunter Publishing, Inc.

—Lanzarote. 3rd ed. (Illus.). 128p. pap. 14.99 *(978-1-85691-232-7(9))* Hunter Publishing, Inc.

—Sunflower Guide Landscapes of Fuerteventura: A Countryside Guide. 4th rev. ed. 2007. (Sunflower Guides Fuerteventura Ser.). (Illus.). 128p. pap. 17.99 *(978-1-85691-320-1(1))* Hunter Publishing, Inc.

Smyth, Charles Piazzi. Teneriffe, an Astronomer's Experiment: Or, Specialities of a Residence above the Clouds. 2010. (Cambridge Library Collection - Physical Sciences Ser.). 512p. pap. 34.99 *(978-1-108-01412-0(7))* Cambridge Univ. Pr.

Thomas, Charles W. Adventures & Observations on the West Coast of Africa, & Its Islands. 2009. 286p. pap. *(978-1-4590-2783-1(3))* Books LLC.

—Adventures & Observations on the West Coast of Africa, & Its Islands Historical & Descriptive Sketches of Madeira, Canary, Biafra, & Cape Ver. 2006. 492p. per. 29.99 *(978-1-4255-5497-2(0))* MPublishing.

Thomas Cook Publishing Staff & Innman, Nick. Gran Canaria & Tenerife. 3rd ed. 2009. (Travellers - Thomas Cook Ser.). (ENG., Illus.). 192p. pap. 16.95 *(978-1-84848-172-5(1))* Cook, Thomas Publishing GBR. Dist: Globe Pequot Pr., The.

Thomas Cook Publishing Staff & Rogers, Barbara. Lanzarote & Fuerteventura. 3rd ed. 2009. (Travellers - Thomas Cook Ser.). (ENG., Illus.). 192p. pap. 16.95 *(978-1-84848-170-1(5))* Cook, Thomas Publishing GBR. Dist: Globe Pequot Pr., The.

CANARY ISLANDS—HISTORY

Bontier, Pierre & Le Verrier, Jean. The Canarian: Or, Book of the Conquest & Conversion of the Canarians in the year 1402, by Messire Jean de Bethencourt, Kt. 2010. (Cambridge Library Collection- Hakluyt First Ser.). (Illus.). 302p. pap. 24.99 *(978-1-108-01139-6(X))* Cambridge Univ. Pr.

Espinosa, Alonso de. The Guanches of Tenerife. 2009. 260p. pap. *(978-0-217-89339-8(2))* Books LLC.

Fitzgerald, Allistair. Air crash investigations: tenerife airport disaster, the world's deadliest plane crash Ever. 2010. 196p. pap. 26.95 *(978-0-557-45179-1(5))* Lulu Enterprises Inc.

Hernández González, Manuel. Francisco de Miranda y Canarias. 2007. (SPA.). 163p. *(978-84-8382-203-6(2))* Centro de la Cultura Popular Canaria.

Romero Pi, Juan. Régimen Económico Fiscal de Canarias. 2010. (SPA.). *(978-84-9903-485-0(3))* Editorial Aranzadi.

Segal, Nancy L. Someone Else's Twin: The True Story of Babies Switched at Birth. 2011. (ENG., Illus.). 250p. 25.00 *(978-1-61614-437-1(8))* Prometheus Bks., Pubs.

CANARY PARROT

see Budgerigar

CANBERRA (A.C.T.)

Locken, E. Travel Journal Canberra. 2010. 192p. pap. 19.99 *(978-0-557-44765-7(8))* Lulu Enterprises Inc.

Reed, Dimity, ed. National Museum of Australia: Building Monographs. 2006. (ENG., Illus.). 180p. 70.00 *(978-1-876907-39-6(8))* Images Publishing Group AUS. Dist: National Bk. Network.

CANBY, EDWARD RICHARD SPRIGG, 1817-1873

Heyman Jr., Max L. & Canby, E. R. S. Prudent Soldier: A Biography of Major General E. R. S. Canby, 1817-1873. 2011. 422p. 54.95 ***(978-1-258-10352-1(4))*** Literary Licensing, LLC.

CANCELLATIONS (PHILATELY)

see also Postmarks

Hall, Richard T. Philately of Switzerland: An Introductory Handbook. 2010. (Illus.). 345p. ***(978-0-9844317-0-0(5))*** A & C Publishing LLC.

Midkiff, Karen. Got the Stamp? Collecting National Park Cancellation Stamps: U. S. Mid-Atlantic Region. 2006. 114p. cd-rom 19.95 *(978-0-9768408-8-6(X))* Lemon Tulip.

—Got the Stamp? Collecting National Park Cancellation Stamps: U. S. Mid-Atlantic Region. 2006. spiral bd. 22.95 *(978-0-9768408-5-5(5))* 2nd ed. 2007. 106p. per. 30.00 *(978-0-9790502-2-0(7))* Lemon Tulip.

—Got the Stamp? Collecting National Park Cancellation Stamps: U. S. National Capital Region. 2006. spiral bd. 22.95 *(978-0-9768408-6-2(3))* 2006. 86p cd-rom 19.95 *(978-0-9768408-9-3(8))* 2nd ec. 2007. 86p. per. 27.00 *(978-0-9790502-3-7(5))* Lemon Tulip.

—Got the Stamp? Collecting National Park Cancellation Stamps: U. S. North Atlantic Region. 2006. 86p. cd-rom 19.95 *(978-0-9768408-7-9(1))* Lemon Tulip.

—Got the Stamp? Collecting National Park Cancellation Stamps: U. S. Southeast Region. 2007. spiral bd. 22.95 *(978-0-9790502-1-3(9))* Lemon Tulip.

CANCER

see also Antineoplastic Agents; Carcinogenesis; Carcinogens; Kaposi's Sarcoma; Leukemia; Melanoma; Tumors in Children

also subdivision Cancer under individual organs or regions of the body, e.g., Breast—Cancer

ABBE Research Division Staff. Minerals & Cancer in Humans: Index & Medical Analysis of New Clinical-Research Information for All Nations. 2006. (Illus.). 160p. ring bd. 74.50 *(978-0-7883-4565-4(6),* 07883-45656) ABBE Pubs. Assn. of Washington, D.C.

Abelmann, Henry W. Cancer As I See It. *(978-0-8022-0002-0(8))* Philosophical Library, Inc.

Abeloff, Martin D., et al. Clinical Oncology & Hematology: Basic Principles & Practices. 4th ed. 2008. (ENG.). 720.00 *(978-1-4160-6236-3(X),* Churchill Livingstone) Elsevier - Health Sciences Div.

Abraham, Jame, et al. The Bethesda Handbook of Clinical Oncology. Abraham, Jame et al, eds. 3rd rev. ed. 2009. (ENG., Illus.). 688p. pap. 63.99 *(978-0-7817-9558-6(3))* Lippincott Williams & Wilkins.

Adams, Peter D. & Sedivy, John M., eds. Cellular Senescence & Tumor Suppression. 2009. (ENG., Illus.). xiii, 272p. 159.00 *(978-1-4419-1074-5(3),* 1441910743) Springer.

Alison, Malcolm R. The Cancer. 2nd ed. 2008. 1616p. 715.00 *(978-0-470-03396-8(7))* Wiley, John & Sons, Inc.

—The Cancer. 2nd rev. ed. 2007. (ENG., Illus.). 1616p. 880.00 *(978-0-470-01852-1(6),* Wiley) Wiley, John & Sons, Inc.

Almeida, Craig A. & Barry, Sheila A. Cancer: Basic Science & Clinical Aspects. 2010. (ENG., Illus.). 424p. pap. 94.95 *(978-1-4051-5606-6(6),* Wiley-Blackwell) Wiley, John & Sons, Inc.

American Cancer Society Staff. Advanced Cancer: What You Need to Know Now. 2008. (QuickFACTS Ser.). (ENG.). 107p. pap. 8.95 *(978-0-944235-68-3(9),* 9780944235683) American Cancer Society, Inc.

Armitage, James O., et al. Clinical Oncology. 4th ed. 2008. (Expert Consult Title: Online + Print Ser.). (ENG., Illus.). 2592p. 330.00 *(978-0-443-06694-9(9),* Churchill Livingstone) Elsevier - Health Sciences Div.

—Clinical Oncology. 4th ed. 2008. (ENG., Illus.). 2592p. 395.00 *(978-0-443-06695-6(7),* Churchill Livingstone) Elsevier - Health Sciences Div.

Arora, Rajesh. Herbal Medicine: A Cancer Chemopreventive & Therapeutic Perspective. 2009. (Illus.). 674p. pap. 110.00 ***(978-81-8448-841-8(6))*** Jaypee Brothers, Medical Pubs. IND. Dist: BookMasters Distribution Services (BDS).

Artiano, Marco. Diagnosis: Death Six Months. 2010. 147p. pap. 12.88 *(978-0-557-50760-3(X))* Lulu Enterprises Inc.

Bald, Alphonso. Mesothelioma from Bench Side to Clinic. 2007. 89.00 *(978-1-60021-789-0(3))* Nova Science Pubs., Inc.

Bapat, Sharmila A. & Huang, Pearl S., eds. Cancer Stem Cells: Identification & Targets. 2008. (ENG., Illus.). 288p. 94.95 *(978-0-470-12201-3(3),* Wiley-Interscience) Wiley, John & Sons, Inc.

Baronzio, Gian F. & Hager, E. Dieter, eds. Hyperthermia in Cancer Treatment: A Primer: A Primer. 2010. (Medical Intelligence Unit Ser.). (Illus.). xxiii, 366p. pap. 259.00 *(978-1-4419-4130-5(4),* 1441941304) Springer.

Bell, Wardean. Cr: Cancer Revelations in America. 2011. 88p. pap. 15.99 ***(978-1-933972-28-2(9))*** PriorityONE Pubns.

Bellenir, Karen, ed. Cancer Sourcebook. 5th ed. 2007. (Health Reference Ser.). (Illus.). 1133p. 87.00 *(978-0-7808-0947-5(5))* Omnigraphics, Inc.

Berg, Deborah T. Pocket Guide to Colorectal Cancer. 2nd rev. ed. 2006. (Illus.). 376p. (C). pap. 49.95 *(978-0-7637-3460-2(8),* 0763734608) Jones & Bartlett Learning, LLC.

Berger, Ann, ed. Myths & Facts about Chronic Cancer Pain. 2006. (Illus.). 32p. pap. 10.95 *(978-1-891483-45-5(5))* PRR, Inc.

Berman, Jules J. Neoplasms: Principles of Development & Diversity. 2008. (Illus.). 429p. pap. 106.95 *(978-0-7637-5570-6(2))* Jones & Bartlett Learning, LLC.

Berstein, Lev M. & Santen, Richard J., eds. Innovative Endocrinology of Cancer. (Advances in Experimental Medicine & Biology Ser.). (Illus.). 2010. xx, 242p. pap. 209.00 *(978-1-4419-2700-2(X),* 144192700X) 2008. XX, 242p. 209.00 *(978-0-387-78817-3(4),* 0387788174) Springer.

Botwell, Brian J., et al. Clinical Malignant Hematology. Kalaycio, Matt E. ed. 2007. (ENG., Illus.). 1024p. 245.00 *(978-0-07-143650-2(2),* 0071436502) McGraw-Hill Professional Publishing.

Bradbury, Rob. Cancer. 2010. (Topics in Medicinal Chemistry Ser.). (Illus.). xiv, 451p. pap. 219.00 *(978-3-642-06966-6(5),* 3642069665) Springer.

Bradlow, H. Leon & Carruba, Guiseppe, eds. Steroid Enzymes & Cancer. 2009. (Annals of the New York Academy of Sciences Ser.). (ENG., Illus.). 352p. pap. 139.95 *(978-1-57331-745-0(4),* Wiley-Blackwell) Wiley, John & Sons, Inc.

Brockstein, Bruce & Masters, Gregory, eds. Head & Neck Cancer. 2010. (Cancer Treatment & Research Ser.). (Illus.). 392p. pap. 179.00 *(978-1-4419-5332-2(9),* 1441953329) Springer.

Bub, David, et al. 100 Questions & Answers about Colorectal Cancer. 2nd rev. ed. 2007. 259p. pap. 22.95 *(978-0-7637-5441-9(2))* Jones & Bartlett Learning, LLC.

Burke, Carol. Hereditary Colorectal Cancer Syndromes. Church, James, ed. 2007. (Illus.). 352p. 125.00 *(978-1-4051-2784-4(8),* Wiley-Blackwell) Wiley, John & Sons, Inc.

Campbell, Rebecca N., ed. Gene Therapy & Cancer Research Focus. 2008. 69.00 *(978-1-60021-970-2(5),* Nova Biomedical Bks.) Nova Science Pubs., Inc.

Cardinni, Dorothy C. Research Focus on Gastric Cancer. 2007. (C). 185.00 *(978-1-60021-726-5(5))* Nova Science Pubs., Inc.

Carr, Kris. Crazy Sexy Cancer Tips. 2007. (ENG., Illus.). 208p. pap. 17.95 *(978-1-59921-231-9(5),* skirt!) Globe Pequot Pr., The.

Casciato, Dennis A. Manual of Clinical Oncology. 6th rev. ed. 2008. (Lippincott Manual Series (Formerly Known As the Spiral Manual Series) Ser.). (ENG., Illus.). 832p. pap. 61.95 *(978-0-7817-6884-9(5))* Lippincott Williams & Wilkins.

Castle Connolly America's Top Doctors for Cancer. 3rd ed. 2007. 648p. per. 29.95 *(978-1-883769-43-7(4))* Castle Connolly Medical, Ltd.

Caughey, Aaron B. Pathophysiology Review. 2nd rev. ed. 2009. (ENG., Illus.). 376p. pap. 45.50 *(978-0-7817-8254-8(6))* Lippincott Williams & Wilkins.

Cefrey, Holly. Coping with Cancer. 2009. (Coping Ser.). 192p. (gr. 7-12). 63.90 *(978-1-61511-993-6(0))* Rosen Publishing Group, Inc., The.

Cesario, Alfredo & Marcus, Frederick, eds. Cancer Systems Biology, Bioinformatics & Medicine: Research & Clinical Applications. 2011. (ENG., Illus.). x, 484p. 129.00 *(978-94-007-1566-0(8),* 9400715668) Springer.

Chen, George G., ed. Female Sex Hormones & Cancers. 2009. (Cancer Etiology, Diagnosis & Treatments Ser.). 195.00 *(978-1-61728-696-4(6),* Nova Biomedical Bks.) Nova Science Pubs., Inc.

Clavien, Pierre-Alain, ed. Malignant Liver Tumors: Current & Emerging Therapies. 3rd ed. 2010. (ENG., Illus.). 576p. 330.00 *(978-1-4051-7976-8(7),* Wiley-Blackwell) Wiley, John & Sons, Inc.

Clymer, R. Swinburne. Cancer, the Killer: Cancer, One of Man's Most Fearful Enemies. 2011. 38p. 35.95 ***(978-1-258-00402-6(X))*** Literary Licensing, LLC.

Coleman, C. Norman. Understanding Cancer: A Patient's Guide to Diagnosis, Prognosis, & Treatment. 2nd ed. 2006. (ENG., Illus.). 232p. 44.00 *(978-0-8018-8417-7(9));* per. 19.95 *(978-0-8018-8418-4(7))* Johns Hopkins Univ. Pr.

Connolly, John J. & Morgan, Jean. America's Top Doctors for Cancer: America's Trusted Source for Identifying Top Doctors. 2nd ed. 2006. 69.95 net. *(978-1-883769-16-1(7))* 3rd ed. 2007. (Illus.). 648p. 79.95 *(978-1-883769-44-4(2))* 5th rev. ed. 2009. (ENG.). 622p. pap. 29.95 *(978-1-883769-08-6(6))* Castle Connolly Medical, Ltd.

Connolly, John J. & Morgan, Jean, eds. America's Top Doctors for Cancer: America's Trusted Source for Identifying Top Doctors. 2010. 625p. 79.95 *(978-1-883769-94-9(9))* Castle Connolly Medical, Ltd.

Connolly, John T., text. America's Top Doctors for Cancer. 2nd ed. 2006. 600p. per. 29.95 *(978-1-883769-10-9(8))* Castle Connolly Medical, Ltd.

Cooper D.C., Alan I, Cancer: The semi-Buddhist answer to dancing with Cancer... YOU LEAD. 2009. 88p. pap. 10.74 *(978-1-4389-4833-1(6))* AuthorHouse.

Corinas, Cristina. Cancer: Herencia y Ambiente. (Ciencia para Todos Ser.). (SPA.). pap. 6.99 *(978-968-16-3572-5(6))* Fondo de Cultura Economica USA.

Courneya, Kerry S. & Friedenreich, Christine M. Physical Activity & Cancer. 2010. (Recent Results in Cancer Research Ser.). (ENG., Illus.). xiii, 387p. 189.00 *(978-3-642-04230-0(9),* 3642042309) Springer.

Craddock, Valda M. Cancer of the Esophagus: Approaches to the Etiology. 2009. (Cambridge Monographs on Cancer Research Ser.). (ENG., Illus.). 300p. pap. 55.00 *(978-0-521-10258-2(8))* Cambridge Univ. Pr.

Cram101 Textbook Reviews. Outlines & Highlights for Head & Neck Cancer by Louis B Harrison, Isbn: 9780781771368 0781771366. 2011. 490p. pap. 37.95 ***(978-1-61490-146-4(5))*** Cram101 Inc.

Cram101 Textbook Reviews & Cram101 Textbook Reviews. Outlines & Highlights for Gynecological Cancer Management: Identification, Diagnosis & Treatment by Daniel Clarke-Pearson, ISBN. 2011. 224p. pap. 30.95 ***(978-1-61461-426-5(1))*** Cram101 Inc.

Cristini, Vittorio & Lowengrub, John. Multiscale Modeling of Cancer: An Integrated Experimental & Mathematical Modeling Approach. 2010. (ENG., Illus.). 298p. 125.00 *(978-0-521-88442-6(X))* Cambridge Univ. Pr.

Curiel, David T. & Douglas, Joanne T., eds. Cancer Gene Therapy. 2010. (Contemporary Cancer Research Ser.). (Illus.). 504p. pap. 209.00 *(978-1-61737-425-8(3),* 1617374253) Humana Pr.

Damjanov, Ivan & Fan, Fang, eds. Cancer Grading Manual. 2007. (Illus.). 126p. pap. 109.00 *(978-0-387-33750-0(4),* 0387337504) Springer.

Das, Dilip K., ed. Viral Cancers: Cytologic Tools in Diagnosis & Management. 2010. (Cancer Etiology, Diagnosis & Treatments Ser.). 96p. pap. 43.00 *(978-1-60876-402-0(8),* Nova Biomedical Bks.) Nova Science Pubs., Inc.

Davis, Mellar P., et al. Supportive Oncology: Expert Consult Online & Print. 2011. (ENG., Illus.). 672p. 149.00 *(978-1-4377-1015-1(8),* Saunders) Elsevier - Health Sciences Div.

De Vries, Jan. Cancer & Leukemia. 160p. pap. 11.95 *(978-1-85158-649-3(0))* Mainstream Publishing Co., Ltd. GBR. Dist: Trafalgar Square Publishing.

C

Deisboeck, Thomas S. & Stamatakos, Georgio S. Multiscale Cancer Modeling. 2010. (Chapman & Hall/CRC Mathematical & Computational Biology Ser.). (ENG., Illus.). 484p. 89.95 *(978-1-4398-1440-6(6)*, CRC Press) Taylor & Francis Group GBR. Dist: Taylor & Francis Group.

Del Rio, Maribel. The Playful Minds Coping Skills Program: A Treatment for Pediatric Oncology Patients. 2008. 136p. pap. *(978-3-8364-8184-7(7))* VDM Verlag Dr. Mueller e.K.

DeVita, Vincent. Cancer: Principles & Practice of Oncology. DePinho, Ronald A. et al, eds. 9th ed. 2011. (ENG.). 2800p. 399.99 *(978-1-4511-0545-2(2))* Lippincott Williams & Wilkins.

DeVita, Vincent T., Jr., et al, eds. Cancer Vol. 2: Principles & Practice of Oncology - Annual Advances in Oncology. 2011. (ENG.). 560p. 99.00 *(978-1-4511-4269-3(2))* Lippincott Williams & Wilkins.

Diaz-Rubio, Eduardo & Schmoll, Hans-Joachim, eds. Critical Role of Anti-Angiogenesis & VEGF Inhibition in Colorectal Cancer, Vol. 69. (Illus.). 56p. pap. *(978-3-8055-8047-2(9))* Karger, S. AG.

Dressler, Demian & Ettinger, Susan. The Dog Cancer Survival Guide: Full Spectrum Treatments to Optimize Your Dog's Life Quality & Longevity. Jacobson, Molly, ed. 2011. (Illus.). 496p. pap. 34.95 *(978-0-9752631-5-0(3))* Maui Media, LLC.

Ekeanyanwu, Chukwuma & NWANKWO, Olisa. Nutritional Pharmacology of Dietary Phytochemicals. 2011. 144p. pap. ***(978-3-8433-9334-8(6))*** Lambert Academic Publishing.

El-Metwally, Tarek H. Cancer Biology: an Updated Global Overview. 2009. (Cancer Etiology, Diagnosis & Treatments Ser.). pap. 43.00 *(978-1-60876-193-7(2)*, Nova Biomedical Bks.) Nova Science Pubs., Inc.

Elit, Laurie, ed. Women & Cancer. 2007. 334p. 89.00 *(978-1-60021-494-3(0))* Nova Science Pubs., Inc.

Ellis, Lee M., et al, eds. Radiofrequency Ablation for Cancer: Current Indications, Techniques & Outcomes. 2010. (ENG., Illus.). 296p. pap. 139.00 *(978-1-4419-3058-3(2)*, 1441930582) Springer.

Erickson, Karen. Together Strong: A Journey of Faith, Community Care & Human Struggles Through Cancer. 2011. 210p. 29.99 ***(978-1-4628-9551-9(4))***; pap. 19.99 ***(978-1-4628-9550-2(6))*** Xlibris Corp.

Eslick, Guy D. Esophageal Cancer, an Issue of Gastroenterology Clinics. 2009. (Clinics: Internal Medicine Ser.: 38-1). (ENG.). 240p. 99.00 *(978-1-4377-0477-8(8)*, Saunders) Elsevier - Health Sciences Div.

Fanti, Stefano, et al. PET-CT Beyond FDG: A Quick Guide to Image Interpretation. 2009. (ENG., Illus.). xiii, 243p. pap. 79.95 *(978-3-540-93908-5(3)*, 3540939083) Springer.

Fantus, I. George, ed. Insulin, Insulin Resistance, Growth Factors & Cancer. 2010. (Energy Balance & Cancer Ser.). (ENG., Illus.). 300p. 189.00 *(978-1-4419-9910-8(8)*, 1441999108) Springer.

Flores, Raja, et al, eds. Atlas of Procedures in Thoracic Cancer. 2009. (Illus.). 240p. 319.95 *(978-0-415-39226-6(8)*, Informa Healthcare) Taylor & Francis Group GBR. Dist: Taylor & Francis Group.

Franco, Eduardo L. & Rohan, Thomas E., eds. Cancer Precursors: Epidemiology, Detection, & Prevention. 2012. (ENG., Illus.). xx, 430p. pap. 144.00 *(978-1-4419-2901-3(0)*, 1441929010) Springer.

Gabriel, Janice Ann, ed. The Biology of Cancer. 2nd ed. 2007. (ENG., Illus.). 216p. pap. 60.99 *(978-0-470-05759-9(9)*, Wiley) Wiley, John & Sons, Inc.

Gearhart, Susan & Ahuja, Nita. Colorectal Cancer. 2010. (Early Diagnosis in Cancer Ser.). (ENG., Illus.). 272p. 152.00 *(978-1-4160-4686-8(0)*, Saunders) Elsevier - Health Sciences Div.

Germanno, Bradley D. Cancer Clusters. 2011. (Cancer Etiology, Diagnosis & Treatments Ser.). 156p. 89.00 *(978-1-61209-516-5(X))* Nova Science Pubs., Inc.

Geyman, John. The Cancer Generation: Baby Boomers Facing a Perfect Storm. 2009. (ENG.). 375p. pap. 18.95 *(978-1-56751-398-1(0))* Common Courage Pr.

Gibson, Faith & Kelly, Daniel, eds. Cancer Care for Adolescents & Young Adults. 2008. (ENG., Illus.). 272p. per. 75.99 *(978-1-4051-3094-3(6)*, Wiley-Blackwell) Wiley, John & Sons, Inc.

Gisselsson, David, ed. Intratumor diversity & clonal evolution in Cancer. 2011. (ENG., Illus.). 368p. 161.00 ***(978-0-12-387688-1(5)***, Academic Pr.) Elsevier Science & Technology Bks.

Glick, Adam B. & Waes, Carter Van, eds. Signaling Pathways in Squamous Cancer. 2010. (ENG., Illus.). xx, 462p. 209.00 *(978-1-4419-7202-6(1)*, 1441972021) Springer.

Godderis, Lode. Cancer Risk Assessment at the Workplace: Cancer Risk of Workers Exposed to Styrene & the Influence of Genetic Polymorphisms of Enzymes Involved in Metabolism & DNA Repair. 2006. (Acta Biomedica Lovaniensia Ser.: Vol. 358). (Illus.). pap. 99.50 *(978-90-5867-535-4(1))* Leuven Univ. Pr. BEL. Dist: Cornell Univ. Pr.

Gross, Ann D. & Sarg, Michael. The Cancer Dictionary. 3rd rev. ed. 2007. (Illus.). 432p. per. 19.95 *(978-0-8160-6412-0(1))*; (C). (gr. 9). 60.00 *(978-0-8160-6411-3(3))* Facts On File, Inc.

Hammer, Gary D. Adrenocortical Carcinoma: Basic Science & Clinical Concepts. 2010. (ENG., Illus.). xv, 546p. 209.00 *(978-0-387-77235-6(9)*, 0387772359) Springer.

Hanna, Louise, et al, eds. Practical Clinical Oncology. 2008. (ENG., Illus.). 512p. pap. 105.00 *(978-0-521-61816-8(9))* Cambridge Univ. Pr.

Harris, Michael K. Oral Cancer: Causes, Diagnosis & Treatment. 2011. (Cancer Etiology, Diagnosis & Treatments Ser.). (Illus.). 327p. 195.00 *(978-1-61209-305-5(1))* Nova Science Pubs., Inc.

Harrison, Louis B., et al, eds. Head & Neck Cancer: A Multidisciplinary Approach. 3rd rev. ed. 2008. (ENG., Illus.). 992p. 288.99 *(978-0-7817-7136-8(6))* Lippincott Williams & Wilkins.

Healy, Bernadine. Living Time: Faith & Facts to Transform Your Cancer Journey. 2008. (ENG.). 352p. per. 14.00 *(978-0-553-38454-3(6)*, Bantam) Random House Publishing Group.

Heathcote, Edwin & Jencks, Charles, eds. Architecture of Hope: Maggie's Cancer Caring Centres. 2010. (ENG., Illus.). 224p. 60.00 *(978-0-7112-2597-8(4))* Lincoln, Frances Ltd. GBR. Dist: Perseus-PGW.

Hesketh, Robin. Betrayed by Nature: The War on Cancer. 2012. (MacSci Ser.). (ENG., Illus.). 272p. 28.00 ***(978-0-230-33848-7(8))*** Palgrave Macmillan.

Higginbotham, Mary Lynn & Henry, Carolyn J. Cancer Management in Small Animal Practice. 2009. (ENG., Illus.). 432p. pap. 86.95 *(978-1-4160-3183-3(9)*, Saunders) Elsevier - Health Sciences Div.

Hino, O., et al, eds. Researches on Hepatocellular Carcinoma in Japan: A Message to the World. (Illus.). *(978-3-8055-7328-3(6))* Karger, S. AG.

Hino, O. & Kudo, M., eds. Recent Progress in Hepatocellular Carcinoma 2007: 90-year Anniversary Issue of Katsusaburo Yamagiwa's Innovative Achievement on Carcinogenesis: Supplement Issue: Oncology 2007, Vol. 72, Suppl. 1. 2008. (Illus.). 140p. (C). pap. *(978-3-8055-8413-5(X))* Karger, S. AG.

Holen, Kyle D. & Chung, Ki Young. Dx/rx: Colorectal Cancer. Shah, Manish A., ed. 2007. (Illus.). 81p. per. 49.95 *(978-0-7637-4744-2(0)*, 0763747440) Jones & Bartlett Learning, LLC.

Houlgatte, Alain. Cancer du Testicule. 2007. (Monographies en Urologie Ser.). 205p. pap. 89.95 *(978-2-287-21243-7(4)*, 2287212434) Springer.

Hunt, Kelly K., et al, eds. Gene Therapy for Cancer. 2010. (Cancer Drug Discovery & Development Ser.). (Illus.). 600p. pap. 219.00 *(978-1-61737-590-3(X)*, 161737590X) Humana Pr.

Hunter, Ross J. & Preedy, Victor R., eds. Nanomedicine & Cancer. 2011. (ENG., Illus.). 370p. 139.95 ***(978-1-57808-727-3(9))*** BIOS Scientific Publishers Ltd. GBR. Dist: Taylor & Francis Group.

Imre, Gabriele. Anti-Apoptotic & Pro-Inflammatory Signaling in Cancer Cells - Status & Modulation by Chemotherapeutic Drugs. 2008. 132p. pap. *(978-3-639-00750-3(6))* VDM Verlag Dr. Mueller e.K.

Institute of Medicine Staff. Extending the Spectrum of Precompetitive Collaboration in Oncology Research: Workshop Summary. 2010. (ENG.). 112p. pap. 29.75 *(978-0-309-15654-7(8))* National Academies Pr.

Institute of Medicine Staff, creator. Asbestos: Selected Cancers. 2006. (ENG., Illus.). 340p. per. 55.00 *(978-0-309-10169-1(7))* National Academies Pr.

Irwin, Melinda L., ed. ACSM's Guide to Exercise & Cancer Survivorship. 2012. (Illus.). 208p. 59.00 ***(978-0-7360-9564-8(0))*** Human Kinetics Pubs.

Jackson, Alisha. My Mommy Has Cancer. 2011. 16p. 8.50 *(978-1-4567-3094-9(0))* AuthorHouse.

Jiang, Wen G., et al, eds. Growth Factors & their Receptors in Cancer Metastasis. 2010. (Cancer Metastasis - Biology & Treatment Ser.). (Illus.). 320p. pap. 169.00 *(978-90-481-5757-0(9)*, 9048157579) Springer.

Jiménez-Ayala, Matías & Jiménez-Ayala Portillo, Beatriz. Endometrial Adenocarcinoma: Prevention & Early Diagnosis. 2008. (Monographs in Clinical Cytology Ser.). (Illus.). 92p. *(978-3-8055-8480-7(6))* Karger, S. AG.

Journal of the National Cancer Institute, September 4, 1996, Vol. 88, No. 7. per. 9.00 *(978-0-16-061574-0(7))* United States Government Printing Office.

Julian-Reynier, C., ed. Risk Communication in Familial Cancer. (Illus.). 82p. *(978-3-8055-7787-8(7))* Karger, S. AG.

Kahn, Michael & Goss, Kathleen H., eds. Targeting the Wnt Pathway in Cancer. 2011. (ENG., Illus.). xi, 241p. 189.00 *(978-1-4419-8022-9(9)*, 1441980229) Springer.

Kang, Kyung A., et al, eds. The Primo Vascular System: Its Role in Cancer & Regeneration. 2011. (ENG., Illus.). xix, 338p. 239.00 ***(978-1-4614-0600-6(5)***, 1461406005) Springer.

Kantarjian, Hagop, et al. The MD Anderson Manual of Medical Oncology. 2nd ed. 2011. *(978-0-07-040106-8(3))* McGraw-Hill Cos., The.

Kardamakis, Dimitrios, et al, eds. Bone Metastases: A translational & clinical Approach. 2009. (Cancer Metastasis - Biology & Treatment Ser.). (ENG., Illus.). xvi, 400p. 219.00 *(978-1-4020-9818-5(9)*, 1402098189) Springer.

Kawakami, Toshiyuki. Cell Differentiation of Neoplastic Cells Originating in the Oral & Craniofacial Regions. 2008. pap. 29.00 *(978-1-60456-932-2(8))* Nova Science Pubs., Inc.

Keen, Alison & Lennan, Elaine, eds. Women's Cancers. 2011. (ENG., Illus.). 288p. pap. 57.99 *(978-1-4051-8851-7(0)*, Wiley-Blackwell) Wiley, John & Sons, Inc.

Kessel, David. 12th World Congress of the International Photodynamic Association: Photodynamic Therapy: Back to the Future: 11-15 June 2009, Seattle, Washington, United States, 2 vols. 2009. (Proceedings of SPIE Ser.). (Illus.). 1142p. pap. 295.00 ***(978-0-8194-7660-9(9))*** SPIE.

Khan, Abdul Arif, ed. Bacteria & Cancer. 2012. (ENG., Illus.). vi, 276p. 189.00 ***(978-94-007-2584-3(1)***, 9400725841) Springer.

Knight, Jeffrey A., et al. Salem Health: Cancer. 2008. 99.00 *(978-1-58765-509-8(8))*; 99.00 *(978-1-58765-508-1(X))*; 99.00 *(978-1-58765-507-4(1))*; 99.00 *(978-1-58765-506-7(3))*; 1408p. 395.00 *(978-1-58765-505-0(5))* Salem Pr., Inc.

Koh, Howard K., ed. Toward the Elimination of Cancer Disparities. 2009. (ENG., Illus.). xii, 384p. 89.95 *(978-0-387-89442-3(X)*, 038789442X) Springer.

Koller, Charles A., et al. Manual of Medical Oncology. 2nd ed. 2011. (ENG., Illus.). 1400p. 228.00 *(978-0-07-170106-8(0)*, 0071701060) McGraw-Hill Professional Publishing.

Kovar, Florian M., et al. Molecular Staging of Colorectal Carcinom. 2010. 88p. pap. *(978-3-639-27548-3(9))* VDM Verlag Dr. Mueller e.K.

Kroemer, Guido. Oncogenes Meet Metabolism. 2008. (Ernst Schering Foundation Symposium Proceedings Ser.). (Illus.). xv, 264p. 139.00 *(978-3-540-79477-6(8))* Springer.

Kroemer, Guido, et al. Oncogenes Meet Metabolism: From Deregulated Genes to a Broader Understanding of Tumour Physiology. 2010. (Ernst Schering Foundation Symposium Proceedings Ser.). (Illus.). xvi, 265p. pap. 139.00 *(978-3-642-09840-6(1)*, 3642098401) Springer.

Krychman, Michael L. 100 Questions & Answers for Women Living with Cancer: A Practical Guide for Survivorship. 2007. (ENG.). 261p. per. 22.95 *(978-0-7637-3924-9(3))* Jones & Bartlett Learning, LLC.

Kyobutungi, Catherine. Ethnic German Immigrants from the Former Soviet Union: Mortality from External Causes & Cancers. 2008. (Challenges in Public Health Ser.). 144p. pap. 49.95 *(978-3-631-56563-6(1))* Lang, Peter GmbH, Europaischer Verlag der Wissenschaften DEU. Dist: Lang, Peter.

Laughlin. Cancer from a to Z: A Dictionary of Cancer-Related Terms. 2008. 432p. pap. 24.00 *(978-1-4343-5465-5(2))* AuthorHouse.

Leopold, Ellen. Under the Radar: Cancer & the Cold War. 2008. (Critical Issues in Health & Medicine Ser.). (ENG., Illus.). 312p. 25.95 *(978-0-8135-4404-5(1))* Rutgers Univ. Pr.

Litchfield, Jennifer E. New Research on Precancerous Conditions. 2007. 268p. 129.00 *(978-1-60021-552-0(1))* Nova Science Pubs., Inc.

Lokeshwar, Vinata B., et al, eds. Bladder Tumors: Molecular Aspects & Clinical Management. 2010. (Cancer Drug Discovery & Development Ser.). (ENG., Illus.). v, 350p. 209.00 *(978-1-60761-927-7(X)*, 160761927X) Humana Pr.

Longe, Jacqueline L. The Gale Encyclopedia of Cancer: A Guide to Cancer & Its Treatments. 3rd ed. 2010. *(978-1-4144-7600-1(0))*; *(978-1-4144-7599-8(3))*; (ENG.). 456.00 *(978-1-4144-7598-1(5))*; (Illus.). xxxvii, 1724p. E-Book 467.80 *(978-1-4144-7601-8(9))* Cengage Gale.

Longo, Dan L. & Harrison, Tinsley Randolph. Hematology & Oncology. 2010. (ENG., Illus.). 788p. pap. 82.00 *(978-0-07-166335-9(5)*, 0071663355) McGraw-Hill Professional Publishing.

Longoria, Miguel Angel & Alcalá, Joris Ismael. Adenocarcinoma: Pathogenesis, Treatment, & Prognosis. 2012. ***(978-1-61942-173-8(9))*** Nova Science Pubs., Inc.

Lucas A.K.A. J.I.M.S. Johnson, Andre Sco. The Cancer Survival Kit Vol. 1: The Power of Three - the Truth. 2008. 108p. pap. 19.95 *(978-1-60441-823-1(0))* PublishAmerica, Inc.

Lyman, Gary H., ed. Oxford American Handbook of Oncology. 2009. (ENG., Illus.). 800p. 44.95 *(978-0-19-536949-6(1))* Oxford Univ. Pr., Inc.

Lynch, Mary Pat. Essentials of Oncology Care. 3rd ed. 2009. *(978-0-9713017-9-5(4))* American College of Obstetricians & Gynecologists.

Markman, Maurie. Atlas of Cancer: Copublished with Current Medicine. 2nd ed. 2007. (Illus.). 642p. 259.00 *(978-1-57340-289-7(3))* Current Medicine Group LLC.

Markman, Maurie, ed. Atlas of Cancer: Copublished with Current Medicine. 2nd ed. 2010. (ENG., Illus.). x, 662p. cd-rom 99.00 *(978-1-57340-316-0(4)*, 1573403164) Current Medicine Group LLC.

Markman, Maurie & Cohen, Lorenzo, eds. Integrative Oncology: Incorporating Complementary Medicine into Conventional Cancer Care. 2010. (Current Clinical Oncology Ser.). (Illus.). xii, 220p. pap. 109.00 *(978-1-61737-817-1(8)*, 1617378178) Humana Pr.

Marshall, Constance E. Surviving the Odds, 1 vol. 2010. 48p. pap. 16.95 *(978-1-60836-624-8(3))* PublishAmerica, Inc.

Martakis, Ignatius K. Cancer Research at the Leading Edge. 2007. 185.00 *(978-1-60021-728-9(1))* Nova Science Pubs., Inc.

McArdle, Orla & O'Mahony, Deirdre. Oncology: An Illustrated Colour Text. 2008. (Illustrated Colour Text Ser.). (ENG., Illus.). 128p. (C). pap. 54.95 *(978-0-443-10374-2(7)*, Churchill Livingstone) Elsevier - Health Sciences Div.

McKinnell, Robert G., et al. The Biological Basis of Cancer. 2nd rev. ed. 2006. (ENG., Illus.). 494p. per. 79.00 *(978-0-521-60633-2(0))* Cambridge Univ. Pr.

Mehta, Shyam. Health: Arabic Edition. 2009. (ARA.). 68p. pap. 21.95 *(978-1-4092-9093-3(X))* Lulu Enterprises Inc.

—Health: Bengali Edition. 2009. (BEN.). 72p. pap. 6.95 *(978-1-4092-9156-5(1))* Lulu Enterprises Inc.

—Health: German Edition. 2009. (GER.). 72p. pap. 21.95 *(978-1-4092-9223-4(1))* Lulu Enterprises Inc.

—Health: Spanish Edition. 2009. (SPA.). 72p. pap. 21.95 *(978-1-4092-9218-0(5))* Lulu Enterprises Inc.

—Health:Italian Edition. 2009. (ITA.). 72p. pap. 21.95 *(978-1-4092-9211-1(8))* Lulu Enterprises Inc.

Missailidis, Sotiris, ed. The Cancer Clock. 2007. (ENG., Illus.). 320p. 169.95 *(978-0-470-06151-0(0))*; pap. 69.95 *(978-0-470-06152-7(9))* Wiley, John & Sons, Inc. (Wiley).

Moorland, Margarite T., ed. Cancer in Female Adolescents. 2008. 120.00 *(978-1-60456-421-1(0))* Nova Science Pubs., Inc.

Mor, Gil & Alvero, Ayesha, eds. Apoptosis & Cancer: Methods & Protocols. 2010. (Methods in Molecular Biology Ser.). (Illus.). xi, 266p. pap. 119.00 *(978-1-61737-582-8(9)*, 1617375829) Humana Pr.

Mortensen, Daniel V. Squamous Cell Carcinoma. 2011. (Cancer Etiology, Diagnosis & Treatments Ser.). 276p. 89.00 *(978-1-61209-929-3(7))* Nova Science Pubs., Inc.

Naff, Clay Farris. Cancer. 2007. (Contemporary Issues Companion Ser.). (ENG., Illus.). 199p. (gr. 10-12). 27.50 *(978-0-7377-2445-5(5)*, Greenhaven Pr., Inc.) Cengage Gale.

Nagarsheth, Nimesh P. Music & Cancer: A Prescription for Healing. 2009. (Illus.). 226p. pap. 22.95 *(978-0-7637-7908-5(3))* Jones & Bartlett Learning, LLC.

Nalwa, Hari Singh. Cancer Nanotechnology: Nanomaterials for Cancer Diagnosis & Therapy. 2006. (Illus.). xxiv, 355p. *(978-1-58883-071-5(3))* American Scientific Pubs.

Neal, Anthony J. & Hoskin, Peter J. Clinical Oncology. 4th ed. 2009. (ENG., Illus.). 432p. pap. 49.95 *(978-0-340-97293-9(9))* Hodder Arnold Pubs.

Oktay, Kutluk H., et al. 100 Questions & Answers about Cancer & Fertility. 2007. (ENG.). 152p. per. 22.95 *(978-0-7637-4049-8(7))* Jones & Bartlett Learning, LLC.

Oncology. Cancer Research, Tumor Markers, Clinical Oncology [Bibliography & Price Not Definite.]: 35Th Meeting of the International Society for Oncodevelopmental Biology & Medicine, Isobm, Prague, September 2007: Abstracts: Supplement Issue: Tumor Biology 2007, Vol. 28, Suppl. 1. Zima, T., ed. 2007. (Illus.). 144p. pap. *(978-3-8055-8400-5(8))* Karger, S. AG.

Parsons, Devon W. Stem Cells & Cancer. 2007. 284p. 129.00 *(978-1-60021-517-9(3))* Nova Science Pubs., Inc.

Pereira, Larissa S. Cancer Research Perspectives. 2008. (Illus.). (C). 69.00 *(978-1-60021-980-1(2)*, Nova Biomedical Bks.) Nova Science Pubs., Inc.

Pesmen, Curtis. Colon Cancer Survivors Gd. 2nd rev. ed. 2009. (ENG.). 220p. pap. 16.00 *(978-0-9776142-6-4(3))* Tatra Pr.

PET/CT in Clinical Practice. 2006. (Illus.). 241p. per. 59.95 *(978-1-84628-430-4(9)*, 1846284309) Springer.

Pierce, Kimberly S. Bridging Cancer, 1 vol. 2010. 124p. pap. 19.95 *(978-1-4489-5648-7(X))* PublishAmerica, Inc.

Pierce, Tanya Harter. Outsmart Your Cancer: Alternative Non-Toxic Treatments That Work. 2009. (ENG.). 506p. pap. 26.95 *(978-0-9728867-8-9(8))* Thoughtworks Publishing.

Platanias, Leonidas C. Cytokines & Cancer. 2010. (Cancer Treatment & Research Ser.). (Illus.). xvi, 378p. pap. 179.00 *(978-1-4419-3728-5(5)*, 1441937285) Springer.

Pullar, Christine E., ed. The Physiology of Bioelectricity in Development, Tissue Regeneration & Cancer. 2011. (ENG., Illus.). 342p. 119.95 *(978-1-4398-3723-8(6)*, CRC Press) Taylor & Francis Group GBR. Dist: Taylor & Francis Group.

Raghav, Krishna & Pandey, P. A Research Project Regarding Stem Cell Therapy & Its Observations: The Subsequent Analysis of the Stem Cell Therapy & Its Research Sensation. 2011. 56p. pap. ***(978-3-639-33785-3(9))*** VDM Verlag Dr. Mueller e.K.

Raghavan, Derek, et al, eds. Textbook of Uncommon Cancer. 3rd rev. ed. 2006. (ENG., Illus.). 878p. 552.00 *(978-0-470-01202-4(1)*, Wiley) Wiley, John & Sons, Inc.

Ramdayal, Kavisha. Single Nucleotide Polymorphisms among Established Ovarian Cancer Genes. 2010. 148p. pap. *(978-3-8383-0882-1(4))* Lambert Academic Publishing.

Reichle, Albrecht. From Molecular to Modular Tumor Therapy: Tumors are Reconstructible Communicatively Evolving Systems. Reichle, Albrecht, ed. 2010. (Tumor Microenvironment Ser.). (Illus.). viii, 566p. 239.00 *(978-90-481-9530-5(6)*, 9048195306) Springer.

Renda, Andrea. Multiple Primary Malignancies. 2008. (Updates in Surgery Ser.). (Illus.). xxii, 290p. 179.00 *(978-88-470-1094-9(2))* Springer.

Renshaw, Rachel & Verville, Kathleen. Lymphoma. 2011. (Biology of Cancer Ser.). (C). 35.00 *(978-0-7910-8823-4(5)*, Chelsea Hse.) Facts On File, Inc.

Rietg, Wolfgang. Living a Longer Active Life! Deacidifying - Cleansing - Detoxing - Cancer - Cancer Prophylaxis. 2009. 100p. pap. *(978-3-8370-3948-1(X))* Books on Demand GmbH.

Rini, Brian I. & Campbell, Steven C. Renal Cell Carcinoma. 2009. (Illus.). 336p. ***(978-1-60795-003-5(0))*** PMPH-USA. Ltd.

R.M, Jayadeepa. Unrevealing Endometrial Cancer. 2011. 116p. pap. ***(978-3-8443-3218-6(9))*** Lambert Academic Publishing.

Rosenbaum, Elana. Here for Now: Living Well with Cancer Through Mindfulness. 2nd rev. ed. 2007. (ENG.). 200p. per. 16.95 *(978-0-9729191-2-8(0))* Satya Hse. Pubns.

Ruddon, Raymond W. Cancer Biology. 4th rev. ed. 2007. (ENG., Illus.). 568p. per. 69.99 *(978-0-19-517544-8(1))* Oxford Univ. Pr., Inc.

Rutten, Lila J. Finney. Building the Evidence Base in Cancer Communication. 2010. 368p. *(978-1-57273-943-7(6))* Hampton Pr., Inc.

Safford, Michael P. & Haines, John G. Follicular Lymphoma & Other Cancer Research. 2009. 254p. pap. 129.00 *(978-1-60741-008-9(7))* Nova Science Pubs., Inc.

Sankaranarayanan, R. & Swaminathan, R. Cancer Survival in Africa, Asia, the Caribbean & Central America. 2011. (IARC Scientific Publications). (ENG., Illus.). 308p. pap. 48.00 ***(978-92-832-2162-3(1))*** World Health Organization.

Satgé, Daniel & Merrick, Joav. Cancer in Children & Adults with Intellectual Disabilities: Current Research Aspects. 2011. (Series: Disability Studies (Joav Merrick - Ser. Editor - National Institute of Child Health & Human Development, Ministry of Social Affairs, Jerusalem Ser.). 195.00 *(978-1-61761-856-7(X))* Nova Science Pubs., Inc.

Schwab, Manfred, ed. Encyclopedia of Cancer, 7 vols. 3rd ed. 2011. (ENG.). lxxxvi, 3984p. 2700.00 ***(978-3-642-16482-8(X)***, 364216482X) Springer.

Shah, Dr. Rupin & Shah, Rupin. Assessment of Oral Pre-Cancer & Cancerous Lesions in Gujarat State. 2011. 68p. pap. ***(978-3-8454-0449-3(3))*** Lambert Academic Publishing.

Shah, Manish A., et al. 100 Questions & Answers about Gastric Cancer. 2007. (Illus.). 168p. pap. 22.95 *(978-0-7637-5367-2(X))* Jones & Bartlett Learning, LLC.

Shepherd, Glenda. Thyroid Cancer for Beginners. 2009. (Illus.). 132p. pap. 10.99 *(978-1-4389-6583-3(4))* AuthorHouse.
Singer, Albert & Monaghan, John. Lower Genital Tract Precancer: Colposcopy, Pathology & Treatment. 2008. 336p. 295.00 *(978-1-4051-5289-1(3),* Wiley-Blackwell) Wiley, John & Sons, Inc.
Singh, Shree Ram. Stem Cell, Regenerative Medicine & Cancer. 2010. (Cell Biology Research Progress Ser.). 195.00 *(978-1-61728-787-9(3))* Nova Science Pubs., Inc.
Skarin, Arthur T. Atlas of Diagnostic Oncology: Expert Consult - Online & Print. 4th ed. 2009. (ENG., Illus.). 654p. 250.00 *(978-0-323-05905-3(8),* Mosby) Elsevier - Health Sciences Div.
Slack, Frank J. Micromas in Development & Cancer. 2010. (Illus.). 300p. 96.00 *(978-1-84816-366-9(5))* World Scientific Publishing Co., Inc.
Slaten, Les. Sadie: A Hunter's Story - My Best Friend. 2010. 76p. pap. 10.99 *(978-1-4490-8555-1(5))* AuthorHouse.
Smith, J. Richard & Del, Priore Guis. Women's Cancers: A Patient's Guide to Dealing with Ovarian & Breast Cancer. 2008. (Illus.). 138p. pap. 19.95 *(978-1-84628-437-3(6),* 1846284376) Springer.
Sonnenberg, Eric van, et al, eds. Tumor Ablation: Principles & Practice. 2010. (ENG., Illus.). xxvi, 600p. pap. 144.00 *(978-1-4419-3046-0(9),* 1441930469) Springer.
Sorenson, Robert V. Progress in Cancer Research. 2007. (C). 129.00 *(978-1-60021-645-9(5))* Nova Science Pubs., Inc.
Spiro, David M., et al. Cancer Emergencies, an Issue of Hematology/Oncology Clinics of North America. 2010. (Clinics: Internal Medicine Ser.: 24-3). (ENG., Illus.). xii, 488p. 99.00 *(978-1-4377-2528-5(7),* Saunders) Elsevier - Health Sciences Div.
Springer, Caroline J., ed. Suicide Gene Therapy: Methods & Reviews. 2010. (Methods in Molecular Medicine Ser.). (Illus.). 560p. pap. 169.00 *(978-1-61737-283-4(8),* 1617372838) Humana Pr.
Stephens, Frederick O., et al. Basics of Oncology. Stephens, Frederick O. & Aigner, Karl Reinhard, eds. 2009. (ENG., Illus.). xxiv, 375p. pap. 69.95 *(978-3-540-92924-6(X),* 354092924X) Springer.
Stockdale, Brenda. You Can Beat the Odds: The Surprising Factors Behind Chronic Illness & Cancer. 2009. (ENG.). 272p. pap. 18.95 *(978-1-59181-079-7(5))* Sentient Pubns.
Stubblefield, Michael D. & O'Dell, Michael W. Synopsis of Clinical Oncology. 2010. *(978-1-936287-00-0(5))* Demos Medical Publishing, LLC.
Surbone, Antonella, et al. Cancer & Pregnancy. 2007. (Recent Results in Cancer Research Ser.). (Illus.). 260p. 189.00 *(978-3-540-71272-5(0),* 3540712720) Springer.
Syse, Astri. Life after Cancer. 2010. 144p. pap. *(978-3-639-18463-1(7))* VDM Verlag Dr. Mueller e.K.
Taktak, Azzam F. G. & Fisher, Anthony C., eds. Outcome Prediction in Cancer. 2007. (ENG., Illus.). 482p. 145.00 *(978-0-444-52855-1(5),* Elsevier Science) Elsevier Science & Technology Bks.
Tannapfel, Andrea. Malignant Mesothelioma. 2011. (Recent Results in Cancer Research Ser.). (Illus.). xi, 193p. 189.00 *(978-3-642-10861-7(X),* 364210861X) Springer.
Tatum, Rita. Sass Cancer Back: Living with Spirit. 2011. 238p. pap. 19.99 ***(978-1-4568-8980-7(X))*** Xlibris Corp.
Tavares, Clement Adams. Cancer & the Atomic Age. 2011. 198p. 42.95 ***(978-1-258-06677-2(7))*** Literary Licensing, LLC.
Taylor, Albina W. Cell Apoptosis & Cancer. 2007. (Illus.). 225.00 *(978-1-60021-505-3(8))* Nova Science Pubs., Inc.
Teicher, Beverly A., et al, eds. Apoptosis & Cancer: Methods & Protocols. 2007. (Methods in Molecular Biology Ser.). (Illus.). 350p. 119.00 *(978-1-58829-457-9(9),* 1588294579) Humana Pr.
Temple, Susan. Contemporary Issues in Women's Cancers. 2008. (Illus.). 349p. (C). 94.95 *(978-0-7637-2602-7(8),* 0763726028) Jones & Bartlett Learning, LLC.
University of National Cancer Registry Association Staff. Cancer Registry Management: Principles & Practice. 2nd rev. ed. 2010. (ENG.). 574p. (C). pap. 114.95 *(978-0-7575-0192-0(3),* 0757501923) Kendall Hunt Publishing Co.
—Central Cancer Registries: Design, Management & Use. 2nd rev. ed. 2007. (ENG.). 468p. (C). pap. 124.95 *(978-0-7575-3120-0(2))* Kendall Hunt Publishing Co.
Vande Woude, George F. & Klein, George, contrib. by. Genomics in Cancer Drug Discovery & Development. 2006. (Advances in Cancer Research Ser.). (ENG., Illus.). 432p. 161.00 *(978-0-12-006696-4(3),* Academic Pr.) Elsevier Science & Technology Bks.
Verma, M., ed. Molecular Signatures of Infectious Agents in Cancer. (Disease Markers Ser.). 202p. pap. 120.00 *(978-1-58603-250-0(X))* IOS Pr., Inc.
Volk, Ruti Malis. The Medical Library Association Guide to Cancer Resources: Authoritative, Patient-Friendly Print & Electronic Sources. 2007. 372p. (C). 85.00 *(978-1-55570-585-5(5))* Neal-Schuman Pubs., Inc.
Waxman, Jonathan. Molecular Endocrinology of Cancer: Volume 1, Part 2, Endocrine Therapies. 2010. (Cancer: Clinical Science in Practice Ser.). (ENG.). 440p. pap. 55.00 *(978-0-521-15949-4(0))* Cambridge Univ. Pr.
Wender, Richard & Snyderman, Danielle. Cancer Pt. 1: What the Primary Care Practitioner Needs to Know, 2 vols. 2009. (Clinics: Internal Medicine Ser.: 36-3). (ENG., Illus.). 88.00 *(978-1-4377-1268-1(1),* Saunders) Elsevier - Health Sciences Div.
Whitten, Pamela, et al. E-Health: The Advent of Online Cancer Information Systems. 2011. *(978-1-57273-752-5(2)); (978-1-57273-753-2(0))* Hampton Pr., Inc.
Wick, Mark, ed. Metastatic Carcinomas of Unknown Origin. 2008. (Illus.). 416p. 150.00 *(978-1-933864-32-7(X))* Demos Medical Publishing, LLC.
Wiginton, Sharon Jean. Abounding Health Naturally. 2010. pap. 12.99 *(978-1-61663-334-9(4))* Tate Publishing & Enterprises, LLC.
Wilkes, Gail M. Colorectal Cancer: Drugs & Treatment. 2nd rev. ed. 2008. (ENG.). 181p. spiral bd. 39.95 *(978-0-7637-6173-8(7))* Jones & Bartlett Learning, LLC.
Xie, Jingwu, ed. Hedgehog signaling activation in human cancer & its clinical Implications. 2011. (ENG., Illus.). ix, 217p. 189.00 *(978-1-4419-8434-0(8),* 1441984348) Springer.
Yao, Tso-Pang & Seto, Edward, eds. Histone Deacetylases: the Biology & Clinical Implication: The Biology & Clinical Implication. 2011. (Handbook of Experimental Pharmacology Ser.). (ENG., Illus.). xi, 260p. 419.00 ***(978-3-642-21630-5(7),*** 3642216307) Springer.
Zänker, Kurt S. & Entschladen, Frank. Neuronal Activity in Tumor Tissue. (Progress in Experimental Tumor Research Ser.: Vol. 39). *(978-3-8055-8246-9(3))* Karger, S. AG.
Zent, Roy & Pozzi, Ambra, eds. Cell-Extracellular Matrix Interactions in Cancer. 2009. (ENG., Illus.). xi, 314p. 159.00 *(978-1-4419-0813-1(7),* 1441908137) Springer.

CANCER—BIOGRAPHY

see Cancer—Patients—Biography

CANCER—CHEMOTHERAPY

Ackerman MSN, Carol L. A Chemotherapy Guide for the Medical-Surgical Nurse. 2007. 52p. pap. 20.00 *(978-1-4303-2870-4(3))* Lulu Enterprises Inc.
Adams, Julian, ed. Proteasome Inhibitors in Cancer Therapy. 2010. (Cancer Drug Discovery & Development Ser.). (Illus.). 328p. pap. 179.00 *(978-1-61737-452-4(0),* 1617374520) Humana Pr.
Adjei, Alex A., ed. Lung Cancer Therapies. 2009. (Cancer Drug Discovery & Development Ser.). 135.00 *(978-1-60327-010-6(8))* Humana Pr.
Aigner, Karl Reinhard & Stephens, Frederick O., eds. Induction Chemotherapy: Integrated Treatment Programs for Locally Advanced Cancers. 2011. (ENG., Illus.). ix, 365p. 139.00 *(978-3-642-18172-6(4),* 3642181724) Springer.
Airley, Rachel. Cancer Chemotherapy: Basic Science to the Clinic. 2009. (ENG., Illus.). 342p. 159.95 *(978-0-470-09254-5(8));* pap. 69.95 *(978-0-470-09255-2(6))* Wiley, John & Sons, Inc. (Wiley).
Anshul, Agarwal. Nanoformulation & Controlled Delivery of Low Solubility Cancer Drugs: A Nanotechnology Based Approach for Formulation of Toxic Therapeutic & Imaging Agents. 2011. 144p. pap. ***(978-3-639-32555-3(9))*** VDM Verlag Dr. Mueller e.K.
Aronson, Jeffrey K., ed. Side Effects of Drugs in Cancer & Immunology. 2010. (ENG.). 780p. 67.95 *(978-0-444-53267-1(6),* Elsevier Science) Elsevier Science & Technology Bks.
Barker, Trey R. The Cancer Chronicles. 2010. 19?p. pap. 14.99 *(978-0-557-35322-4(X))* Lulu Enterprises Inc.
Bermel Mba, Margaret Brennan. The Cancer Odyssey. 2011. 122p. 29.99 ***(978-1-4568-8538-0(3));*** pap. 19.99 ***(978-1-4568-8537-3(5))*** Xlibris Corp.
Bessiel, Jakobe H., ed. Progress in Cancer Prevention. 2008. (Illus.). x, 137p. 69.00 *(978-1-60456-327-6(3),* Nova Biomedical Bks.) Nova Science Pubs., Inc.
Bleuet, Frances & LaMor RMA, Angela, Ncpt. EveryBODY Can Heal. 2010. 130p. pap. 22.50 *(978-0-557-72099-6(0))* Lulu Enterprises Inc.
Blumenthal, Rosalyn D., ed. Chemosensitivity: Volume I: in Vitro Assays. 2010. (Methods in Molecular Medicine Ser.). (Illus.). xiii, 231p. pap. 104.00 *(978-1-61737-508-8(X),* 161737508X) Humana Pr.
—Chemosensitivity: Volume II: in Vivo Models, Imaging, & Molecular Regulators. 2010. (Methods in Molecular Medicine Ser.). (Illus.). 464p. pap. 169.00 *(978-1-61737-660-3(4),* 1617376604) Humana Pr.
Bonavida, Benjamin. Nitric Oxide (NO) & Cancer: Prognosis, Prevention, & Therapy. 2010. (Illus.). xx, 513p. E-Book *(978-1-4419-1432-3(3))* Springer.
Bonavida, Benjamin, ed. Nitric Oxide (NO) & Cancer. 2010. (Cancer Drug Discovery & Development Ser.). (ENG., Illus.). x, 250p. 259.00 *(978-1-4419-1431-6(5),* 1441914315) Springer.
—Sensitization of Cancer Cells for Chemo/Immuno/Radio-Therapy. 2008. (Illus.). 479p. (C). 209.00 *(978-1-934115-29-9(0),* 1934115290) Humana Pr.
Bonetti, Andrea. Platinum & Other Heavy Metal Compounds in Cancer Chemotherapy: Molecular Mechanisms & Clinical Applications. 2009. (Cancer Drug Discovery & Development Ser.). (Illus.). 312p. 189.00 *(978-1-60327-458-6(8))* Humana Pr.
Bradbury, Robert H., ed. Cancer. 2007. (Topics in Medicinal Chemistry Ser.). (Illus.). 451p. 219.00 *(978-3-540-33119-3(0),* 3540331190) Springer.
Bragalone, Diedra L., ed. Drug Information Handbook for Oncology: A Complete Guide to Combination Chemotherapy Regimens. 9th ed. 2011. (Lexi-Comp's Drug Reference Handbooks Ser.). (Illus.). 1707p. pap. 49.95 *(978-1-59195-290-9(5))* Lexi-Comp, Inc.
Brahmer, Julie R., et al, eds. Lung Cancer: Translational & Emerging Therapies. 2007. (Translational Medicine Ser.: Vol. 3). (ENG., Illus.). 280p. 100.00 *(978-0-8493-9021-0(4),* Informa Healthcare) Taylor & Francis Group GBR. Dist: Taylor & Francis Group.
Brown, J. Martin, et al, eds. Beyond Apoptosis: Cellular Outcomes of Cancer Therapy. 2008. (ENG., Illus.). 376p. 230.00 *(978-0-8493-9192-7(X),* Informa Healthcare) Taylor & Francis Group GBR. Dist: Taylor & Francis Group.
Brown, Martin J., et al. Multimodal Concepts for Integration of Cytotoxic Drugs. 2010. (Medical Radiology / Radiation Oncology Ser.). (Illus.). x, 352p. pap. 209.00 *(978-3-642-06505-7(8),* 3642065058) Springer.
Bukowski, Ronald M., et al, eds. Renal Cell Carcinoma: Molecular Targets & Clinical Applications, Second Edition. 2nd ec. 2010. (Illus.). xviii, 506p. pap. 99.95 *(978-1-60761-468-5(5),* 1607614685) Humana Pr.
Butler, Sara Aston & Govindan, Ramaswamy. Essential Cancer Pharmacology: The Prescriber's Guide. 2010. (ENG.). 544p. pap. 74.99 *(978-1-60913-704-5(3))* Lippincott Williams & Wilkins.
Caligiuri, Michael A., ed. Cytokines in the Genesis & Treatment of Cancer. 2007. (Cancer Drug Discovery & Development Ser.). (Illus.). 482p. 229.00 *(978-0-89603-820-2(3),* 0896038203) Humana Pr.
Caligiuri, Michael A. & Lotze, Michael T., eds. Cytokines in the Genesis & Treatment of Cancer. 2010. (Cancer Drug Discovery & Development Ser.). (Illus.). xx, 482p. pap. 229.00 *(978-1-61737-203-2(X),* 161737203X) Humana Pr.
Castoria, Gabriella & Migliaccio, Antimo, eds. Advances in Rapid Sex-Steroid Action: New Challenges & New Chances in Breast & Prostate Cancers. 2011. (ENG., Illus.). xvii, 268p. 189.00 ***(978-1-4614-1763-7(5),*** 1461417635) Springer.
Chabner, Bruce, et al. Harrison's Manual of Oncology. 2008. (Illus.). xxi, 624p. *(978-0-07-150812-4(0)); (978-0-07-150811-7(2))* McGraw-Hill Medical Publishing Div.
Chabner, Bruce A. & Longo, Dan L., eds. Cancer Chemotherapy & Biotherapy: Principles & Practice. 5th rev. ed. 2010. (ENG., Illus.). 848p. 238.99 *(978-1-60547-431-1(2))* Lippincott Williams & Wilkins.
Chen, George G. & Lai, Paul B. S., eds. Apoptosis in Carcinogenesis & Chemotherapy: Apoptosis in Cancer. 2009. (ENG., Illus.). xxii, 386p. 229.00 *(978-1-4020-9596-2(1),* 1402095961) Springer.
Chhipa, Rishi Raj. P53: Old Gene with New Aspects. 2011. 200p. pap. ***(978-3-8443-1113-6(0))*** Lambert Academic Publishing.
Choy, Hak, ed. Chemoradiation in Cancer Therapy. 2010. (Cancer Drug Discovery & Development Ser.). (Illus.). 432p. pap. 154.50 *(978-1-61737-313-8(3),* 1617373133) Humana Pr.
Christie, D.A. The Discovery, Use & Impact of Platinum Salts As Chemotherapy Agents for Cancer. 2007. (Illus.). xxv, 117p. pap. *(978-0-85484-112-7(1))* Wellcome Institute for the History of Medicine.
Chu. Chemotherapy Protocols Poster. rev. ed. 2012. 1p. 31.95 *(978-0-7637-8521-5(0))* Jones & Bartlett Learning, LLC.
Chu, Edward. Chemotherapy Protocols. 5th rev. ed. 2008. (ENG.). 195p. spiral bd. 49.95 *(978-0-7637-7117-1(1))* Jones & Bartlett Learning, LLC.
—Physicians' Cancer Chemotherapy Drug Manual. 10th rev. ed. 2009. 559p. spiral bd. 108.95 *(978-0-7637-8176-7(2))* Jones & Bartlett Learning, LLC.
—Physician's Cancer Chemotherapy Drug Manual 2011. 11th ed. 2010. 591p. spiral bd. 99.95 *(978-1-4496-0197-3(9))* Jones & Bartlett Learning, LLC.
—Physician's Cancer Chemotherapy Drug Manual 2012. 12th ed. 2011. 600p. spiral bd. 93.95 ***(978-1-4496-4683-7(2))*** Jones & Bartlett Learning, LLC.
—Pocket Guide to Chemotherapy Protocols. 6th rev. ed. 2010. 183p. spiral bd. 49.95 *(978-0-7637-8401-0(X))* 7th ed. 2011. 234p. spiral bd. 44.95 ***(978-1-4496-4681-3(6))*** Jones & Bartlett Learning, LLC.
—Pocket Guide to Hematologic Cancer Chemotherapy Protocols. rev. ed. 2012. 170p. spiral bd. 31.95 *(978-0-7637-8520-8(2))* Jones & Bartlett Learning, LLC.
Chu, Edward & DeVita Jr., Vincent T. Physicians' Cancer Chemotheraphy Drug Manual 2012. 12th ed. 2011. 560p. spiral bd. 97.95 ***(978-1-4496-2443-9(X))*** Jones & Bartlett Learning, LLC.
Chu, Edward & DeVita, Vincent T. Physicians' Cancer Chemotherapy Drug Manual 2008. 2007. 552p. pap., spiral bd. 89.95 *(978-0-7637-5562-1(1))* Jones & Bartlett Learning, LLC.
Chu, Edward, et al. Physicians' Cancer Chemotherapy Drug Manual. 2007. (Physicians' Cancer Chemotherapy Drug Manual Ser.). (Illus.). 542p. spiral bd. 77.95 incl. cd-rom *(978-0-7637-4308-6(9))* Jones & Bartlett Learning, LLC.
Clark, Barbara. The Fight of My Life: The Inspiring Story of a Mother's Fight against Breast Cancer. 2007. (ENG., Illus.). 304p. 34.95 *(978-0-340-93809-6(9),* Hodder & Stoughton) Hodder General Publishing Div. GBR. Dist: Independent Pubs. Group.
Clegg, Ellen. ChemoBrain: How Cancer Therapies Can Affect Your Mind. 2008. (ENG., Illus.). 340p. 18.98 *(978-1-59102-669-3(5))* Prometheus Bks., Pubs.
Clendeninn, Neil J. & Appelt, Krzysztof, eds. Matrix Metalloproteinase Inhibitors in Cancer Therapy. 2010. (Cancer Drug Discovery & Development Ser.). (Illus.). 276p. pap. 150.00 *(978-1-61737-123-3(8),* 1617371238) Humana Pr.
Cliffor. Oncogenic Mutations of Tyrosine Kina... 2011. 200p. 111.00 *(978-981-270-546-4(5))* World Scientific Publishing Co., Inc.
Clynes, Martin, ed. Multiple Drug Resistance in Cancer 2: Molecular, Cellular & Clinical Aspects. 2010. 300p. pap. 228.00 *(978-90-481-5108-0(2),* 9048151082) Springer.
Cram101 Textbook Reviews & Cram101 Textbook Reviews. Outlines & Highlights for Medicinal Chemistry of Anticancer Drugs by Carmen Avendano. 2011. 146p. pap. 29.95 ***(978-1-61830-792-7(4))*** Cram101 Inc.
Dannenberg, Andrew J. & DuBois, Raymond N., eds. COX-2: A New Target for Cancer Prevention & Treatment, Vol. 37 (Progress in Experimental Tumor Research Ser.: Vol. 37). (Illus.). *(978-3-8055-7536-2(X))* Karger, S. AG.
Dietel, Manfred. Targeted Therapies in Cancer. 2007. (Recent Results in Cancer Research Ser.). (Illus.). xiv, 262p. 189.00 *(978-3-540-46090-9(X))* Springer.
Dobson, Lelanie. Surviving the Odds. 2010. 54p. pap. 15.99 *(978-1-4500-4163-8(9))* Xlibris Corp.
Ecker, Gerhard & Chiba, Peter. Transporters as Drug Carriers: Structure, Function, Substrates. Ecker, Gerhard & Chiba, Peter, eds. 2009. (Methods & Principles in Medicinal Chemistry Ser.: 112). (ENG., Illus.). 449p. 230.00 *(978-3-527-31661-8(2),* Wiley-VCH) Wiley, John & Sons, Inc.
Fabbro, Doriano & McCormick, Frank, eds. Protein Tyrosine Kinases: From Inhibitors to Useful Drugs. 2010. (Cancer Drug Discovery & Development Ser.). (Illus.). 304p. pap. 259.00 *(978-1-61737-534-7(9),* 1617375349) Humana Pr.
Fojo, Antonio T. & Teicher, Beverly A., eds. Microtubule Targets in Cancer Therapy. 2007. (Cancer Drug Discovery & Developmenttm Ser.). (Illus.). 690p. 259.00 *(978-1-58829-294-0(0),* 1588292940) Humana Pr.
Franciscis, Vittorio de. Signalling Molecules as Targets in Cancer Therapy. 2006. 240p. 89.00 *(978-1-60021-243-7(3),* Nova Biomedical Bks.) Nova Science Pubs., Inc.
Gerritsen, Mary E. & Matthews, David J. Targeting Protein Kinases for Cancer Therapy. 2010. (ENG., Illus.). 702p. 139.00 *(978-0-470-22965-1(9),* Wiley) Wiley, John & Sons, Inc.
Gewirtz, David A., et al, eds. Apoptosis, Senescence & Cancer. 2nd ed. 2010. (Cancer Drug Discovery & Development Ser.). (Illus.). xvii, 599p. pap. 199.00 *(978-1-61737-621-4(3),* 1617376213) Humana Pr.
—Apoptosis, Senescence, & Cancer. 2nd ed. 2007. (Cancer Drug Discovery & Developmenttm Ser.). (Illus.). 599p. 199.00 *(978-1-58829-527-9(3),* 1588295273) Humana Pr.
Giordano, Antonio & Soprano, Kenneth J., eds. Cell Cycle Inhibitors in Cancer Therapy. 2010. (Cancer Drug Discovery & Development Ser.). (Illus.). 326p. pap. 179.00 *(978-1-61737-257-5(9),* 1617372579) Humana Pr.
González, Michael J., et al. I Have Cancer - What Should I Do? Your Orthomolecular Guide for Cancer Management. 2009. 224p. pap. 18.95 *(978-1-59120-243-1(4))* Basic Health Pubns., Inc.
Govindan, Ramaswamy, ed. The Washington Manual of Oncology: Department of Medicine, Division of Oncology, Washington University School of Medicine, St. Louis, Missouri. 2nd rev. ed. 2007. (Lippincott Manual Series (Formerly Known As the Spiral Manual Series) Ser.). (ENG., Illus.). 576p. per. 67.99 *(978-0-7817-8402-3(6))* Lippincott Williams & Wilkins.
Groner, B. Targeted Interference with Signal Transduction Events. 2010. (Recent Results in Cancer Research Ser.). (Illus.). x, 188p. pap. 139.00 *(978-3-642-06834-8(0),* 3642068340) Springer.
Gullatte, Mary Magee, ed. Clinical Guide to Antineoplastic Therapy: A Chemotherapy Handbook. 2nd ed. 2007. (AFA., Illus.). 668p. per. *(978-1-890504-68-7(8))* Oncology Nursing Society.
Haley, John D., ed. EGFR Signaling Networks in Cancer Therapy. 2008. (Cancer Drug Discovery & Development Ser.). 450p. 199.00 *(978-1-58829-948-2(1))* Humana Pr.
Haley, John D. & Gullick, William John, eds. EGFR Signaling Networks in Cancer Therapy. 2010. (Cancer Drug Discovery & Development Ser.). (Illus.). xi, 393p. pap. 199.00 *(978-1-61737-853-9(4),* 1617378534) Humana Pr.
Hickman, John A. & Dive, Caroline, eds. Apoptosis & Cancer Chemotherapy. 2010. (Cancer Drug Discovery & Development Ser.). (Illus.). 360p. pap. 139.00 *(978-1-61737-165-3(3),* 1617371653) Humana Pr.
Hoffer, Abram. Healing Cancer: Complementary Vitamin & Drug Treatments. 2011. (Naturopathic Healing Series, Professional Edition Ser.). (ENG.). 240p. 49.95 ***(978-1-897025-40-6(8))*** Canadian College of Naturopathic Medicine Pr. CAN. Dist: SCB Distributors.
Innocenti, Federico, ed. Genomics & Pharmacogenomics in Anticancer Drug Development & Clinical Response. 2008. (Cancer Drug Discovery & Development Ser.). (Illus.). 730p. 189.00 *(978-1-58829-646-7(6))* Humana Pr.
Jackman, Ann L. & Leamon, Christopher P., eds. Targeted Drug Strategies for Cancer & Inflammation. 2011. (ENG., Illus.). xi, 221p. 189.00 *(978-1-4419-8416-6(X),* 144198416X) Springer.
Jacobsen, Ramune. Barriers to Cancer Pain Management with Opioids. 2010. 100p. pap. *(978-3-8383-5890-1(2))* Lambert Academic Publishing.
Jaroszeski, Mark J., ed. Electrochemotherapy, Electrogenetherapy, & Transdermal Drug Delivery: Electrically Mediated Delivery of Molecules to Cells. 2010. (Methods in Molecular Medicine Ser.). (Illus.). 512p. pap. 143.00 *(978-1-61737-094-6(0),* 1617370940) Humana Pr.
Jellinek, John. Dolores at Fort Hood, Tijuana & Detroit. 2010. 344p. pap. 32.95 *(978-1-4502-4929-4(9))* iUniverse, Inc.
Jordan, V. Craig & Furr, B. J. A., eds. Hormone Therapy in Breast & Prostate Cancer. 2009. (Cancer Drug Discovery & Development Ser.). (ENG., Illus.). xv, 420p. pap. 59.95 *(978-1-60761-471-5(5),* 1607614715) Humana Pr.
Kakar, Manish. Intelligent & Adaptive Systems in Cancer Biomedicine. 2010. 116p. pap. *(978-3-8383-6923-5(8))* Lambert Academic Publishing.
Kaufman, Howard L., et al, eds. Molecular Targeting in Oncology. 2010. (Cancer Drug Discovery & Development Ser.). (Illus.). xvi, 734p. pap. 229.00 *(978-1-61737-653-5(1),* 1617376531) Humana Pr.
Kelland, Lloyd R. & Farrell, Nicholas P., eds. Platinum-Based Drugs in Cancer Therapy. 2010. (Cancer Drug Discovery & Development Ser.). (Illus.). 360p. pap. 160.00 *(978-1-61737-091-5(6),* 1617370916) Humana Pr.
Kelley, Mark R., ed. DNA Repair in Cancer Therapy: Molecular Targets & Clinical Applications. 2011. (ENG.). 330p. 129.95 ***(978-0-12-384999-1(3),*** Academic Pr.) Elsevier Science & Technology Bks.
Kelloff, Gary J., et al, eds. Cancer Chemoprevention: Volume 1: Promising Cancer Chemopreventive Agents. 2010. (Cancer Drug Discovery & Development

C

Ser.). (Illus.). xxxv, 680p. pap. 239.00 *(978-1-61737-342-8(7)*, 1617373427) Humana Pr.

Kelly-Lopez, Catherine. The Cancer Emails - Running Raw in the Wild. 2008. 296p. pap. *(978-3-639-04777-6(X))* VDM Verlag Dr. Mueller e.K.

Khanna, Kum Kum & Shiloh, Yosef, eds. The DNA Damage Response: Implications on Cancer Formation & Treatment: Implications on Cancer Formation & Treatment. 2009. (ENG., Illus.). xii, 449p. 189.00 *(978-90-481-2560-9(X)*, 904812560X) Springer.

Knasmüller, Siegfried. Chemoprevention of Cancer & DNA Damage by Dietary Factors. DeMarini, David M. et al, eds. 2009. (ENG., Illus.). 838p. 275.00 *(978-3-527-32058-5(X)*, Wiley-VCH) Wiley, John & Sons, Inc.

Kratz, Felix, et al, eds. Drug Delivery in Oncology: From Basic Research to Cancer Therapy, 3 vols. 2011. (ENG., Illus.). 1822p. 540.00 ***(978-3-527-32823-9(8)***, Wiley-VCH) Wiley, John & Sons, Inc.

Krohn, Karsten, ed. Anthracycline Chemistry & Biology II: Mode of Action, Clinical Aspects & New Drugs. 2008. (Topics in Current Chemistry Ser.). (Illus.). 223p. 269.00 *(978-3-540-75812-9(7))* Springer.

La Thangue, Nicholas B. & Bandara, Lasantha R., eds. Targets for Cancer Chemotherapy. 2010. (Cancer Drug Discovery & Development Ser.). (Illus.). 360p. pap. 199.00 *(978-1-61737-263-6(3)*, 1617372633) Humana Pr.

Lexi-Comp, creator. Drug Information Handbook for Oncology: A Complete Guide to Combination Chemotherapy Regimens. 8th ed. 2010. (Lexi-Comp's Drug Reference Handbooks Ser.). 1560p. pap. 46.95 *(978-1-59195-277-0(8))* Lexi-Comp, Inc.

Leyland-Jones, Brian, ed. Pharmacogenetics of Breast Cancer: Towards the Individualization of Therapy. 2008. (Translational Medicine Ser.: Vol. 7). (ENG., Illus.). 352p. 200.00 *(978-1-4200-5293-0(4)*, Informa Healthcare) Taylor & Francis Group GBR. Dist: Taylor & Francis Group.

Lyman, Gary H. & Dale, David C., eds. Hematopoietic Growth Factors in Oncology. 2010. (Cancer Treatment & Research Ser.). (Illus.). xv, 433p. 219.00 *(978-1-4419-7072-5(X)*, 144197072X) Springer.

Mahato, Ram I. & Lu, Yi, eds. Pharmaceutical Perspectives of Cancer Therapeutics. 2009. (ENG., Illus.). vi, 596p. 240.00 *(978-1-4419-0130-9(2)*, 1441901302) Springer.

Matray-Devoti, Judith. Cancer Drugs. Triggle, David J., ed. 2006. (Drugs Ser.). (Illus.). 136p. (YA). (gr. 9-12). 30.00 *(978-0-7910-8554-7(6))* Facts On File, Inc.

McKay, Judith & Schacher, Tammy. The Chemotherapy Survival Guide: Everything You Need to Know to Get Through Treatment. 3rd rev. ed. 2009. (ENG.). 280p. pap. 18.95 *(978-1-57224-621-8(9))* New Harbinger Pubns.

Meyer, Tim, ed. Vascular Disruptive Agents for the Treatment of Cancer. 2010. (ENG., Illus.). x, 258p. 189.00 *(978-1-4419-6608-7(0)*, 1441966080) Springer.

Miller, Tani. Chemo & Me: My Hair Loss Experience. 2009. (ENG., Illus.). 48p. 11.95 *(978-1-60443-009-7(5)*, 1604430095) American Cancer Society, Inc.

Missailidis, Sotiris. Anticancer Therapeutics. 2008. (ENG., Illus.). 424p. 188.95 *(978-0-470-72303-6(3)*, Wiley) Wiley, John & Sons, Inc.

M.O., Viji. & K .K. Nair, C. Nanotechnology. 2011. 48p. pap. ***(978-3-8443-1478-6(4))*** Lambert Academic Publishing.

Molenaar, Miranda. Role of Tcf in Body Axis Formation. 2010. 80p. pap. *(978-3-8383-2052-6(2))* Lambert Academic Publishing.

Morrison, Sharon. Even the Eyebrows? 2009. 164p. pap. 13.49 *(978-1-4389-2334-5(1))* AuthorHouse.

Naqvi, Syed Ali Raza, et al. Radiolabelled Compounds for Diagnosis & Therapy. 2010. 204p. pap. *(978-3-639-25892-9(4))* VDM Verlag Dr. Mueller e.K.

Nilon, Cathy. Chemo Cat. 2007. 56p. (J). pap. 9.95 *(978-0-9791921-4-2(5))* Ravenna Pr.

Nowrousian, Mohammad R., ed. Recombinant Human Erythropoietin (rhEPO) in Clinical Oncology: Scientific & Clinical Aspects of Anemia in Cancer. 2nd ed. 2007. (Illus.). 400p. 159.00 *(978-3-211-25223-9(1)*, 3211252231) Springer.

Pagé, Michel, ed. Tumor Targeting in Cancer Therapy. 2010. (Cancer Drug Discovery & Development Ser.). (Illus.). 466p. pap. 179.00 *(978-1-61737-251-3(X)*, 161737251X) Humana Pr.

Panasci, Lawrence C. & Alaoui-Jamali, Moulay A., eds. DNA Repair in Cancer Therapy. 2010. (Cancer Drug Discovery & Development Ser.). (Illus.). xi, 362p. pap. 169.00 *(978-1-61737-480-7(6)*, 1617374806) Humana Pr.

Perry, Michael C., ed. The Chemotherapy Source Book. 4th rev. ed. 2007. (ENG., Illus.). 800p. pap. 99.95 *(978-0-7817-7328-7(8))* Lippincott Williams & Wilkins.

Peters, Godefridus J., ed. Deoxynucleoside Analogs in Cancer Therapy. 2010. (Cancer Drug Discovery & Development Ser.). (Illus.). 496p. pap. 209.00 *(978-1-61737-497-5(0)*, 1617374970) Humana Pr.

Peters, Godefridus Johannes. Deoxynucleoside Analogs in Cancer Therapy. 2006. (Cancer Drug Discovery & Development Ser.). (Illus.). 476p. 209.00 *(978-1-58829-327-5(0)*, 1588293270) Humana Pr.

Peterson, Diolinda. My Village: A Young Family's Story of Cancer, Love, & Gratitude. 2010. pap. 17.99 *(978-1-61663-389-9(1))* Tate Publishing & Enterprises, LLC.

Phillips, Pamela. Tie One On. 2011. 66p. 40.99 ***(978-1-61379-493-7(2))***; 58p. pap. 29.99 ***(978-1-61379-492-0(4))*** Xulon Pr., Inc.

Pinedo, Herbert M. & Giaccone, Giuseppe. Drug Resistance in the Treatment of Cancer. 2007. (Cancer: Clinical Science in Practice Ser.). (ENG.). 340p. pap. 76.00 *(978-0-521-03074-8(9))* Cambridge Univ. Pr.

Polunovsky, Vitaly & Houghton, Peter J. MTOR Pathway & mTOR Inhibitors in Cancer Therapy. 2010. (Cancer Drug Discovery & Development Ser.). (ENG., Illus.). 235p. 239.00 *(978-1-60327-270-4(4))* Humana Pr.

Pommier, Yves, ed. DNA Topoisomerases & Cancer. 2011. (Cancer Drug Discovery & Development Ser.). (ENG., Illus.). xi, 443p. 209.00 *(978-1-4614-0322-7(7)*, 1461403227) Springer.

Prescher-Hughes, Debra S. Nurse's Chemotherapy Quick Pocket Reference. 2008. (ENG.). 208p. pap. 41.95 *(978-0-7637-5824-0(8))* Jones & Bartlett Learning, LLC.

Radisky, Derek C. & Storz, Peter, eds. Reactive Oxygen Species in Cancer Therapy. 2009. (Cancer Drug Discovery & Development Ser.). (ENG.). 300p. 165.00 *(978-1-60327-006-9(X))* Humana Pr.

Raffa, Robert B. & Tallarida, Ronald J., eds. Chemo Fog: Cancer Chemotherapy-Related Cognitive Impairment. 2010. (Advances in Experimental Medicine & Biology Ser.). (ENG., Illus.). xx, 212p. 219.00 *(978-1-4419-6305-5(7)*, 1441963057) Springer.

Rhomberg, Walter & Hellmann, Kurt, eds. Razoxane & Dexrazoxane - Two Multifunctional Agents: Experimental & Clinical Results. 2010. (ENG., Illus.). xiii, 243p. 189.00 *(978-90-481-9167-3(X)*, 904819167X) Springer.

Rubietta, Linda & Rubietta, Tracy. The Chemo Zone: Your Guide to Living & Flourishing During Chemotherapy. 2011. 288p. pap. 24.95 ***(978-1-59298-414-5(2))*** Beaver's Pond Pr., Inc.

Rustum, Youcef M., ed. Fluoropyrimidines in Cancer Therapy. 2010. (Cancer Drug Discovery & Development Ser.). (Illus.). 336p. pap. 199.00 *(978-1-61737-274-2(9)*, 1617372749) Humana Pr.

Sakamoto, Kathleen & Rubin, Eric, eds. Modulation of Protein Stability in Cancer Therapy. (ENG., Illus.). x, 165p. 2010. pap. 129.00 ***(978-1-4419-2401-8(9)***, 1441924019) 2009. 129.00 *(978-0-387-69143-5(X)*, 038769143X) Springer.

Satchi-Fainaro, Ronit & Duncan, Ruth. Polymer Therapeutics II: Polymers as Drugs, Conjugates & Gene Delivery Sytems. 2010. (Advances in Polymer Science Ser.). x, 228p. pap. 279.00 *(978-3-642-06719-8(0)*, 3642067190) Springer.

Schlag, Peter M. & Stein, Ulrike, eds. Regional Cancer Therapy. 2007. (Cancer Drug Discovery & Development Ser.). (Illus.). 455p. 219.00 *(978-1-58829-672-6(5)*, 1588296725) Humana Pr.

Schlag, Peter M. & Stein, Ulrike S., eds. Regional Cancer Therapy. 2010. (Cancer Drug Discovery & Development Ser.). (Illus.). xiv, 462p. pap. 219.00 *(978-1-61737-711-2(2)*, 1617377112) Humana Pr.

Sethuraman, Vijay. Sulfonamide Based Polymeric Systems for Cancer Tumors. 2009. 164p. pap. *(978-3-639-13620-3(9))* VDM Verlag Dr. Mueller e.K.

Shailender, Kanwar. Nsaids As Promising Cancer Chemopreventive Agents: Role of Certain Non Steroidal Anti-Inflammatory Drugs in the Chemoprevention of 1,2-Dimethyl Hydrazine Induced Colon Cancer in Rat Model. 2011. 216p. pap. ***(978-3-639-27403-5(2))*** VDM Verlag Dr. Mueller e.K.

Silverman, Dan & Davidson, Idelle. Your Brain after Chemo: A Practical Guide to Lifting the Fog & Getting Back Your Focus. 2010. (ENG., Illus.). 304p. pap. 16.95 *(978-0-7382-1391-0(8))* Da Capo Pr., Inc.

Simpson, Wallis A. & Smith, Cara Blakley. I Choose to Laugh: Faith in the Midst of Cancer. 2007. 140p. per. 13.95 *(978-0-595-46623-8(0))* iUniverse, Inc.

Skeel, Roland T. & Khleif, Samir. Handbook of Cancer Chemotherapy. 8th rev. ed. 2011. (Lippincott Williams & Wilkins Handbook Ser.). (ENG., Illus.). 832p. pap. 79.99 *(978-1-60831-782-0(X))* Lippincott Williams & Wilkins.

Solimando, Dominic & Waddell, J. Aubrey. Guide to Combination Cancer Chemotherapy Regimens. 2011. 541p. pap. 84.00 net. ***(978-0-615-50763-7(8))*** Thomas Land Pubs., Inc.

Solimando, Dominic A., ed. Drug Information Handbook for Oncology: A Complete Guide to Combination Chemotherapy Regimens. 6th rev. ed. 2007. (Lexi-Comp's Drug Reference Handbooks Ser.). 1335p. per. 42.95 *(978-1-59195-175-9(5))* Lexi-Comp, Inc.

Sullivan, Janet B. & Scotte, Bradley L. Cancer Prevention Research Perspectives. 2011. (Series: Cancer Etiology, Diagnosis & Treatments Ser.). 227p. 89.00 *(978-1-61209-380-2(9))* Nova Science Pubs., Inc.

Teicher, Beverly A., et al, eds. In Vivo Imaging of Cancer Therapy. 2007. (Cancer Drug Discovery & Development Ser.). 494p. 229.00 *(978-1-58829-633-7(4)*, 1588296334) Humana Pr.

Teicher, Beverly A. & Ellis, Lee M., eds. Antiangiogenic Agents in Cancer Therapy. 2nd ed. 2007. (Cancer Drug Discovery & Development (Unnumbered) Ser.). (Illus.). 559p. 199.00 *(978-1-58829-870-6(1))* Humana Pr.

Verdin, Eric, ed. Histone Deacetylases: Transcriptional Regulation & Other Cellular Functions. 2010. (Cancer Drug Discovery & Development Ser.). (Illus.). 352p. pap. 219.00 *(978-1-61737-602-3(7)*, 1617376027) Humana Pr.

Vereecken, Pierre & Awada, Ahmad. Handbook of Skin Care in Cancer Patients. 2012. (Cancer Etiology, Diagnosis & Treatments Ser.). 217p. 59.00 *(978-1-61668-419-8(4))* Nova Science Pubs., Inc.

Vezeau, Sheila. Cancer in the Words of a Child. 2011. 40p. pap. 16.95 ***(978-1-4626-1133-1(8))*** PublishAmerica, Inc.

Viglianti, Benjamin. Chemodosimetry of Invivo Tumor Liposome/Drug Concentration Using Mri. 2010. 220p. pap. *(978-3-639-15540-2(8))* VDM Verlag Dr. Mueller e.K.

Wilkes, Gail & Barton-Burke, Margaret. 2010 Oncology Nursing Drug Handbook. 14th rev. ed. 2009. 1360p. pap. 102.95 *(978-0-7637-8124-8(X))* Jones & Bartlett Learning, LLC.

—2011 Oncology Nursing Drug Handbook. 15th ed. 2010. (Illus.). 1368p. pap. 96.95 *(978-1-4496-0013-6(1))* Jones & Bartlett Learning, LLC.

Wilkes, Gail M. & Barton-Burke, Margaret. Oncology Nursing Drug Handbook. 2006. (Oncology Nursing Drug Handbook Ser.). 1217p. per. 93.95 *(978-0-7637-4306-2(2))* Jones & Bartlett Learning, LLC.

—2008 Oncology Nursing Drug Handbook. 2007. 1220p. pap. 88.95 *(978-0-7637-5563-8(X))* Jones & Bartlett Learning, LLC.

Wilkes, Gail M. & Burke, Margaret Barton. 2012 Oncology Nursing Drug Handbook. 16th ed. 2011. 1418p. pap. 93.95 ***(978-1-4496-4462-8(7))*** Jones & Bartlett Learning, LLC.

Yu, Dihua & Hung, Mien-Chie, eds. Breast Cancer Chemosensitivity. (Advances in Experimental Medicine & Biology Ser.). 2010. xiii, 175p. pap. 189.00 *(978-1-4419-2542-8(2)*, 1441925422) 2007. 190p. 189.00 *(978-0-387-74037-9(6))* Springer.

Zhou, Jun, ed. Multi-Drug Resistance in Cancer. 2009. (Methods in Molecular Biology Ser.). (ENG., Illus.). 504p. 129.00 *(978-1-60761-415-9(4)*, 1607614154) Humana Pr.

Zielinski, Christoph C., et al. Drugs for HER2-positive Breast Cancer. 2010. (Milestones in Drug Therapy Ser.). (Illus.). 250p. 139.00 *(978-3-0346-0093-4(3)*, 3034600933) Birkhauser Verlag AG CHE. Dist: Springer.

CANCER—COMPLICATIONS

see also Cancer Pain

Anker, Stefan, et al, eds. Cachexia & Wasting: A Modern Approach. 2006. (Illus.). xxii, 756p. 339.00 *(978-88-470-0471-9(3)*, 8847004713) Springer.

Aronson, Jeffrey K., ed. Side Effects of Drugs in Cancer & Immunology. 2010. (ENG.). 780p. 67.95 *(978-0-444-53267-1(6)*, Elsevier Science) Elsevier Science & Technology Bks.

Cohen, Eric P. Cancer & the Kidney. 2nd ed. 2010. (ENG., Illus.). 362p. 89.50 *(978-0-19-958019-4(7))* Oxford Univ. Pr., Inc.

Crocker. Betty Crocker's Living with Cancer Cookbook Custom Mgi. 2007. (ENG.). 256p. 24.95 *(978-0-470-18952-8(5)*, Betty Crocker) Wiley, John & Sons, Inc.

Daya, Mohamud & Spiro, David M. Cancer Emergencies Pt. 2: Emergency Medicine Clinics, 2 vols. 2009. (Clinics: Internal Medicine Ser.: 27-3). (ENG., Illus.). 99.00 *(978-1-4377-1211-7(8)*, Saunders) Elsevier - Health Sciences Div.

DeAngelis, Lisa M. & Posner, Jerome B. Neurologic Complications of Cancer. 2nd ed. 2008. (Contemporary Neurology Ser.: Vol. 73). (ENG., Illus.). 656p. 135.00 *(978-0-19-536674-7(3))* Oxford Univ. Pr., Inc.

Donnez, Jacques & Kim, S. Samuel, eds. Principles & Practice of Fertility Preservation. 2011. (Illus.). 536p. 155.00 *(978-0-521-19695-6(7))* Cambridge Univ. Pr.

Ehrlich, Ann B. & McMahon, Elizabeth J., eds. Voices of Lymphedema: Stories, advice, & inspiration from patients & Therapists. 2007. 256p. per. *(978-0-9764806-5-5(4))* Lymph Notes.

Freifeld, Alison. Fever & Neutropenia: In Cancer Patients. 2011. 14p. spiral bd. 11.95 *(978-0-9846290-8-4(4))* International Guidelines Ctr., Inc.

Green, David & Kwaan, Hau C., eds. Coagulation in Cancer. 2009. (Cancer Treatment & Research Ser.). (ENG., Illus.). x, 310p. 169.00 *(978-0-387-79961-2(3))* Springer.

Hou, Mi. Preservation of Fertility in Boys with Cancer. 2010. 76p. pap. *(978-3-639-23827-3(3))* VDM Verlag Dr. Mueller e.K.

Integrative Strategies for Cancer Patients: A Practical Resource for Managing the Side Effects of Cancer Therapy. 2011. pap. 39.00 *(978-981-4313-23-0(8))* World Scientific Publishing Co., Inc.

Jung, Karen. Healthier Eating: & Living with Cancer. 2008. (ENG., Illus.). 304p. pap. *(978-1-894694-57-5(0))* Granville Island Publishing.

Kaplan, Marcelle, ed. Understanding & Managing Oncologic Emergencies: A Resource for Nurses. 2006. (Illus.). 327p. per. 70.00 *(978-1-890504-62-5(9))* Oncology Nursing Society.

Katz, Anne. Breaking the Silence on Cancer & Sexuality: A Handbook for Healthcare Providers. 2007. (Illus.). 280p. per. 70.00 *(978-1-890504-67-0(X))* Oncology Nursing Society.

—Woman Cancer Sex. 2009. (Illus.). 170p. pap. 14.95 *(978-1-890504-80-9(7))* Oncology Nursing Society.

Khorana, Alok A. & Francis, Charles W., eds. Cancer-Associated Thrombosis: New Findings in Translational Science, Prevention, & Treatment. 2007. (ENG., Illus.). 296p. pap. 110.00 *(978-1-4200-7704-9(X)*, Informa Healthcare) Taylor & Francis Group GBR. Dist: Taylor & Francis Group.

Malkin, Mark G. & Newton, Herbert B., eds. Neurological Complications of Systemic Cancer. 2009. (Illus.). 400p. 249.95 *(978-0-8493-9191-0(1)*, Informa Healthcare) Taylor & Francis Group GBR. Dist: Taylor & Francis Group.

Marinella, Mark A. Handbook of Cancer Emergencies. 2009. 413p. pap. 86.95 *(978-0-7637-6989-5(4))* Jones & Bartlett Learning, LLC.

Marr, Kieren A. & Subramanian, Aruna K. Infections in Transplant & Oncology Patients, an Issue of Infectious Disease Clinics. 2010. (Clinics: Internal Medicine Ser.: 24-2). (ENG., Illus.). xv, 258p. 105.00 *(978-1-4377-1831-7(0)*, Saunders) Elsevier - Health Sciences Div.

Meyers, Christina A. & Perry, James R., eds. Cognition & Cancer. 2008. (ENG., Illus.). 353p. 130.00 *(978-0-521-85482-5(2))* Cambridge Univ. Pr.

Mulhall, John P., ed. Fertility Preservation in the Man with Cancer. 2012. (ENG., Illus.). 392p. 165.00 ***(978-1-107-01212-7(0))*** Cambridge Univ. Pr.

Noble, Simon I. R., et al, eds. Venous Thromboembolism in Advanced Disease: A clinical Guide. 2009. (ENG., Illus.). 192p. pap. 59.95 *(978-0-19-923204-8(0))* Oxford Univ. Pr., Inc.

Nowrousian, Mohammad R., ed. Recombinant Human Erythropoietin (rhEPO) in Clinical Oncology: Scientific & Clinical Aspects of Anemia in Cancer. 2nd ed. 2007. (Illus.). 400p. 159.00 *(978-3-211-25223-9(1)*, 3211252231) Springer.

Olver, Ian N., ed. A Textbook of Cancer Supportive Care & Survivorship. 2010. (ENG., Illus.). 420p. 179.00 *(978-1-4419-1224-4(X)*, 144191224X) Springer.

Pastores, Stephen & Halpern, Neil A. Intensive Care of the Cancer Patient, an Issue of Critical Care Clinics. 2009. (Clinics: Internal Medicine Ser.: 26-1). (ENG., Illus.). xiv, 237p. 105.00 *(978-1-4377-1806-5(X)*, Saunders) Elsevier - Health Sciences Div.

Pravinkumar, S. Egbert, et al, eds. Critical Care for Cancer Patients. 2011. (ENG., Illus.). 450p. 99.00 *(978-1-4419-0281-8(3)*, 1441902813) Springer.

Quinn, Gwendolyn P. & Vadaparampil, Susan T., eds. Reproductive Health & Cancer in Adolescents & Young Adults. 2012. (Advances in Experimental Medicine & Biology Ser.). (ENG., Illus.). xv, 220p. 209.00 ***(978-94-007-2491-4(8)***, 9400724918) Springer.

Rubietta, Linda & Rubietta, Tracy. The Chemo Zone: Your Guide to Living & Flourishing During Chemotherapy. 2011. 288p. pap. 24.95 ***(978-1-59298-414-5(2))*** Beaver's Pond Pr., Inc.

Rubin, P. Alert Adverse Late Effects of Cancer Treatment. 2009. (Medical Radiology / Radiation Oncology Ser.). (ENG., Illus.). 410p. 329.00 *(978-3-540-72313-4(7))* Springer.

Rubin, Philip. Alert - Adverse Late Effects of Cancer Treatment. 2009. (Medical Radiology / Radiation Oncology Ser.). (ENG., Illus.). 410p. 329.00 *(978-3-540-75862-4(3))* Springer.

—ALERT - Adverse Late Effects of Cancer Treatment, 2 vols. 2009. (Medical Radiology / Radiation Oncology Ser.). (Illus.). 810p. 449.00 *(978-3-540-76703-9(7))* Springer.

Rubin, Philip, et al. CURED I - LENT Late Effects of Cancer Treatment on Normal Tissues. 2010. (Medical Radiology / Radiation Oncology Ser.). (Illus.). xxii, 144p. pap. 129.00 *(978-3-642-08032-6(4)*, 3642080324) Springer.

—Cured II - LENT Cancer Survivorship Research & Education: Late Effects on Normal Tissues. 2010. (Medical Radiology / Radiation Oncology Ser.). (Illus.). xii, 180p. pap. 109.00 *(978-3-642-09510-8(0)*, 3642095100) Springer.

Rubin, Philip. Cured Ii - Lentcancer Survivorship Research & Education. 2008. (Medical Radiology / Radiation Oncology Ser.). (Illus.). 160p. 109.00 *(978-3-540-76270-6(1)*, 3540762701) Springer.

Safdar, Amar, ed. Management of Infections in Cancer Patients. 2010. (Current Clinical Oncology Ser.). (Illus.). 350p. 239.00 *(978-1-60761-643-6(2)*, 1607616432) Humana Pr.

Schiff, David. Cancer Neurology in Clinical Practice; Neurologic Complications of Cancer & Its Treatment. 2008. 660p. pap. 99.00 *(978-1-60327-512-5(6))* Springer.

Schiff, David, et al, eds. Cancer Neurology in Clinical Practice. 2nd ed. 2008. (Illus.). 513p. 189.00 *(978-1-58829-983-3(X)*, 158829983X) Springer.

Scott-Brown, Martin, et al, eds. Emergencies in Oncology. 2007. (Emergencies in Ser.). (Illus.). 366p. pap. 42.95 *(978-0-19-921563-8(4))* Oxford Univ. Pr., Inc.

Shaw, Gina M. Having Children after Cancer: How to Make Informed Choices Before & after Treatment & Build the Family of Your Dreams. 2011. (ENG., Illus.). 224p. pap. 16.99 *(978-1-58761-054-7(X)*, Celestial Arts) Ten Speed Pr.

Woodruff, Teresa K., et al, eds. Oncofertility: Ethical, Legal, Social, & Medical Perspectives. 2010. (Cancer Treatment & Research Ser.). (Illus.). xvii, 519p. 279.00 *(978-1-4419-6517-2(3)*, 1441965173) Springer.

CANCER—DIAGNOSIS

see also Pap Test

ABBE Scientist Research Division Staff. Analysis of Food Cont aining Cancer-Causing Substances with Index & Medical Analysis of New Clinical & Research Information for All Nations. 2008. (Illus.). 160p. 69.95 *(978-0-7883-4826-6(4))* ABBE Pubs. Assn. of Washington, D.C.

Alemdaroglu, Fikri Emrah. Dna Block Copolymers - Synthesis, Morphologies, & Applications. 2008. 216p. pap. *(978-3-639-03721-0(9))* VDM Verlag Dr. Mueller e.K.

Ali, Amjed & Muhammad Shahid. Diagnosis of Cancer. 2011. 124p. pap. ***(978-3-8443-2372-6(4))*** Lambert Academic Publishing.

American Cancer Society Staff. Breast Cancer: The Essential Guide to Your Breast Cancery Journey. 3rd ed. 2009. (ENG.). 400p. pap., instr.'s gde. ed. 24.95 *(978-0-944235-90-4(5)*, 0944235905) American Cancer Society, Inc.

Aziz, Khalid & Wu, George Y., eds. Cancer Screening. 2010. (Current Clinical Practice Ser.). (Illus.). 344p. pap. 119.00 *(978-1-61737-229-2(3)*, 1617372293) Humana Pr.

Bard, Robert L. Prostate Cancer Decoded: Non-Invasive Breakthrough Treatments. 2007. (ENG., Illus.). 168p. per. 17.95 *(978-1-60037-346-6(1))* Morgan James Publishing.

Barnhardt-Israel, Lillian Elizabeth. Friends in High Places: A Christian Guide to Fighting & Overcoming Cancer. 2011. pap. 12.99 ***(978-1-61346-442-7(8))*** Tate Publishing & Enterprises, LLC.

Berg, Wendie A. Diagnostic Imaging. 2006. (Illus.). *(978-0-8089-2380-0(3))* Harcourt Health Sciences Group.

Bick, Ulrich & Diekmann, Felix. Digital Mammography: Current Concepts. 2009. (Medical Radiology / Diagnostic Imaging Ser.). (ENG., Illus.). xvi, 220p. 319.00 *(978-3-540-78449-4(7)*, 3540784497) Springer.

Bodai, Ernie. I Flunked My PSA! What You Need to Know about Prostate Cancer Now! pap. 11.95 *(978-0-9712070-1-1(1))* B2Z Publishing, Inc.

Bologna, Mauro, ed. Biotargets of Cancer in Current Clinical Practice. 2012. (Current Clinical Pathology Ser.). (ENG., Illus.). xvi, 563p. 239.00 ***(978-1-61779-614-2(X)***, 161779614X) Humana Pr.

Bombardieri, Emilio, et al, eds. Breast Cancer: Nuclear Medicine in Diagnosis & Therapeutic Options. 2010. (Illus.). xiv, 299p. pap. 179.00 *(978-3-642-07186-7(4)*, 3642071864) Springer.

Brennecke, Cecilia M. Breast Imaging: Case Review Series. 2nd ed. 2012. (Case Review Ser.). (ENG., Illus.). 320p. pap. 49.95 ***(978-0-323-08722-3(1)***, Saunders) Elsevier - Health Sciences Div.

Brown, Gina, ed. Colorectal Cancer. 2007. (Contemporary Issues in Cancer Imaging Ser.). (ENG., Illus.). 272p. 99.00 (978-0-521-69291-5(1)) Cambridge Univ. Pr.

brown, stephen. My New Race. 2008. 48p. pap. 16.95 (978-0-557-01762-1(9)) Lulu Enterprises Inc.

Carr, Brian I. Hepatocellular Carcinoma: Diagnosis & Treatment. 2nd ed. 2009. (Current Clinical Oncology Ser.). (ENG., Illus.). xvi, 748p. 219.00 (978-1-60327-373-2(5), 1603273735) Humana Pr.

Carvalho, Lucia Giuggio & Stewart, James A. The Everything Health Guide to Living with Breast Cancer: An Accessible & Comprehensive Resource for Women. 2009. (ENG., Illus.). 304p. pap. 14.95 (978-1-59869-921-0(0)) Adams Media Corp.

Chute, Maureen. Closeness in Crisis - a Proposal for Identifying Resilience in Couples Who Face the Crisis of Cancer in Their Child. 2008. 60p. pap. (978-3-639-10653-4(9)) VDM Verlag Dr. Mueller e.K.

Cleeland, Charles S., et al, eds. Cancer Symptom Science: Measurement, Mechanisms, & Management. 2010. (ENG., Illus.). 376p. 120.00 (978-0-521-86901-0(3)) Cambridge Univ. Pr.

Committee on Developing Biomarker-Based Tools for Cancer Screening, Diagnosis, and Treatment. Cancer Biomarkers: The Promises & Challenges of Improving Detection & Treatment. Nass, Sharyl J. & Moses, Harold L., eds. 2007. (ENG., Illus.). 252p. per. 42.00 (978-0-309-10386-2(X)) National Academies Pr.

Connolly, David, et al. Prostate Specific Antigen. 2010. 272p. pap. (978-3-8383-3877-4(4)) Lambert Academic Publishing.

Cornud, Francois, ed. Clinical Imaging of the Prostate. 2011. (ENG., Illus.). 304p. pap. 99.50 (978-1-84882-096-8(8), 1848820968) Springer.

Dachman, Abraham H., ed. Atlas of Virtual Colonoscopy. 2011. (Illus.). xvi, 276p. pap. 189.00 (978-1-4419-3031-6(0), 1441930310) Springer.

Dachman, Abraham H. & Laghi, Andrea, eds. Atlas of Virtual Colonoscopy. 2nd ed. 2010. (ENG., Illus.). xx, 308p. 189.00 (978-1-4419-5851-8(7), 1441958517) Springer.

DeLong, Lisa Solis. Blood Brothers: A Memoir of Faith & Loss While Raising Two Sons with Cancer. 2011. pap. 19.99 **(978-1-61777-152-1(X))** Tate Publishing & Enterprises, LLC.

Dillon, S. K. Anaplastic Carcinom: But I am Stayin' & Prayin' cause ALL IS WELL. 2011. 66p. pap. 19.95 **(978-1-4626-3140-7(1))** PublishAmerica, Inc.

ENETS Conference for the Diagnosis & Treatment of Neuroendocrine Tumor Disease: 8th Annual Conference, Lisbon, March 2011: Abstracts. Supplement Issue: Neuroendocrinology 2011, Vol. 94, Suppl. 1 2011. (ENG.). 54p. pap. **(978-3-8055-9807-1(6))** Karger, S. AG.

Fitzgerald, Rebecca C., ed. Pre-Invasive Disease: Pathogenesis & Clinical Management: Pathogenesis & Clinical Management. 2010. (ENG., Illus.). xxii, 519p. 189.00 (978-1-4419-6693-3(5), 1441966935) Springer.

Focus Medica Pte Ltd. Colorectal Cancer: An Overview. 2011. 1p. cd-rom 99.00 (978-981-4284-13-4(0)) Focus Medica Pte Ltd. SGP. Dist: Independent Pubs. Group.

Fraim, Nalan Linda. Breast Cancer Awareness & Breast Self-Examination in Northern Cyprus. 2010. 156p. pap. (978-3-8383-5921-2(6)) Lambert Academic Publishing.

Frey, Chris. I'm Sorry, It's Cancer: A Handbook of Help & Hope for Survivors & Caregivers. 2011. 94p. pap. 12.99 **(978-1-257-00692-2(4))** Lulu Enterprises Inc.

Ganjei-Azar, Parvin, et al. Effusion Cytology: A Practical Guide toCancer Diagnosis. 2011. 192p. pap. 85.00 (978-1-933864-65-5(6)) Demos Medical Publishing, LLC.

Ganz, Patricia A., ed. Cancer Survivorship: Today & Tomorrow. 2007. (Illus.). 304p. per. 99.00 (978-0-387-34349-5(0), 0387343490) Springer.

Geschwind, Jean-François H. & Soulen, Michael C., eds. Interventional Oncology: Principles & Practice. 2008. (ENG., Illus.). 636p. 168.00 (978-0-521-86413-8(5)) Cambridge Univ. Pr.

Giordano, Antonio & Normanno, Nicola, eds. Breast Cancer in the Post-Genomic Era. 2009. (Current Clinical Oncology Ser.). (ENG., Illus.). xii, 230p. 219.00 (978-1-60327-944-4(X), 160327944X) Humana Pr.

Govorukhina, Natalia. Biomarker Discovery for Cervical Cancer: Methods & Approaches. 2008. 160p. pap. (978-3-8364-8401-5(3)) VDM Verlag Dr. Mueller e.K.

Greenspan, Adam, et al. Differential Diagnosis in Orthopaedic Oncology. 2nd rev. ed. 2006. (ENG., Illus.). 529p. 288.99 (978-0-7817-7930-2(8)) Lippincott Williams & Wilkins.

Grobmyer, Stephen R. & Moudgil, Brij M. Cancer Nanotechnology: Methods & Protocols. 2010. (Methods in Molecular Biology Ser.). (Illus.). 376p. 159.00 (978-1-60761-608-5(4), 1607616084) Humana Pr.

Guji, Makiko. The Experience of Surviving Terminal Cancer. 2010. 144p. pap. (978-3-8383-0361-1(X)) Lambert Academic Publishing.

Hall, John W. Beating Cancer Can Be Fun: Cancer Fighting Strategies for First Time Diagnosed Cancer Patients. 2011. 108p. 21.23 **(978-1-4634-0362-1(3))**; pap. 15.68 **(978-1-4634-0364-5(X))** AuthorHouse.

Hallman, David G. August Farewell: The Last Sixteen Days of a Thirty-Three-Year Romance. 2011. 180p. 26.95 (978-1-4502-8638-1(0)); pap. 16.95 (978-1-4502-8636-7(4)) iUniverse, Inc.

Hamilton, William & Peters, Tim J., eds. Cancer Diagnosis in Primary Care. 2007. (ENG., Illus.). 208p. pap. 46.95 (978-0-443-10367-4(4), Churchill Livingstone) Elsevier - Health Sciences Div.

Hayat, M. A., ed. Methods of Cancer Diagnosis, Therapy, & Prognosis: Brain Cancer. 2010. (Methods of Cancer Diagnosis, Therapy & Prognosis Ser.). (Illus.). 590p. 239.00 (978-90-481-8664-8(1), 9048186641) Springer.

—Methods of Cancer Diagnosis, Therapy, & Prognosis: Ovarian Cancer, Renal Cancer, Urogenitary tract Cancer, Urinary Bladder Cancer, Cervical Uterine Cancer, Skin Cancer, Leukemia, Multiple Myeloma & Sarcoma. 2009. (Methods of Cancer Diagnosis, Therapy & Prognosis Ser.). (ENG., Illus.). xlvi, 482p. 319.00 (978-90-481-2917-1(6), 9048129176) Springer.

Herold, Keith E. & Rasooly, Avraham, eds. Biosensors for Cancer Diagnostics. 2012. (Series in Sensors Ser.). (ENG., Illus.). 844p. 169.95 (978-1-4398-4165-5(9), Taylor & Francis) Taylor & Francis Group GBR. Dist: Taylor & Francis Group.

Hitchcock, Sandra. The Impact of Cancer. 2011. 92p. pap. **(978-3-8433-8873-3(3))** Lambert Academic Publishing.

Hong, Waun Ki, et al. Holland-Frei Cancer Medicine 8. 8th ed. 2009. (Illus.). 2300p. (978-1-60795-014-1(6)) PMPH-USA. Ltd.

Iland, Harry, et al, eds. Myeloid Leukemia: Methods & Protocols. 2009. (Methods in Molecular Medicine Ser.). 320p. pap. 99.95 (978-1-60761-456-2(1)) Humana Pr.

Imai, K. & Itoh, F., eds. Development of New Molecular Tumor Markers for Diagnosis & Therapy: 36th Meeting of the International Society of Oncology & BioMarkers, ISOBM 2008, Tokyo, October 2008: Abstracts. 2008. 100p. pap. (978-3-8055-8997-0(2)) Karger, S. AG.

Inoue, Tomio. Cancer Staging Diagnosis with PET/CT. Tateishi, Ukihide, ed. 2012. (ENG., Illus.). x, 365p. 219.00 (978-1-4614-0033-2(3), 1461400333) Springer.

Isharwal, Sudhir & Wang, Zhou, eds. Prostate Specific Antigen & Prostate Cancer. 2011. (Cancer Etiology, Diagnosis & Treatments Ser.). pap. 43.00 (978-1-61209-336-4(3), Nova Biomedical Bks.) Nova Science Pubs., Inc.

J. Patrick Daugherty & Edie Hand. Cancer: The Unexpected Gift. 2010. 200p. pap. 16.95 (978-1-4401-8767-4(3)) iUniverse, Inc.

Jackson, Alan, et al. Dynamic Contrast-Enhanced Magnetic Resonance Imaging in Oncology. 2010. (Medical Radiology / Diagnostic Imaging Ser.). (Illus.). xii, 311p. pap. 279.00 (978-3-642-07607-7(6), 3642076076) Springer.

Jacobs, Lisa & Finlayson, Christina. Breast Cancer. 2010. (Early Diagnosis in Cancer Ser.). (ENG., Illus.). 408p. 152.00 (978-1-4160-4932-6(0), Saunders) Elsevier - Health Sciences Div.

Jones, Daniel, ed. Neoplastic Hematopathology: Experimental & Clinical Approaches. 2010. (Contemporary Hematology Ser.). (ENG., Illus.). xiii, 622p. 279.00 (978-1-60761-383-1(2), 1607613832) Humana Pr.

Juraskova, Ilona. Quality of Life / Quality of Sex. 2009. 276p. pap. (978-3-639-04407-2(X)) VDM Verlag Dr. Mueller e.K.

Kah, James C. Y. Gold Nanomaterials. 2011. 252p. pap. **(978-3-8454-0630-5(5))** Lambert Academic Publishing.

Kahán, Zsuzsanna & Tot, Tibor, eds. Breast Cancer, a Heterogeneous Disease Entity: The Very Early Stages. 2011. (ENG.). x, 313p. 209.00 (978-94-007-0488-6(7), 9400704887) Springer.

Knudsen, Steen. Cancer Diagnostics with DNA Microarrays. 2006. (ENG., Illus.). 193p. 178.95 (978-0-471-78407-4(9), Wiley-Liss) Wiley, John & Sons, Inc.

Koch, Wayne. Head & Neck Cancers. 2009. (Early Diagnosis in Cancer Ser.). (ENG., Illus.). 200p. 152.00 (978-1-4160-5202-9(X), Saunders) Elsevier - Health Sciences Div.

Kristoff, Helen C. Cancer Biomarkers. 2010. (Cancer Etiology, Diagnosis & Treatments Ser.). 129.00 (978-1-61761-302-9(9), Nova Biomedical Bks.) Nova Science Pubs., Inc.

Kroon, Rita. You Have Cancer: A Journey Through the Valley of the Shadow of Death. 2011. (ENG.). 107p. pap. 12.95 **(978-1-4327-7789-0(0))** Outskirts Pr., Inc.

Kumar, Challa S. S. R., ed. Nanomaterials for Cancer Diagnosis. 2007. (Nanotechnologies for the Life Sciences Ser.: 5). (ENG., Illus.). 448p. 235.00 (978-3-527-31387-7(7), Wiley-VCH) Wiley, John & Sons, Inc.

Kwabi-Addo, Bernard & Lindstrom, Tia Laura. Cancer Causes & Controversies: Understanding Risk Reduction & Prevention, 1 vol. 241p. 44.95 (978-0-313-37928-4(9), C37928, Praeger Pubs.) Greenwood Publishing Group, Inc.

Laghi, Andrea. New Concepts in Diagnosis & Therapy of Pancreatic Adenocarcinoma. 2010. (Medical Radiology / Diagnostic Imaging Ser.). (ENG., Illus.). x, 178p. 239.00 (978-3-540-85380-0(4), 3540853804) Springer.

Lai, Maode. Intraepithelial Neoplasia. 2009. (ENG., Illus.). 420p. 279.00 (978-3-540-85452-4(5), 3540854525) Springer.

Lenz, Heinz-Josef, ed. Biomarkers in Oncology: Prediction & Prognosis. 2012. (ENG., Illus.). xxii, 491p. 209.00 (978-1-4419-9754-8(7), 1441997547) Springer.

Leong, Anthony S-Y. Quantitative Immunohistology: Problems & Solutions. Leong, Trishe Y-M, ed. 2010. (Immunology & Immune System Disorders Ser.). (Illus.). 70p. pap. 43.00 (978-1-61668-261-3(2)) Nova Science Pubs., Inc.

Lester, Susan C. & Hicks, David G. Breast. 2011. (ENG., Illus.). 500p. 299.00 (978-1-931884-57-0(9)) Lippincott Williams & Wilkins.

Li, Shaoguang & Li, Dongguang. Dna Microarray Technology & Data Analysis in Cancer Research. 2009. 140p. 81.00 (978-981-279-045-3(4)) World Scientific Publishing Co., Inc.

Liu, Steven P., ed. Precancerous Conditions Research Trends. 2007. 129.00 (978-1-60021-551-3(3)) Nova Science Pubs., Inc.

Lyman, Gary H. Oxford American Mini-Handbook of Gastrointestinal Cancers. 2011. (ENG.). 96p. pap. 18.95 (978-0-19-539319-4(8)) Oxford Univ. Pr., Inc.

—Oxford American Mini-handbook of Genitourinary Cancers, 1 vol. 2011. (Oxford American Mini Handbooks Ser.). (ENG.). 128p. pap. 18.95 (978-0-19-539320-0(1)) Oxford Univ. Pr., Inc.

Lyons, Lyman. Diagnosis & Treatment of Cancer. 2007. (Biology of Cancer Ser.). (Illus.). 152p. (C). (gr. 9). lib. bdg. 35.00 (978-0-7910-8826-5(X), Chelsea Hse.) Facts On File, Inc.

Maldonado, Jonathon G. & Cervantes, Mikayla K. Small Cell Carcinomas: Causes, Diagnosis & Treatment. 2009. (Cancer Etiology, Diagnosis & Treatments Ser.). 129.00 (978-1-60741-787-3(1), Nova Biomedical Bks.) Nova Science Pubs., Inc.

Mariani, Giuliano, et al, eds. Radioguided Surgery: A Comprehensive Team Approach. 2007. (Illus.). 297p. 179.00 (978-0-387-33684-8(2), 0387336842) Springer.

Markman, Maurie, et al, eds. Stem Cell Basis of Cancer: Tumorigenesis & Drug Development. 2007. (Cancer Drug Discovery & Development Ser.). 400p. 175.00 (978-1-58829-528-6(1), 1588295281) Humana Pr.

Martin, Linda. No Journey Back. 2011. 152p. 30.95 **(978-1-61507-900-1(9))**; pap. 13.95 **(978-1-61507-899-8(1))** Cross Bks. Publishing.

McKeown, Joshua. The Gift of Cancer: Helping people everywhere realize the potential they have in ministry by using their gifts for His Glory. 2011. 144p. pap. 15.00 **(978-1-4575-0439-6(1))** Dog Ear Publishing, LLC.

McLain, Robert, et al. Cancer in the Spine: Comprehensive Care. McLain, Robert F. et al, eds. 500p. E-Book 399.00 (978-1-59259-971-4(0)) Humana Pr.

McLain, Robert F., et al, eds. Cancer in the Spine: Comprehensive Care. 2010. (Current Clinical Oncology Ser.). (Illus.). 392p. pap. 249.00 (978-1-61737-340-4(0), 1617373400) Humana Pr.

McMillan, Martin L. Balloon Poodles: A step-by-step, chronological guide to not losing your mind over losing your esophagus, & other major Surgeries. 2007. 252p. pap. 19.95 (978-1-60145-153-8(9)) Booklocker.com, Inc.

McSwain, Mark A. Through the Eyes of a Storm: Perspective Gained through a Cancer Journey. 2011. 72p. pap. 8.95 **(978-1-4620-3192-4(7))** iUniverse, Inc.

Meyer, Armin. Alternative Werbung mit Mixed-Reality-Technologie: Konzepte mit Mehrwert für die Kommunikationspolitikdurch den Einsatz von Mixed-Reality-Technologie. 2008. 96p. pap. (978-3-639-02123-3(1)) VDM Verlag Dr. Mueller e.K.

Minigh, J. L., et al. Prompt, Accurate Diagnosis of Pediatric Cancer & Leukemia for Pediatricians, Orthopedists, & Family Practitioners. 2007. 73p. pap. 12.66 (978-1-4303-1175-1(4)) Lulu Enterprises Inc.

Mirzayansfnof;x, Razmik & Murray, David. Cellular Senescence: Implications for Cancer Therapy. 2008. pap. 37.00 (978-1-60692-676-5(4)) Nova Science Pubs., Inc.

Molchan, Kelly. If He Says He's Evil Believe Him! Searching for True Love Can Cause Cancer. 2009. 184p. 26.95 (978-1-4401-4025-9(1)); pap. 16.95 (978-1-4401-4023-5(5)) iUniverse, Inc.

Montgomery, Elizabeth A. & Voltaggio, Lysandra. Biopsy Interpretation of the Gastrointestinal Tract Mucosa Vol. 1: Non-Neoplastic. 2nd rev. ed. 2011. (Biopsy Interpretation Ser.). (ENG., Illus.). 352p. 163.95 **(978-1-4511-0960-3(1))** Lippincott Williams & Wilkins.

Murphy, Michael J. Diagnostic & Prognostic Biomarkers & Therapeutic Targets in Melanoma. 2012. (Current Clinical Pathology Ser.). (Illus.). 300p. 219.00 **(978-1-60761-432-6(4)**, 1607614324) Humana Pr.

Mydlo, Jack H. Penile & Urethral Cancer, an Issue of Urologic Clinics. 2010. (Clinics: Internal Medicine Ser.: 37-3). (ENG., Illus.). x, 328p. 105.00 (978-1-4377-2534-6(1), Saunders) Elsevier - Health Sciences Div.

Nakamura, Robert M., et al, eds. Cancer Diagnostics. 2010. (Contemporary Cancer Research Ser.). (Illus.). 520p. pap. 169.00 (978-1-61737-399-2(0), 1617373990) Humana Pr.

Naqvi, Syed Ali Raza, et al. Radiolabelled Compounds for Diagnosis & Therapy. 2010. 204p. pap. (978-3-639-25892-9(4)) VDM Verlag Dr. Mueller e.K.

Nikiforov, Yuri E. Diagnostic Pathology & Molecular Genetics of the Thyroid: A Comprehensive Guide for Practicing Thyroid Pathology. Nikiforov, Yuri E. et al, eds. 2009. (ENG., Illus.). 448p. 216.00 (978-0-7817-7459-8(4)) Lippincott Williams & Wilkins.

Nilsson, William E., ed. Bladder Cancer: Etymology, Diagnosis, & Treatments. 2010. (Cancer Etiology, Diagnosis & Treatments Ser.). 160.00 (978-1-61728-002-3(X)) Nova Science Pubs., Inc.

Okubo, Jennifer K. No More Cancer for Me! 2009. 28p. pap. 12.95 (978-1-4490-0408-8(3)) AuthorHouse.

Olsson, Louise. Early Detection of Colorectal Cancer. 2009. 52p. pap. (978-3-639-16540-1(3)) VDM Verlag Dr. Mueller e.K.

Olver, Ian N., ed. A Textbook of Cancer Supportive Care & Survivorship. 2010. (ENG., Illus.). 420p. 179.00 (978-1-4419-1224-4(X), 144191224X) Springer.

Optical Detection of Cancer. 2011. 90.00 (978-981-4295-40-6(X)) World Scientific Publishing Co., Inc.

Pasechnikov, Victor D., ed. Gastric Cancer: Diagnosis, Early Prevention, & Treatment. 2010. (Cancer Etiology, Diagnosis & Treatments Ser.). 130.50 (978-1-61668-313-9(9), Nova Biomedical Bks.) Nova Science Pubs., Inc.

Patak, Margie, et al. Implementing Colorectal Cancer Screening: Workshop Summary. 2008. (ENG.). 128p. pap. 30.25 (978-0-309-12139-2(6)) National Academies Pr.

Pegg, Jonathan D. Breast Cancer Screening & Prevention. 2011. (Series: Cancer Etiology, Diagnosis & Treatments Ser.). (Illus.). 132p. 59.00 (978-1-61209-288-1(8), Nova Biomedical Bks.) Nova Science Pubs., Inc.

Prostate Cancer: New Questions about Screening & Treatment: Hearing Before the Committee on Oversight & Government Reform, House of Representatives, One Hundred Eleventh Congress, Second Session, March 4, 2010. 2010. (Illus.). iv, 148p. (978-0-16-086770-5(3), 552-070-41691-9) United States Government Printing Office.

Rankin, Sheila C., ed. Carcinoma of the Esophagus. 2007. (Contemporary Issues in Cancer Imaging Ser.). (ENG., Illus.). 168p. 83.00 (978-0-521-88285-9(0)) Cambridge Univ. Pr.

Riemann, Burkhard & Schober, Otmar, eds. Molecular Imaging in Oncology. 2012. (Recent Results in Cancer Research Ser.: 187). (ENG., Illus.). 250p. 189.00 (978-3-642-10852-5(0), 3642108520) Springer.

Roob, Geoffrey L., et al, eds. Breast Cancer. 2nd ed. 2007. (M. D. Anderson Cancer Care Ser.). (Illus.). 561p. per. 89.95 (978-0-387-34950-3(2)) Springer.

Roberts, Jennifer Tirrell. Opus Magnificat: 1 Cancer Diagnosis. 24 Friends. Magnificent. 2011. 76p. pap. 9.95 **(978-1-4627-0541-2(3))** Cross Bks. Publishing.

Sarmah, Pubalee & C. Deka, Ramesh. Theoretical Aspects of Anticancer Drugs. 2011. 192p. pap. **(978-3-8443-8280-8(1))** Lambert Academic Publishing.

Sauter, Edward & Daly, Mary B. Breast Cancer Risk Reduction & Early Detection. 2010. (ENG., Illus.). viii, 242p. 189.00 (978-0-387-87582-8(4), 0387875824) Springer.

Scardino, Peter. Focal Therapy in Prostate Cancer. Emberton, Mark et al, eds. 2012. (ENG., Illus.). 200p. 124.95 **(978-1-4051-9649-9(1)**, Wiley-Blackwell) Wiley, John & Sons, Inc.

Schmidt, Leslie D., ed. Effectiveness of Core-Needle & Open Surgical Biopsy in Breast Cancer Evaluation. 2011. **(978-1-61209-799-2(5))** Nova Science Pubs., Inc.

Schmoll, Hans-Joachim. ESMO Handbook of Cancer Diagnosis & Treatment Evaluation. 2009. 160p. pap. 99.95 (978-1-84184-703-0(8), Informa Healthcare) Taylor & Francis Group.

Schneider, Andrea. You are Not Alone: Life after a Breast Cancer Diagnosis. 2010. 268p. 29.99 (978-1-4520-3821-6(X)); pap. 18.99 (978-1-4520-3822-3(8)) AuthorHouse.

Shafi, Mahmood I., et al, eds. Gynaecological Oncology. 2nd ed. 2009. (ENG., Illus.). 248p. pap. 65.00 (978-0-521-73024-2(4)) Cambridge Univ. Pr.

Soetikno, Roy & Kaltenbach, Tonya. Non-Polypoid (Flat & Depressed) Colorectal Neoplasms: Gastrointestinal Endoscopy Clincs of North America. 2010. (Clinics: Internal Medicine Ser.: 20-3). (ENG., Illus.). xvi, 408p. 105.00 (978-1-4377-2526-1(0), Saunders) Elsevier - Health Sciences Div.

Soreide, Kjetil & Soiland, Håvard. Clinical, Genetic & Molecular Precursor Features in Colorectal Neoplasia. Soreide, Kjetil & Soiland, Håvard, eds. 2008. (Illus.). 110p. (C). pap. 39.00 (978-1-60456-714-4(7)) Nova Science Pubs., Inc.

Souto, Eliana, et al. Lipid Nanocarriers in Cancer Diagnosis & Therapy. 2011. (Handbook Ser.). pap. **(978-1-84735-478-5(5))**; **(978-1-84735-477-8(7))** iSmithers Rapra Publishing.

Soyer, H. Peter, et al. Dermoscopy: The Essentials. 2nd ed. 2011. (ENG., Illus.). 248p. pap. 75.00 (978-0-7234-3592-1(8), Saunders) Elsevier - Health Sciences Div.

Srivastava, S., ed. The National Cancer Institute Early Detection Research Network: 5th Scientific Workshop - Biomarkers-at-a-Crossroads - Book Edition of Cancer Biomarkers. 2008. 130p. pap. 116.00 (978-1-58603-926-4(1)) IOS Pr., Inc.

Strumpf, Katie. I Never Signed up for This! An Upfront Guide to Dealing with Cancer at a Young Age. 2006. (ENG.). 52p. per. 16.95 (978-1-4241-5611-5(4)) PublishAmerica, Inc.

Su, Li-Ming. Prostate Cancer. 2009. (Early Diagnosis in Cancer Ser.). (ENG., Illus.). 312p. pap. 152.00 (978-1-4160-4575-5(9), Saunders) Elsevier - Health Sciences Div.

Swenson, Lee I. Progress in Tumor Marker Research. 2007. 129.00 (978-1-60021-619-0(6)) Nova Science Pubs., Inc.

Tartar, Marie, et al. Breast Cancer Imaging: A Multidisciplinary, Multimodality Approach. 2008. (ENG., Illus.). 632p. 182.00 (978-0-323-04677-0(0), Mosby) Elsevier - Health Sciences Div.

Thomas, Charles & Fuller, Clifton, eds. Biliary Tract & Gallbladder Cancer: Diagnosis & Therapy. 2008. 336p. 149.00 (978-1-933864-42-6(7)) Demos Medical Publishing, LLC.

Throop, Brian. Stacy's Miracle. 2010. 160p. 25.95 (978-1-4490-7177-6(5)); pap. 19.95 (978-1-4490-7176-9(7)) AuthorHouse.

Tobias, Jeffrey & Hochhauser, Daniel. Cancer & Its Management. 6th ed. 2010. (ENG., Illus.). 576p. pap. 99.95 (978-1-4051-7015-4(8), Wiley-Blackwell) Wiley, John & Sons, Inc.

Tolonen, Teemu. Molecular Biomarkers & Histopathological Parameters in Prostate Cancer Diagnostics & Prognostics. 2011. (Acta Universitatis Tamperensis Ser.). 172p. pap. 85.00 **(978-951-44-8466-7(5))** Tampere Univ. Pr. FIN. Dist: Coronet Bks.

Tuffaha, Muin S. A. Phenotypic & Genotypic Diagnosis of Malignancies: An Immunohistochemical & Molecular Approach. 2008. (ENG.). 298p. 159.95 (978-3-527-31881-0(X), Wiley-VCH) Wiley, John & Sons, Inc.

Twellmann, Thorsten. Data-Driven Analysis of Dynamic Contrast-Enhanced Magnetic Resonance. 2007. 184p. per. (978-3-8364-3316-7(8)) VDM Verlag Dr. Mueller e.K.

Van Meir, Erwin G., ed. CNS Cancer: Models, Markers, Prognostic Factors, Targets, & Therapeutic Approaches. 2009. (Cancer Drug Discovery & Development Ser.). (ENG., Illus.). xii, 1284p. 229.00 (978-1-60327-552-1(5), 1603275525) Humana Pr.

Veenstra, Timothy D. Proteomic Applications in Cancer Detection & Discovery. 2009. 352p. 84.95 (978-0-471-72406-3(8), Wiley-Interscience) Wiley, John & Sons, Inc.

Vuga, Marike. Sequential Therapy in Metastatic Breast Cancer Patients. 2010. 64p. pap. (978-3-639-20970-9(2)) VDM Verlag Dr. Mueller e.K.

C

Waxman, Jonathan. The Elephant in the Room: Stories about Cancer Patients & their Doctors. 2011. (ENG.). xix, 264p. pap. 29.95 (978-0-85729-894-2(1), 0857298941) Springer.

Wender, Richard & Snyderman, Danielle. Cancer - What the Primary Care Clinician Needs to Know Pt. 2: Primary Care - Clinics in Office Practice, 2 vols. 2009. (Clinics: Internal Medicine Ser.: 36-4). (ENG., Illus.). 88.00 (978-1-4377-1269-8(X), Saunders) Elsevier - Health Sciences Div.

Whitten, John T. Cancer of the Gallbladder: New Research. 2006. (Horizons in Cancer Research Ser.: Vol. 38). (Illus.). 158p. 129.00 (978-1-60021-240-6(9), Nova Biomedical Bks.) Nova Science Pubs., Inc.

Williams, Roger & Taylor-Robinson, Simon D., eds. Clinical Dilemmas in Primary Liver Cancer. 2012. (Clinical Dilemmas (UK) Ser.). (ENG., Illus.). 230p. pap. 84.95 (978-0-470-65797-3(9), Wiley-Blackwell) Wiley, John & Sons, Inc.

Willman, Valerie. Victory over Cancer. 2011. 220p. 17.99 (978-1-61379-745-7(1)) Xulon Pr., Inc.

Woodson, Nancy Leake. Hurdles: I find myself viewing the many beautiful colors in the rainbow as if I were looking through the sheer lens of a kaleidoscope, the many shades of color remind me of the Hurdles in my Life. 2010. 248p. 26.95 (978-1-4490-4882-2(X)); pap. 19.95 (978-1-4490-4881-5(1)) AuthorHouse.

Xu, Lei. Microarray Gene Expression Data Integration & Cancer Signatures. 2008. 120p. pap. 78.00 (978-3-639-08553-2(1)) VDM Verlag Dr. Mueller e.K.

Yang, Grace Chia-yu Hsu & Tao, Liang-Che. Transabdominal Fine-Needle Aspiration Biopsy: A Color Atlas & Monograph. 2nd ed. 2007. (Illus.). 461p. 235.00 incl. cd-rom (978-981-256-882-3(4)) World Scientific Publishing Co., Inc.

CANCER—DIET THERAPY

Alschuler, Lise & Gazella, Karolyn A. Five to Thrive: Your Cutting-Edge Cancer Prevention Plan. 2011. (ENG.). 240p. pap. 15.95 (978-1-935297-40-6(6)) Better Nutrition Magazine.

Barnard, Neal D. & Reilly, Jennifer K. The Cancer Survivor's Guide: Foods That Help You Fight Back. 2009. (ENG.). 245p. pap. 19.95 (978-1-57067-225-5(3), Healthy Living) Book Publishing Co.

Béliveau, Richard & Gingras, Denis. Cooking with Foods That Fight Cancer. 2007. (ENG., Illus.). 272p. pap. 24.95 (978-0-7710-1136-8(9), McClelland & Stewart) McClelland & Stewart CAN. Dist: Random Hse., Inc.

Beliveau, Richard & Gingras, Denis. Foods to Fight Cancer: Essential Foods to Help Prevent Cancer. 2007. (ENG., Illus.). 192p. (gr. 12). pap. 19.95 (978-0-7566-2867-3(9)) Dorling Kindersley Publishing, Inc.

Besser, Jeanne, et al. What to Eat During Cancer Treatment: 100 Great-Tasting, Family-Friendly Recipes to Help You Cope. 2009. (ENG.). 158p. pap. 19.95 (978-1-60443-005-9(2), 1604430052) American Cancer Society, Inc.

Betty Crocker Editors, et al. Betty Crocker Living with Cancer Cookbook. 2011. (ENG., Illus.). 288p. pap. 19.99 (978-1-118-08314-7(8), Betty Crocker) Wiley, John & Sons, Inc.

Bloch, Abby S., et al, eds. American Cancer Society Complete Guide to Nutrition for Cancer Survivors: Eating Well, Staying Well During & after Cancer. 2nd ed. 2010. (American Cancer Society Complete Guide T Ser.). (ENG.). 284p. pap. 24.95 (978-0-944235-78-2(6), 0944235786) American Cancer Society, Inc.

Carter, Robert L. & Chosney, Bruce T. Recipes That Won't Kill You: A Living Manual for Cancer Survivors. 2007. ring bd. (978-0-9793810-0-3(2)) Heritage Publishing.

Crocker. Betty Crocker's Living with Cancer Cookbook Custom Mgi. 2007. (ENG.). 256p. 24.95 (978-0-470-18952-8(5), Betty Crocker) Wiley, John & Sons, Inc.

Diet, Nutrition & Cancer Prevention. Date not set. (Illus.). 9p. (978-0-945100-71-3(X)) Parlay International.

Dobic, Mina. My Beautiful Life: How I Conquered Cancer Naturally. 2007. (ENG., Illus.). 1p. pap. 15.95 (978-0-7570-0244-1(7)) Square One Pubs.

Flynn, Mary & Barr, Nancy Verde. The Pink Ribbon Diet: A Revolutionary New Weight Loss Plan to Lower Your Breast Cancer Risk. 2010. (ENG.). 288p. pap. 16.95 (978-0-7382-1394-1(2)) Da Capo Pr., Inc.

Gerson, Charlotte & Bishop, Beata. Healing the Gerson Way: Defeating Cancer & Other Chronic Diseases (with Blu-Ray) Shwed, Joanne, ed. & des. by. 2011. 488p. pap. 44.95 (978-0-9760186-8-1(3)) Gerson Health Media.

—Healing the Gerson Way (with DVD) Defeating Cancer & Other Chronic Diseases. Shwed, Joanne, ed. Kroschel, Stephen. 2011. 488p. pap. 39.95 (978-0-9760186-9-8(1)) Gerson Health Media.

González, Michael J., et al. I Have Cancer - What Should I Do? Your Orthomolecular Guide for Cancer Management. 2009. 224p. pap. 18.95 (978-1-59120-243-1(4)) Basic Health Pubns., Inc.

Greer, Julia B. The Anti-Cancer Cookbook: How to Cut Your Risk with the Most Powerful, Cancer-Fighting Foods. 2008. 224p. pap. 19.95 (978-0-9624814-9-9(1)) Sunrise River Pr.

Hoffer, Abram. Healing Cancer: Complementary Vitamin & Drug Treatments. 2011. (Naturopathic Healing Series, Professional Edition Ser.). (ENG.). 240p. 49.95 (978-1-897025-40-6(8)) Canadian College of Naturopathic Medicine Pr. CAN. Dist: SCB Distributors.

Hofmekler, Ori. The Anti-Estrogenic Diet: How Estrogenic Foods & Chemicals Are Making You Fat & Sick. 2007. (ENG., Illus.). 208p. pap. 16.95 (978-1-55643-684-0(X)) North Atlantic Bks.

Janecek, Herve. Secret to Long Life in Your Dna. 2009. (ENG.). 1p. pap. (978-1-59477-259-7(2), Healing Arts Pr.) Inner Traditions International, Ltd.

Jung, Karen. Healthier Eating: & Living with Cancer. 2008. (ENG., Illus.). 304p. pap. (978-1-894694-57-5(0)) Granville Island Publishing.

Katz, Rebecca & Edelson, Mat. The Cancer-Fighting Kitchen: Nourishing, Big-Flavor Recipes for Cancer Treatment & Recovery. 2009. (ENG., Illus.). 232p. 32.50 (978-1-58761-344-9(1), Celestial Arts) Ten Speed Pr.

—One Bite at Time. 2nd rev. ed. 2008. (ENG., Illus.). 176p. 29.99 (978-1-58761-333-3(6), Celestial Arts) Ten Speed Pr.

Katz, Rebecca, et al. One Bite at a Time: Nourishing Recipes for Cancer Survivors & Their Friends. 2nd rev. ed. 2008. (ENG., Illus.). 176p. pap. 21.99 (978-1-58761-327-2(1), Celestial Arts) Ten Speed Pr.

Katzin, Carolyn F. The Everything Cancer-Fighting Cookbook. 2011. (ENG.). 304p. pap. 16.95 (978-1-4405-0746-5(5)) Adams Media Corp.

Keane, Maureen & Chace, Daniella. What to Eat If You Have Cancer: Healing Foods That Boost Your Immune System. 2nd rev. ed. 2006. (ENG., Illus.). 288p. per. 16.95 (978-0-07-147396-5(3), 0071473963) McGraw-Hill Cos., The.

Knasmüller, Siegfried. Chemoprevention of Cancer & DNA Damage by Dietary Factors. DeMarini, David M. et al, eds. 2009. (ENG., Illus.). 838p. 275.00 (978-3-527-32058-5(X), Wiley-VCH) Wiley, John & Sons, Inc.

Kushi, Michio & Jack, Alex. The Cancer Prevention Diet: The Macrobiotic Approach to Preventing & Relieving Cancer. 3rd rev. ed. 2009. (ENG.). 608p. pap. 23.99 (978-0-312-56106-2(7), St. Martin's Griffin) St. Martin's Pr.

LaMantia, Jean & Berinstein, Neil. The Essential Cancer Treatment Nutrition Guide & Cookbook: Includes 150 Healthy & Delicious Recipes. 2012. (ENG., Illus.). 320p. pap. 24.95 (978-0-7788-0298-3(1)) Rose, Robert Inc. CAN. Dist: Firefly Bks., Ltd.

Marian, Mary & Roberts, Susan. Clinical Nutrition for Oncology Patients. 2009. (Illus.). 463p. 98.95 (978-0-7637-5512-6(5)) Jones & Bartlett Learning, LLC.

Nixon, Daniel, et al. The Prostate Health Program: A Guide to Preventing & Controlling Prostate Cancer. 2007. (ENG., Illus.). 256p. pap. 24.95 (978-0-7432-5432-8(5), Free Pr.) Free Pr.

Prasad, Kedar N. Fighting Cancer with Vitamins & Antioxidants. 4th ed. 2011. (ENG.). 1p. pap. 16.95 (978-1-59477-423-2(4)) Inner Traditions International, Ltd.

Sarkar, Fazlul H., ed. Nutraceuticals & Cancer. 2011. (ENG., Illus.). xii, 379p. 209.00 (978-94-007-2629-1(5), 9400726295) Springer.

Schleicher, Peter & Witzigmann, Eckart. The Alchemy of Food: The Secrets of the Great Art of Cooking & the Healing Effects of Fine Cuisine. 2010. (ENG., Illus.). 160p. 12.99 (978-1-901268-53-9(5), 1901268535) Evans Mitchell Bks. GBR. Dist: MBI Distribution Services/Quayside Distribution.

Seeram, Navindra P. & Stoner, Gary D., eds. Berries & Cancer Prevention. 2010. (ENG., Illus.). xi, 313p. 189.00 (978-1-4419-7553-9(5), 1441975535) Springer.

Seyfried, Thomas. Cancer as a Metabolic Disease: On the Origin, Management, & Prevention of Cancer. 2012. (ENG.). 432p. 135.00 (978-0-470-58492-7(0), Wiley) Wiley, John & Sons, Inc.

Straus, Howard David & Marinacci, Barbara. Dr. Max Gerson: Healing the Hopeless. 2009. (Illus.). 416p. pap. 27.95 (978-0-9760186-1-2(6)) Gerson Health Media.

Surh, Young-Joon, et al. Nutrition & Physical Activity in Aging, Obesity, & Cancer. 2011. (Annals of the New York Academy of Sciences Ser.: 84). (ENG., Illus.). 198p. pap. 130.00 (978-1-57331-842-6(6), Wiley-Blackwell) Wiley, John & Sons, Inc.

Watson, Ronald Ross & Preedy, Victor R., eds. Bioactive Foods & Extracts: Cancer Treatment & Prevention. 2010. (ENG., Illus.). 663p. 169.95 (978-1-4398-1619-6(0), CRC Press) Taylor & Francis Group GBR. Dist: Taylor & Francis Group.

World Cancer Research Fund / American Institute for Cancer Research. Food, Nutrition, Physical Activity, & the Prevention of Cancer: A Global Perspective. 2007. (Illus.). 517p. pap. 69.95 (978-0-9722522-2-5(3)) American Institute For Cancer Research.

CANCER—ECONOMIC ASPECTS

Davis, Devra. The Secret History of the War on Cancer. 2007. (ENG.). 512p. 27.95 (978-0-465-00535-2(7)) Basic Bks.

Gelband, Hellen. Cancer Control Opportunities in Low- & Middle-Income Countries. Sloan, Frank A., ed. 2007. (ENG., Illus.). 340p. pap. 49.00 (978-0-309-10384-8(3)) National Academies Pr.

Moss, Ralph W. The Cancer Industry: The Classic Expose on the Cancer Establishment. pap. 14.95 (978-1-55778-439-1(6)) Equinox Pr.

CANCER—ENVIRONMENTAL ASPECTS

Davis, Devra. The Secret History of the War on Cancer. 2009. (ENG.). 560p. pap. 18.95 (978-0-465-01568-9(9)) Basic Bks.

ICRP Staff. Low-Dose Extrapolation of Radiation Related Cancer Risk. Valentin, J., ed. 2006. (International Commission on Radiological Protection Ser.: 99). (ENG., Illus.). 200p. per. 176.00 (978-0-08-044958-6(1), Elsevier) Elsevier - Health Sciences Div.

Landrigan, Philip, et al, eds. Living in a Chemical World: Framing the Future in Light of the Past. 2006. (Annals of the New York Academy of Sciences Ser.: Vol. 1076). (ENG., Illus.). 500p. pap. 159.95 (978-1-57331-653-8(9), Wiley-Blackwell) Wiley, John & Sons, Inc.

Meliker, Jaymie R. Lifetime Exposure to Arsenic in Drinking Water- Application to a Bladder Cancer Case-Control Study. 2007. 332p. per. (978-3-8364-2942-9(X)) VDM Verlag Dr. Mueller e.K.

Nichols, Nancy A. Lake Effect: Two Sisters & a Town's Toxic Legacy. 2010. (ENG., Illus.). 192p. pap. 25.00 (978-1-59726-821-9(6), Shearwater Bks.) Island Pr.

Obe, Günter, et al, eds. Cancer Risk Evaluation: Methods & Trends. 2011. (ENG., Illus.). 366p. 99.95 (978-3-527-32753-9(3), Wiley-VCH) Wiley, John & Sons, Inc.

Panno, Joseph. Cancer. 2nd rev. ed. 2010. (New Biology Ser.). (Illus.). 264p. (gr. 6-12). 40.00 (978-0-8160-6848-7(8)) Facts On File, Inc.

Panno, Joseph. The New Biology. 2011. (New Biology Ser.). (gr. 6-12). 280.00 (978-0-8160-8487-6(4)) Facts On File, Inc.

Roy, Deodutta & Dorak, M. Tevfik, eds. Environmental Factors, Genes, & the Development of Human Cancers. 2010. (ENG., Illus.). xiii, 300p. 189.00 (978-1-4419-6751-0(6), 1441967516) Springer.

Steingraber, Sandra. Living Downstream: An Ecologist's Personal Investigation of Cancer & the Environment. 2nd ed. 2010. (ENG.). 440p. pap. 16.95 (978-0-306-81869-1(8)) Da Capo Pr., Inc.

CANCER—EPIDEMIOLOGY

Adami, Hans-Olov, et al, eds. Textbook of Cancer Epidemiology. 2nd ed. 2008. (Monographs in Epidemiology & Biostatistics Ser.). (ENG., Illus.). 720p. 95.00 (978-0-19-531117-4(5)) Oxford Univ. Pr., Inc.

Berger, Nathan A., ed. Cancer & Energy Balance, Epidemiology & Overview. 2010. (Energy Balance & Cancer Ser.). (ENG., Illus.). 232p. 209.00 (978-1-4419-5514-2(3), 1441955143) Springer.

Boyle, P. & Levin, B. World Cancer Report 2008. 2009. (IARC Nonserial Publication Ser.). (ENG., Illus.). 512p. pap. 48.00 (978-92-832-0423-7(9)) World Health Organization.

Campbell, Kenneth. Infectious Causes of Cancer: A Guide for Nurses & Healthcare Professionals. 2011. (ENG.). 216p. pap. 62.99 (978-0-470-51805-2(7), Wiley) Wiley, John & Sons, Inc.

Dickman, P. Population-based Cancer Survival Analysis. 2008. (Statistics in Practice Ser.). (ENG.). 320p. 100.00 (978-0-470-02859-9(9), Wiley) Wiley, John & Sons, Inc.

Doll, Richard. The Prevention of Cancer: Pointers from Epidemiology. 2008. (ENG., Illus.). 143p. pap. 29.95 (978-0-202-36220-5(5)) Aldine Transaction.

Faguet, Guy B. The War on Cancer: An Anatomy of Failure, a Blueprint for the Future. 2008. (ENG., Illus.). xvi, 227p. pap. 29.95 (978-1-4020-8620-5(2), 1402086202) Springer.

Frank, Steven A. Dynamics of Cancer: Incidence, Inheritance, & Evolution. 2007. (Princeton Series in Evolutionary Biology). (ENG., Illus.). 400p. (C). 115.00 (978-0-691-13365-2(4)); per. 49.95 (978-0-691-13366-9(2)) Princeton Univ. Pr.

Gastroenterology. Colorectal Cancer Can Be Prevented. Arber, N., ed. 2007. (Illus.). 78p. pap. (978-3-8055-8419-7(9)) Karger, S. AG.

International Agency for Research on Cancer Staff. Atlas of Cancer Mortality in the European Union & the European Economic Area, 1993-1997. Boyle, P., ed. 2009. (IARC Scientific Publication No 159 Ser.). (Illus.). 260p. pap. 30.00 (978-92-832-2159-3(1)) World Health Organization.

Manton, Kenneth G., et al. Cancer Mortality & Morbidity Patterns in the U.S. Population: An Interdisciplinary Approach. 2009. (Statistics for Biology & Health Ser.). (ENG., Illus.). xv, 455p. 89.95 (978-0-387-78192-1(7)) Springer.

Milham, Samuel. Dirty Electricity: Electrification & the Diseases of Civilization. 2010. 120p. 22.95 (978-1-4502-3822-9(X)) iUniverse, Inc.

Nasca, Philip C. Epidemiology of Childhood Cancers. 2011. 122.00 (978-981-4295-79-6(5)) World Scientific Publishing Co., Inc.

Nasca, Philip & Pastides, Harris. Fundamentals of Cancer Epidemiology. 2nd rev. ed. 2007. (Illus.). 541p. (C). 116.95 (978-0-7637-3618-7(X)) Jones & Bartlett Learning, LLC.

Olshan, Andrew F., ed. Epidemiology, Pathogenesis, & Prevention of Head & Neck Cancer. 2010. (ENG., Illus.). xi, 250p. 179.00 (978-1-4419-1471-2(4), 1441914714) Springer.

Rebbeck, Timothy R., et al, eds. Molecular Epidemiology: Applications in Cancer & Other Human Diseases. 2008. (ENG., Illus.). 320p. 200.00 (978-1-4200-5291-6(8), Informa Healthcare) Taylor & Francis Group GBR. Dist: Taylor & Francis Group.

Schottenfeld, David & Fraumeni, Joseph F., eds. Cancer Epidemiology & Prevention. 3rd rev. ed. 2006. (ENG., Illus.). 1416p. 245.00 (978-0-19-514961-6(0)) Oxford Univ. Pr., Inc.

Sunny, Lizzy. Epidemiology of Prostate Cancer in Developing Countries: Epidemiology of Prostate Cancer - Design, Conduct, Analysis & Interpretation of an Original Case Control Study. 2008. 108p. pap. (978-3-639-09856-3(0)) VDM Verlag Dr. Mueller e.K.

Verma, Mukesh. Cancer Epidemiology, 2 vols. 2008. (Methods in Molecular Biology Ser.). (Illus.). 447p. 99.50 (978-1-60327-491-3(X), 160327491X) Humana Pr.

—Cancer Epidemiology: Volume 1, Host Susceptibility Factors, 2 vols. Verma, Mukesh, ed. 2008. (Methods in Molecular Biology Ser.). (Illus.). 300p. 119.00 (978-1-58829-987-1(2)) Humana Pr.

Verma, Mukesh, ed. Cancer Epidemiology: Volume 1, Host Susceptibility Factors. 2010. (Methods in Molecular Biology Ser.). (Illus.). xiv, 484p. pap. 119.00 (978-1-61737-868-3(2), 1617378682) Humana Pr.

—Cancer Epidemiology: Volume 2, Modifiable Factors. 2010. (Methods in Molecular Biology Ser.). (Illus.). xiv, 484p. pap. 99.50 (978-1-61737-902-4(6), 1617379026) Humana Pr.

CANCER—ETIOLOGY

Attributable Causes of Cancer in France in the Year 2000: IARC Working Group Report, No. 3. 2007. (IARC Nonserial Publication). pap. 22.50 (978-92-832-2443-3(4)) World Health Organization.

Boveri, Theodor. Concerning the Origin of Malignant Tumours. Harris, Henry, tr. from GER. annot. ed. 2008. (ENG.). 82p. pap. 25.00 (978-0-87969-788-4(1)) Cold Spring Harbor Laboratory Pr.

Calderwood, Stuart K., et al, eds. Heat Shock Proteins in Cancer. (Heat Shock Proteins Ser.). 2010. x, 406p. pap. 239.00 (978-90-481-7627-4(1), 9048176271) 2007. (Illus.). 398p. 239.00 (978-1-4020-6400-5(4)) Springer.

Cancer Prevention & Early Detection. Date not set. (Illus.). 10p. (978-0-945100-70-6(1)) Parlay International.

Cho, C. H. & Purohit, Vishnudutt. Alcohol, Tobacco, & Cancer. (Illus.). (978-3-8055-8107-3(6)) Karger, S. AG.

Giordano, Antonio & Normanno, Nicola, eds. Breast Cancer in the Post-Genomic Era. (Current Clinical Oncology Ser.). (ENG., Illus.). xii, 230p. 2010. pap. 99.95 (978-1-60761-466-1(9), 1607614669) 2009. 219.00 (978-1-60327-944-4(X), 160327944X) Humana Pr.

Gonzalez, Nicholas J. & Isaacs, Linda L. The Trophoblast & the Origins of Cancer: One solution to the medical enigma of our Time. 2009. (ENG., Illus.). 212p. pap. 49.95 (978-0-9821965-0-2(4)) New Spring Pr., LLC.

Khalili, Kamel & Jeang, Kuan-Teh. Viral Oncology: Basic Science & Clinical Applications. 2009. (ENG., Illus.). 491p. 165.95 (978-0-470-37991-2(X), Wiley-Blackwell) Wiley, John & Sons, Inc.

Kozlov, Serguei V., ed. Inflammation & Cancer: Methods & Protocols: Volume 1, Experimental Models & Practical Approaches, 2 vols. 2009. (Methods in Molecular Biology Ser.). (Illus.). 325p. 129.00 (978-1-934115-14-5(2)) Humana Pr.

Kozlov, Serguei V., ed. Inflammation & Cancer: Methods & Protocols: Volume 2, Molecular Analysis & Pathways. (Methods in Molecular Biology Ser.). (Illus.). xvi, 408p. 2010. (ENG.). pap. 129.00 (978-1-61737-905-5(0), 1617379050) 2009. 129.00 (978-1-60327-529-3(0)) Humana Pr.

Majumder, Sadhan, ed. Stem Cells & Cancer. 2009. (ENG., Illus.). x, 286p. 160.00 (978-0-387-89610-6(4), 0387896104) Springer.

McCormick, Sabrina. No Family History: The Environmental Links to Breast Cancer. 2009. (New Social Formations Ser.). (ENG., Illus.). 192p. 37.50 (978-0-7425-6408-4(8)) Rowman & Littlefield Publishers, Inc.

Mendelsohn, John, et al. The Molecular Basis of Cancer. 3rd ed. 2008. (ENG., Illus.). 704p. 218.00 (978-1-4160-3703-3(9), Saunders) Elsevier - Health Sciences Div.

Ramonde, Pauline R. & Fochas, Eva H., eds. Obesity & Cancer Research. 2009. 129.00 (978-1-60692-388-7(9)) Nova Science Pubs., Inc.

Rohan, Thomas E. & Shah, Keerti V., eds. Cervical Cancer: from Etiology to Prevention: From Etiology to Prevention. 2010. (Cancer Prevention-Cancer Causes Ser.). 436p. pap. 219.00 (978-90-481-6336-6(6), 9048163366) Springer.

Saint Michael's College Staff. The Biology of Cancer Set, 9-Volumes. 2009. (Biology of Cancer Ser.). (C). (gr. 9-18). 315.00 (978-0-7910-9911-7(3), Chelsea Hse.) Facts On File, Inc.

Tompkins, Marilyn B. Gastric Cancer Research Trends. 2007. (C). 185.00 (978-1-60021-725-8(7)) Nova Science Pubs., Inc.

Tu, Shi-Ming. Origin of Cancers: Clinical Perspectives & Implications of a Stem-Cell Theory of Cancer. 2010. (Cancer Treatment & Research Ser.). (ENG., Illus.). cxxxvii, 237p. 219.00 (978-1-4419-5967-6(X), 144195967X) Springer.

United Nations Staff. Effects of Ionizing Radiation: United Nations Scientific Committee on the Effects of Atomic Radiation - UNSCEAR 2006 Report, Volume II - Report to the General Assembly, with Scientific Annexes C, D, & E. 2009. (ENG.). 340p. pap. 80.00 (978-92-1-142270-2(1)) United Nations Pubns.

Weber, Georg F. Molecular Mechanisms of Cancer. (ENG.). xiv, 650p. 2010. pap. 149.00 (978-90-481-7505-5(4), 9048175054) 2007. (Illus.). 149.00 (978-1-4020-6015-1(7), 1402060157) Springer.

Zänker, Kurt S. Diabetes & Cancer: Epidemiological Evidence & Molecular Links. Masur, K. & Thévenod, F., eds. 2008. (Frontiers in Diabetes Ser.). (Illus.). 148p. (978-3-8055-8640-5(X)) Karger, S. AG.

CANCER—GENETIC ASPECTS

see also Oncogenes

American Institute for Cancer Research, ed. Dietary Fat & Cancer: Genetic & Molecular Interactions. 2010. (Advances in Experimental Medicine & Biology Ser.). pap. 219.00 (978-1-4419-3282-2(8), 1441932828) Springer.

Ayesh, Basim. Gene Therapy of Bladder Cancer & Colorectal Metastasis in the Liver. 2009. 156p. pap. (978-3-639-16777-1(5)) VDM Verlag Dr. Mueller e.K.

Bernard, Louane E. & Laurent, Maëlys B. Genetic Predisposition to Disease: New Research. 2008. (C). 185.00 (978-1-60456-836-3(4)) Nova Science Pubs., Inc.

Biava, Pier Mario. Cancer & the Search for Lost Meaning: The Discovery of a Revolutionary New Cancer Treatment. 2009. (ENG., Illus.). 168p. pap. 15.95 (978-1-55643-778-6(1)) North Atlantic Bks.

Boesky, Amy. What We Have: A Memoir. 2011. (ENG.). 336p. (gr. 12). 16.00 (978-1-59240-636-4(X), Gotham) Penguin Group (USA) Inc.

—What We Have: Inspiring Story about Love, Loss, & Survival. 2010. (ENG.). 336p. (gr. 12). 26.00 (978-1-59240-551-0(7), Gotham) Penguin Group (USA) Inc.

Bologna, Mauro, ed. Biotargets of Cancer in Current Clinical Practice. 2012. (Current Clinical Pathology Ser.). (ENG., Illus.). xvi, 563p. 239.00 (978-1-61779-614-2(X), 161779614X) Humana Pr.

Boultwood, Jacqueline & Fidler, Carrie, eds. Molecular Analysis of Cancer. 2010. (Methods in Molecular Medicine Ser.). (Illus.). 328p. pap. 139.00 (978-1-61737-102-8(5), 1617371025) Humana Pr.

Bowcock, Anne M., ed. Breast Cancer: Molecular Genetics, Pathogenesis, & Therapeutics. 2010. (Contemporary Cancer Research Ser.). 608p. pap. 189.00 (978-1-61737-072-4(X), 161737072X) Humana Pr.

Bowen, D. J. & Penchaszadeh, V. B., eds. Minority Recruitment in Cancer Genetics Studies. 2008. (Illus.). 66p. pap. *(978-3-8055-8499-9(7))* Karger, S. AG.

Bronchud, Miguel H., et al, eds. Principles of Molecular Oncology. 3rd ed. 2008. 448p. pap. 99.00 *(978-1-60327-505-7(3))* Springer.

Brown, Anthony M. C. Cancer Genetics. 2011. (Colloquium Series on the Cell Biology of Medicine Ser.). 100p. pap. 35.00 *(978-1-61504-252-4(0))* Morgan & Claypool Life Science Publishers.

Bunz, Fred. Principles of Cancer Genetics. (ENG.). xii, 325p. 2010. pap. 119.00 *(978-90-481-7726-4(X)*, 904817726X) 2008. (Illus.). 119.00 *(978-1-4020-6783-9(6)*, 1402067836) Springer.

Campbell, Lynda J., ed. Cancer Cytogenetics: Methods & Protocols. 2nd ed. 2011. (Methods in Molecular Biology Ser.). (Illus.). x, 273p. 119.00 *(978-1-61779-073-7(7)*, 1617790737) Humana Pr.

Cellular Therapy of Cancer: Development of Gene Therapy Based Approaches. 2011. 96.00 *(978-981-4295-13-0(2))* World Scientific Publishing Co., Inc.

Chung, Daniel C. & Haber, Daniel A., eds. The Massachusetts General Hospital Guide to Clinical Cancer Genetics. 2009. (Illus.). 400p. 149.00 *(978-0-387-93844-8(3))* Springer.

Chung, Leland W. K., et al, eds. Prostate Cancer; Biology, Genetics, & the New Therapeutics. 2008. 532p. pap. 99.00 *(978-1-60327-510-1(X))* Springer.

Clark, Sue, ed. A Guide to Cancer Genetics in Clinical Practice. 2009. (Illus.). 300p. pap. 60.00 *(978-1-903378-54-0(0))* TFM Publishing Ltd. GBR. Dist: JAMCO Distribution.

Cooper, David N. The Molecular Genetics of Lung Cancer. 2010. (ENG., Illus.). xvi, 392p. pap. 149.00 *(978-3-642-06190-5(7)*, 3642061907) Springer.

Croce, Carlo. MicroRNAs & Cancer. 2009. (Current Cancer Research Ser.). 270p. 139.99 *(978-1-60327-268-1(2))* Humana Pr.

Dakubo, Gabriel D. Mitochondrial Genetics & Cancer. 2010. (ENG., Illus.). x, 368p. 209.00 *(978-3-642-11415-1(6)*, 3642114156) Springer.

Devita. Cancer Prin Prac Oncology Mol Biology. 2011. (Illus.). 456p. pap. 89.95 *(978-1-4511-1897-1(X))*, Lippincott Williams & Wilkins.

Doerfler, Walter & Böhm, Petra. DNA Methylation: Basic Mechanisms: Basic Mechanisms. 2010. (Current Topics in Microbiology & Immunology Ser.). (Illus.). viii, 324p. pap. 179.00 *(978-3-642-06708-2(5)*, 3642067085) Springer.

Dumitrescu, Ramona G. & Verma, Mukesh, eds. Cancer Epigenetics: Methods & Protocols. 2012. (Methods in Molecular Biology Ser.). (ENG., Illus.). xiii, 492p. 159.00 ***(978-1-61779-611-1(5)***, 1617796115) Humana Pr.

Dupuy, Adam J. & Largaespada, David A., eds. Insertional Mutagenesis Strategies in Cancer Genetics. 2010. (ENG., Illus.). viii, 200p. 139.00 *(978-1-4419-7655-0(8)*, 1441976558) Springer.

Eiseman. Effects of Preanalytical Variables: On the Quality of Biospecimens Used to Study Genetic Changes in Cancer. 2009. 98p. pap. 35.00 *(978-0-8330-4741-0(8))*, RAND Corp., The.

Ellis, C. Neal, ed. Inherited Cancer Syndromes: Current Clinical Management. 2nd ed. 2010. (ENG., Illus.). viii, 204p. pap. 139.00 *(978-1-4419-6820-3(2)*, 1441968202) Springer.

Fisher, Paul B., ed. Cancer Genomics & Proteomics: Methods & Protocols. 2010. (Methods in Molecular Biology Ser.). (Illus.). xvi, 358p. pap. 99.50 *(978-1-61737-605-4(1)*, 1617376051) Humana Pr.

Foote, MaryAnn, et al, eds. Principles of Molecular Oncology. 3rd ed. 2007. (Illus.). 418p. 179.00 *(978-1-934115-25-1(8))* Humana Pr.

Frank, Steven A. Dynamics of Cancer: Incidence, Inheritance, & Evolution. 2007. (Princeton Series in Evolutionary Biology). (ENG., Illus.). 400p. (C). 115.00 *(978-0-691-13365-2(4))*; per. 49.95 *(978-0-691-13366-9(2))* Princeton Univ. Pr.

Friedman, Sue, et al. Confronting Hereditary Breast & Ovarian Cancer: Identify Your Risk, Understand Your Options, Change Your Destiny. 2012. (Johns Hopkins Press Health Book Ser.). (ENG., Illus.). 288p. pap. 18.95 ***(978-1-4214-0408-0(7))***; (gr. 17). 45.00 ***(978-1-4214-0407-3(9))*** Johns Hopkins Univ. Pr.

Friedmann, Theodore, et al, contrib. by. Advances in Genetics. (ENG.). 2009. 358p. 161.00 *(978-0-12-374831-7(3))* Vol. 69. 2010. (Illus.). 174p. 161.00 *(978-0-12-375022-8(9))*, Elsevier Science & Technology Bks. (Academic Pr.).

Gabriel, Sarah. Eating Pomegranates: A Memoir of Mothers, Daughters, & the BRCA Gene. 2010. (ENG.). 272p. 25.00 *(978-1-4391-4819-8(8)*, Scribner) Scribner.

Gallinger, Steven. Hereditary Colorectal Cancer, an Issue of Surgical Oncology Clinics. 2009. (Clinics: Surgery Ser.: 18-4). (ENG.). 99.00 *(978-1-4377-1390-9(4)*, Saunders) Elsevier - Health Sciences Div.

Genetic counseling in breast Cancer. 2007. pap. 163.00 *(978-1-58603-793-2(5))* IOS Pr., Inc.

Genetics. Cancer Genomics. Cannizzaro, L. A. & Ramesh, K. H., eds. 2007. (Illus.). 282p. *(978-3-8055-8433-3(4))* Karger, S. AG.

Giordano, Antonio & Normanno, Nicola, eds. Breast Cancer in the Post-Genomic Era. (Current Clinical Oncology Ser.). (ENG., Illus.). xii, 230p. 2010. pap. 99.95 *(978-1-60761-466-1(9)*, 1607614669) 2009. 219.00 *(978-1-60327-944-4(X)*, 160327944X) Humana Pr.

Gloscow, Eleanor J. New Research on Genomic Instability. 2006. 302p. 129.00 *(978-1-60021-320-5(0))*, Nova Science Pubs., Inc.

Greene, Diane Tropea Apron Strings: Inheriting Courage, Wisdom and... Breast Cancer. 2007. (ENG., Illus.). 133p. per. 14.00 *(978-1-55825-108-0(4))* Rainbow Bks., Inc.

Gruber, Stephen B., ed. Cancer Genetics. 2010. 384p. 129.00 *(978-0-387-30458-8(4)*, 0387304584) Springer.

Grützmann, Robert & Pilarsky, Christian, eds. Cancer Gene Profiling: Methods & Protocols. 2009. (Methods in Molecular Biology Ser.). (ENG., Illus.). xii, 452p. 129.00 *(978-1-934115-76-3(2)*, 1934115762) Humana Pr.

Gusev, Yuriy, ed. Microrna Profiling in Cancer: A Bioinformatics Perspective. 2009. (ENG., Illus.). 257p. 129.95 *(978-981-4267-01-4(5))* Pan Stanford Publishing SGP. Dist: Taylor & Francis Group.

Gustafsson, Wilma B. New Gene Therapy & Cancer Research. 2008. (Illus.). (C). 129.00 *(978-1-60021-969-6(1)*, Nova Biomedical Bks.) Nova Science Pubs., Inc.

Heim, Sverre, et al. Cancer Cytogenetics: Chromosomal & Molecular Genetic Abberations of Tumor Cells. 3rd ed. 2009. (ENG., Illus.). 756p. 146.95 *(978-0-470-18179-9(6)*, Wiley-Blackwell) Wiley, John & Sons, Inc.

Hodgson, Shirley V., et al. A Practical Guide to Human Cancer Genetics. 3rd rev. ed. 2006. (ENG., Illus.). 410p. per. 112.00 *(978-0-521-68563-4(X))* Cambridge Univ. Pr.

Hunt, Kelly K., et al, eds. Gene Therapy for Cancer. 2007. (Cancer Drug Discovery & Development Ser.). (Illus.). 469p. 219.00 *(978-1-58829-472-2(2)*, 1588294722) Humana Pr.

Innocenti, Federico, ed. Genomics & Pharmacogenomics in Anticancer Drug Development & Clinical Response. 2010. (Cancer Drug Discovery & Development Ser.). (Illus.). xiv, 378p. pap. 189.00 *(978-1-61737-694-8(9)*, 1617376949) Humana Pr.

Jurisica, Igor, et al, eds. Cancer Informatics in the Post Genomic Era: Toward Information-Based Medicine. 2010. (Cancer Treatment & Research Ser.). (Illus.). xx, 180p. pap. 159.00 *(978-1-4419-4344-6(7)*, 1441943447) Springer.

Kazemie, Mirabotalib. The Designs of Biological Forms, Development, & Initiation of Cancer. 2009. 116p. 21.49 *(978-1-4490-1051-5(2))*; pap. 10.99 *(978-1-4490-1050-8(4))* AuthorHouse.

Leyland-Jones, Brian, ed. Pharmacogenetics of Breast Cancer: Towards the Individualization of Therapy. 2008. (Translational Medicine Ser.: Vol. 7). (ENG., Illus.). 352p. 200.00 *(978-1-4200-5293-0(4)*, Informa Healthcare) Taylor & Francis Group GBR. Dist: Taylor & Francis Group.

Masny, Agnes, et al. Genetics & Genomics in Oncology Nursing Practice. 2010. (Illus.). 346p. *(978-1-890504-91-5(2))* Oncology Nursing Society.

Mehta, Jai Prakash, et al. Understanding Breast Cancer Dynamics Using Gene Expression Profiling. 2010. 396p. pap. *(978-3-8383-5931-1(3))* Lambert Academic Publishing.

The Molecular Basis of Human Cancer. 2010. 149.50 *(978-1-934115-18-3(5))* Humana Pr.

Nasheuer, H. P., ed. Genome Stability & Human Diseases. 2009. (Subcellular Biochemistry Ser.). (ENG., Illus.). xvi, 340p. 269.00 *(978-90-481-3470-0(6)*, 9048134706) Springer.

National Cancer Policy Forum (U.S.) Staff, contrib. by. Cancer-Related Genetic Testing & Counseling: Workshop Proceedings. 2007. (ENG., Illus.). 134p. pap. 33.50 *(978-0-309-10997-0(3))* National Academies Pr.

Newman, William G., ed. Pharmacogenetics - Making Cancer Treatment Safer & More Effective. 2010. (ENG., Illus.). vi, 245p. 179.00 *(978-90-481-8617-4(X)*, 904818617X) Springer.

Offit. Clinical Cancer Genetics: Risk Counseling & Mana Gement, Second Edition. 2nd ed. 2009. 448p. 99.95 *(978-0-471-45893-7(7)*, Wiley-Liss) Wiley, John & Sons, Inc.

Offit, Ken & Robson, Mark. Genetic Predisposition to Cancer: Hematology/Oncology Clinics of North America. 2010. (Clinics: Internal Medicine Ser.: 24-5). (ENG.). 99.00 *(978-1-4377-2204-8(0)*, Saunders) Elsevier - Health Sciences Div.

Panno, Joseph. Cancer. 2nd rev. ed. 2010. (New Biology Ser.). (Illus.). 264p. (gr. 6-12). 40.00 *(978-0-8160-6848-7(8))* Facts On File, Inc.

Pasche, Boris. Cancer Genetics. 2010. (Cancer Treatment & Research Ser.). (ENG., Illus.). xii, 112p. 159.00 *(978-1-4419-6032-0(5)*, 1441960325) Springer.

Paull, Tanya. Mechanisms of DNA Damage Recognition. Paull, Tanya, ed. 2009. (Cancer Genetics Ser.). (Illus.). 250p. 139.00 *(978-0-387-69136-7(7))* Springer.

Pestell, Richard G. & Nevalainen, Marja T., eds. Prostate Cancer: Signaling Networks, Genetics, & New Treatment Strategies. 2008. (Current Clinical Oncology Ser.). (Illus.). 455p. 189.00 *(978-1-58829-741-9(1))* Humana Pr.

Poon, Randy Y. C., ed. Polyploidization & Cancer. 2010. (Advances in Experimental Medicine & Biology Ser.). (ENG., Illus.). xvi, 148p. 209.00 *(978-1-4419-6198-3(4)*, 1441961984) Springer.

Potter, John D. & Lindor, Noralane M., eds. Genetics of Colorectal Cancer. 2010. (Cancer Genetics Ser.). (Illus.). xii, 312p. pap. 189.00 *(978-1-4419-1865-9(5)*, 1441918655) Springer.

Queller, Jessica. Pretty Is What Changes: Impossible Choices, the Breast Cancer Gene, & How I Defied My Destiny. 2009. (ENG.). 272p. pap. 14.00 *(978-0-385-52041-6(7))* Spiegel & Grau.

Qureshi, Nadeem & Wilson, Brenda. Collection & Use of Cancer Family History in Primary Care. 2007. (Illus.). ix, 84p. *(978-1-58763-329-4(9))* Agency for Healthcare Research & Quality.

Rasnick, David. The Chromosomal Imbalance Theory of Cancer. 2011. (ENG., Illus.). 330p. 119.95 ***(978-1-57808-737-2(6))*** BIOS Scientific Publishers Ltd. GBR. Dist: Taylor & Francis Group.

Roth, Jack A., ed. Gene-Based Therapies for Cancer. 2010. (Current Cancer Research Ser.). (ENG., Illus.). xiv, 275p. 219.00 *(978-1-4419-6101-3(1)*, 1441961011) Springer.

Roy, Deodutta & Dorak, M. Tevfik, eds. Environmental Factors, Genes, & the Development of Human Cancers. 2010. (ENG., Illus.). xiii, 300p. 189.00 *(978-1-4419-6751-0(6)*, 1441967516) Springer.

Russo, Antonio, et al, eds. Diagnostic, Prognostic & Therapeutic Value of Gene Signatures. 2011. (Current Clinical Pathology Ser.). (ENG., Illus.). xi, 182p 189.00 ***(978-1-61779-357-8(4)***, 1617793574) Humana Pr.

Schneider, Katherine A. Counseling about Cancer: Strategies for Genetic Counseling. 3rd ed. 2011. (ENG., Illus.). 496p. pap. 69.95 ***(978-0-470-08150-1(3)***, Wiley-Blackwell) Wiley, John & Sons, Inc.

Schrijvers, Dirk, et al, eds. ESMO Handbook of Cancer Prevention. 2008. (European Society for Medical Oncology Handbooks Ser.). (Illus.). 172p. pap. 99.95 *(978-0-415-39085-9(0))* Taylor & Francis Group.

Scotting, Paul. Cancer: A Beginner's Guide. 2011. (Beginners Guide (Oneworld) Ser.). (ENG., Illus.). 208p. 14.95 *(978-1-85168-755-8(6))* Oneworld Pubns. GBR. Dist: National Bk. Network.

Senn, Hans-Jörg. Cancer Prevention: 4th International Conference 2006. 2007. (Recent Results in Cancer Research Ser.). (Illus.). xiv, 250p. 189.00 *(978-3-540-37695-8(X))* Springer.

Senn, Hansjörg, et al. Cancer Prevention II. 2008. (Recent Results in Cancer Research Ser.). (ENG., Illus.). xx, 252p. 159.00 *(978-3-540-69296-6(7))* Springer.

Shockney, Lillie. Top Concerns about HER2 Positive Breast Cancer. 2012. 128p. pap. 10.95 *(978-1-4496-0125-6(1))* Jones & Bartlett Learning, LLC.

Singh, Keshav K. & Costello, Leslie, eds. Mitochondria & Cancer. 2009. (ENG., Illus.). xii, 289p. 159.00 *(978-0-387-84834-1(7)*, 0387848347) Springer.

Singh, Shree Ram & Mishra, Manoj K. Signaling, Gene Regulation, & Cancer. 2012. ***(978-1-61942-088-5(0))*** Nova Science Pubs., Inc.

Slaby, Ondrej. MicroRNAs in Solid Cancer: From Biomarkers to Therapeutic Targets. 2012. (DNA & RNA: Properties & Modifications, Functions & Interactions, Recombination & Applications Cancer Etiology, Diagnosis & Treatments Ser.). (Illus.). 200p. 95.00 ***(978-1-61324-514-9(9))*** Nova Science Pubs., Inc.

Soreide, Kjetil & Soiland, Håvard. Clinical, Genetic & Molecular Precursor Features in Colorectal Neoplasia. Soreide, Kjetil & Soiland, Håvard, eds. 2008. (Illus.). 110p. (C). pap. 39.00 *(978-1-60456-714-4(7))* Nova Science Pubs., Inc.

Strausberg, Robert L., ed. Cancer Genomics. (Disease Markers Ser.). 120p. pap. 120.00 *(978-1-58603-251-7(8))* IOS Pr., Inc.

Szyf, Moshe. DNA Methylation & Cancer Therapy. 2010. (Medical Intelligence Unit Ser.). (Illus.). xv, 239p. pap. 209.00 *(978-1-4419-3416-1(2)*, 1441934162) Springer.

Tanguay, Robert M., ed. Aging, Cancer & Age-Related Disease: Common Mechanisms. 2010. (Annals of the New York Academy of Sciences Ser.: 51). (ENG., Illus.). 300p. pap. 130.00 *(978-1-57331-796-2(9)*, Wiley-Blackwell) Wiley, John & Sons, Inc.

Terrian, David M., ed. Cancer Cell Signaling: Methods & Protocols. 2010. (Methods in Molecular Biology Ser.). (Illus.). 352p. pap. 139.00 *(978-1-61737-341-1(9)*, 1617373419) Humana Pr.

Tollefsbol, Trygve O., ed. Cancer Epigenetics. 2008. (ENG., Illus.). 472p. 162.95 *(978-1-4200-4579-6(2)*, CRC Press) Taylor & Francis Group GBR. Dist: Taylor & Francis Group.

Tuffaha, Muin S. A. Phenotypic & Genotypic Diagnosis of Malignancies: An Immunohistochemical & Molecular Approach. 2008. (ENG.). 298p. 159.95 *(978-3-527-31881-0(X)*, Wiley-VCH) Wiley, John & Sons, Inc.

Wang, Timothy, et al, eds. The Biology of Gastric Cancers. 2010. (ENG., Illus.). xx, 332p. pap. 149.00 *(978-1-4419-2405-6(1)*, 1441924051) Springer.

Wang, Timothy, et al. The Biology of Gastric Cancers. 2008. (ENG., Illus.). xx, 332p. 149.00 *(978-0-387-69181-7(2)*, 0387691812) Springer.

Wang, Xin Wei, et al, eds. Molecular Genetics of Liver Neoplasia. 2010. (Cancer Genetics Ser.). (Illus.). 300p. 209.00 *(978-1-4419-6081-8(3)*, 1441960813) Springer.

Webb, Michelle. Cancer Susceptibility: Methods & Protocols. 2010. (Methods in Molecular Biology Ser.). (Illus.). xi, 295p. (ENG.). 139.00 *(978-1-60761-758-7(7)*, 1607617587); E-Book ***(978-1-60761-759-4(5))*** Humana Pr.

Weber, Georg F. Molecular Mechanisms of Cancer. 2010. (ENG.). xiv, 650p. pap. 149.00 *(978-90-481-7505-5(4)*, 9048175054) Springer.

Wei. Dna Repair, Genetic Instability, Cancer. 2006. (Illus.). xx, 253p. 124.00 *(978-981-270-014-8(5))* World Scientific Publishing Co., Inc.

Weinberg, Robert. The Biology of Cancer. 2010. (ENG.). cd-rom 20.00 *(978-0-8153-4458-2(9)*, Garland Science) Taylor & Francis Group.

Weinberg, Robert A. The Biology of Cancer. 2nd rev. ed. 2013. (ENG., Illus.). 864p. 126.00 ***(978-0-8153-4220-5(9))***; 168.00 ***(978-0-8153-4219-9(5))*** Taylor & Francis Group. (Garland Science).

Welcsh, Piri. The Role of Genetics in Breast & Reproductive Cancers. 2009. (Cancer Genetics Ser.). (ENG., Illus.). xiii, 332p. 189.00 *(978-1-4419-0476-8(X)*, 144190476X) Springer.

Wigle, Dennis A. & Wong, Bill, eds. Cancer Informatics in the Post Genomic Era: Toward Information-Based Medicine. 2007. (Cancer Treatment & Research Ser.). (Illus.). 180p. 159.00 *(978-0-387-69320-0(3))* Springer.

Wu, Wei, ed. MicroRNA & Cancer: Methods & Protocols. 2010. (Methods in Molecular Biology Ser.). (ENG., Illus.). x, 273p. 119.00 *(978-1-60761-862-1(1)*, 1607618621) Humana Pr.

CANCER—IMAGING

Alazraki, Naomi P., et al. A Clinician's Guide to Nuclear Oncology: Practical Molecular Imaging & Radionuclide Therapies. 2007. *(978-0-9726478-8-5(0))* SNM Publishing Co.

Bard, Robert L. Prostate Cancer Decoded: Non-Invasive Breakthrough Treatments. 2007. (ENG., Illus.). 168p. per. 17.95 *(978-1-60037-346-6(1))* Morgan James Publishing.

Birdwell, Robyn L. Breast Imaging, an Issue of Radiologic Clinics of North America. 2010. (Clinics: Radiology Ser.: 48-5). (ENG., Illus.). x, 844p. 105.00 *(978-1-4377-2595-7(3)*, Saunders) Elsevier - Health Sciences Div.

Blake, Michael A. & Kalra, Mannudeep K., eds. Imaging in Oncology. 2008. (Cancer Treatment & Research Ser.). (Illus.). XII, 572p. 129.00 *(978-0-387-75586-1(1)*, 0387755861) Springer.

Bombardieri, Emilio, et al, eds. Advances in Nuclear Oncology: Diagnosis & Therapy. 2007. (ENG., Illus.). 544p. 429.95 *(978-1-84184-614-9(7)*, Informa Healthcare) Taylor & Francis Group GBR. Dist: Taylor & Francis Group.

Brennecke, Cecilia M. Breast Imaging: Case Review Series. 2nd ed. 2012. (Case Review Ser.). (ENG., Illus.). 320p. pap. 49.95 ***(978-0-323-08722-3(1)***, Saunders) Elsevier - Health Sciences Div.

Catalano, Orlando, et al. Fundamentals in Oncologic Ultrasound: Sonographic Imaging & Intervention in the Cancer Patient. 2009. (Illus.). xvi, 376p. 219.00 *(978-88-470-1354-4(2))* Springer.

Chen, Xiaoyuan. Molecular Imaging Probes for Cancer Research. 2011. 1100p. 260.00 *(978-981-4293-67-9(9))* World Scientific Publishing Co., Inc.

D'Amico, Anthony V. & Harris, Jay R., eds. Image-Guided Diagnosis & Treatment of Cancer. 2010. (ENG., Illus.). 288p. pap. 125.00 *(978-1-61737-368-8(0)*, 1617373680) Humana Pr.

Davies, A. M., et al. Imaging of Bone Tumors. 2009. (Medical Radiology / Diagnostic Imaging Ser.). (Illus.). 410p. 239.00 *(978-3-540-77982-7(5))* Springer.

Delbeke, Dominique & Israel, Ora, eds. Hybrid PET/CT & SPECT/CT Imaging: A Teaching File. 2011. (ENG., Illus.). 762p. 99.00 *(978-1-4614-0090-5(2)*, 1461400902) Springer.

El-Baz, Ayman S., et al, eds. Multi Modality State-of-the-Art Medical Image Segmentation & Registration Methodologies: Volume 1. 2011. (ENG., Illus.). xii, 410p. 239.00 *(978-1-4419-8194-3(2)*, 1441981942) Springer.

—Multi Modality State-of-the-Art Medical Image Segmentation & Registration Methodologies: Volume II. 2011. (ENG., Illus.). x, 368p. 209.00 *(978-1-4419-8203-2(5)*, 1441982035) Springer.

Hermans, R. Head & Neck Cancer Imaging. 2009. (Medical Radiology / Diagnostic Imaging Ser.). (Illus.). 370p. pap. 149.00 *(978-3-540-68439-8(5))* Springer.

Hermans, Robert, ed. Head & Neck Cancer Imaging. 2nd ed. 2012. (Medical Radiology / Diagnostic Imaging Ser.). (ENG., Illus.). xiv, 413p. 319.00 *(978-3-642-17868-9(5)*, 3642178685) Springer.

—Squamous Cell Cancer of the Neck. 2008. (Contemporary Issues in Cancer Imaging Ser.). (ENG., Illus.). 164p. 83.00 *(978-0-521-88691-8(0))* Cambridge Univ. Pr.

Hoskin, Peter J. & Goh, Vicky. Imaging. 2010. (Radiotherapy in Practice Ser.). (ENG., Illus.). 336p. pap. 79.95 *(978-0-19-923132-4(X))* Oxford Univ. Pr., Inc.

Hricak, Hedvig & Scardino, Peter T. Prostate Cancer. Hricak, Hedvig & Scardino, Peter, eds. 2008. (Contemporary Issues in Cancer Imaging Ser.). (ENG., Illus.). 242p. 81.00 *(978-0-521-88704-5(6))* Cambridge Univ. Pr.

Husband, Janet, ed. Imaging in Oncology, 2 vols. 3rd ed. 2009. (Illus.). 1534p. 855.00 *(978-0-415-45167-3(1)*, Informa Healthcare) Taylor & Francis Group GBR. Dist: Taylor & Francis Group.

Jackson, Alan, et al. Dynamic Contrast-Enhanced Magnetic Resonance Imaging in Oncology. 2010. (Medical Radiology / Diagnostic Imaging Ser.). (Illus.). xii, 311p. pap. 279.00 *(978-3-642-07607-7(6)*, 3642076076) Springer.

Janecek, Martin. Instrumentation for Lesion Detection. 2010. 180p. pap. *(978-3-8383-2192-9(8))* Lambert Academic Publishing.

Kitapci, Mehmet. Atlas of Sectional Radiological Anatomy for PET/CT. 2012. (ENG., Illus.). xiii, 133p. 189.95 ***(978-1-4614-1526-8(8)***, 1461415268) Springer.

Madabhushi, Anant, et al, eds. Prostata Cancer Imaging - Image Analysis & Image-Guided Interventions: International Workshop, Held in Conjunction with MICCAI 2011, Toronto, Canada, September 22, 2011, Proceedings. 2011. (Lecture Notes in Computer Science / Image Processing, Computer Vision, Pattern Recognition, & Graphics Ser.). (ENG., Illus.). ix, 162p. pap. 72.00 ***(978-3-642-23943-4(9)***, 3642239439) Springer.

Mohnike, Wolfgang, et al, eds. Oncologic & Cardiologic PET/CT-Diagnosis: An Interdisciplinary Atlas & Manual. 2008. (Illus.). XVI, 739p. 279.00 *(978-3-540-74090-2(2)*, 3540740902) Springer.

Parvin, Elizabeth, ed. Screening for Breast Cancer. 2008. (Introducing Health Science Ser.). (ENG., Illus.). 104p. pap. 52.50 *(978-0-19-923733-3(6))* Oxford Univ. Pr., Inc.

Patel, Uday, ed. Carcinoma of the Kidney. 2007. (Contemporary Issues in Cancer Imaging Ser.). (ENG., Illus.). 256p. 83.00 *(978-0-521-87838-8(1))* Cambridge Univ. Pr.

Pomper Martin G Staff. Molecular Imaging in Oncology. 2008. (ENG., Illus.). 744p. 400.00 *(978-0-8493-7417-3(0)*, Informa Healthcare) Taylor & Francis Group GBR. Dist: Taylor & Francis Group.

Riemann, Burkhard & Schober, Otmar, eds. Molecular Imaging in Oncology. 2012. (Recent Results in Cancer Research Ser.: 187). (ENG., Illus.). 250p. 189.00 *(978-3-642-10852-5(0)*, 3642108520) Springer.

Rosenthal, Eben & Zinn, Kurt R. Optical Imaging of Cancer: Clinical Applications. 2009. (Illus.). 260p. 159.00 *(978-0-387-93873-8(7)*, 0387938737) Springer.

Rosette, Jean J. M C. H de la, et al, eds. Imaging in Oncological Urology. 2008. (Illus.). 936p. 169.00 *(978-1-84628-514-1(3)*, 1846285143) Springer.

Shaaban, Akram M., et al. Oncology. 2010. (ENG., Illus.). 815p. 339.00 *(978-1-931884-83-9(8))* Lippincott Williams & Wilkins.

Shields, Anthony F. & Price, Pat, eds. In Vivo Imaging of Cancer Therapy. 2010. (Cancer Drug Discovery & Development Ser.). xii, 326p. pap. 229.00 *(978-1-61737-684-9(1)*, 1617376841) Humana Pr.

Tartar, Marie, et al. Breast Cancer Imaging: A Multidisciplinary, Multimodality Approach. 2008. (ENG., Illus.). 632p. 182.00 *(978-0-323-04677-0(0)*, Mosby) Elsevier - Health Sciences Div.

Wang, D. T., ed. Targeted Imaging of Neoplasia in the Digestive Tract: Book Edition of Cancer Biomarkers. 2009. 289p. pap. 116.00 *(978-1-58603-974-5(1))* IOS Pr., Inc.

Yankeelov, Thomas, et al, eds. Quantitative Magnetic Resonance Imaging in Cancer. 2011. (ENG., Illus.). 338p. 129.95 ***(978-1-4398-2057-5(0)***, Taylor & Francis) Taylor & Francis Group GBR. Dist: Taylor & Francis Group.

CANCER—IMMUNOLOGICAL ASPECTS

Alexander, Michael A., ed. Immune-Based Cancer Treatment: The T lymphocyte Response. 2011. (ENG.). 250p. 129.95 *(978-1-57808-703-7(1))* BIOS Scientific Publishers Ltd. GBR. Dist: Taylor & Francis Group.

Bettuzzi, Saverio & Pucci, Sabina. Clusterin, 2 vols. 2009. (Advances in Cancer Research Ser.). (ENG., Illus.). 350p. 161.00 *(978-0-12-374772-3(4)*, Academic Pr.) Elsevier Science & Technology Bks.

Bodey, Bela, et al. Immunological Aspects of Neoplasia - the Role of the Thymus. 2010. (Cancer Growth & Progression Ser.). xi, 207p. pap. 149.00 *(978-90-481-6608-4(X)*, 904816608X) Springer.

Brown, F. & Petricciani, J., eds. Development of Therapeutic Cancer Vaccines Vol. 116: Congress, Los Angeles, Calif. , April 2004. (Developments in Biologicals Ser.). (Illus.). 12;248p. pap. *(978-3-8055-7736-6(2))* Karger, S. AG.

Cancer Prevention & Early Detection. Date not set. (Illus.). 10p. *(978-0-945100-70-6(1))* Parlay International.

Chu, Peiguo & Weiss, Lawrence. Modern Immunohistochemistry. 2009. (Cambridge Illustrated Surgical Pathology Ser.). (ENG., Illus.). 712p. (C). 169.00 *(978-0-521-87430-4(0))* Cambridge Univ. Pr.

Dalgleish, Angus G. & Haefner, Burkhard, eds. The Link Between Inflammation & Cancer: Wounds that do not Heal. 2010. (Cancer Treatment & Research Ser.). xi, 254p. pap. 179.00 *(978-1-4419-3881-7(8)*, 1441938818) Springer.

Dittmar, Thomas, et al. Infection & Inflammation: Impacts on Oncogenesis, Vol. 13. (Contributions to Microbiology Ser.: Vol. 13). (ENG & GER., Illus.). 246p. *(978-3-8055-8064-9(9))* Karger, S. AG.

Garcea, Robert & DiMaio, Daniel, eds. The Papillomaviruses. 2010. (ENG., Illus.). xx, 420p. pap. 149.00 *(978-1-4419-4215-9(7)*, 1441942157) Springer.

Litlekalsoy, Jorunn. Molecular Investigations on Archival Tissues. 2009. 104p. pap. *(978-3-639-16847-1(X))* VDM Verlag Dr. Mueller e.K.

Maio, M., ed. Immunology of Human Melanoma: Tumor-Host Interaction & Immunotherapy. (Biomedical & Health Research Ser.: Vol. 12). (Illus.). 250p. 116.00 *(978-90-5199-253-3(X))* IOS Pr., Inc.

Medin, Jeffrey & Fowler, Daniel H. Experimental & Applied Immunotherapy. 2011. (Illus.). xvii, 442p. E-Book ***(978-1-60761-980-2(6))*** Humana Pr.

Orentas, Rimas, et al. Cancer Vaccines & Tumor Immunity. 2008. (ENG., Illus.). 334p. 148.00 *(978-0-470-07474-9(4)*, Wiley-Liss) Wiley, John & Sons, Inc.

Robins, R. A. & Rees, R. C., eds. Cancer Immunology. 2010. (Immunology & Medicine Ser.). 276p. pap. 149.00 *(978-90-481-5714-3(5)*, 9048157145) Springer.

Singh, Ranjie N. Self-Healing: Powerful Techniques. Date not set. 252p. 24.95 *(978-1-896826-00-4(8))* APG Trade West.

Terabe, Masaki & Berzofsky, Jay A., eds. Natural Killer T Cells: Balancing the Regulation of Tumor Immunity. 2011. (Cancer Drug Discovery & Development Ser.). (ENG., Illus.). xi, 205p. 189.00 ***(978-1-4614-0612-9(9)***, 1461406129) Springer.

CANCER—IMMUNOTHERAPY

Alexander, Michael A., ed. Immune-Based Cancer Treatment: The T lymphocyte Response. 2011. (ENG.). 250p. 129.95 *(978-1-57808-703-7(1))* BIOS Scientific Publishers Ltd. GBR. Dist: Taylor & Francis Group.

Boltz, Agnes. Mimotope Vaccines Against Tumor Antigenes. 2008. 60p. pap. *(978-3-639-04375-4(8))* VDM Verlag Dr. Mueller e.K.

Bunimovich, Svetlana. Diseases of Development. 2009. 120p. pap. *(978-3-639-15113-8(5))* VDM Verlag Dr. Mueller e.K.

Chabner, Bruce A. & Longo, Dan L., eds. Cancer Chemotherapy & Biotherapy: Principles & Practice. 5th rev. ed. 2010. (ENG., Illus.). 848p. 238.99 *(978-1-60547-431-1(2))* Lippincott Williams & Wilkins.

Chanan-Khan, Asher A. A. Immunomodulating Drugs for the Treatment of Cancer. 2011. (ENG., Illus.). 312p. 134.95 *(978-1-60547-333-8(2))* Lippincott Williams & Wilkins.

Cho, William Cs. Immunomodulatory & Anti-Tumor Activities of Astragalus. 2010. 116p. pap. *(978-3-8383-0274-4(5))* Lambert Academic Publishing.

Disis, Mary L., ed. Immunotherapy of Cancer. 2010. (Cancer Drug Discovery & Development Ser.). (Illus.). 528p. pap. 229.00 *(978-1-61737-645-0(0)*, 1617376450) Humana Pr.

Dranoff, Glenn. Cancer Immunology & Immunotherapy. 2011. (Current Topics in Microbiology & Immunology Ser.). (ENG., Illus.). xiii, 304p. 189.00 *(978-3-642-14135-5(8)*, 3642141358) Springer.

Immunotherapy of Cancer. 2007. per. 4250.00 *(978-1-59623-276-1(5))* BCC Research.

Jeannin, Jean-Francois, ed. Lipid A in Cancer Therapy. 2010. (Advances in Experimental Medicine & Biology Ser.). (ENG., Illus.). 152p. 209.00 *(978-1-4419-1602-0(4)*, 1441916024) Springer.

Kaiser, Hans E. & Nasir, Aejaz, eds. Selected Aspects of Cancer Progression: Metastasis, Apoptosis & Immune Response. 2008. (Cancer Growth & Progression Ser.). (Illus.). 249p. 199.00 *(978-1-4020-6728-0(3))* Springer.

—Selected Aspects of Cancer Progression: Metastasis, Apoptosis & Immune Response: Metastasis, Apoptosis & Immune Response. 2010. (Cancer Growth & Progression Ser.). vi, 250p. pap. 199.00 *(978-90-481-7706-6(5)*, 9048177065) Springer.

Kaptzan, Tatiana, et al. Age-Adjusted Cancer Therapy Based on the Reduced Malignancy in the Old. 2010. 180p. pap. *(978-3-8383-3493-6(0))* Lambert Academic Publishing.

Kaufman, Howard L. & Wolchok, Jedd D., eds. General Principles of Tumor Immunotherapy: Basic & Clinical Applications of Tumor Immunology. 2007. (Illus.). 503p. 179.00 *(978-1-4020-6086-1(6))* Springer.

Ludewig, Burkhard & Hoffmann, Matthias W., eds. Adoptive Immunotherapy: Methods & Protocols. 2010. (Methods in Molecular Medicine Ser.). (Illus.). 520p. pap. 169.00 *(978-1-61737-546-0(2)*, 1617375462) Humana Pr.

Lustgarten, Joseph, et al, eds. Targeted Cancer Immune Therapy. 2009. (ENG., Illus.). xi, 343p. 229.00 *(978-1-4419-0169-9(8)*, 1441901698) Springer.

Mazor, Yariv. Recombinant Antibodies for Cancer Immunotherapy. 2009. 200p. pap. *(978-3-639-14586-1(0))* VDM Verlag Dr. Mueller e.K.

Medin, Jeffrey & Fowler, Daniel H. Experimental & Applied Immunotherapy. 2011. (Illus.). xvii, 442p. E-Book ***(978-1-60761-980-2(6))*** Humana Pr.

Oldham, Oldham, ed. Principles of Cancer Biotherapy. 5th ed. 2009. (ENG., Illus.). xii, 744p. 289.00 *(978-90-481-2277-6(5)*, 9048122775) Springer.

Pagé, Michel, ed. Tumor Targeting in Cancer Therapy. 2010. (Cancer Drug Discovery & Development Ser.). (Illus.). 466p. pap. 179.00 *(978-1-61737-251-3(X)*, 161737251X) Humana Pr.

Peper, Erik & Gorter, Phd, Robert. Fighting Cancer: A Nontoxic Approach to Treatment. 2011. (ENG., Illus.). 384p. pap. 22.95 *(978-1-58394-248-2(3))* North Atlantic Bks.

Prendergast, George C. & Jaffee, Elizabeth M., eds. Cancer Immunotherapy: Immune Suppression & Tumor Growth. 2007. (ENG., Illus.). 428p. 114.00 *(978-0-12-372551-6(8)*, Academic Pr.) Elsevier Science & Technology Bks.

Shurin, Michael R. & Salter, Russell David. Dendritic Cells in Cancer. Shurin, Michael R. & Salter, Russell D., eds. 2009. (ENG., Illus.). xviii, 396p. 139.00 *(978-0-387-88610-7(9)*, 0387886109) Springer.

Stigbrand, Torgny. Targeted Radionuclide Tumor Therapy: Biological Aspects. 2008. (ENG., Illus.). xiv, 402p. 219.00 *(978-1-4020-8695-3(4)*, 1402086954) Springer.

Wang, Rongfu, ed. Innate Immune Regulation & Cancer Immunotherapy. 2011. (ENG., Illus.). x, 478p. 209.00 *(978-1-4419-9913-9(2)*, 1441999132) Springer.

Welschof, Martin & Krauss, Jargen, eds. Recombinant Antibodies for Cancer Therapy: Methods & Protocols. 2010. (Methods in Molecular Biology Ser.). (Illus.). 496p. pap. 189.00 *(978-1-61737-250-6(1)*, 1617372501) Humana Pr.

Yotnda, Patricia, ed. Immunotherapy of Cancer: Methods & Protocols. 2010. (Methods in Molecular Biology Ser.). (Illus.). xi, 345p. 159.00 *(978-1-60761-785-3(4)*, 1607617854) Humana Pr.

Zahra, Ghotbi. Piga-Based Nanoparticles in Cancer Immunotherapy & Immunomonitoring: A Versatile Vehicle for Targeting of Dendritic Cells. 2011. 168p. pap. ***(978-3-639-27559-9(4))*** VDM Verlag Dr. Mueller e.K.

CANCER—MOLECULAR ASPECTS

Adjei, Alex A., ed. Lung Cancer Therapies. 2009. (Cancer Drug Discovery & Development Ser.). 135.00 *(978-1-60327-010-6(8))* Humana Pr.

Albitar, Maher. Immunological & Molecular Diagnosis of Cancer. 2011. (Immunology & Immune System Disorders Cancer Etiology, Diagnosis & Treatments Ser.). (Illus.). 293p. 129.00 *(978-1-61728-949-1(3))* Nova Science Pubs., Inc.

American Institute for Cancer Research, ed. Dietary Fat & Cancer: Genetic & Molecular Interactions. 2010. (Advances in Experimental Medicine & Biology Ser.). pap. 219.00 *(978-1-4419-3282-2(8)*, 1441932828) Springer.

Antalis, Toni M. & Bugge, Thomas, eds. Proteases & Cancer. 2009. (Methods in Molecular Biology Ser.). (Illus.). 300p. 129.00 *(978-1-60327-002-1(7)*, 1603270027) Humana Pr.

Barillot, Emmanuel, et al. Computational Systems Biology of Cancer. (Chapman & Hall/CRC Mathematical & Computational Biology Ser.). (Illus.). 2012. (ENG.). 452p. 79.95 *(978-1-4398-3144-1(0))* 2011. 356p. 79.95 *(978-1-4398-3145-8(9))* Taylor & Francis Group GBR. (CRC Press). Dist: Taylor & Francis Group.

Boultwood, Jacqueline & Fidler, Carrie, eds. Molecular Analysis of Cancer. 2010. (Methods in Molecular Medicine Ser.). (Illus.). 328p. pap. 139.00 *(978-1-61737-102-8(5)*, 1617371025) Humana Pr.

Brahmer, Julie R., et al, eds. Lung Cancer: Translational & Emerging Therapies. 2007. (Translational Medicine Ser.: Vol. 3). (ENG., Illus.). 280p. 100.00 *(978-0-8493-9021-0(4)*, Informa Healthcare) Taylor & Francis Group GBR. Dist: Taylor & Francis Group.

Bronchud, Miguel H., et al, eds. Principles of Molecular Oncology. 3rd ed. 2008. 448p. pap. 99.00 *(978-1-60327-505-7(3))* Springer.

Chatterjee, Malay & Kashfi, Khosrow, eds. Cell Signaling & Molecular Targets in Cancer. 2011. (ENG., Illus.). xi, 328p. 189.00 ***(978-1-4614-0729-4(X)***, 146140729X) Springer.

Chiocca, Susanna, et al, eds. Advances in Molecular Oncology. 2007. (Advances in Experimental Medicine & Biology Ser.). (Illus.). 274p. 179.00 *(978-0-387-69114-5(6))* Springer.

Cooper, David N. The Molecular Genetics of Lung Cancer. 2010. (ENG., Illus.). xvi, 392p. pap. 149.00 *(978-3-642-06190-5(7)*, 3642061907) Springer.

Croce, Carlo. MicroRNAs & Cancer. 2009. (Current Cancer Research Ser.). 270p. 139.99 *(978-1-60327-268-1(2))* Humana Pr.

d'Adda di Fagagna, Fabrizio, et al, eds. Advances in Molecular Oncology. 2010. (Advances in Experimental Medicine & Biology Ser.). viii, 274p. pap. 179.00 *(978-1-4419-4338-5(2)*, 1441943382) Springer.

Dai, Wei, ed. Checkpoint Responses in Cancer Therapy. 2008. (Cancer Drug Discovery & Development Ser.). (Illus.). 300p. 219.00 *(978-1-58829-930-7(9))* Humana Pr.

Daoud, Sayed S., ed. Cancer Proteomics: From Bench to Bedside. (Cancer Drug Discovery & Development Ser.). (Illus.). 2010. xii, 264p. pap. 149.00 *(978-1-61737-807-2(0)*, 1617378070) 2007. 264p. 149.00 *(978-1-58829-858-4(2))* Humana Pr.

Devita. Cancer Prin Prac Oncology Mol Biology. 2011. (Illus.). 456p. pap. 89.95 *(978-1-4511-1897-1(X))* Lippincott Williams & Wilkins.

Edwards, Dylan R. The Cancer Degradome: Proteases & Cancer Biology. 2008. (Illus.). 1000p. (C). 225.00 *(978-0-387-69056-8(5))* Springer.

El-Deiry, Wafik S., ed. Death Receptors in Cancer Therapy. 2010. (Cancer Drug Discovery & Development Ser.). (Illus.). 384p. pap. 209.00 *(978-1-61737-401-2(6)*, 1617374016) Humana Pr.

FARID, Nadir R. Molecular Basis of Thyroid Cancer. 2010. (Cancer Treatment & Research Ser.). vii, 444p. pap. 179.00 *(978-1-4419-5476-3(7)*, 1441954767) Springer.

Fisher, Paul B., ed. Cancer Genomics & Proteomics: Methods & Protocols. 2010. (Methods in Molecular Biology Ser.). (Illus.). xvi, 358p. pap. 99.50 *(978-1-61737-605-4(1)*, 1617376051) Humana Pr.

Foote, MaryAnn, et al, eds. Principles of Molecular Oncology. 3rd ed. 2007. (Illus.). 418p. 179.00 *(978-1-934115-25-1(8))* Humana Pr.

Ford, Thomas D. New Cancer Research Developments. 2009. pap. 129.00 *(978-1-60692-447-1(8))* Nova Science Pubs., Inc.

Han, Haiyong & Grippo, Paul, eds. Drug Discovery in Pancreatic Cancer: Models & Techniques. 2010. (ENG., Illus.). x, 352p. 199.00 *(978-1-4419-1159-9(6)*, 1441911596) Springer.

Hiyama, Keiko. Telomeres & Telomerase in Cancer. 2009. (Cancer Drug Discovery & Development Ser.). (Illus.). 300p. 189.00 *(978-1-60327-306-0(9))* Humana Pr.

Innocenti, Federico, ed. Genomics & Pharmacogenomics in Anticancer Drug Development & Clinical Response. 2010. (Cancer Drug Discovery & Development Ser.). (Illus.). xiv, 378p. pap. 189.00 *(978-1-61737-694-8(9)*, 1617376949) Humana Pr.

Jurisica, Igor, et al, eds. Cancer Informatics in the Post Genomic Era: Toward Information-Based Medicine. 2010. (Cancer Treatment & Research Ser.). (Illus.). xx, 180p. pap. 159.00 *(978-1-4419-4344-6(7)*, 1441943447) Springer.

Kaufman, Howard L., et al, eds. Molecular Targeting in Oncology. 2010. (Cancer Drug Discovery & Development Ser.). (Illus.). xvi, 734p. pap. 229.00 *(978-1-61737-653-5(1)*, 1617376531) Humana Pr.

Kiaris, Hippokratis. Understanding Carcinogenesis: An Introduction to the Molecular Basis of Cancer. 2006. (ENG., Illus.). 188p. 109.95 *(978-3-527-31486-7(5)*, Wiley-VCH) Wiley, John & Sons, Inc.

Krupp, Guido & Parwaresch, Reza, eds. Telomerases, Telomeres & Cancer. 2010. (Molecular Biology Intelligence Unit Ser.). 426p. pap. 279.00 *(978-1-4419-3391-1(3)*, 1441933913) Springer.

Ladanyi, Marc & Gerald, William L., eds. Expression Profiling of Human Tumors: Diagnostic & Research Applications. 2010. (Illus.). 416p. pap. 185.00 *(978-1-61737-375-6(3)*, 1617373753) Humana Pr.

Leonard, Debra G. B. Oncology. 2008. (ENG., Illus.). 275p. pap. 89.95 *(978-0-387-87364-0(3))* Springer.

Llombart-Bosch, Antonio, et al, eds. New Trends in Cancer for the 21st Century. 2nd ed. 2010. (Advances in Experimental Medicine & Biology Ser.). (Illus.). xxiv, 396p. pap. 179.00 *(978-90-481-7239-9(X)*, 904817239X) Springer.

Mendelsohn, John, et al. The Molecular Basis of Cancer. 3rd ed. 2008. (ENG., Illus.). 704p. 218.00 *(978-1-4160-3703-3(9)*, Saunders) Elsevier - Health Sciences Div.

Merchant PhD, Kendra, et al. Novel Molecular Targets for Genistein in Prostate Cancer Cells. 2010. 100p. pap. *(978-3-8383-3884-2(7))* Lambert Academic Publishing.

Meyers, Robert A., ed. Cancer: From Mechanisms to Therapeutic Approaches. 2007. (ENG.). 478p. 310.00 *(978-3-527-31768-4(6)*, Wiley-VCH) Wiley, John & Sons, Inc.

Molls, M. The Impact of Tumor Biology on Cancer Treatment & Multidisciplinary Strategies. 2009. (Medical Radiology / Radiation Oncology Ser.). (ENG., Illus.). x, 370p. 199.00 *(978-3-540-74385-9(5))* Springer.

Mydlo, Jack H., ed. Renal Cancer: Methods & Protocols. 2010. (Methods in Molecular Medicine Ser.). (Illus.). 416p. pap. 149.00 *(978-1-61737-208-7(0)*, 1617372080) Humana Pr.

Nakamura, Robert M., et al, eds. Cancer Diagnostics. 2010. (Contemporary Cancer Research Ser.). (Illus.). 520p. pap. 169.00 *(978-1-61737-399-2(0)*, 1617373990) Humana Pr.

Nevalainen, Marja T. Prostate Cancer; Signaling Networks, Genetics, & New Treatment Strategies. Pestell, Richard G., ed. 2008. 472p. pap. 99.00 *(978-1-60327-518-7(5))* Springer.

Potter, John D. & Lindor, Noralane M., eds. Genetics of Colorectal Cancer. 2010. (Cancer Genetics Ser.). (Illus.). xii, 312p. pap. 189.00 *(978-1-4419-1865-9(5)*, 1441918655) Springer.

Rauhala, Hanna. DNA Hypermethylation in Prostate Cancer. 2009. (Acta Universitatis Tamperensis Ser.). 143p. pap. 82.50 *(978-951-44-7883-3(5))* Tampere Univ. Pr. FIN. Dist: Coronet Bks.

Roulston, Joseph E. & Bartlett, John M. S., eds. Molecular Diagnosis of Cancer: Methods & Protocols. 2nd ed. 2010. (Methods in Molecular Medicine Ser.). (Illus.). 408p. pap. 179.00 *(978-1-61737-396-1(6)*, 1617373966) Humana Pr.

Ruddon, Raymond. Molecular Biology of Cancer: Translation to the Clinic. 2010. (ENG.). 400p. 161.00 *(978-0-12-385071-3(1)*, Academic Pr.) Elsevier Science & Technology Bks.

Rudolph, K. Lenhard. Telomeres & Telomerase in Ageing, Disease, & Cancer: Molecular Mechanisms of Adult Stem Cell Ageing. Rudolph, K. Lenhard, ed. 2007. (ENG., Illus.). xiv, 330p. 239.00 *(978-3-540-73708-7(1)*, 3540737081) Springer.

Rudolph, K. Lenhard, ed. Telomeres & Telomerase in Aging, Disease, & Cancer: Molecular Mechanisms of Adult Stem Cell Ageing. 2010. (ENG., Illus.). xiv, 330p. pap. 239.00 *(978-3-642-09288-6(8)*, 3642092888) Springer.

Schulz, Wolfgang Arthur. Molecular Biology of Human Cancers: An Advanced Student's Textbook. 2007. (ENG.). 536p. per. 79.95 *(978-1-4020-6559-0(0))* Springer.

Singh, Shree Ram & Mishra, Manoj K. Signaling, Gene Regulation, & Cancer. 2012. ***(978-1-61942-088-5(0))*** Nova Science Pubs., Inc.

Sobue, et al, eds. Integrated Molecular Medicine for Neuronal & Neoplastic Disorders. 2007. (Annals of the New York Academy of Sciences Ser.: 15). (ENG., Illus.). 200p. pap. 139.95 *(978-1-57331-655-2(5)*, Wiley-Blackwell) Wiley, John & Sons, Inc.

Stewart, David, ed. Molecular Approaches to Controlling Cancer. 2006. (ENG., Illus.). 538p. pap. 126.00 *(978-0-87969-774-7(1))* Cold Spring Harbor Laboratory Pr.

Stillman, Bruce & Stewart, David, eds. Molecular Approaches to Controlling Cancer. 2006. (ENG., Illus.). 538p. 310.00 *(978-0-87969-773-0(3))* Cold Spring Harbor Laboratory Pr.

Szyf, Moshe. DNA Methylation & Cancer Therapy. 2010. (Medical Intelligence Unit Ser.). (Illus.). xv, 239p. pap. 209.00 *(978-1-4419-3416-1(2)*, 1441934162) Springer.

Wang, Timothy, et al, eds. The Biology of Gastric Cancers. 2010. (ENG., Illus.). xx, 332p. pap. 149.00 *(978-1-4419-2405-6(1)*, 1441924051) Springer.

Wang, Timothy, et al. The Biology of Gastric Cancers. 2008. (ENG., Illus.). xx, 332p. 149.00 *(978-0-387-69181-7(2)*, 0387691812) Springer.

Weinberg, Robert. The Biology of Cancer. 2010. (ENG.). cd-rom 20.00 *(978-0-8153-4458-2(9)*, Garland Science) Taylor & Francis Group.

Weinberg, Robert A. The Biology of Cancer. 2nd rev. ed. 2013. (ENG., Illus.). 864p. 126.00 ***(978-0-8153-4220-5(9))***; 168.00 ***(978-0-8153-4219-9(5))*** Taylor & Francis Group. (Garland Science).

Wigle, Dennis A. & Wong, Bill, eds. Cancer Informatics in the Post Genomic Era: Toward Information-Based Medicine. 2007. (Cancer Treatment & Research Ser.). (Illus.). 180p. 159.00 *(978-0-387-69320-0(3))* Springer.

Wilkes, Gail M. Targeted Cancer Therapy: A Handbook for Nurses. rev. ed. 2009. 354p. pap. 67.95 *(978-0-7637-7211-6(9))* Jones & Bartlett Learning, LLC.

Wluf, Carsten & Andersen, Claus L., eds. Statistics & Informatics in Molecular Cancer Research. 2009. (ENG., Illus.). 304p. 85.00 *(978-0-19-953287-2(7))* Oxford Univ. Pr., Inc.

Yegnasubramanian, Srinivasan & Isaacs, William Brewster. Modern Molecular Biology: Approaches for Unbiased Discovery in Cancer Research. 2009. (Applied Bioinformatics & Biostatistics in Cancer Research Ser.). 200p. 219.00 *(978-0-387-69744-4(6))* Springer.

CANCER—NURSING

Bharti, Virendra Kumar & Mills, Shirley. Cancer, Arsenic, Mortality & Their Relationship. 2010. 76p. pap. *(978-3-8383-1974-2(5))* Lambert Academic Publishing.

Brown, Carlton G. Guide to Oncology Symptom Management. 2009. (Illus.). xv, 528p. pap. 105.00 *(978-1-890504-89-2(0))* Oncology Nursing Society.

Brown, Theresa. Critical Care: A New Nurse Faces Death, Life, & Everything in Between. (ENG.). 2011. 256p. pap. 14.99 *(978-0-06-179154-3(7))* 2010. 208p. 19.99 *(978-0-06-179155-0(5))* HarperCollins Pubs. (HarperOne).

Burke, Catherine, ed. Psychosocial Dimensions of Oncology Nursing Care. 2nd ed. 2009. 268p. pap. 67.00 *(978-1-890504-83-0(1))* Oncology Nursing Society.

Chernecky, Cynthia C. & Murphy-Ende, Kathleen. Acute Care Oncology Nursing. 2nd ed. 2008. (ENG., Illus.). 624p. pap. 73.95 *(978-1-4160-3734-7(9)*, Saunders) Elsevier - Health Sciences Div.

Corner, Jessica. Cancer Nursing: Care in Context. Corner, Jessica & Bailey, Christopher D., eds. 2nd rev. ed. 2008. (ENG., Illus.). 736p. pap. 91.99 *(978-1-4051-2253-5(6)*, Wiley-Blackwell) Wiley, John & Sons, Inc.

Cram101 Textbook Reviews & Cram101 Textbook Reviews. Outlines & Highlights for Cancer Nursing: Principles & Practice by Connie Henke Yarbro. 2011. 540p. pap. 38.95 ***(978-1-61812-536-1(2))*** Cram101 Inc.

—Outlines & Highlights for Oncology Nursing by Martha E Langhorne, Janet S Fulton, Shirley E Otto, Isbn: 9780323041850. 2011. 152p. pap. 29.95 ***(978-1-61461-724-2(4))*** Cram101 Inc.

Daya, Mohamud, et al. Cancer Emergencies, Part 1, an Issue of Emergency Medicine Clinics, 2 vols., Pt. 1. 2009. (Clinics: Internal Medicine Ser.: 27-2). (ENG., Illus.). 240p. 99.00 *(978-1-4377-0470-9(0)*, Saunders) Elsevier - Health Sciences Div.

Decker, Georgia M. & Lee, Colleen O. Handbook of Integrative Oncology Nursing: Evidence-Based Practice. 2010. (Illus.). 196p. *(978-1-890504-94-6(7))* Oncology Nursing Society.

Denton, Sylvia, ed. Cancer Nursing. pap. 57.50 *(978-0-7487-3300-2(0))* Nelson Thornes Ltd. GBR. Dist: International Specialized Bk. Services.

Dunleavey, Ruth. Cervical Cancer: A Guide for Nurses. 2009. (ENG., Illus.). 248p. pap. 58.99 *(978-0-470-06101-5(4)*, Wiley) Wiley, John & Sons, Inc.

Eaton, Linda & Tipton, Janelle, eds. Putting Evidence into Practice: Improving Oncology Patient Outcomes. 2009. (Illus.). xvii, 324p. pap. *(978-1-890504-84-7(X))* Oncology Nursing Society.

Eggert, Julie. Cancer Basics. 2010. (Illus.). 608p. *(978-1-890504-90-8(4))* Oncology Nursing Society.

Fawcett, Josephine Tonks N. & McQueen, Anne. Perspectives on Cancer Care. 2011. (ENG., Illus.). 272p. pap. 45.99 *(978-1-4051-9570-6(3),* Wiley-Blackwell) Wiley, John & Sons, Inc.

Fortenbaugh, Cathy & Rummel, Margaret A. Case Studies in Oncology Nursing: Text & OCN Exam Review. 2006. (Illus.). 220p. (C). pap. 63.95 *(978-0-7637-3455-8(1))* Jones & Bartlett Learning, LLC.

Gates, Rose A. & Fink, Regina M. Oncology Nursing Secrets. 3rd rev. ed. 2007. (Secrets Ser.). (ENG., Illus.). 688p. pap. 51.95 *(978-0-323-04457-8(3),* Mosby) Elsevier - Health Sciences Div.

Gibson, Faith & Soanes, Louise. Cancer in Children & Young People. Gibson, Faith, ed. 2008. (Wiley Series in Nursing Ser.: 21). (ENG., Illus.). 432p. pap. 94.99 *(978-0-470-05867-1(6),* Wiley) Wiley, John & Sons, Inc.

Haas, Marilyn & McBride, Deborah L. Managing the Oral Effects of Cancer Treatment: Diagnosis to Survivorship. 2011. 544p. *(978-1-935864-03-5(3))* Oncology Nursing Society.

Haas, Marilyn L., et al. Radiation Therapy: A Guide to Patient Care. 2007. (ENG., Illus.). 786p. 89.95 *(978-0-323-04030-3(6),* Mosby) Elsevier - Health Sciences Div.

Harmer, Victoria. Breast Cancer Nursing Care & Management. 2nd ed. 2011. (ENG., Illus.). 384p. pap. 49.99 *(978-1-4051-9866-0(4),* Wiley-Blackwell) Wiley, John & Sons, Inc.

Holmes Gobel, Barbara, et al, eds. Advanced Oncology Nursing Certification Review & Resource Manual. 2008. 872p. mass mkt. 75.00 *(978-1-890504-75-5(0))* Oncology Nursing Society.

Howard, Penny & Chady, Becky. Placement Learning in Cancer & Palliative Care Nursing: A guide for students in Practice. 2012. (Placement Learning Ser.). (ENG., Illus.). 518p. pap. 15.99 ***(978-0-7020-4300-0(1),*** Bailliere Tindall) Elsevier - Health Sciences Div.

Iwamoto, Ryan R., et al. Manual for Radiation Oncology Nursing Practice & Education. 4th ed. 2011. ***(978-1-935864-12-7(2))*** Oncology Nursing Society.

Jacobs, Léa K., ed. Coping with Cancer. 2008. (Illus.). 154p. 129.00 *(978-1-60456-213-2(7),* Nova Biomedical Bks.) Nova Science Pubs., Inc.

Kaplan, Marcelle, ed. Understanding & Managing Oncologic Emergencies: A Resource for Nurses. 2006. (Illus.). 327p. per. 70.00 *(978-1-890504-62-5(9))* Oncology Nursing Society.

Katz, Anne. Breaking the Silence on Cancer & Sexuality: A Handbook for Healthcare Providers. 2007. (Illus.). 280p. per. 70.00 *(978-1-890504-67-0(X))* Oncology Nursing Society.

King, Cynthia R. Quality of Life: From Nursing & Patient Perspectives. 3rd rev. ed. 2011. 570p. (C). pap. 72.95 *(978-0-7637-4943-9(5))* Jones & Bartlett Learning, LLC.

Lester, Joanne & Schmitt, Patricia. Cancer Rehabilitation & Survivorship: A Transdisciplinary Approach. 2011. 450p. pap. *(978-1-935864-05-9(X))* Oncology Nursing Society.

Mahon, Suzanne M. Breast Cancer. 2nd ed. 2012. 200p. pap. ***(978-1-935864-07-3(6))*** Oncology Nursing Society.

Masny, Agnes, et al. Genetics & Genomics in Oncology Nursing Practice. 2010. (Illus.). 346p. *(978-1-890504-91-5(2))* Oncology Nursing Society.

Newton, Susan, et al. Mosby's Oncology Nursing Advisor: A Comprehensive Guide to Clinical Practice. 2008. (ENG., Illus.). 560p. 66.95 *(978-0-323-04597-1(9),* Mosby) Elsevier - Health Sciences Div.

Otto, Shirley E., et al. Oncology Nursing. 5th rev. ed. 2007. (ENG., Illus.). 816p. per. 86.95 *(978-0-323-04185-0(X),* Mosby) Elsevier - Health Sciences Div.

Peate, Ian. Nursing & Health Survival Guide: Cancer Care. rev. ed. 2012. (ENG.). 74p. spiral bd. ***(978-1-4479-1204-0(7))*** Pearson Bks.

Perry, Beth. More Moments in Time: Images of Exemplary Nursing. 2009. (ENG.). 224p. pap. 32.95 *(978-1-897425-51-0(1))* UBC Pr. CAN. Dist: Univ. of Washington Pr.

Phillips, Janice & King, Cynthia, eds. Advancing Oncology Nursing Science. 2009. pap. 67.50 *(978-1-890504-76-2(9))* Oncology Nursing Society.

Prescher-Hughes, Debra S. Clinical Practice Protocols in Oncology Nursing. 2006. 675p. (C). pap. 72.95 *(978-0-7637-3639-2(2))* Jones & Bartlett Learning, LLC.

—Nurse's Chemotherapy Quick Pocket Reference. 2008. (ENG.). 208p. pap. 41.95 *(978-0-7637-5824-0(8))* Jones & Bartlett Learning, LLC.

Prescher-Hughes, Debra S. & Alkhoudairy, Cynthia J. Clinical Practice Protocols in Oncology Nursing. 2011. 675p. pap. 84.95 ***(978-1-4496-4752-0(9))*** Jones & Bartlett Learning, LLC.

Rancour, Patrice. Tales from the Pager Chronicles. 2008. *(978-1-930538-72-6(3))* Sigma Theta Tau International, Ctr. for Nursing Pr.

Saria, Marlon Garzo. Chemotherapy & Biotherapy Scenarios. 2010. 88p. *(978-1-890504-92-2(0))* Oncology Nursing Society.

Sheldon, Lisa Kennedy, et al. Caring for Cancer Survivors: Prostate Cancer. 2009. (ENG.). 230p. spiral bd. 28.95 *(978-0-7637-7262-8(3))* Jones & Bartlett Learning, LLC.

Shockney, Lillie. Becoming a Breast Center Nurse Navigator. rev. ed. 2009. 148p. pap. 28.95 *(978-0-7637-8494-2(X))* Jones & Bartlett Learning, LLC.

Tadman, Michael & Roberts, David, eds. Oxford Handbook of Cancer Nursing. 2007. (ENG., Illus.). 726p. vinyl bd. 55.50 *(978-0-19-856924-4(6))* Oxford Univ. Pr., Inc.

Videtic, Gregory, et al. Handbook of Radiation Treatment Delivery. 2010. 259.00 *(978-1-933864-52-5(4))* Demos Medical Publishing, LLC.

Wilkes, Gail & Barton-Burke, Margaret. 2010 Oncology Nursing Drug Handbook. 14th rev. ed. 2009. 1360p. pap. 102.95 *(978-0-7637-8124-8(X))* Jones & Bartlett Learning, LLC.

—2011 Oncology Nursing Drug Handbook. 15th ed. 2010. (Illus.). 1368p. pap. 96.95 *(978-1-4496-0013-6(1))* Jones & Bartlett Learning, LLC.

Wilkes, Gail M. Targeted Cancer Therapy: A Handbook for Nurses. rev. ed. 2009. 354p. pap. 67.95 *(978-0-7637-7211-6(9))* Jones & Bartlett Learning, LLC.

Wilkes, Gail M. & Barton-Burke, Margaret. Oncology Nursing Drug Handbook. 2006. (Oncology Nursing Drug Handbook Ser.). 1217p. per. 93.95 *(978-0-7637-4306-2(2))* Jones & Bartlett Learning, LLC.

—2008 Oncology Nursing Drug Handbook. 2007. 1220p. pap. 88.95 *(978-0-7637-5563-8(X))* Jones & Bartlett Learning, LLC.

Wilkes, Gail M. & Burke, Margaret Barton. 2012 Oncology Nursing Drug Handbook. 16th ed. 2011. 1418p. pap. 93.95 ***(978-1-4496-4462-8(7))*** Jones & Bartlett Learning, LLC.

Wilkes, Gail M., et al. 2009 Oncology Nursing Drug Handbook. 13th ed. 2008. 1298p. pap. 104.95 *(978-0-7637-6585-9(6))* Jones & Bartlett Learning, LLC.

Yarbro, Connie Henke, et al. Cancer Nursing: Principles & Practice. 7th rev. ed. 2010. (Illus.). 1946p. 233.95 *(978-0-7637-6357-2(8))* Jones & Bartlett Learning, LLC.

—Oncology Nursing Review. 4th rev. ed. 2007. 294p. pap. 85.95 *(978-0-7637-5030-5(1))* 5th ed. 2011. 280p. pap. 89.95 *(978-1-4496-3178-9(9))* Jones & Bartlett Learning, LLC.

CANCER—NUTRITIONAL ASPECTS

see also Cancer—Diet Therapy

American Institute for Cancer Research, ed. Dietary Fat & Cancer: Genetic & Molecular Interactions. 2010. (Advances in Experimental Medicine & Biology Ser.). pap. 219.00 *(978-1-4419-3282-2(8),* 1441932828) Springer.

Anker, Stefan, et al, eds. Cachexia & Wasting: A Modern Approach. 2006. (Illus.). xxii, 756p. 339.00 *(978-88-470-0471-9(3),* 8847004713) Springer.

Anthc, prod. Traditional Food Guide for Alaska Native Cancer Survivors. 2008. (Illus.). 142p. spiral bd. 24.95 *(978-0-615-19667-1(5))* Alaska Native Tribal Health Consortium.

Bauman, Ed & Waldman, Helayne L. The Whole-Food Guide for Breast Cancer Survivors: A Nutritional Approach to Preventing Reoccurrence. 2012. (New Harbinger Whole-Body Healing Ser.). (ENG., Illus.). 272p. pap. 18.95 ***(978-1-57224-958-5(7))*** New Harbinger Pubns.

Béliveau, Richard & Gingras, Denis. Cooking with Foods That Fight Cancer. 2007. (ENG., Illus.). 272p. pap. 24.95 *(978-0-7710-1136-8(9),* McClelland & Stewart) McClelland & Stewart CAN. Dist: Random Hse., Inc.

Berger, Nathan A., ed. Cancer & Energy Balance, Epidemiology & Overview. 2010. (Energy Balance & Cancer Ser.). (ENG., Illus.). 232p. 209.00 *(978-1-4419-5514-2(3),* 1441955143) Springer.

Bloch, Abby S., et al, eds. American Cancer Society Complete Guide to Nutrition for Cancer Survivors: Eating Well, Staying Well During & after Cancer. 2nd ed. 2010. (American Cancer Society Complete Guide T Ser.). (ENG.). 284p. pap. 24.95 *(978-0-944235-78-2(6),* 0944235786) American Cancer Society, Inc.

Calviello, Gabriella & Serini, Simona, eds. Dietary Omega-3 Polyunsaturated Fatty Acids & Cancer. 2010. (Diet & Cancer Ser.). (ENG., Illus.). xx, 241p. 199.00 *(978-90-481-3578-3(8),* 9048135788) Springer.

Del Fabbro, Egidio, et al. Nutrition & the Cancer Patient. Hopkinson, Jane, ed. 2010. (ENG., Illus.). 600p. 139.95 *(978-0-19-955019-7(0))* Oxford Univ. Pr., Inc.

Greer, Julia B. The Anti-Cancer Cookbook: How to Cut Your Risk with the Most Powerful, Cancer-Fighting Foods. 2008. 224p. pap. 19.95 *(978-0-9624814-9-9(1))* Sunrise River Pr.

Holford, Patrick & Efiong, Liz. Say No to Cancer: The Drug-Free Guide to Preventing & Helping Fight Cancer. 2011. (ENG., Illus.). 414p. pap. 19.95 *(978-0-7499-5411-6(6))* Piatkus Bks. GBR. Dist: Independent Pubs. Group.

Janecek, Herve. Secret to Long Life in Your Dna. 2009. (ENG.). 1p. pap. *(978-1-59477-259-7(2),* Healing Arts Pr.) Inner Traditions International, Ltd.

Katzin, Carolyn F. The Everything Cancer-Fighting Cookbook. 2011. (ENG.). 304p. pap. 16.95 *(978-1-4405-0746-5(5))* Adams Media Corp.

Keane, Maureen & Chace, Daniella. What to Eat if You Have Cancer: Healing Foods That Boost Your Immune System. 2nd rev. ed. 2006. (ENG., Illus.). 288p. per. 16.95 *(978-0-07-147396-5(3),* 0071473963) McGraw-Hill Cos., The.

LaMantia, Jean & Berinstein, Neil. The Essential Cancer Treatment Nutrition Guide & Cookbook: Includes 150 Healthy & Delicious Recipes. 2012. (ENG., Illus.). 320p. pap. 24.95 ***(978-0-7788-0298-3(1))*** Rose, Robert Inc. CAN. Dist: Firefly Bks., Ltd.

Marian, Mary & Roberts, Susan. Clinical Nutrition for Oncology Patients. 2009 (Illus.). 463p. 98.95 *(978-0-7637-5512-6(5))* Jones & Bartlett Learning, LLC.

Milner, John A. & Romagnolo, Donato F., eds. Bioactive Compounds & Cancer. 2010. (Nutrition & Health Ser.). (ENG., Illus.). xiv, 882p. 269.00 *(978-1-60761-626-9(2),* 1607616262) Humana Pr.

Mittelman, Steven D. & Berger, Nathan A., eds. Energy Balance & Hematologic Malignancies. 2012. (Energy Balance & Cancer Ser.). (ENG., Illus.). x, 184p. 139.00 ***(978-1-4614-2402-4(X),*** 146142402X) Springer.

Mutanen, Marja & Pajari, Anne-Maria, eds. Vegetables, Whole Grains, & Their Derivatives in Cancer Prevention. 2010. (Diet & Cancer Ser.). (Illus.). xvii, 250p. 189.00 *(978-90-481-9799-6(6),* 9048197996) Springer.

Ramonde, Pauline R. & Fochas, Eva H., eds. Obesity & Cancer Research. 2009. 129.00 *(978-1-60692-388-7(9))* Nova Science Pubs., Inc.

Renzenbrink, Udo. Diet & Cancer. 68p. pap. 11.95 *(978-0-85440-766-8(9),* 415) Steiner, Rudolf Pr. GBR. Dist: Steiner, Rudolf Pr.

Shankar, Sharmila & Srivastava, Rakesh K., eds. Nutrition, Diet & Cancer. 2012. (ENG., Illus.). xv, 627p. 209.00 ***(978-94-007-2922-3(7),*** 9400729227) Springer.

Shaw, Clare. Nutrition & Cancer. 2011. (ENG., Illus.). 416p. pap. 60.99 *(978-1-4051-9042-8(6),* Wiley-Blackwell) Wiley, John & Sons, Inc.

Watson, Ronald Ross & Preedy, Victor R., eds. Bioactive Foods & Extracts: Cancer Treatment & Prevention. 2010. (ENG., Illus.). 663p. 169.95 *(978-1-4398-1619-6(0),* CRC Press) Taylor & Francis Group GBR. Dist: Taylor & Francis Group.

Weinstein, Jodi Buckman. Tell Me What to Eat Before, During, & after Cancer Treatment: Nutritional Guidelines for Patients & Their Loved Ones. 2010. (Tell Me What to Eat Ser.). (ENG.). 1p. pap. 12.99 *(978-1-60163-109-1(X),* New Page Bks.) Career Pr., Inc.

World Cancer Research Fund / American Institute for Cancer Research. Food, Nutrition, Physical Activity, & the Prevention of Cancer: A Global Perspective. 2007. (Illus.). 517p. pap. 69.95 *(978-0-9722522-2-5(3))* American Institute For Cancer Research.

Zappia, Vincenzo, et al, eds. Advances in Nutrition & Cancer 2. 2010. (Advances in Experimental Medicine & Biology Ser.). 312p. pap. 169.00 *(978-1-4419-3331-7(X),* 144193331X) Springer.

CANCER—PAIN

see Cancer Pain

CANCER—PALLIATIVE TREATMENT

Berger, Ann M., et al, eds. Principles & Practice of Palliative Care & Supportive Oncology. 3rd rev. ed. 2006. (Visual Mnemonics Ser.). (ENG., Illus.). 944p 224.99 *(978-0-7817-9595-1(8))* Lippincott Williams & Wilkins.

Bharti, Virendra Kumar & Mills, Shirley. Cancer, Arsenic, Mortality & Their Relationship. 2010. 76p. pap. *(978-3-8383-1974-2(5))* Lambert Academic Publishing.

Bucher, Julia A., et al. American Cancer Society Complete Guide to Family Caregiving: The Essential Guide to Cancer Caregiving at Home. 2nd ed. 2011. (American Cancer Society Complete Guide T Ser.). (ENG., Illus.). 304p. pap. 24.95 *(978-0-944235-00-3(X),* 094423500X) American Cancer Society, Inc.

Buckley, Jenny. Palliative Care: An Integrated Approach. 2008. (ENG., Illus.). 348p. pap. 73.99 *(978-0-470-05885-5(4),* Wiley) Wiley, John & Sons, Inc.

Chow, Edward & Merrick, Joav, eds. Advanced Cancer. Pain & Quality of Life. 2010. (Health & Human Development (Joav Merrick - Series Editor) Ser.). 89.00 *(978-1-61668-207-1(8),* Nova Biomedical Bks.) Nova Science Pubs., Inc.

Gaba, Nidha. Radioprotectors & Radiosensitizers. 2011. 200p. pap. ***(978-3-8443-0196-0(8))*** Lambert Academic Publishing.

Glare, Paul & Christakis, Nicholas A., eds. Prognosis in Advanced Cancer. 2008. (ENG., Illus.). 432p. pap. 85.00 *(978-0-19-853022-0(6))* Oxford Univ. Pr., Inc.

Held. Delia's Book: Guidance for Cancer Healing. 2009. 80p. pap. 15.95 *(978-1-4490-2998-2(1))* AuthorHouse.

Kissane, David, et al. Handbook of Communication in Oncology & Palliative Care. 2010. (ENG., Illus.). 520p. 125.00 *(978-0-19-923836-1(7))* Oxford Univ. Pr., Inc.

Kissane, David, et al. Handbook of Communication in Oncology & Palliative Care. 2011. (ENG., Illus.). 784p. pap. 75.00 *(978-0-19-923837-8(5))* Oxford Univ. Pr., Inc.

MacDonald, Gayle. Medicine Hands: Massage Therapy for People with Cancer. 2nd ed. 2007. (ENG., Illus.). 240p. pap. 29.95 *(978-1-84409-090-7(6))* Findhorn Pr. GBR. Dist: Independent Pubs. Group.

Mak, J M. Promoting a Good Death for Cancer Patients of Asian Culture: An evidence-based Approach. 2007. (Illus.). 344p. *(978-1-86177-100-1(2))* Whiting & Birch, Ltd.

Menten, Johan. Cancer Pain: Interdisciplinary & comprehensive Management. 2010. 168p. pap. *(978-3-8383-4370-9(0))* Lambert Academic Publishing.

Parker, R. G. & Selch, M. T. Radiation Oncology for Cure & Palliation. 2010. (Medical Radiology / Radiation Oncology Ser.). (Illus.). xii, 282p. pap. 269.00 *(978-3-642-07466-0(9),* 3642074669) Springer.

Pastores, Stephen & Halpern, Neil A. Intensive Care of the Cancer Patient, an Issue of Critical Care Clinics. 2009. (Clinics: Internal Medicine Ser.: 26-1). (ENG., Illus.). xiv, 237p. 105.00 *(978-1-4377-1806-5(X),* Saunders) Elsevier - Health Sciences Div.

Pescatore, Fred. The Science of AHCC: Supplement for 21st Century Cancer Treatment, 1 vol. 2010. 128p. pap. 12.95 *(978-1-59120-280-6(9))* Basic Health Pubns., Inc.

Rankin, Jane L., et al, eds. Rehabilitation in Cancer Care. 2008. (ENG., Illus.). 360p. pap. 82.99 *(978-1-4051-5997-5(9),* Wiley-Blackwell) Wiley, John & Sons, Inc.

CANCER—PATIENTS

Ahmadi, Fereshteh. Culture, Religion & Spirituality in Coping: The Example of Cancer in Patients in Sweden. 2006. (Studia Sociologica Upsaliensia: No.53). 197p. pap. 53.50 *(978-91-554-6589-6(7))* Uppsala Universitet/Acta Universitatis Upsaliensis SWE. Dist: Coronet Bks.

Alam, M. Shabbir & Moshahid A Rizvi, M. Cancer of Uterine Cervix & Pten Tumor Suppressor Gene. 2011. 132p. pap. ***(978-3-8443-0287-5(5))*** Lambert Academic Publishing.

American Cancer Society Staff. Cancer Caregiving A-Z: An At-Home Guide for Patients & Their Loved Ones. 2008. (ENG.). 157p. pap. 14.95 *(978-0-944235-92-8(1),* 9780944235928) American Cancer Society, Inc.

Angelos, M.D., Peter, ed. Ethical Issues in Cancer Patient Care. 2nd ed. 2007. (Cancer Treatment & Research Ser.). (Illus.). 258p. 149.00 *(978-0-387-73638-9(7))* Springer.

Angelos, Peter. Ethical Issues in Cancer Patient Care. 2nd ed. 2008. (Cancer Treatment & Research Ser.). 272p. pap. 59.95 *(978-0-387-87717-4(7))* Springer.

Angelos, Peter, ed. Ethical Issues in Cancer Patient Care. 2nd ed. 2008. pap. ***(978-0-387-78811-1(5))*** Springer Singapore Pte. Ltd.

Arms, Mamie L. C. H. E. M. O. Plan Your Day. 2011. 56p. pap. 8.95 ***(978-1-4620-2215-1(4))*** iUniverse, Inc.

Barry, Michael S. & Barry, Michael. The Art of Caregiving: How to Lend Support & Encouragement to Those with Cancer. 2007. (ENG.). 160p. 14.99 *(978-0-7814-4430-9(6))* Cook, David C.

Battle, Louise A. The Fight Is On! 2010. 214p. pap. 15.99 *(978-1-61579-723-3(8))* Xulon Pr., Inc.

Bellenir, Karen, ed. Cancer Survivorship Sourcebook: Basis Consumer Health Information about the Physical, Educational, Emotional, Social, & Financial Needs of Cancer Patients from Diagnosis, Through Cancer Treatment, & Beyond, Including Facts about Researching Specific Types of Cancer & Learning About. 2007. (Health Reference Ser.). 661p. 87.00 *(978-0-7808-0985-7(8))* Omnigraphics, Inc.

Betty Crocker Editors, et al. Betty Crocker Living with Cancer Cookbook. 2011. (ENG., Illus.). 288p. pap. 19.99 *(978-1-118-08314-7(8),* Betty Crocker) Wiley, John & Sons, Inc.

Beumer, John, et al. Maxillofacial Rehabilitation: Surgical & Prosthodontic Management of Cancer-Related, Acquired, & Congenital Defects of the Head & Neck. 3rd ed. 2011. ***(978-0-86715-498-6(5))*** Quintessence Publishing Co., Inc.

Bosanquet, Nicholas & Sikora, Karol. The Economics of Cancer Care. 2010. (ENG.). 192p. pap. 39.99 *(978-0-521-18380-2(4))* Cambridge Univ. Pr.

Brown, Carlton G. Guide to Oncology Symptom Management. 2009. (Illus.). xv, 528p. pap. 105.00 *(978-1-890504-89-2(0))* Oncology Nursing Society.

Buckman, Robert. Cancer Is a Word, Not a Sentence: A Practical Guide to Help You Through the First Few Weeks. 2006. (ENG., Illus.). 280p. per. 19.95 *(978-1-55407-234-7(4))* Firefly Bks., Ltd.

Canfield, Jack L., et al. Chicken Soup for the Soul: the Cancer Book: 101 Stories of Courage, Support & Love. 2009. (Chicken Soup for the Soul Ser.). (ENG.). 440p. pap. 14.95 *(978-1-935096-30-6(3))* Chicken Soup for the Soul Publishing, LLC.

Carter, Stephanie R. Taking Charge of Fighting Cancer: An easy to use Workbook. 2011. 112p. pap. 17.95 ***(978-1-4620-1377-7(5))*** iUniverse, Inc.

Cooper, Margaret. My Sister's Battle with Pancreatic Cancer. 2011. 38p. pap. 16.95 ***(978-1-4626-0822-5(1))*** PublishAmerica, Inc.

Creative Center Staff. Still Life: Documenting Cancer Survivorship. 2007. (ENG., Illus.). 80p. per. 29.95 *(978-1-884167-65-2(9))* Umbrage Editions.

Cummins, Sherry Taylor. Pink Ribbon Devotions to Go. 2007. pap. 8.95 *(978-0-9789831-3-0(0))* See Media.

Decker, Veronica & Weller-Ferris, Linda. Coping with Cancer: A Patient Pocket Book of Thoughts, Advice, & Inspiration for the Ill. 2009. v, 74p. pap. 9.95 *(978-1-890504-79-3(3))* Oncology Nursing Society.

Del Fabbro, Egidio, et al. Nutrition & the Cancer Patient. Hopkinson, Jane, ed. 2010. (ENG., Illus.). 600p. 139.95 *(978-0-19-955019-7(0))* Oxford Univ. Pr., Inc.

Dellinger, Annetta & Boerger, Karen. Blessings & Prayers for Those with Cancer. 2011. 192p. pap. 5.99 ***(978-0-7586-2672-1(X))*** Concordia Publishing Hse.

Dresser, Rebecca, ed. Malignant: Medical Ethicists Confront Cancer, 1 vol. 2012. (ENG.). 272p. 29.95 ***(978-0-19-975784-8(4))*** Oxford Univ. Pr., Inc.

Dwivedi, Alok, et al. Statistical Models for Treatment Delay & Number of Lymph Nodes. 2011. 304p. pap. ***(978-3-8443-2044-2(X))*** Lambert Academic Publishing.

Eaton, Linda & Tipton, Janelle, eds. Putting Evidence into Practice: Improving Oncology Patient Outcomes. 2009. (Illus.). xvii, 324p. pap. *(978-1-890504-84-7(X))* Oncology Nursing Society.

Eib, Lynn. 50 Days of Hope: Daily Inspiration for Your Journey Through Cancer. 2012. (ENG.). 256p. im. lthr. 13.99 ***(978-1-4143-6449-0(0))*** Tyndale Hse. Pubs.

Ellison, Connie, ed. Chemo Caps & Wraps. 2010. (ENG., Illus.). 80p. pap. 14.95 *(978-1-59635-327-5(9),* Annie's Attic, LLC) Annie's Publishing, LLC.

Ettinger, David S. Supportive Care in Cancer Therapy. Ettinger, David S., ed. 2008. (Illus.). 350p. 179.00 *(978-1-58829-941-3(4))* Humana Pr.

Fawcett, Josephine Tonks N. & McQueen, Anne. Perspectives on Cancer Care. 2011. (ENG., Illus.). 272p. pap. 45.99 *(978-1-4051-9570-6(3),* Wiley-Blackwell) Wiley, John & Sons, Inc.

Feuerstein, Michael & Ganz, Patricia A., eds. Health Services for Cancer Survivors: Practice, Policy & Research. 2011. (ENG., Illus.). xxiii, 395p. 169.00 *(978-1-4419-1347-0(5),* 1441913475) Springer.

Fleishman, Stewart. Learn to Live Through Cancer: What You Need to Know & Do. 2012. (Illus.). xiii, 348p. E-Book ***(978-1-61705-062-6(8))*** 2011. (ENG.). 320p. pap. 18.95 *(978-1-936303-08-3(6))* Demos Medical Publishing, LLC.

Gardner, Sara. Thoughts from My Gift of Cancer. 2010. 335p. pap. 26.51 *(978-1-4457-7006-2(7))* Lulu Enterprises Inc.

Gaudio, James J. Got Cancer? Spring Break Gone Bad. 2009. 168p. pap. 17.65 *(978-1-4251-6448-5(X))* Trafford Publishing.

Gay J. Lindquist. Valley of the Shadow: A Journey Through Cancer & Beyond. 2010. 124p. 23.95 (978-1-4401-9677-5(X)); pap. 13.95 (978-1-4401-9675-1(3)) iUniverse, Inc.

Gionta, Dana. Medical Staff-Family Health Communication in Cancer. 2009. 72p. pap. (978-3-639-11240-5(7)) VDM Verlag Dr. Mueller e.K.

Girard, Vickie. There's No Place Like Hope: A Guide to Berating Cancer in Mind-Sized Bites. Zadra, Dan, ed. 7th rev. ed. 2008. 192p. 14.95 (978-1-932319-70-5(0)) Compendium, Inc., Publishing & Communications.

Graff, Joyce, ed. VHL Handbook Version 3. 1: What You Need to Know about VHL. 2009. (ENG., Illus.). 116p. per. 12.99 (978-1-929539-05-5(3)) V H L Family Alliance.

Guidry, Jeff. An Eagle Named Freedom: My True Story of a Remarkable Friendship. 2011. (ENG.). 224p. pap. 14.99 (978-0-06-201550-1(8), Harper Paperbacks) 2010. 224p. 21.99 (978-0-06-182674-0(X), Morrow, William & Co.) 2010. (ENG.). 240p. pap. 21.99 (978-0-06-194572-4(2), HarperLuxe) HarperCollins Pubs.

Hall, John W. Beating Cancer Can Be Fun: Cancer Fighting Strategies for First Time Diagnosed Cancer Patients. 2011. 108p. 21.23 **(978-1-4634-0362-1(3))**; pap. 15.68 **(978-1-4634-0364-5(X))** AuthorHouse.

Hanks, Jerry & Cordova-Hanks, Bobbi de. Lagrimas de Alegria. 2007. 120p. pap. 12.95 (978-0-7414-3859-1(3)) Infinity Publishing.

Hassey, Patrick. Eyes Through You. 2011. 228p. pap. 15.79 **(978-1-4567-3915-7(8))** AuthorHouse.

Hibbard Willett, Jean. Dear Mom: Why Raising Four Boys Was Neither Boring nor Monotonous. 2008. 242p. per. 19.95 (978-0-9765872-2-4(X)) Caseys World Bks.

Higgins, Erin & Lightbody, Alma. My Wonderful Nightmare: Spiritual Journals Inspired by Cancer. 2010. 196p. pap. 18.00 (978-1-4251-8725-5(0)) Trafford Publishing.

Holland, Jimmie C., et al, eds. Psycho-Oncology, 1 vol. 2nd ed. 2010. (ENG., Illus.). 720p. 149.95 (978-0-19-536743-0(X)) Oxford Univ. Pr., Inc.

Hopko, Derek & Lejuez, Carl. A Cancer Patient's Guide to Overcoming Depression & Anxiety: Getting Through Treatment & Getting Back to Your Life. 2008. (New Harbinger Self-Help Workbook Ser.). (ENG., Illus.). 248p. pap. 19.95 (978-1-57224-504-4(2)) New Harbinger Pubns.

Houchins, Marge. Cheerleader Faith: Team Spirit for the Cancer Patient What to Do When Trouble Comes! 2011. 60p. 24.99 **(978-1-4628-4566-8(5))**; pap. 15.99 **(978-1-4628-4565-1(7))** Xlibris Corp.

Inspirio Staff, creator. What Cancer Cannot Do, 1 vol. 2006. (ENG., Illus.). 128p. 12.99 (978-0-310-81184-8(8)) Inspirio.

Institute of Medicine. Assessing & Improving Value in Cancer Care: Workshop Summary. 2009. (ENG.). 164p. pap. 38.50 (978-0-309-13814-7(0)) National Academies Pr.

Irving, Colm. Anaesthesia, intensive care, & pain management for the cancer Patient. Farquhar-Smith, Paul & Wigmore, Tim, eds. 2011. (ENG., Illus.). 272p. 98.50 (978-0-19-958464-2(8)) Oxford Univ. Pr., Inc.

J. Patrick Daugherty & Edie Hand. Cancer: The Unexpected Gift. 2010. 200p. pap. 16.95 (978-1-4401-8767-4(3)) iUniverse, Inc.

Jennings, Dana. What a Difference a Dog Makes: Big Lessons on Life, Love & Healing from a Small Pooch. 2010. (ENG.). 176p. 21.00 (978-0-385-53283-9(0), Doubleday) Knopf Doubleday Publishing Group.

Jerry Brewer. Gloria's Miracle: A Young Girl, a Deadly Disease & an Enduring Lesson about the Power of Faith. 2009. (Illus.). 237p. 21.95 (978-0-9707399-7-1(4)) San Juan Publishing.

Johnson, Frank E., et al, eds. Patient Surveillance after Cancer Treatment. 2012. (Current Clinical Oncology Ser.). (ENG., Illus.). 950p. 249.00 (978-1-60327-968-0(7), 1603279687) Humana Pr.

Jois, Ramesh. Preoperative Assessment of the Elderly Cancer Patients. 2010. (Illus.). 168p. pap. (978-3-639-23337-7(9)) VDM Verlag Dr. Mueller e.K.

JuKich, Jenene. After Death There Is Life: After Death-Life! Surprises Ahead. 2011. 66p. pap. 11.95 (978-1-4327-6899-7(9)) Outskirts Pr., Inc.

Katz, Anne. Breaking the Silence on Cancer & Sexuality: A Handbook for Healthcare Providers. 2007. (Illus.). 280p. per. 70.00 (978-1-890504-67-0(X)) Oncology Nursing Society.

—Man Cancer Sex. 2009. vii, 169p. pap. 15.00 (978-1-890504-87-8(4)) Oncology Nursing Society.

—Surviving after Cancer: Living the New Normal. (ENG.). 224p. 2012. pap. 21.95 (978-1-4422-0366-2(8)) 2011. 37.95 (978-1-4422-0365-5(X)) Rowman & Littlefield Publishers, Inc.

—Woman Cancer Sex. 2009. (Illus.). 170p. pap. 14.95 (978-1-890504-80-9(7)) Oncology Nursing Society.

King, Samantha. Pink Ribbons, Inc: Breast Cancer & the Politics of Philanthropy. 2008. (Illus.). 208p. pap. 18.95 (978-0-8166-4899-3(9)) Univ. of Minnesota Pr.

Klamerus, Justin F., et al. Johns Hopkins Patients' Guide to Lung Cancer. rev. ed. 2010. 174p. pap. 10.95 (978-0-7637-7436-3(7)) Jones & Bartlett Learning, LLC.

Kneier, Andrew. Finding Your Way Through Cancer: An Expert Cancer Psychologist Helps Patients & Survivors Face the Challenges of Illness. 2010. (ENG., Illus.). 176p. pap. 14.00 (978-1-58761-356-2(5), Celestial Arts) Ten Speed Pr.

Kondor, Karen. Decadron Diary: A Family's Journey Through Hodgkins Disease. 2011. 72p. 24.99 **(978-1-4628-5746-3(9))**; pap. 15.99 **(978-1-4628-5745-6(0))** Xlibris Corp.

Kumar, Nagi B. Nutritional Management of Cancer Treatment Effects. 2012. (ENG., Illus.). xvii, 296p. 189.00 **(978-3-642-27232-5(0)**, 3642272320) Springer.

Ladun, Brenda. Behind the Scenes of Breast Cancer: A News Anchor Tells Her Story of Body & Soul Recovery. 2007. (ENG.). 208p. pap. 16.99 (978-1-59669-091-2(7)) New Hope Pubs.

Lester, Joanne & Schmitt, Patricia. Cancer Rehabilitation & Survivorship: A Transdisciplinary Approach. 2011. 450p. pap. (978-1-935864-05-9(X)) Oncology Nursing Society.

Lindley, Candy. Face of Faith: Discovering a Different Kind of Makeover. 2009. 352p. 22.95 (978-0-9820435-0-9(3)) Exclaim Publishing.

Losciale, Diana. Oraciones de Esperanza: Enfrentando, Sanando, Sobreviviendo, Superando. 2008.Tr. of Pink Prayer Book: Coping, Healing, Surviving, Thriving. (SPA.). 96p. pap. 9.95 (978-0-7648-1775-5(2), Libros Liguori) Liguori Pubns.

—Pink Prayer Book: Coping, Healing, Surviving, Thriving. 2008. 96p. pap. 9.95 (978-0-7648-1767-0(1)) Liguori Pubns.

—Prayers for Coping with Cancer. 2009. 96p. 9.99 (978-0-7648-1829-5(5)) Liguori Pubns.

Mak, J M. Promoting a Good Death for Cancer Patients of Asian Culture: An evidence-based Approach. 2007. (Illus.). 344p. (978-1-86177-100-1(2)) Whiting & Birch, Ltd.

Marston, Dianna Mitchell. Living with Cancer As A New Normal: A Journey with Cancer through the Eyes of a Caregiver. 2007. 108p. per. 11.95 (978-0-595-44899-9(2)) iUniverse, Inc.

Mendes, Dena. A Survivor's Guide to Kicking Cancer's Ass. 2011. (ENG.). 240p. pap. 14.95 (978-1-4019-3154-4(5)) Hay Hse., Inc.

Menten, Johan. Cancer Pain: Interdisciplinary & comprehensive Management. 2010. 168p. pap. (978-3-8383-4370-9(0)) Lambert Academic Publishing.

Miller, Kenneth. Excellent Care for Cancer Survivors: A Guide to Fully Meet Their Needs in Medical Offices & in the Community, 1 vol. 2011. (Praeger Series on Contemporary Health & Living Ser.). (Illus.). 376p. 58.00 (978-0-313-39786-8(4), A3598C) Greenwood Publishing Group, Inc.

Miller, Kenneth D. Excellent Care for Cancer Survivors: A Guide to Fully Meet Their Needs in Medical Offices & in the Community. 2011. (978-0-313-39787-5(2), Praeger Pubs.) Greenwood Publishing Group, Inc.

Miller, Lee. The Cancer Challenge: Sharing the Experience. 2007. 100p. per. 11.95 (978-0-595-42981-3(5)) iUniverse, Inc.

Mossaed, Mahvash. Dear Dr. B. Encounters of a Volunteer at a County Hospital. 2007. (978-0-9796912-1-8(4)) Zodeak G42nd Publishing.

Mulhall, John P., et al, eds. Cancer & Sexual Health. 2011. (Current Clinical Urology Ser.). (ENG., Illus.). xviii, 783p. 279.00 (978-1-60761-915-4(6), 1607619156) Humana Pr.

Murphey, Cecil. When Someone You Love Has Cancer: Comfort & Encouragement for Caregivers & Loved Ones. 2009. (Illus.). 64p. 10.99 (978-0-7369-2428-3(0)) Harvest Hse. Pubs.

Nathan. The Cancer Treatment Revolution: How Smart Drugs & Other New Therapies Are Renewing Our Hope & Changing the Face of Medicine. 2007. (ENG.). 272p. pap. 24.95 (978-0-470-58131-5(X), Wiley) Wiley, John & Sons, Inc.

Nathan, David G. The Cancer Treatment Revolution: How Smart Drugs & Other New Therapies Are Renewing Our Hope & Changing the Face of Medicine. 2007. (ENG.). 272p. 24.95 (978-0-471-94654-0(0), Wiley) Wiley, John & Sons, Inc.

Nguyen, Kim. Between the Tumor & the Tomb: A Diary of Doom & Deliverance. 2007. 206p. per. 16.95 (978-1-59352-332-9(7)) Christian Services Publishing.

Northey, Sue. Pilgrim Prayers for People Living with Cancer. 2010. 140p. pap. 13.00 (978-1-60899-192-1(X), Wipf and Stock) Wipf & Stock Pubs.

Orfali, Robert. Grieving a Soulmate: The Love Story Behind till Death Do Us Part. 2011. 280p. pap. 14.95 **(978-1-936400-66-9(9))** Mill City Pr., Inc.

Ouma, Philip. Coping with Cancer in Keny. 2011. 152p. pap. **(978-3-8433-8619-7(6))** Lambert Academic Publishing.

Owens, Pat. Faith Like Fire: Engulfed by a Great God. 2011. 128p. 28.95 **(978-1-4627-0540-5(5))**; pap. 11.95 **(978-1-4627-0539-9(1))** Cross Bks. Publishing.

Page, Ann E. K., ed. Cancer Care for the Whole Patient: Meeting Psychosocial Health Needs. 2008. (ENG., Illus.). 456p. 46.95 (978-0-309-11107-2(2)) National Academies Pr.

Peltason, Ruth A. & Peltason, Ruth. I Am Not My Breast Cancer: Women Talk Openly about Love & Sex, Hair Loss & Weight Gain, Mothers & Daughters, & Being a Woman with Breast Cancer. 2008. 400p. 25.95 (978-0-06-117410-0(6), Morrow, William & Co.) HarperCollins Pubs.

Pesmen, Curtis. The Colon Cancer Survivors' Guide. 2007. (ENG.). 232p. 22.95 (978-0-9661847-7-8(7)) Tatra Pr.

Phillips, Pamela. Tie One On. 2011. 66p. 40.99 **(978-1-61379-493-7(2))**; 58p. pap. 29.99 **(978-1-61379-492-0(4))** Xulon Pr., Inc.

Piper, John. Don't Waste Your Cancer. 2011. 15p. **(978-1-4335-2331-1(0))** Crossway.

Piper, John. Don't Waste Your Cancer. 2011. 16p. 2.99 (978-1-4335-2322-9(1)) Crossway.

Prida, Mayte. Con Fe: Cómo Transformar Tu Vida y Empezar de Nuevo. 2009. (SPA.). 240p. pap. 14.99 (978-0-06-178014-1(6), Rayo) HarperCollins Pubs.

Razum, Oliver & Spallek, Jacob, eds. Migration-Sensitive Cancer Registration in Europe: Challenges & Potentials. 2011. (Challenges in Public Health Ser.). 138p. 38.95 **(978-3-631-61934-6(0))** Lang, Peter GmbH, Europäischer Verlag der Wissenschaften DEU. Dist: Lang, Peter.

Reissner, Adam J. Conquering Cancer: Pursuing a Cure via Integral Medicine. 2010. 316p. 32.95 (978-1-4502-2458-1(X)); (ENG.). pap. 22.95 (978-1-4502-2456-7(3)) iUniverse, Inc.

Reuben, Suzanne H. Living Beyond Cancer: Finding a New Balance: President's Cancer Panel 2003-2004 Annual Report. Leffall, La Salle D., ed. 2006. (Illus.). 87p. (C). reprint ed. pap. 20.00 (978-1-4223-0586-7(4)) DIANE Publishing Co.

Ricco, John. The Ride of Your Life: Fighting Cancer with Attitude. 2nd ed. 2008. (ENG., Illus.). 152p. pap. 12.95 (978-1-933916-22-4(2)) Nelson Publishing & Marketing.

Rohan, Elizabeth. Laboring at the Edge - Effects of Repeated Exposure to Death & Dying on Oncology Doctors, Nurses, & Social Workers. 2009. 132p. pap. (978-3-639-12099-8(X)) VDM Verlag Dr. Mueller e.K.

Rolfs, Judith. Triumphing over Cancer. 2007. 51p. pap. 14.95 (978-0-9799895-0-6(7)) Wayne & Judith Rolfs.

Rosenthal, Kairol. Everything Changes: The Insider's Guide to Cancer in Your 20's & 30's. 2009. (ENG.). 256p. pap. 16.95 (978-0-470-29402-4(7), Wiley) Wiley, John & Sons, Inc.

Rubenstein, Benjamin. Twice. 2010. (Illus.). 256p. 32.00 (978-0-9786472-9-2(7)) Woodley Bks. LLC.

Rubietta, Linda & Rubietta, Tracy. The Chemo Zone: Your Guide to Living & Flourishing During Chemotherapy. 2011. 288p. pap. 24.95 **(978-1-59298-414-5(2))** Beaver's Pond Pr., Inc.

Sanidad, Benjamin R., Jr. & Murphey, Cecil. Choosing to Live: Dr. Ben's Miracle. (978-0-9720982-0-5(8)) Sanidad, Benjamin.

Sartorius, Norman, et al, eds. Depression & Cancer. 2nd ed. 2011. (World Psychiatric Association Ser.). (ENG., Illus.). 258p. pap. 51.99 (978-0-470-68966-0(8), Wiley) Wiley, John & Sons, Inc.

Saxton, John & Delay, Amanda, eds. Exercise & Cancer Survivorship: Impact on Health Outcomes & Quality of Life. 2010. (ENG., Illus.). x, 202p. 179.00 (978-1-4419-1172-8(3), 1441911723) Springer.

Schafer, Jerry. Angel in My Pocket. 19.99 (978-0-9706847-8-3(9)) Beginning II End Publishing, Inc.

Sessions, Roy B. Cancer Experience: The Doctor, the Patient, the Journey. 2012. (ENG.). 208p. (gr. 17). 59.95 **(978-1-4422-1621-1(2))** Rowman & Littlefield Publishers, Inc.

Sewell, Sue. In the Shadow of Your Wings. 2006. 104p. per. 10.99 (978-0-9759049-8-5(1)) Master Pr.

Shockney, Lillie. Breast Cancer Survivorship Care. rev. ed. 2009. 226p. pap. 28.95 (978-0-7637-8496-6(6)) Jones & Bartlett Learning, LLC.

Siegel, Bernie S. & Sander, Jennifer. Faith, Hope & Healing: Inspiring Lessons Learned from People Living with Cancer. 2009. (ENG.). 240p. 24.95 (978-0-470-28901-3(5), Wiley) Wiley, John & Sons, Inc.

Sirdashney, Erica. Cranes for Christian. 2008. 104p. 9.99 (978-1-60462-788-6(3)) Tate Publishing & Enterprises, LLC.

Smith, Judy Gattis. Fear Not: Learning from Your Cancer. 2008. 128p. pap. 12.00 (978-0-88177-538-9(X)) Upper Room Bks.

Talley, Ronda C., et al, eds. Cancer Caregiving in the United States: Research, Practice, Policy. 2012. (Caregiving: Research bull; Practice bull; Policy Ser.). (ENG., Illus.). xix, 327p. 169.00 **(978-1-4614-3153-4(0)**, 1461431530) Springer.

Thomson, Puja A. J. After Shock: A Step-by-Step Guide to Help You Navigate Your Way: from Cancer Diagnosis to Healing. 2006. (Illus.). xiv, 219p. per. 19.95 (978-1-928663-05-8(2)) Roots & Wings.

Tolbert, Page & Damaskos, Penny. 100 Questions & Answers about Life after Cancer: A Survivor's Guide. 2007. (ENG.). 165p. pap. 22.95 (978-0-7637-5069-5(7)) Jones & Bartlett Learning, LLC.

Waite, Don, et al. Traveling Home: A Young Man's Story of Courage & Faith, 1 vol. 2008. 144p. pap. 11.99 (978-0-8254-2899-9(8)) Kregel Pubns.

Watson, Max, et al. Cancer Care. 2010. (ENG., Illus.). 248p. pap. 24.95 (978-0-19-923203-1(2)) Oxford Univ. Pr., Inc.

Waxman, Jonathan. The Elephant in the Room: Stories about Cancer Patients & their Doctors. 2011. (ENG.). xix, 264p. pap. 29.95 **(978-0-85729-894-2(1)**, 0857298941) Springer.

Wells, Susan. Spiritual Boot Camp: For the Brave Cancer Soldier. 2007. 184p. per. 13.99 (978-1-60266-204-9(5)) Xulon Pr., Inc.

Wilcockson, John. Lance: The Making of the World's Greatest Champion. 2009. (ENG., Illus.). 416p. 26.00 (978-0-306-81587-4(7)) Da Capo Pr., Inc.

Wisdom, Jeff. Through the Valley: Biblical-Theological Reflections on Suffering. 2011. 162p. pap. 19.00 **(978-1-61097-390-8(9)**, Wipf and Stock) Wipf & Stock Pubs.

Yeung, Sai-Ching Jim, et al. Medical Care of the Cancer Patient. 2009. (Illus.). 772p. 99.95 (978-1-60795-008-0(1)) PMPH-USA, Ltd.

Zondervan Publishing Staff & Inspirio Staff. What Cancer Cannot Do, 1 vol. deluxe ed. 2006. (ENG.). 128p. 14.99 (978-0-310-81588-4(6)) Inspirio.

CANCER—PATIENTS—BIOGRAPHY

Achatz, Grant & Kokonas, Nick. Life, on the Line: A Chef's Story of Chasing Greatness, Facing Death, & Redefining the Way We Eat. 2011. (ENG.). 400p. (gr. 12). 27.50 (978-1-59240-601-2(7), Gotham) Penguin Group (USA) Inc.

Adams, Heidi Schultz & Schultz, Christopher. Planet Cancer: The Frequently Bizarre yet Always Informative Experiences & Thoughts of Your Fellow Natives. 2010. (Illus.). 272p. pap. 19.95 (978-0-7627-5901-9(1), Lyons Pr.) Globe Pequot Pr., The.

Adefila, Johnson Ajibade. A Matter of Life & Death: The Testimony of a Heart Attack & Cancer Survivor. 2010. 72p. pap. 21.95 (978-1-4327-5477-8(7)) Outskirts Pr., Inc.

Albon, Ken. Follow Me. 2010. (ENG., Illus.). 157p. pap. (978-1-85756-780-9(3)) Janus Publishing Co.

Allison, Kimberly. Red Sunshine: A Story of Strength & Inspiration from a Doctor Who Survived Stage 3 Breast Cancer. 2011. (ENG.). 192p. pap. 15.95 **(978-1-57826-407-0(3))** Hatherleigh Co., Ltd., The.

Ambrose, Greg. Stories of Rell Sunn. 2010. 176p. pap. 22.95 (978-1-57306-323-4(1)) Bess Pr., Inc.

Ames, Dave. Me, My Cells & I: A Survivor's Seriously Funny Guide to the Science of Cancer. 2011. (ENG.). 332p. pap. 18.95 (978-1-59181-173-2(2)) Sentient Pubns.

Anderson, Taffy A. Treasures in Darkness: A Doctor's Personal Journey Through Breast Cancer. 2007. (ENG.). 192p. per. 13.99 (978-0-8024-8250-1(3), Lift Every Voice) Moody Pubs.

Anglin, Fred. Winning the Battle in Style, 1 vol. 2010. 62p. pap. 19.95 (978-1-4512-8787-5(9)) PublishAmerica, Inc.

Armstrong, Lance. Comeback 2.0: Up Close & Personal. 2009. (ENG., Illus.). 208p. 27.99 (978-1-4391-7314-5(1), Touchstone) Touchstone.

Ayers, Chris, illus. The Daily Zoo Year 2: Keeping the Doctor at Bay with a Drawing a Day. 2009. (ENG.). 160p. 29.95 (978-1-933492-47-6(3)) Design Studio Pr.

B., Annie. The Life I Was Dealt: Right When You Think You Can't Handle Anything Else. 2009. 244p. 29.95 (978-1-4401-2508-9(2)); pap. 19.95 (978-1-4401-2506-5(6)) iUniverse, Inc.

Badgett, Sandy. Remembering Laura: Letting Go of Life with Beauty & Grace. 2009. pap. 14.99 (978-1-60799-078-9(4)) Tate Publishing & Enterprises, LLC.

Baker, Gail Konop. Cancer Is a Bitch: Or, I'd Rather Be Having a Midlife Crisis. 2009. (ENG.). 272p. pap. 14.95 (978-0-7382-1370-5(5)) Da Capo Pr., Inc.

Balwanz, Patti, et al. Nordie's at Noon: The Personal Stories of Four Women Too Young for Breast Cancer. 2007. (ENG.). 304p. per. 12.95 (978-0-7382-1112-1(5)) Da Capo Pr., Inc.

Banks, Deborrah M. Loving Life, I Live. 2011. 124p. pap. 51.99 **(978-1-4568-1577-6(6))** Xlibris Corp.

Barbour, Isabelle. Woman under Construction A Story of Surv. 2007. 81p. pap. 16.95 (978-1-4241-6513-1(X)) PublishAmerica, Inc.

Barker, Trey R. The Cancer Chronicles. 2010. 191p. pap. 14.99 (978-0-557-35322-4(X)) Lulu Enterprises Inc.

Barling, Emanuel. Taking Control of Your Life: A Journey to Wellness. 2010. 275p. pap. 36.95 (978-1-4327-6376-3(8)) Outskirts Pr., Inc.

Bartholomew, Kathleen. What Did I Eat Today? 2011. 364p. pap. 20.82 **(978-1-4457-9858-5(1))** Lulu Enterprises Inc.

Baxter, Meredith. Untied: A Memoir of Family, Fame, & Floundering. (Illus.). 304p. 2012. (ENG.). pap. 15.00 **(978-0-307-71931-7(6)**, Three Rivers Pr.) 2011. 25.00 (978-0-307-71930-0(8), Crown Archetype) Crown Publishing Group.

Beard, Sandra. Laugh When I Cry. 2009. 72p. pap. 15.96 (978-0-557-08404-3(0)) Lulu Enterprises Inc.

Beaulieu, Peter. Kristi: So Thin Is the Veil. 2006. (ENG., Illus.). 400p. pap. 16.95 (978-0-8245-2398-5(9)) Crossroad Publishing Co., The.

Becker, Kim & Becker, Mike. Hello Gorgeous! A Journey of Faith, Love & Hope. 2011. 208p. pap. 19.95 **(978-0-9833586-4-0(8))** Corby Books.

Belcher, Kristen. Hard Times & Holy Places. 2009. 144p. 17.95 (978-1-60641-051-6(2)) Deseret Bk. Co.

Benaroya, Eliezer. Life after Cancer: Coping with a Cancer Verdict. 2008. 128p. 23.95 (978-0-595-71355-4(6)); pap. 13.95 (978-0-595-47759-3(3)) iUniverse, Inc.

Bennett, Amanda. The Cost of Hope: The Story of a Marriage, a Family, & the Quest for Life. 2012. (ENG.). 240p. 26.00 **(978-1-4000-6984-2(X)**, Random House) Random House Publishing Group.

Berman, Jeffrey. Dying to Teach: A Memoir of Love, Loss, & Learning. 2007. (Illus.). 284p. per. 29.95 (978-0-7914-7010-7(5)) State Univ. of New York Pr.

Beukeboom, Marga. The Boy & His Death: A true Story. 2010. 228p. 29.95 (978-1-4502-2843-5(7)); (ENG.). pap. 19.95 (978-1-4502-2841-1(0)) iUniverse, Inc.

Bevier, Bob. Our Journey Through Cancer with God: No Subtitle. 2008. 96p. pap. 9.99 (978-1-60647-597-3(5)) Xulon Pr., Inc.

Beyond the Battle. 2011. 194p. 29.99 **(978-1-4568-4360-1(5))**; pap. 19.99 **(978-1-4568-4359-5(1))** Xlibris Corp.

Bill Murray. Renegade Colonel. 2009. 704p. 47.95 (978-1-4401-6230-5(1)) iUniverse, Inc.

Blackburn, Amy. Caring for Cynthia. 2008. 96p. pap. 24.95 (978-0-9773399-1-4(2)) Channel Photographics.

Blanks, Barbara. Out of the Wreckage: the Pop Stories. 2008. 184p. pap. 13.95 (978-0-557-00909-1(X)) Lulu Enterprises Inc.

Blasutti, Dan. Spiritual Warrior. Date not set. 105p. (978-0-9681262-0-2(0)) Luce, Robert B. Pubs.

Boesky, Amy. What We Have: A Memoir. 2011. (ENG.). 336p. (gr. 12). 16.00 (978-1-59240-636-4(X), Gotham) Penguin Group (USA) Inc.

Bomgaars, Sharon. In His Feathers: The Letters & Journals of Sharon Bomgaars 1956-2002. Schaap, James, ed. 2006. (Illus.). 280p. per. 18.00 (978-0-932914-68-2(3)) Dordt College Pr.

Bomkamp, Jim. The Body of Christ in All Her Glory. 2008. 148p. pap. 11.95 (978-1-59330-544-4(3)) Aventine Pr.

Bone, Pamela. Bad Hair Days. 2007. (ENG.). 256p. per. 21.00 (978-0-522-85369-8(2)) Melbourne Univ. Publishing AUS. Dist: Independent Pubs. Group.

Bousigard-Seepersad, Christine. My life's Journey. 2010. 200p. pap. 19.95 (978-0-557-42675-1(8)) Lulu Enterprises Inc.

—My Life's Journey. l.t. ed. 2010. 166p. pap. 19.95 (978-0-557-35040-7(9)) Lulu Enterprises Inc.

Boynton, Lora Lee. Goodbye Mommy: Memoirs of a Survivor. 2009. (ENG., Illus.). 296p. (978-1-84876-110-0(4)) Troubadour Publishing Ltd.
Brenner, Marie. Apples & Oranges: My Brother & Me, Lost & Found. 2009. (ENG., Illus.). 304p. pap. 15.00 (978-0-312-42880-8(4)) Picador.
Brinker, Nancy G. Promise Me: How a Sister's Love Launched the Global Movement to End Breast Cancer. Lt. ed. 2010. (Illus.). 646p. 31.99 (978-1-4104-3149-3(5)) Thorndike Pr.
Brinker, Nancy G. & Rodgers, Joni. Promise Me: How a Sister's Love Launched the Global Movement to End Breast Cancer. 2010. (ENG., Illus.). 368p. 25.99 (978-0-307-71812-9(3)) Broadway Bks.
—Promise Me: How a Sister's Love Launched the Global Movement to End Breast Cancer. 2011. (ENG.). 368p. pap. 15.00 (978-0-307-71813-6(1), Three Rivers Pr.) Crown Publishing Group.
Brisbois, Maryellen. Why I Hated Pink: Confessions of a Breast Cancer Survivor. 2011. (ENG.). 144p. 17.95 (978-1-936467-01-3(1), vantage*Point) Vantage Pr., Inc.
Broad, Randall & Grushka-Rosen, June. It's an Extraordinary Life: Don't Miss It. 2010. 182p. pap. (978-1-935586-09-8(2)) Aviva Publishing.
Brown, Meg. Dancing with the Enemy: Letting the Good Outweigh the Bad. 2008. (Illus.). 264p. pap. 19.99 (978-0-9818525-1-5(3)) Motivated Proformance, Inc.
Brown, Pamela Marie. The Trees Are Bare. 2007. (ENG.). 140p. per. 12.95 (978-1-58736-812-7(9)) Wheatmark.
Brown, Phyllis Kennedy. His "Time of Refreshing, Behind the Seen! Reflections from the Life of an Ordinary Woman Whom God Loves! 2008. 284p. pap. 15.99 (978-1-60647-366-5(2)) Xulon Pr., Inc.
Brown, Steven G. Living & Loving Through & Past Cancer: A Spouse's Perspective. 2011. pap. 18.99 **(978-1-61777-290-0(9))** Tate Publishing & Enterprises, LLC.
Brunelle, Lorna J. Dirty Bombshell: From Thyroid Cancer Back to Fabulous! 2010. 340p. 29.99 (978-1-4567-1147-4(4)); pap. 19.99 (978-1-4567-1145-0(8)) AuthorHouse.
Bueti, Cathy. Breastless in the City: A Young Woman's Story of Love, Loss, & Breast Cancer. 2006. (ENG.). 200p. pap. 14.95 (978-1-59624-036-0(9)) Cleveland Clinic Pr.
Buff, Keith. Determination: Surviving a Devastating Brain Trauma. 2010. 148p. 24.95 (978-1-4502-2662-2(0)); pap. 14.95 (978-1-4502-2663-9(9)) iUniverse, Inc.
Burnell, Raymond. Personal Growth Through Crises. 2006. (ENG.). 160p. per. 24.95 (978-1-4241-5530-9(4)) PublishAmerica, Inc.
Bush, Fannie B. I've Got to Tell Somebody: A Spiritual Journey Through the Life of a Great Woman of God - A 24 Year Cancer Survivor. 2008. 96p. pap. 18.95 (978-1-4343-6250-6(7)) AuthorHouse.
Butts, Thomas A. Amazing Benefits in Traveling on Someone Else's Dime. 2010. 134p. pap. 45.07 (978-1-4269-4224-2(9)) Trafford Publishing.
Bye, Ronald. Memoirs of a 30-Year Cancer Survivor, 1 vol. 2009. (ENG.). 90p. pap. 16.95 (978-1-60836-255-4(8)) PublishAmerica, Inc.
Campanella, Linda. When All That's Left of Me Is Love: A Daughter's Story of Letting Go. 2011. pap. 17.99 **(978-1-61777-417-1(0))** Tate Publishing & Enterprises, LLC.
Campbell, Mary. Carried in His Arms. 2006. 224p. per. 12.99 (978-0-9759049-7-8(3)) Master Pr.
Campbell, Mary T. Carried in His Arms: An Unexpected Journey Through Cancer. 2007. (ENG.). 223p. per. 14.99 (978-1-60037-360-2(7)) Morgan James Publishing.
Cappello, Mary. Called Back: My Reply to Cancer, My Return to Life. 2009. (ENG.). 220p. pap. 15.95 (978-1-59350-150-1(1)) Alyson Pubns.
Carley, Patricia. Embracing the Moment: Living With, Through & Beyond Cancer. 2011. pap. 12.95 **(978-1-61468-044-4(2))** Troy Book Makers, The.
Carp, Jay. The Gift of Ruth: Love Is gift bestowed from Heaven. 2008. 372p. pap. 16.95 net. (978-0-9758805-9-3(4)) River Pointe Pubns.
Carr, Simon. The Boys Are Back. movie tie-in ed. 2009. (Vintage Ser.). (ENG.). 240p. pap. 14.00 (978-0-307-47627-2(8), Vintage) Knopf Doubleday Publishing Group.
Carter, Kathryn & Elit, Laurie, eds. Bearing Witness: Living with Ovarian Cancer. 2009. (Life Writing Ser.). (ENG., Illus.). 102p. pap. 24.95 (978-1-55458-055-2(2)) Wilfrid Laurier Univ. Pr. CAN. Dist: Univ. of Toronto Pr.
Cash, K. Blake. Surviving: How We Loved Through Pancreatic Cancer. 2011. 80p. pap. 11.99 **(978-1-4634-3889-0(3))** AuthorHouse.
Casperson, Diane & Wakefield, Cynthia. New Breast Friends: Surviving Cancer... Twice. 2011. 140p. 28.95 **(978-1-4497-2217-3(2))**; pap. 11.95 **(978-1-4497-2216-6(4))** Author Solutions, Inc. (WestBow Pr.).
CAT. Love Yourself First. 2011. 80p. pap. 10.97 (978-1-4269-5807-6(2)) Trafford Publishing.
Cathcart, Johnny. Hotpants: A Memoir. 2008. 384p. pap. 16.49 (978-1-4389-0314-9(6)) AuthorHouse.
Charity, Jean. Touch of Cancer. 2009. (Illus.). pap. (978-1-907407-00-0(6)) Black Leaf Publishing Group, The.
Chastain, Jim. I Survived Cancer but Never Won the Tour de France. 2007. 175p. per. 19.95 (978-1-930709-60-7(9)) HAWK Publishing Group.
Chaturvedi, Arvind K. Facing Cancer: An Unforgettable Surviving Experience. 2011. pap. 12.99 **(978-1-61777-817-9(6))** Tate Publishing & Enterprises, LLC.
Cheek, Sigourney. Patient Siggy: Hope & Healing in Cyberspace. 2008. (Illus.). 244p. per. 12.95 (978-1-57736-405-4(8)) Providence Hse Pubs.
—Patient Siggy: Hope & Healing in Cyberspace. 2009. (ENG.). 249p. pap. 13.95 (978-1-59652-503-0(7)) Turner Publishing Co.
Clark, Barbara. The Fight of My Life: The Inspiring Story of a Mother's Fight against Breast Cancer. 2007. (ENG., Illus.). 304p. 34.95 (978-0-340-93809-6(9), Hodder & Stoughton) Hodder General Publishing Div. GBR. Dist: Independent Pubs. Group.
Clark, Carol A. When Our Mom Had Cancer. 2010. (Illus.). 30p. (J). pap. 18.95 (978-1-4327-5129-6(8)) Outskirts Pr., Inc.
Clark, Kim Mcauliffe. Keep Looking Up. 2011. 134p. pap. 12.95 **(978-1-936343-64-5(9))** Peppertree Pr., The.
Cleveland, Paulette. Stories for Emily. 2008. 148p. pap. 13.95 (978-1-4327-2526-6(2)) Outskirts Pr., Inc.
Cody, Joshua. [Sic]: A Memoir. 2011. (ENG., Illus.). 272p. 24.95 (978-0-393-08106-0(0), 8106) Norton, W. W. & Co., Inc.
Conley, Susan. The Foremost Good Fortune. (Vintage Ser.). (ENG., 2012. Illus.). 368p. pap. 15.00 **(978-0-307-73986-5(4)**, Vintage) 2011. 288p. 25.95 (978-0-307-59406-8(8), Knopf) Knopf Doubleday Publishing Group.
Conte, Joseph & Conte, Constance J. Schneider. Down the Yellow Brick Road: An ALS Victim's Quest for Oz. 2006. 150p. per. 12.99 (978-1-59886-553-0(6)) Tate Publishing & Enterprises, LLC.
Conway, Kathlyn. Ordinary Life: A Memoir of Illness. 2007. (Conversations in Medicine & Society Ser.). (ENG.). 280p. per. 20.95 (978-0-472-03235-8(6)) Univ. of Michigan Pr.
Coppinger, Kelli. My Husband, Our Hero. 2008. 179p. pap. 24.95 (978-1-60572-942-7(X)) PublishAmerica, Inc.
Corrigan, Kelly. The Middle Place. 2008. (ENG.). 288p. pap. 14.95 (978-1-4013-4093-3(8)); (Illus.). 272p. 23.95 (978-1-4013-0336-5(6)) Hyperion Pr.
Cosio, Deborah A. Adam's Rib Disorder: A Misconception of Submission. 2009. 188p. 24.99 (978-1-4490-0338-8(9)); pap. 14.99 (978-1-4490-0337-1(0)) AuthorHouse.
Cox, Julie. I Ordered My Future Yesterday: The Julie Cox Story. 2011. 148p. 23.95 **(978-1-4269-7459-5(0))**; pap. 13.95 **(978-1-4269-7458-8(2))** Trafford Publishing.
Cpht, Lucille Hall. Cancer Care. 2008. 128p. pap. 20.99 (978-1-4363-5257-4(6)) Xlibris Corp.
Crump, Galbraith Miller. A Slant of Light. 2009. 312p. pap. 17.95 (978-1-880977-27-9(3)) XOXOX Pr.
Cubrilo, Branka. The Mosaic of the Broken Soul. 2010. 320p. pap. (978-1-907211-97-3(7)) Grosvenor Hse. Publishing Ltd.
Dallaire, Deny. Many Shades of Green: Running Toward the Finish Line, One Cancer at a Time. 2010. (ENG.). 200p. pap. 18.95 (978-0-9865408-0-6(3)) DreamCatcher Publishing CAN. Dist: Univ. of Toronto Pr.
Darke, Steve. Reaching for a Rainbow. 2011. 62p. pap. **(978-0-7552-1371-9(8))** Authors OnLine, Ltd.
Darrow, Estelle. Journey of the Pink Bracelet. 2007. 76p. per. 16.95 (978-1-60441-176-8(7)) PublishAmerica, Inc.
Davis, Phyllis L. Cancer, Now What? 2009. 72p. pap. 10.95 (978-1-4401-8646-2(4)) iUniverse, Inc.
De Gelmont, Evelina. Misha & His Leningrad Diary. 2008. 376p. pap. 19.99 (978-1-60647-320-7(4)) Xulon Pr., Inc.
DeLong, Lisa Solis. Blood Brothers: A Memoir of Faith & Loss While Raising Two Sons with Cancer. 2011. pap. 19.99 **(978-1-61777-152-1(X))** Tate Publishing & Enterprises, LLC.
Dent, Jim. Courage Beyond the Game: The Freddie Steinmark Story. (ENG.). 2012. 368p. pap. 15.99 **(978-1-250-00700-1(3)**, St. Martin's Griffin) 2011. (Illus.). 304p. 25.99 (978-0-312-65285-2(2), Dunne, Thomas Bks.) St. Martin's Pr.
Denton, Flora. The C Word: My Cancer Journey. 2010. 108p. 21.95 (978-1-4520-2758-6(7)); pap. 12.95 (978-1-4520-2757-9(9)) AuthorHouse.
DeSimone, Denise. From Stage IV to Center Stage. 2011. 219p. pap. 17.95 **(978-1-4525-3537-1(X))** Balboa Pr.
Desserich, Brooke & Desserich, Keith. Notes Left Behind. 2010. (ENG.). 288p. pap. 14.99 (978-0-06-188640-9(8), Harper Paperbacks) HarperCollins Pubs.
Dick, David B. A Journal for Lalie: Living Through Prostate Cancer. 2008. 344p. 22.00 (978-0-9755037-2-0(3)) Plum Lick Publishing, Inc.
Dick Grannan. An Unintended Journey. 2010. 140p. pap. 18.00 (978-1-4269-0387-8(1)) Trafford Publishing.
Dietrich, Don, et al. No Guarantees. 2008. (Illus.). 201p. 20.87 (978-1-4251-3072-5(0)) Trafford Publishing.
Divine, Debra. My Private Confessions: An Enlightening Journey through Breast Cancer & Sexual Harassment. 2006. 12.00 (978-0-8059-7311-2(7)) Dorrance Publishing Co., Inc.
Dobic, Mina. My Beautiful Life: How I Conquered Cancer Naturally. 2007. (ENG., Illus.). 1p. pap. 15.95 (978-0-7570-0244-1(7)) Square One Pubs.
Dobson, Apostle Ena. How I Defeated Cancer. 2011. 116p. pap. 11.99 **(978-1-4567-4514-1(X))** AuthorHouse.
Dobson, Lelanie. Surviving the Odds. 2010. 54p. pap. 15.99 (978-1-4500-4163-8(9)) Xlibris Corp.
Douglas, Deborah. Foot Soldiers: Stories from the Breast Cancer 3-Day. 2006. (978-0-944031-24-7(2)) Aslan Publishing.
Duhon-Sells, Rose Marie. Cancer: My Gift of Self-Actualization! 2007. 64p. per. 9.95 (978-0-595-43090-1(2)) iUniverse, Inc.
Dunningham, Christine. Thank You with a Smile: A Personal Battle with Mouth Cancer. 2008. (Illus.). xv, 86p. 7.99 (978-1-4251-7080-6(3)) Trafford Publishing.
Easter, Sheri. Hear My Heart. 2011. 254p. 36.99 **(978-1-61379-821-8(0))** Xulon Pr., Inc.
Ebdell, M. J. Silver Linings: Surviving Breast Cancer. 2007. (Illus.). 88p. per. (978-1-84401-898-7(9)) Athena Pr.
Edmonds, Mark Tiger. Hard Scrabble. 2008. 223p. 26.00 (978-1-60489-000-6(2)); (ENG.). per. 15.95 (978-1-60489-001-3(0)) Livingston Pr.
Edwards, Elizabeth. Resilience: Reflections on the Burdens & Gifts of Facing Life's Adversities. 2010. (ENG.). 256p. pap. 15.00 (978-0-7679-3156-4(4), Random Hse., Inc.
—Resilience: Reflections on the Burdens & Gifts of Facing Life's Adversities. Lt. ed. 2009. 31.95 (978-1-4104-1722-0(0)) Thorndike Pr.
—Saving Graces: Finding Solace & Strength from Friends & Strangers. 2007. (ENG., Illus.). 384p. pap. 14.95 (978-0-7679-2538-9(6), Broadway) Broadway Bks.
Eide, Candace D. Faith, Love, & Laughter: Surviving Cancer. 2008. 161p. pap 24.95 (978-1-4241-9888-7(7)) PublishAmerica, Inc.
Elder, Janet. Huck: The Remarkable True Story of How One Lost Puppy Taught a Family - And a Whole Town - About Hope & Happy Endings. 2010. 304p. 21.00 (978-0-7679-3134-2(3)) Broadway Bks.
Elliott, John and Della. Wendy Update:) in HIS HANDS. 2006. pap. 14.99 (978-1-60034-552-4(2)) Xulon Pr., Inc.
Embrey, Elaine. Breast Cancer. 2009. 112p. pap. 11.99 (978-1-60791-595-9(2)) Xulon Pr., Inc.
Enebrad, Shirley. Over the Rainbow Bridge: My Son's Journey from Here to Heaven. 2009. (ENG., Illus.). 324p. pap. 18.95 (978-1-935359-13-5(4)) Book Pubs. Network.
Erion, Kathleen. Go Bark at the Moon! 2007. 168p. per. 24.95 (978-1-4241-3695-7(4)) PublishAmerica, Inc.
Eszterhas, Joe. Crossbearer: A Memoir of Faith. 2009. (ENG.). 256p. pap. 16.99 (978-0-312-58758-1(9), St. Martin's Griffin) St. Martin's Pr.
Fairchild, Kim. I'D Give My Left Boob for That Oh, Wait, I Already Did. 2009. 156p. 24.95 (978-1-4401-4978-8(X)); pap. 14.95 (978-1-4401-4979-5(8)) iUniverse, Inc.
Farmer, David. The Cancer Diaries, a Journey Through the Crucible. 2009. 200p. pap. 13.95 (978-1-60693-514-9(3), Eloquent Bks.) AEG Literary Publishing Services, Inc.
Fast-Vlaar, Angelina. The Valley of Cancer. 2008. 192p. pap. (978-1-897373-41-5(4)) Word Alive Pr.
Favre, Deanna. Don't Bet Against Me! Beating the Odds Against Breast Cancer & in Life. 2008. (ENG.). 296p. pap. 14.99 (978-1-4143-1908-7(8)) Tyndale Hse. Pubs.
Feiler, Bruce. The Council of Dads: A Story of Family, Friendship, & Learning How to Live. (ENG.). 256p. 2011. pap. 13.99 (978-0-06-177877-3(X), William Morrow Paperbacks) 2010. 22.99 (978-0-06-177876-6(1), Morrow, William & Co.) HarperCollins Pubs.
Ferguson, Marie R. & Sales, Lorraine P. Janessa's Journey Through Her Mother's Eyes. 2009. 186p. pap. 19.99 (978-0-578-02665-7(1)) Ferguson, Marie R.
Ferreira, Melinda. Rays of Grace: A Story of Strength & Spirit. 2010. 148p. pap. 14.99 (978-0-615-30016-0(2)) Hampton Pr., The.
Fesler, Rene A. Alicia's Updates. 2009. 178p. 29.99 (978-1-4415-4368-4(6)); pap. 19.99 (978-1-4415-4367-7(8)) Xlibris Corp.
Fitzpatrick, Andy. Why Mom? A Father's Journal of Mom's Breast Cancer Battle. 2010. 60p. pap. 11.49 (978-1-4520-7925-7(0)) AuthorHouse.
Fitzpatrick-Nager, Laura. Swimming on My Wedding Day: My Cancer. 2008. 95p. pap. 12.95 (978-0-595-86983-1(1), iUniverse, Inc.) iUniverse, Inc.
Floyd, Jeana. An Uninvited Guest: One Woman's Journey from Cancer to Hope. 2007. (Illus.). 128p. 12.99 (978-0-89221-664-2(6)) New Leaf Pr., Inc.
Forbes, Kirk. Love, Kristen: One young woman's courageous battle against Cancer. 2009. 228p. pap. 18.95 (978-1-4401-1384-0(X)) iUniverse, Inc.
Francini. Seeking Freedom & Joy in the Winding Path of Life: A Spiritual Journey of Learning & Self-Discovery. 2007. 164p. per. 15.95 (978-0-595-42531-0(3)) iUniverse, Inc.
Frank, Lauren & Frank, Jennifer. Lauren's Story an Inspirational Cancer Journey. 2007. 52p. per. 17.95 (978-1-934246-48-1(4)) Peppertree Pr., The.
Franz, Carol J. There but for the Grace of God: Surviving Cancer with Adult Stem Cell Transplants. 2009. 236p. 24.99 (978-1-4389-6870-4(1)); pap. 16.95 (978-1-4389-6869-8(8)) AuthorHouse.
Frentz, Thomas S. Trickster in Tweed: The Quest for Quality in a Faculty Life. 2008. (Writing Lives Ser.). (ENG., Illus.). 192p. 94.00 (978-1-59874-317-3(1)); pap. 29.95 (978-1-59874-318-0(X)) Left Coast Pr., Inc.
Frierson, Andrew. Finger Grips Etched in Faith: Staying the Course of Life. 2011. 152p. 24.50 **(978-1-4269-6344-5(0))**; pap. 14.50 **(978-1-4269-6343-8(2))** Trafford Publishing.
Fritz, Robert. What's the Next Step? My Journey with Cancer as a Caregiver & then as a Caretaker. 2011. 168p. 25.95 (978-1-4502-9630-4(0)); pap. 15.95 (978-1-4502-9631-1(9)) iUniverse, Inc.
Fritz, Stephen L. This Is My Story. 2011. 64p. pap. 9.95 **(978-1-4497-2506-8(6)**, WestBow Pr.) Author Solutions, Inc.
Funderburg, Lise. Pig Candy: Taking My Father South, Taking My Father Home - A Memoir. 2009. (ENG.). 320p. pap. 15.00 (978-1-4165-4767-9(3), Free Pr.) Free Pr.
Gabriel, Sarah. Eating Pomegranates: A Memoir of Mothers, Daughters, & the BRCA Gene. 2010. (ENG.). 272p. 25.00 (978-1-4391-4819-8(8), Scribner) Scribner.
Galvez, Eric Anthony. Reversal: When A Therapist Becomes A Patient. 2010. 280p. pap. 20.95 (978-1-4502-2428-4(8)) iUniverse, Inc.
Garlett, Kyle. Heart of Iron: My Journey from Transplant Patient to Ironman Triathlete. 2011. (ENG., Illus.). 336p. 24.95 (978-1-61374-005-7(0)) Chicago Review Pr., Inc.
Gaynel, D. J. Child Abuse, Alcohol & Cancer: I Survived It All. 2008. 108p. 21.49 (978-1-4389-1692-7(2)); pap. 10.99 (978-1-4389-1691-0(4)) AuthorHouse.
Gearin-Tosh, Michael. Living Proof: A Medical Mutiny. 2007. (ENG.). 336p. pap. 22.95 (978-1-4165-7751-5(3), Scribner) Scribner.
Giambra, Jacqueline. Cancer: My Gift from God. 2006. 180p. per. 19.95 (978-1-4120-9724-6(X)) Trafford Publishing.
Gilbert, Laura. Journey to the Dance. 2011. (ENG.). 190p. pap. 14.99 **(978-1-4662-9955-9(X))** CreateSpace.
Gill, Michael Gates. How Starbucks Saved My Life: A Son of Privilege Learns to Live Like Everyone Else. Lt. ed. 2008. (Thorndike Biography Ser.). 353p. 31.95 (978-1-4104-0360-5(2)) Thorndike Pr.
Gilsdorf, Janet R. Inside/Outside: A Physician's Journey with Breast Cancer. 2006. (Conversations in Medicine & Society Ser.). (ENG., Illus.). 256p. 29.95 (978-0-472-11579-2(0)) Univ. of Michigan Pr.
Goldberg, Lori Daly. Gone in a Moment, 1 vol. 2010. 164p. pap. 24.95 (978-1-4489-6812-1(7)) PublishAmerica, Inc.
Good, Deborah. Long after I'm Gone: A Father-Daughter Memoir. 2009. 208p. pap. 13.95 (978-1-931038-55-3(4), DreamSeeker Bks.) Cascadia Publishing Hse., LLC.
Goss, Bill. There's a Flying Squirrel in My Coffee: Overcoming Cancer with the Help of My Pet. 2007. (ENG.). 240p. pap. 17.95 (978-1-4165-7369-2(0), Beyond Words/Atria Bks.) Atria Bks.
Graser, Angeline. Letters along My Journey: My Experience with Cancer & Chemotherapy. 2010. 108p. pap. 14.60 (978-1-4490-9590-1(9)); 26.15 (978-1-4490-9591-8(7)) AuthorHouse.
Gray, Simon. Coda. 2008. (ENG.). 272p. 28.95 (978-1-84708-094-3(4)); pap. 15.95 (978-1-84708-100-1(2)) Granta Bks. GBR. Dist: Independent Pubs. Group.
Grealy, Lucy. Autobiography of a Face. 2011. 13.08 (978-0-7848-3375-9(3), Everbind) Marco Bk. Co.
Greene, Diane Tropea. Apron Strings: Inheriting Courage, Wisdom and... Breast Cancer. 2007. (ENG., Illus.). 133p. per. 14.00 (978-1-56825-108-0(4)) Rainbow Bks., Inc.
Gubar, Susan. Memoir of a Debulked Woman: Enduring Ovarian Cancer. 2012. (ENG., Illus.). 320p. 24.95 **(978-0-393-07325-6(4)**, 7325) Norton, W. W. & Co., Inc.
Guilmette, Bruce. There's More to Life Than Just Living: A Personal Story about Cancer Survival. 2007. 182p. per. 12.99 (978-1-59886-629-2(X)) Tate Publishing & Enterprises, LLC.
Gunther, John. Death Be Not Proud. 2007. (P. S. Ser.). 205p. 21.60 (978-0-7569-8228-7(6)) Perfection Learning Corp.
Guscott, Jan. An Uplifting Experience: Cancer Is Not the End of the World It Just Seems Like It. 2009. (Illus.). 240p. pap. 14.49 (978-1-4490-1217-5(5)) AuthorHouse.
Haag, Ronald. Cancer: The Life & Tribulations of a Two-time Rare Cancer Survivor. 2011. 256p. pap. 27.95 **(978-1-4560-2830-5(8))** PublishAmerica, Inc.
Hagee Tucker, Tish. Hear My Cry: How Grace Conquered Cancer. 2009. pap. 14.99 (978-1-60799-070-3(9)) Tate Publishing & Enterprises, LLC.
Hale, Joe. Hydrangea Waving. 2012. pap. 13.95 **(978-0-7414-7085-0(3))** Infinity Publishing.
Hall, Patsy Moore. The Life of Charles Malachi Mike Moore. 2010. 52p. pap. 9.95 (978-1-934749-66-1(4), CrossHouse Publishing) Hannibal Bks.
Hall, R. Lee. As Normal As Possible: A Breast Cancer Story. 2009. 132p. 23.95 (978-1-4401-5083-8(4)); pap. 13.95 (978-1-4401-5082-1(6)) iUniverse, Inc.
Hallenborg, John C. Life, Sex, & Prostate Cancer Surgery: How One Man Healed & Was Made Whole, 1 vol. 2009. 140p. 34.95 (978-0-275-98135-8(5), C8135); E-Book (978-0-313-38148-5(8)) Greenwood Publishing Group, Inc. (Praeger Pubs.).
Hallman, David G. August Farewell: The Last Sixteen Days of a Thirty-Three-Year Romance. 2011. 180p. 26.95 (978-1-4502-8638-1(0)); pap. 16.95 (978-1-4502-8636-7(4)) iUniverse, Inc.
Hampton, Deborah Lang. Slapped Awake. 2007. 220p. per. 16.95 (978-1-933912-30-1(8)) Westview Publishing Co., Inc.
Harris, Charles. Incurable: A Life after Diagnosis. 2011. 300p. 31.00 (978-1-936113-10-1(4)) Cold Spring Harbor Laboratory Pr.
Harrison, Mary B. And You Will Know the World's Name: A Mother's Memoir. 2006. mass mkt. 15.95 (978-1-58597-393-4(9)) Leathers Publishing.
Hastings, Jeff. Dying Can Change Your Life. 2007. (ENG.). 124p. per. 13.99 (978-1-4141-0825-4(7)) Pleasant Word.
Hatch-Taylor, Karen. Mosaic Life: A Memoir in Verse. 2011. 48p. pap. 9.89 **(978-1-4269-5167-1(1))** Trafford Publishing.
Hayden, Brian M. Death: Living to Talk about It. 2011. 190p. pap. 24.95 **(978-1-4560-6095-4(3))** PublishAmerica, Inc.
Hayward, Kate. From Oncology Nursing to Coping with Breast Cancer. 2008. (Patient Narratives Ser.). 160p. pap. (978-1-84619-273-9(0)) Radcliffe Publishing.
Healing Cancer Peacefully: When the Body's Not a Battlefield, It Can Tell You What It Needs. 2009. (ENG.). 300p. pap. 17.95 (978-0-9823089-0-5(6)) Round House Pr., The.
Healing Project Staff, ed. Voices of Lung Cancer: The Healing Companion: Stories for Courage, Comfort & Strength. 2007. (Voices of Ser.). (ENG., Illus.). 250p. pap. 16.95 (978-1-934184-00-4(4)) Lachance Publishing LLC.
Herron, Tim. Too Soon to Quit! No Subtitle. 2008. 148p. pap. 13.99 (978-1-60647-667-3(X)) Xulon Pr., Inc.

C

Hess, Dave. Hope Beyond Reason: Embraced by God's Presence in the Toughest of Times. 2008. pap. 14.99 (978-0-7684-2697-7(9)) Destiny Image Pubs.

Hicks, Louise. A Hill to Climb: A Teenager's Battle with Cancer, Depression, & Drug Addiction. 2010. pap. 14.99 (978-1-61566-252-4(9)) Tate Publishing & Enterprises, LLC.

Higley, Jim. Bobblehead Dad: 25 Life Lessons I Forgot I Knew. 2011. (Illus.). 202p. pap. 14.95 (978-1-60832-142-1(8)) Greenleaf Book Group.

Hildebrandt, Sherri. More Than Enough. 2011. (978-1-77069-220-6(7)) Word Alive Pr.

Hill, Vince. Another Hill to Climb. 2011. (Illus.). 172p. pap. (978-1-904408-79-6(6)) Bank House Bks.

Hladun, Matt. Brave Will. 2010. 208p. pap. 16.99 (978-0-557-27474-1(5)) Lulu Enterprises Inc.

Ho, Fred. Diary of a Radical Cancer Warrior: Fighting Cancer & Capitalism at the Cellular Level. 2011. (ENG.). 304p. 24.95 (978-1-61608-378-6(6), 608378) Skyhorse Publishing Co., Inc.

Hobin, Lee. God, Why Are You Being So Cruel? 2011. 230p. pap. 14.00 (978-1-60911-872-3(3), Strategic Bk. Publishing) AEG Literary Publishing Services, Inc.

Hoeger, Martin A. One Left Handed Hug. 2009. 160p. pap. 16.50 (978-1-4389-4821-8(2)) AuthorHouse.

Hoeppner, Pamela. The Breast Stays Put ¬. 2008. 268p. per. 15.99 (978-1-60477-103-9(8)) Xulon Pr., Inc.

Hoffman, Sharon J. Tears in My Pocket. 2011. 76p. pap. 10.84 (978-1-4269-6422-0(6)) Trafford Publishing.

Hoge, Merril. Find a Way: Three Words That Changed My Life. 2010. (ENG., Illus.). 224p. 21.99 (978-1-59995-305-2(6)) Center St.

Hollar, Melanie Byrd. Send Forth Your Light. 2006. (Illus.). 232p. pap. 19.95 (978-1-933251-12-7(3)) Parkway Pubs., Inc.

Hong, Leona. There Is Healing in His Hands: A Cancer Story. 2011. 82p. pap. 19.95 (978-1-4560-2235-8(0)) PublishAmerica, Inc.

Hong, Thomas. Dreams with Broken Wings: Memoirs of Dr. Thomas Hong. 2010. 176p. 23.95 (978-1-60911-213-4(X), Eloquent Bks.) AEG Literary Publishing Services, Inc.

Horton, Nancy. Hope in the Midst of Darkness: A Breast Cancer Survivor's Journey. 2011. 400p. pap. (978-1-77069-194-0(4)) Word Alive Pr.

Host, Carrie. Between Me & the River: A Memoir. 2nd ed. 2011. (ENG.). 304p. pap. 14.95 (978-0-373-89246-4(2)) Harlequin Enterprises, Ltd. CAN. Dist: Simon & Schuster, Inc.

Houlette, Marcia S. Alive with Prostate Cancer: Michael's Road. 2010. pap. 9.99 (978-1-61566-465-8(3)) Tate Publishing & Enterprises, LLC.

Huff, Debbi. Holding on for Dear Life. 2007. 260p. per. 27.95 (978-1-4241-5247-6(X)) PublishAmerica, Inc.

Hulliberger, Elaine. Winning the Battle Against Cancer: They Said I Was Going to Die... but, I Didn't. 2008. 220p. pap. 14.99 (978-1-60647-056-5(6)) Xulon Pr., Inc.

Hundley, Steven. The Playground: Noah's Story. 2007. 137p. pap. 11.95 (978-0-7414-4158-4(6)) Infinity Publishing.

Hunter, Cherie. Cancer Made Me Beautiful: A Journey to Recovery. 2011. 140p. pap. 17.95 (978-1-4634-1062-9(X)) AuthorHouse.

Hunter, Lindsey. Unbreakable: My Life with Paul Hunter, a Story of Extraordinary Love, Loss & Courage. 2008. (ENG., Illus.). 352p. pap. 13.95 (978-0-00-726091-1(1)) HarperCollins Pubs. Ltd. GBR. Dist: Independent Pubs. Group.

Ide, Jeffrey. Trail Mix. 2010. 262p. pap. 15.39 (978-0-557-49726-3(4)) Lulu Enterprises Inc.

Ingraham, Brenda. He's Lookin' at You, Kid! A Story of Hope & Faith. 2008. 96p. pap. 11.95 (978-0-595-48116-3(7)) iUniverse, Inc.

Ingram, Nancy. Mission to Remission: A Lighthearted Perspective on the Challenges of Cancer, 1 vol. 2010. 90p. pap. 16.95 (978-1-4489-8457-2(2)) PublishAmerica, Inc.

Iris Sechriest. Sybil's Choice. 2009. 180p. pap. 16.95 (978-1-4401-6858-1(X)) iUniverse, Inc.

Ives, Nanni M. Cancer & the Ecology of Self: Memoirs of a Long-Term Survivor. Bryan, Jessica, ed. 2008. 160p. pap. 18.95 (978-0-9619311-5-5(9)) Lompico Creek Pr.

J. Patrick Daugherty & Edie Hand. Cancer: The Unexpected Gift. 2010. 200p. 26.95 (978-1-4401-8769-8(X)) iUniverse, Inc.

Jackson, Kate. The Smart One. 2013. (ENG., Illus.). 304p. 25.99 (978-1-4516-2156-3(6)) Gallery Pr., The. IRL. Dist: Simon & Schuster, Inc.

Jacobs, Bruce. One Tough Journey. 2009. 92p. pap. 25.00 (978-1-882467-47-1(7)) Wildstone Media.

Jambeck, Nick. Dying to Love Again. 2009. 112p. pap. 14.98 (978-0-557-09767-8(3)) Lulu Enterprises Inc.

James, Eloisa. Paris in Love: A Memoir. 2012. (ENG., Illus.). 272p. 26.00 (978-1-4000-6956-9(4), Random House) Random House Publishing Group.

Jameson, Derek & Jameson, Ellen. Siobhán's Miracle. 2008. (ENG., Illus.). 240p. 24.95 (978-1-84454-566-7(0)) Blake, John Publishing, Ltd. GBR. Dist: Independent Pubs. Group.

—Siobhán's Miracle. 2009. (ENG., Illus.). 288p. pap. 14.95 (978-1-84454-755-5(8)) Blake, John Publishing, Ltd. GBR. Dist: Independent Pubs. Group.

Jamison, Kay Redfield. Nothing Was the Same. 2011. (Vintage Ser.). 224p. pap. 14.95 (978-0-307-27789-3(5), Vintage) Knopf Doubleday Publishing Group.

Jarvis, Debra. It's Not about the Hair: And Other Certainties of Life & Cancer. 2008. (ENG.). 256p. pap. 16.95 (978-1-57061-573-3(X)) Sasquatch Bks.

Jean Schmeling. Miracle Dreams from My Daughter in Heaven. 2010. 48p. pap. 9.95 (978-1-4502-0372-2(8)) iUniverse, Inc.

Jennings, Dana. What a Difference a Dog Makes: Big Lessons on Life, Love, & Healing from a Small Pooch. l.t. ed. 2010. 207p. 31.99 (978-1-4104-3178-3(9)) Thorndike Pr.

Jernigan-Carter, Earlene. When the wheels of faith quit Turning. 2010. 92p. pap. 19.80 (978-0-557-17231-3(4)) Lulu Enterprises Inc.

Joanie Butman. I Don't Buy Green Bananas: (center stage with Cancer) 2010. 208p. pap. 17.95 (978-1-4502-0624-2(7)) iUniverse, Inc.

Jodar, Nannette. Being Held by God: How I Caused My Own Miracle & How You Can Too! 2011. 128p. 23.95 (978-1-4502-9367-9(0)); pap. 13.95 (978-1-4502-9365-5(4)) iUniverse, Inc.

Johanson, Paula. Lance Armstrong: A Biography. 2011. E-Book (978-0-313-38691-6(9), Greenwood Pr.) Greenwood Publishing Group, Inc.

Johanson, Paula Marie. Lance Armstrong: A Biography, 1 vol. 2011. (Greenwood Biographies Ser.). (Illus.). 153p. 35.00 (978-0-313-38690-9(0), A3127C) Greenwood Publishing Group, Inc.

Johnson, Craig. My Prostate Cancer Adventure, & the Lessons Learned. 2011. 80p. pap. 10.95 (978-1-4502-8206-2(7)) iUniverse, Inc.

Johnson, Tara & Schwartz, Meredith Celene. Gestational Trophoblastic Neophasia: A Guide for Women Dealing with Tumors of the Placenta, Such As Choriocarcinoma, Molar Pregnancy & Other Forms of GTN. 2007. (Illus.). 240p. per. 29.95 (978-1-4251-0695-9(1)) Trafford Publishing.

Jones, Michelle. Cancer on Purpose. 2011. 52p. pap. 15.99 (978-1-4568-3855-3(5)) Xlibris Corp.

Jordan, Hope. Princesses Don't Get Cancer: A Heart-wrenching Tale of Horror, Humor & Hope (Spiritual & Practical) 2011. 112p. pap. 11.95 (978-1-61507-793-9(6)) Cross Bks. Publishing.

—Princesses Don't Get Cancer: A Heart-wrenching Tale of Horror, Humor, & Hope (Spiritual & Practical) 2011. 112p. 28.95 (978-1-61507-794-6(4)) Cross Bks. Publishing.

Judge, Pamela Morrow. Naming Horses & Other Short Stories & Poems. 2010. pap. 14.99 (978-1-61566-969-1(8)) Tate Publishing & Enterprises, LLC.

Kalinin, Beverly. Alone on the Yellow Brick Road ~ a Memoir. 2009. 160p. pap. 15.00 (978-1-935125-40-2(0)) Robertson Publishing.

Kantorowicz, Dee. The Handbook of Humor, Survivor Stories, Support, & Hope for People with Inflammatory Breast Cancer: You Are Not Alone. 2007. 52p. per. 8.95 (978-1-4327-1433-8(3)) Outskirts Pr., Inc.

Kathleen Joy. Smile Through It All. 2011. 24p. pap. (978-1-4269-7066-5(8)) Trafford Publishing (UK) Ltd.

Katz, Pina & Katz, Robert. Yes, We Can! 2011. 148p. 29.99 (978-1-4535-4376-4(7)); pap. 19.99 (978-1-4535-4375-7(9)) Xlibris Corp.

Kauder, Bruce M. Daddy, Tell Me a Story about When You Were Little: (A rotten kid grew up to be a Pediatrician) 2009. (Illus.). 151p. (J). (ENG.). 26.95 (978-1-4327-4145-7(4)); pap. 13.95 (978-1-4327-4096-2(2)) Outskirts Pr., Inc.

Kelly-Lopez, Catherine. The Cancer Emails - Running Raw in the Wild. 2008. 296p. pap. (978-3-639-04777-6(X)) VDM Verlag Dr. Mueller e.K.

Kilfeather, Rick. Hope Beyond Diagnosis. 2010. 140p. pap. 14.99 (978-1-61579-791-2(2)) Xulon Pr., Inc.

Kincaid, Hilary. Soaring into Magnificence: -Cancer. 2011. 230p. pap. 24.95 (978-1-4560-8393-9(7)) PublishAmerica, Inc.

Kinney, Trish. Silver Platter Girl. 2009. 380p. 17.95 (978-0-9822293-9-2(9)) Seven Locks Pr.

Kishbaugh, Ryan Patrick. Run Because You Can: My Personal Race with Cancer. 2007. (Illus.). 248p. pap. 19.95 (978-0-9795217-0-6(X)) Humphries, Paul.

Kohl, Carol. The Match of a Lifetime. 2008. 156p. pap. 13.99 (978-1-60477-831-1(8)) Xulon Pr., Inc.

Kohler, Deirdre. Brutal Honesty. 2010. 216p. pap. 15.99 (978-1-4520-7894-6(7)) AuthorHouse.

Kohn, Douglas. Life, Faith, & Cancer: Jewish Journeys Through Diagnosis, Treatment, & Recovery. 2007. 16.95 (978-0-8074-1059-2(4)) URJ Pr.

Koop, David A. Cancer - It's A Good Thing I Got It ! The Life Story of A Very Lucky Man. 2011. 201p. (ENG.). 39.95 (978-1-4327-7578-0(2)); pap. 24.95 (978-1-4327-7448-6(4)) Outskirts Pr., Inc.

Kozar, Richard. The Book of Chad. 2010. (978-1-59556-038-4(6)) OTTN Publishing.

Kramer, Heidi. Through the Fear: Inspiring Stories of Christian Women & Cancer. 2007. spiral bd. 15.00 (978-0-615-14153-4(6)) Life Inspired Speaking.

Krebser, Eldred. Cancer, Thirty One Days. 2011. 124p. pap. 15.36 (978-1-4520-8420-6(3)) AuthorHouse.

Kroon, Rita. You Have Cancer: A Journey Through the Valley of the Shadow of Death. 2011. (ENG.). 107p. pap. 12.95 (978-1-4327-7789-0(0)) Outskirts Pr., Inc.

Kubek, Dora. Insert Breast Here — -A Chronicle of One Woman's Breast Cancer. 2007. 112p. per. 11.95 (978-1-59899-042-3(X)) Long Dash Publishing.

Kunzendorf, Cindy. Finding Rainbows. 2009. 274p. 26.99 (978-1-60860-786-0(0), Eloquent Bks.) AEG Literary Publishing Services, Inc.

Lacey, Sandra, et al. People Like Us: Life with Rob Lacey, 1 vol. 2011. (ENG.). 272p. pap. 14.99 (978-0-310-31904-7(8)) Zondervan.

Lacy, Lizzy. Outside the Box for Good. 2011. 258p. pap. 16.99 (978-1-61379-302-2(2)) Xulon Pr., Inc.

Lalicata, Anthony A., Sr. Tony's Gift: Conquering Life's Battles. 2007. (Illus.). 156p. per. 12.99 (978-1-59886-782-4(2)) Tate Publishing & Enterprises, LLC.

Lampard, Louise. A Year in My Shoes: A Cancer Survivor's Story. 2007. 148p. (ENG.). 24.95 (978-0-595-70586-3(3)); per. 14.95 (978-0-595-46081-6(X)) iUniverse, Inc.

Langa, Beki P. Living & Working with Cancer. 2010. (Illus.). 54p. pap. (978-1-84748-713-1(0)) Athena Pr.

Larry And Delila Woodruff. My Son, My Father, My Hero: One Family's Journey with Cancer. 2010. 132p. pap. 13.95 (978-1-4401-9725-3(3)) iUniverse, Inc.

Latimore, James. Bookwoman: A Cancer Journal. 2008. 404p. pap. 17.99 (978-1-4343-9289-3(9)) AuthorHouse.

Lavelle, Jean. Journey Through Cancer. 2010. (ENG.). 64p. pap. 8.95 (978-1-84730-211-3(4)) Veritas Pubns. IRL. Dist: Dufour Editions, Inc.

Leach, Jean. Oh my goodness it happened to Me. 2007. 107p. pap. 15.51 (978-0-615-15772-6(6)) Leach, Jean.

Lefevers, Jay. Cancer on the Brain: One Man's Journey of Baseball, Business, & Beating the Odds. 2012. (ENG.). 18.95 (978-1-937110-24-6(9)) Emerald Bk. Co.

Lehosit, Darlene. Surviving Lung Cancer: (My Story) 2007. 92p. per. 16.95 (978-1-4241-6344-1(7)) PublishAmerica, Inc.

Leignel, Therese. Fighting the Odds. 2008. 135p. pap. 21.50 (978-1-4092-3963-5(2)) Lulu Enterprises Inc.

Leon Weisman. No Expiration Dates: A Cancer Patient's Strategies for Survival. 2009. 140p. 23.95 (978-1-4401-6869-7(5)); pap. 13.95 (978-1-4401-6868-0(7)) iUniverse, Inc.

Levin (Deceased), Miles Alpern. Keep Fighting, Stop Struggling: The Miles Levin Story. Rice, Dianne, ed. 2011. 189p. pap. 18.95 (978-1-61863-004-9(0)) Bookstand Publishing.

Ley, Erin. The Will to Live: The Perks of Cancer Through the Eyes of a Survivor. 2007. 112p. per. 19.95 (978-1-4241-8229-9(8)) PublishAmerica, Inc.

Light, Beaming. Jumping River: A True Story. 2011. 50p. pap. 16.95 (978-1-4560-2377-5(2)) PublishAmerica, Inc.

Limero, Lorraine Balch. I Won't Be Wearing a Bikini, but I'm Going to Keep on Swimming. 2009. 90p. pap. 9.95 (978-1-60693-585-9(2), Eloquent Bks.) AEG Literary Publishing Services, Inc.

Lipsyte, Robert. In the Country of Illness: Comfort & Advice for the Journey. 2011. (ENG.). 272p. pap. 13.95 (978-1-59687-388-9(4)) IBks., Inc.

Lober, Csp. Still Bigger Than Pink: Alive & Thriving! 2009. 184p. pap. 18.50 (978-1-4389-7016-5(1)) AuthorHouse.

Lorde, Audre. The Cancer Journals. 2006. (ENG., Illus.). 104p. per. 12.95 (978-1-879960-73-2(7)) Aunt Lute Bks.

Lori Lober, Csp Mirm. Still Bigger Than Pink. 2009. 184p. pap. 25.50 (978-1-4389-7017-2(X)) AuthorHouse.

Lorusso, Cosmo. Every Child Needs an Angel. 2010. 188p. (ENG.). 23.95 (978-1-4502-3501-3(8)); pap. 13.95 (978-1-4502-3499-3(2)) iUniverse, Inc.

Lucas, Thomas. Cancer a Love Story. 2009. 84p. pap. 10.49 (978-1-4490-1248-9(5)) AuthorHouse.

Lucey, Angela. Devil Is A Dermatologist. 2007. pap. 12.50 (978-1-59330-449-2(8)) Aventine Pr.

Luth, Sophie A. From Rags to Riches Through Christ. 2008. 202p. pap. 24.95 (978-1-60672-635-8(8)) PublishAmerica, Inc.

Luttrell, Adele Marie. Why Me? 2009. (Illus.). 14.95 (978-0-9788964-0-9(8)) Sand and Sea.

MacDougall, Judy F. Ruby, a Child of the King. 2011. (Illus.). (978-1-77069-174-2(X)) Word Alive Pr.

Maddox, Barbara. Mashed Potatoes & Gravy: A Woman's Journal through Surviving Cancer. 2010. 236p. 28.95 (978-1-4502-1870-2(9)); pap. 18.95 (978-1-4502-1868-9(7)) iUniverse, Inc.

Malden, Carla. Afterimage: A Brokenhearted Memoir of a Charmed Life. (ENG.). 320p. 2012. pap. 16.95 (978-0-7627-8013-6(4)) 2011. 24.95 (978-0-7627-6382-5(5)) Globe Pequot Pr., The. (skirt!).

Mallory, Kevin J. & Lane, Nancy A. John: A Journey Back. 2009. 156p. 24.95 (978-1-4401-5544-4(5)); pap. 14.95 (978-1-4401-5546-8(1)) iUniverse, Inc.

Manahan, Nancy & Bohan, Becky. Living Consciously, Dying Gracefully: A Journey with Cancer & Beyond. 2007. (Illus.). 216p. per. 17.00 (978-1-59298-179-3(8)) Beaver's Pond Pr., Inc.

Marchetto, Marisa Acocella. Cancer Vixen. 2009. (Illus.). 224p. pap. 16.95 (978-0-375-71474-0(X), Pantheon) Knopf Doubleday Publishing Group.

—Cancer Vixen: A True Story. 2006. (ENG., Illus.). 224p. 22.00 (978-0-307-26357-5(6), Knopf) Knopf Doubleday Publishing Group.

—Cancer Vixen: A True Story. 2009. (ENG.). 192p. pap. (978-0-676-97825-4(8), Vintage Canada) Random Hse. of Canada, Ltd. CAN. Dist: Random Hse., Inc.

Mareck, Amy M. Fighting for My Life: Growing up with Cancer. 2007. (ENG.). 192p. (YA). (gr. 4-7). per. 12.95 (978-1-57749-168-2(8)) Taylor Trade Publishing.

Martin, R. Merial. Welford Street Miracles: A Stranger's Touch, A Life Restored. 2009. pap. 13.99 (978-1-60696-049-3(0)) Tate Publishing & Enterprises, LLC.

Martin, Roger H. Racing Odysseus: A College President Becomes a Freshman Again. 280p. 2010. (ENG.). pap. 19.95 (978-0-520-26587-5(4)) 2008. 40.00 (978-0-520-25541-8(0)) Univ. of California Pr.

Masel, Deborah. Soul to Soul: Writings from Dark Places. 2011. (978-965-229-559-0(0)) Gefen Bks.

Matthews, Annie Harmon & Sikora, Karol. Anni's Cancer Companion: An A-Z of Treatments, Therapies & Healing. 2011. (ENG.). 288p. pap. (978-1-84819-067-2(0)) Singing Dragon.

Mazan, Steve. Dying to Do Letterman. 2011. (ENG.). 264p. pap. 14.95 (978-0-7573-1627-2(1)) Health Communications, Inc.

Mazzucchelli, Stella. Silk Flowers Never Die: Love, Death, Mental Illness & Courage in an Internationally Renowned Family. 2009. (Illus.). 405p. (978-0-9553507-2-6(7)) Dynasty Pr., Ltd.

MCcallum, Jim. A Quiet Courage. 2011. 96p. pap. 12.52 (978-1-4567-9366-1(7)) AuthorHouse.

McCaskill, Carole. What Color Is My Ribbon? An Ovarian Cancer Success Story. 2011. 230p. 29.99 (978-1-4653-4513-4(2)); pap. 19.99 (978-1-4653-4512-7(4)) Xlibris Corp.

McClain, Catherine. Cancer Dance. 2008. 185p. pap. 24.95 (978-1-60441-730-2(7)) PublishAmerica, Inc.

McDonnell, Mary. Cancer, Prayer & Survival. 2009. (ENG.). 85p. pap. 15.95 (978-1-85607-639-5(3)) Columba Pr. IRL. Dist: Dufour Editions, Inc.

McFarland, John Robert. Now That I Have Cancer, I Am Whole: Reflections on Life & Healing for Cancer Patients & Those Who Love Them. 2007. (ENG.). 320p. pap. 9.95 (978-0-7407-6372-4(5)) Andrews McMeel Publishing.

McGarry, Aurea. I Won't Survive I'll Thrive! How I Overcame Domestic Violence, Cancer, & Much More. 2007. 148p. (ENG.). 24.95 (978-0-595-69709-0(7)); per. 14.95 (978-0-595-45369-6(4)) iUniverse, Inc.

McGoldrick, Irene. Two Chai Day: One Widow's Story about Living Beyond Grief. 2011. 256p. pap. 16.95 (978-1-936236-79-4(6)) iUniverse, Inc.

McKenna, Marlene Marcello. When Hope Never Dies: The Story of My Recovery from Cancer & the Program I Used to Heal Myself. 2011. 260p. pap. 17.95 (978-1-4567-4567-7(0)) AuthorHouse.

McKeown, Joshua. The Gift of Cancer: Helping people everywhere realize the potential they have in ministry by using their gifts for His Glory. 2011. 144p. pap. 15.00 (978-1-4575-0439-6(1)) Dog Ear Publishing, LLC.

McLaren, Matthew E. The Miracle of Love: The Amazing Journey of a Cancer Survivor. 2010. pap. 20.99 (978-1-61566-904-2(3)) Tate Publishing & Enterprises, LLC.

McNeal, Franne. Off My Chest, but on My Mind: Busting the Barriers of Breast Cancer. 2007. 160p. pap. 21.95 (978-0-9791643-3-0(8)) Significant Business Results LLC.

McWhirt, Karen. Together We Will Win: What Happen's When We Don't Talk about Testicular Cancer: A Young Man's Story. 2010. (Illus.). 360p. pap. 19.95 (978-1-4327-4867-8(X)) Outskirts Pr., Inc.

Melanson, Susan Chapman & Campbell, Archie. Radiation Buddies. 2008. 120p. pap. 17.95 (978-1-4357-2557-7(3)) Lulu Enterprises Inc.

Mendenhall, Donna J. L. Living, Not Dying, with Incurable Cancer: Making Each Day Count. 2011. 164p. pap. 24.95 (978-1-4512-8433-1(0)) PublishAmerica, Inc.

Menzel, Sharon Lynn. A Higher Calling. 2011. 48p. 24.99 (978-1-4653-6798-3(5)); pap. 15.99 (978-1-4653-6797-6(7)) Xlibris Corp.

Mirriam-Goldberg, Caryn. The Sky Begins at Your Feet. 2009. 242p. pap. 21.95 (978-1-888160-43-7(8)) Ice Cube Pr.

Molchan, Kelly. If He Says He's Evil Believe Him! Searching for True Love Can Cause Cancer. 2009. 184p. 26.95 (978-1-4401-4025-9(1)); pap. 16.95 (978-1-4401-4023-5(5)) iUniverse, Inc.

Montanez, Christopher. A True Work of Art. 2011. 26p. pap. 16.95 (978-1-4626-3561-0(X)) PublishAmerica, Inc.

Montenegro, Joana. Sticking it to Cancer. 2011. 116p. pap. 14.95 (978-1-4678-6965-2(1)) AuthorHouse.

Moore, Dwayne. Surviving Wolves at the Door: My Journey Through Cancer. 2008. 384p. pap. 29.95 (978-1-60610-846-8(8)) PublishAmerica, Inc.

Moore, John, Alvett. 2008. 176p. 25.95 (978-0-595-50864-8(2)); pap. 15.95 (978-0-595-52092-3(8)) iUniverse, Inc.

Moorjani, Anita. Dying to Be Me: My Journey from Cancer, to near Death, to True Healing. 2012. (ENG.). xv, 191p. 24.95 (978-1-4019-3751-5(9)) Hay Hse., Inc.

Morgan, Christine L. My Sister Has Breast Cancer. 2009. pap. 11.99 (978-1-60799-030-7(X)) Tate Publishing & Enterprises, LLC.

Morgan, Lindsey & Washington, Linda. Believing That You Belong after Having a Mastectomy: (Follow My Journey, Part 1), 1 vol. 2009. 48p. pap. 16.95 (978-1-60749-394-5(2)) PublishAmerica, Inc.

Morrell, Matthew W. Leukemia & Key Lime Pie. 2006. pap. 10.95 (978-1-890768-77-5(4)) Johnson Bks.

Morris, Kelly W. Pink Ribbons. 2007. 48p. per. 16.95 (978-1-4241-7259-7(4)) PublishAmerica, Inc.

Morrison, Sharon. Even the Eyebrows? 2009. 160p. pap. 13.49 (978-1-4389-2334-5(1)) AuthorHouse.

Mott, Jim. My Walk with the Lord Through the Valley Called Cancer. 2007. 54p. pap. 16.95 (978-1-60441-803-3(6)) PublishAmerica, Inc.

Motyer, Arthur, et al. The Staircase Letters: An Extraordinary Friendship at the End of Life. 2007. (ENG.). 160p. 19.00 (978-0-307-35640-6(X), Random Hse CAN) Random Hse. of Canada, Ltd. CAN. Dist: Random Hse., Inc.

Moutray, Chad. My Life with Laura: A Love Story. 2009. 426p. pap. 24.99 (978-0-557-02869-6(8)) Lulu Enterprises Inc.

Munro, Sandra. It's All about Love. 2010. 193p. pap. 17.99 (978-1-4457-7668-2(5)) Lulu Enterprises Inc.

Munroe, Maria MacHado. It Gets Better! What I Learned from Cancer. 2011. 120p. pap. 19.95 (978-1-4560-5612-4(3)) PublishAmerica, Inc.

Murcer, Bobby & Waggoner, Glen. Yankee for Life: My 40-Year Journey in Pinstripes. 2009. (ENG.). 320p. pap. 14.99 (978-0-06-147342-5(1), Harper Paperbacks) HarperCollins Pubs.

Murphy, Diana. A Woman's Initiation: Women's Experiences with Breast Cancer & How It Transformed Their Lives. 2006. 136p. pap. 14.95 (978-0-9779556-0-2(5)) Synchronicity Bks.

Murphy, Michael. At Five in the Afternoon. 2010. (ENG.). 272p. 39.95 (978-0-86322-407-2(5)) Brandon/Mount Eagle Pubns., Ltd. IRL. Dist: Dufour Editions, Inc.

—At Five in the Afternoon: My Battle with Male Cancer. 2010. (ENG., Illus.). 272p. pap. 14.95 (978-0-86322-426-3(1)) Brandon/Mount Eagle Pubns., Ltd. IRL. Dist: Dufour Editions, Inc.

Murray, Bill. Renegade Colonel. 2009. 704p. pap. 37.95 (978-1-4401-6232-9(8)) iUniverse, Inc.

Naughton, Geraldine. The Perfect Gift. 2010. 52p. pap. 9.95 (978-1-4269-3411-7(4)) Trafford Publishing.

Neave, Veronica. Pieces of Me. 2011. pap. 13.99 (978-1-59955-851-6(3), Bonneville Bks.) Cedar Fort, Inc./CFI Distribution.

Ned Stutman. Facing Up: Grateful Ned's Guide for Living & Dying with Grace. 2009. 152p. pap. 14.95 (978-1-4401-4099-0(5)) iUniverse, Inc.

Nelson, Margy & Nelson, Claire. I'll Stay As Long As I Can: Mother & Daughter Diaries of Love, Tragedy & Remembrance. 2008. 212p. pap. 17.95 (978-0-595-51071-9(X)) iUniverse, Inc.

Nettles, Cherie. Growing My Divine Shrine: Your Way to Live, Love & Laugh Through Life. 2009. (ENG.). 144p. 12.95 (978-0-9817608-7-2(2)) Lifebridge Bks.

Newby, Eleanor M. Don't Count Me Out Yet. 2011. 78p. 24.99 (978-1-4568-3651-1(0)); pap. 15.99 (978-1-4568-3650-4(1)) Xlibris Corp.

Norris, Kathy. Where Does Your Make-up Line Go When You Lose Your Hair? 2006. 112p. per. 10.99 (978-1-59886-523-3(4)) Tate Publishing & Enterprises, LLC.

North, Bradley Dallas. Three Swords of One Light. 2008. 464p. 33.95 (978-1-58909-560-1(X)) Bookstand Publishing.

Northey, Sue. On the Other Side: Journey of A Cancer Survivor. Ivy, Judith, ed. 2007. pap. 11.95 (978-1-59374-722-0(5)) Whiskey Creek Pr., LLC.

Norton, Karen L. Overwhelmed: One Woman's Journey with Breast Cancer. 2011. pap. 10.99 (978-1-61739-068-5(2)) Tate Publishing & Enterprises, LLC.

Norton, Meredith. Lopsided: A Memoir. 2009. (ENG.). 224p. (gr. 12-18). 15.00 (978-0-14-311563-2(4), Penguin (Non-Classics)) Penguin Group (USA) Inc.

O'Brien, Chris. Never Say Die. 2008. 320p. (978-0-7322-8809-9(6)) HarperCollins Pubs. Australia.

O'Brien, Joyce. Choose to Live: Our Journey from Late Stage Cancers to Vibrant Health. 2011. (ENG.). 228p. pap. 17.95 (978-1-60037-836-2(6)) Morgan James Publishing.

O'Connor, Agnes M. Cancer Patience: One Couple's Courageous Battle. 2009. 212p. pap. 17.95 (978-1-4401-2529-4(5)) iUniverse, Inc.

Osborn, Lesa Kelley. 365 Daze. 2011. 104p. pap. 13.95 (978-1-4567-4572-1(7)) AuthorHouse.

O'Shaughnessy, John. The Greatest Gift: A Return to Hope. 2007. (ENG., Illus.). 166p. per. 13.95 (978-1-933916-08-8(7)) Nelson Publishing & Marketing.

Ovitt, Rebecca Sanchez. My Journey of Healing from Cancer. 2006. 101p. per. 9.99 (978-1-59886-529-5(3)) Tate Publishing & Enterprises, LLC.

Pacernick, Gary. A Caregiver's Response: Our Shared Journ. 2006. 135p. pap. 24.95 (978-1-4241-5691-7(2)) PublishAmerica, Inc.

Parenteau, Sharon. I Cry for the Little Girl: a True Story. 2006. (ENG., Illus.). 348p. per. 22.88 (978-1-4120-9604-1(9)) Trafford Publishing.

Parker-Weaver, Stephanie. Rebirth: A Breast Cancer Journey of Many; Survival of Few. 2011. 316p. 29.99 (978-1-4653-4061-0(0)); pap. 19.99 (978-1-4653-4060-3(2)) Xlibris Corp.

Parrish, Darrell W. Cancer & Me: My Personal Journey. 2010. pap. 11.99 (978-1-61579-776-3(5)) Xulon Pr., Inc.

Parrish, Linda. There is no Stage 5: (Blessed with Cancer) 2011. 48p. pap. 15.00 (978-1-4634-2326-1(8)) AuthorHouse.

Partner, Paulo. Amour, Cancer, Combat. 2008. 177p. pap. 23.50 (978-1-4092-2932-2(7)) Lulu Enterprises Inc.

Patricia Meserve Gauvin And Angel Logan. Hope Through the Eyes of Love. 2011. 124p. 29.99 (978-1-4568-6446-0(7)); pap. 19.99 (978-1-4568-6445-3(9)) Xlibris Corp.

Patsy McClendon McDonald (Brown). Cancer & Me: My Cure, My Salvation. 2009. 56p. pap. 9.95 (978-1-4401-6171-1(2)) iUniverse, Inc.

Patterson, Cheryl. Healing in Its Wings. 2007. 84p. per. 9.99 (978-1-60266-135-6(9), Xulon Pr., Inc.

Pausch, Rancy. The Last Lecture. l.t. ed. 2008. (Thorndike Nonfiction Ser.). (Illus.). 285p. 32.95 (978-1-4104-0711-5(X)) Thorndike Pr.

Pausch, Randy & Zaslow, Jeffrey. The Last Lecture. 2008. 224p. pap. 16.00 (978-1-4013-0965-7(8)); (ENG., Illus.). 21.95 (978-1-4013-2325-7(1)) Hyperion Pr.

—La Ultima Lección. 2008. Tr. of Last Lecture. (SPA., Illus.). 232p. 21.95 (978-0-307-39226-8(0), Grijalbo Mondadori, S.A.-Junior ESP. Dist: Random Hse., Inc.

Peaches. How Long Will I Stay? 2011. 52p. pap. 9.99 (978-1-4634-2528-9(7)) AuthorHouse.

Pedicone, Wendi Fox. Hanging Out with Lab Coats: Hope, Humor & Help for Cancer Patients & Their Caregivers. 2007. (Illus.). 348p. 24.95 (978-0-9768997-0-9(1)); per. 17.95 (978-0-9768997-1-6(X)) FoxPress.

Peltason, Ruth A. I Am Not My Breast Cancer: Women Talk Openly about Love & Sex, Hair Loss & Weight Gain, Mothers & Daughters, & Being a Woman with Breast Cancer. 2008. (ENG.). 400p. pap. 15.95 (978-0-06-117407-0(6), Harper Paperbacks) HarperCollins Pubs.

Petersen, Megan. The Poet's Mind, 1 vol. 2010. 62p. pap. 12.95 (978-1-61582-148-8(1)) PublishAmerica, Inc.

Peterson, Diolinda. My Village: A Young Family's Story of Cancer, Love, & Gratitude. 2010. pap. 17.99 (978-1-61663-389-9(1)) Tate Publishing & Enterprises, LLC.

PhotoSensitive. Cancer Connections: Images of Hope & Courage Across Canada. 2011. (ENG., Illus.). 192p. 36.95 (978-0-470-96449-1(9), Wiley) Wiley, John & Sons, Inc.

Piatt, C. Cleveland. A Twenty-Year Fight with Parkinson's Disease. 2011. 354p. pap. 29.95 (978-1-4489-8337-7(1)) PublishAmerica, Inc.

Pietrobono, Patricia. Cancer Check. 2011. 196p. 29.99 (978-1-4568-2931-5(9)); pap. 19.99 (978-1-4568-2930-8(0)) Xlibris Corp.

Poché, Irene L. A Drop of Golden Sun: A Simple Story about an Extraordinary Soul. 2011. 112p. pap. 31.99 (978-1-4567-6833-1(6)) AuthorHouse.

Policastro, Merry. Talk Yourself into a Miracle. 2007. 60p. per. 9.99 (978-1-60266-124-0(3)) Xulon Pr., Inc.

Pontin, Emma. Beating the Blowfish: A candid account of a young yacht skipper's battle with breast Cancer, 1 vol. 2010. (ENG., Illus.). 208p. pap. 19.95 (978-1-57409-294-3(4)) Sheridan Hse., Inc.

Premium Denim and PrivacyWear, Prvcy. Lives Inspired. 2009. 55p. 44.00 (978-0-692-00352-7(5)) Diamond Decisions.

Priddy, Graham. And I Will Trust in You Alone: A Book of Encouragement in My Journey Against Cancer. 2010. (Illus.). 232p. pap. 14.49 (978-1-4490-7335-0(2)) AuthorHouse.

Prodigal, The. Penny's Miracle: Standing on His Promises, 1 vol. 2009. 63p. pap. 16.95 (978-1-4489-9994-1(4)) PublishAmerica, Inc.

Quarrington, Paul. Cigar Box Banjo: Notes on Music & Life, 1 vol. 2011. (ENG.). 256p. pap. 17.95 (978-1-55365-827-6(2), Greystone Bks.) D&M Pubs. Inc. CAN. Dist: Perseus-PGW.

Queller, Jessica. Pretty Is What Changes: Impossible Choices, the Breast Cancer Gene, & How I Defied My Destiny. 2009. (ENG.). 272p pap. 14.00 (978-0-385-52041-6(7)) Spiegel & Grau.

Quinlan, Casey. Cancer for Christmas: Making the Most of a Daunting Gift. 2009. 130p. pap. 12.95 (978-1-936051-41-0(9)) Peppertree Pr., The.

Raab, Diana. Healing with Words: A Writer's Cancer Journey. 2010. pap. (978-1-61599-010-8(0)) Loving Healing Pr., Inc.

Raab, Diana M. Healing with Words: A writer's cancer Journey. 2011. 204p. 32.95 (978-1-61599-110-5(7)) Loving Healing Pr., Inc.

Radner, Gilda. It's Always Something: Twentieth Anniversary Edition. 20th ed. 2009. (ENG., Illus.). 304p. pap. 15.00 (978-1-4391-4886-0(4)) Simon & Schuster.

Rahoul. Living with Cancer Without Fears. 2011. 198p. 29.99 (978-1-4628-6614-4(X)); pap. 19.99 (978-1-4628-6613-7(1)) Xlibris Corp.

Rakoff, Ruth. When My World Was Very Small: A Memoir of Family, Food, Cancer & My Couch. 2010. (ENG.). 224p. 25.95 (978-0-307-35817-2(8), Random Hse CAN) Random Hse. of Canada, Ltd. CAN. Dist: Random Hse., Inc.

Ramos, Sandi. He Carries Me: A Message of Hope & Understanding for the Caregivers of Terminally Ill Loved Ones. 2010. pap. 10.99 (978-1-61663-091-1(4)) Tate Publishing & Enterprises, LLC.

Randall, Brad. The Ld Chronicles: A Story about a Physician & His Missing Prostate. 2011. 114p. pap. 12.95 (978-1-4327-7030-3(6)) Outskirts Pr., Inc.

Rasmussen, Sonja. Doing It with Bling On: Battling Breast Cancer with Style. 2010. 200p. pap. 18.49 (978-1-4490-8622-0(5)) AuthorHouse.

Reeves, William J. Life Alchemy: A Father, A Son & A Transformation. 2009. (Illus.). 138p. pap. 13.95 (978-1-4327-4097-9(0)) Outskirts Pr., Inc.

Regan-Comedy, Maria. If I Have to Fight I Might As Well Win: A Testimony about the Favor of the Lord. 2009. 92p. pap. 10.99 (978-1-60791-470-9(0)) Xulon Pr., Inc.

Reinisch, Nancy. Chemosabee. 2009. 234p. pap. 24.95 (978-0-615-22963-8(8)) NRR Publishing.

Renk, Roberta. Love at Second Sight. 2011. 260p. 35.95 (978-1-4497-1101-6(4)); pap. 19.95 (978-1-4497-1100-9(6)) WestBow Pr. A Div. of Thomas Nelson.

Richardson, Lorna. The Cocktail: That Is What Cured My Colon Cancer. 2011. 108p. 21.23 (978-1-4567-3658-3(2)); pap. 10.68 (978-1-4567-3657-6(4)) AuthorHouse.

Richno, Donna. Cancer, Chemo & Beyond. 2008. 137p. pap. 12.95 (978-1-4357-3035-9(6)) Lulu Enterprises Inc.

Rieff, David. Swimming in a Sea of Death: A Son's Memoir. 2008. (ENG.). 192p. pap. 14.00 (978-0-7432-9947-3(7)) Simon & Schuster.

Roberts, Toni E. It's Okay: Living & Loving Through Cancer. 2009. 108p. pap. 11.95 (978-1-4401-1938-5(4)) iUniverse, Inc.

Robertson, Karen. The Inside Story of Cancer. 2011. 176p. pap. 22.02 (978-1-4567-7759-3(9)) AuthorHouse.

Rocker, Brenda E. From Midnight to Daylight: An Inspiring Autobiography. 2008. 196p. 24.99 (978-1-4389-1267-7(6)); pap. 14.49 (978-1-4389-1268-4(4)) AuthorHouse.

Rockowitz, Glenn. Rodeo in Joliet. 2010. 346p. 23.95 (978-0-578-02543-5(0)) Bennett & Hastings Publishing LLC.

Rockowitz, Glenn. Rodeo in Joliet: A Cancer Memoir. 2011. 346p. pap. 12.95 (978-0-615-39662-0(3)) Bennett & Hastings Publishing LLC.

Roderick, Debbie. Scarred for Life: Diary of a Pink Ribbon Princess. 2011. 120p. pap. 12.95 (978-1-4575-0140-1(6)) Dog Ear Publishing, LLC.

Rogers, Linda Green. Cancer Can't Win. 2007. 64p. per. 15.99 (978-1-4257-9456-9(4)) Xlibris Corp.

Roix, S. R. What's Next, Papa? A Story of Cancer That Awakened Hope & Brought Life. 2011. 108p. 22.95 (978-1-4620-5329-2(7)); pap. 12.95 (978-1-4620-5328-5(9)) iUniverse, Inc.

Romm, Robin. The Mercy Papers: A Memoir of Three Weeks. 2009. (ENG.). 224p. pap. 13.00 (978-1-4165-6792-9(5), Scribner) Scribner.

Roppe, Laura. Rocking the Pink: Finding Myself on the Other Side of Cancer. 2012. (ENG.). 320p. pap. 17.00 (978-1-58005-417-1(X)) Seal Pr.

Rose, Holly. Live & Give: Facebooking My Way Through Breast Cancer. 2011. (ENG.). 338p. pap. 14.99 (978-0-615-43869-6(5)) Holly Rose.

Rosenbaum, Chantal. Pink Wig Will Get You Through It. 2009. 104p. pap. (978-1-905553-06-8(4)) BookPublishingWorld.

Roth, William. Movement: A Memoir of Disability, Cancer, & the Holocaust. 2008. (ENG., Illus.). 200p. pap. 29.95 (978-0-7864-3783-2(9)) McFarland & Co., Inc. Pubs.

Rubenstein, Carolyn. Perseverance: How Young People Turn Fear into Hope-and How They Can Teach Us to Do the Same. 2010. (ENG.). 384p. pap. 18.99 (978-0-7653-1779-7(6), Forge Bks.) Doherty, Tom Assocs., LLC.

Rubey, Jane. Surprise! I'm Still Here!! 2010. 74p. 24.99 (978-1-4535-3529-5(2)); pap. 15.99 (978-1-4535-3528-8(4)) Xlibris Corp.

Rubin, Jane Loeb. Almost a Princess: My Life as a Two-Time Cancer Survivor 2011. 152p. pap. 13.95 (978-1-936236-83-1(4)) iUniverse, Inc.

Ruotsala, Aaron Dean. Cole I Love You to the Moon & Back. 2009. 220p. pap. 15.99 (978-1-60791-444-0(1)) Xulon Pr., Inc.

Russo, Rusty. Three Strikes, You're In. 2009. 112p. pap. 14.95 (978-1-60844-056-6(7)) Dog Ear Publishing, LLC.

Sargent, M. K. Eddie, 1 vol. 2010. 134p. pap. 24.95 (978-1-4489-2116-4(3)) PublishAmerica, Inc.

Saylor, H. Thomas, et al. When One Door Closes: A Teen's Inspiring Journey & Living Legacy. 2008. (Illus.). 248p. 24.95 (978-0-9762012-1-2(6)) Three Dot, L.L.C.

Schneider, Stephen H. & Lane, Janica. The Patient from Hell: How I Worked with My Doctors to Get the Best of Modern Medicine & How You Can Too. annot. ed. 2006. (ENG.). 320p. per. 15.95 (978-0-7382-1078-0(1)) Da Capo Pr., Inc.

Scholz, Mark & Blum, Ralph. Invasion of the Prostate Snatchers: An Essential Guide to Managing Prostate Cancer for Patients & Their Families. 2011. (ENG.). 304p. pap. 16.95 (978-1-59051-515-0(3)) Other Pr., LLC.

Schott, Evonne Stevenson & Rabinowitz, Ed. One More Dance. 2011. 232p. pap. 16.95 (978-1-4685-0066-0(X)) AuthorHouse.

Schrauger, Brian. Walking Taylor Home: A Fatal Disease, a Father's Love, & a Son's Courageous Journey, 1 vol. 2009. (Illus.). 288p. pap. 11.69 (978-0-8254-6291-7(6), Monarch Bks.) Lion Hudson PLC GBR. Dist: Kregel Pubns.

Seager, Maryalice C. The Valley of the Shadow of Death! 2008. 64p. pap. 16.95 (978-1-60563-877-5(3)) PublishAmerica, Inc.

Sell, Colleen. Breast Cancer Survivors: Inspiring Stories of Courage & Triumph. 2008. (ENG.). 336p. pap. 9.95 (978-1-59869-650-9(5)) Adams Media Corp.

—A Cup of Comfort for Breast Cancer Survivors: Inspiring Stories of Courage & Triumph. 2008. (ENG.). 336p. pap. 9.99 (978-1-60550-644-9(3)) Adams Media Corp.

Servan-Schreiber, David. Not the Last Goodbye: On Life, Death, Healing, & Cancer. 2011. (ENG.). 176p. (gr. 12). 22.00 (978-0-670-02591-6(7), Viking Adult) Penguin Group (USA) Inc.

Seward, Clint. Surviving Cancer: Lessons to help you win your Battle. 2009. 107p. pap. 12.96 (978-0-557-14770-0(0)) Lulu Enterprises Inc.

Sewell, Sue Wesley. The Shadow of Your Wings. 2007. (ENG.). 103p. per. 10.99 (978-1-60037-134-9(5)) Morgan James Publishing.

Shahin, Eman. BENEFITS of my CANCER. 2007. 88p. per. 16.95 (978-1-4241-6798-2(1)) PublishAmerica, Inc.

Shelton, Stacy. Me, the Crazy Woman, & Breast Cancer: Strength & Inspiration for the Patient, Survivor, & Those Who Love Them. 2009. 313p. pap. 19.95 (978-0-9825085-9-6(X)) Enlighten Pr.

Sheppard, Arlene Joy. A Princess Meets Her Prince Charming. 2007. 132p. (ENG.). 21.99 (978-1-60477-056-8(2)); per. 13.99 (978-1-60477-055-1(4), Xulon Pr., Inc.

Sheridan, Diane L. Don't Forget the Flippin' E: A Memoir. 2011. 316p. 25.74 (978-1-4520-8866-2(7)); pap. 15.19 (978-1-4520-8865-5(9)) AuthorHouse.

Sheridan, Patrick M. How Come Nothing Ever Kills Granddad? 2009. 408p. 29.49 (978-1-4490-2299-0(5)); pap. 19.99 (978-1-4490-2298-3(7)) AuthorHouse.

Shiller, Romy. Who Knew? A Continuation of You Never Know: A Memoir. 2010. 124p. (ENG.). 24.99 (978-1-4269-2764-5(9)); pap. 14.99 (978-1-4269-2654-9(5)) Trafford Publishing.

Shockney, Lillie. Stealing Second Base: A Breast Cancer Survivor's Experience & Breast Cancer Expert's Story. 2006. (Illus.). 113p. per. 22.95 (978-0-7637-4509-7(X)) Jones & Bartlett Learning, LLC.

Shute, Alesia. Everything's Okay: A Roundtable Comic: My Journey Surviving Childhood Cancer. 2011. (ENG.). 80p. pap. 14.95 (978-1-61066-014-3(5)) Writer of the Round Table Pr.

Sides, Vickie. Vickie's Story: My Cancer Journey. 2010. 48p. pap. 9.95 (978-1-61507-207-1(1)) Cross Bks. Publishing.

Siemientkowski, Ron. Miracle Man Story. 2009. 100p. pap. 14.99 (978-1-60844-145-7(8)) Dog Ear Publishing, LLC.

Silver, Harvey. Oh, Thank God I Have Prostate Cancer! A Patient's View. 2011. 88p. pap. 10.98 (978-1-4567-2165-7(8)) AuthorHouse.

Silver, Julie K. What Helped Get Me Through: Cancer Survivors Share Wisdom & Hope. 2008. (ENG.). 378p. pap. 17.95 (978-1-60443-004-2(4), 1604430044) American Cancer Society, Inc.

Simpson, Robert B. Through the Dark Waters: Searching for Hope & Courage. 2009. 224p. pap. 12.95 (978-1-60594-312-1(6), Llumina Pr.) Aeon Publishing Inc.

Simpson, Wallis A. & Smith, Cara Blakley. I Choose to Laugh: Faith in the Midst of Cancer. 2007. 140p. per. 13.95 (978-0-595-46623-8(0)) iUniverse, Inc.

Skipper, Kathy. A Rose Is God's Autograph. 2007. (YA). per. 15.20 (978-1-932583-37-3(8)) digital@batesjackson llc.

Skloot, Rebeca. Immortal Life of Henrietta. 2011. 15.45 (978-0-7848-3620-0(5), Everbind) Marco Bk. Co.

Skloot, Rebecca. The Immortal Life of Henrietta Lacks. (ENG., Illus.). 2011. 400p. pap. 16.00 (978-1-4000-5218-9(1), Three Rivers Pr.) 2010. 384p. 26.00 (978-1-4000-5217-2(3), Crown) Crown Publishing Group.

—The Immortal Life of Henrietta Lacks. l.t. ed. 604p. 2011. (ENG.). pap. 16.99 (978-1-59413-432-6(4), Large Print Pr.) 2010. 31.99 (978-1-4104-2792-2(7)) Thorndike Pr.

Skowronski, Michael. Unforgettable. 2007. 328p. 33.95 (978-1-4251-6727-1(6)) Trafford Publishing.

Smith, Lester H. You Gotta Dance Like No One's Watching: A two-time cancer survivor & two-time national ballroom dance champion takes life for a Spin. Morille, Trish, ed. 2010. (Illus.). 312p. 34.95 (978-0-9819904-1-5(X)) Bright Sky Pr.

Smith, Manders. A Year with Misty. 2009. (Illus.). 260p. pap. 14.49 (978-1-4490-0747-8(3)) AuthorHouse.

Smith, Marie. Life Music. 2007. 216p. pap. 15.00 (978-0-615-16581-3(8)) Purple Pen Pr.

Smith, Norma J. Walking on Water: Manifestations of the Messiah. 2011. pap. 11.99 (978-1-61346-452-6(5)) Tate Publishing & Enterprises, LLC.

Smith, W. E. (Bill). Later: A Journey of Hope for When Everyone Survives. 2009. 340p. pap. 18.99 (978-1-61579-268-9(6)) Xulon Pr., Inc.

Solomon, Catherine Leah. Diary of a Terminal Woman: I Had Brain Cancer & Lived. 2011. 798p. 34.99 (978-1-4363-6855-1(3)); pap. 23.99 (978-1-4363-6854-4(5)) Xlibris Corp.

Soraya & Soraya. Soraya: A Life of Music, a Legacy of Hope. 2007. (ENG., Illus.). 256p. 19.95 (978-0-470-17127-1(8), Wiley) Wiley, John & Sons, Inc.

Sorbo, Lori A. Eleven Years Later: One Family's Journey to Surviving Cancer. 2009. pap. 9.99 (978-1-60799-932-4(3)) Tate Publishing & Enterprises, LLC.

Spratley, Ian F. It's Not over till the Bag-Lady R. 2008. (Illus.). 176p. 20.00 (978-1-905862-14-6(8)) How To Books GBR. Dist: Parkwest Pubns., Inc.

Springer, Elizabeth M. Struck with Adversity: My Personal Journey with Breast Cancer. 2011. 136p. pap. 24.95 (978-1-4560-7059-5(2)) PublishAmerica, Inc.

Stanley, Barb. The Grace of Living with Cancer. 2011. 60p. pap. 20.95 (978-1-4525-3606-4(6)) Get Published.

Staples. Cancer Ain't Nothing but a Pimple Ta God. 2008. 80p. per. 11.99 (978-1-60477-165-7(8)) Xulon Pr., Inc.

Stewart, Alana. My Journey with Farrah: A Story of Life, Love, & Friendship. 2010. (ENG.). 288p. pap. 14.99 (978-0-06-196059-8(4), Harper Paperbacks) 2009. 288p. 23.99 (978-0-06-196058-1(6), Morrow, William & Co.) 2009. 338p. pap. 23.99 (978-0-06-196636-1(3), HarperLuxe) HarperCollins Pubs.

Stier, Wayne. Stars When the Sun Shines: A Memoir. 2010. (ENG.). 1p. pap. 18.95 (978-1-57863-473-6(3), Weiser Bks.) Red Wheel/Weiser.

Strasser, Judith. Facing Fear: Cancer & Politics, Courage & Hope. 2008. 221p. pap. 19.95 (978-0-9768781-9-3(4)) Borderland Bks.

Streble, Paul. Hello Cancer Remember Me. 2008. 51p. pap. 16.95 (978-1-60441-144-7(9)) PublishAmerica, Inc.

Street, Wayne J. Game, Set, Life: My Match with Crohn's & Cancer. 2010. pap. 14.99 (978-1-61566-260-9(X)) Tate Publishing & Enterprises, LLC.

Stringfield, Michael. Cancer & Me. 2011. 52p. 24.99 (978-1-4628-9014-9(8)); pap. 15.99 (978-1-4628-9015-6(6)) Xlibris Corp.

Sturgeon Williams, Susan. Clipped Wings. 2011. 88p. (978-1-77067-947-4(2)) pap. (978-1-77067-948-1(0)) FriesenPress.

Sullivan, Ester S. Cancer Is Just Right for God: A Twelve Years Survivor. 2011. 108p. 27.49 (978-1-4567-4770-1(3)); pap. 19.99 (978-1-4567-4771-8(1)) AuthorHouse.

Sundquist, Josh. Just Don't Fall: A Hilariously True Story of Childhood, Cancer Amputation, Romantic Yearning, Truth, & Olympic Greatness. 2010. (ENG.). 336p. (gr. 12). 16.00 (978-0-14-311878-7(1), Penguin (Non-Classics)) Penguin Group (USA) Inc.

Supernault, Esther. Blue Diamond Journey: The Healing of a Reluctant Seer. 2010. 268p. pap. 19.75 (978-1-4269-4115-3(3)) Trafford Publishing.

Swarner, Sean. Keep Climbing: How I Beat Cancer & Reached the Top of the World. 2008. (ENG., Illus.). 240p. pap. 16.95 (978-0-7432-9206-1(5), Beyond Words/Atria Bks.) Atria Bks.

Swayze, Lisa Niemi. Worth Fighting For: Love, Loss, & Moving Forward. 2012. (ENG., Illus.). 256p. pap. 14.00 (978-1-4391-9636-6(2)); 336p. 24.00 (978-1-4391-9635-9(4)) Atria Bks. (Beyond Words/Atria Bks.).

—Worth Fighting For: Love, Loss, & Moving Forward. 2012. lib. bdg. (978-1-61173-350-1(2)) Ctr. Point Large Print.

Swayze, Patrick & Swayze, Lisa Niemi. The Time of My Life. 2010. (ENG., Illus.). 256p. pap. 16.00 (978-1-4391-5861-6(4), Beyond Words/Atria Bks.) Atria Bks.

Takala, Sherry. My Healing Path. 2007. pap. 12.95 (978-0-7873-1425-5(0)) Health Research.

Tang, Haitao. A Heart Trace Through the Digital World. 2009. 292p. 28.50 (978-1-60693-759-4(6), Eloquent Bks.) AEG Literary Publishing Services, Inc.

Teall, Sue. Why Not Me? Oh God Why Me? One Woman's Inspirational & Thought-provoking Journey with God through Cancer. 2007. 124p. per. 12.95 (978-0-595-43675-0(7)) iUniverse, Inc.

The Healing Project, ed. Voices of Breast Cancer: The Healing Companion: Stories for Courage, Comfort & Strength. 2007. (Voices of Ser.). (ENG., Illus.). 300p. per. 16.95 (978-1-934184-02-8(0)) Lachance Publishing LLC.

Thomas, Geoff. Riding Through the Storm: My Fight Back to Fitness on the Tour de France. 2008. (ENG., Illus.). 304p. pap. 12.95 (978-0-7528-9343-3(2)) Orion Bks. Ltd. GBR. Dist: Sterling Publishing Co., Inc.

C

Thompson, Janet. Dear God, They Say It's Cancer: A Companion Guide for Women on the Breast Cancer Journey. 2006. (ENG.). 400p. pap. 19.99 (978-1-58229-575-6(1), Howard Bks.) Howard Books.

Tofanelli, Dave. Cancer, a Marriage & a Miracle. 2008. 224p. pap. 15.99 (978-1-60647-724-3(2)) Xulon Pr., Inc.

Treadway, David, et al. Home Before Dark: A Family Portrait of Cancer & Healing. 2010. (ENG.). 256p. 22.95 (978-1-4027-6071-6(X)) Union Square Pr.

Trillin, Calvin. About Alice. 2008. (ENG.). 78p. 15.00 (978-1-4223-9340-6(2)) DIANE Publishing Co.

—About Alice. 2006. (ENG.). 96p. 14.95 (978-1-4000-6615-5(8), Random House) Random House Publishing Group.

Turner, Jerome. Thank God for Cancer! 2008. 136p. per. 13.99 (978-1-60477-665-2(X)) Xulon Pr., Inc.

Tuzinski, Carol. And Then God Spoke to Me. 2007. 252p. per. 24.95 (978-1-4241-7507-9(0)) PublishAmerica, Inc.

Underwood, Judy K. Dying: Finding Comfort & Guidance in a Story of a Peaceful Passing. 2008. 208p. pap. 16.95 (978-0-9794315-1-7(4)) Odyssey Ink.

Urich, Robert. Going the Distance. Date not set. 24.95 (978-0-06-001413-1(X), ReganBooks) HarperCollins Pubs.

Van Doorn, Margreet Jansen. Row, Row, Row My Boat! A Woman's Incredible Journey with Breast Cancer. 2007. (ENG.). 188p. pap. 20.83 (978-1-4120-7993-8(4)) Trafford Publishing.

Van, Mo. Singing off Key. 2006. pap. 15.95 (978-0-9776941-0-5(0)) Sea Wind Publishing.

Vande Berg, Leah & Trujillo, Nick. Cancer & Death: A Love Story in Two Voices. 2008. (978-1-57273-851-5(0)) Hampton Pr., Inc.

VanGinhoven, Thais. Moments with God: Diaries of a Cancer Survivor. 2010. pap. 17.99 (978-1-61663-538-1(X)) Tate Publishing & Enterprises, LLC.

VanSickle, Elizabeth. Crossing Jordan. 2008. 184p. 27.95 (978-0-557-00352-5(0)); pap. 10.95 (978-0-557-00449-2(7)) Lulu Enterprises Inc.

VanSickle, Elizabeth Paige. Conversations with God. 2009. (ENG.). 646p. 45.84 (978-0-557-04954-7(7)); 647p. pap. 28.88 (978-0-557-04937-0(7)) Lulu Enterprises Inc.

Vezeau, Sheila. Cancer in the Words of a Child. 2011. 40p. pap. 16.95 (978-1-4626-1133-1(8)) PublishAmerica, Inc.

Villalba-Navarette, Richard. Cancer's End: Two Months to Live, 1 vol. 2010. 79p. pap. 16.95 (978-1-4489-7116-9(0)) PublishAmerica, Inc.

Vincent, Lorie L. & Vincent, Mark L. Fighting Disease, Not Death: Finding a way through lifelong Struggle. 2011. 112p. pap. 15.00 (978-1-4575-0460-0(X)) Dog Ear Publishing, LLC.

W., Joye. Walking Through the 'C' Word: A Victorious Journey Through Cancer, Divorce & Despair. 2008. 132p. pap. 11.95 (978-1-4327-2561-7(0)) Outskirts Pr., Inc.

Wadeson, Harriet/Claire. Journaling Cancer in Words & Images: Caught in the Clutch of the Crab. 2011. (Illus.). 218p. pap. 36.95 (978-0-398-08672-5(9)) Thomas, Charles C. Pub., Ltd.

Wahlen Tillema, Renee, ed. Leap of Faith: Stories of Courage from the Leroy Butler Foundation. 2007. (Illus.). 178p. 29.95 (978-0-9797905-0-8(6)) LeRoy Butler Foundation, Inc., The.

Walton, Charles. Almost Always Fatal (Surviving Cancer with a Sense of Humor) 2007. 196p. pap. 20.94 (978-0-615-15361-2(5)) KC Creations, Inc.

Wanslee, Sharon. A Desert Daughter's Odyssey. 280p. 30.00 (978-0-930751-00-5(0)); pap. 20.00 (978-0-930751-02-9(7)) New Century Bks.

Ward, Tim B. Surviving & Thriving: A Brain Tumor Survivor's Story. 2010. 260p. pap. 19.95 (978-1-4327-5364-1(9)) Outskirts Pr., Inc.

Ward, William. Traveling Light: Walking the Cancer Path. 2008. 240p. pap. 20.00 (978-1-58420-061-1(8), Lindisfarne Bks.) SteinerBooks, Inc.

Warner, Anna M. My Lipstick Journey Through Cancer: A Journey of Faith & Finding the Right Shade. 2011. 104p. pap. 14.99 (978-1-4567-3003-1(7)) AuthorHouse.

Watts, Ann. How Does It Feel? Reflections on a year in the life of one woman, following a diagnosis of bowel Cancer. 2009. (Illus.). 108p. pap. 35.49 (978-1-4343-8471-3(3)) AuthorHouse.

Weichenthal, Phyllis B. This Is Cancer but You Will Overcome It! 2008. 52p. pap. 10.99 (978-0-88144-308-0(5)) Yorkshire Publishing Group.

Welch, Jill. Time in the Sun: A Record of an Incredible Spiritual Journey. 2010. 148p. pap. 13.95 (978-1-4497-0313-4(5), WestBow Pr.) Author Solutions, Inc.

Wells, Mary Jean. Cancer the Fight of My Life. 2008. 119p. pap. 12.95 (978-1-4357-4512-4(4)) Lulu Enterprises Inc.

Weltz, Nancy A. Another God Moment. 2009. 16p. pap. 12.99 (978-1-4490-3726-0(7)) AuthorHouse.

Westfahl, Carol. Faith, Hope, & Cancer: A Survivor's Tips. 2006. per. 13.95 (978-1-59598-037-3(7)) HenschelHAUS Publishing.

Will, Steve. A Reason to Run: A Personal Journey Through Prostate Cancer & Other Manly Matters. 2007. 191p. per. 15.95 (978-1-930580-93-0(2), Ulyssian Pubns.) Pine Orchard, Inc.

Willets, George. That's Easy for You to Say: Memoirs of a smoker, laryngectomee & public Speaker. 2010. 92p. pap. 11.95 (978-1-4502-3037-7(7)) iUniverse, Inc.

Williams, Steve. Steve Williams: How Dr. Death Became Dr. Life. 2007. (Illus.). 226p. 24.95 (978-1-59670-180-9(3)) Sports Publishing, LLC.

Willis, Jack D. Saving Jack: A Man's Struggle with Breast Cancer. 2008. (ENG.). 208p. pap. 19.95 (978-0-8061-3895-4(5)) Univ. of Oklahoma Pr.

Wilmes, D M. Seven Days of Hospice: A Memoir. 2007. 116p. (ENG.). 22.95 (978-0-595-70150-6(7)); per. 12.95 (978-0-595-46373-2(8)) iUniverse, Inc.

Wilson, Deborah A. Beyond the Boobs: Inspiring & Courageous Stories of Breast Cancer Survival. 2009. (ENG.). 104p. pap. 14.95 (978-0-9841077-3-5(8)) 1 Vision Publishing Co.

Wilson, Jane. A Jar for My Tears: A Journal of Prayer & Healing for Women with Breast Cancer. 2009. pap. 14.99 (978-1-60799-953-9(6)) Tate Publishing & Enterprises, LLC.

Wilson, K. Me, My Cancer, & I. 2007. 48p. per. 16.95 (978-1-4241-8680-8(3)) PublishAmerica, Inc.

Winick, Paul. Cancer Dreams. 2011. 200p. 24.59 (978-1-4634-1841-0(8)); pap. 14.03 (978-1-4634-1842-7(6)) AuthorHouse.

Wisenberg, S. L. The Adventures of Cancer Bitch. 2009. (ENG.). 160p. 25.00 (978-1-58729-802-8(3)) Univ. of Iowa Pr.

Wishart, Adam. One in Three: A Son's Journey into the History & Science of Cancer. 2008. (ENG.). 304p. per. 14.00 (978-0-8021-4348-8(2), Grove Pr.) Grove/Atlantic, Inc.

Woodson, Nancy Leake. Hurdles: I find myself viewing the many beautiful colors in the rainbow as if I were looking through the sheer lens of a kaleidoscope. the many shades of color remind me of the Hurdles in my Life. 2010. 248p. 26.95 (978-1-4490-4882-2(X)); pap. 19.95 (978-1-4490-4881-5(1)) AuthorHouse.

Wyatt, Ellie. I Had Two When I Came In. 2011. 50p. 24.99 (978-1-4653-6044-1(1)); pap. 15.99 (978-1-4653-6043-4(3)) Xlibris Corp.

Yates, David. Cancer Sucks: A True Story. 2011. (ENG.). 224p. pap. 16.95 (978-1-936401-94-9(0)) Two Harbors Pr., Inc.

Zaccone, Suzanne. A Random Interruption: Surviving Breast Cancer with Laughter, Vodka, Smoothies & an Attitude: Surviving Breast Cancer with Laughter, Vodka, Smoothies & an Attitude. 2009. 500p. 34.99 (978-1-4415-8057-3(3)); pap. 23.99 (978-1-4415-8056-6(5)) Xlibris Corp.

Zetterstrom, Charlie. Peggy. 2007. 73p. pap. 16.95 (978-1-60441-788-3(9)) PublishAmerica, Inc.

Zytaruk, Tom. Like a Rock: The Chuck Cadman Story. unabr. ed. 2008. (ENG., Illus.). 304p. pap. 26.95 (978-1-55017-427-4(4)) Harbour Publishing Co., Ltd. CAN. Dist: Ingram Pub. Services.

CANCER—PATIENTS—EMPLOYMENT

Feuerstein, Michael. Work & Cancer Survivors. (ENG.). xxiii, 350p. 2010. pap. 59.95 (978-1-4419-8155-4(1), 1441981551) 2009. (Illus.). 148.00 (978-0-387-72040-1(5), 0387720405) Springer.

CANCER—PATIENTS—FAMILY RELATIONSHIPS

Allen, Jennifer & Allen, ATR-BC Jennifer, Lmft. BONE KNOWING: a true story of coming to life in the face of impending Loss. 2010. 356p. pap. 19.95 (978-0-578-03185-9(X)) Jujupress.

Anderson, John W. Stand by Her: A Breast Cancer Guide for Men, 1 vol. 2009. (ENG.). 272p. pap. 18.95 (978-0-8144-1391-3(9)) Amacom.

Axmann, Martha. She Won the Race: Footprints of Cancer. 2009. 212p. pap. 17.99 (978-1-4141-1249-7(1)) Pleasant Word.

Beach, Wayne A. A Natural History of Family Cancer: Interactional Resources for Managing Illness. 2009. (978-1-57273-691-7(7)); (978-1-57273-690-0(9)) Hampton Pr., Inc.

Benford, Tom & Theis, Andrea Benford. Standing Tall: A Father's Lessons Through His Daughter's Cancer. 2011. 176p. pap. 19.95 (978-1-4520-4395-1(7)) AuthorHouse.

Bolletino, Ruth. How to Talk with Family Caregivers about Cancer. 2009. (ENG.). 304p. pap. 21.95 (978-0-393-70576-8(5), 70576) Norton, W. W. & Co., Inc.

Boynton, Lora Lee. Goodbye Mommy: Memoirs of a Survivor. 2009. (ENG., Illus.). 296p. (978-1-84876-110-0(4)) Troubadour Publishing Ltd.

Bristow, Allen & Kircher, Kim. The Next 15 Minutes: Strength from the Top of the Mountain. 2011. (ENG.). 260p. pap. 15.95 (978-1-933016-11-5(6)) Behler Pubns., LLC.

Brown, Nancy. The Nightmare's Over. 2011. pap. 8.95 (978-0-7414-6678-5(3)) Infinity Publishing.

Brown, Steven G. Living & Loving Through & Past Cancer: A Spouse's Perspective. 2011. pap. 18.99 (978-1-61777-290-0(9)) Tate Publishing & Enterprises, LLC.

Burns, Catherine. Patients with Advanced Cancer. 2010. 284p. pap. (978-3-8383-1272-9(4)) Lambert Academic Publishing.

The Cancer Poetry Project: Poems by Cancer Patients & Those Who Love Them. 2007. 248p. per. 18.95 (978-0-9789946-8-6(X)) Tasora Bks.

Chideme-Munodawafa, Auxilia. Family Functioning in Childhood Cancer among Zimbabwean Families. 2009. 176p. pap. (978-3-639-11184-2(2)) VDM Verlag Dr. Mueller e.K.

Clark, Linda Hovestadt. Valley of the Shadow: A Mother's Journal Through Her Child's Battle with Cancer. 2006. (ENG.). 232p. per. 17.99 (978-1-4141-0693-9(9)) Pleasant Word.

Cohen, Michael E. Mike & Heather: A Young Widower's Short Story. 2009. 60p. pap. 10.49 (978-1-4389-8197-0(X)) AuthorHouse.

Coleman, Susan. For the Love of Bob. 2010. 168p. pap. 14.95 (978-1-936107-38-4(4)) Mill City Pr., Inc.

Collins, Maria Antonieta & Collins, Maria A. Dijiste Que Me Querías: Como Sobrellevar lo Impensable. 2007. (SPA., Illus.). 304p. pap. 14.95 (978-0-06-088471-0(1), Rayo) HarperCollins Pubs.

Coppinger, Kelli. My Husband, Our Hero. 2008. 179p. pap. 24.95 (978-1-60672-942-7(X)) PublishAmerica, Inc.

Corrigan, Kelly. The Middle Place. 2008. (ENG.). 288p. pap. 14.95 (978-1-4013-4093-3(8)); (Illus.). 272p. 23.95 (978-1-4013-0336-5(6)) Hyperion Pr.

DePriest, Jaca C. Blessed & Beyond: A Passage into Widowhood. 2007. 128p. per. 12.95 (978-0-595-41096-5(0)) iUniverse, Inc.

Doyle Spencer, Monique & Levy, Paul F. How Can I Help? Everyday Ways to Help Your Loved Ones Live with Cancer. 2008. (ENG.). 240p. pap. 12.95 (978-1-59869-681-3(5)) Adams Media Corp.

Eggspuehler, Don. Star Benchwarmers: A Family Memoir. 2011. 336p. 28.49 (978-1-4520-8308-7(8)) AuthorHouse.

Ettleman, Shelley. A Family Touched by Cancer, 1 vol. 2009. 52p. pap. 16.95 (978-1-60836-537-1(9)) PublishAmerica, Inc.

Ferreira, Melinda. Rays of Grace: A Story of Strength & Spirit. 2010. 148p. pap. 14.99 (978-0-615-30016-0(2)) Hampton Pr., The.

Fogelson, Hillary. Pale Girl Speaks: A Year Uncovered. 2012. (ENG.). 256p. pap. 16.00 (978-1-58005-444-7(7)) Seal Pr.

Gabriel, Sarah. Eating Pomegranates: A Memoir of Mothers, Daughters, & the BRCA Gene. 2010. (ENG.). 272p. 25.00 (978-1-4391-4819-8(8), Scribner) Scribner.

Garbowski, Anthony J. & Shaw, Lorna J. Don't Walk Through the Mirror. 2007. per. 17.95 (978-1-888223-70-5(7)) McMillen Publishing.

Greene, Diane Tropea. Apron Strings: Inheriting Courage, Wisdom and... Breast Cancer. 2007. (ENG., Illus.). 133p. per. 14.00 (978-1-56825-108-0(4)) Rainbow Bks., Inc.

Hallerman, Victoria & Albert, Peter S. How We Survived Prostate Cancer: What We Did & What We Should Have Done. 2009. (ENG.). 240p. pap. 16.95 (978-1-55704-819-6(3), William Morrow Paperbacks) HarperCollins Pubs.

Hartley, Laura & Palumbo, Mary Lou. Michael's Journey: Michael Hartley's compelling true story of courage, love, & Perseverance. 2009. 136p. 24.99 (978-1-4490-2624-0(9)); pap. 16.99 (978-1-4490-2623-3(0)) AuthorHouse.

Hayward, Kate. From Oncology Nursing to Coping with Breast Cancer. 2008. (Patient Narratives Ser.). 160p. pap. (978-1-84619-273-9(0)) Radcliffe Publishing.

Hermann, Joan F. Cancer in Our Family: Helping Children Cope with a Parent's Illness. 2nd ed. 2012. (ENG.). 218p. pap. 19.95 (978-0-944235-95-9(6), 0944235956) American Cancer Society, Inc.

Johnson, Gwyneth. HELP! My Husband Has Cancer, Now What Do I Do?, 1 vol. 2010. 54p. pap. 16.95 (978-1-4489-5299-1(9)) PublishAmerica, Inc.

Johnson, Kim. Goodnight Lorna Jean. 2011. 144p. 29.99 (978-1-4568-3832-4(6)); pap. 19.99 (978-1-4568-3831-7(8)) Xlibris Corp.

Joy, Louise. Mother & Daughter: (No More Soup) 2009. 104p. pap. 11.95 (978-1-4401-2625-3(9)) iUniverse, Inc.

Kauder, Bruce M. Daddy, Tell Me a Story about When You Were Little: (A rotten kid grew up to be a Pediatrician) 2009. (Illus.). 151p. (J). (ENG.). 26.95 (978-1-4327-4145-7(4)); pap. 13.95 (978-1-4327-4096-2(2)) Outskirts Pr., Inc.

Kayser, Karen & Scott, Jennifer L. Helping Couples Cope with Women's Cancers: An Evidence-Based Approach for Practitioners. 2008. (ENG.). xv, 229p. 49.95 (978-0-387-74802-3(4), 0387748024) Springer.

Kelly, David A. Time Out: A Family's Journey of Faith & Hope Through Childhood Cancer. 2009. pap. 14.99 (978-1-60799-619-4(7)) Tate Publishing & Enterprises, LLC.

King, A. J. Cancer - Diary of a Daughter. 2010. (Illus.). 140p. pap. 11.99 (978-1-4490-3709-3(7)) AuthorHouse.

Larry And Delila Woodruff. My Son, My Father, My Hero: One Family's Journey with Cancer. 2010. 132p. pap. 13.95 (978-1-4401-9725-3(3)) iUniverse, Inc.

Lucas, Thomas. Cancer a Love Story. 2009. 84p. pap. 10.49 (978-1-4490-1248-9(5)) AuthorHouse.

Malden, Carla. Afterimage: A Brokenhearted Memoir of a Charmed Life. (ENG.). 320p. 2012. pap. 16.95 (978-0-7627-8013-6(4)) 2011. 24.95 (978-0-7627-6382-5(5)) Globe Pequot Pr., The. (skirt!).

Marshall, Catherine A., ed. Surviving Cancer As a Family: And Helping Co-Survivors Thrive. 2010. (Disability Insights & Issues Ser.). 189p. 44.95 (978-0-313-37894-2(0), C37894) Greenwood Publishing Group, Inc.

Montgomery, Lee. The Things Between Us: A Memoir. 2007. (ENG.). 256p. pap. 14.00 (978-1-4165-4310-7(4), Free Pr.) Free Pr.

Musser, Robert. The P I N K Primer: For Partners in Need of Koaching. 2009. 116p. pap. 12.95 (978-1-60844-176-1(8)) Dog Ear Publishing, LLC.

Nelson, Margy & Nelson, Claire. I'll Stay As Long As I Can: Mother & Daughter Diaries of Love, Tragedy & Remembrance. 2008. 212p. pap. 17.95 (978-0-595-51071-9(X)) iUniverse, Inc.

Orchard, Anne. Their Cancer - Your Journey: A Traveller's Guide for Carers, Family & Friends. 2008. (Illus.). 246p. pap. (978-0-9559797-0-5(6)) Rainbow Heart Publishing.

O'Shaughnessy, John. The Greatest Gift: A Return to Hope. 2007. (ENG., Illus.). 166p. per. 13.95 (978-1-933916-08-8(7)) Nelson Publishing & Marketing.

Patient Resource - A Cancer Treatment & Facilities Guide for Patients & Their Families. 2007. 128p. per. 6.95 net. (978-0-615-14256-2(7)) Patient Resource Publishing, LLC.

Patterson, Les. Surviving the Beast: (One Man's Walk through His Wife's Cancer) 2011. 58p. pap. 16.95 (978-1-4560-6625-3(0)) PublishAmerica, Inc.

Ricker-White, Heather. A Brand New Beginning, 1 vol. 2009. 85p. pap. 16.95 (978-1-60813-786-2(4)) PublishAmerica, Inc.

Romm, Robin. The Mercy Papers: A Memoir of Three Weeks. 2009. (ENG.). 224p. pap. 13.00 (978-1-4165-6792-9(5), Scribner) Scribner.

Rose, Susannah & Hara, Richard. 100 Questions & Answers about Caring for Family or Friends with Cancer. 2nd rev. ed. 2009. (ENG.). 225p. pap. 22.95 (978-0-7637-6257-5(1)) Jones & Bartlett Learning, LLC.

Saylor, H. Thomas, et al. When One Door Closes: A Teen's Inspiring Journey & Living Legacy. 2008. (Illus.). 248p. 24.95 (978-0-9762012-1-2(6)) Three Dot, L.L.C.

Schafer, Jerry. Angel in My Pocket. 19.99 (978-0-9706847-8-3(9)) Beginning II End Publishing, Inc.

Schwalbe, Will. The End of Your Life Book Club. 2012. (ENG.). 352p. 25.00 (978-0-307-59403-7(3), Knopf) Knopf Doubleday Publishing Group.

Scott, Joyce. The Reason for My Hope: The Father's Compassion in Sickness & Death. 2008. 48p. per. 8.95 (978-1-4327-0751-4(5)) Outskirts Pr., Inc.

Shone, Neville. Cancer: A Family Affair. ix, 133p. (978-0-85969-706-4(1), Sheldon Press) SPCK Publishing.

Shotel, Jay & Shotel, Sue. It's Good to Know a Miracle: Dani's Story - One Family's Struggle with Leukemia. 2008. (ENG., Illus.). 360p. pap. 20.00 (978-1-884092-74-9(8), Gordian Knot Bks.) Altschuler, Richard & Assocs., Inc.

Shute, Alesia. Everything's Okay: A Roundtable Comic: My Journey Surviving Childhood Cancer. 2011. (ENG.). 80p. pap. 14.95 (978-1-61066-014-3(5)) Writer of the Round Table Pr.

Smith, Mary Lu. A Most Excellent Life. 2010. 109p. pap. 17.51 (978-0-557-26393-6(X)) Lulu Enterprises Inc.

Smith, W. E. (Bill). Later: A Journey of Hope for When Everyone Survives. 2009. 340p. pap. 18.99 (978-1-61579-268-9(6)) Xulon Pr., Inc.

Streble, Paul. Hello Cancer Remember Me. 2008. 51p. pap. 16.95 (978-1-60441-144-7(9)) PublishAmerica, Inc.

Tofanelli, Dave. Cancer, a Marriage & a Miracle. 2008. 224p. pap. 15.99 (978-1-60647-724-3(2)) Xulon Pr., Inc.

Treadway, David, et al. Home Before Dark: A Family Portrait of Cancer & Healing. 2010. (ENG.). 256p. 22.95 (978-1-4027-6071-6(X)) Union Square Pr.

Vande Berg, Leah & Trujillo, Nick. Cancer & Death: A Love Story in Two Voices. 2008. (978-1-57273-851-5(0)) Hampton Pr., Inc.

Wilmes, D M. Seven Days of Hospice: A Memoir. 2007. 116p. per. 12.95 (978-0-595-46373-2(8)) iUniverse, Inc.

Young, Linda T. & Ward, Jonathan. Hope for Families of Children with Cancer. 2008. (Illus.). 202p. 15.99 (978-0-9797800-1-1(2)) Kindred Pr.

Young, Lynda. Hope for Families of Children with Cancer. 2010. (ENG.). 224p. pap. 12.99 (978-0-9797800-3-5(9)) Kindred Pr.

Young, Lynda T. & Ward, Jonathan R. Hope for Families of Children with Cancer: You are Not Alone Book Series. 2011. (FRS.). 14.99 (978-0-89112-289-0(3), Leafwood Pubs.) Abilene Christian Univ. Pr.

CANCER—PATIENTS—PAIN

see Cancer Pain

CANCER—PATIENTS—REHABILITATION

Becker, Kim & Becker, Mike. Hello Gorgeous! A Journey of Faith, Love & Hope. 2011. 208p. pap. 19.95 (978-0-9833586-4-0(8)) Corby Books.

Becton, Randy. Everyday Strength: A Cancer Patient's Guide to Spiritual Survival. 2nd ed. 2006. 160p. (Orig.). reprint ed. pap. 12.99 (978-0-8010-6629-0(8)) Baker Bks.

Bye, Ronald. Memoirs of a 30-Year Cancer Survivor, 1 vol. 2009. (ENG.). 90p. pap. 16.95 (978-1-60836-255-4(8)) PublishAmerica, Inc.

Carlson, Linda & Speca, Michael. Mindfulness-Based Cancer Recovery: A Step-by-Step MBSR Approach to Help You Cope with Treatment & Reclaim Your Life. 2011. (ENG.). 200p. pap. 17.95 (978-1-57224-887-8(4)) New Harbinger Pubns.

Cpht, Lucille Hall. Cancer Care. 2008. 128p. 30.99 (978-1-4363-5258-1(4)) Xlibris Corp.

Currin, Morag. Oncology Esthetics: A Practitioner's Guide. 2009. x, 461p. pap. (978-1-932633-49-8(9)) Allured Business Media.

Davey, Julie. Writing for Wellness: A Prescription for Healing. 2007. 340p. per. (978-1-882883-67-7(5)) Idyll Arbor, Inc.

Feuerstein, Michael. Work & Cancer Survivors. (ENG.). xxiii, 350p. 2010. pap. 59.95 (978-1-4419-8155-4(1), 1441981551) 2009. (Illus.). 148.00 (978-0-387-72040-1(5), 0387720405) Springer.

Fitzal, Florian & Schrenk, Peter, eds. Oncoplastic surgery of the Breast: A guide to clinical Practice. 2010. (ENG., Illus.). xiv, 242p. 369.00 (978-3-211-99316-3(9), 3211993169) Springer.

Galgut, Cordelia. The Psychological Impact of Breast Cancer: A Psychologist's Insights As a Patient. 2010. (Illus.). xvi, 187p. pap. (978-1-84619-303-3(6)) Radcliffe Publishing.

Ganz, Patricia A., ed. Cancer Survivorship: Today & Tomorrow. 2007. (Illus.). 304p. per. 99.00 (978-0-387-34349-5(0), 0387343490) Springer.

Gautier, Holly, et al. Everyone's Guide to Cancer Survivorship: A Road Map for Better Health. 2007. (ENG., Illus.). 304p. pap. 19.95 (978-0-7407-6870-5(0)) Andrews McMeel Publishing.

Grekin, Jacqueline. Medicine for the Mind: Coping Skills for People Who Are Surviving Cancer. Date not set. pap. (978-0-9659685-2-2(9)) Grekin, Jacqueline.

Harari, Paul M. Function Preservation & Quality of Life in Head & Neck Radiotherapy. 2009. (Medical Radiology / Radiation Oncology Ser.). (ENG., Illus.). xiii, 325p. 219.00 (978-3-540-73231-0(4)) Springer.

Hart, Jennifer. Marley Rides. 2007. (Illus.). 528p. pap. 20.00 (978-0-9777632-2-1(6)) Lost Borders Pr.

Hartson, John. Please Don't Go: Big John's Journey Back to Life. 2011. (ENG., Illus.). 240p. pap. 14.95 (978-1-84596-709-3(7)) Mainstream Publishing Co., Ltd. GBR. Dist: Independent Pubs. Group.

Hartson, John & Murphy, Richard. Please Don't Go: Big John's Journey Back to Life. 2010. (ENG., Illus.). 240p. 32.95 (978-1-84596-680-5(5)) Mainstream Publishing Co., Ltd. GBR. Dist: Independent Pubs. Group.

Hewitt, Maria Elizabeth & Ganz, Patricia. Implementing Cancer Survivorship Care Planning. 2006. (ENG., Illus.). 320p. pap. 65.00 *(978-0-309-10318-3(5))* National Academies Pr.

Hodgkinson, Katharine, et al. Psychosocial Care of Cancer Patients: A Health Professional's Guide to What to Say & Do. 2008. pap. *(978-0-9775153-9-4(7),* Ausmed Pubns. Pty Ltd.

Kaelin, Carolyn M., et al. The Breast Cancer Survivor's Fitness Plan: Reclaim Health, Regain Strength, Live Longer. 2006. (Harvard Medical School Guides). (ENG., Illus.). 272p. per. 18.95 *(978-0-07-146578-6(2),* 0071465782) McGraw-Hill Cos., The.

Leupold, Nancy & Sciubba, James J., eds. Meeting the Challenges of Oral & Head & Neck Cancer: A Guide for Survivors & Caregivers. 2nd ed. 2011. 217p. pap. 24.99 ***(978-1-59756-454-0(0))*** Plural Publishing, Inc.

Marcus, Dawn A. Therapy Dogs in Cancer Care: A Valuable Complementary Treatment. 2012. (ENG., Illus.). xiv, 193p. pap. 59.95 ***(978-1-4614-3377-4(0),*** 1461433770) Springer.

Melman, Arnold & Newnham, Rosemary. After Prostate Cancer: A What-Comes-Next Guide to a Safe & Informed Recovery, 1 vol. 2011. (ENG., Illus.). 256p. pap. 19.95 *(978-0-19-539966-0(8))* Oxford Univ. Pr., Inc.

Meyers, Christina A. & Perry, James R., eds. Cognition & Cancer. 2008. (ENG., Illus.). 353p. 130.00 *(978-0-521-85482-5(2))* Cambridge Univ. Pr.

Miller, Kenneth D. Medical & Psychosocial Care of the Cancer Survivor. 2009. (Illus.). 479p. 73.95 *(978-0-7637-5770-0(5))* Jones & Bartlett Learning, LLC.

Miller, Tani. Chemo & Me: My Hair Loss Experience. 2009. (ENG., Illus.). 48p. 11.95 *(978-1-60443-009-7(5),* 1604430095) American Cancer Society, Inc.

Musser, Robert. The P I N K Primer: For Partners in Need of Koaching. 2009. 116p. pap. 12.95 *(978-1-60844-176-1(8))* Dog Ear Publishing, LLC.

Nahabedian, Maurice & Nahabedian, Maurice Y. Oncoplastic Surgery of the Breast with DVD. 2009. (ENG., Illus.). 200p. 195.00 *(978-0-7020-3181-6(X),* Saunders) Elsevier - Health Sciences Div.

Olson, Ruth. My Gift to You: Encouragement During a Cancer Crisis. 2009. 56p. pap. 9.95 *(978-1-4401-4574-2(1))* iUniverse, Inc.

Penedo, Frank J., et al. Cognitive-Behavioral Stress Management for Prostate Cancer Recovery. 2008. (Treatments That Work Ser.). (ENG., Illus.). 160p. pap., wbk. ed. 27.95 *(978-0-19-533698-6(4))* Oxford Univ. Pr., Inc.

Post-Ferrante, Pamela. Writing & Healing: A Mindful Guide for Cancer Survivors. 2012. (ENG.). 208p. pap. 35.00 ***(978-1-57826-422-3(7))*** Hatherleigh Co., Ltd., The.

Rankin, Jane L., et al, eds. Rehabilitation in Cancer Care. 2008. (ENG., Illus.). 360p. pap. 82.99 *(978-1-4051-5997-5(9),* Wiley-Blackwell) Wiley, John & Sons, Inc.

Rubenstein, Carolyn. Perseverance: True Voices of Cancer Survivors. 2009. (ENG.). 384p. 24.99 *(978-0-7653-1778-0(8),* Forge Bks.) Doherty, Tom Assocs., LLC.

Saphron. WHOLE: Women Healing Ourselves with Loving Energy: 12 Principles for Rebuilding Life after Breast Cancer. 2007. (Illus.). 251p. *(978-0-9714219-7-4(8))* Conch Shell Pr.

Saunders, Avril Dalziel. Mammograms Save Lives. 2012. (ENG.). 70p. pap. 9.99 ***(978-1-907728-36-5(8),*** PS True Life) Pneuma Springs Publishing GBR. Dist: Lightning Source, Inc.

Savage, Regina E. Mirror Makeovers & Savvy Insights: For the Everyday Gal Surviving Cancer & Baldness with a Sense of Humor. 2009. 32p. 19.95 *(978-0-9823705-0-6(4))* Quiet Angel Publishing, LLC.

Silver, Julie K. After Cancer Treatment: Heal Faster, Better, Stronger. 2006. (Johns Hopkins Press Health Book Ser.). (ENG.). 288p. 47.00 *(978-0-8018-8437-5(3));* per. 17.95 *(978-0-8018-8438-2(1))* Johns Hopkins Univ. Pr.

Silverman, Dan & Davidson, Idelle. Your Brain after Chemo: A Practical Guide to Lifting the Fog & Getting Back Your Focus. 2010. (ENG., Illus.). 304p. pap. 16.95 *(978-0-7382-1391-0(8))* Da Capo Pr., Inc.

Stubblefield, Michael D. Principles & Practice of Cancer Rehabilitation. 2009. 629.00 *(978-1-933864-33-4(8))* Demos Medical Publishing, LLC.

Thiboldeaux, Kim & Golant, Mitch. The Total Cancer Wellness Guide: Reclaiming Your Life after Diagnosis. 2007. (ENG., Illus.). 306p. 24.95 *(978-1-933771-16-8(X))* BenBella Bks.

Van As-Brooks, Corina J. & Ward, Elizabeth C., eds. Head & Neck Cancer: Treatment, Rehabilitation, & Outcomes. 2006. (Illus.). 224p. 99.99 incl. cd-rom *(978-1-59756-061-0(8))* Plural Publishing, Inc.

Walsh, Patrick C. & Worthington, Janet Farrar. Dr. Patrick Walsh's Guide to Surviving Prostate Cancer. 2nd ed. 2007. (ENG., Illus.). 592p. per. 16.99 *(978-0-446-69689-0(7))* Grand Central Publishing.

Weltz, Nancy A. Another God Moment. 2009. 16p. pap. 12.99 *(978-1-4490-3726-0(7))* AuthorHouse.

CANCER—PERSONAL NARRATIVES

see Cancer—Patients—Biography

CANCER—POPULAR WORKS

Abou-Alfa, Ghassan & DeMatteo, Ronald. 100 Questions & Answers about Liver Cancer. 3rd ed. 2011. 138p. pap. 22.95 *(978-1-4496-2289-3(5))* Jones & Bartlett Learning, LLC.

American Cancer Society. QuickFACTS Melanoma Skin Cancer: What You Need to Know-NOW. 2012. (QuickFACTS Ser.). (ENG.). 176p. pap. 8.95 *(978-1-60443-038-7(9))* American Cancer Society, Inc.

American Cancer Society Staff, contrib. by. Quick Facts Lung Cancer: What You Need to Know — Now. 2nd ed. 2012. (QuickFACTS Ser.). (ENG.). 224p. pap. 8.95 ***(978-1-60443-061-5(3))*** American Cancer Society, Inc.

American Cancer Society Staff, ed. QuickFACTS Prostate Cancer: What You Need to Know-NOW. 2nd ed. 2011. (QuickFACTS Ser.). (ENG., Illus.). 152p. pap. 8.95 *(978-1-60443-008-0(7))* American Cancer Society, Inc.

Anderson, Greg. Cancer: 50 Essential Things to Do. 3rd rev. ed. 2009. (ENG.). 224p. (gr. 12-18). 14.00 *(978-0-452-29010-5(4),* Plume) Penguin Group (USA) Inc.

Bazile, Ronald P., Sr., et al. You Have Cancer: A Death Sentence That Four African-American Men Turned into an Affirmation to Remain in the Land of the Living. 2007. (Illus.). 165p. per. 12.00 *(978-0-9639245-2-0(4))* Milligan Bks.

Bellenir, Karen, ed. Breast Cancer Sourcebook. 3rd rev. ed. 2009. (Health Reference Ser.). 93.00 *(978-0-7808-1030-3(9))* Omnigraphics, Inc.

—Cancer Sourcebook. 6th rev. ed. 2011. (Health Reference Ser.). 600p. 95.00 *(978-0-7808-1145-4(3))* Omnigraphics, Inc.

Betty Crocker Editors, et al. Betty Crocker Living with Cancer Cookbook. 2011. (ENG., Illus.). 288p. pap. 19.99 *(978-1-118-08314-7(8),* Betty Crocker) Wiley, John & Sons, Inc.

Bonner, Dede. The 10 Best Questions for Surviving Breast Cancer: The Script You Need to Take Control of Your Health. 2008. (ENG.). 336p. pap. 20.99 *(978-1-4165-6050-0(5),* Touchstone) Touchstone.

Brinker, Nancy G. Promise Me: How a Sister's Love Launched the Global Movement to End Breast Cancer. l.t. ed. 2010. (Illus.). 646p. 31.99 *(978-1-4104-3149-3(5))* Thorndike Pr.

Brinker, Nancy G. & Rodgers, Joni. Promise Me: How a Sister's Love Launched the Global Movement to End Breast Cancer. 2010. (ENG., Illus.). 368p. 25.99 *(978-0-307-71812-9(3))* Broadway Bks.

—Promise Me: How a Sister's Love Launched the Global Movement to End Breast Cancer. 2011. (ENG.). 368p. pap. 15.00 *(978-0-307-71813-6(1),* Three Rivers Pr.) Crown Publishing Group.

Campbell, Steven C., et al. 100 Questions & Answers about Kidney Cancer. 2008. (ENG., Illus.). 197p. pap. 22.95 *(978-0-7637-4993-4(1))* Jones & Bartlett Learning, LLC.

Carr, Kris. Crazy Sexy Cancer Survivor: More Rebellion & Fire for Your Healing Journey. 2008. (ENG., Illus.). 256p. pap. 19.95 *(978-1-59921-370-5(2),* skirt!) Globe Pequot Pr., The.

Charity, Jean. Touch of Cancer. 2009. (Illus.). pap. *(978-1-907407-00-0(6))* Black Leaf Publishing Group, The.

Chodak, Gerald. Winning the Battle Against Prostate Cancer: Get the Treatment That Is Right for You. 2011. (ENG.). 400p. pap. 18.95 *(978-1-936303-03-8(5))* Demos Medical Publishing, LLC.

Coles, L. Stephen. Extraordinary Healing: Restoring Health with the Discoveries of Mirko Beljanski, the World's First Molecular Biologist. 2011. (ENG.). 148p. pap. 15.95 *(978-1-893910-89-8(X))* Freedom Pr., Inc., The.

Cook, Colleen Ryckert. Frequently Asked Questions about Cancer Decisions for You & Your Family. 2011. (FAQ: Teen Life Ser.). (ENG.). 64p. (YA). 29.25 *(978-1-4488-1326-1(3))* Rosen Publishing Group, Inc., The.

Diaz-Montes, Teresa P. Johns Hopkins Patients' Guide to Uterine Cancer. 2009. (ENG.). 156p. pap. 22.95 *(978-0-7637-7460-8(X))* Jones & Bartlett Learning, LLC.

Dizon, Don S. & Duska, Linda R. 100 Q & As about Uterine Cancer. 2nd rev. ed. 2010. 134p. pap. 22.95 *(978-0-7637-7658-9(0))* Jones & Bartlett Learning, LLC.

Dresser, Rebecca, ed. Malignant: Medical Ethicists Confront Cancer, 1 vol. 2012. (ENG.). 272p. 29.95 ***(978-0-19-975784-8(4))*** Oxford Univ. Pr., Inc.

Duncan, Marc D. Patients Guide to Cancer of the Stomach & Esophagus. rev. ed. 2010. 150p. pap. 22.95 *(978-0-7637-7430-1(8))* Jones & Bartlett Learning, LLC.

Ellsworth, Pamela. 100 Questions & Answers about Prostate Cancer. 3rd ed. 2012. 256p. pap. 22.95 ***(978-1-4496-6581-4(0))*** Jones & Bartlett Learning, LLC.

Fesen, Mark R. Surviving the Cancer System: An Empowering Guide to Taking Control of Your Care, 1 vol. 2009. (ENG.). 288p. pap. 18.95 *(978-0-8144-1356-2(0))* Amacom.

Fleishman, Stewart. Learn to Live Through Cancer: What You Need to Know & Do. 2012. (Illus.). xiii, 348p. E-Book ***(978-1-61705-062-6(8))*** 2011. (ENG.). 320p. pap. 18.95 *(978-1-936303-08-3(6))* Demos Medical Publishing, LLC.

Frank, Richard C. Fighting Cancer with Knowledge & Hope: A Guide for Patients, Families, & Health Care Providers. 2009. (Yale University Press Health & Wellness Ser.). (ENG., Illus.). 280p. pap. 18.00 *(978-0-300-15102-2(0))* Yale Univ. Pr.

Friedman, Sue, et al. Confronting Hereditary Breast & Ovarian Cancer: Identify Your Risk, Understand Your Options, Change Your Destiny. 2012. (Johns Hopkins Press Health Book Ser.). (ENG., Illus.). 288p. pap. 18.95 ***(978-1-4214-0408-0(7));*** (gr. 17). 45.00 ***(978-1-4214-0407-3(9))*** Johns Hopkins Univ. Pr.

Galsky, Matthew D. Everything You Need to Know about Cancer in Language You Can Understand. 2009. (ENG.). 136p. pap. 24.95 *(978-0-7637-6454-8(X),* Jones & Bartlett Learning, LLC.

Gonzalgo, Mark. Johns Hopkins Patients' Guide to Bladder Cancer. rev. ed. 2009. 132p. pap. 22.95 *(978-0-7637-7424-0(3))* Jones & Bartlett Learning, LLC.

Graham, Luke & Cefrey, Holly. It's Cancer. Now What? 2011. (Teen Life 411 Ser.). (Illus.). 144p. (YA). (gr. 7-12). lib. bdg. 33.25 *(978-1-4488-4652-8(8))* Rosen Publishing Group, Inc., The.

Holford, Patrick & Efiong, Liz. Say No to Cancer: The Drug-Free Guide to Preventing & Helping Fight Cancer. 2011. (ENG., Illus.). 414p. pap. 19.95 *(978-0-7499-5411-6(6))* Piatkus Bks. GBR. Dist: Independent Pubs. Group.

Hope, Lori. Help Me Live, Revised: 20 Things People with Cancer Want You to Know. 2nd rev. ed. 2011. (ENG., Illus.). 288p. pap. 15.99 *(978-1-58761-149-0(X),* Celestial Arts) Ten Speed Pr.

Howell, Della L. My Child Has Cancer: A Parent's Guide to Diagnosis, Treatment, & Survival, 1 vol. 2008. (Praeger Series on Healing & Managing Injury & Disease Ser.). (Illus.). 216p. 39.95 *(978-0-275-99601-7(8),* C9601, Praeger Pubs.) Greenwood Publishing Group, Inc.

James, Nick. Cancer: A Very Short Introduction. 2011. (ENG., Illus.). 144p. pap. 11.95 *(978-0-19-956023-3(4))* Oxford Univ. Pr., Inc.

Johanson, Paula. Frequently Asked Questions about Testicular Cancer. 2009. (FAQ: Teen Life Ser.). 64p. (gr. 5-6). 58.50 *(978-1-61512-591-3(4))* Rosen Publishing Group, Inc., The.

Katz, Aaron. The Definitive Guide to Prostate Cancer: Everything You Need to Know about Conventional & Integrative Therapies. 2011. (ENG., Illus.). 272p. pap. 16.99 *(978-1-60961-310-5(4))* Rodale Pr., Inc.

Katz, Anne. Surviving after Cancer: Living the New Normal. (ENG.). 224p. 2012. pap. 21.95 *(978-1-4422-0366-2(8))* 2011. 37.95 *(978-1-4422-0365-5(X))* Rowman & Littlefield Publishers, Inc.

Kelvin, Joanne Frankel & Tyson, Leslie. 100 Questions & Answers about Cancer Symptoms & Cancer Treatment Side Effects. 2nd rev. ed. 2010. 240p. pap. 22.95 *(978-0-7637-7760-9(9))* Jones & Bartlett Learning, LLC.

Klein, Eric. The Cleveland Clinic Guide to Prostate Cancer. 2009. (Cleveland Clinic Guides). (ENG.). 160p. pap. 15.99 *(978-1-60714-077-1(2))* Kaplan Publishing.

Lange, Vladimir. Be a Survivor: Your Guide to Breast Cancer Tratement. 5th ed. 2009. 192p. pap. 24.95 *(978-0-9819489-0-4(1))* Lange Productions.

Lyman, Gary. Oxford American Mini-Handbook of Cancer Supportive Care, 1 vol. 2010. (Oxford American Mini Handbooks Ser.). (Illus.). 160p. pap. 18.95 *(978-0-19-539046-9(6))* Oxford Univ. Pr., Inc.

Mendes, Dena. A Survivor's Guide to Kicking Cancer's Ass. 2011. (ENG.). 240p. pap. 14.95 *(978-1-4019-3154-4(5))* Hay Hse., Inc.

Moses, Marsha A., et al. Cancer, 1 vol. 2009. (Biographies of Disease Ser.). (Illus.). 174p. 45.00 *(978-0-313-35979-8(2),* GR5979) Greenwood Publishing Group, Inc.

Mukherjee, Siddhartha. The Emperor of All Maladies: A Biography of Cancer. 2011. (Playaway Adult Nonfiction Ser.). (ENG.). 114.99 ***(978-1-61707-019-8(X))*** Findaway World, LLC.

—The Emperor of All Maladies: A Biography of Cancer. (ENG.). 2011. 608p. pap. 18.00 *(978-1-4391-7091-5(6))* 2010. 592p. 30.00 *(978-1-4391-0795-9(5))* Scribner. (Scribner).

—The Emperor of All Maladies: A Biography of Cancer. l.t. ed. 2012. (ENG.). 944p. 32.99 ***(978-1-4104-4715-9(4))*** Thorndike Pr.

Mulhall, John P. Saving Your Sex Life: A Guide for Men with Prostate Cancer. 2008. (ENG., Illus.). 307p. pap. 17.95 *(978-0-9800649-6-4(1))* Hilton Publishing Co.

O'Brien, Joyce. Choose to Live: Our Journey from Late Stage Cancers to Vibrant Health. 2011. (ENG.). 228p. pap. 17.95 *(978-1-60037-836-2(6))* Morgan James Publishing.

Orchard, Anne. Their Cancer - Your Journey: A Traveller's Guide for Carers, Family & Friends. 2008. (Illus.). 246p. pap. *(978-0-9559797-0-5(6))* Rainbow Heart Publishing.

Raghavan, M D, et al. Bladder Cancer: A Cleveland Clinic Guide. 2008. (Cleveland Clinic Guide Ser.). (ENG.). 187p. pap. 14.95 *(978-1-59624-060-5(1))* Cleveland Clinic Pr.

Robison, Katina & Dizon, Don S. DX-RX: Cervical Cancer. 2nd rev. ed. 2010. 86p. pap. 49.95 *(978-0-7637-9210-7(1))* Jones & Bartlett Learning, LLC.

Scott, Walter. Lung Cancer: A Guide to Diagnosis & Treatment. 2nd ed. 2012. (ENG.). 130p. pap. 19.95 *(978-1-886039-09-4(7))* Addicus Bks.

Scotting, Paul. Cancer: A Beginner's Guide. 2011. (Beginners Guide (Oneworld) Ser.). (ENG., Illus.). 208p. 14.95 *(978-1-85168-755-8(6))* Oneworld Pubns. GBR. Dist: National Bk. Network.

Shaprio. Cancer in Older Adults. rev. ed. 2010. 187p. pap. 22.95 *(978-0-7637-7429-5(4))* Jones & Bartlett Learning, LLC.

Shockney, Lillie. Breast Cancer. 2009. (ENG.). 158p. pap. 11.95 *(978-0-7637-7426-4(X))* Jones & Bartlett Learning, LLC.

—Navigating Breast Cancer: A Guide for the Newly Diagnosed. 2nd rev. ed. 2010. 116p. pap. 22.95 *(978-0-7637-8683-0(7))* Jones & Bartlett Learning, LLC.

—Top Concerns about HER2 Positive Breast Cancer. 2012. 128p. pap. 10.95 *(978-1-4496-0125-6(1))* Jones & Bartlett Learning, LLC.

Shockney, Lillie & Shapiro, Gary R. 100 Questions & Answers about Advanced & Metastatic Breast Cancer. 2nd ed. 2011. *(978-1-4496-3401-8(X))* Jones & Bartlett Publishers.

Shockney, Lillie D. & Shapiro, Gary R. 100 Questions & Answers about Advanced & Metastatic Breast Cancer. 2nd ed. 2011. 152p. pap. 22.95 ***(978-1-4496-4335-5(3))*** Jones & Bartlett Learning, LLC.

Somers, Suzanne. Knockout: Interviews with Doctors Who Are Curing Cancer - And How to Prevent Getting It in the First Place. 2009. (ENG.). 352p. 25.99 *(978-0-307-58746-6(0),* Crown) Crown Publishing Group.

Strasheim, Connie. Defeat Cancer: 15 Doctors of Integrative & Naturopathic Medicine Tell You How. 2011. 444p. pap. 39.95 ***(978-0-9825138-2-8(8))*** BioMed Publishing Group.

Swanson, Cheryl. Busting Loose: Cancer Survivors Tell You What Your Doctor Won't. 2009. (ENG.). 324p. pap. 17.99 *(978-1-934841-74-7(9))* Zumaya Pubns. LLC.

Weinstein, Jodi Buckman. Tell Me What to Eat Before, During, & after Cancer Treatment: Nutritional Guidelines for Patients & Their Loved Ones. 2010. (Tell Me What to Eat Ser.). (ENG.). 1p. pap. 12.99 *(978-1-60163-109-1(X),* New Page Bks.) Career Pr., Inc.

Williams, Penelope M. Breast Cancer: Biography of an Illness. 2008. 300p. pap. *(978-0-9809231-5-5(8))* BPS Bks.

Wright, Jessie. Third Opinion on Prostate Cancer: A Guide to Knowing Your Options. 2010. pap. 12.99 *(978-1-61566-021-6(6))* Tate Publishing & Enterprises, LLC.

Young, Lynda. Hope for Families of Children with Cancer. 2010. (ENG.). 224p. pap. 12.99 *(978-0-9797800-3-5(9))* Kindred Pr.

Young, Lynda T. & Ward, Jonathan R. Hope for Families of Children with Cancer: You are Not Alone Book Series. 2011. (FRS.). 14.99 *(978-0-89112-289-0(3),* Leafwood Pubs.) Abilene Christian Univ. Pr.

Zaccone, Suzanne. A Random Interruption: Surviving Breast Cancer with Laughter, Vodka, Smoothies & an Attitude: Surviving Breast Cancer with Laughter, Vodka, Smoothies & an Attitude. 2009. 500p. 34.99 *(978-1-4415-8057-3(3));* pap. 23.99 *(978-1-4415-8056-6(5))* Xlibris Corp.

CANCER—PREVENTION

see also Cancer—Study and Teaching

ABBE Scientist Research Division Staff. Analysis of Food Cont aining Cancer-Causing Substances with Index & Medical Analysis of New Clinical & Research Information for All Nations. 2008. (Illus.). 160p. 69.95 *(978-0-7883-4826-6(4))* ABBE Pubs. Assn. of Washington, D.C.

Alberts, David S. & Hess, Lisa. Fundamentals of Cancer Prevention. 2nd ed. 2008. (Illus.). 465p. 159.00 *(978-3-540-68985-0(0))* Springer.

Alberts, David S. & Hess, Lisa M., eds. Fundamentals of Cancer Prevention. 2nd ed. 2010. (ENG., Illus.). xx, 536p. pap. 159.00 *(978-3-642-08851-3(1),* 3642088511) Springer.

Alcott, Scott. I'm Not Lance! 2009. 143p. pap. 15.00 *(978-0-557-12233-2(3))* Lulu Enterprises Inc.

Alexander Iii, Arthur Douglass. Overlooked Causes & the Prevention: Cancer, Cardiovascular Heart Disease, Multiple Sclerosis. 2010. 60p. pap. 14.75 *(978-1-4490-5357-4(2))* AuthorHouse.

Alschuler, Lise & Gazella, Karolyn A. Five to Thrive: Your Cutting-Edge Cancer Prevention Plan. 2011. (ENG.). 240p. pap. 15.95 ***(978-1-935297-40-6(6))*** Better Nutrition Magazine.

American Society of Clinical Oncology Staff, contrib. by. Cancer Prevention: An ASCO Curriculum. 2007. *(978-1-932312-33-1(1))* American Society of Clinical Oncology.

Armstrong, Liz, et al. Cancer: 101 Solutions to a Preventable Epidemic. 2007. (Solutions Ser.). (ENG., Illus.). 288p. per. 22.95 *(978-0-86571-542-4(4),* 0865715424) New Society Pubs., Ltd. CAN. Dist: Consortium Bk. Sales & Distribution.

Armstrong, Marc P. Geocoding Health Data: The Use of Geographic Codes in Cancer Prevention & Control, Research & Practice. Gittler, Josephine et al, eds. 2007. (ENG., Illus.). 256p. 113.95 *(978-0-8493-8419-6(2),* CRC Press) Taylor & Francis Group GBR. Dist: Taylor & Francis Group.

Arroye, Raymond P., ed. Cancer Prevention Research Progress. 2008. 79.00 *(978-1-60456-125-8(4),* Nova Biomedical Bks.) Nova Science Pubs., Inc.

Baker, Judyth Vary. Me & Lee: How I Came to Know, Love & Lose Lee Harvey Oswald. 2010. (ENG.). 624p. 24.95 *(978-0-9799886-7-7(5))* Trine Day.

Bartone, John Charles. A-B-C of Cancer Disease Prevention: 30 + Techniques to Avoid Cancers That Have No Cure: Something for Everyone on Planet Earth. 2008. (Illus.). 160p. ring bd. 59.50 *(978-0-7883-4676-7(8))* ABBE Pubs. Assn. of Washington, D.C.

Bartsch, Hans Helge & Weis, Joachim, contrib. by. Gemeinsame Entscheidung in der Krebstherapie: Arzt und Patient im Spannungsfeld der Shared Decision. (GER., Illus.). *(978-3-8055-7785-4(0))* Karger, S. AG.

Bauman, Ed & Waldman, Helayne L. The Whole-Food Guide for Breast Cancer Survivors: A Nutritional Approach to Preventing Reoccurrence. 2012. (New Harbinger Whole-Body Healing Ser.). (ENG., Illus.). 272p. pap. 18.95 ***(978-1-57224-958-5(7))*** New Harbinger Pubns.

Bayor, Marcel. The Bioactivity of Croton Membranaceus - a Traditional Anticancer Herb. 2011. 272p. pap. ***(978-3-8433-8695-1(1))*** Lambert Academic Publishing.

Béliveau, Richard & Gingras, Denis. Cooking with Foods That Fight Cancer. 2007. (ENG., Illus.). 272p. pap. 24.95 *(978-0-7710-1136-8(9),* McClelland & Stewart) McClelland & Stewart CAN. Dist: Random Hse., Inc.

Bellingham, Trevor N. New Topics on Terrorism, Counter-Terrorism, & Preparedness: New Research. Rosenthal, Joel W. et al, eds. 2008. (Illus.). 129.00 *(978-1-60456-196-8(3),* Nova Biomedical Bks.) Nova Science Pubs., Inc.

Bessiel, Jakobe H., ed. Progress in Cancer Prevention. 2008. (Illus.). x, 137p. 69.00 *(978-1-60456-327-6(3),* Nova Biomedical Bks.) Nova Science Pubs., Inc.

Bevis, Larry & Bevis, Shelly. Couple's Answers for Cancer: How to fight & defeat cancer while living a joyful Life. 2009. 148p. pap. 19.95 *(978-1-4401-5072-2(9))* iUniverse, Inc.

Bibb, Robert. Deadly Dairy Deception. 2010. pap. 15.99 *(978-1-61566-773-4(3))* Tate Publishing & Enterprises, LLC.

Bischofová, et al. Colorectal Cancer. 2011. 68p. pap. ***(978-3-8443-2082-4(2))*** Lambert Academic Publishing.

Bosanquet, Nicholas & Sikora, Karol. The Economics of Cancer Care. 2010. (ENG.). 192p. pap. 39.99 *(978-0-521-18380-2(4))* Cambridge Univ. Pr.

Boughton, Barbara & Stefanek, Michael. Reduce Your Cancer Risk: Twelve Steps to a Healthier Life. 2010. (ENG.). 256p. pap. 16.95 *(978-1-932603-92-7(1))* Demos Medical Publishing, LLC.

Boyle, P. & Levin, B. World Cancer Report 2008. 2009. (IARC Nonserial Publication Ser.). (ENG., Illus.). 512p. pap. 48.00 *(978-92-832-0423-7(9))* World Health Organization.

Brandberg, Yvonne, et al, eds. Skin Cancer Prevention. 2006. (Illus.). 462p. 250.00 *(978-0-8493-9889-6(4))* Taylor & Francis Group.

Braun, Louis & Lange, Maximilian, eds. Cancer Prevention Research Trends. 2008. (Illus.). xiv, 137p. 137.00 *(978-1-60456-639-0(6))* Nova Science Pubs., Inc.

Budwig, Johanna. The Budwig Cancer & Coronary Heart Disease Prevention Diet: The Complete Recipes, Updated Research & Protocols for Health & Healing. 2011. (ENG.). 176p. pap. 15.95 *(978-1-893910-42-3(3))* Freedom Pr., Inc., The.

Budwig, Johanna & Himeise, Nexus. Cancer - the Problem & the Solution. 2008. 127p. pap. 14.90 *(978-3-9810502-1-9(5))* Nexus Himeise - Handels GmbH DEU. Dist: AtlasBooks Distribution.

Burns, Peter. Fight Your Cancer Using Nature & Instinct. 2010. 114p. pap. 21.50 *(978-1-4466-4181-1(3))* Lulu Enterprises Inc.

Calviello, Gabriella & Serini, Simona, eds. Dietary Omega-3 Polyunsaturated Fatty Acids & Cancer. 2010. (Diet & Cancer Ser.). (ENG., Illus.). xx, 241p. 199.00 *(978-90-481-3578-3(8)*, 9048135788) Springer.

Cancer: Challenges & Opportunities in the 21st Century: Hearing Before the Committee on Health, Education, Labor, & Pensions, United States Senate, One Hundred Tenth Congress, Second Session, on Examining Cancer Relating to Challenges & Opportunities in the 21st Century, May 8, 2008. 2010. iii, 72p. *(978-0-16-085135-3(1)*, 552-070-40489-9) United States Government Printing Office.

Cantor, David, ed. Cancer in the Twentieth Century. 2008. (ENG., Illus.). 368p. (C). (gr. 13-17). pap. 27.00 *(978-0-8018-8867-0(0))* Johns Hopkins Univ. Pr.

Colditz, Graham A., ed. Encyclopedia of Cancer & Society, 3 vols., Set. 2007. 1616p. 395.00 *(978-1-4129-4989-7(0)*, B49890C) SAGE Pubns., Inc.

Conway, Thomas H. International Journal of Cancer Prevention Compendium: Volume 1. Garcia, Thomas, ed. 2008. (Illus.). pap. 315.00 *(978-1-60456-663-5(9))* Nova Science Pubs., Inc.

Cram101 Textbook Reviews. Outlines & Highlights for Fundamentals of Cancer Prevention by Alberts, Isbn: 9783540689850 3540689850. 2011. 90p. pap. 27.95 ***(978-1-61812-182-0(0))*** Cram101 Inc.

Crump, Sandra, et al, eds. Cervical Cancer Prevention Guidelines for Low-Resource Settings. Kleeman, Frances, tr. 2008. (FRE., Illus.). 212p. spiral bd. 15.00 *(978-0-929817-93-4(1))* JHPIEGO Corp.

Currin, Morag. Oncology Esthetics: A Practitioner's Guide. 2009. x, 461p. pap. ***(978-1-932633-49-8(9))*** Allured Business Media.

Demboski, Karen & McGuire, Lois. Proton Therapy for Prostate Cancer: More Fun Than We Ever Expected. 2010. 127p. pap. 14.95 *(978-0-9824611-5-0(1))* Snow In Sarasota Publishing.

Doll, Richard. The Prevention of Cancer: Pointers from Epidemiology. 2008. (ENG., Illus.). 143p. pap. 29.95 *(978-0-202-36220-5(5))* Aldine Transaction.

Eldridge, Lynne & Borgeson, David. Avoiding Cancer One Day at a Time: Practical Advice for Preventing Cancer. 2006. 320p. per. 19.95 *(978-1-59298-159-5(3))* Beaver's Pond Pr., Inc.

Elwood, J. Mark & Sutcliffe, Simon B., eds. Cancer Control. 2010. (ENG., Illus.). 496p. 110.00 *(978-0-19-955017-3(4))* Oxford Univ. Pr., Inc.

Epstein, Samuel S. National Cancer Institute & American Cancer Society: Criminal Indifference to Cancer Prevention & Conflicts of Interest. 2011. 204p. 29.99 ***(978-1-4628-6135-4(0))***; pap. 19.99 ***(978-1-4628-6134-7(2))*** Xlibris Corp.

Francis, Raymond. Never Fear Cancer Again: The Revolutionary Solution to Turn off Cancer Cells. 2011. (ENG.). 384p. pap. 14.95 *(978-0-7573-1550-3(X))* Health Communications, Inc.

Friedman, Sue, et al. Confronting Hereditary Breast & Ovarian Cancer: Identify Your Risk, Understand Your Options, Change Your Destiny. 2012. (Johns Hopkins Press Health Book Ser.). (ENG., Illus.). 288p. pap. 18.95 ***(978-1-4214-0408-0(7))***; (gr. 17). 45.00 ***(978-1-4214-0407-3(9))*** Johns Hopkins Univ. Pr.

Garcia, Thomas, ed. International Journal of Cancer Prevention Compendium: Volume 2. 2009. (Illus.). 215.00 *(978-1-60456-664-2(7))* Nova Science Pubs., Inc.

Gastroenterology. Colorectal Cancer Can Be Prevented. Arber, N., ed. 2007. (Illus.). 78p. pap. *(978-3-8055-8419-7(9))* Karger, S. AG.

Gelband, Hellen. Cancer Control Opportunities in Low- & Middle-Income Countries. Sloan, Frank A., ed. 2007. (ENG., Illus.). 340p. pap. 49.00 *(978-0-309-10384-8(3))* National Academies Pr.

Greenhaven. Cancer. 2012. (At Issue Ser.). (ENG.). 128p. (gr. 10-12). pap. 33.70 ***(978-0-7377-5559-6(8)***, Greenhaven Pr., Inc.); (YA). (gr. 9-12). lib. bdg. 23.85 ***(978-0-7377-5558-9(X))*** Cengage Gale.

Greer, Julia B. The Anti-Cancer Cookbook: How to Cut Your Risk with the Most Powerful, Cancer-Fighting Foods. 2008. 224p. pap. 19.95 *(978-0-9624814-9-9(1))* Sunrise River Pr.

Harris, Randall E., ed. COX-2 Blockade in Cancer Prevention & Therapy. 2010. (Cancer Drug Discovery & Development Ser.). (Illus.). 384p. pap. 179.00 *(978-1-61737-304-6(4)*, 1617373044) Humana Pr.

Hill, David, et al, eds. Prevention of Skin Cancer. 2010. (Cancer Prevention-Cancer Causes Ser.). 340p. pap. 219.00 *(978-90-481-6346-5(3)*, 9048163463) Springer.

Holford, Patrick & Efiong, Liz. Say No to Cancer: The Drug-Free Guide to Preventing & Helping Fight Cancer. 2011. (ENG., Illus.). 414p. pap. 19.95 *(978-0-7499-5411-6(6))* Piatkus Bks. GBR. Dist: Independent Pubs. Group.

Iarc & WHO. Formaldehyde, 2-Butoxyethanol & 1-Tert-Butoxy-2-Propanol. 2006. (IARC Monographs, Volume 88 Ser.). (ENG.). 483p. pap. 66.00 *(978-92-832-1288-1(6))* World Health Organization.

International Agency for Research on Cancer Staff. Atlas of Cancer Mortality in the European Union & the European Economic Area, 1993-1997. Boyle, P., ed. 2009. (IARC Scientific Publication No 159 Ser.). (Illus.). 260p. pap. 30.00 *(978-92-832-2159-3(1))* World Health Organization.

Janecka, Ivo. Prevention & Management of Colon Cancer Through Physical Activity. 2008. 176p. pap. *(978-3-639-01696-3(3))* VDM Verlag Dr. Mueller e.K.

Katalinic, A. & Borisch, B., eds. Cancer Risk & Prevention at the Molecular Level. 2009. (Illus.). 48p. pap. *(978-3-8055-9128-7(4))* Karger, S. AG.

Katrina, Bos. What If You Could Skip the Cancer? 2009. (ENG.). 144p. pap. 9.95 *(978-1-933916-39-2(7)*, Ferne Pr.) Nelson Publishing & Marketing.

Katzin, Carolyn F. The Everything Cancer-Fighting Cookbook. 2011. (ENG.). 304p. pap. 16.95 *(978-1-4405-0746-5(5))* Adams Media Corp.

Keeney, Sinead. Cancer Prevention Knowledge, Attitudes & Behaviours. 2010. 396p. pap. *(978-3-8383-4548-2(7))* Lambert Academic Publishing.

Kenner, Dan. The Whole-Body Workbook for Cancer: A Complete Integrative Program for Increasing Immunity & Rebuilding Health. 2009. (New Harbinger Whole-Body Healing Ser.). (ENG.). 200p. pap. 21.95 *(978-1-57224-674-4(X))* New Harbinger Pubns.

Khorana, Alok A. & Francis, Charles W., eds. Cancer-Associated Thrombosis: New Findings in Translational Science, Prevention, & Treatment. 2007. (ENG., Illus.). 296p. 230.00 *(978-1-4200-4799-8(X)*, Informa Healthcare) Taylor & Francis Group GBR. Dist: Taylor & Francis Group.

Knasmüller, Siegfried. Chemoprevention of Cancer & DNA Damage by Dietary Factors. DeMarini, David M. et al, eds. 2009. (ENG., Illus.). 838p. 275.00 *(978-3-527-32058-5(X)*, Wiley-VCH) Wiley, John & Sons, Inc.

Koller, Maria H. Tobacco Control Program. 2008. 176p. pap. *(978-3-639-04039-5(2))* VDM Verlag Dr. Mueller e.K.

Krueger, Hans, et al. The Prevention of Second Primary Cancers: A Resource for Clinicians & Health Managers. 2008. (Progress in Experimental Tumor Research Ser.). (Illus.). 148p. *(978-3-8055-8497-5(0))* Karger, S. AG.

Kushi, Michio & Jack, Alex. The Cancer Prevention Diet: The Macrobiotic Approach to Preventing & Relieving Cancer. 3rd rev. ed. 2009. (ENG.). 608p. pap. 23.99 *(978-0-312-56106-2(7)*, St. Martin's Griffin) St. Martin's Pr.

Kwabi-Addo, Bernard & Lindstrom, Tia Laura. Cancer Causes & Controversies: Understanding Risk Reduction & Prevention, 1 vol. 241p. 44.95 *(978-0-313-37928-4(9)*, C37928, Praeger Pubs.) Greenwood Publishing Group, Inc.

Levine, Douglas. Answer to Cancer. 2011. 479p. pap. 24.95 ***(978-0-9819979-0-2(2))*** Levine, Douglas.

Lieberman, D. A., et al, eds. Strategies of Cancer Prevention in Gastroenterology. 2009. (Falk Symposium Ser.). (ENG., Illus.). 128p. 219.00 *(978-90-481-2628-6(2)*, 9048126282) Springer.

Lipscomb, Joseph, et al, eds. Outcomes Assessment in Cancer: Measures, Methods & Applications. 2011. (ENG.). 678p. pap. 80.00 ***(978-1-107-40316-1(2))*** Cambridge Univ. Pr.

Lubecki, John. The End of Cancer. 2nd ed. (Illus.). 198p. reprint ed. *(978-1-884030-00-0(9))* Better Health Bks.

Mahmud, Khalid. Keeping Abreast: Ways to PREVENT Breast Cancer. 2008. 128p. 22.50 *(978-1-60693-313-8(2)*, Strategic Bk. Publishing) AEG Literary Publishing Services, Inc.

McLaren, Matthew E. Life Begins At 65: Words of a Cancer Survivor. 2008. 208p. pap. 18.49 *(978-1-4389-0379-8(0))* AuthorHouse.

Miller, A. B. Cancer Screening. 2011. (ENG.). 458p. pap. 55.00 ***(978-0-521-11694-7(5))*** Cambridge Univ. Pr.

Millwood, Charles L. New Research on Aspirin & Health. 2006. (Nova Biomedical Ser.). (Illus.). 263p. 89.00 *(978-1-60021-244-4(1)*, Nova Biomedical Bks.) Nova Science Pubs., Inc.

Moss, Susan A. Survive Cancer! A Natural Approach to Healing & Prevention. 2009. 401p. pap. 19.95 *(978-0-9642329-2-1(8))* Re:Source Pubns.

Mulshine, James L. & Baer, Thomas M., eds. Quantitative Imaging Tools for Lung Cancer Drug Assessment. 2008. (ENG., Illus.). 162p. 139.00 *(978-0-470-11880-1(6))* Wiley, John & Sons, Inc.

Mutanen, Marja & Pajari, Anne-Maria, eds. Vegetables, Whole Grains, & Their Derivatives in Cancer Prevention. 2010. (Diet & Cancer Ser.). (Illus.). xvii, 250p. 189.00 *(978-90-481-9799-6(6)*, 9048197996) Springer.

Neave, Veronica. Pieces of Me. 2011. pap. 13.99 ***(978-1-59955-851-6(3)***, Bonneville Bks.) Cedar Fort, Inc./CFI Distribution.

Nixon, Daniel, et al. The Prostate Health Program: A Guide to Preventing & Controlling Prostate Cancer. 2007. (ENG., Illus.). 256p. pap. 24.95 *(978-0-7432-5432-8(5)*, Free Pr.) Free Pr.

O'Haynes, Delilah F. Walk Free from Fear of Cancer. 2008. (Illus.). 283p. pap. 19.95 *(978-0-9779282-1-7(7))* Walk Free Pr.

Olshan, Andrew F., ed. Epidemiology, Pathogenesis, & Prevention of Head & Neck Cancer. 2010. (ENG., Illus.). xi, 250p. 179.00 *(978-1-4419-1471-2(4)*, 1441914714) Springer.

Passalaris, Tina M. Cancer Prevention for Life: The Long Talk You Never Had with Your Doctor. 2007. 380p. per. 20.50 *(978-1-59330-461-4(7))* Aventine Pr.

Pecorino, Lauren. Why Millions Survive Cancer: The Successes of Science. 2011. (ENG., Illus.). 256p. 29.95 *(978-0-19-958055-2(3))* Oxford Univ. Pr., Inc.

Pecorino, Lauren. Why Millions Survive Cancer: The successes of Science. 2012. (ENG., Illus.). 256p. pap. 17.95 ***(978-0-19-965875-6(7))*** Oxford Univ. Pr., Inc.

Pegg, Jonathan D. Breast Cancer Screening & Prevention. 2011. (Series: Cancer Etiology, Diagnosis & Treatments Ser.). (Illus.). 132p. 59.00 *(978-1-61209-288-1(8)*, Nova Biomedical Bks.) Nova Science Pubs., Inc.

Piva Demarzo, Marcelo Marcos & Britto Garcia, Sérgio. Exercise & Cancer. 2010. 108p. pap. *(978-3-639-25352-8(3))* VDM Verlag Dr. Mueller e.K.

Rawls, George, et al. Managing Cancer: The African American's Guide to Prevention, Diagnosis & Treatment. rev. ed. 2007. (ENG., Illus.). 362p. per. 16.95 *(978-0-9764443-2-9(1))* Hilton Publishing Co.

Richard, Camille I. & Mercier, Sarah E. Research Progress in Cancer Prevention. 2008. 75.00 *(978-1-60456-765-6(1))* Nova Science Pubs., Inc.

Rocker, Brenda E. From Midnight to Daylight: An Inspiring Autobiography. 2008. 196p. 24.99 *(978-1-4389-1267-7(6))*; pap. 14.49 *(978-1-4389-1268-4(4))* AuthorHouse.

Rohan, Thomas E. & Shah, Keerti V., eds. Cervical Cancer: from Etiology to Prevention: From Etiology to Prevention. 2010. (Cancer Prevention-Cancer Causes Ser.). 436p. pap. 219.00 *(978-90-481-6336-6(6)*, 9048163366) Springer.

Rosenthal, Joel W. & Carey, William J. Prevention of Cancer: New Research. 2008. (Illus.). (C). 185.00 *(978-1-60456-229-3(3))* Nova Science Pubs., Inc.

Roth, Jack A., et al. Lung Cancer. Roth, Jack A. et al, eds. 3rd rev. ed. 2008. (ENG., Illus.). 480p. 209.95 *(978-1-4051-5112-2(9)*, Wiley-Blackwell) Wiley, John & Sons, Inc.

Roy, Swarup & K Bhattacharyya, Dhruba. Data Mining Techniques & Its Application in Medical Imagery. 2010. 120p. pap. *(978-3-639-26746-4(X))* VDM Verlag Dr. Mueller e.K.

Rutten, Lila J. Finney. Building the Evidence Base in Cancer Communication. 2010. 368p. *(978-1-57273-944-4(4))*; *(978-1-57273-943-7(6))* Hampton Pr., Inc.

Saha, Achinto & Kuzuhara, Takashi. Mechanisms of Cancer Prevention with Curcumin & Epicatechin. 2011. 84p. pap. ***(978-3-8443-1642-1(6))*** Lambert Academic Publishing.

Sallum, Christine. Production of Radiolabeled E-Peptide. 2010. 76p. pap. *(978-3-8383-7490-1(8))* Lambert Academic Publishing.

Sardha, Minakshi & ANJUM, Arshad. Early Detection of Cervical Cancer: PAP SMEAR or COLPOSCOPY. 2011. 148p. pap. ***(978-3-8443-1714-5(7))*** Lambert Academic Publishing.

Sarkar, Fazlul H., ed. Nutraceuticals & Cancer. 2011. (ENG., Illus.). xii, 379p. 209.00 ***(978-94-007-2629-1(5)***, 9400726295) Springer.

Schottenfeld, David & Fraumeni, Joseph F., eds. Cancer Epidemiology & Prevention. 3rd rev. ed. 2006. (ENG., Illus.). 1416p. 245.00 *(978-0-19-514961-6(0))* Oxford Univ. Pr., Inc.

Schrijvers, Dirk, et al, eds. ESMO Handbook of Cancer Prevention. 2008. (European Society for Medical Oncology Handbooks Ser.). (Illus.). 172p. pap. 99.95 *(978-0-415-39085-9(0))* Taylor & Francis Group.

Seeram, Navindra P. & Stoner, Gary D., eds. Berries & Cancer Prevention. 2010. (ENG., Illus.). xi, 313p. 189.00 *(978-1-4419-7553-9(5)*, 1441975535) Springer.

Selected papers from the 2nd Haifa cancer prevention Workshop. 2007. pap. 98.00 *(978-1-58603-755-0(2))* IOS Pr., Inc.

Senn, H. J. & Kapp, U. Cancer Prevention. 2010. (Recent Results in Cancer Research Ser.). (Illus.). xiv, 250p. pap. 189.00 *(978-3-642-07235-2(6)*, 3642072356) Springer.

Senn, Hans-Jörg. Cancer Prevention: 4th International Conference 2006. 2007. (Recent Results in Cancer Research Ser.). (Illus.). xiv, 250p. 189.00 *(978-3-540-37695-8(X))* Springer.

Senn, Hans-Jorg & Otto, Florian, eds. Clinical Cancer Prevention. 2010. (Recent Results in Cancer Research Ser.). (Illus.). 200p. 139.00 *(978-3-642-10856-3(3)*, 3642108563) Springer.

Senn, Hansjörg, et al. Cancer Prevention II. 2008. (Recent Results in Cancer Research Ser.). (ENG., Illus.). xx, 252p. 159.00 *(978-3-540-69296-6(7))* Springer.

Servan-Schreiber, David. Anticancer: A New Way of Life. 2009. (ENG.). 288p. (gr. 12-18). 26.95 *(978-0-670-02164-2(4)*, Viking Adult) Penguin Group (USA) Inc.

Seyfried, Thomas. Cancer as a Metabolic Disease: On the Origin, Management, & Prevention of Cancer. 2012. (ENG.). 432p. 135.00 ***(978-0-470-58492-7(0)***, Wiley) Wiley, John & Sons, Inc.

Shahin, Eman. BENEFITS of my CANCER. 2007. 88p. per. 16.95 *(978-1-4241-6798-2(1))* PublishAmerica, Inc.

Shankar, Sharmila & Srivastava, Rakesh K., eds. Nutrition, Diet & Cancer. 2012. (ENG., Illus.). xv, 627p. 209.00 ***(978-94-007-2922-3(7)***, 9400729227) Springer.

Sibtain, Amen. Towards the Prevention of Cancer. 2007. (Illus.). 110p. pap. *(978-1-85315-796-7(1)*, Royal Society of Medicine) Hodder Education.

Srivastava, S., ed. The National Cancer Institute Early Detection Research Network: 5th Scientific Workshop - Biomarkers-at-a-Crossroads - Book Edition of Cancer Biomarkers. 2008. 130p. pap. 116.00 *(978-1-58603-926-4(1))* IOS Pr., Inc.

Stern, Peter L. & Kitchener, Henry C., eds. Vaccines for the Prevention of Cervical Cancer. 2009. (Oxford American Oncology Library). (Illus.). 170p. pap. 24.95 *(978-0-19-954345-8(3))* Oxford Univ. Pr., Inc.

Sullivan, Janet B. & Scotte, Bradley L. Cancer Prevention Research Perspectives. 2011. (Series: Cancer Etiology, Diagnosis & Treatments Ser.). 227p. 89.00 *(978-1-61209-380-2(9))* Nova Science Pubs., Inc.

Tasseff, Tom. Win the Ultimate Battle for Your Health: The Lifesaving Legacy of Tom Tasseff. 2008. 248p. pap. 27.95 *(978-1-4327-2796-3(6))*; pap. 19.95 *(978-1-4327-2741-3(9))* Outskirts Pr., Inc.

The Health Experts of The Doctors' Prescription for Healthy Living, ed. Natural Cancer Cures. 2008. 240p. pap. 15.95 *(978-1-893910-52-2(0))* Freedom Pr., Inc., The.

Vainio, Harri U. & Hietanen, Eino K. Mechanisms in Carcinogenesis & Cancer Prevention. 2010. (Handbook of Experimental Pharmacology Ser.). (Illus.). xxi, 329p. pap. 359.00 *(978-3-642-07859-0(1)*, 3642078591) Springer.

Vilas, Santiago. Prostate Cancer Is Curable. 2006. (Illus.). 185p. per. 17.95 *(978-0-9748946-1-4(3))* Yago Editorial, LLC.

Wagner, Kerstin. Search for Breast Cancer Susceptibility Genes: The Growth Hormone-1 / Insulin-like Growth Factor-1Pathway & its Relationship to Breast Cancer. 2008. 132p. pap. *(978-3-639-02207-0(6))* VDM Verlag Dr. Mueller e.K.

Williams, Xandria. Vital Signs for Cancer Prevention: Protect Yourself from the Onset or Recurrence of Cancer. 2012. (ENG.). 320p. pap. 18.95 ***(978-1-58394-453-0(2))*** North Atlantic Bks.

World Cancer Research Fund / American Institute for Cancer Research. Food, Nutrition, Physical Activity, & the Prevention of Cancer: A Global Perspective. 2007. (Illus.). 517p. pap. 69.95 *(978-0-9722522-2-5(3))* American Institute For Cancer Research.

World Health Organization. Cancer Control: Knowledge into Action. WHO Guide for Effective Programmes: Prevention. 2007. (Nonserial Publication). (ENG.). 54p. pap. 18.00 *(978-92-4-154711-6(1))* World Health Organization.

—Cancer Control: Knowledge into Action. WHO Guide for Effective Programmes. Policy & Advocacy: Policy & Advocacy. 2008. (Nonserial Publication Ser.). (ENG.). 54p. pap. 18.00 *(978-92-4-154752-9(9))* World Health Organization.

Yost, Deborah. The Anti-Cancer Food & Supplement Guide: How to Protect Yourself & Enhance Your Health. 2010. (Healthy Home Library). (ENG.). 256p. 7.99 *(978-0-312-37318-4(X)*, St. Martin's Paperbacks) St. Martin's Pr.

CANCER—PSYCHOLOGICAL ASPECTS

Adams, Heidi Schultz & Schultz, Christopher. Planet Cancer: The Frequently Bizarre yet Always Informative Experiences & Thoughts of Your Fellow Natives. 2010. (Illus.). 272p. pap. 19.95 *(978-0-7627-5901-9(1)*, Lyons Pr.) Globe Pequot Pr., The.

Axmann, Martha. She Won the Race: Footprints of Cancer. 2009. 212p. pap. 17.99 *(978-1-4141-1249-7(1))* Pleasant Word.

Bartley, Trish. Mindfulness-Based Cognitive Therapy for Cancer. 2012. (ENG., Illus.). 420p. pap. 54.95 ***(978-0-470-68383-5(X)***, Wiley-Blackwell) Wiley, John & Sons, Inc.

Bodach, Diane LaRae. Straw into Gold: Illness, Loss, & Hardship As a Path to Inner Peace. 340p. 2012. E-Book *(978-1-57733-332-6(2))* 2011. pap. 19.95 *(978-1-57733-223-7(7))* Blue Dolphin Publishing, Inc.

Bolletino, Ruth. How to Talk with Family Caregivers about Cancer. 2009. (ENG.). 304p. pap. 21.95 *(978-0-393-70576-8(5)*, 70576) Norton, W. W. & Co., Inc.

Bray, Sharon. When Words Heal: Writing Through Cancer. 2006. (ENG.). 160p. pap. 16.95 *(978-1-58394-158-4(4)*, Frog Ltd.) North Atlantic Bks.

Buckman, Robert. Cancer Is a Word, Not a Sentence: A Practical Guide to Help You Through the First Few Weeks. 2006. (ENG., Illus.). 280p. per. 19.95 *(978-1-55407-234-7(4))* Firefly Bks., Ltd.

Carpentier, Melissa Y. & Mullins, Larry Lee. Adolescents with Cancer: The Influence of Close Relationships on Quality of Life, Distress, & Health Behaviors. 2008. 172p. 94.95 *(978-1-60497-580-2(6))* Cambria Pr.

Carter, Stephanie R. Taking Charge of Fighting Cancer: An easy to use Workbook. 2011. 112p. pap. 17.95 ***(978-1-4620-1377-7(5))*** iUniverse, Inc.

Chute, Maureen. Closeness in Crisis - a Proposal for Identifying Resilience in Couples Who Face the Crisis of Cancer in Their Child. 2008. 60p. pap. *(978-3-639-10653-4(9))* VDM Verlag Dr. Mueller e.K.

Cleeland, Charles S., et al, eds. Cancer Symptom Science: Measurement, Mechanisms, & Management. 2010. (ENG., Illus.). 376p. 120.00 *(978-0-521-86901-0(3))* Cambridge Univ. Pr.

Conway, Kathlyn. Ordinary Life: A Memoir of Illness. 2007. (Conversations in Medicine & Society Ser.). (ENG.). 280p. per. 20.95 *(978-0-472-03235-8(6))* Univ. of Michigan Pr.

Currin, Morag. Oncology Esthetics: A Practitioner's Guide. 2009. x, 461p. pap. ***(978-1-932633-49-8(9))*** Allured Business Media.

Daniels, Elisha, et al. You Can Do This! Surviving Breast Cancer Without Losing Your Sanity or Your Style. 2009. (ENG.). 192p. pap. 12.99 *(978-0-7407-8575-7(3))* Andrews McMeel Publishing.

Davis, Cindy. Oncology Social Work Practice in the Care of Breast & Ovarian Cancer Survivors. 2008. 79.00 *(978-1-60692-594-2(6))* Nova Science Pubs., Inc.

Decker, Veronica & Weller-Ferris, Linda. Coping with Cancer: A Patient Pocket Book of Thoughts, Advice, & Inspiration for the Ill. 2009. v, 74p. pap. 9.95 *(978-1-890504-79-3(3))* Oncology Nursing Society.

Derosier, Cynthia Y. H. The Survivor Spirit: The Beauty, Passion, & Power of Breast Cancer Survivors. 2008. 64p. 24.95 *(978-0-9769548-2-8(6))* Good Juju Co., The.

Doyle Spencer, Monique & Levy, Paul F. How Can I Help? Everyday Ways to Help Your Loved Ones Live with Cancer. 2008. (ENG.). 240p. pap. 12.95 *(978-1-59869-681-3(5))* Adams Media Corp.

Duffy, James D. & Valentine, Alan. Psycho-Social Oncology. 2010. (ENG., Illus.). 400p. pap. 75.00 *(978-0-07-162438-1(4)*, 0071624384) McGraw-Hill Professional Publishing.

Ericksen, Julia A. Taking Charge of Breast Cancer. 2008. 319p. per. 24.95 *(978-0-520-25292-9(6))*; (Illus.). 60.00 *(978-0-520-25291-2(8))* Univ. of California Pr.

Fiala, David, illus. God Is Bigger Than Your Cancer: Christian Insights for Cancer Patients. 2008. 128p. 18.99 (978-0-9801591-0-3(5)) Fresh Water Pr.

Fiedler, Craig. Robbery & Redemption: Cancer As Identity Theft. 2011. (ENG.). 48.95 **(978-0-89503-470-0(0))**; 172p. pap. 41.95 **(978-0-89503-473-1(5))** Baywood Publishing Co., Inc.

Fiore, Neil. Coping with the Emotional Impact of Cancer. 2009. (ENG.). 224p. pap. 18.95 (978-0-9801758-3-7(6)) Bay Tree Publishing.

Fogelson, Hillary. Pale Girl Speaks: A Year Uncovered. 2012. (ENG.). 256p. pap. 16.00 **(978-1-58005-444-7(7))** Seal Pr.

Fortson, Leigh. Embrace, Release, Heal: An Empowering Guide to Talking about, Thinking about, & Treating Cancer. 2011. 300p. pap. 17.95 (978-1-60407-431-4(0)) Sounds True, Inc.

Gardner, Daniel S. Cancer in a Dyadic Context. 2009. 160p. pap. (978-3-639-13573-2(3)) VDM Verlag Dr. Mueller e.K.

Gionta, Dana. Medical Staff-Family Health Communication in Cancer. 2009. 72p. pap. (978-3-639-11240-5(7)) VDM Verlag Dr. Mueller e.K.

Grubbs, Ronnie. The Psychological Treatment of Couples Confronting Breast Cancer. 2009. 184p. pap. (978-3-639-11552-9(X)) VDM Verlag Dr. Mueller e.K.

Gubar, Susan. Memoir of a Debulked Woman: Enduring Ovarian Cancer. 2012. (ENG., Illus.). 320p. 24.95 **(978-0-393-07325-6(4)**, 7325) Norton, W. W. & Co., Inc.

Guellati-Salcedo, Sophie. Enhanced Benefit Finding in Women with Early Stage Breast Cancer. 2008. 80p. pap. (978-3-639-07471-0(8)) VDM Verlag Dr. Mueller e.K.

Hefner, Jochen. Psychotherapeutische Interventionen bei Krebskranken: Analyse der Ergebnisse psychoonkologischer Interventionsstudien. 2008. (Europäische Hochschulschriften. Reihe 6: Psychologie Ser.). 116p. pap. 35.95 (978-3-631-58140-7(8)) Lang, Peter GmbH, Europaischer Verlag der Wissenschaften DEU. Dist: Lang, Peter.

Holland, Jimmie C., et al, eds. Psycho-Oncology, 1 vol. 2nd ed. 2010. (ENG., Illus.). 720p. 149.95 (978-0-19-536743-0(X)) Oxford Univ. Pr., Inc.

Hope, Lori. Help Me Live, Revised: 20 Things People with Cancer Want You to Know. 2nd rev. ed. 2011. (ENG., Illus.). 288p. pap. 15.99 (978-1-58761-149-0(X), Celestial Arts) Ten Speed Pr.

International Agency for Research on Cancer Staff & World Health Organization. IARC Code of Good Scientific Practice. 2009. (IARC Nonserial Publication Ser.). (ENG.). 15p. pap. 12.00 (978-92-832-2445-7(0)) World Health Organization.

Jacobs, Léa K., ed. Coping with Cancer. 2008. (Illus.). 154p. 129.00 (978-1-60456-213-2(7), Nova Biomedical Bks.) Nova Science Pubs., Inc.

Jarvis, Debra. It's Not about the Hair: And Other Certainties of Life & Cancer. 2008. (ENG.). 256p. pap. 16.95 (978-1-57061-573-3(X)) Sasquatch Bks.

Kagan, Sarah H. Cancer in the Lives of Older Americans: Blessings & Battles. 2009. 120p. (C). 34.95 (978-0-8122-4143-3(6)) Univ. of Pennsylvania Pr.

Katz, Anne. Breaking the Silence on Cancer & Sexuality: A Handbook for Healthcare Providers. 2007. (Illus.). 280p. per. 70.00 (978-1-890504-67-0(X)) Oncology Nursing Society.

—Man Cancer Sex. 2009. vi, 169p. pap. 15.00 (978-1-890504-87-8(4)) Oncology Nursing Society.

—Woman Cancer Sex. 2009. (Illus.). 170p. pap. 14.95 (978-1-890504-80-9(7)) Oncology Nursing Society.

Kayser, Karen & Scott, Jennifer L. Helping Couples Cope with Women's Cancers: An Evidence-Based Approach for Practitioners. 2008. (ENG.). xv, 229p. 49.95 (978-0-387-74802-3(4), 0387748024) Springer.

King, Cynthia R. Quality of Life: From Nursing & Patient Perspectives. 3rd rev. ed. 2011. 570p. (C). pap. 72.95 (978-0-7637-4943-9(5)) Jones & Bartlett Learning, LLC.

Kissane, David W. & Watson, M. Handbook of Psychotherapy in Cancer Care. 2011. 57.95 (978-1-119-99051-2(3), Wiley-Blackwell) Wiley, John & Sons, Inc.

Kneier, Andrew. Finding Your Way Through Cancer: An Expert Cancer Psychologist Helps Patients & Survivors Face the Challenges of Illness. 2010. (ENG., Illus.). 176p. pap. 14.00 (978-1-58761-356-2(5), Celestial Arts) Ten Speed Pr.

Leidich, Harriet Lerrigo, et al, mems. Our Family Miracle: An Encounter with Cancer. 2006. per. (978-0-9746389-1-1(9)) BERTANI BKS.

Magee, Sherri. Picking up the Pieces: Moving Forward after Surviving Cancer. 2007. (ENG.). 326p. per. 19.95 (978-0-8135-4036-8(4)) Rutgers Univ. Pr.

Manne, Sharon L. & Ostroff, Jamie S. Coping with Breast Cancer: Workbook for Couples. 2008. (Treatments That Work Ser.). (ENG.). 80p. pap. 22.95 (978-0-19-534291-8(7)) Oxford Univ. Pr., Inc.

Marshall, Catherine A., ed. Surviving Cancer As a Family: And Helping Co-Survivors Thrive. 2010. (Disability Insights & Issues Ser.). 189p. 44.95 (978-0-313-37894-2(0), C37894) Greenwood Publishing Group, Inc.

Meyers, Christina A. & Perry, James R., eds. Cognition & Cancer. 2008. (ENG., Illus.). 353p. 130.00 (978-0-521-85482-5(2)) Cambridge Univ. Pr.

Mignone, Robert. Ordinary Valor: How Cancer Saved My Life — Not Once, but Twice. 2011. 164p. (ENG.). 24.95 **(978-1-4327-7322-9(4))**; pap. 19.95 **(978-1-4327-7310-6(0))** Outskirts Pr., Inc.

Miller, Kenneth. Excellent Care for Cancer Survivors: A Guide to Fully Meet Their Needs in Medical Offices & in the Community, 1 vol. 2011. (Praeger Series on Contemporary Health & Living Ser.). (Illus.). 376p. 58.00 (978-0-313-39786-8(4), A3598C) Greenwood Publishing Group, Inc.

Miller, Kenneth D. Excellent Care for Cancer Survivors: A Guide to Fully Meet Their Needs in Medical Offices & in the Community. 2011. **(978-0-313-39787-5(2)**, Praeger Pubs.) Greenwood Publishing Group, Inc.

Miller, Kenneth D. Medical & Psychosocial Care of the Cancer Survivor. 2009. (Illus.). 479p. 73.95 (978-0-7637-5770-0(5)) Jones & Bartlett Learning, LLC.

Miller, Suzanne M. Handbook of Cancer Control & Behavioral Science: A Resource for Researchers, Practitioners, & Policy Makers. 2008. 592p. 49.95 (978-1-4338-0358-1(5)) American Psychological Assn.

Moorey, Stirling & Greer, Steven. Oxford Guide to CBT for People with Cancer. 2nd ed. 2012. (ENG., Illus.). 272p. pap. 59.95 **(978-0-19-960580-4(7))** Oxford Univ. Pr., Inc.

Moorjani, Anita. Dying to Be Me: My Journey from Cancer, to near Death, to True Healing. 2012. (ENG.). xv, 191p. 24.95 **(978-1-4019-3751-5(9))** Hay Hse., Inc.

Murphey, Cecil. When Someone You Love Has Cancer: Comfort & Encouragement for Caregivers & Loved Ones. 2009. (Illus.). 64p. 10.99 (978-0-7369-2428-3(0)) Harvest Hse. Pubs.

Murphy, Diana. A Woman's Initiation: Women's Experiences with Breast Cancer & How It Transformed Their Lives. 2006. 136p. pap. 14.95 (978-0-9779556-0-2(5)) Synchronicity Bks.

Northey, Sue. On the Other Side: Journey of A Cancer Survivor. Ivy, Judith, ed. 2007. pap. 11.95 (978-1-59374-722-0(5)) Whiskey Creek Pr., LLC.

O'Brien, Joyce. Choose to Live: Our Journey from Late Stage Cancers to Vibrant Health. 2011. (ENG.). 228p. pap. 17.95 (978-1-60037-836-2(6)) Morgan James Publishing.

Orchard, Anne. Their Cancer - Your Journey: A Traveller's Guide for Carers, Family & Friends. 2008. (Illus.). 246p. pap. (978-0-9559797-0-5(6)) Rainbow Heart Publishing.

Peltason, Ruth A. I Am Not My Breast Cancer: Women Talk Openly about Love & Sex, Hair Loss & Weight Gain, Mothers & Daughters, & Being a Woman with Breast Cancer. 2008. (ENG.). 400p. pap. 15.95 (978-0-06-117407-0(6), Harper Paperbacks) HarperCollins Pubs.

Penedo, Frank J., et al. Cognitive-Behavioral Stress Management for Prostate Cancer Recovery. 2008. (Treatments That Work Ser.). (ENG., Illus.). 160p. pap., wbk. ed. 27.95 (978-0-19-533698-6(4)) Oxford Univ. Pr., Inc.

Rubenstein, Carolyn. Perseverance: How Young People Turn Fear into Hope-and How They Can Teach Us to Do the Same. 2010. (ENG.). 384p. pap. 18.99 (978-0-7653-1779-7(6), Forge Bks.) Doherty, Tom Assocs., LLC.

Schorn, Joel. Elf-Help for Coping with Cancer. 2007. (Elf Self Help Ser.). (Illus.). 38p. per. 4.95 (978-0-87029-405-1(9)) Abbey Pr.

Servan-Schreiber, David. Anticancer: A New Way of Life. 2009. (ENG.). 288p. (gr. 12-18). 26.95 (978-0-670-02164-2(4), Viking Adult) Penguin Group (USA) Inc.

Sessions, Roy B. Cancer Experience: The Doctor, the Patient, the Journey. 2012. (ENG.). 208p. (gr. 17). 59.95 **(978-1-4422-1621-1(2))** Rowman & Littlefield Publishers, Inc.

Shockney, Lillie. Breast Cancer Survivorship Care. rev. ed. 2009. 226p. pap. 23.95 (978-0-7637-8496-6(6)) Jones & Bartlett Learning, LLC.

Shone, Neville. Cancer: A Family Affair. ix, 133p. (978-0-85969-706-4(1), Sheldon Press) SPCK Publishing.

Silver, Julie K. After Cancer Treatment: Heal Faster, Better, Stronger. 2006. (Johns Hopkins Press Health Book Ser.). (ENG.). 288p. 47.00 (978-0-8018-8437-5(3)); per. 17.95 (978-0-8018-8438-2(1)) Johns Hopkins Univ. Pr.

Watson, Maggie & Kissane, David W., eds. Handbook of Psychotherapy in Cancer Care. 2011. (ENG., Illus.). 284p. pap. 57.95 (978-0-470-66003-4(1), Wiley) Wiley, John & Sons, Inc.

Zaccone, Suzanne. A Random Interruption: Surviving Breast Cancer with Laughter, Vodka, Smoothies & an Attitude: Surviving Breast Cancer with Laughter, Vodka, Smoothies & an Attitude. 2009. 500p. 34.99 (978-1-4415-8057-3(3)); pap. 23.99 (978-1-4415-8056-6(5)) Xlibris Corp.

Zelek, Laurent & Zernik, Nicole. Aider A Vivre Apres un Cancer. 2010. (Oncologie Pratique Ser.). (FRE., Illus.). 296p. pap. 69.95 (978-2-287-79500-8(6)) Springer.

CANCER—RADIOTHERAPY

Alazraki, Naomi P., et al. A Clinician's Guide to Nuclear Oncology: Practical Molecular Imaging & Radionuclide Therapies. 2007. (978-0-9726478-8-5(0)) SNM Publishing Co.

Ang, K. Kian & Garden, Adam S. Radiotherapy for Head & Neck Cancers: Indications & Techniques. 4th rev. ed. 2011. (ENG., Illus.). 304p. 167.99 (978-1-60831-686-1(6)) Lippincott Williams & Wilkins.

Astro & Acr. The ASTRO/ACR Guide to Radiation Oncology Coding 2007. 2007. spiral bd. (978-0-9791723-0-4(6)) ASTRO.

ASTRO & ACR. 2008 Supplement to the ASTRO/ACR Guide to Radiation Oncology Coding 2007. 2008. (978-0-9791723-4-2(9)) ASTRO.

Ataelmannan, Khalid. Radiosensitizing Glioblastoma in a Rat Model. 2009. 72p. pap. (978-3-639-12669-3(6)) VDM Verlag Dr. Mueller e.K.

Ausili Cefaro, Giampiero, et al, eds. A Guide for Delineation of Lymph Nodal Clinical Target Volume in Radiation Therapy. 2010. (ENG., Illus.). xii, 173p. pap. 99.00 (978-3-642-09576-4(3), 3642095763) Springer.

Bentzen, Soren M., et al, eds. Radiation Oncology Advances. 2010. (Cancer Treatment & Research Ser.). (Illus.). xvi, 344p. pap. 179.00 (978-1-4419-4221-0(1), 1441942211) Springer.

Beyzadeoglu, M., et al. Basic Radiation Oncology. 2010. (ENG., Illus.). xxiv, 576p. 139.00 (978-3-642-11665-0(5), 3642116655) Springer.

Bick, Ulrich & Diekmann, Felix. Digital Mammography: Current Concepts. 2009. (Medical Radiology / Diagnostic Imaging Ser.). (ENG., Illus.). xvi, 220p. 319.00 (978-3-540-78449-4(7), 3540784497) Springer.

Blodgett, Todd M. Specialty Imaging - PET/CT: Oncologic Imaging with Correlative Diagnostic CT. 2008. (ENG.). 550p. 229.00 (978-1-931884-18-1(8)) Lippincott Williams & Wilkins.

Bombardieri, Emilio, et al, eds. Advances in Nuclear Oncology: Diagnosis & Therapy. 2007. (ENG., Illus.). 544p. 429.95 (978-1-84184-614-9(7), Informa Healthcare) Taylor & Francis Group GBR. Dist: Taylor & Francis Group.

Brady, Luther W. & frwd. Radiation Oncology: An Evidence-Based Approach. 2010. (Medical Radiology / Radiation Oncology Ser.). (Illus.). xx, 675p. pap. 159.00 (978-3-642-09603-7(4), 3642096034) Springer.

Brady, Luther W. & Yaeger, Theodore E., eds. Encyclopedia of Radiation Oncology, 1 vol. 2012. (ENG., Illus.). xvi, 800p. 549.00 (978-3-540-85513-2(0), 3540855130) Springer.

Brown, Martin J., et al. Multimodal Concepts for Integration of Cytotoxic Drugs. 2010. (Medical Radiology / Radiation Oncology Ser.). (Illus.). x, 352p. pap. 209.00 (978-3-642-06505-7(8), 3642065058) Springer.

Cefaro, Giampiero Ausili. A Guide for Delineation of Lymph Nodal Clinical Target Volume in Radiation Therapy. Genovesi, Domenico et al, eds. 2008. (ENG., Illus.). xii, 173p. 99.00 (978-3-540-77043-5(7), 3540770437) Springer.

Chao, K. S. Clifford, et al. Radiation Oncology: Management Decisions. 3rd rev. ed. 2011. (ENG., Illus.). 880p. pap. 94.95 (978-1-60547-911-8(X)) Lippincott Williams & Wilkins.

Choy, Hak, ed. Chemoradiation in Cancer Therapy. 2010. (Cancer Drug Discovery & Development Ser.). (Illus.). 432p. pap. 154.50 (978-1-61737-313-8(3), 1617373133) Humana Pr.

Cram101 Textbook Reviews & Cram101 Textbook Reviews. Outlines & Highlights for Perez & Bradys Principles & Practice of Radiation Oncology by Edward C Halperin. 2011. 202p. pap. 30.95 **(978-1-61830-774-3(6))** Cram101 Inc.

Curran, Bruce H. & Starkschall, George, eds. Informatics in Radiation Oncology. 2012. (ENG.). 450p. 149.95 (978-1-4398-2582-2(3), CRC Press) Taylor & Francis Group GBR. Dist: Taylor & Francis Group.

Devlin, Phillip M., ed. Brachytherapy: Applications & Techniques. 2006 (Illus.). 448p. 199.99 (978-0-7817-6277-9(4)) Lippincott Williams & Wilkins.

Eary, Janet F. & Brenner, Winfried, eds. Nuclear Medicine Therapy. 2007. (ENG., Illus.). 216p. 200.00 (978-0-8247-2876-2(9), Informa Healthcare) Taylor & Francis Group GBR. Dist: Taylor & Francis Group.

Ernst, Floris. Compensating for Quasi-periodic Motion in Robotic Radiosurgery. 2011. (ENG., Illus.). xi, 244p. 109.00 **(978-1-4614-1911-2(5)**, 1461419115) Springer.

F.A. Calvo, Hospital General Universitario, ed. Atlas for Intraoperative Radiation Therapy. 2011. (Medical Radiology / Radiation Oncology Ser.). 300p. 329.00 (978-3-540-42432-1(6), 3540424326) Springer.

Ford, Thomas D. New Cancer Research Developments. 2009. pap. 129.00 (978-1-60692-447-1(8)) Nova Science Pubs., Inc.

Gewirtz, David A., et al, eds. Apoptosis, Senescence & Cancer. 2nd ed. 2010. (Cancer Drug Discovery & Development Ser.). (Illus.). xvii, 599p. pap. 199.00 (978-1-61737-621-4(3), 1617376213) Humana Pr.

—Apoptosis, Senescence, & Cancer. 2nd ed. 2007. (Cancer Drug Discovery & Developmenttm Ser.). (Illus.). 599p. 199.00 (978-1-58829-527-9(3), 1588295273) Humana Pr.

Goitein, Michael. Radiation Oncology: A Physicist's-Eye View. 2008. (Biological & Medical Physics, Biomedical Engineering Ser.). (Illus.). xii, 330p. 179.00 (978-0-387-72644-1(6)) Springer.

—Radiation Oncology: A Physicist's-Eye View: A Physicist's-Eye View. 2010. (Biological & Medical Physics, Biomedical Engineering Ser.). (Illus.). xii, 330p. pap. 179.00 (978-1-4419-2482-7(5), 1441924825) Springer.

Gregoire, Vincent, et al, eds. Clinical Target Volumes in Conformal & Intensity Modulated Radiation Therapy: A Clinical Guide to Cancer Treatment. 2012. (Medical Radiology / Radiation Oncology Ser.). (ENG., Illus.). xii, 248p. pap. 239.00 (978-3-642-07463-9(4), 3642074634) Springer.

Haas, Marilyn L., et al. Radiation Therapy: A Guide to Patient Care. 2007. (ENG., Illus.). 786p. 89.95 (978-0-323-04030-3(6), Mosby) Elsevier - Health Sciences Div.

Hansen, Eric K. & Roach, I. I. I. Mack, eds. Handbook of Evidence-Based Radiation Oncology. 2006. (Illus.). XII, 540p. pap. 59.95 (978-0-387-30647-6(1), 0387306471) Springer.

Hansen, Eric K. & Roach, Mack, eds. Handbook of Evidence-Based Radiation Oncology. 2nd ed. 2010. (ENG., Illus.). xviii, 786p. pap. 69.95 (978-0-387-92987-3(8), 0387929878) Springer.

Harari, Paul M. Function Preservation & Quality of Life in Head & Neck Radiotherapy. 2009. (Medical Radiology / Radiation Oncology Ser.). (ENG., Illus.). xiii, 325p. 219.00 (978-3-540-73231-0(4)) Springer.

Harris Beitler, Purdie. Radiation Oncology Concepts. 2009. 144p. pap. 17.95 (978-1-4269-1653-3(1)) Trafford Publishing.

Hong, Kelvin & Georgiades, Christos S., eds. Percutaneous Tumor Ablation: Strategies & Techniques. 2010. (ENG., Illus.). 208p. 129.99 (978-1-60406-306-6(8)) Thieme Medical Pubs., Inc.

Hoskin, Peter, ed. External Beam Therapy. (Radiotherapy in Practice Ser.). (ENG., Illus.). 2006. 480p. 115.00 (978-0-19-852929-3(5)) 2nd ed. 2012. 536p. pap. 99.00 **(978-0-19-969656-7(X))** Oxford Univ. Pr., Inc.

Hoskin, Peter & Coyle, Catherine. Radiotherapy in Practice - Brachytherapy. 2nd ed. 2011. (ENG., Illus.). 248p. pap. 79.95 (978-0-19-960090-8(2)) Oxford Univ. Pr., Inc.

Hosmane, Narayan S. Boron & Gadolinium Neutron Capture Therapy for Cancer Treatment. 2011. 300p. 120.00 **(978-981-4338-67-7(2))** World Scientific Publishing Co., Inc.

Hricak, Hedvig, et al. Oncologic Imaging: Essentials of Reporting Common Cancers. 2006. (ENG., Illus.). 320p. pap. 59.95 (978-1-4160-3251-9(7), Saunders) Elsevier - Health Sciences Div.

Hristov, Boris, et al. Radiation Oncology: A Question-Based Review. 2010. (ENG.). 416p. pap. 79.99 (978-1-60831-444-7(8)) Lippincott Williams & Wilkins.

Huang, TzungChi & Zhang, Geoffrey. 4d Study of Thoracic Cancer Radiation Treatment. 2010. 140p. pap. (978-3-639-09318-6(6)) VDM Verlag Dr. Mueller e.K.

Huddart, Robert A. & Shahidi, Mehdi, eds. Cancer Radiotherapy. 2007. (Methods in Molecular Medicine Ser.: Vol. 133). (Illus.). 618p. 149.00 (978-0-89603-831-8(9), 0896038319) Humana Pr.

Hussey, David H. & Beck, Bill. ASTRO: A Celebration of 50 Years. 2008. (978-1-57864-515-2(8)) Donning Co. Pubs.

Jeremic, Branislav, ed. Advances in Radiation Oncology in Lung Cancer. 2010. (Medical Radiology / Radiation Oncology Ser.). (Illus.). xiv, 526p. pap. 329.00 (978-3-642-05600-0(8), 3642056008) Springer.

Kantoff, Philip, ed. Multidisciplinary Treatment for Prostate Cancer. 2007. (Illus.). 100p. pap. 19.95 (978-1-891483-55-4(2)) PRR, Inc.

Kim, Edmund, et al, eds. Clinical PET & PET/CT: Principles & Applications. 2nd ed. 2011. (ENG., Illus.). 350p. 169.00 (978-1-4419-0801-8(3), 1441908013) Springer.

King, Christopher R., et al, eds. Robotic Radiosurgery Treating Prostate Cancer & Related Genitourinary Applications. 2011. (ENG., Illus.). xx, 245p. 179.00 (978-3-642-11494-6(6), 3642114946) Springer.

Langley, Stephen E. M., et al. Prostate Brachytherapy in Clinical Practice. 2009. (Illus.). 150p. pap. 40.00 (978-1-84628-948-4(3)) Springer.

Lemoigne, Yves & Caner, Alessandra, eds. Radiotherapy & Brachytherapy. 2009. (NATO Science for Peace & Security Series B: Physics & Biophysics Ser.). (ENG., Illus.). xviii, 256p. 219.00 (978-90-481-3095-5(6), 9048130956); xviii, 250p. pap. 129.00 (978-90-481-3096-2(4), 9048130964) Springer.

Li, X. Allen, ed. Adaptive Radiation Therapy. 2011. (ENG., Illus.). 427p. 149.95 (978-1-4398-1634-9(4), CRC Press) Taylor & Francis Group GBR. Dist: Taylor & Francis Group.

Lo, William Chun Yip, et al. Computational Acceleration for Medical Treatment Planning. 2010. 116p. pap. (978-3-639-25038-1(9)) VDM Verlag Dr. Mueller e.K.

Lu, Jiade J. Radiation Oncology: An Evidence-Based Approach. 2008. (Medical Radiology / Radiation Oncology Ser.). (Illus.). xx, 675p. 159.00 (978-3-540-77384-9(3)) Springer.

Lu, Jiade J. & Brady, Luther W., eds. Decision Making in Radiation Oncology: Volume 1. 2010. (Medical Radiology / Radiation Oncology Ser.). (Illus.). xxii, 548p. 359.00 (978-3-642-12462-4(3), 3642124623) Springer.

—Decision Making in Radiation Oncology: Volume 2. 2011. (Medical Radiology / Radiation Oncology Ser.). (Illus.). xxii, 592p. 359.00 (978-3-642-16332-6(7), 3642163327) Springer.

Lynes, Barry. Rife's World of Electromedicine: The Story, the Corruption & the Promise. 2009. 88p. pap. 17.95 (978-0-9763797-9-9(1)) BioMed Publishing Group.

Madabhushi, Anant, et al, eds. Prostate Cancer Imaging: Computer-Aided Diagnosis, Prognosis, & Intervention: International Workshop, Held in Conjunction with MICCAI 2010, Beijing, China, September 24, 2010, Proceedings. 2010. (Lecture Notes in Computer Science / Image Processing, Computer Vision, Pattern Recognition, & Graphics Ser.). x, 146p. pap. 72.00 (978-3-642-15988-6(5), 3642159885) Springer.

Mariani, Giuliano, et al, eds. Radioguided Surgery. 2009. (Illus.). xvi, 297p. pap. 59.95 (978-1-4419-1618-1(0), 1441916180) Springer.

McDermott, Patrick N. & Orton, Colin G. The Physics & Technology of Radiation Therapy. 2010. (Illus.). 856p. (978-1-930524-32-3(3)) Medical Physics Publishing.

Mehta, Minesh P., et al, eds. Radiation Oncology Advances. 2007. (Cancer Treatment & Research Ser.). (Illus.). XVI, 344p. 179.00 (978-0-387-36743-9(8), 0387367438) Springer.

Meinel, Lina Arbash. Breast Cancer Characterization Computer-Aided Diagnostic System for Breast Mri Mass Classification. 2008. 120p. pap. (978-3-639-08072-8(6)) VDM Verlag Dr. Mueller e.K.

Metcalfe, Peter, et al. The Physics of Radiotherapy X-Rays & Electrons/By Peter Metcalfe, Tomas Kron, & Peter Hoban. 2007. (978-1-930524-35-4(8)); pap. (978-1-930524-36-1(6)) Medical Physics Publishing.

Metz, James. Proton Therapy. 2010. (978-1-61705-044-2(X)) Demos Medical Publishing, LLC.

Metz, James & Metz, James M. Proton Therapy. 2010. 200p. 85.00 (978-1-936287-15-4(3)) Demos Medical Publishing, LLC.

Meyer, J. L., ed. Imrt, Igrt, Sbrt: Advances in the Treatment Planning & Delivery of Radiotherapy [Bibliography & Price not Definite.]: (Frontiers of Radiation Therapy & Oncology Ser.: Vol. 40). (Illus.). 438p. (978-3-8055-8199-8(8)) Karger, S. AG.

Mundt. Image Guided Radiation Therapy. 2011. (Illus.). 900p. (978-1-60795-042-4(1)) PMPH-USA, Ltd.

Nieder, Carsten & Langendijk, Johannes A., eds. Re-irradiation: New Frontiers. New Frontiers. 2011. (Medical Radiology / Radiation Oncology Ser.). (ENG., Illus.). x, 226p. 239.00 (978-3-642-12467-9(4), 3642124674) Springer.

Nievaart, Victor Alexander. Spectral Tailoring for Boron Neutron Capture Therapy. 2007. (Illus.). xvii, 118p. pap. 59.00 (978-1-58603-762-8(5), Delft University Pr) IOS Pr., Inc.

Paganetti, Harald, ed. Proton Therapy Physics. 2011. (Series in Medical Physics & Biomedical Engineering Ser.). (ENG., Illus.). 704p. 129.95 (978-1-4398-3644-6(2), CRC Press) Taylor & Francis Group GBR. Dist: Taylor & Francis Group.

C

Parker, R. G. & Selch, M. T. Radiation Oncology for Cure & Palliation. 2010. (Medical Radiology / Radiation Oncology Ser.). (Illus.). xii, 282p. pap. 269.00 (978-3-642-07466-0(9), 3642074669) Springer.

Paulino, Arnold C. PET-CT in Radiotherapy Treatment Planning. Teh, Bin S., ed. 2008. (ENG., Illus.). 272p. 166.00 (978-1-4160-3224-3(X), Saunders) Elsevier - Health Sciences Div.

Pazdur, Richard, et al, eds. Cancer Management: A Multidiciplinary Approach Medical, Surgical, & Radiation Oncology. 2007. 1000p. pap. 59.95 (978-1-891483-48-6(X)) PRR, Inc.

Peller, Patrick, et al, eds. PET-CT & PET-MRI in Oncology: A Practical Guide. 2012. (Medical Radiology / Diagnostic Imaging Ser.). (ENG., Illus.). 300p. 329.00 (978-3-642-01138-2(1), 3642011381) Springer.

Phillips, Theodore L., et al. Leibel & Phillips Textbook of Radiation Oncology: Expert Consult - Online & Print. 3rd ed. 2010. (ENG., Illus.). 1664p. 318.00 (978-1-4160-5897-7(4), Saunders) Elsevier - Health Sciences Div.

Reddy, L. Harivardhan & Couvreur, Patrick, eds. Macromolecular Anticancer Therapeutics. 2009. (Cancer Drug Discovery & Development Ser.). (ENG., Illus.). xx, 624p. 229.00 (978-1-4419-0506-2(5), 1441905065) Springer.

Reilly, Raymond M., ed. Monoclonal Antibody & Peptide-Targeted Radiotherapy of Cancer. 2010. (ENG., Illus.). 632p. 158.00 (978-0-470-24372-5(4), Wiley) Wiley, John & Sons, Inc.

Rubin, Philip, et al. CURED I - LENT Late Effects of Cancer Treatment on Normal Tissues. 2010. (Medical Radiology / Radiation Oncology Ser.). (Illus.). xxii, 144p. pap. 129.00 (978-3-642-08032-6(4), 3642080324) Springer.

—Cured II - LENT Cancer Survivorship Research & Education: Late Effects on Normal Tissues. 2010. (Medical Radiology / Radiation Oncology Ser.). (Illus.). xii, 180p. pap. 109.00 (978-3-642-09510-8(0), 3642095100) Springer.

Rubin, Philip. Cured Ii - Lentcancer Survivorship Research & Education. 2008. (Medical Radiology / Radiation Oncology Ser.). (Illus.). 160p. 109.00 (978-3-540-76270-6(1), 3540762701) Springer.

Sanders, Charles L. Radiation Hormesis & the Linear-No-Threshold Assumption: A Story of Benefit & Deception. 2009. (Illus.). xi, 217p. 219.00 (978-3-642-03719-1(4), 3642037194) Springer.

Schoenfeld, Jonathan D. & Kaplan, Irving D. Prostate Brachytherapy: Sowing the Seeds for Success & Salvage. 2010. pap. 49.00 (978-1-61761-197-1(2)) Nova Science Pubs., Inc.

Sibtain, Amen, et al, eds. Physics for Clinical Oncology. 2012. (ENG., Illus.). 272p. pap. 89.95 (**978-0-19-957335-6(2)**) Oxford Univ. Pr., Inc.

Small, William. Combining Targeted Biological Agents with Radiotherapy: Current Status & Future Directions. 2008. (Illus.). 139.00 (978-1-933864-34-1(6)) Demos Medical Publishing, LLC.

Song, William. Image-Guided Radiation Therapy of Prostate Cancer. 2009. 216p. pap. (978-3-639-15392-7(8)) VDM Verlag Dr. Mueller e.K.

Stacy, Scott. Imaging of Bone & Soft Tissue Tumors, an Issue of Radiologic Clinics of North America. 2011. (Clinics: Radiology Ser.: 49-6). (ENG., Illus.). x, 1080p. 110.00 (**978-1-4557-1152-9(7)**, Saunders) Elsevier - Health Sciences Div.

Stanton, Robert & Stinson, Donna. Applied Physics for Radiation Oncology. 2009. pap. (978-1-930524-40-8(4)) Medical Physics Publishing.

Suit, Herman D. & Loeffler, Jay S. Evolution of Radiation Oncology at Massachusetts General Hospital. 2011. (ENG., Illus.). xix, 214p. 139.00 (978-1-4419-6743-5(5), 1441967435) Springer.

Urschel, Harold C., Jr., et al, eds. Treating Tumors That Move with Respiration. 2007. (Robotic Radiosurgery Ser.). (Illus.). 317p. 239.00 (978-3-540-69885-2(X)) Springer.

Videtic, Gregory, et al. Handbook of Radiation Treatment Delivery. 2010. 259.00 (978-1-933864-52-5(4)) Demos Medical Publishing, LLC.

Vijayakumar, Srinivasan et al. Prostate Cancer H/C. 2011. 208p. 289.00 (**978-1-936287-33-8(1)**) Demos Medical Publishing, LLC.

Viswanathan, Akila N., et al, eds. Gynecologic Radiation Therapy: Novel Approaches to Image-Guidance & Management. 2010. (ENG., Illus.). ix, 308p. 139.00 (978-3-540-68954-6(0), 3540689540) Springer.

Wallner, Kent, et al. Prostate Brachytherapy Made Complicated. 3rd ed. 2007. (Illus.). 150.00 (978-0-9648991-6-2(7)) SmartMedicine Pr.

Wazer, David E., et al, eds. Perez & Brady's Principles & Practice of Radiation Oncology. 5th rev. ed. 2007. (ENG., Illus.). 2368p. 324.99 (978-0-7817-6369-1(X)) Lippincott Williams & Wilkins.

Wazer, Wazer, ed. Accelerated Partial Breast Irradiation: Techniques & Clinical Implementation. 2nd ed. 2009. (ENG., Illus.). xviii, 436p. 199.00 (978-3-540-88005-9(4), 3540880054) Springer.

Wiegel, T., et al, eds. Controversies in Gastro-Intestinal Tumor Therapy, Vol. 38. (Frontiers of Radiation Therapy & Oncology Ser.: Vol. 38). (Illus.). 6;26p. (978-3-8055-7690-1(0)) Karger, S. AG.

Yee, Judy. Virtual Colonoscopy. 2007. (ENG., Illus.). 240p. 184.99 (978-0-7817-5770-6(3)) Lippincott Williams & Wilkins.

CANCER—RELIGIOUS ASPECTS

Ahmadi, Fereshteh. Culture, Religion & Spirituality in Coping: The Example of Cancer in Patients in Sweden. 2006. (Studia Sociologica Upsaliensia: No.53). 197p. pap. 53.50 (978-91-554-6589-6(7)) Uppsala Universitet/Acta Universitatis Uppsaliensis SWE. Dist: Coronet Bks.

Anderson, Faith. Help Me, Lord! I'm Too Stressed to Feel Blessed. 2011. 108p. 28.95 (**978-1-4627-0519-1(7)**); pap. 11.95 (**978-1-4627-0518-4(9)**) Cross Bks. Publishing.

Badgett, Sandy. Remembering Laura: Letting Go of Life with Beauty & Grace. 2009. pap. 14.99 (978-1-60799-078-9(4)) Tate Publishing & Enterprises, LLC.

Barnhardt-Israel, Lillian Elizabeth. Friends in High Places: A Christian Guide to Fighting & Overcoming Cancer. 2011. pap. 12.99 (**978-1-61346-442-7(8)**) Tate Publishing & Enterprises, LLC.

Barry, Michael S. & Barry, Michael. The Art of Caregiving: How to Lend Support & Encouragement to Those with Cancer. 2007. (ENG.). 160p. 14.99 (978-0-7814-4430-9(6)) Cook, David C.

Beaulieu, Peter. Kristi: So Thin Is the Veil. 2006. (ENG., Illus.). 400p. pap. 16.95 (978-0-8245-2398-5(9)) Crossroad Publishing Co., The.

Bevier, Bob. Our Journey Through Cancer with God: No Subtitle. 2008. 96p. pap. 9.99 (978-1-60647-597-3(5)) Xulon Pr., Inc.

Bishop, Leslie. Congratulations, You Have Cancer! An empowering, personal encounter with breast cancer & a positive, good feeling & spiritual approach on how you can look at disease differently & recreate your experience of it! 2006. (ENG.). 120p. per. 11.95 (978-1-59800-644-5(4)) Outskirts Pr., Inc.

Blake, Lynnette. The Heavenly cure for Cancer... Is there One? 2009. 126p. pap. 18.29 (978-0-557-19538-1(1)) Lulu Enterprises Inc.

Blue-Salters, Melissa. His Death, My Angel. 2009. 40p. pap. 17.99 (978-1-4389-8871-9(0)) AuthorHouse.

Bomkamp, Jim. The Body of Christ in All Her Glory. 2008. 148p. pap. 11.95 (978-1-59330-544-4(3)) Aventine Pr.

Branson, Joyce. The Ones That Got Away: Seventeen Years of Fishing with Kids Who Have Cancer. 2011. 156p. pap. 15.99 (978-1-4520-9803-6(4)) AuthorHouse.

Carll, Joe. At Peace with Cancer. 2007. 96p. per. 9.99 (978-1-60266-184-4(7)) Xulon Pr., Inc.

Chaffey, Tim. God & Cancer. 2009. 220p. pap. 15.99 (978-1-60791-373-3(9)) Xulon Pr., Inc.

Chevalier, Elena A. In Chemo: Candid Conversations with God. 2010. pap. 14.99 (978-1-61579-561-1(8)) Xulon Pr., Inc.

Clark, Linda Hovestadt. Valley of the Shadow: A Mother's Journal Through Her Child's Battle with Cancer. 2006. (ENG.). 232p. per. 17.99 (978-1-4141-0693-9(9)) Pleasant Word.

Colbert, Don. The New Bible Cure for Cancer. 2010. (ENG.). 128p. pap. 8.99 (978-1-59979-866-0(2), Siloam Pr.) Charisma Media.

Cook, Jerry & Pinkston, Ron. Trusting God When You Have Cancer: Help & Hope for the Road Ahead. 2009. 48p. 13.99 (978-0-7369-2519-8(8)) Harvest Hse. Pubs.

Craig, Eileen. Devotions from the Chemo Room, 1 vol. 2010. 48p. pap. 16.95 (978-1-4489-4343-2(4)) PublishAmerica, Inc.

Cummins, Sherry Taylor. Pink Ribbon Devotions to Go. 2007. pap. 8.95 (978-0-9789831-3-0(0)) See Media.

Demitte, Dien. Getting Through the Night. 2008. pap. 11.99 (978-1-60647-205-7(4)) Xulon Pr., Inc.

DePriest, Jaca C. Blessed & Beyond: A Passage into Widowhood. 2007. 128p. per. 12.95 (978-0-595-41096-5(0)) iUniverse, Inc.

Eide, Candace D. Faith, Love, & Laughter: Surviving Cancer. 2008. 161p. pap. 24.95 (978-1-4241-9888-7(7)) PublishAmerica, Inc.

Evans, Kim. Ribbons of Hope. 2007. per. (978-1-59581-354-1(3), Brentwood Christian Pr.) Brentwood Communications Group.

Fiala, David, illus. God Is Bigger Than Your Cancer: Christian Insights for Cancer Patients. 2008. 128p. 16.99 (978-0-9801591-0-3(5)) Fresh Water Pr.

Floyd, Jeana. An Uninvited Guest: One Woman's Journey from Cancer to Hope. 2007. (Illus.). 128p. 12.99 (978-0-89221-664-2(6)) New Leaf Pr., Inc.

Gast, David. Musing & Muttering Through Cancer. 2008. 108p. per. (978-1-897373-18-7(X)) Word Alive Pr.

George, Brenda. Rejoicing Through the Tears: Embracing God's Hand in Cancer. 2011. 240p. 33.95 (**978-1-4497-2401-6(9)**); pap. 17.95 (**978-1-4497-2402-3(7)**) Author Solutions, Inc. (WestBow Pr.).

Globe Pequot Press Staff. Pink Ribbon Sisterhood: Courage, Hope, & Inspiration from Women Who Battled Breast Cancer. Norris, Mary, ed. 2009. 224p. pap. 14.95 (978-1-59921-820-5(8), skirt!) Globe Pequot Pr., The.

God Mingled with Us. 2006. (Illus.). 134p. per. 12.99 (978-1-59886-269-0(3)) Tate Publishing & Enterprises, LLC.

Hasak, Jan. Mourning Has Broken. 2008. 304p. pap. 17.99 (978-1-60647-252-1(6)) Xulon Pr., Inc.

Hastings, Jeff. Dying Can Change Your Life. 2007. (ENG.). 124p. per. 13.99 (978-1-4141-0825-4(7)) Pleasant Word.

Hess, Dave. Hope Beyond Reason: Embraced by God's Presence in the Toughest of Times. 2008. pap. 14.99 (978-0-7684-2697-7(9)) Destiny Image Pubs.

Higgins, Erin & Lightbody, Alma. My Wonderful Nightmare: Spiritual Journals Inspired by Cancer. 2010. 196p. pap. 18.00 (978-1-4251-8725-5(0)) Trafford Publishing.

Hildebrandt, Sherri. More Than Enough. 2011. (**978-1-77069-220-6(7)**) Word Alive Pr.

Holmes, Karen L. He Provides the Shoes. 2008. 236p. pap. 15.99 (978-1-60647-796-0(X)) Xulon Pr., Inc.

Houchins, Marge. Cheerleader Faith: Team Spirit for the Cancer Patient What to Do When Trouble Comes! 2011. 60p. 24.99 (**978-1-4628-4566-8(5)**); pap. 15.99 (**978-1-4628-4565-1(7)**) Xlibris Corp.

Howard, Deborah. Help! Someone I Love Has Cancer. Tautges, Paul, ed. 2010. (Help! (Day One Publications) Ser.). 62p. pap. (978-1-84625-217-4(2)) DayOne Pubns.

Inspirio Staff, creator. What Cancer Cannot Do, 1 vol. 2006. (ENG., Illus.). 128p. 12.99 (978-0-310-81184-8(8)) Inspirio.

Jameson, Derek & Jameson, Ellen. Siobhan's Miracle. 2008. (ENG., Illus.). 240p. 24.95 (978-1-84454-566-7(0)) Blake, John Publishing, Ltd. GBR. Dist: Independent Pubs. Group.

Kallenbach, JuLee. And Then the Angels Came... . A Teacher's Breast Cancer Story. 2006. per. 5.95 (978-0-9790529-0-3(4)) Kallenbach, JuLee.

Kestner, Patricia. Breast Cancer & God's Word. 2007. 68p. per. 10.99 (978-0-88144-279-3(8)) Yorkshire Publishing Group.

Kilfeather, Rick. Hope Beyond Diagnosis. 2010. 140p. pap. 14.99 (978-1-61579-791-2(2)) Xulon Pr., Inc.

Kohn, Douglas. Life, Faith, & Cancer: Jewish Journeys Through Diagnosis, Treatment, & Recovery. 2007. 16.95 (978-0-8074-1059-2(4)) URJ Pr.

Kugel, James L. In the Valley of the Shadow: On the Foundations of Religious Belief. 2011. (ENG.). 256p. pap. 15.00 (978-1-4391-3010-0(8)); (Illus.). 26.00 (978-1-4391-3009-4(4)) Free Pr. (Free Pr.).

Lacey, Sandra, et al. People Like Us: Life with Rob Lacey, 1 vol. 2011. (ENG.). 272p. pap. 14.99 (978-0-310-31904-7(8)) Zondervan.

Lavelle, Jean. Journey Through Cancer. 2010. (ENG.). 64p. pap. 8.95 (978-1-84730-211-3(4)) Veritas Pubns. IRL. Dist: Dufour Editions, Inc.

Lindley, Candy. Face of Faith: Discovering a Different Kind of Makeover. 2009. 352p. 22.95 (978-0-9820435-0-9(3)) Exclaim Publishing.

Love, Julie Anderson. Disrupted: On Fighting Death & Keeping Faith. 2011. 178p. pap. 20.00 (**978-1-61097-095-2(0)**, Cascade Bks.) Wipf & Stock Pubs.

Lyons, David & Richardson, Linda Lyons. Don't Waste the Pain: Learning to Grow Through Suffering. 2010. (Experience the Life Ser.). 272p. pap. 15.99 (978-1-61521-548-5(4)) NavPress Publishing Group.

MacDougall, Judy F. Ruby, a Child of the King. 2011. (Illus.). (**978-1-77069-174-2(X)**) Word Alive Pr.

Martin, Linda. No Journey Back. 2011. 152p. 30.95 (**978-1-61507-900-1(9)**); pap. 13.95 (**978-1-61507-899-8(1)**) Cross Bks. Publishing.

McDonnell, Mary. Cancer, Prayer & Survival. 2009. (ENG.). 85p. pap. 15.95 (978-1-85607-639-5(3)) Columba Pr. IRL. Dist: Dufour Editions, Inc.

McFarland, John Robert. Now That I Have Cancer, I Am Whole: Reflections on Life & Healing for Cancer Patients & Those Who Love Them. 2007. (ENG.). 320p. pap. 9.95 (978-0-7407-6372-4(5)) Andrews McMeel Publishing.

McSwain, Mark A. Through the Eyes of a Storm: Perspective Gained through a Cancer Journey. 2011. 72p. pap. 8.95 (**978-1-4620-3192-4(7)**) iUniverse, Inc.

Meisenhelder, Melissa Bell. Melissa's Prayer Journal: The Power of Prayer in the Face of Cancer. 2007. (Illus.). 80p. (YA). per. 14.95 (978-0-9796511-0-6(7)) MBM Pubs.

Moore, Dwayne. Surviving Wolves at the Door: My Journey Through Cancer. 2008. 384p. pap. 29.95 (978-1-60610-846-8(8)) PublishAmerica, Inc.

Nettles, Cherie. Growing My Divine Shrine: Your Way to Live, Love & Laugh Through Life. 2009. (ENG.). 144p. 12.95 (978-0-9817608-7-2(2)) Lifebridge Bks.

Nguyen, Kim. Between the Tumor & the Tomb: A Diary of Doom & Deliverance. 2007. 206p. per. 16.95 (978-1-59352-332-9(7)) Christian Services Publishing.

Norris, Kathy. Where Does Your Make-up Line Go When You Lose Your Hair? 2006. 112p. per. 10.99 (978-1-59886-523-3(4)) Tate Publishing & Enterprises, LLC.

North, Bradley Dallas. Three Swords of One Light. 2008. 464p. 33.95 (978-1-58909-560-1(X)) Bookstand Publishing.

Nurse, Ann. From Terror to Love Defined. 2007. 193p. pap. 24.95 (978-1-4241-5270-4(4)) PublishAmerica, Inc.

O'Haynes, Delilah F. Walk Free from Fear of Cancer. 2008. (Illus.). 283p. pap. 19.95 (978-0-9779282-1-7(7)) Walk Free Pr.

Owens, Pat. Faith Like Fire: Engulfed by a Great God. 2011. 128p. 28.95 (**978-1-4627-0540-5(5)**); pap. 11.95 (**978-1-4627-0539-9(1)**) Cross Bks. Publishing.

Pickton, Jennifer. Holding the Light. 2009. (ENG.). 187p. pap. 21.50 (978-0-9558569-1-4(4)) Centre of Light GBR. Dist: Lulu Enterprises Inc.

Piper, John. Don't Waste Your Cancer. 2011. 15p. (**978-1-4335-2331-1(0)**) Crossway.

Piper, John. Don't Waste Your Cancer. 2011. 16p. 2.99 (978-1-4335-2322-9(1)) Crossway.

Prodigal, The. Penny's Miracle: Standing on His Promises, 1 vol. 2009. 63p. pap. 16.95 (978-1-4489-9994-1(4)) PublishAmerica, Inc.

Schultz, Nancy. Mrs. Mattingly's Miracle: The Prince, the Widow, & the Cure That Shocked Washington City. 2011. (ENG., Illus.). 288p. 30.00 (978-0-300-11846-9(5)) Yale Univ. Pr.

Sell, Colleen. Breast Cancer Survivors: Inspiring Stories of Courage & Triumph. 2008. (ENG.). 336p. pap. 9.95 (978-1-59869-650-9(5)) Adams Media Corp.

Sewell, Sue. In the Shadow of Your Wings. 2006. 104p. per. 10.99 (978-0-9759049-8-5(1)) Master Pr.

Sheppard, Arlene Joy. A Princess Meets Her Prince Charming. 2007. 132p. (ENG.). 21.99 (978-1-60477-056-8(2)); per. 13.99 (978-1-60477-055-1(4)) Xulon Pr., Inc.

Simpson, Wallis A. & Smith, Cara Blakley. I Choose to Laugh: Faith in the Midst of Cancer. 2007. 140p. per. 13.95 (978-0-595-46623-8(0)) iUniverse, Inc.

Sirdashney, Erica. Cranes for Christian. 2008. 104p. 9.99 (978-1-60462-788-6(3)) Tate Publishing & Enterprises, LLC.

Smith, Judy Gattis. Fear Not: Learning from Your Cancer. 2008. 128p. pap. 12.00 (978-0-88177-538-9(X)) Upper Room Bks.

Staples. Cancer Ain't Nothing but a Pimple Ta God. 2008. 80p. per. 11.99 (978-1-60477-165-7(8)) Xulon Pr., Inc.

Strange, Wanda. Refined. 2007. 84p. per. 16.95 (978-1-4241-7700-4(6)) PublishAmerica, Inc.

Throop, Brian. Stacy's Miracle. 2010. 160p. 25.95 (978-1-4490-7177-6(5)); pap. 19.95 (978-1-4490-7176-9(7)) AuthorHouse.

Turner, Jerome. Thank God for Cancer! 2008. 136p. per. 13.99 (978-1-60477-665-2(X)) Xulon Pr., Inc.

W., Joye. Walking Through the 'C' Word: A Victorious Journey Through Cancer, Divorce & Despair. 2008. 132p. pap. 11.95 (978-1-4327-2561-7(0)) Outskirts Pr., Inc.

Waite, Don, et al. Traveling Home: A Young Man's Story of Courage & Faith, 1 vol. 2008. 144p. pap. 11.99 (978-0-8254-2899-9(8)) Kregel Pubns.

Walker, Joseph W., III. Life Between Sundays: Living Your Life Outside Church. 2009. pap. 16.99 (978-0-7684-2829-2(7)) Destiny Image Pubs.

Wangerin, Walter, Jr. Letters from the Land of Cancer, 1 vol. 2010. (ENG.). 192p. 16.99 (978-0-310-29281-4(6)) Zondervan.

Weaver, Chris. You Don't Need Nipples to Get into Heaven. 2007. 176p. per. 13.99 (978-1-60477-155-8(0)) Xulon Pr., Inc.

Wisdom, Jeff. Through the Valley: Biblical-Theological Reflections on Suffering. 2011. 162p. pap. 19.00 (**978-1-61097-390-8(9)**, Wipf and Stock) Wipf & Stock Pubs.

Zondervan Publishing Staff & Inspirio Staff. What Cancer Cannot Do, 1 vol. deluxe ed. 2006. (ENG.). 128p. 14.99 (978-0-310-81588-4(6)) Inspirio.

CANCER—RESEARCH

ABBE Scientist Research Division Staff. Methanol & Cancer: Index, Reference & Medical Analysis of New Research Information for All Nations. 2008. (Illus.). 160p. ring bd. 69.95 (978-0-7883-4691-0(1)) ABBE Pubs. Assn. of Washington, D.C.

—Microbiology of Human Cancer: Index, Reference & Medical Analysis of New Research Information. 2008. 160p. ring bd. 69.95 (978-0-7883-4657-6(1)) ABBE Pubs. Assn. of Washington, D.C.

Alvarez, Carlos M. Focus on Cancer Research. 2007. (C). 185.00 (978-1-60021-729-6(X)) Nova Science Pubs., Inc.

Anderson Hospital And Tumor Institute. Radiation Biology & Cancer: A Collection of Papers Presented at the Twelfth Annual Symposium on Fundamental Cancer Research 1958. 2011. 502p. 58.95 (**978-1-258-08526-1(7)**) Literary Licensing, LLC.

Armstrong, Marc P. Geocoding Health Data: The Use of Geographic Codes in Cancer Prevention & Control, Research & Practice. Gittler, Josephine et al, eds. 2007. (ENG., Illus.). 256p. 113.95 (978-0-8493-8419-6(2), CRC Press) Taylor & Francis Group GBR. Dist: Taylor & Francis Group.

Arroye, Raymond P., ed. Cancer Prevention Research Progress. 2008. 79.00 (978-1-60456-125-8(4), Nova Biomedical Bks.) Nova Science Pubs., Inc.

Bal, Harshawardhan & Hujol, Johnny. Java for Bioinformatics & Biomedical Applications. 2010. (ENG., Illus.). xviii, 342p. pap. 115.00 (978-1-4419-4245-6(9), 1441942459) Springer.

Barak, V., ed. Tumor Biology: Tumor Markers, Tumor Targeting & Translational Cancer Research, Vol. 27. 116p. pap. (978-3-8055-8023-6(1)) Karger, S. AG.

Barillot, Emmanuel, et al. Computational Systems Biology of Cancer. 2011. (Illus.). 356p. 79.95 (978-1-4398-3145-8(9), CRC Press) Taylor & Francis Group GBR. Dist: Taylor & Francis Group.

Bartone, John Charles. Cancer Disease for All Americans: Dr. Bartone Rule #1: Food Containing Carcinogens: Index, Reference & Medical Analysis of New Research Information. 2008. (Illus.). 160p. ring bd. 69.95 (978-0-7883-3850-2(1)) ABBE Pubs. Assn. of Washington, D.C.

—Cancer Disease for All Americans: Dr. Bartone Rule #2: Beverages Containing Carcinogens: Index, Reference & Medical Analysis of New Research Information. 2008. (Illus.). 160p. ring bd. 69.95 (978-0-7883-3859-5(5)) ABBE Pubs. Assn. of Washington, D.C.

—Cancer Disease for All Americans: Dr. Bartone Rule #3: Vegetables Containing Carcinogens: Index, Reference & Medical Analysis of New Research Information. 2008. (Illus.). 160p. ring bd. 69.95 (978-0-7883-3875-5(7)) ABBE Pubs. Assn. of Washington, D.C.

Bayor, Marcel. The Bioactivity of Croton Membranaceus - a Traditional Anticancer Herb. 2011. 272p. pap. (**978-3-8433-8695-1(1)**) Lambert Academic Publishing.

Beam, Craig, ed. Biostatistical Applications in Cancer Research. 2010. (Cancer Treatment & Research Ser.). 248p. pap. 199.00 (978-1-4419-5310-0(8), 1441953108) Springer.

Bettuzzi, Saverio & Pucci, Sabina. Clusterin, Part B, 2 vols. 2009. (ENG., Illus.). 350p. 161.00 (978-0-12-381429-6(4), Academic Pr.) Elsevier Science & Technology Bks.

Biava, Pier Mario. Cancer & the Search for Lost Meaning: The Discovery of a Revolutionary New Cancer Treatment. 2009. (ENG., Illus.). 168p. pap. 15.95 (978-1-55643-778-6(1)) North Atlantic Bks.

Borisch, B. & Jacquemier, J., eds. Translational Research in Breast Cancer. 2008. (Illus.). 98p. pap. (978-3-8055-8601-6(9)) Karger, S. AG.

Bringmann, Peter & Weiss, Bertram. Systems Biology: Applications & Perspectives. 2007. (Ernst Schering Foundation Symposium Proceedings Ser.). (Illus.). xvi, 172p. 109.00 (978-3-540-31338-0(9), 3540313389) Springer.

Bryder, Linda. Women's Bodies & Medical Science: An Inquiry into Cervical Cancer. 2010. (Science, Technology & Medicine in Modern History Ser.). (ENG.). 256p. 95.00 (978-0-230-23603-5(0)) Palgrave Macmillan.

Caboux, E., et al. International Network of Biological Resource Centres for Cancer Research. Recommendations on Minimum Technical Standards: IARC Working Group Report, No. 2. 2007. (IARC Nonserial Publication). (ENG.). 56p. pap. 25.00 (978-92-832-2442-6(6)) World Health Organization.

Cancer: Challenges & Opportunities in the 21st Century: Hearing Before the Committee on Health, Education, Labor, & Pensions, United States Senate, One Hundred Tenth Congress, Second Session, on Examining Cancer Relating to Challenges & Opportunities in the 21st Century, May 8, 2008. 2010. iii, 72p. *(978-0-16-085135-3(1)*, 552-070-40489-9) United States Government Printing Office.

Cancer Research: Funding Innovative Research: Hearing Before a Subcommittee of the Committee on Appropriations, United States Senate, One Hundred Eleventh Congress, First Session, Special Hearing, July 6, 2009, Philadelphia, PA. 2010. iii, 37p. ***(978-0-16-085190-2(4)***, 552-070-40543-7) United States Government Printing Office.

Chen, Xiaoyuan. Molecular Imaging Probes for Cancer Research. 2011. 1100p. 260.00 *(978-981-4293-67-9(9))* World Scientific Publishing Co., Inc.

Cho, William C. S., ed. Materia Medica for Various Cancers. 2011. (Evidence-based Anticancer Complementary & Alternative Medicine Ser.). (ENG., Illus.). xii, 406p. 209.00 ***(978-94-007-1982-8(5)***, 9400719825) Springer.

—MicroRNAs in Cancer Translational Research. 2011. (ENG.). xiii, 557p. 189.00 *(978-94-007-0297-4(3)*, 9400702973) Springer.

—An Omics Perspective on Cancer Research. 2009. (ENG., Illus.). viii, 269p. 179.00 *(978-90-481-2674-3(6)*, 9048126746) Springer.

Chute, Maureen. Closeness in Crisis - a Proposal for Identifying Resilience in Couples Who Face the Crisis of Cancer in Their Child. 2008. 60p. pap. *(978-3-639-10653-4(9))* VDM Verlag Dr. Mueller e.K.

Clary, Thomas S., ed. Horizons in Computer Science Research. 2011. (Series: Horizons in Computer Science Ser.). 140.00 *(978-1-61324-262-9(X))* Nova Science Pubs., Inc.

Committee on Cancer Clinical Trials and the NCI Cooperative Group Program & Institute of Medicine. A National Cancer Clinical Trials System for the 21st Century: Reinvigorating the NCI Cooperative Group Program. 2010. (ENG.). 316p. pap. 64.25 *(978-0-309-15186-3(4))* National Academies Pr.

Crowley, John & Hoering, Antje, eds. Handbook of Statistics in Clinical Oncology, Third Edition. 3rd rev. ed. 2012. (ENG., Illus.). 657p. 119.95 *(978-1-4398-6200-1(1)*, Chapman & Hall/CRC) CRC Pr. LLC.

Czlonka, Rod. Decide to Live. 2007. 250p. pap. 22.50 *(978-1-4357-0301-8(4))* Lulu Enterprises Inc.

—Decide to Live - Second Edition. 2010. 263p. pap. 20.00 *(978-0-557-71775-0(2))* Lulu Enterprises Inc.

Daar, Ira. Guidance Molecules in Cancer & Tumor Angiogenesis. 2012. (ENG.). 288p. 161.00 ***(978-0-12-386503-8(4)***, Academic Pr.) Elsevier Science & Technology Bks.

Davis, Devra. Disconnect: The Truth about Cell Phone Radiation, What the Industry Has Done to Hide It, & How to Protect Your Family. 2010. (ENG.). 271p. (gr. 12). 26.95 *(978-0-525-95194-0(6)*, Dutton Adult) Penguin Group (USA) Inc.

Deutsches Krebsforschungszentrum, ed. Current Cancer Research 2006. 2006. (Illus.). 211p. pap. 29.95 *(978-3-7985-1643-4(X)*, 379851643X) Steinkopff, Dietrich DEU. Dist: Springer.

Eiseman. Effects of Preanalytical Variables: On the Quality of Biospecimens Used to Study Genetic Changes in Cancer. 2009. 98p. pap. 35.00 *(978-0-8330-4741-0(8))* RAND Corp., The.

Epstein, Samuel S. National Cancer Institute & American Cancer Society: Criminal Indifference to Cancer Prevention & Conflicts of Interest. 2011. 204p. 29.99 ***(978-1-4628-6135-4(0))***; pap. 19.99 ***(978-1-4628-6134-7(2))*** Xlibris Corp.

Feleppa, E. J., ed. Recent Advances in Imaging the Prostate: Book Edition of Cancer Biomarkers. 2008. 256p. pap. 123.00 *(978-1-58603-938-7(5))* IOS Pr., Inc.

Fisher, Paul & Tew, Ken, contrib. by. Advances in Cancer Research. 2012. (ENG.). 304p. 161.00 ***(978-0-12-394280-7(2)***, Academic Pr.) Elsevier Science & Technology Bks.

Fritz, A., et al. Classification Internationale des maladies pour L'oncologie (CIM-O-3) 2009. 294p. pap. 72.00 *(978-92-4-254534-0(1))* World Health Organization.

Gonzalez, Juan R. Modelling Recurrent Event Data with Application to Cancer Research. 2009. 184p. pap. *(978-3-8364-7464-1(6))* VDM Verlag Dr. Mueller e.K.

Gutiérrez Diez, Pedro J., et al. The Evolution of the Use of Mathematics in Cancer Research. 2012. (ENG., Illus.). xii, 401p. 189.00 ***(978-1-4614-2396-6(1)***, 1461423961) Springer.

Han. Handbook of Cancer Models with Applic. . V9. 2008. 252.00 *(978-981-277-947-2(7))* World Scientific Publishing Co., Inc.

Harrington, David, ed. Designs for Clinical Trials: Perspectives on Current Issues. 2011. (Applied Bioinformatics & Biostatistics in Cancer Research Ser.). (ENG., Illus.). xiv, 204p. 189.00 *(978-1-4614-0139-1(9)*, 1461401399) Springer.

Haslam, Edward T. Dr. Mary's Monkey: How the Unsolved Murder of a Doctor, a Secret Laboratory in New Orleans & Cancer-Causing Monkey Viruses Are Linked to Lee Harvey Oswald, the JFK Assassination & Emerging Global Epidemics. 2007. (ENG., Illus.). 275p. pap. 19.95 *(978-0-9777953-0-7(6))* Trine Day.

Heitman, Joseph, ed. Yeast as a Tool in Cancer Research. 2007. (Illus.). 433p. 209.00 *(978-1-4020-5962-9(0))* Springer.

Hemalatha, Besetti. P21 Ras the Hidden Target for Cancer-an in Silico Analysis. 2011. 76p. pap. ***(978-3-8443-1378-9(8))*** Lambert Academic Publishing.

Hino, O., et al, eds. Researches on Hepatocellular Carcinoma in Japan: A Message to the World. (Illus.). *(978-3-8055-7328-3(6))* Karger, S. AG.

Hu, Yingjie. Gene Selection Based on Consistency Modelling, Algorithms & Applications - Genetic Algorithm Application in Bioinformatics Data Analysis. 2008. 112p. pap. *(978-3-639-00883-8(9))* VDM Verlag Dr. Mueller e.K.

International Agency for Research on Cancer. IARC Biennial Report 2008-2009. 2010. (IARC Scientific Publication). 162p. pap. 30.00 *(978-92-832-0425-1(5))* World Health Organization.

International Agency for Research on Cancer Staff. Centre International de Recherche sur le Cancer: Rapport Biennal 2006-2007. 2008. 164p. pap. 30.00 *(978-92-832-2092-3(7))* World Health Organization.

—IARC Biennial Report 2006-2007. 2007. (IARC Official Publication Ser.). (ENG., Illus.). 279p. pap. 30.00 *(978-92-832-1092-4(1))* World Health Organization.

International Agency for Research on Cancer Staff & World Health Organization. IARC Code of Good Scientific Practice. 2009. (IARC Nonserial Publication Ser.). (ENG.). 15p. pap. 12.00 *(978-92-832-2445-7(0))* World Health Organization.

Jeffries, Lee P. Leading Topics in Cancer Research. 2006. (Horizons in Cancer Research Ser.). 331p. 225.00 *(978-1-60021-332-8(4))* Nova Science Pubs., Inc.

Jones, Robert N. In the Darker Shadow of Science: The Subjugation of Cancer. 2010. 560p. pap. 34.95 *(978-1-4401-7374-5(5))* iUniverse, Inc.

Joshi, Dipti, et al. Anticancer Activity of Casearia Esculenta in Experimental Models. 2011. 68p. pap. ***(978-3-8443-2819-6(X))*** Lambert Academic Publishing.

Kaldis, Philipp, ed. Cell Cycle Regulation. 2010. (Results & Problems in Cell Differentiation Ser.). (Illus.). xii, 374p. pap. 269.00 *(978-3-642-07093-8(0)*, 3642070930) Springer.

Keating, Peter & Cambrosio, Alberto. Cancer on Trial: Oncology as a New Style of Practice. 2012. (ENG., Illus.). 424p. 40.00 *(978-0-226-42891-8(5))* Univ. of Chicago Pr.

Kelly, William Kevin & Halabi, Susan. Oncology Clinical Trials. 2009. 379.00 *(978-1-933864-38-9(9))* Demos Medical Publishing, LLC.

Keranen, Lisa. Scientific Characters: Rhetoric, Politics, & Trust in Breast Cancer Research. 2nd ed. 2010. (Albma Rhetoric Cult & Soc Crit Ser.). (ENG., Illus.). 248p. 45.00 *(978-0-8173-1704-1(X))* Univ. of Alabama Pr.

Krebsforschung Heute. 305p. (C). 24.00 *(978-3-7985-1105-7(5))* Steinkopff, Dietrich DEU. Dist: Springer.

Kumar, Amrendar, et al. Global Cancer Network. 2011. 180p. pap. ***(978-3-8454-0186-7(9))*** Lambert Academic Publishing.

Kutcher, Gerald & Kutcher, G. Contested Medicine: Cancer Research & the Military. 2009. (ENG.). 264p. 35.00 *(978-0-226-46531-9(4))* Univ. of Chicago Pr.

LaFond, Richard, ed. Cancer: The Outlaw Cell, 1 vol. 3rd ed. 2012. (ENG., Illus.). 384p. 99.95 *(978-0-8412-0000-5(9))* American Chemical Society.

Leong, Stanley P. L. Cancer Clinical Trials: Proactive Strategies. 2006. (Cancer Treatment & Research Ser.). (Illus.). 318p. 149.00 *(978-0-387-33224-6(3)*, 0387332243) Springer.

Li, Shaoguang & Li, Dongguang. Dna Microarray Technology & Data Analysis in Cancer Research. 2009. 140p. 81.00 *(978-981-279-045-3(4))* World Scientific Publishing Co., Inc.

Liu, Xin-Yuan, et al, eds. Recent Advances in Cancer Research & Therapy. 2012. (ENG.). 600p. 150.00 ***(978-0-12-397833-2(5))*** Elsevier Science & Technology Bks.

Malinin, Theodore I. Cancer Merchants: History of NCIs, Viruses, & Cancer Programs. 2008. 144p. pap. 14.00 *(978-1-4349-0065-4(7))* Dorrance Publishing Co., Inc.

Martens, Uwe M. Small Molecules in Oncology. 2009. (Recent Results in Cancer Research Ser.). (ENG., Illus.). xvi, 238p. 189.00 *(978-3-642-01221-1(3)*, 3642012213) Springer.

Moehler, Thomas & Goldschmidt, Hartmut. Multiple Myeloma. 2010. (Recent Results in Cancer Research Ser.). (Illus.). 200p. 219.00 *(978-3-540-85771-6(0)*, 3540857710) Springer.

Morrison, Edward P. Horizons in Cancer Research, Vol. 41. 2010. (Horizons in Cancer Research Ser.). 306p. 145.00 *(978-1-60741-790-3(1)*, Nova Biomedical Bks.) Nova Science Pubs., Inc.

Mulshine, James L. & Baer, Thomas M., eds. Quantitative Imaging Tools for Lung Cancer Drug Assessment. 2008. (ENG., Illus.). 162p. 139.00 *(978-0-470-11880-1(6))* Wiley, John & Sons, Inc.

National Cancer Policy Forum & Institute of Medicine. Facilitating Collaborations to Develop Combination Investigational Cancer Therapies: Workshop Summary. 2012. (ENG.). 118p. pap. 38.00 ***(978-0-309-22064-4(5))*** National Academies Pr.

National Cancer Policy Forum (U.S.) Staff, contrib. by. Cancer in Elderly People: Workshop Proceedings. 2007. (ENG., Illus.). 106p. pap. 28.75 *(978-0-309-10476-0(9))* National Academies Pr.

National Cancer Policy Forum Staff & Institute of Medicine Staff. The National Cancer Policy Summit: Summary of a Meeting of the National Cancer Policy Forum. 2011. (ENG.). 60p. pap. 21.00 *(978-0-309-18739-8(7))* National Academies Pr.

Nation's Investment in Cancer Research: A Budget Proposal for Fiscal Years 1997/98. 80p. pap. 25.00 *(978-0-7881-8995-1(6))* DIANE Publishing Co.

Nelson, Jennifer J., et al. Cancer on the Margins: Method & Meaning in Participatory Research. 2009. (ENG., Illus.). 288p. *(978-0-8020-9169-7(5))*; pap. *(978-0-8020-9434-6(1))* Univ. of Toronto Pr.

Ochs, Michael F., et al, eds. Biomedical Informatics in Cancer Research. 2010. (ENG., Illus.). xviii, 354p. 179.00 *(978-1-4419-5712-2(X)*, 144195712X) Springer.

Onuigbo, Wilson. Human Models in Cancer Metastasis Research. 2011. 88p. pap. ***(978-3-8433-7998-4(X))*** Lambert Academic Publishing.

Palladino, Michael A., et al. Biology of Cancer. 2nd rev. ed. 2011. (Special Topics in Biology Ser.). (ENG.). 48p. (C). pap. 13.87 ***(978-0-321-77492-7(2))*** Benjamin-Cummings Publishing Co.

Papadopoulos, V. Stem Cells & Disease: Book Edition of Disease Markers. 2008. 88p. pap. 138.00 *(978-1-58603-875-5(3))* IOS Pr., Inc.

Patel, Manish & Nagl, Sylvia. The Role of Model Integration in Complex Systems Modelling: An Example from Cancer Biology. 2010. (Understanding Complex Systems Ser.). (Illus.). 176p. 159.00 *(978-3-642-15602-1(9)*, 3642156029) Springer.

Rapp, U. R., et al, eds. German Cancer Society: 13th International AEK/AIO Congress of the German Cancer Society, Würzburg, March 2005: Abstracts, Vol. 28. *(978-3-8055-7942-1(X))* Karger, S. AG.

Roboz John Staff. Mass Spectrometry in Cancer Research Second Edition. 2nd ed. 2009. (Illus.). 640p. 199.95 *(978-0-8493-7390-9(5))* CRC Pr. LLC.

Rolland, George Z. New Research on Cervical Cancer. (Illus.). 2007. xii, 247p. *(978-1-62002-130-9(7))* 2006. 248p. 225.00 *(978-1-60021-300-7(6))* Nova Science Pubs., Inc.

Saiko, Philipp. Effects of Naturally Occurring Compounds on Human Cancer Cells. 2008. 212p. pap. *(978-3-639-05897-0(6))* VDM Verlag Dr. Mueller e.K.

Schneider, Katherine A. Counseling about Cancer: Strategies for Genetic Counseling. 3rd ed. 2011. (ENG., Illus.). 496p. pap. 69.95 ***(978-0-470-08150-1(3)***, Wiley-Blackwell) Wiley, John & Sons, Inc.

Schneider, Paul M. Adenocarcinoma of the Esophagogastric Junction. 2010. (Recent Results in Cancer Research Ser.). (ENG., Illus.). xiv, 238p. 159.00 *(978-3-540-70578-9(3)*, 3540705783) Springer.

Schulz, Mandy. Fruit & Vegetable Consumption & Risk of Epithelial Ovarian Cancer. 2008. 120p. pap. *(978-3-639-06087-4(3))* VDM Verlag Dr. Mueller e.K.

Shankar, Udaya. A Fight Without Choice: A Cancer Survivor's Journey from Shock to Treatment to Recovery. 2008. 196p. pap. 24.95 *(978-1-60703-097-3(7))* PublishAmerica, Inc.

Skloot, Rebeca. Immortal Life of Henrietta. 2011. 15.45 ***(978-0-7848-3620-0(5)***, Everbind) Marco Bk. Co.

Skloot, Rebecca. The Immortal Life of Henrietta Lacks. (ENG., Illus.). 2011. 400p. pap. 16.00 *(978-1-4000-5218-9(1)*, Three Rivers Pr.) 2010. 384p. 26.00 *(978-1-4000-5217-2(3)*, Crown) Crown Publishing Group.

—The Immortal Life of Henrietta Lacks. l.t. ed. 604p. 2011. (ENG.). pap. 16.99 *(978-1-59413-432-6(4)*, Large Print Pr.) 2010. 31.99 *(978-1-4104-2792-2(7))* Thorndike Pr.

Srivastava, S., ed. The National Cancer Institute Early Detection Research Network: 5th Scientific Workshop - Biomarkers-at-a-Crossroads - Book Edition of Cancer Biomarkers. 2008. 130p. pap. 116.00 *(978-1-58603-926-4(1))* IOS Pr., Inc.

Tsuruo, Takashi, et al. Cancer Research Front of Japan, 2003 Vol. 52: Special Issue in Commemoration of the 100th Anniversary of the Late Dr. Tomizo Yoshida's Birth. (Gann Monograph on Cancer Research Ser.). (Illus.). 16;280p. *(978-3-8055-7816-5(4))* Karger, S. AG.

Vande Woude, George F., et al, eds. Advances in Cancer Research. 2009. (Advances in Cancer Research Ser.). (ENG.). 450p. 161.00 *(978-0-12-374437-1(7)*, Academic Pr.) Elsevier Science & Technology Bks.

Vande Woude, George F. & Klein, George, eds. Advances in Cancer Research. (ENG.). 2011. 160p. 161.00 *(978-0-12-386469-7(0))* 2011. 200p. 161.00 ***(978-0-12-385524-4(1))*** 2010. 170p. 161.00 *(978-0-12-380888-2(X))* 2010. 244p. 161.00 *(978-0-12-374770-9(8))* 2010. 195p. 161.00 *(978-0-12-374771-6(6))* 2009. 160p. 161.00 *(978-0-12-374773-0(2))* 2008. 480p. 161.00 *(978-0-12-374359-6(1))* 2007. (Illus.). 450p. 161.00 *(978-0-12-374224-7(2))* 2007. (Illus.). 280p. 161.00 *(978-0-12-373896-7(2))* 2007. (Illus.). 368p. 161.00 *(978-0-12-006697-1(1))* 2006. (Illus.). 376p. 161.00 *(978-0-12-006695-7(5))* Vol. 100. 2008. (Illus.). 252p. 161.00 *(978-0-12-374358-9(3))* Elsevier Science & Technology Bks. (Academic Pr.).

Viktorsson, Kajsa. Advancements in Cancer Research. 2012. (Cancer Etiology, Diagnosis & Treatments Ser.). 289p. 95.00 ***(978-1-61470-252-8(7))*** Nova Science Pubs., Inc.

Vonderhaar, B. K. & Smith, G. H., eds. Stem Cells & Breast Cancer - Volume 29 Breast Disease. 2008. 236p. pap. 218.00 *(978-1-58603-912-7(1))* IOS Pr., Inc.

Wagner, Kerstin. Search for Breast Cancer Susceptibility Genes: The Growth Hormone-1 / Insulin-like Growth Factor-1Pathway & its Relationship to Breast Cancer. 2008. 132p. pap. *(978-3-639-02207-0(6))* VDM Verlag Dr. Mueller e.K.

Wang, D. T., ed. Targeted Imaging of Neoplasia in the Digestive Tract: Book Edition of Cancer Biomarkers. 2009. 289p. pap. 116.00 *(978-1-58603-974-5(1))* IOS Pr., Inc.

Wang, Edwin, ed. Cancer Systems Biology. 2010. (Chapman & Hall/CRC Mathematical & Computational Biology Ser.). (ENG., Illus.). 455p. 89.95 *(978-1-4398-1185-6(7)*, CRC Press) Taylor & Francis Group GBR. Dist: Taylor & Francis Group.

Watanabe, Hiroto S. Horizons in Cancer Research. 2011. (Horizons in Cancer Research Ser.). 129.00 *(978-1-61209-377-2(9))*; 129.00 *(978-1-61761-111-7(5))* Nova Science Pubs., Inc.

Watanabe, Hiroto S., ed. Horizons in Cancer Research. 2012. (Horizons in Cancer Research Ser.). 382p. 185.00 ***(978-1-61470-444-7(9))*** Nova Science Pubs., Inc.

Wiuf, Carsten & Andersen, Claus L., eds. Statistics & Informatics in Molecular Cancer Research. 2009. (ENG., Illus.). 304p. 85.00 *(978-0-19-953287-2(7))* Oxford Univ. Pr., Inc.

Woude, George F. Vande & Klein, George, eds. Advances in Cancer Research. 2010. (ENG.). 160p. 161.00 *(978-0-12-380890-5(1)*, Academic Pr.) Elsevier Science & Technology Bks.

Wu, Jane Y., ed. RNA & Cancer. 2009. (Cancer Treatment & Research Ser.). (Illus.). 320p. 129.00 *(978-1-4419-0021-0(7))* Springer.

Xu, Lei. Microarray Gene Expression Data Integration & Cancer Signatures. 2008. 120p. pap. *(978-3-639-08553-2(1))* VDM Verlag Dr. Mueller e.K.

Yeh, I-Yen Richard. Cancer Risk Assessment of Trihalomethanes in Drinking Water. 2008. 148p. pap. *(978-3-639-02915-4(1))* VDM Verlag Dr. Mueller e.K.

25 Jahre im Dienste der Krebsforschung. (Onkologie Ser.: Vol. 25). (GER., Illus.). *(978-3-8055-7393-1(6))* Karger, S. AG.

CANCER—RISK FACTORS

American Society of Clinical Oncology Staff, contrib. by. Cancer Prevention: An ASCO Curriculum. 2007. *(978-1-932312-33-1(1))* American Society of Clinical Oncology.

Attributable Causes of Cancer in France in the Year 2000: IARC Working Group Report, No. 3. 2007. (IARC Nonserial Publication). pap. 22.50 *(978-92-832-2443-3(4))* World Health Organization.

Boughton, Barbara & Stefanek, Michael. Reduce Your Cancer Risk: Twelve Steps to a Healthier Life. 2010. (ENG.). 256p. pap. 16.95 *(978-1-932603-92-7(1))* Demos Medical Publishing, LLC.

Cram101 Textbook Reviews & Cram101 Textbook Reviews. Outlines & Highlights for Cancer Risk Assessment: Chemical Carcinogenesis, Hazard Evaluation, & Risk Quantification by Ching-Hung Hsu, ISBN. 2011. 524p. pap. 38.95 ***(978-1-61461-348-0(6))*** Cram101 Inc.

Elsersawi, Amin. Chemistry, Biology & Cancer: The Bond. 2009. 264p. pap. 81.99 *(978-1-4415-3619-8(1))* Xlibris Corp.

Friedman, Sue, et al. Confronting Hereditary Breast & Ovarian Cancer: Identify Your Risk, Understand Your Options, Change Your Destiny. 2012. (Johns Hopkins Press Health Book Ser.). (ENG., Illus.). 288p. pap. 18.95 ***(978-1-4214-0408-0(7))***; (gr. 17). 45.00 ***(978-1-4214-0407-3(9))*** Johns Hopkins Univ. Pr.

ICRP Staff. Low-Dose Extrapolation of Radiation Related Cancer Risk. Valentin, J., ed. 2006. (International Commission on Radiological Protection Ser.: 99). (ENG., Illus.). 200p. per. 176.00 *(978-0-08-044958-6(1)*, Elsevier) Elsevier - Health Sciences Div.

International Labor Office. Approaches to Attribution of Detrimental Health Effects to Occupational Ionizing Radiation Exposure & Their Application in Compensation Programmes for Cancer: Occupational Safety & Health Series, No. 73. 2010. (ENG.). 140p. pap. 32.00 *(978-92-2-122413-6(9))* International Labour Office.

McTiernan, Anne. Physical Activity, Dietary Calorie Restriction, & Cancer. 2011. (Illus.). viii, 186p. E-Book ***(978-1-4419-7551-5(9))*** Springer.

—Physical Activity, Dietary Calorie Restriction, & Cancer. McTiernan, Anne, ed. 2010. (Energy Balance & Cancer Ser.). (Illus.). viii, 186p. 189.00 *(978-1-4419-7550-8(0)*, 1441975500) Springer.

Mozersky, Jessica. Risky Genes: Genetics, Breast Cancer, & Jewish Identity. 2012. (Genetics & Society Ser.). (ENG.). 200p. (C). 135.00 ***(978-0-415-50228-3(4))*** Routledge.

Obe, Günter, et al, eds. Cancer Risk Evaluation: Methods & Trends. 2011. (ENG., Illus.). 366p. 99.95 *(978-3-527-32753-9(3)*, Wiley-VCH) Wiley, John & Sons, Inc.

Piver, M. Steven & Eltabbakh, Gamal. Myths & Facts about Ovarian Cancer: What You Need to Know. 2007. 10.95 *(978-1-891483-52-3(8))* PRR, Inc.

Schrijvers, Dirk, ed. ESMO Handbook of Cancer in the Senior Patient. 2010. 168p. pap. 99.00 *(978-1-84184-709-2(7)*, Informa Healthcare) Taylor & Francis Group.

Suba, Zsuzsanna. Estrogen Versus Cancer. 2008. 89.00 *(978-1-60456-949-0(2))* Nova Science Pubs., Inc.

CANCER—SOCIAL ASPECTS

Carpentier, Melissa Y. & Mullins, Larry Lee. Adolescents with Cancer: The Influence of Close Relationships on Quality of Life, Distress, & Health Behaviors. 2008. 172p. 94.95 *(978-1-60497-580-2(6))* Cambria Pr.

Colditz, Graham A., ed. Encyclopedia of Cancer & Society, 3 vols., Set. 2007. 1616p. 395.00 *(978-1-4129-4989-7(0)*, B49890C) SAGE Pubns., Inc.

Davis, Cindy. Oncology Social Work Practice in the Care of Breast & Ovarian Cancer Survivors. 2008. 79.00 *(978-1-60692-594-2(6))* Nova Science Pubs., Inc.

Gibbon, Sahra. Breast Cancer Genes & the Gendering of Knowledge: Science & Citizenship in the Cultural Context of the 'New' Genetics. 2007. (ENG.). 256p. 100.00 *(978-1-4039-9901-6(5))* Palgrave Macmillan.

King, Cynthia R. Quality of Life: From Nursing & Patient Perspectives. 3rd rev. ed. 2011. 570p. (C). pap. 72.95 *(978-0-7637-4943-9(5))* Jones & Bartlett Learning, LLC.

Knaul, Felicia, et al. Closing the Cancer Divide: An Equity Imperative. Knaul, Felicia et al, eds. 2012. (Global Health & Equity Ser.). (ENG., Illus.). 250p. pap. 24.95 ***(978-0-9829144-0-3(7))*** Harvard Univ. Pr.

Levy, Sandra M. Behavior & Cancer: Life-Style & Psychological Factors in the Initiation & Progression of Cancer. 2011. 280p. pap. 20.95 *(978-1-4502-8602-2(X))* iUniverse, Inc.

Lowy, Ilana. A Woman's Disease: The history of cervical Cancer. 2011. (ENG.). 256p. 24.95 ***(978-0-19-954881-1(1))*** Oxford Univ. Pr., Inc.

Matthias, Mary E. Will There Be Cows In Heaven? 2010. 140p. pap. 13.95 *(978-1-935097-67-9(9))* Hillcrest Publishing Group, Inc.

McMullin, Juliet Marie & Weiner, Diane, eds. Confronting Cancer: Metaphors, Inequality, & Advocacy. 2009. (School for Advanced Research Advanced Seminar Ser.). pap. 29.95 *(978-1-934691-09-0(7))* School for Advanced Research Pr./SAR Pr.

Miller, Suzanne M. Handbook of Cancer Control & Behavioral Science: A Resource for Researchers, Practitioners, & Policy Makers. 2008. 592p. 49.95 *(978-1-4338-0358-1(5))* American Psychological Assn.

Page, Ann E. K., ed. Cancer Care for the Whole Patient: Meeting Psychosocial Health Needs. 2008. (ENG., Illus.). 456p. 46.95 *(978-0-309-11107-2(2))* National Academies Pr.

Panno, Joseph. Cancer. 2nd rev. ed. 2010. (New Biology Ser.). (Illus.). 264p. (gr. 6-12). 40.00 *(978-0-8160-6848-7(8))* Facts On File, Inc.

Sulik, Gayle A. Pink Ribbon Blues. 2012. (ENG., Illus.). 440p. pap. 21.95 ***(978-0-19-993399-0(5))*** Oxford Univ. Pr., Inc.

CANCER—STATISTICS

Attributable Causes of Cancer in France in the Year 2000: IARC Working Group Report, No. 3. 2007. (IARC Nonserial Publication). pap. 22.50 *(978-92-832-2443-3(4))* World Health Organization.

Crowley, John & Hoering, Antje, eds. Handbook of Statistics in Clinical Oncology, Third Edition. 3rd rev. ed. 2012. (ENG., Illus.). 657p. 119.95 *(978-1-4398-6200-1(1),* Chapman & Hall/CRC) CRC Pr. LLC.

De Andrade, Victor, et al. Perceptions of Ototoxicity in Oncology. 2010. 64p. pap. *(978-3-8383-8831-1(3))* Lambert Academic Publishing.

Edwards, B., et al. Cancer Incidence in Five Continents Volume IX. Curador, M. P., ed. 2009. (IARC Scientific Publication No 160 Ser.). (ENG.). 897p. 300.00 *(978-92-832-2160-9(5))* World Health Organization.

Gutiérrez Diez, Pedro J., et al. The Evolution of the Use of Mathematics in Cancer Research. 2012. (ENG., Illus.). xii, 401p. 189.00 ***(978-1-4614-2396-6(1),*** 1461423961) Springer.

International Agency for Research on Cancer Staff. Atlas of Cancer Mortality in the European Union & the European Economic Area, 1993-1997. Boyle, P., ed. 2009. (IARC Scientific Publication No 159 Ser.). (Illus.). 260p. pap. 30.00 *(978-92-832-2159-3(1))* World Health Organization.

Kelly, William Kevin & Halabi, Susan. Oncology Clinical Trials. 2009. 379.00 *(978-1-933864-38-9(9))* Demos Medical Publishing, LLC.

Office for National Statistics Staff. Cancer Statistics. Date not set. (Illus.). iv, 72p. *(978-0-11-621247-4(0))* Stationery Office, The GBR. Dist: Balogh International, Inc.

Shankar, Udaya. A Fight Without Choice: A Cancer Survivor's Journey from Shock to Treatment to Recovery. 2008. 196p. pap. 24.95 *(978-1-60703-097-3(7))* PublishAmerica, Inc.

Tajima, K., et al, eds. Cancer Mortality & Morbidity Statistics Vol. 51: Japan & the World-2004. (Gann Monograph on Cancer Research Ser.). (Illus.). 8;34p. *(978-3-8055-7747-2(8))* Karger, S. AG.

Wiuf, Carsten & Andersen, Claus L., eds. Statistics & Informatics in Molecular Cancer Research. 2009. (ENG., Illus.). 304p. 85.00 *(978-0-19-953287-2(7))* Oxford Univ. Pr., Inc.

CANCER—STUDY AND TEACHING

American Society of Clinical Oncology Staff, contrib. by. Cancer Prevention: An ASCO Curriculum. 2007. *(978-1-932312-33-1(1))* American Society of Clinical Oncology.

Conner, Lindsey. Learning about Social-Ethical Issues Using Evaluative Constructivism. 2010. 264p. pap. *(978-3-639-22937-0(1))* VDM Verlag Dr. Mueller e.K.

Courtney, Gary D. Carl Janaway - Smartest Bandit of the Cookson Hills. 2008. 364p. pap. 26.15 *(978-1-4259-9588-1(8))* AuthorHouse.

Ohsawa, George. Cancer & the Philosophy of the Far East: Previously Published As Macrobiotics: the Way Healing. Aihara, Herman, ed. 2nd ed. 2011. 148p. pap. 14.95 *(978-0-918860-38-5(5))* Ohsawa, George Macrobiotic Foundation.

CANCER—SURGERY

Audisio. Atlas of Procedures in Surgical. 2009. (Illus.). xxx, 303p. 144.00 *(978-981-283-293-1(9))* World Scientific Publishing Co., Inc.

Bartlett, David, et al. Surgical Oncology. 2012. (ENG., Illus.). 632p. (C). 149.00 ***(978-0-07-178610-2(4),*** 0071786104) McGraw-Hill Professional Publishing.

Bolognese, Antonio & Izzo, Luciano. Surgery in Multimodal Management of Solid Tumors. 2008. (Updates in Surgery Ser.). (Illus.). 250p. 119.00 *(978-88-470-1084-0(5))* Springer.

Bristow, Robert E., et al. Surgery for Ovarian Cancer: Principles & Practice. 2nd rev. ed. 2010. (ENG., Illus.). 460p. *(978-1-84184-706-1(2))* Informa Healthcare.

Butler, Charles E. & Fine, Neil A., eds. Principles of Cancer Reconstructive Surgery. 2008. (Illus.). 267p. 149.00 *(978-0-387-49502-6(9),* 0387495029) Springer.

Carr, Brian I. Hepatocellular Carcinoma: Diagnosis & Treatment. 2nd ed. 2009. (Current Clinical Oncology Ser.). (ENG., Illus.). xvi, 748p. 219.00 *(978-1-60327-373-2(5),* 1603273735) Humana Pr.

Chaudry, M. Asif & Winslet, Marc Christopher, eds. Surgical Oncology. 2009. (Oxford Specialist Handbooks series in Surgery Ser.). (ENG., Illus.). 672p. pap. 89.95 *(978-0-19-923709-8(3))* Oxford Univ. Pr., Inc.

Curley, Steven A. Ablative Procedures in Surgical Oncology, an Issue of Surgical Oncology Clinics. 2011. (Clinics: Surgery Ser.: 20-2). (ENG., Illus.). 208p. 110.00 *(978-1-4557-0511-5(X),* Saunders) Elsevier - Health Sciences Div.

DeMatteo, Ronald P. & Yopp, Adam C. Randomized Clinical Trials in Surgical Oncology, an Issue of Surgical Oncology Clinics. 2009. (Clinics: Surgery Ser.: 19-1). (ENG., Illus.). xx, 234p. 105.00 *(978-1-4377-1878-2(7),* Saunders) Elsevier - Health Sciences Div.

Donald, Paul J. The Difficult Case in Head & Neck Cancer Surgery. 2010. (ENG.). 560p. 209.99 *(978-0-86577-984-6(8))* Thieme Medical Pubs., Inc.

Droller, Michael J., ed. Bladder Cancer: Current Diagnosis & Treatment. 2010. (Current Clinical Urology Ser.). (Illus.). 472p. pap. 169.00 *(978-1-61737-202-5(1),* 1617372021) Humana Pr.

El-Baz, Ayman S., et al, eds. Multi Modality State-of-the-Art Medical Image Segmentation & Registration Methodologies: Volume 1. 2011. (ENG., Illus.). xii, 410p. 239.00 *(978-1-4419-8194-3(2),* 1441981942) Springer.

—Multi Modality State-of-the-Art Medical Image Segmentation & Registration Methodologies: Volume II. 2011. (ENG., Illus.). x, 368p. 209.00 *(978-1-4419-8203-2(5),* 1441982035) Springer.

Fitoussi, A., et al. Oncoplastic & Reconstructive Surgery for Breast Cancer: The Institut Curie Experience. 2009. (ENG., Illus.). xi, 150p. 159.00 *(978-3-642-00143-7(2),* 3642001432) Springer.

Geschwind, Jean-François H. & Soulen, Michael C., eds. Interventional Oncology: Principles & Practice. 2008. (ENG., Illus.). 636p. 168.00 *(978-0-521-86413-8(5))* Cambridge Univ. Pr.

Greene, Frederick L. Surgical Oncology in the Community Cancer Center, an Issue of Surgical Oncology Clinics. 2011. (Clinics: Surgery Ser.: 20-3). (ENG., Illus.). 208p. 110.00 *(978-1-4557-0803-1(8),* Saunders) Elsevier - Health Sciences Div.

Greene, Frederick L. & Heniford, B. Todd, eds. Minimally Invasive Cancer MGMT. 2nd ed. 2009. (Illus.). 385p. 179.00 *(978-1-4419-1237-4(1))* Springer.

Guglielmi, Alfredo, et al, eds. Surgical Treatment of Hilar & Intrahepatic Cholangiocarcinoma. 2007. (Updates in Surgery Ser.). (Illus.). 241p. per. 159.00 *(978-88-470-0728-4(3))* Springer.

Guillem, Jose. Surgical Oncology Clinics of North America: Colorectal Cancer. 2010. (Clinics: Surgery Ser.: 19-4). (ENG., Illus.). xvi, 694p. 105.00 *(978-1-4377-2618-3(6),* Saunders) Elsevier - Health Sciences Div.

Hayat, M. A., ed. Stem Cells & Cancer Stem Cells Vol. 1: Therapeutic Applications in Disease & Injury. 2011. (Stem Cells & Cancer Stem Cells Ser.). (ENG., Illus.). xv, 198p. 189.00 *(978-94-007-1708-4(3),* 9400717083) Springer.

Hayat, M. A., ed. Stem Cells & Cancer Stem Cells Vol. 2: Therapeutic Applications in Disease & Injury. 2011. (Stem Cells & Cancer Stem Cells Ser.: Vol. 2). (ENG., Illus.). xxiv, 384p. 209.00 ***(978-94-007-2015-2(7),*** 9400720157) Springer.

Henderson, John Warren, et al. Henderson's Orbital Tumors. 4th rev. ed. 2006. (ENG., Illus.). 404p. 249.99 *(978-0-7817-3869-9(5))* Lippincott Williams & Wilkins.

Hinkelbein, W., et al, eds. Controversies in the Treatment of Lung Cancer: 12th International Symposium on Special Aspects of Radiotherapy, Berlin, October 2008. 2009. (Frontiers of Radiation Therapy & Oncology Ser.). (Illus.). 214p. *(978-3-8055-9298-7(1))* Karger, S. AG.

Jois, Ramesh. Preoperative Assessment of the Elderly Cancer Patients. 2010. (Illus.). 168p. pap. *(978-3-639-23337-7(9))* VDM Verlag Dr. Mueller e.K.

Kaminishi, M., ed. Surgical Treatment for Digestive Cancer in Japan. 2007. (Illus.). 66p. pap. *(978-3-8055-8274-2(9))* Karger, S. AG.

King, Christopher R., et al, eds. Robotic Radiosurgery Treating Prostate Cancer & Related Genitourinary Applications. 2011. (ENG., Illus.). xx, 245p. 179.00 *(978-3-642-11494-6(6),* 3642114946) Springer.

Krasna, Mark. Lung Cancer, an Issue of Surgical Oncology Clinics. 2011. (Clinics: Surgery Ser.: 20-4). (ENG., Illus.). xvi, 606p. 110.00 ***(978-1-4557-0804-8(6),*** Saunders) Elsevier - Health Sciences Div.

Krebser, Eldred. Cancer, Thirty One Days. 2011. 124p. pap. 15.36 *(978-1-4520-8420-6(3))* AuthorHouse.

Langer, Matthias & Schäfer, Arnd-Oliver. MRI of Rectal Cancer. 2008. (Illus.). 250p. 189.00 *(978-3-540-72832-0(5),* 3540728325) Springer.

Losken, Albert & Hamdi, Moustapha. Partial Breast Reconstruction: Techniques in Oncoplastic Surgery. 2008. *(978-1-57626-283-2(9))* Quality Medical Publishing, Inc.

Löwy, Ilana. Preventive Strikes: Women, Precancer, & Prophylactic Surgery. 2009. (ENG., Illus.). 344p. (gr. 17). 52.00 *(978-0-8018-9364-3(X))* Johns Hopkins Univ. Pr.

Mamounas, Terry B. & Mamounas, Eleftherios P. Early-Stage Breast Cancer - New Developments & Controversies: Surgical Oncology Clinics. 2010. (Clinics: Surgery Ser.: 19-3). (ENG., Illus.). xvi, 465p. 105.00 *(978-1-4377-2617-6(8),* Saunders) Elsevier - Health Sciences Div.

Mariani, Giuliano, et al, eds. Radioguided Surgery: A Comprehensive Team Approach. 2007. (Illus.). 297p. 179.00 *(978-0-387-33684-8(2),* 0387336842) Springer.

Matteotti, R. & Ashley, S. M. Minimally Invasive Surgical Oncology. 2010. (Illus.). 300p. 239.00 *(978-3-540-45018-4(1),* 3540450181) Springer.

Mussa, Antonio. New Technologies in Surgical Oncology. 2009. (Updates in Surgery Ser.). (Illus.). xx, 172p. 139.00 *(978-88-470-1474-9(3),* 8847014743) Springer.

Pasechnikov, Victor D., ed. Gastric Cancer: Diagnosis, Early Prevention, & Treatment. 2010. (Cancer Etiology, Diagnosis & Treatments Ser.). 130.50 *(978-1-61668-313-9(9),* Nova Biomedical Bks.) Nova Science Pubs., Inc.

Pazdur, Richard, et al, eds. Cancer Management: A Multidisciplinary Approach Medical, Surgical, & Radiation Oncology. 2007. 1000p. pap. 59.95 *(978-1-891483-48-6(X))* PRR, Inc.

Poston, Graeme J., et al, eds. Textbook of Surgical Oncology. 2007. (ENG., Illus.). 448p. 250.00 *(978-1-84184-507-4(8),* Informa Healthcare) Taylor & Francis Group GBR. Dist: Taylor & Francis Group.

Prymak, Caroline, et al. Small Animal Oncology: An Introduction. 2009. (ENG., Illus.). 304p. 118.00 *(978-0-7020-2800-7(2),* Saunders) Elsevier - Health Sciences Div.

Saclarides, Theodore J., et al, eds. Surgical Oncology: An Algorithmic Approach. 2010. (Illus.). xxix, 778p. pap. 349.00 *(978-1-4419-2907-5(X),* 144192907X) Springer.

Scardino, Peter. Focal Therapy in Prostate Cancer. Emberton, Mark et al, eds. 2012. (ENG., Illus.). 200p. 124.95 ***(978-1-4051-9649-9(1),*** Wiley-Blackwell) Wiley, John & Sons, Inc.

Shockney. Breast Cancer Surgery. rev. ed. 2011. 149.95 *(978-0-7637-7910-8(5))* Jones & Bartlett Learning, LLC.

Silberman, Howard & Silberman, Allan W., eds. Principles & Practice of Surgical Oncology: A Multidisciplinary Approach to Difficult Problems. 2009. (ENG.). 1200p. 248.99 *(978-0-7817-6546-6(3))* Lippincott Williams & Wilkins.

Snow, Stephen N., et al. Atlas of Skin Cancers Processed by Frozen Sections & Mohs Surgery. 2008. (ENG., Illus.). 354p. 125.00 *(978-1-4276-2318-8(X))* Univ. of Wisconsin Pr.

Spiliotis, John D. & Tepetes, Konstantinos. Cancer Surgery in the Elderly. 2011. (Cancer Etiology, Diagnosis & Treatments Aging Issues, Health & Financial Alternatives Ser.). 354p. 145.00 *(978-1-61209-574-5(7))* Nova Science Pubs., Inc.

Tajima, Yoshitsugu, et al, eds. Hepatobiliary & Pancreatic Carcinogenesis in the Hamster. (ENG., Illus.). xi, 241p. 2010. pap. 189.00 *(978-4-431-99859-4(4),* 4431998594) 2009. 189.00 *(978-4-431-87772-1(X),* 443187772X) Springer.

Xu, Kecheng, et al. Modern Cryosurgery for Cancer. 2012. 900p. 198.00 ***(978-981-4329-65-1(7))*** World Scientific Publishing Co., Inc.

CANCER—TREATMENT

see also Cancer—Diet Therapy

Abel, Emily K. & Subramanian, Saskia K. After the Cure: The Untold Stories of Breast Cancer Survivors. 2008. (ENG.). 208p. 50.00 *(978-0-8147-0725-8(4))* New York Univ. Pr.

Abrams, Donald, et al. Integrative Oncology. 2009. (Weil Integrative Medicine Library). (ENG., Illus.). 350p. 36.99 *(978-0-19-530944-7(8))* Oxford Univ. Pr., Inc.

Adjei, Alex A., ed. Lung Cancer Therapies. 2009. (Cancer Drug Discovery & Development Ser.). 135.00 *(978-1-60327-010-6(8))* Humana Pr.

Ahamed, Shaik Imran. Diagnosis & Treatment of Cancer Using Nanotechnology. 2010. 68p. pap. *(978-3-8383-8174-9(2))* Lambert Academic Publishing.

Alaoui-Jamali, Moulay. Alternative & Complementary Therapies for Cancer. 2010. (Illus.). xx, 722p. pap., instr.'s gde. ed. 49.95 *(978-1-4419-0019-7(5),* 1441900195) Springer.

Alshenawy, Hanan. Immunohistochemical Study of Her-2/Neu & E-Cadherin in Colon Carcinom. 2011. 220p. pap. ***(978-3-8433-9411-6(3))*** Lambert Academic Publishing.

American Cancer Society Staff. Breast Cancer: The Essential Guide to Your Breast Cancer Journey. 3rd ed. 2009. (ENG.). 400p. pap., instr.'s gde. ed. 24.95 *(978-0-944235-90-4(5),* 0944235905) American Cancer Society, Inc.

—Complementary & Alternative Cancer Methods: The Essential Guide for You & Your Doctor. 2nd ed. 2009. (American Cancer Society Complete Guide T Ser.). (ENG.). 893p. pap. 24.95 *(978-0-944235-71-3(9),* 9780944235713) American Cancer Society, Inc.

American Society of Clinical Oncology (ASCO). Antiemetics for Cancer Treatment GUIDELINES Pocketcard (2012) 2011. (ENG.). 10p. spiral bd. 9.95 ***(978-0-9846667-3-7(7))*** International Guidelines Ctr., Inc.

Ames, Dave. Me, My Cells & I: A Survivor's Seriously Funny Guide to the Science of Cancer. 2011. (ENG.). 332p. pap. 18.95 *(978-1-59181-173-2(2))* Sentient Pubns.

Amiji, Mansoor M., ed. Nanotechnology for Cancer Therapy. 2006. (ENG., Illus.). 840p. 205.95 *(978-0-8493-7194-3(5),* CRC Press) Taylor & Francis Group GBR. Dist: Taylor & Francis Group.

Anthuber, Matthias & Spatz, Johann. Laparoscopic Total Mesorectal Excision. 2010. (Operation Primers Ser.). (ENG., Illus.). x, 106p. pap. 49.95 *(978-3-642-04730-5(0),* 3642047300) Springer.

Avendano, Carmen & Menendez, J. Carlos. Medicinal Chemistry of Anticancer Drugs. 2008. (ENG., Illus.). 400p. 195.00 *(978-0-444-52824-7(5),* Elsevier Science) Elsevier Science & Technology Bks.

Azoulay, Élie, ed. Pulmonary Involvement in Patients with Hematological Malignancies. 2011. (Illus.). xix, 827p. 279.00 *(978-3-642-15741-7(6),* 3642157416) Springer.

Bal, Harshawardhan & Hujol, Johnny. Java for Bioinformatics & Biomedical Applications. 2010. (ENG., Illus.). xviii, 342p. pap. 115.00 *(978-1-4419-4245-6(9),* 1441942459) Springer.

Bard, Robert L. Prostate Cancer Decoded: Non-Invasive Breakthrough Treatments. 2007. (ENG., Illus.). 168p. per. 17.95 *(978-1-60037-346-6(1))* Morgan James Publishing.

Baronzio, Gianfranco & Hager, E. Dieter, eds. Hyperthermia in Cancer Treatment: A Primer. 2006. (Medical Intelligence Unit Ser.). (Illus.). xxiii, 366p. 259.00 *(978-0-387-33440-0(8),* 0387334408) Springer.

Barraclough, Jennifer. Enhancing Cancer Care: Complementary Therapy & Support. 2007. (ENG., Illus.). 224p. per. 59.95 *(978-0-19-929755-9(X))* Oxford Univ. Pr., Inc.

Barry, Michael S. & Barry, Michael. The Art of Caregiving: How to Lend Support & Encouragement to Those with Cancer. 2007. (ENG.). 160p. 14.99 *(978-0-7814-4430-9(6))* Cook, David C.

Bayor, Marcel. The Bioactivity of Croton Membranaceus - a Traditional Anticancer Herb. 2011. 272p. pap. ***(978-3-8433-8695-1(1))*** Lambert Academic Publishing.

Becker, Kim & Becker, Mike. Hello Gorgeous! A Journey of Faith, Love & Hope. 2011. 208p. pap. 19.95 ***(978-0-9833586-4-0(8))*** Corby Books.

Berkowitz, Ross S. Gynecologic Cancer, an Issue of Hematology/Oncology Clinics of North America. 2012. (Clinics: Internal Medicine Ser.: 26-1). (ENG., Illus.). 1440p. 109.00 ***(978-1-4557-3874-8(3),*** Saunders) Elsevier - Health Sciences Div.

Berman, Jeff, et al. The Force Program: The Proven Way to Fight Cancer through Physical Activity & Exercise. 2006. 189p. reprint ed. 24.00 *(978-1-4223-5242-7(0))* DIANE Publishing Co.

Berman, Jules J. Precancer: The Beginning & the End of Cancer. 2009. (Illus.). 186p. pap. 56.95 *(978-0-7637-7784-5(6))* Jones & Bartlett Learning, LLC.

Bernier, Jacques, ed. Head & Neck Cancer: Multimodality Management. 2011. (ENG., Illus.). xx, 710p. 239.00 *(978-1-4419-9463-9(7),* 1441994637) Springer.

Bertolotti, Roger. Autologous & Cancer Stem Cell Gene Therapy. 2007. (Progress in Gene Therapy Ser.: Vol. 3). 205.00 *(978-981-277-586-3(2))* World Scientific Publishing Co., Inc.

Bettuzzi, Saverio & Pucci, Sabina. Clusterin, 2 vols. 2009. (Advances in Cancer Research Ser.). (ENG., Illus.). 350p. 161.00 *(978-0-12-374772-3(4),* Academic Pr.) Elsevier Science & Technology Bks.

Betty Crocker Editors, et al. Betty Crocker Living with Cancer Cookbook. 2011. (ENG., Illus.). 288p. pap. 19.99 *(978-1-118-08314-7(8),* Betty Crocker) Wiley, John & Sons, Inc.

Biava, Pier Mario. Cancer & the Search for Lost Meaning: The Discovery of a Revolutionary New Cancer Treatment. 2009. (ENG., Illus.). 168p. pap. 15.95 *(978-1-55643-778-6(1))* North Atlantic Bks.

Blake, Lynnette. The Heavenly cure for Cancer... Is there One? 2009. 126p. pap. 18.29 *(978-0-557-19538-1(1))* Lulu Enterprises Inc.

Blizzard, Merlon. Help! My Child Has Cancer: My Angel on Loan. 2009. 136p. 22.49 *(978-1-4389-4286-5(9))*; pap. 11.99 *(978-1-4389-4285-8(0))* AuthorHouse.

Bodai, Ernie. I Flunked My PSA! What You Need to Know about Prostate Cancer Now! pap. 11.95 *(978-0-9712070-1-1(1))* B2Z Publishing, Inc.

Bolla, Michel & Poppel, Hendrik van, eds. Management of Prostate Cancer: A Multidisciplinary Approach. 2012. (ENG., Illus.). viii, 334p. 159.00 ***(978-3-642-27596-8(6),*** 3642275966) Springer.

Bombardieri, E., et al. Breast Cancer: Nuclear Medicine in Diagnosis & Therapeutic Options. Bombardieri, Emilio et al, eds. 2007. (Illus.). 299p. 179.00 *(978-3-540-36780-2(2))* Springer.

Bosanquet, Nicholas & Sikora, Karol. The Economics of Cancer Care. 2010. (ENG.). 192p. pap. 39.99 *(978-0-521-18380-2(4))* Cambridge Univ. Pr.

Bot, Adrian & Obrocea, Mihail, eds. Cancer Vaccines: Challenges & Opportunities in Translation. 2008. (Translational Medicine Ser.: Vol. 6). (ENG., Illus.). 232p. 230.00 *(978-1-4200-5467-5(8),* Informa Healthcare) Taylor & Francis Group GBR. Dist: Taylor & Francis Group.

Boyiadzis, Michael, et al. Hematology-Oncology Therapy, Second Edition. 2nd ed. 2012. (ENG.). 1008p. pap. 99.00 *(978-0-07-163789-3(3),* 0071637893) McGraw-Hill Professional Publishing.

Brahmer, Julie R., et al, eds. Lung Cancer: Translational & Emerging Therapies. 2007. (Translational Medicine Ser.: Vol. 3). (ENG., Illus.). 280p. 100.00 *(978-0-8493-9021-0(4),* Informa Healthcare) Taylor & Francis Group GBR. Dist: Taylor & Francis Group.

Branson, Joyce. The Ones That Got Away: Seventeen Years of Fishing with Kids Who Have Cancer. 2011. 156p. pap. 15.99 *(978-1-4520-9803-6(4))* AuthorHouse.

Breen, Michael. Medical Image Guided Thermal Ablation. 2008. 100p. pap. *(978-3-8364-6880-0(8))* VDM Verlag Dr. Mueller e.K.

Broom, et al. Therapeutic Pluralism: Exploring the Experiences of Cancer Patients & Professionals. (Illus.). 2008. (ENG.). 168p. (C). 150.00 *(978-0-415-39852-7(5))* 2007. 192p. 47.95 *(978-0-415-39853-4(3))* Routledge.

Brown, Ellen Hodgson. Forbidden Medicine. 2008. pap. *(978-0-9795608-3-5(7))* Third Millennium Pr.

Budwig, Johanna & Himeise, Nexus. Cancer - the Problem & the Solution. 2008. 127p. pap. 14.90 *(978-3-9810502-1-9(5))* Nexus Himeise - Handels GmbH DEU. Dist: AtlasBooks Distribution.

Bukowski, Ronald M. & Novick, Andrew, eds. Clinical Management of Renal Tumors. 2010. (Illus.). xviii, 665p. pap. 99.95 *(978-1-60761-469-2(3),* 1607614693) Humana Pr.

Burnett, Arthur L., II & Morris, Norman. Prostate Cancer Survivors Speak Their Minds: Advice on Options, Treatments, & Aftereffects. 2010. (ENG.). 256p. pap. 16.95 *(978-0-470-57881-0(5),* Wiley) Wiley, John & Sons, Inc.

Burns, Catherine. Patients with Advanced Cancer. 2010. 284p. pap. *(978-3-8383-1272-9(4))* Lambert Academic Publishing.

Cagle, Philip T., et al, eds. Molecular Pathology of Lung Cancer. 2012. (Molecular Pathology Library: 6). (ENG., Illus.). xii, 244p. 189.00 ***(978-1-4614-3196-1(4),*** 1461431964) Springer.

Calbom, Cherie, et al. The Complete Cancer Cleanse: A Proven Program to Detoxify & Renew Body, Mind, & Spirit, 0 vols. 2007. 352p. pap. 14.99 *(978-0-7852-8863-3(5))* Nelson, Thomas Inc.

Calderwood, Stuart K., et al, eds. Heat Shock Proteins in Cancer. (Heat Shock Proteins Ser.). 2010. x, 406p. pap. 239.00 *(978-90-481-7627-4(1),* 9048176271) 2007. (Illus.). 398p. 239.00 *(978-1-4020-6400-5(4))* Springer.

Cancer: Challenges & Opportunities in the 21st Century: Hearing Before the Committee on Health, Education, Labor, & Pensions, United States Senate, One Hundred Tenth Congress, Second Session, on Examining Cancer Relating to Challenges & Opportunities in the 21st Century, May 8, 2008. 2010. iii, 72p. *(978-0-16-085135-3(1),* 552-070-40489-9) United States Government Printing Office.

Carlson, Linda & Speca, Michael. Mindfulness-Based Cancer Recovery: A Step-by-Step MBSR Approach to Help You Cope with Treatment & Reclaim Your Life. 2011. (ENG.). 200p. pap. 17.95 *(978-1-57224-887-8(4))* New Harbinger Pubns.

Carmen Mejia Vazquez, Dra Ma Del & Navarro, Samuel. New Approaches in the Treatment of Cancer. 2011. (Cancer Etiology, Diagnosis & Treatments Ser.). 223p. pap. 79.00 ***(978-1-62100-067-9(2))*** Nova Science Pubs., Inc.

Carter, Albert E. The Cancer Answer. 252p. *(978-0-9619041-1-1(9))* ALM Pubs.

Carter, Ann & Mackereth, Peter A. Massage & Bodywork: Adapting Therapies for Cancer Care. 2006. (ENG., Illus.). 216p. pap. 55.95 *(978-0-443-10031-4(4),* Churchill Livingstone) Elsevier - Health Sciences Div.

Cassileth. Herb-Drug Interactions in Oncology. 2nd ed. 2010. (Illus.). 680p. pap. *(978-1-60795-041-7(3))* PMPH-USA, Ltd.

Cassileth, Barrie R. The Complete Guide to Complementary Therapies in Cancer Care: Essential Information for Patients, Survivors & Health Professionals. 2011. 350p. pap. 39.00 ***(978-981-4335-16-4(9))*** World Scientific Publishing Co., Inc.

Cellular Therapy of Cancer: Development of Gene Therapy Based Approaches. 2011. 96.00 *(978-981-4295-13-0(2))* World Scientific Publishing Co., Inc.

Cham, Bill E. The Eggplant Cancer Cure: A Treatment for Skin Cancer & New Hope for Other Cancers from Nature's Pharmacy. 2008. (ENG., Illus.). 132p. 24.95 *(978-1-890572-21-1(7))* Smart Pubns.

Chamberlain, Jonathan. Cancer Recovery Guide: 15 Alternative & Complementary Strategies for Restoring Health. 2008. 176p. pap. *(978-1-905570-14-0(7))* Clairview Bks.

Chan, Bernard & Halpern, Georges M. The Yin & Yang of Cancer: Breakthroughs from the East & the West. 2007. (ENG.). 224p. pap. 15.95 *(978-0-7570-0207-6(2))* Square One Pubs.

Chan, Helen S. L. Understanding Cancer Therapies. 2007. (ENG.). 213p. 30.00 *(978-1-57806-688-9(3));* per. 14.00 *(978-1-57806-689-6(1))* Univ. Pr. of Mississippi.

Chaplin, Joyce. The First Scientific American: Benjamin Franklin & the Pursuit of Genius. 2007. (ENG., Illus.). 432p. per. 17.50 *(978-0-465-00956-5(5))* Basic Bks.

Chatwin, et al. Complementary & Alter Med Cancer. 2007. (Illus.). 192p. 150.00 *(978-0-415-35993-1(7))* Routledge.

Cho, William C. S., ed. Evidence-based Anticancer Herbal Medicine. 2011. (Evidence-based Anticancer Complementary & Alternative Medicine Ser.). (Illus.). xii, 441p. 209.00 *(978-94-007-0525-8(5),* 9400705255) Springer.

—Materia Medica for Various Cancers. 2011. (Evidence-based Anticancer Complementary & Alternative Medicine Ser.). (ENG., Illus.). xii, 406p. 209.00 ***(978-94-007-1982-8(5),*** 9400719825) Springer.

Cho, William C. S., ed. Supportive Cancer Care with Chinese Medicine. 2010. (ENG., Illus.). viii, 379p. 179.00 *(978-90-481-3554-7(0),* 9048135540) Springer.

Chu, Edward. Pocket Guide to Targeted Therapies in Cancer. rev. ed. 2012. 80p. spiral bd. 31.95 *(978-0-7637-8535-2(0))* Jones & Bartlett Learning, LLC.

Chu, Edward, ed. Multidisciplinary Treatment of Early Colorectal Cancer: A Monograph/AudioCD. 2007. (Illus.). 160p. pap. 24.95 *(978-1-891483-54-7(4))* PRR, Inc.

—New Treatment Strategies for Metastatic Colorectal Cancer. 2008. (Illus.). 96p. pap. 19.95 *(978-1-891483-57-8(9))* PRR, Inc.

Chung, Leland W. K., et al, eds. Prostate Cancer: Biology, Genetics, & the New Therapeutics. 2008. 532p. pap. 99.00 ***(978-1-60327-510-1(X))*** Springer.

Cleeland, Charles S., et al, eds. Cancer Symptom Science: Measurement, Mechanisms, & Management. 2010. (ENG., Illus.). 376p. 120.00 *(978-0-521-86901-0(3))* Cambridge Univ. Pr.

Cohen, Lorenzo & Markman, Maurie. Integrative Oncology: Incorporating Complementary Medicine into Conventional Cancer Care. 2008. (Current Clinical Oncology Ser.). (Illus.). 216p. 109.00 *(978-1-58829-869-0(8))* Humana Pr.

Coles, L. Stephen. Extraordinary Healing: Restoring Health with the Discoveries of Mirko Beljanski, the World's First Molecular Biologist. 2011. (ENG.). 148p. pap. 15.95 *(978-1-893910-89-8(X))* Freedom Pr., Inc., The.

Colotta, Francesco & Mantovani, Alberto, eds. Targeted Therapies in Cancer: Myth or Reality? 2008. (Advances in Experimental Medicine & Biology Ser.: Vol. 610). (Illus.). 222p. 179.00 *(978-0-387-73897-0(5))* Springer.

—Targeted Therapies in Cancer: Myth or Reality? 2010. (Advances in Experimental Medicine & Biology Ser.). (Illus.). viii, 192p. pap. 179.00 *(978-1-4419-2537-4(6),* 1441925376) Springer.

Conley, Susan. The Foremost Good Fortune. (Vintage Ser.). (ENG., 2012. Illus.). 368p. pap. 15.00 ***(978-0-307-73986-5(4),*** Vintage) 2011. 288p. 25.95 *(978-0-307-59406-8(8),* Knopf) Knopf Doubleday Publishing Group.

Constine, Louis S., ed. Cured I - Lent: Late Effects of Cancer Treatment on Normal Tissues. 2007. (Medical Radiology / Radiation Oncology Ser.). (Illus.). 140p. 129.00 *(978-3-540-49069-2(8),* 3540490698) Springer.

Cpht, Lucille Hall. Cancer Care. 2008. 128p. 30.99 *(978-1-4363-5258-1(4));* pap. 20.99 *(978-1-4363-5257-4(6))* Xlibris Corp.

Cram101 Textbook Reviews. Outlines & Highlights for Emerging Cancer Therapy: Microbial Approaches & Biotechnological Tools by A. Fialho. 2011. 116p. pap. 28.95 ***(978-1-61905-346-5(2))*** Cram101 Inc.

Crocker. Betty Crocker's Living with Cancer Cookbook Custom Mgi. 2007. (ENG.). 256p. 24.95 *(978-0-470-18952-8(5),* Betty Crocker) Wiley, John & Sons, Inc.

Currin, Morag. Oncology Esthetics: A Practitioner's Guide. 2009. x, 461p. pap. ***(978-1-932633-49-8(9))*** Allured Business Media.

Dang, Chau, ed. New Treatment Paradigms in Metastatic Breast Cancer. 2008. (Illus.). 96p. pap. 19.95 *(978-1-891483-61-5(7))* PRR, Inc.

Davies, Andrew. Cancer-Related Bone Pain. 2008. (Oxford Pain Management Library Ser.). (ENG., Illus.). 128p. pap. 26.50 *(978-0-19-921573-7(1))* Oxford Univ. Pr., Inc.

—Cancer Related Breakthrough Pain. Davies, Andrew, ed. 2006. (Oxford Pain Management Library Ser.). (Illus.). 128p. per. 29.95 *(978-0-19-921567-6(7))* Oxford Univ. Pr., Inc.

Davis, Darren W., et al, eds. Antiangiogenic Cancer Therapy. 2007. (ENG., Illus.). 864p. 226.95 *(978-0-8493-2799-5(7),* 2799, CRC Press) Taylor & Francis Group GBR. Dist: Taylor & Francis Group.

Davis, Devra. The Secret History of the War on Cancer. (ENG.). 2009. 560p. pap. 18.95 *(978-0-465-01568-9(9))* 2007. 512p. 27.95 *(978-0-465-00535-2(7))* Basic Bks.

Davis, Phyllis L. Cancer, Now What? 2009. 72p. pap. 10.95 *(978-1-4401-8646-2(4))* iUniverse, Inc.

Dawson, Nancy A. & Kelly, W. Kevin, eds. Prostate Cancer: Translational & Emerging Therapies. 2007. (Translational Medicine Ser.: Vol. 1). (ENG., Illus.). 330p. 200.00 *(978-0-8493-7185-1(6))* Taylor & Francis Group.

De Andrade, Victor, et al. Perceptions of Ototoxicity in Oncology. 2010. 64p. pap. *(978-3-8383-8831-1(3))* Lambert Academic Publishing.

Deligdisch, Liane, et al. Early Pathologic Diagnosis of Gynecologic Cancer Including a Clinician's View. 2008. (Illus.). 200p. 112.00 *(978-981-281-895-9(2))* World Scientific Publishing Co., Inc.

Diaz-Montes, Teresa P. Johns Hopkins Patients' Guide to Uterine Cancer. 2009. (ENG.). 156p. pap. 22.95 *(978-0-7637-7460-8(X))* Jones & Bartlett Learning, LLC.

Ding, Xuanfeng. A New Cancer Therapy. 2010. 92p. pap. *(978-3-8383-5297-8(1))* Lambert Academic Publishing.

Dittmer, Dirk P. & Krown, Susan E., eds. Molecular Basis for Therapy of AIDS-Defining Cancers. 2010. (ENG., Illus.). ccivi, 200p. 179.00 *(978-1-4419-1512-2(5),* 1441915125) Springer.

Dittmer, Dirk Peter & Krown, Susan E. Molecular Basis for Therapy of AIDS-Defining Cancers. 2010. (Illus.). xiii, 256p. E-Book ***(978-1-4419-1513-9(3))*** Springer.

Dobic, Mina. My Beautiful Life: How I Conquered Cancer Naturally. 2007. (ENG., Illus.). 1p. pap. 15.95 *(978-0-7570-0244-1(7))* Square One Pubs.

Doerfler, Walter & Böhm, Petra. DNA Methylation: Basic Mechanisms: Basic Mechanisms. 2010. (Current Topics in Microbiology & Immunology Ser.). (Illus.). viii, 324p. pap. 179.00 *(978-3-642-06708-2(5),* 3642067085) Springer.

Dollinger, Malin, et al. Everyone's Guide to Cancer Therapy: How Cancer Is Diagnosed, Treated, & Managed Day to Day. 5th rev. ed. 2008. (ENG., Illus.). 1024p. pap. 29.99 *(978-0-7407-6857-6(3))* Andrews McMeel Publishing.

Douglas H. Gosling. The Wolf at My Door: Cancer in my Body - Cancer in my Mind. 2009. 240p. pap. 23.95 *(978-1-4251-6536-9(2))* Trafford Publishing.

Doyle Spencer, Monique & Levy, Paul F. How Can I Help? Everyday Ways to Help Your Loved Ones Live with Cancer. 2008. (ENG.). 240p. pap. 12.95 *(978-1-59869-681-3(5))* Adams Media Corp.

Dragos, Pal. Holistic Cancer Therapy. 2009. 54p. pap. *(978-3-8391-0463-7(7))* Books on Demand GmbH.

Dunn, Timothy B. & Holmes, Jennifer E., eds. Encyclopedia of Cancer Treatment, 2 vols. 2011. (Series: Cancer Etiology, Diagnosis & Treatments Ser.). 325.00 *(978-1-61324-448-7(7))* Nova Science Pubs., Inc.

Ehrlich, Ann B. & McMahon, Elizabeth J., eds. Voices of Lymphedema: Stories, advice, & inspiration from patients & Therapists. 2007. 256p. per. *(978-0-9764806-5-5(4))* Lymph Notes.

Eisen, Tim. Renal Cancer. 2010. (ENG., Illus.). 120p. pap. 24.95 *(978-0-19-956231-2(8))* Oxford Univ. Pr., Inc.

ENETS Conference for the Diagnosis & Treatment of Neuroendocrine Tumor Disease: 8th Annual Conference, Lisbon, March 2011: Abstracts. Supplement Issue: Neuroendocrinology 2011, Vol. 94, Suppl. 1' 2011. (ENG.). 54p. pap. ***(978-3-8055-9807-1(6))*** Karger, S. AG.

Ermini, M. & Vijayan, R., eds. Asia Pacific Symposium on Pain Control: 4th Symposium, Kuala Lumpur, November 2007: Proceedings. 2008. (Illus.). 112p. pap. *(978-3-8055-8929-1(8))* Karger, S. AG.

Eshowsky, Myron. Peace with Cancer: Shamanism as a Spiritual Approach to Healing. 2010. 186p. pap. 20.00 *(978-0-9793865-0-3(0))* Shoshana Pubns.

Ettinger, David S. Supportive Care in Cancer Therapy. Ettinger, David S., ed. 2008. (Illus.). 350p. 179.00 *(978-1-58829-941-3(4))* Humana Pr.

Ettinger, David S. & Donehower, Ross, eds. Current Cancer Therapeutics. 5th ed. 496p. 2010. pap. 149.00 *(978-1-57340-277-4(X),* 157340277X) 2008. (Illus.). pap. 159.00 *(978-1-57340-285-9(0),* 1573402850) Current Medicine Group LLC.

Faguet, Guy B. The War on Cancer: An Anatomy of Failure, a Blueprint for the Future. 2008. (ENG., Illus.). xvi, 227p. pap. 29.95 *(978-1-4020-8620-5(2),* 1402086202) Springer.

Falanga, A. & ten Cate, H., eds. The Pathophysiology of Cancer & Thrombosis. 2009. (ENG., Illus.). 108p. pap. *(978-3-8055-9075-4(X))* Karger, S. AG.

Fee, John. The Anaemic Leukaemic: A Message of Hope. 2010. 304p. pap. 15.49 *(978-1-4520-3899-5(6))* AuthorHouse.

Feuerstein, Michael, ed. Handbook of Cancer Survivorship. 2006. (Illus.). 504p. 125.00 *(978-0-387-34561-1(2),* 0387345612) Springer.

Fialho, Arsenio & Chakrabarty, Ananda M., eds. Emerging Cancer Therapy: Microbial Approaches & Biotechnological Tools. 2010. (Wiley Series in Biotechnology & Bioengineering Ser.: 2). (ENG., Illus.). 432p. 132.00 *(978-0-470-44467-2(3),* Wiley) Wiley, John & Sons, Inc.

Field Hearing: Philadelphia VA Terminated Cancer Treatment Program: Hearing Before the Committee on Veterans' Affairs, United States Senate, One Hundred Eleventh Congress, First Session, June 29, 2009. 2010. iii, 75p. *(978-0-16-085194-0(7),* 552-070-40547-0) United States Government Printing Office.

Fikus, Sandra. Getting It off My Chest: A Journey through Breast Cancer. 2011. 166p. 29.99 ***(978-1-4568-8506-9(5));*** pap. 19.99 ***(978-1-4568-8505-2(7))*** Xlibris Corp.

Flores Hermosillo, Bernardo David & Phillips, Roger. Virtual Simulation of Radiotherapy Technology for Cancer Treatment. 2011. 124p. pap. ***(978-3-8443-0070-3(8))*** Lambert Academic Publishing.

Floyd, Jeana. An Uninvited Guest: One Woman's Journey from Cancer to Hope. 2007. (Illus.). 128p. 12.99 *(978-0-89221-664-2(6))* New Leaf Pr., Inc.

Focus Medica Pte Ltd. Colorectal Cancer: An Overview. 2011. 1p. cd-rom 99.00 *(978-981-4284-13-4(0))* Focus Medica Pte Ltd. SGP. Dist: Independent Pubs. Group.

Forbat, Liz, et al. Better Cancer Care: A Systemic Approach to Practice. 2009. (Illus.). 166p. 45.00 *(978-1-906716-09-7(9))* Dunedin Academic Pr. GBR. Dist: International Specialized Bk. Services.

Fortson, Leigh. Embrace, Release, Heal: An Empowering Guide to Talking about, Thinking about, & Treating Cancer. 2011. 300p. pap. 17.95 *(978-1-60407-431-4(0))* Sounds True, Inc.

Frank, David, ed. Signaling Pathways in Cancer Pathogenesis & Therapy. 2011. (ENG., Illus.). viii, 148p. 139.00 ***(978-1-4614-1215-1(3),*** 1461412153) Springer.

Frank, David & Mooney, Bernard. Hypnosis & Counselling in the Treatment of Cancer & Chronic Illness. 2007. Orig. Title: Hypnosis & Counselling in the Treatment of Chronic Illness. 160p. pap. *(978-1-84590-080-9(4))* Crown Hse. Publishing.

Freifeld, Alison. Fever & Neutropenia: In Cancer Patients. 2011. 14p. spiral bd. 11.95 *(978-0-9846290-8-4(4))* International Guidelines Ctr., Inc.

Gale, Robert Peter, et al. Blood Stem Cell Transplants. 2011. (ENG.). 200p. pap. 26.99 ***(978-0-521-11693-0(7))*** Cambridge Univ. Pr.

Garrett-Mayer, Elizabeth, ed. Principles of Anticancer Drug Development. 2010. (Cancer Drug Discovery & Development Ser.). (Illus.). xvii, 250p. 189.00 *(978-1-4419-7357-3(5),* 1441973575) Springer.

Gascón, Pere & Morère, Jean-Francois, eds. The Evolving Role of Erythropoietic Therapy in Patients with Cancer: Proceedings of a Roche-Sponsored Symposium: Berlin, Germany, April 29-May 1, 2005, Vol. 69. (Oncology Ser.: Vol. 69, Suppl. 2). (Illus.). *(978-3-8055-8034-2(7))* Karger, S. AG.

Gautier, Gary Steven. Heal Thyself, Optimum Health Forever. 2011. 332p. 36.95 *(978-1-4567-3551-7(9));* pap. 29.95 *(978-1-4567-4320-8(1))* AuthorHouse.

Gazella, Karolyn A. & Alschuler, Lise. Definitive Guide to Cancer: An Integrative Approach to Prevention, Treatment, & Healing. 3rd ed. 2010. (ENG., Illus.). 496p. pap. 25.00 *(978-1-58761-358-6(1),* Celestial Arts) Ten Speed Pr.

Gearin-Tosh, Michael. Living Proof: A Medical Mutiny. 2007. (ENG.). 336p. pap. 22.95 *(978-1-4165-7751-5(3),* Scribner) Scribner.

Gerber, David E. Targeted Therapy in Non-small Cell Lung Cancer, 1 vol. 2011. (Oxford American Pocket Notes Ser.). (ENG.). 88p. pap. 14.95 ***(978-0-19-974308-7(8))*** Oxford Univ. Pr., Inc.

Gerson, Charlotte & Bishop, Beata. Healing the Gerson Way: Defeating Cancer & Other Chronic Diseases. 1. 2007. 450p. pap. 29.95 *(978-0-9760186-0-5(8))* 2nd rev. ed. 2009. (ENG.). 448p. pap. 29.95 net. *(978-0-9760186-2-9(4))* Gerson Health Media.

—Healing the Gerson Way: Defeating Cancer & Other Chronic Diseases (with Blu-Ray) Shwed, Joanne, ed. & des. by. 2011. 488p. pap. 44.95 ***(978-0-9760186-8-1(3))*** Gerson Health Media.

—Healing the Gerson Way (with DVD) Defeating Cancer & Other Chronic Diseases. Shwed, Joanne, ed. Kroschel, Stephen. 2011. 488p. pap. 39.95 ***(978-0-9760186-9-8(1))*** Gerson Health Media.

Giaccone, Giuseppe, ed. Systemic Treatment of Non-Small Cell Lung Cancer. 2011. (ENG., Illus.). 128p. pap. 24.95 *(978-0-19-958048-4(0))* Oxford Univ. Pr., Inc.

Gioeli, Daniel, ed. Targeted Therapies: Mechanisms of Resistance. 2011. (Molecular & Translational Medicine Ser.). (ENG., Illus.). xiv, 201p. 139.00 ***(978-1-60761-477-7(4),*** 1607614774) Humana Pr.

Giordano, Antonio, et al, eds. Cancer Epigenetics: Biomolecular Therapeutics in Human Cancer. 2011. (ENG., Illus.). 436p. 149.95 *(978-0-471-71096-7(2),* Wiley-Blackwell) Wiley, John & Sons, Inc.

Giordano, Antonio & Normanno, Nicola, eds. Breast Cancer in the Post-Genomic Era. (Current Clinical Oncology Ser.). (ENG., Illus.). xii, 230p. 2010. pap. 99.95 *(978-1-60761-466-1(9),* 1607614669) 2009. 219.00 *(978-1-60327-944-4(X),* 160327944X) Humana Pr.

God Mingled with Us. 2006. (Illus.). 134p. per. 12.99 *(978-1-59886-269-0(3))* Tate Publishing & Enterprises, LLC.

González-Moreno, S. Advances in Peritoneal Surface Oncology. 2010. (Recent Results in Cancer Research Ser.). (Illus.). xiii, 176p. pap. 139.00 *(978-3-642-06802-7(2),* 3642068022) Springer.

Gonzalez, Nicholas J. & Isaacs, Linda L. The Trophoblast & the Origins of Cancer: One solution to the medical enigma of our Time. 2009. (ENG., Illus.). 212p. pap. 49.95 *(978-0-9821965-0-2(4))* New Spring Pr., LLC.

Gonzalez, Salvador, et al, eds. Reflectance Confocal Microscopy of Cutaneous Tumors: An Atlas with Clinical, Dermoscopic & Histological Correlations. 2008. (ENG., Illus.). 292p. 260.00 *(978-0-415-45104-8(3),* Informa Healthcare) Taylor & Francis Group GBR. Dist: Taylor & Francis Group.

Goodman, Jordan & Walsh, Vivien. The Story of Taxol: Nature & Politics in the Pursuit of an Anti-Cancer Drug. 2006. (ENG., Illus.). 300p. pap. 38.99 *(978-0-521-03250-6(4))* Cambridge Univ. Pr.

Gordon, Gavin J. Bioinformatics in Cancer & Cancer Therapy. 2008. (Cancer Drug Discovery & Development Ser.). (Illus.). 192p. 179.00 *(978-1-58829-753-2(5))* Humana Pr.

Gordon, Gavin J., ed. Bioinformatics in Cancer & Cancer Therapy. 2012. (Cancer Drug Discovery & Development Ser.). (ENG., Illus.). x, 192p. pap. 179.00 *(978-1-61737-758-7(9),* 1617377589) Humana Pr.

Govidan, Ramaswamy, ed. New Treatment Strategies in Metastatic Lung Cancer. 2008. (Illus.). 96p. pap. 19.95 *(978-1-891483-58-5(7))* PRR, Inc.

Grobmyer, Stephen R. & Moudgil, Brij M. Cancer Nanotechnology: Methods & Protocols. 2010. (Methods in Molecular Biology Ser.). (Illus.). 376p. 159.00 *(978-1-60761-608-5(4),* 1607616084) Humana Pr.

Gross, Carolyn. Treatable & Beatable: Healing Cancer Without Surgery. 2007. (Illus.). 200p. per. 19.95 *(978-0-9718064-1-2(1))* Creative Living Pubns.

Grubbs, Ronnie. The Psychological Treatment of Couples Confronting Breast Cancer. 2009. 184p. pap. *(978-3-639-11552-9(X))* VDM Verlag Dr. Mueller e.K.

Gruver, Kathy. The Alternative Medicine Cabinet. 2010. pap. 11.95 *(978-0-7414-5903-9(5))* Infinity Publishing.

Gugliotti Pt, Mark. Victor Not Victim: My Battle with Hodgkin's Lymphoma. 2009. 96p. pap. 11.95 *(978-1-4401-3452-4(9))* iUniverse, Inc.

Gutiérrez, Lucía M., ed. Neuro-Oncology & Cancer Targeted Therapy. 2010. (Cancer Etiology, Diagnosis & Treatments Ser.). 275p. 129.00 *(978-1-61668-708-3(8))* Nova Science Pubs., Inc.

Haas, Marilyn & McBride, Deborah L. Managing the Oral Effects of Cancer Treatment: Diagnosis to Survivorship. 2011. 544p. *(978-1-935864-03-5(3))* Oncology Nursing Society.

Haley, John D., ed. EGFR Signaling Networks in Cancer Therapy. 2008. (Cancer Drug Discovery & Development Ser.). 450p. 199.00 *(978-1-58829-948-2(1))* Humana Pr.

Haley, John D. & Gullick, William John, eds. EGFR Signaling Networks in Cancer Therapy. 2010. (Cancer Drug Discovery & Development Ser.). (Illus.). xi, 393p. pap. 199.00 *(978-1-61737-853-9(4),* 1617378534) Humana Pr.

Hallerman, Victoria & Albert, Peter S. How We Survived Prostate Cancer: What We Did & What We Should Have Done. 2009. (ENG.). 240p. 24.95 *(978-1-55704-814-1(2),* Morrow, William & Co.) HarperCollins Pubs.

Hansen, Heine H., ed. Lung Cancer Therapy Annual 6th rev. ed. 2008. XII, 212p. 100.00 *(978-0-415-46545-8(1),* Informa Healthcare) Taylor & Francis Group.

Harrington, Kevin J. Viral Therapy of Cancer. Vile, Richard G. & Pandha, Hardev S., eds. 2008. (ENG., Illus.). 432p. 189.95 *(978-0-470-01922-1(0),* Wiley) Wiley, John & Sons, Inc.

Hayat, M. A., ed. Methods of Cancer Diagnosis, Therapy, & Prognosis: Brain Cancer. 2010. (Methods of Cancer Diagnosis, Therapy & Prognosis Ser.). (Illus.). 590p. 239.00 *(978-90-481-8664-8(1),* 9048186641) Springer.

—Methods of Cancer Diagnosis, Therapy & Prognosis: Colorectal Cancer. 2009. (Methods of Cancer Diagnosis, Therapy & Prognosis Ser.). (ENG., Illus.). xxxviii, 506p. 229.00 *(978-1-4020-9544-3(9))* Springer.

—Methods of Cancer Diagnosis, Therapy, & Prognosis: Liver Cancer. 2009. (Methods of Cancer Diagnosis, Therapy & Prognosis Ser.). (ENG., Illus.). xliv, 516p. 289.00 *(978-1-4020-9803-1(0))* Springer.

—Methods of Cancer Diagnosis, Therapy, & Prognosis: Ovarian Cancer, Renal Cancer, Urogenitary tract Cancer, Urinary Bladder Cancer, Cervical Uterine Cancer, Skin Cancer, Leukemia, Multiple Myeloma & Sarcoma. 2009. (Methods of Cancer Diagnosis, Therapy & Prognosis Ser.). (ENG., Illus.). xlvi, 482p. 319.00 *(978-90-481-2917-1(6),* 9048129176) Springer.

—Stem Cells & Cancer Stem Cells Vol. 3: Therapeutic Applications in Disease & Injury. 2011. (Stem Cells & Cancer Stem Cells Ser.). (ENG., Illus.). xxvii, 398p. 209.00 ***(978-94-007-2414-3(4),*** 9400724144) Springer.

—Stem Cells & Cancer Stem Cells, Volume 4: Therapeutic Applications in Disease & Injury. 2012. (Stem Cells & Cancer Stem Cells Ser.). (ENG., Illus.). xix, 319p. 209.00 ***(978-94-007-2827-1(1)*** 9400728271) Springer.

—Stem Cells & Cancer Stem Cells, Volume 5: Therapeutic Applications in Disease & Injury. 2012. (Stem Cells & Cancer Stem Cells Ser.). (ENG., Illus.). xix, 309p. 209.00 ***(978-94-007-2899-8(9)*** 9400728999) Springer.

—Stem Cells & Cancer Stem Cells, Volume 6: Therapeutic Applications in Disease & Injury. 2012. (Stem Cells & Cancer Stem Cells Ser.). (ENG., Illus.). xxiii, 448p. 209.00 ***(978-94-007-2992-6(8),*** 9400729928) Springer.

Helm, C. William & Edwards, Robert P., eds. Intraperitoneal Cancer Therapy. 2007. (Current Clinical Oncology Ser.). (Illus.). 191p. 219.00 *(978-1-58829-878-2(7),* 1588298787) Humana Pr.

—Intraperitoneal Cancer Therapy. 2008. 208p. pap. 99.00 *(978-1-60327-511-8(8))* Springer.

Henderson, Bill. Cancer-Free: Your Guide to Gentle, Non-toxic Healing (Second Edition) 2007. 340p. pap. 37.00 *(978-1-60145-183-5(0))* Booklocker.com, Inc.

Herron, Tim. Too Soon to Quit! No Subtitle. 2008. 148p. pap. 13.99 *(978-1-60647-667-3(X))* Xulon Pr., Inc.

Hester, Joan, et al. Interventional Pain Control in Cancer Pain Management. 2012. (ENG., Illus.). 304p. 160.00 *(978-0-19-921908-7(7))* Oxford Univ. Pr., Inc.

C

Hewitt, Maria Elizabeth & Ganz, Patricia. Implementing Cancer Survivorship Care Planning. 2006. (ENG., Illus.). 320p. pap. 65.00 *(978-0-309-10318-3(5))* National Academies Pr.

Himeise, Lothar. Chemotherapy Heals Cancer & the World Is Flat. 2008. 766p. 49.90 *(978-3-9810502-0-2(7))* Nexus Himeise - Handels GmbH DEU. Dist: AtlasBooks Distribution.

Hirsch, Fred R. & Harper, Peter. Lung Cancer. 2010. (State of the Art Series (Remedica) Ser.). (Illus.). 243p. pap. *(978-1-905721-56-6(0))* Remedica Medical Education & Publishing.

Hjörleifsdóttir, Elísabet. Patients' Experiences of Cancer & Treatment: Distress, Coping & Perception of Care. 2008. 88p. pap. *(978-3-639-08306-4(7))* VDM Verlag Dr. Mueller e.K.

Hoeppner, Pamela. The Breast Stays Put ¬. 2008. 268p. per. 15.99 *(978-1-60477-103-9(8))* Xulon Pr., Inc.

Hong, Waun Ki, et al. Holland-Frei Cancer Medicine 8. 8th ed. 2009. (Illus.). 2300p. *(978-1-60795-014-1(6))* PMPH-USA, Ltd.

Horwich, Alan. Systemic Treatment of Prostate Cancer. 2010. (Oxford Oncology Library). (ENG., Illus.). 128p. pap. 24.95 *(978-0-19-956142-1(7))* Oxford Univ. Pr., Inc.

Hou, Mi. Preservation of Fertility in Boys with Cancer. 2010. 76p. pap. *(978-3-639-23827-3(3))* VDM Verlag Dr. Mueller e.K.

Houghton, Peter J. & Arceci, Robert J., eds. Molecular Targeted Therapy for Childhood Cancer. 2010. (ENG., Illus.). xviii, 538p. 239.00 *(978-0-387-69060-5(3))*, 0387690603) Springer.

Houston, Reagan. Painless Therapy for Major Diseases. 2012. 138p. pap. 11.95 ***(978-0-7414-7112-3(4))*** Infinity Publishing.

Howard, Deborah. Help! Someone I Love Has Cancer. Tautges, Paul, ed. 2010. (Help! (Day One Publications) Ser.). 62p. pap. *(978-1-84625-217-4(2))* DayOne Pubns.

Hoxsey, Harry. Hoxsey Therapy: When Natural Cures for Cancer Became Illegal; the Authobiography of Harry Hoxsey, ND. 2009. 322p. pap. 19.95 *(978-1-929661-32-9(0))* Transpersonal Publishing.

Hricak, Hedvig & Scardino, Peter T. Prostate Cancer. Hricak, Hedvig & Scardino, Peter, eds. 2008. (Contemporary Issues in Cancer Imaging Ser.). (ENG., Illus.). 242p. 81.00 *(978-0-521-88704-5(6))* Cambridge Univ. Pr.

Hricak, Hedvig, et al. Oncologic Imaging: Essentials of Reporting Common Cancers. 2006. (ENG., Illus.). 320p. pap. 59.95 *(978-1-4160-3251-9(7)*, Saunders) Elsevier - Health Sciences Div.

Huber, Brian E. & Magrath, Ian, eds. Gene Therapy in the Treatment of Cancer: Progress & Prospects. 2007. (Cancer: Clinical Science in Practice Ser.). (ENG.). 232p. pap. 58.00 *(978-0-521-03351-0(9))* Cambridge Univ. Pr.

Huck, Frederick Mickel. Cancer Is Your Choice. 2009. 132p. pap. 12.49 *(978-1-4490-0762-1(7))* AuthorHouse.

Icon Health Publications Staff. Official Patients Sourcebook on Hyperthe. 2006. 348p. per. 34.95 *(978-0-497-11189-2(6))* Icon Group International, Inc.

Institute of Medicine. Assessing & Improving Value in Cancer Care: Workshop Summary. 2009. (ENG.). 164p. pap. 38.50 *(978-0-309-13814-7(0))* National Academies Pr.

Institute of Medicine. Patient-Centered Cancer Treatment Planning: Improving the Quality of Oncology Care: Workshop Summary. 2011. (ENG.). 90p. pap. 24.00 ***(978-0-309-21273-1(1))*** National Academies Pr.

Institute of Medicine Staff. A Foundation for Evidence-Driven Practice: A Rapid Learning System for Cancer Care: Workshop Summary. 2010. (ENG.). 124p. pap. 31.75 *(978-0-309-15126-9(0))* National Academies Pr.

—Multi-Center Phase III Clinical Trials & NCI Cooperative Groups: Workshop Summary. 2009. (ENG.). 134p. pap. 33.50 *(978-0-309-12867-4(6))* National Academies Pr.

—Policy Issues in the Development of Personalized Medicine in Oncology: Workshop Summary. 2010. (ENG.). 94p. pap. 21.00 *(978-0-309-14575-6(9))* National Academies Pr.

Integrative Strategies for Cancer Patients: A Practical Resource for Managing the Side Effects of Cancer Therapy. 2011. pap. 39.00 *(978-981-4313-23-0(8))* World Scientific Publishing Co., Inc.

Irving, Colm. Anaesthesia, intensive care, & pain management for the cancer Patient. Farquhar-Smith, Paul & Wigmore, Tim, eds. 2011. (ENG., Illus.). 272p. 98.50 *(978-0-19-958464-2(8))* Oxford Univ. Pr., Inc.

Jacobs, Charlotte. Henry Kaplan & the Story of Hodgkin's Disease. 2010. (ENG., Illus.). 456p. 35.00 *(978-0-8047-6866-5(8)*, Stanford General Bks.) Stanford Univ. Pr.

Jacobs, Lisa & Finlayson, Christina. Breast Cancer. 2010. (Early Diagnosis in Cancer Ser.). (ENG., Illus.). 408p. 152.00 *(978-1-4160-4932-6(0)*, Saunders) Elsevier - Health Sciences Div.

Janecka, Ivo. Prevention & Management of Colon Cancer Through Physical Activity. 2008. 176p. pap. *(978-3-639-01696-3(3))* VDM Verlag Dr. Mueller e.K.

Jemec, Gregor B. E., et al, eds. Non-Surgical Treatment of Keratinocyte Skin Cancer. 2009. (ENG., Illus.). xiii, 218p. 129.00 *(978-3-540-79340-3(2)*, 3540793402) Springer.

Johnson, Frank E., et al, eds. Patient Surveillance after Cancer Treatment. 2012. (Current Clinical Oncology Ser.). (ENG., Illus.). 950p. 249.00 *(978-1-60327-968-0(7)*, 1603279687) Humana Pr.

Johnson, Tara & Schwartz, Meredith Celene. Gestational Trophoblastic Neophasia: A Guide for Women Dealing with Tumors of the Placenta, Such As Choriocarcinoma, Molar Pregnancy & Other Forms of GTN. 2007. (Illus.). 240p. per. 29.95 *(978-1-4251-0695-9(1))* Trafford Publishing.

Jung, Karen. Healthier Eating: & Living with Cancer. 2008. (ENG., Illus.). 304p. pap. *(978-1-894694-57-5(0))* Granville Island Publishing.

Jurisica, Igor, et al, eds. Cancer Informatics in the Post Genomic Era: Toward Information-Based Medicine. 2010. (Cancer Treatment & Research Ser.). (Illus.). xx, 180p. pap. 159.00 *(978-1-4419-4344-6(7)*, 1441934447) Springer.

Kahán, Zsuzsanna & Tot, Tibor, eds. Breast Cancer, a Heterogeneous Disease Entity: The Very Early Stages. 2011. (ENG.). x, 313p. 209.00 *(978-94-007-0488-6(7)*, 9400704887) Springer.

Kalthoff, Holger, ed. Death Receptors & Cognate Ligands in Cancer. 2009. (Results & Problems in Cell Differentiation Ser.). (ENG., Illus.). xiv, 280p. 199.00 *(978-3-642-03044-4(0)*, 3642030440) Springer.

Kantoff, Philip, ed. Multidisciplinary Treatment for Prostate Cancer. 2007. (Illus.). 100p. pap. 19.95 *(978-1-891483-55-4(2))* PRR, Inc.

Karthaus, M. & Ganser, Arnold, eds. Supportive Care in Cancer Patients: Recent Developments, Vol. 50. (Antibiotics & Chemotherapy Ser.: Vol. 50). (Illus.). *(978-3-8055-6910-1(6))* Karger, S. AG.

Katalinic, A. & Borisch, B., eds. Cancer Risk & Prevention at the Molecular Level. 2009. (Illus.). 48p. pap. *(978-3-8055-9128-7(4))* Karger, S. AG.

Katz, MD, Aaron E. The Definitive Guide to Prostate Cancer: Everything You Need to Know about Conventional & Integrative Therapies. l.t. ed. 2012. (ENG.). 371p. 32.99 ***(978-1-4104-4743-2(X))*** Thorndike Pr.

Katz, Aaron. The Definitive Guide to Prostate Cancer: Everything You Need to Know about Conventional & Integrative Therapies. 2011. (ENG., Illus.). 272p. pap. 16.99 *(978-1-60961-310-5(4))* Rodale Pr., Inc.

Kazanietz, Marcelo G., ed. Protein Kinase C in Cancer Signaling & Therapy. 2010. (Current Cancer Research Ser.). (ENG., Illus.). xiv, 494p. 239.00 *(978-1-60761-542-2(8)*, 1607615428) Humana Pr.

Kelley, William D. Cancer Curing the Incurable Without Surgery, Chemotherapy & Radiation. 200p. mass mkt. 29.95 *(978-0-9669422-9-3(9))* College of Metabolic Medicine.

Kelly, David A. Time Out: A Family's Journey of Faith & Hope Through Childhood Cancer. 2009. pap. 14.99 *(978-1-60799-619-4(7))* Tate Publishing & Enterprises, LLC.

Kelly-Lopez, Catherine. The Cancer Emails - Running Raw in the Wild. 2008. 296p. pap. *(978-3-639-04777-6(X))* VDM Verlag Dr. Mueller e.K.

Kelvin, Joanne Frankel & Tyson, Leslie. 100 Questions & Answers about Cancer Symptoms & Cancer Treatment Side Effects. 2nd rev. ed. 2010. 240p. pap. 22.95 *(978-0-7637-7760-9(9))* Jones & Bartlett Learning, LLC.

Kennedy, Bernard N., ed. Stem Cell Transplantation, Tissue Engineering, & Cancer Applications. 2008. 149.00 *(978-1-60692-107-4(X))* Nova Science Pubs., Inc.

Kenner, Dan. The Whole-Body Workbook for Cancer: A Complete Integrative Program for Increasing Immunity & Rebuilding Health. 2009. (New Harbinger Whole-Body Healing Ser.). (ENG.). 200p. pap. 21.95 *(978-1-57224-674-4(X))* New Harbinger Pubns.

Khatib, A-Majid, ed. Regulation of Carcinogenesis, Angiogenesis & Metastasis by the Proprotein Convertases: A New Potential Strategy in Cancer Therapy. 2006. x, 157p. 139.00 *(978-1-4020-4793-0(2)*, 1402047932) Springer.

Khorana, Alok A. & Francis, Charles W., eds. Cancer-Associated Thrombosis: New Findings in Translational Science, Prevention, & Treatment. 2007. (ENG., Illus.). 296p. 230.00 *(978-1-4200-4799-8(X)*, Informa Healthcare) Taylor & Francis Group GBR. Dist: Taylor & Francis Group.

King, Samantha. Pink Ribbons, Inc: Breast Cancer & the Politics of Philanthropy. 2008. (Illus.). 208p. pap. 18.95 *(978-0-8166-4899-3(9))* Univ. of Minnesota Pr.

Kim, David H., et al, eds. Oncolytic Viruses: Methods & Protocols. 2011. (Methods in Molecular Biology Ser.). (ENG., Illus.). x, 241p. 119.00 ***(978-1-61779-339-4(6)***, 1617793396) Humana Pr.

Kissane, David W. & Watson, M. Handbook of Psychotherapy in Cancer Care. 2011. 57.95 *(978-1-119-99051-2(3)*, Wiley-Blackwell) Wiley, John & Sons, Inc.

Kitano, Seigo & Yang, Hang-Kwang, eds. Laparoscopic Gastrectomy for Cancer: Standard Techniques & Clinical Evidences. 2012. (ENG., Illus.). 200p. 139.00 ***(978-4-431-54002-1(4)***, 4431540024) Springer.

Klamerus, Justin F., et al. Johns Hopkins Patients' Guide to Lung Cancer. rev. ed. 2010. 174p. pap. 10.95 *(978-0-7637-7436-3(7))* Jones & Bartlett Learning, LLC.

Knaul, Felicia, et al. Closing the Cancer Divide: An Equity Imperative. Knaul, Felicia et al, eds. 2012. (Global Health & Equity Ser.). (ENG., Illus.). 250p. pap. 24.95 ***(978-0-9829144-0-3(7))*** Harvard Univ. Pr.

Kneece, Judy C. Breast Cancer Treatment Handbook: Understanding the Disease, Treatments, Emotions & Recovery from Breast Cancer. 7th ed. 2009. (Illus.). xiv, 242p. *(978-1-886665-23-1(0))* NAS/UWT.

Kneier, Andrew. Finding Your Way Through Cancer: An Expert Cancer Psychologist Helps Patients & Survivors Face the Challenges of Illness. 2010. (ENG., Illus.). 176p. pap. 14.00 *(978-1-58761-356-2(5)*, Celestial Arts) Ten Speed Pr.

Kondor, Karen. Decadron Diary: A Family's Journey Through Hodgkins Disease. 2011. 72p. 24.99 ***(978-1-4628-5746-3(9))***; pap. 15.99 ***(978-1-4628-5745-6(0))*** Xlibris Corp.

Kristoffersen, Karina. A Functional Study of Notch Signaling in Brain Cancer Stem-Like Cells. 2010. 124p. pap. *(978-3-8383-4614-4(9))* Lambert Academic Publishing.

Kumar, Challa, ed. Nanomaterials for Cancer Therapy. 2006. (Nanotechnologies for the Life Sciences Ser.: 6). (ENG., Illus.). 434p. 225.00 *(978-3-527-31386-0(9)*, Wiley-VCH) Wiley, John & Sons, Inc.

Kumar, Nagi B. Nutritional Management of Cancer Treatment Effects. 2012. (ENG., Illus.). xvii, 296p. 189.00 ***(978-3-642-27232-5(0)***, 3642272320) Springer.

Kurzrock, Razelle & Markman, Maurie, eds. Targeted Cancer Therapy. 2010. (Current Clinical Oncology Ser.). (ENG., Illus.). xii, 452p. pap. 79.95 *(978-1-60761-598-9(3)*, 1607615983) Humana Pr.

—Targeted Cancer Therapy. 2008. (Current Clinical Oncology Ser.). (Illus.). 445p. 179.00 *(978-1-60327-423-4(5)*, 1603274235) Springer.

Lacouture, Mario E. Dermatology & the Cancer Patient: Conditions of the Skin, Hair, & Nails During Cancer Treatment. 2012. (ENG., Illus.). 1200p. 149.95 ***(978-0-470-62188-2(5)***, Wiley-Blackwell) Wiley, John & Sons, Inc.

Laghi, Andrea. New Concepts in Diagnosis & Therapy of Pancreatic Adenocarcinoma. 2010. (Medical Radiology / Diagnostic Imaging Ser.). (ENG., Illus.). x, 178p. 239.00 *(978-3-540-85380-0(4)*, 3540853804) Springer.

Lange, Vladimir. Be a Survivor. Stankovich, Emily, ed. 2nd rev. ed. pap. 24.95 *(978-0-9663610-9-4(1))* Lange Productions.

Lee, Cheryl T. & Wood, David P. Bladder Cancer: Diagnosis, Therapeutics, & Management. 2009. (Current Clinical Urology Ser.). (ENG., Illus.). xvi, 332p. 149.00 *(978-1-58829-988-8(0)*, 1588299880) Humana Pr.

Legrand, Catherine. Assessing Heterogeneity in Clinical Trials Using the Frailty Model. 2009. 188p. pap. *(978-3-639-21334-8(3))* VDM Verlag Dr. Mueller e.K.

Leong, Anthony S-Y. Quantitative Immunohistology: Problems & Solutions. Leong, Trishe Y-M, ed. 2010. (Immunology & Immune System Disorders Ser.). (Illus.). 70p. pap. 43.00 *(978-1-61668-261-3(2))* Nova Science Pubs., Inc.

Leong, Stanley P. L. Cancer Clinical Trials: Proactive Strategies. 2006. (Cancer Treatment & Research Ser.). (Illus.). 318p. 149.00 *(978-0-387-33224-6(3)*, 0387332243) Springer.

Ler, Daria & Riederer, Monika. Establishment of a Diagnostic Test for the Detection of Tumor Markers. 2010. 88p. pap. *(978-3-639-23879-2(6))* VDM Verlag Dr. Mueller e.K.

Leung, Ping-Chung & Fong, Harry, eds. Alternative Treatment for Cancer. 2008. (Annals of Traditional Chinese Medicine Ser.). (Illus.). 363p. 139.00 *(978-981-270-929-5(0))* World Scientific Publishing Co., Inc.

Lewis, Jessica L., ed. Gene Therapy & Cancer Research Progress. 2008. (Illus.). x, 225p. (C). 69.00 *(978-1-60021-811-8(3)*, Nova Biomedical Bks.) Nova Science Pubs., Inc.

Leyland-Jones, Brian, ed. Pharmacogenetics of Breast Cancer: Towards the Individualization of Therapy. 2008. (Translational Medicine Ser.: Vol. 7). (ENG., Illus.). 352p. 200.00 *(978-1-4200-5293-0(4)*, Informa Healthcare) Taylor & Francis Group GBR. Dist: Taylor & Francis Group.

Lipscomb, Joseph, et al, eds. Outcomes Assessment in Cancer: Measures, Methods & Applications. 2011. (ENG.). 678p. pap. 80.00 ***(978-1-107-40316-1(2))*** Cambridge Univ. Pr.

Livingston, Julie. Improvised Medicine: An African Oncology Ward in an Emerging Cancer Epidemic. 2012. (ENG., Illus.). 256p. pap. 23.95 ***(978-0-8223-5342-3(3))*** Duke Univ. Pr.

—Improvising Medicine: An African Oncology Ward in an Emerging Cancer Epidemic. 2012. (ENG., Illus.). 256p. 84.95 ***(978-0-8223-5327-0(X))*** Duke Univ. Pr.

Llombart-Bosch, Antonio, et al, eds. New Trends in Cancer for the 21st Century. 2nd ed. (Advances in Experimental Medicine & Biology Ser.). (Illus.). xxiv, 396p. 2010. pap. 179.00 *(978-90-481-7239-9(X)*, 904817239X) 2006. (ENG., 179.00 *(978-1-4020-4966-8(8)*, 1402049668) Springer.

Lloyd, Michael. How to Survive Lung Cancer - A Practical 12-Step Plan. 2007. 128p. pap. 14.95 *(978-1-4357-0471-8(1))* Lulu Enterprises Inc.

Lowy, Andrew M., et al, eds. Pancreatic Cancer. 2008. (M. D. Anderson Solid Tumor Oncology Ser.). (Illus.). 424p. 119.00 *(978-0-387-69250-0(9))* Springer.

Lyman, Gary. Oxford American Mini-Handbook of Cancer Supportive Care, 1 vol. 2010. (Oxford American Mini Handbooks Ser.). (Illus.). 160p. pap. 18.95 *(978-0-19-539046-9(6))* Oxford Univ. Pr., Inc.

Lyman, Gary H. & Burstein, Harold J., eds. Breast Cancer: Translational Therapeutic Strategies. 2007. (Translational Medicine Ser.: Vol. 2). (ENG., Illus.). 344p. *(978-0-8493-7416-6(2))* Informa Pharmaceuticals & Healthcare.

Lyman, Gary H. & Crawford, Jeffrey. Cancer Supportive Care: Advances in Therapeutic Strategies. Lyman, Gary H. & Crawford, Jeffrey, eds. 2008. (Translational Medicine Ser.: Vol. 5). (ENG., Illus.). 416p. 270.00 *(978-1-4200-5289-3(6)*, Informa Healthcare) Taylor & Francis Group GBR. Dist: Taylor & Francis Group.

Lynes, Barry. Rife's World of Electromedicine: The Story, the Corruption & the Promise. 2009. 88p. pap. 17.95 *(978-0-9763797-9-9(1))* BioMed Publishing Group.

Lyons, Lyman. Diagnosis & Treatment of Cancer. 2007. (Biology of Cancer Ser.). (Illus.). 152p. (C). (gr. 9). lib. bdg. 35.00 *(978-0-7910-8826-5(X)*, Chelsea Hse.) Facts On File, Inc.

M. Matin, Maryam & W. Andrews, Peter. Rna Interference in Human Embryonal Carcinoma & Embryonic Stem Cells. 2010. 144p. pap. *(978-3-8383-7911-1(X))* Lambert Academic Publishing.

MacFarlane, Deborah F. Skin Cancer Management: A Practical Approach. 2009. (ENG., Illus.). xvii, 299p. 99.00 *(978-0-387-88494-3(7)*, 0387884947) Springer.

MacVicar, David, ed. Carcinoma of the Bladder. 2008. (Contemporary Issues in Cancer Imaging Ser.). (ENG., Illus.). 194p. 87.00 *(978-0-521-88456-3(X))* Cambridge Univ. Pr.

Majumder, Sadhan, ed. Stem Cells & Cancer. 2009. (ENG., Illus.). x, 286p. 160.00 *(978-0-387-89610-6(4)*, 0387896104) Springer.

Manegold, Christian, ed. Non-Small Cell Lung Cancer Treatment. 2007. (UNI-MED Science Ser.). (Illus.). 176p. *(978-3-89599-270-4(4))* UNI-MED Verlag AG.

Markes, Martina. Exercise during breast-cancer treatment: A systematic review. 2011. 164p. pap. ***(978-3-8381-2698-2(X))*** Südwestdeutscher Verlag für Hochschulschriften AG & Co. KG.

Markovic, Nenad S. What Every Woman Should Know about Cervical Cancer. 2008. (Illus.). xxv, 220p. 119.00 *(978-1-4020-6936-9(7))* Springer.

Marr, Kieren A. & Subramanian, Aruna K. Infections in Transplant & Oncology Patients, an Issue of Infectious Disease Clinics. 2010. (Clinics: Internal Medicine Ser.: 24-2). (ENG., Illus.). xv, 258p. 105.00 *(978-1-4377-1831-7(0)*, Saunders) Elsevier - Health Sciences Div.

Marsh, Sharon, ed. Cancer Pharmacogenetics. 2009. (ENG., Illus.). 280p. 139.00 *(978-0-387-69133-6(2))* Springer.

Marshall, John L., ed. Encyclopedia of Cancer Therapeutic Targets, 2 vols. 2013. (ENG., Illus.). 1000p. 679.00 *(978-1-4419-0716-5(5)*, 1441907165) Springer.

—Managing Colorectal Cancer: The Resectable & Potentially Resectable Patient, a Multidisciplinary Approach. 2008. (Illus.). 96p. pap. 19.95 *(978-1-891483-60-8(9))* PRR, Inc.

Mazzaferri, Ernest L., et al, eds. Practical Management of Thyroid Cancer: A Multidisciplinary Approach. 2010. (ENG., Illus.). xvi, 448p. pap. 179.00 *(978-1-84996-957-4(4)*, 1849969574) Springer.

McGrath, Henry. The Traditional Chinese Medicine Approach to Cancer: Harmony in the Face of the Tiger. 2009. (ENG., Illus.). 160p. pap. *(978-1-84819-013-9(1))* Kingsley, Jessica Ltd.

Mckenna, Jason. The Secret of Cancer & Aids: Immunological Tolerance in the Lymph System. 2011. (ENG.). 128p. pap. 14.95 ***(978-1-4327-3977-5(8))*** Outskirts Pr., Inc.

McMasters, Kelly M. & Vauthey, Jean-Nicolas, eds. Hepatocellular Carcinoma: Targeted Therapy & Multidisciplinary Care. 2009. (ENG., Illus.). xv, 415p. 219.00 *(978-1-60327-521-7(5)*, 1603275215) Humana Pr.

Means, Reschelle. Intruder: Naturally Kicking Cancer Out. 2011. 128p. 28.95 ***(978-1-4497-1843-5(4))***; pap. 11.95 ***(978-1-4497-1841-1(8))*** Author Solutions, Inc. (WestBow Pr.).

Medeiros, Aloisio & Veloso, Carlitos, eds. Nose & Viral Cancer: Etiology, Pathogenesis & Treatment. 2009. (Cancer Etiology, Diagnosis & Treatments Ser.). 129.00 *(978-1-60741-735-4(9))* Nova Science Pubs., Inc.

Mertens, Gilbert. Cancer: Targeting the Enemy Within. 2009. 462p. pap. 50.00 *(978-1-935383-29-1(9))* Raider Publishing International.

Michell, Michael J., ed. Breast Cancer. 2010. (Contemporary Issues in Cancer Imaging Ser.). (ENG., Illus.). 282p. 99.00 *(978-0-521-51950-2(0))* Cambridge Univ. Pr.

Micozzi, Marc S. Complementary & Integrative Medicine in Cancer Care & Prevention. 2007. (Illus.). 478p. 80.00 *(978-0-8261-0305-5(7))* Springer Publishing Co., Inc.

Miller, Kenneth D. Medical & Psychosocial Care of the Cancer Survivor. 2009. (Illus.). 479p. 73.95 *(978-0-7637-5770-0(5))* Jones & Bartlett Learning, LLC.

Miller, Kenneth D., ed. Choices in Breast Cancer Treatment: Medical Specialists & Cancer Survivors Tell You What You Need to Know. 2008. (Johns Hopkins Press Health Book Ser.). (ENG., Illus.). 416p. 47.00 *(978-0-8018-8684-3(8))*; per. 19.95 *(978-0-8018-8685-0(6))* Johns Hopkins Univ. Pr.

Minev, Boris R., ed. Cancer Management in Man: Chemotherapy, Biological Therapy, Hyperthermia & Supporting Measures: Chemotherapy, Biological Therapy, Hyperthermia & Supporting Measures. 2011. (Cancer Growth & Progression Ser.). (Illus.). x, 650p. 239.00 *(978-90-481-9703-3(1)*, 9048197031) Springer.

Molineux, Graham, et al, eds. Twenty Years of G-CSF: Clinical & Nonclinical Discoveries. 2012. (Milestones in Drug Therapy Ser.). (ENG., Illus.). xxii, 471p. 239.00 ***(978-3-0348-0217-8(X)***, 303480217X) Birkhauser Verlag AG CHE. Dist: Springer.

Molls, M. The Impact of Tumor Biology on Cancer Treatment & Multidisciplinary Strategies. 2009. (Medical Radiology / Radiation Oncology Ser.). (ENG., Illus.). x, 370p. 199.00 *(978-3-540-74385-9(5))* Springer.

Montenegro, Joana. Sticking it to Cancer. 2011. 116p. pap. 14.95 ***(978-1-4678-6965-2(1))*** AuthorHouse.

Moore, Dwayne. Surviving Wolves at the Door: My Journey Through Cancer. 2008. 384p. pap. 29.95 *(978-1-60610-846-8(8))* PublishAmerica, Inc.

Morrison, Sharon. Even the Eyebrows? 2009. 164p. pap. 13.49 *(978-1-4389-2334-5(1))* AuthorHouse.

Mulhall, John P., ed. Fertility Preservation in the Man with Cancer. 2012. (ENG., Illus.). 392p. 165.00 ***(978-1-107-01212-7(0))*** Cambridge Univ. Pr.

Mulhall, John P., et al, eds. Cancer & Sexual Health. 2011. (Current Clinical Urology Ser.). (ENG., Illus.). xviii, 783p. 279.00 *(978-1-60761-915-4(6)*, 1607619156) Humana Pr.

Müller, Gerhard, et al, eds. Protein Kinases as Drug Targets. 2011. (Methods & Principles in Medicinal Chemistry Ser.: 126). (ENG., Illus.). 396p. 190.00 *(978-3-527-31790-5(2)*, Wiley-VCH) Wiley, John & Sons, Inc.

Multiple Myeloma: Translational & Emerging Therapies. 2007. (ENG., Illus.). 320p. 99.95 *(978-1-4200-7801-5(1)*, Informa Healthcare) Taylor & Francis Group GBR. Dist: Taylor & Francis Group.

MYC Network of Growth Regulators & Its Interplay. *(978-91-554-4894-3(1))* Uppsala Universitet/Acta Universitatis Upsaliensis.

Myers, Jeffrey. Oral Cancer Metastasis. 2010. (Illus.). xviii, 346p. E-Book 199.00 *(978-1-4419-0775-2(0))* Springer.

Myers, Jeffrey, ed. Oral Cancer Metastasis. 2010. (ENG., Illus.). xviii, 346p. 199.00 *(978-1-4419-0774-5(2)*, 1441907742) Springer.

Nathan. The Cancer Treatment Revolution: How Smart Drugs & Other New Therapies Are Renewing Our Hope & Changing the Face of Medicine. 2007. (ENG.). 272p. pap. 24.95 *(978-0-470-58131-5(X)*, Wiley) Wiley, John & Sons, Inc.

Nathan, David G. The Cancer Treatment Revolution: How Smart Drugs & Other New Therapies Are Renewing Our Hope & Changing the Face of Medicine. 2007. (ENG.). 272p. 24.95 *(978-0-471-94654-0(0)*, Wiley) Wiley, John & Sons, Inc.

National Cancer Policy Forum & Institute of Medicine. Facilitating Collaborations to Develop Combination Investigational Cancer Therapies: Workshop Summary. 2012. (ENG.). 118p. pap. 38.00 ***(978-0-309-22064-4(5))*** National Academies Pr.

National Cancer Policy Forum, et al. Implementing a National Cancer Clinical Trials System for the 21st Century: A Workshop Summary. 2011. (ENG.). 100p. pap. 39.00 ***(978-0-309-21268-7(5))*** National Academies Pr.

Necula, Virgil. Breast Cancer: Women's Killer. 2008. 161p. pap. 14.95 *(978-0-7414-4558-2(1))* Infinity Publishing.

Nelsen, Robert. Ten Commandments for Surviving Cancer. 2nd rev. ed. 2009. (ENG.). 76p. pap. 9.95 *(978-0-9769865-1-5(5))* Omega-Alpha Pr.

Nieper. The Curious Man: The Life & Works of Dr. Hans Nieper. 2010. 228p. 34.99 *(978-1-4490-6755-7(7))*; pap. 20.30 *(978-1-4490-6752-6(2))* AuthorHouse.

Nikfarjam, Mehrdad. The Effect of Laser Induced Thermal Ablation on Liver Tumours. 2008. 272p. pap. *(978-3-639-04980-0(2))* VDM Verlag Dr. Mueller e.K.

Nilsson, William E., ed. Bladder Cancer: Etymology, Diagnosis, & Treatments. 2010. (Cancer Etiology, Diagnosis & Treatments Ser.). 160.00 *(978-1-61728-002-3(X))* Nova Science Pubs., Inc.

Nwabo Kamdje, Armel Herve. Notch Signaling As a Novel Target for Cancer. 2011. 148p. pap. ***(978-3-8443-9570-9(9))*** Lambert Academic Publishing.

Ochs, Michael F., et al, eds. Biomedical Informatics in Cancer Research. 2010. (ENG., Illus.). xviii, 354p. 179.00 ***(978-1-4419-5712-2(X)***, 144195712X) Springer.

Ofluoglu, Önder & Donthineni, Rakesh. Spine Oncology, an Issue of Orthopedic Clinics. 2008. (Clinics: Orthopedics Ser.: 40-1). (ENG., Illus.). 240p. 99.00 *(978-1-4377-0514-0(6)*, Saunders) Elsevier - Health Sciences Div.

O'Haynes, Delilah F. Walk Free from Fear of Cancer. 2008. (Illus.). 283p. pap. 19.95 *(978-0-9779282-1-7(7))* Walk Free Pr.

Olch, Arthur. Pediatric Radiotherapy Planning & Treatment. 2010. (Illus.). 350p. 99.95 *(978-1-4200-8509-9(3))* CRC Pr. LLC.

Olver, Ian N., ed. A Textbook of Cancer Supportive Care & Survivorship. 2010. (ENG., Illus.). 420p. 179.00 *(978-1-4419-1224-4(X)*, 144191224X) Springer.

Palmer, Jim. Don't Relapse! Building A Healthy Life after Cancer Remission. 2011. 108p. 24.99 ***(978-1-4628-6743-1(X))***; pap. 15.99 ***(978-1-4628-6742-4(1))*** Xlibris Corp.

Pardee, Arthur B. & Stein, Gary S. The Biology & Treatment of Cancer: Understanding Cancer. 2009. (ENG., Illus.). 303p. pap. 81.95 *(978-0-470-00958-1(6)*, Wiley-Blackwell) Wiley, John & Sons, Inc.

Partin, Alan W., et al, eds. Treatment Methods for Early & Advanced Prostate Cancer. 2008. (ENG., Illus.). 424p. 259.95 *(978-0-415-45893-1(5))* CRC Pr. LLC.

Patient Resource - A Cancer Treatment & Facilities Guide for Patients & Their Families. 2007. 128p. per. 6.95 net. *(978-0-615-14256-2(7))* Patient Resource Publishing, LLC.

Patlak, Margie & Levit, Laura. Ensuring Quality Cancer Care Through the Oncology Workforce: Sustaining Care in the 21st Century: Workshop Summary. 2009. (ENG.). 94p. pap. 21.00 *(978-0-309-13671-6(7))* National Academies Pr.

Patlak, Margie & Nass, Sharyl. Improving the Quality of Cancer Clinical Trials: Workshop Summary. 2008. (ENG.). 136p. pap. 33.75 ***(978-0-309-11668-8(6))*** National Academies Pr.

Pazdur, Richard, et al, eds. Cancer Management: A Multidiciplinary Approach Medical, Surgical, & Radiation Oncology. 2007. 1000p. pap. 59.95 *(978-1-891483-48-6(X))* PRR, Inc.

Pecorino, Lauren. Why Millions Survive Cancer: The Successes of Science. 2011. (ENG., Illus.). 256p. 29.95 *(978-0-19-958055-2(3))* Oxford Univ. Pr., Inc.

Pecorino, Lauren. Why Millions Survive Cancer: The successes of Science. 2012. (ENG., Illus.). 256p. pap. 17.95 ***(978-0-19-965875-6(7))*** Oxford Univ. Pr., Inc.

Pérez Gutiérrez, Rosa Martha. Handbook of Compounds with Cytotoxic Activity Isolated from Plants. 2006. (Illus.). 653p. 169.00 *(978-1-60021-369-4(3))* Nova Science Pubs., Inc.

Pesmen, Curtis. The Colon Cancer Survivors' Guide. 2007. (ENG.). 232p. 22.95 *(978-0-9661847-7-8(7))* Tatra Pr.

Peters, Godefridus Johannes. Deoxynucleoside Analogs in Cancer Therapy. 2006. (Cancer Drug Discovery & Development Ser.). (Illus.). 476p. 209.00 *(978-1-58829-327-5(0)*, 1588293270) Humana Pr.

Pham, Tuân, ed. Computational Biology: Issues & Applications in Oncology. 2009. (Applied Bioinformatics & Biostatistics in Cancer Research Ser.). (Illus.). viii, 309p. 209.00 *(978-1-4419-0810-0(2)*, 1441908102) Springer.

Piva Demarzo, Marcelo Marcos & Britto Garcia, Sérgio. Exercise & Cancer. 2010. 108p. pap. *(978-3-639-25352-8(3))* VDM Verlag Dr. Mueller e.K.

Pratt, Dave. Voices from the Prostate Underground. 2008. 108p. pap. 12.95 *(978-1-4401-0148-9(5))* iUniverse, Inc.

Pravinkumar, S. Egbert. et al, eds. Critical Care for Cancer Patients. 2011. (ENG., Illus.). 450p. 99.00 *(978-1-4419-0281-8(3)*, 1441902813) Springer.

Price, Pat, et al. Treatment of Cancer. 5th ed. 2008. (ENG., Illus.). 1248p. 298.50 *(978-0-340-91221-8(9)*, Hodder Arnold) Hodder Education GBR. Dist: Oxford Univ. Pr., Inc.

Prijatel, Patricia. Surviving Triple Negative Breast Cancer: Hope, Treatment, & Recovery. 2012. 256p. 27.95 ***(978-0-19-538762-9(7))*** Oxford Univ. Pr., Inc.

Prostate Cancer: New Questions about Screening & Treatment: Hearing Before the Committee on Oversight & Government Reform, House of Representatives, One Hundred Eleventh Congress, Second Session, March 4, 2010. 2010. (Illus.). iv, 148p. *(978-0-16-086770-5(3)*, 552-070-41691-9) United States Government Printing Office.

Quick, Olivia. Second Chances for Black Halos. 2007. 115p. pap. 15.95 *(978-1-58909-422-2(0))* Bookstand Publishing.

Quintás-Cardama, Alfonso, et al. Targeted Therapy for Solid Tumors & Hematologic Malignancies. 2011. *(978-1-61761-854-3(3))* Nova Science Pubs., Inc.

Rakoff, Ruth. When My World Was Very Small: A Memoir of Family, Food, Cancer & My Couch. 2010. (ENG.). 224p. 25.95 *(978-0-307-35817-2(8)*, Random Hse CAN) Random Hse. of Canada, Ltd. CAN. Dist: Random Hse., Inc.

Ramon, J. & Denis, Louis. Prostate Cancer. 2007. (Recent Results in Cancer Research Ser.). (Illus.). xiv, 272p. 189.00 *(978-3-540-40897-0(5))* Springer.

Randall, Brad. The Ld Chronicles: A Story about a Physician & His Missing Prostate. 2011. 114p. pap. 12.95 ***(978-1-4327-7030-3(6))*** Outskirts Pr., Inc.

Rauhala, Hanna. DNA Hypermethylation in Prostate Cancer. 2009. (Acta Universitatis Tamperensis Ser.). 143p. pap. 82.50 ***(978-951-44-7883-3(5))*** Tampere Univ. Pr. FIN. Dist: Coronet Bks.

Rawls, George, et al. Managing Cancer: The African American's Guide to Prevention, Diagnosis & Treatment. rev. ed. 2007. (ENG., Illus.). 362p. per. 16.95 *(978-0-9764443-2-9(1))* Hilton Publishing Co.

Rayter, Zenon & Mansi, Janine, eds. Medical Therapy of Breast Cancer. 2008. (ENG., Illus.). 416p. pap. 58.00 *(978-0-521-08859-6(3))* Cambridge Univ. Pr.

Reich, Wilhelm. Die Entdeckung des Orgons 2. Der Krebs. (GER.). 349p. pap. *(978-3-462-02378-7(0))* Kiepenheuer & Witsch GmbH & Company KG DEU. Dist: International Bk. Import Service, Inc.

—Die Entdeckung des Orgons I. Die Funktion des Orgasmus: Sexualökonomische Grundprobleme der biologischen Energie. (GER.). 122p. pap. *(978-3-462-01825-7(6))* Kiepenheuer & Witsch GmbH & Company KG DEU. Dist: International Bk. Import Service, Inc.

Rettig, Edward. Through the Valley of the Shadow of Death. 2010. 344p. pap. 22.95 *(978-0-557-49156-8(8))* Lulu Enterprises Inc.

Reuben, Adrian. Diagnosis & Therapy of Hepatocellular Carcinoma: Status Quo & a Glimpse at the Future - Clinics in Liver Disease. 2011. (Clinics: Internal Medicine Ser.: 15-2). (ENG., Illus.). 272p. 99.00 *(978-1-4557-0455-1(2)*, Saunders) Elsevier - Health Sciences Div.

Richno, Donna. Cancer, Chemo & Beyond. 2008. 137p. pap. 12.95 *(978-1-4357-3035-9(6))* Lulu Enterprises Inc.

Riter, Bob. The Elephant in the Room: Practical Advice When the Diagnosis Is Cancer. 2011. 144p. 24.95 ***(978-1-4620-4659-1(2))***; pap. 14.95 ***(978-1-4620-4658-4(4))*** iUniverse, Inc.

Robotin, Monica. When Cancer Crosses Disciplines. 2009. (Illus.). 1196p. 157.00 *(978-1-84816-364-5(9))* Imperial College Pr. GBR. Dist: World Scientific Publishing Co., Inc.

Rolfs, Judith. Triumphing over Cancer. 2007. 51p. pap. 14.95 *(978-0-9799895-0-6(7))* Wayne & Judith Rolfs.

Rosette, Jean J. M C. H de la, et al. Renal Cell Cancer: Diagnosis & Therapy. 2008. (Illus.). 680p. 179.00 *(978-1-84628-385-7(X))* Springer.

Rosu, Claudia A. Race & Patient Perception of Interpersonal Processes of Care. 2008. 300p. pap. *(978-3-639-04834-6(2))* VDM Verlag Dr. Mueller e.K.

Roth, Jack A., et al. Lung Cancer. Roth, Jack A. et al, eds. 3rd rev. ed. 2008. (ENG., Illus.). 480p. 209.95 *(978-1-4051-5112-2(9)*, Wiley-Blackwell) Wiley, John & Sons, Inc.

Rubin, P. Alert Adverse Late Effects of Cancer Treatment. 2009. (Medical Radiology / Radiation Oncology Ser.). (ENG., Illus.). 410p. 329.00 *(978-3-540-72313-4(7))* Springer.

Rubin, Philip. Alert - Adverse Late Effects of Cancer Treatment. 2009. (Medical Radiology / Radiation Oncology Ser.). (ENG., Illus.). 410p. 329.00 *(978-3-540-75862-4(3))* Springer.

—ALERT - Adverse Late Effects of Cancer Treatment, 2 vols. 2009. (Medical Radiology / Radiation Oncology Ser.). (Illus.). 810p. 449.00 *(978-3-540-76703-9(7))* Springer.

Sabe, Chemo. Medical Marijuana Caregiver's Journal. 2007. 110p. pap. 19.95 *(978-0-615-15752-8(1))* Buddha of Compassion.

Safken, Chelsey & Heffron, Melinda. Sweetly Broken, Wholly Surrendered. 2011. pap. 12.99 ***(978-1-61346-686-5(2))*** Tate Publishing & Enterprises, LLC.

Scalapino, Kenneth J. & Thomas, Charles R., Jr. Paraneoplastic & Cancer Treatment-Related Rheumatic Disorders, an Issue of Rheumatic Disease Clinics. 2011. (Clinics: Internal Medicine Ser.: 37-4). (ENG.). 110.00 ***(978-1-4557-1189-5(6)***, Saunders) Elsevier - Health Sciences Div.

Schiff, David. Cancer Neurology in Clinical Practice; Neurologic Complications of Cancer & Its Treatment. 2008. 660p. pap. 99.00 *(978-1-60327-512-5(6))* Springer.

Schiff, David, et al, eds. Cancer Neurology in Clinical Practice. 2nd ed. 2008. (Illus.). 513p. 189.00 *(978-1-58829-983-3(X)*, 158829983X) Springer.

Schmoll, Hans-Joachim. ESMO Handbook of Cancer Diagnosis & Treatment Evaluation. 2009. 160p. pap. 99.95 *(978-1-84184-703-0(8)*, Informa Healthcare) Taylor & Francis Group.

Schneider, Katherine A. Counseling about Cancer: Strategies for Genetic Counseling. 3rd ed. 2011. (ENG., Illus.). 496p. pap. 69.95 ***(978-0-470-08150-1(3)***, Wiley-Blackwell) Wiley, John & Sons, Inc.

Schrijvers, Dirk, ed. ESMO Handbook of Cancer Diagnosis & Treatment Evaluation. 2009. pap. 100.00 *(978-0-415-39086-6(9)*, Informa Healthcare) Taylor & Francis Group GBR. Dist: Taylor & Francis Group.

—ESMO Handbook of Cancer in the Senior Patient. 2010. 168p. pap. 99.00 *(978-1-84184-709-2(7)*, Informa Healthcare) Taylor & Francis Group.

Scott-Brown, Martin, et al, eds. Emergencies in Oncology. 2007. (Emergencies in Ser.). (Illus.). 366p. pap. 42.95 *(978-0-19-921563-8(4))* Oxford Univ. Pr., Inc.

Scott, Catharine Bracken. Only If You Really Want to Know: Breast Cancer: Coping Hints & Treatment Side Effects. 2006. pap. 9.95 *(978-0-9760867-1-0(9))* Fountain City Publishing Co. Enterprise.

Scotting, Paul. Cancer: A Beginner's Guide. 2011. (Beginners Guide (Oneworld) Ser.). (ENG., Illus.). 208p. 14.95 *(978-1-85168-755-8(6))* Oneworld Pubns. GBR. Dist: National Bk. Network.

Sell, Colleen. Breast Cancer Survivors: Inspiring Stories of Courage & Triumph. 2008. (ENG.). 336p. pap. 9.95 *(978-1-59869-650-9(5))* Adams Media Corp.

Servan-Schreiber, David. Anticancer: A New Way of Life. 2009. (ENG.). 288p. (gr. 12-18). 26.95 *(978-0-670-02164-2(4)*, Viking Adult) Penguin Group (USA) Inc.

Shaw, Gina M. Having Children after Cancer: How to Make Informed Choices Before & after Treatment & Build the Family of Your Dreams. 2011. (ENG., Illus.). 224p. pap. 16.99 *(978-1-58761-054-7(X)*, Celestial Arts) Ten Speed Pr.

Shields, Anthony F. & Price, Pat, eds. In Vivo Imaging of Cancer Therapy. 2010. (Cancer Drug Discovery & Development Ser.). xii, 326p. pap. 229.00 *(978-1-61737-684-9(1)*, 1617376841) Humana Pr.

Shoup, Margo & Brown, Kimberly M. Multidisciplinary Approach to Cancer Care, an Issue of Surgical Clinics. 2009. (Clinics: Surgery Ser.: 89-1). (ENG., Illus.). 240p. 90.00 *(978-1-4377-0545-4(6)*, Saunders) Elsevier - Health Sciences Div.

Siddik, Zahid H., ed. Checkpoint Controls & Targets in Cancer Therapy. 2009. (Cancer Drug Discovery & Development Ser.). (ENG., Illus.). xiv, 274p. 259.00 *(978-1-60761-177-6(5)*, 1607611775) Humana Pr.

Singh, Balvinder. Antitumor Activity in Eulophia Campestris & Eulophia Nud: In Vivo. 2011. 112p. pap. ***(978-3-8443-1796-1(1))*** Lambert Academic Publishing.

Slaby, Ondrej. MicroRNAs in Solid Cancer: From Biomarkers to Therapeutic Targets. 2012. (DNA & RNA: Properties & Modifications, Functions & Interactions, Recombination & Applications Cancer Etiology, Diagnosis & Treatments Ser.). (Illus.). 200p. 95.00 ***(978-1-61324-514-9(9))*** Nova Science Pubs., Inc.

Sluyser, Mels. Application of Apoptosis to Cancer Treatment. 2010. (ENG.). vii, 370p. pap. 159.00 *(978-90-481-6833-0(3)*, 9048168333) Springer.

Somers, Suzanne. Knockout: Interviews with Doctors Who Are Curing Cancer - And How to Prevent Getting It in the First Place. (ENG.). 2010. 368p. pap. 16.00 *(978-0-307-58759-6(2)*, Three Rivers Pr.) 2009. 352p. 25.99 *(978-0-307-58746-6(0)*, Crown) Crown Publishing Group.

Souto, Eliana, et al. Lipid Nanocarriers in Cancer Diagnosis & Therapy. 2011. (Handbook Ser.). pap. ***(978-1-84735-478-5(5))***; ***(978-1-84735-477-8(7))*** iSmithers Rapra Publishing.

Spitz, Douglas R., et al, eds. Oxidative Stress in Cancer Biology & Therapy. 2011. (Oxidative Stress in Applied Basic Research & Clinical Practice Ser.). (ENG., Illus.). xvii, 460p. 209.00 ***(978-1-61779-396-7(5)***, 1617793965) Humana Pr.

Springs, Daniel Everett. How to Be Healed of Aids & Cancer. 2007. 82p. pap. 10.00 *(978-1-4257-4647-6(0))* Xlibris Corp.

Srejic & DeMonte. Neurecipes: The MD Anderson Cancer Center Guide to Anesthesia for Neurosurgical Cases. 2008. 116p. pap. 74.99 *(978-1-4389-0547-1(5))* AuthorHouse.

St. Onge, Terri. The St. Onge Survivor's Guide: How to Survive Everyday Life while Battling Cancer. 2008. spiral bd. 24.95 *(978-0-615-23022-1(9))* TSO Company.

Stacker, Steven A. & Achen, Marc G., eds. Lymphangiogenesis in Cancer Metastasis. 2009. (Cancer Metastasis - Biology & Treatment Ser.). (ENG., Illus.). x, 254p. 189.00 *(978-90-481-2246-2(5)*, 9048122465) Springer.

Steinman, Ralph M., et al, eds. Cancer Vaccines. 2009. (Annals of the New York Academy of Sciences Ser.: 33). (ENG., Illus.). 300p. pap. 134.95 *(978-1-57331-759-7(4)*, Wiley-Blackwell) Wiley, John & Sons, Inc.

Stigbrand, Torgny. Targeted Radionuclide Tumor Therapy: Biological Aspects. 2008. (ENG., Illus.). xiv, 402p. 219.00 *(978-1-4020-8695-3(4)*, 1402086954) Springer.

Strasheim, Connie. Defeat Cancer: 15 Doctors of Integrative & Naturopathic Medicine Tell You How. 2011. 444p. pap. 39.95 ***(978-0-9825138-2-8(8))*** BioMed Publishing Group.

Su, Li-Ming. Prostate Cancer. 2009. (Early Diagnosis in Cancer Ser.). (ENG., Illus.). 312p. pap. 152.00 *(978-1-4160-4575-5(9)*, Saunders) Elsevier - Health Sciences Div.

Suryatenggara, Jeremiah. Image Recognition System Based on Pattern Recognition. 2011. 132p. pap. ***(978-3-8433-8924-2(1))*** Lambert Academic Publishing.

Susan G Komen for the Cure. Words for the Cure: Inspiration, Hope, & Comfort for Today & Tomorrow. 2007. (Illus.). 96p. 12.95 *(978-0-696-23812-3(8))* Meredith Bks.

Syed, Abdul Muqeet. Thermometric Calibration of the Heating Effects by 27 12 Mhz. 2011. 68p. pap. ***(978-3-8443-2260-6(4))*** Lambert Academic Publishing.

Szasz, Andras, et al. Oncothermia - Principles & Practices. 2010. (ENG., Illus.). xiii, 565p. 189.00 *(978-90-481-9497-1(0)*, 9048194970) Springer.

Tasseff, Tom. Win the Ultimate Battle for Your Health: The Lifesaving Legacy of Tom Tasseff. 2008. 248p. pap. 27.95 *(978-1-4327-2796-3(6))*; pap. 19.95 *(978-1-4327-2741-3(9))* Outskirts Pr., Inc.

Teicher, Beverly A., et al, eds. In Vivo Imaging of Cancer Therapy. 2007. (Cancer Drug Discovery & Development Ser.). 494p. 229.00 *(978-1-58829-633-7(4)*, 1588296334) Humana Pr.

Teicher, Beverly A. & Ellis, Lee M., eds. Antiangiogenic Agents in Cancer Therapy. 2nd ed. 2007. (Cancer Drug Discovery & Development (Unnumberd) Ser.). (Illus.). 559p. 199.00 *(978-1-58829-870-6(1))* Humana Pr.

Teicher, Beverly A. & Kieber-Emmons, Thomas, eds. Cancer Vaccine Protocols. (Methods in Molecular Medicine Ser.). 300p. 2008. 125.00 *(978-1-58829-271-1(1)*, 1588292711) 2006. 125.00 *(978-1-59745-338-7(2))* Humana Pr.

Thiboldeaux, Kim & Golant, Mitch. The Total Cancer Wellness Guide: Reclaiming Your Life after Diagnosis. 2007. (ENG., Illus.). 306p. 24.95 *(978-1-933771-16-8(X))* BenBella Bks.

Thomas, Charles & Fuller, Clifton, eds. Biliary Tract & Gallbladder Cancer: Diagnosis & Therapy. 2008. 336p. 149.00 *(978-1-933864-42-6(7))* Demos Medical Publishing, LLC.

Thomas, Richard. The Essiac Report: Canada's Remarkable Unknown Cancer Remedy. (Illus.). 256p. (Orig.). 29.95 *(978-0-9639818-2-0(X))*; 29.95 *(978-0-9639818-3-7(8))*; pap. 19.95 *(978-0-9639818-0-6(3))*; lib. bdg. 29.95 *(978-0-9639818-1-3(1))* Alternative Treatment Information Network.

Thompson, Terry. A New Strategy for the War on Cancer: Finally! A New Force Is Entering the Fight & Its Success Depends on Us. 2011. (ENG.). 294p. pap. 19.95 *(978-1-60037-777-8(7))* Morgan James Publishing.

Timmermann, Carsten. Lung Cancer & 20th Century Medicine: The Recalcitrant Disease. 2012. (Science, Technology & Medicine in Modern History Ser.). (ENG.). 272p. 69.95 *(978-1-4039-8802-7(1))* Palgrave Macmillan.

Tobias, Jeffrey & Hochhauser, Daniel. Cancer & Its Management. 6th ed. 2010. (ENG., Illus.). 576p. pap. 99.95 *(978-1-4051-7015-4(8)*, Wiley-Blackwell) Wiley, John & Sons, Inc.

Tovey, Phillip, et al. Traditional, Complementary & Alternative Medicine & Cancer Care: An International Analysis of Grassroots Integration. 2007. (Illus.). 179p. per. 47.95 *(978-0-415-35994-8(5))* Routledge.

Trump, Donald L. & Johnson, Candace S., eds. Vitamin D & Cancer. 2010. (ENG., Illus.). xi, 342p. 189.00 *(978-1-4419-7187-6(4)*, 1441971874) Springer.

Tunn, Per-Ulf. Treatment of Bone & Soft Tissue Sarcomas. 2008. (Recent Results in Cancer Research Ser.). (Illus.). 200p. 199.00 *(978-3-540-77959-9(0))* Springer.

Udeani, George O. Cancer Medicine: Drug Discovery & Development. 2010. 148p. 75.00 *(978-1-4490-3943-1(X))*; pap. 60.00 *(978-1-4490-3944-8(8))* AuthorHouse.

Ullrich, A., ed. Molecular Targets in Cancer Therapy & Their Impact on Cancer Management Vol. 63: 2nd State-of-the-Art Conference, Montreux, February 2002. (Oncology Ser.). (Illus.). *(978-3-8055-7502-7(5))* Karger, S. AG.

Valentini, Vincenzo, et al, eds. Multidisciplinary Management of Rectal Cancer: Questions & Answers. 2012. (ENG., Illus.). xviii, 320p. pap. 69.95 ***(978-3-642-25004-0(1)***, 3642250041) Springer.

Van As-Brooks, Corina J. & Ward, Elizabeth C., eds. Head & Neck Cancer: Treatment, Rehabilitation, & Outcomes. 2006. (Illus.). 224p. 99.99 incl. cd-rom *(978-1-59756-061-0(8))* Plural Publishing, Inc.

VanNucci, Laura. Gene Therapy for Breast Cancer Treatment. 2011. 80p. pap. ***(978-3-8443-2207-1(8))*** Lambert Academic Publishing.

Vazquez, Dra. Ma. Del Camen Mejia & Navarro, Samuel, eds. New Approaches in the Treatment of Cancer. 2011. (Cancer Etiology, Diagnosis & Treatments Ser.). (Illus.). 223p. 79.00 *(978-1-61728-304-8(5))* Nova Science Pubs., Inc.

Vilas, Santiago. Prostate Cancer Is Curable. 2006. (Illus.). 185p. per. 17.95 *(978-0-9748946-1-4(3))* Yago Editorial, LLC.

Vincent, J. Clare Our Story. 2008. 192p. per. *(978-1-84747-591-6(4))* Chipmunkapublishing.

Vuga, Marike. Sequential Therapy in Metastatic Breast Cancer Patients. 2010. 64p. pap. *(978-3-639-20970-9(2))* VDM Verlag Dr. Mueller e.K.

Wachsman, David S. P. C. A Layman's Guide to the Prostate Cancer Experience. 2011. 136p. 23.95 ***(978-1-4620-1064-6(4))***; pap. 13.95 ***(978-1-4620-1063-9(6))*** iUniverse, Inc.

Wallace, W. H. B. & Kelnar, C. J. H., eds. Endocrinopathy after Childhood Cancer Treatment. 2009. (Endocrine Development Ser.). (ENG., Illus.). 186p. *(978-3-8055-9037-2(7))* Karger, S. AG.

Walther, Wolfgang & Stein, Ulrike S., eds. Gene Therapy of Cancer: Methods & Protocols. 2nd ed. 2009. (Methods in Molecular Biology Ser.). (ENG., Illus.). xiv, 738p. 149.00 *(978-1-934115-85-5(1))* Humana Pr.

Wartofsky, Leonard & Van Nostrand, Douglas, eds. Thyroid Cancer: A Comprehensive Guide to Clinical Management. 2nd ed. 2010. (Illus.). 740p. pap. 259.00 *(978-1-61737-583-5(7)*, 1617375837) Humana Pr.

Watson, Maggie & Kissane, David W., eds. Handbook of Psychotherapy in Cancer Care. 2011. (ENG., Illus.). 284p. pap. 57.95 *(978-0-470-66003-4(1)*, Wiley) Wiley, John & Sons, Inc.

Watson, Max, et al. Cancer Care. 2010. (ENG., Illus.). 248p. pap. 24.95 *(978-0-19-923203-1(2))* Oxford Univ. Pr., Inc.

Weber, Randal S. & Moore, Brian A., eds. Cutaneous Malignancy of the Head & Neck: A Multidisciplinary Approach. 2011. (Illus.). 467p. 225.00 *(978-1-59756-338-3(2))* Plural Publishing, Inc.

Weinstein, Jodi Buckman. Tell Me What to Eat Before, During, & after Cancer Treatment: Nutritional Guidelines for Patients & Their Loved Ones. 2010. (Tell Me What to Eat Ser.). (ENG.). 1p. pap. 12.99 *(978-1-60163-109-1(X)*, New Page Bks.) Career Pr., Inc.

Wells, Paula & Halstead, Regina, eds. Rectal Cancer: Etiology, Pathogenesis & Treatment. 2008. (Illus.). xiii, 258p. 129.00 *(978-1-60692-563-8(6))* Nova Science Pubs., Inc.

Wen, Patrick Y., et al. Neurologic Complications of Cancer Therapy. 2011. 390p. ***(978-1-936287-07-9(2))***; E-Book ***(978-1-61705-019-0(9))*** Demos Medical Publishing, LLC.

West, Brandon S. & Stanley, Donna R. Lung Cancer Treatment. 2011. (Cancer Etiology, Diagnosis & Treatments Ser.). (Illus.). 167p. 95.00 *(978-1-61324-131-8(3))* Nova Science Pubs., Inc.

Wiestler, O. D., et al, eds. Cancer Stem Cells: Novel Concepts & Prospects for Tumor Therapy. 2007. (Ernst Schering Foundation Symposium Proceedings Ser.). (Illus.). 263p. 149.00 *(978-3-540-70852-0(9))* Springer.

Wigle, Dennis A. & Wong, Bill, eds. Cancer Informatics in the Post Genomic Era: Toward Information-Based Medicine. 2007. (Cancer Treatment & Research Ser.). (Illus.). 180p. 159.00 *(978-0-387-69320-0(3))* Springer.

Wilkinson, Neal. Management of Gastric Cancer, an Issue of Surgical Oncology Clinics. 2011. (Clinics: Surgery Ser.: 21-1). (ENG.). 115.00 ***(978-1-4557-3940-0(5)***, Saunders) Elsevier - Health Sciences Div.

Williams, Roger & Taylor-Robinson, Simon D., eds. Clinical Dilemmas in Primary Liver Cancer. 2012. (Clinical Dilemmas (UK) Ser.). (ENG., Illus.). 230p. pap. 84.95 ***(978-0-470-65797-3(9)***, Wiley-Blackwell) Wiley, John & Sons, Inc.

Williamson, Steve & Polwart, Calum. The Oral Anticancer Medicine Handbook. 2009. 193p. pap. 21.50 *(978-1-4092-4044-0(4))* Lulu Enterprises Inc.

Woodruff, Teresa K., et al, eds. Oncofertility: Ethical, Legal, Social, & Medical Perspectives. 2010. (Cancer Treatment & Research Ser.). (Illus.). xvii, 519p. 279.00 *(978-1-4419-6517-2(3)*, 1441965173) Springer.

Woodruff, Teresa K. & Snyder, Karrie Ann, eds. Oncofertility: Fertility Preservation for Cancer Survivors. 2007. (Cancer Treatment & Research Ser.). (Illus.). 262p. 169.00 *(978-0-387-72292-4(0))* Springer.

World Health Organization. Cancer Control: Knowledge into Action. WHO Guide for Effective Programmes:Early Detection. 2007. (Nonserial Publication). (ENG.). 48p. pap. 18.00 *(978-92-4-154733-8(2))* World Health Organization.

—Cancer Control: Knowledge into Action. WHO Guide for Effective Programmes:Palliative Care. 2007. (Nonserial Publication). (ENG.). 48p. pap. 18.00 *(978-92-4-154734-5(0))* World Health Organization.

—Cancer Control: Knowledge into Action. WHO Guide for Effective Programmes: Prevention. 2007. (Nonserial Publication). (ENG.). 54p. pap. 18.00 *(978-92-4-154711-6(1))* World Health Organization.

Wright, Jessie. Third Opinion on Prostate Cancer: A Guide to Knowing Your Options. 2010. pap. 12.99 *(978-1-61566-021-6(6))* Tate Publishing & Enterprises, LLC.

Wu, Jane Y., ed. RNA & Cancer. 2009. (Cancer Treatment & Research Ser.). (Illus.). 320p. 129.00 *(978-1-4419-0021-0(7))* Springer.

Yea, Steven & Friedman, Scott L. Regulation of the Krüppel-like Factor 6 Tumor Suppressor: Ras Promotes Cancer Cell Growth via Alternative Splicing-Mediated Inactivation of KLF6. 2008. 168p. pap. *(978-3-639-10335-9(1))* VDM Verlag Dr. Mueller e.K.

Yeung, Sai-Ching Jim, et al. Medical Care of the Cancer Patient. 2009. (Illus.). 772p. 99.95 *(978-1-60795-008-0(1))* PMPH-USA, Ltd.

Yu, Rencun & Hong, Hai. Cancer Management with Chinese Medicine. 2012. 200p. 58.00 ***(978-981-4374-74-3(1))*** World Scientific Publishing Co., Inc.

Zago, Romano. Cancer Can Be Cured! 2008. 264p. 29.95 *(978-1-4401-0910-2(9))* iUniverse, Inc.

—Cancer Can Be Cured. 2008. 264p. pap. 19.95 *(978-1-4401-0911-9(7))* iUniverse, Inc.

Zielinski, Christoph C., et al. Drugs for HER2-positive Breast Cancer. 2010. (Milestones in Drug Therapy Ser.). (Illus.). 250p. 139.00 *(978-3-0346-0093-4(3)*, 3034600933) Birkhauser Verlag AG CHE. Dist: Springer.

25 Jahre im Dienste der Krebsforschung. (Onkologie Ser.: Vol. 25). (GER., Illus.). *(978-3-8055-7393-1(6))* Karger, S. AG.

CANCER CELLS

Acilan, Ceyda. Chromosomal Segregation Defects in Cancer Cells Formation of Anaphase Bridges & Multipolar Spindles. 2008. 168p. pap. *(978-3-639-10677-0(6))* VDM Verlag Dr. Mueller e.K.

Ahamed, Shaik Imran. Diagnosis & Treatment of Cancer Using Nanotechnology. 2010. 68p. pap. *(978-3-8383-8174-9(2))* Lambert Academic Publishing.

Al-Douh, Mohammed, et al. Synthesis, Characterization & Anti-Proliferation Study. 2011. 268p. pap. ***(978-3-8443-3294-0(4))*** Lambert Academic Publishing.

Allan, Alison L., ed. Cancer Stem Cells in Solid Tumors. 2011. (Stem Cell Biology & Regenerative Medicine Ser.). (ENG., Illus.). xvii, 475p. 209.00 *(978-1-61779-245-8(4)*, 1617792454) Humana Pr.

Andre, Lucas H. & Roux, Nathan E., eds. Neuroblastoma Research Trends. 2008. (Illus.). 172p. 98.00 *(978-1-60456-790-8(2))* Nova Science Pubs., Inc.

Arnouk, Hilal. Tumor Secreted Grp170 As a Cancer Vaccine. 2009. 92p. pap. *(978-3-639-15924-0(1))* VDM Verlag Dr. Mueller e.K.

Atchison, Lakshmi & Atchison, Michael. Cell Biology with Cancer Applications, Lab Manual (CPSY) 2008. (ENG.). 336p. (C). spiral bd. 87.33 *(978-0-07-812309-2(7)*, 0078123097) McGraw-Hill Cos., The.

Bagley, Rebecca G. The Tumor Microenvironment. 2010. (Illus.). xviii, 767p. E-Book ***(978-1-4419-6615-5(3))*** Springer.

Baronzio, Gian Franco, et al. Cancer Microenvironment & Therapeutic Implications: Tumor Pathophysiology Mechanisms & Therapeutic Strategies. 2009. (ENG., Illus.). vii, 328p. 169.00 *(978-1-4020-9575-7(9)*, 1402095759) Springer.

Barr, Daniel. Clathrin-Independent Endocytosis of Erbb2 in Human Breast Cancer Cells. 2009. 68p. pap. *(978-3-639-15069-8(4))* VDM Verlag Dr. Mueller e.K.

Bilyak, Andrej. Tumour Invasion & Formation of Metastases Statistical Approach. 2010. 92p. pap. *(978-3-639-26416-6(9))* VDM Verlag Dr. Mueller e.K.

Blumenthal, Rosalyn D., ed. Chemosensitivity: Volume I: in Vitro Assays. 2010. (Methods in Molecular Medicine Ser.). (Illus.). xiii, 231p. pap. 104.00 *(978-1-61737-508-8(X)*, 161737508X) Humana Pr.

Bonavida, Benjamin, ed. Sensitization of Cancer Cells for Chemo/Immuno/Radio-therapy. 2010. (Cancer Drug Discovery & Development Ser.). (Illus.). xxi, 419p. pap. 209.00 ***(978-1-61737-928-4(X)***, 161737928X) Humana Pr.

—Sensitization of Cancer Cells for Chemo/Immuno/Radio-Therapy. 2008. (Illus.). 479p. (C). 209.00 *(978-1-934115-29-9(0)*, 1934115290) Humana Pr.

Briggs, Andre P. & Coburn, Jacob A. Handbook of Cell Proliferation. 2009. (Series: Cell Biology Research Progress Ser.). 195.00 *(978-1-60741-105-5(9))* Nova Science Pubs., Inc.

Brooks, Susan A. & Schumacher, Udo, eds. Metastasis Research Protocols. 2010. (Methods in Molecular Medicine Ser.). 344p. pap. 139.00 *(978-1-61737-096-0(7)*, 1617370967); (Illus.). 336p. pap. 169.00 *(978-1-61737-099-1(1)*, 1617370991) Humana Pr.

Brown, A. M. C. Cell Biology of Cancer. 2011. (Colloquium Series on the Cell Biology of Medicine Ser.). 100p. pap. 35.00 *(978-1-61504-126-8(5))* Morgan & Claypool Life Science Publishers.

Brown, Anthony M. C. Cell Transformation & Proliferation in Cancer. 2011. (Colloquium Series on the Cell Biology of Medicine Ser.). 100p. pap. 35.00 *(978-1-61504-270-8(9))* Morgan & Claypool Life Science Publishers.

Brown, Robert & Böger-Brown, Uta, eds. Cytotoxic Drug Resistance Mechanisms. 2010. (Methods in Molecular Medicine Ser.). 248p. pap. 119.00 *(978-1-61737-093-9(2)*, 1617370932) Humana Pr.

Chatterjee, Malay & Kashfi, Khosrow, eds. Cell Signaling & Molecular Targets in Cancer. 2011. (ENG., Illus.). xi, 328p. 189.00 ***(978-1-4614-0729-4(X)***, 146140729X) Springer.

Conti, Matteo. The Selfish Cell: An Evolutionary Defeat. 2010. xiv, 90p. pap. 119.00 *(978-90-481-7941-1(6)*, 9048179416) 2008. (Illus.). 100p. 119.00 *(978-1-4020-8641-0(5))* Springer.

Cree, Ian A. Cancer Cell Culture: Methods & Protocols. 2nd ed. 2011. (Illus.). xiv, 502p. E-Book ***(978-1-61779-080-5(X))*** Humana Pr.

Cree, Ian A., ed. Cancer Cell Culture: Methods & Protocols. 2nd ed. 2011. (Methods in Molecular Biology Ser.). (Illus.). xiv, 502p. 139.00 *(978-1-61779-079-9(6)*, 1617790796) Humana Pr.

Dai, Wei, ed. Checkpoint Responses in Cancer Therapy. 2008. (Cancer Drug Discovery & Development Ser.). (Illus.). 300p. 219.00 *(978-1-58829-930-7(9))* Humana Pr.

Dittmar, Thomas & Zänker, Kurt S. Cancer & Stem Cells. Dittmar, Thomas & Zander, Kurt S., eds. 2008. (Illus.). viii, 220p. 120.00 *(978-1-60456-478-5(4))* Nova Science Pubs., Inc.

Enders, Greg, ed. Cell Cycle Deregulation in Cancer. 2010. (Contemporary Cancer Research Ser.). (ENG., Illus.). viii, 196p. 219.00 *(978-1-4419-1769-0(1)*, 1441917691) Springer.

Farrar, William L., ed. Cancer Stem Cells. 2009. (ENG., Illus.). 182p. 95.00 *(978-0-521-89628-3(2))* Cambridge Univ. Pr.

Fernandes, Julio A. Focus on Neuroblastoma Research. 2006. (Illus.). 212p. (C). pap. 225.00 *(978-1-60021-484-4(3))* Nova Science Pubs., Inc.

Figgins, Herold C. Trends in Cell Apoptosis Research. 2006. 293p. (C). 225.00 *(978-1-60021-424-0(X))* Nova Science Pubs., Inc.

Franciscis, Vittorio de. Signalling Molecules as Targets in Cancer Therapy. 2006. 240p. 89.00 *(978-1-60021-243-7(3)*, Nova Biomedical Bks.) Nova Science Pubs., Inc.

Fulton, Amy M. Chemokine Receptors in Cancer. 2009. (Cancer Drug Discovery & Development Ser.). (ENG., Illus.). 208p. 189.00 *(978-1-60327-266-7(6))* Humana Pr.

Garrett, Carleton T. & Sell, Stewart, eds. Cellular Cancer Markers. 2010. (Contemporary Biomedicine Ser.). 496p. pap. 189.00 *(978-1-61737-000-7(2)*, 1617370002) Humana Pr.

Gewirtz, David A., et al, eds. Apoptosis, Senescence & Cancer. 2nd ed. 2010. (Cancer Drug Discovery & Development Ser.). (Illus.). xvii, 599p. pap. 199.00 *(978-1-61737-621-4(3)*, 1617376213) Humana Pr.

Gheewala, Nirav K. & N. GHEEWALA, Tejal. Herbal Extract on Cancer Cell Line. 2011. 76p. pap. ***(978-3-8443-9479-5(6))*** Lambert Academic Publishing.

Giordano, Antonio & Soprano, Kenneth J., eds. Cell Cycle Inhibitors in Cancer Therapy. 2010. (Cancer Drug Discovery & Development Ser.). (Illus.). 326p. pap. 179.00 *(978-1-61737-257-5(9)*, 1617372579) Humana Pr.

Gisselsson, David, ed. Intratumor diversity & clonal evolution in Cancer. 2011. (ENG., Illus.). 368p. 161.00 ***(978-0-12-387688-1(5)***, Academic Pr.) Elsevier Science & Technology Bks.

Gogichadze, G. K. & Gogichadze, T. Karyogamic Theory of Cancer Cell Formation from the View of the XXI Century. 2010. (Cancer Etiology, Diagnosis & Treatments Ser.). 125.00 *(978-1-60876-386-3(2)*, Nova Biomedical Bks.) Nova Science Pubs., Inc.

Goldie, James H. & Coldman, Andrew J. Drug Resistance in Cancer: Mechanisms & Models. 2009. (ENG., Illus.). 256p. (C). pap. 56.00 *(978-0-521-11170-6(6))* Cambridge Univ. Pr.

Hayat, M. A., ed. Stem Cells & Cancer Stem Cells Vol. 1: Therapeutic Applications in Disease & Injury. 2011. (Stem Cells & Cancer Stem Cells Ser.). (ENG., Illus.). xv, 198p. 189.00 *(978-94-007-1708-4(3)*, 9400717083) Springer.

Hayat, M. A., ed. Stem Cells & Cancer Stem Cells Vol. 2: Therapeutic Applications in Disease & Injury. 2011. (Stem Cells & Cancer Stem Cells Ser.: Vol. 2). (ENG., Illus.). xxiv, 384p. 209.00 ***(978-94-007-2015-2(7)***, 9400720157) Springer.

Hosseinzadeh, Leila, et al. Curcumin & Doxorubicin. 2011. 148p. pap. ***(978-3-8443-9921-9(6))*** Lambert Academic Publishing.

Jordan, Melissa E., ed. Cancer Stem Cells. 2010. (Cancer Etiology, Diagnosis & Treatments Ser.). 160.00 *(978-1-61668-971-1(4))* Nova Science Pubs., Inc.

Kotlan, Beatrix. Tumor Infiltrating B Lymphocytes: A Novel Approach for Cancer Diagnostics & Therapeutics. 2009. (Illus.). 160p. 139.00 *(978-0-387-69881-6(7))* Springer.

LaFond, Richard, ed. Cancer: The Outlaw Cell, 1 vol. 3rd ed. 2012. (ENG., Illus.). 384p. 99.95 *(978-0-8412-0000-5(9))* American Chemical Society.

LeRoith, Derek, ed. Insulin-like Growth Factors & Cancer: From Basic Biology to Therapeutics. 2011. (Cancer Drug Discovery & Development Ser.). (ENG., Illus.). xii, 284p. 189.00 ***(978-1-4614-0597-9(1)***, 1461405971) Springer.

Li, Willis X., ed. Cell Cycle Checkpoints: Methods & Protocols. 2011. (Methods in Molecular Biology Ser.). (ENG., Illus.). x, 307p. 119.00 *(978-1-61779-272-4(1)*, 1617792721) Humana Pr.

Majumder, Sadhan, ed. Stem Cells & Cancer. 2009. (ENG., Illus.). x, 286p. 160.00 *(978-0-387-89610-6(4)*, 0387896104) Springer.

Mallet, Daniel. Haptotaxis in Tumour Growth & Invasion. 2008. 200p. pap. *(978-3-639-06145-1(4))* VDM Verlag Dr. Mueller e.K.

Margolin, Adam. Computational Inference of Genetic Networks in Human Cancer Cells. 2009. 288p. pap. *(978-3-639-14814-5(2))* VDM Verlag Dr. Mueller e.K.

Markman, Maurie, et al, eds. Stem Cell Basis of Cancer: Tumorigenesis & Drug Development. 2006. (Cancer Drug Discovery & Development Ser.). 400p. 175.00 *(978-1-59745-331-8(5))* Humana Pr.

Masters, John & Palsson, Bernhard, eds. Human Cell Culture: Volume II: Cancer Cell Lines Part 2. 2010. (Human Cell Culture Ser.). (Illus.). 400p. pap. 329.00 *(978-90-481-5286-5(0)*, 9048152860) Springer.

McKinnell, Robert G., et al. The Biological Basis of Cancer. 2nd rev. ed. 2006. (ENG., Illus.). 494p. per. 79.00 *(978-0-521-60633-2(0))* Cambridge Univ. Pr.

Mehta, Kapil & Siddik, Zahid H., eds. Drug Resistance in Cancer Cells. 2009. (ENG., Illus.). xvii, 363p. 149.00 *(978-0-387-89444-7(6)*, 0387894446) Springer.

Meridith, Alan T. Handbook of Prostate Cancer Cell Research: Growth, Signalling & Survival. 2009. (Cancer Etiology, Diagnosis & Treatments Ser.). 129.00 *(978-1-60741-954-9(8)*, Nova Biomedical Bks.) Nova Science Pubs., Inc.

Miettinen, Susanna. Targeting the growth ovarian cancer cells: In vitro effect of vitamin D3, anticancer drugs & p53 gene Therapy. 2009. (Acta Universitatis Tamperensis Ser.). 152p. pap. 82.50 *(978-951-44-7869-7(X))* Tampere Univ. Pr. FIN. Dist: Coronet Bks.

Molls, M. The Impact of Tumor Biology on Cancer Treatment & Multidisciplinary Strategies. 2009. (Medical Radiology / Radiation Oncology Ser.). (ENG., Illus.). x, 370p. 199.00 *(978-3-540-74385-9(5))* Springer.

Mor, Gil & Alvero, Ayesha, eds. Apoptosis & Cancer: Methods & Protocols. 2010. (Methods in Molecular Biology Ser.). (Illus.). xi, 266p. pap. 119.00 *(978-1-61737-582-8(9)*, 1617375829) Humana Pr.

Okudela, Koji, et al. Cancer Stem Cells in Lung Cancer. 2010. (Cancer Etiology, Diagnosis & Treatments Ser.). (Illus.). vi, 65p. pap. 47.00 *(978-1-61728-295-9(2)*, Nova Biomedical Bks.) Nova Science Pubs., Inc.

Palsson, Bernhard & Masters, John, eds. Human Cell Culture: Volume III: Cancer Cell Lines Part 3 Leukemias & Lymphomas. 2010. (Human Cell Culture Ser.). (Illus.). 384p. pap. 379.00 *(978-90-481-5420-3(0)*, 9048154200) Springer.

Parsons, Devon W. Stem Cells & Cancer. 2007. 284p. 129.00 *(978-1-60021-517-9(3))* Nova Science Pubs., Inc.

Parsons, Robert A., ed. Progress in Cancer Drug Resistance Research. 2008. 129.00 *(978-1-60021-822-4(9)*, Nova Biomedical Bks.) Nova Science Pubs., Inc.

Pinedo, Herbert M. & Giaccone, Giuseppe. Drug Resistance in the Treatment of Cancer. 2007. (Cancer: Clinical Science in Practice Ser.). (ENG.). 340p. pap. 76.00 *(978-0-521-03074-8(9))* Cambridge Univ. Pr.

Polunovsky, Vitaly & Houghton, Peter J. MTOR Pathway & mTOR Inhibitors in Cancer Therapy. 2010. (Cancer Drug Discovery & Development Ser.). (ENG., Illus.). 235p. 239.00 *(978-1-60327-270-4(4))* Humana Pr.

Rossi, Silvia. Cell Surface Proteoglycan Signature of Cancer Cells & Role of Gpc-5. 2010. 88p. pap. *(978-3-8383-9391-9(0))* Lambert Academic Publishing.

Saiko, Philipp. Effects of Naturally Occurring Compounds on Human Cancer Cells. 2008. 212p. pap. *(978-3-639-05897-0(6))* VDM Verlag Dr. Mueller e.K.

Scatena, Roberto, et al, eds. Advances in Cancer Stem Cell Biology. 2011. (ENG., Illus.). xii, 343p. 189.00 ***(978-1-4614-0808-6(3)***, 1461408083) Springer.

Schuringa, Jan Jacob & Horton, Sarah J. Genetic & Epigenetic Alterations that Drive Leukemic Stem Cell Self-Renewal. Boom, Vincent van den, ed. 2010. (Stem Cells - Laboratory & Clinical Research Ser.). pap. 49.00 *(978-1-61728-379-6(7)*, Nova Biomedical Bks.) Nova Science Pubs., Inc.

Sheets, Rebecca & Petricciani, John C. Vaccine Cell Substrates 2004: National Institutes of Health (NIH), Doubletree Hotel, Rockville, Md., USA, June 29-July 1, 2004, Vol. 123. (Developments in Biologicals Ser.: Vol. 123). (Illus.). 366p. pap. *(978-3-8055-7999-5(3))* Karger, S. AG.

Siemann, Dietmar W., ed. Tumor Microenvironment. 2010. (ENG., Illus.). 454p. 139.95 *(978-0-470-74996-8(2)*, Wiley) Wiley, John & Sons, Inc.

Stem cells & Cancer. 2007. pap. 130.00 *(978-1-58603-802-1(8))* IOS Pr., Inc.

Terrian, David M., ed. Cancer Cell Signaling: Methods & Protocols. 2010. (Methods in Molecular Biology Ser.). (Illus.). 352p. pap. 139.00 *(978-1-61737-341-1(9)*, 1617373419) Humana Pr.

Torres, Liman S. Cancer Drug Resistance Research Perspectives. 2007. 223p. 129.00 *(978-1-60021-572-8(6))* Nova Science Pubs., Inc.

Ucar, Deniz A. & Moreb, Jan. A New Approach for the Enrichment of Cancer Initiating Cells. 2010. 72p. pap. *(978-3-8383-3965-8(7))* Lambert Academic Publishing.

Verrite, Ethan G. Drug Resistant Neoplasms. 2009. (Cancer Etiology, Diagnosis & Treatments Ser.). 135.00 *(978-1-60741-255-7(1))* Nova Science Pubs., Inc.

Wagner, Josef. The in Vitro Differentiation of Mouse Embryonic Stem Cells. 2010. 320p. pap. *(978-3-8383-6003-4(6))* Lambert Academic Publishing.

Weinberg, Robert. The Biology of Cancer. 2010. (ENG.). cd-rom 20.00 *(978-0-8153-4458-2(9)*, Garland Science) Taylor & Francis Group.

Weinberg, Robert A. The Biology of Cancer. 2nd rev. ed. 2013. (ENG., Illus.). 864p. 126.00 ***(978-0-8153-4220-5(9))***; 168.00 ***(978-0-8153-4219-9(5))*** Taylor & Francis Group. (Garland Science).

Wells, Alan, ed. Cell Motility in Cancer Invasion & Metastasis. 2010. (Cancer Metastasis - Biology & Treatment Ser.). xiii, 351p. pap. 239.00 *(978-90-481-7011-1(7)*, 9048170117) Springer.

Wiestler, O. D., et al, eds. Cancer Stem Cells: Novel Concepts & Prospects for Tumor Therapy. 2007. (Ernst Schering Foundation Symposium Proceedings Ser.). (Illus.). 263p. 149.00 *(978-3-540-70852-0(9))* Springer.

Yea, Steven & Friedman, Scott L. Regulation of the Krüppel-like Factor 6 Tumor Suppressor: Ras Promotes Cancer Cell Growth via Alternative Splicing-Mediated Inactivation of KLF6. 2008. 168p. pap. *(978-3-639-10335-9(1))* VDM Verlag Dr. Mueller e.K.

Yefenof, Eitan, ed. Innate & Adaptive Immunity at the Tumor Microenvironment. 2007. (Tumor Microenvironment Ser.). (Illus.). 335p. 199.00 *(978-1-4020-6749-5(6)*, 1402067496) Springer.

Yu, Dihua & Hung, Mien-Chie, eds. Breast Cancer Chemosensitivity. 2007. (Advances in Experimental Medicine & Biology Ser.: Vol. 608). 190p. 189.00 *(978-0-387-74037-9(6))* Springer.

Yu, John S., ed. Cancer Stem Cells: Methods & Protocols. 2009. (Methods in Molecular Biology Ser.). (ENG., Illus.). xvi, 284p. 149.00 *(978-1-58829-938-3(4)*, 1588299384) Humana Pr.

Yufang Shi, et al, eds. Molecular Mechanisms of Programmed Cell Death. 2010. (ENG.). 220p. pap. 159.00 *(978-1-4419-3404-8(9)*, 1441934049) Springer.

Zhou, Jun, ed. Multi-Drug Resistance in Cancer. 2009. (Methods in Molecular Biology Ser.). (ENG., Illus.). 504p. 129.00 *(978-1-60761-415-9(4)*, 1607614154) Humana Pr.

CANCER EDUCATION

see Cancer—Study and Teaching

CANCER GENES

see Oncogenes

CANCER GENETICS

see Cancer—Genetic Aspects

CANCER IN CHILDREN

see Tumors in Children

CANCER INVASIVENESS

Here are entered works on the ability of cancer to infiltrate and actively destroy surrounding tissue. Works on the transfer of cancer to an organ or part of the body remote from the primary site are entered under Metastasis.

see also Metastasis

Bassi, Pierfrancesco & Pagano, Francesco, eds. Invasive Bladder Cancer. 2006. (Illus.). 303p. 119.00 *(978-1-84628-376-5(0)*, 1846283760) Springer.

Dukubo, Gabriel D., ed. Field Cancerization: Basic Science & Clinical Applications. 2011. ***(978-1-61761-006-6(2))*** Nova Science Pubs., Inc.

Fitzgerald, Rebecca C., ed. Pre-Invasive Disease: Pathogenesis & Clinical Management: Pathogenesis & Clinical Management. 2010. (ENG., Illus.). xxii, 519p. 189.00 *(978-1-4419-6693-3(5)*, 1441966935) Springer.

Kaiser, Hans E. & Nasir, Aejaz, eds. Selected Aspects of Cancer Progression: Metastasis, Apoptosis & Immune Response. 2008. (Cancer Growth & Progression Ser.). (Illus.). 249p. 199.00 *(978-1-4020-6728-0(3))* Springer.

—Selected Aspects of Cancer Progression: Metastasis, Apoptosis & Immune Response: Metastasis, Apoptosis & Immune Response. 2010. (Cancer Growth & Progression Ser.). vi, 250p. pap. 199.00 *(978-90-481-7706-6(5)*, 9048177065) Springer.

Leong, Stanley P. L. From Local Invasion to Metastatic Cancer: Involvement of Distant Sites Through the Lymphovascular System. 2009. (Illus.). xxviii, 637p. *(978-1-60327-087-8(6))* Humana Pr.

CANCER NURSING

see Cancer—Nursing

CANCER PAIN

Bruera, Eduardo D. & Portenoy, Russell K., eds. Cancer Pain: Assessment & Management. 2nd ed. 2009. (ENG., Illus.). 656p. 253.00 *(978-0-521-87927-9(2))* Cambridge Univ. Pr.

Burton, Allen W. & Fisch, Michael J. Cancer Pain Management. 2006. (ENG., Illus.). 544p. 139.00 *(978-0-07-144535-1(8)*, 0071445358) McGraw-Hill Professional Publishing.

Chow, Edward & Merrick, Joav, eds. Advanced Cancer. Pain & Quality of Life. 2010. (Health & Human Development (Joav Merrick - Series Editor) Ser.). 89.00 *(978-1-61668-207-1(8)*, Nova Biomedical Bks.) Nova Science Pubs., Inc.

Cousins, Michael & Gallagher, Rollin. Fast Facts: Fast Facts: Chronic & cancer Pain. 2nd rev. ed. 2011. (ENG., Illus.). 168p. pap. 25.00 ***(978-1-905832-85-9(0))*** Health Pr., Ltd. GBR. Dist: BookMasters Distribution Services (BDS).

Cram101 Textbook Reviews. Outlines & Highlights for Cancer Pain: Assessment & Management by Russell K. Portenoy Edited by Eduardo D. Bruera, ISBN. 2011. 136p. pap. 28.95 ***(978-1-61461-489-0(X))*** Cram101 Inc.

Davies, Andrew. Cancer Related Breakthrough Pain. Davies, Andrew, ed. 2006. (Oxford Pain Management Library Ser.). (Illus.). 128p. per. 29.95 *(978-0-19-921567-6(7))* Oxford Univ. Pr., Inc.
Davis, Mellar P., et al, eds. Opioids in Cancer Pain. 2nd ed. 2009. (ENG., Illus.). 456p. 115.00 *(978-0-19-923664-0(X))* Oxford Univ. Pr., Inc.
Fitzgibbon, Dermot R. & Loeser, John D. Cancer Pain: Assessment, Diagnosis, & Management. 2010. (ENG., Illus.). 464p. 159.99 *(978-1-60831-089-0(2))* Lippincott Williams & Wilkins.
Forbes, Karen. Opioids in Cancer Pain. Forbes, Karen, ed. 2008. (Oxford Pain Management Library Ser.). (ENG., Illus.). 152p. 26.99 *(978-0-19-921880-6(3))* Oxford Univ. Pr., Inc.
Hester, Joan, et al. Interventional Pain Control in Cancer Pain Management. 2012. (ENG., Illus.). 304p. 160.00 *(978-0-19-921908-7(7))* Oxford Univ. Pr., Inc.
Irving, Colm. Anaesthesia, intensive care, & pain management for the cancer Patient. Farquhar-Smith, Paul & Wigmore, Tim, eds. 2011. (ENG., Illus.). 272p. 98.50 *(978-0-19-958464-2(8))* Oxford Univ. Pr., Inc.
Jacobsen, Ramune. Barriers to Cancer Pain Management with Opioids. 2010. 100p. pap. *(978-3-8383-5890-1(2))* Lambert Academic Publishing.
Litot, Monsignor Ed. When Death Comes as A Friend. 2010. 136p. pap. 14.99 *(978-1-4520-7311-8(2))* AuthorHouse.
Menten, Johan. Cancer Pain: Interdisciplinary & comprehensive Management. 2010. 168p. pap. *(978-3-8383-4370-9(0))* Lambert Academic Publishing.
National Cancer Institute. Pain Control Support for People with Cancer. 2009. (Health Psychology Research Focus Ser.). 43.00 *(978-1-60692-848-6(1))*, Nova Biomedical Bks.) Nova Science Pubs., Inc.
Paice, Judith A., et al, eds. Cancer Pain: From Molecules to Suffering. 2010. pap. 75.00 *(978-0-931092-81-7(7))* IASI Pr.
Stannard, Cathy, et al. Opioids in Non-Cancer Pain. 2008. (Oxford Pain Management Library Ser.). (ENG., Illus.). 136p. 24.95 *(978-0-19-923123-2(0))* Oxford Univ. Pr., Inc.
Sykes, Nigel, et al. Cancer Pain, 4 vols. 2nd ed. 2008. (ENG., Illus.). 624p. 195.00 *(978-0-340-94007-5(7)*, Hodder Arnold) Hodder Education GBR. Dist: Oxford Univ. Pr., Inc.

CANCER PATIENTS
see Cancer—Patients

CANCER RESEARCH
see Cancer—Research

CANCUN (MEXICO)
Castellanos, M. Bianet. A Return to Servitude: Maya Migration & the Tourist Trade in Cancun. 2010. (First Peoples: New Directions Indigenous Ser.). (ENG., Illus.). 296p. 75.00 *(978-0-8166-5614-1(2))*; pap. 25.00 *(978-0-8166-5615-8(0))* Univ. of Minnesota Pr.
Rider, Nick. Top 10 Cancun & Yucatan. 2012. (Eyewitness top 10 travel Guide Ser.). (ENG.). 144p. pap. 14.00 ***(978-0-7566-9596-5(1))*** Dorling Kindersley Publishing, Inc.

CANCUN (MEXICO)—GUIDEBOOKS
Baird, David, et al. Frommer's Cancun & the Yucatan 2012. 8th ed. 2011. (Frommer's Color Complete Ser.). (ENG., Illus.). 400p. pap. 19.99 *(978-1-118-02738-7(8)*, Frommers) Wiley, John & Sons, Inc.
Benchwick, Greg. Cancun & the Yucatan. 2011. (Encounter Ser.). (ENG., Illus.). 168p. pap. 14.99 *(978-1-74179-660-5(1))* Lonely Planet Pubns.
Bennett, Lindsay. Cancun & Cozumel. 9th ed. 2008. (Pocket Guide Ser.). (ENG., Illus.). 144p. pap. 8.95 *(978-981-268-270-3(8))* APA Publications Services SGP. Dist: Ingram Pub. Services.
Conord, June & Hepp, Joy. Cancun & the Yucatan. 2nd ed. 2010. (Frommer's Day by Day - Pocket Ser.: 59). (ENG., Illus.). 192p. pap. 14.99 *(978-0-470-49768-5(8)*, Frommers) Wiley, John & Sons, Inc.
Fodor's. Fodor's Cancun & the Riviera Maya 2013: With Cozumel & the Best of the Yucatan. 2012. (Full-color Travel Guide Ser.). (ENG.). 420p. pap. 19.99 ***(978-0-307-92945-7(0)***, Fodor's) Fodor's Travel Pubns.
Gilbert, Jonathan P., et al. Must See Cancun & the Yucatan Michelin. 2009. (Must Sees Ser.). (ENG., Illus.). 160p. pap. 11.99 *(978-1-906261-67-2(9))* Michelin Travel & Lifestyle.
Harris, Richard. Cancún & the Yucatán. 2010. (Hidden Travel Ser.). (ENG., Illus.). 432p. pap. 17.95 *(978-1-56975-716-1(X))* Ulysses Pr.
Lonely Planet Staff & Benchwick, Greg. Cancun, Cozumel & the Yucatan. 5th ed. 2010. (Regional Guide Ser.). (ENG., Illus.). 300p. pap. 21.99 *(978-1-74179-414-4(5))* Lonely Planet Pubns.
Map Group Staff. Cancun InsideOut. 2008. (Illus.). 96p. vinyl bd. *(978-1-84587-040-9(9))* Map Group, The.
Rabinowitz, Eric. People's Choice Guide. Com-Cancun: Travel Survey Guidebook. 2009. (ENG.). 384p. pap. 15.95 *(978-0-942257-46-5(4))* New Chapter Pr., Inc.

CANDIDA INFECTION
see Candidiasis

CANDIDIASIS
Boroch, Ann. The Candida Cure: Yeast, Fungus & Your Health. 2009. 200p. pap. 12.95 *(978-0-9773446-1-1(4))* Quintessential Healing.
Calderone, R., ed. Candida & Candidiasis. 2nd ed. 2011. (ENG.). 480p. ***(978-1-55581-539-4(1))*** ASM Pr.
Cihlar, Ron & Calderone, Richard, eds. Candida Albicans. 2009. (Methods in Molecular Biology Ser.). 119.00 *(978-1-58829-760-0(8))* Humana Pr.
d'Enfert, Christophe & Hube, Bernhard, eds. Candida: Comparative & Functional Genomics. 2007. (Illus.). 428p. 319.00 *(978-1-904455-13-4(1))* Caister Academic Pr. GBR. Dist: International Specialized Bk. Services.
Dixon, Christopher. The Biggest Little Book of Yeast Infections. 2007. (Illus.). 67p. per. 31.99 *(978-0-9793796-9-7(5))* Strategic Publishing Group.
Dua, Amit, et al. Candida Albicans & Complete Dentures - Mystery Unravelled. 2011. 76p. pap. ***(978-3-8433-8795-8(8))*** Lambert Academic Publishing.
Ernst, Erika J., ed. Antifungal Agents. 2010. (Methods in Molecular Medicine Ser.). (Illus.). 224p. pap. 119.00 *(978-1-61737-467-8(9)*, 1617374679) Humana Pr.
Gates, Donna & Schatz, Linda. The Body Ecology Diet: Recovering Your Health & Rebuilding Your Immunity. 2011. (ENG.). 256p. (Orig.). pap. 15.95 *(978-1-4019-3543-6(5))* Hay Hse., Inc.
Gensler, Tracy Olgeaty. Probiotic & Prebiotic Recipes for Health: 100 Recipes That Battle Colitis, Candidiasis, Food Allergies, & Other Digestive Disorders. 2008. (ENG., Illus.). 224p. pap. 19.95 *(978-1-59233-321-9(4)*, 1592333214, Fair Winds Press) Quayside.
Gupta, Nivedita. Epidemiology, Genotyping. 2009. 188p. pap. *(978-3-639-17551-6(4))* VDM Verlag Dr. Mueller e.K.
Silva, Sonia, et al. Virulence Factors of Non-Candida Albicans Candida Species. 2011. 204p. pap. ***(978-3-8433-8881-8(4))*** Lambert Academic Publishing.
Tenney MH, Louise. Candida Albicans. 3rd ed. 2011. (Woodland Health Ser.). 36p. pap. 4.95 *(978-1-58054-194-7(1))* Woodland Publishing, Inc.
Trickett, Shirley. Coping with Candida. (Illus.). 100p. *(978-0-85969-688-3(X))* SPCK Publishing.
Vakil, Ronak. Polymeric Micelle Nanocarriers for the Treatment of Disseminated Candidiasis. 2008. 164p. per. *(978-3-8364-6080-4(7))* VDM Verlag Dr. Mueller e.K.

CANDLEMAKING
Aley, Robert. Candlemaking for Profit: A Practical Guide for Small-Scale Producers. 2011. (ENG.). 80p. pap. 19.95 ***(978-1-85339-721-9(0))*** Practical Action Publishing GBR. Dist: Stylus Publishing, LLC.
Ittner, Rebecca. Candlemaking the Natural Way: 30 Projects Made with Soy, Palm & Beeswax. 2010. (ENG., Illus.). 128p. 19.95 *(978-1-60059-600-1(2))* Lark Bks.
—Candlemaking the Natural Way: 31 Projects Made with Soy, Palm & Beeswax. 2011. (ENG., Illus.). 128p. pap. 14.95 *(978-1-60059-780-0(7))* Lark Bks.
Nicol, Gloria. Candles: An Inspired Guide to Creative Candles with 40 Step-by-Step Projects with Over 325 Specially Commissioned Photographs. 2009. (ENG., Illus.). 160p. pap. 18.99 *(978-1-84476-547-8(4))* Anness Publishing GBR. Dist: National Bk. Network.
Oppenheimer, Betty. Haz Tus Propias Velas. (SPA., Illus.). 226p. *(978-84-7927-509-9(X))* Robinbk., Ediciones S.L. ESP. Dist: Lectorum Pubns., Inc.
Sacchi, Luisa. Creating Candles. 2008. (ENG., Illus.). 224p. pap. 26.95 *(978-0-8117-3476-9(5))* Stackpole Bks.
Stavert, Elaine. Candles. 2010. (Cozy Ser.). (ENG., Illus.). 156p. pap. 14.95 *(978-1-86108-675-4(X))* Guild of Master Craftsman Pubns., Ltd. GBR. Dist: Sterling Publishing Co., Inc.
Thomas, Lynn A. How to Make & Market Gel Candles That Sell Like Wildfire! - Fourth Edition. 2007. 84p. pap. 19.95 *(978-0-9702417-8-8(X))* Booklocker.com, Inc.

CANDLEMAS
see also Candles and Lights
Kollamparampil, Thomas. Jacob of Sarug's Homily on the Presentation of our Lord. 2008. (Texts from Christian Late Antiquity: 15). (ENG & SYR.). pap. 46.00 *(978-1-59333-936-4(4))* Gorgias Pr., LLC.

CANDLES
see also Candlemaking
Eveleigh, David J. Candle Lighting. 2nd ed. 2008. (Shire Library). (ENG., Illus.). 32p. pap. 11.95 *(978-0-7478-0574-8(1))* Shire Pubns., Ltd. GBR. Dist: Random Hse., Inc.
Faraday, Michael. The Chemical History of a Candle. 2008. 116p. 24.99 *(978-0-554-27957-2(6))*; 21.99 *(978-0-554-37260-0(6))* BiblioBazaar.
—The Chemical History of a Candle. 2008. 76p. pap. *(978-1-4068-7535-5(X))* Echo Library.
—The Chemical History of a Candle: A Course of Lectures Delivered before a Juvenile Audience at the Royal Institution. 2007. 106p. pap. 18.99 *(978-1-4346-4397-1(2))*; (ENG.). 114p. pap. 19.99 *(978-1-4346-4398-8(0))* BiblioBazaar.
—A Course of Six Lectures on the Chemical History of a Candle: To Which Is Added A Lecture on Platinum. by Michael Faraday ... Delivered Before A Juve. 2006. 228p. per. 20.99 *(978-1-4255-1974-2(1))* MPublishing.
Faraday, Michael, et al. The Chemical History of a Candle. 2011. (ENG., Illus.). 192p. 24.95 *(978-0-19-969491-4(5))* Oxford Univ. Pr., Inc.
Maffeo, Laura & Mullaney, Colleen. Faux Florals & Candles. 2009. (One-of-a-Kind Weddings Ser.). (ENG., Illus.). 96p. 18.00 *(978-1-58923-392-8(1)*, 1589233921, Creative Publishing International) Quayside.
Matson, Tim. The Book of Non-Electric Lighting: The Classic Guide to the Safe Use of Candles, Fuel Lamps, Lanterns, Gaslights, & Fire-View Stoves. 2nd ed. 2008. (ENG., Illus.). 96p. pap. 13.95 *(978-0-88150-794-2(6)*, *50794) Countryman Pr.
Nolan, Jameel D. The Ultimate Guide to Soy Candlemaking from Hobby Enthusiasts to Business Professionals. 2010. 132p. pap. 39.95 *(978-0-578-03298-6(8))* Nolan, Jameel D.
Ott, Adolph. The Art of Manufacturing Soap & Candles Embracing the Modes of Detecting Frauds. 2006. 200p. per. 18.99 *(978-1-4255-1646-8(7))* MPublishing.

CANDLES—RELIGIOUS ASPECTS
see Candles and Lights

CANDLES, LITURGICAL
see Candles and Lights

CANDLES AND LIGHTS
Here are entered works on the use of candles and lights in religious worship.
see also Menorah
Buckland, Raymond. Buckland doorway to candle Magic. 2007. per. 12.95 *(978-0-9794560-0-8(2))* Buckland Bks.
Dr. Buzzard Spiritual Enchantments: Book 2. 2007. per. 16.95 *(978-0-9758624-5-2(6))* Imperious Publishing.
Mellott, David. I Was & I Am Dust. 2009. 144p. pap. 29.95 *(978-0-8146-6225-0(0)*, Liturgical Pr. Bks.) Liturgical Pr.
Silbiger, Auriel. Bread, Fire, & Water. 96p. 11.99 *(978-1-58330-467-9(3))* Feldheim Pubs.

CANDLES IN INTERIOR DECORATION
Ogboye, Funmi. Soy Candles: the Sentelle Way! Towards Healthy & Stylish Living. 2011. 68p. pap. 13.72 ***(978-1-4567-8659-5(8))*** AuthorHouse.

CANDOMBLE (CULT)
Biebinger, Frank. Auf der Suche nach Gottes Angesicht: Candomble & Katholizismus im Dialog: Eine Fallstudie. (GER., Illus.). xiv, 348p. *(978-3-496-02701-0(0))* Reimer, Dietrich.
Capone, Stefania. Searching for Africa in Brazil: Power & Tradition in Candomblé. Grant, Lucy Lyall, tr. from FRE. 2010. (ENG., Illus.). 336p. 84.95 *(978-0-8223-4625-8(7))*; pap. 23.95 *(978-0-8223-4636-4(2))* Duke Univ. Pr.
Despland, Michel. Bastide on Religion: The Invention of Candomblé. 2008. (Key Thinkers in the Study of Religion Ser.). (ENG.). 224p. (C). 95.00 *(978-1-84553-365-6(8))*; pap. 29.95 *(978-1-84553-366-3(6))* Equinox Publishing Ltd. GBR. Dist: ISD.
Sansi & Sansi-Roca, Roger. Fetishes & Monuments: Afro-Brazilian Art & Culture in the Twentieth Century. 2007. (Remapping Cultural History Ser.: Vol. 6). (Illus.). 224p. 90.00 *(978-1-84545-363-3(8))* Berghahn Bks., Inc.
Theodoro, Helena. Iansã: Rainha DOS Ventos e das Tempestades. 2010. (POR.). 163p. *(978-85-347-0407-6(4))* Pallas Editora e Distribuidora Ltda.
van de Port, Mattijs. Ecstatic Encounters: Bahian Candomblé & the Quest for the Really Real. 2011. (ENG., Illus.). 300p. pap. *(978-90-8964-298-1(6))* Amsterdam Univ. Pr.

CANDY
see also Truffles (Confectionery)
Allen, Lawrence L. Chocolate Fortunes: The Battle for the Hearts, Minds, & Wallets of China's Consumers, 1 vol. 2009. (ENG.). 256p. 27.95 *(978-0-8144-1432-3(X))* Amacom.
Almond, Steve. Candyfreak: A Journey Through the Chocolate Underbelly of America. 2009. 256p. pap. 13.00 *(978-1-4379-6870-5(8))* 2008. 266p. 22.00 *(978-1-4379-5077-9(9))* DIANE Publishing Co.
—Candyfreak: A Journey Through the Chocolate Underbelly of America. 2008. (Playaway Adult Nonfiction Ser.). 44.99 *(978-1-60640-931-2(X))* Findaway World, LLC.
—Candyfreak: A Journey Through the Chocolate Underbelly of America. 2009. 13.09 *(978-0-7848-2124-4(0)*, Everbind) Marco Bk. Co.
Bob, Hippie. Hippie Bob & the Chocolate Factory: A true Fairytale. 2009. 192p. pap. 16.49 *(978-1-4389-7009-7(9))* AuthorHouse.
Bowers, Sharon. Candy Construction: How to Build Race Cars, Castles, & Other Cool Stuff out of Store-Bought Candy. 2010. (ENG., Illus.). 144p. pap. 14.95 *(978-1-60342-548-3(9)*, 1603425489) Storey Publishing, LLC.
Carruthers, Karen. Candy Quilts: Design & Create Custom Candy Molds at Home. 2008. 96p. pap. 19.95 *(978-1-4327-2521-1(1))* Outskirts Pr., Inc.
Chu, Anita. Candy: How to Identify & Make Virtually Every Candy Imaginable. 2009. (Field Guide Ser.). (ENG., Illus.). 352p. pap. 15.95 *(978-1-59474-419-8(X))* Quirk Bks.
CQ Products. Celebrations, Candy Bouquets For: Create Your Own Gifts & Centerpieces. 2009. (ENG.). 60p. spiral bd. 12.00 *(978-1-56383-342-7(5))* G & R Publishing.
CQ Products (Firm) Staff. Candy Bouquets: Create Your Own Gifts & Centerpieces. 2008. (ENG.). 60p. spiral bd. 12.00 *(978-1-56383-299-4(2))* G & R Publishing.
Edelman, Foy Allen. Sweet Carolina: Favorite Desserts & Candies from the Old North State. 2009. (ENG., Illus.). 288p. 26.00 *(978-0-8078-3294-3(4))* Univ. of North Carolina Pr.
Fasolt, Nancy. Clear Toy Candy: All about the Traditional Holiday Treat with Steps for Making Your Own Candy. 2010. (ENG., Illus.). 80p. pap. 14.95 *(978-0-8117-3610-7(5))* Stackpole Bks.
Folster, David. Ganong: A Sweet History of Chocolate. 2006. (ENG., Illus.). 136p. 24.95 *(978-0-86492-480-3(1))* Goose Lane Editions CAN. Dist: Univ. of Toronto Pr.
Hopkins, Kate. Sweet Tooth: The Bittersweet History of Candy. 2012. (ENG.). 320p. 25.99 ***(978-0-312-66810-5(4))*** St. Martin's Pr.
Kimmerle, Beth. Candy: The Sweet History. 2007. (Illus.). 176p. pap. *(978-1-933112-33-6(6))* Collectors Pr., Inc.
Lauren, Dylan. Dylan's Candy Bar: Unwrap Your Sweet Life. 2010. (ENG., Illus.). 224p. 35.00 *(978-0-307-45182-8(8)*, Clarkson Potter) Crown Publishing Group.
Leisure Arts. Celebrating Candy. 2010. (ENG.). 144p. pap. 14.95 *(978-1-60900-004-2(8))* Leisure Arts, Inc.
Mathews, Jennifer P. Chicle: The Chewing Gum of the Americas, from the Ancient Maya to William Wrigley. 2009. (ENG., Illus.). 160p. (C). 50.00 *(978-0-8165-2624-6(9))*; pap. 17.95 *(978-0-8165-2821-9(7))* Univ. of Arizona Pr.
Park, Frances & Park, Ginger. Chocolate Chocolate: The True Story of Two Sisters, Tons of Treats, & the Little Shop That Could. 2011. (ENG.). 288p. 23.99 *(978-0-312-65293-7(3)*, Dunne, Thomas Bks.) St. Martin's Pr.
PMCA Staff, contrib. by. Back to Basics, Confectionery Fundamentals: Volume 1: 2000 - 2006. 2007. 150.00 net. *(978-1-933430-12-6(5)*, PMCA) MC Publishing Co.
Ptak, Claire. The Complete Step-by-Step Guide to Making Sweets, Candy & Chocolates. 2012. (ENG., Illus.). 256p. 29.99 ***(978-0-7548-2473-2(X))*** Anness Publishing GBR. Dist: National Bk. Network.
Ptak, Claire. The Home-Made Sweet Shop: Make Your Own Irresistible Confectionary with 90 Classic Recipes for Sweets, Candies & Chocolates, Shown in More Than 450 Stunning Photographs. 2011. (ENG., Illus.). 160p. 29.99 *(978-1-903141-84-7(2))* Anness Publishing GBR. Dist: National Bk. Network.
Remine, Gayle. Easy Candy Making. 2007. (ENG.). 128p. pap. 8.95 *(978-1-55867-342-7(3))* Bristol Publishing Enterprises.
Rudolph, Marv. Pop Rocks: The Inside Story of America's Revolutionary Candy. 2006. (Illus.). 98p. per. 12.95 *(978-0-9786318-0-2(3))* Specialty Pubs., LLC.
Shotts, Andrew Garrison. Making Artisan Chocolates: Flavor-Infused Chocolates, Truffles, & Confections. 2007. (ENG., Illus.). 176p. pap. 24.99 *(978-1-59253-310-7(8)*, 1592533108, Quarry Books) Quayside.
Vandermeer, Linda. Sweets on a Stick: More Than 150 Kid-Friendly Recipes for Cakes, Candies, Cookies, & Pies on the Go! 2011. (ENG., Illus.). 192p. pap. 16.95 ***(978-1-4405-3005-0(X))*** Adams Media Corp.
Wanat, Nina. Sweet Confections: Beautiful Candy to Make at Home. 2011. (ENG., Illus.). 144p. pap. 17.95 *(978-1-60059-920-0(6))* Lark Bks.
White, Carolyn. Bake Me I'm Yours... Cake Pops: Over 30 Designs for Fun Sweet Treats. 2011. (ENG., Illus.). 128p. 14.99 *(978-1-4463-0137-1(0))* David & Charles Pubs. GBR. Dist: F&W Media, Inc.
Wilson, Dede. Baker's Field Guide to Holiday Candy: Sweet Treats All Year Long. 2011. (Baker's FG Ser.). (ENG., Illus.). 176p. pap. 14.95 *(978-1-55832-753-5(3))* Harvard Common Pr.
Wybauw, Jean-Pierre. Fine Chocolates Vol. 3: Great Experience - Extending Shelf Life. 2010. (ENG., Illus.). 224p. 105.00 *(978-90-209-9020-1(9))* Lannoo Pubs./Racine.

CANE SUGAR
see Sugar

CANES
see Staffs (Sticks, Canes, etc.)

CANETTI, ELIAS, 1905-1994
Canetti, Elias. Party in the Blitz. Hofmann, Michael, tr. 2010. (ENG.). 256p. pap. 13.95 *(978-0-8112-1830-6(9)*, 21830) New Directions Publishing Corp.
Canetti, Vesa & Canetti, Elias. Dearest Georg - Love, Literature, & Power in Dark Times: The Letters of Elias, Veza, & Georges Canetti, 1933-1948. Lauer, Karen & Wachinger, Kristian, eds. Dollenmayer, David, tr. from GER. 2010. (ENG., Illus.). 448p. 24.95 *(978-1-59051-297-5(9))* Other Pr., LLC.
Djoufack, Patrice. Entortung, hybride Sprache und Identitätsbildung: Zur Erfindung von Sprache und Identität bei Franz Kafka, Elias Canetti und Paul Celan. 2010. (GER & ENG.). 443p. (C). 78.00 *(978-3-89971-762-4(7))* Vandenhoeck & Ruprecht GmbH & Co. KG DEU. Dist: ISD.

CANIDAE
Menino, Holly. Darwin's Fox & My Coyote. 2008. (ENG.). 224p. 27.95 *(978-0-8139-2675-9(0))* Univ. Pr. of Virginia.

CANING OF CHAIRS
see Chair Caning

CANISIUS, PETER, SAINT, 1524-1597
Brodrick, James. Saint Peter Canisius, S. J., 1521-1597. reprint ed. 65.00 *(978-0-404-19882-4(1))* AMS Pr., Inc.
Rotsaert, M. & Segaert, B., eds. Markante Jezuïeten uit de Lage Landen: Canisius, Verbiest, Lessius, Regout. 2007. (ENG.). 113p. (C). pap. 58.00 *(978-90-429-2003-3(3))* Peeters Pubs. & Booksellers BEL. Dist: Brown, David Bk. Co., The.

CANNABIS
Here are entered works on the description, culture and use of Cannabis sativa as a drug plant. Works on Cannabis sativa as a fiber plant are entered under Hemp.
see also Hashish; Marijuana
Aston, Maxine, et al. What You Need to Know about Cannabis: Understanding the Facts. 2008. (ENG., Illus.). 144p. (C). pap. *(978-1-84310-697-5(3))* Kingsley, Jessica Ltd.
Bennett, Chris. Cannabis & the Soma Solution. 2010. (ENG., Illus.). 480p. pap. 24.95 *(978-0-9841858-0-1(1))* Trine Day.
Bienenstock, David & High Time Magazine Editors. The Official High Times Pot Smokers Handbook: Featuring 420 Things to Do When You're Stoned. 2008. (ENG., Illus.). 240p. pap. 19.95 *(978-0-8118-6205-9(4))* Chronicle Bks. LLC.
Bott. How-to Marijuan: A Step-by-Step Guide to Medical Marijuana. 2007. 112p. 22.95 *(978-0-595-69191-3(9))*; per. 12.95 *(978-0-595-45086-2(5))* iUniverse, Inc.
Cervantes, Jorge. Marijuana Grow Basics: The Easy Guide for Cannabis Aficionados. 2009. (Illus.). 240p. pap. 21.95 *(978-1-878823-37-3(X))* Van Patten Publishing.

C

Clark, Ethan L., ed. Cannabis Sativa for Health & Hemp. 2011. (Public Health in the 21st Century Ser.). (Illus.). 179p. 95.00 *(978-1-61209-982-8(3))* Nova Science Pubs., Inc.

Crowther, S. M., et al, eds. The Medicalization of Cannabis. 2010. (Illus.). 130p. pap. *(978-0-85484-129-5(6))* Wellcome Institute for the History of Medicine.

Danko, Danny. The Official High Times Field Guide to Marijuana Strains. 2011. (ENG., Illus.). 180p. pap. 14.95 *(978-1-893010-28-4(7),* High Times) Trans-High Corp.

Ditchfield, Jeff. Cannabis Cultivator: A Step-by-Step Guide to Growing Marijuana. 2009. (ENG., Illus.). 112p. pap. 15.00 *(978-1-931160-67-4(8))* Green Candy Pr.

ElSohly, Mahmoud A., ed. Marijuana & the Cannabinoids. 2010. (Forensic Science & Medicine Ser.). (Illus.). 414p. pap. 209.00 *(978-1-61737-581-1(0),* 1617375810) Humana Pr.

Frank, Matthew Gavin. Pot Farm. 2012. (ENG.). 232p. pap. 16.95 ***(978-0-8032-3784-1(7))*** Univ. of Nebraska Pr.

Green, Smokey & McCarthy, Tommy. Growing Marijuana: How to Plant, Cultivate, & Harvest Your Own Weed. 2011. (ENG., Illus.). 224p. pap. 14.95 *(978-1-61608-093-8(0),* 608093) Skyhorse Publishing Co., Inc.

Griffin, Robert, photos by. Naked Girls Smoking Weed: Best of 420 Girls. 2007. (Illus.). 159p. 29.95 *(978-3-936709-26-1(2))* Goliath DEU. Dist: SCB Distributors.

Holland, Julie. The Pot Book: A Complete Guide to Cannabis. 2010. (ENG.). 1p. pap. 19.95 *(978-1-59477-368-6(8),* Park Street Pr.) Inner Traditions International, Ltd.

Jacquette, Dale, ed. Cannabis - Philosophy for Everyone: What Were We Just Talking About. 2010. (Philosophy for Everyone Ser.: 22). (ENG., Illus.). 264p. pap. 19.95 *(978-1-4051-9967-4(9),* Wiley-Blackwell) Wiley, John & Sons, Inc.

Kendall, Dave, et al. Behavioral Neurobiology of the Endocannabinoid System. 2009. (Current Topics in Behavioral Neurosciences Ser.). (ENG., Illus.). xii, 418p. 219.00 *(978-3-540-88954-0(X),* 354088954X) Springer.

Kindbud, Seymour. Grow Your Own Organic Weed! Everything You Need... . . Except the Seeds. 2011. (ENG.). 64p. pap. 10.95 *(978-1-60433-232-2(8))* Cider Mill Pr. Bk. Pubs., LLC.

Kindbud, Seymour & Greenbud, Seymour. Green Weed: The Organic Guide to Growing High Quality Cannabis. 2010. (ENG., Illus.). 224p. pap. 19.95 *(978-1-60433-157-8(7))* Cider Mill Pr. Bk. Pubs., LLC.

King, Jason. The Cannabible 3, Vol. 3. 2006. (ENG., Illus.). 224p. 35.00 *(978-1-58008-786-5(8));* pap. 24.99 *(978-1-58008-784-1(1))* Ten Speed Pr.

Köfalvi, Attila, ed. Cannabinoids & the Brain. 2010. (ENG., Illus.). xvi, 584p. pap. 179.00 *(978-1-4419-4493-1(1),* 1441944931) Springer.

—Cannabinoids & the Brain. 2008. (ENG., Illus.). xvi, 584p. 179.00 *(978-0-387-74348-6(0),* 0387743480) Springer.

Kovach, Chris. Cultivating Cannabis Consistently: A Hydroponic How To. 2008. 224p. pap. 23.99 *(978-1-4357-3690-0(7))* Lulu Enterprises Inc.

—The Hydroponic Bible. 2008. 348p. pap. 17.55 *(978-1-4357-3667-2(2))* Lulu Enterprises Inc.

Lambert, Didier M., ed. Cannabinoids in Nature & Medicine. 2009. (ENG., Illus.). 356p. 200.00 *(978-3-906390-56-7(X),* Wiley-VCH) Wiley, John & Sons, Inc.

Lebigot, Serge. Cannabis, Ce Que les Parents Doivent Savoir. 2010. (FRE., Illus.). 236p. *(978-2-249-62111-6(X))* Lethielleux, Editions.

Marzo, Vincenzo, ed. Cannabinoids. 2011. (Neuroscience Intelligence Unit Ser.). (ENG.). 228p. pap. 219.00 *(978-1-4419-3433-8(2),* 1441934332) Springer.

Mediman. Marijuana Made Simple: A Beginner's Guide to Growing Like a Pro. 2012. (ENG., Illus.). 168p. pap. 18.00 ***(978-1-931160-88-9(0))*** Green Candy Pr.

Newman, Paul. Doctor Feelgood. 2007. (ENG., Illus.). 288p. per. 19.95 *(978-1-84454-412-7(5))* Blake, John Publishing, Ltd. GBR. Dist: Independent Pubs. Group.

Onaivi, Emmanuel S., ed. Marijuana & Cannabinoid Research: Methods & Protocols. 2010. (Methods in Molecular Medicine Ser.). (Illus.). 328p. pap. 149.00 *(978-1-61737-513-2(6),* 1617375136) Humana Pr.

Oner, S. T., ed. Cannabis Indica: The Essential Guide to the World's Finest Marijuana Strains. 2011. (ENG., Illus.). 280p. pap. 20.00 *(978-1-931160-81-0(3))* Green Candy Pr.

Pilcher, Tim. The Cannabis Cookbook: Over 35 Tasty Recipes for Meals, Munchies, & More. 2007. (ENG., Illus.). 128p. pap. 16.95 *(978-0-7624-3090-1(7))* Running Pr. Bk. Pubs.

Pryce, Lord Tayler. The Random Guide to Cannabis Cookery. 2010. 133p. pap. 24.00 *(978-0-557-64954-9(4))* Lulu Enterprises Inc.

Reggio, Patricia H., ed. The Cannabinoid Receptors. 2009. (Receptors Ser.). (Illus.). xiv, 396p. 159.00 *(978-1-58829-712-9(8))* Humana Pr.

Reiman, Amanda. Medical Cannabis Facilities. 2007. 192p. per. *(978-3-8364-2156-0(9))* VDM Verlag Dr. Mueller e.K.

Room, Robin, et al. Cannabis Policy: Moving Beyond Stalemate. 2010. (ENG., Illus.). 244p. pap. 59.95 *(978-0-19-958148-1(7))* Oxford Univ. Pr., Inc.

Rosenthal, Ed. Medical & Personal Marijuana Cultivation. 2010. (ENG., Illus.). 448p. pap., instr.'s hndbk. ed. 29.95 *(978-0-932551-46-7(7))* Quick American.

Rosenthal, Ed, ed. More Marijuana Varieties from the World's Great Seed Breeders. 2007. (Big Book of Buds Ser.: Vol. 3). (ENG., Illus.). 256p. 29.95 *(978-0-932551-82-5(3));* per. 24.95 *(978-0-932551-79-5(3))* Quick American.

—More Marijuana Varieties from the World's Great Seed Breeders Vol. 4, Vol. 4. 2011. (Big Book of Buds Ser.). (ENG., Illus.). 240p. pap. 24.95 *(978-0-932551-48-1(3))* Quick American.

Russo, Ethan B., ed. Handbook of Cannabis Therapeutics: From Bench to Bedside. 2006. (Illus.). 471p. 175.00 *(978-0-7890-3096-2(9));* per. 56.95 *(978-0-7890-3097-9(7))* Routledge.

Ryan, Pat. Sinsemilla Sinsations: Cannabis-Inspired Art Spanning Four Decades: Postcards. 2011. (ENG., Illus.). 60p. pap. 12.95 ***(978-0-86719-766-2(8))*** Last Gasp of San Francisco.

SeeMoreBuds. Let's Grow a Pound: A Day by Day Guide to Growing More Than You Can Smoke. 2012. (ENG., Illus.). 112p. pap. 19.95 *(978-1-936807-01-7(7))* Quick American.

Smith, Mark Haskell. The Heart of Dankness: Underground Botanists, Outlaw Farmers, & the Race for the Cannabis Cup. 2012. (ENG.). 256p. E-Book ***(978-0-307-72055-9(1));*** pap. 14.00 ***(978-0-307-72054-2(3))*** Broadway Bks.

Stitch, J. C. Marijuana Garden Saver: Handbook for Healthy Plants. Rosenthal, Ed, ed. 2008. (ENG., Illus.). 176p. pap. 18.95 *(978-0-932551-91-7(2))* Quick American.

Stolick, Matthew. Otherwise Law-Abiding Citizens: A Scientific & Moral Assessment of Cannabis Use. 2008. (ENG.). 410p. 99.99 *(978-0-7391-2745-2(4))* Lexington Bks.

—Otherwise Law-Abiding Citizens - A Scientific & Moral Assessment of Cannabis Use. 2010. (ENG.). 410p. pap. 45.50 *(978-0-7391-2746-9(2))* Lexington Bks.

Swensen, Greg. The 2004 Cannabis Law Reforms in Western Australia & the United Kingdom: A Case of Too Much Caution? 2008. (Illus.). 380p. pap. *(978-3-639-03177-5(6))* VDM Verlag Dr. Mueller e.K.

T, Brother. Deceived. 2008. 84p. per. 10.00 *(978-1-58961-539-7(5))* PageFree Publishing, Inc.

Thomas, Mel. Cannabis Cultivation: A Complete Grower's Guide. 2012. (ENG., Illus.). 412p. pap. 20.00 *(978-1-931160-83-4(X))* Green Candy Pr.

United Nations Staff. Bulletin on Narcotics: Review of the World Cannabis Situation, Vol. 58, No. 1&2, 2006 (Arabic Language) 2009. (Bulletin on Narcotics Ser.). (ARA.). 164p. pap. 30.00 *(978-92-1-648034-9(3))* United Nations Pubns.

—Recommended Methods for the Identification & Analysis of Cannabis & Cannabis Products. 2009. (ENG.). 56p. pap. 15.00 *(978-92-1-148242-3(9))* United Nations Pubns.

Watson, C. K. Cultivating Cannabis in the 21st Century. 2010. (ENG., Illus.). 580p. pap. 25.00 *(978-1-931160-75-9(9))* Green Candy Pr.

Weinberg, Bill. Cannabis Trips: A Global Guide That Leaves Not Turn Unstoned. 2010. (ENG.). 128p. pap. 16.95 *(978-0-7624-3812-9(6))* Running Pr. Bk. Pubs.

Williamson, Alicia. The Everything Marijuana Book: Your Complete Cannabis Resource, Including History, Growing Instructions, & Preparation. 2010. (ENG.). 304p. pap. 16.95 *(978-1-4405-0687-1(6))* Adams Media Corp.

—Grow Marijuana Now! An Introductory, Step-by-Step Guide to Growing Cannabis. 2010. (ENG.). 240p. pap., instr.'s gde. ed. 12.95 *(978-1-4405-1091-5(1))* Adams Media Corp.

Winterborne, Jeffrey. Medical Marijuana/Cannabis Cultivation. 2008. (ENG., Illus.). 494p. pap. 40.00 *(978-0-9550112-2-1(1))* Pukka Pr. GBR. Dist: AtlasBooks Distribution.

Wishnia, Steven. The Cannabis Companion: The Ultimate Guide to Connoisseurship. 2007. (Illus.). 160p. reprint ed. pap. 27.00 *(978-1-4223-6518-2(2))* DIANE Publishing Co.

Woodford, et al. Street Capital: Black Cannabis Dealers in a White Welfare State. 2009. (Illus.). 200p. 99.00 *(978-1-84742-120-3(2))* Policy Pr. GBR. Dist: Chicago Distribution Ctr.

CANNED FOODS

BCC Staff. Sugars & Sweeteners in Processed Foods & Beverages. 2007. per. 4250.00 *(978-1-59623-298-3(6))* BCC Research.

Bratt, Les. Fish Canning Handbook. 2010. (ENG., Illus.). 320p. 209.99 *(978-1-4051-8099-3(4),* Wiley-Blackwell) Wiley, John & Sons, Inc.

Cabado, Ana G. & Vieites, Juan M., eds. Quality Parameters in Canned Seafoods. 2008. (Illus.). 173p. (C). 79.00 *(978-1-60456-774-8(0))* Nova Science Pubs., Inc.

Eggers, Linda. Spam Cookbook. 2009. 96p. pap. 7.95 *(978-0-9841674-0-1(4))* Gopher Prairie Pr.

Miura, Muriel. Hawai'i Cooks with Spam: Local Recipes Featuring Our Favorite Canned Meat. 2008. 136p. 14.95 *(978-1-56647-853-3(7))* Mutual Publishing LLC.

Patten, Marguerite. Spam - The Cookbook. 2009. (ENG., Illus.). 64p. pap. 7.99 *(978-0-600-62047-1(6),* Hamlyn) Octopus Publishing Group GBR. Dist: Hachette Bk. Group.

Protein Ingredients for Processed Foods. 2006. per. 4250.00 *(978-1-59623-248-8(X))* BCC Research.

CANNED GOODS

see Canned Foods

CANNIBALISM

Anderson, Warwick. The Collectors of Lost Souls: Turning Kuru Scientists into Whitemen. 2008. (ENG., Illus.). 328p. 25.95 *(978-0-8018-9040-6(3))* Johns Hopkins Univ. Pr.

Avramescu, Catalin. Intellectual History of Cannibalism. 2011. (ENG., Illus.). 360p. (C). pap. 26.95 ***(978-0-691-15219-6(5))*** Princeton Univ. Pr.

Avramescu, Catalin. Intellectual History of Cannibalism. Blyth, Alistair Ian, tr. from RUM. 2009. (ENG., Illus.). 360p. (C). 30.95 *(978-0-691-13327-0(1))* Princeton Univ. Pr.

Behrend, Heike. Resurrecting Cannibals: The Catholic Church, Witch-Hunts & the Production of Pagans in Western Uganda. 2011. (Eastern Africa Ser.). 222p. 80.00 *(978-1-84701-039-1(3),* Currey, James) Boydell & Brewer, Ltd. GBR. Dist: Boydell & Brewer, Inc.

Berry-Dee, Christopher. Cannibal Serial Killers: Profiles of Depraved Flesh-Eating Murderers. 2011. (ENG.). 336p. pap. 14.95 *(978-1-56975-902-8(2))* Ulysses Pr.

Bleszynski, Nick. Bloodlust: The Unsavoury Tale of Alexander Pearce, The Convict Cannibal. 2008. (ENG.). 401p. pap. 29.95 ***(978-1-74166-700-4(3))*** Random Hse. Australia AUS. Dist: Independent Pubs. Group.

Blundell, Nigel. Serial Killers: Butchers & Cannibals. 2010. (Illus.). 176p. 39.95 *(978-1-84563-132-1(3))* Wharncliffe Bks. GBR. Dist: Casemate Pubs. & Bk. Distributors, LLC.

Brantlinger, Patrick. Taming Cannibals: Race & the Victorians. 2011. 288p. 45.00 *(978-0-8014-5019-8(5))* Cornell Univ. Pr.

Canibales y Caminantes.Tr. of Cannibals & Travelers. (SPA.). 13.95 *(978-84-348-3387-6(5))* SM Ediciones ESP. Dist: AIMS International Bks., Inc.

Castleden, Chloe. Cannibal Killers: Monsters with an Appetite for Murder & a Taste for Human Flesh. 2010. (ENG.). 320p. pap. 12.95 *(978-1-61608-149-2(X),* 608149) Skyhorse Publishing Co., Inc.

Cram101 Textbook Reviews & Cram101 Textbook Reviews. Outlines & Highlights for Cannibal Tours & Glass Boxes: Anthropology of Museums by Michael M. Ames, ISBN. 2011. 82p. pap. 27.95 ***(978-1-61744-931-4(8))*** Cram101 Inc.

Diehl, Daniel & Donnelly, Mark P. Eat Thy Neighbor: A History of Cannibalism. 2009. (ENG., Illus.). 314p. pap. 17.95 *(978-0-7509-4373-4(4))* History Pr. Ltd.,The GBR. Dist: Independent Pubs. Group.

Donnelly, Mark & Diehl, Daniel. Eat Thy Neighbor: A History of Cannibalism. 2006. (ENG., Illus.). 256p. 19.95 *(978-0-7509-4372-7(6))* History Pr. Ltd.,The GBR. Dist: Independent Pubs. Group.

Ezzo, David A. Cannibalism in Cross Cultural Perspective. 2008. 48p. pap. 10.00 *(978-1-59858-606-0(8))* Dog Ear Publishing, LLC.

Feldman, George Franklin. Cannibalism, Headhunting & Human Sacrifice in North America: A History Forgotten. 2008. (Illus.). 249p. per. 20.00 *(978-0-911469-33-2(8))* Hood, Alan C. & Co., Inc.

Gibson, Walter. Boat. 2007. (ENG.). 152p. pap. 12.95 *(978-981-05-8301-9(X))* Monsoon Bks. Pte. Ltd.

Hogg, Garry. Cannibalism & Human Sacrifice. 2009. (ENG.). 192p. pap. 28.00 *(978-1-4379-6610-7(1))* DIANE Publishing Co.

Jáuregui, Carlos A. Canibalia: Canibalismo, Calibanismo, Antropofagia Cultural y Consumo en América Latina. 2008. (SPA., Illus.). 724p. pap. 44.00 *(978-84-8489-322-6(7));* pap. 98.00 *(978-84-8489-299-1(9))* Iberoamericana Vervuert Publishing Corp.

Martingale, Moira. Cannibal Killers: The Impossible Monsters. 2009. (ENG.). 192p. pap. 14.95 *(978-0-7090-8540-9(0))* Hale, Robert Ltd. GBR. Dist: Independent Pubs. Group.

McLelland, Dennis J. The Avenging Fury of the Plains: John Liver Eating Johnston. 2008. 256p. pap. 16.95 *(978-0-7414-4527-8(1))* Infinity Publishing.

Miles, James. Born Cannibal: Evolution & the Paradox of Man. 2006. 229p. reprint ed. pap. 20.00 *(978-1-4223-5739-2(2))* DIANE Publishing Co.

Nichols, Deborah, et al, eds. Social Violence in the Prehispanic American Southwest. 2008. (ENG., Illus.). 288p. 60.00 *(978-0-8165-2621-5(4))* Univ. of Arizona Pr.

Noble, Louise Christine. Medicinal Cannibalism in Early Modern English Literature & Culture. 2011. (Early Modern Cultural Studies). (ENG., Illus.). 256p. 85.00 *(978-0-230-11027-4(4))* Palgrave Macmillan.

Nunes, Zita. Cannibal Democracy: Race & Representation in the Literature of the Americas. 2008. (Critical American Studies). (Illus.). 240p. 67.50 *(978-0-8166-4840-5(9));* pap. 22.50 *(978-0-8166-4841-2(7))* Univ. of Minnesota Pr.

Parrado, Nando. Miracle in the Andes: 72 Days on the Mountain & My Long Trek Home. 2007. (ENG., Illus.). 291p. 21.60 *(978-0-7569-8847-0(0))* Perfection Learning Corp.

Parrado, Nando & Rause, Vince. Miracle in the Andes. 2011. 14.05 *(978-0-7848-3407-7(5),* Everbind) Marco Bk. Co.

—Miracle in the Andes: 72 Days on the Mountain & My Long Trek Home. 2007. (ENG., Illus.). 304p. pap. 14.00 *(978-1-4000-9769-2(X),* Three Rivers Pr.) Crown Publishing Group.

Raffaele, Paul. Among the Cannibals: Adventures on the Trail of Man's Darkest Ritual. 2008. (Illus.). 288p. 25.95 *(978-0-06-135788-6(X))* Smithsonian Institution Pr.

Richard, Sugg. Mummies Cannibals & Vampires. 2011. (ENG.). 384p. (C). 140.00 *(978-0-415-67416-4(6));* pap. 35.95 *(978-0-415-67417-1(4))* Routledge.

Stampf, Gunter. Interview with a Cannibal: The Secret Life of the Monster of Rotenburg. Brown, Pat, ed. 2008. 380p. 25.95 *(978-1-59777-588-5(6))* Phoenix Bks., Inc.

Strain, Kathy Muskowitz. Giants, Cannibals & Monsters: Bigfoot in Native Culture. 2007. 288p. pap. 39.95 ***(978-0-88839-650-1(3))*** Hancock Hse. Pubs.

Travis-Henikoff, Carole A. Dinner with a Cannibal: The Complete History of Mankind's Oldest Taboo. 2008. (ENG., Illus.). 360p. 24.95 *(978-1-59580-030-5(1))* Santa Monica Pr.

Turner, Christy G., II. Man Corn: Cannibalism & Violence in the Prehistoric American Southwest. 2011. (ENG., Illus.). 552p. pap. 45.00 *(978-0-87480-968-8(1))* Univ. of Utah Pr.

Vierci, Pablo. La sociedad de la Nieve. 2009. (SPA.). 338p. pap. 19.95 *(978-0-307-39281-7(3))* Random House Mondadori ESP. Dist: Random Hse., Inc.

Whitby, Fred. Adventures of a Pinko Commie Bisexual in The 1980s. 2010. 110p. pap. 16.00 *(978-0-557-66781-9(X))* Lulu Enterprises Inc.

Whiteman, Dennis. The Resonant Factor. 2010. 586p. pap. 39.96 *(978-1-4452-1776-5(7))* Lulu Enterprises Inc.

Williamson, Rick. Tavua: The White Cannibal. 2007. (Illus.). 144p. *(978-3-938921-05-0(6))* Hornig, Angelika.

CANNIBALISM IN ANIMALS

Gay, Robert. Notes on Early Mesozoic Theropods. 2010. 44p. pap. 5.38 *(978-0-557-46616-0(4))* Lulu Enterprises Inc.

CANNING, CHARLES JOHN, EARL CANNING, 1812-1862

Cunningham, Henry Stewart. Earl Canning. 2010. 240p. pap. 26.75 *(978-1-143-05986-5(7))* 2009. 224p. 23.99 *(978-1-103-28468-9(1))* 2009. 224p. pap. 17.99 *(978-1-103-28467-2(3))* BiblioBazaar.

—Earl Canning. 2009. 124p. pap. *(978-1-150-66076-4(7))* Books LLC.

—Earl Canning: Rulers of India. 2007. (ENG.). 218p. 39.95 *(978-0-548-21892-1(7));* 220p. per. 24.95 *(978-1-4325-3948-1(5))* Kessinger Publishing, LLC.

—Earl Canning & the Transfer of India from the Company to the Crown. 2010. 244p. pap. 26.75 *(978-1-144-93748-3(5))* BiblioBazaar.

—Earl Canning & the Transfer of India from the Company to the Crown. 2009. 122p. pap. 19.99 *(978-1-150-21143-0(1))* General Bks. LLC.

—Earl Canning & the Transfer of India from the Company to the Crown. 2008. 240p. 41.95 *(978-1-4369-3463-3(X));* pap. 26.95 *(978-1-4368-2713-3(2))* Kessinger Publishing, LLC.

Cunningham, H.S. Earl Canning. 2010. 90p. pap. 20.00 *(978-1-154-98447-7(8))* General Bks. LLC.

Cunningham, Sir Henry Stewart. Earl Canning. 2010. (Illus.). 110p. pap. 20.12 *(978-1-154-34211-6(5))* 2009. 122p. pap. 19.99 *(978-1-151-01977-6(1))* General Bks. LLC.

Money, John. The Chronicles of John Cannon, Excise Officer & Writing Master, Part 2: 1734-43 (Somerset), 2 vols. 2011. (ENG., Illus.). 520p. 99.00 *(978-0-19-726455-3(7))* Oxford Univ. Pr., Inc.

Money, John, ed. The Chronicles of John Cannon, Excise Officer & Writing Master, Part 1: 1684-1733 (Somerset, Oxfordshire, Berkshire), 2 vols. 2011. (ENG., Illus.). 420p. 110.00 *(978-0-19-726454-6(9))* Oxford Univ. Pr., Inc.

CANNING, GEORGE, 1770-1827

Bell, Robert. The Life of the Right Honorable George Canning. 2007. (ENG.). 372p. 48.95 *(978-0-548-11764-4(0))* Kessinger Publishing, LLC.

Hunt, Giles. The Duel: Castlereagh, Canning & Deadly Cabinet Rivalry. 2008. (ENG., Illus.). 224p. 37.00 *(978-1-84511-593-7(7))* I. B. Tauris & Co., Ltd. GBR. Dist: Macmillan.

Lee, Stephen M. George Canning & Liberal Toryism, 1801-27. 2008. (Royal Historical Society Studies in History New Ser.: Volume 62). 222p. 90.00 *(978-0-86193-294-8(3))* Royal Historical Society GBR. Dist: Boydell & Brewer, Inc.

Phillips, W. Alison. George Canning. 2007. (ENG.). 224p. 39.95 *(978-0-548-14332-2(3))* 2006. pap. 24.95 *(978-1-4286-5569-0(7))* Kessinger Publishing, LLC.

CANNING AND PRESERVING

see also Canned Foods; Drying Apparatus; Salmon Canning Industry

Afoakwa, Emmanuel Ohene. Canning Technology: Principles, Applications & Recent Technological Advances. 2008. (Illus.). viii, 85p. pap. 32.00 *(978-1-60456-653-6(1))* Nova Science Pubs., Inc.

Aikman-Smith, Valerie. Salt: Cooking with the World's Favorite Seasoning. 2009. (ENG., Illus.). 64p. *(978-1-84597-912-6(5))* Ryland Peters & Small.

Alfeld, Beverly Ellen Schoonmaker. Pickles to Relish, 1 vol. 2008. (ENG., Illus.). 208p. 24.95 *(978-1-58980-489-0(9))* Pelican Publishing Co., Inc.

Amendt, Linda J. 175 Best Jams, Jellies, Marmalades & Other Soft Spreads. 2008. (ENG., Illus.). 304p. pap. 21.95 *(978-0-7788-0183-2(7))* Rose, Robert Inc. CAN. Dist: Firefly Bks., Ltd.

Australian Women's Weekly Staff. Jams & Jellies. Coleman, Mary, ed. (ENG., Illus.). 80p. pap. 5.95 *(978-1-86396-231-5(X))* ACP Publishing Pty, Ltd. AUS. Dist: Graphic Arts Ctr. Publishing Co.

Barton, Miriam. The Pioneer Cookbook: Recipes for Today's Kitchen. 2011. (ENG., Illus.). 184p. pap. 17.95 ***(978-1-59992-142-6(1))*** Leatherwood Pr.

Better Homes and Gardens Books Staff. Better Homes & Gardens Can It! 2012. (ENG.). 240p. pap. 17.99 ***(978-1-118-21718-4(7),*** Wiley) Wiley, John & Sons, Inc.

—Better Homes & Gardens You Can Can: A Guide to Canning, Preserving, & Pickling. 2011. (Better Homes & Gardens Cooking Ser.). 192p. pap. 14.95 ***(978-1-118-09135-7(3),*** Wiley) Wiley, John & Sons, Inc.

Better Homes and Gardens Editors. You Can Can! A Guide to Canning, Preserving, & Pickling. 2010. (ENG., Illus.). 240p. pap. 17.95 *(978-0-470-60756-5(4),* Wiley) Wiley, John & Sons, Inc.

Better Homes & Gardens You Can Can: Guide to Canning, Preserving, & Pickling. 2010. *(978-0-470-87825-5(8))* Wiley, John & Sons, Inc.

Bratt, Les. Fish Canning Handbook. 2010. (ENG., Illus.). 320p. 209.99 *(978-1-4051-8099-3(4),* Wiley-Blackwell) Wiley, John & Sons, Inc.

Breazeale, James. Economy in the Kitchen. 2007. (Cooking in America Ser.). (ENG.). 116p. per. 9.95 *(978-1-4290-1024-5(X))* Applewood Bks.

Burch, Monte. The Joy of Smoking & Salt Curing: The Complete Guide to Smoking & Curing Meat, Fish, Game, & More. 2011. (Joy of Ser.). (ENG., Illus.). 256p. pap. 14.95 *(978-1-61608-229-1(1),* 608229) Skyhorse Publishing Co., Inc.

Canadian Living Test Kitchen. The Canadian Living Complete Preserving Book. 2012. (ENG., Illus.). 320p. 34.95 ***(978-0-9877474-1-9(X))*** Transcontinental Bks. CAN. Dist: Random Hse., Inc.

Casbeer, Anne. Auntie Anne's Pantry: Preservation in Freezing, Drying, & Canning. 2010. 108p. pap. 11.95 *(978-1-4269-2963-2(3))* Trafford Publishing.

Consumer Dummies Staff. Canning & Preserving All-in-One for Dummies. 2011. (ENG.). 696p. pap. 25.99 *(978-1-118-03419-4(8),* For Dummies) Wiley, John & Sons, Inc.

Cooper, Janet. Home Canning & Preserving: Putting up Small-Batch Jams, Jellies, Pickles, Chutneys, Relishes, & More. 2011. (ENG., Illus.). 208p. 19.95 *(978-1-61608-355-7(7),* 608355) Skyhorse Publishing Co., Inc.

Crocker, Pat. Preserving: The Canning & Freezing Guide for All Seasons. 2012. 552p. 30.00 ***(978-0-06-219144-1(6),*** Morrow, William Cookbooks) HarperCollins Pubs.

Cruess, William. Home & Farm Food Preservation. (Northshire Bookstore Edition Ser.). 2010. 312p. pap. 19.95 *(978-1-4290-4457-8(8))* 2008. (ENG.). 308p. pap. 19.95 *(978-1-4290-1260-7(9))* Applewood Bks.

Department of Agriculture Staff, U. S. Home Canning of Fruits & Vegetables. (Shorey Lost Arts Ser.). (Illus.). 31p. reprint ed. 10.00 *(978-0-8466-6050-7(4))* Shorey's Bookstore.

Dorling Kindersley Publishing Staff. Preserve It! Brown, Lynda, ed. 2010. (ENG.). 352p. 25.00 *(978-0-7566-6208-0(7))* Dorling Kindersley Publishing, Inc.

Dowdney, Steve. Putting Up: A Seasonal Guide to Canning in the Southern Tradition, 1 vol. 2008. (ENG., Illus.). 176p. pap. 19.99 *(978-1-4236-0280-4(3))* Gibbs Smith, Publisher.

—Putting up More: A Guide to Canning Jams, Relishes, Chutneys, Pickles, Sauces, & Salsas, 1 vol. 2011. (ENG., Illus.). 176p. pap. 19.99 *(978-1-4236-0739-7(2))* Gibbs Smith, Publisher.

Dragan, Mary Anne. Well Preserved: Small Batch Preserving for the New Cook. 3rd ed. 2010. (ENG.). 288p. pap. 24.95 *(978-1-55285-988-9(6))* Whitecap Bks., Ltd. CAN. Dist: Midpoint Trade Bks., Inc.

Eales, Mary. Mrs Mary Eales's Receipts. 2007. (Illus.). 60p. per. *(978-1-4065-2499-4(9))* Dodo Pr.

Emery, Carla & Forkner, Lorene Edwards. Canning & Preserving Your Own Harvest: An Encyclopedia of Country Living Guide. 2009. (ENG., Illus.). 208p. pap. 16.95 *(978-1-57061-571-9(3))* Sasquatch Bks.

English, Ashley. Canning & Preserving with Ashley English. 2010. (Homemade Living Ser.). (ENG., Illus.). 136p. 19.95 *(978-1-60059-491-5(3),* 1600594913) Lark Bks.

Farrow, Joanna. Seasonal Preserves. 2010. (ENG., Illus.). 160p. 17.95 *(978-1-84773-436-9(3))* New Holland Pubs., Ltd. GBR. Dist: Sterling Publishing Co., Inc.

Field, Rick, et al. The Williams-Sonoma Art of Preserving. 2010. (ENG.). 240p. 29.95 *(978-1-74089-978-9(4))* Weldon Owen, Inc.

Gasteiger, Daniel. Yes, You Can! And Freeze & Dry It, Too: The Modern Step-by-Step Guide to Preserving Food. 2011. (ENG., Illus.). 256p. pap. 19.95 *(978-1-59186-487-5(9),* 1591864879) Cool Springs Pr.

Geary, Kelly & Knadler, Jessie. Tart & Sweet: 101 Canning & Pickling Recipes for the Modern Kitchen. 2011. (ENG., Illus.). 240p. 24.99 *(978-1-60529-382-0(2))* Rodale Pr., Inc.

Green, Henrietta. A Green Guide to Country Foods. 2011. (ENG., Illus.). 192p. 24.95 *(978-1-907563-29-7(8))* CICO Bks. GBR. Dist: Ryland Peters & Small.

Harrison, John & Harrison, Val. How to Store Your Home-Grown Produce: Canning, Pickling, Jamming, & So Much More. 2010. (ENG., Illus.). 192p. pap. 12.95 *(978-1-61608-144-7(9),* 608144) Skyhorse Publishing Co., Inc.

Hayes, Olive. Preservation of Food. 2007. (Cooking in America Ser.). (ENG.). 56p. per. 9.95 *(978-1-4290-1053-5(3))* Applewood Bks.

Hoff, Archie, compiled by. Dainty Sweets. 2007. (Cooking in America Ser.). (ENG., Illus.). 60p. per. 9.95 *(978-1-4290-1043-6(6))* Applewood Bks.

Hood, Sarah B. We Sure Can! How Jams & Pickles Are Reviving the Lure & Lore of Local Food. 2011. (ENG., Illus.). 272p. pap. 24.95 *(978-1-55152-402-3(3))* Arsenal Pulp Pr. CAN. Dist: Consortium Bk. Sales & Distribution.

Hughes, Mary Catherine. Everywoman's Canning Book. 2007. (Cooking in America Ser.). (ENG.). 112p. per. 9.95 *(978-1-4290-1056-6(8))* Applewood Bks.

James, Ghillie. Jam, Jelly & Relish: Simple Preserves, Pickles & Chutney & Creative Ways to Cook with Them. 2011. (ENG.). 176p. 22.95 *(978-1-906868-18-5(2))* Kyle Bks. GBR. Dist: National Bk. Network.

Jeanroy, Amelia & Ward, Karen. Canning & Preserving for Dummies. 2nd ed. 2009. (ENG., Illus.). 384p. pap. 19.99 *(978-0-470-50455-0(2),* For Dummies) Wiley, John & Sons, Inc.

—Canning & Preserving for Dummies 2nd Edition. 2nd l.t. ed. 2010. (ENG.). 545p. 33.95 *(978-1-4104-2458-7(8))* Thorndike Pr.

Krissoff, Liana. Canning for a New Generation: Bold, Fresh Flavors for the Modern Pantry. 2010. (ENG., Illus.). 304p. pap. 24.95 *(978-1-58479-864-4(5))* Stewart, Tabori & Chang.

Leahy, Kate & Virant, Paul. The Preservation Kitchen: The Craft of Making & Cooking with Pickles, Preserves, & Aigre-Doux. 2012. (ENG., Illus.). 304p. 29.99 ***(978-1-60774-100-8(8))*** Ten Speed Pr.

Meyer, Mary Clemens & Meyer, Susanna. Saving the Seasons: How to Can, Freeze, or Dry Almost Anything. 2010. (ENG.). 288p. pap. 24.99 *(978-0-8361-9512-5(4))* Herald Pr.

Micka, Ana. The Fresh Girl's Guide to Easy Canning & Preserving. 2010. (ENG., Illus.). 128p. pap. 19.99 *(978-0-7603-3846-9(9),* 0760338469, Voyageur Pr) MBI Publishing Co. LLC.

Nargi, Lela, ed. The Farmer's Wife Canning & Preserving Cookbook: Over 250 Blue-Ribbon Recipes! 2009. (ENG., Illus.). 224p. spiral bd. 15.99 *(978-0-7603-3525-3(7),* 0760335257, Voyageur Pr) MBI Publishing Co. LLC.

Norris, Lucy. Pickled: Preserving a World of Tastes & Traditions. (Illus.). pap. 24.95 *(978-1-55054-998-0(7))* D&M Pubs. Inc. CAN. Dist: Perseus-PGW.

Oster, Ken. The Complete Guide to Preserving Meat, Fish, & Game: Step-by-Step Instructions to Freezing, Canning, Curing, & Smoking. 2011. (ENG.). 288p. pap. 24.95 *(978-1-60138-343-3(6))* Atlantic Publishing Co.

Parente, Jackie. Can it! Start Canning & Preserving at Home Today. 2012. (Hobby Farm Home Ser.). (ENG.). 176p. pap. 16.95 ***(978-1-935484-28-8(1),*** Hobby Farms Press) BowTie Pr.

Patten, Marguerite. Jams, Preserves & Chutneys Handbook: All You Need to Know to Prepare & Store over 200 of the World's Best Preserves. 2008. (BASIC BASICS Ser.). (Illus.). 192p. pap. *(978-1-902304-72-4(1))* Grub Street.

Sanders, Moira, et al. The Harrow Fair Cookbook: Prize-Winning Recipes Inspired by One of Canada's Oldest Country Fairs. 2010. 256p. pap. 29.95 *(978-1-77050-020-4(0))* Whitecap Bks., Ltd. CAN. Dist: Midpoint Trade Bks., Inc.

Sandler, Nick. Preserved. 2009. (ENG.). 224p. pap. 22.95 *(978-1-906868-02-4(6))* Cathie, Kyle Ltd. GBR. Dist: National Bk. Network.

Sherman, Jackie. Making the Most of Your Glorious Glut: Cooking, Storing, Freezing, Drying & Preserving Your Garden Pro. 2011. (ENG., Illus.). 256p. pap. 24.95 ***(978-1-900322-96-6(X))*** Green Bks. GBR. Dist: Chelsea Green Publishing.

Shettikere Shivanna, Manohar. Heat Penetration Studies. 2010. 72p. pap. *(978-3-8383-7827-5(X))* Lambert Academic Publishing.

Solomon, Karen. Can It, Bottle It, Smoke It: And Other Kitchen Projects. 2011. (Illus.). 160p. 24.99 *(978-1-58008-575-5(X))* Ten Speed Pr.

—Jam It, Pickle It, Cure It: And Other Cooking Projects. 2009. (ENG., Illus.). 160p. 24.99 *(978-1-58008-958-6(5))* Ten Speed Pr.

Strawbridge, Dick & Strawbridge, James. Preserving: Made at Home. 2012. (Made at Home Ser.). (ENG.). 176p. pap. 19.95 ***(978-1-77085-079-8(1))*** Firefly Bks., Ltd.

Topp, Ellie & Howard, Margaret. The Complete Book of Small-Batch Preserving: Over 300 Recipes to Use Year-Round. 2nd rev. ed. 2007. (ENG., Illus.). 408p. 29.95 *(978-1-55407-267-5(0));* pap. 19.95 *(978-1-55407-256-9(5))* Firefly Bks., Ltd.

Topp, Ellie & Howard, Margaret. Preserving Made Easy: Small Batches & Simple Techniques. 2012. (ENG., Illus.). 320p. pap. 9.99 ***(978-1-77085-094-1(5))*** Firefly Bks., Ltd.

Tremblay, Yvonne. 250 Home Preserving Favorites: From Jams & Jellies to Marmalades & Chutneys. 2010. (ENG., Illus.). 304p. pap. 21.95 *(978-0-7788-0237-2(X))* Rose, Robert Inc. CAN. Dist: Firefly Bks., Ltd.

U.S. Department of Agriculture. The Complete Guide to Home Canning. 2007. (Illus.). 192p. pap. 14.95 *(978-1-60239-077-5(0))* Skyhorse Publishing Co., Inc.

U.S. Dept. Of Agriculture. Complete Guide to Home Canning & Preserving. 2008. 172p. *(978-1-60796-023-2(0));* pap. *(978-965-00-6042-8(1))* Editorial Benei Noaj.

Vassallo, Jody. Preserving Basics: 77 Recipes Illustrated Step by Step. 2011. (My Cooking Class Ser.). (ENG., Illus.). 256p. pap. 24.95 *(978-1-55407-942-1(X))* Firefly Bks., Ltd.

Warren, Piers. How to Store Your Garden Produce, Revised & Enlarged Edition: The key to Self-sufficiency. l.t. ed. 2009. 315p. 30.95 *(978-1-4104-1781-7(6))* Thorndike Pr.

Wildsmith, Lindy. Cured: Slow techniques for flavoring meat, fish & Vegetables. 2010. (ENG.). 250p. pap. 30.00 *(978-1-4402-0512-5(4))* Krause Pubns.

Willis, Kimberley. Canning, Pickling & Preserving: Tools, Techniques & Recipes to Enjoy Fresh Food All Year-Round. 2010. (Knack: Make It Easy Ser.). (ENG., Illus.). 256p. pap. 19.95 *(978-1-59921-950-9(6),* Knack) Globe Pequot Pr., The.

Wilson, Carol. Preserving: Self-Sufficiency. 2009. (Self-Sufficiency Ser.). (ENG., Illus.). 128p. 12.95 *(978-1-60239-789-7(9),* 239789) Skyhorse Publishing Co., Inc.

Ziedrich, Linda. The Joy of Pickling: 225 Flavor-Packed Recipes for Vegetables & More from Garden or Market. 2009. (ENG.). 432p. 29.95 *(978-1-55832-374-2(0))* Harvard Common Pr.

Ziedrich, Linda & Ziedrich. The Joy of Pickling: 250 Flavor-Packed Recipes for Vegetables & More from Garden or Market. rev. ed. 2009. (ENG.). 432p. pap. 18.95 *(978-1-55832-375-9(9))* Harvard Common Pr.

CANNON

see Ordnance

CANOES AND CANOEING

see also Indians of North America—Boats; Kayaking; Kayaks; White-Water Canoeing

Adams, Dave. Season of the Loon. 14.95 *(978-0-87839-145-5(2))* North Star Pr. of St. Cloud.

Adney, Edwin Tappan & Chappelle, Howard I. Bark Canoes & Skin Boats of North America. 2007. (ENG., Illus.). 276p. pap. 19.95 *(978-1-60239-071-3(1),* 239071) Skyhorse Publishing Co., Inc.

Ahrendt, Sue, ed. Becoming a Boundary Waters Family: Woods Wisdom Shared by the Outfitters of the Gunflint Trail. 2009. (Illus.). 76p. spiral bd. 15.99 *(978-1-60743-855-7(0))* Independent Pub.

American Canoe Association Staff. Canoeing. Dillon, Pamela S. & Oyen, Jeremy, eds. 2008. (ENG., Illus.). 264p. 22.95 *(978-0-7360-6715-7(9))* Human Kinetics Pubs.

Anderson, Scott. Distant Fires: Duluth to Hudson Bay. 2008. (Illus.). 176p. pap. 15.95 *(978-0-8166-5503-8(0))* Univ. of Minnesota Pr.

Apps, Jerold W. & Apps, Steve, photos by. Campfires & Loon Calls: Travels in the Boundary Waters. 2011. (ENG., Illus.). 272p. pap. 15.95 *(978-1-936218-07-3(0))* Fulcrum Publishing.

Archer, Laurel. Northern British Columbia Canoe Trips, 1 vol. rev. ed. 2009. (ENG., Illus.). 304p. pap. *(978-1-897522-13-4(4))* Rocky Mountain Bks.

—Northern British Columbia Canoe Trips: Volume Two, 1 vol. 2010. (ENG., Illus.). 396p. pap. *(978-1-926855-04-2(3))* Rocky Mountain Bks.

Audette, Susan T. & Baker, David E. The Old Town Canoe Company: Our First Hundred Years. 2010. (Illus.). 176p. pap. 30.00 *(978-0-88448-203-1(0))* Tilbury Hse. Pubs.

Benson, David. Owls of the North: A Naturalist's Handbook. 2007. (Bird Nerd Natural History Ser.). (Illus.). 86p. per. 19.95 *(978-0-9760313-4-5(5))* Stone Ridge Publishing.

Berger, Jonathan & Terry, Thomas. Canoe Atlas of the Little North. 2007. (ENG., Illus.). 144p. 95.00 *(978-1-55046-496-2(5))* Boston Mills Pr. CAN. Dist: Firefly Bks., Ltd.

Berry, David Chapman. A Week on the Chunky & Chickasawhay. 2009. (ENG.). 200p. pap. 24.95 *(978-1-933896-26-7(4))* Texas Review Pr.

Beymer, Robert & Dzierzak, Louis. Boundary Waters Canoe Area: Western Region. 7th ed. 2009. (ENG.). 288p. pap. 17.95 *(978-0-89997-460-6(0))* Wilderness Pr.

—Boundary Waters Canoe Area - Eastern Region. 5th ed. 2009. (ENG.). 312p. pap. 17.95 *(978-0-89997-461-3(9))* Wilderness Pr.

Bishop, Nathaniel Holmes. Voyage of the Paper Canoe: A geographical journey of 2500 miles from Quebec. 2007. (ENG.). 226p. pap. 20.99 *(978-1-4346-1441-4(7))* BiblioBazaar.

—Voyage of the Paper Canoe: A Geographical Journey of 2500 Miles from Quebec. l.t. ed. 2007. (ENG.). 246p. pap. 22.99 *(978-1-4346-1535-0(9))* BiblioBazaar.

Bowden, Keith. The Tecate Journals: Seventy Days on the Rio Grande. 2007. (ENG., Illus.). 320p. per. 17.95 *(978-1-59485-077-6(1))* Mountaineers Bks., The.

Breining, Greg. Paddle North: Canoeing the Boundary Waters-Quetico Wilderness. 2010. (Illus.). 144p. 29.95 *(978-0-87351-778-2(4))* Minnesota Historical Society Pr.

Brenan, Dan & Sears, George Washington. The Adirondack Letters of George Washington Sears: Whose Pen Name Was Nessmuk. 2011. 204p. 44.95 ***(978-1-258-04215-8(0))*** Literary Licensing, LLC.

Burk, John S. & Kick, Peter. AMC Catskill Mountain Guide, 2nd: AMC's Comprehensive Guide to Hiking Trails in the Catskills. 2nd ed. 2009. (ENG., Illus.). 272p. pap. 23.95 *(978-1-934028-19-3(3))* Appalachian Mountain Club Bks.

Byrd, Dickie. Chandalar 2005. 2008. 193p. pap. 69.50 *(978-1-4357-0723-8(0))* Lulu Enterprises Inc.

Callan, Kevin. A Paddler's Guide to Quetico & Beyond. 2007. (Paddler's Guide Ser.). (ENG., Illus.). 192p. pap. 24.95 *(978-1-55046-500-6(7))* Boston Mills Pr. CAN. Dist: Firefly Bks., Ltd.

—Top 50 Canoe Routes of Ontario. 2011. (ENG., Illus.). 336p. pap. 29.95 *(978-1-55407-834-9(2))* Firefly Bks., Ltd.

Canoe Camping. 2007. (Essential Guides (Heliconia Press) Ser.). (Illus.). 123p. per. *(978-1-896980-22-5(8))* Heliconia Pr., Inc.

Canoeing. (Take up Sports! Ser.). (Illus.). 64p. pap. 4.95 *(978-1-56757-024-3(0))* Appleton Communications, Inc.

Canoeing. cd-rom 11.99 *(978-1-57223-855-8(0),* 8550) Willow Creek Pr., Inc.

Chamberlin, Johnnie. Trails of Little Rock: Hiking, Biking, & Kayaking Trails in Little Rock. 2009. (ENG., Illus.). 80p. (gr. 12). pap. 12.00 *(978-1-935166-10-8(7))* Parkhurst Brothers, Inc., Pubs.

Cilley, David. Adirondack Paddler's Guide: Finding Your Way by Canoe & Kayak in the Adirondack Park. 2008. spiral bd. *(978-0-9746320-2-5(3))* Paddlesports Pr.

Coffey, Maria & Goering, Dag. Visions of the Wild: A Voyage by Kayak Around Vancouver Island. unabr. ed. (ENG., Illus.). 192p. 36.95 *(978-1-55017-264-5(6))* Harbour Publishing Co., Ltd. CAN. Dist: Ingram Pub. Services.

Cole, Jim. Paddling Connecticut & Rhode Island: Southern New England's Best Paddling Routes. 2009. (Paddling Ser.). (ENG., Illus.). 144p. pap. 16.95 *(978-0-7627-3961-5(4),* Falcon Guides) Globe Pequot Pr., The.

Cook, David S. Above the Gravel Bar: The Native Canoe Routes of Maine. 3rd ed. 2007. (Illus.). 142p. per. 12.95 *(978-1-882190-69-0(6))* Polar Bear & Co.

Cook, Sam. Moving Waters: Adventures on Northern Rivers. 2007. (Illus.). 117p. 22.95 *(978-0-9760313-5-2(3))* Stone Ridge Publishing.

Cordes, Jim. The Treasures of Minnesota's North Shore & Gunflint Trail: A Lake Superior Journey. 2008. (ENG., Illus.). 224p. pap. 29.95 *(978-0-9711160-0-9(8))* Cordes, Jim Publishing.

Corliss, Ralph & Chase, Richard. Backpaddlers Guide to the North Umpqua River, 3 bks., Bk. 3: Cable Crossing to Winchester Dam. Date not set. (Illus.). spiral bd. *(978-1-878947-03-1(6))* Walk on Water.

Counts, Jeff. The Paddler's Guide to Michigan. 2011. (ENG., Illus.). 200p. pap. 18.95 *(978-0-88150-930-4(2),* 150930) Countryman Pr.

Coz, Steven. Where Memories Dream: Campfire Stories for the Boundary Waters. 2011. (Illus.). 216p. pap. 14.95 *(978-1-886028-92-0(3))* Savage Pr.

Curran, David. Canoe Trip: North to Athabasca. 2010. pap. 17.95 *(978-1-55571-667-7(9),* Hellgate Pr.) L & R Publishing.

Di Piazza, Anne & Pearthree, Erik. Canoes of the Grand Ocean. 2008. (Bar S Ser.). (Illus.). 154p. (C). 92.50 *(978-1-4073-0289-8(2))* British Archaeological Reports Ltd. GBR. Dist: Brown, David Bk. Co., The.

Diebel, Robert & Diebel, Lynne Smith. Paddling Southern Minnesota: 85 Great Trips by Canoe & Kayak. 2007. (Trails Books Guide Ser.). (Illus.). 198p. per. 19.95 *(978-1-931599-78-8(5))* Big Earth Publishing.

Dierking, Gary. Building Outrigger Sailing Canoes: Modern Construction Methods for Three Fast, Beautiful Boats. 2007. (ENG., Illus.). 192p. per. 22.95 *(978-0-07-148791-7(3),* 0071487913, International Marine/Ragged Mountain Pr.) McGraw-Hill Professional Publishing.

Dunnett, Alastair. The Canoe Boys: The First Epic Scottish Sea Journey by Kayak. 2007. (Illus.). 208p. per. 20.00 *(978-1-903238-99-8(4))* Wilson, Neil Publishing, Ltd. GBR. Dist: Interlink Publishing Group, Inc.

Evans, Doug. Noah's Last Canoe: The Lost Art of Cree Birch Bark Canoe Building. 2008. (ENG.). 104p. pap. 24.95 *(978-1-894283-82-3(1))* Great Plains Pubns. CAN. Dist: Univ. of Toronto Pr.

Faulkner, Steven. Waterwalk: A Passage of Ghosts. 2007. (Illus.). 320p. 16.95 *(978-1-57143-170-7(5))* RDR Bks.

Ferguson, Paul. Paddling Eastern North Carolina. 2nd exp. ed. 2007. (Illus.). 589p. pap. 24.95 *(978-0-9720268-1-9(9))* Pocosin Pr.

Fischer, Hank. Paddling Montana, 2nd. 2nd ed. 2008. (Paddling Ser.). (ENG., Illus.). 224p. pap. 16.95 *(978-0-7627-4352-0(2),* Falcon Guides) Globe Pequot Pr., The.

Fiske, John. AMC River Guide: Maine. 4th ed. 2008. (AMC River Guide Ser.). (ENG., Illus.). 352p. pap. 16.95 *(978-1-934028-15-5(0))* Appalachian Mountain Club Bks.

Fiske, John, ed. River Guide: New Hampshire/Vermont. 4th rev. ed. 2007. (AMC River Guide Ser.). (ENG., Illus.). 328p. pap. 16.95 *(978-1-934028-05-6(3))* Appalachian Mountain Club Bks.

Frye, Bob. Paddling Pennsylvania: A Guide to 50 of the State's Greatest Paddling Adventures. 2011. (ENG., Illus.). 144p. pap. 16.95 *(978-0-7627-4672-9(6),* Falcon Guides) Globe Pequot Pr., The.

Gauthier, Michel. The Nation Lakes Canoe Route: A Paddler's Guide. 2012. (Illus.). 176p. pap. ***(978-0-9865095-2-0(3))*** Dogwood Avenue Bks.

Gazetas, Mary. Around One More Point: A Journal of Paddling Adventures, 1 vol. 2010. (ENG., Illus.). 96p. per. *(978-1-894898-46-1(X))* TouchWood Editions.

Gillette, Bob. Paddling Prince Edward Island: A Guide to the Island's Best Paddling Adventures. 2006. (Falcon Guide Ser.). (ENG., Illus.). 240p. per. 16.95 *(978-0-7627-4117-5(1),* Falcon Guides) Globe Pequot Pr., The.

Gilpatrick, Gil. The Allagash Guide: What You Need to Know to Canoe this Famous Maine Waterway. 2011. (ENG., Illus.). 104p. pap. 11.95 *(978-1-56523-488-8(X))* Fox Chapel Publishing Co., Inc.

—Building a Strip Canoe: Full-Sized Plans & Instructions for Eight Easy-to-Build, Field-Tested Canoes. 2nd rev. expurg. ed. 2010. (Illus.). 112p. pap. 24.95 *(978-1-56523-483-3(9))* Fox Chapel Publishing Co., Inc.

Gilpatrick, Gil. Building Outdoor Gear, 2nd Edition, Revised & Expanded: Easy-to-Make Projects for Camping, Fishing, Hunting & Canoeing (Canoe Paddle, Pack Frame, Reflector Oven, Trip Boxes, Bucksaw, Other Trail-Tested Projects) 2nd rev. ed. 2012. (ENG., Illus.). 120p. pap. 19.95 ***(978-1-56523-484-0(7))*** Fox Chapel Publishing Co., Inc.

Gorman, Stephen & Gray, Daniel A. Canoeing for Everyone: A Step-by-Step Guide to Selecting the Gear, Learning the Strokes, & Planning Your Trip. 2009. (Knack: Make It Easy Ser.). (ENG., Illus.). 256p. pap. 19.95 *(978-1-59921-524-2(1),* Knack) Globe Pequot Pr., The.

Grand River Conservation Authority. Paddling the Grand River: A Trip-Planning Guide to Ontario's Historic Grand River. 2nd rev. ed. 2007. (ENG., Illus.). 96p. pap. 19.95 *(978-1-55028-978-7(0))* Lorimer, James & Co., Ltd., Pubs. CAN. Dist: Casemate Pubs. & Bk. Distributors, LLC.

Grinnell, George James. Death on the Barrens: A True Story of Courage & Tragedy in the Canadian Arctic. 2010. (ENG., Illus.). 296p. pap. 17.95 *(978-1-55643-882-0(6))* North Atlantic Bks.

Hardy, Dunbar. Paddling Colorado: A Guide to the State's Best Paddling Routes. 2009. (Paddling Ser.). (ENG., Illus.). 176p. pap. 16.95 *(978-0-7627-4520-3(7),* Falcon Guides) Globe Pequot Pr., The.

Hayes, John & Wilson, Alex. Quiet Water New Hampshire & Vermont: AMC's Canoe & Kayak Guide to the Best Ponds, Lakes, & Easy Rivers. 3rd ed. 2010. (AMC Quiet Water Ser.). (ENG., Illus.). 336p. pap. 19.95 *(978-1-934028-35-3(5))* Appalachian Mountain Club Bks.

Hodgins, Bruce W. & Hodgins, Carol. Paddling Partners: Fifty Years of Northern Canoe Travel. 2008. (ENG., Illus.). 176p. pap. 24.99 *(978-1-55002-761-7(1))* Natural Heritage/Natural History, Inc. CAN. Dist: Ingram Pub. Services.

Holmes, Tommy. The Hawaiian Canoe. 2nd rev. ed. (Illus.). 220p. 38.00 *(978-0-915013-15-9(0))* Editions, Ltd.

Hoogeveen, Nate. Paddling Iowa: 128 Outstanding Journeys by Canoe & Kayak. Menard, Emily, ed. 2012. 184p. pap. 22.95 ***(978-0-615-57947-4(7))*** Otter Run Media.

Jacobson, Cliff. Basic Illustrated Canoeing. 2008. (Basic Essentials Ser.). (ENG., Illus.). 96p. pap. 9.95 *(978-0-7627-4759-7(5),* Falcon Guides) Globe Pequot Pr., The.

—Boundary Waters Canoe Camping, 3rd. 3rd ed. 2012. (How to Paddle Ser.). (ENG., Illus.). 208p. pap. 18.95 ***(978-0-7627-7344-2(8),*** Falcon Guides) Globe Pequot Pr., The.

—Canoeing. 3rd ed. 2007. (Basic Essentials Ser.). (ENG., Illus.). 80p. per. 8.95 *(978-0-7627-4013-0(2),* Falcon Guides) Globe Pequot Pr., The.

—Canoeing & Camping Beyond the Basics. 3rd ed. 2007. (How to Paddle Ser.). (ENG., Illus.). 224p. pap. 16.95 *(978-0-7627-4018-5(3),* Falcon Guides) Globe Pequot Pr., The.

Jettmar, Karen. The Alaska River Guide: Canoeing, Kayaking, & Rafting in the Last Frontier. 3rd ed. 2008. (Alaska River Guide: Canoeing, Kayaking, &

Rafting in the Last Fronti Ser.). (ENG., Illus.). 328p. pap. 18.95 *(978-0-89732-957-6(0))* Menasha Ridge Pr., Inc.

Jones, Philip N. Canoe & Kayak Routes of Northwest Oregon: Including Southwest Washington. 3rd rev. ed. 2007. (ENG., Illus.). 288p. per. 17.95 *(978-1-59485-032-5(1))* Mountaineers Bks., The.

Keith, Andrew. Afloat Again, Adrift: Three Voyages on the Waters of North America. 2006. per. 15.95 net. *(978-0-9707652-8-4(2))* Aliform Publishing.

Kenley, Kathy. Quiet Water New Jersey & Eastern Pennsylvania: AMC's Canoe & Kayak Guide to the Best Ponds, Lakes, & Easy Rivers. 2010. (AMC Quiet Water Ser.). (ENG., Illus.). 320p. pap. 19.95 *(978-1-934028-34-6(7))* Appalachian Mountain Club Bks.

Kent, Timothy J. A Modern-Day Voyageur Family: Paddling the 3,000 Mile Fur Trade Canoe Route Across the U. S. & Canada. 2009. (Illus.). 760p. 59.95 *(978-0-9657230-6-0(2))* Silver Fox Enterprises.

Kesselheim, Alan S. Let Them Paddle: Coming of Age on the Water. 2012. (ENG., Illus.). 256p. pap. 19.95 ***(978-1-55591-351-9(2))*** Fulcrum Publishing.

Landers, Rich, et al. Paddling Washington: Flatwater & Whitewater Routes in Washington State & the Inland Northwest. 2008. (ENG., Illus.). 384p. pap. 24.95 *(978-1-59485-056-1(9))* Mountaineers Bks., The.

Langford, Ken. The Making of a Canoe Slalom Coach. 2007. 200p. per. 19.11 *(978-1-4251-0769-7(9))* Trafford Publishing.

Laubach, Rene. AMC Best Day Hikes in the Berkshires: Four-Season Guide to 50 of the Best Trails in Western Massachusetts. 2009. (ENG., Illus.). 288p. pap. 18.95 *(978-1-934028-21-6(5))* Appalachian Mountain Club Bks.

Leff, David K. Deep Travel: In Thoreau's Wake on the Concord & Merrimack. 2009. (American Land & Life Ser.). (ENG., Illus.). 230p. 32.00 *(978-1-58729-789-2(2))* Univ. of Iowa Pr.

Letcher, Gary. A Paddler's Guide to the Delaware River: Kayaking, Canoeing, Rafting, Tubing. 3rd ed. 2012. (ENG., Illus.). 256p. pap. 18.95 ***(978-0-8135-5161-6(7)*** , Rivergate Bks.) Rutgers Univ. Pr.

Leverette, Will. A History of Whitewater Paddling in Western North Carolina. 2008. 128p. pap. 14.99 *(978-1-59629-435-6(3))* History Pr., The.

Lindell, Piper L., et al. Allegheny River Paddling Guide: From Kinzua Dam to Tionesta. Brant, Tataboline D., ed. 2007. (Illus.). 36p. ring bd. 28.30 *(978-0-9798528-0-0(3))* Lindell, Piper.

MacGregor, John. The Rob Roy on the Baltic: A Canoe Cruise. 2009. (Illus.). 236p. pap. 14.99 *(978-1-929516-20-9(7))* Dixon-Price Publishing.

MacKay, Bryan. Hiking, Cycling, & Canoeing in Maryland: A Family Guide. 2nd ed. 2008. (ENG., Illus.). 504p. pap. 21.95 *(978-0-8018-8767-3(4))* Johns Hopkins Univ. Pr.

Maclean, Dan. Paddling Alaska: A Guide to the State's Classic Paddling Trips. 2009. (Paddling Ser.). (ENG., Illus.). 160p. pap. 18.95 *(978-0-7627-4229-5(1)*, Falcon Guides) Globe Pequot Pr., The.

Madson, John. Up on the River: People & Wildlife of the Upper Mississippi. 2011. (Bur Oak Book Ser.). (ENG., Illus.). 282p. pap. 19.95 *(978-1-58729-975-9(5))* Univ. of Iowa Pr.

McBride, Beverly Waters. One Foot in Two Canoes. 2009. 304p. pap. 16.95 *(978-1-936051-03-8(6))* Peppertree Pr., The.

McKusick, Marshall B. Aboriginal Canoes in the West Indies: Yale University Publications in Anthropology, No. 63. Mintz, Sidney Wilfred & Rouse, Irving, eds. 2011. 12p. pap. 35.95 ***(978-1-258-09124-8(0))*** Literary Licensing, LLC.

Mitchell, Jeff. Paddling Pennsylvania: Canoeing & Kayaking the Keystone State's Rivers & Lakes. 2010. (ENG., Illus.). 304p. pap. 21.95 *(978-0-8117-3626-8(1))* Stackpole Bks.

Molloy, Johnny. Paddler's Guide to Everglades National Park. 2nd ed. 2009. (ENG., Illus.). 256p. pap. 19.95 *(978-0-8130-3360-0(8))* Univ. Pr. of Florida.

—Paddling Tennessee: A Guide to 38 of the State's Greatest Paddling Adventures. 2011. (ENG., Illus.). 232p. pap. 16.95 *(978-0-7627-4639-2(4)*, Falcon Guides) Globe Pequot Pr., The.

Molloy, Johnny, et al. Canoeing & Kayaking Florida. 2nd ed. 2007. (Canoe & Kayak Ser.). (ENG., Illus.). 312p. per. 17.95 *(978-0-89732-955-2(4))* Menasha Ridge Pr., Inc.

Monkman, Jerry & Monkman, Marcy. Discover Acadia National Park: The Best Hiking, Biking, & Paddling. 3rd ed. 2010. (AMC Discover Ser.). (ENG., Illus.). 288p. pap. 21.95 *(978-1-934028-29-2(0))* Appalachian Mountain Club Bks.

Monkman, Marcy & Monkman, Jerry. AMC Discover the White Mountains, 2nd: AMC's guide to the best hiking, biking, & Paddling. 2nd ed. 2009. (AMC Discover Ser.). (ENG., Illus.). 288p. pap. 18.95 *(978-1-934028-22-3(3))* Appalachian Mountain Club Bks.

Morine, David E. Two Coots in a Canoe: An Unusual Story of Friendship. 2009. (ENG.). 320p. 22.95 *(978-0-7627-5459-5(1))* Globe Pequot Pr., The.

Morrison, Dan. The Black Nile: One Man's Amazing Journey Through Peace & War on the World's Longest River. (ENG.). (gr. 12). 2011. 352p. 16.00 *(978-0-14-311937-1(0)*, Penguin (Non-Classics)) 2010. 320p. 26.95 *(978-0-670-02198-7(9)*, Viking Adult) Penguin Group (USA) Inc.

Mountaineers Books Staff. The Northern Forest Canoe Trail: Enjoy 740 Miles of Canoe & Kayak Destinations in New York, Vermont, Quebec, New Hampshire, & Maine. 2010. (ENG.). 320p. pap. 24.95 *(978-1-59485-061-5(5))* Mountaineers Bks., The.

National Geographic Society Staff. Boundary Waters Canoe Area-East: Trails Illustrated Map. 2010. 11.95 *(978-1-56695-502-7(5))* National Geographic Maps.

—Boundary Waters Canoe Area-West: Trails Illustrated Map. 2010. 11.95 *(978-1-56695-503-4(3))* National Geographic Maps.

Nichols, David L. Lapstrake Canoes: Everything You Need to Know to Build a Light, Strong, Beautiful Boat. 2007. (ENG., Illus.). 160p. pap. 21.95 *(978-1-891369-72-6(5))* Breakaway Bks.

Nielson, Claus Bager. A War Canoe Heading for Christianity. 2007. (Intervention Press Ser.). (ENG., Illus.). 24p. pap. 19.95 *(978-87-89825-77-9(2))* Left Coast Pr., Inc.

Oberholtzer, Ernest Carl. Toward Magnetic North: The Oberholtzer-Magee 1912 Canoe Journey to Hudson Bay. 2008. (ENG., Illus.). 128p. 49.95 *(978-0-87351-623-5(0))* Minnesota Historical Society Pr.

O'Connor, Michael. AMC Discover Cape Cod: AMC's guide to the best hiking, biking, & Paddling. 2009. (ENG., Illus.). 288p. pap. 18.95 *(978-1-934028-17-9(7))* Appalachian Mountain Club Bks.

Oldmixon, Eben. Day Paddling Long Island Sound. 2008. (ENG., Illus.). 240p. per. 16.95 *(978-0-88150-684-6(2)*, 150684) Countryman Pr.

O'Neill, Dan. A Land Gone Lonesome: An Inland Voyage along the Yukon River. 2007. (ENG., Illus.). 272p. per. 15.95 *(978-1-58243-364-6(X))* Basic Bks.

Pelly, David F. The Old Way North: Following the Oberholtzer-Magee Expedition. 2008. (ENG., Illus.). 224p. 27.95 *(978-0-87351-616-7(8)*, Borealis Bk.) Minnesota Historical Society Pr.

Pohl, Herb. The Lure of Faraway Places: Reflections on Wilderness & Solitude. Raffan, James, ed. 2007. (ENG., Illus.). 232p. pap. 23.95 *(978-1-897045-24-4(7))* Natural Heritage/Natural History, Inc. CAN. Dist: Ingram Pub. Services.

Powell, Consie. Leave Only Ripples: A Canoe Country Sketchbook. 2007. (Illus.). 32p. (J). (gr. -1-3). *(978-0-9677057-9-8(7))* Raven Productions, Inc.

Price, Rod. Racing to the Yukon: A Lifetime of Adventure Racing from the Everglades to the Amazon to the World's Longest Canoe Race. 2010. 200p. pap. 19.95 *(978-1-934449-58-5(X))* Legacy Publishing Services, Inc.

Rizzetta, Sam. Canoe & Kayak Building the Light & Easy Way: How to Build Tough, Super-Safe Boats in Kevlar, Carbon, or Fiberglass. 2009. (ENG., Illus.). 256p. pap. 24.95 *(978-0-07-159735-7(2)*, 0071597352, International Marine/Ragged Mountain Pr.) McGraw-Hill Professional Publishing.

Roberts, Harry. Canoe Paddling. Salins, Steve, ed. 3rd ed. 2006. (Basic Essentials Ser.). (ENG., Illus.). 80p. pap. 8.95 *(978-0-7627-4284-4(4)*, Falcon Guides) Globe Pequot Pr., The.

Roberts, Harry, et al. Basic Illustrated Canoe Paddling. Salins, Steve, ed. 2008. (Basic Essentials Ser.). (ENG., Illus.). 96p. pap. 9.95 *(978-0-7627-4758-0(7)*, Falcon Guides) Globe Pequot Pr., The.

Scheibe, Nancy. Ripples of Wisdom. 2010. 288p. pap. 17.95 *(978-0-9819307-5-6(1))* Raven Productions, Inc.

Scobbie, James. From a Canoe. 2007. 176p. pap. 59.50 *(978-1-4303-2282-5(9))* Lulu Enterprises Inc.

Scriver, Mark. Canoe Camping: An Essential Guide. 2011. (ENG., Illus.). 112p. pap. 16.95 *(978-1-56523-646-2(7))* Fox Chapel Publishing Co., Inc.

Seton, Ernest Thompson. The Arctic Prairies. 2008. 220p. 24.99 *(978-0-554-33082-2(2))* 2008. 220p. 27.99 *(978-0-554-23779-4(2))* 2007. (ENG.). 198p. pap. 19.99 *(978-1-4264-5012-9(5))* 2007. (ENG.). 218p. pap. 22.99 *(978-1-4264-5313-7(2))* BiblioBazaar.

—The Arctic Prairies. 2008. (ENG.). 196p. per. *(978-1-4065-9174-3(2))* Dodo Pr.

—The Arctic Prairies. 2006. pap. *(978-1-84702-461-9(0))* Echo Library.

Sinai, Lee. AMC Discover Martha's Vineyard: AMC's guide to the best hiking, biking, & Paddling. 2009. (ENG., Illus.). 256p. pap. 18.95 *(978-1-934028-24-7(X))* Appalachian Mountain Club Bks.

Smith, Clyde H. Northeast Passage: A Photographer's Journey along the Historic Northern Forest Canoe Trail. 2007. 112p. 24.95 *(978-0-9705511-4-6(2))* Thistle Hill Pubns.

Smith, Jason, ed. Ultimate Canoe & Kayak Adventures: 100 Extraordinary Paddling Experiences. 2012. (ENG.). 208p. pap. 34.95 ***(978-1-119-99124-3(2)***, Wiley Nautical) Wiley, John & Sons, Inc.

Stiegelmaier, Kevin. Canoeing & Kayaking New York. 2009. (Canoe & Kayak Ser.). (ENG., Illus.). 320p. pap. 17.95 *(978-0-89732-668-1(7))* Menasha Ridge Pr., Inc.

Stocking, Marion Kingston. To the Wilderness: A Memoir. 2009. 47.50 *(978-0-87413-078-2(6))* Univ. of Delaware Pr.

Stone, Kas. Paddling & Hiking the Georgian Bay Coast. 2008. (ENG., Illus.). 224p. pap. 29.95 *(978-1-55046-477-1(9))* Boston Mills Pr. CAN. Dist: Firefly Bks., Ltd.

Svob, Mike. Paddling Illinois: 64 Great Trips by Canoe & Kayak. 2007. (Trails Books Guide Ser.). (Illus.). 153p. per. 18.95 *(978-1-934553-00-8(X))* Trails Bks.

—Paddling Northern Wisconsin. 2007. (Trails Books Guide). (Illus.). 184p. pap. 22.95 *(978-1-931599-86-3(6))* Big Earth Publishing.

—Paddling Southern Wisconsin: 85 Great Trips by Canoe & Kayak. 2006. (Illus.). 184p. per. 22.95 *(978-1-931599-77-1(7))* Big Earth Publishing.

Tba. Discover the Adirondacks. 2012. (AMC Discover Ser.). (ENG., Illus.). 288p. pap. 18.95 *(978-1-934028-31-5(2))* Appalachian Mountain Club Bks.

Weidemann, Dennis. This Water Goes North. 2008. (ENG.). 256p. 21.95 *(978-0-9796852-0-0(6))* Berens Hse.

Westwood, Andrew. Canoeing: The Essential Skills & Safety. 2011. (ENG., Illus.). 144p. pap. 14.95 *(978-1-56523-634-9(3))* Fox Chapel Publishing Co., Inc.

—Canoeing: The Essential Skills & Safety. 2007. (Essential Guides (Heliconia Press) Ser.). (Illus.). 142p. pap. 14.95 *(978-1-896980-29-4(5))* Heliconia Pr., Inc. CAN. Dist: SCB Distributors.

Westwood, Andrew & Sandiford, Rebecca. Canoeing. 2nd ed. 2012. (Illus.). 144p. ***(978-1-896980-69-0(4))*** Heliconia Pr., Inc.

Whittle, Jamie. White River: A Walk to the Source of the River Findhorn & the Canoe Journey Back. 2007. (Illus.). 192p. *(978-1-905207-16-9(6))* Silvermine International Bks., LLC.

Wilbers, Stephen. A Boundary Waters History: Canoeing Across Time. 2011. 130p. pap. 19.99 ***(978-1-59629-970-2(3))*** History Pr., The.

Wilson, Alex & Hayes, John. Quiet Water New York: Canoe & Kayak Guide. 2nd ed. 2007. (AMC Quiet Water Ser.). (ENG., Illus.). 432p. per. 19.95 *(978-1-929173-73-0(3))* Appalachian Mountain Club Bks.

CANON (LITERATURE)

Here are entered works on the accepted or sanctioned list of works which have achieved recognition in literary history for their superior qualities.

Barton, John. The Canon Literature & Theology: Collected Works of John Barton. 2007. (Society for Old Testament Study Ser.). 308p. 124.95 *(978-0-7546-5451-3(6))* Ashgate Publishing Co.

Beach, Joseph Warren. Making of the Auden Canon. 2009. (ENG.). 323p. pap. 60.00 *(978-0-8166-6022-3(0))* Univ. of Minnesota Pr.

Beam, Alex. A Great Idea at the Time: The Rise, Fall, & Curious Afterlife of the Great Books. 2008. (ENG., Illus.). 256p. 24.95 *(978-1-58648-487-3(7))* Perseus Bks. Group.

—A Great Idea at the Time: The Rise, Fall, & Curious Afterlife of the Great Books. 2009. (ENG., Illus.). 256p. pap. 13.95 *(978-1-58648-776-8(0))* PublicAffairs.

Becker, Eve-Marie, et al. Kanon in Konstruktion und Dekonstruktion: Kanonisierungsprozesse religiöser Texte von der Antike bis zur Gegenwart - Ein Handbuch. 2011. (GER & ENG.). XII, 744p. 196.00 ***(978-3-11-024555-4(8))*** De Gruyter, Walter Inc.

Beilein, Matthias, et al, eds. Kanon, Wertung und Vermittlung: Literatur in der Wissensgesellschaft. 2011. (Studien und Texte zur Sozialgeschichte der Literatur Ser.).Tr. of Canon Formation & Mediation of Literature in the Knowledge Society. (GER.). VII, 350p. 210.00 ***(978-3-11-916346-0(5))***; (Illus.). 140.00 ***(978-3-11-025994-0(X))*** De Gruyter, Walter Inc.

Bowskill, Sarah E. Gender, Nation & the Formation of the Twentieth-Century Mexican Literary Canon. 2011. (Legenda Main Ser.). (ENG.). 133p. (C). 89.50 *(978-1-907975-05-9(5))* European Humanities Research Ctr. GBR. Dist: Brown, David Bk. Co., The.

Brown, Joan L. Confronting Our Canons: Spanish & Latin American Studies in the 21st Century. 2010. (ENG.). 247p. 60.00 *(978-1-61148-351-2(4))* Bucknell Univ. Pr.

Brown, Joan Lipman. Confronting Our Canons: Spanish & Latin American Studies in the 21st Century. 2010. (Illus.). 248p. 54.50 *(978-0-8387-5767-3(7))* Bucknell Univ. Pr.

Brüggemann, Jö. Literarizität und Geschichte als literaturdidaktisches Problem: Eine Studie am Beispiel des Mittelalters. 2008. (Beiträge zur Geschichte des Deutschunterrichts. Begründet und herausgegeben von Joachim S. Hohmann 1988-1998 Ser.). 564p. pap. 124.95 *(978-3-631-58398-2(2))* Lang, Peter GmbH, Europaischer Verlag der Wissenschaften DEU. Dist: Lang, Peter.

Calanchi, Alessandra, et al, eds. The Case & the Canon: Anomalies, discontinuities, metaphors between science & literature. 2011. (Interfacing Science, Literature, & the Humanities Ser.). (ENG.). 309p. (C). 63.00 ***(978-3-89971-681-8(7))*** Vandenhoeck & Ruprecht GmbH & Co. KG DEU. Dist: ISD.

Cammy, J. D., et al. Arguing the Modern Jewish Canon: Essays on Literature & Culture in Honor of Ruth R. Wisse. 2009. (Harvard Center for Jewish Studies). (Illus.). 750p. 75.00 *(978-0-674-02585-1(7))* Harvard Univ. Ctr. for Jewish Studies.

Carlisle, Janice & Schwarz, Daniel R., eds. Narrative & Culture. 2010. (ENG.). 288p. pap. 24.95 *(978-0-8203-3791-3(9))* Univ. of Georgia Pr.

Caton, Lou Freitas. Reading American Novels & Multicultural Aesthetics: Romancing the Postmodern Novel. 2007. (ENG.). 284p. 100.00 *(978-1-4039-8486-9(7))* Palgrave Macmillan.

Cole, Andrew. Literature & Heresy in the Age of Chaucer. 2011. (Cambridge Studies in Medieval Literature Ser.). (ENG.). 324p. pap. 39.99 *(978-0-521-17983-6(1))* Cambridge Univ. Pr.

De Bary, Wm Theodore. Finding Wisdom in East Asian Classics. 2011. (ENG., Illus.). 432p. (gr. 17). pap. 29.50 *(978-0-231-15397-3(X))* Columbia Univ. Pr.

de Bary, Wm. Theodore. Finding Wisdom in East Asian Classics. 2011. (ENG., Illus.). 432p. (gr. 17). 89.50 *(978-0-231-15396-6(1))* Columbia Univ. Pr.

Dirda, Michael. Classics for Pleasure. (ENG.). 352p. 2008. pap. 15.00 *(978-0-15-603385-5(2)*, Mariner Bks.) 2007. 25.00 *(978-0-15-101251-0(2))* Houghton Mifflin Harcourt Trade & Reference Pubs.

Ensslin, Astrid & Ensslin. Canonising Hypertext: Explorations & Constructions. 2007. (Continuum Literary Studies). (ENG., Illus.). 206p. *(978-0-8264-9558-7(3))* Continuum International Publishing Group, Ltd.

Entzminger, Betina. Contemporary Reconfigurations of American Literary Classics: The Origin & Evolution of American Stories. 2012. (Routledge Studies in Twentieth-Century Literature Ser.). (ENG.). 228p. (C). 125.00 ***(978-0-415-53964-7(1))*** Routledge.

Fishelov, David. Dialogues with/and Great Books: The Dynamics of Canon Formation. 2012. 232p. pap. 34.95 ***(978-1-84519-518-2(3))*** Sussex Academic Pr. GBR. Dist: International Specialized Bk. Services.

Gamer, Michael. Romanticism & the Gothic: Genre, Reception, & Canon Formation. 2006. (Cambridge Studies in Romanticism Ser.). (ENG.). 276p. pap. 45.00 *(978-0-521-02693-2(8))* Cambridge Univ. Pr.

Gordinsky, Natasha & Zepp, Susanne. Kanon und Diskurs: Über Literarisierung jüdischer Erfahrungswelten. 2009. (Toldot Ser.). (GER.). 120p. (C). pap. 35.00 *(978-3-525-35093-5(7))* Vandenhoeck & Ruprecht GmbH & Co. KG DEU. Dist: ISD.

Goyens, Michèle, et al, eds. Science Translated: Latin & Vernacular Translations of Scientific Treatises in Medieval Europe. 2008. (Mediaevalia Lovaniensia Ser.). 480p. pap. 80.00 *(978-90-5867-671-9(4))* Leuven Univ. Pr. BEL. Dist: Cornell Univ. Pr.

Graziosi, Barbara & Greenwood, Emily. Homer in the Twentieth Century: Between World Literature & the Western Canon. 2010. (ENG., Illus.). 336p. pap. 45.00 *(978-0-19-959131-2(8))* Oxford Univ. Pr., Inc.

Green, Amy S. The Revisionist Stage: American Directors Reinvent the Classics. 2006. (Cambridge Studies in American Theatre & Drama Ser.). (ENG.). 244p. pap. 48.00 *(978-0-521-02892-9(2))* Cambridge Univ. Pr.

Kelly, Joseph. Our Joyce: From Outcast to Icon. 2010. (ENG., Illus.). 303p. pap. 25.00 *(978-0-292-72376-4(8))* Univ. of Texas Pr.

Kramnick, Jonathan Brody. Making the English Canon: Print-Capitalism & the Cultural Past, 1700-1770. 2008. (ENG.). 296p. (C). pap. 44.00 *(978-0-521-06592-4(5))* Cambridge Univ. Pr.

Kuipers, Christopher. The Canon. 2009. (New Critical Idiom Ser.). 170p. 22.95 *(978-0-415-36924-4(X))* Routledge.

Lambert, Ladina & Ochsner, Andrea, eds. Moment to Monument: The Making & Unmaking of Cultural Significance. 2009. (ENG.). 224p. pap. 39.95 *(978-3-89942-962-6(1))* Transcript Verlag DEU. Dist: Transaction Pubs.

Layman, Bruccoli-Clark & Anderson, George Parker. American Modernism, 1914-1945, 7 vols. 2010. (Research Guide to American Literature Ser.). 328p. (C). (gr. 9-18). 50.00 *(978-0-8160-7865-3(3))* Facts On File, Inc.

Layman, Bruccoli-Clark & Cusatis, John. Post-War Literature, 1945-1970, 7 vols. 2010. (Research Guide to American Literature Ser.). 272p. (C). (gr. 9-18). 50.00 *(978-0-8160-7866-0(1))* Facts On File, Inc.

Layman, Bruccoli-Clark & Franklin, Benjamin. Colonial Literature, 1607-1776, 7 vols. 2010. (Research Guide to American Literature Ser.). 264p. (C). (gr. 9-18). 50.00 *(978-0-8160-7861-5(0))* Facts On File, Inc.

Layman, Bruccoli-Clark & Vietto, Angela. Early American Literature, 1776-1820, 7 vols. 2010. (Research Guide to American Literature Ser.). 224p. (C). (gr. 9-18). 50.00 *(978-0-8160-7862-2(9))* Facts On File, Inc.

Layman, Bruccoli-Clark, et al. Contemporary Literature, 1970-Present, 7 vols. 2010. (Research Guide to American Literature Ser.). 432p. (C). (gr. 9-18). 50.00 *(978-0-8160-7867-7(X))* Facts On File, Inc.

—Realism & Regionalism, 1865-1914, 7 vols. 2010. (Research Guide to American Literature Ser.). 248p. (C). (gr. 9-18). 50.00 *(978-0-8160-7864-6(5))* Facts On File, Inc.

—Romanticism & Transcendentalism, 1820-1865, 7 vols. 2010. (Research Guide to American Literature Ser.). 248p. (C). (gr. 9-18). 50.00 *(978-0-8160-7863-9(7))* Facts On File, Inc.

Mack, Edward Thomas. Manufacturing Modern Japanese Literature: Publishing, Prizes, & the Ascription of Literary Value. 2010. (Asia-Pacific: Culture, Politics, & Society Ser.). (ENG., Illus.). 336p. 84.95 *(978-0-8223-4660-9(5))*; pap. 23.95 *(978-0-8223-4672-2(9))* Duke Univ. Pr.

Nogelmeier, Puakea. Mai Pa'a I Ka Leo: Historical Voice in Hawaiian Primary Materials: Looking Forward & Listening Back. 2010. 26.95 *(978-1-58178-086-4(9))*; pap. 16.95 *(978-1-58178-087-1(7))* Bishop Museum Pr.

Otten, Willemien, et al. How the West Was Won: Essays on the Literary Imagination, the Canon, & the Christian Middle Ages. 2010. (Illus.). 422p. *(978-90-04-18496-1(1))* BRILL.

Renker, Elizabeth. The Origins of American Literature Studies: An Institutional History. 2010. (Cambridge Studies in American Literature & Culture Ser.). (ENG.). 232p. pap. 34.99 *(978-0-521-14199-4(0))* Cambridge Univ. Pr.

Rennison, Nick, et al. 100 Must-Read Classic Novels. 2007. (ENG.). 192p. pap. 9.95 *(978-0-7136-7583-2(7))* A & C Black GBR. Dist: Macmillan.

Research Guide to American Literature, 7 vols., Set. 2010. (Research Guide to American Literature Ser.). (C). (gr. 9). 350.00 *(978-0-8160-8307-7(X))* Facts On File, Inc.

Russett, Margaret. De Quincey's Romanticism: Canonical Minority & the Forms of Transmission. 2006. (Cambridge Studies in Romanticism Ser.). (ENG.). 312p. pap. 66.00 *(978-0-521-03050-2(1))* Cambridge Univ. Pr.

Sanna, Simonetta, ed. Der Kanon in der deutschen Sprach- und Literaturwissenschaft: Akten des IV. Kongresses der Italienischen Germanistenvereinigung. Alghero, 27. -31. 5. 2007. 2009. (IRIS. Ricerche di cultura europea / Forschungen zur europäischen Kultur Ser.). (GER.). 296p. pap. *(978-3-03911-821-2(8))* Lang, Peter.

Spiers, John, ed. Nationalisms & the National Canon, 2 vols., Vol. 2. 2011. (ENG., Illus.). 232p. 80.00 *(978-0-230-28403-6(5))* Palgrave Macmillan.

Stuurman, Siep & Grever, Maria, eds. Beyond the Canon: History for the 21st Century. 2007. (ENG., Illus.). 256p. 95.00 *(978-0-230-51650-2(5))* Palgrave Macmillan.

Thomassen, Einar, ed. Canon & Canonicity: The Formation & Use of Scripture. 2010. 232p. 48.00 *(978-87-635-3027-9(9))* Museum Tusculanum Pr. DNK. Dist: Chicago Distribution Ctr.

Tuite, Clara. Romantic Austen: Sexual Politics & the Literary Canon. 2008. (Cambridge Studies in Romanticism Ser.). (ENG.). 264p. pap. 37.99 *(978-0-521-05439-3(7))* Cambridge Univ. Pr.

Turner, Nick. Post-War British Women Novelists & the Canon. 2012. (ENG.). 202p. pap. 44.95 ***(978-1-4411-8904-2(1))*** Continuum International Publishing Group, Ltd. GBR. Dist: National Bk. Network.

Turner, Nick & Turner. Post-War British Women Novelists & the Canon. 2010. (Continuum Literary Studies). (ENG.). 208p. 110.00 *(978-0-8264-3454-8(1))*

Continuum International Publishing Group, Ltd. GBR. Dist: National Bk. Network.

Zorrilla, J. & Zorrilla, José. El Zapateroy el Rey. (Clasicos Castalia). (SPA., Illus.). 384p. 19.95 *(978-84-7039-310-5(3)*, CC529) Castalia, Editorial S.A. ESP. Dist: Continental Bk. Co., Inc.

CANON (MUSIC)

see Musical Canon

CANON (MUSICAL FORM)

Here are entered works on the canon as a musical form. Music scores are entered under the heading Canons, Fugues, etc.

Carson-Turner, Barrie. Best of Canons & Rounds. 2008. pap. 9.95 *(978-1-84761-116-1(8)*, 1847611168) Schott Music Corp.

Collins, Denis. A Briefe & Short Instruction of the Art of Musicke by Elway Bevin. 2007. (Music Theory in Britain, 1500-1700: Critical Editions Ser.). (Illus.). 146p. 99.95 *(978-0-7546-5053-9(7))* Ashgate Publishing Co.

Harris, Rachel. The Making of a Musical Canon in Chinese Central Asia: The Uyghur Twelve Muqam. 2008. (SOAS Musicology Ser.). (Illus.). 176p. 59.95 *(978-0-7546-6382-9(5)*, Ashgate Publishing Co.

Light, Nathan. Intimate Heritage: Creating Uyghur Muqam Song in Xinjiang. 2011. (ENG.). 352p. pap. 51.50 *(978-3-8258-1120-4(4))* Lit Verlag DEU. Dist: Transaction Pubs.

Norden, Hugo. The Technique of Canon. 2009. (ENG., Illus.). 215p. pap. 23.95 *(978-0-8283-2190-7(6)*, Branden Bks.

Prout, Ebenezer. Double Counterpoint & Canon. 2009. 290p. 43.95 *(978-1-120-81345-9(X))*; pap. 28.95 *(978-1-120-61250-2(0))* Kessinger Publishing, LLC.

Schiltz, Katelijne & Blackburn, Bonnie J. Canons & Canonic Techniques, 14th-16th Centuries: Theory, Practice, & Reception History Proceedings of the International Conference, Leuven, 4-6 October 2005. Blackburn, B. J. & Schiltz, K., eds. 2007. (Leuven Studies in Musicology Ser.). (ENG., Illus.). 498p. (C). 114.00 *(978-90-429-1681-4(8))* Peeters Pubs. & Booksellers BEL. Dist: Brown, David Bk. Co., The.

Wuidar, Laurence. Canons énigmes et hiéroglyphes musicaux dans l'Italie du 17e Siècle. 2008. (Etudes de Musicologie / Musicological Studies). (FRE., Illus.). 265p. pap. 38.95 *(978-90-5201-457-9(4))* PIE - Peter Lang BEL. Dist: Lang, Peter.

CANON CAMERA

Burian, Peter K. Magic Lantern Guides: New MG Camera. 2011. (Magic Lantern Guides). (ENG., Illus.). 208p. pap. 14.95 *(978-1-4547-0136-1(6)*, Pixiq) Sterling Publishing Co., Inc.

Busch, David D. Canon EOS 7D: Digital SLR Photography. 2010. (ENG.). 496p. pap., instr.'s gde. ed. 29.99 *(978-1-4354-5691-4(2))* Delmar Cengage Learning.

—Canon EOS Digital Rebel XSI/450: Digital SLR Photography. 2008. (ENG., Illus.). 328p. pap. 29.99 *(978-1-59863-578-2(6))* Course Technology.

—Canon EOS Digital Rebel XTI/400D Guide to Digital SLR Photography. 2007. (ENG., Illus.). 280p. per. 29.99 *(978-1-59863-456-3(9))* Course Technology.

—Canon EOS Rebel T1i/500D - Digital SLR Photography. 2009. (ENG.). 376p. pap., instr.'s gde. ed. 29.99 *(978-1-4354-5496-5(0))* Course Technology.

—The Canon EOS Rebel T2i/550D. 2011. (ENG.). 144p. pap. 13.99 *(978-1-4354-5876-5(1))* Course Technology.

—Canon EOS Rebel T2i/550D: Digital SLR Photography. 2010. (ENG.). 384p. pap. 29.99 *(978-1-4354-5766-9(8))* Course Technology.

—Canon EOS Rebel XS/1000 Guide to Digital SLR Photography. 2009. (ENG., Illus.). 328p. pap. 29.99 *(978-1-59863-903-2(X))* Course Technology.

—David Busch's Canon EOS 50D Guide to Digital SLR Photography. 2009. (ENG.). 384p. pap. 29.99 *(978-1-59863-904-9(8))* Course Technology.

—David Busch's Canon EOS 60D Guide to Digital SLR Photography. 2011. (ENG.). 430p. pap. 29.99 *(978-1-4354-5938-0(5))* Course Technology.

—David Buschs Canon EOS 7D Gui. 2009. pap. 29.99 *(978-1-4354-5961-8(X))* Course Technology.

—David Busch's Canon EOS Rebel T3/1100D Guide to Digital SLR Photography. 2011. (ENG.). 400p. pap. 29.99 *(978-1-4354-6026-3(X))* Course Technology.

—David Busch's Canon EOS Rebel T3i/600D Guide to Digital SLR Photography. 2011. (ENG.). 480p. pap. 29.99 *(978-1-4354-6028-7(6))* Course Technology.

—David Busch's Canon Powershot G12 Guide to Digital Photography. 2011. (ENG.). 320p. pap. 29.99 *(978-1-4354-5950-2(4))* Course Technology.

—David Busch's Compact Field Guide for the Canon EOS 60D. 2011. (ENG.). 144p. spiral bd. 13.99 *(978-1-4354-5996-0(2))* Course Technology.

—David Busch's Compact Field Guide for the Canon EOS 7D. 2011. (ENG.). 112p. pap. 13.99 *(978-1-4354-5878-9(8))* Course Technology.

—David Busch's Compact Field Guide for the Canon EOS Rebel T3/1100D. 2011. (ENG., Illus.). 144p. spiral bd. 13.99 *(978-1-4354-6030-0(8))* Course Technology.

—David Busch's Compact Field Guide for the Canon EOS Rebel T3i/600D. 2011. (ENG., Illus.). 144p. spiral bd. 13.99 *(978-1-4354-6032-4(4))* Course Technology.

—Digital SLR Photography. 2009. (ENG.). 400p. pap. 29.99 *(978-1-4354-5497-2(9))* Course Technology.

Busch, David D. & White, Alexander S. Canon Powershot G10/G11: Guide to Digital Photography. 2010. (ENG.). 320p. pap. 29.99 *(978-1-4354-5535-1(5))* Course Technology.

Carlson, Jeff. Canon PowerShot G12: From Snapshots to Great Shots. 2011. (Illus.). xi, 227p. ***(978-0-13-265971-0(9))***; (ENG.). 240p. pap. 24.99 *(978-0-321-77161-2(3))* Peachpit Pr.

Dechert, Peter. Canon Rangefinder Cameras 1933-68. 2006. (Hove Collectors Bks.). (ENG., Illus.). 200p. 34.95 *(978-0-906447-30-7(5)*, 0906447305) Hove Bks. GBR. Dist: MBI Distribution Services/Quayside Distribution.

Francke, Harald. Canon Modern Classics F-1, FTB, EF, AE-1, AE-1P. (Modern Classics Ser.). (Illus.). 196p. pap. 19.95 *(978-0-906447-74-1(7)*, Hove Foto Bks, Ltd.) Newpro UK, Ltd. GBR. Dist: Voyageur Pr., Inc.

Garrison, Kerry & Corsentino, Michael. Canon Speedlite System Digital Field Guide. 3rd ed. 2012. (Digital Field Guide Ser.: 253). (ENG.). 320p. pap. 19.99 *(978-1-118-11289-2(X)*, Wiley) Wiley, John & Sons, Inc.

Graves, Russell & Sheppard, Rob. Canon EOS 50D. 2009. (Magic Lantern Guides). (ENG., Illus.). 224p. pap. 19.95 *(978-1-60059-526-4(X))* Lark Bks.

Grey, Christopher. Canon DSLR: The Ultimate Photographer's Guide. 2007. (Digital Workflow Ser.). (ENG., Illus.). 304p. pap. 39.95 *(978-0-240-52040-7(8)*, Focal Pr.) Elsevier Science & Technology Bks.

—Canon EOS Digital Rebel XS/1000D: Focal Digital Camera Guides. 2008. (ENG., Illus.). 256p. pap. 19.95 *(978-0-240-81170-3(4)*, Focal Pr.) Elsevier Science & Technology Bks.

—Canon EOS Digital Rebel XSi/450D. 2008. (Focal Digital Camera Guides). (ENG., Illus.). 256p. pap. 19.95 *(978-0-240-81066-9(X)*, Focal Pr.) Elsevier Science & Technology Bks.

Guncheon, Michael. Canon EOS-1 D Mark III: EOS-1 Ds Mark III. 2008. (Magic Lantern Guides). (ENG., Illus.). 240p. pap. 19.95 *(978-1-60059-205-8(8))* Lark Bks.

—Canon EOS Rebel XTi: EOS 400D. 2007. (Magic Lantern Guides). (Illus.). 192p. pap. 19.95 *(978-1-60059-099-3(3))* Lark Bks.

—Magic Lantern Guides: Canon EOS 5D Mark II. 2009. (Magic Lantern Guides). (ENG., Illus.). 288p. pap. 19.95 *(978-1-60059-536-3(7))* Lark Bks.

—Magic Lantern Guides: Canon EOS 7D. 2010. (Magic Lantern Guides). (ENG., Illus.). 272p. pap. 19.95 *(978-1-60059-664-3(9)*, Pixiq) Sterling Publishing Co., Inc.

—Magic Lantern Guides: Canon EOS Rebel T3i/T3. 2011. (Magic Lantern Guides). (ENG., Illus.). 336p. pap. 19.95 *(978-1-60059-698-8(3)*, Pixiq) Sterling Publishing Co., Inc.

—Magic Lantern Guides: Canon Powershot G11. 2010. (Magic Lantern Guides). (ENG., Illus.). 160p. pap. 14.95 *(978-1-60059-687-2(8))* Lark Bks.

Guncheon, Michael & Guncheon, Michael A. Canon PowerShot Digital Field Guide. 2007. (Digital Field Guide Ser.: 180). (ENG., Illus.). 288p. per. 19.99 *(978-0-470-17461-6(7)*, Wiley) Wiley, John & Sons, Inc.

—Magic Lantern Guides: Canon EOS Rebel XSi, EOS 450D. 2008. (Magic Lantern Guides). (ENG., Illus.). 224p. pap., instr.'s gde. ed. 19.95 *(978-1-60059-416-8(6))* Lark Bks.

Guy, N K. Mastering Canon EOS Flash Photography. 2010. (ENG., Illus.). 432p. pap. 44.95 *(978-1-933952-44-4(X))* Rocky Nook.

Hallett, Tracy. Canon EOS 60D. 2011. (Expanded Guide Ser.). (ENG.). 256p. pap. 19.95 *(978-1-907708-08-4(1)*, Ammonite Pr.) AE Pubns. GBR. Dist: BookMasters Distribution Services (BDS).

Hennings, Harry. Canon EOS 1000/1000FN/Rebel. (User's Guides Bks.). (Illus.). 220p. 19.95 *(978-0-906447-81-9(X)*, Hove Foto Bks, Ltd.) Newpro UK, Ltd. GBR. Dist: Voyageur Pr., Inc.

—Canon EOS 100/Elan. Kopp, Petra, tr. from GER. (User's Guides Bks.). (Illus.). 220p. 19.95 *(978-0-906447-98-7(4)*, Hove Foto Bks, Ltd.) Newpro UK, Ltd. GBR. Dist: Voyageur Pr., Inc.

Inova, Peter. DSLR Canon Digital Rebel XT. 2006. (Illus.). 600p. cd-rom 49.95 *(978-1-882383-29-0(X))* gmbooks.

—DSLR Canon EOS 20D. 2006. (Illus.). 600p. cd-rom 49.95 *(978-1-882383-31-3(1))* gmbooks.

King, Julie Adair. Canon EOS Digital Rebel XSi/450D for Dummies. 2008. (ENG., Illus.). 352p. pap. 29.99 *(978-0-470-38537-1(5)*, For Dummies) Wiley, John & Sons, Inc.

—Canon EOS Rebel T1i/500D for Dummies. 2009. (ENG., Illus.). 368p. pap. 29.99 *(978-0-470-53389-5(7)*, For Dummies) Wiley, John & Sons, Inc.

—Canon Eos Rebel T3i/600D for Dummies: 2011. (ENG., Illus.). 400p. pap. 29.99 *(978-1-118-09498-3(0)*, For Dummies) Wiley, John & Sons, Inc.

—Canon Eos Rebel Xs/1000d. 2008. (ENG., Illus.). 336p. pap. 29.99 *(978-0-470-43392-8(2)*, For Dummies) Wiley, John & Sons, Inc.

King, Julie Adair & Correll, Robert. Canon EOS 60D for Dummies. 2011. (ENG., Illus.). 384p. pap. 29.99 *(978-1-118-00489-0(2)*, For Dummies) Wiley, John & Sons, Inc.

—Canon EOS Rebel T3/1100D for Dummies. 2011. (ENG., Illus.). 400p. pap. 29.99 *(978-1-118-09497-6(2)*, For Dummies) Wiley, John & Sons, Inc.

Kraus, John. Canon Eos-1ds Mark III. 2009. (Digital Field Guide Ser.: 197). (ENG., Illus.). 288p. pap. 24.99 *(978-0-470-40949-7(5)*, Wiley) Wiley, John & Sons, Inc.

Landt, Artur. Canon 40D. Cloot, Jeremy, tr. from GER. rev. ed. 2008. (ENG & GER., Illus.). 200p. pap. 29.95 *(978-1-933952-33-8(4))* Rocky Nook.

Lark Books. Magic Lantern Guides: Canon EOS 60D Multimedia Workshop. 2011. (Magic Lantern Guides). (ENG., Illus.). 64p. 24.95 *(978-1-4547-0128-6(5)*, Pixiq) Sterling Publishing Co., Inc.

—Magic Lantern Guides: Canon EOS Rebel T3i/T3 Multimedia Workshop. 2011. (Magic Lantern Guides). (ENG., Illus.). 64p. 24.95 *(978-1-60059-702-2(5)*, Pixiq) Sterling Publishing Co., Inc.

Lark Books Staff. Canon EOS 50D Multimedia Workshop. 2009. (Magic Lantern Guides). (ENG., Illus.). 64p. 24.95 *(978-1-60059-571-4(5)*, Pixiq) Sterling Publishing Co., Inc.

—Magic Lantern Guides: Canon EOS 7D Multimedia Workshop. 2010. (Magic Lantern Guides). (ENG., Illus.). 64p. 24.95 *(978-1-60059-692-6(4)*, Pixiq) Sterling Publishing Co., Inc.

—Magic Lantern Guides: Canon EOS Rebel T1i/EOS 500D Multimedia Workshop. 2009. (Magic Lantern Guides). (ENG.). 64p. 24.95 *(978-1-60059-611-7(8))* Lark Bks.

—Magic Lantern Guides: Canon EOS Rebel T2i/EOS 550D Multimedia Workshop. 2010. (Magic Lantern Guides). (ENG., Illus.). 64p. 24.95 *(978-1-60059-794-7(7))* Lark Bks.

—Magic Lantern Guides: Canon EOS Rebel XSi EOS 450D EOS Rebel XS EOS 1000D Multimedia Workshop. 2009. (Magic Lantern Guides). (ENG., Illus.). 64p. 24.95 *(978-1-60059-566-0(9))* Lark Bks.

Long, Ben. The Canon EOS Digital Rebel T1i/500D Companion. 2009. (ENG., Illus.). 304p. pap. 24.99 *(978-0-596-80363-6(X))* O'Reilly Media, Inc.

—The Canon EOS Digital Rebel XS/1000D Companion. 2008. (ENG., Illus.). 288p. pap. 24.99 *(978-0-596-15452-3(6))* O'Reilly Media, Inc.

—The Canon Eos Digital Rebel XSi/450D Companion. rev. ed. 2008. (ENG., Illus.). 288p. pap. 24.99 *(978-0-596-52086-1(7))* O'Reilly Media, Inc.

Lowrie, Charlotte K. Canon EOS 30D Digital Field Guide. 2006. (Digital Field Guide Ser.: 179). (ENG., Illus.). 288p. per. 19.99 *(978-0-470-05340-9(2)*, Wiley) Wiley, John & Sons, Inc.

—Canon EOS 40D Digital Field Guide. 2008. (Digital Field Guide Ser.: 186). (ENG., Illus.). 320p. pap. 19.99 *(978-0-470-26044-9(0)*, Wiley) Wiley, John & Sons, Inc.

—Canon EOS 5D. 2008. (Digital Field Guide Ser.: 192). (ENG., Illus.). 283p. pap. 19.99 *(978-0-470-17405-0(6)*, Wiley) Wiley, John & Sons, Inc.

—Canon EOS 60D Digital Field Guide. 2010. (Digital Field Guide Ser.: 226). (ENG., Illus.). 320p. pap. 19.99 *(978-0-470-64862-9(7)*, Wiley) Wiley, John & Sons, Inc.

—Canon EOS 7D. 2009. (Digital Field Guide Ser.: 217). (ENG., Illus.). 304p. pap. 19.99 *(978-0-470-52129-8(5)*, Wiley) Wiley, John & Sons, Inc.

—Canon EOS Digital Rebel XSi/450D. 2008. (Digital Field Guide Ser.: 193). (ENG., Illus.). 288p. pap. 19.99 *(978-0-470-38087-1(X)*, Wiley) Wiley, John & Sons, Inc.

—Canon EOS Rebel T2i/550D Digital Field Guide. 2010. (Digital Field Guide Ser.: 227). (ENG., Illus.). 304p. pap. 19.99 *(978-0-470-64863-6(5)*, Wiley) Wiley, John & Sons, Inc.

—Canon EOS Rebel T3/1100D Digital Field Guide. 2011. (ENG., Illus.). 304p. pap. 19.99 *(978-1-118-09320-7(8)*, Wiley) Wiley, John & Sons, Inc.

—Canon EOS Rebel T3i/600D: Digital Field Guide. 2011. (ENG., Illus.). 304p. pap. 19.99 *(978-0-470-64861-2(9)*, Wiley) Wiley, John & Sons, Inc.

—Canon EOS Rebel XS/1000D. 2008. (Digital Field Guide Ser.: 198). (ENG., Illus.). 272p. pap. 19.99 *(978-0-470-40950-3(9)*, Wiley) Wiley, John & Sons, Inc.

Lowrie, Charlotte K. & Lowrie. Canon EOS Rebel T1i/500D. 2009. (Digital Field Guide Ser.: 207). (ENG., Illus.). 272p. pap. 19.99 *(978-0-470-52128-1(7)*, Wiley) Wiley, John & Sons, Inc.

Lowrie, Charlotte K. & McLemon, Brian. Canon Powershot G11. 2010. (Digital Field Guide Ser.: 210). (ENG., Illus.). 256p. pap. 19.99 *(978-0-470-56508-7(X)*, Wiley) Wiley, John & Sons, Inc.

Lowrie, Charlotte K., et al. Canon EOS 50D. 2009. (Digital Field Guide Ser.: 203). (ENG., Illus.). 288p. pap. 19.99 *(978-0-470-45559-3(4)*, Wiley) Wiley, John & Sons, Inc.

—Canon EOS 5D Mark II. 2009. (Digital Field Guide Ser.: 204). (ENG., Illus.). 288p. pap. 19.99 *(978-0-470-46714-5(2)*, Wiley) Wiley, John & Sons, Inc.

Miller, John D. Tutor at Your Side for the Canon EOS Digital Rebel XTi. 2007. (ENG., Illus.). 151p. pap. 30.00 *(978-0-9649037-2-2(5))* Advantage One, Inc.

Peachpit Press Staff & Carlson, Jeff. Canon PowerShot G10 / G11. 2009. (From Snapshots to Great Shots Ser.). (ENG., Illus.). 240p. pap. 24.99 *(978-0-321-67951-2(2))* Peachpit Pr.

Peachpit Press Staff & Revell, Jeff. Canon Rebel T1i/500D: From Snapshots to Great Shots. 2009. (From Snapshots to Great Shots Ser.). (ENG., Illus.). 288p. pap. 24.99 *(978-0-321-64725-2(4))* Peachpit Pr.

Photo, Llex & Ilex Photo. Canon D-SLR Shooting Modes. 2010. (ENG., Illus.). 128p. pap. 6.95 *(978-1-60433-113-4(5))* Cider Mill Pr. Bk. Pubs., LLC.

Revell, Jeff. Canon 50D: From Snapshots to Great Shots. 2009. (From Snapshots to Great Shots Ser.). (ENG., Illus.). 288p. pap. 24.99 *(978-0-321-61311-0(2))* Peachpit Pr.

—Canon EOS Rebel T2i / 550D: From Snapshots to Great Shots. rev. ed. 2010. (From Snapshots to Great Shots Ser.). (ENG., Illus.). 288p. pap. 24.99 *(978-0-321-73391-7(6))* Peachpit Pr.

—Canon EOS Rebel T3i / 600D: From Snapshots to Great Shots. 2011. (From Snapshots to Great Shots Ser.). (ENG., Illus.). 288p. pap. 24.99 *(978-0-321-77664-8(X))* Peachpit Pr.

Sahlin, Doug & King County Journal staff. Canon EOS 7D for Dummies. 2010. (ENG., Illus.). 352p. pap. 29.99 *(978-0-470-59591-6(4)*, For Dummies) Wiley, John & Sons, Inc.

Schneider, Jason. Magic Lantern Guides: Canon Powershot G10. 2009. (Magic Lantern Guides). (ENG., Illus.). 192p. pap. 14.95 *(978-1-60059-540-0(5))* Lark Bks.

Sheppard, Rob. How to Take Great Photos with the Canon D-SLR System. 2009. (Magic Lantern Guides). (ENG., Illus.). 272p. pap. 19.95 *(978-1-60059-461-8(1))* Lark Bks.

Stansfield, Andy. Canon DSLR System. 2010. (ENG., Illus.). 272p. pap. 19.95 *(978-1-906672-70-6(9)*, Ammonite Pr.) AE Pubns. GBR. Dist: BookMasters Distribution Services (BDS).

—Canon EOS 1000D / Rebel XS. 2009. (Expanded Guide Ser.). (ENG., Illus.). 239p. pap. 19.95 *(978-1-906672-21-8(0)*, Ammonite Pr.) AE Pubns. GBR. Dist: BookMasters Distribution Services (BDS).

—Canon EOS 40D. 2009. (Expanded Guide Ser.). (ENG., Illus.). 256p. pap. 19.95 *(978-1-906672-16-4(4)*, Ammonite Pr.) AE Pubns. GBR. Dist: BookMasters Distribution Services (BDS).

—Canon EOS 50D. 2009. (Expanded Guide Ser.). (ENG., Illus.). 256p. pap. 19.95 *(978-1-906672-39-3(3)*, Ammonite Pr.) AE Pubns. GBR. Dist: BookMasters Distribution Services (BDS).

—Canon EOS 5D Mark II: The Expanded Guide. 2009. (Expanded Guide Ser.). (ENG., Illus.). 240p. pap. 19.95 *(978-1-906672-41-6(5)*, Ammonite Pr.) AE Pubns. GBR. Dist: BookMasters Distribution Services (BDS).

—Canon EOS 7D. 2010. (Expanded Guide Ser.). (ENG., Illus.). 256p. pap. 19.95 *(978-1-906672-72-0(5)*, Ammonite Pr.) AE Pubns. GBR. Dist: BookMasters Distribution Services (BDS).

—Canon EOS System Guide. 2010. (ENG.). 288p. pap. 19.95 *(978-1-86108-650-1(4)*, Ammonite Pr.) AE Pubns. GBR. Dist: BookMasters Distribution Services (BDS).

—Canon Powershot G11. 2010. (Expanded Guide Ser.). (ENG., Illus.). 240p. pap. 19.95 *(978-1-906672-71-3(7)*, Ammonite Pr.) AE Pubns. GBR. Dist: BookMasters Distribution Services (BDS).

—Canon Rebel T1i/EOS 500D. 2009. (Expanded Guide Ser.). (ENG., Illus.). 239p. pap. 19.95 *(978-1-906672-47-8(4)*, Ammonite Pr.) AE Pubns. GBR. Dist: BookMasters Distribution Services (BDS).

Tapp, Eddie. Canon Digital Photo Professional Workflow. 2012. (ENG., Illus.). 240p. pap. 24.99 *(978-1-118-03511-5(9)*, Wiley) Wiley, John & Sons, Inc.

Taylor, David. Canon Rebel T3/EOS 1100D. 2011. (Expanded Guide Ser.). (ENG.). 240p. pap. 19.95 *(978-1-907708-20-6(0)*, Ammonite Pr.) AE Pubns. GBR. Dist: BookMasters Distribution Services (BDS).

—Canon Rebel T3i / EOS 600D. exp. ed. 2011. (Expanded Guide Ser.). (ENG.). 240p. pap. 19.95 *(978-1-907708-19-0(7)*, Ammonite Pr.) AE Pubns. GBR. Dist: BookMasters Distribution Services (BDS).

Watson, Lonzell & Watson. Canon VIXIA HD Camcorder Digital Field Guide. 2009. (Digital Field Guide Ser.: 196). (ENG., Illus.). 272p. pap. 19.99 *(978-0-470-39236-2(3)*, Wiley) Wiley, John & Sons, Inc.

Young, Nicole S. Canon EOS 60D: From Snapshots to Great Shots. 2010. (From Snapshots to Great Shots Ser.). (ENG., Illus.). 288p. pap. 24.99 *(978-0-321-74743-3(7))* Peachpit Pr.

CANON LAW

see also Church Orders, Ancient; Ecclesiastical Courts; Ecclesiastical Law; Privileges and Immunities, Ecclesiastical; Vicars-General

also special legal headings with Canon Law added in parentheses, e.g. Marriage (Canon Law)

Adam, Will. Legal Flexibility & the Mission of the Church: Dispensation & Economy in Ecclesiastical Law. 2011. 264p. 99.95 *(978-1-4094-2055-2(8))* Ashgate Publishing Co.

Adams, Norma & Donahue, Charles, eds. Select Cases from the Ecclesiastical Courts of the Province of Canterbury, c.1200-1301. (Selden Society Annual Ser.: Vol. 95, 1978 & 1979). 95.00 *(978-0-85423-110-2(2))* Selden Society GBR. Dist: Hein, William S. & Co., Inc.

Adamson, Douglas & Reynolds, Roger E. Collectio Toletana: A Canon Law Derivative of the South-Italian Collection in Five Books - An Implicit Edition with Introductory Study. 2008. (Studies & Texts). (LAT & ENG.). 59.95 *(978-0-88844-159-1(2))* Pontifical Institute of Mediaeval Studies, Dept. of Pubns. CAN. Dist: Univ. of Toronto Pr.

Ancient Laws & Institutes of England. 2010. 550p. 175.00 *(978-1-56169-971-1(3))* Gaunt, Inc.

Beozzo Oscar Staff. 2001/3: The Ecumenical Constitution of Churches Concilium June. 2011. pap. ***(978-0-334-03064-5(1)***, SCM Pr.) Hymns Ancient & Modern Ltd.

Bloch, Tamara. Die Stellungnahmen der römisch-katholischen Amtskirche zur Frage der Menschenrechte Seit 1215: Eine historische Untersuchung unter besonderer Berücksichtigung der Gewährleistungen im CIC/1983. 2008. (Schriften zum Staatskirchenrecht Ser.). 276p. pap. 74.95 *(978-3-631-56494-3(5))* Lang, Peter GmbH, Europaischer Verlag der Wissenschaften DEU. Dist: Lang, Peter.

Blumenthal, Uta-Renate, et al, eds. Canon Law, Religion, & Politics: Liber Amicorum Robert Somerville. 2012. (ENG.). 344p. 69.95 ***(978-0-8132-1975-2(2))*** Catholic Univ. of America Pr.

Bradshaw, Paul & Bebawi, Carol, eds. The Canons of Hippolytus. 2009. 88.00 *(978-1-60724-347-2(4))* Gorgias Pr., LLC.

Brooke, C. N. L., et al, eds. Church & Government in the Middle Ages: Essays presented to C. R. Cheney on his 70th Birthday & Edited by C. N. L. Brooke, D. E. Luscombe, G. H. Martin & Dorothy Owen. 2008. (ENG.). 336p. pap. 46.00 *(978-0-521-08929-6(8))* Cambridge Univ. Pr.

Brown, Ralph & Sheehy, Gerard, eds. Canon Law: Letter & Spirit. (Illus.). 1088p. pap. *(978-0-225-66881-0(5)*, Burns & Oates) Continuum International Publishing Group, Ltd.

Coughlin, John J. Canon Law: A Comparative Study with Anglo-American Legal Theory, 1 vol. 2010. (ENG.). 252p. 75.00 *(978-0-19-537297-7(2))* Oxford Univ. Pr., Inc.

Coughlin, John J. Law, Person, & Community: Philosophical, Theological, & Comparative Perspectives on Canon Law, 1 vol. 2012. (ENG.). 288p. (C). 85.00 ***(978-0-19-975677-3(5))*** Oxford Univ. Pr., Inc.

C

Cushing, Kathleen G. & Brasington, Bruce C., eds. Bishops, Texts & the Use of Canon Law Around 1100: Essays in Honour of Martin Brett. 2008. (Church, Faith & Culture in the Medieval West Ser.). (Illus.). 242p. 124.95 (978-0-7546-6015-6(X)) Ashgate Publishing Co.

Cushing, Kathleen G. & Brett, Martin. Readers Texts & Compilers in the Earlier Middle Ages: Studies in Medieval Canon Law in Honour of Linda Folwer-Magerl. 2009. (Church, Faith & Culture in the Medieval West Ser.). (Illus.). 226p. 124.95 (978-0-7546-6235-8(7)) Ashgate Publishing Co.

Dee, Dacian David. The Manifestation of Conscience: The Catholic University of America, Canon Law Studies, No. 410. 2011. 112p. 39.95 **(978-1-258-05289-8(X))** Literary Licensing, LLC.

Diatezulwa-Mbungu, Faustin. Les conciles particuliers dans l'Eglise Latine: Enjeux des canons 439-446 du Code De 1983. 2008. (Europäische Hochschulschriften. Reihe 23: Theologie Ser.). 283p. pap. (978-3-03911-707-9(6)) Lang, Peter.

Dolezalek, Gero. Iuris Historia: Liber Amicorum Gero Dolezalek. Colli, Vincenzo & Conte, Emanuele, eds. 2008. (Studies in Comparative Legal History). (ENG, FRE, GER, ITA & SPA.). 456p. 50.00 (978-1-882239-18-4(0)) Robbins Collection, Schl. of Law, UC Berkeley.

Eichbauer, Melodie H. & Pennington, Kenneth. Law as Profession & Practice in Medieval Europe: Essays in Honor of James A. Brundage. 2011. (Illus.). 436p. 134.95 (978-1-4094-2574-8(6)) Ashgate Publishing Co.

Garnett, George. Marsilius of Padua & 'the Truth of History' 2006. (ENG.). 240p. 110.00 (978-0-19-929156-4(X)) Oxford Univ. Pr., Inc.

Genoese Zerbi, JCL, Federico, JD. Resolving Contract Disputes in Canon Law. 2009. 116p. pap. 14.99 (978-0-557-13070-2(0)) Lulu Enterprises Inc.

Gibson, Margaret Dunlop, ed. The Didascalia Apostolorum in Syriac: Edited from a Mesopotamian Manuscript with Various Readings & Collations of Other MSS. 2011. (Cambridge Library Collection - Religion Ser.). (SYR.). 254p. pap. 23.99 (978-1-108-01896-8(3)) Cambridge Univ. Pr.

Gibson, Margaret Dunlop, tr. The Didascalia Apostolorum in English. 2011. (Cambridge Library Collection - Religion Ser.). (ENG.). 138p. pap. 19.99 (978-1-108-01897-5(1)) Cambridge Univ. Pr.

Harnack, Adolf von. Sources of the Apostolic Canon: With a Treatise on the Origin of the Readership & Other Lower Orders. 2008. 235p. pap. 20.00 (978-1-60608-280-5(9), Wipf and Stock) Wipf & Stock Pubs.

Hartmann, Wilfried & Pennington, Kenneth. History of Byzantine & Eastern Canon Law. 2012. (Hist Medvl Canon Law Ser.). (ENG.). 400p. 59.95 **(978-0-8132-1679-9(6))** Catholic Univ. of America Pr.

Hartmann, Wilfried & Pennington, Kenneth. The History of Medieval Canon Law in the Classical Period, 1140-1234: From Gratian to the Decretals of Pope Gregory IX. 2008. 456p. (C). 64.95 (978-0-8132-1491-7(2)) Catholic Univ. of America Pr.

Heith-Stade, David. Marriage As the Arena of Salvation: An Ecclesiological Study of the Marital Regulation in the Canons of the Council in Trullo. 2011. 206p. pap. 14.95 **(978-1-933275-55-0(3)**, Orthodox Research Institute) Cocheco Falls Publishing.

Helmholz, R. H. The Spirit of Classical Canon Law. 2010. (Spirit of the Laws Ser.). (ENG.). 528p. pap. 28.95 (978-0-8203-3463-9(4)) Univ. of Georgia Pr.

Herbers, Klaus & Fleisch, Ingo. Erinnerung - Niederschrift - Nutzung: Das Papsttum und die Schriftlichkeit im westeuropäischen Mittelalter. 2011. (Abhandlungen der Akademie der Wissenschaften zu Göttingen. Neue Folge Ser.). (GER., Illus.). X, 269p. 140.00 **(978-3-11-025370-2(4))** De Gruyter, Walter Inc.

Jones, Rhidian. The Canon Law of the Roman Catholic Church & the Church of England: A Handbook. 2nd ed. 2011. (ENG.). 208p. 80.00 (978-0-567-61641-8(X), T&T Clark Int'l) Continuum International Publishing Group, Ltd. GBR. Dist: National Bk. Network.

Kelly, Henry Ansgar. Law & Religion in Chaucer's England. 2010. (Variorum Collected Studies). (Illus.). 416p. 165.00 (978-1-4094-0751-5(9)) Ashgate Publishing Co.

Kim, Onyoo Elizabeth. Law & Criminality in the Middle Ages: Academic Essays. 2006. (Hermit Kingdom Studies in History & Religion: Vol. 3). 248p. 75.00 (978-1-59689-067-1(3)); pap. 35.00 (978-1-59689-068-8(1)) Hermit Kingdom Pr., The.

Kottmann, Klaus. Die Freimaurer und die katholische Kirche: Vom geschichtlichen Überblick zur geltenden Rechtslage. 2008. (Adnotationes in Ius Canonicum Ser.). 370p. pap. 70.95 (978-3-631-58484-2(9)) Lang, Peter GmbH, Europaischer Verlag der Wissenschaften DEU. Dist: Lang, Peter.

Library of Congress Staff & Library of Congress, Cataloging Policy and Support Office Staff, contrib. by. Library of Congress Classification. KB. Religious Law. 2008. (978-0-8444-1223-8(6)) Library of Congress.

Lilly, William Samuel. A Manual of the Law Specially Affecting Catholics. 2009. 222p. pap. (978-1-150-32942-5(4)) Books LLC.

Maassen, Friedrich. Geschichte der Quellen und der Literatur des Canonischen Rechts Im Abendlande Bis Zum Ausgange des Mittelalters. 2009. 225.00 (978-1-58477-944-5(6)) Lawbook Exchange, Ltd., The.

Motilla, Agustin. La Administración Española en Materia Religiosa (1808-1977) 2009. (SPA.). x, 207p. (978-84-9836-619-8(4)) Comares, Editorial SL.

Muller, Wolfgang P., ed. Medieval Church Law & the Origins of the Western Legal Tradition: A Tribute to Kenneth Pennington. 2006. (Illus.). 404p. 79.95 (978-0-8132-1462-7(9)) Catholic Univ. of America Pr.

Nwagwu, Mary Gerard Anna. Theology & Methodology of Canon Law. 2006. 251p. per. 25.49 (978-1-59879-188-4(5)) Lifevest Publishing, Inc.

Old Catholic Church, North American. Canons of the North American Old Catholic Church. 2009. 66p. pap. 9.99 (978-0-557-21972-8(8)) Lulu Enterprises Inc.

Owen, Dorothy M., ed. The Medieval Canon Law: Teaching, Literature & Transmission. 2009. (ENG.). 96p. pap. 28.99 (978-0-521-10656-6(7)) Cambridge Univ. Pr.

Pedone, F. Stephen & Donlon, James I., eds. Roman Replies & CLSA Advisory Opinions, 1998. viii, 114p. pap. 14.00 (978-0-943616-82-7(4)) Canon Law Society of America.

Peltzer, Jörg & Peltzer, Jörg Henning. Canon Law, Careers & Conquest: Episcopal Elections in Normandy & Greater Anjou, C.1140-C.1230. 2007. (Cambridge Studies in Medieval Life & Thought). (ENG., Illus.). 352p. 130.00 (978-0-521-88062-6(9)) Cambridge Univ. Pr.

Perczel, Istvan. The Nomocanon of Abdisho of Nisibis. Kaufhold, Hubert, ed. 2nd ed. 2009. (ENG & SYR.). 234.00 (978-1-59333-968-5(2)) Gorgias Pr., LLC.

Peters, Edward N. Excommunication & the Catholic Church: Straight Answers to Tough Questions. 2006. 64p. per. (978-1-932645-45-3(4)) Ascension Pr.

Rodopoulos, Panteleimon. An Overview of Orthodox Canon Law. Dragas, George, ed. 2007. 320p. pap. 18.95 (978-1-933275-15-4(4), Orthodox Research Institute) Cocheco Falls Publishing.

Rolker, Christof. Canon Law & the Letters of Ivo of Chartres. 2010. (Cambridge Studies in Medieval Life & Thought: Fourth Ser.). (ENG., Illus.). 400p. 110.00 (978-0-521-76682-1(6)) Cambridge Univ. Pr.

Schutte, Anne Jacobson. By Force & Fear: Taking & Breaking Monastic Vows in Early Modern Europe. 2011. (Illus.). 304p. 45.00 (978-0-8014-4977-2(4)) Cornell Univ. Pr.

Strauss, Peter L., ed. The Fetha Nagast: The Law of the Kings. Tzadua, Abba Paulos, tr. 2009. 392p. 60.00 (978-1-59460-661-8(7)) Carolina Academic Pr.

Vere, Pete & Truman, Michael. Surprised by Canon Law, Volume 2: More Questions Catholics Ask about Canon Law. 2007. 142p. per. 12.99 (978-0-86716-749-8(1), Servant Bks.) Franciscan Media.

Viscuso, Patrick. Orthodox Canon Law: A Casebook for Study. 2011. (978-1-935317-16-6(4)) Holy Cross Orthodox Pr.

—Orthodox Canon Law: A Casebook for Study. 2007. (978-1-932401-10-3(5)) InterOrthodox Pr.

Winroth, Anders. The Making of Gratian's Decretum. 2007. (Cambridge Studies in Medieval Life & Thought). (ENG., Illus.). 268p. pap. 56.00 (978-0-521-04465-3(0)) Cambridge Univ. Pr.

Woodall, G. J. A Passion for Justice: A Practical Guide to the Code of Canon Law. 2011. 616p. pap. **(978-0-85244-478-8(8))** Gracewing, Ltd.

CANON LAW—CONFLICT OF LAWS

see Conflict of Laws (Canon Law)

CANON LAW—STUDY AND TEACHING

Owen, Dorothy M., ed. The Medieval Canon Law: Teaching, Literature & Transmission. 2009. (ENG.). 96p. pap. 28.99 (978-0-521-10656-6(7)) Cambridge Univ. Pr.

CANONICAL FACULTIES

see Faculties (Canon Law)

CANONIZATION

see also Saints

Catanoso, Justin. My Cousin the Saint: A Story of Love, Miracles, & an Italian Family Reunited. 2009. 368p. pap. 14.99 (978-0-06-172932-4(9), HarperPerennial) HarperCollins Pubs.

Dolgin, Ellen Ecker. Modernizing Joan of Arc: Conceptions, Costumes, & Canonization. 2007. (ENG., Illus.). 207p. per. 35.00 (978-0-7864-3120-5(2)) McFarland & Co., Inc. Pubs.

Finucane, Ronald C. Contested Canonizations: The Last Medieval Saints, 1482-1523. 2011. 288p. 64.95 **(978-0-8132-1875-5(6))** Catholic Univ. of America Pr.

Gaposchkin, M. Cecilia. The Making of Saint Louis: Kingship, Sanctity, & Crusade in the Later Middle Ages. 2010. (Illus.). 352p. pap. 29.95 (978-0-8014-7625-9(9)) Cornell Univ. Pr.

—The Making of Saint Louis: Kingshnp, Sanctity, & Crusade in the Later Middle Ages. 2008. (Illus.). 331p. 47.50 (978-0-8014-4550-7(7)) Cornell Univ. Pr.

Goodich, Michael E. Miracles & Wonders: The Development of the Concept of Miracle 1150-1350. 2007. (Church, Faith & Culture in the Medieval West Ser.). 160p. 114.95 (978-0-7546-5875-7(9)) Ashgate Publishing Co.

Katajala-Peltomaa, S. Gender, Miracles, & Daily Life: The Evidence of Fourteenth-Century Canonization Processes. 2009. (Studies in the history of daily Life (800-1600) Ser.). (ENG & LAT., Illus.). 312p. (C). 123.00 (978-2-503-52958-5(5)) Brepols Pubs. BEL. Dist: ISD.

Leypoldt, Günter. Cultural Authority in the Age of Whitman: A Transnational Perspectives. Manning, Susan & Taylor, Andrew, eds. 2009. (Edinburgh Critical Studies in Transatlantic Literature Ser.). (ENG.). 312p. (gr. 17). 95.00 (978-0-7486-3574-0(2)) Edinburgh Univ. Pr. GBR. Dist: Columbia Univ. Pr.

Parigi, Paolo. The Rationalization of Miracles: How the Catholic Church Created Modern Sainthood. 2012. (ENG., Illus.). 232p. (C). 99.00 **(978-1-107-01368-1(2))** Cambridge Univ. Pr.

CANONS, FUGUES, ETC.

Here are entered collections of miscellaneous canons, fugues and similar compositions.

Bach, Johann Sebastian. The Art of the Fugue BWV 1080. Czerny, Carl, ed. 2008. (Dover Music for Piano Ser.). (ENG.). 96p. per. 9.95 (978-0-486-45731-4(1)) Dover Pubns., Inc.

—Little Preludes & Fugues. 2009. (Dover Music for Piano Ser.). (ENG.). 96p. pap. 8.95 (978-0-486-46916-4(6)) Dover Pubns., Inc.

Czerny, Carl. Carl Czerny: Preludes & Fugues for Organ. Quinn, Iain, ed. 2011. pap. 26.00 net. **(978-0-89579-708-7(9))** A-R Editions, Inc.

Dutkanicz, David, ed. Great Fugues for Solo Keyboard. 2007. (Dover Classical Music for Keyboard Ser.). (ENG., Illus.). 112p. per. 11.95 (978-0-486-45727-7(3)) Dover Pubns., Inc.

Field, Trixi. Harmonic Echoes. 2009. 64p. pap. 12.95 (978-0-9559805-2-7(6)) Voice Confidence GBR. Dist: Lulu Enterprises Inc.

Gorrell, Michelle. Well-Tempered Licks & Grooves Bk. 1: 24 Prelude & Fugues for Piano in Jazz Styles, 2 vols. 2011. (ENG.). 84p. pap. 26.95 incl. audio compact disk (978-0-85162-631-4(9), 0851626319) Boosey & Hawkes, Inc.

Harbison, John. John Harbison - Songs America Loves to Sing: For Flute (Piccolo), Clarinet, Violin, Cello & Piano. 2007. (ENG.). 44p. pap. 35.00 (978-1-4234-1739-2(9), 1423417399) Associated Music Pubs., Inc.

Hinson, Maurice, ed. Debussy — Preludes, Bk 1: By Claude Debussy / ed. Maurice Hinson, Book & CD. 2011. (Alfred Masterwork Edition Ser.). 64p. pap. 10.99 (978-0-7390-7756-6(2)) Alfred Publishing Co., Inc.

—Debussy — Preludes, Bk 2: By Claude Debussy / ed. Maurice Hinson, Book & CD. 2011. (Alfred Masterwork Edition Ser.). 80p. pap. 11.99 (978-0-7390-7757-3(0)) Alfred Publishing Co., Inc.

—George Gershwin — Three Preludes: By George Gershwin / ed. Maurice Hinson, Book & CD. 2011. (Alfred Masterwork Edition Ser.). 16p. pap. 8.99 (978-0-7390-7760-3(0)) Alfred Publishing Co., Inc.

Mazullo, Mark. Shostakovich's Preludes & Fugues: Contexts, Style, Performance. 2010. (ENG., Illus.). 304p. 60.00 (978-0-300-14943-2(3)) Yale Univ. Pr.

Prout, Ebenezer. Double Counterpoint & Canon. 2009. 290p. 43.95 (978-1-120-81345-9(X)); pap. 28.95 (978-1-120-61250-2(0)) Kessinger Publishing, LLC.

Taylor, Justin. Taylor-3 Preludes for the Piano, Op. 1,3,6. 2009. 17p. 12.50 (978-0-557-21643-7(5)) Lulu Enterprises Inc.

Thomas à Kempis. The Chronicle of the Canons Regular of Mount St. Agnes. 2007. (ENG.). 148p. per. 18.99 (978-1-4346-2805-3(1)); 168p. per. 21.99 (978-1-4346-2834-3(5)) BiblioBazaar.

Zeuner, Charles. Charles Zeuner: For Organ & Pianoforte. Clark, J. Bunker, ed. 2007. (Recent Researches in American Music Ser.: A61). 198p. pap. 106.00 net. (978-0-89579-617-2(1)) A-R Editions, Inc.

CANS

see Containers

CANT

see also Slang; Swearing

Coleman, Julie. A History of Cant & Slang Dictionaries: Volume 1: 1567-1784. 2008. (History of Cant & Slang Dictionaries Ser.). (ENG., Illus.). 272p. pap. 50.00 (978-0-19-955709-7(8)) Oxford Univ. Pr., Inc.

—A History of Cant & Slang Dictionaries: Volume II: 1785-1858. 2009. (ENG., Illus.). 352p. pap. 55.00 (978-0-19-955710-3(1)) Oxford Univ. Pr., Inc.

—A History of Cant & Slang Dictionaries: Volume III: 1859-1936. 2008. (History of Cant & Slang Dictionaries Ser.). (ENG., Illus.). 352p. 150.00 (978-0-19-954937-5(0)) Oxford Univ. Pr., Inc.

—A History of Cant & Slang Dictionaries: Volume IV: 1937-1984. 2010. (History of Cant & Slang Dictionaries Ser.). (ENG., Illus.). 416p. 125.00 (978-0-19-956725-6(5)) Oxford Univ. Pr., Inc.

Efing, Christian & Leschber, Corinna, eds. Geheimsprachen in Mittel- und Südosteuropa. 2009. 226p. 66.95 (978-3-631-59943-3(9)) Lang, Peter GmbH, Europaischer Verlag der Wissenschaften DEU. Dist: Lang, Peter.

Farmer, John S. Musa Pedestris: Three Centuries of Canting Songs & Slang Rhymes. 2007. (ENG.). 228p. per. (978-1-4065-1674-6(0)) Dodo Pr.

Gotti, Maurizio. The Language of Thieves & Vagabonds: 17th & 18th Century Canting Lexicography in England. (Lexicographica. Series Maior Ser.). (ENG.). VI, 159p. 135.00 **(978-3-11-186662-8(9))** De Gruyter, Walter Inc.

Green, Jonathon. Crooked Talk: Five Hundred Years of the Language of Crime. 2012. (ENG.). 320p. pap. 14.95 **(978-0-09-954999-4(9))** Random Hse. GBR. Dist: Independent Pubs. Group.

Hotten, John Camden. The Slang Dictionary. 2008. 332p. 28.99 (978-0-559-33415-3(X)); pap. 30.75 (978-0-559-33414-6(1)) BiblioBazaar.

—The Slang Dictionary. 2009. 146p. pap. (978-0-217-37149-0(3)) Books LLC.

Tiffany, Daniel. Infidel Poetics: Riddles, Nightlife, Substance. 2009. (ENG.). 264p. 66.00 (978-0-226-80309-8(0)); pap. 24.00 (978-0-226-80310-4(4)) Univ. of Chicago Pr.

CANTATAS

Cantata #4. (C). pap. (978-0-393-15336-1(3)) Norton, W. W. & Co., Inc.

Canticle of the Sun: Saint Francis of Assisi. 2006. (Illus.). 32p. 11.99 (978-1-58617-164-3(X)) Ignatius Pr.

Cowper, William. John Gilpin. 2006. pap. 9.95 (978-1-4286-8114-9(0)) Kessinger Publishing, LLC.

Craig-Claar, Deborah, narrated by. Look to the Lamb: An Easter Musical for Every Choir: SATB. 2007. (Illus.). 110p. pap. 7.95 (978-5-557-53122-1(X), Word Music) Word Entertainment.

Dennis & Allen, Nan. Lift up the Cross: An Easter Celebration. 2006. (ENG.). 56p. pap. 5.99 (978-0-8341-7546-4(0), 0834175460) Lillenas Publishing Co.

Joseph M. Martin. Winter's Grace: A Cantata for Christmas. 2010. (ENG.). 104p. pap. 8.95 (978-1-4234-7773-0(1), 1423477731, Flammer, Harold Music) Shawnee Pr., Inc.

Lift up the Cross: An Easter Celebration. 2006. (ENG.). 72p. pap. 19.99 (978-0-8341-7549-5(5), 0834175495) Lillenas Publishing Co.

Martin, Joseph. The Song Everlasting: A Sacred Cantata based on Early American Songs. 2011. (ENG.). 100p. pap. 8.95 **(978-1-4584-1550-9(3)**, 1458415503, Flammer, Harold Music) Shawnee Pr., Inc.

Norman, Edward W. The Light Celestial: A Christmas Choir Cantata. 2011. 66p. 36.95 **(978-1-258-03256-2(2))** Literary Licensing, LLC.

Parks, Marty. Risen Indeed: A Worship Service for Easter Sunday. 2006. (ENG.). 32p. pap. 4.99 (978-0-8341-7545-7(2), 0834175452) Lillenas Publishing Co.

Polani, Girolamo. Girolamo Polani: Six Chamber Cantatas for Solo Voice. Talbot, Michael, ed. 2011. pap. 54.00 net. **(978-0-89579-710-0(0))** A-R Editions, Inc.

Salieri, Antonio, et al. Arias for Vincenzo Calvesi: Mozart's First Ferrando. Link, Dorothea, ed. 2011. pap. 130.00 net. **(978-0-89579-717-9(8))** A-R Editions, Inc.

Schram, Scott. The Last Noel: A Christmas Musical for Children. 2007. (ENG.). pap. 22.50 (978-0-7390-4483-4(4)); pap. 16.95 (978-0-7390-4486-5(9)) Alfred Publishing Co., Inc.

Sherry, Fred. 25 Bach Duets from the Cantatas: For Two Cellos. 2011. (ENG.). 64p. pap. 14.99 **(978-1-4584-0793-1(4)**, 1458407934) Boosey & Hawkes, Inc.

Sterling, Robert, contrib. by & creator. I've Seen Jesus: Encountering the Risen Christ: SATB. 2007. (Illus.). 109p. pap. 8.95 (978-5-557-53130-6(0), Word Music) Word Entertainment.

—Peace on Earth: A Christmas Musical; SATB. 2007. 127p. pap. 8.95 (978-5-557-78134-3(X), Word Music) Word Entertainment.

Terry, Charles Sandford. Joh Seb Bach, Cantata Texts, Sacred & Secular. 2009. (GER & ENG., Illus.). 698p. pap. (978-1-906857-20-2(2)) Travis & Emery Music Bookshop.

Worley, Karla. On This Very Night: A Christmas Musical for Every Choir. 2007. (Illus.). 118p. pap. 7.95 (978-5-557-77126-9(3), Word Music) Word Entertainment.

Young, Carlton R., ed. The Good Samaritan: Through the Eyes of the Victim: A Cantata. 2007. 47p. spiral bd. 39.95 (978-1-933663-17-3(0)) General Board of Global Ministries, The United Methodist Church.

CANTATAS—HISTORY AND CRITICISM

Dürr, Alfred. The Cantatas of J. S. Bach: With Their Librettos in German-English Parallel Text. Jones, Richard D. P., tr. from GER. 2006. (ENG., Illus.). 984p. per. 99.00 (978-0-19-929776-4(2)) Oxford Univ. Pr., Inc.

Talbot, Michael. Aspects of the Secular Cantata in Late Baroque Italy. 2009. (Illus.). 452p. 134.95 (978-0-7546-5794-1(9)) Ashgate Publishing Co.

CANTE HONDO

see Flamenco

CANTEENS (RECREATION CENTERS)

see Recreation Areas; Recreation Centers

CANTERBURY (ENGLAND)

Boyle, John & Edwards, Elizabeth. Portrait of Canterbury. 2009. (ENG.). 208p. 32.95 (978-1-86077-532-1(2)) History Pr. Ltd., The GBR. Dist: Independent Pubs. Group.

Crampton, Paul. The Canterbury Book of Days. 2011. (ENG.). 368p. 16.95 **(978-0-7524-5685-0(7))** History Pr. Ltd., The GBR. Dist: Independent Pubs. Group.

—Canterbury Then & Now. 2011. (Then & Now Ser.). (ENG., Illus.). 96p. 24.95 **(978-0-7524-6296-7(2))** History Pr. Ltd., The GBR. Dist: Independent Pubs. Group.

Lyle, Marjorie. Canterbury History You Can See. 2008. (ENG., Illus.). 128p. pap. 29.95 (978-0-7524-4538-0(3)) History Pr. Ltd., The GBR. Dist: Independent Pubs. Group.

Pinnock, Kenneth. A Canterbury Childhood. 2010. (ENG., Illus.). 144p. 24.95 (978-0-7090-8773-1(X)) Hale, Robert Ltd. GBR. Dist: Independent Pubs. Group.

Raju, Alison. The Via Francigena Canterbury to Rome Pt. 1: Canterbury to the Great St Bernard. 2011. 240p. pap. 24.95 **(978-1-85284-487-5(6))** Cicerone Pr. GBR. Dist: Midpoint Trade Bks., Inc.

Stone, John. John Stone's Chronicle: Christchurch Priory, Canterbury, 1417-1472. 2010. pap. 13.00 (978-1-58044-107-0(6)) Medieval Institute Pubns.

CANTERBURY (NEW ZEALAND)

Booth, Robert B. Five Years in New Zealand: 1859 To 1864. 2007. (ENG.). 144p. per. 18.99 (978-1-4346-2946-3(5)); 156p. per. 21.99 (978-1-4346-2947-0(3)) BiblioBazaar.

Butler, Samuel. A First Year in Canterbury Settlement. 2008. 140p. 24.99 (978-0-554-29842-9(2)) 2008. 140p. 21.99 (978-0-554-39145-8(7)) 2007. (ENG.). 124p. pap. 18.99 (978-1-4346-8544-5(6)) 2007. 136p. pap. 19.99 (978-1-4346-8545-2(4)) BiblioBazaar.

—A First Year in Canterbury Settlement. 2011. (Cambridge Library Collection - History Ser.). (ENG., Illus.). 182p. pap. 19.99 **(978-1-108-03938-3(3))** Cambridge Univ. Pr.

—A First Year in Canterbury Settlement. 2008. 108p. pap. (978-1-4065-9562-8(4)) Dodo Pr.

—A First Year in Canterbury Settlement. 2010. (Illus.). 74p. pap. 20.00 (978-1-153-58274-2(0)) General Bks. LLC.

—A First Year in Canterbury Settlement. 2010. 94p. 27.16 (978-1-169-23499-4(2)); pap. 15.16 (978-1-162-64845-3(7)); 33.95 (978-1-161-41710-4(9)) Kessinger Publishing, LLC.

—First Year in Canterbury Settlement Larg. 2006. pap. (978-1-4068-2196-3(9)) Echo Library.

Relph, David. From Tussocks to Tourists: The Story of the Central Canterbury High Country. 2007. (ENG., Illus.). 168p. pap. 19.99 (978-1-877257-46-9(X)) Canterbury Univ. Pr. NZL. Dist: Independent Pubs. Group.

Teal, Jane. Shaping a Colonial Church: Bishop Harper & the Anglican Diocese of Christchurch, 1856-1890. Brown, Colin & Peters, Marie, eds. 2006. (ENG.,

Illus.). 316p. pap. 27.99 (978-1-877257-44-5(3)) Canterbury Univ. Pr. NZL. Dist: Independent Pubs. Group.

CANTERBURY CATHEDRAL

Babington, Margaret. The Romance of Canterbury Cathedral. 2007. 132p. per. (978-1-4067-8904-1(6), Pomona Pr.) Read Bks.

Butler, Derek. Canterbury Cathedral. 2009. (Britain in Old Photographs Ser.). (ENG., Illus.). 128p. pap. 24.95 (978-0-7524-4961-6(3)) History Pr. Ltd.,The GBR. Dist: Independent Pubs. Group.

Foyle, Jonathan. The Architecture of Canterbury Cathedral. 2012. (ENG., Illus.). 208p. pap. 39.95 **(978-1-85759-701-1(X))** Scala, Editions FRA. Dist: National Bk. Network.

Gameson, Richard. The Earliest Books of Canterbury Cathedral. 2008. (ENG., Illus.). 416p. 110.00 (978-0-7123-5008-2(X)) British Library, The GBR. Dist: Chicago Distribution Ctr.

James, M. R., ed. The Verses Formerly Inscribed on Twelve Windows in the Choir of Canterbury Cathedral: Reprinted, from the Manuscript, with Introduction & Notes. 2010. (Cambridge Library Collection - History Ser.). (ENG., Illus.). 176p. pap. 19.99 (978-1-108-01133-4(0)) Cambridge Univ. Pr.

Willis, Robert. The Architectural History of Canterbury Cathedral. 2010. (Cambridge Library Collection - Technology Ser.). (ENG., Illus.). 182p. pap. 19.99 (978-1-108-02308-5(8)) Cambridge Univ. Pr.

CANTICLES

see also Hymns

Collegeville Composers Group. Where Two or Three Are Gathered: Music from Psallite. 2007. (Illus.). 64p. pap. 11.95 (978-0-8146-3077-8(4)) Liturgical Pr.

Mearns, James. The Canticles of the Christian Church: Eastern & Western, in Early & Medieval Times. 2012. (ENG.). 122p. pap. 40.00 **(978-1-107-63823-5(2))** Cambridge Univ. Pr.

O'Neill, George. The Psalms & the Canticles of the Divine Office. Husslein, Joseph, ed. 2011. 326p. 50.95 **(978-1-258-05642-1(9))** Literary Licensing, LLC.

Orthodox Eastern Church Staff, et al, contrib. by. The Psalter of the Prophet & King David: With the Nine Biblical Odes: And an Explanation of How the Psalter Should Be Recited Throughout the Orthodox Liturgical Year: Arranged & Compiled from the King James Version: Emended & Versified According to the Septuagint. 2008. (Illus.). 286p. (978-0-911165-68-5(1)) Ctr. for Traditionalist Orthodox Studies.

CANTILLATION

see also Jewish Chants

Cohen, Judah M. The Making of a Reform Jewish Cantor: Musical Authority, Cultural Investment. 2009. (Helen B. Schwartz Book in Jewish Studies). (ENG., Illus.). 320p. 39.95 (978-0-253-35365-8(3), 0253353653) Indiana Univ. Pr.

Wolfram, Gerda & Wolfram, G., eds. Tradition & Innovation in Late- & Postbyzantine Liturgical Chant: Acta of the Congress Held at Hernen Castle, the Netherlands, in April 2005. 2008. (Eastern Christian Studies). (GER & ENG., Illus.). 381p. (C). pap. 95.00 (978-90-429-2015-6(7)) Peeters Pubs. & Booksellers BEL. Dist: Brown, David Bk. Co., The.

CANTON (CHINA)

see Guangzhou (China)

CANTON (OHIO)

Gup, Ted. A Secret Gift: How One Man's Kindness - And a Trove of Letters - Revealed the Hidden History of the Great Depression. 2010. (ENG.). 368p. (gr. 12). 25.95 (978-1-59420-270-4(2), Penguin Pr. HC, The) Penguin Group (USA) Inc.

—A Secret Gift: How One Man's Kindness — and a Trove of Letters — Revealed the Hidden History of the Great Depression. 2011. (ENG.). 384p. (gr. 12). 16.00 (978-0-14-312000-1(X), Penguin (Non-Classics)) Penguin Group (USA) Inc.

Kenney, Kimberly A. Canton's Pioneers in Flight. 2008. (ENG., Illus.). 160p. per. 19.99 (978-0-7385-2522-8(7)) Arcadia Publishing.

CANTON (OHIO)—NATIONAL PRO FOOTBALL HALL OF FAME

see Pro Football Hall of Fame (U.S.)

CANUTE THE GREAT, KING OF ENGLAND AND DENMARK, 995-1035

Bolton, Timothy. The Empire of Cnut the Great: Conquest & the Consolidation of Power in Northern Europe in the Early Eleventh Century. 2008. (Northern World Ser.). (Illus.). 392p. (978-90-04-16670-7(X)) BRILL.

The Heroes of the Nations Series, 38 vols. reprint ed. (978-0-404-58250-0(8)) AMS Pr., Inc.

Lawson, M. K. Cnut: England's Viking King. 2011. (ENG., Illus.). 256p. pap. 24.95 **(978-0-7524-6069-7(2))** History Pr. Ltd.,The GBR. Dist: Independent Pubs. Group.

CANVAS

Burke, Alisa. Canvas Remix: Techniques for Creating Mixed-Media Accessories. 2008. (ENG., Illus.). 128p. pap. 22.99 (978-1-60061-075-2(7), North Light Bks.) F&W Media, Inc.

MacFarland, Paul. Framing Art on Canvas: Standard Preservation Practice. 2008. (Illus.). 64p. pap. (978-0-9663189-5-1(1)) PFM PubCo.

Stella, Frank. Frank Stella: Irregular Polygons, 1965-66. Kennedy, Brian P., ed. 2010. (Illus.). 150p. 45.00 (978-0-944722-39-8(3)) Univ. Pr. of New England.

CANVAS EMBROIDERY

Alford, Lady M. Needlework As Art. 2008. 614p. 59.95 (978-0-548-96893-2(4)) 2007. (ENG.). 620p. per. 44.95 (978-0-548-64457-7(8)) Kessinger Publishing, LLC.

Awege, Gayna. Kelim Canvaswork. (Craft Library). (Illus.). 48p. pap. 5.50 (978-0-85532-617-3(4), 617-4) Search Pr., Ltd. GBR. Dist: Independent Pubs. Group.

The Canvas Embroidery Notebook: Filling Stitches, Crosses & Eyelets. 42.00 (978-0-9703523-3-0(6)) CENMindy.

The Canvas Embroidery Notebook: Filling Stitches, Tied Variations. 48.00 (978-0-9703523-4-7(4)) CENMindy.

Carter, Jill. New Canvaswork: Creative Techniques in Needlepoint. 2007. (ENG., Illus.). 128p. 24.95 (978-0-7134-8975-0(8), Batsford, B. T. Ltd.) Anova Bks. GBR. Dist: Sterling Publishing Co., Inc.

Crow, Judy & Chamberlain, Glenda, eds. Checkbook Covers. 2008. (ENG.). 22p. pap. 6.95 (978-1-57367-329-7(3)) Annie's Publishing, LLC.

—Christmas Traditions in Plastic Canvas. 2010. (ENG., Illus.). 176p. 24.95 (978-1-57367-336-5(6)) Annie's Publishing, LLC.

Ellison, Connie, ed. Botanical Plaques. 2008. (ENG.). 34p. pap. 6.95 (978-1-57367-310-5(2)) Annie's Publishing, LLC.

Higginson, Susan. Needlepoint Stitches: 52 Stitches Explained & Illustrated. 2008. (ENG., Illus.). 80p. pap. 19.95 (978-1-84448-096-8(8)) Search Pr., Ltd. GBR. Dist: Independent Pubs. Group.

Neubauer, Darlene. Village Bag Holders. 2010. (ENG.). 36p. pap. 7.95 (978-1-59635-319-0(8)) Annie's Publishing, LLC.

Russell, Beth. Art & Craft Needlepoint: 25 Patterns & Projects. 2009. (ENG., Illus.). 128p. pap. 19.95 (978-1-905400-80-5(2)) National Trust, Aylesbury GBR. Dist: Independent Pubs. Group.

SuZy's Portable Stitches II. 2010. 128p. spiral bd. 29.95 (978-0-9701330-6-9(5)) Murphy, Suzy.

CANVAS EMBROIDERY—PATTERNS

Crow, Judy, ed. Classy Kitchens. 2009. 48p. pap. 8.95 (978-1-57367-346-4(3), Needlecraft Shop, The) Annie's Publishing, LLC.

—Plastic Canvas Tapestries. 2010. (ENG.). 16p. pap. 7.95 (978-1-59635-320-6(1)) Annie's Publishing, LLC.

—Quick Stitch Plastic Canvas. 2010. (ENG., Illus.). 48p. pap. 9.95 (978-1-57367-350-1(1), Annie's Attic, LLC) Annie's Publishing, LLC.

—Think Pink in Plastic Canvas. 2009. (ENG.). 34p. pap. 6.95 (978-1-57367-340-2(4)) Annie's Publishing, LLC.

Crow, Judy & Chamberlain, Glenda, eds. Games in Plastic Canvas. 2009. (ENG.). 34p. pap. 6.95 (978-1-57367-338-9(2)) Annie's Publishing, LLC.

Dettelbach, Iona L. Creating Contemporary Bargello. 2007. (Illus.). 122p. per. 34.95 (978-0-9792858-0-6(1)) Capricorn Designs.

Ellison, Connie, ed. Can & Bottle Cozies. 2011. 4p. 5.95 **(978-1-59635-428-9(3)**, Annie's Attic, LLC) Annie's Publishing, LLC.

—Easy to Stitch Tissue Boxes. 2011. 5.99 **(978-1-59635-430-2(5)**, Annie's Attic, LLC) Annie's Publishing, LLC.

—On-the-Go Tissue Toppers. 2011. (ENG., Illus.). 48p. pap. 7.95 **(978-1-59635-413-5(5)**, Annie's Attic, LLC) Annie's Publishing, LLC.

—Plant Accessories. 2011. (ENG.). 4p. 5.99 **(978-1-59635-429-6(1)**, Annie's Attic, LLC) Annie's Publishing, LLC.

Hammet, Barbara. The Art of William Morris in Cross Stitch. (Illus.). 128p. pap. (978-0-7153-1143-1(3)) David & Charles Pubs. GBR. Dist: David & Charles Pubs.

Mullins, Cathy. Plastic Canvas Bazaar Bestsellers. 2008. (Illus.). 176p. (978-1-57367-308-2(0), Needlecraft Shop, The) Annie's Publishing, LLC.

Simon, Jeri & Van Nuys, Sally, eds. Coast to Coast in Punch Needle: The 50 States, State Flowers, Birds & Trees. 2008. (Illus.). 112p. pap. 21.95 (978-0-9793711-4-1(7)) Landauer Publishing, LLC.

Strite-Kurz, Ann. Diaper Patterns: A Study of Diaper Patterns & Related Composite Patterns Used in Canvas & Counted Thread Embroidery. 2007. (Illus.). v, 131p. (978-0-9633259-5-2(7)) Strite-Kurz, Ann.

CANVAS WORK (NEEDLEPOINT)

see Canvas Embroidery

CANYONS

Black, David. Canyoneering: A Guide to Techniques for Wet & Dry Canyons. 2008. (How to Climb Ser.). (ENG., Illus.). 176p. pap. 19.95 (978-0-7627-4519-7(3), Falcon Guides) Globe Pequot Pr., The.

Bull, John. Canyoning in Southern Europe: Classic Canyons in Spain, France & Italy. 2010. (Illus.). 192p. pap. 21.95 (978-1-85284-508-7(2)) Cicerone Pr. GBR. Dist: Midpoint Trade Bks., Inc.

Canyons. pap., stu. ed. (978-0-13-053190-2(1)) Prentice Hall (Schl. Div.).

Dallin, Michael. Ouray Canyoning: Explorations in Colorado's San Juan Mountains. 2010. pap. 16.95 (978-0-615-37086-6(1)) Blue Moon Canyon Pr., LLC.

Hanson, Erik A. Canyons. 2007. (Extreme Earth Ser.). (Illus.). 232p. (YA). (gr. 7-12). 35.00 (978-0-8160-6435-9(0)) Facts On File, Inc.

Holtzclaw, Kenneth M. & Christian, Peggy. San Timoteo Canyon. 2007. (Images of America Ser.). (Illus.). 127p. per. 19.99 (978-0-7385-4744-2(1)) Arcadia Publishing.

Jeffrey, Darren & McDaniel, Travis. Canyoneering Anchors & Basic Rope Systems: WCCM Approved. 2009. 116p. pap. 31.99 (978-1-4389-9364-5(1)) AuthorHouse.

Madsen, Steven K. Exploring Desert Stone: John N. Macomb's 1859 Expedition to the Canyonlands of the Colorado. 2009. (ENG.). 288p. (gr. 13). 34.95 (978-0-87421-707-0(5), Utah State Univ. Pr.) Univ. Pr. of Colorado.

Paulsen, Gary. Canyons. 3rd ed. pap. 3.50 (978-0-13-800186-5(3)) Prentice Hall (Schl. Div.).

Storer, Jay. General Motors Colorado & Canyon — 2004 Thru 2008. 2010. (ENG.). 304p. pap. 29.95 (978-1-56392-798-0(5)) Haynes,Chilton.

CAO, XUEQIN, CA. 1717-1763

see Tsao, Hsueh-chin, ca. 1717-1763

CAOUTCHOUC

see Rubber

CAPA, ROBERT, 1913-1954

Capa, Robert, photos by. This Is War! Robert Capa at Work. 2009. (ENG., Illus.). 288p. pap. 48.00 (978-3-86521-944-2(6)) Steidl, Gerhard Druckerei und Verlag DEU. Dist: D.A.P./Distributed Art Pubs.

Grenier, Roger & Capa, Robert. Robert Capa. 2009. (Photofile Ser.). (ENG., Illus.). 144p. pap. 15.95 (978-0-500-41066-0(6), 541066) Thames & Hudson.

Kershaw, Alex. Blood & Champagne. Date not set. pap. (978-0-312-31565-8(1), St. Martin's Paperbacks) St. Martin's Pr.

Lebrun, Bernard & Lefebvre, Michel. Robert Capa: The Paris Years 1933-54. 2012. (ENG., Illus.). 264p. 40.00 **(978-1-4197-0062-0(6))** Abrams.

Whelan, Richard. Robert Capa at Work: This Is War, 1 vol. 2007. (ENG., Illus.). 288p. 70.00 (978-3-86521-533-8(5)) Steidl, Gerhard Druckerei und Verlag DEU. Dist: D.A.P./Distributed Art Pubs.

Young, Cynthia, ed. The Mexican Suitcase, 1 vol. 2010. (ENG., Illus.). 750p. pap. 98.00 (978-3-86930-141-9(4)) Steidl, Gerhard Druckerei und Verlag DEU. Dist: Innovative Logistics.

CAPABLANCA, JOSE RAUL, 1888-1942

del Rosario, Frisco. Capablanca: A Primer of Checkmate. 2010. (ENG., Illus.). 176p. pap. 19.95 (978-1-936277-02-5(6)) Mongoose Pr.

McDonald, Neil. Chess Secrets: The Giants of Strategy: Learn from Kramnik, Karpov, Petrosian, Capablanca & Nimzowitsch. 2007. (Everyman Chess Ser.). (ENG., Illus.). 192p. per. 26.95 (978-1-85744-541-1(4)) Everyman Chess GBR. Dist: Globe Pequot Pr., The.

Winter, Edward. Capablanca: A Compendium of Games, Notes, Articles, Correspondence, Illustrations & Other Rare Archival Materials on the Cuban Chess Genius Jose Raul Capablanca, 1888-1942. alt. ed. 2011. (ENG., Illus.). 359p. pap. 35.00 (978-0-7864-6634-4(0)) McFarland & Co., Inc. Pubs.

CAPACITORS

Azongha, Sardis. Ultracapacitors & Cascaded Multilevel Converters in Motor Drives. 2009. 116p. pap. (978-3-639-13375-2(7)) VDM Verlag Dr. Mueller e.K.

Brodd, R. J., ed. Electrochemical Capacitors 2006. 2008. (ECS Transactions Ser.). 67p. pap. 60.00 (978-1-60423-913-3(1)) Curran Assocs., Inc.

C37.99-2000 IEEE Guide for the Protection of Shunt Capacitor Banks. 65.00 (978-0-7381-1978-6(4), SH94831-THT) IEEE.

Christians, Marcel. Condensation of R-22 in Horizontal Smooth Tubes. 2009. 248p. pap. (978-3-639-13066-9(9)) VDM Verlag Dr. Mueller e.K.

Dash, Ranjan. Tunable Nanoporous Carbons. 2010. 196p. pap. (978-3-8383-8475-7(X)) Lambert Academic Publishing.

Izadi-Najafabadi, Ali. Carbon Nanotube & Polypyrrole Supercapacitors. 2010. 612p. pap. (978-3-8383-4071-5(X)) Lambert Academic Publishing.

Jain Pushkar & Jain, Pushkar. Tantalum Oxide Thin Films for Embedded Capacitors: Using Pulsed DC Reactive Sputtering. 2008. 212p. pap. (978-3-639-09662-0(2)) VDM Verlag Dr. Mueller e.K.

Jakushokas, Renatas, et al. Power Distribution Networks with on-Chip Decoupling Capacitors. 2nd ed. 2010. (ENG., Illus.). xxv, 644p. 129.00 (978-1-4419-7870-7(4), 1441978704) Springer.

Kumta, Prashant N., ed. Supercapacitors: Fundamentals, Systems, Applications, Emerging Trends. 2009. (Illus.). 300p. 175.00 (978-3-527-31998-5(0), Wiley-VCH) Wiley, John & Sons, Inc.

Popovich, Mikhail, et al. Power Distribution Networks with on-Chip Decoupling Capacitors. 2007. (ENG., Illus.). xxxii, 515p. 109.00 (978-0-387-71600-8(9), 0387716009) Springer.

Power Capacitors: 1994 Edition. 272p. 107.00 (978-1-55937-416-3(0), SH17228) IEEE.

Schulz, Alexander L., ed. Capacitors: Theory, Types & Applications. 2010. (Electrical Engineering Developments Ser.). (Illus.). ix, 119p. 59.00 (978-1-61668-972-8(2)) Nova Science Pubs., Inc.

Su, K. L. Analog Filters. 2nd ed. 2010. (ENG.). 424p. pap. 159.00 (978-1-4419-5277-6(2), 1441952772) Springer.

Technology Research Editors, ed. Multilayer Ceramic Capacitors, 2007 Ed. 2007. pap. 128.50 (978-1-60030-320-3(X), Search-In-Print) CSA Journal Division.

Wang, Yang. Modeling of Ultracapacitor Short-Term & Long-Term Dynamic Behavior. 2009. 84p. pap. (978-3-639-17826-5(2)) VDM Verlag Dr. Mueller e.K.

Xie, Yibing. Nanotube Array Supercapacitor. 2011. (Nanotechnology Science & Technology Ser.). pap. 43.00 (978-1-61209-120-4(2), Nova Novinka) Nova Science Pubs., Inc.

CAPACITY, INDUSTRIAL

see Industrial Capacity

CAPACITY AND DISABILITY

see also Guardian and Ward

Baker, et al, eds. Court of Protection Law Reports: Consolidated Volume (2008-2011) 2011. (ENG.). 1312p. **(978-1-84661-306-7(X))** Jordan Publishing, Ltd.

Barber, Paul, et al. The Mental Capacity Act 2005: A Guide for Practice. 2nd ed. 2009. (Post-Qualifying Social Work Practice Ser.). 288p. pap. (978-1-84445-294-1(8)) Learning Matters Ltd.

Bartlett, Peter. The Mental Capacity Act 2005. 2nd ed. 2008. (Blackstone's Guide Ser.). (ENG.). 416p. 135.00 (978-0-19-923904-7(5), Blackstone Pr.) Oxford Univ. Pr. GBR. Dist: Oxford Univ. Pr., Inc.

Blaufuß, Henning. Rechtsfähige Wohnungseigentümergemeinschaft und nichtrechtsfähige Gemeinschaft der Wohnungseigentümer: Entstehung der rechtsfähigen Wohnungseigentümergemeinschaft als Folge richterlicher Rechtsumgestaltung und ausgewählte Folgeprobleme. 2010. (Schriftenreihe zum Gesellschafts- und Kapitalmarktrecht Ser.). (GER.). 234p. 69.95 (978-3-631-60463-2(7)) Lang, Peter GmbH, Europaischer Verlag der Wissenschaften DEU. Dist: Lang, Peter.

Bourg Carter, Sherrie. Justice for All. 2009. (978-1-60156-089-6(3)) National Institute for Trial Advocacy.

Cipriani, Don. Children's Rights & the Minimum Age of Criminal Responsibility: A Global Perspective. 2009. (Advances in Criminology Ser.). (Illus.). 252p. 124.95 (978-0-7546-7730-7(3)) Ashgate Publishing Co.

Cohen, Lloyd D. & Cohen, Debra Hart. A Lawyer's Guide for Dealing with Disability or Unexpected Events. 2009. (ENG.). pap. 104.95 incl. cd-rom (978-1-60442-116-3(9)) American Bar Assn.

Di Bella, R. C. & McLellan, Hugh S. Adult Guardianship Update: Materials Prepared for the Continuing Legal Education Seminar, Adult Guradianship Update, Held in Vancouver, B.C. on June 14, 2001 & Victoria, B.C. on June 22, 2001. 2010. 19.99 (978-1-155-28190-2(X)) General Bks. LLC.

Drogin, Eric Y., et al. Handbook of Forensic Assessment: Psychological & Psychiatric Perspectives. 2011. (Wiley Desktop Editions Ser.: 209). (ENG.). 824p. 95.00 (978-0-470-48405-0(5), Wiley) Wiley, John & Sons, Inc.

Ewing, Charles Patrick. Insanity: Murder, Madness, & the Law. 2008. (ENG.). 304p. (C). 39.95 (978-0-19-532613-0(X)) Oxford Univ. Pr., Inc.

Goldstein, Alan M. & Goldstein, Naomi E. Sevin. Evaluating Capacity to Waive Miranda Rights. 2010. (Guides to Best Practices for Forensic Mental Health Assessments Ser.). (ENG.). 272p. pap. 39.95 (978-0-19-536617-4(4)) Oxford Univ. Pr., Inc.

Johnson, Dexter/ Reno. You Paternalism & the State: The Mental Capacity Act 2005 & the Capacity Divide. 2008. 154p. pap. 15.00 (978-0-9822338-0-1(9)) Terenshad Publishing Co.

Kent, Grace Helen & Rosanoff, A. J. A Study of Association in Insanity. 2007. 644p. per. (978-1-4065-1902-0(2)) Dodo Pr.

Kent, Grace Helen & Rosanoff, Aaron Joshua. A Study of Association in Insanity. 2009. 144p. 35.95 (978-1-120-21644-1(3)); pap. 20.95 (978-1-120-13147-8(2)) Kessinger Publishing, LLC.

Kitaeff, Jack. Malingering, Lies, & Junk Science in the Courtroom. 2007. (C). 139.95 (978-1-934043-58-5(3)) Cambria Pr.

Mantell, Andy & Scragg, Terry, eds. Safeguarding Adults in Social Work. 2nd rev. ed. 2011. (ENG., Illus.). 224p. pap. (978-0-85725-401-6(4)) Learning Matters Ltd.

Patrick, Hilary & Smith, Nicola. Adult Protection & the Law in Scotland. 2009. (Illus.). 227p. pap. 72.00 (978-1-84766-487-7(3), Bloomsbury Professional) Bloomsbury Publishing Plc GBR. Dist: International Specialized Bk. Services.

Pearce, Nazreen & Jackson, Sue. Urgent Applications in the Court of Protection. 2010. (ENG., Illus.). 584p. pap. (978-1-84661-215-2(2)) Jordan Publishing, Ltd.

Protecting Seniors & Persons with Disabilities: An Examination of Court-Appointed Guardians: Hearing Before the Subcommittee on Administrative Oversight & the Courts of the Committee on the Judiciary, United States Senate, One Hundred Twelfth Congress, First Session, September 22, 2011. 2011. iii, 85p. **(978-0-16-090034-1(4)**, 552-070-43811-4) United States Government Printing Office.

Rispler-Chaim, Vardit. Disability in Islamic Law. 2006. (International Library of Ethics, Law, & the New Medicine: Vol. 32). xiii, 174p. (C). 189.00 (978-1-4020-5051-0(8), 1402050518) Springer.

Roth, Thomas A. Ausgestaltungen der Rechtsfähigkeit im 19. und 20. Jahrhundert: Zur Rechtspersönlichkeit natürlicher Personen in den bedeutenden deutschen Zivilrechtsordnungen. 2008. (Rechtshistorische Reihe Ser.). (GER.). 336p. pap. 81.95 (978-3-631-56999-3(8)) Lang, Peter GmbH, Europaischer Verlag der Wissenschaften DEU. Dist: Lang, Peter.

Saxon, John L. North Carolina Guardianship Manual. 2008. (North Carolina Indigent Defense Manual Ser.). ring bd. 50.00 (978-1-56011-580-9(7)) Schl. of Government.

Schneider, Richard D. The Annotated Ontario Mental Health Statutes. 4th rev. ed. 2007. 78.50 (978-1-55221-127-4(4)) Irwin Law, Inc. CAN. Dist: Gaunt, Inc.

Schopp, Robert F. Mental Disorder & Criminal Law: Responsibility, Punishment & Competence. 2008. (ENG., Illus.). viii, 248p. 89.95 (978-0-387-84844-0(4), 0387848444) Springer.

Teaster, Pamela B., et al. Public Guardianship: In the Best Interest of Incapacitated People?, 1 vol. 2010. 262p. 44.95 (978-0-313-37827-0(4), C37827, Praeger Pubs.) Greenwood Publishing Group, Inc.

Terrell, Martin. A Practitioner's Guide to the Court of Protection. 4th rev. ed. 2012. (ENG.). 420p. pap. 115.00 **(978-1-84766-944-5(1)**, Bloomsbury Professional) Bloomsbury Publishing Plc GBR. Dist: International Specialized Bk. Services.

Transactional Practice: Suzanne T. Carson - Planning for Incapacity. 22.95 (978-1-55681-601-7(4)) National Institute for Trial Advocacy.

Zeng, Xucheng. Si Fa Jing Shen Bing Xue Xin Bian. 2009. (CHI.). (978-7-301-16335-1(5)) Beijing University Pr.

CAPAUKOOS (NEW GUINEAN PEOPLE)

see Kapauku (New Guinean People)

CAPE ANN (MASS.)

see Ann, Cape (Mass.)

CAPE BRETON ISLAND (N.S.)

Caplan, Ron, ed. Magnificent Obsessions: They Wrote about Cape Breton They Wrote about Cape Breton, 1 vol. 2010. (Illus.). 168p. pap. *(978-1-895415-96-4(9))* Breton Bks.

Chiasson, Paul. The Island of Seven Cities: Where the Chinese Settled When They Discovered America. 2007. (ENG., Illus.). 384p. per. 15.99 *(978-0-312-36205-8(6)*, St. Martin's Griffin) St. Martin's Pr.

Danielson, Bill. Cape Breton Weather Watching: For the Naturally Curious. 2007. (Illus.). 260p. pap. *(978-1-897009-13-0(5))* Cape Breton Univ. Pr.

Feintuch, Burt. In the Blood: Cape Breton Conversations on Culture. 2010. E-Book *(978-0-87421-780-3(6))*; (ENG.). 282p. (gr. 13). pap. 28.95 *(978-0-87421-779-7(2))* Univ. Pr. of Colorado. (Utah State Univ. Pr.).

Haynes, Michael. Hiking Trails of Cape Breton, 2nd Edition. 2nd ed. 2012. (ENG., Illus.). 224p. pap. 19.95 ***(978-0-86492-670-8(7))*** Goose Lane Editions CAN. Dist: Univ. of Toronto Pr.

Shaw, John. The Blue Mountains & Other Gaelic Stories from Cape Breton/Na Beanntaichean Gorma Agus Sgeulachdan Eile a Ceap Breatainn. 2007. (Illus.). 240p. *(978-0-7735-3256-4(0))* McGill-Queen's Univ. Pr.

Shaw, John William. The Blue Mountains & Other Gaelic Stories from Cape Breton/Na Beanntaichean Gorma Agus Sgeulachdan Eile a Ceap Breatainn. 2007. (ENG., Illus.). 240p. (C). per. *(978-0-7735-3257-1(9))* McGill-Queen's Univ. Pr.

CAPE CANAVERAL (FLA.)

Davis, Philip H. A Small Skirmish in the Cold War: Cape Canaveral in the Post-Sputnik Period. 2007. 124p. per. 19.95 *(978-1-4241-8711-9(7))* PublishAmerica, Inc.

Marcum, Dianne. Cape Canaveral, Cocoa Beach & Florida's Space Coast. 2nd ed. 2011. (Great Destinations Ser.). (ENG., Illus.). 240p. pap. 19.95 *(978-1-58157-120-2(8)*, 157120) Countryman Pr.

SPENCER, James. CRUISE LINE CONFIDENTIAL - Part 1. 2010. 269p. pap. 20.95 *(978-1-4452-2418-3(6))* Lulu Enterprises Inc.

CAPE CANAVERAL AIR FORCE STATION (FLA.)

Osborne, Ray. Cape Canaveral. 2008. (Images of America (Arcadia Publishing) Ser.). (ENG., Illus.). 128p. pap. 21.99 *(978-0-7385-5327-6(1))* Arcadia Publishing.

CAPE COD (MASS.)

Allison, Robert J. A Short History of Cape Cod. 2010. (Short Histories Ser.). (ENG., Illus.). 128p. pap. 14.95 *(978-1-889833-99-6(1))* Commonwealth Editions.

American Map. Atlas Cape Cod MA Street Atlas. 2008. 160p. 16.95 *(978-1-55751-395-3(3))* Arrow Map, Inc.

Brigham, Albert Perry. Cape Cod & the Old Colony. 2009. (ENG.). 654p. pap. 45.75 *(978-1-117-74566-4(X))* BiblioBazaar.

—Cape Cod & the Old Colony. 2009. 128p. pap. 19.99 *(978-1-150-65319-3(1))* General Bks. LLC.

—Cape Cod & the Old Colony. 2008. 312p. pap. 28.95 *(978-1-4367-9706-1(3))* Kessinger Publishing, LLC.

—Cape Cod & the Old Colony. 284p. reprint ed. 98.00 *(978-0-7222-6663-2(4))* Library Reprints, Inc.

Finch, Robert. A Cape Cod Notebook. 2011. (ENG.). 192p. pap. 9.95 *(978-0-9785766-9-1(1))* On Cape Pubns.

Finch, Robert, ed. A Place Apart: A Cape Cod Reader. 2009. (ENG.). 464p. pap. 21.95 *(978-0-88150-859-8(4)*, 150859) Countryman Pr.

Fodor's Travel Publications, Inc. Staff. Fodor's Cape Cod, Nantucket & Martha's Vineyard, 29th Edition. 29th ed. 2011. (Fodor's Gold Guides). (ENG.). 336p. pap. 17.99 *(978-1-4000-0518-5(3)*, Fodor's) Fodor's Travel Pubns.

Grant, Kim. Cape Cod: Martha's Vineyard & Nantucket. 7th ed. 2007. (Explorer's Guides). (ENG.). 512p. pap. 19.95 *(978-0-88150-771-3(7))* Countryman Pr.

Massachusetts. court. Joint comm. Report of the Joint Committee of 1860 upon the Proposed Canal to Unite Barnstable & Buzzard's Bays, under the Resolve of April 4, 1860, & Subseque. 2006. 168p. per. 18.99 *(978-1-4255-1296-5(8))* MPublishing.

Morse, Ann Liza. Cranberry Kids on Cape Cod. 2006. (Illus.). per. 12.95 *(978-0-9766356-7-3(4))* Rock Village Publishing.

CAPE COD (MASS.)—BIOGRAPHY

Barbo, Theresa Mitchell. The Cape Cod Murder Of 1899: Edwin Ray Snow's Punishment & Redemption. 2007. (True Crime Ser.). (ENG., Illus.). 112p. pap. 19.99 *(978-1-59629-227-7(X))* History Pr., The.

Brunelle, Kathleen. Bellamy's Bride: The Search for Maria Hallett of Cape Cod. 2010. (ENG., Illus.). 128p. pap. 19.99 *(978-1-59629-254-3(7))* History Pr., The.

Clark, Admont G. A Puzzling Pair of Cape Cod Pirates: And Other Stories. 2007. (Illus.). 89p. per. 14.95 *(978-0-9785766-3-9(2))* On Cape Pubns.

CAPE COD (MASS.)—DESCRIPTION AND TRAVEL

Adams, Carol Hamblet. The Gift of Cape Cod. 2010. (Illus.). pap. 12.95 *(978-0-615-28792-8(1))* Adams, Carol Hamblet Communications.

Beston, Henry. The Outermost House: A Year of Life on the Great Beach of Cape Cod. 2007. 34.99 *(978-1-60252-776-8(8))* Findaway World, LLC.

Buckley, Andrew G. Tours of Cape Cod. 2008. (Illus.). 160p. pap. 19.99 *(978-0-7643-3023-0(3))* Schiffer Publishing, Ltd.

Cassidy, Patrick. Cape Cod & the Islands. 8th ed. 2009. (Insiders' Guide Ser.). (ENG.). 352p. pap. 18.95 *(978-0-7627-5311-6(0)*, Insiders' Guide) Globe Pequot Pr., The.

Cote, Paul & Historical Society of Old Yarmouth Staff. Haunted Yarmouth: Ghosts & Legends from the Cape. 2008. (Illus.). 224p. pap. 14.99 *(978-1-59629-430-1(2))* History Pr., The.

Daniels, Ethan. Under Cape Cod Waters. 2010. (Illus.). 152p. 35.00 *(978-1-934598-05-4(4))* Union Park Pr.

DaSilva, John R. & Crosbie, Michael J. Architecture of the Cape Cod Summer: The Work of Polhemus Savery DaSilva. 2008. (ENG., Illus.). 264p. 90.00 *(978-1-86470-280-4(X))* Images Publishing Group AUS. Dist: National Bk. Network.

Drake, Samuel Adams. Nooks & Corners of the New England Coast. 2010. 454p. pap. 33.95 *(978-1-4460-1508-7(4))* Barclay Pr., Inc.

Fields, Charles, photos by. Cape Cod & the National Seashore: A Photographic Essay. 2011. (ENG., Illus.). 144p. 50.00 *(978-0-9829964-0-9(3))* Fields Publishing.

Glassman-Jaffe, Marcia. Are We Almost There? Cape Cod: Where to Go & What to Do with the Kids. 2010. (ENG., Illus.). 64p. 7.95 *(978-0-7627-5283-6(1))* Globe Pequot Pr., The.

Kavanagh, James. Cape Cod Seashore Life: An Introduction to Familiar Plants & Animals in the Cape Cod Region. 2008. (Pocket Naturalist - Waterford Press Ser.). (ENG., Illus.). 1p. 5.95 *(978-1-58355-357-2(6))* Waterford Pr., Inc.

Kennard, Spencer & Kelsey, Richard. Cape Cod & the Islands from Above. 2008. (Illus.). 160p. bds. 39.99 *(978-0-7643-3043-8(8))* Schiffer Publishing, Ltd.

Kleekamp, Kathryn. Cape Cod & the Islands: Where Beauty & History Meet. 2009. (Illus.). 176p. 29.99 *(978-0-7643-3317-0(8))* Schiffer Publishing, Ltd.

Kyi, Tanya Lloyd. Cape Cod & the Islands. 2007. (America Ser.). (ENG., Illus.). 96p. 19.95 *(978-1-55285-862-2(6))* Whitecap Bks., Ltd. CAN. Dist: Midpoint Trade Bks., Inc.

Linder, Chris. The Photographer's Guide to Cape Cod & the Islands: Where to Find the Perfect Shots & How to Take Them. 2007. (ENG., Illus.). 96p. pap. 14.95 *(978-0-88150-767-6(9))* Countryman Pr.

Lombardo, Daniel. Cape Cod National Seashore: The First 50 Years. 2010. (Images of America Ser.). (ENG., Illus.). 128p. pap. 21.99 *(978-0-7385-7284-0(5))* Arcadia Publishing.

Mackie, J. Milton (John Milton). From Cape Cod to Dixie & the Tropics by J Milton MacKie. 2006. 448p. per. 26.99 *(978-1-4255-4906-0(3))* MPublishing.

O'Connor, Michael. AMC Discover Cape Cod: AMC's guide to the best hiking, biking, & Paddling. 2009. (ENG., Illus.). 288p. pap. 18.95 *(978-1-934028-17-9(7))* Appalachian Mountain Club Bks.

Perk, Jeff. Cape Cod: Martha's Vineyard & Nantucket. 2nd ed. 2009. (Moon Handbooks Ser.). (ENG.). 256p. pap. 16.95 *(978-1-56691-829-9(4))* Westview Pr.

Rajs, Jake, photos by. Cape Cod & the Islands. 2008. (ENG., Illus.). 240p. 17.95 *(978-0-8478-3103-6(5))* Rizzoli International Pubns., Inc.

Reckford, Laura M. Cape Cod Day by Day: 24 Smart Ways to See the Region. 2011. (Frommer's Day by Day - Pocket Ser.: 148). (ENG., Illus.). 204p. pap. 13.99 *(978-0-470-87483-7(X)*, Frommers) Wiley, John & Sons, Inc.

Reckford, Laura M. Frommer's Cape Cod, Nantucket & Martha's Vineyard. 16th ed. 2012. (Frommer's Complete Guides). (ENG., Illus.). 320p. pap. 17.99 ***(978-1-118-11999-0(1)**, Frommers)* Wiley, John & Sons, Inc.

Richmond, Arthur P. Cape Cod Wide. 2007. (Illus.). 160p. 39.95 *(978-0-7643-2776-6(3))* Schiffer Publishing, Ltd.

—Harbors of Cape Cod & the Islands. 2008. (Illus.). 208p. bds. 39.99 *(978-0-7643-3007-0(1))* Schiffer Publishing, Ltd.

Rolbein, Seth, ed. The Cape Cod Almanac Second Edition. 2006. per. *(978-0-9773782-1-0(7))* Cape Cod Voice, The.

—The Cape Cod Almanac Third Edition. 2008. per. 5.95 *(978-0-9773782-3-4(3))* Cape Cod Voice, The.

Rothery, Agnes. Cape Cod New & Old. 2010. 288p. pap. 19.95 *(978-1-4290-4001-3(7))* Applewood Bks.

Seufert, Christopher. Cape Cod & the Islands Reflections. 2010. (Illus.). 128p. 24.99 *(978-0-7643-3405-4(0))* Schiffer Publishing, Ltd.

Seufert, Christopher, photos by. Chatham Views: A Photographic Journal from Cape Cod, Massachusetts. 2007. 49.95 *(978-0-9677947-8-5(1))* Mooncusser Films, LLC.

Taber, Gladys. My Own Cape Cod. reprint ed. lib. bdg. 22.95 *(978-0-89190-595-0(2)*, Rivercity Pr.) Amereon LTD.

Thoreau, Henry David. Cape Cod. 2010. 400p. pap. 33.75 *(978-1-142-60540-7(X))* 2009. 264p. pap. 24.99 *(978-1-103-19906-8(4))* 2009. 264p. pap. 18.99 *(978-1-103-19903-7(X))* 2008. 283p. 24.99 *(978-0-554-67764-4(4))* 2008. 349p. 27.99 *(978-0-554-67756-9(3))* 2008. 137p. pap. 23.75 *(978-0-554-67762-0(8))* 2008. 190p. pap. 24.75 *(978-0-554-67758-3(X))* BiblioBazaar.

—Cape Cod. 2009. 94p. pap. *(978-0-217-91720-9(8))*; 148p. pap. *(978-0-217-91722-3(4))*; 94p. pap. *(978-1-4590-5376-2(1))*; 76p. pap. *(978-1-4590-5378-6(8))*; 72p. pap. *(978-0-217-45234-2(5))* Books LLC.

—Cape Cod. 2008. (ENG., Illus.). 272p. 35.00 *(978-0-618-75845-6(3))* Houghton Mifflin Harcourt Trade & Reference Pubs.

—Cape Cod. 2010. 390p. 39.16 *(978-1-163-21042-0(0))*; pap. 27.16 *(978-1-162-75890-9(2))* Kessinger Publishing, LLC.

—Cape Cod. 2008. pap. 7.95 *(978-1-60545-131-2(2))* Quiet Vision Publishing.

—Henry David Thoreau on Cape Cod: His Journeys & the Lost Maps. 2010. *(978-1-929154-42-5(9))* Levenger Pr.

—Thoreau: Cape Cod. 300p. 22.95 *(978-0-8488-1489-2(4))* Amereon LTD.

—Thoreau's Cape Cod. 2008. (ENG., Illus.). 256p. 24.95 *(978-1-933212-60-9(8))* Commonwealth Editions.

Thoreau, Henry David & Marble, Annie Russell. Cape Cod. 2009. 282p. 30.99 *(978-1-116-33073-1(3))*; 28.99 *(978-1-116-33072-4(5))*; pap. 28.75 *(978-1-116-33074-8(1))*; pap. 27.75 *(978-1-116-33075-5(X))* BiblioBazaar.

Thoreau, Henry David & Watson, Amelia Montague. Cape Cod. 2010. 190p. pap. 22.75 *(978-1-141-57136-9(6))* BiblioBazaar.

VanDrimlen, Pamela & Huban, Cheryl Johnson. Best Easy Day Hikes Cape Cod & the Islands. 2nd ed. 2011. (Best Easy Day Hikes Ser.). (ENG., Illus.). 112p. pap. 9.95 *(978-0-7627-6133-3(4)*, Falcon Guides) Globe Pequot Pr., The.

Zagat Survey Staff, ed. Cape Cod & the Islands Restaurants - 2009/10. 2008. (ENG.). 64p. pap. 6.95 *(978-1-60478-145-8(9))* Zagat Survey.

CAPE COD (MASS.)—HISTORY

Barbo, Theresa. True Accounts of Yankee Ingenuity & Grit from the Cape Cod Voice. 2007. (Illus.). 158p. pap., per. 21.99 *(978-1-59629-223-9(7))* History Pr., The.

Barbo, Theresa M. Cape Cod Bay: A History of Salt & Sea. 2008. pap. 21.99 *(978-1-59629-502-5(3))* History Pr., The.

—Nantucket Sound: A Maritime History. 2009. (ENG., Illus.). 160p. pap. 21.99 *(978-1-59629-687-9(9))* History Pr., The.

Brunelle, Kathleen. Bellamy's Bride: The Search for Maria Hallett of Cape Cod. 2010. (ENG., Illus.). 128p. pap. 19.99 *(978-1-59629-254-3(7))* History Pr., The.

Clark, Admont G. A Puzzling Pair of Cape Cod Pirates: And Other Stories. 2007. (Illus.). 89p. per. 14.95 *(978-0-9785766-3-9(2))* On Cape Pubns.

Conway, J. North. The Cape Cod Canal: Breaking Through the Bared & Bended Arm. 2008. (Illus.). 157p. pap. 19.99 *(978-1-59629-374-8(8))* History Pr., The.

Green, Eugene, et al. The Names of Cape Cod: How Cape Cod Places Got Their Names & What They Mean. 2007. (Names Of Ser.). (ENG., Illus.). 208p. per. 12.95 *(978-1-933212-84-5(5))* Commonwealth Editions.

Grigas, Stephen J. Samoset Road - Cape Cod - USA, 1. (Illus.). 2007. 247p. per. 22.95 *(978-0-9789367-0-9(1))* 2nd rev. ed. 2008. 248p. pap. 23.95 *(978-0-9789367-1-6(X))* Francis P. Grigas Foundation.

Krahulik, Karen Christel. Provincetown: From Pilgrim Landing to Gay Resort. 2007. (ENG., Illus.). 288p. per. 22.00 *(978-0-8147-4762-9(0))* New York Univ. Pr.

Lombardo, Daniel. Cape Cod National Seashore: The First 50 Years. 2010. (Images of America Ser.). (ENG., Illus.). 128p. pap. 21.99 *(978-0-7385-7284-0(5))* Arcadia Publishing.

Miller, Stauffer. Cape Cod in the Civil War: The Raised Right Arm. 2010. (ENG., Illus.). 160p. pap. 19.99 *(978-1-59629-984-9(3))* History Pr., The.

Peluso, Charles Tiggie & MacFarlane, Sandy. Tiggie: The Lure & Lore of Commercial Fishing in New England. 2007. (Illus.). 292p. per. 19.95 *(978-1-60008-039-5(1)*, Rooftop Publishing) AuthorHouse.

Richmond, Arthur P. The Evolution of the Cape Cod House: An Architectural History. 2011. (Illus.). 256p. 50.00 ***(978-0-7643-3848-9(X)**, Schiffer Publishing Ltd)* Schiffer Publishing, Ltd.

Richmond, Arthur P. Harbors of Cape Cod & the Islands. 2008. (Illus.). 208p. bds. 39.99 *(978-0-7643-3007-0(1))* Schiffer Publishing, Ltd.

Sicchio, Mary. The Forgotten Cape: 1940-1960. 2007. (Images of America Ser.). (ENG., Illus.). 128p. per. 21.99 *(978-0-7385-5009-1(4))* Arcadia Publishing.

Thoreau, Henry David. Thoreau's Cape Cod. 2008. (ENG., Illus.). 256p. 24.95 *(978-1-933212-60-9(8))* Commonwealth Editions.

Walker, Scott I. & Walker, Robin E. Dennis. 2007. (Postcard History Ser.). (ENG., Illus.). 128p. per. 19.99 *(978-0-7385-4989-7(4))* Arcadia Publishing.

Whalen, Richard F. Everyday Life in Truro: From the Indians to the Victorians. 2007. (Illus.). 119p. pap., per. 16.99 *(978-1-59629-364-9(0))* History Pr., The.

—Truro: The Story of a Cape Cod Town. 2007. (Illus.). 255p. pap., per. 24.99 *(978-1-59629-363-2(2))* History Pr., The.

CAPE COLOURED PEOPLE

see Colored People (South Africa)

CAPE DUTCH LANGUAGE

see Afrikaans Language

CAPE FEAR RIVER VALLEY (N.C.)

Conser, Walter H., Jr. A Coat of Many Colors: Religion & Society along the Cape Fear River of North Carolina. 2009. (Religion in the South Ser.). (ENG.). 384p. pap. 30.00 *(978-0-8131-9281-9(1))* Univ. Pr. of Kentucky.

Sprunt, James. Chronicles of the Cape Fear River, 1660-1916. 2010. 764p. pap. 53.75 *(978-1-147-06013-3(4))* BiblioBazaar.

—Chronicles of the Cape Fear River, 1660-1916. 2009. 600p. pap. *(978-1-150-65663-7(8))* Books LLC.

—Chronicles of the Cape Fear River, 1660-1916. 2010. 762p. 54.36 *(978-1-169-37364-8(X))* 2010. 762p. 67.95 *(978-1-161-77454-2(8))* 2008. 764p. pap. 52.95 *(978-1-4368-0669-5(0))* Kessinger Publishing, LLC.

—Chronicles of the Cape Fear River, 1660-1916. (Illus.). 594p. reprint ed. lib. bdg. 98.00 *(978-0-7222-0781-9(6))* Library Reprints, Inc.

—Tales & Traditions of the Lower Cape Fear, 1661-1896. 215p. reprint ed. lib. bdg. 98.00 *(978-0-7222-0774-1(3))* Library Reprints, Inc.

CAPE HATTERAS (N.C.)

see Hatteras, Cape (N.C.)

CAPE HORN (CHILE)

Hemingway-Douglass, Reanne. Cape Horn: One Man's Dream, One Woman's Nightmare. 2009. (Illus.). 300p. pap. 18.95 *(978-1-934199-02-2(8))* Douglass, Hemingway & Co., LLC.

CAPE MATAPAN, BATTLE OF, 1941

Simmons, Mark. The Battle of Matapan 1941: The Trafalgar of the Mediterranean. 2011. (ENG., Illus.). 192p. pap. 19.95 *(978-0-7524-5829-8(9))* History Pr. Ltd.,The GBR. Dist: Independent Pubs. Group.

CAPE MAY (N.J.)

Biggy, David. Cape May Lighthouse. 2011. (Illus.). 80p. *(978-0-7643-3800-7(5)*, Schiffer Publishing Ltd) Schiffer Publishing, Ltd.

Martino, Vincent, Jr. The Wildwoods: 1920-1970. 2007. (Postcard History Ser.). (Illus.). 127p. per. 21.99 *(978-0-7385-5003-9(5))* Arcadia Publishing.

McManus, Craig. The Ghosts of Cape May, Book 3. 2008. pap. 14.95 *(978-0-9785444-2-3(0))* ChannelCraig, Inc.

Miller, Ben. The First Resort: Fun, Sun, Fire & War in Cape May, Americas Original Seaside Town. 2009. (Illus.). 298p. 29.95 *(978-0-9799051-6-2(8))* Exit Zero Publishing, Inc.

—The First Resort: Fun, Sun, Fire & War in Cape May, America's Original Seaside Town. 2010. (ENG., Illus.). 304p. 34.95 *(978-0-9799051-8-6(4))* Exit Zero Publishing, Inc.

Neith, Jack & Neith, Oleta. Cape May Perspectives. 2011. (Illus.). 80p. *(978-0-7643-3504-4(9))* Schiffer Publishing, Ltd.

Niles, Lawrence, et al. Life along the Delaware Bay: Cape May Gateway to a Million Shorebirds. 2012. (ENG., Illus.). 176p. 32.95 ***(978-0-8135-5246-0(X)**,* Rivergate Bks.) Rutgers Univ. Pr.

Roberts, Russell. Cape May. 2008. (ENG., Illus.). 160p. pap. 19.95 *(978-0-8117-3375-5(0))* Stackpole Bks.

Romm, Richard M. America's First Whaling Industry & the Whaler Yeomen of Cape May. 2011. 56p. pap. ***(978-3-8443-1422-9(9))*** Lambert Academic Publishing.

Wheeler, Edward S. Scheyichbi & the Strand or Early Days along the Delaware. 2007. (ENG.). 146p. 35.95 *(978-0-548-02085-2(X))* Kessinger Publishing, LLC.

CAPE OF GOOD HOPE (SOUTH AFRICA)

Colvin, Ian D. The Cape of Adventure: Strange & Notable Discoveries, Perils, Shipwrecks, Battles upon Sea & Land. 2007. (ENG.). 540p. 57.95 *(978-0-548-00927-7(9))* Kessinger Publishing, LLC.

Prichard, Helen M. Friends & Foes in the Transkei: A Victorian Lady's Experience of Southern Africa During The 1870s. 2009. 172p. *(978-1-84677-758-5(5))*; pap. *(978-1-84677-757-8(7))* Leonaur Ltd.

CAPE OF GOOD HOPE (SOUTH AFRICA)—DESCRIPTION AND TRAVEL

Ballantyne, R. M. Six Months at the Cape. 2007. (ENG.). 112p. per. *(978-1-4065-2062-0(4))* Dodo Pr.

Ballantyne, Robert Michael. Six Months at the Cape. 2008. 124p. 21.99 *(978-0-554-36976-1(1))* 2008. 124p. 24.99 *(978-0-554-27673-1(9))* 2007. (ENG.). 110p. pap. 18.99 *(978-1-4346-3695-9(X))* 2007. (ENG.). 122p. pap. 19.99 *(978-1-4346-3743-7(3))* BiblioBazaar.

Barrow, John. An Account of Travels into the Interior of Southern Africa in the Years 1797 And 1798. 2009. 198p. pap. 19.94 *(978-1-150-01403-1(2))* General Bks. LLC.

—An Account of Travels into the Interior of Southern Africa, in the Years 1797 And 1798: Including Cursory Observations on the Geology & Geography . . 2010. 396p. pap. 33.75 *(978-1-143-06939-0(0))* BiblioBazaar.

—An Account of Travels into the Interior of Southern Africa, in the Years 1797 And 1798: Including Cursory Observations on the Geology & Geography of the Southern Part of that Continent. 2011. (Cambridge Library Collection - Travel & Exploration Ser.). (ENG., Illus.). 442p. pap. 32.99 ***(978-1-108-03277-3(X))*** Cambridge Univ. Pr.

—An Account of Travels into the Interior of Southern Africa, in the years 1797 And 1798: Including Cursory Observations on the Geology & Geography of the Southern Part of that Continent. 2011. (Cambridge Library Collection - Travel & Exploration Ser.). (ENG., Illus.). 506p. pap. 37.99 ***(978-1-108-03278-0(8))*** Cambridge Univ. Pr.

Barrow, Sir John. An Account of Travels into the Interior of Southern Africa, in the Years 1797 & 1798; Including Cursory Observations On. 2010. (Illus.). 194p. pap. 20.40 *(978-1-154-07507-6(9))* General Bks. LLC.

Books. An Account of Travels into the Interior of Southern Africa, in the Years 1797 & 1798; Including Cursory Observations on the Geology And. 2009. (Illus.). 444p. pap. 30.89 *(978-1-150-20518-7(0))* General Bks. LLC.

Huigen, S. & Huigen, Siegfried. Knowledge & Colonialism: Eighteenth-Century Travellers in South Africa. 2009. 308p. *(978-90-04-17743-7(4))* BRILL.

Lenta, Margaret, ed. Paradise, the Castle & the Vineyard: Lady Anne Barnard's Cape Diaries. 2007. (ENG., Illus.). 320p. (gr. 11). pap. 34.95 *(978-1-86814-390-0(2))* Witwatersrand Univ. Pr. Pubns. ZAF. Dist: Transaction Pubs.

CAPE OF GOOD HOPE (SOUTH AFRICA)—HISTORY

Adhikari, Mohamed. Anatomy of A South African Genocide: The Extermination of the Cape San Peoples. 2011. 104p. pap. 14.95 *(978-1-919895-44-4(2))* Double Storey Bks. ZAF. Dist: International Publishers Marketing.

Adhikari, Mohamed. Anatomy of a South African Genocide: The Extermination of the Cape San Peoples. 2011. (ENG.). 120p. pap. 16.95 ***(978-0-8214-1987-8(0))*** Ohio Univ. Pr.

Baker, Harrison Scott. American Prisoners of War Held at Bermuda, Cape of Good Hope,and Jamaica During the War Of 1812. 2007. 324p. pap. 36.50 *(978-0-7884-4499-9(9))* Heritage Bks.

Elbourne, Elizabeth. Blood Ground: Colonialism, Missions, & the Contest for Christianity in the Cape Colony & Britain, 1799-1853. 2008. (McGill-Queen's Studies in the History of Religion Ser.). (ENG., Illus.). 532p. (C). pap. *(978-0-7735-3453-7(9))* McGill-Queen's Univ. Pr.

Fransen, Hans. Old Towns & Villages of the Cape. 2009. (Illus.). 420p. 62.95 *(978-1-86842-227-2(5))* International Publishers Marketing.

Henshilwood, Christopher Stuart. Holocene Prehistory of the Southern Cape, South Africa. 2008. (Bar S Ser.). (Illus.). 171p. (C). 85.00 *(978-1-4073-0343-7(0))* British Archaeological Reports Ltd. GBR. Dist: Brown, David Bk. Co., The.

James, Wilmot & Simons, Mary, eds. Class, Caste & Color: A Social & Economic History of the South African Western Cape. 2009. (ENG., Illus.). 271p. pap. 29.95 *(978-1-4128-0865-1(0))* Transaction Pubs.

Johnson, David. Imagining the Cape Colony: History, Literature, & the South African Nation. 2012. (ENG.). 272p. (gr. 17). 105.00 ***(978-0-7486-4308-0(7))*** Edinburgh Univ. Pr. GBR. Dist: Columbia Univ. Pr.

Lenta, Margaret, ed. Paradise, the Castle & the Vineyard: Lady Anne Barnard's Cape Diaries. 2007. (ENG., Illus.). 320p. (gr. 11). pap. 34.95 *(978-1-86814-390-0(2))* Witwatersrand Univ. Pr. Pubns. ZAF. Dist: Transaction Pubs.

Newton-King, Susan. Masters & Servants on the Cape Eastern Frontier, 1760-1803. 2009. (African Studies). (ENG., Illus.). 352p. pap. 48.00 *(978-0-521-12124-8(8))* Cambridge Univ. Pr.

Price, Richard. Making Empire: Colonial Encounters & the Creation of Imperial Rule in Nineteenth-Century Africa. 2008. (ENG., Illus.). 416p. 95.00 *(978-0-521-88968-1(5))*; 402p. pap. 35.99 *(978-0-521-71819-6(8))* Cambridge Univ. Pr.

Ross, Robert. Status & Respectability in the Cape Colony, 1750-1870: A Tragedy of Manners. 2009. (African Studies). (ENG., Illus.). 220p. (C). pap. 33.99 *(978-0-521-12125-5(6))* Cambridge Univ. Pr.

Strobel, Christoph. The Testing Grounds of Modern Empire: The Making of Colonial Racial Order in the American Ohio Country & the South African Eastern Cape, 1770s-1850s. 2007. 210p. (C). 68.95 *(978-1-4331-0123-6(8))* Lang, Peter Publishing, Inc.

CAPE OF GOOD HOPE (SOUTH AFRICA)—POLITICS AND GOVERNMENT

Elbourne, Elizabeth. Blood Ground: Colonialism, Missions, & the Contest for Christianity in the Cape Colony & Britain, 1799-1853. 2008. (McGill-Queen's Studies in the History of Religion Ser.). (ENG., Illus.). 532p. (C). pap. *(978-0-7735-3453-7(9))* McGill-Queen's Univ. Pr.

Johnson, David. Imagining the Cape Colony: History, Literature, & the South African Nation. 2012. (ENG.). 272p. (gr. 17). 105.00 ***(978-0-7486-4308-0(7))*** Edinburgh Univ. Pr. GBR. Dist: Columbia Univ. Pr.

Mouton, F. A. Prophet Without Honour: F.S. Malan: Afrikaner, South African & Cape Liberal. 2012. (Illus.). 156p. pap. 30.00 ***(978-1-86919-414-7(4))*** International Publishers Marketing.

Sanders, Peter. Throwing down White Man: Cape Rule & Misrule in Colonial Lesotho, 1871-1884. Huws, Ursula, ed. 2011. 306p. pap. 37.95 ***(978-0-85036-654-9(2))*** Merlin Pr. Ltd. GBR. Dist: Independent Pubs. Group.

CAPE OF GOOD HOPE (SOUTH AFRICA)—SOCIAL LIFE AND CUSTOMS

Lenta, Margaret, ed. Paradise, the Castle & the Vineyard: Lady Anne Barnard's Cape Diaries. 2007. (ENG., Illus.). 320p. (gr. 11). pap. 34.95 *(978-1-86814-390-0(2))* Witwatersrand Univ. Pr. Pubns. ZAF. Dist: Transaction Pubs.

Ross, Robert. Status & Respectability in the Cape Colony, 1750-1870: A Tragedy of Manners. 2009. (African Studies). (ENG., Illus.). 220p. (C). pap. 33.99 *(978-0-521-12125-5(6))* Cambridge Univ. Pr.

Simson, Sally & Simpson, Sally. Cape of Good Cooks. 2008. (Illus.). 112p. pap. 27.95 *(978-1-919930-33-6(7))* Double Storey Bks. ZAF. Dist: International Publishers Marketing.

Strobel, Christoph. The Testing Grounds of Modern Empire: The Making of Colonial Racial Order in the American Ohio Country & the South African Eastern Cape, 1770s-1850s. 2007. 210p. (C). 68.95 *(978-1-4331-0123-6(8))* Lang, Peter Publishing, Inc.

CAPE TOWN (SOUTH AFRICA)

Appleson, Trevor. Free Ground. 2006. (ENG., Illus.). 224p. 55.00 *(978-1-86154-262-5(3))* Booth-Clibborn Editions GBR. Dist: Hachette Bk. Group.

Briggs, Philip. Top 10 Cape Town & the Winelands. 2012. (Eyewitness top 10 travel Guide Ser.). (ENG.). 128p. 14.00 ***(978-0-7566-8535-5(4))*** Dorling Kindersley Publishing, Inc.

Coetzer, Toast, et al. Key to Cape Town: Your Insider's Guide to Exploring the Mother City. 2009. (Illus.). 220p. pap. 19.95 ***(978-1-919938-86-8(9))*** Sunbird Publishing ZAF. Dist: International Publishers Marketing.

De Bruyn, Pippa & Bain, Keith. A Hedonist's Guide to Cape Town. 2010. (ENG., Illus.). 208p. im. lthr. 18.00 *(978-1-905428-47-2(2),* HG2) Filmer Ltd. GBR. Dist: Perseus-PGW.

Dorling Kindersley Publishing Staff. Cape Town & the Winelands. 2010. (Eyewitness top 10 travel Guide Ser.). (ENG.). 128p. (gr. 12). 14.00 *(978-0-7566-6147-2(1))* Dorling Kindersley Publishing, Inc.

Englund, Per, photos by. Life Geos On: Snapshots from Cape Town. 2009. (Illus.). 96p. pap. 24.95 *(978-91-85639-22-9(2))* Dokument forlag, Fotograf Malcolm Jacobsson SWE. Dist: SCB Distributors.

Fichte, Andre. A Day in Capetown. Buch + CD. 2006. (ENG., Illus.). 100p. 14.95 incl. lp *(978-3-937406-68-8(9))* Edel Classica Gmbh.

Fox, Justin. Cape Town Calling: From Mandela to Theroux on the Mother City. 2010. 232p. pap. 21.95 *(978-0-624-04297-6(9))* NB Pubs. Ltd. ZAF. Dist: International Publishers Marketing.

Hoberman, Gerald. Cape Town. 2009. (ENG., Illus.). 64p. 18.95 *(978-1-919939-58-2(X))* Hoberman, Gerald Pubns. ZAF. Dist: Perseus Distribution.

Hoberman, Gerald & Hoberman, Marc. Cape Town Mmib X. 2007. 80p. 4.99 *(978-1-919734-52-1(X))* Hoberman, Gerald Pubns. ZAF. Dist: Perseus-PGW.

Insight Guides. Cape Town Insight City Guide. 2nd ed. 2011. (City Guide Ser.). (ENG., Illus.). 272p. pap. 19.99 *(978-981-282-315-1(8))* APA Publications Services SGP. Dist: Ingram Pub. Services.

Jensen, Steffen. Gangs, Politics & Dignity in Cape Town. 2008. (Illus.). 240p. 65.00 *(978-0-226-39833-4(1))*; pap. 24.00 *(978-0-226-39835-8(8))* Univ. of Chicago Pr.

Joyce, Peter. The Best of Cape Town. (Illus.). 96p. 8.95 *(978-1-84330-616-0(6))* New Holland Pubs., Ltd. GBR. Dist: Globe Pequot Pr., The.

—Cape Town. 8th ed. 2011. (Globetrotter Travel Packs Ser.). (ENG., Illus.). 128p. 14.95 *(978-1-84773-887-5(7),* Globetrotter) New Holland Pubs., Ltd. GBR. Dist: Globe Pequot Pr., The.

Karl Baedeker (Firm) Staff, contrib. by. Cape Town: Garden Route. 2012. (Baedeker Guides Ser.). (ENG., Illus.). 350p. pap. 20.00 ***(978-3-8297-6618-0(1))*** Marco Polo Travel Publishing GBR. Dist: Innovative Logistics.

Kearney, Patrick & Kearney. Guardian of the Light: Archbishop Denis Hurley, a Life Against Apartheid. 2009. (ENG., Illus.). 400p. 34.95 *(978-0-8264-1875-3(9))* Continuum International Publishing Group, Ltd. GBR. Dist: National Bk. Network.

Ley, Astrid. Housing as Governance: Interfaces Between Local Government & Civil Society Organisations in Cape Town, South Africa. 2011. (ENG.). 400p. pap. 54.95 *(978-3-643-10330-7(1))* Lit Verlag DEU. Dist: Transaction Pubs.

Makda, Tahira Jehan. Assessment of Risk Management in the Events Industry in Cape Town: Managing risks within the events industry by 2010 in the City of Cape Town. 2010. 560p. pap. *(978-3-639-24503-5(2))* VDM Verlag Dr. Mueller e.K.

Mason, John Edwin. One Love, Ghoema Beat: Inside the Cape Town Carnival. 2010. (Reconsiderations in Southern African History Ser.). (ENG., Illus.). 140p. (gr. 17). pap. 24.50 *(978-0-8139-3059-6(6))* Univ. Pr. of Virginia.

Modern Overland Staff. Cape Town. 2011. (ENG.). 216p. pap. 18.99 *(978-1-60987-122-2(7))* Modern Overland.

Mtakati, Gordon. For Better or Worse! 2010. 248p. pap. 19.99 *(978-1-4500-9219-7(5))* Xlibris Corp.

Norton, Peggy, contrib. by. Found in My Mouth: The Journal of Peggy Norton. viii, 88p. *(978-1-875086-10-8(2))* Fairhead, J. T. & Co. ZAF. Dist: Penton Overseas, Inc.

Organisation for Economic Co-operation and Development Staff. Cape Town, South Africa. 2008. 322p. pap. 61.00 *(978-92-64-04963-5(0))* Organization for Economic Cooperation & Development.

Richmond, Simon & Ranger, Helen. Cape Town. 6th rev. ed. 2009. (City Guide Ser.). (ENG., Illus.). 236p. pap. 19.99 *(978-1-74104-891-9(5))* Lonely Planet Pubns.

Skinner, Mark & Fraser, Sean. Fairest Cape: From the West Coast to the Garden Route. 2009. (Illus.). 112p. 24.95 *(978-1-919938-46-2(X))* International Publishers Marketing.

Thomas Cook Publishing Staff. Cape Town Pocket Guide. 2nd ed. 2010. (Thomas Cook Pocket Guides). (ENG., Illus.). 144p. pap. 9.95 *(978-1-84848-308-8(2))* Cook, Thomas Publishing GBR. Dist: Globe Pequot Pr., The.

Thomas Cook Publishing Staff & Cadman, Mike. Cape Town Pocket Guide. 3rd ed. 2009. (Travellers - Thomas Cook Ser.). (ENG., Illus.). 192p. pap. 16.95 *(978-1-84848-192-3(6))* Cook, Thomas Publishing GBR. Dist: Globe Pequot Pr., The.

Time Out Guides Staff. Time Out Cape Town: Winelands & the Garden Route. 3rd ed. 2009. (Time Out Guides). (ENG., Illus.). 280p. pap. 19.95 *(978-1-84670-156-6(2))* Time Out Guides Ltd. GBR. Dist: Perseus-PGW.

Wallpaper Magazine Editors, ed. Wallpaper* City Guide Cape Town 2012. 2011. (ENG.). 128p. pap. 9.95 ***(978-0-7148-6266-8(5))*** Phaidon Pr., Inc.

Warren-Brown, Gillian, et al. Cape Town Uncovered: A People's City. 2009. (Illus.). 160p. pap. 21.95 *(978-1-919930-75-6(2))* Double Storey Bks. ZAF. Dist: International Publishers Marketing.

Williams, Lizzie. Cape Town - Winelands & Garden Route: Full Colour Regional Travel Guide to Cape Town, the Winelands & Garden Route. 2010. (Footprint - Destination Guides). (Illus.). 288p. pap. 21.95 *(978-1-906098-86-5(7))* Footprint Handbooks GBR. Dist: Globe Pequot Pr., The.

—Frommer's Cape Town Day by Day. 2010. (Frommer's Day by Day - Pocket Ser.: 115). (ENG., Illus.). 184p. pap. 12.99 *(978-0-470-72121-6(9),* Frommers) Wiley, John & Sons, Inc.

Worden, Van Heyningen. Cape Town: Making of City. 2011. 256p. pap. 58.95 *(978-0-86486-656-1(9))* International Publishers Marketing.

CAPE TOWN, UNIVERSITY OF

see University of Cape Town

CAPE VERDE

Carter, Katherine & Aulette, Judy. Cape Verdean Women & Globalization: The Politics of Gender, Culture, & Resistance. 2009. (ENG., Illus.). 208p. 84.00 *(978-0-230-61808-4(1))* Palgrave Macmillan.

Costa, Manuel E. The Making of the Cape Verdean. 2011. 336p. 28.28 ***(978-1-4634-0135-1(3))***; pap. 17.72 ***(978-1-4634-0134-4(5))*** AuthorHouse.

dos Anjos, Jose A. Tavares. Cape Verdean-American Vietnam War Veterans of New Bedford, Massachusetts. 2010. 52p. pap. 9.10 *(978-0-557-17684-7(0))* Lulu Enterprises Inc.

Flood, Callie. Cape Verde (Other Places Travel Guide) 2010. 252p. 18.95 *(978-0-9822619-2-7(6))* Other Places Publishing.

Lobban, Richard Andrew, Jr. & Saucier, Paul Khalil. Historical Dictionary of the Republic of Cape Verde. 4th ed. 2007. (Historical Dictionaries of Africa Ser.). (ENG., Illus.). 360p. 99.00 *(978-0-8108-4906-8(2))* Scarecrow Pr., Inc.

Locken, E. Travel Journal Cape Verde. 2009. 192p. pap. 20.95 *(978-0-557-07966-7(7))* Lulu Enterprises Inc.

Märzhäuser, Christina. Portugiesisch und Kabuverdianu in Kontakt: Muster des Code-switching und lexikalische Innovationen in Raptexten aus Lissabon. 2011. (Rostocker romanistische Arbeiten Ser.). 344p. 82.95 *(978-3-631-61083-1(1))* Lang, Peter GmbH, Europaischer Verlag der Wissenschaften DEU. Dist: Lang, Peter.

Platzer, Stephan J. W. Bringing E Home: Transatlantic Voyage of Schooner Ernestina 1982. 2009. 144p. pap. 27.95 *(978-1-4251-7226-8(1))* Trafford Publishing.

Street, Donald M. Street's Guide to the Cape Verde Islands. 2011. pap. ***(978-1-892399-34-2(2))*** Seaworthy Pubns., Inc.

Thomas Cook Publishing Staff. Cape Verde. 2nd ed. 2010. (Travellers - Thomas Cook Ser.). (ENG., Illus.). 160p. pap. 16.95 *(978-1-84848-234-0(5))* Cook, Thomas Publishing GBR. Dist: Globe Pequot Pr., The.

Wilson, Colum & Irwin, Aisling. Cape Verde. 5th ed. 2011. (ENG., Illus.). 336p. pap. 24.99 *(978-1-84162-350-4(4))* Bradt Travel Guides GBR. Dist: Globe Pequot Pr., The.

CAPE YORK PENINSULA (QLD.)

Heinsohn, Robert & Cermak, Michael. Life in the Cape York Rainforest. 2009. (Illus.). 106p. pap. 35.00 *(978-0-643-09501-4(2))* CSIRO Publishing AUS. Dist: Stylus Publishing, LLC.

CAPEK, KAREL, 1890-1938

Harkins, William Edward. Karel Capek. 2011. 202p. 44.95 ***(978-1-258-07967-3(4))*** Literary Licensing, LLC.

Ohme, Andreas. Karel Capeks Roman der Krieg mit den Molchen: Verfahren - Intention - Rezeption. (Slavische Literaturen - Texte und Abhandlungen Ser.: Vol. 27). (GER., Illus.). 222p. 30.95 *(978-3-631-37477-1(1))* Lang, Peter Publishing, Inc.

Ort, Thomas. Culture & Politics in Modernist Prague, 1911-1938: Karl Capek & His Generation. 2012. (Palgrave Studies in Cultural & Intellectual History Ser.). (ENG.). 256p. 85.00 *(978-0-230-11362-6(1))* Palgrave Macmillan.

CAPILLARIES

Tuma, Ronald F., et al, eds. Microcirculation. 2nd ed. 2008. (ENG., Illus.). 1000p. 210.00 *(978-0-12-374530-9(6),* Academic Pr.) Elsevier Science & Technology Bks.

CAPILLARITY

see also Brownian Movements; Hydrostatics; Permeability; Surface Chemistry; Surface Tension

Berthier, Jean & Brakke, Ken. The Physics of Microdroplets. 2012. (ENG.). 392p. 149.00 ***(978-0-470-93880-5(3),*** Wiley-Scrivener) Wiley, John & Sons, Inc.

Gennes, Pierre-Gilles de, et al. Capillarity & Wetting Phenomena: Drops, Bubbles, Pearls, Waves. 2010. (ENG., Illus.). xv, 291p. pap. 89.95 *(978-1-4419-1833-8(7),* 1441918337) Springer.

Kalliadasis, Serafim, et al. Film Flows, Wave Instabilities & Thermocapillarity. 2010. (Applied Mathematical Sciences Ser.). (ENG., Illus.). 600p. 124.00 *(978-1-84882-366-2(5),* 1848823665) Springer.

Kanegsberg, Barbara & Kanegsberg, Ed, eds. Handbook for Critical Cleaning Second Edition, 2 vols. 2nd rev. ed. 2011. (ENG., Illus.). 1136p. 179.95 *(978-1-4398-2826-7(1),* CRC Press) Taylor & Francis Group GBR. Dist: Taylor & Francis Group.

Lambert, Pierre. Capillary Forces in Microassembly: Modeling, Simulation, Experiments, & Case Study. 2007. (Microtechnology & Mems Ser.). (Illus.). 263p. 129.00 *(978-0-387-71088-4(4))* Springer.

Langbein, Dieter W. Capillary Surfaces: Shape - Stability - Dynamics, in Particular under Weightlessness. 2011. (Springer Tracts in Modern Physics Ser.). (ENG., Illus.). xviii, 392p. pap. 359.00 *(978-3-642-07523-0(1),* 3642075231) Springer.

CAPILLARY ELECTROPHORESIS

Ahuja, Satinder & Jimidar, Mohamedilias, eds. Capillary Electrophoresis Methods for Pharmaceutical Analysis. 2008. (Separation Science & Technology Ser.: 9). (ENG.). 546p. 270.00 *(978-0-12-372573-8(9),* Academic Pr.) Elsevier Science & Technology Bks.

Ali, Imran, et al. Nanochromatography & Nanocapillary Electrophoresis: Pharmaceutical & Environmental Analyses. 2009. (ENG., Illus.). 270p. 99.95 *(978-0-470-17851-5(5),* Wiley) Wiley, John & Sons, Inc.

Altria, Kevin D. Capillary Electrophoresis Guidebook: Principles, Operation, & Applications. 2010. (Methods in Molecular Biology Ser.). 384p. pap. 129.00 *(978-1-61737-011-3(8),* 1617370118) Humana Pr.

Evenhuis, Christopher. Thermal Effects & Temperature Profiles in Capillary Electrophoresis. 2010. 152p. pap. *(978-3-8383-3446-2(9))* Lambert Academic Publishing.

Guttman, Andras. Capillary Gel Electrophoresis & Related Microseparation Techniques. 2008. 350p. 195.00 *(978-0-444-52234-4(4),* Elsevier Science) Elsevier Science & Technology Bks.

Guzman Norberto a Staff. Capillary Electrophoresis & Microchip Technology. 2nd ed. 2008. 169.95 *(978-1-57444-739-2(4))* CRC Pr. LLC.

Hanrahan, Grady & Gomez, Frank A., eds. Chemometric Methods in Capillary Electrophoresis. 2009. (ENG., Illus.). 435p. 122.00 *(978-0-470-39329-1(7),* Wiley) Wiley, John & Sons, Inc.

Henry, Charles, ed. Microchip Capillary Electrophoresis: Methods & Protocols. 2010. (Methods in Molecular Biology Ser.). (Illus.). x, 237p. pap. 139.00 *(978-1-61737-476-0(8),* 1617374768) Humana Pr.

Landers, James P., ed. Handbook of Capillary & Microchip Electrophoresis & Associated Microtechniques. 3rd rev. ed. 2007. (ENG., Illus.). 1592p. 219.95 *(978-0-8493-3329-3(6),* CRC Press) Taylor & Francis Group GBR. Dist: Taylor & Francis Group.

Mitchelson, Keith R. & Cheng, Jing, eds. Capillary Electrophoresis of Nucleic Acids. 2010. (Methods in Molecular Biology Ser.). (Illus.). 432p. pap. 169.00 *(978-1-61737-177-6(7),* 1617371777); 504p. pap. 164.00 *(978-1-61737-186-8(6),* 1617371866) Humana Pr.

Schmitt-Kopplin, Philippe, ed. Capillary Electrophoresis: Methods & Protocols. 2008. (Methods in Molecular Biology Ser.). (Illus.). 809p. 209.00 *(978-1-58829-539-2(7),* 1588295397) Humana Pr.

Strege, Mark A. & Lagu, Avinash L., eds. Capillary Electrophoresis of Proteins & Peptides. 2010. (Methods in Molecular Biology Ser.). (Illus.). 344p. pap. 179.00 *(978-1-61737-307-7(9),* 1617373079) Humana Pr.

Thibault, Pierre & Honda, Susumu, eds. Capillary Electrophoresis of Carbohydrates. 2010. (Methods in Molecular Biology Ser.). (Illus.). 318p. pap. 129.00 *(978-1-61737-206-3(4),* 1617372064) Humana Pr.

Van Eeckhaut, Ann & Michotte, Yvette, eds. Chiral Separations by Capillary Electrophoresis. 2009. (Chromatographic Science Ser.). (ENG., Illus.). 543p. 174.95 *(978-1-4200-6933-4(0),* CRC Press) Taylor & Francis Group GBR. Dist: Taylor & Francis Group.

Volpi, Nicola, ed. Capillary Electrophoresis of Carbohydrates: From Monosaccharides to Complex Polysaccharides. 2010. (ENG., Illus.). xiii, 277p. 209.00 *(978-1-60761-874-4(5),* 1607618745) Humana Pr.

CAPITAL

see also Banks and Banking; Capitalism; Capitalists and Financiers; Human Capital; Infrastructure (Economics); Interest; Liquidity (Economics); Profit; Saving and Investment; Trusts, Industrial; Usury; Wealth

Agyei, Samuel Kwaku. Capital Structure & Performance of Banks in Ghan. 2011. 112p. pap. ***(978-3-8454-0311-3(X))*** Lambert Academic Publishing.

Althusser, Louis & Balibar, Étienne. Reading Capital. Brewster, Ben, tr. 2009. (Radical Thinkers Ser.). (ENG.). 384p. pap. 19.95 *(978-1-84467-347-6(2),* 844347) Verso Bks. GBR. Dist: Norton, W. W. & Co., Inc.

Aspatore Books Staff, compiled by. Understanding Legal Trends in the Private Equity & Venture Capital Market: Top Attorneys on Using the Latest Technology, Complying with Changing Regulations, & Helping Clients Adjust to the New Economic Climate (Inside the Minds) 2011. 132p. pap. 85.00 *(978-0-314-27414-4(6))* Aspatore Bks.

Bartee, RoSusan D. Contemporary Perspectives on Capital in Educational Contexts. 2011. xiii, 224p. *(978-1-61735-364-2(7))*; xiii, 224p. pap. *(978-1-61735-363-5(9))*; E-Book *(978-1-61735-365-9(5))* Information Age Publishing, Inc.

Bentacourt, Roger R., et al. Capital Utilization: A Theoretical & Empirical Analysis. 2008. (ENG., Illus.). 268p. pap. 37.99 *(978-0-521-07028-7(7))* Cambridge Univ. Pr.

Bhatia, Mohan. An Introduction to Economic Capital. 2008. (Illus.). 250p. *(978-1-906348-09-0(X))* Risk Bks.

Böhm-Bawerk, Eugen von. Positive Theory of Capital. 2006. pap. 26.95 *(978-1-60206-039-5(8),* Cosimo Classics) Cosimo, Inc.

Le Centenaire Du 'Capital' Exposés et entretiens sur le Marxisme. (Décades du Centre Culturel International de Cerisy-la-Salle Ser.). (FRE.). 341p. 135.00 ***(978-3-11-130800-5(6))*** De Gruyter, Mouton DEU. Dist: de Gruyter, Walter GmbH & Co. KG.

Cortez, Annette. Winning at Risk: Strategies to Go Beyond Basel. 2011. (Wiley Finance Ser.: 638). (ENG., Illus.). 254p. 60.00 *(978-0-470-92466-2(7),* Wiley) Wiley, John & Sons, Inc.

Cram101 Textbook Reviews Staff. Outlines & Highlights for Understanding Finance: Money, Capital, & Investments by Halpern, ISBN. 2009. 136p. pap. 28.95 *(978-1-4288-3962-5(3))* Cram101 Inc.

Cunningham, William. The Use & Abuse of Money. 248p. 2009. 23.99 *(978-0-559-97422-9(1))* 2009. pap. 17.99 *(978-0-559-97419-9(1))* 2008. 24.99 *(978-0-559-18698-1(3))* 2008. pap. 17.99 *(978-0-559-18696-7(7))* BiblioBazaar.

—The Use & Abuse of Money. 2007. (ENG.). 248p. 41.95 *(978-0-548-08926-2(4))* Kessinger Publishing, LLC.

Dalkir, Kimiz. Knowledge Management in Theory & Practice. 2nd ed. 2011. (ENG., Illus.). 504p. 55.00 *(978-0-262-01508-0(0))* MIT Pr.

Dolfsma, Wilfred. Knowledge Economies: Organization, Location & Innovation. 2009. 160p. pap. 39.95 *(978-0-415-56953-8(2))* Routledge.

Dynamics of Capital Structure. 2010. 96p. pap. *(978-3-8383-6729-3(4))* Lambert Academic Publishing.

Fanno, Marco. Normal & Abnormal International Capital Transfers. 2009. (Studies in Economic Dynamics Ser.). (ENG.). 130p. pap. 40.00 *(978-0-8166-5933-3(8))* Univ. of Minnesota Pr.

Fisher, Irving. The Nature of Capital & Income. 2007. 452p. 44.95 *(978-1-60206-990-9(5))* 2006. pap. 28.95 *(978-1-59605-996-2(6),* Cosimo Classics) Cosimo, Inc.

—The Nature of Capital & Income. 2009. *(978-1-57898-746-7(6))* Martino Publishing.

—The Rate of Interest: Its Nature, Determination & Relation to Economic Phenomena. 2009. pap. *(978-1-57898-745-0(8))* Martino Publishing.

Friedman, Jeffrey & Kraus, Wladimir. Engineering the Financial Crisis: Systemic Risk & the Failure of Regulation. 2011. (Illus.). 224p. (C). 45.00 ***(978-0-8122-4357-4(9))*** Univ. of Pennsylvania Pr.

C

Funk, Christian. Gestaltung effizienter interner Kapitalmärkte in Konglomeraten. 2008. (Controlling und Management Ser.). 268p. pap. 65.95 *(978-3-631-57826-1(1))* Lang, Peter GmbH, Europaischer Verlag der Wissenschaften DEU. Dist: Lang, Peter.

Giffen, Robert. The Growth of Capital. 2009. 180p. 26.99 *(978-1-116-45977-7(9))*; pap. 21.75 *(978-1-116-45979-1(5))*; pap. 22.75 *(978-1-116-45978-4(7))*; 22.99 *(978-1-103-49303-6(5))*; pap. 16.99 *(978-1-103-49300-5(0))* BiblioBazaar.

—The Growth of Capital. 2009. 176p. 37.95 *(978-1-104-42641-5(2))*; pap. 22.95 *(978-1-104-39222-2(4))* Kessinger Publishing, LLC.

Gregoriou, Greg N. & Gregoriou. Operational Risk Toward Basel III: Best Practices & Issues in Modeling, Management, & Regulation. 2009. (Wiley Finance Ser.: 481). (ENG., Illus.). 497p. 95.00 *(978-0-470-39014-6(X)*, Wiley) Wiley, John & Sons, Inc.

Hagemann, Harald. Capital, Time & Transitional Dynamics. 2010. pap. 42.95 *(978-0-415-58863-8(4))* Routledge.

Halpern. Understanding Finance Money Capital and. 2006. pap. 12.95 *(978-1-4288-0621-4(0))* Cram101 Inc.

Haslam, Colin, et al. Redefining Business Models: Strategies for a Financialized World. 2012. (ENG., Illus.). 296p. (C). 145.00 *(978-0-415-67440-9(9))* Routledge.

Hayek, F. A. & White, Lawrence H. The Pure Theory of Capital. 2007. (Collected Works of F. A. Hayek Ser.). (ENG., Illus.). 464p. 65.00 *(978-0-226-32099-1(5))* Univ. of Chicago Pr.

Hayek F a Ed Bartley Staff. Pure Theory Capital: Hayek V15. 2008. (Collected Works of F. A. Hayek Ser.). (ENG.). 480p. 150.00 *(978-0-415-03527-9(9))* Routledge.

Hayek, Friedrich A. von & White, Lawrence H. The Pure Theory of Capital. 2012. pap. ***(978-0-86597-845-4(X))*** Liberty Fund, Inc.

Henry, Peter. Capital Account Liberalization: Theory, Evidence & Speculation. 2006. 0.00 net. *(978-0-9790376-3-4(8))* Brookings Global Economy & Development.

Hofmann, Erik, et al. Ways Out of the Working Capital Trap: Empowering Self-Financing Growth Through Modern Supply Management. 2011. (Advanced Purchasing & SCM Ser.). Orig. Title: Wege aus der Working Capital-Falle. (Illus.). x, 94p. 49.95 *(978-3-642-17270-0(9)*, 3642172709) Springer.

Hollander, Samuel. The Economics of Karl Marx: Analysis & Application. 2008. (Historical Perspectives on Modern Economics Ser.). (ENG.). 550p. 147.00 *(978-0-521-79078-9(6))*; (Illus.). 552p. pap. 75.00 *(978-0-521-79399-5(8))* Cambridge Univ. Pr.

Huxley, Thomas Henry. Evolution & Ethics: Delivered in the Sheldonian Theatre, May 18 1893. Richards, Robert J. & Ruse, Michael, eds. 2009. (ENG.). 176p. (C). 45.00 *(978-0-691-14192-3(4))* Princeton Univ. Pr.

—Evolution & Ethics & Other Essays. 2009. 352p. 31.99 *(978-1-115-70850-0(3))* 2009. 352p. 29.99 *(978-1-115-70851-7(1))* 2009. 352p. pap. 32.75 *(978-1-115-70852-4(X))* 2008. 292p. 25.99 *(978-0-554-36501-5(4))* 2008. 292p. 28.99 *(978-0-554-27198-9(2))* 2007. (ENG.). 258p. per. 21.99 *(978-1-4346-2644-8(X))* 2007. (ENG.). 292p. per. 23.99 *(978-1-4346-2722-3(5))* BiblioBazaar.

—Evolution & Ethics & Other Essays. 2006. pap. *(978-1-4068-1411-8(3))* Echo Library.

IISS. The Military Balance 2010. 2010. (Military Balance Ser.). (ENG., Illus.). 488p. pap. 440.00 *(978-1-85743-557-3(5)*, Routledge) Taylor & Francis Group GBR. Dist: Taylor & Francis Group.

Iiss. The Military Balance 2011. 2nd rev. ed. 2011. (Military Balance Ser.). (ENG., Illus.). 488p. pap. 460.00 *(978-1-85743-606-8(7))* Routledge.

Jameson, Fredric. Representing Capital, Vol. 1. 2011. (ENG.). 176p. 24.95 *(978-1-84467-454-1(1)*, 844454) Verso Bks. GBR. Dist: Norton, W. W. & Co., Inc.

King, Alfred M. Internal Control of Fixed Assets: A Controller & Auditor's Guide. 2011. (Wiley Corporate F&a Ser.: 564). (ENG., Illus.). 192p. 68.50 *(978-0-470-53940-8(2)*, Wiley) Wiley, John & Sons, Inc.

Kirzner, Israel M. Essays on Capital & Interest: An Austrian Perspective. 2012. ***(978-0-86597-780-8(1))***; pap. ***(978-0-86597-781-5(X))*** Liberty Fund, Inc.

Lewitt, Michael E. The Death of Capital: How Creative Policy Can Restore Stability. 2010. (ENG., Illus.). 292p. 27.95 *(978-0-470-46650-6(2)*, Wiley) Wiley, John & Sons, Inc.

Lin, Carol Yeh-Yun & Edvinsson, Leif. National Intellectual Capital: A Comparison of 40 Countries. 2010. (ENG., Illus.). xvii, 392p. 139.00 *(978-1-4419-7376-4(1)*, 1441973761) Springer.

Macrakis, M. S. Scarcity's Ways: the Origins of Capital: A Critical Essay on Thermodynamics, Statistical Mechanics & Economics. 2010. (Boston Studies in the Philosophy of Science Ser.). 240p. pap. 179.00 *(978-90-481-4919-3(3)*, 9048149193) Springer.

Mahura, Kagisho. What Is the Greater Contributor to Total Returns. 2011. 56p. pap. ***(978-3-8443-3435-7(1))*** Lambert Academic Publishing.

Marx, Karl. Capital. 2009. 376p. pap. *(978-1-151-74032-8(2))*; 632p. pap. *(978-0-217-82130-8(8))*; 556p. pap. *(978-0-217-82136-0(7))* Books LLC.

—Capital. McLellan, David, ed. abr. ed. 2008. (Oxford World's Classics Ser.). (ENG.). 544p. pap. 16.95 *(978-0-19-953570-5(1))* Oxford Univ. Pr., Inc.

—Capital: A Critique of Political Economy. Date not set. 464p. 29.95 *(978-0-8488-2366-5(4))* Amereon LTD.

—Capital, Volume One: A Critique of Political Economy. Engels, Friedrich, ed. Moore, Samuel & Aveling, Edward, trs. from GER. 2011. (ENG.). 880p. pap. 14.95 *(978-0-486-47748-0(7))* Dover Pubns., Inc.

—Economic & Philosophic Manuscripts Of 1844. Milligan, Martin, tr. from GER. 2007. (Dover Books on Western Philosophy Ser.). (ENG., Illus.). 208p. per. 6.95 *(978-0-486-45561-7(0))* Dover Pubns., Inc.

—Economic & Philosophic Manuscripts Of 1844. 2011. 212p. pap. 10.50 ***(978-1-891396-56-4(0))*** Martino Publishing.

—The Essential Marx. Trotsky, Leon, ed. 2006. (Dover Books on Western Philosophy Ser.). (ENG., Illus.). 192p. per. 8.95 *(978-0-486-45116-9(X))* Dover Pubns., Inc.

—Das Kapital. 2007. (ENG.). 376p. *(978-1-934568-43-9(0))* Synergy International of The Americas, Ltd.

—Value, Price & Profit. 2008. 64p. pap. 14.95 *(978-1-4344-6311-1(7))* Wildside Pr., LLC.

—Wage-Labor & Capital. Engels, Friedrich, tr. 2009. 56p. pap. *(978-1-4099-6165-9(6))* Dodo Pr.

—Wage-Labor & Capital. 2010. 58p. pap. 16.88 *(978-1-152-14729-4(3))* General Bks. LLC.

—Wage-Labour & Capital & Value, Price & Profit. 2007. 108p. *(978-1-934568-23-1(6))* Synergy International of The Americas, Ltd.

Masciarelli, Francesca. The Strategic Value of Social Capital: How Firms Capitalise on Social Assets. 2011. 192p. 110.00 ***(978-1-84980-296-3(3))*** Elgar, Edward Publishing, Inc.

Mcinnes, Angelique. Working Capital Management. 2010. 128p. pap. *(978-3-8383-6958-7(0))* Lambert Academic Publishing.

Meaney, M. E. Capital as Organic Unity: The Role of Hegel's Science of Logic in Marx's Grundrisse. 2010. (Philosophical Studies in Contemporary Culture Ser.). 208p. pap. 179.00 *(978-90-481-6181-2(9)*, 9048161819) Springer.

Mezaros, I. Beyond Capital. 994p. (C). pap. 29.95 *(978-0-85036-432-3(9))* Merlin Pr. Ltd. GBR. Dist: Paul & Co. Pubs. Consortium, Inc.

Moore, Winston. Small States & Capital Account Liberalization. 2010. 232p. pap. *(978-3-8383-4338-9(7))* Lambert Academic Publishing.

Muzhani, Marin. Controversies in Modern Economic Growth & Capital Theory: A Survey on Mainstream Growth Economists. 2010. *(978-1-60497-708-0(6))* Cambria Pr.

Nicolopoulou, Katerina, et al, eds. Global Knowledge Work: Diversity & Relational Perspectives. 2011. (Illus.). 296p. 125.00 ***(978-1-84844-543-7(1))*** Elgar, Edward Publishing, Inc.

Organisation for Economic Co-operation and Development Staff. Measuring Capital - OECD Manual 2009. 2nd ed. 2009. 232p. pap. 63.00 *(978-92-64-02563-9(4))* Organization for Economic Cooperation & Development.

O'Toole, Paddy. How Organizations Remember: Retaining Knowledge through Organizational Action. 2010. (Organizational Change & Innovation Ser.). (Illus.). xi, 191p. 119.00 *(978-1-4419-7523-2(3)*, 1441975233) Springer.

Parson, Christopher & Titman, Sheridan. Empirical Capital Structure: A Review. 2009. 108p. pap. 75.00 net. *(978-1-60198-202-5(X))* Now Pubs.

Perez-Feliciano, L. A. The American Political Economy & Monopoly Capital. 2009. 184p. pap. *(978-3-639-12925-0(3))* VDM Verlag Dr. Mueller e.K.

Pettit, Justin. Strategic Corporate Finance: Applications in Valuation & Capital Structure. 2007. (Wiley Finance Ser.: 381). (ENG., Illus.). 304p. 90.00 *(978-0-470-05264-8(3)*, Wiley) Wiley, John & Sons, Inc.

Pilling, Geoffrey. Marx's 'Capital' Philosophy & Political Economy. 2009. (Routledge Revivals Ser.). 216p. 110.00 *(978-0-415-57101-2(4))* Routledge.

Preve, Lorenzo A. & Sarria-Allende, Virginia. Working Capital Management, 1 vol. 2010. (Financial Management Association Survey & Synthesis Ser.). (ENG., Illus.). 192p. 39.95 *(978-0-19-973741-3(X))* Oxford Univ. Pr., Inc.

Sagner, James. Essentials of Working Capital Management. 2010. (Essentials Ser.: 55). (ENG., Illus.). 272p. pap. 45.00 *(978-0-470-87998-6(X)*, Wiley) Wiley, John & Sons, Inc.

Sardoni, Claudio, ed. On Political Economists & Modern Political Economy. 2011. (Routledge Revivals Ser.). (ENG.). 440p. 150.00 *(978-0-415-61628-7(X))* Routledge.

Scazzieri, Roberto, et al, eds. Markets, Money & Capital: Hicksian Economics for the Twenty First Century. 2011. (ENG., Illus.). 466p. pap. 55.00 *(978-0-521-18879-1(2))* Cambridge Univ. Pr.

Scazzieri, Roberto, et al. Markets, Money & Capital: Hicksian Economics for the Twenty-First Century. Scazzieri, Roberto et al, eds. 2009. (ENG., Illus.). 466p. 99.00 *(978-0-521-87321-5(5))* Cambridge Univ. Pr.

Schönerwald Da Silva, Carlos Eduardo. Participatory Budgeting & Human Capabilities. 2010. 92p. pap. *(978-3-8383-2102-8(2))* Lambert Academic Publishing.

Shipside, Steve. Karl Marx's das Kapital: A Modern-Day Interpretation of a True Classic. 2009. (Illus.). 128p. pap. 14.00 *(978-1-906821-04-3(6))* Infinite Ideas GBR. Dist: Sony Electronics.

Smith, J. W. Money Hbk: A Mirror Image of the Economy, 2nd Edition. 2nd rev. ed. 2008. 180p. 60.00 *(978-1-933567-13-6(9))* Institute for Economic Democracy Pr., Inc.

Song, Joon-Young. Have We Resolved the Issues Regarding International Capital Structure? 2010. 100p. pap. *(978-3-8383-7309-6(X))* Lambert Academic Publishing.

Stanziani, Alessandro. Rules of Exchange: French Capitalism in Comparative Perspective, Eighteenth to Early Twentieth Centuries. 2012. (ENG., Illus.). 315p. 90.00 *(978-1-107-00386-6(5))* Cambridge Univ. Pr.

Stephan, Gunter. Introduction into Capital Theory: A Neo-Austrian Perspective. 2010. (ENG., Illus.). x, 291p. pap. 69.95 *(978-3-642-08216-0(5)*, 3642082165) Springer.

Suljkanovic, Midran. Corporate Governance in Post-Privatized Bosnia & Herzegovin. 2010. 88p. pap. *(978-3-639-25364-1(7))* VDM Verlag Dr. Mueller e.K.

Sussman, Jason H. The Healthcare Executive's Guide to Allocating Capital. 2007. 70.00 *(978-1-56793-956-9(2))* Health Administration Pr.

TARP Oversight: Is TARP Working for Main Street?: Hearing Before the Subcommittee on Financial Institutions & Consumer Credit of the Committee on Financial Services, U.S. House of Representatives, One Hundred Eleventh Congress, First Session, March 4, 2009. 2009. (Illus.). v, 103p. *(978-0-16-083791-3(X)*, 552-070-39493-1) United States Government Printing Office.

Tarullo, Daniel & Tarullo, Daniel K. Banking on Basel: The Future of International Financial Regulation. 2008. (Illus.). 256p. (C). pap. 26.95 *(978-0-88132-423-5(X))* Peterson Institute for International Economics.

Taylor, Lester D. Capital, Accumulation, & Money: An Integration of Capital, Growth, & Monetary Theory. 2nd ed. 2010. (ENG., Illus.). xxviii, 250p. 189.00 *(978-0-387-98168-0(3)*, 0387981683) Springer.

Valler, Martin & Virovere, Anu. Structural Capital As the Success Factor. 2010. 76p. pap. *(978-3-8383-6204-5(7))* Lambert Academic Publishing.

Wayne, Michael. Marx's das Kapital for Beginners. 2012. (For Beginners Ser.). (ENG., Illus.). 144p. pap. 16.99 *(978-1-934389-59-1(5)*, For Beginners) Steerforth Pr.

Weeks, John. Capital Exploitation & Economic Crisis. 2011. (Routledge Frontiers of Political Economy Ser.). (ENG., Illus.). 208p. (C). 130.00 *(978-0-415-61055-1(9))* Routledge.

Wheen, Francis. Marx's das Kapital: A Biography. 2008. (Books That Changed the World Ser.). (ENG.). 144p. pap. 13.00 *(978-0-8021-4394-5(6)*, Grove Pr.) Grove/Atlantic, Inc.

CAPITAL—TAXATION

see Capital Levy

CAPITAL—ASIA

Davies, Doug & Wei, Liang, eds. Human Resources Management in China: Cases in HR Practice. 2011. (Chandos Asian Studies). (ENG.). 226p. 110.00 ***(978-0-85709-148-2(4)***, Chandos Publishing) Woodhead Publishing Ltd. GBR. Dist: Ingram Pub. Services.

CAPITAL—EUROPE

Apostu, Andreea. The Effects of Diversification Strategies on Capital Structure. 2011. 80p. pap. ***(978-3-8443-2228-6(0))*** Lambert Academic Publishing.

Boldizzoni, Francesco. Means & Ends: The Idea of Capital in the West, 1500-1970. 2008. (ENG., Illus.). 224p. 84.00 *(978-0-230-57257-7(X))* Palgrave Macmillan.

Eimer, Martin. Zeichnungsverträge und Zeichnunsvorverträge: Zu den Rechten und Pflichten aus dem Vertrag über die Vorerhöhungsgesellschaft. 2008. (Osnabrücker Schriften zum Unternehmens- und Wirtschaftsrecht Ser.). 264p. pap. 65.95 *(978-3-631-57811-7(3))* Lang, Peter GmbH, Europaischer Verlag der Wissenschaften DEU. Dist: Lang, Peter.

Fayolle, Alain & Todorov, Kiril, eds. European Entrepreneurship in the Globalizing Economy. 2011. (European Research in Entrepreneurship Ser.). (Illus.). 256p. 115.00 *(978-1-84980-821-7(X))* Elgar, Edward Publishing, Inc.

Pöschke, Moritz. Eigenkapital mittelständischer Gesellschaften nach IAS/IFRS. 2009. (Schriften zum Gesellschafts-, Bilanz- und Unternehmensteuerrecht Ser.). (GER.). 332p. 86.95 *(978-3-631-58868-0(2))* Lang, Peter GmbH, Europaischer Verlag der Wissenschaften DEU. Dist: Lang, Peter.

Rhodes, Martin, et al, eds. Beyond Varieties of Capitalism: Conflict, Contradictions, & Complementarities in the European Economy. 2007. (ENG., Illus.). 456p. 135.00 *(978-0-19-920648-3(1))* Oxford Univ. Pr., Inc.

Rieger, Stefan. Eigenkapitalersatz in mehrstufigen und mehrfachen Beteiligungsverhältnissen: Ein Beitrag zu den Grundlagen und Grenzen des Eigenkapitalersatzgedankens. 2009. (Schriften zum Wirtschafts- und Medienrecht, Steuerrecht und Zivilprozeßrecht Ser.). (GER.). 154p. 54.95 *(978-3-631-59131-4(4))* Lang, Peter GmbH, Europaischer Verlag der Wissenschaften DEU. Dist: Lang, Peter.

Schaumann, Michael. Reform des Eigenkapitalersatzrechts im System der Gesellschafterhaftung: Unter Berücksichtigung der Änderungen durch das MoMiG. 2009. (Schriften zum Verfahrensrecht Ser.). (GER.). 346p. 89.95 *(978-3-631-58614-3(0))* Lang, Peter GmbH, Europaischer Verlag der Wissenschaften DEU. Dist: Lang, Peter.

CAPITAL—NETHERLANDS

Riley, James. International Government Finance & the Amsterdam Capital Market, 1740-1815. 2009. (ENG.). 380p. pap. 51.00 *(978-0-521-10110-3(7))* Cambridge Univ. Pr.

CAPITAL AND LABOR

see Industrial Relations

CAPITAL BUDGET

Baecker, Philipp N. Real Options & Intellectual Property: Capital Budgeting under Imperfect Patent Protection. 2007. (Lecture Notes in Economics & Mathematical Systems Ser.). (Illus.). x, 278p. pap. 129.00 *(978-3-540-48263-5(6))* Springer DEU. Dist: Springer.

Baker, H. Kent & English, Philip, eds. Capital Budgeting Valuation: Financial Analysis for Today's Investment Projects. 2011. (Robert W. Kolb Ser.: 13). (ENG., Illus.). 518p. 95.00 *(978-0-470-56950-4(6)*, Wiley) Wiley, John & Sons, Inc.

Bierman, Harold, Jr. & Smidt, Seymour. The Advanced Capital Budgeting Decision. (Illus.). XVIII, 374p. 2007. 175.00 *(978-0-415-77205-1(2))* 2006. 62.95 *(978-0-415-77206-8(0))* Routledge.

Bierman, Harold, et al. The Capital Budgeting Decision: Economic Analysis of Investment Projects. 9th ed. 2006. (Illus.). (ENG.). 424p. (C). per. 62.95 *(978-0-415-40004-6(X))*; 402p. 175.00 *(978-0-415-40003-9(1))* Routledge.

Ekeha, George. Capital Budgeting Practices & Economic Development. 2011. 76p. pap. ***(978-3-8443-8259-4(3))*** Lambert Academic Publishing.

Khan, Aman. Fundamentals of Public Budgeting. 2012. (Public Administration & Public Policy Ser.). (ENG., Illus.). 500p. (C). 129.95 *(978-1-4200-4657-1(8)*, CRC Press) Taylor & Francis Group GBR. Dist: Taylor & Francis Group.

Marlowe, Justin, et al. Capital Budgeting & Finance: A Guide for Local Governments. 2nd ed. 2009. 110.00 *(978-0-87326-188-3(7))* International City/County Management Assn.

McCrary, Stuart A. Mastering Corporate Finance Essentials: The Critical Quantitative Methods & Tools in Finance. 2010. (Wiley Finance Ser.: 486). (ENG., Illus.). 174p. 49.95 *(978-0-470-39333-8(5)*, Wiley) Wiley, John & Sons, Inc.

Miller, Luke. Development of a Bayesian Real Options Framework. 2010. 192p. pap. *(978-3-639-28292-4(2))* VDM Verlag Dr. Mueller e.K.

CAPITAL CITIES

see Capitals (Cities)

CAPITAL EQUIPMENT

see Industrial Equipment

CAPITAL EXPORTS

see Foreign Exchange; Investments, Foreign

CAPITAL FLIGHT

see Capital Movements

CAPITAL FLOW

see Capital Movements

CAPITAL FORMATION

see Saving and Investment

CAPITAL GAINS TAX

see also Real Property and Taxation

Adams, Rob & Thornton, Grant. Capital Gains Tax Planning 2011/12. 2011. 392p. pap. 165.00 *(978-1-84766-773-1(2)*, Bloomsbury Professional) Bloomsbury Publishing Plc GBR. Dist: International Specialized Bk. Services.

Bayley, Carl. Capital Gains Tax: Emergency Tax Planning Guide. 2010. 116p. pap. *(978-1-907302-19-0(0))* Taxcafe UK Ltd.

—Master Property Capital Gains Tax in 2 Hours. 2008. 100p. pap. *(978-1-904608-75-2(2))* Taxcafe UK Ltd.

—Salary Versus Dividends: How to Extract Company Profits & Cut Your Tax Bill by Thousands. 2008. 296p. pap. *(978-1-904608-83-7(3))*; 276p. pap. *(978-1-904608-77-6(9))* Taxcafe UK Ltd.

—Salary Versus Dividends: How to Extract Company Profits & Slash Your Tax Bill by Thousands. 2009. 312p. pap. *(978-1-904608-99-8(X))* Taxcafe UK Ltd.

Bayley, Carl & Braun, Nick. Property Capital Gains Tax: How to Pay the Absolute Minimum CGT on Rental Properties & Second Homes. 2011. 140p. pap. ***(978-1-907302-36-7(0))*** 2010. 142p. pap. *(978-1-907302-15-2(8))* Taxcafe UK Ltd.

Borden, Bradley T. Tax-Free Like-Kind Exchanges. 2008. (Illus.). ***(978-1-887554-63-3(7))*** Civic Research Institute, Inc.

Borden, Bradley T. Tax-Free Swaps: Using Section 1031 Like-Kind Exchanges to Preserve Investment Net Worth. 2007. (Nuts & Bolts Ser.). (ENG.). 280p. *(978-1-933255-28-6(5))* DNA Pr.

Cameron, David L. & Manning, Elliott. Federal Taxation of Property Transactions. 2012. ***(978-1-59345-886-7(X))*** LexisNexis Matthew Bender.

Cave, Rebecca. Capital Gains Tax Roll-over, Hold-over & Deferral Reliefs 2011/12. 2012. 512p. pap. 195.00 *(978-1-84766-772-4(4)*, Bloomsbury Professional) Bloomsbury Publishing Plc GBR. Dist: International Specialized Bk. Services.

Cave, Rebecca, et al. Capital Gains Tax 2011-12. 2011. 514p. pap. 88.00 *(978-1-84766-757-1(0)*, Bloomsbury Professional) Bloomsbury Publishing Plc GBR. Dist: International Specialized Bk. Services.

CCH Tax Law Editors. Principles of Business Taxation. 2009th ed. 2009. 900p. 149.00 *(978-0-8080-2060-8(9))* Toolkit Media Group.

Fromm, Andreas. Die Investmentaktiengesellschaft mit veränderlichem Kapital: Haftungsfolgen im Falle einer Besteuerung der Anteilseigner nach § 6 InvStG. 2008. (Europäische Hochschulschriften. Reihe 2: Rechtswissenschaft Ser.). 190p. pap. 56.95 *(978-3-631-57466-9(5))* Lang, Peter GmbH, Europaischer Verlag der Wissenschaften DEU. Dist: Lang, Peter.

Hammonds (Firm) Staff & Squire Sanders Hammonds Staff. Tax Aspects of the Purchase & Sale of a Private Company's Shares. 20th ed. 2011. 424p. pap., E-Book 195.00 ***(978-1-84766-863-9(1)***, Bloomsbury Professional) Bloomsbury Publishing Plc GBR. Dist: International Specialized Bk. Services.

Kitson, David. Taper Relief. 6th ed. 2007. 265p. pap. 198.00 *(978-1-84592-486-7(X)*, Bloomsbury Professional) Bloomsbury Publishing Plc GBR. Dist: International Specialized Bk. Services.

Kramer, Andrea S. Financial Products: Taxation, Regulation & Design (2008 Supplement) 2007. 1152p. pap. 306.50 *(978-0-8080-1834-6(5))* Toolkit Media Group.

Simontacchi, Stefano. Taxation of Capital Gains under the OECD Model Convention: With Special Regard to Immovable Property. 2007. xx, 415p. *(978-90-411-2549-1(3))* Kluwer Law International.

Wilson, Martin. Capitol Allowances: Transactions & Planning. *(978-1-86012-812-7(2))* Tolley.

CAPITAL IMPORTS

see Foreign Exchange; Investments, Foreign

CAPITAL INVESTMENTS
see also Art As an Investment
American Association of State Highway and Transportation Officials Staff, contrib. by. The Road to Livability: How State Departments of Transportation Are Using Road Investments to Improve Community Livability. 2010. (Illus.). 16p. pap. *(978-1-56051-482-4(5))* American Assn. of State Highway & Transportation Officials.
Amr, Ahmed. The Sheep & the Guardians: Diary of a SEC Sanctioned Swindle. 2009. 324p. pap. 23.99 *(978-1-4269-1031-9(2))* Trafford Publishing.
Baker, H. Kent & English, Philip, eds. Capital Budgeting Valuation: Financial Analysis for Today's Investment Projects. 2011. (Robert W. Kolb Ser.: 13). (ENG., Illus.). 518p. 95.00 *(978-0-470-56950-4(6),* Wiley) Wiley, John & Sons, Inc.
Baker, H. Kent & Martin, Gerald S. Capital Structure & Corporate Financing Decisions: Theory, Evidence, & Practice. 2011. (Robert W. Kolb Ser.: 15). (ENG., Illus.). 492p. 95.00 *(978-0-470-56952-8(2),* Wiley) Wiley, John & Sons, Inc.
Banik, Arindam & Bhaumik, Pradip K. Foreign Capital Inflows to China, India & the Caribbean: Trends, Assessments & Determinants. rev. ed. 2006. (ENG., Illus.). 232p. 105.00 *(978-1-4039-0040-1(X))* Palgrave Macmillan.
Bierman, Harold, Jr. & Smidt, Seymour. The Advanced Capital Budgeting Decision. (Illus.). XVIII, 374p. 2007. 175.00 *(978-0-415-77205-1(2))* 2006. 62.95 *(978-0-415-77206-8(0))* Routledge.
Bierman, Harold, et al. The Capital Budgeting Decision: Economic Analysis of Investment Projects. 9th ed. 2006. (Illus.). (ENG.). 424p. (C). per. 62.95 *(978-0-415-40004-6(X))*; 402p. 175.00 *(978-0-415-40003-9(1))* Routledge.
Bills, Mark. The IT Value Detective: Corporate Investigations into IT Investment Performance. 2011. (ENG.). 208p. 60.00 *(978-0-470-54034-3(6),* Wiley) Wiley, John & Sons, Inc.
Bradford, Andrew. The Investment Industry for IT Practitioners: An Introductory Guide. 2008. (SII Series on Financial Services Operations Ser.: 1). (ENG., Illus.). 408p. 70.00 *(978-0-470-99780-2(X),* Wiley) Wiley, John & Sons, Inc.
Bromiley, Philip. Corporate Capital Investment: A Behavioral Approach. 2009. (ENG.). 192p. (C). pap. 31.99 *(978-0-521-09212-8(4))* Cambridge Univ. Pr.
Canada and Sull, White. Capital Investment Analysis for Engineer. 2006. pap. 11.95 *(978-1-4288-0721-1(7))* Cram101 Inc.
Carkhuff, Robert. The Science of Freedom. 2007. 270p. pap. 24.95 *(978-1-59996-060-9(5))* Human Resource Development Pr.
Carver, Lorenzo. Venture Capital Valuation: Case Studies & Methodology. 2011. (Wiley Finance Ser.: 631). (ENG., Illus.). 288p. 95.00 *(978-0-470-90828-0(9),* Wiley) Wiley, John & Sons, Inc.
Cram101 Textbook Reviews & Cram101 Textbook Reviews. Outlines & Highlights for Finance for Engineers by F K Crundwell. 2011. 466p. pap. 36.95 *(978-1-61830-346-2(5))* Cram101 Inc.
Cram101 Textbook Reviews Staff. Outlines & Highlights for Valuation: The Art & Science of Corporate Investment Decisions by Sheridan Titman, John Martin, ISBN. 2009. 208p. pap. 30.95 *(978-1-4288-3315-9(3))* Cram101 Inc.
Crundwell, F. K. Finance for Engineers: Evaluation & Funding of Capital Projects. 2008. (ENG., Illus.). xxiv, 622p. 89.95 *(978-1-84800-032-2(4),* 1848000324) Springer.
Crundwell, Frank Kenneth. Finance for Engineers: Evaluation & Funding of Capital Projects. 2010. (ENG., Illus.). xxiv, 622p. pap. 89.95 *(978-1-84996-708-2(3),* 1849967083) Springer.
Danilov, A. I. & Razumova, IU V. Innovatsionno-Investitsionnye Protsessy V Sovremennoi Sisteme Obshchestvennogo Vosproizvodstva: Monografiia. 2010. (RUS.). 250p. *(978-5-7856-0734-7(4))* Marketing, Informacionno-Vnedrenceskij Ctr.
De Mtzerac, Edouard. Cost of Capital in Investment Decisions. 2009. 96p. pap. *(978-3-639-16184-7(X))* VDM Verlag Dr. Mueller e.K.
Deniff, Dominika. Financial Indices & the Atx. 2010. 80p. pap. *(978-3-639-24627-8(6))* VDM Verlag Dr. Mueller e.K.
Eberhard, Anton, et al. Africa's Power Infrastructure: Investment, Integration, Efficiency. 2011. (Directions in Development Ser.). (ENG., Illus.). 336p. pap. 30.00 *(978-0-8213-8455-8(4),* 9780821384558) World Bank Pubns.
Eberhard, Anton A. Africa's Power Infrastructure: Investment, Integration, Efficiency. 2011. *(978-0-8213-8652-1(2))* World Bank Pubns.
Eder, Clemens. Stock Price Bubbles. 2009. 120p. pap. *(978-3-639-16652-1(3))* VDM Verlag Dr. Mueller e.K.
Einhorn, David. Fooling Some of the People All of the Time: A Long Short Story. 2008. (ENG., Illus.). 380p. 29.95 *(978-0-470-07394-0(2),* Wiley) Wiley, John & Sons, Inc.
Ellison, George I. Stock Returns: Cyclicity, Prediction & Economic Consequences. 2009. (Financial Institutions & Services Ser.). 135.00 *(978-1-60741-458-2(9))* Nova Science Pubs., Inc.
Evans, Mervin. ABCs of VC Funding. 2010. cd-rom 19.99 *(978-0-914391-98-2(4))* Community People Pr.
Fabozzi, Frank J. & Mann, Steven V. Introduction to Fixed Income Analytics: Relative Value Analysis, Risk Measures & Valuation. 2nd ed. 2010. (Wiley Desktop Editions Ser.: 191). (ENG., Illus.). 479p. 100.00 *(978-0-470-57213-9(2),* Wiley) Wiley, John & Sons, Inc.
Falkenstein, Eric & Falkenstein. Finding Alpha: The Search for Alpha When Risk & Return Break Down. 2009. (Wiley Finance Ser.: 511). (ENG., Illus.). 298p. 95.00 *(978-0-470-44590-7(4),* Wiley) Wiley, John & Sons, Inc.
Fater, David H. Essentials of Corporate & Capital Formation. 2010. (Essentials Ser.: 59). (ENG., Illus.). 352p. pap. 39.95 *(978-0-470-49656-5(8),* Wiley) Wiley, John & Sons, Inc.
Finnerty, John D. Project Financing: Asset-Based Financial Engineering. 2nd rev. ed. 2007. (Wiley Finance Ser.: 386). (ENG., Illus.). 496p. 95.00 *(978-0-470-08624-7(6),* Wiley) Wiley, John & Sons, Inc.
Friedl, Gunther. Real Options & Investment Incentives. 2010. (ENG., Illus.). xiii, 119p. pap. 109.00 *(978-3-642-08008-1(1),* 3642080081) Springer.
Fu, Jianjing. Capturing the Value of Flexibility in Public Sector Capital Projects. 2011. 112p. pap. *(978-3-8433-9321-8(4))* Lambert Academic Publishing.
Full Committee Hearing on Bonus Depreciation: What It Means for Small Business: Hearing Before the Committee on Small Business, United States House of Representatives, One Hundred Eleventh Congress, Second Session, Hearing Held July 14, 2010. 2010. v, 72p. *(978-0-16-086569-5(7),* 552-070-41567-0) United States Government Printing Office.
Grabowski, Roger J., et al. Cost of Capital , Fourth Edition & Financial Valuation, Third Edition Set. 2011. (ENG.). 310.00 *(978-0-470-93501-9(4),* Wiley) Wiley, John & Sons, Inc.
Grabowski, Roger J., et al. Cost of Capital, Fourth Edition & Financial Valuation, Third Edition Plus Workbooks Set. 2011. (ENG.). 460.00 *(978-0-470-93499-9(9),* Wiley) Wiley, John & Sons, Inc.
Harden, Leland & Heyman, Bob. Marketing by the Numbers: How to Measure & Improve the ROI of Any Campaign, 1 vol. 2010. (ENG., Illus.). 256p. 27.95 *(978-0-8144-1620-4(9))* Amacom.
Hawkins, Daniel. The Struggles over City-Space: Informal Street Vending & Public Space Governance in Medellin, Colombia. 2011. 328p. pap. 71.00 *(978-3-8329-6700-0(1))* Nomos Verlagsgesellschaft DEU. Dist: International Specialized Bk. Services.
Hinz, Richard P., et al, eds. Evaluating the Financial Performance of Pension Funds. 2010. (Directions in Development Ser.). (ENG., Illus.). 296p. pap. 35.00 *(978-0-8213-8159-5(8),* 9780821381595) World Bank Pubns.
Huisman, Kuno J. M. Technology Investment: A Game Theoretic Real Options Approach: A Game Theoretic Real Options Approach. 2010. (Theory & Decision Library C Ser.). 276p. pap. 209.00 *(978-1-4419-4911-0(9),* 1441949119) Springer.
Ilmanen, Antti. Expected Returns: An Investor's Guide to Harvesting Market Rewards. 2011. (Wiley Finance Ser.: 535). (ENG., Illus.). 592p. 75.00 *(978-1-119-99072-7(6),* Wiley) Wiley, John & Sons, Inc.
Im, Yong-Jae & Chon, Song-In. Kiop Chiptan Ui Sunhwan Ch'ulcha: Sijang Kyuyul Kwa Kamdok Kyuyul Ui Yokhal. 2009. (KOR., Illus.). 84p. *(978-89-8063-302-9(5))* KDI.
IT Governance Institute. Enterprise Value: Governance of IT Investments, the Val IT Framework, Version 2. 0. 2008. (Illus.). 118p. per. *(978-1-60420-066-9(9))* Information Systems Audit and Control Assn.
Jones, Russ. Proving Continuous Improvement with Profit Ability. 2008. 46.00 *(978-0-87389-742-6(0))* ASQ Quality Pr.
Jonkhoff, Wouter & Manshanden, Walter, eds. Infrastructure Productivity Evaluation. 2011. (SpringerBriefs in Economics Ser.). (Illus.). viii, 96p. pap. 49.95 *(978-1-4419-8100-4(4),* 1441981004) Springer.
Koirala, Anusha. A Comparative Study of Working Capital Management. 2011. 144p. pap. *(978-3-8454-0229-1(6))* Lambert Academic Publishing.
Külpmann, Mathias. Irrational Exuberance Reconsidered: The Cross Section of Stock Returns. 2nd ed. 2010. (Springer Finance Ser.). (Illus.). xii, 231p. pap. 149.00 *(978-3-642-05726-7(8),* 3642057268) Springer.
Kuraja, Fidan. Investment Appraisal Proposal of a Solid Waste Management Project. 2010. 72p. pap. *(978-3-8383-7793-3(1))* Lambert Academic Publishing.
Kurowski, Lech & Sussman, David. Investment Project Design: A Guide to Financial & Economic Analysis with Constraints. 2011. (Wiley Finance Ser.: 632). (ENG., Illus.). 458p. 85.00 *(978-0-470-91389-5(4),* Wiley) Wiley, John & Sons, Inc.
Larkin, Hoffman, Daly & Lindgren (Firm) Staff, contrib. by. Minnesota's Angel Tax Credit: Small Corporate Offering Registration (SCOR): A "Short Form" Registration Statement. 2011. *(978-1-888404-54-8(X))* Minnesota Dept. of Trade & Economic Development.
Leiderman, Leonardo & Razin, Assaf, eds. Capital Mobility: The Impact on Consumption, Investment & Growth. 2010. (ENG., Illus.). 380p. pap. 42.00 *(978-0-521-14273-1(3))* Cambridge Univ. Pr.
Lerner, Josh, et al. Venture Capital & Private Equity: A Casebook. 4th ed. 2008. (ENG., Illus.). 560p. (C). 149.95 *(978-0-470-22462-5(2),* Wiley) Wiley, John & Sons, Inc.
Lerner, Josh, et al. Venture Capital & Private Equity: A Casebook. 5th ed. 2012. (ENG.). 563p. (C). 158.95 *(978-0-470-65091-2(5),* Wiley) Wiley, John & Sons, Inc.
McCrary, Stuart A. Mastering Corporate Finance Essentials: The Critical Quantitative Methods & Tools in Finance. 2010. (Wiley Finance Ser.: 486). (ENG., Illus.). 174p. 49.95 *(978-0-470-39333-8(5),* Wiley) Wiley, John & Sons, Inc.
Morrison, Rod. The Principles of Project Finance. 2012. 450p. 170.00 *(978-1-4094-3982-0(8),* Gower Publishing Co., Ltd.) Ashgate Publishing, Ltd. GBR. Dist: Ashgate Publishing Co.
O'Byrne, Paul W. TARP in the Crosshairs: Accountability in the Troubled Asset Relief Program. 2009. (Economic Issues, Problems & Perspectives Ser.). (Illus.). 382p. 89.00 *(978-1-60741-807-8(X))* Nova Science Pubs., Inc.
Ohlsson, Gustav. Alpha & the Risk of Failure. 2009. 84p. pap. *(978-3-639-16509-8(8))* VDM Verlag Dr. Mueller e.K.
Organisation For Economic Co-Operation and Development (Oecd). Financing Water & Sanitation: Challenges, Approaches & Tools. 2011. (OECD Co-Publication Ser.). 115p. (C). pap. *(978-1-78040-032-7(2))* IWA Publishing.
Owusu-Manu, De-Graft & Badu, Edward. Capital Structure, Investment Strategy & Financial Decisions. 2011. 340p. pap. *(978-3-8443-1676-6(0))* Lambert Academic Publishing.
Pernick, Ron & Wilder, Clint. The Clean Tech Revolution: Discover the Top Trends, Technologies, & Companies to Watch. 2008. (ENG.). 320p. pap. 15.99 *(978-0-06-089624-9(8),* Collins) HarperCollins Pubs.
Phalippou, Ludovic. Institutional Investors & Equity Markets. 2010. 140p. pap. *(978-3-8383-0440-3(3))* Lambert Academic Publishing.
Phillips, Jack J. & Phillips, Jack. Measuring for Success. 2009. (ENG., Illus.). 296p. pap. 38.95 *(978-1-56286-588-7(9))* American Society for Training & Development.
Phillips, Patricia & Phillips, Jack. The Green Scorecard: Measuring the Return on Investment in Green Initiatives. 2010. (ENG., Illus.). 240p. pap. 29.95 *(978-1-85788-554-5(6))* Ebsco Publishing.
Porras Gonzalez, Eva. The Cost of Capital. 2011. (ENG., Illus.). 250p. 44.00 *(978-0-230-20183-5(0))* Palgrave Macmillan.
Pratt, Shannon P. & Grabowski, Roger J. Cost of Capital. 4th ed. 2010. (ENG., Illus.). 255p. pap., suppl. ed., wbk. ed. 85.00 *(978-0-470-47606-2(0),* Wiley) Wiley, John & Sons, Inc.
—Cost of Capital: Applications & Examples. 4th ed. 2010. (Wiley Finance Ser.: 604). (ENG., Illus.). 754p. 168.00 *(978-0-470-47605-5(2),* Wiley) Wiley, John & Sons, Inc.
—Cost of Capital in Litigation: Applications & Examples. 4th ed. 2010. (ENG., Illus.). 301p. 100.00 *(978-0-470-88094-4(5),* Wiley) Wiley, John & Sons, Inc.
Ralser, Tom & Ralser. ROI for Nonprofits: The New Key to Sustainability. 2009. (ENG.). 176p. pap. 24.95 *(978-0-470-50554-0(0),* Wiley) Wiley, John & Sons, Inc.
Razin, A. & Sadka, Efraim. Foreign Direct Investment. 2007. (ENG., Illus.). 158p. (C). 59.95 *(978-0-691-12706-4(9))* Princeton Univ. Pr.
Read, Tony J. The IT Value Network: From IT Investment to Stakeholder Value. 2009. (ENG., Illus.). 316p. 45.00 *(978-0-470-42279-3(3),* Wiley) Wiley, John & Sons, Inc.
Rechel, B., et al. Investing in Hospitals of the Future. 2009. (Observatory Studies Ser. No. 16 Ser.). (ENG.). 303p. pap. 48.00 *(978-92-890-4304-5(0))* World Health Organization.
Rieger, Stefan. Eigenkapitalersatz in mehrstufigen und mehrfachen Beteiligungsverhältnissen: Ein Beitrag zu den Grundlagen und Grenzen des Eigenkapitalersatzgedankens. 2009. (Schriften zum Wirtschafts- und Medienrecht, Steuerrecht und Zivilprozeßrecht Ser.). (GER.). 154p. 54.95 *(978-3-631-59131-4(4))* Lang, Peter GmbH, Europaischer Verlag der Wissenschaften DEU. Dist: Lang, Peter.
Rienks, Harmen. The Problem of Cooperation & the Savings Based Poverty Trap Model. 2009. 52p. pap. *(978-3-639-18874-5(8))* VDM Verlag Dr. Mueller e.K.
Rogers, Jamie. Strategy, Value & Risk: The Real Options Approach. 2nd ed. 2009. (ENG., Illus.). 208p. 236.00 *(978-0-230-57737-4(7))* Palgrave Macmillan.
Rotzer, Daniel. Momentum Strategies. 2009. 96p. pap. *(978-3-639-20491-9(3))* VDM Verlag Dr. Mueller e.K.
Schniederjans, Marc J. Information Technology Investment: Decision-Making Methodology. 2nd ed. 2010. (Illus.). 468p. 106.00 *(978-981-4262-56-7(1))* World Scientific Publishing Co., Inc.
Shestopaloff, Yuri K. & Shestopaloff, Alexander Yu. Solving the Puzzle of IRR Equation: Choosing the Right Solution to Measure Investment Success. 2011. *(978-0-9813800-9-4(3))* AKVY Pr.
Siegel, Jeremy J. Stocks for the Long Run: The Definitive Guide to Financial Market Returns & Long Term Investment Strategies. 4th rev. ed. 2007. (ENG., Illus.). 436p. 34.95 *(978-0-07-149470-0(7),* 0071494707) McGraw-Hill Cos., The.
Slee, Robert T. Private Capital Markets: Valuation, Capitalization, & Transfer of Private Business Interests. 2nd ed. 2011. (ENG., Illus.). 609p. 95.00 *(978-0-470-92832-5(8),* Wiley) Wiley, John & Sons, Inc.
Soppe, Aloy. Finance As an Instrument to a Sustainable Company. 2008. 192p. pap. *(978-3-639-00913-2(4))* VDM Verlag Dr. Mueller e.K.
Soriano, Jose Lopez. ROI-Based Project Management: From Requirements Management to Value Delivery. 2011. (Advanced & Emerging Communications Technologies Ser.). (ENG., Illus.). 316p. 69.95 *(978-1-4398-4156-3(X),* CRC Press) Taylor & Francis Group GBR. Dist: Taylor & Francis Group.
Tan, Willie. Principles of Project & Infrastructure Finance. 2007. (ENG., Illus.). 296p. (C). 180.00 *(978-0-415-41576-7(4))*; per. 62.95 *(978-0-415-41577-4(2))* Routledge.
Tan, Yinglan. The Way of the VC: Having Top Venture Capitalists on Your Board. 2010. (ENG.). 288p. 39.95 *(978-0-470-82499-3(9),* Wiley) Wiley, John & Sons, Inc.
Thomas, Janice & Mullaly, Mark. Researching the Value of Project Management. 2008. (Illus.). 458p. 49.95 *(978-1-933890-49-4(5))* Project Management Institute.
Titman, Sheridan & Martin, John D. Valuation. 2nd rev. ed. 2010. (ENG.). 552p. (C). 113.33 *(978-0-13-611701-8(5),* Prentice Hall) Prentice Hall PTR.
, Venture Hacks, Venture Hacks. Pitching Hacks: How to pitch startups to Investors. 2009. 86p. pap. 18.99 *(978-0-557-23559-9(6))* Lulu Enterprises Inc.
Weber, Barbara & Alfen, Hans Wilhelm. Infrastructure as an Asset Class: Investment Strategy, Project Finance & PPP. 2010. (Wiley Finance Ser.: 477). (ENG., Illus.). 284p. 75.00 *(978-0-470-68570-9(0),* Wiley) Wiley, John & Sons, Inc.
Wohlfahrt, Uwe. It Investment Evaluation: A Suitability Analysis of Financial Evaluation Measures. 2007. 80p. per. *(978-3-86550-454-8(X))* VDM Verlag Dr. Mueller e.K.
Young, Antony & Aitken, Lucy. Profitable Marketing Communications: A Guide to Marketing Return on Investment. 2007. (ENG.). 212p. 39.95 *(978-0-7494-4942-1(X))* Kogan Page, Ltd. GBR. Dist: Ingram Pub. Services.

CAPITAL INVESTMENTS—MATHEMATICAL MODELS
Back, Kerry. Asset Pricing & Portfolio Choice Theory, 1 vol. 2010. (Financial Management Association Survey & Synthesis Ser.). (ENG., Illus.). 464p. 89.95 *(978-0-19-538061-3(4))* Oxford Univ. Pr., Inc.
Constantinides, George M., et al, eds. Handbook of the Economics of Finance. 2012. (ENG.). Set, Vol 2A,Vol. 2B. (Handbook of the Economics of Finance Ser.: 2A-2B). 2064p. 269.95 *(978-0-444-59416-7(7))* Vol. 2B. (Handbooks in Finance Ser.: 2B). 1032p. 149.95 *(978-0-444-59406-8(X))* Elsevier Science & Technology Bks. (North Holland).
Damodaran, Aswath. Damodaran Valuation Set. 2007. (ENG.). 175.00 *(978-0-470-16839-4(0),* Wiley) Wiley, John & Sons, Inc.
Ghosh, Arvin. Capital Structure & Firm Performance. 2007. (ENG., Illus.). 140p. (gr. 11). 49.95 *(978-1-4128-0710-4(7))* Transaction Pubs.
Lioui, Abraham & Poncet, Patrice. Dynamic Asset Allocation with Forwards & Futures. 2010. (ENG., Illus.). xviii, 256p. pap. 139.00 *(978-1-4419-3689-9(0),* 1441936890) Springer.
Ma, Chenghu. Advanced Asset Pricing Theory. 2011. 816p. 120.00 *(978-1-84816-632-5(X))* Imperial College Pr. GBR. Dist: World Scientific Publishing Co., Inc.
Manos, Ronny. Capital Structure & Dividend Policy. 2008. 228p. pap. *(978-3-639-06162-8(4))* VDM Verlag Dr. Mueller e.K.
Rouah, Fabrice Douglas & Vainberg, Gregory. Option Pricing Models & Volatility Using Excel-VBA. 2007. (Wiley Finance Ser.: 361). (ENG., Illus.). 441p. pap. 100.00 *(978-0-471-79464-6(3),* Wiley) Wiley, John & Sons, Inc.
Semmler, Willi. Asset Prices, Booms & Recessions: Financial Economics from a Dynamic Perspective. 3rd ed. 2011. (ENG., Illus.). xi, 333p. 139.00 *(978-3-642-20679-5(4),* 3642206794) Springer.
Shefrin, Hersh. A Behavioral Approach to Asset Pricing. 2nd ed. 2008. (Academic Press Advanced Finance Ser.). (ENG., Illus.). 618p. 96.95 *(978-0-12-374356-5(7),* Academic Pr.) Elsevier Science & Technology Bks.

CAPITAL INVESTMENTS—INDIA
Rosenstein-Rodan, P. N., ed. Capital Formation & Economic Development. 2011. (ENG.). 176p. 95.00 *(978-0-415-59389-2(1))* Routledge.

CAPITAL LEVY
see also Capital Gains Tax; Property Tax
Aaron, Henry J., et al, eds. Taxing Capital Income. 2007. (ENG., Illus.). 366p. pap. 29.50 *(978-0-87766-737-7(3))* Urban Institute Pr.
Bali, Rifat N. The Varlik Vergisi Affair. 2010. 130.88 *(978-1-61719-124-4(8))* Gorgias Pr., LLC.
Buckley, Michael, ed. Capital Tax Acts 2011: Stamp Duties - Capital Aquisitions Tax - Residential Property Tax. 2011. 1474p. pap. 155.00 *(978-1-84766-691-8(4),* Bloomsbury Professional) Bloomsbury Publishing Plc GBR. Dist: International Specialized Bk. Services.
Buckley, Michael, ed. Capital Tax Acts 2012. 2012. (ENG.). 1240p. pap. 155.00 *(978-1-84766-925-4(5),* Bloomsbury Professional) Bloomsbury Publishing Plc GBR. Dist: International Specialized Bk. Services.
Caldewell, Terrance B., ed. Taxation: 21st Century Issues & Challenges. 2008. 185.00 *(978-1-60456-099-2(1))* Nova Science Pubs., Inc.
Schoutens, Wim & Cariboni, Jessica. Levy Processes in Credit Risk. 2009. (Wiley Finance Ser.: 458). (ENG., Illus.). 200p. 140.00 *(978-0-470-74306-5(9),* Wiley) Wiley, John & Sons, Inc.

CAPITAL MARKET
Ablin, Jack & McGee, Suzanne. Reading Minds & Markets: Minimizing Risk & Maximizing Returns in a Volatile Global Marketplace. 2009. (ENG., Illus.). 224p. 27.99 *(978-0-13-235497-4(7))* FT Press.
Ackert, Lucy & Deaves, Richard. Behavioral Finance: Psychology, Decision-Making, & Markets. 2009. (ENG.). 432p. (C). 165.95 *(978-0-324-66117-0(7))* Cengage South-Western.
Alam, Mohammad Masud. Eu Capital Market Integration. 2010. 72p. pap. *(978-3-639-14873-2(8))* VDM Verlag Dr. Mueller e.K.
Allen, Franklin & Yago, Glenn. Financing the Future: Market-Based Innovations for Growth. 2010. (Wharton School Publishing — Milkin Institute Series on Financial Innovation Ser.). (ENG., Illus.). 256p. 29.99 *(978-0-13-701127-8(X))* Wharton Schl. Publishing.
Alvarez, Marc. Market Data Explained: A Practical Guide to Global Capital Markets Information. 2006. (Elsevier & Mondo Visione World Capital Markets Ser.). (ENG., Illus.). 136p. 66.95 *(978-0-7506-8055-4(5),* Butterworth-Heinemann) Elsevier Science & Technology Bks.
Antelo, Manel & Peon, David. Financial Markets: A Guided Tour. 2011. *(978-1-62100-096-9(6))* Nova Science Pubs., Inc.
Arner, Douglas W., et al, eds. Asia's Debt Capital Markets: Prospects & Strategies for Development. 2010. (Milken Institute Series on Financial Innovation & Economic Growth Ser.). (Illus.). xii, 322p. pap. 209.00 *(978-1-4419-2041-6(2),* 1441920412) Springer.
Asada, Toichiro, et al. Asset Markets, Portfolio Choice & Macroeconomic Activity: A Keynesian Perspective. 2011. (ENG., Illus.). 152p. 100.00 *(978-0-230-29017-4(5))* Palgrave Macmillan.
Aspatore Books Staff, compiled by. Navigating the Subprime Lending Industry: Leading Lawyers on Understanding the Subprime Collapse, the Causes of

C

the Current Lending Climate, & the Industry's Pending Future. 2008. 128p. pap. 150.00 (978-0-314-99175-1(1)) Aspatore Bks.

Atack, Jeremy & Neal, Larry. The Origin & Development of Financial Markets & Institutions: From the Seventeenth Century to the Present. Atack, Jeremy & Neal, Larry, eds. 2009. (ENG., Illus.). 496p. 108.00 (978-0-521-89517-0(0)) Cambridge Univ. Pr.

Atack, Jeremy & Neal, Larry, eds. The Origins & Development of Financial Markets & Institutions: From the Seventeenth Century to the Present. 2010. (ENG.). 496p. pap. 45.00 (978-0-521-15476-5(6)) Cambridge Univ. Pr.

B S, Sumalatha. Indian Mutual Funds in the Liberalized Regime. 2010. 108p. pap. (978-3-639-25375-7(2)) VDM Verlag Dr. Mueller e.K.

Balling, Morten, et al, eds. Corporate Governance, Financial Markets & Global Convergence. 2010. (Financial & Monetary Policy Studies). 372p. pap. 249.00 (978-1-4419-4784-0(1), 1441947841) Springer.

Baums, Theodor & Hutter, Stephan, eds. Gedächtnisschrift für Michael Gruson. 2009.Tr. of In Memory of Michael Gruson. (GER & ENG., Illus.). XII, 484p. 252.00 (978-3-89949-500-3(4)) De Gruyter, Walter Inc.

Belke, Ansgar & Polleit, Thorsten. Monetary Economics in Globalised Financial Markets. 2010. (ENG., Illus.). xiii, 819p. pap. 89.95 (978-3-642-14638-1(4), 3642146384) Springer.

Benning, Joseph F. Trading Stategies for Capital Markets. 2007. (ENG., Illus.). 356p. 79.95 (978-0-07-146496-3(4), 0071464964) McGraw-Hill Cos., The.

Berneburg, Marian. Are European Equity Style Indices Efficient? An Empirical Quest in Three Essays. 2008. 104p. pap. 25.00 (978-3-8329-3855-0(9)) Nomos Verlagsgesellschaft DEU. Dist: International Specialized Bk. Services.

Bernhard, William T. & Leblang, David. Democratic Processes & Financial Markets: Pricing Politics. 2006. (ENG., Illus.). 272p. (C). 80.00 (978-0-521-86122-9(5)); pap. 27.99 (978-0-521-67838-4(2)) Cambridge Univ. Pr.

Blackwell, David W., et al. Modern Financial Markets: Prices, Yields, & Risk Analysis. 2006. (ENG., Illus.). 512p. (C). 194.95 (978-0-470-00010-6(4), Wiley) Wiley, John & Sons, Inc.

Blenman, Lloyd P. Banking & Capital Markets: New International Perspectives. 2010. 400p. 130.00 (978-981-4273-60-2(0)) World Scientific Publishing Co., Inc.

Bookstaber, Richard. A Demon of Our Own Design: Markets, Hedge Funds, & the Perils of Financial Innovation. 2007. (ENG.). 288p. 27.95 (978-0-471-22727-4(7), Wiley) Wiley, John & Sons, Inc.

Borensztein, Eduardo, et al, eds. Bond Markets in Latin America: On the Verge of a Big Bang? 2008. (ENG., Illus.). 320p. (gr. 17). 38.00 (978-0-262-02632-1(5)) MIT Pr.

Brandstätter, Jana. International divergierende demographische Entwicklungen und internationale Kapitalbewegungen. 2008. (Schriften zur Wirtschaftstheorie und Wirtschaftspolitik Ser.). 150p. pap. 49.95 (978-3-631-57906-0(3)) Lang, Peter GmbH, Europaischer Verlag der Wissenschaften DEU. Dist: Lang, Peter.

Brown, Brendan. Bubbles in Credit & Currency: How Hot Markets Cool Down. 2008. (ENG.). 240p. 100.00 (978-0-230-55132-9(7)) Palgrave Macmillan.

Buch, Claudia M. Globalization of Financial Markets: Causes of Incomplete Integration & Consequences for Economic Policy. 2010. (Kieler Studien - Kiel Studies). (Illus.). xv, 249p. pap. 149.00 (978-3-642-07368-7(9), 3642073689) Springer.

Burton, Maureen, et al. An Introduction to Financial Markets & Institutions. 2nd rev. ed. 2009. (ENG., Illus.). 718p. (C). pap. 114.95 (978-0-7656-2276-1(9)) Sharpe, M.E. Inc.

Busby, Thomas L. The Markets Never Sleep: Global Insights for More Consistent Trading. 2007. (Wiley Trading Ser.: 284). (ENG., Illus.). 256p. 60.00 (978-0-470-04946-4(4), Wiley) Wiley, John & Sons, Inc.

Calomiris, Charles W., ed. China's Financial Transition at a Crossroads. 2007. (ENG., Illus.). 432p. (gr. 17). 45.00 (978-0-231-14192-5(0)) Columbia Univ. Pr.

Capital Markets Regulatory Reform: Strengthening Investor Protection, Enhancing Oversight of Private Pools of Capital, & Creating a National Insurance Office: Hearing Before the Committee on Financial Services, U.S. House of Representatives, One Hundred Eleventh Congress, First Session, October 6, 2009. 2010. iv, 319p. (978-0-16-085795-9(3), 552-070-41012-1) United States Government Printing Office.

Casson, Mark. Markets & Market Institutions: Their Origin & Evolution. 2011. (International Library of Critical Writings in Economics Ser.). (Illus.). 768p. 415.00 (978-1-84980-389-2(7)) Elgar, Edward Publishing, Inc.

Cecchetti, Stephen G. Money, Banking, & Financial Markets. 2nd ed. 2007. (ENG., Illus.). 672p. (C). 192.67 (978-0-07-352309-5(7), 0073523097, McGraw-Hill/Irwin) McGraw-Hill Higher Education.

Cecchetti, Stephen G. & Schoenholtz, Kermit L. Money, Banking & Financial Markets. 3rd ed. 2010. (ENG., Illus.). 704p. (C). 192.67 (978-0-07-337590-8(X), 007337590X, McGraw-Hill/Irwin) McGraw-Hill Higher Education.

Cernic, Christian. Finance & Physics. 2010. 128p. pap. (978-3-639-23483-1(9)) VDM Verlag Dr. Mueller e.K.

Cetorelli, Nicola. Trends in Financial Market Concentration & Their Implications for Market Stability: A Reprint from Economic Policy Review. 2007. (Illus.). 19p. (C). pap. 15.00 (978-1-4223-1528-6(2)) DIANE Publishing Co.

Chakrabarti, Debkumar. Investment Behavior of Firms. 2008. 160p. pap. (978-3-639-04508-6(4)) VDM Verlag Dr. Mueller e.K.

Chakrabarti, Rajesh & De, Sankar. Capital Markets in India. 2010. (Response Bks.). (Illus.). 420p. (C). pap. 34.95 (978-81-321-0500-8(1), B05008P) SAGE Pubns., Inc.

Chiu, Iris. Regulatory Convergence in EU Securities Regulation. 2008. xxv, 323p. (978-90-411-2668-9(6)) Kluwer Law International.

Choudhry, Moorad. An Introduction to Bond Markets. 4th ed. 2010. (Wiley Finance Ser.: 16). (ENG., Illus.). 472p. pap. 60.00 (978-0-470-68724-6(X), Wiley) Wiley, John & Sons, Inc.

Choudhry, Moorad, et al. Capital Market Instruments: Analysis & Valuation. 3rd rev. ed. 2010. (ENG., Illus.). 576p. 105.00 (978-0-230-57603-2(6)) Palgrave Macmillan.

Christy, Ralph D. & Bogan, Vicki L. Financial Inclusion, Innovation, & Investments: Biotechnology & Capital Markets Working for the Poor. 2011. (Illus.). 300p. 88.00 (978-981-4329-93-4(2)) World Scientific Publishing Co., Inc.

Coleman, Thomas S. Quantitative Risk Measurement: A Practical Guide to Financial Risk. 2012. (Wiley Finance Ser.: 669). (ENG.). 576p. 95.00 (978-1-118-02658-8(6), Wiley) Wiley, John & Sons, Inc.

Colussi, Marc. Kapitalmarktstrafrecht - Insiderhandel und Marktmanipulation: Einführung, Analyse, Ausblick. 2010. (GER.). 166p. 57.95 (978-3-631-61204-0(4)) Lang, Peter GmbH, Europaischer Verlag der Wissenschaften DEU. Dist: Lang, Peter.

Conti, Vittorio & Hamaui, Rony, eds. Financial Markets Liberalisation & the Role of Banks. 2009. (ENG., Illus.). 400p. pap. 42.00 (978-0-521-11190-4(0)) Cambridge Univ. Pr.

Corcoran, Clive M. Long/Short Market Dynamics: Trading Strategies for Today's Markets. 2007. (Wiley Trading Ser.: 327). (ENG., Illus.). 358p. 80.00 (978-0-470-05728-5(9), Wiley) Wiley, John & Sons, Inc.

Corcoran, Kevin P. Junior mining Investor: 14 natural resource experts show you how to invest profitably in emerging gold, silver, platinum, base metals, & uranium mining & exploration Stocks. 2007. (Illus.). 202p. pap. 22.95 (978-0-9795335-0-1(3)) Corcoran, Kevin.

Cram101 Textbook Reviews. Outlines & Highlights for Money, Banking, & Financial Markets by Stephen Cecchetti. 2011. 272p. pap. 32.95 (978-1-4672-6627-7(2)) Cram101 Inc.

Cram101 Textbook Reviews & Cram101 Textbook Reviews. Outlines & Highlights for the Statistical Mechanics of Financial Markets by Johannes Voit. 2011. 144p. pap. 28.95 (978-1-61830-285-4(X)) Cram101 Inc.

Cram101 Textbook Reviews Staff. Outlines & Highlights for Capital Markets: Institutions & Instruments by Frank J Fabozzi, Franco Modigliani, ISBN. 2009. 186p. pap. 30.95 (978-1-4288-3281-7(5)) Cram101 Inc.

—Outlines & Highlights for Capital Markets by Mcinish, Isbn: 0631211608. 2009. 66p. pap. 27.95 (978-1-4288-3940-3(2)) Cram101 Inc.

—Outlines & Highlights for Financial Markets & Institutions by Jeff Madura, Isbn: 9780324568226. 2009. 308p. pap. 32.95 (978-1-4288-3257-2(2)) Cram101 Inc.

—Outlines & Highlights for Global Business Today by Hill, Isbn: 9780073210544. 2008. 316p. pap. 16.95 (978-1-4288-6423-8(7)) Cram101 Inc.

—Outlines & Highlights for Money & Capital Markets by Rose & Marquis, Isbn: 9780077235802. 2009. 136p. pap. 28.95 (978-1-4288-3827-7(9)) Cram101 Inc.

—Outlines & Highlights for Money & Capital Markets by Rose, Isbn: 9780077235802. 2009. 270p. pap. 32.95 (978-1-4288-6854-0(2)) Cram101 Inc.

—Outlines & Highlights for Money, Banking & Financial Markets by Stephen G Cecchetti, Isbn: 9780073523095. 2009. 238p. pap. 31.95 (978-1-4288-2511-6(8)); 178p. pap. 29.95 (978-1-4288-8947-7(7)) Cram101 Inc.

Cunningham, W. H. (Hank) & Cunningham, W. H. In Your Best Interest: The Ultimate Guide to the Canadian Bond Market. 2nd ed. 2008. Orig. Title: English. (ENG., Illus.). 224p. pap. 26.99 (978-1-55002-876-8(6)) Dundurn CAN. Dist: Ingram Pub. Services.

DACOSTA, LEWIS NIGEL. Mar Ris Man a Prac Gui Wit Ex. 2008. 79.95 (978-1-58488-464-4(9), Chapman & Hall/CRC) CRC Pr. LLC.

Dark Pools, Flash Orders, High-Frequency Trading, & Other Market Structure Issues: Hearing Before the Subcommittee on Securities, Insurance, & Investment of the Committee on Banking, Housing, & Urban Affairs, United States Senate, One Hundred Eleventh Congress, First Session, on Examining the Dark Pools, Flash Orders, High-Frequency Trading, & Other Market Structure Issues, October 28, 2009. 2010. (Illus.). iii, 108p. (978-0-16-086212-0(4), 552-070-41310-3) United States Government Printing Office.

Dash, Atish Kumar. Impact of Financial Liberalisation on Efficiency in Capital Allocation. 2010. 144p. pap. (978-3-639-24080-1(4)) VDM Verlag Dr. Mueller e.K.

Davidson, Alexander. How the Global Financial Markets Really Work: The Definitive Guide to Understanding International Investment & Money Flows. 2009. (ENG., Illus.). 304p. pap. 29.95 (978-0-7494-5393-0(1)) Kogan Page, Ltd. GBR. Dist: Ingram Pub. Services.

Davis, Gerald F. Managed by the Markets: How Finance Re-Shaped America. 2011. (ENG.). 336p. pap. 21.95 (978-0-19-969192-0(4)) Oxford Univ. Pr., Inc.

De Farias Neto, João José. S-Shaped Utility Functions & the Puzzles of the Financial Market. 2010. 112p. pap. (978-3-8383-8316-3(8)) Lambert Academic Publishing.

de Jong, Frank & Rindi, Barbara. The Microstructure of Financial Markets. 2009. (ENG., Illus.). 210p. 95.00 (978-0-521-86784-9(3)); 208p. pap. 42.00 (978-0-521-68727-0(6)) Cambridge Univ. Pr.

De La Torre, Augusto & Schmukler, Sergio L. Emerging Capital Markets & Globalization: The Latin American Experience. 2006. (Latin American Development Forum Ser.). (ENG., Illus.). 220p. per. 35.00 (978-0-8213-6543-4(6)) World Bank Pubns.

De Soto, Jesùs Huerta. The Theory of Dynamic Efficiency. 2008. (Routledge Foundations of the Market Economy Ser.). (Illus.). 288p. 140.00 (978-0-415-42769-2(X)) Routledge.

Dietrich, Benjamin H. German Banking Structure, Pricing & Competition: Implications & International Policy Perspectives. 2009. 246p. 72.95 (978-3-631-59022-5(0)) Lang, Peter GmbH, Europaischer Verlag der Wissenschaften DEU. Dist: Lang, Peter.

Dowd, Kevin K. & Hutchinson, Martin. The Alchemists of Loss: How Modern Finance & Government Intervention Crashed the Financial System. 2010. (ENG., Illus.). 432p. 27.95 (978-0-470-68915-8(3), Wiley) Wiley, John & Sons, Inc.

Durr, Jochen. Active Credit Portfolio Management - Bringing the Capital Market Perspective Into Bank Lending: A Practitioners' View. 2007. XXIV, 429p. pap. 89.95 (978-3-631-56935-1(1)) Lang, Peter Publishing, Inc.

Engel, Eduardo, et al, eds. Economia Spring 2008. 2008. (ENG.). 250p. pap. 36.00 (978-0-8157-2088-1(2)) Brookings Institution Pr.

Fabozzi, Frank J. Capital Markets: Institutions & Instruments. 4th ed. 2008. (ENG.). 696p. (C). pap. 166.67 (978-0-13-602602-0(8), Prentice Hall) Prentice Hall PTR.

Farmer, Roger E. A. Expectations, Employment & Prices. 2010. (ENG., Illus.). 192p. 39.95 (978-0-19-539790-1(8)) Oxford Univ. Pr., Inc.

Fatemi, Khosrow & Salvatore, Dominick, eds. Foreign Exchange Issues, Capital Markets & International Banking in the 1990s (RLE Banking & Finance), Volume 13. 2012. (ENG.). 296p. 115.00 (978-0-415-53880-0(7)) Routledge.

Fater, David H. Essentials of Corporate & Capital Formation. 2010. (Essentials Ser.: 59). (ENG., Illus.). 352p. pap. 39.95 (978-0-470-49656-5(8), Wiley) Wiley, John & Sons, Inc.

Feng, Liling. Saving, Growth & Financial Market Imperfections in Transitional Chin. 2007. 112p. per. (978-3-8364-2992-4(6)) VDM Verlag Dr. Mueller e.K.

Fischer, Veronika. The Sec & Bafin. 2008. 236p. pap. (978-3-8381-0080-7(8)) VDM Verlag Dr. Mueller e.K.

Folkerts-Landau, David. International Capital Markets. 279p. 20.00 (978-1-55775-686-2(4)) International Monetary Fund.

Fontana, Giuseppe, et al, eds. Macroeconomics, Finance & Money: Essays in Honour of Philip Arestis. 2010. (ENG., Illus.). 368p. 126.00 (978-0-230-22906-8(9)) Palgrave Macmillan.

Forbes, Inc. Staff & Groz, Marc M. Forbes Guide to the Markets: Becoming a Savvy Investor. 2nd ed. 2009. (ENG., Illus.). 312p. pap. 22.95 (978-0-470-46338-3(4), Wiley) Wiley, John & Sons, Inc.

French, K. R., et al. The Squam Lake Report: Fixing the Financial System. 2010. (ENG., Illus.). 168p. 19.95 (978-0-691-14884-7(8)) Princeton Univ. Pr.

Garcia, Márcio Gomes Pinto. Financial Markets Volatility & Performance in Emerging Markets. Edwards, Sebastian, ed. 2008. (National Bureau of Economic Research Conference Report). (Illus.). 304p. 75.00 (978-0-226-18495-1(1)) Univ. of Chicago Pr.

Ghosh, Dipasri. Capital Markets & Financial Assets. 2010. 100p. pap. (978-3-8383-4238-2(0)) Lambert Academic Publishing.

Goldberg, Steven H. & Goldberg. Billions of Drops in Millions of Buckets: Why Philanthropy Doesn't Advance Social Progress. 2009. (ENG., Illus.). 302p. 39.95 (978-0-470-45467-1(9), Wiley) Wiley, John & Sons, Inc.

Goldmann, Peter. Fraud in the Markets: Why It Happens & How to Fight It. 2010. (ENG., Illus.). 272p. 39.95 (978-0-470-50789-6(6), Wiley) Wiley, John & Sons, Inc.

Grabowski, Roger J., et al. Cost of Capital , Fourth Edition & Financial Valuation, Third Edition Set. 2011. (ENG.). 310.00 (978-0-470-93501-9(4), Wiley) Wiley, John & Sons, Inc.

Gregoriou, Greg N., et al. The Risk Modeling Evaluation Handbook: Rethinking Financial Risk Management Methodologies in the Global Capital Markets. 2010. (ENG., Illus.). 528p. 95.00 (978-0-07-166370-0(3), 0071663703) McGraw-Hill Cos., The.

Gup, Benton E. Capital Markets, Globalization, & Economic Development. 2010. (Innovations in Financial Markets & Institutions Ser.). xvi, 224p. pap. 229.00 (978-1-4419-3752-0(8), 1441937528) Springer.

Gupta, Saloni. Efficiency of Indian Stock Market. 2010. 252p. pap. (978-3-639-25736-6(7)) VDM Verlag Dr. Mueller e.K.

Hall, Rodney Bruce. Central Banking As Global Governance: Constructing Financial Credibility. 2008. (Cambridge Studies in International Relations). (ENG., Illus.). 278p. 90.00 (978-0-521-89861-4(7)); pap. 36.00 (978-0-521-72721-1(9)) Cambridge Univ. Pr.

Hammen, Horst. BöRsen und Multilaterale Handelssysteme Im Wettbewerb: Eine Wirtschaftsrechtliche Analyse. 2011. (Börsen- und kapitalmarktrechtliche Abhandlungen Ser.). (GER.). 134p. 43.95 (978-3-631-61497-6(7)) Lang, Peter GmbH, Europaischer Verlag der Wissenschaften DEU. Dist: Lang, Peter.

Haugen, Robert A. New Finance. 3rd ed. 2006. pap. 8.95 (978-1-4288-1207-9(5)) Cram101 Inc.

Haugen, Robert A. & HAUGEN, Robert A. The New Finance. 4th ed. 2009. (ENG., Illus.). 160p. (C). pap. 66.67 (978-0-13-603604-3(X), Prentice Hall) Prentice Hall PTR.

Heigl, Andreas. Option Pricing by Means of Genetic Programming. 2008. 68p. pap. (978-3-8364-8520-3(6)) VDM Verlag Dr. Mueller e.K.

Hendy, Ayman. The Impact of Financial Liberalisation on Portfolio Shifts. 2010. 368p. pap. (978-3-639-18264-4(2)) VDM Verlag Dr. Mueller e.K.

Hens, Thorsten & Pilgrim, Beate. General Equilibrium Foundations of Finance: Structure of Incomplete Markets Models. 2010. (Theory & Decision Library C Ser.). 335p. pap. 209.00 (978-1-4419-5333-9(7), 1441953337) Springer.

Hens, Thorsten & Schenk-Hoppé, Klaus Reiner. Handbook of Financial Markets: Dynamics & Evolution. Hens, Thorsten, IV & Schenk-Hoppe, Klaus Reiner, eds. 2009. (Handbooks in Finance Ser.). (ENG., Illus.). 608p. 155.00 (978-0-12-374258-2(7), North Holland) Elsevier Science & Technology Bks.

Hill, Charles W. L. Global Business Today. 3rd ed. 2006. pap. 16.95 (978-1-4288-1212-3(1)) Cram101 Inc.

—Global Business Today. 7th ed. 2010. (ENG., Illus.). 656p. (C). pap. 158.33 (978-0-07-813721-1(7), 0078137217, McGraw-Hill/Irwin) McGraw-Hill Higher Education.

Hillman, Richard J. Financial Market Regulation: Agencies Engaged in Consolidated Supervision Can Strengthen Performance Measurement & Collaboration. 2007. (Illus.). 80p. (C). pap. 25.00 (978-1-4223-1575-0(4)) DIANE Publishing Co.

Ho, Y. K., et al. Asian Pacific Financial Markets. (978-0-409-99591-6(6), MICHIE) LEXIS Publishing.

Hoffman, Philip T., et al. Surviving Large Losses: Financial Crises, the Middle Class, & the Development of Capital Markets. 2009. (Illus.). 272p. pap. 19.00 (978-0-674-03636-9(0), Belknap Pr.) Harvard Univ. Pr.

Horvath, James L. Valuing a Business in Volatile Markets. 2010. (Illus.). x, 835p. (978-0-7798-2286-7(2)) Carswell.

Hubbert, Simon. Essential Mathematics for Market Risk Management. 2nd ed. 2012. (Wiley Finance Ser.). (ENG., Illus.). 350p. 65.00 (978-1-119-97952-4(8), Wiley) Wiley, John & Sons, Inc.

International Monetary Fund. Global Financial Stability Report, October 2008. 2008. (World Economic & Financial Surveys Ser.). (Illus.). 244p. pap. (978-1-58906-757-8(6)) International Monetary Fund.

International Monetary Fund Staff. Integrating Europe's financial Markets. Decressin, Jèrg et al, eds. 2007. (Illus.). 279p. pap. (978-1-58906-623-6(5)) International Monetary Fund.

Irle, Ben M. & Irle, Ben. Convergence of Communications: Implications for Regulating Market Entry. 2009. 393p. pap. 86.00 (978-3-8329-3688-4(2)) Nomos Verlagsgesellschaft DEU. Dist: International Specialized Bk. Services.

Iyengar, Murali. Money Matters: Macroeconomics & Financial Markets. 2011. (Response Bks.). (Illus.). 240p. (C). pap. 30.00 (978-81-321-0532-9(X), B05329P) SAGE Pubns., Inc.

Jankovic, Edward M. Relationships among Country Risk, Investor Expectations, & Financial Variables in Central Europe: A Study of Transitioning Economies. 2010. (Illus.). v, 223p. 109.95 (978-0-7734-1306-1(5)) Mellen, Edwin Pr., The.

Jüngling, Roman. Polnisches Börsen- und Kapitalmarktrecht: Interessenkonflikte bei der Selbstnotierung der Warschauer Börse. 2010. (Börsen- und kapitalmarktrechtliche Abhandlungen Ser.). (GER.). 308p. 83.95 (978-3-631-59894-8(7)) Lang, Peter GmbH, Europaischer Verlag der Wissenschaften DEU. Dist: Lang, Peter.

Kanuk, Alan R. Capital Markets of India: An Investor's Guide. 2007. (Wiley Finance Ser.: 409). (ENG., Illus.). 404p. 85.00 (978-0-470-13763-5(0), Wiley) Wiley, John & Sons, Inc.

Karsai, Judit. Private Equity in Cee. 2010. 68p. pap. (978-3-639-22247-0(4)) VDM Verlag Dr. Mueller e.K.

Karst, Bjö. Das Marktmanipulationsverbot Gem. § 20a Wphg: Unter Besonderer Berücksichtigung der Safe-Harbor -Regelung. 2011. (Schriften zum Gesellschafts-, Bilanz- und Unternehmensteuerrecht Ser.). (GER.). 259p. 76.95 (978-3-631-61839-4(5)) Lang, Peter GmbH, Europaischer Verlag der Wissenschaften DEU. Dist: Lang, Peter.

Kaufman, George G., et al, eds. New Perspectives on Asset Price Bubbles: Theory, Evidence, & Policy, 1 vol. 2012. (ENG., Illus.). 464p. pap. 49.95 (978-0-19-984440-1(2)) Oxford Univ. Pr., Inc.

Kemp, Malcolm. Market Consistency: Model Calibration in Imperfect Markets. 2009. (Wiley Finance Ser.). (ENG., Illus.). 376p. 80.00 (978-0-470-77088-7(0), Wiley) Wiley, John & Sons, Inc.

Kettell, Brian. Islamic Capital Markets. 2009. (ENG., Illus.). 296p. pap. 90.00 (978-0-9558351-1-7(9)) Harriman Hse. Publishing GBR. Dist: Ingram Pub. Services.

King, Mervyn J. Back Office & Operational Risk: Sources, Symptoms & Cures. 3rd ed. 2010. (Illus.). 280p. pap. 89.99 (978-1-906659-36-3(2)) Harriman Hse. Publishing GBR. Dist: Ingram Pub. Services.

Klewes, Joachim & Wreschniok, Robert, eds. Reputation Capital: Building & Maintaining Trust in the 21st Century. 2009. (ENG., Illus.). xii, 408p. 59.95 (978-3-642-01629-5(4), 3642016294) Springer.

Kostolany, André. Weisheit eines Spekulanten. (GER.). 207p. pap. (978-3-612-26610-1(1)) Econ-Verlag GmbH DEU. Dist: International Bk. Import Service, Inc.

Kotz, Sabine. Disclosure in Financial Markets. 2008. 136p. pap. (978-3-8364-9637-7(2)) VDM Verlag Dr. Mueller e.K.

Kurosawa, Yoshitaka. Capital Market & Rating Agencies in Asia: Structuring a Credit Risk Rating Model. 2012. (978-1-61942-121-9(6)) Nova Science Pubs., Inc.

Kürsten, Wolfgang & Nietert, Bernhard, eds. Kapitalmarkt, Unternehmensfinanzierung und rationale Entscheidungen: Festschrift für Jochen Wilhelm. (GER., Illus.). XVI, 574p. 159.00 (978-3-540-27691-3(2), 3540276912) Springer.

Kutlina-Dimitrova, Zornitsa. Finanzmarktentwicklung und Wirtschaftswachstum in den mittel- und osteuropäischen EU-Mitgliedstaaten. 2009. (Europäische Hochschulschriften. Reihe 5: Volks- und Betriebswirtschaft Ser.). (GER.). 208p. pap. 61.95 (978-3-631-59310-3(4)) Lang, Peter GmbH, Europaischer Verlag der Wissenschaften DEU. Dist: Lang, Peter.

Kuznetsov, Alex. The Complete Guide to Capital Markets for Quantitative Professionals. 2006. (McGraw-Hill Library of Investment & Finance Ser.). (ENG., Illus.). 600p. 75.00 (978-0-07-146829-9(3), 007146829X) McGraw-Hill Cos., The.

Kyprianou, Hollington & Adams & Smith: Auctioneers of late-Capitalist Artefacts. 2009. 36p. pap. 18.95 (978-1-4452-0829-9(6)) Lulu Enterprises Inc.

Lanshe, James C., et al. International Capital Markets & Securities Regulation. 2007. (978-1-59460-079-1(1)) Carolina Academic Pr.

Larimore, Taylor, et al. The Bogleheads' Guide to Investing. 2007. (ENG., Illus.). 336p. per. 18.95 (978-0-470-06736-9(5), Wiley) Wiley, John & Sons, Inc.

Lazar, Daniel & G, Saravanan. Fii Investment in Indi. 2010. 104p. pap. (978-3-639-28206-1(X)) VDM Verlag Dr. Mueller e.K.

Lee, Kang-Kook. Capital Account Liberalization & Economic Growth: New Measures, New Estimates & the Experience of South Korea. 2008. 208p. pap. (978-3-639-05660-0(4)) VDM Verlag Dr. Mueller e.K.

Lees, Francis A. Financial Exchanges: A Comparative Approach. 2011. (ENG., Illus.). 320p. (C). 165.00 (978-0-415-89243-8(0)); pap. 69.95 (978-0-415-89244-5(9)) Routledge.

Legislative Proposals to Create a Covered Bond Market in the United States: Hearing Before the Subcommittee on Capital Markets & Government Sponsored Enterprises of the Committee on Financial Services, U.S. House of Representatives, One Hundred Twelfth Congress, First Session, March 11, 2011. 2011. (Illus.). v, 146p. **(978-0-16-089010-9(1)**, 552-070-43042-3) United States Government Printing Office.

Legislative Proposals to Promote Job Creation, Capital Formation, & Market Certainty: Hearing Before the Subcommittee on Capital Markets & Government Sponsored Enterprises of the Committee on Financial Services, U.S. House of Representatives, One Hundred Twelfth Congress, First Session, March 16, 2011. 2011. (Illus.). v, 141p. **(978-0-16-089094-9(2)**, 552-070-43117-9) United States Government Printing Office.

Leinweber, David J. Nerds on Wall Street: Math, Machines & Wired Markets. 2009. (ENG., Illus.). 353p. 39.95 (978-0-471-36946-2(2), Wiley) Wiley, John & Sons, Inc.

Levine, Robert. How to Make Money with Junk Bonds. 2012. (ENG., Illus.). 192p. 22.00 **(978-0-07-179381-0(X)**, 007179381X) McGraw-Hill Cos., The.

Lima, Emanoel Marcos. Disclosure in Philantropic Institutions of Higher Education in Brazil. 2010. 136p. pap. (978-3-639-27760-9(0)) VDM Verlag Dr. Mueller e.K.

Loretz, Michael W. The Stock Market in a Deterministic Overlapping Generations Model. 2010. 136p. pap. (978-3-639-24287-4(4)) VDM Verlag Dr. Mueller e.K.

Lu, Hai. Information Diffusion & the Boundary of Market Efficiency - Theory & Empirical Evidence. 2008. 128p. pap. (978-3-639-04451-5(7)) VDM Verlag Dr. Mueller e.K.

MacKenzie, Donald. An Engine, Not a Camera: How Financial Models Shape Markets. 2008. (Inside Technology Ser.). (ENG., Illus.). 392p. (gr. 17). pap. 25.00 (978-0-262-63367-3(1)) MIT Pr.

Madura, Jeff. Financial Markets & Institutions. 8th rev. ed. 2007. (ENG., Illus.). 800p. (C). 243.95 (978-0-324-56821-9(5)) Cengage South-Western.

—Financial Markets & Institutions, Abridged Edition (Book Only) 8th ed. 2008. (ENG.). 576p. (C). pap. 167.95 (978-0-324-59359-4(7)) Cengage South-Western.

—Financial Markets & Institutions, Abridged Edition (with Stock-Trak Coupon) 9th ed. 2010. (ENG.). 480p. (C). pap. 186.95 (978-0-538-48249-3(4)) Cengage South-Western.

Magill, Michael & Quinzii, Martine, eds. Incomplete Markets, 2 vols. 2008. (International Library of Critical Writings in Economics Ser.). (Illus.). 1176p. 560.00 (978-1-84542-862-4(5)) Elgar, Edward Publishing, Inc.

Mahlknecht, Michael & Hassan, Kabir. Islamic Capital Markets: Products & Strategies. 2011. (Wiley Finance Ser.: 558). (ENG., Illus.). 480p. 75.00 (978-0-470-68957-8(9), Wiley) Wiley, John & Sons, Inc.

Malhotra, Rajeev, ed. A Critical Decade: Policies for India's Development. 2012. (ENG.). 336p. 40.00 **(978-0-19-808013-8(1))** Oxford Univ. Pr., Inc.

Malik, Malieka Farah Deeba. Convergence of Ifrs & Us Gaap. 2011. 72p. pap. **(978-3-8433-8860-3(1))** Lambert Academic Publishing.

Markarian, Garen. Analyst Forecasts, Earnings Management, & Insider Trading Patterns - Incidence & Performance Consequences. 2008. 164p. pap. (978-3-8364-7395-8(X)) VDM Verlag Dr. Mueller e.K.

Markusen, Ann R. Reining in the Competition for Capital. 2007. (Illus.). 225p. 40.00 (978-0-88099-296-1(4)); pap. 18.00 (978-0-88099-295-4(6)) Upjohn, W.E. Institute for Employment Research.

Martinez, Mark A. The Myth of the Free Market: The Role of the State in a Capitalist Economy. 2009. (Illus.). 336p. pap. 24.95 (978-1-56549-267-7(6)) Stylus Publishing, LLC.

McInish, Thomas H. Capital Markets. 2006. pap. 14.95 (978-1-4288-1079-2(X)) Cram101 Inc.

McTague, Jim. Crapshoot Investing: How Tech-Savvy Traders & Clueless Regulators Turned the Stock Market into a Casino. rev. ed. 2011. (ENG., Illus.). 256p. 26.99 (978-0-13-259968-9(6)) FT Press.

Mierzejewski, Fernando. Preference for Liquidity in Markets with Borrowing Restrictions. 2010. 116p. pap. (978-3-8383-4753-0(6)) Lambert Academic Publishing.

Mobius, Mark. Bonds: An Introduction to the Core Concepts. 2012. (Mark Mobius Masterclass Ser.: 1). (ENG.). 250p. 34.95 (978-0-470-82147-3(7), Wiley) Wiley, John & Sons, Inc.

Molyneux, Philip, et al, eds. New Issues in Financial & Credit Markets. 2010. (Palgrave Macmillan Studies in Banking & Financial Institutions Ser.). (ENG., Illus.). 240p. 105.00 (978-0-230-27544-7(3)) Palgrave Macmillan.

Montagu, Gerald & Paul, Colin. Banking & Capital Markets Companion. 5th rev. ed. 2011. (ENG., Illus.). 632p. pap. 95.00 (978-1-84766-308-5(7), Bloomsbury Professional) Bloomsbury Publishing Plc GBR. Dist: International Specialized Bk. Services.

Morris, Charles R. The Trillion Dollar Meltdown Intl. Ed: Easy Money, High Rollers, & the Great Credit Crash. 2008. 224p. pap. 13.95 (978-1-58648-750-8(7)) PublicAffairs.

—The Two Trillion Dollar Meltdown: Easy Money, High Rollers, & the Great Credit Crash. 2009. (ENG., Illus.). 240p. pap. 13.95 (978-1-58648-691-4(8)) PublicAffairs.

Mügge, Daniel. Widen the Market, Narrow the Competition: Banker Interests & the Making of a European Capital Market. 2011. (ECPR Monographs Ser.). (ENG., Illus.). 190p. (gr. 17). pap. 40.00 (978-1-907301-08-7(9)) European Consortium for Political Research GBR. Dist: Columbia Univ. Pr.

Naas, Benjamin & Lysne, Joachim, eds. Financial Markets & the Global Recession. 2010. (Global Recession - Causes, Impacts & Remedies Ser.). 276p. 115.00 (978-1-60741-921-1(1)) Nova Science Pubs., Inc.

Nakku, Victoria Brenda. Capital Market Development & Market Efficiency. 2011. 92p. pap. **(978-3-8433-9080-4(0))** Lambert Academic Publishing.

Nathan, Raj, et al. The New Data Imperative: Managing Real-Time Risk in Capital Markets. 2009. (ENG., Illus.). 128p. 21.95 (978-1-935212-03-4(6)) Easton Studio Pr., LLC.

Nelken, Izzy. Volatility as an Asset Class: A guide to buying, selling & trading third generation volatility Products. 2007. (Illus.). 300p. (978-1-904339-71-7(9)) Risk Bks.

Nelson, Paul. Capital Markets Law & Compliance: The Implications of MiFID. 2008. (Law Practitioner Ser.). (ENG., Illus.). 482p. 165.00 (978-0-521-88936-0(7)) Cambridge Univ. Pr.

Noël, Michel, et al. Development of Capital Markets & Institutional Investors in Russia: Recent Achievements & Policy Challenges Ahead. 2006. (World Bank Working Papers: 87). (ENG., Illus.). 152p. pap. 25.00 (978-0-8213-6794-0(3), 9780821367940) World Bank Pubns.

O'Brien, Gregory & O'Brien, Justin. Private Equity, Corporate Governance & the Dynamics of Capital Market Regulation. 2007. (C). 124.00 (978-1-86094-847-3(2)) Imperial College Pr. GBR. Dist: World Scientific Publishing Co., Inc.

O'Brien, Justin. Engineering a Financial Bloodbath: How Sub-Prime Securitization Destroyed the Legitimacy of Financial Capitalism. 2009. 212p. 38.00 (978-1-84816-216-7(2)) Imperial College Pr. GBR. Dist: World Scientific Publishing Co., Inc.

Organisation for Economic Co-Operation and Development. National Accounts of Oecd Countries: Financial Accounts 2010. 2011. (Illus.). 313p. pap. **(978-92-64-09889-3(5))** Organization for Economic Cooperation & Development.

Ornelas, Jose Renato Haas. Behavior of Equity Foreign Investors on Emerging Markets. 2011. 84p. pap. **(978-3-8443-1382-6(6))** Lambert Academic Publishing.

Ourousoff, Alexandra. Wall Street at War: The Secret Struggle for the Global Economy. 2010. (ENG.). 240p. 49.95 (978-0-7456-4417-2(1)); pap. 14.95 (978-0-7456-4418-9(X)) Polity Pr. GBR. Dist: Wiley, John & Sons, Inc.

Oxley, Lawrence J. Extreme Weather & Financial Markets: Opportunities in Commodities & Futures. 2012. (Wiley Trading Ser.: 538). (ENG., Illus.). 210p. 60.00 **(978-1-118-14721-4(9)**, Wiley) Wiley, John & Sons, Inc.

Patibandla, Murali. Evolution of Markets & Institutions: A Study of an Emerging Economy. 2009. 364p. pap. 44.95 (978-0-415-49403-8(6)) Routledge.

Phalippou, Ludovic. Institutional Investors & Equity Markets. 2010. 140p. pap. (978-3-8383-0440-3(3)) Lambert Academic Publishing.

Pischke, J. D. von, ed. Mobilising Capital for the Poor: What Can Structured Finance Contribute? 2010. (ENG., Illus.). 370p. 119.00 (978-3-540-92224-7(5), 3540922245) Springer.

Posner, Elliot. The Origins of Europe's New Stock Markets. 2009. (Illus.). 264p. 49.00 (978-0-674-03171-5(7)) Harvard Univ. Pr.

Prigent, Jean-Luc. Weak Convergence of Financial Markets. 2010. (Springer Finance Ser.). (Illus.). xiv, 444p. pap. 199.00 (978-3-642-07611-4(4), 3642076114) Springer.

Przytula, Patrycja & Chudzikiewicz, Natalia. The Impact of Estimation Errors on the Option Pricing. 2011. 92p. pap. **(978-3-8443-0604-0(8))** Lambert Academic Publishing.

Raste, Deepak R. Capital Market in India: Reforms & Regulations. 2011. 254p. 42.75 **(978-81-7708-286-9(8))** New Century Publications IND. Dist: International Specialized Bk. Services.

Rebonato, Riccardo. Plight of the Fortune Tellers: Why We Need to Manage Financial Risk Differently. 2007. (ENG., Illus.). 304p. (C). 35.00 (978-0-691-13361-4(1)) Princeton Univ. Pr.

Rechtschaffen, Alan N. Capital Markets, Derivatives & the Law. 2009. (ENG., Illus.). 384p. 247.50 (978-0-19-533908-6(8)) Oxford Univ. Pr., Inc.

Richter, Malte. Die Verwendung von Ratings zur Regulierung des Kapitalmarkts: Eine vergleichende Untersuchung nach US-amerikanischem und deutschem Recht. 2008. (Osnabrücker Schriften zum Unternehmens- und Wirtschaftsrecht Ser.). 336p. pap. 81.95 (978-3-631-57619-9(6)) Lang, Peter GmbH, Europaischer Verlag der Wissenschaften DEU. Dist: Lang, Peter.

Robinson, Joan. The Accumulation of Capital. 2013. (Palgrave Classics in Economics Ser.). (ENG.). 464p. pap. 42.00 (978-0-230-24932-5(9)) Palgrave Macmillan.

Ronackova, Hana. Cross-Listing of Central European Countries. 2010. 60p. pap. (978-3-8383-6189-5(X)) Lambert Academic Publishing.

Rose, Peter S. & Marquis, Milton. Money & Capital Markets. 10th ed. 2008. 840p. (978-0-07-340516-2(7)) McGraw-Hill Cos., The.

Rülke, Jan-Christoph. Expectations in Financial Markets - A Survey Data Approach. 2009. (Studien zu Internationalen Wirtschaftsbeziehungen Ser.). 142p. pap. 39.95 (978-3-631-58560-3(8)) Lang, Peter GmbH, Europaischer Verlag der Wissenschaften DEU. Dist: Lang, Peter.

Sardehi, Nangi. Islamic Capital Markets. 2008. 80p. pap. (978-3-639-00639-1(9)) VDM Verlag Dr. Mueller e.K.

Sauvant, Karl. Foreign Direct Investments from Emerging Markets: The Challenges Ahead. Maschek, Wolfgang & McAllister, Geraldine, eds. 2010. (ENG., Illus.). 492p. 184.00 (978-0-230-10021-3(X)) Palgrave Macmillan.

Schips, Bernd, ed. EMU, Financial Markets & the World Economy. 2010. (ENG.). 336p. pap. 199.00 (978-1-4419-5012-3(5), 1441950125) Springer.

Schlichting, Svenja. Internationalising China's Financial Markets. 2008. (ENG., Illus.). 256p. 89.00 (978-0-230-55198-5(X)) Palgrave Macmillan.

Schmukler, Sergio L. & De La Torre, Augusto. Emerging Capital Markets & Globalization: The Latin American Experience. 2007. (Latin American Development Forum Ser.). (ENG., Illus.). 224p. per. 25.95 (978-0-8047-5719-5(4)) Stanford Univ. Pr.

Schoenhart, Michael. Behavioral Finance & Market Anomalies. 2008. 132p. pap. (978-3-639-01106-7(6)) VDM Verlag Dr. Mueller e.K.

Seeber, Christian. Over- & Underreactions on Capital Markets. 2008. 92p. pap. (978-3-639-05901-4(8)) VDM Verlag Dr. Mueller e.K.

Segre, Sandro. A sociology of business groups & financial Markets: A weberian Perspective. 2008. 142p. 99.95 (978-0-7546-7161-9(5)) Ashgate Publishing Co.

Semmler, Willi. Asset Prices, Booms & Recessions: Financial Economics from a Dynamic Perspective. 3rd ed. 2011. (ENG., Illus.). xi, 333p. 139.00 (978-3-642-20679-5(4), 3642206794) Springer.

Short-Termism in Financial Markets: Hearing Before the Subcommittee on Economic Policy of the Committee on Banking, Housing, & Urban Affairs, United States Senate, One Hundred Eleventh Congress, Second Session, on Examining Short-Termism in Financial Markets, April 29, 2010. 2010. (Illus.). iii, 36p. **(978-0-16-087793-3(8)**, 552-070-42297-8) United States Government Printing Office.

Sipley, Richard. Market Indicators: The Best-Kept Secret to More Effective Trading & Investing. 2009. (Bloomberg Financial Ser.: 38). (ENG., Illus.). 256p. 39.95 (978-1-57660-331-4(8), Bloomberg Pr.) Wiley, John & Sons, Inc.

Smith, Roy C., et al. Global Banking, 1 vol. 3rd ed. 2012. (ENG., Illus.). 456p. 65.00 (978-0-19-533593-4(7)) Oxford Univ. Pr., Inc.

Smithers, Andrew. Wall Street Revalued: Imperfect Markets & Inept Central Bankers. 2009. (ENG., Illus.). 256p. 27.95 (978-0-470-75005-6(7), Wiley) Wiley, John & Sons, Inc.

Solnik, Bruno, et al. Global Investments. 6th ed. 2008. (ENG., Illus.). 688p. (C). pap. 213.33 (978-0-321-52770-7(4)) Addison Wesley.

Sophastienphong, Kiatchai, et al. South Asian Bond Markets: Developing Long-Term Finance for Growth. 2008. (ENG.). 220p. 65.00 (978-0-8213-7718-5(3), 9780821377185); (Illus.). 224p. pap. 35.00 (978-0-8213-7601-0(2), 9780821376010) World Bank Pubns.

Spitzer, Eliot. Government's Place in the Market. 2011. (Boston Review Bks.). (ENG.). 96p. (gr. 17). 14.95 (978-0-262-01570-7(6)) MIT Pr.

Storm, Philipp. Alternative Freiverkehrssegmente im Kapitalmarktrecht: Zugleich ein Beitrag zur rechtsökonomischen Analyse emittentenbezogener Regulierung durch einen Marktveranstalter und zum System der Segmentierung. 2010. (Schriftenreihe zum Gesellschafts- und Kapitalmarktrecht Ser.). (GER.). 420p. 101.95 (978-3-631-60204-1(9)) Lang, Peter GmbH, Europaischer Verlag der Wissenschaften DEU. Dist: Lang, Peter.

Stowell, David. An Introduction to Investment Banks, Hedge Funds, & Private Equity: The New Paradigm. 2010. (ENG.). 592p. (C). 82.95 (978-0-12-374503-3(9), Academic Pr.) Elsevier Science & Technology Bks.

Sylla, Richard, et al, eds. The State, the Financial System & Economic Modernization. 2007. (ENG., Illus.). 312p. pap. 63.00 (978-0-521-03798-3(0)) Cambridge Univ. Pr.

Tang, Yi, et al. Quantitative Analysis, Derivatives Modeling, & Trading Strategies: In the Presence of Counterparty Credit Risk for the Fixed-Income Market. 2006. (Illus.). 498p. 146.00 (978-981-02-4079-0(1)) World Scientific Publishing Co., Inc.

Taylor, Francesca. Market Know How: Finance & Markets. 2009. (ENG., Illus.). 352p. (C). pap. 39.99 (978-0-273-72378-3(2)) FT Press.

Thandaveswar, Vinaya. Trading Strategies Used in Derivatives Market. 2011. 80p. pap. **(978-3-8443-2452-5(6))** Lambert Academic Publishing.

Torre, Augusto de la & Schmukler, Sergio L. Emerging Capital Markets & Globalization: The Latin American Experience. 2006. (Latin American Development Forum Ser.). (ENG.). 224p. 65.00 (978-0-8047-5718-8(6), Stanford Economics & Finance) Stanford Univ. Pr.

Torre, Augusto de la, et al. Innovative Experiences in Access to Finance: Market-Friendly Roles for the Visible Hand? 2012. (Latin American Development Forum Ser.). (ENG.). 200p. pap. 30.00 (978-0-8213-7080-3(4), 9780821370803) World Bank Pubns.

Torrey, Yeram E. Hedge Funds: Regulation & Nonregulation. 2009. pap. 69.00 (978-1-60692-041-1(3)) Nova Science Pubs., Inc.

United Nations. UNCITRAL Legislative Guide on Secured Transaction. 2010. (ENG.). 566p. pap. 85.00 (978-92-1-133675-7(9)) United Nations Pubns.

Valiante, Diego & Lannoo, Karel. MiFID 2. 0: Casting New Light on Europe's Capital Markets. 2011. (ENG., Illus.). 263p. pap. 29.95 **(978-94-6138-081-4(X))** Ctr. for European Policy Studies BEL. Dist: Brookings Institution Pr.

Vardi, Noah. The Integration of European Financial Markets. 2011. 208p. (ENG.). pap. 44.95 **(978-0-415-69561-9(9))**; 125.00 (978-0-415-60263-1(7)) Routledge.

Vaughan-Williams, Leighton, ed. Information Efficiency in Financial & Betting Markets. 2009. (ENG., Illus.). 412p. pap. 53.00 (978-0-521-10817-1(9)) Cambridge Univ. Pr.

Vernon, John A. Economics of Drug R. 2010. 320p. pap. (978-3-639-09597-5(9)) VDM Verlag Dr. Mueller e.K.

Vogel, Harold L. Financial Market Bubbles & Crashes. 2009. (ENG., Illus.). 384p. (C). 35.00 (978-0-521-19967-4(0)) Cambridge Univ. Pr.

Voit, Johannes. The Statistical Mechanics of Financial Markets. 3rd ed. 2010. (Theoretical & Mathematical Physics Ser.). (ABK., Illus.). xv, 378p. pap. 84.95 (978-3-642-06578-1(3), 3642065783) Springer.

Von Gotzen, Richard, et al. The Property Finance Sourcebook 2008. 5th rev. ed. 2008. (ENG.). 400p. 117.00 (978-0-7282-0460-7(6)) Estates Gazette, Ltd. GBR. Dist: Taylor & Francis Group.

Vuong, Quan-Hoang. Financial Markets in Vietnam's Transition Economy. 2010. 448p. pap. (978-3-639-23383-4(2)) VDM Verlag Dr. Mueller e.K.

Wang, Shengzhe. True Sale Securitization: Germany & China. 2007. 84p. per. (978-3-86550-950-5(9)) VDM Verlag Dr. Mueller e.K.

Weert, Frans de. Bank & Insurance Capital Management. 2010. (Wiley Finance Ser.: 516). (ENG., Illus.). 264p. 75.00 (978-0-470-66477-3(0), Wiley) Wiley, John & Sons, Inc.

Welfens, Paul J. J. & Ryan, Cillian, eds. Financial Market Integration & Growth: Structural Change & Economic Dynamics in the European Union. 2011. (ENG.). xxvi, 387p. 189.00 (978-3-642-16273-2(8), 3642162738) Springer.

Whyte, Ann Marie. Financial Markets: Note Taking Guide. rev. ed. 2010. (ENG.). 162p. pap. 28.50 (978-0-7575-6862-6(9)) Kendall Hunt Publishing Co.

Williams, R. "Tee". An Introduction to Trading in the Financial Markets: Global Markets, Risk, Compliance, & Regulation. 2012. (ENG., Illus.). 472p. pap. 39.95 (978-0-12-374837-9(2), Academic Pr.) Elsevier Science & Technology Bks.

—An Introduction to Trading in the Financial Markets: Market Basics. 2010. (ENG., Illus.). 336p. pap. 39.95 (978-0-12-374838-6(0), Academic Pr.) Elsevier Science & Technology Bks.

—An Introduction to Trading in the Financial Markets: Technology - Systems, Data, & Networks. 2011. (ENG., Illus.). 496p. pap. 39.95 (978-0-12-374840-9(2), Academic Pr.) Elsevier Science & Technology Bks.

—An Introduction to Trading in the Financial Markets: Trading, Markets, Instruments, & Processes. 2011. (ENG., Illus.). 464p. pap. 39.95 (978-0-12-374839-3(9), Academic Pr.) Elsevier Science & Technology Bks.

—An Introduction to Trading in the Financial Markets SET, 4 vols. 2012. (ENG., Illus.). 1000p. pap. 119.95 (978-0-12-384972-4(1), Academic Pr.) Elsevier Science & Technology Bks.

Wilson, D. Bloomberg Visual Guide to Financial Markets. 2012. (Bloomberg Financial Ser.: 139). (ENG.). 216p. pap. 60.00 **(978-1-118-20423-8(9)**, Bloomberg Pr.) Wiley, John & Sons, Inc.

Yi, Chun-Ho & Pak, Chan-Ho. Chabon Sijang T'onghapposang Chungkwon Kyuje Wa Chiphap T'uja Kyuje e Kwanhan Pigyopopchok Yon'gu. 2008. 175p. (978-89-8323-889-4(5)) Korea Legislation Research Institute.

Zelenko, Ivan, et al. Catastrophe Bonds: Government Use of Capital Markets as Insurance Against Natural Disasters. 2012. (ENG.). 96p. pap. 15.00 (978-0-8213-8105-2(9), 9780821381052) World Bank Pubns.

Zens, Alexander. External Intervention in Foreign Exchange Markets. 2008. 80p. pap. (978-3-639-01176-0(7)) VDM Verlag Dr. Mueller e.K.

Zhang, Xiaoke. The Political Economy of Capital Market Reforms in South East Asia. 2011. (International Political Economy Ser.). (ENG., Illus.). 272p. 85.00 **(978-0-230-25282-0(6))** Palgrave Macmillan.

Zhu, Qi. The Application of Stakeholder Theory to Post-Trade Industry. 2008. 112p. pap. (978-3-8364-8382-7(3)) VDM Verlag Dr. Mueller e.K.

Zuijderduijn, J. & Zuijderduijn, C. J. Medieval Capital Markets: Markets for Renten, State Formation & Private Investment in Holland (1300-1550) 2009. (Global Economic History Ser.). (Illus.). 310p. (978-90-04-17565-5(2)) BRILL.

CAPITAL MOVEMENTS

see also Investments, Foreign

Abdelal, Rawi. Capital Rules: The Construction of Global Finance. 2009. 320p. pap. 21.00 (978-0-674-03455-6(4)) Harvard Univ. Pr.

Al. Advances in International Investments. 2008. 400p. (C). 124.00 (978-981-270-862-5(6)) World Scientific Publishing Co., Inc.

Alfaro, Laura. Global Capital & National Institutions: Crisis & Choice in the International Financial Architecture. 2009. (Illus.). 700p. 135.00 (978-981-4280-87-7(9)) World Scientific Publishing Co., Inc.

Alogoskoufis, George, et al, eds. External Constraints on Macroeconomic Policy. 2010. (ENG., Illus.). 406p. pap. 42.00 (978-0-521-13407-1(2)) Cambridge Univ. Pr.

Baker, Andrew, et al, eds. Governing Financial Globalization: International Political Economy & Multi-Level Governance. 2008. (Illus.). 272p. 41.95 (978-0-415-47968-4(1)) Routledge.

Beja, L. Hello Flight, Goodbye Capital. 2007. 148p. per. (978-3-8364-3635-9(3)) VDM Verlag Dr. Mueller e.K.

Benyon, Frank S. Direct Investment, National Champions & EU Treaty Freedoms: From Maastricht to Lisbon. 2010. (ENG.). 166p. 90.00

C

(978-1-84946-108-5(2)) Hart Publishing Ltd. GBR. Dist: International Specialized Bk. Services.

Bery, Suman, et al, eds. India Policy Forum 2008-09. 2009. 320p. (C). pap. 29.95 (978-81-321-0149-9(9), B01499P) SAGE Pubns., Inc.

Bonanno, Alessandro & Cavalcanti, Josefa Salete Barbosa. Globalization & the Time-Space Reorganization: Capital Mobility in Agriculture & Food in the Americas. Bonanno, Alessandro & Cavalcanti, Josefa Salete Barbosa, eds. 2011. (Research in Rural Sociology & Development Ser.: Vol. 17). (Illus.). 250p. 114.95 (978-0-85724-317-1(9)) Emerald Group Publishing Ltd. GBR. Dist: Turpin Distribution Services Ltd.

Brender, Anton & Pisani, Florence. Global Imbalances & the Collapse of Globalised Finance. 2010. (ENG., Illus.). 150p. pap. 16.00 (978-92-9079-943-6(9)) Ctr. for European Policy Studies BEL. Dist: Brookings Institution Pr.

Brown, Brendan. What Drives Global Capital Flows? Myth, Speculation & Currency Diplomacy. 2006. (ENG., Illus.). 256p. 110.00 (978-1-4039-4757-4(0)) Palgrave Macmillan.

Cibils, Alan. EXCHANGE RATE POLICY, CAPITAL CONTROLS, AND ECONOMICSTABILITY: A CGE MODEL OF ARGENTINA. 2008. 212p. pap. (978-3-639-10640-4(7)) VDM Verlag Dr. Mueller e.K.

Cohan, Peter & Rangan, U. Srinivasa. Capital Rising: How Capital Flows Are Changing Business Systems All over the World. 2010. (ENG., Illus.). 288p. 37.00 (978-0-230-61231-0(8)) Palgrave Macmillan.

Corrigan, E. Gerald, et al. The Global Economic Crisis. 2011. (ENG.). 64p. pap. 15.00 (978-0-930503-93-2(7)) Trilateral Commission.

Davis, Lance E. & Gallman, Robert E. Evolving Financial Markets & International Capital Flows: Britain, the Americas, & Australia, 1865-1914, 2 vols. 2011. (Japan-US Center UFJ Bank Monographs on International Financial Markets Ser.). (ENG.). 994p. pap. 90.00 (978-0-521-16608-9(X)) Cambridge Univ. Pr.

Dell'Ariccia, Giovanni & International Monetary Fund. Reaping the benefits of financial Globalization. 2008. (Illus.). 42p. pap. (978-1-58906-748-6(7)) International Monetary Fund.

Deshpande, Ashwini, ed. Capital without Borders: Challenges to Development. 2010. (Anthem Studies in Development & Globalization Ser.). (ENG., Illus.). 250p. 99.00 (978-1-84331-838-5(5)) Anthem Pr. GBR. Dist: Books International, Inc.

—Capital Without Borders: Challenges to Development. 2011. (Anthem Press India Ser.). (Illus.). 250p. pap. 40.00 (978-93-80601-16-8(6)) Anthem Pr. GBR. Dist: Books International, Inc.

Edwards, Sebastian, ed. Capital Controls & Capital Flows in Emerging Economies: Policies, Practices, & Consequences. 2007. (National Bureau of Economic Research Conference Report). (Illus.). 584p. 107.50 (978-0-226-18497-5(8)) Univ. of Chicago Pr.

Engelskirchen, H. The Political Economy of Capital. 2011. (Routledge Frontiers of Political Economy Ser.). (ENG.). 240p. (C). 130.00 (978-0-415-77691-2(0)) Routledge.

Garcia, Márcio Gomes Pinto. Financial Markets Volatility & Performance in Emerging Markets. Edwards, Sebastian, ed. 2008. (National Bureau of Economic Research Conference Report). (Illus.). 304p. 75.00 (978-0-226-18495-1(1)) Univ. of Chicago Pr.

Garon, Sheldon. Beyond Our Means: Why America Spends While the World Saves. 2011. (ENG., Illus.). 448p. 29.95 **(978-0-691-13599-1(1))** Princeton Univ. Pr.

Glick, Reuven, ed. Managing Capital Flows & Exchange Rates: Perspectives from the Pacific Basin. 2011. (ENG.). 526p. pap. 65.00 (978-0-521-16934-9(8)) Cambridge Univ. Pr.

Goldin, Ian & Reinert, Kenneth. Globalization for Development: Trade, Finance, Aid, Migration, & Policy. 2nd rev. ed. 2007. (Stand Alones Ser.). (ENG., Illus.). 328p. 90.00 (978-0-8213-7030-8(8), 9780821370308); per. 39.95 (978-0-8213-6929-6(6), 9780821369296) World Bank Pubns.

Goyer, Michel. Contingent Capital: Short-term Investors & the Evolution of Corporate Governance in France & Germany. 2012. (ENG.). 200p. 80.00 (978-0-19-957808-5(7)) Oxford Univ. Pr., Inc.

Handoll, John. Capital, Payments & Money Laundering in the European Union. 2007. 416p. 280.50 (978-1-904501-51-0(6)) Oxford Univ. Pr., Inc.

Harrison, Ann E., ed. Globalization & Poverty. 2007. (National Bureau of Economic Research Conference Report). (Illus.). 536p. 107.50 (978-0-226-31794-6(3)) Univ. of Chicago Pr.

Harvey, John T. Currencies, Capital Flows & Crises: A Post Keynesian Analysis of Exchange Rate Determination. 2009. (Routledge Advances in Heterodox Economics Ser.). (Illus.). 176p. 135.00 (978-0-415-77763-6(1)) Routledge.

—Currencies, Capital Flows & Crises: A post Keynesian analysis of exchange rate Determination. 2010. pap. 42.95 (978-0-415-78120-6(5)) Routledge.

Haufler, Andreas. Taxation in a Global Economy: Theory & Evidence. 2008. (ENG., Illus.). 356p. pap. 42.00 (978-0-521-04759-3(5)) Cambridge Univ. Pr.

Hindelang, Steffen. The Free Movement of Capital & Foreign Direct Investment: The Scope of Protection in EU Law. 2009. (ENG.). 464p. 155.00 (978-0-19-957265-6(8)) Oxford Univ. Pr., Inc.

International Investment Handbook: Moody's. 500p. (Orig.). pap. 2895.00 (978-0-7605-1807-6(6)) Rector Pr., Ltd.

International Monetary Fund Staff. Financial Globalization: A compilation of articles from Finance & Development. Clift, Jeremy et al, eds. 2007. (Illus.). 96p. pap. (978-1-58906-571-0(9)) International Monetary Fund.

Ito, Takatoshi. International Financial Issues in the Pacific Rim: Global Imbalances, Financial Liberalization, & Exchange Rate Policy. Rose, Andrew K., ed. 2008. (National Bureau of Economic Research-East Asia Seminar on Economics Ser.). (Illus.). 368p. 99.00 (978-0-226-38682-9(1)) Univ. of Chicago Pr.

Jeanne, Olivier, et al. Who Needs to Open the Capital Account. 2011. (Illus.). 128p. pap. 25.95 (978-0-88132-511-9(2)) Peterson Institute for International Economics.

Jongwanich, Juthathip. Capital Mobility, Exchange Rate Regimes & Currency Crises: Theory & Evidence from Thailand. 2006. 240p. 169.00 (978-1-60021-448-6(7)) Nova Science Pubs., Inc.

Kawai, Masahiro & Lamberte, Mario B. Managing Capital Flows: The Search for a Framework. 2011. (Illus.). 464p. 185.00 (978-1-84844-787-5(6)) Elgar, Edward Publishing, Inc.

Kohli, Harinder S. Growth & Development in Emerging Market Economies: International Private Capital Flows, Financial Markets & Globalization. 2008. (Illus.). 369p. (978-81-7829-837-5(6)) SAGE Pubns., Inc.

Kohli, Harinder S., ed. Growth & Development in Emerging Economies: International Private Capital Flow, Financial Markets & Globalization. 2008. (Illus.). 378p. (C). 49.95 (978-0-7619-3671-8(8), B4256XC) SAGE Pubns., Inc.

Lee, Kang-Kook. Capital Account Liberalization & Economic Growth: New Measures, New Estimates & the Experience of South Korea. 2008. 208p. pap. (978-3-639-05660-0(4)) VDM Verlag Dr. Mueller e.K.

Markusen, Ann R. Reining in the Competition for Capital. 2007. (Illus.). 225p. 40.00 (978-0-88099-296-1(4)); pap. 18.00 (978-0-88099-295-4(6)) Upjohn, W.E. Institute for Employment Research.

Mauro, Paolo, et al. Emerging Markets & Financial Globalization: Sovereign Bond Spreads in 1870-1913 & Today. 2008. (ENG., Illus.). 208p. per. 49.95 (978-0-19-922613-9(X)) Oxford Univ. Pr., Inc.

Moschella, Manuela. Governing Risk: The IMF & Global Financial Crises. 2010. (International Political Economy Ser.). (ENG.). 256p. 95.00 (978-0-230-23687-5(1)) Palgrave Macmillan.

Mostrous, Yiannis G., et al. The Rise of the State: Profitable Investing & Geopolitics in the 21st Century. 2010. (ENG., Illus.). 304p. 25.99 (978-0-13-715387-9(2)) FT Press.

Ninkovic, Jasminka. Determinants of International Flows. 2008. 120p. pap. (978-3-639-07866-4(7)) VDM Verlag Dr. Mueller e.K.

Organisation for Economic Co-operation and Development. OECD Code of Liberalisation of Capital Movements. 2011. 182p. pap. 67.00 **(978-92-64-11076-2(3))** Organization for Economic Cooperation & Development.

Organisation for Economic Co-operation and Development Staff. Oecd Codes of Liberalisation: User's Guide 2007. 2007. 129p. pap. 52.00 (978-92-64-03556-0(7)) Organization for Economic Cooperation & Development.

Perea, José Ramón. An Evaluation of the Conventional Wisdom on Capital Flow Volatility. 2008. 124p. pap. (978-3-639-02700-6(0)) VDM Verlag Dr. Mueller e.K.

Perry, Guillermo. Beyond Lending: How Multilateral Banks Can Help Developing Countries Manage Volatility. 2009. (ENG., Illus.). 98p. pap. 18.95 (978-1-933286-32-7(6)) Ctr. for Global Development.

Proctor, Bob. Contact Capital: How toTurn Your Contacts into Cash Flow. 2008. 70p. pap. 12.95 (978-1-891279-25-6(4)) INTI Publishing & Resource Bks., Inc.

Rao, D. Tripati & Correa, Romar. Financial Liberalisation. 2008. 116p. pap. (978-3-639-04459-1(2)) VDM Verlag Dr. Mueller e.K.

Razin, A. & Sadka, Efraim. Foreign Direct Investment. 2007. (ENG., Illus.). 158p. (C). 59.95 (978-0-691-12706-4(9)) Princeton Univ. Pr.

Rockefeller, Barbara & Schmelzer, Vicki. The Foreign Exchange Matrix: A new framework for traders to understand currency Movements. 2012. (ENG.). 250p. pap. 55.00 **(978-0-85719-130-4(6))** Harriman Hse. Publishing GBR. Dist: Ingram Pub. Services.

Satyanath, Shanker. Globalization, Politics, & Financial Turmoil: Asia's Banking Crisis. 2009. (Political Economy of Institutions & Decisions Ser.). (ENG., Illus.). 176p. pap. 26.99 (978-0-521-10743-3(1)) Cambridge Univ. Pr.

Sercu, Piet & Uppal, Raman. Exchange Rate Volatility, Trade, & Capital Flows under Alternative Exchange Rate Regimes. 2006. (Japan-US Center UFJ Bank Monographs on International Financial Markets Ser.). (ENG.). 176p. pap. 38.99 (978-0-521-03423-4(X)) Cambridge Univ. Pr.

Smit, et al. Ec Free Movement of Capital, Corporate Income Taxation & Third Countries. 2008. pap. 119.00 (978-90-411-2710-5(0)) Wolters Kluwer Law & Business.

Snowden, P. N. Emerging Risk in International Banking (RLE Banking & Finance) Origins of Financial Vulnerability in The 1980s, Volume 31. 2012. (ENG.). 160p. 100.00 **(978-0-415-52942-6(5))** Routledge.

Sovereign Wealth Funds: New Challenges from a Changing Landscape: Hearing Before the Subcommittee on Domestic & International Monetary Policy, Trade, & Technology of the Committee on Financial Services, U.S. House of Representatives, One Hundred Tenth Congress, Second Session, September 10, 2008. 2008. v, 87p. (978-0-16-082294-0(7), 552-070-38356-5) United States Government Printing Office.

Tiberghien, Yves. Entrepreneurial States: Reforming Corporate Governance in France, Japan, & Korea. 2007. (Cornell Studies in Political Economy). (Illus.). 255p. 39.95 (978-0-8014-4593-4(0)) Cornell Univ. Pr.

Tobin, James B. & Parker, Lawrence R., eds. Joint Ventures, Mergers & Acquisitions, & Capital Flow. 2008. 120.00 (978-1-60692-795-3(7)) Nova Science Pubs., Inc.

United Nations Conference on Trade and Development, Secretariat Staff. The Global Economic Crisis: Systemic Failures & Multilateral Remedies. 2009. (ENG., Illus.). 80p. pap. 22.00 (978-92-1-112765-2(3)) United Nations Pubns.

Vaccani, Matteo. Alternative Remittance Systems & Terrorism Financing: Issues in Risk Management. 2009. (World Bank Working Papers: 180). (ENG., Illus.). 40p. pap. 15.00 (978-0-8213-8178-6(4), 9780821381786) World Bank Pubns.

Watson, Matthew. The Political Economy of International Capital Mobility. 2007. (ENG., Illus.). 256p. 105.00 (978-0-230-00124-4(6)) Palgrave Macmillan.

CAPITAL OUTPUT RATES

see Cost Effectiveness

CAPITAL PUNISHMENT

see also Death Row; Hanging

ABBE Research Division Staff. Capital Punishment-World Controversy & the Challenge to Physicians as Participants of Medical Conflict with Index & Medical Analysis of New Research Information for All Nations. 2007. (Illus.). 160p. 69.95 (978-0-7883-4636-1(9), 0-7883-4646-9) ABBE Pubs. Assn. of Washington, D.C.

—The Death Penalty, Executions & Is the Pain of Lethal Injections Torture or Humane Treatments? With Index of New Information for All Nations. 2006. (Illus.). 160p. 69.95 (978-0-7883-4609-5(1), 0-7883-4609-1) ABBE Pubs. Assn. of Washington, D.C.

Acca. Towards Abolition of the Death Penalty in Uganda. (Illus.). lv, 160p. (978-9970-02-615-9(1)) Fountain Pubs. Ltd.

Akins, Jerry. Hangin' Times in Fort Smith: A History of Executions in Judge Parker's Court. 2012. (ENG.). 268p. pap. 22.50 **(978-1-935106-34-0(1))** Butler Ctr. for Arkansas Studies.

Allen, Howard W. & Clubb, Jerome M. Race, Class, & the Death Penalty: Capital Punishment in American History. 2008. pap. 24.95 (978-0-7914-7438-9(0)); (Illus.). 239p. 65.00 (978-0-7914-7437-2(2)) State Univ. of New York Pr.

Atwell, Mary Welek. Wretched Sisters: Examining Gender & Capital Punishment. 2007. (Studies in Crime & Punishment). 264p. (C). pap. 32.95 (978-0-8204-7883-8(0)) Lang, Peter Publishing, Inc.

Badinter, Robert. Abolition: One Man's Battle Against the Death Penalty. Mercer, Jeremy, tr. from FRE. 2008. (ENG.). 244p. lib. bdg. 29.95 (978-1-55553-692-3(1), Northeastern University Pr.) Univ. Pr. of New England.

Bae, Sangmin. When the State No Longer Kills: International Human Rights Norms & Abolition of Capital Punishment. 2008. xv, 178p. pap. 29.95 (978-0-7914-7208-8(6)) 2007. (Illus.). 178p. 65.00 (978-0-7914-7207-1(8)) State Univ. of New York Pr.

Baird, Robert. Death Penalty: Debating the Moral, Legal, & Political Issues. Rosenbaum, Stuart E., ed. 2010. (ENG.). 300p. pap. 19.00 (978-1-59102-760-7(8)) Prometheus Bks., Pubs.

Bakken, Gordon Morris. Invitation to an Execution: A History of the Death Penalty in the United States. 2010. (ENG., Illus.). 480p. 75.00 (978-0-8263-4856-2(4)) Univ. of New Mexico Pr.

Baldwin, Maria T. Amnesty International & U. S. Foreign Policy: Human Rights Campaigns in Guatemala, the United States, & China. 2008. (Law & Society Ser.). 314p. 75.00 (978-1-59332-329-5(8)) LFB Scholarly Publishing LLC.

Baldwin, Robert. Life & Death Matters: Seeking the Truth about Capital Punishment. 2008. 24.95 (978-1-58838-234-4(6), NewSouth Bks.) NewSouth, Inc.

Bastien, Pascal. Une Histoire de la Peine de Mort: Bourreaux et Supplices: Paris, Londres, 1500-1800. 2011. (FRE.). 339p. (978-2-02-079754-2(2)) Editions du Seuil.

Baumgartner, Frank R., et al. The Decline of the Death Penalty & the Discovery of Innocence. 2008. (ENG., Illus.). 308p. pap. 26.00 (978-0-521-71524-9(5)); 292p. 82.00 (978-0-521-88734-2(8)) Cambridge Univ. Pr.

Beccaria, Cesare. On Crimes & Punishments. Newman, Graeme & Marongiu, Pietro, eds. & trs. by. from ITA. 5th ed. 2009. (ENG.). 193p. 39.95 (978-1-4128-1015-9(9)) Transaction Pubs.

—On Crimes & Punishments & Other Writings. Parzen, Jeremy, tr. from ITA. 2008. (Lorenzo Da Ponte Italian Library). (ENG.). 224p. (978-0-8020-8990-8(9)) Univ. of Toronto Pr.

Beck, Elizabeth, et al. In the Shadow of Death: Restorative Justice & Death Row Families. (ENG., Illus.). 336p. 2009. pap. 21.99 (978-0-19-537569-5(6)) 2007. (C). 42.50 (978-0-19-517941-5(2)) Oxford Univ. Pr., Inc.

Becker, David A., ed. Problems with Death. 2006. (Opposing Viewpoints Ser.). (ENG., Illus.). 247p. (gr. 10-12). (J). pap. 39.70 (978-0-7377-2953-5(8)); 27.50 (978-0-7377-2954-2(6)) Cengage Gale. (Greenhaven Pr., Inc.).

Berman. Death Penalty Law & Policy: Theories Doctrines & Practices. 2010. pap., stu. ed. (978-0-7355-8259-0(9)) Wolters Kluwer Law & Business.

Bessler, John D. Cruel & Unusual: The American Death Penalty & the Founders' Eighth Amendment. 2012. (ENG., Illus.). 464p. 39.95 (978-1-55553-716-6(2), Northeastern University Pr.) Univ. Pr. of New England.

Bienen, Leigh Buchanan. Murder & Its Consequences: Essays on Capital Punishment in America. (ENG.). 256p. 2011. pap. 34.95 **(978-0-8101-2834-7(9))** 2010. 89.95 (978-0-8101-2697-8(4)) Northwestern Univ. Pr.

Blaskovich, Dagny A. & Simon, Rita J. A Comparative Analysis of Capital Punishment: Statutes, Policies, Frequencies, & Public Attitudes the World Over. 2007. (Global Perspectives on Social Issues Ser.). (ENG.). 128p. pap. 26.50 (978-0-7391-2091-0(3)) Lexington Bks.

Bohm, Robert, ed. The Death Penalty Today. 2008. (ENG., Illus.). 240p. (C). pap. 77.95 (978-1-4200-7011-8(8), CRC Press) Taylor & Francis Group GBR. Dist: Taylor & Francis Group.

Bohm, Robert M. DeathQuest: An Introduction to the Theory & Practice of Capital Punishment in the United States. 4th ed. 2011. (ENG.). 446p. (C). pap. 44.95 (978-1-4377-3493-5(6)) Anderson Publishing Co.

Bohm, Robert M. The Past as Prologue: The Supreme Court's Pre-Modern Death Penalty Jurisprudence & Its Influence on the Supreme Court's Modern Death Penalty Decisions. 2012. pap. **(978-1-61163-091-6(6))** Carolina Academic Pr.

Brandon, Craig. The Electric Chair: An Unnatural American History. alt. ed. 2009. (ENG., Illus.). 285p. pap. 35.00 (978-0-7864-4493-9(2)) McFarland & Co., Inc. Pubs.

Brook, Timothy, et al. Death by a Thousand Cuts. 2008. (Illus.). 336p. 33.00 (978-0-674-02773-2(6)) Harvard Univ. Pr.

Burkhead, Michael Dow. A Life for a Life: The American Debate over the Death Penalty. 2009. (ENG., Illus.). 215p. pap. 39.95 (978-0-7864-3368-1(X)) McFarland & Co., Inc. Pubs.

Burnett, Cathleen. Wrongful Death Sentences: Rethinking Justice in Capital Cases. 2010. 250p. 52.50 (978-1-58826-716-0(4)) Rienner, Lynne Pubs.

Cahill, Thomas. A Saint on Death Row: How a Forgotten Child Became a Man & Changed a World. 2010. (ENG.). 160p. pap. 14.00 (978-0-7679-2646-1(3), Anchor) Knopf Doubleday Publishing Group.

Calvet, Livia. Capital Punishment in the United States. 2010. 72p. pap. (978-3-8383-5507-8(5)) Lambert Academic Publishing.

Capfield, Steven. It Took a Village. 2007. 251p. pap. 15.95 (978-0-9759968-0-5(0)) Capfield's Pr.

Capital Punishment. 2010. (Information Plus Reference Ser.). (ENG.). 160p. 58.00 (978-1-4144-4115-3(0)) Cengage Gale.

Carcara, D. 15,543 & Counting. 2007. 140p. per. 24.95 (978-1-4241-9592-3(6)) PublishAmerica, Inc.

Carter, Linda E., et al. Understanding Capital Punishment Law. 2nd ed. 2008. pap. (978-1-4224-2386-8(7)) LexisNexis Matthew Bender.

Cheever, George Barrell. Punishment by Death: Its Authority & Expediency. (Capital Punishment Ser.). reprint ed. 37.50 (978-0-404-62409-5(X)) AMS Pr., Inc.

—Punishment by Death: Its Authority & Expediency. 2007. (ENG.). 158p. 36.95 (978-0-548-17698-6(1)); 160p. per. 21.95 (978-1-4304-7660-3(5)) Kessinger Publishing, LLC.

Christianson, Scott. The Last Gasp: The Rise & Fall of the American Gas Chamber. (Illus.). 344p. 2011. (ENG.). pap. 18.95 (978-0-520-27121-0(1)) 2010. 55.00 (978-0-520-25562-3(3)) Univ. of California Pr.

Clark, Richard. Women & the Noose: A History of Female Execution. 2008. (ENG.). 288p. 34.95 (978-0-7524-4489-5(1)) History Pr. Ltd., The GBR. Dist: Independent Pubs. Group.

Clarke, Alan W. & Whitt, Laurelyn. The Bitter Fruit of American Justice: International & Domestic Resistance to the Death Penalty. 2007. (ENG.). 280p. lib. bdg. 40.00 (978-1-55553-682-4(4), Northeastern University Pr.) Univ. Pr. of New England.

Clarke, Phil. Executioners. 2008. 512p. 9.99 (978-0-7088-0366-0(0)) Little, Brown Bk. Group Ltd. GBR. Dist: Book Sales, Inc.

Cohen, Bernard L. Law Without Order: Capital Punishment & the Liberals. reprint ed. 30.00 (978-0-404-62410-1(3)) AMS Pr., Inc.

Connell, Nadine M. Death by Jury: Group Dynamics & Capital Sentencing. 2009. (Criminal Justice). 222p. 62.00 (978-1-59332-334-9(4)) LFB Scholarly Publishing LLC.

Connors, Paul G., ed. Capital Punishment. 2007. (Current Controversies Ser.). (ENG.). 220p. (gr. 10-12). per. 27.50 (978-0-7377-3712-7(3), Greenhaven Pr., Inc.); (Illus.). (YA). (gr. 9-12). pap. 38.50 (978-0-7377-3711-0(5)) Cengage Gale.

Cotton, Allison M. Effigy: Images of Capital Defendants. 2010. (Issues in Crime & Justice Ser.). (ENG.). 230p. pap. 29.95 (978-0-7391-2552-6(4)) Lexington Bks.

—Effigy: Images of Capital Defendents. 2008. (Issues in Crime & Justice Ser.). (ENG.). 230p. 73.50 (978-0-7391-2551-9(6)) Rowman & Littlefield Publishers, Inc.

Coyne, Lorraine V., ed. Capital Punishment Update. 2008. pap. 39.00 (978-1-60456-133-3(5)) Nova Science Pubs., Inc.

Coyne, Randall & Entzeroth, Lyn. Capital Punishment & the Judicial Process, Third Edition, 2007 Supplement. 2007. 142p. per. 15.00 (978-1-59460-327-3(8)) Carolina Academic Pr.

Crew, Bob. The Beheading: And Other True Stories. 2011. (ENG.). 280p. pap. 13.95 **(978-1-84358-345-5(3))** Blake, John Publishing, Ltd. GBR. Dist: Independent Pubs. Group.

Culbert, Jennifer Louise. Dead Certainty: The Death Penalty & the Problem of Judgment. 2007. (Cultural Memory in the Present Ser.). (ENG.). 248p. per. 21.95 (978-0-8047-5746-1(1)) Stanford Univ. Pr.

Cunningham, Mark. Evaluation for Capital Sentencing, 1 vol. 2010. (Guides to Best Practices for Forensic Mental Health Assessments Ser.). (ENG., Illus.). 240p. pap. 39.95 (978-0-19-534155-3(4)) Oxford Univ. Pr., Inc.

Day, Mary. Death Penalty USA: 2009-2010. 2012. 350p. 49.95 (978-0-9725141-9-4(8), MoBeta, Inc.) MoBeta Publishing.

Del Carmen, Rolando V., et al. The Death Penalty: Constitutional Issues, Commentaries & Case Briefs. 2nd ed. 2008. (ENG.). 325p. (C). pap. 32.95 (978-1-59345-575-0(5)) Anderson Publishing Co.

Delfino, Michelangelo & Day, Mary. Death Penalty USA: 2001-2002. 2009. 463p. 49.95 (978-0-9725141-7-0(1), MoBeta, Inc.) MoBeta Publishing.

—Death Penalty USA: 2003-2004. 2008. 373p. 49.95 (978-0-9725141-3-2(9), MoBeta, Inc.) MoBeta Publishing.

—Death Penalty USA: 2005 - 2006. 2007. (ENG.). 374p. 49.95 (978-0-9725141-2-5(0), MoBeta, Inc.) MoBeta Publishing.

—Death Penalty USA: 2007 - 2008. 2009. 275p. 49.95 (978-0-9725141-8-7(X), MoBeta, Inc.) MoBeta Publishing.

DeMatteo, David, et al. Forensic Mental Health Assessments in Death Penalty Cases, 1 vol. 2011. (ENG.). 440p. 65.00 (978-0-19-538580-9(2)) Oxford Univ. Pr., Inc.

Derrida, Jacques. The Beast & the Sovereign, Volume I, 2 vols. Bennington, Geoffrey, tr. from FRE. 2009. (Seminars of Jacques Derrida Ser.). (ENG.). 368p. 35.00 (978-0-226-14428-3(3)) Univ. of Chicago Pr.

—The Beast & the Sovereign, Volume I. Bennington, Geoffrey, tr. from FRE. 2011. (Seminars of Jacques Derrida Ser.). (ENG.). 368p. pap. 22.50 (978-0-226-14429-0(1)) Univ. of Chicago Pr.

—The Beast & the Sovereign, Volume II. Bennington, Geoffrey, tr. from FRE. 2011. (Seminars of Jacques Derrida Ser.). 320p. 35.00 (978-0-226-14430-6(5)) Univ. of Chicago Pr.

Dicks, Shirley. Death Row: Interviews with Inmates, Their Families & Opponenets of Capital Punishment. alt. ed. 2012. (ENG.). 158p. pap. 25.00 **(978-0-7864-6943-7(9))** McFarland & Co., Inc. Pubs.

Disalle, Michael V. The Power of Life or Death. (Capital Punishment Ser.). reprint ed. 28.50 (978-0-404-62411-8(1)) AMS Pr., Inc.

Donovan, Tom D. Hanging Around the Big Sky: The Unofficial Guide to Lynching, Strangling & Legal Hangings of Montana, 2 vols. 2007. (Illus.). (978-0-9769718-2-5(8)); (978-0-9769718-1-8(X)) Portage Meadows Publishing.

Dow, David R. The Autobiography of an Execution. 2011. (ENG.). 288p. pap. 14.99 (978-0-446-56207-2(6), Twelve) Grand Central Publishing.

—The Autobiography of an Execution. l.t. ed. 2010. (ENG.). 356p. 30.95 (978-1-4104-2579-9(7)) Thorndike Pr.

Duffy, Clinton T. Eighty-Eight Men & Two Women. reprint ed. 32.50 (978-0-404-62412-5(X)) AMS Pr., Inc.

Edds, Margaret. An Expendable Man: The near-Execution of Earl Washington, Jr. 2006. (ENG., Illus.). 288p. per. 23.00 (978-0-8147-2239-8(3)) New York Univ. Pr.

Ekland-Olson, Sheldon. Who Lives Who Dies Who Decides? Abortion Neonatal Care Assisted Dying & Capital Punishment. 2011. (Contemporary Sociological Perspectives Ser.). (ENG., Illus.). 448p. 155.00 (978-0-415-89246-9(5)) Routledge.

—Who Lives, Who Dies, Who Decides?: Abortion, Neonatal Care, Assisted Dying, & Capital Punishment. 2011. (Contemporary Sociological Perspectives Ser.). (ENG.). 448p. pap. 39.95 (978-0-415-89247-6(3)) Routledge.

The Electric Chair. 2008. mass mkt. 25.00 (978-1-60388-214-9(6)) JonesHarvest Publishing.

Evans, Kim Masters. Capital Punishment: Cruel & Unusual? 2009. (Information Plus Ser.). (ENG., Illus.). 160p. pap. 53.00 (978-1-4144-0747-0(5)) Cengage Gale.

Farb, Robert L. 2007 Supplement to North Carolina Capital Case Law Handbook (Second Edition 2004) 2007. 11.00 net. (978-1-56011-561-8(0)) Schl. of Government.

Finsterbusch, Karin, et al, eds. Human Sacrifice in Jewish & Christian Tradition. 2006. (Numen Book Series-Studies in the History of Religions). (Illus.). 365p. (978-90-04-15085-0(4)) BRILL.

Frazier, Harriet C. Death Sentences in Missouri, 1803-2005: A History & Comprehensive Registry of Legal Executions, Pardons, & Commutations. 2006. (ENG., Illus.). 279p. per. 75.00 (978-0-7864-2719-2(1)) McFarland & Co., Inc. Pubs.

Friedland, Paul. Seeing Justice Done: The Age of Spectacular Capital Punishment in France. 2012. (ENG., Illus.). 344p. 65.00 **(978-0-19-959269-2(1))** Oxford Univ. Pr., Inc.

Friedman, Lauri S. The Death Penalty. 2007. (Compact Research Ser.). (Illus.). 112p. (YA). (gr. 7-12). lib. bdg. 25.95 (978-1-60152-008-1(5)) ReferencePoint Pr., Inc.

Gaie, Joseph B. R. The Ethics of Medical Involvement in Capital Punishment: A Philosophical Discussion. 2010. (International Library of Ethics, Law, & the New Medicine Ser.). 174p. pap. 139.00 (978-90-481-6494-3(X), 904816494X) Springer.

Gardiner, Gerald A. Capital Punishment As a Deterrent, & the Alternative. reprint ed. 32.50 (978-0-404-62415-6(4)) AMS Pr., Inc.

Garland, David. Peculiar Institution: America's Death Penalty in an Age of Abolition. 2010. (Illus.). 432p. 35.00 (978-0-674-05723-4(6), Belknap Pr.) Harvard Univ. Pr.

—Peculiar Institution: America's Death Penalty in an Age of Abolition. 2010. (Illus.). 432p. (978-0-19-959499-3(6)) Oxford Univ. Pr., Inc.

Gerber, Rudolph J. & Johnson, John M. The Top Ten Death Penalty Myths: The Politics of Crime Control, 1 vol. 2007. 256p. 49.95 (978-0-275-99780-9(4), C9780, Praeger Pubs.) Greenwood Publishing Group, Inc.

Goodheart, Lawrence B. Solemn Sentence of Death. 2011. 328p. pap. 28.95 (978-1-55849-847-1(8)) Univ. of Massachusetts Pr.

—The Solemn Sentence of Death: Capital Punishment in Connecticut. 2011. 328p. (978-1-55849-846-4(X)) Univ. of Massachusetts Pr.

Gowers, Ernest A. A Life for a Life? The Problem of Capital Punishment. (Illus.). reprint ed. 22.50 (978-0-404-62416-3(2)) AMS Pr., Inc.

Greenhaven Editor, ed. The Death Penalty. 2012. (Opposing Viewpoints Ser.). (ENG., Illus.). 240p. (gr. 10-12). 41.70 (978-0-7377-4960-1(1)); pap. 28.90 (978-0-7377-4961-8(X)) Cengage Gale. (Greenhaven Pr., Inc.).

Grisham, John. The Innocent Man: Murder & Injustice in a Small Town. 2006. cd-rom 44.99 (978-1-59895-381-7(8)) Findaway World, LLC.

—The Innocent Man: Murder & Injustice in a Small Town. 2006. (ENG., Illus.). 368p. 28.95 (978-0-385-51723-2(8), Doubleday) Knopf Doubleday Publishing Group.

—The Innocent Man: Murder & Injustice in a Small Town. 2007. (ENG., Illus.). 400p. pap. 16.00 (978-0-385-34091-5(5), Delta); 448p. mass mkt. 7.99 (978-0-440-24383-0(1), Dell) Random House Publishing Group.

Guernsey, Joann Bren. Death Penalty: Fair Solution or Moral Failure? 2009. (USA TODAY's Debate: Voices & Perspectives Ser.). 160p. (YA). (gr. 9-12). 35.93 (978-0-7613-4079-9(3)) Lerner Publishing Group.

Hale, Leslie. Hanged in Error. reprint ed. 24.50 (978-0-404-62420-0(0)) AMS Pr., Inc.

Hammel, Andrew. Ending the Death Penalty: The European Experience in Global Perspective. 2010. (ENG., Illus.). 272p. 89.00 (978-0-230-23198-6(5)) Palgrave Macmillan.

Hartnett, Stephen J. Executing Democracy: Capital Punishment & the Making of America, 1683-1807. 2010. (Rhetoric & Public Affairs Ser.). (ENG.). 331p. 59.95 (978-0-87013-869-0(3)) Michigan State Univ. Pr.

Heard, Alex. The Eyes of Willie McGee: A Tragedy of Race, Sex, & Secrets in the Jim Crow South. 2011. (ENG.). 432p. pap. 15.99 (978-0-06-128416-8(5), HarperPerennial) 2010. 416p. 26.99 (978-0-06-128415-1(7)) HarperCollins Pubs.

Heilbrun, Alfred. The Death Penalty: Beyond the Smoke & Mirrors. 2006. (ENG.). 274p. per. 44.50 (978-0-7618-3472-4(9)) Univ. Pr. of America, Inc.

Hodgkinson, Peter & Schabas, William. Capital Punishment: Strategies for Abolition. Hodgkinson, Peter & Schabas, William A., eds. 2009. (ENG., Illus.). 392p. pap. 53.00 (978-0-521-11559-9(0)) Cambridge Univ. Pr.

Hornby, Jim. In the Shadow of the Gallows No. 5: Capital Punishment in Prince Edward Island, 1769-1941. (Illus.). 152p. pap. 12.95 (978-0-919013-30-8(9)) Univ. of Prince Edward Island, Institute of Island Studies CAN. Dist: Goose Lane Editions.

Hoshowsky, Robert J. The Last to Die: Ronald Turpin, Arthur Lucas, & the End of Capital Punishment in Canada. 2007. (ENG., Illus.). 224p. pap. 24.99 (978-1-55002-672-6(0), Hounslow Pr.) Dundurn CAN. Dist: Ingram Pub. Services.

Hoyle, Carolyn & Hood, Roger. The Death Penalty: A Worldwide Perspective. 4th rev. ed. 2008. (ENG.). 350p. (C). pap. 65.00 (978-0-19-922847-8(7)) Oxford Univ. Pr., Inc.

Hussain, Nasser & Sarat, Austin, eds. Forgiveness, Mercy, & Clemency. 2006. (ENG.). 256p. 70.00 (978-0-8047-5332-6(6)); per. 25.95 (978-0-8047-5333-3(4)) Stanford Univ. Pr.

Impact of Federal Habeas Corpus Limitations on Death Penalty Appeals: Hearing Before the Subcommittee on the Constitution, Civil Rights, & Civil Liberties of the Committee on the Judiciary, House of Representatives, One Hundred Eleventh Congress, First Session, December 8, 2009. 2010. iv, 69p. (978-0-16-085512-2(8), 552-070-40775-8) United States Government Printing Office.

Ingle, Joseph B. Last Rights: 13 Fatal Encounters with the State's Justice. 2008. (ENG., Illus.). 320p. pap. 12.95 (978-1-4027-5449-4(3)) Union Square Pr.

Jackson, Bruce & Christian, Diane. In This Timeless Time: Living & Dying on Death Row in America. 2012. (Documentary Arts & Culture, Published in association with the Center for Documentary Studies at Duke University Ser.). (ENG., Illus.). 256p. 35.00 **(978-0-8078-3539-5(0))** Univ. of North Carolina Pr.

Jacobs, Helmut C., ed. Gegen Folter und Todesstrafe: Aufklarerischer Diskurs und europaische Literatur Vom 18. Jahrhundert Bis Zur Gegenwart. (GER., Illus.). 326p. 53.95 (978-3-631-55009-0(X)) Lang, Peter GmbH, Europaischer Verlag der Wissenschaften DEU. Dist: Lang, Peter Publishing, Inc.

Jacquette, Dale. Dialogues on the Ethics of Capital Punishment. (New Dialogues in Philosophy Ser.). (ENG.). 2009. 148p. pap. 16.95 (978-0-7425-6144-1(5)) 2008. 128p. 32.95 (978-0-7425-6143-4(7)) Rowman & Littlefield Publishers, Inc.

Jasper, Margaret C. The Law of Capital Punishment. 2nd ed. 2008. (Legal Almanac Ser.). (ENG.). 124p. 47.00 (978-0-19-537655-5(2)) Oxford Univ. Pr., Inc.

Johnsen, Julia E., ed. Capital Punishment. (Capital Punishment Ser.). reprint ed. 32.50 (978-0-404-62421-7(9)) AMS Pr., Inc.

Johnson, David T. & Zimring, Franklin E. The Next Frontier: National Development, Political Change, & the Death Penalty in Asia. 2009. (Studies in Crime & Public Policy Ser.). (Illus.). 544p. 99.00 (978-0-19-533740-2(9)); (ENG., pap. 35.00 (978-0-19-538245-7(5)) Oxford Univ. Pr., Inc.

Jones, Mark R. South Carolina Killers: Crimes of Passion. 2007. (True Crime Ser.). (ENG., Illus.). 96p. pap. 14.99 (978-1-59629-395-3(0)) History Pr., The.

Jones, Paul Christian. Against the Gallows: Antebellum American Writers & the Movement to Abolish Capital Punishment. 2011. 256p. pap. 35.00 (978-1-60938-048-9(7)) Univ. of Iowa Pr.

Jones, Sandra J. Coalition Building in the Anti-Death Penalty Movement: Privileged Morality, Race Realities. 2010. (ENG.). 314p. 83.99 (978-0-7391-2038-5(7)) Lexington Bks.

Joyce, James A. Capital Punishment: A World View. (Capital Punishment Ser.). (Illus.). reprint ed. 34.50 (978-0-404-62422-4(7)) AMS Pr., Inc.

Kaplan, Paul. Murder Stories: Ideological Narratives in Capital Punishment. 2012. (Issues in Crime & Justice Ser.). (ENG.). 218p. (gr. 17). 65.00 **(978-0-7391-7170-7(4))** Lexington Bks.

Keyzer, Amy. Does Capital Punishment Deter Crime? 2007. (At Issue Ser.). (ENG., Illus.). 128p. (YA). (gr. 9-12). pap. 30.85 (978-0-7377-3675-5(5)) Cengage Gale.

Keyzer, Amy Marcaccio, ed. Does Capital Punishment Deter Crime? 2007. (At Issue Ser.). (ENG.). 91p. (gr. 10-12). per. 22.50 (978-0-7377-3676-2(3), Greenhaven Pr., Inc.) Cengage Gale.

King, Gilbert. The Execution of Willie Francis: Race, Murder, & the Search for Justice in the American South. 2009. (ENG.). 400p. pap. 17.95 (978-0-465-01378-4(3), Basic Civitas Bks.) Basic Bks.

Koestler, Arthur. Reflections on Hanging. reprint ed. 30.00 (978-0-404-62423-1(5)) AMS Pr., Inc.

Kramer, Matthew H. The Ethics of Capital Punishment: A Philosophical Investigation of Evil & Its Consequences. 2012. (ENG.). 448p. 100.00 **(978-0-19-964218-2(4))** Oxford Univ. Pr., Inc.

Krogh, Tyge. A Lutheran Plague: Murdering to Die in the Eighteenth Century. 2012. (ENG., Illus.). 236p. **(978-90-04-22115-4(8))** BRILL.

Kudlac, Christopher S. Public Executions: The Death Penalty & the Media, 1 vol. 2007. (Crime, Media, & Popular Culture Ser.). (Illus.). 200p. 49.95 (978-0-275-99307-8(8), C9307, Praeger Pubs.) Greenwood Publishing Group, Inc.

Kukathas, Uma. Death Penalty. 2007. (Contemporary Issues Companion Ser.). (ENG., Illus.). 240p. (gr. 10-12). 27.50 (978-0-7377-3250-4(4), Greenhaven Pr., Inc.); (YA). (gr. 9-12). pap. 39.70 (978-0-7377-3249-8(0)) Cengage Gale.

Kunerth, Jeff. Trout: A True Story of Murder, Teens, & the Death Penalty. 2012. (ENG., Illus.). 216p. 24.95 **(978-0-8130-3981-7(9))** Univ. Pr. of Florida.

Kurtis, Bill. Death Penalty on Trial: Crisis in American Justice. 2008. (ENG.). 218p. 25.00 (978-1-4223-9236-2(8)) DIANE Publishing Co.

Lane, Charles. Stay of Execution: Saving the Death Penalty from Itself. 2010. (ENG.). 160p. 19.95 (978-1-4422-0378-5(1)) Rowman & Littlefield Publishers, Inc.

Lanier, Charles S., et al. The Future of America's Death Penalty: An Agenda for the Next Generation of Capital Punishment Research. 2009. 582p. pap. 54.00 (978-1-59460-426-3(6)) Carolina Academic Pr.

Laska, Lewis L. Legal Executions in Tennessee: A Comprehensive Registry, 1782-2009. 2011. (ENG., Illus.). 490p. pap. 95.00 (978-0-7864-5975-9(1)) McFarland & Co., Inc. Pubs.

Latzer, Barry & McCord, David. Death Penalty Cases: Leading U. S. Supreme Court Cases on Capital Punishment. 3rd ed. 2010. (ENG., Illus.). 456p. pap. 44.95 (978-0-12-382024-2(3), Butterworth-Heinemann) Elsevier Science & Technology Bks.

Lietzman, Hans. Apollinaris von Laodicea und seine Schule: Texte und Untersuchungen. (Orthodoxies & Heresies in the Early Church Ser.). reprint ed. 37.50 (978-0-404-62390-6(5)) AMS Pr., Inc.

Lu, Hong & Miethe, Terance D. Chinas Death Penalty: History, Law, & Contemporary Practices. 2007. (Routledge Advances in Criminology Ser.). (ENG., Illus.). 192p. 125.00 (978-0-415-95569-0(6)) Routledge.

Lyon, Andrea. Angel of Death Row: My Life as a Death Penalty Defense Lawyer. 2010. (ENG., Illus.). 288p. 24.95 (978-1-60714-434-2(4)) Kaplan Publishing.

Mandery, Evan J. Capital Punishment: A Balanced Examination. 2nd ed. 2011. (Illus.). 568p. pap. 64.95 (978-1-4496-0598-8(2)) Jones & Bartlett Learning, LLC.

Martschukat, Jürgen. Is the Death Penalty Dying? European & American Perspectives. Sarat, Austin, ed. 2011. (ENG., Illus.). 342p. 90.00 (978-0-521-76351-6(7)) Cambridge Univ. Pr.

Massingill, Ruth, et al. Prison City: Life with the Death Penalty in Huntsville, Texas. 2007. (Illus.). 280p. (C). 89.95 (978-0-8204-8891-2(7)); pap. 32.95 (978-0-8204-8890-5(9)) Lang, Peter Publishing, Inc.

McCafferty, James, ed. Capital Punishment. 2009. (ENG.). 273p. pap. 29.95 (978-0-202-36328-8(7)) Aldine Transaction.

McDougall, Colin. Execution. 2010. (ENG.). 312p. pap. 18.95 (978-0-7710-9439-2(6), New Can Library) McClelland & Stewart CAN. Dist: Random Hse., Inc.

McGowen, Randall & Meranze, Michael. America's Death Penalty: Between Past & Present. Garland, David et al, eds. 2011. (ENG., Illus.). 256p. pap. 22.00 (978-0-8147-3267-0(4)) New York Univ. Pr.

Melusky, Joseph A. & Pesto, Keith A. Capital Punishment, 1 vol. 2011. (Historical Guides to Controversial Issues in America Ser.). (Illus.). 207p. 55.00 (978-0-313-33558-7(3), GR3558) Greenwood Publishing Group, Inc.

Melusky, Joseph Anthony & Pesto, Keith A. Capital Punishment. 2011. (Illus.). x, 207p. E-Book **(978-1-4408-0057-3(X)**, Greenwood Pr.) Greenwood Publishing Group, Inc.

Merriner, James L. The Man Who Emptied Death Row: Governor George Ryan & the Politics of Crime. 2008. (Elmer H Johnson & Carol Holmes Johnson Series in Criminology Ser.). (ENG., Illus.). 240p. 29.95 (978-0-8093-2865-9(8)) Southern Illinois Univ. Pr.

Miller, Kenneth W. & Niven, David. Death Justice: Rehnquist, Scalia, Thomas, & the Contradictions of the Death Penalty. 2009. 246p. pap. 39.95 (978-1-59332-340-0(9)) LFB Scholarly Publishing LLC.

Montagu, Basil. The Opinions of Different Authors upon the Punishment of Death. 2008. 324p. 28.99 (978-0-554-52059-9(1)); 29.99 (978-0-554-52052-0(4)); pap. 30.75 (978-0-554-52053-7(2)); pap. 29.75 (978-0-554-52057-5(5)) BiblioBazaar.

—The Opinions of Different Authors upon the Punishment of Death. 2008. 324p. pap. 30.95 (978-1-4373-1403-8(1)) Kessinger Publishing, LLC.

Morgan, David T. A Blue Voice Crying in the Wilderness of a Red State. 2010. 336p. pap. 21.44 (978-0-557-19484-1(9)) Lulu Enterprises Inc.

Mulvey-Roberts, Marie, ed. Writing for Their Lives: Death Row USA. 2006. 336p. 47.00 (978-0-252-02793-2(0)); per. 20.95 (978-0-252-07099-0(2)) Univ. of Illinois Pr.

Naish, Camille. Death Comes to the Maiden: Sex & Execution 1431-1933, Volume 29. 2012. (Routledge Library Editions). (ENG.). 296p. (C). 115.00 **(978-0-415-62371-1(5))** Routledge.

Oshinsky, David M. Capital Punishment on Trial: Furman V. Georgia & the Death Penalty in Modern America. 2010. 29.95 (978-0-7006-1710-4(8)); 160p. pap. 14.95 (978-0-7006-1711-1(6)) Univ. Pr. of Kansas.

Osler, Mark. Jesus on Death Row: The Trial of Jesus & American Capital Punishment. 2009. 157p. pap. 17.00 (978-0-687-64756-9(8)) Abingdon Pr.

Palmer, Louis J., Jr. Encyclopedia of Capital Punishment in the United States. 2nd rev. ed. 2008. (ENG., Illus.). 631p. 95.00 (978-0-7864-3263-9(2)) McFarland & Co., Inc. Pubs.

Parrish, Michael. The Supreme Court & Capital Punishment: Designing Death, 00 vols. rev. ed. 2009. 488p. 135.00 (978-0-87289-773-1(7)) CQ Pr.

Paternoster, Raymond, et al. The Death Penalty: America's Experience with Capital Punishment. 2007. (ENG., Illus.). 362p. (C). pap. 49.95 (978-0-19-533242-1(3)) Oxford Univ. Pr., Inc.

—The Death Penalty: America's Experience with Capital Punishment. 2007. (Illus.). xviii, 314p. (978-1-933220-14-7(7)) Roxbury Publishing Co.

Peppers, Todd C. & Anderson, Laura Trevett. Anatomy of an Execution: The Life & Death of Douglas Christopher Thomas. 2009. (ENG., Illus.). 340p. 29.95 (978-1-55553-713-5(8), Northeastern University Pr.) Univ. Pr. of New England.

Perry, Michael J. Constitutional Rights, Moral Controversy, & the Supreme Court. (ENG.). 2010. 266p. pap. 35.99 (978-0-521-18441-0(X)) 2008. 264p. 79.00 (978-0-521-75595-5(6)) Cambridge Univ. Pr.

Pfeifer, Michael J. The Roots of Rough Justice: Origins of American Lynching. 2011. (ENG., Illus.). 160p. 40.00 (978-0-252-03613-2(1)) Univ. of Illinois Pr.

Quinby, G. W. (George Washington). The Gallows, the Prison, & the Poor-House. 2006. 332p. per. 23.99 (978-1-4255-3349-6(3)) MPublishing.

Reauthorization & Improvement of DNA Initiatives of the Justice for All ACT of 2004: Hearing Before the Subcommittee on Crime, Terrorism, & Homeland Security of the Committee on the Judiciary, House of Representatives, One Hundred Tenth Congress, Second Session, April 10, 2008. 2009. (Illus.). iv, 266p. (978-0-16-082681-8(0), 552-070-38698-0) United States Government Printing Office.

Redekop, John H. & Martens, Elmer A. La Peine Capitale. 32p. pap. 2.50 (978-0-919797-86-4(5)) Kindred Productions.

Rivkind, Nina & Shatz, Steven F. Cases & Materials on the Death Penalty. 2nd rev. ed. 2008. 144p. pap. 23.00 (978-0-314-19126-7(7), West Legalworks) West.

—Cases & Materials on the Death Penalty. 3rd ed. 2009. xviii, 960p. (978-0-314-19955-3(1)) West Publishing Co., College & Schl. Div.

Robinson, Matthew B. Death Nation: The Experts Explain American Capital Punishment. 2007. (ENG., Illus.). 352p. per. 54.60 (978-0-13-158693-2(9), Prentice Hall) Prentice Hall PTR.

Rogers, Alan. Murder & the Death Penalty in Massachusetts. 2008. 480p. pap. 34.95 net. (978-1-55849-633-0(5)); lib. bdg. 98.00 net. (978-1-55849-632-3(7)) Univ. of Massachusetts Pr.

Ryan, Katy, ed. Demands of the Dead: Executions, Storytelling, & Activism in the United States. 2012. (ENG., Illus.). 320p. pap. 39.95 **(978-1-60938-088-5(6))** Univ. of Iowa Pr.

Sarat, Austin. Mercy on Trial: What It Means to Stop an Execution. 2007. (ENG., Illus.). 352p. (C). per. 29.95 (978-0-691-13399-7(9)) Princeton Univ. Pr.

—The Road to Abolition? The Future of Capital Punishment in the United States. Ogletree, Charles, Jr., ed. 2009. (ENG.). 368p. pap. 22.00 (978-0-8147-6218-9(2)) New York Univ. Pr.

Sarat, Austin & Culbert, Jennifer, eds. States of Violence: War, Capital Punishment, & Letting Die. 2009. (ENG.). 332p. 88.00 (978-0-521-87627-8(3)); pap. 31.00 (978-0-521-69976-1(2)) Cambridge Univ. Pr.

Sarat, Austin & Shoemaker, Karl. Who Deserves to Die? Constructing the Executable Subject. 2011. viii, 312p. (978-1-55849-882-2(6)); 320p. pap. 28.95 (978-1-55849-883-9(4)) Univ. of Massachusetts Pr.

Sayward, Amy L. & Vandiver, Margaret. Tennessee's New Abolitionists: The Fight to End the Death Penalty in the Volunteer State. 2010. (ENG.). 300p. pap. 24.95 (978-1-57233-704-6(4)) Univ. of Tennessee Pr.

Schabas, William. War Crimes & Human Rights: Essays on the Death Penalty, Justice, & Accountability. 2010. 1158p. 190.00 (978-1-905017-63-8(4)) Gaunt, Inc.

Schmidt, Geraldine. The Violence of Capital Punishment - a Deterrent to Justice. 2008. 108p. pap. (978-3-639-04585-7(8)) VDM Verlag Dr. Mueller e.K.

Scott, George R. The History of Capital Punishment: Including An Examination of the Case for & Against Capital Punishment. (Capital Punishment Ser.). (Illus.). reprint ed. 38.50 (978-0-404-62428-6(6)) AMS Pr., Inc.

Segrave, Kerry. Women & Capital Punishment in America, 1840-1899: Death Sentences & Executions in the United States & Canada. 2008. (ENG.). 218p. pap. 39.95 (978-0-7864-3823-5(1)) McFarland & Co., Inc. Pubs.

Shere, Dennis. The Last Meal: Defending an Accused Mass Murderer. 2010. 220p. pap. 16.95 (978-0-9827206-2-2(9)) Titletown Publishing, LLC.

Sinclair, Billy Wayne & Sinclair, Jodie. Capital Punishment: An Indictment by a Death-Row Survivor. 2011. (ENG.). 264p. pap. 14.95 (978-1-61145-034-7(9), 611034, Arcade Publishing) Skyhorse Publishing Co., Inc.

Slack, James D. Abortion, Execution, & the Consequences of Taking Life. 2011. (ENG., Illus.). 228p. pap. 24.95 (978-1-4128-4222-8(0)) Transaction Pubs.

Spear, Charles. Essays on the Punishment of Death. 2010. 260p. pap. 26.75 (978-1-141-36723-8(8)) 2010. 264p. pap. 26.75 (978-1-141-69914-8(1)) 2009. 244p. 23.99 (978-1-103-61805-7(9)) 2009. 244p. pap. 17.99 (978-1-103-61801-9(6)) BiblioBazaar.

—Essays on the Punishment of Death. 2009. 170p. pap. *(978-0-217-20696-9(4))*; 166p. pap. *(978-1-4590-4824-9(5))* Books LLC.

—Essays on the Punishment of Death. 2008. 252p. 41.95 *(978-1-4366-3696-4(5))*; pap. 26.95 *(978-0-548-86782-2(8))* Kessinger Publishing, LLC.

Stack, Richard A. Dead Wrong: Violence, Vengeance, & the Victims of Capital Punishment, 1 vol. 2006. (Illus.). 320p. 49.95 *(978-0-275-99221-7(7)*, C9221, Praeger Pubs.) Greenwood Publishing Group, Inc.

Sundby, Scott E. A Life & Death Decision: A Jury Weighs the Death Penalty. 2007. (ENG.). 240p. pap. 17.95 *(978-0-230-60063-8(8))* Palgrave Macmillan.

Temple, John. The Last Lawyer: The Fight to Save Death Row Inmates. 2009. (ENG.). 224p. 25.00 *(978-1-60473-355-6(1))* Univ. Pr. of Mississippi.

Thurshwell, Adam. Capital Punishment. 2013. (ENG.). 240p. 150.00 *(978-0-415-42423-3(2))*; pap. 37.95 *(978-1-84568-111-1(8))* Taylor & Francis Group GBR. (Routledge Cavendish). Dist: Taylor & Francis Group.

Tórrez, Robert J. Myth of the Hanging Tree: Stories of Crime & Punishment in Territorial New Mexico. 2008. (ENG., Illus.). 200p. pap. 19.95 *(978-0-8263-4379-6(1))* Univ. of New Mexico Pr.

Trevaskes, Susan. The Death Penalty in Contemporary China. 2012. (Palgrave Series in Asian Goverance Ser.). (ENG., Illus.). 320p. 90.00 ***(978-0-230-61354-6(3))*** Palgrave Macmillan.

U. S. Congress, House Committee on the Judiciary Staff. Abolition of Capital Punishment. (Capital Punishment Ser.). reprint ed. 39.50 *(978-0-404-62430-9(8))* AMS Pr., Inc.

—Capital Punishment. (Capital Punishment Ser.). reprint ed. 49.50 *(978-0-404-62431-6(6))* AMS Pr., Inc.

U. S. Congress Senate Committee on the Judiciary Staff. Imposition of Capital Punishment. (Capital Punishment Ser.). reprint ed. 40.00 *(978-0-404-62432-3(4))* AMS Pr., Inc.

—To Abolish the Death Penalty. (Capital Punishment Ser.). reprint ed. 44.00 *(978-0-404-62433-0(2))* AMS Pr., Inc.

—To Establish Constitutional Procedures for the Imposition of Capital Punishment. (Capital Punishment Ser.). reprint ed. 40.00 *(978-0-404-62434-7(0))* AMS Pr., Inc.

—To Establish Rational Criteria for the Imposition of Capital Punishment. (Capital Punishment Ser.). reprint ed. 47.50 *(978-0-404-62435-4(9))* AMS Pr., Inc.

Urbina, Martin G. Capital Punishment in America: Race & the Death Penalty over Time. 2012. pap. ***(978-1-59332-445-2(6))*** LFB Scholarly Publishing LLC.

VanLandingham, Frances. Back on Nowhere Road. 2007. per. 14.95 *(978-1-59712-080-7(4))* Catawba Publishing Co.

Vaughn, Courtney. To Be among the Living. 2009. 468p. pap. *(978-3-639-14971-5(8))* VDM Verlag Dr. Mueller e.K.

Vollum, Scott. Last Words & the Death Penalty: Voices of the Condemned & their Co-Victims. 2007. (Criminal Justice). 314p. lib. bdg. 75.00 *(978-1-59332-264-9(X))* LFB Scholarly Publishing LLC.

—Last Words & the Death Penalty: Voices of the Condemned & Their Co-Victims. 2010. (Illus.). 316p. pap. 35.95 *(978-1-59332-436-0(7))* LFB Scholarly Publishing LLC.

Walker, Ida. The Death Penalty. 2008. (Essential Viewpoints Set 2 Ser.). (Illus.). 112p. (YA). (gr. 7-12). 34.22 *(978-1-60453-055-1(3))* ABDO Publishing Co.

Walker, Thomas. Eligible for Execution: Daryl Atkins & the Death Penalty, 00 vols. rev. ed. 2008. 320p. (C). pap. 33.00 *(978-0-87289-418-1(5))* CQ Pr.

Walsh, Dermot. Beneath Cannock's Clock: The Last Man Hanged in Ireland. 2009. (ENG., Illus.). 160p. pap. 19.95 *(978-1-85635-627-5(2))* Mercier Pr., Ltd., The IRL. Dist: Dufour Editions, Inc.

Waterkeyn, Xavier. Death Row: Profiles of People Who Face the Ultimate Penalty. 2006. (ENG., Illus.). 208p. per. 14.95 *(978-1-74110-387-8(8))* New Holland Pubs. Pty. Ltd. AUS. Dist: Tuttle Publishing.

Williams, Kenneth. Most Deserving Death? An Analysis of the Supreme Court's Death Penalty Jurisprudence. 2012. (Law, Justice & Power Ser.). (Illus.). 226p. 99.95 ***(978-0-7546-7885-4(7))*** Ashgate Publishing Co.

Wilson, R. Michael. Legal Executions after Statehood in North Dakota, South Dakota, Wyoming, Montana, Idaho, Washington & Oregon: A Comprehensive Registry. 2010. (ENG., Illus.). 416p. pap. 95.00 *(978-0-7864-6126-4(8))* McFarland & Co., Inc. Pubs.

—Legal Executions in Nebraska, Kansas & Oklahoma Including the Indian Territory: A Comprehensive History. 2012. (ENG.). pap. 125.00 ***(978-0-7864-6651-1(0))*** McFarland & Co., Inc. Pubs.

Wilson, R. Michael. Legal Executions in the Western Territories, 1847-1911: Arizona, Colorado, Idaho, Kansas, Montana, Nebraska, Nevada, New Mexico, North Dakota, Oklahoma, Oregon, South Dakota, Utah, Washington & Wyoming. 2010. (ENG., Illus.). 228p. pap. 95.00 *(978-0-7864-4825-8(3))* McFarland & Co., Inc. Pubs.

Wolfe, Burton H. Pileup on Death Row. (Capital Punishment Ser.). (Illus.). reprint ed. 46.50 *(978-0-404-62436-1(7))* AMS Pr., Inc.

Wollschlager, Nicholas. Capital Punishment Through Political Affiliation. 2011. 56p. pap. ***(978-3-8443-0613-2(7))*** Lambert Academic Publishing.

Wright, Valerie L. Could Quicker Executions Deter Homicides? The Relationship Between Celerity, Capital Punishment, & Murder. 2011. (ENG.). 180p. 65.00 *(978-1-59332-460-5(X))* LFB Scholarly Publishing LLC.

Yorke, Jon. Against the Death Penalty: International Initiatives & Implications. 2008. (Law, Justice & Power Ser.). (Illus.). 334p. 134.95 *(978-0-7546-7413-9(4))* Ashgate Publishing Co.

CAPITAL PUNISHMENT—RELIGIOUS ASPECTS

Attridge, Harold W. The Bible & the Death Penalty. 2007. (ENG.). 224p. 25.00 *(978-0-300-11178-1(9))* Yale Univ. Pr.

Lukenbill, David. Capital Punishment & Catholic Social Teaching: A Tradition of Support. 2009. (Illus.). 121p. pap. 14.95 *(978-0-9791670-7-2(8))* LampStand Foundation, The.

Seay, Scott D. Hanging Between Heaven & Earth. 2009. 232p. 36.00 *(978-0-87580-402-6(0))* Northern Illinois Univ. Pr.

Yoder, John Howard & Nugent, John C. The End of Sacrifice: The Capital Punishment Writings of John Howard Yoder. 2011. 286p. pap. ***(978-0-8361-9464-7(0))*** Herald Pr.

CAPITAL PUNISHMENT—GREAT BRITAIN

Clark, Richard. Capital Punishment in Britain. 2009. (ENG., Illus.). 336p. 32.95 *(978-0-7110-3413-6(3))* Allan, Ian Publishing GBR. Dist: BookMasters Distribution Services (BDS).

Gregory, James. Victorians Against the Gallows: Capital Punishment & the Abolitionist Movement in Nineteenth Century Britain. 2011. (Library of Victorian Studies). (ENG., Illus.). 384p. 105.00 ***(978-1-84885-694-3(6))*** I. B. Tauris & Co., Ltd. GBR. Dist: Macmillan.

McKenzie, Andrea. Tyburn's Martyrs: Execution in England, 1675-1775. 2007. (Hambledon Continuum Ser.). (ENG., Illus.). 336p. 65.00 *(978-1-84725-171-8(4)*, Hambledon Continuum) Continuum International Publishing Group, Ltd. GBR. Dist: National Bk. Network.

Skene, Felicia. Scenes from a Silent World: Or, Prisons & their Inmates. 2010. (Cambridge Library Collection - Women's Writing Ser.). 276p. pap. 23.99 *(978-1-108-02191-3(3))* Cambridge Univ. Pr.

Webb, Simon. Execution: A History of Capital Punishment in Britain. 2012. (ENG., Illus.). 160p. pap. 16.95 ***(978-0-7524-6407-7(8))*** History Pr. Ltd.,The GBR. Dist: Independent Pubs. Group.

Yetter, Leigh, ed. Public Execution in England, 1563-1868: A History in Documents, 4 vols. 2009. (ENG., Illus.). 1728p. 625.00 *(978-1-85196-942-5(X))* Pickering & Chatto Pubs., Ltd. GBR. Dist: Ashgate Publishing Co.

—Public Execution in England, 1563-1968, 4 vols., Pt. 2. 2010. (ENG., Illus.). 1734p. 625.00 *(978-1-85196-944-9(6))* Pickering & Chatto Pubs., Ltd. GBR. Dist: Ashgate Publishing Co.

CAPITAL SINS

see Deadly Sins

CAPITALISM

see also Capital; Christianity and Economics; Entrepreneurship; Mixed Economy; Technocracy

Abbott, Richard H. Cotton & Capital. 2009. 306p. pap. 29.95 *(978-1-55849-745-0(5))* Univ. of Massachusetts Pr.

Aburdene, Patricia. Megatrends 2010: The Rise of Conscious Capitalism. 2007. (ENG., Illus.). 248p. per. 16.95 *(978-1-57174-539-2(4))* Hampton Roads Publishing Co., Inc.

Adamovsky, Ezequiel. Anti-Capitalism. Trigona, Marie, tr. from SPA. 2011. (ENG., Illus.). 192p. pap. 14.95 ***(978-1-60980-087-1(7))*** Seven Stories Pr.

Adams, Jessica. Wounds of Returning: Race, Memory, & Property on the Postslavery Plantation. 2007. (New Directions in Southern Studies). (ENG., Illus.). 256p. 73.95 *(978-0-8078-3104-5(2))*; per. 24.95 *(978-0-8078-5801-1(3))* Univ. of North Carolina Pr.

Aglietta, Michel & Bai, Guo. China's Development: Capitalism & Empire. 2012. (Rethinking Globalizations Ser.). (ENG., Illus.). 320p. (C). 135.00 ***(978-0-415-53502-1(6))*** Routledge.

Aitken, Rob. Performing Capital: Toward a Cultural Economy of Popular & Global Finance. 2007. (ENG.). 256p. 95.00 *(978-1-4039-7733-5(X))* Palgrave Macmillan.

Akerlof, George A. & Shiller, Robert J. Animal Spirits: Wie Wirtschaft Wirklich Funktioniert. (ENG., Illus.). 2010. 256p. pap. 16.95 *(978-0-691-14592-1(X))* 2009. 264p. (C). 24.95 *(978-0-691-14233-3(5))* Princeton Univ. Pr.

Al-Sadr, Muhammad. The Islamic Economic Doctrine: A Comparative Study. Shubber, Kadom, tr. from ARA. 2010. 422p. pap. *(978-0-9566093-0-4(9))* MECI Ltd.

Albo, Greg, et al. In & Out of Crisis: The Global Financial Meltdown & Left Alternatives. 2010. (Spectre Ser.). (ENG.). 144p. pap. 13.95 *(978-1-60486-212-6(2))* PM Pr.

Albritton, Robert. Let Them Eat Junk: How Capitalism Creates Hunger & Obesity. 2009. (ENG.). 288p. 95.00 *(978-0-7453-2807-2(5))* Pluto Pr. GBR. Dist: Macmillan.

Albritton, Robert, et al, eds. Political Economy & Global Capitalism: The 21st Century, Present & Future. 2010. (Anthem Politics & IR Ser.). (ENG., Illus.). 259p. pap. 40.00 *(978-1-84331-875-0(X))* Anthem Pr. GBR. Dist: Books International, Inc.

Albritton, Robert, told to. Let Them Eat Junk: How Capitalism Creates Hunger & Obesity. 2009. (ENG., Illus.). 259p. pap. 24.95 *(978-1-894037-38-9(3))* Arbeiter Ring Publishing CAN. Dist: AK Pr. Distribution.

Allen, Kieran. Marx & the Alternative to Capitalism, 1 vol. 2011. (ENG.). 224p. pap. 24.00 *(978-0-7453-3002-0(9))* Pluto Pr. GBR. Dist: Macmillan.

Allen, Matthew M. C. & Allen, Matthew. The Varieties of Capitalism Paradigm: Explaining Germany's Comparative Advantage? 2006. (ENG., Illus.). 184p. 110.00 *(978-1-4039-9526-1(5))* Palgrave Macmillan.

Allman, Paula. Critical Education Against Global Capitalism: Karl Marx & Revolutionary Critical Education. 2010. 306p. pap. *(978-94-6091-263-4(X))* Sense Pubs.

Amin, Ash. The Social Economy: Alternative Ways of Thinking about Capitalism & Welfare. 2009. (ENG., Illus.). 288p. 139.95 *(978-1-84813-281-8(6))*; pap. 37.95 *(978-1-84813-282-5(4))* Zed Bks., Ltd. GBR. Dist: Macmillan.

Amin, Samir. Ending the Crisis of Capitalism or Ending Capitalism. 2010. 208p. pap. 27.95 ***(978-1-906387-80-8(X))*** Pambazuka Pr. GBR. Dist: Independent Pubs. Group.

—Global History: A View from the South. 2010. 200p. pap. 24.95 ***(978-1-906387-96-9(6))*** Pambazuka Pr. GBR. Dist: Independent Pubs. Group.

Amin, Samir. The Law of Worldwide Value. 2nd ed. 2010. (ENG.). 160p. 75.00 *(978-1-58367-234-1(6))* Monthly Review Pr.

Amin, Samir & Membrez, James. The World We Wish to See: Revolutionary Objectives in the Twenty-First Century. 2008. (ENG.). 160p. (C). 60.00 *(978-1-58367-172-6(2))*; pap. 15.95 *(978-1-58367-171-9(4))* Monthly Review Pr.

Andersen, Birgitte, ed. Intellectual Property Rights in Contemporary Capitalism. 2011. (Routledge Studies in the Modern World Economy Ser.). (ENG.). 288p. (C). 150.00 *(978-0-415-48346-9(8))* Routledge.

Anderson, Brian C. Democratic Capitalism & Its Discontents. 2007. 225p. (C). 25.00 *(978-1-933859-24-8(5))* ISI Bks.

Anderson, Mark. Japan & the Specter of Imperialism. 2009. (ENG.). 272p. 95.00 *(978-0-230-61922-7(3))* Palgrave Macmillan.

Andreski, Stanislav, ed. Max Weber on Capitalism, Bureaucracy & Religion. 2008. 272p. 39.95 *(978-0-415-48953-9(9))* 2006. 176p. 180.00 *(978-0-415-40214-9(X))* Routledge.

Andreu, Jose Miguel & Rahman, Rita Dulci. Global Democracy for Sustaining Global Capitalism: The Way to Solve Current Global Problems. 2009. (ENG.). 362p. 49.95 *(978-81-7188-730-9(9))* Academic Foundation IND. Dist: Independent Pubs. Group.

Angus, Ian, ed. The Global Fight for Climate Justice: Anticapitalist Responses to Global Warming & Environmental Destruction. 2011. (ENG.). 284p. pap. 24.95 *(978-1-55266-344-8(2))* Fernwood Publishing Co., Ltd. CAN. Dist: Independent Pubs. Group.

Antony, Wayne & Guard, Julie, eds. Bankruptcies & Bailouts. 2009. (ENG.). 168p. pap. 18.95 *(978-1-55266-313-4(2))* Fernwood Publishing Co., Ltd. CAN. Dist: Independent Pubs. Group.

Appleby, Joyce. The Relentless Revolution: A History of Capitalism. (ENG.). 2011. 512p. pap. 17.95 *(978-0-393-33939-0(4)*, 33939) 2010. 494p. 29.95 *(978-0-393-06894-8(3)*, 6894) Norton, W. W. & Co., Inc.

Arnold, Thurman W., et al. The Future of Democratic Capitalism: Benjamin Franklin Lectures, Second Series 1949. 2011. 120p. 39.95 ***(978-1-258-08726-5(X))*** Literary Licensing, LLC.

Arrighi, Giovanni. Long Twentieth Century: Money, Power & the Origins of Our Time. rev. ed. 2010. (ENG., Illus.). 432p. pap. 26.95 *(978-1-84467-304-9(9)*, 844304) Verso Bks. GBR. Dist: Norton, W. W. & Co., Inc.

—Long Twentieth Century: Money, Power & the Origins of Our Time, New Edition Money, Power & the Origins of Our Time. rev. ed. 2010. (ENG., Illus.). 400p. 110.00 *(978-1-84467-321-6(9)*, 844321) Verso Bks. GBR. Dist: Norton, W. W. & Co., Inc.

Ashworth, John. Slavery, Capitalism, & Politics in the Antebellum Republic: The Coming of the Civil War, 1850-1861, 2 vols. 2008. (ENG.). 694p. per. 34.99 *(978-0-521-71369-6(2))* Cambridge Univ. Pr.

—Slavery, Capitalism, & Politics in the Antebellum Republic: Volume 2: the Coming of the Civil War, 1850-1861, 2 vols. 2008. (ENG.). 694p. 135.00 *(978-0-521-88592-8(2))* Cambridge Univ. Pr.

Aslund, Anders. Russia's Capitalist Revolution: Why Market Reform Succeeded & Democracy Failed. 2007. (Illus.). 356p. per. 26.95 *(978-0-88132-409-9(4))* Peterson Institute for International Economics.

Atherton, John. Transfiguring Capitalism: An Enquiry into Religion & Global Change. 2008. 342p. pap. *(978-0-334-02831-4(0))* Hymns Ancient & Modern Ltd.

Aubauer, Hans Peter & Knoflacher, Hermann, eds. Kapitalismus gezähmt? Sozialer Wohlstand innerhalb der Naturgrenzen: Mit Beiträgen von Rudolf Edlinger, Franz Fischler, Mathias Binswanger, Hermann Knoflacher, Manfred Sliwka, Markus Knoflacher, Gerlind Weber, Armin Reller, Hans Peter Aubauer und Klaus Woltron. 2010. 298p. pap. 43.95 *(978-3-631-58919-9(0))* Lang, Peter GmbH, Europaischer Verlag der Wissenschaften DEU. Dist: Lang, Peter.

Aymard, Maurice. Dutch Capital & World Capitalism: Capitalisme hollondais et capitalisme Mondial. 2008. (Studies in Modern Capitalism Ser.). (FRE & ENG.). 324p. pap. 42.00 *(978-0-521-08607-3(8))* Cambridge Univ. Pr.

Slavoj. Living in the End Times. 2011. (ENG.). 520p. pap. 22.95 *(978-1-84467-702-3(8)*, 844702) Verso Bks. GBR. Dist: Norton, W. W. & Co., Inc.

Backhaus, Jürgen G. The Reformation: As a Pre-Condition for Modern Capitalism. 2011. 280p. pap. 34.95 ***(978-3-643-10737-4(4))*** Lit Verlag DEU. Dist: Transaction Pubs.

Bagchi, Amiya Kumar. Perilous Passage: Mankind & the Global Ascendancy of Capital. 2008. (World Social Change Ser.). (ENG., Illus.). 422p. pap. 37.95 *(978-0-7425-3921-1(0))* Rowman & Littlefield Publishers, Inc.

Bajorek, Jennifer. Counterfeit Capital: Poetic Labor & Revolutionary Irony. 2008. (ENG.). 160p. 50.00 *(978-0-8047-5824-6(7))* Stanford Univ. Pr.

Balakrishnan, Gopal. Antagonistics: Capitalism & Power in an Age of War. 2009. (ENG.). 200p. 110.00 *(978-1-84467-268-4(9)*, 844268); pap. 26.95 *(978-1-84467-269-1(7)*, 844269) Verso Bks. GBR. Dist: Norton, W. W. & Co., Inc.

Ball, Stephen J., et al, eds. Education, Capitalism & the Global Crisis. 2012. (ENG.). 112p. 125.00 ***(978-0-415-69342-4(X))*** Routledge.

Barbalet, Jack. Weber, Passion & Profits: 'The Protestant Ethic & the Spirit of Capitalism' in Context. 2008. (ENG., Illus.). 264p. 96.99 *(978-0-521-89509-5(X))* Cambridge Univ. Pr.

—Weber, Passion & Profits: 'the Protestant Ethic & the Spirit of Capitalism' in Context. 2011. (ENG.). 264p. pap. 39.99 *(978-0-521-17444-2(9))* Cambridge Univ. Pr.

Barber, Benjamin R. & Barber, Benjamin. Consumed: How Markets Corrupt Children, Infantilize Adults, & Swallow Citizens Whole. 2008. (ENG.). 416p. per. 16.95 *(978-0-393-33089-2(3)*, 33089) Norton, W. W. & Co., Inc.

Barbera, Robert. The Cost of Capitalism: Understanding Market Mayhem & Stabilizing Our Economic Future. 2009. (ENG., Illus.). 240p. 27.95 *(978-0-07-162844-0(4)*, 0071628444) McGraw-Hill Cos., The.

Barbour, Violet. Capitalism in Amsterdam in the Seventeenth Century. (Johns Hopkins University. Studies in the Social Sciences, Thirtieth Ser.: 1). reprint ed. 39.50 *(978-0-404-61313-6(6))* AMS Pr., Inc.

Barma, Naazneen H. & Vogel Steven, K., eds. The Political Economy Reader: Markets as Institutions. 2007. (ENG., Illus.). 584p. 143.00 *(978-0-415-95492-1(4))* Routledge.

Barnes, Jack. Capitalism's Long Hot Winter Has Begun. 2009. (PER., Illus.). 144p. pap. 10.00 *(978-964-5783-13-4(5))* Pathfinder Pr.

—The Working Class & the Transformation of Learning: The Fraud of Education Reform under Capitalism. 2007. (GRE.). 65p. 5.00 *(978-960-88214-6-0(0))* Pathfinder Pr.

Barnes, Peter. Capitalism 3. 0: A Guide to Reclaiming the Commons. 2006. (BK Currents Ser.). (ENG., Illus.). 195p. 22.95 *(978-1-57675-361-3(1))* Berrett-Koehler Pubs., Inc.

Bartels, Anke, et al, eds. Re/defining the Matrix: Reflections on Time - Space - Agency, Vol. 3. 2006. (Transpects Ser.). (Illus.). 248p. pap. *(978-0-8204-8706-9(6))* Lang, Peter AG.

Bauman, Zygmunt. Living on Borrowed Time: Conversations with Citlali Rovirosa-Madrazo. 2010. (ENG.). 100p. 64.95 *(978-0-7456-4738-8(3))*; pap. 22.95 *(978-0-7456-4739-5(1))* Polity Pr. GBR. Dist: Wiley, John & Sons, Inc.

Baumol, William J., et al. Good Capitalism, Bad Capitalism, & the Economics of Growth & Prosperity. 2009. (ENG., Illus.). 336p. pap. 22.00 *(978-0-300-15832-8(7))* Yale Univ. Pr.

Beatty, Jack. Age of Betrayal: The Triumph of Money in America, 1865-1900. 2008. (Vintage Ser.). (ENG., Illus.). 512p. pap. 16.95 *(978-1-4000-3242-6(3)*, Vintage) Knopf Doubleday Publishing Group.

Becker, Juergen. Da Wissen Sie Mehr als Ich! Das Mysterium des Rheinischen Kapitalismus. (GER.). 511p. pap. *(978-3-462-02766-2(2))* Kiepenheuer & Witsch GmbH & Company KG DEU. Dist: International Bk. Import Service, Inc.

Becker, Uwe. Open Varieties of Capitalism: Continuity, Change & Performances. 2009. (ENG., Illus.). 240p. 89.00 *(978-0-230-20164-4(4))* Palgrave Macmillan.

Bedogne, Vincent Frank. Economics of Fulfillment: The Obsolescence of Socialism & Capitalism & an Economic Philosophy for the Future. 2009. (Threshold to Meaning Ser.). 168p. pap. 19.00 *(978-1-55635-925-5(X)*, Wipf and Stock) Wipf & Stock Pubs.

Bell, Daniel A. Beyond Liberal Democracy: Political Thinking for an East Asian Context. 2006. (ENG.). 408p. (C). per. 30.95 *(978-0-691-12308-0(X))*; 379p. 67.50 *(978-0-691-12307-3(1))* Princeton Univ. Pr.

Bell, John R. Capitalism & the Dialectic: The Uno-Sekine Approach to Marxian Political Economy. 2009. (ENG.). 256p. 95.00 *(978-0-7453-2934-5(9))*; pap. 39.95 *(978-0-7453-2933-8(0))* Pluto Pr. GBR. Dist: Macmillan.

Bellamy Foster, John & Magdoff, Fred. What Every Environmentalist Needs to Know about Capitalism. 2011. (ENG.). 160p. pap. 13.95 *(978-1-58367-241-9(9))* Monthly Review Pr.

Berberoglu, Berch. Beyond the Global Capitalist Crisis: The World Economy in Transition. 2011. (Globalization, Crises, & Change Ser.). (Illus.). 236p. 99.95 ***(978-1-4094-1239-7(3))*** Ashgate Publishing Co.

Berberoglu, Berch, ed. Globalization in the 21st Century: Labor, Capital, & the State on a World Scale. 2010. (ENG.). 248p. 84.00 *(978-0-230-61852-7(9))* Palgrave Macmillan.

Bernstein, Andrew. Capitalism Unbound: The Incontestable Moral Case for Individual Rights. 2009. (ENG.). 146p. pap. 20.99 *(978-0-7618-4969-8(6))* Univ. Pr. of America, Inc.

—Capitalist Solutions: A Philosophy of American Moral Dilemmas. 2011. (ENG.). 180p. 34.95 *(978-1-4128-4294-5(8))* Transaction Pubs.

Bernstein, Ann. The Case for Business in Developing Economies. (ENG.). 2012. 408p. (gr. 12). pap. 20.00 ***(978-0-14-352799-2(1))*** 2010. 412p. 34.95 *(978-0-14-302652-5(6))* Penguin Group (USA) Inc. (Penguin Global).

Bernstein, Henry. Agrarian Change Today: Bringing Class Back In. 2010. (Agrarian Change & Peasant Studies Ser.). 160p. pap. 17.95 *(978-1-56549-356-8(7))* Stylus Publishing, LLC.

Best, Beverley. Marx & the Dynamic of the Capital Formation: An Aesthetics of Political Economy. 2010. (ENG.). 252p. 89.00 *(978-0-230-10239-2(5))* Palgrave Macmillan.

Best/Kahn, ed. The Global Industrial Complex: Systems of Domination. 2011. (ENG., Illus.). 344p. 85.00 ***(978-0-7391-3697-3(6))*** Lexington Bks.

Bhengu, Mfuniselwa J. African Economic Humanism: The Rise of an African Economic Philosophy. 2011. (Transformation & Innovation Ser.). 242p. 114.95 *(978-1-4094-0435-4(8)*, Gower Publishing Co., Ltd.) Ashgate Publishing, Ltd. GBR. Dist: Ashgate Publishing Co.

Bhidé, Amar. A Call for Judgment: Sensible Finance for a Dynamic Economy, 1 vol. 2010. (ENG.). 384p. 29.95 *(978-0-19-975607-0(4))* Oxford Univ. Pr., Inc.

Bichler, Shimshon & Nitzan, Jonathan. Capital as Power: A Study of Order & Creorder. 2009. (RIPE Series in Global Political Economy Ser.). (ENG., Illus.). 464p. (C). 140.00 *(978-0-415-47719-2(0))* Routledge.

Biel, Robert. The Entropy of Capitalism. 2011. (Studies in Critical Social Sciences Ser.). (Illus.). 384p. ***(978-90-04-20430-0(X))*** BRILL.

Bindman, Stephen. Pseudo-Capitalism. 2008. 276p. 29.99 *(978-1-4363-6833-9(2))*; pap. 19.99 *(978-1-4363-6832-2(4))* Xlibris Corp.

Birchfield, Vicki L. & Birchfield, Vicki. Income Inequality in Capitalist Democracies: The Interplay of Values & Institutions. 2009. (ENG., Illus.). 232p. 45.00 *(978-0-271-03440-9(8))* Pennsylvania State Univ. Pr.

Bishop, Matthew & Green, Michael. The Road from Ruin: How to Revive Capitalism & Put America Back on Top. 2011. (ENG.). 400p. pap. 15.00 *(978-0-307-46423-1(7)*, Crown Business) Crown Publishing Group.

Bittelman, Alexander & Jerome, V. J. Leninism, the Only Marxism Today: A Discussion of the Characteristics of Declining Capitalism. 2011. 66p. 36.95 ***(978-1-258-03053-7(5)***, Literary Licensing, LLC.

Blanchard, Kathryn D. The Protestant Ethic or the Spirit of Capitalism: Christians, Freedom, & Free Markets. 2010. 262p. pap. 29.00 *(978-1-60608-659-9(6)*, Cascade Bks.) Wipf & Stock Pubs.

Blaney, David L. & Inayatullah, Naeem. Savage Economics: Wealth, Poverty & the Temporal Walls of Capitalism. 2010. (RIPE Series in Global Political Economy Ser.). (ENG.). 248p. (C). 130.00 *(978-0-415-54847-2(0))*; pap. 39.95 *(978-0-415-54848-9(9))* Taylor & Francis Group GBR. (Routledge). Dist: Taylor & Francis Group.

Bloom, Howard. Genius of the Beast: A Radical Re-Vision of Capitalism. 2009. (ENG.). 528p. 29.00 *(978-1-59102-754-6(3))* Prometheus Bks., Pubs.

Bloom, Howard. The Genius of the Beast: A Radical Re-Vision of Capitalism. 2011. (ENG.). 607p. pap. 21.00 ***(978-1-61614-478-4(5))*** Prometheus Bks., Pubs.

Bluhm, Katharina & Schmidt, Rudi, eds. Change in SMEs: The New European Capitalism. 2008. (ENG., Illus.). 320p. (C). 105.00 *(978-0-230-51589-5(4))* Palgrave Macmillan.

Bober, Stanley. Marx & the Meaning of Capitalism: Introduction & Analyses. 2008. (ENG., Illus.). 224p. 89.00 *(978-0-230-60679-1(2))* Palgrave Macmillan.

Bogle, John C. The Battle for the Soul of Capitalism. 2006. (ENG.). 288p. per. 16.00 *(978-0-300-11971-8(2))* Yale Univ. Pr.

Bojicic, Savo. America ... America ... or Is It? 2010. 484p. 30.99 *(978-1-4520-3435-5(4))*; pap. 20.49 *(978-1-4520-3433-1(8))* AuthorHouse.

Boltanski, Luc & Chiapello, Eve. The New Spirit of Capitalism. Elliott, Gregory, tr. from FRE. 2007. (ENG.). 656p. per. 49.95 *(978-1-84467-165-6(8)*, 844165) Verso Bks. GBR. Dist: Norton, W. W. & Co., Inc.

Bonsell, Thomas. Saving America: Using Democratic Capitalism to Rescue the Nation from Economic Folly. 2011. 260p. pap. 22.95 ***(978-0-87586-868-4(1))***; pap. 22.95 ***(978-0-87586-867-7(3))*** Algora Publishing.

Bootle, R. P. The Trouble with Markets: Saving Capitalism from Itself. 2nd ed. 2011. (ENG., Illus.). 256p. pap. 21.99 ***(978-1-85788-558-3(9))*** Ebsco Publishing.

Bootle, Roger. The Trouble with Markets: Saving Capitalism from Itself. 2009. (ENG.). 282p. 29.95 *(978-1-85788-537-8(6))* Ebsco Publishing.

Bottomore, Tom. Theories of Modern Capitalism (Routledge Revivals) 2010. (Routledge Revivals Ser.). 98p. 85.00 *(978-0-415-57894-3(9))* Routledge.

Bowles, Paul. Capitalism. 2006. (Short Histories of Big Ideas Ser.). (ENG.). 224p. pap. 24.95 *(978-0-582-50609-1(3))* Longman Publishing Group.

—Capitalism. 2nd rev. ed. 2012. (Seminar Studies in History Ser.). (ENG.). 192p. (C). pap. 28.00 *(978-1-4082-6922-0(8))* Longman Publishing Group.

Bowles, Samuel & Gintis, Herbert. Democracy & Capitalism: Property, Community, & the Contradictions of Modern Social Thought. 2010. (Routledge Revivals Ser.). (ENG.). 256p. 115.00 *(978-0-415-60881-7(3))* Routledge.

Bowles, Samuel & Gintis, Herbert. Schooling in Capitalist America: Educational Reform & the Contradictions of Economic Life. 2011. (ENG.). 380p. pap. 22.00 ***(978-1-60846-131-8(9))*** Haymarket Bks.

Bowman, John R. Capitalist Collective Action: Competition, Cooperation & Conflict in the Coal Industry. 2006. (Studies in Marxism & Social Theory Ser.). (ENG.). 272p. pap. 55.00 *(978-0-521-02882-0(5))* Cambridge Univ. Pr.

Bowyer, Jerry. The Free Market Capitalist's Survival Guide: How to Invest & Thrive in an Era of Rampant Socialism. 2012. (ENG.). 240p. pap. 16.99 ***(978-0-06-182484-5(4))*** Broadside Bks. GBR. Dist: HarperCollins Pubs.

Bradley, Robert L., Jr. Capitalism at Work: Business, Government, & Energy, 3 vols., Vol. 1. 2008. (ENG., Illus.). 500p. 39.95 *(978-0-9764041-7-0(6))* M & M Scrivener Pr.

Braithwaite, John. Regulatory Capitalism: How It Works, Ideas for Making It Work Better. (Illus.). 264p. 2009. pap. 50.00 *(978-1-84844-471-3(0))* 2008. (C). 125.00 *(978-1-84720-002-0(8))* Elgar, Edward Publishing, Inc.

Branden, Barbara. The Moral Antagonism of Capitalism & Socialism. 2011. 8p. pap. 35.95 ***(978-1-258-04960-7(0))*** Literary Licensing, LLC.

Brass, Tom. Labour Regime Change in the Twenty-First Century: Unfreedom, Capitalism & Primitive Accumulation. 2011. (Studies in Critical Social Sciences Ser.). (Illus.). 352p. ***(978-90-04-20247-4(1))*** BRILL.

Bratton, John, et al. Capitalism & Classical Sociological Theory. 2009. (ENG., Illus.). 325p. pap. *(978-0-8020-9681-4(6))* Univ. of Toronto Pr.

Bremmer, Ian. The End of the Free Market: Who Wins the War Between States & Corporations? (ENG.). 240p. (gr. 12). 2011. 16.00 *(978-1-59184-440-2(1)*, Portfolio Trade) 2010. 26.95 *(978-1-59184-301-6(4)*, Portfolio (Hardcover)) Penguin Group (USA) Inc.

Brennan, James & Rougier, Marcelo. The Politics of National Capitalism: Peronism & the Argentine Bourgeoisie 1946-1947. 2009. (ENG.). 224p. 60.00 *(978-0-271-03571-0(4))* Pennsylvania State Univ. Pr.

Brenner, Robert. Property & Progress: The Historical Origins & Social Foundations of Self-Sustaining. 2009. (ENG.). 400p. 34.95 *(978-1-84467-318-6(9))* Verso Bks. GBR. Dist: Norton, W. W. & Co., Inc.

Brick, Howard. Transcending Capitalism. 2006. 304p. 43.95 *(978-0-8014-2590-5(5))* Cornell Univ. Pr.

Brockelman, Thomas. Zizek & Heidegger: The Question Concerning Techno-Capitalism. (ENG.). 198p. 2012. pap. 44.95 ***(978-1-4411-9929-4(2))*** 2009. (Illus.). 130.00 *(978-0-8264-9777-2(2))* Continuum International Publishing Group, Ltd. GBR. Dist: National Bk. Network.

Brockington, Daniel & Duffy, Rosaleen, eds. Capitalism & Conservation. 2011. (Antipode Book Ser.: 17). (ENG.). 344p. pap. 34.95 *(978-1-4443-3834-8(X)*, Wiley-Blackwell) Wiley, John & Sons, Inc.

Brook, Yaron & Watkins, Don. Free Market Revolution: How Ayn Rand's Ideas Can End Big Government. 2012. (ENG.). 272p. 27.00 ***(978-0-230-34169-2(1))*** Palgrave Macmillan.

Brooks, Arthur & Wehner, Peter. Wealth & Justice: The Morality of Democratic Capitalism Common Sense Concepts. 2010. (ENG.). 88p. pap. 9.95 *(978-0-8447-4377-6(1)*, AEI Pr.) American Enterprise Institute for Public Policy Research.

Brooks, Arthur C. The Road to Freedom: How to Win the Fight for Free Enterprise. 2012. (ENG.). 224p. (gr. 9). 25.99 ***(978-0-465-02940-2(X))*** Basic Bks.

Brooks, Arthur C. & Wehner, Peter. Wealth & Justice: The Morality of Democratic Capitalism. 2010. E-Book *(978-0-8447-4378-3(X)*, AEI Pr.) American Enterprise Institute for Public Policy Research.

Brubaker, Pamela K., et al, eds. Justice in a Global Economy: Strategies for Home, Community, & World. 2006. (ENG.). 165p. per. 20.00 *(978-0-664-22955-9(7))* Westminster John Knox Pr.

Bruff, Ian. Culture & Consensus in European Varieties of Capitalism: A Common Sense Analysis. 2008. (ENG.). 208p. 89.00 *(978-0-230-54932-6(2))* Palgrave Macmillan.

Buchanan, Ian & Buchanan. Deleuze & Guattari's Anti-Oedipus. 2008. (Reader's Guides). (ENG.). 182p. 19.95 *(978-0-8264-9149-7(9))*; 100.00 *(978-0-8264-9148-0(0))* Continuum International Publishing Group, Ltd. GBR. Dist: National Bk. Network.

Buchholz, Rogene & Buchholz, Rogene A. Rethinking Capitalism: Community & Responsibility in Business. 2009. (Routledge Studies in Business Ethics Ser.). (ENG., Illus.). 258p. (C). 150.00 *(978-0-415-99721-6(6))* Routledge.

Buck, Daniel. Constructing China's Capitalism: Urban-Rural Industries in the Shanghai Region. 2012. (China in Transformation Ser.). (ENG., Illus.). 272p. 85.00 ***(978-0-230-34095-4(4))*** Palgrave Macmillan.

Buder, Stanley. Capitalizing on Change: A Social History of American Business. 2009. (Published for the Omohundro Institute of Early American History & Culture, Williamsburg, VA Ser.). (ENG., Illus.). 568p. 47.50 *(978-0-8078-3231-8(6))* Univ. of North Carolina Pr.

Budgen, Sebastian, et al, eds. Lenin Reloaded: Toward a Politics of Truth. Fernbach, David, tr. 2007. (SIC Ser.). (ENG.). 352p. per. 25.95 *(978-0-8223-3941-0(2))*; 94.95 *(978-0-8223-3929-8(3))* Duke Univ. Pr.

Bugra, Ayse & Agartan, Kaan. Reading Karl Polanyi for the Twenty-First Century: Market Economy as a Political Project. 2007. (ENG.). 284p. 100.00 *(978-1-4039-8393-0(3))* Palgrave Macmillan.

Bunker, Stephen G. & Ciccantell, Paul S. East Asia & the Global Economy: Japan's Ascent, with Implications for China's Future. 2007. (Johns Hopkins Studies in Globalization Ser.). (ENG.). 264p. (gr. 17). 47.00 *(978-0-8018-8593-8(0))* Johns Hopkins Univ. Pr.

Burawoy, Michael. The Extended Case Method: Four Countries, Four Decades, Four Great Transformations, & One Theoretical Tradition. 2009. 288p. 55.00 *(978-0-520-25900-3(9))*; pap. 24.95 *(978-0-520-25901-0(7))* Univ. of California Pr.

Bush, Ray. Poverty & Neoliberalism: Persistence & Reproduction in the Global South, 1 vol. 2007. (Third World in Global Politics Ser.). (ENG., Illus.). 237p. 36.00 *(978-0-7453-1960-5(2))*; 256p. lib. bdg. 100.00 *(978-0-7453-1961-2(0))* Pluto Pr. GBR. Dist: Macmillan.

Caffentzis, George. In Letters of Blood & Fire: Work, Machines, & Value in the Bad Infinity of Capitalism. 2012. (Common Notions Ser.). (ENG.). 300p. pap. 19.95 ***(978-1-60486-335-2(8))*** PM Pr.

Cairnie, Julie & Walls, Marion. Revisiting Robert Tressell's Mugsborough: New Perspectives on the Ragged Trousered Philanthropists. 2008. 240p. 99.95 *(978-1-60497-551-2(2))* Cambria Pr.

Calhoun, Craig & Derluguian, Georgi, eds. Business as Usual: The Roots of the Global Financial Meltdown. 2011. (ENG., Illus.). 312p. 65.00 *(978-0-8147-7277-5(3))* New York Univ. Pr.

Callinicos, Alex. Bonfire of Illusions: The Twin Crises of the Liberal World. 2010. (ENG., Illus.). 144p. 59.95 *(978-0-7456-4875-0(4))*; pap. 19.95 *(978-0-7456-4876-7(2))* Polity Pr. GBR. Dist: Wiley, John & Sons, Inc.

Capitalism Nature Socialism. 2006. (ENG.). pap. 41.95 ***(978-0-415-40085-5(6)***, Taylor & Francis) Taylor & Francis Group GBR. Dist: Taylor & Francis Group.

Capitalism Nature Socialism, 16.2. 2008. pap. 41.95 *(978-0-415-37396-8(4))* Routledge.

Capitalism Nature Socialism, 16.3. 2008. pap. 41.95 *(978-0-415-37397-5(2))* Routledge.

Capitalism Nature Socialism, 16.4. 2008. (ENG.). pap. 41.95 *(978-0-415-37398-2(0))* Routledge.

Carney, Richard & Carney, Richard W. Contested Capitalism: The Political Origins of Financial Institutions. 2009. (Routledge Advances in International Political Economy Ser.). (ENG., Illus.). 208p. (C). 128.00 *(978-0-415-54734-5(2))* Routledge.

Carroll, William K. The Making of a Transnational Capitalist Class: Corporate Power in the 21st Century. 2010. (ENG., Illus.). 320p. 134.95 *(978-1-84813-442-3(8))*; pap. 37.95 *(978-1-84813-443-0(6))* Zed Bks., Ltd. GBR. Dist: Macmillan.

Castillo, Greg. Cold War on the Home Front: The Soft Power of Midcentury Design. 2010. (ENG., Illus.). 304p. pap. 24.95 *(978-0-8166-4692-0(9))* Univ. of Minnesota Pr.

Catherwood, Christopher & DiVanna, Joseph. Merchants of Fear: Why They Want Us to Be Afraid. 2008. (ENG., Illus.). 272p. 24.95 *(978-1-59921-281-4(1)*, Lyons Pr.) Globe Pequot Pr., The.

Cato, Molly Scott. Market, Schmarket: Building the Post-Capitalist Economy. 2006. (Illus.). 206p. 44.95 *(978-1-873797-51-8(6))*; per. 26.95 *(978-1-873797-50-1(8))* New Clarion Pr., Ltd. GBR. Dist: SPD-Small Pr. Distribution.

Cazdyn, Eric. The Already Dead: The New Time of Politics, Culture, & Illness. 2012. (ENG., Illus.). 248p. 84.95 ***(978-0-8223-5203-7(6))***; pap. 23.95 ***(978-0-8223-5228-0(1))*** Duke Univ. Pr.

Cedroni, Lorella. Italian Critics of Capitalism. 2010. (ENG.). 190p. 63.50 *(978-0-7391-4234-9(8))*; pap. 28.50 *(978-0-7391-4235-6(6))* Lexington Bks.

Centeno, Miguel A. & Cohen, Joseph N. Global Capitalism: A Sociological Perspective. 2010. (PESS - Polity Economy & Society Ser.: 7). (ENG., Illus.). 180p. 69.95 *(978-0-7456-4450-9(3))*; pap. 22.95 *(978-0-7456-4451-6(1))* Polity Pr. GBR. Dist: Wiley, John & Sons, Inc.

Center for Socialist History, compiled by. Neither Capitalism nor Socialism: Theories of Bureaucratic Collectivism. 2007. 349p. pap. 19.99 *(978-0-916695-15-6(8))* Ctr. for Socialist History.

Chang, Claude. Aggressive Capitalism: The Overleveraging of America's Wealth, Integrity, & Dollar. 2010. (ENG.). 198p. pap. 29.50 *(978-0-7618-5294-0(8))* Univ. Pr. of America, Inc.

Chang, Dae-oup. Capitalist Development in Korea: Labour, Capital & the Myth of the Developmental State. (Routledge Advances in Korean Studies). (ENG., Illus.). 224p. (C). 2012. pap. 42.95 ***(978-0-415-54100-8(X))*** 2009. 158.00 *(978-0-415-45940-2(0))* Routledge.

Chang, Ha-Joon. Bad Samaritans: The Myth of Free Trade & the Secret History of Capitalism. 2008. (ENG.). 288p. pap. 17.00 *(978-1-59691-598-5(6))* Bloomsbury Publishing.

—23 Things They Don't Tell You about Capitalism. 2011. (ENG.). 304p. 25.00 *(978-1-60819-166-6(4))* Bloomsbury Publishing.

Chang, Yun-shik. Transformations in Twentieth Century Korea. 2009. 382p. pap. 39.95 *(978-0-415-54695-9(8))* Routledge.

Chartier, Gary & Johnson, Charles W., eds. Markets Not Capitalism: Individualist Anarchism Against Bosses, Inequality, Corporate Power, & Structural Poverty. 2011. (ENG.). 440p. pap. 32.00 ***(978-1-57027-242-4(5))*** Autonomedia.

Cheah, Pheng. Inhuman Conditions: On Cosmopolitanism & Human Rights. 2007. (Illus.). 336p. per. 30.50 *(978-0-674-02394-9(3))* Harvard Univ. Pr.

Chen, Jie & Dickson, Bruce J. Allies of the State: China's Private Entrepreneurs & Democratic Change. 2010. (Illus.). 232p. 45.00 *(978-0-674-04896-6(2))* Harvard Univ. Pr.

Chess, James M. How to Create Overwhelming Republican Majorities. Chess, James M., ed. 2007. 196p. pap. 19.95 *(978-0-9675399-5-9(1))* Okay Enterprises.

Chilcote, Ronald H. Power & the Ruling Classes in Northeast Brazil: Juazeiro & Petrolina in Transition. 2006. (Cambridge Latin American Studies). (ENG.). 404p. pap. 75.00 *(978-0-521-02881-3(7))* Cambridge Univ. Pr.

Choate, Pat. Saving Capitalism: Keeping America Strong. 2009. (Vintage Ser.). (ENG., Illus.). 288p. pap. 15.00 *(978-0-307-47483-4(6)*, Vintage) Knopf Doubleday Publishing Group.

Chu, Yin-Wah. Chinese Capitalisms: Historical Emergence & Political Implications. 2010. (International Political Economy Ser.). (ENG., Illus.). 272p. 89.00 *(978-0-230-57649-0(4))* Palgrave Macmillan.

Ciochetto, Lynne. Globalisation & Advertising in Emerging Economies: Brazil, Russia, India & China. 2011. (Routledge Studies in International Business & the World Economy Ser.). (ENG., Illus.). 200p. (C). 145.00 *(978-0-415-56200-3(7))* Routledge.

Çizakça, Murat. Islamic Capitalism & Finance: Origins, Evolution & the Future. 2011. (Studies in Islamic Finance, Accounting & Governance Ser.). (Illus.). 360p. 150.00 ***(978-0-85793-147-4(4))*** Elgar, Edward Publishing, Inc.

Clarke, John Henrik. Christopher Columbus & the Afrikan Holocaust: Slavery & the Rise of European Capitalism. 2011. (ENG.). 123p. pap. 10.95 ***(978-1-61759-030-6(4))*** EWorld, Inc.

Clarke, Linda. Building Capitalism (Routledge Revivals) 2011. (Routledge Revivals Ser.). (ENG.). 336p. 140.00 ***(978-0-415-68788-1(8))*** Routledge.

Clarke, Simon. The Development of Capitalism in Russia. 2009. 258p. pap. 39.95 *(978-0-415-54577-8(3))* 2007. 250p. 160.00 *(978-0-415-36825-4(1))* Routledge.

Coase, Ronald & Wang, Ning. How China Became Capitalist. 2012. (International Economic Association Ser.). (ENG., Illus.). 272p. 100.00 ***(978-1-137-01936-3(0))*** Palgrave Macmillan.

Coates, Ken & Simpson, Tony, eds. Reinventing Socialism. 2010. (Illus.). 96p. pap. *(978-0-85124-779-3(2))* Spokesman Bks. GBR. Dist: Coronet Bks.

Coffey, Dan & Thornley, Carole. Globalization & Varieties of Capitalism: New Labour, Economic Policy & the Abject State. 2009. (ENG., Illus.). 208p. 89.00 *(978-0-230-55309-5(5))* Palgrave Macmillan.

Cohen, G. A. & Otsuka, Michael. On the Currency of Egalitarian Justice, & Other Essays in Political Philosophy. 2011. (ENG.). 288p. (C). 85.00 *(978-0-691-14870-0(8))*; pap. 22.95 *(978-0-691-14871-7(6))* Princeton Univ. Pr.

Coleman, Daniel & Kamboureli, Smaro, eds. Retooling the Humanities: The Culture of Research in Canadian Universities. 2011. (ENG.). 336p. pap. 49.95 *(978-0-88864-541-8(4))* Univ. of Alberta Pr. CAN. Dist: Michigan State Univ. Pr.

Connolly, William E. Capitalism & Christianity, American Style. 2008. (ENG.). 192p. 79.95 *(978-0-8223-4249-6(9))*; pap. 22.95 *(978-0-8223-4272-4(3))* Duke Univ. Pr.

Cooper, Melinda. Life as Surplus: Biotechnology & Capitalism in the Neoliberal Era. 2008. (In Vivo Ser.). (ENG.). 208p. pap. 25.00 *(978-0-295-98791-0(X))* Univ. of Washington Pr.

Corey, Lewis. The Decline of American Capitalism. 2010. 436p. pap. *(978-1-152-02105-1(2))* Books LLC.

Corfe, Robert. The Death of Socialism: The Irrelevance of the Traditional Left & the Call for a Progressive Politics of Universal Humanity. 2009. (ENG.). 190p. pap. 20.99 ***(978-1-906791-16-2(3))*** Arena Bks. GBR. Dist: Lightning Source UK, Ltd.

—Egalitarianism of the Free Society: And the End of Class Conflict. 2008. (ENG.). 335p. per. 32.99 *(978-0-9556055-2-9(0))* Arena Bks. GBR. Dist: Lightning Source UK, Ltd.

—Social Capitalism in Theory & Practice: Emergence of the New Majority, 3 vols. 2008. (ENG.). 324p. per. 32.99 *(978-0-9556055-3-6(9))* Arena Bks. GBR. Dist: Lightning Source UK, Ltd.

—Social Capitalism in Theory & Practice: Prosperity in a Stable World, 3 vols. 2008. (ENG.). 496p. per. 32.99 *(978-0-9556055-5-0(5))* Arena Bks. GBR. Dist: Lightning Source UK, Ltd.

—Social Capitalism in Theory & Practice: The People's Capitalism, 3 vols. 2008. (ENG.). 484p. per. 32.99 *(978-0-9556055-4-3(7))* Arena Bks. GBR. Dist: Lightning Source UK, Ltd.

Cornwall, John & Cornwall, Wendy. Capitalist Development in the Twentieth Century: An Evolutionary-Keynesian Analysis. 2007. (Modern Cambridge Economics Ser.). (ENG.). 304p. pap. 64.00 *(978-0-521-34942-0(7))* Cambridge Univ. Pr.

Corradi, Juan E. South of the Crisis: A Latin American Perspective on the Late Capitalist World. 2010. (Anthem Studies in Development & Globalization Ser.). (ENG.). 172p. 99.00 *(978-1-84331-853-8(9))* Anthem Pr. GBR. Dist: Books International, Inc.

Courvisanos. The Political Economy of Innovation a Kaleckian Perspective. 2012. 336p. 145.00 ***(978-1-84720-596-4(8))*** Elgar, Edward Publishing, Inc.

Cowling, Keith & Cowley, Sue. Beyond Capitalism. (ENG., Illus.). 1p. *(978-1-85567-301-4(0)*, Burns & Oates) Continuum International Publishing Group, Ltd.

Cox, Oliver C. Capitalism & American Leadership. 2011. 350p. 51.95 ***(978-1-258-07054-0(5))*** Literary Licensing, LLC.

Cox, Oliver Cromwell. Foundations of Capitalism. 2011. 512p. 60.95 ***(978-1-258-08066-2(4))*** Literary Licensing, LLC.

Craig, Béatrice & Craig, Beatrice. Backwoods Consumers & Homespun Capitalists: The Rise of a Market Culture in Eastern Canada. 2009. 320p. *(978-0-8020-9317-2(5))* Univ. of Toronto Pr.

Cram101 Textbook Reviews. Outlines & Highlights for a Cultural History of Finance by Irene Finel-Honigman. 2011. 184p. pap. 29.95 ***(978-1-61905-229-1(6))*** Cram101 Inc.

Cram101 Textbook Reviews. Outlines & Highlights for Essentials of Comparative Politics by Patrick Oneil, Isbn: 9780393928761. 2010. 222p. pap. 30.95 *(978-1-61654-999-2(8))* Cram101 Inc.

Cram101 Textbook Reviews & Cram101 Textbook Reviews. Outlines & Highlights for Global Problems & the Culture of Capitalism by Richard Robbins, Isbn: 9780205801053. 2011. 324p. pap. 33.95 ***(978-1-61461-699-3(X))*** Cram101 Inc.

—Outlines & Highlights for the Sociology of Economic Life by Mark Granovetter. 2011. 194p. pap. 30.95 ***(978-1-61830-259-5(0))*** Cram101 Inc.

Cram101 Textbook Reviews Staff. Outlines & Highlights for Global Problems & the Culture of Capitalism by Robbins, Isbn: 0205407412. 2008. 140p. pap. 11.95 *(978-1-4288-6237-1(4))* Cram101 Inc.

—Outlines & Highlights for Global Problems & the Culture of Capitalism by Robbins, Isbn: 0205524877. 2008. 96p. pap. 10.95 *(978-1-4288-6240-1(4))* Cram101 Inc.

Cremin, Colin. Capitalism's New Clothes: Enterprise, Ethics & Enjoyment in Times of Crisis, 1 vol. 2011. (ENG.). 224p. 32.00 *(978-0-7453-2814-0(8))*; lib. bdg. 115.00 *(978-0-7453-2815-7(6))* Pluto Pr. GBR. Dist: Macmillan.

Cucer, Stela. Funding Opportunities of the Companies. 2011. 80p. pap. ***(978-3-8443-1018-4(5))*** Lambert Academic Publishing.

Cudd, Ann & Holmstrom, Nancy. Capitalism, for & Against: A Feminist Debate. 2011. (ENG., Illus.). 360p. 99.00 *(978-0-521-11407-3(1))*; pap. 29.99 *(978-0-521-13211-4(8))* Cambridge Univ. Pr.

Cuddy, Thomas W. Revolutionary Economies: What Archaeology Reveals about the Birth of American Capitalism. 2008. (ENG.). 166p. 80.00 *(978-0-7591-1178-3(2))* Rowman & Littlefield Publishers, Inc.

Cuddy, Thomas Willia. Revolutionary Economies: What Archaeology Reveals about the Birth of American Capitalism. 2008. (ENG.). 166p. pap. 32.95 *(978-0-7591-1179-0(0))* Rowman & Littlefield Publishers, Inc.

Dahlberg, Arthur A. Jobs, Machines & Capitalism. (BCL Ser. I). reprint ed. 20.00 *(978-0-404-01917-4(X))* AMS Pr., Inc.

C

Daianu, Daniel. Which Way Goes Capitalism? In Search of Adequate Policies in a Dramatically Changing World. 2009. (Illus.). 298p. 45.00 *(978-963-9776-47-0(5))* Central European Univ. Pr.

Damroth, George. We've Lost Our Way: Why Political Change Is Necessary & What We Must Do about It. 2011. pap. 20.99 ***(978-1-61739-988-6(4))*** Tate Publishing & Enterprises, LLC.

Daunton, Martin. State & Market in Victorian Britain: War, Welfare & Capitalism. 2008. 352p. 99.00 *(978-1-84383-383-3(2),* Boydell Press) Boydell & Brewer, Ltd. GBR. Dist: Boydell & Brewer, Inc.

D'Aveni. Strategic Capitalism: The New Economic Strategy for Winning the Capitalist Cold War. 2012. (ENG., Illus.). 304p. 30.00 ***(978-0-07-178116-9(1),*** 0071781161) McGraw-Hill Cos., The.

Davenport, Stewart. Friends of the Unrighteous Mammon: Northern Christians & Market Capitalism, 1815-1860. 2008. 256p. 45.00 *(978-0-226-13706-3(6))* Univ. of Chicago Pr.

Davis, Mike & Monk, Daniel Bertrand, eds. Evil Paradises: Dreamworlds of Neoliberalism. (ENG., Illus.). 336p. 2008. pap. 18.95 *(978-1-59558-392-5(0))* 2007. 26.95 *(978-1-59558-076-4(X))* New Pr., The.

De Beuckelaer, Gerard. It's Broken, Let's Fix It: The Zeitgeist & Modern Enterprise. 2010. (ENG., Illus.). xi, 282p. pap. 69.95 *(978-3-642-08672-4(1),* 3642086721) Springer.

de Lange, Deborah E. Cliques & Capitalism: A Modern Networked Theory of the Firm. 2011. (ENG., Illus.). 256p. 95.00 *(978-0-230-11454-8(7))* Palgrave Macmillan.

De Lottinville, Michel. Your Career, Your Money, Your Life: How to Set Yourself Free from Capitalism. 2011. 92p. pap. 11.95 ***(978-1-60976-650-4(4),*** Strategic Bk. Publishing) AEG Literary Publishing Services, Inc.

De Sousa Santos, Boaventura, ed. Another Production Is Possible: Beyond the Capitalist Canon. (ENG.). 2007. 488p. per. 34.95 *(978-1-84467-148-9(8),* 844148) 2006. 512p. 95.00 *(978-1-84467-078-9(3),* 844078) Verso Bks. GBR. Dist: Norton, W. W. & Co., Inc.

Dedelow, Ew. Why Capitalism Works & Government Doesn't: Or, How Government Is Recycling the American Workforce to Pay Its Bills & How the Rich Profit from Big. 2009. 260p. pap. 26.95 *(978-1-4389-7370-8(5))* AuthorHouse.

Degen, Robert. The Triumph of Capitalism. 2009. (ENG.). 217p. pap. 24.95 *(978-1-4128-1145-3(7))* Transaction Pubs.

Degen, Robert A. & Degen, Robert. The Triumph of Capitalism. 2007. (ENG.). 217p. (gr. 11). 39.95 *(978-1-4128-0689-3(5))* Transaction Pubs.

Deleuze, Gilles & Guattari, Felix. Anti-Oedipus: Capitalism & Schizophrenia. (Illus.). 432p. pap. *(978-0-485-30018-5(4))* Continuum International Publishing Group, Ltd.

—Anti-Oedipus: Capitalism & Schizophrenia. Seem, Mark et al, trs. 2009. (ENG.). 432p. (gr. 12-18). 22.00 *(978-0-14-310582-4(5),* Penguin Classics) Penguin Group (USA) Inc.

Demsetz, Harold. From Economic Man to Economic System: Essays on Human Behavior & the Institutions of Capitalism. (ENG.). 198p. (C). 2011. pap. 34.99 ***(978-1-107-64085-6(7))*** 2008. 68.00 *(978-0-521-50997-8(1))* Cambridge Univ. Pr.

Derber, Charles. Greed to Green: Solving Climate Change & Remaking the Economy. 2010. 272p. 125.00 *(978-1-59451-811-9(4));* (ENG.). pap. 23.95 *(978-1-59451-812-6(2))* Paradigm Pubs.

Derber, Charles. Marx's Ghost: Midnight Conversations on Changing the World. 2011. 176p. 93.00 ***(978-1-61205-065-2(4));*** pap. 18.95 ***(978-1-61205-066-9(2))*** Paradigm Pubs.

Derluguian, Georgi. Business as Usual: The Roots of the Global Financial Meltdown. Calhoun, Craig, ed. 2011. (ENG., Illus.). 312p. pap. 19.00 *(978-0-8147-7278-2(1))* New York Univ. Pr.

Desai, Radhika, ed. Revitalizing Marxist Theory for Today's Capitalism. 2011. (Research in Political Economy Ser.). (Illus.). 300p. ***(978-1-78052-254-8(1))*** Emerald Group Publishing Ltd.

Devine, Pat. Democracy Adn Economic Planning. 2010. (ENG.). 320p. pap. 29.95 *(978-0-7456-3479-1(6))* Polity Pr. GBR. Dist: Wiley, John & Sons, Inc.

Dickson, Bruce. Wealth & Power in Contemporary China: The Communist Party's Embrace of the Private Sector. 2008. (ENG., Illus.). 292p. pap. 28.00 *(978-0-521-70270-6(4))* Cambridge Univ. Pr.

—Wealth into Power: The Communist Party's Embrace of China's Private Sector. 2008. (ENG., Illus.). 292p. 80.00 *(978-0-521-87845-6(4))* Cambridge Univ. Pr.

Dirlik, Arif, et al. Global Capitalism & the Future of Agrarian Society. 2012. pap. ***(978-1-61205-038-6(7))*** Paradigm Pubs.

Dobb, Maurice. Capitalist Enterprise & Social Progress. 2012. (ENG.). 424p. 150.00 ***(978-0-415-52635-7(3))*** Routledge.

—Political Economy & Capitalism. 2012. (ENG.). 376p. 130.00 ***(978-0-415-52363-9(X))*** Routledge.

Dobb, Maurice. Studies in the Development of Capitalism. 408p. (Orig.). 2010. pap. 27.96 *(978-1-163-13365-1(5))* 2008. 49.95 *(978-1-4367-1022-0(7))* 2007. (ENG.). per. 34.95 *(978-1-4304-6421-1(6))* Kessinger Publishing, LLC.

Doerr, Harold L. A Square of Daffodils, Capitalism, & Why Children Don't Learn: The Story of Building a Wonderful, Loving Family. 2011. 256p. 29.95 ***(978-1-4502-9342-6(5));*** pap. 19.95 ***(978-1-4502-9340-2(9))*** iUniverse, Inc.

Doherty, Brian. Radicals for Capitalism: A Freewheeling History of the Modern American Libertarian Movement. 2008. (ENG.). 752p. pap. 21.95 *(978-1-58648-572-6(5))* PublicAffairs.

Domar, Evsey D. Capitalism, Socialism, & Serfdom: Essays by Evsey D. Domar. 2008. (ENG.). 320p. pap. 42.00 *(978-0-521-07020-1(1))* Cambridge Univ. Pr.

Doogan, Kevin. New Capitalism? The Transformation of Work. 2009. (ENG., Illus.). 240p. 69.95 *(978-0-7456-3324-4(2))* Polity Pr. GBR. Dist: Wiley, John & Sons, Inc.

Doogan, Kevin & Doogan. New Capitalism? The Transformation of Work. 2009. (ENG., Illus.). 240p. pap. 28.95 *(978-0-7456-3325-1(0))* Polity Pr. GBR. Dist: Wiley, John & Sons, Inc.

Doran, Christopher. Making the World Safe for Capitalism: How Iraq Threatened the US Economic Empire & had to be Destroyed, 1 vol. 2012. (ENG.). 296p. lib. bdg. 99.00 ***(978-0-7453-3223-9(4))*** Pluto Pr. GBR. Dist: Macmillan.

Dowd, Douglas, ed. Inequality & the Global Economic Crisis. 2009. (ENG.). 272p. 90.00 *(978-0-7453-2944-4(6));* pap. 32.95 *(978-0-7453-2943-7(8))* Pluto Pr. GBR. Dist: Macmillan.

Dragos, Pal. Structure of Global Capitalism Volume 1. 2006. pap. *(978-3-8334-5310-6(9))* Books on Demand GmbH.

—Structure of Global Capitalism Volume 2. 2006. pap. *(978-3-8334-5311-3(7))* Books on Demand GmbH.

Dreyer, Wayne. Foucault & the Politics of Development Aid. 2010. 388p. pap. *(978-3-8383-4888-9(5))* Lambert Academic Publishing.

D'Souza, Rohan. Drowned & Dammed: Colonial Capitalism & Flood Control in Eastern India. 2006. (ENG., Illus.). 292p. 55.00 *(978-0-19-568217-5(3))* Oxford Univ. Pr., Inc.

Dubbink, W. Assisting the Invisible Hand: Contested Relations Between Market, State & Civil Society. 2010. (Issues in Business Ethics Ser.). 240p. pap. 179.00 *(978-90-481-6353-3(6),* 9048163536) Springer.

Dufour, Dany-Robert. The Art of Shrinking Heads: The New Servitude of the Liberated in the Age of Total Capitalism. Macey, David, tr. from FRE. 2008. (ENG.). 200p. pap. 22.95 *(978-0-7456-3690-0(X));* 64.95 *(978-0-7456-3689-4(6))* Polity Pr. GBR. Dist: Wiley, John & Sons, Inc.

Duke, Philip & Hamilakis, Yannis, eds. Archaeology & Capitalism: From Ethics to Politics. 2007. (One World Archaeology Ser.). (ENG., Illus.). 298p. 89.00 *(978-1-59874-270-1(1))* Left Coast Pr., Inc.

Dullien, Sebastian, et al. Decent Capitalism: A Blueprint for Reforming our Economies, 1 vol. 2011. (ENG., Illus.). 256p. 28.00 *(978-0-7453-3109-6(2));* lib. bdg. 90.00 *(978-0-7453-3110-2(6))* Pluto Pr. GBR. Dist: Macmillan.

Duménil, Gérard & Lévy, Dominique. The Crisis of Neoliberalism. 2011. (Illus.). 400p. 49.95 *(978-0-674-04988-8(8))* Harvard Univ. Pr.

Dunn, Stephen P. The Fall & Rise of the Asiatic Mode of Production. (ENG.). 180p. 2012. pap. 42.95 ***(978-0-415-61862-5(2))*** 2011. 95.00 *(978-0-415-61621-8(2))* Routledge.

Dunning. Global Capitalism at Bay. 2007. (ENG.). 384p. (C). 44.95 *(978-0-415-43964-0(7))* Routledge.

During, Simon. Cultural Turns Essay Cult Crit. 2009. (ENG.). 208p. 125.00 *(978-0-415-24654-5(7));* pap. 42.95 *(978-0-415-24655-2(5))* Routledge.

Dutt, Rajani Palme. Fascism & Social Revolution. 2011. 310p. 48.95 ***(978-1-258-02072-9(6))*** Literary Licensing, LLC.

Dyer-Witheford, Nick & de Peuter, Greig. Games of Empire: Global Capitalism & Video Games. 2009. (Electronic Mediations Ser.). (ENG.). 320p. pap. 19.95 *(978-0-8166-6611-9(3))* Univ. of Minnesota Pr.

Eagleton, Terry. Why Marx Was Right. 272p. 2012. (ENG.). pap. 16.00 ***(978-0-300-18153-1(1))*** 2011. 25.00 *(978-0-300-16943-0(4))* Yale Univ. Pr.

Eaton, J. L. Personal Capital. 2009. 206p. pap. 14.99 *(978-0-557-09289-5(2))* Lulu Enterprises Inc.

Ebeling, Richard M., et al. In Defense of Capitalism Volume II, Vol. 2. Ebeling, Richard M. et al, eds. 2011. 108p. pap. 15.00 ***(978-0-87359-059-4(7))*** Northwood Univ. Pr.

Eberle, Harold R. Compassionate Capitalism: A Judeo-Christian Value. 2010. 136p. pap. *(978-1-882523-35-1(0))* Worldcast Publishing.

Egbert, Henrik & Esser, Clemens. Aspects in Varieties of Capitalism. 2010. (Illus.). 236p. pap. *(978-3-8383-4045-6(0))* Lambert Academic Publishing.

Eisenberg, Christiane. Englands Weg in die Marktgesellschaft. 2009. (Kritische Studien Zur Geschichtswissenschaft Ser.). (GER., Illus.). 166p. (C). 45.00 *(978-3-525-37008-7(3))* Vandenhoeck & Ruprecht GmbH & Co. KG DEU. Dist: ISD.

Eisenlohr, Emily. Fairy Tale Capitalism: Fact & Fiction Behind Too Big to Fail. 2010. 272p. 27.95 *(978-1-4520-3406-5(0))* AuthorHouse.

Elliott, Gregory. Ends in Sight: Marx/Fukuyama/Hobsbawm/Anderson. 2008. (ENG.). 160p. per. 26.00 *(978-0-7453-2762-4(1))* Pluto Pr. GBR. Dist: Macmillan.

—Senses of an Ending. 2008. (ENG.). 160p. 80.00 *(978-0-7453-2763-1(X))* Pluto Pr. GBR. Dist: Macmillan.

Elliott, Larry & Atkinson, Dan. The Gods that Failed: How Blind Faith in Markets Has Cost Us Our Future. 2010. (ENG.). 304p. (gr. 9). pap. 16.95 *(978-1-56858-440-9(7))* Basic Bks.

Elsner, Wolfram & Hanappi, Gerhard. Varieties of Capitalism & New Institutional Deals: Regulation, Welfare & the New Economy. Elsner, Wolfram & Hanappi, Hardy, eds. 2009. (Studies in Evolutionary Political Economy Ser.). (Illus.). 392p. 167.00 *(978-1-84720-473-8(2))* Elgar, Edward Publishing, Inc.

Emerson, Peter J., ed. Towards an Inclusive Democracy: Consensual Voting Procedures for Use in Parliaments, Councils & Committees. 2007. (Illus.). XVI, 186p. (C). 129.00 *(978-3-540-33163-6(8),* 3540331638) Springer.

Emigh, Rebecca & Emigh, Rebecca Jean. The Undevelopment of Capitalism: Sectors & Markets in Fifteenth-Century Tuscany. 2008. (Politics History & Social Chan Ser.). (ENG., Illus.). 288p. 91.50 *(978-1-59213-618-6(4));* pap. 31.95 *(978-1-59213-619-3(2))* Temple Univ. Pr.

Engler, Allan. Economic Democracy: The Working Class Alternative to Capitalism. 2010. (ENG.). 112p. pap. 15.95 *(978-1-55266-346-2(9))* Fernwood Publishing Co., Ltd. CAN. Dist: Independent Pubs. Group.

Epstein, Richard A. Free Markets under Siege: Cartels, Politics, & Social Welfare. 2008. (Hoover Classics Ser.). 14.95 *(978-0-8179-4611-1(X))* Hoover Institution Pr.

Ertl, Alan. The Political Economic Foundation of Democratic Capitalism: From Genesis to Maturation. 2007. 468p. per. 37.95 *(978-1-59942-424-8(X),* Brown Walker Pr.) Universal Pubs.

Ertuna, Ibrahim Ozer. Wealth Welfare & the Global Free Market: A Social Audit of Capitalist Economies. 2009. (Corporate Social Responsibility Ser.). 244p. 124.95 *(978-0-566-08905-3(X),* Gower Publishing Co., Ltd.) Ashgate Publishing, Ltd. GBR. Dist: Ashgate Publishing Co.

Espinosa De Godos, Eusebio. Popular Capitalism. 2010. 254p. pap. *(978-0-7552-0601-8(0))* Authors OnLine, Ltd.

Eubank, Lawrence. Why Marx Was Wrong: A Refutation of the Major Tenets of Marxist Economics. 2011. 516p. (gr. 10-12). pap. 20.95 ***(978-1-4634-3415-1(4))*** AuthorHouse.

Everling, Clark. Dialectics of Class Struggle in the Global Economy. 2009. (ENG.). 208p. 145.00 *(978-0-415-77810-7(7))* Routledge.

Falasca-Zamponi, Simonetta. Waste & Consumption: Capitalism, the Environment, & the Life of Things. 2010. (Framing 21st Century Social Issues Ser.). 76p. pap. 9.95 *(978-0-415-89210-0(4))* Routledge.

Fan, Joseph P. H. & Morck, Randall, eds. Capitalizing China. 2012. (National Bureau of Economic Research Conference Report). (Illus.). 368p. 110.00 ***(978-0-226-23724-4(9))*** Univ. of Chicago Pr.

Fasenfest, D. & Fasenfest, David. Engaging Social Justice: Critical Studies of 21st Century Social Transformation. Fasenfest, D., ed. 2009. (Illus.). 300p. *(978-90-04-17654-6(3))* BRILL.

Fasenfest, David, ed. Engaging Social Justice: Critical Studies of Twenty-First Century Social Transformation. 2011. (Studies in Critical Social Sciences Ser.). (ENG.). 356p. pap. 28.00 ***(978-1-60846-124-0(6))*** Haymarket Bks.

Federici, Silvia. Revolution at Point Zero: Housework, Reproduction, & Feminist Struggle. 2012. (Common Notions Ser.). (ENG.). 208p. pap. 15.95 ***(978-1-60486-333-8(1))*** PM Pr.

Fellman, Susanna, et al, eds. Creating the Nordic Model of Capitalism: The Business History of a Competitive Periphery. 2008. (ENG., Illus.). 252p. pap. 46.00 *(978-0-230-54553-3(X))* Palgrave Macmillan.

Fernando, Jude L. The Political Economy of NGOs: State Formation in Sri Lanka & Bangladesh, 1 vol. 2011. (ENG.). 352p. lib. bdg. 100.00 *(978-0-7453-2172-1(0));* 30.00 *(978-0-7453-2171-4(2))* Pluto Pr. GBR. Dist: Macmillan.

Fichter, James R. So Great a Proffit: How the East Indies Trade Transformed Anglo-American Capitalism. 2010. (Illus.). 400p. 35.00 *(978-0-674-05057-0(6))* Harvard Univ. Pr.

Figueroa, Adolfo. Capitalist Development & the Peasant Economy in Peru. 2009. (Cambridge Latin American Studies). (ENG.). 156p. pap. 31.99 *(978-0-521-10160-8(3))* Cambridge Univ. Pr.

Filho. The Value of Marx. 2007. 192p. pap. 43.95 *(978-0-415-45926-6(5))* Routledge.

Fine, Ben. Women's Employment & the Capitalist Family. (ENG.). 2012. 264p. pap. 42.95 ***(978-0-415-61411-5(2))*** 2011. 262p. 115.00 *(978-0-415-61410-8(4))* Routledge.

Finel-Honigman, Irene. A Cultural History of Finance. 2009. xiii, 338p. (C). 110.00 *(978-0-203-86661-0(4))* Routledge.

Fioretos, Orfeo. Creative Reconstructions: Multilateralism & European Varieties of Capitalism After 1950. 2011. (Cornell Studies in Political Economy Ser.). (Illus.). 264p. 49.95 *(978-0-8014-4969-7(3))* Cornell Univ. Pr.

Fisher, Eran. Media & New Capitalism in the Digital Age: The Spirit of Networks. 2010. (ENG., Illus.). 272p. 89.00 *(978-0-230-61607-3(0))* Palgrave Macmillan.

Fisher, Melissa S. & Downey, Greg, eds. Frontiers of Capital: Ethnographic Reflections on the New Economy. 2006. (ENG.). 392p. per. 26.95 *(978-0-8223-3739-3(8));* (Illus.). 94.95 *(978-0-8223-3727-0(4))* Duke Univ. Pr.

Fiske, John. Reading the Popular. 2nd rev. ed. 2010. (ENG., Illus.). 256p. 115.00 *(978-0-415-59650-3(5));* pap. 31.95 *(978-0-415-59651-0(3))* Routledge.

—Understanding Popular Culture. 2nd rev. ed. 2010. (ENG., Illus.). 232p. 120.00 *(978-0-415-59652-7(1));* pap. 33.95 *(978-0-415-59653-4(X))* Routledge.

Flank, Lenny. Contradictions of Capitalism: An Introduction to Marxist Economics. 2007. 122p. per. 11.99 *(978-0-9791813-9-9(9))* Red & Black Pubs.

—Hegemony & Counter-Hegemony: Marxism, Capitalism, & their Relation to Sexism, Racism, Nationalism & Authoritarianism. 2007. 173p. per. 11.99 *(978-0-9791813-7-5(2))* Red & Black Pubs.

Flaschel, Peter. The Macrodynamics of Capitalism: Elements for a Synthesis of Marx, Keynes & Schumpeter. 2nd ed. (ENG., Illus.). xiv, 399p. 2010. pap. 189.00 *(978-3-642-09971-7(8),* 3642099718) 2008. 189.00 *(978-3-540-87931-2(5),* 3540879315) Springer.

Flaschel, Peter & Greiner, Alfred. Flexicurity Capitalism: Foundations, Problems & Perspectives, 1 vol. 2012. (ENG., Illus.). 240p. 55.00 *(978-0-19-975158-7(7))* Oxford Univ. Pr., Inc.

Flaschel, Peter & Greiner, Alfred. A Future for Capitalism: Classical, Neoclassical & Keynesian Perspectives. 2011. (Illus.). 368p. 150.00 ***(978-1-84980-855-2(4))*** Elgar, Edward Publishing, Inc.

Flaschel, Peter & Landesmann, Michael A. Mathematical Economics & the Dynamics of Capitalism: Goodwin's Legacy Continued. Flaschel, Peter & Landesmann, Michael A., eds. 2008. (Illus.). CCCII, 18p. 160.00 *(978-0-415-45145-1(0))* Routledge.

Flaschel, Peter, et al. Roads to Social Capitalism: Theory, Evidence, & Policy. 2012. (Illus.). 384p. 160.00 ***(978-1-78100-287-2(8))*** Elgar, Edward Publishing, Inc.

Flax, Bill. The Courage to do Nothing: A Moral Defense of Markets & Freedom. 2010. pap. 21.99 *(978-1-61663-527-5(4))* Tate Publishing & Enterprises, LLC.

Fleisher, Belton M., et al, eds. Policy Reform & Chinese Markets: Progress & Challenges. 2008. (Advances in Chinese Economic Studies). 352p. (C). 150.00 *(978-1-84720-396-0(5))* Elgar, Edward Publishing, Inc.

Floyd, Kevin. The Reification of Desire: Toward a Queer Marxism. 2009. (ENG., Illus.). 304p. 75.00 *(978-0-8166-4395-0(4))* Univ. of Minnesota Pr.

Foley, Douglas E. Learning Capitalist Culture: Deep in the Heart of Tejas. 2nd ed. 2010. (Contemporary Ethnography Ser.). 272p. (C). pap. 24.95 *(978-0-8122-2098-8(6))* Univ. of Pennsylvania Pr.

Forbes, Steve & Ames, Elizabeth. Freedom Manifesto: Why Markets Are Moral & Big Government Isn't. 2012. (ENG.). 288p. 26.00 ***(978-0-307-95157-1(X),*** Crown Business) Crown Publishing Group.

Forbes, Steve & Ames, Elizabeth. How Capitalism Will Save Us: Why Free People & Free Markets Are the Best Answer in Today's Economy. 2011. (ENG.). 400p. pap. 15.00 *(978-0-307-46310-4(9),* Three Rivers Pr.) Crown Publishing Group.

Forbes, Steve & Ames, Elizabeth S. How Capitalism Will Save Us: Why Free People & Free Markets Are the Best Answer in Today's Economy. 2009. (ENG.). 368p. 25.00 *(978-0-307-46309-8(5),* Crown Business) Crown Publishing Group.

Foster, John Bellamy & Magdoff, Fred. The Great Financial Crisis: Causes & Consequences. 2009. (ENG.). 144p. 50.00 *(978-1-58367-185-6(4));* pap. 12.95 *(978-1-58367-184-9(6))* Monthly Review Pr.

—What Every Environmentalist Needs to Know about Capitalism. 2011. (ENG.). 160p. 55.00 *(978-1-58367-242-6(7))* Monthly Review Pr.

Fougeres, Dorian. Aquarian Capitalism & Transition in Indonesia. 2008. 296p. pap. *(978-3-8364-8653-8(9))* VDM Verlag Dr. Mueller e.K.

Frankel, Hyman. Socialism: Vision & Reality. 2010. (ENG.). 341p. pap. 32.99 ***(978-1-906791-57-5(0))*** Arena Bks. GBR. Dist: Lightning Source UK, Ltd.

Fraser, Andrew. The Wasp Question. 2011. 422p. pap. ***(978-1-907166-29-7(7))*** Arktos Media Ltd.

Freyer, Tony A. Antitrust & Global Capitalism, 1930-2004. 2009. (Cambridge Historical Studies in American Law & Society Ser.). (ENG.). 452p. pap. 35.99 *(978-0-521-74727-1(9))* Cambridge Univ. Pr.

Frieden, Jeffry A. & Frieden, Jeffry. Global Capitalism: Its Fall & Rise in the Twentieth Century. annot. ed. 2007. (ENG.). 576p. pap. 19.95 *(978-0-393-32981-0(X),* 32981) Norton, W. W. & Co., Inc.

Friedland, Julian. Doing Well & Good: The Human Face of the New Capitalism. 2009. 258p. *(978-1-59311-788-7(4))* Information Age Publishing, Inc.

Friedland, Julian, ed. Doing Well & Good: The Human Face of the New Capitalism (PB) 2009. 260p. pap. 45.99 *(978-1-59311-787-0(6))* Information Age Publishing, Inc.

Friedman, Daniel. Morals & Markets: An Evolutionary Account of the Modern World. 2008. (ENG.). 268p. 40.00 *(978-0-230-60097-3(2))* Palgrave Macmillan.

Fry, Lewis Cass. Catechism of Karl Marx's Capital: A Beginner's Introduction to the Socialist Analysis of Capitalism. 2010. *(978-1-934941-99-7(9))* Red & Black Pubs.

Frye, Timothy. Building States & Markets after Communism: The Perils of Polarized Democracy. 2010. (Cambridge Studies in Comparative Politics Ser.). (ENG., Illus.). 312p. 90.00 *(978-0-521-76773-6(3));* pap. 29.00 *(978-0-521-73462-2(2))* Cambridge Univ. Pr.

Fumagalli, Andrea. Crisis in the Global Economy: Financial Markets, Social Struggles, & New Political Scenarios. Mezzadra, Sandro, ed. Mc Gimsey, Jason Francis, tr. from ITA. 2010. (Semiotext(e) / Active Agents Ser.). (ENG., Illus.). 304p. (gr. 17). pap. 17.95 *(978-1-58435-087-3(3))* Semiotexte/Smart Art.

Funnell, Warwick, et al. In Government We Trust: Market-Failure & the Delusions of Privatisation. 2009. (ENG.). 336p. 95.00 *(978-0-7453-2908-6(X))* Pluto Pr. GBR. Dist: Macmillan.

Gabrisch, Hubert & Hölscher, Jens. Successes & Failures of Economic Transition: The European Experience. 2006. (ENG., Illus.). 256p. 116.00 *(978-1-4039-3493-2(2))* Palgrave Macmillan.

Gaido, Daniel. The Formative Period of American Capitalism: A Materialist Interpretation. 2006. (Routledge International Studies in Business History Ser.). (ENG.). 176p. (C). 143.00 *(978-0-415-39173-3(3))* Routledge.

Gallas, Alexander. Dichotomy, Dualism, Duality. 2010. 96p. pap. *(978-3-639-11929-9(0))* VDM Verlag Dr. Mueller e.K.

Gamble, Andrew. The Spectre at the Feast: Capitalist Crisis & the Politics of Recession. 2009. (ENG., Illus.). 208p. 90.00 *(978-0-230-23074-3(1));* pap. 31.00 *(978-0-230-23075-0(X))* Palgrave Macmillan.

Ganßmann, Heiner. Doing Money. 2011. (Routledge International Studies in Money & Banking Ser.). (ENG., Illus.). 200p. (C). 140.00 *(978-0-415-67738-7(6))* Routledge.

Gao, Mobo. The Battle for China's Past: Mao & the Cultural Revolution. 2008. (ENG.). 280p. 95.00 *(978-0-7453-2781-5(8));* pap. 27.95 *(978-0-7453-2780-8(X))* Pluto Pr. GBR. Dist: Macmillan.

Garofalo, Daniela. Women, Love, & Commodity Culture in British Romanticism. 2012. 190p. 99.95 ***(978-1-4094-4102-1(4))*** Ashgate Publishing Co.

Garrido, Aleksandro Palomo. La Crisis de Los Valores en la Globalizaci=N. 2008. 428p. pap. *(978-3-639-10300-7(9))* VDM Verlag Dr. Mueller e.K.

Gat, Azar. Victorious & Vulnerable: Why Democracy Won in the 20th Century & How It Is Still Imperiled. 2009. (Hoover Studies in Politics, Economics, &

Society Ser.). (ENG.). 140p. 29.95 *(978-1-4422-0114-9(2))* Rowman & Littlefield Publishers, Inc.

Geier. Rust, Wheat, & Beige: Consequences of Teamwork. 2008. 274p. 24.95 *(978-0-9779186-3-8(7),* Books On Fire) Corporations Unlimited.

Gelinas, Nicole. After the Fall: Saving Capitalism from Wall Street - And Washington. 2009. (ENG.). 250p. 23.95 *(978-1-59403-261-5(0))* Encounter Bks.

—After the Fall: Saving Capitalism from Wall Street-and Washington. 2011. (ENG.). 240p. pap. 16.95 *(978-1-59403-525-8(3))* Encounter Bks.

Gelso, Aldo. Mafia: Capitalism & Democracy. 2007. (Illus.). 227p. 31.99 *(978-1-4257-7692-3(2))*; pap. 21.99 *(978-1-4257-7686-2(8))* Xlibris Corp.

Gencel Bek, Mine. Communicating Capitalism. 2010. 220p. pap. *(978-3-8383-7697-4(8))* Lambert Academic Publishing.

Geuha, Ashok S., ed. Markets & Morals: Ethical Issues in Economics. 2011. (History of Science Philosophy & Culture in Indian Civilization Ser.). (Illus.). 263p. 77.50 ***(978-81-87586-51-7(6))*** Munshiram Manoharlal Pubs. Private, Ltd. IND. Dist: Coronet Bks.

Ghate, Debi & Ralston, Richard E., eds. Why Businessmen Need Philosophy: The Capitalist's Guide to the Ideas Behind Ayn Rand's Atlas Shrugged. 2011. (ENG.). 336p. (gr. 12). 15.00 *(978-0-451-23269-4(0),* N A L Trade) Penguin Group (USA) Inc.

Ghoreishi, Minoo & Goreshi, Renato. Conscience Capitalism: Stakeholder's Approach to Business. rev. ed. 2012. (ENG.). 150p. pap. 45.00 ***(978-0-7575-9550-9(2))*** Kendall Hunt Publishing Co.

Gidwani, Vinay & Gidwani, Vinay K. Capital, Interrupted: Agrarian Development & the Politics of Work in India. 2008. (Illus.). 368p. 75.00 *(978-0-8166-4958-7(8))*; pap. 25.00 *(978-0-8166-4959-4(6))* Univ. of Minnesota Pr.

Gilbert, Jeremy. Anticapitalism & Culture: Radical Theory & Popular Politics. 2008. (Culture Machine Ser.). (ENG.). 224p. pap. 29.95 *(978-1-84520-230-9(9))* Berg Pubs. GBR. Dist: Macmillan.

Gilman-Opalsky, Richard. Spectacular Capitalism: Guy Debord & the Practice of Radical Philosophy. 2011. 134p. pap. 18.00 ***(978-1-57027-228-8(X))*** Autonomedia.

Girling, John. Capital & Power (Routledge Revivals) 2010. (Routledge Revivals Ser.). (ENG.). 244p. 105.00 *(978-0-415-58937-6(1),* Routledge) Taylor & Francis Group GBR. Dist: Taylor & Francis Group.

Giroux, Henry A. Zombie Politics & Culture in the Age of Casino Capitalism. 2010. (Popular Culture & Everyday Life Ser.). (C). 182p. pap. 32.95 *(978-1-4331-1226-3(4))*; 184p. 129.95 *(978-1-4331-1227-0(2))* Lang, Peter Publishing, Inc.

Gladstein, Mimi Reisel. Ayn Rand. Meadowcroft, John, ed. 2009. (Major Conservative & Libertarian Thinkers Ser.). (ENG.). 176p. 130.00 *(978-0-8264-4513-1(6))* Continuum International Publishing Group, Ltd. GBR. Dist: National Bk. Network.

Glezos, Simon. The Politics of Speed: Capitalism, the State & War in an Accelerating World. 2011. (Interventions Ser.). (ENG., Illus.). 224p. (C). 130.00 *(978-0-415-78261-6(9))* Routledge.

Glyn, Andrew. Capitalism Unleashed: Finance, Globalization, & Welfare. 2007. (ENG., Illus.). 272p. per. 21.95 *(978-0-19-922679-5(2))* Oxford Univ. Pr., Inc.

Goheen, Michael W. & Glanville, Erin. The Gospel & Globalization: Exploring the Religious Roots of a Globalized World. 2009. 384p. pap. *(978-1-57383-440-7(8))* Regent College Publishing.

Gonzaga, Elmo. Globalization & Becoming-Nation: Subjectivity, Nationhood, & Narrative in the Period of Global Capitalism. 2010. 141p. pap. 15.00 *(978-971-542-561-2(5))* Univ. of the Philippines Pr. PHL. Dist: Univ. of Hawaii Pr.

Gooding-Williams, Robert. Crediting God: Sovereignty & Religion in the Age of Global Capitalism. Vatter, Miguel, ed. (ENG.). 336p. 2010. 80.00 *(978-0-8232-3319-9(7),* 3rd ed. 2011. pap. 32.00 *(978-0-8232-3320-5(0))* Fordham Univ. Pr.

Gordon, Todd. Cops, Crime & Capitalism: The Law & Order Agenda in Canada. 2006. (ENG.). 176p. pap. 21.95 *(978-1-55266-185-7(7))* Fernwood Publishing Co., Ltd. CAN. Dist: Independent Pubs. Group.

Gore, Lance. The Chinese Communist Party & China's Capitalist Revolution: The Political Impact of Market. 2010. (Routledge Contemporary China Ser.). (ENG., Illus.). 200p. (C). 125.00 *(978-0-415-58744-0(1))* Routledge.

Gorski, Philip S. The Protestant Ethic Revisited. 2011. (Politics History & Social Chan Ser.). (ENG.). 360p. 74.50 ***(978-1-4399-0189-2(9))*** Temple Univ. Pr.

Graeber, David. Possibilities: Essays on Hierarchy, Rebellion & Desire. 2007. (ENG.). 400p. per. 22.95 *(978-1-904859-66-6(6))* AK Pr. GBR. Dist: Consortium Bk. Sales & Distribution.

Graeff, Peter. Capitalism, Democracy & the Prevention of War & Poverty: Perpspectives on Economic & Political Freedom. Mehlkop, Guido, ed. 2008. (Routledge Advances in International Relations & Global Politics Ser.). (Illus.). XII, 228p. 140.00 *(978-0-415-46740-7(3))* Routledge.

Granovetter, Mark & Swedberg, Richard, eds. The Sociology of Economic Life. 3rd ed. 2011. (ENG.). 592p. (C). pap. 59.00 *(978-0-8133-4455-3(7))* Westview Pr.

Gratzer, David. The Cure: How Capitalism Can Save American Health Care. (ENG.). 2008. 250p. pap. 17.95 *(978-1-59403-219-6(X))* 2006. (Illus.). 325p. 25.95 *(978-1-59403-153-3(3))* Encounter Bks.

Greeman, Richard. Beware of Vegetarian Sharks. 2009. 358p. pap. 19.97 *(978-1-4303-2307-5(8))* Lulu Enterprises Inc.

Green, Michael & Bishop, Matthew. The Road from Ruin: How to Revive Capitalism & Put America Back on Top. 2010. (ENG.). 384p. 27.00 *(978-0-307-46422-4(9),* Crown Business) Crown Publishing Group.

Green, Stephen. Good Value: Reflections on Money, Morality & an Uncertain World. (ENG.). 2011. 256p. pap. 14.95 *(978-0-8021-4525-3(6),* Grove Pr.) 2010. 288p. 25.00 *(978-0-8021-1917-9(4),* Atlantic Monthly Pr.) Grove/Atlantic, Inc.

Greider, William. The Soul of Capitalism: Opening Paths to a Moral Economy. abr. ed. 2009. (Playaway Adult Nonfiction Ser.). (ENG.). 49.99 *(978-1-60812-729-0(X))* Findaway World, LLC.

Gu, George Zhibin. China & the New World Order: How Entrepreneurship, Globalization, & Borderless Business Are Reshaping China & the World. 2006. 248p. 29.99 *(978-1-59682-108-8(6))*; pap. 22.99 *(978-1-59682-107-1(8))* Fultus Corp. (Fultus Publishing).

—China's Global Reach: (Revised & Updated Edition) rev. ed. 2006. 252p. *(978-1-59682-094-4(2),* Fultus Publishing) Fultus Corp.

Guattari, Félix. Chaosophy: Texts & Interviews, 1972-1977. Lotringer, Sylvere, ed. 2008. (Semiotext(e) / Foreign Agents Ser.). (ENG.). 336p. (gr. 17). pap. 18.95 *(978-1-58435-060-6(1))* Semiotexte/Smart Art.

Gulamhusein, Nevine. Acuity of Poverty: Looking into the Inequality of Access. 2011. 129p. pap. 47.95 *(978-1-4327-4008-5(3))* Outskirts Pr., Inc.

Gulli, Bruno. Earthly Plenitudes: A Study on Sovereignty & Labor. 2009. (ENG.). 200p. 59.50 *(978-1-59213-979-8(5))* Temple Univ. Pr.

Guo, Qiang. Xin Xin Xiang Ying: Xin Zi Ben Zhu Yi - Xin She Hui Zhu Yi = Xinxin Xiangying: Xinzibenzhuyi Xinshehuizhuyi. 2010. (CHI.). *(978-7-5119-0092-0(5))* China Modern Economic & Electronic Publishing Hse.

Gwyn, Douglas. The Covenant Crucified. 2006. 416p. per. *(978-0-85245-397-1(3))* Quaker Books.

Hacker, Jacob S. & Pierson, Paul. Winner-Take-All Politics: How Washington Made the Rich Richer-And Turned Its Back on the Middle Class. (ENG.). 368p. 2011. pap. 15.00 *(978-1-4165-8870-2(1))* 2010. 27.00 *(978-1-4165-8869-6(8))* Simon & Schuster.

Halewood, Michael. A. N. Whitehead & Social Theory: Tracing a Culture of Thought. 2011. (Key Issues in Modern Sociology Ser.). 198p. 99.00 *(978-0-85728-796-0(6))* Anthem Pr. GBR. Dist: Books International, Inc.

Halteman, James. The Clashing Worlds of Economics & Faith. annot. ed. 2007. 224p. pap. 24.00 *(978-1-55635-170-9(4),* Wipf and Stock) Wipf & Stock Pubs.

Hamilakis, Yannis & Duke, Philip, eds. Archaeology & Capitalism: From Ethics to Politics. 2009. (One World Archaeology, Vol. 54 Ser.). (ENG.). 298p. pap. 36.95 *(978-1-59874-271-8(X))* Left Coast Pr., Inc.

Hancké, Bob, ed. Debating Varieties of Capitalism: A Reader. 2009. (ENG.). 320p. 125.00 *(978-0-19-956967-0(3))*; pap. 55.00 *(978-0-19-956966-3(5))* Oxford Univ. Pr., Inc.

Hancké, Bob, et al, eds. Beyond Varieties of Capitalism: Conflict, Contradictions, & Complementarities in the European Economy. 2008. (ENG., Illus.). 448p. pap. 55.00 *(978-0-19-954701-2(7))* Oxford Univ. Pr., Inc.

Hanieh, Adam. Capitalism & Class in the Gulf Arab States. 2011. (ENG.). 266p. 85.00 *(978-0-230-11077-9(0))* Palgrave Macmillan.

Hankel, Wilhelm & Isaak, Robert. Brave New World Economics: Global Finance Threatens Our Future. 2011. (ENG., Illus.). 270p. 29.95 *(978-1-118-00441-8(8),* Wiley) Wiley, John & Sons, Inc.

Hann, Chris & Hart, Keith, eds. Market & Society: The Great Transformation Today. 2011. (ENG., Illus.). 334p. pap. 43.00 *(978-0-521-29508-6(4))* Cambridge Univ. Pr.

Hanna, Nelly. Artisan Entrepreneurs in Cairo & Early-Modern Capitalism (1600-1800) 2011. 280p. ***(978-0-8156-3279-5(7))*** Syracuse Univ. Pr.

Haque, Umair. The New Capitalist Manifesto: Building a Disruptively Better Business. 2011. (ENG., Illus.). 256p. 26.95 *(978-1-4221-5858-6(6))* Harvard Business Review Pr.

Häring, Norbert & Douglas, Niall. Economists & the Powerful: Convenient Theories, Distorted Facts, Ample Rewards. 2012. (Anthem Other Canon Ser.). 275p. pap. 29.95 ***(978-0-85728-459-4(2))*** Anthem Pr. GBR. Dist: Books International, Inc.

Harland Prechel Staff. Politics & Public Policy. 2008. (Illus.). xviii, 206p. 110.99 *(978-1-84855-178-7(9))* Emerald Group Publishing Ltd. GBR. Dist: Turpin Distribution Services Ltd.

Hart, Keith & Hann, C. M. Market & Society: The Great Transformation Today. Hann, Chris & Hart, Keith, eds. 2009. (ENG., Illus.). 332p. 113.00 *(978-0-521-51965-6(9))* Cambridge Univ. Pr.

Hart, Stuart L. Capitalism at the Crossroads: Next Generation Business Strategies for a Post-Crisis World. 3rd rev. ed. 2010. (ENG., Illus.). 352p. pap. 19.99 *(978-0-13-704232-6(9))* Wharton Schl. Publishing.

Harvey, David. The Enigma of Capital: And the Crises of Capitalism, 1 vol. 2nd ed. (ENG., Illus.). 304p. 2011. pap. 16.95 *(978-0-19-983684-0(1))* 2010. 24.95 *(978-0-19-975871-5(9))* Oxford Univ. Pr., Inc.

—The Limits to Capital. rev. ed. 2007. (ENG., Illus.). 478p. pap. 34.95 *(978-1-84467-095-6(3),* 844095) Verso Bks. GBR. Dist: Norton, W. W. & Co., Inc.

Harvey, David. Rebel Cities: From the Right to the City to the Urban Revolution. 2012. (ENG., Illus.). 112p. 19.95 ***(978-1-84467-882-2(2),*** 844882) Verso Bks. GBR. Dist: Norton, W. W. & Co., Inc.

Hass, Jeffrey. Rethinking the Post-Soviet Experience: Markets, Moral Economies, & Cultural Contradictions of Post-Socialist Russia. 2011. (Euro-Asian Studies). (ENG., Illus.). 296p. 100.00 ***(978-0-230-28466-1(3))*** Palgrave Macmillan.

Hatfield, Zester J. Progressivism: Our Road to Serfdom: Arise America: Rebuild Your God-Given Capitalist Foundations. 2010. (ENG.). 284p. 27.89 *(978-1-4269-3387-5(8))* Trafford Publishing.

Hatfield, Zester J. & Hatfield, Marilyn J. Progressivism: Our Road to Serfdom: Arise America: Rebuild Your God-Given Capitalist Foundations. 2010. 284p. pap. 17.89 *(978-1-4269-3386-8(X))* Trafford Publishing.

Haymarket Books. Zombie Capitalism: Global Crisis & the Relevance of Marx. 2010. (ENG., Illus.). 425p. pap. *(978-1-60846-104-2(1))* Pluto Pr.

Haynes, Douglas E. Small Town Capitalism in Western India: Artisans, Merchants & the Making of the Informal Economy, 1870-1960. 2012. (Cambridge Studies in Indian History & Society Ser.). (ENG., Illus.). 376p. 99.00 ***(978-0-521-19333-7(8))*** Cambridge Univ. Pr.

Heck, Gene W. Charlemagne, Muhammad, & the Arab Roots of Capitalism. 2006. (Studien Zur Geschichte und Kultur des Islamischen Orients. Neue Folge Ser.). (ENG.). XIV, 381p. 119.00 *(978-3-11-019229-2(2))* De Gruyter, Walter Inc.

Heller, Henry. The Transition from Feudalism to Capitalism: A 21st Century Perspective, 1 vol. 2011. (Future of World Capitalism Ser.). (ENG.). 320p. 35.00 *(978-0-7453-2959-8(4))*; lib. bdg. 110.00 ***(978-0-7453-2960-4(8))*** Pluto Pr. GBR. Dist: Macmillan.

Heller, Michael G. Capitalism, Institutions, & Economic Development. 2011. (ENG.). 336p. (C). pap. 44.95 ***(978-0-415-69445-2(0))*** Routledge.

Herod, James. Getting Free: Creating an Association of Democratic Autonomous Neighborhoods. 2007. 144p. pap. 14.00 *(978-0-9794264-0-7(5))* Parsons, Lucy Ctr.

Herrmann-Pillath, Carsten. The Economics of Identity & Creativity. 2010. (ENG., Illus.). 259p. pap. 29.95 *(978-1-4128-1101-9(5))* Transaction Pubs.

Hill, Michael C. Cannibal Capitalism: How Big Business & the Feds Are Ruining America. 2011. (ENG., Illus.). 256p. 27.95 ***(978-1-118-17531-6(X),*** Wiley) Wiley, John & Sons, Inc.

Hinton, Mary. Commercial Church: Black Churches & the New Religious Marketplace in America. 2011. (ENG.). 170p. 60.00 *(978-0-7391-3772-7(7))* Lexington Bks.

Hirsch, Yale. The Capitalist Spirit: How Each & Every One of us Can Make a Giant Difference in Our Fast-Changing World. 2009. (ENG.). 320p. 19.95 *(978-0-470-40737-0(9),* Wiley) Wiley, John & Sons, Inc.

Hobson, John A. The Evolution of Modern Capitalism. 2009. 466p. 33.99 *(978-1-113-93157-3(4))*; 31.99 *(978-1-113-93156-6(6))*; pap. 36.75 *(978-1-113-93151-1(5))* BiblioBazaar.

Hoenig, Jonat. Greed Is Good: The Capitalist Pig Guide to Investing. 10.00 *(978-0-88730-985-4(2))* Harper Business Systems.

Holloway, John. Crack Capitalism, 1 vol. 2010. (ENG.). 272p. 95.00 *(978-0-7453-3009-9(6))*; pap. 30.00 *(978-0-7453-3008-2(8))* Pluto Pr. GBR. Dist: Macmillan.

Hölscher, Jens & Tomann, Hörst. Varieties of Capitalism in Post-Communist Countries. Lane, David & Myant, Martin R., eds. 2007. (Studies in Economic Transition Ser.). (ENG.). 288p. 126.00 *(978-1-4039-9641-1(5))* Palgrave Macmillan.

Hosking, Geoffrey. Trust: Money, Markets & Society. 2010. (Manifestos for the 21st Century Ser.). 92p. 14.95 *(978-1-906497-75-0(3))* Seagull Bks. GBR. Dist: Chicago Distribution Ctr.

Howard-Hassmann, Rhoda E. & Welch, Claude E., eds. Economic Rights in Canada & the United States. 2009. (Pennsylvania Studies in Human Rights Ser.). 288p. (C). pap. 24.95 *(978-0-8122-2093-3(5))* Univ. of Pennsylvania Pr.

Howard, M. C. & King, J. E. The Rise of Neoliberalism in Advanced Capitalist Economies: A Materialist Analysis. 2008. (ENG.). 328p. 100.00 *(978-0-230-53703-3(0))* Palgrave Macmillan.

Howie, Gillian. Between Feminism & Materialism: A Question of Method. 2010. (Breaking Feminist Waves Ser.). (ENG.). 280p. 89.00 *(978-0-230-10269-9(7))* Palgrave Macmillan.

Huang, Yasheng. Capitalism with Chinese Characteristics: Entrepreneurship & the State. 2008. (ENG., Illus.). 366p. (C). 40.00 *(978-0-521-89810-2(2))* Cambridge Univ. Pr.

Hughes, John. The End of Work: Theological Critiques of Capitalism. (Illuminations: Theory & Religion Ser.). (ENG., Illus.). 264p. 2007. 116.95 *(978-1-4051-5892-3(1))* 2006. pap. 48.95 *(978-1-4051-5893-0(X))* Wiley, John & Sons, Inc. (Wiley-Blackwell).

Hung, Ho-Fung, ed. China & the Transformation of Global Capitalism. 2009. (Themes in Global Social Change Ser.). (ENG., Illus.). 224p. 50.00 *(978-0-8018-9307-0(0))*; (C). (gr. 13-17). pap. 27.00 *(978-0-8018-9308-7(9))* Johns Hopkins Univ. Pr.

Hunter, James Davison. Thrift & Thriving in America: Capitalism & Moral Order from the Puritans to the Present, 1 vol. Yates, Joshua J., ed. 2011. (ENG., Illus.). 640p. 35.00 *(978-0-19-976906-3(0))* Oxford Univ. Pr., Inc.

Huntley, Somer. Redefining Economics. 2011. 172p. pap. ***(978-3-8443-8610-3(6))*** Lambert Academic Publishing.

Hutton, Will. Them & Us: Changing Britain - Why We Need a Fair Society. 2011. (ENG.). 448p. pap. 17.95 ***(978-0-349-12148-2(6))*** Little, Brown Bk. Group Ltd. GBR. Dist: Independent Pubs. Group.

Hwang, Richard Ruey-Chyi. Recent Interpretations of Karl Marx's Social Theory: An Essay on Habermas, Cohen & Elster, Vol. 531. 2006. (European University Studies: Vol. 31). (Illus.). 145p. pap. *(978-0-8204-7664-3(1))* Lang, Peter AG.

Ido, Masanobu, ed. Variety of Capitalism Types of Democracy & Globalization. 2012. (Routledge Advances in International Political Economy Ser.). (ENG., Illus.). 248p. (C). 125.00 *(978-0-415-67150-7(7))* Routledge.

Illouz, Eva. Cold Intimacies: The Making of Emotional Capitalism. 2007. (ENG.). 144p. 64.95 *(978-0-7456-3904-8(6))*; pap. 19.95 *(978-0-7456-3905-5(4))* Polity Pr. GBR. Dist: Wiley, John & Sons, Inc.

Ingham, Geoffrey. Capitalism: With a New Postscripts on the Financial Crisis & Its Aftermath. 2008. (Key Concepts Ser.). (ENG.). 200p. pap. 24.95 *(978-0-7456-3648-1(9))*; 74.95 *(978-0-7456-3647-4(0))* Polity Pr. GBR. Dist: Wiley, John & Sons, Inc.

Jackson, Arthur. Chaos, Synchronicity, & Capitalism: the Phases in the Evolution of a Natural System. 2007. 215p. pap. 27.95 *(978-0-615-15190-8(6))* Jackson, Arthur.

Jacoby, Sanford. The Embedded Corporation: Corporate Governance & Employment Relations in Japan & the United States. 2007. (ENG., Illus.). 236p. (C). per. 23.95 *(978-0-691-13384-3(0))* Princeton Univ. Pr.

James, C. Boyd. Garvey, Garveyism, & the Problem of Black Redemption. 2008. *(978-1-59221-654-3(4))*; 416p. pap. *(978-1-59221-655-0(2))* Africa World Pr.

James, C. L. R. A New Notion: Two Works by C. L. R. James: Every Cook Can Govern & the Invading Socialist Society. Ignatiev, Noel, ed. 2010. (ENG.). 160p. pap. 16.95 *(978-1-60486-047-4(2))* PM Pr.

Jarnagin, Laura. A Confluence of Transatlantic Networks: Elites, Capitalism, & Confederate Migration to Brazil. 2008. (Atlantic Crossings Ser.). (ENG.). 448p. 49.75 *(978-0-8173-1624-2(8))* Univ. of Alabama Pr.

Jentz, John B. & Schneirov, Richard. Chicago in the Age of Capital: Class, Politics, & Democracy During the Civil War & Reconstruction. 2012. (Working Class in American History Ser.). (ENG., Illus.). 320p. 55.00 ***(978-0-252-03683-5(2))*** Univ. of Illinois Pr.

Jessop, Bob & Sum, Ngai-Ling. Beyond the Regulation Approach: Putting Capitalist Economies in Their Place. 2007. 496p. pap. 66.00 *(978-1-84720-319-9(1))* Elgar, Edward Publishing, Inc.

Joel Kovel. Capitalism Nature Socialism. 2007. pap. 41.95 *(978-0-415-43138-5(7))*; pap. 41.95 *(978-0-415-43137-8(9))*; pap. 41.95 *(978-0-415-43139-2(5))*; pap. 41.95 *(978-0-415-43140-8(9))* Routledge.

—Capitalism Nature Socialism. 2007. (ENG.). pap. 41.95 *(978-0-415-40086-2(4),* Taylor & Francis) Taylor & Francis Group GBR. Dist: Taylor & Francis Group.

John E. Jones. Faces of Capitalism & Socialism. 2010. 112p. pap. 13.35 *(978-1-4269-0175-1(5))* Trafford Publishing.

Johnson, Paul. Making the Market: Victorian Origins of Corporate Capitalism. 2010. (Cambridge Studies in Economic History - Second Ser.). (ENG., Illus.). 266p. 99.00 *(978-0-521-85783-3(X))* Cambridge Univ. Pr.

Jones, Geoffrey & Wadhwani, R. Daniel. Entrepreneurship & Global Capitalism, 2 vols., Set. 2007. (International Library of Entrepreneurship Ser.). (Illus.). 1088p. (C). 495.00 *(978-1-84542-407-7(7))* Elgar, Edward Publishing, Inc.

Juris, Jeffrey S. Networking Futures: The Movements Against Corporate Globalization. 2008. (Experimental Futures Ser.). (ENG., Illus.). 400p. pap. 26.95 *(978-0-8223-4269-4(3))*; (C). 94.95 *(978-0-8223-4250-2(2))* Duke Univ. Pr.

Juvin, Hervé. The Coming of the Body. Howe, John, tr. from FRE. 2010. (ENG., Illus.). 272p. 27.95 *(978-1-84467-310-0(3),* 844310) Verso Bks. GBR. Dist: Norton, W. W. & Co., Inc.

Kü, et al. Anständig wirtschaften: Warum Ökonomie Moral braucht. 2010. 342p. *(978-3-492-05424-9(2))* Piper Verlag GmbH.

Kahan, Alan. Mind vs. Money: The War between Intellectuals & Capitalism. 2010. (ENG.). 311p. 39.95 *(978-1-4128-1063-0(9))* Transaction Pubs.

Kaletsky, Anatole. Capitalism 4. 0: The Birth of a New Economy in the Aftermath of Crisis. 2011. (ENG., Illus.). 448p. pap. 17.99 *(978-1-58648-962-5(3))* PublicAffairs.

—Capitalism 4.0: The Birth of a New Economy in the Aftermath of Crisis. 2010. (ENG., Illus.). 416p. 28.95 *(978-1-58648-871-0(6))* PublicAffairs.

Kassimeris, Christos & Gouliamos, Kostas, eds. The Marketing of War in the Age of Neo-Militarism. 2011. (Routledge Advances in Sociology Ser.). (ENG., Illus.). 290p. (C). 125.00 *(978-0-415-88513-3(2))* Routledge.

Kaufmann, Franz-Xaver. Variations of the Welfare State: Great Britain, Sweden, France & Germany Between Capitalism & Socialism. 2012. (German Social Policy Ser.). Orig. Title: Geschichte der Sozialpolitik in Deutschland seit 1945, volume 1: Grundlagen der Sozialpolitik. (ENG., Illus.). x, 241p. 139.00 ***(978-3-642-22548-2(9),*** 3642225489) Springer.

Kelly, Jane & Malone, Shelia, eds. Ecosocialism or Barbarism - Expanded Second Edition. 2008. 176p. per. *(978-0-902869-88-2(4))* International Marxist Grp. (IMG).

Kennedy, Geoff. Diggers, Levellers, & Agrarian Capitalism: Radical Political Thought in Seventeenth Century England. 2008. (ENG.). 276p. 73.50 *(978-0-7391-2374-4(2))* Lexington Bks.

Kennedy, Scott, ed. Beyond the Middle Kingdom: Comparative Perspectives on China's Capitalist Transformation. 2011. (Contemporary Issues in Asia & Pacific Ser.). (ENG.). 280p. 65.00 *(978-0-8047-6957-0(5))*; pap. 22.95 *(978-0-8047-6958-7(3))* Stanford Univ. Pr.

Kenworthy, Lane. Egalitarian Capitalism: Jobs, Income, & Growth in Affluent Countries. 2007. (Illus.). 222p. per. 18.95 *(978-0-87154-452-0(0))* Russell Sage Foundation.

Kernen, Joe & Kernen, Blake. Your Teacher Said What?! Defending Our Kids from the Liberal Assault on Capitalism. 2011. (ENG.). 256p. (gr. 12). 25.95 *(978-1-59523-077-5(7),* Sentinel) Penguin Group (USA) Inc.

Keskin, Tugrul, ed. The Sociology of Islam: Secularism, Economy & Politics. 2012. 528p. pap. 34.95 ***(978-0-86372-425-1(6),*** Ithaca Pr.) Garnet Publishing, Ltd. GBR. Dist: International Specialized Bk. Services.

Kim, Annette Miae. Learning to Be Capitalists: Entrepreneurs in Vietnam's Transition Economy. 2008. (ENG., Illus.). 160p. 35.00 *(978-0-19-536939-7(4))* Oxford Univ. Pr., Inc.

C

Kim, Kyong-Dong & Lim, Hyun-Chin, eds. East Meets West: Civilizational Encounters & the Spirit of Capitalism in East Asia. 2007. (Social Sciences in Asia Ser.). (Illus.). 200p. pap. (978-90-04-16021-7(3)) BRILL.

Kinsley, Michael, ed. Creative Capitalism: A Conversation with Bill Gates, Warren Buffett, & Other Economic Leaders. 2009. (ENG.). 336p. pap. 20.99 (978-1-4165-9942-5(8)) Simon & Schuster.

Kirby, Peadar & Murphy, Mary P. Towards a Second Republic: Irish Politics & the Celtic Tiger, 1 vol. 2011. (ENG.). 240p. lib. bdg. 95.00 (978-0-7453-3056-3(8)); (Illus.). 30.00 (978-0-7453-3055-6(X)) Pluto Pr. GBR. Dist: Macmillan.

Klein, Naomi. The Shock Doctrine: The Rise of Disaster Capitalism. 2007. (ENG.). 576p. 30.00 (978-0-8050-7983-8(1), Metropolitan Bks.) Holt, Henry & Co.

—The Shock Doctrine: The Rise of Disaster Capitalism. 2008. (ENG.). 720p. pap. 16.00 (978-0-312-42799-3(9)) Picador.

Kliman, Andrew. The Failure of Capitalist Production: Underlying Causes of the Great Recession, 1 vol. 2011. (ENG., Illus.). 256p. 95.00 (978-0-7453-3240-6(4)) Pluto Pr. GBR. Dist: Macmillan.

Knoedler, Janet T., et al, eds. Thorstein Veblen & the Revival of Free Market Capitalism. 2007. 264p. (C). 127.00 (978-1-84542-540-1(5)) Elgar, Edward Publishing, Inc.

Knoflacher, Hermann & Rosik-Kölbl, Agnieszka, eds. Kapitalismus - gezähmt? Technologie und Kapitalismus: Mit Beiträgen von Dennis Meadows, Klaus Woltron, Markus Knoflacher, Hans Peter Aubauer, Tadej Brezina, Hermann Knoflacher und Armin Reller. 2008. 170p. pap. 28.95 (978-3-631-57161-3(5)) Lang, Peter GmbH, Europaischer Verlag der Wissenschaften DEU. Dist: Lang, Peter.

Kobrin, Rebecca, ed. Chosen Capital: The Jewish Encounter with American Capitalism. 2012. (ENG.). 288p. 70.00 (978-0-8135-5307-8(5)); (Illus.). pap. 26.95 (978-0-8135-5308-5(3)) Rutgers Univ. Pr.

Koch, Max. Capitalism & Climate Change: Theoretical Discussion, Historical Development & Policy Responses. 2011. (ENG., Illus.). 224p. 85.00 (978-0-230-27251-4(7)) Palgrave Macmillan.

Kolodko, Grzegorz W., et al, eds. Transition & Beyond. 2007. (Studies in Economic Transition Ser.). (ENG., Illus.). 288p. 126.00 (978-0-230-54697-4(8)) Palgrave Macmillan.

Konzelmann, Suzanne J. & Fovargue-Davies, Marc, eds. Banking Systems in the Crisis. 2012. (Routledge Critical Studies in Finance & Stability Ser.). (ENG., Illus.). 304p. (C). 130.00 (978-0-415-51789-8(3)) Routledge.

Kopelas, George. Society in a Market Economy. 2011. 84p. pap. 14.03 (978-1-4520-7184-8(5)) AuthorHouse.

Korkotsides, Anastasios S. Consumer Capitalism. 2007. (Routledge Frontiers of Political Economy Ser.). (Illus.). 258p. 150.00 (978-0-415-37518-4(5)) Routledge.

Kornai, Janos. From Socialism to Capitalism. 2008. (ENG., Illus.). 200p. 35.00 (978-963-9776-16-6(5)) Central European Univ. Pr.

Koslowski, Peter. Ethics of Capitalism & Critique of Sociobiology: Two Essays with a Comment by James M. Buchanan. 2010. (Studies in Economic Ethics & Philosophy Ser.). ix, 142p. pap. 129.00 (978-3-642-08246-7(7), 3642082467) Springer.

Koslowski, Peter, ed. The Theory of Capitalism in the German Economic Tradition: Historism, Ordo-Liberalism, Critical Theory, Solidarism. 2010. (Studies in Economic Ethics & Philosophy Ser.). (ENG., Illus.). xii, 596p. pap. 239.00 (978-3-642-08592-5(X), 364208592X) Springer.

Kovel, Joel. The Enemy of Nature: The End of Capitalism or the End of the World? 2nd rev. ed. 2007. (ENG.). 336p. 99.00 (978-1-84277-870-8(6)); 354p. per. 27.00 (978-1-84277-871-5(4)) Zed Bks., Ltd. GBR. Dist: Macmillan.

Kram, Lo. The Kite & the Kingdom: Getting Crisis under Control! 2009. 492p. 39.95 (978-1-4401-3119-6(8)); pap. 29.95 (978-1-4401-3117-2(1)) iUniverse, Inc.

Krane, Jim. City of Gold: Dubai & the Dream of Capitalism. 2010. (ENG., Illus.). 384p. pap. 16.00 (978-0-312-65543-3(6)) Picador.

Krigbaum, Edward J. Relentless: The Socialist Attack on American Freedom. 2009. 244p. 26.50 (978-1-60693-938-3(6), Strategic Bk. Publishing) AEG Literary Publishing Services, Inc.

Kristensen, Peer Hull & Lilja, Kari. Nordic Capitalisms & Globalization: New Forms of Economic Organization & Welfare Institutions. 2011. (ENG., Illus.). 300p. 99.00 (978-0-19-959453-5(8)) Oxford Univ. Pr., Inc.

Kristensen, Peer Hull & Lilja, Kari, eds. Nordic Capitalisms & Globalization: New Forms of Economic Organization & Welfare Institutions. 2012. (ENG.). 328p. pap. 45.00 (978-0-19-965584-7(7)) Oxford Univ. Pr., Inc.

Krug, Barbara & Hendrischke, Hans, eds. The Chinese Economy in the 21st Century: Enterprise & Business Behaviour. 2007. (Illus.). 264p. (C). 119.00 (978-1-84542-750-4(5)) Elgar, Edward Publishing, Inc.

Kuo, Tai-chun & Myers, Ramon H. Taiwan's Economic Transformation: Leadership, property rights & institutional Change. 2011. (Routledge Research on Taiwan Ser.). (ENG., Illus.). 176p. (C). 125.00 (978-0-415-66590-2(6)) Routledge.

Kusljic, Dorde. Transition in Bosni. 2009. 54p. pap. (978-3-639-16343-8(5)) VDM Verlag Dr. Mueller e.K.

Lacher. Beyond Globalization. 2007. pap. 41.95 (978-0-415-46000-2(X)) Routledge.

Lacher, Hannes. Beyond Globalization: Capitalism, Territoriality & the International Relations of Modernity. 2006. (Routledge/RIPE Studies in Global Political Economy Ser.). (ENG., Illus.). 224p. (C). 150.00 (978-0-415-32193-8(X), RU26929) Routledge.

Laibman, David. Deep History: A Study in Social Evolution & Human Potential. (SUNY Series in Radical, Social, & Political Theory). 224p. 2008. per. 29.95 (978-0-7914-6930-9(1)) 2006. (Illus.). 65.00 (978-0-7914-6929-3(8)) State Univ. of New York Pr.

Laine, Jorge. El híbrido entre la Revolución y el Imperio. 2010. (SPA.). 64p. pap. 9.99 (978-1-59835-220-7(2), CBH Bks.) Cambridge BrickHouse, Inc.

Lal, Deepak. Reviving the Invisible Hand: The Case for Classical Liberalism in the Twenty-First Century. 2008. (ENG., Illus.). 336p. (C). pap. 35.00 (978-0-691-13638-7(6)) Princeton Univ. Pr.

Lange, Matthew. Antisemitic Elements in the Critique of Capitalism in German Culture, 1850-1933. 348p. pap. 83.95 (978-3-03911-040-7(3)) Lang, Peter Publishing, Inc.

Langlois, Richard N. The Dynamics of Industrial Capitalism: Schumpeter, Chandler, & the New Economy. 2007. (Graz Schumpeter Lectures). (Illus.). 122p. 140.00 (978-0-415-77167-2(6)) Routledge.

Lanz, Tobias J., ed. Beyond Capitalism & Socialism: A New Statement of an Old Ideal. 2008. (ENG., Illus.). 240p. 25.95 (978-1-932528-10-7(5)) IHS Pr.

Larsen, Wolf. Capitalism Sucks! 2011. 224p. 24.95 (978-1-4567-2639-3(0)); pap. 14.95 (978-1-4567-2640-9(4)) AuthorHouse.

Larson, John Lauritz. The Market Revolution in America: Liberty, Ambition, & the Eclipse of the Common Good. 2009. (Cambridge Essential Histories Ser.). (ENG., Illus.). 222p. (C). 75.00 (978-0-521-88365-8(2)); pap. 20.99 (978-0-521-70989-7(X)) Cambridge Univ. Pr.

Larsson, Tomas. Land & Loyalty: Security & the Development of Property Rights in Thailand. 2012. (Cornell Studies in Political Economy Ser.). (ENG., Illus.). 224p. 45.00 (978-0-8014-5081-5(0)) Cornell Univ. Pr.

Lash, Scott M. Intensive Culture: Social Theory, Religion & Contemporary Capitalism. 2010. (Published in Association with Theory, Culture & Society Ser.). 256p. 135.00 (978-1-4129-4516-5(X), B4516XC); pap. 51.00 (978-1-4129-4517-2(8), B4516XP) SAGE Pubns., Ltd. GBR. Dist: SAGE Pubns., Inc.

Laski, Harold J. Democracy in Crisis. reprint ed. 37.50 (978-0-404-03882-3(4)) AMS Pr., Inc.

Laski, John. Capitalism & Christianity: A Moral & Ethical Struggle. 2008. 108p. pap. 16.95 (978-1-60441-624-4(6)) PublishAmerica, Inc.

Lee, Steven Hugh, ed. Transformations in Twentieth Century Korea. 2006. (RoutledgeCurzon Advances in Korean Studies: Vol. 7). (ENG., Illus.). 384p. (C). 160.00 (978-0-415-38065-2(0)) Routledge.

Lenin, Nikolai. Imperialism: The State & Revolution. 2011. 234p. 46.95 (978-1-258-02697-4(X)) Literary Licensing, LLC.

Lenin, V. Fight Against Stalinism & Imperialism: The Highest Stage of Capitalism. 2007. 264p. 35.95 (978-0-9793363-7-9(6)) Ellis, Frederick.

Lepper, John. An Enquiry into the Ideology & Reality of Markets & Market Systems. 2012. (ENG., Illus.). 304p. 100.00 (978-0-230-32097-0(X)) Palgrave Macmillan.

Lester, David, ed. The Gruesome Acts of Capitalism. 2nd rev. ed. 2007. (ENG., Illus.). 112p. pap. 10.95 (978-1-894037-30-3(8)) Arbeiter Ring Publishing CAN. Dist: AK Pr. Distribution.

Leuschel, Roland, et al. The Global Debt Trap: How to Escape the Danger & Build a Fortune. 2010. (ENG., Illus.). 230p. 29.95 (978-0-470-76723-8(5), Wiley) Wiley, John & Sons, Inc.

Lewis, Paul H. The Agony of Argentine Capitalism: From Menem to the Kirchners, 1 vol. 2009. 221p. 65.00 (978-0-313-37877-5(0), C37877); pap. 29.95 (978-0-313-37879-9(7), B37879) Greenwood Publishing Group, Inc. (Praeger Pubs.).

Lewitt, Michael E. The Death of Capital: How Creative Policy Can Restore Stability. 2010. (ENG., Illus.). 292p. 27.95 (978-0-470-46650-6(2), Wiley) Wiley, John & Sons, Inc.

Leys, Colin. Total Capitalism: Market Politics, Market State. 2007. 156p. pap. 22.95 (978-0-85036-590-0(2)) Merlin Pr. Ltd. GBR. Dist: Independent Pubs. Group.

Li, Minqi. The Rise of China & the Demise of the Capitalist World Economy. 2009. (ENG.). 240p. 75.00 (978-1-58367-183-2(8)); pap. 16.95 (978-1-58367-182-5(X)) Monthly Review Pr.

—The Rise of China & the Demise of the Capitalist World Economy. 2008. (Illus.). 192p. 95.00 (978-0-7453-2773-0(7)) Pluto Pr. GBR. Dist: Univ. of Michigan Pr.

Li, Xiaoxi, ed. Assessing the Extent of China's Marketization. 2006. (Chinese Trade & Industry Ser.). (Illus.). 350p. 130.00 (978-0-7546-4878-9(8)) Ashgate Publishing Co.

Lichtenstein, Nelson, ed. American Capitalism: Social Thought & Political Economy in the Twentieth Century. 2007. (Politics & Culture in Modern America Ser.). (Illus.). 392p. (C). per. 24.95 (978-0-8122-1940-1(6)) Univ. of Pennsylvania Pr.

Light Brigade Publishing House. The Manifesto of Capitalism, 9th Edition: An Analysis & Summary of Adam Smith's the Wealth of Nations. 9th ed. 2008. 210p. pap. 10.00 incl. audio (978-0-9625163-6-8(8)) Light Brigade Publishing Hse.

Lilley, Sasha, ed. Capital & Its Discontents: Conversations with Radical Thinkers in a Time of Tumult. 2011. (Spectre Ser.). (ENG.). 320p. pap. 20.00 (978-1-60486-334-5(X)) PM Pr.

Lind, Christopher. Rumours of a Moral Economy: Ethics & Capitalism. 2011. (ENG., Illus.). 144p. pap. 18.95 (978-1-55266-373-8(6)) Fernwood Publishing Co., Ltd. CAN. Dist: Independent Pubs. Group.

Lingle, Christopher. Singapore's Authoritarian Capitalism: Asian Values, Free Market Illusions, & Political Dependency. xxii, 168p. (978-84-85809-52-3(1)) Sirocco, Edicions, Societat Anonima.

Liodakis, George. Totalitarian Capitalism & Beyond. 2010. (Illus.). 248p. 99.95 (978-0-7546-7557-0(2)) Ashgate Publishing Co.

Lippit. Capitalism. 2007. 224p. 43.95 (978-0-415-43506-2(4)) Routledge.

Lipschutz, Ronnie D. Political Economy, Capitalism, & Popular Culture. 2010. (ENG.). 230p. 79.00 (978-0-7425-5650-8(6)); pap. 26.95 (978-0-7425-5651-5(4)) Rowman & Littlefield Publishers, Inc.

Litan, Robert E. & Schramm, Carl J. Better Capitalism: Renewing the Entrepreneurial Strength of the American Economy. 2012. (ENG., Illus.). 288p. 32.50 (978-0-300-14678-3(7)) Yale Univ. Pr.

Liu, Xin. The Mirage of China: Anti-Humanism, Narcissism, & Corporeality of the Contemporary World. 2009. 222p. 90.00 (978-1-84545-545-3(2)) Berghahn Bks., Inc.

Lloyd-Jones, Roger, et al. Corporate Governance & Personal Capitalism: British Manufacturing in the First Half of the Twentieth Century. 2011. (Modern Economic & Social History Ser.). (Illus.). 250p. 124.95 (978-0-7546-5587-9(3)) Ashgate Publishing Co.

Lloyd, Tom. Business at a Crossroads: The Crisis of Corporate Leadership. 2009. (ENG.). 216p. 44.00 (978-0-230-23094-1(6)) Palgrave Macmillan.

Long, Susan & Sievers, Burkard, eds. Towards a Socioanalysis of Money, Finance & Capitalism: Beneath the Surface of the Financial Industry. 2011. (Routledge International Studies in Money & Banking Ser.). (ENG., Illus.). 416p. (C). 155.00 (978-0-415-60031-6(6)) Routledge.

López G, Julio. La Economía de Michal Kalecki y el Capitalismo Actual: Ensayos de Teoría Económica y Economía Aplicada. 2008. (Economía Ser.). (SPA., Illus.). 295p. pap. (978-968-16-8343-6(9)) Fondo de Cultura Economica.

Lough, Joseph W. H. Weber & the Persistence of Religion: Social Theory, Capitalism & the Sublime. annot. ed. 2006. (Routledge Advances in Sociology Ser.). 140p. 133.00 (978-0-415-34352-7(6), RU3526X) Routledge.

Lovins, L. Hunter & Cohen, Boyd. Climate Capitalism: Capitalism in the Age of Climate Change, 1 vol. 2011. (ENG., Illus.). 400p. 27.95 (978-0-8090-3473-4(5), Hill & Wang) Farrar, Straus & Giroux.

Lovins, L. Hunter & Cohen, Boyd. Way Out: Capitalism in the Age of Climate Change, 1 vol. 2012. (ENG., Illus.). 400p. pap. 16.95 (978-0-8090-3469-7(7), Hill & Wang) Farrar, Straus & Giroux.

Lukomnik, Jon, et al. The New Capitalists: How Citizen Investors Are Reshaping the Corporate Agenda. 2006. (ENG., Illus.). 288p. 29.95 (978-1-4221-0101-8(0)) Harvard Business Review Pr.

Lynn, Barry C. Cornered: The New Monopoly Capitalism & the Economics of Destruction. 2010. (ENG.). 336p. 26.95 (978-0-470-18638-1(0), Wiley) Wiley, John & Sons, Inc.

Lynn, Barry C. Cornered: The New Monopoly Capitalism & the Economics of Destruction. 2011. (ENG.). 336p. pap. 16.95 (978-0-470-92856-1(5), Wiley) Wiley, John & Sons, Inc.

Macartney, Huw. Variegated Neoliberalism: EU varieties of capitalism & International Political Economy. 2011. (Routledge/RIPE Studies in Global Political Economy Ser.). (ENG., Illus.). 208p. (C). 130.00 (978-0-415-60150-4(9)) Routledge.

Macdonald, Kate, et al, eds. New Visions for Market Governance: Crisis & Renewal. 2012. (Challenges of Globalisation Ser.). (ENG., Illus.). 256p. (C). 130.00 (978-0-415-69111-6(7)) Routledge.

MacGilvray, Eric. The Invention of Market Freedom. 2011. (ENG.). 216p. 90.00 (978-1-107-00136-7(6)); pap. 26.99 (978-0-521-17189-2(X)) Cambridge Univ. Pr.

Mack-Tucker, Patti. What You Should Know Before Starting a Business. 2010. 144p. 29.95 (978-1-4520-2666-4(1)); pap. 24.95 (978-1-4520-2667-1(X)) AuthorHouse.

Magnuson, Joel. Mindful Economics: How the U. S. Economy Works, Why It Matters, & How It Could Be Different. 2008. (ENG., Illus.). 432p. pap. 24.95 (978-1-58322-847-0(0)) Seven Stories Pr.

Magnuson, Joel, text. Mindful Economics: Understanding American Capitalism, Its Consequences & Alternatives. 2006. pap. 29.99 (978-0-9790822-0-7(X)) Pilot Light Bks.

Mah, Ben. China & the World: Global Crisis of Capitalism. 2011. 376p. pap. 24.95 (978-1-4620-5680-4(6)) iUniverse, Inc.

Mainwaring, Simon. We First: How Brands & Consumers Use Social Media to Build a Better World. (ENG.). 256p. 2012. pap. 17.00 (978-0-230-34163-0(2)) 2011. (Illus.). 26.00 (978-0-230-11026-7(6)) Palgrave Macmillan.

Malisa, Mark. Out of These Ashes. 2009. 244p. pap. (978-3-639-18553-9(6)) VDM Verlag Dr. Mueller e.K.

Mander, Jerry. The Capitalism Papers: Six Fatal Flaws of an Obsolete System. 2012. (ENG.). 256p. 26.00 (978-1-58243-717-0(3), Counterpoint) Counterpoint LLC.

Mann, James. The China Fantasy: Why Capitalism Will Not Bring Democracy to China. 2008. (ENG.). 160p. (gr. 12-18). 13.00 (978-0-14-311292-1(9), Penguin (Non-Classics)) Penguin Group (USA) Inc.

Manokha, Ivan. The Political Economy of Human Rights Enforcement: Moral & Intellectual Leadership in the Context of Global Hegemony. 2008. (Global Ethics Ser.). (ENG.). 304p. 100.00 (978-0-230-55072-8(X)) Palgrave Macmillan.

Marazzi, Christian. The Violence of Financial Capitalism. Lebedeva, Kristina & Mc Gimsey, Jason Francis, trs. from ITA. 2011. (Semiotext(e) / Intervention Ser.). (ENG.). 136p. (gr. 17). pap. 12.95 (978-1-58435-102-3(0)) Semiotexte/Smart Art.

Marfany, Julie. Land Proto-Industry & Population in Catalonia C. 1680-1829: An Alternative Transition to Capitalism? 2012. (Modern Economic & Social History Ser.). (Illus.). 190p. 124.95 (978-1-4094-4465-7(1)) Ashgate Publishing Co.

Martel, James. Textual Conspiracies: Walter Benjamin, Idolatry, & Political Theory. 2011. (ENG.). 318p. 75.00 (978-0-472-11772-7(6)) Univ. of Michigan Pr.

Martel, James R. Textual Conspiracies: Walter Benjamin, Idolatry, & Political Theory. 2011. 314p. E-Book (978-0-472-02819-1(7)) Univ. of Michigan Pr.

Martin, Roger L. Fixing the Game: Bubbles, Crashes, & What Capitalism Can Learn from the NFL. 2011. (ENG.). 272p. 24.95 (978-1-4221-7164-6(7)) Harvard Business Review Pr.

—Fixing the Game: How Runaway Expectations Broke the Economy, & How to Get Back to Reality. 2011. (Illus.). 198p. (978-1-4221-7229-2(5)) Harvard Business Review Pr.

Martin, William G., ed. Making Waves: Worldwide Social Movements, 1750-2005. 2007. (Fernand Braudel Center Ser.). (Illus.). 226p. 125.00 (978-1-59451-480-7(1)) Paradigm Pubs.

Martinez, Mark A. The Myth of the Free Market: The Role of the State in a Capitalist Economy. 2009. (Illus.). 336p. 69.95 (978-1-56549-284-4(6)) Stylus Publishing, LLC.

Marwood, Maurice E. Professional Nomad. 2009. 274p. pap. 25.00 (978-1-4251-8035-5(3)) Trafford Publishing.

Mason, Matt. The Pirate's Dilemma: How Youth Culture Is Reinventing Capitalism. 2009. (ENG., Illus.). 288p. pap. 18.99 (978-1-4165-3220-0(X), Free Pr.) Free Pr.

Mason, Paul. Meltdown: The End of the Age of Greed. 2nd ed. 2010. (ENG.). 288p. pap. 14.95 (978-1-84467-653-6(6), 844653) Verso Bks. GBR. Dist: Norton, W. W. & Co., Inc.

Matthews, Christopher N. Archaeology of American Capitalism. 2010. (American Experience in Archaeological Pespective Ser.). (ENG., Illus.). 256p. 69.95 (978-0-8130-3524-6(4)) Univ. Pr. of Florida.

Matthews, Gary. Moral Power & the Capitalist Dilemm. 2010. 392p. pap. (978-3-8383-5311-1(0)) Lambert Academic Publishing.

Mattick, Paul. Business as Usual: The Economic Crisis & the Failure of Capitalism. 2011. (ENG.). 126p. pap. 17.95 (978-1-86189-801-2(0)) Reaktion Bks., Ltd. GBR. Dist: Chicago Distribution Ctr.

Mautner, Gerlinde. Language & the Market Society. 2010. (Illus.). viii, 215p. (C). 120.00 (978-0-203-85599-7(X)) Routledge.

—Language & the Market Society: Critical Reflections on Discourse & Dominance. 2010. (Routledge Critical Studies in Discourse Ser.). (ENG., Illus.). 230p. (C). 128.00 (978-0-415-99814-7(X)) Routledge.

Mavroudeas, S. The Limits of Regulation: A Critical Analysis of Capitalist Development. 2012. 224p. 110.00 (978-0-85793-863-3(0)) Elgar, Edward Publishing, Inc.

Mazumdar, Sucheta. From Orientalism to Postcolonialism: Asia-Europe & the Lineages of Difference. 2009. (Routledge Contemporary Asia Ser.). (ENG.). 256p. 130.00 (978-0-415-54740-6(7)) Routledge.

Mazumdar, Sucheta, et al. From Orientalism to Postcolonialism. 2011. 256p. pap. 42.95 (978-0-415-67169-9(8)) Routledge.

McCloskey, Deirdre N. The Bourgeois Virtues: Ethics for an Age of Commerce. (Illus.). 634p. 2007. pap. 22.50 (978-0-226-55664-2(6)) 2006. 32.50 (978-0-226-55663-5(8)) Univ. of Chicago Pr.

McCraw, Thomas K. Prophet of Innovation: Joseph Schumpeter & Creative Destruction. 2010. (Illus.). 736p. pap. 21.00 (978-0-674-03481-5(3), Belknap Pr.) Harvard Univ. Pr.

McDaniel, Charles. God & Money: The Moral Challenge of Capitalism. 2006. (ENG.). 352p. 30.95 (978-0-7425-5222-7(5)) Rowman & Littlefield Publishers, Inc.

McDonald, David A. Electric Capitalism: Recolonising Africa on the Power Grid. McDonald, David A. & McDonald David, eds. 2008. (ENG., Illus.). 536p. 136.50 (978-1-84407-714-4(4)) Routledge.

McDonald, Patrick J. The Invisible Hand of Peace: Capitalism, the War Machine, & International Relations Theory. 2009. (ENG., Illus.). 352p. (C). 85.00 (978-0-521-76136-9(0)); pap. 27.99 (978-0-521-74412-6(1)) Cambridge Univ. Pr.

McDonough, Terrence, et al, eds. Contemporary Capitalism & Its Crises: Social Structure of Accumulation Theory for the 21st Century. 2010. (ENG., Illus.). 374p. 95.00 (978-0-521-51516-0(5)); pap. 32.99 (978-0-521-73580-3(7)) Cambridge Univ. Pr.

McFarlane, George. Behind the Rhetoric. 2010. 153p. pap. 55.00 (978-1-4092-9826-7(4)) Lulu Enterprises Inc.

McGuigan, Jim. Cool Capitalism. 2009. (ENG., Illus.). 256p. 80.00 (978-0-7453-2640-5(4)); pap. 26.95 (978-0-7453-2678-8(1)) Pluto Pr. GBR. Dist: Macmillan.

Mclaren/Best/Kahn/No. The Global Industrial Complex: Systems of Domination. 2011. (ENG., Illus.). 344p. pap. 36.95 (978-0-7391-3698-0(4)) Lexington Bks.

McMahon, Christopher. Public Capitalism: The Political Authority of Corporate Executives. 2012. (Haney Foundation Ser.). 208p. (C). 39.95 (978-0-8122-4444-1(3)) Univ. of Pennsylvania Pr.

McMillan, Chris. Zizek & Communist Strategy: On the Disavowed Foundations of Global Capitalism. 2012. (ENG.). 192p. (gr. 17). 105.00 (978-0-7486-4664-7(7)) Edinburgh Univ. Pr. GBR. Dist: Columbia Univ. Pr.

McNally, David. Another World Is Possible: Globalization & Anti-Capitalism. 2nd rev. annot. ed. 2006. (ENG., Illus.). 408p. per. 28.95 (978-1-894037-27-3(8)) Arbeiter Ring Publishing CAN. Dist: AK Pr. Distribution.

—Global Slump: The Economics & Politics of Crisis & Resistance. 2010. (Spectre Ser.). (ENG.). 176p. pap. 17.00 (978-1-60486-332-1(3)) PM Pr.

—Monsters of the Market: Zombies, Vampires & Global Capitalism. 2011. (Illus.). 272p. (978-90-04-20157-6(2)) BRILL.

Medaille, John C. Toward a Truly Free Market: A Distributist Perspective on the Role of Government, Taxes, Health Care, Deficits, & More. (ENG.). 2011. pap. 18.00 (978-1-61017-027-7(X)) 2010. (Illus.). vi, 282p. 26.95 (978-1-935191-81-0(0)) ISI Bks.

Medved, Michael. The 5 Big Lies about American Business: Combating Smears Against the Free-Market Economy. 2010. (ENG.). 272p. pap. 15.00 (978-0-307-58747-3(9), Three Rivers Pr.) Crown Publishing Group.

Mellor, Mary. The Future of Money: From Financial Crisis to Public Resource, 1 vol. 2010. (ENG.). 176p. 90.00 (978-0-7453-2995-6(0)); pap. 30.00 (978-0-7453-2994-9(2)) Pluto Pr. GBR. Dist: Macmillan.

Meltzer, Allan H. Why Capitalism?, 1 vol. 2012. (ENG., Illus.). 168p. 21.95 (978-0-19-985957-3(4), Oxford Univ. Pr., Inc.

Menshikov, Stanislav M. The Anatomy of Russian Capitalism. Douglas, Rachel B., tr. from RUS. 2007. pap. 30.00 (978-0-943235-22-6(7), EIRBK-2006-1, EIRNS) Executive Intelligence Review.

Mentan, Tatah. Understanding Contemporary Capitalism: A Marxist Historical/Materialist Interpretation. 2011. (ENG.). 152p. lib. bdg. (978-1-936320-37-0(1)) Academica Pr., LLC.

Mészáros, István & Foster, John Bellamy. The Structural Crisis of Capital. 2010. (ENG.). 218p. 79.00 (978-1-58367-209-5(5)); pap. 26.95 (978-1-58367-208-2(7)) Monthly Review Pr.

Meszaros, Istvan, et al. The Challenge & Burden of Historical Time: Socialism in the Twenty-First Century. 2008. (ENG.). 480p. 89.00 (978-1-58367-170-2(6)); (C). pap. 29.95 (978-1-58367-169-6(2)) Monthly Review Pr.

Micocci, Andrea. The Metaphysics of Capitalism. (ENG.). 280p. 2010. pap. 31.50 (978-0-7391-2838-1(8)) 2009. 78.99 (978-0-7391-2837-4(X)) Lexington Bks.

Micocci, Andrea. Moderation & Revolution. 2011. (ENG.). 390p. 85.00 (978-0-7391-6713-2(9)) Lexington Bks.

Mielants, Eric H. & Mielants, Eric. The Origins of Capitalism & the Rise of the West. 2008. (ENG.). 256p. pap. 26.95 (978-1-59213-576-9(5)) Temple Univ. Pr.

Mielants, Eric M. The Origins of Capitalism & the Rise of the West. 2007. 256p. 68.50 (978-1-59213-575-2(7)) Temple Univ. Pr.

Mikhailov, Boris, photos by. Boris Mikhailov. Tea Coffee Capuccino. 2011. (ENG., Illus.). 240p. 85.00 (978-3-86560-877-2(9)) Verlag der Buchhandlung Walther Konig DEU. Dist: D.A.P./Distributed Art Pubs.

Milhaupt, Curtis J. & Pistor, Katharina. Law & Capitalism: What Corporate Crises Reveal about Legal Systems & Economic Development Around the World. (ENG.). 2010. 280p. pap. 25.00 (978-0-226-52528-0(7)) 2008. (Illus.). 272p. 39.00 (978-0-226-52527-3(9)) Univ. of Chicago Pr.

Miliband, Ralph. The State in Capitalist Society. 2009. 360p. pap. 29.95 (978-0-85036-668-4(7)) Merlin Pr. Ltd. GBR. Dist: Independent Pubs. Group.

Millos, John, et al. Rethinking Imperialism: A Study of Capitalist Rule. 2009. (ENG., Illus.). 272p. 105.00 (978-0-230-22100-0(9)) Palgrave Macmillan.

Mises, Ludwig von. The Anti-Capitalistic Mentality. (ENG.). 84p. (C). (gr. 12). 2009. pap. 12.00 (978-0-86597-671-9(6)) 2006. 20.00 (978-0-86597-670-2(8)) Liberty Fund, Inc.

Mizruchi, Susan L. The Rise of Multicultural America: Economy & Print Culture, 1865-1915. 2009. (ENG., Illus.). 352p. 69.95 (978-0-8078-3250-9(2)); pap. 26.95 (978-0-8078-5912-4(5)) Univ. of North Carolina Pr.

MjoSet, Lars, ed. The Nordic Varieties of Capitalism. 2011. (Comparative Social Research Ser.). (Illus.). 420p. (978-0-85724-777-3(8)) Emerald Group Publishing Ltd.

Mjoset, Lars & Nordhaug, Kristen, eds. Capitalism Compared. 2007. (Comparative Social Research Ser.). 424p. 111.95 (978-0-7623-1313-6(7)) Emerald Group Publishing Ltd. GBR. Dist: Turpin Distribution Services Ltd.

Model, David & Model, Lesley. Selling Out: Consuming Ourselves to Death. 2010. 168p. 22.49 (978-1-4520-4317-3(5)); pap. 11.99 (978-1-4520-4316-6(7)) AuthorHouse.

Moore, Karl. The Origins of Globalization. 2009. (Routledge International Studies in Business History Ser.). (ENG., Illus.). 292p. (C). 44.95 (978-0-415-80598-8(8)) Routledge.

Moore, Stanley Williams. The Critique of Capitalism Democracy: An Introduction to the Theory of the State in Marx, Engels, & Lenin. 2011. 180p. 42.95 (978-1-258-04657-5(3)) Literary Licensing, LLC.

Moreta, Angel. Capitalismo y Descampesinización en el Suroeste Dominicano. 2009. (SPA., Illus.). 369p. (978-9945-02-065-6(X)) Archivo General de la Nacion.

Morgan, Glenn & Whitley, Richard, eds. Capitalisms & Capitalism in the Twenty-First Century. 2012. (ENG., Illus.). 400p. 110.00 (978-0-19-969476-1(1)) Oxford Univ. Pr., Inc.

Morgenson, Gretchen. The Capitalist's Bible. 2009. (ENG., Illus.). 320p. pap. 16.99 (978-0-06-156098-9(7), Harper Paperbacks) HarperCollins Pubs.

Moulier-Boutang, Yann. Cognitive Capitalism. (ENG.). 200p. 2012. pap. 22.95 (978-0-7456-4733-3(2)) 2011. 64.95 (978-0-7456-4732-6(4)) Polity Pr. GBR. Dist: Wiley, John & Sons, Inc.

Mrozowicki, Adam. Coping with Social Change: Life Strategies of Workers in Poland's New Capitalism. 2011. 284p. pap. 65.00 (978-90-5867-865-2(2)) Leuven Univ. Pr. BEL. Dist: Cornell Univ. Pr.

Mueller, Dennis C. The Oxford Handbook of Capitalism, 1 vol. 2012. (Oxford Handbooks Ser.). (ENG., Illus.). 576p. 150.00 (978-0-19-539117-6(9)) Oxford Univ. Pr., Inc.

Mueller, Dennis C. & Cantner, Uwe, eds. Capitalism & Democracy in the 21st Century: Proceedings of the International Joseph A. Schumpeter Society Conference, Vienna 1998 Capitalism & Socialism in the 21st Century. 2010. (ENG., Illus.). v, 375p. pap. 123.00 (978-3-7908-2480-3(1), 3790824801) Physica-Verlag DEU. Dist: Springer.

Muller. Disenchantment with Market Economics: East Germans & Western Capitalism. 2007. (European Anthropology in Translation Ser.: Vol. 1). 254p. 27.95 (978-1-84545-506-4(1)) Berghahn Bks., Inc.

Muller, Jerry Z. Capitalism & the Jews. (ENG.). 2011. 272p. pap. 19.95 (978-0-691-15306-3(X)) 2010. 280p. (C). 24.95 (978-0-691-14478-8(8)) Princeton Univ. Pr.

Munford, Clarence J. American Crucible: Black Enslavement, White Capitalism, & Imperial Globalization: An Interpretation of Western Civilization since 1441. 2009. (978-1-59221-670-3(6)); 426p. pap. (978-1-59221-671-0(4)) Africa World Pr.

Murphy, John W. & Callaghan, Karen A. Toward a Post-Market Society. 2011. (Business Economics in a Rapidly-Changing World Ser.). viii, 190p. 89.00 (978-1-61209-646-9(8)) Nova Science Pubs., Inc.

Murphy, Robert P. The Politically Incorrect Guide to Capitalism. 2007. (Politically Incorrect Guides). (ENG., Illus.). 206p. per. 19.95 (978-1-59698-504-9(6)) Regnery Publishing, Inc., An Eagle Publishing Co.

Muzi D'Amico, Nicolás. The False Emancipation of Intellectual Labour in the Knowledge Economy. 2010. 64p. pap. (978-3-639-22842-7(1)) VDM Verlag Dr. Mueller e.K.

Nakano, Akira. Iwasaki Yataro "Mitsubishi" No Kigyoron: Nippon Kabushiki-Gaisha No Genten. 2010. (JPN., Illus.). 319p. (978-4-02-330497-0(2)) Asahi Shimbun-Sha.

Nance, Susan. How the Arabian Nights Inspired the American Dream, 1790-1935. 2009. (ENG., Illus.). 360p. 52.95 (978-0-8078-3274-5(X)) Univ. of North Carolina Pr.

Nasr, Vali. Forces of Fortune: The Rise of the New Muslim Middle Class & What It Will Mean for Our World. 2009. (ENG., Illus.). 320p. 26.00 (978-1-4165-8968-6(6), Free Pr.) Free Pr.

—The Rise of Islamic Capitalism: Why the New Muslim Middle Class Is the Key to Defeating Extremism. 2010. (ENG.). 320p. pap. 16.00 (978-1-4165-8969-3(4), Free Pr.) Free Pr.

Navarro, Armando. Global Capitalist Crisis & the Second Great Depression: Egalitarian Systemic Models for Change. 2012. (978-0-7391-7017-5(1)) 2011. (ENG.). 452p. (gr. 17). 90.00 (978-0-7391-7016-8(3)) Lexington Bks.

Nearing, Scott, et al. Which Offers More for the Future? Communism, Socialism, Capitalism. 2011. 64p. 36.95 (978-1-258-05995-8(9)) Literary Licensing, LLC.

Nee, Victor, et al, eds. On Capitalism. 2007. (ENG., Illus.). 368p. 70.00 (978-0-8047-5664-8(3)); per. 24.95 (978-0-8047-5665-5(1)) Stanford Univ. Pr.

Nee, Victor & Opper, Sonja. Capitalism from Below: Markets & Institutional Change in China. 2012. (ENG., Illus.). 456p. 45.00 (978-0-674-05020-4(7)) Harvard Univ. Pr.

Neuhaus, Richard J. Doing Well & Doing Good: The Challenge to the Christian Capitalist. 2012. (ENG.). 320p. pap. 15.00 (978-0-307-95560-9(5), Image) Doubleday Religious Publishing Group, The.

Nickerson, Mike. Life, Money & Illusion: Living on Earth As If We Want to Stay. rev. ed. 2009. (ENG., Illus.). 464p. pap. 22.95 (978-0-86571-659-9(5), 9780865716599) New Society Pubs., Ltd. CAN. Dist: Consortium Bk. Sales & Distribution.

Nitzan, Jonathan & Bichler, Shimshon. Capital as Power: A Study of Order & Creorder. 2009. (RIPE Series in Global Political Economy Ser.). (ENG., Illus.). 464p. (C). pap. 39.95 (978-0-415-49680-3(2)) Routledge.

Nolan, Peter. Capitalism & Freedom: The Contradictory Character of Globalisation. (Anthem Studies in Development & Globalization Ser.). (ENG., Illus.). 358p. 2008. pap. 35.00 (978-1-84331-282-6(4)) 2007. 80.00 (978-1-84331-280-2(8)) Anthem Pr. GBR. Dist: Books International, Inc.

—Crossroads: The End of Capitalism & the Future of Humanity. 2010. (Illus.). 304p. 26.95 (978-0-462-09968-2(7)) Marshall Cavendish GBR. Dist: Midpoint Trade Bks., Inc.

Noonan, Jeff. Democratic Society & Human Needs: Towards a Renewed Critique of Liberal Capitalism. 2006. (McGill-Queen's Studies in the History of Religion Ser.). (ENG.). 288p. (C). (978-0-7735-3120-8(3)) McGill-Queen's Univ. Pr.

North, Charles M. & Smietana, Bob. Good Intentions: Nine Hot-Button Issues Viewed Through the Eyes of Faith. 2008. (ENG., Illus.). 224p. per. 13.99 (978-0-8024-3462-3(2)) Moody Pubs.

Nwoko, Matthew I. Foundational Theories of International & Transnational Relations. 2010. 304p. 31.95 (978-1-4502-0190-2(3)) iUniverse, Inc.

O'Flynn, M. Profitable Ideas: The Ideology of the Individual in Capitalist Development. 2009. (Studies in Critical Social Sciences Ser.). 200p. (978-90-04-17804-5(X)) BRILL.

O'Flynn, Michael. Profitable Ideas: The Ideology of the Individual in Capitalist Development. 2012. (Studies in Critical Social Sciences Ser.). (ENG., Illus.). 200p. pap. 28.00 (978-1-60846-199-8(8)) Haymarket Bks.

O'Lalor, Peter. Alexander Hamilton & the Duty & Obligation of Government. 2009. 248p. pap. (978-3-639-12440-8(5)) VDM Verlag Dr. Mueller e.K.

O'Neil, Patrick H. Comparative Politics. 3rd ed. 2009. (ENG., Illus.). 384p. (C). pap. 67.57 (978-0-393-93376-5(8), 93376) Norton, W. W. & Co., Inc.

Our Schools/Our Selves, ed. Breaking the Iron Cage: Resistance to the Schooling of Global Capitalism. 2009. 264p. pap. 12.00 (978-0-88627-474-0(5)) Canadian Centre for Policy Alternatives/Centre canadien de recherche en politiques de rechange CAN. Dist: Gibson Publishing Connections.

Overman, Steven J. The Protestant Ethic & the Spirit of Sport: How Calvinism & Capitalism Shaped America's Games. 2011. (Sports & Religion Ser.). 276p. pap. 35.00 (978-0-88146-226-5(8)) Mercer Univ. Pr.

Oyvin Descoyvin. The Race: Human that Is. 2009. 56p. pap. 9.95 (978-1-4401-7861-0(5)) iUniverse, Inc.

Pack, Spencer J. Capitalism As a Moral System: Adam Smith's Critique of the Free Market Economy. 2010. (Illus.). 208p. pap. 36.00 (978-1-84980-129-4(0)) Elgar, Edward Publishing, Inc.

Paczýnska, Agnieszka. State, Labor, & the Transition to a Market Economy: Egypt, Poland, Mexico, & the Czech Republic. 2009. (ENG.). 256p. 55.00 (978-0-271-03436-2(X)) Pennsylvania State Univ. Pr.

Palicki, Bernard. A Capitalist Manifesto. 2009. 132p. 29.99 (978-1-4415-2444-7(4)); pap. 19.99 (978-1-4415-2443-0(6)) Xlibris Corp.

Palmer, Tom G., ed. The Morality of Capitalism: What Your Professors Won't Tell You. 2011. pap. 8.95 (978-0-89803-170-6(2)) Jameson Bks., Inc.

Panayotakis, Costas. Rationalization & Capitalism's Dialectic of Scarcity. 2009. 560p. pap. (978-3-639-15971-4(3)) VDM Verlag Dr. Mueller e.K.

Panayotakis, Costas. Remaking Scarcity: From Capitalist Inefficiency to Economic Democracy, 1 vol. 2011. (Future of World Capitalism Ser.). (ENG.). 240p. 30.00 (978-0-7453-3099-0(1)); lib. bdg. 95.00 (978-0-7453-3100-3(9)) Pluto Pr. GBR. Dist: Macmillan.

Parenti, Michael. Contrary Notions: The Michael Parenti Reader. 2007. (ENG.). 304p. per. 18.95 (978-0-87286-482-5(0)) City Lights Bks.

Parijs, Philippe van. Marxism Recycled. 2009. (Studies in Marxism & Social Theory Ser.). (ENG., Illus.). 264p. pap. 38.99 (978-0-521-12214-6(7)) Cambridge Univ. Pr.

Park, Julie. The Self & It: Novel Objects in Eighteenth-Century England. 2009. (ENG., Illus.). 312p. 50.00 (978-0-8047-5696-9(1)) Stanford Univ. Pr.

Parks, Robert H., et al. The End of Capitalism: Destructive Forces of an Economy Out of Control. 2009. (ENG., Illus.). 304p. 26.98 (978-1-59102-717-1(9)) Prometheus Bks., Pubs.

Patriquin, Larry. Agrarian Capitalism & Poor Relief in England, 1500-1860: Rethinking the Origins of the Welfare State. 2007. (ENG.). 280p. 100.00 (978-0-230-51693-9(9)) Palgrave Macmillan.

Paul, Ellen Frankel, et al. Liberalism & Capitalism. 2011. (Social Philosophy & Policy Ser.). (ENG.). 312p. (C). pap. 36.99 (978-1-107-64026-9(1)) Cambridge Univ. Pr.

Paul Zarembka. Why Capitalism Survives Crises: The Shock Absorbers. 2009. 299p. 144.95 (978-1-84855-586-0(5)) Emerald Group Publishing Ltd. GBR. Dist: Turpin Distribution Services Ltd.

Peet, Richard, et al. Theories of Development: Contentions, Arguments, Alternatives. 2nd ed. 2009. (ENG., Illus.). 324p. 70.00 (978-1-60623-066-4(2)); pap. 45.00 (978-1-60623-065-7(4)) Guilford Pubns., Inc.

Pejovich, Svetozar & Colombatto, Enrico. Law, Informal Rules & Economic Performance: The Case for Common Law. 192p. 2010. pap. 36.00 (978-1-84980-027-3(8)) 2008. (C). 119.00 (978-1-84542-873-0(0)) Elgar, Edward Publishing, Inc.

Pelley, William Dudley. No More Hunger. 2011. 236p. 26.26 (978-1-4269-5113-8(2)); pap. 16.26 (978-1-4269-5111-4(6)) Trafford Publishing.

Penny, Laurie. Meat Market: Female Flesh under Capitalism. 2011. (ENG.). 79p. pap. 12.95 (978-1-84694-521-2(6)) O Bks., John Hunt.

Perelman, Michael. The Invisible Handcuffs of Capitalism: How Market Tyranny Stifles the Economy by Stunting Workers. 2011. (ENG.). 280p. 75.00 (978-1-58367-230-3(3)); pap. 19.95 (978-1-58367-229-7(X)) Monthly Review Pr.

Pérez Díaz, Víctor, ed. Markets & Civil Society: The European Experience in Comparative Perspective. 2009. 278p. 95.00 (978-1-84545-607-8(6)) Berghahn Bks., Inc.

Perlman, Fredy. The New Freedom: Corporate Capitalism. 2008. (Illus.). 233p. per. 20.00 (978-1-60001-999-9(4), Southpaw Culture) Factory Schl.

Peston, Robert. The New Capitalism: How & Why the Economic World Has Changed Forever - And How It Affects Us All. 2012. (ENG.). 368p. pap. 19.95 (978-0-340-99861-8(X), Hodder & Stoughton) Hodder General Publishing Div. GBR. Dist: Independent Pubs. Group.

Peters, Michael A. Neoliberalism & after? Education, Social Policy, & the Crisis of Western Capitalism. 2011. (Global Studies in Education Ser.). (C). pap. 32.95 (978-1-4331-1205-8(1)) Lang, Peter Publishing, Inc.

—Neoliberalism & after? Education, Social Policy, & the Crisis of Western Capitalism (CB) 2011. (Global Studies in Education Ser.). x, 222p. (C). 129.95 (978-1-4331-1206-5(X)) Lang, Peter Publishing, Inc.

Peters, Michael A. & Bulut, Ergin. Cognitive Capitalism, Education, & Digital Labor. 2011. (Illus.). 384p. (C). 149.95 (978-1-4331-0982-9(4)); pap. 38.95 (978-1-4331-0981-2(6)) Lang, Peter Publishing, Inc.

Petit, Patrick U., ed. Earth Capitalism: Creating a New Civilization Through a Responsible Market Economy. 2010. (ENG., Illus.). 244p. pap. 29.95 (978-1-4128-1106-4(6)) Transaction Pubs.

Petras, James F. Global Depression & Regional Wars. 2009. (Illus.). 236p. (978-0-932863-68-3(X)) Clarity Pr., Inc.

Phillips, Nicola, ed. Migration in the Global Political Economy. 2011. 290p. 65.00 (978-1-58826-762-7(8)) Rienner, Lynne Pubs.

Picciotto, Sol. Regulating Global Corporate Capitalism. 2011. (International Corporate Law & Financial Market Regulation Ser.). (ENG., Illus.). 602p. 130.00 (978-1-107-00501-3(9)); pap. 65.00 (978-0-521-18196-9(8)) Cambridge Univ. Pr.

Pilling, Geoff & Pilling, Doria, eds. Marxist Political Economy: Essays in Retrieval: Selected Works of Geoff Pilling. 2012. (Routledge Studies in the History of Economics Ser.). (ENG., Illus.). 288p. (C). 130.00 (978-0-415-67852-0(8)) Routledge.

Pirenne, Henri. The Stages in the Social History of Capitalism. 2011. 34p. pap. 7.99 (978-1-61203-106-4(4)) Bottom of the Hill Publishing.

Piveronus, Peter J. The Reinvention of Capitalism: Russia's Alternative to Corporate Concentration & to the Command Economy. 2006. 182p. (978-0-7734-5580-1(9)) Mellen, Edwin Pr., The.

Pollard, John F. Money & the Rise of the Modern Papacy: Financing the Vatican, 1850-1950. 2008. (ENG., Illus.). 288p. pap. 38.99 (978-0-521-09211-1(6)) Cambridge Univ. Pr.

Pollard, Vincent Kelly. State Capitalism, Contentious Politics & Large-Scale Social Change. 2011. 248p. (978-90-04-19445-8(2)) BRILL.

Pollard, Vincent Kelly, ed. State Capitalism, Contentious Politics & Large-Scale Social Change. 2012. (Studies in Critical Social Sciences Ser.). (ENG., Illus.). 236p. pap. 28.00 (978-1-60846-208-7(0)) Haymarket Bks.

Poole, Eve. The Church on Capitalism: Theology & the Market. 2010. (ENG., Illus.). 240p. 100.00 (978-0-230-27516-4(8)) Palgrave Macmillan.

Porritt, Jonathon. Capitalism: As If the World Matters. 2007. (ENG., Illus.). 288p. per. 34.95 (978-1-84407-193-7(6)) Routledge.

Posner, Richard A. The Crisis of Capitalist Democracy. (Illus.). 408p. 2011. (ENG.). pap. 18.95 (978-0-674-06219-1(1)) 2010. 25.95 (978-0-674-05574-2(8)) Harvard Univ. Pr.

—A Failure of Capitalism: The Crisis of '08 & the Descent into Depression. 2011. (ENG.). 368p. pap. 17.95 (978-0-674-06039-5(3)) Harvard Univ. Pr.

Post, Charles. The American Road to Capitalism: Studies in Class-Structure, Economic Development & Political Conflict, 1620-1877. 2012. (Historical Materialism Book Ser.). (ENG., Illus.). 300p. pap. 28.00 (978-1-60846-198-1(X)) Haymarket Bks.

Pozuelo-Monfort, Jaime & Buchwalter, David. The Monfort Plan: The New Architecture of Capitalism. 2010. (Wiley Finance Ser.). (ENG., Illus.). 504p. 60.00 (978-0-470-29363-8(2), Wiley) Wiley, John & Sons, Inc.

Prasch, R. E. How Markets Work: Supply, Demand & the 'Real World' 2008. (Illus.). 192p. pap. 25.00 (978-1-84720-614-5(X)) Elgar, Edward Publishing, Inc.

—How Markets Work: Supply, Demand & the 'real World' 2008. (Illus.). 192p. 119.00 (978-1-84720-613-8(1)) Elgar, Edward Publishing, Inc.

Prashad, Vijay. Fat Cats & Running Dogs: The Enron Stage of Capitalism. (Illus.). 144p. (978-1-84277-260-7(0)); pap. (978-1-84277-261-4(9)) Zed Bks., Ltd. GBR. Dist: Palgrave Macmillan.

Prechel, Harland, ed. Politics & Neoliberalism: Structure, Process & Outcome. 2007. (Illus.). 268p. 111.95 (978-0-7623-1435-5(4)) Emerald Group Publishing Ltd. GBR. Dist: Turpin Distribution Services Ltd.

Preda, Alex. Framing Finance: The Boundaries of Markets & Modern Capitalism. 2009. (ENG., Illus.). 328p. 65.00 (978-0-226-67931-0(4)); pap. 25.00 (978-0-226-67932-7(2)) Univ. of Chicago Pr.

Prempeh, E. Osei Kwadwo. Against Global Capitalism: African Social Movements Confront Neoliberal Globalization. 2006. (Illus.). 198p. 120.00 (978-0-7546-4764-5(1)) Ashgate Publishing Co.

Prindle, David F. The Paradox of Democratic Capitalism: Politics & Economics in American Thought. 2006. (ENG.). 392p. (gr. 17). 49.95 (978-0-8018-8411-5(X)) Johns Hopkins Univ. Pr.

Pring, Beryl. Education (Rle Edu L) 2011. (Routledge Library Editions: Education Ser.). (ENG.). 296p. 115.00 (978-0-415-50587-1(9)) Routledge.

Procaccia, Uriel. Russian Culture, Property Rights, & the Market Economy. 2011. (ENG.). 310p. pap. 60.00 (978-0-521-29262-7(X)) Cambridge Univ. Pr.

Proudhon, P-J. The Philosophy of Misery: The Evolution of Capitalism. 2006. (ENG.). 372p. pap. 25.99 (978-1-4264-0898-4(6)); 352p. pap. 26.99 (978-1-4264-0908-0(7)) BiblioBazaar.

Pryor, Frederic L. Capitalism Reassessed. 2010. (ENG., Illus.). 454p. 80.00 (978-0-521-19020-6(7)) Cambridge Univ. Pr.

Radice, Hugo. The Political Economy of Global Capitalism. 2007. (Routledge/RIPE Studies in Global Political Economy Ser.). 240p. 140.00 (978-0-415-29646-5(3)); pap. 37.95 (978-0-415-29647-2(1), RU25287) Routledge.

Rand, Ayn. Conservatism: An Obituary. 2011. 16p. pap. 35.95 (978-1-258-00229-9(9)) Literary Licensing, LLC.

Rani, S. Women & Global Economic Order: A Feminist Perspective. 2010. 307p. 59.50 (978-81-7533-319-2(7)) M. D. Pubns. Pvt. Ltd. IND. Dist: Coronet Bks.

Rao, Hayagreeva & Rao, H. Market Rebels: How Activists Make or Break Radical Innovations. 2008. (ENG., Illus.). 222p. (C). 24.95 (978-0-691-13456-7(1)) Princeton Univ. Pr.

Rappaport, Alfred & Bogle, John C. Saving Capitalism from Short-Termism: How to Build Long-Term Value & Take Back Our Financial Future. 2011. (ENG., Illus.). 256p. 30.00 (978-0-07-173636-7(0), 0071736360) McGraw-Hill Cos., The.

Raquiza, Antoinette R. State Structure & Economic Development in Southeast Asia. 2011. (Routledge Studies in the Growth Economies of Asia Ser.). (ENG., Illus.). 224p. (C). 140.00 (978-0-415-61767-3(7)) Routledge.

Rasmussen, Dennis. The Problems & Promise of Commercial Society: Adam Smith's Response to Rousseau. (ENG.). 192p. pap. 27.50 (978-0-271-03349-5(5)) Pennsylvania State Univ. Pr.

Rasmussen, Dennis Carl & Rasmussen, Dennis. The Problems & Promise of Commercial Society: Adam Smith's Response to Rousseau. 2008. (ENG.). 192p. 45.00 (978-0-271-03348-8(7)) Pennsylvania State Univ. Pr.

Redding, Gordon & Witt, Michael A. The Future of Chinese Capitalism. 2008. (ENG., Illus.). 275p. 75.00 (978-0-19-921813-4(7)) Oxford Univ. Pr., Inc.

C

—The Future of Chinese Capitalism: Choices & Chances. 2010. (ENG., Illus.). 280p. pap. 34.95 *(978-0-19-957587-9(8))* Oxford Univ. Pr., Inc.

Reed, Lawrence W. & Haywood, Dale M. When We Are Free. 3rd ed. 403p. 17.50 *(978-0-87359-054-9(6))* Northwood Univ. Pr.

Reekie, W. Duncan. Spiritual Capital, Natural Law & the Secular Market Place. 2007. 187p. (Orig.). (C). pap. 36.50 *(978-1-903386-55-2(1))* Civitas:Institute for the Study of Civil Society GBR. Dist: Coronet Bks.

Reich, Robert B. Supercapitalism: The Transformation of Business, Democracy, & Everyday Life. 2008. (Vintage Ser.). (ENG.). 288p. pap. 15.95 *(978-0-307-27799-2(2)*, Vintage) Knopf Doubleday Publishing Group.

Renton, David, et al. The Congo: Plunder & Resistance. 2007. (ENG., Illus.). 256p. per. 35.95 *(978-1-84277-485-4(9))*; 104.95 *(978-1-84277-484-7(0))* Zed Bks., Ltd. GBR. Dist: Macmillan.

Residual & Sustainable Economy: A Distributive System in the Market Economy for Sustainability. 2011. 65.00 *(978-981-4304-51-1(4))* World Scientific Publishing Co., Inc.

Reynolds, Ryan. Moving Targets: Political Theatre in a Post-Political Age. 2008. 212p. pap. *(978-3-639-03334-2(5))* VDM Verlag Dr. Mueller e.K.

Rhodes, David. Capitalism, Sustainability & the Big Society: Meeting the Global Challenge of Ensuring a Sustainable Future. 2011. 192p. pap. 18.81 *(978-1-4567-7580-3(4))* AuthorHouse.

Richards, Jay W. Money, Greed, & God: Why Capitalism Is the Solution & Not the Problem. (ENG.). 2010. 192p. pap. 13.99 *(978-0-06-190057-0(5))* 2009. 272p. 24.99 *(978-0-06-137561-3(6))* HarperCollins Pubs. (HarperOne).

Richter, Rudolf. New Institutional Economics of Markets. Furubotn, Eirik G., ed. 2010. (International Library of Critical Writings in Economics series Ser.). (Illus.). 688p. 381.00 *(978-1-84720-983-2(1))* Elgar, Edward Publishing, Inc.

Riegel, Edwin C. The New Approach to Freedom. 2011. 50p. 35.95 ***(978-1-258-09761-5(3))*** Literary Licensing, LLC.

Rieger, Joerg. Grace under Pressure: Negotiating the Heart of the Methodist Traditionsnull. 2011. 108p. pap. 12.95 ***(978-0-938162-77-3(2))*** United Methodist Board of Higher Education & Ministry.

Riley, Stephen V. Capitalism, Democracy & Emerging Christianity: An Essay by A Catholic Activist. 2010. 96p. pap. 12.00 *(978-1-4520-0567-6(2))* AuthorHouse.

Robbins, Richard H. Global Problems & the Culture of Capitalism. 5th rev. ed. 2010. (ENG.). 408p. (C). pap. 91.00 *(978-0-205-80105-3(6)*, Prentice Hall) Prentice Hall PTR.

Roberts, Alasdair. The Logic of Discipline: Global Capitalism & the Architecture of Government, 1 vol. 2011. (ENG.). 220p. pap. 24.95 ***(978-0-19-984614-6(6))*** Oxford Univ. Pr., Inc.

Roberts, Michael. The Great Recession. 2009. 334p. pap. 31.50 *(978-1-4452-4408-2(X))* Lulu Enterprises Inc.

Robinson, Jonathan D. The Right View. 2006. 124p. per. *(978-1-84401-725-6(7))* Athena Pr.

Robinson, William I. Latin America & Global Capitalism: A Critical Globalization Perspective. (Johns Hopkins Studies in Globalization Ser.). (ENG., Illus.). 444p. (gr. 17). 2010. pap. 35.00 *(978-0-8018-9834-1(X))* 2008. 57.00 *(978-0-8018-9039-0(X))* Johns Hopkins Univ. Pr.

Rogge, Benjamin A. A Maverick's Defense of Freedom: Selected Writings & Speeches of Benjamin A. Rogge. 2010. (ENG.). 440p. (C). (gr. 12). 25.00 *(978-0-86597-784-6(4))*; pap. 15.00 *(978-0-86597-785-3(2))* Liberty Fund, Inc.

Rosefielde, Steven. Red Holocaust. 2010. (ENG., Illus.). 360p. 190.00 *(978-0-415-77756-8(9))*; pap. 37.95 *(978-0-415-77757-5(7))* Routledge.

Rosenberg, Jordana & Villarejo, Amy. Queer Studies & the Crises of Capitalism. 2011. (ENG.). 225p. pap. 12.00 ***(978-0-8223-6757-4(2))*** Duke Univ. Pr.

Rothkopf, David. Power Inc: The Epic Rivalry Between Big Business & Government-and the Reckoning That Lies Ahead. 2012. (ENG., Illus.). 448p. 30.00 ***(978-0-374-15128-7(8))*** Farrar, Straus & Giroux.

Rousseas, S. Capitalism & Catastrophe. 2008. (ENG., Illus.). 156p. pap. 38.99 *(978-0-521-06851-2(7))* Cambridge Univ. Pr.

Roy, Ravi K. Neoliberalism: National & Regional Experiments with Global Idea. Denzau, Arthur T. & Willett, Thomas D., eds. 2007. (Illus.). 272p. 43.95 *(978-0-415-45866-5(8))* Routledge.

Ryn, Claes. America the Virtuous: The Crisis of Democracy & the Quest for Empire. 2009. (ENG.). 234p. pap. 24.95 *(978-1-4128-1331-0(X))* Transaction Pubs.

Saez, Patricia & Pareras, Luis. Capitalismo 2. 0: El poder del ciudadano para cambiar el Mundo. 2011. (Plataforma Empresa Ser.). (SPA.). 400p. pap. 32.95 ***(978-84-15115-16-8(4))*** Plataforma Editorial SL ESP. Dist: Independent Pubs. Group.

Saltman, Kenneth J. Capitalizing on Disaster: Taking & Breaking Public Schools. 2007. (Cultural Politics & the Promise of Democracy Ser.). (ENG.). 184p. per. 38.95 *(978-1-59451-382-4(1))*; 125.00 *(978-1-59451-381-7(3))* Paradigm Pubs.

Samli, A. Coskun. Globalization from the Bottom Up: A Blueprint for Modern Capitalism. (ENG., Illus.). xxiv, 148p. 2009. pap. 49.95 *(978-1-4419-1042-4(5)*, 1441910425) 2008. 89.95 *(978-0-387-77097-0(6)*, 0387770976) Springer.

Samuels, Warren J. Erasing the Invisible Hand: Essays on an Elusive & Misused Concept in Economics. 2011. (ENG.). 352p. 95.00 *(978-0-521-51725-6(7))* Cambridge Univ. Pr.

Sandel, Michael J. What Money Can't Buy: The Moral Limits of Markets, 1 vol. 2012. (ENG., Illus.). 256p. 27.00 ***(978-0-374-20303-0(2))*** Farrar, Straus & Giroux.

Sandlin, Jennifer A. Critical Pedagogies of Consumption: Living & Learning in the Shadow of the Shopocalypse. 2009. (Sociocultural, Political, & Historical Studies in Education Ser.). (ENG., Illus.). 278p. 145.00 *(978-0-415-99789-8(5))* Routledge.

Sanyal & Sanyal, Kalyan K. Rethinking Capitalist Development: Primitive Accumulation, Governmentality & Post-Colonial Capitalism. 2007. 275p. 110.00 *(978-0-415-44087-5(4))* Routledge.

Saul, John S. Decolonization & Empire: Contesting the Rhetoric & Reality of Resubordination in Southern Africa & Beyond. 2008. (ENG.). 196p. pap. 22.95 *(978-0-85036-592-4(9))* Merlin Pr. Ltd. GBR. Dist: Independent Pubs. Group.

—Revolutionary Traveller: Freeze-Frames from a Life. 2010. (ENG., Illus.). 436p. pap. 26.95 *(978-1-894037-37-2(5))* Arbeiter Ring Publishing CAN. Dist: AK Pr. Distribution.

Savage, Mike & Williams, Karel, eds. Remembering Elites. 2008. (Sociological Review Monographs). (ENG., Illus.). 312p. pap. 34.95 *(978-1-4051-8546-2(5)*, Wiley-Blackwell) Wiley, John & Sons, Inc.

Schaeffer, Robert. Red Inc: Dictatorship & the Development of Capitalism in China, 1949-2009. 2011. (Illus.). 272p. 117.00 *(978-1-59451-711-2(8))* Paradigm Pubs.

Schaeffer, Robert K. Red: Dictatorship & the Development of Capitalism in China,1949-2009. 2012. (Illus.). 272p. pap. 29.95 *(978-1-59451-712-9(6))* Paradigm Pubs.

Schiwy, Freya, et al, eds. Digital Media, Cultural Production & Speculative Capitalism. 2011. (ENG.). 128p. (C). 125.00 *(978-0-415-61449-8(X))* Routledge.

Schneider, Gerald & Gleditsch, Nils Petter, eds. The Capitalist Peace. 2012. (ENG.). 128p. (C). 140.00 ***(978-0-415-52989-1(1))*** Routledge.

Schramm, Carl J. The Entrepreneurial Imperative: How America's Economic Miracle Will Reshape the World (And Change Your Life) 2006. (ENG.). 256p. 24.95 *(978-0-06-084163-8(X)*, Collins) HarperCollins Pubs.

Schroeter, Daniel J. Merchants of Essaouira: Urban Society & Imperialism in Southwestern Morocco, 1844-1886. 2009. (Cambridge Middle East Library). (ENG.). 348p. pap. 46.00 *(978-0-521-10540-8(4))* Cambridge Univ. Pr.

Schumpeter, Joseph A. Can Capitalism Survive? 2011. 108p. pap. 7.50 ***(978-1-891396-76-2(5))*** Martino Publishing.

—Can Capitalism Survive? Creative Destruction & the Future of the Global Economy. 2009. (ENG.). 208p. pap. 10.00 *(978-0-06-192801-7(1)*, HarperPerennial) HarperCollins Pubs.

—Capitalism, Socialism & Democracy. 2010. 424p. 51.95 *(978-1-169-83215-2(6))*; 51.95 *(978-1-169-83213-8(X))*; pap. 36.95 *(978-1-169-83214-5(8))*; pap. 36.95 *(978-1-169-83212-1(1))* Kessinger Publishing, LLC.

—Capitalism, Socialism & Democracy. 2010. 426p. pap. 9.95 ***(978-1-891396-51-9(X))*** Martino Publishing.

—Capitalism, Socialism & Democracy. 2010. (Routledge Classics Ser.). (ENG.). 456p. pap. *(978-0-415-56789-3(0)*, Routledge) Taylor & Francis Group.

—Capitalism, Socialism, & Democracy. 3rd ed. 2008. (ENG.). 448p. pap. 15.99 *(978-0-06-156161-0(4)*, HarperPerennial) HarperCollins Pubs.

Schumpeter, Joseph Alois. Capitalism, Socialism & Democracy. 6th ed. 2006. 464p. 70.00 *(978-0-415-10762-4(8))* Routledge.

Schweickart, David. After Capitalism. 2nd ed. 2011. ***(978-0-7425-6499-2(1))*** Rowman & Littlefield Education.

—After Capitalism. 2nd rev. ed. 2011. (New Critical Theory Ser.). (ENG.). 280p. (C). (gr. 13-17). 80.00 ***(978-0-7425-6497-8(5))***; pap. 29.95 ***(978-0-7425-6498-5(3))*** Rowman & Littlefield Publishers, Inc.

Scott, Allen J. The Social Economy of the Metropolis: Cognitive-Cultural Capitalism & the Global Resurgence of Cities. 2009. (ENG., Illus.). 200p. 55.00 *(978-0-19-954930-6(3))* Oxford Univ. Pr., Inc.

Scott, Bruce R. Capitalism: Its Origins & Evolution as a System of Governance. 2011. (ENG., Illus.). xxxv, 670p. 49.95 ***(978-1-4614-1878-8(X)***, 146141878X) Springer.

—Capitalism, democracy & Development. 2009. 300p. 239.00 *(978-3-540-44762-7(8))* Springer.

—The Concept of Capitalism. 2009. (ENG., Illus.). viii, 76p. pap. 14.95 *(978-3-642-03109-0(9)*, 3642031099) Springer.

Sedgwick, Peter H. The Market Economy & Christian Ethics. 2007. (New Studies in Christian Ethics Ser.). (ENG.). 340p. pap. 69.00 *(978-0-521-04484-4(7))* Cambridge Univ. Pr.

Seliger, Bernhard & Sepp, Jüri, eds. Das Konzept der Sozialen Marktwirtschaft und seine Anwendung: Deutschland im internationalen Vergleich. 2009. (Ordnungspolitische Dialoge Ser.). (GER.). 314p. 72.95 *(978-3-631-58772-0(4))* Lang, Peter GmbH, Europaischer Verlag der Wissenschaften DEU. Dist: Lang, Peter.

Seligman, Edwin Robert Anderson & Nearing, Scott. Debate on Capitalism vs. Socialism. Haldeman-Julius, E., ed. 2011. 66p. 36.95 ***(978-1-258-01928-0(0))*** Literary Licensing, LLC.

Seligson, Mitchell A. & Passe-Smith, John T., eds. Development & Underdevelopment: The Political Economy of Global Inequality, 4th Edition. 4th ed. 2008. 500p. (C). pap. 26.50 *(978-1-58826-584-5(6))* Rienner, Lynne Pubs.

Selwyn, Ben. Workers State & Development in Brazil: Powers of Labour, Chains of Value. 2012. (ENG., Illus.). 256p. 100.00 ***(978-0-7190-8531-4(4))*** Manchester Univ. Pr. GBR. Dist: Macmillan.

Sender, John & Smith, Sheila. The Development of Capitalism in Africa. 2011. (ENG.). 192p. 95.00 *(978-0-415-60196-2(7))* Routledge.

Sennett, Richard, ed. The Culture of the New Capitalism. 2007. (Castle Lectures in Ethics, Politics, & Economics). (ENG.). 224p. per. 15.00 *(978-0-300-11992-3(5))* Yale Univ. Pr.

Shannon, Deric, et al, eds. Accumulation of Freedom: Writings on Anarchist Economics. 2012. (ENG., Illus.). 320p. pap. 21.00 ***(978-1-84935-094-5(9))*** AK Pr. GBR. Dist: Consortium Bk. Sales & Distribution.

Shapiro, Stephen. How to Read Marx's Capital. 2008. (How to Read Theory Ser.). (ENG.). 192p. 80.00 *(978-0-7453-2562-0(9))*; (Illus.). pap. 24.00 *(978-0-7453-2561-3(0))* Pluto Pr. GBR. Dist: Macmillan.

Sharafutdinova. Political Consequences of Cron. 2011. (ND Contemporary European Politics Ser.). (ENG., Illus.). 312p. pap. 38.00 *(978-0-268-04135-9(0))* Univ. of Notre Dame Pr.

Shaw, George Bernard. The Intelligent Woman's Guide to Socialism & Capitalism. 2012. (ENG.). 450p. pap. 18.95 *(978-1-56649-053-5(7))* Welcome Rain Pubs.

Shelton, Eugene N. Capitalism in Business, Politics & Society. 2011. (Series: Economic Issues, Problems & Perspectives Ser.). pap. 129.00 *(978-1-61122-547-1(7))* Nova Science Pubs., Inc.

Shionoya, Yuichi & Nishizawa, Tamotsu, eds. Marshall & Schumpeter on Evolution: Economic Sociology of Capitalist Development. 2009. 296p. 145.00 *(978-1-84720-813-2(4))* Elgar, Edward Publishing, Inc.

Shutt, Harry. The Trouble with Capitalism: An Inquiry into the Causes of Global Economic Failure. 2nd rev. ed. 2009. (ENG., Illus.). 256p. pap. 26.95 *(978-1-84813-422-5(3))* Zed Bks., Ltd. GBR. Dist: Macmillan.

Silva Michelena, Héctor. Ética y Economía: Con Referencias Al Capitalismo y Al Socialismo. 2010. (SPA.). 132p. *(978-980-336-016-0(7))* Academia Nacional de Ciencias Economicas.

Sim, Stuart. Addicted to Profit: Reclaiming Our Lives from the Free Market. 2012. (ENG.). 240p. (gr. 17). pap. 37.50 ***(978-0-7486-4671-5(X))*** Edinburgh Univ. Pr. GBR. Dist: Columbia Univ. Pr.

Simpson, Tony, ed. What's Happening at Fukushima? 2011. (Spokesman Ser.). 96p. pap. 17.50 ***(978-0-85124-800-4(4))*** Spokesman Bks. GBR. Dist: Coronet Bks.

Sinclair, Upton. Letters to Judd: An American Workingman. 2011. 68p. 36.95 ***(978-1-258-03351-4(8))*** Literary Licensing, LLC.

Sitton, John F. Marx Today: Selected Works & Recent Debates. Sitton, John F., ed. 2010. (ENG.). 272p. 116.00 *(978-0-230-10240-8(9))* Palgrave Macmillan.

Skoll, Geoffrey R. Contemporary Criminology & Criminal Justice Theory: Evaluating Justice Systems in Capitalist Societies. 2009. (ENG.). 244p. 89.00 *(978-0-230-61598-4(8))* Palgrave Macmillan.

Skousen, W. Cleon. Naked Capitalist. Date not set. 152p. 18.95 *(978-0-8488-2662-8(0))* Amereon LTD.

Sloterdijk, Peter. Rage & Time: A Psychopolitical Investigation. Wenning, Mario, tr. from GER. (Insurrections: Critical Studies in Religion, Politics, & Culture Ser.). (ENG.). 256p. (gr. 17). 2012. pap. 25.00 ***(978-0-231-14523-7(3))*** 2010. (Illus.). 34.50 *(978-0-231-14522-0(5))* Columbia Univ. Pr.

Small, Michael Duane. A Letter to the Class Of '65. 2011. 108p. pap. 17.45 ***(978-1-257-91177-6(5))*** Lulu Enterprises Inc.

Smith, Andrew. British Businessmen & Canadian Confederation: Constitution Making in an Era of Anglo-Globalization. 2008. (ENG.). 240p. (C). *(978-0-7735-3405-6(9))* McGill-Queen's Univ. Pr.

Smith, Murray E. G. Global Capitalism in Crisis: Karl Marx & the Decline of the Profit System. 2010. (ENG.). 172p. pap. 24.95 *(978-1-55266-353-0(1))* Fernwood Publishing Co., Ltd. CAN. Dist: Independent Pubs. Group.

Smith, Neil. Uneven Development: Nature, Capital, & the Production of Space. 3rd ed. 2008. (ENG., Illus.). 344p. pap. 22.95 *(978-0-8203-3099-0(X))* Univ. of Georgia Pr.

Smith, Paul. Primitive America: The Ideology of Capitalist Democracy. 2007. 176p. 54.00 *(978-0-8166-2826-1(2))*; per. 17.95 *(978-0-8166-2827-8(0))* Univ. of Minnesota Pr.

Sobrino & Sobrino, Jon. Fuera de Los Pobres No Hay Salvación: Pequeños Ensayos Utópico-Proféticos. (SPA.). 164p. *(978-84-8164-918-5(X))* Trotta, Editorial S.A.

Soederberg, Susanne. Global Governance in Question: Empire, Class, & the New Common Sense in Managing North-South Relations. 2009. (ENG., Illus.). 206p. pap. 24.95 *(978-1-894037-26-6(X))* Arbeiter Ring Publishing CAN. Dist: AK Pr. Distribution.

Song, Jesook. Millennium South Korea. 2010. (Routledge Advances in Korean Studies). (ENG., Illus.). 176p. (C). 125.00 *(978-0-415-58265-0(2))* Routledge.

Soros, George. The Soros Lectures: At the Central European University. 2011. (ENG., Illus.). 144p. pap. 11.99 *(978-1-58648-944-1(5))* PublicAffairs.

Spence, Martin. The Making of a London Suburb: Capital Comes to Penge. 2007. (Illus.). 96p. pap. 22.95 *(978-0-85036-589-4(9))* Merlin Pr. Ltd. GBR. Dist: Independent Pubs. Group.

Speth, James Gustave. The Bridge at the End of the World. 2008. 476p. pap. 45.00 *(978-0-300-14463-5(6))* Yale Univ. Pr.

Speth, James Gustave & Speth, J. G. The Bridge at the Edge of the World: Capitalism, the Environment, & Crossing from Crisis to Sustainability. 2009. (ENG., Illus.). 320p. pap. 18.00 *(978-0-300-15115-2(2))* Yale Univ. Pr.

Stafford, David. Around the World in Several Pieces: A Country by Country Guide to Emerging Markets in Southeast Asia & Africa. 2010. (Illus.). 50p. pap. 19.95 *(978-1-4327-6383-1(0))* Outskirts Pr., Inc.

Stanford, Jim. Economics for Everyone: A Short Guide to the Economics of Capitalism, 1 vol. 2008. (ENG., Illus.). 360p. 21.00 *(978-0-7453-2750-1(8))*; lib. bdg. 72.00 *(978-0-7453-2751-8(6))* Pluto Pr. GBR. Dist: Macmillan.

Stanziani, Alessandro. Rules of Exchange: French Capitalism in Comparative Perspective, Eighteenth to Early Twentieth Centuries. 2012. (ENG., Illus.). 315p. 90.00 *(978-1-107-00386-6(5))* Cambridge Univ. Pr.

Stark, Rodney. The Victory of Reason: How Christianity Led to Freedom, Capitalism, & Western Success. annot. ed. 2006. (ENG., Illus.). 304p. per. 15.95 *(978-0-8129-7233-7(3)*, Random Hse. Trade Paperbacks) Random House Publishing Group.

Stehr, Nico. Moral Markets: How Knowledge & Affluence Change Consumers & Products. 288p. 2008. pap. 45.95 *(978-1-59451-457-9(7))* 2007. 125.00 *(978-1-59451-456-2(9))* Paradigm Pubs.

Stehr, Nico, et al, eds. The Moralization of Markets. 2009. (ENG., Illus.). 378p. pap. 34.95 *(978-1-4128-1089-0(2))* Transaction Pubs.

Stengers, Isabella, et al. Capitalist Sorcery: Breaking the Spell. 2011. (ENG.). 224p. 80.00 *(978-0-230-23762-9(2))* Palgrave Macmillan.

Stiles, Paul. Is the American Dream Killing You? How the Market Rules Our Lives. 2006. (Illus.). 320p. per. 13.95 *(978-0-06-059379-7(2))* HarperCollins Pubs.

Strauss, William. The myth of endless growth: exposing capitalism's Insustainability. 2010. 369p. 39.95 *(978-0-557-62496-6(7))* Lulu Enterprises Inc.

Streeck, Wolfgang. Re-Forming Capitalism: Institutional Change in the German Political Economy. 2010. (ENG., Illus.). 304p. 39.95 *(978-0-19-957398-1(0))* Oxford Univ. Pr., Inc.

Suarez-Villa, Luis. Globalization & Technocapitalism. 2012. 250p. 99.95 ***(978-1-4094-3915-8(1))*** Ashgate Publishing Co.

Suarez-Villa, Luis. Technocapitalism: A Critical Perspective on Technological Innovation & Corporatism. (ENG.). 230p. 2012. pap. 29.95 ***(978-1-4399-0043-7(4))*** 2009. (Illus.). 56.50 *(978-1-4399-0042-0(6))* Temple Univ. Pr.

Sumner, Jennifer. Sustainability & the Civil Commons: Rural Communities in the Age of Globalization. 2007. (ENG., Illus.). 188p. pap. *(978-0-8020-9527-5(5))* Univ. of Toronto Pr.

Suneja, Vivek. Understanding Business: A Multidimensional Approach to the Market Economy. Suneja, Vivek, ed. 2nd rev. ed. 2006. (Understanding Business Behaviour Ser.). (ENG., Illus.). 304p. (C). per. 51.95 *(978-0-415-40501-0(7))* Routledge.

Suresh, R. R. Economy & Society: Evolution of Capitalism. 2010. 332p. (C). pap. 29.95 *(978-81-321-0404-9(8)*, B04049P) SAGE Pubns., Inc.

Swader, Christopher. The Capitalist Personality: Face-to-Face Sociality & Economic Change in the Post-Communist World. 2012. (Routledge Advances in Sociology Ser.). (ENG.). 240p. (C). 125.00 *(978-0-415-89221-6(X))* Routledge.

Tabb, William K. The Restructuring of Capitalism in Our Time. 2011. (ENG.). 352p. (gr. 17). 35.00 *(978-0-231-15842-8(4))* Columbia Univ. Pr.

Táíwò, Olúfẹ́mi. How Colonialism Preempted Modernity in Africa. 2010. (ENG.). 368p. pap. 27.95 *(978-0-253-22130-8(7)*, 0253221307) Indiana Univ. Pr.

Tawney, R. H. Religion & the Rise of Capitalism. 2008. 352p. *(978-1-4437-2373-2(8))* 2006. (ENG.). 348p. per. *(978-1-4067-2418-9(1))* Read Bks. (Hesperides Pr.).

Tawney, Richard H. Religion & the Rise of Capitalism. 2008. 32.00 *(978-0-8446-1446-5(7))* Smith, Peter Pub., Inc.

Taylor, James. Creating Capitalism: Joint-Stock Enterprise in British Politics & Culture, 1800-1870. 2006. (Royal Historical Society Studies in History New Ser.: Volume 53). (Illus.). 266p. 80.00 *(978-0-86193-284-9(6))* Royal Historical Society GBR. Dist: Boydell & Brewer, Inc.

Thompson, Joseph P. The Workman: His False Friends & His True Friends. 2008. 260p. pap. 20.00 *(978-1-59925-201-8(5))* Solid Ground Christian Bks.

Tomasi, John. Free Market Fairness. 2012. (ENG., Illus.). 368p. (C). 35.00 ***(978-0-691-14446-7(X))*** Princeton Univ. Pr.

Tony Cutler, et al. Marx's Capital & Capitalism Today. 2009. 348p. 140.00 *(978-0-415-55594-4(9))* Routledge.

Tripp, Charles. Islam & the Moral Economy: The Challenge of Capitalism. 2006. (ENG.). 240p. 90.00 *(978-0-521-86377-3(5))*; per. 34.99 *(978-0-521-68244-2(4))* Cambridge Univ. Pr.

Tugal, Cihan. Passive Revolution: Absorbing the Islamic Challenge to Capitalism. 2009. (ENG.). 320p. 70.00 *(978-0-8047-6144-4(2))*; pap. 24.95 *(978-0-8047-6145-1(0))* Stanford Univ. Pr.

Turrell, Robert Vicat. Capital & Labour on the Kimberley Diamond Fields, 1871-1890. 2008. (African Studies). (ENG.). 316p. pap. 42.00 *(978-0-521-07179-6(8))* Cambridge Univ. Pr.

Tutino, John. Making a New World: Founding Capitalism in the Bajío & Spanish North America. 2011. (ENG., Illus.). 712p. 99.95 *(978-0-8223-4974-7(4))*; pap. 29.95 *(978-0-8223-4989-1(2))* Duke Univ. Pr.

Tyler, Colin. Civil Society, Capitalism & the State Pt. 2. 2011. (British Idealist Studies). (ENG.). 250p. 49.90 *(978-1-84540-217-4(0))* Imprint Academic GBR. Dist: Ingram Pub. Services.

Ukpere, Wilfred. Capitalist Globalisation in Limbo. 2010. 572p. pap. *(978-3-8383-5179-7(7))* Lambert Academic Publishing.

Vagnone, Joe. So You Want to Buy a Small Business. 2011. 132p. 23.99 ***(978-1-4567-1957-9(2))*** AuthorHouse.

Vail, Mark. Recasting Welfare Capitalism: Economic Adjustment in Contemporary France & Germany. 2009. (ENG., Illus.). 248p. 56.50 *(978-1-59213-967-5(1))* Temple Univ. Pr.

Vanderbeeken, Robrecht, et al, eds. Drunk on Capitalism: An Interdisciplinary Reflection on Market Economy, Art & Science. 2011. (Einstein Meets Magritte: an Interdisciplinary Reflection on Science, Nature, Art, Human Action & Society Ser.). (ENG., Illus.). xxiii, 180p. 139.00 ***(978-94-007-2081-7(5)***, 9400720815) Springer.

Varoufakis. Modern Political Economy. 2011. (ENG., Illus.). 552p. 165.00 (978-0-415-42875-0(0)); pap. 65.00 (978-0-415-42888-0(2)) Routledge.
Vasapollo, Luciano. Crisis of Capitalism: Compendium of Applied Economics (Global Capitalism) 2011. xi, 372p. (978-90-04-21032-5(6)) BRILL.
Veblen, Thorstein. The Engineers & the Price System. 2009. 72p. pap. (978-0-217-62480-0(4)) Books LLC.
—The Engineers & the Price System. 2006. pap. 11.95 (978-1-59605-892-7(7), Cosimo Classics) Cosimo, Inc.
—The Theory of Business Enterprise. 2009. 236p. pap. (978-1-4099-6559-6(7)) Dodo Pr.
—The Theory of Business Enterprise. 2007. (ENG.). 416p. per. 24.45 (978-1-59462-874-0(2), Book Jungle) Standard Pubns., Inc.
Veltmeyer, Henry. Imperialism, Crisis & Class Struggle: The Enduring Verities & Contemporary Face of Capitalism. 2010. (Illus.). 272p. (978-90-04-18414-5(7)) BRILL.
Veltmeyer, Henry. Imperialism, Crisis & Class Struggle: The Enduring Verities & Contemporary Face of Capitalism: Essays in Honor of James Petras. 2012. (Studies in Critical Social Sciences Ser.). (ENG., Illus.). 324p. pap. 28.00 (978-1-60846-146-2(7)) Haymarket Bks.
Vickers, Tom. Refugees Capitalism & the British State: Implications for Social Workers Volunteers & Activists. 2012. (Illus.). 200p. 99.95 (978-1-4094-4152-6(0)) Ashgate Publishing Co.
Vogel, Steven K. Japan Remodeled: How Government & Industry Are Reforming Japanese Capitalism. 2006. (Cornell Studies in Political Economy). (Illus.). 250p. per. 21.95 (978-0-8014-7371-5(3)) Cornell Univ. Pr.
Vogel, Steven K. & Barma, Naazneen H., eds. A Political Economy Reader: Markets as Institutions. 2007. (Illus.). 569p. per. 51.95 (978-0-415-95493-8(2)) Routledge.
Von Mises, Ludwig. The Anti-Capitalistic Mentality. 2010. 124p. pap. 6.95 (978-1-891396-21-2(8)) Martino Publishing.
Wagner, Walter C. Moral Capitalism & The Essential Economy, As Managed by the Workable Market. 2006. 260p. 24.95 (978-0-9776834-6-8(X)) Wagner Book LLC.
Walker, Andrew. Tai Lands & Thailand: Community & State in Southeast Asia. 2009. (C). pap. 29.00 (978-0-8248-3359-6(7)) Univ. of Hawaii Pr.
Wallerstein, Immanuel. Historical Capitalism with Capitalist Civilization. 3rd ed. 2011. (ENG.). 176p. pap. 16.95 (978-1-84467-766-5(4), 844766) Verso Bks. GBR. Dist: Norton, W. W. & Co., Inc.
—Making Waves: Worldwide Social Movements, 1750-2005. Martin, William G., ed. 2008. (Fernand Braudel Center Ser.). (Illus.). 226p. pap. 47.95 (978-1-59451-481-4(X), Paradigm Pubs.
—The Modern World-System I: Capitalist Agriculture & the Origins of the European World-Economy in the Sixteenth Century, with a New Prologue. 2011. (ENG., Illus.). 440p. pap. 29.95 (978-0-520-26757-2(5)) Univ. of California Pr.
—The Modern World-System II: Mercantilism & the Consolidation of the European World-Economy, 1600-1750, with a New Prologue. 2011. (ENG., Illus.). 397p. pap. 29.95 (978-0-520-26758-9(3)) Univ. of California Pr.
—The Modern World-System III: The Second Era of Great Expansion of the Capitalist World-Economy, 1730s-1840s with a New Prologue. 2011. (ENG., Illus.). 390p. pap. 29.95 (978-0-520-26759-6(1)) Univ. of California Pr.
—The Modern World-System IV: Centrist Liberalism Triumphant, 1789-1914. 2011. (ENG., Illus.). 384p. 65.00 (978-0-520-26760-2(5)); pap. 26.95 (978-0-520-26761-9(3)) Univ. of California Pr.
Waters, Mary-Alice & Koppel, Martin. Capitalism & the Transformation of Africa: Reports from Equatorial Guinea. 2009. (Illus.). 150p. pap. 10.00 (978-1-60488-016-8(3)) Pathfinder Pr.
Webber, M. Making Capitalism in Rural China. 2012. (Illus.). 336p. 150.00 (978-0-85793-409-3(0)) Elgar, Edward Publishing, Inc.
Weber, Max. The Protestant Ethic & the Spirit of Capitalism. 2006. pap. 8.95 (978-1-4288-1499-8(X)) Cram101 Inc.
—The Protestant Ethic & the Spirit of Capitalism. Swedberg, Richard, ed. 2009. (Norton Critical Editions Ser.). (ENG.). 312p. (C). pap. 14.00 net. (978-0-393-93068-9(8), 93068) Norton, W. W. & Co., Inc.
—The Protestant Ethic & the Spirit of Capitalism. 2008. 96p. pap. 8.99 (978-1-4209-3181-5(4)) Digireads.com.
—The Protestant Ethic & the Spirit of Capitalism. 2009. 316p. (978-1-60796-098-0(2)); pap. (978-1-60796-097-3(4)) Editorial Benei Noaj.
—The Protestant Ethic & the Spirit of Capitalism. 2008. 308p. pap. (978-1-4097-2763-7(7)) Read Bks.
—The Protestant Ethic & the Spirit of Capitalism with Other Writings on the Rise of the West. Kalberg, Stephen, ed. 4th ed. 2008. (ENG.). 608p. (C). pap. 44.95 (978-0-19-533253-7(9)) Oxford Univ. Pr., Inc.
Weber, Max & Kalberg, Stephen. The Protestant Ethic & the Spirit of Capitalism, 1 vol. 2010. (ENG.). 448p. (C). pap. 19.95 (978-0-19-974725-2(3)) Oxford Univ. Pr., Inc.
Wee, C. J. Wan-Ling. The Asian Modern: Culture, Capitalist Development, Singapore. 2007. (Illus.). 224p. (978-9971-69-392-3(5)) Hong Kong Univ. Pr.
Weeks, John. Capital Exploitation & Economic Crisis. 2011. (Routledge Frontiers of Political Economy Ser.). (ENG., Illus.). 208p. (C). 130.00 (978-0-415-61055-1(9)) Routledge.
Weems, Robert. Business in Black & White: American Presidents & Black Entrepreneurs in the Twentieth Century. 2009. (ENG., Illus.). 352p. 55.00 (978-0-8147-7517-2(9)) New York Univ. Pr.
Wei, Shulin. Zhongguo Shi Chang Jing Ji Fa Zhan de Zhi du Zhang Ai Tan Yuan: Wang Yanan Jing Ji Si Xiang de Qi Shi. 2009. (CHI., Illus.). (978-7-218-05866-5(3)) Guangdong Peoples Publishing Hse.
Wesbury, Brian S. It's Not as Bad as You Think: Why Capitalism Trumps Fear & the Economy Will Thrive. 2009. (ENG., Illus.). 224p. 24.95 (978-0-470-23833-2(X), Wiley) Wiley, John & Sons, Inc.
Westra, Richard, et al. Political Economy & Global Capitalism: The 21st Century, Present & Future. Westra, Richard et al, eds. 2007. (Anthem Politics & IR Ser.). (ENG., Illus.). 259p. 80.00 (978-1-84331-279-6(4)) Anthem Pr. GBR. Dist: Books International, Inc.
White, Leslie A., , Leslie A & White, Leslie A. Modern Capitalist Culture. 2008. (ENG.). 700p. 79.95 (978-1-59874-157-5(8)) Left Coast Pr., Inc.
White, Curtis. The Barbaric Heart: Faith, Money, & the Crisis of Nature. 2009. 208p. pap. 16.95 (978-0-9817091-2-3(5)) Paradigm Pubns.
White, Leslie A. Modern Capitalist Culture. abr. ed. 2009. (ENG., Illus.). 212p. pap. 34.95 (978-1-59874-158-2(6)) Left Coast Pr., Inc.
Williams, Chris. Ecology & Socialism: Capitalism & the Environment. 2010. (ENG.). 220p. pap. (978-1-60846-091-5(6)) Pluto Pr.
Williams, Evan Calder. Combined & Uneven Apocalypse: Luciferian Marxism. 2011. (ENG., Illus.). 261p. pap. 24.95 (978-1-84694-468-0(6)) O Bks.,John Hunt.
Willmott, Glenn. Modernist Goods: Primitivism, the Market, & the Gift. 2008. (ENG., Illus.). 384p. (978-0-8020-9769-9(3)) Univ. of Toronto Pr.
Witt, Michael A. Changing Japanese Capitalism: Societal Coordination & Institutional Adjustment. (ENG., Illus.). 2011. 239p. pap. 39.99 (978-0-521-18282-9(4)) 2006. 240p. 118.00 (978-0-521-86860-0(2)) Cambridge Univ. Pr.
Wolff, Edward N. Growth, Accumulation, & Unproductive Activity: An Analysis of the Postwar US Economy. 2006. (ENG., Illus.). 216p. pap. 48.00 (978-0-521-03475-3(2)) Cambridge Univ. Pr.
Wolff, Richard D. Capitalism Hits the Fan: The Global Economic Meltdown & What to Do about It. 2009. (ENG.). 256p. pap. 18.00 (978-1-56656-784-8(X), Olive Branch Pr.) Interlink Publishing Group, Inc.
Wolff, Richard D. & Barsamian, David. Occupy the Economy: Why Capitalism Can't Win. 2012. (City Lights Open Media Ser.). (ENG.). 190p. pap. 14.95 (978-0-87286-567-9(3)) City Lights Bks.
Wood, Geoffrey T. & Lane, Christel, eds. Capitalist Diversity & Diversity Within Capitalism. 2011. (Routledge Frontiers of Political Economy Ser.). (ENG., Illus.). 272p. (C). 140.00 (978-0-415-58344-2(6)) Routledge.
Woods, Thomas E. Beyond Distributism. 2008. 79p. pap. (978-1-880595-29-9(X)) Acton Institute for the Study of Religion & Liberty.
Woods, Thomas E., Jr. Meltdown: A Free-Market Look at Why the Stock Market Collapsed, the Economy Tanked, & Government Bailouts Will Make Things Worse. 2009. (ENG.). 194p. 27.95 (978-1-59698-587-2(9)) Regnery Publishing, Inc., An Eagle Publishing Co.
Wyatt, Chris. Defetishised Society: New Economic Democracy as a Libertarian Alternative to Capitalism. 2011. (ENG.). 256p. 120.00 (978-1-4411-5933-5(9)) Continuum International Publishing Group, Ltd. GBR. Dist: National Bk. Network.
Xiaoxi, Li, et al. Emerging Markets Reform & Development in China. 2010. (Illus.). ix, 49p. pap. 49.00 (978-1-61668-769-4(X)) Nova Science Pubs., Inc.
Xing, Li. The Rise of China & Its Implication on World Order. 2010. (International Political Economy of New Regionalisms Ser.). (Illus.). 222p. 99.95 (978-0-7546-7913-4(6)) Ashgate Publishing Co.
Xing, Li & Winther, Gorm, eds. Globalization & Transnational Capitalism: Crisis, Opportunities & Alternatives. 2009. 258p. pap. 44.95 (978-87-7307-956-0(1)) Aalborg Universitetsforlag DNK. Dist: International Specialized Bk. Services.
Yagi, Kiichiro, et al, eds. The Crisis of 2008 & the Future of Capitalism. 2012. (Routledge Studies in the Modern World Economy Ser.). (ENG.). 256p. (C). 152.00 (978-0-415-68733-1(0)) Routledge.
Yavlinsky, Grigory. Realeconomik: The Hidden Cause of the Great Recession (and How to Avert the Next One) Bouis, Antonina W., tr. 2011. (ENG.). 192p. 26.00 (978-0-300-15910-3(2)) Yale Univ. Pr.
Yip, Francis Ching-Wah. Capitalism as Religion - A Study of Paul Tillich's Interpretation of Modernity. 2010. (Harvard Theological Studies: 59). (Illus.). 240p. pap. 22.95 (978-0-674-02147-1(9)) Harvard Univ. Pr.
Younkins, Edward W. Champions of a Free Society: Ideas of Capitalism's Philosophers & Economists. 2008. (ENG.). 408p. 99.99 (978-0-7391-2647-9(4)); pap. 41.99 (978-0-7391-2648-6(2)) Lexington Bks.
Yunus, Muhammad. Building Social Business: The New Kind of Capitalism That Serves Humanity's Most Pressing Needs. (ENG., Illus.). 256p. 2011. pap. 15.99 (978-1-58648-956-4(9)) 2010. 25.95 (978-1-58648-824-6(4)) PublicAffairs.
Zakim, Michael. Accounting for Capitalism: The Business Clerk as Social Revolutionary. 2012. 272p. 35.00 (978-0-226-97797-3(8)) Univ. of Chicago Pr.
Zakim, Michael & Kornblith, Gary J. Capitalism Takes Command: The Social Transformation of Nineteenth-Century America. 2012. (ENG., Illus.). 368p. 90.00 (978-0-226-45109-1(7)) Univ. of Chicago Pr.
Zakim, Michael & Kornblith, Gary J., eds. Capitalism Takes Command: The Social Transformation of Nineteenth-Century America. 2012. (ENG., Illus.). 368p. pap. 30.00 (978-0-226-45110-7(0)) Univ. of Chicago Pr.
Zarembka, Paul, ed. Transitions in Latin America & in Poland & Syria. 2007. 360p. 111.95 (978-0-7623-1383-9(8)) Emerald Group Publishing Ltd. GBR. Dist: Turpin Distribution Services Ltd.
Zentai, Violetta & Kovács, János Mátyás, eds. Capitalism from Outside? Economic Cultures in Central & Eastern Europe after 1989. 2012. (ENG.). 320p. 55.00 (978-615-5211-33-1(7)) Central European Univ. Pr.
Zieba, Maciej. Papal Economics: The Catholic Church on Democratic Capitalism, from Rerum Novarum to Caritas in Veritate. 2012. (Culture of Enterprise Ser.). (ENG.). 26.95 (978-1-933859-97-2(0)) ISI Bks.
Zimra, Georges. Résiter [sic] à la Servitude. 2009. 207p. (978-2-917191-25-5(2)) Berg Pubs.
Zingales, Luigi. A Capitalism for the People: Recapturing the Lost Genius of American Prosperity. 2012. (ENG.). 336p. (gr. 9). 27.99 (978-0-465-02947-1(7)) Basic Bks.
Zizek, Slavoj. First As Tragedy, Then As Farce. 2009. (ENG.). 158p. pap. 14.95 (978-1-84467-428-2(2), 844428) Verso Bks. GBR. Dist: Norton, W. W. & Co., Inc.
—In Defense of Lost Causes. 2009. (ENG.). 530p. pap. 22.95 (978-1-84467-429-9(0), 844429) Verso Bks. GBR. Dist: Norton, W. W. & Co., Inc.
Zumbansen, Peer & Williams, Cynthia, eds. The Embedded Firm: Corporate Governance, Labor, & Finance Capitalism. 2011. (ENG., Illus.). 498p. 105.00 (978-1-107-00601-0(5)) Cambridge Univ. Pr.
Zündorf, Irmgard. Der Preis der Marktwirtschaft: Staatliche Preispolitik und Lebensstandard in Westdeutschland 1948 Bis 1963. 2006. (Vierteljahrschrift fur Sozial- und Wirtschaftsgeschichte - Beihefte (VSWG-B) Ser.). (GER., Illus.). 33p. (C). 94.00 (978-3-515-08861-9(X)) Steiner, Franz Verlag Wiesbaden GmbH DEU. Dist: Brown, David Bk. Co., The.

CAPITALISTS AND FINANCIERS

see also Bondholders; Businesspeople; Capitalism; Stockholders

Allen, Robert G. & Nelson Bell, Karen. Nothing down for Women: The Smart Woman's Quick-Start Guide to Real Estate Investing. 2011. (ENG.). 480p. pap. 28.99 (978-0-7432-9785-1(7), Free Pr.) Free Pr.
Ammann, Daniel. The King of Oil: The Secret Lives of Marc Rich. 2010. (ENG., Illus.). 336p. pap. 16.99 (978-0-312-65068-1(X), St. Martin's Griffin) St. Martin's Pr.
Aynalem, Muluneh. The Law Applicable to Concession Agreements. 2010. 128p. pap. (978-3-639-26792-1(3)) VDM Verlag Dr. Mueller e.K.
Barnard, Zenia. Online Community Portals for Enhanced Customer Relationship Management. 2010. 316p. pap. (978-3-8383-6281-6(0)) Lambert Academic Publishing.
Barrow, Colin. The Global Property Investor's Toolkit: A Sourcebook for Successful Decision Making. 2008. (ENG., Illus.). 464p. pap. 39.95 (978-1-84112-763-7(9), Capstone) Wiley, John & Sons, Inc.
Bartmann, Bill & Rozek, Jonathan. Bailout Riches! How Everyday Investors Can Make a Fortune Buying Bad Loans for Pennies on the Dollar. 2009. (ENG., Illus.). 240p. 34.95 (978-0-470-47825-7(X), Wiley) Wiley, John & Sons, Inc.
Beauchamp, Cari. Joseph P. Kennedy Presents: His Hollywood Years. 2010. (Vintage Ser.). (ENG., Illus.). 528p. pap. 18.95 (978-0-307-47522-0(0), Vintage) Knopf Doubleday Publishing Group.
Black, Conrad. A Matter of Principle. 2011. (ENG., Illus.). 592p. 35.00 (978-0-7710-1670-7(0), McClelland & Stewart) McClelland & Stewart CAN. Dist: Random Hse., Inc.
Boubakri, Narjess & Cosset, Jean-Claude, eds. Institutional Investors in Global Capital Markets. 2011. (International Finance Review Ser.). (Illus.). 350p. (978-1-78052-242-5(8)) Emerald Group Publishing Ltd.
Bowyer, Jerry. The Free Market Capitalist's Survival Guide: How to Invest & Thrive in an Era of Rampant Socialism. 2011. (ENG.). 240p. 25.99 (978-0-06-182483-8(6)) Broadside Bks. GBR. Dist: HarperCollins Pubs.
Brands. The Money Men: Capitalism, Democracy, & the Hundred Years' War over the American Dollar. (Enterprise Ser.). (ENG., Illus.). 224p. 2007. per. 14.95 (978-0-393-33050-2(8), 33050) 2006. 23.95 (978-0-393-06184-0(1)) Norton, W. W. & Co., Inc.
Brands, H. W. The Murder of Jim Fisk for the Love of Josie Mansfield: A Tragedy of the Gilded Age. 2011. (ENG., Illus.). 224p. pap. 15.00 (978-0-307-74325-1(X), Anchor) Knopf Doubleday Publishing Group.
Brown, Eddie. Beating the Odds: Edition Brown's Investing & Life Strategies. 2011. (ENG., Illus.). 215p. 27.95 (978-0-470-93662-7(2), Wiley) Wiley, John & Sons, Inc.
Buffett, Mary & Clark, David. Warren Buffett & the Art of Stock Arbitrage: Proven Strategies for Arbitrage & Other Special Investment Situations. 2010. (ENG.). 176p. 25.00 (978-1-4391-9882-7(9), Scribner) Scribner.
Chen, Jie & Dickson, Bruce J. Allies of the State: China's Private Entrepreneurs & Democratic Change. 2010. (Illus.). 232p. 45.00 (978-0-674-04896-6(2)) Harvard Univ. Pr.
Chien, Chia-Li. Show Me the Money: Run Your Business like a Prosperous Investor. 2010. 184p. 28.00 (978-1-4502-1521-3(1)) iUniverse, Inc.
—Show Me the Money: Run Your Business like a Prosperous Investor. 2010. 184p. pap. 18.00 (978-1-4502-1519-0(X)) iUniverse, Inc.
Choudhry, Moorad. Bonds: A Concise Guide for Investors. 2006. (ENG., Illus.). 192p. 46.00 (978-0-230-00649-2(3)) Palgrave Macmillan.
Chu, Cindy Yik-Yi. Chinese Communists & Hong Kong Capitalists: 1937-1997. 2010. (ENG., Illus.). 208p. 89.00 (978-0-230-10799-1(0)) Palgrave Macmillan.
City Girl Staff & S., Suzana. Confessions of a City Girl: The Devil Wears Pinstripes. 2010. (ENG.). 282p. pap. 14.95 (978-0-7535-1981-3(X)) Virgin Bks. Ltd. GBR. Dist: Independent Pubs. Group.
Conde, Mario. Los Días de Gloria. 2010. (SPA.). 860p. (978-84-270-3675-8(2)) Ediciones Martínez Roca.
Crisafulli, Patricia. The House of Dimon: How JPMorgan's Jamie Dimon Rose to the Top of the Financial World. 2011. (ENG.). 242p. pap. 16.95 (978-0-470-92469-3(1), Wiley) Wiley, John & Sons, Inc.
Crisafulli, Patricia & Crisafulli. The House of Dimon: How JPMorgan's Jamie Dimon Rose to the Top of the Financial World. 2009. (ENG.). 256p. 24.95 (978-0-470-41296-1(8), Wiley) Wiley, John & Sons, Inc.
Damodaran, Harish. India's New Capitalists: Caste, Business, & Industry in a Modern Nation. 2008. (ENG.). 368p. 110.00 (978-0-230-20507-9(0)) Palgrave Macmillan.
Daniels, John B. Every Young Investor's Handbook. 2011. 140p. 29.99 (978-1-4568-8186-3(8)); pap. 19.99 (978-1-4568-8185-6(X)) Xlibris Corp.
Davis, Forrest. What Price Wall Street? 2011. 384p. 53.95 (978-1-258-05991-0(6)) Literary Licensing, LLC.
De Brouwer, Philippe J. S. Maslowian Portfolio Theory: A Coherent Approach to Strategic Asset Allocation. 2012. (ENG.). 470p. pap. 61.95 (978-90-5487-897-1(5)) VUB Univ. Pr. BEL. Dist: Independent Pubs. Group.
Dinkelspiel, Frances. Towers of Gold: How One Jewish Immigrant Named Isaias Hellman Created California. 2010. (ENG., Illus.). 400p. pap. 16.99 (978-0-312-35527-2(0), St. Martin's Griffin) St. Martin's Pr.
Douglas, Thompson. Inside the Muslim Brotherhood. 2012. (ENG., Illus.). 288p. 32.95 (978-1-85782-687-6(6)) Blake, John Publishing, Ltd. GBR. Dist: Independent Pubs. Group.
Draper, William H., III. The Startup Game: Inside the Partnership Between Venture Capitalists & Entrepreneurs. 2011. (ENG.). 272p. 28.00 (978-0-230-10486-0(X)) Palgrave Macmillan.
Draper, William H. H., III. The Startup Game: Inside the Partnership between Venture Capitalists & Entrepreneurs. 2012. (ENG.). 272p. pap. 17.00 (978-0-230-33994-1(8)) Palgrave Macmillan.
Fellner, Gerlinde. Investor Behaviour. 2008. 144p. pap. (978-3-639-07567-0(6)) VDM Verlag Dr. Mueller e.K.
Fenberg, Steven. Unprecedented Power: Jesse Jones, Capitalism, & the Common Good. 2011. (Illus.). 616p. 35.00 (978-1-60344-434-7(3)) Texas A&M Univ. Pr.
Fong, William. J. W. McConnell: Financier, Philanthropist, Patriot. 2008. (ENG., Illus.). 752p. (C). (978-0-7735-3270-0(6)) McGill-Queen's Univ. Pr.
Forbes, Bertie Charles. Men Who Are Making America. 442p. reprint ed. 98.00 (978-0-7222-8391-2(1)) Library Reprints, Inc.
Foxman, Abraham H. Jews & Money: The Story of a Stereotype. (ENG., 256p. 2012. Illus.). pap. 17.00 (978-0-230-12064-8(4)) 2010. 26.00 (978-0-230-62385-9(9)) Palgrave Macmillan.
Franch, John. Robber Baron: The Life of Charles Tyson Yerkes. 2008. (ENG., Illus.). 384p. per. 24.95 (978-0-252-07517-9(X)) Univ. of Illinois Pr.
Franks, Sandy & Nunnally, Sarah. Barbarians of Wealth: Protecting Yourself from Today's Financial Attilas. 2010. (Agora Ser.: 20). (ENG., Illus.). 448p. 29.95 (978-0-470-76814-3(2), Wiley) Wiley, John & Sons, Inc.
Fraser, Steve. Wall Street: America's Dream Palace. 2009. (Icons of America Ser.). (ENG., Illus.). 208p. pap. 14.00 (978-0-300-15143-5(8)) Yale Univ. Pr.
Freud, David. Freud in the City. 2008. (ENG.). 418p. pap. 19.95 (978-1-903071-19-9(4)) Bene Factum Publishing, Ltd. GBR. Dist: Independent Pubs. Group.
Gage, Lyman J. Memoirs of Lyman J Gage. 2007. (ENG.). 256p. 42.95 (978-0-548-14210-3(6)) 2006. pap. 27.95 (978-1-4286-5428-0(3)) Kessinger Publishing, LLC.
Glowrey, Mark. Sterling Fixed Income for the Private Investor. 2012. (ENG.). 176p. pap. 27.99 (978-0-85719-042-0(3)) Harriman Hse. Publishing GBR. Dist: Ingram Pub. Services.
Green, David R., et al, eds. Men, Women, & Money: Perspectives on Gender, Wealth, & Investment 1850-1930. 2011. (ENG., Illus.). 368p. 99.00 (978-0-19-959376-7(0)) Oxford Univ. Pr., Inc.
Griffin, G. Edward. The Creature from Jekyll Island: A Second Look at the Federal Reserve. 5th ed. 2010. pap. 24.50 (978-0-912986-45-6(X)) American Media.
Grodinsky, Julius. Jay Gould: His Business Career, 1867-1892. 2011. 640p. 65.95 (978-1-258-02729-2(1)) Literary Licensing, LLC.
Häberlein, Mark. The Fuggers of Augsburg: Pursuing Wealth & Honor in Renaissance Germany. 2012. E-Book (978-0-8139-3258-3(0)); (ENG., Illus.). 304p. (gr. 17). 39.50 (978-0-8139-3244-6(0)) Univ. Pr. of Virginia.
Henry Baldwin Hyde: A Biographical Sketch. 2007. (ENG.). 264p. 42.95 (978-0-548-04650-0(6)) Kessinger Publishing, LLC.
Henry Baldwin Hyde: A Biographical Sketch. 244p. reprint ed. 48.00 (978-0-7950-2322-4(7)) New Library Press LLC.
Hirsch, Melvin. How Not to Lose a Million Dollars in Stocks. 2011. 128p. pap. 21.40 (978-1-60746-281-1(8)) FastPrncl, Inc.
Holbrook, Stewart. The Age of the Moguls. 2010. (ENG., Illus.). 395p. pap. 32.95 (978-1-4128-1082-1(5)) Transaction Pubs.
Horowitz, Andrew. The Winning Investor's Guide to Making Money in Any Market. 2010. 240p. pap. 14.99 (978-0-8050-9097-0(5), Holt Paperback) Holt, Henry & Co.
Hunt, James L. Relationship Banker: Eugene W. Stetson, Wall Street, & American Business, 1916-1959. 2009. (Illus.). 400p. 35.00 (978-0-86554-915-9(X)) Mercer Univ. Pr.
Jacob, Margaret C. & Secretan, Catherine. Self-Perception of Early Modern Capitalists. 2008. (ENG., Illus.). 288p. 95.00 (978-0-230-60447-6(1)) Palgrave Macmillan.
Jankovsky, Jason Alan & Trader X. The Art of the Trade: What I Learned (and Lost) Trading the Chicago Futures Markets. 2008. (ENG.). 208p. 29.95 (978-0-470-13899-1(8), Wiley) Wiley, John & Sons, Inc.
Jennings, Walter Wilson. A Dozen Captains of American Industry. 2011. 238p. 46.95 (978-1-258-06023-7(X)) Literary Licensing, LLC.
Josephson, Matthew. The Robber Barons: The Great American Capitalists, 1861-1901. 30.95 (978-0-8488-0091-8(5)) Amereon LTD.

—The Robber Barons: The Great American Capitalists, 1861-1901. 2010. (ENG.). 482p. pap. 39.95 *(978-1-4128-1125-5(2))* Transaction Pubs.

Kantilal R. Patel. Stock Market Investors Companion: Winning Methodology for Making Money. 2009. 276p. pap. 30.95 *(978-1-4401-8638-7(3))* iUniverse, Inc.

Kaplan, Herbert. Nathan Mayer Rothschild & the Creation of a Dynasty: The Critical Years 1806-1816. 2010. (ENG.). 224p. pap. 21.95 *(978-0-8047-7361-4(0))* Stanford Univ. Pr.

Klein, Maury. The Life & Legend of E. H. Harriman. 2011. (ENG., Illus.). 544p. pap. 50.00 ***(978-0-8078-6553-8(2))*** Univ. of North Carolina Pr.

Knowles, Valerie. From Telegrapher to Titan: The Life of William C. Van Horne. 2010. (Railroads Past & Present Ser.). (ENG., Illus.). 504p. pap. 29.95 *(978-0-253-22250-3(8)*, 0253222508) Indiana Univ. Pr.

—William C. Van Horne: Railway Titan. 2010. (Quest Biography Ser.). (ENG., Illus.). 216p. pap. 19.99 *(978-1-55488-702-6(X))* Dundurn CAN. Dist: Ingram Pub. Services.

Konanykhin, Alex. Defiance: Or How to Succeed in Business Despite Being Hounded by the FBI, the KGB, the INS, the Department of Homeland Security, the Department of Justice, Interpol & Mafia Hit Men; A True Story. 2008. 240p. 27.95 *(978-0-9727377-1-5(5)*, Renaissance Publishing) KMGI Publishing.

Labitan, Bud. The Four Filters Invention of Warren Buffett & Charlie Munger. 2009. 148p. pap. 30.47 *(978-0-615-24129-6(8))* Acalmix.

—The Four Filters Invention of Warren Buffett & Charlie Munger (Large Print Edition) 2010. 150p. pap. 29.95 *(978-0-557-36677-4(1))* Lulu Enterprises Inc.

—Valuations - 30 Intrinsic Value Estimations in the style of Warren Buffett & Charlie Munger. 2010. 186p. pap. 39.99 *(978-0-557-48333-4(6))* Lulu Enterprises Inc.

Labor Research Association. Monopoly Today. 2011. 128p. 40.95 ***(978-1-258-01140-6(9))*** Literary Licensing, LLC.

Lake, Amielle, et al. The Elephant Hunters: Chronicles of the Moneymen. 2008. (ENG., Illus.). 184p. 53.00 *(978-0-230-55369-9(9))* Palgrave Macmillan.

Lammertink, Steven. Business Angels. 2011. 64p. pap. ***(978-3-8443-0996-6(9))*** Lambert Academic Publishing.

Larkin, Hoffman, Daly & Lindgren (Firm) Staff, contrib. by. Minnesota's Angel Tax Credit: Small Corporate Offering Registration (SCOR): A "Short Form" Registration Statement. 2011. ***(978-1-888404-54-8(X))*** Minnesota Dept. of Trade & Economic Development.

Laurence, Anne, et al, eds. Women & Their Money 1700-1950: Essays on Women & Finance. 2012. (Routledge International Studies in Business History Ser.). (ENG., Illus.). 336p. (C). pap. 42.95 ***(978-0-415-54255-5(3))*** Routledge.

Lauria, Thomas J. Investor Relations: the Art & Philosophy of Effective Corporate Communications. 2008. 122p. 34.95 *(978-0-557-02862-7(0))*; pap. 19.95 *(978-0-557-00763-9(1))* Lulu Enterprises Inc.

Lay, Jeffery. TOPGUN on Wall Street: Why the United States Military Should Run Corporate America. 2012. (ENG.). 336p. 25.99 ***(978-1-59315-717-3(7))*** Vanguard Pr.

Lopez-Morell, Miguel A. The House of Rothschild in Spain 1812-1941. 2012. (Illus.). 350p. ***(978-0-7546-6800-8(2))*** Ashgate Publishing, Ltd.

Loving, Rush, Jr., ed. The Men Who Loved Trains: The Story of Men Who Battled Greed to Save an Ailing Industry. 2008. (Railroads Past & Present Ser.). (ENG., Illus.). 384p. pap. 17.95 *(978-0-253-22031-8(9)*, 0253220319) Indiana Univ. Pr.

Lowe, Janet C. Warren Buffett Speaks: Wit & Wisdom from the World's Greatest Investor. 2nd rev. ed. 2007. (ENG., Illus.). 288p. 19.95 *(978-0-470-15262-1(1)*, Wiley) Wiley, John & Sons, Inc.

Lowenstein, Roger. Buffett: The Making of an American Capitalist. 2008. (ENG., Illus.). 512p. pap. 19.00 *(978-0-8129-7927-5(3)*, Random Hse. Trade Paperbacks) Random House Publishing Group.

Lowes, David E. The Anti-Capitalist Dictionary: Movements, Histories, & Motivations. 2006. (ENG.). 320p. 113.95 *(978-1-84277-682-7(7))*; per. 31.95 *(978-1-84277-683-4(5))* Zed Bks., Ltd. GBR. Dist: Macmillan.

Makley, Michael J. The Infamous King of the Comstock: William Sharon & the Gilded Age in the West. 2009. (Wilber S. Shepperson Series in Nevada History Ser.). (ENG., Illus.). 328p. pap. 24.95 *(978-0-87417-779-4(0))* Univ. of Nevada Pr.

—John Mackay: Silver King in the Gilded Age. 2009. (Wilber S. Shepperson Series in Nevada History Ser.). (ENG., Illus.). 296p. 34.95 *(978-0-87417-770-1(7))* Univ. of Nevada Pr.

Mallaby, Sebastian. More Money Than God: Hedge Funds & the Making of a New Elite. 2010. (ENG., Illus.). 496p. (gr. 12). 29.95 *(978-1-59420-255-1(9)*, Penguin Pr. HC, The) Penguin Group (USA) Inc.

Mangot, Mickaël & Mangot. 50 Psychological Experiments for Investors. 2009. (ENG.). 200p. pap. 24.95 *(978-0-470-82383-5(6)*, Wiley) Wiley, John & Sons, Inc.

Marquis Who's Who, creator. Who's Who in Corporate America. 2011. (Who's Who in Finance & Business Ser.). 1323p. 412.25 ***(978-0-8379-3575-1(X))*** Marquis Who's Who, LLC.

Marquis Who's Who Staff. Who's Who in Finance & Business 2008-2009. 36th ed. 2007. 1100p. 349.00 *(978-0-8379-0356-9(4))* Marquis Who's Who, LLC.

Mars, Laura. Financial Services Canada 2010. Lang, Robert, ed. 2010. pap. 350.00 *(978-1-59237-571-4(5))* Grey Hse. Publishing.

Martin, Roderick, et al. Investor Engagement: Investors & Management Practice under Shareholder Value. 2007. (ENG., Illus.). 240p. 95.00 *(978-0-19-920260-7(5))* Oxford Univ. Pr., Inc.

McAlpine, R. W. (Robert W.). The Life & Times of Col James Fisk, Jr , Being a Full & Impartial Account of the Remarkable Career of a Most Remarkable Man; Together with Sketch. 2006. 512p. per. 29.99 *(978-1-4255-5705-8(8))* MPublishing.

Mcclellan, James E., et al. The Little Book of Trading: Trend Following Strategy for Big Winnings. 2011. (Little Books. Big Profits Ser.: 33). (ENG., Illus.). 210p. 19.95 *(978-1-118-06350-7(3)*, Wiley) Wiley, John & Sons, Inc.

McDonald, Duff. Last Man Standing: The Ascent of Jamie Dimon & JPMorgan Chase. 2010. (ENG., Illus.). 352p. pap. 16.00 *(978-1-4165-9954-8(1))* Simon & Schuster.

McMacken, David. Built on Pines: The Sgtory of Ammi Willard Wright, Michigan Lumberman, Capitalist, & Philanthrapist. (Illus.). vii, 210p. *(978-0-9728304-0-9(5))* Alma Public Library.

McNeese, Tim. The Robber Barons & the Sherman Anti-Trust ACT: Reshaping American Business. 2008. (Milestones in American History Ser.). (Illus.). 128p. (YA). (gr. 7-12). 35.00 *(978-1-60413-008-9(3))* Facts On File, Inc.

Means, Howard. Money & Power: The History of Business. 2006. 274p. reprint ed. pap. 17.00 *(978-1-4223-5795-8(3))* DIANE Publishing Co.

Mellon, James. The Judge: A Life of Thomas Mellon, Founder of a Fortune. 2011. (Illus.). 592p. 38.00 *(978-0-300-16714-6(8))* Yale Univ. Pr.

Michie, Ranald C. Guilty Money: The City of London in Victorian & Edwardian Culture, 1815-1914, 1 vol. 2009. (Financial History Ser.). (ENG.). 288p. 99.00 *(978-1-85196-892-3(X))* Pickering & Chatto Pubs., Ltd. GBR. Dist: Ashgate Publishing Co.

Mitchell, Mark. The Dendreon Effect: How Felons, con-men & Wall Street Insiders Manipulate High-tech Stocks. 2011. (ENG.). 288p. pap. 19.95 *(978-1-56343-141-8(6))* Silver Lake Publishing.

Moody, John. The Masters of Capital. 2009. 236p. 23.99 *(978-1-103-83456-3(8))*; pap. 17.99 *(978-1-103-83446-4(0))* BiblioBazaar.

—The Masters of Capital. 2007. 35.00 *(978-1-4344-8953-1(1))*; 244p. per. 19.95 *(978-1-4344-8952-4(3))* Wildside Pr., LLC.

—The Masters of Capital: A Chronicle of Wall Street. 2007. (ENG.). 240p. 41.95 *(978-0-548-23958-2(4))*; 244p. per. 26.95 *(978-1-4326-4106-1(9))* Kessinger Publishing, LLC.

—The Masters of Capital: A Chronicle of Wall Street. (Chronicles of America Ser.). 234p. reprint ed. 98.00 *(978-0-7222-7117-9(4))* Library Reprints, Inc.

Mosbacher, Robert A., Sr. & McGrath, James Gerald. Going to Windward: A Mosbacher Family Memoir. 2010. (ENG., Illus.). 336p. 30.00 *(978-1-60344-221-3(9))* Texas A&M Univ. Pr.

Munsell, F. Darrell. From Redstone to Ludlow: John Cleveland Osgood's Struggle Against the United Mine Workers of America. (Mining the American West Ser.). (Illus.). 2011. (ENG.). 392p. (C). pap. 29.95 *(978-1-60732-100-2(9))* 2009. xi, 392p. *(978-0-87081-934-0(0))* Univ. Pr. of Colorado.

Nairn, Alasdair & Davis, Jonathan. Templeton's Way with Money: Strategies & Philosophy of a Legendary Investor. 2012. (ENG.). 256p. 39.95 ***(978-1-118-14961-4(0)***, Wiley) Wiley, John & Sons, Inc.

Nakano, Akira. Iwasaki Yataro "Mitsubishi" No Kigyoron: Nippon Kabushiki-Gaisha No Genten. 2010. (JPN., Illus.). 319p. *(978-4-02-330497-0(2))* Asahi Shimbun-Sha.

Nasr, Vali. Forces of Fortune: The Rise of the New Muslim Middle Class & What It Will Mean for Our World. 2009. (ENG., Illus.). 320p. 26.00 *(978-1-4165-8968-6(6)*, Free Pr.) Free Pr.

—The Rise of Islamic Capitalism: Why the New Muslim Middle Class Is the Key to Defeating Extremism. 2010. (ENG.). 320p. pap. 16.00 *(978-1-4165-8969-3(4)*, Free Pr.) Free Pr.

Newcomb, Simon. A Plain Man's Talk on the Labor Question. 2009. 200p. 26.99 *(978-1-110-71135-2(2))*; pap. 22.75 *(978-1-110-71133-8(6))*; 26.99 *(978-1-110-52425-9(0))*; pap. 22.75 *(978-1-110-52424-2(2))* BiblioBazaar.

—A Plain Man's Talk on the Labor Question. 2009. 98p. pap. *(978-0-217-15437-6(9))* Books LLC.

—A Plain Man's Talk on the Labor Question. 2009. 204p. 39.95 *(978-1-104-00732-4(0))*; pap. 24.95 *(978-1-4374-6298-2(7))* Kessinger Publishing, LLC.

Nocera, Joe. Good Guys & Bad Guys: Behind the Scenes with the Saints & Scoundrels of American Business (and Everything in Between) 2011. (ENG.). 304p. (gr. 12). 16.00 *(978-1-59184-439-6(8)*, Portfolio Trade) Penguin Group (USA) Inc.

Oppenheimer, Jerry. Madoff with the Money. (ENG., Illus.). 2010. 256p. pap. 16.95 *(978-0-470-62459-3(0))* 2009. 280p. 24.95 *(978-0-470-50498-7(6))* Wiley, John & Sons, Inc. (Wiley).

Partnoy, Frank. The Match King: Ivar Kreuger, the Financial Genius Behind a Century of Wall Street Scandals. 2010. (ENG., Illus.). 288p. pap. 15.95 *(978-1-58648-812-3(0))* PublicAffairs.

Payment, Simone. Donald Trump: Profile of a Real-Estate Tycoon. 2009. (Career Profiles Ser.). 112p. (gr. 9-10). 63.90 *(978-1-61511-793-2(8))* Rosen Publishing Group, Inc., The.

Price, John. The Conscious Investor: Profiting from the Timeless Value Approach. 2010. (Wiley Finance Ser.: 586). (ENG., Illus.). 366p. 49.95 *(978-0-470-60438-0(7)*, Wiley) Wiley, John & Sons, Inc.

Renehan, Edward J., Jr. Dark Genius of Wall Street: The Misunderstood Life of Jay Gould, King of the Robber Barons. 2007. (Illus.). 352p. reprint ed. 30.00 *(978-1-4223-6837-4(8))* DIANE Publishing Co.

Rockefeller, John Davison. Random Reminiscences of Men & Events. 2009. 200p. 22.99 *(978-1-103-97423-8(8))* 2009. 200p. pap. 16.99 *(978-1-103-97416-0(5))* 2008. 120p. 24.99 *(978-0-554-27902-2(9))* 2008. 120p. 21.99 *(978-0-554-37205-1(3))* 2007. 108p. pap. 18.99 *(978-1-4346-4279-0(8))* 2007. (ENG.). 118p. pap. 19.99 *(978-1-4346-4280-6(1))* BiblioBazaar.

—Random Reminiscences of Men & Events. 2009. 204p. 39.95 *(978-1-104-42982-9(9))*; pap. 24.95 *(978-1-104-37112-8(X))* Kessinger Publishing, LLC.

Rohatyn, Felix G. Dealings: A Political & Financial Life. 2010. (ENG., Illus.). 304p. 27.00 *(978-1-4391-8196-6(9))* Simon & Schuster.

Roodman, David. Due Diligence: An Impertinent Inquiry into Microfinance. 2011. (ENG., Illus.). 275p. pap. 24.95 *(978-1-933286-48-8(2))* Ctr. for Global Development.

Ross, Brian. The Madoff Chronicles: Inside the Secret World of Bernie & Ruth. 2010. 269p. 20.00 *(978-1-4379-7436-2(8))* DIANE Publishing Co.

—The Madoff Chronicles: Inside the Secret World of Bernie & Ruth. 2009. (ENG.). 288p. 19.99 *(978-1-4013-1029-5(X))* Hyperion Pr.

Rotblut, Charles. Better Good than Lucky: How Savvy Investors Create Fortune with the Risk-Reward Ratio. Golden, Karris, ed. 2010. (ENG., Illus.). 195p. 29.95 *(978-1-934354-14-8(7))* W&A Publishing.

Saito, William Hiroyuki. An Unprogrammed Life: Adventures of an Incurable Entrepreneur. 2012. (ENG.). 320p. pap. 24.95 ***(978-1-118-07703-0(2)***, Wiley) Wiley, John & Sons, Inc.

Sawler, Harvey. Twenty-First Century Irvings. 2007. (ENG., Illus.). 192p. 29.95 *(978-1-55109-608-7(0))* Down East Bks.

Schacht, Hjalmar Horace Greeley. Confessions of the Old Wizard: The Autobiography of Hjalmar Horace Greeley Schacht. Pyke, Diana, tr. 2011. 520p. 60.95 ***(978-1-258-01696-8(6))*** Literary Licensing, LLC.

Schroeder, Alice. The Snowball: Warren Buffett & the Business of Life. (ENG., Illus.). 2009. 832p. pap. 20.00 *(978-0-553-38461-1(9))* 2008. 976p. 35.00 *(978-0-553-80509-3(6)*, Bantam) Random House Publishing Group.

—The Snowball: Warren Buffett & the Business of Life. l.t. ed. 2008. (ENG.). 1664p. pap. 35.00 *(978-0-7393-2798-2(4))* Random Hse. Large Print.

Scott, James Brown. Robert Bacon: Life & Letters. 2007. (ENG.). 518p. 55.95 *(978-0-548-04740-8(5))* Kessinger Publishing, LLC.

Shashoua, Roger. Dancing with the Bear: A Serial Entrepreneur Goes East. 2007. (ENG., Illus.). 195p. 25.00 *(978-1-84673-076-4(7)*, GMB Publishing Ltd.) Blue Ibex Ltd. GBR. Dist: Ingram Pub. Services.

Sherwood, Tim. Charles Tyson Yerkes: Railway Tycoon. 2009. (ENG., Illus.). 192p. pap. 34.95 *(978-0-7524-4622-6(3))* History Pr. Ltd.,The GBR. Dist: Independent Pubs. Group.

Shore, Laurence. Southern Capitalists: The Ideological Leadership of an Elite, 1832-1885. 2011. (ENG.). 294p. pap. 40.00 *(978-0-8078-9779-9(5))* Univ. of North Carolina Pr.

Simko, Ladislav. The Bear, the Bull & the Types of Sentiment. 2011. 112p. pap. ***(978-3-8443-0918-8(7))*** Lambert Academic Publishing.

Singh, Saurabh. Mutual Funds Marketing & Mccarthy. 2011. 88p. pap. ***(978-3-8383-7332-4(4))*** Lambert Academic Publishing.

Skrabec, Quentin R. Henry Clay Frick: The Life of the Perfect Capitalist. 2010. (ENG., Illus.). 270p. pap. 45.00 *(978-0-7864-4383-3(9))* McFarland & Co., Inc. Pubs.

Slater, Robert. Soros: The World's Most Influential Investor. 2nd ed. 2008. (ENG., Illus.). 336p. 27.95 *(978-0-07-160844-2(3)*, 0071608443) McGraw-Hill Cos., The.

Smith, George David & Dalzell, Frederick. Wisdom from the Robber Barons: Enduring Business Lessons from Rockefeller, Morgan, & the First Industrialists. 160p. 7.99 *(978-0-7858-1566-2(X))* Book Sales, Inc.

Soppe, Aloy. Finance As an Instrument to a Sustainable Company. 2008. 192p. pap. *(978-3-639-00913-2(4))* VDM Verlag Dr. Mueller e.K.

Speier, Torben. Insiderhandel und Ad-hoc-Publizität nach Anlegerschutzverbesserungsgesetz: Rechtliche Grundlagen und ausgewählte Fragen in einem veränderten kapitalmarktrechtlichen Gewand. 2009. (Schriften zum Wirtschafts- und Medienrecht, Steuerrecht und Zivilprozeßrecht Ser.). (GER.). 444p. pap. 99.95 *(978-3-631-58595-5(0))* Lang, Peter GmbH, Europaischer Verlag der Wissenschaften DEU. Dist: Lang, Peter.

Straney, Louis L. Investor's Guide to Loss Recovery: Rights, Mediation, Arbitration, & Other Strategies. 2011. (Wiley Finance Ser.: 12). (ENG.). 210p. 75.00 *(978-0-470-93762-4(9)*, Wiley) Wiley, John & Sons, Inc.

Strauch, Carl F. Emerson's New England Capitalist: Harvard Library Bulletin, V10, No. 2, Spring 1956. 2011. 16p. pap. 35.95 ***(978-1-258-07270-4(X))*** Literary Licensing, LLC.

Sudetic, Chuck. The Philanthropy of George Soros: Building Open Societies. 2011. *(978-1-58648-859-8(7))* PublicAffairs.

Suljkanovic, Midran. Corporate Governance in Post-Privatized Bosnia & Herzegovin. 2010. 88p. pap. *(978-3-639-25364-1(7))* VDM Verlag Dr. Mueller e.K.

Train, John. The Midas Touch: The Strategies That Have Made Warren Buffett the World's Most Successful Investor. 2nd ed. 2009. (ENG.). 190p. 19.99 *(978-1-906659-18-9(4))* Harriman Hse. Publishing GBR. Dist: Ingram Pub. Services.

Twist, Anthony. A Life of John Julius Angerstein, 1735-1823: Widening Circles in Finance, Philanthropy & the Arts in Eighteenth Century London. 2006. (Illus.). 620p. 149.95 *(978-0-7734-5583-2(3))* Mellen, Edwin Pr., The.

Veneziani, Vincent W. The Greatest Trades of All Time: Top Traders Making Big Profits from the Crash of 1929 to Today. 2011. (Wiley Trading Ser.: 483). (ENG., Illus.). 166p. 45.00 *(978-0-470-64599-4(7)*, Wiley) Wiley, John & Sons, Inc.

Villette, Michel & Vuillermot, Catherine. From Predators to Icons: Exposing the Myth of the Business Hero. Holoch, George & Kimberly, John R., trs. from FRE. 2009. (Illus.). 224p. 62.95 *(978-0-8014-4700-6(3))*; pap. 24.95 *(978-0-8014-7566-5(X))* Cornell Univ. Pr.

Wang, Xiaoli. Private Equity, Asset Allocation & Risk Perception - Entrepreneur Spirit & Asset Allocation from a Risk Perspective. 2008. 140p. pap. *(978-3-639-11496-6(5))* VDM Verlag Dr. Mueller e.K.

Ward, Geoffrey C. A Disposition to Be Rich: How a Small-Town Pastor's Son Ruined an American President, Brought on a Wall Street Crash, & Made Himself the Best-Hated Man in the United States. 2012. (ENG., Illus.). 432p. 28.95 ***(978-0-679-44530-2(7)***, Knopf) Knopf Doubleday Publishing Group.

Weikert, Sascha. Option Warrants vs. Turbo Certificates. 2010. 112p. pap. *(978-3-639-26351-0(0))* VDM Verlag Dr. Mueller e.K.

Weiss, Stephen L. The Big Win: Learning from the Legends to Become a More Successful Investor. 2012. (ENG.). 240p. 29.95 *(978-0-470-91610-0(9)*, Wiley) Wiley, John & Sons, Inc.

—The Billion Dollar Mistake: Learning the Art of Investing Through the Missteps of Legendary Investors. 2010. (ENG.). 272p. 29.95 *(978-0-470-48106-6(4)*, Wiley) Wiley, John & Sons, Inc.

Without Risk There's No Reward. 2008. 23.95 *(978-0-9801270-9-6(2))* Seven Locks Pr.

Woods, Ngaire & Martinez-Diaz, Leonardo, eds. Networks of Influence?: Developing Countries in a Networked Global Order. 2009. (ENG., Illus.). 256p. 99.00 *(978-0-19-956442-2(6))* Oxford Univ. Pr., Inc.

CAPITALIZATION

see also subdivision Capitalization under names of languages, e.g. German Language—Capitalization

Pacella, Andrea. We Have What We Are. 2009. 208p. pap. *(978-3-639-19580-4(9))* VDM Verlag Dr. Mueller e.K.

CAPITALIZATION (FINANCE)

see Corporations—Finance; Securities; Valuation

CAPITALS (CITIES)

see also Capitols

Almandoz, Arturo, ed. Planning Latin America's Capital Cities 1850-1950. 2009. (Planning, History & Environment Ser.). (ENG., Illus.). 296p. 44.95 *(978-0-415-55308-7(3))* Routledge.

Cotterell, Arthur. The Imperial Capitals of China: A Dynastic History of the Celestial Empire. 2008. (ENG., Illus.). 336p. (gr. 12). 27.95 *(978-1-59020-007-0(1))* Overlook Pr., The.

De Frantz, Monika. Capital City Cultures: Reconstructing Contemporary Europe in Vienna & Berlin. 2011. (Europe plurielle - Multiple Europes Ser.). 260p. pap. 57.95 *(978-90-5201-739-6(5))* PIE - Peter Lang BEL. Dist: Lang, Peter.

Hall, Thomas. Planning Europe's Capital Cities: Aspects of Nineteenth-Century Urban Development. 2009. (Planning, History & Environment Ser.). (ENG., Illus.). 408p. (C). 44.95 *(978-0-415-55249-3(4))* Routledge.

Hamilton, Alice C. Traveling Mercies: My Personal Prayer Journey to the 50 State Capitols. 2008. (ENG.). 70p. pap. 8.99 *(978-0-9762730-5-9(5))* Vision Publishing.

Hull, Matthew S. Government of Paper: The Materiality of Bureaucracy in Urban Pakistan. 2012. (ENG.). 320p. 65.00 ***(978-0-520-27214-9(5))***; pap. 26.95 ***(978-0-520-27215-6(3))*** Univ. of California Pr.

Kovacevic, Igor, ed. Urbanity: Twenty Years Later: Projects for Central European Capitals. 2011. 233p. pap. *(978-80-254-8170-7(0))* Actar Birkhauser Distribution.

Krüger, Jens. Die Finanzierung der Bundeshauptstadt Bonn. 2006. (Veröffentlichungen der Historischen Kommission zu Berlin Ser.). (GER., Illus.). X, 283p. 154.00 *(978-3-11-019090-8(7))* De Gruyter, Walter Inc.

Maitland, Robert, et al, contrib. by. City Tourism: National Capital Perspectives. 2010. (Illus.). 304p. 145.00 *(978-1-84593-546-7(2))* CABI GBR. Dist: Stylus Publishing, LLC.

Manzanilla, Linda & Chapdelaine, Claude, eds. Domestic Life in Prehispanic Capitals: A Study of Specialization, Hierarchy, & Ethnicity. 2009. (Memoirs Series, Studies in Latin American Ethnohistory & Archaeology: 46). (Illus.). 280p. 38.00 *(978-0-915703-71-5(8))* Univ. of Michigan, Museum of Anthropology, Pubns. Dept.

Monaco Books. Capital Cities Europe, 1 vol. 2010. (ENG., Illus.). 240p. 24.95 *(978-3-89944-622-7(4)*, Monaco Bks.) Verlag Wolfgang Kunth GmbH & Co. KG DEU. Dist: Innovative Logistics.

Slack, Enid & Chattopadhyay, Rupak. Finance & Governance of Capital Cities in Federal Systems. 2009. (Thematic Issues in Federalism Ser.). 342p. *(978-0-7735-3564-0(0))*; (ENG.). (C). pap. *(978-0-7735-3565-7(9))* McGill-Queen's Univ. Pr.

CAPITOL (WASHINGTON, D.C.)

see United States Capitol (Washington, D.C.)

CAPITOLS

see also United States Capitol (Washington, D.C.)

Hamilton, Alice C. Traveling Mercies: My Personal Prayer Journey to the 50 State Capitols. 2008. (ENG.). 70p. pap. 8.99 *(978-0-9762730-5-9(5))* Vision Publishing.

Kimathi, James. Parliaments & Their Architecture: Design Art Technology. 2011. (ENG., Illus.). 1p. 59.95 *(978-1-86470-349-8(0))* Images Publishing Group AUS. Dist: National Bk. Network.

Stembridge, Jim. Fifty State Capitols: The Architecture of Representative Government. 2011. (ENG., Illus.). 128p. pap. 27.95 *(978-0-9830292-0-5(2)*, Coho Publishing) Cohographics.

Vale, Lawrence J. Architecture, Power, & National Identity. 2nd rev. ed. 2008. (Illus.). (ENG.). 400p. (C). 160.00 *(978-0-415-95514-0(9))*; XIV, 386p. 44.95 *(978-0-415-95515-7(7))* Routledge.

CAPITULATIONS, MILITARY
see also Prisoners of War

Afflerbach, Holger & Strachan, Hew, eds. How Fighting Ends: A History of Surrender. 2012. (ENG.). 520p. 125.00 ***(978-0-19-969362-7(5))*** Oxford Univ. Pr., Inc.

Gordin, Michael D. Five Days in August: How World War II Became a Nuclear War. 2007. (ENG., Illus.). 226p. (C). 24.95 *(978-0-691-12818-4(9))* Princeton Univ. Pr.

International Institute for St. The Military Balance 2009. 2009. (Military Balance Ser.). (ENG., Illus.). 486p. pap. 412.00 *(978-0-415-49846-3(5))* Routledge.

Young, Donald J. Final Hours in the Pacific: The Allied Surrenders of Wake Island, Bataan, Corregidor, Hong Kong & Singapore. 2011. (ENG., Illus.). 191p. pap. 38.00 *(978-0-7864-5938-4(7))* McFarland & Co., Inc. Pubs.

CAPONE, AL, 1899-1947

Balsamo, William & Balsamo, John. Young Al Capone: The Untold Story of Scarface in New York, 1899-1925. 2011. (ENG., Illus.). 288p. 24.95 *(978-1-61608-085-3(X)*, 608085) Skyhorse Publishing Co., Inc.

Eig, Jonathan. Get Capone: The Secret Plot That Captured America's Most Wanted Gangster. (ENG., Illus.). 480p. 2011. pap. 16.00 *(978-1-4165-8060-7(3))* 2010. 28.00 *(978-1-4165-8059-1(X))* Simon & Schuster.

—Get Capone: The Secret Plot That Captured America's Most Wanted Gangster. l.t. ed. 2010. 710p. 31.99 *(978-1-4104-2743-4(9))* Thorndike Pr.

Helmer, William J. & Bilek, Arthur J. The St. Valentine's Day Massacre: The Untold Story of the Gangland Bloodbath That Brought down Al Capone. 2006. (ENG., Illus.). 317p. per. 18.95 *(978-1-58182-549-7(8))* Turner Publishing Co.

Hoffman, Dennis E. Scarface Al & the Crime Crusaders: Chicago's Private War Against Capone. 2010. (ENG., Illus.). 208p. pap. 19.95 *(978-0-8093-3004-1(0))* Southern Illinois Univ. Pr.

CAPORETTO, BATTLE OF, KOBARID, SLOVENIA, 1917

Macdonald, John. Caporetto & the Isonzo Campaign: The Italian Front 1915-1918. 2012. (Illus.). 208p. 39.95 ***(978-1-84884-671-5(1))*** Pen & Sword Bks. Ltd. GBR. Dist: Casemate Pubs. & Bk. Distributors, LLC.

Morselli, Mario. Caporetto 1917: Victory or Defeat? 2007. CLXXXVIp. 39.95 *(978-0-415-44937-3(5))* Routledge.

CAPOTE, TRUMAN, 1924-1984

Baumli, Diana. Truman Capote, The Fascination of Gothic: Gothic Characters & Motifs Inspired by Reality. 2008. 68p. pap. *(978-3-639-07024-8(0))* VDM Verlag Dr. Mueller e.K.

Bloom, Harold, ed. Truman Capote, New Edition. 2nd rev. ed. 2009. (Bloom's Modern Critical Views Ser.). 216p. (C). (gr. 9-18). 45.00 *(978-1-60413-398-1(8)*, Chelsea Hse.) Facts On File, Inc.

Center for Learning Staff. The Member of the Wedding/A Christmas Memory: Curriculum Unit. 2007. (Novel Ser.). 65p. (YA). spiral bd. 19.95 *(978-1-56077-850-9(4))* Center for Learning, The.

Clarke, Gerald. Capote: A Biography. 2010. (ENG., Illus.). 656p. pap. 17.99 *(978-1-4391-8750-0(9))* Simon & Schuster.

—Truman Capote. Pozanco, Victor, tr. 2006. (SPA & ENG.). 624p. per. 18.95 *(978-84-666-2061-9(8))* Ediciones B ESP. Dist: Independent Pubs. Group.

Davis, Deborah. Party of the Century: The Fabulous Story of Truman Capote & His Black & White Ball. 2007. (ENG., Illus.). 320p. per. 17.95 *(978-0-470-09821-9(X)*, Wiley) Wiley, John & Sons, Inc.

Gale, Robert L. Truman Capote Encyclopedia. 2010. (ENG., Illus.). 187p. 75.00 *(978-0-7864-4296-6(4))* McFarland & Co., Inc. Pubs.

Guest, David. Sentenced to Death: The American Novel & Capital Punishment. 2007. (ENG.). 179p. per. 25.00 *(978-1-60473-015-9(3))* Univ. Pr. of Mississippi.

Long, Robert Emmet & Long. Truman Capote, Enfant Terrible. 2008. (ENG.). 144p. 24.95 *(978-0-8264-2763-2(4))* Continuum International Publishing Group, Ltd. GBR. Dist: National Bk. Network.

Moates, Marianne. Truman Capote's Southern Years: Stories from a Monroeville Cousin. 2008. (ENG., Illus.). 256p. pap. 19.95 *(978-0-8173-5527-2(8))* Univ. of Alabama Pr.

Rudisill, Marie. Fruitcake: Heirloom Recipes & Memories of Truman Capote & Cousin Sook. 2010. (ENG., Illus.). 80p. pap. 15.00 *(978-0-8078-9930-4(5))* Univ. of North Carolina Pr.

Schultz, William Todd. Tiny Terror: Why Truman Capote (Almost) Wrote Answered Prayers. 2011. (Inner Lives Ser.). (ENG.). 190p. 17.95 *(978-0-19-975204-1(4))* Oxford Univ. Pr., Inc.

Voss, Ralph F. Truman Capote & the Legacy of In Cold Blood. 2011. ***(978-0-8173-8588-0(6))*** Univ. of Alabama Pr.

—Truman Capote & the Legacy of In Cold Blood. 3rd ed. 2011. (ENG., Illus.). 264p. 34.95 ***(978-0-8173-1756-0(2))*** Univ. of Alabama Pr.

CAPPADOCIAN LANGUAGE

Limberis, Vasiliki. Architects of Piety: The Cappadocian Fathers & the Cult of the Martyrs. 2011. (ENG., Illus.). 256p. 74.00 *(978-0-19-973088-9(1))* Oxford Univ. Pr., Inc.

CAPPELLA SISTINA (VATICAN PALACE, VATICAN CITY)

Blech, Benjamin & Doliner, Roy. The Sistine Secrets: Michelangelo's Forbidden Messages in the Heart of the Vatican. (ENG.). 336p. 2009. pap. 19.99 *(978-0-06-146905-3(X))* 2008. (Illus.). 26.95 *(978-0-06-146904-6(1))* HarperCollins Pubs. (HarperOne).

Graham-Dixon, Andrew. Michelangelo & the Sistine Chapel. 2009. 240p. 24.95 *(978-1-60239-358-4(0))* Skyhorse Publishing Co., Inc.

Panyard, Christine M. & Michelangelo Buonarroti. A Biblical Tour Through the Sistine Chapel: Celebrating 500 Years under the Ceiling of Michelangelo. 2011. (Illus.). 96p. *(978-0-8091-0593-9(4))* Paulist Pr.

Pfeiffer, Heinrich W. The Sistine Chapel. Lindberg, Steven, tr. from ITA. 2007. (ENG., Illus.). 352p. 125.00 *(978-0-7892-0934-4(9))* Abbeville Pr., Inc.

CAPRA, FRANK, 1897-1991

McBride, Joseph. Frank Capra: The Catastrophe of Success. 2011. (ENG., Illus.). 800p. pap. 40.00 *(978-1-60473-838-4(3))* Univ. Pr. of Mississippi.

CAPRI AUTOMOBILE

Morgan Jones, Martyn. Ford Capri. 2011. (Haynes Enthusiast Guide Ser.). (ENG., Illus.). 160p. 34.95 *(978-1-84425-637-2(5)*, 1844256375) Haynes Publishing PLC GBR. Dist: MBI Distribution Services/Quayside Distribution.

Robson, Graham. Ford Capri. 2008. (Crowood Autoclassics Ser.). (ENG., Illus.). 192p. 34.95 *(978-1-86126-978-2(1)*, 1861269781) Crowood Pr., Ltd. GBR. Dist: MBI Distribution Services/Quayside Distribution.

CAPRI ISLAND (ITALY)

Bonechi, Casa. Art & History of Capri: English Edition. pap. *(978-88-7009-281-3(X))* Casa Editrice Bonechi.

Capri. 64p. *(978-88-8029-510-5(1))* Casa Editrice Bonechi.

Fiori, Pamela. In the Spirit of Capri. 2009. 144p. *(978-2-7594-0406-3(4))* Assouline.

Fisher, Robert. Close to Paradise: The Gardens of Naples, Capri & the Amalfi Coast. 2011. (ENG., Illus.). 208p. 45.00 *(978-0-7112-3038-5(2))* Lincoln, Frances Ltd. GBR. Dist: Perseus-PGW.

Fodor's Travel Publications, Inc. Staff. The Amalfi Coast, Capri & Naples. 6th ed. 2011. (Fodor's Ser.). (ENG., Illus.). 392p. pap. 22.99 *(978-0-679-00933-7(7)*, Fodor's) Fodor's Travel Pubns.

Gold Guide to Capri. (Illus.). 96p. 12.95 *(978-88-7009-860-0(5))* Casa Editrice Bonechi ITA. Dist: CPG Publishing, Inc.

Swallow, Nicky. Frommer's the Amalfi Coast with Naples, Capri & Pompeii. 4th ed. 2012. (Frommer's Color Complete Ser.). (ENG., Illus.). 384p. pap. 21.99 ***(978-1-118-07467-1(X)***, Frommers) Wiley, John & Sons, Inc.

CAPS AND GOWNS
see Academic Costume

CAPSAICIN

Salazar, Mario Alfonso & Ortega, Jose Miguel. Peppers: Nutrition, Consumption, & Health. 2012. ***(978-1-61942-085-4(6))*** Nova Science Pubs., Inc.

CAPTAINS OF SHIPS
see Ship Captains

CAPTIVATE (COMPUTER PROGRAM)

Huettner, Brenda. Adobe Captivate 3: The Definitive Guide. 2008. (ENG., Illus.). 442p. pap. 32.95 *(978-1-59822-049-0(7))* Jones & Bartlett Learning, LLC.

—Adobe Captivate 4: The Definitive Guide. rev. ed. 2009. 464p. pap. 44.95 *(978-0-7637-8137-8(1))* Jones & Bartlett Learning, LLC.

Siegel, Kevin A. Essentials of Adobe Captivate 2: Skills & Drills Workbook. 2006. 264p. spiral bd., training bk. ed. 35.00 *(978-1-932733-12-9(4))* IconLogic, Inc.

—Essentials of Adobe Captivate 3: Skills & Drills Workbook. 2007. (Illus.). 298p. spiral bd. 35.00 *(978-1-932733-17-4(5))* IconLogic, Inc.

Virtual Training Company, prod. Adobe Captivate 2. 2007. cd-rom 99.95 *(978-1-933736-86-2(6))* VTC, Inc.

CAPTIVITIES, INDIAN
see Indian Captivities

CAPTURE AT SEA
see Enemy Property; Privateering; Prize Law

CAPTURED PROPERTY
see Enemy Property

CAPUCHIN MONKEYS

Perry, Susan & Manson, Joseph H. Manipulative Monkeys: The Capuchins of Lomas Barbudal. 2011. (ENG., Illus.). 368p. pap. 22.95 *(978-0-674-06038-8(5))* Harvard Univ. Pr.

Rogers, Ellen. Kasey to the Rescue: The Remarkable Story of a Monkey & a Miracle. 2010. (ENG.). 288p. 23.99 *(978-1-4013-2341-7(3))* Hyperion Pr.

CAPUCHINS

Crosby, Michael. Thank God Ahead of Time. 2009. 320p. pap. 16.95 *(978-0-86716-919-5(2))* Franciscan Media.

Falanga, Agostino. The Venerable Maria Lorenza Longo: Foundress of the Hospital of the Incurables & of the Capuchin Poor Clares of Naples, 1463-1542. Giannone, Ronald, tr. from ITA. 2009. (Illus.). 176p. pap. 18.95 *(978-0-8091-4595-9(2))* Paulist Pr.

Odell, Catherine M. Solanus Casey: The Story of Father Solanus. rev. ed. 2007. (Illus.). 266p. per. 14.95 *(978-1-59276-181-4(X))* Our Sunday Visitor, Publishing Div.

Pio, Padre. Words of Light: Inspiration from the Letters of Padre Pio. 2008. (ENG.). 206p. 23.95 *(978-1-55725-569-3(5))* Paraclete Pr., Inc.

—Words of Light: Inspiration from the Letters of Padre Pio. 2009. (ENG.). 206p. (gr. 13). pap. 14.99 *(978-1-55725-643-0(8))* Paraclete Pr., Inc.

Tosti, Mario. La Chiesa Sul Fiume: La Missione Dei Cappuccini Dell'Umbria in Amazzonia, 1909-2009. 2010. (ITA., Illus.). 363p. *(978-88-88001-68-5(9))* Ist. Storico dei Cappuccini.

Treece, Patricia, compiled by. Quiet Moments with Padre Pio: 120 Daily Readings. 2007. 123p. per. 10.99 *(978-0-86716-841-9(2)*, Servant Bks.) Franciscan Media.

CAPUCHINS (MAMMALS)
see Capuchin Monkeys

CAR BUYING
see Automobiles—Purchasing

CAR SERVICE (FREIGHT)
see Railroads—Freight

CAR WORKERS
see Railroads—Employees

CARAIB INDIANS
see Carib Indians

CARAIB LANGUAGE
see Carib Language

CARATHEODORY MEASURE

Cushman, Richard H. Geometry of Nonholonomically Constrained Systems, Vol. 26. 2009. (Illus.). 424p. 111.00 *(978-981-4289-48-1(5))* World Scientific Publishing Co., Inc.

CARAVAGGIO, MICHELANGELO MERISI DA, 1573-1610

Bal, Mieke. Quoting Caravaggio. *(978-0-8047-3210-9(8))* Stanford Univ. Pr.

Caravaggio, Michelangelo Merisi da, et al. Caravaggio & Painters of Realism in Malta. Sciberras, Keith & de Giorgio, Cynthia, eds. 2007. (ENG., Illus.). 236p. (C). pap. 90.00 *(978-99932-7-163-5(2))* Midsea Bks. Ltd. MLT. Dist: Brown, David Bk. Co., The.

—Caravaggio & Paintings of Realism in Malta. 2007. (ENG., Illus.). 236p. (C). 112.00 *(978-99932-7-162-8(4))* Midsea Bks. Ltd. MLT. Dist: Brown, David Bk. Co., The.

Debobno, Sandro. Understanding Caravaggio & His Art in Malta. 2007. 56p. (C). pap. 9.95 *(978-99932-7-164-2(0))* Midsea Bks. Ltd. MLT. Dist: Brown, David Bk. Co., The.

Dette, Gabriel, et al, eds. Caravaggio in Holland: Musik und Genre bei Caravaggio und den Utrechter Caravaggisten. 2009. (GER., Illus.). 192p. (C). pap. 59.00 *(978-3-7774-8065-7(7))* Hirmer Verlag GmbH DEU. Dist: Brown, David Bk. Co., The.

Ebert-Schifferer, Sybille. Caravaggio: The Artist & His Work. 2012. (ENG., Illus.). 320p. 59.95 ***(978-1-60606-095-7(3)***, J. Paul Getty Museum) Getty Pubns.

Franklin, David & Schütze, Sebastian. Caravaggio & His Followers in Rome. 2011. (Illus.). x, 333p. ***(978-0-88884-891-8(9))*** Yale Univ. Pr.

Franklin, David & Schutze, Sebastian. Caravaggio & His Followers in Rome. 2011. (ENG., Illus.). 224p. 50.00 *(978-0-300-17072-6(6))* Yale Univ. Pr.

Franklin, David & Schütze, Sebastian. Caravaggio & les Peintres Caravagesques à Rome. 2011. (FRE., Illus.). x, 333p. ***(978-0-88884-892-5(7))*** Yale Univ. Pr.

Fried, Michael. The Moment of Caravaggio. 2010. (A. W. Mellon Lectures in the Fine Arts Ser.). (ENG., Illus.). 328p. 49.50 *(978-0-691-14701-7(9))* Princeton Univ. Pr.

Graham-Dixon, Andrew. Caravaggio: A Life Sacred & Profane. 2011. (ENG., Illus.). 514p. 39.95 *(978-0-393-08149-7(4)*, 8149) Norton, W. W. & Co., Inc.

Gregori, Mina, et al. The First Medusa: Caravaggio. 2012. (Illus.). 160p. 75.00 *(978-88-7439-582-8(5))* 5 Continents ITA. Dist: Abrams.

Harr, Jonathan. The Lost Painting: The Quest for a Caravaggio Masterpiece. 2006. (ENG.). 320p. pap. 16.00 *(978-0-375-75986-4(7)*, Random Hse. Trade Paperbacks) Random House Publishing Group.

Hout, Guus van den. The Last Caravaggio. Treffers, Bert, ed. 2011. (ENG., Illus.). 96p. pap. 37.50 *(978-90-400-7794-4(0))* Waanders B.V., Uitgeverij NLD. Dist: National Bk. Network.

Hunt, Patrick. Caravaggio. (Life & Times Ser.). (Illus.). 192p. 15.95 *(978-1-904341-74-1(8))* Haus Publishing GBR. Dist: Consortium Bk. Sales & Distribution.

Jover, Manuel. Caravaggio. 2007. (Illus.). 256p. pap. *(978-2-87939-322-3(1))* Terrail, Pierre Editions.

Konig, Eberhard. Caravaggio: Michelangelo Merisi Da: 1571-1610. 2008. (Masters of Italian Art Ser.). (Illus.). 140p. pap. 9.95 *(978-0-8416-0077-5(5))* American Map Corp.

Néret, Gilles & Caravaggio, Michelangelo Merisi da. Caravaggio. 2010. (25 Ser.). (ENG., Illus.). 96p. 14.99 *(978-3-8365-2381-3(7))* TASCHEN DEU. Dist: Ingram Pub. Services.

Nicolson, Benedict. Caravaggism in Europe, 3 vols. Vertova, Luisa, ed. 2nd ed. (Illus.). 1020p. *(978-88-422-0233-2(9))* Allemandi.

Patrizi, M. L. & Witting, Felix. Caravaggio. 2012. (Mega Square Ser.). (ENG., Illus.). 256p. 12.95 ***(978-1-906981-43-3(4))*** Parkstone Pr. USA, Ltd.

Pericolo, Lorenzo. Caravaggio & Pictorial Narrative. 2011. (Studies in Baroque Art Ser.). (ENG., Illus.). 654p. (C). 290.00 *(978-1-905375-48-6(4))* Miller, Harvey Pubs. GBR. Dist: Brown, David Bk. Co., The.

Prose, Francine. Caravaggio: Painter of Miracles. 2010. (ENG., Illus.). 160p. pap. 13.99 *(978-0-06-176890-3(1)*, HarperPerennial) HarperCollins Pubs.

Rowland, Ingrid D. Caravaggio in One Square Mile. 2006. 184p. 20.00 *(978-0-226-73021-9(2))* Univ. of Chicago Pr.

Saggio, Antonino. The Instrument of Caravaggio. 2010. 42p. pap. 9.34 *(978-1-4461-2228-0(X))* Lulu Enterprises Inc.

Schutze, Sebastian. Caravaggio: Complete Work. 2009. (ENG., Illus.). 306p. 150.00 *(978-3-8365-0183-5(X))* TASCHEN DEU. Dist: Ingram Pub. Services.

Spike, John T. Caravaggio. rev. ed. 2010. (ENG., Illus.). 280p. 95.00 *(978-0-7892-1059-3(2))* Abbeville Pr., Inc.

Strinati, Claudio, et al, eds. Caravaggio. 2010. (Illus.). 247p. 70.00 *(978-88-572-0458-1(8))* Skira Editore ITA. Dist: Random Hse., Inc.

Strinati, Claudio Massimo, et al. Caravaggio Bacon. 2010. (ITA & ENG., Illus.). 224p. 60.00 *(978-88-7179-623-9(3)*, Ore Cultura Srl (Acc)) Antique Collectors' Club GBR. Dist: National Bk. Network.

Varriano, John. Caravaggio: The Art of Realism. (Illus.). 2010. (ENG.). 304p. pap. 40.95 *(978-0-271-02718-0(5))* 2006. 272p. 75.00 *(978-0-271-02717-3(7))* Pennsylvania State Univ. Pr.

Vodret Adamo, Rossella. Caravaggio: The Mystery of the Two Saint Francis in Meditation. 2009. (Illus.). 70p. *(978-88-366-1611-4(9))* Silvana.

Vodret Adamo, Rossella & Caravaggio, Michelangelo Merisi da. I Doppi Di Caravaggio: Il Mistero Svelato Dei Due San Francesco in Meditazione. 2010. (ITA., Illus.). 77p. *(978-88-498-2822-1(5))* Rubbettino.

Vodret, Rossella, ed. & text. Caravaggio: The Complete Works, 1 vol. 2010. (ENG.). 216p. 60.00 *(978-88-366-1662-6(3))* Silvana ITA. Dist: D.A.P./Distributed Art Pubs.

VV Staff. Caravaggio. (Colección Art Book). (SPA., Illus.). 144p. (Orig.). *(978-84-8156-182-1(7))* Sociedad Editorial Electa Espana ESP. Dist: Lectorum Pubns., Inc.

Warwick, Genevieve & Caravaggio, Michelangelo Merisi da. Caravaggio: Realism, Rebellion, Reception. 2007. (University of Delaware Press Studies in 17th- & 18th- Century Art & Culture). (Illus.). 145p. 52.50 *(978-0-87413-936-5(8))* Univ. of Delaware Pr.

Whitfield, Clovis. Caravaggio's Eye. 2011. (ENG., Illus.). 264p. 65.00 *(978-1-907372-10-0(5))* Holberton, Paul Publishing GBR. Dist: Univ. of Washington Pr.

Witting, Felix & Patrizi, M. L. Micheli da Carravaggio. 2012. (Best Of Ser.). (ENG., Illus.). 200p. 19.95 ***(978-1-906981-83-9(3))*** Parkstone Pr. USA, Ltd.

Zuffi, Stefano. Caravaggio: Masters of Art. 2012. (Illus.). 160p. pap. 12.95 ***(978-3-7913-4656-4(3))*** Prestel Publishing.

Zuffi, Stefano, text. Discovering Caravaggio: The Art Lover's Guide to Understanding the Paintings. 2010. (ENG., Illus.). 256p. 45.00 *(978-0-8478-3529-4(4))* Rizzoli International Pubns., Inc.

CARAVAN SITES
see Trailer Camps

CARAVANS

Field-Lewis, Jane & Haddon, Chris. My Cool Caravan: All You Need to Know about Retro Caravans. 2010. (ENG., Illus.). 160p. 24.95 *(978-1-86205-878-1(4))* Chrysalis Children's Bks. GBR. Dist: Independent Pubs. Group.

Hammond, Richard. A Short History of Caravans in the UK. (ENG.). 2010. 144p. pap. 16.95 *(978-0-7538-2671-3(2)*, Phoenix) 2009. (Illus.). 140p. 24.95 *(978-0-297-84446-4(6))* Orion Publishing Group, Ltd. GBR. Dist: Independent Pubs. Group.

Rockel, Stephen J. Carriers of Culture: Labor on the Road in Nineteenth-Century East Africa, 1 vol. 2006. (Social History of Africa Ser.). (Illus.). 368p. per. 41.25 *(978-0-325-07133-6(0)*, E07133) Heinemann.

Rockel, Stephen J., ed. Carriers of Culture: Labor on the Road in Nineteenth-Century East Africa, 1 vol. 2006. (Social History of Africa Ser.). (Illus.). 368p. 124.95 *(978-0-325-07116-9(0)*, E07116, Praeger Pubs.) Greenwood Publishing Group, Inc.

CARAVANS (TRAILERS)
see Mobile Homes; Travel Trailers

CARBANIONS

Snieckus, Victor, ed. Advances in Carbanion Chemistry, Vol. 3. Date not set. 109.50 *(978-0-7623-0344-1(1)*, JAI Pr.) Elsevier Science & Technology Bks.

CARBAZOLE

Adhikari, Ravi & Neckers, Douglas C. Carbazole-Based Emitting Compounds. 2010. 192p. pap. *(978-3-639-24918-7(6))* VDM Verlag Dr. Mueller e.K.

CARBENES

Anwarul Haque, Rosenani S.M. Metal Complexes of N-Heterocyclic Carbene. 2009. 164p. pap. *(978-3-639-18404-4(1))* VDM Verlag Dr. Mueller e.K.

Cazin, Catherine S. J. Heterocyclic Carbenes in Transition Metal Catalysis & Organocatalysis. 2010. (Catalysis by Metal Complexes Ser.). (ENG., Illus.). xvi, 336p. 189.00 *(978-90-481-2865-5(X)*, 904812865X) Springer.

Dötz, Karl Heinz. Metal Carbenes in Organic Synthesis. 2010. (Topics in Organometallic Chemistry Ser.). (ENG., Illus.). ix, 377p. pap. 449.00 *(978-3-642-06003-8(X)*, 364206003X) Springer.

Díez-González, Silvia & Royal Society of Chemistry Staff. N-Heterocyclic Carbenes: From Laboratory Curiosities to Efficient Synthetic Tools. 2010. (RSC Catalysis Ser.). (ENG., Illus.). 468p. (C). 195.00 ***(978-1-84973-042-6(3))*** Royal Society of Chemistry, The GBR. Dist: Ingram Pub. Services.

Gillingham, Dennis. A Synthesis of Baconipyrone Through New Catalytic Asymmetric Methods. 2008. 148p. pap. *(978-3-8364-9216-4(4))* VDM Verlag Dr. Mueller e.K.

Glorius, Frank. N-Heterocyclic Carbenes in Transition Metal Catalysis. 2010. (Topics in Organometallic Chemistry Ser.). xii, 231p. pap. 319.00 *(978-3-642-07197-3(X)*, 364207197X) Springer.

—N-Heterocyclic Carbenes (NHC) in Transition Metal Catalysis. 2006. (Topics in Organometallic Chemistry Ser.: Vol. 21). (Illus.). xii, 231p. 319.00 *(978-3-540-36929-5(5)*, 3540369295) Springer.

C

McGuinness, David. Heterocyclic Carbene Complexes. 2010. 172p. pap. *(978-3-8383-2136-3(7))* Lambert Academic Publishing.

Nolan, Steven P., ed. N-Heterocyclic Carbenes in Synthesis. 2006. (ENG., Illus.). 319p. 229.00 *(978-3-527-31400-3(8)*, Wiley-VCH) Wiley, John & Sons, Inc.

O'Brien, Julie S. Main Group Compounds with P-Conjugated Nitrogen Support. 2009. 120p. pap. *(978-3-639-18779-3(2))* VDM Verlag Dr. Mueller e.K.

CARBIDES

see also Silicon Carbide

Gusev, A. I., et al. Disorder & Order in Strongly Nonstoichiometric Compounds: Transition Metal Carbides, Nitrides & Oxides. 2010. (Springer Series in Materials Science Ser.). (Illus.). xv, 607p. pap. 199.00 *(978-3-642-07524-7(X)*, 364207524X) Springer.

Kriven, Waltraud M., et al. Strategic Materials & Computational Design. 2010. (Ceramic Engineering & Science Proceedings Ser.: 538). (ENG.). 204p. 89.95 *(978-0-470-92191-3(9)*, Wiley-American Ceramic Society) Wiley, John & Sons, Inc.

Technology Research Editors, ed. Cemented Carbides for Cutting Tool Applications in Metal, 2007 Ed. 2007. pap. 128.50 *(978-1-60030-438-5(9)*, Search-In-Print) CSA Journal Division.

Vanger, Sofia H. Silicon Carbide: New Materials, Production Methods & Applications. 2011. (Series: Materials Science & Technologies Ser.). 129.00 *(978-1-61122-312-5(1))* Nova Science Pubs., Inc.

CARBINES

see Rifles

CARBOHYDRATE METABOLISM

see Carbohydrates—Metabolism

CARBOHYDRATES

see also Dextran; Food—Carbohydrate Content; Low-Carbohydrate Diet
also names of compounds belonging to this group, e.g. Cellulose, Dextrose

BeMiller, James N. & Whistler, Roy Lester. Carbohydrate Chemistry for Food Scientists. 2nd ed. 2007. (Illus.). 389p. *(978-1-891127-53-3(5))* AACC International.

Bewley, C. A. Protein-Carbohydrate Interactions in Infectious Diseases. 2006. (RSC Biomolecular Sciences Ser.). (ENG., Illus.). 364p. 232.00 *(978-0-85404-802-1(2)*, 0854048022) Royal Society of Chemistry, The GBR. Dist: Ingram Pub. Services.

Brand-Miller, Jennie, et al. The Low GI Handbook: The New Glucose Revolution Guide to the Long-Term Health Benefits of Low GI Eating. 2010. (ENG.). 400p. pap. 16.95 *(978-0-7382-1389-7(6))* Da Capo Pr., Inc.

Brockhausen, Inka, ed. Glycobiology Protocols. 2010. (Methods in Molecular Biology Ser.). (Illus.). 400p. pap. 179.00 *(978-1-61737-638-2(8)*, 1617376388) Humana Pr.

Bucke, Christopher, ed. Carbohydrate Biotechnology Protocols. 2010. (Methods in Biotechnology Ser.). (Illus.). 352p. pap. 149.00 *(978-1-61737-074-8(6)*, 1617370746) Humana Pr.

Chen, Xi, et al. Chemical Glycobiology I: Glycoconjugates & Carbohydrate — Protein Interactions. 2008. (ACS Symposium Ser.). (ENG., Illus.). 340p. 175.00 *(978-0-8412-7440-2(1))* American Chemical Society.

Chevolot, Yann, ed. Carbohydrate Microarrays: Methods & Protocols. 2011. (Methods in Molecular Biology Ser.). (ENG., Illus.). xvi, 427p. 139.00 ***(978-1-61779-372-1(8)**, 1617793728)* Humana Pr.

Codee, Jeroen & Marel, Gijsbert van der. Carbohydrate Chemistry Vol. 2: Proven Synthetic Methods. 2012. (Carbohydrate Chemistry Ser.). (ENG., Illus.). 500p. 149.95 ***(978-1-4398-7594-0(4)**, CRC Press)* Taylor & Francis Group GBR. Dist: Taylor & Francis Group.

Complex Carbohydrate Therapeutics Market: Companies-Products-Services. 325p. (Orig.). pap. *(978-0-7605-2327-8(4))* Rector Pr., Ltd.

Corfield, Anthony P., ed. Glycoprotein Methods & Protocols: The Mucins. 2010. (Methods in Molecular Biology Ser.). 528p. pap. 189.00 *(978-1-61737-149-3(1)*, 1617371491) Humana Pr.

Coxon, James Morriss, ed. Advances in Carbocation Chemistry, Vol. 3. Date not set. 109.50 *(978-0-7623-0345-8(X)*, JAI Pr.) Elsevier Science & Technology Bks.

Demchenko, Alexei V., ed. Frontiers in Modern Carbohydrate Chemistry. 2007. (ACS Symposium Ser.). (ENG., Illus.). 448p. (C). 165.00 *(978-0-8412-3970-8(3))* American Chemical Society.

Eggleston, Gillian & Vercellotti, John R. Industrial Application of Enzymes on Carbohydrate Based Materials. 2007. (ACS Symposium Ser.). (ENG., Illus.). 260p. (C). 135.00 *(978-0-8412-7406-8(1))* American Chemical Society.

El Ashry, E. S. H. Heterocycles from Carbohydrate Precursors. 2007. (Topics in Heterocyclic Chemistry Ser.). (Illus.). xii, 354p. 499.00 *(978-3-540-72956-3(9))* Springer.

El Ashry, El Sayed H. Heterocycles from Carbohydrate Precursors. 2010. (Topics in Heterocyclic Chemistry Ser.). (Illus.). xii, 354p. pap. 499.00 *(978-3-642-09205-3(5)*, 3642092055) Springer.

Finch, P., ed. Carbohydrates: Structures, Syntheses & Dynamics. 2010. 352p. pap. 198.00 *(978-90-481-4033-6(1)*, 9048140331) Springer.

Fukuda, Minoru, contrib. by. Glycobiology, Pt. A. 2010. (ENG., Illus.). 664p. 187.00 *(978-0-12-381001-4(9)*, Academic Pr.) Elsevier Science & Technology Bks.

Gabius, Hans-Joachim, ed. Sugar Code: Fundamentals of Glycosciences. 2009. (ENG., Illus.). 597p. 95.00 *(978-3-527-32089-9(X)*, Wiley-VCH) Wiley, John & Sons, Inc.

Garg, Hari G., et al, eds. Carbohydrate Chemistry, Biology & Medical Applications. 2008. (ENG.). 432p. 136.00 *(978-0-08-054816-6(4)*, Elsevier Science) Elsevier Science & Technology Bks.

Grunwald, Peter, ed. Carbohydrate-Modifying Biocatalysts. 2011. (ENG., Illus.). 846p. 299.95 *(978-981-4241-67-0(9))* Pan Stanford Publishing SGP. Dist: Taylor & Francis Group.

Guo, Zhongwu & Boons, Geert-Jan, eds. Carbohydrate-Based Vaccines & Immunotherapies. 2009. (Wiley Series in Drug Discovery & Development Ser.: 8). (ENG., Illus.). 416p. 139.00 *(978-0-470-19756-1(0)*, Wiley) Wiley, John & Sons, Inc.

Horton, Derek. Advances in Carbohydrate Chemistry & Biochemistry. (ENG.). 2011. 338p. 241.00 ***(978-0-12-385518-3(7))*** 2011. 314p. 241.00 *(978-0-12-385520-6(9))* 2010. 562p. 241.00 *(978-0-12-380854-7(5))* 2010. 456p. 241.00 *(978-0-12-380856-1(1))* 2009. 422p. 241.00 *(978-0-12-374743-3(0))* 2007. 460p. 241.00 *(978-0-12-373920-9(9))* Elsevier Science & Technology Bks. (Academic Pr.).

Hounsell, Elizabeth F., ed. Glycoanalysis Protocols. 2nd ed. 2010. (Methods in Molecular Biology Ser.). 272p. pap. 119.00 *(978-1-61737-016-8(9)*, 1617370169) Humana Pr.

Huang, Xuefei & Barchi, Joseph J. Petite & Sweet: Glyco-Nanotechnology As a Bridge to New Medicines. 2012. (ACS Symposium Ser.: 1091). (ENG.). 240p. 150.00 ***(978-0-8412-2688-3(1))*** American Chemical Society.

Ito, Ryouichi & Matsuo, Youta, eds. Handbook of Carbohydrate Polymers: Development, Properties & Applications. 2010. (Polymer Science & Technology Ser.). 295.00 *(978-1-60876-367-2(6))* Nova Science Pubs., Inc.

Kamerling, J. P. Comprehensive Glycoscience: From Chemistry to Systems Biology, 4 Vols., Set. 2007. 4000p. 1595.00 *(978-0-444-51967-2(X)*, Elsevier Science) Elsevier Science & Technology Bks.

—Comprehensive Glycoscience Set: From Chemistry to Systems Biology, 4 vols. 2007. (ENG., Illus.). 3600p. 2195.00 *(978-0-444-52746-2(X)*, Elsevier Science) Elsevier Science & Technology Bks.

Kovac, Paul, ed. Carbohydrate Chemistry: Proven Synthetic Methods. 2011. (Carbohydrate Chemistry Ser.). (ENG., Illus.). 468p. 149.95 *(978-1-4398-6689-4(9)*, CRC Press) Taylor & Francis Group GBR. Dist: Taylor & Francis Group.

Lawoko, Martin. Lignin Carbohydrate Complexes in Softwood & Chemical Pulps: Characterisation, Structure & Reactivity. 2008. 68p. pap. *(978-3-639-10239-0(8))* VDM Verlag Dr. Mueller e.K.

Li, Jianjun, ed. Functional Glycomics: Methods & Protocols. 2009. (Methods in Molecular Biology Ser.). (ENG., Illus.). xi, 284p. 119.00 *(978-1-60761-453-1(7)*, 1607614537) Humana Pr.

Lindhorst, Thisbe K. Essentials of Carbohydrate Chemistry & Biochemistry. 3rd ed. 2007. (ENG., Illus.). 332p. pap. 90.00 *(978-3-527-31528-4(4)*, Wiley-VCH) Wiley, John & Sons, Inc.

McDougall, John & McDougall, Mary. The Starch Solution: Eat the Foods You Love, Regain Your Health, & Lose the Weight for Good! 2012. (ENG.). 368p. 26.99 ***(978-1-60961-393-8(7))*** Rodale Pr., Inc.

Miljkovic, Momcilo. Carbohydrates: Synthesis, Mechanisms, & Stereoelectronic Effects. 2009. (ENG., Illus.). x, 450p. 199.00 *(978-0-387-92264-5(4)*, 0387922644) Springer.

Moreira, Susana. Carbohydrate Binding Modules: Functions & Applications. Gama, Miguel, ed. 2010. (Biotechnology in Agriculture, Industry & Medicine Ser.). 76p. pap. 43.00 *(978-1-60876-979-7(8))* Nova Science Pubs., Inc.

Narain, Ravin, ed. Engineered Carbohydrate-Based Materials for Biomedical Applications: Polymers, Surfaces, Dendrimers, Nanoparticles, & Hydrogels. 2011. (ENG., Illus.). 424p. 125.00 *(978-0-470-47235-4(9)*, Wiley) Wiley, John & Sons, Inc.

Packer, Nicolle & Karlsson, Niclas G. Glycomics. 2009. (Methods in Molecular Biology Ser.). (Illus.). xiv, 389p. 129.00 *(978-1-58829-774-7(8))* Humana Pr.

Packer, Nicolle H. & Karlsson, Niclas G., eds. Glycomics: Methods & Protocols. 2010. (Methods in Molecular Biology Ser.). (Illus.). xiv, 386p. pap. 129.00 ***(978-1-61737-769-3(4)**, 1617377694)* Humana Pr.

Patton, R. The Paradox of Animal Nutrition: Perfected by Lack, Beset by Excess. 2011. (ENG., Illus.). 278p. pap. 24.00 *(978-1-904761-72-3(0))* Nottingham Univ. Pr. GBR. Dist: Independent Pubs. Group.

Penades, Soledad. Host-Guest Chemistry: Mimetic Approaches to Study Carbohydrate Recognition. 2010. (Topics in Current Chemistry Ser.). (Illus.). x, 241p. pap. 269.00 *(978-3-642-07566-7(5)*, 3642075665) Springer.

Rauter, Amélia P., et al, eds. Carbohydrates in Sustainable Development I, 2 vols. 2010. (Topics in Current Chemistry Ser.). (Illus.). xiv, 200p. 299.00 *(978-3-642-14836-1(0)*, 3642148360) Springer.

—Carbohydrates in Sustainable Development II, 2 vols. 2010. (Topics in Current Chemistry Ser.). (Illus.). xi, 201p. 299.00 *(978-3-642-15160-6(4)*, 3642151604) Springer.

Rauter, Amélia Pilar. Carbohydrate Chemistry. 2011. (Specialist Periodical Reports). (ENG., Illus.). 410p. 480.00 ***(978-1-84973-154-6(3))*** Royal Society of Chemistry, The GBR. Dist: Ingram Pub. Services.

Rauter, Amélia Pilar & Royal Society of Chemistry Staff. Carbohydrate Chemistry. Lindhorst, Thisbe, ed. 2010. (Specialist Periodical Reports). (ENG., Illus.). 208p. 480.00 ***(978-1-84755-044-6(4))*** Royal Society of Chemistry, The GBR. Dist: Ingram Pub. Services.

Rosati, Kitty Gurkin. The Rice Diet Renewal: A Healing 30-Day Program for Lasting Weight Loss. 2010. (ENG., Illus.). 304p. 25.95 *(978-0-470-52544-9(4)*, Wiley) Wiley, John & Sons, Inc.

Sinnott, Michael L. Carbohydrate Chemistry & Biochemistry: Structure & Mechanisms. 2007. (ENG., Illus.). 766p. (C). 115.00 ***(978-0-85404-256-2(3))*** Royal Society of Chemistry, The GBR. Dist: Ingram Pub. Services.

Statz, Arnold E., ed. Glycoscience: Epimerisation, Isomerisation & Rearrangement Reactions of Carbohydrates. 2010. (Topics in Current Chemistry Ser.). (Illus.). xii, 351p. pap. 419.00 *(978-3-642-07465-3(0)*, 3642074650) Springer.

Stick, Robert V. & Williams, Spencer. Carbohydrates: The Essential Molecules of Life. 2nd ed. 2008. (ENG., Illus.). 496p. 93.95 *(978-0-240-52118-3(8)*, Elsevier Science) Elsevier Science & Technology Bks.

Stulik, Jiri, et al, eds. BSL3 & BSL4 Agents: Proteomics, Glycomics, & Antigenicity. 2011. (ENG., Illus.). 256p. 139.95 ***(978-3-527-32780-5(0)**, Wiley-VCH)* Wiley, John & Sons, Inc.

Sugrue, Richard J., ed. Glycovirology Protocols. 2010. (Methods in Molecular Biology Ser.). (Illus.). 256p. pap. 129.00 *(978-1-61737-664-1(7)*, 1617376647) Humana Pr.

Thibault, Pierre & Honda, Susumu, eds. Capillary Electrophoresis of Carbohydrates. 2010. (Methods in Molecular Biology Ser.). (Illus.). 318p. pap. 129.00 *(978-1-61737-206-3(4)*, 1617372064) Humana Pr.

Volpi, Nicola, ed. Capillary Electrophoresis of Carbohydrates: From Monosaccharides to Complex Polysaccharides. 2010. (ENG., Illus.). xiii, 277p. 209.00 *(978-1-60761-874-4(5)*, 1607618745) Humana Pr.

Wang, Binghe & Boons, Geert-Jan, eds. Carbohydrate Recognition: Biological Problems, Methods, & Applications. 2011. (Wiley Series in Drug Discovery & Development Ser.: 13). (ENG., Illus.). 448p. 135.00 *(978-0-470-59207-6(9)*, Wiley) Wiley, John & Sons, Inc.

Wang, Ping, Slim & Recovered: With the Qualitative Method. 2010. 184p. pap. 63.00 *(978-1-4269-2773-7(8))* Trafford Publishing.

Wong, Simon & Arsequell, Gemma, eds. Immunobiology of Carbohydrates. 2010. (Molecular Biology Intelligence Unit Ser.). 332p. pap. 189.00 *(978-1-4419-3414-7(6)*, 1441934146) Springer.

Wu, Albert M. The Molecular Immunology of Complex Carbohydrates-3. 2011. (Illus.). xxxv, 809p. ***(978-1-4419-7877-6(1))*** Springer.

Wu, Albert M., ed. The Molecular Immunology of Complex Carbohydrates-3. 2011. (Advances in Experimental Medicine & Biology Ser.). (Illus.). xxxv, 809p. 279.00 *(978-1-4419-7876-9(3)*, 1441978763) Springer.

Yeo, Wee Kian & Hawley, John A. Nutrient Availability & Skeletal Muscle Training Adaptation: Interactions of Nutrient Availability & Endurance Training on Skeletal Muscle Adaptation. 2011. 136p. pap. ***(978-3-639-29867-3(5))*** VDM Verlag Dr. Mueller e.K.

CARBOHYDRATES—METABOLISM

Abdelaleim, Elsayed & Ewald, Komor. Sugarcane Yellow Leaf Virus. 2011. 112p. pap. ***(978-3-639-29946-5(9))*** VDM Verlag Dr. Mueller e.K.

Candy, David J. Biological Functions of Carbohydrates. 2007. (ENG., Illus.). 208p. per. 92.00 *(978-0-216-91011-9(0))* Springer.

Elwins, Dannie. Secrets to Handling & Controlling Your Glycemic Index. 2009. 36p. pap. 16.99 *(978-0-557-15749-5(8))* Lulu Enterprises Inc.

Garg, Hari G., et al, eds. Carbohydrate Chemistry, Biology & Medical Applications. 2008. (ENG.). 432p. 136.00 *(978-0-08-054816-6(4)*, Elsevier Science) Elsevier Science & Technology Bks.

Tate, Suresh. Metabolism of Carbohydrates: Glucose Homeostasis in Fasting & Diabetes. 2012. (Colloquium Series on the Cell Biology of Medicine Ser.). 100p. pap. 35.00 *(978-1-61504-300-2(4))* Morgan & Claypool Life Science Publishers.

CARBOHYDRATES IN HUMAN NUTRITION

Barbosa, Aneli M., et al. Bioactive Oligosaccharides: Production, Biological Functions & Potential Commercial Applications. 2010. (Biotechnology in Agriculture, Industry & Medicine Ser.). 75p. pap. 43.00 *(978-1-61668-149-4(7))* Nova Science Pubs., Inc.

Biliaderis, Costas G. & Izydorczyck, Marta S., eds. Functional Food Carbohydrates. 2006. (Functional Foods & Nutraceuticals Ser.). (ENG., Illus.). 570p. 167.95 *(978-0-8493-1822-1(X)*, 1822, CRC Press) Taylor & Francis Group GBR. Dist: Taylor & Francis Group.

Brand-Miller, Jennie & Foster-Powell, Kaye. The New Glucose Revolution Shopper's Guide to GI Values 2010: The Authoritative Source of Glycemic Index Values for More Than 1,000 Foods. 2010. (Glucose Revolution Ser.). (ENG.). 304p. 7.99 *(978-0-7382-1368-2(3))* Da Capo Pr., Inc.

Cheung. Living with Glycaemic Factor. 2007. 128p. pap. 13.95 *(978-0-85969-975-4(7)*, Sheldon Press) SPCK Publishing GBR. Dist: Westminster John Knox Pr.

Churms, Shirley C. & Ravenscroft, Neil. Chromatographic Analysis of Carbohydrates. 2008. (Illus.). 420p. 159.95 *(978-0-8493-7068-7(X))* CRC Pr. LLC.

Conrad, Kendall. Eat Well, Feel Well: More Than 150 Delicious Specific Carbohydrate Diet - Compliant Recipes. 2010. (ENG.). 240p. pap. 16.00 *(978-0-307-59060-2(7)*, Three Rivers Pr.) Crown Publishing Group.

Garg, Hari G., et al, eds. Carbohydrate Chemistry, Biology & Medical Applications. 2008. (ENG.). 432p. 136.00 *(978-0-08-054816-6(4)*, Elsevier Science) Elsevier Science & Technology Bks.

Kress, Diane. The Metabolism Miracle: 3 Easy Steps to Regain Control of Your Weight... Permanently. 2009. (ENG.). 320p. 25.00 *(978-0-7382-1277-7(6))* Da Capo Pr., Inc.

Montignac, Michel. French Diet, 1 vol. 2010. (ENG., Illus.). 255p. 24.99 *(978-2-35934-040-2(9))* Alpen Editions FRA. Dist: Innovative Logistics.

Taubes, Gary. Good Calories, Bad Calories: Fats, Carbs, & the Controversial Science of Diet & Health. 2008. (Vintage Ser.). (ENG.). 640p. pap. 17.00 *(978-1-4000-3346-1(2)*, Vintage) Knopf Doubleday Publishing Group.

Wolever, Thomas M. S. The Glycaemic Index: A Physiological Classification of Dietary Carbohydrate. 2010. (Illus.). 240p. pap. 57.50 *(978-1-84593-722-5(8))* CABI GBR. Dist: Stylus Publishing, LLC.

CARBOHYDRATES IN THE BODY

Candy, David J. Biological Functions of Carbohydrates. 2007. (ENG., Illus.). 208p. per. 92.00 *(978-0-216-91011-9(0))* Springer.

Elwins, Dannie. Secrets to Handling & Controlling Your Glycemic Index. 2009. 36p. pap. 16.99 *(978-0-557-15749-5(8))* Lulu Enterprises Inc.

Zhang, Lijuan. Glycosaminoglycans in Development, Health & Disease. 2010. (ENG.). 408p. 161.00 *(978-0-12-381282-7(8)*, Academic Pr.) Elsevier Science & Technology Bks.

CARBON

see also Charcoal; Coal; Diamonds; Fullerenes; Graphite

Agarwal, Arvind, et al. Carbon Nanotubes: Reinforced Metal Matrix Composites. 2010. (Nanomaterials & their Applications Ser.). (ENG., Illus.). 325p. 159.95 *(978-1-4398-1149-8(0)*, CRC Press) Taylor & Francis Group GBR. Dist: Taylor & Francis Group.

Agrawal, Pratik. Review of Carbon Markets. 2011. 64p. pap. ***(978-3-8443-0677-4(3))*** Lambert Academic Publishing.

Ali, Nasar, et al. Carbon Based Nanomaterials. 2010. (Illus.). 322p. pap. *(978-0-87849-155-1(4))* Trans Tech Pubns., Ltd.

American Carbon Society Staff, compiled by. International Conference on Carbon (Carbon 2007) 2008. 2369p. pap. 150.00 *(978-1-60423-946-1(8))* Curran Assocs., Inc.

Bandaru, Prabhakar R., et al. Nanotubes, Nanowires, Nanobelts & Nanocoils — Promise, Expectations & Status: Symposium Held December 1-4, 2008, Boston, Massachusetts, U.S.A. 2009. (MRS Proceedings Ser.). (ENG., Illus.). 235p. (C). 125.00 *(978-1-60511-114-8(7))* Materials Research Society.

Baranowski, Bogdan, et al, eds. Carbon Nanomaterials in Clean Energy Hydrogen Systems. 2008. (NATO Science for Peace & Security Series C: Environmental Security Ser.). (Illus.). xxxiv, 910p. 299.00 *(978-1-4020-8896-4(5))*; pap. 139.00 *(978-1-4020-8897-1(3))* Springer.

Barsukov, Igor V., et al, eds. New Carbon Based Materials for Electrochemical Energy Storage Systems. 2006. (NATO Science Ser.: Vol. 229). (Illus.). xxiv, 523p. 289.00 *(978-1-4020-4810-4(6)*, 1402048106); XXIV, 524p. pap. 149.00 *(978-1-4020-4811-1(4)*, 1402048114) Springer.

Bellucci, Stefano, ed. Physical Properties of Ceramic & Carbon Nanoscale Structures: The INFN Lectures, Vol. II. 2011. (Lecture Notes in Nanoscale Science & Technology Ser.). (ENG., Illus.). xiv, 280p. 129.00 *(978-3-642-15777-6(7)*, 3642157777) Springer.

Belval, Brian. The Carbon Elements: Carbon, Silicon, Germanium, Tin, Lead. 2009. (Understanding the Elements of the Periodic Table Ser.). (ENG., Illus.). 48p. (YA). (gr. 5-9). lib. bdg. 26.50 *(978-1-4358-5334-8(2))* Rosen Publishing Group, Inc., The.

Bennett, Charles J. & Whiting, Meredith. Managing for a Carbon-Concerned Future: A Decision-Making Framework. 2007. (Illus.). 65p. *(978-0-8237-0896-3(9))* Conference Board, Inc., The.

Boeckl, John J., et al, eds. Fundamentals of Low-Dimensional Carbon Nanomaterials: Volume 1284. 2011. (MRS Proceedings Ser.). (Illus.). 200p. (C). 109.00 ***(978-1-60511-261-9(5))*** Cambridge Univ. Pr.

Bosch, Pedro. El Carbono: Cuentos Orientales. (Ciencia para Todos Ser.). (SPA.). pap. 6.99 *(978-968-16-4733-9(5))* Fondo de Cultura Economica USA.

Botti, Sabina. Physical Properties of Carbon Nanotube. 2007. (Illus.). 107p. *(978-81-7895-282-6(3))* Transworld Research Network.

Clearing the Smoke: Understanding the Impacts of Black Carbon Pollution: Hearing Before the Select Committee on Energy Independence & Global Warming, House of Representatives, One Hundred Eleventh Congress, Second Session, March 16, 2010. 2010. (Illus.). iii, 116p. ***(978-0-16-087581-6(1)**, 552-070-42212-9)* United States Government Printing Office.

Colombo, Luciano & Fasolino, Anna Lisa, eds. Computer-Based Modeling of Novel Carbon Systems & Their Properties: Beyond Nanotubes. 2010. (Carbon Materials: Chemistry & Physics Ser.). (ENG., Illus.). 250p. 159.00 *(978-1-4020-9717-1(4)*, 1402097174) Springer.

Donaldson, Kenneth, et al, eds. The Toxicology of Carbon Nanotubes. 2012. (ENG., Illus.). 264p. 140.00 ***(978-1-107-00837-3(9))*** Cambridge Univ. Pr.

Fiorito, Silvana. Carbon Nanotubes: Angels or Demons? 2008. (ENG., Illus.). 164p. pap. 119.95 *(978-981-4241-01-4(6))* Pan Stanford Publishing SGP. Dist: Taylor & Francis Group.

Furimsky, Edward. Carbons & Carbon Supported Catalysts in Hydroprocessing. 2008. (RSC Catalysis Ser.). (ENG., Illus.). 174p. (C). 160.00 ***(978-0-85404-143-5(5))*** Royal Society of Chemistry, The GBR. Dist: Ingram Pub. Services.

Gelencsér, András. Carbonaceous Aerosol. 2010. (Atmospheric & Oceanographic Sciences Library). ix, 350p. pap. 189.00 *(978-90-481-6740-1(X)*, 904816740X) Springer.

Gössling, Stefan. Carbon Management in Tourism: Mitigating the Impacts on Climate Change. 2011. (Routledge International Series in Tourism, Business & Management Ser.). (ENG., Illus.). 368p. (C). 155.00 *(978-0-415-56632-2(0))*; pap. 59.95 *(978-0-415-56633-9(9))* Routledge.

Grady, Brian P. Carbon Nanotube-Polymer Composites: Manufacture, Properties, & Applications. 2011. (ENG., Illus.). 352p. 125.00 *(978-0-470-59641-8(4)*, Wiley) Wiley, John & Sons, Inc.

Guldi, Dirk M. & Martín, Nazario, eds. Carbon Nanotubes & Related Structures: Synthesis, Characterization, Functionalization, & Applications. 2010. (ENG., Illus.). 562p. 215.00 *(978-3-527-32406-4(2)*, Wiley-VCH) Wiley, John & Sons, Inc.

Harris, Peter J. F. Carbon Nanotube Science: Synthesis, Properties & Applications. 2nd rev. ed. (ENG.). 2011. 313p. pap. 39.99 (978-0-521-53585-4(9)) 2009. (Illus.). 314p. 87.00 (978-0-521-82895-6(3)) Cambridge Univ. Pr.

Hierold, Christofer. Carbon Nanotube Devices: Properties, Modeling, Integration & Applications. 2008. (Advanced Micro & Nanosystems Ser.). (ENG., Illus.). 376p. 260.00 (978-3-527-31720-2(1), Wiley-VCH) Wiley, John & Sons, Inc.

Hoffman, Andrew J. Carbon Strategies: How Leading Companies Are Reducing Their Climate Change Footprint. 2007. (ENG., Illus.). 192p. pap. 37.50 (978-0-472-03265-5(8)) Univ. of Michigan Pr.

Javey, Ali & Kong, Jing, eds. Carbon Nanotube Electronics. 2008. (Series on Integrated Circuits & Systems Ser.). 350p. 129.00 (978-0-387-36833-7(7), 0387368337) Springer.

Jenkins, G. M. & Kawamura, K. Polymeric Carbons: Carbon Fibre, Glass & Char. 2011. (ENG.). 188p. pap. 26.99 (978-0-521-10678-6(8)) Cambridge Univ. Pr.

Jorio, Ado, et al., eds. Carbon Nanotubes: Advanced Topics in the Synthesis, Structure, Properties & Applications. 2010. (Topics in Applied Physics Ser.). (Illus.). xxiv, 720p. pap. 269.00 (978-3-642-09195-7(4), 3642091954) Springer.

—Carbon Nanotubes: Advanced Topics in the Synthesis, Structure, Properties & Applications. 2008. (Topics in Applied Physics Ser.). (Illus.). 720p. 269.00 (978-3-540-72864-1(3)) Springer.

Koning, Cor, et al, eds. Polymer Carbon Nanotube Composites. 2012. (ENG., Illus.). 256p. 149.95 (978-981-4310-93-2(X)) Pan Stanford Publishing SGP. Dist: Taylor & Francis Group.

Kutsch, Werner, et al, eds. Soil Carbon Dynamics: An Integrated Methodology. 2010. (ENG., Illus.). 298p. 110.00 (978-0-521-86561-6(1)) Cambridge Univ. Pr.

Leonard, Francois. The Physics of Carbon Nanotube Devices. 2008. (Micro & Nano Technologies Ser.). (ENG., Illus.). 300p. 165.00 (978-0-8155-1573-9(1)) William Andrew, Inc.

Loiseau, Annick, et al, eds. Understanding Carbon Nanotubes: From Basics to Applications. (Lecture Notes in Physics Ser.). (Illus.). xvi, 555p. 2010. pap. 199.00 (978-3-642-06598-9(8), 3642065988) 2006. (ENG., 199.00 (978-3-540-26922-9(3), 3540269223) Springer.

Lorenz, Klaus & Lal, Rattan. Carbon Sequestration in Forest Ecosystems. 2009. (ENG., Illus.). xix, 277p. 199.00 (978-90-481-3265-2(7), 9048132657) Springer.

MacKenzie, Fred T., ed. Carbon in the Geobiosphere: Earth's Outer Shell. 2006. (Topics in Geobiology Ser.). (Illus.). 402p. 269.00 (978-1-4020-4044-3(X), 140204044X) Springer.

Mahler, Erne & Seiler, Detlev. Carbon Nanotube & Nanocomposite Research. 2011. (Materials Science & Technologies/Nanotechnology Science & Technology Ser.). 111p. 95.00 (978-1-61470-510-9(0)) Nova Science Pubs., Inc.

Marsh, Harry & Rodríguez Reinoso, Francisco. Activated Carbon. 2006. (ENG., Illus.). 554p. 250.00 (978-0-08-044463-5(6), Elsevier Science) Elsevier Science & Technology Bks.

McNally, T. & Potschke, P., eds. Polymer Carbon Nanotube Composites: Preparation, Properties & Applications. 2011. (Woodhead Publishing in Materials Ser.). (ENG., Illus.). 848p. 305.00 (978-1-84569-761-7(8)) Woodhead Publishing Ltd. GBR. Dist: Ingram Pub. Services.

Messina, Giacomo & Santangelo, Saveria, eds. Carbon: The Future Material for Advanced Technology Applications. 2010. (Topics in Applied Physics Ser.). (Illus.). xxii, 529p. pap. 299.00 (978-3-642-06733-4(6), 3642067336) Springer.

Mirabella, Salvo. Self-Interstitial Diffusion & Clustering in Crystalline Si. 2010. 236p. pap. (978-3-8383-9023-0(1)) Lambert Academic Publishing.

Monthioux, Marc. Carbon Meta-Nanotubes: Synthesis, Properties & Applications. 2012. (ENG., Illus.). 448p. 165.00 (978-0-470-51282-1(2), Wiley) Wiley, John & Sons, Inc.

Nemes, Laszlo. Spectroscopy, Dynamics & Molecular Theory of Carbon Plasmas & Vapors: Advances in the Understanding of the Most Complex High-Temperature Elemental System. 2011. (Illus.). 500p. 138.00 (978-981-283-764-6(7)) World Scientific Publishing Co., Inc.

Oâ€(tm)Connell, Michael J. Carbon Nanotubes: Properties, Applications, & Commercialization. 2nd rev. ed. 2012. (Illus.). 525p. 119.95 (978-1-4398-1320-1(5), CRC Press) Taylor & Francis Group GBR. Dist: Taylor & Francis Group.

Osawa, Eiji, ed. Perspectives of Fullerene Nanotechnology. 2012. (ENG., Illus.). 400p. pap. 182.00 (978-90-481-5766-2(8), 9048157668) Springer.

Ottenhouse, Avery P., ed. Carbon Nanotubes: New Research. 2009. 98.00 (978-1-60692-236-1(X)) Nova Science Pubs., Inc.

Pastorin, Giorgia, ed. Carbon Nanotubes: From Bench Chemistry to Promising Biomedical Applications. 2011. (ENG., Illus.). 156p. 129.95 (978-981-4241-68-7(7)) Pan Stanford Publishing SGP. Dist: Taylor & Francis Group.

Peng, Kem. Processing Carbon Nanotube/Thermoplastic Composites. 2009. 112p. pap. (978-3-639-13028-7(6)) VDM Verlag Dr. Mueller e.K.

Pribat, Didier, et al. Carbon Nanotubes, Graphene, & Associated Devices IV. 2011. (Proceedings of SPIE Ser.). 94p. pap. 80.00 (978-0-8194-8711-7(2)) SPIE.

Radovic, Ljubisa R., ed. Chemistry & Physics Carbon. 2012. (Chemistry & Physics of Carbon Ser.). (ENG., Illus.). 360p. 199.95 (978-1-4398-2094-0(5), CRC Press) Taylor & Francis Group GBR. Dist: Taylor & Francis Group.

—Chemistry & Physics of Carbon, Volume 30, Vol. 30. 2007. (Chemistry & Physics of Carbon Ser.). (ENG., Illus.). 264p. 205.95 (978-1-4200-4298-6(X), CRC Press) Taylor & Francis Group GBR. Dist: Taylor & Francis Group.

Rafii-Tabar, Hashem. Computational Physics of Carbon Nanotubes. 2007. (Illus.). 504p. 130.00 (978-0-521-85300-2(1)) Cambridge Univ. Pr.

Rafii-Tabar, Hashem & Rafii-Tabar, H. Computational Physics of Carbon Nanotubes. 2009. (Illus.). 508p. pap. 69.00 (978-0-521-11571-1(X)) Cambridge Univ. Pr.

Razeghi, M., et al. Carbon Nanotubes & Associated Devices: 10-12 August 2008, San Diego, California, USA. 2008. (Proceedings of SPIE Ser.). (Illus.). 322p. pap. 105.00 (978-0-8194-7257-1(3)) SPIE.

—Carbon Nanotubes, Graphene, & Associated Devices II: 5-6 August 2009, San Diego, California, United States. 2009. (Proceedings of SPIE Ser.). (Illus.). 114p. pap. 80.00 (978-0-8194-7689-0(7)) SPIE.

Rietmeijer, Frans J. M., ed. Natural Fullerenes & Related Structures of Elemental Carbon. 2010. (Developments in Fullerene Science Ser.). xxii, 295p. pap. 219.00 (978-90-481-7054-8(0), 9048170540) Springer.

Rodrigues, Joo & Domingos, Tiago M. D. Carbon Responsibility & Embodied Emissions: Theory & Measurement. 2008. (Routledge Studies in Ecological Economics Ser.). (Illus.). 288p. 120.00 (978-0-415-47020-9(X)) Routledge.

Saito, Susumu & Zettl, Alex. Carbon Nanotubes: Quantum Cylinders of Graphene. 2008. (Contemporary Concepts of Condensed Matter Science Ser.: 3). (ENG.). 232p. 205.00 (978-0-444-53276-3(5), Elsevier Science) Elsevier Science & Technology Bks.

Saito, Yahachi. Carbon Nanotube & Related Field Emitters: Fundamentals & Applications. 2010. (ENG.). 288p. 180.00 (978-0-470-82417-7(4), Wiley) Wiley, John & Sons, Inc.

Saito, Yahachi, ed. Carbon Nanotube & Related Field Emitters: Fundamentals & Applications. 2010. (ENG., Illus.). 504p. 175.00 (978-3-527-32734-8(7), Wiley-VCH) Wiley, John & Sons, Inc.

Serp, Philippe & Figueiredo, José Luís, eds. Carbon Materials for Catalysis. 2008. (ENG., Illus.). 579p. 178.00 (978-0-470-17885-0(X), Wiley) Wiley, John & Sons, Inc.

Servantie, James. Dynamics & Friction in Double Walled Carbon Nanotubes. 2009. 184p. pap. (978-3-8364-6421-5(7)) VDM Verlag Dr. Mueller e.K.

Shima, Hiroyuki & Sato, Motohiro, eds. Elastic & Plastic Deformation of Carbon Nanotubes. 2012. (ENG.). 300p. 149.95 (978-981-4310-75-8(1)) Pan Stanford Publishing SGP. Dist: Taylor & Francis Group.

Sibler, Sabine. Analyzes of the Carbon Fluxes in a Central Brazilian Floodplain. 2008. 80p. pap. (978-3-639-09115-1(9)) VDM Verlag Dr. Mueller e.K.

Stoft, Steven. Carbonomics: How to Fix the Climate & Charge It to OPEC. 2008. (Illus.). viii, 297p. pap. (978-0-9818775-0-1(8)) Heaphy, Mary Lou Pubns.

Sun, Xiaogang. Aligned Carbon Nanotubes. 2011. 64p. pap. (978-3-8443-8694-3(7)) Lambert Academic Publishing.

Tagmatarchis, Nikos, ed. Advances in Carbon Nanomaterials: Science & Applications. 2012. (ENG., Illus.). 400p. 149.95 (978-981-4267-87-8(2)) Pan Stanford Publishing SGP. Dist: Taylor & Francis Group.

Tjong, Sie Chin, et al. Carbon Nanotube Reinforced Composites: Metal & Ceramic Matrices. 2009. (ENG., Illus.). 242p. 220.00 (978-3-527-40892-4(4), Wiley-VCH) Wiley, John & Sons, Inc.

Wu, Wan-Yu. Metal-Containing Hydrogenated Amorphous Carbon Thin Films. 2009. 192p. pap. (978-3-639-14095-8(8)) VDM Verlag Dr. Mueller e.K.

Yoshimura, Susumu & Chang, R. P. H., eds. Supercarbon: Synthesis, Properties & Applications. 2010. (Springer Series in Materials Science Ser.). (Illus.). xvi, 250p. pap. 219.00 (978-3-642-08405-8(2), 3642084052) Springer.

Zhou, Xinjian. Carbon Nanotube Transistors, Sensors, & Beyond. 2008. 196p. pap. (978-3-639-08891-5(3)) VDM Verlag Dr. Mueller e.K.

CARBON—ISOTOPES

see also Radiocarbon Dating

Heys, J. Richard, et al. Preparation of Compounds Labeled with Tritium & Carbon-14. 2009. (ENG., Illus.). 682p. 210.00 (978-0-470-51607-2(0), Wiley) Wiley, John & Sons, Inc.

Mikhova, Bozhana. Organic Metalloid Compounds: Subvolume D: NMR Data for Carbon-13, Part 6. Lechner, Manfred Dieter & Gupta, Vandana, eds. 2011. (Landolt-Börnstein: Numerical Data & Functional Relationships in Science & Technology - New Series / Physical Chemistry Ser.). (ENG.). viii, 230p. 4989.00 (978-3-642-14248-2(6), 3642142486) Springer.

Vlad, Daniela. Mudgases Geochemistry & Factors Controlling Their Variability. 2010. 420p. pap. (978-3-639-24265-2(3)); 316p. pap. (978-3-639-25351-1(5)) VDM Verlag Dr. Mueller e.K.

West, Jason B., et al, eds. Isoscapes: Understanding movement, pattern, & process on Earth through isotope Mapping. 2009. (ENG., Illus.). xxiv, 487p. 79.00 (978-90-481-3353-6(X), 904813353X) Springer.

CARBON—SPECTRA

see also Radiocarbon Dating

West, Jason B., et al, eds. Isoscapes: Understanding movement, pattern, & process on Earth through isotope Mapping. 2009. (ENG., Illus.). xxiv, 487p. 79.00 (978-90-481-3353-6(X), 904813353X) Springer.

CARBON, ACTIVATED

Abu Foul, Ahmed. Physical-Chemical Treatment of Stabilized Leachate. 2011. 324p. pap. (978-3-8443-3004-5(6)) Lambert Academic Publishing.

Aghamohammadi, Nasrin. Leachate Treatment Using Powdered Activated Carbon- Activated Sludge. 2010. 172p. pap. (978-3-639-22460-3(4)) VDM Verlag Dr. Mueller e.K.

Cecen, Ferhan & Aktas, Özgür. Activated Carbon for Water & Wastewater Treatment: Integration of Adsorption & Biological Treatment. 2011. (ENG., Illus.). 406p. 155.00 (978-3-527-32471-2(2), Wiley-VCH) Wiley, John & Sons, Inc.

Committee to Examine the Disposal of Activated Carbon from the Heating, Ventilation, and Air Conditioning Systems at Chemical Agent Disposal Facilities & National Research Council Staff. The Disposal of Activated Carbon from Chemical Agent Disposal Facilities. 2009. (ENG.). 86p. pap. 21.00 (978-0-309-13818-5(3)) National Academies Pr.

Ilango, siva & Ilango, Siva. Adsorption & Activated Carbons. 2011. 212p. pap. (978-3-8433-8531-2(9)) Lambert Academic Publishing.

Kwiatkowski, James F., ed. Activated Carbon: Classifications, Properties & Applications. 2011. (Chemical Engineering Methods & Technology Ser.). (Illus.). xv, 555p. 129.00 (978-1-61209-684-1(0)) Nova Science Pubs., Inc.

Terranova, Maria Letizia, et al, eds. Carbon Nanomaterials for Gas Adsorption. 2012. (ENG.). 300p. 149.95 (978-981-4316-43-9(1)); 149.95 (978-981-4361-43-9(7)) Pan Stanford Publishing SGP. Dist: Taylor & Francis Group.

CARBON-BLACK

Sager, Tina. Defining the Role of Particle Surface Area in Pulmonary Toxicity - an Examination of the Pulmonary Toxicity of Ultrafine & Fine-Sized Carbon Black. 2008. 264p. pap. (978-3-639-11090-6(0)) VDM Verlag Dr. Mueller e.K.

Sanders, Ian J. & Peeten, Thomas L. Carbon Black: Production, Properties & Uses. 2011. (Materials Science & Technologies Ser.). (Illus.). 305p. 129.00 (978-1-61209-535-6(6)) Nova Science Pubs., Inc.

CARBON COMPOUNDS

see also Organic Compounds

Akiba, Kin-ya. Organo Main Group Chemistry. 2011. (ENG., Illus.). 285p. pap. 79.95 (978-0-470-45033-8(9), Wiley) Wiley, John & Sons, Inc.

Bauhofer, C. Compounds with 1 to 7 Carbon Atoms: Index of Organic Compounds, Vol. 3J. 2008. (Landolt-Börnstein: Numerical Data & Functional Relationships in Science & Technology Ser.). (Illus.). 7279.00 (978-3-540-73081-1(8), 3540730818) Springer.

Bauhofer, C., et al. Compounds with 1 to 7 Carbon Atoms. 2007. (Landolt-Börnstein: Numerical Data & Functional Relationships in Science & Technology Ser.). (Illus.). vi, 382p. 5199.00 (978-3-540-23066-3(1), 3540230661) Springer.

—Compounds with 8 to 12 Carbon Atoms (Supplement to Subvolume B & E) 2007. (Landolt-Börnstein: Numerical Data & Functional Relationships in Science & Technology Ser.). (Illus.). vi, 517p. 7400.00 (978-3-540-27307-3(7), 3540273077) Springer.

BCC Research Staff. Diamond & Diamond-like & CBN Films & Coating Products. 2007. per. 4250.00 (978-1-59623-305-8(2)) BCC Research.

Beguin, Francois & Frackowiak, Elzbieta. Carbons for Electrochemical Energy Storage & Conversion Systems. 2009. (Advanced Materials & Technologies Ser.). (ENG., Illus.). 529p. 154.95 (978-1-4200-5307-4(8), CRC Press) Taylor & Francis Group GBR. Dist: Taylor & Francis Group.

Carbon Nanotubes: Technologies & Commercial Prospects. 2007. per. 4250.00 (978-1-59623-283-9(8)) BCC Research.

Chauvin, Remi & Canac, Yves. Transition Metal Complexes of Neutral eta1-Carbon Ligands. 2010. (Topics in Organometallic Chemistry Ser.). (ENG.). xi, 256p. 359.00 (978-3-642-04721-3(1), 3642047211) Springer.

Delhaès, Pierre. Solids & Carbonated Materials. 2010. (Iste Ser.: 480). (ENG., Illus.). 650p. 211.00 (978-1-84821-200-8(3), Wiley-ISTE) Wiley, John & Sons, Inc.

Fiorito, Silvana. Carbon Nanotubes: Angels or Demons? 200p. 59.00 (978-981-270-710-9(7)) World Scientific Publishing Co., Inc.

Goruganthu, Srikanth. Degradation of Carbon/Epoxy Composites Due to Environmental Effects. 2010. 100p. pap. (978-3-639-24002-3(2)) VDM Verlag Dr. Mueller e.K.

Haley, Michael M. & Tykwinski, Rik R., eds. Carbon-Rich Compounds: From Molecules to Materials. 2006. 663p. 230.00 (978-3-527-60799-0(4), Wiley-VCH) Wiley, John & Sons, Inc.

Hirota, E., et al, contrib. by. Molecules containing Five or More Carbon Atoms. 2007. (Landolt-Börnstein: Numerical Data & Functional Relationships in Science & Technology - New Series / Molecules & Radicals Ser.). viii, 229p. 3750.00 (978-3-540-44741-2(5), 3540447415) Springer.

—Molecules containing Three or Four Carbon Atoms. 2007. (Landolt-Börnstein: Numerical Data & Functional Relationships in Science & Technology - New Series / Molecules & Radicals Ser.). viii, 187p. 3100.00 (978-3-540-44739-9(3), 3540447393) Springer.

Hirota, E., et al. Molecules containing One or Two Carbon Atoms: (Supplement to II/7, II/15, II/21, II/23, II/25) 2006. (Landolt-Börnstein: Numerical Data & Functional Relationships in Science & Technology Ser.). viii, 192p. 2849.00 (978-3-540-37488-6(4), 3540374884) Springer.

Krüger, Anke. Carbon Materials & Nanotechnology. 2010. (ENG., Illus.). 490p. pap. 115.00 (978-3-527-31803-2(8), Wiley-VCH) Wiley, John & Sons, Inc.

Meijere, Armin De. Carbon Rich Compounds I. 2010. (Topics in Current Chemistry Ser.). (Illus.). xi, 231p. pap. 289.00 (978-3-642-08381-5(1), 3642083811) Springer.

Sabetraftar, Karim. Comparison of GPP & Hydrological Organic Carbon Flux: A Catchment Scale Approach. 2010. 432p. pap. (978-3-8383-0069-6(6)) Lambert Academic Publishing.

Saddow, Stephen E. Silicon Carbide Biotechnology: A Biocompatible Semiconductor for Advanced Biomedical Devices & Applications. 2011. (ENG., Illus.). 495p. 195.95 (978-0-12-385906-8(9), Elsevier Science) Elsevier Science & Technology Bks.

Sharon, et al. Carbon Nano Forms & Applications. 2009. (ENG., Illus.). 544p. 150.00 (978-0-07-163960-6(8), 0071639608) McGraw-Hill Professional Publishing.

Shuai, Zhigang, et al. Theory of Charge Transport in Carbon Electronic Materials. 2012. (SpringerBriefs in Molecular Science Ser.). (ENG., Illus.). ix, 90p. pap. 49.95 (978-3-642-25075-0(0), 3642250750) Springer.

Veziroglu, T. Nejat, et al, eds. Hydrogen Materials Science & Chemistry of Carbon Nanomaterials. 2007. (NATO Science for Peace & Security Series / NATO Science for Peace & Security Series A: Chemistry & Biology Ser.). XLI, 878p. pap. 159.00 (978-1-4020-5513-3(7), 1402055137); xli, 878p. 249.00 (978-1-4020-5512-6(9), 1402055129) Springer.

Vigalok, Arkadi, ed. C-X Bond Formation. 2010. (Topics in Organometallic Chemistry Ser.). (ENG., Illus.). xi, 187p. 299.00 (978-3-642-12072-5(5), 3642120725) Springer.

Yudin, Andrei K., ed. Catalyzed Carbon-Heteroatom Bond Formation. 2010. (ENG., Illus.). 522p. 215.00 (978-3-527-32428-6(3), Wiley-VCH) Wiley, John & Sons, Inc.

CARBON DATING

see Radiocarbon Dating

CARBON DIOXIDE

Abdulagatov, Aziz I., et al, eds. Binary Aqueous & CO2 Containing Mixtures & the Krichevskii Parameter. 2010. (Chemistry Research & Applications Ser.). 235p. pap. 43.00 (978-1-60876-990-2(9)) Nova Science Pubs., Inc.

Al-Fattah, Saud M., et al. Carbon Capture & Storage: Technologies, Policies, Applications & Implementation Strategy. 2011. (ENG.). 404p. 159.95 (978-0-415-62084-0(8), CRC Press) Taylor & Francis Group GBR. Dist: Taylor & Francis Group.

Alexander, Ralph B. Global Warming False Alarm: The Bad Science Behind the United Nations' Assertion that Man-made CO2 Causes Global Warming. 2009. (Illus.). 178p. pap. 18.95 (978-0-9840989-0-3(9)) Canterbury Publishing.

Andersen, Mikael Skou & Ekins, Paul, eds. Carbon-Energy Taxation: Lessons from Europe. 2010. (ENG., Illus.). 256p. 99.00 (978-0-19-957068-3(X)) Oxford Univ. Pr., Inc.

Approaching Midnight: Oversight of the Bush Administration's Last Minute Rulemakings: Hearing Before the Select Committee on Energy Independence & Global Warming, House of Representatives, One Hundred Tenth Congress, Second Session, December 11, 2008. 2010. (Illus.). iii, 131p. (978-0-16-087415-4(7), 552-070-42108-4) United States Government Printing Office.

Aresta, M., ed. Carbon Dioxide Recovery & Utilization. 2010. (Illus.). 384p. pap. 169.00 (978-90-481-6335-9(8), 9048163358) Springer.

Aresta, Michele, ed. Carbon Dioxide as Chemical Feedstock. 2010. (ENG., Illus.). 414p. 215.00 (978-3-527-32475-0(5), Wiley-VCH) Wiley, John & Sons, Inc.

Aydiner, Kerim, et al. Carbon Dioxide Storage in Geological Medi. 2011. 68p. pap. (978-3-8443-0522-7(X)) Lambert Academic Publishing.

Balaban, Murat O. & Ferrentino, Giovanna, eds. Dense Phase Carbon Dioxide: Food & Pharmaceutical Applications. 2012. (ENG.). 336p. 199.95 (978-0-8138-0649-5(6), Wiley-Blackwell) Wiley, John & Sons, Inc.

Bernard, James P. Technological Issues in Carbon Capture. 2011. (Energy Policies, Politics & Prices Ser.). 89.00 (978-1-61122-845-8(X)) Nova Science Pubs., Inc.

Berners-Lee, Mike. How Bad Are Bananas? The Carbon Footprint of Everything 1 vol. 2011. (ENG., Illus.). 240p. pap. 16.95 (978-1-55365-831-3(0), Greystone Bks.) D&M Pubs. Inc. CAN. Dist: Perseus-PGW.

Bolland, Olav. Power Generation: CO2 Capture & Storage. 2009. 416p. 150.00 (978-0-470-77071-9(6), Wiley) Wiley, John & Sons, Inc.

Bond, Patrick, et al, eds. Climate Change, Carbon Trading & Civil Society: Negative Returns on South African Investments. 2009. 231p. pap. 38.95 (978-1-86914-141-7(5)) Univ. of Natal Pr. ZAF. Dist: International Specialized Bk. Services.

Bond, Patrick & Dada, Rehana, eds. Climate Change, Carbon Trading & Civil Society: Negative Returns on South African Investments. 2007. 208p. pap. (978-1-86914-123-3(7)) University of Kwazulu-Natal Press ZAF. Dist: International Specialized Bk. Services.

Boykoff, Maxwell, ed. The Politics of Climate Change: A Survey. 2009. (Illus.). 320p. 260.00 (978-1-85743-496-5(0)) Routledge.

Brassington, Mark. How to Go Carbon Neutral: A Practical Guide to Treading More Lightly upon the Earth. 2008. (Illus.). 119p. pap. (978-1-84528-250-9(7)) How To Books.

Bulkeley, Harriet A., et al, eds. Cities & Low Carbon Transitions. 2011. (Routledge Studies in Human Geography Ser.). (ENG., Illus.). 256p. (C). 140.00 (978-0-415-58697-9(6)) Routledge.

Cap, Auction, & Trade: Auctions & Revenue Recycling under Carbon Cap & Trade: Hearing Before the Select Committee on Energy Independence & Global Warming, House of Representatives, One Hundred Tenth Congress, Second Session, January 23, 2008. 2010. (Illus.). iii, 217p. (978-0-16-086997-6(8), 552-070-41856-3) United States Government Printing Office.

Carbon Capture & Sequestration Legislation: Hearing Before the Committee on Energy & Natural Resources, United States Senate, One Hundred Twelfth Congress, First Session, to Receive Testimony on Carbon Capture & Sequestration Legislation, Including S. 699 & S. 757, May 12, 2011. 2011. iii

44p. *(978-0-16-089022-2(5)*, 552-070-43054-7) United States Government Printing Office.

Carbon Dioxide. 73p. pap. *(978-0-662-13649-1(7))* Canadian Government Publishing.

Carroll, John J., et al, eds. Carbon Dioxide Sequestration & Related Technologies. 2011. (ENG., Illus.). 508p. 195.00 *(978-0-470-93876-8(5)*, Wiley-Scrivener) Wiley, John & Sons, Inc.

Carroll, John J. & Anwar, Sara. Carbon Dioxide Thermodynamic Properties Handbook: Covering Temperatures from -20 Degrees to 250 Degrees Celcius & Pressures up to 1000 Bar. 2011. (ENG.). 568p. 310.00 *(978-1-118-01298-7(4)*, Wiley-Scrivener) Wiley, John & Sons, Inc.

Clark, Woodrow W. II, ed. Sustainable Communities: Toward Energy Independence & Carbon Neutral Communities. 2009. (ENG., Illus.). x, 314p. 89.95 *(978-1-4419-0218-4(X)*, 144190218X) Springer.

Collins Publishers Staff. Carbon Counter: Calculate Your Carbon Footprint. 2008. (Collins Gem Ser.). (ENG.). 192p. pap. 7.95 *(978-0-00-724812-4(1))* HarperCollins Pubs. Ltd. GBR. Dist: Independent Pubs. Group.

Committee on Energy Futures and Air Pollution in Urban China and the United States, et al. Energy Futures & Urban Air Pollution: Challenges for China & the United States. 2008. (ENG.). 386p. pap. 76.25 *(978-0-309-11140-9(4))* National Academies Pr.

Dangerous Climate Change: Hearing Before the Select Committee on Energy Independence & Global Warming, House of Representatives, One Hundred Tenth Congress, First Session, April 26, 2007. 2010. (Illus.). iii, 206p. *(978-0-16-086904-4(8)*, 552-070-41814-8) United States Government Printing Office.

The Department of Energy's FutureGen Program: Hearing Before the Subcommittee on Energy & Environment, Committee on Science & Technology, House of Representatives, One Hundred Tenth Congress, Second Session, April 15, 2008. 2008. (Illus.). iv, 272p. *(978-0-16-081938-4(5)*, 552-070-38111-2) United States Government Printing Office.

Easterbrook, Don. Evidence-Based Climate Science: Data opposing CO2 emissions as the primary source of global Warming. 2011. (ENG., Illus.). 416p. 119.95 ***(978-0-12-385956-3(5))*** Elsevier Science & Technology Bks.

Ebune, Guilbert. Carbon Dioxide Capture from Powerplant Flue Gas Using Activated Carbon. 2010. 60p. pap. *(978-3-8383-5214-5(9))* Lambert Academic Publishing.

The Economics of Global Warming: Shaping How U.S. Companies Are Doing Business: Field Hearing Before the Select Committee on Energy Independence & Global Warming, House of Representatives, One Hundred Tenth Congress, Second Session, July 28, 2008. 2010. iii, 72p. ***(978-0-16-087216-7(2)**,* 552-070-42054-1) United States Government Printing Office.

Eyre, Nick, et al. Carbon Markets: An International Business Guide. 2009. (Environmental Market Insights Ser.). (ENG., Illus.). 328p. 58.50 *(978-1-84407-727-4(6))* Routledge.

Fukuoka, Shinsuke. Non-Phosgene Polycarbonate from CO2 - Industrialization of Green Chemical Process. 2011. (Environmental Research Advances Ser.). 165.00 ***(978-1-61470-877-3(0))*** Nova Science Pubs., Inc.

Future of Coal: Hearing Before the Committee on Energy & Natural Resources, United States Senate, One Hundred Tenth Congress, First Session ... March 22, 2007. 2007. iii, 53p. *(978-0-16-078978-6(8)*, 552-070-36093-0) United States Government Printing Office.

The Future of Fossil Fuels: Geological & Terrestrial Sequestration of Carbon Dioxide: Joint Oversight Hearing Before the Subcommittee on Energy & Mineral Resources, Joint with the Subcommittee on National Parks, Forests, & Public Lands of the Committee on Natural Resources, U.S. House of Representatives, One Hundred Tenth Congress, First Session, Tuesday, May 1, 2007. 2007. (Illus.). v, 82p. *(978-0-16-079941-9(4)*, 552-070-36768-3) United States Government Printing Office.

FutureGen & the Department of Energy's Advanced Coal Programs: Hearing Before the Subcommittee on Energy & Environment, Committee on Science & Technology, House of Representatives, One Hundred Eleventh Congress, First Session, March 11, 2009. 2009. iv, 155p. *(978-0-16-084375-4(8)*, 552-070-39918-6) United States Government Printing Office.

Ganapathy, Hullathy Subban. Supercritical Carbon Dioxide. 2011. 140p. pap. ***(978-3-8454-0440-0(X))*** Lambert Academic Publishing.

Gellings, Clark W. Saving Energy & Reducing CO2 Emissions with Electricity. 2011. *(978-0-88173-667-0(8))* Fairmont Pr., Inc.

—Saving Energy & Reducing Co2 with Electricity. 2011. (ENG.). 275p. 129.95 *(978-1-4398-7012-9(8))* Fairmont Pr., Inc.

Gershon, David. Low Carbon Diet: A 30 Day Program to Lose 5000 Pounds. 2007. (ENG., Illus.). 80p. pap. 12.95 *(978-0-9630327-2-0(0))* Empowerment Institute.

Goodall, Chris. How to Live a Low-Carbon Life: The Individual's Guide to Stopping Climate Change. 2007. (ENG., Illus.). 320p. per. 24.95 *(978-1-84407-426-6(9))* Routledge.

—How to Live a Low-Carbon Life: The Individual's Guide to Tackling Climate Change. 2nd rev. ed. 2010. (ENG., Illus.). 320p. 82.50 *(978-1-84407-909-4(0))*; pap. 24.95 *(978-1-84407-910-0(4))* Routledge.

Gruden, Dusan. Traffic & Environment. 2010. (Handbook of Environmental Chemistry / Anthropogenic Compounds Ser.). (Illus.). xiv, 294p. pap. 279.00 *(978-3-642-05506-5(0)*, 3642055060) Springer.

Gupta, Ram B. & Shim, Jae-Jin. Solubility in Supercritical Carbon Dioxide. 2006. (ENG., Illus.). 960p. 226.95 *(978-0-8493-4240-0(6)*, 4240, CRC Press) Taylor & Francis Group GBR. Dist: Taylor & Francis Group.

Hall, Linley Erin. Reducing Your Carbon Footprint in the Kitchen. 2009. (Your Carbon Footprint Ser.). 48p. (gr. 5-5). 53.00 *(978-1-60854-912-2(7)*, Rosen Central) Rosen Publishing Group, Inc., The.

Harrington, Jonathan. The Climate Diet: How You Can Cut Carbon, Cut Costs, & Save the Planet. 2008. (ENG., Illus.). 208p. pap. 15.95 *(978-1-84407-533-1(8))* Routledge.

Harrison, E. Bruce. Corporate Greening 2. 0: Create & Communicate Your Company's Climate Change & Sustainability Strategies. 2008. (ENG.). 230p. 24.95 *(978-1-933002-70-5(0))* PublishingWorks.

Hayden, Howard C. A Primer on CO2 & Climate, 2nd Edition. 2008. (Illus.). 87p. pap. 14.95 *(978-0-9714845-6-6(2))* Vales Lake Publishing, LLC.

He, Manchao, et al, eds. Co2 Storage in Carboniferous Formations & Abandoned Coal Mines. 2011. (ENG.). 216p. (C). 134.00 ***(978-0-415-62079-6(1)**,* CRC Press) Taylor & Francis Group GBR. Dist: Taylor & Francis Group.

Hemsath, Klaus H. Climate Change - Gold Rush or Disaster? Facts, Causes, Technologies, Opportunities. 2007. 360p. per. 27.95 *(978-1-4327-1345-4(0))* Outskirts Pr., Inc.

Henderson, Rachel. Partitioning Soil Carbon Dioxide Efflux Through Vertical Profiles. 2008. 48p. pap. *(978-3-639-01275-0(5))* VDM Verlag Dr. Mueller e.K.

Hester, Ronald E. & Harrison, Roy M., eds. Carbon Capture & Storage. 2009. (Issues in Environmental Science & Technology Ser.). (ENG., Illus.). 324p. (C). 96.00 *(978-1-84755-917-3(4))* Royal Society of Chemistry, The GBR. Dist: Ingram Pub. Services.

Homer-Dixon, Thomas & Garrison, Nick. Carbon Shift: How Peak Oil & the Climate Crisis Will Change Canada (And Our Lives) 2010. (ENG., Illus.). 240p. pap. 18.50 *(978-0-307-35719-9(8)*, Vintage Canada) Random Hse. of Canada, Ltd. CAN. Dist: Random Hse., Inc.

Hong, Lei. Development of Oxygenated Hydrocarbon-Based Co2- Soluble Polymers - Using Co2 As a Green Solvent. 2008. 168p. pap. *(978-3-639-10800-2(0))* VDM Verlag Dr. Mueller e.K.

Hou, Michael Z., et al, eds. Underground Storage of CO2 & Energy. 2010. (ENG.). 384p. 145.95 *(978-0-415-60049-1(9)*, CRC Press) Taylor & Francis Group GBR. Dist: Taylor & Francis Group.

The Implications of the Supreme Court's Decision Regarding EPA's Authorities with Respect to Greenhouse Gases under the Clean Air ACT: Hearing Before the Committee on Environment & Public Works, United States Senate, One Hundred Tenth Congress, First Session, April 24, 2007. 2011. iii, 86p. ***(978-0-16-089899-0(4)**,* 552-070-43745-2) United States Government Printing Office.

International Energy Agency Staff. Transport Energy & CO2: Moving Towards Sustainability. 2009. (Illus.). 414p. pap. 63.00 *(978-92-64-07316-6(7))* Organization for Economic Cooperation & Development.

Jackson, Felicia. Conquering Carbon. 2010. (ENG., Illus.). 256p. pap. 14.95 *(978-1-84773-425-9(1))* New Holland Pubs., Ltd. GBR. Dist: National Bk. Network.

Jankovic, Ljubomir. Designing Zero Carbon Buildings Using Dynamic Simulation Methods. 2012. (ENG., Illus.). 336p. (C). pap. 59.95 ***(978-1-84971-294-1(8))*** Routledge.

Lu, Jiemin. Natural Analogue of Carbon Dioxide Geological Storage. 2009. 188p. pap. *(978-3-639-20751-4(3))* VDM Verlag Dr. Mueller e.K.

Mackenzie, Fred T. & Lerman, Abraham. Carbon in the Geobiosphere: - Earth's Outer Shell - 2010. (Topics in Geobiology Ser.). (Illus.). xxi, 402p. pap. 269.00 *(978-90-481-7022-7(2)*, 9048170222) Springer.

Marini, Luigi. Geological Sequestration of Carbon Dioxide: Thermodynamics, Kinetics, & Reaction Path Modeling. 2006. (Developments in Geochemistry Ser.: 11). (ENG., Illus.). 470p. 175.00 *(978-0-444-52950-3(0)*, Elsevier Science) Elsevier Science & Technology Bks.

Markusson, Nils, et al, eds. The Social Dynamics of Carbon Capture & Storage. 2012. (Earthscan Science in Society Ser.). (ENG., Illus.). 352p. 140.00 ***(978-1-84971-314-6(6))***; pap. 49.95 ***(978-1-84971-315-3(4))*** Routledge.

Maroto-Valer, M. M., ed. Developments & Innovation in Carbon Dioxide (Co2) Capture & Storage Technology, 2 vols. 2010. (ENG., Illus.). 512p. 249.95 *(978-1-4398-3101-4(7))*; 528p. 249.95 *(978-1-4398-3099-4(1))* Taylor & Francis Group GBR. (CRC Press). Dist: Taylor & Francis Group.

—Developments & Innovation in Carbon Dioxide (CO2) Capture & Storage Technology: Carbon Dioxide (CO2) Capture, Transport & Industrial Applications, 2 vols. 2010. (Illus.). 560p. 265.00 *(978-1-84569-533-0(X))* Woodhead Publishing Ltd. GBR. Dist: Taylor & Francis Group.

—Developments & Innovation in Carbon Dioxide (CO2) Capture & Storage Technology: Carbon Dioxide (CO2) Storage & Utilisation, 2 vols., Vol. 2. 2010. (Illus.). 544p. 265.00 *(978-1-84569-797-6(9))* Woodhead Publishing Ltd. GBR. Dist: Taylor & Francis Group.

Massachusetts V. U.S. EPA: Implications of the Supreme Court Decision: Hearing Before the Select Committee on Energy Independence & Global Warming, House of Representatives, One Hundred Tenth Congress, First Session, June 8, 2007. 2010. (Illus.). iii, 90p. *(978-0-16-086841-2(6)*, 552-070-41755-9) United States Government Printing Office.

Massachusetts V. U.S. EPA, Part II: Implications of the Supreme Court Decision: Hearing Before the Select Committee on Energy Independence & Global Warming, House of Representatives, One Hundred Tenth Congress, Second Session, March 13, 2008. 2010. (Illus.). iv, 157p. ***(978-0-16-087422-2(X)**,* 552-070-42115-7) United States Government Printing Office.

Meadowcroft, James & Langhelle, Oluf, eds. Caching the Carbon: The Politics & Policy of Carbon Capture & Storage. 2011. 320p. pap. 50.00 *(978-0-85793-387-4(6))* Elgar, Edward Publishing, Inc.

Meadowcroft, James R. & Langhelle, Oluf, eds. Caching the Carbon: The Politics & Policy of Carbon Capture & Storage. 2010. (Illus.). 320p. 139.00 *(978-1-84844-412-6(5))* Elgar, Edward Publishing, Inc.

Mills, Robin. Capturing Carbon: The New Weapon in the War Against Climate Change. 2011. (Columbia/Hurst Ser.). (ENG.). 288p. (gr. 17). 35.00 *(978-0-231-70186-0(1))* Columbia Univ. Pr.

Mohitpour, Mo. Pipeline Transportation of Carbon Dioxide Containing Impurities. 2011. ***(978-0-7918-5983-4(5))*** American Society of Mechanical Engineers, The.

Musil, Robert K. Hope for a Heated Planet: How Americans Are Fighting Global Warming & Building a Better Future. 2008. (ENG.). 264p. 24.95 *(978-0-8135-4411-3(4))* Rutgers Univ. Pr.

MWH Americas. Potential Groundwater Quality Impacts Resulting from Geologic Carbon Sequestration. 2009. (Illus.). 302p. pap. *(978-1-60573-060-8(2))* Water Research Foundation.

National Council for Science and the Environment. The Climate Solutions Consensus: What We Know & What to Do about It. Blockstein, David & Wiegman, Leo, eds. 2009. (ENG., Illus.). 336p. 50.00 *(978-1-59726-636-9(1))*; pap. 35.00 *(978-1-59726-674-1(4))* Island Pr.

Neelameggham, Neale R., et al, eds. Energy Technology 2010: Conservation, Greenhouse Gas Reduction & Management, Alternative Energy Sources. 2010. (ENG.). 252p. pap. 152.00 *(978-0-87339-749-0(5)*, Wiley) Wiley, John & Sons, Inc.

—Energy Technology Perspectives: Conservation, Carbon Dioxide Reduction & Production from Alternative Sources. 2009. (ENG.). 282p. pap. 94.00 *(978-0-87339-733-9(9)*, Wiley) Wiley, John & Sons, Inc.

Neelameggham, Neale R. & Reddy, Ramana G., eds. Carbon Dioxide Reduction Metallurgy. 2008. (ENG., Illus.). 218p. pap. 154.00 *(978-0-87339-713-1(4)*, Wiley) Wiley, John & Sons, Inc.

Neuhoff, Karsten. Climate Policy after Copenhagen: The Role of Carbon Pricing. 2011. (ENG., Illus.). 290p. 99.00 *(978-1-107-00893-9(X))*; 296p. pap. 34.99 *(978-1-107-40141-9(0))* Cambridge Univ. Pr.

Nösberger, Josef, et al. Managed Ecosystems & CO2: Case Studies, Processes, & Perspectives. 2010. (Ecological Studies). (Illus.). xl, 459p. pap. 269.00 *(978-3-642-06835-5(9)*, 3642068359) Springer.

Organisation for Economic Co-operation and Development Staff. Co2 Capture & Storage: A Key Carbon Abatement Option. 2008. pap. 63.00 *(978-92-64-04140-0(0))* Organization for Economic Cooperation & Development.

—Cutting Transport CO2 Emissions: What Progress? 2007. pap. *(978-92-821-0382-1(X))* European Conference of Ministers of Transportation.

—Transports et éMissions de CO2: Quels Progrès ? 2007. pap. *(978-92-821-2379-9(0))* European Conference of Ministers of Transportation.

Özgür, Emre. Carbon Dioxide Sequestration into Deep Saline Aquifers. 2010. 128p. pap. *(978-3-8383-5968-7(2))* Lambert Academic Publishing.

Parag, Yael & Fawcett, Tina, eds. Personal Carbon Trading. 2010. (Climate Policy Ser.). (ENG., Illus.). 144p. 99.95 *(978-1-84971-196-8(8))* Routledge.

Pearce, Joshua, et al. Green Ontario: Can the Province Make the Conversion? 2012. (ENG.). 250p. (C). *(978-1-55339-288-0(4))*; pap. *(978-1-55339-287-3(6))* McGill-Queen's Univ. Pr.

Pontin, John. The Converging World: How One Community's Path to Zero Waste Is Helping Save Our Planet. 2008. (ENG., Illus.). 224p. pap. 24.95 *(978-0-7499-5170-2(2))* Piatkus Bks. GBR. Dist: Independent Pubs. Group.

Pontin, John & Roderick, Ian. Converging World: Connecting Communities in Global Change. 2007. (Schumacher Briefings Ser.: 13). (Illus.). 80p. pap. *(978-1-903998-92-2(1))* Green Bks. GBR. Dist: Central Bks. Ltd.

Preparing for Copenhagen: How Developing Countries Are Fighting Climate Change: Hearing Before the Select Committee on Energy Independence & Global Warming, House of Representatives, One Hundred Eleventh Congress, First Session, March 4, 2009. 2010. (Illus.). iii, 166p. ***(978-0-16-087440-6(8)**,* 552-070-42133-1) United States Government Printing Office.

Qiu, Guang-Ming, et al, eds. Modification & Preparation of Membrane in Supercritical Carbon Dioxide. 2010. (Chemistry Research & Applications Ser.). 125p. 43.00 *(978-1-60876-905-6(4))* Nova Science Pubs., Inc.

Rackley, Steve. Carbon Capture & Storage: Engineering Technologies. 2009. (ENG., Illus.). 408p. 155.00 *(978-1-85617-636-1(3)*, Butterworth-Heinemann) Elsevier Science & Technology Bks.

Range of Innovative, Non-Geologic Applications for the Beneficial Reuse of Carbon Dioxide from Coal & Other Fossil Fuel Facilities: Hearings Before a Subcommittee of the Committee on Appropriations, United States Senate, One Hundred Eleventh Congress, First Session, Special Hearing, May 6, 2009, Washington, DC. 2009. (Illus.). iii, 74p. *(978-0-16-084590-1(4)*, 552-070-40096-6) United States Government Printing Office.

Raschi, A., et al, eds. Plant Responses to Elevated CO2: Evidence from Natural Springs. 2008. (ENG., Illus.). 288p. pap. 58.00 *(978-0-521-08729-2(5))* Cambridge Univ. Pr.

Rebalancing the Carbon Cycle: Hearing Before the Subcommittee on Energy & Resources of the Committee on Government Reform, House of Representatives, One Hundred Ninth Congress, Second Session, September 27, 2006. 2008. (Illus.). iii, 140p. *(978-0-16-082518-7(0)*, 552-070-38553-3) United States Government Printing Office.

Regulatory Aspects of Carbon Capture, Transportation, & Sequestration: Hearing Before the Committee on Energy & Natural Resources, United States Senate, One Hundred Tenth Congress, First Session, to Receive Testimony on the Regulatory Aspects of Carbon Capture, Transportation, & Sequestration & to Receive Testimony on Two Related Bills, S. 2323 ... & S. 2144 ... January 31, 2007 [i.e. 2008]. 2008. iii, 96p. *(978-0-16-080861-6(8)*, 552-070-37413-2) United States Government Printing Office.

Reynolds, Larry. The Business Leader's Guide to the Low Carbon Economy. 2012. 250p. ***(978-1-4094-2351-5(4)**,* Gower Publishing Co., Ltd.) Ashgate Publishing, Ltd.

Robertson, John. Carbon Dioxide Feeds the World: CO2 - the Marvel Molecule. 2011. 50p. pap. 25.00 ***(978-1-60746-640-6(6))*** FastPrncil, Inc.

Russell, Sasha. Carbon Capture & Storage Projects Within Emissions Trading Systems. 2011. 180p. pap. ***(978-3-8443-8131-3(7))*** Lambert Academic Publishing.

Schafer, Karina. Water & Carbon Relations under Ambient & Elevated Atmospheric Co2. 2009. 144p. pap. *(978-3-639-12075-2(2))* VDM Verlag Dr. Mueller e.K.

Schütze, Michael, et al, eds. Corrosion Protection Against Carbon Dioxide. 2011. (Kreysa Continuation Ser.). (ENG., Illus.). 230p. 165.00 ***(978-3-527-33145-1(X)**,* Wiley-VCH) Wiley, John & Sons, Inc.

Snook, Jim. Ice Age Extinction: Cause & Human Consequences. 2007. 32.95 *(978-0-87586-558-4(5))*; pap. 21.95 *(978-0-87586-557-7(7))* Algora Publishing.

Strengths & Weaknesses of Regulating Greenhouse Gas Emissions Using Existing Clean Air ACT Authorities: Hearing Before the Subcommittee on Energy & Air Quality of the Committee on Energy & Commerce, House of Representatives, One Hundred Tenth Congress, Second Session, April 10, 2008. 2008. v, 168p. *(978-0-16-084014-2(7)*, 552-070-39686-1) United States Government Printing Office.

Terry, Nicola. Energy & Carbon Emissions: the Way We Live Today. 2011. (Illus.). 256p. pap. 19.95 *(978-1-906860-14-1(9))* UIT Cambridge GBR. Dist: Independent Pubs. Group.

Toth, Ferenc L. Geological Disposal of Carbon Dioxide & Radioactive Waste: A Comparative Assessment. Comparative Assessment. 2009. (Advances in Global Change Research Ser.). (Illus.). 350p. 229.00 *(978-90-481-8711-9(7)*, 9048187117) Springer.

Towards Ecological Taxation: The Efficacy of Emissions- Related Motor Taxation Regimes. 2011. (Corporate Social Responsibility Ser.). (Illus.). 256p. 124.95 *(978-0-566-08979-4(3)*, Gower Publishing Co., Ltd.) Ashgate Publishing, Ltd. GBR. Dist: Ashgate Publishing Co.

Tremblay, William O. Barriers to Climate Change Mitigation Technologies & Energy Efficiency. 2011. (Climate Change & its Causes, Effects & Prediction Ser.). 115.00 *(978-1-61761-558-0(7))* Nova Science Pubs., Inc.

United Nations Staff. Investor Interest & Capacity Building Needs. 2010. (ECE Energy Ser.). (ENG.). 180p. pap. 38.00 *(978-92-1-117013-9(3))* United Nations Pubns.

Volk, Tyler. CO2 Rising: The World's Greatest Environmental Challenge. (ENG., Illus.). 240p. (gr. 17). 2010. pap. 12.95 *(978-0-262-51521-4(0))* 2008. 23.95 *(978-0-262-22083-5(0))* MIT Pr.

Voluntary Carbon Offsets: Getting What You Pay for: Hearing Before the Select Committee on Energy Independence & Global Warming, House of Representatives, One Hundred Tenth Congress, First Session, July 18, 2007. 2010. (Illus.). iii, 180p. *(978-0-16-086773-6(8)*, 552-070-41694-3) United States Government Printing Office.

Williams, Jo. Zero-Carbon Homes: A Road Map. 2011. (Illus.). 224p. E-Book ***(978-0-203-15352-9(9))*** Earthscan.

Wilson, Elizabeth J. & Gerard, David, eds. Carbon Capture & Sequestration: Integrating Technology, Monitoring & Regulation. 2007. (ENG., Illus.). 296p. 238.00 *(978-0-8138-0207-7(5)*, Wiley-Blackwell) Wiley, John & Sons, Inc.

Winkler, Harold. Taking Action on Climate Change: Long-Term Mitigation Scenarios for South Africa. 2010. 228p. pap. 54.95 *(978-1-919895-25-3(6))* Double Storey Bks. ZAF. Dist: International Publishers Marketing.

World Bank. Climate Change & the World Bank Group: Phase I I - the Challenge of Low-Carbon Development. 2011. (Independent Evaluation Group Studies). (ENG.). 164p. pap. 20.00 *(978-0-8213-8653-8(0)*, 9780821386538) World Bank Pubns.

Yao, Takeshi, ed. Zero-Carbon Energy Kyoto 2010: Proceedings of the Second International Symposium of Global COE Program Energy Science in the Age of Global Warming - Toward CO2 Zero-emission Energy System. 2011. (Green Energy & Technology Ser.). xii, 321p. 259.00 *(978-4-431-53909-4(3)*, 4431539093) Springer.

CARBON MONOXIDE

Carbon Monoxide Poisoning: Sounding the Alarm on a Silent Killer: Hearing Before the Subcommittee on Consumer Protection, Product Safety, & Insurance of the Committee on Commerce, Science, & Transportation, United States Senate, One Hundred Eleventh Congress, First Session, December 17, 2009. 2010. iii, 33p. *(978-0-16-086553-4(0)*, 552-070-41550-5) United States Government Printing Office.

Committee on Combined Exposures to Hydrogen Cyanide and Carbon Monoxide in Army Operations, et al. Combined Exposures to Hydrogen Cyanide & Carbon Monoxide in Army Operations: Initial Report. 2008. (ENG.). 42p. pap. 18.00 *(978-0-309-11366-3(0))* National Academies Pr.

Committee on Toxicology Staff & Committee on Exposures to Hydrogen Cyanide and Carbon Monoxide in Army Operations. Exposures to Hydrogen Cyanide & Carbon Monoxide in Army Operations: Final Report. 2008. (ENG.). 50p. pap. 15.00 *(978-0-309-12560-4(X))* National Academies Pr.

Davis, B. H. & Occelli, Mario L. Advances in Fisher-Tropsch Synthesis, Catalysts, & Catalysis. 2009. (Chemical Industries Ser.). (ENG., Illus.). 424p. 236.95 *(978-1-4200-6256-4(5)*, CRC Press) Taylor & Francis Group GBR. Dist: Taylor & Francis Group.

DiLoreto, Dante & Corcoran, Idina. Carbon Monoxide: Sources, Uses, & Hazards. 2012. ***(978-1-61942-055-7(4))*** Nova Science Pubs., Inc.

Furimsky, Edward, ed. Catalysis in the Refining of Fischer-Tropsch Syncrude. 2010. (RSC Catalysis Ser.). (Illus.). 294p. 195.00 *(978-1-84973-080-8(6))* Royal Society of Chemistry, The GBR. Dist: Ingram Pub. Services.

Kristinsson, Hordur G., et al, eds. Modified Atmospheric Processing & Packaging of Fish: Filtered Smokes, Carbon Monoxide, & Reduced Oxygen Packaging. 2006. (ENG., Illus.). 243p. 220.00 *(978-0-8138-0768-3(9)*, Wiley-Blackwell) Wiley, John & Sons, Inc.

Penney, David G., ed. Carbon Monoxide Poisoning. 2007. (ENG., Illus.). 808p. 188.00 *(978-0-8493-8417-2(6))* CRC Pr. LLC.

Rojas, S. Biofuels from Fischer-Tropsch Synthesis. Ojeda, M., ed. 2010. (Energy Science, Engineering & Technology Ser.). (Illus.). 73p. pap. 43.00 *(978-1-61668-366-5(X))* Nova Science Pubs., Inc.

Sheldon, R.A. Chemicals from Synthesis Gas: Catalytic Reactions of CO & H2. 2010. (Catalysis by Metal Complexes Ser.). 240p. pap. 309.00 *(978-90-481-8378-4(2)*, 9048183782) Springer.

Wang, Rui, ed. Signal Transduction & the Gasotransmitters: NO, CO, & H2S in Biology & Medicine. 2010. (Illus.). 392p. pap. 155.00 *(978-1-61737-512-5(8)*, 1617375128) Humana Pr.

Watts, Ralph. The Effect of No & Co on Cellular Iron Metabolism. 2009. 196p. pap. *(978-3-639-14658-5(1))* VDM Verlag Dr. Mueller e.K.

Yoshikawa, Toshikazu & Naito, Yuji, eds. Gas Biology Research in Clinical Practice. 2011. (ENG., Illus.). 148p. *(978-3-8055-9664-0(2))* Karger, S. AG.

CARBONATE ROCKS

see also Limestone

Ahr, W. M. & Ahr, Wayne M. Geology of Carbonate Reservoirs: The Identification, Description & Characterization of Hydrocarbon Reservoirs in Carbonate Rocks. 2008. (ENG., Illus.). 296p. 99.95 *(978-0-470-16491-4(3)*, Wiley-Interscience) Wiley, John & Sons, Inc.

Alsharhan, Abdulrahman S. & Kendall, Christopher G., eds. Quaternary Carbonate & Evaporite Sedimentary Facies & Their Ancient Analogues: A Tribute to Douglas James Shearma. 2011. (International Association of Sedimentologists Ser.: 96). (ENG., Illus.). 496p. 120.00 *(978-1-4443-3910-9(9)*, Wiley-Blackwell) Wiley, John & Sons, Inc.

Avdeev, Boris. Statistical Analysis of Rock Fabric: Point Estimation, Smoothing & Regression. 2008. 56p. pap. *(978-3-639-10082-2(4))* VDM Verlag Dr. Mueller e.K.

de Boer, Poppe, et al, eds. Analogue & Numerical Modelling of Sedimentary Systems: From Understanding to Prediction. 2008. (International Association of Sedimentologists Ser.: 8). (ENG., Illus.). 328p. 169.95 *(978-1-4051-8930-9(4)*, Wiley-Blackwell) Wiley, John & Sons, Inc.

Draut, Amy E., et al. Formation & Applications of the Sedimentary Record in Arc Collision Zones. 2008. pap. *(978-0-8137-2436-2(8))* United States Geological Survey.

Flügel, Erik. Microfacies of Carbonate Rocks: Analysis, Interpretation & Application. 2nd ed. 2009. (Illus.). xxiii, 984p. 179.00 *(978-3-642-03795-5(X)*, 364203795X) Springer.

Foubert, Anneleen & Henriet, Jean-Pierre. Nature & Significance of the Recent Carbonate Mound Record: The Mound Challenger Code. 2009. (Lecture Notes in Earth Sciences Ser.). (ENG., Illus.). xx, 298p. 209.00 *(978-3-642-00289-2(7)*, 3642002897) Springer.

James, Noel P. & Bone, Yvonne. Neritic Carbonate Sediments in a Temperate Realm: Southern Australia. 2010. (ENG., Illus.). x, 240p. 139.00 *(978-90-481-9288-5(9)*, 9048192889) Springer.

Johnson, Markes E. & Ledesma-Vázquez, Jorge, eds. Atlas of Coastal Ecosystems in the Western Gulf of California: Tracking Limestone Deposits on the Margin of a Young Sea. 2009. (ENG., Illus.). 192p. 70.00 *(978-0-8165-2530-0(7))* Univ. of Arizona Pr.

LaMoreaux, Philip E., ed. Hydrology of Limestone Terranes: Annotated Bibliography of Carbonate Rocks. (IAH Contributions to Hydrogeology Ser.: Vol. 10). 268p. pap. *(978-3-922705-14-7(6))* Heise, Heinz, GmbH & Company KG, Verlag.

McKenzie, Judith A., et al, eds. Perspectives in Carbonate Geology: A Tribute to the Career of Robert Nathan Ginsburg. 2009. (International Association of Sedimentologists Ser.: 39). (ENG., Illus.). 400p. 159.95 *(978-1-4051-9380-1(8)*, Wiley-Blackwell) Wiley, John & Sons, Inc.

Mutti, Maria, et al, eds. Carbonate Systems During the Oligocene-Miocene Climatic Transition. 2010. (International Association of Sedimentologists Ser.: 97). (ENG., Illus.). 312p. 129.95 *(978-1-4443-3791-4(2)*, Wiley-Blackwell) Wiley, John & Sons, Inc.

Scesi, Laura & Gattinoni, Paola. Water Circulation in Rocks. 2009. (ENG., Illus.). vii, 165p. 129.00 *(978-90-481-2416-9(6)*, 9048124166) Springer.

Van Buchem, F. S. P., et al, eds. Mesozoic & Cenozoic Carbonate Systems of the Mediterranean & the Middle East: Stratigraphic & Diagenetic Reference Models. 2010. (Illus.). 424p. *(978-1-86239-292-2(7))* Geological Society Publishing Hse.

Wisshak, Max. High-Latitude Bioerosion: the Kosterfjord Experiment: The Kosterfjord Experiment. 2010. (Lecture Notes in Earth Sciences Ser.). (Illus.). xii, 202p. pap. 159.00 *(978-3-642-07195-9(3)*, 3642071953) Springer.

CARBONATED BEVERAGES

see also Advertising—Carbonated Beverages

Appleton, Nancy & Jacobs, G. N. Killer Colas: The Hard Truth about Soft Drinks. 2011. 192p. pap. 15.95 ***(978-0-7570-0341-7(9))*** Square One Pubs.

Ashurst, P. & Hargitt, R., eds. Soft drink & fruit juice problems Solved. 2009. (ENG.). 208p. 195.00 *(978-1-4200-7437-6(7))* Taylor & Francis Group GBR. Dist: Taylor & Francis Group.

Baumer, Jim. Moxie: Maine in a Bottle. 2012. (ENG., Illus.). 96p. 14.95 ***(978-1-60893-043-2(2))*** Down East Bks.

Faygo Beverages' Centennial Recipe Book. 2007. 9.95 *(978-0-9792673-0-7(7))* Faygo Beverages, Inc.

Foster, Robert John & Robert, Foster J. Coca-Globalization: Following Soft Drinks from New York to New Guinea. 2008. (ENG., Illus.). 304p. pap. 32.00 *(978-0-230-60386-8(6))* Palgrave Macmillan.

Fralia, Tom, creator. Sodalicious. 2007. 240p. per. 16.95 *(978-0-9616340-0-1(6))* SodaLicious, LLC.

Saxe, De Forest. Saxe's New Guide. 2007. (Cooking in America Ser.). (ENG.). 156p. per. 11.95 *(978-1-4290-1048-1(7))* Applewood Bks.

Schloss, Andrew. Homemade Soda: 200 Recipes for Making & Using Fruit Sodas & Fizzy Juices, Sparkling Waters, Root Beers & Cola Brews, Herbal & Healing Waters, Sparkling Teas & Coffees, Shrubs & Switchels, Cream Sodas & Floats, & Other Carbonated Concoctions. 2011. (ENG., Illus.). 336p. pap. 18.95 *(978-1-60342-796-8(1)*, 1603427961) Storey Publishing, LLC.

Steen, David P. & Ashurst, Philip R., eds. Carbonated Soft Drinks: Formulation & Manufacture. 2006. (ENG., Illus.). 368p. 245.00 *(978-1-4051-3435-4(6)*, Wiley-Blackwell) Wiley, John & Sons, Inc.

CARBONATES

see also Carbonate Rocks

Alonso-Zarza, A. M. & Tanner, Lawrence H. Carbonates in Continental Settings: Facies, Environments, & Processes. 2009. (Developments in Sedimentology Ser.: 61). (ENG., Illus.). 400p. 165.00 *(978-0-444-53025-7(8)*, Elsevier Science) Elsevier Science & Technology Bks.

—Carbonates in Continental Settings: Geochemistry, Diagenesis & Applications. 2009. (Developments in Sedimentology Ser.: 62). (ENG.). 336p. 180.00 *(978-0-444-53526-9(8))* Elsevier Science & Technology Bks.

Halvorson, Christine. Arm & Hammer Pure Baking Soda: Over 100 Helpful Household Hints. 2007. (Illus.). 80p. 8.98 *(978-1-4127-1547-8(4))* Publications International, Ltd.

Keys, Ryan. Matrix Acidizing of Heterogeneous Carbonates. 2011. 120p. pap. ***(978-3-8443-1432-8(6))*** Lambert Academic Publishing.

Obeida, Tawfiq. Dynamic Reservoir Simulation for Carbonates. 2011. 76p. pap. ***(978-3-8443-1805-0(4))*** Lambert Academic Publishing.

CARBONIC ACID

see Carbon Dioxide

CARBONIC OXIDE

see Carbon Monoxide

CARBONIFEROUS PERIOD

see Geology, Stratigraphic—Carboniferous

CARBONIUM IONS

see also Radicals (Chemistry)

Olah, George A., et al. Hypercarbon Chemistry. 2nd ed. 2011. (ENG., Illus.). 480p. 125.00 *(978-0-470-93568-2(5)*, Wiley) Wiley, John & Sons, Inc.

CARBONIZATION

see also Charcoal; Coal Gasification; Coal-Tar Products

Wan Ali, Wan Shabuddin. Properties of Oil Palm Shell-Based Activated Carbon. 2010. 164p. pap. *(978-3-639-23378-0(6))* VDM Verlag Dr. Mueller e.K.

CARBONYL COMPOUNDS

Beller, Matthias. Catalytic Carbonylation Reactions. 2010. (Topics in Organometallic Chemistry Ser.). (Illus.). xii, 283p. pap. 259.00 *(978-3-642-06955-0(X)*, 364206955X) Springer.

Castillon, S. & Cavinato, G., contrib. by. Catalytic Carbonylation Reactions. 2006. (Topics in Organometallic Chemistry Ser.: Vol. 18). (Illus.). 283p. 259.00 *(978-3-540-33002-8(X)*, 354033002X) Springer.

Cenini, S. & Ragaini, F. Catalytic Reductive Carbonylation of Organic Nitro Compounds. 2010. (Catalysis by Metal Complexes Ser.). 356p. pap. 349.00 *(978-90-481-4766-3(2)*, 9048147662) Springer.

Chebanov, Valentin A. Azaheterocycles Based on a,ß-Unsaturated Carbonyls. 2008. (ENG., Illus.). viii, 212p. 239.00 *(978-3-540-68361-2(5)*, 3540683615) Springer.

Chebanov, Valentin A., et al. Azaheterocycles Based on a,ß-Unsaturated Carbonyls. 2010. (ENG., Illus.). viii, 212p. pap. 239.00 *(978-3-642-08796-7(5)*, 3642087965) Springer.

Kollár, László, ed. Modern Carbonylation Methods. 2008. (ENG., Illus.). 383p. 255.00 *(978-3-527-31896-4(8)*, Wiley-VCH) Wiley, John & Sons, Inc.

Lin, Zhi-Ping & Li, Ji-Tai. Some Applications of Ultrasound Irradiation in Pinacol Coupling of Carbonyl Compounds. 2010. pap. 49.00 *(978-1-61728-978-1(7))* Nova Science Pubs., Inc.

Maser, Edmund. Enzymology & Molecular Biology of Carbonyl Metabolism, No. 13. Weiner, Henry et al, eds. 2007. (Enzymology & Molecular Biology of Carbonyl Metabolism Ser.). (Illus.). 414p. (C). pap. 324.95 *(978-1-55753-447-7(0))* Purdue Univ. Pr.

CARBORUNDUM

see Silicon Carbide

CARBOXYLIC ACIDS

see also Fatty Acids

Auras, Rafael A., et al, eds. Poly: Synthesis, Structures, Properties, Processing, & Applications. 2010. (Wiley Series on Polymer Engineering & Technology Ser.: 6). (ENG., Illus.). 528p. 158.00 *(978-0-470-29366-9(7)*, Wiley) Wiley, John & Sons, Inc.

Holder, Alvin A., et al, eds. Dipicolinic Acid, Its Analogues & Derivatives: Aspects of their Coordination Chemistry. 2011. (Illus.). 80p. pap. ***(978-1-61209-770-1(7))*** Nova Science Pubs., Inc.

Kato, Shinzi. Chalcogenocarboxylic Acid Derivatives. 2010. (Topics in Current Chemistry Ser.). (Illus.). x, 280p. pap. 349.00 *(978-3-642-06193-6(1)*, 3642061931) Springer.

Liebman, Joel F. & Rappoport, Zvi Z., eds. The Chemistry of Hydroxylamines, Oximes & Hydroxamic Acids, 2 vols., Vol. 2. 2011. (Patai's Chemistry of Functional Groups Ser.). (ENG., Illus.). 1118p. 1115.00 *(978-0-470-68263-0(9)*, Wiley-Blackwell) Wiley, John & Sons, Inc.

Piemonte, Vincenzo. Polylactic Acid: Synthesis, Properties & Applications. 2012. (Chemistry Research & Applications Ser.). 354p. 165.00 ***(978-1-62100-348-9(5))*** Nova Science Pubs., Inc.

Rappoport, Zvi & Liebman, Joel F. The Chemistry of Hydroxylamines, Oximes & Hydroxamic Acids, 2 vols. 2009. (Patai's Chemistry of Functional Groups Ser.). (ENG., Illus.). 1078p. 1950.00 *(978-0-470-51261-6(X)*, Wiley) Wiley, John & Sons, Inc.

Segla, Peter, et al. Structures, Physico-Chemical Properties & Biological Activities of Copper (II) Pyridinecarboxylates. 2011. (Chemical Engineering Methods & Technology Ser.). (Illus.). x, 82p. 43.00 *(978-1-61761-831-4(4))* Nova Science Pubs., Inc.

Tojo, Gabriel & Fernandez, Marcos I. Oxidation of Primary Alcohols to Carboxylic Acids: A Guide to Current Common Practice. 2010. (Basic Reactions in Organic Synthesis Ser.). (Illus.). xvi, 116p. pap. 99.00 *(978-1-4419-2254-0(7)*, 1441922547) Springer.

CARBURETORS

Hammill, Des. SU Carburettor High-Performance Manual. 2007. (SpeedPro Ser.). (ENG., Illus.). 96p. reprint ed. per. 29.95 *(978-1-84584-073-0(9)*, 1845840739) Veloce Publishing Ltd. GBR. Dist: MBI Distribution Services/Quayside Distribution.

Helt, Bob. How to Identify & Rebuild Carter YH Carburetors Used on Corvair Turbocharged Engines. 2010. 92p. pap. 25.00 *(978-1-4269-2834-5(3))* Trafford Publishing.

Lake, Charles S. The Motorcyclist's Handbook. 2011. 344p. pap. 29.95 ***(978-1-935700-55-5(3))*** Periscope Film, LLC

Passini, John. Weber Carburettors Tuning Tips & Techniques. 2008. (ENG., Illus.). 128p. pap. 19.95 *(978-1-85520-759-2(1)*, 1855207591) Brooklands Bks. GBR. Dist: MBI Distribution Services/Quayside Distribution.

Ruggles, Cliff. How to Rebuild & Modify Rochester Quadrajet Carburetors. 2006. (ENG., Illus.). 128p. pap. 24.95 *(978-1-932494-18-1(9)*, S-A Design) CarTech, Inc.

CARCINOGENESIS

see also Carcinogens

Air Pollution & Cancer. 2009. (IARC Scientific Publication No 161 Ser.). (ENG.). pap. 250.00 *(978-92-832-2161-6(3))* International Agency for Research on Cancer (IARC) (UN) FRA. Dist: World Health Organization.

Backman, V. & Roy, K. H., eds. Optical Spectroscopic Markers of Cancer: Book Edition of Disease Markers. 2009. 135p. pap. 102.00 *(978-1-58603-982-0(2))* IOS Pr., Inc.

Bagley, Rebecca G. The Tumor Microenvironment. 2010. (Illus.). xvii, 767p. E-Book ***(978-1-4419-6615-5(3))*** Springer.

Baronzio, Gian Franco, et al. Cancer Microenvironment & Therapeutic Implications: Tumor Pathophysiology Mechanisms & Therapeutic Strategies. 2009. (ENG., Illus.). vii, 328p. 169.00 *(978-1-4020-9575-7(9)*, 1402095759) Springer.

Bauer & Susanne. The Local Health Impact of Atmospheric Nuclear Weapons: Cancer Epidemiology in Areas Adjacent to the Semipalatinsk Test Site, Kazakhstan. 2006. (European University Studies Ser.: Vol. 33). 233p. (C). *(978-3-631-53730-5(1))* Lang, Peter AG.

Bauser & Susanne. The Local Health Impact of Atmospheric Nuclear Weapons: Cancer Epidemiology in Areas Adjacent to the Semipalatinsk Test Site, Kazakhstan. 2006. (European University Studies Ser.: Vol. 33). 233p. (C). pap. *(978-0-8204-7705-3(2))* Lang, Peter AG.

Bogomolny, Evgeny. Study of Early Spectral Changes in Cell Transformation. 2009. 124p. pap. *(978-3-639-14436-9(8))* VDM Verlag Dr. Mueller e.K.

Boorman, G. A. Genetically Modified Model Report on Toxicology & Carcinogeneticity Studies of Dichloroacetic Acid (CAS No. 79-43-6) in Genetically Modified (FVB Tb. ACV Hemizygous) Mice (Dermal & Drinking Water Studies) & Carcinogenecity Studies of Dichloroacetic Acid in Genetically Modified [B6. 129-Trp53tm1Brd (N5) Haploinsufficient] Mice (Drinking Water Studies) 2007. (Illus.). 167p. (C). pap. 45.00 *(978-1-4223-1520-0(7))* DIANE Publishing Co.

—Genetically Modified Model Report on Toxicology Studies of Bromodichloromethane (CAS No. 75-27-4) in Genetically Modified (FVB Tb. AC Hemizygous) Mice (Dermal, Drinking Water, & Gavage Studies) & Carcinogenicity Studies of Bromodichloromethane in Genetically Modified [B6. 129-Trp53tm1Brd (N5) Haploinsufficient] Mice (Drinking Water & Gavage Studies) 2007. (Illus.). 227p. (C). pap. 45.00 *(978-1-4223-1522-4(3))* DIANE Publishing Co.

Bronchud, Miguel H., et al, eds. Principles of Molecular Oncology. 3rd ed. 2008. 448p. pap. 99.00 *(978-1-60327-505-7(3))* Springer.

Caligiuri, Michael A., ed. Cytokines in the Genesis & Treatment of Cancer. 2007. (Cancer Drug Discovery & Development Ser.). (Illus.). 482p. 229.00 *(978-0-89603-820-2(3)*, 0896038203) Humana Pr.

Caligiuri, Michael A. & Lotze, Michael T., eds. Cytokines in the Genesis & Treatment of Cancer. 2010. (Cancer Drug Discovery & Development Ser.). (Illus.). xx, 482p. pap. 229.00 *(978-1-61737-203-2(X)*, 161737203X) Humana Pr.

Chen, George G. & Lai, Paul B. S., eds. Apoptosis in Carcinogenesis & Chemotherapy: Apoptosis in Cancer. 2009. (ENG., Illus.). xxii, 386p. 229.00 *(978-1-4020-9596-2(1)*, 1402095961) Springer.

Committee for Evaluation of Space Radiation Cancer Risk Model, et al. Technical Evaluation of the NASA Model for Cancer Risk to Astronauts Due to Space Radiation. 2012. (ENG.). 86p. pap. 36.00 ***(978-0-309-25305-5(5))*** National Academies Pr.

Committee on Applications of Toxicogenomic Technologies to Predictive Toxicology and Risk Assessment & National Research Council. Applications of Toxicogenomic Technologies to Predictive Toxicology & Risk Assessment. 2007. (ENG.). 300p. pap. 61.50 *(978-0-309-11298-7(2))* National Academies Pr.

Coppola, Domenico, ed. Mechanisms of Oncogenesis: An update on Tumorigenesis. 2010. (Cancer Growth & Progression Ser.). (ENG., Illus.). xii, 304p. 269.00 *(978-90-481-3724-4(1)*, 9048137241) Springer.

Dalgleish, Angus G. & Haefner, Burkhard, eds. The Link Between Inflammation & Cancer: Wounds that do not Heal. 2010. (Cancer Treatment & Research Ser.). xii, 254p. pap. 179.00 *(978-1-4419-3881-7(8)*, 1441938818) Springer.

Dittmar, Thomas, et al. Infection & Inflammation: Impacts on Oncogenesis, Vol. 13. (Contributions to Microbiology Ser.: Vol. 13). (ENG & GER., Illus.). 246p. *(978-3-8055-8064-9(9))* Karger, S. AG.

Dukubo, Gabriel D., ed. Field Cancerization: Basic Science & Clinical Applications. 2011. ***(978-1-61761-006-6(2))*** Nova Science Pubs., Inc.

Foote, MaryAnn, et al, eds. Principles of Molecular Oncology. 3rd ed. 2007. (Illus.). 418p. 179.00 *(978-1-934115-25-1(8))* Humana Pr.

Ford, Thomas D. New Cancer Research Developments. 2009. pap. 129.00 *(978-1-60692-447-1(8))* Nova Science Pubs., Inc.

Frank, David, ed. Signaling Pathways in Cancer Pathogenesis & Therapy. 2011. (ENG., Illus.). viii, 148p. 139.00 ***(978-1-4614-1215-1(3)***, 1461412153) Springer.

Frank, Steven A. Dynamics of Cancer: Incidence, Inheritance, & Evolution. 2007. (Princeton Series in Evolutionary Biology). (ENG., Illus.). 400p. (C). 115.00 *(978-0-691-13365-2(4))*; per. 49.95 *(978-0-691-13366-9(2))* Princeton Univ. Pr.

Giraldez, Fernando & Herrero, Miguel A., eds. Mathematics, Developmental Biology & Tumour Growth. 2009. (Contemporary Mathematics Ser.). (Illus.). 123p. pap. 49.00 *(978-0-8218-4663-6(9))* American Mathematical Society.

Gogichadze, G. K. & Gogichadze, T. Karyogamic Theory of Cancer Cell Formation from the View of the XXI Century. 2010. (Cancer Etiology, Diagnosis & Treatments Ser.). 125.00 *(978-1-60876-386-3(2)*, Nova Biomedical Bks.) Nova Science Pubs., Inc.

Heldin, Carl-Henrik, frwd. Transforming Growth Factor-ß in Cancer Therapy: Cancer Treatment & Therapy, 2 vols. 2008. (Cancer Drug Discovery & Development (Unnumbered) Ser.). (Illus.). 786p. 199.00 *(978-1-58829-715-0(2))* Humana Pr.

Hickman, John A. & Dive, Caroline, eds. Apoptosis & Cancer Chemotherapy. 2010. (Cancer Drug Discovery & Development Ser.). (Illus.). 360p. pap. 139.00 *(978-1-61737-165-3(3)*, 1617371653) Humana Pr.

Hoffman Edward J Staff. Cancer & the Search for Selective Biochemical Inhibitors Second. 2nd rev. ed. 2007. (ENG., Illus.). 480p. 162.95 *(978-1-4200-4593-2(8)*, CRC Press) Taylor & Francis Group GBR. Dist: Taylor & Francis Group.

Hooth, M. J., ed. Toxicology & Carcinogenesis Studies of Sodium Chlorate in F344/N Rats & B6C3F1 Mice. 2006. (Illus.). 255p. (C). pap. 45.00 *(978-1-4223-0612-3(7))* DIANE Publishing Co.

IARC Staff. 1,3-Butadiene, Ethylene Oxide & Vinyl Halides (Vinyl Fluoride, Vinyl Chloride & Vinyl Bromide) 2009. (IARC Monographs on the Evaluation of the Carcinogenic Risks to Humans Ser.). (ENG.). 519p. pap. 66.00 *(978-92-832-1297-3(5))* World Health Organization.

ICRP Staff. Low-Dose Extrapolation of Radiation Related Cancer Risk. Valentin, J., ed. 2006. (International Commission on Radiological Protection Ser.: 99). (ENG., Illus.). 200p. per. 176.00 *(978-0-08-044958-6(1)*, Elsevier) Elsevier - Health Sciences Div.

International Agency for Research on Cancer Staff. Household Combustion of Solid Fuels & High Temperature Frying: IARC Monographs on the Evaluation of Carcinogenic Risks to Humans. 2010. (IARC Monographs Volume 95 Ser.). (ENG.). 400p. pap. 66.00 *(978-92-832-1295-9(9))* World Health Organization.

Jakowlew, Sonia B., ed. Transforming Growth Factor-Beta in Cancer Therapy, Volume I: Basic & Clinical Biology. 2010. (Cancer Drug Discovery & Development Ser.). (Illus.). xxiv, 735p. pap. 199.00 *(978-1-61737-735-8(X)*, 161737735X) Humana Pr.

—Transforming Growth Factor-Beta in Cancer Therapy, Volume II: Cancer Treatment & Therapy. 2010. (Cancer Drug Discovery & Development Ser.). (Illus.). xxvi, 786p. pap. 199.00 *(978-1-61737-736-5(8)*, 1617377368) Humana Pr.

Kaminishi, Michio, ed. Research Advances in Gastroenterological Carcinogenesis: Highlights from the Proceedings of the 3rd International Conference on Gastroenterological Carcinogenesis, Sapporo, Japan, August 19-20, 2004,

C

Vol. 69. (Oncology Ser.: Vol. 69, Suppl. 1). (Illus.). *(978-3-8055-8003-8(7))* Karger, S. AG.
Karcher, Walter. Dibenzanthracenes & Environmental Carcinogenesis. 2009. (Cambridge Monographs on Cancer Research Ser.). (ENG.). 284p. pap. 55.00 *(978-0-521-10588-0(9))* Cambridge Univ. Pr.
Khatib, A-Majid, ed. Regulation of Carcinogenesis, Angiogenesis & Metastasis by the Proprotein Convertases: A New Potential Strategy in Cancer Therapy. 2006. x, 157p. 139.00 *(978-1-4020-4793-0(2)*, 1402047932) Springer.
Kiaris, Hippokratis. Understanding Carcinogenesis: An Introduction to the Molecular Basis of Cancer. 2006. (ENG., Illus.). 188p. 109.95 *(978-3-527-31486-7(5)*, Wiley-VCH) Wiley, John & Sons, Inc.
Kudo, Masatoshi, ed. Imaging Human Hepatocarcinogenesis. (Intervirology Ser.: Vol. 47, Nos. 3-5). (Illus.). 168p. pap. *(978-3-8055-7788-5(5))* Karger, S. AG.
Majumder, Sadhan, ed. Stem Cells & Cancer. 2009. (ENG., Illus.). x, 286p. 160.00 *(978-0-387-89610-6(4)*, 0387896104) Springer.
Markman, Maurie, et al, eds. Stem Cell Basis of Cancer: Tumorigenesis & Drug Development. 2006. (Cancer Drug Discovery & Development Ser.). 400p. 175.00 *(978-1-59745-331-8(5))* Humana Pr.
McKinnell, Robert G., et al. The Biological Basis of Cancer. 2nd rev. ed. 2006. (ENG., Illus.). 494p. per. 79.00 *(978-0-521-60633-2(0))* Cambridge Univ. Pr.
Melnick, R. L., ed. Toxicology & Carcinogenesis Studies of Bromodichloromethane No 75-27-4) in Male F344/N Rats & Female B6C3Fl Mice. 2006. (Illus.). 248p. (C). pap. 45.00 *(978-1-4223-0633-8(X))* DIANE Publishing Co.
Mercier, Isabelle, et al, eds. Caveolins in Cancer Pathogenesis, Prevention & Therapy. 2011. (Current Cancer Research Ser.). (ENG., Illus.). xi, 123p. 139.00 ***(978-1-4614-1000-3(2)***, 1461410002) Springer.
Meyers, Craig, ed. AIDS-Associated Viral Oncogenesis. 2010. (Cancer Treatment & Research Ser.). (Illus.). ix, 270p. pap. 159.00 *(978-1-4419-4287-6(4)*, 1441942874) Springer.
Meyers, Robert A., ed. Cancer: From Mechanisms to Therapeutic Approaches. 2007. (ENG.). 478p. 310.00 *(978-3-527-31768-4(6)*, Wiley-VCH) Wiley, John & Sons, Inc.
The Molecular Basis of Human Cancer. 2010. 149.50 *(978-1-934115-18-3(5))* Humana Pr.
Mor, Gil & Alvero, Ayesha, eds. Apoptosis & Cancer: Methods & Protocols. 2010. (Methods in Molecular Biology Ser.). (Illus.). xi, 266p. pap. 119.00 *(978-1-61737-582-8(9)*, 1617375829) Humana Pr.
Penning, Trevor M., ed. Chemical Carcinogenesis. 2011. (Current Cancer Research Ser.). (Illus.). xv, 440p. 189.00 *(978-1-61737-994-9(8)*, 1617379948) Humana Pr.
Rasnick, David. The Chromosomal Imbalance Theory of Cancer. 2011. (ENG., Illus.). 330p. 119.95 ***(978-1-57808-737-2(6))*** BIOS Scientific Publishers Ltd. GBR. Dist: Taylor & Francis Group.
Ruddon, Raymond W. Cancer Biology. 4th rev. ed. 2007. (ENG., Illus.). 568p. per. 69.99 *(978-0-19-517544-8(1))* Oxford Univ. Pr., Inc.
Schönthal, Axel H., ed. Checkpoint Controls & Cancer: Volume 1: Reviews & Model Systems. 2010. (Methods in Molecular Biology Ser.). (Illus.). xvi, 318p. pap. 119.00 *(978-1-61737-426-5(1)*, 1617374261) Humana Pr.
—Checkpoint Controls & Cancer: Volume 2: Activation & Regulation Protocols. 2010. (Methods in Molecular Biology Ser.). (Illus.). 348p. pap. 139.00 *(978-1-61737-603-0(5)*, 1617376035) Humana Pr.
Siemann, Dietmar W., ed. Tumor Microenvironment. 2010. (ENG., Illus.). 454p. 139.95 *(978-0-470-74996-8(2)*, Wiley) Wiley, John & Sons, Inc.
Simon, M. Celeste, ed. Diverse Effects of Hypoxia on Tumor Progression. 2010. (Current Topics in Microbiology & Immunology Ser.). (Illus.). x, 143p. 219.00 *(978-3-642-13328-2(2)*, 3642133282) Springer.
Singal. Nanoparticle Induced Inflammatory Signaling in the Lung. 2010. 232p. pap. *(978-3-639-21552-6(4))* VDM Verlag Dr. Mueller e.K.
Sporn, Michael B., frwd. Transforming Growth Factor-B in Cancer Therapy, Volume I: Basic & Clinical Biology. 2008. (Cancer Drug Discovery & Development (Unnumbered) Ser.). (Illus.). 735p. 199.00 *(978-1-58829-714-3(4))* Humana Pr.
Stavridis, John C. Oxidation: the Cornerstone of Carcinogenesis: Oxidation & Tobacco Smoke Carcinogenesis. A Relationship Between Cause & Effect. 2010. xxii, 258p. pap. 159.00 *(978-90-481-7702-8(2)*, 9048177022) 2008. (Illus.). 258p. 159.00 *(978-1-4020-6703-7(8))* Springer.
Stern, Robert, ed. Hyaluronan in Cancer Biology. 2009. (ENG., Illus.). 468p. 82.95 *(978-0-12-374178-3(5)*, Academic Pr.) Elsevier Science & Technology Bks.
The International Agency for Research on Cancer. Ingested Nitrates & Nitrites: On the Evaluation of Carcinogenic Risks to Humans. 2011. (IARC Monographs Volume 94 Ser.). (ENG.). 457p. pap. 66.00 *(978-92-832-1294-2(0))* World Health Organization.
Tumors & Cell Phone Use: What the Science Says: Hearing Before the Subcommittee on Domestic Policy of the Committee on Oversight & Government Reform, House of Representatives, One Hundred Tenth Congress, Second Session, September 25, 2008. 2009. (Illus.). iii, 226p. *(978-0-16-083848-4(7)*, 552-070-39545-8) United States Government Printing Office.
Vainio, Harri U. & Hietanen, Eino K. Mechanisms in Carcinogenesis & Cancer Prevention. 2010. (Handbook of Experimental Pharmacology Ser.). (Illus.). xxi, 329p. pap. 359.00 *(978-3-642-07859-0(1)*, 3642078591) Springer.
Walker, N. J., ed. Toxicology & Carcinogenesis Studies of 3,3', 4,4', 5-Pentachlorobiphenyl in Female Harlan Sprague-Dawley Rats. 2006. (Illus.). 246p. (C). pap. 45.00 *(978-1-4223-0613-0(5))* DIANE Publishing Co.
Wong, David K., ed. Tumorigenesis Research Advances. 2007. (C). 129.00 *(978-1-60021-817-0(2))* Nova Science Pubs., Inc.
Yadav, Vipin & Denning, Mitchell F. Molecular Signaling Pathways in Human Skin Carcinogenesis. 2011. 192p. pap. ***(978-3-8454-1453-9(7))*** Lambert Academic Publishing.
Zakhari, Samir, et al, eds. Alcohol & Cancer. 2011. (ENG., Illus.). xvi, 243p. 189.00 *(978-1-4614-0039-4(2)*, 1461400392) Springer.

CARCINOGENS

Bartone, John Charles. Cancer Disease for All Americans: Dr. Bartone Rule #1: Food Containing Carcinogens: Index, Reference & Medical Analysis of New Research Information. 2008. (Illus.). 160p. ring bd. 69.95 *(978-0-7883-3850-2(1))* ABBE Pubs. Assn. of Washington, D.C.
—Cancer Disease for All Americans: Dr. Bartone Rule #2: Beverages Containing Carcinogens: Index, Reference & Medical Analysis of New Research Information. 2008. (Illus.). 160p. ring bd. 69.95 *(978-0-7883-3859-5(5))* ABBE Pubs. Assn. of Washington, D.C.
—Cancer Disease for All Americans: Dr. Bartone Rule #3: Vegetables Containing Carcinogens: Index, Reference & Medical Analysis of New Research Information. 2008. (Illus.). 160p. ring bd. 69.95 *(978-0-7883-3875-5(7))* ABBE Pubs. Assn. of Washington, D.C.
Coombs, Maurice M. & Bhatt, Tarlochan S. Cyclopenta[a]phenanthrenes. 2008. (Cambridge Monographs on Cancer Research Ser.). (ENG.). 288p. pap. 58.00 *(978-0-521-10192-9(1))* Cambridge Univ. Pr.
Davis, Devra. The Secret History of the War on Cancer. 2009. (ENG.). 560p. pap. 18.95 *(978-0-465-01568-9(9))* Basic Bks.
Greenhaven. Cancer. 2012. (At Issue Ser.). (ENG.). 128p. (gr. 10-12). pap. 33.70 ***(978-0-7377-5559-6(8)***, Greenhaven Pr., Inc.); (YA). (gr. 9-12). lib. bdg. 23.85 ***(978-0-7377-5558-9(X))*** Cengage Gale.
Hsu, Ching-Hung & Stedeford, Todd, eds. Cancer Risk Assessment: Chemical Carcinogenesis, Hazard Evaluation, & Risk Quantification. 2010. (ENG., Illus.). 832p. 195.00 *(978-0-470-23822-6(4)*, Wiley) Wiley, John & Sons, Inc.
Iarc & WHO. Inorganic & Organic Lead Compounds: IARC Monographs on the Evaluation of Carcinogenic Risks to Human. 2006. (IARC Monographs, Volume 87 Ser.). (ENG.). 519p. pap. 66.00 *(978-92-832-1287-4(8))* World Health Organization.
IARC Staff. 1,3-Butadiene, Ethylene Oxide & Vinyl Halides (Vinyl Fluoride, Vinyl Chloride & Vinyl Bromide) 2009. (IARC Monographs on the Evaluation of the Carcinogenic Risks to Humans Ser.). (ENG.). 519p. pap. 66.00 *(978-92-832-1297-3(5))* World Health Organization.
IARC Working Group on the Evaluation of Carcinogenic Risks to Humans, Meeting Staff & International Agency for Research on Cancer Staff, contrib. by. Smokeless Tobacco & Some Tobacco-Specific N-Nitrosamines: IARC Monographs on the Evaluation of Carcinogenic Risks to Human. 2007. (IARC Monographs, Volume 89 Ser.). (ENG.). 635p. pap. 66.00 *(978-92-832-1289-8(4))* World Health Organization.
ICRP Staff. Low-Dose Extrapolation of Radiation Related Cancer Risk. Valentin, J., ed. 2006. (International Commission on Radiological Protection Ser.: 99). (ENG., Illus.). 200p. per. 176.00 *(978-0-08-044958-6(1)*, Elsevier) Elsevier - Health Sciences Div.
Institute of Medicine Staff, creator. Asbestos: Selected Cancers. 2006. (ENG., Illus.). 340p. per. 55.00 *(978-0-309-10169-1(7))* National Academies Pr.
International Agency for Research on Cancer Staff. Human Papillomaviruses - IARC Monographs on the Evaluation of Carcinogenic Risks to Humans. 2007. (IARC Monographs). 678p. pap. 66.00 *(978-92-832-1290-4(8))* World Health Organization.
—Some Non-Heterocyclic Polycyclic Aromatic Hydrocarbons & Some Related Exposures. 2010. (IARC Monographs Volume 92 Ser.). (ENG.). 861p. pap. 66.00 *(978-92-832-1292-8(4))* World Health Organization.
Jacob, Jürgen. Sulfur Analogues of Polycyclic Aromatic Hydrocarbons (Thiaarenes) Environmental Occurrence, Chemical & Biological Properties. 2008. (Cambridge Monographs on Cancer Research Ser.). (ENG.). 296p. pap. 58.00 *(978-0-521-10356-5(8))* Cambridge Univ. Pr.
Karcher, Walter. Dibenzanthracenes & Environmental Carcinogenesis. 2009. (Cambridge Monographs on Cancer Research Ser.). (ENG.). 284p. pap. 55.00 *(978-0-521-10588-0(9))* Cambridge Univ. Pr.
Mishra, Vivek, et al. Edible Oil Adulterants: Exposure Risk. 2011. 180p. pap. ***(978-3-8443-1736-7(8))*** Lambert Academic Publishing.
Newman, M. S., et al. The Chemistry & Biology of Benz[a]anthracenes. 2009. (Cambridge Monographs on Cancer Research Ser.). (ENG.). 244p. pap. 51.00 *(978-0-521-10589-7(7))* Cambridge Univ. Pr.
Pohanish, Richard P. Sittig's Handbook of Toxic & Hazardous Chemicals & Carcinogens. 6th ed. 2011. (ENG.). 3096p. 595.00 *(978-1-4377-7869-4(0))* William Andrew, Inc.
Steinman, David. Diet for a Poisoned Planet: How to Choose Safe Foods for You & Your Family. 2006. (ENG.). 640p. per. 17.95 *(978-1-56025-922-0(1))* Running Pr. Bk. Pubs.
The International Agency for Research on Cancer. IARC Monographs on the Evaluation of Carcinogenic Risks to Humans. 2011. (IARC Monographs). 460p. pap. 66.00 *(978-92-832-1293-5(2))* World Health Organization.
—Shift-Work Painting & Fire-Fighting: On the Evaluation of Carcinogenic Risks to Humans. 2011. (IARC Monographs Ser.). 608p. pap. 66.00 *(978-92-832-1298-0(3))* World Health Organization.
—Some Industrial & Cosmetic Dyes & Related Exposures. 2011. (IARC Monographs Ser.). 624p. pap. 66.00 *(978-92-832-1299-7(1))* World Health Organization.
Wildavsky, Aaron. Regulation of Carcinogens: Are Animal Tests a Sound Foundation? (Illus.). 38p. pap. 5.95 *(978-0-945999-57-7(7)*, 1009) Independent Institute, The.
Wiwanitkit, Viroj. Melamine & Other Problematic Food Carcinogens. 2008. 120p. pap. 43.00 *(978-1-60692-940-7(2))* Nova Science Pubs., Inc.
World Health Organization. IPCS Mode of Action Framework - IPCS Harmonization Project Document, No. 4. 2008. (Nonserial Publication). 127p. pap. 48.00 *(978-92-4-156349-9(4))* World Health Organization.
Zain Khan, Mohammad. Bioremediation of Chlorophenols by Aerobic Granulation Technology. 2011. 156p. pap. ***(978-3-8443-8240-2(2))*** Lambert Academic Publishing.

CARCINOMA

see Cancer; Tumors

CARD CATALOGS

Division, Library Of Congress Catalog. Handbook of Card Distribution. 2009. 168p. pap. *(978-0-217-21727-9(3))* Books LLC.
Krajewski, Markus & Krapp, Peter. Paper Machines: About Cards & Catalogs, 1548-1929. 2011. (History & Foundations of Information Science Ser.). (ENG., Illus.). 224p. (gr. 17). 30.00 *(978-0-262-01589-9(7))* MIT Pr.

CARD GAMES

see also Cardsharping; Contract Bridge; Fortune-Telling; Playing Cards; Poker; Solitaire (Game); Whist

AEG. Legend of the Burning Sands. 2008. 39.95 *(978-1-59472-046-8(0))* Alderac Entertainment Group.
Arnold, Peter. Card Games. 2007. (ENG., Illus.). 400p. pap. 16.95 *(978-0-550-10336-9(8))* Chambers Harrap Pubs., Ltd. GBR. Dist: Independent Pubs. Group.
—Card Games for Families. 2010. (ENG., Illus.). 176p. pap. 11.95 *(978-0-550-10470-0(4))* Chambers Harrap Pubs., Ltd. GBR. Dist: Independent Pubs. Group.
—Card Games for Gambling. 2008. (ENG., Illus.). 176p. pap. 9.95 *(978-0-550-10408-3(9))* Chambers Harrap Pubs., Ltd. GBR. Dist: Independent Pubs. Group.
—Card Games for One. 2010. (ENG., Illus.). 176p. pap. 9.95 *(978-0-550-10407-6(0))* Chambers Harrap Pubs., Ltd. GBR. Dist: Independent Pubs. Group.
—Chambers Card Games. 3rd ed. 2011. (ENG., Illus.). 412p. pap. 19.95 *(978-0-550-10179-2(9)*, Hodder & Stoughton) Hodder General Publishing Div. GBR. Dist: Independent Pubs. Group.
—Chambers Card Games for Families: The Ultimate Family Pastime. 2nd ed. 2011. (ENG., Illus.). 168p. pap. 12.95 ***(978-0-550-10184-6(5)***, Hodder & Stoughton) Hodder General Publishing Div. GBR. Dist: Independent Pubs. Group.
—Complete Book of Card Games. 2012. (ENG.). 256p. pap. 9.99 ***(978-0-600-62395-3(5)***, Hamlyn) Octopus Publishing Group GBR. Dist: Hachette Bk. Group.
Barnes, Hugh & Williams, Lance. Stupidiel Stupidtool Expansion: Stupidtool Expansion. 2007. 60p. (YA). 8.95 *(978-0-9749627-3-3(2))* Lost Adept Distractions.
Benjamin, Fred. Euchre Strategies. 2008. 92p. pap. 16.95 *(978-1-4303-1497-4(4))* Lulu Enterprises Inc.
Bing-O-Cards Game. 84.00 *(978-0-88079-384-1(8)*, DBOC12) U.S. Games Systems, Inc.
Bis Card Game. (FRE.). 24.95 *(978-88-8148-072-2(7))* European Language Institute ITA. Dist: Distribooks, Inc.
Bleach. Bleach TCG Bounts Booster. 2008. 3.29 *(978-1-934112-61-8(5))* Diamond Bk. Distributors.
Bleach Staff. Bankai TCG Starter. 2008. 11.99 *(978-1-59396-935-6(X))* Diamond Comic Distributors, Inc.
Bleach Staff, creator. Bankai TCG Booster. 2008. 3.29 *(978-1-59396-934-9(1))* Diamond Comic Distributors, Inc.
Bourke Smith Staff. Countdown to Winning Bridge. 2007. cd-rom *(978-1-897106-31-0(9))* Master Point Pr.
Boyett, Mark. The Bar & Lounge Deck: 2010. 2009. pap. 19.95 *(978-1-61584-999-4(8))* Independent Pub.
—The Diners Deck: Downtown/Brooklyn Zoo. 2009. pap. 29.95 *(978-1-61584-998-7(X))* Independent Pub.
—The Diners Deck: Manhattan 2010. 2009. pap. 29.95 *(978-1-61584-997-0(1))* Independent Pub.
Burger, Robert E. & McClain, Guthrie. Pro Bridge - the Hall of Fame. 2011. (Illus.). 176p. pap. 19.95 ***(978-4-87187-456-4(7))*** Ishi Pr. International.
Cambias, James & Kelly, Diane. Parasites Unleashed. 2007. (J). 9.95 *(978-0-9770419-2-3(1))* Zygote Games LLC.
Cappelletti, Mike & Caro, Mike. Mastering Hold'em & Omaha Poker. 2007. (ENG., Illus.). 448p. pap. 19.95 *(978-1-58042-139-3(3))* Cardoza Publishing.
Cardoza, Avery, et al. World Series of Poker Offical Guidebook. 2010. (ENG.). 176p. pap. 9.95 *(978-1-58042-245-1(4))* Cardoza Publishing.
Chronicle Books Staff. I Dare You: 30 Sealed Seductions. Bright, Susie, ed. 2010. (ENG.). 30p. 14.95 *(978-0-8118-6991-1(1))* Chronicle Bks. LLC.
Cline, Mike & Yi-Cline, Nancy, creators. Franky Fox's A1 Game Card Set. 2007. 52p. (J). 7.99 *(978-0-9777419-2-2(3))* Lingo Pr. LLC.
Cummings, Michelle & Training Wheels Inc. Staff. Playing with A Full Deck: 52 Team Activities Using A Deck of Cards! rev. ed. 2011. (ENG.). 122p. pap. 27.55 *(978-0-7575-4094-3(5))* Kendall Hunt Publishing Co.
Dawson, Lawrence H. Hoyle's Games Modernized - Cards - Board Games & Billiards. 2008. 480p. *(978-1-4437-3296-3(6))* 2007. 476p. per. *(978-1-4067-8954-6(2))* Read Bks. (Home Farm Bks.).
Diagram Group. The Ultimate Book of Card Games. 2006. (ENG., Illus.). 464p. pap. 9.95 *(978-1-4027-4093-0(X))* Sterling Publishing Co., Inc.
Diagram Group Staff. Little Giant Encyclopedia: Card Games. 2009. (ENG., Illus.). 512p. pap. 9.95 *(978-1-4027-6417-2(0)*, Sterling Innovation) Sterling Publishing Co., Inc.
Dillman, Erika & Van Tilburg, Christopher. Don't Die Out There Deck. 2007. (ENG.). n/ap. 6.95 *(978-1-59485-071-4(2))* Mountaineers Bks., The.
Downtown Bookworks Inc. Staff & Bergen, Marty. Pocket Posh Tips for Bridge Players. 2011. (ENG.). 128p. pap. 7.99 *(978-1-4494-0764-3(1))* Andrews McMeel Publishing.
Dragon Ball Staff, ed. Destructive Fury Starter. 2009. 9.99 *(978-1-60584-126-7(9))* Diamond Bk. Distributors.
Fantasy Flight Games, creator. Warhammer Invasion Card Game: The Chaos Moon Battle Pack. 2011. 14.95 ***(978-1-61661-027-2(1))*** Fantasy Flight Games.
FASA Corporation Staff. Shadowrun: The Trading Card Game. (Shadowrun Ser.). pap. 89.90 *(978-1-55560-332-8(7)*, 03327F) FASA Corp.
Fitzgerald, Mike, creator. The PEZ Card Game. 60.00 *(978-1-57281-261-1(3)*, DPZS6); 120.00 *(978-1-57281-262-8(1)*, DPZ60) U.S. Games Systems, Inc.
Fox, Debbie & Beane, Allan L. Good-Bye Bully Machine Card Game. 2010. (ENG.). 60p. (J). (gr. 3-12). 12.99 *(978-1-57542-356-2(1))* Free Spirit Publishing, Inc.
Frontiersmen of the Old West. (Old West Series Card Games Ser.). 6.00 *(978-1-57281-015-0(7)*, OWF54) U.S. Games Systems, Inc.
Frost-Sharratt, Cara. 101 Clever Card Tricks. 2007. (ENG., Illus.). 128p. pap. 7.95 *(978-0-600-61388-6(7)*, Hamlyn) Octopus Publishing Group GBR. Dist: Hachette Bk. Group.
Froud, Wendy. Heart of the Faerie Oracle. 2010. (ENG., Illus.). 138p. 25.00 *(978-0-8109-8823-1(2))* Abrams.
Gollehon, John. Attack the Casino's Vulnerable Games! 2006. (Illus.). 243p. per. 7.99 *(978-0-914839-80-4(2))* Gollehon Pr.
Gordon, Lynn & Chronicle Books Staff. Things to Try Once in Your Life. 2008. (ENG., Illus.). 54p. 6.95 *(978-0-8118-6373-5(5))* Chronicle Bks. LLC.
—Tokens of Affection. rev. ed. 2008. (ENG., Illus.). 54p. 6.95 *(978-0-8118-6375-9(1))* Chronicle Bks. LLC.
Grabbi, Thrusti Kicki, et al. Kiss & Tell: The Outrageous Party Game of Sexy Stories & Tall Tales. 2010. (ENG.). 120p. 18.95 *(978-0-8118-7543-1(1))* Chronicle Bks. LLC.
Grant, Audrey Grant. 2 over 1 Game Force. 2009. (ENG.). 254p. pap. 19.95 *(978-0-939460-84-7(X))* American Contract Bridge League.
Greenblatt, Kim. Forty Dollar No Limit Texas Hold'em Ring & Tournament Games. 2007. per. 20.00 *(978-0-9777282-7-5(7))* Greenblatt, Kim.
Halwas, Shawn. Go Fish: Seven Speaking & Listening Games for Learning Languages. 2007. (gr. k-12). pap. 22.00 *(978-0-86647-238-8(X))* Pro Lingua Assocs., Inc.
Harwood, Jeremy. How to Play Winning Card Games. 2008. (ENG., Illus.). 256p. 29.99 *(978-0-7548-1817-5(9))* Anness Publishing GBR. Dist: National Bk. Network.
Heinsoo, Rob, des. Three-Dragon Ante: Emperor's Gambit: A D&D Game. 2010. (4th Edition D&D Ser.). (ENG.). 14.99 *(978-0-7869-5478-0(7))* Wizards of the Coast.
Heitman, Bethany & Ruderman, Zoe. Cosmo's Truth or Dare: Our Naughtiest Sex Game Ever! 2010. (ENG., Illus.). 120p. 9.95 *(978-1-58816-544-2(2))* Hearst Communications, Inc.
Hoffmann, Professor. The Illustrated Book of Patience Games. 2008. pap. *(978-1-84830-028-6(X)*, Wildhern Pr.) Echo Library.
Hoyle's Official Rules of Card Games. (Illus.). 576p. pap. *(978-1-86515-153-3(X))* Hinkler Bks. Pty. Ltd.
Indian Chiefs of the Old West. (Old West Series Card Games Ser.). 6.00 *(978-1-57281-013-6(0)*, OWC54) U.S. Games Systems, Inc.
Jacobs, Byon. Think Like a Poker Pro: How to study, plan & play like a Professional. 2011. (ENG., Illus.). 304p. pap. 34.95 *(978-1-904468-55-4(1))* D & B Publishing GBR. Dist: Globe Pequot Pr., The.
Jay, Joshua. Magic: The Complete Course. 2008. (ENG., Illus.). 288p. 19.95 *(978-0-7611-4987-3(2)*, 0761149872) Workman Publishing Co., Inc.
Kovalic, John, illus. The Good, the Bad, & the Munchkin. 2007. (Munchkin Ser.). 24.95 *(978-1-55634-769-6(3))* Jackson, Steve Games, Inc.
Lawmen of the Old West. (Old West Series Card Games Ser.). 6.00 *(978-1-57281-014-3(9)*, OWL54) U.S. Games Systems, Inc.
Lee, Stuart. Magic Aces: A Complete Routine of Amazing Card Tricks. 2011. 100p. pap. 11.65 ***(978-1-4269-6201-1(0))*** Trafford Publishing.
Lohner, Henry. Poker, Blackjack, Faro: Internationale Bibliographie des Kartenglücksspiels; International Bibliography of Gambler's Card Games. 2010. 246p. pap. 49.50 *(978-3-8391-2508-3(1))* Bks. on Demand.
Louie, Laughing. The SideKick to Basic Blackjack Strategy: The SideKick was Developed to Enhance Basic Blackjack Strategy. 2011. 56p. pap. 14.99 ***(978-1-4567-6614-6(7))*** AuthorHouse.
Marks, Arnold. Card Games Properly Explained: Poker, Canasta, Cribbage, Gin Rummy, Whist, & Much More. 2010. (ENG., Illus.). 176p. pap. 12.95 *(978-1-61608-145-4(7)*, 608145) Skyhorse Publishing Co., Inc.
McCaulay, Philip Martin. Blackjack Card Counting. 2009. 48p. pap. 14.95 *(978-0-557-17893-3(2))* Lulu Enterprises Inc.
McEvoy, Tom & Cloutier, T. J. Championship No-Limit & Pot-Limit Hold'em. 2009. (ENG.). 304p. pap. 19.95 *(978-1-58042-258-1(6))* Cardoza Publishing.

—Championship Omaha: Omaha High-Low, Pot-Limit Omaha & Limit Omaha High. 2009. (ENG.). 336p. pap. 19.95 (978-1-58042-259-8(4)) Cardoza Publishing.

McNeely, Scott. Card Games: The Comprehensive Guide to More Than 350 Games. 2009. (ENG., Illus.). 400p. 19.95 (978-0-8118-6642-2(4)) Chronicle Bks. LLC.

Mew, Matt. Fruits & Veggies Makin' Faces Card Game. 2007. (J). 12.99 (978-0-9747064-2-9(6), ABridge Club) Russ Invision.

Moran, Mark. 52,000 Hands Later. 2007. 56p. pap. 14.99 (978-1-4303-1299-4(8)) Lulu Enterprises Inc.

MTG. MTG Shadowmoor Blister. 2008. 3.99 (978-0-7869-4904-5(X)) Wizards of the Coast.

—MTG Shadowmoor Fat Pack. 2008. 34.99 (978-0-7869-4907-6(4)) Wizards of the Coast.

—MTG Shadowmoor Theme Deck. 2008. 12.29 (978-0-7869-4894-9(9)) Wizards of the Coast.

Naruto. Naruto Shippuden Theme Deck. 2008. 9.99 (978-1-60584-079-6(3)) Diamond Bk. Distributors.

Naruto, ed. Naruto Broken Promises Blister. 2010. bds. 4.99 (978-1-60584-210-3(9)) Diamond Comic Distributors, Inc.

—Naruto Fierce Ambitions Tin. 2010. 14.99 (978-1-60584-209-7(5)) Diamond Comic Distributors, Inc.

Neil H. Timm. Precision Simplified: For 2/1 Game Force Players. 2010. 172p. pap. 13.96 (978-1-4269-2430-9(5)) Trafford Publishing.

—2/1 Game Force a Modern Approach: For Beginning & Intermediate Players. 2010. 308p. pap. 19.96 (978-1-4269-2429-3(1)) Trafford Publishing.

Newell, Eric. Minnesota Whist. 2010. 98p. pap. 8.99 (978-0-557-76334-4(7)) Lulu Enterprises Inc.

Nodwick: The Card Game. 18.00 (978-0-9658694-6-1(6)) Impressions.

Olarnick, Daniel. The Prometheus Stratagem. 2008. 63p. pap. 14.95 (978-0-7414-4555-1(7)) Infinity Publishing.

Old West Card Games. (Old West Series Card Games Ser.). 72.00 (978-1-57281-072-3(6), DOLW12) U.S. Games Systems, Inc.

Orbanes, Philip E. Deluxe Rook with a Book: Includes Cards. Date not set. 80p. pap. 7.95 (978-1-891056-24-6(7)) Winning Moves.

—Rook in a Book. Date not set. (Illus.). 80p. mass mkt. 5.95 (978-1-891056-25-3(5)) Winning Moves.

Orijinz. 2007. 14.95 (978-0-9723349-1-4(2)) 2nd ed. 2008. 14.95 (978-0-9723349-0-7(4)) Entspire LLC.

Outlaws of the Old West. (Old West Series Card Games Ser.). 6.00 (978-1-57281-016-7(5), OWO54) U.S. Games Systems, Inc.

Parlett, David. Teach Yourself Card Games. 3rd ed. 2006. (Teach Yourself: Games/Hobbies/Sports Ser.). (ENG., Illus.). 228p. per. 11.95 (978-0-07-148258-5(X), 007148258X) McGraw-Hill Cos., The.

Phillips, Hubert. The Complete Book of Card Games. 2008. 272p. (978-1-4437-3761-6(5), Home Farm Bks.) Read Bks.

Pokemon. Legends Awakened Blister. 2008. 3.79 (978-1-60438-025-5(X)) Pokemon, USA, Inc.

Reese, Terence & Bird, David. Miracles of Card Play. 2009. (Master Bridge Ser.). (ENG.). 160p. pap. 27.95 (978-0-297-84494-5(6)) Orion Publishing Group, Ltd. GBR. Dist: Independent Pubs. Group.

Ringel, Howard. Make the Winning Bid: Bidding Guidelines for the Advancing Player. 2008. 224p. pap. 15.95 (978-1-60264-279-9(6)) Virtualbookworm.com Publishing, Inc.

Riot Card Game. 11.99 (978-0-9719484-0-2(2)) Impressions.

Rosen, Jennifer & Smith, Stefan. Cork Jester's Wine Teasers Wine Game. 2007. (Illus.). 12.95 (978-0-9801319-0-1(1)) Fine Wine Games, Inc.

Ryvah Coloring Book. 2006. (YA). per. 19.95 (978-0-9787693-3-8(3)) Leonard, Michael.

Sager, Mike. Journeys in Time: Highlander Character Creation Aid. 14.95 (978-1-887032-27-8(4)) Thunder Castle Games, Inc.

—Journeys in Time: Highlander GM Screen. 9.95 (978-1-887032-26-1(6)) Thunder Castle Games, Inc.

—Journeys in Time: Highlander the RPG. 24.95 (978-1-887032-25-4(8)) Thunder Castle Games, Inc.

—Journeys in Time No. 3: Highlander Source Book. 19.95 (978-1-887032-31-5(2)) Thunder Castle Games, Inc.

—Sword Master: Highlander 56 Card Deck. 8.95 (978-1-887032-32-2(0)) Thunder Castle Games, Inc.

—Sword Master: Highlander Box of 12 Decks. 107.40 (978-1-887032-33-9(9)) Thunder Castle Games, Inc.

—Sword Master: Highlander Box of 36 Packs. 88.20 (978-1-887032-34-6(7)) Thunder Castle Games, Inc.

—Towers in Time: T in T Amazon 54 Card Decks. 6.95 (978-1-887032-09-4(6)) Thunder Castle Games, Inc.

—Towers in Time: T in T Amazon 8 Card Decks. 1.45 (978-1-887032-10-0(X)) Thunder Castle Games, Inc.

—Towers in Time: T in T Greek Edition 54 Card Deck. 6.95 (978-1-887032-05-6(3)) Thunder Castle Games, Inc.

—Towers in Time: T in T Greek Edition Box of 12 Decks. 83.40 (978-1-887032-07-0(X)) Thunder Castle Games, Inc.

—Towers in Time: T in T Greek Edition Box of 60 Packs. 87.00 (978-1-887032-08-7(8)) Thunder Castle Games, Inc.

—Towers in Time: T in T Norse 54 Card Deck. 6.95 (978-1-887032-17-9(7)) Thunder Castle Games, Inc.

—Towers in Time: T in T Norse Box of 12 Decks. 83.40 (978-1-887032-19-3(3)) Thunder Castle Games, Inc.

—Towers in Time: T in T Original Edition 54 Card Deck. 6.95 (978-1-887032-01-8(0)) Thunder Castle Games, Inc.

—Towers in Time: T in T Original Edition Box of 12 Decks. 83.40 (978-1-887032-03-2(7)) Thunder Castle Games, Inc.

—Towers in Time: T in T Original Edition Box of 60 Packs. 87.00 (978-1-887032-04-9(5)) Thunder Castle Games, Inc.

—Towers in Time: T in T Original Edition Promo Deck. (One Thousand One Ser.). 9.95 (978-1-887032-00-1(2)) Thunder Castle Games, Inc.

—Towers in Time: T in T Zodiac 54 Card Deck. 6.95 (978-1-887032-13-1(4)) Thunder Castle Games, Inc.

—Towers in Time: T in T Zodiac Box of 12 Decks. 83.40 (978-1-887032-15-5(0)) Thunder Castle Games, Inc.

Schaffner, Karl. The Yantra Deck: The Art of Being Present. 2008. (Illus.). 150p. 35.00 (978-0-615-17550-8(3)) Vayu Publishing.

Schulman, Heidi. The Original Dog Tarot: Divine the Canine Mind. 2012. (ENG., Illus.). 64p. 14.95 (978-0-307-98493-7(1), Potter Style) Crown Publishing Group.

Shaain, Michael. Man Bites Dog. 2012. (Spinner Bks.). (ENG.). pap. 9.95 (978-1-57561-707-7(2)) Univ. Games.

Sleeper, Ryan. The Ultimate Hold 'Em Book: The Ultimate Winners Guide for No Limit Hold 'Em Players. 2009. 392p. pap. 24.99 (978-1-4389-5483-7(2)) AuthorHouse.

Spanish Playing Cards. 60.00 (978-1-57281-362-5(8), DSP50) U.S. Games Systems, Inc.

Sper, Emily. Hanukkah Card Games. 2006. (J). 14.95 (978-0-9754902-0-4(6)) Sper, Emily.

—Hanukkah Crazy 8's. 2006. (J). 4.95 (978-0-9754902-2-8(2)) Sper, Emily.

—Hanukkah Go Fish. 2006. (J). 4.95 (978-0-9754902-1-1(4)) Sper, Emily.

—Hanukkah Rummy. 2006. (J). 4.95 (978-0-9754902-3-5(0)) Sper, Emily.

—Passover Go Fish. 2006. (J). 4.95 (978-0-9754902-4-2(9)) Sper, Emily.

Summers, Jake. Dangerous Hands in Texas Holdem. 2007. 277p. pap. 19.93 (978-0-615-14977-6(4)) Tae Bks.

Tucker, Rob. Playing No-Limit Hold'em as a Business. 2010. (ENG.). 304p. pap. 19.95 (978-1-58042-263-5(2)) Cardoza Publishing.

—Playing Sit & Go Poker as a Business. 2011. (ENG.). 176p. pap. 19.95 (978-1-58042-265-9(9)) Cardoza Publishing.

U S Games Systems. Wizard Junior Card Game. 2006. (Wizard Card Games Ser.). (J). (gr. 3-7). 6.00 (978-1-57281-559-9(0), WZJR36) U.S. Games Systems, Inc.

U S Games Systems, creator. Historical Signals & Semaphores Collector's Set. 2006. (Illus.). 60p. pap. 16.95 (978-1-57281-563-6(9), SFS108) U.S. Games Systems, Inc.

Upper Deck. Ult Battles Booster. 2008. 2.99 (978-1-59945-656-0(7)) Upper Deck Co., LLC,The.

—Ult Battles Hulk Starter. 2008. 9.99 (978-1-59945-654-6(0)) Upper Deck Co., LLC,The.

—Ult Battles Iron Man Starter. 2008. 9.99 (978-1-59945-652-2(4)) Upper Deck Co., LLC,The.

Upper Deck Entertainment Staff. World of Warcraft Heroes of Azeroth Booster. 2006. 3.99 (978-1-59945-031-5(3)) Upper Deck Co., LLC,The.

—World of Warcraft Heroes of Azeroth Starter Deck. 2006. 15.99 (978-1-59945-029-2(1)) Upper Deck Co., LLC,The.

—WoW Molten Core Raid Deck. 2007. 29.99 (978-1-59945-091-9(7)) Upper Deck Co., LLC,The.

Villarreal, N. R. No Limit Hold 'Em: 15 Costly Mistakes to Avoid while Playing No Limit Texas Hold 'EM: The Book of Blunders. 2006. (ENG.). 68p. per. 9.95 (978-1-59800-723-7(8)) Outskirts Pr., Inc.

Walker, Katarina. The Pro's Guide to Spanish 21 & Australian Pontoon. 2008. 208p. pap. 25.00 (978-1-4357-1065-8(7)) Lulu Enterprises Inc.

Warren, Ken. Ken Warren Teaches - 7-Card Stud: High - High-Low - Razz. 2008. (ENG., Illus.). 240p. pap. 14.95 (978-1-58042-221-5(7)) Cardoza Publishing.

Wheeler, Ralph. 333 Winning Hold'em Tips. 2009. (ENG.). 176p. pap. 9.95 (978-1-58042-260-4(8)) Cardoza Publishing.

Wiedman, Charlie. Lunch Money. 2007. pap. 19.95 (978-1-887801-47-8(2), Atlas Games) Trident, Inc.

Wizards of the Coast Staff. Magic Worldwake Fat Pack. 2010. pap. 34.99 (978-0-7869-5431-5(0)) Wizards of the Coast.

—Magic Worldwake Intro Pack. 2010. pap. 12.29 (978-0-7869-5424-7(8)) Wizards of the Coast.

WOW Naxxramas Treasure Pack. 2009. 11.99 (978-1-60806-041-2(1)) Upper Deck Co., LLC,The.

Zerner, Amy & Farber, Monte. Little Reminders - The law of Attraction: 36 Oracle Cards to Guide You to Wealth & Prosperity: the Law of Attraction. 2008. (ENG., Illus.). 80p. 14.95 (978-0-9786968-8-7(3)) Sterling Publishing Co., Inc.

—Little Reminders about Love & Relationships. 2007. (ENG., Illus.). 36p. 12.95 (978-0-9786968-4-9(0)) Sterling Publishing Co., Inc.

30 Minutes or Less: Favorite Food. (Illus.). 96p. (978-1-4054-7306-4(1)) Parragon, Inc.

CARD GAMES—HISTORY

Harwood, Jeremy & Sippetts, Trevor. The Step-by-Step Guide to Playing World's Best 250 Card Games: Including Bridge, Poker, Family Games & Solitaires. 2010. (ENG., Illus.). 512p. 35.00 (978-0-7548-2086-4(6)) Anness Publishing GBR. Dist: National Bk. Network.

Sherman, Wynn A. Miles of Heart: The Story of the Dan Deangelo Invitational Hearts Tournament. 2008. 229p. pap. 24.95 (978-1-60474-139-1(2)) PublishAmerica, Inc.

Topsfield, Andrew. The Art of Play: Board & Card Games of India. 2007. 168p. 66.00 (978-81-502-6769-6(7)) Marg Pubns. IND. Dist: National Bk. Network.

CARD SHARPING

see Cardsharping

CARD SYSTEM IN BUSINESS

see also Punched Card Systems

Arnold, Horace Lucian, ed. The Complete Cost Keeper: Some Original Systems of Shop Cost Keeping or Factory Accounting (1899) 2009. 430p. pap. 36.95 (978-1-120-73909-4(8)) Kessinger Publishing, LLC.

Byles, R. B. The Card Index System; Its Principles, Uses, Operation, & Component Parts. 2008. 152p. pap. (978-1-4097-9530-8(6)) Read Bks.

Spencer, Donna. Card Sorting: Designing Usable Categories. 2009. (ENG., Illus.). 161p. pap. 36.00 (978-1-933820-02-6(0)) Rosenfeld Media, LLC.

CARD TRICKS

see also Fortune-Telling

Chartwell Books Staff, creator. Card & Magic Tricks: Over 100 Tricks Guaranteed to Amaze & Entertain. 2009. (ENG., Illus.). 224p. spiral bd., instr.'s hndbk. ed. 14.99 (978-0-7858-2539-5(8), 0785825398, Chartwell) Book Sales, Inc.

Coppini, Mark. 15 Great Card Forces. 2010. (ENG., Illus.). 53p. (978-1-907629-08-2(4)) ShieldCrest.

Diaconis, Persi & Graham, Ron. Magical Mathematics: The Mathematical Ideas that Animate Great Magic Tricks. 2011. (ENG., Illus.). 258p. 29.95 (978-0-691-15164-9(4)) Princeton Univ. Pr.

Diagram Group Staff. Little Giant Encyclopedia: Card & Magic Tricks. 2008. (ENG., Illus.). 512p. pap. 9.95 (978-1-4027-6005-1(1)) Sterling Publishing Co., Inc.

Einhorn, Nicholas. Card Magic: How to Shuffle, Control & Force Cards, Including Special Gimmicks & Advanced Flourishes. 2009. (ENG., Illus.). 96p. pap. 16.99 (978-1-84476-749-6(3)) Anness Publishing GBR. Dist: National Bk. Network.

Eldin, Peter. Card Tricks. 2010. (ENG., Illus.). 160p. pap. 9.95 (978-0-550-10471-7(2)) Chambers Harrap Pubs., Ltd. GBR. Dist: Independent Pubs. Group.

Elliott, James William. Elliott's Last Legacy: Secrets of the King of All Kard Kings. Houdini, Harry, ed. 2011. 326p. 50.95 (978-1-258-09921-3(7)) Literary Licensing, LLC.

Fulves, Karl. Foolproof Card Tricks for the Amateur Magician. 2009. (Dover Magic Bks.). (ENG.). 304p. pap. 11.95 (978-0-486-47270-6(1)) Dover Pubns., Inc.

Giobbi, Roberto. Card College Light. 2006. (Illus.). 174p. 35.00 (978-0-945296-54-6(1)) Hermetic Pr., Inc.

Hartman, J. K. Card Dupery. 2007. (Illus.). 408p. 52.00 (978-0-945296-56-0(8)) Hermetic Pr., Inc.

Hugard, Jean. The Royal Road to Card Magic. 2008. 308p. (978-1-4437-3454-7(3), Pomona Pr.) Read Bks.

Jay, Joshua. Joshua Jay's Amazing Book: Tricks, Shuffles, Games & Hustles Plus Bets You Can't Lose. 2010. (ENG., Illus.). 208p. (J). 16.95 (978-0-7611-5842-4(1), 0761158421) Workman Publishing Co., Inc.

Lane, Mike. Card Magic. 2012. (Miraculous Magic Tricks Ser.). (ENG., Illus.). 32p. (gr. 3-6). pap. 11.75 (978-1-4488-6731-8(2)); lib. bdg. 25.25 (978-1-61533-512-1(9)) Windmill Bks.

—Coin Magic. 2012. (Miraculous Magic Tricks Ser.). (ENG., Illus.). 32p. (gr. 3-6). pap. 11.75 (978-1-4488-6727-1(4)); lib. bdg. 25.25 (978-1-61533-510-7(2)) Windmill Bks.

Lee, Stuart. Old Wine in a New Bottle: Classic Card Tricks Spectacularly Re-Worked. 2010. 180p. pap. 16.50 (978-1-4251-8660-9(2)) Trafford Publishing.

Ritchey, David. 26 Card Tricks: For the Intermediate Level Magician Using a Standard Deck. 2010. (978-0-929915-52-4(6)) Headline Bks.

Roterberg, A. New Era Card Tricks - Magic with Cards. 2008. (Illus.). 296p. (978-1-4437-3776-0(3), Home Farm Bks.) Read Bks.

CARDANO, GIROLAMO, 1501-1576

Morley, Henry. Life of Girolamo Cardano of Milan Physic. 2006. (ENG.). pap. 30.95 (978-1-4286-4691-9(4)); pap. 30.95 (978-1-4286-4690-2(6)) Kessinger Publishing, LLC.

Siraisi, Nancy G. The Clock & the Mirror: Girolamo Cardano & Renaissance Medicine. 2012. (ENG., Illus.). 336p. (C). pap. 29.95 (978-0-691-14433-7(8)) Princeton Univ. Pr.

Waters, George William. Jerome Cardan. 2007. 212p. (ENG.). 42.99 (978-1-4280-7476-7(7)); per. 36.99 (978-1-4280-7471-2(6)) IndyPublish.com.

—Jerome Cardan: A Biographical Study. 2007. (ENG.). 228p. pap. 20.99 (978-1-4346-3250-0(4)); 258p. pap. 23.99 (978-1-4346-3251-7(2)) BiblioBazaar.

CARDBOARD

see Paperboard

CARDENAS, LAZARO, 1895-1970

Ashby, Joe C. Organized Labor & the Mexican Revolution under Lázaro Cárdenas. 2011. (ENG.). 362p. pap. 50.00 (978-0-8078-9609-9(8)) Univ. of North Carolina Pr.

González, Samuel. El Cardenismo, 1932-1940. León, ed. 2010. (Historia Ser.). (SPA.). 519p. pap. 31.95 (978-607-16-0410-1(9)) Fondo de Cultura Económica.

Hurtado Martín, Santiago. Justicia, Desarrollo y Equidad: Los Diez Pilares Fundacionales Del Estado y la Política Social de Lázaro Cárdenas. 2009. (SPA.). 153p. 13.00 (978-970-722-712-5(5)) Plaza y Valdes, S.A. de C.V. MEX. Dist: Sony Electronics.

Kiddle, Amelia M. & Muñoz, María L. O., eds. Populism in Twentieth Century Mexico: The Presidencies of Lázaro Cárdenas & Luis Echeverría. 2010. (ENG., Illus.). 320p. 55.00 (978-0-8165-2918-6(3)) Univ. of Arizona Pr.

CARDIA

Chandrasoma, Parakrama T. Diagnostic Atlas of Gastroesophageal Reflux Disease: A New Histology-Based Method. 2007. (ENG., Illus.). 320p. 185.00 (978-0-12-373605-5(6), Academic Pr.) Elsevier Science & Technology Bks

Evaluating GERD Symptoms: ReQuest: 2007. pap. (978-3-8055-8315-2(X)) Karger, S. AG.

Fass, FACP, FACG, FACG, Ronnie, Ronnie. Gastroesophageal Reflux Disease (GERD) PocketGuide (2010) 2010. 6p. 7.95 (978-0-9845053-1-9(8)) International Guidelines Ctr., Inc.

Fielding, John Wl & Hallissey, Michael T., eds. Upper Gastrointestinal Surgery. 2010. (Springer Specialist Surgery Ser.). (ENG., Illus.). xii, 396p. pap. 239.00 (978-1-84996-888-1(8), 1849968888) Springer.

Magee, Elaine. If I Have Acid Reflux: Nutrition You Can Live With. rev. ed. 2008. (Tell Me What to Eat Ser.). (ENG.). 1p. pap. 12.99 (978-1-60163-019-3(0)) Career Pr., Inc.

Mittal, Ravinder. Motor Function of the Pharynx, Esophagus, & Its Sphincters. 2011. (Colloquium Series on Integrated Systems Physiology: from Molecule to Function to Disease Ser.). 100p. pap. 35.00 (978-1-61504-333-0(0)) Morgan & Claypool Pubs.

The Reflux Book: A Parent's Guide to Gastroesophageal Reflux. 2007. (Illus.). 288p. pap. 20.00 (978-0-615-18269-8(0)) Intensive Care Parenting, LLC.

Rodriguez, Jorge E. & Wyler, Susan. The Acid Reflux Solution: A Cookbook & Lifestyle Guide for Healing Heartburn Naturally. 2012. (ENG.). 224p. (978-1-60774-228-9(4)); (Illus.). pap. 21.99 (978-1-60774-227-2(6)) Ten Speed Pr.

CARDIAC ARREST

see also Cardiac Resuscitation; CPR (First Aid); Heart Failure

Aehlert, Barbara. Rapid ACLS on PDA with ACLS Quick Review Study Guide. 3rd ed. 2007. pap. 42.95 (978-0-323-05274-0(6), Mosby/JEMS) Elsevier - Health Sciences Div.

Aehlert, Barbara J. ACLS Study Cards. 3rd ed. 2008. (ENG., Illus.). 144p. 31.95 (978-0-323-05810-0(8), Mosby) Elsevier - Health Sciences Div.

—RAPID ACLS - CD-ROM PDA Software Powered by Skyscape. 2nd rev. ed. 2007. (Rapid Ser.). (ENG.). cd-rom 24.95 (978-0-323-04972-6(9), Mosby/JEMS) Elsevier - Health Sciences Div.

Ahmad, Rashidi, et al. Adult Cardiopulmonary Resuscitation. 2010. 128p. pap. (978-3-8383-8635-5(3)) Lambert Academic Publishing.

Al-Ahmad, Amin, et al, eds. Ventricular Arrhythmias & Sudden Cardiac Death: Mechanism, Ablation, & Defibrillation. 2008. (ENG., Illus.). 360p. 185.95 (978-1-4051-6114-5(0), Wiley-Blackwell) Wiley, John & Sons, Inc.

American College of Emergency Physicians (ACEP). EACLS Study Guide. 2nd rev. ed. 2006. 130p. (C). pap. 26.95 (978-0-7637-4954-5(0)) Jones & Bartlett Learning, LLC.

—EACLS Study Guide - Express PDF. 2nd rev. ed. 2009. pap. 15.95 (978-0-7637-8613-7(6)) Jones & Bartlett Learning, LLC.

American Heart Association, creator. Advanced Cardiovascular Life Support Provider Manual. 2011. pap. 53.75 (978-1-61669-010-6(0)) American Heart Assn., Inc.

Baker, Paul W. & Grantham, Hugh J. M., eds. Resuscitation of Patients in Ventricular Fibrillation from the Perspective of Emergency Medical Services. 2010. (Cardiology Research & Clinical Developments Ser.). 72p. pap. 43.00 (978-1-60876-668-0(3), Nova Biomedical Bks.) Nova Science Pubs., Inc.

Bakris, George L., ed. The Kidney in Heart Failure. 2012. (ENG., Illus.). xii, 248p. 209.00 (978-1-4614-3693-5(1), 1461436931) Springer.

Basson, Craig T. & Lerman, Bruce B. Ischemic Heart Disease & Arrhythmias. 2009. 379.00 (978-1-933864-58-7(3)) Demos Medical Publishing, LLC.

Bayés de Luna, Antonio, et al, eds. Arrhythmias & Sudden Death in Athletes. 2010. (Developments in Cardiovascular Medicine Ser.). 176p. pap. 105.00 (978-90-481-5470-8(7), 9048154707) Springer.

Brady, Bill, et al. Cardiac Arrest, an Issue of Emergency Medicine Clinics. 2011. (Clinics: Internal Medicine Ser.: 30-1). (ENG., Illus.). 960p. 115.00 (978-1-4557-3854-0(9), Saunders) Elsevier - Health Sciences Div.

Brugada, Josep, et al, eds. Cardiac Resynchronization Therapy. 2007. (ENG., Illus.). 338p. 269.95 (978-1-84184-637-8(6), Informa Healthcare) Taylor & Francis Group GBR. Dist: Taylor & Francis Group.

Brugada, Ramon. Clinical Approach to Sudden Cardiac Death Syndromes. 2010. (Illus.). xvi, 340p. 139.00 (978-1-84882-926-8(4), 1848829264) Springer.

Capucci. Sudden Cardiac Death. 2006. (ENG., Illus.). 212p. 160.00 (978-1-84184-578-4(7)) Taylor & Francis Group.

Derr, Paula & Criddle, Laura M. Emergency & Critical Care: Pocket Guide ACLS Version. 7th ed. 2012. (Illus.). 193p. spiral bd. 21.95 (978-1-890495-58-9(1)) Jones & Bartlett Learning, LLC.

Doyle, Leonard J. & Saltsman, Richard A. Cardiopulmonary Resuscitation: Procedures & Challenges. 2011. (978-1-62100-139-3(3)) Nova Science Pubs., Inc.

Eisenberg, Mickey S. Resuscitate! How Your Community Can Improve Survival from Sudden Cardiac Arrest. 2009. (ENG., Illus.). 288p. pap. 29.95 (978-0-295-98889-4(4)) Univ. of Washington Pr.

Fix, Shaun & Lezon, Kathleen. Success! in ACLS: Tips & Tricks for Passing the ACLS Course. 2007. (ENG., Illus.). 192p. (C). pap. 34.00 (978-0-13-117621-8(8), Prentice Hall) Prentice Hall PTR.

C

Gossman, William, et al. ACLS Review. 3rd ed. 2007. (Pearls of Wisdom Medicine Ser.). (ENG., Illus.). 116p. per. 28.00 *(978-0-07-149257-7(7),* 0071492577, McGraw-Hill/Appleton & Lange) McGraw-Hill Professional Publishing.

Grauer, Ken. Arrhythmia Management & Cardiac Arrest: Arrhythmia Management & Cardiac Arrest: A Pocket Brain Approach. 2007. (ENG., Illus.). 106p. pap. 16.00 *(978-0-9663389-1-1(X))* KG/EKG Pr.

Hartpence, Craig. Early Access to Automated External Defibrillators. 2010. 98p. pap. 18.90 *(978-0-557-50577-7(1))* Lulu Enterprises Inc.

Johnson, C. Bruce. Heart to Heart: 12 People Discover Better Lives after Their Heart Attacks. 2009. 220p. 27.95 *(978-1-4401-7074-4(6))*; pap. 17.95 *(978-1-4401-7075-1(4))* iUniverse, Inc.

Kunz, Michele G. Zombie Notes ACLS Certification Exam Prep. Kunz, Joseph C., Jr., ed. & des. by. 2011. 2p. mass mkt. 4.99 *(978-1-933230-47-4(9))* Dickson Keanaghan, LLC.

—Zombie Notes BCLS Certification Exam Prep. Kunz, Joseph C., Jr., ed. & des. by. 2011. 2p. mass mkt. 4.99 *(978-1-933230-48-1(7))* Dickson Keanaghan, LLC.

Lippincott. ACLS Review Made Incredibly Easy. 2nd rev. ed. 2012. (Incredibly Easy! Ser.). (ENG.). 352p. pap. 43.99 *(978-1-60831-288-7(7))* Lippincott Williams & Wilkins.

Mandell, Joyce E., ed. Ventricular Fibrillation & Acute Coronary Syndrome. 2010. (Cardiology Research & Clinical Developments Ser.). 129.00 *(978-1-61728-969-9(8))* Nova Science Pubs., Inc.

O'Keefe, James H., et al. The ECG Criteria Book. 2nd rev. ed. 2009. 186p. pap. 20.95 *(978-0-7637-6252-0(0))* Jones & Bartlett Learning, LLC.

Pagaduan, Angel N. Survival Lessons from a Heart Attack. 2009. 54p. pap. 15.99 *(978-1-4415-4179-6(9))* Xlibris Corp.

Podesser, Bruno K. & Chambers, David J., eds. New solutions for the Heart: An update in advanced perioperative Protection. 2010. (ENG., Illus.). 400p. 209.00 *(978-3-211-85547-8(5),* 3211855475) Springer.

Sato, Atsuko & Hayashi, Seiji. Coronary Artery Disease, Cardiac Arrest, & Bypass Surgery: Risk Factors, Health Effects, & Outcomes. 2012. ***(978-1-62100-976-4(9))*** Nova Science Pubs., Inc.

Weiss, Raul & Daoud, Emile. Sudden Cardiac Death: Heart Failure Clinics. 2011. (Clinics: Internal Medicine Ser.: 7-2). (ENG., Illus.). 176p. 99.00 *(978-1-4557-0458-3(X),* Saunders) Elsevier - Health Sciences Div.

Xanthos, Theodoros. Drugs in Cardiopulmonary Resuscitation. 2011. (Series: Cardiology Research & Clinical Developments Ser.). 145.00 *(978-1-61122-512-9(4))* Nova Science Pubs., Inc.

CARDIAC CATHETERIZATION

Askari, Arman T. Introductory Guide to Cardiac Catheterization. Askari, Arman T. et al, eds. 2nd rev. ed. 2010. (ENG., Illus.). 224p. pap. 64.99 *(978-1-60547-885-2(7))* Lippincott Williams & Wilkins.

Bergersen, Lisa. Congenital Heart Disease: The Catheterization Manual. 2008. (ENG., Illus.). viii, 200p. pap. 69.95 *(978-0-387-77291-2(X),* 038777291X) Springer.

Brusch, John L., ed. Infective Endocarditis: Management in the Era of Intravascular Devices. 2007. (Infectious Disease & Therapy Ser.: Vol. 41). (ENG., Illus.). 388p. 300.00 *(978-0-8493-7097-7(3),* Informa Healthcare) Taylor & Francis Group GBR. Dist: Taylor & Francis Group.

Butman, Samuel M., ed. Complications of Percutaneous Coronary Interventions. 2010. (Illus.). xvi, 170p. pap. 124.00 *(978-1-4419-2031-7(5),* 1441920315) Springer.

Casella, Michela & Dello Russo, Antonio. An Atlas of Radioscopic Catheter Placement for the Electrophysiologist. 2008. (Illus.). 160p. 279.00 *(978-1-84800-226-5(2))* Springer.

Huber, Christoph. Transcatheter Valve Therapies. 2009. (ENG.). 272p. 250.00 *(978-1-4398-1078-1(8),* Informa Healthcare) Taylor & Francis Group.

Kern, Morton L. The Cardiac Catheterization Handbook. 5th ed. 2011. (ENG., Illus.). 432p. pap. 69.95 *(978-0-323-07902-0(4),* Mosby) Elsevier - Health Sciences Div.

Lemos. Diagnostic Methods in the Catheterization Laboratory. 2009. (ENG., Illus.). 288p. 250.00 *(978-1-84184-658-3(9),* Informa Healthcare) Taylor & Francis Group.

Mitchell, Andrew, et al. Cardiac Catheterization & Coronary Intervention. 2008. (Oxford Specialist Handbooks in Cardiology Ser.). (ENG., Illus.). 336p. pap. 75.00 *(978-0-19-929579-1(4))* Oxford Univ. Pr., Inc.

Mukherjee. Cardiac Catheterization, Coronary & Peripheral Angioplasty, and. 2010. (Illus.). 1000p. *(978-1-84184-664-4(3))* Informa Healthcare.

Ragosta, Michael. Cardiac Catheterization: An Atlas & DVD. 2009. (ENG., Illus.). 208p. 182.00 *(978-1-4160-3999-0(6),* Saunders) Elsevier - Health Sciences Div.

Redwood, Simon, et al, eds. Oxford Textbook of Interventional Cardiology. 2010. (ENG., Illus.). 700p. 225.00 *(978-0-19-956908-3(8))* Oxford Univ. Pr., Inc.

Sharma, Samin K. & Palacios, Igor. Percutaneous Approaches to Valvular Heart Disease, an Issue of Interventional Cardiology Clinics. 2012. (Clinics: Internal Medicine Ser.: 1-1). (ENG.). 110.00 ***(978-1-4557-3881-6(6)***, Saunders) Elsevier - Health Sciences Div.

Thakur, Ranjan & Natale, Andrea, eds. Transseptal Catheterization & Interventions. 2010. (ENG., Illus.). 256p. 115.00 *(978-0-9790164-1-7(X))* Cardiotext Publishing.

Waksman, Ron & Ajani, Andrew A. E., eds. Pharmacology in the Catheterization Laboratory. 2009. (ENG., Illus.). 400p. 165.95 *(978-1-4051-5704-9(6),* Wiley-Blackwell) Wiley, John & Sons, Inc.

Widimsky, Petr, et al. Catheterization & Interventional Cardiology in Adult Patients. 2010. (ENG., Illus.). 152p. pap. 24.95 *(978-0-19-955887-2(6))* Oxford Univ. Pr., Inc.

CARDIAC DIAGNOSTIC IMAGING
see Heart—Imaging

CARDIAC DISEASES
see Heart—Diseases

CARDIAC FUNCTION TESTS
see Heart Function Tests

CARDIAC IMAGING
see Heart—Imaging

CARDIAC MUSCLE
see Myocardium

CARDIAC NERVES
see Heart—Innervation

CARDIAC PACEMAKER, ARTIFICIAL
see Pacemaker, Artificial (Heart)

CARDIAC PACING
see also Pacemaker, Artificial (Heart)

Abbas, Abbas K. & Bassam, Rasha. Adaptive Controlling Aspects of Cardiac Pacemaker. 2011. (Synthesis Lectures on Biomedical Engineering Ser.). 100p. pap. 40.00 *(978-1-60845-154-8(2))* Morgan & Claypool Pubs.

Abraham, William. Cardiac Resynchronization Therapy in Heart Failure. Abraham, William T. & Baliga, Ragavendra R., eds. 2009. (ENG., Illus.). 208p. 154.99 *(978-0-7817-9844-0(2))* Lippincott Williams & Wilkins.

Barold, S. Serge, et al. Cardiac Pacemakers & Resynchronization Step by Step: An Illustrated Guide. 2nd ed. 2010. (ENG., Illus.). 480p. pap. 78.95 *(978-1-4051-8636-0(4),* Wiley-Blackwell) Wiley, John & Sons, Inc.

The Beat Goes On: A book for young adults living with a pacemaker or ICD. 2007. 7.20 *(978-1-933638-12-6(5))* Pritchett & Hull Assocs., Inc.

Bongiorni, Maria Grazia, ed. Transvenous Lead Extraction: From Simple Traction to Internal Transjugular Approach. 2010. (ENG., Illus.). 250p. pap. 139.00 *(978-88-470-1465-7(4),* 8847014654) Springer.

Curtis, Anne B. & Cardiovascular Services University of South Florida Staff. Fundamentals of Cardiac Pacing. 2009. 245p. pap. 76.95 *(978-0-7637-5630-7(X))* Jones & Bartlett Learning, LLC.

Delfino, Jana. Magnetic Resonance Imaging of Cardiac Dyssynchrony. 2009. 236p. pap. *(978-3-639-13166-6(5))* VDM Verlag Dr. Mueller e.K.

Edwards, Andrew & Polman, Remco. Pacing in Sport & Exercise: A Psychophysiological Perspective. 2012. ***(978-1-61942-420-3(7))*** Nova Science Pubs., Inc.

Efimov, Igor R., et al. Cardiac Bioelectric Therapy: Mechanisms & Practical Implications. 2008. (Illus.). 704p. 199.00 *(978-0-387-79402-0(6))* Springer.

Ellenbogen, Kenneth & Auricchio, Angelo, eds. Pacing to Support the Failing Heart. 2008. (American Heart Association Clinical Ser.: 5). (ENG., Illus.). 392p. 138.95 *(978-1-4051-7534-0(6),* Wiley-Blackwell) Wiley, John & Sons, Inc.

Ellenbogen, Kenneth A. & Wood, Mark A. Cardiac Pacing & ICDs. 5th ed. 2008. (ENG., Illus.). 568p. pap. 68.95 *(978-1-4051-6350-7(X),* Wiley-Blackwell) Wiley, John & Sons, Inc.

Ellenbogen, Kenneth A., et al. Clinical Cardiac Pacing, Defibrillation & Resynchronization Therapy: Expert Consult Premium Edition - Enhanced Online Features & Print. 4th ed. 2011. (ENG., Illus.). 1104p. 299.00 *(978-1-4377-1616-0(4),* Saunders) Elsevier - Health Sciences Div.

Hayes, David L. Cardiac Pacing, Defibrillation & Resynchronization. 3rd ed. 2012. (ENG.). 700p. 99.95 ***(978-0-470-65833-8(9)***, Wiley-Blackwell) Wiley, John & Sons, Inc.

Hayes, David L. & Asirvatham, Samuel J. Dictionary of Cardiac Pacing, Defibrillation, Resynchronization & Arrhythmias. 2nd ed. 2007. (ENG., Illus.). 320p. 49.00 *(978-0-9790164-0-0(1))* Cardiotext Publishing.

Hayes, David L. & Friedman, Paul A. Cardiac Pacing, Defibrillation & Resynchronization: A Clinical Approach. 2nd ed. 2008. (ENG., Illus.). 640p. 104.95 *(978-1-4051-6748-2(3),* Wiley-Blackwell) Wiley, John & Sons, Inc.

Kenny, Tom. Cardiac Pacing. 2nd ed. 2008. (Nuts & Bolts Ser.: 1). (ENG., Illus.). 184p. pap. 76.95 *(978-1-4051-8403-8(5),* Wiley-Blackwell) Wiley, John & Sons, Inc.

—The Nuts & Bolts of Cardiac Resynchronization Therapy. 2007. (Nuts & Bolts Ser.: 2). (ENG., Illus.). 224p. per. 70.95 *(978-1-4051-5372-0(5),* Wiley-Blackwell) Wiley, John & Sons, Inc.

—Paced ECG Interpretation. 2009. (Nuts & Bolts Ser.: 4). (ENG., Illus.). 488p. pap. 87.95 *(978-1-4051-8404-5(3),* Wiley-Blackwell) Wiley, John & Sons, Inc.

Kusumoto, Fred M. & Goldschlager, Nora F., eds. Cardiac Pacing for the Clinician. 2nd rev. ed. 2007. (Illus.). 742p. 99.00 *(978-0-387-72762-2(0))* Springer.

McAlister, Finlay. Cardiac Resynchronization Therapy & Implantable Cardiac Defibrillators in Left Ventricular Systolic Dysfunction. 2007. (AHRQ Publication Ser.: No. 152). (Illus.). x, 199p. *(978-1-58763-258-7(6))* Agency for Healthcare Research & Quality.

Mestan, Miroslav & Kvasnicka, Jiri. Optimization of Paced AV Delay Using Atrial Contribution Index. 2008. (Illus.). viii, 81p. pap. 50.00 *(978-1-60456-604-8(3))* Nova Science Pubs., Inc.

Mond, Harry G. & Karpawich, Peter P. Pacing Options in the Adult Patient with Congenital Heart Disease. 2006. (ENG., Illus.). 152p. 75.95 *(978-1-4051-5569-4(8),* Wiley-Blackwell) Wiley, John & Sons, Inc.

Moses, H. Weston & Mullin, James C. A Practical Guide to Cardiac Pacing. 6th rev. ed. 2007. (ENG., Illus.). 240p. pap. 84.99 *(978-0-7817-8881-6(1))* Lippincott Williams & Wilkins.

Rzavi, Mehdi & Razavi, Mehdi. Cardiac Rhythm Devices: A Case-Based Approach to Management. 2011. (Illus.). xiv, 175p. pap. 199.00 *(978-1-933864-67-9(2))* Demos Medical Publishing, LLC.

Saksena, Sanjeev & Camm, A. John. Electrophysiological Disorders of the Heart: Expert Consult - Online & Print. 2nd ed. 2011. (ENG., Illus.). 1488p. 279.00 *(978-1-4377-0285-9(6),* Saunders) Elsevier - Health Sciences Div.

Yu, Cheuk-Man, et al, eds. Cardiac Resynchronization Therapy. 2nd ed. 2008. (ENG., Illus.). 464p. 124.95 *(978-1-4051-7739-9(X),* Wiley-Blackwell) Wiley, John & Sons, Inc.

CARDIAC PATIENTS
see Heart—Diseases—Patients

CARDIAC RESUSCITATION
see also CPR (First Aid)

Aehlert, Barbara J. ACLS Study Cards. 3rd ed. 2008. (ENG., Illus.). 144p. 31.95 *(978-0-323-05810-0(8),* Mosby) Elsevier - Health Sciences Div.

—ACLS Study Guide. 4th ed. 2011. (ENG., Illus.). 424p. (C). pap. 29.95 *(978-0-323-08449-9(4),* Mosby) Elsevier - Health Sciences Div.

—Rapid ACLS. 2nd rev. ed. 2011. (ENG.). 208p. spiral bd. 24.95 *(978-0-323-08320-1(X),* Mosby/JEMS) Elsevier - Health Sciences Div.

—RAPID ACLS - CD-ROM PDA Software Powered by Skyscape. 2nd rev. ed. 2007. (Rapid Ser.). (ENG.). cd-rom 24.95 *(978-0-323-04972-6(9),* Mosby/JEMS) Elsevier - Health Sciences Div.

American Academy of Orthopaedic Surgeons (AAOS), et al. First Aid, CPR, & AED. 6th ed. 2011. 480p. pap. 51.95 *(978-1-4496-0946-7(5))* Jones & Bartlett Learning, LLC.

American College of Emergency Physicians (ACEP). EACLS Study Guide. 2nd rev. ed. 2006. 130p. (C). pap. 26.95 *(978-0-7637-4954-5(0))* Jones & Bartlett Learning, LLC.

—EACLS Study Guide - Express PDF. 2nd rev. ed. 2009. pap. 15.95 *(978-0-7637-8613-7(6))* Jones & Bartlett Learning, LLC.

American Heart Association, creator. Advanced Cardiovascular Life Support Provider Manual. 2011. pap. 53.75 ***(978-1-61669-010-6(0))*** American Heart Assn., Inc.

—Heartsaver Child & Infant CPR AED Wallet Card. 2011. (ENG., Illus.). ring bd. 17.50 ***(978-1-61669-064-9(X))*** American Heart Assn., Inc.

Gossman, William, et al. ACLS Review. 3rd ed. 2007. (Pearls of Wisdom Medicine Ser.). (ENG., Illus.). 116p. per. 28.00 *(978-0-07-149257-7(7),* 0071492577, McGraw-Hill/Appleton & Lange) McGraw-Hill Professional Publishing.

Hazinski, Mary Fran, et al, eds. Handbook of Emergency Cardiovascular Care: For Healthcare Providers. 2008. (Illus.). 99p. spiral bd. 27.75 *(978-0-87493-540-0(7))* American Heart Assn., Inc.

Keng Sheng, Chew. Cardiopulmonary Resuscitation in Malaysi: What's the Outcomes? 2010. 112p. pap. *(978-3-8383-8508-2(X))* Lambert Academic Publishing.

Kraus, William & Keteyian, Steven, eds. Cardiac Rehabilitation. 2007. (Contemporary Cardiology Ser.). (Illus.). 314p. 129.00 *(978-1-58829-770-9(5))* Humana Pr.

Kunz, Michele G. Zombie Notes ACLS Certification Exam Prep. Kunz, Joseph C., Jr., ed. & des. by. 2011. 2p. mass mkt. 4.99 *(978-1-933230-47-4(9))* Dickson Keanaghan, LLC.

—Zombie Notes BCLS Certification Exam Prep. Kunz, Joseph C., Jr., ed. & des. by. 2011. 2p. mass mkt. 4.99 *(978-1-933230-48-1(7))* Dickson Keanaghan, LLC.

Lippincott. ACLS Review Made Incredibly Easy. 2nd rev. ed. 2012. (Incredibly Easy! Ser.). (ENG.). 352p. pap. 43.99 *(978-1-60831-288-7(7))* Lippincott Williams & Wilkins.

McKenna, Kim. ACLS Essentials: Basics & More. 2008. (Illus.). xxiii, 246p. *(978-0-07-301791-4(4))* 2007. 160p. (C). pap. 51.56 *(978-0-07-299932-7(2),* 9780072999327) McGraw-Hill Cos., The.

Paradis, Norman, et al, eds. Cardiac Arrest: The Science & Practice of Resuscitation Medicine. 2nd rev. ed. 2007. (ENG., Illus.). 1374p. 208.00 *(978-0-521-84700-1(1))* Cambridge Univ. Pr.

Thygerson, Steven M. & Thygerson, Alton L. First Aid, CPR, & AED Essentials. 6th ed. 2011. 270p. pap. 34.95 ***(978-1-4496-2662-4(9))*** Jones & Bartlett Learning, LLC.

CARIDAC VALVES
see Heart Valves

CARDIACS
see Heart—Diseases—Patients

CARDIACS, COOKING FOR
see Heart—Diseases—Diet Therapy—Recipes

CARDIGAN WELSH CORGI

Beauchamp, Richard G. Welsh Corgis: Pembroke & Cardigan. 2nd rev. ed. 2010. (Complete Pet Owner's Manual Ser.). (ENG., Illus.). 112p. pap. 8.99 *(978-0-7641-4242-0(9))* Barron's Educational Series, Inc.

CARDINAL ARITHMETIC
see Cardinal Numbers

CARDINAL NUMBERS
see also Three (The Number)

Cram101 Textbook Reviews. Outlines & Highlights for the Mathematics of Infinity: A Guide to Great Ideas by Theodore G. Faticoni. 2011. 92p. pap. 27.95 ***(978-1-61830-509-1(3))*** Cram101 Inc.

Dannon, H. /Vic. The Continuum Hypothesis. 2008. (Illus.). 140p. per. 40.00 *(978-0-9801287-1-0(4))* Gauge Institute.

Eastis, David M. 7. 2011. (ENG., Illus.). 224p. pap. 16.00 *(978-1-4405-0652-9(3))* Adams Media Corp.

Faticoni, Theodore G. The Mathematics of Infinity: A Guide to Great Ideas. 2nd ed. 2012. (Pure & Applied Mathematics: a Wiley Series of Texts, Monographs & Tracts Ser.: 111). (ENG.). 358p. 79.95 ***(978-1-118-20448-1(4)***, Wiley) Wiley, John & Sons, Inc.

Holz, Michael, et al. Introduction to Cardinal Arithmetic. 2009. (Modern Birkhäuser Classics Ser.). Orig. Title: 978-3-7643-6124-2 (bat). 312p. pap. 39.95 *(978-3-0346-0327-0(4),* 3034603274) Birkhauser Verlag AG CHE. Dist: Springer.

MacQueen, Donald Sims. The Integration of MILLION into the English System of Number Words: A Diachronic Study. 2010. (Illus.). 320p. 80.95 *(978-3-631-60156-3(5))* Lang, Peter GmbH, Europaischer Verlag der Wissenschaften DEU. Dist: Lang, Peter.

Marohn, Mariel. One Million ... & More, 1 vol. 2011. (DUT, FRE & ENG., Illus.). 224p. pap. 49.95 *(978-90-79761-00-5(1))* Tectum B.V.B.A. BEL. Dist: Innovative Logistics.

Mengden, Ferdinand von. Cardinal Numerals: Old English from a Cross-Linguistic Perspective. 2010. (Topics in English Linguistics [TIEL] Ser.). (ENG., XIII, 329p. Illus.). 140.00 *(978-3-11-022034-6(2))*; 210.00 ***(978-3-11-173374-6(2))*** De Gruyter, Mouton DEU. Dist: de Gruyter, Walter GmbH & Co. KG.

Monk, J. Donald. Cardinal Invariants on Boolean Algebras. 2009. (Modern Birkhäuser Classics Ser.). Orig. Title: 978-3-7643-5402-2 (pm). 308p. pap. 59.95 *(978-3-0346-0333-1(9),* 3034603339) Birkhauser Verlag AG CHE. Dist: Springer.

CARDINAL VIRTUES
see Virtue and Virtues

CARDINALS

Arthur, James, et al. John Henry Newman. 2008. (Continuum Library of Education Thought Ser.). (ENG.). 256p. 140.00 *(978-0-8264-8407-9(7))* Continuum International Publishing Group, Ltd. GBR. Dist: National Bk. Network.

Bargrave, John. Pope Alexander the Seventh & the College of Cardinals. Robertson, James C., ed. (Camden Society, London, Publications, First Ser.: No. 92). reprint ed. 37.50 *(978-0-404-50192-1(3))* AMS Pr., Inc.

—Pope Alexander the Seventh & the College of Cardinals. Robertson, James C., ed. 2007. (ENG.). 172p. 37.95 *(978-0-548-20632-4(5))*; 176p. per. 22.95 *(978-1-4325-2411-1(9))* Kessinger Publishing, LLC.

Beaumont, Keith. Blessed John Henry Newman: Theologian & Spiritual Guide for Our Times. 2010. (Illus.). 100p. 17.95 *(978-1-58617-552-8(1))* Ignatius Pr.

Blanchard, Jean-Vincent. Eminence: Cardinal Richelieu & the Rise of France. 2011. (ENG., Illus.). 320p. 30.00 *(978-0-8027-1704-7(7))* Walker & Co.

Brady, Sean. The Making of a Cardinal. 2008. (ENG., Illus.). 56p. pap. 10.95 *(978-1-84730-106-2(1))* Veritas Pubns. IRL. Dist: Dufour Editions, Inc.

Broadley, Martin John, ed. Bishop Herbert Vaughan & the Jesuits: Education & Authority. 2010. (Catholic Record Society: Records Ser.: Volume 82). (Illus.). 286p. 80.00 *(978-0-902832-25-1(5))* Catholic Record Society GBR. Dist: Boydell & Brewer, Inc.

Busi, Davide. I Primi Passi Di un Erudito: Angelo Maria Querini, Firenze e L'Oratio de Mosaicae Historiae Praestantia. 2008. (ITA.). 140p. *(978-88-8486-338-6(4))* La Compagnia della Stampa.

Charles, William, ed. Basil Hume: Ten Years On. 2009. (ENG., Illus.). 232p. 22.95 *(978-0-8264-3941-3(1),* Burns & Oates) Continuum International Publishing Group, Ltd. GBR. Dist: National Bk. Network.

Chisnall, Peter M. John Henry Newman: A Very English Saint. 2010. (Illus.). 328p. pap. *(978-0-85244-683-6(7))* Gracewing, Ltd.

Cornwell, John. Newman's Unquiet Grave: The Reluctant Saint. (ENG.). 288p. 2011. pap. 16.95 *(978-1-4411-7323-2(4))* 2010. (Illus.). 24.95 *(978-1-4411-5084-4(6))* Continuum International Publishing Group, Ltd. GBR. Dist: National Bk. Network.

De Castro, Rosalia. En las Orillas del Mar. (Clasicos Castalia). (SPA., Illus.). 152p. 9.95 *(978-84-7039-274-0(3),* CC524) Castalia, Editorial S.A. ESP. Dist: Continental Bk. Co., Inc.

De, Conihout Isabelle. Mazarin. 2010. (FRE., Illus.). 480p. *(978-2-903824-53-2(3))* Hayot, Monelle, Editions d'art.

Dulles, Avery. John Henry Newman: New Edition Introduction by Ian Ker. 2009. (ENG.). 192p. 19.95 *(978-0-8264-3564-4(5))* Continuum International Publishing Group, Ltd. GBR. Dist: National Bk. Network.

Erb, Peter C. The Correspondence of Henry Edward Manning & William Ewart Gladstone, 1844-1853, Vol. 2. 2012. (ENG.). 640p. 180.00 *(978-0-19-957733-0(1))* Oxford Univ. Pr., Inc.

—The Correspondence of Henry Edward Manning & William Ewart Gladstone, 1861-1875, Vol. 3. 2012. (ENG.). 640p. 180.00 *(978-0-19-957734-7(X))* Oxford Univ. Pr., Inc.

Erb, Peter C., ed. The Correspondence of Henry Edward Manning & William Ewart Gladstone, 1833-1844, Vol. 1. 2012. (ENG.). 640p. 180.00 *(978-0-19-957732-3(3))* Oxford Univ. Pr., Inc.

—The Correspondence of Henry Edward Manning & William Ewart Gladstone, 1882-1891, Vol. 4. 2012. (ENG.). 640p. 180.00 *(978-0-19-957735-4(8))* Oxford Univ. Pr., Inc.

Farley, John. The Life of John Cardinal Mccloskey: First Prince of the Church in America. 2007. 432p. per. 29.95 *(978-1-60206-760-8(0))* Cosimo, Inc.

Fischer, Andreas. Kardinale Im Konklave: Die Lange Sedisvakanz der Jahre 1268 Bis 1271. 2008. (Bibliothek des Deutschen Historischen Instituts in ROM Ser.). (GER.). X, 533p. *(978-3-484-82118-7(3))* Verlag Max Niemeyer.

Fletcher, Stella. Cardinal Wolsey: A Life in Renaissance Europe. 2009. (ENG., Illus.). 240p. 34.95 *(978-1-84725-245-6(1))* Continuum International Publishing Group, Ltd. GBR. Dist: National Bk. Network.

Golaszewski, Marcin. Clemens August Graf von Galen: Ein Politischer Prediger im Nationalsozialismus. 2010. (Gießener Arbeiten zur neueren deutschen Literatur und Literaturwissenschaft Ser.). (GER.). 292p. 72.95 *(978-3-631-61228-6(1))* Lang, Peter GmbH, Europaischer Verlag der Wissenschaften DEU. Dist: Lang, Peter.

Golway, Terry. Full of Grace: An Oral Biography of John Cardinal O'Connor. 2007. (ENG.). 256p. pap. 18.95 *(978-1-4165-7364-7(X)*, Beyond Words/Atria Bks.) Atria Bks.

Haile, Martin. Life of Reginald Pole. 2009. (ENG.). 585p. 44.99 *(978-1-117-39372-8(0))*; pap. 43.75 *(978-1-117-39373-5(9))* BiblioBazaar.

—Life of Reginald Pole. 2007. (ENG.). 570p. 58.95 *(978-0-548-15125-9(3))*; 572p. per. 43.95 *(978-1-4304-4470-1(3))* Kessinger Publishing, LLC.

Hyde, Helen. Cardinal Bendinello Sauli & Church Patronage in Sixteenth-Century Italy. 2009. (Royal Historical Society Studies in History New Ser.: Volume 68). (Illus.). 223p. 90.00 *(978-0-86193-301-3(X))* Royal Historical Society GBR. Dist: Boydell & Brewer, Inc.

—Church, Commerce & Patronage in Early Sixteenth-Century Rome: The Career of Cardinal Bandinello Sauli, C. 1481-1518. 2009. 95.00 *(978-0-86193-290-0(0))* Royal Historical Society GBR. Dist: Boydell & Brewer, Inc.

Johnson, Terry. Cardinal Fever. 2010. pap. 9.99 *(978-1-60799-769-6(X))* Tate Publishing & Enterprises, LLC.

Keogh, Daire & McDonnell, Albert, eds. Cardinal Paul Cullen & His World. 2011. (Illus.). 470p. 70.00 *(978-1-84682-235-3(1))* Four Courts Pr. IRL. Dist: International Specialized Bk. Services.

Ker, Ian. John Henry Newman: A Biography. 2010. (ENG., Illus.). 784p. pap. 35.00 *(978-0-19-959659-1(X))* Oxford Univ. Pr., Inc.

Ker, Ian & Merrigan, Terrence, eds. The Cambridge Companion to John Henry Newman. 2009. (Cambridge Companions to Religion Ser.). (ENG.). 298p. (C). 81.00 *(978-0-521-87186-0(7))*; pap. 30.99 *(978-0-521-69272-4(5))* Cambridge Univ. Pr.

Mansfield, Dermot. Heart Speaks to Heart: The Story of Blessed John Henry Newman. 2011. (ENG.). 224p. pap. 26.95 *(978-1-84730-242-7(4))* Veritas Pubns. IRL. Dist: Dufour Editions, Inc.

Mayer, Thomas F. Reginald Pole: Prince & Prophet. 2007. (ENG.). 488p. pap. 61.00 *(978-0-521-03369-0(3))* Cambridge Univ. Pr.

Mayer, Thomas F. & Walters, Courtney B. The Correspondence of Reginald Pole - A Biographical Companion Vol. 4: The British Isles. Gordon, Bruce et al, eds. 2008. (St Andrews Studies in Reformation History: Vol. 4). (LAT & ENG.). 656p. 165.00 *(978-0-7546-0329-0(6))* Ashgate Publishing Co.

Murphy, Paul V. Ruling Peacefully: Cardinal Ercole Gonzaga & Patrician Reform in Sixteenth-Century Italy. 2007. 290p. 79.95 *(978-0-8132-1478-8(5))* Catholic Univ. of America Pr.

Newman, Cardinal John Henry. Apologia Pro Vita Sua. 2007. 444p. per. *(978-1-4067-8832-7(5)*, Pomona Pr.) Read Bks.

Newman, Henry John. Apologia Pro Vita Sua. 2007. 284p. (ENG.). 44.99 *(978-1-4280-7547-4(X))*; per. 37.99 *(978-1-4280-7535-1(6))* IndyPublish.com.

Newman, John Henry. Apologia pro Vita Sua. 2007. (ENG.). 326p. pap. 23.99 *(978-1-4346-4275-2(5))*; 362p. pap. 26.99 *(978-1-4346-4276-9(3))* BiblioBazaar.

—Apologia Pro Vita Sua: Being a Reply to a Pamphlet Entitled 'What, Then, Does Dr. Newman Mean?' 2010. (Cambridge Library Collection - Religion Ser.). 566p. pap. 39.99 *(978-1-108-02147-0(6))* Cambridge Univ. Pr.

Newman, John Henry C., ed. Apologia Pro Vita Sua & Six Sermons. 2007. Tr. of Apologia Pro Vita Sua. (ENG.). 312p. per. *(978-1-4065-4966-9(5))* Dodo Pr.

—Apologia Pro Vita Sua & Six Sermons. 2007. Tr. of Apologia Pro Vita Sua. (ENG.). pap. *(978-1-4068-3519-9(6))* Echo Library.

Newman, John Henry C. & Turner, Frank M. Apologia Pro Vita Sua & Six Sermons. 2012. Tr. of Apologia Pro Vita Sua. (ENG., Illus.). 528p. pap. 30.00 *(978-0-300-17786-2(0))* Yale Univ. Pr.

Newman, John Henry C. & Turner, Frank M., eds. Apologia Pro Vita Sua & Six Sermons. 2008. Tr. of Apologia Pro Vita Sua. 528p. 55.00 *(978-0-300-11507-9(5))* Yale Univ. Pr.

Norris, Thomas J. Cardinal Newman for Today. 2010. pap. *(978-1-56548-365-1(0))* New City Community Pr.

O'Carroll, Ciaran. Paul Cardinal Cullen: Profile of a Practicial Nationalist. 2009. (ENG., Illus.). 321p. 39.95 *(978-1-84730-131-4(2))* Veritas Pubns. IRL. Dist: Dufour Editions, Inc.

Pereiro, James. Cardinal Manning: From Anglican Archdeacon to Council Father at Vatican I. 2008. 376p. pap. *(978-0-85244-405-4(2))* Gracewing, Ltd.

Richardson, Carol. The Possessions of a Cardinal: Art, Piety, & Politics, 1450-1700. 2010. (ENG., Illus.). 456p. 85.00 *(978-0-271-03468-3(8))* Pennsylvania State Univ. Pr.

Richardson, Carol M. Reclaiming Rome: Cardinals in the Fifteenth Century. 2009. *(978-90-04-17183-1(5))* BRILL.

Robinson, Adam Patrick. Reforming Bishop Papal Diplomat Suspect Heretic & Presiding Legate at the Council of Trent: A Reassessment of the Career of Cardinal Giovanni Morone (1509-1580) 2012. (Illus.). 248p. 124.95 ***(978-1-4094-1783-5(2))*** Ashgate Publishing Co.

Silanos, Pietro. Gerardo Bianchi Da Parma (1302) La Biografia Di un Cardinale-Legato Duecentesco. 2010. xxxvi, 512p. *(978-88-89670-51-4(7))* Herder, Editorial S.A.

Slawson, Douglas J. Ambition & Arrogance: Cardinal William O'Connell of Boston & the American Catholic Church. 2007. (ENG.). 248p. per. *(978-0-9787855-0-5(9))* Cobalt Productions.

Turner, Frank M. John Henry Newman: The Challenge to Evangelical Religion. 2011. (Illus.). 752p. pap. 27.50 *(978-0-300-17309-3(1))* Yale Univ. Pr.

Veritas, ed. Reflections on the Pilgrim's Journey: Remembering Cahal B. Cardinal Daly. 2010. (ENG., Illus.). 64p. pap. 12.95 *(978-1-84730-225-0(4))* Veritas Pubns. IRL. Dist: Dufour Editions, Inc.

Walsh, Michael J. The Cardinals: Thirteen Centuries of the Men Behind the Papal Throne. 2011. 256p. pap. 23.00 *(978-0-8028-2941-2(4)*, Eerdmans, William B. Publishing Co.

Williams, Folkestone. The Lives of the English Cardinals V1: Including Historical Notices Of 2007. pap. 38.95 *(978-1-4304-8250-5(8))* Kessinger Publishing, LLC.

Williams, Robert Folkestone. Lives of the English Cardinals, Including Historical Notices of the Papal Court, from Nicholas Breakspear to Thomas Wolsey, Cardinal. 2006. 500p. per. 29.99 *(978-1-4255-5577-1(2))*; (ENG.). 552p. per. 32.99 *(978-1-4255-6087-4(3))* MPublishing.

Zacour, Norman P. Talleyrand: The Cardinal of Perigord, 1301-1364. 2011. 84p. 37.95 ***(978-1-258-04345-2(9))*** Literary Licensing, LLC.

CARDINALS (BIRDS)

Stratton-Porter, Gene. The Song of the Cardinal. 2006. pap. *(978-1-4068-3139-9(5))* Echo Library.

—The Song of the Cardinal. 2007. 156p. (ENG.). 29.95 *(978-1-4344-9385-9(7))*; per. 14.95 *(978-1-4344-9384-2(9))* Wildside Pr., LLC.

CARDIO-PULMONARY RESUSCITATION

see CPR (First Aid)

CARDIOGRAPHY

see also Echocardiography

Benson, Roy & Connolly, Declan. Heart Rate Training. 2011. (ENG., Illus.). 224p. pap. 18.95 *(978-0-7360-8655-4(2))* Human Kinetics Pubs.

Hottenrott, Kuno. Training with the Heart Rate Monitor. 2007. (Illus.). 152p. (J). pap. 16.95 *(978-1-84126-213-0(7))* Meyer & Meyer Sport, Ltd. GBR. Dist: Cardinal Pubs. Group.

Kudrynski, Krzysztof. Analysis of Heart Rate Variability Signal. 2010. 80p. pap *(978-3-8383-7236-5(0))* Lambert Academic Publishing.

Maron, Barry J. & Salberg, Lisa. Hypertrophic Cardiomyopathy: For Patients, Their Families & Interested Physicians. 2nd rev. ed. 2006. (ENG., Illus.). 128p. pap. 37.95 *(978-1-4051-4710-1(5)*, Wiley-Blackwell) Wiley, John & Sons, Inc.

Sevelius, Gunnar. An Untold Medical Story, Coronary Blood Flow, Heart Attack Prediction, Prevention & Treatment. 2011. 180p. 25.00 *(978-1-4567-4891-3(2))*; pap. 15.00 *(978-1-4567-4892-0(0))* AuthorHouse.

CARDIOLOGICAL MANIFESTATIONS OF GENERAL DISEASES

Barbaro, Giuseppe, ed. HIV Infection & the Cardiovascular System, Vol. 40. (Advances in Cardiology Ser.: Vol. 40). (Illus.). *(978-3-8055-7606-2(4))* Karger, S. AG.

Milan, Zoka. Cardiovascular Diseases & Liver Transplantation. 2011. (Cardiology Research & Clinical Developments Ser.). 129.00 *(978-1-61122-910-3(3))* Nova Science Pubs., Inc.

Nixon, J. V., ed. The AHA Clinical Cardiac Consult. 3rd ed. 2010. (5-Minute Consult Ser.). (ENG.). 400p. 94.99 *(978-1-60831-622-9(X))* Lippincott Williams & Wilkins.

Nixon, J. V. (Ian), et al, eds. The AHA Clinical Cardiac Consult Mobile: Powered by Skyscape, Inc. 3rd rev. ed. 2011. (5-Minute Consult Ser.). (ENG.). 89.00 ***(978-1-4511-7326-0(1))*** Lippincott Williams & Wilkins.

CARDIOLOGY

see also Heart—Diseases; Pediatric Cardiology

Abbott, Jonathan A. Topics in Cardiology: Veterinary Clinics of North America - Small Animal Practice. 2010. (Clinics: Veterinary Medicine Ser.: 40-4). (ENG., Illus.). xiv, 530p. 80.00 *(978-1-4377-2506-3(6)*, Saunders) Elsevier - Health Sciences Div.

Abedin, Zainul & Conner, Robert. Essential Cardiac Electrophysiology: With Self-Assessment. 2007. (ENG., Illus.). 312p. pap. 55.95 *(978-1-4051-5108-5(0)*, Wiley-Blackwell) Wiley, John & Sons, Inc.

Abraham, William T. & Krum, Henry. Heart Failure: A Practical Approach to Treatment. 2007. (ENG., Illus.). 332p. (C). 103.00 *(978-0-07-144315-9(0)*, 0071443150) McGraw-Hill Professional Publishing.

The American College of Cardiology's CPT Guide 2007. 2006. 191p. pap. 145.00 *(978-1-58397-065-2(7)*, OP593707CSD) American College of Cardiology.

American College of Clinical Pharmacy Staff, contrib. by. PSAP-VI Cardiology Bk. 1: Cardiology. 6th ed. 2007. 226p. pap. 80.00 *(978-1-932658-31-6(9))* American College of Clinical Pharmacy.

Apple, Fred S., et al, eds. Markers in Cardiology: A Case-Oriented Approach. 2007. (ENG., Illus.). 272p. 125.95 *(978-1-4051-3418-7(6)*, Wiley-Blackwell) Wiley, John & Sons, Inc.

Ardehali, Reza, et al, eds. Practical Approach to Cardiovascular Medicine. 2011. (ENG., Illus.). 408p. pap. 69.95 *(978-1-4051-8039-9(0)*, Wiley-Blackwell) Wiley, John & Sons, Inc.

Arnar, D. O. & Andersen, K., eds. Nordic-Baltic Congress of Cardiology: 22nd Congress, Reykjavik, June 2009: Abstracts & Program. 2009. (Illus.). 134p. pap. *(978-3-8055-9143-0(8))* Karger, S. AG.

Bader, Rima, et al. The Perinatal Cardiology Handbook. 2008. (Mobile Medicine Ser.). (ENG., Illus.). 544p. pap., instr.'s hndbk. ed. 52.95 *(978-0-323-04206-2(6)*, Mosby) Elsevier - Health Sciences Div.

Baliga, Ragavendra R. McGraw-Hill Specialty Board Review Cardiology. 2011. (McGraw-Hill Specialty Board Review Ser.). (ENG., Illus.). 1078p. 179.00 incl. cd-rom *(978-0-07-161408-5(7)*, 0071614087) McGraw-Hill Professional Publishing.

Bengel, Frank M. Nuclear Cardiology from Perfusion to Tissue Biology: Cardiology Clinics. 2009. (Clinics: Internal Medicine Ser.: 27-2). (ENG., Illus.). 240p. 99.00 *(978-1-4377-0457-0(3)*, Saunders) Elsevier - Health Sciences Div.

Bonow, Robert O., et al. Braunwald's Heart Disease: A Textbook of Cardiovascular Medicine, 2-Volume Set: Expert Consult Premium Edition - Enhanced Online Features & Print, 2 vols. 9th ed. 2011. (ENG., Illus.). 2136p. 269.00 *(978-1-4377-2708-1(5)*, Saunders) Elsevier - Health Sciences Div.

Braunwald, Eugene & Bonow, Robert O. Braunwald's Heart Disease: A Textbook of Cardiovascular Medicine. 9th ed. 2011. *(978-0-8089-2436-4(2)*, Saunders) Elsevier Australia.

Braunwald, Eugene & Loscalzo, Joseph. Harrison's Cardiovascular Medicine. 2010. (ENG., Illus.). 636p. pap. 82.00 *(978-0-07-170291-1(1)*, 0071702911) McGraw-Hill Professional Publishing.

Cannon, Christopher P. & O'Gara, Patrick T., eds. Critical Pathways in Cardiovascular Medicine. 2nd rev. ed. 2006. (Board Review Ser.). (ENG., Illus.). 336p. 84.99 *(978-0-7817-9439-8(0))* Lippincott Williams & Wilkins.

Carroll, John D. & Chen, S. James. Advances in Coronary Angiography, an Issue of Cardiology Clinics. 2009. (Clinics: Internal Medicine Ser.: 27-3). (ENG., Illus.). 240p. 99.00 *(978-1-4377-1197-4(9)*, Saunders) Elsevier - Health Sciences Div.

Cheitlin, Melvin D. Clinical Cardiology. 7th ed. Date not set. (C). pap. 43.95 *(978-0-8385-1385-9(9)*, Medical Examination Publishing Co.) Appleton & Lange.

Chizner, Michael A. Clinical Cardiology Made Ridiculously Simple. 2nd ed. 2007. (Medmaster Ridiculously Simple Ser.). (Illus.). 354p. pap. 34.95 incl. cd-rom *(978-0-940780-82-8(8))* MedMaster, Inc.

Cho, Leslie, et al, eds. The Cardiology Intensive Board Review Question Book. 2nd rev. ed. 2008. (ENG., Illus.). 384p. pap. 99.00 *(978-0-7817-7467-3(5))* Lippincott Williams & Wilkins.

Coding Companion for Cardiology/Cardiothoracic Surgery/Vascular Surgery. 2007. per. 199.95 *(978-1-56337-897-3(3))* OptumInsight, Inc.

Colombo, Antonio & Stankovic, Goran, eds. Problem Oriented Approaches in Interventional Cardiology. 2007. (ENG., Illus.). 592p. 249.95 *(978-1-84184-631-6(7)*, Informa Healthcare) Taylor & Francis Group GBR. Dist: Taylor & Francis Group.

Crawford, Michael H. Current Diagnosis & Treatment in Cardiology. 3rd ed. 2009. (LANGE CURRENT Ser.). (ENG., Illus.). 556p. pap. 82.00 *(978-0-07-144211-4(1)*, 0071442111) McGraw-Hill Medical Publishing Div.

Crawford, Michael H., et al. Cardiology. 3rd ed. 2009. (ENG., Illus.). 1984p. 250.00 *(978-0-7234-3485-6(9)*, Mosby) Elsevier - Health Sciences Div.

Dalen. University Hospitals: Doctors & Patients. 2009. 236p. pap. 14.95 *(978-1-59330-603-8(2))* Aventine Pr.

Daniels, David V. Concise Cardiology: An Evidence-Based Handbook. Daniels David V., ed. 2008. (ENG., Illus.). 288p. pap. 51.99 *(978-0-7817-8509-9(X))* Lippincott Williams & Wilkins.

Davidson, Michael H., et al, eds. Therapeutic Lipidology. 2007. (Contemporary Cardiology Ser.). (Illus.). 487p. 219.00 *(978-1-58829-551-4(6)*, 1588295516) Humana Pr.

Dawkins, Keith D., et al. Cardiology. 5th rev. ed. 2008. (Lecture Notes Ser.: 28). (ENG., Illus.). 312p. pap. 45.95 *(978-1-4051-5708-7(9)*, Wiley-Blackwell) Wiley, John & Sons, Inc.

Despres, Jean-Pierre & Di Marzo, Vincenzo, eds. Abdominal Obesity & the Endocannabinoid System: From Basic Aspects to Clinical Management of Related Cardiometabolic Risk. 2008. (ENG., Illus.). 264p. 200.00 *(978-1-4200-6084-3(8)*, Informa Healthcare) Taylor & Francis Group GBR. Dist: Taylor & Francis Group.

Dornelas, Ellen A. Psychotherapy with Cardiac Patients: Behavioral Cardiology in Practice. 2008. 280p. 49.95 *(978-1-4338-0356-7(9))* American Psychological Assn.

Driscoll, David J., et al. Interpretation of Intracardiac Electrograms: The Fundamentals. 2011. (ENG.). 138.99 ***(978-1-4511-1195-8(9))*** Lippincott Williams & Wilkins.

Duckers, Henricus J., et al, eds. Essentials of Restenosis: For the Interventional Cardiologist. 2007. (Contemporary Cardiology Ser.). (Illus.). 458p. 199.00 *(978-1-58829-491-3(9)*, 1588294919) Humana Pr.

Eagle, Kim A., et al, eds. Practical Cardiology: Evaluation & Treatment of Common Cardiovascular Disorders. 2nd rev. ed. 2008. (ENG., Illus.). 720p. pap. 84.99 *(978-0-7817-7294-5(X))* Lippincott Williams & Wilkins.

Eeckhout, Eric, et al, eds. Handbook of Complications During Percutaneous Cardiovascular Interventions. 2006. (ENG., Illus.). 334p. 210.00 *(978-1-84184-380-3(6))* Taylor & Francis Group.

European Society of Cardiology, E. S. C., ed. ESC Guidelines Desk Reference 2011: Compendium of Abridged ESC Guidelines 2011. 2011. (ENG., Illus.). xvi, 391p. pap. 109.00 ***(978-1-908517-29-6(8)***, 1908517298) Springer DEU. Dist: Springer.

Fellows, Dennis. Cardiac Telemetry Basics Test Book. 2010. 56p. pap. 15.20 *(978-1-4357-5474-4(3))* Lulu Enterprises Inc.

Ferenczi, Emily, et al. Cardiology. Puri, Basant K. & Smock, Elliott, eds. 2007. (ENG., Illus.). 128p. pap. 22.95 *(978-0-340-92557-7(4))* Hodder Arnold Pubs.

Final Report of the Pooling Project on CHD. (AHA Monograph Ser.: No. 60). pap. 4.80 *(978-0-87493-095-5(2)*, 73-046A) American Heart Assn., Inc.

Fisher, Nick. Frontline Cardiology: An Off-the-Fence Guide for Those Who Need a Definitive Answer to What Do I Do Next? 2006. (ENG., Illus.). 196p. pap., instr.'s gde. ed. 37.95 *(978-0-7234-3425-2(5)*, Mosby) Elsevier - Health Sciences Div.

Focus Medica Pte Ltd, ed. Animated Dictionary of Cardiology, 1 vol. 2010. (Dictionary Ser.). (ENG.). 80p. 99.00 *(978-981-4284-06-6(8))* Focus Medica Pte Ltd. SGP. Dist: Independent Pubs. Group.

Foult, Jean-Marc, et al, eds. Exercise testing in Cardiology. Hoffman, Olivier, tr. 2010. 100p. pap. 19.95 *(978-2-287-99498-2(X)*, 228799498X) Springer.

Fuchs, Christina. Gender & Aortic Stenosis. 2008. 60p. pap. *(978-3-639-06449-0(6))* VDM Verlag Dr. Mueller e.K.

Fuster, Valentin, ed. The AHA Guidelines & Scientific Statements Handbook. 2009. (ENG., Illus.). 408p. 104.95 *(978-1-4051-8463-2(9)*, Wiley-Blackwell) Wiley, John & Sons, Inc.

Fuster, Valentin & Narula, Jagat. Update on Coronary Risk Factors, an Issue of Medical Clinics of North America. 2012. (Clinics: Internal Medicine Ser.: 96-5). (ENG.). 83.00 ***(978-1-4557-2292-1(8)***, Saunders) Elsevier - Health Sciences Div.

Gardner. Return of Blood to the Heart. 2nd ed. (Illus.). 268p. 62.00 *(978-0-86196-387-4(3))* Libbey, John Eurotext Ltd. FRA. Dist: Books International, Inc.

Gersh, Bernard. Year Book of Cardiology 2011 - E-Book1. 2011. E-Book ***(978-0-323-08729-2(9)***, Mosby Canada) Elsevier - Health Sciences Div.

Gersh, Bernard J. Year Book of Cardiology 2010. 2010. (Year Bks.: 2010). (ENG.). 176.00 *(978-0-323-06825-3(1)*, Mosby) Elsevier - Health Sciences Div.

—Year Book of Cardiology 2011. 2011. (Year Bks.: 2011). (ENG.). 520p. 159.00 *(978-0-323-08408-6(7)*, Mosby) Elsevier - Health Sciences Div.

Gersh, Bernard J. Year Book of Cardiology 2012. 2012. (Year Bks.: 2012). (ENG.). 640p. 173.00 ***(978-0-323-08874-9(0)***, Mosby) Elsevier - Health Sciences Div.

Gray, Rosaire & Pack, Louise. Cardiovascular Disease in the Elderly. 2011. (Oxford Care Manuals Ser.). (ENG., Illus.). 336p. pap. 45.00 *(978-0-19-957059-1(0))* Oxford Univ. Pr., Inc.

Grech, Ever D. ABC of Interventional Cardiology. 2nd ed. 2011. (ABC Ser.: 149). (ENG., Illus.). 120p. pap. 40.95 *(978-1-4051-7067-3(0))* Wiley, John & Sons, Inc.

Greenfield, Joseph C., Jr. Duke Cardiology Fellows Training Program: Sixty-three Years of Excellence. 2011. 158p. 27.00 *(978-1-59460-969-5(1))* Carolina Academic Pr.

Griffin, Brian P., et al, eds. The Cleveland Clinic Cardiology Board Review. 2006. (ENG., Illus.). 896p. 145.00 *(978-0-7817-5942-7(0))* Lippincott Williams & Wilkins.

—Manual of Cardiovascular Medicine. 3rd rev. ed. 2008. (ENG., Illus.). 1024p. pap. 94.99 *(978-0-7817-7854-1(9))* Lippincott Williams & Wilkins.

Herrick, James B. A Short History of Cardiology. reprint ed. 49.50 *(978-0-404-13278-1(2))* AMS Pr., Inc.

Higgins, John, et al. Cardiology Clinical Questions. 2011. (Clinical Science Ser.). (ENG., Illus.). 260p. pap. 45.00 ***(978-0-07-174898-8(9)***, 0071748989) McGraw-Hill Professional Publishing.

Hijazi, Ziyad M., et al, eds. Complications in Percutaneous Interventions for Congenital & Structural Heart Disease. 2008. (Illus.). XII, 364p. 350.00 *(978-0-415-45107-9(8))* CRC Pr. LLC.

Hollenberg, Steve, ed. Cardiology in Family Practice: A Practical Guide. 2010. (Current Clinical Practice Ser.). (Illus.). 184p. pap. 69.95 *(978-1-61737-608-5(6)*, 1617376086) Humana Pr.

Hollenberg, Steven & Heitner, Stephen. Cardiology in Family Practice: A Practical Guide. 2nd ed. 2011. (Current Clinical Practice Ser.). (ENG., Illus.). xii, 159p. pap. 59.95 ***(978-1-61779-384-4(1)***, 1617793841) Humana Pr.

Holler, Teresa. Cardiology Essentials. 2007. (ENG., Illus.). 284p. per. 63.95 *(978-0-7637-5076-3(X))* Jones & Bartlett Learning, LLC.

Iaizzo, Paul A., ed. Handbook of Cardiac Anatomy, Physiology, & Devices. 2nd ed. 2009. (ENG., Illus.). x, 700p. 179.00 *(978-1-60327-371-8(9)*, 1603273719) Humana Pr.

Ingenix, creator. Coding Companion Cardiology/Cardiothoracic Surgery/Vascular Surgery. 2008. (Coding Companion Ser.). (Illus.). 786p. spiral bd. 199.95 *(978-1-60151-164-5(7))* OptumInsight, Inc.

Ingenix, Inc. Staff. Coding Companion for Cardiology 2001. (Illus.). spiral bd. 179.95 *(978-1-56329-717-5(5))* OptumInsight, Inc.

Kamkin, Andre & Kiseleva, Irina, eds. Mechanosensitivity of the Heart. 2009. (Mechanosensitivity in Cells & Tissues Ser.). (ENG., Illus.). xxxvii, 471p. 269.00 *(978-90-481-2849-5(8)*, 9048128498) Springer.

Kjeldsen, Sverre Erik. 2003 European Society of Hypertension - European Society of Cardiology Guidelines for the Management of Arterial Hypertension: Guidelines Committee. (Illus.). 54p. *(978-3-8055-7754-0(0))* Karger, S. AG

Klaidman, Stephen. Coronary: A True Story of Medicine Gone Awry. 2008. (ENG.). 320p. pap. 15.00 *(978-0-7432-6755-7(9)*, Scribner) Scribner.

Klein, Lloyd W. & Kern, Morton J., eds. SCAI Interventional Cardiology Board Review Book. 2006. (ENG., Illus.). 496p. 164.99 *(978-0-7817-6197-0(2))* Lippincott Williams & Wilkins.

Kowalski, Robert E. Die 8-Wochen-Cholesterinkur. (GER.). *(978-3-612-20636-7(2))* Econ-Verlag GmbH DEU. Dist: International Bk. Import Service, Inc.

Kumar, A. Sampath. Thoracic Park: (Musings of a Heart Surgeon) 2006. 196p. pap. 18.95 *(978-81-7017-459-2(7))* Abhinav Pubns. IND. Dist: Independent Pubs. Group.

Lenihan, Daniel & Sawyer, Douglas B. Cardio-oncology Related to Heart Failure, an Issue of Heart Failure Clinics. 2011. (Clinics: Internal Medicine Ser.: 7-3). (ENG., Illus.). 168p. 99.00 *(978-1-4557-1101-7(2)*, Saunders) Elsevier - Health Sciences Div.

Leon, Martin B., et al. Interventional Cardiology Self-Assessment & Review. Date not set. 380p. (C). pap. 45.00 *(978-1-890114-04-6(9))* Physician's Pr.

Levine, Glenn N. & Adair, Olivia Vynn. Cardiology Secrets. 3rd ed. 2009. (Secrets Ser.). (ENG., Illus.). 488p. pap. 54.95 *(978-0-323-04525-4(1)*, Mosby) Elsevier - Health Sciences Div.

Levula, Mari. Gene Expression Profiling of Human Lipoprotein-Loaded Macrophages & Atherosclerotic Lesions with Special Emphasis on ADAMs. 2009. (Acta Universitatis Tamperensis Ser.). 154p. pap. 82.50 *(978-951-44-7942-7(4))* Tampere Univ. Pr. FIN. Dist: Coronet Bks.

Libby, Peter & Braunwald, Eugene. Braunwald's Heart Disease: A Textbook of Cardiovascular Medicine. 8th ed. 2008. (Illus.). *(978-0-8089-2385-5(4)*, Saunders) Elsevier - Health Sciences Div.

Lipsky, Martin S., et al. American Medical Association Guide to Preventing & Treating Heart Disease: Essential Information You & Your Family Need to Know about Having a Healthy Heart. 2008. (ENG., Illus.). 336p. 25.95 *(978-0-471-75024-6(7)*, Wiley) Wiley, John & Sons, Inc.

Lyon, Alexander R., et al. Cardiology: Churchill's Ready Reference. 2011. (ENG., Illus.). 136p. (C). pap. 35.95 *(978-0-443-06842-3(9)*, Churchill Livingstone) Elsevier - Health Sciences Div.

Massad, Malek G., ed. Surgical Options for the Management of Congestive Heart Failure. (Cardiology Ser.: Vol. 101, Nos. 1-3). (Illus.). 156p. *(978-3-8055-7739-7(7))* Karger, S. AG.

Matheis, G., et al, eds. Leukocyte Depletion in Cardiac Surgery & Cardiology. (Illus.). *(978-3-8055-7281-1(6))* Karger, S. AG.

Mather, Paul J. Jefferson Heart Institute Handbook of Cardiology. rev. ed. 2010. 528p. pap. 86.95 *(978-0-7637-6049-6(8))* Jones & Bartlett Learning, LLC.

Mayo Clinic Cardiovascular Fellows. Mayo Clinic Cardiology: Board Review Questions & Answers. 2007. (ENG., Illus.). 352p. per. 80.00 *(978-1-4200-6746-0(X)*, Informa Healthcare) Taylor & Francis Group GBR. Dist: Taylor & Francis Group.

McCarthy, Patrick M. & Young, James B., eds. Heart Failure: A Combined Medical & Surgical Approach. 2007. (ENG., Illus.). 328p. 128.95 *(978-1-4051-2203-0(X)*, Wiley-Blackwell) Wiley, John & Sons, Inc.

Medical Learning Corporation. Peripheral & Cardiology Coder 2010: An Easy-to-Use Tool for Coding & Reimbursement Compliance. 2010. (Illus.). 213p. spiral bd. 231.00 *(978-1-934826-48-5(0))* Medical Learning, Inc.

Moussa, Issam D., et al, eds. Asymptomatic Carotid Artery Stenosis: Risk Stratification & Management. 2007. (ENG., Illus.). 256p. 159.95 *(978-1-84184-613-2(9))* Taylor & Francis Group.

Movahed, Assad, et al, eds. Integrating Cardiology for Nuclear Medicine Physicians: A Guide to Nuclear Medicine Physicians. 2008. (ENG., Illus.). xiv, 546p. 229.00 *(978-3-540-78673-3(2)*, 3540786732) Springer.

Murphy, Joseph G., ed. Mayo Clinic Cardiology Review. 3rd rev. ed. 2006. (ENG., Illus.). 1608p. 170.00 *(978-0-8493-9057-9(5)*, Informa Healthcare) Taylor & Francis Group GBR. Dist: Taylor & Francis Group.

Murphy, Joseph G. & Lloyd, Margaret A. Mayo Clinic Cardiology Concise Textbook & Mayo Clinic Cardiology Board Review Questions & Answers: (text & q&a Set) 2007. (ENG.). 400p. 200.00 *(978-1-4200-6748-4(6)*, Informa Healthcare) Taylor & Francis Group GBR. Dist: Taylor & Francis Group.

Myerson, Saul, et al. Emergencies in Cardiology. 2nd ed. 2010. (ENG., Illus.). 464p. 42.95 *(978-0-19-955438-6(2))* Oxford Univ. Pr., Inc.

Nixon, J. V., ed. The AHA Clinical Cardiac Consult. 3rd ed. 2010. (5-Minute Consult Ser.). (ENG.). 400p. 94.99 *(978-1-60831-622-9(X))* Lippincott Williams & Wilkins.

Nixon, J. V. (Ian), et al, eds. The AHA Clinical Cardiac Consult Mobile: Powered by Skyscape, Inc. 3rd rev. ed. 2011. (5-Minute Consult Ser.). (ENG.). 89.00 ***(978-1-4511-7326-0(1))*** Lippincott Williams & Wilkins.

Noordergraaf, Abraham. Blood in Motion. 2011. (ENG., Illus.). xvii, 323p. 79.95 *(978-1-4614-0004-2(X)*, 146140004X) Springer.

Norell, Michael S. The Oblique View: Cardiology from a Different Angle. 2007. (Illus.). 154p. pap. 38.00 *(978-1-903378-53-3(2))* TFM Publishing Ltd. GBR. Dist: JAMCO Distribution.

Norell, Michael S., et al. Essential Interventional Cardiology. 2nd ed. 2008. (ENG., Illus.). 560p. 120.00 *(978-0-7020-2981-3(5)*, Saunders) Elsevier - Health Sciences Div.

Oates, Crispian, ed. Cardiovascular Haemodynamics & Doppler Waveforms Explained. 2008. (ENG., Illus.). 192p. (C). pap. 64.00 *(978-0-521-73473-8(8))* Cambridge Univ. Pr.

Patel, Anil M. EKGs & Cardiac Studies: Essential Evidence-Based Data for Common Clinical Encounters. 2009. (LANGE Instant Access Ser.). (ENG., Illus.). 164p. pap. 34.00 *(978-0-07-154523-5(9)*, 0071545239) McGraw-Hill Medical Publishing Div.

Pollock, Anne. Medicating Race: Heart Disease & Durable Preoccupations with Difference. 2012. (Experimental Futures Ser.). (ENG.). 280p. pap. 23.95 ***(978-0-8223-5344-7(X))***; (Illus.). 84.95 ***(978-0-8223-5329-4(6))*** Duke Univ. Pr.

Prasad, Rajnish, et al. Cardiology. 2006. (In a Page Ser.). 272p. per. 41.99 *(978-0-7817-6496-4(3))* Lippincott Williams & Wilkins.

Ramrakha, Punit & Hill, Jonathan, eds. Oxford Handbook of Cardiology. 2nd ed. 2012. (ENG., Illus.). 808p. 65.00 ***(978-0-19-964321-9(0))*** Oxford Univ. Pr., Inc.

Ramsdale, David R. & Modi, Simon. 100 Challenges in Cardiology. 2010. (Illus.). 250p. pap. 68.00 *(978-981-4307-14-7(9))* World Scientific Publishing Co., Inc.

Rimmerman, Curtis M. You & Your Cardiologist: A Cleveland Clinic Guide. 2008. (ENG.). 200p. pap. 14.95 *(978-1-59624-081-0(4))* Cleveland Clinic Pr.

Rosenbloom, Judy. Cardiovascular Coding Reference Guide 2007. 2007. spiral bd. 95.00 *(978-0-9749842-9-2(9))* JR Assocs.

—Cardiovascular Coding Reference Guide 2007 - CD. 2007. cd-rom 95.00 *(978-0-9792812-1-1(0))* JR Assocs.

Rosenthal, Lawrence S. Dx/Rx: Arrhythmias. Tighe, Dennis A., ed. 2007. (Illus.). 122p. per. 55.95 *(978-0-7637-2354-5(1)*, 0763723541) Jones & Bartlett Learning, LLC.

Rowlands, Derek & Clarke, Bernard. Recent Advances in Cardiology, Vol. 14. 2007. (ENG., Illus.). 264p. pap. 69.00 *(978-1-85315-715-8(5))* Hodder Arnold Pubs.

Runge, Marschall S., et al. Netter's Cardiology. 2nd ed. 2010. (Netter Clinical Science Ser.). (ENG., Illus.). 672p. 195.00 *(978-1-4377-0638-3(X))*; 99.95 *(978-1-4377-0637-6(1))* Elsevier - Health Sciences Div. (Saunders).

Sabharwal, Nikant, et al. Nuclear Cardiology. 2008. (Oxford Specialist Handbooks in Cardiology Ser.). (ENG., Illus.). 256p. pap. 69.50 *(978-0-19-920644-5(9))* Oxford Univ. Pr., Inc.

Saksena, Franklin B. The Art & Science of Cardiac Physical Examination. 2006. (Contemporary Cardiology Ser.). (Illus.). 411p. 149.00 incl. audio compact disk *(978-1-58829-776-1(4)*, 1588297764) Humana Pr.

San, Tan Ru & Zhong, Liang. Cardiac Science & Engineering. Ghista, Dhanjoo N., ed. 2012. (ENG., Illus.). 600p. 139.95 *(978-1-4200-8806-9(8)*, CRC Press) Taylor & Francis Group GBR. Dist: Taylor & Francis Group.

Saw, Jacqueline, et al, eds. Handbook of Complex Percutaneous Carotid Intervention. 2006. (Contemporary Cardiology Ser.). (Illus.). 400p. 259.00 *(978-1-58829-605-4(9)*, 1588296059) Humana Pr.

Schoenhagen, Paul, et al. IVUS Made Easy, 2 vols. 2008. (Illus.). 128p. 229.95 *(978-1-84184-683-5(X)*, Informa Healthcare) Taylor & Francis Group GBR. Dist: Taylor & Francis Group.

Shepard, Donald S. Lifestyle Modification to Control Heart Disease: Evidence & Policy. 2009. 232p. pap. 61.95 *(978-0-7637-4947-7(8))* Jones & Bartlett Learning, LLC.

Simon, Stewart & Strang, Geoff. A Clinician's Guide to Pulmonary Arterial Hypertension. 2nd rev. ed. 2008. (ENG., Illus.). 64p. pap. 40.00 *(978-1-84184-665-1(1)*, Informa Healthcare) Taylor & Francis Group GBR. Dist: Taylor & Francis Group.

Springhouse Publishing Company Staff. Cardiology Subspecialty Consult. Washington University School of Medicine Staff et al, eds. 2nd rev. ed. 2008. (Washington Manual® Subspecialty Consult Ser.: No. 174). (ENG., Illus.). 480p. pap. 47.99 *(978-0-7817-9151-9(0))* Lippincott Williams & Wilkins.

Stedman's Medical Dictionary Staff. Cardiovascular & Pulmonary Words. 5th rev. ed. 2008. (Stedman's Ser.). (ENG.). cd-rom 45.99 *(978-0-7817-7630-1(9))* Lippincott Williams & Wilkins.

Stedman's Medical Dictionary Staff, ed. Stedman's Cardiovascular & Pulmonary Words: With Respiratory Words. 5th rev. ed. 2007. (Stedman's Word Book Ser.). (ENG., Illus.). 1072p. per. 43.99 *(978-0-7817-7611-0(2))* Lippincott Williams & Wilkins.

Steinberg, Jonathan S. An Electrophysiology: The Basics - A Companion Guide for the Cardiology Fellow During the EP Rotation. Steinberg, Jonathan S. & Mittal, Suneet, eds. 2009. (ENG.). 240p. pap. 78.99 *(978-1-60547-343-7(X))* Lippincott Williams & Wilkins.

Sutton, Paul & Fagan, Toby. Cardiovascular System. 3rd rev. ed. 2007. (Crash Course-UK Ser.). (Illus.). 252p. pap. *(978-0-7234-3430-6(1))* Mosby GBR. Dist: Elsevier - Health Sciences Div.

Swanton, R. Howard & Banerjee, Shrilla. Swanton's Cardiology. 6th rev. ed. 2008. (ENG., Illus.). 696p. pap. 125.95 *(978-1-4051-7819-8(1)*, Wiley-Blackwell) Wiley, John & Sons, Inc.

Takeuchi, Satoru & Mala, J. Geraldine Sandana. Heat Shock Proteins in Cardiovascular Diseases. 2011. (Cardiology Research & Clinical Developments Ser.). 94p. pap. 47.00 *(978-1-61324-589-7(0))* Nova Science Pubs., Inc.

Tanaka, Paul K. ICD-9 CM Easy Coder Cardiology. 2008. (Easy Coder Ser.). 258p. spiral bd. 69.00 *(978-1-56781-441-5(7))* Unicor Medical, Inc.

Tanaka, Paul K. ICD-9-CM Easy Coder: Cardiology. 2011. (ENG.). spiral bd. 79.00 ***(978-1-56781-444-6(1))*** Unicor Medical, Inc.

Tcheng, James E. Primary Angioplasty in Acute Myocardial Infarction. 2nd ed. 2008. (Contemporary Cardiology Ser.). (Illus.). 270p. 119.00 *(978-1-60327-496-8(0))* Humana Pr.

Thakur, Ranjan & Natale, Andrea, eds. Transseptal Catheterization & Interventions. 2010. (ENG., Illus.). 256p. 115.00 *(978-0-9790164-1-7(X))* Cardiotext Publishing.

Topol, Eric J. & Teirstein, Paul S. Textbook of Interventional Cardiology. 6th ed. 2011. (ENG., Illus.). 928p. 279.00 ***(978-1-4377-2358-8(6)***, Saunders) Elsevier - Health Sciences Div.

Tse, Hung-Fat, et al, eds. Cardiology. 2011. (ENG., Illus.). 464p. 149.50 *(978-0-19-956809-3(X))* Oxford Univ. Pr., Inc.

Tubaro, Marco, et al. The ESC Textbook of Intensive & Acute Cardiac Care. 2011. (ENG., Illus.). 848p. 325.00 *(978-0-19-958431-4(1))* Oxford Univ. Pr., Inc.

Turner, Kimberli, ed. Coders' Desk Reference for Cardiology Diagnoses. 2010. 561p. pap. 171.50 *(978-1-60151-458-5(1))* OptumInsight, Inc.

Ubogagu, Edith. Cardiology to Impress Vol. 2: The Ultimate Guide for Students & Junior Doctors. 2010. (Illus.). 240p. pap. 49.00 *(978-1-84816-538-0(2))* Imperial College Pr. GBR. Dist: World Scientific Publishing Co., Inc.

Watson, Sandy & Gorski, Kenneth A. Invasive Cardiology: A Manual for Cath Lab Personnel. 3rd rev. ed. 2010. 646p. pap. 91.95 *(978-0-7637-6468-5(X))* Jones & Bartlett Learning, LLC.

Wazni, Oussama, ed. Handbook of Cardiac Electrophysiology. 2007. (ENG., Illus.). 412p. 190.00 *(978-1-84184-620-0(1))* Taylor & Francis Group.

Willerson, James, et al, eds. Cardiovascular Medicine. 3rd rev. ed. 2007. (Illus.). XXXII, 2928p. 215.00 *(978-1-84628-188-4(1)*, 1846281881) Springer.

Willius, Fredrick A. & Dry, Thomas Jan. A History of the Heart & the Circulation. 2006. *(978-1-57898-605-7(2))* Martino Publishing.

Yagel, Simcha, et al, eds. Cardiology: Embryology, Genetics, Physiology, Echocardiographic Evaluation, Diagnosis & Perinatal Management of Cardiac Diseases. 2nd rev. ed. 2008. (Series in Maternal-Fetal Medicine). (ENG., Illus.). 818p. 500.00 *(978-0-415-43265-8(0)*, Informa Healthcare) Taylor & Francis Group GBR. Dist: Taylor & Francis Group.

Yusuf, Salim, et al, eds. Evidence-Based Cardiology. 3rd ed. 2009. (Evidence-Based Medicine Ser.: 25). (ENG., Illus.). 1240p. 330.95 *(978-1-4051-5925-8(1))* Wiley, John & Sons, Inc.

Zimetbaum, Peter J. & Josephson, Mark E., eds. Practical Clinical Electrophysiology. 2008. (ENG., Illus.). 320p. 136.99 *(978-0-7817-6603-6(6))* Lippincott Williams & Wilkins.

CARDIOPULMONARY ARREST

see Cardiac Arrest

CARDIOPULMONARY BYPASS

Cram101 Textbook Reviews. Outlines & Highlights for Cardiopulmonary Bypass: Principles & Practice by Glenn P Gravlee, ISBN. 2011. 338p. pap. 28.95 *(978-1-61490-407-6(3))* Cram101 Inc.

Gasz, Balazs. Inflammatory Response & Oxidative Stress Related to Cardiopulmonary Bypass. 2008. 80p. pap. *(978-3-639-03614-5(X))* VDM Verlag Dr. Mueller e.K.

Ghosh, Sunit, et al. Cardiopulmonary Bypass. 2009. (Cambridge Clinical Guides). (ENG., Illus.). 216p. pap. 66.00 *(978-0-521-72199-8(7))* Cambridge Univ. Pr.

Gravlee, Glenn P., et al, eds. Cardiopulmonary Bypass: Principles & Practice. 3rd rev. ed. 2007. (ENG., Illus.). 816p. 225.99 *(978-0-7817-6815-3(2))* Lippincott Williams & Wilkins.

Walker, Lawrence. My New Life! A Survivor's Story! 2006. (ENG.). 156p. per. 24.95 *(978-1-4241-4511-9(2))* PublishAmerica, Inc.

CARDIOPULMONARY SYSTEM

see also Heart; Lungs

American Academy of Orthopaedic Surgeons (AAOS) & Thygerson, Alton L. First Aid, CPR, & AED, Standard. 6th ed. 2011. 112p. pap. 14.25 *(978-1-4496-0944-3(9))* Jones & Bartlett Learning, LLC.

Colbert, Bruce J. & Kennedy, Barbara L. Integrated Cardiopulmonary Pharmacology. 2nd ed. 2007. (ENG.). 408p. (C). pap. 80.40 *(978-0-13-228541-4(X)*, Prentice Hall) Prentice Hall PTR.

Colbert, Bruce J., et al. Integrated Cardiopulmonary Pharmacology. 3rd ed. 2011. (ENG., Illus.). 384p. (C). pap. 77.20 *(978-0-13-256872-2(1)*, Prentice Hall) Prentice Hall PTR.

Cram101 Textbook Reviews. Outlines & Highlights for Cardiopulmonary Anatomy & Physiology: Essentials for Respiratory Care -with CD by Terry des Jardins, ISBN. 2010. 106p. pap. 28.95 *(978-1-61698-033-7(8))* Cram101 Inc.

Cram101 Textbook Reviews & Cram101 Textbook Reviews. Outlines & Highlights for Essentials of Cardiopulmonary Physical Therapy by Ellen Hillegass, Isbn: 9781437703818. 2011. 336p. pap. 33.95 ***(978-1-61461-139-4(4))*** Cram101 Inc.

Darowski, Marek & Ferrari, Gianfranco. Comprehensive Models of Cardiovascular & Respiratory Systems: Their Mechanical Support & Interactions. 2009. (Cardiology Research & Clinical Developments Ser.). 98.00 *(978-1-60876-212-5(2))* Nova Science Pubs., Inc.

Delmar. Case Studies for Respiratory Care. 2010. (ENG.). (C). 764.95 *(978-1-4354-8095-7(3))* Delmar Cengage Learning.

Delmar Learning, Cengage. Case Studies for Respiratory Care. 2010. (ENG.). (C). 133.95 *(978-1-4354-8096-4(1))* Delmar Cengage Learning.

Des Jardins, Terry. Cardiopulmonary Anatomy & Physiology. 5th rev. ed. 2007. (ENG.). 664p. (C). pap. 105.95 *(978-1-4180-4278-3(1))* Delmar Cengage Learning.

DeTurk, William E. & Cahalin, Lawrence P. Cardiovascular & Pulmonary Physical Therapy: An Evidence-Based Approach. 2nd ed. 2010. (ENG., Illus.). 778p. 99.00 *(978-0-07-159812-5(X)*, 007159812X) McGraw-Hill Medical Publishing Div.

—Cardiovascular & Pulmonary Physical Therapy: An Evidence-Based Approach. 2nd ed. 2010. (Illus.). xi, 778p. *(978-0-07-159815-6(4))*; *(978-0-07-159814-9(6))* McGraw-Hill Professional Publishing.

Fillyaw, Mike J. Netter's Cardiopulmonary Physical Therapy. 2007. (Illus.). (C). pap. 39.95 *(978-1-933247-12-0(6)*, Saunders) Elsevier - Health Sciences Div.

Fuentes, Virginia Luis, et al, eds. Canine & Feline Cardiorespiratory Medicine. 2nd ed. 2010. (ENG., Illus.). 328p. pap. 157.99 *(978-1-905319-12-1(6))* British Small Animal Veterinary Assn. (BSAVA) GBR. Dist: Wiley, John & Sons, Inc.

Hazinski, Mary Fran, et al, eds. Handbook of Emergency Cardiovascular Care: For Healthcare Providers. 2008. (Illus.). 99p. spiral bd. 27.75 *(978-0-87493-540-0(7))* American Heart Assn., Inc.

Hillegass, Ellen. Essentials of Cardiopulmonary Physical Therapy. 3rd ed. 2010. (ENG., Illus.). 784p. (C). pap. 94.95 *(978-1-4377-0381-8(X)*, Saunders) Elsevier - Health Sciences Div.

Martin, Justin McCory. Heart. 2010. 16p. ***(978-0-545-24799-3(3))*** Scholastic, Inc.

Moffat, Marilyn & Frownfelter, Donna, eds. Cardiovascular/Pulmonary Essentials: Applying the Preferred Physical Therapist Practice Patterns. 2007. (Essentials in Physical Therapy Ser.). (ENG., Illus.). 400p. (C). per. 58.95 *(978-1-55642-668-1(2))* SLACK, Inc.

Obst, Glenn & Bryant, Stanley. Living with Your Heart & Lungs. 2008. 147p. pap. 25.95 *(978-0-615-24001-5(1))* Bryant, Stanley L.

Singal. Nanoparticle Induced Inflammatory Signaling in the Lung. 2010. 232p. pap. *(978-3-639-21552-6(4))* VDM Verlag Dr. Mueller e.K.

Stedman's Medical Dictionary Staff. Cardiovascular & Pulmonary Words. 5th rev. ed. 2008. (Stedman's Ser.). (ENG.). cd-rom 45.99 *(978-0-7817-7630-1(9))* Lippincott Williams & Wilkins.

Stedman's Medical Dictionary Staff, ed. Stedman's Cardiovascular & Pulmonary Words: With Respiratory Words. 5th rev. ed. 2007. (Stedman's Word Book Ser.). (ENG., Illus.). 1072p. per. 43.99 *(978-0-7817-7611-0(2))* Lippincott Williams & Wilkins.

Thygerson, Alton L. First Aid, CPR, & AED. 2007. 150p. (C). pap. 13.50 *(978-0-7637-5146-3(4))* Jones & Bartlett Learning, LLC.

Vesalius, Andreas, et al. On the Fabric of the Human Body: A Translation of de Humani Corporis Fabrica Libri Septem. 2009. *(978-0-930405-90-8(0))* Norman Publishing.

Ware, Wendy A., ed. Small Animal Cardiopulmonary Medicine. 2012. (ENG., Illus.). 224p. pap. 44.95 ***(978-1-84076-164-1(4))*** Manson Publishing, Ltd. GBR. Dist: Thieme Medical Pubs., Inc.

Watchie, Joanne. Cardiovascular & Pulmonary Physical Therapy: A Clinical Manual. 2nd ed. 2009. (ENG., Illus.). 448p. pap. 64.95 *(978-0-7216-0646-0(6)*, Saunders) Elsevier - Health Sciences Div.

Webb, W. Richard & Higgins, Charles B. Thoracic Imaging: Pulmonary & Cardiovascular Radiology. 2nd rev. ed. 2010. (ENG.). 928p. 239.00 *(978-1-60547-976-7(4))* Lippincott Williams & Wilkins.

CARDIORESPIRATORY SYSTEM

see Cardiopulmonary System

CARDIOSPASM

Youssef (, Mrcs. Results of Endoscopic Dilatation Versus Cardiomyotomy in Achalasi. 2011. 216p. pap. ***(978-3-8443-0806-8(7))*** Lambert Academic Publishing.

CARDIOVASCULAR AGENTS

see also Vasodilators

Aronson, Jeffrey K. Meyler's Side Effects of Cardiovascular Drugs. 2009. (ENG.). 840p. 63.95 *(978-0-444-53268-8(4)*, Elsevier Science) Elsevier Science & Technology Bks.

Baliga, Ragavendra R. Statin Prescribing Guide. 2010. (Oxford American Pocket Notes Ser.). (ENG., Illus.). 80p. pap. 14.95 *(978-0-19-539234-0(5))* Oxford Univ. Pr., Inc.

Billman, George Edward. Novel Therapeutic Targets for Antiarrhythmic Drugs. 2010. (ENG., Illus.). 586p. 166.00 *(978-0-470-26100-2(5)*, Wiley) Wiley, John & Sons, Inc.

Chirkov, Yuliy Y., et al. Beneficial Effects of Perhexiline in Cardiovascular Disease States. 2010. (Cardiology Research & Clinical Developments Ser.). viii, 43p. pap. 43.00 *(978-1-61668-977-3(3)*, Nova Biomedical Bks.) Nova Science Pubs., Inc.

Cohen, Jay S. Natural Alternatives to Lipitor, Zocor & Other Statin Drugs: What to Use & Do to Help Lower Bad Cholesterol. 2006. (Squareone Health Guides). (ENG.). 160p. pap. 7.95 *(978-0-7570-0286-1(2))* Square One Pubs.

Colbert, Bruce J. & Kennedy, Barbara L. Integrated Cardiopulmonary Pharmacology. 2nd ed. 2007. (ENG.). 408p. (C). pap. 80.40 *(978-0-13-228541-4(X)*, Prentice Hall) Prentice Hall PTR.

Colbert, Bruce J., et al. Integrated Cardiopulmonary Pharmacology. 3rd ed. 2011. (ENG., Illus.). 384p. (C). pap. 77.20 *(978-0-13-256872-2(1)*, Prentice Hall) Prentice Hall PTR.

Crouch, Michael A. Cardiovascular Pharmacotherapy: A Point-Of-Care Guide. 2010. *(978-1-58528-215-9(4))* American Society of Health-System Pharmacists.

Ferrara, Napoleone, ed. Angiogenesis: From Basic Science to Clinical Applications. 2006. (ENG., Illus.). 280p. 179.95 *(978-0-8493-2844-2(6)*, 2844, CRC Press) Taylor & Francis Group GBR. Dist: Taylor & Francis Group.

Fogoros, Richard N. Antiarrhythmic Drugs: A Practical Guide. 2nd rev. ed. 2007. (ENG., Illus.). 192p. (Orig.). pap. 83.95 *(978-1-4051-6351-4(8)*, Wiley-Blackwell) Wiley, John & Sons, Inc.

Frishman, William H. & Sica, Domenic A., eds. Cardiovascular Pharmacotherapeutics. 3rd ed. 2011. (ENG., Illus.). 800p. 199.00 *(978-0-9790164-3-1(6))* Cardiotext Publishing.

Graveline, Duane. The Statin Damage Crisis. 2009. 192p. pap. 20.00 *(978-1-4243-3869-6(7))* Graveline, Duane E.

—Statin Drugs Side Effects. 2008. 196p. pap. 20.00 *(978-0-9700817-9-7(0))* Graveline, Duane E.

Holmqvist, Gunnar N., ed. Statins. 2009. 89.00 *(978-1-60692-103-6(7))* Nova Science Pubs., Inc.

Housmans, Philippe R., ed. Advances in Cardiovascular Pharmacology: A Society of Cardiovascular Anesthesiologists Monograph. 2008. (ENG., Illus.). 280p. 68.00 *(978-1-60547-060-3(0))* Lippincott Williams & Wilkins.

Kaski, Juan Carlos, et al. Drugs in Cardiology. 2011. (ENG., Illus.). 784p. pap. 75.00 *(978-0-19-955746-2(2))* Oxford Univ. Pr., Inc.

Khan, M. Gabriel. Cardiac Drug Therapy. 7th ed. 2007. (Contemporary Cardiology Ser.). (ENG., Illus.). xiv, 420p. 179.00 *(978-1-58829-904-8(X)*, 158829904X) Humana Pr.

Kipshidze, Nicholas N., et al. Textbook of Interventional Cardiovascular Pharmacology. Kennedy, Cathy, ed. 2007. (ENG., Illus.). 704p. 420.00 *(978-1-84184-438-1(1)*, Informa Healthcare) Taylor & Francis Group GBR. Dist: Taylor & Francis Group.

Moini. Cardiopulmonary Pharmacology for Respiratory Care. rev. ed. 2010. 320p. pap. 69.95 *(978-0-7637-8437-9(0))* Jones & Bartlett Learning, LLC.

Moini, Jahangir. Cardiopulmonary Pharmacology for Respiratory Care with Companion Web Site. 2010. 320p. pap. 75.95 *(978-1-4496-1560-4(0))* Jones & Bartlett Learning, LLC.

Roberts, Barbara H. The Truth about Statins: Risks & Alternatives to Cholesterol-Lowering Drugs. 2012. (ENG., Illus.). 304p. pap. 15.00 ***(978-1-4516-6097-5(9))*** Gallery Pr., The IRL. Dist: Simon & Schuster, Inc.

Robles, Nicolás Roberto. Calcium Channel Blockers & Renal Disease. 2009. (Cerebrovascular Research & Disorders Ser.). 89.00 *(978-1-60741-975-4(0),* Nova Biomedical Bks.) Nova Science Pubs., Inc.

Schmitt, Carol G., et al, eds. Handbook of Pediatric Cardiovascular Drugs. 2008. (Illus.). 356p. per. 86.95 *(978-1-84628-952-1(1))* Springer.

Springhouse Publishing Company Staff & Lippincott Williams and Wilkins Staff, eds. Nursing Cardiovascular Drug Handbook 2011. 2010. (ENG.). 288p. pap. 25.99 *(978-1-4511-0311-3(5))* Lippincott Williams & Wilkins.

Tighe, Dennis A., et al. Cardiology Drug Guide 2010. rev. ed. 2010. 558p. spiral bd. 67.95 *(978-0-7637-5807-3(8))* Jones & Bartlett Learning, LLC.

Waksman, Ron & Ajani, Andrew A. E., eds. Pharmacology in the Catheterization Laboratory. 2009. (ENG., Illus.). 400p. 165.95 *(978-1-4051-5704-9(6),* Wiley-Blackwell) Wiley, John & Sons, Inc.

Wu, Alan H. B. & Yeo, Kiang-Teck J., eds. Pharmacogenomic Testing in Current Clinical Practice: Implementation in the Clinical Laboratory. 2011. (Molecular & Translational Medicine Ser.). (Illus.). xiv, 272p. 219.00 *(978-1-60761-282-7(8),* 1607612828) Humana Pr.

Xanthos, Theodoros. Drugs in Cardiopulmonary Resuscitation. 2011. (Series: Cardiology Research & Clinical Developments Ser.). 145.00 *(978-1-61122-512-9(4))* Nova Science Pubs., Inc.

Yang, Cui. Pge2 Receptors, Chloride Channels. 2011. 196p. pap. ***(978-3-8443-8404-8(9))*** Lambert Academic Publishing.

CARDIOVASCULAR DISEASE NURSING

see Cardiovascular System—Diseases—Nursing

CARDIOVASCULAR DRUGS

see Cardiovascular Agents

CARDIOVASCULAR PATIENT

see Heart—Diseases—Patients

CARDIOVASCULAR RESEARCH

see Cardiovascular System—Research

CARDIOVASCULAR SYSTEM

see also Blood—Circulation; Blood-Vessels; Heart

Abbara, Suhny, et al. Diagnostic Imaging. 2008. (Illus.). *(978-0-8089-2383-1(8))* Harcourt Health Sciences Group.

Ameer, Omar Z. Characterization of Loranthus Ferrugineus Cardiovascular Activities. 2011. 288p. pap. ***(978-3-8443-1925-5(5))*** Lambert Academic Publishing.

Azóia, Nuno & Dobreiro, Pedra, eds. Treadmill Exercise & Its Effects on Cardiovascular Fitness, Depression & Muscle Aerobic Function. 2010. (Public Health in the 21st Century Ser.). 129.00 *(978-1-60876-857-8(0))* Nova Science Pubs., Inc.

Beachey, Will. Respiratory Care Anatomy & Physiology: Foundations for Clinical Practice. 2nd rev. ed. 2007. (ENG., Illus.). 448p. (C). pap. 67.95 *(978-0-323-02740-3(7),* Mosby) Elsevier - Health Sciences Div.

Belanger, Ann C. Vascular Anatomy & Physiology: An Introductory Text. 2nd ed. Date not set. pap. 39.95 *(978-0-941022-40-8(4))* Davies Publishing, Inc.

Bell, Christopher. Cardiovascular Physiology in Exercise & Sport. 2008. (ENG., Illus.). 200p. (C). pap. 41.95 *(978-0-443-06965-9(4),* Churchill Livingstone) Elsevier - Health Sciences Div.

Bodmer, Rolf, ed. Cardiovascular Development: Advances in Developmental Biology. 2007. (Advances in Developmental Biology Ser.). (ENG., Illus.). 454p. 133.00 *(978-0-444-53014-1(2),* Elsevier Science) Elsevier Science & Technology Bks.

Brecker, Stephen J. D., ed. Percutaneous Device Closure of the Atrial Septum. 2006. (ENG., Illus.). 198p. 209.95 *(978-1-84184-596-8(5))* Taylor & Francis Group.

Competence Assurance Systems Staff. Cardiovascular Education Course: Acute Care. (Illus.). 195p. pap. 75.00 *(978-0-89147-112-7(X))* Competence Assurance Systems.

Courneya, Carol-Ann, et al. Cardiovascular Physiology: A Clinical Approach. 2010. (ENG.). 206p. pap. 44.99 *(978-0-7817-7485-7(3))* Lippincott Williams & Wilkins.

Cram101 Textbook Reviews. Outlines & Highlights for Phlebotomy for Health Care Personnel by Kathryn a Booth. 2011. 56p. pap. 26.95 ***(978-1-61905-718-0(2))*** Cram101 Inc.

Cram101 Textbook Reviews & Cram101 Textbook Reviews. Outlines & Highlights for Braunwalds Heart Disease: A Textbook of Cardiovascular Medicine, Single Volume by Peter Libby MD, ISBN. 2011. 390p. pap. 34.95 ***(978-1-61461-700-6(7))*** Cram101 Inc.

—Outlines & Highlights for Cardiovascular & Pulmonary Physical Therapy: Evidence & Practice by Donna Frownfelter, ISBN. 2011. 128p. pap. 28.95 ***(978-1-61461-340-4(0))*** Cram101 Inc.

—Outlines & Highlights for Respiratory Care Anatomy & Physiology by Will Beachey. 2011. 396p. pap. 35.95 ***(978-1-61830-763-7(0))*** Cram101 Inc.

Davies, Mark G., et al, eds. Pumps & Pipes: Proceedings of the Annual Conference. 2010. (ENG., Illus.). x, 300p. 129.00 *(978-1-4419-6011-5(2),* 1441960112) Springer.

Dilsizian, Vasken & Pohost, Gerald M., eds. Cardiac CT, PET & MR. 2nd ed. 2010. (ENG., Illus.). 384p. 104.95 *(978-1-4051-8553-0(8),* Wiley-Blackwell) Wiley, John & Sons, Inc.

Fallon, Anna. Platelet Activation & Procoagulant Evaluation in an in Vitro System. 2009. 276p. pap. *(978-3-639-13794-1(9))* VDM Verlag Dr. Mueller e.K.

Fillyaw, Mike J. Netter's Cardiopulmonary Physical Therapy. 2007. (Illus.). (C). pap. 39.95 *(978-1-932247-12-0(6),* Saunders) Elsevier - Health Sciences Div.

Fix, Shaun & Lezon, Kathleen. Success! in ACLS: Tips & Tricks for Passing the ACLS Course. 2007. (ENG., Illus.). 192p. (C). per. 34.00 *(978-0-13-117621-8(8),* Prentice Hall) Prentice Hall PTR.

Formaggia, L., et al. Cardiovascular Mathematics. 2009. (Ms&a Ser.). (Illus.). xx, 550p. 99.00 *(978-88-470-1151-9(5))* Springer.

Freyschmidt, Jürgen, ed. Handbuch Diagnostische Radiologie: Kardiovaskuläres System. 2007. (Handbuch diagnostische Radiologie Ser.). (Illus.). XIV, 477p. 249.00 *(978-3-540-41420-9(7),* 3540414207) Springer.

Fürtinger, Stefan. Comparison of Cardiovascular Controls under Orthostatic Stress. 2010. 88p. pap. *(978-3-639-27482-0(2))* VDM Verlag Dr. Mueller e.K.

Gerecht, Sharon, ed. Biophysical Regulation of Vascular Differentiation & Assembly. 2011. (Biological & Medical Physics, Biomedical Engineering Ser.). (ENG., Illus.). xiii, 232p. 129.00 *(978-1-4419-7834-9(8),* 1441978348) Springer.

Giordano, Antonio & Galderisi, Umberto, eds. Cell Cycle Regulation & Differentiation in Cardiovascular & Neural Systems. 2009. (Illus.). 300p. 189.00 *(978-1-60327-152-3(X))* Humana Pr.

Granger, Harris I. Vascular Permeability. Granger, Joey & Granger, Neil, eds. 2012. (Colloquium Series on Integrated Systems Physiology: from Molecule to Function Ser.). 100p. pap. 40.00 *(978-1-61504-024-7(2))* Morgan & Claypool Life Science Publishers.

Gropler, Robert J., et al, eds. Cardiovascular Molecular Imaging. 2007. (ENG., Illus.). 368p. 330.00 *(978-0-8493-3377-4(6))* Taylor & Francis Group.

Hannon, Kathleen. Network Theory & Vascular Laboratories. 2008. 56p. pap. *(978-3-639-08347-7(4))* VDM Verlag Dr. Mueller e.K.

HealthTank, creator. The Heart Deck. 2007. 10.95 *(978-0-9801083-0-9(6))* HealthTank, LLC.

Homeister, Jonathon W. & Willis, Monte S., eds. Molecular & Translational Vascular Medicine. 2012. (Molecular & Translational Medicine Ser.). (ENG., Illus.). vi, 388p. 209.00 ***(978-1-61779-905-1(X),*** 161779905X) Humana Pr.

Housmans, Philippe R., ed. Advances in Cardiovascular Pharmacology: A Society of Cardiovascular Anesthesiologists Monograph. 2008. (ENG., Illus.). 280p. 68.00 *(978-1-60547-060-3(0))* Lippincott Williams & Wilkins.

Humphrey, Jay D. Cardiovascular Solid Mechanics: Cells, Tissues, & Organs. 2010. (ENG., Illus.). xvi, 757p. pap. 149.00 *(978-1-4419-2897-9(9),* 1441928979) Springer.

Hunter, Ross J. & Preedy, Victor R., eds. Nanomedicine & the Cardiovascular System. 2011. (ENG., Illus.). 486p. 149.95 *(978-1-57808-726-6(0))* BIOS Scientific Publishers Ltd. GBR. Dist: Taylor & Francis Group.

Hutchison, Stuart J. Complications of Myocardial Infarction: Clinical Diagnostic Imaging Atlas. 2008. (Cardiovascular Emergencies: Atlas & Multimedia Ser.). (ENG., Illus.). 296p. 185.00 *(978-1-4160-5272-2(0),* Saunders) Elsevier - Health Sciences Div.

—Principles of Cardiovascular Computed Tomography: Expert Consult - Online & Print. 2012. (ENG., Illus.). 304p. pap. 99.00 *(978-1-4377-0407-5(7),* Saunders) Elsevier - Health Sciences Div.

Hutchison, Stuart J. & Strohm, Oliver. Principles of Cardiovascular Magnetic Resonance Imaging: Expert Consult - Online & Print. 2012. (ENG., Illus.). 400p. 99.00 *(978-1-4377-0406-8(9),* Saunders) Elsevier - Health Sciences Div.

Jain, Kewal K. Applications of Biotechnology in Cardiovascular Therapeutics. 2011. (Illus.). xxviii, 350p. 209.00 *(978-1-61779-239-7(X),* 161779239X) Humana Pr.

Kamkin, Andre & Kiseleva, Irina, eds. Mechanosensitivity of the Heart. 2009. (Mechanosensitivity in Cells & Tissues Ser.). (ENG., Illus.). xxxvii, 471p. 269.00 *(978-90-481-2849-5(8),* 9048128498) Springer.

Kang, Kyung A., et al, eds. The Primo Vascular System: Its Role in Cancer & Regeneration. 2011. (ENG., Illus.). xix, 338p. 239.00 ***(978-1-4614-0600-6(5)*** 1461406005) Springer.

Kheradvar, Arash & Pedrizzetti, Gianni. Vortex Formation in the Cardiovascular System. 2012. (ENG., Illus.). xiii, 164p. 189.00 ***(978-1-4471-2287-6(9),*** 1447122879) Springer.

Klabunde, Richard E. Cardiovascular Physiology Concepts. 2nd rev. ed. 2011. (ENG., Illus.). 256p. pap. 45.99 ***(978-1-4511-1384-6(6))*** Lippincott Williams & Wilkins.

Kupinski, Ann Marie. Diagnostic Medical Sonography: The Vascular System. 2012. (Diagnostic Medical Sonography Ser.). (ENG.). 704p. 129.95 ***(978-1-60831-350-1(6))*** Lippincott Williams & Wilkins.

Leahy, Martin J., ed. Microcirculation Imaging. 2012. (ENG.). 411p. 199.95 ***(978-3-527-32894-9(7),*** Wiley-VCH) Wiley, John & Sons, Inc.

Leondes. Biomechanical Systems Technology (V2) 2007. 139.00 *(978-981-270-982-0(7))* World Scientific Publishing Co., Inc.

Levick, J. R. An Introduction to Cardiovascular Physiology. 5th ed. 2010. (ENG., Illus.). 384p. (Orig.). pap. 49.95 *(978-0-340-94204-8(5))* Hodder Arnold Pubs.

Levick, J. Rodney. Cardiovascular Physiology: Questions for Self Assessment. 2010. (ENG., Illus.). 272p. pap. 34.95 *(978-0-340-98511-3(9))* Hodder Arnold Pubs.

Levy, Matthew N., et al. Cardiovascular Physiology. 9th rev. ed. 2006. (Mosby's Physiology Monograph Ser.). (ENG., Illus.). 288p. (C). pap. 44.95 *(978-0-323-03446-3(2),* Mosby) Elsevier - Health Sciences Div.

Liu, Yi-Hwa & Wackers, Frans J. Cardiovascular Imaging. 2010. (ENG., Illus.). 176p. 89.95 *(978-1-84076-109-2(1))* Manson Publishing, Ltd. GBR. Dist: Thieme Medical Pubs., Inc.

Loscalzo, Joseph & Vita, Joseph A., eds. Nitric Oxide & the Cardiovascular System. 2010. (Contemporary Cardiology Ser.). (Illus.). 616p. pap. 209.00 *(978-1-61737-101-1(7),* 1617371017) Humana Pr.

Martin, Justin McCory. Heart. 2010. 16p. ***(978-0-545-24799-3(3))*** Scholastic, Inc.

Matata, Bashir M. & Elahi, Maqsood M., eds. Oxidative Stress: A Focus on Cardiovascular Disease Pathogenesis. 2010. (Cardiology Research & Clinical Developments Ser.). 125.00 *(978-1-61668-157-9(8),* Nova Biomedical Bks.) Nova Science Pubs., Inc.

Michalski, Jacek & Nowak, Isabela, eds. Menopause: Vasomotor Symptoms, Systematic Treatments & Self-Care Measures. 2010. (Aging Issues, Health & Financial Alternatives Ser.). (Illus.). 209p. 145.00 *(978-1-60876-930-8(5),* Nova Biomedical Bks.) Nova Science Pubs., Inc.

Miyazaki, Akira & Imawari, Michio, eds. New Frontiers in Lifestyle-Related Diseases. 2010. (ENG., Illus.). xxii, 160p. pap. 79.95 *(978-4-431-99839-6(X),* 443199839X) Springer.

Mohrman, David E. & Heller, Lois Jane. Cardiovascular Physiology, Seventh Edition. 7th ed. 2010. (LANGE Physiology Ser.). (ENG., Illus.). 304p. pap. 42.00 *(978-0-07-170120-4(6),* 0071701206) McGraw-Hill Professional Publishing.

Moneta, Gregory L. Year Book of Vascular Surgery 2011. 2011. (Year Bks.: 2011). (ENG.). 384p. 159.00 ***(978-0-323-08429-1(X),*** Mosby) Elsevier - Health Sciences Div.

Neilan, Alex. Effects of Green Tea on Cardiovascular Risk. 2011. 120p. pap. ***(978-3-8443-0068-0(6))*** Lambert Academic Publishing.

Neumyer, Marsha M. & Thiele, Brian L. Techniques of Abdominal Vascular Sonography. Date not set. *(978-0-941022-27-9(7))* Davies Publishing, Inc.

Neumyer, Marsha M., et al. Vascular Laboratory Physician's Manual: Indications, Interpretation, & Clinical Decision Making. Date not set. *(978-0-941022-29-3(3))* Davies Publishing, Inc.

Nicol, Ed, et al. Cardiovascular Computed Tomography. 2012. (ENG., Illus.). 540p. 78.95 ***(978-0-19-957259-5(3))*** Oxford Univ. Pr., Inc.

Noble, Alan, et al. The Cardiovascular System. 2nd ed. 2010. (Systems of the Body Ser.). (ENG., Illus.). 192p. pap. 54.95 *(978-0-7020-3374-2(X),* Churchill Livingstone) Elsevier - Health Sciences Div.

Noraza, Abdul Rahman, et al. Optimal Cardiovascular Screening Activities: Prevalence & Its Associated Factors among Apparently Healthy School Teachers in Kota Bharu, Malaysia. 2011. 80p. pap. ***(978-3-639-34001-3(9))*** VDM Verlag Dr. Mueller e.K.

Oates, Crispian, ed. Cardiovascular Haemodynamics & Doppler Waveforms Explained. 2008. (ENG., Illus.). 192p. (C). pap. 64.00 *(978-0-521-73473-8(8))* Cambridge Univ. Pr.

Peng, Xu & Antonyak, Marc, eds. Cardiovascular Development: Methods & Protocols. 2012. (Methods in Molecular Biology Ser.). (ENG., Illus.). xiv, 341p. 139.00 ***(978-1-61779-522-0(4),*** 1617795224) Humana Pr.

Pervitsky, Dmitry. Hno Adducts of Horse Myoglobin & Human Hemoglobin. 2010. 108p. pap. *(978-3-8383-0158-7(7))* Lambert Academic Publishing.

Regar, Evelyn, et al, eds. Optical Coherence Tomography in Cardiovascular Research. 2006. (ENG., Illus.). 372p. 350.00 *(978-1-84184-611-8(2))* Taylor & Francis Group.

Ribes, Ramón. Cardiovascular English. 2008. spiral bd. 39.95 *(978-3-540-73141-2(5),* 3540731415) Springer.

Rogers, Kara, ed. The Cardiovascular System. 2010. (Human Body Ser.). 248p. (YA). (ENG.). lib. bdg. 45.00 *(978-1-61530-128-7(3));* (Illus.). 90.00 *(978-1-61530-258-1(1))* Rosen Publishing Group, Inc., The.

Rosenwasser, Robert H., ed. Interventional Neuroradiology. 2007. (ENG., Illus.). 440p. 330.00 *(978-0-8493-9562-8(3),* Informa Healthcare) Taylor & Francis Group GBR. Dist: Taylor & Francis Group.

Rudman, Jack. ARRT Examination in Cardiovascular - Interventional Technology (CIT) Date not set. (Admission Test Ser.). 69.95 *(978-0-8373-5867-3(1),* ATS117) National Learning Corp.

Rychik, Jack & Tian, Zhiyun. Fetal Cardiovascular Imaging. 2011. (ENG., Illus.). 544p. 149.00 *(978-1-4160-3172-7(3),* Saunders) Elsevier - Health Sciences Div.

Sablayrolles, Jean-Louis. Low Dose Coronary CTA in Ischemic Disease. 2008. 300p. 189.00 *(978-88-470-0863-2(8))* Springer.

Salvi, Paolo. Pulse Waves: How Vascular Hemodynamics Affect Blood Pressure. 2012. (ENG., Illus.). xii, 138p. pap. 69.95 ***(978-88-470-2438-0(2),*** 8847024382) Springer.

Schools, Cats Careers, et al. CATS Cardiovascular Technologist. 2010. 57p. pap. 79.99 *(978-0-557-12694-1(0))* Lulu Enterprises Inc.

Sideman, Samuel, et al, eds. Control & Regulation of Transport Phenomena in the Cardiac System. 2008. (Annals of the New York Academy of Sciences Ser.: Vol. 1420). (ENG., Illus.). 300p. pap. 139.95 *(978-1-57331-706-1(3),* Wiley-Blackwell) Wiley, John & Sons, Inc.

Smith, Denise L. & Fernhall, Bo. Advanced Cardiovascular Exercise Physiology. 2010. (ENG., Illus.). 240p. (C). 71.00 *(978-0-7360-7392-9(2))* Human Kinetics Pubs.

Stouffer, George A., ed. Cardiovascular Hemodynamics for the Clinician. 2007. (ENG., Illus.). 312p. per. 81.95 *(978-1-4051-6917-2(6),* Wiley-Blackwell) Wiley, John & Sons, Inc.

Sutton, Paul & Fagan, Toby. Cardiovascular System. 3rd rev. ed. 2007. (Crash Course-UK Ser.). (Illus.). 252p. pap. *(978-0-7234-3430-6(1))* Mosby GBR. Dist: Elsevier - Health Sciences Div.

Ter Horst, Gert J., ed. The Nervous System & the Heart. 2010. (Illus.). 584p. pap. 165.00 *(978-1-61737-139-4(4),* 1617371394) Humana Pr.

Thiriet, Marc. Biology & Mechanics of Blood Flows: Part I: Biology, 2 vols. 2007. (CRM Series in Mathematical Physics Ser.). (Illus.). XIII, 657p. 149.00 *(978-0-387-74846-7(6),* 0387748466) Springer.

—Cell & Tissue Organization in the Circulatory & Ventilatory Systems. 2011. (Biomathematical & Biomechanical Modeling of the Circulatory & Ventilatory Systems Ser.). (ENG., Illus.). xii, 735p. 199.00 *(978-1-4419-9757-9(1),* 1441997571) Springer.

—Control of Cell Fate in the Circulatory & Ventilatory Systems. 2011. (Biomathematical & Biomechanical Modeling of the Circulatory & Ventilatory Systems Ser.). (ENG., Illus.). x, 536p. 199.00 *(978-1-4614-0328-9(6),* 1461403286) Springer.

Thiriet, Marc. Signaling at the Cell Surface in the Circulatory & Ventilatory Systems. 2011. (Biomathematical & Biomechanical Modeling of the Circulatory & Ventilatory Systems Ser.). (Illus.). xv, 982p. 219.00 ***(978-1-4614-1990-7(5),*** 1461419905) Springer.

Varghese, Anitha & Pennell, Dudley J. Cardiovascular Magnetic Resonance Made Easy. 2007. (Made Easy Ser.). (ENG., Illus.). 176p. pap. 74.95 *(978-0-443-10301-8(1),* Churchill Livingstone) Elsevier - Health Sciences Div.

Waite, Lee & Fine, Jerry. Applied Biofluid Mechanics. 2007. (ENG., Illus.). 314p. (C). 115.00 *(978-0-07-147217-3(7),* 0071472177) McGraw-Hill Professional Publishing.

Waldstein, Shari, et al, eds. Cardiovascular Behavioral Medicine. 2010. (ENG.). 1000p. 349.00 *(978-0-387-85959-0(4),* 0387859594) Springer.

Wang, Donna H. Molecular Sensors for Cardiovascular Homeostasis. 2007. (Illus.). viii, 216p. 149.00 *(978-0-387-47528-8(1))* Springer.

Webb, David. Endothelin & Cardiovascular Regulation. 2011. (Colloquium Series on Integrated Systems Physiology: from Molecule to Function Ser.). 100p. pap. 35.00 *(978-1-61504-159-6(1))* Morgan & Claypool Life Science Publishers.

Zamorano, Jose Luis & Rademakers, Frank E. The ESC Textbook of Cardiovascular Imaging. Bax, Jeroen J. & Knuuti, Juhani, eds. 2010. (ENG., Illus.). 568p. 199.00 *(978-1-84882-420-1(3),* 1848824203) Springer.

CARDIOVASCULAR SYSTEM—DISEASES

see also Blood Circulation Disorders

also specific diseases, e.g. Varicose Veins

Aaronson, Philip Irving & Ward, Jeremy P. T. The Cardiovascular System at a Glance. 3rd rev. ed. 2007. (At a Glance Ser.: 1). (ENG., Illus.). 136p. per. 44.95 *(978-1-4051-5044-6(0),* Wiley-Blackwell) Wiley, John & Sons, Inc.

Abraham, David, et al, eds. Advances in Vascular Medicine. 2010. (ENG., Illus.). xvi, 451p. 219.00 *(978-1-84882-636-6(2),* 1848826362) Springer.

Achenbach, Stephan, et al. Atlas of Cardiovascular Computed Tomography. 2007. (ENG., Illus.). x, 278p. 189.00 *(978-1-57340-257-5(2),* 1573402672) Current Medicine Group LLC.

Acosta, Daniel, Jr., ed. Cardiovascular Toxicology, Fourth Edition. 4th rev. ed. 2008. (Target Organ Toxicology Ser.: Vol. 25). (ENG., Illus.). 684p. 230.00 *(978-1-4200-4473-7(7))* CRC Pr. LLC.

Alexander Iii, Arthur Douglass. Overlooked Causes & the Prevention: Cancer, Cardiovascular Heart Disease, Multiple Sclerosis. 2010. 60p. pap. 14.75 *(978-1-4490-5357-4(2))* AuthorHouse.

Almeida, Jose. Atlas of Endovascular Venous Surgery: Expert Consult - Online & Print. 2011. (ENG., Illus.). 512p. 279.00 ***(978-1-4377-1790-7(X),*** Saunders) Elsevier - Health Sciences Div.

Amarenco, Pierre, ed. Cardiovascular Risk Factor Management in the Prevention of Stroke Vol. 16: Satellite Symposium Held on the Occasion of the 11th European Stroke Conference, Geneva, Switzerland, May 31, 2002: Proceedings. (Cerebrovascular Diseases Ser.: Vol. 16, Suppl. 3). (Illus.). *(978-3-8055-7587-4(4))* Karger, S. AG.

American Heart Association Staff. The AHA Mentoring Handbook. 2nd ed. 2008. (ENG., Illus.). 192p. pap. 14.99 *(978-1-60547-625-4(0))* Lippincott Williams & Wilkins.

American Medical Association, creator. CPT Reference Guide for Cardiovascular Coding. 2011. (Illus.). 244p. pap. 175.00 ***(978-1-60359-303-8(9))*** American Medical Assn.

Antman, Elliott M. Cardiovascular Therapeutics: A Companion to Braunwald's Heart Disease. 3rd rev. ed. 2006. (ENG., Illus.). 984p. 188.00 *(978-1-4160-3358-5(0),* Saunders) Elsevier - Health Sciences Div.

Aparicio-Sánchez, José Luis. Curso de Reanimación Cardiopulmonar Neonatal Avanzada. 2008. 66p. pap. 28.50 *(978-1-4357-0838-9(5))* Lulu Enterprises Inc.

Aronow, Wilbert S., et al, eds. Cardiovascular Disease in the Elderly. 4th rev. ed. 2008. (Fundamental & Clinical Cardiology Ser.: Vol. 63). (ENG., Illus.). 888p. 300.00 *(978-1-4200-6170-3(4),* Informa Healthcare) Taylor & Francis Group GBR. Dist: Taylor & Francis Group.

Ascher, Enrico. Haimovici's Vascular Surgery. 6th ed. 2012. (ENG.). 1306p. 399.95 ***(978-1-4443-3071-7(3),*** Wiley-Blackwell) Wiley, John & Sons, Inc.

Askari, Arman T. & Lincoff, A. Michael. Antithrombotic Drug Therapy in Cardiovascular Disease. 2009. (Contemporary Cardiology Ser.). (Illus.). 450p. 309.00 *(978-1-60327-234-6(8))* Humana Pr.

ASM International Staff, contrib. by. Materials & Coatings for Medical Devices: Cardiovascular. 2009. (Illus.). viii, 444p. ***(978-1-61503-000-2(X))*** ASM International, Inc.

Baars, H. F., et al. Clinical Cardiogenetics. 2011. (ENG., Illus.). xv, 455p. 219.00 *(978-1-84996-470-8(X),* 184996470X) Springer.

Bader, Michael, ed. Cardiovascular Hormone Systems: From Molecular Mechanisms to Novel Therapeutics. 2008. (ENG., Illus.). 456p. 250.00 *(978-3-527-31920-6(4)*, Wiley-VCH) Wiley, John & Sons, Inc.

Badylak, S. F., et al, eds. Cells Tissues Organs Vol. 195, No. 1-2: Cardiovascular Regenerative Biology. 2011. (ENG., Illus.). 184p. pap. ***(978-3-8055-9872-9(6))*** Karger, S. AG.

Baker, Andrew H., ed. Vascular Disease: Molecular Biology & Gene Transfer Protocols. 2010. (Methods in Molecular Medicine Ser.). 456p. pap. 149.00 *(978-1-61737-155-4(6)*, 1617371556) Humana Pr.

Bakris, George L. Diabetes, the Kidney, & Cardiovascular Risk, an Issue of Cardiology Clinics. 2010. (Clinics: Internal Medicine Ser.: 28-3). (ENG., Illus.). viii, 428p. 105.00 *(978-1-4377-2430-1(2)*, Saunders) Elsevier - Health Sciences Div.

Bakris, George L., ed. Managing the Kidney when the Heart Is Failing. 2012. (ENG., Illus.). x, 114p. pap. 49.95 ***(978-1-4614-3690-4(7)***, 1461436907) Springer.

Balestra, Constantino. PFO & the Diver: Patency of Cardiac Foramen Ovale: A Risk Factor for Dysbaric Disorders? 2007. xiii, 146p. *(978-1-930536-39-5(9))* Best Publishing Co.

Baliga, Ragavendra R. Introductory Guide to Cardiac CT Imaging. 2009. (ENG., Illus.). 168p. pap., instr.'s gde. ed. 36.00 *(978-1-58255-938-4(4))* Lippincott Williams & Wilkins.

Barbaro, Giuseppe. Cardiovascular Disease in Aids. 2nd ed. 2008. (Illus.). 246p. spiral bd. 199.00 *(978-88-470-0760-4(7))* Springer.

Barbaro, Giuseppe, ed. HIV Infection & the Cardiovascular System, Vol. 40. (Advances in Cardiology Ser.: Vol. 40). (Illus.). *(978-3-8055-7606-2(4))* Karger, S. AG.

Beck, G. Ronald, et al, eds. Manual of Outpatient Cardiology. 2011. (ENG., Illus.). xiii, 505p. pap. 49.95 ***(978-0-85729-943-7(3)***, 0857299433) Springer.

Bender, Jeffrey R. Oxford American Handbook of Cardiology. 2010. (Oxford American Handbooks in Medicine Ser.). (ENG., Illus.). 744p. pap. 49.95 *(978-0-19-538969-2(7))* Oxford Univ. Pr., Inc.

Bennington, Eleanor H. Horizons in World Cardiovascular Research. 2009. 175.00 *(978-1-60876-447-1(8))* Nova Science Pubs., Inc.

Bennington, Eleanor H., ed. Horizons in World Cardiovascular Research. 2011. (Series: Horizons in World Cardiovascular Research Ser.). 245p. 95.00 *(978-1-61324-243-8(3))* Nova Science Pubs., Inc.

—Horizons in World Cardiovascular Research. Volume 2. 2010. (Horizons in World Cardiovascular Research Ser.). 145.00 *(978-1-61668-610-9(3)*, Nova Biomedical Bks.) Nova Science Pubs., Inc.

Bermudes, Richard A., et al, eds. Managing Metabolic Abnormalities in the Psychiatrically Ill: A Clinical Guide for Psychiatrists. 2007. (Illus.). 314p. 69.00 *(978-1-58562-241-2(9))* American Psychiatric Publishing, Inc.

Bhatt, Deepak L., ed. Platelets in Cardiovascular Disease. 2008. (Illus.). 218p. 124.00 *(978-1-86094-826-8(X))* Imperial College Pr. GBR. Dist: World Scientific Publishing Co., Inc.

Bhave, Swati Y. & Saini, Sunil, eds. AHA Syndrome & Cardiovascular Disease. 2009. (ENG., Illus.). 300p. 120.00 *(978-1-84829-023-5(3))* Anshan GBR. Dist: Publishers Storage & Shipping.

Biederman, Robert W. W., et al. Cardiac MRI: Guide Book on the Go. 2009. (ENG., Illus.). 160p. spiral bd. 53.99 *(978-1-60547-606-3(4))* Lippincott Williams & Wilkins.

Blei. Vascular Anomalies. rev. ed. 2010. 146p. pap. 22.95 *(978-0-7637-6659-7(3))* Jones & Bartlett Learning, LLC.

Blumenthal, Roger, et al. Preventive Cardiology: Companion to Braunwald's Heart Disease: Expert Consult - Online & Print. 2011. (ENG., Illus.). 632p. 159.00 *(978-1-4377-1366-4(1)*, Saunders) Elsevier - Health Sciences Div.

Bohan, J. Stephen & Kosowsky, Joshua. Cardiovascular Emergencies, an Issue of Emergency Medicine Clinics. 2011. (Clinics: Internal Medicine Ser.: 29-4). (ENG.). 110.00 ***(978-1-4557-1095-9(4)***, Saunders) Elsevier - Health Sciences Div.

Bradley, T. Douglas. Sleep Apnea: Implications in Cardiovascular & Cerebrovascular Disease. 2nd rev. ed. 2008. (ENG., Illus.). 416p. 300.00 *(978-0-8493-4150-2(7))* Taylor & Francis Group.

Brady, William J., et al. Cardiovascular Problems in Emergency Medicine: A Discussion-Based Review. Grossman, Shamai & Rosen, Peter, eds. 2nd ed. 2012. (CTEM - Current Topics in Emergency Medicine Ser.: 1). (ENG., Illus.). 408p. pap. 99.95 ***(978-0-470-67067-5(3)***, Wiley-Blackwell) Wiley, John & Sons, Inc.

Bragg, Paul C. & Bragg, Patricia. Healthy Heart: Keep Your Cardiovascular System Healthy & Fit at Any Age. 16th ed. 2007. (ENG., Illus.). 256p. pap. 11.95 *(978-0-87790-097-9(3))* Health Science.

Brataas, Jorgen & Nanstveit, Viggo. Handbook of Cardiovascular Research. 2009. (Cardiology Research & Clinical Developments Ser.). 195.00 *(978-1-60741-792-7(8)*, Nova Biomedical Bks.) Nova Science Pubs., Inc.

Braunwald, Eugene & Loscalzo, Joseph. Harrison's Cardiovascular Medicine. 2010. (ENG., Illus.). 636p. pap. 82.00 *(978-0-07-170291-1(1)*, 0071702911) McGraw-Hill Professional Publishing.

Breddin, Hans K. & Walenga, Jeanine M., eds. Clinical Management of Thrombotic & Cardiovascular Disorders with Thrombin Inhibitors - The Role of Argatroban Vol. 32: Satellite Symposium Held at the International Society of Thrombosis & Haemostasis, Paris, July 11, 2001. (Pathophysiology of Haemostasis & Thrombosis Ser.: Vol. 32, Suppl. 3). (Illus.). *(978-3-8055-7558-4(0))* Karger, S. AG.

Broad, Mary Ann, et al, eds. Cardiorespiratory Assessment of the Adult Patient: A Clinician's Guide. 2012. (Physiotherapist's Tool Box Ser.). (ENG., Illus.). 212p. (C). spiral bd. 38.95 ***(978-0-7020-4345-1(1)***, Churchill Livingstone) Elsevier - Health Sciences Div.

Budoff, Matthew J., et al, eds. Atlas of Cardiovascular Computed Tomography: Includes narrated Videos. 2008. cd-rom 129.00 *(978-1-57340-292-7(3))* Current Medicine Group LLC.

Budoff, Matthew J. & Shinbane, Jerold S., eds. Cardiac CT Imaging: Diagnosis of Cardiovascular Disease. 2nd ed. 2010. (ENG., Illus.). xxvi, 412p. 159.00 *(978-1-84882-649-6(4)*, 1848826494) Springer.

Budoff, Matthew J., et al. Atlas of Cardiovascular Computed Tomography. 2007. *(978-1-57340-259-0(1))* Current Medicine Group LLC.

Burgess, John H. Doctor to the North: Thirty Years Treating Heart Disease among the Inuit. 2008. (Footprints Ser.). (ENG., Illus.). 178p. (C). *(978-0-7735-3431-5(8))* McGill-Queen's Univ. Pr.

Burke, Allen. Practical Cardiovascular Pathology. Tavora, Fabio, ed. 2010. (ENG., Illus.). 608p. 245.99 *(978-1-60547-841-8(5))* Lippincott Williams & Wilkins.

Butlin, Mark. Structural & Functional Effects on Large Artery Stiffness. 2008. 228p. pap. *(978-3-8364-9788-6(3))* VDM Verlag Dr. Mueller e.K.

Camm, A. John, et al, eds. The ESC Textbook of Cardiovascular Medicine. 2nd ed. 2009. (ENG., Illus.). 1300p. 475.00 *(978-0-19-956699-0(2))* Oxford Univ. Pr., Inc.

Cannon, Christopher P. & Kwong, Raymond Y., eds. Cardiovascular Magnetic Resonance Imaging. 2006. (Contemporary Cardiology Ser.). 300p. 175.00 *(978-1-59745-306-6(4))* Humana Pr.

Carmel, Ralph & Jacobsen, Donald W., eds. Homocysteine in Health & Disease. 2011. (ENG., Illus.). 536p. pap. 95.00 *(978-1-107-40242-3(5))* Cambridge Univ. Pr.

Cho, Leslie, et al, eds. The Cardiology Intensive Board Review Question Book. 2nd rev. ed. 2008. (ENG., Illus.). 384p. pap. 99.00 *(978-0-7817-7467-3(5))* Lippincott Williams & Wilkins.

Clark, Luther T. Cardiovascular Disease & Diabetes. 2006. (ENG., Illus.). 400p. 101.00 *(978-0-07-143681-6(2)*, 0071436812) McGraw-Hill Professional Publishing.

Clerico, Aldo & Emdin, Michele. Natriuretic Peptides: The Hormones of the Heart. 2006. (ENG., Illus.). xiv, 184p. 189.00 *(978-88-470-0497-9(7)*, 8847004977) Springer.

Coghlan, Gerry & Handler, Clive E. Preventing Cardiovascular Disease in Primary Care. 2nd ed. 2008. 197p. pap. *(978-1-84619-145-9(9))* Radcliffe Publishing.

Cohen, Ronald & Gunstad, John. Neuropsychology & Cardiovascular Disease. 2009. (ENG., Illus.). 432p. 85.00 *(978-0-19-534118-8(X))* Oxford Univ. Pr., Inc.

Committee on a National Surveillance System for Cardiovascular and Select Chronic Diseases & Institute of Medicine. A Nationwide Framework for Surveillance of Cardiovascular & Chronic Lung Diseases. 2011. (ENG.). 260p. pap. 49.50 ***(978-0-309-21216-8(2))*** National Academies Pr.

Committee on Preventing the Global Epidemic of Cardiovascular Disease: Meeting the Challenges in Developing Countries & Institute of Medicine. Promoting Cardiovascular Health in the Developing World: A Critical Challenge to Achieve Global Health. Fuster, Valentin & Kelly, Bridget B., eds. 2010. (ENG.). 484p. pap. 93.00 *(978-0-309-14774-3(3))* National Academies Pr.

Committee on Social Security Cardiovascular Disability Criteria, et al. Cardiovascular Disability: Updating the Social Security Listings. 2010. (ENG.). 304p. pap. 62.25 *(978-0-309-15698-1(X))* National Academies Pr.

Cram101 Textbook Reviews. Outlines & Highlights for Cardiovascular Genetics & Genomics for the Cardiologist by Victor J Dzau MD. 2011. 198p. pap. 30.95 ***(978-1-61812-061-8(1))*** Cram101 Inc.

—Outlines & Highlights for Management of Complex Cardiovascular Problems by Thach Nguyen, Isbn: 9781405140317. 2011. 138p. pap. 28.95 ***(978-1-61744-936-9(9))*** Cram101 Inc.

Cram101 Textbook Reviews & Cram101 Textbook Reviews. Outlines & Highlights for Cardiovascular Development: Advances in Developmental Biology by Elsevier Science, ISBN. 2011. 426p. pap. 35.95 ***(978-1-61461-286-5(2))*** Cram101 Inc.

—Outlines & Highlights for Neurovascular Neuropsychology by Joanne Fest. 2011. 112p. pap. 28.95 ***(978-1-61830-602-9(2))*** Cram101 Inc.

Creager, Mark, ed. Atlas of Vascular Disease. 3rd ed. 2009. (ENG.). cd-rom 99.00 *(978-1-57340-318-4(0)*, 1573403180) Current Medicine Group LLC.

Creager, Mark A. Atlas of Vascular Disease. Creager, Mark, ed. 3rd ed. 2008. (ENG., Illus.). vii, 296p. 199.00 *(978-1-57340-269-9(9)*, 1573402699) Current Medicine Group LLC.

Crook, Martin A., et al. Problem Solving in Cardiovascular Risk. 2011. (Illus.). 276p. pap. ***(978-1-904392-98-9(9))*** Clinical Publishing Services.

Cruickshank, John Malcolm. The Modern Role of Beta-Blockers in Cardiovascular Medicine. 2010. (Illus.). 271p. pap. *(978-1-60795-108-7(8))* PMPH-USA. Ltd.

Da?kapan, Arzu, ed. Cardiac Rehabilitation in Women. 2010. (Cardiology Research & Clinical Developments Ser.). pap. 43.00 *(978-1-61668-146-3(2)*, Nova Biomedical Bks.) Nova Science Pubs., Inc.

Dauphinee, Shauna & Karsan, Aly. Endothelial Dysfunction & Inflammation. 2010. (Progress in Inflammation Research Ser.). (Illus.). xii, 234p. 219.00 *(978-3-0346-0167-2(0)*, 3034601670) Birkhauser Verlag AG CHE. Dist: Springer.

Davidson, Andrew. Vascular Access. 2nd ed. (Handbooks Ser.). (Illus.). 500p. 45.00 *(978-1-57059-627-8(1))* Landes Bioscience.

Davies, Alun H., et al, eds. Venous Disease Simplified. 2007. (Illus.). 240p. pap. 58.00 *(978-1-903378-25-0(7))* TFM Publishing Ltd. GBR. Dist: JAMCO Distribution.

DeBakey, Michael E. & Gotto, Antonio, Jr. The Living Heart in the 21st Century. 2012. (ENG., Illus.). 320p. pap. 20.00 ***(978-1-61614-563-7(3))*** Prometheus Bks., Pubs.

Deindl, Elisabeth & Kupatt, Christian, eds. Therapeutic Neovascularization - Quo Vadis? 2007. (ENG., Illus.). x, 262p. 159.00 *(978-1-4020-5954-4(X)*, 140205954X) Springer.

deLeon, Antonio C. Cardiac Auscultation. 29p. 9.75 *(978-1-886128-00-2(6))* Laennec Publishing, Inc.

DeMello, Walmor C. & Frohlich, Edward D., eds. Renin Angiotensin System & Cardiovascular Disease. 2009. (Contemporary Cardiology Ser.). (ENG., Illus.). xii, 248p. 219.00 *(978-1-60761-185-1(6)*, 1607611856) Humana Pr.

Desai, Milind Y. & Schoenhagen, Paul, eds. Cardiac Computed Tomography: Problem-Based Learning. 2011. (ENG., Illus.). 272p. pap. 129.00 ***(978-1-60831-565-9(7))*** Lippincott Williams & Wilkins.

DeTurk, William E. & Cahalin, Lawrence P. Cardiovascular & Pulmonary Physical Therapy: An Evidence-Based Approach. 2nd ed. 2010. (ENG., Illus.). 778p. 99.00 *(978-0-07-159812-5(X)*, 007159812X) McGraw-Hill Medical Publishing Div.

DeVries, Stephen & Dalen, James, eds. Integrative Cardiology. 2010. (Weil Integrative Medicine Library). (ENG., Illus.). 400p. 39.95 *(978-0-19-538346-1(X))* Oxford Univ. Pr., Inc.

Dewey, Marc. Cardiac CT. 2010. (Illus.). xiii, 333p. 179.00 *(978-3-642-14021-1(1)*, 3642140211) Springer.

DiPetrillo, Keith, ed. Cardiovascular Genomics: Methods & Protocols. 2009. (Methods in Molecular Biology Ser.). (ENG., Illus.). x, 350p. 129.00 *(978-1-60761-246-9(1)*, 1607612461) Humana Pr.

Doevendans, P. A. F. M., et al, eds. Cardiovascular Specific Gene Expression. 2010. (Developments in Cardiovascular Medicine Ser.). (Illus.). 340p. pap. 249.00 *(978-90-481-5189-9(9)*, 9048151899) Springer.

Doyle, Mark, et al. The Cardiovascular MRI Tutorial: Lectures & Learning. 2007. (ENG., Illus.). 400p. 209.99 *(978-0-7817-7216-7(8))* Lippincott Williams & Wilkins.

Durstine, J. Larry, et al. Pollock's Textbook of Cardiovascular Disease & Rehabilitation. 2008. (ENG., Illus.). 432p. (C). 96.00 *(978-0-7360-5967-1(9))* Human Kinetics Pubs.

Dzau, Victor J. & Liew, Choong-Chin, eds. Cardiovascular Genetics & Genomics for the Cardiologist. 2007. (ENG., Illus.). 328p. 185.95 *(978-1-4051-3394-4(5)*, Wiley-Blackwell) Wiley, John & Sons, Inc.

Eagle, Kim A., et al, eds. Practical Cardiology: Evaluation & Treatment of Common Cardiovascular Disorders. 2nd rev. ed. 2008. (ENG., Illus.). 720p. pap. 84.99 *(978-0-7817-7294-5(X))* Lippincott Williams & Wilkins.

Eckel, Robert H., ed. Metabolic Risk for Cardiovascular Disease. 2010. (American Heart Association Clinical Ser.: 17). (ENG., Illus.). 264p. 131.95 *(978-1-4051-8104-4(4)*, Wiley-Blackwell) Wiley, John & Sons, Inc.

Erdmann, Volker A., et al, eds. RNA Technologies in Cardiovascular Medicine & Research. 2008. (ENG., Illus.). xiv, 358p. 239.00 *(978-3-540-78708-2(9)*, 3540787089) Springer.

European Society of Cardiology, E. S. C., ed. ESC Guidelines Desk Reference 2011: Compendium of Abridged ESC Guidelines 2011. 2011. (ENG., Illus.). xvi, 391p. pap. 109.00 ***(978-1-908517-29-6(8)***, 1908517298) Springer DEU. Dist: Springer.

European Society of Cardiology Staff. Esc Compendium of Abridged Guidelines. 2007. (ENG.). 374p. pap. 50.00 *(978-0-7817-6421-6(1))* Lippincott Williams & Wilkins.

Fenske, Theodore. While You Quit: A Smoker's Guide to Reducing the Risk of Heart Disease & Stroke. 2009. (ENG., Illus.). 256p. pap. 24.99 *(978-1-55002-939-0(8)*, Dundurn Pr.) Dundurn CAN. Dist: Ingram Pub. Services.

Ferdinand, Keith C., ed. Racial & Ethnic Minorities & Cardiovascular Disease. 2009. (Contemporary Cardiology Ser.). (Illus.). 400p. 179.00 *(978-1-58829-981-9(3))* Humana Pr.

Ferdinand, Keith C. & Armani, Annemarie. Cardiovascular Disease in Racial & Ethnic Minorities. 2009. (Illus.). xviii, 331p. *(978-1-60761-778-5(1))*; E-Book 129.00 *(978-1-59745-410-0(9))* Humana Pr.

Ferenczi, Emily, et al. Cardiology. Puri, Basant K. & Smock, Elliott, eds. 2007. (ENG., Illus.). 128p. pap. 22.95 *(978-0-340-92557-7(4))* Hodder Arnold Pubs.

Field, John M., ed. ACLS Resource Text for Instructors & Experienced Providers: Professional. 2008. (Illus.). 444p. pap. 59.75 *(978-0-87493-541-7(5))* American Heart Assn., Inc.

Finck, Brian N., et al, eds. Ars/Rxrs in Cardiovascular Physiology & Disease. 2008. 140p. pap. 22.00 *(978-977-454-021-9(2))* Hindawi Publishing Corp.

Finn, J. Paul & Lohan, Derek G. Cardiovascular MRI & MRA: from Seating Area to Signed Report: Volume 2: Interpretation Atlas. 2010. (Illus.). 450p. 189.00 *(978-1-60761-017-5(5))* Humana Pr.

Fischer, Evelyn. Cardiovascular Forward Programming of ES cells: Gezielte Differenzierung von pluripotenten Stammzellen zu spezifischen kardiovaskulären Zelltypen. 2011. 124p. pap. ***(978-3-8381-2535-0(5))*** Südwestdeutscher Verlag für Hochschulschriften AG & Co. KG.

Fisher, Miles. Diabetes & Heart Disease. 2009. (Oxford Drama Library). (ENG., Illus.). 160p. pap. 24.95 *(978-0-19-954372-4(0))* Oxford Univ. Pr., Inc.

Fisman, E. Z. & Tenenbaum, A., eds. Cardiovascular Diabetology: Clinical, Metabolic & Inflammatory Facets [Bibliography & Price not Definite.]: 2008. (Advances in Cardiology Ser.). (Illus.). 220p. *(978-3-8055-8427-2(X))* Karger, S. AG.

Fitridge, Robert & Thompson, Matthew, eds. Mechanisms of Vascular Disease: A reference book for vascular Specialists. 2011. (Illus.). 582p. pap. ***(978-0-9871718-2-5(8))*** Univ. of Adelaide Pr.

Florian, Maria. Estrogen's Role in Cardiovascular Health. 2009. 252p. pap. *(978-3-639-15299-9(9))* VDM Verlag Dr. Mueller e.K.

Fonseca, Vivian A. Cardiovascular Endocrinology: Shared Pathways & Clinical Crossroads. Fonseca, Vivian A., ed. 2008. (Illus.). 400p. (C). 159.00 *(978-1-58829-850-8(7))* Humana Pr.

Frank W. Cawood and Associates Staff, contrib. by. The Healthy Heart Handbook: Flush Your Arteries, Heal Your Heart, & Lower High Blood Pressure, Without Dangerous Drugs or Risky Surgery. 2009. (Illus.). viii, 376p. *(978-1-932470-74-1(3))* FC&A Publishing.

Frishman, William H. & Sica, Domenic A., eds. Cardiovascular Pharmacotherapeutics. 3rd ed. 2011. (ENG., Illus.). 800p. 199.00 *(978-0-9790164-3-1(6))* Cardiotext Publishing.

Fuster, Valentin. Hurst's the Heart. 12th ed. 2008. (Illus.). xxxi, 2477p. *(978-0-07-154942-4(0))* McGraw-Hill Medical Publishing Div.

Garcia, Mario J. Noninvasive Cardiovascular Imaging: A Multimodality Approach. 2011. (ENG., Illus.). 752p. 209.99 *(978-0-7817-9535-7(4))* Lippincott Williams & Wilkins.

Gillum, Richard F., et al, eds. Stroke in Blacks: A Guide to Management & Prevention. (Illus.). *(978-3-8055-6713-8(8))* Karger, S. AG.

Glesby, Marshall. HIV & Cardiovascular Risk. 2010. (Oxford American Pocket Notes Ser.). 80p. pap. 14.95 *(978-0-19-973730-7(4))* Oxford Univ. Pr., Inc.

Gotto Jr Antonio M Staff. Comprehensive Management of High Risk Cardiovascular Patients. 2007. (ENG., Illus.). 770p. 99.95 *(978-1-4200-6677-7(3)*, Informa Healthcare) Taylor & Francis Group GBR. Dist: Taylor & Francis Group.

Gourlay, T. & Black, R., eds. Biomaterials & Devices for the Circulatory System. 2010. (Woodhead Publishing Series in Biomaterials Ser.). (ENG., Illus.). 400p. 230.00 *(978-1-84569-464-7(3))* Woodhead Publishing Ltd. GBR. Dist: Ingram Pub. Services.

Griffin, Brian, et al. Cleveland Clinic Cardiology Board. 2nd rev. ed. 2012. (ENG., Illus.). 952p. 159.00 ***(978-1-4511-0537-7(1))*** Lippincott Williams & Wilkins.

Griffin, Brian P., et al, eds. The Cleveland Clinic Cardiology Board Review. 2006. (ENG., Illus.). 896p. 145.00 *(978-0-7817-5942-7(0))* Lippincott Williams & Wilkins.

—Manual of Cardiovascular Medicine. 3rd rev. ed. 2008. (ENG., Illus.). 1024p. pap. 94.99 *(978-0-7817-7854-1(9))* Lippincott Williams & Wilkins.

Grizzard, John D., et al. Cardiovascular MRI in Practice: A Teaching File Approach. 2008. (Illus.). 288p. 179.00 *(978-1-84800-089-6(8)*, 1848000898) Springer.

Gross, David R. Animal Models in Cardiovascular Research. 3rd ed. 2009. (ENG., Illus.). xxvi, 431p. 159.00 *(978-0-387-95961-0(0)*, 0387959610) Springer.

Haase, Jürgen, et al, eds. Cardiovascular Interventions in Clinical Practice. 2010. (ENG., Illus.). 744p. 332.00 *(978-1-4051-8277-5(6)*, Wiley-Blackwell) Wiley, John & Sons, Inc.

Hampl, H. & Besarab, A., eds. Cardiovascular Disease in the Uremic Patient, Vol. 28. (Illus.). 116p. pap. *(978-3-8055-8058-8(4))* Karger, S. AG.

Harrington, Robert, et al. Hurst's the Heart, Set. 13th ed. 2010. (ENG., Illus.). 2500p. 228.00 *(978-0-07-163646-9(3)*, 0071636463) McGraw-Hill Professional Publishing.

Hawken, C. M. Chelation Therapy. 3rd ed. 2011. (Woodland Health Ser.). 32p. pap. 4.95 ***(978-1-58054-198-5(4))*** Woodland Publishing, Inc.

Heagerty Anthony Staff, et al. Cardiovascular Biology in Health & Disease. 2009. 139.95 *(978-0-8493-9887-2(8)*, Informa Healthcare) Taylor & Francis Group GBR. Dist: Taylor & Francis Group.

The Hearthy Heart Handbook for Women - 2006. 2006. mass mkt. 4.00 *(978-1-933236-11-7(6))* National Heart, Lung, & Blood Institute.

Heller, Gary V., et al. Nuclear Cardiology: Technical Applications. 2008. (ENG., Illus.). 352p. 88.00 *(978-0-07-146475-8(1)*, 0071464751) McGraw-Hill Cos., The.

Hiremath, Shobha Rani R. & Murthy, S. Narasimha, eds. Drug Delivery Systems for Cardiovascular Diseases. 2012. (Drug Delivery Ser.). (Illus.). 304p. 149.95 *(978-1-4398-5275-0(8)*, CRC Press) Taylor & Francis Group GBR. Dist: Taylor & Francis Group.

Hjemdahl, Paul, et al, eds. Stress & Cardiovascular Disease. 2011. (ENG., Illus.). 300p. 219.00 *(978-1-84882-418-8(1)*, 1848824181) Springer.

Ho, Vincent & Reddy, Gautham P. Cardiovascular Imaging, 2 vols., Vol. 1, Set. 2010. (Expert Radiology Ser.). (ENG., Illus.). 1832p. 329.00 *(978-1-4160-5335-4(2)*, Saunders) Elsevier - Health Sciences Div.

Hobbs, Richard & Arroll, Bruce, eds. Cardiovascular Risk Management. 2008. (ENG., Illus.). 100p. pap. 52.95 *(978-1-4051-5575-5(2)*, Wiley-Blackwell) Wiley, John & Sons, Inc.

Hoffman, Julian I. E. & Moller, James H., eds. Pediatric Cardiovascular Medicine. 2nd ed. 2012. (ENG.). 1094p. 324.95 ***(978-1-4443-3589-7(8)***, Wiley-Blackwell) Wiley, John & Sons, Inc.

Hogan, Carl P. Cardiovascular Health & Disease Research Trends. 2007. 129.00 *(978-1-60021-757-9(5))* Nova Science Pubs., Inc.

Hollenberg, Steve, ed. Cardiology in Family Practice: A Practical Guide. 2010. (Current Clinical Practice Ser.). (Illus.). 184p. pap. 69.95 *(978-1-61737-608-5(6)*, 1617376086) Humana Pr.

Hu, Dayi, et al, eds. Management of Complex Cardiovascular Problems: The Evidence-Based Medicine Approach. 3rd rev. ed. 2007. (ENG., Illus.). 464p. per. 93.95 *(978-1-4051-4031-7(3)*, Wiley-Blackwell) Wiley, John & Sons, Inc.

Hubbard, Sean T. The Search for Wellness: A Holistic Approach to Stroke, Heart Disease, & Other Lifestyle-Related Conditions. 2006. 96p. per. 14.95 *(978-0-9777792-3-9(8))* Neu Age Publishing Co.

Hurst, John Willis, et al. Hurst's the Heart, 2 vols. 13th ed. 2010. (Illus.). xxix, 2444p. *(978-0-07-163647-6(1)); (978-0-07-174758-5(3)); (978-0-07-163649-0(8))* McGraw-Hill Cos., The.

Hutchison, Stuart J. Principles of Cardiovascular Radiology: Expert Consult - Online & Print. 2011. (Principles of Cardiovascular Imaging Ser.). (ENG., Illus.). 464p. pap. 99.00 *(978-1-4377-0405-1(0),* Saunders) Elsevier - Health Sciences Div.

Hwang, Ned H. C., et al, eds. Advances in Cardiovascular Engineering. 2010. (Nato Science Series: A: Ser.). 452p. pap. 349.00 *(978-1-4419-3228-0(3),* 1441932283) Springer.

Iacobellis, Gianluca. Obesity & Cardiovascular Disease. 2009. (ENG., Illus.). 240p. pap. 59.95 *(978-0-19-954932-0(X))* Oxford Univ. Pr., Inc.

Ingelsson, E., ed. Circulating Biomarkers in Cardiovascular Disease - Book Edition of Disease Markers. 2009. 94p. pap. 131.00 *(978-1-60750-057-5(4))* IOS Pr., Inc.

Ingenix, Inc. Staff. Coding Illustrated Cardiovascular & Respiratory 2001. (Illus.). pap. 149.95 *(978-1-56337-358-9(0))* OptumInsight, Inc.

Institute of Medicine Staff & Committee on Secondhand Smoke Exposure and Acute Coronary Events. Secondhand Smoke Exposure & Cardiovascular Effects: Making Sense of the Evidence. 2010. (ENG.). 240p. pap. 39.00 *(978-0-309-13839-0(6))* National Academies Pr.

Jain, Kewal K. Applications of Biotechnology in Cardiovascular Therapeutics. 2011. (Illus.). xxviii, 350p. ***(978-1-61779-240-3(3))*** Humana Pr.

Janecek, Martin. Instrumentation for Lesion Detection. 2010. 180p. pap. *(978-3-8383-2192-9(8))* Lambert Academic Publishing.

Januzzi, James L. Cardiac Biomarkers in Clinical Practice. rev. ed. 2009. (Illus.). 900p. pap. 86.95 *(978-0-7637-6161-5(3))* Jones & Bartlett Learning, LLC.

Jobbágy, Ákos. Early Diagnosis & Objective Assessment of Patients. 2010. 152p. pap. *(978-3-8383-5316-5(1))* Lambert Academic Publishing.

Johnstone, Michael T. & Veves, Aristidis, eds. Diabetes & Cardiovascular Disease. 2nd ed. 2010. (Contemporary Cardiology Ser.). (Illus.). 672p. pap. 189.00 *(978-1-61737-549-1(7),* 1617375497) Humana Pr.

Joseph, Jacob, ed. Mast Cells & Cardiovascular Disease. 2009. 116.10 *(978-1-61668-593-5(X))* Nova Science Pubs., Inc.

Junien, Jean-Louis & Staels, B. Nuclear Receptors as Molecular Targets for Cardiometabolic & Central Nervous System Diseases, 8. 2008. (Illus.). ix, 117p. 126.00 *(978-1-58603-857-1(5))* IOS Pr., Inc.

Kado, Hideaki & Masuda, Munetaka, eds. Cardiovascular Surgery for Congenital Heart Disease. 2009. (ENG., Illus.). xviii, 270p. 259.00 *(978-4-431-99469-5(6),* 4431994696) Springer.

Kaski, J. C. & Holt, David W., eds. Myocardial Damage: Early Detection by Novel Biochemical Markers. 2010. (Developments in Cardiovascular Medicine Ser.). 212p. pap. 169.00 *(978-90-481-5056-4(6),* 9048150566) Springer.

Kastler, Bruno, ed. MRI of Cardiovascular Malformations. 2009. 179.00 *(978-3-540-30701-3(X))* Springer.

King, Spencer B., III & Yeung, Alan. Interventional Cardiology. 2006. (ENG., Illus.). 600p. (C). 185.00 *(978-0-07-141527-9(0),* 0071415270) McGraw-Hill Professional Publishing.

Kipshidze, Nicholas N., et al. Textbook of Interventional Cardiovascular Pharmacology. Kennedy, Cathy, ed. 2007. (ENG., Illus.). 704p. 420.00 *(978-1-84184-438-1(1),* Informa Healthcare) Taylor & Francis Group GBR. Dist: Taylor & Francis Group.

Kirkham, Fenella & Ganesan, Vijeya, eds. Stroke & Cerebrovascular Disease in Childhood. 2011. (ENG., Illus.). 248p. 199.95 *(978-1-898683-34-6(4))* Mac Keith Pr. GBR. Dist: Wiley, John & Sons, Inc.

Kleinman, Charles S. & Seri, Istvan. Hemodynamics & Cardiology: Neonatology Questions & Controversies: Expert Consult - Online & Print. 2nd ed. 2012. (Neonatology: Questions & Controversies Ser.). (ENG., Illus.). 576p. 89.95 ***(978-1-4377-2763-0(8),*** Saunders) Elsevier - Health Sciences Div.

Klimczak, Christophe & Nihoyannopoulos, Petros. 100 Challenges in Echocardiography. 2008. (ENG., Illus.). 256p. (C). pap. 44.95 *(978-0-443-06927-7(1),* Churchill Livingstone) Elsevier - Health Sciences Div.

Kokkinos, Peter. Physical Activity & Cardiovascular Disease Prevention. 2009. 418p. 101.95 *(978-0-7637-5612-3(1))* Jones & Bartlett Learning, LLC.

Kontush, Anatol & Chapman, M. John. High-Density Lipoproteins: Structure, Metabolism, Function & Therapeutics. 2012. (ENG., Illus.). 648p. 135.00 ***(978-0-470-40821-6(9),*** Wiley) Wiley, John & Sons, Inc.

Koster, Nancy. Cardiovascular Imaging Review: Expert Consult - Online & Print. 2011. (ENG., Illus.). 192p. pap. 99.00 *(978-1-4160-6250-9(5),* Saunders) Elsevier - Health Sciences Div.

Kramer, Christopher M. Multimodality Imaging in Cardiovascular Medicine. 2011. (Illus.). xiv, 343p. 509.00 *(978-1-933864-74-7(5))* Demos Medical Publishing, LLC.

Kramer, Christopher M. & Hundley, W. Greg. Atlas of Cardiovascular Magnetic Resonance Imaging: Imaging Companion to Braunwald's Heart Disease. 2009. (Imaging Techniques to Braunwald's Heart Disease Ser.). (ENG., Illus.). 376p. 195.00 *(978-1-4160-6135-9(5),* Saunders) Elsevier - Health Sciences Div.

Krentz, Andrew & Wong, Nathan, eds. Metabolic Syndrome & Cardiovascular Disease: Epidemiology, Assessment, & Management. 2007. (ENG.). 344p. 99.95 *(978-1-4200-6676-0(5),* Informa Healthcare) Taylor & Francis Group GBR. Dist: Taylor & Francis Group.

Krentz, Andrew J. & Wong, Nathan D., eds. Metabolic Syndrome & Cardiovascular Disease: Epidemiology, Assessment, & Management. 2007. (Illus.). 313p. 230.00 *(978-0-8493-9373-0(6),* Informa Healthcare) Taylor & Francis Group GBR. Dist: Taylor & Francis Group.

Krings, Timo, et al. Case-Based Interventional Neuroradiology. 2011. (ENG., Illus.). 464p. 99.99 *(978-1-60406-373-8(4))* Thieme Medical Pubs., Inc.

Kumar, Dhavendra & Elliott, Perry. Principles & Practice of Clinical Cardiovascular Genetics. 2010. (ENG., Illus.). 624p. *(978-0-19-536895-6(9))* Oxford Univ. Pr.

Kwiterovich, Peter O., ed. The Johns Hopkins Textbook of Dyslipidemia. 2009. (ENG.). 320p. 114.99 *(978-0-7817-8265-4(1))* Lippincott Williams & Wilkins.

Kwong, Raymond Y., ed. Cardiovascular Magnetic Resonance Imaging. 2008. (Contemporary Cardiology Ser.). (Illus.). 749p. 239.00 incl. cd-rom *(978-1-58829-673-3(3),* 1588296733) Humana Pr.

Labarthe, Darwin. Epidemiology & Prevention of Cardiovascular Disease. 2nd rev. ed. 2010. 710p. pap. 120.95 *(978-0-7637-4689-6(4))* Jones & Bartlett Learning, LLC.

Lawless, Christine, ed. Sports Cardiology in Practice: Evaluation, Management & Case Studies. 2010. (ENG., Illus.). x, 465p. pap. 69.95 *(978-0-387-92774-9(3),* 0387927743) Springer.

Lawton, Michael T., et al, eds. Controversies in Neurological Surgery: Neurovascular Diseases. 2006. (ENG., Illus.). 304p. 149.99 *(978-1-58890-344-0(3))* Thieme Medical Pubs., Inc.

Layton, Kevin G. & Percelle, Raymond A., eds. Angioplasty Research Progress. 2008. (Illus.). xii, 522p. 215.00 *(978-1-60456-422-8(9))* Nova Science Pubs., Inc.

Leone, Aurelio. Passive Smoking & Cardiovascular Pathology: Mechanisms & Physiopathological Bases of Damage. 2007. 79.00 *(978-1-60021-644-2(7))* Nova Science Pubs., Inc.

Libby, Peter. Essential Atlas of Cardiovascular Disease. Libby, Peter, ed. 4th ed. 2009. (ENG.). 432p. 159.00 *(978-1-57340-309-2(1),* 1573403091) Current Medicine Group LLC.

Lim, Michael. Catheterization Hemodynamics, an Issue of Cardiology Clinics. 2011. (Clinics: Internal Medicine Ser.: 29-2). (ENG., Illus.). 160p. 110.00 *(978-1-4557-0425-5(3),* Saunders) Elsevier - Health Sciences Div.

Lincoff, A. Michael, ed. Platelet Glycoprotein IIb/IIIa Inhibitors in Cardiovascular Disease. 2nd ed. 2010. (Contemporary Cardiology Ser.). (Illus.). 440p. pap. 179.00 *(978-1-61737-408-1(3),* 1617374083) Humana Pr.

Littarru, P. G., ed. The Fifth Conference of the International CoQ10 Association BioFactors: Kobe 2007 - 50th Anniversary of CoQ10 Discovery - Book Edition Of. 2008. 197p. pap. 348.00 *(978-1-58603-963-9(6))* IOS Pr., Inc.

Lu, Jing. Detection of Endoleaks in Ct Data for Monitoring of Aaa Stents. 2008. (Illus.). 108p. pap. *(978-3-639-01367-2(0))* VDM Verlag Dr. Mueller e.K.

Lurie, A., ed. Obstructive Sleep Apnea in Adults: Relationship with Cardiovascular & Metabolic Disorders. 2011. (Advances in Cardiology Ser.). (ENG., Illus.). 272p. ***(978-3-8055-9645-9(6))*** Karger, S. AG.

Maj, Mario. Depression & Heart Disease. Glassman, Alexander & Sartorius, Norman, eds. 2011. (ENG., Illus.). 190p. pap. 51.99 *(978-0-470-71057-9(6),* Wiley) Wiley, John & Sons, Inc.

Mancini, Mario, et al, eds. Nutritional & Metabolic Bases of Cardiovascular Disease. 2011. (ENG., Illus.). 488p. 167.95 *(978-1-4051-8276-8(8),* Wiley-Blackwell) Wiley, John & Sons, Inc.

Manning, Warren J. Atlas of Cardiovascular Magnetic Resonance Imaging. 2008. *(978-1-57340-291-0(5))* Current Medicine Group Ltd.

Marín-García, José. Signaling in the Heart. 2011. (Illus.). xx, 507p. 169.00 *(978-1-4419-9460-8(2),* 1441994602) Springer.

Marín-García, José, ed. Post-Genomic Cardiology. 2007. (ENG., Illus.). 688p. 185.00 *(978-0-12-373698-7(6),* Academic Pr.) Elsevier Science & Technology Bks.

McAllister, Hugh A., Jr. Ten Years of Images from Circulation: Journal of the American Heart Association. Willerson, James T., ed. 2006. (Illus.). 310p. 81.50 *(978-0-7817-6706-4(7))* Lippincott Williams & Wilkins.

McBride, Patrick E. Contemporary Diagnosis & Mangement in Preventive Cardiology. 2nd ed. 2009. 485p. pap. 27.75 *(978-1-935103-17-2(2),* Handbooks in Health Care Co.) Assocs. in Medical Marketing Co., Inc.

McKenna, Kim. ACLS Essentials: Basics & More. 2007. 160p. (C). pap. 51.56 *(978-0-07-299932-7(2),* 9780072999327) McGraw-Hill Cos., The.

McKinsey, James F., ed. Minimally Invasive Vascular Surgery. 2009. (Current Cardiac Surgery Ser.). 175.00 *(978-1-58829-804-1(3))* Humana Pr.

McManus, Bruce M. Atlas of Cardiovascular Pathology for the Clinician. 2nd ed. 2008. *(978-1-57340-273-6(7))* Current Medicine Group Ltd.

McManus, Bruce M. & Braunwald, Eugene, eds. Atlas of Cardiovascular Pathology for the Clinician. 2nd ed. 2008. 300p. 199.00 *(978-1-57340-279-8(6))* Current Medicine Group LLC.

Mehran, Roxana & Kini, Annapoorna S. Percutaneous Interventions in Women an Issue of Interventional Cardiology Clinics. 2012. (Clinics: Internal Medicine Ser.: 1-2). (ENG.). 110.00 ***(978-1-4557-3882-3(4),*** Saunders) Elsevier - Health Sciences Div.

Meier, Bernhard, ed. Current Best Practice in Interventional Cardiology. 2010. (ENG., Illus.). 232p. 165.95 *(978-1-4051-8255-3(5),* Wiley-Blackwell) Wiley, John & Sons, Inc.

Mendis, S., et al. Global Atlas on Cardiovascular Disease Prevention & Control. 2012. (Nonserial Publications Ser.). (ENG.). 161p. pap. 48.00 ***(978-92-4-156437-3(7))*** World Health Organization.

Mendizabal Ruiz, Eduardo Gerardo. Probabilistic Segmentation of Intravascular Ultrasound Sequences. 2011. 64p. pap. ***(978-3-8443-2540-9(9))*** Lambert Academic Publishing.

Mensah, George A. & Rich, Michael W. Preventive Cardiology in the Elderly, an Issue of Clinics in Geriatric Medicine. 2009. (Clinics: Internal Medicine Ser.: 25-4). (ENG.). 99.00 *(978-1-4377-1386-2(6),* Saunders) Elsevier - Health Sciences Div.

Messiah, Sarah. Prevalence of the Metabolic Syndrome in Us Adolescents. 2008. 176p. pap. *(978-3-639-06930-3(7))* VDM Verlag Dr. Mueller e.K.

Milan, Zoka. Cardiovascular Diseases & Liver Transplantation. 2011. (Cardiology Research & Clinical Developments Ser.). 129.00 *(978-1-61122-910-3(3))* Nova Science Pubs., Inc.

Minotti, Giorgio. Cardiotoxicity of Non-Cardiovascular Drugs. 2010. (ENG., Illus.). 360p. 155.00 *(978-0-470-77274-4(3),* Wiley) Wiley, John & Sons, Inc.

Miyazaki, Akira. New Frontiers in Lifestyle-Related Diseases. 2008. (ENG., Illus.). xxii, 160p. 79.95 *(978-4-431-76427-4(5),* 4431764275) Springer.

Moghadisian, Mohammed H. & Eskin, Michael N. A., eds. Functional Foods & Cardiovascular Disease. 2012. (ENG., Illus.). 296p. 129.95 *(978-1-4200-7110-8(6),* CRC Press) Taylor & Francis Group GBR. Dist: Taylor & Francis Group.

Moini, Jahangir. Cardiopulmonary Pharmacology for Respiratory Care with Companion Web Site. 2010. 320p. pap. 75.95 *(978-1-4496-1560-4(0))* Jones & Bartlett Learning, LLC.

Montoya, Lorraine. The Experience of Making Lifestyle Change. 2010. 92p. pap. *(978-3-639-22768-0(9))* VDM Verlag Dr. Mueller e.K.

Morrow, David A., ed. Cardiovascular Biomarkers: Pathophysiology & Disease Management. 2010. (Contemporary Cardiology Ser.). (Illus.). 640p. pap. 229.00 *(978-1-61737-620-7(5),* 1617376205) Humana Pr.

Mosca, Lori J. Contemporary Diagnosis & Management of Dyslipidemias in Women. 2009. 195p. pap. 24.99 *(978-1-935103-10-3(5))* Assocs. in Medical Marketing Co., Inc.

Moscucci, Mauro. Complications of Cardiovascular Procedures: Risk Factors, Management & Bailout Techniques. 2010. (ENG., Illus.). 624p. 156.99 *(978-0-7817-7588-5(4))* Lippincott Williams & Wilkins.

Mukherjee, Debabrata, et al, eds. Interventional Cardiology: 1001 Questions - An Interventional Cardiology Board Review. 2011. (ENG.). 528p. pap. 129.00 ***(978-1-4511-1299-3(8))*** Lippincott Williams & Wilkins.

Muthorst, Sonja. TAPSE: Evaluierung eines neuen echokardiographischen Parameters. 2011. 108p. pap. ***(978-3-8381-2461-2(8))*** Südwestdeutscher Verlag für Hochschulschriften AG & Co. KG.

Myat, Aung, et al, eds. Challenging Concepts in Cardiovascular Medicine: A Case-Based Approach with Expert Commentary. 2011. (ENG., Illus.). 288p. pap. 98.50 ***(978-0-19-969554-6(7))*** Oxford Univ. Pr., Inc.

National Council on Radiation Protection and Measurements, Scientific Committee 1-17 Staff, contrib. by. Second Primary Cancers & Cardiovascular Disease after Radiation Therapy. 2011. (NCRP Reports: No. 170). ***(978-0-9823843-9-8(4))*** National Council on Radiation Protection & Measurements.

Navar, Gabriel. Renin-Angiotensin System. 2011. (Colloquium Series on Integrated Systems Physiology: from Molecule to Function Ser.). 100p. pap. 35.00 *(978-1-61504-234-0(2))* Morgan & Claypool Life Science Publishers.

Nayak, Krishna S., ed. Handbook of Cardiovascular Magnetic Resonance Imaging. 2006. (Fundamental & Clinical Cardiology Ser.: Vol. 60). (ENG., Illus.). 480p. 230.00 *(978-0-8247-5841-7(2),* Informa Healthcare) Taylor & Francis Group GBR. Dist: Taylor & Francis Group.

Nicholls, Stephen J. & Worthley, Stephen G. Cardiovascular Imaging for Clinical Practice. rev. ed. 2010. 386p. pap. 117.95 *(978-0-7637-5622-2(9))* Jones & Bartlett Learning, LLC.

Norell, Michael S., et al. Essential Interventional Cardiology. 2nd ed. 2008. (ENG., Illus.). 560p. 120.00 *(978-0-7020-2981-3(5),* Saunders) Elsevier - Health Sciences Div.

O'Byrne, Paul. Red Wine & Health. 2009. (Illus.). xvii, 527p. 89.00 *(978-1-60692-718-2(3))* Nova Science Pubs., Inc.

Oostra, R. J. Viragh's & Steding's Scanning Electron Microscopy Atlas of the Developing Human Heart. 2006. (Illus.). 365p. 175.00 *(978-0-8176-4344-7(3),* 0817643443) Birkhauser Boston.

O'Rourke, Robert, et al. Hurst's the Heart Manual of Cardiology. 13th ed. 2012. (ENG., Illus.). 656p. (C). pap. 65.00 ***(978-0-07-177315-7(0),*** 0071773150) McGraw-Hill Professional Publishing.

O'Rourke, Robert A., et al. Hurst's the Heart: Manual of Cardiology. 12th ed. 2009. (ENG., Illus.). 784p. (C). pap. 63.00 *(978-0-07-159298-7(9),* 0071592989) McGraw-Hill Professional Publishing.

Patterson, David & Treasure, Tom. Disorders of the Cardiovascular System. (ENG., Illus.). 368p. *(978-0-340-53593-6(8),* Hodder Arnold) Hodder Education.

Pelliccia, Antonio, ed. Sports Cardiology Casebook. 2009. (ENG., Illus.). xviii, 242p. 109.00 *(978-1-84882-041-8(0),* 1848820410) Springer.

Perelles, Scott & Goldman, Jeffery. Cardiac Imaging Cases. 2009. (Illus.). 768p. pap. 179.00 *(978-0-07-147714-7(4),* 9780071477147) McGraw-Hill Professional Publishing.

Perk, Joep, et al, eds. Cardiovascular Prevention & Rehabilitation. 2007. (ENG., Illus.). xvii, 517p. pap. 129.00 *(978-1-84628-993-4(9),* 1846289939); 249.00 *(978-1-84628-462-5(7),* 1846284627) Springer.

Pollard, Tessa. Western Diseases: An Evolutionary Perspective. 2008. (Cambridge Studies in Biological & Evolutionary Anthropology Ser.). (ENG., Illus.). (C). 236p. 133.99 *(978-0-521-85180-0(7));* 223p. pap. 66.00 *(978-0-521-61737-6(5))* Cambridge Univ. Pr.

Poller, Wolfgang & Barciszewski, Jan, eds. RNA Technologies in Cardiovascular Medicine & Research. 2010. (ENG., Illus.). xiv, 358p. pap. 239.00 *(978-3-642-09746-1(4),* 3642097464) Springer.

Poulter, Neil. Clinical Manual of Total Cardiovascular Risk. 2009. (Illus.). 96p. 39.95 *(978-1-84800-252-4(1))* Springer.

Prevention of Cardiovascular Disease. 2007. (Nonserial Publication). (ENG.). 30p. pap. 15.00 *(978-92-4-154725-3(1));* 31p. pap. 15.00 *(978-92-4-154729-1(4));* 31p. pap. 15.00 *(978-92-4-154728-4(6))* World Health Organization.

Pritchett & Hull Assoc., illus. Moving Right along after Heart Surgery. 2007. (ENG & SPA.). 14.95 *(978-1-933638-22-5(2))* Pritchett & Hull Assocs., Inc.

Psychological Factors & Cardiovascular Disorders: The Role of Stress & Psychosocial Influences. 2009. 468p. 87.00 *(978-1-60456-923-0(9))* Nova Science Pubs., Inc.

Ragosta, Michael. Cases in Interventional Cardiology. 2010. (ENG., Illus.). 352p. 99.95 *(978-1-4377-0583-6(9),* Saunders) Elsevier - Health Sciences Div.

—Textbook of Clinical Hemodynamics. 2008. (ENG., Illus.). 264p. 99.95 *(978-1-4160-4000-2(5),* Saunders) Elsevier - Health Sciences Div.

Raizada, Mohan K., et al, eds. Cardiovascular Genomics. 2010. (Contemporary Cardiology Ser.). (Illus.). 376p. pap. 189.00 *(978-1-61737-542-2(X),* 161737542X) Humana Pr.

Rastogi, Sanjeev, ed. Evidence-Based Practice in Complementary & Alternative Medicine: Perspectives, Protocols, Problems & Potential in Ayurveda. 2012. (ENG., Illus.). xiv, 245p. 189.00 ***(978-3-642-24564-0(1),*** 3642245641) Springer.

Rathbond, Jackson E., ed. Handbook of Lipoprotein Research. 2010. (Protein Biochemistry, Synthesis, Structure & Cellular Functions Ser.). 129.00 *(978-1-61668-186-9(1))* Nova Science Pubs., Inc.

Rea, William J. Reversibility of Chronic Degenerative Disease & Hypersensitivity Vol. 1: Regulating Mechanisms. 2010. (ENG., Illus.). 594p. 139.95 *(978-1-4398-1342-3(6),* CRC Press) Taylor & Francis Group GBR. Dist: Taylor & Francis Group.

Reanimacion Cardiopulmonar Avanzada (Advanced Cardiac Life Support). 1997-99. Date not set. (Emergency Cardiovascular Care Programs Ser.). (SPA.). 386p. pap. 25.00 *(978-0-87493-633-9(0))* American Heart Assn., Inc.

Rémy-Jardin, Martine & Remy, Jacques. Integrated Cardiothoracic Imaging with MDCT. 2010. (Medical Radiology / Diagnostic Imaging Ser.). (Illus.). xii, 444p. pap. 139.00 *(978-3-642-09146-9(6),* 3642091466) Springer.

Riba, Michelle, et al. Psychiatry & Heart Disease: The Mind, Brain & Heart. 2012. (ENG., Illus.). 272p. 99.95 ***(978-0-470-68580-8(8),*** Wiley-Blackwell) Wiley, John & Sons, Inc.

Roden, Dan M., et al. Cardiovascular Genetics & Genomics. 2009. (American Heart Association Clinical Ser.: 10). (ENG., Illus.). 288p. 138.95 *(978-1-4051-7540-1(0),* Wiley-Blackwell) Wiley, John & Sons, Inc.

Ronco, C., et al. Cardiovascular Disorders in Hemodialysis, Vol. 149. (Contributions to Nephrology Ser.: Vol. 149). (Illus.). *(978-3-8055-7938-4(1))* Karger, S. AG.

Ronellenfitsch, Ulrich. Cardiovascular Mortality among Ethic German Immigrants from the Former Soviet Union to Germany. 2007. (Challenges in Public Health Ser.: Vol. 51). XV, 182p. pap. 46.95 *(978-3-631-55704-4(3))* Lang, Peter GmbH, Europaischer Verlag der Wissenschaften DEU. Dist: Lang, Peter Publishing, Inc.

RuDusky, Basil. Forensic Cardiovascular Medicine. 2009. (ENG., Illus.). 210p. 102.95 *(978-1-4200-9431-2(9),* CRC Press) Taylor & Francis Group GBR. Dist: Taylor & Francis Group.

Runge, Marschall S., et al. Netter's Cardiology. 2nd ed. 2010. (Netter Clinical Science Ser.). (ENG., Illus.). 572p. 195.00 *(978-1-4377-0638-3(X));* 99.95 *(978-1-4377-0637-6(1))* Elsevier - Health Sciences Div. (Saunders).

Russo, Robert J. Intravascular Ultrasound Pocket Guide. 7th rev. ed. 2010. 108p. spiral bd. 26.95 *(978-0-7637-6600-9(3))* Jones & Bartlett Learning, LLC.

Rymer, Marilyn M., et al. The Stroke Center Handbook: Organizing Care for Better Outcomes: A Guide to Stroke Center Development & Operations. 2006. (ENG., Illus.). 128p. 119.95 *(978-1-84214-286-8(0),* Informa Healthcare) Taylor & Francis Group GBR. Dist: Taylor & Francis Group.

Safian, Robert. Manual of Interventional Cardiology. 3rd rev. ed. 2008. 1050p. pap. 104.95 *(978-1-890114-39-8(1))* Physician's Pr.

Saksena, Franklin B. Color Atlas of Local & Systemic Signs of Cardiovascular Disease. 2008. (ENG., Illus.). 128p. per. 93.95 *(978-1-4051-5976-0(6),* Wiley-Blackwell) Wiley, John & Sons, Inc.

Sauer, Heinrich, et al, eds. Studies on Cardiovascular Disorders. 2010. (Oxidative Stress in Applied Basic Research & Clinical Practice Ser.). (Illus.). 400p. 239.00 *(978-1-60761-599-6(1),* 1607615991) Humana Pr.

Schmitt, Carol G., et al, eds. Handbook of Pediatric Cardiovascular Drugs. 2008. (Illus.). 356p. per. 89.95 *(978-1-84628-952-1(1))* Springer.

Schmitt, Lukas & König, Timm, eds. Advances in Cardiovascular Research, Volume 1. 2010. (Cardiology Research & Clinical Developments Ser.). 195.00 *(978-1-60741-720-0(0))* Nova Science Pubs., Inc.

Schneider, Diana M. The Coumadin (Warfarin) Help Book: Anticoagulation Therapy to Prevent & Manage Strokes, Heart Attacks, & Other Vascular Conditions. 2008. (ENG., Illus.). 112p. pap. 16.95 *(978-0-9793564-2-1(3))* DiaMed, LLC.

Schoenhagen, Paul, et al. Cardiac CT Made Easy: An Introduction to Cardiovascular Multidetector Computer Tomography (Combined Book & DVD Set), 2 vols. 2007. (ENG.). 140p. 299.95 *(978-1-84184-659-0(7)* Informa Healthcare) Taylor & Francis Group GBR. Dist: Taylor & Francis Group.

Schools, Cats Careers & Cardiovascular Technology, School of. CATS Cardiovascular Technologist. 2010. 62p. pap. 99.99 *(978-0-557-12185-4(X))* Lulu Enterprises Inc.

Schul. Starting & Managing a Phlebology Practice. 2010. (ENG., Illus.). 208p. 99.00 *(978-1-85315-940-4(9))* Hodder Arnold Pubs.

C

Sellke, Frank W. & Ruel, Marc. Atlas of Cardiac Surgical Techniques. 2009. (Surgical Techniques Atlas Ser.). (ENG., Illus.). 456p. 285.00 (978-1-4160-4065-1(X), Saunders) Elsevier - Health Sciences Div.

Shaaban, Juwita, et al. Ambulatory Blood Pressure Monitoring. 2011. 80p. pap. **(978-3-8443-0201-1(8))** Lambert Academic Publishing.

Shaddy, Robert, et al. Pediatric Practice Cardiology. 2012. (Pediatric Practice Ser.). (ENG., Illus.). 400p. 89.00 **(978-0-07-176320-2(1)**, 0071763201) McGraw-Hill Professional Publishing.

Shaheen, Dr. Ghazala, et al. Cardiovascular Diseases. 2011. 196p. pap. **(978-3-8454-0643-5(7))** Lambert Academic Publishing.

Sharma, Samin K. & Kini, Annapoorna S. Advanced Applied Interventional Cardiology , an Issue of Cardiology Clinics. 2010. (Clinics: Internal Medicine Ser.: 28-1). (ENG., Illus.). xii, 189p. 105.00 (978-1-4377-1800-3(0), Saunders) Elsevier - Health Sciences Div.

Sheppard, Mary. Practical Cardiovascular Pathology. 2nd ed. 2011. (ENG., Illus.). 352p. 198.50 (978-0-340-98193-1(8)) Hodder Arnold Pubs.

Sher, Leo, ed. Psychological Factors & Cardiovascular Disorders: The Role of Psychiatric Pathology & Maladaptive Personality Features. 2008. 365p. 79.00 (978-1-60456-871-4(2)) Nova Science Pubs., Inc.

Shi, Wenyu. Adaptive Control of a Total Artificial Heart. 2010. 108p. pap. (978-3-8383-1961-2(3)) Lambert Academic Publishing.

Sideman, Samuel, et al, eds. Control & Regulation of Transport Phenomena in the Cardiac System. 2008. (Annals of the New York Academy of Sciences Ser.: Vol. 1420). (ENG., Illus.). 300p. pap. 139.95 (978-1-57331-706-1(3), Wiley-Blackwell) Wiley, John & Sons, Inc.

Simon, Daniel I. & Rogers, Campbell, eds. Vascular Disease & Injury: Preclinical Research. 2010. (Contemporary Cardiology Ser.). (Illus.). 368p. pap. 169.00 (978-1-61737-169-1(6), 1617371696) Humana Pr.

Sjögren, Per. Diet & Cardiometabolic Risk. 2009. 80p. pap. (978-3-639-16995-9(6)) VDM Verlag Dr. Mueller e.K.

Smith, D. Cardiovascular Risk Factors, an Issue of Clinics in Laboratory Medicine. 2006. 240p. 79.00 (978-1-4160-3878-8(7), Saunders) Elsevier - Health Sciences Div.

Smith, Timothy William & Pinto, Duane S. Tarascon Pocket Cardiologica. 2011. 400p. pap. 19.95 **(978-1-4496-1516-1(3)**, Tarascon) Jones & Bartlett Learning, LLC.

Sniderman, Allan, ed. The Atherogenic Dyslipoproteinemias: A Clinical Manual. 2007. (Illus.). 248p. 110.00 (978-1-4051-2446-1(6), Wiley-Blackwell) Wiley, John & Sons, Inc.

Springhouse Publishing Company Staff. Disease & Drug Consult - Respiratory Disorders. 2009. (ENG., Illus.). 480p. pap. 41.99 (978-1-60547-053-5(8)) Lippincott Williams & Wilkins.

Springhouse Publishing Company Staff & Lippincott Williams and Wilkins Staff, eds. Hemodynamic Monitoring. 2nd rev. ed. 2010. (Incredibly Easy! Ser.). (ENG., Illus.). 160p. pap. 46.99 (978-1-60831-340-2(9)) Lippincott Williams & Wilkins.

Sreejayan, Nair & Ren, Jun, eds. Vascular Biology Protocols. 2010. (Methods in Molecular Medicine Ser.). xii, 372p. pap. 179.00 (978-1-61737-650-4(7), 1617376507) Humana Pr.

Stedman's Medical Dictionary Staff. Cardiovascular & Pulmonary Words. 5th rev. ed. 2008. (Stedman's Ser.). (ENG.). cd-rom 45.99 (978-0-7817-7630-1(9)) Lippincott Williams & Wilkins.

Stedman's Medical Dictionary Staff, ed. Stedman's Cardiovascular & Pulmonary Words: With Respiratory Words. 5th rev. ed. 2007. (Stedman's Word Book Ser.). (ENG., Illus.). 1072p. per. 43.99 (978-0-7817-7611-0(2)) Lippincott Williams & Wilkins.

Stone, Martin & Hoffmann, Candace. Cranberries: Nature's Nutrient Powerhouse. 2007. (Woodland Health Ser.). 30p. pap. 4.95 (978-1-58054-461-0(4)) Woodland Publishing, Inc.

Stoner, Lee & McCully, Kevin. Blood Velocity Parameters That Contribute to Flow-Mediated Dilation. 2011. 132p. pap. **(978-3-8433-9381-2(8))** Lambert Academic Publishing.

Sun, Jing Ping, et al, eds. Practical Handbook of Echocardiography: 101 Case Studies. 2010. (ENG.). 368p. pap. 138.95 (978-1-4051-9556-0(8), Wiley-Blackwell) Wiley, John & Sons, Inc.

Sun, John. Cardiac Evaluation of the Developmental Origins of Adult Cardiovascular Diseases. 2008. 128p. pap. (978-3-639-03207-9(1)) VDM Verlag Dr. Mueller e.K.

Sutton, Amy, ed. Cardiovascular Diseases & Disorders. 4th rev. ed. 2010. (Health Reference Ser.). 640p. lib. bdg. 93.00 (978-0-7808-1080-8(5)) Omnigraphics, Inc.

Tadeusiewicz, Ryszard & Augustyniak, Piotr. Ubiquitous Cardiology: Emerging Wireless Telemedical Applications. 2009. (Illus.). 430p. 165.00 (978-1-60566-080-6(9)) IGI Global.

Taylor, Allen J. Atlas of Cardiovascular Computed Tomography. 2009. (Imaging Techniques to Braunwald's Heart Disease Ser.). (ENG., Illus.). 304p. 195.00 (978-1-4160-6136-6(3), Saunders) Elsevier - Health Sciences Div.

Thacher, Tyler. Autonomous Effects of Shear & Stretch on the Arterial Wall. 2010. 108p. pap. (978-3-8383-6711-8(1)) Lambert Academic Publishing.

Thubrikar, Mano J. Vascular Mechanics & Pathology. 2007. (ENG., Illus.). xxiv, 496p. 124.00 (978-0-387-33816-3(0), 0387338160) Springer.

Topol, Eric J., ed. The Topol Solution: Textbook of Cardiovascular Medicine. 3rd rev. ed. 2006. (ENG., Illus.). 1664p. 256.50 (978-0-7817-7012-5(2)) Lippincott Williams & Wilkins.

Toth, Peter & Cannon, Christopher P., eds. Comprehensive Cardiovascular Medicine in the Primary Care Setting. 2010. (Contemporary Cardiology Ser.). (ENG., Illus.). xiii, 580p. 279.00 (978-1-60327-962-8(8), 1603279628) Humana Pr.

Toth, Peter P. & Cannon, Christopher P., eds. Comprehensive Cardiovascular Medicine in the Primary Care Setting. 2011. (Contemporary Cardiology Ser.). (Illus.). xiii, 580p. pap. 99.00 (978-1-60761-982-6(2), 1607619822) Humana Pr.

Turner, J. Rick & Durham, Todd A. Integrated Cardiac Safety: Assessment Methodologies for Noncardiac Drugs in Discovery, Development, & Postmarketing Surveillance. 2008. (ENG., Illus.). 470p. 94.95 (978-0-470-22964-4(0), Wiley) Wiley, John & Sons, Inc.

Unterseher, Jeanne. Cardiovascular Health Risk Management in the Primary Care Setting: Cardiovascular Health Risk Management. 2008. 68p. pap. (978-3-639-09489-3(1)) VDM Verlag Dr. Mueller e.K.

Vascular Biology Protocols. 2008. (Methods in Molecular Medicine Ser.). 179.00 (978-1-58829-574-3(5)) Humana Pr.

Vikstedt, Riikka. Phospholipid Transfer Protein & Cholesteryl Ester Transfer Protein. 2010. 112p. pap. (978-3-8383-1854-7(4)) Lambert Academic Publishing.

Vivanco, Fernando. Cardiovascular Proteomics: Methods & Protocols. Vivanco, Fernando, ed. 2007. (Methods in Molecular Biology Ser.: Vol. 357). (Illus.). 432p. 159.00 (978-1-58829-535-4(4), 1588295354) Humana Pr.

Vivanco, Fernando, ed. Cardiovascular Proteomics: Methods & Protocols. 2010. (Methods in Molecular Biology Ser.). (Illus.). 432p. pap. 159.00 (978-1-61737-627-6(2), 1617376272) Humana Pr.

Vogel, John H. K. & Krucoff, Mitchell. Integrative Cardiology: Complementary & Alternative Medicine for the Heart. 2007. (ENG., Illus.). 624p. (C). 83.95 (978-0-07-144337-1(1), 0071443371) McGraw-Hill Medical Publishing Div.

Wagner, Galen & Pahlm, Olle. Cardiovascular Multimodal Image-Guided Diagnosis & Therapy. 2011. (ENG., Illus.). 444p. 155.00 (978-0-07-161346-0(3), 0071613463) McGraw-Hill Professional Publishing.

Wang, Qing. Cardiovascular Disease: Methods & Protocols, 2 vols. 2007. (Methods in Molecular Medicine Ser.: Vols. 128-129). (Illus.). 184p. 35.00 (978-1-58829-845-4(0), 1588298450) Humana Pr.

Wang, Qing, ed. Cardiovascular Disease, Volume 1: Genetics. 2010. (Methods in Molecular Medicine Ser.). (Illus.). 264p. pap. 139.00 (978-1-61737-649-8(3), 1617376493) Humana Pr.

—Cardiovascular Disease, Volume 2: Molecular Medicine. 2010. (Methods in Molecular Medicine Ser.). (Illus.). 376p. pap. 179.00 (978-1-61737-829-4(1), 1617378291) Humana Pr.

Wang, Qing K., ed. Cardiovascular Disease: Methods & Protocols, Volume 1: Genetics, 2 vols. 2006. (Methods in Molecular Medicine Ser.: Vols. 128-129). (Illus.). 237p. 139.00 (978-1-58829-572-9(9), 1588295729) Humana Pr.

—Cardiovascular Disease, Volume 2: Methods & Protocols: Molecular Medicine, 2 vols. 2006. (Methods in Molecular Medicine Ser.: Vols. 128-129). (Illus.). 363p. 179.00 (978-1-58829-892-8(2), 1588298922) Humana Pr.

Waring, W. Stephen, ed. Cardiovascular Risk Management. 2006. (Churchill's in Clinical Practice Ser.). (ENG., Illus.). 160p. pap. 37.95 (978-0-443-10174-8(4), Churchill Livingstone) Elsevier - Health Sciences Div.

Watson, Sandy & Gorski, Kenneth A. Invasive Cardiology: A Manual for Cath Lab Personnel. 3rd rev. ed. 2010. 646p. pap. 91.95 (978-0-7637-6468-5(X)) Jones & Bartlett Learning, LLC.

Weiss, Stuart & Milas, Bonnie L. Anesthesia Pocket Consult: Cardiac Anesthesia: Print + IPod. 2008. (Illus.). pap. 69.95 (978-1-4160-4651-6(8), Saunders) Elsevier - Health Sciences Div.

Westveer, Douglas & Jordan, Sandra. The Heart of the Matter: Questions to Ask Your Cardiologist. 2009. (ENG.). pap. 14.95 (978-1-60037-633-7(9)) Morgan James Publishing.

Wheeler, Derek S., et al. Cardiovascular Pediatric Critical Illness & Injury. Wheeler, Derek S. et al, eds. 2008. (ENG., Illus.). xiii, 298p. pap. 69.95 (978-1-84800-922-6(4)) Springer.

Wilkins, Martin R. Cardiovascular Pharmacogenetics. 2011. (Handbook of Experimental Pharmacology Ser.). (Illus.). x, 407p. pap. 489.00 (978-3-642-07291-8(7), 3642072917) Springer.

Willerson, James T., et al, eds. Cardiovascular Medicine, Vol. 1. 3rd ed. 2007. 1500p. 99.99 (978-1-84800-012-4(X)) Springer.

Willius, Fredrick A. & Dry, Thomas Jan. A History of the Heart & the Circulation. 2006. (978-1-57898-605-7(2)) Martino Publishing.

Wittram, Conrad. Atlas of Pulmonary Vascular Imaging: A Multimodality Approach. 2010. (ENG., Illus.). 176p. 99.99 (978-1-60406-312-7(2)) Thieme Medical Pubs., Inc.

Wood, David, ed. Prevention of Cardiovascular Disease: A Handbook for Clinical Practice. 2007. (European Society of Cardiology Ser.). (Illus.). 224p. 65.00 (978-1-4051-2940-4(9), Wiley-Blackwell) Wiley, John & Sons, Inc.

World Health Organization. Prevention of Cardiovascular Disease. 2007. (Nonserial Publication). (ENG.). 30p. pap. 18.00 (978-92-4-154724-6(3)); 32p. pap. 18.00 (978-92-4-154727-7(8)); 30p. pap. 18.00 (978-92-4-154726-0(X)) World Health Organization.

World Health Organization Staff, contrib. by. Prevention of Cardiovascular Disease: Guidelines for Assessment & Management of Cardiovascular Risk. 2007. (Nonserial Publication). (ENG., Illus.). 92p. pap. 36.00 (978-92-4-154717-8(0)) World Health Organization.

Xie, Fang & von Dadelszen, Peter. Infection & Immune Genetics in Preeclampsi. 2011. 140p. pap. **(978-3-8443-9321-7(8))** Lambert Academic Publishing.

Xu, Qingbo, ed. A Handbook of Mouse Models of Cardiovascular Disease. 2006. (ENG., Illus.). 402p. 240.00 (978-0-470-01610-7(8), Wiley) Wiley, John & Sons, Inc.

Yim, Peter J. Vascular Hemodynamics: Bioengineering & Clinical Perspectives. 2008. (ENG., Illus.). 354p. 148.00 (978-0-470-08947-7(4), Wiley-Blackwell) Wiley, John & Sons, Inc.

Yusuf, Salim, et al, eds. Evidence-Based Cardiology. 3rd ed. 2009. (Evidence-Based Medicine Ser.: 25). (ENG., Illus.). 1240p. 330.95 (978-1-4051-5925-8(1)) Wiley, John & Sons, Inc.

Zimmerman, Marcia & Kroner, Jayson. 7-Syndrome Healing. 2009. (ENG.). 368p. pap. 17.95 (978-0-7570-0317-2(6)) Square One Pubs.

CARDIOVASCULAR SYSTEM—DISEASES—NURSING

American Nurses Credentialing Center Staff, contrib. by. Cardiac/Vascular Nursing Review & Resource Manual. 2nd ed. 2006. xiii, 405p. (978-0-9768213-8-0(9)) American Nurses Credentialing Ctr.

Baas, Linda. Cardiac Vascular Review & Resource Manual. 3rd ed. 2010. pap. 85.00 (978-1-935213-07-9(5)) American Nurses Credentialing Ctr.

Basson, Craig T. & Lerman, Bruce B. Structural Heart Disease. 2009. 379.00 (978-1-933864-59-4(1)) Demos Medical Publishing, LLC.

Budoff, Matthew J. & Shinbane, Jerold S. Handbook of Cardiovascular CT: Essentials for Clinical Practice. Budoff, Matthew J. & Shinbane, Jerold S., eds. 2008. (Illus.). X, 260p. pap. 79.95 (978-1-84800-091-9(X), 184800091X) Springer.

Concepts in Critical & High Acuity Nursing: Sg. 2008. (C). pap. 21.95 (978-1-4018-5680-9(2)) Delmar Cengage Learning.

Cook, Kerry & Langton, Helen, eds. Cardiothoracic Care for Children & Young People: A Multidisciplinary Approach. 2009. (ENG., Illus.). 240p. pap. 61.99 (978-0-470-51841-0(3), Wiley) Wiley, John & Sons, Inc.

Cram101 Textbook Reviews & Cram101 Textbook Reviews. Outlines & Highlights for Cardiac Nursing: A Companion to Braunwalds Heart Disease by Debra K. Moser DNSc RN FAHA FAAN, ISBN. 2011. 230p. pap. 31.95 **(978-1-61461-705-1(8))** Cram101 Inc.

Critical & High Acuity Nursing Sg. 2008. (C). pap. 25.95 (978-1-4018-4264-2(X)) Delmar Cengage Learning.

Ekeanyanwu, Chukwuma & NWANKWO, Olisa. Nutritional Pharmacology of Dietary Phytochemicals. 2011. 144p. pap. **(978-3-8433-9334-8(6))** Lambert Academic Publishing.

Guidelines Center, International. Primary Prevention of Cardiovascular Disease & Type 2 Diabetes in Patients at Metabolic Risk GUIDELINES Pocketcard: The Endocrine Society (TES) 2010. (Illus.). 12p. pap. 9.95 (978-0-9846167-9-4(9)) International Guidelines Ctr., Inc.

Hatchett, Richard & Thompson, David R. Cardiac Nursing: A Comprehensive Guide. 2nd ed. 2008. (ENG., Illus.). 674p. 134.00 (978-0-443-10214-1(7), Churchill Livingstone) Elsevier - Health Sciences Div.

Hodge, Tanya. Fast Facts for the Cardiac Surgery Nurse: Everything You Need to Know in a Nutshell. 2011. **(978-0-8261-0832-6(6))**; 200p. pap. **(978-0-8261-0831-9(8))** Springer.

Jacobson, Carol, et al. Cardiovascular Nursing Practice: A Comprehensive Resource Manual & Study Guide for Clinical Nurses. 2007. (Illus.). 942p. per. 75.00 (978-0-9785045-0-2(X)) Cardiovascular Nursing Education Assocs.

Jevon, Philip. Advanced Cardiac Life Support: A Guide for Nurses. 2nd ed. 2009. (ENG., Illus.). 328p. pap. 47.99 (978-1-4051-8566-0(X), Wiley-Blackwell) Wiley, John & Sons, Inc.

Kumar, Dhavendra & Elliott, Perry. Principles & Practice of Clinical Cardiovascular Genetics. 2010. (ENG., Illus.). 624p. (978-0-19-536895-6(9)) Oxford Univ. Pr.

Lippincott Williams and Wilkins Staff. ECG Facts. Springhouse Publishing Company Staff, ed. 2nd rev. ed. 2009. (Incredibly Easy! Ser.). (ENG., Illus.). 128p. spiral bd. 27.99 (978-1-60547-476-2(2)) Lippincott Williams & Wilkins.

Lippincott Williams and Wilkins Staff, creator. ECG Strip Ease: An Arrhythmia Interpretation Workbook. 2006. (ENG., Illus.). 384p. per., wbk. ed. 41.99 (978-1-58255-558-4(3)) Lippincott Williams & Wilkins.

Maisch, Bernhard. Pericardiocentesis & Intrapericardial Treatment. 2010. 200p. pap. 139.00 (978-3-642-11334-5(6), 3642113346) Springer.

Maisel, William H., ed. Device Therapy in Heart Failure. 2009. (Contemporary Cardiology Ser.). (Illus.). 300p. 279.00 (978-1-58829-994-9(5)) Humana Pr.

Miceli, G., et al, eds. European Stroke Services: From Evidence to Practice: Satellite Symposium to the 11th European Stroke Conference, Geneva, Switzerland, May 29-June 1, 2002, Vol. 15. (Illus.). (978-3-8055-7553-9(X)) Karger, S. AG.

Munoz, Ricardo, et al, eds. Critical Care of Children with Heart Disease: Basic Medical & Surgical Concepts. 2010. (ENG., Illus.). xxx, 700p. 199.00 (978-1-84882-261-0(8), 1848822618) Springer.

Osman, Faizel. The Cardiovascular Consequences of Hyperthyroidism. 2010. 268p. pap. (978-3-8383-5222-0(X)) Lambert Academic Publishing.

Quinn, Louise & Springhouse Publishing Company Staff, eds. Cardiovascular Care. 2007. (RN Expert Guide Ser.). (ENG., Illus.). 512p. pap. 46.99 (978-1-58255-704-5(7)) Lippincott Williams & Wilkins.

Springhouse Publishing Company Staff. Cardiovascular Disorders. 2009. (ENG.). 512p. pap. 41.99 (978-1-60547-049-8(X)) Lippincott Williams & Wilkins.

Springhouse Publishing Company Staff, ed. Cardiovascular Care Made Incredibly Easy! 2nd rev. ed. 2008. (Incredibly Easy! Ser.). (ENG., Illus.). 352p. pap. 46.95 (978-0-7817-8824-3(2)) Lippincott Williams & Wilkins.

—Nursing Know-How: Evaluating Heart & Breath Sounds. 2008. (ENG., Illus.). 384p. 47.99 (978-0-7817-9203-5(7)) Lippincott Williams & Wilkins.

Stone, Martin. Nattokinase: A Natural Weapon Against Cardiovascular Disease. 2007. (Woodland Health Ser.). 28p. pap. 4.95 (978-1-58054-172-5(0)) Woodland Publishing, Inc.

Woods, Susan L., et al, eds. Cardiac Nursing. 6th rev. ed. 2009. (ENG., Illus.). 960p. 102.95 (978-0-7817-9280-6(0)) Lippincott Williams & Wilkins.

CARDIOVASCULAR SYSTEM—RADIOGRAPHY

Achenbach, Stephan, ed. Atlas of Cardiovascular Computed Tomography. 2007. (ENG., Illus.). x, 278p. 189.00 (978-1-57340-267-5(2), 1573402672) Current Medicine Group LLC.

Baliga, Ragavendra R. Introductory Guide to Cardiac CT Imaging. 2009. (ENG., Illus.). 168p. pap., instr.'s gde. ed. 36.00 (978-1-58255-938-4(4)) Lippincott Williams & Wilkins.

Berman, Daniel S. & Germano, Guido. Clinical Gated Cardiac SPECT. 2nd rev. ed. 2006. (ENG., Illus.). 384p. 162.95 (978-1-4051-3155-1(1), Wiley-Blackwell) Wiley, John & Sons, Inc.

Braunwald, Eugene & Manning, Warren, eds. Atlas of Cardiovascular Magnetic Resonance Imaging. 2009. (Illus.). 256p. 159.00 (978-1-57340-299-6(0), 1573402990) Current Medicine Group LLC.

Budoff, Matthew J., et al, eds. Atlas of Cardiovascular Computed Tomography: Includes narrated Videos. 2008. cd-rom 129.00 (978-1-57340-292-7(3)) Current Medicine Group LLC.

Budoff, Matthew J., et al. Atlas of Cardiovascular Computed Tomography. 2007. (978-1-57340-259-0(1)) Current Medicine Group LLC.

Chen, Wengen & Takalkar, Amol M. Cardiovascular PET Imaging, an Issue of PET Clinics. 2012. (Clinics: Radiology Ser.: 6-4). (ENG., Illus.). XI, 383p. 83.00 **(978-1-4557-1120-8(9)**, Saunders) Elsevier - Health Sciences Div.

Danias, Peter G. Cardiovascular MRI: 150 Multiple-Choice Questions & Answers. 2008. (Contemporary Cardiology Ser.). (Illus.). XI, 192p. pap. 89.95 (978-1-934115-59-6(2), 1934115592) Springer.

Doyle, Mark, et al. The Cardiovascular MRI Tutorial: Lectures & Learning. 2007. (ENG., Illus.). 400p. 209.99 (978-0-7817-7216-7(9)) Lippincott Williams & Wilkins.

Fialová, Katerina & Nováková, Marie. Effects of Sigma Receptor Ligands in Mammalian Myocardium. 2011. 156p. pap. **(978-3-8443-8233-4(X))** Lambert Academic Publishing.

Finck, Brian N., et al, eds. Ars/Rxrs in Cardiovascular Physiology & Disease. 2008. 140p. pap. 22.00 (978-977-454-021-9(2)) Hindawi Publishing Corp.

Finn, J. Paul & Lohan, Derek G. Cardiovascular MRI & MRA: from Seating Area to Signed Report: Volume 2: Interpretation Atlas. 2010. (Illus.). 450p. 189.00 (978-1-60761-017-5(5)) Humana Pr.

Grizzard, John D., et al. Cardiovascular MRI in Practice: A Teaching File Approach. 2008. (Illus.). 288p. 179.00 (978-1-84800-089-6(8), 1848000898) Springer.

Johnson, Bonnie L. & Fogarty, Thomas J., eds. Vascular Imaging: Principles & Techniques. Date not set. (Illus.). 400p. 89.00 (978-1-56757-063-2(1)) Appleton Communications, Inc.

Kantor, Birgit & Williamson, Eric E., eds. Computed Tomography of the Cardiovascular System. 2007. (ENG., Illus.). 556p. 309.95 (978-1-84184-625-5(2), Informa Healthcare) Taylor & Francis Group GBR. Dist: Taylor & Francis Group.

Kerckhoffs, Roy C. P., ed. Patient-Specific Modeling of the Cardiovascular System: Technology-Driven Personalized Medicine. 2010. (ENG., Illus.). xxii, 242p. 189.00 (978-1-4419-6690-2(0), 1441966900) Springer.

Pelberg, Robert & Mazur, Wojciech. Vascular CT Angiography Manual. 2010. (ENG., Illus.). xviii, 377p. pap. 59.95 (978-1-84996-259-9(6), 1849962596) Springer.

Schoenhagen, Paul, et al. Cardiac CT Made Easy: An Introduction to Cardiovascular Multidetector Computer Tomography (Combined Book & DVD Set), 2 vols. 2007. (ENG.). 140p. 299.95 (978-1-84184-659-0(7), Informa Healthcare) Taylor & Francis Group GBR. Dist: Taylor & Francis Group.

Taylor, Allen J. Atlas of Cardiovascular Computed Tomography. 2009. (Imaging Techniques to Braunwald's Heart Disease Ser.). (ENG., Illus.). 304p. 195.00 (978-1-4160-6136-6(3), Saunders) Elsevier - Health Sciences Div.

CARDIOVASCULAR SYSTEM—RESEARCH

Collins, James A., ed. Encyclopedia of Cardiovascular Research (3 Volume Set), 3 vols. 2011. (Cardiology Research & Clinical Developments Ser.). 395.00 **(978-1-61324-960-4(8)**, Nova Biomedical Bks.) Nova Science Pubs., Inc.

French, Roger. William Harvey's Natural Philosophy. 2006. (ENG., Illus.). 408p. pap. 56.00 (978-0-521-03108-0(7)) Cambridge Univ. Pr.

Gross, David R. Animal Models in Cardiovascular Research. 3rd ed. 2009. (ENG., Illus.). xxvi, 431p. 159.00 (978-0-387-95961-0(0), 0387959610) Springer.

Halberg, Franz & Singh, R. B., eds. World Heart Research Yearbook. Volume 1. 2010. (World Heart Research Yearbook Ser.). 145.00 (978-1-60741-881-8(9)) Nova Science Pubs., Inc.

Kaithwas, Gaurav, et al. Aloe Vera Gel: Antioxidant with Cholinergic Innervations. 2011. 76p. pap. **(978-3-639-31723-7(8))** VDM Verlag Dr. Mueller e.K.

Needham, Terence. Vascular Laboratory Quality Assurance Manual. Date not set. (978-0-941022-26-2(9)) Davies Publishing, Inc.

Neumyer, Marsha M. & Auer, Arthur I., eds. The Noninvasive Vascular Laboratory: Current Issues & Clinical Developments. Date not set. (978-0-941022-28-6(5)) Davies Publishing, Inc.

Sehgal, Gaurav & Gregson, Peter. 2d Coordinate System of the Heart. 2008. 96p. pap. (978-3-639-04975-6(6)) VDM Verlag Dr. Mueller e.K.

Takeuchi, Satoru & Mala, J. Geraldine Sandana. Heat Shock Proteins in Cardiovascular Diseases. 2011. (Cardiology Research & Clinical Developments Ser.). 94p. pap. 47.00 (978-1-61324-589-7(0)) Nova Science Pubs., Inc.

Tshambuluka, Noxolo Doris, et al. Cardiovascular Effects of Leonotis Leonurus in Anesthesized Rats. 2011. 124p. pap. **(978-3-8443-2046-6(6))** Lambert Academic Publishing.

CARDIOVASCULAR SYSTEM—SURGERY

Berdajs, Denis & Turina, Marko, eds. Operative Anatomy of the Heart. 2009. (Illus.). 580p. 199.00 *(978-3-540-69227-0(4))* Springer.

Cannon, Christopher P., et al, eds. On Bypass: Advanced Perfusion Techniques. (Current Cardiac Surgery Ser.). 400p. 2007. (Illus.). 179.00 *(978-1-58829-636-8(9)*, 1588296369) 2006. 149.00 *(978-1-59745-305-9(6))* Humana Pr.

Davis, James, ed. 2008 Coding Guide Cardiology/Cardiovascular Surgery. 2007. per. 129.95 *(978-1-57066-466-3(8))* Practice Management Information Corp.

DiNardo, James A. & Zvara, David A. Anesthesia for Cardiac Surgery. 3rd rev. ed. 2007. (ENG., Illus.). 472p. 217.95 *(978-1-4051-5363-8(6)*, Wiley-Blackwell) Wiley, John & Sons, Inc.

Earnshaw, J. J. & Murie, J. A. The Evidence for Vascular Surgery. 2nd ed. 2007. (Illus.). 276p. 115.00 *(978-1-903378-45-8(1))* TFM Publishing Ltd. GBR. Dist: JAMCO Distribution.

English, Terence. Follow Your Star: From Mining to Heart Transplants - A Surgeon's Story. 2011. (Illus.). 252p. 32.12 *(978-1-4567-7130-0(2))*; pap. 19.58 *(978-1-4567-7131-7(0))* AuthorHouse.

Huang, Shoei K. Stephen & Wood, Mark A. Catheter Ablation of Cardiac Arrhythmias. 2nd ed. 2010. (ENG., Illus.). 672p. 195.00 *(978-1-4377-1368-8(8)*, Saunders) Elsevier - Health Sciences Div.

Kandarpa, Krishna, ed. Peripheral Vascular Interventions. 2007. (ENG., Illus.). 720p. 215.99 *(978-0-7817-8687-4(8))* Lippincott Williams & Wilkins.

Kern, John A. & Kron, Irving L. Advances in Cardiac & Aortic Surgery, an Issue of Surgical Clinics. 2009. (Clinics: Surgery Ser.: 89-4). (ENG.). 90.00 *(978-1-4377-1387-9(4)*, Saunders) Elsevier - Health Sciences Div.

Massad, Malek G., ed. Surgical Options for the Management of Congestive Heart Failure. (Cardiology Ser.: Vol. 101, Nos. 1-3). (Illus.). 156p. *(978-3-8055-7739-7(7))* Karger, S. AG.

Mather, Paul J. Jefferson Heart Institute Handbook of Cardiology. rev. ed. 2010. 528p. pap. 86.95 *(978-0-7637-6049-6(8))* Jones & Bartlett Learning, LLC.

Mavroudis, Constantine. Pediatric Cardiac Surgery. 4th ed. 2012. (ENG.). 928p. 299.95 **(978-1-4051-9652-9(1)**, Wiley-Blackwell) Wiley, John & Sons, Inc.

McKinsey, James F., ed. Minimally Invasive Vascular Surgery. 2009. (Current Cardiac Surgery Ser.). 175.00 *(978-1-58829-804-1(3))* Humana Pr.

Medicine Group (Education) Ltd Staff, et al. Interventional Cardiology: Essential Clinician's Guide, 1 vol. Mukherjee, Debabrata & Bavry, Anthony A., eds. 2011. (Oxford American Cardiology Library). (ENG., Illus.). 160p. pap. 39.95 *(978-0-19-973260-9(4))* Oxford Univ. Pr., Inc.

Moneta, Gregory L. Year Book of Vascular Surgery 2011 - E-Book1. 2011. E-Book **(978-0-323-08753-7(1)**, Mosby) Elsevier - Health Sciences Div.

Nayak, Krishna S., ed. Handbook of Cardiovascular Magnetic Resonance Imaging. 2006. (Fundamental & Clinical Cardiology Ser.: Vol. 60). (ENG., Illus.). 480p. 230.00 *(978-0-8247-5841-7(2)*, Informa Healthcare) Taylor & Francis Group GBR. Dist: Taylor & Francis Group.

Ragosta, Michael. Cases in Interventional Cardiology. 2010. (ENG., Illus.). 352p. 99.95 *(978-1-4377-0583-6(9)*, Saunders) Elsevier - Health Sciences Div.

Reinterventions in Vascular & Endovascular Surgery. 2007. 150p. pap. *(978-960-399-540-1(1))* Iatrikes Ekdoseis, Periklis Ch. Paschalidis GRC. Dist: Elsevier - Health Sciences Div.

Reves, J. G., et al. Atlas of Cardiothoracic Anesthesia. 2nd ed. 2009. (Illus.). 230p. 319.00 *(978-1-57340-278-1(8))* Current Medicine Group LLC.

Safian, Robert. Manual of Interventional Cardiology. 3rd rev. ed. 2008. 1050p. pap. 104.95 *(978-1-890114-39-8(1))* Physician's Pr.

CARDS

see Card Games; Playing Cards

CARDS, ADVERTISING

see Advertising Cards

CARDS, BUSINESS

see Business Cards

CARDS, CATALOG

see Catalog Cards

CARDS, GREETING

see Greeting Cards

CARDS, PLAYING

see Playing Cards

CARDS, SMART

see Smart Cards

CARDS, SPORTS

see Sports Cards

CARDSHARPING

James, Grosjean. Exhibit CAA Beyond Counting. 2009. 250.00 *(978-0-9790061-4-2(7))* South Side Advantage Pr.

Kronzek, Allan Zola. 52 Ways to Cheat at Poker: How to Spot Them, Foil Them, & Defend Yourself Against Them. 2008. (ENG., Illus.). 208p. (gr. 12-18). 13.00 *(978-0-452-28911-6(4)*, Plume) Penguin Group (USA) Inc.

Mezrich, Ben. 21 - Bringing down the House: The Inside Story of Six M. I. T. Students Who Took Vegas for Millions. movie tie-in ed. 2008. (ENG.). 288p. pap. 15.00 *(978-1-4165-6419-5(5)*, Free Pr.) Free Pr.

CARDWELL, EDWARD CARDWELL, VISCOUNT, 1813-1886

Erickson, Arvel B. Edward T Cardwell, Peelite: Transactions of the American Philosophical Society, V49, Part 2, April 1959. 2011. 108p. 39.95 **(978-1-258-07616-0(0))** Literary Licensing, LLC.

CARE, INSTITUTIONAL

see Institutional Care

CARE, RESPITE

see Respite Care

CARE GIVERS

see Caregivers

CARE OF CHILDREN

see Child Care

CARE OF SOULS

see Pastoral Counseling; Pastoral Theology

CARE OF THE SICK

see also Bed Rest; Home Care Services; Home Nursing; Hospitals; Nursing; Patients—Positioning; Self-Care, Health; Terminal Care

Acello, Barbara. The Long-Term Card Nursing Assistant's Guide to Advanced Restorative Skills. 2010. (Illus.). 295p. spiral bd. incl. cd-rom *(978-1-60146-727-0(3))* Opus Communications.

Acello, Barbara. The Long-Term Care Nursing Desk Reference. 2nd ed. 2009. xiii, 481p. 298.00 **(978-1-60146-275-6(1))** HCPro, Inc.

Beresford, Peter, et al, eds. Palliative Care, Social Work & Service Users: Making Life Possible. 2007. (ENG.). 32p. per. *(978-1-84310-465-0(2))* Kingsley, Jessica Ltd.

Boog, Kathryn M. & Tester, Claire Y. Palliative Care: A Practical Guide for the Health Professional: Finding Meaning & Purpose in Life & Death. 2007. (ENG., Illus.). 240p. pap. 60.95 *(978-0-443-10380-3(1)*, Churchill Livingstone) Elsevier - Health Sciences Div.

Bouwer, J., ed. Spirituality & Meaning in Health Care: A Dutch Contribution to an Ongoing Discussion. 2008. (Studies in Spirituality Supplements Ser.). (ENG.). 151p. (C). pap. 57.00 *(978-90-429-2054-5(8))* Peeters Pubs. & Booksellers BEL. Dist: Brown, David Bk. Co., The.

Bowlby, Sophia. Interdependency & Care over the Lifecourse. 2009. (Relationships & Resources Ser.). (Illus.). 224p. 110.00 *(978-0-415-43466-9(1))* Routledge.

Bowlby, Sophia, et al. Interdependency & Care over the Lifecourse. 2010. (Relationships & Resources Ser.). (ENG., Illus.). 200p. (C). 40.95 *(978-0-415-43467-6(X))* Routledge.

Conlon, Patrick. The Essential Hospital Handbook: How to Be an Effective Partner in a Loved One's Care. 2009. (Yale University Press Health & Wellness Ser.). (ENG.). 384p. instr.'s hndbk. ed. 30.00 *(978-0-300-14575-5(6))*; pap., wbk. ed., instr.'s hndbk. ed. 18.00 *(978-0-300-14576-2(4))* Yale Univ. Pr.

Corr, Charles A., et al. Death & Dying, Life & Living With InfoTrac College Edition. 3rd ed. *(978-0-534-74506-6(7))* Wadsworth.

Cram101 Textbook Reviews. Outlines & Highlights for Nursing Assistant: Nursing Process Approach by Hegner, Barbara, ISBN. 2011. 422p. pap. 35.95 **(978-1-61812-524-8(9))** Cram101 Inc.

Cram101 Textbook Reviews Staff. Outlines & Highlights for Death & Dying: Life & Living by Corr ISBN. 2008. 192p. per. 13.95 *(978-1-4288-5761-2(3))* Cram101 Inc.

—Outlines & Highlights for Death & Dying, Life & Living by Charles a Corr, Isbn: 9780495506461. 2009. 100p. pap. 27.95 *(978-1-4288-9838-7(7))* Cram101 Inc.

Curtis, Anthony M. & Werthel, Danielle P., eds. Religion & Healthcare. 2011. (Religion & Spirituality Health Care in Transition Ser.). (Illus.). 147p. 95.00 *(978-1-61324-256-8(5))* Nova Science Pubs., Inc.

Dellinger, Annetta & Boerger, Karen. JOY-spirations for Caregivers: A Dialogue with God. 2010. 304p. pap. 19.99 *(978-1-60615-026-9(X))* WinePress Publishing.

Delmar, (Delmar). Delmar's Nursing Assistant Skills & Procedures. 2011. (ENG.). (C). 1897.95 *(978-1-4390-5778-0(8))* Delmar Cengage Learning.

deWit, Susan C. Fundamental Concepts & Skills for Nursing - Text & Virtual Clinical Excursions 3. 0 Package. 3rd ed. 2008. (ENG.). (C). pap. 108.95 *(978-1-4160-6225-7(4)*, Saunders) Elsevier - Health Sciences Div.

—Student Learning Guide for Fundamental Concepts & Skills for Nursing. 3rd ed. 2008. (ENG.). 544p. (C). pap. 27.95 *(978-1-4160-6234-9(3)*, Saunders) Elsevier - Health Sciences Div.

Dugan, Diana L. Successful Nursing Assistant Care, 2nd Edition. 2nd ed. 2007. (Illus.). 544p. (C). *(978-1-888343-94-6(X))*; per. *(978-1-888343-97-7(4))* Hartman Publishing, Inc.

Dunlap, Susan J. Caring Cultures: How Congregations Respond to the Sick. 2009. (ENG.). 260p. pap. 24.95 *(978-1-932792-87-4(2))* Baylor Univ. Pr.

Fredriksen-Goldsen, Karen I., ed. Caregiving with Pride. 2007. (ENG., Illus.). 180p. pap. 54.95 *(978-1-56023-759-4(7))* Routledge.

Giannone, Richard. Hidden: Reflections on Gay Life, AIDS, & Spiritual Desire. 2012. (ENG., Illus.). 224p. 27.95 **(978-0-8232-4184-2(X))** Fordham Univ. Pr.

Goldberg, Stan. Leaning into Sharp Points: Practical Guidance & Nurturing Support for Caregivers. 2012. (ENG.). 232p. pap. 14.95 **(978-1-60868-067-2(3))** New World Library.

Gordon, Suzanne, ed. The Complexities of Care: Nursing Reconsidered. 2006. (Culture & Politics of Health Care Work Ser.). 211p. per. 19.95 *(978-0-8014-7322-7(5))* Cornell Univ. Pr.

—The Complexities of Care: Nursing Reconsidered. 2006. (Culture & Politics of Health Care Work Ser.). 211p. 60.95 *(978-0-8014-4505-7(1))* Cornell Univ. Pr.

Hall, M. Alice. North Carolina Nursing Aide I Practice: The Essentials of Caring. 2007. (C). pap. *(978-0-89089-363-0(2))* Carolina Academic Pr.

Hegner, Acello. Nursing Assistant A Nursing Process Appr. 2007. pap. 19.95 *(978-1-4288-1929-0(0))* Cram101 Inc.

Hegner, Barbara, et al. Workbook for Hegner/Acello/Caldwell's Nursing Assistant: A Nursing Process Approach - Basics. 2009. (ENG.). 336p. (C). pap. 44.95 *(978-1-4283-1747-5(3))* Delmar Cengage Learning.

Howard, Gay. How to Comply with CMS & Joint Commission Restraint & Seclusion Requirements. 2007. v, 147p. **(978-1-60146-086-8(4))** Opus Communications.

Karpinski, Marion. Quick Tips for Caregivers. 2010. (CHI., Illus.). xvi, 217p. mass mkt. 139.00 *(978-0-9798245-8-6(3))* Medifecta Healthcare Training.

Kelly, Relda T., et al. Workbook & Competency Evaluation Review for Mosby's Textbook for Nursing Assistants. 7th ed. 2007. (ENG., Illus.). 544p. (C). per. 29.95 *(978-0-323-05250-4(9)*, Mosby) Elsevier - Health Sciences Div.

Kentley, Laura E., ed. Time Out: Examining Seclusion & Restraint in Schools. 2010. (Education in a Competitive & Globalizing World Ser.). 137p. 89.00 *(978-1-60876-932-2(1))* Nova Science Pubs., Inc.

Locsin, Rozzano C. & Purnell, Marguerite J. A Contemporary Nursing Process: The (Un)bearable Weight of Knowing in Nursing. 2009. 448p. pap. *(978-0-8261-2578-1(6))* Springer.

Martin, William & Martin, Nancy. The Caregiver's Tao Te Ching: Compassionate Caring for Your Loved Ones & Yourself. 2011. (ENG.). 144p. pap. 14.00 *(978-1-57731-888-0(9))* New World Library.

McGlinn, Christopher. Reducing the Use of Physical Restraints - the Effect of Federal Legislation. 2008. 92p. pap. *(978-3-639-10401-1(3))* VDM Verlag Dr. Mueller e.K.

Meszler, Rabbi Joseph B. Facing Illness, Finding God: How Judaism Can Help You & Caregivers Cope when Body or Spirit Fails. 2010. 150p. pap. 16.99 *(978-1-58023-423-8(2))* Jewish Lights Publishing.

Mol, Annemarie, et al, eds. Care in Practice: On Tinkering in Clinics, Homes & Farms. 2010. (ENG., Illus.). 300p. pap. 49.95 *(978-3-8376-1447-3(6))* Transcript Verlag DEU. Dist: Transaction Pubs.

Munro, Ian. The Lived Experience of Gay Men Caring for Others with Hiv/Aids. 2008. 324p. pap. *(978-3-639-03581-0(X))* VDM Verlag Dr. Mueller e.K.

O'Neal, Cynthia. Talk Softly: A Memoir. 2010. (ENG.). 240p. 22.00 *(978-1-58322-906-4(X))* Seven Stories Pr.

Pierron, Jean-Philippe. Vulnérabilité: Pour une Philosophie du Soin. 2010. (FRE.). 208p. *(978-2-13-058109-3(9))* Presses Universitaires de France.

Pulliam, Jolynn. The Nursing Assistant: Acute, Subacute, & Long-Term Care. 5th ed. 2011. (ENG., Illus.). 448p. (C). pap. 50.67 **(978-0-13-262255-4(6)**, Prentice Hall) Prentice Hall PTR.

Ruffman, Jill V. & Sladek, Marjorie B. Now, What Do We Do? Successfully Manage Your Hospital Stay: A Guided Journal for Patients & Those Who Care for Them. 2007. (ENG., Illus.). 165p. spiral bd. 19.95 *(978-0-9766323-1-3(4))* Ruffman, Sladek Publishing Co.

Scalia, Elizabeth. Caring for the Dying with the Help of Your Catholic Faith. 2008. (With the Help of Your Catholic Faith Ser.). 63p. per. 5.95 *(978-1-59276-239-2(5))* Our Sunday Visitor, Publishing Div.

Schweizer, Harold. Patient. 2010. (Bucknell Apercus Histori Ser.). (ENG.). pap. 25.00 *(978-1-61148-346-8(8))* Bucknell Univ. Pr.

Sorrentino, Sheila A. Mosby's Essentials for Nursing Assistants - Text & Workbook Package. 4th ed. 2009. (ENG.). (C). pap. 62.95 *(978-0-323-06988-5(6)*, Mosby) Elsevier - Health Sciences Div.

—Nursing Assistants. 7th ed. 2007. (ENG., Illus.). 880p. (C). 65.95 *(978-0-323-04998-6(2)*, Mosby) Elsevier - Health Sciences Div.

Sorrentino, Sheila A. & Mosby. Mosby's Essentials for Nursing Assistants - Text & Mosby's Nursing Assistant Skills DVD - Student Version 3. 0 Package. 4th ed. 2009. (ENG.). (C). pap. 62.95 *(978-0-323-07216-8(X)*, Mosby) Elsevier - Health Sciences Div.

—Mosby's Essentials for Nursing Assistants - Text & Mosby's Nursing Assistant Video Skills: Student Online Version 3. 0 (User Guide & Access Code) Package. 4th ed. 2009. (ENG.). (C). pap. 62.95 *(978-0-323-07217-5(8)*, Mosby) Elsevier - Health Sciences Div.

—Mosby's Essentials for Nursing Assistants - Text, Workbook & Mosby's Nursing Assistant Skills DVD - Student Version 3. 0 Package. 4th ed. 2009. (ENG.). (C). pap. 77.95 *(978-0-323-07218-2(6)*, Mosby) Elsevier - Health Sciences Div.

—Mosby's Essentials for Nursing Assistants - Text, Workbook & Mosby's Nursing Assistant Video Skills: Student Online Version 3. 0 (User Guide & Access Code) Package. 4th ed. 2009. (ENG.). (C). pap. 77.95 *(978-0-323-07215-1(1)*, Mosby) Elsevier - Health Sciences Div.

Sorrentino, Sheila A., et al. Mosby's Essentials for Nursing Assistants. 4th ed. 2009. (ENG., Illus.). 576p. (C). pap. 46.95 *(978-0-323-06621-1(6)*, Mosby) Elsevier - Health Sciences Div.

CAREER CHANGES

Abel, C. P. C. Congratulations! You're Unemployed a Complete Guide to Finding Your First Job Out of College. 2009. 180p. pap. 12.95 *(978-1-934925-53-9(5)*, Strategic Bk. Publishing) AEG Literary Publishing Services, Inc.

Adams, Stephen. Back to Work! Create New Opportunities in the Wake of Job Loss. 2009. (ENG.). 144p. pap. 9.99 *(978-0-8024-4261-1(7))* Moody Pubs.

Armstrong, James. Now What? Discovering Your New Life & Career After 50. 2007. 196p. per. 13.99 *(978-1-933656-06-9(9))* Lighthouse Pubns., Inc.

Arnold, Camilla & Barrett, Jane. If Not Now, When? How to Take Charge of Your Career. 2010. (ENG., Illus.). 192p. pap. 14.95 *(978-1-4081-2505-2(0))* A & C Black GBR. Dist: Macmillan.

Barnson, William. Bounce Back Like A Champion. 2010. 108p. 23.49 *(978-1-4520-2429-5(4))* AuthorHouse.

—Bounce Back Like A Champion: The Dynamic Step-by-step System Used by the U. S. Military Transition Program for Getting a New Civilian Job Fast. 2010. 108p. pap. 13.99 *(978-1-4520-2430-1(8))* AuthorHouse.

Barranger, Jack. Knowing When to Quit. 2011. 200p. (Orig.). pap. 18.95 **(978-1-58509-138-6(3))** Book Tree, The.

Basalla, Susan & Debelius, Maggie. So What Are You Going to Do with That? Finding Careers Outside Academia. 2nd ed. 2007. (ENG., Illus.). 160p. per. 14.00 *(978-0-226-03882-7(3))* Univ. of Chicago Pr.

Basalla, Susan Elizabeth & Debelius, Maggie. What Are You Going to Do with That? Finding Careers Outside Academia. 2nd ed. 2007. (ENG., Illus.). 160p. 32.50 *(978-0-226-03881-0(5))* Univ. of Chicago Pr.

Baugh, S. Gayle & Sullivan, Sherry E. Maintaining Focus, Energy, & Options over the Career. 2009. *(978-1-59311-958-4(5))*; pap. *(978-1-59311-957-7(7))* Information Age Publishing, Inc.

Baur, Jean. Eliminated! Now What? Finding Your Way from Job-Loss Crisis to Career Resilience. 2010. 240p. pap. 14.95 *(978-1-59357-816-9(4)*, JIST Works) JIST Publishing.

Bench, Marcia. Career Coaching: An Insider's Guide - Study Guide. 2008. 196p. pap. 34.95 *(978-0-9817005-1-9(9))* High Flight Pr.

Bench, Marcia A. Career Coaching: An Insider's Guide - Second Edition. 2nd ed. 2008. (Illus.). 444p. pap. 39.95 *(978-0-9817005-0-2(0))* High Flight Pr.

Betof, Edward & Betof, Nila. Just Promoted! A 12-Month Road Map for Success in Your New Leadership Role. 2nd ed. 2010. (ENG., Illus.). 320p. pap. 16.95 *(978-0-07-174525-3(4)*, 0071745254) McGraw-Hill Cos., The.

Bloch, Thomas M. Stand for the Best: What I Learned after Leaving My Job As CEO of H & R Block to Become a Teacher & Founder of an Inner-City Charter School. 2008. (ENG., Illus.). 256p. 24.95 *(978-0-470-18896-5(0)*, Jossey-Bass) Wiley, John & Sons, Inc.

Bolles, Richard Nelson. What Color Is Your Parachute? 3rd rev. ed. 2010. (ENG., Illus.). 64p. pap., wbk. ed. 11.99 *(978-1-58008-009-5(X))* Ten Speed Pr.

—What Color Is Your Parachute? 2009: A Practical Manual for Job-Hunters & Career-Changers. 2008. (ENG., Illus.). 456p. pap. 18.95 *(978-1-58008-930-2(5))* Ten Speed Pr.

—What Color Is Your Parachute? 2010: A Practical Manual for Job-Hunters & Career-Changers. 2009. (ENG., Illus.). 336p. 28.99 *(978-1-58008-989-0(5))*; pap. 18.99 *(978-1-58008-987-6(9))* Ten Speed Pr.

—What Color Is Your Parachute? 2012: A Practical Manual for Job-Hunters & Career-Changers. 40th ed. 2011. (ENG., Illus.). 384p. 29.99 *(978-1-60774-011-7(7))*; pap. 18.99 *(978-1-60774-010-0(9))* Ten Speed Pr.

Brewer, Sonny, ed. Don't Quit Your Day Job: Acclaimed Authors & the Day Jobs they Quit. 2011. (ENG.). 432p. pap. 15.95 *(978-1-84982-136-0(4))* MP Publishing Ltd. GBR. Dist: Perseus-PGW.

Cain, George. Turning Points, Second Edition: New Paths & Second Careers for Lawyers. 2nd ed. 2010. (ENG.). 79p. pap. 29.95 *(978-1-60442-713-4(2))* American Bar Assn.

Castleberry, Wayne. Fresh Start - Transition: Employment vs. Self-Employment A Guide to Greater Opportunities. 2010. 132p. pap. 19.98 *(978-1-4520-4662-4(X))* AuthorHouse.

Chen, Charles P. Career Endeavour: Pursuing a Cross-Cultural Life Transition. 2006. (Cross-Cultural Management Ser.). 176p. 130.00 *(978-0-7546-4621-1(1))* Ashgate Publishing Co.

Cleaver, Joanne. The Career Lattice: How Lateral Move Strategies Can Grow Careers & Companies. 2012. (ENG., Illus.). 272p. pap. 28.00 **(978-0-07-179169-4(8)**, 0071791698) McGraw-Hill Cos., The.

Conklin, Linda. Career Coach - Getting the Right Job Right Now! 2008. 108p. pap. 19.98 *(978-0-615-23664-3(2))* Conklin, Linda.

Cooper, Charles. Later-in-Life Lawyers: Tips for the Non-Traditional Law Student. 2nd ed. 2012. 360p. pap. 18.95 **(978-1-888960-16-7(7))** Fine Print Pr, The.

DeCarlo, Laura. Job Search Bloopers. 2008. (ENG.). 1p. pap. 15.99 *(978-1-60163-016-2(6))* Career Pr., Inc.

Degraff, Jeff & Lichtenberg, Greg. Innovation You: Four Steps to Becoming New & Improved. 2011. 256p. 25.00 *(978-0-345-53069-1(1)*, Ballantine Bks.) Random House Publishing Group.

Drucker, Peter F. Managing Oneself. 2007. (Harvard Business Review Classics Ser.). (ENG.). 72p. per. 8.95 *(978-1-4221-2312-6(X))* Harvard Business Review Pr.

Dzuro, Joan. Starting Over: Getting a Job You Love. 2009. pap. 9.99 *(978-1-60799-020-8(2))* Tate Publishing & Enterprises, LLC.

Ellsworth, Thomas. The Rat, the Race, & the Cage: A Simple Way to Guarantee Job Satisfaction & Success: for Christians. 2006. 80p. 19.95 *(978-1-57921-869-0(5))* WinePress Publishing.

Enelow, Wendy & Kursmark, Louise. Expert Resumes for Military to Civilian Transitions Second Edition. 2nd ed. 2009. (ENG.). 288p. pap. 16.95 *(978-1-59357-732-2(X)*, JIST Works) JIST Publishing.

Enelow, Wendy S. & Kursmark, Louise M. Expert Resumes for Career Changers. 2nd ed. 2010. 304p. pap. 16.95 *(978-1-59357-781-0(8)*, JIST Works) JIST Publishing.

Entrepreneur Press Staff & Sandlin, Eileen. Start Your Own Consulting Business, Third Edition. 3rd ed. 2010. (ENG.). 224p. pap. 19.95 *(978-1-59918-373-2(0)*, 1599183730) Entrepreneur Pr. dba Entrepreneur Media, Inc.

C

Etherington, Matthew. Changing Careers to Become a School Teacher: A study of mature age preservice teachers in career transition. 2009. 308p. pap. *(978-3-639-15295-1(6))* VDM Verlag Dr. Mueller e.K.

Evans, Vaughan. Backing U! A Business-Oriented Guide to Backing Your Passion & Achieving Career Success. 2009. 333p. pap. 24.95 *(978-0-9561391-0-8(8))* Business & Careers Pr GBR. Dist: AtlasBooks Distribution.

—Backing U! Lite: A Quick-Read Guide to Backing Your Passion & Achieving Business Success. 2009. 186p. pap. 14.95 *(978-0-9561391-1-5(6))* Business & Careers Pr GBR. Dist: AtlasBooks Distribution.

Farley, Janet I. Military-to-Civilian Career Transition Guide, Second Edition: The Essential Job Search Handbook for Service Members. 2nd ed. 2009. 208p. pap. 14.95 *(978-1-59357-731-5(1),* JIST Works) JIST Publishing.

Feistritzer, Emily C. & Haar, Charlene K. Alternative Routes to Teacher Certification. 2007. (ENG.). 224p. (C). pap. 39.95 *(978-0-13-175041-8(0),* Prentice Hall) Prentice Hall PTR.

Fifty Lessons Management Collection Staff, compiled by. Loving Your Work. 2010. (Lessons Learned: Ser.). (ENG.). 112p. pap. 9.95 *(978-1-4221-3986-8(7))* Harvard Business Review Pr.

Ghilani, Mary E. Second Chance: How Career Changers Can Find a Great Job, 1 vol. 2010. 184p. 34.95 *(978-1-59884-358-3(3),* A2638C) Greenwood Publishing Group, Inc.

—10 Strategies for Reentering the Workforce: Career Advice for Anyone Who Needs a Good (Or Better) Job Now. 2008. 192p. 39.95 *(978-0-313-35696-4(3),* C35696, Praeger Pubs.) Greenwood Publishing Group, Inc.

Grace, Corina. Take Charge of Your Career... & Find a Job You Really Love! The Essential Resource Pack for Career Planning. 2010. (ENG.). 250p. pap. 31.95 *(978-1-905785-33-9(X))* Liffey Pr., The IRL. Dist: Dufour Editions, Inc.

Green, Graham. The Career Change Handbook. 3rd ed. 2006. (Illus.). 190p. per. 26.00 *(978-1-84528-137-3(3))* How To Books GBR. Dist: Parkwest Pubns., Inc.

Hannon, Kerry. What's Next? Follow Your Passion & Find Your Dream Job. 2010. (ENG., Illus.). 216p. 22.95 *(978-0-8118-7115-0(0))* Chronicle Bks. LLC.

Hansen, J. P. The Bliss List: The Ultimate Guide to Living the Dream at Work & Beyond! 2010. 240p. pap. 19.95 *(978-0-9840934-1-0(9))* Career Bliss Pubns., Inc.

Harvard Business School Publishing Corporation Staff, creator. Shaping Your Career: Expert Solutions to Everyday Challenges. 2008. (Pocket Mentor Ser.). (ENG., Illus.). 88p. per. 9.95 *(978-1-4221-1876-4(2))* Harvard Business Review Pr.

Henderson, David G. & Henderson, David. Job Search: Marketing Your Military Experience. 5th rev. ed. 2009. (ENG., Illus.). 272p. pap. 19.95 *(978-0-8117-3590-2(7))* Stackpole Bks.

Herrick, Scot. I've Landed My Dream Job — Now What??? How to Achieve Success in the First 30 Days in a New Job. 2010. 116p. pap. 19.95 *(978-1-60005-168-5(5))* Happy About.

Hill, Janelle, et al. Life after the Military: A Handbook for Transitioning Veterans. 2011. (Military Life Ser.). (ENG.). 324p. 34.95 *(978-1-60590-740-6(5))* Government Institutes.

Hite, Don. The Advice of a Headhunter: How to Land the Perfect Job in Today's Competitive Job Market. 2008. (ENG.). 594p. pap. 24.95 *(978-0-9779863-0-9(6))* Durban House Pr., Inc.

Hoffman, Reid & Casnocha, Ben. The Start-Up of You: Adapt to the Future, Invest in Yourself, & Transform Your Career. 2012. ***(978-0-307-88891-4(6))***; (ENG.). 272p. 26.00 ***(978-0-307-88890-7(8))*** Crown Publishing Group. (Crown Business).

Holmes Hedrick, Camille. Retaining Career Switchers. 2008. 132p. pap. *(978-3-639-08966-0(9))* VDM Verlag Dr. Mueller e.K.

Jansen, Julie. I Don't Know What I Want, but I Know It's Not This: A Step-by-Step Guide to Finding Gratifying Work. rev. ed. 2010. (ENG.). 304p. (gr. 12-18). 15.00 *(978-0-14-311699-8(1),* Penguin (Non-Classics)) Penguin Group (USA) Inc.

Jewell, Catherine. New Resume New Career: Get the Job You Want with the Skills & Experience You Already Have. 2010. (ENG.). 272p. (gr. 12-18). 16.95 *(978-1-59257-975-4(2),* Alpha Bks.) Penguin Group (USA) Inc.

Johnstone, Judith. Planning a Career Change. 6th rev. ed. 2006. (Illus.). 160p. per. 20.00 *(978-1-84528-100-7(4))* Parkwest Pubns., Inc.

Joiner, Steven. The Idealist Guide to Nonprofit Careers for Sector Switchers. 2010. (Hundreds of Heads Survival Guides). (ENG., Illus.). 252p. pap. 18.95 *(978-1-933512-22-8(9))* Hundreds of Heads Bks., Inc.

Kay, Andrea. Work's a Bitch & Then You Make It Work: 6 Steps to Go from Pissed off to Powerful. 2009. (ENG.). 272p. pap. 15.95 *(978-1-58479-708-1(8))* Stewart, Tabori & Chang.

Knadler, Jessie. Rurally Screwed: My Life off the Grid with the Cowboy I Love. 2012. (ENG.). 336p. (gr. 12). 24.95 ***(978-0-425-24568-2(3),*** Berkley Hardcover) Penguin Group (USA) Inc.

Lawler, Edward E. & O'Toole, James, eds. America at Work: Choices & Challenges. 2008. (ENG.). 368p. pap. 29.95 *(978-0-230-60680-7(6))* Palgrave Macmillan.

Lees. Career Reboot: 24 Tips for Tough Times. 2009. (ENG.). 120p. pap. 17.00 *(978-0-07-712758-9(7),* 0077127587) McGraw-Hill Cos., The.

—How to Get A Job You'll Love 2011-2012 E: Dition. 6th ed. 2010. (ENG., Illus.). 312p. pap. 25.00 *(978-0-07-712993-4(8),* 0077129938) McGraw-Hill Cos., The.

Levinson, Jay Conrad & Neitlich, Andrew. Guerrilla Marketing for a Bulletproof Career: How to Attract Ongoing Opportunities in Perpetually Gut Wrenching Times, for Entrepreneurs, Employees, & Everyone in Between. 2011. (Guerilla Marketing Press Ser.). (ENG.). 250p. pap. 19.95 *(978-1-60037-815-7(3))* Morgan James Publishing.

Lillenstein, David J. The Role of the School Psychologist in Transition Planning. 2009. 184p. pap. *(978-3-639-14173-3(3))* VDM Verlag Dr. Mueller e.K.

Lore, Nicholas. The Pathfinder: How to Choose or Change Your Career for a Lifetime of Satisfaction & Success. rev. ed. 2012. (ENG.). 448p. pap. 16.99 *(978-1-4516-0832-8(2),* Touchstone) Touchstone.

Lovett, C. Academics & Career Change. Date not set. *(978-0-275-90016-8(9),* C0016, Praeger Pubs.) Greenwood Publishing Group, Inc.

Maestas, Lily. Unlimited Options. rev. ed. 2009. (ENG.). 266p. pap. 46.47 *(978-0-7575-6143-6(8))* Kendall Hunt Publishing Co.

Mainiero, Lisa A. & Sullivan, Sherry E. The Opt-Out Revolt: Why People Are Leaving Companies to Create Kaleidoscope Careers. 2006. (ENG., Illus.). 400p. 28.95 *(978-0-89106-186-1(X))* Ebsco Publishing.

Mandell, Fred & Jordan, Kathleen. Becoming a Life Change Artist: 7 Creative Skills to Reinvent Yourself at Any Stage of Life. 2010. (ENG.). 320p. (gr. 12). 18.00 *(978-1-58333-404-1(1),* Avery) Penguin Group (USA) Inc.

Mangelsdorf, Martha E. Strategies for Successful Career Change: Finding Your Very Best Next Work Life. 2009. (ENG.). 224p. pap. 16.99 *(978-1-58008-824-4(4))* Ten Speed Pr.

Mannering, Karen. Get the Career You Want: A Teach Yourself Guide. 2011. (Teach Yourself: General Reference Ser.). (ENG.). 208p. pap. 15.00 ***(978-0-07-177522-9(6),*** 0071775226) McGraw-Hill Cos., The.

Maples, Lucy. Selected Perceptions of Second Career Novice Teachers. 2011. 204p. pap. ***(978-3-8383-7494-9(0))*** Lambert Academic Publishing.

Marsh, Rosalie. Release Your Potential: Making Sense of Personal & Professional Development. 2011. (ENG., Illus.). 118p. pap. ***(978-1-908302-08-3(9))*** Christal Publishing.

Martin, Thomas L. Jr. Career Change Management. 2008. 232p. 29.99 *(978-1-4363-7645-7(9))*; pap. 19.99 *(978-1-4363-7644-0(0))* Xlibris Corp.

Martinez, Luis A. Getting There. 2010. 220p. 29.99 *(978-1-4500-2626-0(5))*; pap. 19.99 *(978-1-4500-2625-3(7))* Xlibris Corp.

Martini, Kitty & Reed, Candice. Thank You for Firing Me! How to Catch the Next Wave of Success after You Lose Your Job. 2010. (ENG.). 240p. pap. 14.95 *(978-1-4027-6956-6(3))* Sterling Publishing Co., Inc.

McCorkindale, Susan. Confessions of a Counterfeit Farm Girl. 2008. (ENG.). 368p. (gr. 12-18). 15.00 *(978-0-451-22493-4(0),* N A L Trade) Penguin Group (USA) Inc.

McKnight, William. 90 Days to Success in Consulting. 2009. (ENG., Illus.). 256p. pap. 19.99 *(978-1-4354-5442-2(1))* Course Technology.

McNeal, Delatorro, II. Caught Between a Dream & a Job: How to Leave the 9-to-5 Behind & Step into the Life You've Always Wanted. 2007. (ENG.). 238p. 21.99 *(978-1-59979-217-0(6))* Charisma Media.

Metro Resource Publications Staff. Retraining: Twenty-First Century Key to Success. (Keep it Simple Ser.). (Illus.). 132p. (Orig.). pap. 14.95 *(978-0-945376-99-6(5))* Metro Resource Pubns.

Miedaner, Talane. Coach Yourself to a New Career: 7 Steps to Reinventing Your Professional Life. 2010. (ENG.). 240p. pap. 18.95 *(978-0-07-170309-3(8),* 0071703098) McGraw-Hill Cos., The.

Miners, Rick & Sedlar, Jeri. Don't Retire,REWIRE!, 2E. 2nd ed. 2007. (ENG.). 304p. (gr. 12-18). 18.95 *(978-1-59257-689-0(3),* Alpha Bks.) Penguin Group (USA) Inc.

Mitchell, Pamela. The 10 Laws of Career Reinvention: Essential Survival Skills for Any Economy. 2011. (ENG.). 272p. (gr. 12). 15.00 *(978-0-7352-0453-9(5))* Prentice Hall Pr.

Mittapalli, Kavita. What Makes Public School Teachers Stay, Leave or Become Non-Teachers? 2009. 80p. pap. *(978-3-639-14249-5(7))* VDM Verlag Dr. Mueller e.K.

MORE magazine. MORE Magazine 287 Secrets of Reinventing Your Life: Big & Small Ways to Embrace New Possibilities. 2011. (ENG.). 272p. pap. 16.95 *(978-1-118-01262-8(3),* Wiley) Wiley, John & Sons, Inc.

Murdock, Ken. Your Complete Guide to Job Search & Career Change. 2010. 108p. pap. 14.95 *(978-0-557-37363-5(8))* Lulu Enterprises Inc.

Newman, Rick. Rebounders: How Winners Pivot from Setback to Success. 2012. (ENG.). 256p. 26.00 ***(978-0-345-52783-7(6),*** Ballantine Bks.) Random House Publishing Group.

O'Brien, Marcia. Why Do Teachers Stay? 2009. 136p. pap. *(978-3-639-16939-3(5))* VDM Verlag Dr. Mueller e.K.

Paton, Nick. The Complete Career Makeover. 2010. (ENG., Illus.). 230p. pap. 26.95 *(978-0-85265-149-0(X))* Random Hse. GBR. Dist: Independent Pubs. Group.

Piotrowski, Katy. The Career Coward's Guide to Changing Careers: Sensible Strategies for Overcoming Job Search Fears. 2007. (Career Coward's Guides). (Illus.). 224p. per. 10.95 *(978-1-59357-390-4(1),* J3904, JIST Works) JIST Publishing.

Power, Sally J. The Mid-Career Success Guide: Planning for the Second Half of Your Working Life, 1 vol. 2006. (Illus.). 216p. 39.95 *(978-0-275-98801-2(5),* C8801, Praeger Pubs.) Greenwood Publishing Group, Inc.

Remling, Jennifer. Carve Your Own Road. 2009. (ENG.). 1p. pap. 14.99 *(978-1-60163-052-0(2))* Career Pr., Inc.

Rigdon, L. How to Change Your Career & Do the Work You Really Love: A Step-by-Step Plan for Making It Happen. 2009. (ENG.). 360p. pap. 24.95 *(978-1-60138-288-7(X))* Atlantic Publishing Co.

Riklan, David & Riklan, Michelle A., selected by. 101 Great Ways to Enhance Your Career. 2011. (Illus.). 389p. pap. 19.95 ***(978-0-9794992-7-2(5))*** Self Improvement Online, Inc.

Rolle, Linda K. Getting Back to Work: Everything You Need to Bounce Back & Get a Job After a Layoff. 2009. (ENG., Illus.). 288p. pap. 15.95 *(978-0-07-163867-8(9),* 0071638679) McGraw-Hill Cos., The.

Rowan, Sophie. Brilliant Career Coach: How to Find & Follow Your Dream Career. 2nd rev. ed. 2011. (ENG., Illus.). 256p. pap. 19.99 ***(978-0-273-75014-7(3))*** FT Press.

Rowlett, Paula & Rowlett, Tom. Swallowed by the Whale: Surviving & Managing Change in the Workplace. 2010. 212p. pap. 19.95 *(978-1-4520-8566-1(8))* AuthorHouse.

Sammons, Mary Beth. Second Acts That Change Lives: Making a Difference in the World. 2009. (ENG.). 176p. pap. 14.95 *(978-1-57324-368-1(X),* Conari Pr.) Red Wheel/Weiser.

Savino, Carl S., et al. Military-to-Civilian Resumes & Letters: How to Best Communicate Your Strengths to Employers. 3rd ed. 2007. (ENG., Illus.). 268p. pap. 21.95 *(978-1-57023-267-1(9))* Impact Pubns.

Schatt, S. & Lobl, M. Paint Your Career Green. 2011. 208p. pap. 12.95 *(978-1-59357-859-6(8))* JIST Publishing.

Scott-Lennon, Frank, et al. Redundancy: A Development Opportunity for You! 2008. (ENG., Illus.). 104p. pap. 14.95 ***(978-1-906946-00-5(0))*** Management Briefs Ltd.

Shatkin, Laurence. The Sequel: How to Change Your Career Without Starting Over. 2011. 224p. pap. 12.95 *(978-1-59357-865-7(2))* JIST Publishing.

Smith, Dennis. Outplace: Career Change, Real World Stories, Real World Answers, 1 vol. 2009.Tr. of Outplace. 83p. pap. 16.95 *(978-1-4489-8548-7(X))* PublishAmerica, Inc.

Snodgrass, S. Gary. Stepping Up: 12 Ways to Rev up, Revitalize, or Renew Your Career. 2007. 87p. 13.95 *(978-1-929774-41-8(9),* Greenleaf Book Group Pr.) Greenleaf Book Group.

Spector, Stan. Baby Boomers' Official Guide to Retirement Income. 2007. 128p. per. 16.95 *(978-1-59858-342-7(5))* Dog Ear Publishing, LLC.

Storlie, Chad. Combat Leader to Corporate Leader: 20 Lessons to Advance Your Civilian Career, 1 vol. 2010. (Illus.). 184p. 34.95 *(978-0-313-38332-8(4),* A2726C, Praeger Pubs.) Greenwood Publishing Group, Inc.

Strankowski, Donald J. New Strategies for a New Job Market. 2008. 264p. pap. 21.95 *(978-0-595-49604-4(0),* iUniverse, Inc.) iUniverse, Inc.

Tanner, Ken. The Boomers' Career Survival Guide: Achieving Success & Contentment from Middle Age through Retirement, 1 vol. 2009. (Illus.). 165p. 29.95 *(978-0-313-36521-8(0),* C36521, Praeger Pubs.) Greenwood Publishing Group, Inc.

Teller, Mark. Screw the Recruiter: Beat Corporate America at its Own Game. 2011. (ENG.). 200p. (YA). pap. 19.95 *(978-0-9819723-0-5(6))* Screw, Inc., The.

Viola, Marc Anthony. A Spy's Resume: Confessions of a Maverick Intelligence Professional & Misadventure Capitalist. 2008. (Scarecrow Professional Intelligence Education Ser.). (ENG.). 318p. pap. 52.00 *(978-0-8108-6098-8(8))* Scarecrow Pr., Inc.

Wagner, Tamara. Hair Is MY Business. 2008. 178p. pap. 34.95 *(978-1-4303-2885-8(1))* Lulu Enterprises Inc.

Wall, Janet E., frwd. 150 Best Jobs Through Military Training. (Best Jobs Ser.). (Illus.). 402p. per. 19.95 *(978-1-59357-462-8(2),* J4628) JIST Publishing.

Wang, Mo, et al. Mid & Late Career Issues. 2012. (Applied Psychology Ser.). (ENG., Illus.). 320p. 62.95 ***(978-0-415-80495-0(7),*** Routledge) Taylor & Francis Group GBR. Dist: Taylor & Francis Group.

Watkins, Michael D. Your Next Move: The Leader's Guide to Navigating Major Career Transitions. 2009. (ENG., Illus.). 240p. 26.95 *(978-1-4221-4763-4(0))* Harvard Business Review Pr.

Wellenstein, Carl. 12 Steps to a New Career. 2009. (ENG.). 1p. pap. 16.99 *(978-1-60163-062-9(X))* Career Pr., Inc.

Wenschlag, Roger. We Hug in the Hallways Here. 2008. 176p. pap. 19.95 *(978-1-59298-262-2(X))* Beaver's Pond Pr., Inc.

Whiteman, Lily Madeleine. How to Land a Top-Paying Federal Job: Your Complete Guide to Opportunities, Internships, Resumes & Cover Letters, Networking, Interviews, Salaries, Promotions, & More!, 1 vol. 2nd ed. 2012. (ENG.). 288p. pap. 24.95 incl. audio compact disk ***(978-0-8144-2022-5(2))*** Amacom.

Wolfe, Tom. Out of Uniform: Your Guide to a Successful Military-to-Civilian Career Transition. 2011. 249p. pap. 24.95 *(978-1-59797-715-9(2))* Potomac Bks., Inc.

Wolfelt, Alan D. & Duvall, Kirby J. Healing after Job Loss: 100 Practical Ideas. 2010. (Healing Your Grieving Heart Ser.). (ENG.). 128p. pap. 11.95 *(978-1-879651-69-2(6))* Companion Pr.

Worthing, Marcia L. & Buck, Charles A. Escape the Mid-Career Doldrums: What to Do Next When You're Bored, Burned Out, Retired or Fired. 2007. (ENG.). 224p. per. 18.95 *(978-0-470-11515-2(7),* Wiley) Wiley, John & Sons, Inc.

Wring, et al. Transferring Your Teaching Skills into the Wider World: Life Beyond the Classroom. 2007. (Illus.). X, 270p. 31.95 *(978-0-415-42870-5(X))*; 130.00 *(978-0-415-42867-5(X))* Routledge.

Zhan, Yujie. Antecedents & Health Outcomes of Bridge Employment. 2010. 80p. pap. *(978-3-639-12611-2(4))* VDM Verlag Dr. Mueller e.K.

CAREER COUPLES

see Dual-Career Families

CAREER DEVELOPMENT

Here are entered works on the occupational and professional growth of individuals within their chosen fields and on that aspect of personnel management concerned with increasing an employee's potential for advancement and career changes within related fields.

Aaron, Raymond & Lacher, Sue. Double Your Income Doing What You Love: Raymond Aaron's Guide to Power Mentoring. 2008. (ENG., Illus.). 191p. 24.95 *(978-0-470-17370-1(X),* Wiley) Wiley, John & Sons, Inc.

Abboud, Sharon Reed. All Moms Work: Short-Term Career Strategies for Long-Range Success. 2009. (Capital Ideas for Business & Personal Development Ser.). 248p. pap. 15.95 *(978-1-933102-68-9(3))* Capital Bks., Inc.

Abraham, Joel. Hired! Networking to Land the Job YOU Want. 2011. 100p. pap. 14.99 ***(978-1-4567-4564-6(6))*** AuthorHouse.

Adams, Margaret. How to Take Charge of Your Teaching Career. 2008. (ENG., Illus.). 176p. 34.95 *(978-1-84706-031-0(5))* Continuum International Publishing Group, Ltd. GBR. Dist: National Bk. Network.

Adams, Stephen P. Reinventing Your Career: Surviving a Layoff & Creating New Opportunities. pap. 9.99 *(978-0-8024-7361-5(X))* Northfield Publishing.

Adkins-Spears, Judith. Jump-Start Your Merchandising Career. 2011. 226p. 29.99 ***(978-1-4568-4217-8(X))***; pap. 19.99 ***(978-1-4568-4216-1(1))*** Xlibris Corp.

Aiken, Sean. One-Week Job Project: One Man, One Year, 52 Jobs. 2010. (ENG., Illus.). 320p. pap. 15.00 *(978-0-345-50803-4(3),* Villard Bks.) Random House Publishing Group.

Alexander, Laurel. 675 Ways to Develop Yourself & Your People. 2007. 244p. pap. 99.95 *(978-1-59996-053-1(2))* Human Resource Development Pr.

Altilla, Tony. I Wish Someone Had Told Me That: Ten Kernals of Experience for Those Starting Their Careers from Those Ending Theirs. 2008. *(978-0-9809231-7-9(4))* BPS Bks.

And Smith, Mr & Mrs Smith's Employment Survival Guide. 2009. 74p. pap. 12.99 *(978-1-4389-7970-0(3))* AuthorHouse.

Anderson, Nancy Range. Job Search Skills for Moms. 2010. 102p. pap. 16.95 *(978-0-557-31707-3(X))* Lulu Enterprises Inc.

Andersson, Cristina. Winning Helix: The Art of Learning & Manifesting Your True Potential. Hunt, Marie, ed. 2006. (Illus.). 196p. per. 25.00 *(978-0-9769689-2-4(4))* Free Educational Publications International, Inc.

Andrews, Brad. How to Land a Top-Paying Aerospace Engineer, Aerospace Product & Parts Manufacturing Services Job: Your Complete Guide to Opportunities, Resumes & Cover Letters, Interviews, Salaries, Promotions, What to Expect from Recruiters & More! 2010. 160p. pap. *(978-1-74244-559-5(4))* Emereo Pty Ltd.

—The Truth about Advertising & Public Relations Jobs - How to Job-Hunt & Career-Change for Advertising & Public Relations Jobs - the Facts You Should Know. 2009. (Illus.). 196p. pap. *(978-1-74244-169-6(6))* Emereo Pty Ltd.

Aretakis, Nicholas. No More Ramen: The 20-Something's Real World Survival Guide: Straight Talk on Jobs, Money, Balance, Life, & More. 2006. (ENG., Illus.). 236p. pap. 14.95 *(978-0-9776224-0-5(1))* Next Stage Pr.

Arnold, Camilla & Barrett, Jane. If Not Now, When? How to Take Charge of Your Career. 2010. (ENG., Illus.). 192p. pap. 14.95 *(978-1-4081-2505-2(6))* A & C Black GBR. Dist: Macmillan.

Asher, Donald. Cracking the Hidden Job Market: How to Find Opportunity in Any Economy. 2010. (ENG., Illus.). 208p. pap. 14.99 *(978-1-58008-494-9(X))* Ten Speed Pr.

—How to Get Any Job: Career Launch & Re-Launch for Everyone under 30 (Or How to Avoid Living in Your Parents' Basement) 2nd rev. ed. 2009. (ENG., Illus.). 240p. pap. 15.99 *(978-1-58008-947-0(X))* Ten Speed Pr.

—Who Gets Promoted, Who Doesn't, & Why: 10 Things You'd Better Do If You Want to Get Ahead. 2007. (ENG., Illus.). 176p. pap. 14.99 *(978-1-58008-820-6(1))* Ten Speed Pr.

Ashley, Rod. Get a Better Job. 2011. (Teach Yourself Ser.). (ENG., Illus.). 256p. pap. 15.95 *(978-1-4441-1593-2(6),* Hodder & Stoughton) Hodder General Publishing Div. GBR. Dist: Independent Pubs. Group.

Askew, Jennifer P. From Student to Pharmacist: Making the Transition. 2010. 192p. pap. 29.95 *(978-1-58212-142-0(7))* American Pharmacists Assn.

ASTD. Addressing the Skills Gap. 2010. (ENG.). 16p. pap. 24.95 *(978-1-56286-731-7(8))* American Society for Training & Development.

Atkins, Robert. Getting the Most from Nursing School: A Guide to Becoming a Nurse. 2008. (ENG.). 256p. pap. 45.95 *(978-0-7637-5581-2(8))* Jones & Bartlett Learning, LLC.

Axelrod, Wendy & Coyle, Jeannie. Make Talent Your Business: How Exceptional Managers Develop People While Getting Results. 2011. (Bk Business Ser.). (ENG., Illus.). 210p. pap. 22.95 *(978-1-60509-931-6(7))* Berrett-Koehler Pubs., Inc.

Aylward, Scott & Moore, Pattye. Confessions from the Corner Office: 15 Instincts That Will Help You Get There. 2007. (ENG.). 229p. 24.95 *(978-0-470-12678-3(7),* Wiley) Wiley, John & Sons, Inc.

Azzarello, Patty. Rise: 3 Practical Steps for Advancing Your Career, Standing Out as a Leader, & Liking Your Life. 2012. (ENG., Illus.). 288p. pap. 15.99 ***(978-1-60774-260-9(8))*** Ten Speed Pr.

Baber, Anne & Waymon, Lynne. Make Your Contacts Count: Networking Know-How for Business & Career Success. 2nd rev. ed. 2007. (ENG., Illus.). 272p. pap. 14.95 *(978-0-8144-7402-0(0))* Amacom.

Badasch, Shirley A. & Chesebro, Doreen S. Health Science Fundamentals. 2008. (ENG.). 656p. (C). pap., stu. ed., act. bk. ed. 40.60 *(978-0-13-504372-1(7),* Prentice Hall) Prentice Hall PTR.

Baggett, Byrd. 97 Things to Take Your Sales Career to the Next Level. 2010. (Good Things to Know Ser.). (ENG.). 270p. pap. 9.99 *(978-1-59652-749-2(8))* Turner Publishing Co.

Bailey, Mary Ann. Finding the Right Career Path. 2006. (Wetfeet Insider Guides). (Illus.). 126p. per. 21.95 *(978-1-58207-554-9(9))* WetFeet, Inc.

Baines, Bernard. The Deal - Take Ownership of Your Career. 2008. 104p. per. *(978-1-84549-298-4(6))* arima publishing.

Ball, James. Professionalism Is for Everyone: 5 Keys to Being a True Professional. 2008. 80p. pap. 9.95 *(978-1-887570-05-3(5))* Goals Institute, Inc., The.

Barber, Gloria. Mastering the Workplace: Rediscovering Passion in Your Workforce. 2010. 252p. pap. 19.95 *(978-1-934449-42-4(3))* Legacy Publishing Services, Inc.

Barnes, Anthony, et al. An Introduction to Career Learning & Development 11-19. 2010. (ENG., Illus.). 168p. (C). 130.00 *(978-0-415-57777-9(2))*; pap. 37.95 *(978-0-415-57778-6(0))* Taylor & Francis Group GBR. (Routledge). Dist: Taylor & Francis Group.

Barnes, Eric B. Why Volunteers Get All the Breaks. 2009. 96p. pap. 11.95 *(978-1-4401-4474-5(5))* iUniverse, Inc.

Baruch, Yehuda & Reis, Christina, eds. Careers without Borders: Critical Perspectives. 2012. (ENG., Illus.). 376p. (C). 200.00 ***(978-0-415-50116-3(4))*** Routledge.

—Careers Without Borders: Critical Perspectives. 2012. (ENG., Illus.). 376p. (C). pap. 59.95 ***(978-0-415-50115-6(6))*** Routledge.

Baugh, S. Gayle & Sullivan, Sherry E. Maintaining Focus, Energy, & Options over the Career. 2009. *(978-1-59311-958-4(5))*; pap. *(978-1-59311-957-7(7))* Information Age Publishing, Inc.

Bedell, Gene. The Millionaire in the Mirror: How to Find Your Passion & Make a Fortune Doing It — Without Quitting Your Day Job. 2008. (ENG., Illus.). 288p. 23.95 *(978-0-06-147348-7(0)*, Collins) HarperCollins Pubs.

Beilke, Ines T. & Beilke, Mariah. Career Motivation & Self-Concept: On Track on Purpose. 7th rev. ed. 2010. (ENG.). 506p. pap. 94.75 *(978-0-7575-7313-2(4))* Kendall Hunt Publishing Co.

Belbin Associates Staff & Belbin Associates. The Belbin Guide to Succeeding at Work. 2009. (ENG., Illus.). 112p. pap. 14.95 *(978-1-4081-1501-5(8))* A & C Black GBR. Dist: Macmillan.

Belding, Shaun. Win at Work: Navigate the Nasties, Get Things Done, & Get Ahead. 2010. (ENG.). 192p. pap. 19.95 *(978-0-7494-5711-2(2))* Kogan Page, Ltd. GBR. Dist: Ingram Pub. Services.

Bench, Marcia. Career Coaching: An Insider's Guide - Study Guide. 2008. 196p. pap. 34.95 *(978-0-9817005-1-9(9))* High Flight Pr.

Bench, Marcia A. Career Coaching: An Insider's Guide - Second Edition. 2nd ed. 2008. (Illus.). 444p. pap. 39.95 *(978-0-9817005-0-2(0))* High Flight Pr.

Benjamin, Susan. Professional Networking: Hundreds of Ready-to-Use Phrases for Meeting & Keeping Helpful Contacts Everywhere You Go. 2009. (Perfect Phrases Ser.). (ENG.). 208p. pap. 10.95 *(978-0-07-162916-4(5)*, 0071629165) McGraw-Hill Cos., The.

Benko, Cathleen & Anderson, Molly. The Corporate Lattice: Achieving High Performance in the Changing World of Work. 2010. (ENG., Illus.). 224p. 29.95 *(978-1-4221-5516-5(1))* Harvard Business Review Pr.

Benko, Cathleen & Weisberg, Anne Cicero. Mass Career Customization: Aligning the Workplace with Today's Nontraditional Workforce. 2007. (ENG., Illus.). 230p. 29.95 *(978-1-4221-1033-1(8))* Harvard Business Review Pr.

Bennett, Nathan & Miles, Stephen. Your Career Game: How Game Theory Can Help You Achieve Your Professional Goals. 2011. (ENG.). 272p. pap. 17.95 *(978-0-8047-7872-5(8)*, Stanford Business Bks.) Stanford Univ. Pr.

Bennett, Nathan & Miles, Stephen A. Your Career Game: How Game Theory Can Help You Achieve Your Professional Goals. 2010. (ENG., Illus.). 272p. 24.95 *(978-0-8047-5628-0(7)*, Stanford Business Bks.) Stanford Univ. Pr.

Berger, Dorothy & Berger, Lance A. The Talent Management Handbook: Creating Organizational Excellence by Identifying, Developing, & Promoting Your Best People. 2nd ed. 2010. (ENG., Illus.). 576p. instr.'s hndbk. ed. 60.00 *(978-0-07-173905-4(X)*, 007173905X) McGraw-Hill Cos., The.

Bergstrom, Barbara B. Don't Forget Your Keys: Each Key Holds the Power to Your Career Advancement. 2010. 188p. 24.95 *(978-1-4269-3027-0(5))*; pap. 14.95 *(978-1-4269-3088-1(7))* Trafford Publishing.

Bilanich, Bud. 42 Rules to Jumpstart Your Professional Success: A Guide to Common Sense Career Development & Entrepreneurial Achievement. Lowell, Laura, ed. 2009. 134p. pap. 19.95 *(978-1-60773-026-2(X)*, Super Star Pr.) Happy About.

Binder, Libuse. Ten Ways to Change the World in Your 20's. 2009. (ENG.). 352p. pap. 14.99 *(978-1-4022-2109-5(6))* Sourcebooks, Inc.

Black, Cathie. Basic Black. 2008. 340p. pap. 18.99 *(978-1-60396-211-7(5))* Aguilar, S. A. de Ediciones-Grupo Santillana ESP. Dist: Santillana USA Publishing Co., Inc.

—Basic Black: The Essential Guide for Getting Ahead at Work (and in Life) (ENG.). 304p. 2008. pap. 14.95 *(978-0-307-35113-5(0)*, Three Rivers Pr.) 2007. 24.95 *(978-0-307-35110-4(6)*, Crown Business) Crown Publishing Group.

Blackett, Karine. Career Achievement: Growing Your Goals. 2010. (ENG., Illus.). 336p. (C). pap. 72.00 *(978-0-07-337700-1(7)*, 0073377007) McGraw-Hill Higher Education.

Blanck, Terese Corey, et al. The College to Career Roadmap: A Four Year Guide to Coaching Your Student. 2006. pap. *(978-1-891859-65-6(X))* Atwood Publishing.

—The College to Career Roadmap: A Four Year Guide to Finding Your Path. 2006. pap. *(978-1-891859-66-3(8))* Atwood Publishing.

Bly, Robert. 88 Money-Making Writing Jobs. 2009. (ENG.). 336p. pap. 20.99 *(978-1-4022-1507-0(X))* Sourcebooks, Inc.

Boags, Rita S. Mentorship: A Pathway to Career Success. 2008. 116p. pap. 14.95 *(978-1-4343-9715-7(7))* AuthorHouse.

Bobrowitz, Art. The Harmony of Science & Soul: Finding Meaning in the 21st Century Workplace. 2012. (ENG., Illus.). 342p. pap. 23.95 ***(978-0-615-47013-9(0))*** Compass Rose Consulting, Inc.

Bolles, Richard Nelson. What Color Is Your Parachute? 2011: A Practical Manual for Job-Hunters & Career-Changers. 2010. (ENG., Illus.). 368p. 28.99 *(978-1-58008-267-9(X))*; pap. 18.99 *(978-1-58008-270-9(X))* Ten Speed Pr.

Bolles, Richard Nelson & Figler, Howard. The Career Counselor's Handbook. 2nd rev. ed. 2007. (Parachute Library). (ENG., Illus.). 320p. pap. 19.99 *(978-1-58008-870-1(8))* Ten Speed Pr.

Bolton, Gillie E. J. Reflective Practice: Writing & Professional Development. 3rd ed. 2010. (Illus.). 304p. (C). 98.00 *(978-1-84860-211-3(1)*, B02113C); pap. 46.00 *(978-1-84860-212-0(X)*, B02113P) SAGE Pubns., Ltd. GBR. Dist: SAGE Pubns., Inc.

Bopp, Mary Ann, et al. Agile Career Development: Lessons & Approaches from IBM. 2009. (ENG.). 272p. 39.99 *(978-0-13-715364-0(3))* Pearson Education.

Borchard, David C., et al. Your Career Planner. 10th rev. ed. 2010. (ENG.). 352p. pap. 65.39 *(978-0-7575-5338-7(9))* Kendall Hunt Publishing Co.

Borthwick, Arlene & Pierson, Melissa. Transforming Classroom Practice: Professional Development Strategies in Educational Technology. 2008. (Illus.). xiii, 241p. pap. 44.95 *(978-1-56484-246-6(0))* International Society for Technology in Education.

Boyd, Sandra & Rosenberg, Michael. The Flexible Thinker Guide to Extreme Career Performance. 200p. *(978-0-9736361-0-9(6))* Orange You Glad, Incorporated.

Bradbury, Helen. Beyond Reflective Practice: New Approaches to Professional Lifelong Learning. Bradbury, Helen et al, eds. 2009. (ENG., Illus.). 240p. pap. 45.95 *(978-0-415-46793-3(4))* Routledge.

Braley, Larry D. & Gragg, Ray D. Working from the Heart - A Way of Life. 2008. 191p. pap. 19.95 *(978-0-557-02696-8(2))* Lulu Enterprises Inc.

Branch, Treivor. The Drama-Free Workweek: How to Manage Difficult People for Workplace & Career Success. 2011. 76p. pap. 12.95 *(978-1-4269-5433-7(5))* Trafford Publishing.

Branson, Douglas M. No Seat at the Table: How Corporate Governance & Law Keep Women Out of the Boardroom. 2008. (ENG.). 256p. pap. 23.00 *(978-0-8147-9105-9(0))* New York Univ. Pr.

Brauner, Marygail K., et al. Improving Development & Utilization of U. S. Air Force Intelligence Officers. 2009. 84p. pap. 23.50 *(978-0-8330-4716-8(7)*, tr-628) RAND Corp., The.

Breen, Howard J. The Toothpick Factory: Ten Guideposts to help students get the right Job. 2010. 144p. 29.95 *(978-1-4520-0337-5(8))*; pap. 21.95 *(978-1-4520-0336-8(X))* AuthorHouse.

Bremner, Trevor. Personality & Success in a Russian University. 2009. 92p. pap. *(978-3-639-16297-4(8))* VDM Verlag Dr. Mueller e.K.

Brewer, Gayle. Career Planning & Awareness. 2009. 64p. pap. *(978-3-639-14929-6(7))* VDM Verlag Dr. Mueller e.K.

Bridgstock, Ruth. The Protean Careers of Artists. 2011. 440p. pap. ***(978-3-8443-2254-5(X))*** Lambert Academic Publishing.

Brolin & Loyd & Cram101 Textbook Reviews Staff. Career Developement & Transition Services. 2007. 80p. per. 10.95 *(978-1-4288-1988-7(6)*, Cram101 Inc.

Brown, Anne & Zefo, Beth. Grad to Great: Discover the Secrets to Success in Your First Career, 1 vol. 2010. (ENG.). 173p. pap. 18.50 *(978-0-9798018-0-8(X))* New Year Publishing.

Brown, Diane. Restorying Ourselves - Using Currere to Examine Teachers' Careers. 2008. 148p. pap. *(978-3-639-00251-5(2))* VDM Verlag Dr. Mueller e.K.

Brown III, Adolph. Championship Habits: Soft Skills in Hard Times for Leaders & Managers. 2009. 92p. pap. 14.95 *(978-1-4401-4360-1(9))* iUniverse, Inc.

Browne, Steven E. Getting that Job in Hollywood: The Motion Picture, Cable & Television Industry. 2007. 178p. pap. 12.95 *(978-0-7414-4325-0(2))* Infinity Publishing.

Brubaker, Dale L. & Coble, Larry D. Staying on Track: An Educational Leader's Guide to Preventing Derailment & Ensuring Personal & Organizational Success. 2nd rev. ed. 2006. 200p. 72.95 *(978-1-4129-3935-5(6)*, B39356C); pap. 31.95 *(978-1-4129-3936-2(4)*, B39356P) Corwin Pr.

Bruce, Andy & Birchall, David. Innovation: Fast Track to Success. 2012. (ENG., Illus.). 240p. pap. 24.99 ***(978-0-13-296483-8(X))*** FT Press.

Bruce, Anne. Employee Development Plans. 2010. (Perfect Phrases Ser.). (ENG., Illus.). 176p. pap. 10.95 *(978-0-07-171509-6(6)*, 0071715096) McGraw-Hill Cos., The.

Bryon, Mike. Great Answers to Tough Career Dilemmas: Test Your Aptitude, Be Inspired & Discover Your Ideal Career. 2011. (ENG., Illus.). 252p. pap. 29.95 *(978-0-7494-5413-5(X))* Kogan Page, Ltd. GBR. Dist: Ingram Pub. Services.

Bubb, Sara & Earley, Peter. Helping Staff Develop in Schools. 2010. (Illus.). 136p. 68.00 *(978-1-84920-025-7(4)*, B00257C); pap. 32.00 *(978-1-84920-026-4(2)*, B00257P) SAGE Pubns., Ltd. GBR. Dist: SAGE Pubns., Inc.

—Leading & Managing Continuing Professional Development: Developing People, Developing Schools. 2nd ed. 2007. (Illus.). 208p. 79.00 *(978-1-4129-4827-2(4)*, B48272C) SAGE Pubns., Ltd. GBR. Dist: SAGE Pubns., Inc.

Building Your Dream Life: Career, Sex & Leisure. 14.95 *(978-0-9643699-9-3(0))* Effective Living Publishing.

Buraimoh, Michael. The Mind of Success: Your Guide to Career Building & Self-Actualisation. 2011. 120p. pap. 18.42 *(978-1-4567-7119-5(1))* AuthorHouse.

Burchell, Michael & Robin, Jennifer. The Great Workplace Poster. 2011. (ENG.). 1p. pap. 10.00 ***(978-0-470-90288-2(4)***, Pfeiffer) Wiley, John & Sons, Inc.

Burge, Ryan C. College Is Just a Game. 2008. 188p. pap. 24.95 *(978-1-4241-9019-5(3))* PublishAmerica, Inc.

Burgess, Tobin, et al. The Personal Vision Workbook. 2006. (ENG., Illus.). 224p. (C). per. 26.95 *(978-1-4018-9939-4(0))* Delmar Cengage Learning.

Burley, Suzanne & Pomphrey, Cathy. Mentoring & Coaching in Secondary Schools. 2011. (ENG., Illus.). 152p. 120.00 *(978-0-415-56361-1(5))*; pap. 31.95 *(978-0-415-56363-5(1))* Routledge.

Burns, Karen. The Amazing Adventures of Working Girl: Real-Life Career Advice You Can Actually Use. 2009. (ENG.). 288p. 14.95 *(978-0-7624-3348-3(5)*, Running Pr.) Running Pr. Bk. Pubs.

Burrows, David & Laing, Zhivargo. College Career & Money: A Guide for Teens & Young People. 11.99 *(978-1-56229-204-1(8)*, Christian Living Bks., Inc.) Pneuma Life Publishing, Inc.

Burtnett, Frank. Bound for Career Guidebook: A Student Guide to Career Exploration, Decision Making, & the Job Search. 2011. (ENG.). 154p. pap., stu. ed. 17.95 *(978-1-60709-760-0(5))* Rowman & Littlefield Education.

—Bound-for-Career Guidebook: A Student Guide to Career Exploration, Decision Making, & the Job Search. 2010. (ENG.). 154p. stu. ed. 28.00 *(978-1-60709-759-4(1))* Rowman & Littlefield Education.

Bustamente, Gerald Gilbert & Bustamente, Linda Taylor. From College to Career: Making a Successful Transition to the Corporate World. 2007. (ENG.). 258p. per. 19.95 *(978-0-595-43157-1(7))* iUniverse, Inc.

Cahill, Danny. Harper's Rules: A Recruiter's Guide to Finding a Dream Job & the Right Relationship. 2011. 156p. 21.95 *(978-1-60832-100-1(2))* Greenleaf Book Group.

Cairns, Len & Stephenson, John. Capable Workplace Learning. 2009. 210p. *(978-90-8790-969-7(1))*; (Illus.). pap. *(978-90-8790-968-0(3))* Sense Pubs.

Calamela, Patricia, et al. Smashing Apples' Guide to Teaching: Know Where You're Going Before You Get There. 2008. 88p. pap. 14.95 *(978-1-4327-3132-8(7))* Outskirts Pr., Inc.

Caligiuri, Paula. Get a Life, Not a Job: Do What You Love & Let Your Talents Work for You. 2010. (ENG.). 208p. pap. 19.99 *(978-0-13-705849-5(7))* FT Press.

Callahan, Terry. Goal Oriented. 2006. (Cocurricular Activities Ser.). (Illus.). 64p. (YA). lib. bdg. 19.95 *(978-1-59084-890-6(X))* Mason Crest Pubs.

Cambridge University Press Staff. Success on the Job. *(978-0-8359-4642-1(6))* Cambridge Adult Education.

Campbell Thornton, Kim. Careers with Dogs: The Comprehensive Guide to Finding Your Dream Job. 2011. (ENG.). 488p. (gr. 6). pap. 24.95 *(978-1-933958-19-4(7))* BowTie Pr.

Canter, Rachelle J. Make the Right Career Move: 28 Critical Insights & Strategies to Land Your Dream Job. 2006. (ENG.). 242p. 29.95 *(978-0-470-05236-5(8)*, Wiley) Wiley, John & Sons, Inc.

Cardinale, Kristin. The 9-to-5 Cure: Work on Your own Terms & Reinvent Your Life. 2011. 224p. pap. 14.95 *(978-1-59357-807-7(5)*, JIST Works) JIST Publishing.

Career Confidential: Success Secrets No One Ever Told You. 260p. pap. *(978-1-891984-44-0(6))* Entrepreneur Pr. dba Entrepreneur Media, Inc.

Careerbuilder.com Editors & Cook's Illustrated Magazine Editors. Career Building: Your Total Handbook for Finding a Job & Making It Work. 2009. (ENG.). 288p. pap. 16.99 *(978-0-06-157910-3(6)*, Harper Paperbacks) HarperCollins Pubs.

Carlisle, Jim & Gill, Alex. A. I. M. The Powerful 10-Step Personal & Career Success Program. 2010. (ENG., Illus.). 272p. 32.95 *(978-0-470-73760-6(3)*, Wiley) Wiley, John & Sons, Inc.

Carnes, Barbara. Make Learning Stick: 20 Proven Techniques That Produce Results. 2010. (ENG.). 192p. pap. 32.95 *(978-1-55286-679-2(6))* American Society for Training & Development.

Carpenter, Heather. Older Workers. 2010. 308p. pap. *(978-3-8383-5822-2(8))* Lambert Academic Publishing.

Carroll, Steve & Gill, Jim. Don't Sell Yourself Short! Be All You Can Be! 2009. 168p. 34.50 *(978-1-4269-1588-8(8))* Trafford Publishing.

Carson, Nacie. The Finch Effect: The Five Strategies to Adapt & Thrive in Your Working Life. 2012. (ENG.). 208p. 25.95 ***(978-1-118-13428-3(*)***, Jossey-Bass) Wiley, John & Sons, Inc.

Carter, Carol. Sophomore Guide to College & Career: Preparing for Life after High School. 2007. (Illus.). 163p. per. 16.95 *(978-0-9742044-6-8(3))* LifeBound.

Carter, Carol J., et al. Keys to Success: Building Analytical, Creative, & Practical Skills. 7th ed. 2011. (ENG.). 416p. (C). pap. 80.40 *(978-0-13-707360-3(7)*, Prentice Hall) Prentice Hall PTR.

—Keys to Success: Building Analytical, Creative & Practical Skills, Brief Edition. 6th ed. 2011. (ENG., Illus.). 336p. (C). pap. 59.80 *(978-0-13-707355-9(0)*, Prentice Hall) Prentice Hall PTR.

CCDC Guide. 7th ed. pap. *(978-0-660-12333-2(9))* Canadian Government Publishing.

Cengage Learning Staff & Haroun, Lee. Professional Skills in Action. 2008. (ENG.). (C). 47.95 *(978-1-4180-5567-7(0))* Cengage South-Western.

Cengage South-Western. Resume Generator Plus. 2nd ed. 2010. (ResumeGenerator Ser.). (ENG.). (C). 39.95 *(978-1-111-48056-1(7))* Cengage South-Western.

Chandler, Dawn E. Relational Savvy. 2009. 308p. pap. *(978-3-639-12202-2(X))* VDM Verlag Dr. Mueller e.K.

Chartrand, Judy M. Now You're Thinking about College. rev. ed. 2011. (IDentity Ser.). (ENG.). 32p. (C). pap. 13.33 ***(978-0-13-282574-0(0)***, Prentice Hall) Prentice Hall PTR.

—Now You're Thinking about Your Career. rev. ed. 2011. (IDentity Ser.). (ENG.). 32p. (C). pap. 13.33 ***(978-0-13-281967-1(8)***, Prentice Hall) Prentice Hall PTR.

Chen, Charles P. & Lee, Wendy. Ethnicity & Careers of Chinese-Canadian Young Adults. 2012. pap. ***(978-1-61324-268-1(9))*** Nova Science Pubs., Inc.

Childress Consulting. 4-Square Human Development System: A Comprehensive Process for Human Behavior & Performance Development. 2007. (ENG.). 148p. per. 13.95 *(978-1-58736-728-1(9))* Wheatmark.

Chua, Rogelio Saldo. Jumpstart. 2011. 134p. 29.99 ***(978-1-4568-6690-7(7))***; pap. 19.99 ***(978-1-4568-6689-1(3))*** Xlibris Corp.

Ciletti, Dorene. Marketing Yourself. 2nd ed. 2010. (Bpa Ser.). (ENG., Illus.). 368p. (C). 94.95 *(978-0-538-45011-9(8))* Cengage South-Western.

Clancy, Teri, et al. A Taste for Work. 2010. (ENG.). 187p. pap. 14.95 *(978-0-557-08554-5(3))* Lulu Enterprises Inc.

Clark, Timothy, et al. Business Model You: A One-Page Method for Reinventing Your Career. 2012. (ENG.). 264p. pap. 27.95 ***(978-1-118-15631-5(5)***, Wiley) Wiley, John & Sons, Inc.

Clark, Tom. Career Strategies. rev. ed. 2010. (ENG.). 170p. pap. 88.37 *(978-0-7575-7987-5(6))* Kendall Hunt Publishing Co.

Coleman, Harvey J. Empowering Yourself: The Organizational Game Revealed. 2010. (ENG.). 216p. pap. 33.00 *(978-1-4490-8034-1(0))* AuthorHouse.

Coleman, Harvey J. Empowering Yourself: The Organizational Game Revieled. 2010. (Illus.). x, 202p. ***(978-1-4490-8036-5(7))*** AuthorHouse.

College Board Editors. Book of Majors 2012: The Only Book That Describes Majors in Depth & Lists the Colleges That Offer Them. 2011. (ENG.). 1300p. pap. 26.99 *(978-0-87447-968-3(1))* College Board, The.

Collin, Audrey & Patton, Wendy, eds. Vocational Psychological & Organisational Perspectives on Career. 2009. 264p. *(978-90-8790-916-1(0))*; pap. *(978-90-8790-915-4(2))* Sense Pubs.

Columbus, Gene & Goldblatt, Joe. The Complete Guide to Careers in Special Events. 2010. (ENG., Illus.). 240p. pap. 42.95 *(978-0-470-46325-3(2)*, Wiley) Wiley, John & Sons, Inc.

Combs, Patrick. Major in Success: Make College Easier, Fire up Your Dreams, & Get a Great Job. 5th rev. ed. 2007. (ENG., Illus.). 208p. pap. 14.99 *(978-1-58008-865-7(1))* Ten Speed Pr.

Conklin, Linda. Career Coach - Getting the Right Job Right Now! 2008. 108p. pap. 19.98 *(978-0-615-23664-3(2))* Conklin, Linda.

Conklin, Wendy. Applying Differentiation Strategies Professional Development DVD. 2008. (Applying Differentiation Strategies Ser.). (gr. k-12). pap. 199.99 *(978-1-4258-0079-6(3))* Teacher Created Materials, Inc.

Connor, Elizabeth. An Introduction to Staff Development in Academic Libraries. 2009. (ENG., Illus.). 248p. 132.00 *(978-0-7890-3844-9(7))*; pap. 41.95 *(978-0-7890-3845-6(5))* Routledge.

Consumer Dummies Staff. Thriving in the Workplace All-in-One for Dummies. 2010. (ENG., Illus.). 696p. pap. 29.99 *(978-0-470-57525-3(5)*, For Dummies) Wiley, John & Sons, Inc.

Coombe, Christine, et al, eds. Reigniting, Retooling, & Retiring in English Language Teaching. 2012. (ENG.). 208p. (C). pap. 30.95 ***(978-0-472-03386-7(7))*** Univ. of Michigan Pr.

Corey, Gerald. Creating Your Professional Path: Lessons from My Journey. 2010. *(978-1-55620-309-1(8))* American Counseling Assn.

Cortini, Michela, et al, eds. Boundaryless Careers & Occupational Wellbeing. 2011. (ENG & ITA., Illus.). 288p. 100.00 *(978-0-230-23660-8(X))* Palgrave Macmillan.

Couper, David. Outsiders on the Inside: How to Create a Winning Career... Even When You Don't Fit In! 2010. (ENG., Illus.). 1p. pap. 15.99 *(978-1-60163-127-5(8))* Career Pr., Inc.

Covey, Stephen R. & Colosimo, Jennifer. Great Work, Great Career: How to Create Your Ultimate Job & Make an Extraordinary Contribution. 2009. (Illus.). 162p. *(978-1-936111-10-7(1))* Franklin Covey Co.

Cox Aka: Bigg, Randy. Selling Made Simple. 2008. 64p. pap. 16.99 *(978-1-4389-1119-9(X))* AuthorHouse.

Coyle, John. Outside the Nutshell: Success vs Completion. 2011. (Illus.). 152p. pap. 14.88 *(978-1-4520-4471-2(6))* AuthorHouse.

Craig, Randall M. Personal Balance Sheet: A Practical Career Planning Guide. 2007. (Illus.). 220p. *(978-0-9735404-3-7(5))* Knowledge to Action Pr.

Cram101 Textbook Reviews. Outlines & Highlights for Applying Career Development Theory to Counseling by Richard Sharf, Isbn: 9780495804703. 2011. 108p. pap. 28.95 ***(978-1-4288-2665-6(3))*** Cram101 Inc.

—Outlines & Highlights for Career Development & Planning: A Comprehensive Approach by Robert C. Reardon. 2011. 140p. pap. 28.95 ***(978-1-61905-202-4(4))*** Cram101 Inc.

—Outlines & Highlights for Career Development Interventions in the 21st Century by Spencer G Niles. 2011. 146p. pap. 29.95 ***(978-1-61905-186-7(9))*** Cram101 Inc.

Cram101 Textbook Reviews Staff. Outlines & Highlights for from Day: Success Secrets for Starting You Career by White, ISBN. 2009. 58p. pap. 26.95 *(978-1-4288-3857-4(0))* 2008. 64p. pap. 9.95 *(978-1-4288-6398-9(2))* Cram101 Inc.

—Outlines & Highlights for Human Resource Development by Werner, Isbn: 0324578741. 2008. 108p. pap. 11.95 *(978-1-4288-6275-3(7))* Cram101 Inc.

—Outlines & Highlights for Mobilizing Minds: Creating Wealth from Talent in the 21st Century Organization by Bryan, ISBN. 2008. 72p. pap. 10.95 *(978-1-4288-6566-2(7))* Cram101 Inc.

—Outlines & Highlights for Your Career: How to Make it Happen by Julie Levitt, ISBN. 2009. 58p. pap. 26.95 *(978-1-4288-2959-6(8))*; 66p. pap. 27.95 *(978-1-4288-7970-6(6))* Cram101 Inc.

Cromack, William & Young, Matt. Hire Me! 2006. (Illus.). 125p. per. 15.95 *(978-1-932226-53-9(2))* Wizard Academy Pr.

C

Cross, Andy. Talent Management Pocketbook. 2007. (Illus.). 112p. pap. 12.95 *(978-1-903776-47-6(3))* Management Pocketbooks GBR. Dist: Ware-Pak, Inc.

Cutshaw, Oliver. Recovery, Reframing, & Renewal: Surviving an Information Science Career Crisis in a Time of Change. 2011. 168p. 75.00 *(978-1-84334-632-6(X)*, Chandos Publishing) Woodhead Publishing Ltd. GBR. Dist: Neal-Schuman Pubs., Inc.

Dabbah, Mariela & Poire, Arturo. The Latino Advantage in the Workplace: Use Who You Are to Get Where You Want to Be. 2006. (ENG.). 224p. per. 17.95 *(978-1-57248-569-3(8)*, Sphinx Publishing) Sourcebooks, Inc.

D'Alessandro, David F. Career Warfare: 10 Rules for Building a Sucessful Personal Brand on the Business Battlefield. 2nd ed. 2008. (ENG.). 240p. pap. 16.95 *(978-0-07-159729-6(8)*, 0071597298) McGraw-Hill Cos., The.

Dalton, Kevin. Leadership & Management Development: Developing Tomorrow's Managers. 2010. (ENG., Illus.). 520p. pap. *(978-0-273-70470-6(2))* Prentice Hall PTR.

Dalton, Steve. The 2-Hour Job Search: Using Technology to Get the Right Job Faster. 2012. (ENG., Illus.). 240p. pap. 12.99 ***(978-1-60774-170-1(9))*** Ten Speed Pr.

Darling, Diane. The Networking Survival Guide: Practical Advice to Help You Gain Confidence, Approach People, & Get the Success You Want. 2nd ed. 2010. (ENG.). 288p. pap. 16.95 *(978-0-07-171758-8(7)*, 0071717587) McGraw-Hill Cos., The.

Dashwood-Quick, Wendy. Discover Yourself on the Yellow Brick Road: 7 Core Principles of Career Success. 2009. (Illus.). 192p. pap. *(978-1-905430-59-8(0))* Lean Marketing Pr.

Davies, Philippa. Irresistibility: Secrets of Selling Yourself. 224p. pap. 22.95 *(978-0-340-75156-5(8)*, Hodder & Stoughton) Hodder General Publishing Div. GBR. Dist: Trafalgar Square Publishing.

Davis-Ali, Susan. How to Become Successful Without Becoming a Man. 2009. 300p. 24.99 *(978-1-4363-9215-0(2))*; pap. 17.99 *(978-1-4363-9214-3(4))* Xlibris Corp.

Day-MacLeod, Deirdre. Career Building Through Blogging. 2009. (Digital Career Building Ser.). 64p. (gr. 6-6). 58.50 *(978-1-61512-163-2(3))* Rosen Publishing Group, Inc., The.

De La Rosa, Bianca. Empower Yourself for an Amazing Career. 2011. 160p. 30.95 ***(978-1-4525-3797-9(6))***; pap. 13.95 ***(978-1-4525-3757-3(7))*** Balboa Pr.

Deems, Richard & Deems, Terri A. Make Job Loss Work for You: Get over It & Get Your Career Back on Track. 2009. 208p. pap. 12.95 *(978-1-59357-740-7(0)*, JIST Works) JIST Publishing.

Deign, Jason & Potts, Keith. Why Should I Work for You? How to Turn the Tables on the World of Work. 2010. (ENG., Illus.). 195p. pap. 22.00 *(978-1-84528-347-6(3))* How To Books GBR. Dist: Parkwest Pubns., Inc.

Deitche, Scott M. Green Collar Jobs: Environmental Careers for the 21st Century, 1 vol. 2010. (Illus.). 170p. 34.95 *(978-0-313-38014-3(7)*, A2053C, Praeger Pubs.) Greenwood Publishing Group, Inc.

Dennen, Vanessa L. & Myers, Jennifer B. Virtual Professional Development & Informal Learning Via Social Networks. 2012. ***(978-1-4666-1817-6(5))*** IGI Global.

Dennen, Vanessa P. & Myers, Jennifer B., eds. Virtual Professional Development & Informal Learning via Social Networks. 2012. 311p. 175.00 ***(978-1-4666-1815-2(9)***, Information Science Reference) IGI Global.

Desimone and We, Harris. Human Resource Development. 2006. pap. 12.95 *(978-1-4288-0784-6(5))* Cram101 Inc.

Dibinga, Muadi Bijimba. Put Your Shoes On! A Step-by-step Guide for Young People Entering the Workforce. 2007. (YA). per. 19.95 *(978-0-9760056-2-9(X))* Free Your Mind Publishing.

Dickmann. Global Careers. 2010. (Global HRM Ser.). (ENG., Illus.). 352p. (C). pap. 49.95 *(978-0-415-44628-0(7))* Routledge.

Digiovanni, Mark. 6,000,000 Minutes on the Clock: Discovering the What, Where & Why of Your Ideal Career. 2008. 144p. pap. 14.95 *(978-0-595-51900-2(8))* iUniverse, Inc.

Direct, Animal Jobs. Working with Animals. 2010. 198p. pap. 27.50 *(978-1-4452-3890-6(X))* Lulu Enterprises Inc.

DiSesa, Nina. Seducing the Boys Club: Uncensored Tactics from a Woman at the Top. 2008. (ENG.). 256p. pap. 16.00 *(978-0-345-49699-7(X)*, Ballantine Bks.) Random House Publishing Group.

Dixson, Kirsten & Arruda, William. Career Distinction: Stand Out by Building Your Brand. 2007. (ENG., Illus.). 224p. 22.95 *(978-0-470-12818-3(6)*, Wiley) Wiley, John & Sons, Inc.

Donald Ford. How to Control Your Career for Life: Helpful Techniques for Getting, Keeping, & Changing Employment Opportunities. 2010. 156p. 24.95 *(978-1-4401-8274-7(4))*; pap. 14.95 *(978-1-4401-8272-3(8))* iUniverse, Inc.

Donner, Gail J. & Wheeler, Mary M. Taking Control of Your Career: A Handbook for Health Professionals. 2008. (ENG.). 144p. (C). pap. 31.95 *(978-1-897422-16-8(4)*, Mosby) Elsevier - Health Sciences Div.

Donovan, Georgie L. & Figueroa, Miguel A. Staff Development Strategies That Work! Stories & Strategies from New Librarians. 2008. 230p. 75.00 *(978-1-55570-644-9(4))* Neal-Schuman Pubs., Inc.

Dorio, Marc. The Complete Idiot's Guide to Career Advancement. 2009. (Complete Idiot's Guide Ser.). (ENG.). 336p. (gr. 12-18). 18.95 *(978-1-59257-832-0(2)*, Alpha Bks.) Penguin Group (USA) Inc.

Doris Sims, Sphr. The 30-Minute Guide to Talent & Succession Management: A Quick Reference Guide for Business Leaders. 2009. 40p. pap. 22.95 *(978-1-4389-5571-1(5))* AuthorHouse.

Doty, Elizabeth J. The Compromise Trap: How to Thrive at Work Without Selling Your Soul. 2009. (ENG.). 216p. pap. 17.95 *(978-1-57675-576-1(2))* Berrett-Koehler Pubs., Inc.

Douglas, Max E., et al. The Ultimate Book of Perfect Phrases for Job Seekers. 2008. (Perfect Phrases Ser.). (ENG.). 544p. pap. 19.95 *(978-0-07-148566-1(X)*, 007148566X) McGraw-Hill Cos., The.

Draper, Robert E. The Other Side of Success: ... & all its empty Promises. 2009. 224p. 29.95 *(978-0-595-51571-4(1))*; pap. 19.95 *(978-0-595-52735-9(3))* iUniverse, Inc.

Driskill, Edie Milligan. Pink Slipped: A Post-Layoff Survival Guide. 2009. (ENG.). 288p. (gr. 12-18). 15.00 *(978-1-59257-962-4(0)*, Alpha Bks.) Penguin Group (USA) Inc.

Drucker, Peter F. Managing Oneself. 2007. (Harvard Business Review Classics: Ser.). (ENG.). 72p. per. 8.95 *(978-1-4221-2312-6(X))* Harvard Business Review Pr.

DuBrin, Andrew J. Impression Management in the Workplace. 2010. (ENG., Illus.). 256p. 120.00 *(978-0-415-87173-0(5)*, Routledge) Taylor & Francis Group GBR. Dist: Taylor & Francis Group.

—Impression Management in the Workplace: Research, Theory, & Practice. 2010. (ENG., Illus.). 256p. 59.95 *(978-0-415-87174-7(3)*, Routledge) Taylor & Francis Group GBR. Dist: Taylor & Francis Group.

Duggan, Molly H. & Jurgens, Jill C. Career Interventions & Techniques: A Complete Guide for Human Service Professionals. 2006. (Interventions that Work Ser.). (ENG., Illus.). 512p. (C). per. 107.80 *(978-0-205-45238-5(8))* Allyn & Bacon, Inc.

Dunning, Donna. 10 Career Essentials: Using Your Personality Type to Excel at Work. 2010. (ENG.). 224p. pap. 19.95 *(978-1-85788-542-2(2))* Ebsco Publishing.

Eaton, John. Life Is Now! - How to Make it Happen: An Autobiography by John Eaton a Simple Countryboy Makes Good. 2011. 252p. pap. 68.17 *(978-1-4520-8683-5(4))* AuthorHouse.

Eberts, Marjorie & Gisler, Margaret. Careers for Bookworms & Other Literary Types. 4th ed. 2008. (ENG.). 176p. pap. 14.95 *(978-0-07-154539-6(5)*, 0071545395) McGraw-Hill Cos., The.

Eccles, Simon & Sanders, Stephanie, eds. So you want to be a brain Surgeon? 3rd ed. 2009. (ENG., Illus.). 320p. pap. 35.00 *(978-0-19-923196-6(6))* Oxford Univ. Pr., Inc.

Edds, Carol A. How to Market Career Development Programs & Services. 2008. *(978-1-885333-23-0(4))* National Career Development Assn.

Eikenberry, Kevin. Championing Change: Creating Remarkable Leaders. 2010. (ENG.). 32p. pap., wbk. ed. 15.00 *(978-0-470-50183-2(9)*, Pfeiffer) Wiley, John & Sons, Inc.

Eisenberg, Mark J. The Physician-Scientist's Career Guide. 2010. (ENG., Illus.). xxiii, 272p. pap. 29.95 *(978-1-60327-907-9(5)*, 1603279075) Humana Pr.

Elefant, Carolyn. Solo by Choice: How to Be the Lawyer You Always Wanted to Be. 2007. pap. *(978-0-940675-58-2(7)*, DecisionBooks) LawyerAvenue Pr.

Eliason, Grafton & Patrick, John. Career Development in the Schools. 2008. *(978-1-59311-534-0(2))*; pap. *(978-1-59311-533-3(4))* Information Age Publishing, Inc.

Ellig, Janice Reals. Driving the Career Highway, 0 vols. 2009. 288p. pap. 13.99 *(978-1-59555-278-5(2))* Nelson, Thomas Inc.

Elsdon, Ron, ed. Building Workforce Strength: Creating Value through Workforce & Career Development, 1 vol. 2010. 234p. 44.95 *(978-0-313-37926-0(2)*, C37926, Praeger Pubs.) Greenwood Publishing Group, Inc.

Empson, Lila. 100 Answers to 100 Questions Every Graduate Should Know. 2009. (ENG.). 224p. pap. 10.99 *(978-1-59979-479-2(9))* Charisma Media.

Epstein, Susan & Lenz, Janet G. Developing & Managing Career Resources. 2008. pap. *(978-1-885333-19-3(6))* National Career Development Assn.

Erickson, Tamara J. Plugged In: The Generation Y Guide to Thriving at Work. 2008. (ENG., Illus.). 278p. 16.95 *(978-1-4221-2060-6(0))* Harvard Business Review Pr.

—What's Next, Gen X? Keeping up, Moving Ahead, & Getting the Career You Want. 2009. (ENG., Illus.). 224p. 19.95 *(978-1-4221-2064-4(3))* Harvard Business Review Pr.

Evans, Vaughan. Backing You, MBA! How Thinking of Yourself as a Business Can Advance or Transform Your Career. 2011. (Illus.). 400p. pap. 19.95 ***(978-0-9561391-2-2(4))*** Business & Careers Pr GBR. Dist: AtlasBooks Distribution.

Evarts, Jeff. Making Good Money in A Bad Economy: 35 Self-Employed Options. 2011. 168p. pap. 15.95 ***(978-1-4620-1592-4(1))*** iUniverse, Inc.

Facts on File, Inc. Staff. Career Skills Library: Problem Solving, Third Edition. 3rd rev. ed. 2009. (Career Skills Library). (Illus.). 192p. (gr. 6-12). 25.95 *(978-0-8160-7773-1(8)*, Ferguson Publishing Co.) Facts On File, Inc.

Faimon, Peg. The Designer's Guide to Business & Careers: How to Succeed on the Job or on Your Own. 2009. (ENG., Illus.). 320p. pap. 19.99 *(978-1-60061-156-8(7)*, HOW Bks.) F&W Media, Inc.

Farol, Alexander V. Career Combat: A Field Manual for Winning & Advancing in the American Work Place. Hampson, Glenn C., ed. 98p. 15.00 *(978-0-9653869-5-1(3))* Castle Pacific Publishing.

Farr, Michael & Shatkin, Laurenc. Best Jobs for the 21st Century Fifth Edition. 5th ed. 2008. 704p. pap. 19.95 *(978-1-59357-536-6(X)*, JIST Works) JIST Publishing.

Ferguson, et al. The Hero's Journey: An Introspective & Critical Thinking Approach to Life/Career Planning. 3rd rev. ed. 2011. (ENG.). 246p. pap. 60.95 *(978-0-7575-7909-7(4))* Kendall Hunt Publishing Co.

Ferguson-Nanos. The Hero's Journey: An Introspective & Critical Thinking Approach to Life/Career Planning. 3rd rev. ed. 2011. (ENG.). 246p. pap. 61.00 ***(978-0-7575-9567-7(7))*** Kendall Hunt Publishing Co.

Fernando, Rashika. 101 Secrets to Career Success. 2010. (ENG.). 208p. pap. 12.99 *(978-1-4354-5722-5(6))* Course Technology.

Ferrett, Sharon. Peak Performance: Success in College & Beyond. 6th rev. ed. 2006. 552p. (C). pap. 61.00 *(978-0-07-312549-7(0)*, 9780073125497, McGraw-Hill Humanities, Social Sciences & World Languages) McGraw-Hill Higher Education.

Ferrett, Sharon & Ferrett, Sharon K. Peak Performance: Success in College & Beyond. 7th ed. 2009. (ENG., Illus.). 568p. (C). pap. 80.00 *(978-0-07-337512-0(8)*, 0073375128) McGraw-Hill Higher Education.

Ferrett, Sharon K. Peak Performance: Success in College & Beyond. (Illus.). 5th ed. 2009. (ENG.). pap., pap. 86.50 *(978-0-07-329386-8(5))* 7th ed. 2010. xxxvii, 530p. pap. *(978-0-07-722771-5(9))* 8th ed. 2012. xxxii, 493p. *(978-0-07-747154-5(7))* McGraw-Hill Cos., The.

—Peak Performance: Success in College & Beyond. 8th ed. 2011. (ENG., Illus.). 528p. (C). pap. 80.00 *(978-0-07-337519-9(5)*, 0073375195) McGraw-Hill Higher Education.

Fetzer, John. Career Management for Chemists: A Guide to Success in a Chemistry Career. 2010. (ENG., Illus.). xi, 266p. pap. 69.95 *(978-3-642-05886-8(8)*, 3642058868) Springer.

Ficco, Mike. What Every Engineer Should Know about Career Management. 2008. (What Every Engineer Should Know Ser.). (ENG., Illus.). 264p. 54.95 *(978-1-4200-7682-0(5)*, CRC Press) Taylor & Francis Group GBR. Dist: Taylor & Francis Group.

Fields, Jonathan. Career Renegade: How to Make a Great Living Doing What You Love. 2009. (ENG.). 288p. pap. 14.00 *(978-0-7679-2741-3(9))* Broadway Bks.

Fifty Lessons Management Collection Staff, compiled by. Loving Your Work. 2010. (Lessons Learned: Ser.). (ENG.). 112p. pap. 9.95 *(978-1-4221-3986-8(7))* Harvard Business Review Pr.

Fifty Lessons Staff, compiled by. Managing Your Career. 2007. (Lessons Learned: Ser.). (ENG.). 112p. per. 9.95 *(978-1-4221-1861-0(4))* Harvard Business Review Pr.

Finney, Martha I. Rebound: A Proven Plan for Starting over after Job Loss. 2009. (ENG.). 208p. pap. 17.99 *(978-0-13-702114-7(3))* FT Press.

Fireside, Bryna J. Choices for the High School Graduate. 5th rev. ed. 2009. 280p. pap. 16.95 *(978-0-8160-7618-5(9)*, Checkmark Bks.) Facts On File, Inc.

Firkola, Peter. Working for the Kaish. 2010. 112p. pap. *(978-3-639-10561-2(3))* VDM Verlag Dr. Mueller e.K.

Fitzpatrick, Corine & Costantini, Kathleen. Counseling 21St Century Students for Optimal College & Career R. 2011. (ENG., Illus.). 254p. pap. 29.95 *(978-0-415-87612-4(5))* Routledge.

Fletcher, Molly & Kincaid, Steve. Your Dream Job Game Plan: Five Tools for Becoming Your Own Career Agent. 2008. (ENG.). 208p. 14.95 *(978-1-59357-612-7(9)*, JIST Works) JIST Publishing.

Flores, Lorenzo G. Executive Career Advancement: How to Understand the Politics of Promotion the X Factor. 2009. 320p. pap. 18.25 *(978-1-4208-0755-4(2))* AuthorHouse.

Fogarty, Robin. From Staff Room to Classroom: A Guide for Planning & Coaching Professional Development. Pete, Brian M., ed. 2006. (Illus.). 176p. 62.95 *(978-1-4129-2603-4(3)*, B26033C) Corwin Pr.

Fogarty, Robin J. & Pete, Brian M., eds. From Staff Room to Classroom II: The One-Minute Professional Development Planner. 2009. (Illus.). 200p. pap. 34.95 *(978-1-4129-7499-8(2)*, B74998P) Corwin Pr.

Fogel, Peter. Reboot Your Career: 27 Ways to Invent Yourself in the Workplace (If You STILL Have a Job!) 2011. 224p. pap. *(978-0-88391-195-2(7))* Fell, Frederick Pubs., Inc.

Forsyth, Patrick. Detox Your Career: 10 Steps to Revitalizing Your Job & Career. 2007. (Career Makers Ser.). (ENG.). 190p. pap. 19.95 *(978-1-904879-51-0(9))* Cyan Communications GBR. Dist: Independent Pubs. Group.

—Disaster Proof Your Career: Tactics to Survive, Thrive & Keep Ahead in the Workplace. 2010. (ENG.). 160p. pap. 17.95 *(978-0-7494-5954-3(9))* Kogan Page, Ltd. GBR. Dist: Ingram Pub. Services.

—Manage Your Boss: 10 Steps to Creating the Ideal Working Relationship. 2007. (Career Makers Ser.). (ENG.). 173p. per. 19.95 *(978-1-904879-53-4(5))* Cyan Communications GBR. Dist: Independent Pubs. Group.

Fowler, Chad. The Passionate Programmer: Creating a Remarkable Career in Software Development. 2009. (Pragmatic Life Ser.). (ENG.). 200p. pap. 23.95 *(978-1-934356-34-0(4)*, Pragmatic Bookshelf, The) Pragmatic Programmers, LLC, The.

Fox, Jeffrey J. How to Get to the Top: Business Lessons Learned at the Dinner Table. 2007. (Fox Business Library). 224p. 17.95 *(978-1-4013-0330-3(7))* Hyperion Pr.

Fralick & Fralick, Marsha. College & Career Success. 4th rev. ed. 2009. (ENG.). pap. 75.41 *(978-0-7575-5216-8(1))* Kendall Hunt Publishing Co.

Frederick, Sue. I See Your Dream Job: A Career Intuitive Shows You How to Discover What You Were Put on Earth to Do. 2009. (ENG.). 272p. 19.99 *(978-0-312-55420-0(6))* St. Martin's Pr.

Freemantle, David. Wanted: How to Become the Most Wanted Employee Around. 2010. (ENG., Illus.). 232p. (C). pap. 19.99 *(978-0-273-72491-9(6))* FT Press.

Friedman, Andrew. Continuing Professional Development. (Illus.). 288p. (C). 2012. pap. 63.95 *(978-0-415-67925-1(7))* 2011. (ENG., 135.00 *(978-0-415-67791-2(2))* Routledge.

Fry, Ron. 101 Great Resumes. 3rd ed. 2009. (ENG.). 224p. pap. 12.99 *(978-1-59863-855-4(6))* Course Technology.

Gamage, David. Professional Development for Leaders & Managers of Self-Governing Schools. 2006. (ENG.). xvi, 306p. 219.00 *(978-1-4020-4928-6(5)*, 1402049285) Springer.

Garber, Peter R. Winning the Rat Race at Work. 2006. (Illus.). 184p. per. 29.95 *(978-1-895186-68-0(4))* Multi-Media Pubns., Inc. CAN. Dist: Ingram Pub. Services.

Gardner, Garth. Gardner's Guide to Pitching & Selling Animation. 2010. (Gardner's Guide Ser.). (ENG.). 275p. pap. 34.95 *(978-1-58965-057-2(3))* Gardner, Garth Co., Inc. (GGC).

Garfinkle, Joel A. Getting Ahead: Three Steps to Take Your Career to the Next Level. 2011. (ENG.). 271p. 24.95 *(978-0-470-91587-5(0)*, Wiley) Wiley, John & Sons, Inc.

Garner, Randy & Willis, Ethan. Prosper: Create the Life You Really Want. 2011. (ENG.). 168p. pap. 15.95 *(978-1-60994-070-6(9))* Berrett-Koehler Pubs., Inc.

Garton, Jeffrey. Career Contentment: Don't Settle for Anything Less! 2008. (ENG.). 250p. per. 22.95 *(978-1-56286-506-1(4))* American Society for Training & Development.

Geary, Gail. Your Next Career: Do What You've Always Wanted to Do. 2nd ed. 2009. (ENG.). 240p. pap. 14.95 *(978-1-59357-671-4(4)*, JIST Works) JIST Publishing.

Gelardin, Sally D. Starting & Growing a Business in the Global Marketplace: Career Entrepreneurs Share Stories & Strategies. 2006. pap. *(978-1-885333-16-2(1))* National Career Development Assn.

George Ojie-Ahamiojie. Upward Mobility: Interviewing, Career Management, & Managing my Manager & Taking His Job! 2009. 104p. pap. 12.99 *(978-1-4389-4738-9(0))* AuthorHouse.

Gerdes, Lindsey. The Best Places to Launch a Career. 2008. (ENG.). 330p. (C). pap. 18.95 *(978-0-07-149655-1(6)*, 0071496556) McGraw-Hill Cos., The.

Gershberg, Ilene L. Fit & Powerful Professionals ~ Smart Focus, Food & Fitness Strategies. McCabe, Denise, ed. 2007. 212p. per. 19.95 *(978-0-9789205-0-0(3))* Ilene on Health, LLC.

Gisler, Margaret. Careers for Hard Hats & Other Construction Types, 2nd Ed. 2nd ed. 2008. (ENG.). 160p. pap. 16.95 *(978-0-07-154538-9(7)*, 0071545387) McGraw-Hill Cos., The.

Gitman, Lawrence J. & McDaniel, Carl. The Future of Business: The Essentials. 4th ed. 2008. (ENG.). 528p. (C). pap. 132.95 *(978-0-324-59076-0(8))* Cengage South-Western.

Globe-Fearon Staff. Getting a Job & Keeping It. pap., instr.'s gde. ed. 5.50 *(978-0-8359-0697-5(3))* Globe Fearon Educational Publishing.

Glube, Nancy E. & Hartman, Phyllis G. Never Get Lost Again: Navigating Your HR Career. 2009. (ENG.). 224p. pap. 27.95 *(978-1-58644-136-4(1))* Society for Human Resource Management.

Goetchius, Alex. Career Building Through Social Networking. 2007. (Digital Career Building Ser.). (Illus.). 64p. (YA). (gr. 7-12). lib. bdg. 29.25 *(978-1-4042-1943-4(9))* Rosen Publishing Group, Inc., The.

Goetsch, David. Building a Winning Career in Business, 25 Proven St. 2007. 200p. pap. 33.33 *(978-0-13-119015-3(6)*, Prentice Hall) Prentice Hall PTR.

Goldfarb, Robert. What's Stopping Me from Getting Ahead? What Your Manager Won't Tell You about What It Really Takes to Be Successful. 2010. (ENG.). 208p. pap. 18.95 *(978-0-07-174126-2(7)*, 0071741267) McGraw-Hill Cos., The.

Goodman, Michelle. The Anti 9 to 5 Guide: Practical Career Advice for Women Who Think Outside the Cube. 2007. (ENG.). 240p. per. 14.95 *(978-1-58005-186-6(3))* Seal Pr.

—My So-Called Freelance Life: How to Survive & Thrive as a Creative Professional for Hire. 2008. (ENG.). 240p. pap. 15.95 *(978-1-58005-259-7(2))* Seal Pr.

Gore, Paul A. & Carter, Louisa P. Students in Transition: Research & Practice in Career Development. 2011. *(978-1-889271-73-6(X))* National Resource Ctr. for The First Year Experience & Students in Transition.

Govindan, Ramu. Reflections on Career Planning. 2010. 129p. pap. 10.95 *(978-0-557-31428-7(3))* Lulu Enterprises Inc.

Graber, Geoff. All In: Poker Night Lessons for Winning Big at Your Career. 2006. (Illus.). 224p. pap. 13.95 *(978-0-06-113944-4(0)*, ReganBooks) HarperCollins Pubs.

Grace, Corina. Take Charge of Your Career... & Find a Job You Really Love! The Essential Resource Pack for Career Planning. 2010. (ENG.). 250p. pap. 31.95 *(978-1-905785-33-9(X))* Liffey Pr., The IRL. Dist: Dufour Editions, Inc.

Graen, George. Jessica's Web: Womens Advantages in the Knowledge Era (PB) 2007. 280p. per. 39.99 *(978-1-59311-655-6(4))* Information Age Publishing, Inc.

Graham, Bridget & Reidy, Monique. Working World 101: The New Grad's Guide to Getting a Job. 2009. (ENG.). 256p. pap. 13.95 *(978-1-59869-495-6(2))* Adams Media Corp.

Green, Gordon W. Making Your Education Work for You: A Proven System for Success in School & for Getting the Job of Your Dreams. 2010. (ENG.). 304p. 26.99 *(978-0-7653-1952-4(7)*, Forge Bks.) Doherty, Tom Assocs., LLC.

Green, Gordon W., Jr. Making Your Education Work for You: A Proven System for Success in School & for Getting the Job of Your Dreams. 2010. (ENG.). 304p. pap. 12.99 *(978-0-7653-1953-1(5)*, Forge Bks.) Doherty, Tom Assocs., LLC.

Greene, Jake. Whoa, My Boss Is Naked... A Career Book for People Who Would Never Be Caught Dead Reading a Career Book. 2008. (ENG.). 240p. pap.

12.95 *(978-0-385-52337-0(8)*, Broadway Business) Knopf Doubleday Publishing Group.

Grill, Johannes. Die strategische Bedeutung des Human Capital und seine Bewertung: Ein Bezugsrahmen zur Evaluation ambitionierter mittlerer Unternehmen. 2008. (Bildung und Organisation Ser.). 436p. pap. 99.95 *(978-3-631-57519-2(X))* Lang, Peter GmbH, Europaischer Verlag der Wissenschaften DEU. Dist: Lang, Peter.

Grinbaum, Andrew. Cha Ching! 2010. 184p. pap. 24.95 *(978-0-557-61321-2(3))* Lulu Enterprises Inc.

Grogan, Miriam Bamberger & Bradley, Heather. Judge for Yourself: Clarity, Choice, & Action in Your Legal Career. 2007. (ENG., Illus.). 100p. per. 24.95 *(978-1-59031-599-6(5))* American Bar Assn.

Grose, Ray. How to Sell Yourself. 2010. (Sunday Times Creating Success Ser.). (ENG.). 144p. pap. 14.95 *(978-0-7494-5638-2(8))* Kogan Page, Ltd. GBR. Dist: Ingram Pub. Services.

Growing Professionals. 20.00 *(978-0-9718958-0-5(5))* Singleton, Gloria E.

Gubbin, Dianne & Ashman, Joann W. Powerladder: Network Your Way to Career Success: A Women's Fast Track Guide. 2008. (ENG.). pap. 13.99 *(978-1-59932-054-0(1))* Advantage Media Group.

Gunn, Eileen. Your Career Is an Extreme Sport: Focus. Drive. Excel. 2006. (ENG., Illus.). 192p. per. 14.95 *(978-1-59337-611-6(1))* Adams Media Corp.

Gunn, Robert W. & Gullickson, Betsy Raskin. On the High Wire: How to Survive Being Promoted, 1 vol. 2008. (Illus.). 184p. pap. 19.95 *(978-0-313-35155-6(4)*, B35155, Praeger Trade) Greenwood Publishing Group, Inc.

Gunz, Hugh & Peiperl, Maury, eds. Handbook of Career Studies. 2007. (Illus.). 648p. 150.00 *(978-0-7619-3039-6(6)*, B30396C) SAGE Pubns., Inc.

Gurney, Darrell. Never Apply for a Job Again! Break the Rules, Cut the Line, Beat the Rest. 2012. (ENG.). 1p. pap. 14.99 *(978-1-60163-202-9(9))* Career Pr., Inc.

Gurney, Darrell W. Never Apply for a Job Again! Break the Rules, Cut the Line, Beat the Rest. 2012. E-Book ***(978-1-60163-625-6(3))*** Career Pr., Inc.

Gustafsson, Siv & Kalwij, Adriaan, eds. Education & Postponement of Maternity: Economic Analyses for Industrialized Countries. 2010. (European Studies of Population Ser.). xii, 325p. pap. 249.00 *(978-90-481-7177-4(6)*, 9048171776) Springer.

Gutmann, Joanna & Grose, Ray. How to Sell Yourself. 2nd ed. 2010. (Creating Success Ser.). (ENG.). 144p. pap. 14.95 *(978-0-7494-6031-0(8))* Kogan Page, Ltd. GBR. Dist: Ingram Pub. Services.

Hager, Jodene "Dene". Building an Amazing Career. 2011. 256p. pap. 19.95 ***(978-1-935586-34-0(3))*** Aviva Publishing.

Hall, Richard. The Secrets of Success at Work: 10 Steps to Accelerating Your Career. 2nd rev. ed. 2010. (ENG., Illus.). 184p. (C). pap. 24.99 ***(978-0-273-74294-4(9))*** FT Press.

Halstead, David H. Make It Happen: Create Your Career Control Your Life. 2007. (ENG., Illus.). per. 14.95 *(978-1-933596-75-4(9))* Morgan James Publishing.

—Make It Happen: Create Your Career, Control Your Life. 2007. (ENG.). 252p. 24.95 *(978-1-60037-247-6(3))* Morgan James Publishing.

Haneberg, Lisa. Middle Management Acumen. 2011. 20p. pap. 24.95 *(978-1-56286-789-8(X))* American Society for Training & Development.

Hanna, Sharon P., et al. Career by Design: Communicating Your Way to Success. 4th ed. 2007. (ENG., Illus.). 368p. (C). per. 56.60 *(978-0-13-233090-9(3)*, Prentice Hall) Prentice Hall PTR.

Hannon, Kerry. What's Next? Follow Your Passion & Find Your Dream Job. 2010. (ENG., Illus.). 216p. 22.95 *(978-0-8118-7115-0(0))* Chronicle Bks. LLC.

Hansen, Carol D. & Lee, Yih-teen, eds. The Cultural Context of Human Resource Development. 2009. (ENG., Illus.). 288p. (C). 105.00 *(978-0-230-55134-3(3))* Palgrave Macmillan.

Hansen, J. P. The Bliss List: The Ultimate Guide to Living the Dream at Work & Beyond! 2010. 240p. pap. 19.95 *(978-0-9840934-1-0(9))* Career Bliss Pubns., Inc.

Hansen, Mark D. Climbing the Corporate Ladder — Safely! 2011. *(978-1-885581-57-0(2))* American Society of Safety Engineers.

Harlan, Mary Ann. Personal Learning Networks: Professional Development for the Isolated School Librarian, 1 vol. 2009. (Illus.). 96p. pap. 30.00 *(978-1-59158-790-3(5)*, LU8790) Libraries Unlimited, Inc.

Harrington, Brad & Hall, Douglas T. Career Management & Work-Life Integration: Using Self-Assessment to Navigate Contemporary Careers. 2007. (Illus.). 248p. (C). 108.00 *(978-1-4129-5410-5(X)*, B37450C); per. 57.00 *(978-1-4129-3745-0(0)*, B37450P) SAGE Pubns., Inc.

Harris, Carla. Expect to Win: 10 Proven Strategies for Thriving in the Workplace. 2010. (ENG.). 240p. (gr. 12-18). 15.00 *(978-0-452-29590-2(4)*, Plume) Penguin Group (USA) Inc.

—Expect to Win: Proven Strategies for Success from a Wall Street Vet. 2009. (ENG.). 240p. (gr. 12-18). 24.95 *(978-1-59463-051-4(8)*, Hudson Street Pr.) Penguin Group (USA) Inc.

Harris, Quinn. The Quinn Harris Story: From Funky Blues to Good News. 2011. 272p. pap. 15.19 ***(978-1-4567-6960-4(X))*** AuthorHouse.

Hartley, Gregory & Karinch, Maryann. The Most Dangerous Business Book You'll Ever Read. 2011. (ENG., Illus.). 206p. 24.95 *(978-0-470-88802-5(4)*, Wiley) Wiley, John & Sons, Inc.

Hartman, Kathleen & Stewart, Thomas. 35 Ways to Discover a Major. 2nd ed. 2009. (ENG.). 160p. (C). pap. 23.95 *(978-0-547-19990-0(2))* Wadsworth.

Hartung, Paul J. & Subich, Linda Mezydlo. Developing Self in Work & Career: Concepts, Cases, & Contexts. 2010. (Illus.). viii, 245p. 59.95 *(978-1-4338-0861-6(7))* American Psychological Assn.

Harvard Business Review. Harvard Business Review on Advancing Your Career. 2011. (Harvard Business Review Paperback Ser.). (ENG.). 224p. pap. 22.00 *(978-1-4221-7223-0(6))* Harvard Business Review Pr.

Harvard Business School Press Staff. Managing Up: Expert Solutions to Everyday Challenges. 2008. (Pocket Mentor Ser.). (ENG.). 96p. pap. 9.95 *(978-1-4221-2277-8(8))* Harvard Business Review Pr.

Harvard Business School Publishing Corporation Staff, creator. Shaping Your Career: Expert Solutions to Everyday Challenges. 2008. (Pocket Mentor Ser.). (ENG., Illus.). 88p. per. 9.95 *(978-1-4221-1876-4(2))* Harvard Business Review Pr.

Harvey, Carolyn & Herrild, Beth. Comfortable Chaos: Forget "Balance & Make career & Family Choices That Work for You. 2010. (ENG.). 280p. mass mkt. 14.95 *(978-1-55180-604-4(5))* Self-Counsel Pr., Inc. CAN. Dist: Midpoint Trade Bks., Inc.

Harvey, Stephanie, et al. Staff Development with the Comprehension Toolkits: Implementing & Sustaining Comprehension Instruction Across the Curriculum. 2011. 192p. pap. 47.50 ***(978-0-325-02884-2(2)***, E02884, Firsthand) Heinemann.

Harwood, Tracy, et al. Study Skills for Marketing Students. 2008. 176p. (C). 102.95 *(978-0-335-22280-3(3)*, 9780335222803); pap. 34.95 *(978-0-335-22279-7(X)*, 9780335222797) McGraw-Hill Education GBR. (Open University Pr.). Dist: McGraw-Hill Cos., The.

Hawley, Casey. 10 Make-or-Break Career Moments: Navigate, Negotiate, & Communicate for Success. 2010. (ENG., Illus.). 224p. pap. 13.99 *(978-1-58008-723-0(X))* Ten Speed Pr.

Hecklinger, Fred J. & Black, Bernadette M. Training for Life: A Practical Guide to Career & Life Planning. 10th rev. ed. 2010. (ENG.). 350p. pap. 63.16 *(978-0-7575-6048-4(2))* Kendall Hunt Publishing Co.

Heffelfinger, William. Management Yang. 2009. 100p. pap. 14.95 *(978-0-557-08548-4(9))* Lulu Enterprises Inc.

Henry, Carl. 15 Hot Tips That Will Supercharge Your Sales Career. 2008. 172p. 24.95 *(978-0-9657626-6-3(1))* Henry Assocs.

Herrick, Scot. I've Landed My Dream Job — Now What??? How to Achieve Success in the First 30 Days in a New Job. 2010. 116p. pap. 19.95 *(978-1-60005-168-5(5))* Happy About.

Hershey, April. Factors Affecting the Career Path & Aspiration Level of a School Leader - Men Versus Women. 2007. 168p. per. *(978-3-8364-2787-6(7))* VDM Verlag Dr. Mueller e.K.

Heska, Linda. Enhancing the Employee Experience. 2009. 104p. pap. *(978-3-639-13816-0(3))* VDM Verlag Dr. Mueller e.K.

Hess, Peter M. Career Success: Right Here, Right Now! 2nd rev. ed. 2007. (ENG.). 336p. (C). pap. 105.95 *(978-1-4180-4927-0(1))* Delmar Cengage Learning.

Hess, Vicki. Shift to Professional Paradise: 5 Steps to Less Stress, More Energy & Remarkable Results at Work. 2008. per. 14.95 *(978-0-9798009-5-5(1))* CornerStone Leadership Institute.

Highlands: Matching Your Abilities with College & Career: the Right Choice. 2nd ed. 2006. Orig. Title: Same. (YA). per. 12.95 *(978-0-9755112-2-0(X))* Highlands Co. LLC, The.

Hilliard, Denise. Momager Notes: What You Should Know If You're Considering Managing Your Child's Talent in Preparation for A Career in Tv, Film or Broadway. 2011. 152p. pap. 18.50 ***(978-1-4634-4119-7(3))*** AuthorHouse.

Hirasaki, Parrish. Corporate Climbing: An Accurate (and Irreverent) Guide. 2009. 148p. pap. 16.95 *(978-1-59858-866-8(4))* Dog Ear Publishing, LLC.

Hirsh, Wendy & Jackson, Charles. Planning Your Career: Learn in a Week, What the Leading Experts Learn in a Lifetime. 2012. (Teach Yourself: Business Ser.). (ENG., Illus.). 128p. pap. 12.00 ***(978-1-4441-5922-6(4)***, 1444159224) McGraw-Hill Cos., The.

Hoffman, Reid & Casnocha, Ben. The Start-Up of You: Adapt to the Future, Invest in Yourself, & Transform Your Career. 2012. ***(978-0-307-88891-4(6))***; (ENG.). 272p. 26.00 ***(978-0-307-88890-7(8))*** Crown Publishing Group. (Crown Business).

Hoggan, James & Littlemore, Rich. Do the Right Thing. 2009. 176p. 19.95 *(978-1-933102-85-6(3))* Capital Bks., Inc.

Hoggan, James & Littlemore, Richard. Do the Right Thing: PR Tips for a Skeptical Public. 2009. 176p. pap. 10.00 *(978-1-933102-86-3(1))* Capital Bks., Inc.

Holland, R. William. Are There Any Good Jobs Left? Career Management in the Age of the Disposable Worker, 1 vol. 2006. (Illus.). 176p. 34.95 *(978-0-275-99044-2(3)*, C9044, Praeger Pubs.) Greenwood Publishing Group, Inc.

—Cracking the New Job Market: The 7 Rules for Getting Hired in Any Economy, 1 vol. 2011. (ENG.). 256p. pap. 17.95 *(978-0-8144-1734-8(5))* Amacom.

Holmes, Dvid. Smart Guide to the Perfect Job Interview. 2012. (Smart Guide Ser.). (ENG.). 272p. pap. 19.95 ***(978-0-9834421-6-5(9))*** Smart Guide Pubns., Inc.

Holt, Jim. The Career-Savvy College Student. 2007. 92p. per. 12.95 *(978-1-59858-307-6(7))* Dog Ear Publishing, LLC.

Hood, Beth & Hood, Jim. Test Drive Your Future, College Student Edition: 12 Simple Steps to Choosing Your Perfect Career. 2011. 148p. pap. 14.95 ***(978-0-9799262-2-8(X))*** Little Bit More Fun, Inc., A.

Hood, Darryl. Small Market. 2007. 65p. pap. 10.95 *(978-1-4357-0054-3(6))* Lulu Enterprises Inc.

Hoover, John & Gorrell, Paul J. The Coaching Connection: A Manager's Guide to Developing Individual Potential in the Context of the Organization, 1 vol. 2009. (ENG.). 272p. 29.95 *(978-0-8144-1414-9(1))* Amacom.

Horney, Mark. Organization Men. 2011. 244p. pap. ***(978-3-8443-8558-8(4))***, Lambert Academic Publishing.

Hoschette, John A. The Career Guide Book for Engineers. 2010. (ENG., Illus.). 609p. pap. 69.95 *(978-0-470-50350-8(5)*, Wiley) Wiley, John & Sons, Inc.

Huang, Catherine & Rosenberg, Arthur D. Women & the Art of War: Sun Tzu's Strategies for Winning Without Confrontation. 2012. (ENG.). 224p. 17.95 ***(978-0-8048-4254-9(X))*** Tuttle Publishing.

Hughey, Kenneth F., et al. The Handbook of Career Advising. 2009. (ENG., Illus.). 420p. 65.00 *(978-0-470-37368-2(7)*, Jossey-Bass) Wiley, John & Sons, Inc.

Hunt. Career Development for Managers. 96p. pap. *(978-0-304-33410-0(3))* Continuum International Publishing Group, Ltd.

Hunt, James M. & Weintraub, Joseph R. The Coaching Organization: A Strategy for Developing Leaders. 2006. 272p. per. 50.00 *(978-1-4129-0576-3(1)*, B05753P) SAGE Pubns., Inc.

Hustad, Megan. How to Be Useful: A Beginner's Guide to Not Hating Work. 2008. (ENG.). 256p. 19.95 *(978-0-618-71350-9(6))* Houghton Mifflin Harcourt Trade & Reference Pubs.

Husted, Seward W. George C. Marshall. 2007. (J). 23.95 *(978-0-9709682-3-4(X))* Army War College Foundation Pr.

Inkson, Kerr. Understanding Careers: The Metaphors of Working Lives. 2006. (Illus.). 344p. (C). 106.00 *(978-1-4129-4007-8(9)*, B29509C); per. 61.00 *(978-0-7619-2950-5(9)*, B29509P) SAGE Pubns., Inc.

Jackson, Ericka D. When God Calls: A Step-by-Step Plan to Live God's Vision as Your Full-time Vocation. 2008. 216p. pap. 15.95 *(978-1-4303-1373-1(0))* Lulu Enterprises Inc.

Jackson, Norman J. Learning for A Complex World: A Lifewide Concept of Learning, Education & Personal Development. 2011. (Illus.). 388p. 97.18 ***(978-1-4567-9371-5(3))***; pap. 35.27 ***(978-1-4567-9370-8(5))*** AuthorHouse.

Jacoway, Kristen. I'm in a Job Search — Now What??? Using LinkedIn, Facebook, & Twitter as Part of Your Job Search Strategy. Alba, Jason, ed. 2010. 136p. pap. 19.95 *(978-1-60005-170-8(7))* Happy About.

Jacques, Roy & Hobson, Mary. The Sergeant Major Syndrome: A Book for People Who Want to Advance Their Careers. 2011. 140p. 23.95 ***(978-1-4620-2209-0(X))***; pap. 13.95 ***(978-1-4620-2207-6(3))*** iUniverse, Inc.

Jansen, Julie. I Don't Know What I Want, but I Know It's Not This: A Step-by-Step Guide to Finding Gratifying Work. rev. ed. 2010. (ENG.). 304p. (gr. 12-18). 15.00 *(978-0-14-311699-8(1)*, Penguin (Non-Classics)) Penguin Group (USA) Inc.

Jasper, Melanie. Professional Development, Reflection & Decision-Making. 2007. (Vital Notes for Nurses Ser.: 4). (ENG., Illus.). 264p. per. 40.99 *(978-1-4051-3261-9(2)*, Wiley-Blackwell) Wiley, John & Sons, Inc.

Jeffries, Mark. The Art of Business Seduction: A 30-Day Plan to Get Noticed, Get Promoted, & Get Ahead. 2010. (ENG.). 213p. 22.95 *(978-0-470-59618-0(X)*, Wiley) Wiley, John & Sons, Inc.

Jellison, Jerald. Life after Grad School: Getting from A to B, 1 vol. 2010. (ENG.). 240p. pap. 21.95 *(978-0-19-973430-6(5))* Oxford Univ. Pr., Inc.

Jennings, Stephen L. Graduate with a Job: Getting College Students Hired & Equipping them for Career & Life Success. 2009. 124p. pap. 14.95 *(978-1-60844-210-2(1))* Dog Ear Publishing, LLC.

JIST Publishing Editors. Your Career & Life Plan Portfolio Instructor's Resources CD-ROM, Third Edition. 3rd ed. 2007. (ENG.). 25.95 *(978-1-59357-435-9(3)*, J4369, JIST Works) JIST Publishing.

—Your Career & Life Plan Portfolio, Third Edition. 3rd ed. 2007. (ENG.). 144p. 15.95 *(978-1-59357-435-2(5)*, J4352, JIST Works) JIST Publishing.

Johnson, David & Maclean, Rupert. Teaching - Professionalization, Development & Leadership. 2008. (ENG.). xiv, 318p. 169.00 *(978-1-4020-8185-9(5)*, 1402081855) Springer.

Johnson, David & Maclean, Rupert, eds. Teaching: Professionalisation, Development & Leadership: Festschrift for Professor Eric Hoyle. 2010. (ENG.). xiv, 318p. pap. 169.00 *(978-90-481-7798-1(7)*, 9048177987) Springer.

Johnson, Robin Denise. Career by Design: Tools & techniques for empowering your work Life. 2007. per., wbk. ed. 30.00 *(978-0-9787831-2-9(3))* Novus Publishing, LLC.

Johnson, Scott. Platforms of Success. 2009. 260p. 39.99 *(978-1-4389-7384-5(5))*; pap. 34.49 *(978-1-4389-7365-4(9))* AuthorHouse.

Johnson, Tory & Spizman, Robyn Freedman. Take This Book to Work: How to Ask for (and Get) Money, Fulfillment, & Advancement. 2007. (ENG.). 272p. pap. 15.95 *(978-0-312-35886-0(5)*, St. Martin's Griffin) St. Martin's Pr.

Johnstone, Judith. Planning a Career Change. 6th rev. ed. 2006. (Illus.). 160p. per. 20.00 *(978-1-84528-100-7(4))* Parkwest Pubns., Inc.

Jordan, Ann & Whaley, Lynne. Investigating Your Career. 3rd ed. 2012. (Middle School Solutions Ser.). (ENG.). 384p. (C). 80.95 ***(978-1-111-57550-2(9))*** Cengage South-Western.

Jordan, Ann K. & Whaley, Lynne T. Investigating Your Career. 2nd rev. ed. 2007. (Title 1 Ser.). (ENG., Illus.). 312p. (C). 84.95 *(978-0-538-44476-7(2)*, Cengage South-Western.

Kaiser, Hermann. Career Booster Kit. 2006. 64p. per. 14.95 *(978-0-9744276-2-1(4))* Value Added Resources, Inc.

Kamara, Lamin Tombekai. The Hr Companion: Human Resource Management. 2011. 298p. pap. 27.95 ***(978-1-4560-6502-7(5))*** PublishAmerica, Inc.

Kanaga, Kim, et al. Development Planning Workbook: Six Steps to Successful Change. 2009. *(978-1-60491-071-1(2))* Ctr. for Creative Leadership.

Kappesser, Lisa Caldas. The Smart New Way to Get Hired: Use Emotional Intelligence & Land the Right Job. 2010. (ENG.). 240p. pap. 14.95 *(978-1-59357-664-6(1)*, JIST Works) JIST Publishing.

Kaputa, Catherine. You Are a Brand! How Smart People Brand Themselves for Business Success. 2009. (ENG.). 208p. pap. 19.95 *(978-1-85788-545-3(7))* Ebsco Publishing.

Karlsberg, Robert. Accelerate Your Career: 133 Ways to Perform Better & Get Promoted Faster. 2007. (Illus.). 16p. *(978-0-9773593-2-5(8))* NeoVista Health.

—How to Become a Rising Star in Your Career in 60 Days or Less. 2007. pap. 47.00 *(978-0-9773593-3-2(6))* NeoVista Health.

Kasomo, Daniel W. Career & Aids Counselling for University Students. 2010. 60p. pap. *(978-3-8383-8681-2(7))* Lambert Academic Publishing.

Katz, Janet R., et al. Keys to Nursing Success. 3rd rev. ed. 2009. (ENG., Illus.). 480p. (C). pap. 74.20 *(978-0-13-703684-4(1)*, Prentice Hall) Prentice Hall PTR.

Kaufman, Judith. Steps to Success: The Fairleigh Dickinson Way. rev. ed. 2010. (ENG.). 434p. pap. 54.59 *(978-0-7575-4753-9(2))* Kendall Hunt Publishing Co.

Kay, Frances. New Kid on the Block: 10 Steps to Help You Survive & Thrive in the First 100 Days of Your New Job. 2007. (Career Makers Ser.). (ENG., Illus.). 191p. per. 19.95 *(978-1-904879-52-7(7))* Cyan Communications GBR. Dist: Independent Pubs. Group.

—Successful Networking: How to Build New Networks for Career & Company Progression. 2010. (ENG.). 208p. pap. 17.95 *(978-0-7494-5879-9(6))* Kogan Page, Ltd. GBR. Dist: Ingram Pub. Services.

Kearney, Nunnery. Making Transition from LPN To. 2009. 256p. pap. 34.95 *(978-0-8036-2188-6(4))* Davis, F. A. Co.

Kearney-Nunnery, Rose & Kearney-Nunnery, Rose. Making the Transition from LPN to RN. 2009. (Illus.). 256p. pap. 42.95 *(978-0-8036-2148-0(5))* Davis, F. A. Co.

Keehn, Kelley. She Inc. A Woman's Guide to Maximizing Her Career Potential. 2009. (ENG., Illus.). 224p. pap. *(978-1-897178-64-5(6))* Insomniac Pr.

Kellaway, Lucy. I did a Very Silly Thing at the Office Party: And Other Work/Life Dilemmas. 2007. 224p. pap. 17.95 *(978-1-84668-039-7(5))* Profile Bks. Ltd. GBR. Dist: Independent Pubs. Group.

Kelloway, Karen. Nail It! Six Steps to Transform Your Career. 2010. 152p. pap. 16.95 *(978-1-4269-0363-2(4))* Trafford Publishing.

Kelly, Kevin. Top Jobs: How They Are Different & What You Need to Succeed. 2009. (ENG.). 208p. 22.99 *(978-0-13-712781-8(2))* FT Press.

Kentli, Fulya Damla. Influence of Hidden Curriculum on Career Choice. 2009. 168p. pap. *(978-3-639-12992-2(X))* VDM Verlag Dr. Mueller e.K.

King, Eden & Knight, Jennifer L. How Women Can Make It Work: The Science of Success, 1 vol. 2011. (Women & Careers in Management Ser.). (Illus.). 327p. 54.95 *(978-0-313-39309-9(5)*, A3335C); xxi, 327p. E-Book *(978-0-313-39310-5(9)*, Praeger Pubs.) Greenwood Publishing Group, Inc.

King, Joan C. A Life on Purpose: Wisdom at Work. 2011. 260p. pap. 20.00 *(978-0-9785393-7-5(0)*, Bibliocast) Word Keepers, Inc.

Kirpal, Simone R. Labour Market Flexibility & Individual Careers: A Comparative Study. 2011. (Technical & Vocational Education & Training: Issues, Concerns & Prospects Ser.). (ENG.). xiii, 271p. 139.00 *(978-94-007-0233-2(7)*, 9400702337) Springer.

Kitson, Michael J., et al. How to Keep Your Job in a Tough Competitive Market. 2009. (ENG.). 240p. pap. 12.95 *(978-1-60550-651-7(6))* Adams Media Corp.

Kjarsgaard, Robert. Rapid Prototyping In Action: A Prototype Career Facilitator Training ModuleDeveloped In a Distributed Learning Format. 2008. 120p. pap. *(978-3-639-04401-0(0))* VDM Verlag Dr. Mueller e.K.

Kleiman, Jessica & Weinsaft Cooper, Meryl. Be Your Own Best Publicist: How to Use PR Techniques to Get Noticed, Hired & Rewarded at Work. 2011. (ENG.). 1p. pap. 15.99 *(978-1-60163-148-0(0))* Career Pr., Inc.

Klein, Robert H., et al, eds. On Becoming a Psychotherapist: The Personal & Professional Journey, 1 vol. 2011. (ENG.). 352p. 45.00 *(978-0-19-973639-3(1))* Oxford Univ. Pr., Inc.

Komisarjevsky, Chris. The Power of Reputation: Strengthen the Asset That Will Make or Break Your Career, 1 vol. 2012. (ENG.). 224p. 22.00 ***(978-0-8144-1797-3(3))*** Amacom.

Kooy, Mary. Telling Stories in Book Clubs: Women Teachers & Professional Development. 2010. xii, 244p. pap. 109.00 *(978-1-4419-4158-9(4)*, 1441941584) Springer.

Kotadia, Sam. 52 Ways To Discover Your Dream Job. 2011. 70p. 14.95 *(978-0-9558760-7-3(9))* Mindsport Ltd. Pubns. GBR. Dist: Cardinal Pubs. Group.

Kourdi, Jeremy & Davies, Jacqueline. The Truth about Talent: A Guide to Building a Dynamic Workforce, Realizing Potential & Helping Leaders Succeed. 2010. (ENG., Illus.). 272p. 39.95 *(978-0-470-74882-4(6)*, Jossey-Bass) Wiley, John & Sons, Inc.

Krannich, Caryl & Krannich, Ron. No One Will Hire Me! Avoid 17 Mistakes & Win the Job. 3rd ed. 2006. (ENG., Illus.). 208p. per. 15.95 *(978-1-57023-266-4(0))* Impact Pubns.

Krannich, Ron & Krannich, Caryl. You Should Hire Me! Interview Secrets to Get the Job You Love. 2008. (ENG., Illus.). 208p. pap. 15.95 *(978-1-57023-270-1(9))* Impact Pubns.

Krantz, Steven G. The Survival of a Mathematician: From Tenure-Track to Emeritus. 2008. 310p. pap. 40.00 *(978-0-8218-4629-2(9))* American Mathematical Society.

Krista, Pearson. Shifting from Traditional to Professional Studies - a Review of Undergraduate Curriculum Development in Ontario. 2008. 100p. pap. *(978-3-639-11157-6(5))* VDM Verlag Dr. Mueller e.K.

Kroth, Michael & Christensen, McKay. Career Development Basics. 2009. (ENG.). 160p. pap. 29.95 *(978-1-56286-546-7(3))* American Society for Training & Development.

C

Krumboltz, John D. & Levin, Al S. Luck Is No Accident: Making the Most of happenstance in Your Life & Career. 2nd ed. 2010. (Illus.). 176p. pap. 18.95 (978-1-886230-03-3(X)) Impact Pubs., Inc.

Kuhnhanss, Christoph. El Arte de Saber Venderse. 2008. (Masterclass (Robin Book) Ser.). (Illus.). 285p. pap. (978-84-7927-863-2(3)) Robinbk., Ediciones S.L.

Kumar, Arti. Personal, Academic & Career Development in Higher Education: Soaring to Success. 2008. (Illus.). 296p. 165.00 (978-0-415-42359-5(7)); 45.95 (978-0-415-42360-1(0)) Routledge.

Kursmark, Louise. Directory of Professional Resume Writers: How to Find & Work with a Pro to Accelerate Your Job Search. 2008. (Illus.). 296p. per. 19.95 (978-1-59357-519-9(X), JIST Works) JIST Publishing.

Kurth, Brian. Test-Drive Your Dream Job: A Step-by-Step Guide to Finding & Creating the Work You Love. 2008. (ENG.). 256p. pap. 20.99 (978-0-446-69888-7(1), Business Plus) Grand Central Publishing.

Lab-Volt Staff. Building Career Success: Tech-Design ESeries. 2010. 122p. 12.00 (978-1-60533-152-2(X)); 82p. ring bd. 9.00 (978-1-60533-153-9(8)) Lab-Volt Systems, Inc.

Laffler, David. Career Diary of a Private Investigator: Gardner's Guide Series. 2008. (Gardner's Guide Ser.). (ENG.). 180p. pap. 14.95 (978-1-58965-046-6(8)) Gardner, Garth Co., Inc. (GGC).

Lais, Toni. Career Diary of a Physical Therapist: Gardner's Guide Series. 2008. (Gardner's Guide Ser.). (ENG.). 150p. pap. 11.95 (978-1-58965-055-8(7)) Gardner, Garth Co., Inc. (GGC).

Lambert, Stephen. Great Jobs for Business Majors. 3rd ed. 2008. (ENG.). 240p. pap. 16.95 (978-0-07-154483-2(6), 0071544836) McGraw-Hill Cos., The.

—Great Jobs for Sociology Majors. 3rd ed. 2008. (ENG.). 192p. pap. 16.95 (978-0-07-154482-5(8), 0071544828) McGraw-Hill Cos., The.

Lassiter, Pam. The New Job Security: The 5 Best Strategies for Taking Control of Your Career. rev. ed. 2010. (ENG., Illus.). 224p. pap. 14.99 (978-1-58008-377-5(3)) Ten Speed Pr.

LaVerne, Ludden. Job Savvy, Fourth Edition. 4th ed. 2008. 240p. wbk. ed. 18.95 (978-1-59357-553-3(X), JIST Works) JIST Publishing.

Lawrence, Annee. The Job Seekers Handbook. 2nd rev. ed. 2006. Orig. Title: Job Seeking: It's a Game of Skill. (ENG., Illus.). 192p. per. (978-0-947205-94-2(2)) Univ. of New South Wales.

Lazzari, Margaret. The Practical Handbook for the Emerging Artist, Enhanced Edition. 2nd ed. 2010. (ENG.). 352p. (C). pap. 87.95 (978-0-495-91026-8(0)) Wadsworth.

LearningExpress Editors. Best Careers for Veterans. 2009. (ENG.). 210p. pap. 14.95 (978-1-57685-670-3(4)) LearningExpress, LLC.

Leatherman, Dick. Is Coffee Break the Best Part of Your Day? How to Keep Your Job in Today's Turbulent Environment! - Job Skills for You - Includes Simple, Tested, Step-by-Step Instructions. 2nd ed. 2010. (Illus.). 288p. pap. 24.95 (978-1-59996-214-6(4)) Human Resource Development Pr.

Lechter, Sharon L. & Reid, Greg S. Three Feet from Gold: Turn Your Obstacles into Opportunities! 2009. (Think & Grow Rich Ser.). (ENG.). 256p. 22.95 (978-1-4027-6764-7(1)) Sterling Publishing Co., Inc.

Lee, Mary Price. Opportunities in Animal & Pet Care Careers. 2nd ed. 2008. (ENG.). 160p. pap. 14.95 (978-0-07-154534-1(4), 0071545344) McGraw-Hill Cos., The.

Lees. Career Reboot: 24 Tips for Tough Times. 2009. (ENG.). 120p. pap. 17.00 (978-0-07-712758-9(7), 0077127587) McGraw-Hill Cos., The.

Lees, Kirsten. Let Go of My Leg! How to Get the Working Life You Want after Having Children. 2006. (ENG., Illus.). 224p. pap. (978-0-273-70657-1(8), Financial Times/Prentice Hall) Pearson Education, Ltd.

Legrand, Audrey. How to Get Out of Job Jail. 2007. 97p. pap. 14.95 (978-0-615-20171-9(7)) Innovators & Motivators, Inc.

Leibold, Frank B. The Key to Job Success in Any Career: Developing Six Competencies That Close America's Global Skills Gap. 2010. (Illus.). 200p. pap. 19.95 (978-1-4327-6046-5(7)) Outskirts Pr., Inc.

Lencioni, Patrick. The Three Signs of a Miserable Job: A Fable for Managers (and Their Employees) 2007. (J-B Lencioni Ser.: 2). (ENG., Illus.). 272p. 24.95 (978-0-7879-9531-7(2), Jossey-Bass) Wiley, John & Sons, Inc.

Lencioni, Patrick M. Managing for Employee Engagement: A Workshop Based on the Three Signs of a Miserable Job. 2011. (ENG.). 8p. ring bd. 20.00 (978-0-470-52074-1(4), Pfeiffer) Wiley, John & Sons, Inc.

—Managing for Employee Engagement Set: A Workshop Based on the Three Signs of a Miserable Job. 2011. (ENG.). ring bd. 695.00 (978-0-470-92706-9(2), Pfeiffer) Wiley, John & Sons, Inc.

—Managing for Employee Engagement Facilitator's Guide - Flash Drive Replacement Only. 2011. 100.00 (978-0-470-62187-5(7), Pfeiffer) Wiley, John & Sons, Inc.

—Managing for Employee Engagement Facilitator's Guide Package - Non-Saleable! 2011. 160p. ring bd. 80.00 (978-0-470-53707-7(8), Pfeiffer) Wiley, John & Sons, Inc.

—The Three Signs of a Miserable Job: Anonymity, Irrelevance, Immeasurement. 2011. (J-B Lencioni Ser.: 39). (ENG.). 1p. pap. 10.00 (978-0-470-92962-9(6), Pfeiffer) Wiley, John & Sons, Inc.

Lenz, Janet G., et al. Career Development & Planning: A Comprehensive Approach. 3rd ed. 2008. (ENG., Illus.). 352p. (C). pap. 124.95 (978-1-4266-3135-1(9)) CENGAGE Learning Custom Publishing.

Levinson, Jay Conrad & Neitlich, Andrew. Guerrilla Marketing for a Bulletproof Career: How to Attract Ongoing Opportunities in Perpetually Gut Wrenching Times, for Entrepreneurs, Employees, & Everyone in Between. 2011. (Guerilla Marketing Press Ser.). (ENG.). 250p. pap. 19.95 (978-1-60037-815-7(3)) Morgan James Publishing.

Levinson, Jay Conrad & Perry, David E. Guerrilla Marketing for Job Hunters 3. 0: How to Stand Out from the Crowd & Tap into the Hidden Job Market Using Social Media & 999 Other Tactics Today. 3rd ed. 2011. (ENG., Illus.). 315p. pap. 21.95 (978-1-118-01909-2(1), Wiley) Wiley, John & Sons, Inc.

Levit, Alexandra. Blind Spots: 10 Business Myths You Can't Afford to Believe on Your New Path to Success. 2011. (ENG.). 272p. (gr. 12). 15.00 (978-0-425-24306-0(0), Berkley Trade) Penguin Group (USA) Inc.

Lewis, Thomas N., et al. The 16 Career Clusters: A Project-Based Orientation. 2008. (Middle School Solutions Ser.). (ENG., Illus.). 192p. pap. 48.95 (978-0-538-44957-1(8)) Cengage South-Western.

Liburdi, John C. Flying Start: Mentoring for Air Force Company Grade Officers. 2009. 119p. pap. 15.26 (978-0-557-06065-8(6)) Lulu Enterprises Inc.

Lim, Gary. Dive into ACTION! Find Your Niche in Times of Uncertainty. 2009. 92p. pap. 14.95 (978-0-578-01823-2(3)) Dorato Pr.

Lindenfield, Stuart. Confident Networking for Career Success. 2010. (ENG., Illus.). 288p. pap. 15.95 (978-0-7499-4170-3(7)) Piatkus Bks. GBR. Dist: Independent Pubs. Group.

Lineberg, Skip & Bennington, Emily. Effective Immediately: How to Fit In, Stand Out, & Move up on Your First Real Job. 2010. (ENG., Illus.). 224p. pap. 14.99 (978-1-58008-999-9(2)) Ten Speed Pr.

Liptak, John. Overcoming Barriers to Employment Success. 2008. 80p. pap. 13.95 (978-1-59357-615-8(3), JIST Works) JIST Publishing.

Liptak, John J. Job Search Knowledge Scale. (YA). 34.95 (978-1-59357-105-4(4), C6-JA1054) JIST Publishing.

Little, Sean David. What You Won't Learn in Your Teacher Education Program. 2008. 76p. pap. 16.95 (978-1-60474-447-7(2)) PublishAmerica, Inc.

Llewellyn, A. Bronwyn, et al. Green Jobs: A Guide to Eco-Friendly Employment. 2008. (ENG.). 240p. pap. 12.95 (978-1-59869-872-5(9)) Adams Media Corp.

Lobosco, Charles. C. A. R. E. - Courage to Take Action Relevant to Everyone: Building a Better Workplace Starts with You! 2010. 192p. 24.95 (978-1-4502-5066-5(1)); pap. 14.95 (978-1-4502-5065-8(3)) iUniverse, Inc.

Lombardo, Michael M. & Eichinger, Robert W. Career Architect Development Planner Book German Language: A Systematic Approach to Development. 2011. 1411p. pap. 119.00 (978-1-933578-34-7(3)) Korn/Ferry International: powered by Lominger.

—Career Architect Development Planner Book Italian Language: A Systematic Approach to Development. 2011. pap. 119.00 (978-1-933578-38-5(6)) Korn/Ferry International: powered by Lominger.

—Career Architect Development Planner Book Portuguese (Brazil) Language. 2011. pap. 119.00 (978-1-933578-35-4(1)) Korn/Ferry International: powered by Lominger.

—Career Architect Development Planner Book Simplified Chinese Language: A Systematic Approach to Development. 2011. pap. 119.00 (978-1-933578-36-1(X)) Korn/Ferry International: powered by Lominger.

Lombardo, Michael M. & Eichinger, Robert W. Eighty-Eight Assignments for Development in Place. 2010. 48p. pap. 15.00 (978-1-60491-078-0(X)) Ctr. for Creative Leadership.

London, Manuel. Employee Engagement Through Effective Performance Management: A Manager's Guide to Psychological Principles of Team Leadership. 2009. (ENG., Illus.). 272p. 49.95 (978-1-84872-820-2(4), Routledge) Taylor & Francis Group GBR. Dist: Taylor & Francis Group.

Longson, Sally. Life after... Engineering & Built Environment: A Practical Guide to Life after Your Degree. 2006. (Illus.). 200p. per. 21.95 (978-0-415-37592-4(4)) Routledge.

—Returning to Work. 4th ed. 2008. 265p. pap. 26.00 (978-1-84528-075-8(X)) How To Books GBR. Dist: Parkwest Pubns., Inc.

Luke, H. Medical Education & Sociology of Medical Habitus: It's not about the Stethoscope! It's not about the Stethoscope! 2010. (ENG.). 350p. pap. 129.00 (978-90-481-6273-4(4), 9048162734) Springer.

Lurie, Steven. Handbook for Early Career Success. 2009. 192p. pap. 16.95 (978-1-59858-809-5(5)) Dog Ear Publishing, LLC.

Lyles, Dick. Pearls of Perspicacity: Proven Wisdom to Help You Find Career Satisfaction & Success. 2010. 132p. 23.95 (978-1-4502-4478-7(5)); pap. 13.95 (978-1-4502-4479-4(3)) iUniverse, Inc.

Mabey, Christopher & Finch Lees, Tim. Management & Leadership Development. 2007. (Illus.). 280p. (C). per. 60.00 (978-1-4129-2902-8(4), B29016P) SAGE Pubns., Ltd. GBR. Dist: SAGE Pubns., Inc.

MacInnis, Lyman. How to Succeed in Anything by Really Trying. 2010. (ENG.). 224p. pap. 14.95 (978-0-307-35725-0(2), Vintage Canada) Random Hse. of Canada, Ltd. CAN. Dist: Random Hse., Inc.

Maestas, Lily. Unlimited Options. rev. ed. 2009. (ENG.). 266p. pap. 46.47 (978-0-7575-6143-6(8)) Kendall Hunt Publishing Co.

Magaw, Amy. To Teach, or Not to Teach. 2007. 148p. pap. 15.00 (978-0-615-14013-1(0)) Victory Christian Publishing.

Magdalene Chooi Hwa, Ang. Managerial Success, Mentoring & Goal Orientation. 2010. 104p. pap. (978-3-639-22548-8(1)) VDM Verlag Dr. Mueller e.K.

Mahafza, Bassem R. Portrait of a CEO: A Guide to Starting & Growing a Small Business. 2010. 168p. pap. 15.49 (978-1-4520-8459-6(9)) AuthorHouse.

Maitland, Alison & Thomson, Peter. Future Work: How Businesses Can Adapt & Thrive in the New World of Work. 2011. (ENG., Illus.). 192p. 30.00 (978-0-230-28422-7(1)) Palgrave Macmillan.

Makela, Julia Panke. A Case Study Approach to Ethics in Career Development: Exploring Shades of Gray. 2009. pap. (978-1-885333-27-8(7)) National Career Development Assn.

Malis, Mark D. Gap Odyssey: Navigating the Business Highway. 2009. 96p. pap. 18.50 (978-1-4490-2483-3(1)) AuthorHouse.

Mander, Rosemary. Becoming a Midwife: Mander & Flemi. Fleming, Valerie, ed. 2009. (ENG., Illus.). 248p. (C). 135.00 (978-0-415-46437-6(4)) Routledge.

—Becoming a Midwife - Mander & Flemi. Fleming, Valerie, ed. 2009. (ENG., Illus.). 248p. (C). 38.95 (978-0-415-46438-3(2)) Routledge.

Mannering, Karen. Get the Career You Want: A Teach Yourself Guide. 2011. (Teach Yourself: General Reference Ser.). (ENG.). 208p. pap. 15.00 (978-0-07-177522-9(6), 0071775226) McGraw-Hill Cos., The.

Manning, Mark. FINDING a Job Is Good; Finding 86 of Them Is Just NUTS!, 1 vol. 2010. 174p. pap. 24.95 (978-1-4489-4623-5(9)) PublishAmerica, Inc.

Margulis, Alexander R. The Road to Success: A Career Manual - How to Advance to the Top. 2006. (ENG., Illus.). 120p. per. 39.95 (978-0-12-370587-7(8), Academic Pr.) Elsevier Science & Technology Bks.

Marsh, Rosalie. Lifelong Learning: A View from the Coal Face. 2011. (ENG., Illus.). 108p. pap. (978-1-908302-04-5(6)) Christal Publishing.

—Release Your Potential: Making Sense of Personal & Professional Development. 2011. (ENG., Illus.). 118p. pap. (978-1-908302-08-3(9)) Christal Publishing.

—Skills for Employability Part One Part One: Pre-Employment. 2012. (Lifelong Learning Personal Effectiveness Guides: No. 3). (ENG., Illus.). 138p. pap. 11.50 (978-1-908302-16-8(X)) Christal Publishing GBR. Dist: Lightning Source, Inc.

Marshall, Lois. Take Charge of Your Nursing Career: Conquer the Challenges & Realize the Rewards. 2010. (978-1-930538-85-6(5)) Sigma Theta Tau International, Ctr. for Nursing Pr.

Martin, Chuck L., et al. Work Your Strengths: A Scientific Process to Identify Your Skills & Match Them to the Best Career for You, 1 vol. 2010. (ENG.). 256p. 21.95 (978-0-8144-1407-1(9)) Amacom.

Martin, Thomas L. Jr. Career Change Management. 2008. 232p. 29.99 (978-1-4363-7645-7(9)); pap. 19.99 (978-1-4363-7644-0(0)) Xlibris Corp.

Martinez, Luis A. Getting There. 2010. 220p. 29.99 (978-1-4500-2626-0(5)); pap. 19.99 (978-1-4500-2625-3(7)) Xlibris Corp.

Martner, Knud. Mahler's Concerts. 2010. (ENG., Illus.). 416p. (gr. 12). 50.00 (978-1-59020-392-7(5)) Overlook Pr., The.

Mathieu, Chris, ed. Careers in Creative Industries. 2011. (Routledge Advances in Management & Business Studies). (ENG., Illus.). 312p. (C). 125.00 (978-0-415-80826-2(X)) Routledge.

Max, Douglas & Bacal, Robert. Setting Performance Goals: Hundred of Ready-To-Use Phrases for Comunicating Any Performance Plan or Review. 2nd ed. 2010. (Perfect Phrases Ser.). (ENG.). 208p. pap. 12.00 (978-0-07-174505-5(X), 007174505X) McGraw-Hill Cos., The.

McCabe, Linda L. & McCabe, Edward R. B. How to Succeed in Academics. 2nd ed. 2010. (ENG.). 294p. pap. 25.95 (978-0-520-26268-3(9)) Univ. of California Pr.

McCann, Greg. When Your Parents Sign the Paychecks: Finding Career Success Inside or Outside the Family Business. 2007. 272p. pap. 19.95 (978-1-59357-323-2(5), J3232, JIST Works) JIST Publishing.

McCauley, Cynthia D. Developmental Assignments: Creating Learning Experiences without Changing Jobs (Chinese) 2008. 80p. pap. 25.00 (978-1-60491-050-6(X)) Ctr. for Creative Leadership.

—Developmental Assignments: Creating Learning Experiences without Changing Jobs (Dutch) 2008. 80p. pap. 25.00 (978-1-60491-049-0(6)) Ctr. for Creative Leadership.

—Developmental Assignments: Creating Learning Experiences without Changing Jobs (French) 2008. 80p. pap. 25.00 (978-1-60491-045-2(3)) Ctr. for Creative Leadership.

—Developmental Assignments: Creating Learning Experiences without Changing Jobs (German) 2008. 80p. pap. 25.00 (978-1-60491-048-3(8)) Ctr. for Creative Leadership.

—Developmental Assignments: Creating Learning Experiences without Changing Jobs (Japanese) 2008. 80p. pap. 25.00 (978-1-60491-051-3(8)) Ctr. for Creative Leadership.

—Developmental Assignments: Creating Learning Experiences without Changing Jobs (Russian) 2008. 80p. pap. 25.00 (978-1-60491-047-6(X)) Ctr. for Creative Leadership.

—Developmental Assignments: Creating Learning Experiences without Changing Jobs (Spanish) 2008. (SPA.). 80p. pap. 25.00 (978-1-60491-046-9(1)) Ctr. for Creative Leadership.

McClain, James. Successful Career Development A Game Pla. 2007. 372p. 29.95 (978-1-4241-2421-3(2)) PublishAmerica, Inc.

McDermott, Eoghan. The Career Doctor: How to Get - And Keep - The Job You Want. 2010. (ENG.). 192p. pap. 27.95 (978-1-85607-982-2(1)) Currach Pr. IRL. Dist: Dufour Editions, Inc.

McDermott, Steve. How to Be a Complete & Utter Failure in Life, Work & Everything: 44 1/2 Steps to Lasting Underachievement. 2008. (ENG., Illus.). 208p. per. 14.99 (978-0-13-813810-3(9)) FT Press.

—How to Be a Complete & Utter Failure in Life, Work & Everything: 44 1/2 Steps to Lasting Underachievement. 2nd rev. ed. 2007. (ENG., Illus.). 208p. (C). pap. (978-0-273-70607-6(1)) Pearson Education Canada.

McDonald, Sean. Stop Complaining! Start Growing! Lessons on Growing Your Business & Career. 2009. 120p. pap. 15.95 (978-1-4389-1407-7(5)) AuthorHouse.

McGovern, Patricia M. The Career That Ate My Life. 2007. (Illus.). 116p. per. 19.95 (978-1-84753-534-4(8)) Lulu Enterprises Inc.

McGraw-Hill Editors. The big book of Jobs 2012-2013. 2011. (ENG.). 960p. pap. 19.00 (978-0-07-177351-5(7), 0071773517) McGraw-Hill Cos., The.

Mchenry, Sherene. The Busy Students' Guide to College & Career Success. 3rd rev. ed. 2010. (ENG.). 154p. pap. 55.37 (978-0-7575-6783-4(5)) Kendall Hunt Publishing Co.

McIvor, Brian. Career Detection: Finding & Managing Your Career. 2008. (ENG., Illus.). 126p. pap. 14.95 (978-0-9519738-5-1(1)) Management Briefs Ltd.

McKee, John M. Career Wisdom: 101 Proven Strategies to Ensure Workplace Success. 2007. (ENG.). 128p. per. 8.95 (978-1-58736-828-8(5)) Wheatmark.

McKnight, Michelynn. The Agile Librarian's Guide to Thriving in Any Institution, 1 vol. 201p. pap. 30.00 (978-1-59158-668-5(2), LU8668) Libraries Unlimited, Inc.

McMullin, Julie & Marshall, Victor W., eds. Aging & Working in the New Economy: Changing Career Structures in Small IT Firms. 2010. (Illus.). 256p. 112.00 (978-1-84844-177-4(0)) Elgar, Edward Publishing, Inc.

McNeal, Delatorro, II. Caught Between a Dream & a Job: How to Leave the 9-to-5 Behind & Step into the Life You've Always Wanted. 2007. (ENG.). 238p. 21.99 (978-1-59979-217-0(6)) Charisma Media.

Meers, Sharon & Strober, Joanna. Getting To 50/50: How Working Couples Can Have It All by Sharing It All. 2009. (ENG., Illus.). 320p. 26.00 (978-0-553-80655-7(6)) Random House Publishing Group.

Mello, Brad, et al, eds. Pathways to Careers & Communication in the 21st Century. 8th ed. 2011. (C). (978-0-944811-28-3(0)) National Communication Assn. (NCA).

Mepham, John. Super Salesmanship + Convincing Advertising = Lucrative Business. 2011. 342p. pap. 25.50 (978-1-4466-0366-6(0)) Lulu Enterprises Inc.

Merino Tejedor, Enrique. Career Planning Techniques. 2011. 72p. pap. (978-3-8443-0667-5(6)) Lambert Academic Publishing.

Merritt, Jennifer. The Wall Street Journal Guide to Building Your Career. 2012. (ENG.). 208p. pap. 15.00 (978-0-307-71956-0(1), Crown Business) Crown Publishing Group.

Miedaner, Talane. Coach Yourself to a New Career: 7 Steps to Reinventing Your Professional Life. 2010. (ENG.). 240p. pap. 18.95 (978-0-07-170309-3(8), 0071703098) McGraw-Hill Cos., The.

Mike Holt's Master/Contractor Simulated Exam 2008 Edition. 2008. per. (978-1-932685-44-2(8)) Holt, Mike Enterprises, Inc.

Milady Publishing Company Staff. Career Management for Barbers. 2006. (ENG., Illus.). 80p. per. 54.50 (978-1-4180-5088-7(1), Milady Publishing Co.) Delmar Cengage Learning.

Miller, Dan. No More Dreaded Mondays: Ignite Your Passion - And Other Revolutionary Ways to Discover Your True Calling at Work. 2009. (ENG.). 272p. pap. 14.99 (978-0-307-58877-7(7), Broadway Business) Knopf Doubleday Publishing Group.

—No More Dreaded Mondays: Ignite Your Passion — And Other Revolutionary Ways to Discover Your True Calling at Work. 2009. (ENG.). 272p. pap. 14.99 (978-1-4000-7385-6(5), WaterBrook Pr.) Doubleday Religious Publishing Group, The.

Miller, David C. The Influential Actuary: How Actuaries & Other Technically-Oriented Professionals Set Themselves Apart. 2010. (978-1-56698-761-5(X)) Actex Pubns.

Miller, Lee E. Get More Money on Your Next Job... in Any Economy. 2nd ed. 2009. (ENG.). 208p. pap. 14.95 (978-0-07-162138-0(5), 0071621385) McGraw-Hill Cos., The.

Miller, Nelson. A Law Graduate's Guide: Navigating Law School's Hidden Career & Professional-Development Curriculum. 2011. xv, 239p. pap. (978-1-935220-39-8(X)) Bridge Publishing Group LLC.

Mitchell, Joan & Walker-Mitchell, Nancy. Dr. Joan's Mentoring Book: Straight Talk about Taking Charge of Your Career. 2007. per. (978-0-9795240-0-4(8)) Mitchell & Mitchell, LLC.

Mitchell, Karrie D. Finding Their Way - Cultural Capital Facilitators & First-Generation Community College Students. 2008. 188p. pap. (978-3-639-01962-9(8)) VDM Verlag Dr. Mueller e.K.

Miyake, Lisa & Pham, Vu H. Impressive First Impressions: A Guide to the Most Important 30 Seconds (and 30 Years) of Your Career, 1 vol. 2010. 224p. 29.95 (978-0-313-37594-1(1), C37594, Praeger Pubs.) Greenwood Publishing Group, Inc.

Mohd Rasdi, Rozlah. Career Success of Managers. 2010. 260p. pap. (978-3-8383-4459-1(6)) Lambert Academic Publishing.

Moneypenny & McGregor, Heather. Sharpen Your Heels: Mrs. Moneypenny's Career Advice for Women. 2012. (ENG.). 256p. (gr. 12). 27.95 (978-1-59184-466-2(5), Portfolio (Hardcover)) Penguin Group (USA) Inc.

Monroe, Kara. Evaluation of an Online Professional Development Program for Part-Time Faculty. 2008. 196p. pap. (978-3-639-06303-5(1)) VDM Verlag Dr. Mueller e.K.

Montgomery, Rhonda, et al. Solving the Professional Development Puzzle: 101 Solutions for Career & Life Planning. 2008. (ENG.). 240p. (C). pap. 39.20 (978-0-13-500365-7(2), Prentice Hall) Prentice Hall PTR.

Montoya, Peter & Vandehey, Tim. The Brand Called You: Make Your Business Stand Out in a Crowded Marketplace. 2008. (ENG., Illus.). 288p. pap. 16.95 (978-0-07-159750-0(6), 0071597506) McGraw-Hill Cos., The.

Moody, Judy. Career Decisions in Computer Technology Fields. 2008. 208p. pap. (978-3-639-01892-9(3)) VDM Verlag Dr. Mueller e.K.

Morem, Susan. How to Get a Job & Keep It: Career & Life Skills You Need to Succeed. 2nd rev. ed. 2007. 224p. pap. 16.95 (978-0-8160-6776-3(7)); (C). (gr. 9). 35.00 (978-0-8160-6775-6(9)) Facts On File, Inc. (Ferguson Publishing Co.).

Morrison, Marcy. Finding Your Passion: The Easy Guide to Your Dream Career. 2009. (ENG.). pap. 14.95 *(978-1-60037-545-3(6))* Morgan James Publishing.
Moss, Wes. Make More, Worry Less: Secrets from 18 Extraordinary People Who Created a Bigger Income & a Better Life. 2008. (ENG.) 272p. 24.99 *(978-0-13-234686-3(9))* FT Press.
Mshick, Paula. Mapping Gender in Academic Workplaces - Ways of Reproducing Gender Inequality Within the Discourse of Equality. 2008. 184p. pap. *(978-3-639-03545-2(3))* VDM Verlag Dr. Mueller e.K.
Mulligan, Michael V. Helping Your Children Launch a Successful Career before Age 30: Working with Your Son & Daughter to Get Them off the Family Payroll. 2011. 280p. pap. 28.95 *(978-1-4502-8921-4(5))* iUniverse, Inc.
Myers, Ford R. & Myers. Get the Job You Want, Even When No One's Hiring: Take Charge of Your Career, Find a Job You Love, & Earn What You Deserve. 2009. (ENG., Illus.). 224p. pap. 19.95 *(978-0-470-45741-2(4),* Wiley) Wiley, John & Sons, Inc.
Nash, Ron. How to Find Your Dream Job, Even in a Recession. 2008. 172p. pap. 14.64 *(978-0-557-02826-9(4))* Lulu Enterprises Inc.
Navarro, Joe & Poynter, Toni Sciarra. Louder Than Words: Take Your Career from Average to Exceptional with the Hidden Power of Nonverbal Intelligence. 256p. 2011. (ENG.). pap. 16.99 *(978-0-06-201504-4(4),* 2010. (Illus.). 24.99 *(978-0-06-177139-2(2))* HarperCollins Pubs. (Collins).
Neimeyer, Greg J. & Taylor, Jennifer M. Continuing Professional Development & Lifelong Learning: Issues, Impacts & Outcomes. 2012. ***(978-1-62100-767-8(7))*** Nova Science Pubs., Inc.
Newman, Katherine S. Chutes & Ladders: Navigating the Low-Wage Labor Market. (Russell Sage Foundation Books at Harvard University Press Ser.). (Illus.). 432p. 2008. pap. 22.50 *(978-0-674-02753-4(1))* 2006. 35.00 *(978-0-674-02336-9(6))* Harvard Univ. Pr.
Nicholas, Mark. I Come First: How the Ego Rules Every Business Decision. 2010. 21.95 *(978-0-9826888-0-9(6))* Barely Lit Spaces Pubns.
Nichols & Nichols College Professional. The Professional Development Seminar: First-Year Course. 3rd rev. ed. 2010. (ENG.). 338p. spiral bd. 58.89 *(978-0-7575-7696-6(6))* Kendall Hunt Publishing Co.
Nichols College Professional Development Staff. The Professional Development Seminar Junior & Senior Course Workbook. 2nd rev. ed. 2010. (ENG.). 202p. spiral bd. 39.45 *(978-0-7575-7416-0(5))* Kendall Hunt Publishing Co.
Niles, Harris-Bowlsbey & Cram101 Textbook Reviews Staff. Career Development Interventions in the Twenty First Century. 2007. 116p. per. 11.95 *(978-1-4288-2068-5(X))* Cram101 Inc.
Niles, Spencer, et al. Career Flow: A Hope-Centered Approach to Career Development. 2010. (ENG., Illus.). 264p. (C). pap. 37.80 *(978-0-13-224190-8(0),* Prentice Hall) Prentice Hall PTR.
Niles, Spencer G. & Harris-Bowlsbey, JoAnn. Career Development Interventions in the 21st Century. (Pearson Custom Education Ser.). (ENG.). (C). 3rd ed. 2008. 528p. 134.67 *(978-0-13-225438-0(7))* 4th rev. ed. 2012. 544p. 132.00 ***(978-0-13-265859-1(3))*** Prentice Hall PTR. (Prentice Hall).
Niles, Spencer G., et al. Essential Elements of Career Counseling: Processes & Techniques. 2nd ed. 2008. (ENG.). 192p. (C). pap. 36.00 *(978-0-13-158218-7(6),* Prentice Hall) Prentice Hall PTR.
Nizankiewicz, Michael J. I Did it My Way: ... & it Wasn't Always the Right Way. 2010. 100p. pap. 17.99 *(978-1-4520-3060-9(X))* AuthorHouse.
Nowak, Lily. The Medicine Wheel: A Balanced Approach to Employment Counseling. 2007. 176p. per. 15.95 *(978-0-595-44396-3(6))* iUniverse, Inc.
Ohlsson, Hjalmar & Borg, Hanne, eds. Career Development. 2009. (Education in a Competitive & Globalizing World Ser.). 129.00 *(978-1-60741-464-3(3))* Nova Science Pubs., Inc.
Ojie-Ahamiojie, George. Professional Development: Strategies for Interviewing, Career Management, & Diplomacy in the Workplace. 2008. 72p. pap. 11.99 *(978-1-4389-1308-7(7))* AuthorHouse.
Osborn, Debra S. Teaching Career Development: A Primer for Presenters & Instructors. 2008. pap. *(978-1-885333-22-3(6))* National Career Development Assn.
Osborn, Debra S. & Zunker, Vernon G. Using Assessment Results for Career Development. 8th ed. 2011. (Graduate Career Counseling Ser.). (ENG., Illus.). 416p. (C). pap. 95.95 *(978-1-111-52127-1(1))* Brooks/Cole.
Osborn, Debra S., et al. The Internet: A Tool for Career Planning. 3rd ed. 2011. *(978-1-885333-30-8(7))* National Career Development Assn.
Owen, Hilarie. The Complete Guide to Mentoring: How to Design, Implement & Evaluate Effective Mentoring Programmes. 2011. (ENG., Illus.). 160p. pap. 39.95 *(978-0-7494-6114-0(4))* Kogan Page, Ltd. GBR. Dist: Ingram Pub. Services.
Ozbilgin, Mustafa & Pines, Ayala Malach. Career Choice in Management & Entrepreneurship a Research Companion. 2007. (Illus.). 616p. (C). 240.00 *(978-1-84542-844-0(7))* Elgar, Edward Publishing, Inc.
Palumbo, Michael. Your Career Tips! 2011. 298p. pap. 19.95 ***(978-1-257-15596-5(2))*** Lulu Enterprises Inc.
Panitkuljukkrawal, Rome. Life Planning: How to make a plan for your own future for your own Life. 2010. (Illus.). 152p. pap. 15.49 *(978-1-4490-8605-3(5))* AuthorHouse.
Parker, Glenn R. Capitol Investments: The Marketability of Political Skills. 2011. (Economics, Cognition, & Society Ser.). (ENG., Illus.). 216p. pap. 27.95 *(978-0-472-05037-6(0))* Univ. of Michigan Pr.
Parrillo Iii, Albert. A Study of Adolescent Career Thoughts. 2009. 180p. pap. *(978-3-639-15895-3(4))* VDM Verlag Dr. Mueller e.K.
Parvin, Cordell. Prepare to Win: A Lawyer's Guide to Rainmaking, Career Success & Life Fulfillment. 2007. (ENG.). 160p. 39.95 *(978-0-9791519-1-0(0))* Life Career Publishing.
Patton, Wendy & McMahon, Mary. Career Development & Systems Theory. 2008. 408p. *(978-90-77874-63-9(1))* Sense Pubs.
Paul D. Camp Community College Staff. Pdccc Your Ticket to Success: A Customized Version of College & Career Success by Marsha Fralick for Paul D. Camp Community College. 2nd rev. ed. 2010. (ENG.). 322p. pap. 43.00 *(978-0-7575-7915-8(9))* Kendall Hunt Publishing Co.
Pearson, Fenorris. How to Play the Game at the Top: The 9 Rules for Consummate Corporate Effectiveness. 2010. (ENG.). 256p. 27.50 *(978-1-932841-52-7(0))* Agate Publishing, Inc.
Pennings, Johannes M., et al. Human Capital, Inter-Firm Mobility & Organizational Evolution. 2007. (Illus.). 304p. 130.00 *(978-1-84542-757-3(2))* Elgar, Edward Publishing, Inc.
Perigo, Julie. Winners in the Second Half: A Guide for Executives at the Top of Their Game. 2008. (ENG., Illus.). 218p. 39.95 *(978-0-470-72537-5(0),* Jossey-Bass) Wiley, John & Sons, Inc.
Peroni, Gwen. CICD 2010 - Book Only. 2010. pap. *(978-1-4426-1088-0(3))* Univ. of Toronto Pr.
Peruniak, Geoffrey. A Quality of Life Approach to Career Development. 2010. (Illus.). 240p. *(978-1-4426-4136-5(3));* pap. *(978-1-4426-1064-4(6))* Univ. of Toronto Pr.
Peterson's. Green Careers in Energy. DeAngelis, Therese, ed. 2010. (ENG.). 358p. (YA). pap. 21.95 *(978-0-7689-2860-0(5))* Peterson's.
—Green Jobs for a New Economy: The Career Guide to Emerging Opportunities. DeAngelis, Therese, ed. 2009. (ENG.). 300p. (YA). pap. 21.95 *(978-0-7689-2815-0(X))* Peterson's.
Peterson's Guides Staff. Green Careers in Building & Landscaping: Your Guide to Jobs in Sustainable Contruction, Retrofitting, & Landscape Design. DeAngelis, Therese, ed. 2010. (ENG.). 400p. (YA). pap. 21.95 *(978-0-7689-2911-9(3))* Peterson's.
Pfeffer, Markus. E-Recruitment. 2008. 152p. pap. *(978-3-639-03230-7(6))* VDM Verlag Dr. Mueller e.K.
Phillips, Jean & Gully, Stanley Morris. Assessing Internal Job Candidates. 2010. (Staffing Strategically Ser.). (ENG., Illus.). 72p. pap. 18.95 *(978-1-58644-159-3(0))* Society for Human Resource Management.
Pierce, James G. Is the Organizational Culture of the U. S. Army Congruent with the Professional Development of Its Senior Level Corps? 2010. (Letort Papers). pap. *(978-1-58487-459-1(7))* Strategic Studies Institute, U.S. Army War College Commandant (AWCC-DSI/Pubns.).
Piña, Tinabeth. Cha-Ching!!! 2008. 56p. pap. 10.00 *(978-1-4257-7183-6(1))* Xlibris Corp.
Pink, Daniel H. The Adventures of Johnny Bunko: The Last Career Guide You'll Ever Need. 2008. (ENG., Illus.). 160p. (gr. 12-18). 15.00 *(978-1-59448-291-5(8),* Riverhead Trade (Paperbacks)) Penguin Group (USA) Inc.
Piotrowski, Katy. The Career Coward's Guide to Career Advancement: Sensible Strategies for Overcoming Career Fears. 2009. (ENG.). 192p. pap. 10.95 *(978-1-59357-393-5(6),* JIST Works) JIST Publishing.
Pippen, Delois. The Right Career. 2008. 72p. pap. 10.00 *(978-1-4257-3602-6(5))* Xlibris Corp.
Plunkett, Niamh. Professional Development of Healthcare Assistants in Northwest Ireland. 2011. 276p. pap. ***(978-3-8433-7967-0(X))*** Lambert Academic Publishing.
Pollan, Stephen M. & Levine, Mark. Lifelines for Money Misfortunes: How to Overcome Life's Greatest Challenges. 2007. (ENG.). 244p. 24.95 *(978-0-470-13907-3(2),* Wiley) Wiley, John & Sons, Inc.
Pols, Laurens. Organizational Career Management in the Netherlands. 2011. 96p. pap. ***(978-3-8433-9090-3(8))*** Lambert Academic Publishing.
Poole, Jon. Your Career from Here: Getting to the Job You Want. 2010. (In Easy Steps Ser.). (ENG., Illus.). 216p. pap. 14.99 *(978-1-84078-387-2(7))* Computer Step GBR. Dist: Perseus-PGW.
Port, Whitney & Berk, Sheryl. True Whit: Designing a Life of Style, Beauty, & Fun. 2011. (ENG.). 224p. 19.99 *(978-0-06-199686-3(6))* HarperCollins Pubs.
Powell, Edward. How to Get the Job You've Always Dreamed Of: (It's Marketing, It's Job Coaching, It's How to Get Results!) 2006. (ENG.). 56p. per. 16.95 *(978-1-4241-5681-8(5))* PublishAmerica, Inc.
Pradere, Steven. Effective Staff Development Connected to Increased Student Achievement - Building a Measureable Connection Between Effective. 2008. 132p. pap. *(978-3-639-02689-4(6))* VDM Verlag Dr. Mueller e.K.
Pryor, Robert. The Chaos Theory of Careers. 2011. (ENG., Illus.). 256p. (C). 160.00 *(978-0-415-55188-5(9))* Routledge.
Pryor, Robert & Bright, Jim. The Chaos Theory of Careers: A New Perspective on Working in the Twenty-First Century. 2011. (ENG., Illus.). 256p. (C). pap. 49.95 *(978-0-415-80634-3(8))* Routledge.
Ptolomey, Joanna. Taking Charge of Your Career: A Guide for the Library & Information Professional. 2009. 200p. pap. 85.00 ***(978-1-84334-465-0(3))*** Neal-Schuman Pubs., Inc.
Punch, Renee. Career Development of Deaf & Hard of Hearing Adolescents. 2008. 212p. pap. *(978-3-639-02557-6(1))* VDM Verlag Dr. Mueller e.K.
Pyle, K. Richard. Group Career Counseling: Practices & Principles. 2007. *(978-1-885333-17-9(X))* National Career Development Assn.
Quast, Lisa. Your Career, Your Way: Personal Strategies to Achieve Your Career Aspirations. 2006. (ENG., Illus.). 148p. per. *(978-1-59594-042-1(1),* Wingspan Pr.) WingSpan Publishing.
Ragland, Tom. How to Find a Job in a Bad Economy. 2009. 48p. pap. 15.95 *(978-1-4327-3007-9(X))* Outskirts Pr., Inc.
Ramsey, Dan. The Everything Start Your Own Consulting Business Book: Expert, step-by-step advice for a successful & profitable Career. 2009. (ENG.). 304p. pap. 15.95 *(978-1-60550-365-3(7))* Adams Media Corp.
Reece, Barry & Brandt, Rhonda. Human Relationsfirst. 2008. (ENG.). 312p. (C). pap. 77.95 *(978-0-618-97599-0(3),* 1024656) CENGAGE Learning.
Reitman, Annabelle. Career Moves: Take Charge of Your Training Career NOW! 2006. (ENG., Illus.). 200p. pap. 28.95 *(978-1-56286-456-9(4))* American Society for Training & Development.
Remling, Jennifer. Carve Your Own Road. 2009. (ENG.). 1p. pap. 14.99 *(978-1-60163-052-0(2))* Career Pr., Inc.
Renicks, Elizabeth. Preparing Today's Kids for Tomorrow's Jobs: What Should Our Community Do? Tebbetts, Ilse, ed. 2008. (Illus.). 30p. 3.90 *(978-0-945639-40-4(6))* National Issues Forums Institute.
Ress, Patricia Griffin. How to Generate Income Without a Job. 2011. 30p. pap. 16.95 ***(978-1-4626-2992-3(X))*** PublishAmerica, Inc.
Richard A. Wittmeyer. What You Should Know When Looking for a Job in Today's Marketplace: A Step-by-Step Approach to the Job Search. 2009. 80p. pap. 13.45 *(978-1-4269-2009-7(1))* Trafford Publishing.
Riegelman, Nancy. Collezioni Directions. 2009. (ENG.). 512p. (C). spiral bd. 207.40 *(978-0-13-509387-0(2),* Prentice Hall) Prentice Hall PTR.
Rigby, Rhymer. The Careerist: 100 Ways to Get Ahead at Work. 2012. (ENG.). 240p. pap. 19.95 ***(978-0-7494-6592-6(1))*** Kogan Page, Ltd. GBR. Dist: Ingram Pub. Services.
Rigdon, L. How to Change Your Career & Do the Work You Really Love: A Step-by-Step Plan for Making It Happen. 2009. (ENG.). 360p. pap. 24.95 *(978-1-60138-288-7(X))* Atlantic Publishing Co.
Riklan, David & Riklan, Michelle A., selected by. 101 Great Ways to Enhance Your Career. 2011. (Illus.). 389p. pap. 19.95 ***(978-0-9794992-7-2(5))*** Self Improvement Online, Inc.
Roach, Sean. Get off Your Duff & Make Your Own @#$! Cheese: It's up to You to Make Things Happen for Yourself. 2009. (ENG.). 105p. pap. 14.97 *(978-1-60037-530-9(8))* Morgan James Publishing.
Robbins, Mel. Professionalism: Reaching the Heights of Success in Your Career. 2010. (Illus.). xviii, 238p. pap. ***(978-1-60714-175-4(2))*** Kaplan Publishing.
Robert-Ribes, Jordi. Connecting Forward: Advanced networking for executives changing jobs, company, industry or Country. 2011. (ENG.). 136p. pap. ***(978-1-78088-049-5(9))*** Troubadour Publishing Ltd.
Roberts, et al. Career Discoveries: Career Planning Workbook. 2nd rev. ed. 2011. (ENG.). 338p. pap. 45.00 ***(978-0-7575-9122-8(1))*** Kendall Hunt Publishing Co.
Robinson, Steven T. Student Activity Workbook Business & Career Exploration Program. 2011. 56p. pap. 21.00 ***(978-1-4670-2468-6(6))*** AuthorHouse.
Robinson, William. The Keeping It Real Guide to Employment. 2008. 119p. pap. 10.01 *(978-0-557-02587-9(7))* Lulu Enterprises Inc.
Roche-Tarry, Dona & Roche-Lebrec, Dale. What's Next? Redefining Retirement. 2011. (ENG., Illus.). 224p. 40.00 *(978-0-230-29125-6(2))* Palgrave Macmillan.
Rodenkirch, John J., 1st. Lifetime Career Guidebook. 2008. (Illus.). per. *(978-0-9798353-1-5(3))* Explanation Pr.
Rodenkirch, John/Jeffrey. Lifetime Career Guidebook. 2007. per. *(978-0-9798353-0-8(5))* Explanation Pr.
Roffer, Robin Fisher. The Fearless Fish Out of Water: How to Succeed When You're the Only One Like You. 2009. (ENG.). 224p. 24.95 *(978-0-470-31668-9(3),* Wiley) Wiley, John & Sons, Inc.
Ronnestad, Michael Helge & Skovholt, Thomas. The Developing Practitioner. 2012. (ENG., Illus.). 384p. 39.95 *(978-0-415-88459-4(4))* Routledge.
Rosenberg, Arthur D. 101 Ways to Stand Out at Work: How to Get the Recognition & Rewards You Deserve. 2009. (ENG.). 256p. pap. 9.95 *(978-1-59869-981-4(4))* Adams Media Corp.
Ross, John D. Online Professional Development: Design, Deliver, Succeed! 2011. (Illus.). 208p. pap. 38.95 *(978-1-4129-8712-7(1),* B87127P) Corwin Pr.
Rothwell, William J. The Manager's Guide to Maximizing Employee Potential: Quick & Easy Strategies to Develop Talent Every Day, 1 vol. 2009. (ENG., Illus.). 272p. pap. 17.95 *(978-0-8144-1430-9(3))* Amacom.
Rounds, Mike. Executive Authorship: Write Your Way to Career Advancement. 2009. (Illus.). vi, 114p. pap. *(978-1-891440-57-1(8))* CPM Systems.
Rowan, Sophie. Brilliant Career Coach: How to Find & Follow Your Dream Career. 2nd rev. ed. 2011. (ENG., Illus.). 256p. pap. 19.99 ***(978-0-273-75014-7(3))*** FT Press.
Rowden, Robert W. Workplace Learning: Principles & Practice. 2007. (Professional Practices in Adult Education & Lifelong Learning Ser.). (Illus.). 146p. (C). *(978-1-57524-268-2(0))* Krieger Publishing Co.
Rowlett, Paula & Rowlett, Tom. Swallowed by the Whale: Surviving & Managing Change in the Workplace. 2010. 212p. pap. 19.95 *(978-1-4520-8566-1(8))* AuthorHouse.
Royer, Todd. Workination: Are You Fascinated with Your Career? 2007. 100p. per. 19.95 *(978-0-9789782-2-8(6))* Open Door Pubns.
Roßnagel, Christian Stamov, et al, eds. A Competence Perspective on Lifelong Workplace Learning. 2010. (Professions - Training, Education & Demographics Ser.). pap. 49.00 *(978-1-61668-686-4(3),* Nova Novinka) Nova Science Pubs., Inc.
Rudman, Jack. Career Counselor. (Career Examination Ser.: C-3698). pap. 29.95 *(978-0-8373-3698-5(8))* National Learning Corp.
Russell, Linda. Engage Your Workforce: Infoline. 2010. (ENG.). 16p. pap. 24.95 *(978-1-56286-724-9(5))* American Society for Training & Development.
Russell, Nan S. Hitting Your Stride: Your Work, Your Way. 2008. (Capital Career & Personal Development Ser.). 264p. per. 16.95 *(978-1-933102-56-6(X))* Capital Bks., Inc.
—Nibble Your Way to Success: 56 Winning Tips for Taking Charge of Your Career. 2007. 10.95 *(978-0-9792802-0-7(6))* MountainWorks Pr.
Safir, Rose. Moving on Up! Female Career Advancement & the Senior Intelligence Executive Service. 2008. (Illus.). xv, 75p. 61.99 *(978-1-4363-5565-0(6))* Xlibris Corp.
Salpeter, Miriam M. Social Networking for Career Success. 2011. (ENG.). 368p. pap. 18.95 *(978-1-57685-782-3(4))* LearningExpress, LLC.
Sampson, James P. Designing & Implementing Career Programs: A Handbook for Effective Practice. 2008. pap. *(978-1-885333-21-6(8))* National Career Development Assn.
Sanders, Ian & Sloly, David. Mash-up! How to Use Your Multiple Skills to Give You the Edge, Earn More Money & Be Happier. 2012. (ENG.). 192p. pap. 19.95 ***(978-0-7494-6590-2(5))*** Kogan Page, Ltd. GBR. Dist: Ingram Pub. Services.
Savickas, Mark L. Career Counseling. 2011. (Illus.). 160p. pap. 24.95 *(978-1-4338-0980-4(X))* American Psychological Assn.
Saylor-Marchant, Linda/Diane & 44 Enterprises, eds. Mentors You Should Know: Selected Essays & biographies about recession 21, careers, challenges Family- life the future & More. 2011. pap. 17.95 ***(978-1-4276-5259-1(7))*** Aardvark Global Publishing.
Scanlan, John B. Careers in Action. 3rd rev. ed. 2009. (ENG.). 290p. spiral bd. 60.69 *(978-0-7575-5259-5(5))* Kendall Hunt Publishing Co.
Schawbel, Dan. Me 2. 0, Revised & Updated Edition: 4 Steps to Building Your Future. rev. ed. 2010. (ENG.). 288p. pap. 14.99 *(978-1-60714-712-1(2))* Kaplan Publishing.
Schuh, Lexi. How to Get the Promotion You Want in 90 Days or Less: A Step-by-Step Plan for Making It Happen. 2009. (ENG.). 288p. pap. 24.95 *(978-1-60138-285-6(5))* Atlantic Publishing Co.
Schuman, Amy M. Nurturing the Talent to Nurture the Legacy: Career Development in the Family Business. 2010. (Family Business Leadership Ser.). (ENG., Illus.). 108p. pap. 23.00 *(978-0-230-11113-4(0))* Palgrave Macmillan.
Schuster, John P. The Power of Your Past: The Art of Reclaiming, Recalling, & Recasting. 2011. (BK Life Ser.). (ENG.). 240p. pap. 15.95 *(978-1-60509-826-5(4))* Berrett-Koehler Pubs., Inc.
Schutt, Donald A. A Strength-Based Approach to Career Development Using Appreciative Inquiry. 2007. *(978-1-885333-18-6(8))* National Career Development Assn.
Schwaiger, John. In Search of a Good Fit. 2009. 112p. pap. 13.99 *(978-1-60791-291-0(0))* Xulon Pr., Inc.
Schwartzkroin, Philip A. So You Want to be a Scientist? 2009. (ENG.). 208p. pap. 19.95 *(978-0-19-533354-1(3))* Oxford Univ. Pr., Inc.
Scott-Lennon, Frank, et al. Redundancy: A Development Opportunity for You! 2008. (ENG., Illus.). 104p. pap. 14.95 ***(978-1-906946-00-5(0))*** Management Briefs Ltd.
Scumaci, Dondi. Designed for Success: The 10 Commandments for Women in the Workplace. 2007. (ENG.). 256p. 21.99 *(978-1-59979-237-8(0))* Charisma Media.
Sdn Consulting. Increase Your Career Possibilities: An Insider's Guide to Interview Success. 2009. 92p. pap. 12.95 *(978-1-4389-6273-3(8))* AuthorHouse.
Searcy, Linda. PayDay Principles Does What I Do Really Matter. 2007. 160p. pap. 14.95 *(978-0-615-16493-9(5))* JustWrite Publishing.
Sears, Susan J. & Gordon, Virginia N. Building Your Career: A Guide to Your Future. 4th ed. 2010. (ENG., Illus.). 144p. (C). pap. 45.00 *(978-0-13-708452-4(8),* Prentice Hall) Prentice Hall PTR.
Seiden, Jason. How to Self-Destruct: Making the Least of What's Left of Your Career. 2008. (Illus.). 186p. per. 12.95 *(978-0-9799431-0-2(8))* 2009. pap. 18.95 *(978-1-929774-97-5(4))* Greenleaf Book Group.
Seitz, Victoria A. I Don't Wear A Suit! A Guide to Style for All of Us. 2011. 172p. pap. 11.70 ***(978-1-4634-6831-6(8))*** AuthorHouse.
Seldman, Marty & Seldman, Joshua. Executive Stamina: How to Optimize Time, Energy, & Productivity to Achieve Peak Performance. 2008. (ENG., Illus.). 320p. 24.95 *(978-0-470-22290-4(5),* Wiley) Wiley, John & Sons, Inc.
Sember, Terrance & Sember, Brette McWhorter. Bad Apples: How to Manage Difficult Employees, Encourage Good Ones to Stay, & Boost Productivity. 2009. (ENG.). 256p. pap. 14.95 *(978-1-60550-004-1(6))* Adams Media Corp.
Sharf, Richard S. Applying Career Development Theory to Counseling. 5th ed. 2009. (Graduate Career Counseling Ser.). (ENG.). 544p. (C). 166.95 *(978-0-495-80470-3(3))* Brooks/Cole.
—Applying Career Development Theory to Counseling. 5th ed. 2009. (ENG.). 192p. (C). pap. 49.95 *(978-0-495-80478-9(9))* Brooks/Cole.
Shatkin, L. & Farr, M. Top 100 Careers Without a Four-Year Degree. 10th ed. 2011. 400p. pap. 18.95 *(978-1-59357-784-1(2))* JIST Publishing.
Shatkin, Laurenc. Your $100,000 Career Plan: Match Your Personality to a Six-Figure Job. 2009. (ENG.). 240p. pap. 14.95 *(978-1-59357-668-4(4),* JIST Works) JIST Publishing.
Shatkin, Laurence. Quick Guide to College Majors & Careers. 2nd ed. 2008. (ENG.). 368p. pap. 18.95 *(978-1-59357-637-0(4),* JIST Works) JIST Publishing.
—The Sequel: How to Change Your Career Without Starting Over. 2011. 224p. pap. 12.95 *(978-1-59357-865-7(2))* JIST Publishing.
Shatkin, Laurence & Farr, Michael. Overnight Career Choice: Discover Your Ideal Job in Just a Few Hours. 2nd ed. 2011. 208p. pap. 9.95 *(978-1-59357-810-7(5),* JIST Works) JIST Publishing.

C

Shaw, Peter. The Four vs of Leadership: Vision, Values, Value-Added & Vitality. 2nd rev. ed. 2006. (ENG., Illus.). 226p. per. 29.95 *(978-1-84112-698-2(5),* Capstone) Wiley, John & Sons, Inc.

Sheldon, Pj Bme Mm. Career Strategies for Success. 2010. 152p. 29.99 *(978-1-4535-1656-0(5));* pap. 19.99 *(978-1-4535-1655-3(7))* Xlibris Corp.

Shepard, Molly D., et al. Breaking into the Boys' Club: 8 Ways for Women to Get Ahead in Business. 2009. (ENG.). 240p. pap. 15.95 *(978-1-59077-143-3(5))* Evans, M. & Co., Inc.

Sherfield, Robert M. & Moody, Patricia. Cornerstone: Opening Doors to Career Success. 2nd ed. 2009. (ENG.). 368p. (C). pap. 53.80 *(978-0-13-503003-5(X),* Prentice Hall) Prentice Hall PTR.

Shigley, Debra. The Go-Getter Girl's Guide: Get What You Want in Work & Life (and Look Great While You're at It) 2009. (ENG., Illus.). 256p. pap. 16.99 *(978-0-312-55575-7(X),* St. Martin's Griffin) St. Martin's Pr.

Signorelli, Paul & Reed, Lori. Workplace Learning & Leadership: A Handbook for Library & Nonprofit Trainers. 2011. 192p. pap. *(978-0-8389-1082-5(3))* American Library Assn.

Silvis, Carol A. & DuVivier, Roxanne L. 100% Externship Success: Success in Your Externship & Beyond. 2008. (ENG., Illus.). 384p. (C). pap. 52.95 *(978-1-4180-1549-7(0))* Delmar Cengage Learning.

Simeon, Roblyn. Working in the Global Economy: How to Develop & Manage Your Career Across Borders. 2012. (ENG., Illus.). 350p. 120.00 *(978-0-415-89130-1(2));* pap. 89.95 *(978-0-415-89131-8(0))* Routledge.

Simoneau, Carol Brooks & Bailey, Gerald D. A Facilitator's Guide to Online Professional Development: Establishing Communities of Learning & Cultures of Thinking. 2010. (Illus.). 216p. pap. 29.95 *(978-1-933760-34-6(6))* Christopher-Gordon Pubs., Inc.

Sims, Michelle R. The Power & Joy of Giving: A spiritual guide to empowering individuals & the church without investing a dime in stocks & Bonds. 2009. 72p. pap. 10.95 *(978-1-4401-3260-5(7))* iUniverse, Inc.

Sindell, Milo & Sindell, Thuy. The End of Work as You Know It: 8 Strategies to Redefine Work in Your Own Terms. 2009. (ENG., Illus.). 144p. pap. 14.99 *(978-1-58008-997-5(6))* Ten Speed Pr.

—Job Spa: 12 Weeks to Refresh, Refocus, & Recommit to Your Career. 2008. (ENG., Illus.). 288p. pap. 14.95 *(978-1-59869-473-4(1))* Adams Media Corp.

Skillings, Pamela. Escape from Corporate America: A Practical Guide to Creating the Career of Your Dreams. 2008. (ENG., Illus.). 352p. pap. 15.00 *(978-0-345-49974-5(3),* Ballantine Bks.) Random House Publishing Group.

Skorikov, Vladimir & Patton, Wendy, eds. Career Development in Childhood & Adolescence. 2007. 360p. per. *(978-90-8790-159-2(3))* Sense Pubs.

Slaughter, Patricia Susan. You Sitting on Top of the World-Instead of the World Sitting on Top of You! 2011. 102p. 24.99 ***(978-1-4653-6107-3(3));*** pap. 15.99 ***(978-1-4653-6106-6(5))*** Xlibris Corp.

Slomka, Beverly. Teens & the Job Game: Prepare Today-Win It Tomorrow. 2011. 120p. pap. 11.95 *(978-1-936236-45-9(1))* iUniverse, Inc.

Slowinski, Gene. Finding the Perfect Career. 2008. (Illus.). 74p. pap. 16.95 *(978-0-9768327-1-3(2))* Alliance Pr.

Smith, Norm. Got Progress? 2011. 108p. pap. 24.95 ***(978-1-257-07866-0(6))*** Lulu Enterprises Inc.

Smith, Roger Dean & Smith, Roger D. Advice Written on the Back of a Business Card: Leaders Share Their Most Valued Words of Guidance. 2009. (Illus.). 299p. ***(978-0-9823040-3-7(X))*** Modelbenders Pr.

Smoke Your Firefighter Interview: Strengthening Your Approach to the Fire Department Interview. 4th ed. 2008. 330p. pap. 24.95 *(978-0-9729934-4-9(4))* Freespool Enterprises.

Smolen, Dan. Tailoring the Green Suit: Empowering Yourself for an Executive Career in the New Green Economy. 2010. 136p. 21.99 *(978-1-4490-5980-4(5))* AuthorHouse.

Snelgrove, Shawn. Essentially You @ Work: A Career Transition Guide. 2009. 108p. pap. 28.50 *(978-0-578-00505-8(0))* Brainstorming a la Mode, Inc.

Snieder, Roel & Larner, Ken. The Art of Being a Scientist: A Guide for Graduate Students & Their Mentors. 2009. (ENG., Illus.). 296p. (C). pap. 34.99 *(978-0-521-74352-5(4))* Cambridge Univ. Pr.

Snyder, Didiayer. On Your Mark - an Insight Guide to Modeling. 2008. 236p. pap. 30.00 *(978-1-4389-2305-5(8))* AuthorHouse.

Solomon, Amy, et al. 100% Career Success. 2006. (ENG.). 208p. (C). pap. 34.95 *(978-1-4180-1632-6(2))* Delmar Cengage Learning.

Solomon, Michael R., et al. Brand You for Marketing: Real People Real Choices. 7th rev. ed. 2011. (ENG.). 312p. (C). pap. 42.67 *(978-0-13-038853-7(X),* Prentice Hall) Prentice Hall PTR.

Solomon, Nancy D. Impact! What Every Woman Needs to Know to Go from Invisible to Invincible. 2009. (ENG., Illus.). 304p. 24.95 *(978-0-470-48439-5(X),* Wiley) Wiley, John & Sons, Inc.

Sözüdogru, Oytun & Yaratan, Hüseyin. An Investigation on Multiple Intelligences. 2011. 76p. pap. ***(978-3-8443-3305-3(3))*** Lambert Academic Publishing.

Spector, Donald. The Self Improved: The Scientific Way to Get What You Want. 2009. (ENG.). 272p. 25.00 *(978-1-57826-335-6(2))* Hatherleigh Co., Ltd., The.

Spence, Marina. Make Every Day a Friday! The Joy of Connecting Who You Are with What You Do. 2009. (ENG.). pap. 12.95 *(978-1-60037-450-0(6))* Morgan James Publishing.

Sprouse, Mike. The Greatness Gap: Personal Strategies to Boost Your Professional Potential. 2011. (ENG.). 196p. pap. 15.99 *(978-1-59932-266-7(8))* Advantage Media Group.

Staley, Constance C. & Staley, Steve. FOCUS on College & Career Success. 2011. (ENG., Illus.). 384p. (C). pap. 44.95 *(978-1-4390-8390-1(8))* Wadsworth.

Statum, Ronald. Improving the Odds of Getting Beyond the Door. 2008. 292p. pap. 16.95 *(978-1-4327-1998-2(X))* Outskirts Pr., Inc.

Stebleton, Michael & Henle, Michael. Hired! the Job Hunting & Career Planning Guide. 4th ed. 2010. (ENG.). 360p. (C). pap. 53.80 *(978-0-13-502325-9(4),* Prentice Hall) Prentice Hall PTR.

Steele, Markell. Fast Track Your Career: Three Steps for Finding Work you Love. 2007. 64p. pap. 33.95 *(978-0-615-15870-9(6))* Futures in Motion, Inc.

Steinberg, Paul D. Making Yourself Marketable Insider Tips from A New York Career Consultant on Standing Out from the Crowd. 2009. 68p. pap. 14.97 *(978-0-557-05589-0(X))* Lulu Enterprises Inc.

Stewart, Susan. Have You Had Lunch? 2011. 60p. pap. 12.52 *(978-1-4567-7434-9(4))* AuthorHouse.

Stone, Gladys & Whelan, Fred. Goal! Your 30-Day Game Plan for Business & Career Success. 2009. (ENG.). 152p. pap. 14.95 *(978-1-884956-95-9(5))* Linden Publishing Co., Inc.

Strobel, Leny Mendoza & Gochuico, Nancy Figueroa, eds. From Our Hearts to Yours: Letters to a Young Student. 2008. 100p. per. *(978-0-9779438-2-1(8))* Phoenix Publishing Hse. International.

Stutz, Elinor. Hired! How to Use Sales Techniques to Sell Yourself on Interviews. 2010. E-Book 14.99 *(978-1-60163-685-0(7))* Career Pr., Inc.

Sun, Sanxing. The Key to Career Success. 2nd ed. 2007. per. 15.95 *(978-0-9785590-0-7(2))* TL Tower.

—The Key to Success: Shape A Superb Perception of You. 2007. 320p. 18.95 *(978-0-9785590-3-8(7))* TL Tower.

Sutton, Gary. Launch! Rate Your Job Skills vs. Other Grads. 2007. (Illus.). 350p. (C). pap. 39.00 *(978-0-9759625-1-0(5))* Sutton, Gary.

Tahmincioglu, Eve. From the Sandbox to the Corner Office: Lessons Learned on the Journey to the Top. 2006. (ENG.). 225p. 22.95 *(978-0-471-78883-6(X),* Wiley) Wiley, John & Sons, Inc.

Tait, Ruth. Global Roads to the Top. 2012. (ENG., Illus.). 256p. 42.00 *(978-0-230-27440-2(4))* Palgrave Macmillan.

Tallman, David. Laid off & Loving It: How to Survive A Catastrophe. 2011. pap. 11.99 *(978-1-61739-119-4(0))* Tate Publishing & Enterprises, LLC.

Tanner, Ken. The Boomers' Career Survival Guide: Achieving Success & Contentment from Middle Age through Retirement, 1 vol. 2009. (Illus.). 165p. 29.95 *(978-0-313-36521-8(0),* C36521, Praeger Pubs.) Greenwood Publishing Group, Inc.

—Never Order Barbecue in Maine: Proven Career Strategies from People Who've Been There, Done That, 0 vols. 2006. 240p. 18.99 *(978-0-7852-1349-9(X))* Nelson, Thomas Inc.

Taylor, Diane S. Career Work Experience: A Career Development Workbook. 3rd rev. ed. (ENG.). 2012. pap. 49.99 ***(978-0-7575-9851-7(X))*** 2010. 198p. pap. 49.27 *(978-0-7575-1436-4(7))* Kendall Hunt Publishing Co.

Templin, Joseph. Financial Mistakes of New College Grads: the Seminar. 2009. 38p. pap. 15.00 *(978-0-557-07476-1(2))* Lulu Enterprises Inc.

Thayer, Lee. How Executives Fail: 25 Surefire Recipes for Sabotaging Your Career. 2007. per. 24.95 *(978-1-934229-00-2(8))* Windsor Media Enterprises, Inc.

Thomas, Sherri. Career Smart: Five Steps to a Powerful Personal Brand. 2007. 108p. 21.95 *(978-1-60145-366-2(3))* Booklocker.com, Inc.

Thomson, Peninah, et al. A Woman's Place in the Boardroom: The Roadmap. 2008. (ENG., Illus.). 224p. 53.00 *(978-0-230-53712-5(X))* Palgrave Macmillan.

Tobin, Daniel R. Learn Your Way to Success: How to Customize Your Professional Learning Plan to Accelerate Your Career. 2011. (ENG., Illus.). 240p. pap. 20.00 ***(978-0-07-178225-8(7),*** 0071782257) McGraw-Hill Cos., The.

Tomorrow's Young Achievers: 31 Career Defining Insights for a Radically Different Tomorrow. 2010. 141p. pap. 5.00 *(978-81-7806-204-4(6))* Unicorn Bks. Pvt Ltd. IND. Dist: Mahal, Pustak Pubs., Booksellers & Order Suppliers.

Tonhäuser, Cornelia. Implementierung von Coaching als Instrument der Personalentwicklung in deutschen Großunternehmen. 2010. (Forum Personalmanagement / Human Resource Management Ser.). (GER.). 380p. 79.95 *(978-3-631-60289-8(8))* Lang, Peter GmbH, Europaischer Verlag der Wissenschaften DEU. Dist: Lang, Peter.

Tracy, Brian. Earn What You're Really Worth: Maximize Your Income at Any Time in Any Market. 2012. (ENG.). 272p. 25.99 *(978-1-59315-630-5(8))* Vanguard Pr.

Tracy, Brian. Earn What You're Really Worth: Maximize Your Income in Any Market. 2012. E-Book ***(978-1-59315-670-1(7),*** Vanguard Press) Pegasus Elliot Mackenzie Publishers.

Trochiano, William. Successful Career Management in a Downsizing Organization. 2008. 136p. pap. *(978-3-639-08608-9(2))* VDM Verlag Dr. Mueller e.K.

Trotta, Marcia. Staff Development on a Shoestring: A How-To-Do-It Manual for Librarians. 2010. x, 117p. 70.00 *(978-1-55570-730-9(0))* Neal-Schuman Pubs., Inc.

Trunk, Penelope. Brazen Careerist: The New Rules for Success. 2007. (ENG.). 224p. 25.99 *(978-0-446-57864-6(9),* Business Plus) Grand Central Publishing.

Tuch, C.L. & Tuch, C.V. Student Success Guide. 2007. 4p. *(978-1-55431-187-3(X))* Permacharts, Inc.

—Student Success Guide: Learning & Studying Tools. 2007. 6p. *(978-1-55431-246-7(9))* Permacharts, Inc.

Turbane, Ronnie Gale. Knowledge Is POWER series - the Beginning: The Resume, the Interview, the New Hire, Six Skills with Stratgies for Success. 2007. 98p. per. *(978-0-9797149-0-0(7))* Turbane, Ronnie Gale.

Turienzo, Rubén. The Wisdom of Oz: The Road to Motivation, Courage & Talent. 2011. (SPA., Illus.). 192p. pap. 24.99 ***(978-1-907794-04-9(2))*** LID Publishing GBR. Dist: AtlasBooks Distribution.

Turner, Joe & Swenson, Sue. Paycheck 911: Don't Panic... Power Your Job Search! 2008. 192p. pap. 17.00 *(978-0-9779804-4-4(8))* OPA Author Services.

Tymorek, Stan. Career Launcher. 2012. (Career Launcher Ser.). (C). (gr. 9). 768.90 ***(978-0-8160-8416-6(5),*** Ferguson Publishing Co.) Facts On File, Inc.

Ugwuoke, Chigbo A. Time to Decide: A Career Choice Manual. 2011. 64p. pap. 12.10 ***(978-1-4520-6256-3(0))*** AuthorHouse.

University of Nevada, Las Vegas Staff. Academic & Career Connections at Univ. rev. ed. 2009. (ENG.). 376p. pap. 58.76 *(978-0-7575-6721-6(5))* Kendall Hunt Publishing Co.

Varlejs, Jana, et al, eds. Strategies for Regenerating the Library & Information Profession. 2009. (IFLA Publications). (ENG.). 415p. *(978-3-598-22044-9(8))* Saur, K. G. Verlag GmbH & Co.

Vincent, Aaltje & Valkenburg, Jacco. Career Management via LinkedIn. 2011. (ENG., Illus.). 128p. pap. *(978-90-491-0439-9(8),* Lannoo Pubs. (Acc)) Antique Collectors' Club.

Viscusi, Stephen. Bulletproof Your Job: 4 Simple Strategies to Ride Out the Rough Times & Come Out on Top at Work. 2008. (Illus.). 192p. 19.95 *(978-0-06-171360-6(0),* Collins) HarperCollins Pubs.

Waddell, Janice, et al. Building Your Nursing Career: A Guide for Students. 3rd ed. 2008. (ENG., Illus.). 80p. (C). spiral bd. 24.95 *(978-1-897422-15-1(6),* Mosby) Elsevier - Health Sciences Div.

Wade, Sarah. Find Your Dream Job: True Stories & Guaranteed for Getting a Job You Love. 2010. (Illus.). 235p. pap. 15.95 *(978-1-905736-47-8(9))* Marshall Cavendish GBR. Dist: Midpoint Trade Bks., Inc.

Wall, Bob. Coaching for Emotional Intelligence: The Secret to Developing the Star Potential in Your Employees. 2006. (ENG.). 240p. 24.95 *(978-0-8144-0890-2(7))* Amacom.

Wallace, Wanda T. Reaching the Top: Factors That Impact the Careers & Retention of Senior Women Leaders. 2008. 136p. pap. 12.95 *(978-1-4303-1196-6(7))* Lulu Enterprises Inc.

Wallin, Peter. Living the Dream: The Four Pillars to Life Mastery. 2010. 175p. pap. 15.00 *(978-1-59571-515-9(0))* Word Association Pubs.

Walton. African-American Managers' Perceptions about Factors That Impact Their Career Development & Job Opportunities. 2008. 80p. pap. 13.49 *(978-1-4343-2281-4(5))* AuthorHouse.

Wang, Hsiou-Huai. Between Self & Others. 2011. 492p. pap. ***(978-3-8383-9174-8(8))*** Lambert Academic Publishing.

Wang, Ling. Preservice Teachers' Self-Efficacy for Technology Integration. 2009. 108p. pap. *(978-3-639-14229-7(2))* VDM Verlag Dr. Mueller e.K.

Wasson, Christina, et al. Making History at the Frontier: Women Creating Careers As Practicing Anthropologists, Number 26. 2006. (NAPA Bulletin Ser.: Vol. 26). (ENG., Illus.). 232p. pap. 31.95 *(978-1-931303-29-3(0),* Wiley-Blackwell) Wiley, John & Sons, Inc.

Watson, Joe. Where the Jobs Are Now: The Fastest-Growing Industries & How to Break into Them. 2009. (ENG.). 288p. pap. 18.95 *(978-0-07-170339-0(X),* 007170339X) McGraw-Hill Cos., The.

Watson, Mark & McMahon, Mary, eds. Career Development: Global Issues & Challenges. 2012. (Professions - Training, Education & Demographics Ser.). 181p. 75.00 *(978-1-61324-852-2(0))* Nova Science Pubs., Inc.

Wellenstein, Carl. 12 Steps to a New Career. 2009. (ENG.). 1p. pap. 16.99 *(978-1-60163-062-9(X))* Career Pr., Inc.

Werdlow Rogers, June. Cracking the Double Standard Code: A Guide to Successful Navigation in the Workplace. 2010. 278p. 24.95 *(978-1-934980-45-3(5));* (ENG.). pap. 17.95 *(978-1-934980-46-0(3))* Cable Publishing.

Werner, Jon M. & DeSimone, Randy L. Human Resource Development. 6th ed. 2011. (ENG.). 688p. (C). 212.95 *(978-0-538-48099-4(8))* Cengage South-Western.

Whitcomb, Susan B. & Bryan, Chandlee. The Twitter Job Search Guide: Find a Job & Advance Your Career in Just 15 Minutes a Day. 2010. 256p. pap. 14.95 *(978-1-59357-791-9(5),* JIST Works) JIST Publishing.

White, Andrea. Healthy, Wealthy, & Wise: Planning for yOur Encore Years. 2009. pap. 9.95 *(978-1-61623-870-4(4))* Independent Pub.

—Shooting It Straight from the Hip: YOU Are Your Best Feature. 2007. 76p. per. 16.95 *(978-1-4241-9508-4(X))* PublishAmerica, Inc.

Wibbenmeyer, Kelly. Any Tom, Dick, or Harry Can Get A Job: A Sure Fire Way to Land A Job. 2009. (Illus.). 120p. pap. 12.95 *(978-1-4327-5306-1(1))* Outskirts Pr., Inc.

Wichert, Ines. Where Have All the Senior Women Gone? 9 Critical Job Assignments for Women Leaders. 2011. (ENG., Illus.). 248p. 40.00 *(978-0-230-30129-0(0))* Palgrave Macmillan.

Widener, Chris. The Angel Inside: Michelangelo's Secrets for Following Your Passion & Finding the Work You Love. 2010. (ENG.). 128p. pap. 9.99 *(978-0-307-71953-9(7),* Broadway Business) Knopf Doubleday Publishing Group.

Wilkes. Professional Development. 4th ed. Date not set. (Freshman Orientation/College Success Ser.). tchr. ed. 2.25 *(978-0-534-51158-6(9))* Wadsworth.

Williams, Anna Graf & Hall, Karen J. Creating Your Career Portfolio: At-A-Glance Guide for Students. 3rd ed. 2007. (ENG., Illus.). 176p. pap. 29.95 incl. cd-rom *(978-0-9796434-0-8(6))* Learnovation, LLC.

Williams, John. Screw Work, Let's Play: How to Do What You Love & Get Paid for It. rev. ed. 2010. (ENG.). 248p. (C). pap. 19.99 *(978-0-273-73093-4(2))* FT Press.

Williams, Mark. Career & Life Development. rev. ed. 2012. (ENG.). 244p. spiral bd. 50.00 ***(978-0-7575-9613-1(4))*** Kendall Hunt Publishing Co.

Wilson, Alissa, et al. Practical Idealists: Changing the World & Getting Paid. 2008. (Practical Idealism Ser.). 228p. pap. 15.00 *(978-0-674-03207-1(1))* Harvard Univ. Pr.

Wilson, Joni. The Voice of Success: A Woman's Guide to a Powerful & Persuasive Voice, 1 vol. 2009. (ENG., Illus.). pap. 17.95 *(978-0-8144-1280-0(7))* Amacom.

Wilson, Randall D. Undecided? A Workbook for Career Decision Making & Life Planning. (C). pap. *(978-1-884155-01-7(4))* Day & Nite Publishing.

Wilson, Yusuf. Time to Get Hired! Strategies for Your Job Search, Job Transition, & Finding Green Jobs. 2010. 188p. 26.50 *(978-1-4269-4188-7(9));* pap. 16.50 *(978-1-4269-4187-0(0))* Trafford Publishing.

Wong, Anny, et al. The Use of Standardized Scores in Officer Career Management & Selection, 1 vol. 2012. (ENG.). 90p. pap. 19.50 ***(978-0-8330-5902-4(5))*** RAND Corp., The.

Woods, Edward. Employee Development at the Workplace: Achieving Empowerment in a Continuous Learning Environment. 2nd rev. ed. 2010. (ENG.). 190p. pap. 50.89 *(978-0-7575-1687-0(4),* 0757516874) Kendall Hunt Publishing Co.

Woodward, Marti. The 10 Power Protocols. 2009. 108p. pap. 12.99 *(978-1-60860-137-0(4),* Strategic Bk. Publishing) AEG Literary Publishing Services, Inc.

Woodward, Michael. The YOU Plan: A 5-Step Guide to Taking Charge of Your Career in the New Economy. 2010. (ENG.). 176p. pap. 14.99 *(978-1-59932-175-2(0),* Keynote Publishing) Advantage Media Group.

Yarnall, Jane. Strategic Career Management: Developing Your Talent. 2007. (ENG., Illus.). 264p. per. 46.95 *(978-0-7506-8369-2(4))* Routledge.

Yeung, Rob. Job Hunting for Rookies. 2009. (Illus.). 192p. pap. *(978-0-462-09956-9(3))* Marshall Cavendish.

—Job Hunting the New Rules. 2009. 192p. pap. *(978-0-462-09928-6(8))* Marshall Cavendish.

Yorio, Kimberly & Friedman, Caitlin. The Big Bold Moves for Career Success: How to Build Confidence, Conquer Fear, Manage up, Navigate Change & Much, Much More. 2009. (ENG.). 240p. pap. 13.99 *(978-0-7679-2767-3(2))* Broadway Bks.

York, Norman J. & York, Madeleine A. Thriving in the Changing Lab Market. Reardon, Madeliene, ed. Date not set. 225p. pap. *(978-0-9661547-1-9(1),* Entheos Pubns.) York Career Development, Inc.

Zabel, Diane. Career Paths & Career Development of Business Librarians. 2009. (ENG.). 256p. 150.00 *(978-0-7890-3794-7(7));* pap. 45.95 *(978-0-7890-3795-4(5))* Routledge.

Zaugra, John. Liberal Eduation: Your Intentional Career Path. rev. ed. 2010. (ENG.). 72p. pap. 17.90 *(978-0-7575-6132-0(2))* Kendall Hunt Publishing Co.

Zeiss, Tony. Build Your Own Ladder: 4 Secrets to Making Your Career Dreams Come True. 2010. 178p. pap. 12.99 *(978-1-4016-0527-8(3))* Nelson, Thomas Inc.

Zelinski, Ernie & Zelinski, Ernie J. Career Success Without a Real Job: The Career Book for People Too Smart to Work in Corporations. 2009. (ENG.). 240p. pap. 16.95 *(978-1-58008-967-8(4))* Ten Speed Pr.

Zelinski, Ernie J. Career Success Without a Real Job: The Career Book for People Too Smart to Work in Corporations. 2009. (ENG.). 240p. pap. 16.95 *(978-0-9694194-7-1(3))* Visions International Publishing CAN. Dist: National Bk. Network.

—Real Success Without a Real Job: There Is No Life Like It! 2006. (ENG., Illus.). 229p. per. 16.95 *(978-1-58008-800-8(7))* Ten Speed Pr.

Zepeda, Sally J. Professional Development: What Works. 2nd ed. 2011. (Illus.). xxiii, 327p. ***(978-1-59667-193-5(9))*** Eye On Education, Inc.

Zepeda, Sally J. Professional Development: What Works. 2008. 300p. 39.95 *(978-1-59667-086-0(X))* Eye On Education, Inc.

Zlton, David E. The Power Move: Accelerate Your Professional Advancement through the Power of Knowledge. 2010. 132p. 24.95 *(978-1-4502-5182-2(X));* pap. 14.95 *(978-1-4502-5181-5(1))* AuthorHouse.

CAREER EDUCATION

Here are entered works on the efforts of educational institutions and the community to teach individuals the values of a work-oriented society in preparation for meaningful employment. Works on vocational instruction within the standard educational system, usually at the secondary level, are entered under Vocational Education. Works on the process of training individuals in a particular skill after termination of their formal education are entered under Occupational Training. Works on retraining persons with obsolete vocational skills are entered under Occupational Retraining. Works on on-the-job training of employees are entered under Employees—Training of.

see also Vocational Education

Allen, Jim, et al, eds. Competencies, Higher Education & Career in Japan & the Netherlands. (Higher Education Dynamics Ser.). 2010. vi, 271p. pap. 169.00 *(978-90-481-7514-7(3),* 9048175143) 2007. (Illus.). 268p. 169.00 *(978-1-4020-6043-4(2))* Springer.

Archambault, Dennis R. YourfirstCareerJob. com: The Adventure of Your Life. 2007. (Illus.). 72p. per. 17.95 *(978-0-9729752-1-6(7))* danc-N-life: pub.

Aronowitz, Stanley. The Last Good Job in America: Work & Education in the New Global Technoculture. 2007. (Critical Perspectives Series: a Book Series Dedicated to Paulo Freire Ser.). (ENG.). 282p. per. 21.95 *(978-0-7425-6026-0(0))* Rowman & Littlefield Publishers, Inc.

Barnes, Anthony, et al. An Introduction to Career Learning & Development 11-19. 2010. (ENG., Illus.). 168p. (C). 130.00 *(978-0-415-57777-9(2))*; pap. 37.95 *(978-0-415-57778-6(0))* Taylor & Francis Group GBR. (Routledge). Dist: Taylor & Francis Group.

Barrett, Janet R. Constructing a Personal Orientation to Music Teaching. 2010. (ENG., Illus.). 208p. 140.00 *(978-0-415-87183-9(2))* Routledge.

Bly, Robert. 88 Money-Making Writing Jobs. 2009. (ENG.). 336p. pap. 20.99 *(978-1-4022-1507-0(X))* Sourcebooks, Inc.

Career & Technical Education. 2010. 32p. lib. bdg. 151.60 *(978-1-60279-965-3(2), 200494)* Cherry Lake Publishing.

Chronicle Guidance Publishers, creator. Chronicle Career College & Technology School Databook: Schools Offering Programs That Result in an Occupational Certificate/Diploma or a Technical Associate Degree. 2008. (Chronicle Career College & Technology School Databook Ser.). 148p. pap. 35.00 *(978-1-55631-352-3(7))* Chronicle Guidance Pubns., Inc.

—Chronicle Two-Year College Databook: Schools Offering Programs That Result in an Occupational Certificate/Diploma or an Associate Degree. 2008. (Chronicle Two-Year College Databook Ser.). 478p. pap. 35.50 *(978-1-55631-350-9(0))* Chronicle Guidance Pubns., Inc.

Colozzi, Edward. Creating Careers with Confidence. 2008. (ENG.). 144p. (C). pap. 27.40 *(978-0-13-515789-3(7),* Prentice Hall) Prentice Hall PTR.

Derrickson, Dale R. Career & Technical Student Organizations: Purpose & Possibility. 2007. 100p. pap. 19.95 *(978-0-7414-4306-9(6))* Infinity Publishing.

Eliason, Grafton & Patrick, John. Career Development in the Schools. 2008. *(978-1-59311-534-0(2))*; pap. *(978-1-59311-533-3(4))* Information Age Publishing, Inc.

Fay, Charles. Parenting Kids - To Become the People Employers Really Want and... America Desperately Needs! 2008. pap. 17.95 *(978-1-930429-96-3(7))* Love & Logic Institute, Inc.

Feng, Anwei, et al, eds. Becoming Interculturally Competent through Education & Training. 2009. (Languages for Intercultural Communication & Education Ser.). (ENG., Illus.). 192p. 39.95 *(978-1-84769-162-0(5))* Multilingual Matters GBR. Dist: Univ. of Toronto Pr.

Gore, Paul A. & Carter, Louisa P. Students in Transition: Research & Practice in Career Development. 2011. *(978-1-889271-73-6(X))* National Resource Ctr. for The First Year Experience & Students in Transition.

Hager, Paul & Holland, Susan, eds. Graduate Attributes, Learning & Employability. 2010. (Lifelong Learning Book Ser.). xiv, 307p. pap. 179.00 *(978-90-481-7349-5(3),* 9048173493) Springer.

Hernàndez-Gantes, Victor & Blank, William. Teaching English Language Learners in Career & Technical Education Programs. 2008. (ENG., Illus.). 256p. 145.00 *(978-0-415-95758-8(3))* Routledge.

Hernàndez-Gantes, Victor, et al. Teaching English Language Learners in Career & Technical Education Programs. 2008. (Illus.). XIV, 242p. 36.95 *(978-0-415-95757-1(5))* Routledge.

Keleher, Patrick, et al, eds. Work-Integrated Learning in Engineering, Built Environment & Technology: Diversity of Practice in Practice. 2011. (Illus.). 350p. 180.00 *(978-1-60960-547-6(0),* Information Science Reference) IGI Global.

Kinard, Lee. Guilford Technical Community College History, 1958-2008: Creating Entrepreneurial Partnerships for Workforce Preparedness. 2008. (ENG.). 548p. 24.95 *(978-1-59460-558-1(0))* Carolina Academic Pr.

Lewis, Thomas N. & South-Western Educational Publishing Staff. The 16 Career Clusters: A Project-Based Orientation (with IMPACT Interactive CD-ROM) 2008. (Bpa Ser.). (ENG.). 192p. 76.95 *(978-0-538-44971-7(3))* Cengage South-Western.

Littrell, Ed.D., J.J., JJ, et al. School to Career. 9th ed. 2011. (ENG.). (gr. 9-12). pap. 20.00 ***(978-1-60525-529-3(7))*** Goodheart-Willcox Pub.

Littrell, J. J., et al. School to Career. 9th ed. 2011. (ENG.). 640p. (gr. 9-12). 88.00 *(978-1-60525-528-6(9))* Goodheart-Willcox Pub.

Maestas, Lily. Get Clear on Your Career. rev. ed. 2009. (ENG.). 130p. pap. 29.77 *(978-0-7575-6142-9(X))* Kendall Hunt Publishing Co.

Marzetti, Matthew J. The Law School Gamble: Things You Must Consider Before Placing Your Bet. 2009. 156p. pap. 17.95 *(978-1-4490-2102-3(6))* AuthorHouse.

McCutcheon Jr, Moses. Planning Today for Success Tomorrow Hel. 2007. (ENG.). 164p. 30.95 *(978-1-4327-0072-0(3))*; pap. 19.95 *(978-1-4327-0013-3(8))* Outskirts Pr., Inc.

Mulligan, Michael V. My High School, College & Post College Plans: Placing Myself on the Right Career Path before Age 30. 2011. 316p. pap. 30.95 *(978-1-4620-0053-1(3))* iUniverse, Inc.

Neumark, David. Improving School-to-Work Transitions. 2007. (Illus.). 294p. *(978-0-87154-642-5(6))* Russell Sage Foundation.

Nijhof, W. J. & Brandsma, Jittie, eds. Bridging the Skills Gap between Work & Education. 2010. (Illus.). 244p. pap. 110.00 *(978-90-481-5197-4(X),* 904815197X) Springer.

Oakes, Elizabeth H. Ferguson Career Resource Guide to Apprenticeship Programs, 2 vols., Set. 2nd rev. ed. 2006. (Ferguson Career Resource Guide Ser.). 1056p. (C). (gr. 9-18). 150.00 *(978-0-8160-5573-9(4),* Ferguson Publishing Co.) Facts On File, Inc.

Orrell, Janice. Work Integrated Learning. 2010. (ENG., Illus.). 240p. pap. 42.95 *(978-0-415-55677-4(5))* Routledge.

Orrell, Janice, et al. Work Integrated Learning. 2010. (ENG., Illus.). 240p. 130.00 *(978-0-415-55676-7(7),* Routledge) Taylor & Francis Group GBR. Dist: Taylor & Francis Group.

Reed, Susan C., et al. Linking Adults with Community: Promoting Civic Engagement Through Community Based Learning, No. 118. 2008. (J-B ACE Single Issue Adult & Continuing Education Ser.: 93). (ENG.). 96p. pap. 29.00 *(978-0-470-38531-9(6),* Jossey-Bass) Wiley, John & Sons, Inc.

Sampson, James P. Designing & Implementing Career Programs: A Handbook for Effective Practice. 2008. pap. *(978-1-885333-21-6(8))* National Career Development Assn.

Schomburg, Harald & Teichler, Ulrich. Higher Education & Graduate Employment in Europe: Results from Graduates Surveys from Twelve Countries. 2010. (Higher Education Dynamics Ser.). vii, 169p. pap. 149.00 *(978-90-481-7297-9(7),* 9048172977) Springer.

Schomburg, Harald & Teichler, Ulrich, eds. Higher Education & Graduate Employment in Europe: Results from Graduates Surveys from Twelve Countries. 2006. (Higher Education Dynamics Ser.: Vol. 27). (Illus.). 168p. 149.00 *(978-1-4020-5153-1(0),* 1402051530) Springer.

Schutt, Donald A., Jr. How to Plan & Develop a Career Center. 2nd rev. ed. 2007. (Illus.). 240p. 35.00 *(978-0-8160-7135-7(7),* Ferguson Publishing Co.) Facts On File, Inc.

Seddon, Terri, et al, eds. Learning & Work & the Politics of Working Life: Global Transformations & Collective Identities in Teaching, Nursing & Social Work. 2010. (ENG.). 248p. 140.00 *(978-0-415-55752-8(6))* Routledge.

Seddon, Terri, et al. Learning & Work & the Politics of Working Life: Global Transformations & Collective Identities in Teaching, Nursing & Social Work. 2010. (ENG.). 248p. pap. 47.95 *(978-0-415-55753-5(4))* Routledge.

Seelig, Tina. What I Wish I Knew When I Was 20 Intl: A Crash Course on Making Your Place in the World. 2010. (ENG.). 208p. pap. 12.00 *(978-0-06-204741-0(8),* HarperOne) HarperCollins Pubs.

Shaffer, David Williamson. How Computer Games Help Children Learn. 2008. (ENG., Illus.). 256p. pap. 17.00 *(978-0-230-60252-6(5))* Palgrave Macmillan.

Sutton, Gary. Launch! Rate Your Job Skills vs. Other Grads. 2007. (Illus.). 350p. (C). pap. 39.00 *(978-0-9759625-1-0(5))* Sutton, Gary.

Synatschk, Katherine O. & Clark, Gary M. Employment & Career Planning. 2007. iii, 135p. pap. *(978-1-4164-0239-8(X))* PRO-ED, Inc.

Tancos, Kathryn. Your Gateway to Success. 2009. pap. *(978-1-61623-128-6(9))* Independent Pub.

Teichler, Ulrich. Careers of University Graduates. 2007. (Higher Education Dynamics Ser.). (Illus.). 288p. 189.00 *(978-1-4020-5925-4(6))* Springer.

—Higher Education & the World of Work. 2008. 340p. *(978-90-8790-755-6(9))*; pap. *(978-90-8790-754-9(0))* Sense Pubs.

Teichler, Ulrich, ed. Careers of University Graduates: Views & Experiences in Comparative Perspectives. 2010. (Higher Education Dynamics Ser.). vi, 284p. pap. 189.00 *(978-90-481-7477-5(5),* 9048174775) Springer.

Tomlinson, Michael. Higher Education & Graduate Employability. 2009. 200p. pap. *(978-3-639-12665-5(3))* VDM Verlag Dr. Mueller e.K.

Turner, Kathy, et al. Essential Academic Skills. rev. ed. 2009. (ENG., Illus.). x, 294p. pap. 55.00 *(978-0-19-556836-3(2))* Oxford Univ. Pr., Inc.

Wang, Victor. Definitive Readings in the History, Philosophy, Theories & Practice of Career & Technical Education. Wang, Victor C. X., ed. 2010. 350p. 180.00 *(978-1-61520-747-3(3))* IGI Global.

Wang, Victor C. X. Handbook of Research on E-Learning Applications for Career & Technical Education: Technologies for Vocational Training, 2 vols. Wang, Victor C. X., ed. 2009. (Illus.). 1028p. 495.00 *(978-1-60566-739-3(0),* Information Science Reference) IGI Global.

Wang, Victor C. X. & King, Kathleen P. Building Workforce Competencies in Career & Technical Education. 2009. (Adult Education Special Topics Ser.). (Illus.). xxi, 269p. *(978-1-60752-030-6(3))*; 292p. pap. *(978-1-60752-029-0(X))* Information Age Publishing, Inc.

Zendel, Azita. Hollywood Apprentice: How to Break into Hollywood & Survive the Toxic Boss Syndrome. 2006. (Hollywood Apprentice Ser.). 326p. per. 19.95 *(978-0-9759016-4-9(8),* AZ1836) Azita Bks. & Films, Inc.

CAREER MANAGEMENT
see Career Development

CAREER PLANNING
see Career Development

CAREER WOMEN
see Women—Employment

CAREERS
see Occupations; Professions; Success; Vocational Guidance

CAREGIVERS
Here are entered works on family or friends who provide personal home care for the elderly, ill, or people with disabilities on an informal voluntary basis.

Abingdon. What's in the Bible about God? What's in the Bible & Why Should I Care? 2008. (Why Is That in the Bible & Why Should I Care? Ser.). 80p. pap. 8.00 *(978-0-687-65363-8(0))* Abingdon Pr.

—What's in the Bible about Jesus? What's in the Bible & Why Should I Care? 2008. (Why Is That in the Bible & Why Should I Care? Ser.). 84p. pap. 8.00 *(978-0-687-65383-6(5))* Abingdon Pr.

—What's in the Bible about Us? What's in the Bible & Why Should I Care? 2008. (Why Is That in the Bible & Why Should I Care? Ser.). 82p. pap. 8.00 *(978-0-687-65373-7(8))* Abingdon Pr.

Abingdon Press. What's in the Bible & How Do I Use It? Real Help for Regular People. 2008. (Why Is That in the Bible & Why Should I Care? Ser.). 109p. pap. 10.00 *(978-0-687-65403-1(3))* Abingdon Pr.

Abrams, Grant & Elizabeth, Patricia. Caregiver Revolution: 5 Steps to Enlightened Caregiving. 2011. (ENG., Illus.). 180p. pap. 19.95 *(978-0-89556-148-0(4))* Gateways Bks. & Tapes.

Abramson, Alexis & Dunkin, Mary Anne. The Caregiver's Survival Handbook: How to Care for Your Aging Parent Without Losing Yourself. rev. ed. 2011. (ENG.). 288p. (gr. 12). 15.95 *(978-0-399-53642-7(6),* Perigee Trade) Penguin Group (USA) Inc.

Activities en Espanol. Activities en Espanol. 2010.Tr. of Acitvities in Spanish. (SPA., Illus.). 107p. 14.95 *(978-0-615-37470-3(0))* Fernandez, Alberto.

AgeWiseLiving LLC. The Ultimate Caregiver's Survival Guide: The Step by Step Blueprint for Resolving Your Eldercare Issues by Choice, Not Crisis. 2008. 151p. spiral bd. 97.00 *(978-0-9796879-1-4(8))* AgeWiseLiving.

Agronin, Marc E. Alzheimer Disease & Other Dementias: A Practical Guide. 2nd rev. ed. 2007. (Practical Guides in Psychiatry Ser.). (ENG., Illus.). 336p. pap. 49.99 *(978-0-7817-6770-5(9))* Lippincott Williams & Wilkins.

Alt, Betty L. & Wells, Sandra. When Caregivers Kill: Understanding Child Murder by Parents & Other Guardians. 2010. (ENG.). 160p. 44.95 *(978-1-4422-0077-7(4))* Rowman & Littlefield Publishers, Inc.

Alterra, Aaron. The Caregiver: A Life with Alzheimer's. 2008. (Culture & Politics of Health Care Work Ser.). 213p. per. 20.95 *(978-0-8014-7434-7(5))* Cornell Univ. Pr.

American Cancer Society Staff. Cancer Caregiving A-Z: An At-Home Guide for Patients & Their Loved Ones. 2008. (ENG.). 157p. pap. 14.95 *(978-0-944235-92-8(1),* 9780944235928) American Cancer Society, Inc.

American Institute of Architects Staff. Design for Aging Post-Occupancy Evaluations: Lessons Learned from Senior Living Environments Featured in the AIA's Design for Aging Review. Anderzhon, Jeffrey W. et al, eds. 2007. (Wiley Series in Healthcare & Senior Living Design Ser.: 8). (ENG., Illus.). 328p. 85.00 *(978-0-471-75714-6(4),* Wiley) Wiley, John & Sons, Inc.

Amerson, Kathryn Smaw. The Caregivers. 2010. 276p. pap. 15.95 *(978-1-60911-460-2(4),* Eloquent Bks.) AEG Literary Publishing Services, Inc.

Are the Explosive Costs of Elder Care Hurting Family Finances & Business Competition?: Hearing Before the Joint Economic Committee, Congress of the United States, One Hundred Tenth Congress, First Session, May 16, 2007. 2007. iii, 46p. *(978-0-16-079658-6(X),* 552-070-36610-5) United States Government Printing Office.

Aronson, Miriam K. & Weiner, Marcella Bakur. Aging Parents, Aging Children: How to Stay Sane & Survive. 2007. (ENG.). 160p. per. 22.99 *(978-0-7425-4746-9(9),* Aronson, Jason) Rowman & Littlefield Publishers, Inc.

Await, Jane Kriete. The Stranger Comes at Sundown: Living & Dying with Parkinson's Disease. 2008. (Illus.). xiv, 185p. pap. 17.95 *(978-1-890689-33-9(5),* Rio Grande Bks.) LPD Pr.

Baldassar, Loretta, et al. Families Caring Across Borders: Migration, Ageing & Transnational Caregiving. 2007. (ENG., Illus.). 288p. 110.00 *(978-1-4039-4776-5(7))* Palgrave Macmillan.

Banister, Katie Rodriguez & Demos Medical Publishing Staff. The Personal Care Attendant Guide: The Art of Finding, Keeping, or Being One. 2006. (ENG.). 140p. per. 16.95 *(978-1-932603-28-6(X))* Demos Medical Publishing, LLC.

Barbanell, Les. Breaking the Addiction to Please: Goodbye Guilt. 2009. (ENG.). 120p. 28.50 *(978-0-7657-0674-4(1),* Aronson, Jason) Rowman & Littlefield Publishers, Inc.

—Removing the Mask of Kindness: Diagnosis & Treatment of the Caretaker Personality Disorder. 2006. (ENG., Illus.). 212p. 86.50 *(978-0-7657-0409-2(9))* Rowman & Littlefield Publishers, Inc.

—Removing the Mask of Kindness: Diagnosis & Treatment of the Caretaker Personality Syndrome. 2006. (ENG., Illus.). 212p. per. 41.99 *(978-0-7657-0410-8(2))* Rowman & Littlefield Publishers, Inc.

Barry, Michael S. & Barry, Michael. The Art of Caregiving: How to Lend Support & Encouragement to Those with Cancer. 2007. (ENG.). 160p. 14.99 *(978-0-7814-4430-9(6))* Cook, David C.

Barsamian, Gloria G. Sustenance & Hope for Caregivers of Elderly Parents: The Bread of Angels. 2009. (Praeger Series on Contemporary Health & Living Ser.). 34.95 *(978-0-313-36011-4(1))*; E-Book *(978-0-313-36012-1(X))* Greenwood Publishing Group, Inc. (Praeger Pubs.).

Bartlett, Angel. Wounded, but Not Broken: The Life of A Therapeutic Foster Child. 2010. 132p. 21.95 *(978-1-4520-5404-9(5))*; pap. 12.95 *(978-1-4520-5405-6(3))* AuthorHouse.

Bartocci, Barbara. Quick Prayers for Compassionate Caregivers. 2008. (Grace on the Go Ser.). (Illus.). 96p. pap. 10.00 *(978-0-8192-2286-2(0),* Morehouse Publishing) Church Publishing, Inc.

Baumgardner, Frances Garrett. Surviving Illness & Death. 2007. 72p. per. 9.99 *(978-1-60266-143-1(X))* Xulon Pr., Inc.

Beach, Shelly. Ambushed by Grace: Help & Hope on the Caregiving Journey. 2008. (ENG.). 208p. pap. 11.99 *(978-1-57293-242-5(2))* Discovery Hse. Pubs.

—Precious Lord, Take My Hand: Meditations for Caregivers. 2007. (ENG.). 240p. per. 11.99 *(978-1-57293-195-4(7))* Discovery Hse. Pubs.

Beaugez, Sarah. Outer Edge of Grace. 2011. 96p. pap. 15.99 ***(978-1-4653-4667-4(8))*** Xlibris Corp.

Beckett, Joyce & Beckett, Joyce Octavia. Lifting Our Voices: The Journeys into Family Caregiving of Professional Social Workers. 2008. (ENG., Illus.). 384p. (gr. 17). 90.00 *(978-0-231-14060-7(6))*; pap. 29.50 *(978-0-231-14061-4(4))* Columbia Univ. Pr.

Beckett, Joyce Octavia. Lifting Our Voices: The Journeys into Family Caregiving of Professional Social Workers. 2008. (Illus.). 286p. E-Book 23.99 *(978-0-231-51195-7(7))* Columbia Univ. Pr.

Beechem, Kathy. So Far, So Good: A Memoir of a Brain Tumor Patient & His Caregiver. 2011. 278p. pap. 16.95 ***(978-1-60976-995-6(3),*** Eloquent Bks.) AEG Literary Publishing Services, Inc.

Beerman, Susan. Eldercare 911: The Caregiver's Complete Handbook for Making Decisions. rev. ed. 2008. (ENG., Illus.). 640p. pap. 26.98 *(978-1-59102-616-7(4))* Prometheus Bks., Pubs.

Bell, David. The Dynamics of Connection: How Evolution & Biology Create Caregiving & Attachment. 2010. (ENG.). 286p. 78.99 *(978-0-7391-4352-0(2))* Lexington Bks.

Berman, Raeann & Shulman, Bernard H. Caring for Your Aging Parents. 2009. (ENG.). 256p. pap. 14.99 *(978-1-4022-1861-3(3))* Sourcebooks, Inc.

Bernhard, Toni. How to Be Sick: A Buddhist-Inspired Guide for the Chronically Ill & Their Caregivers. 2010. (ENG.). 216p. pap. 15.95 *(978-0-86171-626-5(4))* Wisdom Pubns.

Bertini, Kristine. Strength for the Sandwich Generation: Help to Thrive While Simultaneously Caring for Our Kids & Our Aging Parents, 1 vol. 2011. 144p. 34.95 *(978-1-59884-356-4(8),* A2641C) Greenwood Publishing Group, Inc.

Biederman, Billie. Hello Mama Goodbye. 2008. 312p. pap. 18.98 *(978-0-615-22352-0(4))* LopsideDown Pr.

Blackburn, Amy. Caring for Cynthia. 2008. 96p. pap. 24.95 *(978-0-9773399-1-4(2))* Channel Photographics.

Bloom, Jack H. Jewish Relational Care A-Z: We Are Our Other's Keeper. 2006. (ENG.). 484p. 124.00 *(978-0-7890-2705-4(4))* Routledge.

Bloom, Jack H., ed. Jewish Relational Care A-Z: We Are Our Other's Keeper. 2006. (ENG.). 484p. per. 50.50 *(978-0-7890-2706-1(2))* Routledge.

Blyton, Ben. Going Home: A Caregiver's Guide. 2010. 340p. pap. 24.95 *(978-1-4520-2764-7(1))* AuthorHouse.

Boggatz, Thomas. Growing Old in Egypt: The Supply & Demand of Care for Older Persons. 2011. (ENG., Illus.). 160p. 27.95 *(978-977-416-455-2(5))* American Univ. in Cairo Pr. EGY. Dist: Oxford Univ. Pr., Inc.

Boileau, Jean. Chasing the Wind. 2008. 168p. pap. 16.95 *(978-1-4357-3083-0(6))* Lulu Enterprises Inc.

Boise, Phil. Go Green Rating Scale for Early Childhood Settings Handbook: Improving Your Score. 2010. (ENG.). 200p. pap. 29.95 *(978-1-60554-007-8(2))* Redleaf Pr.

Booth, Alan, et al, eds. Intergenerational Caregiving. 2008. (Illus.). 415p. pap. 29.50 *(978-0-87766-747-6(0))* Urban Institute Pr.

Boyer, Kim & Shapiro, Mary. Alzheimer's & Dementia: A Practical & Legal Guide for Nevada Caregivers. 2011. 176p. pap. 21.95 ***(978-0-87417-858-6(4))*** Univ. of Nevada Pr.

Boyer, Sue. Als, a Daughter's View. 2009. 80p. pap. 16.95 *(978-1-60749-011-1(0))* PublishAmerica, Inc.

Brackey, Jolene. Creating Moments of Joy: A Journal for Caregivers. 4th ed. 2008. 331p. per. 24.95 *(978-1-55753-462-0(4))* Purdue Univ. Pr.

Bradshaw, Diane. I Am Arnold. 2011. 148p. 22.99 ***(978-1-4670-2503-4(8))***; pap. 15.99 ***(978-1-4670-2504-1(6))*** AuthorHouse.

Breitung, Joan Carson. Forgetting: When to Worry, What to Do. 2008. (ENG.). 175p. pap. 19.98 *(978-1-59102-617-4(2))* Prometheus Bks., Pubs.

Brouhard, Rod. Life's Little Emergencies: A Handbook for Active Independent Seniors & Caregivers. 2011. E-Book ***(978-1-61705-074-9(1))***; (ENG.). 250p. pap. 16.95 ***(978-1-936303-15-1(9))*** Demos Medical Publishing, LLC.

Bucher, Julia A., et al. American Cancer Society Complete Guide to Family Caregiving: The Essential Guide to Cancer Caregiving at Home. 2nd ed. 2011. (American Cancer Society Complete Guide T Ser.). (ENG., Illus.). 304p. pap. 24.95 *(978-0-944235-00-3(X),* 094423500X) American Cancer Society, Inc.

Budlender, Deborah, ed. Time Use Studies & Unpaid Care Work. 2010. (Routledge/UNRISD Research in Gender & Development Ser.). (ENG., Illus.). 256p. (C). 125.00 *(978-0-415-88224-8(9))* Routledge.

Bugg, William. Soaring above Adversity. 2006. (ENG.). 128p. per. 19.95 *(978-1-4241-0880-0(2))* PublishAmerica, Inc.

Burau, Viola, et al. Governing Home Care: A Cross-national Comparison. 2007. (Globalization & Welfare Ser.). (Illus.). 240p. 119.00 *(978-1-84542-752-8(1))* Elgar, Edward Publishing, Inc.

Burns, Catherine. Patients with Advanced Cancer. 2010. 284p. pap. *(978-3-8383-1272-9(4))* Lambert Academic Publishing.

Busby, Nicole. A Right to Care? Unpaid Care Work in European Employment Law. 2011. (ENG.). 248p. 140.00 *(978-0-19-957902-0(4))* Oxford Univ. Pr., Inc.

Butler, Debbye. Patient in Affliction: Tips, Tears & Laughter for the in-Home Family Caregiver of A Dying Parent. 2010. 212p. pap. 14.49 *(978-1-4520-0285-9(1))* AuthorHouse.

Caine, Carrie. Who Is Taking Care of My Mother. 2011. 66p. 24.99 ***(978-1-4568-4068-6(1))***; pap. 15.99 ***(978-1-4568-4067-9(3))*** Xlibris Corp.

Calo-oy, Starr. Caregiving Tips A-Z: Everything you need to know to care for your loved one at Home! 2007. per. 29.95 *(978-0-9753195-2-9(3))* Orchard Pubns.

—Caregiving Tips A-Z Alzheimer's & Other Dementias: Everything you need to know to care for your loved one at Home. 2007. per. 29.95 *(978-0-9753195-3-6(1))* Orchard Pubns.

Cannon, Geneva Gertrude. Ready-to-Use Planners & Record Keeping Forms for Family Caregivers: A Companion CD-ROM to the Book, Caring for Your Loved One Who Is Ill at Home. 2006. cd-rom 14.95 *(978-0-9785091-5-6(3))* Avenegg, Inc.

C

The Caregiver Meditations: Reflections on Loving Presence. 2007. 16.00 (978-0-9747366-9-3(4)) Erie Chapman Foundation.

Carey, Louise. The Hedge People: How I Kept My Sanity & Sense of Humor As an Alzheimer's Caregiver. 2009. (ENG.). 128p. pap. 11.99 (978-0-8341-2468-4(8), 9780834124684) Beacon Hill Pr. of Kansas City.

Caring for Our Seniors: How Can We Support Those on the Frontlines?: Hearing Before the Special Committee on Aging, United States Senate, One Hundred Tenth Congress, Second Session, Washington, DC, April 16, 2008. 2009. (Illus.). iii, 231p. (978-0-16-082704-4(3), 552-070-38721-8) United States Government Printing Office.

Carl, Glenys & Rada, Steve. Hold My Hand: A Mother's Journey. 2006. 310p. per. 12.50 (978-0-330-43761-5(5)) Macmillan Pubs., Ltd. GBR. Dist: Independent Pubs. Group.

Caro, Francis G. Family & Aging Policy. 2007. (Illus.). 237p. 175.00 (978-0-7890-3373-4(9)); per. 54.95 (978-0-7890-3374-1(7)) Routledge.

Carol L. Russell Ed.D. Sandwiched! Tales, Tips, & Tools to Balance Life in the Sandwich Generation. 2009. 384p. pap. 24.95 (978-1-4401-5482-9(1)) iUniverse, Inc.

Carter, Lois. Boundless Grace: Devotions from a Caregiver's Heart. 2010. pap. 8.99 (978-1-61663-500-8(2)) Tate Publishing & Enterprises, LLC.

Carter, Pamela J. & McGreer, Marilyn. Personal Support Workers- Canada: A Humanistic Approach to Caregiving. 2010. 944p. pap. 69.95 (978-1-60831-170-5(8)) Lippincott Williams & Wilkins.

Casey, Nell. An Uncertain Inheritance: Writers on Caring for Family. 2008. 304p. pap. 14.99 (978-0-06-087531-2(3), HarperPerennial) HarperCollins Pubs.

Cerasoli, Lisa. As Nora Jo Fades Away: Confessions of a Caregiver: A Memoir. 2010. 180p. 15.95 (978-1-58985-190-0(0)) Five Star Pubns., Inc.

Chan, Anna. A Carer's Odyssey: Life as Mother, Wife, Carer. 2011. 256p. pap. (978-1-84876-573-3(8)) Troubadour Publishing Ltd.

Child, Brenda's. The Right Amount of Sunshine... Cultivating Little Girls into Young Ladies. 2010. 136p. pap. 19.00 (978-0-557-37996-5(2)) Lulu Enterprises Inc.

Colmer, Rebecca. Caring for Caregiver. 2008. 95p. pap. 3.95 (978-0-9765465-6-6(6)) Eklektika Pr.

—Family Caregiver Organizer: A Personal & Medical Journal for both the Care-receiver & their Caregiver(s) 2007. 288p. pap. 26.95 (978-0-9765465-3-5(1)) Eklektika Pr.

Colmer, Rebecca Sharp. Family Caregiver Answer Book. 2008. (Illus.). 111p. per. 12.95 (978-0-9765465-4-2(X)) Eklektika Pr.

—Family Caregiver Starter Kit: Caregiving Preparedness. 2008. 49.95 (978-0-9765465-5-9(8)) Eklektika Pr.

Committee on the Future Health Care Workforce for Older Americans & Institute of Medicine Staff. Retooling for an Aging America: Building the Health Care Workforce. 2008. (ENG., Illus.). 316p. 29.95 (978-0-309-11587-2(6)) National Academies Pr.

Committee on the Role of Human Factors in Home Healthcare & National Research Council. The Role of Human Factors in Home Health Care: Workshop Summary. 2010. (ENG.). 322p. pap. 65.00 (978-0-309-15629-5(7)) National Academies Pr.

Copolov, David L., et al, eds. Pharmacological & Psychosocial Treatments in Schizophrenia. 2nd rev. ed. 2008. (ENG., Illus.). 272p. pap. 260.00 (978-0-415-42156-0(X), Informa Healthcare) Taylor & Francis Group GBR. Dist: Taylor & Francis Group.

Corbett, Margo. The Savvy Patient's Toolkit. 2008. 250p. pap. 24.95 (978-0-7414-4479-0(8)) Infinity Publishing.

—The Savvy Patient's Toolkit - 1-Hour Audio. 2010. pap. (978-0-7414-6118-6(8)) Infinity Publishing.

—The Savvy Patient's Toolkit with Audio CD. 2008. 250p. pap. 29.95 (978-0-7414-4571-1(9)) Infinity Publishing.

Coste, Joanne Koenig. Learning to Speak Alzheimer's: The New Approach to Living Positively with Alzheimer's Disease. 2007. 244p. reprint ed. pap. 20.00 (978-1-4223-9027-6(6)) DIANE Publishing Co.

Cress, Cathy Jo. Care Managers: Working with the Aging Family. 2008. 342p. pap. 103.95 (978-0-7637-5585-0(0)) Jones & Bartlett Learning, LLC.

Cromer, Janet M. Professor Cromer Learns to Read: A Couple's New Life after Brain Injury. 2010. 304p. 25.99 (978-1-4490-6420-4(5)); pap. 15.99 (978-1-4490-6419-8(1)) AuthorHouse.

Currie, Diane. Before My Eyes: A Daughter's Personal Journey with her Mother into Alzheimer's Disease. 2010. 88p. pap. 10.95 (978-1-4502-1678-4(1)) iUniverse, Inc.

Davey, Adam & Szinovacz, Maximiliane E. Caregiving Contexts: Cultural, Familial, & Societal Implications. 2007. (Illus.). 294p. 65.00 (978-0-8261-0287-4(5)) Springer Publishing Co., Inc.

Davis, Nanette J. Blessed Is She: ELDER CARE - Women's Stories of Choice, Challenge & Commitment. 2008. 308p. pap. 18.95 (978-1-60145-466-9(X)) Booklocker.com, Inc.

De Klerk-Rubin, Vicki. Validation Techniques for Dementia Care: The Family Guide to Improving Communication. 2007. (Illus.). 132p. per. 18.95 (978-1-932529-37-1(3)) Health Professions Pr.

Dellinger, Annetta & Boerger, Karen. Blessings and Prayers for Caregivers. 2010. 208p. pap. 4.99 (978-0-7586-1868-9(9)) Concordia Publishing Hse.

—JOY-spirations for Caregivers: A Dialogue with God. 2010. 304p. pap. 19.99 (978-1-60615-026-9(X)) WinePress Publishing.

Denholm, Diana B. The Caregiving Wife's Handbook: Caring for Your Seriously Ill Husband, Caring for Yourself. 2012. (ENG.). 168p. pap. 14.95 (978-0-89793-605-7(1)) Hunter Hse., Inc.

Djedje, Derahonon/Adrienne, creator. Caregiver Timesheet Pad. 2007. (ENG., Illus.). 200p. spiral bd. 13.89 (978-0-9749007-0-4(2)) Business Mind, Inc.

Doblhammer, Gabriele & Scholz, Rembrandt D. Ageing, Care Need & Quality of Life: The Perspective of Care Givers & People in Need of Care. 2010. (Demografischer Wandel - Hintergründe und Herausforderungen Ser.). (Illus.). 243p. pap. 49.95 (978-3-531-16626-1(3), 3531166263) VS Verlag fur Sozialwissenschaften GmbH DEU. Dist: Springer.

Dodds, Monica. A Catholic Guide to Caring for Your Aging Parent. 2006. (ENG.). 360p. per. 14.95 (978-0-8294-1872-9(5)) Loyola Pr.

Dolen, Carolyn E. Brain Injury Rewiring for Loved Ones: A Lifeline to New Connections. 2009. 316p. 19.00 (978-1-882883-71-4(3)) Idyll Arbor, Inc.

Dowe, Roberta. A Simple Plan. 2008. 176p. pap. (978-1-55452-316-0(8)) Essence Publishing.

Dresser, Rebecca, ed. Malignant: Medical Ethicists Confront Cancer, 1 vol. 2012. (ENG.). 272p. 29.95 (978-0-19-975784-8(4)) Oxford Univ. Pr., Inc.

Driscoll, Marilyn. Devotions for Caregivers: A Month's Supply of Prayer. 2006. (Illumination Bks.). 86p. per. 6.95 (978-0-8091-4394-8(1), 4394-1) Paulist Pr.

Duarte, Cynthia. Yet, I Will Love Thee: The Hard Truth of Alzheimer's Caregiving. 2008. 64p. per. 16.95 (978-1-4241-9904-4(2)) PublishAmerica, Inc.

Duda, Deborah. Coming Home: A Practical & Compassionate Guide to Caring for a Dying Loved One. 2010. pap. 16.95 (978-0-9842358-9-6(2)) Synergy Bks.

Duffy, Mignon. Making Care Count: A Century of Gender, Race, & Paid Care Work. 2011. (ENG., Illus.). 204p. (C). 72.00 (978-0-8135-4960-6(4)); pap. 24.95 (978-0-8135-4961-3(2)) Rutgers Univ. Pr.

Dullaert, Ricus. Care for the Caregivers: Manual. Ach, Johann S. & Siep, Ludwig, eds. 2007. (ENG.). 89p. (gr. 11). pap. 22.50 (978-90-5589-274-7(2)) Het Spinhuis NLD. Dist: Transaction Pubs.

Edmunson, Janet. Finding Meaning with Charles: Caregiving with Love Through a Degenerative Disease. 2006. 291p. per. 15.95 (978-0-9778133-0-8(4)) Edmunson, Janet.

Ehlert, Mary Anne. The Gift I Was Given: The Journey of a Caregiver Through the Stages of What Now?, Why Me?, & Ah Ha! 2009. (ENG.). pap. 14.95 (978-1-60037-504-0(9)) Morgan James Publishing.

Emlet, Michael R. Help for the Caregiver: Facing the Challenges with Understanding & Strength. 2008. (ENG.). 24p. 3.99 (978-1-934885-50-5(9)) New Growth Pr.

Englander, Joan. Joy in the Evening of our Lives: Nurturing the Elderly Soul. 2008. per. 19.95 (978-0-9794681-0-0(8)) Healing River Pr.

Epstein, Lita. The 250 Eldercare Questions Everyone Should Ask. 2009. (ENG.). 192p. pap. 10.95 (978-1-59869-890-9(7)) Adams Media Corp.

Eriksen, John. The Power of Institutions. Addis, Elisabetta et al, eds. 2011. (Gender & Well-Being Ser.). (Illus.). 290p. 114.95 (978-1-4094-0705-8(5)) Ashgate Publishing Co.

Farrell, Richard J. Alzheimer's Caregiving: Lessons from a Surviving Spouse. 2011. 92p. pap. 11.95 (978-1-4502-7645-0(8)) iUniverse, Inc.

Fazio, Sam. The Enduring Self in People with Alzheimer's: Getting to the Heart of Individualized Care. 2008. (Illus.). 175p. pap. 26.95 (978-1-932529-38-8(1)) Health Professions Pr.

Fell-Carlson, Deborah L. Working Safely in Health Care: A Practical Guide. 2007. (Safety & Regulatory for Health Science Ser.). (ENG., Illus.). 464p. (C). per. 68.95 (978-1-4180-0623-5(8)) Delmar Cengage Learning.

—Working Safely in Health Care: A Quick Reference. 2007. (Safety & Regulatory for Health Science Ser.). (ENG., Illus.). 216p. (C). spiral bd. 38.95 (978-1-4180-0625-9(4)) Delmar Cengage Learning.

Fleming, David A. & Hagan, John C., III, eds. The Care of the Dying Patient. 2010. (ENG.). 170p. 39.95 (978-0-8262-1874-2(1)); pap. 19.95 (978-0-8262-1890-2(3)) Univ. of Missouri Pr.

Foerster, Denise. Understanding Pain When You're Not the Patient: Helping Caregivers & Patients to Better Understand the Phases of Patient Recovery after the Hospital. 2007. 48p. per. 16.95 (978-1-4241-8118-6(6)) PublishAmerica, Inc.

Folbre, Nancy, et al, eds. Warm Hands in Cold Age: Gender & Aging. 2006. (Illus.). 206p. (978-0-415-39676-9(X)) Routledge, Chapman & Hall, Inc.

—Warm Hands in Cold Age: Gender & Aging. 2006. (Illus.). 206p. per. 52.99 (978-0-415-41559-0(4)) Taylor & Francis Group.

Forrester, Rachel & Broadhurst, Sarah, eds. Autism & Loss. 2007. (ENG., Illus.). 208p. per. (978-1-84310-433-9(4)) Kingsley, Jessica Ltd.

Fountain & O'Donnell, D. O. Helping Hurting People. 2008. 152p. pap. 15.99 (978-1-58930-223-5(0)) Selah Publishing Group, LLC.

Francis, Paulette. Caring with a Difference: A Guide to Caring with Compassion, Respect & Professionalism. 2011. 64p. pap. 15.56 (978-1-4567-8052-4(2)) AuthorHouse.

Fraser, J. W. Caregiver or Taker. 2007. 238p. pap. 17.95 (978-1-4303-1038-9(3)) Lulu Enterprises Inc.

French, Barbara. Someday Street: A Memoir. 2008. 280p. pap. 27.95 (978-1-60703-637-1(1)) PublishAmerica, Inc.

Frey, Chris. I'm Sorry, It's Cancer: A Handbook of Help & Hope for Survivors & Caregivers. 2011. 94p. pap. 12.99 (978-1-257-00692-2(4)) Lulu Enterprises Inc.

Fridays with Eva: Caring for & Learning from My Mother-in-law, a Holocaust Survivor. 2009. pap. 17.95 (978-1-935232-11-7(8)) ComteQ Publishing.

Friedman, Joseph H. Making the Connection Between Brain & Behavior: Coping with Parkinson's Disease. 2007. (ENG.). 250p. per. 19.95 (978-1-932603-42-2(5)) Demos Medical Publishing, LLC.

Fritz, Robert. What's the Next Step? My Journey with Cancer as a Caregiver & then as a Caretaker. 2011. 168p. 25.95 (978-1-4502-9630-4(0)); pap. 15.95 (978-1-4502-9631-1(9)) iUniverse, Inc.

Gaboury, Melinda A. Home Health Pocket Guide to OASIS-C: A Reference for Field Staff. 2010. (Illus.). 172p. spiral bd. 39.00 (978-1-60146-674-7(9)) Opus Communications.

Gelardin, Sally D. Career & Caregiving: Empowering the Shadow Workforce of Family Caregivers. 2009. pap. (978-1-885333-28-5(5)) National Career Development Assn.

Gibson, Janet. SeniVision: The New Outlook on Senior Lifestyle & Care. 2007. 439p. ring bd. (978-0-9789568-0-6(X)) WiseLife Pr., Inc.

Gilbert, Peter, et al, eds. Spirituality, Values & Mental Health: Jewels for the Journey. 2007. (Illus.). 336p. per. (978-1-84310-456-8(3)) Kingsley, Jessica Ltd.

Gillies, Andrea. Keeper: One House, Three Generations, & a Journey into Alzheimer's. 2010. (ENG.). 336p. 25.00 (978-0-307-71911-9(1)) Broadway Bks.

—Keeper: One House, Three Generations, & a Journey into Alzheimer's. 2011. (ENG.). 336p. pap. 15.00 (978-0-307-71912-6(X), Three Rivers Pr.) Crown Publishing Group.

Givens, Janet L. Mom... Can You Move My Legs? 2010. 128p. (ENG.). 28.95 (978-1-4497-0258-8(9)); pap. 11.95 (978-1-4497-0257-1(0)) Author Solutions, Inc. (WestBow Pr.).

Glendinning, Caroline & Kemp, Peter, eds. Cash & Care: Policy Challenges in the Welfare State. 2006. 336p. pap. 39.95 (978-1-86134-856-2(8)) Policy Pr. GBR. Dist: Chicago Distribution Ctr.

Glenn, Evelyn Nakano. Forced to Care: Coercion & Caregiving in America. (Illus.). 272p. 2012. (ENG.). pap. 19.95 (978-0-674-06415-7(1)) 2010. 29.95 (978-0-674-04879-9(2)) Harvard Univ. Pr.

Glennon, Kathleen. Healing & Wholeness: Reflections & Rituals for the Sick & Dying. 2010. (ENG.). 151p. pap. 18.95 (978-1-85607-674-6(1)) Columba Pr. IRL. Dist: Dufour Editions, Inc.

Godwin, Latrise. For the Love of the Wise: A Caregivers Guide to Dementia. 2008. 66p. pap. 7.99 (978-1-60604-157-4(6)) Tate Publishing & Enterprises, LLC.

Goldberg, Stan. Leaning into Sharp Points: Practical Guidance & Nurturing Support for Caregivers. 2012. (ENG.). 232p. pap. 14.95 (978-1-60868-067-2(3)) New World Library.

Gracey, Marilyn J. A Story of the OWMC: The Wasted Years. 2008. (978-1-55452-306-1(0)) Essence Publishing.

Green, Cynthia R. & Beloff, Joan. Through the Seasons: An Activity Book for Memory-Challenged Adults & Caregivers. 2008. (ENG., Illus.). 64p. act. bk. ed. 20.95 (978-0-8018-8844-1(1)) Johns Hopkins Univ. Pr.

Green, Eboni Ivory. At the Heart of the Matter: A Spiritual Journey for Caregivers. 2011. 180p. 30.95 (978-1-4497-1597-7(4)); pap. 13.95 (978-1-4497-1596-0(6)) Author Solutions, Inc. (WestBow Pr.).

Greenberg, Tamara McClintock. When Someone You Love Has a Chronic Illness: Hope & Help for Those Providing Support. 2012. pap. 13.99 (978-1-59955-939-1(0), Plain Sight Publishing) Cedar Fort, Inc./CFI Distribution.

Greene, Roberta R. Contemporary Issues of Care. 2007. (ENG.). 430p. 175.00 (978-0-7890-3241-6(4)) Routledge.

Greene, Roberta R., ed. Contemporary Issues of Care. 2007. (ENG., Illus.). 430p. pap. 54.95 (978-0-7890-3242-3(2)) Routledge.

Gross, Jane. A Bittersweet Season: Caring for Our Aging Parents — and Ourselves. 2012. (ENG.). 448p. pap. 15.95 (978-0-307-47240-3(X), Vintage) Knopf Doubleday Publishing Group.

Gutter, Janice Baldon. Caregiving: A Daughter's Story: Life after Loss - Surviving Caregiving. 2010. 108p. 23.49 (978-1-4490-2504-5(8)); pap. 12.99 (978-1-4490-2503-8(X)) AuthorHouse.

Hamilton, Jane Meier. Journey of a Lifetime. 2010. pap. 11.95 (978-0-7414-5802-5(0)) Infinity Publishing.

Hanks, Jerry & Cordova-Hanks, Bobbi de. Lagrimas de Alegria. 2007. 120p. pap. 12.95 (978-0-7414-3859-1(3)) Infinity Publishing.

Harris, Catina. Windows of a Woman. 2009. 56p. pap. 10.49 (978-1-4389-3315-3(0)) AuthorHouse.

Harris, Marilyn D. & Harris, Marilyn. Handbook of Home Health Care Administration. 5th rev. ed. 2009. 1000p. pap. 186.95 (978-0-7637-5582-9(6)) Jones & Bartlett Learning, LLC.

Harris, Roy W. Caring for the Caregiver. 2009. pap. 10.99 (978-1-60799-843-3(2)) Tate Publishing & Enterprises, LLC.

Haymon, Sandra W. Baby Boomers: Sandwiched Between Retirement & Caregiving. 2009. pap. 29.99 (978-1-60696-861-1(0)) Tate Publishing & Enterprises, LLC.

Haynali, Carolyn. I Was Once Like You: Before I Got Alzheimer's. 2011. 308p. 24.95 (978-1-4678-4952-4(9)); pap. 16.95 (978-1-4678-4953-1(7)) AuthorHouse.

Hayslip, Jr., Bert, Bert & Smith, Gregory C., eds. Resilient Grandparent Caregivers: A Strengths-Based Perspective. 2012. (ENG.). 352p. 95.95 (978-0-415-89754-9(8)); pap. 44.95 (978-0-415-89755-6(6)) Routledge.

Heard & Lake. Challenge of Attachment Caregiving. 2009. 240p. pap. 34.95 (978-1-85575-728-8(1)) Karnac Bks. GBR. Dist: Stylus Publishing, LLC.

Heffron, Mary Claire & Murch, Trudi. Reflective Supervision & Leadership for Infant & Early Childhood Programs. 2010. (978-1-934019-90-0(9)) Zero To Three Pr.

Henry, Linda Gambee & Henry, James Douglas. Transformational Eldercare from the Inside Out: Strengths-Based Strategies for Caring. 2007. xxvi, 196p. pap. (978-1-55810-229-3(9)) American Nurses Publishing.

Hermann, Luke & Summers Hermann, Tara. Toddler Medbasics: Lifesaving Action Steps at Your Fingertips: Ages 1-5. 2011. (ENG.). 64p. 12.00 (978-0-7624-4205-8(0)) Running Pr. Bk. Pubs.

Herring, Jonathan. Caring & the Law. 2013. (ENG.). 264p. pap. 45.00 (978-1-84946-106-1(6)) Hart Publishing Ltd. GBR. Dist: International Specialized Bk. Services.

Hewitt-Taylor, Jaqui. Children with Complex & Continuing Health Needs: The Experiences of Children, Families & Care Staff. 2007. (ENG.). 240p. pap. (978-1-84310-502-2(0)) Kingsley, Jessica Ltd.

Hohler, Sharon E. Caregiver's Guide: Care for Yourself While You Care for Your Loved Ones. 2011. (McFarland Health Topics Ser.). (ENG.). 284p. pap. 35.00 (978-0-7864-4962-0(4)) McFarland & Co., Inc. Pubs.

Hryniuk, Michael. Theology, Disability, & Spiritual Transformation: Learning from the Communities of L'Arche. 2010. (978-1-60497-694-6(2)) Cambria Pr.

Huddleston, Kathryn. There's A Storm Coming: the Journey to Rescue & Save My Father: Helping My Father Achieve His Mental, Physical, & Spiritual Potential During His Alzheimer's Disease. 2010. 372p. 39.95 (978-1-4497-0599-2(5)); pap. 24.95 (978-1-4497-0597-8(9)) Author Solutions, Inc. (WestBow Pr.).

Hudson, Peter & Payne, Sheila, eds. Family Carers in Palliative Care: A guide for health & social care professionals. 2009. (ENG.). 336p. pap. 57.50 (978-0-19-921690-1(8)) Oxford Univ. Pr., Inc.

Hutchison, Joyce & Rupp, Joyce. May I Walk You Home-Rev. 10th ed. 2009. 192p. pap. 12.95 (978-1-59471-214-2(X)) Ave Maria Pr.

Implementation of Caregiver Assistance: Moving Forward: Hearing Before the Subcommittee on Health of the Committee on Veterans' Affairs, U.S. House of Representatives, One Hundred Twelfth Congress, First Session, July 11, 2011. 2011. iii, 84p. (978-0-16-090118-8(9), 552-070-43825-4) United States Government Printing Office.

International Council of Nurses Staff, et al. Notes on Nursing: A Guide for Today's Caregivers. 2009. (ENG., Illus.). 200p. pap. 21.95 (978-0-7020-3423-7(1), Bailliere Tindall) Elsevier - Health Sciences Div.

Isaksen, Lise Widding, ed. Global Care Work: Gender & Migration in Nordic Societies. 2011. (ENG., Illus.). 240p. 49.95 (978-91-85509-48-5(5)) Nordic Academic Pr., Sweden SWE. Dist: Independent Pubs. Group.

Jacinto, George. Caregivers' Self-Forgiveness. 2010. 144p. pap. (978-3-639-24154-9(1)) VDM Verlag Dr. Mueller e.K.

Jacobs, Léa K., ed. Coping with Cancer. 2008. (Illus.). 154p. 129.00 (978-1-60456-213-2(7), Nova Biomedical Bks.) Nova Science Pubs., Inc.

Jacobs, Rick. Life Has Begun. 2007. 260p. per. 19.95 (978-0-595-38540-9(0)) iUniverse, Inc.

Jamakaya & Jamakaya, eds. A Celebration of Caregiving: Portraits & Stories. 2007. (Illus.). 95p. 29.95 (978-0-9794997-0-8(4)) IndependenceFirst.

James W. Ramage, M. S. W. A Caregiver's Training Manual for the Elderly: Alzheimer's & other Dementia. 2009. 212p. pap. 19.49 (978-1-4389-2366-6(X)) AuthorHouse.

Jegermalm, Magnus. Informal Care & Support for Carers. 2008. 76p. pap. (978-3-639-07225-9(1)) VDM Verlag Dr. Mueller e.K.

Jenkins, Cheryl. She Just Wanted to Dance Again: My Journey to Parenting My Parent & A Simplified Guide to Becoming a Parent's Caregiver. 2009. 100p. pap. 11.95 (978-1-4401-0775-7(0)) iUniverse, Inc.

Joint United Nations Programme on HIV/AIDS (UNAIDS) & World Health Organization. Preventing Carer Burnout: Inter-Mission Care & Rehabilitation Society (IMCARES) 2009. (UNAIDS Publication Ser.). (ENG.). 48p. pap. 18.00 (978-92-9173-638-6(4)) World Health Organization.

Kalina, Kathy. Midwife for Souls: Spiritual Care for the Dying: A Pastoral Guide for Hospice Care Workers & All Who Live with the Terminally Ill. 2nd ed. 2007. 145p. per. 10.95 (978-0-8198-4856-7(5)) Pauline Bks. & Media.

Kaminski, Patricia, et al. Parenting the Custodial Grandchild: Implications for Clinical Practice. Hayslip, Bert, Jr. & Kaminski, Patricia, eds. 2nd ed. 2008. (Illus.). 304p. pap. 49.00 (978-0-8261-1685-7(X)) Springer Publishing Co., Inc.

Kane, Robert L. The Good Caregiver: A One-of-a-Kind Compassionate Resource for Anyone Caring for an Aging Loved One. 2011. (ENG.). 336p. (gr. 12). 17.00 (978-1-58333-422-5(X), Avery) Penguin Group (USA) Inc.

Karpinski, Marion. Quick Tips for Caregivers. 2010. (CHI., Illus.). xvi, 217p. mass mkt. 139.00 (978-0-9798245-8-6(3)) Medifecta Healthcare Training.

Kearse, Mary Kathleen, et al. Lymphedema Caregiver's Guide: Arranging & Providing Home Care. 2009. (Illus.). 472p. pap. 34.95 (978-0-9764806-7-9(0)) Lymph Notes.

Kelly, Jo Anna. Dementia & Caregiving. 2008. 204p. pap. (978-3-639-03270-3(5)) VDM Verlag Dr. Mueller e.K.

Kelly, Lois. Be the Noodle: Fifty Ways to Be a Compassionate, Courageous, Crazy-Good Caregiver. 2010. 126p. pap. 20.00 (978-1-935444-69-5(7)) World Audience Pubs.

Kenemore, Paula. My Life, My Care, My Way: My Advance Personal Care Plan. 2007. 77p. per. 14.95 (978-0-9800579-6-6(5)) Lake Effect Media.

Kincheloe, Donna. I Never Walk the Halls Alone. 2007. (ENG.). 160p. pap. 18.95 (978-1-932124-90-3(X)) ACW Pr.

King, Pamela Ayer. The 10-Step Guide for the Caregiver, 1 vol. 2009. 55p. pap. 12.95 (978-1-4489-2637-4(8)) PublishAmerica, Inc.

Kinnell, Herbert G. Killer Carers. 2007. (Illus.). 132p. per. (978-1-84401-945-8(4)) Athena Pr.

Kivanc, D. Y. May I Call You Mommy. 2010. 36p. pap. 15.49 (978-1-4520-1125-7(7)) AuthorHouse.

Knutson, Lois D. & Knutson, Lois. Compassionate Caregiving: Practical Help & Spiritual Encouragement. 2007. 256p. pap. 14.99 (978-0-7642-0371-8(1)) Bethany Hse. Pubs.

Krull, Catherine & Sempruch, Justyna, eds. A Life in Balance? Reopening the Family-Work Debate. 2011. (ENG., Illus.). 280p. pap. 37.95

(978-0-7748-1968-8(5)) Univ. of British Columbia Pr. CAN. Dist: Univ. of Washington Pr.

Kubesch, Nadine. Work & Caregiving: Theory & Good Practice for a greater Reconcilability. 2007. 64p. per. *(978-3-8364-2547-6(5))* VDM Verlag Dr. Mueller e.K.

Lampert, Ron. Everything Happens for a Reason: Thirty Years as a Caregiver/Advocate. 2011. 108p. 21.23 *(978-1-4567-1382-9(5))*; pap. 10.68 *(978-1-4567-1380-5(9))* AuthorHouse.

Laverty, Cindy. Caregiving: Eldercare Made Clear & Simple. 2010. 230p. pap. 19.95 *(978-0-9827765-0-6(0))* CLW Publishing.

LeBlanc, Gary Joseph & Leblanc, Gary Joseph. Staying Afloat in a Sea of Forgetfulness: Common Sense Caregiving Expanded Edition. 2011. 332p. 29.99 ***(978-1-4628-7706-5(0))***; pap. 19.99 ***(978-1-4628-7705-8(2))*** Xlibris Corp.

Lee, Nancy. This Is Their Story. 2010. 152p. pap. *(978-3-639-20418-6(2))* VDM Verlag Dr. Mueller e.K.

Lehrke, Joan. Your Loved One Is Coming Home: Ways to Help Prepare Yourself to Take Care of a Loved One During Their Last Days. 2009. 52p. pap. 10.49 *(978-1-4490-3484-9(5))* AuthorHouse.

Lemonius, Hilary. A Caregiver's Diary. 2011. 50p. pap. 16.95 ***(978-1-4560-5472-4(4))*** PublishAmerica, Inc.

Levine, Carol & Murray, Thomas H., eds. The Cultures of Caregiving: Conflict & Common Ground among Families, Health Professionals, & Policy Makers. 2007. (ENG., Illus.). 216p. (gr. 17). per. 25.00 *(978-0-8018-8771-0(2))* Johns Hopkins Univ. Pr.

Levine, Kathryn. Against All Odds: Resilience in Single Mothers of Children with Disabilities. 2008. 172p. pap. *(978-3-639-07986-9(8))* VDM Verlag Dr. Mueller e.K.

Lewis, Fran. Because We Care. 2011. 76p. 24.99 ***(978-1-4568-9131-2(6))***; pap. 15.99 ***(978-1-4568-9130-5(8))*** Xlibris Corp.

Lewis, Zoë A. I Hope They Know. the Essential Handbook on Alzheimer's Disease & Care. 2008. (ENG.). 240p. pap. 24.95 *(978-1-60264-177-8(3))* Virtualbookworm.com Publishing, Inc.

LifeLight for Little Ones: Caregivers Manual. pap. 7.95 *(978-0-570-09251-3(5), 20-2245)* Concordia Publishing Hse.

Lightwater, Rheanni. Whose Problem Is It? Taking the Pressure off of Personal Responsibility. 2009. (ENG., Illus.). 15p. spiral bd. 15.95 *(978-0-9777080-9-3(8))* Soul Resources.

Lima, Julie C. & Allen, Susan. The Availability of Care for Late-Middle-Aged Adults with Chronic Conditions. 2008. 208p. 99.95 *(978-1-60497-576-5(8))* Cambria Pr.

Lipsyte, Robert. In the Country of Illness: Comfort & Advice for the Journey. 2011. (ENG.). 272p. pap. 13.95 *(978-1-59687-388-9(4))* IBks., Inc.

Lockhart, Sybil. Mother in the Middle: A Biologist's Story of Caring for Parent & Child. 2009. (ENG.). 320p. 25.00 *(978-1-4165-4155-4(1),* Touchstone) Touchstone.

Long, Elaine. The Caregiver's Choice: Find Strength & Serenity by Changing Your Mind. 2008. 112p. 20.95 *(978-0-595-49363-0(7))*; pap. 10.95 *(978-0-595-49018-9(2))* iUniverse, Inc.

Long, Janice Evans. Dying the Right Way: A System of Care Giving & Planning for Families. 2010. (ENG.). 328p. pap. 19.95 *(978-1-60037-700-6(9))* Morgan James Publishing.

Lord, Janice Harris. Spiritually Sensitive Caregiving: A Multi-Faith Handbook. 2008. 175p. pap. 12.95 *(978-1-878321-32-9(3))* Compassion Bks., Inc.

Loverde, Joy. The Complete Eldercare Planner, Revised & Updated Edition: Where to Start, Which Questions to Ask, & How to Find Help. 2009. (ENG.). 400p. pap. 19.95 *(978-0-307-40962-1(7),* Three Rivers Pr.) Crown Publishing Group.

Lovern, Sandy. Finding Your Way: A Spiritual GPS for Caregivers. 2010. (ENG.). 176p. pap. 14.99 *(978-1-59669-246-6(4))* New Hope Pubs.

Luke, Richard D. The Long Wait: The Caregiver's Guide to Survival. 2011. 96p. pap. 11.95 ***(978-1-4620-4126-8(4))*** iUniverse, Inc.

Lynch, Terry. But I Don't Want Eldercare! Helping Your Parents Stay As Strong As They Can As Long As They Can. 2008. 328p. per. 17.95 *(978-0-9770179-6-6(6))* Legal Ctr. for People with Disabilities, The.

MacEnulty, Pat & Titus, Tamara. This Is the Way We Say Goodbye. 2011. *(978-1-55861-772-8(8))* Feminist Pr. at The City Univ. of New York.

March, Artemis. Dying into Grace: Mother & Daughter ... a Dance of Healing. 2007. (ENG., Illus.). 358p. per. 19.95 *(978-0-9793967-9-3(4))* Quantum Lens Pr.

Marrella, Dee. Everything about ME: A Guide for My Future Caregivers. 2011. 280p. pap. 19.95 *(978-1-932021-60-8(4))* DC Pr. LLC.

—Everything about ME for Military Personnel & Families: A Guide for My Future Caregivers. 2011. 280p. pap. 19.95 *(978-1-932021-62-2(0))* DC Pr. LLC.

Marriott, Hugh & MARRIOTT, Hugh. Caring: How to Cope with the Emotional & Practical Aspects of Caring for Someone. 2009. (ENG., Illus.). 400p. pap. 16.95 *(978-0-7499-2986-2(3))* Piatkus Bks. GBR. Dist: Independent Pubs. Group.

Marshall, Constance E. Surviving the Odds, 1 vol. 2010. 48p. pap. 16.95 *(978-1-60836-624-8(3))* PublishAmerica, Inc.

Marston, Dianna Mitchell. Living with Cancer As A New Normal: A Journey with Cancer through the Eyes of a Caregiver. 2007. 108p. per. 11.95 *(978-0-595-44899-9(2))* iUniverse, Inc.

Mathieu, Françoise. The Compassion Fatigue Workbook: Creative Tools for Transforming Compassion Fatigue & Vicarious Traumatization. 2011. (Routledge Psychosocial Stress Ser.). (ENG., Illus.). 179p. pap. 39.95 ***(978-0-415-89790-7(4))*** Routledge.

Matthews, Jane. The Carer's Handbook: Essential Information & Support for All Those in a Caring Role. 2006. 182p. per. 22.00 *(978-1-84528-096-3(2))* Parkwest Pubns., Inc.

—The Carer's Handbook 2e. 2nd ed. 2007. 182p. pap. 22.00 *(978-1-84528-194-6(2))* Parkwest Pubns., Inc.

McBee, Lucia. Mindfulness-Based Elder Care: Communicating & Embodying Mindfulness for Frail Elders & Their Caregivers. 2008. 40.00 *(978-0-8261-1511-9(X))* Springer Publishing Co., Inc.

McCann-Beranger, Judith. A Caregiver's Guide to Alzheimer's & Related Diseases. 2008. (B& B Personal Wellness Ser.). (Illus.). 111p. pap. 10.00 *(978-1-933480-20-6(3))* Bunim and Bannigan Ltd.

McDermott, Annika. Addressing the Needs of Informal Carers. 2010. 76p. pap. *(978-3-8383-4245-0(3))* Lambert Academic Publishing.

McKenna, David Loren & Seraydarian, Patricia McKenna. A Stroke of Grace. 2008. 116p. pap. 11.99 *(978-1-60647-795-3(1))* Xulon Pr., Inc.

McMahon, Fran. To Love a Stranger: A Caregiver's Perspective. 2007. (ENG.). 160p. per. 15.99 *(978-1-4141-0862-9(1))* Pleasant Word.

McQuellon, Richard & Cowan, Michael. The Art of Conversation Through Serious Illness: Lessons for Caregivers, 1 vol. 2010. (ENG., Illus.). 144p. pap. 15.95 *(978-0-19-538922-7(0))* Oxford Univ. Pr., Inc.

Meeting the Needs of Family Caregivers of Veterans: Hearing Before the Subcommittee on Health of the Committee on Veterans' Affairs, U.S. House of Representatives, One Hundred Eleventh Congress, First Session, June 4, 2009. 2010. iii, 87p. *(978-0-16-085071-4(1),* 552-070-40428-7) United States Government Printing Office.

Meyer, Maria M. & Derr, Paula. The Comfort of Home: A Complete Guide for Caregivers. 3rd ed. 2007. (Comfort of Home Ser.). (ENG., Illus.). 400p. per. 24.95 *(978-0-9664767-9-8(4))* CareTrust Pubns., LLC.

—The Comfort of Home for Stroke: A Guide for Caregivers. 2007. (Comfort of Home Ser.). (ENG., Illus.). 342p. per. 24.95 *(978-0-9664767-8-1(6))* CareTrust Pubns., LLC.

Meyer, Maria M., et al. The Comfort of Home for Parkinson Disease: A Guide for Caregivers. 2007. (Comfort of Home Ser.). (ENG., Illus.). 298p. pap. 24.95 *(978-0-9664767-7-4(8))* CareTrust Pubns., LLC.

—Multiple Sclerosis: Multiple Sclerosis Caregivers. 2006. (Comfort of Home Ser.). (ENG., Illus.). 336p. per., instr.'s gde. ed. 24.95 *(978-0-9664767-5-7(X))* CareTrust Pubns., LLC.

Miller, Darleen. Yes! It Really Is All about Me: The Journey of a Lifetime. 2011. 132p. pap. 16.95 ***(978-1-4525-3575-3(2))*** Get Published.

MillerSimard, Laurienne, BC. Caregiver Rx. 2010. 214p. pap. 39.95 *(978-0-557-18266-4(2))* Lulu Enterprises Inc.

Mintz, Suzanne Geffen. A Family Caregiver Speaks Up: It Doesn't Have to Be This Hard. 2007. (Capital Cares Ser.). (Illus.). 232p. per. 14.95 *(978-1-933102-46-7(2))* Capital Bks., Inc.

Moeller, Mary. Generation Dances: A Caregiver's Journe. 2006. 194p. pap. 24.95 *(978-1-4241-3874-6(4))* PublishAmerica, Inc.

Monroe, Barbara & Oliviere, David, eds. Resilience in Palliative Care: Achievement in Adversity. 2007. (ENG., Illus.). 272p. pap. 69.95 *(978-0-19-920641-4(4))* Oxford Univ. Pr., Inc.

Morse, Louise. Worshipping with Dementia: Selected Scriptures & Prayers for Sufferers & Carers, 1 vol. 2010. 272p. pap. 14.99 *(978-1-85424-931-9(2),* Monarch Bks.) Lion Hudson PLC GBR. Dist: Kregel Pubns.

Mottet, Louann M. Caregiving @ Home Series: Activities of Daily Living. rev. ed. 2008. (ENG.). 122p. (C). spiral bd. 125.00 *(978-1-58254-037-5(3))* Kendall Hunt Publishing Co.

Mrykalo, Frank. Caregiving & Elderly Parents: Concerns, Issues, & Recommendations: A Psychologist's Perspective. 2008. 271p. pap. 27.95 *(978-1-60441-703-6(X))* PublishAmerica, Inc.

Mulkey, Sarah. Footnotes: Lessons from a Baby-in-Residence. 2010. 68p. pap. 9.95 *(978-1-4502-6304-7(6))* iUniverse, Inc.

Munday, Barbara. A Jug Full of Caring. 2008. 304p. pap. 19.95 *(978-1-84799-586-5(1))* Lulu Enterprises Inc.

Munitich, Brenda. The Little Book of Positive Thoughts for Carers. 2009. 68p. pap. *(978-1-84923-425-2(6))* YouWriteOn.

Munro, Ian. The Lived Experience of Gay Men Caring for Others with Hiv/Aids. 2008. 324p. pap. *(978-3-639-03581-0(X))* VDM Verlag Dr. Mueller e.K.

Murphey, Cecil. When Someone You Love Has Cancer: Comfort & Encouragement for Caregivers & Loved Ones. 2009. (Illus.). 64p. 10.99 *(978-0-7369-2428-3(0))* Harvest Hse. Pubs.

Murphy, Betsy. Guide to Caregiving in the Final Months of Life. 2007. 64p. 5.00 *(978-0-9798701-0-1(0))* TM Brown.

Myers, Robin. A Caregiver's Journey. 2008. 48p. pap. 16.95 *(978-1-4137-7330-9(3))* PublishAmerica, Inc.

Nelham, Carolyn. I Love You What's Your Name? 2009. 200p. pap. *(978-3-639-07272-3(3))* VDM Verlag Dr. Mueller e.K.

Neuman, Fredric. Caring: Home Caregiving for A Loved One with Emotional Illness. 2008. 256p. pap. 16.95 *(978-0-9814843-8-9(7))* Simon & Brown.

Nicol, Colleen. Senior Days: Insightful Tales & No-Nonsense Help from the Frontlines of Eldercare. 2008. (ENG., Illus.). 134p. pap. 14.95 *(978-0-9794896-0-0(1))* Long Lake Pr.

Noonan, Nell E. Not Alone: Encouragement for Caregivers. 2009. 320p. 20.00 *(978-0-8358-9982-6(9))* Upper Room Bks.

Noonan, Nell E. The Struggles of Caregiving. 2012. ***(978-0-8358-1091-3(7))*** Upper Room Bks.

Nouwen, Henri J. M. A Spirituality of Caregiving. 2011. 64p. pap. 12.00 *(978-0-8358-1045-6(3))* Upper Room Bks.

Nowicki, Karen A. Spiritual Triage: Timely Meditations for Health-care Workers. 2010. 106p. pap. 13.00 *(978-1-60899-188-4(1),* Resource Pubns.) Wipf & Stock Pubs.

Oliva-Hemker, Maria, et al, eds. Your Child with Inflammatory Bowel Disease: A Family Guide for Caregiving. 2010. (Johns Hopkins Press Health Book Ser.). (ENG., Illus.). 304p. pap. 19.95 *(978-0-8018-9556-2(1))*; (gr. 17). 45.00 *(978-0-8018-9555-5(3))* Johns Hopkins Univ. Pr.

Our Unsung Heroes: Grandparents & Relative Caregivers-As-Parents. 2006. (Illus.). 114p. per. 13.95 *(978-1-58597-389-7(0))* Leathers Publishing.

Owens, Alistair. Gender Inequalities, Households & the Production of Well-Being in Modern Europe. Borderias, Cristina et al, eds. 2010. (Gender & Well-Being Ser.). (Illus.). 340p. 124.95 *(978-0-7546-7968-4(3))* Ashgate Publishing Co.

Owens, Virginia Stem. Caring for Mother: A Daughter's Long Goodbye. 2007. (ENG.). 163p. per. 17.00 *(978-0-664-23152-1(7))* Westminster John Knox Pr.

Pagdi, Gayatri. Walking with Chris. 2008. 228p. pap. 25.95 *(978-1-84747-772-9(0))* Chipmunkapublishing.

Palm Beach Community College & Children and Families Research Group Staff. Introduction to Child Care Worker Certification. rev. ed. 2010. (ENG.). 450p. spiral bd. 37.56 *(978-0-7575-5481-0(4))* Kendall Hunt Publishing Co.

Parker, Charlotte. Return to Joy. 2010. 176p. 24.95 *(978-0-9822851-0-7(8))* Dancing Horse Publishing.

Parker, Lillian. African American Spousal Caregivers. 2010. 104p. pap. *(978-3-8383-5915-1(1))* Lambert Academic Publishing.

Patricia Cox. We Keep Our Potato Chips in the Refrigerator: A Memoir of an Alzheimer's Victim. 2010. 136p. pap. 13.95 *(978-1-4502-0256-5(X))* iUniverse, Inc.

Pausch, Jai. Dream New Dreams: Reimagining My Life after Loss. 2012. (ENG., Illus.). 240p. 24.00 ***(978-0-307-88850-1(9),*** Crown Archetype) Crown Publishing Group.

Pearce, Nancy. Inside Alzheimer's: How to Hear & Honor Connections with a Person who has Dementia. rev. ed. 2011. (ENG., Illus.). 336p. pap. 19.95 *(978-0-9788299-1-9(3))* Forrason Pr.

Pearson, Glenn A. Prepare to Meet Your God: Scriptural Meditations for the Terminally Ill & Their Caregivers. enl. l.t. ed. 2007. 212p. per. 14.95 incl. cd-rom *(978-0-9765222-1-8(7),* Trestle Pr.) Ekklesia Pr.

Pfeiffer, Eric. The Art of Caregiving in Alzheimer's Disease. 2011. 136p. pap. 14.95 ***(978-1-257-76112-8(9))*** Lulu Enterprises Inc.

Phillips, Kathy J. The Moon in the Water: Reflections on an Aging Parent. 2008. (Illus.). (ENG.). 160p. 19.95 *(978-0-8265-1586-5(X))*; xii, 139p. pap. *(978-0-8265-1587-2(8))* Vanderbilt Univ. Pr.

Piercy, Kathleen W. Working with Aging Families: Therapeutic Solutions for Caregivers, Spouses, & Adult Children. 2010. (ENG.). 288p. 27.95 *(978-0-393-73282-5(7),* 73282) Norton, W. W. & Co., Inc.

Pinchot, Laura J. Help Wanted Caregiver: A Guide to Helping Your Loved One Cope with Serious Illness. 2010. 112p. pap. 13.00 *(978-1-890504-97-7(1))* Oncology Nursing Society.

Powell, Carol. Reflections on the Spiritual Journey of Caregivers: A Collection of Inspiring Anecdotes by Family Members Experiencing the Challenges & Lessons of Care Giving. 2010. 260p. pap. 14.49 *(978-1-4520-1002-1(1))* AuthorHouse.

Power, Andrew. Landscapes of Care: Comparative Perspectives on Family Caregiving. 2010. (Illus.). 260p. 124.95 *(978-0-7546-7950-9(0))* Ashgate Publishing Co.

Praver, Frances Cohen. Crossroads at Midlife: Your Aging Parents, Your Emotions & Your Self. 2008. 184p. pap. 19.95 *(978-0-313-36316-0(1),* B36316, Praeger Trade) Greenwood Publishing Group, Inc.

Prieto, Emily. Home Health Care Provider: A Guide to Essential Skills. 2008. (Illus.). 35.00 *(978-0-8261-2852-2(1))* Springer Publishing Co., Inc.

Pringle-Reid, Vertie. Smile Bandages: Loving the Unlovable. 2009. 176p. 22.95 *(978-1-4389-3740-3(7))*; pap. 15.95 *(978-1-4389-3739-7(3))* AuthorHouse.

Qualls, Sara H. & Zarit, Steven H., eds. Aging Families & Caregiving. 2009. (Wiley Series in Clinical Geropsychology Ser.: 3). (ENG., Illus.). 338p. 64.00 *(978-0-470-00855-3(5),* Wiley) Wiley, John & Sons, Inc.

Rafool, Gordon J. Communicating for Care: How to Form a Successful Team with the Alzheimer's Patient, Caregiver, & Doctor. 2007. 72p. per. 16.95 *(978-1-4241-7718-9(9))* PublishAmerica, Inc.

Raunea, Auna. The Innocent & the Merciless. 2011. 176p. 24.23 ***(978-1-4269-6276-9(2))***; pap. 14.23 ***(978-1-4269-6275-2(4))*** Trafford Publishing.

Raynor, Vanessa. Training Caregivers in Feeding Geriatric Residents. 2009. 172p. pap. *(978-3-639-19333-6(4))* VDM Verlag Dr. Mueller e.K.

Razavi, Shahra, ed. Seen, Heard & Counted: Rethinking Care in a Development Context. 2012. (Development & Change Special Issues Ser.: 4). (ENG.). 276p. pap. 34.95 ***(978-1-4443-6153-7(8),*** Wiley-Blackwell) Wiley, John & Sons, Inc.

Razavi, Shahra & Staab, Silke, eds. Global Variations in the Political & Social Economy of Care. 2012. (Routledge/UNRISD Research in Gender & Development Ser.). (ENG., Illus.). 286p. (C). 125.00 ***(978-0-415-52250-2(1))*** Routledge.

Reed, Emma. The Other Woman Is AD: A Behavior Log on an Alzheimer's Patient, My Husband. 2011. 100p. pap. 15.49 *(978-1-4567-2212-8(3))* AuthorHouse.

Reed, Gayle L. Caregiver's Checklist: A Personal Experience. Shade, Zoe & Goodman, Kathy, eds. 2006. 69p. spiral bd. 19.95 *(978-0-9768637-0-0(7))* In Memory Of, Inc.

Reimer, Kevin Scott. Living L'Arche: Stories of Compassion, Love & Disability. 2009. 192p. *(978-1-84706-435-6(3))* Continuum International Publishing Group, Ltd.

Renzenbrink, Irene. Caregiver Stress & Staff Support in Illness, Dying & Bereavement. 2011. (ENG., Illus.). 248p. pap. 57.95 *(978-0-19-959040-7(0))* Oxford Univ. Pr., Inc.

Reynolds, Joanne. Search for Light: Ten Crucial Lessons for Caregivers. 2010. pap. 24.99 *(978-1-60799-968-3(4))* Tate Publishing & Enterprises, LLC.

Risseeuw, Carla, et al. Care, Culture & Citizenship: Revisiting the Politics of the Dutch Welfare State. 2008. (ENG.). 232p. pap. 49.95 *(978-90-5589-239-6(4))* Het Spinhuis NLD. Dist: Transaction Pubs.

Robison, Susan, et al. Communication for the Cognizant, Nonverbal Patient. 2011. pap. 8.99 ***(978-1-61739-917-6(5))*** Tate Publishing & Enterprises, LLC.

Rogers, Chrissie & Weller, Susie, eds. Critical Approaches to Care: Understanding Caring Relations, Identities & Cultures. 2012. (Relationships & Resources Ser.). (ENG., Illus.). 240p. (C). 135.00 *(978-0-415-61329-3(9))* Routledge.

Rogers, Sloan. And Then There Was Me: A Memoir: Living with a Dying Loved One. 2011. pap. 15.99 *(978-1-61739-852-0(7))* Tate Publishing & Enterprises, LLC.

Rose, Charles. In the Midst of Life: A Hospice Volunteer's Story. 2007. pap. 19.95 *(978-1-60306-020-2(0))* NewSouth, Inc.

Sadler, Shelly & Speaker, Joanna. Home Caregiver Guide. rev. ed. 2009. (ENG.). 168p. (C). pap. 10.95 *(978-0-7575-6579-3(4))* Kendall Hunt Publishing Co.

Saito, Yayoi, ed. Meeting the Challenges of Elder Care: Japan & Norway. 2010. 223p. 84.95 *(978-1-920901-95-0(7))* Trans Pacific Pr. AUS. Dist: International Specialized Bk. Services.

Salach, Susan. Just When U Think U Know What You're Talking about ... along Comes Grandpa! Caregiving Resources for People in the Real World. 2006. pap. 19.95 *(978-1-58736-666-6(5))* Wheatmark.

Sammons, Mary Beth, et al. We Carry Each Other: Getting Through Life's Toughest Times. 2007. (ENG.). 184p. pap. 16.95 *(978-1-57324-311-7(6),* Conari Pr.) Red Wheel/Weiser.

Samu, Zsazsa. Our Caregivers Stories from Our Nursing. 2007. pap. 9.95 *(978-1-4327-0189-5(4))* Outskirts Pr., Inc.

Sanchez, Elaine K. Letters from Madelyn: Chronicles of a Caregiver. 2007. (Illus.). 271p. pap. *(978-0-89802-777-8(2))* Beautiful America Publishing Co.

Sanders, Delia González & Fortinsky, Richard H. Dementia Care with Black & Latino Families: A Social Work Problem-Solving Approach. 2011. ***(978-0-8261-0677-3(3))*** Springer.

Scalia, Elizabeth. Caring for the Dying with the Help of Your Catholic Faith. 2008. (With the Help of Your Catholic Faith Ser.). 63p. per. 5.95 *(978-1-59276-239-2(5))* Our Sunday Visitor, Publishing Div.

Schmall, Vicki L., et al. Manuel de Ayuda para Cuidadores: Herramientas valiosas para Cuidadores. 2006. (SPA.). pap. *(978-0-9785448-1-2(1))* Legacy Health System, Caregiver Services.

Schonhoff, Shelly & Speaker, Joanna. Family Caregivers Guide. rev. ed. 2008. (ENG.). 168p. (C). pap. 10.95 *(978-1-58254-035-1(7))* Kendall Hunt Publishing Co.

Seegmiller, Judy. Life with Big Al: Early Alzheimer's; A Caregiver's Diary. 174p. pap. 12.95 *(978-1-57636-108-5(X))* SunRise Publishing.

Setne, Jean. Default Caregivers. 2011. 136p. 24.95 ***(978-1-4567-6698-6(8))***; pap. 14.99 ***(978-1-4567-6699-3(6))*** AuthorHouse.

Shaaban, Juwita, et al. Caregiver Burden in Dementi. 2011. 64p. pap. ***(978-3-8443-1373-4(7))*** Lambert Academic Publishing.

Sharpe, Charles C. Online Resources for Caregivers of the Elderly. 2010. (ENG.). 199p. pap. 39.95 *(978-0-7864-5941-4(7))* McFarland & Co., Inc. Pubs.

Sheehan, James. The Father Who Didn't Know My Name. 2006. pap. 15.95 *(978-0-9672801-1-0(7))* Coy Publishing Co.

Sheehy, Gail. Passages in Caregiving: Turning Chaos into Confidence. (ENG.). 2011. 416p. pap. 16.99 *(978-0-06-166121-1(X),* Harper Paperbacks) 2010. 368p. 27.99 *(978-0-06-166120-4(1),* Morrow, William & Co.) HarperCollins Pubs.

—Passages in Caregiving: Turning Chaos into Confidence. l.t. ed. 2010. (ENG.). 732p. 33.99 *(978-1-4104-2989-6(X))* Thorndike Pr.

Sheldon, Joyce Marie. From Fear to Faith, A Caregiver's Journey: Reflections on Finding Hope in the Midst of Despair. 2006. 19.95 *(978-0-9704651-8-4(1))* Lorimer Pr.

Shifren, Kim. How Caregiving Affects Development: Psychological Implications for Child, Adolescent, & Adult Caregivers. 2008. (Illus.). 248p. 49.95 *(978-1-4338-0393-2(3))* American Psychological Assn.

Shouse, Deborah. Love in the Land of Dementia: Finding Hope in the Caregiver's Journey. 2006. (Illus.). 179p. per. 14.95 *(978-0-9777590-4-0(0))* Creativity Connection, The.

Shriver, Maria. Alzheimer's in America: The Shriver Report on Women & Alzheimer's. 2011. (ENG., Illus.). 320p. pap. 12.99 *(978-1-4516-3987-2(2),* Free Pr.) Free Pr.

Shulman, Neil, et al. The Real Truth about Aging: A Survival Guide for Older Adults & Caregivers. 2009. (ENG., Illus.). 368p. pap. 21.98 *(978-1-59102-719-5(5))* Prometheus Bks., Pubs.

Siles, Madonna. Eureka! Memories & Motivations: A Strategy for Creating a Healing Home for the Stroke / Brain Injury Patient & Caregiver. 2010. (ENG., Illus.). 216p. pap. 17.95 *(978-0-9825518-0-6(0))* Third Step Pr.

Silin, Jonathan G. My Father's Keeper: The Story of a Gay Son & His Aging Parents. 2007. (ENG.). 184p. per. 16.00 *(978-0-8070-7965-2(0))* Beacon Pr.

Silin, Peter S. Nursing Homes & Assisted Living: The Family's Guide to Making Decisions & Getting Good Care. 2nd ed. 2009. (ENG.). 388p. pap. 25.00

C

(978-0-8018-9352-0(6)); (gr. 17). 47.00 (978-0-8018-9351-3(8)) Johns Hopkins Univ. Pr.

Singer, George H. S., et al, eds. Family Support & Family Caregiving Across Disabilities. 2011. (ENG.). 216p. (C). 125.00 (978-0-415-68268-8(1)) Routledge.

Singer, Jonathan. The Special Needs Parent Handbook: Critical Strategies & Practical Advice to Help You Survive & Thrive. 2010. (ENG.). 82p. pap. 14.99 (978-1-4520-7446-7(1)) AuthorHouse.

Skillin, Joseph. Confessions of a Caregiver: When Alzheimer's Comes to Your Home. 2009. 120p. pap. 10.99 (978-1-60799-503-6(4)) Tate Publishing & Enterprises, LLC.

Smith, Edward Arthur Warwick & Smith, Edward. An Apple a Day: A People's History of Sickness, Survival, Healing & Health Care in Canada. 2010. (ENG., Illus.). 96p. pap. 16.95 (978-1-55277-017-7(6)) Lorimer, James & Co., Ltd., Pubs. CAN. Dist: Casemate Pubs. & Bk. Distributors, LLC.

Smith, Gina, et al. An Integrated Approach to Family Work for Psychosis: A Manual for Family Workers. 2007. (ENG., Illus.). 28p. per. (978-1-84310-369-1(9)) Kingsley, Jessica Ltd.

Smith, Lilian. Lilies in the Valley. 2010. 96p. pap. 10.99 (978-1-60957-896-1(1)) Xulon Pr., Inc.

Smith M.S., Barbara A., OTR/L. Still Giving Kisses: A Guide to Helping & Enjoying the Alzheimer's Victim You Love. 2008. 136p. pap. 12.50 (978-1-4357-1025-2(8)) Lulu Enterprises Inc.

Solimeo, Samantha. With Shaking Hands: Aging with Parkinson's Disease in America's Heartland. 2009. (Studies in Medical Anthropology). (ENG., Illus.). 232p. 72.00 (978-0-8135-4543-1(9)); pap. 24.95 (978-0-8135-4544-8(7)) Rutgers Univ. Pr.

Somers, Marion. Elder Care Made Easier: Doctor Marion's 10 Steps to Help You Care for an Aging Loved One. 2006. (ENG., Illus.). 177p. pap. 16.95 (978-1-886039-80-3(1)) Addicus Bks.

Spainhour, Polly L. The Color of Gray: (Living & Dying with Alzheimer's) 2011. 318p. pap. 29.95 **(978-1-4560-9134-7(4))** PublishAmerica, Inc.

Spreiter, Mary. Comfort for the Caregiver. 2007. 69p. pap. (978-0-9797673-0-2(X)) Spreiter, Mary.

Spring, Janis Abrahms, PhD & Spring, Michael. Life with Pop: Lessons on Caring for an Aging Parent. 2010. (ENG.). 240p. (gr. 12). 16.00 (978-1-58333-395-2(9), Avery) Penguin Group (USA) Inc.

Stahl, Michael Wayne K. Health Care - Are You Ready? A Handbook for Care Givers. 2010. 240p. pap. 16.95 (978-1-4490-2096-5(8)) AuthorHouse.

Steinberg. Forgetting the Memories: A Caregiver's Journey Through Alzheimer's Disease. 2010. 120p. 24.49 (978-1-4490-5589-9(3)); pap. 15.95 (978-1-4490-5588-2(5)) AuthorHouse.

Stevens, Judith. Senior Secrets: Caregiving Advice from the Front Lines. 2007. 120p. per. 12.95 (978-0-595-44788-6(0)) iUniverse, Inc.

Stewart, Jamye. Last Trip Home. 2010. 237p. pap. 14.95 (978-1-4327-2231-9(X)) Outskirts Pr., Inc.

Sutherland Millmann, Anita. Fluffy, My Yellow Dog: A Unlikely Care Giver. 2010. 40p. pap. 16.99 (978-1-4490-6215-6(6)) AuthorHouse.

Swayze, Lisa Niemi. Worth Fighting For: Love, Loss, & Moving Forward. 2012. (ENG., Illus.). 256p. pap. 14.00 **(978-1-4391-9636-6(2))**; 336p. 24.00 (978-1-4391-9635-9(4)) Atria Bks. (Beyond Words/Atria Bks.).

—Worth Fighting For: Love, Loss, & Moving Forward. 2012. lib. bdg. **(978-1-61173-350-1(2))** Ctr. Point Large Print.

Tarnow, Georgette H. When Your Parent Becomes Your Child: Advice for Caregivers... from a Daughter Who Spent 23 Years Dealing with Aging & Dementia. 2011. 142p. pap. 14.95 **(978-1-60910-741-3(1))** Booklocker.com, Inc.

Taylor, Jonathan. Take Me Home: Parkinson's, My Father, Myself. 2008. (ENG., Illus.). 288p. 29.95 (978-1-86207-955-7(2)) Granta Bks. GBR. Dist: Independent Pubs. Group.

Telling My Life's Story. 2006. 3.00 (978-0-9788913-0-5(9)) Sacred Vigil Pr.

The Healing Project. Voices of Caregiving: The Healing Companion: Stories for Courage, Comfort & Strength. 2008. (Voices of Ser.). (ENG.). 288p. pap. 16.95 (978-1-934184-06-6(3)) Lachance Publishing LLC.

Thibault, Jane Marie & Morgan, Richard. No Act of Love Is Ever Wasted: The Spirituality of Caring for Persons with Dementia. 2009. 160p. pap. 16.00 (978-0-8358-9995-6(0)) Upper Room Bks.

Tirabassi, Maren C., et al. Caring for Ourselves While Caring for Our Elders. 2007. 134p. per. (978-0-8298-1717-1(4)) Pilgrim Pr., The/United Church Pr.

Todd, Linda. Tales from the Third Floor. 2010. 136p. pap. 10.99 (978-1-4520-0343-6(2)) AuthorHouse.

Tofanelli, Dave. Cancer, a Marriage & a Miracle. 2008. 224p. pap. 15.99 (978-1-60647-724-3(2)) Xulon Pr., Inc.

Toseland, Ronald W., et al, eds. Education & Support Programs for Caregivers: Research, Practice, Policy. 2011. (Caregiving: Research, Policy, & Practice Ser.). xvi, 165p. 129.00 (978-1-4419-8030-4(X), 144198030X) Springer.

Townsend, Terry F. Living Alone with Dementia — Alzheimer's. 2008. 106p. pap. 16.95 (978-1-60672-256-5(5)) PublishAmerica, Inc.

Treasure, Janet, et al. The Clinician's Guide to Collaborative Caring in Eating Disorders: The New Maudsley Method. 2009. (ENG., Illus.). 304p. (C). 42.95 (978-0-415-48425-1(1)); 115.00 (978-0-415-48424-4(3)) Routledge.

—Skills-Based Learning for Caring for a Loved One with an Eating Disorder: The New Maudsley Method. 2007. (ENG., Illus.). 248p. per. 24.95 (978-0-415-43158-3(1)) Routledge.

Trickett, Donna M. Caregiving 101: 101 Easy-to-Understand bits of Vital Information. 2011. 228p. 29.99 **(978-1-4568-8751-3(3))**; pap. 19.99 **(978-1-4568-8750-6(5))** Xlibris Corp.

Tuell, Ra'ufa Sherry. Islamic Approaches to Patient Care: Muslim Beliefs & Healthcare Practices for Caregivers. 2011. **(978-1-59008-070-2(X))** amana pubns.

Turner, Isaac Croom. Here It Is: The Cutting Edge of Church Respite Care. 2007. per. 16.95 (978-0-9796978-4-5(0)) G Publishing LLC.

University of Health Care, creator. End of Life Care Issues: Death, Dying, & Grief. 2006. (End of Life Care Issues (University of Health Care) Ser.). cd-rom 49.95 (978-1-59491-282-5(3)) UniversityOfHealthCare.

Until There's a Cure: How to Help Alzheimer's Patients & Families Now: Forum Before the Special Committee on Aging, United States Senate, One Hundred Eleventh Congress, Second Session, Washington, DC, December 8, 2010. 2011. (Illus.). iii, 219p. **(978-0-16-088374-3(1)**, 552-070-42647-7) United States Government Printing Office.

van Belle-Kusse, Patty & Zadoks, Judith. Supporting Survivors & Caregivers after Brain Injury: A program for psychosocial Support. 2011. 126p. pap. 35.00 **(978-1-931117-59-3(4))** Lash & Assocs. Publishing/Training, Inc.

Van der Zande, Irene & Santa Cruz Toddler Care Center Staff. 1,2,3... the Toddler Years: A Practical Guide for Parents & Caregivers. 3rd rev. ed. 2011. (ENG.). 208p. pap. 14.95 (978-0-940953-25-3(0)) Toddler Ctr. Pr., The.

Wagner, Patti. Did I Forget to Tell You? 2008. 60p. pap. 9.95 (978-1-4401-1208-9(8)) iUniverse, Inc.

Walton. Compassionate Care: An inspirational guide for caregivers of the seriously ill. 2009. 236p. pap. 15.99 (978-1-60791-455-6(7)) Xulon Pr., Inc.

Waring, Marilyn, et al, eds. Who Cares? The Economics of Dignity. 2011. (ENG., Illus.). 200p. pap. 24.95 (978-1-84929-019-7(9)) Commonwealth Secretariat GBR. Dist: Stylus Publishing, LLC.

Watkins, Grant. CPR for Caregivers: Connect, Project, & Reflect Through Mind, Body, & Spirit. 2008. 75p. per. 18.95 (978-1-934690-01-7(5)) Tasora Bks.

Weisstub, D. N., et al, eds. Aging: Caring for our Elders: Caring for our Elders. 2010. (International Library of Ethics, Law, & the New Medicine Ser.). 264p. pap. 149.00 (978-90-481-5897-3(4), 9048158974) Springer.

Wheeler, Doris Speigner. The Ultimate Care Giver. 2010. 260p. pap. 16.99 (978-1-60957-450-5(8)) Xulon Pr., Inc.

Wicks, Laurel A. Lessons from a Caregiver: Caring for an Elder with Love & Compassion, 1 vol. 2009. (ENG.). 152p. pap. 12.99 (978-1-4236-0553-9(5)) Gibbs Smith, Publisher.

Wilson, Rowena Grice & Crewe, Sandra Edmonds. Tradition & Policy Perspectives in Kinship Care. 2007. (ENG., Illus.). 268p. 125.00 (978-0-7890-3551-6(0)); per. 54.50 (978-0-7890-3552-3(9)) Routledge.

Winakur, Jerald. Memory Lessons: A Doctor's Story. 2008. 304p. 24.95 (978-1-4013-0302-0(1)) Hyperion Pr.

Wisniewski, Linda C. Off Kilter: A Woman's Journey to Peace with Scoliosis, Her Mother & Her Polish Heritage. 2008. (ENG.). 164p. pap. 18.95 (978-1-59719-012-1(8)) Pearlsong Pr.

Wittenberg-Lyles, Elaine. Dying with Comfort: Family Illness Narratives & Early Palliative Care. 2010. (Illus.). 280p. (978-1-57273-984-0(3)); (978-1-57273-985-7(1)) Hampton Pr., Inc.

Wolfelt, Alan D. & Duvall, Kirby J. Healing Your Grieving Heart When Someone You Care about Has Alzheimer's: 100 Practical Ideas for Families, Friends, & Caregivers. 2011. (Healing Your Grieving Heart Ser.). (ENG.). 128p. pap. 11.95 **(978-1-61722-148-4(1))** Companion Pr.

Woodson, Cheryl E. To Survive Caregiving: A Daughter's Experience, A Doctor's Advice on Finding Hope, Help & Health. 2007. (ENG.). 180p. per. 18.95 (978-0-7414-3725-9(2)) Infinity Publishing.

Wornell, Doug. Wandering Explorers: Practical Dementia for Families & Caregivers. 2011. 162p. pap. **(978-1-84991-456-7(7))** Chipmunkapublishing.

Yeates, Nicola. Globalizing Care Economies & Migrant Workers: Explorations in Global Care Chains. 2009. (ENG., Illus.). 256p. 89.00 (978-0-230-00534-1(9)) Palgrave Macmillan.

Yurth, David. Sliding Home: A Memoir. 2007. 124p. per. 19.95 (978-1-4241-7672-4(7)) PublishAmerica, Inc.

Zucker, Elana. Being a Caregiver in a Home Setting. rev. ed. 2012. (ENG., Illus.). 416p. (C). pap. 21.95 **(978-0-13-274189-7(X)**, Prentice Hall) Prentice Hall PTR.

CAREW, ROD, 1945-

Carew, Rod & Berkow, Ira. Carew. 2010. (Fesler-Lampert Minnesota Heritage Ser.). (ENG., Illus.). 268p. pap. 18.95 (978-0-8166-7009-3(9)) Univ. of Minnesota Pr.

CAREX

Hipp, Andrew L. Field Guide to Wisconsin Sedges: An Introduction to the Genus Carex (Cyperaceae) 2008. (ENG., Illus.). 280p. pap. 27.95 (978-0-299-22594-0(1)) Univ. of Wisconsin Pr.

Mohlenbrock, Robert H. Sedges: Carex. 2nd ed. 2011. (Illus.). 193p. E-Book (978-0-8093-8627-7(5)); 456p. 65.00 (978-0-8093-3024-9(5)) Southern Illinois Univ. Pr.

Wilson, Barbara L., et al. Field Guide to the Sedges of the Pacific Northwest 2008. (ENG., Illus.). 432p. pap. 35.00 (978-0-87071-197-8(0)) Oregon State Univ. Pr.

CAREY, MARIAH, 1970-

Dominguez, Pier. Mariah Carey: The Making of an American Diva. 2010. (ENG.). 272p. pap. (978-1-926745-54-1(X)) Transit Publishing (Transit Editeur Inc.).

CAREY, MATHEW, 1760-1839

Bradsher, Earl L. Mathew Carey: Editor, Author & Publisher. (BCL Ser. I). reprint ed. 31.50 (978-0-404-00969-4(7)) AMS Pr., Inc.

Vogeley, Nancy J. The Bookrunner: A History of Inter-American Relations: Print, Politics, & Commerce in the United States & Mexico, 1800-1830. 2011. **(978-1-60618-011-2(8))** American Philosophical Society.

CAREY, WILLIAM, 1761-1834

Appleby, John. I Can Plod... William Carey & the Early Years of the First Baptist Missionary Society. 2008. (Illus.). 309p. (978-0-946462-74-2(7)) Evangelical Pr.

Belcher, Joseph. William Carey: A Biography. 2006. 308p. per. 23.99 (978-1-4255-3221-5(7)) MPublishing.

Marshman, John Clark. The Life & Labours of Carey, Marshman, & Ward: The Serampore Missionaries. 2010. (Cambridge Library Collection - Religion Ser.). (ENG.). 408p. pap. 31.99 (978-1-108-00826-6(7)) Cambridge Univ. Pr.

Smith, George. The Life of William Carey. 2010. 504p. pap. 38.75 (978-1-146-87611-7(4)) BiblioBazaar.

—The Life of William Carey. 2009. 306p. pap. (978-1-150-51673-3(9)) Books LLC.

—The Life of William Carey. 2008. (ENG.). 348p. pap. 21.95 (978-1-60597-610-5(5), Book Jungle) Standard Pubns., Inc.

—Life of William Carey. 2010. (Illus.). 238p. pap. 32.01 (978-1-153-74077-7(X)) General Bks. LLC.

—The Life of William Carey, D. D: Shoemaker & Missionary. 2011. (Cambridge Library Collection - History Ser.). (ENG., Illus.). 500p. pap. 37.99 (978-1-108-02918-6(3)) Cambridge Univ. Pr.

—The Life of William Carey, Shoemaker & M. 2006. pap. (978-1-84702-485-5(8)) Echo Library.

CARGO AIRCRAFT

see Transport Planes

CARGO CULTS

Denicola, Lane. Reading the Ipod as an Anthropological Artifact: Click Wheels & Cargo Cults. 2010. (Routledge Series for Creative Teaching & Learning Ser.). (ENG.). 128p. 130.00 (978-0-415-80166-9(4)); pap. 19.95 (978-0-415-80167-6(2)) Taylor & Francis Group GBR. (Routledge India). Dist: Taylor & Francis Group.

Jebens, Holger. After the Cult: Perceptions of Other & Self in West New Britain (Papua New Guinea) 2010. (Illus.). 250p. 90.00 (978-1-84545-674-0(2)) Berghahn Bks., Inc.

Lattas, Andrew. Dreams, Madness & Fairy Tales in New Britain. 2010. (Illus.). 394p. pap. 50.00 (978-1-59460-727-1(3)) Carolina Academic Pr.

CARGO HANDLING

see also Ships—Cargo; Stowage; Unitized Cargo Systems

Aviation Security: Are We Truly Protected?, Part I & a Frontline Perspective on the Need for Enhanced Human Resources & Equipment, Part II: Hearing Before the Subcommittee on Transportation Security & Infrastructure Protection of the Committee on Homeland Security, House of Representatives, One Hundred Tenth Congress, First Session, October 16, 2007 & November 1, 2007. 2009. (Illus.). iv, 117p. (978-0-16-084141-5(0), 552-070-39748-5) United States Government Printing Office.

Bonacich, Edna & Wilson, Jake B. Getting the Goods: Ports, Labor, & the Logistics Revolution. 2008. 336p. 75.50 (978-0-8014-4572-9(8)); 273p. per. 24.95 (978-0-8014-7425-5(6)) Cornell Univ. Pr.

Brodie, Peter. Illustrated Dictionary of Cargo Handling. 3rd rev. ed. 2010. 223p. 207.00 (978-1-84311-882-4(3)) Informa Professional GBR. Dist: International Specialized Bk. Services.

Closing the Gaps in Air Cargo Security: Hearing Before the Committee on Homeland Security & Governmental Affairs, United States Senate, One Hundred Eleventh Congress, Second Session, November 16, 2010. 2011. iii, 64p. **(978-0-16-090027-3(1)**, 552-070-43804-1) United States Government Printing Office.

Günther, Hans-Otto. Container Terminals & Cargo Systems: Design, Operations Management, & Logistics Control Issues. Kim, Kap Hwan & Günther, Hans-Otto, eds. 2007. (ENG., Illus.). vi, 381p. 159.00 (978-3-540-49549-9(5), 3540495495) Springer.

Kim, Kap Hwan & Günther, Hans-Otto, eds. Container Terminals & Cargo Systems: Design, Operations Management, & Logistics Control Issues. 2010. (ENG., Illus.). vi, 381p. pap. 159.00 (978-3-642-08049-4(9), 3642080499) Springer.

Lawyer, Anthony B. Savannah Guide to Lashing: For All Deep Sea Vessels, Vol. III. 2011. 72p. 24.99 **(978-1-4628-6231-3(4))**; pap. 15.99 **(978-1-4628-6230-6(6))** Xlibris Corp.

Lighthouse Press, prod. U. S. C. G. Oil Record Book for Ships. 2007. pap. 9.95 (978-1-57785-644-3(9), Lighthouse Pr.) ProStar Pubns., Inc.

Markarian, Garik, et al. Aviation Security Engineering: A Holistic Approach. 2011. (Illus.). 280p. 109.00 (978-1-60807-072-5(7)) Artech Hse., Inc.

Meurn, Robert J. Marine Cargo Operations: A Guide to Stowage. 2011. (Illus.). 512p. 50.00 (978-0-87033-623-2(1), Schiffer Publishing Ltd) Schiffer Publishing, Ltd.

The Next Step in Aviation Security — Cargo Security: Is DHS Implementing the Requirements of the 9/11 Law Effectively?: Hearing Before the Subcommittee on Transportation Security & Infrastructure Protection of the Committee on Homeland Security, House of Representatives, One Hundred Tenth Congress, Second Session, July 15, 2008. 2008. iii, 91p. (978-0-16-082113-4(4), 552-070-38260-7) United States Government Printing Office.

Rowbotham, J. Mark. Introduction to Marine Cargo Management. 2008. (Lloyd's Practical Shipping Guides Ser.). (Illus.). 298p. 306.00 (978-1-84311-756-8(8)) Informa Professional GBR. Dist: International Specialized Bk. Services.

100 Percent Air Cargo Screening: Remaining Steps to Secure Passenger Aircraft: Hearing Before the Subcommittee on Transportation Security & Infrastructure Protection of the Committee on Homeland Security, House of Representatives, One Hundred Eleventh Congress, Second Session, June 30, 2010. 2011. (Illus.). iii, 70p. **(978-0-16-088765-9(8)**, 552-070-42905-1) United States Government Printing Office.

CARGO INSURANCE, MARINE

see Marine Insurance

CARGO MOVEMENT

see Cargo Cults

CARGO PLANES

see Transport Planes

CARGO SHIPS

see also Barges; Tankers

Bawal, Raymond Aloysious, Jr. Superships of the Great Lakes: Thousand-Foot Ships on the Great Lakes. Jerlecki, Constance Marie, ed. 2010. (Illus.). 106p. pap. 19.95 (978-0-9818157-4-9(X)) Inland Expressions.

Carroll, Paul. The Wexford: Elusive Shipwreck of the Great Storm 1913. 2010. (ENG., Illus.). 328p. pap. 30.00 (978-1-55488-736-1(4)) Dundurn CAN. Dist: Ingram Pub. Services.

Cope, Tony. On the Swing Shift: Building Liberty Ships in Savannah. 2009. (Illus.). 288p. 26.95 (978-1-59114-123-5(0)) Naval Institute Pr.

Cudahy, Brian J. Box Boats: How Container Ships Changed the World. 2nd ed. 2007. (ENG., Illus.). 352p. per. 25.00 (978-0-8232-2569-9(0)) Fordham Univ. Pr.

Curley, Stephen J. The Ship That Would Not Die: USS Queens, SS Excambion, & USTS Texas Clipper. 2011. (Centennial Series of the Association of Former Students, Texas A&M University Ser.). (Illus.). 256p. 29.95 (978-1-60344-427-9(0)) Texas A&M Univ. Pr.

Greenberg, Michael D., et al. Maritime Terrorism: Risk & Liability. 2007. (Illus.). 206p. per. 30.00 (978-0-8330-4030-5(8), MG520) RAND Corp., The.

Greenway, Ambrose. The Cargo Liners. 2008. (Illus.). 176p. 50.00 (978-1-84832-006-2(X)) Pen & Sword Bks. Ltd. GBR. Dist: Casemate Pubs. & Bk. Distributors, LLC.

Jaffee, Walter W. The Freighters from A (Adabelle Lykes) to Z (Zoella Lykes) 2010. (Illus.). 672p. 150.00 (978-1-889901-50-3(4)) Glencannon Pr.

Kadar, Wayne Louis. Great Lakes Collisions, Wrecks & Disasters. 2008. pap. 16.95 (978-1-892384-47-8(7)) Avery Color Studios, Inc.

Lafferty, William & van Heest, Valerie. Buckets & Belts: The Evolution of Great Lakes Self-Unloaders. 2009. (Illus.). 300p. pap. 22.95 (978-0-9801750-0-4(3)) In-Depth Editions.

Lemper, Burkhard & Zachcial, Manfred, eds. Trends in Container Shipping: Proceedings of the ISL Maritime Conference 2008. 2009. (Maritime Logistik. Maritime Logistics Ser.). 154p. 57.95 (978-3-631-59780-4(0)) Lang, Peter GmbH, Europaischer Verlag der Wissenschaften DEU. Dist: Lang, Peter.

Malcolm, Ian & Wood, Alan C. Life Aboard a Wartime Liberty Ship. 2010. (Illus.). 256p. pap. 34.95 (978-1-4456-0020-8(X)) Amberley Publishing GBR. Dist: Casemate Pubs. & Bk. Distributors, LLC.

Mattson, Arthur. Water & Ice: The Tragic Wrecks of the Bristol & the Mexico on the South Shore of Long Island. 2009. (Illus.). viii, 280p. **(978-0-615-29439-1(1))** Lynbrook Historical Bks.

Moise, Leicester R. Gainard Against the Odds. 2008. (Illus.). v, 78p. **(978-1-58374-185-6(2))** Chicago Spectrum Pr.

November 2007 San Francisco Oil Spill: Causes & Response: Field Hearing Before the Subcommittee on Coast Guard & Maritime Transportation of the Committee on Transportation & Infrastructure, House of Representatives, One Hundred Tenth Congress, First Session, November 19, 2007 (San Francisco, CA) 2007. (Illus.). xx, 113p. (978-0-16-081365-8(4), 552-070-37743-3) United States Government Printing Office.

Peetoom, Adrian. Vacation Adventures on a Cargo Ship, 1 vol. 2008. (ENG., Illus.). 288p. pap. 24.95 (978-1-897252-28-4(5)) Fitzhenry & Whiteside, Ltd. CAN. Dist: Ingram Pub. Services.

Plowman, Peter. Coast to Coast: The Great Australian Coastal Liners. 2007. (Illus.). 196p. pap. 29.95 (978-1-877058-60-8(2)) Rosenberg Publishing Pty, Ltd. AUS. Dist: International Specialized Bk. Services.

Rumberg, Hester. Ten Degrees of Reckoning: A True Story of Survival. 2010. (ENG.). 272p. (gr. 12-18). 15.00 (978-0-425-23210-1(7), Berkley Trade) Penguin Group (USA) Inc.

The Safe Port ACT: A Six-Month Review: Hearing Before the Subcommittee on Border, Maritime, & Global Counterterrorism of the Committee on Homeland Security, House of Representatives, One Hundred Tenth Congress, First Session, April 26, 2007. 2009. (Illus.). iv, 89p. (978-0-16-083601-5(8), 552-070-39319-6) United States Government Printing Office.

Staecker, Del. The Lady Gangster: A Sailor's Memoir. 2009. (Illus.). 180p. 23.95 (978-1-934980-21-7(8)) Cable Publishing.

—The Lady Gangster: A Sailor's Memoir. 2009. (Illus.). 176p. pap. 16.95 (978-1-934980-22-4(6)) Cable Publishing.

Walker, Spike. On the Edge of Survival: A Shipwreck, a Raging Storm, & the Harrowing Alaskan Rescue That Became a Legend. 2011. (ENG., Illus.). 304p. pap. 14.99 (978-0-312-60459-2(9), St. Martin's Griffin) St. Martin's Pr.

Williams, David L. & De Kerbrech, Richard P. Coastal Vessels: A Colour Portfolio. 2008. (ENG., Illus.). 80p. 24.95 (978-0-7110-3205-7(X)) Allan, Ian Publishing GBR. Dist: BookMasters Distribution Services (BDS).

CARIB INDIANS

Boucher, Philip P. Cannibal Encounters: Europeans & Island Caribs, 1492-1763. 2009. (Johns Hopkins Studies in Atlantic History & Culture Ser.). (ENG., Illus.). 232p. (gr. 17). pap. 27.00 *(978-0-8018-9099-4(3))* Johns Hopkins Univ. Pr.

Schwerin, Karl H. Oil & Steel: Processes of Karinya Culture Change in Response to Industrial Development. 2009. 288p. 68.00 *(978-1-59740-782-3(8))* ACLS Humanities E-Book.

Schwerin, Karl H. & Pleck, Elizabeth H. Oil & Steel: Processes of Karinya Culture Change in Response to Industrial Development. 2008. 288p. pap. 29.00 *(978-1-59740-659-8(7))* ACLS Humanities E-Book.

Staiano, Kathryn V. Interpreting Signs of Illness: A Case Study in Medical Semiotics. (Approaches to Semiotics [AS] Ser.). (ENG.). XVII, 284p. 196.00 ***(978-3-11-176422-1(2))*** De Gruyter, Mouton DEU. Dist: de Gruyter, Walter GmbH & Co. KG.

CARIB LANGUAGE

Courtz, Henk. A Carib grammar & Dictionary. 2008. (ENG & CAR.). 516p. pap. *(978-0-9781707-6-9(8))* Magoria Bks.

CARIBAN LANGUAGES

see also Carib Language

Icon Group International, Inc. Staff, compiled by. Webster's Jamaican - English Thesaurus Dictionary. 2008. 95p. ring bd. 28.95 incl. audio compact disk *(978-0-497-83530-9(4))* Icon Group International, Inc.

CARIBBEAN, ENGLISH-SPEAKING

Here are entered works on the English-speaking states comprising the British West Indies, as well as Belize, Guyana, and the Virgin Islands of the United States. Works limited to the British West Indies are entered under the heading West Indies, British.

Henry, Jones Mills & Lefranc. Institutional Aspects of West Indian Development. 210p. pap. *(978-976-8123-21-3(4))* Randle, Ian Pubs.

Higman, B. W. & Monteith, Kathleen E. A., eds. West Indian Business History: Enterprise & Entrepreneurship. 2010. (Illus.). 236p. pap. *(978-976-640-240-2(X))* Univ. of the West Indies Pr.

Mills, Charles W. Radical Theory, Caribbean Reality: Race, Class & Social Domination. 2010. 284p. pap. *(978-976-640-227-3(2))* Univ. of the West Indies Pr.

Rahim, Jennifer, ed. Beyond Borders: Cross-Culturalism & the Caribbean Canon. 2009. (Illus.). 267p. pap. *(978-976-640-216-7(7))* Univ. of the West Indies Pr.

Roopnarine, Lomarsh. Indo-Caribbean Indenture: Resistance & Accommodation, 1838-1920. 2006. (Illus.). 176p. per. *(978-976-640-185-6(3))* Univ. of the West Indies Pr.

CARIBBEAN AREA

Here are entered works on the region that lies between continental North and South America and consists of the archipelago of the West Indies, the Caribbean Sea and the adjacent mainland regions, including Southern Mexico, the countries of Central America, Colombia and Venezuela.

see also Caribbean, English-Speaking; West Indies

Clawson, David L. Latin America & the Caribbean: Lands & Peoples. 5th ed. 2011. (ENG., Illus.). 480p. (C). pap. 92.00 ***(978-0-19-975924-8(3))*** Oxford Univ. Pr., Inc.

Hunt. Caribbean Chemistry. Date not set. (Illus.). 312p. pap. 40.76 *(978-0-582-02949-1(X))* Addison-Wesley Longman, Ltd. GBR. Dist: Trans-Atlantic Pubns., Inc.

Hunte, Nicola. Omeros & Beloved Through Wilson Harris's Cross-Cultural Imagination. 2010. 292p. pap. *(978-3-8383-5831-4(7))* Lambert Academic Publishing.

Mintz, Sidney Wilfred & Rouse, Irving, eds. Papers in Caribbean Anthropology: Yale University Publications in Anthropology, No. 57-64. 2011. 270p. 47.95 ***(978-1-258-09117-0(8))*** Literary Licensing, LLC.

Routledge Staff, creator. South America, Central America & the Caribbean. 15th rev. ed. 2006. (South America, Central America & the Caribbean Ser.). (Illus.). 1076p. 615.00 *(978-1-85743-392-0(0))* Routledge.

Wright, Irene A., ed. Global & Regional Problems: Towards an Interdisciplinary Study. 2010. (Hakluyt Society, Second Ser.). 224p. 69.95 *(978-1-4094-1429-2(9))* Hakluyt Society GBR. Dist: Ashgate Publishing Co.

CARIBBEAN AREA—ANTIQUITIES

Bari, Hubert. The Pink Pearl: A Natural Treasure of the Caribbean. 2007. (ENG., Illus.). 176p. 58.00 *(978-88-6130-013-2(8))* Skira Editore ITA. Dist: Random Hse., Inc.

Fraginals, Manual Moreno. Autochthonous Societies, Vol. 1. Sued-Badillo, Jalil, ed. 2007. (ENG.). 442p. 31.00 *(978-1-4039-7589-8(2))* Palgrave Macmillan.

Goggin, John M. The Spanish Olive Jar, an Introductory Study: Yale University Publications in Anthropology, No. 62. Mintz, Sidney Wilfred & Rouse, Irving, eds. 2011. 50p. 35.95 ***(978-1-258-09123-1(2))*** Literary Licensing, LLC.

Hayward, Michele H., et al. Rock Art of the Caribbean. 2009. (Caribbean Archaeology & Ethnohistory Ser.). (ENG.). 304p. pap. 30.95 *(978-0-8173-5530-2(8))*; (Illus.). 51.75 *(978-0-8173-1650-1(7))* Univ. of Alabama Pr.

Hicks, Dan. The Garden of the World: An Historical Archaeology of Sugar Landscapes in the Eastern Caribbean. 2011. (Bar S Ser.). (ENG., Illus.). 119p. (C). pap. 75.00 *(978-1-4073-0046-7(6))* British Archaeological Reports Ltd. GBR. Dist: Brown, David Bk. Co., The.

Jiménez, Jaime R. Pagán. De Antiquos Pueblos BAR S1687: El Archipiélago Borincano y la Llegada de los Primeros Pobladores Agroceramistas. 2007. (Bar S Ser.). (SPA., Illus.). 268p. (C). pap. 105.00 *(978-1-4073-0125-9(X))* British Archaeological Reports Ltd. GBR. Dist: Brown, David Bk. Co., The.

Kepecs, Susan, et al, eds. Beyond the Blockade: New Currents in Cuban Archaeology. 2nd ed. 2010. (Caribbean Archaeology & Ethnohistory Ser.). (ENG., Illus.). 224p. 35.00 *(978-0-8173-1720-1(1))*; pap. 22.95 *(978-0-8173-5633-0(9))* Univ. of Alabama Pr.

Kepecs, Susan, et al. Beyond the Blockade: New Currents in Cuban Archaeology. 2010. (Illus.). ix, 206p. *(978-0-8173-8492-0(8))* Univ. of Alabama Pr.

Lammers. Tracing Traces from the Present. 2009. (Archaeological Studies Leiden University Ser.). 182p. per. *(978-90-8728-028-4(9)*, Leiden Univ. Pr.) Amsterdam Univ. Pr.

Leshikar-Denton, Margaret E. & Luna Erreguerena, Pilar, eds. Underwater & Maritime Archaeology in Latin America & the Caribbean. 2011. (One World Archaeology Ser.). (ENG., Illus.). 316p. pap. 34.95 ***(978-1-59874-263-3(9))*** Left Coast Pr., Inc.

Reid, Basil A., ed. Archaeology & Geoinformatics: Case Studies from the Caribbean. 2nd ed. 2008. (Caribbean Archaeology & Ethnohistory Ser.). (ENG., Illus.). 296p. 54.75 *(978-0-8173-1601-3(9))*; pap. 34.95 *(978-0-8173-5470-1(0))* Univ. of Alabama Pr.

Siegel, Peter E. & Righter, Elizabeth, eds. Protecting Heritage in the Caribbean. 3rd ed. 2011. (Caribbean Archaeology & Ethnohistory Ser.). (ENG., Illus.). 216p. pap. 27.50 *(978-0-8173-5667-5(3))* Univ. of Alabama Pr.

Wilson, Samuel M. The Archaeology of the Caribbean. 2007. (Cambridge World Archaeology Ser.). (ENG., Illus.). (C). 224p. 99.99 *(978-0-521-62333-9(2))*; 222p. pap. 30.99 *(978-0-521-62622-4(6))* Cambridge Univ. Pr.

CARIBBEAN AREA—BIOGRAPHY

Baptiste, Lyndon. Ooh My Testicles! A tale of Entanglement. 2009. 108p. pap. 12.95 *(978-1-4401-4989-4(5))* iUniverse, Inc.

Blanchard, Robert & Blanchard, Melinda. Live What You Love: Notes from a Passionate Life. 2010. (ENG., Illus.). 216p. pap. 14.95 *(978-1-4027-7376-1(5))* Sterling Publishing Co., Inc.

Block, Kristen. Ordinary Lives in the Early Caribbean: Religion, Colonial Competition, & the Politics of Profit. 2012. (Early American Places Ser.). (ENG.). 312p. 69.95 ***(978-0-8203-3867-5(2))***; (Illus.). pap. 24.95 ***(978-0-8203-3868-2(0))*** Univ. of Georgia Pr.

Bodden, Jackie. A Cayman Childhood Remembered. 2007. 288p. im. lthr. 24.95 *(978-0-9785936-4-3(2))* Bodden, Jackie.

Cook, Nick & Beharry, Johnson. Barefoot Soldier: A Story of Extreme Valour. 2007. (ENG., Illus.). 448p. pap. 13.95 *(978-0-7515-3879-3(5))* Little, Brown Bk. Group Ltd. GBR. Dist: Independent Pubs. Group.

Cottingham, John & Hacker, Peter, eds. Mind, Method, & Morality: Essays in Honour of Anthony Kenny. 2010. (ENG.). 360p. 99.00 *(978-0-19-955612-0(1))* Oxford Univ. Pr., Inc.

Davis, Stephen. Bob Marley: Conquering Lion of Reggae. 3rd ed. 2012. (ENG., Illus.). 336p. pap. 16.95 *(978-0-85965-467-8(2))* Plexus Publishing, Ltd. GBR. Dist: Perseus-PGW.

Frank, Maraj & Diana, Maraj. Snapshots. 2009. 412p. 40.00 *(978-1-4269-0386-1(3))* Trafford Publishing.

Frankson, A. S. A Caribbean Identity: Memoirs of the Colonial Service. 2nd ed. 2008. (ENG., Illus.). 264p. 52.00 *(978-1-84511-591-3(0)*, Radcliffe Pr., The) I. B. Tauris & Co., Ltd. GBR. Dist: Macmillan.

Gaetjens, Lesly. The Shot Heard Around the World: the Joe Gaetjens Story. 2010. 116p. pap. 12.99 *(978-0-557-61231-4(4))* Lulu Enterprises Inc.

Gould, J. Duncan. Never a Dull Moment. 2010. 223p. pap. 19.79 *(978-1-4452-5650-4(9))* Lulu Enterprises Inc.

Gurley, Rudy. A Caribbean Tale. 2006. 404p. pap. 11.99 *(978-1-4276-0535-1(1))* Aardvark Global Publishing.

Hobson, Jeanette. At the Foot of Rawlins Mountain. 2006. 135p. pap. 24.95 *(978-1-4241-1979-0(0))* PublishAmerica, Inc.

Irene S. Prospere. Memories of Montserrat. 2009. 72p. pap. 15.00 *(978-1-4269-1944-2(1))* Trafford Publishing.

James, Willie. Charismatic Crisis-Prone Caribbean Leaders of Our Era. 2011. 24.99 *(978-1-57197-504-1(7)*, Ivy House Publishing Group) Pentland Pr., Inc.

Justin, Augustus (Gus). The One-Pound Baby, Gusandra, & Other Spiritual Journeys. 2008. 98p. pap. 9.00 *(978-0-8059-7760-8(0))* Dorrance Publishing Co., Inc.

Lewis, Phyllis. Island Memories: My Life in Trinidad. 2010. 104p. pap. 12.99 *(978-1-4269-0758-6(3))* Trafford Publishing.

Maraj, Frank. Snapshots. Maraj, Diana, ed. & told to by. 2008. 412p. pap. 25.55 *(978-1-4251-8544-2(4))* Trafford Publishing.

Markham, E. A. Against the Grain: A 1950s Memoir. 2008. (ENG.). 220p. pap. 24.95 *(978-1-84523-030-2(2))* Peepal Tree Pr., Ltd. GBR. Dist: Independent Pubs. Group.

Marksman, Donna. See You Later Darlin' 2009. (Illus.). 108p. 23.99 *(978-1-4389-5966-5(4))*; pap. 13.99 *(978-1-4389-5965-8(6))* AuthorHouse.

McCall, G. J. H. The Pilkington Gene. 2011. (Illus.). 168p. pap. ***(978-0-7552-1331-3(9))*** Authors OnLine, Ltd.

McCaslin, John. Weed Man: The Remarkable Journey of Jimmy Divine. 2011. 320p. pap. 15.99 ***(978-1-4016-0535-3(4))*** Nelson, Thomas Inc.

Morris, Dennis. Bob Marley: A Rebel Life. 3rd ed. 2012. (ENG., Illus.). 160p. pap. 19.95 *(978-0-85965-468-5(0))* Plexus Publishing, Ltd. GBR. Dist: Perseus-PGW.

O'Reilly, Sean. 21st Century Pirate. 2007. pap. 12.99 *(978-1-934248-20-1(7))* Mill City Pr., Inc.

Ortega, Rafael. Yo Fui Del Servicio Secreto de la Policia Dominican. 2008. 232p. pap. 31.45 *(978-1-59754-398-9(5))* Editorial Libros en Red.

Ortiz, David & Massarotti, Tony. Big Papi: My Story of Big Dreams & Big Hits. 2008. (ENG., Illus.). 288p. pap. 14.95 *(978-0-312-38344-2(4)*, St. Martin's Griffin) St. Martin's Pr.

Parfitt, George. Being Anglo-Caribbean. 2009. 148p. pap. 20.95 *(978-1-4092-5484-3(4))* Lulu Enterprises Inc.

Parker, Gabrielle. Aimé Césaire. 2010. (Inspirations Ser.). (ENG.). 100p. pap. 10.95 *(978-1-906413-24-8(X))* Arcadia Bks. Ltd. GBR. Dist: Independent Pubs. Group.

Perreira, Joseph 'Reds'. Living My Dreams. 2011. 156p. pap. 11.70 ***(978-1-4567-4169-3(1))*** AuthorHouse.

Purcell, Joan M. Memoirs of a Woman in Politics: Spiritual Struggle. 2009. 316p. pap. 15.99 *(978-1-4389-0468-9(1))* AuthorHouse.

Richardson, B. Louis. Late Dream: Finding Purpose. 2011. 108p. 20.95 ***(978-1-4620-0092-0(4))***; pap. 10.95 ***(978-1-4620-0091-3(6))*** iUniverse, Inc.

Sanders, Richard. If a Pirate I Must Be... The True Story of Black Bart, King of the Caribbean Pirates. 2009. (ENG., Illus.). 288p. pap. 14.95 *(978-1-60239-624-1(8)*, 239624) Skyhorse Publishing Co., Inc.

Scheeres, Julia. Jesus Land: A Memoir. 2006. (ENG.). 384p. per. 15.95 *(978-1-58243-354-7(2))* Counterpoint LLC.

Sims, Lowery Stokes, frwd. Llewellyn Xavier: His Life & Work. 2007. (ENG., Illus.). 224p. *(978-1-4050-8649-3(1))* Macmillan Caribbean.

Snell, Tony. Spitfire Troubadour. 2009. 252p. pap. 25.08 *(978-1-4251-7187-2(7))* Trafford Publishing.

Stockhausen Bazliel, Yvonne & Bazliel, Yvonne Stockhausen. Miracle or Coincidence. 2007. 52p. per. *(978-1-84748-192-4(2))* Athena Pr.

Strong, Ezra, ed. Infamous Pirates: Their Lives & Bloody Exploits. 2007. (Dover Maritime Ser.). (ENG., Illus.). 320p. per. 10.95 *(978-0-486-46185-4(8))* Dover Pubns., Inc.

Thompson-Hall, Doris. Life in Chateaubelair, 1 vol. 2010. 48p. pap. 16.95 *(978-1-4489-4312-8(4))* PublishAmerica, Inc.

White, Marjorie Victoria. Stars in the Sky at Dawn: Enduring Memories of Childhood. 2011. 264p. 29.99 ***(978-1-4653-4221-8(4))***; pap. 19.99 ***(978-1-4653-4220-1(6))*** Xlibris Corp.

Wild, Raimund Johannes. Little Heroes: Boys of the Barrio. 2008. 116p. pap. 12.95 *(978-1-4401-0436-7(0))* iUniverse, Inc.

CARIBBEAN AREA—CLIMATE

Duncan, Samuel B. Implications of Climate Change in Mexico, the Caribbean & Central America. 2011. (Climate Change & its Causes, Effects & Prediction Ser.). 89.00 *(978-1-61122-849-6(2))* Nova Science Pubs., Inc.

Rivers, Chelsea M. Hurricane Ivan: The Experience. 2009. 244p. pap. 15.99 *(978-1-61579-124-8(8))* Xulon Pr., Inc.

Simms, Andrew. Up in Smoke? Latin America & the Caribbean: The Threat from Climate Change to the Environment & Human Development. 2006. (Up in Smoke? Ser.). (ENG., Illus.). 48p. pap. 12.75 *(978-1-904882-12-1(9))* Oxfam Publishing GBR. Dist: Stylus Publishing, LLC.

Torre, Augusto de la, et al. Desarrollo con Menos Carbono: Respuestas Latinoamericanas al Desafío del Cambio Climático - Síntesis. 2009. (Latin America & Caribbean Studies). (SPA.). 96p. pap. 35.00 *(978-0-8213-7920-2(8)*, 9780821379202) World Bank Pubns.

CARIBBEAN AREA—DESCRIPTION AND TRAVEL

Architecture, Supersudaca. The Caribbean Total Resort: A Handbook of Mass Tourism. 2011. 304p. pap. *(978-84-96540-81-1(2))* Actar Birkhauser Distribution.

Bailey. Caribbean Lands. Date not set. pap. 27.69 *(978-0-582-03987-2(8))* Addison-Wesley Longman, Ltd. GBR. Dist: Trans-Atlantic Pubns., Inc.

Blouet, Brian W. & Blouet, Olwyn M. Latin America & the Caribbean: A Systematic & Regional Survey. 6th ed. 2009. (ENG., Illus.). 480p. (C). pap. 123.95 *(978-0-470-38773-3(4)*, Wiley) Wiley, John & Sons, Inc.

Bonsal, Stephen. The American Mediterranean. 2010. 542p. pap. 40.75 *(978-1-177-74368-6(X))*; 544p. pap. 40.75 *(978-1-142-33063-7(X))* BiblioBazaar.

—The American Mediterranean. 2009. 256p. pap. 22.54 *(978-1-150-71176-3(0))* General Bks. LLC.

—American Mediterranean. 2010. 248p. pap. *(978-1-151-88027-7(2))* Books LLC.

—American Mediterranean. 488p. reprint ed. 98.00 *(978-0-7222-9499-4(9))* Library Reprints, Inc.

Breton, André. Martinique: Snake Charmer. Seaman, David, tr. from FRE. 2008. (Surrealist Revolution Ser.). (ENG., Illus.). 96p. 19.95 *(978-0-292-71765-7(2))* Univ. of Texas Pr.

Bright, Michael, et al. Wild Caribbean: The Hidden Wonders of the World's Most Famous Islands. 2007. (ENG., Illus.). 224p. pap. 25.00 *(978-0-300-12549-8(6))* Yale Univ. Pr.

Douglas, Matthew & Caldwell, Mary. Mary's Voyage: The Adventures of John & Mary Caldwell A Sequel to Desperate Voyage. 2008. (ENG., Illus.). 256p. pap. 19.95 *(978-1-57409-267-7(7))* Sheridan Hse., Inc.

Fernández, Eladio. Hispaniola: A Photographic Journey Through Island Biodiversity. Ferreras, Irina P. & Romero, Gustavo, trs. 2007. (SPA & ENG., Illus.). 396p. 60.00 *(978-0-674-02628-5(4)*, Belknap Pr.) Harvard Univ. Pr.

Flowers of the Caribbean. 96p. 15.99 *(978-88-476-0626-5(8))* Casa Editrice Bonechi ITA. Dist: Puerto Rico Postcard.

Gajek, Margaret. Exotic Gardens of the Eastern Caribbean. 2010. (ENG., Illus.). 250p. 37.95 *(978-0-9813279-1-4(5))* Ozone Zone Bks. CAN. Dist: Independent Pubs. Group.

Gillespie, Spike. Quilty as Charged: Undercover in a Material World. 2007. (Surrealist Revolution Ser.). (ENG., Illus.). 200p. pap. 19.95 *(978-0-292-70599-9(9))* Univ. of Texas Pr.

Hanna, Nick & Stanford, Emma. National Geographic Traveler - The Carribean. 2nd rev. ed. 2007. (National Geographic Traveler Ser.). (ENG., Illus.). 400p. pap. 27.95 *(978-1-4262-0141-7(9)*, National Geographic) National Geographic Society.

Henderson, James. Caribbean & the Bahamas. 6th ed. (Country & Regional Guides). (ENG., Illus.). 340p. per. 22.95 *(978-1-86011-212-6(9))* Cadogan Guides GBR. Dist: Globe Pequot Pr., The.

Jain, Jasbir & Agarwal, Supriya, eds. Writers of the Caribbean Diaspora: Shifting Homelands, Travelling Identities. 2008. 300p. 34.95 *(978-1-932705-77-5(5))* New Dawn Pr., Inc.

Jordan, Craig. The Travelling Triathlete: A Middle - Aged Man's Journey to Fitness. 2011. 300p. pap. 19.95 ***(978-1-4670-0080-2(9))*** AuthorHouse.

Kamyab, Armin. Dominic: A Tropical Paradise. 2009. 100p. pap. 34.99 *(978-1-4389-1567-8(5))* AuthorHouse.

Kiegler, Richard & Kahn, Edward. The Hell with Working Let's Go Sailing. 2007. 194p. 25.95 *(978-1-59824-487-8(5))*; 196p. per. 12.95 *(978-1-59824-486-1(8))* E-BookTime LLC.

Kretschmer, John & Krestschmer, John. At the Mercy of the Sea: The True Story of Three Sailors in a Caribbean Hurricane. 2006. (Illus.). 223p. 24.95 *(978-0-07-147507-5(9)*, 9780071475075, International Marine/Ragged Mountain Pr.) McGraw-Hill Professional Publishing.

Lambton, Lucinda. Lucinda Lambton's Colonial Caribbean. 2012. (Illus.). 224p. 55.95 ***(978-1-906768-37-9(4)***, Stacey International) Stacey Publishing GBR. Dist: Midpoint Trade Bks., Inc.

Ligon, Richard. True & Exact History of the Island of Barbados. Kupperman, Karen Ordahl, ed. & intro. by. 2011. 201p. (C). pap. 15.95 *(978-1-60384-620-2(4))*; lib. bdg. 48.00 *(978-1-60384-621-9(2))* Hackett Publishing Co., Inc.

Locken, E. Travel Journal Antigua & Barbuda. 2010. 192p. pap. 19.99 *(978-0-557-43257-8(X))* Lulu Enterprises Inc.

—Travel Journal Dominica. 2010. 192p. pap. 19.99 *(978-0-557-43466-4(1))* Lulu Enterprises Inc.

Luntta, Karl. The Caribbean: Lesser Antilles. 2nd ed. pap. 22.95 *(978-962-217-690-4(9))* Airphoto International/Odyssey HKG. Dist: Norton, W. W. & Co., Inc.

Mashaw, Jerry L. & MacClintock, Anne U. Seasoned by Salt: A Voyage in Search of the Caribbean. 2007. (ENG., Illus.). 276p. per. 16.95 *(978-1-57409-246-2(4))* Sheridan Hse., Inc.

Myers, Paul. What I Did in Cuba. 2008. 104p. pap. 12.50 *(978-1-84799-485-1(7))* Lulu Enterprises Inc.

Pavlidis, Stephen J. Life at Sea Level: Tales of Island Adventures from a Travel Guide Author's Perspective. 2011. pap. *(978-1-892399-33-5(4))* Seaworthy Pubns., Inc.

Pearce, Pauline. Bajan Affair. 2007. 140p. per. *(978-1-84747-390-5(3))* Chipmunkapublishing.

Pegas, Bette Blaydes. Chasing a Dream in the Galápagos: A Personal Evolution. 2009. 14.95 *(978-0-916251-97-0(7))* Sunbelt Pubns., Inc.

Reesema, Meg Nolan Van. Caribbean Hideaways: Discovering Enchanting Rooms & Private Villas. 2010. (ENG., Illus.). 202p. 50.00 *(978-0-8478-3292-7(9))* Rizzoli International Pubns., Inc.

Rodionov, Viktor. Vas Zdes Ne Bylo! 2010. (RUS., Illus.). 448p. ***(978-0-557-80749-9(2))*** Lulu Enterprises Inc.

Rowlandson, Leonard. The 'Novel' Story of Redonda. 2008. 90p. pap. 30.00 *(978-1-4357-5799-8(8))* Lulu Enterprises Inc.

Schomburgk, Robert Hermann. The History of Barbados: Comprising a Geographical & Statistical Description of the Island; a Sketch of the Historical Events since the Settlement; & an Account of its Geology & Natural Productions. 2010. (Cambridge Library Collection - History Ser.). (Illus.). 770p. pap. 50.00 *(978-1-108-02331-3(2))* Cambridge Univ. Pr.

Sprauve, Gilbert A. Vagabondages Au Soleil. 2007. (FRE & ENG., Illus.). 156p. per. 15.00 *(978-1-4251-1041-3(X))* Trafford Publishing.

Sullivan, Lynne. Pocket Adventures St. Martin & St. Barts. 2009. 360p. pap. 13.99 *(978-1-58843-696-2(9))* Hunter Publishing, Inc.

Thompson, Krista. Eye for the Tropics: Tourism, Photography, & Framing the Caribbean Picturesque. 2007. (Objects/Histories Ser.). (ENG., Illus.). 392p. (C). 99.95 *(978-0-8223-3751-5(7))* Duke Univ. Pr.

Thompson, Krista A. An Eye for the Tropics: Tourism, Photography, & Framing the Caribbean Picturesque. 2007. (Objects/Histories Ser.). (ENG., Illus.). 392p. per. 27.95 *(978-0-8223-3764-5(9))* Duke Univ. Pr.

Tomei, Karel. Flying over ABC (Aruba, Bonaire, Curaçao) 2011. 256p. 27.90 ***(978-90-5594-692-1(3)***, Scriptum Pubs.) Midpoint Trade Bks., Inc.

Tyson, Ben, et al. Sports Events Management: The Caribbean Experience. 2010. (New Directions in Tourism Analysis Ser.). (Illus.). 238p. 89.95 *(978-1-4094-1855-9(3))* Ashgate Publishing Co.

Vanderhoof, Ann. The Spice Necklace: My Adventures in Caribbean Cooking, Eating, & Island Life. (ENG.). 480p. 2011. pap. 14.95 *(978-0-547-42316-6(0)*, Mariner Bks.) 2010. 25.00 *(978-0-618-68537-0(5))* Houghton Mifflin Harcourt Trade & Reference Pubs.

Ward, Evan R. Packaged Vacations: Tourism Development in the Spanish Caribbean. 2008. (ENG., Illus.). 352p. 69.95 *(978-0-8130-3229-0(6))* Univ. Pr. of Florida.

Weatheritt, Les. Caribbean Passagemaking, 1 vol. 2nd rev. ed. 2011. (ENG., Illus.). 224p. pap. 27.95 *(978-1-57409-308-7(8))* Sheridan Hse., Inc.

Weissmann, Amie, ed. Ports of Call: The Caribbean & North America. rev. ed. (Weissmann Travel Reports). ring bd. 329.00 *(978-0-945305-20-0(6))* Weissmann Travel Reports.

Whitcomb, Edgar D. Cilin II: A Solo Sailing Odyssey. 2011. 304p. pap. 17.95 ***(978-1-4567-6808-9(5))*** AuthorHouse.

—Cilin Ii: A Solo Sailing Odyssey: The Closest Point to Heaven. 2011. 304p. 27.95 ***(978-1-4567-6807-2(7))*** AuthorHouse.

Wylie, Brian D. The Long Trip Home: A South American & Caribbean Adventure Through the Past. 2009. (Illus.). xii, 93p. ***(978-0-595-63025-7(1))*** iUniverse, Inc.

Zimmer, Robert L. Nuff Nuff Niceness: Rediscovering the Mother Colony. 2010. 108p. 23.99 *(978-1-4520-5062-1(7))*; pap. 13.99 *(978-1-4520-5061-4(9))* AuthorHouse.

CARIBBEAN AREA—DIRECTORIES

Routledge, creator. South America, Central America & the Caribbean. 16th rev. ed. 2007. (Europa Regional Surveys of the World Ser.). (Illus.). 1103p. 720.00 *(978-1-85743-432-3(3))* Routledge.

CARIBBEAN AREA—DISCOVERY AND EXPLORATION

see America—Discovery and Exploration

CARIBBEAN AREA—ECONOMIC CONDITIONS

Alleyne, Doddridge H. N. Export/Import Trends & Economic Development in Trinidad, 1919-1939. 2010. (Illus.). 355p. pap. *(978-976-8125-91-0(8))* Canoe Pr. Univ. of the West Indies.

Baker, Gordon, ed. No Island Is an Island: The Impact of Globalization on the Commonwealth Caribbean. 2007. (ENG.). 135p. per. 19.95 *(978-1-86203-172-2(X))* Royal Institute of International Affairs GBR. Dist: Brookings Institution Pr.

Barros, Ricardo Paes de, et al. Measuring Inequality of Opportunities in Latin America & the Caribbean. 2008. (Latin American Development Forum Ser.). (ENG., Illus.). 220p. pap. 30.00 *(978-0-8213-7745-1(0)*, 9780821377451) World Bank Pubns.

Baum, Daniel J. The Banks of Canada in the Commonwealth Caribbean: Economic Nationalism & Multinational Enterprises of a Medium Power. 2007. 176p. per. 16.95 *(978-0-595-47603-9(1)*, Backinprint.com) iUniverse, Inc.

Birchwood, Anthony & Goto, Marielle. Issues in Monetary & Fiscal Policy in Small Developing States: A Case Study of the Caribbean. 2011. (ENG., Illus.). 90p. pap. 24.95 ***(978-1-84929-061-6(X))*** Commonwealth Secretariat GBR. Dist: Stylus Publishing, LLC.

Brereton, Bridget. General History of the Caribbean — Unesco: The Caribbean in the Twentieth Century. 2007. (ENG.). 788p. 231.00 *(978-1-4039-7593-5(0))* Palgrave Macmillan.

Brewster, Erwin E. Finance for Small & Medium-Sized Enterprises in the Caribbean. 2006. (Economic Paper Ser.). (ENG., Illus.). 128p. per. 28.50 *(978-0-85092-843-3(5))* Iwokrama International Rain Forest Programme GUY. Dist: Stylus Publishing, LLC.

Bulmer-Thomas, Victor. The Economic History of the Caribbean since the Napoleonic Wars. 2012. (ENG., Illus.). 375p. (C). 120.00 ***(978-0-521-19889-9(5))***; pap. 44.99 ***(978-0-521-14560-2(0))*** Cambridge Univ. Pr.

Chambers, Donna, et al, eds. New Perspectives in Caribbean Tourism. 2008. (Routledge Advances in Tourism Ser.). (ENG., Illus.). 278p. 125.00 *(978-0-415-95838-7(5))* Routledge.

Claude M. Jonnard. Islands in the Wind: The political economy of the English East Caribbean. 2009. 228p. pap. 19.95 *(978-1-4401-9426-9(2))* iUniverse, Inc.

Conrad. Education, Human Capital Accumulation, & Economic Growth. 2009. 116p. pap. *(978-3-8364-9033-7(1))* VDM Verlag Dr. Mueller e.K.

Cooper, Andrew F. Internet Gambling Offshore: Caribbean Struggles over Casino Capitalism. 2011. (ENG., Illus.). 224p. 85.00 *(978-0-230-29345-8(X))* Palgrave Macmillan.

David, Peggy Ann & Lange, Brenda. The Caribbean Community & Common Market. 2009. (Global Organizations Ser.). (Illus.). 128p. (YA). (gr. 7-12). 35.00 *(978-0-7910-9541-6(X))* Facts On File, Inc.

De Monie, Gustaaf, et al. Strategies for Global & Regional Ports: The Case of Caribbean Container & Cruise Ports. 2010. 252p. pap. 159.00 *(978-1-4419-5075-8(3)*, 1441950753) Springer.

Demas. West Indian Development. 160p. pap. *(978-976-8123-02-2(8))* Randle, Ian Pubs.

Demas, William G. The Economics of Development in Small Countries: With Special Reference to the Caribbean. 2010. (Illus.). 150p. pap. *(978-976-640-223-5(X))* Univ. of the West Indies Pr.

Eneas, Godfrey. The New Caribbean: A Region in Transition. 2009. 260p. pap. 15.99 *(978-1-4343-9012-7(8))* AuthorHouse.

Erriah, Paul J. Quo Vadis: Perspectives on the Commonwealth Caribbean from Colonial Times to Present. 2011. 176p. 29.95 ***(978-1-4575-0203-3(8))***; pap. 24.95 ***(978-1-60844-959-0(9))*** Dog Ear Publishing, LLC.

Europa Publications, ed. South America Central America & the Caribbean 2012. 20th rev. ed. 2011. (ENG.). 1148p. 880.00 *(978-1-85743-619-8(9))* Routledge.

Europa Publications Staff, ed. South America, Central America & the Caribbean 2009. 17th rev. ed. 2008. (ENG., Illus.). 1120p. 760.00 *(978-1-85743-467-5(6))* Routledge.

Fajnzylber, Pablo & López, J. Humberto. Remittances & Development: Lessons from Latin America. Fajnzylber, Pablo & López, J. Humberto, eds. 2008. (Latin American Development Forum Ser.). (ENG., Illus.). 408p. per. 30.00 *(978-0-8213-6870-1(2)*, 9780821368701) World Bank Pubns.

Fay, Marianne & Morrison, Mary. Infrastructure in Latin America & the Caribbean: Recent Developments & Key Challenges. 2006. (Directions in Development Ser.). (ENG., Illus.). 144p. per. 25.00 *(978-0-8213-6676-9(9)*, 9780821366769) World Bank Pubns.

Fortin, Henri, et al. Accounting for Growth in Latin America & the Caribbean: Improving Corporate Financial Reporting to Support Regional Economic Development. 2009. (Directions in Development Ser.). (ENG., Illus.). 196p. pap. 29.95 *(978-0-8213-8108-3(3)*, 9780821381083) World Bank Pubns.

Gale. Major Companies of Latin America & the Caribbean. 15th ed. 2011. (Major Companies of Latin America & the Caribbean Ser.). 1350p. lib. bdg. 1350.00 ***(978-1-86099-704-4(X))*** Graham & Whiteside, Ltd. GBR. Dist: Cengage Gale.

Gootnick, David. Foreign Assistance: Usaid Completed Many Caribbean Disaster Recovery Activities, but Several Challenges Hampered Efforts. 2006. (Illus.). 51p. (C). pap. 20.00 *(978-1-4223-0785-4(9))* DIANE Publishing Co.

Henry, Jones Mills & Lefranc. Institutional Aspects of West Indian Development. 210p. pap. *(978-976-8123-21-3(4))* Randle, Ian Pubs.

Holder, Jean S. Don't Burn Our Bridges: The Case for Owning Airlines. 2010. (Illus.). 296p. pap. *(978-976-640-232-7(9))* Univ. of the West Indies Pr.

Icon Group International, Inc. Staff, compiled by. The 2006 Economic & Product Market Databook for Arima, Trinidad & Tobago. 2006. 618p. ring bd. 95.00 *(978-0-497-80083-3(7))* Icon Group International, Inc.

—The 2006 Economic & Product Market Databook for Castries, St. Lucia. 2006. 618p. ring bd. 95.00 *(978-0-497-80319-3(4))* Icon Group International, Inc.

—The 2006 Economic & Product Market Databook for Fort-de-France, Martinique. 2006. 618p. ring bd. 95.00 *(978-0-497-80547-0(2))* Icon Group International, Inc.

—The 2006 Economic & Product Market Databook for Gouyave, Grenada. 2006. 618p. ring bd. 95.00 *(978-0-497-80613-2(4))* Icon Group International, Inc.

—The 2006 Economic & Product Market Databook for Kingstown, St. Vincent & the Grenadines. 2006. 618p. ring bd. 95.00 *(978-0-497-81999-6(6))* Icon Group International, Inc.

—The 2006 Economic & Product Market Databook for Kralendijk, Netherlands Antilles. 2006. 618p. ring bd. 95.00 *(978-0-497-80773-3(4))* Icon Group International, Inc.

—The 2006 Economic & Product Market Databook for la Trinité, Martinique. 2006. 618p. ring bd. 95.00 *(978-0-497-80806-8(4))* Icon Group International, Inc.

—The 2006 Economic & Product Market Databook for le François, Martinique. 2006. 618p. ring bd. 95.00 *(978-0-497-80830-3(7))* Icon Group International, Inc.

—The 2006 Economic & Product Market Databook for le Gosier, Guadeloupe. 2006. 618p. ring bd. 95.00 *(978-0-497-80831-0(5))* Icon Group International, Inc.

—The 2006 Economic & Product Market Databook for le Lamentin, Martinique. 2006. 618p. ring bd. 95.00 *(978-0-497-80833-4(1))* Icon Group International, Inc.

—The 2006 Economic & Product Market Databook for les Abymes, Guadeloupe. 2006. 618p. ring bd. 95.00 *(978-0-497-80845-7(5))* Icon Group International, Inc.

—The 2006 Economic & Product Market Databook for Marigot, Dominica. 2006. 618p. ring bd. 95.00 *(978-0-497-80954-6(0))* Icon Group International, Inc.

—The 2006 Economic & Product Market Databook for Morne-a-l'Eau, Guadeloupe. 2006. 618p. ring bd. 95.00 *(978-0-497-81056-6(5))* Icon Group International, Inc.

—The 2006 Economic & Product Market Databook for Port-of-Spain, Trinidad & Tobago. 2006. 618p. ring bd. 95.00 *(978-0-497-81279-9(7))* Icon Group International, Inc.

—The 2006 Economic & Product Market Databook for Portsmouth, Dominica. 2006. 618p. ring bd. 95.00 *(978-0-497-81283-6(5))* Icon Group International, Inc.

—The 2006 Economic & Product Market Databook for Schoelcher, Martinique. 2006. 618p. ring bd. 95.00 *(978-0-497-81486-1(2))* Icon Group International, Inc.

—The 2006 Economic & Product Market Databook for Sint Nicolaas, Aruba. 2006. 618p. ring bd. 95.00 *(978-0-497-81542-4(7))* Icon Group International, Inc.

—The 2006 Economic & Product Market Databook for Vieux Fort, St. Lucia. 2006. 618p. ring bd. 95.00 *(978-0-497-81247-8(9))* Icon Group International, Inc.

—The 2006 Economic & Product Market Databook for Willemstad, Netherlands Antilles. 2006. 618p. ring bd. 95.00 *(978-0-497-81824-1(8))* Icon Group International, Inc.

Inter-American Development Bank. Room for Development: Housing Markets in Latin America & the Caribbean. 2012. (ENG., Illus.). 344p. 110.00 ***(978-1-137-00564-9(5))***; pap. 38.00 ***(978-1-137-00563-2(7))*** Palgrave Macmillan.

Inter-American Development Bank Staff. Development Connections: Unveiling the Impact of New Information Technologies. 2011. (ENG.). 352p. pap. 38.00 *(978-0-230-11194-3(7))* Palgrave Macmillan.

—Development Connections: Unveiling the Impact of New Information Technologies. Chong, Alberto, ed. 2011. (ENG., Illus.). 352p. 110.00 *(978-0-230-11193-6(9))* Palgrave Macmillan.

Inter-American Development Bank Staff, et al. The Local Alternative: Decentralization & Economic Development. 2011. (ENG., Illus.). 336p. 110.00 *(978-0-230-11175-2(0))*; pap. 38.00 *(978-0-230-11176-9(9))* Palgrave Macmillan.

International Monetary Fund. Regional Economic Outlook: Western Hemisphere, Nov 06. 2006. (World Economic & Financial Surveys Ser.). (Illus.). 47p. per. *(978-1-58906-594-9(8))* International Monetary Fund.

Knight, Franklin W. The Caribbean: The Genesis of a Fragmented Nationalism, 1 vol. 3rd ed. 2011. (Latin American Histories Ser.). (ENG., Illus.). 304p. (C). pap. 44.95 *(978-0-19-538133-7(5))* Oxford Univ. Pr., Inc.

Lewis, Colin, et al. South America, Central America & the Caribbean 2010. 18th rev. ed. 2009. (ENG.). 1136p. 810.00 *(978-1-85743-525-2(7))* Routledge.

Lomborg, Bjorn, ed. Latin American Development Priorities: Costs & Benefits. 2010. (ENG., Illus.). 724p. 129.00 *(978-0-521-76690-6(7))*; pap. 49.99 *(978-0-521-74752-3(X))* Cambridge Univ. Pr.

MacDonald, Scott B. & Novo, Andrew R. When Small Countries Crash. 2011. (ENG.). 223p. 39.95 *(978-1-4128-1483-6(9))* Transaction Pubs.

Major Companies of Latin America & the Caribbean. 2011th ed. 2010. 1250.00 *(978-1-86099-650-4(7))* Graham & Whiteside, Ltd. GBR. Dist: Cengage Gale.

Mandle, Jay. Patterns of Caribbean Development: An Interpretive Essay on Economic Change. 2011. (ENG.). 176p. 95.00 *(978-0-415-59366-3(2))* Routledge.

McGregor, Duncan, et al, eds. Global Change & Caribbean Vulnerability: Environment, Economy & Society at Risk. 2009. (Illus.). 389p. pap. *(978-976-640-221-1(3))* Univ. of the West Indies Pr.

Mesa-Lago, Carmelo. World Crisis Effects on Social Security in Latin America & the Caribbean: Lessons & Policies. 2010. (ENG., Illus.). 200p. pap. 28.95 *(978-1-900039-97-0(4))* Institute of Latin American Studies GBR. Dist: Brookings Institution Pr.

Moberg & Moberg, Mark. Slipping Away: Banana Politics & Fair Trade in the Eastern Caribbean. 2009. (Illus.). 272p. 90.00 *(978-1-84545-145-5(7))* Berghahn Bks., Inc.

Moberg, Mark. Slipping Away: Banana Politics & Fair Trade in the Eastern Caribbean. 2010. (DISL Ser.). (Illus.). 272p. 32.95 *(978-1-84545-197-4(X))* Berghahn Bks., Inc.

Molinas Vega, Jose R., et al. Do Our Children Have a Chance? The 2010 Human Opportunity Report for Latin America & the Caribbean. 2011. (Directions in Development Ser.). (ENG., Illus.). 170p. pap. 25.00 ***(978-0-8213-8699-6(9)***, 9780821386996) World Bank Pubns.

Momsen, Janet & Besson, Jean, eds. Caribbean Land & Development Revisited. 2007. (Studies of the Americas Ser.). (ENG., Illus.). 292p. 95.00 *(978-1-4039-7392-4(X))* Palgrave Macmillan.

Olwig, Karen Fog. Caribbean Journeys: An Ethnography of Migration & Home in Three Family Networks. 2007. (ENG., Illus.). 336p. 89.95 *(978-0-8223-3977-9(3))*; pap. 24.95 *(978-0-8223-3994-6(3))* Duke Univ. Pr.

Palmer, Ransford W. The Caribbean Economy in the Age of Globalization. 2009. (ENG.). 192p. 89.00 *(978-0-230-60380-6(7))* Palgrave Macmillan.

Pollard, Walker A., et al. Economic Growth & Development in the Caribbean Region. 2009. (Global Economic Studies). (Illus.). viii, 342p. 89.00 *(978-1-60741-030-0(3))* Nova Science Pubs., Inc.

Rampersad, Frank. The New World Trade Order: Uruguay Round Agreements & Implications for Caricom States. pap. *(978-976-8123-03-9(6))* Randle, Ian Pubs.

Rigobón, Roberto, ed. Economia: Spring 2010 - Journal of the Latin American & Caribbean Economic Association. 2010. (ENG.). 164p. pap. 36.00 *(978-0-8157-0470-6(4))* Brookings Institution Pr.

Rigobón, Roberto, et al, eds. Economia: Fall 2010 - Journal of the Latin American & Caribbean Economic Association. 2011. (ENG.). 152p. pap. 36.00 *(978-0-8157-2159-8(5))* Brookings Institution Pr.

Smith, Frederick H. Caribbean Rum: A Social & Economic History. 2008. (ENG., Illus.). 368p. pap. 29.95 *(978-0-8130-3315-0(2))* Univ. Pr. of Florida.

South America Central America & the Caribbean 2011. 19th rev. ed. 2010. (ENG.). 1152p. 835.00 *(978-1-85743-562-7(1))* Routledge.

Sport for Development in Latin America & the Caribbean. 2006. 32p. *(978-92-806-4114-1(X))* United Nations Children's Fund, The (UNICEF).

Torre, Augusto de la, et al. Financial Development in Latin America & the Caribbean: The Road Ahead. 2011. ***(978-0-8213-8936-2(X))*** World Bank Pubns.

Tuitt, Austin. Caribbean-American Trade Connection: Green Pages. lib. bdg. *(978-0-944981-06-1(2))* Let Go & Let God.

Underwood, Frances W. The Marketing System in Peasant Haiti: Yale University Publications in Anthropology, No. 60. Mintz, Sidney Wilfred & Rouse, Irving, eds. 2011. 40p. 35.95 ***(978-1-258-09121-7(6))*** Literary Licensing, LLC.

United Nations. Economic Impact of Disasters: Evidence from DALA Assessments by ECLAC in Latin America & the Caribbean. 2010. (Estudios y Perspectivas Ser.). (ENG.). 52p. pap. 10.00 *(978-92-1-121731-5(8))* United Nations Pubns.

—Economic Survey of Latin America & the Caribbean 2008-2009: Policies for Creating Quality Jobs. 2010. (ENG.). 148p. pap. 75.00 *(978-92-1-121711-7(3))* United Nations Pubns.

—Latin America & the Caribbean in the World Economy 2007: 2008 Trends (Includes CD-ROM) 2009. (ENG., Illus.). 187p. pap. 25.00 incl. lp *(978-92-1-121676-9(1))* United Nations Pubns.

—Preliminary Overview of the Economies of Latin America & the Caribbean: 2007. 2008. (ENG., Illus.). 188p. pap. 20.00 *(978-92-1-121663-9(X))* United Nations Pubns.

—Quality of Latin American & Caribbean Industrialization & Integration into the Global Economy. 2010. (Comercio Internacional Ser.). (ENG.). 84p. pap. 10.00 *(978-92-1-121718-6(0))* United Nations Pubns.

United Nations & United Nations: Economic Commission for Latin America and the Caribbean. Economic Survey of Latin America & the Caribbean 2007-2008: Macroeconomic Policy & Volatility. 2009. (ENG., Illus.). 148p. pap. 75.00 incl. cd-rom *(978-92-1-121677-6(X))* United Nations Pubns.

United Nations Environment Programme Staff, contrib. by. Hydropolitical Vulnerability & Resilience along International Waters: Latin America & the Caribbean. 2008. (ENG., Illus.). 152p. pap. 30.00 *(978-92-807-2863-7(6))* United Nations Environment Programme KEN. Dist: National Bk. Network.

United Nations Staff. Cepal Review, April 2009. 2010. (ENG.). 204p. pap. 20.00 *(978-92-1-121685-1(0))* United Nations Pubns.

—Preliminary Overview of the Economies of Latin America & the Caribbean: 2008. 2009. (ENG.). 176p. pap. 20.00 *(978-92-1-121684-4(2))* United Nations Pubns.

—Social Panorama of Latin America 2008 (Includes CD-ROM) 2010. (ENG.). 256p. pap. 35.00 incl. lp *(978-92-1-121680-6(X))* United Nations Pubns.

Velasco, Andris, ed. Spring 2003. Date not set. 250p. pap. 36.00 *(978-0-8157-2071-3(8))* Brookings Institution Pr.

Verrest, Hebe. Home-Based Economic Activities & Caribbean Urban Livelihoods. 2007. (UvA Proefschriften Ser.). 332p. per. *(978-90-5629-490-8(3)*, Leiden Univ. Pr.) Amsterdam Univ. Pr.

Wiley, James. The Banana: Empires, Trade Wars, & Globalization. 2010. (At Table Ser.). (ENG., Illus.). 316p. pap. 29.95 *(978-0-8032-3285-3(3))* Univ. of Nebraska Pr.

World Bank Publications Staff, et al. Job Creation in Latin America & the Caribbean: Recent Trends & the Policy Challenges. 2009. (Latin American Development Forum Ser.). (ENG., Illus.). 480p. pap. 40.00 *(978-0-8213-7623-2(3)*, 9780821376232) World Bank Pubns.

Wynter, Sylvia & Eudell, Demetrius L. We Must Learn to Sit down Together & Talk about a Little Culture: Decolonizing Essays, 1967-1984. 2012. 260p. pap. 32.95 *(978-1-84523-108-8(2))* Peepal Tree Pr., Ltd. GBR. Dist: Independent Pubs. Group.

Yépez-García, Rigoberto Ariel, et al. Meeting the Balance of Electricity Supply & Demand in Latin America & the Caribbean. 2011. (Directions in Development Ser.). (ENG.). 210p. pap. 25.00 ***(978-0-8213-8819-8(3)***, 9780821388198) World Bank Pubns.

CARIBBEAN AREA—ECONOMIC INTEGRATION

Andic, Fuat, et al. A Theory of Economic Integration for Developing Countries. 2011. (ENG.). 176p. 95.00 *(978-0-415-59381-6(6))* Routledge.

Demas. West Indian Development. 160p. pap. *(978-976-8123-02-2(8))* Randle, Ian Pubs.

Mullerleile, Christophe. Caricom Integration. (Illus.). 374p. pap. *(978-976-625-070-6(7))* Kingston Publishing, Ltd.

United Nations. Latin America & the Caribbean in the World Economy: A Crisis Generated in the Centre & a Recovery Driven by the Emerging Economies. 2011. (ENG.). 168p. pap. 30.00 ***(978-92-1-121742-1(3))*** United Nations Pubns.

United Nations Staff. Cepal Review, April 2009. 2010. (ENG.). 204p. pap. 20.00 *(978-92-1-121685-1(0))* United Nations Pubns.

World Bank Staff, et al, contrib. by. Accelerating Trade & Integration in the Caribbean: Policy Options for Sustained Growth, Job Creation, & Poverty Reduction. 2009. (Country Studies). (ENG., Illus.). 364p. pap. 35.00 *(978-0-8213-8017-8(6)*, 9780821380178) World Bank Pubns.

CARIBBEAN AREA—ECONOMIC POLICY

Engel, Eduardo, et al, eds. Economia, Volume 8: Fall 2007, Number 1. 2008. (ENG., Illus.). 250p. pap. 36.00 *(978-0-8157-2087-4(4))* Brookings Institution Pr.

Henry, Jones Mills & Lefranc. Institutional Aspects of West Indian Development. 210p. pap. *(978-976-8123-21-3(4))* Randle, Ian Pubs.

Inter-American Development Bank Staff. The Age of Productivity: Transforming Economies from the Bottom Up. 2010. (ENG., Illus.). 368p. pap. 36.00 *(978-0-230-62352-1(2))* Palgrave Macmillan.

Inter-American Development Bank Staff & MacMillan, Palgrave. The Age of Productivity: Transforming Economies from the Bottom Up. 2010. (ENG., Illus.). 368p. 105.00 *(978-0-230-62350-7(6))* Palgrave Macmillan.

International Trade Centre. EC-CARIFORUM Economic Partnership Agreement: Services & Investment Commitments. 2010. (ENG.). 256p. pap. 70.00 *(978-92-9137-371-0(0))* United Nations Pubns.

Osuala, Dickson Chiedozie. Carbon Markets; Prospects for the Caribbean. 2011. 116p. pap. ***(978-3-8454-0233-8(4))*** Lambert Academic Publishing.

Pagés, Carmen, et al. Job Creation in Latin America & the Caribbean: Recent Trends & Policy Challenges. 2009. (Latin American Development Forum Ser.). (ENG., Illus.). 450p. 80.00 *(978-0-8213-7688-1(8)*, 9780821376881) World Bank Pubns.

Rampersad, Frank. The New World Trade Order: Uruguay Round Agreements & Implications for Caricom States. pap. *(978-976-8123-03-9(6))* Randle, Ian Pubs.

Rigobón, Roberto, ed. Economia: Spring 2010 - Journal of the Latin American & Caribbean Economic Association. 2010. (ENG.). 164p. pap. 36.00 *(978-0-8157-0470-6(4))* Brookings Institution Pr.

Rigobón, Roberto, et al, eds. Economia: Fall 2010 - Journal of the Latin American & Caribbean Economic Association. 2011. (ENG.). 152p. pap. 36.00 *(978-0-8157-2159-8(5))* Brookings Institution Pr.

Rigobon, Roberto, et al, eds. Economia: Journal of the Latin American & Caribbean Economic Assocation; Number 2. 2008. (Economía Ser.). (ENG., Illus.). 250p. per. 36.00 *(978-0-8157-2082-9(3))* Brookings Institution Pr.

Stevens, Christopher, et al. The CARIFORUM & Pacific ACP Economic Partnership Agreements: Challenges Ahead? 2009. (Economic Paper Ser.).

(ENG., Illus.). 232p. pap. 32.95 *(978-1-84929-000-5(8))* Commonwealth Secretariat GBR. Dist: Stylus Publishing, LLC.

Taylor, Kenwyn M. How Caribbean Political Leaders Successfully Managed Needed Economic Entreprenurial & Social Adjustments, 1981-1995: The Importance of Understanding All the Factors Affecting Change. 2011. (Illus.). 512p. 149.95 *(978-0-7734-1525-6(4))* Mellen, Edwin Pr., The.

United Nations. Latin America & the Caribbean in the World Economy: A Crisis Generated in the Centre & a Recovery Driven by the Emerging Economies. 2011. (ENG.). 168p. pap. 30.00 ***(978-92-1-121742-1(3))*** United Nations Pubns.

—Latin America & the Caribbean in the World Economy: Crisis & Opportunities for Regional Cooperation (Includes CD-ROM) 2010. (ENG.). 108p. pap. 25.00 incl. lp *(978-92-1-121710-0(5))* United Nations Pubns.

—Status & Potential of Commercial Bioprospecting Activities in Latin America & the Caribbean. 2007. (Medio Ambiente y Desarrollo Ser.). (ENG.). 68p. pap. 10.00 *(978-92-1-121648-6(6))* United Nations Pubns.

World Bank Publications Staff, et al. Measuring Inequality of Opportunities in Latin America & the Caribbean. 2008. (Latin American Development Forum Ser.). (ENG., Illus.). 180p. 80.00 *(978-0-8213-7747-5(7)*, 9780821377475) World Bank Pubns.

World Bank Staff, et al, contrib. by. Accelerating Trade & Integration in the Caribbean: Policy Options for Sustained Growth, Job Creation, & Poverty Reduction. 2009. (Country Studies). (ENG., Illus.). 364p. pap. 35.00 *(978-0-8213-8017-8(6)*, 9780821380178) World Bank Pubns.

CARIBBEAN AREA—EMIGRATION AND IMMIGRATION

Brotherton, David C. & Barrios, Luis. Banished to the Homeland: Dominican Deportees & Their Stories of Exile. 2011. (ENG., Illus.). 384p. (gr. 17). 79.50 ***(978-0-231-14934-1(4))***; pap. 29.50 ***(978-0-231-14935-8(2))*** Columbia Univ. Pr.

Byron, Margaret & Condon, Stephanie. Migration in Comparative Perspective: Caribbean Communities in Britain & France. 2012. (Routledge Research in Population & Migration Ser.). (ENG., Illus.). 304p. (C). pap. 42.95 ***(978-0-415-54289-0(8))*** Routledge.

Cervantes-Rodríguez, Margarita. International Migration in Cuba: Accumulation, Imperial Designs, & Transnational Social Fields. 2011. 344p. pap. 29.95 ***(978-0-271-03539-0(0))*** 2010. (ENG., Illus.). 328p. 75.00 *(978-0-271-03538-3(2))* Pennsylvania State Univ. Pr.

Dessens, Nathalie. From Saint-Domingue to New Orleans: Migration & Influences. (Southern Dissent Ser.). (ENG., Illus.). 272p. 2010. pap. 27.95 *(978-0-8130-3567-3(8))* 2007. 65.00 *(978-0-8130-3037-1(4))* Univ. Pr. of Florida.

Dobson, David. Scots in Jamaica, 1655-1855. 2011. 178p. pap. 18.00 ***(978-0-8063-5540-5(9))*** Clearfield Co.

Dobson, David. Transatlantic Voyages, 1600-1699. 2nd rev. ed. 2008. pap. 18.50 *(978-0-8063-5369-2(4))* Clearfield Co.

Duany, Jorge. Blurred Borders: Transnational Migration Between the Hispanic Caribbean & the United States. 2011. (ENG., Illus.). 352p. 65.00 *(978-0-8078-3497-8(1))*; pap. 29.95 *(978-0-8078-7203-1(2))* Univ. of North Carolina Pr.

Eckstein, Susan. The Immigrant Divide: How Cuban Americans Changed the U. S. & Their Homeland. 2009. (ENG., Illus.). 312p. 148.00 *(978-0-415-99922-9(7))* Routledge.

Falconi, José Luis & Mazzotti, José Antonio, eds. The Other Latinos: Central & South Americans in the United States. 2008. (Series on Latin American Studies: 20). (Illus.). 313p. per. 24.95 *(978-0-674-02589-9(X))* Americas Society.

Fletcher-Anthony, Wilma. 'My Mother Is a Stranger' & Other Themes of Reunification. 2009. 120p. pap. *(978-3-639-09194-6(9))* VDM Verlag Dr. Mueller e.K.

Jackson, Regine O., ed. Geographies of the Haitian Diaspora. 2011. (Routledge Studies on African & Black Diaspora Ser.). (ENG., Illus.). 348p. (C). 125.00 *(978-0-415-88708-3(9))* Routledge.

Jones, Terry-Ann. Jamaican Immigrants in the United States & Canada: Race, Transnationalism, & Social Capital. 2007. (New Americans). 198p. lib. bdg. 62.00 *(978-1-59332-237-3(2))* LFB Scholarly Publishing LLC.

Mielants, Eric H., et al, eds. Caribbean Migration to Western Europe & the United States: Essays on Incorporation, Identity, & Citizenship. 2009. (ENG., Illus.). 270p. 63.50 *(978-1-59213-954-5(X))* Temple Univ. Pr.

Miller, O. Alexander. Migration Can Fall Apart: Life Stories from Voluntary & Deportee Return Migrants. 2008. (ENG., Illus.). 160p. pap. 31.50 *(978-0-7618-4000-8(1))* Univ. Pr. of America, Inc.

Newton, Darrell M. M. Paving the Empire Road: BBC Television & Black Britons. 2012. (ENG., Illus.). 224p. 80.00 *(978-0-7190-8167-5(X))* Manchester Univ. Pr. GBR. Dist: Macmillan.

Page, Kezia. Transnational Negotiations in Caribbean Diasporic Literature: Remitting the Text. 2010. (Routledge Research in Postcolonial Literatures Ser.). (ENG.). 168p. (C). 125.00 *(978-0-415-87362-8(2))* Routledge.

Pedraza, Silvia. Political Disaffection in Cuba's Revolution & Exodus. 2007. (Cambridge Studies in Contentious Politics Ser.). (ENG.). 382p. 86.00 *(978-0-521-86787-0(8))*; (Illus.). per. 29.99 *(978-0-521-68729-4(2))* Cambridge Univ. Pr.

Regis, Helen A., ed. Caribbean & Southern: Transnational Perspectives on the U. S. South. 2006. (Southern Anthropological Society Proceedings Ser.: No. 38). (ENG., Illus.). 168p. 59.95 *(978-0-8203-2831-7(6))*; pap. 22.95 *(978-0-8203-2832-4(4))* Univ. of Georgia Pr.

The Role of Remittances in Leveraging Sustainable Development in Latin America & the Caribbean: Hearing Before the Subcommittee on Domestic & International Monetary Policy, Trade, & Technology of the Committee on Financial Services, U.S. House of Representatives, One Hundred Tenth Congress, First Session, March 7, 2007. 2007. (Illus.). v, 84p. *(978-0-16-078915-1(X)*, 552-070-36041-7) United States Government Printing Office.

Shemak, April. Asylum Speakers: Caribbean Refugees & Testimonial Discourse. 2nd ed. 2010. (American Literatures Initiative Ser.). (ENG., Illus.). 320p. 48.00 *(978-0-8232-3355-7(3))* Fordham Univ. Pr.

Tinker, Keith L. The Migration of Peoples from the Caribbean to the Bahamas. 2011. (ENG., Illus.). 168p. 69.95 *(978-0-8130-3531-4(7))* Univ. Pr. of Florida.

Zacair, Philippe, ed. Haiti & the Haitian Diaspora in the Wider Caribbean. 2011. (New World Diasporas Ser.). (ENG.). 218p. pap. 22.95 ***(978-0-8130-4018-9(3))*** Univ. Pr. of Florida.

CARIBBEAN AREA—FOREIGN RELATIONS

Association for International Arbitration Staff, ed. Arbitration & Mediation in the ACP-EU Relations. 2008. 193p. pap. 40.00 *(978-90-466-0202-7(8))* Maklu Uitgevers N.V. BEL. Dist: International Specialized Bk. Services.

Bangura, Abdul K. Pan-Africanism Caribbean Connections. 2007. 176p. per. 15.95 *(978-0-595-45193-7(4))* iUniverse, Inc.

Byron, Margaret & Condon, Stephanie. Migration in Comparative Perspective: Caribbean Communities in Britain & France. 2007. (Routledge Research in Population & Migration Ser.). (ENG., Illus.). 304p. (C). 125.00 *(978-0-415-31045-1(6)*, RU26231) Routledge.

Cooper, Andrew F. Internet Gambling Offshore: Caribbean Struggles over Casino Capitalism. 2011. (ENG., Illus.). 224p. 85.00 *(978-0-230-29345-8(X))* Palgrave Macmillan.

Erriah, Paul J. Quo Vadis: Perspectives on the Commonwealth Caribbean from Colonial Times to Present. 2011. 176p. 29.95 ***(978-1-4575-0203-3(8))***; pap. 24.95 ***(978-1-60844-959-0(9))*** Dog Ear Publishing, LLC.

Ghahremani, Nuschin. The Eu-Cariforum Economic Partnership Agreement. 2009. 136p. pap. *(978-3-639-13925-9(9))* VDM Verlag Dr. Mueller e.K.

Janssen, Roger. In Search of A Path: An. 2010. 250p. pap. 44.00 *(978-90-6718-334-5(2))* KITLV Pr. NLD. Dist: Univ. of Hawaii Pr.

Meehan, Kevin. People Get Ready: African American & Caribbean Cultural Exchange. (Caribbean Studies Ser.). (ENG.). 256p. 2011. pap. 30.00 ***(978-1-61703-201-1(8))*** 2009. 50.00 *(978-1-60473-281-8(4))* Univ. Pr. of Mississippi.

Mulerielle, Christophe. Caricom Integration. (Illus.). 374p. pap. *(978-976-625-070-6(7))* Kingston Publishing, Ltd.

New Direction or Old Path? Caribbean Basin Security Initiative (CBSI): Hearing Before the Subcommittee on the Western Hemisphere of the Committee on Foreign Affairs, House of Representatives, One Hundred Eleventh Congress, First Session, December 9, 2009. 2010. iii, 117p. *(978-0-16-085518-4(7)*, 552-070-40781-2) United States Government Printing Office.

Niblett, Michael & Oloff, Kerstin, eds. Perspectives on the 'Other America' Comparative Approaches to Caribbean & Latin American Culture. 2009. (Illus.). 272p. pap. 78.00 *(978-90-420-2704-6(5))* Rodopi.

Palmer, David Scott. U. S. Relations with Latin America during the Clinton Years: Opportunities Lost or Opportunities Squandered? 2010. (ENG., Illus.). 144p. (C). pap. 19.50 *(978-1-61610-142-8(3))* Orange Grove Bks.

Paravisini-Gebert, Lizabeth & Romero-Cesareo, Ivette, eds. Displacements & Transformations in Caribbean Cultures. 2008. (ENG., Illus.). 256p. 59.95 *(978-0-8130-3218-4(0))* Univ. Pr. of Florida.

Shah, Ramona. Caribbean-European International Economic Relations. 2010. 244p. pap. *(978-3-639-21749-0(7))* VDM Verlag Dr. Mueller e.K.

Wohlstetter, Albert & Wohlstetter, Roberta. Latin America & the Caribbean. 2006. (Adelphi Paper Ser.). (Illus.). 233p. 200.00 *(978-0-415-39857-2(6))* Routledge.

CARIBBEAN AREA—GENEALOGY

Crooks, Paul. A Tree Without Roots: The Guide to Tracing British, African & Asian-Caribbean Ancestry. 2008. (ENG., Illus.). 206p. pap. 18.95 *(978-1-905147-81-6(3)*, Black Amber) Arcadia Bks. Ltd. GBR. Dist: Dufour Editions, Inc.

Dobson, David. Scots in Jamaica, 1655-1855. 2011. 178p. pap. 18.00 ***(978-0-8063-5540-5(9))*** Clearfield Co.

O'Sullivan-Sirjue, Jennifer. Researching your Jamaican Family. 2007. 142p. pap. *(978-976-8189-48-6(7))* Arawak Pubns.

Our caribbean heritage in Context. 2006. (YA). per. *(978-1-59872-520-9(3))* Instant Pub.

CARIBBEAN AREA—GUIDEBOOKS

Bryant, Sue & Cameron, Sarah. Caribbean Cruises. 2nd ed. 2012. (Insight Guides). (Illus.). 400p. pap. 24.99 ***(978-1-78005-021-8(6))*** APA Publications Services SGP. Dist: Ingram Pub. Services.

Cameron, Sarah. Barbados. 2nd ed. 2006. (Pocket Guides). (ENG., Illus.). 224p. per. 12.95 *(978-1-904777-58-8(9))* Footprint Handbooks GBR. Dist: Globe Pequot Pr., The.

—Caribbean - Insight Guides. 6th ed. 2012. (Insight Guides). (Illus.). 368p. pap. 24.99 ***(978-1-78005-037-9(2))*** APA Publications Services SGP. Dist: Ingram Pub. Services.

Cameron, Sarah. Footprint Caribbean Islands. 17th ed. 2007. (Travel Guides). (ENG., Illus.). 864p. per. 24.95 *(978-1-904777-97-7(X))* Footprint Handbooks GBR. Dist: Globe Pequot Pr., The.

The Caribbean. 592p. Random Hse., Inc.

Colas, Antony & Sutherland, Bruce. Central America & the Caribbean. 2010. (ENG., Illus.). 120p. pap. 19.95 *(978-0-9562455-0-2(1))* Wilderness Pr.

Colón, Christina Paulette. Caribbean Ports of Call. 8th ed. 2010. (Frommer's Complete Guides: 819). (ENG., Illus.). 384p. pap. 17.99 *(978-0-470-64015-9(4)*, Frommers) Wiley, John & Sons, Inc.

—Frommer's Portable Aruba, Bonaire & Curacao. 6th ed. 2011. (Frommer's Portable Ser.: 274). (ENG.). 216p. pap. 12.99 *(978-1-118-07472-5(6)*, Frommers) Wiley, John & Sons, Inc.

Crask, Paul. Dominica. 2008. (Bradt Travel Guide Ser.). (ENG., Illus.). 256p. pap. 24.99 *(978-1-898323-92-1(5))* Bradt Travel Guides GBR. Dist: Globe Pequot Pr., The.

—Grenada, Carriacou & Petite Martinique. 2009. (ENG., Illus.). 256p. pap. 23.99 *(978-1-84162-274-3(5))* Bradt Travel Guides GBR. Dist: Globe Pequot Pr., The.

Fiori, Pamela. In the in the SPIRIT of ST. BARTHS. 2011. (ENG.). 144p. 45.00 *(978-2-7594-0517-6(6))* Assouline FRA. Dist: Perseus Distribution.

Fodor's. Fodor's Caribbean 2013. 2012. (Full-color Travel Guide Ser.). (ENG.). 1168p. pap. 24.99 ***(978-0-307-92934-1(5)***, Fodor's) Fodor's Travel Pubns.

—Fodor's Caribbean Ports of Call 2013. 15th ed. 2012. (Travel Guide Ser.). (ENG.). 416p. pap. 17.99 ***(978-0-307-92940-2(X)***, Fodor's) Fodor's Travel Pubns.

Fodor's Travel Publications, Inc. Staff. Barbados & St. Lucia. 2nd ed. 2010. (In Focus-Color Ser.). (ENG.). 236p. pap. 11.99 *(978-1-4000-0466-9(7)*, Fodor's) Fodor's Travel Pubns.

—The Complete Guide to Caribbean Cruises: A Cruise Lover's Guide to Selecting the Right Trip, with All the Best Ports of Call. 4th ed. 2011. (Fodor's Ser.). (ENG., Illus.). 688p. pap. 23.99 *(978-0-679-00973-3(6))* Fodor's Travel Pubns.

—Fodor's Caribbean 2012. 2011. (Full-Color Travel Guide Ser.). (ENG.). 1168p. pap. 24.99 *(978-0-679-00926-9(4)*, Fodor's) Fodor's Travel Pubns.

—Fodor's Caribbean Ports of Call 2012. 2011. (Fodor's Ser.). (ENG.). 416p. pap. 17.99 *(978-0-679-00938-2(8))* Fodor's Travel Pubns.

—St. Maarten, St. Barth & Anguilla. 2nd ed. 2010. (In Focus-Color Ser.). (ENG.). 216p. pap. 11.99 *(978-1-4000-0467-6(5))* Fodor's Travel Pubns.

—535 Best Beaches: In the U. S., Caribbean, & Mexico. 2010. (Full-Color Gold Guides). (ENG., Illus.). 328p. pap. 18.99 *(978-1-4000-0505-5(1)*, Fodor's) Fodor's Travel Pubns.

Gmelch, George. Behind the Smile: The Working Lives of Caribbean Tourism. 2nd ed. 2012. ***(978-0-253-00129-0(3))*** Indiana Univ. Pr.

—Behind the Smile, Second Edition: The Working Lives of Caribbean Tourism. 2nd ed. 2012. (ENG., Illus.). 280p. pap. 24.00 ***(978-0-253-00123-8(4)***, 0253001234) Indiana Univ. Pr.

Greenberg, Harriet. St. Martin & St. Barts Alive! 2nd ed. 2008. (Illus.). 312p. pap. 16.99 *(978-1-58843-356-5(0))* Hunter Publishing, Inc.

Groene, Janet. Personal Paradise: Caribbean. 2006. (ENG., Illus.). 224p. pap. 14.95 *(978-1-59360-076-1(3))* Open Road Publishing.

Henry, L. Every Student's Handbook. 2007. 184p. per. *(978-976-8202-45-1(9))* LMH Publishing, Ltd.

Hinsdale, Joshua Eden. Playa del Carmen, Tulum & the Riviera Maya. 3rd ed. 2011. (Explorer's Great Destinations Ser.). (ENG., Illus.). 256p. pap. 19.95 *(978-1-58157-132-5(1)*, 157132) Countryman Pr.

Huber, Joyce & Huber, Jon. Best Dives of the Caribbean. 3rd rev. ed. 2006. (Best Dives of the Caribbean Ser.). (Illus.). 364p. per. 19.99 *(978-1-58843-585-9(7))* Hunter Publishing, Inc.

Huggins-Cooper, Lynn. The Caribbean. 2008. (Travel Through (QEB) Ser.). (Illus.). 32p. (J). (gr. 3-6). lib. bdg. 18.95 *(978-1-59566-355-9(X))* QEB Publishing Inc.

Ig Caribbean Cruises. 2009. (GUIDE Ser.). 23.95 *(978-981-282-061-7(2))* Insight Guides.

Johansens, creator. Conde Nast Johansens the Americas: Atlantic, Caribbean & Pacific. 2007. (Recommended Hotels, Inns, Resorts, & Spas-the Americas, Atlantic, Caribbean & Pacific Ser.). (Illus.). 448p. per. 36.00 *(978-1-903665-36-7(1))* Conde Nast Johansens Ltd. GBR. Dist: Casemate Pubs. & Bk. Distributors, LLC.

Kucharikova, Irena. North Caribbean Cruising Companion. 2010. 256p. 49.95 *(978-0-470-72176-6(6))* Wiley, John & Sons, Inc.

Lee, Alfonso Silva & Dooley, Roger E. Coral Reefs: Of the Caribbean, the Bahamas, & Florida. 2007. (ENG., Illus.). 80p. per. *(978-0-333-67402-4(2))* Macmillan Caribbean.

Nausbaum, Donald. Aruba, Bonnaire & Curacao. 2006. (ENG., Illus.). 220p. pap. 40.00 *(978-1-4050-6565-8(6))* Macmillan Caribbean GBR. Dist: Interlink Publishing Group, Inc.

Pavlidis, Stephen J. The Northern Bahamas Guide: From Grand Bahama & the Abacos South to Cat Island. 2009. pap. *(978-1-892399-28-1(8))* Seaworthy Pubns., Inc.

Peachin, Mary L. Scuba Caribbean. 2009. (ENG., Illus.). 288p. pap. 24.95 *(978-0-8130-3287-0(3))* Univ. Pr. of Florida.

Permenter, Paris & Bigley, John. Caribbean with Kids. 5th ed. 2008. (ENG., Illus.). 248p. pap. 14.95 *(978-1-59360-109-6(3))* Open Road Publishing.

—Open Road's Best of the Caribbean. 2010. (ENG., Illus.). 224p. pap. 9.95 *(978-1-59360-137-9(9))* Open Road Publishing.

Philpott, Don & Landmarks Staff. Antigua. 2nd rev. ed. 2008. (Illus.). 96p. 11.99 *(978-1-84306-368-1(9))* Landmark Publishing Ltd. GBR. Dist: Hunter Publishing, Inc.

Porter, Darwin, et al. Frommer's Caribbean. 23rd ed. 2011. (Frommer's Complete Guides). (ENG., Illus.). 800p. pap. 24.99 *(978-1-118-00427-2(2)*, Frommers) Wiley, John & Sons, Inc.

Prince, Danforth & Porter, Darwin. Jamaica. 6th ed. 2010. (Frommer's Complete Guides: 820). (ENG., Illus.). 288p. pap. 17.99 *(978-0-470-61444-0(7)*, Frommers) Wiley, John & Sons, Inc.

Radula-Scott, Caroline. Caribbean. 5th ed. 2009. (Insight Guides). (ENG., Illus.). 384p. pap. 24.99 *(978-981-282-060-0(4))* APA Publications Services SGP. Dist: Ingram Pub. Services.

Recommended Hotels/Inns in America 2007. 2007. (Illus.). 436p. pap. 35.00 *(978-1-903665-31-2(0))* Conde Nast Johansens Ltd. GBR. Dist: Casemate Pubs. & Bk. Distributors, LLC.

Rock, Tim & Lonely Planet Staff. Diving & Snorkeling Cayman Islands. 2nd rev. ed. 2007. (Lonely Planet Diving & Snorkeling Guides). (ENG., Illus.). 144p. pap. 24.99 *(978-1-74059-897-2(0))* Lonely Planet Pubns.

Runge, Jonathan. Rum & Reggae's Caribbean. 5th ed. 2006. (Rum & Reggae Ser.). (ENG., Illus.). 864p. per. 21.95 *(978-1-893675-14-8(9))* Rum & Reggae Guidebooks, Inc.

Shales, Melissa. Barbados Travel Pack, 3rd. 3rd ed. 2011. (Globetrotter Travel Packs Ser.). (ENG., Illus.). 128p. 14.95 *(978-1-84773-851-6(6)*, Globetrotter) New Holland Pubs., Ltd. GBR. Dist: Globe Pequot Pr., The.

Showker, Kay. Caribbean Ports of Call: A Guide for Today's Cruise Passengers. 2010. (ENG., Illus.). 592p. pap. 18.95 *(978-0-7627-6035-0(4))* Globe Pequot Pr., The.

—Caribbean Ports of Call: Western Region: A Guide for Today's Cruise Passengers. 9th ed. 2008. (Caribbean Ports of Call: Western Region Ser.). (ENG., Illus.). 256p. pap. 17.95 *(978-0-7627-4539-5(8))* Globe Pequot Pr., The.

—100 Best Resorts of the Caribbean, 9th. 2011. (100 Best Ser.). (ENG., Illus.). 400p. pap. 19.95 *(978-0-7627-7152-3(6))* Globe Pequot Pr., The.

Thomas Cook Publishing. Barbados Pocket Guide, 2nd: Compact & practical pocket guides for sun seekers & city Breakers. 2nd ed. 2011. (Thomas Cook Pocket Guides). (ENG., Illus.). 128p. pap. 9.95 *(978-1-84848-451-1(8))* Cook, Thomas Publishing GBR. Dist: Globe Pequot Pr., The.

—Travellers Caribbean Cruising, 4th. 2010. (Travellers - Thomas Cook Ser.). (ENG., Illus.). 192p. pap. 16.95 *(978-1-84848-196-1(9))* Cook, Thomas Publishing GBR. Dist: Globe Pequot Pr., The.

Thomas, Polly & Dorling Kindersley Publishing Staff. Caribbean. 2011. (Eyewitness Travel Guides). (ENG., Illus.). 552p. 30.00 *(978-0-7566-7018-4(7))* Dorling Kindersley Publishing, Inc.

Vipond, Anne. Caribbean by Cruise Ship: The Complete Guide to Cruising the Caribbean. 5th ed. 2007. (Caribbean by Cruise Ship: the Complete Guide to Cruising the Caribbean Ser.). (Illus.). 352p. pap. *(978-0-9688389-8-3(7))* Ocean Cruise Guides, Ltd.

Warren, Andrew. Condé Nast Johansens the Americas Atlantic Caribbean & Pacific: Recommended Hotels Inns Resorts & Spas 2009. 2008. (Illus.). 452p. pap. 25.00 *(978-1-903665-42-8(6))* Conde Nast Johansens Ltd. GBR. Dist: Casemate Pubs. & Bk. Distributors, LLC.

CARIBBEAN AREA—HISTORY

Alleyne - Cumberbatch, Ayaana. Evaluating Two Library Associations of the English Speaking Caribbean. 2011. 128p. pap. ***(978-3-8454-1386-0(7))*** Lambert Academic Publishing.

Armitage, David. The British Atlantic World, 1500-1800. Braddick, Michael J., ed. 2nd rev. ed. 2009. (ENG., Illus.). 384p. pap. 32.00 *(978-0-230-20235-1(7))* Palgrave Macmillan.

Armitage, David & Braddick, Michael J., eds. The British Atlantic World, 1500-1800. 2nd rev. ed. 2009. (ENG., Illus.). 384p. 100.00 *(978-0-230-20234-4(9))* Palgrave Macmillan.

Benson, Michael. Ballparks of North America: A Comprehensive Historical Reference to Baseball Grounds, Yards & Stadiums, 1845 To 1988. alt. ed. 2009. (ENG., Illus.). 505p. pap. 39.95 *(978-0-7864-4421-2(5))* McFarland & Co., Inc. Pubs.

Bercuson, D. H., et al. Long Night of the Tankers: Hitler's War Against Carribean Oil, 1942-1944. 2012. (ENG.). 352p. 34.95 ***(978-1-77087-094-9(6))*** McArthur & Co. CAN. Dist: National Bk. Network.

Bisnauth. History of Religions in the Caribbean. (Illus.). pap. *(978-976-625-003-4(0))* Kingston Publishing, Ltd.

Block, Kristen. Ordinary Lives in the Early Caribbean: Religion, Colonial Competition, & the Politics of Profit. 2012. (Early American Places Ser.). (ENG.). 312p. 69.95 ***(978-0-8203-3867-5(2))***; (Illus.). pap. 24.95 ***(978-0-8203-3868-2(0))*** Univ. of Georgia Pr.

Blouet, Olwyn M. The Contemporary Caribbean: History, Life & Culture since 1945. 2007. (Reaktion Books - Contemporary Worlds Ser.). (ENG., Illus.). 224p. per. 24.95 *(978-1-86189-313-0(2))* Reaktion Bks., Ltd. GBR. Dist: Chicago Distribution Ctr.

Bolland, Nigel O. Struggles for Freedom: Essays on Slavery, Colonialism, & Culture in the Caribbean & Central America. pap. *(978-976-8111-16-6(X))* Randle, Ian Pubs.

Boucher, Philip P. France & the American Tropics to 1700: Tropics of Discontent? (ENG., Illus.). 392p. (C). (gr. 13-17). 2008. 57.00 *(978-0-8018-8725-3(9))* 2007. per. 28.00 *(978-0-8018-8726-0(7))* Johns Hopkins Univ. Pr.

Brereton, Bridget. General History of the Caribbean — Unesco: The Caribbean in the Twentieth Century. 2007. (ENG.). 788p. 231.00 *(978-1-4039-7593-5(0))* Palgrave Macmillan.

Bronfman, Alejandra. On the Move: The Caribbean Since 1989. 2007. (Global History of the Present Ser.). (ENG., Illus.). 256p. 80.00

C

(978-1-84277-766-4(1)); per. 25.95 (978-1-84277-767-1(X)) Zed Bks., Ltd. GBR. Dist: Macmillan.

Brothers, Timothy S., et al. Caribbean Landscapes: An Interpretive Atlas. 2008. (Illus.). 249p. spiral bd. 59.00 (978-1-58432-459-1(7)) Educa Vision.

Buhle, Paul. Tim Hector: A Caribbean Radical's Story. 2006. (ENG., Illus.). 272p. 32.00 (978-1-57806-851-7(7)) Univ. Pr. of Mississippi.

Burney, James. History of the Buccaneers of America. 2010. (Cambridge Library Collection - Travel & Exploration Ser.). (Illus.). 320p. pap. 24.99 (978-1-108-02524-9(2)) Cambridge Univ. Pr.

—History of the Buccaneers of America. 2007. (ENG.). 396p. per. 16.75 (978-1-60206-253-5(6)) Cosimo, Inc.

—History of the Buccaneers of America. 2008. 340p. 46.95 (978-0-548-93211-7(5)) 2007. (ENG.). 344p. per. 31.95 (978-0-548-59238-0(1)) Kessinger Publishing, LLC.

Cañete Quesada, Carmen. El Exilio Español Ante Los Programas de la Identidad Cultural en el Caribe Insular (1934-1956) 2011. (Ediciones de Iberoamericana Ser.). pap. 29.80 **(978-84-8489-573-2(4))** Iberoamericana Vervuert Publishing Corp.

Cram101 Textbook Reviews & Cram101 Textbook Reviews. Outlines & Highlights for Latin America & the Caribbean by Brian W Blouet, Isbn: 9780470387733 0470387734. 2011. 172p. pap. 29.95 **(978-1-61490-023-8(X))** Cram101 Inc.

—Outlines & Highlights for Latin America & the Caribbean by David L Clawson, Isbn: 9780072826944 0072826940. 2011. 368p. pap. 34.95 **(978-1-61654-136-1(9))** Cram101 Inc.

Curtis, Wayne. And a Bottle of Rum: A History of the New World in Ten Cocktails. 2007. (ENG.). 304p. pap. 14.95 (978-0-307-33862-4(2), Three Rivers Pr.) Crown Publishing Group.

de Jong, Nanette. Tambú: Curaçao's African-Caribbean Ritual & the Politics of Memory. 2012. (Ethnomusicology Multimedia Ser.). (ENG., Illus.). 182p. 70.00 (978-0-253-35654-3(7), 0253356547); pap. 25.00 (978-0-253-22337-1(7), 0253223377) Indiana Univ. Pr.

Dunkley, Daive A., ed. Readings in Caribbean History & Culture: Breaking Ground. 2011. (ENG.). 324p. 80.00 **(978-0-7391-6846-2(0))** Lexington Bks.

Emmer, Pieter C. General History of the Caribbean — UNESCO Vol. 2: New Societies - The Caribbean in the Long Sixteenth Century. 2007. (ENG.). 344p. 231.00 (978-1-4039-7590-4(6)) Palgrave Macmillan.

Eneas, Godfrey. The New Caribbean: A Region in Transition. 2009. 260p. pap. 15.99 (978-1-4343-9012-7(8)) AuthorHouse.

Erriah, Paul J. Quo Vadis: Perspectives on the Commonwealth Caribbean from Colonial Times to Present. 2011. 176p. 29.95 **(978-1-4575-0203-3(8))**; pap. 24.95 **(978-1-60844-959-0(9))** Dog Ear Publishing, LLC.

Esquemeling, John. The Buccaneers of Americ. 2008. 128p. pap. 14.99 (978-1-60459-520-8(5)) Wilder Pubns., Ltd.

—The Buccaneers of America: A True Account of the Most Remarkable Assaults Committed of Late Years upon the Coasts of the West Indies by the Buccaneers of Jamaica & Tortuga. Powell, Henry, ed. 2010. (Cambridge Library Collection - History Ser.). (Illus.). 566p. pap. 39.99 (978-1-108-02481-5(5)) Cambridge Univ. Pr.

—The Buccaneers of America: In the Original English Translation Of 1684. 2007. 296p. per. 18.95 (978-1-60206-100-2(9)) Cosimo, Inc.

Ette, Ottmar, ed. Caribbean(s) on the Move - Archipiélagos Literarios del Caribe: A Transarea Symposium. 2007. 168p. pap. 40.95 (978-3-631-56716-6(2)) Lang, Peter Publishing, Inc.

Exquemelin, A. O. The Buccaneers of America: A Firsthand Account of Life with the Caribbean Pirates Captain Henry Morgan, Francis Lolonois, & Pierra la Grande. 2009. (Illus.). 192p. pap. (978-1-934941-72-0(7)) Red & Black Pubs.

Ferguson, James. Travellers History: The Caribbean. 2nd ed. 2008. (Traveller's History Ser.). (ENG., Illus.). 288p. pap. 14.95 (978-1-56656-690-2(8)) Interlink Publishing Group, Inc.

Foote, Nicola. The Caribbean History Reader. 2012. (Routledge Readers in History Ser.). (ENG., Illus.). 480p. 125.00 (978-0-415-80022-8(6)) Routledge.

Foote, Nicola, ed. The Caribbean History Reader. 2012. (Routledge Readers in History Ser.). (ENG., Illus.). 480p. pap. 49.95 (978-0-415-80023-5(4)) Routledge.

Fraginals, Manual Moreno. Autochthonous Societies, Vol. 1. Sued-Badillo, Jalil, ed. 2007. (ENG.). 442p. 31.00 (978-1-4039-7589-8(2)) Palgrave Macmillan.

Fraginals, Manual Moreno & Sued-Badillo, Jalil. General History of the Caribbean — UNESCO: The Complete Set. 2009. (ENG.). 3400p. 800.00 (978-1-4039-7608-6(2)) Palgrave Macmillan.

—General History of the Caribbean — UNESCO Vol. 4: The Long Nineteenth Century: Nineteenth-Century Transformations. 2009. (ENG.). 500p. 150.00 (978-1-4039-7592-8(2)) Palgrave Macmillan.

Gedda, George. Dominican Connection: Talent from the Tropics Changes Face of National Pastime. 2009. 160p. pap. 12.95 (978-1-60693-023-6(0), Eloquent Bks.) AEG Literary Publishing Services, Inc.

Hairr, John. Caribbean Monk Seals: Lost Seals of the Gulf of Mexico & Caribbean Sea. 2011. 198p. pap. 14.95 **(978-1-61646-063-1(6))** Coachwhip Pubns.

Hamilton, Douglas. Scotland, the Caribbean & the Atlantic World, 1750-1820. 2010. (ENG., Illus.). 264p. pap. 30.95 (978-0-7190-7183-6(0)) Manchester Univ. Pr. GBR. Dist: Macmillan.

Higman, B. W. A Concise History of the Caribbean. 2010. (Cambridge Concise Histories Ser.). (ENG., Illus.). 372p. 80.00 (978-0-521-88854-7(9)); pap. 24.99 (978-0-521-04348-9(4)) Cambridge Univ. Pr.

—General History of the Caribbean — UNESCO Vol. 6: Methodology & Historiography of the Caribbean. 2007. (ENG.). 950p. 231.00 (978-1-4039-7594-2(9)) Palgrave Macmillan.

Inocent, Lionel. A Carib Son a Brooklyn Story. 2010. 476p. pap. 23.50 (978-1-59330-651-9(2)) Aventine Pr.

Irwin, Raymond D. Books on Early American History & Culture, 1961-1970: An Annotated Bibliography, 1 vol. annot. ed. 2007. (Bibliographies & Indexes in American History Ser.: No. 54). 336p. 89.95 (978-0-313-31432-2(2), GR1432, Praeger Pubs.) Greenwood Publishing Group, Inc.

Jain, Jasbir & Agarwal, Supriya, eds. Writers of the Caribbean Diaspora: Shifting Homelands, Travelling Identities. 2008. 300p. 34.95 (978-1-932705-77-5(5)) New Dawn Pr., Inc.

Jong, Nanette de. Tambú: Curaçao's African-Caribbean Ritual & the Politics of Memory. 2012. **(978-0-253-00572-4(8))** Indiana Univ. Pr.

Kelly, Kenneth G. & Hardy, Meredith D., eds. French Colonial Archaeology in the Southeast & Caribbean. 2011. (Florida Museum of Natural History: Ripley P. Bullen Ser.). (ENG., Illus.). 256p. 74.95 (978-0-8130-3680-9(1)) Univ. Pr. of Florida.

Kinkor, Kenneth J. & Simpson, Sharon. Real Pirates: The Untold Story of the Whydah from Slave Ship to Pirate Ship. 2007. (ENG., Illus.). 176p. per. 19.95 (978-1-4262-0262-9(8)) National Geographic Society.

Kordac, Lubos. Historic Shipwrecks of the Dominican Republic & Haiti. 2009. pap. (978-1-61623-639-7(6)) Independent Pub.

Kritzler, Edward. Jewish Pirates of the Caribbean: How a Generation of Swashbuckling Jews Carved Out an Empire in the New World in Their Quest for Treasure, Religious Freedom — and Revenge. 2008. (ENG., Illus.). 336p. 26.00 (978-0-385-51398-2(4)) Knopf Doubleday Publishing Group.

Landers, Jane G. Atlantic Creoles in the Age of Revolutions. (Illus.). 352p. 2011. (ENG.). pap. 19.95 (978-0-674-06204-7(3)) 2010. 31.50 (978-0-674-03591-1(7)) Harvard Univ. Pr.

Latimer, Jon. Buccaneers of the Caribbean: How Piracy Forged an Empire. 2009. (Illus.). 368p. 27.95 (978-0-674-03403-7(1)) Harvard Univ. Pr.

Lopez Acevedo, Gladys & Tan, Hong. Impact Evaluation of Small & Medium Enterprise Programs in Latin America & the Caribbean. 2011. **(978-0-8213-8776-4(6))** World Bank Pubns.

López-Acevedo, Gladys & Tan, Hong W., eds. Impact Evaluation of Small & Medium Enterprise Programs in Latin America & the Caribbean. 2011. (ENG.). 144p. pap. 20.00 (978-0-8213-8775-7(8), 9780821387757) World Bank Pubns.

Luis, William. Las Vanguardias Literarias en el Caribe: Cuba, Puerto Rico y República Dominicana. 2010. (Bibliografía y Antología Crítica de las Vanguardias en el Mundo Ibérico Ser.). pap. 44.00 **(978-84-8489-564-0(5))** Iberoamericana Vervuert Publishing Corp.

Martin, Tony. Caribbean History. 2011. (ENG., Illus.). 384p. (C). pap. 44.00 **(978-0-13-220860-4(1),** Prentice Hall) Prentice Hall PTR.

Martinez-Fernandez, Luis. Frontiers, Plantations, & Walled Cities: Essays on Culture & Society. 2010. (Illus.). 260p. pap. 24.95 (978-1-55876-512-2(3)) Wiener, Markus Pubs., Inc.

—Frontiers, Plantations, & Walled Cities: Essays on Society, Culture, & Politics in the Hispanic Caribbean (1800-1945) 2010. (Illus.). 320p. 68.95 (978-1-55876-511-5(5)) Wiener, Markus Pubs., Inc.

McGarrity, Maria. Washed by the Gulf Stream: The Historic & Geographic Relation of Irish & Caribbean Literature. 2008. (Illus.). 196p. 40.00 (978-0-87413-028-7(X)) Univ. of Delaware Pr.

Metzgen, Humphrey & Graham, John. Caribbean Wars Untold: A Salute to the British West Indies. 2007. (Illus.). 256p. per. (978-976-640-203-7(5)) Univ. of the West Indies Pr.

Moreman, Christopher M. & Rushton, Cory James, eds. Race, Oppression & the Zombie: Essays on Cross-Cultural Appropriations of the Caribbean Tradition. 2011. (ENG.). 240p. pap. 45.00 **(978-0-7864-5911-7(5))** McFarland & Co., Inc. Pubs.

Morgan, Kenneth, ed. The Bright-Meyler Papers: A Bristol-West India Connection, 1732-1837. 2008. (Records of Social & Economic History, New Ser.). (ENG., Illus.). 650p. 175.00 (978-0-19-726405-8(0)) Oxford Univ. Pr., Inc.

Moulin Civil, Françoise, et al. De la Isla Al Archipiélago en el Mundo Hispano. 2010. (SPA.). 272p. (978-84-00-08931-3(6)) Centro de Estudios Historicos Jerezanos.

Moya Pons, Frank. History of the Caribbean: Plantation, Trade, War in the Atlantic World. 2007. (Illus.). xiii, 402p. pap. 28.95 (978-1-55876-415-6(1)) Wiener, Markus Pubs., Inc.

—History of the Caribbean: Plantations, Trade, & War in the Atlantic World. 2007. (Illus.). 460p. 88.95 (978-1-55876-414-9(3)) Wiener, Markus Pubs., Inc.

Opie, Frederick Douglass. Black Labor Migration in Caribbean Guatemala, 1882-1923. 2009. (Working in the Americas Ser.). (ENG., Illus.). 192p. 65.00 (978-0-8130-3371-6(3)) Univ. Pr. of Florida.

Ott, Bernhard. Beyond Fragmentation: Integrating Mission & Theological Education: A Critical Assessment of Some Recent Developments in Evangelical Theological Education. 2011. (Regnum Studies in Mission Ser.). 416p. pap. 47.00 **(978-1-61097-595-7(2),** Wipf and Stock) Wipf & Stock Pubs.

Our caribbean heritage in Context. 2006. (YA). per. (978-1-59872-520-9(3)) Instant Pub.

Palmie, Stephen & Scarano, Francisco A., eds. The Caribbean: A History of the Region & Its Peoples. 2011. (ENG., Illus.). 624p. 95.00 (978-0-226-64506-3(1)) Univ. of Chicago Pr.

Paravisini-Gebert, Lizabeth & Romero-Cesareo, Ivette, eds. Displacements & Transformations in Caribbean Cultures. 2008. (ENG., Illus.). 256p. 59.95 (978-0-8130-3218-4(0)) Univ. Pr. of Florida.

Parfitt, George. Being Anglo-Caribbean. 2009. 148p. pap. 20.95 (978-1-4092-5484-3(4)) Lulu Enterprises Inc.

Petrillo, Renee. A Sail of Two Idiots: 100 Hard-Won Lessons from a Non-Sailor (and Her Husband) Who Quit the Rat Race & Sailed Safely To. 2012. (ENG.). 304p. pap. 22.00 **(978-0-07-177984-5(1),** 0071779841, International Marine/Ragged Mountain Pr.) McGraw-Hill Professional Publishing.

Pickering, David & Collins Staff. Pirates. 2006. (Collins Gem Ser.). (Illus.). 256p. pap. 7.95 (978-0-06-113712-9(X), Harper Paperbacks) HarperCollins Pubs.

Pinel, Elsa. Secrets of the House of Dahomy: Guarded Secrets of the Caribbean Elders. 2007. 192p. (ENG.). 26.95 (978-0-595-69189-0(7)); per. 16.95 (978-0-595-44980-4(8)) iUniverse, Inc.

Poisonous Plants of the Caribbean. 2009. (Illus.). 120p. pap. (978-1-929440-03-0(0)) Nautilus Publishing Co.

Reid, Basil A. Myths & Realities of Caribbean History. 2009. (Caribbean Archaeology & Ethnohistory Ser.). (ENG., Illus.). 168p. pap. 19.95 (978-0-8173-5534-0(0)) Univ. of Alabama Pr.

Rodriguez Julia, Edgardo. Caribenos. (SPA., Illus.). xiii, 330p. (978-0-86581-584-1(4)) Instituto de Cultura Puertorriquena.

Routledge, creator. South America, Central America & the Caribbean. 16th rev. ed. 2007. (Europa Regional Surveys of the World Ser.). (Illus.). 1103p. 720.00 (978-1-85743-432-3(3)) Routledge.

Sanders, Richard. If a Pirate I Must Be... The True Story of Black Bart, King of the Caribbean Pirates. 2007. (Illus.). 278p. 19.95 (978-1-60239-019-5(3)) Skyhorse Publishing Co., Inc.

Scarano, Francisco A. & Palmie, Stephan, eds. The Caribbean: A History of the Region & Its Peoples. 2011. (ENG., Illus.). 624p. pap. 35.00 (978-0-226-64508-7(8)) Univ. of Chicago Pr.

Schloss, Rebecca Hartkopf. Sweet Liberty: The Final Days of Slavery in Martinique. 2009. (Early American Studies). 312p. (C). 39.95 (978-0-8122-4172-3(X)) Univ. of Pennsylvania Pr.

Schomburgk, Robert Hermann. The History of Barbados: Comprising a Geographical & Statistical Description of the Island; a Sketch of the Historical Events since the Settlement; & an Account of its Geology & Natural Productions. 2010. (Cambridge Library Collection - History Ser.). (Illus.). 770p. pap. 50.00 (978-1-108-02331-3(2)) Cambridge Univ. Pr.

Sealy. Sealy's Caribbean Leaders. (Illus.). 207p. pap. (978-976-625-034-8(0)) Kingston Publishing, Ltd.

Smith, Aaron. The Atrocities of the Pirates: A Faithful Narrative of the Unparalleled Suffering of the Author During his Captivity among the Pirates. 2011. (ENG.). 144p. pap. 12.95 (978-1-61608-194-2(5), 608194) Skyhorse Publishing Co., Inc.

Smith, Frederick H. The Archaeology of Alcohol & Drinking. 2008. (American Experience in Archaeological Perspective Ser.). (ENG., Illus.). 176p. pap. 24.95 (978-0-8130-3290-0(3)) Univ. Pr. of Florida.

Snitkovsky, Victor. Jewish Communities of Caribbean Islands, Central & South America: History & Today. 2009. (RUS., Illus.). 254p. (978-1-934881-12-5(0), M-Graphics) M-Graphics Publishing.

Strong, Ezra, ed. Infamous Pirates: Their Lives & Bloody Exploits. 2007. (Dover Maritime Ser.). (ENG., Illus.). 320p. per. 10.95 (978-0-486-46185-4(8)) Dover Pubns., Inc.

Talty, Stephan. Empire of Blue Water: Captain Morgan's Great Pirate Army, the Epic Battle for the Americas, & the Catastrophe That Ended the Outlaws' Bloody Reign. 2008. (ENG., Illus.). 352p. pap. 14.95 (978-0-307-23661-6(7), Three Rivers Pr.) Crown Publishing Group.

Taylor, Christopher. The Black Carib Wars: Freedom, Survival, & the Making of the Garifuna. 2012. (Caribbean Studies Ser.). (ENG.). 216p. 55.00 **(978-1-61703-310-0(3))** Univ. Pr. of Mississippi.

Tillis, Antonio D., ed. Critical Perspectives on Afro-Latin American Literature. 2011. (Routledge Studies on African & Black Diaspora Ser.). (ENG.). 272p. (C). 125.00 (978-0-415-89627-6(4)) Routledge.

United Nations. Statistical Yearbook for Latin America & the Caribbean 2008. 2009. (FRE & MUL., Illus.). 430p. pap. 95.00 (978-92-1-021066-9(2)) United Nations Pubns.

UTE Wartenberg Staff. Money of the Caribbean: COAC Proceedings 15. 2006. (Coinage of the Americas Conference Ser.: Vol. 15). (ENG., Illus.). 328p. (C). 65.00 (978-0-89722-285-3(7)) American Numismatic Society.

Walne, Peter. A Guide to Manuscript Sources for the History of Latin America & the Caribbean in the British Isles. xx, 580p. (978-0-19-818152-1(3)) Bow Historical Bks.

Walvin, James. The Trader, the Owner, the Slave: Parallel Lives in the Age of Slavery. (ENG., Illus.). 2008. 304p. pap. 15.95 (978-0-7126-6763-0(6)) 2007. 320p. 32.95 (978-0-224-06144-5(5)) Random Hse. GBR. Dist: Independent Pubs. Group.

CARIBBEAN AREA—MAPS

Blouet, Brian W. & Blouet, Olwyn M. Latin America & the Caribbean: A Systematic & Regional Survey. 6th ed. 2009. (ENG., Illus.). 480p. (C). pap. 123.95 (978-0-470-38773-3(4), Wiley) Wiley, John & Sons, Inc.

MacPherson. Map Reading for the Caribbean. 2nd ed. Date not set. (Illus.). 50p. pap. 9.95 (978-0-582-76609-9(5)) Addison-Wesley Longman, Ltd. GBR. Dist: Trans-Atlantic Pubns., Inc.

MapEasy Inc Staff. Guidemap to the Caribbean - Northern Islands. 2006. 6.95 (978-1-878979-66-7(3)) Mapeasy, Inc.

Solutions, NVision, Inc. Port-au-Prince Relief Map Book ISBN. 2010. 125p. pap. 66.50 (978-0-557-30340-3(0)) Lulu Enterprises Inc.

CARIBBEAN AREA—POLITICS AND GOVERNMENT

Best, Curwen. The Politics of Caribbean Cyberculture. 2008. (ENG.). 260p. 95.00 (978-0-230-60376-9(9)) Palgrave Macmillan.

Braveboy-Wagner, Jacqueline Anne & Braveboy-wagner, Jacqueli. Small States in Global Affairs: The Foreign Policies of the Caribbean Community (Caricom) 2007. (ENG., Illus.). 288p. 100.00 (978-1-4039-8001-4(2)) Palgrave Macmillan.

Carruthers, David V., ed. Environmental Justice in Latin America: Problems, Promise, & Practice. 2008. (Urban & Industrial Environments Ser.). (ENG., Illus.). 344p. (gr. 17). 62.00 (978-0-262-03372-5(0)); per. 28.00 (978-0-262-53300-3(6)) MIT Pr.

Conrad. Education, Human Capital Accumulation, & Economic Growth. 2009. 116p. pap. (978-3-8364-9033-7(1)) VDM Verlag Dr. Mueller e.K.

Devonish, Hubert. Language & Liberation: Creole Language Politics in the Caribbean. 2nd exp. ed. 2007. 270p. pap. (978-976-8189-26-4(6)) Arawak Pubns.

Erriah, Paul J. Quo Vadis: Perspectives on the Commonwealth Caribbean from Colonial Times to Present. 2011. 176p. 29.95 **(978-1-4575-0203-3(8))**; pap. 24.95 **(978-1-60844-959-0(9))** Dog Ear Publishing, LLC.

Europa Publications Staff, ed. South America, Central America & the Caribbean 2009. 17th rev. ed. 2008. (ENG., Illus.). 1120p. 760.00 (978-1-85743-467-5(6)) Routledge.

Fanning, Lucia, et al, eds. Towards Marine Ecosystem-Based Management in the Wider Caribbean. 2011. (MARE Publication Ser.). (ENG.). 425p. pap. (978-90-8964-242-4(0)) Amsterdam Univ. Pr.

Francois, Martinus. St. Lucia's Julius Caesar & Marcus Brutus. 2010. 120p. pap. 15.00 (978-1-4251-8996-9(2)) Trafford Publishing.

Frankson, A. S. A Caribbean Identity: Memoirs of the Colonial Service. 2nd ed. 2008. (ENG., Illus.). 264p. 52.00 (978-1-84511-591-3(0), Radcliffe Pr., The) I. B. Tauris & Co., Ltd. GBR. Dist: Macmillan.

Ghahremani, Nuschin. The Eu-Cariforum Economic Partnership Agreement. 2009. 136p. pap. (978-3-639-13925-9(9)) VDM Verlag Dr. Mueller e.K.

Hillman, Richard S. & D¿Agostino, Thomas J., eds. Understanding the Contemporary Caribbean. 2nd ed. 2009. (Illus.). 475p. (C). pap. 27.50 (978-1-58826-663-7(X)) Rienner, Lynne Pubs.

Inniss, Abiola. Essays in Caribbean Law & Policy. 2011. 112p. pap. **(978-3-8443-3147-9(6))** Lambert Academic Publishing.

Jain, Jasbir & Agarwal, Supriya, eds. Writers of the Caribbean Diaspora: Shifting Homelands, Travelling Identities. 2008. 300p. 34.95 (978-1-932705-77-5(5)) New Dawn Pr., Inc.

James, Willie. Charismatic Crisis-Prone Caribbean Leaders of Our Era. 2011. 24.99 (978-1-57197-504-1(7), Ivy House Publishing Group) Pentland Pr., Inc.

Joseph, Tennyson S. D. Decolonization in St. Lucia: Politics & Global Neoliberalism, 1945-2010. 2011. (Caribbean Studies Ser.). (ENG.). 240p. 55.00 (978-1-61703-117-5(8)) Univ. Pr. of Mississippi.

Knight, Franklin W. The Caribbean: The Genesis of a Fragmented Nationalism, 1 vol. 3rd ed. 2011. (Latin American Histories Ser.). (ENG., Illus.). 304p. (C). pap. 44.95 (978-0-19-538133-7(5)) Oxford Univ. Pr., Inc.

Laurent, Edwin, ed. Trade Policy for Parliamentarians: A Guide for the Caribbean. 2012. (ENG.). 100p. pap. 24.95 (978-1-84929-040-1(7)) Commonwealth Secretariat GBR. Dist: Stylus Publishing, LLC.

Leshikar-Denton, Margaret E. & Erreguerena, Pilar Luna, eds. Underwater & Maritime Archeology in Latin America & the Caribbean. 2008. (One World Archaeology Ser.). (ENG., Illus.). 316p. 94.00 (978-1-59874-262-6(0)) Left Coast Pr., Inc.

Lomborg, Bjorn, ed. Latin American Development Priorities: Costs & Benefits. 2010. (ENG., Illus.). 724p. 129.00 (978-0-521-76690-6(7)); pap. 49.99 (978-0-521-74752-3(X)) Cambridge Univ. Pr.

Martinez-Fernandez, Luis. Frontiers, Plantations, & Walled Cities: Essays on Culture & Society. 2010. (Illus.). 260p. pap. 24.95 (978-1-55876-512-2(3)) Wiener, Markus Pubs., Inc.

—Frontiers, Plantations, & Walled Cities: Essays on Society, Culture, & Politics in the Hispanic Caribbean (1800-1945) 2010. (Illus.). 320p. 68.95 (978-1-55876-511-5(5)) Wiener, Markus Pubs., Inc.

Mowforth. Tourism & Responsibility: Perspectives from Latin America & the Caribbean. 2007. (Illus.). X, 246p. 180.00 (978-0-415-42364-9(3)) Routledge.

Mowforth, Martin, et al. Tourism & Responsibility: Perspectives from Latin America & the Caribbean. 2007. (Illus.). X, 246p. 51.95 (978-0-415-42366-3(X)) Routledge.

Osei, Philip D. & Nwasike, Joan N. The Contract System of Employment for Senior Government Officials: Experiences from the Caribbean. 2011. (Managing the Public Service: Strategies for Improvement Ser.). (ENG.). 120p. pap. 33.00 (978-1-84929-046-3(6)) Commonwealth Secretariat GBR. Dist: Stylus Publishing, LLC.

Purcell, Joan M. Vision of Change: A Caribbean Perspective. 2011. 208p. 24.75 **(978-1-4634-3259-1(3))**; pap. 14.95 **(978-1-4634-3260-7(7))** AuthorHouse.

Puri, Shalini, ed. The Legacies of Caribbean Radical Politics. 2010. (ENG.). 160p. (C). 125.00 (978-0-415-58689-4(5)) Routledge.

Rosselló, Pedro. El derecho a la Salud: La lucha en busca de un Ideal. 2009. (Illus.). 200p. lib. bdg. (978-0-9823230-1-4(8)) Sistema Universitaria Ana G. Mendez.

Seligson, Mitchell. Challenges to Democracy in Latin America & the Caribbean 2006: Evidence from the AmericasBarometer 2006. 2007. 30.00 (978-0-9792178-7-6(3)) LAPOP (Latin American Public Opinion Project).

Siegel, Peter E. & Righter, Elizabeth, eds. Protecting Heritage in the Caribbean. 3rd ed. 2011. (Caribbean Archaeology & Ethnohistory Ser.). (ENG., Illus.). 216p. pap. 27.50 (978-0-8173-5667-5(3)) Univ. of Alabama Pr.

Simmonds, Keith. Electoral Reform in the English Speaking Caribbean. 2010. 111p. pap. 20.00 (978-0-557-18466-8(5)) Lulu Enterprises Inc.

Stavridis, James G. Partnership for the Americas: Western Hemisphere Strategy & U. S. Southern Command: Western Hemisphere Strategy & U. S. Southern Command. National Defense University (U.S.), ed. 2010. (ENG., Illus.). 288p. pap. 27.00 (978-0-16-087042-2(9), Dept. of the Army) United States Government Printing Office.

Torre, Augusto de la, et al. Desarrollo con Menos Carbono: Respuestas Latinoamericanas al Desafío del Cambio Climático - Síntesis. 2009. (Latin America & Caribbean Studies). (SPA.). 96p. pap. 35.00 (978-0-8213-7920-2(8), 9780821379202) World Bank Pubns.

United Nations. Exploring Policy Linkages Between Poverty, Crime & Violence: A look at Three Caribbean States. 2009. (Studies & Perspectives Ser.). (ENG.). 48p. pap. 10.00 (978-92-1-121674-5(5)) United Nations Pubns.

CARIBBEAN AREA—POPULATION

United Nations. Latin America & the Caribbean Demographic Observatory: Internal Migration - Year IV (Includes CD-ROM), 1 vol. 2011. (ENG & SPA.). 478p. pap. 15.00 (**978-92-1-021075-1(1)**) United Nations Pubns.

—Latin America & the Caribbean Demographic Observatory: Population Projection. 2008. (MUL.). 196p. pap. 25.00 incl. lp (978-92-1-021063-8(8)) United Nations Pubns.

—Latin America & the Caribbean Demographic Observatory N. 9: Mortality - Year V (Includes CD-ROM) 2011. (ENG.). 252p. pap. 15.00 incl. cd-rom (**978-92-1-021074-4(3)**) United Nations Pubns.

—Latin America & the Caribbean Demographic Observatory: Urbanization Prospects - Year IV (Includes CD-ROM) 2011. (ENG & SPA.). 294p. pap. 25.00 incl. cd-rom (**978-92-1-021071-3(9)**) United Nations Pubns.

CARIBBEAN AREA—RELIGION

Bisnauth. History of Religions in the Caribbean. (Illus.). pap. (978-976-625-003-4(0)) Kingston Publishing, Ltd.

Bisnauth, Dale. History of Religions. 2006. 244p. per. (978-976-8202-15-4(7)) LMH Publishing, Ltd.

The Caribbean: A Legacy of Love. 2008. 96p. pap. 8.50 (978-0-8341-2346-5(0), 083-412-3460) Beacon Hill Pr. of Kansas City.

Davis, Kortright. Cross & Crown in Barbados: Caribbean Political Religion in the Late 19th Century. 2011. 196p. pap. 22.00 (978-1-61097-061-7(6), Wipf and Stock) Wipf & Stock Pubs.

Edmonds, Ennis & Gonzalez, Michelle. Caribbean Religious History: An Introduction. 2010. (ENG., Illus.). 288p. pap. 22.00 (978-0-8147-2235-0(0)) New York Univ. Pr.

Fernandez Olmos, Margarite & Paravisini-Gebert, Lizabeth. Creole Religions of the Caribbean: An Introduction from Vodou & Santeria to Obeah & Espiritismo, Second Edition Foreword by Joseph M. Murphy. 2nd ed. 2011. (ENG.). 324p. 79.00 (978-0-8147-6227-1(1)); pap. 23.00 (978-0-8147-6228-8(X)) New York Univ. Pr.

Filan, Kenaz. Vodou Money Magic: The Way to Prosperity Through the Blessings of the Lwa. 2010. (ENG.). 1p. pap. (978-1-59477-331-0(9), Destiny Bks.) Inner Traditions International, Ltd.

George, Milton. Laying down the Foundations for Caribbean Theologies. 2010. 68p. pap. (978-3-8383-4081-4(7)) Lambert Academic Publishing.

Henry, Steinberg. As She Returns, 1 vol. 2009. 300p. pap. 27.95 (978-1-60813-096-2(7)) PublishAmerica, Inc.

Lopez-Gale, Myrna. Haiti: God Has Not Forsaken You. 2011. 36p. pap. 15.50 (**978-1-4634-0613-4(4)**) AuthorHouse.

McNeal, Keith E. Trance & Modernity in the Southern Caribbean: African & Hindu Popular Religions in Trinidad & Tobago. 2011. (New World Diasporas Ser.). (ENG., Illus.). 400p. 74.95 (978-0-8130-3736-3(0)) Univ. Pr. of Florida.

Miller, Michael St. A. Reshaping the Contextual Vision in Caribbean Theology: Theoretical Foundations for Theology Which Is Contextual, Pluralistic, & Dialectical. 2007. (ENG.). 414p. 89.50 (978-0-7618-3784-8(1)); per. 57.99 (978-0-7618-3785-5(X)) Univ. Pr. of America, Inc.

Mitchell, Mozella G. Crucial Issues in Caribbean Religions. 2006. (Martin Luther King, Jr. Memorial Studies in Religion, Culture, & Social Development: Vol. 10). (Illus.). 288p. (C). 79.95 (978-0-8204-8191-3(2)); pap. 32.95 (978-0-8204-8863-9(1)) Lang, Peter Publishing, Inc.

Murrell, Nathaniel Samuel. Afro-Caribbean Religions: An Introduction to Their Historical, Cultural, & Sacred Traditions. 2009. (ENG., Illus.). 432p. 89.50 (978-1-4399-0040-6(X)); pap. 40.95 (978-1-4399-0041-3(8)) Temple Univ. Pr.

Parfitt, George. Being Anglo-Caribbean. 2009. 148p. pap. 20.95 (978-1-4092-5484-3(4)) Lulu Enterprises Inc.

Paton, Diana & Forde, Maarit, eds. Obeah & Other Powers: The Politics of Caribbean Religion & Healing. 2012. (ENG., Illus.). 392p. 99.95 (**978-0-8223-5124-5(2)**); pap. 27.95 (**978-0-8223-5133-7(1)**) Duke Univ. Pr.

Ramsey, Kate. The Spirits & the Law: Vodou & Power in Haiti. 2011. (ENG., Illus.). 448p. 45.00 (978-0-226-70379-4(7)) Univ. of Chicago Pr.

Schmidt, Bettina E. Caribbean Diaspora in USA: Diversity of Caribbean Religions in New York City. 2008. (Vitality of Indigenous Religions Ser.). (Illus.). 208p. 99.95 (978-0-7546-6365-2(5)) Ashgate Publishing Co.

Straub, Gerard Thomas. Hidden in the Rubble: A Haitian Pilgrimage to Compassion & Resurrection. 2010. (Illus.). 192p. pap. 18.00 (978-1-57075-897-3(2)) Orbis Bks.

Tann, Mambo Chita. Haitian Vodou: An Introduction to Haiti's Indigenous Spiritual Tradition. 2012. (ENG., Illus.). 264p. pap. 15.95 (**978-0-7387-3069-1(6)**) Llewellyn Pubns.

Wielzen, Duncan. Popular Religiosity & Roman Liturgy. 2010. 404p. pap. (978-3-8383-0334-5(2)) Lambert Academic Publishing.

CARIBBEAN AREA—SOCIAL CONDITIONS

Abraham, Sara. Labour & the Multiracial Project in the Caribbean: Its History & Its Promise. 2007. (Caribbean Studies (Lexington Books) Ser.). (ENG., Illus.). 258p. 78.99 (978-0-7391-1685-2(1)); per. 34.99 (978-0-7391-1686-9(X)) Lexington Bks.

Aird, Sheila Marie Cecilia. The Forgotten Ones - Enslaved Children in Caribbean Societies, 1673-1838. 2008. 204p. pap. (978-3-8364-9424-3(8)) VDM Verlag Dr. Mueller e.K.

Alexander, Leo. Putas of the Caribbean (Prostitutes of the Caribbean) 2011. 140p. pap. 14.95 (**978-1-4634-0523-6(5)**) AuthorHouse.

Barnes, Natasha. Cultural Conundrums: Gender, Race, Nation, & the Making of Caribbean Cultural Politics. 2006. (ENG., Illus.). 232p. 80.00 (978-0-472-09939-9(5)); per. 27.95 (978-0-472-06939-2(X)) Univ. of Michigan Pr.

Block, Kristen. Ordinary Lives in the Early Caribbean: Religion, Colonial Competition, & the Politics of Profit. 2012. (Early American Places Ser.). (ENG.). 312p. 69.95 (**978-0-8203-3867-5(2)**); (Illus.). pap. 24.95 (**978-0-8203-3868-2(0)**) Univ. of Georgia Pr.

Bolland, Nigel O. Struggles for Freedom: Essays on Slavery, Colonialism, & Culture in the Caribbean & Central America. pap. (978-976-8111-16-6(X)) Randle, Ian Pubs.

Branche, Jerome. Race, Colonialism, & Social Transformation in Latin America & the Caribbean. 2008. (ENG., Illus.). 288p. 69.95 (978-0-8130-3264-1(4)) Univ. Pr. of Florida.

Brereton, Bridget. General History of the Caribbean — Unesco: The Caribbean in the Twentieth Century. 2007. (ENG.). 788p. 231.00 (978-1-4039-7593-5(0)) Palgrave Macmillan.

Bush, Barbara. Slave Women in Caribbean Society, 1650-1838. 208p. 2009. (Illus.). 15.00 (978-1-59740-342-9(3)) 2008. pap. 20.00 (978-1-59740-557-7(4)) ACLS Humanities E-Book.

Clawson, David L. Latin America & the Caribbean: Lands & Peoples, 1 vol. 4th ed. 2010. (ENG.). 464p. (C). pap. 99.95 (978-0-19-976624-6(X)) Oxford Univ. Pr., Inc.

Cook, Loraine D. Teacher Locus of Control. 2010. 84p. pap. (978-3-639-25118-0(0)) VDM Verlag Dr. Mueller e.K.

Cotlear, Daniel. Demographic Transition & Social Policy in Latin America & the Caribbean. 2010. (Directions in Development Ser.). (ENG., Illus.). 320p. pap. 35.00 (978-0-8213-8487-9(2), 9780821384879); E-Book (978-0-8213-8469-5(4)) World Bank Pubns.

Curtis, Debra. Pleasures & Perils: Girls' Sexuality in a Caribbean Consumer Culture. 2009. (Rutgers Series in Childhood Studies). (ENG., Illus.). 256p. 68.00 (978-0-8135-4429-8(7)); pap. 23.95 (978-0-8135-4430-4(0)) Rutgers Univ. Pr.

David, Peggy Ann & Lange, Brenda. The Caribbean Community & Common Market. 2009. (Global Organizations Ser.). (Illus.). 128p. (YA). (gr. 7-12). 35.00 (978-0-7910-9541-6(X)) Facts On File, Inc.

Donato, Katharine M., et al, eds. Continental Divides: International Migration in the Americas: International Migration in the Americas. 2010. (ANNALS of the American Academy of Political & Social Science Ser.: 630). (Illus.). 324p. (C). 47.00 (978-1-4129-9186-5(2), 295630C); pap. 34.95 (978-1-4129-9187-2(0), 295630P) SAGE Pubns., Inc.

Erriah, Paul J. Quo Vadis: Perspectives on the Commonwealth Caribbean from Colonial Times to Present. 2011. 176p. 29.95 (**978-1-4575-0203-3(8)**); pap. 24.95 (**978-1-60844-959-0(9)**) Dog Ear Publishing, LLC.

Ette, Ottmar, ed. Caribbean(s) on the Move - Archipiélagos Literarios del Caribe: A Transarea Symposium. 2007. 168p. pap. 40.95 (978-3-631-56716-6(2)) Lang, Peter Publishing, Inc.

Europa Publications, ed. South America Central America & the Caribbean 2012. 20th rev. ed. 2011. (ENG.). 1148p. 880.00 (978-1-85743-619-8(9)) Routledge.

Gacitúa-Marió, Estanislao, et al. Exclusión Social y Reducción de la Pobreza en América Latina y Caribe. (SPA., Illus.). 310p. (978-9977-68-110-8(4)) Facultad Latinoamericana de Ciencias Sociales.

Goldish, Josette C. Once Jews: Stories of Caribbean Sephardim. 2009. (Illus.). 360p. 88.95 (978-1-55876-493-4(3)); 380p. pap. 34.95 (978-1-55876-494-1(1)) Wiener, Markus Pubs., Inc.

Gomez, Cathy. Coping with Sudden Job Loss. 2010. 112p. pap. (978-3-639-23696-5(3)) VDM Verlag Dr. Mueller e.K.

Gordon-Strachan, Georgiana. Micronutrient Deficiencies in the Caribbean. 2010. 324p. pap. (978-3-639-22252-4(0)) VDM Verlag Dr. Mueller e.K.

Hailey, Adrian, et al. Conservation of Caribbean Island Herpetofaunas. 2011. (978-90-04-19410-6(X)) BRILL.

Hayward, Michele H., et al. Rock Art of the Caribbean. 2009. (Caribbean Archaeology & Ethnohistory Ser.). (ENG.). 304p. pap. 30.95 (978-0-8173-5530-2(8)); (Illus.). 51.75 (978-0-8173-1650-1(7)) Univ. of Alabama Pr.

Hillman, Richard S. & D¿Agostino, Thomas J., eds. Understanding the Contemporary Caribbean. 2nd ed. 2009. (Illus.). 475p. (C). pap. 27.50 (978-1-58826-663-7(X)) Rienner, Lynne Pubs.

Hitchen, Peter. Education & Multicultural Cohesion in the Caribbean:the Case of Belize, 1931 - 1981. 2008. 458p. 48.50 (978-1-4116-6994-9(0)) Lulu Enterprises Inc.

Jones, Cecily. Engendering Whiteness: White Women & Colonialism in Barbados & North Carolina, 1627-1865. 2007. (Studies in Imperialism Ser.). (ENG.). 272p. 89.00 (978-0-7190-6432-6(5)) Manchester Univ. Pr. GBR. Dist: Macmillan.

Knight, Franklin W. The Caribbean: The Genesis of a Fragmented Nationalism, 1 vol. 3rd ed. 2011. (Latin American Histories Ser.). (ENG., Illus.). 304p. (C). pap. 44.95 (978-0-19-538133-7(5)) Oxford Univ. Pr., Inc.

Kritzler, Edward. Jewish Pirates of the Caribbean: How a Generation of Swashbuckling Jews Carved Out an Empire in the New World in Their Quest for Treasure, Religious Freedom — and Revenge. 2009. (ENG.). 352p. pap. 15.95 (978-0-7679-1952-4(1), Anchor) Knopf Doubleday Publishing Group.

Kronik, Jakob & Verner, Dorte. Indigenous Peoples & Climate Change in Latin America & the Caribbean. 2010. (Directions in Development Ser.). (ENG., Illus.). 200p. pap. 35.00 (978-0-8213-8237-0(3), 9780821382370) World Bank Pubns.

Lewis, Colin, et al. South America, Central America & the Caribbean 2010. 18th rev. ed. 2009. (ENG.). 1136p. 810.00 (978-1-85743-525-2(7)) Routledge.

Milner, Josh. Piracy in the Americas, 1775-1865: A Short History. 2010. pap. (978-0-89824-597-4(4)) Royal Fireworks Publishing Co.

Misir, Prem, ed. & frwd. Ethnic Cleavage & Closure in the Caribbean Diaspora: Essays on Race, Ethnicity & Class. 2006. (Illus.). 236p. 109.95 (978-0-7734-5552-8(3)) Mellen, Edwin Pr., The.

Mohammed, Patricia. Imaging the Caribbean: Culture & Visual Translation. 2010. (ENG., Illus.). 416p. pap. 41.00 (978-0-230-10449-5(5)) Palgrave Macmillan.

Molines Vega, Jose R., et al. Do Our Children Have a Chance? The 2010 Human Opportunity Report for Latin America & the Caribbean. 2011. (Directions in Development Ser.). (ENG., Illus.). 170p. pap. 25.00 (**978-0-8213-8699-6(9)**, 9780821386996) World Bank Pubns.

Moreman, Christopher M. & Rushton, Cory James, eds. Race, Oppression & the Zombie: Essays on Cross-Cultural Appropriations of the Caribbean Tradition. 2011. (ENG.). 240p. pap. 45.00 (**978-0-7864-5911-7(5)**) McFarland & Co., Inc. Pubs.

Newton, Melanie J. The Children of Africa in the Colonies: Free People of Color in Barbados in the Age of Emancipation. 2008. (Antislavery, Abolition, & the Atlantic World Ser.). (Illus.). 322p. 42.50 (978-0-8071-3326-2(4)) Louisiana State Univ. Pr.

O'Loughlin, K. F. & Lander, James F. Caribbean Tsunamis: A 500-Year History From 1498-1998. 2010. (Advances in Natural & Technological Hazards Research Ser.). 280p. pap. 139.00 (978-90-481-6467-7(2), 9048164672) Springer.

Olwig, Karen Fog. Caribbean Journeys: An Ethnography of Migration & Home in Three Family Networks. 2007. (ENG., Illus.). 336p. 89.95 (978-0-8223-3977-9(3)); pap. 24.95 (978-0-8223-3994-6(3)) Duke Univ. Pr.

Oostindie, Gert. Ethnicity in the Caribbean: Essays in Honor of Harry Hoetink. 2006. (Amsterdam Academic Archive Ser.). 258p. pap. (978-90-5356-851-4(4), Leiden Univ. Pr.) Amsterdam Univ. Pr.

Publishing, Lmh, compiled by. The Jamaican Handbook for the Elderly. 2010. 190p. pap. (978-976-8202-73-4(4)) LMH Publishing, Ltd.

Purcell, Joan M. Vision of Change: A Caribbean Perspective. 2011. 208p. 24.75 (**978-1-4634-3259-1(3)**); pap. 14.95 (**978-1-4634-3260-7(7)**) AuthorHouse.

Ribe, Helena, et al. From Right to Reality: Incentives, Labor Markets, & the Challenge of Achieving Universal Social Protection in Latin America & the Caribbean. 2012. (Latin American Development Forum Ser.). (ENG.). 449p. pap. 39.95 (**978-0-8213-8687-3(5)**, 9780821386873) World Bank Pubns.

Ruck, Rob. Raceball: How the Major Leagues Colonized the Black & Latin Game. 2012. (ENG., Illus.). 288p. pap. 18.00 (**978-0-8070-4807-8(0)**) Beacon Pr.

Ruggiero, Kristin, ed. The Jewish Diaspora in Latin America & the Caribbean: Fragments of Memory. 2010. (Illus.). 270p. pap. 34.50 (978-1-84519-414-7(4)) Sussex Academic Pr. GBR. Dist: International Specialized Bk. Services.

Sheller, Mimi. Citizenship from Below: Caribbean Agency & Embodied Freedom. 2012. (Next Wave: New Directions in Women's Studies). (ENG., Illus.). 368p. 94.95 (**978-0-8223-4934-1(5)**) Duke Univ. Pr.

—Citizenship from Below: Erotic Agency & Caribbean Freedom. 2012. (Next Wave: New Directions in Women's Studies). (ENG., Illus.). 368p. pap. 25.95 (**978-0-8223-4953-2(1)**) Duke Univ. Pr.

Smith, Frederick H. Caribbean Rum: A Social & Economic History. 2008. (ENG., Illus.). 368p. pap. 29.95 (978-0-8130-3315-0(2)) Univ. Pr. of Florida.

South America Central America & the Caribbean 2011. 19th rev. ed. 2010. (ENG.). 1152p. 835.00 (978-1-85743-562-7(1)) Routledge.

United Nations. Exploring Policy Linkages Between Poverty, Crime & Violence: A look at Three Caribbean States. 2009. (Studies & Perspectives Ser.). (ENG.). 48p. pap. 10.00 (978-92-1-121674-5(5)) United Nations Pubns.

—Handbook on Planning & Action for Crime Prevention in Southern Africa & the Caribbean Regions. 2009. (Criminal Justice Handbook Ser.). (ENG.). 126p. pap. 26.00 (978-92-1-130269-1(2)) United Nations Pubns.

Various Bills & Resolutions: Markup Before the Committee on Foreign Affairs, House of Representatives, One Hundred Tenth Congress, First Session, on H.R. 2828, H.R. 3432, H.Res. 405, H. Res. 624, H. Res. 635, H. Res. 651, H. con. Res. 200, & H. con. Res. 203, H.R. 2003, S. 1612 & H. Res. 676, September 26, 2007. 2008. iv, 169p. (978-0-16-080144-0(3), 552-070-36884-1) United States Government Printing Office.

Whitmarsh, Ian. Biomedical Ambiguity: Race, Asthma, & the Contested Meaning of Genetic Research in the Caribbean. 2008. 232p. 68.95 (978-0-8014-4686-3(4)); pap. 22.95 (978-0-8014-7441-5(8)) Cornell Univ. Pr.

Widgen, Quirin. Aimé Césaire Zwischen Poesie und Politik: Identität und Gesellschaft Auf Martinique. 2010. (GER.). 120p. (978-3-631-60185-3(9)) Lang, Peter Publishing, Inc.

Wolfert, Sinaya. Curaçao: Religions, Rituals & Traditions. 2010. 224p. 65.00 (978-94-6022-046-3(0)) Royal Tropical Institute Pr. (KIT (Koninklijk Instituut voor de Tropen) NLD. Dist: Stylus Publishing, LLC.

World Bank Group Staff, et al. The Promise of Early Childhood Development in Latin America & the Caribbean. 2009. (Latin American Development Forum Ser.). (ENG., Illus.). 220p. pap. 40.00 (978-0-8213-7759-8(0), 9780821377598) World Bank Pubns.

CARIBBEAN AREA—SOCIAL LIFE AND CUSTOMS

Accilien, Cécile, et al, eds. Just below South: Intercultural Performance in the Caribbean & the U. S. South. 2007. (New World Studies). (ENG.). 288p. (C). (gr. 13-17). per. 22.50 (978-0-8139-2600-1(9)); (gr. 17). 59.50 (978-0-8139-2599-8(1)) Univ. Pr. of Virginia.

Brickhouse, Anna. Transamerican Literary Relations & the Nineteenth-Century Public Sphere. 2009. (Cambridge Studies in American Literature & Culture Ser.). (ENG.). 344p. pap. 46.00 (978-0-521-10101-1(8)) Cambridge Univ. Pr.

Burke, Suzanne. Policing the Transnational. 2010. 352p. pap. (978-3-8383-3508-7(2)) Lambert Academic Publishing.

Curet, L. Antonio & Hauser, Mark W. Islands at the Crossroads: Migration, Seafaring, & Interaction in the Caribbean. 2011. (Illus.). 352p. (**978-0-8173-8537-8(1)**) Univ. of Alabama Pr.

Curet, L. Antonio & Hauser, Mark W., eds. Islands at the Crossroads: Migration, Seafaring, & Interaction in the Caribbean. 2011. (Caribbean Archaeology & Ethnohistory Ser.). (ENG., Illus.). 328p. pap. 35.00 (978-0-8173-5655-2(X)) Univ. of Alabama Pr.

Emoff, Ron. Music & the Performance of Identity on Marie-Galante, French Antilles. 2009. (SOAS Musicology Ser.). (Illus.). 210p. 99.95 (978-0-7546-6565-6(8)) Ashgate Publishing Co.

Green, Garth L. & Scher, Philip W., eds. Trinidad Carnival: The Cultural Politics of a Transnational Festival. 2007. (ENG., Illus.). 272p. pap. 21.95 (978-0-253-21883-4(7), 0253218837) Indiana Univ. Pr.

Henke, Holger. Constructing Vernacular Culture in the Trans-Caribbean. 2007. (Caribbean Studies). (ENG.). 432p. 94.50 (978-0-7391-2160-3(X)) Lexington Bks.

Henke, Holger & Magister, Karl-Heinz. Constructing Vernacular Culture in the Trans-Caribbean. 2007. (Caribbean Studies (Lexington Books) Ser.). (ENG.). 432p. per. 47.50 (978-0-7391-2161-0(8)) Lexington Bks.

Henke/Magister, ed. Constructing Vernacular Culturcb. 2007. 432p. 90.00 (978-0-7391-2060-6(3)) Lexington Bks.

Henry, Steinberg. As She Returns, 1 vol. 2009. 300p. pap. 27.95 (978-1-60813-096-2(7)) PublishAmerica, Inc.

Hofman, Corinne L. & van Duijvenbode, Anne, eds. Communities in Contact: Essays in archaeology, ethnohistory & ethnography of the Amerindian Circum-Caribbean. 2011. (ENG., Illus.). 512p. (C). pap. 116.00 (**978-90-8890-063-1(9)**) Sidestone Pr. NLD. Dist: Brown, David Bk. Co., The.

Lamming, George & University of the West Indies (Mona, Jamaica), Centre for Caribbean Thought Staff. Sovereignty of the Imagination: Conversations III. 2009. 82p. pap. 15.00 (978-0-913441-46-6(5)) House of Nehesi Pubs. ANT. Dist: SPD-Small Pr. Distribution.

Levy, Horace, ed. The African Caribbean Worldview & the Making of Caribbean Society: History, Biology, Culture. 2009. 248p. pap. (978-976-640-210-5(8)) Univ. of the West Indies Pr.

Lewis, Stanford O. Nothing but Time. 2008. 290p. pap. (978-0-9785066-1-2(8)) Old Mountain Pr.

Maharajh, Hari D. & Merrick, Joav, eds. Social & Cultural Psychiatry Experience from the Caribbean Region. 2010. (Disability Studies (Joav Merrick - Series Editor - National Institute of Child Health & Human Development, Ministry of Social Affairs, Jerusalem Ser.). 235.00 (978-1-61668-506-5(9)) Nova Science Pubs., Inc.

Martinez-Fernandez, Luis. Frontiers, Plantations, & Walled Cities: Essays on Culture & Society. 2010. (Illus.). 260p. pap. 24.95 (978-1-55876-512-2(3)) Wiener, Markus Pubs., Inc.

—Frontiers, Plantations, & Walled Cities: Essays on Society, Culture, & Politics in the Hispanic Caribbean (1800-1945) 2010. (Illus.). 320p. 68.95 (978-1-55876-511-5(5)) Wiener, Markus Pubs., Inc.

Mihatsch, Wiltrud, ed. Language Contact & Language Change in the Caribbean & Beyond. (Sprachen, Gesellschaften und Kulturen in Lateinamerika: Vol. 9). (SPA & ENG., Illus.). 263p. pap. 47.95 (978-3-631-54554-6(1)) Lang, Peter GmbH, Europaischer Verlag der Wissenschaften DEU. Dist: Lang, Peter Publishing, Inc.

Miller, Rebecca S. Carriacou String Band Serenade: Performing Identity in the Eastern Caribbean. 2008. (Music Culture Ser.). (ENG., Illus.). 312p. lib. bdg. 49.95 (978-0-8195-6858-8(9)) Wesleyan Univ. Pr.

Mitchell, Ernest Roy. Public Relations - a 40-Year Journey. 2009. 364p. pap. (978-976-8054-79-1(4)) Paria Publishing Co., Ltd.

Mohammed, Patricia. Imaging the Caribbean: Culture & Visual Translation. 2010. (ENG., Illus.). 416p. pap. 41.00 (978-0-230-10449-5(5)) Palgrave Macmillan.

Montgomery, Michael, ed. The Crucible of Carolina: Essays in the Development of Gullah Language & Culture. 2008. (ENG., Illus.). 252p. pap. 24.95 (978-0-8203-3115-7(5)) Univ. of Georgia Pr.

Paravisini-Gebert, Lizabeth. Literature of the Caribbean, 1 vol. 2008. (Literature as Windows to World Cultures Ser.). 256p. 49.95 (978-0-313-32845-9(5), GR2845, Greenwood Pr.) Greenwood Publishing Group, Inc.

Regis, Helen A., ed. Caribbean & Southern: Transnational Perspectives on the U. S. South. 2006. (Southern Anthropological Society Proceedings Ser.: No. 38). (ENG., Illus.). 168p. 59.95 (978-0-8203-2831-7(6)); pap. 22.95 (978-0-8203-2832-4(4)) Univ. of Georgia Pr.

Reiss, Timothy J., ed. Music, Writing, & Cultural Unity in the Caribbean. 540p. 109.95 (978-1-59221-176-0(3)) Africa World Pr.

C

Roberts, Peter. The Roots of Caribbean Identity: Language, Race, & Ecology. 2008. (ENG., Illus.). 518p. pap. 32.00 (978-0-521-72745-7(6)) Cambridge Univ. Pr.

Rush, Anne Spry. Bonds of Empire: West Indians & Britishness from Victoria to Decolonization. 2011. (ENG.). 272p. 99.00 (978-0-19-958855-8(4)) Oxford Univ. Pr., Inc.

Sanabria, Harry. The Anthropology of Latin America & the Caribbean. 2006. (ENG., Illus.). 448p. (C). per. 76.80 (978-0-205-38099-2(9)) Allyn & Bacon, Inc.

Skervin, Hyacinth. Culture in Regional Geography Education. 2011. 156p. pap. **(978-3-8443-3131-8(X))** Lambert Academic Publishing.

Smart, Ian & Bedeau, Koren Allyson. Decoding Carnival: Creole Bacchanal, Pan-African Festival. 2010. (Illus.). xiv, 183p. pap. **(978-0-939423-26-2(X))** Original World Pr.

Sprauve, Gilbert A. Pell-Mell: ... So We Live! 2011. 156p. 23.42 (978-1-4269-5563-1(4)); pap. 13.42 (978-1-4269-5562-4(6)) Trafford Publishing.

Tewari, Laxmi G. Music of the Indian Diaspora in Trinidad. 2010. (ENG.). 290p. 40.00 (978-1-58432-647-2(6), Caribbean Studies Pr.) Educa Vision.

Wolfert, Sinaya. Curaçao: Religions, Rituals & Traditions. 2010. 224p. 65.00 (978-94-6022-046-3(0)) Royal Tropical Institute Pr. (KIT (Koninklijk Instituut voor de Tropen) NLD. Dist: Stylus Publishing, LLC.

Wynter, Sylvia & Eudell, Demetrius L. We Must Learn to Sit down Together & Talk about a Little Culture: Decolonizing Essays, 1967-1984. 2012. 260p. pap. 32.95 (978-1-84523-108-8(2)) Peepal Tree Pr., Ltd. GBR. Dist: Independent Pubs. Group.

CARIBBEAN ART

see Art, Caribbean

CARIBBEAN COOKING

see Cooking, Caribbean

CARIBBEAN DRAMA

Dawes, Kwame & Stephenson, Olivier H. P. Visions & Voices: Conversations with Fourteen Caribbean - Playwrights. Dawes, Kwame, ed. 2012. (ENG.). 400p. pap. 39.95 (978-1-84523-173-6(2)) Peepal Tree Pr., Ltd. GBR. Dist: Independent Pubs. Group.

Marzette, DeLinda. Africana Women Writers: Performing Diaspora, Staging Healing. 2012. **(978-1-4331-1380-2(5))** Lang, Peter Publishing, Inc.

CARIBBEAN ISLANDS

see West Indies

CARIBBEAN LITERATURE

Charles, Delpha. A Caribbean Accent to Shakespeare's Voice. 2012. 21.95 **(978-0-7414-7216-8(3))**; pap. 19.95 **(978-0-7414-7215-1(5))** Infinity Publishing.

Dabydeen, Cyril, ed. Beyond Sangre Grande: Caribbean Writing Today. 2011. (ENG.). 200p. pap. 28.95 (978-1-894770-66-8(8)) TSAR Pubns. CAN. Dist: Univ. of Toronto Pr.

D'Costa, Jean & Lalla, Barbara, eds. Voices in Exile: Jamaican Texts of the 18th & 19th Centuries. 2nd ed. 2009. (ENG.). 176p. pap. 22.00 (978-0-8173-5566-1(9)) Univ. of Alabama Pr.

Debrot, Cola, et al. Founding Fictions of the Dutch Caribbean: Cola Debrot's "My Black Sister" & Boeli Van Leeuwen's "A Stranger on Earth" 2007. 168p. (C). pap. 29.95 (978-0-8204-8819-6(4)) Lang, Peter Publishing, Inc.

Donnell, Alison & Bucknor, Michael Andrew, eds. The Routledge Companion to Caribbean Literature in English. 2011. (Routledge Literature Companions Ser.). (ENG.). 704p. 185.00 (978-0-415-48577-7(0)) Routledge.

Dur_n, V'ctor Manuel. An Anthology of Belizean Literature: English, Creole, Spanish, Garifuna. 2007. (CRP, CAI, SPA & ENG.). 140p. 56.99 (978-0-7618-3725-1(6)) Univ. Pr. of America, Inc.

Glave, Thomas, ed. Our Caribbean: A Gathering of Lesbian & Gay Writing from the Antilles. 2008. (ENG.). 416p. 94.95 (978-0-8223-4208-3(1)) Duke Univ. Pr.

Glave, Thomas, ed. & contrib. by. Our Caribbean: A Gathering of Lesbian & Gay Writing from the Antilles. 2008. (ENG.). 416p. pap. 26.95 (978-0-8223-4226-7(X)) Duke Univ. Pr.

Hewitt. Voices Out of Africa in Twentieth Century. 2009. (Illus.). 402p. 80.00 (978-0-8387-5729-1(4)) Bucknell Univ. Pr.

Hopkins, David & Martindale, Charles, eds. The Oxford History of Classical Reception in English Literature: Volume 3 (1660-1790) 2012. (Oxford History of Classical Reception in English Literature Ser.). (ENG.). 776p. 185.00 **(978-0-19-921981-0(8))** Oxford Univ. Pr., Inc.

Irele, Abiola. The Négritude Moment: Explorations in Francophone African & Caribbean Literature & Thought. 2010. 256p. pap. (978-1-59221-798-4(2)) Africa World Pr.

McGarrell, Shirley. The Debate about the Teaching of Literature. 2010. 236p. pap. (978-3-639-24511-0(3)) VDM Verlag Dr. Mueller e.K.

Plasa, Carl. Slaves to Sweetness: British & Caribbean Literatures of Sugar. 2012. (Liverpool University Press - Studies in European Regional Cultures Ser.). (ENG.). 256p. pap. 39.95 **(978-1-84631-749-1(5))** Liverpool Univ. Pr. GBR. Dist: Chicago Distribution Ctr.

Schwarz, Bill, ed. Caribbean Literature after Independence: The Case of Earl Lovelace. 2008. (ENG.). 220p. pap. 30.00 (978-1-900039-91-8(5)) Institute of Latin American Studies GBR. Dist: Brookings Institution Pr.

Weir-Soley, Donna & Adisa, Opal Palmer, eds. Caribbean Erotic: Poetry, Prose & Essays. 2011. (ENG.). 256p. pap. 22.95 (978-1-84523-089-0(2)) Peepal Tree Pr., Ltd. GBR. Dist: Independent Pubs. Group.

CARIBBEAN LITERATURE—HISTORY AND CRITICISM

Accilien, Cecile. Rethinking Marriage in Francophone African & Caribbean Literatures. 2008. (After the Empire: the Francophone World & Postcolonial France Ser.). (ENG.). 206p. pap. 28.50 (978-0-7391-1658-6(4)); 202p. 68.50 (978-0-7391-1657-9(6)) Lexington Bks.

Accilien, Cécile, et al, eds. Just below South: Intercultural Performance in the Caribbean & the U. S. South. 2007. (New World Studies). (ENG.). 288p. (C). (gr. 13-17). per. 22.50 (978-0-8139-2600-1(9)); (gr. 17). 59.50 (978-0-8139-2599-8(1)) Univ. Pr. of Virginia.

Alcocer, Rudyard J. Time Travel in the Latin American & Caribbean Imagination: Re-reading History. 2011. (ENG., Illus.). 254p. 85.00 (978-0-230-11798-3(8)) Palgrave Macmillan.

Anim-Addo, Joan. Touching the Body: African Caribbean Women's Writing. 2007. (Illus.). 356p. pap. 37.99 (978-1-902294-23-0(8)) Mango Publishing GBR. Dist: SPD-Small Pr. Distribution.

Antoine, Régis. Rayonnants écrivains de la Caraïbe: Haïti, Guadeloupe, Martinique, Guyane: Anthologie et Analyses. (FRE.). 292p. (978-2-7068-1333-7(4)) Maisonneuve et Larose.

Arthur, Kevyn, ed. Caribbean Treasure Vol. 1: A Trove of 18th Century Barbadian Poetry & Prose. 2009. (ENG.). 300p. pap. 39.95 (978-1-84523-010-4(8)) Peepal Tree Pr., Ltd. GBR. Dist: Independent Pubs. Group.

—Caribbean Treasure Vol. 2: A Trove of 18th-Century Barbadian Poetry & Prose-From the Barbados Gazette & the Barbados Mercury, 1783-1789. 2012. 400p. pap. 39.95 (978-1-84523-011-1(6)) Peepal Tree Pr., Ltd. GBR. Dist: Independent Pubs. Group.

Birbalsingh, Frank. Passion & Exile: Essays in Caribbean Literature. 260p. 7.95 (978-1-870518-16-1(0)) Penguin Group (USA) Inc.

Bragard, Véronique. Transoceanic Dialogues: Coolitude in Caribbean & Indian Ocean Literatures. 2008. 282p. 45.95 (978-90-5201-418-0(3)) PIE - Peter Lang BEL. Dist: Lang, Peter.

Brathwaite, Kamau. LX Vol. 1: The Love Axe/L - Developing a Caribbean Aesthetic. 2011. 280p. pap. 39.95 (978-1-84523-175-0(9)) Peepal Tree Pr., Ltd. GBR. Dist: Independent Pubs. Group.

—LX Vol. 2: The Love Axe/L - Notes & Commentary. 2011. 330p. pap. 39.95 (978-1-84523-176-7(7)) Peepal Tree Pr., Ltd. GBR. Dist: Independent Pubs. Group.

Britton, Celia. The Sense of Community in French Caribbean Fiction. (Liverpool University Press - Contemporary French & Francophone Cultures Ser.). (ENG.). 256p. 2011. pap. 32.95 (978-1-84631-500-8(X)) 2009. 85.00 (978-1-84631-137-6(3)) Liverpool Univ. Pr. GBR. Dist: Chicago Distribution Ctr.

Campbell, Kofi Omoniyi Sylvanus & Campbell, Kofi. Literature & Culture in the Black Atlantic: From Pre-To Postcolonial. 2006. (ENG.). 208p. 84.00 (978-1-4039-7223-1(0)) Palgrave Macmillan.

Cancel, Robert & Woodhull, Winifred. African Diasporas: Ancestors, Migrations & Borders. 2008. (978-1-59221-648-2(X)); pap. (978-1-59221-649-9(8)) Africa World Pr.

Cañete Quesada, Carmen. El Exilio Español Ante Los Programas de la Identidad Cultural en el Caribe Insular (1934-1956) 2011. (Ediciones de Iberoamericana Ser.). pap. 29.80 **(978-84-8489-573-2(4))** Iberoamericana Vervuert Publishing Corp.

Casteel, Sarah Phillips. Second Arrivals: Landscape & Belonging in Contemporary Writing of the Americas. 2007. (New World Studies). (ENG.). 272p. (gr. 17). 59.50 (978-0-8139-2638-4(6)); (Illus.). per. 22.50 (978-0-8139-2639-1(4)) Univ. Pr. of Virginia.

Cesaire, Suzanne. The Great Camouflage: Writings of Dissent (1941-1945) Maximin, Daniel, ed. Walker, Keith L., tr. from FRE. & contrib. by. by. 2012. (ENG & FRE., Illus.). 156p. (C). 60.00 **(978-0-8195-7088-8(5))**; pap. 18.95 **(978-0-8195-7275-2(6))** Wesleyan Univ. Pr.

Costello, Kathleen. The Composition of Culture. 2008. 104p. pap. (978-3-639-08593-8(0)) VDM Verlag Dr. Mueller e.K.

Cox, Juanita, ed. In the Eye of the Storm: Edgar Mittelholzer, 1909-2009 - Critical Perspectives. 2012. 352p. pap. 35.95 (978-1-84523-128-6(7)) Peepal Tree Pr., Ltd. GBR. Dist: Independent Pubs. Group.

Dalleo, Raphael. Caribbean Literature & the Public Sphere: From the Plantation to the Postcolonial. 2011. xv, 296p. E-Book **(978-0-8139-3202-6(5))**; (ENG., Illus.). 320p. (C). (gr. 13-17). pap. 29.50 **(978-0-8139-3199-9(1))**; (ENG., Illus.). 320p. (gr. 17). 59.50 **(978-0-8139-3198-2(3))** Univ. Pr. of Virginia.

Dance, Daryl C. New World Adams: Interviews with West Indian Writers. 2nd ed. 2008. (ENG., Illus.). 366p. pap. 29.95 (978-1-900715-04-1(X)) Peepal Tree Pr., Ltd. GBR. Dist: Independent Pubs. Group.

Dawes, Neville. Fugue & Other Writings. 2011. 230p. pap. 22.95 (978-1-84523-109-5(0)) Peepal Tree Pr., Ltd. GBR. Dist: Independent Pubs. Group.

De Ferrari, Guillermina. Vulnerable States: Bodies of Memory in Contemporary Caribbean Fiction. 2007. (New World Studies). (ENG.). 272p. (gr. 17). 69.50 (978-0-8139-2646-9(7)); per. 24.50 (978-0-8139-2647-6(5)) Univ. Pr. of Virginia.

Deena, Seodial Frank H. Situating Caribbean Literature & Criticism in Multicultural & Postcolonial Studies. 2008. (Caribbean Studies). 72.95 (978-0-8204-6222-6(5)) Lang, Peter Publishing, Inc.

Deloughrey, Elizabeth M. Routes & Roots: Navigating Caribbean & Pacific Island Literatures. 2007. (Illus.). 334p. 51.00 (978-0-8248-3122-6(5)) Univ. of Hawaii Pr.

D'Hulst, L., et al. Caribbean Interfaces. 2007. 372p. (C). per. 100.00 (978-90-420-2184-6(5)) Rodopi.

Dieke, Ikenna. Allegory & Meaning: Reading African, African American, & Caribbean Literature. 2010. (ENG.). 188p. pap. 28.00 (978-0-7618-5121-9(6)) Univ. Pr. of America, Inc.

Donnell, Alison. Una Marson & Louise Bennett. (Writers & Their Work Ser.). (ENG.). (C). 2012. pap. 26.00 (978-0-7463-0990-2(2)) 2011. 80.00 (978-0-7463-1073-1(0)) Northcote Hse. Publishers, Ltd. GBR. Dist: Brown, David Bk. Co., The.

Doring, Tobias. Caribbean-English Passages: Intertexuality in a Postcolonial Tradition. 2006. (Routledge Research in Postcolonial Literatures Ser.). 256p. 34.00 (978-0-415-41856-0(9)) Routledge.

Edmondson, Belinda. Caribbean Middlebrow: Leisure Culture & the Middle Class. 2009. (Illus.). 232p. 45.00 (978-0-8014-4814-0(X)) Cornell Univ. Pr.

Emery, Mary Lou. Modernism, the Visual, & Caribbean Literature. (ENG., Illus.). 304p. 2009. pap. 42.00 (978-0-521-11709-8(7)) 2007. 110.00 (978-0-521-87213-3(8)) Cambridge Univ. Pr.

Ferly, Odile. A Poetics of Relation: Caribbean Women Writing at the Millennium. 2012. (ENG., Illus.). 222p. 85.00 **(978-0-230-12044-0(X))** Palgrave Macmillan.

Francis, Donette. Fictions of Feminine Citizenship: Sexuality & the Nation in Contemporary Caribbean Literature. 2010. (ENG.). 200p. 84.00 (978-0-230-61987-6(8)) Palgrave Macmillan.

François, Anne M. Rewriting the Return of Africa: Voices of Francophone Caribbean Women Writers. 2011. (ENG.). 146p. 60.00 (978-0-7391-4826-6(5)) Lexington Bks.

François, Anne M. Rewriting the Return to Africa: Voices of Francophone Caribbean Women Writers. 2011. xxxiii, 111p. E-Book **(978-0-7391-4828-0(1))** Lexington Bks.

Frindéthié, K. Martial. The Black Renaissance in Francophone African & Caribbean Literatures. 2008. (ENG., Illus.). 215p. pap. 39.95 (978-0-7864-3663-7(8)) McFarland & Co., Inc. Pubs.

Fumagalli, Maria Cristina. Caribbean Perspectives on Modernity: Returning Medusa's Gaze. 2009. (New World Studies). (ENG., Illus.). 216p. (C). (gr. 13-17). pap. 22.50 (978-0-8139-2858-6(3)); (gr. 17). 59.50 (978-0-8139-2857-9(5)) Univ. Pr. of Virginia.

Glaser, Marlies & Pausch, Marioan, eds. Caribbean Writers: Between Orality & Writing. 2009. 250p. 63.00 (978-90-5183-735-3(6)) Rodopi.

Glover, Kaiama L. Haiti Unbound: A Spiralist Challenge to the Postcolonial Canon. 2011. (Liverpool University Press - Contemporary French & Francophone Cultures Ser.). (ENG.). 262p. 95.00 (978-1-84631-499-5(2)) Liverpool Univ. Pr. GBR. Dist: Chicago Distribution Ctr.

Goldman, Dara E. Out of Bounds: Islands & the Demarcation of Identity in the Hispanic Caribbean. 2008. (Bucknell Studies in Latin American Literature & Theory). (Illus.). 249p. 52.50 (978-0-8387-5677-5(8)) Bucknell Univ. Pr.

Goluch, Dorota. I Rather Dead: A Spivakian Reading of Indo-Caribbean Women's Narratives. 2011. 108p. 39.95 (978-93-80905-03-7(3)) ROMAN Bks. IND. Dist: Lightning Source, Inc.

González, Ann. Resistance & Survival: Children's Narrative from Central America & the Caribbean. 2009. (ENG., Illus.). 196p. 45.00 (978-0-8165-2824-0(1)) Univ. of Arizona Pr.

Halloran, Vivian Nun. Exhibiting Slavery: The Caribbean Postmodern Novel as Museum. 2009. (New World Studies). (ENG.). 224p. (C). (gr. 13-17). pap. 21.50 (978-0-8139-2866-1(4)); (Illus.). (gr. 17). 55.00 (978-0-8139-2865-4(6)) Univ. Pr. of Virginia.

Heady, Margaret. Marvelous Journeys: Routes of Identity in the Caribbean Novel. 2008. (Caribbean Studies). (C). 59.95 (978-0-8204-7610-0(2)) Lang, Peter Publishing, Inc.

Henke, Holger. Constructing Vernacular Culture in the Trans-Caribbean. 2007. (Caribbean Studies). (ENG.). 432p. 94.50 (978-0-7391-2160-3(X)) Lexington Bks.

Henke, Holger & Magister, Karl-Heinz. Constructing Vernacular Culture in the Trans-Caribbean. 2007. (Caribbean Studies (Lexington Books) Ser.). (ENG.). 432p. per. 47.50 (978-0-7391-2161-0(8)) Lexington Bks.

Henke/Magister, ed. Constructing Vernacular Culturcb. 2007. 432p. 90.00 (978-0-7391-2060-6(3)) Lexington Bks.

Johnson, Erica L. Caribbean Ghostwriting. 2009. 152p. 43.00 (978-0-8386-4222-1(5)) Fairleigh Dickinson Univ. Pr.

Jurney, Florence Ramond. Representations of the Island of Caribbean Literature: Caribbean Women Redefine Their Homelands. 2009. 228p. 109.95 (978-0-7734-4909-1(4)) Mellen, Edwin Pr., The.

Karem, Jeff. The Purloined Island: Caribbean-U. S. Crosscurrents in Literature & Culture, 1880-1959. 2011. (New World Studies). (ENG., Illus.). 320p. (gr. 17). 69.50 (978-0-8139-3086-2(3)) Univ. Pr. of Virginia.

—The Purloined Islands: Caribbean-U. S, Crosscurrents in Literature & Culture, 1880-1959. 2011. (New World Studies). (ENG., Illus.). 320p. (C). (gr. 13-17). pap. 35.00 (978-0-8139-3087-9(1)) Univ. Pr. of Virginia.

Kaussen, Valerie. Migrant Revolutions: Haitian Literature, Globalization, & U. S. Imperialism. 2007. (After the Empire: The Francophone World & Postcolonial France Ser.). (ENG.). 290p. 78.99 (978-0-7391-1636-4(3)) Rowman & Littlefield Publishers, Inc.

King-Aribisala, Karen. The Hangman's Game. 2007. (ENG.). 220p. per. 19.95 (978-1-84523-046-3(9)) Peepal Tree Pr., Ltd. GBR. Dist: Independent Pubs. Group.

Knepper, Wendy. Patrick Chamoiseau: A Critical Introduction. 2012. (Caribbean Studies Ser.). (ENG.). 256p. 55.00 **(978-1-61703-154-0(2))** Univ. Pr. of Mississippi.

Lamming, George & University of the West Indies (Mona, Jamaica), Centre for Caribbean Thought Staff. Sovereignty of the Imagination: Conversations III. 2009. 82p. pap. 15.00 (978-0-913441-46-6(5)) House of Nehesi Pubs. ANT. Dist: SPD-Small Pr. Distribution.

Larrier, Renee. Autofiction & Advocacy in the Francophone Caribbean. 2006. (ENG.). 200p. 59.95 (978-0-8130-3005-0(6)) Univ. Pr. of Florida.

Lee-Loy, Anne-Marie. Searching for Mr. Chin: Constructions of Nation & the Chinese in West Indian Literature. 2010. (ENG.). 198p. 42.00 (978-1-4399-0130-4(9)) Temple Univ. Pr.

Lewis, Shireen K. Race, Culture, & Identity: Francophone West African & Caribbean Literature & Theory from Negritude to Creolite. 2006. (Caribbean Studies (Lexington Books) Ser.). (ENG.). 188p. per. 27.50 (978-0-7391-1473-5(5)) Lexington Bks.

Loichot, Valérie. Orphan Narratives: The Postplantation Literature of Faulkner, Glissant, Morrison, & Saint-John Perse. 2007. (New World Studies). (ENG., Illus.). 256p. (C). (gr. 13-17). per. 19.50 (978-0-8139-2641-4(6)) Univ. Pr. of Virginia.

Luis, William. Las Vanguardias Literarias en el Caribe: Cuba, Puerto Rico y República Dominicana. 2010. (Bibliografía y Antología Crítica de las Vanguardias en el Mundo Ibérico Ser.). pap. 44.00 **(978-84-8489-564-0(5))** Iberoamericana Vervuert Publishing Corp.

Mackey, Nathaniel. Discrepant Engagement: Dissonance, Cross-Culturality & Experimental Writing. 2009. (Cambridge Studies in American Literature & Culture Ser.). (ENG.). 328p. pap. 42.00 (978-0-521-10999-4(X)) Cambridge Univ. Pr.

Malouf, Michael G. Transatlantic Solidarities: Irish Nationalism & Caribbean Poetics. 2009. (New World Studies). (ENG., Illus.). 272p. (C). (gr. 13-17). pap. 22.50 (978-0-8139-2780-0(3)); (gr. 17). 55.00 (978-0-8139-2779-4(X)) Univ. Pr. of Virginia.

Márquez, Robert. A World among These Islands: Essays on Literature, Race, & National Identity in Antillean America. 2010. 272p. (978-1-55849-850-1(8)) Univ. of Massachusetts Pr.

Marquez, Roberto. World among These Islands. 2010. 272p. pap. 26.95 (978-1-55849-851-8(6)) Univ. of Massachusetts Pr.

M'Baye, Babacar. The Trickster Comes West: Pan-African Influence in Early Black Diasporan Narratives. (ENG.). 272p. 2011. pap. 30.00 **(978-1-61703-210-3(7))** 2009. 50.00 (978-1-60473-233-7(4)) Univ. Pr. of Mississippi.

McCleod, Corinna. Mapmaker: Kwame Dawes & the Caribbean Literary Aesthetic. 2012. 272p. pap. 32.95 (978-1-84523-162-0(7)) Peepal Tree Pr., Ltd. GBR. Dist: Independent Pubs. Group.

McCusker, Maeve. Patrick Chamoiseau: Recovering Memory. 2007. (Liverpool University Press - Contemporary French & Francophone Cultures Ser.). (ENG.). 256p. 80.00 (978-1-84631-048-5(2)) Liverpool Univ. Pr. GBR. Dist: Chicago Distribution Ctr.

McGarrity, Maria. Washed by the Gulf Stream: The Historic & Geographic Relation of Irish & Caribbean Literature. 2008. (Illus.). 196p. 40.00 (978-0-87413-028-7(X)) Univ. of Delaware Pr.

Mehta, Brinda. Notions of Identity, Diaspora, & Gender in Caribbean Women's Writing. 2009. (ENG.). 242p. 89.00 (978-0-230-61881-7(2)) Palgrave Macmillan.

Melas, Natalie. All the Difference in the World: Postcoloniality & the Ends of Comparison. 2006. (Cultural Memory in the Present Ser.). (ENG.). 304p. 57.00 (978-0-8047-3197-3(7)); per. 22.95 (978-0-8047-3198-0(5)) Stanford Univ. Pr.

Miller, Paul B. Elusive Origins: The Enlightenment in the Modern Caribbean Historical Imagination. 2010. (New World Studies). (ENG.). 248p. (C). (gr. 13-17). pap. 21.50 (978-0-8139-2980-4(6)); (Illus.). (gr. 17). 49.50 (978-0-8139-2979-8(2)) Univ. Pr. of Virginia.

Mortimer, Mildred. Writing from the Hearth: Public, Domestic, & Imaginative Space in Francophone Women's Fiction of Africa & the Caribbean. 2007. (After the Empire: The Francophone World & Postcolonial France Ser.). (ENG.). 224p. per. 31.50 (978-0-7391-1907-5(9)) Lexington Bks.

Mortimer, Mildred P. Writing from the Hearth: Public, Domestic, & Imaginative Space in Francophone Women's Fiction of Africa & the Caribbean. 2007. (After the Empire: The Francophone World & Postcolonial France Ser.). (ENG.). 224p. 78.99 (978-0-7391-1906-8(0)) Lexington Bks.

Mukundi, Paul M. Preventing Things from Falling Further Apart: The Preservation of Cultural Identities in Postcolonial African, Indian, & Caribbean Literatures. 2010. 204p. pap. (978-1-906704-71-1(6)) Adonis & Abbey Publishers Ltd.

—Preventing Things from Falling Further Apart: The Preservation of Cultural Identities in Postcolonial African, Indian, & Caribbean Literatures (HB) 2010. 204p. (978-1-906704-70-4(8)) Adonis & Abbey Publishers Ltd.

Murdoch, H. Adlai. Creole Identity in the French Caribbean Novel. 2009. (ENG.). 320p. (C). pap. 29.50 (978-1-61610-127-5(X)) Orange Grove Bks.

Murdoch, H. Adlai. Creolizing the Metropole: Migrant Caribbean Identities in Literature & Film. 2012. (Blacks in the Diaspora Ser.). (ENG., Illus.). 408p. 80.00 **(978-0-253-00118-4(8)**, 0253001188); pap. 30.00 **(978-0-253-00120-7(X)**, 025300120X) Indiana Univ. Pr.

Niblett, Michael. The Caribbean Novel since 1945: Cultural Practice, Form, & the Nation-State. 2012. (Caribbean Studies Ser.). (ENG.). 304p. 60.00 **(978-1-61703-247-9(6))** Univ. Pr. of Mississippi.

Niblett, Michael & Oloff, Kerstin, eds. Perspectives on the 'Other America' Comparative Approaches to Caribbean & Latin American Culture. 2009. (Illus.). 272p. pap. 78.00 (978-90-420-2704-6(5)) Rodopi.

Noland, Carrie & Watten, Barrett, eds. Diasporic Avant-Gardes: Experimental Poetics & Cultural Displacement. 2009. (ENG., Illus.). 288p. 100.00 *(978-0-230-61629-5(1))* Palgrave Macmillan.

Olliz-Boyd, Antonio. The Latin American Identity & the African Diaspora: Ethnogenesis in Context. 2010. *(978-1-60497-704-2(3))* Cambria Pr.

Opoku-Agyemang, Naana Jane, et al. Africa & Trans-Atlantic Memories: Literary & Aesthetic Manifestations of Diaspora & History. 2008. 496p. *(978-1-59221-633-8(1))*; pap. *(978-1-59221-632-1(3))* Africa World Pr.

Ossers Cabrera, Manuel Augusto & Buckley, Milagros Montiel de. La Expresividad en la Cuentística de Juan Bosch: Análisis Estilístico: Expressiveness in Juan Bosch's Short Stories: A Stylistic Analysis. 2010. 356p. 119.00 *(978-0-7734-1382-5(0))* Mellen, Edwin Pr., The.

Page, Kezia. Transnational Negotiations in Caribbean Diasporic Literature: Remitting the Text. 2010. (Routledge Research in Postcolonial Literatures Ser.). (ENG.). 168p. (C). 125.00 *(978-0-415-87362-8(2))* Routledge.

Paravisini-Gebert, Lizabeth. Literature of the Caribbean, 1 vol. 2008. (Literature as Windows to World Cultures Ser.). 256p. 49.95 *(978-0-313-32845-9(5)*, GR2845, Greenwood Pr.) Greenwood Publishing Group, Inc.

Patteson, Richard F. The Fiction of Robert Antoni: Writing in the Estuary. 2010. 221p. pap. *(978-976-640-229-7(9))* Univ. of the West Indies Pr.

Pearson, Nels & Singer, Marc. Detective Fiction in a Postcolonial & Transnational World. 2009. 224p. 99.95 *(978-0-7546-6848-0(7))* Ashgate Publishing Co.

Peyma, Nasser Dasht. Postcolonial Drama: A Comparative Study of Wole Soyinka, Derek Walcott & Girish Kamad. 2009. 258p. 45.00 *(978-81-316-0282-9(6))* Rawat Pubns. IND. Dist: International Specialized Bk. Services.

Pirbhai, Mariam & Mahabir, Joy, eds. Critical Perspectives on Indo-Caribbean Womens Literature. 2012. (Routledge Research in Postcolonial Literatures Ser.). (ENG.). 228p. (C). 125.00 ***(978-0-415-50967-1(X))*** Routledge.

Plasa, Carl. Slaves to Sweetness: British & Caribbean Literatures of Sugar. 2009. (Liverpool University Press - Studies in European Regional Cultures Ser.). (ENG.). 192p. 95.00 *(978-1-84631-184-0(5))* Liverpool Univ. Pr. GBR. Dist: Chicago Distribution Ctr.

Ramchand & Salick, Roydon. Samuel Selvon. 2012. (Writers & Their Work Ser.). (ENG.). 120p. (C). 80.00 *(978-0-7463-1089-2(7))* Northcote Hse. Publishers, Ltd. GBR. Dist: Brown, David Bk. Co., The.

Ramchand, Kenneth & Salick, Roydon. Sam Selvon. 2012. (Writers & Their Work Ser.). (ENG.). 120p. (C). pap. 26.00 *(978-0-7463-0974-2(0))* Northcote Hse. Publishers, Ltd. GBR. Dist: Brown, David Bk. Co., The.

Reiss, Timothy J., ed. Music, Writing, & Cultural Unity in the Caribbean. 540p. 109.95 *(978-1-59221-176-0(3))* Africa World Pr.

Rosell, Sara. La Novela de Escritoras Dominicanas de 1990 a 2007. 2007. (SPA.). 180p. *(978-0-7734-5359-3(8))* Mellen, Edwin Pr., The.

Russ, Elizabeth Christine. The Plantation in the Postslavery Imagination. 2009. (Imagining the Americas Ser.). (ENG.). 224p. 65.00 *(978-0-19-537715-6(X))* Oxford Univ. Pr., Inc.

Russell, Heather. Legba's Crossing: Narratology in the African Atlantic. (ENG.). 216p. 2011. pap. 24.95 *(978-0-8203-3879-8(6))* 2009. 44.95 *(978-0-8203-2867-6(7))* Univ. of Georgia Pr.

Sandiford, Keith. Theorizing A Colonial Caribbean-Atlantic Imaginary. 2010. (ENG., Illus.). 204p. (C). 125.00 *(978-0-415-87689-6(3))* Routledge.

Santiago-Díaz, Eleuterio. Escritura Afropuertorriqueña y Modernidad. 2007. (Serie Nuevo Siglo Ser.). (SPA.). 269p. *(978-1-930744-30-1(7))* Instituto Internacional de Literatura Iberoamericana (IILI).

Saunders, Patricia Joan. Alien-Nation & Repatriation: Translating Identity in Anglophone Caribbean Literature. 2007. (Caribbean Studies (Lexington Books) Ser.). (ENG.). 212p. 68.50 *(978-0-7391-1469-8(7))*; per. 31.50 *(978-0-7391-1470-4(0))* Lexington Bks.

Smith, Faith. Sex & the Citizen: Interrogating the Caribbean. 2011. (New World Studies). (ENG., Illus.). 304p. (C). (gr. 13-17). pap. 35.00 *(978-0-8139-3113-5(4))*; (gr. 17). 69.50 *(978-0-8139-3112-8(6))* Univ. Pr. of Virginia.

Tagirova-Daley, Tatiana A. Claude McKay's Liberating Narrative: Russian & Anglophone Caribbean Literary Connection. 2012. 156p. (C). 70.95 ***(978-1-4331-1820-3(3))*** Lang, Peter Publishing, Inc.

Thébia-Melsan, Annick & Aliker, Pierre. Aimé Césaire, le Legs: "Nous Sommes de Ceux Qui Disent Non à L'ombre" 2009. (FRE., Illus.). 474p. *(978-2-915978-52-0(2))* Argol Editions.

Thomas, Bonnie. Breadfruit or Chestnut? Gender Construction in the French Caribbean Novel. (After the Empire: The Francophone World & Postcolonial France Ser.). (ENG.). 212p. 2007. per. 34.99 *(978-0-7391-1584-8(7))* 2006. 62.99 *(978-0-7391-1583-1(9))* Lexington Bks.

Tinsley, Omise'eke Natasha. Thiefing Sugar: Eroticism Between Women in Caribbean Literature. 2010. (Perverse Modernities Ser.). (ENG., Illus.). 288p. 84.95 *(978-0-8223-4756-9(3))*; pap. 23.95 *(978-0-8223-4777-4(6))* Duke Univ. Pr.

Torres, Benjamin. Para Llegar a la Isla Verde. 2007. (SPA.). 288p. pap. 13.95 *(978-0-8477-3192-3(8))* Univ. of Puerto Rico Pr.

Vásquez, Sam. Humor in the Caribbean Literary Canon. 2012. (New Caribbean Studies). (ENG.). 224p. 85.00 ***(978-1-137-01028-5(2))*** Palgrave Macmillan.

Watson, Tim. Caribbean Culture & British Fiction in the Atlantic World, 1780-1870. (Cambridge Studies in Nineteenth-Century Literature & Culture Ser.). (ENG., Illus.). 2011. 286p. pap. 36.99 *(978-0-521-18871-5(7))* 2008. 288p. 90.00 *(978-0-521-87626-1(5))* Cambridge Univ. Pr.

Wilson, Lucy. In Due Season: Essays on Novels of Development by Caribbean Women Writers. 2008. (ENG.). 100p. pap. 26.50 *(978-0-7618-4112-8(1))* Univ. Pr. of America, Inc.

Winks, Christopher. Symbolic Cities in Caribbean Literature. 2009. (ENG.). 212p. 89.00 *(978-0-230-61218-1(0))* Palgrave Macmillan.

Zahoor, Asiya. Diaspora & the Caribbean Aesthetics. 2011. 104p. pap. ***(978-3-8383-7771-1(0))*** Lambert Academic Publishing.

CARIBBEAN LITERATURE—WOMEN AUTHORS

Anim-Addo, Joan. Touching the Body: African Caribbean Women's Writing. 2007. (Illus.). 356p. pap. 37.99 *(978-1-902294-23-0(8))* Mango Publishing GBR. Dist: SPD-Small Pr. Distribution.

Covi, Giovanna. Modernist Women Race Nation: Networking Women 1890-1950 Circum-Atlantic Connections. 2006. (Illus.). 214p. pap. 29.99 *(978-1-902294-29-2(7))*, Mango Publishing GBR. Dist: SPD-Small Pr. Distribution.

Ferly, Odile. A Poetics of Relation: Caribbean Women Writing at the Millennium. 2012. (ENG., Illus.). 222p. 85.00 ***(978-0-230-12044-0(X))*** Palgrave Macmillan.

Francis, Donette. Fictions of Feminine Citizenship: Sexuality & the Nation in Contemporary Caribbean Literature. 2010. (ENG.). 200p. 84.00 *(978-0-230-61987-6(8))* Palgrave Macmillan.

François, Anne M. Rewriting the Return to Africa: Voices of Francophone Caribbean Women Writers. 2011. xxxiii, 111p. E-Book ***(978-0-7391-4828-0(1))*** Lexington Bks.

Jurney, Florence Ramond. Representations of the Island of Caribbean Literature: Caribbean Women Redefine Their Homelands. 2009. 228p. 109.95 *(978-0-7734-4909-1(4))* Mellen, Edwin Pr., The.

Ligon, Alison D. Traversing Caribbean Thresholds: Coming of Age Stories in Selected Works of Anglophone Fiction. 2009. *(978-1-4331-0629-3(9))* Lang, Peter Publishing, Inc.

Mehta, Brinda. Notions of Identity, Diaspora, & Gender in Caribbean Women's Writing. 2009. (ENG.). 242p. 89.00 *(978-0-230-61881-7(2))* Palgrave Macmillan.

Mortimer, Mildred. Writing from the Hearth: Public, Domestic, & Imaginative Space in Francophone Women's Fiction of Africa & the Caribbean. 2007. (After the Empire: The Francophone World & Postcolonial France Ser.). (ENG.). 224p. per. 31.50 *(978-0-7391-1907-5(9))* Lexington Bks.

Mortimer, Mildred P. Writing from the Hearth: Public, Domestic, & Imaginative Space in Francophone Women's Fiction of Africa & the Caribbean. 2007. (After the Empire: The Francophone World & Postcolonial France Ser.). (ENG.). 224p. 78.99 *(978-0-7391-1906-8(0))* Lexington Bks.

Ngue, Julie Nack. Critical Conditions: Reading Illness & Disability in Francophone African & Caribbean Women's Writing. 2011. (ENG.). 208p. (gr. 17). 60.00 ***(978-0-7391-5114-3(2))*** Lexington Bks.

Pirbhai, Mariam & Mahabir, Joy, eds. Critical Perspectives on Indo-Caribbean Womens Literature. 2012. (Routledge Research in Postcolonial Literatures Ser.). (ENG.). 228p. (C). 125.00 ***(978-0-415-50967-1(X))*** Routledge.

Ramirez, Dolores Alcaide. Violencia, Género y Migración en el Caribe Hispano: Reescribiendo la Nación. 2011. (Caribbean Studies). (Illus.). 220p. (C). 77.95 ***(978-1-4331-1546-2(8))*** Lang, Peter Publishing, Inc.

Rosell, Sara. La Novela de Escritoras Dominicanas de 1990 a 2007. 2007. (SPA.). 180p. *(978-0-7734-5359-3(8))* Mellen, Edwin Pr., The.

Scott, Helen. Caribbean Women Writers & Globalization: Fictions of Independence. 2006. (Illus.). 202p. 110.00 *(978-0-7546-5134-5(7))* Ashgate Publishing Co.

Wilson, Lucy. In Due Season: Essays on Novels of Development by Caribbean Women Writers. 2008. (ENG.). 100p. pap. 26.50 *(978-0-7618-4112-8(1))* Univ. Pr. of America, Inc.

CARIBBEAN POETRY

Brown, Stewart, et al. The Oxford Book of Caribbean Verse. 2nd ed. 2009. (Oxford Books of Prose & Verse Ser.). (ENG., Illus.). 448p. (Orig.). pap. 19.95 *(978-0-19-956159-9(1))* Oxford Univ. Pr., Inc.

Dawes, Kwame, ed. So Much Things to Say: 100 Poets from the First Ten Years of the Calabash International Literary Festival. 2010. (ENG.). 275p. pap. 16.95 *(978-1-936070-07-7(3))* Akashic Bks.

CARIBBEAN POETRY—HISTORY AND CRITICISM

Arthur, Kevyn, ed. Caribbean Treasure Vol. 1: A Trove of 18th Century Barbadian Poetry & Prose. 2009. (ENG.). 300p. pap. 39.95 *(978-1-84523-010-4(8))* Peepal Tree Pr., Ltd. GBR. Dist: Independent Pubs. Group.

—Caribbean Treasure Vol. 2: A Trove of 18th-Century Barbadian Poetry & Prose- From the Barbados Gazette & the Barbados Mercury, 1783-1789. 2012. 400p. pap. 39.95 *(978-1-84523-011-1(6))* Peepal Tree Pr., Ltd. GBR. Dist: Independent Pubs. Group.

Badiane, Mamadou. The Changing Face of Afro-Caribbean Cultural Identity: Negrismo & NZgritude. 2009. (ENG.). 198p. 68.50 *(978-0-7391-2553-3(2))* Lexington Bks.

Breiner, Laurence A. Black Yeats: Eric Roach & the Politics of Caribbean Poetry. 2008. (Peepal Tree Caribbean Poetry Ser.). (ENG.). 400p. pap. 34.95 *(978-1-84523-047-0(7))* Peepal Tree Pr., Ltd. GBR. Dist: Independent Pubs. Group.

Figueroa, Victor. Not at Home in One's Home: Caribbean Self-Fashioning in the Poetry of Luis Palés Matos, Aimé Césaire, & Derek Walcott. 2009. 239p. 51.50 *(978-0-8386-4177-4(6))* Fairleigh Dickinson Univ. Pr.

Griffith, Paul A. Afro-Caribbean Poetry & Ritual. 2010. (ENG.). 236p. 84.00 *(978-0-230-62364-4(6))* Palgrave Macmillan.

Hodges, Hugh. Soon Come: Jamaican Spirituality, Jamaican Poetics. 2008. (ENG.). 256p. (C). (gr. 13-17). pap. 21.50 *(978-0-8139-2683-4(1))*; (gr. 17). 59.50 *(978-0-8139-2682-7(3))* Univ. Pr. of Virginia.

Otto, Melanie. A Creole Experiment: Utopian Space in Kamau Brathwaite's Video-Style Works. 2009. *(978-1-59221-562-1(9))*; 329p. pap. *(978-1-59221-563-8(7))* Africa World Pr.

Patterson, Anita. Race, American Literature & Transnational Modernisms. 2011. (Cambridge Studies in American Literature & Culture Ser.). (ENG.). 248p. pap. 48.00 *(978-0-521-34956-7(7))* Cambridge Univ. Pr.

CARIBBEAN SEA

Blakeslee, George Hubbard. Mexico & the Caribbean. 2009. 256p. pap. *(978-0-217-23651-5(0))* Books LLC.

—Mexico & the Caribbean. 363p. reprint ed. 98.00 *(978-0-7222-9454-3(9))*; 98.00 *(978-0-7222-9498-7(0))* Library Reprints, Inc.

Blakeslee, George Hubbard, ed. Mexico & the Caribbean. 2008. 376p. pap. 33.95 *(978-1-4371-3201-4(4))* Kessinger Publishing, LLC.

Gambrill, Anthony. In Search of the Buccaneers. 2007. (Illus.). 258p. *(978-0-333-97652-4(5))* Macmillan Caribbean.

Kepner, Charles D. Social Aspects of the Banana Industry. (Columbia University, Studies in the Social Sciences: No. 414). reprint ed. 27.50 *(978-0-404-51414-3(6))* AMS Pr., Inc.

CARIBOU

see also Reindeer

Confer, Dennis. Hunt Alaska Now: Self-Guiding for Trophy Moose & Caribou. O'Loughlin, Diane & Russ, Tony, eds. 2006. (Illus.). 368p. per. 29.95 *(978-0-9741684-5-6(9))* Northern Publishing.

Georgeson, C. C. Reindeer & Caribou. (Shorey Historical Ser.). (Illus.). 24p. reprint ed. pap. 10.00 *(978-0-8466-0159-3(1)*, S159) Shorey's Bookstore.

Haugen, Scott. Hunting the Alaskan High Arctic: Big-Game Hunting for Grizzly, Dall Sheep, Moose, Caribou, & Polar Bear in the Arctic Circle. 2008. (ENG.). 240p. 34.95 *(978-1-57157-295-0(3))* Safari Pr., Inc.

Heuer, Karsten. Being Caribou: Five Months on Foot with an Arctic Herd. 2008. (World As Home Ser.). (ENG., Illus.). 240p. per. 15.00 *(978-1-57131-308-9(7))* Milkweed Editions.

Luttich, Stuart N. & Camps, Lodewijk. The Return of Caribou to Ungava. 2007. (McGill-Queen's Native & Northern Ser.). (ENG., Illus.). 656p. (C). *(978-0-7735-3233-5(1))* McGill-Queen's Univ. Pr.

Seton, Ernest Thompson. The Arctic Prairies. 2007. (ENG.). 198p. pap. 19.99 *(978-1-4264-5012-9(5))*; 218p. pap. 22.99 *(978-1-4264-5313-7(2))* BiblioBazaar.

CARICATURE

see also Caricatures and Cartoons; Cartooning; Grotesque; Parody; Wit and Humor

Eyre, Doug. Drawing Caricatures. 2007. (ENG., Illus.). 160p. pap. 37.95 *(978-1-86126-951-5(X))* Crowood Pr., Ltd. GBR. Dist: Independent Pubs. Group.

Humphreys, Eldon. Carving MacGolfers. (Illus.). 76p. *(978-0-9683448-8-0(7))* Chipping Away.

McLees, Ainslie Armstrong. Baudelaire's Argot Plastique: Poetic Caricature & Modernism. 2010. (ENG., Illus.). 216p. pap. 24.95 *(978-0-8203-3486-3(3))* Univ. of Georgia Pr.

Rauser, Amelia F. Caricature Unmasked: Irony, Authenticity, & Individualism in Eighteenth-Century English Prints. 2008. (ENG., Illus.). 60.00 *(978-1-61149-323-8(4))* Univ. of Delaware Pr.

Smith, Mitchell. The Art of Caricature. 2007. 96p. per. 9.95 *(978-1-4344-0140-3(5))* Wildside Pr., LLC.

—The Art of Caricaturing: Making Comics. 2007. 104p. per. *(978-956-291-531-1(X))* Editorial Benei Noaj.

CARICATURE—HISTORY

Bills, Mark. The Art of Satire: London in Caricature. 2006. (ENG., Illus.). 240p. 74.00 *(978-0-85667-613-0(6))* Wilson, Philip Pubs., Ltd. GBR. Dist: Macmillan.

Porterfield, Todd, ed. The Efflorescence of Caricature, 1715-1838. 2010. (Illus.). 240p. 99.95 *(978-0-7546-6591-5(7))* Ashgate Publishing Co.

Wright, Thomas. A History of Caricature & Grotesque in Literature & Art. 2010. 288p. pap. *(978-1-152-83309-8(X))* Books LLC.

—A History of Caricature & Grotesque in Literature & Art. 2007. (ENG.). 512p. per. 40.95 *(978-1-4304-8817-0(4))* Kessinger Publishing, LLC.

CARICATURES AND CARTOONS

see also Animated Films; Caricature; Cartooning; Comic Books, Strips, etc.; Mazarinades; Wit and Humor, Pictorial

also American Wit and Humor, Pictorial; English Wit and Humor, Pictorial; and similar headings

American Caricatures Pertaining to the Civil War. reprint ed. 150.00 *(978-0-7222-7988-5(4))* Library Reprints, Inc.

Arakawa, Hiromu. The Anime. Searleman, Eric, ed. 2006. (Fullmetal Alchemist Ser.). (ENG., Illus.). 96p. 19.99 *(978-1-4215-0766-8(8))* Viz Media.

Bacon, Peggy, et al. Off with Their Heads! 2011. 86p. 38.95 ***(978-1-258-04761-0(6))*** Literary Licensing, LLC.

Beck, Jerry. The Hanna-Barbera Treasury: Rare Art & Mementos from Your Favorite Cartoon Classics. 2007. (ENG., Illus.). 155p. 45.00 *(978-1-933784-28-1(8))* Palace Publishing Group, LP.

Beck, Jerry, ed. The 100 Greatest Looney Tunes Cartoons. 2010. (ENG., Illus.). 256p. 24.95 *(978-1-60887-003-5(0))* Palace Pr. International.

Blanche, Jon. Warhammer 40,000: the Emperor's Will. 2011. (ENG.). 144p. 40.00 *(978-1-84970-114-3(8)*, Games Workshop) Simon & Schuster.

Botes, Conrad, et al, illus. Bitterkomix, No. 15. 2009. (ENG.). 96p. pap. 30.00 *(978-1-77009-527-4(6))* Jacana Media ZAF. Dist: Independent Pubs. Group.

Brady, Pat & Wimmer, Don. 100% Whole Grin Rose Is Rose: A Collection of Rose Is Rose Comics. 2008. (ENG., Illus.). 128p. pap. 12.99 *(978-0-7407-7094-4(2))* Andrews McMeel Publishing.

Brooks, Charles, ed. Best Editorial Cartoons of the Year: 2009 Edition, 1 vol. 2009th ed. 2008. (Best Editorial Cartoons Ser.). (ENG., Illus.). 208p. pap. 14.95 *(978-1-58980-665-8(4))* Pelican Publishing Co., Inc.

Burciaga, José Antonia. Last Supper of Chicano Heroes: Selected Works of Jose Antonio Burciaga. Gladstein, Mimi R. & Chacon, Daniel, eds. 2008. (Camino del Sol Ser.). (ENG., Illus.). 256p. pap. 16.95 *(978-0-8165-2662-8(1))* Univ. of Arizona Pr.

Burciaga, Jose Antonio. Last Supper of Chicano Heroes: Selected Works of Jose Antonio Burciaga. Gladstein, Mimi R. & Chacon, Daniel, eds. 2008. (Camino del Sol Ser.). (ENG., Illus.). 256p. 35.00 *(978-0-8165-2661-1(3))* Univ. of Arizona Pr.

Byrnes, Gene. The Complete Guide to Professional Cartooning. 2011. 256p. 47.95 ***(978-1-258-10435-1(0))*** Literary Licensing, LLC.

Caricature Carvers of America. Caricatures in Motion: Caricature Carvers of America. 2011. (Illus.). 96p. pap. 19.99 ***(978-0-7643-3873-1(0)***, Schiffer Publishing Ltd) Schiffer Publishing, Ltd.

Chadburn, Steve, et al. Draw Caricature. 2007. (Illus.). 96p. pap. 14.95 *(978-1-84537-675-8(7))* New Holland Pubs., Ltd. GBR. Dist: Sterling Publishing Co., Inc.

Crumb, R. The Complete Crumb Comics Vol. 1: The Early Years of Bitter Struggle. 2nd ed. 2012. (Complete Crumb Ser.). (ENG., Illus.). 208p. pap. 24.99 ***(978-1-60699-558-7(8)***, 699558) Fantagraphics Bks.

Crumb, R. R. Crumb Draws the Blues. (Illus.). 56p. 16.95 *(978-0-86166-101-5(X))* Last Gasp of San Francisco.

Curtis, John & Mason, Andy, eds. Just for Kicks: The Year in Cartoons. 2nd ed. 2011. (ENG., Illus.). 96p. pap. 27.00 *(978-1-77009-926-5(3))* Jacana Media ZAF. Dist: Independent Pubs. Group.

Danjoux, Ilan. Political Cartoons & the Israeli-Palestinian Conflict. 2012. (New Approaches to Conflict Analysis Ser.). (ENG., Illus.). 144p. 100.00 ***(978-0-7190-8362-4(1))*** Manchester Univ. Pr. GBR. Dist: Macmillan.

Editorial Cartoons by Kids 2000. (Illus.). 60p. 6.95 *(978-1-55933-287-3(5))* Zino Pr. Children's Bks.

Eide, Elisabeth & Kunelius, Risto, eds. Transnational Media Events: The Mohammed Cartoons & the Imagined Clash of Civilizations. 2008. (Illus.). 290p. pap. 99.50 *(978-91-89471-64-1(4))* International Clearinghouse on Childrennordicom SWE. Dist: Coronet Bks.

Fantagraphics Staff. Norman Pettingill: Backwoods Humorist. Groth, Gary, ed. 2010. (ENG., Illus.). 136p. 39.99 *(978-1-60699-319-4(4)*, 699319) Fantagraphics Bks.

Francis, Stephen. Mother Anderson's Secret Book of Wit & Wisdom. 2011. (ENG., Illus.). 96p. pap. 14.95 ***(978-1-4314-0107-9(2))*** Jacana Media ZAF. Dist: Independent Pubs. Group.

—Strike While the Iron Is Hot: A New Madam & Eve Collection. 2010. (ENG.). 152p. pap. 20.00 *(978-1-77009-779-7(1))* Jacana Media ZAF. Dist: Independent Pubs. Group.

—Twilight of the Vuvuzelas. 2011. (ENG., Illus.). 136p. pap. 20.95 *(978-1-77009-878-7(X))* Jacana Media ZAF. Dist: Independent Pubs. Group.

Geisel, Theodore Seuss. Theodor Seuss Geisel Vol. 2: The Early Works of Dr. Seuss. 2006. (Illus.). 170p. 22.95 *(978-1-933160-19-1(5))* Devil's Due Digital, Inc. - A Checker Digital Co.

Gifford. Encyclopedia of Comic Characters. Date not set. (Illus.). 256p. 4.95 *(978-0-582-89294-1(5))* Addison-Wesley Longman, Ltd. GBR. Dist: Trans-Atlantic Pubns., Inc.

Grondahl, Calvin. Freeway to Perfection: A Collection of Mormon Cartoons. (Illus.). 96p. (Orig.). reprint ed. pap. 6.95 *(978-0-9606760-1-9(5))* Sunstone Foundation.

Gross, Sam. I Am Blind & My Dog Is Dead. 2007. (ENG., Illus.). 136p. (gr. 12). 13.95 *(978-1-58567-989-8(5))* Overlook Pr., The.

Habit, Franklin. It Itches: A Stash of Knitting Cartoons. 2008. (ENG., Illus.). 112p. 12.95 *(978-1-59668-093-7(8))* Interweave Pr., LLC.

Halford, Randy. Left Field, Reloaded: More Cartoons by Randy Halford. 2010. 176p. pap. 13.99 *(978-1-4490-7503-3(7))* AuthorHouse.

Harris, Sidney. There Goes the Neighborhood: Cartoons on the Environment. 2008. (ENG.). 152p. pap. 22.95 *(978-0-8203-3243-7(7))* Univ. of Georgia Pr.

Harrison, John & Harrison, Edward. Idle Idol: The Japanese Mascot. 2010. (ENG., Illus.). 144p. 16.95 *(978-0-9841906-1-4(9))* Batty, Mark Pub., LLC.

Harrison, Scott. Undigested Kernel: The Vacation Pictures of Scott Harrison. 2008. (Illus.). 96p. 19.95 *(978-0-86719-695-5(5))* Last Gasp of San Francisco.

Hart, Chris. Cartooning: The Ultimate Character Design Book. 2008. (ENG., Illus.). 131p. (J). (gr. 5-13). pap. 19.95 *(978-1-933027-42-5(6)*, Hart, Chris Bks.) Sixth&Spring Bks.

Hess, Stephen & Northrop, Sandy. American Political Cartoons, 1754-2010: The Evolution of a National Identity. 2010. (ENG., Illus.). 203p. pap. 24.95 *(978-1-4128-1119-4(8))* Transaction Pubs.

Janus Publishing Company Staff. Quotes 'n' Jokes. 2010. 209p. pap. *(978-1-85756-659-8(9))* Janus Publishing Co.

Johnston, Lynn. In the Beginning, There Was Chaos: For Better or for Worse 2nd Treasury. 2011. (ENG.). 416p. 25.99 *(978-1-4494-0954-8(7))* Andrews McMeel Publishing.

Joseph, Franco. 9 to 90 Ticklers: Cartoon Jokes for All Ages. 2010. 44p. pap. 21.99 *(978-1-4500-7890-0(7))* Xlibris Corp.

C

Kahn, Michael Alexander. Political Cartoons & Caricatures: From the collection of Michael Alexander Kahn. 2007. (ENG., Illus.). 62p. lib. bdg. 25.00 *(978-0-910672-72-6(5))* Grolier Club of New York, The.
Kaplan, Bruce Eric. This Is A Bad Time: A Collection of Cartoons. 2011. (ENG., Illus.). 192p. pap. 13.99 *(978-1-4516-3641-3(5))* Simon & Schuster.
Kayanan, Rafael. Isolated Incidents. 2008. 88p. pap. 19.99 *(978-1-4357-3327-5(4))* Lulu Enterprises Inc.
Keely, Jack. Cool Cars: Learn the Art of Cartooning Step by Step. 2008. (How to Draw & Paint Ser.). (ENG., Illus.). 32p. pap. 8.95 *(978-1-60058-064-2(5), 1600580645)* Foster, Walter Publishing, Inc.
Klausen, Jytte. The Cartoons That Shook the World. 2009. (Illus.). 240p. 35.00 *(978-0-300-12472-9(4))* Yale Univ. Pr.
Kosen & KOSEN. The Artwork of Kosen. 2008. (Illus.). 64p. pap. 14.95 *(978-1-933664-28-6(2))* Yaoi Pr.
Kotek, Joel. Cartoons & Extremism: Israel & the Jews in Arab & Western Media. 2009. (Illus.). 201p. (C). pap. 19.95 *(978-0-85303-752-1(3))* Vallentine Mitchell Pubs. GBR. Dist: International Specialized Bk. Services.
Kraus, Jerelle. All the Art That's Fit to Print: Inside the New York Times Op-Ed Page. 2008. (ENG., Illus.). 280p. (gr. 17). 49.95 *(978-0-231-13824-6(5))* Columbia Univ. Pr.
Lancaster, Osbert. Cartoons & Coronets: The Genius of Osbert Lancaster. 2009. (ENG., Illus.). 224p. pap. 30.00 *(978-0-7112-2938-9(4))* Lincoln, Frances Ltd. GBR. Dist: Perseus-PGW.
Leiknes, Mark. Cow & Boy. 2008. (ENG., Illus.). 128p. (gr. 3-18). pap. 12.99 *(978-0-7407-7098-2(5))* Andrews McMeel Publishing.
Li, Yishan. 500 Manga Villains & Heroes. 2010. (ENG.). 528p. pap. 19.99 *(978-0-06-196880-8(3), Collins Design)* HarperCollins Pubs.
Lynde, Stan. Grass Roots, 1998-1999. (Illus.). 128p. pap. 15.95 *(978-1-886370-15-9(X), 1417)* Cottonwood Publishing, Inc.
Martin, Dan. See You in the Funny Papers: The Rich Tradition of St. Louis Cartooning. 2008. 128p. pap. 19.95 *(978-1-933370-27-9(0))* Reedy Pr.
Mason, Andy, ed. Don't Joke! The Year in Cartoons. 2010. (ENG., Illus.). 160p. pap. 20.00 *(978-1-77009-758-2(9))* Jacana Media ZAF. Dist: Independent Pubs. Group.
Mayoral, Avelino R. Wacky Barbershop Cartoons. 2010. 101p. pap. 19.52 *(978-0-557-52724-3(4))* Lulu Enterprises Inc.
McGill, Donald Fraser Gould. The Michael Winner Collection of Donald McGill. 2007. (ENG., Illus.). 82p. pap. *(978-1-871136-96-8(2))* Beetles, Chris Ltd.
McLain, Bonnie. More Doodles to Dangle With. 2008. 53p. pap. 22.50 *(978-0-557-01887-1(0))* Lulu Enterprises Inc.
McManus, George. Bringing up Father: From Sea to Shining Sea. 2010. (Illus.). 272p. (YA). 49.99 *(978-1-60010-508-1(4))* Idea & Design Works, LLC.
McPhee, Constance C. & Orenstein, Nadine. Infinite Jest: Caricature & Satire from Leonardo to Levine. 2011. 45.00 ***(978-1-58839-429-3(8))*** Metropolitan Museum of Art, The.
McPhee, Constance C. & Orenstein, Nadine M. Infinite Jest: Caricature & Satire from Leonardo to Levine. 2011. (Illus.). 224p. 45.00 *(978-0-300-17581-3(7))* Yale Univ. Pr.
Miguel, Mark San. Wannababies: Birth Pangs. 2011. 148p. pap. 14.95 *(978-1-4502-7648-1(2))* iUniverse, Inc.
Millard, Travis. Hey Fudge. 2007. 30.00 *(978-0-9760388-1-8(1))* Narrow Bks.
Moss, Marie. Hello Kitty Sweet, Happy, Fun Book! A Sneak Peek into Her Supercute World. 2010. (ENG.). 128p. 29.95 *(978-0-7624-3770-2(7), Running Pr.)* Running Pr. Bk. Pubs.
Mouly, Françoise. Blown Covers: New Yorker Covers You Were Never Meant to See. 2012. (ENG., Illus.). 128p. 24.95 ***(978-1-4197-0209-9(2))*** Abrams.
New Yorker Magazine Staff & Mankoff, Robert. The New Yorker Cartoon Caption Contest. 2008. (ENG.). 216p. 24.99 *(978-0-7407-7750-9(5))* Andrews McMeel Publishing.
Newman, Stanley. Comic & Cartoon Crosswords to Keep You Sharp. 2011. (ENG.). 64p. spiral bd. 6.95 *(978-1-4027-8010-3(9), Puzzlewright)* Sterling Publishing Co., Inc.
Page One, creator. Great New Characters. 2008. (Cube Collection Ser.). (Illus.). 672p. *(978-981-245-578-9(7))* Page One Publishing.
Paskowitz, Richard. Soldier joker the Cartoons. 2008. 115p. pap. 17.95 *(978-1-4357-5475-1(1))* Lulu Enterprises Inc.
Phi Delta Kappa International. Head of the Class: The Collected Kappan Cartoons for Educators. 2009. 176p. pap. 16.95 *(978-1-935249-36-8(3))* Solution Tree.
Phillips, Irving W. Classic Mr. Mum: 100 cartoons from the Strange World of Mr. Mum. 2010. 108p. pap. 10.95 *(978-1-4502-4489-3(0))* iUniverse, Inc.
Pizz, The. The Dizzy Dictionary: A Lowbrow Guide to Kustom Kulture. 2008. (ENG., Illus.). 56p. 10.95 *(978-0-86719-705-1(6))* Last Gasp of San Francisco.
Post, Lee. The Very Best of Your Square Life. 2007. 152p. per. 14.95 *(978-1-934443-09-5(3))* ExpandingBooks.com.
Prestbury, David. The DONKEY STONE & DOLLY BLUE DAYS. 2008. (Illus.). 95p. pap. 23.50 *(978-0-9559777-1-8(1))* Prestbury, David GBR. Dist: Lulu Enterprises Inc.
Preston, Margaret (Junkin). Cartoons, by Margaret J Preston. 2006. 240p. per. 20.99 *(978-1-4255-2070-0(7))* MPublishing.
Radcliffe, Russ, ed. Best Australian Political Cartoons 2007. 2008. (Best Australian Political Cartoons Ser.). (ENG.). 192p. pap. 24.95 *(978-1-921215-56-8(9))* Scribe Pubns. AUS. Dist: Independent Pubs. Group.
—Best Australian Political Cartoons 2008. 2009. (Best Australian Political Cartoons Ser.). (ENG.). 192p. pap. 24.95 *(978-1-921372-32-2(X))* Scribe Pubns. AUS. Dist: Independent Pubs. Group.
Renard, Jules. Types Militaires. 2008. 140p. pap. 59.95 *(978-2-914417-32-7(2))* Herissey, Charles FRA. Dist: Casemate Pubs. & Bk. Distributors, LLC.
Ristaino, Marcia R. China's Intrepid Muse. 2009. (ENG.). 176p. pap. 40.00 *(978-1-891640-57-5(7))* Floating World Editions.
Rius, Jorge. The Communist Manifesto in Cartoon Form. Edelson, Morris, tr. from SPA. 3rd ed. (Illus.). reprint ed. pap. 1.50 *(978-0-9600306-1-3(1))* Quixote Pr.
Scarfe, Gerald. Heroes & Villains. 2006. (Illus.). 40.00 *(978-1-85514-338-8(0))* National Portrait Gallery Pubns. GBR. Dist: Antique Collectors' Club.
Sempe, Jean-Jacques. A Little Bit of Paris. 2007. (ENG., Illus.). 128p. 24.95 *(978-0-7893-1571-7(8))* Universe Publishing.
Shaw, Karl. The Giant Bathroom Book of Cartoons. 2009. (Giant Bathroom Reader Ser.). (ENG., Illus.). 400p. 9.99 *(978-1-84901-211-9(3), 1849012113)* Book Sales, Inc.
Silverstein, Shel. Different Dances. 25th anniv. ed. 21.95 *(978-0-8488-1168-6(2))* Amereon LTD.
Smith, Jim. Deadly Are the Mighty: The Art of Jim Smith. 2011. (ENG., Illus.). 160p. 29.95 ***(978-1-61724-052-2(4))*** Asylum Pr.
Sneyd, Doug & Johnson, Lynn. The Art of Doug Sneyd. 2011. (Illus.). 248p. 39.99 *(978-1-59582-725-8(0))* Dark Horse Comics.
Sparrow, Keith & Li, Yishan. Manga Tips: The Pocket Reference to Drawing Manga. 2010. (Mini Manga Ser.). (ENG., Illus.). 192p. pap. 7.95 *(978-1-84448-520-8(X))* Search Pr., Ltd. GBR. Dist: Independent Pubs. Group.
Stevens, Dave. Dave Stevens: the Complete Sketchbook Collection: The Complete Sketchbook Collection. 2011. 256p. 50.00 ***(978-1-61377-037-5(5))*** Idea & Design Works, LLC.
Sweatdrop Studios Staff & Li, Yishan. 500 Manga Characters. 2007. (ENG., Illus.). 528p. pap. 19.99 *(978-0-06-125652-3(8), Collins Design)* HarperCollins Pubs.
Talbot, Bryan. The Art of Bryan Talbot. 2007. (ENG., Illus.). 96p. pap. 19.95 *(978-1-56163-512-2(X))* NBM Publishing Co.
The Cartoon Bank, creator. Empire State Building Book of New Yorker Cartoons. 2008. (Illus.). 100p. per. *(978-0-9755738-8-4(8))* Cartoon Bank, The.
Tibbals, Geoff, ed. The Mammoth Book of the Funniest Cartoons of All Time. 2006. (Mammoth Book Of Ser.). (ENG., Illus.). 512p. per. 13.95 *(978-0-7867-1831-3(5))* Running Pr. Bk. Pubs.
Truman, Vincent. This Is My First Time So Please Be Brutal. 2008. (Illus.). 224p. pap. 12.98 *(978-1-4357-0685-9(4))* Lulu Enterprises Inc.
Weller, Alan. The Mexican Prints of Posada & Manilla. 2012. (Dover Pictorial Archive Ser.). (ENG.). 128p. pap. 19.95 ***(978-0-486-99177-1(6))*** Dover Pubns., Inc.
West, Richard V. The Line That Roars: Editorial Cartoons in the Age of Anxiety. 2007. (Illus.). 63p. *(978-0-9763771-3-9(6))* LSU Museum of Art.
Wheeler, Shannon. I Thought You Would Be Funnier. 2011. (ENG.). 128p. pap. 17.99 *(978-1-60886-094-4(9))* Boom! Studios.
Wolf, Edwin. Benjamin Franklin's Stamp Act Cartoon. 2011. 12p. pap. 35.95 ***(978-1-258-01665-4(6))*** Literary Licensing, LLC.
Wood, Ashley. Sketches & Ideas. 2008. (Illus.). 96p. 16.99 *(978-1-60010-340-7(5))* Idea & Design Works, LLC.
Yoe, Craig. Arf Museum: The Unholy Marriage of Art & Comics, No. 2. 2006. (ENG., Illus.). 120p. pap. 19.95 *(978-1-56097-732-2(9), 56732)* Fantagraphics Bks.
Zapiro. Da Zuma Code. 2009. 160p. pap. 25.95 *(978-1-77013-101-9(9))* Double Storey Bks. ZAF. Dist: International Publishers Marketing.
—Do You Know Who I Am?! 2011. (ENG., Illus.). 136p. pap. 20.95 *(978-1-77009-879-4(8))* Jacana Media ZAF. Dist: Independent Pubs. Group.

CARICATURES AND CARTOONS—FRANCE

McWilliam, Neil, ed. Lines of Attack: Conflicts in Caricature. 2010. (ENG., Illus.). 96p. pap. 18.95 *(978-0-938989-32-5(4))* Duke Univ. Pr.

CARICATURES AND CARTOONS—GERMANY

Vetter-Liebnow, Gisela. Friedrich Karl Waechter: Zeichenkunst. 2009. (GER., Illus.). 384p. (C). 72.00 *(978-3-7774-9095-3(4))* Hirmer Verlag GmbH DEU. Dist: Brown, David Bk. Co., The.

CARICATURES AND CARTOONS—GREAT BRITAIN

Bryant, Mark. Wars of Empire in Cartoons. 2008. (Illus.). 160p. 34.95 *(978-1-902304-40-3(3))* Grub Street GBR. Dist: Casemate Pubs. & Bk. Distributors, LLC.
Burgerman, Jon. Pens Are My Friends. 2010. (ENG., Illus.). 310p. 55.00 *(978-988-99591-4-2(3))* Systems Design, Ltd. HKG. Dist: D.A.P./Distributed Art Pubs.
Cruikshank, George. Bachelors Own Book or the Progress of Mr. 2006. pap. 15.95 *(978-1-4286-3875-4(X))* Kessinger Publishing, LLC.
Maddocks, Peter. Hate Men Who. (Illus.). 64p. 7.95 *(978-1-85479-709-4(3))* O'Mara, Michael Bks., Ltd. GBR. Dist: Trans-Atlantic Pubns., Inc.
Myrone, Martin, ed. Rude Britannia: From Hogarth to Now. 2010. (ENG., Illus.). 160p. pap. 34.95 *(978-1-85437-886-6(4))* Tate Publishing, Ltd. GBR. Dist: Hachette Bk. Group.
Rauser, Amelia F. Caricature Unmasked: Irony, Authenticity, & Individualism in Eighteenth-Century English Prints. 2008. (Illus.). 160p. 60.00 *(978-0-87413-986-0(4))* Univ. of Delaware Pr.
Wyman, Bill. The Stones: A History in Cartoons. 2009. (ENG.). 192p. pap. 30.95 *(978-0-7509-4249-2(5))* History Pr. Ltd., The GBR. Dist: Independent Pubs. Group.

CARICATURES AND CARTOONS—SOVIET UNION

Kutuzova, Anna. An Imperialist Hawk. 2008. 76p. pap. *(978-3-639-08514-3(0))* VDM Verlag Dr. Mueller e.K.

CARICATURISTS

see Cartoonists

CARIES, DENTAL

see Dental Caries

CARILLONS

see also Handbell Ringing

Johnston, Jill. England's Child: The Carillon & the Casting of Big Bells. 2008. (ENG., Illus.). 304p. 27.95 *(978-0-932274-71-7(4))* Cadmus Editions.

CARING

see also Empathy; Helping Behavior; Sympathy

Armstrong, Karen. Twelve Steps to a Compassionate Life. (ENG.). 240p. 2011. pap. 14.00 *(978-0-307-74288-9(1), Anchor)* 2010. 22.95 *(978-0-307-59559-1(5), Knopf)* Knopf Doubleday Publishing Group.
—Twelve Steps to a Compassionate Life. l.t. ed. 2011. (ENG.). 289p. 31.99 *(978-1-4104-3503-3(2))* Thorndike Pr.
Barasch, Marc Ian & Barasch, Marc Ian. The Compassionate Life: Walking the Path of Kindness. 2nd ed. 2009. (BK Life Ser.). (ENG.). 288p. pap. 16.95 *(978-1-57675-756-7(0))* Berrett-Koehler Pubs., Inc.
Barry, Michael S. & Barry, Michael. The Art of Caregiving: How to Lend Support & Encouragement to Those with Cancer. 2007. (ENG.). 160p. 14.99 *(978-0-7814-4430-9(6))* Cook, David C.
Beach, Shelly. Ambushed by Grace: Help & Hope on the Caregiving Journey. 2008. (ENG.). 208p. pap. 11.99 *(978-1-57293-242-5(2))* Discovery Hse. Pubs.
—Precious Lord, Take My Hand: Meditations for Caregivers. 2007. (ENG.). 240p. per. 11.99 *(978-1-57293-195-4(7))* Discovery Hse. Pubs.
Bloom, Jack H. Jewish Relational Care A-Z: We Are Our Other's Keeper. 2006. (ENG.). 484p. 124.00 *(978-0-7890-2705-4(4))* Routledge.
Bloom, Jack H., ed. Jewish Relational Care A-Z: We Are Our Other's Keeper. 2006. (ENG.). 484p. per. 50.50 *(978-0-7890-2706-1(2))* Routledge.
Bloom, Pamela, ed. The Power of Compassion: Stories That Open the Heart, Heal the Soul, & Change the World. 2010. (ENG.). 256p. pap. 15.95 *(978-1-57174-629-0(3))* Hampton Roads Publishing Co., Inc.
Boff, Leonardo. Essential Care: An Ethics of Human Nature. Guilherme, Alexandre, tr. from POR. 2008. 192p. pap. 29.95 *(978-1-60258-142-5(8))* Baylor Univ. Pr.
Braley, Larry D. & Gragg, Ray D. Managing from the Heart - A Way of Life (Abbreviated Edition) 2009. 283p. pap. 17.97 *(978-0-557-04379-8(4))* Lulu Enterprises Inc.
Briskin, Alan & Boller, Jan. Daily Miracles: Stories & Practices of Humanity & Excellence in Healthcare. 2006. *(978-1-930538-44-3(8))* Sigma Theta Tau International, Ctr. for Nursing Pr.
Brown, Stephanie L., et al. Moving Beyond Self-Interest: Perspectives from Evolutionary Biology, Neuroscience, & the Social Sciences. 2011. (ENG., Illus.). 320p. 49.95 ***(978-0-19-538810-7(0))*** Oxford Univ. Pr., Inc.
Burk, Connie & Lipsky, Laura van Dernoot. Trauma Stewardship: An Everyday Guide to Caring for Self While Caring for Others. 2009. (BK Life Ser.). (ENG., Illus.). 264p. pap. 19.95 *(978-1-57675-944-8(X))* Berrett-Koehler Pubs., Inc.
Canfield, Jack L., et al. Celebrating People Who Make a Difference: The Headlines You'll Never Read. 2008. (Chicken Soup for the Soul Ser.). (ENG., Illus.). 320p. pap. 14.95 *(978-0-7573-0667-9(5))* Health Communications, Inc.
Carey, Louise. The Hedge People: How I Kept My Sanity & Sense of Humor As an Alzheimer's Caregiver. 2009. (ENG.). 128p. pap. 11.99 *(978-0-8341-2468-4(8), 9780834124684)* Beacon Hill Pr. of Kansas City.
Casey, Nell. An Uncertain Inheritance: Writers on Caring for Family. 2008. 304p. pap. 14.99 *(978-0-06-087531-2(3), HarperPerennial)* HarperCollins Pubs.
Chinmaya Publications Staff, contrib. by. Compassion. 2007. (Illus.). xiv, 124p. pap. *(978-1-880687-94-9(1))* Chinmaya Pubns.
Clark Miller, Sarah. The Ethics of Need: Agency, Dignity, & Obligation. 2011. (ENG.). 200p. (C). 125.00 *(978-0-415-88268-2(0))* Routledge.
Clinton, Tim, et al, eds. Caring for People God's Way: Personal & Emotional Issues, Addictions, Grief, & Trauma, 0 vols. 2009. 576p. pap. 22.99 *(978-0-7852-9775-8(8))* Nelson, Thomas Inc.
Dalai Lama XIV. The Dalai Lama's Little Book of Compassion. 2011. 224p. 12.95 *(978-1-57174-670-2(6))* Hampton Roads Publishing Co., Inc.
—How to Be Compassionate: A Handbook for Creating Inner Peace & a Happier World. Hopkins, Jeffrey, ed. & tr. by. 2011. (ENG.). 160p. pap. 14.00 *(978-1-4516-2391-8(7), Beyond Words/Atria Bks.)* Atria Bks.
—How to Be Compassionate: A Handbook for Creating Inner Peace & a Happier World. 2011. (ENG., Illus.). 160p. 20.00 *(978-1-4516-2390-1(9), Beyond Words/Atria Bks.)* Atria Bks.
—How to Expand Love: Widening the Circle of Loving Relationships. 2006. (ENG.). 224p. pap. 15.00 *(978-0-7432-6969-8(1), Beyond Words/Atria Bks.)* Atria Bks.
Dellinger, Annetta & Boerger, Karen. JOY-spirations for Caregivers: A Dialogue with God. 2010. 304p. pap. 19.99 *(978-1-60615-026-9(X))* WinePress Publishing.
Deshotel, Minnie. Striving for Compassion While Gazing at Life. 2009. 128p. pap. 15.99 *(978-1-4490-2416-1(5))* AuthorHouse.
Discovery House Publishers Staff & Branon, Dave. When You Don't Know What to Say: Words of Caring for All Occasions. 2007. (ENG.). 160p. per. 9.99 *(978-1-57293-254-8(6))* Discovery Hse. Pubs.
Dobrin, Arthur. Lost Art of Happiness. 2011. (ENG.). 240p. pap. 17.00 *(978-1-61614-255-1(3))* Prometheus Bks., Pubs.
Dodds, Monica. A Catholic Guide to Caring for Your Aging Parent. 2006. (ENG.). 360p. per. 14.95 *(978-0-8294-1872-9(5))* Loyola Pr.
Duncan Oliver, Joan. The Meaning of Nice: How Compassion & Civility Can Change Your Life (And the World) 2012. (ENG.). 272p. (gr. 12). 14.00 ***(978-0-425-24087-8(8)***, Berkley Trade) Penguin Group (USA) Inc.
Ekman, Paul & Dalai Lama XIV. Emotional Awareness: Overcoming the Obstacles to Psychological Balance & Compassion. 2008. (ENG., Illus.). 288p. 23.00 *(978-0-8050-8712-3(5), Times Bks.)* Holt, Henry & Co.
Emlet, Michael R. Help for the Caregiver: Facing the Challenges with Understanding & Strength. 2008. (ENG.). 24p. 3.99 *(978-1-934885-50-5(9))* New Growth Pr.
Fargo, Donna. I Thanked God for You Today, 1 vol. 2010. (Illus.). 96p. pap. 13.95 *(978-1-59842-474-4(2))* Blue Mountain Arts Inc.
Fehr, Beverley, et al, eds. The Science of Compassionate Love: Theory, Research, & Applications. 2008. (ENG., Illus.). 488p. 110.95 *(978-1-4051-5393-5(8))*; pap. 52.95 *(978-1-4051-5394-2(6))* Wiley, John & Sons, Inc. (Wiley-Blackwell).
Ferrare, D. Michael. Walking the Unmarked Path: Notes from My Journey to Personhood in the New Millennium. 2010. *(978-1-58982-770-7(8))* American Bk. Publishing Group.
Francis, Paulette. Caring with a Difference: A Guide to Caring with Compassion, Respect & Professionalism. 2011. 64p. pap. 15.56 ***(978-1-4567-8052-4(2))*** AuthorHouse.
Galvin, Kathleen & Todres, Les. Caring & Well-Being: A Lifeworld Approach. 2012. (ENG.). 192p. (C). 125.00 ***(978-0-415-50460-7(0))*** Routledge.
Ganis, Richard. The Politics of Care in Habermas & Derrida: Between Measurability & Immeasurability. 2010. viii, 163p. *(978-0-7391-5011-5(1))*; (ENG.). 172p. 60.00 *(978-0-7391-5009-2(X))* Lexington Bks.
Germer, Christopher K. The Mindful Path to Self-Compassion: Freeing Yourself from Destructive Thoughts & Emotions. 2009. (ENG.). 306p. 40.00 *(978-1-60623-284-2(3))*; (Illus.). 15.95 *(978-1-59385-975-6(9))* Guilford Pubns., Inc.
Giannone, Richard. Hidden: Reflections on Gay Life, AIDS, & Spiritual Desire. 2012. (ENG., Illus.). 224p. 27.95 ***(978-0-8232-4184-2(X))*** Fordham Univ. Pr.
Gilbert, Paul. Compassion-Focused Therapy. 2011. 232p. (C). pap. 34.00 *(978-0-415-48533-3(9))* Routledge.
Goldberg, Stan. Leaning into Sharp Points: Practical Guidance & Nurturing Support for Caregivers. 2012. (ENG.). 232p. pap. 14.95 ***(978-1-60868-067-2(3))*** New World Library.
Gordon, Gus. Solitude & Compassion: The Path to the Heart of the Gospel. 2009. 200p. 18.00 *(978-1-57075-830-0(1))* Orbis Bks.
Gordon, Mary. Roots of Empathy: Changing the World Child by Child. 2009. (ENG.). 312p. pap. 15.95 *(978-1-61519-007-2(4), 1615190074)* Experiment LLC, The.
Gorman, Mary Jane. Tending Body, Heart, Mind & Soul: Following Jesus in Caring for Ourselves. 2006. 136p. per. 10.00 *(978-0-687-49210-7(6))* Abingdon Pr.
Hanh, Thich Nhat. The Novice: A Story of True Love. (ENG.). 2012. 256p. pap. 14.99 ***(978-0-06-200584-7(7))*** 2011. 208p. 23.99 *(978-0-06-200583-0(9))* HarperCollins Pubs. (HarperOne).
Hanh, Thich Nhat. True Love: A Practice for Awakening the Heart. Kohn, Sherab Chodzin, tr. 2011. (ENG., Illus.). 128p. pap. 11.00 *(978-1-59030-939-1(1))* Shambhala Pubns., Inc.
Hanh, Thich Nhat & Parallax Press Staff. Teachings on Love. 2nd ed. 2006. (ENG.). 195p. per. 16.95 *(978-1-888375-00-8(0))* Parallax Pr.
Held, Virginia. The Ethics of Care: Personal, Political, & Global. 2007. (ENG.). 224p. per. 45.00 *(978-0-19-532590-4(7))* Oxford Univ. Pr., Inc.
Huff, Tim. Dancing with Dynamite: Celebrating Against the Odds. 2010. (Illus.). ***(978-1-894860-49-9(7))*** BayRidge Bks.
Jones, David A. A Biblical Guide to Caregiving. 2011. 284p. pap. 24.99 ***(978-1-4583-9600-6(2))*** Lulu Enterprises Inc.
Kentel, Jeanne Adèle. Educating the Young: The Ethics of Care. 2011. (New International Studies in Applied Ethics Ser.). 293p. pap. 61.95 *(978-3-03911-984-4(2))* Lang, Peter AG GBR. Dist: Lang, Peter.
Kok, James R. 90% of Helping Is Just Showing Up. 2nd ed. 2007. 128p. per. 11.95 *(978-1-59255-413-3(4))* Faith Alive Christian Resources.
Lake, Robert, ed. Dear Nel: Opening the Circles of Care (Letters to Nel Noddings) 2012. 168p. ***(978-0-8077-5299-9(1))***; (ENG.). pap. 27.95 ***(978-0-8077-5298-2(3))*** Teachers College Pr., Teachers College, Columbia Univ.
Lampe, Karen. The Caring Congregation: How to Become One & Why it Matters. 2011. 112p. pap. 13.00 *(978-1-4267-2733-7(X))* Abingdon Pr.
Leighton, Jonathan. The Battle for Compassion: Ethics in an Apathetic Universe. 2011. 260p. pap. 22.95 *(978-0-87586-871-4(1))*; pap. 22.95 ***(978-0-87586-870-7(3))*** Algora Publishing.
Leloup, Jean-Yves. Compassion & Meditation: The Spiritual Dynamic Between Buddhism & Christianity. 2009. (ENG.). 1p. pap. 14.95 *(978-1-59477-277-1(0))* Inner Traditions International, Ltd.
Levine, Noah. The Heart of the Revolution: The Buddha's Radical Teachings of Forgiveness, Compassion, & Kindness. 2011. (ENG.). 224p. pap. 15.99 *(978-0-06-171124-4(1), HarperOne)* HarperCollins Pubs.
Levine, Susan S. Loving Psychoanalysis: Technique & Theory in the Therapeutic Relationship. 2008. (ENG.). 170p. 41.99 *(978-0-7657-0624-9(5), Aronson, Jason)* Rowman & Littlefield Publishers, Inc.
Lovern, Sandy. Finding Your Way: A Spiritual GPS for Caregivers. 2010. (ENG.). 176p. pap. 14.99 *(978-1-59669-246-6(4))* New Hope Pubs.

Lynch, Kathleen, et al. Affective Equality: Love, Care & Injustice. Lynch, Kathleen et al, eds. 2009. (ENG., Illus.). 272p. 89.00 *(978-0-230-21249-7(2))* Palgrave Macmillan.

MacGregor, Sherilyn. Beyond Mothering Earth: Ecological Citizenship & the Politics of Care, 1 vol. 2007. (ENG., Illus.). 296p. per. 29.95 *(978-0-7748-1202-3(8))* UBC Pr. CAN. Dist: Univ. of Washington Pr.

Masson, Cheryl. Dare to Care: Reflections on the Art of Caring. 2009. 104p. pap. 13.99 *(978-1-4389-2444-1(5))* AuthorHouse.

Metzler, Barbara R. Passionaries: Turning Compassion into Action. 2006. (Illus.). 272p. per. 19.95 *(978-1-59947-105-1(1))* Templeton Pr.

Miller, Jonathan. The Compassionate Community: Ten Values to Unite America. (ENG.). 256p. 2007. pap. 14.95 *(978-1-4039-8495-1(6))* 2006. 24.95 *(978-1-4039-7408-2(X))* Palgrave Macmillan.

Moeller, Bob & Moeller, Cheryl. The Marriage Miracle: How Soft Hearts Can Make a Couple Strong. 2010. 256p. pap. 13.99 *(978-0-7369-2710-9(7))* Harvest Hse. Pubs.

Mol, Annemarie, et al, eds. Care in Practice: On Tinkering in Clinics, Homes & Farms. 2010. (ENG., Illus.). 300p. pap. 49.95 *(978-3-8376-1447-3(6))* Transcript Verlag DEU. Dist: Transaction Pubs.

Möller, Christian. Kirche, Die Bei Trost Ist: Plädoyer Für eine Seelsorgliche Kirche. 2007. (GER.). 205p. (C). pap. 27.00 *(978-3-525-60419-9(X))* Vandenhoeck & Ruprecht GmbH & Co. KG DEU. Dist: ISD.

Naoe, Fumitada. Live with Meaning. Die with Passion. 2009. (ENG., Illus.). 160p. 19.95 *(978-0-9785084-5-6(9))* One Peace Bks., Inc.

Neff, Kristin. Self-Compassion: Stop Beating Yourself up & Leave Insecurity Behind. (ENG.). 320p. 2012. pap. 14.99 ***(978-0-06-173352-9(0)**, William Morrow Paperbacks)* 2011. 24.99 *(978-0-06-173351-2(2)*, Morrow, William & Co.) HarperCollins Pubs.

Noddings, Nel. The Maternal Factor: Two Paths to Morality. 2010. (ENG.). 304p. 55.00 *(978-0-520-26549-3(1))*; pap. 24.95 *(978-0-520-26550-9(5))* Univ. of California Pr.

Nouwen, Henri J. M. A Spirituality of Caregiving. 2011. 64p. pap. 12.00 *(978-0-8358-1045-5(3))* Upper Room Bks.

Nugent, Madeline Pecora & Stead, Julian. Love-Ability: Becoming Lovable by Caring for Yourself & Others. 2007. 175p. per. 13.95 *(978-1-56548-268-5(9))* New City Pr.

O'Connell, Maureen H. Compassion: Loving Our Neighbor in an Age of Globalization. 2009. 208p. pap. 32.00 *(978-1-57075-845-4(X))* Orbis Bks.

Pennel, Joe E. The Gift of Presence: A Guide to Helping Those Who Suffer. 2009. 141p. 10.00 *(978-1-4267-0214-3(0))* Abingdon Pr.

Poole Hicks, Allidah, et al. When Crisis Strikes... What to Do, What to Say, How to Help: What to Do, What to Say, How to Help. 2011. 356p. pap. 27.95 ***(978-0-9824028-0-1(5))*** Good Neighbors Publishing LLC.

Preece, Rob. The Courage to Feel: Buddhist Practices for Opening to Others. 2009. (ENG.). 160p. pap. 14.95 *(978-1-55939-333-1(5))* Snow Lion Pubns., Inc.

Ralston, Deb. Golden Lunches. 2009. 28p. pap. 13.50 *(978-1-60693-542-2(9)*, Eloquent Bks.) AEG Literary Publishing Services, Inc.

Ranheim, Albertine Elisabeth. Expanding Caring. 2011. 72p. pap. ***(978-3-8454-0788-3(3))*** Lambert Academic Publishing.

Richards, Marty. Caresharing: A Reciprocal Approach to Caregiving & Care Receiving in the Complexities of Aging, Illness or Disability. 2010. 256p. pap. 16.99 *(978-1-59473-286-7(8))* 2008. 250p. 24.99 *(978-1-59473-247-8(7))* SkyLight Paths Publishing.

Roach, M. Simone. The Human Act of Caring: A Blueprint for the Health Professions. xi, 163p. *(978-0-919100-64-0(3))* CHA Pr.

Robert, Ellsberg, ed. Modern Spiritual Masters: Writings on Contemplation & Compassion. 2008. 192p. pap. 18.00 *(978-1-57075-788-4(7))* Orbis Bks.

Robinson, Amber. Mercy Rising: Simple Ways to Practice Justice & Compassion. 2010. (ENG.). 192p. pap. 14.99 *(978-0-8341-2497-4(1)*, 9780834124974) Beacon Hill Pr. of Kansas City.

Robinson, Fiona. The Ethics of Care: A Feminist Approach to Human Security. 2011. (Global Ethics & Politics Ser.). (ENG.). 200p. 74.50 *(978-1-4399-0065-9(5))*; (ENG.). 200p. pap. 24.95 *(978-1-4399-0066-6(3))*; 208p. E-Book ***(978-1-4399-0067-3(1))*** Temple Univ. Pr.

Robinson, Simon. Spirituality, Ethics, & Care. 2007. (ENG.). 208p. per. *(978-1-84310-498-8(9))* Kingsley, Jessica Ltd.

Sander, Dorothy. Caring for Mom. 2010. 127p. pap. 13.95 *(978-0-557-32423-1(8))* Lulu Enterprises Inc.

Schuette, Sarah L. I Am Caring. 2008. (Character Values Ser.). (ENG.). 24p. (gr. k-1). pap. 35.70 *(978-1-4296-2969-0(X)*, Pebble Bks.) Capstone Pr., Inc.

—I Am Caring. 2007. (Character Values Ser.). (ENG.). 24p. (gr. k-1). pap. 5.95 *(978-1-4296-1560-0(5)*, Pebble Bks.) Capstone Pr., Inc.

Shah Kazemi, Reza, et al. Common Ground Between Islam & Buddhism: Spiritual & Ethical Affinities. 2010. (ENG.). 174p. pap. 16.95 *(978-1-891785-62-7(1))* Fons Vitae of Kentucky, Inc.

Shel, Tammy. The Ethics of Caring: Bridging Pedagogy & Utopia. 2007. 160p. per. *(978-90-8790-209-4(3))* Sense Pubs.

Shel, Tammy A. The Ethics of Caring: Between Utopia & Pragmatism. 2007. pap. *(978-0-8204-9742-6(8))* Lang, Peter Publishing, Inc.

Skog, Susan. Radical Acts of Love: How Compassion Is Transforming Our World. 2006. 288p. reprint ed. 22.00 *(978-1-4223-5265-6(X))* DIANE Publishing Co.

Slote. The Ethics of Care & Empathy. 2007. XIV, 138p. 35.95 *(978-0-415-77201-3(X))*; 90.00 *(978-0-415-77200-6(1))* Routledge.

Slote, Michael A. Moral Sentimentalism, 1 vol. 2010. (ENG.). 184p. 65.00 *(978-0-19-539144-2(6))* Oxford Univ. Pr., Inc.

Smith, Heather & Smith, Mark K. The Art of Helping Others: Being Around, Being There, Being Wise. 2008. (ENG.). 176p. pap. *(978-1-84310-638-8(8))* Kingsley, Jessica Ltd.

Stafford, Wess & Merrill, Dean. Just a Minute: In the Heart of a Child, One Moment... Can Last Forever. 2012. (ENG.). 224p. 19.99 ***(978-0-8024-0472-5(3))*** Moody Pubs.

Sternberg, Rachel Hall. Tragedy Offstage: Suffering & Sympathy in Ancient Athens. 2009. (ENG.). 250p. pap. 25.00 *(978-0-292-72238-5(9))* Univ. of Texas Pr.

Straub, Gail. The Rhythm of Compassion: Caring for Self, Connecting with Society. 2008. (ENG.). 240p. pap. 14.95 *(978-0-9630327-3-7(9))* Empowerment Institute.

Sumner, Jane. The Moral Construct of Caring in Nursing As Communicative Action. 2008. 272p. pap. *(978-3-639-08137-4(4))* VDM Verlag Dr. Mueller e.K.

Temes, Ivan. Care: You Have the Power! 2008. 136p. pap. 19.95 *(978-1-60005-126-5(X))* Happy About.

Thibault, Jane Marie & Morgan, Richard. No Act of Love Is Ever Wasted: The Spirituality of Caring for Persons with Dementia. 2009. 160p. pap. 16.00 *(978-0-8358-9995-6(0))* Upper Room Bks.

Watson, Jean. Assessing & Measuring Caring in Nursing & Health Sciences. 2nd ed. 2008. 350p. 60.00 *(978-0-8261-2196-7(9))* Springer Publishing Co., Inc.

—Human Caring Science: A Theory of Nursing. 2nd ed. 2011. 122p. pap. 49.95 *(978-1-4496-2810-9(9))* Jones & Bartlett Learning, LLC.

White, Richard J. Radical Virtues: Moral Wisdom & the Ethics of Contemporary Life. 2008. (ENG.). 212p. 70.00 *(978-0-7425-6099-4(6))*; pap. 24.95 *(978-0-7425-6100-7(3))* Rowman & Littlefield Publishers, Inc.

Wilson, Amy Lyles, ed. Compassion: Cultivating a Good Heart. 2008. 96p. pap. 12.00 *(978-0-8358-9955-0(1))* Upper Room Bks.

Wilson, Michael Todd & Hoffmann, Brad. Preventing Ministry Failure: A ShepherdCare Guide for Pastors, Ministers & Other Caregivers. 2007. (ENG., Illus.). 265p. per. 18.00 *(978-0-8308-3444-0(3)*, IVP Bks.) InterVarsity Pr.

Wilson, Rod. How Do I Help a Hurting Friend? Practical Help for Leaders & Laypeople. 2010. *(978-1-57383-448-3(3))* Regent College Publishing.

Wiseman, Neil B. Contagious Compassion: The Life & Ministry of Tom Nees. 2010. (Illus.). 92p. *(978-0-8341-2479-0(3))* Nazarene Publishing Hse.

Wolf, Joanne, et al. Teaching Kids to Care: Nurturing Character & Compassion. 2007. (ENG., Illus.). 248p. per. 16.95 *(978-1-57174-548-4(3))* Hampton Roads Publishing Co., Inc.

CARINTHIA

Leitner, Friedrich. Die Inschriften des Bundeslandes Karnten: Teil 2: Die Inschriften des Politischen Bezirks St. Veit an der Glan. 2008. (Die Deutschen Inschriften Ser.). (GER., Illus.). 729p. (C). 119.00 *(978-3-7001-6052-6(6))* Austrian Academy of Sciences Press AUT. Dist: Brown, David Bk. Co., The.

CARLETON, GUY, SIR, 1724-1808

see Dorchester, Guy Carleton, Baron, 1724-1808

CARLETON COLLEGE

Rutz, Carol & Savina, Mary, eds. Building Intellectual Community Through Collaboration. 2007. per. 18.95 *(978-0-9746379-4-5(7))* College City Pubns.

Senghor, Lingerr & Zang, Adam. Carleton College 2012: Off the Record. 2011. 188p. pap. 16.95 ***(978-1-4274-0368-1(6))*** College Prowler, Inc.

CARLETON'S INVASION, 1776

Hadden, James. Hadden's Journal & Orderly Books. 2009. (Revolutionary War Ser.). (ENG.). 700p. pap. 40.95 *(978-1-4290-1685-8(X))* Applewood Bks.

Hadden, James M. A Journal Kept in Canada & upon Burgoy. 2006. pap. 50.95 *(978-1-4286-4782-4(1))* Kessinger Publishing, LLC.

Jones, Charles Henry. History of the Campaign for the Conquest of Canada in 1776: From the Death of Montgomery to the Retreat of the British Army under Sir Guy Carleton. 234p. reprint ed. 98.00 *(978-0-7222-6808-7(4))* Library Reprints, Inc.

CARLISLE (ENGLAND)

Eley, C. King. The Cathedral Church of Carlisle. 2007. (Illus.). 104p. per. *(978-1-4065-1791-0(7))* Dodo Pr.

McCarthy, Michael R. Roman Carlisle & the Post-Roman Kingdoms. (Illus.). 176p. pap. 35.00 *(978-0-7524-1955-8(2))* History Pr. Ltd.,The GBR. Dist: Trafalgar Square Publishing.

CARLISLE (PA.)

Ridner, Judith E. A Town In-Between: Carlisle, Pennsylvania, & the Early Mid-Atlantic Interior. 2010. (Early American Studies). (Illus.). 320p. (C). 49.95 *(978-0-8122-4236-2(X))* Univ. of Pennsylvania Pr.

CARLISLE INDIAN SCHOOL (CARLISLE, PA.)

see United States Indian School (Carlisle, Pa.)

CARLISTS

Blinkhorn, Martin. Carlism & Crisis in Spain 1931-1939. 2008. (ENG.). 412p. pap. 53.00 *(978-0-521-08634-9(5))* Cambridge Univ. Pr.

Imágenes: El Carlismo en Las Artes. 2010. (SPA., Illus.). 410p. *(978-84-235-3227-8(5))* Navarra, Comunidad Autonoma, Servicio de Prensa, Publicaciones y Relaciones Sociales.

Kennett-Barrington. Letters from the Carlist War, 1874-1876. Lascelles & Alberich, eds. Date not set. (Hispanic Text Ser.: No. 43). (Illus.). 133p. pap. 17.95 *(978-0-85989-264-3(6))* Univ. of Exeter Pr. GBR. Dist: Brown, David Bk. Co., The.

Moral Roncal, Antonio M. & Moral Roncal, Antonio Manuel. La Cuestión Religiosa en la Segunda República Española: Iglesia y Carlismo. 2009. (SPA., Illus.). 263p. *(978-84-9742-905-4(2))* Biblioteca Nueva, Editorial, S.L.

CARLO BORROMEO, SAINT, 1538-1584

see Charles Borromeo, Saint, 1538-1584

CARLOS, PRINCE OF ASTURIAS, 1545-1568—DRAMA

Schiller, Frederich. Don Carlos. 2008. 332p. 29.99 *(978-0-554-23766-4(0))* 2008. 332p. 28.99 *(978-0-554-33069-3(5))* 2006. 278p. pap. 21.99 *(978-1-4264-4999-4(2))* 2006. 330p. pap. 24.99 *(978-1-4264-5300-7(0))* BiblioBazaar.

CARLOS, THE JACKAL

Follain, John. Jackal: The Complete Story of the Legendary Terrorist, Carlos the Jackal. 2011. (ENG.). 344p. pap. 14.95 *(978-1-61145-026-2(8)*, 611026, Arcade Publishing) Skyhorse Publishing Co., Inc.

CARLOS V, HOLY ROMAN EMPEROR, 1500-1558

see Charles V, Holy Roman Emperor, 1500-1558

CARLOTA, EMPRESS, CONSORT OF MAXIMILIAN, EMPEROR OF MEXICO, 1840-1927

Hall, Frederic. Life of Maximilian I , Late Emperor of Mexico, with a Sketch of the Empress Carlota by Frederic Hall. 2006. 336p. per. 23.99 *(978-1-4255-3368-7(X))* MPublishing.

Harding, Bertita. Phantom Crown: The Story of Maximilian & Carlota of Mexico. 2008. 384p. 29.95 *(978-1-4344-6893-2(3))*; pap. 19.95 *(978-1-4344-6892-5(5))* Wildside Pr., LLC.

Hyde, H. Montgomery. Mexican Empire - the History of Maximilian & Carlota of Mexico. 2007. 388p. per. *(978-1-4067-3709-7(7))* Read Bks.

Ibsen, Kristine. Maximilian, Mexico, & the Invention of Empire. 2010. (ENG., Illus.). 232p. 55.00 *(978-0-8265-1688-6(2))* Vanderbilt Univ. Pr.

Igler, Susanne. De la Intrusa Infame a la Loca Del Castillo: Carlota de Mexico en la Literatura de Su 'patria' Adoptiva. 2007. (Studien und Dokumente Zur Geschichte der Romanischen Literaturen Ser.: Vol. 58). (SPA., Illus.). 480p. (C). pap. 89.95 *(978-3-631-55029-8(4))* Lang, Peter Publishing, Inc.

Tomo, Grandes de, ed. Los Grandes - Carlota Emperatriz. 2007. 112p. pap. 5.95 *(978-970-666-806-6(3))* Grupo Editorial Tomo, S.A. de C.V. MEX. Dist: Giron Bks.

CARLOVINGIAN ARCHITECTURE

see Architecture, Carolingian

CARLOVINGIAN ART

see Art, Carolingian

CARLOVINGIANS

see Carolingians

CARLOW (IRELAND)

Luddy, Maria. Matters of Deceit: Breach of Promise to Marry Cases 19th- & 20th-Century Limerick. 2011. 64p. pap. 14.95 ***(978-1-84682-294-0(7))*** Four Courts Pr. IRL. Dist: International Specialized Bk. Services.

CARLSBAD CAVERNS (N.M.)

Blake-Birchell, Donna, et al. Carlsbad & Carlsbad Caverns. 2010. (Images of America Ser.). (ENG., Illus.). 128p. pap. 21.99 *(978-0-7385-7884-2(3))* Arcadia Publishing.

CARLSEN, KURT

Delaney, Frank. Simple Courage: A True Story of Peril on the Sea. 2007. (ENG., Illus.). 320p. per. 14.95 *(978-0-8129-7595-6(2)*, Random Hse. Trade Paperbacks) Random House Publishing Group.

CARLYLE, JANE WELSH, 1801-1866

Carlyle, Jane Welsh. Letters & Memorials of Jane Welsh Carlyle. Carlyle, Thomas & Froude, James Anthony, eds. 2011. (Cambridge Library Collection - Literary Studies). (ENG.). 410p. pap. 31.99 *(978-1-108-02925-4(6))*; 352p. pap. 28.99 *(978-1-108-02927-8(2))*; 410p. pap. 31.99 *(978-1-108-02926-1(4))* Cambridge Univ. Pr.

Carlyle, Thomas. Thomas Carlyle: Letters to His Wife. Bliss, Trudy, ed. 2011. 418p. 54.95 ***(978-1-258-08732-6(4))*** Literary Licensing, LLC.

Kerry, Paul E. & Hill, Marylu. Thomas Carlyle Resartus: Reappraising Carlyle's Contribution to the Philosophy of History, Political Theory, & Cultural Criticism. 2010. 67.50 *(978-0-8386-4223-8(3))* Fairleigh Dickinson Univ. Pr.

Simpson, Alan & McQueen Simpson, Mary, intros. I Too am Here: Selections from the Letters of Jane Welsh Carlyle. 2010. (ENG.). 336p. pap. 29.99 *(978-0-521-13498-9(6))* Cambridge Univ. Pr.

CARLYLE, THOMAS, 1795-1881

Arnold, A. S. The Story of Thomas Carlyle. 2009. 380p. 33.99 *(978-1-116-22166-4(7))*; 38.99 *(978-1-116-22165-7(9))*; pap. 32.75 *(978-1-116-22168-8(3))* BiblioBazaar.

—The Story of Thomas Carlyle. 2008. 400p. 49.95 *(978-1-4374-1201-7(7))*; pap. 34.95 *(978-1-4373-2520-1(3))* Kessinger Publishing, LLC.

Blunt, Reginald. The Carlyles' Chelsea Home. 2009. 160p. 36.95 *(978-1-104-54447-8(4))*; pap. 21.95 *(978-1-104-48197-1(9))* Kessinger Publishing, LLC.

Campbell, Ian. Thomas Carlyle. 2011. 192p. pap. ***(978-1-84921-089-8(6))*** Kennedy & Boyd.

Carlyle, Jane Welsh. Letters & Memorials of Jane Welsh Carlyle. Carlyle, Thomas & Froude, James Anthony, eds. 2011. (Cambridge Library Collection - Literary Studies). (ENG.). 410p. pap. 31.99 *(978-1-108-02925-4(6))*; 410p. pap. 31.99 *(978-1-108-02926-1(4))*; 352p. pap. 28.99 *(978-1-108-02927-8(2))* Cambridge Univ. Pr.

Carlyle, Thomas. Collectanea Thomas Carlyle, 1821-1855. 2009. 148p. 21.99 *(978-1-103-95457-5(1))*; pap. 15.99 *(978-1-103-95447-6(4))* BiblioBazaar.

—Collectanea Thomas Carlyle, 1821-1855. Jones, Samuel Arthur, ed. 2007. (ENG.). 142p. 35.95 *(978-0-548-27238-1(7))*; 144p. per. 20.95 *(978-1-4326-7698-8(9))* Kessinger Publishing, LLC.

—Collectanea Thomas Carlyle, 1821-1855. 2008. 144p. pap. *(978-1-4086-9560-9(X))* Read Bks.

—Correspondence of Thomas Carlyle & Ral. 2007. pap. *(978-1-4065-1272-4(9))* Dodo Pr.

—The Correspondence of Thomas Carlyle & Ralph Waldo Emerson, 1834-1872. 2009. 384p. 26.99 *(978-1-103-16530-8(5))* 2009. 384p. pap. 20.99 *(978-1-103-16529-2(1))*1. 2006. (ENG.). 298p. pap. 23.99 *(978-1-4264-7372-2(9))*2. 2006. (ENG.). 324p. pap. 24.99 *(978-1-4264-7373-9(7))* BiblioBazaar.

—The Correspondence of Thomas Carlyle & Ralph Waldo Emerson, 1834-1872. 2009. 272p. pap. *(978-0-217-75195-7(4))*; 222p. pap. *(978-0-217-75194-0(6))*; 204p. pap. *(978-0-217-07535-0(5))* Books LLC.

—Early Letters of Thomas Carlyle. 2008. 392p. pap. 32.75 *(978-0-559-52299-4(1))* BiblioBazaar.

—Early Letters of Thomas Carlyle. 2009. 288p. pap. *(978-0-217-83149-9(4))* Books LLC.

—Early Letters of Thomas Carlyle: 1814-1826. Norton, Charles Eliot, ed. 2007. pap. 33.95 *(978-1-4304-5097-9(5))* Kessinger Publishing, LLC.

—Letters of Thomas Carlyle to His Younges. 2006. pap. 28.95 *(978-1-4286-5341-2(4))* Kessinger Publishing, LLC.

—The Love Letters of Thomas Carlyle & Jane Welsh. 2009. 296p. pap. 20.03 *(978-1-4589-2888-7(8))*; pap. 20.12 *(978-1-4589-2890-0(X))* General Bks. LLC.

—New Letters of Thomas Carlyle V1. Carlyle, Alexander, ed. 2007. (ENG.). 356p. 46.95 *(978-0-548-10698-3(3))* Kessinger Publishing, LLC.

—New Letters of Thomas Carlyle V2. Carlyle, Alexander, ed. 2007. (ENG.). 376p. 48.95 *(978-0-548-10699-0(1))* Kessinger Publishing, LLC.

—On Heroes & Hero Worship & the Heroic in History. 2008. 240p. 24.99 *(978-0-554-35894-9(8))* 2008. 240p. 27.99 *(978-0-554-26591-9(5))* 2007. (ENG.). 214p. pap. 20.99 *(978-1-4346-1445-2(X))* 2007. (ENG.). 236p. pap. 22.99 *(978-1-4346-1539-8(1))* BiblioBazaar.

—Reminiscences. 2009. 352p. 25.99 *(978-1-103-80204-3(6))*; pap. 19.99 *(978-1-103-80196-1(1))* BiblioBazaar.

—Reminiscences. 2009. 66p. pap. *(978-0-217-85249-4(1))* Books LLC.

—Reminiscences. Campbell, Ian & Fielding, K. J., eds. 2009. 488p. pap. *(978-1-84921-000-3(4))* Kennedy & Boyd.

—Thomas Carlyle: Letters to His Wife. Bliss, Trudy, ed. 2011. 418p. 54.95 ***(978-1-258-08732-6(4))*** Literary Licensing, LLC.

Carlyle, Thomas. Thomas Carlyle Table Talk. 2006. pap. 16.95 *(978-1-4286-5583-6(2))* Kessinger Publishing, LLC.

Carlyle, Thomas & Emerson, Ralph Waldo. The Correspondence of Thomas Carlyle & Ralph Waldo Emerson, 1834-1872. 2008. 300p. 28.99 *(978-0-554-24731-1(3))*; 328p. 28.99 *(978-0-554-34035-7(6))*; 300p. 25.99 *(978-0-554-34034-0(8))*; 328p. 29.99 *(978-0-554-24732-8(1))* BiblioBazaar.

Carlyle, Thomas & Norton, Charles Eliot. Reminiscences. 2009. 618p. 38.99 *(978-1-115-49199-0(7))*; 45.99 *(978-1-115-49198-3(9))*; pap. 44.75 *(978-1-115-49201-0(2))*; pap. 45.75 *(978-1-115-49200-3(4))* BiblioBazaar.

Chesterton, G. K. Simplicity & Tolstoy. reprint ed. lib. bdg. 98.00 *(978-0-7426-3005-5(6))* Classic Bks.

Chesterton, G. K. & Hodder-Willams, J. E. Thomas Carlyle. 2010. 54p. 31.95 *(978-1-161-72643-5(8))* 2007. (ENG.). 52p. per. 16.95 *(978-0-548-78604-8(6))* Kessinger Publishing, LLC.

Chesterton, G. K. & Hodder-Williams, J. E. Thomas Carlyle. 2010. 50p. pap. 16.75 *(978-1-146-38726-2(1))* BiblioBazaar.

Christie, William, ed. The Letters of Francis Jeffrey to Thomas & Jane Welsh Carlyle, 1 vol. 2008. (Pickering Masters Ser.). (ENG.). 240p. 195.00 *(978-1-85196-982-1(9))* Pickering & Chatto Pubs., Ltd. GBR. Dist: Ashgate Publishing Co.

Conway, Moncure Daniel. Thomas Carlyle. 2009. 276p. 24.99 *(978-1-103-94322-7(7))* 2009. 276p. pap. 18.99 *(978-1-103-94314-2(6))* 2009. 276p. 24.99 *(978-1-103-62223-8(4))* 2009. 276p. pap. 18.99 *(978-1-103-62219-1(6))* 2008. 236p. 24.99 *(978-0-559-70508-3(5))* 2008. 236p. pap. 25.75 *(978-0-559-70505-2(0))* BiblioBazaar.

—Thomas Carlyle. 2009. 166p. pap. *(978-0-217-40538-6(X))* Books LLC.

—Thomas Carlyle. 2009. 196p. pap. 19.99 *(978-1-4590-0733-8(6))* General Bks. LLC.

Dickerson, Vanessa D. Dark Victorians. 2008. 176p. 37.00 *(978-0-252-03256-1(X))* Univ. of Illinois Pr.

Elbert Hubbard. Little Journeys to the Homes of the Great, Volume I: Little Journeys to the Homes of Good Men & Great. 2006. (ENG.). 206p. pap. 20.99 *(978-1-4264-6534-5(3))* BiblioBazaar.

Forster, Joseph. Four Great Teachers: John Ruskin, Thomas Carlyle, Ralph Waldo. 2007. pap. 20.95 *(978-1-4304-9879-7(X))* Kessinger Publishing, LLC.

Froude, James Anthony. Thomas Carlyle: A History of his Life in London, 1834-1881. 2011. (Cambridge Library Collection - Literary Studies). (ENG.). 500p. pap. 35.99 *(978-1-108-02933-9(7))*; (Illus.). 476p. pap. 34.99 *(978-1-108-02932-2(9))* Cambridge Univ. Pr.

—Thomas Carlyle: A History of the First Forty Years of his Life, 1795-1835. 2011. (Cambridge Library Collection - Literary Studies). (ENG.). 508p. pap. 37.99 *(978-1-108-02930-8(2))*; (Illus.). 462p. pap. 34.99 *(978-1-108-02929-2(9))* Cambridge Univ. Pr.

—Thomas Carlyle V1 A History of His Life. 2006. pap. 37.95 *(978-1-4286-3587-6(4))* Kessinger Publishing, LLC.

—Thomas Carlyle V2 A History of His Life. 2006. pap. 38.95 (978-1-4286-3589-0(0)) Kessinger Publishing, LLC.
Garnett, Richard. Life of Thomas Carlyle. 2009. 188p. 30.99 (978-1-115-91113-9(9)); 26.99 (978-1-115-91114-6(7)); pap. 21.75 (978-1-115-91116-0(3)) BiblioBazaar.
—Life of Thomas Carlyle. 2009. 132p. pap. (978-1-150-56806-0(2)) Books LLC.
—Life of Thomas Carlyle. 2006. (ENG.). pap. 26.95 (978-1-4286-3536-4(X)) Kessinger Publishing, LLC.
—The Life of Thomas Carlyle. 2007. (ENG.). 228p. 41.95 (978-0-548-12561-8(9)) Kessinger Publishing, LLC.
Helming, Steven. The Esoteric Comedies of Carlyle, Newman, & Yeats. 2009. (ENG.). 288p. pap. 38.99 (978-0-521-10969-7(8)) Cambridge Univ. Pr.
Hubbard, Elbert. Little Journeys to the Homes of Good Men & Great. 2009. 36p. pap. 15.75 (978-1-113-05901-7(X)) BiblioBazaar.
—Little Journeys to the Homes of Good Men & Great. 2009. 104p. pap. (978-1-151-35597-3(6)) Books LLC.
—Little Journeys to the Homes of Good Men & Great. 2008. 160p. pap. (978-1-4086-8456-6(X)) Read Bks.
—Little Journeys to the Homes of the Great: Little Journeys to the Homes of Good Men, 1. l.t. ed. 2007. 226p. pap. 22.99 (978-1-4264-6593-2(9)) BiblioBazaar.
Jenkins, Ellen J. Eighteenth-Century British Historians. 2007. (Dictionary of Literary Biography Ser.). (ENG., Illus.). 512p. 315.00 (978-0-7876-8154-8(7)) Cengage Gale.
Johnson, William Savage. Thomas Carlyle: A Study of His Literary Apprenticeship, 1814-1831. 2008. 148p. 21.99 (978-0-559-20857-7(X)); pap. 20.75 (978-0-559-20854-6(5)) BiblioBazaar.
Kerry, Paul E. & Hill, Marylu. Thomas Carlyle Resartus: Reappraising Carlyle's Contribution to the Philosophy of History, Political Theory, & Cultural Criticism. 2010. 67.50 (978-0-8386-4223-8(3)) Fairleigh Dickinson Univ. Pr.
Larkin, Henry. Carlyle & the Open Secret of His Life. 2010. 424p. pap. 35.75 (978-1-178-35868-1(2)); 394p. pap. 33.75 (978-1-177-14991-4(5)); 390p. pap. 33.75 (978-1-143-02633-1(0)) BiblioBazaar.
—Carlyle & the Open Secret of His Life. 2009. 222p. pap. (978-1-4590-3820-2(7)) Books LLC.
—Carlyle & the Open Secret of His Life. 2008. 384p. 48.95 (978-1-4365-3584-7(0)) 2007. (ENG.). 388p. per. 33.95 (978-0-548-73458-2(5)) Kessinger Publishing, LLC.
Lehman, Benjamin H. Carlyle's Theory of the Hero. reprint ed. 24.50 (978-0-404-03949-3(9)) AMS Pr., Inc.
Lippincott, Benjamin Evans. Victorian Critics of Democracy: Carlyle, Ruskin, Arnold, Stephen, Maine, Lecky. 2009. (ENG.). 292p. pap. 50.00 (978-0-8166-5928-9(1)) Univ. of Minnesota Pr.
MacCunn, John. Six Radical Thinkers: Bentham, J. S. Mill, Cobden, Carlyle, Mazzini, T. H. Green. 2007. (ENG.). 274p. 42.95 (978-0-548-18676-3(6)); 276p. per. 27.95 (978-1-4304-9028-9(4)) Kessinger Publishing, LLC.
Masson, David. Memories of London in the Forties. 2007. (ENG.). 258p. 42.95 (978-0-548-21479-4(4)); 260p. per. 27.95 (978-1-4325-3444-8(0)) Kessinger Publishing, LLC.
Morrow, John. Thomas Carlyle. 2007. (ENG., Illus.). 304p. per. 29.95 (978-1-85285-544-4(4), Hambledon Continuum) Continuum International Publishing Group, Ltd. GBR. Dist: National Bk. Network.
Nichol, John. Thomas Carlyle. Morley, John, ed. (English Men of Letters Ser.). reprint ed. lib. bdg. 27.50 (978-0-404-51723-6(4)) AMS Pr., Inc.
—Thomas Carlyle. 2010. 282p. pap. 28.75 (978-1-178-35788-2(0)) 2010. 260p. 34.99 (978-1-117-94439-5(5)) 2010. 260p. pap. 26.75 (978-1-117-94440-1(9)) 2009. 260p. 24.99 (978-1-103-08854-6(8)) 2009. 268p. 24.99 (978-1-103-15445-6(1)) 2009. 268p. pap. 18.99 (978-1-103-15443-2(5)) 2009. 260p. pap. 18.99 (978-1-103-08851-5(3)) 2008. 155p. 28.99 (978-0-554-89472-0(6)) 2008. 244p. 27.99 (978-0-554-26871-2(X)) 2008. 244p. 24.99 (978-0-554-36174-1(4)) 2008. 236p. 25.99 (978-0-554-89482-9(3)) 2008. 236p. pap. 26.75 (978-0-554-89480-5(7)) 2008. 155p. pap. 27.75 (978-0-554-89475-1(0)) 2007. 214p. pap. 20.99 (978-1-4346-2037-8(9)) 2007. (ENG.). 240p. pap. 22.99 (978-1-4346-2066-8(2)) BiblioBazaar.
—Thomas Carlyle. 2011. (Cambridge Library Collection - English Men of Letters Ser.). (ENG.). 264p. pap. 23.99 **(978-1-108-03447-0(0))** Cambridge Univ. Pr.
—Thomas Carlyle. 2007. (ENG.). 196p. per. (978-1-4065-4041-3(2)) Dodo Pr.
—Thomas Carlyle. 2010. (Illus.). 138p. pap. 22.72 (978-1-153-72764-8(1)) General Bks. LLC.
—Thomas Carlyle. 2010. 176p. pap. (978-1-4076-5444-7(6)) HardPr.
Ralli, Augustus. Guide to Carlyle. 2009. 326p. pap. 24.76 (978-0-217-31534-0(8)) General Bks. LLC.
—Guide to Carlyle. 2008. 454p. 52.95 (978-0-548-94053-2(3)) 2007. (ENG.). 456p. per. 37.95 (978-0-548-60868-5(7)) Kessinger Publishing, LLC.
Roe, Frederick William. Thomas Carlyle As a Critic of Literature. 2008. 172p. 36.95 (978-1-4374-2683-0(2)); pap. 21.95 (978-1-4373-5061-6(5)) Kessinger Publishing, LLC.
Scurr, Ruth. Carlyle's the French Revolution: Continuum Histories 5. 2010. (Continuum Histories Ser.). (ENG.). 208p. 16.95 (978-0-8264-4052-5(5)) Continuum International Publishing Group, Ltd. GBR. Dist: National Bk. Network.
Taylor, Jonathan. Science & Omniscience in Nineteenth-Century Literature. 2007. (ENG.). 202p. (C). 69.50 (978-1-84519-125-2(0)) Sussex Academic Pr. GBR. Dist: International Specialized Bk. Services.
Thrall, Miriam M. Rebellious Fraser's: Nol Yorke's Magazine in the Days of Maginn, Thackeray & Carlyle. reprint ed. 29.50 (978-0-404-06458-7(2)) AMS Pr., Inc.
Wilson, David Alec. Carlyle till Marriage 1795 To 1826. 2007. (ENG.). 464p. 52.95 (978-0-548-01657-2(7)) Kessinger Publishing, LLC.
Wylie, William Howie. Thomas Carlyle: The Man & His Books. 2007. (ENG.). 464p. 52.95 (978-0-548-03876-5(7)) Kessinger Publishing, LLC.

CARMAN, WILLIAM BLISS, 1861-1929

Bliss Carman & Richard Hovey. Short Works of Bliss Carman & Richard Hovey. 2007. (ENG.). 256p. per. 21.99 (978-1-4346-0981-6(2)); 306p. pap. 24.99 (978-1-4346-1080-5(2)) BiblioBazaar.

CARMEL (CALIF.)

Brown, Ann Marie. Monterey & Carmel: Including Santa Cruz & Big Sur. 3rd ed. 2009. (Moon Handbooks Ser.). (ENG., Illus.). 250p. pap. 16.95 (978-1-56691-995-1(9)) Westview Pr.
Seavey, Kent. Carmel: A History in Architecture. 2007. (Images of America Ser.). (ENG., Illus.). 128p. per. 19.99 (978-0-7385-4705-3(0)) Arcadia Publishing.

CARMELITE NUNS

Mason, Agnes, tr. Saint Theresa: The History of her Foundations. 2011. (ENG.). 326p. pap. 22.99 (978-1-107-65545-4(5)) Cambridge Univ. Pr.
Of the Blessed Trinity, Sister Elizabeth. The Praise of Glory: Sister Elizabeth of the Blessed Trinity. 2007. 15.95 (978-1-930278-51-6(9)) Loreto Pubns.
Traflet, Dianne Marie. Saint Edith Stein: A Spiritual Portrait. 2008. (Illus.). 208p. pap. 16.95 (978-0-8198-7108-4(7)) Pauline Bks. & Media.

CARMELITES

Bernanos, Georges. Dialogue des Carmelites. (Coll. Le Livre de Vie). (FRE.). pap. 10.95 (978-0-8288-9079-3(X), F87641) French & European Pubns., Inc.
Boyce, James John. Carmelite Liturgy & Spiritual Identity: The Choir Books of Krakow. 2009. (Medieval Church Studies). (ENG, FRE & LAT., Illus.). 524p. (C). 152.00 (978-2-503-51714-8(5)) Brepols Pubs. BEL. Dist: ISD.
Brice, Father & Brice. Teresa, John, & Therese: A Family Portrait of Three Great Carmelites. 2011. 336p. 50.95 **(978-1-258-04232-5(0))** Literary Licensing, LLC.
Chick, H., ed. & tr. A Chronicle of the Carmelites in Persia: The Safavids & the Papal Mission of the 17th & 18th Centuries. 2012. (ENG.). 1424p. 349.00 **(978-1-84885-768-1(3))** I. B. Tauris & Co., Ltd. GBR. Dist: Macmillan.
Culligan, Kevin G., ed. A Better Wine: Essays Celebrating Kieran Kavanaugh, O. C. D. 2007. (Carmelite Studies: Vol. 10). (Illus.). pap. (978-0-935216-41-7(3)) I C S Pubns.
Deeney, Aloysius. Welcome to the Secular Order of Discalced Carmelites. 2009. pap. 12.95 (978-0-935216-75-2(8)) I C S Pubns.
Esteve, Enrique Maria & Guarch, Joaquin M. Carmel, Mary's Own, Part: A History of the Carmelite Order. Pausback, Gabriel N., tr. 2011. 72p. 36.95 **(978-1-258-01867-2(5))** Literary Licensing, LLC.
Irish Carmelites, ed. Meeting God: Carmelite Reflections & Prayers. 2008. (ENG., Illus.). 155p. 26.95 (978-1-85607-587-9(7)) Columba Pr. IRL. Dist: Dufour Editions, Inc.
Jotischky, Andrew. The Perfection of Solitude. 2008. pap. 28.95 (978-0-271-02831-6(9)) Pennsylvania State Univ. Pr.
Payne, Steven. The Carmelite Tradition. 2011. E-Book (978-0-8146-3953-5(4)) Liturgical Pr.
Rohrbach, Peter-Thomas. Journey to Carith: The Sources & Story of the Discalced Carmelites. 2007. 228p. pap. (978-0-935216-45-5(6)) I C S Pubns.
Teresa, Mary. The Servant of God: Mother Mary Teresa of St. Joseph. Bittle, Berchmans, tr. 2011. 316p. 50.95 **(978-1-258-02099-6(8))** Literary Licensing, LLC.

CARMICHAEL, STOKELY, 1941-1998

Joseph, Peniel E. Dark Days, Bright Nights: From Black Power to Barack Obama. 2010. (ENG.). 288p. (gr. 13). 26.00 (978-0-465-01366-1(X), Basic Civitas Bks.) Basic Bks.

CARNAP, RUDOLF, 1891-1970

Bonk, Thomas, ed. Language, Truth & Knowledge: Contributions to the Philosophy of Rudolf Carnap. 2010. (Vienna Circle Institute Library). 216p. pap. 139.00 (978-90-481-6258-1(0), 9048162580) Springer.
Butrick, Richard. Carnap on meaning & Analyticity. (Janua Linguarum. Series Minor Ser.). (ENG.). 77p. 210.00 **(978-3-11-213364-4(1))**; 135.00 **(978-3-11-129213-7(4))** De Gruyter, Mouton DEU. Dist: de Gruyter, Walter GmbH & Co. KG.
Carus, A. W. Carnap & Twentieth-Century Thought: Explication as Enlightenment. (ENG.). 2010. 364p. pap. 42.00 (978-0-521-13086-8(7)) 2008. 360p. 93.00 (978-0-521-86227-1(2)) Cambridge Univ. Pr.
Creath, Richard & Friedman, Michael, eds. The Cambridge Companion to Carnap. 2008. (Cambridge Companions to Philosophy Ser.). (ENG.). 390p. per. 28.99 (978-0-521-54945-5(0)) Cambridge Univ. Pr.
—The Cambridge Companion to Carnap. 2008. (Cambridge Companions to Philosophy Ser.). (ENG.). 390p. 84.99 (978-0-521-84015-6(5)) Cambridge Univ. Pr.
Haddock, Guillermo E. Rosado. The Young Carnap's Unknown Master: Husserl's Influence on der Raum & der Logische Aufbau der Welt. 2008. 150p. 99.95 (978-0-7546-6158-0(X)) Ashgate Publishing Co.
Kazemier, B. H. & Vuysje, D., eds. Logic & Language: Studies dedicated to Professor Rudolf Carnap on the Occasion of his Seventieth Birthday. 2010. (Synthese Library). 256p. pap. 139.00 (978-90-481-8319-7(7), 9048183197) Springer.
Richardson, Alan W. Carnap's Construction of the World: The Aufbau & the Emergence of Logical Empiricism. 2008. (ENG.). 256p. pap. 40.00 (978-0-521-05200-9(9)) Cambridge Univ. Pr.
Uebel, Thomas. Empiricism at the Crossroads: The Vienna Circle's Protocol-Sentence Debate. 2007. (Full Circle Ser.). (ENG.). 650p. per. 89.95 (978-0-8126-9640-0(9)) Open Court Publishing Co.
Wagner, Pierre. Carnap's Logical Syntax of Language. 2009. (History of Analytic Philosophy Ser.). (ENG., Illus.). 304p. 100.00 (978-0-230-20151-4(2)) Palgrave Macmillan.
Wagner, Pierre, ed. Carnap's Ideal of Explication & Naturalism. 2012. (History of Analytic Philosophy Ser.). (ENG., Illus.). 288p. 85.00 **(978-0-230-28259-9(8))** Palgrave Macmillan.

CARNATACA LANGUAGE

see Kannada Language

CARNATIONS

Brotherston, R. & Smith, Martin. The Book of the Carnation. 2008. (Gardening in America Ser.). (ENG.). 148p. pap. 11.95 (978-1-4290-1462-5(8)) Applewood Bks.
Cook, Ernest, ed. Carnations, Picotees, & the Wild & Garden Pinks. 2009. (Gardening in America Ser.). (ENG.). 216p. pap. 15.95 (978-1-4290-1380-2(X)) Applewood Bks.
Lamborn, Levi. American Carnation Culture. 2008. (Gardening in America Ser.). (ENG.). 188p. pap. 13.95 (978-1-4290-1375-8(3)) Applewood Bks.
McLeod, J., et al. Carnations & Pinks. 2010. (Gardening in America Ser.). (ENG., Illus.). 132p. pap. 9.95 (978-1-4290-9117-6(7)) Applewood Bks.
Roychowdhury, Rajib. Effect of Chemical Mutagens on Carnation. 2011. 276p. pap. **(978-3-8443-0840-2(7))** Lambert Academic Publishing.
Ward, Charles. The American Carnation. 2008. (Gardening in America Ser.). (ENG.). 308p. pap. 20.95 (978-1-4290-1385-7(0)) Applewood Bks.

CARNEGIE, ANDREW, 1835-1919

Carnegie, Andrew. Andrew Carnegie's Own Story for Boys & Girls. Tappan, Eva March, ed. 2011. 170p. 41.95 **(978-1-258-00244-2(2))** Literary Licensing, LLC.
—Autobiography of Andrew Carnegie. 2010. (ENG.). 408p. pap. 34.75 (978-1-176-20901-5(9)) 2010. 470p. pap. 37.75 (978-1-148-90878-6(1)) 2008. 360p. 31.99 (978-0-554-26556-8(7)) 2008. 360p. 29.99 (978-0-554-35859-8(X)) 2007. (ENG.). 326p. per. 23.99 (978-1-4346-1341-7(0)) BiblioBazaar.
—Autobiography of Andrew Carnegie. 2007. (ENG.). 400p. 32.95 (978-1-60206-964-0(6)) Cosimo, Inc.
—Autobiography of Andrew Carnegie. 2007. (Illus.). pap. (978-1-4065-1286-1(9)) Dodo Pr.
—Autobiography of Andrew Carnegie. 2007. (ENG.). 228p. per. (978-1-4068-1523-8(3)) Echo Library.
—Autobiography of Andrew Carnegie. 2010. (Illus.). 218p. pap. 9.65 (978-1-77045-267-1(2)) 2009. 232p. pap. 9.65 (978-1-150-06095-3(6)) General Bks. LLC.
—Autobiography of Andrew Carnegie. 2007. (ENG.). 400p. 49.95 (978-0-548-21317-9(8)); per. 34.95 (978-1-4325-3244-4(8)) Kessinger Publishing, LLC.
—The Autobiography of Andrew Carnegie. 2007. 412p. 22.99 (978-1-59986-695-6(1)) Filiquarian Publishing, LLC.
—The Autobiography of Andrew Carnegie. 2011. (ENG.). 416p. pap. 19.99 (978-1-61039-082-8(2)); (Illus.). 35.00 (978-1-61039-080-4(6)) PublicAffairs.
—Autobiography of Andrew Carnegie. l.t. ed. 2007. (ENG.). 360p. per. 26.99 (978-1-4346-1393-6(3)) BiblioBazaar.
—The Autobiography of Andrew Carnegie & the Gospel of Wealth. 2009. 192p. pap. 8.99 (978-1-4209-3296-6(9)) Digireads.com.
—The Autobiography of Andrew Carnegie & the Gospel of Wealth. 2006. (ENG.). 352p. (gr. 12-18). 6.95 (978-0-451-53038-7(1), Signet Classics) Penguin Group (USA) Inc.
Carnegie, Andrew & Van Dyke, John Charles. Autobiography of Andrew Carnegie. 2010. (ENG.). 466p. pap. 37.75 (978-1-176-44745-5(9)); 468p. pap. 37.75 (978-1-141-90070-1(X)) BiblioBazaar.
Derbyshire, Wyn. Six Tycoons: Lives of John Astor, Vanderbilt, Carnegie, Henry Ford & J. D. Rockefeller. 2008. (Illus.). 251p. 36.95 (978-1-904905-84-4(6)) Spiramus Pr. GBR. Dist: International Specialized Bk. Services.
—Six Tycoons: The Lives of John Jacob Astor, Cornelius Vanderbilt, Andrew Carnegie, John D. Rockefeller, Henry Ford & Joseph P. Kennedy. 2009. 251p. pap. 14.95 (978-1-904905-85-1(4)) Spiramus Pr. GBR. Dist: International Specialized Bk. Services.
Eisenstadt, A. S. Carnegie's Model Republic: Triumphant Democracy & the British-American Relationship. 2008. xv, 204p. pap. 24.95 (978-0-7914-7224-8(8)) State Univ. of New York Pr.
Gangewere, Robert J. Palace of Culture: Andrew Carnegie's Museums & Library in Pittsburgh. 2011. (ENG., Illus.). 360p. 35.00 **(978-0-8229-4397-6(2))** Univ. of Pittsburgh Pr.
Hill, Dave & Hill, Napoleon. Think & Grow Rich: The Original Classic. deluxe ed. 2009. (ENG.). 388p. 14.95 (978-1-906465-59-9(2), Capstone) Wiley, John & Sons, Inc.
Hill, Napoleon. Earl Nightingale Reads Think & Grow Rich. 2009. 308p. 28.99 (978-0-559-07955-9(9)); 29.99 (978-0-559-07940-5(0)); pap. 28.75 (978-0-559-07951-1(6)); pap. 25.99 (978-0-559-07944-3(3)) BiblioBazaar.
—Earl Nightingale Reads Think & Grow Rich. 2009. 236p. pap. 18.95 (978-1-58509-333-5(5)) Book Tree, The.
—Earl Nightingale Reads Think & Grow Rich. 2007. (Dover Empower Your Life Ser.). (ENG.). 272p. per. 6.95 (978-0-486-45946-2(2)) Dover Pubns., Inc.
—Earl Nightingale Reads Think & Grow Rich. 2009. 248p. pap. 14.95 (978-1-4341-0252-2(1)) Editorium, The.
—Earl Nightingale Reads Think & Grow Rich. 2007. (ENG.). 260p. 19.99 (978-1-59986-685-7(4)) Filiquarian Publishing, LLC.
—Earl Nightingale Reads Think & Grow Rich. Hartley, Bill & Hartley, Ann, eds. 21st ed. 2007. (ENG., Illus.). 256p. pap., wbk. ed. 19.95 (978-1-932429-32-9(8)) Highroads Media, Inc.
—Earl Nightingale Reads Think & Grow Rich. 2009. 329p. pap. 20.01 (978-0-557-08320-6(6)) Lulu Enterprises Inc.
—Earl Nightingale Reads Think & Grow Rich. 2007. 310p. pap. 13.50 (978-1-59280-260-9(5)) Marketplace Bks., Inc.
—Earl Nightingale Reads Think & Grow Rich. 2011. (ENG.). 238p. pap. 12.80 (978-1-936594-22-1(6)) Tribeca Bks.
—Earl Nightingale Reads Think & Grow Rich. 204p. 2008. (ENG.). per. 7.49 (978-1-60459-187-3(0)) 2007. 29.95 (978-1-934451-34-2(7)) 2007. (ENG.). per. 6.99 (978-1-934451-35-9(5)) Wilder Pubns., Ltd.
—Piense y hágase Rico. 2010. (Vintage Espanol Ser.). (SPA & ENG.). 368p. pap. 15.00 (978-0-307-47582-4(4), Vintage) Knopf Doubleday Publishing Group.
—Think & Grow Rich. 2010. (ENG.). 238p. pap. 11.80 (978-1-4414-0789-4(8)) CreateSpace.
—Think & Grow Rich: Complete Original, Unaltered Text: Special 70th Anniversary Edition. 2007. (ENG.). 200p. per. 9.99 (978-0-9794154-7-0(0)) Arc Manor.
—Think & Grow Rich: Hard Cover: Complete Original Text: Special 70th Anniversary Edition. 2007. 244p. 29.99 (978-1-60450-015-8(8)) Arc Manor.
—Think & Grow Rich: Original Version. 2007. (ENG.). 148p. per. (978-956-9569-61-6(1)); 232p. (978-956-291-042-2(3)) Editorial Benei Noaj.
—Think & Grow Rich: The 21st-Century. rev. ed. 2008. (ENG.). 352p. pap. 19.95 (978-1-932429-35-0(2)) Highroads Media, Inc.
—Think & Grow Rich: The Original Version. 2007. 232p. per. (978-956-291-324-9(4)) Editorial Benei Noaj.
—Think & Grow Rich Deluxe Edition. deluxe ed. 2008. (ENG.). 400p. (gr. 12-18). 19.95 (978-1-58542-659-1(8), Tarcher) Penguin Group (USA) Inc.
—Think & Grow Rich. Hardcover with Dust-Jacket. Complete Original Text of the Classic 1937 Edition. 2007. 244p. 37.79 (978-1-60450-007-3(7)) Arc Manor.
—Think Your Way to Wealth. 2011. (ENG.). 384p. (gr. 12). 12.95 (978-1-58542-894-6(9), Tarcher) Penguin Group (USA) Inc.
Hill, Napoleon & Clason, George. Think & Grow Rich by Napoleon Hill & Richest Man in Babylon by George S Clason. 2007. 256p. (978-956-291-510-6(7)) Editorial Benei Noaj.
—Think & Grow Rich by Napoleon Hill & the Richest Man in Babylon by George S Clason. 2007. 264p. per. (978-956-291-511-3(5)) Editorial Benei Noaj.
Hill, Napoleon & Maupassant, Guy de. My Uncle Jules & Other Stories(Mon Oncle Jules et Autres Contes) Appelbaum, Stanley, ed. & tr. by. 2007. (Dover Dual Language French Ser.). (FRE & ENG.). 224p. per. 12.95 (978-0-486-45753-6(2)) Dover Pubns., Inc.
Lamont-Brown, Raymond. Carnegie: The Richest Man in the World. 2006. (ENG., Illus.). 284p. per. 14.95 (978-0-7509-3371-1(2)) Sutton Publishing.
Morris, Charles R. The Tycoons: How Andrew Carnegie, John D. Rockefeller, Jay Gould, & J. P. Morgan Invented the American Supereconomy. 2006. (ENG., Illus.). 400p. pap. 18.00 (978-0-8050-8134-3(8), Owl Bks.) Holt, Henry & Co.
Think & Grow Rich. 2008. 29.90 (978-1-60591-038-3(4)) Title Player, Inc.
Winkler, John K. Incredible Carnegie. 2006. 320p. per. (978-1-4067-2946-7(9), Hesperides Pr.) Read Bks.

CARNEGIE CORPORATION OF NEW YORK

Keppel, Frederick P. Philanthropy & Learning with Other Papers. reprint ed. 20.00 (978-0-404-03660-7(0)) AMS Pr., Inc.

CARNEGIE ENDOWMENT FOR INTERNATIONAL PEACE

Hesperides. Carnegie Endowment for International Peace Year Book For 1915. 2007. 204p. per. (978-1-4067-5706-4(3), Hesperides Pr.) Read Bks.

CARNEGIE HALL (NEW YORK, N.Y.)

Page, Tim & Hall, Carnegie. Carnegie Hall Treasures. 2011. (ENG., Illus.). 192p. 75.00 (978-0-06-170367-6(2), Collins Design) HarperCollins Pubs.
Tackley, Catherine. Benny Goodman: The Famous 1938 Carnegie Hall Jazz Concert. 2012. (Oxford Studies in Recorded Jazz Ser.). (ENG.). 240p. 74.00 **(978-0-19-539830-4(0))**; pap. 18.95 **(978-0-19-539831-1(9))** Oxford Univ. Pr., Inc.

CARNEGIE-MELLON UNIVERSITY

Hirata, Lauren & Liebermann, Dan. Carnegie Mellon University 2012: Off the Record. 2011. 188p. pap. 16.95 **(978-1-4274-0369-8(4))** College Prowler, Inc.

CARNITINE

Sinatra, Stephen T. The Sinatra Solution: Metabolic Cardiology. 2008. (ENG., Illus.). 272p. pap. 25.95 (978-1-59120-216-5(7)) Basic Health Pubns., Inc.

CARNIVAL

Here are entered works on festivals, merrymaking, and revelry before Lent. Works on traveling amusement enterprises, consisting of sideshows, games of chance, merry-go-rounds, etc. are entered under Carnivals.

see also Masks; Mumming

Crichlow, Michaeline, ed. Carnival Art Culture & Politics. 2012. (ENG., Illus.). 200p. (C). 125.00 **(978-0-415-69276-2(8))** Routledge.
Falke, Stephen & Holder, Geoffrey. Moko Jumbies: The Dancing Spirits of Trinidad. 2006. (ENG., Illus.). 216p. 65.00 (978-0-9727661-3-5(8)) Pointed Leaf Pr.

Galembo, Phyllis, photos by. Maske. 2010. (ENG., Illus.). 208p. 45.00 *(978-1-905712-17-5(0))* Boot, Chris GBR. Dist: D.A.P./Distributed Art Pubs.
Gray, John. From Vodou to Zouk: A Bibliographic Guide to Music of the French-speaking Caribbean & Its Diaspora. 2010. (Black Music Reference Ser.: Vol. 1). 240p. 79.95 *(978-0-9844134-0-9(5))* African Diaspora Pr.
Horsman, Paul V. The Fabulous World of the Carnival. Goldsack, Bob, ed. 88p. pap. 26.95 *(978-1-880545-07-2(1))* Midway Museum Pubns.
Innes, C. D., et al. Carnival: Theory & Practice. 2011. ***(978-1-59221-848-6(2))***; 486p. pap. ***(978-1-59221-849-3(0))*** Africa World Pr.
Mason, John Edwin. One Love, Ghoema Beat: Inside the Cape Town Carnival. 2010. (Reconsiderations in Southern African History Ser.). (ENG., Illus.). 140p. (gr. 17). pap. 24.50 *(978-0-8139-3059-6(6))* Univ. Pr. of Virginia.
Smart, Ian & Bedeau, Koren Allyson. Decoding Carnival: Creole Bacchanal, Pan-African Festival. 2010. (Illus.). xiv, 183p. pap. ***(978-0-939423-26-2(X))*** Original World Pr.
Tanco, Valeria & Cardozo, Yamandú. Agarrate Catalina: El Libro. 2010. (SPA., Illus.). 154p. *(978-9974-95-368-0(5)*, Aguilar) Santillana USA Publishing Co., Inc.

CARNIVAL—EUROPE
Peeren, Esther. Intersubjectivities & Popular Culture: Bakhtin & Beyond. 2007. (Cultural Memory in the Present Ser.). (ENG.). 304p. 60.00 *(978-0-8047-5669-3(4))* Stanford Univ. Pr.

CARNIVAL—ITALY
Bertin, Marco. Masquerade: Una Festa Privata Veneziana. 2006. (ENG.). 80p. 14.95 incl. lp *(978-3-937406-59-6(X))* Edel Classica Gmbh.

CARNIVAL—LOUISIANA—NEW ORLEANS
Gotham, Kevin Fox. Authentic New Orleans: Tourism, Culture, & Race in the Big Easy. 2007. (ENG., Illus.). 288p. 75.00 *(978-0-8147-3185-7(6))*; pap. 24.00 *(978-0-8147-3186-4(4)*, New York Univ. Pr.
Hardy, Arthur. Mardi Gras in New Orleans: An Illustrated History. 3rd ed. 2007. (Illus.). 124p. *(978-0-930892-71-5(2))* Hardy, Arthur Enterprises, Inc.
Jewell, Edwin. Jewell's Crescent City, Illustrated. 2011. (ENG.). 198p. pap. 13.95 ***(978-1-4585-0094-6(2))*** Univ. of Michigan Library.
Kennedy, Al. Big Chief Harrison & the Mardi Gras Indians, 1 vol. 2010. (ENG., Illus.). 416p. 35.00 *(978-1-58980-696-2(4))* Pelican Publishing Co., Inc.
Mistretta, Andrea. Mardi Gras Parade of Posters, 1 vol. 2009. (ENG., Illus.). 96p. 19.95 *(978-1-58980-778-5(2))* Pelican Publishing Co., Inc.
Schindler, Henri. Mardi Gras Treasures: Jewelry of the Golden Age, 1 vol. 2006. (Mardi Gras Treas Ser.). (ENG., Illus.). 160p. 35.00 *(978-1-56554-725-4(X))* Pelican Publishing Co., Inc.
Swirynsky, Vladimir. Mardi Gras 2000. Hassenzahl, Susan L., ed. (Illus.). 52p. pap. 5.00 *(978-1-881786-44-3(7))* New Kiev Publishing.

CARNIVAL—SOUTH AMERICA
George, Terry. Carnival in Rio: Samba, Samba, Samba. 2006. (ENG.). 14.95 incl. lp *(978-3-937406-55-8(7))* Edel Classica Gmbh.
Green, Garth L. & Scher, Philip W., eds. Trinidad Carnival: The Cultural Politics of a Transnational Festival. 2007. (ENG., Illus.). 272p. 60.00 *(978-0-253-34823-4(4)*, 0253348234) Indiana Univ. Pr.
Guilbault, Jocelyne. Governing Sound: Cultural Politics of Trinidad's Carnival Musics. 2007. (Chicago Studies in Ethnomusicology Ser.). (Illus.). 352p. 67.50 *(978-0-226-31059-6(0))* Univ. of Chicago Pr.
—Governing Sound: The Cultural Politics of Trinidad's Carnival Musics. 2007. (Chicago Studies in Ethnomusicology Ser.). (ENG., Illus.). 352p. 30.00 *(978-0-226-31060-2(4))* Univ. of Chicago Pr.
Scott, Anna B. A Fala Que Faz Words That Work. 2010. 328p. pap. *(978-3-639-23512-8(6))* VDM Verlag Dr. Mueller e.K.
Sterzi, Valeria. Deconstructing Gender in Carnival: A Cross Cultural Investigation of a Social Ritual. 2010. (ENG.). 182p. pap. 39.95 *(978-3-8376-1348-3(8))* Transcript Verlag DEU. Dist: Transaction Pubs.

CARNIVAL—UNITED STATES
Chemers, Michael M. Staging Stigma: A Critical Examination of the American Freak Show. 2008. (Palgrave Studies in Theatre & Performance History Ser.). (ENG., Illus.). 192p. 89.00 *(978-0-230-61066-8(8))* Palgrave Macmillan.
Diamond, Heather A. American Aloha: Cultural Tourism & the Negotiation of Tradition. 2008. 288p. (C). 55.00 *(978-0-8248-3171-4(3))* Univ. of Hawaii Pr.
Gabbert, Lisa. Winter Carnival in a Western Town: Identity, Change & the Good of the Community. 2011. 232p. (gr. 13). 26.95 *(978-0-87421-829-9(2)*, Utah State Univ. Pr.) Univ. Pr. of Colorado.
Hunter, Virginia Lee, photos by. Carny: Americana on the Midway. 2007. (ENG., Illus.). 100p. 35.00 *(978-1-884167-66-9(7))* Umbrage Editions.

CARNIVAL PLAYS
Forbes, Bronwen. Make Merry in Step & Song: A Seasonal Treasury of Music, Mummer's Plays & Celebrations in the English Folk Tradition. 2009. (ENG., Illus.). 264p. pap. 19.95 *(978-0-7387-1500-1(X))* Llewellyn Pubns.
Scott, Anna B. A Fala Que Faz Words That Work. 2010. 328p. pap. *(978-3-639-23512-8(6))* VDM Verlag Dr. Mueller e.K.

CARNIVALS
Here are entered works on traveling amusement enterprises, consisting of sideshows, games of chance, merry-go-rounds, etc. Works on festivals, merrymaking, and revelry before Lent, are entered under Carnival.
Bodnar, Les. Carnie. 2010. (ENG., Illus.). 192p. 26.00 *(978-1-58731-101-7(1))* St. Augustine's Pr., Inc.
Bruce, Frank. Showfolk: An Oral History of a Fairground. 2011. (ENG., Illus.). 288p. pap. 14.95 *(978-1-905267-45-3(2))* NMS Enterprises Ltd. - Publishing GBR. Dist: National Bk. Network.
Green, Garth L. & Scher, Philip W., eds. Trinidad Carnival: The Cultural Politics of a Transnational Festival. 2007. (ENG., Illus.). 272p. pap. 21.95 *(978-0-253-21883-4(7)*, 0253218837) Indiana Univ. Pr.
Innes, C. D., et al. Carnival: Theory & Practice. 2011. ***(978-1-59221-848-6(2))***; 486p. pap. ***(978-1-59221-849-3(0))*** Africa World Pr.
Korol-Evans, Kimberly Tony. Renaissance Festivals: Merrying the Past & Present. 2009. (ENG., Illus.). 218p. pap. 35.00 *(978-0-7864-4014-6(7))* McFarland & Co., Inc. Pubs.
Stencell, A. W. Circus & Carnival Ballyhoo: Sideshow Freaks, Jabbers & Blade Box Queens. 2010. (ENG.). 300p. pap. 22.95 *(978-1-55022-880-9(3))* ECW Pr. CAN. Dist: Independent Pubs. Group.
West, Rick & Loika, Mason. Pickled Punks & Girlie Shows: A Life Spent on the Midways of America. 2011. (Illus.). 160p. *(978-0-7643-3703-1(3)*, Schiffer Publishing Ltd) Schiffer Publishing, Ltd.

CARNIVORA
see also names of carnivorous animals
Arment, Chad. Varmints: Mystery Carnivores of North America. 2010. 686p. pap. 29.95 *(978-1-61646-019-8(9))* Coachwhip Pubns.
Aubry, Keith Baker. Biology & Conservation of Martens, Sables, & Fishers: A New Synthesis. 2012. ***(978-0-8014-5088-4(8)***, Comstock Publishing Assocs.) Cornell Univ. Pr.
Bothma, Jacobus du P. Carnivore Ecology in Arid Lands. 2010. (Adaptations of Desert Organisms Ser.). (Illus.). x, 209p. pap. 201.00 *(978-3-642-08213-9(0)*, 3642082130) Springer.
Downes, Jonathan. Smaller Mystery Carnivores of the Westco. 2006. 136p. per. *(978-1-905723-05-8(9))* CFZ Pr.
Gehrt, Stanley D., et al, eds. Urban Carnivores: Ecology, Conflict, & Conservation. 2010. (ENG., Illus.). 304p. (gr. 17). 75.00 *(978-0-8018-9389-6(5))* Johns Hopkins Univ. Pr.
Goswami, Anjali & Friscia, Anthony, eds. Carnivoran Evolution: New Views on Phylogeny, Form & Function. 2010. (Cambridge Studies in Morphology & Molecules: New Paradigms in Evolutionary Bio Ser.). (ENG., Illus.). 506p. 135.00 *(978-0-521-51529-0(7))*; pap. 59.00 *(978-0-521-73586-5(6))* Cambridge Univ. Pr.
Hatler, David F., et al. Carnivores of British Columbia, 1 vol. 2010. (ENG.). 416p. pap. *(978-0-7726-5869-2(2))* Royal British Columbia Museum.
Hunter, Luke. Carnivores of the World. 2011. (Princeton Field Guides). (ENG., Illus.). 240p. pap. 29.95 ***(978-0-691-15228-8(4))*** Princeton Univ. Pr.
Long, Robert, et al, eds. Noninvasive Survey Methods for Carnivores. 2008. (ENG., Illus.). 400p. 90.00 *(978-1-59726-119-7(X))* Island Pr.
MacKay, Paula, et al, eds. Noninvasive Survey Methods for Carnivores. 2008. (ENG., Illus.). 400p. pap. 50.00 *(978-1-59726-120-3(3))* Island Pr.
Rosalino, Luís M. & Gheler-Costa, Carla. Middle-Sized Carnivores in Agricultural Landscapes. 2011. *(978-1-61122-033-9(5))* Nova Science Pubs., Inc.

CARNIVOROUS PLANTS
Barthlott, Wilhelm, et al. Woody Cut Stems for Growers & Florists: Production & Post-Harvest Handling of Branches for Flowers, Fruit, & Foliage. 2008. (ENG., Illus.). 576p. 39.95 *(978-0-88192-892-1(5)*, 0881928925) Timber Pr., Inc.
Darwin, Charles. Insectivorous Plants. 2007. (ENG.). 404p. pap. 26.99 *(978-1-4264-1995-9(3))* BiblioBazaar.
—Insectivorous Plants. 2007. (ENG.). 472p. 52.95 *(978-0-548-16436-5(3))*; 476p. per. 37.95 *(978-1-4304-6068-8(7))* Kessinger Publishing, LLC.
—Insectivorous Plants. 2011. 490p. pap. 38.75 ***(978-1-178-61030-7(6))*** 2011. 480p. pap. 37.75 ***(978-1-172-94343-2(5))*** 2010. (ENG.). 488p. pap. 38.75 *(978-1-171-77239-2(4))* 2010. 482p. pap. 37.75 *(978-1-176-71725-1(1))* 2010. (ENG.). 400p. pap. 34.75 *(978-1-177-46989-0(8))* 2010. 474p. 42.99 *(978-1-117-89580-2(7))* 2010. 474p. pap. 37.75 *(978-1-117-89581-9(5))* 2010. 486p. pap. 38.75 *(978-1-146-35839-2(3))* 2010. 490p. pap. 38.75 *(978-1-147-71466-1(5))* 2010. 484p. pap. 38.75 *(978-1-144-84655-6(2))* 2010. 490p. pap. 38.75 *(978-1-144-73817-2(2))* 2010. 482p. pap. 37.75 *(978-1-145-25180-9(3))* 2010. 478p. pap. 37.75 *(978-1-145-10578-3(1))* 2010. 488p. pap. 38.75 *(978-1-142-76834-8(1))* 2008. 436p. 30.99 *(978-0-554-31617-8(X))* 2008. 436p. 32.99 *(978-0-554-22314-8(7))* BiblioBazaar.
—Insectivorous Plants. 2009. (Illus.). 294p. pap. *(978-1-150-06997-0(X))* Books LLC.
—Insectivorous Plants. 2009. (Cambridge Library Collection - Life Sciences Ser.). (Illus.). 476p. pap. 29.99 *(978-1-108-00484-8(9))* Cambridge Univ. Pr.
—Insectivorous Plants. 2010. (Illus.). 260p. pap. 33.96 *(978-1-153-63101-3(6))* General Bks. LLC.
—Insectivorous Plants. 2010. 356p. 37.56 *(978-1-169-32789-4(3))*; 474p. 42.36 ***(978-1-163-46940-8(8))***; 356p. pap. 25.56 ***(978-1-162-66824-6(3))***; 474p. pap. 30.36 ***(978-1-163-12141-2(X))***; 356p. 46.95 *(978-1-161-43589-1(8))* Kessinger Publishing, LLC.
—Insectivorous Plants. l.t. ed. 2007. (ENG.). 432p. pap. 28.99 *(978-1-4264-2106-8(0))* BiblioBazaar.
—Insectivorous Plants. (Illus.). 377p. reprint ed. lib. bdg. 98.00 *(978-0-7222-3079-4(6))* Library Reprints, Inc.
Darwin, Charles & Darwin, Francis. Insectivorous Plants. 2010. (ENG.). 428p. pap. 35.75 *(978-1-171-67117-6(2))* BiblioBazaar.
McPherson, Stewart. Pitcher Plants of the Americas. 2006. (Illus.). 320p. 44.95 *(978-0-939923-75-5(0))*; pap. 34.95 *(978-0-939923-74-8(2))* McDonald & Woodward Publishing Co., The.
Parks, Samantha & Phillips, Sara. Grow Your Own Venus Fly Trap: Just Add Flies! 2007. (ENG.). 32p. pap. 6.95 *(978-0-7624-2941-7(0))* Running Pr. Bk. Pubs.
Rice, Barry A. Growing Carnivorous Plants. 2006. (ENG., Illus.). 224p. 39.95 *(978-0-88192-807-5(0)*, 0881928070) Timber Pr., Inc.
Schnell, Donald E. Carnivorous Plants of the United States & Canada. 2009. (ENG.). 468p. pap. 39.95 *(978-1-60469-108-5(5)*, 1604691085) Timber Pr., Inc.
Theisen, Inge, et al. The Curious World of Carnivorous Plants: A Comprehensive Guide to Their Biology & Cultivation. 2007. (ENG., Illus.). 224p. 39.95 *(978-0-88192-792-4(9)*, 0881927929) Timber Pr., Inc.
Walters, Martin & Lavelle, Michael. The Illustrated Encyclopedia of Wild Flowers & Flora of the World: An Expert Reference & Identification Guide to over 1730 Wild Flowers & Plants from Every Continent. Walters, Martin, ed. 2012. (ENG., Illus.). 512p. 35.00 *(978-0-7548-1972-1(8))* Anness Publishing GBR. Dist: National Bk. Network.

CARO, JOSEPH, 1488-1575
Epstein, Yechiel M. Aruch Hashulchan, 8 Vols. (HEB.). 65.00 *(978-0-87559-097-4(7))* Shalom, P. Pubns., Inc.

CAROLINA
Reis, Alda Almeida Miranda & Pereira, Maria Rita Brandão. Carolina: Apogeu, Declínio e Ressurgência. 2nd ed. 2007. (POR., Illus.). 94p. *(978-85-88172-52-4(6))* Etica Servicos Editoriais Ltda.
Salley, Alexander S. Narratives of Early Carolina, 1650-1708. 2007. (ENG.). 406p. 49.95 *(978-0-548-25202-4(5))*; 408p. per. 34.95 *(978-1-4326-5490-0(X))* Kessinger Publishing, LLC.

CAROLINA HURRICANES (HOCKEY TEAM)
Codagnone, Brian. The Hartford Whalers. 2007. (Images of Sports Ser.). (ENG., Illus.). 128p. per. 21.99 *(978-0-7385-5501-0(0))* Arcadia Publishing.

CAROLINA MARIA, QUEEN, CONSORT OF FERDINAND I, KING OF THE TWO SICILIES, 1752-1814
Cordy, Jeaffreson. The Queen of Naples & Lord Nelson. 2009. 392p. 33.99 *(978-1-110-73643-0(6))*; pap. 32.75 *(978-1-110-73641-6(X))* BiblioBazaar.
Jeaffreson, John Cordy. The Queen of Naples & Lord Nelson V1: An Historical Biography Based on Manuscripts in the British Museum (1889) 2008. 376p. 48.95 *(978-1-4374-0946-8(6))*; pap. 33.95 *(978-1-4373-2247-7(5))* Kessinger Publishing, LLC.

CAROLINA PANTHERS (FOOTBALL TEAM)
Fowler, Scott & Chandler, Charles. The Year of the Cat. 2007. (ENG., Illus.). 304p. pap. 21.95 *(978-1-4165-7798-0(X))* Simon & Schuster.
Rosinski, Bill & Yasinskas, Pat. Bill Rosinski's Tales from the Carolina Panthers. 2007. (Tales Ser.). (Illus.). 192p. 19.95 *(978-1-59670-178-6(1))* Sports Publishing, LLC.
Tolan, Pamilla S. Mike Minter: Driven by Purpose... the Power of a Dream. Warder, James, ed. 2008. 210p. 21.99 *(978-0-9802051-0-7(7))* Comfort Publishing Services, LLC.

CAROLINA PLAYMAKERS
Koch, Frederick H. Carolina Folk Plays. 2007. (ENG.). 204p. 39.95 *(978-0-548-04529-9(1))* Kessinger Publishing, LLC.

CAROLINE, QUEEN, CONSORT OF GEORGE IV, KING OF GREAT BRITAIN, 1768-1821
Fraser, Flora. The Unruly Queen: The Life of Queen Caroline. 2009. (ENG.). 560p. pap. 16.95 *(978-0-307-45636-6(6)*, Anchor) Knopf Doubleday Publishing Group.
Robins, Jane. The Trial of Queen Caroline: The Scandalous Affair That Nearly Ended a Monarchy. 2006. (ENG., Illus.). 384p. 58.00 *(978-0-7432-5590-5(9)*, Free Pr.) Free Pr.
Swanson, Margaret. George & Caroline. 2011. 124p. pap. ***(978-3-8383-4728-8(5))*** Lambert Academic Publishing.

CAROLINE MATHILDE, QUEEN, CONSORT OF CHRISTIAN VII, KING OF DENMARK, 1751-1775
Henry, Wilkins. A Queen of Tears, Caroline Matilde, Queen of Denmark & Norway & Princess of Great Britain & Ir. 2009. 420p. 34.99 *(978-1-113-45878-0(X))*; pap. 33.75 *(978-1-113-45874-2(7))* BiblioBazaar.
Smyth, Gillespie. The Romance of Diplomacy V2: Historical Memoir of Queen Carolina Matilda of Denmark, Sister to King George the Third. 2007. 496p. 53.95 *(978-0-548-27538-2(6))*; (ENG.). 500p. per. 38.95 *(978-1-4326-8025-1(0))* Kessinger Publishing, LLC.
Smyth, Gillespie & Keith, Robert Murray. The Romance of Diplomacy V1: Historical Memoir of Queen Carolina Matilda of Denmark, Sister to King George the Third (1861) 2009. 518p. 55.95 *(978-1-104-71592-2(9))*; pap. 40.95 *(978-1-104-66485-5(2))* Kessinger Publishing, LLC.
Wraxall, Lascelles. Life & Times of Her Majesty Caroline Matild. 2009. 244p. pap. *(978-0-217-50355-6(1))* Books LLC.

CAROLINE COUNTY (VA.)
Collins, Herbert Ridgeway. Bible Records of Caroline County, Virginia Families. 2008. x, 361p. *(978-0-7884-7508-5(8))*; 372p. pap. 40.00 *(978-0-7884-4758-7(0))* Heritage Bks.

CAROLINE UNIVERSITY
see Univerzita Karlova

CAROLINGIAN ARCHITECTURE
see Architecture, Carolingian

CAROLINGIAN ART
see Art, Carolingian

CAROLINGIANS
see also France—History—to 987
Airlie, Stuart. The Making & Unmaking of the Carolingian World. 2012. (Variorum Collected Studies). 300p. 154.95 ***(978-1-4094-4600-2(X))*** Ashgate Publishing Co.
Booker, Courtney M. Past Convictions: The Penance of Louis the Pious & the Decline of the Carolingians. 2009. (Middle Ages Ser.). (Illus.). 432p. (C). 75.00 *(978-0-8122-4168-6(1))* Univ. of Pennsylvania Pr.
Contreni, John J. Learning & Culture in Carolingian Europe: Letters Numbers Exegesis & Manuscripts. 2011. (Variorum Collected Studies). (Illus.). 336p. 139.95 *(978-1-4094-2041-5(8))* Ashgate Publishing Co.
Dutton, Paul Edward. Charlemagne's Mustache: And Other Cultural Clusters of a Dark Age. 2008. (New Middle Ages Ser.). (ENG., Illus.). 320p. pap. 32.00 *(978-0-230-60247-2(9))* Palgrave Macmillan.
Garipzanov, Ildar H. Symbolic Language of Authority in the Carolingian World (C.751-877) 2008. (Brill's Ser. on the Early Middle Ages Ser.). (Illus.). 544p. *(978-90-04-16669-1(6))* BRILL.
Garver, Valerie L. Women & Aristocratic Culture in the Carolingian World. 2009. (Illus.). 328p. 49.95 *(978-0-8014-4771-6(2))* Cornell Univ. Pr.
Hammer, Carl I. From Ducatus to Regnum: Ruling Bavaria under the Merovingians & Early Carolingians. 2007. (Haute Moyen Age Ser.). (ENG., Illus.). 384p. (C). pap. 87.00 *(978-2-503-52582-2(2))* Brepols Pubs. BEL. Dist: ISD.
Koziol, Geoffrey. The Politics of Memory & Identity in Carolingian Royal Diplomas: The West Frankish Kingdom (840-987) 2012. (Utrecht Studies in Medieval Literacy Ser.). (ENG., Illus.). 661p. (C). 203.00 ***(978-2-503-53595-1(X))*** Brepols Pubs. BEL. Dist: Brown, David Bk. Co., The.
MacLean, Simon, ed. History & Politics in Late Carolingian & Ottonian Europe: The Chronicle of Regino of Prum & Adalbert of Magdeburg. 2009. (Manchester Medieval Sources Ser.). (ENG., Illus.). 328p. 94.00 *(978-0-7190-7134-8(8))*; mass mkt. 34.00 *(978-0-7190-7135-5(6))* Manchester Univ. Pr. GBR. Dist: Macmillan.
McKitterick, Rosamond. Charlemagne: The Formation of a European Identity. 2008. (ENG., Illus.). 478p. (C). pap. 29.99 *(978-0-521-71645-1(4))* Cambridge Univ. Pr. GBR. Dist: Cambridge Univ. Pr.
—Charlemagne: The Formation of Carolingian Identity. 2008. (ENG., Illus.). 478p. (C). 88.00 *(978-0-521-88672-7(4))* Cambridge Univ. Pr.
Nelson, Janet L. Courts, Elites, & Gendered Power in the Early Middle Ages. 2007. (Variorum Collected Studies Series: CS878 Ser.). 346p. 165.00 *(978-0-7546-5933-4(X))* Ashgate Publishing Co.
Noble, Thomas F. X. Images, Iconoclasm, & the Carolingians. 2009. (Middle Ages Ser.). 496p. (C). 69.95 *(978-0-8122-4141-9(X))* Univ. of Pennsylvania Pr.
Scholz, Sebastian. Politik - Selbstverständnis - Selbstdarstellung: Die Päpste in Karolingischer und Ottonischer Zeit. 2006. (Historische Forschungen Ser.). (GER., Illus.). 514p. (C). 87.00 *(978-3-515-08933-3(0))* Steiner, Franz Verlag Wiesbaden GmbH DEU. Dist: Brown, David Bk. Co., The.
Smith, Julia M. H. Province & Empire: Brittany & the Carolingians. 2006. (Cambridge Studies in Medieval Life & Thought). (ENG.). 260p. pap. 53.00 *(978-0-521-03030-4(7))* Cambridge Univ. Pr.
Stone, Rachel. Morality & Masculinity in the Carolingian Empire. 2011. (Cambridge Studies in Medieval Life & Thought: Fourth Ser.). (ENG., Illus.). 420p. 99.00 ***(978-1-107-00674-4(0))*** Cambridge Univ. Pr.
Ullmann, Walter. The Carolingian Renaissance & the Idea of Kingship (Routledge Revivals) 2010. 202p. 115.00 *(978-0-415-57159-3(6)*, Routledge) Taylor & Francis Group GBR. Dist: Taylor & Francis Group.
—The Carolingian Renaissance & the Idea of Kingship the Birkbeck Lectures 1968-9. 2008. 220p. pap. 22.00 *(978-1-59740-541-6(8))* ACLS Humanities E-Book.
Wormald, Patrick & Nelson, Janet L., eds. Lay Intellectuals in the Carolingian World. (ENG.). 278p. 2011. pap. 36.99 *(978-0-521-17409-1(0))* 2007. (Illus.). 104.00 *(978-0-521-83453-7(8))* Cambridge Univ. Pr.

CAROLS
see also Christmas—Poetry; Christmas Music
Ada, Alma Flor & Campoy, F. Isabel. Merry Navidad! Villancicos en Espanol E Ingles/Christmas Carols in Spanish & English. 2007. (ENG & SPA., Illus.). 63p. (J). (gr. k-5). lib. bdg. 17.89 *(978-0-06-058435-1(1)*, Rayo) HarperCollins Pubs.
Ada, Alma Flor, et al. Merry Navidad! Villancicos en Español E Inglés - Christmas Carols in Spanish & English. 2007. (ENG & SPA., Illus.). 64p. (J). (gr. k-5). 16.99 *(978-0-06-058434-4(3)*, Rayo) HarperCollins Pubs.
Albrecht, Sally K., ed. Carols for Solo Singers: 10 Seasonal Favorites Arranged for Solo Voice & Piano for Recitals & Concerts. 2011. (For Solo Singers Ser.). 64p. pap. 24.99 *(978-0-7390-7658-3(2))* Alfred Publishing Co., Inc.
—Carols for Solo Singers: 10 Seasonal Favorites Arranged for Solo Voice & Piano for Recitals & Concerts (Medium High Voice) 2011. (For Solo Singers Ser.). 64p. pap. 15.99 *(978-0-7390-7656-9(6))* Alfred Publishing Co., Inc.
—Carols for Solo Singers: 10 Seasonal Favorites Arranged for Solo Voice & Piano for Recitals & Concerts (Medium Low Voice) 2011. (For Solo Singers Ser.). 64p. pap. 15.99 *(978-0-7390-7659-0(0))*; (ENG.). pap. 24.99 *(978-0-7390-7661-3(2))* Alfred Publishing Co., Inc.
Alexander, Dennis. Especially for Christmas, Book 1: 8 Christmas Favorites Arranged for Early Intermediate to Intermediate Pianists. 2008. (Especially for

C

Christmas Ser.). (ENG.). 24p. pap. 6.95 *(978-0-7390-5576-2(3))* Alfred Publishing Co., Inc.

—Especially for Christmas, Book 2: 8 Christmas Favorites Arranged for Intermediate Pianists. 2008. (Especially for Christmas Ser.). (ENG.). 24p. pap. 6.95 *(978-0-7390-5577-9(1))* Alfred Publishing Co., Inc.

—Especially for Christmas, Book 3: 8 Christmas Favorites Arranged for Late Intermediate Pianists. 2008. (Especially for Christmas Ser.). (ENG.). 24p. pap. 6.95 *(978-0-7390-5578-6(X))* Alfred Publishing Co., Inc.

Alfred Publishing, creator. Christmas Carols from Around the World: A Celebration of International Carols & Regional Traditions. 2007. (ENG., Illus.). 112p. per. 14.95 *(978-0-7390-4899-3(6))* Alfred Publishing Co., Inc.

—Christmas Ukulele. 2010. (Just for Fun (Alfred) Ser.). (ENG.). 120p. pap. 16.99 *(978-0-7390-6973-8(X))* Alfred Publishing Co., Inc.

Alfred Publishing, ed. Christmas Instrumental Solos — Popular Christmas Songs: Cello (with Piano Acc.) 2007. (ENG.). 64p. pap. 14.95 *(978-0-7390-4876-4(7))* Alfred Publishing Co., Inc.

—A Stained Glass Christmas with Heavenly Carols: Piano/Vocal/Chords. 2007. (ENG.). 80p. pap. 12.95 *(978-0-7390-4901-3(1))* Alfred Publishing Co., Inc.

Alfred Publishing Staff. The Best Easy Book of Christmas Guitar: Over 100 Christmas Favorites Including a Special Easy Solo Guitar TAB Section! 2008. (ENG.). 152p. pap. 19.95 *(978-0-7390-5525-0(9))* Alfred Publishing Co., Inc.

—The Carol Singer's Carol: Choral Octavo. 2011. (Faber Edition: Choral Signature Ser.). (ENG.). pap. 3.95 ***(978-0-571-53671-9(9))*** Faber & Faber, Ltd. GBR. Dist: Alfred Publishing Co., Inc.

—Christmas Song Essentials: Piano/Vocal/Chords. 2007. (ENG., Illus.). 172p. pap. 16.95 *(978-0-7390-4898-6(8))* Alfred Publishing Co., Inc.

—Classic FM — Silent Nights. 2011. (Faber Edition Ser.). (ENG.). pap. 13.80 *(978-0-571-53569-9(0))* Faber & Faber, Ltd. GBR. Dist: Alfred Publishing Co., Inc.

—The Complete Christmas Suites: Intermediate to Advanced Arrangements for Solo Piano. 2009. (ENG.). 96p. pap. 12.99 *(978-0-7390-6272-2(7))* Alfred Publishing Co., Inc.

—Mirabile Dictu: From Manchester Carols, Choral Octavo. 2010. (Faber Edition: Choral Signature Ser.). (ENG.). pap. 3.95 *(978-0-571-53567-5(4))* Faber & Faber, Ltd. GBR. Dist: Alfred Publishing Co., Inc.

—Piano Stylings of Classic Christmas Carols. Shanaphy, Edward, ed. 2011. (Ekay Edition Ser.). (ENG.). pap. 16.95 ***(978-1-929006-66-3(7))*** Alfred Publishing Co., Inc.

—Susan Boyle — the Gift: Piano/Vocal/Guitar. 2011. 48p. pap. 14.99 *(978-0-7390-7785-6(6))* Alfred Publishing Co., Inc.

—World's Most Beloved Christmas Songs: Piano/Vocal/Chords. 2008. (ENG.). 272p. pap. 24.95 *(978-0-7390-5593-9(3))* Alfred Publishing Co., Inc.

Amsco Publications, creator. Christmas Favorites: Playalong for Alto Saxophone. 2007. (CenterStage Ser.). (ENG., Illus.). 32p. pap. 12.95 incl. audio compact disk *(978-0-8256-3569-4(1)*, 0825635691) Music Sales Corp.

—Christmas Favorites: Playalong for Clarinet. 2007. (CenterStage Ser.). (ENG.). 32p. pap. 12.95 incl. audio compact disk *(978-0-8256-3570-0(5)*, 0825635705) Music Sales Corp.

—Christmas Favorites: Playalong for Flute. 2007. (CenterStage Ser.). (ENG.). 32p. pap. 12.95 incl. audio compact disk *(978-0-8256-3571-7(3)*, 0825635713) Music Sales Corp.

—Christmas Favorites: Playalong for Trumpet. 2007. (CenterStage Ser.). (ENG.). 32p. pap. 12.95 incl. audio compact disk *(978-0-8256-3572-4(1)*, 0825635721) Music Sales Corp.

—Christmas Favorites: Playalong for Violin. 2007. (Christmas Favorites Ser.). (ENG.). 32p. pap. 12.95 incl. audio compact disk *(978-0-8256-3573-1(X)*, 082563573X) Music Sales Corp.

Andrews, Lee, contrib. by. Mel Bay Presents Dobro Christmas Songbook, 1 vol. 2007. (ENG.). 32p. pap. 7.95 *(978-0-7866-7620-0(5))* Mel Bay Pubns., Inc.

Atkinson, Catherine, et al. The Spirit of Christmas: Traditional Recipes, Crafts & Carols. 2009. (ENG., Illus.). 128p. pap. 17.95 *(978-1-84773-640-6(8))* New Holland Pubs., Ltd. GBR. Dist: Sterling Publishing Co., Inc.

BarlowGirl. BarlowGirl - Home for Christmas. 2008. (ENG.). 128p. pap. 16.95 *(978-1-4234-6879-0(1)*, 1423468791) Leonard, Hal Corp.

Baumgartner, Eric. Christmas. 2007. (ENG.). 24p. pap. 9.95 incl. audio compact disk *(978-1-4234-3156-5(1)*, 1423431561) Willis Music Co.

Bay, William. Mel Bay's Caroling Book, Spanish Edition, 1 vol. 2006. (ENG.). 16p. pap. 3.95 *(978-0-7866-7609-5(4)*, 20313BCD) Mel Bay Pubns., Inc.

Bennett, Jeff. O Night Divine! Celebrating the Birth of Christ. 2009. (ENG.). 48p. pap. 15.99 *(978-0-8341-7744-4(7)*, 9780834177444) Lillenas Publishing Co.

Berlin, Irving. White Christmas. Date not set. 32p. pap. 5.99 *(978-0-06-443719-6(1))* HarperCollins Pubs.

Berry, Cindy. O Little Town of Bethlehem: Carols for the Christ Child. 2011. (ENG.). 40p. pap. 15.99 ***(978-0-8341-7910-3(5)***, 9780834179103) Lillenas Publishing Co.

Blessings of Christmas. 2007. audio compact disk *(978-5-557-58510-1(9))* Alpha Omega Publications.

Bob Dylan - Christmas in the Heart. 2009. (ENG.). pap. 17.99 *(978-1-4234-9022-7(3)*, 1423490223); 56p. pap. 17.99 *(978-0-8256-3730-8(9)*, 0825637309) Music Sales Corp.

Bober, Melody. Christmas Memories. 2007. (ENG.). 24p. pap. 6.95 *(978-0-7390-4916-7(X))*; pap. 6.95 *(978-0-7390-4915-0(1))*; pap. 6.95 *(978-0-7390-4914-3(3))* Alfred Publishing Co., Inc.

Bordon, David & Winters, Tom. Everything Christmas. 2010. (ENG., Illus.). 320p. 14.99 *(978-0-307-72929-3(X)*, WaterBrook Pr.) Doubleday Religious Publishing Group, The.

Boston Music Company & Hal Leonard Corporation Staff, creators. Beginning Christmas for Piano. 2008. (ENG.). 32p. pap. 9.95 *(978-0-8256-3683-7(3)*, 0825636833) Music Sales Corp.

Bradley, Ian. The Daily Telegraph Book of Carols. 2006. (ENG.). 450p. 37.95 *(978-0-8264-9240-1(1))* Continuum International Publishing Group, Ltd. GBR. Dist: National Bk. Network.

Burlingham, Jan, illus. & adapted by. The Friendly Beasts: A Medieval French Carol. 2009. 28p. (J). 14.95 *(978-0-8091-6742-5(5)*, Ambassador Bks.) Paulist Pr.

Carson Turner, Barrie, ed. Bassoons for Christmas. 2008. (ENG.). 32p. pap. 24.95 incl. audio compact disk *(978-1-902455-74-7(6)*, 1902455746) Schott Music Corp.

Cathcart, Cynthia. Carols for Christmas: Arranged for the Clarsach. 2006. spiral bd. 34.95 *(978-0-9743126-5-1(7))* Highland Circle Publishing.

Celtic Woman. A Christmas Celebration: Piano/Vocal/Chords. 2008. (ENG.). 96p. pap. 21.95 *(978-0-7390-5680-6(8))* Alfred Publishing Co., Inc.

Chilcott, Bob. Bob Chilcott Carols 2: 10 carol arrangements for mixed Voices. 2009. 72p. pap. 12.95 *(978-0-19-336507-0(3))* Oxford Univ. Pr., Inc.

Christmas Is a Birthday: A Musical for Senior Adult Choir. 2008. (ENG.). 88p. pap. 7.99 *(978-0-8341-7645-4(9)*, 9780834176454) Lillenas Publishing Co.

Christmas Mosaic: A Festival of Carols for Any Choir. 2009. (ENG.). 104p. pap. 6.99 *(978-0-8341-7694-2(7)*, 9780834176942) Lillenas Publishing Co.

The Christmas Story: In Carols & Poetry. 2009. (ENG.). 80p. pap. 7.99 *(978-0-8341-7697-3(1)*, 9780834176973) Lillenas Publishing Co.

Chung, Brian. Expressions of Christmas: 8 Inventive Explorations of Classic Carols for Solo Piano. 2011. (Sacred Performer Collections). 40p. pap. 12.99 ***(978-0-7390-8032-0(6))*** Alfred Publishing Co., Inc.

Clancy, Ronald M. Best-Loved Christmas Carols: The Stories Behind Twenty-Five Yuletide Favorites. 2006. (ENG., Illus.). 112p. 19.95 *(978-1-4027-4187-6(1))* Sterling Publishing Co., Inc.

Coates, Dan, contrib. by. Simply Christmas: 30 Favorite Christmas Songs & Carols. 2008. (Simply Ser.). (ENG.). 80p. pap. 12.95 *(978-0-7390-5183-2(0))* Alfred Publishing Co., Inc.

—The World's Most-Beloved Christmas Songs: 60 Heart-Warming Holiday Favorites. 2010. (ENG.). 176p. pap. 19.99 *(978-0-7390-7340-7(0))* Alfred Publishing Co., Inc.

Curnow, James, ed. Hymns & Carols for Worship: Vocal Solos for All Medium Range Voices. 2007. (ENG.). 52p. pap. 14.95 incl. audio compact disk *(978-90-431-2438-6(9)*, 9043124389) de Haske Pubns. B.V. NLD. Dist: Leonard, Hal Corp.

Curry, Craig. Christmas Themes & Variations: Creative Settings for Solo Piano. 2008. (ENG.). 56p. pap. 16.95 *(978-1-4234-6719-9(1)*, 1423467191) Leonard, Hal Corp.

Davis, Chip. Mannheim Steamroller Christmas. 2008. (ENG.). 192p. pap. 14.95 *(978-1-4391-5259-1(4))* Pocket Books.

—Mannheim Steamroller Christmas: The Season for Joy, 0 vols. 2007. (Illus.). 64p. 14.99 *(978-1-4041-0511-9(5))* Nelson, Thomas Inc.

Day, Janet, contrib. by. The Christmas Caroling Songbook: 50 Christmas Favorites for Church, School & Community. 2009. 56p. pap. 3.95 *(978-5-552-43035-2(2))* Leonard, Hal Corp.

De Vito, Carlo. The Christmas Carols Kit: Everything You Need to Bring Out that Holiday Sound & Cheer! 2014. (ENG.). 128p. pap. 14.95 *(978-1-60433-089-2(9))* Cider Mill Pr. Bk. Pubs., LLC.

Deneff, Peter, contrib. by. Christmas Carols: Cello. 2006. (ENG.). 24p. pap. 10.95 incl. audio compact disk *(978-1-4234-1363-9(6)*, 1423413636) Leonard, Hal Corp.

—Christmas Carols for Flute. 2006. (Hal Leonard Instrumental Play-along Ser.). (ENG.). 24p. pap. 10.95 incl. audio compact disk *(978-1-4234-1353-0(9)*, 1423413539) Leonard, Hal Corp.

—Christmas Carols: Viola. 2006. (Instrumental Play-along Ser.). (ENG.). 24p. pap. 10.95 incl. audio compact disk *(978-1-4234-1362-2(8)*, 1423413628) Leonard, Hal Corp.

Duffy, Carol Ann. The Manchester Carols: A Re-Telling of the Christmas Story, Vocal Score. 2009. (Faber Edition Ser.). (ENG.). pap. 14.95 *(978-0-571-52121-0(5))* Faber & Faber, Ltd. GBR. Dist: Alfred Publishing Co., Inc.

Duncan, Edmondstoune. The Story of the Carol. 2009. (ENG.). 278p. 34.99 *(978-1-117-47314-7(7)*, BiblioLife); pap. 26.75 *(978-1-117-47315-4(5))* BiblioBazaar.

—The Story of the Carol. 2010. 110p. pap. 20.12 *(978-1-152-61830-5(X))* General Bks. LLC.

—The Story of the Carol. 2009. 276p. 42.95 *(978-1-104-69182-0(5))*; pap. 27.95 *(978-1-104-66755-9(X))* Kessinger Publishing, LLC.

Esmond, Doug. Irish You a Merry Christmas: The Many Moods of Celtic Christmas Arranged for Solo Guitar. 2010. (ENG.). 32p. pap. 15.99 incl. audio compact disk *(978-1-57424-259-1(8)*, 1574242598) Centerstream Publishing.

Faber, Nancy. Joy to the World: The Collaborative Artist Chamber Music Series. 2011. (ENG.). 24p. pap. 9.95 ***(978-1-61677-706-7(0)***, 1616777060) Faber Piano Adventures(r).

Fettke, Tom. The Heart of Christmas: Inspirational Carol Medleys for Solo Piano. 2007. (ENG.). 72p. pap. 14.95 *(978-1-4234-5529-5(0)*, 1423455290) Leonard, Hal Corp.

Fox, Daniel. World's Greatest Christmas Songs: 65 of the World's Most Popular & Best Loved Traditional & Contemporary Christmas Songs. rev. ed. 2008. (World's Greatest Ser.). (ENG.). 144p. pap. 17.95 *(978-0-7390-5585-4(2))* Alfred Publishing Co., Inc.

Giles, Gordon. O Come Emmanuel: A Musical Tour of Daily Readings for Advent & Christmas. 2006. (ENG.). 168p. (gr. 13). per. 16.99 *(978-1-55725-515-0(6))* Paraclete Pr., Inc.

Goss, Louise & Holland, Sam. The Music Tree Christmas: 4 Solos & 2 Duets for Student & Teacher. 2007. (ENG.). 16p. pap. 6.95 *(978-0-7390-4912-9(7))* Alfred Publishing Co., Inc.

—The Music Tree Christmas: 6 Solos & 1 Duet for Student & Teacher. 2007. (ENG.). 16p. pap. 6.95 *(978-0-7390-4911-2(9))* Alfred Publishing Co., Inc.

Grant, Natalie. Believe. 2006. (ENG.). 90p. per. 22.95 *(978-1-59235-146-6(8)*, 1592351468) Shawnee Pr., Inc.

Hakes, Derek K. He Is Born! 2 or 3 Octaves, Level 2+ 2011. 8p. pap. 4.50 ***(978-1-4291-2326-6(5))*** Lorenz Corp., The.

Hal Leonard. Chris Tomlin - Glory in the Highest: Christmas Songs of Worship, 1 vol. 2010. (ENG.). 112p. pap. 16.99 *(978-1-935288-08-4(3)*, 1935288083) Leonard, Hal Corp.

Hal Leonard Corp. Christmas Songs. 2011. (ENG.). 144p. pap. 12.99 ***(978-1-4584-1159-4(1)***, 1458411591) Leonard, Hal Corp.

—Christmas Strumming: Ukulele Play-along Volume 11. 2011. (ENG.). 16p. pap. 12.99 incl. audio compact disk ***(978-1-4584-1003-0(X)***, 145841003X) Leonard, Hal Corp.

—Glee: The Music - The Christmas Album. 2011. (ENG.). 80p. pap. 14.99 ***(978-1-4584-0820-4(5)***, 1458408205) Leonard, Hal Corp.

Hal Leonard Corp., creator. Christmas: Easy Pieces for Acoustic Guitar. 2010. 24p. pap. 12.99 incl. audio compact disk *(978-1-84938-327-1(8)*, 1849383278) Music Sales Corp.

—Christmas Carols. 2011. (ENG.). 152p. pap. 14.99 ***(978-1-4584-1100-6(1)***, 1458411001) Leonard, Hal Corp.

—Christmas Carols for Easy Classical Guitar. 2010. (ENG.). 40p. pap. 9.99 incl. audio compact disk *(978-1-60378-248-7(6)*, 1603782486) Cherry Lane Music Co.

—Christmas Carols for Gospel Piano. 2011. (ENG.). 52p. pap. 9.99 ***(978-1-60378-361-3(X)***, 160378361X) Cherry Lane Music Co.

—Christmas Classics: Essential Elements Guitar Ensembles Mid-Intermediate Level. 2011. (ENG.). 32p. pap. 9.99 ***(978-1-4584-1005-4(6)***, 1458410056) Leonard, Hal Corp.

—Christmas Hits: Beginning Piano Solo Play-along Volume 4. 2011. (ENG.). 16p. pap. 14.99 incl. audio compact disk ***(978-1-4584-0828-0(0)***, 1458408280) Leonard, Hal Corp.

Hal Leonard Corp., creator. The World's Greatest Christmas Carols: Stories & Music of the Best Loved Carols. 2007. (ENG.). 63p. pap. 14.95 incl. audio compact disk *(978-1-59235-178-7(6)*, 1592351786) Shawnee Pr., Inc.

Hal Leonard Corporation Staff. Christmas Carols: 10 Holiday Favorites. 2007. (Jazz Play-along Ser.). (ENG.). 80p. pap. 14.95 incl. audio compact disk *(978-1-4234-3165-7(0)*, 1423431650) Leonard, Hal Corp.

Hal Leonard Corporation Staff, creator. Christmas Carols. 2006. (ENG.). (Piano Play-along Ser.: Vol. 48). 23p. pap. 14.95 incl. audio compact disk *(978-1-4234-1402-5(0)*, 1423414020); (Guitar Play-along Ser.: Vol. 62). 24p. pap. 12.95 incl. audio compact disk *(978-1-4234-1394-3(6)*, 1423413946) Leonard, Hal Corp.

—Christmas Carols: Alto Sax. 2006. (ENG.). 24p. pap. 10.95 incl. audio compact disk *(978-1-4234-1355-4(5)*, 1423413555) Leonard, Hal Corp.

—Christmas Carols: Clarinet. 2006. (ENG.). 24p. pap. 10.95 incl. audio compact disk *(978-1-4234-1354-7(7)*, 1423413547) Leonard, Hal Corp.

—Christmas Carols: Easy Piano CD Play-along Volume 28. 2009. (ENG.). 32p. pap. 14.99 incl. audio compact disk *(978-1-4234-8298-7(0)*, 1423482980) Leonard, Hal Corp.

—Christmas Carols: Harmonica Play-along Volume 11. 2009. (ENG.). 24p. pap. 12.99 incl. audio compact disk *(978-1-4234-8259-8(X)*, 142348259X) Leonard, Hal Corp.

—Christmas Carols: Horn. 2006. (ENG.). 24p. pap. 10.95 incl. audio compact disk *(978-1-4234-1359-2(8)*, 1423413598) Leonard, Hal Corp.

—Christmas Carols: Piano Duet Play-along Volume 24. 2008. (ENG.). 64p. pap. 14.95 incl. audio compact disk *(978-1-4234-5671-1(8)*, 1423456718) Leonard, Hal Corp.

—Christmas Carols: Pro Vocal Male/Female Edition Volume 7. 2009. (ENG.). 12p. pap. 14.99 incl. audio compact disk *(978-1-4234-8322-9(7)*, 1423483227) Leonard, Hal Corp.

—Christmas Carols: Sing with the Choir Volume 13. 2009. (ENG.). 40p. pap. 14.99 incl. audio compact disk *(978-1-4234-8480-6(0)*, 1423484800) Leonard, Hal Corp.

—Christmas Carols: Tenor Sax. 2006. (ENG.). 24p. pap. 10.95 incl. audio compact disk *(978-1-4234-1356-1(3)*, 1423413563) Leonard, Hal Corp.

—Christmas Carols: Trombone. 2006. (ENG.). 24p. pap. 10.95 incl. audio compact disk *(978-1-4234-1360-8(1)*, 1423413601) Leonard, Hal Corp.

—Christmas Carols: Trumpet. 2006. (ENG.). 24p. pap. 10.95 incl. audio compact disk *(978-1-4234-1358-5(X)*, 142341358X) Leonard, Hal Corp.

—Christmas Carols: Violin. 2006. (ENG.). 24p. pap. 10.95 incl. audio compact disk *(978-1-4234-1361-5(X)*, 142341361X) Leonard, Hal Corp.

—Christmas Carols: Violin Play-along Volume 5. 2006. (ENG.). 16p. pap. 14.99 incl. audio compact disk *(978-1-4234-1381-3(4)*, 1423413814) Leonard, Hal Corp.

—Christmas Carols: Volume 9. 2007. (Play with the CD Piano Ser.). (ENG.). 64p. pap. 19.95 incl. audio compact disk *(978-1-4234-5196-9(1)*, 1423451961) Leonard, Hal Corp.

—Christmas Carols for Mandolin. 2006. (ENG.). 56p. pap. 8.95 *(978-1-4234-1398-1(9)*, 1423413989) Leonard, Hal Corp.

—Christmas Carols for Ukulele. 2008. (ENG.). 48p. pap. 7.95 *(978-1-4234-5651-3(3)*, 1423456513) Leonard, Hal Corp.

—Christmas Classics. (ENG.). 2008. 40p. pap. 6.95 *(978-1-4234-5647-6(5)*, 1423456475) 2007. 64p. pap. 14.95 incl. audio compact disk *(978-1-4234-3162-6(6)*, 1423431626) Leonard, Hal Corp.

—Christmas Classics for Bass: 20 Melodies Arranged for 4-String Electric Bass. 2007. (ENG.). 56p. pap. 9.95 *(978-1-4234-3158-9(8)*, 1423431588) Leonard, Hal Corp.

—Christmas Favorites - Alto Sax: Big Band Play-along Volume 5. 2008. (ENG.). 24p. pap. 14.95 incl. audio compact disk *(978-1-4234-5849-4(4)*, 1423458494) Leonard, Hal Corp.

—Christmas Guitar Collection: 20 Songs Arranged for Solo Fingerstyle Guitar. 2007. (ENG.). 65p. pap. 17.95 incl. audio compact disk *(978-1-4234-3154-1(5)*, 1423431545) Leonard, Hal Corp.

—Christmas Tradition: 7 Arrangements for Brass Quintet - Conductor's Score. 2008. (ENG.). 32p. pap. 16.95 *(978-1-4234-6378-8(1)*, 1423463781) Leonard, Hal Corp.

—Christmas Tradition: 7 Arrangements for Brass Quintet - Horn in F. 2008. (ENG.). 16p. pap. 8.95 *(978-1-4234-6381-8(1)*, 1423463811) Leonard, Hal Corp.

—Christmas Tradition: 7 Arrangements for Brass Quintet - Trombone. 2008. (ENG.). 16p. pap. 8.95 *(978-1-4234-6382-5(X)*, 142346382X) Leonard, Hal Corp.

—Christmas Tradition: 7 Arrangements for Brass Quintet - Trumpet I in B-flat. 2008. (ENG.). 16p. pap. 8.95 *(978-1-4234-6379-5(X)*, 142346379X) Leonard, Hal Corp.

—Christmas Tradition: 7 Arrangements for Brass Quintet - Trumpet II in B-flat. 2008. (ENG.). 16p. pap. 8.95 *(978-1-4234-6380-1(3)*, 1423463803) Leonard, Hal Corp.

—Christmas Tradition: 7 Arrangements for Brass Quintet - Tuba. 2008. (ENG.). 16p. pap. 8.95 *(978-1-4234-6383-2(8)*, 1423463838) Leonard, Hal Corp.

—Cool Christmas: Jazz Play-along Volume 111. 2009. (ENG.). 72p. pap. 15.99 incl. audio compact disk *(978-1-4234-8253-6(0)*, 1423482530) Leonard, Hal Corp.

—Guitars for Christmas: 20 Christmas Carols for One or Two Guitars. 2007. 32p. pap. 17.95 incl. audio compact disk *(978-1-902455-75-4(4)*, 1902455754) Schott Music Corp.

—The Real Christmas Book: C Edition, 1 vol. 2008. (ENG.). 216p. pap. 25.00 *(978-1-4234-3387-3(4)*, 1423433874) Leonard, Hal Corp.

—Trumpets for Christmas: 20 Christmas Carols for One or Two Trumpets. 2008. (ENG.). 32p. pap. 19.95 incl. audio compact disk *(978-1-84761-050-8(1)*, 1847610501) Schott Music Corp.

—Worship Songs for Kids Songbook: With Easy Instructions. 2008. (ENG.). 24p. (J). (gr. -1-3). pap. 9.95 *(978-1-4234-3461-0(7)*, 1423434617) Leonard, Hal Corp.

—50 Christmas Piano Solos. 2008. (ENG.). 194p. pap. 16.95 *(978-1-4234-5652-0(1)*, 1423456521) Leonard, Hal Corp.

Hal Leonard Corporation Staff, ed. The Christmas Caroling Songbook, 1 vol. 2006. (ENG.). 96p. pap. 9.99 *(978-1-4234-1419-3(5)*, 1423414195) Leonard, Hal Corp.

Hal Leonard Publications Staff. Christmas Carols: Essential Songs Series, 1 vol. 2009. (ENG.). 248p. pap. 19.99 *(978-1-4234-8251-2(4)*, 1423482514) Leonard, Hal Corp.

Hammerly, Jim. Cool Chords for Christmas: Basic Jazz Harmonies for Piano. 2007. (ENG.). 48p. pap. 14.95 *(978-1-4234-5528-8(2)*, 1423455282) Leonard, Hal Corp.

—Cool Chords for Christmas: Basic Jazz Harmonies for Piano. Tornquist, Carol, ed. 2007. 48p. pap. 14.95 *(978-5-557-58263-6(0)*, Word Music) Word Entertainment.

Harnsberger, L. C. Christmas Favorites for Recorder. 2007. (ENG.). 24p. pap. 5.99 *(978-0-7390-4918-1(6))* Alfred Publishing Co., Inc.

Harrison, House. Christmas Joy. 2006. 32p. pap. 1.99 *(978-1-57794-824-7(6))* Harrison House Pubs.

Hayes, Mark, et al. Christmas Evergreens: Timeless Piano Arrangements of Classic Carols. 2007. (ENG.). 72p. pap. 18.95 *(978-1-59235-175-6(1)*, 1592351751) Shawnee Pr., Inc.

Healey, Bruce. Season of Carols: Easy Solo Cello & Piano. 2007. (ENG.). 44p. pap. 9.95 *(978-1-4234-2625-7(8)*, 1423426258) Leonard, Hal Corp.

—Season of Carols: Easy Solo Viola & Piano. 2007. (ENG.). 44p. pap. 9.95 *(978-1-4234-2624-0(X)*, 142342624X) Leonard, Hal Corp.

Hill, Helen, et al. The Saintons Go to Bethlehem. 2011. 66p. 36.95 ***(978-1-258-08557-5(7))*** Literary Licensing, LLC.

Hogan, Ed. Creative Carols for Alto Sax: Traditional Carols with a Popular Twist. 2010. (ENG.). 28p. cd-rom 29.99 *(978-0-8341-7805-2(2)*, 0834178052) Lillenas Publishing Co.

—Creative Carols for Brass Quartet Vol. 2: Traditional Carols with a Popular Twist. 2011. (ENG.). 32p. pap. 59.99 ***(978-0-8341-7812-0(5)***, 9780834178120) Lillenas Publishing Co.

—Creative Carols for Brass Quartet, Volume 1: Traditional Carols with a Popular Twist. 2010. (ENG.). 36p. cd-rom 59.99 *(978-0-8341-7811-3(7)*, 0834178117) Lillenas Publishing Co.

—Creative Carols for Cello: Traditional Carols with a Popular Twist. 2010. (ENG.). 28p. cd-rom 29.99 *(978-0-8341-7810-6(9)*, 0834178109) Lillenas Publishing Co.

—Creative Carols for Clarinet: Traditional Carols with a Popular Twist. 2010. (ENG.). 28p. cd-rom 29.99 *(978-0-8341-7804-5(4)*, 0834178044) Lillenas Publishing Co.
—Creative Carols for Flute: Traditional Carols with a Popular Twist. 2010. (ENG.). 28p. cd-rom 29.99 *(978-0-8341-7803-8(6)*, 0834178036) Lillenas Publishing Co.
—Creative Carols for French Horn: Traditional Carols with a Popular Twist. 2010. (ENG.). 28p. cd-rom 29.99 *(978-0-8341-7808-3(7)*, 0834178087) Lillenas Publishing Co.
—Creative Carols for String Quartet Vol. 2: Traditional Carols with a Popular Twist. 2011. (ENG.). 32p. pap. 59.99 ***(978-0-8341-7816-8(8)***, 9780834178168) Lillenas Publishing Co.
—Creative Carols for String Quartet, Volume 1: Traditional Carols with a Popular Twist. 2010. (ENG.). 36p. pap. 59.99 *(978-0-8341-7815-1(X)*, 9780834178151) Lillenas Publishing Co.
—Creative Carols for Trombone: Traditional Carols with a Popular Twist. 2010. (ENG.). 28p. cd-rom 29.99 *(978-0-8341-7807-6(9)*, 0834178079) Lillenas Publishing Co.
—Creative Carols for Trumpet: Traditional Carols with a Popular Twist. 2010. (ENG.). 28p. cd-rom 29.99 *(978-0-8341-7806-9(0)*, 0834178060) Lillenas Publishing Co.
—Creative Carols for Violin: Traditional Carols with a Popular Twist. 2010. (ENG.). 28p. cd-rom 29.99 *(978-0-8341-7809-0(5)*, 0834178095) Lillenas Publishing Co.
—Creative Carols for Woodwind Trio Vol. 2: Traditional Carols with a Popular Twist. 2011. (ENG.). 32p. pap. 59.99 ***(978-0-8341-7814-4(1)***, 9780834178144) Lillenas Publishing Co.
Hogan, Ed. Creative Carols for Woodwind Trio, Volume 1: Traditional Carols with a Popular Twist. 2010. (ENG.). 40p. cd-rom 59.99 *(978-0-8341-7813-7(3)*, 0834178133) Lillenas Publishing Co.
Honey, Paul. A Jazzy Christmas: Alto Sax. 2010. (ENG.). 24p. pap. 10.99 incl. audio compact disk *(978-1-4234-9568-0(3)*, 1423495683) Music Sales Corp.
—A Jazzy Christmas: Clarinet. 2010. (ENG.). 24p. pap. 10.99 incl. audio compact disk *(978-1-4234-9567-3(5)*, 1423495675) Music Sales Corp.
—A Jazzy Christmas: Flute. 2010. (ENG.). 24p. pap. 10.99 incl. audio compact disk *(978-1-4234-9566-6(7)*, 1423495667) Music Sales Corp.
—A Jazzy Christmas: Tenor Sax. 2010. (ENG.). 24p. pap. 10.99 incl. audio compact disk *(978-1-4234-9569-7(1)*, 1423495691) Music Sales Corp.
—A Jazzy Christmas: Trumpet. 2010. (ENG.). 24p. pap. 10.99 incl. audio compact disk *(978-1-4234-9570-3(5)*, 1423495705) Music Sales Corp.
Janszen, Matthew. A Seasoned Christmas: Advanced Piano Solo. 2009. (ENG.). 56p. pap. 14.99 incl. audio compact disk *(978-1-4234-8376-2(6)*, 1423483766) Leonard, Hal Corp.
Johnson, Victor C. Christ the Babe Is Lord of All: SATB/SAB with Opt. Flute. 2011. 8p. pap. 1.85 ***(978-1-4291-2556-7(X))*** Lorenz Corp., The.
Joseph M. Martin. Season of Wonders: Celebrating the Miracle of Christmas. 2007. (ENG.). 100p. pap. 7.95 *(978-1-59235-170-1(0)*, 1592351700, Flammer, Harold Music) Shawnee Pr., Inc.
Joseph M. Martin & Joseph M. Martin. Tapestry of Light. 2011. (ENG.). 1p. pap. 59.99 ***(978-1-4584-0023-9(9)***, 1458400239, Flammer, Harold Music) Shawnee Pr., Inc.
Joy to the World. Date not set. 5.95 *(978-0-88271-572-8(0)*, 10206) Regina Pr., Malhame & Co.
Joyce, Anna, ed. Christmas Songs. 2009. (Take the Lead Ser.). 19p. pap. incl. audio compact disk *(978-1-84328-830-5(3))* International Music Pubns. Ltd.
Keats, Ezra Jack, illus. The Little Drummer Boy. 2007. (ENG.). 32p. (J). (gr. -1-18). bds. 6.99 *(978-0-670-06282-9(0)*, Viking Juvenile) Penguin Group (USA) Inc.
Keveren, Phillip. Santa Swings: Phillip Keveren Series. 2010. (ENG.). 64p. pap. 12.99 *(978-1-4234-9551-2(9)*, 1423495519) Leonard, Hal Corp.
Lehman, Clayton. Sacred Music for Christmas. 2010. 93p. pap. 25.00 *(978-0-578-04320-3(3))* Harmonies for Life.
Line, Lorie. Lorie Line - Christmas Around the World. 2008. 88p. pap. 34.95 *(978-1-891195-22-8(0)*, 1891195220) Leonard, Hal Corp.
—Lorie Line - the Glory of Christmas. 2007. (ENG.). 94p. pap. 34.95 *(978-1-4234-5475-5(8)*, 1423454758) Leonard, Hal Corp.
Love's Pure Light: Yuletide Classics for the Piano Soloist. 2008. (ENG.). 56p. pap. 16.99 *(978-0-8341-7650-8(5)*, 9780834176508) Lillenas Publishing Co.
Martin, Pamela. Echo Christmas Joy: SAB with Opt. Orchestra or Instrumental Ensemble. 2011. 11p. pap. 1.95 ***(978-1-4291-2480-5(6))*** Lorenz Corp., The.
—Echo Christmas Joy: SATB with Opt. Orchestra or Instrumental Ensemble. 2011. 11p. pap. 1.95 ***(978-1-4291-2479-9(2))*** Lorenz Corp., The.
Meisner, Gary, contrib. by. Christmas Carols for Accordion. 2007. (ENG.). 48p. per. 9.95 *(978-1-4234-3177-0(4)*, 1423431774) Leonard, Hal Corp.
Merrill, Bob & Styne, Jule. Mr. Magoo's Christmas Carol: Sheet Music from the First Animated Christmas Special. 2011. (ENG.). 44p. pap. 14.99 ***(978-0-7390-7663-7(9))*** Alfred Publishing Co., Inc.
A Merry Christmas. 4.50 *(978-0-687-02276-2(2))*; 4.50 *(978-0-687-02337-0(8))*; 4.50 *(978-0-687-02357-8(2))*; 5.00 *(978-0-687-02487-2(0))* Abingdon Pr.
Miller, Carolyn. Merry Christmas! 8 Simple Solos for the Season. 2011. (ENG.). 16p. pap. 6.99 ***(978-1-4584-0803-7(5)***, 1458408035) Willis Music Co.
Miller, Donald. Mel Bay Presents Christmas Strings: Cello & Bass with Piano Accompaniment: for Solo Ensemble, 1 vol. 2007. (ENG., Illus.). 60p. pap. 9.95 *(978-0-7866-7559-3(4))* Mel Bay Pubns., Inc.
MMO, creator. Christmas Memories: Sing or Play-along to Your Favorite Christmas Songs. 2006. (ENG., Illus.). 40p. pap. 14.98 incl. audio compact disk *(978-1-59615-218-2(4)*, 1596152184) Music Minus One.
Niles, John Jacob. Christmas Songs & Carols Pack: High Voice. 2008. (ENG.). 48p. pap. 19.95 incl. audio compact disk *(978-1-4234-3694-2(6)*, 1423436946, G Schirmer, Inc.) Leonard, Hal Corp.
—Christmas Songs & Carols Pack: Low Voice. 2008. (ENG.). 48p. pap. 19.95 incl. audio compact disk *(978-1-4234-3695-9(4)*, 1423436954, G Schirmer, Inc.) Leonard, Hal Corp.
Overman, Kathy M. Fun Family Christmas Devotions: Advent Guide for Busy Parents. 2007. per. 19.95 *(978-0-9743425-6-6(4))* Ablaze Pubns.
Pace, Cynthia. Easy Christmas Melodies Piano: With Duet Accompaniments. 2007. (ENG.). 32p. pap. 12.95 incl. audio compact disk *(978-1-4234-2603-5(7)*, 1423426037) Leonard, Hal Corp.
Page, Anna Laura, et al. A Christmas Carol — Scrooge in Bethlehem (A Musical for Children Based upon a Story by Charles Dickens) Director's Score, Score. 2008. (ENG.). 32p. pap. 24.95 *(978-0-7390-5060-6(5))* Alfred Publishing Co., Inc.
—A Christmas Carol — Scrooge in Bethlehem (A Musical for Children Based upon a Story by Charles Dickens) Performance Pack, Score & 10 Books. 2008. (ENG.). pap. 64.95 *(978-0-7390-5065-1(6))* Alfred Publishing Co., Inc.
—A Christmas Carol — Scrooge in Bethlehem (A Musical for Children Based upon a Story by Charles Dickens) Preview Pack, Book & CD. 2008. (ENG.). pap. 16.95 *(978-0-7390-5064-4(8))* Alfred Publishing Co., Inc.
—A Christmas Carol — Scrooge in Bethlehem (A Musical for Children Based upon a Story by Charles Dickens) Singer's Edition 5-Pack, 5 Books. 2008. (ENG.). pap. 22.50 *(978-0-7390-5061-3(3))* Alfred Publishing Co., Inc.
Peat, Frank Edwin. Christmas Carols: 44 Favorites with Easy Piano Arrangements. 2010. (Dover Song Collections). (ENG.). 80p. (gr. 5). pap. 9.95 *(978-0-486-47823-4(8))* Dover Pubns., Inc.
Pethel, Stan. He Is Born, the Divine Christ Child: Christmas Portraits Arranged for Solo Piano. 2007. (ENG., Illus.). 48p. pap. 15.99 *(978-0-8341-7582-2(7)*, 0834175827) Lillenas Publishing Co.
Reed, Edward Bliss. Christmas Carols Printed in the Sixteenth Century. Reed, Edward Bliss, ed. 2011. 168p. 41.95 ***(978-1-258-01870-2(5))*** Literary Licensing, LLC.
Reimer, Marilyn. Worship Christ, the Newborn King: Blending Carols & Classics. 2010. (ENG.). 56p. pap. 16.99 *(978-0-8341-7792-5(7)*, 9780834177925) Lillenas Publishing Co.
Renbourn, John & Grossman, Stefan. Deluxe Anthology of O'Carolan Music for Fingerstyle Guitar, 1 vol. 2008. (Mel Bay Archive Editions Ser.). (ENG., Illus.). 160p. pap. 17.95 *(978-0-7866-0104-2(3)*, 95266) Mel Bay Pubns., Inc.
Riley, Lavawan. Love's Pure Light: Yuletide Classics for the Piano Soloist. 2008. (ENG.). 56p. pap. 15.99 *(978-1-4234-6149-4(5)*, 1423461495) Lillenas Publishing Co.
Rollin, Catherine. Dances for Christmas, Bk 1: 6 Early Intermediate to Intermediate Christmas Favorites Arranged in Dance Styles. 2008. (Dances for Christmas Ser.). (ENG.). 24p. pap. 6.95 *(978-0-7390-5626-4(3))* Alfred Publishing Co., Inc.
Ryan, Michael. Prayer at the Manger: 2 or 3 Octaves (Handbells or Handchimes), Level 2. 2011. 8p. pap. 4.50 ***(978-1-4291-2365-5(6))*** Lorenz Corp., The.
Sinatra, Frank. 132. Frank Sinatra Christmas Collection: E-Z Play Today #132. 2008. (ENG.). 40p. pap. 9.99 *(978-1-4234-6363-4(3)*, 1423463633) Leonard, Hal Corp.
Skempton, Howard. The Virgin's Name Was Mary. 2009. 4p. pap. 1.85 *(978-0-19-336570-4(7))* Oxford Univ. Pr., Inc.
Smalko, Emilia. It's Time to Act! Working to Re-Humanize the Fetus in A New Era of Promising New Solutions & Alternatives to Abortion: 2011. 174p. pap. 21.95 ***(978-1-4327-7134-8(5))*** Outskirts Pr., Inc.
Smith, Gail. Christmas Carols for Piano Made Easy, 1 vol. 2006. (ENG.). 16p. pap. 4.95 *(978-0-7866-7351-3(6)*, 21086) Mel Bay Pubns., Inc.
Takahashi, Masa. Christmas Carols: Jazz Guitar Chord Melody Solos. 2010. (ENG.). 40p. pap. 12.99 *(978-1-4234-9478-2(4)*, 1423494784) Leonard, Hal Corp.
Tempelman-Kluit, Anne, ed. Sleds, Sleighs & Snow: A Canadian Christmas Carol. 2007. (ENG., Illus.). 292p. pap. 19.95 *(978-1-55285-905-6(3))* Whitecap Bks., Ltd. CAN. Dist: Midpoint Trade Bks., Inc.
These Are Special Times: Piano/Vocal/Chords. 2008. (ENG.). 100p. pap. 21.95 *(978-0-7390-5400-0(7))* Alfred Publishing Co., Inc.
Tomlin, Chris. Chris Tomlin - Glory in the Highest: Christmas Songs of Worship. 2010. (ENG.). 64p. pap. 14.99 *(978-1-4234-9480-5(6)*, 1423494806) Leonard, Hal Corp.
Tornquist, Carol. Christmas Carols for Today: 10 Contemporary Arrangements of Traditional Carols. 2009. (Sacred Performer Collections). (ENG.). 40p. pap. 12.99 *(978-0-7390-6301-9(4))* Alfred Publishing Co., Inc.
Tornquist, Carol. Medleys for Blended Worship — Christmas. 2011. (Sacred Performer Collections). 40p. pap. 12.99 ***(978-0-7390-7318-6(4))*** Alfred Publishing Co., Inc.
Tranchell, Peter. If Ye Would Hear the Angels Sing. 2009. 4p. pap. 2.50 *(978-0-19-395018-4(9))* Oxford Univ. Pr., Inc.
Treasury of Christmas. 2007. audio compact disk *(978-5-557-58301-5(7))* Alpha Omega Publications.
Tsitsaros, Christos. Fantasia on Polish Christmas Carols: A Medley of Seven Traditional Kolendy for Late Intermediate Piano. 2011. (ENG.). 16p. pap. 6.99 ***(978-1-4584-1188-4(5)***, 1458411885) Leonard, Hal Corp.
Upper Room Book of Christmas Carols. 33p. pap. 2.00 *(978-0-8358-0199-7(3))* Upper Room Bks.
Wagner, Douglas E. The Rose of Bethlehem: SATB with Opt. Instrumental Ensemble. 2011. 12p. pap. 1.95 ***(978-1-4291-2476-8(8))*** Lorenz Corp., The.
White, Marilyn. O Holy Child of Bethlehem: Christmas Carols Arranged for Solo Piano. 2008. (ENG.). 48p. pap. 14.99 *(978-1-4234-6151-7(7)*, 1423461517) Lillenas Publishing Co.
101 Strings Orchestra, contrib. by. Treasury of Christmas. 2007. audio compact disk *(978-5-558-03355-7(X))* Alpha Omega Publications.

CAROLS—HISTORY AND CRITICISM

Griffin, Pam. The Sounds of Christmas. 2011. pap. 2.99 ***(978-1-59955-923-0(4)***, Bonneville Bks.) Cedar Fort, Inc./CFI Distribution.
Lawson-Jones, Mark. Why Was the Partridge in the Pear Tree? The History of Christmas Carols. 2012. (ENG., Illus.). 128p. pap. 13.95 ***(978-0-7524-5957-8(0))*** History Pr. Ltd.,The GBR. Dist: Independent Pubs. Group.
Newell, Lloyd D. & Newell, Karmel H. I Heard the Bells on Christmas Day. 2009. *(978-1-60641-154-4(3)*, Shadow Mountain) Deseret Bk. Co.
Nobbman, Dale. The Ultimate Christmas Music Companion Fact Book. 2007. (ENG.). 152p. pap. 19.99 *(978-1-57424-228-7(8)*, 1574242288) Centerstream Publishing.
Smith, Andrew W. The Fallowfield Carol: Or the Adventure of Messrs. Wiggin & Clarke, Concerning Their Search for an Ancient Carol of Christm. 2010. pap. 11.99 *(978-1-61566-250-0(2))* Tate Publishing & Enterprises, LLC.
St. Amour, Mary Paulina. Study of the "Villancico" up to Lope de Vega. (Catholic University of America, Studies in Romance Languages & Literatures: No. 21). reprint ed. 37.50 *(978-0-404-50321-5(7))* AMS Pr., Inc.

CAROTENES

see also Vitamin A

Gutierrez, Rosa Martha Perez, et al, eds. Biological Effects of B - Carotene. 2010. (Nutrition & Diet Research Progress Ser.). 87p. pap. 43.00 *(978-1-61668-256-9(6))* Nova Science Pubs., Inc.
Haugen, Leiv & Bjornson, Terje. Beta Carotene: Dietary Sources, Cancer & Cognition. 2009. (Nutrition & Diet Research Progress Ser.). 129.00 *(978-1-60741-611-1(5)*, Nova Biomedical Bks.) Nova Science Pubs., Inc.
Preedy, Victor R. & Watson, Ronald R. Lycopene: Nutritional, Medicinal & Therapeutic Properties. 2009. (ENG., Illus.). 472p. 119.95 *(978-1-57808-538-5(1))* BIOS Scientific Publishers Ltd. GBR. Dist: Taylor & Francis Group.

CAROTENOIDS

see also Carotenes; Retinoids

Astaxanthin: Natural Astaxanthin, King of the Carotenoids. 2007. 6.95 *(978-0-9792353-0-6(8))* Cyanotech Corp.
Barredo, José-Luis, ed. Microbial Carotenoids from Bacteria & Microalgae: Methods & Protocols. 2012. (Methods in Molecular Biology Ser.: 892). (ENG., Illus.). x, 352p. 139.00 ***(978-1-61779-878-8(9)***, 1617798789) Humana Pr.
—Microbial Carotenoids from Fungi: Methods & Protocols. 2012. (Methods in Molecular Biology Ser.). (ENG., Illus.). xiii, 310p. 119.00 ***(978-1-61779-917-4(3)***, 1617799173) Humana Pr.
Britton, George, et al, eds. Carotenoids Vol. 4: Natural Functions. 2008. (Carotenoids Ser.). 350p. 159.00 *(978-3-7643-7498-3(5)*, 3764374985) Birkhauser Verlag AG CHE. Dist: Springer.
—Carotenoids Vol. 5: Nutrition & Health. 2009. (Carotenoids Ser.). (Illus.). 350p. 139.00 *(978-3-7643-7500-3(0))* Birkhauser Boston.
de la Rosa, Laura A., et al, eds. Fruit & Vegetable Phytochemicals: Chemistry, Nutritional Value & Stability. 2010. (ENG., Illus.). 384p. 219.95 *(978-0-8138-0320-3(9)*, Wiley-Blackwell) Wiley, John & Sons, Inc.
Frank, H. A., et al, eds. The Photochemistry of Carotenoids. 2010. (Advances in Photosynthesis & Respiration Ser.). (Illus.). 420p. pap. 379.00 *(978-90-481-5310-7(7)*, 9048153107) Springer.
Landrum, John T., ed. Carotenoids: Physical, Chemical, & Biological Functions & Properties. 2009. (ENG., Illus.). 568p. 195.95 *(978-1-4200-5230-5(6)*, CRC Press) Taylor & Francis Group GBR. Dist: Taylor & Francis Group.
Yamaguchi, Masaycshi, ed. Carotenoids: Properties, Effects & Diseases. 2011. (Biochemistry Research Trends Ser.). 195.00 *(978-1-61209-713-8(8)*, Nova Biomedical Bks.) Nova Science Pubs., Inc.

CAROTID ARTERY

Cho, Byung-Kyu & Tominaga, Teiji. Moyamoya Disease Update. 2010. (ENG., Illus.). 350p. 219.00 *(978-4-431-99702-3(4)*, 4431997024) Springer.
Frickey, Nathalie. Spontaneous Dissection & Stroke in Young Adults. 2008. 92p. pap. *(978-3-639-06915-0(3))* VDM Verlag Dr. Mueller e.K.
Heiser, Angela. Rat Jugular Vein & Carotid Artery Catheterization for Acute Survival Studies: A Practical Guide. 2007. (Illus.). 115p. spiral bd. 114.00 *(978-0-387-49414-2(6))* Springer.
Henry, Michel. The Carotid & Supra-Aortic Trunks: Diagnosis, Angioplasty & Stenting. 2nd ed. 2011. (ENG., Illus.). 520p. 209.95 *(978-1-4051-9854-7(0)*, Wiley-Blackwell) Wiley, John & Sons, Inc.
Hopkins, L. Nelson, et al, eds. Carotid Atherosclerotic Disease: Pathologic Basis for Treatment. 2008. (Illus.). 362p. 180.00 *(978-1-84184-149-6(8)*, Informa Healthcare) Taylor & Francis Group GBR. Dist: Taylor & Francis Group.
Macdonald, Sumaira & Stansby, Gerald. Practical Carotid Artery Stenting: I 2009. (ENG., Illus.). xiv, 208p. 119.00 *(978-1-84800-298-2(X)*, 184800298X) Springer.
Moussa. Essentials in Carotid Duplex Ultrasound. Salameh, Maya Jean, ed. 2009. 196p. 280.00 *(978-0-415-45524-4(3)*, Informa Healthcare) Taylor & Francis Group.
Schaller, Bernhard, ed. Imaging of Carotid Artery Stenosis. 2006. (Illus.). 272p. 259.00 *(978-3-211-32332-8(5)*, 3211323325) Springer.
Sturzenegger, M., et al, eds. European Society of Neurosonology & Cerebral Hemodynamics: 7th Meeting, Bern, May 2002: Final Program & Abstracts. (Illus.). *(978-3-8055-7455-6(X))* Karger, S. AG.
Yao & Pearce. Modern Trends in Vascular Surgery: Carotid Artery Disease. 2010. 600p. ***(978-1-60795-052-3(9))*** PMPH-USA. Ltd.
Yount, Professor Ray, et al. Different Strokes for Different Folks: The Dilemma over Writing Styles. 2011. (C). lib. bdg. ***(978-0-9711516-3-5(6))*** Grand Old Pr.

CAROTIN

see Carotenes

CAROTINOIDS

see Carotenoids

CAROUSEL ART

see Merry-Go-Round Art

CARP

see also Koi

Asian Carp: Hearing Before the Subcommittee on Water & Power of the Committee on Energy & Natural Resources, United States Senate, One Hundred Eleventh Congress, Second Session, to Examine the Science & Policy Behind the Federal Framework & Nonfederal Efforts to Prevent Introduction of the Aquatic Invasive Asian Carp into the Great Lakes, February 25, 2010. 2010. iii, 75p. *(978-0-16-085807-9(0)*, 552-070-41024-4) United States Government Printing Office.
Asian Carp & the Great Lakes: Hearing Before the Subcommittee on Water Resources & Environment of the Committee on Transportation & Infrastructure, House of Representatives, One Hundred Eleventh Congress, First [i.e. Second] Session, February 9, 2010. 2010. (Illus.). xiv, 204p. *(978-0-16-086376-9(7)*, 552-070-41455-0) United States Government Printing Office.
Ball, Chris, et al. Big Carp. Church, Bob, ed. 2007. (ENG., Illus.). 200p. 49.95 *(978-1-86126-911-9(0))* Crowood Pr., Ltd. GBR. Dist: Independent Pubs. Group.
David, Lior. Inheritance of Colors & Evolution of Koi & Carp. 2009. 108p. pap. *(978-3-639-15475-7(4))* VDM Verlag Dr. Mueller e.K.
Deborah M. Maeda. Troubled Waters: Asian Carp & the Great Lakes. 2011. (Series: Environmental Science, Engineering & Technology Ser.). 89.00 *(978-1-61761-766-9(0))* Nova Science Pubs., Inc.
Driver, Patrick. Carp Ecosystem Impacts. 2008. 192p. pap. *(978-3-639-07284-6(7))* VDM Verlag Dr. Mueller e.K.
Invasive Species: Hearing Before the Subcommittee on Water & Power of the Committee on Energy & Natural Resources, United States Senate, One Hundred Eleventh Congress, Second Session, to Examine the Federal Response to the Discovery of the Aquatic Invasive Species Asian Carp in Lake Calumet, Illinois, July 14, 2010. 2010. iii, 58p. ***(978-0-16-087213-6(8)***, 552-070-42051-7) United States Government Printing Office.
Kolar, Cynthia. Asian Carps: A Biological Synopsis & Risk Assessment. 33rd ed. 2007. 204p. 60.00 *(978-1-888569-79-7(4))* American Fisheries Society.
Sanders, Jennifer D. & Peterson, Sam B., eds. Carp: Habitat, Management & Diseases. 2011. (Fish, Fishing, & Fisheries Marine Biology Ser.). (Illus.). 215p. 95.00 ***(978-1-61324-525-5(4))*** Nova Science Pubs., Inc.

CARPAL TUNNEL SYNDROME

Luchetti, R. & Amadio, P., eds. Carpal Tunnel Syndrome. 2006. (Illus.). 405p. 339.00 *(978-3-540-22387-0(8)*, 3540223878) Springer.
Luchetti, Riccardo & Amadio, Peter, eds. Carpal Tunnel Syndrome. 2010. (Illus.). xxii, 410p. pap. 339.00 *(978-3-642-06119-6(2)*, 3642061192) Springer.
Worseg, A. P., et al. Endoscopic Carpal Tunnel Release. 2007. (Illus.). 250p. 399.00 *(978-3-211-83237-0(8)*, 3211832378) Springer.

CARPATHIAN MOUNTAINS

Kozak, Jacek & Ostapowicz, Katarzyna Anna, eds. Integrating Nature & Society towards Sustainability. 2012. (Environmental Science & Engineering Ser.). (ENG.). x, 290p. 139.00 ***(978-3-642-12724-3(X)***, 364212724X) Springer.

CARPATHIAN MOUNTAINS—DESCRIPTION AND TRAVEL

Crosse, Andrew F. Round about the Carpathians. 2008. 256p. 25.99 *(978-0-554-35858-1(1))* 2008. 256p. 28.99 ***(978-0-554-26555-1(9))*** 2007. 230p. pap. 20.99 *(978-1-4346-1340-0(2))* 2007. 252p. pap. 23.99 *(978-1-4346-1392-9(5))* BiblioBazaar.
—Round about the Carpathians. 2008. 386p. pap. 33.95 ***(978-1-4371-3441-4(6))*** Kessinger Publishing, LLC.
O'Toole, Edward. Carpathian Ghost Hunter. 2008. 148p. pap. *(978-1-59146-160-9(X)*, Crystal Dreams Publishing) Multi-Media Pubns., Inc.

CARPATHIAN MOUNTAINS—HISTORY

Kienlin, Tobias L. Traditions & Transformations: Approaches to Eneolithic (Copper Age) & Bronze Age Metalworking & Society in Eastern Central Europe & the Carpathian Basin. 2011. (Bar S Ser.). (ENG., Illus.). 405p. (C). pap. 152.50 *(978-1-4073-0740-4(1))* British Archaeological Reports Ltd. GBR. Dist: Brown, David Bk. Co., The.
Tunstall, Graydon A. Blood on the Snow: The Carpathian Winter War, 1915. 2010. 29.95 *(978-0-7006-1720-3(5))* Univ. Pr. of Kansas.
Zalai-Gaál, István et al. Zur Herkunft des Schädelkults Im Neolithikum des Karpatenbeckens. 2009. (Series Minor Ser.). (GER., Illus.). 138p. (C). pap. 38.00 *(978-963-9911-08-6(9))* Archaeolingua Alapitvany HUN. Dist: Brown, David Bk. Co., The.

C

CARPATHO-RUSYNS
Here are entered works on Ruthenian inhabitants of Transcarpathia.
Plishkova, Anna. Language & National Identity: Rusyns South of Carpathians. 2010. (ENG.). (gr. 17). 55.00 *(978-0-88033-646-8(3))* Eastern European Monographs.
Rusinko, Elaine, ed. Committing Community: Carpatho-Rusyn Studies as an Emerging Scholarly Discipline. 2009. (ENG., Illus.). 416p. (gr. 17). 70.00 *(978-0-88033-645-1(5))* Eastern European Monographs.
Rusinko, Elaine, et al, eds. God Is a Rusyn: Anthology of Contemporary Carpatho-Rusyn Literature. 2011. 322p. pap. 29.95 ***(978-0-89357-381-2(7))*** Slavica Pubs.

CARPENTER, EDWARD, 1844-1929
Carpenter, Edward. My Days & Dreams. 2008. 380p. *(978-1-4437-2423-4(8),* Hesperides Pr.) Read Bks.
Copley, Antony. A Spiritual Bloomsbury: Hinduism & Homosexuality in the Lives & Writings of Edward Carpenter, E. M. Forster, & Christopher Isherwood. 2006. (ENG.). 410p. per. 32.50 *(978-0-7391-1465-0(4));* 89.50 *(978-0-7391-1464-3(6))* Lexington Bks.
Rowbotham, Sheila. Edward Carpenter: A Life of Liberty & Love. 2009. (ENG., Illus.). 548p. pap. 24.95 *(978-1-84467-421-3(5),* 844421) Verso Bks. GBR. Dist: Norton, W. W. & Co., Inc.
Swan, Tom. Edward Carpenter the Man & His Message. 2006. pap. 16.95 *(978-1-4286-3735-1(4))* Kessinger Publishing, LLC.

CARPENTER, MARY, 1807-1877
Carpenter, Joseph E. The Life & Work of Mary Carpenter. 495p. reprint ed. 98.00 *(978-0-7222-1738-2(2))* Library Reprints, Inc.

CARPENTER, MATTHEW HALE, 1824-1881
Flower, Frank Abial. Life of Matthew Hale Carpenter. 2007. (ENG.). 588p. 58.95 *(978-0-548-10830-7(7))* Kessinger Publishing, LLC.

CARPENTER FAMILY
Usher, J. Genealogy & Historical Record of the Carpenter Family, with a Brief Genealogy of Some Descendants of William Carpenter of Weymouth & Rehoboth, Massachusetts, William of Providence, Rhode Island, Samuel of Pennsylvania & Ephraim, Timothy & Josias of Long Island. fac. ed. 70p. reprint ed. pap. 14.00 *(978-0-7404-0203-6(0X))* Higginson Bk. Co.

CARPENTERS
see also Cabinetmakers
Beechert, Edward D. Aupuni I La'au: A History of Hawai'i's Carpenters Union Local 745. pap. 7.95 *(978-0-681-02743-5(6))* Booklines Hawaii, Ltd.
Broughton, Ralph. All in a Lifetime. 2006. (ENG., Illus.). 164p. per. 19.57 *(978-1-4120-9720-8(7))* Trafford Publishing.
Brown, John Fulton. The Bushwhackers: The Story of a Reluctant Rebel During the Civil War. 2009. 420p. 36.95 *(978-1-4401-5446-1(5));* pap. 26.95 *(978-1-4401-5448-5(1))* iUniverse, Inc.
Carroll, John. Working Alone. (Illus.). 160p. pap. *(978-1-56158-425-3(8),* 070539) Taunton Pr., Inc.
Gaines, Pat. The Journal of Amos Hannah. (Illus.). 2008. (ENG.). 254p. pap. 14.99 *(978-0-9817049-7-5(2))* 2007. 256p. 34.00 *(978-0-9787421-5-7(X))* Dragonfly Publishing, Inc.
Garrison, J. Ritchie. Two Carpenters: Architecture & Building in Early New England, 1799-1859. 2006. (Illus.). 240p. 48.95 *(978-1-57233-485-4(1))* Univ. of Tennessee Pr.
Haddlesey, Richard. Virtual Meccano. 2010. 100p. pap. *(978-3-8383-6291-5(8))* Lambert Academic Publishing.
Harrison, Douglas. First Watch: Seawater in My Veins. 2007. (Illus.). 14.95 *(978-1-4120-5784-4(1))* Trafford Publishing.

CARPENTERS COMPANY
Carpenters' Company Of The City And Coun. Carpenters' Hall, & Its Historic Memories. 2011. 22p. pap. 11.99 ***(978-1-4181-9092-7(6))*** MPublishing.

CARPENTIER, ALEJO, 1904-1980
Campuzano, Luisa. Alejo Carpentier: Acá y Allá. 2007. (Serie Antonio Cornejo Polar Ser.: Vol. 5). (SPA., Illus.). 374p. *(978-1-930744-31-8(5))* Instituto Internacional de Literatura Iberoamericana (ILLI).
Viala, Fabienne. Marguerite Yourcenar, Alejo Carpentier: Ecritures de L'histoire. 2008. (Yourcenar Ser.). (FRE & SPA.). 185p. pap. 54.95 *(978-90-5201-400-5(0))* PIE - Peter Lang BEL. Dist: Lang, Peter.

CARPENTRY
see also Doors and Doorways; Floors; Joinery; Roofs; Scaffolding; Walls; Woodwork; Woodworking Machinery
Ankerson, Katherine S. Elements of Interior & Lightframe Construction. 68p. instr.'s gde. ed. *(978-1-56367-299-6(5))* Fairchild Bks.
Bailey, R. F. The Pocket Size Carpenter's Helper. 3rd ed. 2008. (ENG., Illus.). 124p. spiral bd. 14.95 *(978-1-933502-19-9(3))* Linden Publishing Co., Inc.
Benjamin, Asher. The Country Builder's Assistant. 2007. 68p. per. 8.50 *(978-1-60206-769-1(4))* Cosimo, Inc.
—Country Builders Assistant Containing A. 2006. 64p. per. *(978-1-4067-9587-5(9),* Hesperides Pr.) Read Bks.
Berry, Nancy E. Architectural Trim: Ideas, Inspiration & Practical Advice for Adding Wainscoting, Mantels, Built-Ins, Baseboards, Cornices, Casings & Columns to Your Home. 2007. (Home Design Details Ser.). (ENG., Illus.). 160p. pap. 24.99 *(978-1-59253-326-8(4),* 1592533264, Quarry Books) Quayside.
Brackett, Gary. DEWALT Carpentry & Framing Complete Handbook. 2011. (ENG.). 240p. pap. 24.95 *(978-1-111-13613-0(0),* DEWALT) CENGAGE Learning.
Brackett, Gary. DeWALT Carpentry & Framing Complete Handbook (1st Print Run) 2011. (ENG.). 240p. pap. 24.95 ***(978-1-133-28238-9(5),*** DEWALT) CENGAGE Learning.
Cram101 Textbook Reviews. Outlines & Highlights for Principles & Practices of Light Construction by Ronald C Smith. 2011. 94p. pap. 27.95 ***(978-1-61812-804-1(3))*** Cram101 Inc.
Creative Homeowner Press Editors, ed. Trim. 2nd ed. 2009. (Home Improvement Ser.). (ENG., Illus.). 112p. pap. 10.95 *(978-1-58011-445-5(8))* Creative Homeowner.
Creative Homeowner Press Staff. Trimwork. Creative Homeowner Press Editors, ed. 2010. (Home Improvement Ser.). (ENG., Illus.). 288p. (gr. 5). pap. 19.95 *(978-1-58011-477-6(6))* Creative Homeowner.
Creative Publishing International Editors. Black & Decker Here's How... Trimwork: 24 Quick & Easy Makeovers for Walls, Windows & Doors. 2010. (Black & Decker Here's How Ser.). (ENG., Illus.). 96p. pap. 9.99 *(978-1-58923-488-8(X),* 158923488X, Creative Publishing International) Quayside.
—Trim & Finish Carpentry: Tips & Techniques from the Pros. 2nd ed. 2010. (Black & Decker Ser.). (ENG., Illus.). 160p. 19.99 *(978-1-58923-523-6(1),* 1589235231) Quayside.
Cushman, Ted & DeKorne, Clayton. Finish Carpentry. 2008. (For Pros by Pros Ser.). (ENG., Illus.). 250p. pap. 24.95 *(978-1-56158-818-3(0),* Taunton) Taunton Pr., Inc.
DeKorne, Clayton. Trim Carpentry. 2008. (Taunton's Build Like a Pro Ser.). (ENG., Illus.). 186p. pap. 19.95 *(978-1-56158-943-2(8))* Taunton Pr., Inc.
Douglas, W. B. Carpentry & Joinery: A Comprehensive Self-Teaching Text in the Fine Art of Carpentry, Complete Home Building Instructions. 25.50 *(978-0-87559-109-4(4))* Shalom, P. Pubns., Inc.
Durbahn & Sundberg. Fundamentals of Carpentry, No. 2. *(978-0-8269-0571-0(4))* American Technical Pubs., Inc.
Eadie, Wallace. How to Build Your Own Bentwood Chair: A Guide to Building & Selling Rustic Furniture. 2011. 84p. pap. 15.95 ***(978-1-4620-1055-4(5))*** iUniverse, Inc.
Ellis, George. A Treasury of Carpentry. 2008. 460p. pap. *(978-1-905217-99-1(4))* Mills, Jeremy Publishing.
Engel, Andy. Building Stairs. 2007. (For Pros by Pros Ser.). (ENG., Illus.). 234p. per. 24.95 *(978-1-56158-892-3(X),* Taunton) Taunton Pr., Inc.
Engel, Andy. Carpentry Complete: Expert Advice from Start to Finish. 2012. (Taunton's Complete Ser.). (ENG., Illus.). 272p. pap. 21.95 ***(978-1-60085-146-9(0))*** Taunton Pr., Inc.
Fine Homebuilding. Trim Carpentry. 2012. (For Pros by Pros Ser.). (ENG., Illus.). 240p. pap. 24.95 ***(978-1-60085-502-3(4))*** Taunton Pr., Inc.
Fine Homebuilding Editors, ed. Carpentry. 2007. (For Pros by Pros Ser.). (ENG., Illus.). 313p. per. 24.95 *(978-1-56158-915-9(2),* Taunton) Taunton Pr., Inc.
—Framing Floors, Walls, & Ceilings. 2009. (For Pros by Pros Ser.). (ENG., Illus.). 281p. pap. 24.95 *(978-1-60085-069-1(3))* Taunton Pr., Inc.
Goring, Les. Manual of First & Second Fixing Carpentry. 3rd rev. ed. 2010. (ENG., Illus.). 280p. pap. 42.95 *(978-1-85617-768-9(8))* Routledge.
Goss, Ralph & Mindham, Chris N. Goss's Roofing Ready Reckoner: Metric Cutting & Sizing Tables for Timber Roof Members. 4th rev. ed. 2007. (ENG., Illus.). 192p. pap. 29.99 *(978-1-4051-5921-0(9),* Wiley-Blackwell) Wiley, John & Sons, Inc.
Hull, Brent & Hull Historical Staff. Hull Historical Molding Catalog. 2009. (ENG.). 79p. pap. 19.95 *(978-1-56523-385-0(9))* Fox Chapel Publishing Co., Inc.
Huth, Mark. Practical Problems in Mathematics for Carpenters. 9th ed. 2011. (Practical Problems in Mathematics Ser.). (ENG.). 208p. (C). pap. 72.95 *(978-1-111-31342-5(3))* Delmar Cengage Learning.
Kossow, Greg. Trim Complete: Expert Advice from Start to Finish. 2008. (Taunton's Complete Ser.). (ENG., Illus.). 235p. per. 21.95 *(978-1-56158-869-5(5))* Taunton Pr., Inc.
Maguire, Byron W. Carpentry Framing & Finishing. 4th ed. 2007. (Illus.). *(978-0-13-228596-4(7))* Prentice Hall PTR.
Manual de Carpinteria I.Tr. of Carpentry Guide One. (SPA.). 32.48 *(978-968-24-5645-9(2))* Trillas Editorial, S. A. MEX. Dist: Continental Bk. Co., Inc.
Marshall, Chris. Trim Carpentry Projects. 2008. (Illus.). 160p. pap. 14.95 *(978-1-58159-363-1(5),* Shady Oak Pr.) North American Media Group.
McDowell, Josh. Mas Que un Carpintero. 2009.Tr. of More Than a Carpenter. (SPA., Illus.). 185p. pap. 3.99 *(978-0-7899-1712-6(2))* Editorial Unilit.
Meredith Books Staff & Better Homes and Gardens Books Staff. Carpentry & Trimwork: Step-by-Step Instructions. 2008. (Do It Yourself Ser.). (ENG., Illus.). 144p. pap. 12.95 *(978-0-696-23661-7(3),* Wiley) Wiley, John & Sons, Inc.
Miller, Mark, et al. Carpentry & Construction, Fifth Edition. 5th ed. 2009. (ENG., Illus.). 784p. pap. 49.95 *(978-0-07-162471-8(6),* 0071624716) McGraw-Hill Professional Publishing.
Moon, Philip. Trim Carpentry. 2nd ed. 2006. (ENG., Illus.). 240p. per. 58.95 *(978-1-4180-2864-0(9))* Delmar Cengage Learning.
NCCER. Carpentry: Trainee Guide Level 4. 4th ed. 2008. pap. ***(978-0-13-614411-3(X))*** Prentice Hall PTR.
NCCER. Carpentry Fundamentals. 4th ed. 2006. (ENG.). 496p. (C). 89.33 *(978-0-13-229268-9(8),* Prentice Hall) Prentice Hall PTR.
Osborn, Roe. Finishing a House: A Complete Guide from Installing Insulation to Running Trim. 2012. (ENG., Illus.). 240p. pap. 21.95 ***(978-1-60085-393-7(5))*** Taunton Pr., Inc.
Pollan, Michael. A Place of My Own: The Architecture of Daydreams. 2008. (ENG.). 352p. (gr. 12-18). 16.00 *(978-0-14-311474-1(3),* Penguin (Non-Classics)) Penguin Group (USA) Inc.
Popular Woodworking Editors, ed. Spons on Carpentry & Joinery: A Manual for Handicraftsmen & Amateurs. 2010. (ENG.). 276p. pap. 21.99 *(978-1-4403-1411-7(X),* Popular Woodworking Bks.) F&W Media, Inc.
Porter, Brian & Tooke, Chris. Carpentry & Joinery 1. 2012. (ENG.). (C). pap. 34.95 ***(978-0-08-097154-4(7),*** Butterworth-Heinemann) Elsevier Science & Technology Bks.
—Carpentry & Joinery 2. 2012. (ENG.). (C). pap. 37.95 ***(978-0-08-097156-8(3),*** Butterworth-Heinemann) Elsevier Science & Technology Bks.
—Carpentry & Joinery 3. 2012. (ENG.). (C). pap. 41.95 ***(978-0-08-097158-2(X),*** Butterworth-Heinemann) Elsevier Science & Technology Bks.
—Carpentry & Joinery 3, Vol. 3. 2nd rev. ed. 2007. (ENG., Illus.). 400p. per. 36.95 *(978-0-7506-6505-6(X))* Routledge.
Prince, Chris. DEWALT Carpentry Quick Check: Extreme Duty Edition. 2011. (ENG.). 42p. pap. 14.95 *(978-1-111-13587-4(8),* DEWALT) CENGAGE Learning.
Rudman, Jack. Carpentry. (Occupational Competency Examination Ser.: Vol. 10). 49.95 *(978-0-8373-5760-7(8),* Passbooks) National Learning Corp.
—Carpentry Workbook. (Workbook Ser.: Vol. 3020). 49.95 *(978-0-8373-7929-6(6),* Passbooks) National Learning Corp.
—Introduction to Carpentry. (Dantes Subject Standardized Tests Ser.: Vol. 40). 49.95 *(978-0-8373-6540-4(6))* National Learning Corp.
Sunset Books Staff. Trimwork. 2009. (ENG., Illus.). 240p. pap. 21.95 *(978-0-376-01270-8(6),* Sunset Bks./Sunset Publishing Corp.) Oxmoor Hse., Inc.
Vogt, Floyd. Carpentry. 5th ed. 2009. (ENG., Illus.). 944p. 158.95 *(978-1-4354-8405-4(3))* Delmar Cengage Learning.
—Residential Construction Academy. 2nd ed. 2007. (ENG.). 144p. (C). pap., wbk. ed. 34.95 *(978-1-4283-2364-3(3))* Delmar Cengage Learning.
—Residential Construction Academy: Carpentry. 2nd ed. 2007. (ENG.). (C). 1158.95 *(978-1-4180-0188-9(0))* Delmar Cengage Learning.
—Residential Construction Academy: Carpentry. 2nd ed. 2007. (ENG.). (C). 1158.95 *(978-1-4180-0187-2(2));* (Illus.). 624p. 111.95 *(978-1-4180-0183-4(X))* Delmar Cengage Learning.
—Workbook for Vogt's Carpentry, 5th. 5th ed. 2009. (ENG.). 336p. (C). pap. 47.95 *(978-1-4354-8406-1(1))* Delmar Cengage Learning.
Wagner, Willis H. & Kicklighter, Clois E. Modern Woodworking. tchr. ed. 6.00 *(978-1-56637-620-4(3))* Goodheart-Willcox Pub.
Wagner, Willis H. & Smith, Howard Bud. Modern Carpentry: Essential Skills for the Building Trades. 11th ed. 2007. (ENG., Illus.). (gr. 9-14). 182p. per., wbk. ed. 24.00 *(978-1-59070-649-7(8));* 1006p. 93.28 *(978-1-59070-648-0(X))* Goodheart-Willcox Pub.
Wakeling, Arthur, ed. Things to Make in Your Home Workshop. 2011. (Illus.). 256p. 47.95 ***(978-1-258-10188-6(2))*** Literary Licensing, LLC.
Webster, Alfred P. & Bright, Kathryn E. Mathematics for Carpentry & the Construction Trades. 3rd ed. 2011. (ENG.). 408p. (C). pap. 107.00 *(978-0-13-511400-1(4),* Prentice Hall) Prentice Hall PTR.
Wood Lake Books Staff. Finish Carpentry & Trimwork: Tools, Tips, Techniques, & Projects. Allen, Benjamin et al, eds. 2008. (Do It Yourself Ser.). (ENG., Illus.). 240p. pap. 19.95 *(978-0-696-23737-9(7),* Wiley) Wiley, John & Sons, Inc.
Zerbe, J. S. Carpentry for Boys. 2007. (ENG.). 208p. per. *(978-1-4065-6806-6(6))* Dodo Pr.

CARPENTRY—ESTIMATES
Atcheson, Dan. National Framing & Finish Carpentry Estimator. 3rd ed. 2008. (National Framing & Finish Carpentry Estimator Ser.). (Illus.). 402p. pap. 62.95 incl. cd-rom *(978-1-57218-211-0(3))* Craftsman Bk. Co.
Atcheson, Daniel Benn. National Framing & Finish Carpentry Estimator. 2006. (National Framing & Finish Carpentry Estimator Ser.). (Illus.). 398p. pap. 52.25 incl. cd-rom *(978-1-57218-183-0(4))* Craftsman Bk. Co.
Rsmeans, compiled by. Means CPG Residential Detailed Costs. 2007. (Illus.). 403p. per. 39.95 *(978-0-87629-056-9(X))* Means, R.S. Co., Inc.

CARPENTRY—TOOLS
see also Lathes; Planes (Hand Tools); Saws
American Society of Mechanical Engineers Staff, ed. Glazier's Chisels & Wood Chisels-Safety Requirements. 16p. 32.00 *(978-0-7918-2491-7(8))* ASME Pr.
—Hatchets: Safety Requirements. 16p. 28.00 *(978-0-7918-2460-3(8))* ASME Pr.
—Ripping Chisels & Flooring/Electricians' Chisels: Safety Requirements. 16p. 32.00 *(978-0-7918-2484-9(5))* ASME Pr.
Anthony, Paul. Tablesaws. 2009. (Complete Illustrated Guides). (ENG., Illus.). 220p. pap. 24.95 *(978-1-60085-011-0(1))* Taunton Pr., Inc.
Anthony, Paul & Fine Woodworking Magazine Editors, eds. Working with Power Tools. 2007. (New Best of Fine Woodworking Ser.). (ENG., Illus.). 284p. pap. 21.95 *(978-1-56158-872-5(5),* Taunton) Taunton Pr., Inc.
Arnold, Bob. Sunswumthru a Building. 2006. (Illus.). 123p. *(978-1-929048-06-9(8))* Longhouse, Pubs. & Booksellers.
English, John. Woodworker's Guide to Sharpening: All You Need to Know to Keep Your Tools Sharp. 2008. (ENG., Illus.). 155p. pap. 19.95 *(978-1-56523-309-6(3))* Fox Chapel Publishing Co., Inc.
Horner, Ken. Essential Guide to the Steel Square: Facts, Short-Cuts, & Problem-Solving Secrets for Carpenters, Woodworkers & Builders. 2007. (Woodworker's Essentials & More Ser.). (ENG., Illus.). 181p. per. 19.95 *(978-1-56523-342-3(5))* Fox Chapel Publishing Co., Inc.
Zerbe, J. S. How to Do It!: A Hands-on Introduction to the Essential Woodworking, Electrical & Mechanical Skills Every Handyman, Craftsman & Inventor Needs. 2008. 436p. pap. 29.95 *(978-0-557-00045-6(9))* Lulu Enterprises Inc.

CARPENTRY—VOCATIONAL GUIDANCE
Cruising Guide to Belize & Mexico's Caribbean Coast, Including Guatemala's Rio Dulce: Third Edition. 3rd ed. 2007. per. 39.95 *(978-0-9755753-1-4(7))* Windmill Hill Bks.
Sheldon, Roger. Opportunities in Carpentry Careers. 2007. (Opportunities in... Ser.). (ENG.). 221p. per. 13.95 *(978-0-07-147606-5(7),* 0071476067) McGraw-Hill Cos., The.

CARPET AND RUG INDUSTRY
see Rug and Carpet Industry

CARPETBAG RULE (U.S. HISTORY, 1865-1877)
see Reconstruction (U.S. History, 1865-1877)

CARPETS
see also Rug and Carpet Industry; Rugs; Weaving
Barbatti, Bruno. Berber Carpets of Morocco: The Symbols Origin & Meaning. 2009. (ENG., Illus.). 344p. 120.00 *(978-2-86770-184-9(8))* ACR Edition FRA. Dist: Antique Collectors' Club.
Borka, Max. Art of the Loom, 1 vol. 2011. (ENG., Illus.). 160p. 92.50 ***(978-94-90693-09-1(X))*** Exhibitions International BEL. Dist: Innovative Logistics.
Goswami, K. K., ed. Advances in Carpet Manufacture. 2009. (Illus.). 320p. 222.95 *(978-1-4200-9491-6(2))* CRC Pr. LLC.
—Advances in Carpet Manufacture. 2009. (Illus.). 336p. *(978-1-84569-333-6(7))* Woodhead Publishing Ltd.
Style Name Directory for Carpets & Rugs. 96p. pap. 30.00 *(978-0-89275-016-0(2))* Carpet & Rug Institute, Inc.

CARRACCI, ANNIBALE, 1560-1609
Dickerson, C. D., III. Raw Painting: The Butcher's Shop by Annibale Carracci. 2010. (Kimbell Masterpiece Ser.). (ENG., Illus.). 100p. pap. 16.95 *(978-0-300-16640-8(0))* Kimbell Art Museum.

CARRACCI, LODOVICO, 1555-1619
Loisel, Catherine. Ludovico Carracci. 2008. (Drawing Gallery Ser.). (ENG., Illus.). 84p. pap. 15.95 *(978-88-7439-129-5(3))* 5 Continents ITA. Dist: Hachette Bk. Group.

CARREL, ALEXIS, 1873-1944
Friedman, David M. The Immortalists: Charles Lindbergh, Dr. Alexis Carrel, & Their Daring Quest to Live Forever. 2008. (ENG.). 368p. pap. 14.95 *(978-0-06-052816-4(8),* HarperPerennial) 2007. (Illus.). 352p. 26.95 *(978-0-06-052815-7(X),* Ecco) HarperCollins Pubs.
Reggiani, Andrés Horacio. God's Eugenicist: Alexis Carrel & the Sociobiology of Decline. 2006. (Berghahn Monographs in French Studies: Vol. 6). (Illus.). 268p. (C). 90.00 *(978-1-84545-172-1(4))* Berghahn Bks., Inc.

CARRERA VERDUGO, JOSE MIGUEL, 1785-1821
Dolores Luna Guinot. Conspiracy in Mendoz. 2009. 340p. pap. 25.00 *(978-1-4269-2185-8(3))* Trafford Publishing.

CARRIAGE AND WAGON MAKING
see also Wheels
Bourn, Daniel. A treatise upon wheel-carriages; showing their present Defects: With a plan & description of a new constructed waggon: which will effectually preserve & improve the public Roads â¿. 2007. 39.95 *(978-1-4255-8883-0(2))* MPublishing.
Felton, William. A Treatise on Carriages. 2009. 114p. pap. *(978-1-4432-5368-0(5))* Books LLC.
FitzGerald, William N. The Carriage Trimmers' Manual: Guide Book & Illustrated Technical Dictionary. 2007. reprint ed. pap. 32.95 *(978-1-931626-23-1(5),* Astragal Pr.) Finney Co., Inc.
Holmstrom, J. G. Traditional Blacksmithing: The Fine Art of Horseshoeing & Wagon Making. 2012. (ENG., Illus.). 204p. pap. 12.95 ***(978-1-61608-551-3(7),*** 608551) Skyhorse Publishing Co., Inc.
Riker, Ben. Pony Wagon Town, along U S 1890. 2011. 312p. 50.95 ***(978-1-258-07982-6(8))*** Literary Licensing, LLC.
Sturt, George. The Wheelwright's Shop. 2008. 144p. *(978-1-4437-3887-3(5),* Home Farm Bks.) Read Bks.

CARRIAGES AND CARTS
see also Coaching (Transportation); Omnibuses; Vehicles
Bourn, Daniel. A treatise upon wheel-carriages; showing their present Defects: With a plan & description of a new constructed waggon: which will effectually preserve & improve the public Roads â¿. 2007. 39.95 *(978-1-4255-8883-0(2))* MPublishing.
Crouwel, J. H. Chariots & Other Wheeled Vehicles in Italy Before the Roman Empire. 2012. (ENG., Illus.). 248p. (C). pap. 80.00 ***(978-1-84217-467-8(3))*** Oxbow Bks., Ltd. GBR. Dist: Brown, David Bk. Co., The.
Mynard, Dennis C. Salmons & Sons: The Tickford Coachbuilders. 2007. (ENG.). 192p. 49.95 *(978-1-86077-422-5(9))* History Pr. Ltd.,The GBR. Dist: Independent Pubs. Group.
Scott, N. M. The British Hearse & the British Funeral. 2011. (Illus.). 160p. 42.50 ***(978-1-84624-512-1(5))*** Book Guild, Ltd. GBR. Dist: Trans-Atlantic Pubns., Inc.
Smith, D. J. Discovering Horse-Drawn Carriages. 3rd ed. 2011. (Shire Discovering Ser.). (ENG., Illus.). 80p. pap. 11.95 *(978-0-85263-720-3(9))* Shire Pubns., Ltd. GBR. Dist: Random Hse., Inc.
Swift, Jan & Swift, Geoff. Perambulators. 2008. (Shire Library). (ENG.). 64p. pap. 12.95 *(978-0-7478-0684-4(5))* Shire Pubns., Ltd. GBR. Dist: Random Hse., Inc.

Vickers, Hugh. The Royal Mews at Buckingham Palace: Official Guidebook. 2010. (ENG.). 56p. pap. 7.95 *(978-1-902163-26-0(5))* Royal Collection Enterprises Ltd. GBR. Dist: Chicago Distribution Ctr.

Viner, David. Wagons & Carts. 2009. (Shire Library). (ENG., Illus.). 64p. pap. 12.95 *(978-0-7478-0676-9(4))* Shire Pubns., Ltd. GBR. Dist: Random Hse., Inc.

Wachsmann, Shelley. The Gurob Ship-Cart Model & Its Mediterranean Context/Shelley Wachsmann. 2012. ***(978-1-60344-429-3(7))*** Texas A&M Univ. Pr.

Wackernagel, Rudolph H. & Wackernagel, Rudolf H. Staats- und Galawagen der Wittelsbacher: Kutschen, Schlitten und Sänften aus dem Marstallmuseum Schloss Nymphenburg, 2 vols. 2007. (ENG., Illus.). 416p. 190.00 *(978-3-925369-87-2(2))* Arnoldsche Art Pubs. DEU. Dist: Antique Collectors' Club.

Waldbaum, Laura. Carting with Your Dog: Positive Draft Training for Fun & Competition. 2011. 168p. pap. 14.95 *(978-1-61781-024-4(X))* Dogwise Publishing.

Wood, Jonathan. Coachbuilding: The Hand-Crafted Car Body. 2009. (Shire Library). (ENG., Illus.). 48p. pap. 12.95 *(978-0-7478-0688-2(8))* Shire Pubns., Ltd. GBR. Dist: Random Hse., Inc.

CARRIER LANGUAGE

Hargus, Sharon. Witsuwit'en Grammar: Phonetics, Phonology, Morphology. 2007. (ENG., Illus.). 850p. 150.00 *(978-0-7748-1382-2(2))* UBC Pr. CAN. Dist: Univ. of Washington Pr.

CARRIER PIGEONS

see Pigeons

CARRIERS

Here are entered works on individuals or companies engaged in the transportation of passengers or goods.

see also Bus Lines; Express Service; Postal Service; Taxicabs

Basedow, Jürgen, et al, eds. The Hamburg Lectures on Maritime Affairs 2007 And 2008. 2009. (Hamburg Studies on Maritime Affairs Ser.). (Illus.). xi, 196p. pap. 139.00 *(978-3-642-04063-4(2),* 3642040632) Springer.

Bergoffen, Gene. Commercial Motor Vehicle Carrier Safety Management Certification. 2007. (Illus.). 52p. 45.00 *(978-0-309-09878-6(5))* Transportation Research Board.

Federal Communications Commission (U.S.), compiled by. Statistics of Communications Common Carriers. 2006/2007. 2011. (ENG.). 268p. pap. 39.00 *(978-0-16-086612-8(X),* Federal Communications Commission) United States Government Printing Office.

Gerhold, Dorian. Road Transport before the Railways: Russell's London Flying Waggons. 2008. (ENG., Illus.). 336p. pap. 46.00 *(978-0-521-09014-8(8))* Cambridge Univ. Pr.

Güner-Özbek, Meltem Deniz, ed. The United Nations Convention on Contracts for the International Carriage of Goods Wholly or Partly by Sea: An Appraisal of the Rotterdam Rules. 2011. (ENG.). x, 289p. 139.00 *(978-3-642-19649-2(7),* 3642196497) Springer.

Harris, Brian. Ridley's Law of the Carriage of Goods by Land, Sea & Air. 8th rev. ed. 2010. 512p. pap. *(978-0-414-04502-6(5))* Sweet & Maxwell, Ltd.

Hicks, Tyler G. Directory of Freight Forwarders & Custom House Brokers. 2010. (ENG.). 106p. pap. 17.50 *(978-1-56150-982-9(5))* International Wealth Success, Inc.

—Directory of Freight Forwarders & Custom House Brokers. 2009. pap. 17.50 *(978-1-56150-978-2(7))* 17th ed. 2007. pap. 17.50 *(978-1-56150-853-2(5))* International Wealth Success, Inc.

Hoeks, Marian. Multimodal Transport Law: Law Applicable to Multimodal Contract. 2010. xxviii, 530p. *(978-90-411-3246-8(5))* Kluwer Law International.

LexisNexis (Firm) Staff, contrib. by. Goods in Transit: Selected Statutes & Treaties. 2009. pap. *(978-1-4224-7569-0(7))* LexisNexis Matthew Bender.

Reynolds, George G. The Distribution of Power to Regulate Interstate Carriers Between the Nation & the States. (Columbia University, Studies in the Social Sciences: No. 295). reprint ed. 34.50 *(978-0-404-51295-8(X))* AMS Pr., Inc.

Rogers, R. Vashon (Robert Vashon). The Law of the Road; or, Wrongs & Rights of a Traveller. 2006. 288p. per. 23.99 *(978-1-4255-2617-7(9))* MPublishing.

Singh, Lachmi. The Law of Carriage of Goods by Sea. 2012. (Illus.). 498p. pap. 75.00 *(978-1-84766-703-8(1),* Bloomsbury Professional) Bloomsbury Publishing Plc GBR. Dist: International Specialized Bk. Services.

CARRIERS—RATES

see Transportation—Rates

CARRIERS, AIRPLANE

see Aircraft Carriers

CARROLL, ANNA ELLA, 1815-1894

Blackwell, Sarah Ellen. A Military Genius: Life of Anna Ella Carroll of Maryland. 2007. (ENG.). 156p. pap. 19.99 *(978-1-4346-4523-4(1));* 180p. pap. 21.99 *(978-1-4346-4524-1(X),* BiblioBazaar.

Greenbie, Sydney & Greenbie, Marjorie Barstow. Anna Ella Carroll & Abraham Lincoln: A Biography. 2011. 570p. 63.95 ***(978-1-258-07198-1(3))*** Literary Licensing, LLC.

Marks, Carole C. Moses & the Monster & Miss Anne. 2009. (ENG., Illus.). 256p. 37.00 *(978-0-252-03394-0(9))* Univ. of Illinois Pr.

CARROLL, CHARLES, 1737-1832

Birzer, Bradley J. American Cicero: The Life of Charles Carroll. 2010. (Lives of the Founders Ser.). (ENG.). 230p. 25.00 *(978-1-933859-89-7(X))* ISI Bks.

Rowland, Kate Mason. The Life of Charles Carroll of Carrollton 1737-1832: Correspondence & Public Papers, 2 vol., set. reprint ed. 250.00 *(978-0-7222-9030-9(6))* Library Reprints, Inc.

CARROLL, LEWIS, 1832-1898

Berg, R. J. Art of Alice: Madness Returns. 2011. (Illus.). 184p. 34.99 *(978-1-59582-697-8(1))* Dark Horse Comics.

Carroll, Lewis, pseud. Alice au Pays des Merveilles.Tr. of Alice in Wonderland. (FRE.). pap. 16.95 *(978-2-07-051366-6(1))* Gallimard, Editions FRA. Dist: Distribooks, Inc.

—Alice au Pays des Merveilles.Tr. of Alice in Wonderland. pap. 17.95 *(978-2-266-09945-5(0))* Presses Pocket FRA. Dist: Distribooks, Inc.

—The Annotated Hunting of the Snark. 2006. (Annotated Bks.). (ENG., Illus.). 192p. 27.95 *(978-0-393-06242-7(2),* 6242) Norton, W. W. & Co., Inc.

—Lewis Carroll. 2009. (Photofile Ser.). (ENG., Illus.). 144p. pap. 15.95 *(978-0-500-41098-1(4),* 541098) Thames & Hudson.

—Lewis Carroll & the House of Macmillan. Cohen, Morton N. & Gandolfo, Anita, eds. 2007. (Cambridge Studies in Publishing & Printing History Ser.). (ENG., Illus.). 396p. pap. 79.00 *(978-0-521-04471-4(5))* Cambridge Univ. Pr.

Collingwood, Stuart Dodgson. The Life & Letters of Lewis Carroll. 2009. 396p. 31.99 *(978-0-559-12569-0(0));* 29.99 *(978-0-559-12579-9(8));* pap. 32.75 *(978-0-559-12577-5(1));* pap. 26.99 *(978-0-559-12572-0(0))* BiblioBazaar.

—The Life & Letters of Lewis Carroll. 2007. (ENG.). 232p. per. *(978-1-4068-4707-9(0))* Echo Library.

Collingwood, Stuart Dodgson. The Life & Letters of Lewis Carroll (Rev. C. L. Dodgson) 2011. (Cambridge Library Collection - Life Sciences Ser.). (ENG., Illus.). 474p. pap. 34.99 ***(978-1-108-03388-6(1))*** Cambridge Univ. Pr.

Davies, Mark. Alice in Waterland: Lewis Carroll & the River Thames in Oxford. 2011. (ENG., Illus.). 130p. pap. *(978-1-904955-72-6(X))* Signal Bks.

Dickens, Charles. Household Words, Volume 8 (German Edition) (Collected Works of Lewis Carroll). reprint ed. lib. bdg. 98.00 *(978-0-7426-2353-8(X))* Classic Bks.

Dodgson, Charles Lutwidge. The Dynamics of a Particle. reprint ed. lib. bdg. 98.00 *(978-0-7426-2269-2(X))* Classic Bks.

Dusinberre, Juliet, contrib. by. Alice to the Lighthouse: Children's Books & Radical Experiments in Art. (Illus.). 19.95 *(978-0-333-65850-5(7))* Macmillan Pubs., Ltd. GBR. Dist: Trans-Atlantic Pubns., Inc.

Gardner, Martin. Sphere Packing, Lewis Carroll, & Reversi: Martin Gardner's New Mathematical Diversions. 2009. (New Martin Gardner Mathematical Library). (ENG., Illus.). 296p. 55.00 *(978-0-521-75607-5(3))* Cambridge Univ. Pr.

Higonnet, Anne. Lewis Carroll. 2008. (ENG., Illus.). 128p. 39.95 *(978-0-7148-4282-0(6))* Phaidon Pr., Inc.

Hollingsworth, Cristopher, ed. Alice beyond Wonderland: Essays for the Twenty-first Century. 2009. (ENG., Illus.). 256p. 42.95 *(978-1-58729-819-6(8))* Univ. of Iowa Pr.

Hubbard, Tom, et al. Lives of Victorian Literacy Figures: Carroll, Stevenson & Swinburne by Their Contemporaries, 3 vols., Set. Pite, Ralph, ed. 2008. (Lives of Victorian Literary Figures Ser.: Vols. 1-3). (ENG.). 1360p. 495.00 *(978-1-85196-905-0(5))* Pickering & Chatto Pubs., Ltd. GBR. Dist: Ashgate Publishing Co.

Irwin, William & Davis, Richard Brian. Alice in Wonderland & Philosophy: Curiouser & Curiouser. 2010. (Blackwell Philosophy & Pop Culture Ser.: 20). (ENG., Illus.). 240p. pap. 17.95 *(978-0-470-55836-2(9),* Wiley) Wiley, John & Sons, Inc.

Leach, Karoline. In the Shadow of the Dreamchild: The Myth & Reality of Lewis Carroll. 2nd rev. ed. 2009. (ENG.). 256p. pap. 23.95 *(978-0-7206-1318-6(3))* Owen, Peter Ltd. GBR. Dist: Independent Pubs. Group.

Lennon, Florence B. Victoria Through the Looking Glass: The Life of Lewis Carroll. 27.95 *(978-0-89190-991-0(5))* Amereon LTD.

Menges, Jeff A., ed. Alice Illustrated: 110 Images from the Classic Tales of Lewis Carroll. 2012. (Dover Fine Art, History of Art Ser.). (ENG., Illus.). 128p. pap. 19.95 *(978-0-486-48204-0(9))* Dover Pubns., Inc.

Rubin, C M & Rubin, Gabriela. The Real Alice in Wonderland: A Role Model for the Ages. 2010. 144p. 29.95 *(978-1-4490-8131-7(2))* AuthorHouse.

Sewell, Byron S., et al. An Annotated International Bibliography of Lewis Carroll's Sylvie & Bruno Books. 2008. (Illus.). 95.00 *(978-1-58456-212-2(9))* Oak Knoll Pr.

Smith, Geoffrey. Charles Blackman. 2009. (ENG.). 144p. 34.95 *(978-0-7241-0274-7(4))* National Gallery of Victoria AUS. Dist: National Bk. Network.

Smith, Geoffrey & St John Moore, Felicity. Charles Blackman: Alice in Wonderland. 2007. (ENG., Illus.). 144p. pap. 26.50 *(978-0-7241-0272-3(8))* National Gallery of Victoria AUS. Dist: National Bk. Network.

Walker, George A. A Is for Alice. 2009. (ENG., Illus.). 64p. pap. 12.95 *(978-0-88984-323-3(6))* Porcupine's Quill, Inc. CAN. Dist: Univ. of Toronto Pr.

Whatley, Charlotte. Alice in Wonderland Paper Dolls: Through an All New Looking Glass. 2010. (Dover Paper Dolls Ser.). (ENG., Illus.). 32p. (J). (gr. 6). pap. 9.99 *(978-0-486-47958-3(7))* Dover Pubns., Inc.

Wilson, Robin. Lewis Carroll in Numberland: His Fantastical Mathematical Logical Life. (ENG.). 2010. 237p. pap. 15.95 *(978-0-393-30452-7(3),* 30452) 2008. (Illus.). 208p. 24.95 *(978-0-393-06027-0(6),* 6027) Norton, W. W. & Co., Inc.

Winchester, Simon. The Alice Behind Wonderland. 2011. (ENG., Illus.). 192p. 16.95 *(978-0-19-539619-5(7))* Oxford Univ. Pr., Inc.

Woolf, Jenny. The Mystery of Lewis Carroll: Discovering the Whimsical, Thoughtful, & Sometimes Lonely Man Who Created Alice in Wonderland. (ENG., Illus.). 336p. 2011. pap. 16.99 *(978-0-312-67371-0(X),* St. Martin's Griffin) 2010. 27.99 *(978-0-312-61298-6(2))* St. Martin's Pr.

CARROLL COUNTY (MD.)

ADC, the Map People Staff, creator. Carroll County, Maryland Street Atlas. 2007. (Illus.). 52p. 12.95 *(978-0-87530-889-0(9))* ADC The Map People.

Baty, Catherine & Jerry Trescott on behalf of the Historical Society. Carroll County. 2011. (Then & Now Ser.). (ENG., Illus.). 96p. pap. 21.99 ***(978-0-7385-8801-8(6))*** Arcadia Publishing.

Blackpool, Stephen. Maryland Historical Markers Carroll & Frederick Counties. 2008. (ENG.). per. 49.95 *(978-0-9742554-6-0(7))* Blackpool, Stephen Inc.

Bonner, James C. Georgia's Last Frontier: The Development of Carol County. 2010. (ENG., Illus.). 268p. pap. 24.95 *(978-0-8203-3525-4(8))* Univ. of Georgia Pr.

Carroll County Genealogical Society. Carroll County, Maryland Cemeteries, Volume 2: East-Central. 2007. pap. 22.00 *(978-0-7884-4056-4(X))* Heritage Bks.

CARROLL FAMILY

Hoffman, Ronald. The Carroll Family of Maryland. 2008. *(978-1-929545-52-0(5))* American Antiquarian Society.

Stevenson, K. History of the William Carroll Family of Alleghany County, New York. fac. ed. 100p. reprint ed. pap. 19.00 *(978-0-7404-2286-7(3));* pap. 19.00 *(978-0-7404-2287-4(1))* Higginson Bk. Co.

CARROTENES

see Carotenes

CARROUSEL ART

see Merry-Go-Round Art

CARS (AUTOMOBILES)

see Automobiles

CARS, ANTIQUE

see Antique and Classic Cars

CARS, ARMORED (TANKS)

see Tanks (Military Science)

CARS, CLASSIC

see Antique and Classic Cars

CARS, RAILROAD

see Railroads—Cars

CARS, VINTAGE

see Antique and Classic Cars

CARS AND CAR BUILDING

see Railroads—Cars

CARSON, KIT, 1809-1868

Abbott, John S. C. Christopher Carson. 2008. 236p. 27.99 *(978-0-554-28635-8(1));* 24.99 *(978-0-554-37938-8(4))* BiblioBazaar.

—Christopher Carson. 2007. (ENG.). 152p. per. *(978-1-4068-4772-7(0))* Echo Library.

—Christopher Carson. (American Pioneers & Patriots Ser.). 348p. reprint ed. 98.00 *(978-0-7222-8369-1(5));* 98.00 *(978-0-7222-8462-9(4))* Library Reprints, Inc.

—Christopher Carson Familiarly Known As Kit Carson by John S C Abbott with Illustrations by Eleanor Greatorex. 2006. 364p. per. 26.99 *(978-1-4255-3734-0(0))* MPublishing.

Bate, W. n. & Bate, W. N. Frontier Legend: Texas Finale of Captain William F. Drannan, Pseudo Frontier Comrade of Kit Carson. 2011. 76p. 37.95 ***(978-1-258-02297-6(4))*** Literary Licensing, LLC.

Bradley, Glenn Danford. Winning the Southwest: A Story of Conquest. 2008. 244p. 24.99 *(978-0-559-84504-8(9));* pap. 25.75 *(978-0-559-84502-4(2))* BiblioBazaar.

—Winning the Southwest: A Story of Conquest. 225p. reprint ed. 98.00 *(978-0-7222-9286-0(4))* Library Reprints, Inc.

Burdett, Charles. Life of Kit Carson: The Great Western Hunter & Guide. Comprising Wild & Romantic Exploits As A Hunter & Trapper in the Rocky Mountains; Thrillin. 2006. 396p. per. 26.99 *(978-1-4255-4258-0(1))* MPublishing.

Carson, Kit & Grant, Blanche C. Kit Carson's Own Story of His Life: Facsimile of Original 1926 Edition. 2006. (ENG., Illus.). 180p. per. 22.95 *(978-0-86534-568-3(6))* Sunstone Pr.

De Witt C. Peters. The Life & Adventures of Kit Carson; the Nestor of the Rocky Mountains- from Facts Narrated by Him. 2007. (ENG.). 388p. pap. 25.99 *(978-1-4346-0001-1(7))* BiblioBazaar.

Greatorex, Eleanor. Christopher Carson: Familiarly Known as Kit Carson the Pioneer of The. 2007. (ENG.). 212p. pap. 20.99 *(978-1-4346-5945-3(3));* 234p. pap. 22.99 *(978-1-4346-5946-0(1))* BiblioBazaar.

Peters, De Witt C. The Life & Adventures of Kit Carson, the Nestor of the Rocky. 2006. pap. *(978-1-4068-2092-8(X))* Echo Library.

Peters, De Witt Clinton. The Life & Adventures of Kit Carson; the Nestor of the Rocky Mountains- from Facts Narrated by Himself. l.t. ed. 2007. 426p. pap. 28.99 *(978-1-4346-0086-8(6))* BiblioBazaar.

Peters, DeWitt C. Kit Carson's Wild West. 2007. (ENG.). 632p. 60.95 *(978-0-548-04687-6(5))* Kessinger Publishing, LLC.

Sabin, Edwin L. Kit Carson Days, 1809-1868: Adventures in the Path of Empire. (Illus.). 669p. reprint ed. lib. bdg. 128.00 *(978-0-7222-0759-8(X))* Library Reprints, Inc.

Sides, Hampton. Blood & Thunder: An Epic of the American West. 2006. (Illus.). 480p. 35.00 *(978-0-385-50777-6(1),* Doubleday) Doubleday Religious Publishing Group, The.

—Blood & Thunder: The Epic Story of Kit Carson & the Conquest of the American West. 2007. (ENG., Illus.). 624p. pap. 17.00 *(978-1-4000-3110-8(9),* Anchor) Knopf Doubleday Publishing Group.

Simmons, Marc. Kit Carson & His Three Wives: A Family History. 2011. (Calvin P. Horn Lectures in Western History & Culture Ser.). (ENG., Illus.). 240p. pap. 21.95 ***(978-0-8263-3297-4(8))*** Univ. of New Mexico Pr.

CARSON, KIT, 1809-1868—JUVENILE LITERATURE

Ellis, Edward Sylvest & Ellis, Edward Sylvester. The Life of Kit Carson: Hunter, Trapper, Guide, Indian Agent, & Colonel U. S. a. 2010. 276p. pap. 27.75 *(978-1-148-61393-2(5))* BiblioBazaar.

Ellis, Edward Sylvester. The Life of Kit Carson: Hunter, Trapper, Guide, Indian Agent, & Colonel U. S. A. 2010. 268p. pap. 27.75 *(978-1-146-66083-9(9))* BiblioBazaar.

—The Life of Kit Carson: Hunter, Trapper, Guide, Indian Agent, & Colonel U. S. a. 2010. 274p. pap. 27.75 *(978-1-145-99337-2(0))* BiblioBazaar.

—The Life of Kit Carson, Hunter, Trapper, Guide, Indian Agent, & Colonel U S A. 2010. 112p. pap. 17.69 *(978-1-152-78382-9(3))* General Bks. LLC.

Ellis, Edward Sylvester 1840-1916 [Fro. The Life of Kit Carson, Hunter, Trapper, Guide, Indian Agent, & Colonel U S A. 2010. 282p. pap. 27.75 *(978-1-149-44723-9(0))* BiblioBazaar.

CARSON, RACHEL, 1907-1964

Biographiq. Rachel Carson - Environmental Pioneer (Biography) 2008. 68p. pap. 9.99 *(978-1-59986-384-9(7),* Biographiq) Filiquarian Publishing, LLC.

Brooks, Paul. Rachel Carson: The Writer at Work. 2008. (ENG.). 359p. pap. 18.00 *(978-1-4379-5193-6(7))* DIANE Publishing Co.

Carson, Rachel. Courage for the Earth: Writers, Scientists, & Activists Celebrate the Life & Writing of Rachel Carson. Matthiessen, Peter, ed. 2007. (Writers, Scientists, & Activists Celebrate the Life & Writing of Rachel Carson Ser.). (ENG.). 224p. pap. 14.95 *(978-0-618-87276-3(0))* Houghton Mifflin Harcourt Trade & Reference Pubs.

Dunlap, Thomas R., ed. DDT, Silent Spring, & the Rise of Environmentalism: Classic Texts. 2008. (Weyerhaeuser Environmental Classics Ser.). (ENG., Illus.). 160p. pap. 16.95 *(978-0-295-98834-4(7))* Univ. of Washington Pr.

Lear, Linda. Rachel Carson: Witness for Nature. 2009. (ENG.). 688p. pap. 17.95 *(978-0-547-23823-4(1),* Mariner Bks.) Houghton Mifflin Harcourt Trade & Reference Pubs.

Lytle, Mark H. The Gentle Subversive: Rachel Carson, Silent Spring, & the Rise of the Environmental Movement. 2007. (New Narratives in American History Ser.). (ENG., Illus.). 288p. (C). per. 19.95 *(978-0-19-517247-8(7))* Oxford Univ. Pr., Inc.

Murphy, Priscilla Coit. What a Book Can Do: The Publication & Reception of Silent Spring. 2007. (Studies in Print Culture & the History of the Book). (Illus.). 254p. per. 22.95 *(978-1-55849-582-1(7))* Univ. of Massachusetts Pr.

Quaratiello, Arlene R. Rachel Carson: A Biography. 2010. (ENG.). 152p. pap. 18.00 *(978-1-61614-187-5(5))* Prometheus Bks., Pubs.

Sideris, Lisa H. & Moore, Kathleen Dean, eds. Rachel Carson: Legacy & Challenge. 2008. (SUNY Series in Environmental Philosophy & Ethics). 287p. 74.50 *(978-0-7914-7471-6(2));* pap. 29.95 *(978-0-7914-7472-3(0))* State Univ. of New York Pr.

Souder, William. On a Farther Shore: The Life & Legacy of Rachel Carson. 2012. (ENG., Illus.). 544p. 30.00 ***(978-0-307-46220-6(X),*** Crown) Crown Publishing Group.

CARSON, RACHEL, 1907-1964—JUVENILE LITERATURE

Ehrlich, Amy. Rachel: The Story of Rachel Carson. 2008. (ENG., Illus.). (J). 13.65 *(978-1-60686-063-2(1))* Perfection Learning Corp.

CARSON CITY (NEV.)

Ballew, Susan J. & Dolan, L. Trent. Early Carson City. 2010. (Images of America Ser.). (ENG., Illus.). 128p. pap. 21.99 *(978-0-7385-7158-4(X))* Arcadia Publishing.

Harpster, Jack. 100 Years in the Nevada's Governor's Mansion. 2009. (Illus.). 256p. 39.95 *(978-1-935043-00-3(5))* Stephens Pr. LLC.

Ibanez, Florante Peter & Estepa Ibanez, Roselyn. Filipinos in Carson & the South Bay. 2009. (Images of America Ser.). (ENG., Illus.). 128p. pap. 21.99 *(978-0-7385-7036-5(2))* Arcadia Publishing.

Moreno, Richard. A Short History of Carson City. 2011. (Illus.). 192p. pap. 21.95 *(978-0-87417-836-4(3))* Univ. of Nevada Pr.

CARTE, RICHARD D'OYLY, 1844-1901

Cellier, Francois. Gilbert & Sullivan & Their Operas. 2009. 318p. pap. *(978-0-217-25640-7(6))* Books LLC.

Oost, Regina B. Gilbert & Sullivan: Class & the Savoy Tradition 1875-1896. 2009. (Nineteenth Century Ser.). (Illus.). 180p. 99.95 *(978-0-7546-6412-3(0))* Ashgate Publishing Co.

CARTEL FOR EXCHANGE OF PRISONERS, 1862-1864

see United States—History—Civil War, 1861-1865—Prisoners and Prisons

CARTELS

Here are entered works on combinations in restraint of trade in which independent business enterprises formally agree among themselves to control or limit output, prices, and-or markets so as to achieve monopolistic power. Works on combinations in which stock ownership is transferred to trustees, who in turn issue trust certificates and dividends and who attempt to achieve monopolistic control over output, prices, or markets, are entered under Trusts, Industrial.

see also Commodity Control; Holding Companies; Trusts, Industrial

Beaton-Wells, Caron, et al, eds. Criminalising Cartels: Critical Studies of an International Regulatory Movement. 2011. (ENG.). 471p. 180.00 (978-1-84946-025-5(6)) Hart Publishing Ltd. GBR. Dist: International Specialized Bk. Services.

Beaton-Wells, Caron & Fisse, Brent. Australian Cartel Regulation: Law, Policy & Practice in an International Context. 2011. (ENG.). 685p. 185.00 (978-0-521-76089-8(5)) Cambridge Univ. Pr.

Beith, Malcolm. The Last Narco: Inside the Hunt for el Chapo, the World's Most Wanted Drug Lord. 2010. (ENG., Illus.). 368p. 24.00 (978-0-8021-1952-0(2), Grove Pr.) Grove/Atlantic, Inc.

Bellodi, Leonardo & Tosato, Gian Luigi, eds. Eu Competition Law: Procedure - Antitrust - Merger - State Aid. 2nd ed. 2011. 850p. 385.00 (978-90-77644-19-5(9)) Claeys & Casteels Publishing BEL. Dist: International Specialized Bk. Services.

Blanke. Global Cartel Litigation. 2011. ring bd. (978-90-411-2712-9(7)) Wolters Kluwer Law & Business.

Connor, John M. Global Price Fixing. 2nd ed. (Studies in Industrial Organization Ser.). (Illus.). 2008. xvi, 484p. spiral bd. 129.00 (978-3-540-78669-6(4)) 2007. xvi, 503p. 289.00 (978-3-540-34217-5(6), 3540342176) Springer.

Dabbah, Maher M. & Hawk, Barry E. Anti-Cartel Enforcement Worldwide 3 Volume Set, 3 vols. 2009. (Antitrust & Competition Law Ser.). (ENG., Illus.). 3000p. 895.00 (978-0-521-89721-1(1)) Cambridge Univ. Pr.

Drauz, Götz & Jones, Christopher, eds. EU Competition Law Vol. II: Mergers & Acquisitions. 2nd ed. 2012. 1690p. 490.00 (978-90-77644-18-8(0)) Claeys & Casteels Publishing BEL. Dist: International Specialized Bk. Services.

Gonta, Cristina. Export Cartels. 2011. 60p. pap. **(978-3-8433-7308-1(6))** Lambert Academic Publishing.

Grayson, George W. La Familia Drug Cartel: Implications for U. S. -Mexican Security. 2010. (Illus.). xi, 111p. pap. (978-1-58487-471-3(6)) Strategic Studies Institute, U.S. Army War College Commandant (AWCC-DSI/Pubns.).

Harding, Christopher & Joshua, Julian. Regulating Cartels in Europe. 2nd ed. 2011. (ENG., Illus.). 424p. 120.00 (978-0-19-955148-4(0)) Oxford Univ. Pr., Inc.

Harrington, Joseph E., Jr. How Do Cartels Operate? 2006. 120p. pap. 80.00 (978-1-933019-40-6(9)) Now Pubs.

Hillman, John. The International Tin Cartel. 2010. (Routledge Explorations in Economic History Ser.). (ENG., Illus.). 496p. (C). 190.00 (978-0-415-55412-1(8)) Routledge.

Jephcott, Mark. The Law of Cartels. 2nd rev. ed. 2011. (ENG.). 552p. (978-1-84661-276-3(4)) Jordan Publishing, Ltd.

LeClair, Mark S. Cartelization Antitrust & Globalization in the Us & Europe. 2010. (Routledge Studies in the Modern World Economy Ser.). (ENG., Illus.). 196p. (C). 145.00 (978-0-415-57343-6(2), Routledge) Taylor & Francis Group GBR. Dist: Taylor & Francis Group.

Longmire, Sylvia. Cartel: The Coming Invasion of Mexico's Drug Wars. 2011. (ENG., Illus.). 256p. 26.00 (978-0-230-11137-0(8)) Palgrave Macmillan.

Marshall, Robert C. & Marx, Leslie M. The Economics of Collusion: Cartels & Bidding Rings. 2012. (ENG., Illus.). 304p. (gr. 17). 35.00 **(978-0-262-01732-9(6))** MIT Pr.

McGowan, Lee. The Anti-Trust Revolution in Europe: The European Commission. S Cartel Policy. 2010. (Illus.). 240p. 112.00 (978-1-84720-146-1(6)) Elgar, Edward Publishing, Inc.

Mobley, Samantha & Denton, Ross, eds. Global Cartels Handbook: Leniency - Policies & Procedure. 2012. (ENG.). 816p. pap. 190.00 **(978-0-19-964100-0(5))** Oxford Univ. Pr., Inc.

Rees, Martin, ed. Cartel Enforcement Worldwide. 2010. x, 1082p. 330.00 **(978-1-907174-07-0(9))** Gaunt, Inc.

Riesenkampff, Alexander & Lehr, Stefan. European Cartel Law. Date not set. pap. 50.00 (978-0-86640-062-6(1)) German American Chamber of Commerce, Inc.

Rizza, Cesare & Siragusa, Mario, eds. EU Competition Law Vol. III: Cartels & Collusive Behaviour - Restrictive Agreements & Practices Between Competitors. 2nd ed. 2012. 1567p. 385.00 (978-90-77644-20-1(2)) Claeys & Casteels Publishing BEL. Dist: International Specialized Bk. Services.

Sakkers, Ewoud. European Cartel Digest, 2 vols. 2008. (FRE, GER & ENG., Illus.). ring bd. (978-90-411-2660-3(0)) Kluwer Law International.

Simonsson, Ingeborg. Legitimacy in EU Cartel Control. 2010. (ENG.). 439p. 170.00 (978-1-84946-005-7(1)) Hart Publishing Ltd. GBR. Dist: International Specialized Bk. Services.

Utton, Michael A. Cartels & Economic Collusion: The Persistence of Corporate Conspiracies. 2011. 192p. 110.00 (978-1-84980-770-8(1)) Elgar, Edward Publishing, Inc.

Wurm, Clemens. Business, Politics & International Relations: Steel, Cotton & International Cartels in British Politics, 1924-1939. Salmon, Patrick, tr. 2009. (ENG., Illus.). 420p. pap. 53.00 (978-0-521-10876-8(4)) Cambridge Univ. Pr.

CARTER, ANGELA, 1940-1992

Cavallaro, Dani. The World of Angela Carter: A Critical Investigation. 2011. (ENG.). 208p. pap. 40.00 (978-0-7864-6128-8(4)) McFarland & Co., Inc. Pubs.

Clapp, Susannah. A Card from Angela Carter. 2012. (ENG., Illus.). 112p. 19.99 **(978-1-4088-2690-4(9))** Bloomsbury Publishing.

Gamble, Sarah. Angela Carter: A Literary Life. 2009. (Literary Lives Ser.). (ENG.). 240p. pap. 36.00 (978-0-230-58098-5(X)) Palgrave Macmillan.

Gorga, Gemma. Seductions in Narrative: Subjectivity & Desire in the Works of Angela Carter & Jeanette Winterson. 2007. (C). 109.95 (978-1-934043-85-1(0)) Cambria Pr.

Gruss, Susanne. The Pleasure of the Feminist Text: Reading Michèle Roberts & Angela Carter. 2009. (Illus.). 356p. pap. 101.00 (978-90-420-2531-8(X)) Rodopi.

Kerchy, Anna. Body Texts in the Novels of Angela Carter: Writing from a Corporeagraphic Point of View. 2008. 372p. 119.95 (978-0-7734-4892-6(6)) Mellen, Edwin Pr., The.

Munford, Rebecca, ed. Re-Visiting Angela Carter: Texts, Contexts, Intertexts. 2006. (ENG.). 224p. 84.00 (978-1-4039-9705-0(5)) Palgrave Macmillan.

Ozyurt Kilic, Mine. Gender-Bending Fantasies in Women's Writing. 2009. 228p. pap. (978-3-639-13969-3(0)) VDM Verlag Dr. Mueller e.K.

Peach, Linden. Angela Carter. 2nd rev. ed. 2009. (ENG.). 208p. 85.00 (978-0-230-20282-5(9)); pap. 29.00 (978-0-230-20283-2(7)) Palgrave Macmillan.

Sage, Lorna, ed. Essays on the Art of Angela Carter: Flesh & the Mirror. 2009. (ENG., Illus.). 384p. pap. 17.95 (978-1-84408-471-5(X), Virago Press) Little, Brown Bk. Group Ltd. GBR. Dist: Independent Pubs. Group.

Tonkin, Maggie. Angela Carter & Decadence: Critical Fictions/Fictional Critiques. 2012. (ENG., Illus.). 236p. 85.00 **(978-0-230-28415-9(9))** Palgrave Macmillan.

CARTER, ELLIOTT COOK, 1908-

Boland, Marguerite & Link, John, eds. Elliott Carter Studies. 2012. (ENG., Illus.). 392p. 99.00 **(978-0-521-11362-5(8))** Cambridge Univ. Pr.

Carter, Elliott, et al. Elliott Carter: A Centennial Celebration. 2008. (978-1-57647-135-7(7)) Pendragon Pr.

Cervino, Alessandro & Laws, Catherine. The Practice of Practising. 2012. (ENG., Illus.). 92p. pap. 34.00 **(978-90-5867-848-5(2))** Leuven Univ. Pr. BEL. Dist: Cornell Univ. Pr.

Meyer, Felix & Shreffler, Anne C. Elliott Carter: A Centennial Portrait in Letters & Documents. 2008. (Illus.). 380p. 45.00 (978-1-84383-404-5(9), Boydell Press) Boydell & Brewer, Ltd. GBR. Dist: Boydell & Brewer, Inc.

Wierzbicki, James. Elliott Carter. 2011. (American Composers Ser.). (ENG.). 136p. pap. 20.00 (978-0-252-07800-2(4)) Univ. of Illinois Pr.

CARTER, HOWARD, 1874-1939

Hawass, Zahi. King Tutankhamun: The Treasures of the Tomb. 2008. (ENG., Illus.). 296p. 80.00 (978-0-500-05151-1(8)) Thames & Hudson.

James, T. G. H. Howard Carter: The Path to Tutankhamun. 2nd ed. 2012. (ENG., Illus.). 544p. pap. 23.00 **(978-1-84511-258-5(X)**, Tauris Parke Paperbacks) I. B. Tauris & Co., Ltd. GBR. Dist: Macmillan.

Meyerson, Daniel. In the Valley of the Kings: Howard Carter & the Mystery of King Tutankhamun's Tomb. 2009. (ENG., Illus.). 256p. 26.00 (978-0-345-47693-7(X), Ballantine Bks.) Random House Publishing Group.

Winstone, H. V. F. Howard Carter: And the Discovery of the Tomb of Tutankhamun. 2007. (Illus.). 428p. pap. 20.00 (978-1-905521-05-0(7)) Barzan Publishing Company GBR. Dist: Interlink Publishing Group, Inc.

CARTER, JIMMY, 1924-

Auten, Brian J. Carter's Conversion: The Hardening of American Defense Policy. 2009. (ENG.). 360p. (C). 44.95 (978-0-8262-1816-2(4)) Univ. of Missouri Pr.

Carter, Jimmy. Beyond the White House. l.t. ed. 2007. (Thorndike Nonfiction Ser.). (Illus.). 411p. 31.95 (978-1-4104-0270-7(3)) Thorndike Pr.

—Beyond the White House: Waging Peace, Fighting Disease, Building Hope. 2008. (ENG., Illus.). 288p. pap. 15.00 (978-1-4165-5881-1(0)) Simon & Schuster.

—Palestine Peace Not Apartheid. 2007. (ENG.). 288p. pap. 15.00 (978-0-7432-8503-2(4)) Simon & Schuster.

—Palestine Peace Not Apartheid. rev. l.t. ed. 2007. (Thorndike Nonfiction Ser.). 313p. 31.95 (978-0-7862-9408-4(6)) Thorndike Pr.

—A Remarkable Mother. 2010. (ENG.). 240p. pap. 15.99 (978-1-4516-1298-1(2), Scribner) Scribner.

—A Remarkable Mother. l.t. ed. 2008. (Thorndike Biography Ser.). (Illus.). 232p. 31.95 (978-1-4104-0657-6(1)) Thorndike Pr.

—Remarkable Mother. l.t. ed. 2009. (ENG.). 240p. pap. 15.95 (978-1-59413-297-1(6), Kennebec Large Print) Cengage Gale.

—We Can Have Peace in the Holy Land: A Plan That Will Work. 2010. (ENG., Illus.). 256p. pap. 15.00 (978-1-4391-4069-7(3)) Simon & Schuster.

—White House Diary. 2010. (ENG., Illus.). 592p. 30.00 (978-0-374-28099-4(1)) Farrar, Straus & Giroux.

—White House Diary. 2011. (ENG., Illus.). 592p. pap. 20.00 (978-0-312-57719-3(2)) Picador.

Castile, George Pierre. Taking Charge: Native American Self-Determination & Federal Indian Policy, 1975-1993. 2006. (ENG.). 168p. 35.00 (978-0-8165-2542-3(0)) Univ. of Arizona Pr.

Clymer, Adam. Drawing the Line at the Big Ditch: The Panama Canal Treaties & the Rise of the Right. 2008. (Illus.). 286p. 29.95 (978-0-7006-1582-7(2)) Univ. Pr. of Kansas.

Evans, Mike. Jimmy Carter: The Liberal Left & World Chaos. 2009. 550p. 35.00 (978-0-935199-33-8(0)) TimeWorthy Bks.

Flippen, J. Brooks. Jimmy Carter, the Politics of Family, & the Rise of the Religious Right. 2011. (Since 1970: Histories of Contemporary America Ser.). (ENG., Illus.). 456p. 69.95 (978-0-8203-3769-2(2)); pap. 26.95 (978-0-8203-3770-8(6)) Univ. of Georgia Pr.

Frisch, Scott A. & Kelly, Sean Q. Jimmy Carter & the Water Wars: Presidential Influence & the Politics of Pork. 2011. 236p. pap. 29.99 **(978-1-60497-778-3(7))** 2008. 99.95 (978-1-934043-89-9(3)) Cambria Pr.

Gaillard, Frye. Prophet from Plains: Jimmy Carter & His Legacy. (Wormsloe Foundation Publications Ser.). (ENG.). 144p. 2009. pap. 18.95 (978-0-8203-3332-8(8)) 2007. 22.95 (978-0-8203-2914-7(2)) Univ. of Georgia Pr.

Glad, Betty. An Outsider in the White House: Jimmy Carter, His Advisors, & the Making of American Foreign Policy. 2009. (Illus.). 392p. 29.95 (978-0-8014-4815-7(8)) Cornell Univ. Pr.

Godbold, E. Stanly, Jr. Jimmy & Rosalynn Carter: The Georgia Years, 1924-1974, 1 vol. 2010. (ENG., Illus.). 400p. 29.95 (978-0-19-975344-4(X)) Oxford Univ. Pr., Inc.

Jackson, Donna R. Jimmy Carter & the Horn of Africa: Cold War Policy in Ethiopia & Somalia. annot. ed. 2007. (ENG., Illus.). 240p. per. 39.95 (978-0-7864-2987-5(9)) McFarland & Co., Inc. Pubs.

Kaufman, Scott. Plans Unraveled: The Foreign Policy of the Carter Administration. 2008. (Illus.). 308p. 38.00 (978-0-87580-390-6(3)) Northern Illinois Univ. Pr.

Kaufman, Scott & Kaufman, Burton Ira. The Presidency of James Earl Carter, Jr. 2nd ed. 2006. (American Presidency Ser.). (Illus.). 302p. 35.00 (978-0-7006-1470-7(2)); per. 17.95 (978-0-7006-1471-4(0)) Univ. Pr. of Kansas.

Mattson, Kevin. What the Heck Are You up to, Mr. President? Jimmy Carter, America's 'Malaise,' & the Speech That Should Have Changed the Country. 2009. (ENG.). 272p. 25.00 (978-1-59691-521-3(8)) Bloomsbury Publishing.

—What the Heck Are You Up To, Mr. President? Jimmy Carter, America's 'Malaise,' & the Speech That Should Have Changed the Country. 2010. (ENG.). 288p. pap. 16.00 (978-1-60819-206-9(7)) Bloomsbury Publishing.

Michael, Deanna L. Jimmy Carter As Educational Policymaker: Equal Opportunity & Efficiency. 2008. viii, 191p. 60.00 (978-0-7914-7529-4(8)) State Univ. of New York Pr.

—Jimmy Carter as Educational Policymaker: Equal Opportunity & Efficiency. 2009. 176p. pap. 21.95 (978-0-7914-7530-0(1), Suny Pr.) State Univ. of New York Pr.

Milnes, Arthur, ed. Jimmy & Rosalynn Carter: A Canadian Tribute. 2011. (Library of Political Leadership Ser.). (ENG.). 232p. (C). (978-1-55339-301-6(5)); pap. (978-1-55339-300-9(7)) McGill-Queen's Univ. Pr.

Ribuffo, Leo P. The Limits of Moderation: Jimmy Carter & the Ironies of American Liberalism. 2008. 640p. 39.95 (978-0-300-11839-1(2)) Yale Univ. Pr.

Ruddy, T. Michael. Jimmy Carter: Politician with Principles (First Men, America's Presidents Series) 2011. (First Men, America's Presidents Ser. - Peterson, Barbara Bennett (Oregon State University Ser.). 49.00 (978-1-61761-850-5(0)) Nova Science Pubs., Inc.

Sneh, Itai Nartzizenfield. The Future Almost Arrived: How Jimmy Carter Failed to Change U.S. Foreign Policy. 2007. (Studies in International Relations Ser.). (C). pap. 34.95 (978-0-8204-8185-2(8)) Lang, Peter Publishing, Inc.

Stanley, Timothy. Kennedy vs. Carter: The 1980 Battle for the Democratic Party's Soul. 2010. 320p. 34.95 (978-0-7006-1702-9(7)) Univ. Pr. of Kansas.

Stuckey, Mary E. Jimmy Carter, Human Rights, & the National Agenda. 2009. (Presidential Rhetoric Ser.: No. 20). (ENG.). 232p. 39.95 (978-1-60344-074-5(7)) Texas A&M Univ. Pr.

Thornton, Richard C. Carter Years: Toward a New Global Order. 2007. (ENG., Illus.). 586p. pap. 19.95 (978-1-55778-871-9(5)) Paragon Hse. Pubs.

Zelizer, Julian. Jimmy Carter: The 39th President, 1977-1981. Schlesinger, Arthur M. & Wilentz, Sean, eds. 2010. (American Presidents Ser.). (ENG., Illus.). 208p. 23.00 (978-0-8050-8957-8(8), Times Bks.) Holt, Henry & Co.

Zelizer, Julian E. Jimmy Carter. l.t. ed. 2010. (American Presidents Ser.). 262p. 31.99 (978-1-4104-3247-6(5)) Thorndike Pr.

CARTER, LILLIAN, 1898-1983

Carter, Jimmy. Remarkable Mother. l.t. ed. 2009. (ENG.). 240p. pap. 15.95 (978-1-59413-297-1(6), Kennebec Large Print) Cengage Gale.

Carter, Lillian & Spann, Gloria Carter. Away from Home: Letters to My Family. 2008. (ENG., Illus.). 160p. pap. 12.00 (978-1-4165-7660-0(6)) Simon & Schuster.

CARTER, ROBERT, 1728-1804

Levy, Andrew. The First Emancipator: Slavery, Religion, & the Quiet Revolution of Robert Carter. 2007. (ENG.). 336p. pap. 15.95 (978-0-375-76104-1(7), Random Hse. Trade Paperbacks) Random House Publishing Group.

CARTER, ROSALYNN, 1927-

Godbold, E. Stanly, Jr. Jimmy & Rosalynn Carter: The Georgia Years, 1924-1974, 1 vol. 2010. (ENG., Illus.). 400p. 29.95 (978-0-19-975344-4(X)) Oxford Univ. Pr., Inc.

Kaufman, Scott. Rosalynn Carter: Equal Partner in the White House. 2007. (Modern First Ladies Ser.). (Illus.). 206p. 29.95 (978-0-7006-1544-5(X)) Univ. Pr. of Kansas.

Milnes, Arthur, ed. Jimmy & Rosalynn Carter: A Canadian Tribute. 2011. (Library of Political Leadership Ser.). (ENG.). 232p. (C). (978-1-55339-301-6(5)); pap. (978-1-55339-300-9(7)) McGill-Queen's Univ. Pr.

CARTER COUNTY (MO.)

West Carter County, compiled by. History & Families of Carter County Missouri: 1859-2006. 2006. 185p. lib. bdg. 60.00 (978-1-932439-61-8(7)) M.T. Publishing Co., Inc.

CARTER FAMILY

Carter, R. R. & Randolph, R. I. The Carter Tree: Tabulated & Indexed. fac. ed. 241p. reprint ed. pap. 38.00 (978-0-7404-2268-1(X)); pap. 38.00 (978-0-7404-2269-8(8)) Higginson Bk. Co.

CARTER FAMILY (MUSICAL GROUP)

Lasky, David. The Carter Family: Don't Forget This Song. 2012. (ENG., Illus.). 192p. 24.95 (978-0-8109-8836-1(4)) Abrams.

CARTERET, JOHN, EARL, 1690-1763

see Granville, John Carteret, Earl, 1690-1763

CARTHAGE (EXTINCT CITY)

see also Punic Wars

Beyer, Brian & Eutropius. War with Hannibal: Authentic Latin Prose for the Beginning Student. 2008. (LAT & ENG., Illus.). 128p. (C). pap. 30.00 (978-0-300-13918-1(7)) Yale Univ. Pr.

CAILLER, Bernadette. Carthage ou la flamme du Brasier: Mémoire et échos chez Virgile, Senghor, Mellah, Ghachem, Augustin, Ammi, Broch et Glissant. 2007. (Francopolyphonies Ser.: 6). (FRE.). 238p. pap. 65.00 (978-90-420-2201-0(9)) Rodopi.

Church, Alfred John. The Story of Carthage. 2009. 126p. pap. (978-1-151-12889-8(9)) Books LLC.

Church, Alfred John & Gilman, Arthur. The Story of Carthage. 2007. (ENG.). 328p. per. 30.95 (978-1-4304-4224-0(7)) Kessinger Publishing, LLC.

Davis, Nathan. Carthage & Her Remains. 2009. 360p. pap. (978-0-217-82224-4(X)) Books LLC.

Freed, Joann. Bringing Carthage Home: The Excavations of Nathan Davis, 1856-1859. 2011. (University of British Columbia Studies in the Ancient World Ser.). (ENG., Illus.). 264p. (C). 96.00 (978-1-84217-992-5(6)) Oxbow Bks., Ltd. GBR. Dist: Brown, David Bk. Co., The.

Garland, Robert. Hannibal. 2010. (Illus.). 144p. pap. 24.95 (978-1-85399-725-9(0)) Duckworth Publishers GBR. Dist: International Publishers Marketing.

Gärtner, Thomas. Untersuchungen zur Gestaltung und zum historischen Stoff der Johannis Corippis. 2008. (Untersuchungen Zur Antiken Literatur und Geschichte Ser.). (GER.). 136p. 91.00 (978-3-11-020107-9(0)) De Gruyter, Walter Inc.

Hoyos, Dexter. The Carthaginians. 2010. (Peoples of the Ancient World Ser.). (ENG., Illus.). 288p. 110.00 (978-0-415-43644-1(3)) Routledge.

—Truceless War: Carthages Fight for Survival, 241 to 237 BC. 2007. (History of Warfare Ser.). (Illus.). 286p. (978-90-04-16076-7(0)) BRILL.

Miles, Richard. Carthage Must Be Destroyed: The Rise & Fall of an Ancient Civilization. 2012. (ENG., Illus.). 544p. (gr. 12). pap. 20.00 **(978-0-14-312129-9(4)**, Penguin (Non-Classics)) Penguin Group (USA) Inc.

O'Connell, Robert L. The Ghosts of Cannae: Hannibal & the Darkest Hour of the Roman Republic. 2011. (ENG., Illus.). 336p. pap. 17.00 (978-0-8129-7867-4(6), Random Hse. Trade Paperbacks) Random House Publishing Group.

Stevens, Susan T., et al. A Cemetery of Vandalic Date at Carthage, JRA Supplement #75. 2009. (Illus.). 366p. 125.00 (978-1-887829-75-5(X)) Journal of Roman Archaeology, LLC.

Zimmermann, Klaus. Karthago: Aufstieg und Fall einer Großmacht. 2010. (GER., Illus.). 159p. (978-3-8062-2281-4(9)) Theiss, Konrad Verlag, GmbH.

CARTHUSIANS

Carthusian, A. Way of Silent Love. 2006. 148p. per. (978-0-85244-034-6(0)) Gracewing, Ltd.

Coppack, Glyn & Aston, Michael. Christ's Poor Men: The Carthusians in Britain. (Illus.). 176p. 35.00 (978-0-7524-1961-9(7)) History Pr. Ltd.,The GBR. Dist: Trafalgar Square Publishing.

Cre, Marleen, ed. The Medieval Translator Traduire Au Moyen Age Volume 9: Vernacular Mysticism in the Charterhouse. 2006. (Medieval Translator Ser.). (FRE & ENG., Illus.). 373p. (C). pap. 94.00 (978-2-503-52132-9(0)) Brepols Pubs. BEL. Dist: ISD.

Dillon, Anne. Michelangelo & the English Martyrs: The Images of the Martyrdom of the Carthusian Fathers. 2012. (Illus.). 337p. 124.95 **(978-0-7546-6447-5(3))** Ashgate Publishing Co.

Gaens, T. & De Grauwe, J. De kracht van de Stilte: Geest en geschiedenis van de Kartuizerorde. 2007. (ENG.). 153p. (C). pap. 29.00 (978-90-429-1835-1(7)) Peeters Pubs. & Booksellers BEL. Dist: Brown, David Bk. Co., The.

Luxford, J. H., ed. Studies in Carthusian Monasticism in the Late Middle Ages. 2009. (Medieval Church Studies). (ENG., Illus.). 367p. (C). 123.00 (978-2-503-51699-8(8)) Brepols Pubs. BEL. Dist: ISD.

Maguire, Nancy Klein & Public Affairs Committee Staff. An Infinity of Little Hours: Five Young Men & Their Trial of Faith in the Western World's Most Austere Monastic Order. 2007. (ENG., Illus.). 304p. per. 13.95 (978-1-58648-432-3(X)) PublicAffairs.

Märker, Almuth. Das Prohemium longum des Erfurter Kartäuserkatalogs aus der Zeit Um 1475: Edition und Untersuchung, 2 vols. 2008. (Lateinische Sprache und Literatur des Mittelalters Ser.). (LAT & GER., Illus.). 602p. pap. (978-3-906769-97-4(6)) Lang, Peter.

CARTIER, GEORGE ETIENNE, SIR, 1814-1873

Papineau, L. J. Sir G. E. Cartier. reprint ed. 150.00 (978-0-7222-6955-8(2)) Library Reprints, Inc.

CARTIER, JACQUES, 1491-1557

Baxter, James Phinney. A Memoir of Jacques Cartier, Sieur de Limoilou. 464p. reprint ed. 98.00 (978-0-7222-6429-4(1)) Library Reprints, Inc.

Gordon, Alan. The Hero & the Historians: Historiography & the Uses of Jacques Cartier. 2010. (ENG., Illus.). 248p. (C). pap. 32.95 (978-0-7748-1742-4(9)) UBC Pr. CAN. Dist: Univ. of Washington Pr.

Leacock, Stephen. The Mariner of St. Malo: Chronicle of the Voyages of Jacques Cartier. (Chronicles of Canada Ser.). 125p. reprint ed. 88.00 (978-0-7222-6774-5(6)) Library Reprints, Inc.

CARTIER-BRESSON, HENRI, 1908-2004

Assouline, Pierre. Henri Cartier-Bresson: A Biography. 2012. (ENG., Illus.). 280p. pap. 24.95 **(978-0-500-29052-1(0)**, 529052) Thames & Hudson.

Bravo, M. Alvarez. Documentary & Anti Graphic Photographs, 1 vol. 2008. (ENG., Illus.). 192p. 35.00 *(978-3-86521-072-2(4))* Steidl, Gerhard Druckerei und Verlag DEU. Dist: Innovative Logistics.

Cartier-Bresson, Henri. Henri Cartier-Bresson. 2007. (Photofile Ser.). (ENG., Illus.). 144p. pap. 15.95 *(978-0-500-41060-8(7)*, 541060) Thames & Hudson.

Cartier-Bresson, Henri, photos by. The Modern Century. 2010. (ENG., Illus.). 376p. 75.00 *(978-0-87070-778-0(7))* Museum of Modern Art.

Cartier-Bresson, Henri & Cartier-Bresson, Henri, photos by. Scrapbook: Photographs 1932-1946. 2007. (ENG., Illus.). 256p. 100.00 *(978-0-500-54333-7(X)*, 554333) Thames & Hudson.

Cartier-Bresson, Henri & Evans, Walker. Photographing America, 1929-1947. Sire, Agnès, ed. 2009. (ENG., Illus.). 180p. 50.00 *(978-0-500-54370-2(4)*, 554370) Thames & Hudson.

Cartier-Bresson, Henri & Galassi, Peter. Henri Cartier-Bresson: The Modern Century. 2010. (Illus.). 376p. pap. *(978-0-87070-777-3(9))* Museum of Modern Art.

Chéroux, Clément. Discoveries: Henri Cartier-Bresson. 2008. (ENG., Illus.). 144p. pap. 14.95 *(978-0-8109-9826-1(2))* Abrams.

Clair, Jean, et al. Henri Cartier-Bresson: The Man, the Image & the World - A Retrospective. 2006. (ENG., Illus.). 432p. pap. 55.00 *(978-0-500-28642-5(6)*, 528642) Thames & Hudson.

Sire, Agnes & Nancy, Jean-Luc. An Inner Silence: The Portraits of Henri Cartier-Bresson. 2010. (ENG., Illus.). 160p. pap. 34.95 *(978-0-500-28875-7(5)*, 528875) Thames & Hudson.

CARTILAGE

An, Yuehuei H. & Martin, Kylie L., eds. Handbook of Histology Methods for Bone & Cartilage. 2010. (ENG., Illus.). 588p. pap. 189.00 *(978-1-61737-277-3(3)*, 1617372773) Humana Pr.

Athanasiou, Kyriacos A. & Sanchez-Adams, Johanna. Engineering the Knee Meniscus. 2009. (Synthesis Lectures on Tissue Engineering Ser.). 97p. pap. 35.00 *(978-1-59829-872-7(0))* Morgan & Claypool Pubs.

Athanasiou, Kyriacos A., et al. Articular Cartilage Tissue Engineering. 2009. (Synthesis Lectures on Tissue Engineering Ser.). 182p. pap. 45.00 *(978-1-59829-875-8(5))* Morgan & Claypool Pubs.

Brittberg, Mats & Gersoff, Wayne. Cartilage Surgery: An Operative Manual, Expert Consult: Online & Print. 2010. (ENG., Illus.). 320p. 250.00 *(978-1-4377-0878-3(1)*, Saunders) Elsevier - Health Sciences Div.

Camacho-Huebner, C., et al, eds. Cartilage & Bone Development & Its Disorders: 4th ESPE Advanced Seminar in Developmental Endocrinology, Stockholm, June-July 2010. 2011. (Endocrine Development Ser.). (ENG., Illus.). 120p. ***(978-3-8055-9792-0(4))*** Karger, S. AG.

Carter, Dennis R. & Beaupré, Gary S. Skeletal Function & Form: Mechanobiology of Skeletal Development, Aging, & Regeneration. 2007. (ENG., Illus.). 332p. pap. 69.00 *(978-0-521-71475-4(3))* Cambridge Univ. Pr.

Culebras, Antonio, ed. Sleep Disorders & Neurologic Diseases. 2nd rev. ed. 2007. (Neurological Disease & Therapy Ser.). (ENG., Illus.). 456p. 250.00 *(978-0-8493-4324-7(0)*, Informa Healthcare) Taylor & Francis Group GBR. Dist: Taylor & Francis Group.

Daniels, A. U. & Wirz, Dieter, eds. Mechanical Properties of Articular Cartilage, Meniscus & Related Materials. 2011. (Orthopedic Biology & Medicine Ser.). (ENG., Illus.). 400p. 179.00 *(978-1-60327-994-9(6)*, 1603279946) Humana Pr.

Erggelet, Christoph & Mandelbaum, Bert. Principals of Cartilage Repair. 2008. (Illus.). VIII, 124p. 129.00 *(978-3-7985-1590-1(5)*, 3798515905) Steinkopff, Dietrich DEU. Dist: Springer.

Fuortes, Michelle. Cartilage: Keeping Joints Functioning. 2011. (Colloquium Series on the Cell Biology of Medicine Ser.). 100p. pap. 35.00 *(978-1-61504-258-6(X))* Morgan & Claypool Life Science Publishers.

Gahunia, Harpal & Babyn, Paul. Cartilage Injuries in the Pediatric Knee, an Issue of Orthopedic Clinics. 2012. (Clinics: Orthopedics Ser.: 43-2). (ENG.). 115.00 ***(978-1-4557-3905-9(7)***, Saunders) Elsevier - Health Sciences Div.

Kien Hui, Chua, et al. Growing Human Chondrocytes & Cartilage Tissue Engineering. 2010. 156p. pap. *(978-3-639-26246-9(8))* VDM Verlag Dr. Mueller e.K.

Kijowski, Richard. Magnetic Resonance Imaging Clinics of North America. 2011. (Clinics: Radiology Ser.: 19-2). (ENG., Illus.). 232p. 110.00 *(978-1-4557-0742-3(2)*, Saunders) Elsevier - Health Sciences Div.

Link, Thomas M., ed. Cartilage Imaging: Significance, Techniques, & New Developments. 2011. (ENG., Illus.). xi, 245p. 189.00 *(978-1-4419-8437-1(2)*, 1441984372) Springer.

Martin, R. Bruce, et al. Skeletal Tissue Mechanics. 2010. (ENG., Illus.). xiv, 392p. pap. 149.00 *(978-1-4419-3128-3(7)*, 1441931287) Springer.

Mauck, Robert & Elliott, Dawn. Fibrocartilage Tissue Engineering. 2011. (Synthesis Lectures on Tissue Engineering Ser.). 100p. pap. 40.00 *(978-1-60845-166-1(6))* Morgan & Claypool Pubs.

Mehl, Stephanie. Articular Cartilage. 2009. 100p. pap. *(978-3-639-13220-5(3))* VDM Verlag Dr. Mueller e.K.

Meyer, Ulrich & Wiesmann, Hans Peter. Bone & Cartilage Engineering. 2010. (ENG., Illus.). xiv, 264p. pap. 249.00 *(978-3-642-06468-5(X)*, 364206468X) Springer.

Minas, Tom. A Primer in Cartilage Repair & Joint Preservation of the Knee: Expert Consult. 2011. (ENG., Illus.). 288p. 199.00 *(978-1-4160-6654-5(3)*, Saunders) Elsevier - Health Sciences Div.

Mlejnek, Matej. Medical Visualization for Orthopedic Applications. 2008. 100p. pap. *(978-3-8364-9385-7(3))* VDM Verlag Dr. Mueller e.K.

Seibel, Markus J., et al, eds. Dynamics of Bone & Cartilage Metabolism: Principles & Clinical Applications. 2nd rev. ed. 2006. (ENG., Illus.). 920p. 260.00 *(978-0-12-088562-6(X)*, Academic Pr.) Elsevier Science & Technology Bks.

Shakibaei, Mehdi. Diverse Roles of Integrin Receptors in Articular Cartilage. 2008. (Advances in Anatomy, Embryology & Cell Biology Ser.). (Illus.). 85p. pap. 139.00 *(978-3-540-78770-9(4)*, 3540787704) Springer.

Stoltz, J. F., ed. Mechanobiology: Cartilage & Chondrocyte - Volume 5 - Volume 73 Biomedical & Health Research - Book Edition of Biorheology. 2008. (Illus.). 104p. 240.00 *(978-1-58603-927-1(X))* IOS Pr., Inc.

Williams, Riley J., III, ed. Cartilage Repair Strategies. 2007. (ENG., Illus.). xviii, 374p. 249.00 *(978-1-58829-629-0(6)*, 1588296296) Humana Pr.

Zaidi, Mone. Skeletal Biology & Medicine II: Bone & Cartilage Homeostasis & Bone Disease. 2012. (Annals of the New York Academy of Sciences Ser.: 93). (ENG., Illus.). 252p. pap. 75.00 ***(978-1-57331-856-3(6)***, Wiley-Blackwell) Wiley, John & Sons, Inc.

Zur Nieden, Nicole I. Embryonic Stem Cell Therapy for Osteo-Degenerative Diseases: Methods & Protocols. 2011. (Illus.). xii, 336p. E-Book ***(978-1-60761-962-8(8))*** Humana Pr.

CARTOGRAPHY

Here are entered works on the general science of map-making, including map projection and the mapping of large areas. Works on the mapping of small areas and the drawing of maps in elementary schools are entered under Map Drawing. Works on cartography applied to a particular subject are entered under that subject subdivided by the subdivision Maps, e.g. Geology—Maps.

see also Map Projection; Military Topography; Nautical Charts; Vegetation Mapping

Abrahamsson, Christian & Gren, Martin. Go: On the Geographies of Gunner Olsson. 2012. (Illus.). 380p. 134.95 ***(978-1-4094-1238-0(5))*** Ashgate Publishing Co.

Alai, Cyrus. General Maps of Persia 1477 - 1925. 2nd ed. 2010. (Handbook of Oriental Studies). (Illus.). 324p. *(978-90-04-18627-9(1))* BRILL.

Antique Collectors' Club. Atlas Ferraris. 2011. (ENG., Illus.). 600p. 150.00 *(978-90-209-9292-2(9))* Lannoo Pubs./Racine.

Appel, Carl L. Provenzalische Lautlehre: Mit Einer Karte. (Provenzalische Chrestomathie Ser.). reprint ed. 37.50 *(978-0-404-19027-9(8))* AMS Pr., Inc.

Baddeley, John F. Russia, Mongolia, China: Being Some Record of the Relations Between Them from the Beginning of the XVIIth Century to the Death of the Tsar Alexei Mikhailovich, A. D. 1602-1676, Rendered Mainly in the Form of Narratives Dictated or Written by the Envoys Sent by the Russian Tsars, or Their Voevodas in Siberia to the Kalmuk & Mongol Khans & Princes: & to the Emperors of China: with Introductions, Historical & Geograp, 2 vols. 2008. (Illus.). 350.00 *(978-1-57898-641-5(9))* Martino Publishing.

Bagrow, Leo. History of Cartography: Enlarged Second Edition. Skelton, R. A., ed. 2nd ed. 2009. (ENG., Illus.). 312p. pap. 179.95 *(978-1-4128-1154-5(6))* Transaction Pubs.

Bartlett, John. Mapping Jordan through Two Millennia. 2008. (Palestine Exploration Fund Annuals Ser.). (ENG., Illus.). 175p. (C). 96.00 *(978-1-905981-40-3(6))* Maney Publishing GBR. Dist: Brown, David Bk. Co., The.

Belletti, Adrian. Structures & Strategies. 2008. (Routledge Leading Linguists Ser.). (Illus.). 304p. 141.00 *(978-0-415-96201-8(3))* Routledge.

Bennison, George M., et al. An Introduction to Geological Structures & Maps. 8th rev. ed. 2011. (ENG., Illus.). 192p. pap. 41.50 ***(978-1-4441-1212-2(0))*** Hodder Education GBR. Dist: Oxford Univ. Pr., Inc.

Blevins, Bruce H. Mapping Wyoming. 2007. (Illus.). 390p. 125.00 *(978-1-57898-660-6(5))* Martino Publishing.

Boettinger, Janis L., et al, eds. Digital Soil Mapping: Bridging Research, Production, & Environmental Application. 2010. (Progress in Soil Science Ser.). (ENG., Illus.). 473p. 199.00 *(978-90-481-8862-8(8)*, 9048188628) Springer.

Brewer, Cynthia. Designed Maps: A Sourcebook for GIS Users. 2008. (ENG., Illus.). 170p. pap. 39.95 *(978-1-58948-160-2(7)*, ESRI Pr.) ESRI, Inc.

Broeders, P. W. A. Gijsbert Franco, Baron Von Derfelden Van Hinderstein, 1783-1857: Leven en Werk Van "Eene Ware Specialiteit" in Kaart Gebracht. 2007. (DUT., Illus.). 548p. 220.00 *(978-90-6194-409-6(0))* HES & DE GRAAF Pubs. BV NLD. Dist: Oak Knoll Pr.

Buchroithner, Manfred, ed. True-3D in Cartography: Autostereoscopic & Steric Visualisation of Geodata. 2011. (Lecture Notes in Geoinformation & Cartography Ser.). (ENG.). x, 290p. 229.00 *(978-3-642-12271-2(X)*, 364212271X) Springer.

Cadhla, Stiofan O. Civilizing Ireland: Ordnance Survey 1824-1842 Ethnography, Cartography, Translation. 2007. (Illus.). 280p. (C). 75.00 *(978-0-7165-3372-6(3))*; pap. 32.50 *(978-0-7165-2881-4(9))* Irish Academic Pr. IRL. Dist: International Specialized Bk. Services.

Caquard, Sébastien, et al, eds. Mapping Environmental Issues in the City: Arts & Cartography Cross Perspectives. 2011. (Lecture Notes in Geoinformation & Cartography Ser.). (ENG., Illus.). xiv, 273p. 129.00 ***(978-3-642-22440-9(7)***, 3642224407) Springer.

Carter, Paul. Dark Writing: Geography, Performance, Design. 2008. (Illus.). (C). 328p. 64.00 *(978-0-8248-3246-9(9))*; 306p. pap. 28.00 *(978-0-8248-3312-1(0))* Univ. of Hawaii Pr.

Cartwright, William. Cartography & Art. 2009. (Lecture Notes in Geoinformation & Cartography Ser.). (Illus.). 400p. 199.00 *(978-3-540-68567-8(7))* Springer.

Cartwright, William, et al, eds. Cartography & Art. 2010. (Lecture Notes in Geoinformation & Cartography Ser.). (ENG., Illus.). xix, 391p. pap. 199.00 ***(978-3-642-08810-0(4)***, 3642088104) Springer.

Cartwright, William, et al, eds. Multimedia Cartography. 2nd ed. (ENG., Illus.). xxvi, 546p. 2010. pap. 239.00 *(978-3-642-07173-7(2)*, 3642071732) 2006. 239.00 *(978-3-540-36650-8(4)*, 3540366504) Springer.

Cauvin, Colette. Thematic Cartography, 3 vols. 2010. (ENG., Illus.). 512p. 180.00 *(978-1-84821-110-0(4)*, Wiley-ISTE) Wiley, John & Sons, Inc.

Cauvin, Colette, et al. Thematic Cartography, 3 vols. 2010. (ENG., Illus.). 320p. 130.00 *(978-1-84821-112-4(0))*; 448p. 180.00 *(978-1-84821-111-7(2))*;3-Volume Set. (Iste Ser.: 389). 625.00 *(978-1-84821-109-4(0))* Wiley, John & Sons, Inc. (Wiley-ISTE).

Clarke, H. B. & Prunty, Jacinta. Reading the Maps: A Guide to the Irish Historic Towns Atlas. 2011. (Illus.). 264p. pap. 35.00 ***(978-1-904890-70-6(9))*** Royal Irish Academy IRL. Dist: International Specialized Bk. Services.

Conley, Tom. Cartographic Cinema. 2007. (Illus.). 336p. 75.00 *(978-0-8166-4356-1(3))*; per. 26.50 *(978-0-8166-4357-8(1))* Univ of Minnesota Pr.

Copeta, Clara. Cartografie, Immagini, Metafore. 2009. (ITA., Illus.). 300p. *(978-88-8063-593-2(X))* Longo Angelo.

Crampton, Jeremy W. Mapping: A Critical Introduction to Cartography & GIS. 2010. (Critical Introductions to Geography Ser.: 4). (ENG., Illus.). 232p. pap. 39.95 *(978-1-4051-2173-6(4)*, Wiley-Blackwell) Wiley, John & Sons, Inc.

Crampton, Jeremy W. & Krygier, John B. Mapping: A Critical Introduction to Cartography & GIS. 2010. (Critical Introductions to Geography Ser.: 5). (ENG., Illus.). 232p. 104.95 *(978-1-4051-2172-9(6)*, Wiley-Blackwell) Wiley, John & Sons, Inc.

Cram101 Textbook Reviews. Outlines & Highlights for Cartography: Thematic Map Design by Dent, ISBN. 2011. 288p. pap. 32.95 ***(978-1-6181-2-980-2(5))*** Cram101 Inc.

—Outlines & Highlights for Thematic Cartography & Geographic Visualization by Terry a Slocum. 2011. 128p. pap. 28.95 ***(978-1-61490-791-6(9))*** Cram101 Inc.

Dalla Zuanna, Gianpiero & Micheli, Giuseppe A. Strong family & low fertility:a Paradox? New perspectives in interpreting contemporary family & reproductive Behaviour. 2010. (European Studies of Population Ser.). 179p. pap. 179.00 *(978-90-481-6730-2(2)*, 9048167302) Springer.

Delazari, Luciene. The Design of an Electronic Interactive Atlas. 2010. 112p. pap. *(978-3-639-25746-5(4))* VDM Verlag Dr. Mueller e.K.

Denny, Mark. The Science of Navigation: From Dead Reckoning to GPS. 2012. (ENG., Illus.). 272p. (gr. 17). 65.00 ***(978-1-4214-0511-7(3))***; pap. 30.00 ***(978-1-4214-0512-4(1))*** Johns Hopkins Univ. Pr.

Dodge, Martin, ed. Classics in Cartography: Reflections on Influential Articles from Cartographica. 2011. (ENG., Illus.). 430p. 119.95 *(978-0-470-68174-9(8)*, Wiley) Wiley, John & Sons, Inc.

Dodge, Martin, et al, eds. The Map Reader: Theories of Mapping Practice & Cartographic Representation. 2011. (ENG., Illus.). 504p. 119.95 ***(978-0-470-74283-9(6)***, Wiley) Wiley, John & Sons, Inc.

Dodge, Martin, et al, eds. Rethinking Maps: New Frontiers in Cartographic Theory. 2011. (Routledge Studies in Human Geography Ser.). (ENG., Illus.). 272p. (C). pap. 52.95 *(978-0-415-67667-0(3))* Routledge.

Ermacora, Beate, ed. Simon Wachsmuth: Aporia/Europa. 2011. (ENG., Illus.). 104p. 37.50 ***(978-3-86678-448-2(1))*** Kerber Verlag DEU. Dist: D.A.P./Distributed Art Pubs.

Esri. Esri Map Book, Volume 26. 2011. (ENG., Illus.). 120p. pap. 24.95 *(978-1-58948-284-5(0)*, ESRI Pr.) ESRI, Inc.

Evans, R. T. & Frye, H. M. History of the Topographic Branch (Division) 2009. (Illus.). xvi, 196p. *(978-1-4113-2612-5(1))* United States Geological Survey.

Fawcett - Tang, Roger. Mapping Graphic Navigational Systems. 2008. (ENG., Illus.). 208p. pap. 35.00 *(978-2-88893-036-5(6)*, 2888930366) RotoVision SA CHE. Dist: Quayside.

Fenna, Donald. Cartographic Science a Compendium of Map Projections with Derivat. 2006. (ENG., Illus.). 504p. (C). 107.95 *(978-0-8493-8169-0(X)*, CRC Press) Taylor & Francis Group GBR. Dist: Taylor & Francis Group.

Foxell, Simon. Mapping London: Making Sense of the City. 2011. (ENG., Illus.). 288p. pap. 39.95 *(978-1-906155-45-2(3))* Black Dog Publishing Ltd. GBR. Dist: Perseus Distribution.

Gartner, Georg & Ortag, Felix, eds. Cartography in Central & Eastern Europe: Cee 2009. 2009. (Lecture Notes in Geoinformation & Cartography Ser.). (ENG., Illus.). xix, 570p. 249.00 *(978-3-642-03293-6(1)*, 3642032931) Springer.

Gartner, Georg F. & Ortag, Felix. Cartography in Central & Eastern Europe: Selected Papers of the 1st ICA Symposium on Cartography for Central & Eastern Europe. 2010. (Illus.). xix, 570p. E-Book *(978-3-642-03294-3(X))* Springer.

Ginsberg, William B. Maps & Mapping of Norway, 1602-1855. 2009. (Illus.). 332p. 145.00 *(978-0-9787900-2-8(2))*; 295.00 *(978-0-9787900-3-5(0))* Septentrionalium Pr.

Grafarend, Erik W. & Krumm, Friedrich W. Map Projections: Cartographic Information Systems. 2010. (Illus.). xviii, 714p. pap. 219.00 *(978-3-642-07178-2(3)*, 3642071783) Springer.

Harmon, Katharine A. & Clemans, Gayle. The Map as Art: Contemporary Artists Explore Cartography. 2009. (ENG., Illus.). 256p. 45.00 *(978-1-56898-762-0(5))* Princeton Architectural Pr.

Hartemink, Alfred E., et al, eds. Digital Soil Mapping with Limited Data. 2010. (Illus.). xxiv, 445p. pap. 159.00 *(978-90-481-7925-1(4)*, 9048179254) Springer.

Haywood, Carl W. Sometimes Only Horses to Eat. 2008. 392p. pap. 24.95 *(978-0-9802279-0-1(9))* Rockman's Trading Post, Inc.

Hegglund, Jon. World Views: Metageographies of Modernist Fiction, 1 vol. 2012. (Modernist Literature & Culture Ser.). (ENG., Illus.). 256p. 49.95 ***(978-0-19-979610-6(6))*** Oxford Univ. Pr., Inc.

Heller, Michelle. Synapse EHR 1. 1 an Electronic Charting Simulation Exercise. 2009. (ENG.). 72p. (C). pap. 23.95 *(978-1-4354-9817-4(8))* Delmar Cengage Learning.

hf Ullmann, compiled by. Peters World Atlas: The Earth in Its True Proportions, 1 vol. 2010. (ENG., Illus.). 232p. pap. 29.99 *(978-3-8331-5560-4(4))* h.f.ullmann DEU. Dist: Innovative Logistics.

Higgins, Hannah B. The Grid Book. 2009. (ENG., Illus.). 312p. (gr. 17). pap. 26.95 *(978-0-262-51240-4(8))* MIT Pr.

Hillstrom, Laurie. Gps. 2010. (Technology 360 Ser.). (ENG.). 128p. (YA). (gr. 7-12). 33.45 *(978-1-4205-0325-8(1))* Cengage Gale.

Hollingum, Ben. Maps & Measurement. 2010. (Understanding Maps of Our World Ser.). (ENG.). 48p. (gr. 6-8). pap. 14.05 *(978-1-4339-3504-6(X)*, Stevens, Gareth Secondary Library) Stevens, Gareth Publishing LLLP.

Hoogvliet, Margriet. Pictura et Scriptura: Textes, Images et Hermeneutique des Mappae Mundi (XIIIe-XVIe Siecle) 2007. (Terrarum Orbis Ser.). (FRE., Illus.). 391p. (C). 116.00 *(978-2-503-52065-0(0))* Brepols Pubs. BEL. Dist: ISD.

Hunt, Ashley. Geography Map. 2007. 0.01 net. *(978-1-60402-334-3(1))* Independent Pub.

Jennings, Ken. Maphead: Charting the Wide, Weird World of Geography Wonks. 2011. (ENG.). 54.99 ***(978-1-61587-890-1(4))*** Findaway World, LLC.

—Maphead: Charting the Wide, Weird World of Geography Wonks. (ENG.). 2012. 304p. pap. 15.00 ***(978-1-4391-6718-2(4))*** 2011. 288p. lib. bdg. 25.00 *(978-1-4391-6717-5(6))* Scribner. (Scribner).

Johnson, Linda. The Kandik Map. 2011. (ENG.). 232p. pap. 19.95 *(978-1-60223-042-2(0))* Univ. of Alaska Pr.

Karimi, Hassan A. & Akinci, Burcu. CAD & GIS Integration. 2009. (ENG., Illus.). 247p. 92.95 *(978-1-4200-6805-4(9))* Auerbach Pubs., Inc.

Kivelson, V. Cartographies of Tsardom. 2006. (Illus.). 344p. 79.95 *(978-0-8014-4409-8(8))* Cornell Univ. Pr.

Kivelson, Valerie A. Cartographies of Tsardom: The Land & Its Meanings in Seventeenth-Century Russia. 2006. (Illus.). 263p. per. 29.95 *(978-0-8014-7253-4(9))* Cornell Univ. Pr.

Kohlstock, Peter. Topographie: Methoden und Modelle der Landesaufnahme. 2011. (De Gruyter Studium Ser.). (GER.). (C). 49.00 ***(978-3-11-022675-1(8))*** De Gruyter, Walter Inc.

Konecny, Milan, et al, eds. Geographic Information & Cartography for Risk & Crises Management: Towards Better Solutions. 2010. (Lecture Notes in Geoinformation & Cartography Ser.). (ENG.). xxii, 429p. 169.00 *(978-3-642-03441-1(1)*, 3642034411) Springer.

Konstam, Angus. The World Atlas of Pirates: Treasures & Treachery on the Seven Seas, in Maps, Tall Tales, & Pictures. 2009. (ENG., Illus.). 256p. 29.95 *(978-1-59921-474-0(1)*, Lyons Pr.) Globe Pequot Pr., The.

Kordan, Bohdan S. The Mapping of Ukraine: European Cartography & Maps of Early Modern Ukraine, 1150-1799. 2008.Tr. of Kartohrafuvannia Ukrainy: Evropeiska Kartohrafiia Ta Karty Rannomodernoï Ukrainy. (UKR & ENG., Illus.). 1043p. *(978-0-9660621-4-4(0))* Ukrainian Museum, The.

Kraak, Menno-Jan & Ormeling, Ferjan. Cartography: Visualization of Spatial Data. 3rd ed. 2010. (ENG., Illus.). 198p. pap. 87.50 *(978-0-273-72279-3(4))* Pearson Education, Ltd. GBR. Dist: Trans-Atlantic Pubns., Inc.

—Cartography, Third Edition: Visualization of Spatial Data. 3rd ed. 2010. (ENG.). 199p. pap. 55.00 *(978-1-60918-193-2(X))* Guilford Pubns., Inc.

Kriz, Karel, et al, eds. Mapping Different Geographies. 2010. (Lecture Notes in Geoinformation & Cartography Ser.). xii, 255p. 159.00 *(978-3-642-15536-9(7)*, 3642155367) Springer.

Krygier, John & Wood, Denis. Making Maps, Second Edition: A Visual Guide to Map Design for GIS. 2nd rev. ed. 2011. (ENG., Illus.). 256p. pap. 50.00 *(978-1-60918-166-6(2))* Guilford Pubns., Inc.

Lai, Poh Chin, et al. Spatial Epidemiological Approaches in Disease Mapping & Analysis. 2008. (ENG., Illus.). 194p. 99.95 *(978-1-4200-4546-8(6)*, CRC Press) Taylor & Francis Group GBR. Dist: Taylor & Francis Group.

Lasater, Brian. The Dream of the West, Pt II. 2008. 600p. pap. 39.95 *(978-1-4303-1382-3(X))* Lulu Enterprises Inc.

Lisle, Richard J., et al. Basic Geological Mapping. 5th ed. 2011. (Geological Field Guide Ser.: 35). (ENG., Illus.). 230p. pap. 39.95 ***(978-0-470-68634-8(0)***, Wiley) Wiley, John & Sons, Inc.

Lockett, Jerry. Captain James Cook in Atlantic Canada: The Adventurer & Map Maker's Formative Years. 2010. (ENG., Illus.). 200p. 29.95 *(978-0-88780-920-0(0))* Formac Publishing Co., Ltd. CAN. Dist: Casemate Pubs. & Bk. Distributors, LLC.

Mancilla, Blanca. Intensional Collaborative Web Environments: A New Approach to Map Making. 2008. 152p. pap. *(978-3-639-10442-4(0))* VDM Verlag Dr. Mueller e.K.

McCoy, Roger. On the Edge: Mapping North America's Coasts. 2012. (ENG., Illus.). 256p. 29.95 ***(978-0-19-974404-6(1))*** Oxford Univ. Pr., Inc.

Meng, Liqiu, et al. Map-Based Mobile Services: Interactivity & Usability. 2007. (Lecture Notes in Geoinformation & Cartography Ser.). (Illus.). 260p. 239.00 *(978-3-540-37109-0(5))* Springer.

Mers, Adelheid, ed. Useful Pictures. 2009. (Illus.). 128p. pap. 20.00 *(978-0-945323-17-4(4))* WhiteWalls, Inc.

Mitchell, Peta. Cartographic Strategies of Postmodernity: The Figure of the Map in Contemporary Theory & Fiction. 2007. (Routledge Studies in Twentieth-Century Literature Ser.). (ENG., Illus.). 192p. (C). 125.00 *(978-0-415-95597-3(1))* Routledge.

Mogel, Lize & Bhagat, Alexis. An Atlas of Radical Cartography, 1 vol. 2008. (ENG., Illus.). 160p. 35.00 (978-0-9791377-2-3(1)) Journal of Aesthetics and Protest Pr./Herbst.
Monmonier, Mark S. No Dig, No Fly, No Go: How Maps Restrict & Control. 2010. (Illus.). 242p. 65.00 (978-0-226-53467-1(7)); (ENG., pap. 18.00 (978-0-226-53468-8(5)) Univ. of Chicago Pr.
Montemerlo, Michael & Thrun, Sebastian. FastSLAM: A Scalable Method for the Simultaneous Localization & Mapping Problem in Robotics. (Springer Tracts in Advanced Robotics Ser.). (Illus.). 2010. xv, 119p. pap. 119.00 (978-3-642-07978-8(4), 3642079784) 2007. XV, 119p. (C). 119.00 (978-3-540-46399-3(2), 3540463992) Springer.
Moore, Antoni & Drecki, Igor, eds. Geospatial Vision 2: Proceedings of the GeoCart' 2010 Conference. 2011. (Lecture Notes in Geoinformation & Cartography Ser.). (ENG.). x, 280p. 139.00 (978-3-642-12288-0(4), 3642122884) Springer.
Nebenzahl, Kenneth. Mapping the Silk Road & Beyond: 2,000 Years of Exploring the East. 2011. (ENG.). 176p. pap. 29.95 **(978-0-7148-6320-7(3))** Phaidon Pr., Inc.
Nimmo, Alexander & Wilkins, Noël P. Inverness Survey & Journal 1806. 2011. (Illus.). 208p. 49.25 **(978-1-904890-74-4(1))** Royal Irish Academy IRL. Dist: International Specialized Bk. Services.
Norment, Christopher. In the Memory of the Map: A Cartographic Memoir. 2012. (Sightline Bks.). (ENG., Illus.). 262p. pap. 22.50 **(978-1-60938-077-9(0))** Univ. of Iowa Pr.
Nyerges, Timothy L. & Jankowski, Piotr. Regional & Urban GIS: A Decision Support Approach. 2009. (ENG., Illus.). 299p. 60.00 (978-1-60623-336-8(X)) Guilford Pubns., Inc.
Olsson, Gunnar. Abysmal: A Critique of Cartographic Reason. 2007. (ENG., Illus.). 584p. 42.50 (978-0-226-62930-8(9)) Univ. of Chicago Pr.
Painho, Marco, et al, eds. Geospatial Thinking. 2010. (Lecture Notes in Geoinformation & Cartography Ser.). xviii, 418p. 199.00 (978-3-642-12325-2(2), 3642123252) Springer.
Perkins, Chris & Parry, Bob, eds. Information Sources in Cartography. (Guides to Information Sources Ser.). (ENG.). 540p. **(978-3-11-187418-0(4))** Saur, K. G. Verlag GmbH & Co.
Peter Eredics, ed. Mapping Forestry. 2010. (Mapping Industries Ser.). (ENG., Illus.). 100p. pap. 12.95 (978-1-58948-209-8(3), ESRI Pr.) ESRI, Inc.
Peterson, Gretchen N. GIS Cartography: A Guide to Effective Map Design. 2009. (ENG., Illus.). 248p. 96.95 (978-1-4200-8213-5(2), CRC Press) Taylor & Francis Group GBR. Dist: Taylor & Francis Group.
Peterson, Michael P., ed. Online Maps with APIs & WebServices. 2012. (Lecture Notes in Geoinformation & Cartography Ser.). (ENG., Illus.). ix, 318p. 129.00 **(978-3-642-27484-8(6)**, 3642274846) Springer.
Propen, Amy D. Locating Visual-Material Rhetorics: The Map, the Mill, & the GPS. 2011. **(978-1-60235-257-5(7))**; **(978-1-60235-255-1(0))**; pap. **(978-1-60235-254-4(2))** Parlor Pr.
Rijke, P. J. de. Frisia Dominium: Kaarten Van de Provincie Friesland Tot 1850: Geschiedenis en Cartobibliografie. 2006. (DUT & ENG.). 452p. 155.00 (978-90-6194-419-5(8)) HES & DE GRAAF Pubs. BV NLD. Dist: Oak Knoll Pr.
Robinson, Arthur Howard. The Look of Maps: An Examination of Cartographic Design. 2010. (ENG., Illus.). 128p. pap. 18.95 (978-1-58948-262-3(X), ESRI Pr.) ESRI, Inc.
Rowntree, Lester, et al. Mapping Workbook. 4th ed. 2008. (ENG.). 88p. (C). pap. 23.40 (978-0-13-601174-3(8), Prentice Hall) Prentice Hall PTR.
—Mapping Workbook for Globaization & Diversity: Geography of a Changing World. 3rd ed. 2010. (ENG.). 240p. (C). pap. 25.40 (978-0-321-66739-7(5), Prentice Hall) Prentice Hall PTR.
Ruas, Anne, ed. Advances in Cartography & GIScience. Volume 1: Selection from ICC 2011, Paris. 2011. (Lecture Notes in Geoinformation & Cartography Ser.). (ENG., Illus.). xvi, 558p. 229.00 (978-3-642-19142-8(8), 3642191428) Springer.
—Advances in Cartography & GIScience. Volume 2: Selection from ICC 2011, Paris. 2011. (Lecture Notes in Geoinformation & Cartography / Publications of the International Cartographic Association (ICA) Ser.). (ENG., Illus.). xvi, 487p. 179.00 (978-3-642-19213-5(0), 3642192130) Springer.
Ruggles, Richard I. A Country So Interesting: The Hudson's Bay Company & Two Centuries of Mapping, 1670-1870. 2011. (Rupert's Land Record Society Ser.). (ENG., Illus.). 320p. (C). pap. **(978-0-7735-3885-6(2))** McGill-Queen's Univ. Pr.
Rush, Mary. Apocryphal Irish Texts. 2010. 228p. pap. (978-3-639-21530-4(3)) VDM Verlag Dr. Mueller e.K.
Sappington, Nancy, ed. Mapping for Congress: Supporting Public Policy with GIS: Library of Congress, Congressional Cartography Program. 2007. (ENG., Illus.). 83p. per. 14.95 (978-1-58948-145-9(3), ESRI Pr.) ESRI, Inc.
Scafi, Alessandro. Mapping Paradise: A History of Heaven on Earth. 2006. (Illus.). 400p. 60.00 (978-0-226-73559-7(1)) Univ. of Chicago Pr.
Seegel, Steven. Mapping Europe's Borderlands: Russian Cartography in the Age of Empire. 2012. (ENG., Illus.). 384p. 55.00 **(978-0-226-74425-4(6))** Univ. of Chicago Pr.
Seegel, Steven. Ukraine under Western Eyes: The Bohdan & Neonila Krawciw Ucrainica Map Collection. 2009. (Harvard Series in Ukrainian Studies). (Illus.). 248p. 95.00 (978-1-932650-04-4(0)) Harvard Ukrainian Research Institute.
Shelef, Nadav G. Evolving Nationalism: Homeland, Identity, & Religion in Israel, 1925-2005. 2010. (Illus.). 296p. 69.95 (978-0-8014-4870-6(0)) Cornell Univ. Pr.
Sherwood, Robert. The Cartography of Alexander von Humboldt: Images of the Enlightenment in America. 2008. (Illus.). 216p. pap. (978-3-639-03967-2(X)) VDM Verlag Dr. Mueller e.K.
Slavick, Elin O'Hara. Bomb after Bomb: A Violent Cartography, 1 vol. 2007. (ENG., Illus.). 112p. pap. 34.95 (978-88-8158-633-2(9)) Charta ITA. Dist: D.A.P./Distributed Art Pubs.
Slocum, Terry A., et al. Thematic Cartography & Geovisualization. Clarke, Keith C., ed. 3rd ed. 2008. (ENG., Illus.). 576p. (C). 157.80 (978-0-13-229834-6(1), Prentice Hall) Prentice Hall PTR.
Smith, Richard J. Mapping China & Managing the World: Culture, Cartography & Cosmology in Late Imperial Times. 2012. (Asia's Transformations/Critical Asian Scholarship Ser.). (ENG., Illus.). 304p. (C). 150.00 (978-0-415-68509-2(5)); pap. 49.95 (978-0-415-68510-8(9)) Routledge.
Spencer, Edgar W. Geologic Maps: A Practical Guide to the Preparation & Interpretation of Geologic Maps. 2nd ed. 2006. (Illus.). 148p. (C). pap. 33.95 (978-1-57766-462-8(0)) Waveland Pr., Inc.
Springer, Nick. Cartography Design Annual #1. 2009. 78p. pap. 39.95 (978-0-615-22116-8(5)) Springer Cartographics, LLC.
Staatsbibliothek Zu Berlin - Preussischer Kulturbesitz Staff, ed. Bibliographia Cartographica Vol. 32: Internationale Dokumentation des Kartographischen Schrifttums International Documentation of Cartographical Literature Documentation Internationale de la Litterature Cartographique. 2009. XXVI, 355p. pap. (978-3-598-20650-4(X)) Saur, K. G. Verlag GmbH & Co.
Strandsbjerg, Jeppe. Territory, Globalization & International Relations: The Cartographic Reality of Space. 2010. (ENG., Illus.). 208p. 84.00 (978-0-230-58083-1(1)) Palgrave Macmillan.
Talbert, Richard J. A. Ancient Perspectives: Maps & Their Place in Mesopotamia, Egypt, Greece, & Rome. 2012. (Kenneth Nebenzahl, Jr. , Lectures in the History of Cartography Ser.). (Illus.). 272p. 65.00 **(978-0-226-78937-8(3))** Univ. of Chicago Pr.
Tally, Robert T., Jr. & Tally, Robert T. Melville, Mapping & Globalization: Literary Cartography in the American Baroque Writer. 2009. (Continuum Literary Studies). (ENG.). 192p. 120.00 (978-0-8264-7151-2(X)) Continuum International Publishing Group, Ltd. GBR. Dist: National Bk. Network.
Thrower, Norman J. W. Maps & Civilization: Cartography in Culture & Society. 3rd ed. 2008. Orig. Title: Maps & Man. (Illus.). 362p. per. 30.00 (978-0-226-79974-2(3)) Univ. of Chicago Pr.
Turchi, Peter. Maps of the Imagination: The Writer As Cartographer. 2007. (ENG., Illus.). 246p. pap. 22.95 (978-1-59534-041-2(6)) Trinity Univ. Pr.
Tyner, Judith A. Principles of Map Design. 2010. (ENG., Illus.). 259p. 60.00 (978-1-60623-544-7(3)) Guilford Pubns., Inc.
United Nations Staff. Ninth United Nations Regional Cartographic Conference for the Americas: Report of the Conference - New York, 10-14 August 2009. 2009. (ENG.). 28p. pap. 8.00 (978-92-1-101204-0(X)) United Nations Pubns.
Waldseemuller, Martin & Hessler, John W. The Naming of America: Martin Waldseemuller's 1507 World Map & the Cosmographiae Introductio. 2008. (ENG., Illus.). 128p. 24.95 (978-1-904832-49-2(0)) Giles, D. Ltd. GBR. Dist: Antique Collectors' Club.
Wallis, H. Cartographical Innovations. xx, 353 p. (978-0-906430-04-0(6)) Bow Historical Bks.
Wilkinson, Henry Robert. Maps & Politics: A Review of the Ethnographic Cartography of Macedonia. 2009. 404p. 60.00 (978-1-59740-742-7(9)); pap. 40.00 (978-1-59740-764-9(X)) ACLS Humanities E-Book.
Wood, Denis & Fels, John. The Natures of Maps: Cartographic Constructions of the Natural World. 2009. (ENG., Illus.). 231p. 49.00 (978-0-226-90604-1(3)) 2008. pap. (978-0-226-90605-8(1)) Univ. of Chicago Pr.
Wright, Dawn J., et al. Coastal Informatics: Web Atlas Design & Implementation. 2010. (Illus.). 350p. 180.00 (978-1-61520-815-9(1)) IGI Global.
Yang, Xiaojun, ed. Remote Sensing & Geospatial Technologies for Coastal Ecosystem Assessment & Management. 2009. (Lecture Notes in Geoinformation & Cartography Ser.). (Illus.). xiv, 561p. 239.00 (978-3-540-88182-7(4)) Springer.
Zentai, László & Nunez, Jesús Reyes, eds. Maps for the Future: Children, Education & Internet. 2012. (Lecture Notes in Geoinformation & Cartography / Publications of the International Cartographic Association (ICA) Ser.). (ENG., Illus.). vii, 316p. 129.00 (978-3-642-19521-1(0), 3642195210) Springer.

CARTOGRAPHY—DATA PROCESSING

see also Digital Mapping

Blaser, A., ed. Data Base Techniques for Pictorial Application: Florence, June 20-22 1979. 2007. (Lecture Notes in Computer Science Ser.). XI, 599p. pap. 49.95 (978-3-540-09763-1(5), 3540097635) Springer.
ESRI, compiled by. ESRI Map Book, Volume 24. 2009. (ESRI Map Bks.). (ENG., Illus.). 120p. pap. 24.95 (978-1-58948-230-2(1), ESRI Pr.) ESRI, Inc.
Gartner, Georg, ed. Location Based TeleCartography & Services. 2007. (Lecture Notes in Geoinformation & Cartography Ser.). (Illus.). XXII, 605p. 329.00 (978-3-540-36727-7(6), 3540367276) Springer.
Gartner, Georg, et al, eds. Location Based Services & TeleCartography. 2010. (Lecture Notes in Geoinformation & Cartography Ser.). (Illus.). xxii, 605p. pap. 329.00 (978-3-642-07179-9(1), 3642071791) Springer.
Gartner, Georg & Li, Yan, eds. Location Based Services & TeleCartography III: From New Theories to LBS 2. 0. 2010. (Lecture Notes in Geoinformation & Cartography Ser.). x, 290p. 139.00 (978-3-642-12370-2(8), 3642123708) Springer.
Hazzard, Erik. OpenLayers 2. 10 Beginner's Guide. 2011. (Illus.). 351p. pap. (978-1-84951-412-5(7)) Packt Publishing, Ltd.
Mackaness, William A., et al, eds. Generalisation of Geographic Information: Cartographic Modelling & Applications. 2007. (International Cartographic Association Ser.). (ENG.). 386p. 200.00 (978-0-08-045374-3(0), Elsevier Science) Elsevier Science & Technology Bks.
Meng, Liqiu, et al. Map-based Mobile Services: Design, Interaction & Usability. 2010. (Lecture Notes in Geoinformation & Cartography Ser.). (Illus.). xiv, 352p. pap. 239.00 (978-3-642-07204-8(6), 3642072046) Springer.
Murayama, Y. & Thapa, Rajesh Bahadur, eds. Spatial Analysis & Modeling in Geographical Transformation Process: GIS-based Applications. 2011. (GeoJournal Library). (ENG., Illus.). x, 300p. 139.00 (978-94-007-0670-5(7), 9400706707) Springer.
Peterson, Michael P. International Perspectives on Maps & the Internet. 2008. (Lecture Notes in Geoinformation & Cartography Ser.). (Illus.). 441p. 239.00 (978-3-540-72028-7(6)) Springer.
—International Perspectives on Maps & the Internet. 2010. (Lecture Notes in Geoinformation & Cartography Ser.). (Illus.). xviii, 442p. pap. 239.00 (978-3-642-09121-6(0), 3642091210) Springer.
Tomlinson, Roger. Pensando en el Sig: Planificacion del Sistema de Informacion Geografica Dirigida a Gerentes. 3rd ed. 2008. (ENG.). pap. 9.95 (978-1-58948-229-6(8), ESRI Pr.) ESRI, Inc.
Van Sickle, Jan. Basic GIS Coordinates. 2nd rev. ed. 2010. (ENG., Illus.). 200p. 94.95 (978-1-4200-9231-8(6), CRC Press) Taylor & Francis Group GBR. Dist: Taylor & Francis Group.

CARTOGRAPHY—HISTORY

Akerman, J. R. The Imperial Map: Cartography & the Mastery of Empire. Akerman, James R., ed. 2009. (Kenneth Nebenzahl, Jr. , Lectures in the History of Cartography Ser.). (Illus.). 384p. 60.00 (978-0-226-01076-2(7)) Univ. of Chicago Pr.
Alai, Cyrus. Special Maps of Persia 1477-1925, 2 vols. 2010. (Illus.). 420p. (978-90-04-18401-5(5)) BRILL.
Andrews, John. Maps in Those Days: Carthographic Methods Before 1850. 2009. (Illus.). 549p. 85.00 (978-1-84682-188-2(6)) Four Courts Pr. IRL. Dist: International Specialized Bk. Services.
Barrow, Ian J. Colonial Sri Lanka, 1800-1900. 2008. (ENG., Illus.). 232p. 39.95 (978-0-19-569191-7(1)) Oxford Univ. Pr., Inc.
Baynton-Williams, Ashley & Baynton-Williams, Miles. New Worlds: Maps from the Age of Discovery. 2009. (ENG., Illus.). 224p. 14.99 (978-1-84866-018-2(9), 1848660189) Quercus GBR. Dist: Book Sales, Inc.
Betz, Richard L. The Mapping of Africa: A Cartobibliography of Printed Maps of the African Continent to 1700. 2007. (Illus.). 540p. 235.00 (978-90-6194-489-8(9)) HES & DE GRAAF Pubs. BV NLD. Dist: Oak Knoll Pr.
Birkholz, Daniel. The King's Two Maps: Cartography & Culture in Thirteenth-Century England. 2009. 258p. 39.95 (978-0-415-80342-7(X)) Routledge.
Bremmer, Rolf H., et al, eds. Foundations of Learning: The Transfer of Encyclopaedic Knowledge in the Early Middle Ages. 2007. (Mediaevalia Groningana New Ser.). (ENG., Illus.). 393p. (C). pap. 101.00 (978-90-429-1979-2(5)) Peeters Pubs. & Booksellers BEL. Dist: Brown, David Bk. Co., The.
Brincken, Anna Dorothee von den. Studien zur Universalkartographie des Mittelalters: Veröffentlichungen des Max-Planck-Instituts für Geschichte 229. 2008. (Veröffentlichungen des Max-Planck-Instituts Für Geschichte Ser.). (ITA, GER & ENG., Illus.). 868p. (C). 164.00 (978-3-525-35884-9(9)) Vandenhoeck & Ruprecht GmbH & Co. KG DEU. Dist: ISD.
Bruckner, Martin, ed. Early American Cartographies. 2011. (Published for the Omohundro Institute of Early American History & Culture, Williamsburg, Virginia Ser.). (ENG., Illus.). 496p. 60.00 (978-0-8078-3469-5(6)) Univ. of North Carolina Pr.
Carrera, Magali M. Traveling from New Spain to Mexico: Mapping Practices of Nineteenth-Century Mexico. 2011. (ENG., Illus.). 352p. 89.95 (978-0-8223-4976-1(0)); pap. 24.95 (978-0-8223-4991-4(4)) Duke Univ. Pr.
Conley, Tom. The Self-Made Map: Cartographic Writing in Early Modern France. 2011. (ENG., Illus.). 392p. pap. 25.00 (978-0-8166-7448-0(5)) Univ. of Minnesota Pr.
Conzen, Michael P. & Dillon, Diane, eds. Mapping Manifest Destiny: Chicago & the American West. 2008. (Illus.). 120p. pap. 27.95 (978-0-911028-81-2(1)) Newberry Library.
Doherty, Gillian M. The Irish Ordnance Survey: History, Culture & Memory. 2006. (Illus.). 237p. pap. 29.95 (978-1-84682-036-6(7)) Four Courts Pr. IRL. Dist: International Specialized Bk. Services.
Dym, Jordana. Mapping Latin America: A Cartographic Reader. Offen, Karl, ed. 2011. (ENG., Illus.). 360p. 125.00 (978-0-226-61821-0(8)) Univ. of Chicago Pr.
Dym, Jordana & Offen, Karl, eds. Mapping Latin America: A Cartographic Reader. 2011. (ENG., Illus.). 360p. pap. 39.00 (978-0-226-61822-7(6)) Univ. of Chicago Pr.
Edson, Evelyn. The World Map, 1300-1492: The Persistence of Tradition & Transformation. 2007. (ENG., Illus.). 312p. (gr. 17). 52.00 (978-0-8018-8589-1(2)) Johns Hopkins Univ. Pr.
Etherington, Norman, ed. Mapping European Conquest: Australia & Southern Africa. 2007. (Illus.). 230p. (C). pap. 31.00 (978-0-9802964-4-0(7)) UWA Publishing AUS. Dist: International Specialized Bk. Services.
Fernández García, Álvaro. Cartografía Medieval: El Enigma Del Mapamundi de 1375. 2009. (SPA., Illus.). 229p. (978-84-9742-906-1(0)) Biblioteca Nueva, Editorial, S.L.
Ginsberg, William B. Printed Maps of Scandinavia & the Arctic, 1482-1601. 2006. (Illus.). 232p. 95.00 (978-0-9787900-0-4(6)); 225.00 (978-0-9787900-1-1(4)) Septentrionalium Pr.
Goffart, Walter. Barbarians, Maps, & Historiography: Studies on the Early Medieval West. 2009. (Variorum Collected Studies). (Illus.). 344p. 165.00 (978-0-7546-5984-6(4)) Ashgate Publishing Co.
Gordon, Andrew, et al, eds. Literature, Mapping, & the Politics of Space in Early Modern Britain. 2010. (ENG., Illus.). 292p. pap. 36.99 (978-0-521-16943-1(7)) Cambridge Univ. Pr.
Harrisse, Henry. The Discovery of North America: A Critical, Documentary, & Historic Investigation: with an Essay on the Early Cartography of the New World, Including Descriptions of Two Hundred & Fifty Maps or Globes Existing or Lost, Constructed Before the Year 1536: to Which Are Added a Chronology of One Hundred Voyages Westward, Projected, Attempted, or Accomplished Between 1431 & 1504: Biographical Accounts of the Three Hundred Pilots. 2007. (Illus.). 812p. 125.00 (978-1-57898-596-8(X)) Martino Publishing.
Harvey, P. D. A. Manors & Maps in Rural England, from the Tenth Century to the Seventeenth. 2010. (Variorum Collected Studies). (Illus.). 352p. 165.00 (978-1-4094-0241-1(X)) Ashgate Publishing Co.
Hiatt, Alfred. Terra Incognita: Mapping the Antipodes Before 1600. 2008. (ENG., Illus.). 224p. 60.00 (978-0-226-33303-8(5)) Univ. of Chicago Pr.
Jacob, Christian. The Sovereign Map: Theoretical Approaches in Cartography Throughout History. Dahl, Edward H., ed. Conley, Tom, tr. from FRE. 2006. (Illus.). 464p. 65.00 (978-0-226-38953-0(7)) Univ. of Chicago Pr.
Jacobs, Frank. Strange Maps: An Atlas of Cartographic Curiosities. 2009. (ENG., Illus.). 256p. (gr. 12-18). 30.00 (978-0-14-200525-5(8), Studio) Penguin Group (USA) Inc.
Jenish, D'Arcy. Epic Wanderer: David Thompson & the Mapping of the Canadian West. 2009. (ENG., Illus.). 320p. pap. 18.95 (978-0-8032-2452-0(4), Bison Bks.) Univ. of Nebraska Pr.
Johnson, Linda. The Kandik Map. 2009. (Illus.). 160p. 34.95 (978-1-60223-032-3(3)) Univ. of Alaska Pr.
Kain, Roger J. P. & Oliver, Richard R. The Tithe Maps of England & Wales: A Cartographic Analysis & County-by-County Catalogue. 2011. (ENG., Illus.). 898p. pap. 98.00 (978-0-521-18880-7(6)) Cambridge Univ. Pr.
Laffon, Caroline & Laffon, Martine. Mapping the World: Stories of Geography. 2009. (ENG., Illus.). 192p. 39.95 (978-1-55407-525-6(4)); pap. 24.95 (978-1-55407-781-6(8)) Firefly Bks., Ltd.
Liebenberg, Elri & Demhardt, Imre Josef, eds. History of Cartography: International Symposium of the ICA Commission 2010. 2011. (Lecture Notes in Geoinformation & Cartography Ser.). (ENG., Illus.). ix, 303p. 129.00 (978-3-642-19087-2(1), 3642190871) Springer.
Macleod, David I., ed. Mapping in Michigan & the Great Lakes Region. 2007. (ENG., Illus.). 375p. (C). 69.95 (978-0-87013-807-2(3)) Michigan State Univ. Pr.
Manners, Ian. European Cartographers & the Ottoman World, 1500-1750: Maps from the Collection of O. J. Sopranos. 2010. (Oriental Institute Museum Publications). (ENG., Illus.). 144p. (C). 44.95 (978-1-885923-75-2(9)) Oriental Institute of the Univ. of Chicago, The.
McCorquodale, Duncan & Kessler, Fritz C. Mapping America: Exploring the Continent. 2010. (ENG., Illus.). 240p. 45.00 (978-1-907317-08-8(2)) Black Dog Publishing Ltd. GBR. Dist: Perseus Distribution.
Metailie, Georges, ed. Graphics & Text in the Production of Technical Knowledge in China: The Warp & the Weft. 2007. (Sinica Leidensia Ser.). (Illus.). 772p. (978-90-04-16063-7(9)) BRILL.
Peter Barber, Tom Harper. Magnificent Maps: Power, Propaganda & Art. 2012. (Illus.). 176p. pap. 24.95 (978-0-7123-5093-8(4)) British Library, The GBR. Dist: Chicago Distribution Ctr.
Petto, Christine Marie. When France Was King of Cartography: The Patronage & Production of Maps in Early Modern France. 2007. (Toposophia Ser.). (ENG., Illus.). 232p. 73.50 (978-0-7391-1440-7(9)) Lexington Bks.
Rees, Tony. Arc of the Medicine Line: Mapping the World's Largest Undefended Border Across the Western Plains. 2007. (Illus.). 384p. (978-1-55365-278-6(9)) D&M Pubs. Inc.
—Arc of the Medicine Line: Mapping the World's Longest Undefended Border Across the Western Plains. 2008. (ENG., Illus.). 426p. 29.95 (978-0-8032-1791-1(9)) Univ. of Nebraska Pr.
Riffenburgh, Beau. The Men Who Mapped the World: The Treasures of Cartography. 2011. (ENG., Illus.). 96p. 39.95 **(978-1-84732-877-9(6))** Carlton Bks., Ltd. GBR. Dist: Sterling Publishing Co., Inc.
Schramm, Manuel. Digitale Landschaften: Pallas Athene - 30. 2009. (Pallas Athene. Beitrage zur Universitats- und Wissenschaftsgeschichte Ser.). (GER., Illus.). 212p. (C). 54.00 (978-3-515-09346-0(X)) Steiner, Franz Verlag Wiesbaden GmbH DEU. Dist: Brown, David Bk. Co., The.
Schulten, Susan. Mapping the Nation: History & Cartography in Nineteenth-Century America. 2012. (ENG., Illus.). 272p. 45.00 **(978-0-226-74068-3(4))** Univ. of Chicago Pr.
Schwartz, Seymour I. Putting America on the Map: The Story of the Most Important Graphic Document in the History of the United States. 2007. (ENG., Illus.). 1p. 29.98 (978-1-59102-513-9(3)) Prometheus Bks., Pubs.
Scott, Anne M., et al. European Perceptions of Terra Australis. 2012. (Illus.). 334p. 124.95 **(978-1-4094-2605-9(X))** Ashgate Publishing Co.
Short, John Rennie. Cartographic Encounters: Indigenous Peoples & the Exploration of the New World. 2009. (ENG., Illus.). 224p. 45.00 (978-1-86189-436-6(8)) Reaktion Bks., Ltd. GBR. Dist: Chicago Distribution Ctr.

Short, John Rennie. Korea: A Cartographic History. 2012. (ENG., Illus.). 160p. 45.00 (**978-0-226-75364-5(6)**) Univ. of Chicago Pr.

Stachurski, Richard. Longitude by Wire: Finding North America. 2009. (Illus.). 264p. (978-1-57003-801-3(5)) Univ. of South Carolina Pr.

Talbert, Richard J. A. & Unger, Richard W. Cartography in Antiquity & the Middle Ages: Fresh Perspectives, New Methods. 2008. (Technology & Change in History Ser.). 352p. (C). (978-90-04-16663-9(7)) BRILL.

van Egmond, Marco. Covens & Mortier: A Map Publishing House in Amsterdam, 1685-1866. 2009. (Utrecht Studies in the History of Cartography Ser.). 600p. 240.00 (978-90-6194-220-7(9)) HES & DE GRAAF Pubs. BV NLD. Dist: Oak Knoll Pr.

Viles, Donald M. Hidden Heritage of New Spain. 2006. (Illus.). 220p. per. 15.95 (978-1-892076-25-0(X)) Dancing Moon Pr.

Virga, Vincent. Cartographia: Mapping Civilizations. 2007. (ENG., Illus.). 272p. 60.00 (978-0-316-99766-9(8)) Little Brown & Co.

Whitfield, Peter. Image of the World: 20 Centuries of World Maps. rev. ed. 2010. (ENG., Illus.). 144p. pap. 30.00 (978-0-7123-5069-1(6)) British Library, The GBR. Dist: Chicago Distribution Ctr.

Wigal, Donald. Historic Maritime Maps, 1290-1699. 2007. (ENG., Illus.). 255p. 39.95 (978-1-85995-693-9(9)) Parkstone International GBR. Dist: Ingram Pub. Services.

Wigen, Kären. A Malleable Map: Geographies of Restoration in Central Japan, 1600-1912. 2010. (Asia: Local Studies / Global Themes Ser.). (ENG., Illus.). 340p. 45.00 (978-0-520-25918-8(1)) Univ. of California Pr.

Wigen, Kären. A Malleable Map: Geographies of Restoration in Central Japan, 1600-1912. 2012. (Asia: Local Studies / Global Themes Ser.). (ENG., Illus.). 340p. pap. 34.95 (**978-0-520-27276-7(5)**) Univ. of California Pr.

Woodward, David. The History of Cartography Vol. 3, Pt. 1: Cartography in the European Renaissance. 2007. (History of Cartography Ser.). (Illus.). 1120p. 200.00 (978-0-226-90733-8(3)) Univ. of Chicago Pr.

—The History of Cartography Vol. 3, Pt. 2: Cartography in the European Renaissance. 2007. (History of Cartography Ser.). (Illus.). 1152p. 200.00 (978-0-226-90734-5(1)) Univ. of Chicago Pr.

Wooldridge, William C. Mapping Virginia: From the Age of Exploration to the Civil War. 2012. (**978-0-8139-3267-5(X)**); (ENG., Illus.). 392p. (gr. 17). 200.00 (**978-0-8139-3268-2(8)**) Univ. Pr. of Virginia.

CARTOGRAPHY—JUVENILE LITERATURE

Gonzales, Doreen. Are We There Yet? Using Map Scales. 2008. (Map Mania Ser.). (ENG.). 24p. (gr. 1-2). pap. 41.70 (978-1-4296-2883-9(9), First Facts) Capstone Pr., Inc.

CARTOMANCY

see Fortune-Telling

CARTONS

see Paper Coatings

CARTOONING

Abe, Yoshitoshi. Yoshitoshi Abe Lain Illustration Limited Edition. 2006. (Illus.). 144p. (YA). 39.95 (978-1-56970-880-4(0)) Digital Manga Publishing.

Abel, Jessica & Madden, Matt. Mastering Comics: Drawing Words & Writing Pictures Continued. 2012. (ENG., Illus.). 336p. (YA). pap. 34.99 (**978-1-59643-617-6(4)**, First Second Bks.) Roaring Brook Pr.

Acosta, Robert & Espinosa, Rod. How to Draw Chibi Pocket Manga. 2009. (Illus.). 144p. pap. 14.95 (978-0-9816647-0-5(9)) Antarctic Pr., Inc.

Adams, Neal, illus. Neal Adams by Design. deluxe ed. 2009. (ENG.). 192p. 39.99 (978-1-4012-1917-8(9)) DC Comics.

Altabe, Joan. Cartooning Behind the Scenes. 2011. 280p. pap. 15.99 (978-1-59092-374-0(X)) Orchard House Pr.

Amberlyn, J. C. Drawing Manga Animals, Chibis, & Other Adorable Creatures. 2009. (ENG., Illus.). 160p. pap. 21.99 (978-0-8230-9533-9(9)) Watson-Guptill Pubns., Inc.

Baugh, Bryan. Swords & Sorcery! How to Draw Fantastic Fantasy Adventure Comics. 2007. (ENG., Illus.). 144p. pap. 19.95 (978-0-8230-1666-2(8)) Watson-Guptill Pubns., Inc.

Bishop, Franklin. The Cartoonist's Bible: An Essential Reference for the Practicing Artist. 2009. (Quarto Book Ser.). (ENG., Illus.). 192p. spiral bd. 14.99 (978-0-7858-2085-7(X), 078582085X, Chartwell) Book Sales, Inc.

Brunetti, Ivan. Cartooning: Philosophy & Practice. 2011. (Illus.). 88p. pap. 13.00 (978-0-300-17099-3(8)) Yale Univ. Pr.

Buckler, Rich. How to Draw Dynamic Comic Books, 1 vol. 2007. (ENG., Illus.). 128p. 34.95 (978-1-934331-07-1(4)); per. 19.95 (978-1-887591-95-9(8)) Vanguard Productions.

Buhle, Paul, ed. Jews & American Comics: An Illustrated History of an American Art Form. 2008. (ENG., Illus.). 198p. 29.95 (978-1-59558-331-4(9)) New Pr., The.

Byrne, John. Cartooning: Create Your Own World of Cartoons, Caricatures, Comic Strips & Manga. 2009. (Collins Need to Know? Ser.). (ENG., Illus.). 192p. pap. 15.95 (978-0-00-726392-9(9)) HarperCollins Pubs. Ltd. GBR. Dist: Independent Pubs. Group.

Byrne, John M. Cartooning: The Best One-Stop Guide to Drawing Cartoons, Caricatures, Comic Strips, & Manga. 2008. 192p. pap. 16.95 (978-0-06-147794-2(X), HarperPerennial) HarperCollins Pubs.

Camara, Sergi & Duran, Vanessa. Art of Drawing Manga. 2007. (SPA & ENG., Illus.). 192p. pap. 17.95 (978-1-4027-4706-9(3)) Sterling Publishing Co., Inc.

Capullo, Greg. Art of Greg Capullo. 2007. 160p. pap. 24.99 (978-1-58240-839-2(4)) Image Comics.

Celli, Dan. "sir, Is This Where I Catch the Cellitoons?" 2011. 144p. 29.99 (**978-1-4568-9442-9(0)**) Xlibris Corp.

Cheeseman-Meyer, Jason. Vanishing Point: Perspective for Comics from the Ground Up. 2007. (ENG., Illus.). 128p. pap. 19.99 (978-1-58180-954-1(9), Impact) F&W Media, Inc.

Cogeval, Guy, et al. Walt Disneys Wunderbare Welt und Ihre Wurzeln in der Europäischen Kunst. 2008. (GER., Illus.). 304p. (C). 63.00 (978-3-7774-4375-1(1)) Hirmer Verlag GmbH DEU. Dist: Brown, David Bk. Co., The.

Comickers Magazine Staff. Comickers Art No. 1: Tools & Techniques for Drawing Amazing Manga. 2008. (ENG., Illus.). 128p. pap. 24.99 (978-0-06-144153-0(8), Collins Design) HarperCollins Pubs.

—Comickers Art No. 2: Create Amazing Manga Characters. 2008. (ENG., Illus.). 128p. pap. 24.95 (978-0-06-145254-3(8), Collins Design) HarperCollins Pubs.

—Comickers Coloring Book. 2008. (ENG.). 144p. pap. 18.95 (978-0-06-124204-5(7), Collins Design) HarperCollins Pubs.

Cowan, Finlay. Fantasy Artist's Pocket Reference Dragons & Beasts. 2008. (ENG., Illus.). 224p. 19.99 (978-1-60061-050-9(1), Impact) F&W Media, Inc.

Crilley, Mark. Mastering Manga with Mark Crilley: 30 drawing lessons from the creator of Akiko. 2012. (ENG., Illus.). 128p. pap. 22.99 (**978-1-4403-0931-1(0)**, Impact) F&W Media, Inc.

Danner, Alexander & Withrow, Steven. Character Design for Graphic Novels. 2007. (Character Design Library). (ENG., Illus.). 192p. pap. 29.95 (978-0-240-80902-1(5), Focal Pr.) Elsevier Science & Technology Bks.

Darvas, Lou. You Can Draw Cartoons. 2011. 160p. 41.95 (**978-1-258-09774-5(5)**) Literary Licensing, LLC.

Doran, Colleen. Manga Pro Superstar Workshop: How to Create & Sell Comics & Graphic Novels. 2007. (ENG., Illus.). 128p. pap. 19.99 (978-1-58180-985-5(9), Impact) F&W Media, Inc.

Dunn, Ben. How to Draw Manga Pocket Manga Volume 4. 2008. (Illus.). 144p. pap. 12.95 (978-0-9797719-8-9(6)) Antarctic Pr., Inc.

—How to Draw Manga Pocket Manga Volume 5. 2009. (Illus.). 144p. pap. 12.95 (978-0-9801255-6-6(1)) Antarctic Pr., Inc.

—How to Draw Vampires. 2010. 128p. pap. 19.99 (978-0-9841107-6-6(3)) Antarctic Pr., Inc.

—How to Draw Vampires Pocket Manga. 2011. (Illus.). 128p. pap. 12.99 (978-0-9843375-8-3(X)) Antarctic Pr., Inc.

Espinosa, Rod. How to Draw Steampunk Pocket Manga. 2012. 128p. pap. 14.95 (**978-0-9837934-0-3(9)**) Antarctic Pr., Inc.

Fairrington, Brian & Dummies Press Staff. Drawing Cartoons & Comics for Dummies. 2009. (ENG., Illus.). 368p. pap. 19.99 (978-0-470-42683-8(7), For Dummies) Wiley, John & Sons, Inc.

Fingeroth, Danny. How to Create Comics from Script to Print. 2010. (Illus.). 108p. pap. 15.95 (978-1-893905-60-3(8)) TwoMorrows Publishing.

Ford, Noel, et al. Draw Cartoons: Basic Techniques*cartoons & Strips*exercises. 2006. (Illus.). 96p. pap. (978-1-84537-417-4(7)) New Holland Pubs., Ltd. GBR. Dist: Sterling Publishing Co., Inc.

Garvin, John, ed. The Landon School of Illustrating & Cartooning: 1922 Facsimile Edition. 2008. (Illus.). 246p. per. 21.95 (978-0-9785946-0-2(6)) Enchanted Images.

Gianni, Gary. Prince Valiant Page. 2008. (Illus.). 112p. 29.95 (978-1-933865-04-1(0)) Flesk Pubns.

Go Office. More How to Draw Manga Vol. 2: Penning Characters. 128p. pap. (978-4-88996-146-1(1)) Graphic-Sha JPN. Dist: Diamond Comic Distributors, Inc.

Graphic-Sha. How to Draw Manga: Sketching Manga-Style Volume 5 - Sketching Sports Basics: Sketching Manga-Style Volume 5 - Sketching Sports Basics. 2008. 200p. pap. 29.99 (978-4-7661-1915-2(0)) Graphic-Sha JPN. Dist: Diamond Bk. Distributors.

Hamernik, Harry. Cartoon 360: Secrets to Drawing Cartoon People. 2010. (ENG., Illus.). 128p. pap. 19.99 (978-1-60061-913-7(4), Impact) F&W Media, Inc.

—Cartoonimals: How to Draw Amazing Cartoon Animals. 2008. (ENG., Illus.). 128p. pap. 19.99 (978-1-60061-114-8(1), Impact) F&W Media, Inc.

—Face Off: How to Draw Amazing Caricatures & Comic Portraits. 2006. (ENG., Illus.). 128p. pap. 19.99 (978-1-58180-759-2(7), Impact) F&W Media, Inc.

Hart, Chris. Cartooning: The Ultimate Character Design Book. 2008. (ENG., Illus.). 131p. (J). (gr. 5-13). pap. 19.95 (978-1-933027-42-5(8), Hart, Chris Bks.) Sixth&Spring Bks.

—Manga Mania: Chibi Sketchbook. 2007. (Manga Mania Ser.). (ENG., Illus.). 144p. (J). (gr. 5-12). 12.95 (978-1-933027-31-9(2), Hart, Chris Bks.) Sixth&Spring Bks.

—Manga Mania: Fantasy Sketchbook. 2007. (Manga Mania Ser.). (ENG., Illus.). 144p. (J). (gr. 5-12). 12.95 (978-1-933027-33-3(9), Hart, Chris Bks.) Sixth&Spring Bks.

Hart, Christopher. Cartoon Cute Animals: How to Draw the Most Irresistible Creatures on the Planet. 2010. (ENG., Illus.). 160p. pap. 21.99 (978-0-8230-8556-9(2)) Watson-Guptill Pubns., Inc.

—Drawing Shape by Shape: Create Cartoon Animals, Characters & More with Circles, Squares & Triangles. 2012. (ENG., Illus.). 192p. (J). (gr. -1-4). spiral bd. 14.95 (**978-1-936096-41-1(2)**, Hart, Chris Bks.) Sixth&Spring Bks.

—Humongous Book of Cartooning. 2009. (ENG., Illus.). 224p. pap. 21.99 (978-0-8230-5036-9(X)) Watson-Guptill Pubns., Inc.

—Manga for the Beginner: Everything You Need to Start Drawing Right Away! 2008. (ENG., Illus.). 192p. pap. 21.95 (978-0-8230-3083-5(0)) Watson-Guptill Pubns., Inc.

—Manga for the Beginner Chibis: Everything You Need to Start Drawing the Super-Cute Characters of Japanese Comics. 2010. (ENG., Illus.). 192p. pap. 21.99 (978-0-8230-1488-0(6)) Watson-Guptill Pubns., Inc.

—Manga for the Beginner Shoujo: Everything You Need to Start Drawing the Most Popular Style of Japanese Comics. 2010. (ENG., Illus.). 192p. pap. 21.99 (978-0-8230-3329-4(5)) Watson-Guptill Pubns., Inc.

—Manga Mania Magical Girls & Friends: How to Draw the Super-Popular Action Fantasy Characters of Manga. 2006. (Manga Mania Ser.). (ENG., Illus.). 144p. pap. 19.95 (978-0-8230-2968-6(9)) Watson-Guptill Pubns., Inc.

—Manga Mania Occult & Horror: How to Draw the Elegant & Seductive Characters of the Dark. 2007. (ENG., Illus.). 144p. pap. 19.95 (978-0-8230-1422-4(3)) Watson-Guptill Pubns., Inc.

—Simplified Anatomy for the Comic Book Artist: How to Draw the New Streamlined Look of Action-Adventure Comics! 2007. (ENG., Illus.). 160p. pap. 19.95 (978-0-8230-4773-4(3)) Watson-Guptill Pubns., Inc.

Hissey, Ivan. How to Draw Cartoons: A step-by-step guide with 1000 Illustrations. 2011. (ENG., Illus.). 160p. pap. 19.99 (978-1-84476-954-4(2)) Anness Publishing GBR. Dist: National Bk. Network.

Hissey, Ivan & Tappenden, Curtis. How to Draw Digital Cartoons: A Step-by-Step Guide with 200 Illustrations - from Getting Started to Advanced Techniques, with 70 Practical Exercises & Projects. 2011. (ENG., Illus.). 96p. pap. 16.99 (978-1-84476-989-6(5)) Anness Publishing GBR. Dist: National Bk. Network.

—The Practical Encyclopedia of Cartooning: Learn to Draw Cartoons Step by Step With Over 1500 Illustrations. 2009. (ENG., Illus.). 256p. 35.00 (978-0-7548-1897-7(7)) Anness Publishing GBR. Dist: National Bk. Network.

Hissey, Ivan, et al. The Complete Step-by-Step Guide to Drawing Cartoons, Manga & Anime: Expert Techniques & Projects, Shown in More Than 2000 Illustrations. 2012. (ENG., Illus.). 512p. 29.99 (**978-0-7548-2373-5(3)**) Anness Publishing GBR. Dist: National Bk. Network.

Hodgson, Jon. Fantasy Art for Beginners. 2009. (ENG., Illus.). 128p. pap. 22.99 (978-1-60061-342-5(X)) David & Charles Pubs. GBR. Dist: F&W Media, Inc.

Home Room Staff. Samurai & Ninja Action Scene Collection. 2007. (Illus.). 176p. (YA). per. 24.99 (978-4-7661-1742-4(5)) Graphic-Sha JPN. Dist: Diamond Bk. Distributors.

Hooks, Ed. Acting for Animators. 3rd ed. 2011. (ENG., Illus.). 192p. 100.00 (978-0-415-58023-6(4)); pap. 31.95 (978-0-415-58024-3(2)) Routledge.

Hughes, David. Walking the Dog. 2011. (ENG., Illus.). 304p. 39.95 (978-0-224-08229-7(9)) Random Hse. GBR. Dist: Independent Pubs. Group.

Hutchison, David, et al. How to Draw Manga, Vol. 3. 2008. (How to Draw Manga Ser.). (Illus.). 144p. pap. 12.95 (978-0-9797719-1-0(9)) Antarctic Pr., Inc.

Ikari Studio Staff. Erotic Manga: Draw Like the Experts. 2006. (ENG., Illus.). 384p. pap. 25.99 (978-0-06-089322-4(2), Collins Design) HarperCollins Pubs.

—The Monster Book of Manga: Girls. 2008. (ENG., Illus.). 384p. pap. 25.99 (978-0-06-153794-3(2), Collins Design) HarperCollins Pubs.

—Monster Book of Manga - Boys. 2010. (ENG.). 384p. pap. 25.99 (978-0-06-173298-0(2), Collins Design) HarperCollins Pubs.

Ikari Studio Staff, creator. Fairies & Magical Creatures: Draw Like the Experts. 2007. (ENG., Illus.). 384p. pap. 25.99 (978-0-06-124203-8(9), Collins Design) HarperCollins Pubs.

James, Andrew & Li, Yishan. One Million Manga Figures: Over One Million Characters to Create & Color. 2010. (ENG.). 128p. 19.99 (978-0-7407-9755-2(7)) Andrews McMeel Publishing.

Jones, Richard & Santillan, Jorge. Manga Monsters. 2012. (Learn to Draw Manga Ser.). (ENG.). 32p. (J). (gr. 4-6). pap. 11.75 (**978-1-4488-7947-2(7)**); (Illus.). lib. bdg. 26.50 (**978-1-4488-7876-5(4)**) Rosen Publishing Group, Inc., The. (PowerKids Pr.).

Jordan, Andre. Heaven Knows I'm Miserable Now. 2009. (ENG.). 256p. pap. 13.99 (978-0-06-154730-0(1), HarperPerennial) HarperCollins Pubs.

Kamikaze Factory Studio. Shojo Manga: Pop & Romance. 2011. (ENG., Illus.). 352p. pap. 25.99 (978-0-06-202351-3(9), Collins Design) HarperCollins Pubs.

Kane, Bob, creator. Batman: The Dailies 1943-1946. 2007. (ENG., Illus.). 544p. 20.00 (978-1-4027-4717-5(9)) Sterling Publishing Co., Inc.

Khoury, George. The Extraordinary Works of Alan Moore: Indispensable Edition: Indispensable Edition. 2009. 240p. pap. 29.95 (978-1-60549-009-0(1)) TwoMorrows Publishing.

Kitchen, Alexa. Drawing Comics Is Easy! Except When It's Hard. 2006. (Illus.). 176p. 19.95 (978-0-9710080-6-9(X)) Kitchen, Denis Publishing Co.

Kitchen, Denis & Buhle, Paul. The Art of Harvey Kurtzman: The Mad Genius of Comics. 2009. (ENG., Illus.). 256p. 45.00 (978-0-8109-7296-4(4)) Abrams.

Komanoya, Rico. Gothic Lolita Punk: Draw Like the Hottest Japanese Artists. 2009. (ENG.). 176p. pap. 24.99 (978-0-06-114995-5(0), Collins Design) HarperCollins Pubs.

Krainak, Paul. Kartoon Kings: The Graphic Work of Simon Grennan & Christopher Sperandio. 2007. (ENG., Illus.). 120p. 29.95 (978-1-933202-24-2(6)) West Virginia Univ. Pr.

Kubert, Joe. How to Draw from Life, 1 vol. Spurlock, J. David, ed. 2009. (ENG., Illus.). 128p. 34.95 (978-1-934331-15-6(5)); pap. 24.95 (978-1-934331-14-9(7)) Vanguard Productions.

Lawrence, Chris. Legends: the History of Painted Comics HC: The History of Painted Comics HC. 2012. 200p. (YA). 29.99 (978-1-60690-087-1(0), Dynamite Entertainment) Dynamic Forces, Inc.

Lee, Stan. Stan Lee's Complete How to Draw Comics. 2012. (Illus.). 200p. 29.99 (978-1-933305-75-2(4), Dynamite Entertainment) Dynamic Forces, Inc.

Lent, John A. Cartooning in Africa. 2008. (Illus.). 304p. (C). (978-1-57273-553-8(8)); pap. (978-1-57273-554-5(6)) Hampton Pr., Inc.

Lent, John A., ed. Southeast Asian Cartooning. 2012. (ENG., Illus.). 304p. pap. 38.95 (**978-0-87580-678-5(3)**) Northern Illinois Univ. Pr.

Li, Yishan. Faces & Hair: The Pocket Guide to Drawing All Manga Face & Hair Styles. 2010. (Mini Manga Ser.). (ENG., Illus.). 192p. pap. 7.95 (978-1-84448-523-9(4)) Search Pr., Ltd. GBR. Dist: Independent Pubs. Group.

—Hands & Feet: The Pocket Guide to Drawing Hands & Feet from Every Angle. 2010. (Mini Manga Ser.). (ENG., Illus.). 192p. pap. 7.95 (978-1-84448-522-2(6)) Search Pr., Ltd. GBR. Dist: Independent Pubs. Group.

—Manga Females Clip Art: Everything you need to create your own professional-looking manga Artwork. 2009. (ENG.). 128p. 19.99 (978-0-7407-7934-3(6)) Andrews McMeel Publishing.

Locarno Film Festival Staff. Manga Impact: The World of Japanese Animation. 2010. (ENG., Illus.). 304p. pap. 39.95 (978-0-7148-5741-1(6)) Phaidon Pr., Inc.

Longhurst, Terry. Dibujos Comicos. (SPA.). 256p. (978-1-4054-3552-9(6)) Parragon, Inc.

Lunning, Frenchy, ed. Emerging Worlds of Anime & Manga. 2006. (Illus.). 184p. per. 19.95 (978-0-8166-4945-7(6)) Univ. of Minnesota Pr.

Manley, Mike. The Best of Draw! Volume 3, Vol. 3. 2008. (Best of Draw! Ser.). (Illus.). 256p. pap. 29.95 (978-1-893905-91-7(8)) TwoMorrows Publishing.

Marschall, Richard. Mail-Order Geniuses. Bernard, Warren, ed. 2012. (ENG., Illus.). 224p. 28.99 (978-1-60699-453-5(0), 699453) Fantagraphics Bks.

Martin, Dan. See You in the Funny Papers: The Rich Tradition of St. Louis Cartooning. 2008. 128p. pap. 19.95 (978-1-933370-27-9(0)) Reedy Pr.

Martinbrough, Shawn. How to Draw Noir Comics: The Art & Technique of Visual Storytelling. 2007. (ENG., Illus.). 144p. pap. 19.95 (978-0-8230-2406-3(7)) Watson-Guptill Pubns., Inc.

Mason, Andy. What's So Funny? Under the Skin of South African Cartooning. 2011. 256p. pap. 24.95 (978-1-77013-071-5(3)) Double Storey Bks. ZAF. Dist: International Publishers Marketing.

Matsumoto, Mio & Matsumoto, Min. My Diary. 2009. (ENG., Illus.). 200p. 24.95 (978-0-224-08443-7(7)) Random Hse. GBR. Dist: Independent Pubs. Group.

McCloud, Scott. Making Comics: Storytelling Secrets of Comics, Manga & Graphic Novels. 2006. (ENG., Illus.). 272p. pap. 22.99 (978-0-06-078094-4(0), William Morrow Paperbacks) HarperCollins Pubs.

Meadows, Joel & Marshall, Gary. Studio Space. 2008. (Illus.). 320p. pap. 29.99 (978-1-58240-908-5(0)) Image Comics.

More HTDM Vol 1 the Basics of Character Drawing. 114p. pap. (978-4-7661-1336-5(5)) Japan Pubns. (U.S.A.), Inc.

Murdock, Kelly L. Anime Studio: The Official Guide. 2008. (ENG., Illus.). 512p. pap. 39.99 (978-1-59863-432-7(1)) Course Technology.

—Anime Studio 6. 2009. (ENG.). 560p. pap. 39.99 (978-1-4354-5561-0(4)) Course Technology.

Nagatomo, Haruno. Draw Your Own Manga: Honing Your Style, 1 vol. 2007. (Draw Your Own Manga Ser.). (ENG., Illus.). 96p. pap. 19.95 (978-4-7700-3045-0(2)) Kodansha America, Inc.

Nguyen, Tom. Incredible Comics with Tom Nguyen: The Ultimate Guide to Creating Kick-Ass Comic Art. 2007. (ENG., Illus.). 128p. pap. 19.99 (978-1-58180-946-6(8), Impact) F&W Media, Inc.

Nishida, Masaki. Drawing Manga Medieval Castles & Knights. 2009. (How to Draw Manga Ser.). 24p. (gr. 3-3). 47.90 (978-1-61513-441-0(7), PowerKids Pr.) Rosen Publishing Group, Inc., The.

Nolen-Weathington, Eric. Jeff Smith. 2011. 120p. pap. 15.95 (978-1-60549-024-3(5)) TwoMorrows Publishing.

Nolen-Weathington, Eric & Ash, Roger. Modern Masters Volume 19: Mike Ploog. 2008. (Modern Masters Ser.). (Illus.). 120p. pap. 14.95 (978-1-60549-007-6(5)) TwoMorrows Publishing.

Nolen-Weathington, Eric & Field, Tom. Modern Masters Volume 17: Lee Weeks. 2008. 128p. pap. 14.95 (978-1-893905-94-8(2)) TwoMorrows Publishing.

Nolen-Weathington, Eric & Wilson, Nathan. Modern Masters Volume 26: Frazer Irving: Frazer Irving. 2011. 120p. pap. 15.95 (978-1-60549-039-7(3)) TwoMorrows Publishing.

Norman, Dean. The Invisible Bear on Bunchgrass Mountain: And Wally's Woods, Vol. 9. 2010. 240p. pap. 17.00 (978-1-4269-4332-4(6)) Trafford Publishing.

Oda, Eiichiro. One Piece Color Walk Art Book Vol. 2. 2012. (One Piece Ser.). (ENG.). 110p. pap. 19.99 (**978-1-4215-4113-6(0)**) Viz Media.

Okum, David. Manga Martial Arts: Over 50 Basic Lessons for Drawing the World's Most Popular Fighting Style. 2008. (ENG., Illus.). 128p. pap. 19.99 (978-1-60061-029-5(3), Impact) F&W Media, Inc.

Perry, Fred, et al. How to Draw Manga: Next Generation Pocket Manga Volume 1: Next Generation Pocket Manga Volume 1. 2009. (Illus.). 144p. pap. 12.95 (978-0-9816647-8-1(4)) Antarctic Pr., Inc.

Picture Box Inc, creator. Cartoon Workshop/Pig Tales, 1 vol. 2007. (ENG., Illus.). 96p. per. 14.95 (978-0-9789722-0-2(1)) PictureBox, Inc.

Prestel Publishing, creator. Once upon a Time: Walt Disney: The Sources of Inspiration for the Disney Studios. 2007. (Illus.). 353p. 75.00 (978-3-7913-3770-8(X)) Prestel Publishing.

Quarto Publishing, prod. How to Draw Manga Style. 2011. (ENG.). 224p. spiral bd. 14.99 (978-0-7858-2668-2(8), 0785826688, Chartwell) Book Sales, Inc.

Reid, Chris & Kantz, John. How Not to Draw Manga, Vol. 1. 2007. (Illus.). 144p. (YA). pap. 14.95 (978-0-9776424-9-6(6)) Antarctic Pr., Inc.

Rhodes, Michael & Hills, Doug. Manga Studio for Dummies. 2008. (ENG., Illus.). 384p. pap. 24.99 (978-0-470-12986-9(7), For Dummies) Wiley, John & Sons, Inc.

C

Roche, Nick. Transformers: How to Draw Transformers: How to Draw Transformers. 2012. (Illus.). 32p. pap. 4.99 ***(978-1-61377-149-5(5))*** Idea & Design Works, LLC.

Sacks, Terence J. Opportunities in Cartooning & Animation Careers. 2007. (ENG.). 160p. per. 14.95 *(978-0-07-148206-6(7),* 0071482067) McGraw-Hill Cos., The.

Scalera, Buddy. Comic Artist's Photo Reference Men & Boys. 2008. (ENG., Illus.). 144p. pap. 24.99 *(978-1-60061-004-2(8),* Impact) F&W Media, Inc.

Schelly, Bill. Man of Rock: A Biography of Joe Kubert. 2008. (ENG., Illus.). 320p. pap. 19.99 *(978-1-56097-928-9(3),* 56928) Fantagraphics Bks.

Schooner, Carl. Carl Allen Schoner's Big Cartoon Sketchbook. 2007. 408p. pap. 29.95 *(978-1-4116-3792-4(5))* Lulu Enterprises Inc.

Scraper, Katherine, et al. Cartooning 101. 2011. (J). pap. ***(978-1-4509-5322-1(0))*** Benchmark Education Co.

Seelig, Tim & Li, Yishan. The Practical Encyclopedia of Manga: Learn to Draw Manga Step by Step with More than 1500 Illustrations. 2010. (ENG., Illus.). 256p. 35.00 *(978-0-7548-1958-5(2))* Anness Publishing GBR. Dist: National Bk. Network.

Seelig, Tim, et al. How to Draw Digital Manga & Anime. 2012. (ENG., Illus.). 96p. pap. 15.99 ***(978-1-78019-141-6(3))*** Anness Publishing GBR. Dist: National Bk. Network.

Seelig, Timothy & Li, Yishan. How to Draw Manga: A Step-by-Step Guide with over 750 Illustrations: Expert Techniques for Creating Your Own Manga Characters & Stories, with More Than 50 Exercises & Projects. 2012. (ENG., Illus.). 160p. pap. 19.99 ***(978-1-78019-014-3(X))*** Anness Publishing GBR. Dist: National Bk. Network.

Semisow, Inga. Draw Shojo Girls & Bishie Boys. 2011. (ENG., Illus.). 80p. pap. 17.95 *(978-1-84448-529-1(3))* Search Pr., Ltd. GBR. Dist: Independent Pubs. Group.

Shelbourn, Colin. Drawing Cartoons, 1 vol. 2010. (ENG., Illus.). 160p. 34.95 *(978-1-84797-172-2(5))* Crowood Pr., Ltd. GBR. Dist: Independent Pubs. Group.

Silke, Jim. Dames, Dolls, & Gun Molls. 2010. (Illus.). 96p. (YA). pap. 24.99 *(978-1-59582-272-7(0))* Dark Horse Comics.

Simpson, Terry L. Dibujar Comics. (SPA.). 194p. *(978-84-7927-326-2(7))* Robinbk., Ediciones S.L. ESP. Dist: Lectorum Pubns., Inc.

Silva, Jin. Jam Session. 2009. (ENG.). 112p. 19.95 *(978-80-7391-016-7(0),* Art Stock Bks. Ltd/Csi) Continental Sales, Inc.

Smith, Jamie & Helfferich, Deirdre, eds. Cartoon North: Sequential Art in Alaska. 2007. (Illus.). 56p. 12.00 *(978-0-9749221-3-3(7))* Ester Republic Pr.

Smith, Jeff. The Art of Bone. 2007. (Illus.). 200p. 39.95 *(978-1-59307-441-8(7))* Dark Horse Comics.

Southgate, Anna & Sparrow, Keith. Drawing Manga Girls. 2011. 84.30 *(978-1-4488-4806-5(7));* pap. 14.05 *(978-1-4488-4802-7(4));* lib. bdg. 31.95 *(978-1-4488-4798-3(2))* Rosen Publishing Group, Inc., The. (Rosen Central).

Sparrow, Keith. Bishoujo Manga: Draw Amazing Girls. 2007. (Easel Does It Ser.). (Illus.). 96p. pap. 18.95 *(978-0-06-113932-1(7),* Collins Design) HarperCollins Pubs.

Sparrow, Keith. Mega Manga. 2011. (Illus.). 288p. pap. 19.95 ***(978-1-84448-387-7(8))*** Search Pr., Ltd. GBR. Dist: Independent Pubs. Group.

Sparrow, Keith & Li, Yishan. Manga Tips: The Pocket Reference to Drawing Manga. 2010. (Mini Manga Ser.). (ENG., Illus.). 192p. pap. 7.95 *(978-1-84448-520-8(X))* Search Pr., Ltd. GBR. Dist: Independent Pubs. Group.

—Mecha Manga: The Pocket Guide to Drawing all Manga Robots & Machines. 2010. (Mini Manga Ser.). (ENG., Illus.). 192p. pap. 7.95 *(978-1-84448-521-5(8))* Search Pr., Ltd. GBR. Dist: Independent Pubs. Group.

Starkings, Richard, et al. Tim Sale: Black & White. rev. exp. ed. 2008. (Illus.). 272p. 39.99 *(978-1-58240-880-4(7))* Image Comics.

Steelriver Studio Staff. Mangaka America: Manga by America's Hottest Artists. 2006. (ENG., Illus.). 148p. pap. 24.95 *(978-0-06-113769-3(3),* Collins Design) HarperCollins Pubs.

Stevens, Dave. Brush with Passion: The Art & Life of Dave Stevens. Fenner, Arnie & Fenner, Cathy, eds. 2008. (ENG., Illus.). 288p. 39.95 *(978-1-59929-010-2(3))* Underwood Books.

Style School Volume 4. 2009. (Illus.). 176p. (YA). pap. 16.95 *(978-1-59582-197-3(X))* Dark Horse Comics.

Sweatdrop Studios Staff. Draw Manga. 2006. (ENG., Illus.). 96p. pap. 14.95 *(978-1-84537-416-7(9))* New Holland Pubs., Ltd. GBR. Dist: Sterling Publishing Co., Inc.

Tsukamoto, Hiroyoshi. Manga Matrix: Create Unique Characters Using the Japanese Matrix System. 2006. (ENG., Illus.). 172p. pap. 24.99 *(978-0-06-089341-5(9),* Collins Design) HarperCollins Pubs.

Vacation from Reality: The Art of Anthony Ausgang. 2007. (Illus.). 139p. pap. 34.95 *(978-0-9766325-0-4(0))* 9mm Bks.

Wagner, Matt. The Art of Grendel. Schutz, Diana, ed. 2007. (Illus.). 200p. 39.95 *(978-1-59307-789-1(0))* Dark Horse Comics.

Wilson, Rowland B. Rowland B. Wilson's Trade Secrets: Notes for Cartooning & Animation. Lemieux-Wilson, Suzanne, ed. 2012. (ENG., Illus.). 320p. pap. 39.95 ***(978-0-240-81734-7(6),*** Focal Pr.) Elsevier Science & Technology Bks.

Woodcock, Vincent. How to Draw & Paint Crazy Cartoon Characters: Create Original Characters with Lots of Personality. 2007. (ENG., Illus.). 128p. pap. 21.99 *(978-0-7641-3573-6(2))* Barron's Educational Series, Inc.

Yaniger, Derek. Wildsville: The Art of Derek Yaniger. 2008. (Masters of Lowbrow Ser.). (ENG., Illus.). 112p. 27.95 *(978-0-9558336-3-2(9))* Korero Books LLP GBR. Dist: Independent Pubs. Group.

Zhou, Joanna. Super-Cute Chibis to Draw & Paint: Giant-Sized Fun from a Micro-Sized World. 2011. (ENG.). 128p. pap. 21.99 *(978-0-7641-4677-0(7))* Barron's Educational Series, Inc.

CARTOONING—JUVENILE LITERATURE

Al-Kinani, Maarja. Cartoon. 2010. 100p. pap. 69.50 *(978-1-4461-5949-1(3))* Lulu Enterprises Inc.

Publications International Staff, ed. Disney Phineas & Ferb (Look & Find Soft Cover) 2011. 20p. (J). pap. 5.98 ***(978-1-4508-1454-6(9))*** Publications International, Ltd.

CARTOONISTS

Aamodt, Britt. Superheroes, Strip Artists, & Talking Animals: Minnesota's Contemporary Cartoonists. 2010. (ENG., Illus.). 240p. pap. 29.95 *(978-0-87351-777-5(6))* Minnesota Historical Society Pr.

Alaniz, José. Komiks: Comic Art in Russia. 2010. (ENG., Illus.). 288p. 55.00 *(978-1-60473-366-2(7))* Univ. Pr. of Mississippi.

Amash, Jim & Nolen-Weathington, Eric. Carmine Infantino: Penciler, Publisher, Provocateur. 2010. 224p. pap. 26.95 *(978-1-60549-025-0(3))* TwoMorrows Publishing.

Andrae, Thomas. Creators of the Superheroes. 2011. (Illus.). 224p. pap. 39.99 *(978-1-932563-53-5(9))* Hermes Pr.

Andrae, Tom. Masters of Comic Art. 2007. (Illus.). 224p. (YA). pap. 29.99 *(978-1-932563-95-5(4))* Hermes Pr.

Andre, Thomas, et al. Walt Kelly: The Life & Art of the Creator of Pogo. 2012. (Illus.). 244p. (YA). 49.99 *(978-1-932563-89-4(X))* Hermes Pr.

Assouline, Pierre. Hergé: The Man Who Created Tintin. Ruas, Charles, tr. from FRE. 2009. (ENG.). 288p. pap. 24.95 *(978-0-19-539759-8(2))* Oxford Univ. Pr., Inc.

Assouline, Pierre. Herge: The Man Who Created Tintin, 1 vol. Ruas, Charles, tr. from FRE. 2011. (ENG.). 288p. pap. 15.95 ***(978-0-19-983727-4(9))*** Oxford Univ. Pr., Inc.

Baker, Bill. Michael Avon Oeming on His Work & Career. 2009. (Talking with Graphic Novelists Ser.). 164p. (gr. 9-9). 61.20 *(978-1-60853-260-5(7))* Rosen Publishing Group, Inc., The.

Ball, David M. & Kuhlman, Martha B., eds. The Comics of Chris Ware. 2010. (ENG., Illus.). 288p. 55.00 *(978-1-60473-442-3(6))* Univ. Pr. of Mississippi.

—The Comics of Chris Ware: Drawing Is a Way of Thinking. 2010. (ENG., Illus.). 288p. pap. 28.00 *(978-1-60473-443-0(4))* Univ. Pr. of Mississippi.

Beauchamp, Monte, ed. The Life & Times of R. Crumb: Comments from Contemporaries. 2007. (Illus.). 182p. reprint ed. pap. 18.00 *(978-1-4223-6268-6(X))* DIANE Publishing Co.

Bechdel, Alison. Are You My Mother? 2012. (ENG., Illus.). 304p. 22.00 *(978-0-618-98250-9(7))* Houghton Mifflin Harcourt Trade & Reference Pubs.

Bell, Blake. The World of Steve Ditko. 2008. (ENG.). 220p. 39.99 *(978-1-56097-921-0(6),* 56921) Fantagraphics Bks.

Block, Herbert. Herblock: The Life & Work of the Great Political Cartoonist. Katz, Harry, ed. 2009. (ENG., Illus.). 304p. 35.00 *(978-0-393-06772-9(6),* 6772) Norton, W. W. & Co., Inc.

Bocquet, José-Louis, et al. The Adventures of Herge. 2011. (ENG., Illus.). 64p. 19.95 *(978-1-77046-059-1(4))* Drawn & Quarterly Pubns. CAN. Dist: Macmillan.

Bray, Glenn. The Original Art of Basil Wolverton: From the Collection of Glenn Bray. 2007. (Illus.). 271p. 35.00 *(978-0-86719-687-0(4))* Last Gasp of San Francisco.

Brower, Steven. From Shadow to Light: The Life & Art of Mort Meskin. 2010. (ENG., Illus.). 224p. 39.99 *(978-1-60699-358-3(5),* 699358) Fantagraphics Bks.

Brown, Jeffrey. Little Things: A Memoir in Slices. 2008. (ENG., Illus.). 352p. pap. 14.00 *(978-1-4165-4946-8(3),* Touchstone) Touchstone.

Brown, Jeffrey A. Funny Misshapen Body: A Memoir. 2009. (ENG.). 320p. pap. 16.00 *(978-1-4165-4947-5(1),* Touchstone) Touchstone.

Bryant, Mark. Illingworth's War in Cartoons. 2009. (Illus.). 128p. 29.95 *(978-1-906502-54-6(4))* Grub Street GBR. Dist: Casemate Pubs. & Bk. Distributors, LLC.

Bryant, Mark. The World's Greatest War Cartoonists, 1792-1945: An A-Z. 2011. (Illus.). 192p. 39.95 ***(978-1-908117-08-3(7))*** Grub Street GBR. Dist: Casemate Pubs. & Bk. Distributors, LLC.

Bryant, Robert L. The Thin Black Line: Perspectives on Vince Colletta, Comics' Most Controversial Inker. 2010. (Illus.). 112p. pap. 14.95 *(978-1-60549-028-1(8))* TwoMorrows Publishing.

Buenaventura, Alvin. The Art of Daniel Clowes: Modern Cartoonist. 2012. (ENG., Illus.). 224p. 40.00 ***(978-1-4197-0208-2(4))*** Abrams.

Cebulski, C. B., et al. X-Factor - Second Coming, Vol. 10. 2011. (ENG., Illus.). 112p. (YA). (gr. 8-17). pap. 14.99 *(978-0-7851-4369-7(6))* Marvel Worldwide, Inc.

Cetaka, Natubhai Mistri. Kalama Ane Kenvasa. 2008. (GUJ., Illus.). viii, 192p. *(978-81-8480-016-6(9))* Gurjar Granthratna Karyalaya.

Chaykin, Howard V. Howard Chaykin: Conversations. Costello, Brannon, ed. 2011. (Conversations with Comic Artists Ser.). (ENG., Illus.). 304p. 40.00 *(978-1-60473-975-6(4))* Univ. Pr. of Mississippi.

Chute, Hillary L. Graphic Women: Life Narrative & Contemporary Comics. 2010. (Gender & Culture Ser.). (ENG., Illus.). 316p. (gr. 17). pap. 26.50 *(978-0-231-15063-7(6))* Columbia Univ. Pr.

Ciment, Gilles & Groensteen, Thierry. 100 Cases de Maîtres: Un Art Graphique, la Bande Dessinée. 2010. (FRE., Illus.). 235p. *(978-2-7324-4140-5(6))* Editions de la Martiniere.

Comickers Magazine Staff. Comickers Art No. 3: Write Amazing Manga Stories. 2008. (ENG., Illus.). 128p. pap. 24.95 *(978-0-06-145207-9(6),* Collins Design) HarperCollins Pubs.

Conrad, Paul. I, Con: The Autobiography of Paul Conrad, Editorial Cartoonist. 2006. (Illus.). 190p. per. 25.00 *(978-1-883318-72-7(6))* Angel City Pr.

Cooper, Dave. Bent. 2010. (ENG., Illus.). 80p. 22.99 *(978-1-60699-378-1(X),* 699378) Fantagraphics Bks.

Covey, Jacob & Ketcham, Hank. Where's Dennis? Chun, Alex & Glines, Shane, eds. 2007. (ENG., Illus.). 200p. pap. 19.95 *(978-1-56097-853-4(8),* 56853) Fantagraphics Bks.

Crumb, Sophie & Crumb, R. Sophie Crumb: Evolution of a Crazy Artist. Kominsky-Crumb, Aline, ed. 2010. (ENG., Illus.). 304p. 350.00 *(978-0-393-08014-8(5),* 8014) Norton, W. W. & Co., Inc.

Crumb, Sophie & Crumb, Robert. Sophie Crumb: Evolution of a Crazy Artist. Kominsky-Crumb, Aline, ed. 2010. (ENG., Illus.). 272p. 27.95 *(978-0-393-07996-8(1),* 7996) Norton, W. W. & Co., Inc.

Davies, Russell. Ronald Searle: A Biography. 2006. (ENG., Illus.). 194p. *(978-1-871136-82-1(2))* Beeties, Chris Ltd.

Delisle, Guy. Burma Chronicles. 2010. (ENG., Illus.). 240p. pap. 16.95 *(978-1-77046-025-6(X))* Drawn & Quarterly Pubns. CAN. Dist: Macmillan.

DePastino, Todd. Bill Mauldin: A Life up Front. 2009. (ENG., Illus.). 384p. pap. 16.95 *(978-0-393-33488-3(0),* 33488) Norton, W. W. & Co., Inc.

Ditko, Steve, et al. The Art of Steve Ditko. 2009. (Illus.). 208p. (YA). 29.99 *(978-1-60010-542-5(4))* Idea & Design Works, LLC.

Doucet, Julie. 365 Days. 2008. (ENG., Illus.). 360p. 29.95 *(978-1-897299-15-9(X))* Drawn & Quarterly Pubns. CAN. Dist: Macmillan.

Duffy, Damian & Jennings, John. Out of Sequence: Underrepresented Voices in American Comics. 2009. (ENG., Illus.). 152p. pap. 25.00 *(978-1-883015-42-8(1))* Krannert Art Museum.

Durham, Dick. Peyton: The World's Greatest Yachting Cartoonist. 2011. (ENG., Illus.). 176p. 25.95 *(978-1-4081-2440-6(8))* A & C Black GBR. Dist: Macmillan.

Eisner, Will. Will Eisner: Conversations. Inge, M. Thomas, ed. 2011. (Conversations with Comic Artists Ser.). (ENG.). 224p. 65.00 *(978-1-61703-126-7(7));* (Illus.). pap. 25.00 *(978-1-61703-127-4(5))* Univ. Pr. of Mississippi.

Evanier, Mark. Kirby: King of Comics. 2008. (ENG., Illus.). 224p. 45.00 *(978-0-8109-9447-8(X))* Abrams.

Farmer, Joyce. Special Exits: A Memoir. 2010. (ENG., Illus.). 208p. 26.99 *(978-1-60699-381-1(X),* 699381) Fantagraphics Bks.

Farr, Michael. The Adventures of Herge: Creator of Tintin. 2008. (Illus.). 128p. 29.95 *(978-0-86719-679-5(3))* Last Gasp of San Francisco.

Feiffer, Jules. Backing into Forward: A Memoir. 2010. (ENG., Illus.). 464p. 30.00 *(978-0-385-53158-0(3),* Talese, Nan A.) Knopf Doubleday Publishing Group.

Fingeroth, Danny. Disguised as Clark Kent: Jews, Comics, & the Creation of the Superhero. 2008. (ENG., Illus.). 216p. pap. 22.95 *(978-0-8264-3014-4(7))* Continuum International Publishing Group, Ltd. GBR. Dist: National Bk. Network.

Fingeroth, Danny & Fingeroth. Disguised as Clark Kent: Jews, Comics, & the Creation of the Superhero. 2007. (ENG., Illus.). 216p. 29.95 *(978-0-8264-1767-1(1))* Continuum International Publishing Group, Ltd. GBR. Dist: National Bk. Network.

Fitzgerald, Paul. Will Eisner & PS Magazine. 2008. (Illus.). 320p. pap. 29.99 *(978-1-932563-01-6(6))* Hermes Pr.

Flemig, Kurt. Karikaturisten-Lexikon. (GER.). XIV, 325p. ***(978-3-11-186496-9(0))*** Saur, K. G. Verlag GmbH & Co.

Getty. Diary of J. J. Grandville. 2010. 57.50 *(978-0-8386-4200-9(4))* Fairleigh Dickinson Univ. Pr.

Getty, Clive F. The Diary of J. J. Grandville & the Missouri Album: The Life of an Opposition Caricaturist & Romantic Book Illustrator in Paris under the July Monarchy. 2010. (ENG.). 57.50 *(978-1-61147-407-7(8))* Fairleigh Dickinson Univ. Pr.

Gianni, Gary. Prince Valiant Page. 2008. (Illus.). 112p. 29.95 *(978-1-933865-04-1(0))* Flesk Pubns.

Gill, Tom. The Misadventures of a Roving Cartoonist: The Lone Ranger's Secret Sidekick. 2008. (Illus.). 246p. 29.95 *(978-1-58985-021-7(1))* Five Star Pubns., Inc.

Goede, Don & Yazdani, Tarssa. Hi, How Are You? The Life, Art, & Music of Daniel Johnston. 2nd rev. ed. 2006. (Illus.). 225p. pap. 24.95 *(978-0-86719-667-2(X))* Last Gasp of San Francisco.

Goldstein, Nancy. Jackie Ormes: The First African American Woman Cartoonist. 2008. (ENG., Illus.). 240p. 40.00 *(978-0-472-11624-9(X))* Univ. of Michigan Pr.

Groth, Gary. The Comics Journal. 2008. (Comics Journal Ser.). (ENG.). No. 291. 216p. pap. 11.99 *(978-1-56097-937-1(2),* 56937)No. 292. 200p. pap. 11.99 *(978-1-56097-938-8(0),* 56938) Fantagraphics Bks.

Halford, Randy. Left Field, Reloaded: More Cartoons by Randy Halford. 2010. 176p. pap. 13.99 *(978-1-4490-7503-3(7))* AuthorHouse.

Haspiel, Dean & Irving, Christopher. Graphic NYC Presents: Dean Haspiel: The Early Years. 2010. (Illus.). 192p. pap. 19.99 *(978-1-60010-825-9(3))* Idea & Design Works, LLC.

Hatfield, Charles. Hand of Fire: The Comics Art of Jack Kirby. 2011. (Great Comics Artists Ser.). (ENG., Illus.). 304p. 65.00 ***(978-1-61703-177-9(1));*** pap. 25.00 ***(978-1-61703-178-6(X))*** Univ. Pr. of Mississippi.

Heatley, David. My Brain Is Hanging Upside Down. 2008. (ENG., Illus.). 128p. 24.95 *(978-0-375-42539-4(X),* Pantheon) Knopf Doubleday Publishing Group.

Hignite, Todd. In the Studio: Visits with Contemporary Cartoonists. 2007. (ENG., Illus.). 320p. pap. 19.95 *(978-0-300-13387-5(1))* Yale Univ. Pr.

Irving, Christopher. Comics Introspective Volume 1: Peter Bagge, Vol. 1. 2007. (Comics Introspective Ser.). (Illus.). 128p. pap. 16.95 *(978-1-893905-83-2(7))* TwoMorrows Publishing.

—Comics Introspective Volume Two: Dean Haspiel. 2008. 128p. pap. 16.95 *(978-1-893905-90-0(X))* TwoMorrows Publishing.

Jennings, John & Duffy, Damian. Black Comix: African American Independent Comics, Art & Culture. 2010. (ENG., Illus.). 176p. 45.00 *(978-0-9841906-5-2(1))* Batty, Mark Pub., LLC.

Jones, Gerard. Men of Tomorrow: Geeks, Gangsters, & the Birth of the Comic Book. (ENG.). 384p. 2009. *(978-1-4379-6721-0(3))* 2008. pap. 15.00 *(978-1-4379-6456-1(7))* DIANE Publishing Co.

Jordan, Andre. Heaven Knows I'm Miserable Now. 2009. (ENG.). 256p. pap. 13.99 *(978-0-06-154730-0(1),* HarperPerennial) HarperCollins Pubs.

Jusko, Joe. Art of Joe Jusko. 2009. 200p. 49.99 *(978-0-9795939-7-0(2))* Desperado Publishing.

Kamagurka. The Holy Kama! 2012. (ENG., Illus.). 896p. 55.00 ***(978-90-5856-386-6(3))*** Stichting Kunstboek Bvba BEL. Dist: National Bk. Network.

Kaplan, Arie. From Krakow to Krypton: Jews & Comic Books. 2008. (ENG., Illus.). 240p. pap. 25.00 *(978-0-8276-0843-6(8))* Jewish Pubn. Society.

Keiji, Nakazawa. Hiroshima: The Autobiography of Barefoot Gen. 2010. (Asian Voices Ser.). (ENG.). 216p. 39.95 *(978-1-4422-0747-9(7))* Rowman & Littlefield Publishers, Inc.

Kirtley, Susan E. & Barry, Lynda. Lynda Barry: Girlhood Through the Looking Glass. 2012. (Great Comics Artists Ser.). (ENG., Illus.). 208p. 65.00 ***(978-1-61703-234-9(4));*** pap. 25.00 ***(978-1-61703-235-6(2))*** Univ. Pr. of Mississippi.

Kitchen, Denis & Buhle, Paul. The Art of Harvey Kurtzman: The Mad Genius of Comics. 2009. (ENG., Illus.). 256p. 45.00 *(978-0-8109-7296-4(4))* Abrams.

Kominsky Crumb, Aline. Need More Love: A Graphic Memoir. 2007. (Illus.). 383p. 30.00 *(978-1-84601-133-7(7))* M Q Pubns. GBR. Dist: Ingram Pub. Services.

Korshikova, Irina & Peskov, Vitalii. Vitaliu Ot Iriny: Pamiati Khudozhnika Vitaliia Peskova. 2007. (RUS., Illus.). 317p. *(978-1-893552-50-0(0))* Mir Collection Publishing Hse.

Koterba, Jeffrey. Inklings. (ENG., Illus.). 272p. 2010. pap. 14.95 *(978-0-547-38650-8(8),* Mariner Bks.) 2009. 25.00 *(978-0-15-101492-7(2))* Houghton Mifflin Harcourt Trade & Reference Pubs.

Kushner, Seth, photos by. Leaping Tall Buildings: The Origins of American Comics. 2012. (ENG., Illus.). 240p. 35.00 ***(978-1-57687-591-9(1))*** powerHouse Cultural Entertainment, Inc.

Lasiuta, Tim. Brush Strokes with Greatness: The Life & Art of Joe Sinnott. 2007. (Illus.). 136p. pap. 17.95 *(978-1-893905-72-6(1))* TwoMorrows Publishing.

Lee, Jim & Baker, Bill. Icons: The DC Comics & Wildstorm Art of Jim Lee. 2010. (Illus.). 296p. 39.95 *(978-1-84576-519-4(2),* Titan Bks.) Titan Bks. Ltd. GBR. Dist: Random Hse., Inc.

Lenox, Emi. Emitown. 2011. (Illus.). 400p. (YA). pap. 24.99 *(978-1-60706-318-6(2))* Image Comics.

Lent, John A. Cartooning in Africa. 2008. (Illus.). 304p. (C). *(978-1-57273-553-8(8));* pap. *(978-1-57273-554-5(6))* Hampton Pr., Inc.

Levi, Antonia, et al, eds. Boys' Love Manga: Essays on the Sexual Ambiguity & Cross-Cultural Fandom of the Genre. 2010. (ENG., Illus.). 280p. pap. 39.95 *(978-0-7864-4195-2(X))* McFarland & Co., Inc. Pubs.

Levin, Bob. Most Outrageous: The Trials & Trespasses of Dwaine Tinsley & Chester the Molester. 2008. (ENG., Illus.). 200p. pap. 19.99 *(978-1-56097-919-7(4),* 56919) Fantagraphics Bks.

Mark Schultz: Various Drawings Volume One. 2006. (Illus.). 47p. pap. 19.95 *(978-0-9723758-6-3(4))* Flesk Pubns.

Marshall, Monica. Joe Sacco. 2009. (Library of Graphic Novelists Ser.). 112p. (gr. 7-12). 63.90 *(978-1-60853-655-9(6))* Rosen Publishing Group, Inc., The.

Martell, Nevin. Looking for Calvin & Hobbes: The Unconventional Story of Bill Watterson & His Revolutionary Comic Strip. (ENG., Illus.). 272p. 2010. pap. 16.95 *(978-1-4411-0685-8(5))* 2009. 27.95 *(978-0-8264-2984-1(X))* Continuum International Publishing Group, Ltd. GBR. Dist: National Bk. Network.

Martin, Dan. See You in the Funny Papers: The Rich Tradition of St. Louis Cartooning. 2008. 128p. pap. 19.95 *(978-1-933370-27-9(0))* Reedy Pr.

Masters of Comic Art. 2007. 224p. (YA). 49.99 *(978-1-932563-96-2(2))* Hermes Pr.

McCay, Winsor. Early Works. 2007. (Winsor Mccay: Early Works). 200p. Vol. 9. (Illus.). pap. 19.95 *(978-1-933160-07-8(1))* Vol. 10. pap. 19.95 *(978-1-933160-08-5(X))* Devil's Due Digital, Inc. - A Checker Digital Co.

McLaughlin, Jeff, ed. Stan Lee: Conversations. 2007. (ENG., Illus.). 237p. 50.00 *(978-1-57806-984-2(X));* per. 22.00 *(978-1-57806-985-9(8))* Univ. Pr. of Mississippi.

Meadows, Joel & Marshall, Gary. Studio Space. 2008. (Illus.). 320p. 49.99 *(978-1-58240-909-2(9));* pap. 29.99 *(978-1-58240-908-5(0))* Image Comics.

Michaelis, David. Schulz & Peanuts: A Biography. 2007. (ENG., Illus.). 672p. 34.95 *(978-0-06-621393-4(2))* HarperCollins Pubs.

Micheal Turner Tribute. 2008. 80p. (YA). pap. 8.99 *(978-0-9774821-7-7(0))* Aspen MLT, Inc.

Morrow, John. Kirby Five-Oh! Celebrating 50 Years of the King of Comics. 2008. (Illus.). 168p. pap. 19.95 *(978-1-893905-89-4(6))* TwoMorrows Publishing.

Mullaney, Dean. Caniff HC. 2011. (Illus.). 360p. 49.99 *(978-1-60010-920-1(9))* Idea & Design Works, LLC.

Nadel, Dan. Art in Time: Unknown Comic Book Adventures, 1940-1980. 2010. (ENG., Illus.). 304p. 40.00 *(978-0-8109-8824-8(0))* Abrams.

Nolen-Weathington, Eric. Jeff Smith. 2011. 120p. pap. 15.95 *(978-1-60549-024-3(5))* TwoMorrows Publishing.

—Modern Masters Volume 12: Michael Golden. 2007. (Modern Masters Ser.: Vol. 12). (Illus.). 120p. pap. 14.95 *(978-1-893905-74-0(8))* TwoMorrows Publishing.

—Modern Masters Volume 14: Frank Cho, Vol. 14. 2010. (Modern Masters Ser.). (Illus.). 120p. pap. 15.95 *(978-1-893905-84-9(5))* TwoMorrows Publishing.

—Modern Masters Volume 15: Mark Schultz. 2008. (Modern Masters Ser.: Vol. 15). (Illus.). 128p. pap. 14.95 *(978-1-893905-85-6(3))* TwoMorrows Publishing.

—Modern Masters Volume 16: Mike Allred. 2008. (Modern Masters Ser.). (Illus.). 120p. pap. 14.95 *(978-1-893905-86-3(1))* TwoMorrows Publishing.

—Modern Masters Volume 2: George Perez. 2007. (Modern Masters Ser.: Vol. 2). 128p. pap. 14.95 *(978-1-893905-25-2(X))* TwoMorrows Publishing.

—Nick Cardy: Behind the Art. 2008. 128p. 34.95 *(978-1-893905-99-3(3))* TwoMorrows Publishing.

Nolen-Weathington, Eric & Ash, Roger. Modern Masters Volume 19: Mike Ploog. 2008. (Modern Masters Ser.). (Illus.). 120p. pap. 14.95 *(978-1-60549-007-6(5))* TwoMorrows Publishing.

Nolen-Weathington, Eric & Field, Tom. Modern Masters Volume 17: Lee Weeks. 2008. 128p. pap. 14.95 *(978-1-893905-94-8(2))* TwoMorrows Publishing.

Nolen-Weathington, Eric & Wilson, Nathan. Modern Masters Volume 26: Frazer Irving: Frazer Irving. 2011. 120p. pap. 15.95 *(978-1-60549-039-7(3))* TwoMorrows Publishing.

O'Connell, Jean Gould. Chester Gould: A Daughter's Biography of the Creator of Dick Tracy. 2007. (ENG., Illus.). 231p. 45.00 *(978-0-7864-2825-0(2))* McFarland & Co., Inc. Pubs.

Oriol, Anja Llorella, et al. Color & Layout: From Asparagus White to Burnt Olive. 2008. (Illus.). 256p. 45.00 *(978-0-06-153790-5(X)*, Collins Design) HarperCollins Pubs.

Otfinoski, Steven. Stan Lee: Comic Book Genius. 2006. (Great Life Stories Ser.). (ENG., Illus.). 112p. (J). (gr. 6-8). lib. bdg. 30.50 *(978-0-531-13873-1(9))* Scholastic Library Publishing.

Ovcharova, Maria. Beshkov & Altmaier: Fragments of a Friendship 1934-1955. 2006. (Illus.). 83p. 69.50 *(978-954-463-024-9(4))* Bulgarian Bestseller - National Museum of Bulgarian Books & Polygraphy BGR. Dist: Coronet Bks.

Parille, Ken & Cates, Isaac, eds. Daniel Clowes: Conversations. 2010. (Conversations with Comics Artists Ser.). (ENG., Illus.). 240p. 50.00 *(978-1-60473-440-9(X))*; pap. 22.00 *(978-1-60473-441-6(8))* Univ. Pr. of Mississippi.

Peck, Brian. John Buscema: Michelangelo of Comics. deluxe ed. 2010. (Illus.). 176p. (YA). 60.00 *(978-1-932563-55-9(5))*; pap. 39.99 *(978-1-932563-50-4(4))* Hermes Pr.

Peeters, Benoit. Hergé, Son of Tintin. Kover, Tina A., tr. from FRE. 2011. (ENG., Illus.). 424p. 29.95 ***(978-1-4214-0454-7(0))*** Johns Hopkins Univ. Pr.

Pendergast, Tom & Pendergast, Sara. U-X-L Graphic Novelists, 3 vols. 2006. (Illus.). lxii, 634p. *(978-1-4144-0441-7(7))*; lxii, 634p. *(978-1-4144-0443-1(3))*; lxii, 634p. *(978-1-4144-0442-4(5))*;Set. (ENG., 720p. 225.00 *(978-1-4144-0440-0(9))* Cengage Gale. (UXL).

Perez, George. Art of George Perez. 2012. (Illus.). 256p. (YA). 49.99 *(978-1-60010-859-4(8))* Idea & Design Works, LLC.

—Art of George Perez S&N Limited Edition. 2012. (Illus.). 256p. (YA). 79.99 *(978-1-60010-860-0(1))* Idea & Design Works, LLC.

Reardon, Michael T. Foxo Reardon. 2008. 260p. pap. 24.95 *(978-1-59393-149-0(2))* BearManor Media.

Reibel, Olivier. La Vie Secrète D'Hergé: Biographie Inattendue. 2010. (FRE.). 484p. *(978-2-84454-638-8(2))* Dervy, Editions.

Ristaino, Marcia R. China's Intrepid Muse. 2009. (ENG.). 176p. pap. 40.00 *(978-1-891640-57-5(7))* Floating World Editions.

Russell, P. Craig. Art of P. Craig Russell. 2010. (Illus.). 256p. 49.99 *(978-0-9795939-1-8(3))* Idea & Design Works, LLC.

Sacco, Kevin. The Plane Story. 2011. (Illus.). 128p. (YA). pap. 19.99 *(978-1-60010-867-9(9))* Idea & Design Works, LLC.

Sadowski, Greg. Harvey Kurtzman. 2006. (Comics Journal Ser.). (ENG., Illus.). 124p. pap. 19.95 *(978-1-56097-755-1(8)*, 56755) Fantagraphics Bks.

Saylor, Harry T. Edgycute: From Neo Pop to Low Brow & Back Again. 2009. (ENG., Illus.). 176p. 45.00 *(978-0-9817805-9-7(8))* Batty, Mark Pub., LLC.

Schelly, Bill. Founders of Comic Fandom: Profiles of 90 Publishers, Dealers, Collectors, Writers, Artists & Other Luminaries of the 1950s And 1960s. 2010. (ENG., Illus.). 236p. pap. 40.00 *(978-0-7864-4347-5(2))* McFarland & Co., Inc. Pubs.

—Man of Rock: A Biography of Joe Kubert. 2008. (ENG., Illus.). 320p. pap. 19.99 *(978-1-56097-928-9(3)*, 56928) Fantagraphics Bks.

Schrag, Ariel. Awkward & Definition: The High School Comic Chronicles of Ariel Schrag. 2008. (ENG., Illus.). 144p. pap. 16.95 *(978-1-4165-5231-4(6)*, Touchstone) Touchstone.

Schulz, Charles M. My Life with Charlie Brown. Inge, M. Thomas, ed. 2010. (ENG., Illus.). 144p. 25.00 *(978-1-60473-447-8(7))* Univ. Pr. of Mississippi.

Schumacher, Michael. Will Eisner: A Dreamer's Life in Comics. 2010. (ENG., Illus.). 368p. 28.00 *(978-1-60819-013-3(7))* Bloomsbury Publishing.

Shelbourn, Colin. Drawing Cartoons, 1 vol. 2010. (ENG., Illus.). 160p. 34.95 *(978-1-84797-172-2(5))* Crowood Pr., Ltd. GBR. Dist: Independent Pubs. Group.

Simon, Joe. Joe Simon: My Life in Comics - The Illustrated Autobiography. 2011. (ENG., Illus.). 256p. 24.95 *(978-1-84576-930-7(9)*, Titan Bks.) Titan Bks. Ltd. GBR. Dist: Random Hse., Inc.

Sliva, Jiri. Jam Session. 2009. (ENG.). 112p. 19.95 *(978-80-7391-016-7(0)*, Art Stock Bks. Ltd/Csi) Continental Sales, Inc.

Soper, Kerry D. We Go Pogo: Walt Kelly, Politics, & American Satire. 2012. (Great Comics Artists Ser.). (ENG.). 272p. 65.00 ***(978-1-61703-283-7(2))***; pap. 25.00 ***(978-1-61703-284-4(0))*** Univ. Pr. of Mississippi.

Spiegelman, Art. Breakdowns: Portrait of the Artist as a Young %@&*! 2008. (ENG., Illus.). 72p. 27.50 *(978-0-375-42395-6(8)*, Pantheon) Knopf Doubleday Publishing Group.

—MetaMaus: A Look Inside a Modern Classic, Maus. 2011. (ENG., Illus.). 300p. 35.00 *(978-0-375-42394-9(X)*, Pantheon) Knopf Doubleday Publishing Group.

Spurgeon, Tom & Covey, Jacob. Comics As Art: We Told You So. 2007. (Illus.). 192p. 28.95 *(978-1-56097-738-4(8))* Fantagraphics Bks.

Starkings, Richard, et al. Tim Sale: Black & White. rev. exp. ed. 2008. (Illus.). 272p. 39.99 *(978-1-58240-880-4(7))* Image Comics.

Steadman, Ralph. The Joke's Over: Bruised Memories: Gonzo, Hunter S. Thompson, & Me. 2007. (ENG., Illus.). 416p. pap. 15.00 *(978-0-15-603250-6(3)*, Mariner Bks.) Houghton Mifflin Harcourt Trade & Reference Pubs.

Stevens, Alec. E. J. Pace: Christian Cartoonist. 2007. (Illus.). 250p. pap. 19.95 *(978-0-9778214-1-9(2))* Calvary Comics.

Stevens, Dave. Dave Stevens: the Complete Sketchbook Collection: The Complete Sketchbook Collection. 2011. 256p. 50.00 ***(978-1-61377-037-5(5))*** Idea & Design Works, LLC.

Szasz, Ferenc Morton. Atomic Comics: Cartoonists Confront the Nuclear World. 2012. E-Book ***(978-0-87417-879-1(7))***; (Illus.). 200p. 34.95 ***(978-0-87417-874-6(6))*** Univ. of Nevada Pr.

Taylor, Anthony & Trim, Mike. The Future Was Fab: The Art of Mike Trim. 2006. (Illus.). 160p. 75.00 *(978-1-932563-83-2(0))* Hermes Pr.

Thomas, John Rhett. The Marvel Art of Joe Quesada. 2010. (ENG., Illus.). 240p. (YA). (gr. 8-17). 49.99 *(978-0-7851-4629-2(6))* Marvel Worldwide, Inc.

Thomas, Roy & Amash, Jim. John Romita... & All That Jazz! 2007. 208p. 44.95 *(978-1-893905-76-4(4))*; (Illus.). 192p. pap. 24.95 *(978-1-893905-75-7(6))* TwoMorrows Publishing.

Thurber, James. My Life & Hard Times. 17.95 *(978-0-8488-0338-4(8))* Amereon LTD.

Tolvanen, Juhani. Moomin Every Day: Tove & Lars Jansson & the Creation of the Moomin Comic Strip. 2012. (ENG., Illus.). 136p. 22.95 ***(978-1-77046-043-0(8))*** Drawn & Quarterly Pubns. CAN. Dist: Macmillan.

Töpffer, Rodolphe, et al. Correspondance Complète. 2009. (HISTOIRE des IDeES et CRITIQUE LITTeRAIRE Ser.). (FRE., Illus.). 528p. (C). pap. 96.00 *(978-2-600-01296-6(0))* Droz, Librairie CHE. Dist: Brown, David Bk. Co., The.

Toth, Alex, et al. Genius, Isolated: the Life & Art of Alex Toth: The Life & Art of Alex Toth. 2011. (Illus.). 328p. 49.99 *(978-1-60010-828-0(8))* Idea & Design Works, LLC.

Vess, Charles. Drawing down the Moon: The Art of Charles Vess. 2011. 212p. pap. 29.99 ***(978-1-59582-765-4(X))*** Dark Horse Comics.

Ware, Chris. Uninked: Paintings, Sculpture & Graphic Works by Five Cartoonists. 2007. *(978-0-910407-59-5(2))* Phoenix Art Museum.

Weisman, Mary-Lou. Al Jaffee's Mad Life: A Biography. 2010. (ENG., Illus.). 240p. 27.99 *(978-0-06-186448-3(X))* HarperCollins Pubs.

—Al Jaffee's Mad Life: A Biography. 2011. (ENG., Illus.). 240p. pap. 16.99 *(978-0-06-186449-0(8))* HarperCollins Pubs.

Wertz, Julia. Drinking at the Movies. 2010. (ENG., Illus.). 192p. pap. 15.00 *(978-0-307-59183-8(2)*, Three Rivers Pr.) Crown Publishing Group.

Williams, Paul & Lyons, James, eds. The Rise of the American Comics Artist: Creators & Contexts. 2010. (ENG., Illus.). 256p. 55.00 *(978-1-60473-791-2(3))*; pap. 28.00 *(978-1-60473-792-9(1))* Univ. Pr. of Mississippi.

Wilson, Tom. Zig-Zagging: Loving Madly, Losing Badly - How Ziggy Saved My Life. 2009. (ENG., Illus.). 212p. 17.95 *(978-0-7573-0793-5(0))* Health Communications, Inc.

Witek, Joseph, ed. Art Spiegelman: Conversations. 2007. (ENG., Illus.). 318p. 50.00 *(978-1-934110-11-9(6))*; per. 22.00 *(978-1-934110-12-6(4))* Univ. Pr. of Mississippi.

Wootton, David & Nickerson, Fiona. The Definitive Thelwell. 2010. (ENG., Illus.). 104p. pap. *(978-1-905738-14-4(5))* Beetles, Chris Ltd.

Wright, Doug. The Collected Doug Wright Vol. 1: Canada's Master Cartoonist. Mackay, Seth & Mackay, Brad, eds. 2009. (ENG., Illus.). 240p. 39.95 *(978-1-897299-52-4(4))* Drawn & Quarterly Pubns. CAN. Dist: Macmillan.

Yeagle, Dean. Melange. 2011. (ENG., Illus.). 160p. 40.00 *(978-2-35574-076-3(3))* Editions Akileos FRA. Dist: SCB Distributors.

Yoe, Craig. Krazy Kat & the Art of George Herriman: A Celebration. 2011. (ENG., Illus.). 224p. 29.95 *(978-0-8109-9594-9(8))* Abrams.

CARTOONS

see Caricatures and Cartoons

CARTOONS, ANIMATED

see Animated Films

CARTRIDGES

Barnes, Frank C. Cartridges of the World: A Complete & Illustrated Reference for over 1500 Cartridges. Bodinson, Holt, ed. 12th ed. 2009. (ENG., Illus.). 568p. pap. 32.99 *(978-0-89689-936-0(5)*, Gun Digest) Krause Pubns.

Behn, Jack. 45-70 Rifles. 2008. (Stackpole Classic Gun Book Ser.). (ENG., Illus.). 160p. 16.95 *(978-0-8117-0446-5(7))* Stackpole Bks.

Bredsten, George B. Handgun Bullet Stopping Power: Beyond the Hyperbole of Cartridge Advocacy. 2008. (Illus.). 212p. pap. *(978-1-926585-03-1(8)*, CCB Publishing) CCB Publishing.

Bussard, Michael. Ammo Encyclopedia. Allen, John B. et al, eds. 2nd ed. 2010. (Illus.). 840p. pap. 29.95 *(978-1-936120-01-7(1))* Blue Bk. Pubns., Inc.

Bussard, Mike, et al. Ammo Encyclopedia. 3rd ed. 2011. (Illus.). 912p. pap. ***(978-1-936120-10-9(0))*** Blue Bk. Pubns., Inc.

Giles, Ray T. & Shuey, Daniel L. 100 Years of Winchester Cartridge Boxes, 1856-1956. 2006. (Illus.). 352p. 69.95 *(978-0-7643-2541-0(8))* Schiffer Publishing, Ltd.

Harding, C. W. The Birmingham Cartridge Manufact. 2012. (ENG., Illus.). 288p. 75.00 ***(978-1-84689-064-2(0))*** Quiller Publishing, Ltd. GBR. Dist: Stackpole Bks.

—British Cartridge Manufacturers, Loaders & Retailers Including Ironmongers & Gunsmiths. 2012. (ENG., Illus.). 288p. 75.00 ***(978-1-84689-145-8(0))*** Quiller Publishing, Ltd. GBR. Dist: Stackpole Bks.

Hoyem, George A., ed. Cartridge Catalogues. Date not set. (Illus.). 480p. 95.00 *(978-0-939683-17-8(2))* Armory Pubns.

Keith, Elmer. Big Game Rifles & Cartridges. 2011. 184p. 42.95 ***(978-1-258-01433-9(5))*** Literary Licensing, LLC.

Krasnickas, Frank. Cartridges of South Coventry. 2006. (ENG., Illus.). 432p. per. 49.95 *(978-1-4120-8949-4(2))* Trafford Publishing.

Nonte, George C. The Home Guide to Cartridge Conversions. rev. ed. 24.95 *(978-0-88227-005-0(2))* Gun Room Pr.

Rutterford, Ken. Cartridge Drawings Now & Then from the Pen of Ken. 2007. (Illus.). 196p. per. *(978-1-84549-213-7(7))* arima publishing.

Rutterford, Ken J. Stampings on Shotshells. 2011. 394p. pap. ***(978-1-84549-475-9(X))*** arima publishing.

CARTS

see Carriages and Carts

CARTULARIES

see also Archives; Charters; Diplomatics

Hey, David, et al. A Monastic Community in Local Society: The Beauchief Abbey Cartulary. 2012. (Camden Fifth Ser.). (Illus.). viii, 304p. 80.00 ***(978-1-107-01646-0(0))*** Cambridge Univ. Pr.

Vitali, David. Mit dem Latein am Ende? Volkssprachlicher Einfluss in lateinischen Chartularen aus der Westschweiz. 2008. (Lateinische Sprache und Literatur des Mittelalters Ser.). (LAT, FRE & GER., Illus.). 643p. *(978-3-03910-866-4(2))* Lang, Peter.

CARTWRIGHT, ALEXANDER JOY, 1820-1892

Martin, Jay. Live All You Can: Alexander Joy Cartwright & the Invention of Modern Baseball. 2009. (ENG., Illus.). 168p. (gr. 17). 22.95 *(978-0-231-14794-1(5))* Columbia Univ. Pr.

Nucciarone, Monica. Alexander Cartwright: The Life Behind the Baseball Legend. 2009. (ENG., Illus.). 326p. 27.95 *(978-0-8032-3353-9(1))* Univ. of Nebraska Pr.

CARTWRIGHT, JOHN, 1740-1829

Cartwright, John. The Life & Correspondence of Major Cartwright. 2009. 194p. pap. *(978-1-150-62616-6(X))*; 264p. pap. *(978-0-217-09062-9(1))* Books LLC.

Osborne, John W. John Cartwright. 2008. (Conference on British Studies Biographical Ser.). (ENG.). 188p. pap. 31.99 *(978-0-521-08814-5(3))* Cambridge Univ. Pr.

CARTWRIGHT, PETER, 1785-1872

Cartright, Peter. Autobiography of Peter Cartright: The Backwoods Preacher. Strickland, W. P., ed. (Illus.). 525p. reprint ed. lib. bdg. 98.00 *(978-0-7222-4828-7(8))* Library Reprints, Inc.

Cartwright, Peter. Autobiography of Peter Cartwright. 2009. 260p. 24.99 *(978-1-103-11556-3(1))*; pap. 18.99 *(978-1-103-11555-6(3))* BiblioBazaar.

—Autobiography of Peter Cartwright. 2009. 296p. pap. *(978-0-217-18008-5(6))* Books LLC.

—Autobiography of Peter Cartwright, the Backwoods Preacher. 2009. 286p. pap. *(978-1-151-17051-4(8))* Books LLC.

—Autobiography of Peter Cartwright, the Backwoods Preacher. 2006. 532p. per. 29.99 *(978-1-4255-5933-5(6))* MPublishing.

Cartwright, Peter & Strickland, William Peter. Autobiography of Peter Cartwright. 2010. 340p. pap. 31.75 *(978-1-144-32360-6(6))* BiblioBazaar.

CARUSO, ENRICO, 1873-1921

Fucito, Salvatore. Caruso & the Art of Singing. 2009. 86p. pap. *(978-1-4590-3836-3(3))* Books LLC.

CARVER, GEORGE WASHINGTON, 1864?-1943

Beene, Gary. The Seeds We Sow: Kindness That Fed a Hungry World. 2011. (ENG.). pap. 26.95 *(978-0-86534-788-5(3))* Sunstone Pr.

Clark, Glenn. Man Who Talks with the Flowers. pap. 4.95 *(978-0-910924-09-2(0))* Macalester Park Publishing Co., Inc.

—The Man Who Talks with the Flowers: The Intimate Life Story of Dr. George Washington Carver. 2010. 68p. pap. 10.95 *(978-1-57898-877-8(2))* Martino Publishing.

—The Man Who Talks with the Flowers: The Intimate Life Story of Dr. George Washington Carver. 2011. 40p. pap. 6.49 ***(978-1-61720-418-0(8))*** Wilder Pubns., Ltd.

—The Man Who Talks with the Flowers-the Intimate Life Story of Dr George Washington Carver. 2011. 68p. pap. 6.95 ***(978-1-61427-066-9(X))*** Martino Publishing.

George Washington Carver National Monument (Mo.) Staff & George Washington Carver Birthplace Association Staff, contrib. by. George Washington Carver: His Life & Legacy. 2010. pap. *(978-1-57864-628-9(6))* Donning Co. Pubs.

Kremer, Gary R. George Washington Carver: A Biography, 1 vol. 2011. (Greenwood Biographies Ser.). (Illus.). 202p. 35.00 *(978-0-313-34796-2(4)*, GR4796); E-Book *(978-0-313-34797-9(2)*, Greenwood Pr.) Greenwood Publishing Group, Inc.

Mayberry, B. D., ed. A George Washington Carver Handbook. 2007. 92p. pap. 15.95 *(978-1-60306-016-5(2))* NewSouth, Inc.

Smith, Alvin D. & Edmunds, Henry E. George Washington Carver: Man of God. 2011. 76p. 36.95 ***(978-1-258-06113-5(9))*** Literary Licensing, LLC.

CARVER, GEORGE WASHINGTON, 1864?-1943—JUVENILE LITERATURE

Macceca, Stephanie & Doak, Robin S. George Washington Carver: Agriculture Pioneer. 2010. (Mission: Science Biographies Ser.). (ENG.). 40p. (gr. 5-6). lib. bdg. 27.99 *(978-0-7565-4305-1(3)*, Exploring Science) Compass Point Bks.

CARVER, RAYMOND, 1938-1988

Amir, Ayala. The Visual Poetics of Raymond Carver. (ENG.). 2011. 238p. pap. 34.99 ***(978-0-7391-3922-6(3))*** 2010. (Illus.). 230p. 65.00 *(978-0-7391-3921-9(5))* Lexington Bks.

Bethea, Arthur F. Technique & Sensibility in the Fiction & Poetry of Raymond Carver. 2009. 334p. 39.95 *(978-0-415-80354-0(3))* Routledge.

Jingqiong, Zhou. Raymond Carver's Short Fiction in the History of Black Humor. 2006. 158p. (C). 60.95 *(978-0-8204-8620-8(5))* Lang, Peter Publishing, Inc.

Miltner, Robert & Kleppe, Sandra Lee, eds. New Paths to Raymond Carver: Critical Essays on His Life, Fiction, & Poetry. 2008. 208p. 39.95 *(978-1-57003-724-5(8))* Univ. of South Carolina Pr.

Sklenicka, Carol. Raymond Carver: A Writer's Life. (ENG., Illus.). 592p. 2010. pap. 20.00 *(978-0-7432-6246-0(8))* 2009. 35.00 *(978-0-7432-6245-3(X))* Scribner. (Scribner).

CARVER, WILLIAM F., 1840-1927

Thorp, Raymond W. Spirit Gun of the West: The Story of Doc W. F. Carver. 2011. 268p. 47.95 ***(978-1-258-04411-4(0))*** Literary Licensing, LLC.

CARVING (DECORATIVE ARTS)

see also Bone Carving; Glyptics; Ice Carving; Ivory Carving; Scrimshaws; Stone Carving; Wood-Carving

Arenski, Jay, et al. Swiss Carvings: Art of the Black Forest. 2007. (ENG., Illus.). 184p. *(978-1-85149-493-4(6)*, Antique Collectors Club Dist) Antique Collectors' Club.

Benson, Peter. The Art of Carving Netsuke. 2010. 168p. pap. 27.95 *(978-1-56523-512-0(6))* Fox Chapel Publishing Co., Inc.

Bisco, Steve. Twenty Decorative Carving Projects in Period Styles. 2011. (ENG.). 192p. pap. 24.95 *(978-1-56523-535-9(5))* Fox Chapel Publishing Co., Inc.

Bowers, Bill & Wolfe, Tom. Carving Golf Ball Spirits. 2008. (Illus.). 64p. pap. 14.99 *(978-0-7643-3148-0(5))* Schiffer Publishing, Ltd.

Carving Melon Sculptures. 2008. (Illus.). 110p. mass mkt. 16.95 *(978-0-9629277-6-8(7))* Lynch, Lonnie.

Carving Watermelon Sculptures: Watermelon Carving. 2008. (Illus.). 110p. mass mkt. *(978-0-9629277-7-5(5))* Lynch, Lonnie.

Clift, Jon & Cuthbert, Amanda. How to Grow Your Food: A Guide for Brand-New Gardeners. 2011. (ENG., Illus.). 132p. pap. 12.95 *(978-1-900322-68-3(4))* Green Bks. GBR. Dist: Chelsea Green Publishing.

Daisey, Rosalyn. Carving Animals — Bunnies & Chipmunks. 2011. (Illus.). 256p. 45.00 ***(978-0-7643-3885-4(4))*** Schiffer Publishing, Ltd.

de Guitaut, Caroline. Fabergé's Animals: A Royal Farm in Miniature. 2010. (Illus.). 119p. 24.95 *(978-1-905686-12-4(9))* Royal Collection Enterprises Ltd. GBR. Dist: Chicago Distribution Ctr.

Hall, Nora. Relief Carving with Nora Hall. 2011. (Illus.). 112p. pap. 24.99 ***(978-0-7643-3938-7(9)***, Schiffer Publishing Ltd) Schiffer Publishing, Ltd.

Harde, Michael. Contemporary Gunning Decoys. 2007. (ENG., Illus.). 44p. spiral bd. 24.95 *(978-1-881982-53-1(X))* Stackpole Magazines.

Jubb, Robert. Carving Japanese Netsuke for Beginners. 2011. (ENG., Illus.). 176p. pap. 21.95 *(978-1-86108-693-8(8))* Guild of Master Craftsman Pubns., Ltd. GBR. Dist: Sterling Publishing Co., Inc.

Lynch, Lonnie T. Carving Melon Sculptures: The Art of Turning Ordinary Melons into Elegant Sculptures. 2008. 116p. pap. 16.95 *(978-1-4389-1501-2(2))* AuthorHouse.

Miller, Tony & Hui, Humphrey K. F. Elegance in Relief: Carved Porcelain from Jingdezhen of the 19th to early 20th Centuries. (CHI & ENG., Illus.). 358p. 55.00 *(978-962-7101-75-8(3))* Art Media Resources, Inc.

Moore, Harris W. Chip Carving. 2010. 58p. pap. 17.75 *(978-1-148-99870-1(5))* BiblioBazaar.

—Chip Carving. 56p. 2010. 31.95 *(978-1-161-98279-4(5))* 2009. pap. 16.95 *(978-1-104-63241-0(1))* Kessinger Publishing, LLC.

Nagashima, Hiroshi. The Decorative Art of Japanese Food Carving: Elegant Garnishes for All Occasions, 1 vol. 2009. (ENG., Illus.). 112p. 24.95 *(978-4-7700-3087-0(8))* Kodansha America, Inc.

Pumpkins (cust) 2007. 15.95 *(978-0-8118-6092-5(2))* Chronicle Bks. LLC.

Pye, Chris. Carving on Turning. 2009. (ENG.). 166p. pap. 24.95 *(978-1-56523-404-8(9))* Fox Chapel Publishing Co., Inc.

Quick, Lelande & Leiper, Hugh. Gemcraft: How to Cut & Polish Gemstones. 2007. (ENG.). 192p. per. 22.95 *(978-0-548-44063-6(8))* Kessinger Publishing, LLC.

C

Rottger, Ernst. Creative Wood Design. 2007. 108p. per. 19.95 *(978-0-548-38629-3(3))* Kessinger Publishing, LLC.
Scariano, Nicolo. Sculpting Cane Handles. 2008. (Illus.). 64p. pap. 14.95 *(978-0-7643-2823-7(9))* Schiffer Publishing, Ltd.
Sparrow, Andy. The Complete Caving Manual. 2010. (ENG., Illus.). 192p. 36.95 *(978-1-84797-146-3(6))* Crowood Pr., Ltd. GBR. Dist: Independent Pubs. Group.
The Spirit of Carving Clocks. 2008. (Illus.). 52p. pap. 20.00 *(978-0-9800283-0-0(2))* Zelt, William O.
Stevens, Jim. Powder Horns: Fabrication & Decoration. 2010. (Illus.). 176p. pap. 29.99 *(978-0-7643-3489-4(1))* Schiffer Publishing, Ltd.
Varner, Gary. Strangely Wrought Creatures of Life Dea. 2007. 160p. pap. 15.95 *(978-1-4303-0261-2(5))* Lulu Enterprises Inc.
Woodard, Greg & Robinette, Kurt. Workbench Projects: Lifesize Merlin. 2007. (ENG.). 40p. (J). spiral bd. 24.95 *(978-1-881982-36-4(X))* Stackpole Magazines.
Yu, Ming. Chinese Jade. 3rd ed. 2011. (Introductions to Chinese Culture Ser.). (ENG., Illus.). 152p. pap. 19.99 ***(978-0-521-18684-1(6))*** Cambridge Univ. Pr.

CARVING (MEAT, ETC.)

Hertzmann, Peter. Knife Skills ILLUS. 2007. 29.95 *(978-0-7930-6178-5(4))* Norton, W. W. & Co., Inc.
—Knife Skills Illustrated: A User's Manual. 2007. (ENG., Illus.). 384p. 29.95 *(978-0-393-06178-9(7),* 6178) Norton, W. W. & Co., Inc.
Lincoln, D. A. & Lincoln, Mary Johnson. Carving & Serving. 2008. (Cooking in America Ser.). (ENG.). 60p. per. 9.95 *(978-1-4290-1255-3(2))* Applewood Bks.
Lincoln, Mary Johnson. Carving & Serving. 2009. 48p. pap. *(978-0-217-45308-0(2))* Books LLC.
—Carving & Serving. 2008. 56p. pap. 16.95 *(978-1-4367-9800-6(0))* Kessinger Publishing, LLC.
Wright, Clarissa Dickson & Scott, Johnny. Sunday Roast: Cooking & Carving. 2010. (ENG., Illus.). 192p. pap. 22.95 *(978-1-85626-957-5(4))* Cathie, Kyle Ltd. GBR. Dist: National Bk. Network.

CARY, JOYCE, 1888-1957

Bloom, Robert. The Indeterminate World: A Study of the Novels of Joyce Cary. 2011. 232p. 46.95 ***(978-1-258-08588-9(7))*** Literary Licensing, LLC.

CARY, LOTT, 1780-1828

Thomas, Perry. From Slave to Governor: The Unlikely Life of Lott Cary. 2010. (ENG.). 228p. (YA). pap. 12.50 *(978-0-9786567-9-9(2))* Parson Place Pr., LLC.

CARY, LUCIUS

see Falkland, Lucius Cary, Viscount, 1610?-1643

CARYOCINESIS

see Karyokinesis

CASALS, PABLO, 1876-1973

Casals, Pablo. Joys & Sorrows. Date not set. 316p. 24.95 *(978-0-8488-2231-6(5))* Amereon LTD.
Siblin, Eric. The Cello Suites: J. S. Bach, Pablo Casals, & the Search for a Baroque Masterpiece. (ENG.). 336p. 2011. pap. 15.95 *(978-0-8021-4524-6(8),* Grove Pr.) 2009. 24.00 *(978-0-8021-1929-2(8),* Atlantic Monthly Pr.) Grove/Atlantic, Inc.

CASANOVA, GIACOMO, 1725-1798

Casanova de Seingalt, Jacques. The Memoirs of Casanova: Venetian Years. 2007. 432p. per. *(978-1-4068-4414-6(4))* Echo Library.
Casanova, Giacomo. History of My Life. Trask, Willard R., tr. from FRE. 2007. (ENG.). 1512p. 37.50 *(978-0-307-26557-9(9),* Everyman's Library) Knopf Doubleday Publishing Group.
—Storia della Mia Vita. *(978-88-8289-028-5(7))* Newton & Compton.
Endore, S. Guy. Casanova the World's Greatest Lover: His Known & Unknown Life. 2007. (ENG.). 418p. 49.95 *(978-0-548-05912-8(8))* Kessinger Publishing, LLC.
Kelly, Ian. Casanova: Actor, Lover, Priest, Spy. (ENG.). 416p. (gr. 12). 2011. 15.95 *(978-1-58542-844-1(2))* 2008. 28.95 *(978-1-58542-658-4(X))* Penguin Group (USA) Inc. (Tarcher).
Nettl, Paul. The Other Casanov: A Contribution to Eighteenth-Century Music & Manners. 2011. 320p. 50.95 ***(978-1-258-07912-3(7))*** Literary Licensing, LLC.
Whibley, Charles. Literary Portraits. 2009. 326p. 36.99 *(978-1-116-99105-5(5))* BiblioBazaar.
—Literary Portraits. 2009. 148p. pap. 19.99 *(978-1-151-21235-1(0))* General Bks. LLC.
Zweig, Stefan. Casanova: A Study in Self-Portraiture. Paul, Eden & Paul, Cedar, trs. from GER. 2009. (ENG.). 160p. pap. 17.95 *(978-1-906548-06-3(4))* Pushkin Pr., Ltd. GBR. Dist: Consortium Bk. Sales & Distribution.
Zweig, Stefan, intro. Casanova, Stendhal, Tolstoy: Adepts in Self-Portraiture, 3. 2012. (ENG.). 410p. pap. 34.95 ***(978-1-4128-4595-3(5))*** Transaction Pubs.

CASAS, BARTOLOME DE LAS, 1474-1566

Castro, Daniel. Another Face of Empire: Bartolomé de Las Casas, Indigenous Rights, & Ecclesiastical Imperialism. 2007. (Latin America Otherwise Ser.). (ENG.). 248p. 79.95 *(978-0-8223-3930-4(7));* per. 22.95 *(978-0-8223-3939-7(0))* Duke Univ. Pr.
Clayton, Lawrence A. Bartolomé de las Casas: A Biography. 2012. (ENG., Illus.). 502p. 75.00 ***(978-1-107-00121-3(8))*** Cambridge Univ. Pr.
Clayton, Lawrence A., ed. Bartolome de Las Casas & the Conquest of the Americas. 2011. (Viewpoints / Puntos de Vista Ser.: 6). (ENG.). 208p. pap. 24.95 *(978-1-4051-9428-0(6));* 90.95 *(978-1-4051-9427-3(8))* Wiley, John & Sons, Inc. (Wiley-Blackwell).
De Las Casas, Bartolome. A Brief Account of the Destruction of the Indies. 2007. (ENG.). 88p. per. *(978-1-4068-4415-3(2))* Echo Library.
—A Brief Account of the Destruction of the Indies. Gordons, Sara, tr. 2011. 108p. pap. ***(978-1-60796-371-4(X))*** Editorial Benei Noaj.
De Las Casas, Bartolome & Gordons, Sara. A Brief Account of the Destruction of the Indies. 2011. 108p. ***(978-1-60796-342-4(6))*** Editorial Benei Noaj.
Friede, Juan & Keen, Benjamin, eds. Bartolome de las Casas in History: Toward an Understanding of the Man & His Work. 2008. 648p. pap. 35.00 *(978-0-87580-987-8(1))* Northern Illinois Univ. Pr.
Hanke, Lewis. Aristotle & the American Indians: A Study in Race Prejudice in the Modern World. 2011. 176p. 42.95 ***(978-1-258-01394-3(0))*** Literary Licensing, LLC.
Helps, Arthur. Life of Las Casas the Apostle of the Ind. 2006. pap. 30.95 *(978-1-4286-3436-7(3))* Kessinger Publishing, LLC.
Merediz, Eyda M. Approaches to Teaching the Writings of Bartolomé de Las Casas. Arias, Santa, ed. 2008. (SPA & ENG.). 37.50 *(978-0-87352-944-0(8));* pap. 19.75 *(978-0-87352-945-7(6))* Modern Language Assn. of America.

CASAUBON, ISAAC, 1559-1614

Grafton, Anthony & Weinberg, Joanna. I Have Always Loved the Holy Tongue: Isaac Casaubon, the Jews, & a Forgotten Chapter in Renaissance Scholarship. 2011. (Carl Newell Jackson Lectures). (Illus.). 392p. 35.00 *(978-0-674-04840-9(7),* Belknap Pr.) Harvard Univ. Pr.
Parenty, Helene. Isaac Casaubon Helleniste: Des studia humanitatis a la Philologie. 2009. (Travaux d'Humanisme et Renaissance Ser.). 488p. (C). 249.00 *(978-2-600-01093-1(9))* Droz, Librairie CHE. Dist: Brown, David Bk. Co., The.
Pattison, Mark. Isaac Casaubon, 1559-1614. 2011. (Cambridge Library Collection - Literary Studies). (ENG.). 552p. pap. 39.99 ***(978-1-108-03487-6(X))*** Cambridge Univ. Pr.

CASCADE RANGE

Beckey, Fred. Cascade Alpine Guide, 3rd Edition: Vol. 3: Rainy Pass to Fraser River. 2009. (ENG.). 416p. pap. 34.95 *(978-1-59485-136-0(0))* Mountaineers Bks., The.
Lat-Kla, Loo Wit & Lat-Kla, Loo-Wit. Gold Hunting in the Cascade Mountains. 2011. 30p. 35.95 ***(978-1-258-07561-3(X))*** Literary Licensing, LLC.
McQuaide, Mike. Day Hike! Central Cascades: The Best Trails You Can Hike in a Day. 2nd ed. 2008. (Day Hike! Ser.). (ENG., Illus.). 304p. pap. 16.95 *(978-1-57061-539-9(X))* Sasquatch Bks.
Rinehart, Mary Roberts. Tenting To-Night. 2007. (ENG.). 124p. per. *(978-1-4065-6280-4(7))* Dodo Pr.
—Tenting To-Night. 2007. (ENG.). 100p. per. *(978-1-4068-3924-1(8))* Echo Library.
Romano, Craig. Day Hiking Central Cascades. 2009. (Day Hiking Ser.). (ENG.). 140p. pap. 18.95 *(978-1-59485-094-3(1))* Mountaineers Bks., The.
—Day Hiking North Cascades: Mount Baker/Mountain Loop Highway/San Juan Islands. 2008. (Day Hiking Ser.). (ENG., Illus.). 320p. pap. 18.95 *(978-1-59485-048-6(8))* Mountaineers Bks., The.

CASCADING STYLE SHEETS

Here are entered works on a set of standard stylistic rules specified by the World Wide Web Consortium to describe how HTML documents are presented to users.

Andrew, Rachel & Yank, Kevin. Everything You Know about CSS Is Wrong! 2008. (ENG., Illus.). 130p. pap. 29.95 *(978-0-9804552-2-9(7))* SitePoint Pty, Ltd. AUS. Dist: Ingram Pub. Services.
Baker, Donna L. CSS for Web Designers Only. 2006. (ENG., Illus.). 278p. pap. 39.99 *(978-0-471-78867-6(8),* Wiley) Wiley, John & Sons, Inc.
Bartlett, Kynn & Montoya, Chris. CSS. 3rd ed. 2013. (Sams Teach Yourself Ser.). (ENG., Illus.). 450p. pap. 34.99 *(978-0-672-33102-2(0))* Sams.
Batschelet, Margaret W. XHTML/CSS Basics for Web Writers. 2006. (ENG., Illus.). 304p. (C). per. 77.40 *(978-0-13-172014-5(7),* Prentice Hall) Prentice Hall PTR.
Bowers, Michael. Pro CSS & HTML Design Patterns. 2007. (Expert's Voice in Web Development Ser.). (ENG.). 494p. pap. 44.99 *(978-1-59059-804-7(0))* Apress L. P.
Bowers, Michael, et al. Pro HTML5 & CSS3 Design Patterns. 2011. (ENG.). 532p. pap. 44.99 *(978-1-4302-3780-8(5))* Apress L. P.
Budd, Andy, et al. CSS Mastery: Advanced Web Standards Solutions. 2nd ed. 2009. (ENG., Illus.). 384p. pap. 39.99 *(978-1-4302-2397-9(9),* Friends of Ed) Apress L. P.
Casciano, Chris. The CSS Pocket Guide. 2010. (Pocket Guide Ser.). (ENG., Illus.). 288p. pap. 14.99 *(978-0-321-73227-9(8))* Peachpit Pr.
Catlin, Hampton & Catlin, Michael Lintorn. Pragmatic Guide to Sass. 2011. (ENG.). 128p. pap. 25.00 ***(978-1-934356-84-5(0),*** Pragmatic Bookshelf, The) Pragmatic Programmers, LLC, The.
Cederholm, Dan. Bulletproof Web Design: Improving Flexibility & Protecting Against Worst-Case Scenarios with HTML5 & CSS3. 3rd rev. ed. 2011. (Voices That Matter Ser.). (ENG., Illus.). 320p. pap. 44.99 ***(978-0-321-80835-6(5))*** New Riders Publishing.
—Bulletproof Web Design: Improving Flexibility & Protecting Against Worst-Case Scenarios with XHTML & CSS. 2nd rev. ed. 2007. (Voices That Matter Ser.). (ENG., Illus.). 312p. per. 39.99 *(978-0-321-50902-4(1))* New Riders Publishing.
—Handcrafted CSS: Bulletproof Essentials. 2009. (Voices That Matter Ser.). (ENG.). 34.99 *(978-0-321-65812-8(4))* New Riders Publishing.
Cederholm, Dan & Marcotte, Ethan. Handcrafted CSS Pack: More Bulletproof Web Design. 2009. (Voices That Matter Ser.). (ENG., Illus.). 240p. pap. 44.99 *(978-0-321-64338-4(0));* pap. 54.99 *(978-0-321-65853-1(1))* New Riders Publishing.
Clarke, Andy. CSS Artistry: A Web Design Master Class. 2008. (ENG., Illus.). 384p. 99.99 *(978-0-321-58484-7(8))* New Riders Publishing.
—CSS Artistry: A Web Design Master Class: Includes Full-Color Transcending CSS Book & 2 1/2-Hour Inspired CSS DVD Video Training. 2008. (Voices That Matter Ser.). (ENG., Illus.). ix, 371p. 69.99 *(978-0-321-57265-3(3))* New Riders Publishing.
—Designing with CSS for a Beautiful Web, DVD. 2009. (Voices That Matter Ser.). (ENG.). 34.99 *(978-0-321-68013-6(8))* New Riders Publishing.
Clarke, Andy & Holzschlag, Molly E. CSS Artistry: A Web Design Master Class: Includes Full-Color Transcending CSS Book & 2 1/2-Hour Inspired CSS DVD Video Training. 2006. (Voices That Matter Ser.). (ENG., Illus.). 384p. pe. 54.99 *(978-0-321-41097-9(1))* New Riders Publishing.
Collison, Simon. Beginning CSS Web Development: From Novice to Professional. 2006. (Expert's Voice in Web Development Ser.). (ENG., Illus.). 448p. per. 34.99 *(978-1-59059-689-0(7))* Apress L. P.
Collison, Simon, et al. Web Standards Creativity: Innovations in Web Design with XHTML, CSS, & DOM Scripting. 2007. (ENG., Illus.). 288p. per. 49.99 *(978-1-59059-803-0(2),* Friends of Ed) Apress L. P.
Cook, Craig, et al. Foundation HTML5 with CSS3: A Modern Guide & Reference. 2012. (ENG.). 400p. pap. 34.99 ***(978-1-4302-3876-8(3),*** Friends of Ed) Apress L. P.
Course Technology. HTML 5 & CSS Illustrated Complete Review, Pack. 2011. (ENG.). (C). 10.95 *(978-1-111-52785-3(7))* Course Technology.
—HTML, XHTML, & CSS. 2nd ed. 2009. (ENG.). 12.95 *(978-0-538-74605-2(X))* Course Technology.
Cram101 Textbook Reviews. Outlines & Highlights for New Perspectives on Blended Html, Xhtml, & Css by Henry Bojack, Isbn: 9781423906513 1423906519. 2011. 272p. pap. 32.95 ***(978-1-61490-750-3(1))*** Cram101 Inc.
Cram101 Textbook Reviews & Cram101 Textbook Reviews. Outlines & Highlights for New Orleans after the Civil War: Race, Politics, & a New Birth of Freedom by Justin A. Nystrom, ISBN. 2011. 132p. pap. 28.95 ***(978-1-61461-922-2(0))*** Cram101 Inc.
Croft, Jeff, et al. Pro CSS Techniques. 2006. (Expert's Voice Ser.). (ENG., Illus.). 408p. per. 39.99 *(978-1-59059-732-3(X))* Apress L. P.
Crowther, Rob. Quick & Easy Html5 & Css3: A User Friendly Reference Guide. 2012. (ENG.). 325p. pap. 34.99 ***(978-1-935182-89-4(7))*** Manning Pubns. Co.
CSS Site Design. 2006. cd-rom 149.95 ***(978-1-59671-279-9(1))*** Lynda.com, LLC.
Debolt, Virginia. Mastering Integrated HTML & CSS. 2007. (ENG., Illus.). 616p. pap. 39.99 *(978-0-470-09754-0(X),* Sybex) Wiley, John & Sons, Inc.
DeLoach, Scott. CSS to the Point. 2008. 155p. pap. 21.00 *(978-0-615-21213-5(1))* ClickStart, Inc.
Duckett, Jon. Beginning HTML, XHTML, CSS & JavaScript. 2009. (ENG., Illus.). 864p. pap. 34.99 *(978-0-470-54070-1(2),* Wrox) Wiley, John & Sons, Inc.
—HTML & CSS: Design & Build Websites. 2011. (ENG., Illus.). 512p. pap. 29.99 *(978-1-118-00818-8(9),* Wiley) Wiley, John & Sons, Inc.
Felke-Morris, Terry. Basics of Web Design: HTML5 & CSS3. rev. ed. 2011. (ENG., Illus.). 368p. (C). pap. 78.00 *(978-0-13-700338-9(2))* Addison Wesley.
Ford, Jerry Lee, Jr. HTML, XHTML, & CSS for the Absolute Beginner. 2009. (ENG.). 432p. pap. 29.99 *(978-1-4354-5423-1(5))* Course Technology.
Gasston, Peter. The Book of CSS3: A Developer's Guide to the Future of Web Design. 2011. (ENG.). 304p. pap. 34.95 *(978-1-59327-286-9(3))* No Starch Pr., Inc.
Gillenwater, Zoe Mickley. Stunning CSS3: A Project-Based Guide to the Latest in CSS. rev. ed. 2010. (Voices That Matter Ser.). (ENG., Illus.). 320p. pap. 44.99 *(978-0-321-72213-3(2))* New Riders Publishing.
Gillenwater, Zoe Mickley & Gillenwater, Zoe. Flexible Web Design: Creating Liquid & Elastic Layouts with CSS. 2008. (ENG., Illus.). 336p. pap. 44.99 *(978-0-321-55384-3(5))* New Riders Publishing.
Goldstein, Alexis. Learning CSS3 Animations & Transitions: A Hands-on Guide to Animating in CSS3 with Transforms, Transitions, Keyframes, & JavaScript. 2012. (Learning Ser.). (ENG.). 480p. pap. 39.99 ***(978-0-321-83960-2(9))*** Addison Wesley Professional.
Graffam, J. D. CSS for Print Designers. rev. ed. 2011. (ENG., Illus.). 176p. pap. 29.99 *(978-0-321-76588-8(5))* New Riders Publishing.
Grannell, Craig. The Essential Guide to CSS & HTML Web Design. 2007. (ENG., Illus.). 600p. pap. 34.99 *(978-1-59059-907-5(1),* Friends of Ed) Apress L. P.
Griffiths, Patrick. HTML Dog: The Best-Practice Guide to XHTML & CSS. 2006. (ENG., Illus.). 368p. per. 49.99 *(978-0-321-31139-9(6))* New Riders Publishing.
Harrel, Bill & Harrel, William. HTML, CSS, & JavaScript Mobile Development for Dummies. 2011. (ENG.). 432p. pap. 29.99 *(978-1-118-02622-9(5),* For Dummies) Wiley, John & Sons, Inc.
Harris, Andy. HTML, XHTML & CSS All-in-One for Dummies. (ENG., 1080p. 2nd ed. 2010. Illus.). pap. 39.99 *(978-0-470-53755-8(8))* 3rd ed. 2013. pap. 39.99 ***(978-1-118-28938-9(2))*** Wiley, John & Sons, Inc. (For Dummies).
Hart-Davis, Guy. HTML, XTML, & CSS. 2009. (QuickSteps Ser.). (ENG., Illus.). 224p. pap. 19.99 *(978-0-07-163317-8(0),* 0071633170) McGraw-Hill Osborne.
Henick, Ben. HTML & CSS: The Good Parts. 2010. (Animal Guide Ser.). (ENG., Illus.). 352p. pap. 34.99 *(978-0-596-15760-9(6))* O'Reilly Media, Inc.
Hilgraves, Rebekkah & Boumphrey, Frank. HTML5 eLearning Kit for Dummies. 2012. (ENG.). 408p. pap. 39.99 ***(978-1-118-07475-6(0),*** For Dummies) Wiley, John & Sons, Inc.
Hill, Josh & Brannan, James A. Brilliant HTML5 & CSS3. rev. ed. 2011. (ENG., Illus.). 300p. pap. 67.50 *(978-0-273-74712-3(6))* Pearson Education, Ltd. GBR. Dist: Trans-Atlantic Pubns., Inc.
Huddleston, Rob. HTML, XHTML, & CSS: Your Visual Blueprint for Designing Effective Web Pages. 2008. (Wiley Desktop Editions Ser.: 11). (ENG., Illus.). 369p. pap. 29.99 *(978-0-470-27436-1(0),* Visual) Wiley, John & Sons, Inc.
Jacobs, Denise R. CSS Detective Guide: The Tricks for Solving Tough CSS Mysteries. 2010. (ENG., Illus.). 288p. pap. 34.99 *(978-0-321-68394-6(3))* New Riders Publishing.
Kennedy, Antony & de Leon, Inayaili. Pro CSS for High Traffic Websites. 2011. (ENG.). 432p. pap. 49.99 *(978-1-4302-3288-9(9))* Apress L. P.
Kraynak, Joe. The Complete Idiot's Guide to HTML5 & CSS3. 2011. (Complete Idiot's Guide Ser.). (ENG., Illus.). 448p. (gr. 12). 24.95 *(978-1-61564-084-3(3),* Alpha Bks.) Penguin Group (USA) Inc.
Lalwani, Rajesh. Web Widgets with CSS, DOM, JSON & Ajax. 2008. 350p. pap. 39.99 *(978-0-470-24664-1(2),* Wiley) Wiley, John & Sons, Inc.
Lane, Jonathan, et al. Foundation Website Creation with CSS, XHTML, & JavaScript. 2008. (ENG., Illus.). 275p. pap. 34.99 *(978-1-4302-0991-1(7),* Friends of Ed) Apress L. P.
Mandal, Jyotsna Kumar. Algorithmic Design of Compression Schemes & Correction Techniques. 2011. 164p. pap. ***(978-3-8433-9274-7(9))*** Lambert Academic Publishing.
McFarland, David. Css: The Missing Manual. 2nd ed. 2009. (Missing Manual Ser.). (ENG., Illus.). 560p. pap. 34.99 *(978-0-596-80244-8(7),* Pogue Pr.) O'Reilly Media, Inc.
McGrath, Mike. CSS in Easy Steps. 2nd ed. 2009. (In Easy Steps Ser.). (ENG., Illus.). 192p. pap. 14.99 *(978-1-84078-364-3(8))* Computer Step GBR. Dist: Perseus-PGW.
Meersman, Jonathan & Vodnik, Sasha. HTML 5 CSS Illustrated Introductory. 2011. (Illustrated Ser.). (ENG., Illus.). 232p. (C). pap. 51.95 *(978-1-111-52789-1(X))* Course Technology.
Meloni, Julie. Sams Teach Yourself HTML5 & CSS3 in 24 Hours. 9th rev. ed. 2012. (ENG.). 456p. pap. 34.99 ***(978-0-672-33614-0(6))*** Sams.
Meyer, Eric A. Css: The Definitive Guide. 3rd rev. ed. 2006. (ENG., Illus.). 538p. per. 44.99 *(978-0-596-52733-4(0))* O'Reilly Media, Inc.
—CSS Pocket Reference. 4th ed. 2011. (ENG.). 252p. pap. 14.99 *(978-1-4493-9903-0(7))* O'Reilly Media, Inc.
—Smashing CSS. 2010. (Smashing Magazine Book Ser.). (ENG., Illus.). 304p. pap. 44.99 *(978-0-470-68416-0(X),* Wiley) Wiley, John & Sons, Inc.
Mills, Chris. CSS3 Interface Design: Develop & Design. rev. ed. 2012. (ENG.). 320p. pap. 44.99 ***(978-0-321-82372-4(9))*** Peachpit Pr.
Moll, Cameron. Mobile Web Design. 2008. (Illus.). 108p. pap. 19.95 *(978-0-615-18591-0(6))* Moll, Cameron.
Montoya, Chris & Bartlett, Kynn. CSS Fundamentals LiveLessons Bundle. 2009. pap. 69.99 *(978-0-13-704383-5(X))* Prentice Hall PTR.
Moscovitz, Meitar, et al. AdvancED CSS. 2009. (ENG.). 384p. pap. 39.99 *(978-1-4302-1932-3(7),* Friends of Ed) Apress L. P.
Murphy, Christopher & Persson, Nicklas. HTML & CSS Web Standards Solutions: A Web Standardistas' Approach. 2008. (ENG., Illus.). 400p. pap. 39.99 *(978-1-4302-1606-3(9),* Friends of Ed) Apress L. P.
Murphy, Christopher, et al. Beginning HTML5 & CSS3: The Web Evolved. 2012. (ENG.). 450p. pap. 39.99 *(978-1-4302-2874-5(1))* Apress L. P.
Negrino, Tom & Smith, Dori. Styling Web Pages with CSS. 2009. (Visual QuickProject Guide Ser.). (ENG., Illus.). 144p. pap. 24.99 *(978-0-321-55557-1(0))* Peachpit Pr.
Netherland, Wynn, et al. Sass & Compass in Action. 2012. (ENG.). 300p. pap. 44.99 ***(978-1-61729-014-5(9))*** Manning Pubns. Co.
Nixon, Robin. Plug-in CSS 100 Power Solutions. 2011. (ENG., Illus.). 320p. pap. 40.00 *(978-0-07-174876-6(8),* 0071748768) McGraw-Hill Osborne.
Nortown Press. HTML & CSS Easy Web Design. 2007. 200p. per. *(978-0-9737214-8-5(0))* Nortown Pr.
Nortown Press, Mahmood Shanbedi. HTML & CSS Easy Web Design with XHTML Second Edition. 2008. (Illus.). 216p. per. *(978-0-9737214-9-2(9))* Nortown Pr.
Olsson, Tommy & O'Brien, Paul. The Ultimate CSS Reference. 2008. (ENG., Illus.). 440p. 44.95 *(978-0-9802858-5-7(2))* SitePoint Pty, Ltd. AUS. Dist: Ingram Pub. Services.
Powell, Thomas. HTML & CSS. 5th ed. 2010. (ENG., Illus.). 856p. pap. 39.99 *(978-0-07-149629-2(7),* 0071496297) McGraw-Hill Osborne.
Powers, David. The Essential Guide to Dreamweaver CS3 with CSS, Ajax, & PHP. 2007. (Friends of ED Adobe Learning Library). (ENG.). 784p. pap. 49.99 *(978-1-59059-859-7(8),* Friends of Ed) Apress L. P.
—Getting StartED with CSS. 2009. (ENG.). 350p. pap. 24.99 *(978-1-4302-2543-0(2),* Friends of Ed) Apress L. P.
Powers, David & Video2brain Staff. HTML5, CSS3, & jQuery with Adobe Dreamweaver CS5. 5. 2011. (Learn by Video Ser.). (ENG.). 48p. 74.99 ***(978-0-321-78811-5(7))*** Adobe Pr.
Purvis, Michael, et al. Beginning Google Maps API 3. 2nd ed. 2010. (ENG.). 328p. pap. 39.99 *(978-1-4302-2802-8(4))* Apress L. P.
Sams Publishing Staff. Sams Teach Yourself HTML & CSS: Video Learning Starter Kit. 2009. (Sams Teach Yourself Ser.). (ENG.). 50p. 39.99 *(978-0-672-33059-9(8))* Sams.

Schafer, Steven M. HTML, XHTML, & CSS Bible. 5th ed. 2010. (Bible Ser.: 615). (ENG., Illus.). 792p. pap. 39.99 *(978-0-470-52396-4(4)*, Wiley) Wiley, John & Sons, Inc.

Schmitt, Christopher. CSS Cookbook. 3rd ed. 2009. (Animal Guide Ser.). (ENG., Illus.). 732p. pap. 49.99 *(978-0-596-15593-3(X))* O'Reilly Media, Inc.

Schmitt, Christopher, et al. Professional CSS: Cascading Style Sheets for Web Design. 2nd ed. 2008. (ENG., Illus.). 301p. pap. 49.99 *(978-0-470-17708-2(X)*, Wrox) Wiley, John & Sons, Inc.

Shelly, Gary B. & Woods, Denise M. HTML, XHTML, & CSS. 6th ed. 2010. (Shelly Cashman Ser.). (ENG., Illus.). 440p. pap. 93.95 *(978-0-538-74745-5(5))* Course Technology.

Shelly, Gary B. & Woods, Denise M. HTML5 & CSS: Introductory. 7th ed. 2012. (HTML Ser.). (ENG.). 288p. pap. 58.95 ***(978-1-133-52613-1(6))*** Course Technology.

Shelly, Gary B., et al. HTML, XHTML, & CSS: Comprehensive. 6th ed. 2010. (Available Titles Skills Assessment Manager (SAM) - Office 2010 Ser.). (ENG., Illus.). 744p. pap. 125.95 *(978-0-538-74754-7(4))* Course Technology.

Shreves, Ric. Drupal 5 Themes: Create a new theme for your Drupal website with a clean layout & powerful CSS Styling. 2007. (Illus.). 250p. per. *(978-1-84719-182-3(7))* Packt Publishing, Ltd.

Sikos, Leslie. Web Standards: Mastering HTML5, CSS3, & XML. 2011. (ENG., Illus.). 524p. pap. 44.99 ***(978-1-4302-4041-9(5))*** Apress L. P.

Snook, Jonathan, et al. The Art & Science of CSS. 2007. (ENG., Illus.). 224p. per. 39.95 *(978-0-9758419-7-6(1))* SitePoint Pty, Ltd. AUS. Dist: Ingram Pub. Services.

Stark, Jonathan. Building iPhone Apps with HTML, CSS, & JavaScript: Making App Store Apps Without Objective-C or Cocoa. 2010. (ENG., Illus.). 186p. pap. 29.99 *(978-0-596-80578-4(0))* O'Reilly Media, Inc.

Stark, Jonathan & Jepson, Brian. Building Android Apps with HTML, CSS, & JavaScript: Making Native Apps with Standards-Based Web Tools. 2nd ed. 2012. (ENG.). 178p. pap. 29.99 ***(978-1-4493-1641-9(7))*** O'Reilly Media, Inc.

Sujak, Sulaimi. Make It Simple. 2008. 132p. 22.00 *(978-1-60693-283-4(7)*, Eloquent Bks.) AEG Literary Publishing Services, Inc.

Sullivan, Stephanie & Rewis, Greg. Mastering CSS with Dreamweaver CS4. 2008. (Voices That Matter Ser.). (ENG., Illus.). 368p. pap. 49.99 *(978-0-321-60503-0(9))* New Riders Publishing.

Teague, Jason Cranford. CSS, DHTML, & Ajax: Visual QuickStart Guide. 4th rev. ed. 2006. (Visual Quickstart Guide Ser.). (ENG., Illus.). 584p. per. 29.99 *(978-0-321-44325-0(X))* Peachpit Pr.

—Speaking in Styles: Fundamentals of CSS for Web Designers. 2009. (Voices That Matter Ser.). (Illus.). 360p. pap. 44.99 *(978-0-321-57416-9(8))* New Riders Publishing.

Vodnik, Sasha & Meersman, Jonathan. HTML5 & CSS3, Illustrated Complete. 2011. (Illustrated Ser.). (ENG., Illus.). 432p. (C). pap. 94.95 *(978-1-111-52798-3(9))* Course Technology.

Warner, Janine C. & LaFontaine, David. Mobile Web Design for Dummies. 2010. (ENG., Illus.). 384p. pap. 24.99 *(978-0-470-56096-9(7)*, For Dummies) Wiley, John & Sons, Inc.

Weakley, Russ. Sams Teach Yourself CSS3 in 10 Minutes. 2nd rev. ed. 2012. (Sams Teach Yourself — Minutes Ser.). (ENG.). 272p. pap. 24.99 ***(978-0-672-33568-6(9))*** Sams.

Wenz, Christian. HTML5 & CSS3 Developer's Phrasebook. rev. ed. 2012. (Developer's Library). (ENG.). 275p. pap. 29.99 *(978-0-321-77639-6(9))* Addison Wesley Professional.

Westfall, Jon, et al. Android Web Apps Development: Develop for Android Using HTML5, CSS3, JavaScript & More Web Standards. 2012. (ENG.). 284p. pap. 34.99 ***(978-1-4302-3957-4(3))*** Apress L. P.

Weyl, Estelle, et al. HTML5 & CSS3 for the Real World. 2011. (ENG., Illus.). 400p. pap. 39.95 *(978-0-9808469-0-4(0))* SitePoint Pty, Ltd. AUS. Dist: Ingram Pub. Services.

Wiley Publications Staff & W3Schools Staff. Learn CSS with W3School. 2010. (ENG., Illus.). 288p. pap. 29.99 *(978-0-470-61192-0(8)*, Wiley) Wiley, John & Sons, Inc.

Wooldridge, Mike & Wooldridge, Linda. HTML & CSS. 2008. (Teach Yourself VISUALLY (Tech) Ser.: 6). (ENG., Illus.). 334p. pap. 29.99 *(978-0-470-28588-6(5)*, Visual) Wiley, John & Sons, Inc.

Wyke-Smith, Charles. CSS with CWS: An Introduction to Professional XHTML & CSS Coding Techniques. 2008. (Voices That Matter Ser.). (ENG.). 14.99 *(978-0-321-61849-8(1))* New Riders Publishing.

—Stylin' with CSS: A Designer's Guide. 2nd ed. 2007. (Voices That Matter Ser.). (ENG., Illus.). 312p. per. 44.99 *(978-0-321-52556-7(6))* New Riders Publishing.

W3Schools. Learn HTML & CSS with W3Schools. 2010. (ENG., Illus.). 240p. pap. 29.99 *(978-0-470-61195-1(2)*, Wiley) Wiley, John & Sons, Inc.

York, Richard & Pouncey, Ian. Beginning CSS: Cascading Style Sheets for Web Design. 3rd ed. 2011. (ENG., Illus.). 464p. pap. 39.99 *(978-0-470-89152-0(1)*, Wrox) Wiley, John & Sons, Inc.

York, Richard & York. Beginning JavaScript & CSS Development with JQuery. 2009. (ENG., Illus.). 560p. pap. 44.99 *(978-0-470-22779-4(6)*, Wrox) Wiley, John & Sons, Inc.

CASCO BAY

Tyler, David A. Maine's Casco Bay Islands: A Guide. 2007. (ENG., Illus.). 80p. pap. 15.95 *(978-0-89272-743-8(8))* Down East Bks.

CASE (COMPUTER SCIENCE)

see Computer-Aided Software Engineering

CASE HARDENING

Technology Research Editors, ed. Surface Mechanical Properties of Plasma Nitrided Steels, 2007 Ed. 2007. pap. 128.50 *(978-1-60030-357-9(9)*, Search-In-Print) CSA Journal Division.

CASE MANAGEMENT IN HOSPITALS

see Hospitals—Case Management Services

CASE METHOD

Here are entered works on the use of recorded cases as a method of instruction. see also subdivision Case Studies under subjects

Adler, Gordon & Amann, Wolfgang. Case Writing for Executive Education: A Survival Guide. 2011. (Illus.). x, 116p. *(978-1-61735-361-1(2))*; pap. *(978-1-61735-360-4(4))*; E-Book *(978-1-61735-362-8(0))* Information Age Publishing, Inc.

Bhat, Sushma Seth. Inter-Organisational Cooperation & Networks in Destination Marketing. 2010. 292p. pap. *(978-3-639-13753-8(1))* VDM Verlag Dr. Mueller e.K.

Billingsly, Felix, et al. Single Case Research Methods. 2010. (ENG.). 240p. (C). pap. 40.40 *(978-0-13-062321-8(0)*, Prentice Hall) Prentice Hall PTR.

Capps, Donald & Fowler, Gene. The Pastoral Care Case: Learning about Care in Congregations. 2010. 178p. pap. 20.00 *(978-1-60899-448-9(1)*, Wipf and Stock) Wipf & Stock Pubs.

Cram101 Textbook Reviews & Cram101 Textbook Reviews. Outlines & Highlights for Single-Case Research Designs: Methods for Clinical & Applied Settings by Alan Kazdin, ISBN. 2011. 140p. pap. 28.95 ***(978-1-4288-5981-4(0))*** Cram101 Inc.

DeHorse, David S. The Why of It: Langdell's Generation Speaks to Today's Law Students. 2010. (Illus.). xvii, 137p. pap. ***(978-0-9827645-2-7(9))*** Sondheim Group, LLC.

Farquhar, Jillian. Case Study Research for Business. 2012. 144p. (C). 120.00 ***(978-1-84920-776-8(3)***, B07768C); pap. 44.95 ***(978-1-84920-777-5(1)***, B07768P) SAGE Pubns., Ltd. GBR. Dist: SAGE Pubns., Inc.

Fenstermacher, Gary D., et al. Approaches to Teaching. 5th rev. ed. 2009. (ENG.). 144p. pap. 19.95 *(978-0-8077-4982-1(6))* Teachers College Pr., Teachers College, Columbia Univ.

Gerring, John. Case Study Research: Principles & Practices. 2006. (ENG., Illus.). 278p. 85.00 *(978-0-521-85928-8(X))*; per. 29.99 *(978-0-521-67656-4(8))* Cambridge Univ. Pr.

Giordano, Gerard. Cockeyed Education: A Case Method Primer. 2010. (ENG.). 174p. 70.00 *(978-1-60709-434-0(7))*; pap. 29.95 *(978-1-60709-435-7(5))* Rowman & Littlefield Education.

—Lopsided Schools: Case Method Briefings. 2011. (ENG.). 232p. 70.00 *(978-1-60709-786-0(9))* 2011. (ENG.). 232p. pap. 34.95 *(978-1-60709-787-7(7))* 2010. *(978-1-60709-788-4(5))* Rowman & Littlefield Education.

—Solving Education's Problems Effectively: A Guide to Using the Case Method. 2009. (ENG.). 252p. 99.95 *(978-1-57886-998-5(6))*; pap. 39.95 *(978-1-57886-999-2(4))* Rowman & Littlefield Education.

Green, Ravonne A. Case Study Research: A Program Evaluation Guide for Librarians. 2011. E-Book ***(978-1-59158-861-0(8))*** Libraries Unlimited, Inc.

—Case Study Research: A Program Evaluation Guide for Librarians, 1 vol. 2011. 116p. pap. 45.00 ***(978-1-59158-860-3(X)***, LU8860) Pearson Education GBR. Dist: ABC-CLIO, LLC.

Hancock, Dawson R. & Algozzine, Bob. Doing Case Study Research: A Practical Guide for Beginning Researchers. 2nd ed. 2011. (ENG.). 128p. pap. 24.95 ***(978-0-8077-5268-5(1))*** Teachers College Pr., Teachers College, Columbia Univ.

Hunger, J. David & Wheelen, Thomas L. Essentials of Strategic Management. 5th rev. ed. 2010. (ENG., Illus.). 208p. (C). pap. 104.00 *(978-0-13-600669-5(8)*, Prentice Hall) Prentice Hall PTR.

Kauffman, James M., et al. Managing Classroom Behaviors: A Reflective Case-Based Approach. 5th ed. 2010. (ENG.). 240p. (C). pap. 74.60 *(978-0-13-705679-8(6)*, Prentice Hall) Prentice Hall PTR.

Kazdin, Alan E. Single-Case Research Designs: Methods for Clinical & Applied Settings, 1 vol. 2nd ed. 2010. (ENG., Illus.). 464p. (C). pap. 79.95 *(978-0-19-534188-1(0))* Oxford Univ. Pr., Inc.

Marschan-Piekkari, Rebecca & Welch, Catherine. Rethinking the Case Study in International Business & Management Research. 2011. (Illus.). 576p. 210.00 *(978-1-84844-184-2(3))* Elgar, Edward Publishing, Inc.

Mauffette-Leenders, Louise A., et al. Apprendre Cas Par Cas. (FRE., Illus.). x, 148p. *(978-0-7714-2496-0(5))* Univ. of Western Ontario.

Merriam, Sharan B. & Merriam. Qualitative Research: A Guide to Design & Implementation. 3rd ed. 2009. (ENG., Illus.). 320p. pap. 47.00 *(978-0-470-28354-7(8)*, Jossey-Bass) Wiley, John & Sons, Inc.

Naumes, William & Naumes, Margaret J. The Art & Craft of Case Writing. 3rd ed. 2011. (ENG.). 336p. 99.95 *(978-0-7656-2776-6(0))*; pap. 44.95 ***(978-0-7656-2777-3(9))*** Sharpe, M.E. Inc.

Pitton, Debra E. Developing Preservice Problem. 2010. (ENG.). 228p. 80.00 *(978-1-60709-461-6(4))* Rowman & Littlefield Education.

Pitton, Debra Eckerman. Developing Preservice Problem-Solving Skills. 2010. (ENG.). 228p. pap. 36.95 *(978-1-60709-462-3(2))* Rowman & Littlefield Education.

Redman, George L. & Redman, Angela. A Casebook for Exploring Diversity. 4th ed. 2010. (ENG.). 224p. (C). pap. 37.40 *(978-0-13-706128-0(5))* Allyn & Bacon, Inc.

Sandeen, Arthur. Enhancing Leadership in Colleges & Universities: A Case Approach. 2011. 236p. 54.95 *(978-0-398-08600-8(1))*; pap. 34.95 *(978-0-398-08601-5(X))* Thomas, Charles C. Pub., Ltd.

Schmidt, Steven W. Case Studies & Activities in Adult Education & Human Resource Development. 2010. E-Book *(978-1-61735-075-7(3))*; (Illus.). 198p. *(978-1-61735-074-0(5))*; (Illus.). 198p. pap. *(978-1-61735-073-3(7))* Information Age Publishing, Inc.

Weishaar, Mary Konya, et al. Inclusive Educational Administration: A Case-Study Approach. 2nd ed. 2007. 258p. (C). pap. 42.95 *(978-1-57766-498-7(1))* Waveland Pr., Inc.

Welch, Catherine. Rethinking the Case Study in International Business & Management Research. Piekkari, Rebecca, ed. 2012. (Illus.). 576p. pap. 39.95 ***(978-0-85793-333-1(7))*** Elgar, Edward Publishing, Inc.

Wiebe, Elden, et al, eds. Encyclopedia of Case Study Research, 2 vols. 2009. (Illus.). 1152p. 370.00 *(978-1-4129-5670-3(6)*, B56706C) SAGE Pubns., Inc.

Yin, Robert K. Case Study Research: Design & Methods. 4th ed. 2008. (Applied Social Research Methods Ser.: 5). (Illus.). 240p. (C). pap. 50.00 *(978-1-4129-6099-1(1)*, B60984P) SAGE Pubns., Inc.

CASE WESTERN RESERVE UNIVERSITY

Case Western Reserve University: Michelson-morley Experiment, Case Western Reserve University School of Medicine. 2010. 168p. pap. 14.14 *(978-1-157-02906-9(X))* General Bks. LLC.

Case Western Reserve University Alumni: Donald Knuth, Roger Zelazny, Edward Morley, Dennis Kucinich, Jerome Corsi, Peter Breggin. 2010. 596p. pap. 14.14 *(978-1-157-02907-6(8))* General Bks. LLC.

Case Western Reserve University Faculty: Melvin Kranzberg, Albert Abraham Michelson, Frederick Reines, Roman Vishniac, Russell L. Ackoff. 2010. 210p. pap. 19.99 *(978-1-155-33404-2(3))* General Bks. LLC.

Case Western Spartans Football: Case Western Spartans Football Coaches, Lou Saban, Jim Gilstrap, Wesley Englehorn, Charley Winner. 2010. 32p. pap. 14.14 *(978-1-157-79485-1(8))* General Bks. LLC.

Case Western Spartans Football Coaches: Lou Saban, Jim Gilstrap, Wesley Englehorn, Charley Winner, Walter D. Powell, Bill Edwards. 2010. 28p. pap. 14.14 *(978-1-157-36678-2(3))* General Bks. LLC.

Llc, Books. Case Western Reserve University Alumni: Case Western Reserve University School of Law Alumni, Donald Knuth, Roger Zelazny, Edward Morley. 2010. 648p. pap. 19.99 *(978-1-156-04857-3(5))* General Bks. LLC.

Locci, Ana B. & Bond, Chris. Case Western Reserve University: Squire Valleevue & Valley Ridge Farms. 2011. (Campus History Ser.). (Illus.). 128p. pap. 21.99 ***(978-0-7385-8275-7(1))*** Arcadia Publishing.

CASE WORK, SOCIAL

see Social Case Work

CASEIN PAINTING

Quiller, Stephen. Watermedia Painting with Stephen Quiller: The Complete Guide to Working in Watercolor, Acrylics, Gouache, & Casein. 2008. (ENG., Illus.). 176p. pap. 24.95 *(978-0-8230-9688-6(2))* Watson-Guptill Pubns., Inc.

CASEMENT, ROGER, SIR, 1864-1916

Bryant, William. Roger Casement: A Biography. 2007. 312p. per. 21.95 *(978-0-595-44795-4(3))* iUniverse, Inc.

Casement, Roger. Sir Roger Casement Gesammelte Schriften. 2009. 266p. 42.95 *(978-1-120-80886-8(3))*; pap. 27.95 *(978-1-120-70807-6(9))* Kessinger Publishing, LLC.

—Trial of Sir Roger Casement. 2009. 314p. pap. *(978-0-217-65002-1(3))* Books LLC.

—Trial of Sir Roger Casement. Knott, George H., ed. 2009. 370p. 48.95 *(978-1-104-96399-6(X))*; pap. 33.95 *(978-1-104-92722-6(5))* Kessinger Publishing, LLC.

—The Trial of Sir Roger Casement. 2010. 326p. pap. *(978-1-152-08663-0(4))* Books LLC.

Goodman, Jordan. The Devil & Mr. Casement: One Man's Battle for Human Rights in South America's Heart of Darkness. 2011. (ENG., Illus.). 336p. pap. 18.00 *(978-0-312-68058-9(9))* Picador.

Knott, George H. Trial of Sir Roger Casement. 2008. 362p. 46.95 *(978-1-4365-6467-0(0))* 2007. 364p. per. 31.95 *(978-0-548-75939-4(1))* Kessinger Publishing, LLC.

Knott, George H., ed. The Trial of Sir Roger Casement. 2008. 360p. 46.95 *(978-0-548-98906-7(0))* 2007. (ENG.). 364p. per. 31.95 *(978-0-548-65832-1(3))* Kessinger Publishing, LLC.

Laubscher, Michael. Who Is Roger Casement? 2012. (ENG.). 288p. pap. 24.95 ***(978-1-84588-982-1(7))*** History Pr. Ltd., The GBR. Dist: Independent Pubs. Group.

CASES OF CONSCIENCE

see Casuistry

CASH, JOHNNY, 1932-2003

Batchelor, Bob. Literary Cash: Unauthorized Writings Inspired by the Legendary Johnny Cash. 2006. (Smart Pop Ser.). (ENG.). 257p. pap. 17.95 *(978-1-933771-03-8(8))* BenBella Bks.

Cash, John Carter. Anchored in Love: An Intimate Portrait of June Carter Cash, 0 vols. 2007. (Illus.). 224p. 24.99 *(978-0-8499-0187-4(1))* Nelson, Thomas Inc.

—House of Cash: The Legacies of my Father, Johnny Cash. 2011. (ENG., Illus.). 160p. 39.95 *(978-1-60887-028-8(6))* Palace Pr. International.

Cash, Johnny. Johnny Cash Anthology. 2011. (ENG.). 320p. pap. 29.99 ***(978-1-4584-0346-9(7)***, 1458403467) Leonard, Hal Corp.

Cash, Vivian & Sharpsteen, Ann. I Walked the Line: My Life with Johnny. 2008. (ENG., Illus.). 352p. pap. 15.00 *(978-1-4165-3295-8(1)*, Scribner) Scribner.

Clapp, Rodney. Johnny Cash & the Great American Contradiction: Christianity & the Battle for the Soul of a Nation. 2008. (ENG.). 159p. pap. 17.00 *(978-0-664-23088-3(1))* Westminster John Knox Pr.

D'Ambrosio, Antonino. A Heartbeat & a Guitar: Johnny Cash & the Making of Bitter Tears. 2011. (ENG.). 296p. (gr. 9). pap. 16.99 *(978-1-56858-637-3(X))* Basic Bks.

Edwards, Leigh H. Johnny Cash & the Paradox of American Identity. 2009. (Profiles in Popular Music Ser.). (ENG.). 256p. pap. 19.95 *(978-0-253-22061-5(0)*, 0253220610) Indiana Univ. Pr.

Huss, John & Werther, David, eds. Johnny Cash & Philosophy: The Burning Ring of Truth. 2008. (Popular Culture & Philosophy Ser.). (ENG.). 288p. pap. 18.95 *(978-0-8126-9645-5(X))* Open Court Publishing Co.

Kleist, Reinhardt. Johnny Cash: I See a Darkness. Waaler, Michael, tr. from GER. 2009. (ENG., Illus.). 224p. pap. 17.95 *(978-0-8109-8463-9(6))* Abrams.

Noles, Randy. Fiddler's Curse: The Untold Story of Ervin T. Rouse, Chubby Wise, Johnny Cash & the Orange Blossom Special. 2007. (ENG., Illus.). 226p. per. 14.95 *(978-1-57424-214-0(8)*, 1574242148) Centerstream Publishing.

Silverman, Jonathan. Nine Choices: Johnny Cash & American Culture. 2010. (Illus.). 288p. (ENG.). pap. 26.95 *(978-1-55849-827-3(3))*; lib. bdg. 80.00 *(978-1-55849-826-6(5))* Univ. of Massachusetts Pr.

Streissguth, Michael. Johnny Cash: The Biography. 2007. (ENG., Illus.). 368p. per. 15.95 *(978-0-306-81565-2(6))* Da Capo Pr., Inc.

Streissguth, Michael, ed. Ring of Fire: The Johnny Cash Reader. 2006. 310p. reprint ed. pap. 17.00 *(978-1-4223-5448-3(2))* DIANE Publishing Co.

Thomson, Graeme. The Resurrection of Johnny Cash: Hurt, Redemption, & American Recordings. 2011. (ENG., Illus.). 254p. pap. 19.95 *(978-1-906002-36-7(3)*, 1906002363, Jawbone) Outline Pr., Ltd. GBR. Dist: Leonard, Hal Corp.

Tost, Tony. Johnny Cash's American Recordings. 2011. (33 1/3 Ser.). (ENG.). 224p. pap. 12.95 *(978-1-4411-7461-1(3))* Continuum International Publishing Group, Ltd. GBR. Dist: National Bk. Network.

CASH FLOW

Allman, Keith A. Modeling Structured Finance Cash Flows with Microsoft Excel: A Step-by-Step Guide. 2007. (Wiley Finance Ser.: 370). (ENG., Illus.). 224p. pap. 80.00 *(978-0-470-04290-8(7)*, Wiley) Wiley, John & Sons, Inc.

Bissessur, Sanjay. Earnings Quality & Earnings Management: The Role of Accounting Accruals. 2008. 216p. pap. *(978-3-639-05544-3(6))* VDM Verlag Dr. Mueller e.K.

Brott, Rich. Basic Principles for Maximizing Your Cash Flow: 7 Steps to Financial Freedom! 2008. 120p. per. 14.99 *(978-1-60185-019-5(0)*, 1001) ABC Book Publishing.

—Biblical Principles for Financial Success - Student Workbook. 2008. 228p. per. 17.99 *(978-1-60185-016-4(6))* ABC Book Publishing.

—Biblical Principles for Financial Success - Teacher Workbook. 2008. 228p. per. 19.99 *(978-1-60185-015-7(8))* ABC Book Publishing.

Cagan, Michele. The Everything Accounting Book: Balance Your Budget, Manage Your Cash Flow, & Keep Your Books in the Black. 2006. (ENG., Illus.). 304p. per. 15.95 *(978-1-59337-718-2(5))* Adams Media Corp.

Chen, Jianguo, et al. The Corporate Cost of Capital & Financial Investment in New Zealand. 2008. 52p. pap. *(978-3-639-01116-6(3))* VDM Verlag Dr. Mueller e.K.

Christy, George C. & Christy. Free Cash Flow: Seeing Through the Accounting Fog Machine to Find Great Stocks. 2009. (Wiley Finance Ser.: 484). (ENG., Illus.). 181p. 49.95 *(978-0-470-39175-4(8)*, Wiley) Wiley, John & Sons, Inc.

Damodaran, Aswath. Damodaran Valuation Set. 2007. (ENG.). 175.00 *(978-0-470-16839-4(0)*, Wiley) Wiley, John & Sons, Inc.

Day, Alastair. Mastering Cash Flow & Valuation Modelling. rev. ed. 2011. (Financial Times Ser.). (ENG., Illus.). 344p. pap. 99.99 ***(978-0-273-73281-5(1))*** FT Press.

Epstein, Lita. The Business Owner's Guide to Reading & Understanding Financial Statements: How to Budget, Forecast, & Monitor Cash Flow for Better Decision Making. 2012. (ENG.). 192p. pap. 19.95 ***(978-1-118-14351-3(5)***, Wiley) Wiley, John & Sons, Inc.

Gallinelli, Frank. What Every Real Estate Investor Needs to Know about Cash Flow... & 36 Other Key Financial Measures. 2008. (ENG., Illus.). 312p. pap. 22.95 *(978-0-07-160327-0(1)*, 0071603271) McGraw-Hill Cos., The.

Goldstein, Harvey. Don't Bust the Budget: Toss It! 2007. (Illus.). 148p. per. 15.95 *(978-0-9767575-9-7(1))* Topos Bks.

Granof, Michael H., et al. How to Cost Your Labor Contract. 2nd ed. 2011. ***(978-1-57018-928-9(5))*** BNA Bks.

Gray, David. Finance Arts Guide to Nonprofit Cash Flow: A Guide for You & Your Nonprofit Organization. 2010. (ENG.). 178p. pap. 19.95 *(978-0-9828124-0-2(X))* Finance Arts, LLC.

Hackel, Kenneth S. Security Valuation & Risk Analysis: Assessing Value in Investment Decision-Making. 2010. (ENG., Illus.). 614p. 85.00 *(978-0-07-174435-5(5)*, 0071744355) McGraw-Hill Cos., The.

Hölzlwimmer, Andrea. Optimizing Value Flows with SAP ERP. 2009. (Illus.). 350p. 79.95 *(978-1-59229-298-1(4)*, SAP PR.) Galileo Pr., Inc.

Im, Yong-Jae & Chon, Song-In. Kiop Chiptan Ui Sunhwan Ch'ulcha: Sijang Kyuyul Kwa Kamdok Kyuyul Ui Yokhal. 2009. (KOR., Illus.). 84p. *(978-89-8063-302-9(5))* KDI.

Johar, Khalid L. Venture Appraisal. 2010. 240p. pap. *(978-3-8383-8607-2(8))* Lambert Academic Publishing.

Jury, Timothy. Cash Flow Analysis & Forecasting: The Definitive Guide to Understanding & Using Published Cash Flow Data. 2nd ed. 2012. (Wiley

Finance Ser.). (ENG.). 334p. 75.00 ***(978-1-119-96265-6(X)***, Wiley) Wiley, John & Sons, Inc.

Linzer, Richard & Linzer, Anna O. Cash Flow Strategies: Innovation in Nonprofit Financial Management. 2007. (ENG., Illus.). 272p. 90.00 *(978-0-7879-8147-1(8)*, Jossey-Bass) Wiley, John & Sons, Inc.

Linzer, Richard S. & Linzer, Anna O. The Cash Flow Forecaster. 2007. cd-rom 60.00 *(978-0-7879-8626-1(7))* Wiley, John & Sons, Inc.

—The Cash Flow Forecaster & Real Estate Calculator. 2007. 50.00 *(978-0-7879-9605-5(X)*, Jossey-Bass) Wiley, John & Sons, Inc.

Liu, Cathy Zishang. The Relation Between Long-Term Accruals & Operating Cash Flows. 2008. 92p. pap. *(978-3-8364-9787-9(5))* VDM Verlag Dr. Mueller e.K.

Lütolf-Carroll, Constance, et al. From Innovation to Cash Flows: Value Creation by Structuring High Technology Alliances. 2009. (Wiley Finance Ser.: 527). (ENG., Illus.). 618p. 110.00 *(978-0-470-11809-2(1)*, Wiley) Wiley, John & Sons, Inc.

Mccallion, Robert & Warner, Alan. Improve Your Cash Flow. 2nd ed. 2010. (Teach Yourself Ser.). (ENG.). 304p. pap. 19.95 *(978-1-4441-0863-7(8)*, Hodder & Stoughton) Hodder General Publishing Div. GBR. Dist: Independent Pubs. Group.

O'Berry, Denise. Small Business Cash Flow: Strategies for Making Your Business a Financial Success. 2006. (ENG., Illus.). 224p. per. 29.95 *(978-0-470-04097-3(1)*, Wiley) Wiley, John & Sons, Inc.

Platt, Harlan D. Lead with Cash: Cash Flow for Corporate Renewal. 2010. (Illus.). 250p. 45.00 *(978-1-84816-375-1(4))* Imperial College Pr. GBR. Dist: World Scientific Publishing Co., Inc.

Priest, William W. & McClelland, Lindsay H. Free Cash Flow & Shareholder Yield: New Priorities for the Global Investor. 2007. (ENG., Illus.). 192p. 29.95 *(978-0-470-12833-6(X)*, Wiley) Wiley, John & Sons, Inc.

Rowley, Lee. How to Market & Sell Your Art, Music, Photographs, & Handmade Crafts Online: Turn Your Hobby into a Cash Machine. 2008. (ENG.). 288p. per. 24.95 *(978-1-60138-146-0(8))* Atlantic Publishing Co.

Rutherford, Douglass. The Complete Guide to Real Estate Cash Flow Analysis. 2007. per. *(978-1-59872-900-9(4))* Instant Pub.

Scholze, Andreas. Discounted Cashflow und Jahresabschlußanalyse: Zur Berücksichtigung externer Rechnungslegungsinformationen in der Unternehmensbewertung. 2009. (Betriebswirtschaftliche Studien. Rechnungs- und Finanzwesen, Organisation und Institution Ser.). (GRE.). 214p. pap. 56.95 *(978-3-631-57999-2(3))* Lang, Peter GmbH, Europaischer Verlag der Wissenschaften DEU. Dist: Lang, Peter.

Shim, Jae. Managing & Improving Your Cash Flow. 2011. (Illus.). 180p. pap. 39.95 *(978-1-906403-63-8(5))* Global Professional Publishing GBR. Dist: Stylus Publishing, LLC.

Terrani, Davide & Davide, Terrani. Dcf & Risk-Neutral Valuation: A Comparison. 2011. 152p. pap. ***(978-3-639-31899-9(4))*** VDM Verlag Dr. Mueller e.K.

Witte, Katja. Wertkonzeption einer nutzenbasierten Bewertung von Patenten: Konzeptualisierung eines Handlungsrahmens zur Separierung patentspezifischer Cash Flows. 2009. (Europäische Hochschulschriften. Reihe 5: Volks- und Betriebswirtschaft Ser.). (GER.). 296p. pap. 76.95 *(978-3-631-58783-6(X))* Lang, Peter GmbH, Europaischer Verlag der Wissenschaften DEU. Dist: Lang, Peter.

CASH MANAGEMENT

Aidamenbor, Jaunty & Mgbemena, Chikanayo. Valuing Companies in Emerging Markets. 2010. 120p. pap. *(978-3-8383-7097-2(X))* Lambert Academic Publishing.

Alinvi, Fatima. Customers' Expectations of Banks Becoming Cashless. 2010. 104p. pap. *(978-3-639-27511-7(X))* VDM Verlag Dr. Mueller e.K.

Allen, Billy. Fast Cash. 2010. 112p. pap. 16.49 *(978-1-4520-9143-3(9))* AuthorHouse.

Allman, Keith A. Modeling Structured Finance Cash Flows with Microsoft Excel: A Step-by-Step Guide. 2007. (Wiley Finance Ser.: 370). (ENG., Illus.). 224p. pap. 80.00 *(978-0-470-04290-8(7)*, Wiley) Wiley, John & Sons, Inc.

Allman-Ward, Michele & Allman-Ward, A. Peter. Optimizing Company Cash: A Guide for Financial Professionals. 2007. (Illus.). xxiii, 271p. *(978-0-87051-654-2(X))* American Institute of Certified Public Accountants.

Bauer, Brigitte. Untreue durch Cash-Pooling im Konzern. 2008. (Criminalia. Abhandlungen aus den gesamten Strafrechtswissenschaften Ser.). 320p. pap. 74.95 *(978-3-631-57842-1(3))* Lang, Peter GmbH, Europaischer Verlag der Wissenschaften DEU. Dist: Lang, Peter.

Berman, Karen & Knight, Joe. Financial Intelligence for Entrepreneurs: What You Really Need to Know about the Numbers. 2008. (Financial Intelligence: Ser.). (ENG., Illus.). 304p. pap. 30.00 *(978-1-4221-1915-0(7))* Harvard Business Review Pr.

—Financial Intelligence for HR Professionals: What You Really Need to Know about the Numbers. 2008. (Financial Intelligence: Ser.). (ENG., Illus.). 320p. pap. 30.00 *(978-1-4221-1913-6(0))* Harvard Business Review Pr.

Berman, Karen, et al. Financial Intelligence for IT Professionals: What You Really Need to Know about the Numbers. 2008. (Financial Intelligence: Ser.). (ENG., Illus.). 296p. pap. 24.95 *(978-1-4221-1914-3(9))* Harvard Business Review Pr.

Breslin, Mark. Million Dollar Blue Collar: Managing Your Money for Work & Life Success. 2008. (Illus.). 152p. pap. 19.95 *(978-0-9741662-6-1(X))* McAlly International Pr.

Carter, Matthew M. The 90% Rule. 2010. pap. 13.95 *(978-0-7414-5984-8(1))* Infinity Publishing.

—The 90% Rule: Workbook. 2010. pap. 9.95 *(978-0-7414-5985-5(X))* Infinity Publishing.

Chapman, Meyrick. Don't Be Fooled Again: Lessons in the Good, Bad & Unpredictable Behaviour of Global Finance. 2010. (Financial Times Ser.). (ENG.). 296p. (C). pap. 26.99 ***(978-0-273-72789-7(3))*** FT Press.

Christy, George C. & Christy. Free Cash Flow: Seeing Through the Accounting Fog Machine to Find Great Stocks. 2009. (Wiley Finance Ser.: 484). (ENG., Illus.). 181p. 49.95 *(978-0-470-39175-4(8)*, Wiley) Wiley, John & Sons, Inc.

Dalton, Tony. Cash Management: Making Your Business Cash-Rich... Without Breaking the Bank. 2011. (Business on a Shoestring Ser.). (ENG.). 208p. pap. 14.95 ***(978-1-4081-3984-4(7))*** A & C Black GBR. Dist: Macmillan.

Eusani, Guido. Die Erfassung verdeckter Vermögensverlagerungen im Rahmen eines bilanzgestützten Kapitalschutzes bei der GmbH de lege lata et Ferenda: Eine Untersuchung unter besonderer Berücksichtigung des Cash Poolings im faktischen GmbH-Konzern sowie des Regierungsentwurfs eines Gesetzes zur Modernisierung des GmbH-Rechts und zur Bekämpfung von Missbräuchen (MoMiG) 2008. (Studien zum deutschen und europäischen Gesellschafts- und Wirtschaftsrecht Ser.). 222p. pap. 56.95 *(978-3-631-58335-7(4))* Lang, Peter GmbH, Europaischer Verlag der Wissenschaften DEU. Dist: Lang, Peter.

Fauzan, Arief & Pratama, Indra. Set-up Cash Pool Structure. 2010. 72p. pap. *(978-3-8383-8583-9(7))* Lambert Academic Publishing.

Freidhof, Jan. The Dilemma of Cash Management in China. 2007. 52p. per. *(978-3-8364-0841-7(4))* VDM Verlag Dr. Mueller e.K.

Goldstein, Harvey. Don't Bust the Budget: Toss It! 2007. (Illus.). 148p. per. 15.95 *(978-0-9767575-9-7(1))* Topos Bks.

Hall, Alvin. Before You Spend That Money: Priceless Ways to Manage Your Money. 2014. (ENG., Illus.). 256p. pap. 16.00 *(978-0-7432-7956-7(5)*, Beyond Words/Atria Bks.) Atria Bks.

Hangebrauck Ralf. Kapitalaufbringung, Kapitalerhaltung und Existenzschutz bei konzernweiten Cash-Pooling-Systemen. 2008. (Europäische Hochschulschriften. Reihe 2: Rechtswissenschaft Ser.). 602p. pap. 141.95 *(978-3-631-57589-5(0))* Lang, Peter GmbH, Europaischer Verlag der Wissenschaften DEU. Dist: Lang, Peter.

Hassan, Sajjad. Tax Audit Techniques in Cash Based Economies: A Practical Guide. 2nd ed. 2010. (ENG.). 100p. pap. 19.95 *(978-0-9553540-4-5(8))* Commonwealth Secretariat GBR. Dist: Stylus Publishing, LLC.

Jansen, Justus, ed. International Cash Pooling: Cross-border Cash Management Systems & Intra-group Financing. 2011. 306p. pap. 109.00 ***(978-3-86653-192-5(3))*** Sellier - European Law Publishers GmbH DEU. Dist: International Specialized Bk. Services.

Jury, Timothy. Cash Flow Analysis & Forecasting: The Definitive Guide to Understanding & Using Published Cash Flow Data. 2nd ed. 2012. (Wiley Finance Ser.). (ENG.). 334p. 75.00 ***(978-1-119-96265-6(X)***, Wiley) Wiley, John & Sons, Inc.

Linzer, Richard & Linzer, Anna. The Cash Flow Solution: The Nonprofit Board Member's Guide to Financial Success. 2006. (ENG., Illus.). 160p. per. 24.95 *(978-0-7879-7833-4(7)*, Jossey-Bass) Wiley, John & Sons, Inc.

Linzer, Richard & Linzer, Anna O. Cash Flow Strategies: Innovation in Nonprofit Financial Management. 2007. (ENG., Illus.). 272p. 90.00 *(978-0-7879-8147-1(8)*, Jossey-Bass) Wiley, John & Sons, Inc.

Masson, Dubos J., et al. Essentials of Treasury Management. 2006. pap. 16.95 *(978-1-4288-1122-5(2))* Cram101 Inc.

Riddick-Grisham, Susan & Deming, Laura, eds. Pediatric Life Care Planning & Case Management, Second Edition. 2nd rev. ed. 2011. (ENG., Illus.). 1051p. 159.95 *(978-1-4398-0358-5(7)*, CRC Press) Taylor & Francis Group GBR. Dist: Taylor & Francis Group.

Shim, Jae. Managing & Improving Your Cash Flow. 2011. (Illus.). 180p. pap. 39.95 *(978-1-906403-63-8(5))* Global Professional Publishing GBR. Dist: Stylus Publishing, LLC.

Thompson-Wells, Christine. Making Cash Flow: The Game of Money & How to Play It! 2010. (ENG., Illus.). 224p. pap. 22.95 *(978-0-9551498-6-7(6))* Planet Press Ltd. GBR. Dist: Independent Pubs. Group.

Travis, Ron. Synergistic Management Control Systems. 2010. 484p. pap. 26.00 *(978-1-4520-0922-3(8))* AuthorHouse.

Travis Sr., Ron. Synergistic Management Control Systems. 2010. 484p. pap. 34.00 *(978-1-4520-0921-6(X))* AuthorHouse.

Tumwine, Emmanuel, et al. Cash Management & Financial Performance of Hotels. 2011. 112p. pap. ***(978-3-8443-2688-8(X))*** Lambert Academic Publishing.

van Ortega, Eleazar. Maximizing Cash Management with SAP ERP Financials. 2010. (Illus.). 460p. 79.95 *(978-1-59229-324-7(7)*, SAP PR.) Galileo Pr., Inc.

CASH REGISTERS

Vargas, Camilo. Universal Design of a Future Grocery Retail Checkstand. 2009. 96p. pap. *(978-3-639-13137-6(1))* VDM Verlag Dr. Mueller e.K.

CASH TAKEOVER BID

see Tender Offers (Securities)

CASINOS

Anonymous. Casino Confidential: A Pit Boss's Guide to Beating the House. 2007. (ENG., Illus.). 176p. pap. 15.95 *(978-1-59474-195-1(6))* Quirk Bks.

Berkus, E. Casino Caged: An inside perspective on the behind-the-scenes world of casino wild Life. 2007. 172p. per. 24.95 *(978-1-4241-7803-2(7))* PublishAmerica, Inc.

Binkley, Christina. Winner Takes All: Steve Wynn, Kirk Kerkorian, Gary Loveman, & the Race to Own Las Vegas. 2009. (ENG.). 320p. pap. 15.99 *(978-1-4013-0976-3(3))* Hyperion Pr.

Blackwood, Kevin. Casino Gambling for Dummies. 2nd rev. ed. 2006. (ENG., Illus.). 384p. pap. 19.99 *(978-0-471-75286-8(X)*, For Dummies) Wiley, John & Sons, Inc.

Bloom, Steve, ed. Casino City's Casino Vendors Guide. 2007. (ENG.). 432p. pap. 49.95 *(978-1-931732-90-1(6))* 2006. 458p. per. 49.95 net. *(978-1-931732-72-7(8))* Casino City Pr.

—Casino City's Casino Vendors Guide CD. 2007. (ENG.). cd-rom 149.95 *(978-1-931732-91-8(4))*; cd-rom 149.95 net. *(978-1-931732-79-6(5))* Casino City Pr.

—Casino City's Gaming Business Directory. 2007. 750p. (ENG.). spiral bd. 199.95 *(978-1-931732-94-9(9))*; spiral bd. 169.95 net. *(978-1-931732-84-0(1))* Casino City Pr.

—Casino City's Gaming Business Directory CD. 2007. (ENG.). cd-rom 374.95 *(978-1-931732-95-6(7))*;Summer 2007. cd-rom 324.95 net. *(978-1-931732-85-7(X))* Casino City Pr.

—Casino City's Global Gaming Almanac. 2007. 520p. ring bd. 374.95 net. *(978-1-931732-82-6(5))*; cd-rom 449.95 net. *(978-1-931732-83-3(3))* Casino City Pr.

Bodinger De Uriarte, John J. Casino & Museum: Representing Mashantucket Pequot Identity. 2007. (ENG., Illus.). 256p. 50.00 *(978-0-8165-2545-4(5))* Univ. of Arizona Pr.

Boss, Derk J. & Zajic, Alan W. Casino Security & Gaming Surveillance Handbook. 2010. (ENG., Illus.). 322p. 83.95 *(978-1-4200-8782-6(7))* Auerbach Pubs., Inc.

Bourie, Steve. American Casino Guide. (American Casino Guide Ser.). (Illus.). 496p. 2008. pap. 18.95 *(978-1-883768-18-8(7))* 2006. per. 16.95 *(978-1-883768-16-4(0))* Casino Vacations.

Bourie, Steve. American Casino Guide 2012 Edition. 2012th ed. 2011. (American Casino Guide Ser.). 496p. pap. 18.95 ***(978-1-883768-21-8(7))*** Casino Vacations.

Bracey, Earnest N. The Moulin Rouge & Black Rights in Las Vegas: A History of the First Racially Integrated Hotel-Casino. 2008. (ENG., Illus.). 227p. pap. 45.00 *(978-0-7864-3992-8(0))* McFarland & Co., Inc. Pubs.

Cardoza, Avery. Casino Craps for the Winner. 2010. (ENG.). 160p. pap. 12.95 *(978-1-58042-241-3(1))* Cardoza Publishing.

Castleman, Deke. Whale Hunt in the Desert: Secrets of a Vegas Superhost. exp. rev. ed. 2009. (Illus.). 330p. pap. 16.95 *(978-0-929712-89-5(7))* Huntington Pr.

Chandler, Susan Kerr & Jones, Jill B. Casino Women: Courage in Unexpected Places. 2011. 240p. 29.95 *(978-0-8014-5014-3(4)*, ILR Pr.) Cornell Univ. Pr.

Ciciarelli, Alan. Play Smart & Enjoy Your Stay: How to Play Smart at a Casino Without Complicated Strategies. 2012. ***(978-1-58982-650-2(7)***, Millennial Mind Publishing) American Bk. Publishing Group.

Currie, Billye B. The Gambler: Romancing Lady Luck. 2007. (Studies in Jungian Psychology by Jungian Analysts Ser.). (Illus.). 124p. per. 25.00 *(978-1-894574-19-8(2)*, 012-171) Inner City Bks. CAN. Dist: Bookworld Trade, Inc.

Einiger, Ken. Play to Win: A World Champion's Guide to Winning Blackjack Tournaments. 2006. (Illus.). 172p. per. 14.95 *(978-0-929712-38-3(2)*, 376-044) Huntington Pr.

Eng, Richard. The Complete Guide to U. S. Casinos & Racinos. 2007. (ENG.). 450p. per. 19.95 *(978-1-932910-89-6(1))* Daily Racing Form.

Fischer, Steve. When the Mob Ran Vegas: Stories of Money, Mayhem & Murder. 2007. (ENG.). cd-rom 39.95 *(978-0-9770658-1-3(2))* Berkline Pr.

French, Peter. The Gambling Handbook: The Illustrated Step-by-Step Guide to Playing & Winning on-Line & in the Casino. 2006. (Illus.). 192p. *(978-1-905204-71-7(X))* Quercus.

GARDNER, Mayo. Casino Games You Can Beat: Baccarat, Blackjack & Craps. 2008. 95p. pap. 14.95 *(978-1-4357-4679-4(1))* Lulu Enterprises Inc.

Gollehon, John. Attack the Casino's Vulnerable Games! 2006. (Illus.). 243p. per. 7.99 *(978-0-914839-80-4(2))* Gollehon Pr.

—Strike the Casino with Winning Strategies! 2007. (Illus.). 237p. per. 7.99 *(978-0-914839-81-1(0))* Gollehon Pr.

Goss, Ernest P. & Morse, Edward A. Governing Fortune: Casino Gambling in America. 2007. (ENG., Illus.). 344p. 90.00 *(978-0-472-09965-8(5))* Univ. of Michigan Pr.

Greenlees, E. Malcolm. Casino Accounting & Financial Management. 2nd ed. 2008. (Gambling Studies). (ENG., Illus.). 480p. 60.00 *(978-0-87417-767-1(7))* Univ. of Nevada Pr.

Hagen, Tom & Weiss, Sonia. 101 Ways to Win Blackjack: Includes Tips to Win at the Casino & Online. 2009. (ENG.). 192p. pap. 10.95 *(978-1-4405-0005-3(3))* Adams Media Corp.

Hart, Rick. Sin City Rider. 2011. 220p. 29.99 ***(978-1-4568-7092-8(0))***; pap. 19.99 ***(978-1-4568-7091-1(2))*** Xlibris Corp.

Hashimoto, Kathryn. Casino Management: A Strategic Approach. 2007. (Casino Essential Ser.). (ENG., Illus.). 432p. (C). 62.40 *(978-0-13-192672-1(1)*, Prentice Hall) Prentice Hall PTR.

—Casino Marketing: Theories & Applications. 2009. (Casino Essential Ser.). (ENG.). 160p. (C). pap. 62.40 *(978-0-13-199614-4(2)*, Prentice Hall) Prentice Hall PTR.

Hashimoto, Kathryn & Durham, Steve. Casino Financial Controls: Tracking the Flow of Money. 2009. (Casino Essential Ser.). (ENG.). 176p. (C). pap. 62.40 *(978-0-13-174809-5(2)*, Prentice Hall) Prentice Hall PTR.

Hashimoto, Kathryn & Roberts, Chris. Casinos: Organization & Culture. 2009. (Casino Essential Ser.). (ENG.). 160p. (C). pap. 62.40 *(978-0-13-174812-5(2)*, Prentice Hall) Prentice Hall PTR.

Hashimoto, Kathryn, et al. Casino Gaming Methods: An Inside Look at Casino Games, Probabilities, Security & Surveillance. 2009. (Casino Essential Ser.). (ENG.). 192p. (C). pap. 62.40 *(978-0-13-222897-8(1)*, Prentice Hall) Prentice Hall PTR.

Huddy, John. Storming Las Vegas: How a Cuban-Born, Soviet-Trained Commando Took down the Strip to the Tune of Five World-Class Hotels, Three Armored Cars, & Millions of Dollars. 2009. (Illus.). 384p. pap. 15.00 *(978-0-345-51441-7(6)*, Ballantine Bks.) Random House Publishing Group.

Illar, Lou. Believe Me or Your Lying Eyes with Hind Sight! An Entertaining History of Casinos, Corruption, & Charities in America (Second Edition) 2009. 416p. pap. 28.99 *(978-1-4490-0751-5(1))* AuthorHouse.

International Tennis Hall of Fame & Museum. Tennis & the Newport Casino. 2011. (Images of Sports Ser.). (Illus.). 128p. pap. 21.99 *(978-0-7385-7482-0(1))* Arcadia Publishing.

Karmel, James R. Gambling on the American Dream: Atlantic City & the Casino Era, 1 vol. 2008. (Financial History Ser.). (ENG., Illus.). 256p. 99.00 *(978-1-85196-926-5(8))* Pickering & Chatto Pubs., Ltd. GBR. Dist: Ashgate Publishing Co.

Kling, Dwayne. The Rise of the Biggest Little City: An Encyclopedic History of Reno Gaming, 1931-1981. 2010. (Gambling Studies Ser.). (Illus.). 256p. pap. 29.95 *(978-0-87417-829-6(0))* Univ. of Nevada Pr.

Knapp Rinella, Heidi. The Stardust of Yesterday: Reflections on a Las Vegas Legend. Weatherford, Mike, ed. 2006. (Illus.). 186p. 39.95 *(978-1-932173-70-3(6))* Stephens Pr. LLC.

Lax, Rick. Fool Me Once: Hustlers, Hookers, Headliners, & How Not to Get Screwed in Vegas. 2011. (ENG.). 304p. pap. 15.99 *(978-0-312-54570-3(3)*, St. Martin's Griffin) St. Martin's Pr.

Light, Steven Andrew & Rand, Kathryn R.L. Indian Gaming & Tribal Sovereignty: The Casino Compromise. 2007. 240p. per. 17.95 *(978-0-7006-1553-7(9))* Univ. Pr. of Kansas.

Marquez, Ernest. Noir Afloat: Tony Cornero & the Notorious Gambling Ships of Southern California. 2011. *(978-1-883318-66-6(1))* Angel City Pr.

Meister, Alan. Casino City's Indian Gaming Industry Report. (ENG.). 2008. 132p. spiral bd. 249.95 *(978-1-60627-008-0(7))* 2007. spiral bd. 199.95 net. *(978-1-931732-80-2(9))* 2007. cd-rom 199.95 net. *(978-1-931732-81-9(7))*2007-2008 Edition. 2007. spiral bd. 225.00 net. *(978-1-931732-86-4(8))* Casino City Pr.

—Casino City's Indian Gaming Industry Report CD. 2007. (ENG.). cd-rom 225.00 net. *(978-1-931732-87-1(6))* Casino City Pr.

Mendelson, Paul. The Mammoth Book of Casino Games. 2010. (ENG.). 480p. pap. 13.95 *(978-0-7624-3847-1(9))* Running Pr. Bk. Pubs.

Mitchell, Gayle. Easy Casino Gambling: Winning Strategies for the Beginner. 2007. (ENG., Illus.). 224p. per. 17.95 *(978-1-60239-011-9(8))* Skyhorse Publishing Co., Inc.

Moss, Laurence S. Perspectives on Gambling: Lotteries, Wagers, & Casinos. 2008. (AJES - Studies in Economic Reform & Social Justice Ser.). (ENG., Illus.). 200p. 116.95 *(978-1-4051-7949-2(X))*; pap. 50.95 *(978-1-4051-7943-0(0))* Wiley, John & Sons, Inc. (Wiley-Blackwell).

Nersesian, Bob. Beat the Players: Casinos, Cops & the Game Inside the Game. 2006. 320p. per. 19.95 *(978-0-935926-28-6(3))* Pi Yee Pr.

Nestor, Basil. The Unofficial Guide to Slots, Blackjack, Poker & Other Casino Games. 2006. (Unofficial Guides). 384p. pap. 16.99 *(978-0-7645-8494-7(4)*, Wiley) Wiley, John & Sons, Inc.

Pileggi, Nicholas & Shandling, Larry. Casino: Love & Honor in Las Vegas. 2011. (ENG.). 432p. pap. 9.99 *(978-1-4516-3567-6(2))* Pocket Books.

Rosinski, Robert, Sr. Las Vegas Lean: How Las Vegas Casinos have taken Lean Manufacturing concepts to a whole new Level. 2007. 200.00 *(978-0-9679593-7-5(3))* Anitech, Inc.

Royer, Victor H. New Casino Slots: How to Play bull; Have Fun bull; & Win! 2010. 196p. pap. 16.95 *(978-1-4502-3801-4(7))* iUniverse, Inc.

Sallaz, Jeff. The Labor of Luck: Casino Capitalism in the United States & South Africa. 2009. (ENG., Illus.). 320p. 55.00 *(978-0-520-25948-5(3))*; pap. 24.95 *(978-0-520-25949-2(1))* Univ. of California Pr.

Scoblete, Frank. The Virgin Kiss & Other Adventures. 2008. 303p. pap. 17.95 *(978-0-912177-17-5(9))* Research Services Unlimited.

Sheehan, Jack. Forgotten Man: How Circus Circus's Bill Bennett Brought Middle America to Las Vegas. 2010. (Illus.). 244p. 29.95 *(978-1-935043-32-4(3))* Stephens Pr. LLC.

Smith, John L. Bluegrass Days, Neon Nights: High Rolling with Happy Chandler's Wayward Son, Dan Chandler. 2010. (Las Vegas Review-Journal Book Ser.). (Illus.). 256p. 24.95 *(978-1-932173-43-7(9))* Stephens Pr. LLC.

Stevens, Mark. Bet your Life. 2008. 130p. pap. 14.95 *(978-1-4357-4663-3(5))* Lulu Enterprises Inc.

Stone, Peter H. Casino Jack & the United States of Money: Superlobbyist Jack Abramoff, His Republican Allies, & the Buying of Washington. 2010. (ENG.). 224p. 15.95 *(978-1-933633-69-5(7))* Melville Hse. Publishing.

Suzuki, Sylvester. The Intelligent Guide to Casino Gaming. 2011. 220p. pap. 15.95 *(978-0-9677551-5-1(8)*, Intelligent Games Publishing) Chartley Publishing, LLC.

Walker, Douglas M. The Economics of Casino Gambling. (ENG., Illus.). xii, 207p. 2010. pap. 139.00 *(978-3-642-07119-5(8)*, 3642071198) 2007. 139.00 *(978-3-540-35102-3(7)*, 3540351027) Springer.

Zajak, Barbara & Burman, Howard. You Can't Win: One Woman's Struggle with the Casinos. 2010. 160p. pap. 14.95 *(978-1-4502-0449-1(X))* iUniverse, Inc.

CASKETS

see Boxes

CASKETS (COFFINS)
see Coffins

CASS, LEWIS, 1782-1866

McLaughlin, Andrew. Lewis Cass. 363p. reprint ed. 98.00 *(978-0-7222-8495-7(0))* Library Reprints, Inc.

McLaughlin, Andrew C. Lewis Cass. 2009. 376p. 29.99 *(978-1-116-52869-5(X))*; 38.99 *(978-1-116-52868-8(1))*; pap. 33.75 *(978-1-116-52870-1(3))*; pap. 32.75 *(978-1-116-52871-8(1))* BiblioBazaar.

—Lewis Cass. 2007. 376p. 48.95 *(978-0-548-55115-8(4))*; (ENG.). per. 33.95 *(978-0-548-50102-3(5))* Kessinger Publishing, LLC.

McLaughlin, Andrew Cunningham. Lewis Cass. 2009. 170p. pap. *(978-1-150-56675-2(2))*; 186p. pap. *(978-0-217-50083-8(8))*; 240p. pap. *(978-0-217-30269-2(6))* Books LLC.

—Lewis Cass. (American Statesmen Ser.). 363p. reprint ed. 98.00 *(978-0-7222-9031-6(4))* Library Reprints, Inc.

McLaughlin, Andrew C. Lewis Cass. (Illus.). reprint ed. lib. bdg. 125.00 *(978-0-7222-0102-2(8))* Library Reprints, Inc.

Silbey, Joel H. Party over Section: The Rough & Ready Presidential Election of 1848. 2009. (Illus.). 224p. 34.95 *(978-0-7006-1640-4(3))* Univ. Pr. of Kansas.

CASSADY, NEAL, 1926-1968

Creighton, David. Ecstasy of the Beats: On the Road to Understanding. 2007. (ENG., Illus.). 320p. pap. 26.99 *(978-1-55002-734-1(4))* Dundurn CAN. Dist: Ingram Pub. Services.

Nicosia, Gerald & Santos, Anne Marie. One & Only: The Untold Story of on the Road. 2011. (ENG., Illus.). 242p. 22.95 *(978-1-936740-04-8(4)*, Viva Editions) Cleis Pr.

Sandison, David & Vickers, Graham. Neal Cassady: The Fast Life of a Beat Hero. 2006. (ENG., Illus.). 368p. 24.95 *(978-1-55652-615-2(6))* Chicago Review Pr., Inc.

CASSATT, MARY, 1845-1926

Adelson, Warren, et al. Art in a Mirror. 2007. (ENG., Illus.). 96p. pap. 35.00 *(978-0-9741621-1-9(6))* Adelson Galleries, Inc.

Mathews, Nancy Mowll & Cantor, Jay E. Mary Cassatt: Friends & Family. 2008. pap. *(978-0-939384-34-1(5))* Shelburne Museum, Inc.

Pinsky, Susan, et al. Mary Cassatt: Prints & Drawings from the Collection of Ambroise Vollard. 2008. (Illus.). 136p. 50.00 *(978-0-9741621-8-8(3))* Adelson Galleries, Inc.

Roach Jr., John P. Absin: A Biographical Novel of Edgar Degas. 2009. 140p. 29.95 *(978-1-4343-7879-8(9))*; pap. 24.95 *(978-1-4343-7878-1(0))* AuthorHouse.

Webster, Sally. Eve's Daughter/Modern Woman: A Mural by Mary Cassatt. 2008. (ENG., Illus.). 176p. pap. 25.95 *(978-0-252-07596-4(X))* Univ. of Illinois Pr.

CASSAVA

Ephraim, Nuwamanya, et al. Descriptive & Comparative Analysis of Cassava Starches. 2010. 84p. pap. *(978-3-8383-8918-9(2))* Lambert Academic Publishing.

Fermont, Anneke. Cassava & Soil Fertility in East Afric. 2010. 180p. pap. *(978-3-8383-5327-2(7))* Lambert Academic Publishing.

Lokko, Yvonne. The Cassava Mosaic Virus Disease. 2010. 184p. pap. *(978-3-8383-7909-8(8))* Lambert Academic Publishing.

Mengue Feniman, Cristane. Cooking Cassav. 2010. 64p. pap. *(978-3-639-24034-4(0))* VDM Verlag Dr. Mueller e.K.

Pace, Colleen M. Cassava: Farming, Uses, & Economic Impact. 2011. (Agriculture Issues & Policies Ser.). (Illus.). 222p. 89.00 *(978-1-61209-655-1(7))* Nova Science Pubs., Inc.

CASSEROLE COOKERY
see Casserole Cooking

CASSEROLE COOKING
see also Dutch Oven Cooking; Electric Cooking, Slow

Alley, Lynn. The Gourmet Slow Cooker Vol. 2: Regional Comfort-Food Classics. 2006. (ENG., Illus.). 112p. pap. 18.95 *(978-1-58008-732-2(9))* Ten Speed Pr.

Atkinson, Catherine & Bleu, Cordon. The Classic Casseroles for Your Slow Cooker. 2010. (ENG.). 256p. pap. 16.95 *(978-0-572-03541-9(1))* Foulsham, W. Co., Ltd. GBR. Dist: APG Sales & Distribution Services.

Atkinson, Catherine & Fleetwood, Jenni. 500 Slow Recipes: A Collection of Delicious Slow-cooked & One-pot Recipes, Including Casseroles, Stews, Soups, Pot Roasts, Puddings & Desserts, Shown in 500 Photographs. 2009. (ENG., Illus.). 256p. 29.99 *(978-0-7548-1889-2(6))* Anness Publishing GBR. Dist: National Bk. Network.

—500 Slow Recipes: A Collection of Delicious Slow-Cooked One-Pot Recipes, Including Casseroles, Stews, Soups, Pot Roasts, Puddings & Desserts. 2011. (ENG., Illus.). 264p. pap. 18.99 *(978-1-78019-003-7(4))* Anness Publishing GBR. Dist: National Bk. Network.

Australian Women's Weekly Staff. Casseroles & One Pot Wonders. Blacker, Maryanne, ed. (Illus.). 128p. pap. 12.95 *(978-1-86396-043-4(0))* ACP Publishing Pty, Ltd. AUS. Dist: Graphic Arts Ctr. Publishing Co.

Baugniet, Rebecca. 500 Casseroles: The Only Casserole Compendium You'll Ever Need. 2009. (Illus.). 288p. 16.95 *(978-1-4162-0769-6(4))* Sellers Publishing, Inc.

Beard, Jim. The Casserole Cookbook. 2011. 148p. 40.95 ***(978-1-258-07651-1(9))*** Literary Licensing, LLC.

Better Homes and Gardens Books Staff. The Ultimate Casseroles Book: More Than 400 Comfort Food Classics. 2011. (Better Homes & Gardens Ultimate Ser.: 28). (ENG., Illus.). 480p. pap. 19.99 *(978-1-118-02035-7(9)*, Wiley) Wiley, John & Sons, Inc.

Better Homes and Gardens Books Staff, contrib. by. Dinner in a Bowl: 160 Recipes for Simple, Satisfying Meals. 2012. (ENG.). 256p. pap. 17.99 ***(978-1-118-03815-4(0)***, Wiley) Wiley, John & Sons, Inc.

Betty Crocker Editors. Betty Crocker One-Dish Family Favorites: Casseroles, Skillet Meals, Stir-Fries, & More Easy, Everyday Dinners. 2006. (Illus.). 383p. *(978-1-59486-503-9(5))* Rodale Pr., Inc.

Burckhardt, Ann L. Hot Dish Heaven: Classic Casseroles from Midwest Kitchens. 2006. (Illus.). 160p. per. 16.95 *(978-0-87351-568-9(4))* Minnesota Historical Society Pr.

Canadian Living Test Kitchen. Canadian Living: The One-Dish Collection. 2012. (ENG., Illus.). 288p. pap. 26.95 ***(978-0-9813938-9-6(6))*** Transcontinental Bks. CAN. Dist: Random Hse., Inc.

Cassidy, Peter & Brigdale, Martin, photos by. Tagines & Couscous. 2010. (ENG., Illus.). 144p. *(978-1-84597-948-5(6))* Ryland Peters & Small.

Catanzaro, Angela. Italian Casserole Cooking. 2007. pap. 19.95 *(978-0-87140-191-5(6))* Liveright Publishing Corp.

Coleman, Mary, ed. Healthy Life. (Illus.). 64p. pap. *(978-1-86396-125-7(9)*, Australian Women's Weekly) ACP Publishing Pty, Ltd.

Collins, Tiffany. 300 Best Casserole Recipes. 2010. (ENG., Illus.). 352p. pap. 24.95 *(978-0-7788-0246-4(9))* Rose, Robert Inc. CAN. Dist: Firefly Bks., Ltd.

Cookbook Resources, contrib. by. 365 Easy Casserole Recipes. 2008. *(978-1-59769-005-8(8))* Cookbook Resources, LLC.

Cooper, Cinnamon. The Everything Cast-Iron Cookbook. 2010. (ENG.). 304p. pap. 15.95 *(978-1-4405-0225-5(0))* Adams Media Corp.

Delicious Casseroles. 96p. *(978-1-4054-9557-8(X))* Parragon, Inc.

Durand, Faith. Not Your Mother's Casseroles. 2011. (NYM Ser.). (ENG.). 336p. 24.95 *(978-1-55832-483-1(6))*; pap. 16.95 *(978-1-55832-484-8(4))* Harvard Common Pr.

Erasmus, Christelle. One-Dish Winners. 2011. 144p. pap. 21.95 *(978-0-7981-4869-6(1))* NB Pubs. Ltd. ZAF. Dist: International Publishers Marketing.

Eyring, Janet & Ashcraft, Stephanie. 200 Casseroles, 1 vol. 2011. (ENG.). 208p. 12.99 *(978-1-4236-2334-2(7))* Gibbs Smith, Publisher.

Farrow, Joanna. 200 One Pot Meals: Hamlyn All Color. 2009. (ENG.). 240p. pap. 7.99 *(978-0-600-61948-2(6)*, Hamlyn) Octopus Publishing Group GBR. Dist: Hachette Bk. Group.

Favorite Brand Name Recipes Editors. Campbell's Casseroles & One-Dish Favorites. 2010. 96p. 7.98 *(978-1-60553-889-1(2))* Publications International, Ltd.

—Country Casseroles. 2010. 144p. spiral bd. 10.98 *(978-1-60553-706-1(3))* Publications International, Ltd.

Favorite Brand Name Recipes Editors, ed. Casseroles. 2010. 384p. pap. 15.98 *(978-1-60553-168-7(5))* Publications International, Ltd.

—Casseroles; Skillets; Soups; Slow Cooker. 2010. 320p. spiral bd. 16.98 *(978-1-60553-715-3(2))* Publications International, Ltd.

—Down-Home Cooking 3 Books In 1: Meat & Potatoes, Casseroles, & Desserts. 2010. 238p. 14.98 *(978-1-4508-0781-4(X))* Publications International, Ltd.

—Simple 1-2-3 One-Dish Meals. 2010. 144p. spiral bd. 10.98 *(978-1-60553-119-9(7)*, PIL Kids) Publications International, Ltd.

Favorite Recipes Press, creator. Casseroles. 2007. (Favorite Recipes of Home Economic Teachers Ser.). (Illus.). 382p. 19.95 *(978-0-87197-538-6(6))* Southwestern Publishing Group, Inc.

Favorite Recipes Press Staff, contrib. by. Casseroles. 2009. (Illus.). 382p. ***(978-0-87197-842-4(3))*** FRP.

Good Food Magazine Staff. Good Food: 201 One-Pot Favourites. 2011. (ENG., Illus.). 192p. pap. 23.95 ***(978-1-84990-141-3(4))*** BBC Worldwide GBR. Dist: Independent Pubs. Group.

Hoffman, Mable. The Crockery Cook. 2006. (ENG., Illus.). 160p. per. 14.95 *(978-0-7624-2600-3(4))* Running Pr. Bk. Pubs.

Hornby, Jane. 101 More One-Pot Dishes: Triple-Tested Recipes. 2010. (Good Food 101 Ser.). (ENG., Illus.). 216p. pap. 9.95 *(978-1-84607-767-8(2))* BBC Worldwide GBR. Dist: Independent Pubs. Group.

Jones, Barbara C. Casseroles to the Rescue: Easy-To-Make Home-Cooked Casseroles. (Illus.). 285p. pap. *(978-1-931294-50-8(X))* Cookbook Resources, LLC.

Larsen, Linda Johnson, et al. Church Potluck Best-Loved Slow Cooker & Casserole Recipes. 2010. *(978-1-60529-297-7(4))* Rodale Pr., Inc.

Let's Cook One Pot. Date not set. (Let's Cook Ser.). 48p. pap. 4.98 *(978-1-4054-0844-8(8))* Parragon, Inc.

McKee, Gwen & Moseley, Barbara. Recipe Hall of Fame One-Dish Wonders: Winning Recipes from Hometown America. 2011. ***(978-1-934193-68-6(2))*** Quail Ridge Pr., Inc.

Miller, Norma. One-Pot Dishes for Every Season: Over 100 Delicious Recipes. 2010. (ENG., Illus.). 192p. pap. 12.95 *(978-1-61608-016-7(7)*, 608016) Skyhorse Publishing Co., Inc.

Mumm, Debbie, illus. Debbie Mumm 3 Books In 1: Old-Fashioned Cookies Cookbook, Country Casseroles Cookbook, Grilling & More Cookbook. 2007. (3 Books In 1 Ser.). 12.98 *(978-1-4127-2878-2(9))* Publications International, Ltd.

Musetti-Carlin, Monica. Casserole Cooking: Over 100 Easy & Delicious One-Dish Recipes. Krusinski, Anna, ed. 2012. (Country Comfort Ser.). (ENG.). 192p. pap. 12.50 ***(978-1-57826-404-9(9))*** Hatherleigh Co., Ltd., The.

One Pot Cooking. Date not set. (Essentials Collection Cooking). 96p. 5.98 *(978-1-4054-2023-5(5))* Parragon, Inc.

Ono, Tadashi & Salat, Harris. Japanese Hot Pots: Comforting One-Pot Meals. 2009. (ENG., Illus.). 160p. pap. 25.00 *(978-1-58008-981-4(X))* Ten Speed Pr.

Paré, Jean. One Dish Wonders: 2-In-1 Cookbook Collection. 2008. *(978-1-897069-87-5(1))* Recipe Factory, Inc.

Pillsbury Company Staff. The Best of the Bake-Off Casseroles. 2010. (ENG., Illus.). 160p. pap. 17.95 *(978-0-470-48577-4(9)*, Wiley) Wiley, John & Sons, Inc.

Pollock, Sandy & Cook, Crystal. The Casserole Queens Cookbook: Put Some Lovin' in Your Oven with 100 Easy One-Dish Recipes. 2011. (ENG., Illus.). 208p. pap. 17.99 *(978-0-307-71785-6(2)*, Clarkson Potter) Crown Publishing Group.

Publications International Staff. Busy Family Campbell's Casserole. Favorite Brand Name Recipes Editors, ed. 2010. 192p. spiral bd. 10.98 *(978-1-60553-182-3(0)*, PIL Kids) Publications International, Ltd.

—One Dish Slow Cooker 3 In 1. 2006. (Illus.). 288p. spiral bd. 10.98 *(978-1-4127-2486-9(4)*, PIL Kids) Publications International, Ltd.

—Recipes to Share Casseroles. 2009. 144p. spiral bd. 10.98 *(978-1-4127-9796-2(9)*, PIL Kids) Publications International, Ltd.

Publications International Staff, creator. Favorite Brand Name Slow Cooker Recipes. 2007. (Favorite Brand Name Ser.). (Illus.). 383p. 15.98 *(978-1-4127-2811-9(8))* Publications International, Ltd.

Publications International Staff, ed. Campbell's Casseroles. 2008. spiral bd. 4.98 *(978-1-4127-2868-3(1))* Publications International, Ltd.

—The One-Dish Bible. 2010. 256p. 14.98 *(978-1-60553-722-1(5))* Publications International, Ltd.

Reader's Digest Association Staff, contrib. by. Easy Everyday Favorites: From the World's #1 Cooking Website. 2007. (Illus.). 256p. 21.95 *(978-0-7621-0844-2(4))* Reader's Digest Assn., Inc., The.

Reader's Digest Editors & Jackson, Gram. Just One Pot: Over 320 Simple & Delicious Recipes, from Hearty Stews to Tasty Tangines. 2010. (ENG.). (gr. 12). 19.95 *(978-1-60652-160-1(8))* Reader's Digest Assn., Inc., The.

Rice Hahn, Pamela. The Everything One-Pot Cookbook: Delicious & Simple Meals That You Can Prepare in Just One Dish - 300 All-New Recipes! 2nd ed. 2009. (ENG.). 304p. pap. 15.95 *(978-1-59869-836-7(2))* Adams Media Corp.

Rosenthal, Alan. Stewed! Nourish Your Soul. 2010. (ENG., Illus.). 160p. 29.95 ***(978-0-09-193802-4(3))*** Ebury Publishing GBR. Dist: Independent Pubs. Group.

Ryland Peters & Small, creator. Easy One-Pot: Frugal recipes for busy Cooks. 2009. (ENG., Illus.). 240p. *(978-1-84597-896-9(X))* Ryland Peters & Small.

Taste of Home. Taste of Home - Casseroles: 377 Dishes for Families, Potlucks & Parties. 2011. (ENG.). 256p. (gr. 12). 15.95 *(978-0-89821-876-3(4))* Reader's Digest Assn., Inc., The.

Taste of Home Casseroles Slow Cooker & Soups: 3 Books in 1: 536 Family-Pleasing Recipes. 2007. (Illus.). 384p. *(978-0-89821-596-0(X))* Reiman Pubns., L.P.

The Ultimate Casserole Cookbook. 2010. (Illus.). 320p. ***(978-0-89821-798-8(9))*** Reiman Pubns., L.P.

Washburn, Laura. Home-Cooked Comforts: Oven Bakes, Casseroles & Other One-Pot Dishes. 2006. (ENG.). 144p. *(978-1-84975-037-0(8))* Ryland Peters & Small.

Weight Watchers Editors. Weight Watchers One Pot Cookbook. 2011. (ENG., Illus.). 384p. 29.99 ***(978-1-118-03812-3(6)***, Wiley) Wiley, John & Sons, Inc.

Widican, Kristen. The Everything Healthy Casserole Cookbook: Includes - Bubbly Black Bean & Cheese Dip, Chicken Jambalaya, Seitan Shepard's Pie, Turkey & Summer Squash Mousska, Harvest Fruit Cake. 2011. (ENG., Illus.). 304p. pap. 16.95 ***(978-1-4405-2932-0(9))*** Adams Media Corp.

Wilson, Mitzie & Taylor, Genevieve. Stew! 100 Splendidly Simple Recipes. 2011. (ENG., Illus.). 160p. pap. 19.95 *(978-1-906650-47-6(0))* Absolute Pr. GBR. Dist: Independent Pubs. Group.

Wright, Clifford A. Bake until Bubbly: The Ultimate Casserole Cookbook. 2008. (ENG.). 464p. pap. 22.95 *(978-0-471-75447-3(1)*, Wiley) Wiley, John & Sons, Inc.

CASSEROLE RECIPES
see Casserole Cooking

CASSETTE BOOKS
see Audiobooks

CASSIAN, JOHN, CA. 360-CA. 435

Chadwick, Owen. John Cassian. 2nd ed. 2008. (ENG.). 180p. pap. 42.00 *(978-0-521-08020-0(7))* Cambridge Univ. Pr.

Goodrich, Richard J. Contextualizing Cassian: Aristocrats, Asceticism, & Reformation in Fifth-Century Gaul. 2008. (Oxford Early Christian Studies). (ENG., Illus.). 320p. 125.00 *(978-0-19-921313-9(5))* Oxford Univ. Pr., Inc.

Kelly, Christopher J. Cassian's Conferences: Scriptural Interpretation & the Monastic Ideal. 2012. (New Critical Thinking in Religion, Theology & Biblical Studies). 196p. 79.95 ***(978-1-4094-0559-7(1))*** Ashgate Publishing Co.

Schaff, Philip, ed. Nicene & Post-Nicene Fathers: Second Series, Volume XI Sulpitius Severus, Vincent of Lerins, John Cassian. 2007. 652p. (ENG.). 37.95 *(978-1-60206-528-4(4))*; per. 27.95 *(978-1-60206-527-7(6))* Cosimo, Inc.

CASSIDY, BUTCH, B. 1866

Betenson, W. J. Butch Cassidy, My Uncle: A Family Portrait. 2012. ***(978-1-937147-02-0(9))***; pap. ***(978-1-937147-03-7(7))*** High Plains Pr.

Casson, Simon. Riding the Outlaw Trail: An Eye Classic. 2nd rev. ed. 2011. (Eye Classics Ser.). (ENG., Illus.). 306p. pap. 12.95 *(978-1-903070-65-9(1))* Eye Bks. GBR. Dist: Independent Pubs. Group.

Warner, Matt, et al. Last of the Bandit Riders... Revisited. Date not set. (Illus.). 252p. reprint ed. pap. 24.95 *(978-0-9656694-1-2(6))* Big Moon Traders.

CASSIDY, DAVID, 1950-

Cassidy, David. Could It Be Forever? My Story. 2009. (ENG., Illus.). 448p. pap. 13.95 *(978-0-7553-1580-2(4))* Headline Bk. Publishing GBR. Dist: Independent Pubs. Group.

CASSIDY, HOPALONG, 1895-1972
see Boyd, William, 1895-1972

CASSINO, BATTLE OF, CASSINO, ITALY, 1944

Dear, Ian. Ten Commando. 2011. 224p. pap. 24.95 *(978-1-84884-400-1(X))* Pen & Sword Bks. Ltd. GBR. Dist: Casemate Pubs. & Bk. Distributors, LLC.

CASSIODORUS, SENATOR, CA.. 487-CA. 580

Andrews, Clarence L. Wrangell & the Gold of the Cassiar. 61p. reprint ed. pap. 10.00 *(978-0-8466-0267-5(9)*, S267) Shorey's Bookstore.

CASSIRER, ERNST, 1874-1945

Barash, Jeffrey Andrew, ed. The Symbolic Construction of Reality: The Legacy of Ernst Cassirer. 2008. (Studies in German-Jewish Cultural History & Literature, Franz Rosenzweig Miner Ser.). 248p. 45.00 *(978-0-226-03686-1(3))* Univ. of Chicago Pr.

Bishop, Paul & Stephenson, R. H., eds. The Paths of Symbolic Knowledge. 2006. (Cultural Studies & the Symbolic Ser.). 140p. (C). 49.00 *(978-1-904350-27-9(5))* Northern Universities Pr. GBR. Dist: Brown, David Bk. Co., The.

Cornell, Drucilla. Symbolic Forms for a New Humanity: Cultural & Racial Reconfigurations of Critical Theory. 4th ed. 2010. (Just Ideas Ser.). (ENG.). 224p. 70.00 *(978-0-8232-3250-5(6))* Fordham Univ. Pr.

Cornell, Drucilla & Panfilio, Kenneth Michael. Symbolic Forms for a New Humanity: Cultural & Racial Reconfigurations of Critical Theory. 4th ed. 2010. (Just Ideas Ser.). (ENG.). 224p. pap. 26.00 *(978-0-8232-3251-2(4))* Fordham Univ. Pr.

Coskun, Deniz. Law as Symbolic Form: Ernst Cassirer & the Anthropocentric View of Law. (Law & Philosophy Library). 2010. xii, 381p. pap. 179.00 *(978-90-481-7584-0(4)*, 9048175844) 2007. 381p. 179.00 *(978-1-4020-6255-1(9))* Springer.

Gordon, Peter E. Continental Divide: Heidegger, Cassirer, Davos. 2012. (ENG., Illus.). 448p. pap. 21.95 ***(978-0-674-06417-1(8))*** Harvard Univ. Pr.

Hoel, Aud Sissel & Folkvord, Ingvild, eds. Ernst Cassirer on Form & Technology: Contemporary Readings. 2012. (ENG., Illus.). 272p. 85.00 ***(978-0-230-36547-6(7))*** Palgrave Macmillan.

Irgens, Eirik. Pluralism in Management: Organizational Theory, Management Education, & Ernst Cassirer. 2011. (Routledge Studies in Management, Organizations & Society Ser.). (ENG., Illus.). 172p. (C). 125.00 *(978-0-415-88617-8(1))* Routledge.

Mawanzi Ndombe, César. Das symbolische Denken als Schlüssel zum Verständnis der Negro-afrikanischen (Bantu-)Weltanschauung: Eine religionsphilosophische Deutung im Anschluss an die Kulturphilosophie Ernst Cassirers. 2008. (Europäische Hochschulschriften. Reihe 23: Theologie Ser.). (GRE & GER.). 420p. pap. 99.95 *(978-3-631-58531-3(4))* Lang, Peter GmbH, Europaischer Verlag der Wissenschaften DEU. Dist: Lang, Peter.

Skidelsky, Edward. Ernst Cassirer: The Last Philosopher of Culture. 2008. (ENG.). 304p. (C). 45.00 *(978-0-691-13134-4(1))* Princeton Univ. Pr.

Skidelsky, Edward. Ernst Cassirer - the Last Philosopher of Culture. 2011. (ENG.). 304p. (C). pap. 24.95 ***(978-0-691-15235-6(7))*** Princeton Univ. Pr.

Verene, Donald Phillip. The Origins of the Philosophy of Symbolic Forms. 2011. (Topics in Historical Philosophy Ser.). (ENG.). 168p. 69.95 *(978-0-8101-2778-4(4))* Northwestern Univ. Pr.

CASSIUS DIO COCCEIANUS

Simons, Benedikt. Cassius Dio und die Römische Republik: Untersuchungen zum Bild des römischen Gemeinwesens in den Büchern 3â€"35 der Romaika. 2009. (Beiträge zur Altertumskunde Ser.). Tr. of Cassius Dio & the Roman Republic. (GER.). X, 337p. 210.00 ***(978-3-11-174140-6(0))*** De Gruyter, Walter Inc.

Simons, Benedikt. Cassius Dio und die Römische Republik: Das Bild Cassius Dios von der Römische Republik in der Bachern 3-35 der Romaika. 2009. (Beiträge zur Altertumskunde Ser.). Tr. of Cassius Dio & the Roman Republic. (GER.). X, 337p. 140.00 *(978-3-11-022586-0(7))* De Gruyter, Walter Inc.

CAST-IRON
see also Columns, Iron and Steel; Decorative Cast-Ironwork; Iron Founding

American Society of Mechanical Engineers Staff, ed. Cast Iron Fittings for Sovent Drainage Systems. 24p. 35.00 *(978-0-7918-2580-8(9))* ASME Pr.

—Cast Iron Pipe Flanges & Flanged Fittings. 44p. 65.00 *(978-0-7918-2573-0(6))* ASME Pr.

—Cast Iron Threaded Drainage Fittings. 28p. 42.00 *(978-0-7918-2576-1(0))* ASME Pr.

Berns, Hans & Theisen, Werner. Ferrous Materials: Steel & Cast Iron. Scheibelein, Gillian, tr. 2010. (ENG., Illus.). xii, 418p. pap. 189.00 *(978-3-642-09093-6(1)*, 3642090931) Springer.

—Ferrous Materials: Steels & Cast Iron. 2008. (ENG., Illus.). xii, 418p. 189.00 *(978-3-540-71847-5(8)*, 3540718478) Springer.

Durand-Charre, Madeleine. Microstructure of Steels & Cast Irons. 2010. (Engineering Materials & Processes Ser.). (Illus.). xii, 404p. pap. 279.00 *(978-3-642-05897-4(3)*, 3642058973) Springer.

C

Forsythe, Robert. The Blast Furnace & the Manufacture of Pig Iron. 2007. 368p. 84.95 *(978-1-4276-1461-2(X))* Wexford College Pr.

Goodrich, George, ed. Casting Defects Handbook: Iron & Steel. 2008. (Illus.). 242p. pap. 60.00 *(978-0-87433-314-5(8))* American Foundry Society.

Technology Research Editors, ed. Surface Hardening of Cast Iron by Laser Beam, 2007 Ed. 2007. pap. 128.50 *(978-1-60030-430-9(3)*, Search-In-Print) CSA Journal Division.

Trans Tech Publications Staff. Science & Processing of Cast Iron IX. 2010. pap. *(978-0-87849-227-5(5))* Trans Tech Pubns., Ltd.

Unglik, Henry. Cast Irons from les Forges du Saint-Maurice, Quebec: A Metallurgical Study. (Illus.). 55p. pap. *(978-0-660-13598-4(1))* Canadian Government Publishing.

Woodward, Joseph H., III & Woodward, Joseph H. Alabama Blast Furnaces. 2nd ed. 2006. (Library Alabama Classics Ser.). (ENG., Illus.). 176p. per. 19.95 *(978-0-8173-5432-9(8))* Univ. of Alabama Pr.

CAST-IRON—COLLECTORS AND COLLECTING

Smith, David G. & Wafford, Chuck. The Book of Griswold & Wagner: Favorite * Wapak * Sidney Hollow Ware. 5th enl. ed. 2011. (Illus.). 328p. *(978-0-7643-3729-1(7)*, Schiffer Publishing Ltd) Schiffer Publishing, Ltd.

CAST-IRON COOKING

see Skillet Cooking

CASTANEDA, CARLOS, 1931-1998

Patterson, Wm Patrick, et al. The Life & Teachings of Carlos Castaneda. 2008. *(978-1-879514-97-3(4))* Arete Communications.

Wagner, Roy. Coyote Anthropology. 2010. (ENG., Illus.). 216p. 40.00 *(978-0-8032-1082-0(5))* Univ. of Nebraska Pr.

Wolf, Felix. The Art of Navigation: Travels with Carlos Castaneda & Beyond. 2010. (ENG.). 324p. pap. 20.00 *(978-0-9822900-1-9(2))* Millichap Bks., LLC.

CASTAWAYS

Crampton, Hazel. The Sunburnt Queen. 2006. (ENG., Illus.). 420p. per. 19.95 *(978-0-86356-545-8(X))* Saqi Bks. GBR. Dist: Consortium Bk. Sales & Distribution.

Fuller, Elizabeth E. Nakahama Manjiro's Hyosen Kiryaku: A Companion Book: Exhibition Catalogue. 2007. (Illus.). 116p. pap. 30.00 *(978-1-4223-6652-3(9))* DIANE Publishing Co.

Rogers, Stanley. Crusoes & Castaways: True Stories of Survival & Solitude. 2011. (ENG., Illus.). 272p. pap. 10.95 *(978-0-486-47897-5(1))* Dover Pubns., Inc.

CASTE

see also Social Classes

Amos, Timothy D. Embodying Difference: The Making of Burakumin in Modern Japan. 2011. 66.00 *(978-0-8248-3578-1(6))*; pap. 33.00 *(978-0-8248-3579-8(4))* Univ. of Hawaii Pr.

Bansode, Prashant, et al, eds. Globalization & Social Justice: Perspectives, Challenges & Praxis. 2008. 318p. 35.00 *(978-81-316-0212-6(5))* Rawat Pubns. IND. Dist: International Specialized Bk. Services.

Caube, Kamala Nayana. Jatiyom Ka Rajanitikarana: [Bihara Mem Pichari Jatiyom Ke Ubhara Ki Dastana]. 2008. (HIN.). 279p. *(978-81-8143-735-8(7)*, Library of Congress — New Delhi Overseas Office) Vani Prakashan.

Dike, Victor. The Osu Caste Discrimination in Igboland: Impact on Igbo Culture & Civilization. 2007. 108p. per. 11.95 *(978-0-595-45921-6(8))* iUniverse, Inc.

Jayanntha, Dilesh. Electoral Allegiance in Sri Lanka. 2006. (Cambridge South Asian Studies: Vol. 48). (ENG.). 232p. pap. 48.00 *(978-0-521-02975-9(9))* Cambridge Univ. Pr.

Jiggins, Janice. Caste & Family Politics Sinhalese, 1947-1976. 2010. (ENG.). 204p. pap. 22.99 *(978-0-521-13378-4(5))* Cambridge Univ. Pr.

McGilvray, Dennis B. Crucible of Conflict: Tamil & Muslim Society on the East Coast of Sri Lanka. 2008. (ENG., Illus.). 448p. (C). 99.95 *(978-0-8223-4137-6(9))*; pap. 27.95 *(978-0-8223-4161-1(1))* Duke Univ. Pr.

McGilvray, Dennis B., ed. Caste Ideology & Interaction. 2009. (Cambridge Papers in Social Anthropology Ser.). (ENG., Illus.). 268p. pap. 36.99 *(978-0-521-10500-2(5))* Cambridge Univ. Pr.

Meigs, Benjamin. Caste, in the Island of Ceylon. 2011. 30p. pap. 11.99 *(978-1-4181-9338-6(0))* MPublishing.

O'Toole, Rachel Sarah. Bound Lives: Africans, Indians, & the Making of Race in Colonial Peru. 2012. (Pitt Latin American Studies). (ENG.). 280p. pap. 25.95 *(978-0-8229-6193-2(8))* Univ. of Pittsburgh Pr.

Taylor, McComas. The Fall of the Indigo Jackal: The Discourse of Division & Purnabhadra's Pancatantra. 2008. xiv, 236p. pap. 29.95 *(978-0-7914-7178-4(0))* State Univ. of New York Pr.

CASTE—INDIA

see also Brahmans; Dalits; Jats

Anderson, J. D. The Peoples of India. 2011. (ENG.). 150p. pap. 19.99 *(978-1-107-40162-4(3))* Cambridge Univ. Pr.

Bairy, Ramesh. Being Brahmin Being Modern. 2010. (ENG.). 304p. (C). 95.00 *(978-0-415-58576-7(7)*, Routledge India) Taylor & Francis Group GBR. Dist: Taylor & Francis Group.

Banerjee-Dube, Ishita, ed. Caste in History. 2010. (Themes in Indian History Ser.). (ENG.). 350p. 29.95 *(978-0-19-806678-1(3))* Oxford Univ. Pr., Inc.

Bhagavan, Manu & Feldhaus, Anne. Speaking Truth to Power: Religion Caste, & the Subaltern Question in India. 2008. (ENG., Illus.). 288p. 29.95 *(978-0-19-569305-8(1))* Oxford Univ. Pr., Inc.

Çalikoglu, Melih Rüstü. Transformation of the Caste System & the Dalit Movement. 2009. 100p. pap. *(978-3-639-13738-5(8))* VDM Verlag Dr. Mueller e.K.

Chalam, K. S. Caste-Based Reservations & Human Development in India. 2007. 210p. *(978-81-7829-742-2(6))* SAGE Pubns., Inc.

Charsley, Simon R. & Kadekar, Laxmi Narayan, eds. Performers & Their Arts in India. 2007. (Illus.). 312p. 95.00 *(978-0-415-40113-5(5))* Routledge.

Chaturvedi, Vinayak. Peasant Pasts: History & Memory in Western India. 2007. (Illus.). 288p. 55.00 *(978-0-520-25076-5(1))*; 307p. per. 26.95 *(978-0-520-25078-9(8))* Univ. of California Pr.

Deshpande, Ashwini. Deshpande: The Grammar of Caste - Economic Discrimination in Contemporary India, 1 vol. 2011. (ENG., Illus.). 272p. 45.00 *(978-0-19-807203-4(1))* Oxford Univ. Pr., Inc.

Doron, Assa. Caste, Occupation & Politics on the Ganges: Passages of Resistance. 2008. (Anthropology & Cultural History in Asia & the Indo-Pacific Ser.). (Illus.). 216p. 114.95 *(978-0-7546-7550-1(5))* Ashgate Publishing Co.

Elliot, Robert H. Gold, Sport, & Coffee Planting in Mysore. 2007. 388p. pap. 25.99 *(978-1-4264-7329-6(X))* 2006. (ENG.). 436p. pap. 28.99 *(978-1-4264-7402-6(4))* BiblioBazaar.

Ganguly, Debjani. Caste, Colonialism & Counter-Modernity: Notes on a Postcolonial Hermeneutics of Caste. 2009. 292p. pap. 39.95 *(978-0-415-54435-1(1))* Routledge.

Gough, Kathleen. Rural Society in Southeast India. 2008. (Cambridge Studies in Social & Cultural Anthropology Ser.). (ENG.). 476p. pap. 84.00 *(978-0-521-04019-8(1))* Cambridge Univ. Pr.

Gupt, Bharat. India: A Cultural Decline or Revival? 2008. 236p. *(978-81-246-0459-5(2))*; pap. *(978-81-246-0460-1(6))* D. K. Print World (P) Ltd.

Guru, Gopal & Sarukkai, Sundar. The Cracked Mirror: An Indian Debate on Experience & Theory. 2012. (ENG.). 264p. 39.95 *(978-0-19-807831-9(5))* Oxford Univ. Pr., Inc.

Hasan, Zoya. Politics of Inclusion: Castes, Minorities, & Affirmative Action. 2009. (ENG.). 300p. 50.00 *(978-0-19-569695-0(6))* Oxford Univ. Pr., Inc.

Hiebert, Paul G. Konduru: Structure & Integration in a South Indian Village. 2009. (ENG.). 208p. pap. 50.00 *(978-0-8166-5787-2(4))* Univ. of Minnesota Pr.

Holmström, Lakshmi & Bama. Karukku. 2nd ed. 2012. (ENG., Illus.). 168p. 19.95 *(978-0-19-807830-2(7))* Oxford Univ. Pr., Inc.

Hunt, W. S. Indias Outcasts A New Era. 2006. 132p. per. *(978-1-4067-2719-7(9)*, Hesperides Pr.) Read Bks.

Jenkins, Laura Dudley. Identity & Identification in India. 2009. 266p. pap. 39.95 *(978-0-415-56062-7(4))* Routledge.

Khare, R. S., ed. Caste, Hierarchy, & Individualism: Indian Critiques of Louis Dumont's Contributions. 2009. (Oxford in India Readings in Sociology & Social Anthropology Ser.). (ENG.). 304p. 29.95 *(978-0-19-806277-6(X))* Oxford Univ. Pr., Inc.

Kumar, Ashwani. Community Warriors: State, Peasants & Caste Armies in Bihar. 2009. (Anthem Press India Ser.). (ENG.). 240p. pap. 40.00 *(978-1-84331-709-8(5))* Anthem Pr. GBR. Dist: Books International, Inc.

Lakshman, Narayan. Patrons of the Poor: Caste Politics & Policymaking in India. 2011. (ENG., Illus.). 328p. 49.95 *(978-0-19-806998-0(7))* Oxford Univ. Pr., Inc.

Life Bliss Foundation Staff. Indian Community System. 2007. 19.99 *(978-1-934364-40-6(1))* Life Bliss Foundation.

Makavana, Manubhai Eca, et al, eds. Backward Classes & Social Justice. 2011. 348p. 50.00 ***(978-81-316-0406-9(3))*** Rawat Pubns. IND. Dist: International Specialized Bk. Services.

Mayer, Adrian C. Caste & Kinship in Central India: A Study of Fiji Indian Rural Society. 2008. 256p. pap. 39.95 *(978-0-415-48757-3(9))* Routledge.

Menon, Dilip M. Caste, Nationalism & Communism in South India: Malabar 1900-1948. 2007. (Cambridge South Asian Studies). (ENG.). 232p. (C). pap. 36.99 *(978-0-521-05195-8(9))* Cambridge Univ. Pr.

Mines, Diane P. Caste in India. 2009. *(978-0-924304-55-2(3))* Assn. for Asian Studies, Inc.

Narayan, Deepa, ed. The Promise of Empowerment & Democracy in India. 2009. (Moving Out of Poverty Ser.: 3). (ENG., Illus.). 432p. 90.00 *(978-0-8213-7838-0(4)*, 9780821378380) World Bank Pubns.

Natrajan, Balmurli. The Culturalization of Caste in India: Identity & Inequality in a Multicultural Age. 2011. (Routledge Contemporary South Asia Ser.). (ENG., Illus.). 232p. (C). 130.00 *(978-0-415-77997-5(9))* Routledge.

Pandian, M. S. S. Brahmin & Non-Brahmin: Genealogies of the Tamil Political Present. 2007. xi, 274p. *(978-81-7824-162-3(5))* Permanent Black.

Patra, Benudhar & Singhania, Kanta. Dalits in Historical Perspective in North-Western India. 2010. (Illus.). xxii, 263p. *(978-81-7702-225-4(3)*, Library of Congress — New Delhi Overseas Office) Pratibha Prakashan, Oriental Pubs. & Distributors.

Radhakrishnan, P. Religion, Caste, & State. 2007. 308p. 32.00 *(978-81-316-0063-4(7))* Rawat Pubns. IND. Dist: International Specialized Bk. Services.

Rao, Anupama & Rao, A. The Caste Question: Dalits & the Politics of Modern India. 2009. (ENG., Illus.). 352p. 65.00 *(978-0-520-25559-3(3))*; pap. 26.95 *(978-0-520-25761-0(8))* Univ. of California Pr.

Rawat, Ramnarayan S. Reconsidering Untouchability: Chamars & Dalit History in North India. 2011. (Contemporary Indian Studies). (ENG., Illus.). 298p. 70.00 *(978-0-253-35558-4(3)*, 0253355583); pap. 24.95 *(978-0-253-22262-6(1)*, 0253222621) Indiana Univ. Pr.

Scoville, James G., ed. Status Influences in Third World Labor Markets: Caste, Gender, & Custom. (De Gruyter Studies in Organization Ser.). (ENG.). VIII, 329p. 196.00 ***(978-3-11-179123-4(8))*** De Gruyter, Walter Inc.

Sekine, Yasumasa. Pollution, Untouchability & Harijans. 2011. 416p. 60.00 ***(978-81-316-0385-7(7))*** Rawat Pubns. IND. Dist: International Specialized Bk. Services.

Shah, Ghanshyam, et al. Untouchability in Rural India. 2006. (Illus.). 216p. (C). per. 34.00 *(978-0-7619-3507-0(X)*, B3507XP) SAGE Pubns., Inc.

Shyamlal. Studies in Social Protest. 2010. (HIN., Illus.). 372p. 55.00 *(978-81-316-0331-4(8))* Rawat Pubns. IND. Dist: International Specialized Bk. Services.

Singer, Milton & Cohn, Bernard, eds. Structure & Change in Indian Society. 2007. (ENG., Illus.). 523p. (gr. 11). pap. 39.95 *(978-0-202-36138-3(1))* Aldine Transaction.

Singh, Birinder Pal. Criminal Tribes of Punjab. 2010. (ENG.). lix, 151p. (C). 95.00 *(978-0-415-55147-2(1)*, Routledge India) Taylor & Francis Group GBR. Dist: Taylor & Francis Group.

Srinivas, Mysore Narasimhachar, intro. Caste, Its Twentieth Century Avatar. xxxvii, 306p. *(978-0-670-86956-5(2))* Penguin Group (USA) Inc.

Sunar, Aasha. Untouchable Jivan. Richburg, Shirley, ed. 2006. pap. 11.95 *(978-0-9710139-4-0(2))* People's Pr., The.

Teltumbde, Anand. The Persistence of Caste: India's Hidden Apartheid & the Khairlanji Murders. 2011. (ENG.). 214p. 116.95 *(978-1-84813-448-5(7))* Zed Bks., Ltd. GBR. Dist: Macmillan.

Thorat, Sukhadeo & Newman, Katherine S., eds. Blocked by Caste: Economic Discrimination & Social Exclusion in Modern India. 2010. (ENG., Illus.). 400p. 29.95 *(978-0-19-806080-2(7))* Oxford Univ. Pr., Inc.

Thorat, Sukhadeo & Newman, Katherine S., eds. Blocked by Caste: Economic Discrimination in Modern India. 2012. (ENG., Illus.). 400p. 24.95 ***(978-0-19-808169-2(3))*** Oxford Univ. Pr., Inc.

Thurston, Edgar. Castes & Tribes of Southern India. 2010. 234p. pap. *(978-1-151-74048-9(9))* 2010. 228p. pap. *(978-1-151-95186-1(2))* 2009. 248p. pap. *(978-1-151-40370-4(9))* Books LLC.

—Castes & Tribes of Southern India. 2009. 256p. pap. 33.59 *(978-1-151-40365-0(2))* General Bks. LLC.

Thurston, Edgar & Rangachari, K. Castes & Tribes of Southern India. 2010. 556p. 44.99 *(978-1-140-18765-3(1))* 2010. 556p. pap. 42.75 *(978-1-140-18766-0(X))* 2009. (ENG.). 557p. pap. 30.99 *(978-1-116-42915-2(2)*, BiblioLife) 2009. (ENG.). 551p. pap. 32.99 *(978-1-116-55286-7(8)*, BiblioLife) 2009. (ENG.). 551p. pap. 30.99 *(978-1-116-55287-4(6)*, BiblioLife) 2009. (ENG.). 557p. pap. 32.99 *(978-1-116-42914-5(4)*, BiblioLife) BiblioBazaar.

Wilson, John. Indian Caste. 2009. 194p. pap. *(978-0-217-48916-4(8))* Books LLC.

CASTIGLIONE, BALDASSARE, CONTE, 1478-1529

Castiglione, Baldassare. Book of the Courtier. Hoby, Thomas, tr. (Tudor Translations, First Ser.: No. 23). reprint ed. 57.50 *(978-0-404-51854-7(0))* AMS Pr., Inc.

Roeder, Ralph. Renaissance Lawgivers: Savonarola, Machiavelli, Castiglione, & Aretino. 2011. (ENG., Illus.). 558p. pap. 49.95 *(978-1-4128-1824-7(9))* Transaction Pubs.

White, John Simon. Renaissance Cavalier. 2011. 78p. 37.95 ***(978-1-258-03768-0(8))*** Literary Licensing, LLC.

CASTILE (SPAIN)

Hay, John M. Castilian Days. reprint ed. 24.50 *(978-0-404-03157-2(9))* AMS Pr., Inc.

O'Callaghan, Joseph F. The Gibraltar Crusade: Castile & the Battle for the Strait. 2011. (Middle Ages Ser.). (Illus.). 392p. (C). 55.00 *(978-0-8122-4302-4(1))* Univ. of Pennsylvania Pr.

CASTILE (SPAIN)—HISTORY

Chabás, José & Goldstein, B. R. The Alfonsine Tables of Toledo. 2012. (Archimedes Ser.). (ENG.). 356p. pap. 219.00 *(978-90-481-6404-2(4)*, 9048164044) Springer.

Dodds, Jerrilynn D., et al. The Arts of Intimacy: Christians, Jews, & Muslims in the Making of Castilian Culture. 2009. (ENG., Illus.). 416p. pap. 25.95 *(978-0-300-15838-0(6))* Yale Univ. Pr.

Dodds, Jerrilynn Denise, et al. The Arts of Intimacy: Christians, Jews, & Muslims in the Making of Castilian Culture. 2009. (ENG., Illus.). 416p. pap. 24.00 *(978-0-300-14214-3(5))* Yale Univ. Pr.

Echevarria, Ana & Beagles, Martin. The Moorish Guard of the Kings of Castile (1410-1467) 2008. (Illus.). 384p. *(978-90-04-17110-7(X))* BRILL.

Espinosa, Aurelio. The Empire of the Cities: Emperor Charles V, the Comunero Revolt, & the Transformation of the Spanish System. 2008. (Studies in Medieval & Reformation Traditions: History, Culture, Religion, Ideas). (Illus.). 368p. (C). *(978-90-04-17136-7(3))* BRILL.

Palomero, Félix. Alfonso VI: ¿del Ocaso de lo Hispano Al Mundo Romano-Frances? 2009. (SPA., Illus.). 302p. *(978-84-9849-409-9(5))* Dykinson, S.L.

Procter, Evelyn S. Curia & Cortes in León & Castile, 1072-1295. 2010. (Cambridge Iberian & Latin American Studies). (ENG.). 340p. pap. 36.99 *(978-0-521-13532-0(X))* Cambridge Univ. Pr.

Rodríguez-Velasco, Jesús D. Order & Chivalry: Knighthood & Citizenship in Late Medieval Castile. Ferguson, Eunice Rodriguez, tr. from SPA. 2010. (Middle Ages Ser.). 304p. (C). 65.00 *(978-0-8122-4212-6(2))* Univ. of Pennsylvania Pr.

Salvador Martinez, H. Alfonso X, the Learned: A Biography. 2010. *(978-90-04-18147-2(4))* BRILL.

CASTILIAN LANGUAGE

see Spanish Language

CASTING

see Founding; Iron Founding; Plaster Casts; Plastics—Molding; Steel Castings

CASTING (FISHING)

see Fly-Casting; Spin Fishing

CASTINGS, METAL

see Metal Castings

CASTLE, IRENE

Golden, Eve. Vernon & Irene Castle's Ragtime Revolution. 2007. (ENG., Illus.). 360p. 40.00 *(978-0-8131-2459-9(X))* Univ. Pr. of Kentucky.

CASTLE, VERNON

Golden, Eve. Vernon & Irene Castle's Ragtime Revolution. 2007. (ENG., Illus.). 360p. 40.00 *(978-0-8131-2459-9(X))* Univ. Pr. of Kentucky.

CASTLES

see also Palaces

also names of castles, e.g. Windsor Castle

AA Publishing. Exploring Britain's Castles: Celebrating Britain's Magnificent Legacy. 2012. (ENG., Illus.). 224p. 34.95 ***(978-0-7495-7075-0(X))*** Automobile Assn. GBR. Dist: Independent Pubs. Group.

Abaka, Edmund Kobina. "House of Slaves & 'door of No Return'" Gold Coast/Ghana Slave Forts, Castles & Dungeons & the Atlantic Slave Trade. 2011. ***(978-1-59221-825-7(3))*** Africa World Pr.

Alex, Erdmute & Spindler, Barbara. Time to Travel-Travel in Time to Germany's Finest Stately Homes, Gardens, Castles, Abbeys & Roman Remains: Official Joint Guide of the Heritage Administrations Baden-Wurttemberg, Bavaria, Berlin-Brandenburg, Dessau-Worlitz, Hesse, Rhineland-Palatinate, Saxony, Saxony-Anhalt, Thuringia. 2nd ed. 2007. (Illus.). 256p. pap. 29.95 *(978-3-7954-1411-5(3))* Schnell und Steiner GmbH, Verlag DEU. Dist: Independent Pubs. Group.

Andrews, Kevin & Bugh, Glenn R. Castles of the Morea. 2nd ed. 2006. (Gennadeion Monograph Ser.). (ENG., Illus.). 306p. 75.00 *(978-0-87661-406-8(3))* American Schl. of Classical Studies at Athens.

Ashcombe, Elizabeth. My Life in a Cotswold Castle: How I Saved Sudeley. 2010. (Illus.). 128p. pap. 22.95 *(978-1-84868-801-8(6))* Amberley Publishing GBR. Dist: Casemate Pubs. & Bk. Distributors, LLC.

Avery, Tracey. Tattershall Castle. 2006. (National Trust Guidebooks Ser.). (ENG.). 32p. pap. 10.95 *(978-1-84359-119-1(7))* History Pr. Ltd., The GBR. Dist: Independent Pubs. Group.

Beissel, Jeannette. Luxury Houses. 2007. (Illus.). 220p. 59.95 *(978-3-8327-9173-5(6))* teNeues Publishing Co.

Bischoff, Michael. Castles of the Weser Renaissance. 2009. (ENG.). 304p. 138.00 *(978-3-936681-23-9(6))* Edition Axel Menges GmbH DEU. Dist: National Bk. Network.

Bonechi, Casa. Chateau of Amboise. 48p. pap. *(978-88-7009-225-7(9))* Casa Editrice Bonechi.

—Golden Book Chateaux: The Loire. (Illus.). 128p. *(978-88-7009-380-3(8))* Casa Editrice Bonechi.

Brown, Michael. Scottish Baronial Castles 1250-1450. 2009. (Fortress Ser.). (ENG., Illus.). 64p. pap. 18.95 *(978-1-84603-286-8(5))* Osprey Publishing, Ltd. GBR. Dist: Random Hse., Inc.

Castles. 2007. (Nonfiction Collection). (J). 5.50 *(978-1-60343-007-4(5))* Pioneer Valley Educational Pr., Inc.

Chapman, Charles & Brown, Alexandra. Windsor Ablaze! The Windsor Castle Fire & Restoration. 2007. (ENG., Illus.). 64p. pap. 23.00 *(978-0-7188-3082-3(2))* Lutherworth Pr., The GBR. Dist: Brown, David Bk. Co., The.

Chateau of Blois. 48p. pap. *(978-88-7009-726-9(9))* Casa Editrice Bonechi.

Coe, Graham S. Edinburgh & the Lothians. 2007. (Castle Touring Guides Ser.: Vol. 4). (ENG., Illus.). 224p. pap. 21.95 *(978-1-899874-37-8(2))* Goblinshead GBR. Dist: Dufour Editions, Inc.

Corazza, Giacomo. The Castle of Tabiano: A thousand years of history, legends, in the Pallavicino Fiefs. 2011. 80p. pap. 24.95 *(978-88-492-1869-5(9))* Gangemi ITA. Dist: International Publishers Marketing.

Correia, Luís Miguel Maldonado de Vasconcelos. Castelos Em Portugal: Retrato Do Seu Perfil Arquitectónico (1509-1949) 2010. (POR., Illus.). 469p. *(978-989-26-0022-2(3))* Coimbra Editora.

Countess of Carnarvon Staff. Lady Almina & the Real Downton Abbey: The Lost Legacy of Highclere Castle. 2011. (ENG., Illus.). 320p. pap. 15.99 ***(978-0-7704-3562-2(9))*** Broadway Bks.

Coventry, Martin. Castles of the Clans: The Strongholds & Seats of 750 Scottish Families & Clans. 2008. (ENG., Illus.). 640p. pap. 38.95 *(978-1-899874-36-1(4))* Goblinshead GBR. Dist: Dufour Editions, Inc.

Davis, Paul R. Castles of the Welsh Princes. 2011. (ENG., Illus.). 108p. pap. 14.95 ***(978-0-86243-970-5(1))*** Y Lolfa GBR. Dist: Dufour Editions, Inc.

De Montclos, Jean-Marie Pérouse. Chateaux of the Loire Valley, 1 vol. 2011. (ENG.). 360p. 19.99 ***(978-3-8331-6234-3(1))*** h.f.ullmann DEU. Dist: Innovative Logistics.

Dover Publications Inc. Staff, creator. Castles. 2007. (Electronic Clip Art Ser.). (ENG., Illus.). 48p. pap. 14.95 *(978-0-486-99828-2(2))* Dover Pubns., Inc.

Dubois, Adrien. Caen Castle: A Ten Centuries Old Fortress Within the Town. 2010. (Publications du Crahm Ser.). (Illus.). 128p. (C). 22.00 *(978-2-902685-75-2(0))* Brepols Pubs. BEL. Dist: Brown, David Bk. Co., The.

Ellenblum, Ronnie. Crusader Castles & Modern Histories. (ENG.). 2009. 376p. pap. 50.00 *(978-0-521-12364-8(X))* 2007. (Illus.). 374p. 114.00 *(978-0-521-86083-3(0))* Cambridge Univ. Pr.

Ettel, P., et al, eds. Chateau et Representations: Actes du colloque international de Stirling (Ecosse). 2008. 2010. (Chateau Gaillard Ser.). (ENG, FRE & GER.). 280p. (C). 65.00 *(978-2-902685-77-6(7))* Brepols Pubs. BEL. Dist: Brown, David Bk. Co., The.

Ettel, P., et al. Chateau et Peuplement: Etudes de Castellologie Medievale. 2007. (Chateau Gaillard Ser.). (Illus.). 373p. 62.00 *(978-2-902685-34-9(3))* Brepols Pubs. BEL. Dist: Brown, David Bk. Co., The.

Etting, Vivian. Royal Castles of Denmark During the 14th Century: An Analysis of the Major Royal Castles with Special Regard to Their Functions & Strategic Importance. 2010. (Illus.). 217p. 55.00 *(978-87-7602-138-2(6))* Univ. Pr. of Southern Denmark DNK. Dist: International Specialized Bk. Services.

Farah, Caesar E. The Ottoman Forts & Castles of Yemen: A Photographic & Architectural Analysis. 2011. (Illus.). 180p. 109.95 *(978-0-7734-1291-0(3))* Mellen, Edwin Pr., The.

Fawcett, Richard & Rutherford, Allan. Renewed Life for Scottish Castles. 2011. (CBA Research Report). (Illus.). 178p. (C). pap. 40.00 *(978-1-902771-86-1(9))* Council for British Archaeology GBR. Dist: Brown, David Bk. Co., The.

Ferrand, Franck. Highland Living: Landscape, Style, & Traditions of Scotland. 2010. (ENG., Illus.). 160p. 39.95 *(978-2-08-030133-8(0))* Flammarion et Cie FRA. Dist: Random Hse., Inc.

Fitzgerald, Mairéad. Castles of Ireland. 2007. (ENG., Illus.). 48p. pap. 12.95 ***(978-0-86278-988-6(5))*** O'Brien Pr., Ltd., The IRL. Dist: Dufour Editions, Inc.

Friar, Stephen. The Sutton Companion to Castles. 2008. (ENG., Illus.). 352p. pap. 34.95 *(978-0-7509-3994-2(X))* History Pr. Ltd.,The GBR. Dist: Independent Pubs. Group.

Fry, Plantagenet Somerset. Castles of Britain & Ireland. (Illus.). 312p. pap. *(978-0-7153-1255-1(3))* David & Charles Pubs. GBR. Dist: David & Charles Pubs.

Gaens, T. & Nijssen, R., eds. Schoon Volk: Kasteelbewoners in West-Limburg in de 19e eeuw Eby T. Gaens, R. Nijssen. 2010. (DUT.). 155p. (C). pap. 35.00 *(978-90-429-2462-8(4))* Peeters Pubs. & Booksellers BEL. Dist: Brown, David Bk. Co., The.

Garnett, Oliver. Dunster Castle. 2006. (National Trust Guidebooks Ser.). (ENG., Illus.). 48p. pap. 11.95 *(978-1-84359-049-1(2))* History Pr. Ltd.,The GBR. Dist: Independent Pubs. Group.

Gibson, Scott W. The Curse of Castle Caernarfon. 162p. 22.95 *(978-0-9704483-0-9(9))* M.I. Pubs.

Gondoin Castellant Staff. French Castles of 100 Years War, Vol. 1. 2006. (Illus.). 128p. 39.95 *(978-2-915239-80-5(0))* Histoire et Collections FRA. Dist: Casemate Pubs. & Bk. Distributors, LLC.

Gondoin, Stephane W. Twilight of the Medieval Castles. 2008. (Fortresses Ser.). (Illus.). 128p. 44.95 *(978-2-35250-069-8(9))* Histoire et Collections FRA. Dist: Casemate Pubs. & Bk. Distributors, LLC.

Goodall, John. The English Castle, 1066-1650. 2011. (Paul Mellon Centre for Studies in Britis Ser.). (Illus.). 480p. 75.00 *(978-0-300-11058-6(8))* Yale Univ. Pr.

Gravett, Christopher. Castles & Fortifications from Around the World. 2007. (ENG., Illus.). 192p. pap. 24.95 *(978-1-59921-110-7(6)*, Lyons Pr.) Globe Pequot Pr., The.

—The Castles of Edward I in Wales 1277-1307. Cowper, Marcus & Bogdanovic, Nikolai, eds. 2007. (Fortress Ser.). (ENG., Illus.). 64p. pap. 16.95 *(978-1-84603-027-7(7))* Osprey Publishing, Ltd. GBR. Dist: Random Hse., Inc.

—English Castles 1200-1300. 2009. (Fortress Ser.). (ENG., Illus.). 64p. pap. 18.95 *(978-1-84603-374-2(8))* Osprey Publishing, Ltd. GBR. Dist: Random Hse., Inc.

Green, Michelin. Michelin Green Gd Chateaux of Loire. 9th rev. ed. 2010. (Green Guide Ser.). (ENG., Illus.). 336p. pap. 21.99 *(978-1-906261-76-4(8))* Michelin Travel & Lifestyle.

Harrington, Peter. The Castles of Henry VIII. 2007. (Fortress Ser.). (ENG., Illus.). 96p. pap. 16.95 *(978-1-84603-130-4(3))* Osprey Publishing, Ltd. GBR. Dist: Random Hse., Inc.

Heritage House Group Staff. Hudson's Historic Houses & Gardens, Castles & Heritage Sites. 2009. (Illus.). 608p. pap. 24.95 *(978-0-85101-886-7(6))* Heritage Hse. Group Ltd. GBR. Dist: Globe Pequot Pr., The.

Holliday, Christopher. Houses of the Lake District. 2012. (ENG., Illus.). 208p. 50.00 ***(978-0-7112-3161-0(3))*** Lincoln, Frances Ltd. GBR. Dist: Perseus-PGW.

Hull, Lise. Great Castles of Britain & Ireland. 2009. (ENG., Illus.). 160p. pap. 19.95 *(978-1-84773-130-2(9))* New Holland Pubs., Ltd. GBR. Dist: National Bk. Network.

—The Great Castles of Britain & Ireland. 2006. (ENG., Illus.). 160p. 45.00 *(978-1-84330-898-0(3))* New Holland Pubs., Ltd. GBR. Dist: National Bk. Network.

—Understanding the Castle Ruins of England & Wales: How to Interpret the History & Meaning of Masonry & Earthworks. 2008. (ENG., Illus.). 228p. 49.95 *(978-0-7864-3457-2(0))* McFarland & Co., Inc. Pubs.

Impey, Edward, ed. The White Tower. 2009. (ENG., Illus.). 406p. 85.00 *(978-0-300-11293-1(9))* Yale Univ. Pr.

Kenyon, John & Williams, Diane, eds. The Impact of the Edwardian Castles in Wales. 2010. (ENG., Illus.). 240p. (C). 70.00 *(978-1-84217-380-0(4))* Oxbow Bks., Ltd. GBR. Dist: Brown, David Bk. Co., The.

Kenyon, John R. The Medieval Castles of Wales. 2011. (ENG., Illus.). 166p. pap. 25.00 *(978-0-7083-2180-5(1))* Univ. of Wales Pr. GBR. Dist: Chicago Distribution Ctr.

Kuhler, Michael. The Castles of King Ludwig II. 2011. (Castles & Palaces Ser.). (ENG., Illus.). 128p. 32.95 *(978-3-8003-1868-1(7))* Verlagshaus Wurzburg GmbH & Co. KG DEU. Dist: Independent Pubs. Group.

Langenscheidt Publishers Staff. Michelin Travel Guide Chateaux of the Loire. 8th rev. ed. 2008. (Michelin Travel Guide Chateauz of the Loire Ser.). (Illus.). 335p. 21.95 *(978-1-906261-25-2(3))* Michelin.

Leith Hay, Andrew. Castles of Aberdeenshire: Historical & Descriptive Notices. 2011. (Illus.). 250p. reprint ed. pap. ***(978-1-84530-113-2(7))*** Grimsay Pr.

Lepage, Jean-Denis G.G. Castles & Fortified Cities of Medieval Europe: An Illustrated History. alt. ed. 2010. (ENG., Illus.). 335p. pap. 39.95 *(978-0-7864-6099-1(7))* McFarland & Co., Inc. Pubs.

Lewis, Brenda. Life in a Medieval Castle. 2008. (ENG.). 96p. pap. *(978-0-7509-4602-5(4))* History Pr. Ltd.,The.

Lindsay, Maurice. The Castles of Scotland. (Illus.). 482p. pap. 24.95 *(978-0-09-473430-2(5)*, Arrow Bks., Ltd.) Random Hse. GBR. Dist: Trafalgar Square Publishing.

Mattingly, Alan. The Cathar Way: A Walker's Guide to the Sentier Cathare, a Trail Linking Cathar Castles in Southern France. 2010. (Illus.). 192p. pap. 19.95 *(978-1-85284-486-8(8))* Cicerone Pr. GBR. Dist: Midpoint Trade Bks., Inc.

Mcneill. Small Castles in the British Isles. 2008. (Illus.). 224p. 108.00 *(978-0-415-37834-5(6))* Routledge.

Mézin, Louis. La Villa Masséna: Du Premier Empire à la Belle Époque. 2010. (FRE., Illus.). 183p. *(978-2-7572-0387-3(8))* Somogy Editions d'Art.

Miltoun, Francis. Castles & Chateaux of Old Navarre and. 2006. (Illus.). pap. 42.95 *(978-1-4286-6337-4(1))* Kessinger Publishing, LLC.

Mol, Eva. Hidden Complexities of the Frankish Castle: Social Aspects of Space in the Configurational Architecture of Frankish Castles in the Holy Land, 1099-1291. 2012. (Archaeological Studies Leiden University Ser.: 25). (ENG.). 220p. pap. *(978-90-8728-119-9(6)*, Leiden Univ. Pr.) Amsterdam Univ. Pr.

Morgan, Gerald. Castles in Wales. 2010. (ENG., Illus.). 262p. pap., instr.'s hndbk. ed. 12.95 ***(978-1-84771-031-4(X))*** Y Lolfa GBR. Dist: Dufour Editions, Inc.

Morris, Marc. Castle. (Illus.). 288p. 35.00 *(978-0-7522-1536-5(1)*, Boxtree) Pan Macmillan GBR. Dist: Trafalgar Square Publishing.

Nash, George & Redwood, Brian. Looking Beyond the Castle Walls: The Weobley Castle Project. 2006. (Bar S Ser.). (Illus.). xv, 199p. (C). pap. 90.00 *(978-1-84171-954-2(4))* British Archaeological Reports Ltd. GBR. Dist: Brown, David Bk. Co., The.

Nicolle, David. Crusader Castles in Cyprus, Greece & the Aegean 1191-1571. 2007. (Fortress Ser.). (ENG., Illus.). 64p. pap. 18.95 *(978-1-84176-976-9(2))* Osprey Publishing, Ltd. GBR. Dist: Random Hse., Inc.

Nossov, Konstantin. Indian Castles 1206-1526: The Rise & Fall of the Delhi Sultanate. 2006. (Fortress Ser.: Vol. 51). (ENG., Illus.). 64p. pap. 16.95 *(978-1-84603-065-9(X))* Osprey Publishing, Ltd. GBR. Dist: Random Hse., Inc.

Perouse De Montclos, Jean-Marie. Chateaux of the Loire Valley. 2008. (Art & Architecture Ser.). (Illus.). 359p. pap. 24.95 *(978-0-8416-0060-7(0))* American Map Corp.

Phillips, Charles. Medieval Castles, Stately & Historic Houses of Great Britain & Northern Ireland: From Ancient Times to the Wars of the Roses & 1485. 2009. (ENG., Illus.). 96p. pap. 14.99 *(978-1-84476-563-8(6))* Anness Publishing GBR. Dist: National Bk. Network.

Phillips, Charles & Wilson, Richard. The Complete Illustrated Guide to the Castles, Palaces & Stately Houses of Britain & Ireland: Britain's Magnificent Architectural, Cultural & Historical Heritage Is Celebrated in over 500 Photographs, Fine-Art Paintings, Maps & Drawings. 2008. (ENG., Illus.). 256p. 35.00 *(978-0-7548-1740-6(7))* Anness Publishing GBR. Dist: National Bk. Network.

Phillips, Charles & Wilson, Richard G. The Illustrated Encyclopedia of the Castles, Palaces & Stately Houses of Britain & Ireland: A Magnificent Visual Account of Britain's Architectural & Historical Heritage Celebrated in over 500 Beautiful Photographs, Fine-Art Paintings, Drawings & Maps. 2012. (ENG., Illus.). 264p. 18.99 ***(978-0-7548-2475-6(6))*** Anness Publishing GBR. Dist: National Bk. Network.

Phillips, Charles & Wilson, Richard G. The Stately Houses Palaces & Castles of Georgian, Victorian & Modern Britain: From George I to Elizabeth II, 1714 to the Present Day. 2011. (ENG., Illus.). 96p. pap. 16.99 *(978-1-84476-800-4(7))* Anness Publishing GBR. Dist: National Bk. Network.

Phillips, Neil. Earthwork Castles of Gwent & Ergyng AD 1050-1250. 2006. (Bar S Ser.). (Illus.). ix,258p. (C). 100.00 *(978-1-84171-977-1(3))* British Archaeological Reports Ltd. GBR. Dist: Brown, David Bk. Co., The.

Pratt, Lord Michael. Hungary. 2008. (Great Country Houses Of... Ser.). (ENG., Illus.). 143p. 39.95 *(978-0-7892-0891-0(1))* Abbeville Pr., Inc.

Prior, Stuart. The Norman Art of War: A Few Well-Positioned Castles. 2006. (ENG., Illus.). 176p. per. 37.95 *(978-0-7524-3651-7(1))* History Pr. Ltd.,The GBR. Dist: Independent Pubs. Group.

Reid, Alan. The Castles of Wales. 2nd ed. (Illus.). 140p. pap. 13.95 *(978-1-871083-41-5(9))* Jones, John Publishing GBR. Dist: Dufour Editions, Inc.

Samuel, Mark & Hamlyn, Kate. Blarney Castle: Its History, Development & Purpose. 2008. (Illus.). 166p. 39.00 *(978-1-85918-411-0(1))* Cork Univ. Pr. IRL. Dist: Stylus Publishing, LLC.

Sarramon Christian, photos by. Bordeaux Chateaux: A History of the Grands Crus Classés since 1855. rev. ed. 2009. (ENG., Illus.). 320p. pap. 34.95 *(978-2-08-030121-5(7))* Flammarion et Cie FRA. Dist: Random Hse., Inc.

Scala Publishing. Leeds Castle: Queen of Castles, Castle of Queens. 2010. (ENG., Illus.). 64p. pap. 10.00 *(978-1-85759-590-1(4))* Scala, Editions FRA. Dist: National Bk. Network.

Simpson, W. Douglas, ed. The Building Accounts of Tattershall Castle, 1434-1472. 2010. (Publications of the Lincoln Record Society Ser.: Volume 55). (Illus.). 118p. pap. 45.00 *(978-0-901503-89-3(4))* Lincoln Record Society GBR. Dist: Boydell & Brewer, Inc.

Stephenson, Charles. Castles: A Global History of Fortified Structures - Ancient, Medieval, & Modern. 2011. (ENG., Illus.). 288p. pap. 29.99 *(978-0-312-54140-8(6)*, St. Martin's Griffin) St. Martin's Pr.

Struthers, Jane & Frances Lincoln Staff. Castles from the Air. 2006. (Illus.). 256p. 40.00 *(978-0-7112-2447-6(1))* Lincoln, Frances Ltd. GBR. Dist: Perseus-PGW.

Sudbury, Richard. Two Gentlemen in Touraine. 2007. (ENG.). 348p. 46.95 *(978-0-548-07292-9(2))* Kessinger Publishing, LLC.

Svec, Joseph W. Toy Castles & Knights: A Guide to Toy Castles from Around the World. 2012. pap. 26.95 ***(978-0-7414-7323-3(2))*** Infinity Publishing.

Tabraham, Chris. Castles of Scotland: A Voyage Through the Centuries. 2006. (Historic Scotland Ser.). (ENG., Illus.). 208p. 24.95 *(978-0-7134-8976-7(6)*, Batsford, B. T. Ltd.) Anova Bks. GBR. Dist: Sterling Publishing Co., Inc.

Taylor, T. Saint Michael's Mount. 2010. (ENG.). 212p. pap. 23.99 *(978-0-521-13796-6(9))* Cambridge Univ. Pr.

Thomas, Anabel. Garrisoning the Borderlands of Medieval Siena: Sant'angelo in Colle - Frontier Castle under the Government of the Nine (1287-1355) 2011. (Illus.). 444p. 124.95 *(978-1-4094-2603-5(3))* Ashgate Publishing Co.

Thompson, M. W. The Decline of the Castle. 2008. (ENG., Illus.). 224p. pap. 32.99 *(978-0-521-08397-3(4))* Cambridge Univ. Pr.

—The Rise of the Castle. 2008. (ENG., Illus.). 216p. pap. 32.99 *(978-0-521-08853-4(4))* Cambridge Univ. Pr.

Turnbull, Stephen. Japanese Castles AD 250 — 1540. 2008. (Fortress Ser.). (ENG., Illus.). 64p. pap. 18.95 *(978-1-84603-253-0(9))* Osprey Publishing, Ltd. GBR. Dist: Random Hse., Inc.

—Japanese Castles in Korea 1592-98. 2007. (Fortress Ser.). (ENG., Illus.). 64p. pap. 16.95 *(978-1-84603-104-5(4))* Osprey Publishing, Ltd. GBR. Dist: Random Hse., Inc.

—Strongholds of the Samurai: Japanese Castles 250-1877. 2009. (General Military Ser.). (ENG., Illus.). 272p. 24.95 *(978-1-84603-413-8(2))* Osprey Publishing, Ltd. GBR. Dist: Random Hse., Inc.

Wagener, Olaf, ed. Vmbringt mit starcken turnen, Mum: Ortsbefestigungen im Mittelalter. 2011. (Beihefte zur Mediaevistik. Monographien, Editionen, Sammelbände Ser.). (GER.). 452p. pap. 108.95 *(978-3-631-60664-3(8))* Lang, Peter GmbH, Europaischer Verlag der Wissenschaften DEU. Dist: Lang, Peter.

Wagener, Olaf & Laß, Heiko, eds. Die imaginäre Burg. 2009. (Beihefte zur Mediaevistik. Monographien, Editionen, Sammelbände Ser.). (GER.). 216p. pap. 53.95 *(978-3-631-58008-0(8))* Lang, Peter GmbH, Europaischer Verlag der Wissenschaften DEU. Dist: Lang, Peter.

Wardle, Terry. England's First Castle: The Story of a 1000-Year-Old Mystery. 2009. (ENG., Illus.). 160p. pap. 32.95 *(978-0-7524-4797-1(1))* History Pr. Ltd.,The GBR. Dist: Independent Pubs. Group.

Weirter, Louis. The Story of Edinburgh Castle. 2009. (Illus.). 136p. pap. 39.99 *(978-1-4389-5398-4(4))* AuthorHouse.

Westerberg, Ann. Castles of Colorado: Scandals, Hauntings, & Tales of the Past. 2008. (Illus.). 190p. pap. 22.95 *(978-1-55566-417-6(2))* Johnson Bks.

Wilsdon, Bill. Plantation Castles on the Erne. 2010. (ENG., Illus.). 256p. pap. 32.95 ***(978-1-84588-980-7(0))*** History Pr. Ltd.,The GBR. Dist: Independent Pubs. Group.

CASTLES—JUVENILE LITERATURE

Jovinelly, Joann. The Crafts & Culture of a Medieval Castle. 2006. 52p. (gr. 3-7). pap. 29.25 *(978-1-4358-3771-3(1))* Rosen Publishing Group, Inc., The.

CASTLETON (VT.)

Thompson, Donald H. Castleton, Vermont: Its Industries, Enterprises & Eateries. 2010. (Illus.). 160p. pap. 19.99 *(978-1-60949-096-6(7))* History Pr., The.

CASTOR (RODENT)

see Beavers

CASTRATION

ABBE Scientist Research Division Staff. Castration of Humans in Sex, Health, Disease & Law: Index & Medical Analysis of New Clinical / Research Information for All Nations. 2006. (Illus.). 160p. ring bd. 74.50 *(978-0-7883-3783-3(1)*, 07883-37521) ABBE Pubs. Assn. of Washington, D.C.

Ward, Ivan. Castration: Ideas in Psychoanalysis. 2006. 80p. reprint ed. pap. 8.00 *(978-1-4223-5783-5(X))* DIANE Publishing Co.

CASTRATION OF CRIMINALS AND DEFECTIVES

see Involuntary Sterilization

CASTRO, FIDEL, 1927-

Absher, Kenneth Michael. Mind-Sets & Missiles: A First Hand Account of the Cuban Missile Crisis. 2009. (Letort Papers). pap. *(978-1-58487-400-3(7))* Strategic Studies Institute, U.S. Army War College Commandant (AWCC-DSI/Pubns.).

Balfour, S. & Balfour, Sebastian. Castro. 3rd ed. 2008. (Profiles in Power Ser.). (ENG., Illus.). 232p. (C). pap. 42.80 *(978-1-4058-7318-5(3))* Longman Publishing Group.

Bardach, Ann Louise. Without Fidel: A Death Foretold in Miami, Havana, & Washington. 2009. (ENG., Illus.). 352p. 28.00 *(978-1-4165-5150-8(6)*, Scribner) Scribner.

Betancourt, Luis A. & Betancourt, Luis Adrián. Fidel en la Mira: Testimonio de un Acoso. 2010. (SPA.). 374p. *(978-84-96797-35-2(X))* Foca, Ediciones y Distribuciones Generales S.L., Grupo Akal.

Bugge, Brian K. The Mystique of Conspiracy: Oswald, Castro, & the CIA. 2007. (Illus.). 167p. 23.95 *(978-0-9601708-1-4(2))* Bugge, Brian K.

Castro, Fidel. The Declarations of Havana. 2008. (Revolutions Ser.). (ENG.). 160p. pap. 14.95 *(978-1-84467-156-4(9)*, 844156) Verso Bks. GBR. Dist: Norton, W. W. & Co., Inc.

—Fidel Castro: Antologa Mnima. Deutschmann, David & Shnookal, Deborah, eds. 2008. (SPA & ENG.). 600p. pap. 19.95 *(978-1-921438-01-1(0))* Ocean Pr. AUS. Dist: Consortium Bk. Sales & Distribution.

—Fidel Castro Reader. Deutschmann, David & Shnookal, Deborah, eds. rev. ed. 2007. (ENG., Illus.). 524p. per. 19.95 *(978-1-920888-88-6(8))* Ocean Pr. AUS. Dist: Consortium Bk. Sales & Distribution.

—Fidel Castro Speaks with the People of Cub. 2011. 34p. 35.95 ***(978-1-258-04025-3(5))*** Literary Licensing, LLC.

—Political Portraits: Fidel Castro Reflects on Famous Figures in History. Acosta-Matos, Eliades, ed. 2010. (ENG.). 200p. pap. 16.95 *(978-1-920888-94-7(2))* Ocean Pr. AUS. Dist: Consortium Bk. Sales & Distribution.

—Strategic Victory: The War Against Batista in the Sierra Maestra. 2012. (ENG., Illus.). 600p. pap. 29.95 *(978-0-9870779-0-5(2))* Ocean Pr. AUS. Dist: Consortium Bk. Sales & Distribution

Castro, Fidel & Betto, Frei. Fidel y la Religion: Conversaciones con Frei Betto Sobre el Marxismo y la Teologia de la Liberacion. 2006. (Ocean Sur Ser.). (SPA & ENG.). 324p. pap. 19.95 *(978-1-920888-77-0(2))* Ocean Pr. AUS. Dist: Consortium Bk. Sales & Distribution.

Córdova, Efrén. 50 Años de Revolución en Cuba: El Legado de Los Castro 1959-2009. Córdova, Efrén, ed. 2009. (SPA., Illus.). 557p. pap. 39.00 *(978-1-59388-157-3(6))* Ediciones Universal.

DePalma, Anthony. The Man Who Invented Fidel: Castro, Cuba, & Herbert L. Matthews of the New York Times. 2007. (ENG., Illus.). 320p. per. 16.95 *(978-1-58648-442-2(7))* PublicAffairs.

Erikson, Daniel P. The Cuba Wars: Fidel Castro, the United States, & the Next Revolution. 2009. (ENG., Illus.). 384p. pap. 18.00 *(978-1-60819-012-6(9))* Bloomsbury Publishing.

Escalante, Fabian. Executive Action: 634 Ways to Kill Fidel Castro. rev. ed. 2006. (Secret War Ser.). (ENG.). 232p. pap. 16.95 *(978-1-920888-72-5(1))* Ocean Pr. AUS. Dist: Consortium Bk. Sales & Distribution.

Esteban, Angel & Panichelli, Stephanie. Fidel & Gabo: A Portrait of the Legendary Friendship Between Fidel Castro & Gabriel Garcia Marquez. Stockwell, Diane, tr. from SPA. 2009. (ENG.). 352p. 26.00 *(978-1-60598-058-4(7)*, 605058) Pegasus Bks.

—Fidel & Gabo: A Portrait of the Legendary Friendship Between Fidel Castro & Gabriel Garcia Marqueza. 2011. (ENG.). 352p. pap. 15.95 *(978-1-60598-258-8(X)*, 605258) Pegasus Bks.

Fernández, Gonzalo. Cuba's Primer - Castro's Earring Economy. 2009. 168p. pap. 19.72 *(978-0-557-06573-8(9))* Lulu Enterprises Inc.

Fontova, Humberto E. Fidel: Hollywood's Favorite Tyrant. 2006. 229p. reprint ed. 28.00 *(978-1-4223-5325-7(7))* DIANE Publishing Co.

Foss, Clive. Fidel Castro. rev. ed. 2006. (ENG.). 176p. per. 16.95 *(978-0-7509-4175-4(8))* History Pr. Ltd.,The GBR. Dist: Independent Pubs. Group.

—Fidel Castro. 2009. (SPA.). 160p. pap. 8.95 *(978-84-96746-04-6(6))* Robinbk., Ediciones S.L. ESP. Dist: Independent Pubs. Group.

Garibaldi, Luciano & Manferto De Fabianis, Valeria. Fidel Castro. 2007. (ENG., Illus.). 272p. pap. 30.00 *(978-88-544-0340-6(7)*, White Star) Rizzoli International Pubns., Inc.

Guayasamín, Oswaldo & Castro, Fidel. Abrazo de Guayasamin Para Fidel. 2007. (ENG & SPA.). 64p. pap. 9.95 *(978-1-920888-87-9(X))* Ocean Pr. AUS. Dist: Consortium Bk. Sales & Distribution

Hicks, Conchita Hernandez. Leaving Havana. 2011. 236p. 24.95 *(978-1-4520-8607-1(9))*; pap. 14.95 *(978-1-4520-8606-4(0))* AuthorHouse.

Jayatilleka, Dayan. Fidel's Ethics of Violence: The Moral Dimension of the Political Thought of Fidel Castro. 2007. (ENG.). 248p. 100.00 *(978-0-7453-2697-9(8))*; per. 30.00 *(978-0-7453-2696-2(X))* Pluto Pr. GBR. Dist: Macmillan.

Kohan, Nestor. Fidel. 2010. (Siete Cuentos Ser.). (SPA & ENG., Illus.). 192p. pap. 13.95 *(978-1-58322-783-1(0))* Seven Stories Pr.

—Fidel: A Graphic Novel Life of Fidel Castro. Buchman, Elisex, tr. from SPA. 2010. (ENG., Illus.). 192p. pap. 14.95 *(978-1-58322-782-4(2))* Seven Stories Pr.

Latell, Brian. Castro's Secrets: The CIA & Cuba's Intelligence Machine. 2012. (ENG., Illus.). 288p. 27.00 ***(978-0-230-62123-7(6))*** Palgrave Macmillan.

Lockwood, Lee. Fidel Castro. 2012. (Illus.). 320p. ***(978-3-8365-2998-3(X))*** TASCHEN.

Losada, Pescador Luis. El Legado de Fidel Castro. 2007. 224p. pap. *(978-84-935056-4-6(1))* Ediciones Urano S. A.

Minà, Gianni. El Papa y Fidel.Tr. of Pope & Fidel. (SPA., Illus.). 367p. 16.98 *(978-970-05-1050-7(6))* Grijalbo, Editorial MEX. Dist: Continental Bk. Co., Inc.

Montaner, Carlos Alberto. Fidel Castro & the Cuban Revolution: Age, Position, Character, Destiny, Personality, & Ambition. 2007. (ENG.). 255p. (gr. 11). pap. 24.95 *(978-1-4128-0731-9(X))* Transaction Pubs.

Moral, Alberto. Fidel Castro Y El 9-11. 2007. 398p. pap. 30.89 *(978-1-4251-2315-4(5))* Trafford Publishing.

Negrone, Jos Bendinelli. Fidel Castro. 2007. (ENG., Illus.). 128p. 50.00 (978-3-940004-17-8(0), Earbooks) edel classics GmbH DEU. Dist: AtlasBooks Distribution.

Rafael de La Cova, Antonio. The Moncada Attack: Birth of the Cuban Revolution. 2007. (Illus.). 391p. 59.95 (978-1-57003-672-9(1)) Univ. of South Carolina Pr.

Ramonet, Ignacio & Castro, Fidel. Fidel Castro: My Life: A Spoken Autobiography. 2009. (ENG., Illus.). 736p. pap. 22.00 (978-1-4165-6233-7(8), Scribner) Scribner.

Rasenberger, Jim. The Brilliant Disaster: JFK, Castro, & America's Doomed Invasion of Cuba's Bay of Pigs. (ENG., Illus.). 480p. 2012. pap. 18.00 **(978-1-4165-9653-0(4))** 2011. 32.00 (978-1-4165-9650-9(X)) Scribner. (Scribner).

Reid-Henry, Simon. Fidel & Che: A Revolutionary Friendship. 2009. (ENG., Illus.). 448p. 28.00 (978-0-8027-1573-9(7)) Walker & Co.

Rivera Quintana, Juan Carlos. Breve Historia de Fidel Castro. 2010. (SPA., Illus.). 242p. pap. (978-84-9763-762-6(3)) Nowtilus, S.L., Ediciones.

Robinson, Eugene. Last Dance in Havana: The Final Days of Fidel & the Start of the New Cuban Revolution. 2007. (ENG., Illus.). 288p. pap. 19.95 (978-1-4165-6826-1(3), Free Pr.) Free Pr.

Russo, Gus & Molton, Stephen. Brothers in Arms: The Kennedys, the Castros, & the Politics of Murder. 2009. (ENG., Illus.). 560p. pap. 20.00 (978-1-59691-645-6(1)) Bloomsbury Publishing.

Showe, Jonathan. Cuba Rising: An American Insider's Perspective. 2009. (ENG.). 26.95 (978-0-615-32361-9(8)) Insights Pr.

Skierka, Volker. Fidel Castro: A Biography. Camiller, Patrick, tr. 2006. (ENG., Illus.). 488p. pap. 17.95 (978-0-7456-4081-5(8)) Polity Pr. GBR. Dist: Wiley, John & Sons, Inc.

Sweig, Julia E. Cuba: What Everyone Needs to Know. 2009. (What Everyone Needs to Know Ser.). (ENG.). 208p. pap. 16.95 (978-0-19-538380-5(X)) Oxford Univ. Pr., Inc.

Symmes, Patrick. The Boys from Dolores: Fidel Castro's Schoolmates from Revolution to Exile. 2008. (Vintage Departures Ser.). (ENG.). 368p. pap. 15.95 (978-1-4000-7644-4(7), Vintage) Knopf Doubleday Publishing Group.

Todd, Allan & Waller, Sally. History for the IB Diploma: Origins & Development of Authoritarian & Single Party States. 2011. (Ib Ser.). (ENG.). 240p. pap. 32.00 (978-0-521-18934-7(9)) Cambridge Univ. Pr.

Valdes, Zoe. La ficcion Fidel. 2008. (SPA.). 368p. pap. 15.99 (978-0-06-175551-4(6), Rayo) HarperCollins Pubs.

Villafaña, Frank. Cold War in the Congo: The Confrontation of Cuban Military Forces, 1960-1967. 2009. (ENG., Illus.). 236p. 39.95 (978-1-4128-1007-4(8)) Transaction Pubs.

Vision Publisher. Fidel Castro & the Americas. 2011. 20p. pap. 35.95 **(978-1-258-02522-9(1))** Literary Licensing, LLC.

von Tunzelmann, Alex. Red Heat: Conspiracy, Murder, & the Cold War in the Caribbean. 2011. (ENG., Illus.). 464p. 30.00 (978-0-8050-9067-3(3)) Holt, Henry & Co.

Welch, Robert Henry Winborne & Francis, Dale. Fidel Castro: Communist. 2011. 50p. 35.95 **(978-1-258-00299-2(X))** Literary Licensing, LLC.

With Castro Stepping down, What Is Next for Cuba & the Western Hemisphere? Hearing Before the Subcommittee on the Western Hemisphere of the Committee on Foreign Affairs, House of Representatives, One Hundred Tenth Congress, Second Session, March 5, 2008. 2008. iii, 72p. (978-0-16-080789-3(1), 552-070-37378-1) United States Government Printing Office.

Wong-Diaz, Francisco R. Castro's Cuba: Quo Vadis? 2006. (Letort Papers). pap. (978-1-58487-267-2(5)) Strategic Studies Institute, U.S. Army War College Commandant (AWCC-DSI/Pubns.).

CASTRO, THOMAS, 1834-1898
see Orton, Arthur, 1834-1898

CASTS, SURGICAL
see Plaster Casts, Surgical

CASUAL LABOR
see also Migrant Labor; Seasonal Variations (Economics)

Bosse. Extension Protection by Labour Law: Comparative Study. 2011. 240p. (978-90-411-3289-5(9)) Kluwer Law International.

Standing, Guy. The Precariat: The New Dangerous Class. 2011. (ENG.). 192p. 90.00 (978-1-84966-352-6(1)); pap. 29.95 (978-1-84966-351-9(3)) Bloomsbury Publishing.

CASUALTIES, DISASTER
see Mass Casualties

CASUALTIES IN FIRES
see Fires—Casualties

CASUALTY INSURANCE
see also Accident Insurance; Disaster Insurance; Flood Insurance

Aylward, Michael F. Problem Issues in CGL. 2nd ed. 2008. x, 230p. pap. (978-0-87218-744-3(6)) National Underwriter Co.

Economic Impacts of Global Warming: Insurance: Hearing Before the Select Committee on Energy Independence & Global Warming, House of Representatives, One Hundred Tenth Congress, First Session, May 3, 2007. 2010. (Illus.). iii, 184p. **(978-0-16-086747-7(9)**, 552-070-41669-2) United States Government Printing Office.

Fleischhaker, Cpcu Karin A. The Savvy Businessperson's Guide to Property & Casualty Insurance. 2008. 552p. pap. 34.99 (978-1-4343-9482-8(4)) AuthorHouse.

Gore, Ernest H. Property/Casualty Insurance: A Basic Guide for Adjustors, Underwriters, Agents, Brokers, Attorneys, Entrepreneurs, & Business Managers. 2008. 200p. pap. 19.95 (978-1-60585-164-8(7)) Independent Pub.

Grey House Publishing, creator. The Street. com Ratings' Guide to Property & Casualty Insurers: A Quarterly Compilation of Insurance Company Ratings & Analyses. 2007. (Street. com Guide to Property & Casualty Insurers Ser.). 443p. per. 249.00 (978-1-59237-263-8(5)) Grey Hse. Publishing.

Insurance Research Council. Municipal Bond Holdings of Property-Casualty Insurance Companies. 2007. 61p. pap. 100.00 (978-1-56594-045-1(8)) Insurance Research Council.

Kain, Cole Stephen & Glovach, Lana M. Annotated Commercial Crime Policy. 2nd ed. 2006. xiii, 818p. (978-1-59031-791-4(2)) American Bar Assn.

Mars-Proietti, Laura. Street. com Ratings' Guide to Property & Casualty Insurers: A Quarterly Compilation of Insurance Company Ratings & Analyses. 2008. (Street. com Guide to Property & Casualty Insurers Ser.). 470p. pap. 249.00 (978-1-59237-333-8(X)) Grey Hse. Publishing.

Mars-Proietti, Laura, ed. TheStreet. com Ratings Guide to Property & Casualty Insurers: 2007. 2007. pap. 249.00 (978-1-59237-262-1(7)) Grey Hse. Publishing.

—TheStreet. com Ratings Guide to Property & Casualty Insurers: 2008. 2008. pap. 249.00 (978-1-59237-334-5(8)) Grey Hse. Publishing.

—TheStreet. com Ratings Guide to Property & Casualty Insurers: 2009. 2009. pap. 249.00 (978-1-59237-467-0(0)) 2009. pap. 249.00 (978-1-59237-466-3(2)) 2008. pap. 249.00 (978-1-59237-335-2(6)) Grey Hse. Publishing.

—TheStreet.com Ratings' Guide to Property & Casualty Insurers: Spring 2008. 2008. pap. 249.00 (978-1-59237-276-8(7)) Grey Hse. Publishing.

National Underwriter Company Staff, contrib. by. FCandS QandA Book. 2007. vi, 132p. pap. (978-0-87218-736-8(5)) National Underwriter Co.

Public Attitude Monitor 2006, Issue 1, Natural Disasters. 2006. 48p. pap. 50.00 (978-1-56594-042-0(3), IRC167) Insurance Research Council.

Statistical Compilation for Property/Casualty Insurance Companies In 2005. 2007. spiral bd. (978-1-59917-102-9(3)) National Assn. of Insurance Commissioners.

Stephenson, John B. Climate Change: Financial Risks to Federal & Private Insurers in Coming Decades are Potentially Significant. 2007. (Illus.). 68p. (C). pap. 25.00 (978-1-4223-1559-0(2)) DIANE Publishing Co.

TheStreet. com Ratings Guide to Property & Casualty Insurers: A Quarterly Compilation of Insurance Company Ratings & Analyses. 2007. pap. 249.00 (978-1-58773-343-7(9)); 53rd ed. pap. 249.00 (978-1-58773-341-3(2)); 54th ed. pap. 249.00 (978-1-58773-342-0(0)) TheStreet.com Ratings, Inc.

TheStreet.com Ratings, ed. TheStreet. com Ratings Guide to Property & Casualty Insurers. 2010. pap. 249.00 (978-1-59237-527-1(8)) 2009. pap. 249.00 (978-1-59237-526-4(X)) Grey Hse. Publishing.

—TheStreet. com Ratings Guide to Property & Casualty Insurers: Fall 2009. 2009. pap. 249.00 (978-1-59237-468-7(9)) Grey Hse. Publishing.

TheStreet.com Ratings Staff & Weiss Ratings Inc. Staff, eds. TheStreet. com Ratings Guide to Property & Casualty Insurers. 2010. pap. 249.00 (978-1-59237-529-5(4)); pap. 249.00 (978-1-59237-528-8(6)) Grey Hse. Publishing.

United States, Congress House Committee on Financial Services Subcommittee on Capital Markets, Insurance, and Government Sponsored Enterprises Staff, contrib. by. Stabilizing Insurance Markets for Coastal Consumers: Hearing Before the Subcommittee on Capital Markets, Insurance, & Government Sponsored Enterprises of the Committee on Financial Services, U.S. House of Representatives, One Hundred Ninth Congress, Second Session, September 13, 2006. 2007. v, 177p. (978-0-16-078467-5(0), 552-070-35753-0) United States Government Printing Office.

Ward's Insurance Results, Property-Casualty 2006. 2006. (978-1-928967-14-9(0)) Ward Group.

Ward's Insurance Results, Property-Casualty 2007. 2007. 600p. (978-1-928967-16-3(7)) Ward Group.

Weiss Ratings, ed. Weiss Ratings Guide to Property & Casualty Insurers. 2011. pap. 249.00 (978-1-59237-801-2(3)) 2011. pap. 249.00 (978-1-59237-800-5(5)) 2011. pap. 249.00 (978-1-59237-799-2(8)) 2010. pap. 249.00 (978-1-59237-798-5(X)) Grey Hse. Publishing.

Weiss Ratings Inc, creator. The Street. com Ratings' Guide to Property & Casualty Insurers: A Quarterly Compilation of Insurance Company Ratings & Analyses. (Street. com Guide to Property & Casualty Insurers Ser.). (Illus.). 446p. 51st ed. 2006. per. 249.00 (978-1-58773-273-7(4)) 52nd ed. 2007. per. 249.00 (978-1-58773-340-6(4)) TheStreet.com Ratings, Inc.

—Weiss Ratings' Guide to Property & Casualty Insurers: A Quarterly Compilation of Insurance Company Ratings & Analyses. 50th ed. 2006. (Street. com Guide to Property & Casualty Insurers Ser.). (Illus.). 452p. per. 249.00 (978-1-58773-272-0(6)) TheStreet.com Ratings, Inc.

2005 Invested Assets Report for Property/Casualty. 2007. spiral bd. 175.00 (978-1-59917-090-9(6)) National Assn. of Insurance Commissioners.

CASUISTRY
see also Applied Ethics; Conscience; Pastoral Counseling; Responsa

Burke, Edward F. Acute Cases in Moral Medicine. 2009. 74p. pap. (978-0-217-90945-7(0)) Books LLC.

—Acute Cases in Moral Medicine. 2007. (ENG.). 148p. 35.95 (978-0-548-04141-3(5)) Kessinger Publishing, LLC.

Cherry, Mark & Iltis, Ana Smith, eds. Pluralistic Casuistry: Moral Arguments, Economic Realities, & Political Theory. 2007. (Philosophy & Medicine Ser.). 272p. (C). 159.00 (978-1-4020-6259-9(1)) Springer.

Cherry, Mark J. & Smith Iltis, Ana, eds. Pluralistic Casuistry: Moral Arguments, Economic Realities, & Political Theory. 2010. (Philosophy & Medicine Ser.). xii, 260p. pap. 159.00 (978-90-481-7586-4(0), 9048175860) Springer.

Kallendorf, Hilaire & Kallendorf, Hillaire. Conscience on Stage: The Comedia as Casuistry in Early Modern Spain. 2007. (University of Toronto Romance Ser.). (SPA & ENG.). 320p. (978-0-8020-9229-8(2)) Univ. of Toronto Pr.

Kiener, Mary Aloysi. Hearts Shall Be Enlightened: Reflections for the Examination of Conscience. 2011. 190p. 42.95 **(978-1-258-02575-5(2))** Literary Licensing, LLC.

Lachmann, Rainer, et al. Ethische Schlüsselprobleme: Lebensweltlich -systematisch - didaktisch. 2006. (Theologie fur lehrerinnen und Lehrer Ser.). (GER.). 384p. (C). pap. 38.00 (978-3-525-61423-5(3)) Vandenhoeck & Ruprecht GmbH & Co. KG DEU. Dist: ISD.

Mayes, Benjamin Tg. Counsel & Conscience: Lutheran Casuistry & Moral Reasoning After the Reformation. 2011. (Refo500 Academic Studies (R5AS) Ser.). (ENG.). 250p. (C). 95.00 (978-3-525-55027-4(8)) Vandenhoeck & Ruprecht GmbH & Co. KG DEU. Dist: ISD.

Rupnik, Marko Ivan. Human Frailty, Divine Redemption: The Theology & Practice of the Examen. 2011. pap. 8.95 **(978-0-8198-3410-2(6))** Pauline Bks. & Media.

Two Sisters Of Notre Dame. Soul Clinic: An Examination of Conscience for Religious Teachers. 2011. 212p. 44.95 **(978-1-258-04175-5(8))** Literary Licensing, LLC.

CAT
see Cats

CAT BREEDS

Alderton, David. The Cat Selector: How to Choose the Right Cat for You. 2011. (ENG.). 176p. 24.99 (978-0-7641-6424-8(4)) Barron's Educational Series, Inc.

Bacchella, Adriano, photos by. Cats, Cats... & more Cats! 2010. (ENG., Illus.). 256p. 29.95 (978-88-544-0479-3(9)) White Star ITA. Dist: Random Hse., Inc.

Davis, Karen Leigh. The Everything Cat Book. 2nd ed. 2006. (ENG., Illus.). 304p. per. 15.95 (978-1-59337-577-5(8)) Adams Media Corp.

Gould, Laura L. Cats Are Not Peas: A Calico History of Genetics. 2nd rev. ed. 2008. (ENG.). 312p. 39.00 (978-1-56881-320-2(1)) AK Peters, Ltd.

Rixon, Angela. The Illustrated Encyclopedia of Cat Breeds: The Comprehensive Visual Directory of all the World's Cat Breeds, Plus Invaluable Practical Information on Breeding, Training, Care, & Showing. 2011. (Illustrated Encyclopedias Ser.). (ENG., Illus.). 256p. 14.99 (978-0-7858-0364-5(5), 0785803645, Wellfleet) Book Sales, Inc.

Stroud, Jon. The DVD Book of Cats. 2009. (DVDBook Ser.). (ENG., Illus.). 128p. 17.99 (978-1-905828-82-1(9), 1905828829) G2 Entertainment Ltd. GBR. Dist: MBI Distribution Services/Quayside Distribution.

Tobias, Phyllis. The Personal Maine Coon. 2009. 80p. pap. 24.50 (978-1-60860-915-4(4), Eloquent Bks.) AEG Literary Publishing Services, Inc.

Witt, Monty. Cat Puzzles. 2009. 124p. pap. 18.96 (978-0-557-17611-3(5)) Lulu Enterprises Inc.

CAT FAMILY (MAMMALS)
see Felidae

CAT OWNERS

Becker, Marty & Spadafori, Gina. Meowwow! Curiously Compelling Facts, True Tales, & Trivia Even Your Cat Won't Know. 2007. (ENG., Illus.). 224p. pap. 14.95 (978-0-7573-0622-8(5)) Health Communications, Inc.

Bicket, Tammy L., et al. Hugs for Cat Lovers: Stories, Sayings, & Scriptures to Encourage & Inspire. 2008. (Hugs Ser.). (ENG., Illus.). 128p. 11.99 (978-1-4165-5705-0(9), Howard Bks.) Howard Books.

Brokering, Herbert. More Cat Psalms: Prayers My Cats Have Taught Me. 2008. (Illus.). 64p. per. 8.99 (978-0-8066-8035-4(0), Augsburg Bks.) Augsburg Fortress, Pubs.

Canfield, Jack, et al. Chicken Soup for the Soul: My Cat's Life: 101 Stories about All the Ages & Stages of Our Feline Family Members. 2011. (ENG.). 400p. pap. 14.95 (978-1-935096-66-5(4)) Chicken Soup for the Soul Publishing, LLC.

Canfield, Jack L., et al. What I Learned from the Cat: 101 Stories about Life, Love & Lessons. 2009. (Chicken Soup for the Soul Ser.). (ENG.). 400p. pap. 14.95 (978-1-935096-37-5(0)) Chicken Soup for the Soul Publishing, LLC.

Catscapades: True Cat Tales. 2010. (Illus.). 136p. pap. 12.95 (978-0-9773576-6-6(X)) Matilija Pr.

Day, Christopher. Natural Cat Care. 2010. (ENG., Illus.). 96p. 9.95 (978-1-60710-097-3(5), Thunder Bay Pr.) Advantage Pubs. Group.

Duno, Steve. Be the Cat! Secrets of the Natural Cat Owner. 2008. (ENG., Illus.). 160p. pap. 14.95 (978-1-4027-5278-0(4)) Sterling Publishing Co., Inc.

Eilert-Overbeck, Brigitte. Kittens. 2008. (Complete Pet Owner's Manual Ser.). (ENG., Illus.). 64p. pap. 8.99 (978-0-7641-3962-8(2)) Barron's Educational Series, Inc.

Fleishauer, Connie & Adams, Dottie P. Purr-ables from Heaven: Devotions for Cat Lovers. 2008. (Illus.). 252p. per. 11.99 (978-0-7369-2057-5(9)) Harvest Hse. Pubs.

Grant, Callie Smith, ed. A Dickens of a Cat: And Other Stories of the Cats We Love. 2007. 192p. pap. 12.99 (978-0-8007-5846-2(3)) Revell.

Hampshire, Kristen, et al. Cat Lover's Daily Companion: 365 Days of Insight & Guidance for Living a Joyful Life with Your Cat. 2011. (ENG., Illus.). 320p. pap. 15.99 (978-1-59253-749-5(9), 1592537499) Quayside.

Hawkins, Lorrie Bell. Jolicure Cats. 2009. (ENG., Illus.). 76p. 19.95 (978-0-920187-09-8(9)) Percheron Pr. Pubs. CAN. Dist: Univ. of Toronto Pr.

Korda, Michael & Korda, Margaret. Cat People. 2006. (Illus.). 176p. per. 12.95 (978-0-06-075664-2(0), HarperPerennial) HarperCollins Pubs.

Longden, Deric. Enough to Make a Cat Laugh. 2008. (ENG.). 288p. pap. 16.95 (978-0-552-15620-2(5)) Transworld Publishers Ltd. GBR. Dist: Independent Pubs. Group.

Mitchell, Patricia. Best Friends Forever: Me & My Cat: What I've Learned about Life, Love, & Faith from My Cat. 2010. 14.99 (978-0-7642-0774-7(1)) Bethany Hse. Pubs.

Parker, Carolyn. Squeaky's Farm: Our Lives in Rural Spain. 2011. (ENG., Illus.). 288p. pap. 11.95 (978-1-892076-82-3(9)) Dancing Moon Pr.

Schaffer, Clair. Cats in the Parsonage: Book 1. 2009. 192p. pap. 13.99 (978-1-58169-324-9(9), Evergreen Pr.) Genesis Communications, Inc.

Sell, Colleen. Cat Lovers: Stories That Celebrate Our Feline Friends. 2008. (ENG.). 336p. pap. 9.95 (978-1-59869-654-7(8)) Adams Media Corp.

Steiger, Brad & Steiger, Sherry Hansen. Cat Miracles: Inspirational True Stories of Remarkable Felines. 2008. (ENG.). 272p. pap. 12.95 (978-1-60550-016-4(X)) Adams Media Corp.

Sutherland Millmann, Anita. Checky the Feral Cat. 2009. 32p. pap. 12.99 (978-1-4389-5719-7(X)) AuthorHouse.

Tovey, Doreen. Double Trouble. 2007. (ENG.). 160p. pap. 12.95 **(978-1-84024-569-1(7))** Summerdale Pubs. GBR. Dist: Independent Pubs. Group.

—New Boy. 2006. (ENG.). 160p. pap. 12.95 **(978-1-84024-517-2(4))** Summerdale Pubs. GBR. Dist: Independent Pubs. Group.

—Raining Cats & Donkeys. 2012. (ENG.). 176p. pap. 12.95 **(978-1-84953-064-4(5))** Summerdale Pubs. GBR. Dist: Independent Pubs. Group.

Wells, M. R., et al. The Cat Lover's Devotional. 2011. (Illus.). 240p. pap. 12.99 (978-0-7369-2881-6(2)) Harvest Hse. Pubs.

—Purr-ables from Heaven Gift Edition: Inspirational Stories for Cat Lovers. 2008. 32p. 12.99 (978-0-7369-2204-3(0)) Harvest Hse. Pubs.

What Now Mama? or Feral Cat Goes Domestic. 7.95 (978-0-9785446-0-7(9)) Hedwig Pr.

Willems Snopek, Roxanne. More Great Cat Stories: Incredible Tales about Exceptional Cats, 1 vol. 2008. (Amazing Stories Ser.). (ENG., Illus.). 128p. pap. (978-1-894974-55-4(7)) Heritage Hse.

CAT OWNERS—FICTION

Andrews, Donna. Cockatiels at Seven. l.t. ed. 2008. (Meg Langslow Mystery Ser.: Vol. 9). 372p. 31.50 (978-1-4104-0932-4(5)) Thorndike Pr.

Babson, Marian. Only the Cat Knows. l.t. ed. 2007. (Thorndike Mystery Ser.). 347p. 30.95 (978-0-7862-9753-5(0)) Thorndike Pr.

Braun, Lilian Jackson. The Cat Who Dropped a Bombshell, 28 vols. 2006. (Cat Who... Ser.). (ENG.). 304p. (gr. 12-18). 7.99 (978-0-515-14241-9(7), Jove) Penguin Group (USA) Inc.

—The Cat Who Dropped a Bombshell. l.t. ed. 2006. (Cat Who... Ser.). 224p. per. 12.95 (978-1-59413-164-6(3), Large Print Pr.) Thorndike Pr.

—The Cat Who Had 60 Whiskers. l.t. ed. 2007. (Cat Who... Ser.). 186p. per. 13.95 (978-1-59413-242-1(9), Large Print Pr.) Thorndike Pr.

—The Cat Who Had 60 Whiskers. 2008. (Cat Who... Ser.). 228p. 18.45 (978-1-4178-1458-9(6), Turtleback) Turtleback Bks.

Brown, Rita Mae. The Big Cat Nap. l.t. ed. 2012. (Mrs. Murphy Mystery Ser.). (ENG.). 33.99 **(978-1-4104-4695-4(6))** Thorndike Pr.

—Cat of the Century. 2011. (ENG., Illus.). 320p. mass mkt. 7.99 (978-0-553-59160-6(6)) Random House Publishing Group.

—Hiss of Death. 2011. (Illus.). 240p. 26.00 (978-0-553-80708-0(0)) Random House Publishing Group.

—The Purrfect Murder. 2009. (Mrs. Murphy Mystery Ser.). (ENG., Illus.). 368p. mass mkt. 7.50 (978-0-553-58683-1(1)) Random House Publishing Group.

Brown, Rita Mae & Brown, Sneaky Pie. The Big Cat Nap. 2012. (Mrs. Murphy Mystery Ser.). (ENG.). 240p. 26.00 **(978-0-345-53044-8(6))** Random House Publishing Group.

—Cat of the Century. l.t. ed. 2010. (Mrs. Murphy Mystery Ser.). (ENG.). 33.95 (978-1-4104-2319-1(0)) Thorndike Pr.

—Hiss of Death. l.t. ed. 2011. (Mrs. Murphy Mystery Ser.). 33.99 (978-1-4104-3515-6(6)) Thorndike Pr.

—The Purrfect Murder. l.t. ed. 2008. (Mrs. Murphy Mystery Ser.). (Illus.). 405p. 33.95 (978-1-4104-0326-1(2)) Thorndike Pr.

—Puss 'n Cahoots. 2008. (Mrs. Murphy Mystery Ser.). (ENG., Illus.). 352p. mass mkt. 7.99 (978-0-553-58682-4(3), Bantam) Random House Publishing Group.

—Santa Clawed. 2009. (Mrs. Murphy Mystery Ser.). (ENG.). 288p. mass mkt. 7.99 (978-0-553-59159-0(2)) Random House Publishing Group.

—Santa Clawed. l.t. ed. 2008. (Mrs. Murphy Mystery Ser.). 490p. 30.95 (978-1-4104-0929-4(5)) Thorndike Pr.

Claire, Edie. Never Buried: A Leigh Koslow Mystery. 2008. 260p. pap. 15.95 (978-0-595-52387-0(0)) iUniverse, Inc.

Douglas, Carole Nelson. Cat in a Red Hot Rage. 2008. (Midnight Louie Mysteries Ser.: No. 19). (ENG.). 384p. pap. 6.99 (978-0-7653-5270-5(2), Forge Bks.) Doherty, Tom Assocs., LLC.

—Cat in a Topaz Tango. rev. l.t. ed. 2010. (Midnight Louie Ser.). 648p. 31.50 (978-1-4104-2119-7(8)) Thorndike Pr.

—Cat in an Ultramarine Scheme. l.t. ed. 2010. (Midnight Louie Ser.). 578p. 32.99 (978-1-4104-3059-5(6)) Thorndike Pr.

Downey, Brigitte. Diaries of a Cultured Cat. 2006. 356p. per. (978-1-905529-68-1(6)) Grosvenor Hse. Publishing Ltd.

Freeman, Kathie. Catwalk: A Feline Odyssey. l.t. ed. 2006. 304p. per. 14.95 *(978-0-9742062-6-4(1))* McPugh, Kathleen.
Hale, Rebecca M. How to Wash a Cat. l.t. ed. 2010. lib. bdg. 32.95 *(978-1-60285-733-9(4))* Ctr. Point Large Print.
—How to Wash a Cat. 2008. 302p. 21.95 *(978-0-9796344-0-6(7))* Green Vase Publishing.
—How to Wash a Cat. 1 vol. 2010. (Cats & Curios Mystery Ser.). (ENG.). 304p. (gr. 12-18). 6.99 *(978-0-425-23204-0(2),* Berkley) Penguin Group (USA) Inc.
Heebner, Jacque. First Person Cat. 2009. 280p. 29.95 *(978-1-936051-45-8(1))* Peppertree Pr., The.
James, Miranda. File M for Murder. 2012. (Cat in the Stacks Mystery Ser.). (ENG.). 304p. (gr. 12). 7.99 ***(978-0-425-24618-4(3),*** Berkley) Penguin Group (USA) Inc.
Kelly, Sofie. Curiosity Thrilled the Cat: A Magical Cats Mystery, 1 vol. 2012. (Magical Cats Ser.). (ENG.). 336p. (gr. 12). 7.99 ***(978-0-451-23754-5(4),*** Signet) Penguin Group (USA) Inc.
King, Ron S. ME & CAT. 2008. 114p. pap. 23.50 *(978-1-4092-1997-2(6))* Lulu Enterprises Inc.
Macomber, Debbie. Family Affair. 2011. (ENG.). 112p. 16.99 *(978-0-06-199712-9(9),* Morrow, William & Co.); 176p. pap. 16.99 *(978-0-06-201767-3(5),* HarperLuxe) HarperCollins Pubs.
Millionaire, Tony. Billy Hazelnuts & the Crazy Bird. 2010. (ENG., Illus.). 104p. 19.99 *(978-1-56097-917-3(8),* 56917) Fantagraphics Bks.
Morris, Gilbert. What the Cat Dragged In. l.t. ed. 2007. (Jacques & Cleo: Cat Detectives Ser.). 463p. 28.95 *(978-0-7862-9927-0(4))* Thorndike Pr.
—When the Cat's Away. l.t. ed. 2008. (Jacques & Cleo Cat Detectives Ser.). 447p. 29.95 *(978-1-4104-0603-3(2))* Thorndike Pr.
Pollee Freier. Snickers, the Preacher Cat. 2009. 100p. pap. 11.95 *(978-1-4401-8000-2(8))* iUniverse, Inc.
Sweeney, Leann. The Cat, the Lady & the Liar. l.t. ed. 2011. (Cats in Trouble Mystery Ser.). (ENG.). 467p. pap. 26.99 ***(978-1-4104-4092-1(3),*** Kennebec Large Print) Cengage Gale.
—The Cat, the Lady & the Liar: A Cats in Trouble Mystery. 2011. (Cats in Trouble Mystery Ser.). (ENG.). 288p. (gr. 12). 6.99 *(978-0-451-23302-8(6),* Signet) Penguin Group (USA) Inc.
—The Cat, the Professor & the Poison. l.t. ed. 2010. (Cats in Trouble Mystery Ser.). 445p. pap. 26.99 *(978-1-4104-2844-8(3),* Kennebec Large Print) Cengage Gale.
Walters, Minette & Walters, Minette. The Shape of Snakes. 2008. (Vintage Crime/Black Lizard Ser.). (ENG.). 384p. pap. 13.95 *(978-0-307-27711-4(9),* Vintage) Knopf Doubleday Publishing Group.

CAT-WORSHIP
see Cats—Folklore

CAT, DOMESTIC
see Cats

CATABAPTISTS
see Anabaptists

CATABOLISM
see Metabolism

CATACOMBS
see also Christian Art and Symbolism; Church History—Primitive and Early Church, ca. 30-600

Becker, Erich. Malta Sotterranea: Studies of its Early Christian & Jewish Sepulchural Art. Fenech, Katrin, ed. & tr. by. from GER. 2009. (Maltese social studies Ser.). (ENG., Illus.). 268p. (C). 40.00 *(978-99932-7-247-2(7))* Midsea Bks. Ltd. MLT. Dist: Brown, David Bk. Co., The.
Cappelletti, Sylvia. The Jewish Community in Rome: From the Second Century B.C. to the Third Century C.E. 2006. (Supplements to the Journal for the Study of Judaism Ser.: Vol. 113). (Illus.). 250p. *(978-90-04-15157-4(5))* BRILL.
Farris, John. Catacombs. 2008. 492p. *(978-1-933618-35-7(3))* Cocytus Pr.
The Martyr of the Catacombs. 2008. 84p. pap. 9.45 *(978-1-60459-408-9(X))* Wilder Pubns., Ltd.
Nicolai, Vincenzo F., et al. The Christian Catacombs of Rome. 2009. (ENG.). 208p. pap. 39.95 *(978-3-7954-2212-7(4),* Art Stock Bks. Ltd/Csi) Continental Sales, Inc.

CATAL MOUND (TURKEY)

Benigni, Helen & Carter, Barbara. The Goddess & the Bull: A Study in Minoan-Mycenaean Mythology. Dexter, Miriam Robbins, ed. 2007. (ENG., Illus.). 110p. per. 25.50 *(978-0-7618-3834-0(1))* Univ. Pr. of America, Inc.
Dural, Sadrettin. Protecting Çatalhöyük: Memoir of an Archaeological Site Guard. 2007. (ENG., Illus.). 160p. 89.00 *(978-1-59874-049-3(0))* Left Coast Pr., Inc.
—Protecting Çatalhöyük: Memoir of an Archaeological Site Guard. Cleere, Duygu Camurcuoglu, tr. from TUR. 2007. (ENG., Illus.). 160p. pap. 36.95 *(978-1-59874-050-9(4))* Left Coast Pr., Inc.
Hodder, Ian, ed. Religion in the Emergence of Civilization: Çatalhöyük as a Case Study. 2010. (ENG., Illus.). 372p. 95.00 *(978-0-521-19260-6(9));* pap. 40.00 *(978-0-521-15019-4(1))* Cambridge Univ. Pr.

CATALAN DRAMA—HISTORY AND CRITICISM

Foguet i Boreu, Francesc & Santamaria, Núria. La Revolució Teatral Dels Setanta. 2010. (CAT.). 241p. *(978-84-937371-5-3(1))* Punctum Editions.

CATALAN LANGUAGE

Assimil Staff. Catalan sin Esfuerzo: Catalan for Spanish Speakers. (CAT & SPA.). 28.95 incl. audio *(978-0-8288-4498-7(4),* S38601) French & European Pubns., Inc.
Bargalló Valls, Josep, et al. Manual de Mètrica I Versificació Catalanes. 2nd ed. 2007. (CAT.). 270p. *(978-84-9787-227-0(4))* Empúries, S.A., Editorial.
Brew Vocabulari Catala-Castella-Angles de Comerc Exterior. (CAT, ENG & SPA.). 43p. 13.50 *(978-0-7859-0718-3(1),* S33058) French & European Pubns., Inc.
Britton, A. Scott. Catalan Dictionary & Phrasebook. 2011. (CAT & ENG.). 204p. pap. *(978-0-7818-1258-0(5))* Hippocrene Bks., Inc.
Canigo Staff. Canigo Diccionari Castella-Catala, Catala-Castella. (CAT & SPA.). 878p. pap. 59.95 *(978-0-8288-1757-8(X),* S31565) French & European Pubns., Inc.
Catalan/English/Catalan Dictionary. (CAT & ENG.). 688p. *(978-0-320-00765-1(0))* French & European Pubns., Inc.
Coromines Vigneaux, Joan. Diccionari Etimologic Complementaride la Llengua Catalana, 9 vols. (CAT.). 8594p. *(978-84-7256-173-1(9))* Bow Historical Bks.
Euro Talk. Talk More Catalan. 2008. 29.99 *(978-1-60077-218-4(8))* TOPICS Entertainment.
—Talk Now! Catalan. 2008. 29.99 *(978-1-84352-364-2(7))* TOPICS Entertainment.
Fabra, Pompeu & Yates, Alan. The Architect of Modern Catalan: Selected Writings. 2009. (Illus.). xxxii, 240p. *(978-90-272-3264-9(4))* Benjamins, John Publishing Co.
García de Toro, Cristina. La traducción entre lenguas en Contacto: Catalán y Español. 2010. (Europäische Hochschulschriften. Reihe 21: Linguistik Ser.). (SPA.). 182p. pap. *(978-3-03911-493-1(X))* Lang, Peter.
Gimeno Ugalde, Esther. La Identidad Nacional Catalana: Ideologías Lingüísticas Entre 1833 y 1932. 2010. (SPA.). 371p. pap. 56.00 *(978-84-8489-540-4(8))* Iberoamericana Vervuert Publishing Corp.
Icon Group International, Inc. Staff, compiled by. Webster's Catalan - English Thesaurus Dictionary. 2008. 687p. ring bd. 28.95 incl. audio compact disk *(978-0-497-83463-0(4))* Icon Group International, Inc.
Mas, Marta. Digui, Digui- Curs de Català per a Estrangers. (CAT., Illus.). ix, 365p. *(978-84-393-2117-0(1))* Generalitat de Catalunya.
Megerdoomian, Karine. Beyond Words & Phrases. 2009. 216p. pap. *(978-3-639-15763-5(X))* VDM Verlag Dr. Mueller e.K.
Montaña i Martí, Maria Teresa & Escatllar i Torrent, Francesc. Tarragona: Una Passejada Pel Terme, una Retrobada Amb la Gent: Onomàstica Tarragona Amb Anotacions Multidisciplinars, 2 vols. 2007. (CAT., Illus.). *(978-84-96639-38-6(X)); (978-84-96639-39-3(8))* Arola Editors, S.L.
Monzó, Quim. Guadalajara. Bush, Peter, tr. from CAT. 2011. (ENG.). 135p. pap. 12.95 *(978-1-934824-19-1(4))* Open Letter.
Munch, Christian H. Sprachpolitik und Gesellschaftliche Alphabetisierung: Zur Entwicklung der Schreibkompetenz in Katalonien Seit 1975. (GER., Illus.). 254p. 50.95 *(978-3-631-53763-3(8))* Lang, Peter Publishing, Inc.
Palou, Jordi & Vidal, Pau. RodaMots. 2009. (CAT.). 292p. *(978-84-9787-414-4(5))* Empúries, S.A., Editorial.
Payrató, Lluís & Cots, Josep Maria, eds. The Pragmatics of Catalan. 2011. (Mouton Series in Pragmatics [MSP] Ser.). (ENG.). VI, 391p. 140.00 ***(978-3-11-023868-6(3))*** De Gruyter, Mouton DEU. Dist: de Gruyter, Walter GmbH & Co. KG.
Poch Gasau, Anna & Yates, Alan. Complete Catalan. 3rd ed. 2011. (TY: Language Guides). (ENG.). 336p. pap. 32.00 *(978-0-07-176066-9(0),* 0071760660) McGraw-Hill Cos., The.
—Complete Catalan with Two Audio CDs: A Teach Yourself Guide. 3rd ed. 2011. (TY: Language Guides). (ENG.). 336p. pap. 46.00 incl. audio compact disk, audio compact disk *(978-0-07-176065-2(2),* 0071760652) McGraw-Hill Cos., The.
Raspall i Juanola, Joana & Martí i Castell, Joan. Diccionari de Frases Fetes. 2009. (CAT.). 429p. *(978-84-297-6181-8(0))* Edicions Península 62.
Strubell, Miquel. Democratic Policies for Language Revival: The Case of Catalan. Boix-Fuster, Emili, ed. 2011. (ENG., Illus.). 256p. 85.00 *(978-0-230-28512-5(0))* Palgrave Macmillan.
Vann, Robert E. Materials for the Sociolinguistic Description & Corpus-Based Study of Spanish in Barcelona: Toward a Documentation of Colloquial Spanish in Naturally Occurring Groups. 2009. (Illus.). 300p. 109.95 *(978-0-7734-4871-1(3))* Mellen, Edwin Pr., The.
Wieland, Katharina. Jugendsprache in Barcelona: Eine Untersuchung zum Katalanischen im Spannungsfeld zwischen normalisiertem und autonomem Sprachgebrauch. 2008. (Beihefte Zur Zeitschrift Für Romanische Philologie Ser.).Tr. of Youth Language in Barcelona. (GER.). IX, 433p. 168.00 ***(978-3-11-916110-7(1))*** De Gruyter, Walter Inc.
—Jugendsprache in Barcelona: Eine Untersuchung zum Katalanischen im Spannungsfeld zwischen normalisiertem und autonomem Sprachgebrauch. 2008. (Beihefte Zur Zeitschrift Für Romanische Philologie Ser.).Tr. of Youth Language in Barcelona. (GER.). IX, 433p. *(978-3-484-52345-6(X))* Verlag Max Niemeyer.

CATALAN LITERATURE
see also Catalan Poetry

Buj Alfara, Angela. Monsieur Binoix I Altres Contes. 2010. (CAT.). 108p. *(978-84-9791-665-3(4))* Cossetània, Imatge-9, S.L., Edicions.
Krummrich, Philip. The Hero & Leander Theme in Iberian Literature, 1500-1800: An Anthology of Translations. 2006. 412p. *(978-0-7734-5694-5(5))* Mellen, Edwin Pr., The.
Lafarga, Francisco & Pegenaute, Luis, eds. Interacciones Entre las Literaturas Ibéricas. 2011. (Relaciones literarias en el Ambito Hispanico. Traduccion, Literatura y Cultura Ser.). (SPA & MUL., Illus.). 526p. pap. *(978-3-0343-0448-1(X))* Lang, Peter.
Pique, Ramon, ed. Silenci? 2009. 310p. *(978-84-96954-45-8(5))* Actar Birkhauser Distribution.
Roca, Maria Carme. El Monestir Proscrit. 2008. (CAT.). 277p. *(978-84-664-0905-6(X))* Columna Edicions.

CATALAN LITERATURE—HISTORY AND CRITICISM

Ferrater, Gabriel & Ponsatí-Murlà, Oriol. Tres Prosistes: Joaquim Ruyra, Caterina Albert, Josep Pla. 2010. (CAT.). 137p. *(978-84-9787-666-7(0))* Empúries, S.A., Editorial.
Forner, Climent. Paraules Sobre Paraules: Pròlegs I Discursos. 2010. (L'Oreneta Ser.: Vol. 19). (CAT.). 382p. *(978-84-89751-89-7(7))* L'Albí, Ediciones.
Friedlein, Roger. Der Dialog bei Ramon Llull: Literarische Gestaltung als apologetische Strategie. (Beihefte zur Zeitschrift far romanische Philologie Ser.).Tr. of Dialogue in the Works of Ramon Llull. Literature as an apologetic Strategy. (GER.). VIII, 348p. 165.00 ***(978-3-11-186161-6(9))*** De Gruyter, Walter Inc.
Léglu, Catherine. Multilingualism & Mother Tongue in Medieval French, Occitan, & Catalan Narratives. 2010. (Penn State Romance Studies). (Illus.). 216p. 65.00 *(978-0-271-03672-4(9));* pap. 35.00 *(978-0-271-03673-1(7))* Pennsylvania State Univ. Pr.
London, John. Contextos de Joan Brossa: L'acció, la Imatge I la Paraula. 2010. (CAT., Illus.). 245p. *(978-84-475-3428-9(6))* Univ. de Barcelona Pubns.
Malé i Pegueroles, Jordi & Miralles, Eulàlia. Mites Clàssics en la Literatura Catalana Moderna I Contemporània. 2007. (CAT.). 219p. *(978-84-475-3112-7(0))* Univ. de Barcelona Pubns.

CATALAN POETRY

Crowe, Anna, ed. Lights off Water. Pelegri, Iolanda, tr. from CAT. 2007. (ENG.). 128p. per. 16.95 *(978-1-85754-916-4(3))* Carcanet Pr., Ltd. GBR. Dist: Independent Pubs. Group.

CATALAN POETRY—HISTORY AND CRITICISM

Broch, Alex & Broch, Alex. Sobre Poesia Catalana: Lectures Crítiques, 1973-2006. 2007. (CAT.). 394p. *(978-84-8437-081-9(X))* Proa, Ediciones, S.A.
Cocozzella, Peter. Fra Francesc Moner's Bilingual Poetics of Love & Reason: The 'Wisdom Text' by a Catalan Writer of the Early Renaissance. 2010. (Currents in Comparative Romance Languages & Literatures Ser.). 248p. (C). 75.95 *(978-1-4331-0805-1(4))* Lang, Peter Publishing, Inc.

CATALINA, LUCIUS SERVIUS, CA. 108-62 B.C.

Sallust. Sallust's History of the War Against Jugurtha, & of the Conspiracy of Catiline: With A Dictionary & Notes. by Prof. E. A. Andrews. 2006. 356p. per. 26.99 *(978-1-4255-3635-0(2))* MPublishing.

CATALINA ISLAND (CALIF.)
see Santa Catalina Island (Calif.)

CATALOG CARDS

Krajewski, Markus & Krapp, Peter. Paper Machines: About Cards & Catalogs, 1548-1929. 2011. (History & Foundations of Information Science Ser.). (ENG., Illus.). 224p. (gr. 17). 30.00 *(978-0-262-01589-9(7))* MIT Pr.

CATALOGING
see also Anglo-American Cataloguing Rules; Bibliography; Catalog Cards; Classification—Books; Colophons; Cooperative Cataloging; Descriptive Cataloging; Indexing; Library Science; Processing (Libraries); Searching, Bibliographical; Shelflisting; Subject Cataloging

Baca, Murtha, et al. Cataloging Cultural Objects: A Guide to Describing Cultural Works & Their Images. 2006. (Illus.). 396p. per. 75.00 *(978-0-8389-3564-4(8))* American Library Assn.
Bade, David. Responsible Librarianship: Library Policies for Unreliable Systems. 2008. (Illus.). 192p. pap. 22.00 *(978-0-9778617-6-7(7),* Library Juice Pr.) Litwin Bks., LLC.
Blum, Rudolf. Kallimachos: The Alexandrian Library & the Origins of Bibliography. Wellisch, Hans H., tr. from GER. 2011. (Wisconsin Studies in Classics Ser.). 288p. pap. 35.00 *(978-0-299-13174-6(2))* Univ. of Wisconsin Pr.
Caemmerer, Christiane & Jungmayr, Jorg, eds. Flugblätter von der frühen Neuzeit bis zur Gegenwart als kulturhistorische Quellen und bibliothekarische Sondermaterialien. 2010. (GER & ENG., Illus.). 302p. pap. 72.95 *(978-3-631-56122-5(9))* Lang, Peter GmbH, Europaischer Verlag der Wissenschaften DEU. Dist: Lang, Peter.
Chan, Lois Mai. Cataloging & Classification: An Introduction. 3rd ed. 2007. (ENG., Illus.). 600p. per. 65.00 *(978-0-8108-6000-1(7))* Scarecrow Pr., Inc.
Dewey, Melvil. A Classification & Subject Index for Cataloguing & Arranging the Books & Pamphlets of a Library. 2008. 112p. pap. *(978-1-4068-7005-3(6))* Echo Library.
—A Classification & Subject Index for Cataloguing & Arranging the Books & Pamphlets of a Library. 2010. (Illus.). 158p. pap. 7.87 *(978-1-4432-0037-0(9))* General Bks. LLC.
Division, Library Of Congress Catalog. Handbook of Card Distribution. 2009. 168p. pap. *(978-0-217-21727-9(3))* Books LLC.
Fletcher, Jain. Collection-level Cataloging: Bound-with Books, 1 vol. 2010. (Third Millennium Cataloging Ser.). (Illus.). 95p. pap. 45.00 *(978-1-59158-543-5(0),* LU8543) Libraries Unlimited, Inc.
Guo, Jingzhi. Collaborative Concept Exchange. 2008. 200p. pap. *(978-3-639-01064-0(7))* VDM Verlag Dr. Mueller e.K.
Hider, Philip & Harvey, D. R. Organising Knowledge in a Global Society: Principles & Practice in Libraries & Information Centres. rev. ed. 2008. 376p. pap. 110.00 ***(978-1-876938-67-3(6),*** Centre for Information Studies, Charles Sturt University) Woodhead Publishing Ltd. GBR. Dist: Neal-Schuman Pubs., Inc.
Holley, Robert P. & Carter, Ruth C. Cataloger, Editor, & Scholar: Essays in Honor of Ruth C. Carter. 2007. (ENG.). 440p. 125.00 *(978-0-7890-3622-3(3))* Routledge.
Intner, Sheila I., et al. Cataloging Correctly for Kids: An Introduction to the Tools. 5th ed. 2010. (Illus.). 232p. *(978-0-8389-3589-7(3))* American Library Assn.
Intner, Sheila S. Beginning Cataloging, 1 vol. 2009. (Illus.). 184p. pap. 40.00 *(978-1-59158-839-9(1),* LU8839) Libraries Unlimited, Inc.
Intner, Sheila S. & Weihs, Jean. Beginning Cataloging, 1 vol. 2009. (Illus.). 184p. 65.00 *(978-1-59158-687-6(9),* LU8687) Libraries Unlimited, Inc.
Jewett, Charles Coffin. On the Construction of Catalogues of Libraries, & of a General Catalogue; & Their Publication by Means of Separate, Stereotyped Titles with Rules. 2006. 112p. per. 16.99 *(978-1-4255-0738-1(7))* MPublishing.
Kaplan, Allison G. Crash Course in Cataloging for Non-Catalogers: A Casual Conversation on Organizing Information, 1 vol. 2009. (Crash Course Ser.). (Illus.). 140p. pap. 30.00 *(978-1-59158-401-8(9),* LU4019) Libraries Unlimited, Inc.
Krogh, Peter & Krogh, P. The Dam Book: Digital Asset Management for Photographers. 2nd rev. ed. 2009. (ENG., Illus.). 496p. pap. 49.99 *(978-0-596-52357-2(2))* O'Reilly Media, Inc.
Library of Congress, Copyright Office Staff & Library of Congress, Cataloging Distribution Service Staff, contrib. by. Library of Congress Copyright Data As Distributed in the MARC 21 Format: Record Format Documentation for the Copyright Cataloging Distribution Service. 2008. *(978-0-8444-1202-3(3))* Library of Congress.
Lubas, Rebecca L. Practical Strategies for Cataloging Departments. 2011. E-Book *(978-1-59884-493-1(8))* Libraries Unlimited, Inc.
Lubas, Rebecca L., ed. Practical Strategies for Cataloging Departments, 1 vol. 2011. (Third Millennium Cataloging Ser.). (Illus.). 117p. pap. 45.00 *(978-1-59884-492-4(X),* A2998P) Libraries Unlimited, Inc.
McIntosh, Joyce, ed. Cataloging & Indexing: Challenges & Solutions. 2011. (ENG.). 319p. 59.95 *(978-1-926692-76-0(4))* Apple Academic Pr., Inc. CAN. Dist: Taylor & Francis Group.
Miller, William & Pellen, Rita M. Adapting to E-Books. Pellen, Rita, ed. 2009. (Illus.). VI, 290p. 150.00 *(978-0-415-48377-3(8))* Routledge.
Oversight Hearing on the Library of Congress: Current Issues in Library Management: Hearing Before the Committee on House Administration, House of Representatives, One Hundred Tenth Congress, First Session, Hearing Held in Washington, DC, October 24, 2007. 2008. ii, 102p. *(978-0-16-080631-5(3),* 552-070-37241-5) United States Government Printing Office.
Ranganathan, S. R. Cataloguing Practice. 2nd ed. 517p. reprint ed. 50.00 *(978-81-85273-14-3(6))* Sarada Ranganathan Endowment for Library Science IND. Dist: Advent Bks. Div., Stosius, Inc.
Roberto, K. R., ed. Radical Cataloging: Essays at the Front. 2008. (ENG., Illus.). 321p. pap. 45.00 *(978-0-7864-3543-2(7))* McFarland & Co., Inc. Pubs.
Sanchez, Elaine. Emerging Issues in Academic Library Cataloging & Technical Services. 2007. per. 72.95 *(978-1-57440-086-1(X))* Primary Research Group.
Sanchez, Elaine R., ed. Conversations with Catalogers in the 21st Century, 1 vol. 2010. (Libraries Unlimited Library Management Collection). (Illus.). 283p. pap. 50.00 *(978-1-59884-702-4(3),* A3279P) Libraries Unlimited, Inc.
Saye, Jerry D. Manheimer's Cataloging & Classification. 5th ed. 2010. (Books in Library & Information Science Ser.). 450p. 139.95 *(978-0-8247-2681-2(2),* DK3003) Taylor & Francis Group.
Svenonius, Elaine. The Intellectual Foundation of Information Organization. 2009. (Digital Libraries & Electronic Publishing Ser.). (ENG.). 280p. (gr. 17). pap. 26.00 *(978-0-262-51261-9(0))* MIT Pr.
Taylor, Arlene G. Understanding FRBR: What It Is & How It Will Affect Our Retrieval Tools, 1 vol. 2007. (Illus.). 192p. per. 45.00 *(978-1-59158-509-1(0),* LU5090) Libraries Unlimited, Inc.
Tillett, Barbara, ed. IFLA Cataloguing Principles: The Statement of International Cataloguing Principles (ICP) & its Glossary. 2009. (IFLA Series on Bibliographic Control Ser.). (ENG.). 304p. *(978-3-598-24285-4(9))* Saur, K. G. Verlag GmbH & Co.
Weihs, Jean & Intner, Sheila S. Standard Cataloging for School & Public Libraries, 1 vol. 4th rev. ed. 2007. (Illus.). 296p. per. 50.00 *(978-1-59158-378-3(0),* LU3780) Libraries Unlimited, Inc.
Wheatley, Henry Benjamin. How to Catalogue a Library. 2010. (Cambridge Library Collection - Printing & Publishing History Ser.). 288p. pap. 23.99 *(978-1-108-02148-7(4))* Cambridge Univ. Pr.
—How to Make an Index. 2010. (Cambridge Library Collection - Printing & Publishing History Ser.). 252p. pap. 17.99 *(978-1-108-02150-0(6))* Cambridge Univ. Pr.
Zhang, Yin & Salaba, Athena. Implementing FRBR in Libraries: Key Issues & Future Directions. 2009. (Illus.). xiv, 154p. 80.00 *(978-1-55570-661-6(4))* Neal-Schuman Pubs., Inc.

CATALOGING, COOPERATIVE
see Cooperative Cataloging

CATALOGING OF AUDIO-VISUAL MATERIALS
see Cataloging of Non-Book Materials

CATALOGING OF COMPUTER FILES

Williams, Sarah Bay. Digital Shoebox: The How to Organize, Find, & Share Your Photos. 2009. (ENG., Illus.). 168p. pap. 24.99 *(978-0-321-66049-7(8))* Peachpit Pr.

CATALOGING OF EDUCATIONAL MEDIA

The Child of the World: Michael Olaf's Essential Montessori for Ages 3 to 12+ at Home & at School. 2007. pap. 7.00 net. *(978-1-879264-01-4(3))* Olaf, Michael Montessori Co.

Nehmer, Kathleen Suttles, ed. Middle School Teachers Guide to Free Curriculum Materials. (Middle School Teachers Guide to Free Curriculum Materials Ser.). 9th ed. 2006. 278p. per. 57.00 *(978-0-87708-432-7(7))* 10th ed. 2007. 242p. per. 57.00 *(978-0-87708-449-5(1))* Educators Progress Service, Inc.

Stephenson, Susan Mayclin. The Joyful Child: Michael Olaf's Essential Montessori for Birth to Three Years. 2007. 6.00 net. *(978-1-879264-16-8(1))* Olaf, Michael Montessori Co.

—The Joyful Child, 2008-2009: From Birth to Three Years. 2008. (Illus.). 72p. 7.00 net. *(978-1-879264-13-7(7))* Olaf, Michael Montessori Co.

CATALOGING OF MACHINE-READABLE DATA FILES

see Cataloging of Computer Files

CATALOGING OF MOTION PICTURES

Yee, Martha M. Moving Image Cataloging: How to Create & How to Use a Moving Image Catalog, 1 vol. 2007. (Third Millennium Cataloging Ser.). (Illus.). 288p. per. 45.00 *(978-1-59158-438-4(8),* LU4388) Libraries Unlimited, Inc.

CATALOGING OF MUSIC

Dean, Roger & Thorgerson, Storm. The Album Cover Album. 2008. (ENG.). 160p. 29.95 *(978-0-06-162695-1(3),* Collins Design) HarperCollins Pubs.

Koth, Michelle S. Uniform Titles for Music. 2008. (Music Library Association Technical Reports). (ENG., Illus.). 292p. pap. 53.00 *(978-0-8108-5281-5(0))* Scarecrow Pr., Inc.

Lisius, Peter H. & Griscom, Richard, eds. Directions in Music Cataloging. 2012. pap. 50.00 ***(978-0-89579-719-3(4))*** A-R Editions, Inc.

CATALOGING OF NON-BOOK MATERIALS

see also cataloging of individual types of materials, e.g. Cataloging of Maps

Karpuk, Deborah. KidzCat: A How-to-Do-It Manual for Cataloging Children's Materials & Instructional Resources. 2007. (How To-Do-It Manuals for Librarians Ser.). 275p. pap. 59.95 *(978-1-55570-590-9(1))* Neal-Schuman Pubs., Inc.

Olson, Nancy B., et al. Cataloging of Audiovisual Materials & Other Special Materials: A Manual Based on AACR2 & MARC 21, 1 vol. 5th ed. 2008. (Illus.). 332p. pap. 45.00 *(978-1-59158-635-7(6),* LU5863) Libraries Unlimited, Inc.

Weber, Mary Beth & Austin, Fay Angela. Describing Electronic, Digital, & Other Media Using AACR2 & RDA: A How-To-Do-It Manual & CD-ROM for Librarians. 2010. (Illus.). xviii, 301p. 75.00 *(978-1-55570-668-5(1))* Neal-Schuman Pubs., Inc.

Yee, Martha M. Moving Image Cataloging: How to Create & How to Use a Moving Image Catalog, 1 vol. 2007. (Third Millennium Cataloging Ser.). (Illus.). 288p. per. 45.00 *(978-1-59158-438-4(8),* LU4388) Libraries Unlimited, Inc.

CATALOGING OF PERIODICALS

see Cataloging of Serial Publications

CATALOGING OF SERIAL PUBLICATIONS

Association of College and Research Libraries, Rare Books and Manuscripts Section Bibliographic Standards Committee Staff & Library of Congress, Cataloging Policy and Support Office Staff, contrib. by. Descriptive Cataloging of Rare Materials (Serials) 2008. *(978-0-8444-1217-7(1))* Library of Congress.

Black, Steve. Serials in Libraries: Issues & Practices, 1 vol. 2006. 208p. per. 45.00 *(978-1-59158-258-8(X),* LU258X) Libraries Unlimited, Inc.

Genereux, Cecilia & Moeller, Paul, eds. Notes for Serials Cataloging, 1 vol. 3rd rev. ed. 2009. 196p. pap. 55.00 *(978-1-59158-653-1(4),* LU8653) Libraries Unlimited, Inc.

Rosenberg, Frieda B. & Saudargas, Thom. Serials Holdings Workshop. 3rd ed. 2008. *(978-0-8444-1198-9(1))* Library of Congress.

CATALOGS

see also Commercial Catalogs; Library Catalogs

also subdivision Catalogs under specific subjects, e.g. Engravings—Catalogs; Manuscripts—Catalogs

Allured, Michael, ed. McCutcheon's Emulsifiers & Detergents: North American & International Edition. 2007. *(978-1-933430-15-7(X))* MC Publishing Co.

—McCutcheon's Functional Materials: North American & International Edition. 2007. *(978-1-933430-18-8(4))* MC Publishing Co.

Allured, Michael Allured, ed. McCutcheon's Emulsifiers & Detergents: North American Edition. 2007. pap. *(978-1-933430-13-3(3))* MC Publishing Co.

Delmar. 2008 PDR Nurse's Drug Handbook. Thomson Healthcare Staff, ed. 2007. 1800p. pap. 39.95 *(978-1-56363-665-3(4))* PDR Network, LLC.

Hood, Karen Jean Matsko. Mountain Valley View Farm, Inc. Catalog. 2010. 9.95 *(978-1-59210-311-9(1))*; pap. 9.95 *(978-1-59210-252-5(2))*; cd-rom 9.95 *(978-1-59210-268-6(9))* Whispering Pine Pr. International, Inc.

Index Nominum: International Drug Directory, Nineteenth Edition. 19th rev. ed. 2008. 1982p. 410.00 *(978-3-8047-5042-5(7))* Medpharm Scientific Pubs. DEU. Dist: Taylor & Francis Group.

Kirwin, Liza & Princeton Architectural Press Staff. Lists: To-Dos, Illustrated Inventories, Collected Thoughts, & Other Artists' Enumerations from the Smithsonian's Archives of American Art. 2010. (ENG., Illus.). 208p. 24.95 *(978-1-56898-888-7(5))* Princeton Architectural Pr.

POS 2007 Classics Catalog. 2007. pap. *(978-0-415-95878-3(4))* Routledge.

Rhee, Douglas J., et al, contrib. by. PDR for Ophthalmic Medicines. 36th ed. 2007. (Physicians' Desk Reference for Ophthalmic Medicines Ser.). (Illus.). 291p. 69.95 *(978-1-56363-663-9(8))* PDR Network, LLC.

Schaap, Ella. Delft Ceramics at the Philadelphia Museum of Art. 2006. (ENG., Illus.). 32.00 *(978-0-87633-168-2(1))* Philadelphia Museum of Art.

Shepard, Judy. The Catalog Book: Designs for Catalogs & Direct Mail. 2007. (Illus.). 175p. 40.00 *(978-1-58471-097-4(7))* Visual Reference Pubns., Inc.

Thomson, creator. Red Book: Pharmacy's Fundamental Reference. 112th ed. 2008. (Red Book: Pharmacy's Fundamental Reference Ser.). (Illus.). 1012p. pap. 76.95 *(978-1-56363-671-4(9))* PDR Network, LLC.

Thomson Healthcare, creator. PDR Guide to Drug Interactions, Side Effects, & Indications. 62nd rev. ed. 2007. (Physicians' Desk Reference Guide to Drug Interactions, Side Effects, & Indications Ser.). 2298p. 73.95 *(978-1-56363-664-6(6))* PDR Network, LLC.

Thomson Healthcare Staff, ed. 2008 Red Book Update. 112th ed. 2007. 50p. pap. 99.00 *(978-1-56363-682-0(4))* PDR Network, LLC.

Tucker, Annie, ed. Super 7: The Book. 2008. (Illus.). 277p. pap. 39.95 *(978-0-9796678-1-7(X))* Super7 Media, Inc.

Wanamaker. Wanamaker's New Hats & Bonnets 1891 Vintage Millinery Catalog. 2007. pap. 10.95 *(978-1-934268-28-5(3))* Bramcost Pubns., LLC.

CATALOGS—PRINTING

Finch, Richard D. & Rives, Veda M., eds. Marks from the Matrix: Normal Editions Workshop Collaborative Limited Edition Prints 1976-2006. 2007. (Illus.). 196p. *(978-0-9795884-0-2(5))*; (ENG., pap. *(978-0-9795884-1-9(3))* Normal Editions Workshop Illinois State Univ.

Kermes, Constantine J. Work in Progress: Paintings & Other Works of Constantine Kermes. 2008. (Illus.). 80p. 65.00 *(978-0-9776414-8-2(1))* LifeReloaded.

Musacchio, Humberto. El Taller de Gráfica Popular. 2007. (Tezontle Ser.). (SPA.). 214p. 49.95 *(978-968-16-7703-9(X))* Fondo de Cultura Economica USA.

Whitesell, David R. First Supplement to James E. Walsh's Catalogue of the Fifteenth-Century Printed Books in the Harvard University Library. 2006. (Harvard Library Bulletin Ser.: 16). (Illus.). 236p. 29.95 *(978-0-674-02145-7(2))* Harvard Univ. Library.

CATALOGS, BOOKSELLERS'

see Booksellers' Catalogs

CATALOGS, CARD

see Card Catalogs

CATALOGS, CLASSIFIED

see Classified Catalogs

CATALOGS, CLASSIFIED (DEWEY DECIMAL)

see Classified Catalogs (Dewey Decimal)

CATALOGS, COMMERCIAL

see Commercial Catalogs

CATALOGS, FILM

see Motion Pictures—Catalogs

CATALOGS, LIBRARY

see Library Catalogs

CATALOGS, ONLINE

see Online Catalogs

CATALOGS, PUBLISHERS'

see Publishers' Catalogs

CATALOGS, STAR

see Stars—Catalogs

CATALOGS, SYSTEMATIC

see Classified Catalogs

CATALOGS, SUBJECT

see Subject Catalogs

CATALOGS, UNION

see Union Catalogs

CATALOGS, UNIVERSAL

see Bibliography, International

CATALONIA (SPAIN)

Alarcón, Amado & Garzón, Luis G. Language, migration & social mobility in Catalonia. 2011. (International Studies in Sociology & Social Anthropology Ser.). (Illus.). 170p. ***(978-90-04-21123-0(3))*** BRILL.

Almirall, Josep & Almirall Rill, Josep. Human Towers: Touching the Sky with the Hand, 1 vol. 2011. (ENG.). 240p. pap. 16.95 *(978-84-8478-473-9(8))* Triangle Postals, S.L. ESP. Dist: Innovative Logistics.

Andrews, Sarah & Thomas Cook Publishing Staff. Catalonia. 3rd ed. 2009. (Travellers - Thomas Cook Ser.). (ENG., Illus.). 192p. pap. 16.95 *(978-1-84848-142-8(X))* Cook, Thomas Publishing GBR. Dist: Globe Pequot Pr., The.

Buffery, Helena. Historical Dictionary of the Catalans. 2010. (Historical Dictionaries of Peoples & Cultures Ser.). (ENG., Illus.). 454p. 85.00 *(978-0-8108-5483-3(X))* Scarecrow Pr., Inc.

Buffery, Helena & Marcer, Elisenda. Historical Dictionary of the Catalans. 2011. E-Book *(978-0-8108-7514-2(4))* Scarecrow Pr., Inc.

Catlos, Brian A. The Victors & the Vanquished: Christians & Muslims of Catalonia & Aragon, 1050-1300. 2007. (Cambridge Studies in Medieval Life & Thought). (ENG., Illus.). 480p. pap. 61.00 *(978-0-521-03644-3(5))* Cambridge Univ. Pr.

Colom Gorgues, Antonio, et al. Les Dones Al Món Rural en Catalunya. 2009. (CAT., Illus.). 232p. *(978-84-9876-604-2(4))* Tirant lo Blanch.

Dalmau, Antoni. Jocs, Cançons I Costums Que No Hem de Prerdre. 2008. (CAT., Illus.). 166p. *(978-84-664-0873-8(8))* Columna Edicions.

Dowling, Andrew. Catalonia since the Spanish Civil War: Reconstructing the Nation. 2012. (ENG.). 272p. 74.95 ***(978-1-84519-530-4(2))*** Sussex Academic Pr. GBR. Dist: International Specialized Bk. Services.

Eaude, Michael. Catalonia: A Cultural History. 2008. (Landscapes of the Imagination Ser.). (ENG., Illus.). 256p. 25.00 *(978-0-19-532797-7(7))* Oxford Univ. Pr., Inc.

Edwards, Siân. Catalonia. 192p. *(978-0-7083-2039-6(2))*; pap. *(978-0-7083-2038-9(4))* Univ. of Wales Pr.

Facaros, Dana & Pauls, Michael. Barcelona & Catalonia. 2009. (Illus.). 320p. pap. *(978-1-86011-421-2(0))* Cadogan Guides GBR. Dist: Globe Pequot Pr., The.

—Barcelona & Catalonia. 2009. (ENG., Illus.). 352p. pap. 21.95 *(978-1-56656-768-8(8))* Interlink Publishing Group, Inc.

Farràs, Andreu, et al. El Ascensor: Charnegos Al Poder. 2009. (SPA.). 303p. *(978-84-92758-30-2(9))* Angle Editorial, S.L.

Fodor's. Fodor's Barcelona, 4th Edition: With Highlights of Catalonia & Bilbao. 2012. (Full-color Travel Guide Ser.). (ENG.). 408p. pap. 19.99 ***(978-0-307-92917-4(5)***, Fodor's) Fodor's Travel Pubns.

Gallagher, Mary-Ann, et al. Eyewitness Travel Guides - Barcelona & Catalonia. 2011. (Eyewitness Travel Guides). (ENG.). 208p. 20.00 *(978-0-7566-6936-2(7))* Dorling Kindersley Publishing, Inc.

Greer, Scott L. Nationalism & Self-Government: The Politics of Autonomy in Scotland & Catalonia. 2007. (SUNY Series in National Identities). 223p. 65.00 *(978-0-7914-7047-3(4))* State Univ. of New York Pr.

Guise, Richard. Two Wheels over Catalonia. 2011. (ENG., Illus.). 320p. pap. 13.95 ***(978-1-84953-144-3(7))*** Summerdale Pubs. GBR. Dist: Independent Pubs. Group.

Henders, Susan J. Territoriality, Asymmetry, & Autonomy: Catalonia, Corsica, Hong Kong, & Tibet. 2010. (ENG.). 288p. 95.00 *(978-1-4039-7062-6(9))* Palgrave Macmillan.

Illa, Oriol & Illa i Garcia, Oriol. Independentisme Català: Entre el Símbol I la Institució. 2010. (SPA.). 135p. *(978-84-15002-22-2(X))* Angle Editorial, S.L.

Jarrett, Jonathan. Rulers & Ruled in Frontier Catalonia, 880-1010: Pathways of Power. 2010. (Royal Historical Society Studies in History New Ser.: Volume 75). (Illus.). 220p. 90.00 *(978-0-86193-309-9(5))* Royal Historical Society GBR. Dist: Boydell & Brewer, Inc.

Keown, Dominic, ed. A Companion to Catalan Culture. 2011. (Monografías A Ser.: Volume 293). (Illus.). 282p. 95.00 *(978-1-85566-227-8(2),* Tamesis Bks.) Boydell & Brewer, Ltd. GBR. Dist: Boydell & Brewer, Inc.

Kleiner-Liebau, Désirée. Migration & the Construction of National Identity in Spain. 2009. 272p. pap. 29.80 *(978-84-8489-476-6(2))* Iberoamericana Vervuert Publishing Corp.

Marfany, Julie. Land Proto-Industry & Population in Catalonia C. 1680-1829: An Alternative Transition to Capitalism? 2012. (Modern Economic & Social History Ser.). (Illus.). 190p. 124.95 ***(978-1-4094-4465-7(1))*** Ashgate Publishing Co.

Mendonsa, Eugene. The Scripting of Domination in Medieval Catalonia: An Anthropological View. 2008. 236p. 40.00 *(978-1-59460-486-7(X))* Carolina Academic Pr.

Milton, Gregory B. Market Power: Lordship, Society, & Economy in Medieval Catalonia (1276-1313) 2012. ***(978-0-230-39141-3(9))***; (ENG., Illus.). 272p. 90.00 ***(978-0-230-39170-3(2))*** Palgrave Macmillan.

Pla Boada, Ricard. Catalonia, 1 vol. 2007. (ENG., Illus.). 431p. pap. 26.00 *(978-84-8478-310-7(3))* Triangle Postals, S.L. ESP. Dist: Innovative Logistics.

Pla, Maurici & Pla i Serra, Maurici. Catalonia: A Guide to Modern Architecture, 1880-2007, 1 vol. 2007. (ENG., Illus.). 488p. pap. 63.00 *(978-84-8478-009-0(0))* Triangle Postals, S.L. ESP. Dist: Innovative Logistics.

Roller, Elisa. Nationalist Movements & European Integration. 2007. 256p. 120.00 *(978-0-415-34800-3(5),* RU42416) Routledge.

Stolz, Klaus. Towards a Regional Political Class? Professional Politicians & Regional Institutions in Catalonia & Scotland. 2010. (Devolution Ser.). (ENG.). 256p. 90.00 *(978-0-7190-7979-5(9))* Manchester Univ. Pr. GBR. Dist: Macmillan.

Thomas Cook Publishing Staff. Driving Guides Catalonia & the Spanish Pyrenees. 4th ed. 2011. (Drive Around - Thomas Cook Ser.). (ENG., Illus.). 288p. pap. 26.95 *(978-1-84848-377-4(5))* Cook, Thomas Publishing GBR. Dist: Globe Pequot Pr., The.

White, Gary & Aviva, Elyn. Powerfull Places in Catalonia. 2010. 124p. pap. 8.95 *(978-0-9826233-1-2(3))* Pilgrims Process, Inc.

CATALYSIS

see also Fluidization; Heterogeneous Catalysis; Platinum Catalysts

A. D'yakonov, Vladimir, ed. Dzhemilev Reaction in Organic & Organometallic Synthesis. 2010. (Chemistry Research & Applications Ser.). 105p. pap. 43.00 *(978-1-60876-683-3(7))* Nova Science Pubs., Inc.

Adam, Waldemar, et al. Oxidation of Organic Compounds by Dioxiranes. 2009. (ENG., Illus.). 670p. pap., instr.'s hndbk. ed. 111.00 *(978-0-470-45407-7(5),* Wiley-Interscience) Wiley, John & Sons, Inc.

Anderson, J. R. & Boudart, M., eds. Catalysis: Science & Technology, 11 vols. Incl. Vol. 5. 281p. (C). 1984. 136.00 *(978-0-387-12665-4(1))*; Vol. 6. 313p. (C). 1984. 145.00 *(978-0-387-12815-3(8))*; Vol. 1. 309p. (C). 1981. 136.00 *(978-0-387-10353-2(8))*; Vol. 2. 280p. (C). 1982. 117.00 *(978-0-387-10593-2(X))*; Vol. 4. 289p. (C). 1983. 136.00 *(978-0-387-11855-0(1))*; Vol. 7. 223p. (C). 1985. 135.00 *(978-0-387-15035-2(8))*; Vol. 8. 262p. (C). 1987. 117.00 *(978-0-387-15034-5(X))*; Vol. 9. Burwell, R. L., et al, contrib. by. 190p. (C). 1991. 111.00 *(978-0-387-52972-1(1))*; Vol. 10. 164p. 1996. 134.00 *(978-3-540-60109-8(0))*; Vol. 3. 289p. 1983. 127.00 *(978-0-387-11634-1(6))*; (Illus.). 289p. 999.00 *(978-3-540-11634-9(6))* Springer.

Andersson, Pher G., ed. Iridium Catalysis. 2011. (Topics in Organometallic Chemistry Ser.). (Illus.). x, 220p. 259.00 *(978-3-642-15333-4(X),* 364215333X) Springer.

Andreea, Gluhoi. Fundamental Studies Focused on Understanding of Gold Catalysis: Potential Use of Gold Based Catalysts for Various Environmentally Friendly Applications, in Particular Automotive Catalysis & Hydrogen Fuel Cells. 2011. 216p. pap. ***(978-3-639-32000-8(X))*** VDM Verlag Dr. Mueller e.K.

Astruc, Didier, ed. Nanoparticles & Catalysis. 2007. (ENG., Illus.). 663p. 500.00 *(978-3-527-31572-7(1),* Wiley-VCH) Wiley, John & Sons, Inc.

Augugliaro, Vincenzo. Clean by Light Irradiation: Practical Applications of Supported TiO2. 2010. (ENG., Illus.). 282p. (C). 160.00 ***(978-1-84755-870-1(4))*** Royal Society of Chemistry, The GBR. Dist: Ingram Pub. Services.

Baerns, Manfred. Basic Principles in Applied Catalysis. 2010. (Springer Series in Chemical Physics Ser.). (Illus.). x, 557p. pap. 319.00 *(978-3-642-07310-6(7),* 3642073107) Springer.

Balbuena, Perla B. & Subramanian, Venkat R., eds. Theory & Experiment in Electrocatalysis. 2010. (Modern Aspects of Electrochemistry Ser.). (Illus.). xxiv, 578p. 259.00 *(978-1-4419-5593-7(3),* 1441955933) Springer.

Barbaro, Pierluigi & Bianchini, Claudio, eds. Catalysis for Sustainable Energy Production. 2009. (ENG., Illus.). 474p. 235.00 *(978-3-527-32095-0(4),* Wiley-VCH) Wiley, John & Sons, Inc.

Barbaro, Pierluigi & Liguori, Francesca, eds. Heterogenized Homogeneous Catalysts for Fine Chemicals Production: Materials & Processes. 2010. (Catalysis by Metal Complexes Ser.). (ENG., Illus.). xvii, 400p. 219.00 *(978-90-481-3695-7(4),* 9048136954) Springer.

Bargon, J., et al, contrib. by. In situ NMR Methods in Catalysis. 2007. (Topics in Current Chemistry Ser.). (Illus.). xii, 169p. 219.00 *(978-3-540-71426-2(X))* Springer.

Bargon, Joachim & Kuhn, Lars T. In situ NMR Methods in Catalysis. 2010. (Topics in Current Chemistry Ser.). (Illus.). xii, 169p. pap. 219.00 *(978-3-642-09060-8(5),* 3642090605) Springer.

Behr, Arno & Neubert, Peter. Applied Homogeneous Catalysis. 2012. (ENG., Illus.). 716p. 185.00 ***(978-3-527-32641-9(3))***; pap. 95.00 ***(978-3-527-32633-4(2))*** Wiley, John & Sons, Inc. (Wiley-VCH).

Beller, Matthias, et al, eds. Catalysis: From Principles to Applications. 2012. (ENG.). 615p. 90.00 ***(978-3-527-32349-4(X)***, Wiley-VCH) Wiley, John & Sons, Inc.

Benaglia, Maurizio, ed. Recoverable & Recyclable Catalysts. 2009. (ENG., Illus.). 500p. 175.00 *(978-0-470-68195-4(0),* Wiley) Wiley, John & Sons, Inc.

Bignozzi, Carlo Alberto, ed. Photocatalysis. 2011. (Topics in Current Chemistry Ser.). (ENG., Illus.). xi, 220p. 259.00 ***(978-3-642-22293-1(5)***, 3642222935) Springer.

Blaser, Hans Ulrich & Federsel, Hans-Jürgen, eds. Asymmetric Catalysis on Industrial Scale: Challenges, Approaches & Solutions. 2nd ed. 2010. (ENG., Illus.). 580p. 360.00 *(978-3-527-32489-7(5),* Wiley-VCH) Wiley, John & Sons, Inc.

Bolm, Carsten & Hahn, F. Ekkehardt, eds. Activating Unreactive Substrates: The Role of Secondary Interactions. 2009. (ENG., Illus.). 481p. 240.00 *(978-3-527-31823-0(2),* Wiley-VCH) Wiley, John & Sons, Inc.

Bonakdarpour, Arman & Dahn, Jeff R. Combinatorial Studies of Pt-Based Oxygen Reduction Electrocatalysts. 2008. (Illus.). 224p. pap. *(978-3-639-04465-2(7))* VDM Verlag Dr. Mueller e.K.

Bond, Geoffrey C. Metal-Catalysed Reactions of Hydrocarbons. 2010. (Fundamental & Applied Catalysis Ser.). (Illus.). xxii, 666p. pap. 139.00 *(978-1-4419-3694-3(7),* 1441936947) Springer.

Bond, Geoffrey C., et al. Catalysis by Gold. 2006. (Catalytic Science Ser.: Vol. 6). (Illus.). 366p. 150.00 *(978-1-86094-658-5(5))* Imperial College Pr. GBR. Dist: World Scientific Publishing Co., Inc.

Bullock, R. Morris, ed. Catalysis Without Precious Metals. 2010. (ENG., Illus.). 306p. 215.00 *(978-3-527-32354-8(6),* Wiley-VCH) Wiley, John & Sons, Inc.

Caprio, Vittorio & Williams, Jonathan M. J. Catalysis in Asymmetric Synthesis. 2nd ed. 2009. (Postgraduate Chemistry Ser.). (ENG., Illus.). 408p. pap. 75.00 *(978-1-4051-7519-7(2))*; 160.00 *(978-1-4051-9091-6(4))* Wiley, John & Sons, Inc. (Wiley-Blackwell).

Carley, Albert F., et al, eds. Surface Chemistry & Catalysis. 2010. (Fundamental & Applied Catalysis Ser.). 400p. pap. 269.00 *(978-1-4419-3387-4(5),* 1441933875) Springer.

Cejka, Jiri, et al, eds. Zeolites & Catalysis: Synthesis, Reactions & Applications, 2 vols. 2010. (ENG., Illus.). 918p. 390.00 *(978-3-527-32514-6(X),* Wiley-VCH) Wiley, John & Sons, Inc.

Chaloner, P. A., et al. Homogeneous Hydrogenation. 2010. (Catalysis by Metal Complexes Ser.). (Illus.). 288p. pap. 289.00 *(978-90-481-4323-8(3),* 9048143233) Springer.

Chiusoli, G. P. Metal-Catalysis in Industrial Organic Processes. 2008. (ENG., Illus.). 312p. (C). pap. 72.00 *(978-0-85404-150-3(8))* Royal Society of Chemistry, The GBR. Dist: Ingram Pub. Services.

Chorkendorff, I. & Niemantsverdriet, J. W. Concepts of Modern Catalysis & Kinetics. 2nd ed. 2007. (ENG.). 477p. 100.00 *(978-3-527-31672-4(8),* Wiley-VCH) Wiley, John & Sons, Inc.

Církva, Vladimír & Žabová, Hana, eds. Photocatalysis on Titania-coated Electrode-less Discharge Lamps. 2010. (Chemical Engineering Methods & Technology Ser.). x, 76p. pap. 43.00 *(978-1-60876-842-4(2))* Nova Science Pubs., Inc.

Copéret, C. & Chaudret, Bruno. Surface & Interfacial Organometallic Chemistry & Catalysis. 2010. (Topics in Organometallic Chemistry Ser.). (Illus.). x, 292p. pap. 319.00 *(978-3-642-06584-2(8),* 3642065848) Springer.

Cordova, Armando, ed. Catalytic Asymmetric Conjugate Reactions. 2010. (ENG., Illus.). 464p. 200.00 *(978-3-527-32411-8(9)*, Wiley-VCH) Wiley, John & Sons, Inc.

Cornils, Boy, et al, eds. Catalysis from A to Z: A Concise Encyclopedia, 3 vols. 3rd ed. 2007. (ENG., Illus.). 1560p. 895.00 *(978-3-527-31438-6(5)*, Wiley-VCH) Wiley, John & Sons, Inc.

Cottilard, Sophie A., ed. Catalytic Combustion. 2011. (Series: Chemical Engineering Methods & Technology Ser.). (Illus.). 208p. 140.00 *(978-1-61324-279-7(4))* Nova Science Pubs., Inc.

Cram101 Textbook Reviews & Cram101 Textbook Reviews. Outlines & Highlights for Catalysis in Asymmetric Synthesis by Vittorio Caprio, Isbn: 9781405175197. 2011. 426p. pap. 35.95 ***(978-1-61461-493-7(8))*** Cram101 Inc.

Crawley, Matthew L. & Trost, Barry M. Applications of Transition Metal Catalysis in Drug Discovery & Development: An Industrial Perspective. 2012. (ENG., Illus.). 376p. 99.95 ***(978-0-470-63132-4(5)***, Wiley) Wiley, John & Sons, Inc.

Dai, Li-Xin & Hou, Xue-Long, eds. Chiral Ferrocenes in Asymmetric Catalysis: Synthesis & Applications. 2010. (ENG., Illus.). 431p. 215.00 *(978-3-527-32280-0(9)*, Wiley-VCH) Wiley, John & Sons, Inc.

Davis, B. H. & Occelli, Mario L. Advances in Fisher-Tropsch Synthesis, Catalysts, & Catalysis. 2009. (Chemical Industries Ser.). (ENG., Illus.). 424p. 236.95 *(978-1-4200-6256-4(5)*, CRC Press) Taylor & Francis Group GBR. Dist: Taylor & Francis Group.

Davis, Burtron H. & Occelli, Mario L. Fischer-Tropsch Synthesis, Catalysts & Catalysis. 2006. (Studies in Surface Science & Catalysis Ser.: 163). (ENG., Illus.). 430p. 255.00 *(978-0-444-52221-4(2)*, Elsevier Science) Elsevier Science & Technology Bks.

De Lasa, Hugo & Serrano-Rosales, Benito. Advances in Chemical Engineering: Photocatalytic Technologies. 2009. (Advances in Chemical Engineering Ser.: 36). (ENG.). 250p. 231.00 *(978-0-12-374763-1(5)*, Academic Pr.) Elsevier Science & Technology Bks.

Degnan, Thomas F. & Chen, Nai Y. Handbook of Experimental Catalysis. 2008. 880p. 175.00 *(978-0-471-38416-8(X)*, Wiley-Interscience) Wiley, John & Sons, Inc.

D'Elia, Valeric. Synthesis, Characterization & Application of A/ß-Oligopeptides. 2010. 176p. pap. *(978-3-639-25344-3(2))* VDM Verlag Dr. Mueller e.K.

Derouane, E. G., et al, eds. Catalytic Activation & Functionalisation of Light Alkanes: Advances & Challenges. 2010. (NATO Science Partnership Sub-Series: 3: Ser.). 504p. pap. 419.00 *(978-90-481-4999-5(1)*, 9048149991) Springer.

Dixneuf, Pierre & Bruneau, Christian, eds. Metal Vinylidenes & Allenylidenes in Catalysis: From Reactivity to Applications in Synthesis. 2008. (ENG., Illus.). 356p. 235.00 *(978-3-527-31892-6(5)*, Wiley-VCH) Wiley, John & Sons, Inc.

Dragutan, Valerian, et al, eds. Green Metathesis Chemistry: Great Challenges in Synthesis, Catalysis & Nanotechnology. 2009. (NATO Science for Peace & Security Series A: Chemistry & Biology Ser.). (Illus.). xix, 425p. 269.00 *(978-90-481-3431-1(5)*, 9048134315); (ENG., pap. 139.00 *(978-90-481-3432-8(3)*, 9048134323) Springer.

Drauz, Karlheinz, et al, eds. Enzyme Catalysis in Organic Synthesis, 3 vols., Vol. 3. 3rd rev. ed. 2012. (ENG., Illus.). 2038p. 605.00 ***(978-3-527-32547-4(6)***, Wiley-VCH) Wiley, John & Sons, Inc.

Duca, Gheorghe. Homogeneous Catalysis with Metal Complexes: Fundamentals & Applications. 2012. (Springer Series in Chemical Physics Ser.). (ENG., Illus.). xii, 478p. 169.00 ***(978-3-642-24628-9(1)***, 3642246281) Springer.

Eguchi, Koichi, et al, eds. Science & Technology in Catalysis: 5th Tokyo Conference on Advanced Catalytic Science & Technology. 2007. (Studies in Surface Science & Catalysis Ser.: 172). (ENG., Illus.). 652p. 260.00 *(978-0-444-53202-2(1)*, Elsevier Science) Elsevier Science & Technology Bks.

El-Seidy, Ahmed M. A. Synthesis, Characterization & Catalysis of Schiff Bases Complexes. 2011. 284p. pap. ***(978-3-8443-8287-7(9))*** Lambert Academic Publishing.

Fessner, Wolf-Dieter & Anthonsen, Thorleif, eds. Modern Biocatalysis: Stereoselective & Environmentally Friendly Reactions. 2009. (ENG., Illus.). 400p. 220.00 *(978-3-527-32071-4(7)*, Wiley-VCH) Wiley, John & Sons, Inc.

Frey, Perry A. & Hegeman, Adrian D. Enzymatic Reaction Mechanisms. 2007. (ENG., Illus.). 848p. (C). 225.00 *(978-0-19-512258-9(5))* Oxford Univ. Pr., Inc.

Fuentes, Serio. Catalizadores. (Ciencia para Todos Ser.). (SPA.). pap. 6.99 *(978-968-16-2859-8(4))* Fondo de Cultura Economica USA.

Furimsky, Edward, ed. Catalysis in the Refining of Fischer-Tropsch Syncrude. 2010. (RSC Catalysis Ser.). (Illus.). 294p. 195.00 *(978-1-84973-080-8(6))* Royal Society of Chemistry, The GBR. Dist: Ingram Pub. Services.

Gade, Lutz H. Dendrimer Catalysis. 2010. (Topics in Organometallic Chemistry Ser.). (Illus.). xii, 189p. pap. 239.00 *(978-3-642-07083-9(3)*, 3642070833) Springer.

Garcia-Junceda, Eduardo, ed. Multi-Step Enzyme Catalysis: Biotransformations & Chemoenzymatic Synthesis. 2008. (ENG.). 256p. 168.00 *(978-3-527-31921-3(2)*, Wiley-VCH) Wiley, John & Sons, Inc.

Gates, Bruce C., contrib. by. Advances in Catalysis. 2007. (Advances in Catalysis Ser.). (ENG., Illus.). 406p. 231.00 *(978-0-12-373897-4(0)*, Academic Pr.) Elsevier Science & Technology Bks.

Gates, Bruce C., et al, contrib. by. Advances in Catalysis. 2011. (ENG.). 352p. 231.00 ***(978-0-12-387772-7(5)***, Academic Pr.) Elsevier Science & Technology Bks.

Gates, Bruce C., et al, eds. Advances in Catalysis. 2010. (ENG.). 644p. 231.00 *(978-0-12-380852-3(9)*, Academic Pr.) Elsevier Science & Technology Bks.

Ghang, Minjae & Ramel, Bjo. Focus on Catalysis Research: New Developments. 2012. (Chemistry Research & Applications Chemical Engineering Methods & Technology Ser.). (Illus.). 417p. 185.00 ***(978-1-62100-444-8(9))*** Nova Science Pubs., Inc.

Grogan, Gideon. Practical Biotransformations: A Beginner's Guide. 2009. (Postgraduate Chemistry Ser.: 2). (ENG., Illus.). 344p. pap. 75.00 *(978-1-4051-7125-0(1)*, Wiley-Blackwell) Wiley, John & Sons, Inc.

Grunwald, Peter. Biocatalysis. 2008. (Illus.). 700p. 163.00 *(978-1-86094-744-5(1))*; pap. 86.00 *(978-1-86094-771-1(9))* Imperial College Pr. GBR. Dist: World Scientific Publishing Co., Inc.

Gruttadauria, Michelangelo & Giacalone, Francesco, eds. Catalytic Methods in Asymmetric Synthesis: Advanced Materials, Techniques, & Applications. 2011. (ENG., Illus.). 720p. 149.95 *(978-0-470-64136-1(3)*, Wiley) Wiley, John & Sons, Inc.

Guczi, László & Erdőhelyi, András, eds. Catalysis for Alternative Energy Generation. 2012. (ENG., Illus.). 325p. 179.00 *(978-1-4614-0343-2(X)*, 146140343X) Springer.

Gulyás, Henrik & Fernández, Elena. Influence of the Borane Reagent Structure on Catalytic Synthesis of Organoboranes. 2011. pap. *(978-1-61209-340-6(X))* Nova Science Pubs., Inc.

H & Baerns, Manfred. Combinatorial Development of Solid Catalytic Materials: Design of High-Throughput Experiments, Data Analysis, Data Mining. 2009. (Illus.). 180p. 77.00 *(978-1-84816-343-0(6))* Imperial College Pr. GBR. Dist: World Scientific Publishing Co., Inc.

Hashmi, A. Stephen K. & Toste, Dean F., eds. Modern Gold Catalyzed Synthesis. 2012. (ENG.). 418p. 200.00 ***(978-3-527-31952-7(2)***, Wiley-VCH) Wiley, John & Sons, Inc.

Heiz, U. & Landman, U., eds. Nanocatalysis. 2007. (Nanoscience & Technology Ser.). (Illus.). 503p. per. 139.00 *(978-3-540-74551-8(3))*; 249.00 *(978-3-540-32645-8(6)*, 3540326456) Springer.

Hou, C. T. & Shaw, Jei-Fu. Biocatalysis & Bioenergy. 2008. (ENG., Illus.). 608p. 178.00 *(978-0-470-13404-7(6)*, Wiley-Interscience) Wiley, John & Sons, Inc.

Islamova, Regina M., et al, eds. Kinetics, Catalysis & Mechanism of Chemical Reactions. from Pure to Applied Science - Today & Tomorrow. 2012. (Chemistry Research & Applications Ser.). 324p. 140.00 ***(978-1-61470-696-0(4))*** Nova Science Pubs., Inc.

Islamova, Regina M., et al. Kinetics, Catalysis & Mechanism of Chemical Reactions: From Pure to Applied Science - Tomorrow & Perspectives. 2012. (Chemistry Research & Applications/Polymer Science & Technology Ser.). 460p. 165.00 ***(978-1-61470-712-7(X))*** Nova Science Pubs., Inc.

Jacobsen, Eric N., et al, eds. Comprehensive Asymmetric Catalysis: Supplement 1. 2010. (ENG., Illus.). xiv, 238p. pap. 279.00 *(978-3-642-05562-1(1)*, 3642055621) Springer.

—Comprehensive Asymmetric Catalysis: Supplement 2. 2010. (ENG., Illus.). xvi, 135p. pap. 179.00 *(978-3-642-05901-8(5)*, 3642059015) Springer.

Joó, Ferenc. Aqueous Organometallic Catalysis. 2010. (Catalysis by Metal Complexes Ser.). 312p. pap. 219.00 *(978-90-481-5904-8(0)*, 9048159040) Springer.

Kaneko, Masao & Okura, Ichiro, eds. Photocatalysis: Science & Technology. 2010. (Biological & Medical Physics, Biomedical Engineering Ser.). (Illus.). xvi, 356p. pap. 189.00 *(978-3-642-07794-4(3)*, 3642077943) Springer.

Kirschning, Andreas, ed. Immobilized Catalysts: Solid Phases, Immobilization & Applications. 2010. (Topics in Current Chemistry Ser.). (ENG.). ix, 336p. pap. 419.00 *(978-3-642-05889-9(2)*, 3642058892) Springer.

Knoezinger, Helmut, et al, eds. Advances in Catalysis. 2009. (ENG., Illus.). 488p. 231.00 *(978-0-12-374336-7(2)*, Academic Pr.) Elsevier Science & Technology Bks.

Kolasinski, Kurt K. Surface Science: Foundations of Catalysis & Nanoscience. 3rd ed. 2012. (ENG.). 574p. 195.00 ***(978-1-119-99036-9(X))***; pap. 80.00 ***(978-1-119-99035-2(1))*** Wiley, John & Sons, Inc. (Wiley).

Kolasinski, Kurt W. Surface Science: Foundations of Catalysis & Nanoscience. 2nd ed. 2008. (ENG., Illus.). 500p. 230.00 *(978-0-470-03304-3(5)*, Wiley) Wiley, John & Sons, Inc.

—Surface Science: Foundations of Catalysis & Nanoscience. 2nd ed. 2008. (ENG., Illus.). 500p. pap. 85.00 *(978-0-470-03308-1(8)*, Wiley) Wiley, John & Sons, Inc.

Koper, Marc, et al. Fuel Cell Catalysis: A Surface Science Approach. Koper, Marc, ed. 2009. (Wiley Series on Electrocatalysis & Electrochemistry Ser.: 1). (ENG., Illus.). 720p. 166.00 *(978-0-470-13116-9(0)*, Wiley-Interscience) Wiley, John & Sons, Inc.

Kotschy, András & Timári, Géza. Heterocycles from Transition Metal Catalysis: Formation & Functionalization. 2010. (Catalysis by Metal Complexes Ser.). xii, 199p. pap. 249.00 *(978-90-481-6912-2(7)*, 9048169127) Springer.

Krische, Michael J. Metal Catalyzed Reductive C-C Bond Formation: A Departure from Preformed Organometallic Reagents. 2010. (Topics in Current Chemistry Ser.). (Illus.). xii, 264p. pap. 295.00 *(978-3-642-09198-8(9)*, 3642091989) Springer.

Kulprathipanja, Santi, ed. Zeolites in Industrial Separation & Catalysis. 2010. (ENG., Illus.). 618p. 235.00 *(978-3-527-32505-4(0)*, Wiley-VCH) Wiley, John & Sons, Inc.

Lasa, Hugo de, et al. Photocatalytic Reaction Engineering. 2010. (Illus.). xii, 187p. pap. 129.00 *(978-1-4419-3627-1(0)*, 1441936270) Springer.

Lee, Jeehiun K. & Tantillo, Dean J. Orotidine Monophosphate Decarboxylase: A Mechanistic Dialogue. 2010. (Topics in Current Chemistry Ser.). (Illus.). x, 151p. pap. 189.00 *(978-3-642-05819-6(1)*, 3642058191) Springer.

Leeuwen, Piet van. Phosphorus(III)Ligands in Homogeneous Catalysis: Design & Synthesis. Kamer, Paul C. J., ed. 2012. (ENG.). 384p. 180.00 ***(978-0-470-66627-2(7)***, Wiley) Wiley, John & Sons, Inc.

Leeuwen, Piet W. N. M. Van. Supramolecular Catalysis. Leeuwen, Piet W. N. M. Van, ed. 2008. (ENG., Illus.). 318p. 235.00 *(978-3-527-32191-9(8)*, Wiley-VCH) Wiley, John & Sons, Inc.

Leitner, Walter & Hölscher, Markus. Regulated Systems for Multiphase Catalysis. 2010. (Topics in Organometallic Chemistry Ser.). (Illus.). xvi, 208p. pap. 249.00 *(978-3-642-09015-8(X)*, 364209015X) Springer.

Leitner, Walter & Hölscher, Markus. Regulated Systems for Multiphase Catalysis. 2008. (Topics in Organometallic Chemistry Ser.). (Illus.). 300p. 249.00 *(978-3-540-71074-5(4)*, 3540710744) Springer.

Likhtenshtein, Gertz I. New Trends in Enzyme Catalysis & Biomimetic Chemical Reactions. 2012. (ENG.). 240p. pap. 144.00 *(978-1-4419-5234-9(9)*, 1441952349) Springer.

List, Benjamin, ed. Asymmetric Organocatalysis. 2010. (Topics in Current Chemistry Ser.). (ENG., Illus.). I, 400p. 389.00 *(978-3-642-02814-4(4)*, 3642028144) Springer.

Lloyd, Lawrie. Handbook of Industrial Catalysts. 2008. (Fundamental & Applied Catalysis Ser.). (Illus.). 394p. 129.00 *(978-0-387-24682-6(7)*, 0387246827) Springer.

Lopes, Pietro. Electrocatalysis on Fuel Cells Fed with Hydrogen. 2010. 88p. pap. *(978-3-639-22382-8(9))* VDM Verlag Dr. Mueller e.K.

Ma, Shengming, ed. Asymmetric Catalysis from a Chinese Perspective. 2011. (Topics in Organometallic Chemistry Ser.). (ENG., Illus.). xii, 280p. 309.00 *(978-3-642-19471-9(0)*, 3642194710) Springer.

María, Pablo Domínguez De. Ionic Liquids in Biotransformations & Organocatalysis: Solvents & Beyond. 2012. (ENG.). 456p. 149.95 ***(978-0-470-56904-7(2)***, Wiley) Wiley, John & Sons, Inc.

María, Pablo Domínguez De, et al. Redox Biocatalysis: Fundamentals & Applications. 2012. (ENG.). 526p. 149.95 ***(978-0-470-87420-2(1)***, Wiley) Wiley, John & Sons, Inc.

Maruoka, Keiji, ed. Asymmetric Phase Transfer Catalysis. 2008. (ENG., Illus.). 228p. 175.00 *(978-3-527-31842-1(9)*, Wiley-VCH) Wiley, John & Sons, Inc.

Maseras, Feliu & Lledós, Agustí, eds. Computational Modeling of Homogeneous Catalysis. 2010. (Catalysis by Metal Complexes Ser.). 384p. pap. 199.00 *(978-1-4419-5232-5(2)*, 1441952322) Springer.

Matienko, Ludmila I., et al, eds. Selective Catalytic Hydrocarbons Oxidation: New Perspectives. 2010. (Illus.). 166p. 145.00 *(978-1-60876-385-6(4))* Nova Science Pubs., Inc.

Matsuda, Tomoko, ed. Future Directions in Biocatalysis. 2007. (ENG., Illus.). 364p. 240.00 *(978-0-444-53059-2(2)*, Elsevier Science) Elsevier Science & Technology Bks.

McReynolds, David K. New Topics in Catalysis Research. 2006. (Illus.). 228p. 119.00 *(978-1-60021-286-4(7))* Nova Science Pubs., Inc.

Meyer, Franc & Limberg, Christian. Organometallic Oxidation Catalysis. 2010. (Topics in Organometallic Chemistry Ser.). xii, 253p. pap. 279.00 *(978-3-642-07206-2(2)*, 3642072062) Springer.

Mikami, Koichi & Lautens, Mark, eds. New Frontiers in Asymmetric Catalysis. 2007. (ENG., Illus.). 418p. 139.00 *(978-0-471-68026-0(5)*, Wiley-Interscience) Wiley, John & Sons, Inc.

Montanari, F. & Casella, L., eds. Metalloporphyrins Catalyzed Oxidations. 2010. (Catalysis by Metal Complexes Ser.). 372p. pap. 269.00 *(978-90-481-4355-9(1)*, 9048143551) Springer.

Morokuma, Keiji & Musaev, Djamaladdin G., eds. Computational Modeling for Homogeneous & Enzymatic Catalysis: A Knowledge-Base for Designing Efficient Catalysts. 2008. (ENG., Illus.). 398p. 249.00 *(978-3-527-31843-8(7)*, Wiley-VCH) Wiley, John & Sons, Inc.

Niemantsverdriet, J. W. Spectroscopy in Catalysis: An Introduction. 3rd ed. 2007. (ENG., Illus.). 344p. 159.00 *(978-3-527-31651-9(5)*, Wiley-VCH) Wiley, John & Sons, Inc.

Nieuwoudt, Josias Jakobus. Modelling of Catalytic Distillation. 2011. 236p. pap. ***(978-3-8454-1376-1(X))*** Lambert Academic Publishing.

Ohama, Yoshihiko & Van Gemert, Dionys, eds. Applications of Titanium Dioxide Photocatalysis to Construction Materials: State-of-the-Art Report of the RILEM Technical Committee 194-TDP. 2011. (RILEM State-of-the-Art Reports). (ENG., Illus.). xii, 48p. 129.00 *(978-94-007-1296-6(0)*, 9400712960) Springer.

O'Hayre, Ryan. Probing Electrochemistry at the Micro Scale. 2008. 180p. pap. *(978-3-639-11334-1(9))* VDM Verlag Dr. Mueller e.K.

Ojima, Iwao, ed. Catalytic Asymmetric Synthesis. 3rd ed. 2010. (ENG., Illus.). 998p. 195.00 *(978-0-470-17577-4(X)*, Wiley) Wiley, John & Sons, Inc.

Ono, Yoshio & Hattori, Hideshi. Solid Base Catalysis. 2011. (Springer Series in Chemical Physics Ser.). (ENG., Illus.). 409p. 169.00 *(978-3-642-18338-6(7)*, 3642183387) Springer.

ORNSTEIN. Improving Enzyme Cata. 2009. 169.95 *(978-0-8247-0251-9(4))* CRC Pr. LLC.

Oyama, S. Ted. Mechanisms in Homogeneous & Heterogeneous Epoxidation Catalysis. Oyama, S. Ted, ed. 2008. (ENG., Illus.). 528p. 205.00 *(978-0-444-53188-9(2)*, Elsevier Science) Elsevier Science & Technology Bks.

Patti, Angela. Green Approaches to Asymmetric Catalytic Synthesis. 2011. (SpringerBriefs in Molecular Science / Green Chemistry for Sustainability Ser.). (ENG., Illus.). xiv, 140p. pap. 49.95 *(978-94-007-1453-3(X)*, 940071453X) Springer.

Pellissier, Hélène. Chiral Sulfur-Containing Ligands: Asymmetric Catalysis. 2009. (RSC Catalysis Ser.). (ENG., Illus.). 402p. (C). 224.00 *(978-1-84755-924-1(7))* Royal Society of Chemistry, The GBR. Dist: Ingram Pub. Services.

Pellissier, Hélène, ed. Recent Developments in Asymmetric Organocatalysis. 2010. (RSC Catalysis Ser.). (Illus.). 260p. (C). 195.00 ***(978-1-84973-054-9(7))*** Royal Society of Chemistry, The GBR. Dist: Ingram Pub. Services.

Pignataro, Bruno, ed. New Strategies in Chemical Synthesis & Catalysis. 2012. (ENG.). 406p. 140.00 ***(978-3-527-33090-4(9)***, Wiley-VCH) Wiley, John & Sons, Inc.

Plietker, Bernd, ed. Iron Catalysis: Fundamentals & Applications. 2011. (Topics in Organometallic Chemistry Ser.). (Illus.). xi, 200p. 259.00 *(978-3-642-14669-5(4)*, 3642146694) Springer.

—Iron Catalysis in Organic Chemistry: Reactions & Applications. 2008. (ENG., Illus.). 295p. 210.00 *(978-3-527-31927-5(1)*, Wiley-VCH) Wiley, John & Sons, Inc.

Prunier, Michael L., ed. Catalysis of Organic Reactions: Twenty-Second Conference. 2008. (Chemical Industries Ser.). (ENG., Illus.). 548p. 185.95 *(978-1-4200-7076-7(2)*, CRC Press) Taylor & Francis Group GBR. Dist: Taylor & Francis Group.

Reetz, Manfred. Combinatorial Methods in Homogeneous Metal Catalysis. 2009. 250p. 279.00 *(978-3-540-88270-1(7))* Springer.

Reetz, Manfred, et al. Organocatalysis. 2010. (Ernst Schering Foundation Symposium Proceedings Ser.). (Illus.). xiv, 342p. pap. 149.00 *(978-3-642-09261-9(6)*, 3642092616) Springer.

Reetz, Manfred T., et al. Organocatalysis. 2008. (Ernst Schering Foundation Symposium Proceedings Ser.). (Illus.). 256p. 149.00 *(978-3-540-73494-9(5)*, 3540734945) Springer.

Review of the Basic Energy Sciences Committee, et al. Catalysis for Energy: Fundamental Science & Long-Term Impacts of the U. S. Department of Energy Basic Energy Science Catalysis Science Program. 2009. (ENG.). 138p. pap. 34.00 *(978-0-309-12856-8(0))* National Academies Pr.

Rioux, Robert, ed. Model Systems in Catalysis: Single Crystals to Supported Enzyme Mimics. 2009. (ENG., Illus.). xix, 526p. 199.00 *(978-0-387-98041-6(5)*, 0387980415) Springer.

Roberts, Stanley M. Catalysts for Fine Chemical Synthesis, , Set, Volumes 1-5. 2007. (ENG.). 1314p. 1200.00 *(978-0-470-51605-8(4)*, Wiley-Interscience) Wiley, John & Sons, Inc.

Romano, Francesco H. & Russo, Andrea, eds. Biocatalysis Research Progress. 2008. (Illus.). xv, 365p. 185.00 *(978-1-60456-619-2(1))* Nova Science Pubs., Inc.

Rothenberg, Gadi. Catalysis: Concepts & Green Applications. 2008. (ENG., Illus.). 292p. 80.00 *(978-3-527-31824-7(0)*, Wiley-VCH) Wiley, John & Sons, Inc.

Royal Society of Chemistry Staff. Catalysis, Vol. 20. Spivey, J. J., ed. 2007. (Specialist Periodical Reports). (ENG.). 414p. 448.00 *(978-0-85404-244-9(X))* Royal Society of Chemistry, The GBR. Dist: Ingram Pub. Services.

—Catalysis, Vol. 23. 2011. (Specialist Periodical Reports). (ENG., Illus.). 360p 480.00 *(978-1-84973-142-3(X))* Royal Society of Chemistry, The GBR. Dist: Ingram Pub. Services.

—Catalysis: Volume 22. Spivey, James J. & Dooley, K. M., eds. 2010. (Specialist Periodical Reports). (ENG., Illus.). 328p. 480.00 *(978-1-84755-951-7(4))* Royal Society of Chemistry, The GBR. Dist: Ingram Pub. Services.

—Catalysis: Volume 24. Spivey, J. J. & Gupta, Mayank, eds. 2012. (ENG.). 370p. 480.00 ***(978-1-84973-375-5(9))*** Royal Society of Chemistry, The GBR. Dist: Ingram Pub. Services.

—Chemical & Biochemical Catalysis for Next Generation Biofuels. Simmons, Blake A., ed. 2011. (RSC Energy & Environment Ser.). (ENG., Illus.). 206p. 202.00 ***(978-1-84973-030-3(X))*** Royal Society of Chemistry, The GBR. Dist: Ingram Pub. Services.

Royal Society of Chemistry Staff. Quantum Tunnelling in Enzyme-Catalysed Reactions. Allemann, Rudolf & Scrutton, Nigel S., eds. 2009. (RSC Biomolecular Sciences Ser.). (ENG., Illus.). 412p. 232.00 *(978-0-85404-122-0(2))* Royal Society of Chemistry, The GBR. Dist: Ingram Pub. Services.

Santos, Elizabeth & Schmickler, Wolfgang, eds. Catalysis in Electrochemistry: From Fundamental Aspects to Strategies for Fuel Cell Development. 2011. (Wiley Series on Electrocatalysis & Electrochemistry Ser.: 3). (ENG., Illus.). 536p. 135.00 *(978-0-470-40690-8(9)*, Wiley) Wiley, John & Sons, Inc.

Schiavello, Mario, ed. Photoelectrochemistry, Photocatalysis & Photoreactors Fundamentals & Developments. 2010. (NATO Science Series C: (closed) Ser.). 660p. pap. 469.00 *(978-90-481-8414-9(2)*, 9048184142) Springer.

Schmal, Martin. Chemical Reaction Engineering: Essentials, Exercises & Examples. 2012. (ENG.). 550p. (C). pap. 89.95 ***(978-0-415-69538-1(4)***, CRC Press) Taylor & Francis Group GBR. Dist: Taylor & Francis Group.

Schmidt, Stephen R., ed. Catalysis of Organic Reactions. 2006. (Chemical Industries Ser.). (ENG., Illus.). 552p. 199.95 *(978-0-8493-7557-6(6)*, CRC Press) Taylor & Francis Group GBR. Dist: Taylor & Francis Group.

Schulzke, Carola & Samuel, Prinson P., eds. Molybdenum & Tungsten Cofactor Model Chemistry. 2010. (Chemistry Research & Applications Ser.). pap. 43.00 *(978-1-61668-750-2(9))* Nova Science Pubs., Inc.

Serp, Philippe & Figueiredo, José Luís, eds. Carbon Materials for Catalysis. 2008. (ENG., Illus.). 579p. 178.00 *(978-0-470-17885-0(X)*, Wiley) Wiley, John & Sons, Inc.

Severn, John R. & Chadwick, John C., eds. Tailor-Made Polymers: Via Immobilization of Alpha-Olefin Polymerization Catalysts. 2008. (ENG., Illus.). 374p. 235.00 *(978-3-527-31782-0(1)*, Wiley-VCH) Wiley, John & Sons, Inc.

C

Sheldon, Roger Arthur, et al. Green Chemistry & Catalysis. 2007. (ENG., Illus.). 448p. 230.00 (978-3-527-30715-9(X), Wiley-VCH) Wiley, John & Sons, Inc.

Shem, Diana. Catalysis of Orotidine 5'-Monophosphate. 2011. 68p. pap. (978-3-8443-8088-0(4)) Lambert Academic Publishing.

Shiono, Takeshi, et al, eds. Progress in Olefin Polymerization Catalysts & Polyolefin Materials: Proceedings of the First Asian Polyolefin Workshop, Nara, Japan, December 7-9 2005. 2006. (Studies in Surface Science & Catalysis Ser.: 161). (ENG., Illus.). 298p. 240.00 (978-0-444-52751-6(6), Elsevier Science) Elsevier Science & Technology Bks.

Simándi, László I., ed. Advances in Catalytic Activation of Dioxygen by Metal Complexes. 2010. (Catalysis by Metal Complexes Ser.). 352p. pap. 199.00 (978-1-4419-5238-7(1), 1441952381) Springer.

Soai, Kenso. Amplification of Chirality. 2010. (Topics in Current Chemistry Ser.). (Illus.). xii, 206p. pap. 289.00 (978-3-642-09668-6(9), 3642096689) Springer.

Soai, Kenso, ed. Amplification of Chirality. 2008. (Topics in Current Chemistry Ser.). (Illus.). 205p. 289.00 (978-3-540-77868-4(3)) Springer.

Somorjai, Gabor A. & Li, Yimin. Introduction to Surface Chemistry & Catalysis. 2nd ed. 2010. (ENG., Illus.). 800p. 158.00 (978-0-470-50823-7(X), Wiley) Wiley, John & Sons, Inc.

Song, Minsuh. Catalysis: Principles, Types & Applications. 2011. (Chemistry Research & Applications Ser.). 495p. 295.00 (978-1-61209-654-4(9)) Nova Science Pubs., Inc.

Soriano, Elena & Marco-Contelles, José, eds. Computational Mechanisms of Au & Pt Catalyzed Reactions. 2011. (Topics in Current Chemistry Ser.). (Illus.). xiii, 252p. 309.00 (978-3-642-21082-2(1), 3642210821) Springer.

Spivey, James J. & Dooley, K. M., eds. Catalysis, Vol. 21. 2009. (Specialist Periodical Reports). (ENG.). 250p. 480.00 (978-0-85404-249-4(0)) Royal Society of Chemistry, The GBR. Dist: Ingram Pub. Services.

Steinborn, Dirk. Fundamentals of Organometallic Catalysis. Harmsen, Alexander, tr. from GER. 2012. (ENG., Illus.). 472p. 140.00 (978-3-527-32716-4(9)); pap. 70.00 (978-3-527-32717-1(7)) Wiley, John & Sons, Inc. (Wiley-VCH).

Strukul, G., ed. Catalytic Oxidations with Hydrogen Peroxide as Oxidant. 2010. (Catalysis by Metal Complexes Ser.). 300p. pap. 349.00 (978-90-481-4163-0(X), 904814163X) Springer.

Swiegers, Gerhard. Mechanical Catalysis: Methods of Enzymatic, Homogeneous, & Heterogeneous Catalysis. 2008. (ENG., Illus.). 352p. 117.00 (978-0-470-26202-3(8), Wiley-Interscience) Wiley, John & Sons, Inc.

Tachibana, Yasuhiro. Solar Hydrogen & Nanotechnology VI. 2011. (Proceedings of SPIE Ser.). 182p. pap. 80.00 (978-0-8194-8719-3(8)) SPIE.

Temkin, Oleg N. Homogeneous Catalysis with Metal Complexes: Kinetic Aspects & Mechanisms. Pozdeev, P. P., tr. 2nd ed. 2012. (ENG.). 830p. 315.00 (978-0-470-66699-9(4), Wiley) Wiley, John & Sons, Inc.

Van Santen, Christa. Computational Methods in Catalysis & Materials Science: An Introduction for Scientists & Engineers. Sautet, Philippe & Santen, Rutger A. van, eds. 2009. (ENG., Illus.). 472p. 150.00 (978-3-527-32032-5(6), Wiley-VCH) Wiley, John & Sons, Inc.

Vannice, M. Albert. Kinetics of Catalytic Reactions. 2010. (ENG., Illus.). xviii, 240p. pap. 109.00 (978-1-4419-3758-2(7), 1441937587) Springer.

Vayenas, Constantinos G., ed. Interfacial Phenomena in Electrocatalysis. 2011. (Modern Aspects of Electrochemistry Ser.). (ENG., Illus.). xvi, 373p. 189.00 (978-1-4419-5579-1(8), 1441955798) Springer.

Vayssieres, Lionel. On Solar Hydrogen & Nanotechnology. 2010. (ENG., Illus.). 704p. 295.00 (978-0-470-82397-2(6), Wiley) Wiley, John & Sons, Inc.

Vazquez-Duhalt, R., ed. Environmental Biotransformations: A Written Symposium. 2008. (Illus.). 154p. pap. (978-3-8055-8513-2(6)) Karger, S. AG.

Vicario, Jose L., et al. Organocatalytic Enantioselective Conjugate Addition Reactions: A Powerful Tool for the Stereocontrolled Synthesis of Complex Molecules. 2010. (RSC Catalysis Ser.). (ENG., Illus.). 368p. (C). 195.00 (978-1-84973-024-2(5)) Royal Society of Chemistry, The GBR. Dist: Ingram Pub. Services.

Vries, Johannes G. de & Elsevier, Cornelis J., eds. Handbook of Homogeneous Hydrogenation, 3 vols. 2007. (ENG., Illus.). 1641p. 795.00 (978-3-527-31161-3(0), Wiley-VCH) Wiley, John & Sons, Inc.

Wang, Ping. Nanoscale Biocatalysis: Methods & Protocols. 2011. (Illus.). xi, 241p. E-Book (978-1-61779-132-1(6)) Humana Pr.

Wang, Ping, ed. Nanoscale Biocatalysis: Methods & Protocols. 2011. (Methods in Molecular Biology Ser.). (Illus.). xi, 241p. 119.00 (978-1-61779-131-4(8), 1617791318) Humana Pr.

Waser, Mario. Asymmetric Organocatalysis in Natural Product Syntheses. 2012. (Progress in the Chemistry of Organic Natural Products Ser.: 96). (ENG., Illus.). vi, 200p. 259.00 (978-3-7091-1162-8(5), 3709111625) Springer.

Wegner, Patrick. Catalyst: Online Mastery Learning System for Chemistry. 2008. (Wiley Plus Products Ser.). (ENG.). (C). pap. 19.95 (978-0-470-12675-2(2), Wiley) Wiley, John & Sons, Inc.

Weitkamp, Jens & Puppe, Lothar, eds. Catalysis & Zeolites: Fundamentals & Applications. 2010. (Illus.). xviii, 564p. pap. 569.00 (978-3-642-08347-1(1), 3642083471) Springer.

Westin, Gunnar. Solar Hydrogen & Nanotechnology III: 13-14 August 2008, San Diego, California, USA. 2008. (Proceedings of SPIE Ser.). (Illus.). 118p. pap. 70.00 (978-0-8194-7264-9(6)) SPIE.

Whittall, John & Sutton, Peter. Practical Methods for Biocatalysis & Biotransformations. 2010. (ENG., Illus.). 432p. 175.00 (978-0-470-51927-1(4), Wiley) Wiley, John & Sons, Inc.

Whittall, John & Sutton, Peter, eds. Practical Methods for Biocatalysis & Biotransformations, No. 2. 2012. (ENG.). 392p. 160.00 (978-1-119-99139-7(0), Wiley) Wiley, John & Sons, Inc.

Yanming, Gong & Yeboah, Yaw D. Electrocatalysts for PEM Fuel Cells: Synthesis, Characterization, & Performance Testing. 2008. 120p. pap. (978-3-639-10446-2(3)) VDM Verlag Dr. Mueller e.K.

Yardimci, Ozlem. Plasma Catalysis in Hydrocarbon Processing. 2010. 112p. pap. (978-3-639-26425-8(8)) VDM Verlag Dr. Mueller e.K.

Zhou, Qi-Lin, ed. Privileged Chiral Ligands & Catalysts. 2011. (ENG., Illus.). 484p. 175.00 (978-3-527-32704-1(5), Wiley-VCH) Wiley, John & Sons, Inc.

Zinola, Carlos Fernando, ed. Electrocatalysis: Computational, Experimental, & Industrial Aspects. 2010. (Surfactant Science Ser.). (ENG., Illus.). 664p. 159.95 (978-1-4200-4544-4(X), CRC Press) Taylor & Francis Group GBR. Dist: Taylor & Francis Group.

CATALYSTS

Ackrine, Whitney J., ed. Polymer Initiators. 2010. (Biochemistry Research Trends Ser.). 129.00 (978-1-61761-304-3(5)) Nova Science Pubs., Inc.

Akah, Aaron. The Remediation of Ammonia in Waste Streams. 2010. 188p. pap. (978-3-8383-7546-5(7)) Lambert Academic Publishing.

Andersson, Pher G., ed. Innovative Catalysis in Organic Synthesis: Oxidation, Hydrogenation,and C-X Bond Forming Reactions. 2012. (ENG.). 374p. 185.00 (978-3-527-33097-3(6), Wiley-VCH) Wiley, John & Sons, Inc.

Anpo, M. & Kamat, Prashant V. Environmentally Benign Catalysts. 2009. (Nanostructure Science & Technology Ser.). (Illus.). xi, 757p. 259.00 (978-0-387-48441-9(8)) Springer.

Astruc, D. Organometallic Chemistry & Catalysis. 2007. (Illus.). xii, 608p. 109.00 (978-3-540-46128-9(0), 3540461280) Springer.

Baugh, Lisa S. & Canich, Jo Ann M., eds. Stereoselective Polymerization with Single-Site Catalysts. 2007. (ENG., Illus.). 696p. 236.95 (978-1-57444-579-4(0), CRC Press) Taylor & Francis Group GBR. Dist: Taylor & Francis Group.

BCC Research Staff. Catalysts for Environmental & Energy Applications. 2007. per. 4250.00 (978-1-59623-301-0(X)) BCC Research.

Bharali, Pankaj & Mahipal Reddy, Benjaram. Design of Ceria-Based Nanocomposite Oxides for Catalytic Applications. 2011. 168p. pap. (978-3-8443-1791-6(0)) Lambert Academic Publishing.

Boyadjian, Cassia. Oxidative Cracking of N-Hexane. 2011. 144p. pap. (978-3-8433-8963-1(2)) Lambert Academic Publishing.

Burness, Lynn T., ed. Mesoporous Materials: Properties, Preparation & Applications. 2009. (Illus.). xiv, 370p. 145.00 (978-1-60741-051-5(6)) Nova Science Pubs., Inc.

Capers Jr., William T. Now Faith: The Catalyst to Everything. 2011. 108p. pap. 11.95 (978-1-61507-889-9(4)) Cross Bks. Publishing.

Chadwick, John C., et al. Homogeneous Catalysts: Activity - Stability - Deactivation. 2011. (ENG., Illus.). 418p. 180.00 (978-3-527-32329-6(5), Wiley-VCH) Wiley, John & Sons, Inc.

Che, Michel & Vedrine, Jacques C., eds. Characterization of Solid Materials & Heterogeneous Catalysts: From Structure to Surface Reactivity. 2012. (ENG.). 1284p. 405.00 (978-3-527-32687-7(1), Wiley-VCH) Wiley, John & Sons, Inc.

Clatworthy, Jonathan. Liberal Faith in a Divided Church. 2008. (ENG.). 320p. pap. 29.95 (978-1-84694-116-0(4)) Hunt, John Publishing Ltd. GBR. Dist: National Bk. Network.

Cybulski, Andrzej, et al, eds. Novel Concepts in Catalysis & Chemical Reactors: Improving the Efficiency for the Future. 2010. (ENG., Illus.). 398p. 200.00 (978-3-527-32469-9(0), Wiley-VCH) Wiley, John & Sons, Inc.

Davis, Burtron H. & Occelli, Mario L. Fischer-Tropsch Synthesis, Catalysts & Catalysis. 2006. (Studies in Surface Science & Catalysis Ser.: 163). (ENG., Illus.). 430p. 255.00 (978-0-444-52221-4(2), Elsevier Science) Elsevier Science & Technology Bks.

Davis, Robert. International Assessment of Research & Development in Catalysis by Nanostructured Materials. 2011. 328p. 99.00 (978-1-84816-689-9(3)) Imperial College Pr. GBR. Dist: World Scientific Publishing Co., Inc.

de Jong, Krijn P., ed. Synthesis of Solid Catalysts. 2009. (ENG., Illus.). 422p. 225.00 (978-3-527-32040-0(7), Wiley-VCH) Wiley, John & Sons, Inc.

Derouane, Eric G. & Roberts, Stanley M., eds. Microporous & Mesoporous Solid Catalysts, Vol. 4. 2007. (Catalysts for Fine Chemicals Synthesis Ser.: 4). (ENG., Illus.). 258p. 269.00 (978-0-471-49054-8(7), Wiley-Interscience) Wiley, John & Sons, Inc.

Figlus, Marek. Recoverable Catalysts for Asymmetric Reduction of Imines. 2010. 184p. pap. (978-3-639-25071-8(0)) VDM Verlag Dr. Mueller e.K.

Furimsky, Edward. Carbons & Carbon Supported Catalysts in Hydroprocessing. 2008. (RSC Catalysis Ser.). (ENG., Illus.). 174p. (C). 160.00 (978-0-85404-143-5(5)) Royal Society of Chemistry, The GBR. Dist: Ingram Pub. Services.

Furimsky, Edward. Catalysts for Upgrading Heavy Petroleum Feeds. 2007. (Studies in Surface Science & Catalysis Ser.: 169). (ENG., Illus.). 404p. 215.00 (978-0-444-53084-4(3), Elsevier Science) Elsevier Science & Technology Bks.

Gaigneaux, E., et al, eds. Scientific Bases for the Preparation of Heterogeneous Catalysts: Proceedings of the 9th International Symposium Louvain-la-Neuve, Belgium, September 10-14 2006. 2006. (Studies in Surface Science & Catalysis Ser.: 162). (ENG., Illus.). 1070p. 405.00 (978-0-444-52827-8(X), Elsevier Science) Elsevier Science & Technology Bks.

Gayen, Arup. Investigations on Metal-Ceria Interaction in Auto-Exhaust Catalysis. 2010. 280p. pap. (978-3-639-24527-1(X)) VDM Verlag Dr. Mueller e.K.

Ghorannevis, Zohreh. Nonmagnetic Growth of Swnts. 2011. 124p. pap. (978-3-8443-1187-7(4)) Lambert Academic Publishing.

Gil, Antonio, et al, eds. Pillared Clays & Related Catalysts. 2010. (ENG., Illus.). xvi, 550p. 259.00 (978-1-4419-6669-8(2), 1441966692) Springer.

Global Market for Catalyst Regeneration. 2006. per. 4250.00 (978-1-59623-226-6(9)) BCC Research.

Granger, Pascal & Pârvulescu, Vasile, eds. Past & Present in DeNOx Catalysis: From Molecular Modelling to Chemical Engineering. 2007. (Studies in Surface Science & Catalysis Ser.: 171). (ENG., Illus.). 418p. 215.00 (978-0-444-53058-5(4), Elsevier Science) Elsevier Science & Technology Bks.

Griffith, W. P. Ruthenium Oxidation Complexes: Their uses as homogenous organic Catalysts. 2010. (Catalysis by Metal Complexes Ser.). (ENG., Illus.). xv, 330p. 159.00 (978-1-4020-9376-0(4), 1402093764) Springer.

Guisnet, Michel & Ribeiro, Fernando Ramoa. Deactivation & Regeneration of Zeolite Catalysts. 2011. (Illus.). 360p. 90.00 (978-1-84816-637-0(0)) Imperial College Pr. GBR. Dist: World Scientific Publishing Co., Inc.

Haberlandt, Reinhold, et al, eds. Molecules in Interaction with Surfaces & Interfaces. 2010. (Lecture Notes in Physics Ser.). xviii, 511p. pap. 179.00 (978-3-642-05813-4(2), 3642058132) Springer.

Harmata, Michael, ed. Silver in Organic Chemistry. 2010. (ENG., Illus.). 402p. 116.00 (978-0-470-46611-7(1), Wiley) Wiley, John & Sons, Inc.

Heck, Ronald M., et al. Catalytic Air Pollution Control: Commercial Technology. 3rd ed. 2009. (ENG., Illus.). 544p. 122.00 (978-0-470-27503-0(0), Wiley) Wiley, John & Sons, Inc.

Hello, Kasim, et al. Heterogeneous Catalysts for Esterification Reaction. 2011. 212p. pap. (978-3-8433-8845-0(8)) Lambert Academic Publishing.

Khanaev, Valeri M., et al. Fixed Bed Reactors with Gradient Catalysts. 2008. 103p. 29.00 (978-1-60456-780-9(5)) Nova Science Pubs., Inc.

Kulprathipanja, Santi, ed. Zeolites in Industrial Separation & Catalysis. 2010. (ENG., Illus.). 618p. 235.00 (978-3-527-32505-4(0), Wiley-VCH) Wiley, John & Sons, Inc.

Kung. Geometry & Phase Transitions in Collo... 2009. (Illus.). xxii, 191p. 79.00 (978-981-283-496-6(6)) World Scientific Publishing Co., Inc.

Litto, Rajab. Catalytic Combustion for Mitigation of Lean Methane Emission. 2011. 412p. pap. (978-3-8443-9518-1(0)) Lambert Academic Publishing.

Lloyd, Lawrie. Handbook of Industrial Catalysts. 2007. (Illus.). xxii, 490p. (978-0-387-49962-8(8)) Springer.

Marafi, Meena, et al. Handbook of Spent Hydroprocessing Catalysts: Regeneration, Rejuvenation, Reclamation, Environment & Safety. 2010. (ENG., Illus.). 362p. 235.00 (978-0-444-53556-6(X)) Elsevier Science & Technology Bks.

Maschmeyer, Thomas, ed. Heterogeneous Catalyst Preparation: Concepts, Challenges & Opportunities. 2006. 400p. 190.00 (978-3-527-31153-8(X)) Wiley, John & Sons, Inc.

Mason, Elena C. & Weber, Allison P. Polypyrrole: Properties, Performance & Applications. 2011. (Materials Science & Technologies Ser.). (Illus.). 296p. 165.00 (978-1-61209-143-3(1)) Nova Science Pubs., Inc.

Molander, Gary. Catalyst Components for Coupling Reactions. 2008. (Hdbk of Reagents for Organic Synthesis Ser.). (ENG., Illus.). 690p. 220.00 (978-0-470-51811-3(1), Wiley) Wiley, John & Sons, Inc.

Narayana Rao, Komateedi. New Generation Non-Noble Bimetallic Catalysts for Twc Applications. 2011. 152p. pap. (978-3-8443-2368-9(6)) Lambert Academic Publishing.

Niemantsverdriet, J. W. Spectroscopy in Catalysis: An Introduction. 3rd ed. 2007. (ENG., Illus.). 344p. 159.00 (978-3-527-31651-9(5), Wiley-VCH) Wiley, John & Sons, Inc.

Niwa, Miki, et al. Characterization & Design of Zeolite Catalysts: Solid Acidity, Shape Selectivity & Loading Properties. 2010. (Springer Series in Materials Science Ser.). (Illus.). x, 184p. 159.00 (978-3-642-12619-2(7), 3642126197) Springer.

Nuyken, Oskar. Neodymium Based Ziegler Catalysts - Fundamental Chemistry. 2010. (Advances in Polymer Science Ser.). (Illus.). xii, 287p. pap. 349.00 (978-3-642-07112-6(0), 3642071120) Springer.

Occelli, Mario L. Fluid Catalytic Cracking VII: Materials, Methods & Process Innovations. 2007. (Studies in Surface Science & Catalysis Ser.: 166). (ENG., Illus.). 356p. 215.00 (978-0-444-53060-8(6), Elsevier Science) Elsevier Science & Technology Bks.

Okada, Tatsuhiro & Kaneko, Masao, eds. Molecular Catalysts for Energy Conversion. (Springer Series in Materials Science Ser.). (Illus.). 2010. xxiv, 434p. pap. 239.00 (978-3-642-08965-7(8), 3642089658) 2008. 458p. 239.00 (978-3-540-70730-1(1)) Springer.

Parmon, V. Thermodynamics of Non-Equilibrium Processes for Chemists with a Particular Application to Catalysis. 2009. (ENG., Illus.). 340p. 260.00 (978-0-444-53028-8(2), Elsevier Science) Elsevier Science & Technology Bks.

Parmon, V. M., et al. Photocatalysis: Catalysts, Kinetics & Reactors. 2012. (ENG.). 400p. 190.00 (978-3-527-31784-4(8), Wiley-VCH) Wiley, John & Sons, Inc.

Peruzzini, Maurizio & Gonsalvi, Luca, eds. Phosphorus Chemistry: Catalysis & Material Science Applications. 2011. (Catalysis by Metal Complexes Ser.). (Illus.). 500p. 189.00 (978-90-481-3816-6(7), 9048138167) Springer.

Plietker, Bernd, ed. Iron Catalysis: Fundamentals & Applications. 2011. (Topics in Organometallic Chemistry Ser.). (Illus.). xi, 200p. 259.00 (978-3-642-14669-5(4), 3642146694) Springer.

Poehler, Andrew C. Homogeneous Catalysts: Types, Reactions & Applications. 2011. (Chemical Engineering Methods & Technology Ser.). (Illus.). 523p. 165.00 (978-1-61122-894-6(8)) Nova Science Pubs., Inc.

Potyrailo, Radislav A., ed. Combinatorial & High-Throughput Discovery & Optimization of Catalysts & Materials. 2006. (Combinatorial Chemistry Ser.). (ENG., Illus.). 473p. 226.95 (978-0-8493-3669-0(4), CRC Press) Taylor & Francis Group GBR. Dist: Taylor & Francis Group.

Ranjbar, Abbas. Hydrogen Storage Properties of Magnesium Hydride. 2011. 144p. pap. (978-3-8443-8772-8(2)) Lambert Academic Publishing.

Regalbuto John Staff. Handbook of Catalyst Preparation. 2006. (ENG., Illus.). 488p. 191.95 (978-0-8493-7088-5(4), CRC Press) Taylor & Francis Group GBR. Dist: Taylor & Francis Group.

Roberts, Stanley M. Catalysts for Fine Chemical Synthesis, , Set, Volumes 1-5. 2007. (ENG.). 1314p. 1200.00 (978-0-470-51605-8(4), Wiley-Interscience) Wiley, John & Sons, Inc.

Roberts, Stanley M. & Whittall, John, eds. Regio- And Stereo-Controlled Oxidations & Reductions, Vol. 5. 2007. (Catalysts for Fine Chemicals Synthesis Ser.: 5). (ENG., Illus.). 336p. 250.00 (978-0-470-09022-0(7), Wiley-Interscience) Wiley, John & Sons, Inc.

Royal Society of Chemistry Staff. Nanostructured Catalsts: Selective Oxidations. Hess, Christian & Schlogl, Robert, eds. 2011. (RSC Nanoscience & Nanotechnology Ser.). (ENG., Illus.). 452p. 232.00 (978-0-85404-186-2(9)) Royal Society of Chemistry, The GBR. Dist: Ingram Pub. Services.

—Turning Points in Solid-State, Materials & Surface Science: A Book in Celebration of the Life & Work of Sir John Meurig Thomas. Edwards, Peter P. & Harris, Kenneth D. M., eds. 2007. (ENG.). 946p. 480.00 (978-0-85404-114-5(1)) Royal Society of Chemistry, The GBR. Dist: Ingram Pub. Services.

Sadykov, Vladislav. Syngas Generation from Hydrocarbons & Oxygenates with Structured Catalysts. 2010. (Energy Science, Engineering & Technology Ser.). pap. 43.00 (978-1-60876-323-8(4)) Nova Science Pubs., Inc.

Sagala, Sophia L. Promoters of Supported Iron Catalysts. 2011. 72p. pap. (978-3-639-33344-2(6)) VDM Verlag Dr. Mueller e.K.

Saha, B. Recent Developments in Heterogeneous Catalytic Reactors. 2012. (Studies in Surface Science & Catalysis Ser.). (ENG.). 180.00 (978-0-444-53008-0(8)) Elsevier Science & Technology Bks.

Saikia, Pranjal & M. REDDY, BENJARAM. Ceria Based Nano Catalysts. 2011. 168p. pap. (978-3-8443-2899-8(8)) Lambert Academic Publishing.

Shaw, Anthony Peter Gordon. Half-Sandwich Ruthenium Complexes. 2009. 108p. pap. (978-3-639-19809-6(3)) VDM Verlag Dr. Mueller e.K.

Stroyuk, Olexsander L., et al. Semiconductor Catalysis & Photocatalysis on the Nanoscale. 2010. (Nanotechnology Science & Technology Ser.). 69.00 (978-1-61728-788-6(1)) Nova Science Pubs., Inc.

Technology Research Editors, ed. Metal Recovering & Recycling of Catalysts, 2007 Ed. 2007. pap. 128.50 (978-1-60030-413-2(3), Search-In-Print) CSA Journal Division.

Twigg, Martyn V. The Catalyst Handbook. 3rd rev. ed. 2011. (ENG.). 624p. 129.95 (978-1-84076-087-3(7)) Manson Publishing, Ltd. GBR. Dist: Thieme Medical Pubs., Inc.

Wang, Jin-An & Esquivel, Jose Manuel Dominguez, eds. New Catalytic Materials & Applications: Volume 1279. 2011. (MRS Proceedings Ser.). (ENG.). (C). 112.00 (978-1-60511-256-5(9)) Cambridge Univ. Pr.

Weber, Th., et al, eds. Transitional Metal Sulphides: Chemistry & Catalysis. 2010. (NATO Science Partnership Sub-Series: 3: Ser.). 364p. pap. 299.00 (978-90-481-5100-4(7), 9048151007) Springer.

Welker-Nieuwoudt, Cathrin. Ruthenium Based Fischer-Tropsch Synthesis. 2011. 216p. pap. (978-3-8443-2127-2(6)) Lambert Academic Publishing.

Wirth, Thomas, ed. Microreactors in Organic Synthesis & Catalysis. 2008. (ENG., Illus.). 297p. 229.00 (978-3-527-31869-8(0), Wiley-VCH) Wiley, John & Sons, Inc.

Zhang, Jiujun, ed. PEM Fuel Cell Electrocatalysts & Catalyst Layers: Fundamentals & Applications. 2008. (Illus.). xxii, 1137p. 219.00 (978-1-84800-935-6(6)) Springer.

Zhang, Weicheng. Development of Effective Chiral Ligands for Asymmetric Hydrogenation. 2009. 160p. pap. (978-3-639-19545-3(0)) VDM Verlag Dr. Mueller e.K.

Zhou, Bing, et al, eds. Nanotechnology in Catalysis 3. 2010. (Nanostructure Science & Technology Ser.). xxii, 338p. pap. 159.00 (978-1-4419-2243-4(1), 1441922431) Springer.

Zhou, Qi-Lin, ed. Privileged Chiral Ligands & Catalysts. 2011. (ENG., Illus.). 484p. 175.00 (978-3-527-32704-1(5), Wiley-VCH) Wiley, John & Sons, Inc.

CATAMARANS

Tarjan, Gregor. Catamarans: The Complete Guide for Cruising Sailors. 2007. (ENG., Illus.). 304p. 39.95 (978-0-07-149885-2(0), 0071498850, International Marine/Ragged Mountain Pr.) McGraw-Hill Professional Publishing.

—Catamarans: Tomorrow's Superyachts. 2009. (ENG., Illus.). 280p. 65.00 (978-1-57409-286-8(3)) Sheridan Hse., Inc.

CATAMOUNTS

see Puma

CATAPHORESIS

see Electrophoresis

CATAPULT

Catapults GS Teacher's Guide. 2006. spiral bd. 24.95 (978-1-58651-927-8(1)) Pitsco/Pitsco LEGO Dacta.

Gurstelle, William. Whoosh Boom Splat: The Garage Warrior's Guide to Building Projectile Shooters. 2007. (ENG., Illus.). 160p. per. 16.95 (978-0-307-33948-5(3), Three Rivers Pr.) Crown Publishing Group.

Payne-Gallwey, Ralph. The Crossbow: Its Military & Sporting History, Construction & Use. 2007. (ENG., Illus.). 400p. per. 19.95 *(978-1-60239-010-2(X)*, 239010) Skyhorse Publishing Co., Inc.

Rihll, Tracey. The Catapult: A History. 2007. (Illus.). 408p. 29.95 *(978-1-59416-035-6(X))* Westholme Publishing.

—The Catapult: A History, Second Edition. 2nd ed. 2012. (ENG., Illus.). 392p. pap. 19.95 *(978-1-59416-103-2(8))* Westholme Publishing.

CATARACT

Agarwal, Amar. Illustrative Guide to Cataract Surgery: A Step-by-Step Approach to Refining Surgical Skills. 2011. (ENG., Illus.). 240p. 149.95 *(978-1-55642-981-1(9))* SLACK, Inc.

Agarwal, Amar & Lindstrom, Richard L. Microincisional Cataract Surgery: The Art & Science. 2010. (ENG.). 240p. pap. 103.95 *(978-1-55642-943-9(6))* SLACK, Inc.

Alio y Sanz, Jorge L. & Azar, Dimitri T., eds. Management of Complications in Refractive Surgery. 2010. (Illus.). xxvi, 362p. pap. 159.00 *(978-3-642-07228-4(3)*, 3642072283) Springer.

Apple, David J. Sir Harold Ridley & His Fight for Sight: He Changed the World So That We May Better See It. 2006. (ENG., Illus.). 352p. 49.95 *(978-1-55642-786-2(7))* SLACK, Inc.

Benjamin, Larry. Cataract Surgery. 2007. (Surgical Techniques in Ophthalmology Ser.). (ENG., Illus.). 180p. 160.00 *(978-1-4160-2969-4(9)*, Saunders) Elsevier - Health Sciences Div.

Chang, David F. Cataracts: A Patient's Guide to Treatment. 2nd ed. 2011. (ENG., Illus.). 144p. pap. 22.95 ***(978-1-61711-038-2(8))*** SLACK, Inc.

Chang, David F., ed. Curbside Consultation in Cataract Surgery: 49 Clinical Questions. 2007. (Curbside Consultation in Ophthalmology Ser.). (Illus.). 288p. pap. 83.95 *(978-1-55642-799-2(9))* SLACK, Inc.

Devgan, Uday. Cataract Surgery: A Patient's Guide to Cataract Treatment. 2009. (ENG., Illus.). 120p. pap. 19.95 *(978-1-886039-94-0(1)*, 1294454) Addicus Bks.

Fine, I. Howard. Minimizing Incision & Maximizing Outcomes in Cataract Surgery. Alió y Sanz, Jorge L., ed. 2009. (ENG., Illus.). xvi, 314p. 139.00 *(978-3-642-02861-8(6)* 3642028616) Springer.

Garg. Mini Atlas of Manual Small Incisions in Cateract Surgery. 2008. (Anshan Gold Standard Mini Atlas Ser.). (ENG., Illus.). 350p. pap. 34.95 *(978-1-905740-46-8(8))* Anshan GBR. Dist: Publishers Storage & Shipping.

Garg, Ashok. Mastering Phaco Chop Techniques. 2009. (ENG.). 302p. 104.00 *(978-0-07-163441-0(X)*, 007163441X) McGraw-Hill Professional Publishing.

Gogate, Parikshit. Manual Small Incision Cataract Surgery in Indi. 2010. 64p. pap. *(978-3-639-22384-2(5))* VDM Verlag Dr. Mueller e.K.

Hernandez, Camila M., ed. Cataracts: Causes, Symptoms, & Surgery. 2010. (Eye & Vision Research Developments Ser.). (Illus.). 216p. 116.10 *(978-1-61668-955-1(2)*, Nova Biomedical Bks.) Nova Science Pubs., Inc.

Hockwin, O., et al, eds. Progress in Lens & Cataract Research: In Honour of Professor Kazuyuki Sasaki, Vol. 35. (Developments in Ophthalmology Ser.: Vol. 35). (Illus.). *(978-3-8055-7367-2(7))* Karger, S. AG.

Hovanesian, John. Premium Cataract Surgery: A Step-by-Step Guide. 2012. (ENG.). 192p. 139.95 ***(978-1-61711-022-1(1))*** SLACK, Inc.

Johnson, Sandra. Cataract Surgery in the Glaucoma Patient. 2009. (Illus.). 264p. 159.00 *(978-0-387-09407-6(5)*, 0387094075) Springer.

Koch, Douglas, ed. Cataract & Refractive Surgery: Progress III. 2008. (Essentials in Ophthalmology Ser.). (Illus.). xiv, 122p. 109.00 *(978-3-540-76378-9(3)*, 3540763783) Springer.

Kohnen, Thomas, ed. Modern Cataract Surgery Update, Vol. 34. (Developments in Ophthalmology Ser.: Vol. 34). (Illus.). *(978-3-8055-7364-1(2))* Karger, S. AG.

Kohnen, Thomas & Koch, Douglas D. Cataract & Refractive Surgery. 2010. (Essentials in Ophthalmology Ser.). (Illus.). xvi, 178p. pap. 159.00 *(978-3-642-06805-8(7)*, 3642068057) Springer.

Krueger, Ronald R., et al, eds. Laser Refractive Cataract Surgery. 2012. (ENG., Illus.). 250p. 189.00 ***(978-1-4614-1009-6(6)***, 1461410096) Springer.

Kyselova, Zuzana. Experimental Approaches in Diabetic Cataract Research. 2009. 108p. pap. *(978-3-639-20646-3(0))* VDM Verlag Dr. Mueller e.K.

Nanayakkara, Shyama. Vision Related Quality of Life among Elders with Cataract in Sri Lank. 2011. 256p. pap. ***(978-3-8443-0280-6(8))*** Lambert Academic Publishing.

Nussdorf, Jonathan D., ed. Eye on the Bayou: New Concepts in Glaucoma, Cataract & Neuro-Ophthalmology. 2006. (Illus.). 253p. lib. bdg. *(978-90-6299-209-6(9))* Kugler Pubns.

Olson, Randall J., et al. Cataract Surgery from Routine to Complex: A Practical Guide. 2011. (ENG., Illus.). 272p. 169.95 *(978-1-55642-947-7(9))* SLACK, Inc.

Reddy, K. Ravi Kumar & Satyavani, P. Atlas of Cataract Surgery. 2009. (ENG.). 198p. 135.00 *(978-0-07-163445-8(2)*, 0071634452) McGraw-Hill Professional Publishing.

Roshdy, Maged. Microincision Bimanual Phacoemulsification Safety & Efficacy. 2011. 68p. pap. ***(978-3-8454-0413-4(2))*** Lambert Academic Publishing.

Scott, Ingrid U. Diabetes & Ocular Disease: Past, Present, & Future Therapies. 2nd ed. 2009. (American Academy of Ophthalmology Monograph Ser.: Vol. 14). (ENG., Illus.). 352p. 95.00 *(978-0-19-534023-5(X))* Oxford Univ. Pr., Inc.

Steinert, Roger F. Cataract Surgery. 3rd ed. 2009. (ENG., Illus.). 704p. 274.00 *(978-1-4160-3225-0(8)*, Saunders) Elsevier - Health Sciences Div.

CATARRH

see Cold (Disease)

CATASTRAL SURVEYS

see Real Property

CATASTROPHE INSURANCE

see Disaster Insurance

CATASTROPHES

see Disasters

CATASTROPHES (GEOLOGY)

see also Deluge; Geology—History

Adushkin, Vitaly & Nemchinov, Ivan, eds. Catastrophic Events Caused by Cosmic Objects. 2010. (Illus.). xii, 358p. pap. 139.00 *(978-90-481-7644-1(1)*, 9048176441) Springer.

Alvarez, Walter. The Mountains of Saint Francis: Discovering the Geologic Events That Shaped Our Earth. 2008. (ENG., Illus.). 288p. 25.95 *(978-0-393-06185-7(X)*, 6185) Norton, W. W. & Co., Inc.

—T. rex & the Crater of Doom. 2008. (Princeton Science Library). (ENG., Illus.). 216p. pap. 16.95 *(978-0-691-13103-0(1))* Princeton Univ. Pr.

Cockell, Charles, et al. Biological Processes Associated with Impact Events. 2010. (Impact Studies). (Illus.). xvi, 376p. pap. 169.00 *(978-3-642-06515-6(5)*, 3642065155) Springer.

Erwin, Douglas H. Extinction: How Life on Earth Nearly Ended 250 Million Years Ago. 2008. (ENG., Illus.). 320p. pap. 24.95 *(978-0-691-13628-8(9))* Princeton Univ. Pr.

Firestone, Richard, et al. The Cycle of Cosmic Catastrophes: Flood, Fire, & Famine in the History of Civilization. 2006. (ENG., Illus.). 1p. per. 18.00 *(978-1-59143-061-2(5)*, 1253698) Inner Traditions International, Ltd.

Froede, Carl R., Jr. Geology by Design: Interpreting Rocks & Their Catastrophic Record. 2007. (Illus.). 160p. per. 14.99 *(978-0-89051-503-7(4))* Master Bks.

Ginenthal, Charles. The Extinction of the Mammoth. Date not set. 305p. 24.95 *(978-0-9639759-2-8(7))* Ginenthal, Charles Ivy Pr. Bks.

Hanslmeier, Arnold. Habitability & Cosmic Catastrophes. 2008. (Advances in Astrobiology & Biogeophysics Ser.). (Illus.). xiv, 248p. 139.00 *(978-3-540-76944-6(7))* Springer.

Palmer, Trevor. Perilous Planet Earth: Catastrophes & Catastrophism through the Ages. 2010. 536p. pap. 50.00 *(978-0-521-17464-0(3))* Cambridge Univ. Pr.

Prothero, Donald R. Catastrophes! Earthquakes, Tsunamis, Tornadoes, & Other Earth-Shattering Disasters. 2011. (ENG., Illus.). 360p. 30.00 *(978-0-8018-9692-7(4))* Johns Hopkins Univ. Pr.

Shustov, B. M. & Rykhlova, L. V. Asteroidno-Kometnaia Opasnost: Vchera, Segodnia, Zavtra. 2010. (RUS., Illus.). 383p. *(978-5-9221-1241-3(4))* Fiziko-Matematiceskaja Literatura.

Thomas, Chan. The Adam & Eve Story: The History of Cataclysms. 2nd ed. 243p. (Orig.). pap. 12.95 *(978-1-884600-07-4(7))* Bengal Tiger Pr.

Whitcomb, John C. The World That Perished: An Introduction to Biblical Catastrophism. 3rd ed. 2009. (Illus.). 178p. pap. 18.00 *(978-0-88469-266-9(3))* BMH Bks.

Whittington, Carla & Baer, Eric. Workbook for Geologic Catastrophes. 3rd rev. ed. 2010. (ENG.). 182p. spiral bd. 44.06 *(978-0-7575-5575-6(6))* Kendall Hunt Publishing Co.

CATASTROPHES (MATHEMATICS)

Deffuant, Guillaume & Gilbert, Nigel, eds. Viability & Resilience of Complex Systems: Concepts, Methods & Case Studies from Ecology & Society. 2011. (Understanding Complex Systems Ser.). (ENG., Illus.). xii, 221p. 129.00 *(978-3-642-20422-7(8)*, 3642204228) Springer.

Wildgen, Wolfgang & Brandt, Per Aage. Semiosis & Catastrophes: René Thom's Semiotic Heritage. 2010. (FRE & ENG., Illus.). 185p. pap. *(978-3-0343-0467-2(6))* Lang, Peter.

Wilson, Alan. Catastrophe Theory & Bifurcation (Routledge Revivals) 2011. (Routledge Revivals Ser.). (ENG.). 354p. 140.00 ***(978-0-415-68782-9(9))*** Routledge.

Woodcock, Alexander E. & Poston, T. A Geometrical Study of the Elementary Catastrophes. 2008. (Lecture Notes in Mathematics Ser.). (Illus.). v, 257p. pap. 46.00 *(978-3-540-06681-1(0))* Springer.

CATASTROPHICAL, THE

see also Change

Burstein, Joseph. Professionals of Catastrophic Realm. 2007. v, 60p. *(978-0-9765949-3-2(5))* Metrics Pr.

Cerulo, Karen A. Never Saw It Coming: Cultural Challenges to Envisioning the Worst. 2006. (Illus.). 336p. 80.00 *(978-0-226-10032-6(4))*; pap. 30.00 *(978-0-226-10033-3(2))* Univ. of Chicago Pr.

Danelek, J. Allan. Extinction or Utopia - 2012: Doomsday Prophecies Explored. 2009. (ENG.). 216p. pap. 16.95 *(978-0-7387-1464-6(X))* Llewellyn Pubns.

Greenfield, Jill & Latymer-Sayers, William. Quantifying Catastrophic Injuries. 2011. pap. 250.00 *(978-1-84766-547-8(0)*, Bloomsbury Professional) Bloomsbury Publishing Plc GBR. Dist: International Specialized Bk. Services.

Hoens, Dominiek, et al, eds. The Catastrophic Imperative: Subjectivity, Time & Memory in Contemporary Thought. 2009. (ENG.). 288p. 100.00 *(978-0-230-55285-2(4))* Palgrave Macmillan.

Joseph, Lawrence E. Aftermath: Prepare for & Survive Apocalypse 2012. 2011. (ENG.). 288p. pap. 15.00 *(978-0-7679-3079-6(7)*, Three Rivers Pr.) Crown Publishing Group.

—Apocalipsis 2012: Un Estudio Sobre el Fin de la Civilizacion. 2008. 352p. pap. 14.99 *(978-0-06-156561-8(X))* HarperCollins Pubs.

—Apocalypse 2012: An Investigation into Civilization's End. 2008. (ENG.). 272p. pap. 14.95 *(978-0-7679-2448-1(7))* Broadway Bks.

Kerner, Aaron. Representing the Catastrophic: Coming to Terms with "Unimaginable" Suffering & "Incomprehensible" Horror in Visual Culture. 2007. (Illus.). 332p. 119.95 *(978-0-7734-5410-1(1))* Mellen, Edwin Pr., The.

Maatallah, Prof. Magid. The Islamic Insurance. 2011. 148p. pap. ***(978-3-8454-0095-2(1))*** Lambert Academic Publishing.

Rickert, Donald R. The Parallax: See Yourself with New Understanding. 2011. 116p. 28.95 ***(978-1-4582-0059-4(0))***; pap. 11.95 ***(978-1-4582-0058-7(2))*** Author Solutions, Inc. (Abbott Pr.).

van der Worp, Jacco & Masters, Marshall. Planet X Forecast & 2012 Survival Guide. Manning, Janice, ed. & contrib. by. 2nd ed. 2007. (Illus.). 308p. pap. 19.95 *(978-1-59772-075-5(5)*, Your Own World Bks.) Your Own World, Inc.

CATATONIA

Fink, Max & Taylor, Michael Alan. Catatonia: A Clinician's Guide to Diagnosis & Treatment. 2006. (ENG.). 276p. pap. 62.00 *(978-0-521-03236-0(9))* Cambridge Univ. Pr.

CATAWBA INDIANS

see Indians of North America—East (U.S.)

CATAWBA LANGUAGE

Speck, Frank G. Catawba Texts. (Columbia University, Contributions to Anthropology Ser.: Vol. 24). reprint ed. 27.50 *(978-0-404-50574-5(0))* AMS Pr., Inc.

CATCHES

see Glees, Catches, Rounds, etc.

CATCHING (BASEBALL)

Bennett, Bob. Catching Fundamentals & Techniques. 2nd ed. 2007. (Coaches Choice Ser.). (Illus.). 111p. pap. 24.95 *(978-1-58518-054-7(8))* Coaches Choice.

—101 Catching Drills. 2008. (Illus.). 222p. pap. 19.95 *(978-1-60679-004-5(8))* Coaches Choice.

Leyritz, Jim, et al. Catching Heat: The Jim Leyritz Story. 2011. (Illus.). 244p. 24.95 *(978-0-7573-1566-4(6))* Health Communications, Inc.

Mayne, Brent. The Art of Catching: The Secrets & Techniques of Baseball's Most Demanding Position. 2008. (Illus.) 102p. pap. 25.00 *(978-0-9815386-5-5(7))* Cleanline Bks.

CATECHETICAL ILLUSTRATIONS

see Homiletical Illustrations

CATECHETICAL SERMONS

Rust, Henry R., ed. The Church in Today's World. pap. 8.95 *(978-1-877871-29-0(X)*, 3544) Educational Ministries, Inc.

Siggins, Ian D. K. A Harvest of Medieval Preaching: The Sermon Books of Johann Herolt, OP (Discipulus) 2009. 344p. 29.99 *(978-1-4415-8042-9(5))*; pap. 19.99 *(978-1-4415-8041-2(7))* Xlibris Corp.

CATECHETICS

see also Catechetical Sermons; Catechisms; Christian Education; First Communion; Questioning

also subdivision Catechisms and Creeds under names of Christian denominations, e.g. Catholic Church—Catechisms and Creeds

Andrewes, Lancelot. A Pattern of Catechistical Doctrine, & Other Minor Works of Lancelot Andrewes, Sometime Lord Bishop of Winchester. 2008. 457p. pap. 38.00 *(978-1-60608-123-5(3)*, Wipf and Stock) Wipf & Stock Pubs.

Farey, Caroline, et al, eds. The Pedagogy of God: It's Centrality in Catechesis & Catechist Formation: Its Centrality in Catechesis & Catechist Formation. 2011. 188p. 13.95 ***(978-1-931018-72-2(3))*** Emmaus Road Publishing.

Kurth, Erwin W. Catechetical Helps. (CHI.). 187p. pap. 5.00 *(978-0-570-09979-6(X)*, 16-6038) Concordia Publishing Hse.

White, Joseph D. Multisensory Methods in Catechesis. 2007. (Catechist's Companion Ser.). (Illus.). 7p. pap. 2.95 *(978-1-59276-289-7(1))* Our Sunday Visitor, Publishing Div.

CATECHETICS—CATHOLIC CHURCH

Bandas, Rudolph G. Contents & Methods of Catechization. 2009. 340p. pap. 37.00 *(978-1-60899-134-1(2)*, Wipf and Stock) Wipf & Stock Pubs.

Catholic Church, United States Conference of Catholic Bishops Committee on Evangelization and Catechesis Staff, contrib. by. Catechetical Formation in Chaste Living: Guidelines for Curriculum Design & Publication. 2008. 27p. pap. *(978-1-60137-043-3(1))* United States Conference of Catholic Bishops.

—Doctrinal Elements of a Curriculum Framework for the Development of Catechetical Materials for Young People of High School Age. 2008. iv, 53p. pap. *(978-1-60137-042-6(3))* United States Conference of Catholic Bishops.

Fox, Mary. Journals of the Catechesis of the Good Shepherd, 2003-2008. 2009. (Illus.). 198p. pap. *(978-1-56854-274-4(7))* Good Shepherd Pubns.

Gaupin, Linda L. Embracing the Vision: Sacramental Catechesis for First Reconciliation & First Communion. 2008. 193p. pap. 69.95 incl. cd-rom *(978-1-58595-644-9(9))* Twenty-Third Pubns./Bayard.

Hailer, Gretchen. Echoing the Word: An Introductory Catechist Formation Process. 2008. 96p. pap. 19.95 *(978-0-8091-4563-8(4))* Paulist Pr.

Hoffmann, Mary Byrne. Catechesis in a Multi-Media World: Connecting to Today's Students. 2011. pap. *(978-0-8091-4708-3(4))* Paulist Pr.

Hofinger, Johannes. The Art of Teaching Christian Doctrine: The Good News & Its Proclamation. 2011. 290p. 48.95 ***(978-1-258-08325-0(6))*** Literary Licensing, LLC.

Hughes, Monica. Planning Your Teaching Year: A Catechist's Guide to Developing Effective Goals. 2009. (Catechists Guide Ser.). 80p. pap. 8.95 *(978-0-8091-4569-0(3))* Paulist Pr.

Infantino, Ginger. Handbook for Today's Catechist: The Role of the Catechist: Planning Effective Lessons, Sharing the Faith. 2009. 5.99 *(978-0-7648-1846-2(5))* Liguori Pubns.

—Manual para el Catequista de Hoy: El Papel Del Catequista Planificar Lecciones Eficaces Compartir la Fe. 2010.Tr. of Handbook for Today's Catechist: Role of the Catechist: Planning Effective Lessons, Sharing the Faith. (SPA.). 5.99 *(978-0-7648-1871-4(6)*, Libros Liguori) Liguori Pubns.

Kelly, Francis D. The Mystery We Proclaim: Catechesis for the Third Millennium. 2nd ed. 2008. 158p. pap. 18.00 *(978-1-55635-684-1(6))* Wipf & Stock Pubs.

Kelly, Maureen. Sacraments Source Book. 2007. ***(978-0-15-901641-1(X))*** Harcourt Religion Pubs.

Moran, Gabriel. Fashioning a People Today: The Educational Insights of Maria Harris. 2007. 185p. per. 16.95 *(978-1-58595-605-0(8))* Twenty-Third Pubns./Bayard.

Naaeke, Anthony Y. Kaleidoscope Catechesis: Missionary Catechesis in Africa, Particularly in the Diocese of Wa in Ghana. 2006. 174p. (C). 62.95 *(978-0-8204-8685-7(X))* Lang, Peter Publishing, Inc.

Neuberger, Anne E. To Walk Humbly: Stories & Activities for Teaching Compassion & Justice for Ages 10-13. 2007. 138p. per. 19.95 *(978-1-58595-616-6(3))* Twenty-Third Pubns./Bayard.

O'Leary, Daniel J. Begin with the Heart: Recovering a Sacramental Vision. 2009. (ENG., Illus.). 183p. pap. 38.95 *(978-1-85607-611-1(3))* Columba Pr. IRL. Dist: Dufour Editions, Inc.

Paprocki, Joe. La Caja de Herramientas Del Catequista: Cómo Triunfar en el Ministerio de la Catequesis Arias, Miguel, tr. from ENG. 2009. (SPA.). 152p. pap. 9.95 *(978-0-8294-2767-7(8))* Loyola Pr.

—The Catechist's Toolbox: How to Thrive as a Religious Education Teacher. 2007. (ENG., Illus.). 152p. per. 9.95 *(978-0-8294-2451-5(2))* Loyola Pr.

Peterfy, Ida. Catechist Companion: Ready-To-Use Lesson Plans: Creed, Sacraments, Commandments, & Saints. 2009. (Illus.). vii, 226p. pap. *(978-1-56854-797-8(8))* Liturgy Training Pubns.

Schonborn, Christoph. Living the Catechism of the Catholic Church, Vol. 3. 160p. 10.95 *(978-0-89870-835-6(4))* Ignatius Pr.

United States Conference of Catholic Bishops, creator. United States Catholic Catechism for Adults. 2006. (Illus.). 637p. per. 24.95 *(978-1-57455-450-2(6))* United States Conference of Catholic Bishops.

Wagner, Nick. The Way of Faith: A Field Guide for the RCIA Process. 2008. 200p. pap. *(978-1-58595-710-1(0))* Twenty-Third Pubns./Bayard.

CATECHETICS—LUTHERAN CHURCH

Ohlemacher, Andreas. Lateinische Katechetik der frühen lutherischen Orthodoxie. 2010. (Forschungen Zur Kirchen- und Dogmengeschichte Ser.). (GER., Illus.). 510p. (C). 137.00 *(978-3-525-56399-1(X))* Vandenhoeck & Ruprecht GmbH & Co. KG DEU. Dist: ISD.

CATECHISMS

see also Bible—Catechisms; Catechetical Sermons; Catechetics; Creeds

also subdivision Catechisms and Creeds under names of religions, religious denominations, etc., e.g. Catholic Church—Catechisms and Creeds

Aldridge, Mark. Calling All Catholics: A Message from the Word of God. 2009. pap. 14.99 *(978-1-60799-942-3(0))* Tate Publishing & Enterprises, LLC.

Anon & Anon. Creeds & Catechisms: Apostles' Creed, Nicene Creed, Athanasian Creed, the Heidelberg Catechism, the Canons of Dordt, the Belgic Confession, & The. 2011. 140p. ***(978-1-84902-449-5(9))*** Benediction Classics.

An Arabic Catechism on Biblical History. 2010. pap. 26.32 ***(978-1-61719-625-6(8))*** Gorgias Pr., LLC.

Arquidiocesis de Cali Staff. Catequesis para Primera Comunion (Catechesis for First Communion) (SPA.). 96p. pap. 3.95 *(978-958-607-815-3(9))* Sociedad de San Pablo COL. Dist: St Pauls/Alba Hse. Pubs.

—Catequetica Parroquial.Tr. of Catechesis for the Catechists. (SPA.). 96p. pap. 3.95 *(978-958-607-325-7(4))* Sociedad de San Pablo COL. Dist: St Pauls/Alba Hse. Pubs.

Bradshaw, Paul, ed. Essays in Early Eastern Initiation. 2009. 88.00 *(978-1-60724-363-2(6))* Gorgias Pr., LLC.

Brown, John. Questions & Answers on the Shorter Catechism. 2006. Org. Title: An Essay towards an Easy, Plain, Practical, & Extensive Explication of the Assembly's Shorter Catechism. (ENG.). 384p. per. 22.00 *(978-1-60178-004-1(4))* Reformation Heritage Bks.

—Short Catechism for Young Children. 2006. pap. 15.95 *(978-1-4286-4641-4(8))* Kessinger Publishing, LLC.

Catechism. deluxe ed. 5.15 *(978-0-89870-492-1(8))* Ignatius Pr.

CATECHIST Magazine's Prayers for Catechists. 2006. 2.25 *(978-1-933178-39-4(6))* Pflaum Publishing Group.

Catholic Catechism in the Mosul Dialect of Aramaic (Sureth) 2010. (SYR.). pap. 22.00 *(978-1-61719-623-2(1))* Gorgias Pr., LLC.

Catholic Catechism in Urmia Aramaic. 2010. (SYR.). pap. 27.28 *(978-1-61719-622-5(3))* Gorgias Pr., LLC.

Cuellar, Gloria. Veo A Jesus Con Ojos Jovenes. 120p. 11.95 *(978-958-607-823-8(X))* Sociedad de San Pablo COL. Dist: St Pauls/Alba Hse. Pubs.

Devitt, Patrick M. Faith Languages: Thoughts for Each Day. 2009. (ENG.). 267p. pap. 22.95 *(978-1-84730-121-5(5))* Veritas Pubns. IRL. Dist: Dufour Editions, Inc.

Durand, Casimir F. The Old Catholic Church & Other Writings. Serge, A. Therault, ed. 2011. 192p. pap. 16.95 ***(978-1-937002-16-9(0))*** Apocryphile Pr.

Eyes, Ears, & All My Senses. 64p. 13.75 *(978-0-570-00782-1(8))* Concordia Publishing Hse.

C

Fabrizius, Karl F. Bible Stories for Daily Prayer: Catechism Stories, 10 vols., Vol. 7. Bender, Peter C., ed. 2006. 230p. (J). ring bd. 20.00 *(978-0-9725687-7-7(8))* Concordia Catechetical Academy.

Farah, Charles. Catechism for New Christians. Farah Jr., Charles, ed. 2011. 66p. 36.95 ***(978-1-258-08220-8(9))*** Literary Licensing, LLC.

Farrell, Martin W. The Parish Catechism: Written Especially for Instructing Non-Catholic People in the Basic Teachings of Religion. 2011. 146p. 40.95 ***(978-1-258-09255-9(7))*** Literary Licensing, LLC.

Fti, Brother Anthony Josemaria. The Blessed Virgin Mary in England: A Mary-Catechism with Pilgrimage to Her Holy Shrines. 2008. 520p. pap. 35.95 *(978-0-595-50074-1(9))* iUniverse, Inc.

Grace, Richard W. The Triple Catechism, Part. 2011. 146p. 40.95 ***(978-1-258-05616-2(X))*** Literary Licensing, LLC.

Grosvenor, Vernon. Catechism for Catechumens. 2011. 130p. pap. 19.99 ***(978-1-4568-5143-9(8))*** Xlibris Corp.

Headlam, Stewart. The Laws of Eternal Life Being Studies in the Church Catechism. 2007. (ENG.). 112p. 34.95 *(978-0-548-05204-4(2))* Kessinger Publishing, LLC.

Heidelberg Catechism: Khmer. (Bibles Ser.). 3.95 *(978-1-56212-700-8(4),* 155291) Faith Alive Christian Resources.

Jehlicka, Francis. Graded Catechism: According to the Instruction of the Motu Proprio Orbem Catholicum of Pius XI, June 29 1923. 2011. 242p. 46.95 ***(978-1-258-01563-3(3))*** Literary Licensing, LLC.

John Paul II, pseud. On Catechesis in Our Time: Catechesi Tradendae. 67p. pap. 3.95 *(978-0-8198-1486-9(5),* 332-035) Pauline Bks. & Media.

Kasomo, Daniel W. The Permanence of Catholic Priesthood. 2011. 324p. pap. ***(978-3-8443-1220-1(X))*** Lambert Academic Publishing.

Kingswood, Jeff. From the Lips of Little Ones. 2008. 164p. (J). pap. 10.00 *(978-1-884527-24-1(8))* Crown & Covenant Pubns.

Living Luther's Catechism: 52 Interactive Devotions. 64p. 9.99 *(978-0-570-06847-1(9),* 20-2723) Concordia Publishing Hse.

Lloyd Csp, James B. Catholicism & Same Sex Attraction. 2011. 124p. pap. 14.95 ***(978-1-60844-942-2(4))*** Dog Ear Publishing, LLC.

Luther, Martin. El Catecismo Menor de Martin Lutero con Explicaciones: Luther's Small Catechism with Explanation, 1997 Edition. rev. exp. ed. (SPA.). 144p. pap. 4.50 *(978-0-570-09977-2(3),* 16-6037); pap. 8.90 *(978-0-570-05139-8(8),* 16-6050); 144p. pap. 4.50 *(978-0-570-09976-5(5),* 16-6036); pap. 8.90 *(978-0-570-05113-8(4),* 16-1914) Concordia Publishing Hse.

—Luther's Small Catechism. (VIE.). 64p. 2.50 *(978-0-570-05014-8(6),* 16-1106); (LAO.). 87p. pap. 4.50 *(978-0-570-05001-8(4),* 16-5001) Concordia Publishing Hse.

Madden, Charles. The Mini-Catechism: 388 Fundamental Questions & Answers on the Catholic Faith. 2006. 48p. 4.50 *(978-0-9788687-1-0(4))* Requiem Pr.

Madden, Maureen. Reflections on the Catechism. 2006. 56p. 4.95 *(978-1-58595-598-5(1))* Twenty-Third Pubns./Bayard.

Marcel, Pierre Ch. In God's School: Foundations for a Christian Life. 2009. 212p. pap. 23.00 *(978-1-60608-116-7(0),* Wipf and Stock) Wipf & Stock Pubs.

Marrocchi, Mario. Los Jubileos.Tr. of Jubilees. (SPA.). 112p. 4.95 *(978-958-692-001-8(1))* Sociedad de San Pablo COL. Dist: St Pauls/Alba Hse. Pubs.

McDonald, William P. Christian Catechetical Texts: Book 1: Medieval & Reformation, 1357-1579/Book 2: Orthodoxy & Pietism, 1618-1778/Book 3: Modern & Missionary, 1790-1908, 3 vols. 2011. (Illus.). 1334p. 229.95 *(978-0-7734-1536-2(X))* Mellen, Edwin Pr., The.

Mcquade, Paula. Early Modern Catechisms Written for Mothers Schoolmistresses & Children: Essential Works for the Study of Early Modern Englishwomen. 2008. (Early Modern Englishwoman: A Facsimile Library of Essential Works ndash; Essential Works Ser. III, Part Three Ser.). 326p. 165.00 *(978-0-7546-5165-9(7))* Ashgate Publishing Co.

Memory Book for Lutheran Schools. 178p. 5.50 *(978-0-570-00694-7(5),* 22-1039) Concordia Publishing Hse.

Methodist Episcopal Church Catechisms. The Catechism of the Methodist Episcopal Church Numbers 1, 2, & 3, in One Volume, Designed for Consecutive Study in Sunday Schools & Families. 2006. 164p. per. 18.99 *(978-1-4255-1238-5(0))* MPublishing.

Meyer, Dietrich, et al. Katechismen. 2008. (Texte Zur Geschichte des Pietismus Ser.). (GER., Illus.). 581p. (C). 128.00 *(978-3-525-55854-6(6))* Vandenhoeck & Ruprecht GmbH & Co. KG DEU. Dist: ISD.

Morgan, Barbara, et al. Catechism of the Catholic Church & the Craft of Catechesis. 2008. 158p. pap. 15.95 *(978-1-58617-221-3(2))* Ignatius Pr.

Murphy, Joe. Echoes in the Gangway: A Catholic Boy's Trek Through the Fifties - Memories of My Family & St. Leo Parish. 2010. 304p. pap. 21.95 *(978-1-4401-3748-8(X))* iUniverse, Inc.

Murrell, Adam. The Young Baptist's Catechism: A Beginner's Guide to the Baptist Confession of Faith Of 1689. 2007. 52p. pap. 7.00 *(978-1-55635-261-4(1),* Resource Pubns.) Wipf & Stock Pubs.

My Life in Jesus. 80p. tchr. ed. 19.50 *(978-0-570-00759-3(3),* 22-2873) Concordia Publishing Hse.

Nicholson, William. Exposition of the Catechism. (Library of Anglo-Catholic Theology: No. 14). reprint ed. 32.50 *(978-0-404-52106-6(1))* AMS Pr., Inc.

Nuevo Catecismo para Indios Remisos.Tr. of New Catechism for Reluctant Natives. (SPA.). 140p. reprint ed. *(978-968-411-396-1(X))* Ediciones Era MEX. Dist: Continental Bk. Co., Inc.

of the Southwest, Anglo-Catholic Archdiocese. The Southwest Anglo-Catholic Catechism (Catechismus Meridionalis-Occidentalis) - Paperback Edition. 2009. 132p. pap. 13.28 *(978-0-557-19159-8(9))* Lulu Enterprises Inc.

Pablo, Juan, II. Catecismo de la Iglesia Catolica: Catechism of the Catholic Church. (SPA.). 704p. 12.95 *(978-958-607-957-0(0))* Sociedad de San Pablo ESP. Dist: St Pauls/Alba Hse. Pubs.

Partners in Learning Family Kit. 19.99 *(978-0-570-00786-9(0),* 22-2906); 12.95 *(978-0-570-00781-4(X),* 22-2894) Concordia Publishing Hse.

Penagos, Jose Arturo. Libro Basico Del Catequista. 80p. 3.95 *(978-958-607-585-5(0))* Sociedad de San Pablo COL. Dist: St Pauls/Alba Hse. Pubs.

Peters, Albrecht. Commentary on Luther's Catechism: Creeds. Schaum, Charles P., ed. Trapp, Thomas H., tr. 2011. (ENG.). 332p. pap. 42.99 ***(978-0-7586-1149-9(8))*** Concordia Publishing Hse.

Pham, John-Peter. A Primer for the Catechism of the Catholic Church. 2nd ed. Date not set. 112p. reprint ed. pap. 4.95 *(978-1-890177-01-0(6))* Midwest Theological Forum.

Philipps, James. Understanding St. Paul. 2006. 56p. 4.95 *(978-1-58595-600-5(7))* Twenty-Third Pubns./Bayard.

Piechowski, Otto R. & Shannon, William Henry. The Catechism of the Catholic Church: A Second Look. 2009. xiv, 76p. ***(978-1-56077-899-8(7))*** Center for Learning, The.

Poust, Mary DeTurris, et al. The Complete Idiot's Guide to the Catholic Catechism. 2008. (Complete Idiot's Guide Ser.). (ENG., Illus.). 336p. (gr. 12-18). 14.95 *(978-1-59257-707-1(5),* Alpha Bks.) Penguin Group (USA) Inc.

Presbyterian Board of Publication & Presbyterian Board Of Publication. The Intermediate Catechism with Proofs with Proofs from the Scriptures in English & German. 2011. 52p. 36.95 ***(978-1-258-05096-2(X))*** Literary Licensing, LLC.

Resines, Luis & Resines Llorente, Luis. De la Fe Maltratada a la Fe Bien Tratada: Lo Peor y lo Mejor de los Catecismos Españoles. 2009. (SPA.). 254p. *(978-84-288-2146-9(1))* Promoción Popular Cristiana.

Ruhland, Thomas. Understanding the Catechism: Prayer. 2006. (Illus.). 128p. per. 7.50 *(978-0-7829-0878-7(0))* RCL Benziger Publishing.

Schonborn, Christoph. Living the Catechism of the Catholic Church, Vol. 3. 160p. 10.95 *(978-0-89870-835-6(4))* Ignatius Pr.

Seyer, Herman D., compiled by. Working Through Luther's Small Catechism. 62p. 5.50 *(978-0-570-03908-2(8),* 12-2990) Concordia Publishing Hse.

Singer-Towns, Brian. The Catholic Faith Handbook for Youth. 2nd ed. 2008. (Illus.). 474p. per. 19.95 *(978-0-88489-987-7(X))* St. Mary's Pr.

Singer-Towns, Brian, et al. The Catholic Faith Handbook for Youth. 2nd ed. 2008. (Illus.). 474p. 28.25 *(978-0-88489-988-4(8))* St. Mary's Pr.

The Small Catechism: 1943 Translation. 16p. 2.00 *(978-0-570-01500-0(6),* 22-2154) Concordia Publishing Hse.

The Small Catechism: 1943 Translation, Tract Edition. 16p. 3.75 *(978-0-570-08154-8(8),* 22-1015) Concordia Publishing Hse.

The Small Catechism: 1986 Translation. 221p. 2.50 *(978-0-570-09889-8(0),* 22-2273) Concordia Publishing Hse.

Smyth, Thomas. An Ecclesiastical Catechism of the Presbyterian Church. 2008. 132p. 21.99 *(978-0-559-40864-9(1));* pap. 19.75 *(978-0-559-40862-5(5))* BiblioBazaar.

—An Ecclesiastical Catechism of the Presbyterian Church. Donnan, Geoffrey, ed. 2007. 104p. pap. 14.50 *(978-0-9773442-3-9(1))* Reformation Media & Pr.

Stewart, C. The Church History Catechism: The German Reformation. 2011. 64p. pap. 12.84 *(978-1-4520-2821-7(4))* AuthorHouse.

A Summary Catechism for the Present Time. 2010. (ARA.). 104.48 *(978-1-61719-760-4(2))* Gorgias Pr., LLC.

A Summary Catechism in Arabic. 2010. (ARA.). 113.84 *(978-1-61719-762-8(9))* Gorgias Pr., LLC.

Trost, Frederick R. Evangelism Catechism: A New Approach for the 21st Century. 2009. *(978-0-8298-1815-4(4))* Pilgrim Pr., The/United Church Pr.

Tucker, Beverley D. & Swatos, William H., Jr. Questions on the Way: A Catechism Based on the Book of Common Prayer. 3rd rev. ed. 128p. pap. 7.95 *(978-0-88028-164-5(2),* 887) Forward Movement Pubns.

Velicu, Adrian. Civic Catechisms & Reason in the French Revolution. 2010. 180p. 114.95 *(978-0-7546-6998-2(X))* Ashgate Publishing Co.

CATECHISMS—BIBLIOGRAPHY

Eames, Wilberforce. Early New England Catechisms. 2009. 68p. pap. 12.18 *(978-1-151-56144-2(4))* General Bks. LLC.

—Early New England Catechisms. 2008. 114p. 34.95 *(978-1-4365-7453-2(6))* 2007. (ENG.). 116p. per. 19.95 *(978-0-548-80578-7(4))* Kessinger Publishing, LLC.

CATECHOLAMINES

see also Adrenaline; Dopamine; Hormones; Noradrenaline

Nagatsu, Toshiharu, et al, eds. Catecholamine Research: From Molecular Insights to Clinical Medicine. 2010. (Advances in Behavioral Biology Ser.). 560p. pap. 279.00 *(978-1-4419-3388-1(3),* 1441933883) Springer.

Pacak, Karel, et al. Stress, Neurotransmitters, & Hormones: Neuroendocrine & Genetic Mechanisms. 2009. (Annals of the New York Academy of Sciences Ser.). (ENG., Illus.). 452p. pap. 154.95 *(978-1-57331-692-7(X),* Wiley-Blackwell) Wiley, John & Sons, Inc.

Ritsner, Michael S. & Weizman, Abraham, eds. Neuroactive Steroids in Brain Function, Behavior & Neuropsychiatric Disorders: Novel Strategies for Research & Treatment. 2010. (Illus.). xx, 564p. pap. 239.00 *(978-90-481-7738-7(3),* 9048177383) Springer.

Vaudry, Hubert & Shioda, Seiji, eds. Phylogenetic Aspects of Neuropeptides: From Invertebrates to Humans. 2010. (Annals of the New York Academy of Sciences Ser.: 54). (ENG., Illus.). 300p. pap. 130.00 *(978-1-57331-798-6(5),* Wiley-Blackwell) Wiley, John & Sons, Inc.

CATECHUMENS

Duty, Kim. Teaching the Faith: A Catechist's Guide to Classroom Management. 2007. (Catechists Guide Ser.). 68p. per. 8.95 *(978-0-8091-4400-6(X),* 4400-6) Paulist Pr.

Galipeau, Jerry. Apprenticed to Christ: Activities for Practicing the Catholic Way of Life. 2007. (Illus.). 112p. per. 12.95 *(978-1-58459-327-0(X))* World Library Pubns.

Leijssen, Lambert, ed. Initiation Chretienne et la Liturgie - Christian Initiation & the Liturgy. 2008. (Textes et Etudes Liturgiques / Studies in Liturgy Ser.). (FRE.). 234p. (C). pap. 51.00 *(978-90-429-2051-4(3))* Peeters Pubs. & Booksellers BEL. Dist: Brown, David Bk. Co., The.

Ralph, Margaret Nutting. Breaking Open the Lectionary: Lectionary Readings in their Biblical Context for RCIA, Faith Sharing Groups & Lectors - Cycle A. 2007. 240p. pap. 19.95 *(978-0-8091-4471-6(9),* 4471-6) Paulist Pr.

Wagner, Nick. The Heart of Faith: A Field Guide for Catechumens & Candidates. 2010. 120p. pap. 12.95 *(978-1-58595-817-7(4))* Twenty-Third Pubns./Bayard.

CATEDRAL DE SANTIAGO DE COMPOSTELA

Watson, Christabel & Watson, Katherine. The Romanesque Cathedral of Santiago de Compostela: A Reassessment. 2009. (Bar S Ser.). (ENG., Illus.). 117p. (C). pap. 80.00 *(978-1-4073-0511-0(5))* British Archaeological Reports Ltd. GBR. Dist: Brown, David Bk. Co., The.

CATEGORIAL GRAMMAR

Jäger, Gerhard. Anaphora & Type Logical Grammar. 2010. (Trends in Logic Ser.). xiv, 289p. pap. 219.00 *(978-90-481-6992-4(5),* 9048169925) Springer.

Morrill, Glyn. Categorial Grammar: Logical Syntax, Semantics, & Processing. 2010. (ENG., Illus.). 320p. pap. 55.00 *(978-0-19-958986-9(0));* 150.00 *(978-0-19-958985-2(2))* Oxford Univ. Pr., Inc.

CATEGORIES (MATHEMATICS)

see also Functor Theory

Adamek, Jiri, et al. Abstract & Concrete Categories: The Joy of Cats. 2009. (Dover Books on Mathematics Ser.). (ENG.). 528p. (C). pap. 24.95 *(978-0-486-46934-8(4))* Dover Pubns., Inc.

Adámek, Jiri, et al. Algebraic Theories: A Categorical Introduction to General Algebra. 2010. (Cambridge Tracts in Mathematics Ser.). (ENG., Illus.). 258p. 80.00 *(978-0-521-11922-1(7))* Cambridge Univ. Pr.

Aguiar, Marcelo & Mahajan, Swapneel Arvind. Monoidal Functors, Species, & Hopf Algebras. 2010. (CRM Monograph Ser.). (Illus.). 784p. 169.00 *(978-0-8218-4776-3(7))* American Mathematical Society.

Andre, M., et al. Reports of the Midwest Category Seminar II. 2007. (Lecture Notes in Mathematics Ser.). 96p. per. 39.95 *(978-3-540-04231-0(8))* Springer.

André, M., et al. Reports of the Midwest Category Seminar V. 2008. (Lecture Notes in Mathematics Ser.). 255p. 46.00 *(978-3-540-05442-9(1))* Springer.

Awodey, Steve. Category Theory. 2nd ed. 2010. (Oxford Logic Guides). (ENG., Illus.). 320p. 125.00 *(978-0-19-958736-0(1));* pap. 55.00 *(978-0-19-923718-0(2))* Oxford Univ. Pr., Inc.

Baez, John C. & May, J. Peter, eds. Towards Higher Categories. 2009. (IMA Volumes in Mathematics & its Applications Ser.). xiii, 283p. 119.00 *(978-1-4419-1523-8(0),* 1441915230) Springer.

Banaschewski, B., ed. Categorical Aspects of Topology & Analysis: Proceedings of an International Conference Held at Carleton University, Ottawa, August 11-15, 1981. 2008. (Lecture Notes in Mathematics Ser.). pap. 46.00 *(978-3-540-11211-2(1))* Springer.

Banaschewski, B. & Hoffmann, R. E., eds. Continuous Lattices: Proceedings of the Conference on Topological & Categorical Aspects of Continuous Lattices (Workshop IV) Held at the University of Bremen, Germany, November 9-11, 1979. 2008. (Lecture Notes in Mathematics Ser.). pap. 69.95 *(978-3-540-10848-1(3))* Springer.

Barr, M. *-Autonomous Categories. 2008. (Lecture Notes in Mathematics Ser.). 152p. pap. 39.95 *(978-3-540-09563-7(2))* Springer.

Barr, M., et al. Exact Categories & Categories of Sheaves. 2008. (Lecture Notes in Mathematics Ser.). (ENG.). 256p. pap. 59.95 *(978-3-540-05678-2(5),* 3540056785) Springer.

—Reports of the Midwest Category Seminar III. 2008. (Lecture Notes in Mathematics Ser.). 252p. pap. 59.95 *(978-3-540-04625-7(9),* 3540046259) Springer.

Baues, Hans-Joachim. Algebraic Homotopy. 2008. (Cambridge Studies in Advanced Mathematics). (ENG.). 488p. pap. 95.00 *(978-0-521-05531-4(8))* Cambridge Univ. Pr.

Bautista, R., et al. Differential Tensor Algebras & their Module Categories. 2009. (London Mathematical Society Lecture Note Ser.). (ENG., Illus.). 462p. pap. 80.00 *(978-0-521-75768-3(1))* Cambridge Univ. Pr.

Bechtel, William & Richardson, Robert C. Discovering Complexity: Decomposition & Localization As Strategies in Scientific Research. 2010. (ENG., Illus.). 340p. (gr. 17). pap. 27.00 *(978-0-262-51473-6(7))* MIT Pr.

Binz, E. & Herrlich, H., eds. Categorical Topology: Proceedings of the Conference held at Mannheim, 21-25 July 1975. 2008. (Lecture Notes in Mathematics Ser.). 736p. pap. 69.95 *(978-3-540-07859-3(2))* Springer.

Bold, S., et al, eds. Foundations of the Formal Sciences V: Infinite Games. 2007. 368p. per. *(978-1-904987-75-8(3))* College Pubns.

Borceux, F. & Vandenbossche, G. Algebra in a Localic Topos with Applications to Ring Theory. 2008. (Lecture Notes in Mathematics Ser.). pap. 59.95 *(978-3-540-12711-6(9))* Springer.

Borceux, Francis. Handbook of Categorical Algebra: Volume 1, Basic Category Theory. 2008. (Encyclopedia of Mathematics & its Applications Ser.). (ENG.). 364p. pap. 74.00 *(978-0-521-06119-3(9))* Cambridge Univ. Pr.

—Handbook of Categorical Algebra: Volume 2, Categories & Structures. 2008. (Encyclopedia of Mathematics & its Applications Ser.). (ENG., Illus.). 464p. pap. 84.00 *(978-0-521-06122-3(9))* Cambridge Univ. Pr.

—Handbook of Categorical Algebra: Volume 3, Sheaf Theory. 2008. (Encyclopedia of Mathematics & its Applications Ser.). (ENG., Illus.). 544p. pap. 100.00 *(978-0-521-06124-7(5))* Cambridge Univ. Pr.

Borceux, Francis & Bourn, Dominique. Mal'cev, Protomodular, Homological & Semi-Abelian Categories. 2010. (Mathematics & Its Applications Ser.). xiv, 479p. pap. 209.00 *(978-90-481-6551-3(2),* 9048165512) Springer.

Broughan, K. A. Invariants for Real-Generated Uniform Topological & Algebraic Categories. 2008. (Lecture Notes in Mathematics Ser.). 212p. pap. 26.00 *(978-3-540-07418-2(X))* Springer.

Brümmer, Guillaume & Gilmour, Christopher, eds. Papers in Honour of Bernhard Banaschewski. 2010. 512p. pap. 189.00 *(978-90-481-5540-8(1),* 9048155401) Springer.

Bunge, Marta & Funk, Jonathon. Singular Coverings of Toposes: The Geometry of Lawvere Distributions. 2006. (Lecture Notes in Mathematics Ser.). (Illus.). XII, 225p. 69.95 *(978-3-540-36359-0(9),* 3540363599) Springer.

Canonaco, Alberto. The Beilinson Complex & Canonical Rings of Irregular Surfaces. 2006. (Memoirs of the American Mathematical Society Ser.: No. 862). 99p. pap. 60.00 *(978-0-8218-4193-8(9))* American Mathematical Society.

Categorical Algebra & its Applications: Proceedings of a Conference, Held in Louvain-la-Neuve, Belgium, July 26 - August 1, 1987. 2008. (Lecture Notes in Mathematics Ser.). pap. 59.95 *(978-3-540-50362-0(5))* Springer.

Diers, Y. Categories of Boolean Sheaves of Simple Algebras. 2008. (Lecture Notes in Mathematics Ser.). pap. 39.95 *(978-3-540-16459-3(6))* Springer.

Dikranjan, D. & Tholen, Walter. Categorical Structure of Closure Operators: With Applications to Topology, Algebra & Discrete Mathematics. 2010. (Mathematics & Its Applications Ser.). 376p. pap. 189.00 *(978-90-481-4631-4(3),* 9048146313) Springer.

Dosen, K. Cut Elimination in Categories. 2010. (Trends in Logic Ser.). (Illus.). 244p. pap. 219.00 *(978-90-481-5226-1(7),* 9048152267) Springer.

Dubuc, Eduardo J. Kan Extensions in Enriched Category Theory. 2008. (Lecture Notes in Mathematics Ser.). 192p. pap. 39.95 *(978-3-540-04934-0(7),* 3540049347) Springer.

Ehrig, Hartmut, et al. Fundamentals of Algebraic Graph Transformation. 2010. (Monographs in Theoretical Computer Science. an EATCS Ser.). (Illus.). xiv, 388p. pap. 139.00 *(978-3-642-06831-7(6),* 3642068316) Springer.

Fiadeiro, Jose Luiz. Categories for Software Engineering. 2010. (ENG.). xiv, 250p. pap. 109.00 *(978-3-642-05888-2(4),* 3642058884) Springer.

Fossum, R. M., et al. Trivial Extensions of Abelian Categories. 2008. (Lecture Notes in Mathematics Ser.). 140p. pap. 26.00 *(978-3-540-07159-4(8))* Springer.

Fresse, Benoit. Modules over Operads & Functors. 2009. (Lecture Notes in Mathematics Ser.). (ENG., Illus.). ix, 308p. pap. 79.95 *(978-3-540-89055-3(6))* Springer.

Ghilardi, Silvio & Zawadowski, M. Sheaves, Games, & Model Completions: A Categorical Approach to Nonclassical Propositional Logics. 2010. (Trends in Logic Ser.). 254p. pap. 179.00 *(978-90-481-6036-5(7),* 9048160367) Springer.

Gillibert, Pierre & Wehrung, Friedrich. From Objects to Diagrams for Ranges of Functors. 2011. (Lecture Notes in Mathematics Ser.). (ENG., Illus.). civiii, 10p. pap. 49.95 ***(978-3-642-21773-9(7),*** 3642217737) Springer.

Gray, J. W. Formal Category Theory: Adjointness For 2-Categories. 2008. (Lecture Notes in Mathematics Ser.). 300p. pap. 59.95 *(978-3-540-06830-3(9))* Springer.

Harper, L. H. Global Methods for Combinatorial Isoperimetric Problems. 2010. (Cambridge Studies in Advanced Mathematics Ser.). (ENG.). 250p. pap. 39.99 *(978-0-521-18383-3(9))* Cambridge Univ. Pr.

Hart, Bradd, et al, eds. Models, Logics, & Higher-Dimensional Categories: A Tribute to the Work of Mihaly Makkai. 2011. (CRM Proceedings & Lecture Notes Ser.). (Illus.). 426p. pap. 130.00 ***(978-0-8218-7281-9(8))*** American Mathematical Society.

Hartshorne, Robin. Residues & Duality. 2007. (Lecture Notes in Mathematics Ser.). 432p. per. 69.95 *(978-3-540-03603-6(2))* Springer.

He, Jingrui. Analysis of Rare Categories. 2012. (Cognitive Technologies Ser.). (ENG., Illus.). viii, 135p. 99.00 ***(978-3-642-22812-4(7),*** 3642228127) Springer.

Herrlich, H. & Preu_, G., eds. Categorical Topology: Proceedings of the International Conference, Berlin, August 27th to September 2nd 1978. 2008. (Lecture Notes in Mathematics Ser.). 436p. pap. 59.00 *(978-3-540-09503-3(9))* Springer.

Herrlich, Horst. Topologische Reflexionen und Coreflexionen. 2007. (Lecture Notes in Mathematics Ser.). (GER.). 192p. per. 29.95 *(978-3-540-04247-1(4))* Springer.

Hilton, P. J., ed. Category Theory, Homology Theory & Their Applications Proceedings of the Conference Held at the Seattle Research Center of the Battelle Memorial In. 2007. (Lecture Notes in Mathematics Ser.). 324p. per. 59.95 *(978-3-540-04611-0(9));* 224p. per. 59.95 *(978-3-540-04605-9(4))* Springer.

—Category Theory, Homology Theory & Their Applications Proceedings of the Conference Held at the Seattle Research of the Battelle Memorial Institute. 2007. (Lecture Notes in Mathematics Ser.). 496p. per. 69.95 *(978-3-540-04618-9(6))* Springer.

Hofmann, Karl H. The Duality of Compact Semigroups & C*-Bigebras. 2008. (Lecture Notes in Mathematics Ser.). 160p. pap. 26.00 *(978-3-540-04918-0(5)*, 3540049185) Springer.

Holm, Thorsten, et al. eds. Triangulated Categories. 2010. (London Mathematical Society Lecture Note Ser.). (ENG., Illus.). 472p. pap. 75.00 *(978-0-521-74431-7(8))* Cambridge Univ. Pr.

Humphreys, James E. Representations of Semisimple Lie Algebras in the BGG Category O. 2008. (Graduate Studies in Mathematics Ser.: Vol. 94). (Illus.). 289p. (C). 61.00 *(978-0-8218-4678-0(7))* American Mathematical Society.

Ingram, W. T. & Mahavier, William S. Inverse Limits: From Continua to Chaos. 2011. (Developments in Mathematics Ser.). (ENG., Illus.). xv, 217p. 99.00 ***(978-1-4614-1796-5(1)***, 1461417961) Springer.

Johnstone, P. I., et al. Indexed Categories & Their Applications. 2008. (Lecture Notes in Mathematics Ser.). 272p. pap. 59.95 *(978-3-540-08914-8(4))* Springer.

Kashiwara, Masaki & Schapira, Pierre. Categories & Sheaves. 2010. (Grundlehren der mathematischen Wissenschaften Ser.). x, 497p. pap. 119.00 *(978-3-642-06620-7(8)*, 3642066208) Springer.

Kelly, G. M., ed. Category Seminar. 2008. (Lecture Notes in Mathematics Ser.). 388p. pap. 59.95 *(978-3-540-06966-9(6))* Springer.

Kozlov, Dmitry. Combinatorial Algebraic Topology. (Algorithms & Computation in Mathematics Ser.). (Illus.). 389p. 2008. pap. 59.95 *(978-3-540-73051-4(6))* 2007. 109.00 *(978-3-540-71961-8(X))* Springer.

Krömer, Ralf. Tool & Object: A History & Philosophy of Category Theory. 2007. (Science Networks. Historical Studies). xxxvi, 367p. (C). 149.00 *(978-3-7643-7523-2(X)*, 376437523X) Birkhauser Boston.

Lambek, Joachim. Completions of Categories. 2007. (Lecture Notes in Mathematics Ser.). (ENG.). 80p. (Orig.). per. 39.95 *(978-3-540-03607-4(5))* Springer.

Lawvere, F. W., ed. Toposes, Algebraic Geometry & Logic. 2008. (Lecture Notes in Mathematics Ser.). 200p. pap. 39.95 *(978-3-540-05920-2(2)*, 3540059202) Springer.

Lawvere, F. William & Schanuel, Stephen H. Conceptual Mathematics: A First Introduction to Categories. 2nd ed. 2009. (ENG., Illus.). 408p. (C). pap. 63.00 *(978-0-521-71916-2(X))* Cambridge Univ. Pr.

Lazard, M. P. Commutative Formal Groups. 2008. (Lecture Notes in Mathematics Ser.). 240p. pap. 59.95 *(978-3-540-07145-7(8))* Springer.

Lipman, Joseph & Hashimoto, Mitsuyasu. Foundations of Grothendieck Duality for Diagrams of Schemes. 2009. (Lecture Notes in Mathematics Ser.). x, 478p. pap. 99.00 *(978-3-540-85419-7(3))* Springer.

Lurie, Jacob. Higher Topos Theory. 2009. (Annals of Mathematics Studies). (ENG., Illus.). 960p. (C). 115.00 *(978-0-691-14048-3(0))*; pap. 69.95 *(978-0-691-14049-0(9))* Princeton Univ. Pr.

Mac Lane, Saunders. Categories for the Working Mathematician. 2nd ed. 2010. (Graduate Texts in Mathematics Ser.). (Illus.). xii, 314p. pap. 74.95 *(978-1-4419-3123-8(6)*, 1441931236) Springer.

Mac Lane, Saunders, ed. Coherence in Categories. 2008. (Lecture Notes in Mathematics Ser.). 248p. pap. 59.95 *(978-3-540-05963-9(6)*, 3540059636) Springer.

Maclane, S. Reports of the Midwest Category Seminar Iv. 2008. (Lecture Notes in Mathematics Ser.). pap. 39.95 *(978-3-540-04926-5(6))* Springer.

Magid, Andy R. Module Categories of Analytic Groups. 2008. (Cambridge Tracts in Mathematics Ser.). (ENG.). 148p. pap. 33.99 *(978-0-521-09027-8(X))* Cambridge Univ. Pr.

Maher, Carolyn A., et al, eds. Combinatorics & Reasoning: Representing, Justifying & Building Isomorphisms. 2010. (Mathematics Education Library). (ENG., Illus.). 125p. 139.00 *(978-0-387-98131-4(4)*, 0387981314) Springer.

Makkai, M. & Reyes, G. E. First Order Categorical Logic. 2008. (Lecture Notes in Mathematics Ser.). 312p. pap. 59.95 *(978-3-540-08439-6(8))* Springer.

Manes, E. G., ed. Category Theory Applied to Computation & Control. 2007. (Lecture Notes in Computer Science Ser.). 260p. pap. 29.95 *(978-3-540-07142-6(3)*, 3540071423) Springer.

Markl, Martin, et al. Operads in Algebra, Topology & Physics. 2007. (Mathematical Surveys & Monographs). 349p. pap. 98.00 *(978-0-8218-4362-8(1))* American Mathematical Society.

Marquis, Jean-Pierre. From a Geometrical Point of View: A Study of the History & Philosophy of Category Theory. 2009. (Logic, Epistemology, & the Unity of Science Ser.). (ENG., Illus.). x, 310p. 219.00 *(978-1-4020-9383-8(7)*, 1402093837) Springer.

Michor, P. W. Functors & Categories of Banach Spaces. 2008. (Lecture Notes in Mathematics Ser.). 112p. pap. 39.95 *(978-3-540-08764-9(8))* Springer.

Petrich, M. Categories of Algebraic Systems. 2008. (Lecture Notes in Mathematics Ser.). 232p. pap. 59.95 *(978-3-540-07998-9(X))* Springer.

Pitt, D., ed. Category Theory & Computer Programming. 2007. (Lecture Notes in Computer Science Ser.). 532p. per. 59.95 *(978-3-540-17162-1(2))* Springer.

Pitt, David. Category Theory & Computer Science: Manchester, UK, September 5-8, 1989. Proceedings. 2007. (Lecture Notes in Computer Science Ser.). 376p. per. 44.95 *(978-3-540-51662-0(X))* Springer.

Pitt, David H., et al., eds. Category Theory & Computer Science: Edinburgh, UK, September 7-9, 1987. Proceedings. 2007. (Lecture Notes in Computer Science Ser.). 312p. per. 59.95 *(978-3-540-18508-6(9))* Springer.

Prest, Mike. Definable Additive Categories: Purity & Model Theory. 2011. (Memoirs of the American Mathematical Society Ser.). 109p. pap. 70.00 *(978-0-8218-4767-1(8))* American Mathematical Society.

Saavedra Rivano, N. Categories Tannakiennes. 2008. (Lecture Notes in Mathematics Ser.). (FRE.). 424p. per. 59.00 *(978-3-540-05844-1(3))* Springer.

Salmon, P. Categories & Commutative Algebra: Lectures given at the Centro Internazionale Matematico Estivo (C. I. M. E.) held in Varenna (Como), Italy, September 11-21,1971. 2010. (CIME Summer Schools Ser.). 338p. pap. 49.95 *(978-3-642-10978-2(0)*, 3642109780) Springer.

Seip, Ulrich. Kompakt erzeugte Vektorräume und Analysis. 2008. (Lecture Notes in Mathematics Ser.). (GER.). ix, 118p. 29.95 *(978-3-540-05909-7(1))* Springer.

Simmons, Harold. An Introduction to Category Theory. 2011. (ENG., Illus.). 236p. 90.00 ***(978-1-107-01087-1(X))***; pap. 29.99 ***(978-0-521-28304-5(3))*** Cambridge Univ. Pr.

Simpson, Carlos. Homotopy Theory of Higher Categories: From Segal Categories to n-Categories & Beyond. 2011. (New Mathematical Monographs). (ENG., Illus.). 652p. 105.00 ***(978-0-521-51695-2(1))*** Cambridge Univ. Pr.

Soille, Pierre. Morphological Image Analysis: Principles & Applications. 2nd ed. 2010. (Illus.). xvi, 391p. pap. 149.00 *(978-3-642-07696-1(3)*, 3642076963) Springer.

Strooker, J. R. Introduction to Categories, Homological Algebra & Sheaf Cohomology. 2009. (ENG.). 260p. pap. 36.99 *(978-0-521-09525-9(5))* Cambridge Univ. Pr.

Toën, Bertrand & Vezzosi, Gabriele. Homotopical Algebraic Geometry II: Geometric Stacks & Applications. 2008. (Memoirs of the American Mathematical Society Ser.). 224p. pap. 81.00 *(978-0-8218-4099-3(1))* American Mathematical Society.

Tutz, Gerhard. Structured Regression for Categorical Data. 2011. (Cambridge Series in Statistical & Probabilistic Mathematics Ser.). (ENG., Illus.). 576p. 90.00 *(978-1-107-00965-3(0))* Cambridge Univ. Pr.

Ulmer, Friedrich. Lokal präsentierbare Kategorien. 2008. (Lecture Notes in Mathematics Ser.). (GER.). 208p. pap. 29.95 *(978-3-540-05578-5(9)*, 3540055789) Springer.

Verity, Dominic. Complicial Sets Characterising the Simplicial Nerves of Strict [Omega]-Categories. 2008. (Memoirs of the American Mathematical Society Ser.). 184p. pap. 76.00 *(978-0-8218-4142-6(4))* American Mathematical Society.

Xue, W. Rings with Morita Duality. 2008. (Lecture Notes in Mathematics Ser.). 177p. pap. 39.95 *(978-3-540-55770-8(9))* Springer.

CATEGORIES (PHILOSOPHY)

see also Predicate (Logic)

Alvarez-Pereyre, F., ed. Categories et categorisation. une perspective Interdisciplinaire. 2008. (Societe d'Etudes Linguistiques et Anthropologiques de France Ser.). (FRE.). 358p. (C). pap. 94.00 *(978-90-429-2133-7(1))* Peeters Pubs. & Booksellers BEL. Dist: Brown, David Bk. Co., The.

Apolloni, David Bruc. The Self-Predication Assumption in Plato. 2011. (ENG.). 290p. 75.00 ***(978-0-7391-4484-8(7))*** Lexington Bks.

Aristotle. The Categories. 2007. (ENG.). 48p. pap. 8.45 *(978-1-60424-572-1(7)*, Book Jungle) Standard Pubns., Inc.

Beebee, Helen, et al, eds. The Semantics & Metaphysics of Natural Kinds. 2010. (Routledge Studies in Metaphysics Ser.). (ENG., Illus.). 250p. (C). 125.00 *(978-0-415-87366-6(5))* Routledge.

Benthem, Johan van, et al, eds. The Age of Alternative Logics: Assessing Philosophy of Logic & Mathematics Today. 2009. (Logic, Epistemology, & the Unity of Science Ser.). (Illus.). x, 350p. pap. 69.95 *(978-90-481-2485-5(9))* Springer.

Carr, Jeffrey. Aristotle's Use of Genos in Logic, Philosophy, & Science. 2009. *(978-1-4331-0321-6(4))* Lang, Peter Publishing, Inc.

Engelhardt Jr., H. Tristram & Pinkard, T., eds. Hegel Reconsidered: Beyond Metaphysics & the Authoritarian State. 2010. (Philosophical Studies in Contemporary Culture Ser.). 256p. pap. 199.00 *(978-90-481-4349-8(7)*, 9048143497) Springer.

Haaparanta, Leila & Koskinen, Heikki J., eds. Categories of Being: Essays on Metaphysics & Logic, 1 vol. 2012. (ENG.). 496p. 99.00 ***(978-0-19-989057-6(9))*** Oxford Univ. Pr., Inc.

Hannan, Michael, et al. Logics of Organization Theory: Audiences, Codes, & Ecologies. 2007. (ENG., Illus.). 384p. (C). 105.00 *(978-0-691-13106-1(6))* Princeton Univ. Pr.

King, Daniel. The Earliest Syriac Translation of Aristotle's Categories: Text, Translation & Commentary. 2010. (Aristoteles Semitico-Latinus Ser.). (ENG.). 330p. *(978-90-04-18660-6(3))* BRILL.

Klimmek, Nikolai F. Kants System der transzendentalen Ideen. (Kantstudien-Ergänzungshefte Ser.). (GER.). IX, 235p. 180.00 ***(978-3-11-182209-9(5))*** De Gruyter, Walter Inc.

Newton, Lloyd A. Medieval Commentaries on Aristotle's Categories. 2008. (Brill's Companions to the Christian Tradition Ser.). 448p. *(978-90-04-16752-0(8))* BRILL.

Pólos, László, et al. Logics of Organization Theory: Audiences, Codes, & Ecologies. 2007. (ENG., Illus.). 384p. (C). per. 37.50 *(978-0-691-13450-5(2))* Princeton Univ. Pr.

Studtmann, Paul. The Foundations of Aristotle's Categorial Scheme. 2008. pap. *(978-0-87462-761-9(3))* Marquette Univ. Pr.

CATEGORY THEORY (MATHEMATICS)

see Categories (Mathematics)

CATERERS AND CATERING

see also Breakfasts; Buffets (Cooking); Dinners and Dining; Luncheons; Menus; Stewards; Table

Allen, Graham. Catering & Food Services Recipe for Fifty: Kitchen Operation & Management & European & Asia Culinary. 2010. 428p. pap. 30.00 *(978-1-4269-1877-3(1))* Trafford Publishing.

Brown, Warren. World Recipes for a Home Catering Business. 2010. 80p. pap. 17.50 *(978-1-4092-7074-4(2))* Lulu Enterprises Inc.

Burton, Mary. Bravo! 2010 Event Resource Guide. 2009. 368p. pap. 9.95 *(978-1-884471-47-6(1))* Bravo Pubns., Inc.

Cavey, Kevin. The Republic of Paradise: A Fairytale of the Heavens & a Myth of the Gods. 2010. 312p. pap. 18.95 *(978-1-4251-8781-1(1))* Trafford Publishing.

Connolly, Kevin. The Last Irish Cowboy. 2010. (Illus.). 220p. pap. 14.49 *(978-1-4490-8652-7(7))* AuthorHouse.

De Herrera, Christine. I'm Cookin' on Your Range: A Guide to In-Home Personal Chef Services. 2008. (Illus.). 59p. spiral bd. 129.95 *(978-0-9801579-0-1(0))* I'M COOKIN ON YOUR RANGE.

Dodgshun, Graham, et al. Cookery for the Hospitality Industry. 6th ed. 2011. (ENG., Illus.). 704p. (C). pap. 89.95 *(978-0-521-15632-5(7))* Cambridge Univ. Pr.

Erdosh, George. Start & Run a Catering Business. 3rd rev. ed. 2010. (Start & Run ... Ser.). (ENG., Illus.). 248p. pap. 17.95 *(978-1-55180-736-2(X))* Self-Counsel Pr., Inc. CAN. Dist: Midpoint Trade Bks., Inc.

Foskett, David & Ceserani, Victor. Ceserani & Kinton's the Theory of Catering: Tutor Resource Dynamic Learning. 11th ed. 2007. (ENG.). 342p. pap., tchr. ed. 750.00 *(978-0-340-94176-8(6))* Hodder Education GBR. Dist: Oxford Univ. Pr., Inc.

—Ceserani & Kinton's the Theory of Catering. 11th ed. 2007. (ENG., Illus.). 720p. pap. 49.95 *(978-0-340-93926-0(5))* Hodder Education GBR. Dist: Oxford Univ. Pr., Inc.

Foskett, David & Paskins, Patricia. The Theory of Hospitality & Catering. 12th ed. 2011. (ENG., Illus.). 448p. pap. 47.00 ***(978-1-4441-2376-0(9))*** Hodder Education GBR. Dist: Oxford Univ. Pr., Inc.

George, Erdosh. Tried & True Recipes from a Caterer's Kitchen - the Secrets of Great Foods. 2008. 252p. 26.50 *(978-1-60693-198-1(9)*, Eloquent Bks.) AEG Literary Publishing Services, Inc.

Godsmark, C. & Godsmark, Carol. Starting & Running a Catering Business. 2nd ed. 2008. (Illus.). 264p. 26.00 *(978-1-84528-266-0(3))* How To Books GBR. Dist: Parkwest Pubns., Inc.

Godsmark, Carol. Starting & Running a Catering Business: How to Start & Manage a Successful Enterprise. 2006. (Illus.). 247p. per. 26.00 *(978-1-84528-090-1(3))* Parkwest Pubns., Inc.

Heigl, Jennifer. Career Diary of a Caterer: Thirty Days Behind the Scenes with a Professional. 2007. (Gardner's Guide Ser.). (ENG., Illus.). 150p. per. 11.95 *(978-1-58965-031-2(X))* Gardner, Garth Co., Inc. (GGC).

Liang, Xixiong. Aomen Yin Shi Ye Jin Xi. 2009. (CHI., Illus.). 87p. *(978-962-04-2893-7(5))* Joint Publishing Co.

Mattel, Bruce & Culinary Institute of America Staff. Catering: A Guide to Managing a Successful Business Operation. 2008. (ENG., Illus.). 368p. 45.00 *(978-0-7645-5798-9(X)*, Wiley) Wiley, John & Sons, Inc.

Norman, Phillip. Sex, Drugs & Hospitality. 2008. (Illus.). 92p. per. *(978-1-84748-101-6(9))* Athena Pr.

Rowley, Carla & Rowley, Lee. How to Open & Operate a Financially Successful Personal Chef Business: With Companion CD-ROM. 2008. (ENG.). 288p. per. 39.95 *(978-1-60138-141-5(7))* Atlantic Publishing Co.

Scanlon. Catering Management 3E with Buffets Set. 2011. 134.95 *(978-1-118-09922-3(2))* Wiley, John & Sons, Inc.

Scanlon, Nancy Loman. Catering Management. (ENG., 3rd rev. ed. 2006. Illus.). 304p. 75.00 *(978-0-471-42981-4(3))* 4th ed. 2012. 320p. 70.00 ***(978-1-118-09149-4(3))*** Wiley, John & Sons, Inc. (Wiley).

Shock. On-premise Catering: Hotels, Convention & Conference Centers, & Clubs with Buffets Set. 2011. 144.95 *(978-1-118-09926-1(5))* Wiley, John & Sons, Inc.

—On-premise Catering: Hotels, Convention Centers, Arenas, Clubs, & More 2E with Buffets Set. 2011. 134.95 *(978-1-118-09923-0(0))* Wiley, John & Sons, Inc.

Shock, Patti J. & Stefanelli, John M. A Meeting Planner's Guide to Catered Events. 2008. (ENG., Illus.). 324p. pap., instr.'s gde. ed. 45.00 *(978-0-470-12411-6(3)*, Wiley) Wiley, John & Sons, Inc.

Shock, Patti J., et al. On-Premise Catering: Hotels, Convention Centers, Arenas, Clubs, & More. 2nd ed. 2011. (ENG., Illus.). 496p. 70.00 *(978-0-470-55175-2(5)*, Wiley) Wiley, John & Sons, Inc.

Stott, Trish. Highly Recommended 2: Student's Book. 2010. (ENG., Illus.). 112p. pap. *(978-0-19-457750-2(3))* Oxford Univ. Pr., Inc.

—Highly Recommended 2: Teacher's Book. 2010. (ENG., Illus.). 64p. pap. *(978-0-19-457752-6(X))* Oxford Univ. Pr., Inc.

Stott, Trish & Pohl, Alison. Highly Recommended 2: Workbook. 2010. (ENG., Illus.). 64p. pap. *(978-0-19-457751-9(1))* Oxford Univ. Pr., Inc.

Strange, Frances. Don Strange of Texas: His Life & Recipes. 2010. 34.95 *(978-0-940672-81-9(2))* Shearer Publishing.

Thomas, Chris. Off-Premise Catering Management. 3rd ed. 2012. (ENG.). 512p. ***(978-0-470-88971-8(3))*** Wiley, John & Sons, Inc.

Vivaldo, Denise. How to Start a Home-Based Catering Business: *Become the Top Caterer in Your Area *Organize Menus for Parties, Corporate Events, & Weddings *Market Your Business on the Internet *Hire & Manage Staff *Handle Paperwork, Invoicing, & Taxes with Ease *Become an Eco-Friendly Caterer. 6th ed. 2010. (Home-Based Business Ser.). (Illus.). 256p. pap. 18.95 *(978-0-7627-5267-6(X))* Globe Pequot Pr., The.

—How to Start a Home-Based Personal Chef Business. 2nd ed. 2011. (Home-Based Business Ser.). (ENG.). 240p. pap. 18.95 *(978-0-7627-6366-5(3))* Globe Pequot Pr., The.

Weinberg, Joyce. Starting & Running a Catering Business: Insider Advice on Turning Your Talent into a Lucrative Career. 2007. (ENG.). 304p. per. 14.95 *(978-1-59869-384-3(0))* Adams Media Corp.

Wyatt, Rawdon & Riley, David. Leisure, Travel & Tourism: All You Need to Improve Your Vocabulary. 2nd ed. 2007. (ENG.). 80p. per. 14.95 *(978-0-7136-8736-1(3))* A & C Black GBR. Dist: Macmillan.

CATERINA, DA GENOVA, SAINT, 1447-1510

see Catherine, of Genoa, Saint, 1447-1510

CATERINA, DA SIENA, SAINT, 1347-1380

see Catherine, of Siena, Saint, 1347-1380

CATERPILLARS

see also Silkworms

Miller, Jeffrey C., et al. 100 Caterpillars: Portraits from the Tropical Forests of Costa Rica. 2010. (Illus.). 272p. pap. 26.50 *(978-0-674-03482-2(1)*, Belknap Pr.) Harvard Univ. Pr.

Shi, Zhe, et al. Plants vs. Caterpillars- Is Trypsin Inhibitor a Plant Defense Against the Larvae of the Forest Tent Caterpillar ? 2008. 88p. pap. *(978-3-639-03494-3(5))* VDM Verlag Dr. Mueller e.K.

Sodergaard, Jim. Moths & Caterpillars of the North Woods. 2009. pap. 18.95 *(978-0-9792006-6-3(0))* Kollath-Stensaas Pubs.

The Mailbox Books Staff. The Best of the Mailbox Themes: Caterpillars & Butterflies. 2010. 48p. 7.95 *(978-1-56234-919-6(8)*, Mailbox Bks., The) Education Ctr., Inc.

Wagner, David. Owlet Caterpillars of Eastern North America. 2011. (ENG., Illus.). 576p. pap. 35.00 *(978-0-691-15042-0(7))* Princeton Univ. Pr.

CATESBY, MARK, 1679-1749

American Museum of Natural History. The Natural History of America. 2008. 288p. 39.95 *(978-0-06-124207-6(1))* HarperCollins Pubs.

Frick, George Frederick & Stearns, Raymond Phineas. Mark Catesby: The Colonial Audubon. 2011. 162p. 41.95 ***(978-1-258-03897-7(8))*** Literary Licensing, LLC.

CATFISHES

Bussolini, Jake & Byrum, Mac. The Catfish Hunters: Techniques, Science, & Personal Bests. 2011. (Illus.). 340p. 23.04 ***(978-1-4670-7663-0(5))*** AuthorHouse.

Clarke, Simon. Catfishing. 2008. (ENG., Illus.). 192p. 49.95 *(978-1-84797-001-5(X))* Crowood Pr., Ltd. GBR. Dist: Independent Pubs. Group.

Finley, Lee. Catfishes: The Complete Guide to the Successful Care & Breeding of More Than 100 Catfish Species, 1 vol. 2009. (ENG., Illus.). 128p. pap. *(978-0-7938-1577-4(7))* TFH Pubns., Inc.

Kin, Sovann. Food Ingredients Affect off-Flavor Compounds in Catfish Fillets. 2009. 132p. pap. *(978-3-639-17214-0(0))* VDM Verlag Dr. Mueller e.K.

Ly, Xuan Anh. Vietnamese Catfish Industry. 2011. 68p. pap. ***(978-3-8443-0335-3(9))*** Lambert Academic Publishing.

Michaletz, Paul H. & Travnichek, Vincent H. Conservation, Ecology, & Management of Catfish: The Second International Symposium. 2011. (Illus.). xx, 780p. ***(978-1-934874-25-7(6))*** American Fisheries Society.

Sands, David. Fishkeeper's Guide to South American Catfishes. (Illus.). 117p. 10.95 *(978-3-923880-97-3(9)*, 16036) Tetra Pr.

Sayed, Alaa El-Din, et al. Effect of Ultraviolet Radiation on Catfish Embryos. 2011. 120p. pap. ***(978-3-8443-8894-7(X))*** Lambert Academic Publishing.

CATHARINA, SAINT, OF ALEXANDRIA

Logan, H. M. The dialect of the Life of Saint Katherine: A linguistic study of the phonology & inflections. (Janua Linguarum. Series Practica Ser.). (ENG.). 259p. 210.00 ***(978-3-11-195523-0(0))***; 135.00 ***(978-3-11-099962-4(5))*** De Gruyter, Mouton DEU. Dist: de Gruyter, Walter GmbH & Co. KG.

Marker, Gary. Imperial Saint: The Cult of St. Catherine & the Dawn of Female Rule in Russia. 2007. (Illus.). 327p. 42.00 *(978-0-87580-375-3(X))* Northern Illinois Univ. Pr.

Parker, Margaret. The Spanish Santa Catalina de Alejandría: The Many Lives of a Saint's Life. 2010. (Estudios de Literatura Medieval Ser.: 7). 208p. lib. bdg. 24.95 *(978-1-58871-174-8(9)*, Juan de la Cuesta-Hispanic Monographs) LinguaText, Ltd.

Sands, Tracey Renée. The Company She Keeps: The Medieval Swedish Cult of Saint Katherine of Alexandria & Its Transformations. 2009. (Illus.). xxii, 276p. *(978-0-86698-410-2(0))* Arizona State Univ., Arizona Ctr. for Medieval & Renaissance Studies.

Walsh, Christine. The Cult of St Katherine in Early Medieval Europe. 2007. (Church, Faith & Culture in the Medieval West Ser.). (Illus.). 244p. 124.95 *(978-0-7546-5861-0(9))* Ashgate Publishing Co.

CATHARINE, OF ARAGON, QUEEN, CONSORT OF HENRY VIII, KING OF ENGLAND, 1485-1536

Froude, J. A. Divorce of Catherine of Aragon the Story. 2006. pap. 38.95 *(978-1-4286-5316-0(3))* Kessinger Publishing, LLC.

Froude, James. The Divorce of Catherine of Aragon. 2007. (ENG.). 492p. 53.95 *(978-0-548-05029-3(5))* Kessinger Publishing, LLC.

Mattingly, Garrett. Catherine of Aragon. reprint ed. 32.50 *(978-0-404-20169-2(5))* AMS Pr., Inc.

Tremlett, Giles. Catherine of Aragon: The Spanish Queen of Henry VIII. 2010. (ENG., Illus.). 448p. 28.00 *(978-0-8027-7916-8(6))* Walker & Co.

C

Williams, Patrick. Catherine of Aragon. 2012. (Illus.). 512p. 39.95 **(978-1-84868-325-9(1))** Amberley Publishing GBR. Dist: Casemate Pubs. & Bk. Distributors, LLC.

CATHARINE HOWARD, QUEEN, CONSORT OF HENRY VIII, KING OF ENGLAND, D. 1542

Cato, Anne. An Unchaste Life: Memoir of a Tudor Queen. 2006. 248p. pap. (978-0-9781146-0-2(4)) Lyon-Rampant Publishing.

Denny, Joanna. Katherine Howard: A Tudor Conspiracy. 2008. (ENG., Illus.). 304p. per. 17.95 (978-0-7499-5120-7(6)) Platkus Bks. GBR. Dist: Independent Pubs. Group.

Smith, Lacey Baldwin. Catherine Howard: The Queen Whose Adulteries Made a Fool of Henry VIII. 2009. (Illus.). 240p. 29.95 (978-1-84868-214-6(X)) Amberley Publishing GBR. Dist: Casemate Pubs. & Bk. Distributors, LLC.

CATHARINE PARR, QUEEN, CONSORT OF HENRY VIII, KING OF ENGLAND, 1512-1548

James, Susan E. Catherine Parr: Henry VIII's Last Love. 2009. (ENG., Illus.). 352p. pap. 24.95 (978-0-7524-4853-4(6)); 336p. 34.95 (978-0-7524-4591-5(X)) History Pr. Ltd., The GBR. Dist: Independent Pubs. Group.

Muhlbach, L. Henry Viii & His Court. Pierce, H. N., tr. 2007. (ENG.). 404p. per. (978-1-4065-2188-7(4)) Dodo Pr.

Muhlbach, Louise. Henry Viii & His Court. 2010. 376p. 39.16 (978-1-169-33163-1(7)); pap. 27.16 (978-1-162-66569-6(6)); 48.95 (978-1-161-43434-7(8)) Kessinger Publishing, LLC.

Muhlbach, Luise. Henry Viii & His Court. 2008. 432p. 30.99 (978-0-554-38681-2(X)); 32.99 (978-0-554-29378-3(1)) BiblioBazaar.

Mühlbach, Luise. Henry Viii & His Court. 2009. 304p. pap. (978-0-217-22078-1(9)) Books LLC.

Norton, Elizabeth. Catherine Parr. 2011. (Illus.). 416p. pap. 19.95 **(978-1-4456-0383-4(7))** Amberley Publishing GBR. Dist: Casemate Pubs. & Bk. Distributors, LLC.

Parr, Katherine. Katherine Parr: Complete Works & Correspondence. Mueller, Janel, ed. 2011. (Illus.). 656p. 65.00 (978-0-226-64724-1(2)) Univ. of Chicago Pr.

Porter, Linda. Katherine the Queen: The Remarkable Life of Katherine Parr, the Last Wife of Henry VIII. (ENG., Illus.). 2011. 416p. pap. 19.99 (978-0-312-61696-0(1), St. Martin's Griffin) 2010. 400p. 27.99 (978-0-312-38438-8(6)) St. Martin's Pr.

Withrow, Brandon & Catharine Parr. Katherine Parr: A Guided Tour of the Life & Thought of a Reformation Queen. 2009. pap. (978-1-59638-117-9(5)) P & R Publishing.

CATHARISTS

see Albigenses

CATHARSIS

hler, Martin. Grenzen der Katharsis in den modernen Künsten: Transformationen des aristotelischen Modells seit Bernays, Nietzsche und Freud. Vöhler, Martin & Linck, Dirck, eds. 2009. Tr. of Boundaries of Catharsis in the Modern Arts. (GER., Illus.). XIV, 391p. 109.00 (978-3-11-020624-1(2)) De Gruyter, Walter Inc.

O'Shea, Stephen. The Friar of Carcassonne: Revolt Against the Inquisition in the Last Days of the Cathars. 2011. (ENG.). 304p. 28.00 (978-0-8027-1994-2(5)) Walker & Co.

Szczeklik, Andrzej. Catharsis: On the Art of Medicine. Lloyd-Jones, Antonia, tr. from POL. 2007. (ENG., Illus.). 174p. per. 13.00 (978-0-226-78868-5(7)) Univ. of Chicago Pr.

CATHARTICS

see Purgatives

CATHEDRAL CHURCH OF ST. PAUL'S (LONDON, ENGLAND)

see St. Paul's Cathedral (London, England)

CATHEDRAL OF SANTIAGO DE COMPOSTELA

see Catedral de Santiago de Compostela

CATHEDRALE D'AMIENS

Ruskin, John. Our Fathers Have Told Us. Part I. the Bible of Amiens. 2010. 336p. 68.50 (978-1-4092-2546-1(1)); (ENG.). pap. 50.95 (978-1-4092-2547-8(X)) Lulu Enterprises Inc.

CATHEDRALE DE CHARTRES

Adams, Henry. Mont-Saint-Michel & Chartres. 2008. 432p. 30.99 (978-0-554-31382-5(0)) 2008. 432p. 32.99 (978-0-554-22079-6(2)) 2007. (ENG.). 390p. pap. 25.99 (978-1-4264-1611-8(3)) 2007. (ENG.). 568p. pap. 32.99 (978-1-4264-1699-6(7)) BiblioBazaar.

—Mont-Saint-Michel & Chartres. 2007. 284p. per. (978-1-4068-4767-3(4)) Echo Library.

—Mont-Saint-Michel & Chartres. 2007. 324p. per. 19.99 (978-1-59547-788-0(8)) NuVision Pubns., LLC.

—Mont-Saint-Michel & Chartres. 2007. 452p. per. 14.45 (978-1-60424-143-3(8), Book Jungle) Standard Pubns., Inc.

—Mont-Saint Michel & Chartres - Henry Adams. 2007. 448p. pap. 14.95 (978-1-60424-414-4(3), Book Jungle) Standard Pubns., Inc.

Burckhardt, Titus. Chartres & the Birth of the Cathedral. 2010. (ENG., Illus.). 160p. pap. 24.95 (978-1-933316-77-2(2)) World Wisdom, Inc.

Sweeney, Jon M. Beauty Awakening Belief: How the Medieval Worldview Inspires Faith Today. 2009. 160p. pap. 20.00 (978-0-8192-2370-8(0), Morehouse Publishing) Church Publishing, Inc.

CATHEDRALS

see also Architecture, Gothic

also subdivision Churches under names of cities, e.g. New York (N.Y.)—Churches

Akinsha, Konstantin, et al. The Holy Place: Architecture, Ideology, & History in Russia. 2007. (ENG., Illus.). 224p. 38.00 (978-0-300-11027-2(8)) Yale Univ. Pr.

Aldsworth, F. & Shaw, Ian. Qasr Ibrim: The Cathedral Church. 2010. (Excavation Memoirs Ser.). (ENG., Illus.). 169p. (C). pap. 130.00 (978-0-85698-187-6(7)) Egypt Exploration Society GBR. Dist: Brown, David Bk. Co., The.

Andas, Margrete Syrstad, et al, eds. The Medieval Cathedral of Trondheim: Architectural & Ritual Constructions in Their European Context. 2007. (Ritus et Artes Ser.). (GER & ENG., Illus.). 375p. (C). 102.00 (978-2-503-52301-9(3)) Brepols Pubs. BEL. Dist: ISD.

Aubert, Marcel & Goubet. Cathedrales et Tresors Gothiques en France. 153.25 (978-0-7859-0344-4(5), F22241) French & European Pubns., Inc.

Beeson, Trevor. Window on Westminster. 336p. pap. 35.00 (978-0-334-02745-4(4)) Hymns Ancient & Modern Ltd GBR. Dist: Morehouse Publishing.

Crawford, John & Gillespie, Raymond, eds. St Patrick's Cathedral, Dublin: A History. 2009. (Illus.). 424p. 70.00 (978-1-84682-044-1(8)) Four Courts Pr. IRL. Dist: International Specialized Bk. Services.

Deguara, Aloysius. The Metropolitan Cathedral: Mdina. 2008. (Insight heritage Guides). 48p. (C). pap. 12.00 (978-99932-7-172-7(1)) Midsea Bks. Ltd. MLT. Dist: Brown, David Bk. Co., The.

Erlande-Brandenburg, Alain. The Cathedral: The Social & Architectural Dynamics of Construction. 2009. (Cambridge Studies in the History of Architecture Ser.). (ENG., Illus.). 404p. pap. 42.00 (978-0-521-11037-2(8)) Cambridge Univ. Pr.

Giurgola, Romaldo. Luminous Simplicity: The Architecture & Art of St. Patrick's Cathedral, Parramatta. rev. ed. 2006. (Illus.). 192p. (C). 99.00 (978-1-876832-83-4(5)) Macmillan Art Publishing AUS. Dist: Brown, David Bk. Co., The.

Hall, Edward. A Guide to the Cathedral Church. 2011. 164p. pap. 12.95 **(978-1-4585-0118-9(3))** Univ. of Michigan Library.

James, John. In Search of the Unknown in Medieval Architecture. 2007. (Illus.). 686p. (C). 300.00 (978-1-904597-36-0(X)) Pindar Pr. GBR. Dist: Brown, David Bk. Co., The.

Lloyd, Samuel Thames, 3rd, et al. Living Stones: Washington National Cathedral At 100. Babcock, Amy Carson, ed. 2007. (Illus.). 128p. 34.95 (978-0-9745299-3-6(1)) Washington National Cathedral.

Prentice, Sartell. The Voices of the Cathedral: Tales in Stone & Legends in Glass. 2007. (ENG.). 390p. 48.95 (978-0-548-03678-5(0)) Kessinger Publishing, LLC.

Prevas, Nicholas M. House of God... Gateway to Heaven: A Centennial History of the Greek Orthodox Cathedral of the Annunciation. 2007. (Illus.). 460p. 60.00 (978-0-9790235-0-7(5)) Greek Orthodox Cathedral of the Annunciation.

Puig, Jordi & Pla Boada, Ricard. Gaudi in the Cathedral of Mallorca, 1 vol. Vivas, Pere, ed. 2008. (ENG., Illus.). 144p. pap. 16.95 (978-84-8478-148-6(8)) Triangle Postals, S.L. ESP. Dist: Innovative Logistics.

Recht, Roland. Believing & Seeing: The Art of Gothic Cathedrals. Whittall, Mary, tr. from FRE. (ENG., Illus.). 392p. 2010. pap. 27.50 (978-0-226-70607-8(9)) 2008. 45.00 (978-0-226-70606-1(0)) Univ. of Chicago Pr.

Scott, Robert A. The Gothic Enterprise: A Guide to Understanding the Medieval Cathedral - With a New Preface. 2nd ed. 2011. (ENG., Illus.). 306p. pap. 21.95 (978-0-520-26999-6(3)) Univ. of California Pr.

Stanford, Charlotte A. Commemorating the Dead in Late Medieval Strasbourg: The Cathedral Book of Benefactors, 1320-1520. 2011. (Church, Faith & Culture in the Medieval West Ser.). (Illus.). 348p. 124.95 **(978-1-4094-0136-0(7))** Ashgate Publishing Co.

Sudek, Josef, photos by. Josef Sudek: Saint Vitus's Cathedral. 2011. (ENG., Illus.). 104p. 60.00 (978-80-7215-386-2(2)) TORST CZE. Dist: D.A.P./Distributed Art Pubs.

Tan Books, creator. St. Michael the Archangel. 2006. 60p. pap. 3.00 (978-0-89555-844-2(0), 2173, TAN Bks.) St. Benedict Pr., LLC.

Thaler, Manfred Josef. Das Salzburger Domkapitel in der Frühen Neuzeit (1514 Bis 1806) Verfassung und Zusammensetzung. 2011. (Wissenschaft und Religion Ser.). (GER.). 688p. 115.95 (978-3-631-60601-8(X)) Lang, Peter GmbH, Europaischer Verlag der Wissenschaften DEU. Dist: Lang, Peter.

Toker, Franklin. On Holy Ground: Liturgy, Architecture & Urbanism in the Cathedrals & the Streets of Medieval Florence. 2009. (Florence duomo Project Ser.). (ENG., Illus.). 324p. (C). 160.00 (978-1-905375-51-6(4)) Miller, Harvey Pubs. GBR. Dist: Brown, David Bk. Co., The.

Vroom, Wim. Financing Cathedral Building in the Middle Ages: The Generosity of the Faithful. 2010. (ENG., Illus.). 734p. (978-90-8964-035-2(5)) Amsterdam Univ. Pr.

CATHEDRALS—GREAT BRITAIN

Anonymous. Ely Cathedral. 2008. (ENG.). 144p. per. 20.75 (978-1-4375-2044-6(8)); 160p. pap. 21.75 (978-1-4375-1241-0(0)); 144p. pap. 20.75 (978-1-4375-1240-3(2)) BiblioBazaar.

Barrett, C. K. Barchester. (Illus.). 499p. 51.00 (978-0-281-04667-6(0)) SPCK Publishing GBR. Dist: Pilgrim Pr., The/United Church Pr.

Batsford, Harry & Fry, Charles. The Cathedrals of England. 2012. (ENG., Illus.). 224p. 24.95 **(978-1-84994-029-0(0),** Batsford, B. T. Ltd.) Anova Bks. GBR. Dist: Sterling Publishing Co., Inc.

Billings, Robert William. Baronial & Ecclesiastical Antiquities of Scotland, The - 2008. (Illus.). 792p. pap. (978-1-84530-058-6(0)) Grimsay Pr.

—The Baronial & Ecclesiastical Antiquities of Scotland (1901) 2008. (Illus.). 224p. pap. (978-1-84530-054-8(8)) Grimsay Pr.

Bond, Francis. The Cathedrals of England & Wales. 2007. 516p. per. (978-1-905217-82-3(X)) Mills, Jeremy Publishing.

Bünker, Michael & Binski, Paul. Peterborough Cathedral: Five Years after 22 November 2001. 2006. (ENG., Illus.). 128p. 50.00 **(978-1-903470-55-8(2))** Holberton, Paul Publishing GBR. Dist: Casemate Pubs. & Bk. Distributors, LLC.

Cannon, Jon & Williamson, Beth, eds. The Medieval Art, Architecture & History of Bristol Cathedral: An Enigma Explored. 2011. (Bristol Studies in Medieval Cultures Ser.: Volume 2). (Illus.). 376p. 95.00 (978-1-84383-680-3(7), Boydell Press) Boydell & Brewer, Ltd. GBR. Dist: Boydell & Brewer, Inc.

Corlette, Hubert C. The Cathedral Church of Chichester. 2008. (Illus.). pap. (978-1-84830-917-3(1), Wildhern Pr.) Echo Library.

Dalton, Paul, et al, eds. Cathedrals, Communities & Conflict in the Anglo-Norman World. 2011. (Studies in the History of Medieval Religion Ser.: Volume 38). (Illus.). 274p. 90.00 (978-1-84383-620-9(3), Boydell Press) Boydell & Brewer, Ltd. GBR. Dist: Boydell & Brewer, Inc.

Dimock, Arthur. Cathedral Church of Saint Paul an Accoun. 2006. pap. 21.95 (978-1-4286-6321-3(5)) Kessinger Publishing, LLC.

Ely Cathedral. 2008. (ENG.). 160p. per. 21.75 (978-1-4375-2219-8(X)) BiblioBazaar.

Hubert C. Corlette. Bell's Cathedrals: Chichester: Short History & Description of Its Fabric with An. I.t. ed. 2007. (ENG.). 144p. pap. 19.99 (978-1-4264-7000-4(2)) BiblioBazaar.

Hume, Peter. England's Cathedrals in Watercolour. 2007. (ENG., Illus.). 64p. pap. 15.00 (978-0-7459-5253-6(4)) Lion Hudson PLC GBR. Dist: Independent Pubs. Group.

Humphrey, Stephen & Morris, James. Churches & Cathedrals of London. 2nd ed. 2007. (ENG., Illus.). 160p. per. 24.95 (978-1-84537-337-5(5)) New Holland Pubs., Ltd. GBR. Dist: National Bk. Network.

Hutton, Edward. England of My Heart: Spring. 2011. 400p. pap. 34.75 **(978-1-178-53088-9(4))** 2008. 288p. 25.99 (978-0-554-32529-3(2)) 2008. 288p. 28.99 (978-0-554-23226-3(X)) 2007. (ENG.). 258p. pap. 21.99 (978-1-4264-3949-0(0)) 2006. 284p. pap. 23.99 (978-1-4264-4007-6(3)) BiblioBazaar.

—England of My Heart: Spring. 2009. (Illus.). 258p. pap. (978-1-4099-8558-7(X)) Dodo Pr.

—England of My Heart: Spring. 2010. 192p. pap. (978-1-4076-0655-2(7)) HardPr.

—England of My Heart: Spring. 2010. (Illus.). 156p. pap. 24.30 (978-1-153-60429-1(9)) General Bks. LLC.

King, Richard John. Handbook to the Cathedrals of England; Northern Division - Part. 2011. 272p. pap. 29.95 **(978-1-4460-8307-9(1))** Thorndike Pr.

Lawrence, David & Wilson, Ann, eds. The High Victorian Cathedral of St Fin Barre, Cork: William Burges in Ireland. 2006. (Illus.). 200p. (C). 65.00 (978-1-84682-023-6(5)) Four Courts Pr. IRL. Dist: International Specialized Bk. Services.

Lewis, Richard, et al. Wells Cathedral. 2006. (ENG., Illus.). 128p. pap. 29.95 (978-1-85759-370-9(7)) Scala, Editions FRA. Dist: National Bk. Network.

Maude, Thomas. Guided by a Stone-Mason: Exploring the Cathedrals, Abbeys & Churches of Britain. 2011. (ENG., Illus.). 176p. pap. 17.00 (978-1-84885-547-2(8), Tauris Parke Paperbacks) I. B. Tauris & Co., Ltd. GBR. Dist: Macmillan.

Pepin, David. Discovering Cathedrals. 7th ed. 2008. (Shire Discovering Ser.). (ENG., Illus.). 176p. pap. 17.95 (978-0-7478-0597-7(0)) Shire Pubns., Ltd. GBR. Dist: Random Hse., Inc.

Perkins, Thomas. The Cathedral Church of Saint Albans. 2007. (ENG.). 128p. 35.95 (978-0-548-03706-5(X)) Kessinger Publishing, LLC.

Reeve, Matthew M. Thirteenth-Century Wall Painting of Salisbury Cathedral: Art, Liturgy, & Reform. 2008. (Illus.). 230p. 80.00 (978-1-84383-331-4(X), Boydell Press) Boydell & Brewer, Ltd. GBR. Dist: Boydell & Brewer, Inc.

Scala Publishing. Chester Cathedral. 2010. (ENG., Illus.). 48p. pap. 10.00 (978-1-85759-591-8(2)) Scala, Editions FRA. Dist: National Bk. Network.

CATHER, WILLA, 1873-1947

Azzarello, Robert. Queer Environmentality: Ecology, Evolution, & Sexuality in American Literature. 2012. 160p. 89.95 **(978-1-4094-2664-6(5))** Ashgate Publishing Co.

Bims, Nicholas. Willa Cather. 2011. **(978-1-58765-826-6(7))** Salem Pr., Inc.

Cather Studies. Willa Cather & Modern Cultures. Reynolds, Guy J. & Homestead, Melissa J., eds. 2011. (Cather Studies). (ENG., Illus.). 328p. pap. 40.00 (978-0-8032-3772-8(3)) Univ. of Nebraska Pr.

Cather Studies Staff. History, Memory, & War. Trout, Steven, tr. 2006. (Cather Studies: Vol. 6). (ENG., Illus.). 316p. pap. 35.00 (978-0-8032-9464-6(6)) Univ. of Nebraska Pr.

Chinery, Mary C. Carnival in the Novels of Willa Cather: When the World Becomes Grotesque. 2011. 165p. 109.95 (978-0-7734-1550-8(5)) Mellen, Edwin Pr., The.

Cumberland, Debra L., ed. Willa Cather¿s the Song of the Lark. 2010. (Illus.). 306p. pap. 84.00 (978-90-420-3203-3(0)) Rodopi.

Durrans, Stephanie. The Influence of French Culture on Willa Cather: Intertextual References & Resonances. 304p. 119.95 (978-0-7734-5239-8(7)) Mellen, Edwin Pr., The.

Kephart, Christine. The Catherian Cathedral: Gothic Cathedral Iconography in Willa Cather's Fiction. 2011. (ENG., Illus.). 164p. 60.00 (978-1-61147-016-1(1)) Fairleigh Dickinson Univ. Pr.

Lee, Hermione. Willa Cather: A Life Saved Up. 2008. (ENG., Illus.). 416p. pap. 16.95 (978-1-84408-492-0(2)) Little, Brown Bk. Group Ltd. GBR. Dist: Independent Pubs. Group.

Murphy, John J. & Skaggs, Merrill Maguire, eds. Willa Cather: New Facts, New Glimpses, Revisions. 2008. (Willa Cather Ser.). (Illus.). 345p. 65.00 (978-0-8386-4135-4(0)) Fairleigh Dickinson Univ. Pr.

Nourse, Joan T. Monarch Notes on Cather's My Antonia & Other Works. (C). 3.50 (978-0-671-00604-4(5), Arco) Peterson's.

O'Connor, Margaret Anne, ed. Willa Cather: The Contemporary Reviews. 2009. (American Critical Archives Ser.). (ENG., Illus.). 576p. (C). pap. 56.00 (978-0-521-11209-3(5)) Cambridge Univ. Pr.

Palleau-Papin, Françoise, et al. Willa Cather Vol. 8: A Writer's Worlds. Murphy, John J. & Thacker, Robert, eds. 2010. (Cather Studies). (ENG., Illus.). 492p. pap. 40.00 (978-0-8032-3025-5(7)) Univ. of Nebraska Pr.

Perriman, Wendy K. Willa Cather & the Dance: A Most Satisfying Elegance. 2009. 75.00 (978-0-8386-4203-0(9)) Fairleigh Dickinson Univ. Pr.

Porter, David. On the Divide: The Many Lives of Willa Cather. 2010. (ENG., Illus.). 416p. pap. 29.95 (978-0-8032-3279-2(9)) Univ. of Nebraska Pr.

Porter, David H. On the Divide: The Many Lives of Willa Cather. 2008. (ENG., Illus.). 416p. 29.95 (978-0-8032-3755-1(3)) Univ. of Nebraska Pr.

Porter, David H. & Marks, Lucy. Seeking Life Whole: Willa Cather & the Brewsters. 2009. 45.00 (978-0-8386-4199-6(7)) Fairleigh Dickinson Univ. Pr.

Quirk, Thomas. Bergson & American Culture: The Worlds of Willa Cather & Wallace Stevens. 2011. (ENG.). 318p. pap. 40.00 (978-0-8078-9756-0(6)) Univ. of North Carolina Pr.

Reynolds, Guy J. & Reynolds, Guy, eds. Willa Cather as Cultural Icon. 2007. (Cather Studies: Vol. 7). (ENG., Illus.). 366p. pap. 35.00 (978-0-8032-6011-5(3)) Univ. of Nebraska Pr.

Russell, Danielle. Between the Angle & the Curve: Mapping Gender, Race, Space, & Identity in Willa Cather & Toni Morrison. 2009. 230p. 39.95 (978-0-415-80296-3(2)) Routledge.

Shively, Steven B. & Albertini, Virgil, eds. Teaching the Works of Willa Cather. 2009. (Illus.). 288p. 35.00 (978-0-9822730-0-5(2)); (ENG.). pap. 25.00 (978-0-9822730-1-2(0)) GreenTower Pr.

Skaggs, Merrill Maguire. Axes: Willa Cather & William Faulkner. 2009. (ENG., Illus.). 224p. pap. 24.95 (978-0-8032-2801-6(5)) Univ. of Nebraska Pr.

Stout, Janis P. Picturing a Different West: Vision, Illustration, & the Tradition of Cather & Austin. 2007. (Grover E. Murray Studies in the American Southwest Ser.). (Illus.). 352p. 40.00 (978-0-89672-610-9(X)) Texas Tech Univ. Pr.

Stout, Janis P., ed. & contrib. by. Willa Cather & Material Culture: Real-World Writing, Writing the Real World. 2012. (Amer Lit Realism & Naturalism Ser.). (ENG.). 256p. pap. 29.95 **(978-0-8173-5731-3(9))** Univ. of Alabama Pr.

Trout, Steven. Memorial Fictions: Willa Cather & the First World War. 2008. (ENG.). 225p. pap. 19.95 (978-0-8032-1837-6(0)) Univ. of Nebraska Pr.

Urgo, Joseph R. & Skaggs, Merrill Maguire, eds. Violence, the Arts, & Willa Cather. 2007. (Willa Cather Ser.). 320p. (C). 61.50 (978-0-8386-4157-6(1)) Fairleigh Dickinson Univ. Pr.

Van Ghent. Willa Cather-Aw V36. 2009. (ENG.). 48p. pap. 25.00 (978-0-8166-0321-3(9)) Univ. of Minnesota Pr.

CATHERINE, OF ARAGON, QUEEN, CONSORT OF HENRY VIII, KING OF ENGLAND, 1485-1536

see Catharine, of Aragon, Queen, Consort of Henry VIII, King of England, 1485-1536

CATHERINE, OF GENOA, SAINT, 1447-1510

Hugel, Friedrich Von. Mystical Element of Religion, 2 vols. 2009. (ENG., Illus.). Set. 888p. pap. 104.50 (978-0-227-17263-6(9)) Vol. 2. 422p. pap. 64.00 (978-0-227-17262-9(0)) Clarke, James Co., Ltd. GBR. Dist: Brown, David Bk. Co., The.

Von Hugel, Friedrich. The Mystical Element of Religion, As Studied in Saint Catherine of Genoa & Her Friends. 2008. 428p. 51.95 (978-1-4365-4011-7(9)) 2007. 432p. per. 36.95 (978-0-548-73060-7(1)) Kessinger Publishing, LLC.

Von Hugel, Friedrich, ed. Mystical Element of Religion, 2 vols., Vol. 1. 2009. (ENG., Illus.). 466p. pap. 64.00 (978-0-227-17261-2(2)) Clarke, James Co., Ltd. GBR. Dist: Brown, David Bk. Co., The.

CATHERINE, OF SIENA, SAINT, 1347-1380

Benincasa, Catherine. Letters of Catherine Benincasa. 2008. 328p. 29.99 (978-0-554-22446-6(1)) BiblioBazaar.

—Letters of Catherine Benincasa. Vida D. Scudder, tr. 2007. (ENG.). 294p. pap. 21.99 (978-1-4264-2347-5(0)); 324p. pap. 24.99 (978-1-4264-2395-6(0)) BiblioBazaar.

—Letters of Catherine Benincasa. 2006. pap. (978-1-4065-1217-5(6)) Dodo Pr.

—Letters of Catherine Benincasa, Saint Catherine of Vienna. 2007. 192p. per. (978-1-4068-4425-2(X)) Echo Library.

Benson, Robert Hugh. The History of Richard Raynal, Solitary. 2006. 136p. (ENG.). per. 10.95 (978-1-59818-997-1(2)); 24.95 (978-1-59818-564-5(0)) Aegypan.

—The History of Richard Raynal, Solitary. 2007. (ENG.). 108p. per. (978-1-4065-4838-9(3)) Dodo Pr.

—The History of Richard Raynal, Solitary. 2008. 258p. 42.95 (978-1-4365-8258-2(X)) 2007. (ENG.). 260p. per. 27.95 (978-0-548-79172-1(4)) Kessinger Publishing, LLC.

Brophy, Don. Catherine of Siena: A Passionate Life. (ENG.). 304p. 2011. pap. 14.95 (978-1-933346-37-3(X)) 2010. (Illus.). 24.95 (978-1-933346-28-1(0)) BlueBridge.

Catherine. Path of Holiness: Wisdom from Catherine of Siena. 2011. pap. (978-0-8198-5963-1(X)) Pauline Bks. & Media.

Catherine & Noffke, Suzanne. Catherine of Siena: An Anthology. 2011. *(978-0-86698-454-6(2))* ACMRS.

Catherine of Siena. Little Talks with God. Carrigan, Henry L., Jr., ed. 2007. 144p. per. 9.95 *(978-1-55725-531-0(8))* Paraclete Pr., Inc.

Hilkert, Mary C. Speaking with Authority: Catherine of Siena & the Voices of Women Today. 2008. 176p. pap. 15.95 *(978-0-8091-4586-7(3))* Paulist Pr.

McDermott, Thomas. Catherine of Siena: Spiritual Development in Her Life & Teaching. 2008. 368p. pap. 27.95 *(978-0-8091-4547-8(2))* Paulist Pr.

Il Processo Castellano: Santa Caterina Da Siena Nelle Testimonianze Al Processo Di Canonizzazione Di Venezia. 2009. (ITA.). 404p. *(978-88-88625-95-9(X))* Nerbini.

Ryley, M. Beresford. Queens of the Renaissance. 2009. 372p. 38.99 *(978-1-116-80850-6(1))*; 33.99 *(978-1-116-80851-3(X))*; pap. 32.75 *(978-1-116-80852-0(8))*; pap. 31.75 *(978-1-116-80853-7(6))* BiblioBazaar.

—Queens of the Renaissance. 2007. (ENG.). 412p. per. 34.95 *(978-0-548-78699-4(2))* Kessinger Publishing, LLC.

Siena, Catherine. The Letters of Catherine of Siena, Vol. 3. Noffke, Suzanne, tr. & intro. by. 2007. (Medieval & Renaissance Texts & Studies: 329). *(978-0-86698-377-8(5))* Arizona State Univ., Arizona Ctr. for Medieval & Renaissance Studies.

Sweeney, Jon M., notes. The Road to Siena: The Essential Biography of St. Catherine. 2009. (ENG., Illus.). 204p. (gr. 13). 21.99 *(978-1-55725-621-8(7))* Paraclete Pr., Inc.

Tylus, Jane. Reclaiming Catherine of Siena: Literacy, Literature, & the Signs of Others. 2009. (ENG., Illus.). 344p. 45.00 *(978-0-226-82128-3(5))* Univ. of Chicago Pr.

Undset, Sigrid. Catherine of Siena. 2009. 300p. (C). pap. 17.95 *(978-1-58617-408-8(8))* Ignatius Pr.

van der Plancke, Chantal & Knockaert, Andre. 15 Days of Prayer with Saint Catherine of Siena. 2009. (15 Days of Prayer Ser.). 144p. pap. 12.95 *(978-1-56548-310-1(3))* New City Pr.

Williams, Joan. Three Saints: Women Who Changed History: Genevieve of Paris, Catherine of Siena, Teresa of Avila. 2006. (Illus.). 159p. per. 9.95 *(978-0-87946-315-1(5))* ACTA Pubns.

CATHERINE, THE GREAT, 1729-1796

see Catherine II, Empress of Russia, 1729-1796

CATHERINE II, EMPRESS OF RUSSIA, 1729-1796

Bruess, Gregory L. Religion, Identity & Empire: A Greek Archbishop in the Russia of Catherine the Great. (East European Monographs). (Illus.). 308p. 45.00 *(978-0-88033-371-9(5))* Eastern European Monographs.

Dixon, Simon. Catherine the Great. 2010. (ENG.). 352p. pap. 16.99 *(978-0-06-078628-1(0)*, Ecco) HarperCollins Pubs.

Dukes, Paul. Catherine the Great & the Russian Nobility: A Study Based on the Materials of the Legislative Commission Of 1767. 2008. (ENG.). 284p. pap. 38.99 *(978-0-521-08400-0(8))* Cambridge Univ. Pr.

Johnson, Anthony P. The Original Diva: the Life & Times of Catherine II the Great. 2009. 75p. (ENG.). pap. 18.50 *(978-0-557-05754-2(X))*; pap. 19.70 *(978-0-557-05463-3(X))* Lulu Enterprises Inc.

Kaus, Gina. Catherine: The Portrait of an Empress. 2010. 424p. 41.56 *(978-1-163-36932-6(2))* Kessinger Publishing, LLC.

—Catherine: The Portrait of an Empress. Head, June, tr. 2010. 426p. 41.56 *(978-1-169-34087-9(3))* 2010. 426p. 51.95 *(978-1-161-68748-4(3))* 2007. (ENG.). 424p. per. 36.95 *(978-0-548-45426-8(4))* Kessinger Publishing, LLC.

—Catherine: The Portrait of an Empress. 2007. (ENG.). 422p. 51.95 *(978-0-548-05916-6(0))* Kessinger Publishing, LLC.

Massie, Robert K. Catherine the Great: Portrait of a Woman. 2011. (ENG., Illus.). 656p. 35.00 *(978-0-679-45672-8(4)*, Random House) Random House Publishing Group.

Munro, George E. The Most Intentional City: St. Petersburg in the Reign of Catherine the Great. 2008. (Illus.). 372p. 69.50 *(978-0-8386-4146-0(6))* Fairleigh Dickinson Univ. Pr.

O'Malley, Lurana Donnels. The Dramatic Works of Catherine the Great: Theatre & Politics in Eighteenth-Century Russia. 2006. (Performance in the Long Eighteenth Century: Studies in Theatre, Music & Dance Ser.). (Illus.). 242p. 110.00 *(978-0-7546-5628-9(4))* Ashgate Publishing Co.

Proskurina, Vera. Creating the Empress: Politics & Poetry in the Age of Catherine II. 2011. (Ars Rossika Ser.). (ENG.). 250p. 55.00 *(978-1-936235-50-6(1))* Academic Studies Pr.

Rounding, Virginia. Catherine the Great: Love, Sex, & Power. 2008. (ENG., Illus.). 592p. pap. 18.99 *(978-0-312-37863-9(7)*, St. Martin's Griffin) St. Martin's Pr.

—A Life of Catherine the Great: Love, Sex & Power. Date not set. mass mkt. *(978-0-312-99746-5(9)*, St. Martin's Paperbacks); pap. *(978-0-312-32888-7(5))* St. Martin's Pr.

Streeter, Michael. Catherine the Great. 2007. (Life× Ser.). (ENG., Illus.). 176p. per. 15.95 *(978-1-905791-06-4(2))* Haus Publishing GBR. Dist: Consortium Bk. Sales & Distribution.

CATHERINE DE MEDICIS, QUEEN, CONSORT OF HENRY II, KING OF FRANCE, 1519-1589

Costello, Louisa S. Catherine de Medici. (Bentley's Standard Novels Ser.: No. 112). reprint ed. 37.50 *(978-0-404-54512-3(2))* AMS Pr., Inc.

Scott, Virginia & Sturm-Maddox, Sara. Performance Poetry & Politics on the Queen's Day: Catherine de Medicis & Pierre de Ronsard at Fontainbleau. 2007. (Studies in Performance & Early Modern Drama Ser.). (Illus.). 278p. 114.95 *(978-0-7546-5839-9(2))* Ashgate Publishing Co.

CATHETERS

Aliot, Etienne, et al, eds. Catheter Ablation of Atrial Fibrillation. 2008. (ENG., Illus.). 280p. 185.95 *(978-1-4051-6349-1(6)*, Wiley-Blackwell) Wiley, John & Sons, Inc.

Bodenham, Andy. Central Venous Catheters. Hamilton, Helen, ed. 2009. (Wiley Series in Nursing Ser.). (ENG., Illus.). 266p. pap. 55.99 *(978-0-470-01994-8(8)*, Wiley) Wiley, John & Sons, Inc.

Davies, Alun H. & Gibbons, Christopher, eds. Vascular Access Simplified. 2nd ed. 2007. (Illus.). 246p. pap. 60.00 *(978-1-903378-52-6(4))* TFM Publishing Ltd. GBR. Dist: JAMCO Distribution.

Diggery, Robert C. & Grint, Daniel T. Catheters: Types, Applications, & Potential Complications. 2012. pap. *(978-1-62100-630-5(1))* Nova Science Pubs., Inc.

Heiser, Angela. Rat Jugular Vein & Carotid Artery Catheterization for Acute Survival Studies: A Practical Guide. 2007. (Illus.). 115p. spiral bd. 114.00 *(978-0-387-49414-2(6))* Springer.

Natale, Andrea & Jalife, Jose, eds. Atrial Fibrillation: From Bench to Bedside. 2008. (Contemporary Cardiology Ser.). (Illus.). 453p. 119.00 *(978-1-58829-856-0(6))* Springer.

Natale, Andrea & Raviele, Antonio. Atrial Fibrillation Ablation: The State of the Art Based on the Venicechart International Consensus Document. 2007. (ENG., Illus.). 104p. pap. 62.95 *(978-1-4051-8038-2(2)*, Wiley-Blackwell) Wiley, John & Sons, Inc.

Norell, Michael S., et al. Essential Interventional Cardiology. 2nd ed. 2008. (ENG., Illus.). 560p. 120.00 *(978-0-7020-2981-3(5)*, Saunders) Elsevier - Health Sciences Div.

Stoneham, Mark & Westbrook, Jon. Invasive Medical Skills: A Multimedia Approach. 2007. (ENG., Illus.). 160p. pap. 52.95 *(978-1-4051-5986-9(3)*, Wiley-Blackwell) Wiley, John & Sons, Inc.

Wilber, David J., et al, eds. Catheter Ablation of Cardiac Arrhythmias: Basic Concepts & Clinical Applications. 3rd rev. ed. 2008. (ENG., Illus.). 392p. 165.95 *(978-1-4051-3117-9(9)*, Wiley-Blackwell) Wiley, John & Sons, Inc.

CATHODE RAYS

see also Electric Discharges through Gases; Electrons; X-Rays

Anders, André. Cathodic Arcs: From Fractal Spots to Energetic Condensation. 2010. (Springer Series on Atomic, Optical, & Plasma Physics Ser.). (Illus.). xviii, 540p. pap. 179.00 *(978-1-4419-2711-8(5)*, 1441927115) Springer.

Anders, André. Cathodic Arcs: From Fractal Spots to Energetic Condensation. 2008. (Springer Series on Atomic, Optical, & Plasma Physics Ser.). (Illus.). 294p. 179.00 *(978-0-387-79107-4(8))* Springer.

Oks, Efim. Plasma Cathode Electron Sources: Physics, Technology, Applications. 2006. (ENG., Illus.). 181p. 190.00 *(978-3-527-40634-0(4)*, Wiley-VCH) Wiley, John & Sons, Inc.

CATHODIC PROTECTION

Chess, Paul M. & Palmer, Richard. Cathodic Protection of Steel in Concrete & Masonry. 2nd rev. ed. 2012. (ENG., Illus.). 336p. 180.00 *(978-0-415-39503-8(8)*, CRC Press) Taylor & Francis Group GBR. Dist: Taylor & Francis Group.

Holtsbaum, W. Brian. Cathodic Protection Survey Procedures. 2009. pap. *(978-1-57590-219-7(2))* NACE International.

Schweitzer, P.E., Philip A. Corrosion of Linings & Coatings: Cathodic & Inhibitor Protection & Corrosion Monitoring, 3 vols. 2nd ed. 2006. (Corrosion Engineering Handbook, Second Edition Ser.). (ENG., Illus.). 568p. 99.95 *(978-0-8493-8247-5(5)*, CRC Press) Taylor & Francis Group GBR. Dist: Taylor & Francis Group.

CATHOLIC ACTION

see also Christian Democracy; Laity

Cleary, Maureen. Management Dilemmas in Catholic Human Service: Health Care, Welfare, & Education. 2007. (Illus.). 304p. *(978-0-7734-5462-0(4))* Mellen, Edwin Pr., The.

Congregation for Institutes of Consecrated Life and Societies of Apostolic Life Staff & Societies of Apostolic Life Staff. Letter to the Bishops of the United States & Essential Elements in the Church's Teaching on Religious Life As Applied to Works of the Apostolate. 55p. pap. 0.50 *(978-0-8198-2323-6(6))* Pauline Bks. & Media.

Correa de Oliveira, Plinio. In Defense of Catholic Action. American Society for the Defense of Tradition Staff, tr. from POR. 2006. Orig. Title: Em Defesa da Acao Catolica. 422p. 25.00 *(978-1-877905-36-0(4))* American Society for the Defense of Tradition, Family & Property, The (TFP).

Gauvreau, Michael. The Catholic Origins of Quebec's Quiet Revolution, 1931-1970. 2007. (McGill-Queen's Studies in the History of Religion Ser.). (ENG.). 522p. (C). per. *(978-0-7735-3371-4(0))* McGill-Queen's Univ. Pr.

Issel, William. For Both Cross & Flag: Catholic Action, Anti-Catholicism, & National Security Politics in World War II San Francisco. 2009. (Urban Life, Landscape & Policy Ser.). (ENG., Illus.). 216p. 42.00 *(978-1-4399-0028-4(0))* Temple Univ. Pr.

Meyer, Bernard F. The Mystical Body in Action: A Workbook of Parish Catholic Action. 2011. 212p. 44.95 ***(978-1-258-05406-9(X))*** Literary Licensing, LLC.

Murphy, John Francis. The Moral Obligation of the Individual to Participate in Catholic Action. 2011. 270p. 47.95 ***(978-1-258-05276-8(8))*** Literary Licensing, LLC.

Seebold, Andrew L. Social Moral Reconstruction According to the Writings & Works of William Joseph Chaminade, 1761-1850. 2011. 196p. 42.95 ***(978-1-258-04255-4(X))*** Literary Licensing, LLC.

Wolpert, Andrew. Change in a Changing World: Golden Blade 1993. (Illus.). 160p. pap. 14.95 *(978-0-86315-150-7(7)*, 754) Floris Bks. GBR. Dist: SteinerBooks, Inc.

CATHOLIC APOSTOLIC CHURCH

Irving, Edward. Sermons & Lectures. Carlyle, M. A., G, ed. 2011. 650p. pap. 55.00 *(978-1-61097-236-9(8)*, Wipf and Stock) Wipf & Stock Pubs.

Narrative of Facts, characterizing the supernatural manifestations in members of Mr. Irving's congregation, & other individuals in England & Scotland; & formerly in the writer Himself. 2010. pap. 19.00 *(978-1-61143-193-3(X))* Gorgias Pr., LLC.

The Purpose of God in Creation & Redemption. 2007. (ENG.). 382p. 48.95 *(978-0-548-05165-8(6))* Kessinger Publishing, LLC.

Spruit, Herman Adrian. The Rule of Antioch. 3rd ed. 2010. pap. *(978-1-57733-255-8(5))*; E-Book *(978-1-57733-327-2(6))* Blue Dolphin Publishing, Inc.

CATHOLIC AUTHORS

see also subdivision Catholic Authors under names of literatures, e.g. English Literature—Catholic Authors

Burton, Patricia A. More Than Silence: A Bibliography of Thomas Merton. 2008. (ATLA Bibliography Ser.). (ENG.). 234p. 75.00 *(978-0-8108-6095-7(3))* Scarecrow Pr., Inc.

Kaczor, Christopher, ed. O Rare Ralph McInerny: Stories & Reflections on a Legendary Notre Dame Professor. 2011. (ENG., Illus.). 155p. pap. 18.00 *(978-1-58731-585-5(8))* St. Augustine's Pr., Inc.

McInerny, Ralph. I Alone Have Escaped to Tell You: My Life & Pastimes. 2011. (ENG., Illus.). 192p. pap. 22.00 ***(978-0-268-03523-5(7))*** Univ. of Notre Dame Pr.

McInerny, Ralph. Some Catholic Writers. 2007. 166p. 23.00 *(978-1-58731-777-4(X))* St. Augustine's Pr., Inc.

Robbins, Harold. The Last of the Realists: A Distributist Biography of G. K. Chesterton. 2010. (Illus.). 160p. pap. 22.95 *(978-1-932528-01-5(6))* IHS Pr.

CATHOLIC CHURCH

see also Anglo-Catholicism; Canon Law; Catholic Apostolic Church; Councils and Synods; Fasts and Feasts; Oxford Movement; Salvation Outside the Catholic Church

Aillet, Bishop Marc. The Old Mass & the New: Explaining the Moto Proprio Summorum Pontificum of Pope Benedict XVI. 2010. 109p. pap. 11.95 *(978-1-58617-362-3(6))* Ignatius Pr.

Alzati, Cesare & Guiver, George, CR. Ambrosianum Mysterium. 2009. 88.00 *(978-1-60724-394-6(6))*; 88.00 *(978-1-60724-397-7(0))* Gorgias Pr., LLC.

American and Foreign Christian Union. The Story of the Madiai; with Notices of Efforts Made, in Europe & America in Their Behalf Comp & Ed by the Secretaries of the American & For. 2006. 308p. per. 23.99 *(978-1-4255-2960-4(7))* MPublishing.

Ankerberg, John, et al. The Facts on Roman Catholicism. 2009. (Facts on Ser.). 96p. pap. 5.99 *(978-0-7369-2403-0(5))* Harvest Hse. Pubs.

Avila, St. Teresa of. Selected Writings of St Teresa of Avil: A Synthesis of Her Writings. Doheny, William J., ed. 2011. 480p. 58.95 ***(978-1-258-00713-3(4))*** Literary Licensing, LLC.

Bailey, James. Rethinking Poverty: Income, Assets, & the Catholic Social Justice Tradition. 2010. (Catholic Social Tradition Ser.). (ENG., Illus.). 216p. pap. 30.00 *(978-0-268-02223-5(2))* Univ. of Notre Dame Pr.

Bascio, Patrick & Caso, Adolph. Pedophilia: The Cancer Within. 2010. pap. *(978-0-8283-2201-0(5))* Branden Bks.

Basile, Alex. Finding Faith in a Godless World: A Catholic Path to God. 2008. *(978-0-8189-1265-8(0))* St Pauls/Alba Hse. Pubs.

Batson, Beatrice, ed. Shakespeare's Christianity: The Protestant & Catholic Poetics of Julius Caesar, Macbeth, & Hamlet. 2006. 150p. per. 29.95 *(978-1-932792-36-2(8))* Baylor Univ. Pr.

Beazley, Frank. The Gap in Catholic Healthcare Chaplaincy. 2011. 80p. pap. ***(978-3-8443-9560-0(1))*** Lambert Academic Publishing.

Being CRC: What It Means, Why It Matters. (Bibles Ser.). *(978-1-59255-205-4(5)*, 165440) Faith Alive Christian Resources.

Bell, Randall. QuickMarks: Roman Catholic. 2006. (Illus.). 6p. vinyl bd. 4.99 *(978-0-9765486-2-1(3))* Owners Manual Pr.

Belloc Hilaire. Europe & the Faith: Sine auctoritate nulla Vita. 2007. (ENG.). 186p. pap. 19.99 *(978-1-4264-2943-9(6))*; 198p. pap. 21.99 *(978-1-4264-2996-5(7))* BiblioBazaar.

Berrigan, Daniel. They Call Us Dead Men: Reflections on Life & Conscience. 2009. (Daniel Berrigan Reprint Ser.). 192p. pap. 22.00 *(978-1-60608-517-2(4)*, Wipf and Stock) Wipf & Stock Pubs.

Besant, Annie Wood & Besant, Annie. Five Sermonettes. 2011. 32p. 35.95 ***(978-1-258-00991-5(9))*** Literary Licensing, LLC.

Betterton, Robert J. Saving the Catholic Church While Sitting in a Pew. 2011. 260p. pap. 16.99 ***(978-1-61379-719-8(2))*** Xulon Pr., Inc.

Boora, Kulwant Singh. The Roman Catholic Church & Its Recognition of the Validity of Baptism in the Name of Jesus (Acts 2: 38) from 100 A. D. to 500 A. D. 2011. 112p. pap. 20.00 ***(978-1-4634-2906-5(1))*** AuthorHouse.

Boscani Leoni, Simona. Essor et fonctions des images religieuses dans les Alpes: L'exemple de l'ancien diocèse de Coire (1200-1530 Env.) 2008. 703p. pap. *(978-3-03911-167-1(1))* Lang, Peter.

Bossung-Winkler, Monika. Gottes Geist im Armenviertel: Protestantische Pfingstbewegung und Katholische Charismatische Erneuerung in Ecuador. (Europaische Hochschulschriften Ser.: Vol. 747). (GER., Illus.). 302p. 39.95 *(978-3-631-39545-5(0))* Lang, Peter Publishing, Inc.

Bouyer, Louis. Liturgical Piety. 2011. 294p. 48.95 ***(978-1-258-09148-4(8))*** Literary Licensing, LLC.

Brighenti, Kenneth, et al. John Paul II for Dummies. 2006. (ENG., Illus.). 364p. pap. 19.99 *(978-0-471-77382-5(4)*, For Dummies) Wiley, John & Sons, Inc.

Brown, Ralph & Sheehy, Gerard, eds. Canon Law: Letter & Spirit. (Illus.). 1088p. pap. *(978-0-225-66881-0(5)*, Burns & Oates) Continuum International Publishing Group, Ltd.

Buckenmaier, Achim. Universale Kirche vor Ort: Zum Verhältnis von Universalkirche und Ortskirche. 2009. (GER.). 444p. *(978-3-7917-2193-4(3))* Pustet, Friedrich GmbH & Co. KG.

Buckley, James, et al, eds. The Blackwell Companion to Catholicism. 2010. (Wiley-Blackwell Companions to Religion Ser.: 69). (ENG.). 544p. pap. 46.95 *(978-1-4443-3732-7(7)*, Wiley-Blackwell) Wiley, John & Sons, Inc.

Bunson, Mathew, ed. Our Sunday Visitor's Catholic Almanac. 2007. 640p. per. 6.95 *(978-1-59276-443-3(6))* Our Sunday Visitor, Publishing Div.

Burns, M. P. Credo: the Battered Bride: One Catholic looks at the Church he Loves. 2008. 348p. pap. 27.50 *(978-1-4092-1184-6(3))* Lulu Enterprises Inc.

—The Vision of Faith: Love & the Renewal of the Church. 2009. 221p. pap. 18.95 *(978-1-4092-7227-4(3))* Lulu Enterprises Inc.

Butler, Sheila. Roman Catholicism: Ethics. 2nd ed. 2009. 152p. pap. 36.50 *(978-0-340-98657-8(3))* Hodder Education GBR. Dist: Trans-Atlantic Pubns., Inc.

—Roman Catholicism - Ethics. 2009. (Illus.). 64p. pap. 20.00 *(978-0-340-98717-9(0))* Hodder Education GBR. Dist: Trans-Atlantic Pubns., Inc.

Byron, William J. Faith-Based Reflections on American Life. 2010. 208p. pap. 14.95 *(978-0-8091-4638-3(X))* Paulist Pr.

—Next-Generation Leadership: A Toolkit for Those in Their Teens, Twenties, & Thirties, Who Want to be Successful Leaders. 2010. 291p. pap. 25.00 *(978-1-58966-221-6(0))* Univ. of Scranton Pr.

Caron, Gerald. Mark in the Lectionary: An Ecumenical Guide to the Sunday Gospels. 2008. 208p. pap. 19.95 *(978-0-8091-4591-1(X))* Paulist Pr.

Carroll, John J. Engaging Society: The Sociologist in a War Zone. 2007. (Illus.). 330p. (C). 62.00 *(978-971-550-505-5(8))* Univ. of Hawaii Pr.

Chesterton, G. K. The Catholic Church & Conversion. 2006. 141p. pap. 11.95 *(978-1-58617-073-8(2))* Ignatius Pr.

Cifres, Alejandro & Pizzo, Marco, eds. Rari e Preziosi: Modern & Contemporary Documents from the Archives of the Holy Office. 2010. (ITA & ENG., Illus.). 208p. 56.95 *(978-88-492-1617-2(3))* Gangemi ITA. Dist: International Publishers Marketing.

Collins, Michael. The Vatican. 2011. (ENG.). 320p. 22.95 *(978-0-7566-8900-1(7))* Dorling Kindersley Publishing, Inc.

Collins, Paul, ed. From Inquisition to Freedom: Hans Kung & Others. 256p. pap. *(978-0-8264-5415-7(1))* Continuum International Publishing Group, Ltd.

Corden, James A. The Rights of Catholics in the Church. 2007. 145p. per. 14.95 *(978-0-8091-4433-4(6)*, 4433-4) Paulist Pr.

Crosby, Michael H. The Dysfunctional Church: Addiction & Codependency in the Family of Catholicism. 2011. 256p. (Orig.). pap. 28.00 *(978-1-61097-147-8(7)*, Wipf and Stock) Wipf & Stock Pubs.

Cullen. Catholic Social Justice: Theological & Practical Explorations. Hoose, Bernard & Mannion, Gerard, eds. 2007. (ENG.). 272p. 41.95 *(978-0-567-04542-3(0))* Continuum International Publishing Group, Ltd. GBR. Dist: National Bk. Network.

Czerwon, Ariane. Predigt gegen Ketzer: Studien zu den lateinischen Sermones Bertholds von Regensburg. 2011. (Spatmittelalter, Humanismus, Reformation Ser.). (GER.). 265p. 177.50 ***(978-3-16-150141-8(1))*** Mohr Siebeck GmbH & Co. KG DEU. Dist: Coronet Bks.

Davies, Michael. Pope Paul's New Mass. 2009. xxxi, 713p. *(978-1-892331-73-1(X))* Angelus Pr.

Davies, Wendy. Welsh History in the Early Middle Ages: Texts & Societies. 2009. (Variorum Collected Studies). (Illus.). 362p. 170.00 *(978-0-7546-5971-6(2))* Ashgate Publishing Co.

Dawes, N. Gamil. A Besieged Church: An Overview from the Pew of an Ordinary Catholic. 2006. 224p. per. 17.35 *(978-1-4120-9658-4(8))* Trafford Publishing.

del Rio Sanchez, Francisco, ed. Catalogue des manuscrits de la fondation Georges et Mathilde Salem (Alep, Syrie) 2008. (Sprachen und Kulturen des Christlichen Orients Ser.). (GER., Illus.). 352p. (C). 167.00 *(978-3-89500-628-9(9))* Reichert, Ludwig Dr. DEU. Dist: Brown, David Bk. Co., The.

Dellosso, Joseph. Anything but Catholic: An Archbishop - A Deacon - & Celibacy What Every Catholic Should Know. 2006. 13.00 *(978-0-8059-8328-9(7))* Dorrance Publishing Co., Inc.

Dianich, Severino. A Short Introduction to the Catholic Church. pap. 11.50 *(978-0-8189-9490-6(8))* St Pauls/Alba Hse. Pubs.

Doran, Robert M., et al. Early Works on Theological Method 1. 2010. (Collected Works of Bernard Lonergan Ser.). (ENG.). 688p. *(978-1-4426-4086-3(3))*; pap. *(978-1-4426-1020-0(4))* Univ. of Toronto Pr.

Dowling, John. The History of Romanism. 2009. 650p. pap. 39.53 *(978-1-150-31127-7(4))* General Bks. LLC.

Driver, Jack M. The Vatican. 2007. (Illus.). 192p. 12.99 *(978-1-904756-91-0(3)*, Chartwell) Book Sales, Inc.

Drossbach, Gisela & Schmidt, Hans-Joachim, eds. Zentrum und Netzwerk: Kirchliche Kommunikationen und Raumstrukturen im Mittelalter. 2008. (Scrinium Friburgense Ser.).Tr. of Centre & Network. (GER.). 396p. 147.00 *(978-3-11-019660-3(3))* De Gruyter, Walter Inc.

Edwards, Mark. Catholicity & Heresy in the Early Church. 2009. 208p. 99.95 (978-0-7546-6291-4(8)); pap. 29.95 (978-0-7546-6297-6(7)) Ashgate Publishing Co.

Eppstein, John. The Catholic Tradition of the Law of Nations. 2007. 110.00 (978-1-58477-822-6(9)) Lawbook Exchange, Ltd., The.

Equale, Tony. An Unknown God: Essays in Pursuit of the Sacred. 2009. 317p. (ENG.). (978-1-933567-27-3(9)); pap. 25.00 (978-1-933567-26-6(0)) Institute for Economic Democracy Pr., Inc.

Erlandson, Greg. En la Cabina de Votacion: Una Guia Catolica. Estenger, Vilma G., tr. 2008. 1p. 14.95 (978-1-59276-347-4(2)) Our Sunday Visitor, Publishing Div.

Ernst, Cornelius. Multiple Echo: Explorations in Theology. Kerr, Fergus & Radcliffe, Timothy, eds. 2007. 262p. pap. 28.00 (978-1-59752-992-1(3), Wipf and Stock) Wipf & Stock Pubs.

Fantoli, Annibale. Galileo & the Catholic Church: A Critique of the Closure of the Galileo Commission's Work. Coyne, George V., tr. 2008. (From vatican Observa Ser.). (ENG.). 36p. pap. 8.00 (978-88-209-6848-9(7)) Libreria Editrice Vaticana VAT. Dist: Chicago Distribution Ctr.

Father Leopoldo. (978-1-929291-11-3(6)) Roman Catholic Bks.

Ferrara, Jennifer & Sodano Ireland, Patricia. Women in Search of the Truth: Converts to Catholism Tell Their Stories. 2009. 299p. pap. 14.95 (978-1-59276-523-2(8)) Our Sunday Visitor, Publishing Div.

Fireside Catholic Publishing, creator. Thematic Plans & Activities for Catholic Youth: A Guide for Catholic Youth Ministers. 2007. 47p. pap. 19.95 (978-1-55665-051-2(5)) Fireside Catholic Bibles.

Fitz, Raymond, frwd. Black Belt Leader, Peaceful Leader: An Introduction to Catholic Servant Leadership. 2008. 140p. per. 19.95 (978-0-9768627-5-8(1)) Asogomi Publishing International.

Flinn, Juliana. Mary, the Devil, & Taro: Catholicism & Women's Work in a Micronesian Society. 2009. (C). 47.00 (978-0-8248-3374-9(0)) Univ. of Hawaii Pr.

From to Pope to Pope. Date not set. pap. (978-0-312-28319-3(9), St. Martin's Griffin) St. Martin's Pr.

Fusting, Daniel. The Catholic Church in the Third Millennium. 2011. 182p. pap. 14.99 (978-1-61215-838-9(2)) Xulon Pr., Inc.

Gendron, Mike. Preparing Catholics for Eternity. l.t. ed. 2008. 208p. per. 12.99 (978-0-9717009-3-2(1)) 21st Century Pr.

Giago, Tim. Children Left Behind: The Dark Legacy of Indian Mission Boarding Schools. 2006. (Illus.). 166p. per. (978-1-57416-086-4(9)) Clear Light Pubs.

Gibbons, Eric. Christian Voodoo: A Guide to Luck, Omens, Recipes for Homemade Miracles, & Exorcism. 2007. (Illus.). 128p. pap. 14.95 (978-0-7643-2566-3(3)) Schiffer Publishing, Ltd.

Gibson, Christine. Saints on Call: Everyday Devotions for Moms. 2011. (978-0-7648-2034-2(6)) Liguori Pubns.

Gill, Nicholas. Spiritual Prefect in Clerical Religious. 2006. pap. 21.95 (978-1-4286-5681-9(2)) Kessinger Publishing, LLC.

Gilsdorf, Richard W. & Beno, Patrick F. The Signs of the Times: Understanding the Church since Vatican II. 2008. (Illus.). ix, 542p. pap. (978-0-615-21961-5(6)) Star of the Bay Pr.

Glavich SND, Mary Kathleen. Handbook for Catholics: Our Catholic Tradition (Revised Edition) 2009. 3.50 (978-0-8294-2855-1(0)) Loyola Pr.

Glenn, Paul J. Apologetics: A Class Manual in the Philosophy of the Catholic Religion. 2011. 326p. 50.95 (978-1-258-06655-0(6)) Literary Licensing, LLC.

Goan, Sean. Let the Reader Understand: The Sunday Readings of Year A. 2007. (ENG.). 125p. pap. 18.95 (978-1-85607-590-9(7)) Columba Pr. IRL. Dist: Dufour Editions, Inc.

Goan, Sean & Hogan, Martin. Jesus Our Servant: Reflections on the Sunday Readings for Mark's Year. 2009. (ENG.). 147p. pap. 18.95 (978-1-85607-632-6(6)) Columba Pr. IRL. Dist: Dufour Editions, Inc.

Graham, William C. A Catholic Handbook: Essentials for the 21st Century. 2010. 101p. pap. 9.95 (978-0-8091-4639-0(8)) Paulist Pr.

Griffin, Susan M. Anti-Catholicism & Nineteenth-Century Fiction. 2009. (Cambridge Studies in American Literature & Culture Ser.). (ENG., Illus.). 296p. pap. 38.99 (978-0-521-09352-1(X)) Cambridge Univ. Pr.

Guindon, Kenneth. History Is Not Enough! 2007. 348p. per. 17.99 (978-1-60477-006-3(6)) Xulon Pr., Inc.

Hammonds, Richard. The Pentecostal Movement. 2009. 80p. pap. 11.99 (978-1-4389-5727-2(0)) AuthorHouse.

Hanna, Tony. With Respect: Authority in the Catholic Church. 2008. (ENG.). 95p. pap. 19.95 (978-1-85607-609-8(1)) Columba Pr. IRL. Dist: Dufour Editions, Inc.

Hederman, Mark Patrick. Dancing with Dinosaurs: A Spirituality for the 21st Century. 2011. (ENG.). 100p. pap. 17.95 (978-1-85607-735-4(7)) Columba Pr. IRL. Dist: Dufour Editions, Inc.

Helmick, Raymond G. Living Catholic Faith in a Contentious Age. 2010. (ENG.). 176p. 19.95 (978-1-4411-5219-0(9)) Continuum International Publishing Group, Ltd. GBR. Dist: National Bk. Network.

Henderson Davis, Claire. After the Church: Divine Encounter in a Sexual Age. 2007. 79p. per. 15.99 (978-1-85311-736-7(6)) Canterbury Pr.

Hession, Anne & Kieran, Patricia, eds. Exploring Theology: Making Sense of the Catholic Tradition. 2008. (ENG.). 320p. pap. 32.95 (978-1-84730-025-6(1)) Veritas Pubns. IRL. Dist: Dufour Editions, Inc.

Hickey, Liam. Finding Delight in People. 232p. pap. 16.50 (978-0-85439-588-0(1)) St. Paul Pubns. GBR. Dist: St Pauls/Alba Hse. Pubs.

Hughes, J. B., ed. The Register of Walter Langton, Bishop of Coventry & Lichfield, 1296-1321, 2 vols., Vol. 2. 2007. (Canterbury & York Society Ser.: Volume 97). (LAT & ENG.). 382p. 45.00 (978-0-907239-67-3(6)) Boydell & Brewer, Inc.

Indigo Custom Publishing, creator. Saint Joseph Catholic Church: A Living History. 2006. (Illus.). 192p. 39.95 (978-0-9776711-6-8(X)) Sphinx Publishing.

Inglessis, E.M.Jung-. Holy Year in Rome. (Illus.). 326p. pap. (978-88-209-2400-3(5)) International Scholars Pubns.

Jodock, Darrell, ed. Catholicism Contending with Modernity: Roman Catholic Modernism & Anti-Modernism in Historical Context. 2011. (ENG.). 360p. pap. 39.99 (978-0-521-17502-9(X)) Cambridge Univ. Pr.

Johnson, Angela S. Seasons of Faith: A Walk through the History of the Roman Catholic Diocese of Marquette 1900-2000. 2006. (Illus.). 341p. (978-0-9786970-0-6(6)) Roman Catholic Diocese of Marquette.

Jolly, Karen Louise. The Community of St. Cuthbert in the Late Tenth Century: The Chester-Le-Street Additions to Durham Cathedral Library A.IV.19. 2012. (Text & Context Ser.). 536p. 99.95 (978-0-8142-1181-6(X)); cd-rom 39.95 (978-0-8142-9282-2(8)) Ohio State Univ. Pr.

Kasomo, Daniel W. In-Depth Study of the Catholic Church. 2011. 188p. pap. (978-3-8443-1217-1(X)) Lambert Academic Publishing.

Kelly, Matthew. Rediscover Catholicism: A Spiritual Guide to Living with Passion & Purpose. 2011. 324p. 27.95 (978-0-9841318-9-1(2)) Beacon Publishing.

Kelly, Thomas Forrest. The Beneventan Chant. 2008. (Cambridge Studies in Music Ser.). (ENG.). 368p. pap. 53.00 (978-0-521-06597-9(6)) Cambridge Univ. Pr.

Kemper, Mary Ann. Flowers for the Triumph: Flower Miracles in the Life of the Catholic Church. 2009. 283p. pap. 15.95 (978-1-4327-4808-1(4)) Outskirts Pr., Inc.

Kennedy, Eugene. Blogging Towards Bethlehem: Discovering the Eternal in the Seasons of Ordinary Time. 2007. (Illus.). 320p. 25.00 (978-1-58768-042-7(4), 042-7, HiddenSpring) Paulist Pr.

Kessler, Mathew, compiled by. Living the Ten Commandments as a Catholic Today. 2009. 96p. pap. 10.95 (978-0-7648-1849-3(X), Liguori) Liguori Pubns.

Koncel, Ed. Views from the Pew, Pulpit & Women Religious. 2010. 166p. 29.99 (978-1-4535-3691-9(4)); pap. 19.99 (978-1-4535-3690-2(6)) Xlibris Corp.

Krall, Johannes. Kirchenvermögen - Nachhaltigkeit - Wirtschaftsethik: Rechtliche Gestaltungsmöglichkeiten bei der Verwaltung von Kirchenvermögen unter nachhaltigen und Wirtschaftsethischen Überlegungen. 2008. (Wissenschaft und Religion. Veröffentlichungen des Internationalen Forschungszentrums für Grundfragen der Wissenschaften Salzburg Ser.). (GRE.). 322p. 83.95 (978-3-631-59122-2(5)) Lang, Peter GmbH, Europaischer Verlag der Wissenschaften DEU. Dist: Lang, Peter.

Kubelbeck, William J. The Sacred Penitentiaria & Its Relations to Faculties of Ordinaries & Priests. 2007. (ENG.). 130p. 35.95 (978-0-548-04533-6(X)) Kessinger Publishing, LLC.

LaBelle, Jeffrey & Kendall, Daniel. Being Catholic in a Changing World. 2009. 88p. pap. 9.95 (978-0-8091-4611-6(8)) Paulist Pr.

Leedom, Tim C. & Churchville, Maryjane. The Book No Pope Would Want You to Read. 2011. (Illus.). 366p. pap. 19.95 (978-1-61759-029-0(0)) EWorld, Inc.

Liderbach, Daniel. Roman Catholic Belief Seeking Understanding. 2011. 88p. pap. 19.95 (978-1-4560-8310-6(4)) PublishAmerica, Inc.

Longenecker, Dwight. More Christianity: Finding the Fullness of the Faith - Expanded Revised Edition. 2010. 275p. pap. 16.95 (978-1-58617-342-5(1)) Ignatius Pr.

Lukefahr, Oscar. We Live: To Know, Love, & Serve God. 2010. (978-0-7648-1856-1(2)) Liguori Pubns.

Lundin, Roger. Believing Again: Doubt & Faith in a Secular Age. 2009. 320p. pap. 26.00 (978-0-8028-3077-7(3)) Eerdmans, William B. Publishing Co.

Lytton, Timothy D. Holding Bishops Accountable: How Lawsuits Helped the Catholic Church Confront Clergy Sexual Abuse. 2008. (Illus.). 304p. 38.50 (978-0-674-02810-4(4)) Harvard Univ. Pr.

Maher, Eamon. The Church & Its Spire: John Mcgahern & the Catholic Question. 2011. (ENG.). 218p. 44.95 (978-1-85607-728-6(4)) Columba Pr. IRL. Dist: Dufour Editions, Inc.

Makepeace, Francis. Spinning Wheels. 2010. 644p. pap. 37.95 (978-1-4461-5970-5(1)) Lulu Enterprises Inc.

Maquet, Julien. 'Faire justice' dans le diocese de Liege au Moyen Age (VIII-XII Siecles) Essai de droit judiciaire Reconstitue. 2009. (BIBLIOTHeQUE de la FACULTe de PHILOSOPHIE et LETTRES de L'UNIVERSITe de LIeGE Ser.). (FRE., Illus.). 832p. (C). pap. 130.00 (978-2-87019-290-0(8)) Droz, Librairie CHE. Dist: Brown, David Bk. Co., The.

March, Kenneth. Is God Calling His People to Leave the un-Holy Roman Catholic Church. 2010. 116p. pap. 11.99 (978-1-60957-417-8(6)) Xulon Pr., Inc.

Mathews, Constantine. Eastern Orthodoxy Compared: Her Main Teachings & Significan Differences with Roman Catholicism & the Major Protestant Denominations. 2006. (ENG.). 128p. pap. 12.95 (978-1-933654-01-0(5)) Light & Life Publishing Co.

Maye, Brian. The Search for Justice: Trocaire: A History. 2010. (ENG., Illus.). 376p. pap. 24.95 (978-1-84730-167-3(3)) Veritas Pubns. IRL. Dist: Dufour Editions, Inc.

McCarthy, David Matzko. The Good Life: Genuine Christianity for the Middle Class. 2006. (Christian Practice of Everyday Life (Wipf & Stock) Ser.). 176p. pap. 21.00 (978-1-55635-068-9(6), Wipf and Stock) Wipf & Stock Pubs.

McCarthy, David Matzko & Lysaught, M. Therese, eds. Gathered for the Journey: Moral Theology in Catholic Perspective. 2007. 356p. per. 28.00 (978-0-8028-2595-7(8)) Eerdmans, William B. Publishing Co.

McCloskey, C. John & Shaw, Russell. Good News, Bad News: Evangelization, Conversion & the Crisis of Faith. 2007. 134p. pap. 15.95 (978-1-58617-125-4(9)) Ignatius Pr.

McGlone, Mary M. & Lowery, Daniel L. A Basic Catholic Dictionary. 2011. (978-0-7648-2055-7(9)) Liguori Pubns.

McLaughlin, Gerald T. The Bishop of Lipoppo: A Fable. 2009. 248p. pap. 16.95 (978-1-4401-3465-4(0)) iUniverse, Inc.

McLees, Nectaria, ed. Bright Faith: Father Artemy Vladimirov Talks with Western Orthodox Christians. 2010. (Illus.). 191p. pap. 12.95 (978-0-916700-13-3(5)) Christ the Saviour Brotherhood Publishing.

McNamara, Denis R. Catholic Church Architecture & the Spirit of the Liturgy. 2009. (Illus.). xiii, 225p. (978-1-59525-027-8(1)) Hillenbrand Bks.

Meara, David. Pugin & Revival of Memorial Brasse. (Illus.). 192p. pap. (978-0-7201-2171-1(X), Burns & Oates) Continuum International Publishing Group, Ltd.

Merkur, Dan. Crucified with Christ: Meditation on the Passion, Mystical Death, & the Medieval Invention of Psychotherapy. 2008. pap. 24.95 (978-0-7914-7106-7(3)) State Univ. of New York Pr.

Merton, T. Dos Semanas en Alaska. (SPA.). 242p. 9.50 (978-84-89920-88-0(5), 86922) Ediciones Oniro S.A. ESP. Dist: Lectorum Pubns., Inc.

Milfull, Inge B. The Hymns of the Anglo-Saxon Church: A Study & Edition of the 'Durham Hymnal' 2007. (Cambridge Studies in Anglo-Saxon England Ser.). (ENG.). 512p. pap. 84.00 (978-0-521-03081-6(1)) Cambridge Univ. Pr.

Miller, J. Bleecker. Leo Xiii & Modern Civilization. 2007. (ENG.). 196p. 37.95 (978-0-548-14614-9(4)) 2006. pap. 22.95 (978-1-4286-5946-9(3)) Kessinger Publishing, LLC.

—Leo Xiii & Modern Civilization. 2008. 192p. pap. (978-1-4086-7698-1(2)) Read Bks.

Montez, Lola. Lectures of Lola Montez Including Her Autobiography. 2006. 304p. per. 23.99 (978-1-4255-2943-7(7)) MPublishing.

Morgan, Barbara, et al. Catechism of the Catholic Church & the Craft of Catechesis. 2008. 158p. pap. 15.95 (978-1-58617-221-3(2)) Ignatius Pr.

Mullins, Patrick. What We Believe: Understanding the Faith That We Share with the Saints. 2010. (ENG.). 271p. pap. 23.95 (978-1-84730-214-4(9)) Veritas Pubns. IRL. Dist: Dufour Editions, Inc.

Munoz, Hector. Alabanzas a la Iglesia (Praises to the Church) (SPA.). 144p. 2.95 (978-958-692-010-0(0)) Sociedad de San Pablo COL. Dist: St Pauls/Alba Hse. Pubs.

Naaman, Paul. The Maronites: The Origins of an Antiochene Church: A Historical & Geographical Study of the Fifth to Seventh Centuries. 2011. E-Book (978-0-87907-794-5(8)) Cistercian Pubns., Inc.

Neuhaus, Richard John. Appointment in Rome: The Church in America Awakening. 2011. (ENG.). 184p. pap. 19.95 (978-0-8245-2697-9(X)) Crossroad Publishing Co., The.

Neuhaus, Richard John. Catholic Matters: Confusion, Controversy, & the Splendor of Truth. 2007. (ENG.). 272p. per. 15.95 (978-0-465-04936-3(2)) Basic Bks.

Nolan, C. D. Betrayal: A Fiction Novel. 2008. 260p. 26.95 (978-0-595-51663-6(7)); pap. 16.95 (978-0-595-52601-7(2)) iUniverse, Inc.

O'Hagan, Thomas. Essays on Catholic Life. 2010. 174p. pap. 21.75 (978-1-141-06461-8(8)) BiblioBazaar.

—Essays on Catholic Life. 2009. 66p. pap. 14.14 (978-1-151-67770-9(1)) General Bks. LLC.

—Essays on Catholic Life. 2007. (ENG.). 168p. 36.95 (978-0-548-09114-2(5)) Kessinger Publishing, LLC.

—Essays on Catholic Life. 2008. (ENG.). 168p. per. (978-1-4086-6184-0(5)) Read Bks.

O'Hanlon, John. Life & Scenery in Missouri: Reminiscences of a Missionary Priest. (Illus.). 293p. reprint ed. lib. bdg. 98.00 (978-0-7222-0705-5(0)) Library Reprints, Inc.

O'Keefe, Mark. Deciding to Be Christian: A Daily Commitment. 2012. (978-0-7648-2118-9(0)) Liguori Pubns.

Osborne, Kenan B. The Permanent Diaconate: Its History & Place in the Sacrament of Orders. 2007. 224p. pap. 18.95 (978-0-8091-4448-8(4), 4448-8) Paulist Pr.

Pable, Martin. Reclaim the Fire: A Parish Guide to Evangelization. 2009. (Illus.). 168p. pap. 12.95 (978-0-87946-395-3(3)) ACTA Pubns.

Paris, Edmond. Genocide in Satellite Croatia, 1941-1945: A Record of Racial & Religious Persecutions & Massacres. Perkins, Lois, tr. 2011. 324p. 50.95 (978-1-258-05936-1(3)) Literary Licensing, LLC.

Pearce, Joseph. The Quest for Shakespeare. 2008. 216p. 21.95 (978-1-58617-224-4(7)) Ignatius Pr.

Pedone, F. Stephen & Donlon, James I., eds. Roman Replies & CLSA Advisory Opinions, 1998. viii, 114p. pap. 14.00 (978-0-943616-82-7(4)) Canon Law Society of America.

Pellitero, Ramiro, et al. La Iglesia Como Familia de Dios. 2010. (SPA.). 263p. (978-84-321-3792-1(8)) Rialp, Ediciones, S.A.

Peltzer, Jörg & Peltzer, Jörg Henning. Canon Law, Careers & Conquest: Episcopal Elections in Normandy & Greater Anjou, C.1140-C.1230. 2007. (Cambridge Studies in Medieval Life & Thought). (ENG., Illus.). 352p. 130.00 (978-0-521-88062-6(9)) Cambridge Univ. Pr.

Pennock, Michael. This Is Our Church: A History of Catholicism. 2007. (Illus.). 352p. stu. ed., per. 19.95 (978-1-59471-075-9(9)); 416p. pap., stu. ed. 19.95 (978-1-59471-169-5(0)) Ave Maria Pr.

Peri, Paul F. Catholic Parish Administration: A Handbook. 2012. viii, 72p. (978-1-61643-092-4(3)); 80p. pap. 9.95 (978-0-8091-4752-6(1)) Paulist Pr.

Perry, Alan R. The Don Camillo Stories of Giovannino Guareschi: A Humorist Portrays the Sacred. 2008. (Toronto Italian Studies). (ENG., Illus.). 224p. (978-0-8020-9756-9(1)) Univ. of Toronto Pr.

Pratt, Douglas. The Church & Other Faiths: The World Council of Churches, the Vatican, & Interreligional Dialogue. 2010. (ENG.). 386p. pap. (978-3-0343-0454-2(4)) Lang, Peter.

Quispel, Gilles. Gnostica, Judaica, Catholica. 2008. (Nag Hammadi & Manichaean Studies). (GER & ENG.). 900p. (978-90-04-13945-9(1)) BRILL.

Ratzinger, Joseph, et al. Gottes Projekt: Nachdenken über Schöpfung und Kirche. 2009. (GER.). 140p. (978-3-7917-2174-3(7)) Pustet, Friedrich GmbH & Co. KG.

Rausch, Thomas P. Being Catholic in a Culture of Choice. 2006. (Michael Glazier Bks.). 123p. per. 19.95 (978-0-8146-5984-7(5)) Liturgical Pr.

Resines, Luis & Resines Llorente, Luis. De la Fe Maltratada a la Fe Bien Tratada: Lo Peor y lo Mejor de Los Catecismos Españoles. 2009. (SPA.). 254p. (978-84-288-2146-9(1)) Promoción Popular Cristiana.

Rigsby, Sandy & Mason, Steve. Exploring the Sunday Lectionary: A Teenager's Guide to the Readings - Cycle A. 2007. 208p. pap. 19.95 (978-0-8091-9583-1(6), 9583-1) Paulist Pr.

Rojas, Ronald R. A Relational Identity for Deacon Spirituality. 2009. 256p. pap. 15.50 (978-1-59330-616-8(4)) Aventine Pr.

Roman Catholicism. 2010. pap. 18.52 (978-1-61143-182-7(4)) Gorgias Pr., LLC.

Saint Francis. The Words of Saint Francis, from His Works & the Early Legends. 2007. 108p. per. 14.95 (978-1-60206-394-5(X)) Cosimo, Inc.

Salvatore, Nick, ed. Faith & the Historian: Catholic Perspectives. 2007. (Illus.). 208p. per. 26.00 (978-0-252-07382-3(7)) Univ. of Illinois Pr.

Salzmann, Andrew & Narendran, Sabitha. Catholic & Loving It: Traditions for a New Generation. annot. ed. 2007. 178p. per. (978-0-86716-807-5(2)) Franciscan Media.

Sampson, Holden E. Progressive Redemption: The Catholic Church its Functions & Offices in the World. 2007. 642p. 60.95 (978-0-548-05459-8(2)) Kessinger Publishing, LLC.

Scaperlanda, Michael A. & Collett, Teresa S. Recovering Self-Evident Truths: Catholic Perspectives on American Law. 2007. 403p. per. 34.95 (978-0-8132-1482-5(3)) Catholic Univ. of America Pr.

Schillebeeckx, Edward. Revelation & Theology: Schillebeeckx Collected Works 2. 2013. (ENG.). 352p. 110.00 (978-0-567-65308-6(0), T&T Clark Int'l) Continuum International Publishing Group, Ltd. GBR. Dist: National Bk. Network.

—World & Church: Schillebeeckx Collected Works 4. 2013. (ENG.). 272p. 110.00 (978-0-567-05422-7(5), T&T Clark Int'l) Continuum International Publishing Group, Ltd. GBR. Dist: National Bk. Network.

Scholl, Edith. Words for the Journey: A Monastic Vocabulary. 2009. (LAT & ENG.). pap. (978-0-87907-021-2(8)) Cistercian Pubns., Inc.

Scott, David. The Catholic Passion: Rediscovering the Power & Beauty of the Faith. 2007. (ENG.). 280p. pap. 12.95 (978-0-8294-2477-5(6)) Loyola Pr.

Scott, James Brown. The Catholic Conception of International Law: Francisco de Vitoria, Founder of the Modern Law of Nations, Francisco Suarez, Founder of the Modern Philosophy of Law in General & in Particular of the Laws of Nations: A Critical Examination & a Justified Appreciation. 2007. 125.00 (978-1-58477-821-9(0)) Lawbook Exchange, Ltd., The.

Secrecy, Sophistry & Gay Sex in the Catholic Church. 2011. 254p. pap. 19.95 (978-1-61098-212-2(6)) Nazca Plains Corp., The.

Shedd, William G. T. Discourses & Essays. 2007. (ENG.). 326p. 45.95 (978-0-548-17247-6(1)); pap. 30.95 (978-1-4304-7073-1(9)) Kessinger Publishing, LLC.

Sicard, Augustin. The Soul of the Sacred Liturgy. Benson, R. J. & Raemers, Sydney Albert, trs. 2011. 112p. 39.95 (978-1-258-04994-2(5)) Literary Licensing, LLC.

Singer-Towns, Brian, ed. Catholic Youth Bible. 2007. (Illus.). 1600p. (YA). lthr. 39.95 (978-0-88489-664-7(1)); lthr. 45.95 (978-0-88489-663-0(3)) St. Mary's Pr.

Skrocki, Michael. Historical Roots of the Extraordinary Form of Marriage in the 1990 Codex Canonum Ecclesiarum Orientalium. 2008. 252p. pap. (978-3-639-04022-7(8)) VDM Verlag Dr. Mueller e.K.

Smith, Claire Furia. Can I Confess By E-Mail? What Catholics May & May Not Do. 2010. (978-0-8189-1312-9(6)) St Pauls/Alba Hse. Pubs.

Staley, Vernon. The Catholic Religion. 2009. 254p. pap. (978-0-217-34474-6(7)); 228p. pap. (978-1-4589-7819-6(2)) Books LLC.

Stanford, Peter. Catholicism — an Introduction: A Teach Yourself Guide. 2nd ed. 2010. (Teach Yourself: Reference Ser.). (ENG.). 208p. pap. 15.00 (978-0-07-174754-7(0), 0071747540) McGraw-Hill Cos., The.

Stanley, Joseph. Dreaming of the Future of a Failing Church. 2011. 244p. pap. 12.99 (978-1-61667-296-6(X)) Raider Publishing International.

Staples, Tim. Nuts & Bolts: A Practical, How to Guide for explaining & defending the Catholic Faith. 2007. 128p. pap. (978-0-9642610-2-0(2)) Basilica Pr.

Summitt, Margaret. Catholic Literature: An Introduction. 2007. 252p. pap. 12.95 (978-0-9791600-3-5(0)) Tumblar Hse.

Taylor, John. Catholics along the Rio Grande. 2011. (Images of America Ser.). (ENG., Illus.). 128p. pap. 21.99 (978-0-7385-7975-7(0)) Arcadia Publishing.

Turner, Paul. When Other Christians Become Catholic. 2007. (Illus.). 172p. per. 23.95 (978-0-8146-6216-8(1)) Liturgical Pr.

Tyrrell, George. Essays on Faith & Immortality. 2009. 142p. pap. (978-0-217-47269-2(9)) Books LLC.

—The Faith of the Millions. 2008. 240p. 27.99 (978-0-554-23236-2(7)) 2008. 240p. 24.99 (978-0-554-32539-2(X)) 2007. (ENG.). 442p. pap. 28.99 (978-1-4264-4017-5(0)) BiblioBazaar.

—The Faith of the Millions: Second Series. l.t. ed. 2007. (ENG.). 210p. pap. 20.99 (978-1-4264-3959-9(8)) BiblioBazaar.

Wagner, Abp Wynn. A Pilgrims Guide to the Old Catholic Church. 2009. 124p. pap. 14.99 *(978-0-557-21617-8(6))* Lulu Enterprises Inc.
Wagner, Nick. The Way of Faith: A Field Guide for the RCIA Process. 2008. 200p. pap. *(978-1-58595-710-1(0))* Twenty-Third Pubns./Bayard.
Wallace, Peter John. A Roman Catholicism. Bartlett, Cynthia, ed. 2009. (ENG., Illus.). pap., stu. ed. 37.50 *(978-1-4085-0457-4(X))* Nelson Thornes Ltd. GBR. Dist: Trans-Atlantic Pubns., Inc.
Walsh, James J. Catholic Churchmen in Science. 2007. (ENG.). 252p. per. *(978-1-4067-5734-7(9))* Read Bks.
Warneka, Timothy. Black Belt Leader, Peaceful Leader: An Introduction to Catholic Servant Leadership. 2008. 144p. 29.95 net. *(978-0-9768627-9-6(4))* Asogomi Publishing International.
Watton, Victor & Kolka, Diane. Catholic Christianity for Edexcel Second Edition. 2nd rev. ed. 2007. (Illus.). 240p. pap. 47.50 *(978-0-340-92933-9(2)*, Hodder Murray) Hodder Education GBR. Dist: Trans-Atlantic Pubns., Inc.
Watton, Victor W. Catholic Christianity for Edexcel: Revision Guide 2ed. 2nd ed. 2007. (Illus.). 116p. pap. 17.95 *(978-0-340-93977-2(X)*, Hodder Murray) Hodder Education GBR. Dist: Trans-Atlantic Pubns., Inc.
Weigel, George. God's Choice: Pope Benedict XVI & the Future of the Catholic Church. annot. ed. 2006. 320p. pap. 16.95 *(978-0-06-093759-1(9)*, HarperPerennial) HarperCollins Pubs.
The Well & the Shallows. 2007. 203p. pap. 14.95 *(978-1-58617-126-1(7))* Ignatius Pr.
Wilson, Todd. John Henry Newman: Prayers, Poems, Meditations. 2007. pap. *(978-0-281-05973-7(X))* SPCK Publishing.
Wood, Regina Beauvais. A Reply to Once a Catholic. 2007. 100p. per. 10.00 *(978-1-4257-4124-2(X))* Xlibris Corp.
Woodall, G. J. A Passion for Justice: A Practical Guide to the Code of Canon Law. 2011. 616p. pap. ***(978-0-85244-478-8(8))*** Gracewing, Ltd.
Wright, Dudley. Roman Catholicism & Freemasonry. 2010. 260p. 42.95 *(978-1-161-37087-4(0))* Kessinger Publishing, LLC.
Wright, Wendy M. Sacred Dwelling: An Everyday Family Spirituality. annot. ed. 2007. 223p. per. *(978-0-8198-7098-8(6))* Pauline Bks. & Media.
Zech, Charles. Best Practices in Parish Stewardship. 2008. per. 24.95 *(978-1-59276-492-1(4))* Our Sunday Visitor, Publishing Div.

CATHOLIC CHURCH—APOLOGETIC WORKS

Alexander, Anthony F. College Apologetics. 2011. 256p. 47.95 ***(978-1-258-02013-2(0))*** Literary Licensing, LLC.
Armstrong, Dave. Bible Proofs for Catholic Truths: A Source Book for Apologists & Inquirers. 2009. xiv, 445p. pap. 15.95 *(978-1-933184-57-9(4))* Sophia Institute Pr.
—More Biblical Evidence for Catholicism. 2007. 188p. per. 15.95 *(978-1-4303-2243-6(8))* Lulu Enterprises Inc.
—The One-Minute Apologist: Essential Catholic Replies to over Sixty Common Protestant Claims. 2007. 143p. per. 14.95 *(978-1-933184-23-4(X))* Sophia Institute Pr.
Brown, Beth Dotson. Yes! I Am Catholic: How Faith Plays a Role in My Life. 2007. (Illus.). 190p. per. 17.75 *(978-0-88489-964-8(0))* St. Mary's Pr.
Cahill, Daniel William. First American Ed of the Works of the Rev D W Cahill, D D the Highly Distinguished Irish Priest, Patriot & Scholar. 2006. 404p. per. 26.99 *(978-1-4255-4332-7(4))* MPublishing.
Campion, Edmund. Ten Reasons Proposed to His Adversaries for Disputation in the Name of the Faith & Presented to the Illustrious Members of Our Universities. 2007. (ENG.). 124p. pap. 18.99 *(978-1-4264-4794-5(9))*; 138p. pap. 19.99 *(978-1-4264-2535-6(X))* BiblioBazaar.
Chesterton, G. K. The Everlasting Man. 2011. 224p. pap. 12.99 ***(978-1-61203-254-2(0))*** Bottom of the Hill Publishing.
—The Everlasting Man. 2008. (ENG.). 232p. per. *(978-1-4065-9100-2(9))* Dodo Pr.
—The Everlasting Man. 2007. (Dover Books on Western Philosophy Ser.). (ENG.). 288p. per. 9.95 *(978-0-486-46036-9(3))* Dover Pubns., Inc.
—The Everlasting Man. 2007. 262p. per. 14.95 *(978-1-59856-016-9(6))* Hendrickson Pubs. Marketing, LLC.
—The Everlasting Man. 2008. 180p. 29.99 *(978-1-60459-247-4(8))*; per. 8.99 *(978-1-60459-246-7(X))* Wilder Pubns., Ltd.
Crean, Thomas. God Is No Delusion: A Refutation of Richard Dawkins. 2007. 160p. pap. 12.95 *(978-1-58617-231-2(X))* Ignatius Pr.
da Costa, Alexandra. Reforming Printing: Syon Abbey's Defence of Orthodoxy 1525-1534. 2012. (Oxford English Monographs). (ENG.). 288p. 110.00 ***(978-0-19-965356-0(9))*** Oxford Univ. Pr., Inc.
Dunn, George T. Roman Catholic Church Versus 2nd Vatican Council Reformation: Hoping to Save Souls. 2011. 112p. 29.99 ***(978-1-4628-4866-9(4))***; pap. 19.99 ***(978-1-4628-4865-2(6))*** Xlibris Corp.
Fenelon, Marge. When's God Gonna Call Me Back? 2010. xi, 131p. pap. *(978-0-7648-1914-8(3))* Liguori Pubns.
Fichter, Joseph H. Textbook in Apologetics. 2011. 336p. 50.95 ***(978-1-258-04147-2(2))*** Literary Licensing, LLC.
Finley, Mitch. The Joy of Being Catholic: A Resounding Affirmation of Our Faith. 2010. (ENG.). 128p. 12.95 *(978-0-8245-2572-9(8))* Crossroad Publishing Co., The.
—The Seeker's Guide to Being Catholic. 2010. (Illus.). 204p. pap. 23.00 *(978-1-60899-264-5(0)*, Wipf and Stock) Wipf & Stock Pubs.
Fireside Catholic Publishing, creator. The New Catholic Answer Bible-NAB. l.t. ed. 2009. (Illus.). 1394p. pap. 34.95 *(978-1-55665-484-3(7))* Fireside Catholic Bibles.
Gibbons, James. The Faith of Our Fathers: Being a Plain Exposition & Vindication of the Church Founded by Our Lord Jesus Christ. 2010. 490p. pap. 38.75 *(978-1-142-03149-7(7))* BiblioBazaar.
Gilbey, A.N. We Believe. 2011. 264p. pap. ***(978-0-85244-770-3(1))*** Gracewing, Ltd.
Hahn, Scott & Flaherty, Regis J., eds. Catholic for a Reason IV: Scripture & the Mystery of Marriage & Family Life. 2007. (Catholic for a Reason Ser.). 199p per. 15.95 *(978-1-931018-44-9(8))* Emmaus Road Publishing.
Kenrick, Francis Patrick. A Vindication of the Catholic Church, in a Series of Letters Addressed to the Rt Rev John Henry Hopkins by Francis Patrick Kenrick. 2006. 340p. per. 23.99 *(978-1-4255-3474-5(0))* MPublishing.
Knox, Ronald. In Soft Garments: Classic Catholic Apologetics. 2010. 215p. pap. 14.95 *(978-1-58617-300-5(6))* Ignatius Pr.
Kreeft, Peter. Ecumenical Jihad: Ecumenism & the Culture War. 2012. (ENG.). 184p. pap. 17.00 ***(978-1-58731-216-8(6))*** St. Augustine's Pr., Inc.
Kreeft, Peter & Tacelli, Ronald. Handbook of Catholic Apologetics: Reasoned Answers to Questions of Faith. 2009. 600p. pap. 21.95 *(978-1-58617-279-4(4))* Ignatius Pr.
Lams, Victor J. The Rhetoric of Newman's Apologia Pro Catholica, 1845-1864. 2007. 220p. (C). 68.95 *(978-1-4331-0015-4(0))* Lang, Peter Publishing, Inc
Leach, Michael. Why Stay Catholic? Unexpected Answers to a Life-Changing Question. 2011. (ENG.). 360p. pap. 14.95 *(978-0-8294-3537-5(9))* Loyola Pr.
Lehner, Ulrich, ed. Beda Mayr, Vertheidigung der katholischen Religion (1789) Sammt einem Anhange von der Möglichkeit einer Vereinigung zwischen unserer, und der Evangelisch-Lutherischen Kirche. 2009. (Brill's Studies in Intellectual History). (GER & ENG.). 434p. *(978-90-04-17318-7(8))* BRILL.
Linden, James V. & Costello, William T. The Fundamentals of Religion. 2011. 352p. 51.95 ***(978-1-258-08364-9(7))*** Literary Licensing, LLC.
Madrid, Patrick. Does the Bible Really Say That? Discovering Catholic Teaching in Scripture. 2006. 186p. per. 13.99 *(978-0-86716-774-0(2)*, Servant Bks.) Franciscan Media.
McNeely, Maurice G. Catholicism Without the Guilt. 2006. (ENM., Illus.). 196p. 24.95 *(978-1-59800-764-0(5))* Outskirts Pr., Inc.
Micek, Adam A. The Apologetics of Martin John Spalding. 2011. 148p. 40.95 ***(978-1-258-04351-3(3))*** Literary Licensing, LLC.
Michael, Sheehan. Apologetics & Catholic Doctrine: Catholic Clasics. 2009. (Illus.). 686p. pap. *(978-1-905574-45-2(2))* Baronius Pr. Ltd.
More, Thomas & Gottschalk, Mary. Dialogue Concerning Heresies. 2006. *(978-1-59417-044-7(4))* Scepter Pubs., Inc.
Newman, Cardinal John Henry. Apologia Pro Vita Sua. 2007. 444p. per. *(978-1-4067-8832-7(5)*, Pomona Pr.) Read Bks.
Newman, Henry John. Apologia Pro Vita Sua. 2007. 284p. (ENG.). 44.99 *(978-1-4280-7547-4(X))*; per. 37.99 *(978-1-4280-7535-1(6))* IndyPublish.com.
Newman, John Henry. Apologia pro Vita Sua. 2007. (ENG.). 326p. pap. 23.99 *(978-1-4345-4275-2(5))*; 362p. pap. 26.99 *(978-1-4346-4276-9(3))* BiblioBazaar.
—Apologia Pro Vita Sua: Being a Reply to a Pamphlet Entitled 'What, Then, Does Dr. Newman Mean?' 2010. (Cambridge Library Collection - Religion Ser.). 566p. pap. 39.99 *(978-1-108-02147-0(6))* Cambridge Univ. Pr.
—Lectures on the Present Position of Catholics in England: Addressed to the Brothers of the Oratory in the Summer Of 1851 (1908) 2008. 454p. 52.95 *(978-1-4365-9471-4(5))* 2007. 456p. per. 37.95 *(978-0-548-79152-3(X))* Kessinger Publishing, LLC.
Newman, John Henry C., ed. Apologia Pro Vita Sua & Six Sermons. 2007.Tr. of Apologia Pro Vita Sua. (ENG.). 312p. per. *(978-1-4065-4966-9(5))* Dodo Pr.
—Apologia Pro Vita Sua & Six Sermons. 2007.Tr. of Apologia Pro Vita Sua. (ENG.). pap. *(978-1-4068-3519-9(6))* Echo Library.
Newman, John Henry C. & Turner, Frank M. Apologia Pro Vita Sua & Six Sermons. 2012.Tr. of Apologia Pro Vita Sua. (ENG., Illus.). 528p. pap. 30.00 *(978-0-300-17786-2(0))* Yale Univ. Pr.
Newman, John Henry C. & Turner, Frank M., eds. Apologia Pro Vita Sua & Six Sermons. 2008.Tr. of Apologia Pro Vita Sua. 528p. 55.00 *(978-0-300-11507-9(5))* Yale Univ. Pr.
Parker, Kenneth L. Catholic & Cornered: Answers to Common Questions about Your Faith. 2011. 10.99 ***(978-0-7648-2025-0(7))*** Liguori Pubns.
Poole, Matthew & Kistler, Don. A Discussion Between a Catholic Priest & a Protestant: Wherein the Principal Points & Arguments of Both Religions Are Truly Proposed & Fully Examined. 2010. *(978-0-9826155-3-9(1))* Northampton Pr., The.
Rutler, George W. A Crisis of Saints: The Call to Heroic Faith in an Unheroic World. 2nd ed. 2009. (ENG.). 224p. pap. 19.95 *(978-0-8245-2525-5(6))* Crossroad Publishing Co., The.
Salza, John. The Biblical Basis for the Papacy. 2007. 223p. per. 13.95 *(978-1-59276-284-2(0))* Our Sunday Visitor, Publishing Div.
Schreck, Alan. Catholic & Christian for Young Adults: Questions & Answers about the Faith. 2007. 181p. per. 13.99 *(978-0-86716-602-6(9)*, Servant Bks.) Franciscan Media.
Stanford, Edward. Foundations of Christian Belief: An Introductory Course in Apologetics. 2011. 262p. 47.95 ***(978-1-258-01936-5(1))*** Literary Licensing, LLC.
Stanford, Peter & Stanford. Why I Am Still a Catholic: Essays in Faith & Perseverance. 2006. (ENG.). 154p. 23.95 *(978-0-8264-9145-9(6))* Continuum International Publishing Group, Ltd. GBR. Dist: National Bk. Network.
Witherup, Ronald D. Fundamentalismo Biblico: Lo que todo catolico debe Saber. 2009. (ENG & SPA.). 96p. pap. 10.95 *(978-0-8146-1890-5(1))* Liturgical Pr.

CATHOLIC CHURCH—ASCETICISM

see Asceticism

CATHOLIC CHURCH—BENEFICES

see Benefices, Ecclesiastical

CATHOLIC CHURCH—BIBLIOGRAPHY

see also Catholic Literature

Finotti, Joseph Maria. Bibliographia Catholica Americana: A List of Works Written by Catholic Authors, 2006. 324p. per. 23.99 *(978-1-4255-3207-9(1))* MPublishing.
Langlois, Claude & Sorrel, Christian. Le Temps des Congrès Catholiques: Bibliographie Raisonnée des Actes de Congrès Tenus en France de 1870 à Nos Jours. 2010. (FRE.). 437p. *(978-2-503-53183-0(0))* Brepols Pubs.

CATHOLIC CHURCH—BIOGRAPHY

Aronica, Paul. Rose of the Andes: A Biography of A Servant of God, Laura Vicuna. 2011. 126p. 40.95 ***(978-1-258-09192-7(5))*** Literary Licensing, LLC.
Beattie, Blake R. Angelus Pacis: The Legation of Cardinal Giovanni Gaetano Orsini, 1326-1334. 2006. (Medieval Mediterranean Ser.: Vol. 67). (Illus.). 245p. *(978-90-04-15393-6(4))* BRILL.
Beaulieu, Peter. Kristi: So Thin Is the Veil. 2006. (ENG., Illus.). 400p. pap. 16.95 *(978-0-8245-2398-5(9))* Crossroad Publishing Co., The.
Beaumont, Keith. Blessed John Henry Newman: Theologian & Spiritual Guide for Our Times. 2010. (Illus.). 100p. 17.95 *(978-1-58617-552-8(1))* Ignatius Pr.
Bonner, Jeremy. The Road to Renewal: Victor Joseph Reed & Oklahoma Catholicism, 1905-1971. 2007. (Illus.). 425p. 34.95 *(978-0-8132-1507-5(2))* Catholic Univ. of America Pr.
Brann, Henry Athanasius. Most Reverend John Hughes: First Archbishop of New York. (Makers of America Ser.). 182p. reprint ed. 88.00 *(978-0-7222-8557-2(4))* Library Reprints, Inc.
Briere, Emile. Katia: A Personal Vision of Catherine de Hueck Doherty. 175p. pap. *(978-2-89039-159-8(0))* Madonna Hse. Pubns.
Buck, Mark. Politics, Finance & the Church in the Reign of Edward II. 2008. (Cambridge Studies in Medieval Life & Thought: Third Ser.). (ENG.). 264p. pap. 37.99 *(978-0-521-09119-0(5))* Cambridge Univ. Pr.
Building Bridges: Pope John Paul II & the Horizon of Life, THIRD EDITION. 3rd ed. 2007. per. 39.95 *(978-1-885938-35-0(7))* Cathedral Foundation Pr.
Caponigri, Aloysius R. Modern Catholic Thinkers: An Anthology. (Essay Index Reprint Ser.). 650p. reprint ed. lib. bdg. 40.50 *(978-0-8290-0784-8(9))* Irvington Pubs.
Chater, Veronica & Chater, V. Waiting for the Apocalypse: A Memoir of Faith & Family. 2009. (ENG.). 336p. 23.95 *(978-0-393-06603-6(7)*, 6603) Norton, W. W. & Co., Inc.
Comiskey, John P. In My Heart's Best Wishes for You: A biography of Archbishop John Walsh. 2012. (McGill-Queen's Studies in the History of Religion Ser.). (ENG., Illus.). 304p. (C). ***(978-0-7735-4013-2(X))*** McGill-Queen's Univ. Pr.
Cruz, Moira. Misery- 2006. (Illus.). 125p. pap. 14.25 *(978-1-4120-8219-8(6))* Trafford Publishing.
Curley, Michael J. John Neumann, a Biography: Fourth Bishop of Philadelphia. 2011. 568p. 63.95 ***(978-1-258-08953-5(X))*** Literary Licensing, LLC.
Doherty, Eddie. Tumbleweed: A Biography of Catherine Doherty. 2nd ed. (Illus.). 203p. pap. *(978-0-921440-12-3(X))* Madonna Hse. Pubns.
Driver, Jenny, et al, eds. Women of Opus Dei: In Their Own Words. 2009. (ENG.). 224p. pap. 24.95 *(978-0-8245-2425-8(X))* Crossroad Publishing Co., The.
Fernández Gracia, Ricardo. Varia Palafoxiana: Doce Estudios en Torno a Don Juan de Palafox y Mendoza. 2010. (SPA.). 380p. *(978-84-235-3236-0(4))* Navarra, Comunidad Autonoma, Servicio de Prensa, Publicaciones y Relaciones Sociales.
Gamboa, Eduardo. Virtuous Healers: Models of Faith in Medicine. 2008. 176p. pap. 15.95 *(978-0-86716-693-4(2))* Franciscan Media.
Hahn, Scott. Ordinary Work, Extraordinary Grace: My Spiritual Journey in Opus Dei. 2006. (ENG.). 176p. 21.95 *(978-0-385-51924-3(9)*, Doubleday Religion) Doubleday Religious Publishing Group, The.
—Ordinary Work, Extraordinary Grace: My Spiritual Journey in Opus Dei. 2008 155p. *(978-0-385-51948-9(6))* Knopf Doubleday Publishing Group.
Hemesath, Sister Caroline. From Slave to Priest: The Inspirational Story of Fr. Augustine Tolton. 2010. 255p. pap. 16.95 *(978-1-58617-524-5(6))* Ignatius Pr.
Hogan, John Joseph. On the Mission in Missouri & Fifty Years Ago: Two Irish-American Classics by Father John Joseph Hogan. Payton, Crystal, ed. 2009. (ENG., Illus.). 224p. pap. 24.95 *(978-0-9673925-5-4(1))* Lens & Pen Pr.
Jolliffe, John, ed. English Catholic Heroes. 2008. (Illus.). 252p. pap. *(978-0-85244-604-1(7))* Gracewing, Ltd.
Kardel, Troels & Maquet, Paul, eds. Nicolaus Steno: Biography & Original Papers of a 17th Century Scientist. 2012. (ENG., Illus.). xx, 900p. 139.00 ***(978-3-642-25078-1(5)***, 3642250785) Springer.
Kenworthy-Browne CJ, Christina, ed. Mary Ward, 1585-1645: A Briefe Relation, with Autobiographical Fragments & a Selection of Letters. 2008. (Catholic Record Society: Records Ser.: Volume 81). (Illus.). 208p. 80.00 *(978-0-902832-24-4(7))* Catholic Record Society GBR. Dist: Boydell & Brewer, Inc.
McGowan, Mark G. Michael Power: The Struggle to Build the Catholic Church on the Canadian Frontier. 2007. (McGill-Queen's Studies in the History of Religion Ser.). (ENG., Illus.). 392p. (C). per. *(978-0-7735-3248-9(X))* McGill-Queen's Univ. Pr.
Moore, Jim. What Is Christian Truth for You? 2007. 348p. per. 17.99 *(978-1-60266-089-2(1))* Xulon Pr., Inc.
O'Donnell, James J. Augustine Confessions: Augustine Confessions: Volume 1: Introduction & Text. 2012. (ENG.). 287p. pap. 45.00 ***(978-0-19-966072-8(7))*** Oxford Univ. Pr., Inc.
Pruter, Bishop. Blue Jellybean Hedy Lamarr & We Dont E. 2006. 172p. per. 14.95 *(978-0-912134-23-9(2)*, Borgo Pr.) Wildside Pr., LLC.
Smith, Julia. The Elusive Father Brown. 2010. (Illus.). 240p. pap. *(978-0-85244-698-0(5))* Gracewing, Ltd.
Swander, Mary. The Desert Pilgrim: En Route to Mysticism & Miracles. 2008. pap. 19.95 *(978-1-888160-33-8(0))* Ice Cube Pr.
Vidler, Alec R. A Variety of Catholic Modernists. 2009. (ENG.). 256p. pap. 34.99 *(978-0-521-10027-4(5))* Cambridge Univ. Pr.

CATHOLIC CHURCH—CATECHISMS AND CREEDS

see also Baltimore Catechism

Anderson, William A. In His Light. 2011. (ENG., Illus.). 326p. pap. 17.40 ***(978-1-59276-981-0(0))*** Our Sunday Visitor, Publishing Div.
Anderson, William A. & Anderson, William Angor. In His Light: A Path Into Catholic Belief. 2009. (Illus.). ix, 326p. pap. *(978-0-15-902409-6(9))* Harcourt Religion Pubs.
Annunziata, Sister & McGuire. Sister Annunziata's First Communion Catechism. 2011. 48p. 35.95 ***(978-1-258-03711-6(4))*** Literary Licensing, LLC.
Anonymous. Baltimore Catechism No. 3: A Catechism of Christian Doctrine. 2007. (ENG.). 286p. pap. 21.99 *(978-1-4346-2490-1(0))*; 320p. pap. 24.99 *(978-1-4346-2532-8(X))* BiblioBazaar.
—Doctrina Christiana: The first book printed in the Philippines, Manila, 1593. A Facsimile of the copy in the Lessing J. Rosenwald Collection, Library. 2007. (ENG.). 154p. pap. 21.99 *(978-1-4264-2470-0(1))* BiblioBazaar.
Baker, S.J., Kenneth. Doctrinal Sermons on the Catechism of the Catholic Church. 2012. (ENG.). 272p. pap. 22.00 ***(978-1-58731-189-5(5))*** St. Augustine's Pr., Inc.
Barry, John F. Una Sola Fe, un Solo Señor: Creencias Catolicas Basicas = One Faith, One Lord. 2009. (Illus.). 224p. *(978-0-8215-5565-1(0))* Sadlier, William H. Inc.
Bowman, Wayne B. Hidden in Plain Sight: Catechism versus the Bible. 2009. (J). pap. 15.99 *(978-1-60799-779-5(7))* Tate Publishing & Enterprises, LLC.
Buela, Carlos Miguel. Catechism for Youth. 2008. 331p. (YA). pap. 16.95 *(978-1-933871-48-6(2))* IVE Pr.
Catechism of the Catholic Church. 29.95 *(978-1-58617-550-4(5))* Ignatius Pr.
The Catechism of the Council of Trent. 2010. pap. 19.60 *(978-1-61143-194-0(8))* Gorgias Pr., LLC.
Catholic Church Staff & Catholic Church, Canadian Conference of Catholic Bishops Publications Service Staff, contrib. by. Catechism of the Catholic Church. (Illus.). 698p. *(978-0-88997-281-0(8))* Canadian Conference of Catholic Bishops/Conference des Eveques Catholiques du Canada.
Cecchetto-Capani, Marina. Dios con Nosotros para el Ano Liturgico B: Recursos para una Catequesis para Toda la Comunidad. 2006. 339.00 *(978-1-58595-581-7(7))* Twenty-Third Pubns./Bayard.
Confraternity of Christian Doctrine & Confraternity Of Christian Doctrine. This We Believe, by This We Live. 2011. 442p. 56.95 ***(978-1-258-05895-1(2))*** Literary Licensing, LLC.
Connell, Francis J. & Sharrock, David. The New Confraternity Edition, Revised Baltimore Catechism No. 2011. 320p. 50.95 ***(978-1-258-07006-9(5))*** Literary Licensing, LLC.
Connell, Francis J., et al. Father Connell's the New Baltimore Catechism, No. 2011. 418p. 54.95 ***(978-1-258-02559-5(0))*** Literary Licensing, LLC.
Crouch, Marlene C. Whose Voice Are You Listening To? A Comparison of the Catholic Catechism to the Bible. 2010. pap. 22.99 *(978-1-61566-261-6(8))* Tate Publishing & Enterprises, LLC.
Deharbe, Joseph. A Full Catechism of the Catholic Religion. 2009. 238p. pap. *(978-0-217-66568-1(3))* Books LLC.
Deharbe, Joseph & Lynch, Patrick N. A Full Catechism of the Catholic Religion. Fander, John, tr. 2007. (ENG.). 336p. 45.95 *(978-0-548-34801-7(4))*; per. 30.95 *(978-0-548-29025-5(3))* Kessinger Publishing, LLC.
Deharbe, Joseph, et al. A Full Catechism of the Catholic Religion. 2009. 338p. 36.99 *(978-1-116-70272-1(1))*; 32.99 *(978-1-116-70272-9(X))*; pap. 31.75 *(978-1-116-70273-6(8))*; pap. 30.75 *(978-1-116-70274-3(6))* BiblioBazaar.
Doctrina Christiana: The first book printed in the Philippines, Manila, 1593. A Facsimile of the copy in the Lessing J. Rosenwald Collection, Library. l.t. ed. 2006. 148p. pap. 18.99 *(978-1-4264-2427-4(2))* BiblioBazaar.
Doherty, Catherine de Hueck. Beginning Again: Recovering Your Joy & Innocence Through Confession. 160p. pap. *(978-0-921440-94-9(4))* Madonna Hse. Pubns.
Duffy, Regis A. The Liturgy in the Catechism: Celebrating God's Wisdom & Love. 2010. 104p. pap. 14.00 *(978-1-60899-612-4(3)*, Wipf and Stock) Wipf & Stock Pubs.
Elijah. Divine & Healing Path: Old Catholic Catechism. 2009. 189p. pap. 15.99 *(978-0-557-17424-9(4))* Lulu Enterprises Inc.
Groeschel, Benedict. Experiencing the Mystery of Christ: Praying with the Creed. 2008. per. 14.95 *(978-1-59276-404-4(5))* Our Sunday Visitor, Publishing Div.
Groeschel, Benedict J. Praying with the Creed: Meditations from the Oratory. 2007. (Illus.). 192p. pap. 14.95 *(978-1-59276-321-4(9))* Our Sunday Visitor, Publishing Div.
Haas, David. Increase Our Faith: Year C: Parish Prayer Services for Whole Community Catechesis. 2006. 220p. per. 24.95 *(978-1-58595-569-5(8))* Twenty-Third Pubns./Bayard.
Jung, Scott. The Complete Christian Catechism. 2010. 244p. pap. 17.00 *(978-0-557-04725-3(0))* Lulu Enterprises Inc.

C

Kelly, William Roswell, et al. Living in God's Grace: Living My Religion Series, Book 3. 2011. 364p. 51.95 ***(978-1-258-09316-7(2))*** Literary Licensing, LLC.

—Living in God's Holiness: Living My Religion Series, Book 8. 2011. 368p. 53.95 ***(978-1-258-09317-4(0))*** Literary Licensing, LLC.

—Living in God's Love: Living My Religion Series, Book 1. 2011. 162p. 41.95 ***(978-1-258-09150-7(X))*** Literary Licensing, LLC.

Kinkead, Thomas L. Baltimore Catechism: An Explanation of the Baltimore Catechism of Chris, 4. l.t. ed. 2007. (ENG.). 412p. pap. 28.99 *(978-1-4264-8097-3(0))* BiblioBazaar.

—Baltimore Catechism No. 4: An Explanation of the Baltimore Catechism of Chris. 2007. 368p. pap. 25.99 *(978-1-4264-8040-9(7))* BiblioBazaar.

—An Explanation of the Baltimore Catechism of Christian Doctrine. 2009. 404p. 32.99 *(978-1-115-70674-2(8))*; pap. 21.99 *(978-1-115-70677-3(2))*; pap. 27.99 *(978-1-115-70676-6(4))* BiblioBazaar.

—An Explanation of the Baltimore Catechism of Christian Doctrine. 2007. 340p. per. *(978-1-4065-2893-0(5))* Dodo Pr.

Lillig, Tina. The Catechesis of the Good Shepherd in a Parish Setting. 2010. 88p. pap. 12.00 *(978-1-56854-262-1(3)*, CGSPAR, Catechesis of the Good Shepherd) Liturgy Training Pubns.

Lonneux, Martin J. The Graded Catechism in Inuit. 2011. 298p. 48.95 ***(978-1-258-05232-4(6))*** Literary Licensing, LLC.

Malloy, Joseph I. A Catechism for Inquirers. 2011. 98p. 38.95 ***(978-1-258-07652-8(7))*** Literary Licensing, LLC.

McHugh, John A. & Callan, Charles J. Catechism of the Council of Trent for Parish Priests. 2011. 662p. 68.95 ***(978-1-258-10116-9(5))*** Literary Licensing, LLC.

McKeating, Michael. O Timothy! Guard the Deposit of Faith. 2007. 176p. per. 13.99 *(978-1-60266-426-5(9))* Xulon Pr., Inc.

Mniler, Michael. Familiar Explanation of Christian Doctrine Adapted for the Family & More Advanced Students in Catholic Schools & Colleges No III. 2006. 528p. per. 29.99 *(978-1-4255-5823-9(2))* MPublishing.

Paprocki, Joe. The Catechist's Toolbox Leader Guide. 2008. 48p. pap. 2.95 *(978-0-8294-2724-0(4))* Loyola Pr.

Piechowski, Otto R. & Shannon, William Henry. The Catechism of the Catholic Church: A Second Look. 2009. xiv, 76p. ***(978-1-56077-899-8(7))*** Center for Learning, The.

Schonborn, Christoph. Living the Catechism of the Catholic Church. 130p. 10.95 *(978-0-89870-956-8(3))* Ignatius Pr.

Simon, M. La vie dans le Christ dans le catechisme de Jean-Paul II. 2010. (Bibliotheca Ephemeridum Theologicarum Lovaniensium Ser.). (FRE.). 651p. (C). pap. 122.00 *(978-90-429-2309-6(1))* Peeters Pubs. & Booksellers BEL. Dist: Brown, David Bk. Co., The.

Simon, Maurice & Simon, M. La celebration du mystere chretien dans le catechisme de Jean-Paul II. 2006. (Bibliotheca Ephemeridum Theologicarum Lovaniensium Ser.). (FRE & ENG.). 638p. (C). pap. 124.00 *(978-90-429-1734-7(2))* Peeters Pubs. & Booksellers BEL. Dist: Brown, David Bk. Co., The.

Singer-Towns, Brian. The Catholic Faith Handbook for Youth. 2nd ed. 2008. (Illus.). 474p. per. 19.95 *(978-0-88489-987-7(X))* St. Mary's Pr.

Singer-Towns, Brian, et al. The Catholic Faith Handbook for Youth. 2nd ed. 2008. (Illus.). 474p. 28.25 *(978-0-88489-988-4(8))* St. Mary's Pr.

Sosa, Juan J. Manual para Entender y Participar en la Misa. 2009. (SPA.). 96p. 5.99 *(978-0-7648-1800-4(7)*, Libros Liguori) Liguori Pubns.

United States Conference of Catholic Bishops, creator. United States Catholic Catechism for Adults. 2006. (Illus.). 637p. per. 24.95 *(978-1-57455-450-2(6))* United States Conference of Catholic Bishops.

Wagner III, Bishop Wynn. A Catechism of the Liberal Catholic Church. 2008. 273p. pap. 19.99 *(978-0-557-00662-5(7))* Lulu Enterprises Inc.

Zanotto, Luigi. Profundizando y Madurando Nuestra Fe: Para la Formacion de Catequistas y Agentes de Pastoral. 2006. (SPA.). 184p. pap. 19.95 *(978-1-58595-618-0(X))* Twenty-Third Pubns./Bayard.

CATHOLIC CHURCH—CEREMONIES AND PRACTICES

see Catholic Church—Customs and Practices

CATHOLIC CHURCH—CHARITIES

Cushing, Richard. Pope Pius Xii. 2011. 184p. 42.95 ***(978-1-258-03905-9(2))*** Literary Licensing, LLC.

Fadica, ed. The Catholic Funding Guide: A Directory of Resources for Catholic Activities. 6th ed. 2009. (ENG.). 568p. pap. 150.00 *(978-1-891646-06-5(0))* Foundations & Donors Interested in Catholic Activities, Inc.

FADICA, Inc. Staff. The Catholic Funding Guide: A Directory of Resources for Catholic Activities. 2007. 530p. per. 110.00 *(978-1-891646-05-8(2))* Foundations & Donors Interested in Catholic Activities, Inc.

Gonzalez-Balado, Jose Luis. Teresa of Calcutta: A Personal Memoir. 2007. (Illus.). 185p. per. 12.95 *(978-0-7648-1547-8(4))* Liguori Pubns.

Hayes, Patrick. Pope Pius Xi. 2011. 20p. pap. 35.95 ***(978-1-258-03759-8(9))*** Literary Licensing, LLC.

Hehir, J. Bryan. Catholic Charities USA: 100 Years at the Intersection of Charity & Justice. 2010. E-Book 9.95 *(978-0-8146-3930-6(5))*; 19.95 *(978-0-8146-3339-7(0))* Liturgical Pr.

Ilo, Stan Chu. The Church & Development in Africa: Aid & Development from the Perspective of Catholic Social Ethics. 2011. (African Christian Studies). 342p. pap. 38.00 ***(978-1-60899-779-4(0)***, Pickwick Pubns.) Wipf & Stock Pubs.

Kammer, Fred. Faith. Works. Wonders: An Insider's Guide to Catholic Charities. 2009. 220p. pap. 24.00 *(978-1-60608-927-9(7)*, Pickwick Pubns.) Wipf & Stock Pubs.

Korgen, Jeffry Odell. Solidarity Will Transform the World: Stories of Hope from Catholic Relief Services. 2007. (Illus.). 161p. per. 16.00 *(978-1-57075-744-0(5))* Orbis Bks.

Mother Teresa of Calcutta & Kolodiejchuk, Brian. Mother Teresa: Come Be My Light. 2007. (ENG.). 416p. 24.00 *(978-0-385-52037-9(9)*, Doubleday) Doubleday Religious Publishing Group, The.

Pullan, Brian. Rich & Poor in Renaissance Venice: The Social Institutions of a Catholic State, To 1620. 2008. 728p. pap. 72.00 *(978-1-59740-375-7(X))* ACLS Humanities E-Book.

Skok, Deborah A. More Than Neighbors: Catholic Settlements & Day Nurseries in Chicago, 1893-1930. 2007. (Illus.). 251p. 38.00 *(978-0-87580-374-6(1))* Northern Illinois Univ. Pr.

Zwick, Mark & Zwick, Louise. Mercy Without Borders: The Catholic Worker & Immigration. 2010. 288p. pap. 24.00 *(978-0-8091-4689-5(4))* Paulist Pr.

CATHOLIC CHURCH—CLERGY

see also Apostolic Succession; Bishops; Cardinals; Episcopacy; Ex-Priests, Catholic; Priests; Privileges and Immunities, Ecclesiastical

Aquinas, Thomas. St. Thomas Aquinas & the Mendicant Controversies: Three Translations. Proctor, John, tr. from LAT. rev. ed. 2007. 570p. 65.00 *(978-1-934182-00-0(1))* Alethes Pr.

Balboni, Jennifer M. Clergy Sexual Abuse Litigation: Survivors Seeking Justice. 2011. 170p. 59.95 *(978-1-935049-37-1(2))* FirstForumPress.

Bergquist, Patrick. The Long Dark Winter's Night: Reflections of a Priest in a Time of Pain & Privilege. 2010. 144p. pap. 16.95 *(978-0-8146-3301-4(3))* Liturgical Pr.

Berry, Jason & Renner, Gerald. Vows of Silence: The Abuse of Power in the Papacy of John Paul II. 2010. (ENG.). 368p. pap. 16.00 *(978-0-7432-8706-7(1)*, Free Pr.) Free Pr.

Bobic, Pavlina. War & Faith: The Catholic Church in Slovenia, 1914-1918. 2012. (Illus.). xviii, 261p. ***(978-90-04-20219-1(6))*** BRILL.

Bohr, David. The Diocesan Priest: Consecrated & Sent. 2009. pap. 24.95 *(978-0-8146-3278-9(5))* Liturgical Pr.

Brandmuller, Walter. Light & Shadows: Defending Church History amid Faith, Facts & Legends. 2009. 160p. pap. 16.95 *(978-1-58617-273-2(5))* Ignatius Pr.

Browne, Right Rev G. F. Alcuin of York. 2008. 380p. *(978-1-4437-2301-5(0))* 2006. 376p. per. *(978-1-4067-1835-5(1))* Read Bks. (Hesperides Pr.).

Burkhardt, Johannes. Abschied Vom Religionskrieg: Der Siebenjährige Krieg und die Päpstliche Diplomatie. (GER.). VIII, 487p. 210.00 ***(978-3-11-181779-8(2))*** De Gruyter, Walter Inc.

Cafardi, Nicholas P. Before Dallas: The U. S. Bishops' Response to Clergy Sexual Abuse of Children. 2008. 255p. 27.95 *(978-0-8091-0580-9(2)*, 0580-9) Paulist Pr.

Catholic Church Staff, et al, contrib. by. Rite of Penance: Approved for Use in the Dioceses of the United States of America by the United States Conference of Catholic Bishops & Confirmed by the Holy See with Readings from the Revised Lectionary for Mass. 2010. xxv, 329p. ***(978-1-60137-095-2(4))*** United States Conference of Catholic Bishops.

Chinnici, Joseph P. When Values Collide: The Catholic Church, Sexual Abuse & the Challenges of Leadership. 2009. 240p. pap. 25.00 *(978-1-57075-873-7(5))* Orbis Bks.

Colahan, Clark A. & Masferrer, Roberto. Díaz de Luco's Guide for Bishops: Spanish Reform & the Lazarillo. 2007. (C). *(978-0-86698-379-2(1))* Arizona State Univ., Arizona Ctr. for Medieval & Renaissance Studies.

Congregation for Catholic Education. Directives Concerning the Preparation of Seminary Educators. 60p. pap. 1.75 *(978-0-8198-1871-3(2))* Pauline Bks. & Media.

Congregation for Institutes of Consecrated Life and Societies of Apostolic Life Staff & Societies of Apostolic Life Staff. Directives for Mutual Relations Between Bishops & Religious in the Church: Mutuae Relationes. 65p. pap. 0.50 *(978-0-8198-1860-7(7))* Pauline Bks. & Media.

Cozzens, Donald B. Freeing Celibacy. 2006. 115p. 15.95 *(978-0-8146-3160-7(6))* Liturgical Pr.

Doherty, Catherine. Dear Father: A Message of Love for Priests. 3rd exp. ed. 138p. pap. *(978-0-921440-76-5(6))* Madonna Hse. Pubns.

Donahue, George Joseph. The Secular Priesthood: A Book of Letters. 2011. 230p. 46.95 ***(978-1-258-05456-4(6))*** Literary Licensing, LLC.

Donnelly, D., et al, eds. The Belgian Contribution to the Second Vatican Council: International Research Conference at Mechelen, Leuven & Louvain-la-Neuve (September 12-16, 2005) 2008. (Bibliotheca Ephemeridum Theologicarum Lovaniensium Ser.). (ENG.). 728p. (C). pap. 124.00 *(978-90-429-2101-6(3))* Peeters Pubs. & Booksellers BEL. Dist: Brown, David Bk. Co., The.

Dullea, Gearoid, ed. Deacons: Ministers of Christ & of God's Mysteries. 2010. (ENG.). 101p. pap. 15.95 *(978-1-84730-217-5(3))* Veritas Pubns. IRL. Dist: Dufour Editions, Inc.

—On Shepherding: Reflections on the Priesthood. 2011. (ENG.). 112p. pap. 24.95 *(978-1-85607-681-4(4))* Columba Pr. IRL. Dist: Dufour Editions, Inc.

Dziwisz, Stanislaw. A Life with Karol: My Forty-Year Friendship with the Man Who Became Pope. Walker, Adrian J., tr. from ITA. 2008. (ENG., Illus.). 272p. 25.00 *(978-0-385-52374-5(2)*, Doubleday) Doubleday Religious Publishing Group, The.

Eberley, Ronald N. The Unnatural Law of Celibacy: One Married Man's Struggle to Become a Catholic Priest. 2006. 204p. reprint ed. 23.00 *(978-1-4223-5340-0(0))* DIANE Publishing Co.

Edwards, Lisa Marie. Roman Virtues: The Education of Latin American Clergy in Rome, 1858-1962. 2011. (Latin America: Interdisciplinary Studies). 150p. (C). 68.95 ***(978-1-4331-1306-2(6))*** Lang, Peter Publishing, Inc.

Egan, Kevin. Remaining a Catholic after the Murphy Report. 2011. (ENG.). 168p. pap. 25.95 ***(978-1-85607-740-8(3))*** Columba Pr. IRL. Dist: Dufour Editions, Inc.

Figueiredo, Anthony J. A Priest for All Liturgical Seasons: Changing Calendar, Unchanging Virtue. 2009. *(978-0-8189-1298-6(7))* St Pauls/Alba Hse. Pubns.

Fleming, Patrick, et al. Broken Trust: Stories of Pain, Hope, & Healing from Clerical Abuse Survivors & Abusers. 2007. (ENG.). 240p. 19.95 *(978-0-8245-2410-4(1))* Crossroad Publishing Co., The.

Frawley-O'Dea, Mary Gail. Perversion of Power: Sexual Abuse in the Catholic Church, 1 vol. 2007. (ENG.). 336p. lib. bdg. 59.95 *(978-0-8265-1546-9(0))*; per. 24.95 *(978-0-8265-1547-6(9))* Vanderbilt Univ. Pr.

Galasso, Carmine. Crosses: Portraits of Clergy Abuse. 2007. (Illus.). 200p. 50.00 *(978-1-904563-59-4(7))* Trolley GBR. Dist: Prestel Publishing.

Gautier, Mary, et al. Same Call, Different Men: The Evolution of the Priesthood since Vatican II. 2012. ***(978-0-8146-3429-5(X))*** Liturgical Pr.

Goldner, Virginia & Frawley-O'Dea, Mary G., eds. Predatory Priests, Silenced Victims: The Sexual Abuse Crisis & the Catholic Church. 2007. (ENG.). 259p. 44.50 *(978-0-88163-424-2(7))* Routledge.

Gonzalez, Fernando M. Marcial Maciel: Los Legionarios de Cristo. 2006. (SPA.). 480p. pap. 24.95 *(978-970-699-150-8(6))* Tusquets Editores ESP. Dist: Ediciones Urano S. A.

Green, T. Pitt. Restoring Sanctuary. 2010. 224p. pap. 14.00 *(978-1-60844-690-2(5))* Dog Ear Publishing, LLC.

Gula, Richard M. Just Ministry: Professional Ethics for Pastoral Ministers. 2010. 288p. pap. 19.95 *(978-0-8091-4631-4(2))* Paulist Pr.

Hidalgo, Myra L. Sexual Abuse & Catholicism: How Priests & Nuns Become Perpetrators. 2007. (ENG., Illus.). 164p. 125.00 *(978-0-7890-2955-3(3))* Routledge.

—Sexual Abuse & the Culture of Catholicism: How Priests & Nuns Become Perpetrators. 2007. (ENG., Illus.). 164p. per. 18.95 *(978-0-7890-2956-0(1))* Routledge.

Hill, Harvey, et al. By Those Who Knew Them: French Modernists Left, Right, & Center. 2008. 200p. (C). 59.95 *(978-0-8132-1537-2(4))* Catholic Univ. of America Pr.

Hogan, John Joseph. On the Mission in Missouri & Fifty Years Ago: Two Irish-American Classics by Father John Joseph Hogan. Payton, Crystal, ed. 2009. (ENG., Illus.). 224p. pap. 24.95 *(978-0-9673925-5-4(1))* Lens & Pen Pr.

Ike, Roberto Marie. Advocacy Coalition & Welfare Policy: Analyzing Coalition Consensus. 2007. (ENG., Illus.). 220p. per. 38.99 *(978-0-7618-3479-3(6))* Univ. Pr. of America, Inc.

International Jesuit Network Development Staff. The Development of Peoples: Challenges for Today & Tomorrow. 2007. (ENG.). 220p. per. 29.95 *(978-1-85607-574-9(5))* Columba Pr. IRL. Dist: Dufour Editions, Inc.

John Paul II, pseud. I Will Give You Shepherds: Pastores Dabo Vobis. 168p. pap. 5.95 *(978-0-8198-3665-6(6)*, 332-129) Pauline Bks. & Media.

Johrendt, Jochen. Die Diener des Apostelfürsten: Das Kapitel von St. Peter im Vatikan (11.-13. Jahrhundert) 2011. (Bibliothek des Deutschen Historischen Instituts in Rom Ser.). (GER.). X, 564p. 112.00 ***(978-3-11-023407-7(6))*** De Gruyter, Walter Inc.

Kammer, Fred. Salted with Fire: Spirituality for the Faithjustice Journey. 2008. 154p. pap. 18.00 *(978-1-55635-998-9(5)*, Wipf and Stock) Wipf & Stock Pubs.

Kasomo, Daniel W. Personal Ordinariate & Personal Prelature. 2011. 440p. pap. ***(978-3-8443-0712-2(5))*** Lambert Academic Publishing.

—Vocation to Catholic Priesthood & Religious Life. 2011. 376p. pap. ***(978-3-8443-8011-8(6))*** Lambert Academic Publishing.

Kasomo, Rt. Rev. Daniel W & Kasomo, Rt. Rev. Daniel W. The Association of Catholic Priests the Society of St Peter & Paul. 2011. 352p. pap. ***(978-3-8454-1689-2(0))*** Lambert Academic Publishing.

Keenan, Marie. Child Sexual Abuse & the Catholic Church: Gender, Power, & Organizational Culture. 2011. (ENG.). 400p. 59.95 ***(978-0-19-989567-0(8))*** Oxford Univ. Pr., Inc.

Klaiber, Jeffrey. The Church, Dictatorships, & Democracy in Latin America. 2009. 336p. pap. 40.00 *(978-1-60608-947-7(1)*, Wipf and Stock) Wipf & Stock Pubs.

Lea, Henry Charles. An Historical Sketch of Sacerdotal Celibacy in the Christian Church. 2006. 612p. per. 34.99 *(978-1-4255-6505-3(0))* MPublishing.

Leahy, Brendan & Michael, Mulvey, eds. Priests Today: Reflections on Identity, Life & Ministry. 2010. 120p. pap. 9.95 *(978-1-56548-346-0(4))* New City Pr.

Ledbetter, Donald E. Deacon Relationships Through the Body of Christ. 2009. 232p. pap. 15.99 *(978-1-60791-710-6(6))* Xulon Pr., Inc.

Levering, Matthew. Christ & the Catholic Priesthood: Ecclesial Hierarchy & the Pattern of the Trinity. 2010. x, 340p. *(978-1-59525-029-2(8))* Hillenbrand Bks.

Lind, Christopher. Priestly Studies in Modern Papal Teachin. 2006. pap. 19.95 *(978-1-4286-6131-8(X))* Kessinger Publishing, LLC.

Loiero, Salvatore. Priesterliche Existenz: Gemeinsamer Studientag der Bayerischen Priesterseminare und der Theologischen Fakultät der Katholischen Universität Eichstätt-Ingolstadt. 2010. (GER.). 106p. *(978-3-7917-2298-6(0))* Pustet, Friedrich GmbH & Co. KG.

Majilla, Gerard. Don't Canonize Mother Teres: Save Mother Teresa from Pope & the crafty Catholic Clergy. 2009. 124p. pap. 12.49 *(978-1-4389-6122-4(7))* AuthorHouse.

Martínez, Sanjuana. Prueba de Fe: La Red de Cardenales y Obispos en la Pederastía Clerical. 2009. (SPA.). 273p. 18.95 *(978-970-37-0713-3(0))* Editorial Planeta, S. A. ESP. Dist: Giron Bks.

McDonnell, Eunan. The Concept of Freedom in the Writings of St. Francis de Sales. 2009. 482p. 84.95 *(978-3-03911-963-9(X))* Lang, Peter AG GBR. Dist: Lang, Peter.

McGovern, Thomas J. Priestly Identity: A Study in the Theology of Priesthood. 2010. 320p. pap. 35.00 *(978-1-60899-532-5(1))* Wipf & Stock Pubs.

McGrath, Elsie Hainz, et al, eds. Women Find a Way: The Movement & Stories of Roman Catholic Womenpriests. 2008. 160p. pap. 19.95 *(978-1-60264-223-2(0))* Virtualbookworm.com Publishing, Inc.

Mooney, Tom. All the Bishops' Men: Clerical Abuse in an Irish Diocese. 2011. (ENG., Illus.). 288p. pap. 23.95 *(978-1-84889-099-2(0))* Collins Pr., The IRL. Dist: Dufour Editions, Inc.

Mukuka, Dominic Mulenga. Catholic & Protestant Churches' Views on Women Ordination: Women Ordination in South Africa. 2011. 96p. pap. ***(978-3-639-34294-9(1))*** VDM Verlag Dr. Mueller e.K.

Murphy, Charles M. Models of Priestly Formation: Past, Present & Future. 2006. (Crossroad Faith & Formation Book Ser.). (ENG.). 96p. pap. 14.95 *(978-0-8245-2402-9(0)*, Herder & Herder) Crossroad Publishing Co., The.

Mwerihari Musings: '1964 Southern Rhodesia to Zimbabwe 1999' 2007. (Illus.). 216p. per. *(978-1-84401-804-8(0))* Athena Pr.

Nuzzi, Ronald James, et al. Faith, Finances, & the Future: The Notre Dame Study of U. S. Pastors. 2008. (ENG.). 88p. pap. 10.00 *(978-0-9788793-5-8(X))* Alliance for Catholic Education Pr.

O'Brien, David J. & Shannon, Thomas A., eds. Catholic Social Thought: The Documentary Heritage. 2010. 824p. pap. 30.00 *(978-1-57075-891-1(3))* Orbis Bks.

Peter. The Moral Treatise on the Eye. Newhauser, Richard, tr. from LAT. 2012. (Mediaeval Sources in Translation Ser.). (ENG.). 306p. pap. 35.00 ***(978-0-88844-301-4(3))*** Pontifical Institute of Mediaeval Studies, Dept. of Pubns. CAN. Dist: Univ. of Toronto Pr.

Pierre, Simone M. The Struggle to Serve: The Ordination of Women in the Roman Catholic Church. alt. ed. 2011. (ENG.). 215p. pap. 30.00 ***(978-0-7864-6716-7(9))*** McFarland & Co., Inc. Pubs.

Pifko, John M. My Favorite Priest: A Convert Maker. 2011. 146p. pap. 24.95 ***(978-1-4560-6747-2(8))*** PublishAmerica, Inc.

Plante, Ph.D., Thomas G & McChesney, Kathleen L., eds. Sexual Abuse in the Catholic Church: A Decade of Crisis, 2002-2012, 1 vol. 2011. (Abnormal Psychology Ser.). 270p. 48.00 ***(978-0-313-39387-7(7)***, A3405C) Greenwood Publishing Group, Inc.

Plante, Thomas G. & McChesney, Kathleen. Sexual Abuse in the Catholic Church: A Decade of Crisis, 2002-2012. 2011. E-Book ***(978-0-313-39388-4(5)***, Praeger Pubs.) Greenwood Publishing Group, Inc.

Podles, Leon J. Sacrilege: Sexual Abuse in the Catholic Church. 2008. (ENG.). 676p. 22.95 *(978-0-9790279-9-4(3)*, (800) 462-6420) Crossland Foundation Pr.

Porteous, Julian. After the Heart of God: The Life & Ministry of Priests at the Beginning of the Third Millennium. 2011. (ENG.). 154p. pap. 14.95 *(978-1-58979-579-2(2))* Taylor Trade Publishing.

Power, David. Mission, Ministry, Order: Reading the Tradition in the Present Context. 2008. (ENG.). 416p. pap. 39.95 *(978-0-8264-2853-0(3))* Continuum International Publishing Group, Ltd. GBR. Dist: National Bk. Network.

Power, David Noel. Mission, Ministry, Order: Reading the Tradition in the Present Context. 2008. (ENG.). 416p. 120.00 *(978-0-8264-2852-3(5))* Continuum International Publishing Group, Ltd. GBR. Dist: National Bk. Network.

Robinson, Denis & Abbey Press (Saint Meinrad, Ind.) Staff. Sacerdos in Aeternum — Prayers & Blessings for Priests. 2010. viii, 407p. *(978-0-87029-436-5(9))* Abbey Pr.

Robinson, Geoffrey. Confronting Power & Sex in the Catholic Church: Reclaiming the Spirit of Jesus. 2008. 307p. (Orig.). pap. *(978-1-920721-47-3(9))* Liturgical Pr.

Rossetti, Stephen J. Our Journey into Joy: Ten Steps to Priestly Holiness. 2009. 32p. pap. 2.50 *(978-1-59471-219-7(0))* Ave Maria Pr.

Ruddy, Christopher. Tested in Every Way: The Catholic Priesthood in Today's Church. 2007. (ENG.). 192p. pap. 16.95 *(978-0-8245-2427-2(6))* Crossroad Publishing Co., The.

Rutherford, Janet & Twomey, D. Vincent, eds. The Holy Spirit in the Fathers of the Church. 2010. 203p. 65.00 *(978-1-84682-255-1(6))* Four Courts Pr. IRL. Dist: International Specialized Bk. Services.

Shaw, Russell. To Hunt, to Shoot, to Entertain: Clericalism & the Catholic Laity. 2011. 202p. pap. 23.00 ***(978-1-61097-203-1(1)***, Wipf and Stock) Wipf & Stock Pubs.

Spicer, Kevin P. Hitler's Priests: Catholic Clergy & National Socialism. 2008. (Illus.). 385p. 34.95 *(978-0-87580-384-5(9))* Northern Illinois Univ. Pr.

Suárez, Federico. About Being a Priest. 2nd ed. 2009. 219p. pap. *(978-1-59417-083-6(5))* Scepter Pubs., Inc.

Suhard, Emmanuel. Priests among Men. 2011. 116p. 39.95 ***(978-1-258-03692-8(4))*** Literary Licensing, LLC.

Toups, David L. Reclaiming Our Priestly Character. 2008. per. 17.95 *(978-0-9800455-0-5(9))* IPF Pubns.

Van Der Borght, Eduardus. Theology of Ministry: A Reformed Contribution. 2007. (Studies in Reformed Theology Ser.). 470p. *(978-90-04-15805-4(7))* BRILL.

Vaughan, John S. The Minister of Christ V1: Or Ascetical Notes & Reflections for Priests. 2011. 310p. 50.95 ***(978-1-258-05072-6(2))*** Literary Licensing, LLC.

William. William of Ockham - Dialogu Pts. 2 & 3, Pts. 2 & 3. Ballweg, Jan et al, eds. 2011. (Auctores Britannici Medii Aevi Ser.). (LAT & ENG.). 200p. 75.00 *(978-0-19-726480-5(8))* Oxford Univ. Pr., Inc.

Witherup, Ronald D. Gold Tested in Fire: A New Pentecost for the Catholic Priesthood. 2012. ***(978-0-8146-3382-3(X))*** Liturgical Pr.

Witherup, Ronald D. Ministerial Priesthood in the Third Millennium: Faithfulness of Christ, Faithfulness of Priests. 2009. 24.95 *(978-0-8146-3326-7(9))* Liturgical Pr.

Zech, Charles. Best Practices in Catholic Church Ministry Performance Management. 2010. (ENG.). 130p. 57.99 *(978-0-7391-4523-4(1))* Lexington Bks.

CATHOLIC CHURCH—CLERGY—APPOINTMENT, CALL AND ELECTION

Carr, Aidan. Vocation to the Priesthood Its Canonical. 2006. pap. 20.95 *(978-1-4286-5831-8(9))* Kessinger Publishing, LLC.

Cushing, Richard. That They May Know Thee. Kane, George L., ed. 2011. 226p. 46.95 **(978-1-258-07993-2(3))** Literary Licensing, LLC.

Lawlor, David. Divine Right? The Parnell Split in Meath. 2007. (Illus.). 286p. 59.95 *(978-1-85918-426-4(X))* Cork Univ. Pr. IRL. Dist: Stylus Publishing, LLC.

O'Callaghan, Joseph. Is He Worthy? Election of Bishops in the Catholic Church. 2007. (ENG.). 210p. 68.00 *(978-0-7425-5819-9(3))*; pap. 24.95 *(978-0-7425-5820-5(7))* Rowman & Littlefield Publishers, Inc.

Rollo-Koster, Joëlle. Raiding Saint Peter: Empty Sees, Violence, & the Initiation of the Great Western Schism (1378) 2008. (Brill's Ser.). 288p. *(978-90-04-16560-1(6))* BRILL.

Ryan, Robin. Catholics on Call: Discerning a Life of Service in the Church. 2010. 19.95 *(978-0-8146-3270-3(X))* Liturgical Pr.

CATHOLIC CHURCH—CLERGY—BIOGRAPHY

Abislaimán, Rafael B. Peregrinando a San Agustín: Al Encuentro Del Siervo de Dios, Padre Félix Varela. 2008. (Félix Varela Ser.). (SPA., Illus.). 448p. pap. 29.95 *(978-1-59388-123-7(7))* Ediciones Universal.

Almond, Kenneth Alfred. Saint John Almond & the Society of his Time. 2008. (Illus.). 96p. pap. *(978-1-84748-366-9(6))* Athena Pr.

Andrews, Gregory John. Making God Laugh. 2011. pap. 16.95 *(978-0-7414-6485-9(3))* Infinity Publishing.

Beagle, Donald Robert. Poet of the Lost Cause: A Life of Father Ryan. 2008. (ENG., Illus.). 48.95 *(978-1-57233-606-3(4))* Univ. of Tennessee Pr.

Beriger, Andreas. Windesheimer Klosterkultur Um 1500: Vita, Werk und Lebenswelt des Rutger Sycamber. (Frahe Neuzeit Ser.).Tr. of Monastery Culture in Windesheim around 1500. the biography, works, & life-world of Rutger Sycamber. (GER.). XI, 371p. 180.00 **(978-3-11-187175-2(4))** De Gruyter, Walter Inc.

Biographiq. John Wycliffe - the Morning Star of the Reformation (Biography) 2008. 60p. pap. 9.99 *(978-1-59986-075-6(9)*, Biographiq) Filiquarian Publishing, LLC.

Boresky, Theodosia. Life of St Josaphat: Martyr of the Union. 2011. 388p. 53.95 **(978-1-258-03017-9(9))** Literary Licensing, LLC.

Braun, Leopold. In Lubianka's Shadow: The Memoirs of an American Priest in Stalin's Moscow, 1934-1945. Hamburg, G. M., ed. 2006. (Illus.). 456p. 35.00 *(978-0-268-02199-3(6))* Univ. of Notre Dame Pr.

Brinkley, Douglas & Fenster, Julie. Parish Priest: Father Michael McGivney & American Catholicism. 2007. (ENG., Illus.). 272p. pap. 13.99 *(978-0-06-077685-5(4)*, HarperPerennial) HarperCollins Pubs.

Campbell, Bernadette. Jock Dalrymple: And the Path to Holiness. 2013. (ENG.). 224p. pap. 19.95 *(978-0-86012-441-2(X)*, Burns & Oates) Continuum International Publishing Group, Ltd. GBR. Dist: National Bk. Network.

Cassidy, Edward Idris Cardinal & Cassidy, Edward Idris. My Years in Vatican Service. 2009. (Illus.). 176p. pap. 18.95 *(978-0-8091-4593-5(6))* Paulist Pr.

Cox, Gerald F. Radical Peasant. 2006. (Illus.). 153p. pap. 15.00 *(978-1-4120-9557-0(3))* Trafford Publishing.

Dalarun, J., et al. The Two Lives of Robert of Arbrissel, Founder of Fontevraud: Legends, Writings & Testimonies. 2007. (Disciplina Monastica Ser.). (ENG, FRE & LAT., Illus.). 772p. (C). pap. 218.00 *(978-2-503-52419-1(2))* Brepols Pubs. BEL. Dist: ISD.

Daly, Edward & Devlin, Kieran, eds. The Clergy of the Diocese of Derry - An Index. 2nd ed. 2009. (Illus.). 244p. 70.00 *(978-1-84682-168-4(1))* Four Courts Pr. IRL. Dist: International Specialized Bk. Services.

Daly, Michael. The Book of Mychal: The Surprising Life & Heroic Death of Father Mychal Judge. 2009. (ENG., Illus.). 416p. pap. 17.99 *(978-0-312-58744-4(9)*, St. Martin's Griffin) St. Martin's Pr.

De Castro, Rosalía. En las Orillas del Mar. (Clasicos Castalia). (SPA., Illus.). 152p. 9.95 *(978-84-7039-274-0(3)*, CC524) Castalia, Editorial S.A. ESP. Dist: Continental Bk. Co., Inc.

De Mullenheim, Sophie. John Mary Vianney: The Holy Cure of Ars. 2010. 36p. 14.99 *(978-1-58617-509-2(2))* Ignatius Pr.

Dear, John. A Persistent Peace: One Man's Struggle for a Nonviolent World. 2008. (ENG.). 456p. 22.95 *(978-0-8294-2720-2(1))* Loyola Pr.

Dorman, Marianne. Lancelot Andrewes 1555-1626: Teacher & Preacher in the Post-Reformation English Church. 2006. pap. 28.95 *(978-1-58736-639-0(8))* Wheatmark.

Foley, Thomas W. & Foley, Thomas. Father Francis M. Craft: Missionary to the Sioux. 2007. (ENG., Illus.). 1p. pap. 17.95 *(978-0-8032-6925-5(0)*, Bison Bks.) Univ. of Nebraska Pr.

Fushek, Dale. The Unexpected Life. 2011. 160p. pap. 15.00 **(978-1-881276-05-0(8))** Serey/Jones Pubs.

Gribble, Richard. Father of the Fatherless: The Authorized Biography of Father Nelson Baker. 2011. 432p. 29.95 *(978-0-8091-0596-0(9))* Paulist Pr.

Groeschel, Benedict & Groeschel, Benedict J. Travelers along the Way: The Men & Women Who Shaped My Life. 2010. pap. *(978-0-86716-984-3(2)*, Servant Bks.) Franciscan Media.

Harley, Thomas. Matthew Poole: His Life, His Times, His Contributions along with His Argument against the Infallibility of the Roman Catholic Church. 2009. 232p. pap. 18.95 *(978-0-595-52502-7(4))* iUniverse, Inc.

Harrington, Thomas J. A Call to Save: The Memoir of a Fire Chaplain. McCabe, Marsha L., ed. 2006. (Illus.). 72p. per. 12.95 *(978-0-932027-97-9(0))* Spinner Pubns., Inc.

Hemsath, Sister Caroline. From Slave to Priest: A Biography of the Reverend Augustine Tolton (1854-1897) First Black American Priest of the United States. 2006. (Illus.). 251p. 17.95 *(978-1-58617-097-4(X))* Ignatius Pr.

In Memoriam Mar Ignatius Afram II Rahmani. 2010. (ARA.). pap. 29.68 *(978-1-61143-008-0(9))* Gorgias Pr., LLC.

Jestice, Phyllis & Sherry, Matthew, trs. from FRE. A Life Poured Out: Pierre Claverie of Algeria. 2007. Orig. Title: Pierre claverie: un Algerien par Alliance. (FRE., Illus.). 286p. per. 30.00 *(978-1-57075-706-8(2))* Orbis Bks.

Josaitis, Marvin. Breaking Grand Silence: A Former Catholic Priest Speaks Out. 2011. pap. 10.99 **(978-1-61346-678-0(1))** Tate Publishing & Enterprises, LLC.

Lavigne, Ruth H. The Life of St. Claude de la Colombiere: Spiritual Director of St. Margaret Mary Alacoque. 135p. pap. 7.95 *(978-0-8189-4467-3(6))* St Pauls/Alba Hse. Pubs.

Lewis, C. S. & Calabria, Giovanni. The Latin Letters of C. S. Lewis. Moynihan, Martin, tr. from LAT. 2009. Orig. Title: Letters: A Study in Friendship. 126p. pap. 12.00 *(978-1-58731-455-1(X))* St. Augustine's Pr., Inc.

Maguire, Connell. Foibles of Father Joe. 2008. per. 14.95 *(978-0-9727330-3-8(5))* Chi Chi Pr.

Mahieu-De Praetere, Marthe. Kurisumala: Francis Mahieu Acharya, Pioneer in Christian Monasticism in India. Van Winkle, Susan, tr. from FRE. 2008. (Cistercian Father Ser.). (Illus.). 394p. per. 79.95 *(978-0-87907-614-6(3))* Cistercian Pubns., Inc.

Malloy, Edward A. Monk's Tale: The Pilgrimage Begins, 1941-1975. 2009. (ENG., Illus.). 256p. 25.00 *(978-0-268-03516-7(4))* Univ. of Notre Dame Pr.

Malloy, Edward A. Monk's Tale: Way Stations on the Journey. 2011. (Illus.). 280p. 25.00 **(978-0-268-03522-8(9))** Univ. of Notre Dame Pr.

Maxfield, Leo. I Am the Holy Land ... & so are You. 2008. 160p. pap. *(978-0-9715270-4-1(0))* Avalini.

Mccarthy, Monsignor William. The Conspiracy: An Innocent Priest. 2010. 340p. 33.95 *(978-1-4502-3965-3(X))*; pap. 23.95 *(978-1-4502-3964-6(1))* iUniverse, Inc.

McGovern, Thomas. Generations of Priests. 2010. 456p. 60.00 *(978-1-84682-256-8(4))*; pap. 30.00 *(978-1-84682-257-5(2))* Four Courts Pr. IRL. Dist: International Specialized Bk. Services.

McMullen, John William. The Last Blackrobe of Indiana: And the Potawatomi Trail of Death. 2006. 420p. per. 16.95 *(978-0-9791304-0-3(9))* Charles River Pr.

McMurren, Irving. The Abernathy Chronicles, Part One. 2008. 296p. pap. 17.50 *(978-1-4357-1388-8(5))* Lulu Enterprises Inc.

McWilliams, Steve. Green Bananas: My Days with Father Bill Atkinson. 2010. (Illus.). 176p. pap. 14.95 *(978-0-915180-45-5(6)*, 0988) Harrowood Bks.

—Green Bananas: The Wisdom of Father Bill. deluxe ed. 2010. 25.00 *(978-0-915180-44-8(8))* Harrowood Bks.

Merton, Thomas. Passion for Peace: Reflections on War & Nonviolence. Shannon, William H., ed. abr. ed. 2006. (ENG.). 176p. pap. 14.95 *(978-0-8245-2415-9(2)*, Crossroad) Crossroad Publishing Co., The.

Meyer, James L. I Loved a Boy: Confessions of a Roman Catholic Priest. 2007. (Illus.). 240p. 24.95 *(978-0-9759416-3-8(1))* Van Antwerp & Beale Pubs.

Morgan, Frank. Both Sides of the Altar. 2011. (ENG.). 208p. pap. 19.00 *(978-1-58731-080-5(5))* St. Augustine's Pr., Inc.

Mugridge, Christine Anne & Usher, Jerry, eds. Called by Name: The Inspiring Stories of 12 Men Who Became Catholic Priests. 2008. 189p. per. 12.99 *(978-1-934217-36-8(0))* Ascension Pr.

Murray, Paul Edward. Life in Paradox: The Story of a Gay Catholic Priest. 2008. (ENG.). 272p. pap. 24.95 *(978-1-84694-112-2(1))* Hunt, John Publishing Ltd. GBR. Dist: National Bk. Network.

Nowicki, Tomasz. Plebani Archidiakonatu Pomorskiego W XVIII Wieku: Studium Prozopograficzne. 2008. (POL., Illus.). 188p. *(978-83-7306-409-6(5))* Towarzystwo Naukowe Katolickiego Uniwersytetu Lubelskiego.

O Madagain, Murchadh. By the Word of Their Testimony: The Journey of a Priest. 2009. 192p. pap. 12.00 *(978-1-59056-119-5(8))* Lantern Bks.

O'Connell, David. Furl That Banner: The Life of Abram J. Ryan, Poet-Priest of the South. 2006. (Illus.). 251p. 35.00 *(978-0-88146-035-3(4))* Mercer Univ. Pr.

Oldfield, John. El Obispo del Barrio: Una Biografico del Obispo Alphonso Gallegos, OAR. Alvarez, Beatriz O., tr. from ENG. 2007. (SPA., Illus.). 101p. per. 12.95 *(978-0-8091-4431-0(X)*, 4431-x) Paulist Pr.

O'Rourke, Michelle. Befriending Death: Henri Nouwen & a Spirituality of Dying. 2009. 160p. pap. 18.00 *(978-1-57075-840-9(9))* Orbis Bks.

Pine, M. S. John Bannister Tabb the PriestPoet. 2006. pap. 21.95 *(978-1-4286-4665-0(5))* Kessinger Publishing, LLC.

Prindiville, Raymond J. G. Damien, Martyr of Molokai. 2011. 26p. 35.95 **(978-1-258-01593-0(5))** Literary Licensing, LLC.

Rafferty, Kevin. Fragments of a Life. 2009. (ENG.). 306p. 47.95 *(978-1-85607-621-0(0))* Columba Pr. IRL. Dist: Dufour Editions, Inc.

Richards, Virginia Helen & Halpin, D. Thomas. Saint Damien of Molokai: Hero of Hawaii. 2009. (Illus.). 128p. (J). pap. 7.95 *(978-0-8198-7126-8(5))* Pauline Bks. & Media.

Rodriguez, Fidel. Félix Varela: Profundidad Manifiesta. 2007. (SPA., Illus.). pap. 24.95 *(978-1-59388-074-3(X))* Ediciones Universal.

Rodriguez, P. Fidel. Felix Varela: Profundidad Manifiesta Vol. 1: Primeros Anos de la Vida del Padre Felix Varela y Morales. Infancia, Adolescencia y Juventud (1785-1821), 3 vols. 2007. (Coleccion Felix Varela Ser.: Vol. 28). (Illus.). 347p. pap. 24.95 *(978-1-59388-075-0(8))* Ediciones Universal.

Rotelli, Richard L. Let Me Be a Light: The Faith Journey of Father Ron Lawson. 2010. pap. 21.95 *(978-0-7414-6021-9(1))* Infinity Publishing.

Rubio-Boitel, Fernando. La Pecera de la Habana: Recuento de un Pedro Pan: Desde Cuba hasta Nuevo México. 2009. (SPA.). 441p. pap. 25.00 *(978-1-61584-051-9(6))* Independent Pub.

Ryan, Patrick. Archbishop Patrick John Ryan His Life & Times: Ireland - St. Louis - Philadelphia 1831-1911. 2010. (Illus.). 372p. pap. 17.99 *(978-1-4389-9822-0(8))* AuthorHouse.

Schroth, Raymond. Bob Drinan: The Controversial Life of the First Catholic Priest Elected to Congress. 2nd ed. 2010. (ENG.). 432p. 32.95 *(978-0-8232-3304-5(9))* Fordham Univ. Pr.

Seed, Michael & Botham, Noel. Sinners & Saints: The Irreverent Diaries of Britain's Most Controversial Priest. 2009. (ENG., Illus.). 278p. 29.95 *(978-1-84454-770-8(1))* Blake, John Publishing, Ltd. GBR. Dist: Independent Pubs. Group.

Stacey, John. John Wycliff & Reform. 2009. 170p. pap. 20.00 *(978-1-60608-761-9(4)*, Wipf and Stock) Wipf & Stock Pubs.

Studer, Louis. Farmer to Father: Finding God in People, Places & Events. 2007. (Illus.). iv, 183p. *(978-0-9795561-0-4(4))* Missionnaires Oblats de Marie Immaculee.

Sullivan, Karen. The Inner Lives of Medieval Inquisitors. 2011. (ENG.). 312p. 45.00 *(978-0-226-78167-9(4))* Univ. of Chicago Pr.

Tapia, Maria Del Carmen. Inside Opus Dei: A True, Unfinished Story. 2006. (ENG., Illus.). 378p. pap. 22.95 *(978-0-8264-1930-9(5))* Continuum International Publishing Group, Ltd. GBR. Dist: National Bk. Network.

Tedesco, Mark. Undeniable Longing. 2010. (ENG.). 208p. pap. 16.95 *(978-0-89733-599-7(6))* Academy Chicago Pubs., Ltd.

Trepanier, Claire. A Woman of Valour: The Biography of Marie-Louise Bouchard Labelle. 2010. 240p. pap. 24.95 *(978-1-897425-84-8(8))* Univ. of Washington Pr.

Upton, Julia. Worship in Spirit & Truth: The Life & Legacy of H.A. Reinhold. 2010. 24.95 *(978-0-8146-6220-5(X))* Liturgical Pr.

Voderholzer, Rudolf. Meet Henri de Lubac: His Life & Work. Miller, Michael J., tr. from GER. 2008. 222p. pap. 24.95 *(978-1-58617-128-5(3))* Ignatius Pr.

Walbridge, Linda. The Christians of Pakistan. 2009. 262p. pap. 39.95 *(978-0-415-57088-6(3))* Routledge.

Walsh, Michael J. The Cardinals: Thirteen Centuries of the Men Behind the Papal Throne. 2011. 256p. pap. 23.00 *(978-0-8028-2941-2(4))* Eerdmans, William B. Publishing Co.

Weakland, Rembert G. A Pilgrim in a Pilgrim Church: Memoirs of a Catholic Archbishop. 2009. (Illus.). 450p. 35.00 *(978-0-8028-6382-9(5))* Eerdmans, William B. Publishing Co.

Weigel, George. The End & the Beginning: Pope John Paul II - The Victory of Freedom, the Last Years, the Legacy. l.t. ed. 2010. 1152p. pap. 33.00 *(978-0-7393-7761-1(2))* Random Hse. Large Print.

Weinstein, Gregory. Savonarol: Italian Reformer & Martyr of the Fifteenth Century. 2011. 64p. 36.95 **(978-1-258-00679-2(0))** Literary Licensing, LLC.

Williams, Sue. World Beyond Tears: The Ongoing Story of Father Chris Riley. 2007. 304p. (Orig.). *(978-0-7322-8265-3(9))* HarperCollins Pubs. Australia.

Wright, Scott. Oscar Romero & the Communion of Saints: A Biography. 2009. (Illus.). 160p. pap. 20.00 *(978-1-57075-839-3(5))* Orbis Bks.

Yallop, David. The Power & the Glory: Inside the Dark Heart of Pope John Paul II's Vatican. 2009. (ENG.). 560p. pap. 18.00 *(978-0-465-01542-9(5))* Basic Bks.

CATHOLIC CHURCH—CLERGY—CORRESPONDENCE

Eudes, John. Letters & Shorter Works. Hauser, Ruth, tr. 2011. 380p. 53.95 **(978-1-258-08799-9(5))** Literary Licensing, LLC.

Frassati, Pier Giorgio, et al. Letters to His Friends & Family. 2009. *(978-0-8189-1305-1(3))* St Pauls/Alba Hse. Pubs.

Lewis, C. S. & Calabria, Giovanni. The Latin Letters of C. S. Lewis. Moynihan, Martin, tr. from LAT. 2009. Orig. Title: Letters: A Study in Friendship. 126p. pap. 12.00 *(978-1-58731-455-1(X))* St. Augustine's Pr., Inc.

Lord, Daniel A. Played by Ear: The Autobiography of Daniel A. Lord. 2011. 414p. 54.95 **(978-1-258-03490-0(5))** Literary Licensing, LLC.

McGrath, Francis J., ed. The Final Step, 1 November 1843 — 6 October 1845. 2006. (Newman Letters & Diaries). (ENG.). 864p. 350.00 *(978-0-19-925459-0(1))* Oxford Univ. Pr., Inc.

Merton, Thomas, et al. A Meeting of Angels: The Correspondence of Thomas Merton with Edward Deming & Faith Andrews. 2008. (Illus.) 118p. 25.00 *(978-0-9721144-9-3(1))* Broadstone Media LLC.

CATHOLIC CHURCH—CONFIRMATION

see Confirmation—Catholic Church

CATHOLIC CHURCH—CONTROVERSIAL LITERATURE

Here are entered works which argue against the philosophy, doctrines and practices of the Catholic Church.

see also Anti-Catholicism

Alvarez Recio, Leticia. Fighting the Antichrist: A Cultural History of Anti-Catholicism in Tudor England. 2011. (ENG., Illus.). 238p. 69.95 *(978-1-84519-427-7(6)*, Sussex Academic Pr. GBR. Dist: International Specialized Bk. Services.

Anderson, Robert. The Buddha of Christendom. 2007. 344p. per. 21.95 *(978-1-60206-204-7(8))* Cosimo, Inc.

Balmes, Jaime Luciano. European Civilization: Protestantism & Catholicity Compared... by Rev. J. Balmes. 2006. 512p. per. 29.99 *(978-1-4255-5716-4(3))* MPublishing.

Beecher, Lyman. A Plea for the West. 2009. 58p. pap. 14.14 *(978-1-151-70983-0(6))* General Bks. LLC.

Beecher, Lyman, abr. A Plea for the West. 2009. (Amer Philosophy, Religion Ser.). (ENG.). 196p. pap. 14.95 *(978-1-4290-1837-1(2))* Applewood Bks.

Beeke, Joel R. & Kistler, Don. Sola Scriptura! The Protestant Position on the Bible. 2nd ed. 2009. *(978-1-56769-183-2(8))* Reformation Pubs.

Benson, Robert Hugh. Paradoxes of Catholicism. 2007. (ENG.) 96p. per. *(978-1-4065-4947-1(2))* Dodo Pr.

Berry, E. Sylvester. The Church of Christ: An Apologetic & Dogmatic Treatise. 2009. 344p. pap. 38.00 *(978-1-60608-802-9(5)*, Wipf and Stock) Wipf & Stock Pubs.

Bowman, Wayne B. Hidden in Plain Sight: Catechism versus the Bible. 2009. (J). pap. 15.99 *(978-1-60799-779-5(7))* Tate Publishing & Enterprises, LLC.

Brantl, George, ed. Catholicism. 2007. (ENG.). 254p. 42.95 *(978-0-548-08028-3(3))* Kessinger Publishing, LLC.

Buttrose, Larry. Tales of the Popes: From Eden to el Dorado, an Infamous History. 2009. (ENG.). 224p. pap. 19.95 *(978-1-74110-666-4(4))* New Holland Pubs. Pty, Ltd. AUS. Dist: Tuttle Publishing.

Eskrich, Pierre & Trento, Jean-Baptiste. Mappe-monde nouvelle Papistique: Histoire de la mappe-monde papistique, en laquelle est declaire tout ce qui est contenu et pourtraict en la grande table, ou carte de la Mappe-monde (Geneve, 1566) Lestringant, Frank & Preda, Alessandra, eds. 2009. (Travaux d'Humanisme et Renaissance Ser.). (FRE., Illus.). 486p. (C). 181.00 *(978-2-600-01265-2(6))* Droz, Librairie CHE. Dist: Brown, David Bk. Co., The.

Garvin, Joseph N. & Corbett, James A. The Summa Contra Haereticos: Ascribed to Praepositinus of Cremona. Moore, Philip S., ed. 2011. 358p. 51.95 **(978-1-258-08935-1(1))** Literary Licensing, LLC.

Gaudron, Matthias. The Catechism of the Crisis in the Church. 2010. *(978-1-892331-79-3(9))* Angelus Pr.

Gibbons, James. The Faith of Our Fathers. 2009. 260p. pap. *(978-0-217-89071-7(7))* Books LLC.

—The Faith of Our Fathers. (Early Best Sellers Ser.). reprint ed. lib. bdg. 48.00 *(978-0-7426-1027-9(6))* Classic Bks.

Gohdes, C. B. Does the Modern Papacy Require a New Evaluation? 2011. 264p. 47.95 **(978-1-258-02117-7(X))** Literary Licensing, LLC.

Goldstein, David. Letters, Hebrew-Catholic, to Mr Isaacs. 2011. 314p. 50.95 **(978-1-258-09141-5(0))** Literary Licensing, LLC.

Gore, Charles. Roman Catholic Claims. 2009. 210p. 28.99 *(978-1-113-59435-8(7))*; pap. 23.75 *(978-1-113-59434-1(9))*; pap. 24.75 *(978-1-113-60785-0(8))* BiblioBazaar.

—Roman Catholic Claims. 2009. 126p. pap. *(978-0-217-27947-5(3))* Books LLC.

—Roman Catholic Claims. 224p. 2008. 39.95 *(978-1-4365-8066-3(8))* 2007. (ENG.). per. 24.95 *(978-0-548-79463-0(4))* Kessinger Publishing, LLC.

—Roman Catholic Claims. 7th ed. 2008. 225p. pap. 19.00 *(978-1-60608-117-4(9))* Wipf & Stock Pubs.

Guimaraes, Atila Sinke. Ecclesia: The Church, 11 vols., Vol. 11. 2009.Tr. of Church. (LAT & ENG.). 320p. pap. 20.00 *(978-0-9819793-0-4(0))* Tradition in Action, Inc.

Guinness, H. Grattan. Romanism & the Reformation: From the Standpoint of Prophecy. 2009. 408p. pap. 33.00 *(978-1-55635-618-6(8)*, Wipf and Stock) Wipf & Stock Pubs.

Hislop, Alexander. The Two Babylons. 2007. 356p. per. 16.45 *(978-1-60206-139-2(4))* Cosimo, Inc.

—The Two Babylons. 2007. 360p. per. 31.95 *(978-1-4209-2942-3(9))* Digireads.com.

—The Two Babylons: Or the Papal Worship... [Complete Book Edition, not pamphlet Edition]. 2010. 354p. pap. 10.00 *(978-1-57898-900-3(0))* Martino Publishing.

—The Two Babylons: Or the Papal Worship Proved to be the Worship of Nimrod & His Wife. 2006. (Illus.). 356p. per. 27.95 *(978-1-58509-273-4(8))* Book Tree, The.

—The Two Babylons: Or, the Papal Worship Proved to be the Worship of Nimrod & His Wife. 2007. 528p. 24.99 *(978-1-59986-636-9(6))*; (ENG.). pap. 16.99 *(978-1-59986-654-3(4))* Filiquarian Publishing, LLC.

—The Two Babylons - Alexander Hislop. 2007. 360p. pap. 21.95 *(978-1-60424-486-1(0)*, Book Jungle) Standard Pubns., Inc.

—Two Babylons or the Papal Worship Proved to Be the Worship of Nimrod & His Wife. 2007. 356p. 46.95 *(978-0-548-00202-5(9))* Kessinger Publishing, LLC.

—The Two Babylons or the Papal Worship Proved to Be the Worship of Nimrod & His Wife. 2009. 412p. 39.99 *(978-1-61534-009-5(2))*; pap. 24.99 *(978-1-61534-008-8(4))* EZreads Pubns., LLC.

Ironside, H. A. Letters to a Roman Catholic Priest. 2011. 50p. 35.95 **(978-1-258-03890-3(8))** Literary Licensing, LLC.

Jewel, John. The Works of John Jewel, Bishop of Salisbury. Ayre, John, ed. 2010. (Parker Society Ser.). 596p. pap. 50.00 *(978-1-60608-064-1(4)*, Wipf and Stock) Wipf & Stock Pubs.

Johnson, Frederick A. Christ & Catholicism. 2011. 298p. 48.95 **(978-1-258-07061-8(8))** Literary Licensing, LLC.

La Rocque, Patrick de. John Paul II: Doubts about a Beatification. 2011. pap. **(978-1-892331-91-5(8))** Angelus Pr.

McCabe, Joseph. Hitler Dupes the Vatican: How the Papacy Was Sold in Austria & Sold Civilization in Czechoslovakia. 2011. 34p. 35.95 **(978-1-258-02584-7(1))** Literary Licensing, LLC.

—The Pope Helps Hitler to World Power: How the Cross Courted the Swastika for Eight Years. Haldeman-Julius, E., ed. 2011. 34p. 35.95 **(978-1-258-04942-3(2))** Literary Licensing, LLC.

—Rome's Syllabus of Condemned Opinions: The Last Blast of the Catholic Church's Medieval Trumpet. Haldeman-Julius, E., ed. 2011. 34p. 35.95 **(978-1-258-09639-7(0))** Literary Licensing, LLC.

—The Totalitarian Church of Rome: Its Fuehrer, Its Gauleiter, Its Gestabo, & Its Money-Box. Haldeman-Julius, E., ed. 2011. 34p. 35.95 ***(978-1-258-05584-4(8))*** Literary Licensing, LLC.

McCabe, Joseph. Twelve Years in a Monastery. 2009. 256p. 24.99 *(978-1-103-68772-5(7))*; pap. 18.99 *(978-1-103-68771-8(9))* BiblioBazaar.

McCrossen, Vincent A. The Empty Room. 2011. 166p. 41.95 ***(978-1-258-07428-9(1))*** Literary Licensing, LLC.

McIlvaine, Charles Pettit. Righteousness by Faith: Nature & Means of Our Justification Before God. 2nd ed. 2007. 494p. pap. 42.00 *(978-1-55635-708-4(7))* Wipf & Stock Pubs.

—Righteousness by Faith; or, the Nature & Means of Our Justification Before God; Illustrated by a Comparison of the Doctrine of the Oxford Tracts Wit. 2006. (Illus.). 500p. per. 29.99 *(978-1-4255-5582-5(9))* MPublishing.

Mediaeval & Modern Saints & Miracles. 2007. (ENG.). 316p. 45.95 *(978-0-548-08135-8(2))* Kessinger Publishing, LLC.

M'Gavin, William. Protestant V1 A Series of Essays. 2006. pap. 36.95 *(978-1-4286-4564-6(0))* Kessinger Publishing, LLC.

—Protestant V2 A Series of Essays. 2006. pap. 40.95 *(978-1-4286-4565-3(9))* Kessinger Publishing, LLC.

Müller, Michael. The Catholic Dogma: Extra Ecclesiam Nullus omnino Salvatur. 2007. 304p. per. 24.95 *(978-0-9782985-1-7(9))* Catholic Authors Pr.

Murray, Nicholas. Letters to the Rt Rev John Hughes, Roman Catholic Bishop of New York by Kirwan [Pseud.]. 2006. 316p. per. 23.99 *(978-1-4255-3085-3(0))* MPublishing.

—Romanism at Home: Letters to the Hon. Roger B. Taney / by Kirwan [Pseud.]. 2006. 292p. per. 23.99 *(978-1-4255-2627-6(6))* MPublishing.

Newman, Cardinal John Henry. An Essay on the Development of Christian Doctrine. 2007. 468p. per. 21.95 *(978-1-60206-575-8(6))* Cosimo, Inc.

O'Clock, Jr. Isaiah's Leper: A spiritual Odyssey. 2008. 328p. pap. 22.95 *(978-0-595-50983-6(5))* iUniverse, Inc.

Owen, Olin Marvin. Rum, Rags, & Religion or, in Darkest America & the Way Out. 2007. (ENG.). 128p. 35.95 *(978-0-548-14995-9(X))*; per. 20.95 *(978-1-4304-4321-6(9))* Kessinger Publishing, LLC.

Pascal, Blaise. Pascal's Pensees. 2008. 400p. 29.99 *(978-0-554-36613-5(4))*; 31.99 *(978-0-554-27310-5(1))* BiblioBazaar.

—Pensees. 2007. (ENG.). 256p. per. 16.99 *(978-1-59547-915-0(5))* NuVision Pubns., LLC.

—Pensees. (FRE.). pap. 9.95 *(978-2-266-05452-2(X))* Presses Pocket FRA. Dist: Distribooks, Inc.

Pope, or President? 2006. 368p. per. 26.99 *(978-1-4255-3834-7(7))* MPublishing.

Rafferty, Oliver. George Tyrrell & Catholic Modernism. 2010. 187p. 65.00 *(978-1-84682-236-0(X))* Four Courts Pr. IRL. Dist: International Specialized Bk. Services.

Ranke-Heinemann, Uta. Eunuchs for the Kingdom of Heaven: Women, Sexuality, & the Catholic Church. 2006. 360p. reprint ed. 22.00 *(978-1-4223-5378-3(8))* DIANE Publishing Co.

Raupert, J. Godfrey. Supreme Problem an Examination of Histor. 2006. pap. 31.95 *(978-1-4286-3821-1(0))* Kessinger Publishing, LLC.

Rutherford, J. F. Enemies. 2007. (ENG.). 380p. 48.95 *(978-0-548-03685-3(3))* Kessinger Publishing, LLC.

Rutherford, Joseph F. Face the Facts & Learn the Only One Way of Escape. 2008. 68p. pap. 9.90 *(978-1-4357-0775-7(3))* Lulu Enterprises Inc.

Scheeben, Matthias Joseph. The Mysteries of Christianity. 2008. (ENG.). 834p. pap. 69.95 *(978-0-8245-2430-2(6))* Crossroad Publishing Co., The.

—Nature & Grace. Vollert, Cyril, tr. 2009. 386p. pap. 42.00 *(978-1-60608-949-1(8)*, Wipf and Stock) Wipf & Stock Pubs.

Shaffern, Robert W. The Penitents' Treasury: Indulgences in Latin Christendom, 1175-1375. 2007. (ENG.). 275p. 40.00 *(978-1-58966-139-4(7))*; pap. 25.00 *(978-1-58966-136-3(2))* Univ. of Scranton Pr.

Shamon, Albert J. Three Steps to Sanctity. pap. 3.00 *(978-1-891280-18-4(X))* CMJ Marian Pubs.

Shelton, Rick. John: 16. 2009. 160p. pap. 17.00 *(978-1-4389-8362-2(X))* AuthorHouse.

Soames, Henry. The Latin Church During Anglo Saxon Times. 2007. (ENG.). 528p. 55.95 *(978-0-548-04761-3(8))* Kessinger Publishing, LLC.

Southwell, Robert. An Humble Supplication to her Maiestie. Bald, R. C., ed. 2011. (ENG.). 106p. pap. 19.99 *(978-1-107-66833-1(6))* Cambridge Univ. Pr.

Tettemer, John Moynihan. I Was a Monk: The Autobiography of John Tettemer. Mabie, Janet, ed. 2011. 304p. 48.95 ***(978-1-258-03341-5(0))*** Literary Licensing, LLC.

Tyrrell, SJ, George. Lex Credendi: A Sequel to Lex Orandi. 2009. 274p. pap. 24.00 *(978-1-60608-390-1(2)*, Wipf and Stock) Wipf & Stock Pubs.

—Lex Orandi: Or, Prayer & Creed. 2009. 240p. pap. 21.00 *(978-1-60608-388-8(0)*, Wipf and Stock) Wipf & Stock Pubs.

White, Joseph Blanco. Second Travels of an Irish Gentleman in Search of a Religion V1. 2007. (ENG.). 264p. 42.95 *(978-0-548-15007-8(9))*; per. 27.95 *(978-1-4304-4334-6(0))* Kessinger Publishing, LLC.

Williams, Walter Dakin & Stewart, Walter Robert. Nails of Protest: A Critical Comparison of Modern Protestant & Catholic Beliefs. 2011. 102p. 39.95 ***(978-1-258-08702-9(2))*** Literary Licensing, LLC.

Winzet, Ninian. Certane Tractatis for Reformatioun of Doctryne & Maneris in Scotland. (Maitland Club, Glasgow Publications: No. 33). reprint ed. 37.50 *(978-0-404-53001-3(X))* AMS Pr., Inc.

—Certane Tractatis for Reformatioun of Doctryne & Maneris in Scotland. 2010. 214p. pap. 24.75 *(978-1-148-37482-6(5))* BiblioBazaar.

CATHOLIC CHURCH—CONTROVERSIAL LITERATURE—PROTESTANT AUTHORS

Beecher, Lyman. A Plea for the West. 2008. 188p. 37.95 *(978-1-4366-0501-4(6))*; (ENG.). 192p. per. 22.95 *(978-0-548-81367-6(1))* Kessinger Publishing, LLC.

Blakeney, R. P. Popery in Its Social Aspect Being A Com. 2006. pap. 30.95 *(978-1-4286-4465-6(2))* Kessinger Publishing, LLC.

Chiniquy. The Priest the Woman & the Confessional. 2008. 168p. 22.99 *(978-0-554-36913-6(3))* 2008. 168p. 25.99 *(978-0-554-27610-6(0))* 2007. 152p. pap. 19.99 *(978-1-4346-3590-7(2))* BiblioBazaar.

—The Priest the Woman & the Confessional. 140p. 2009. pap. 10.95 *(978-1-4385-1911-1(7))* 2008. (ENG.). pap. 13.95 *(978-1-4385-1203-7(1))* Standard Pubns., Inc. (Book Jungle).

—The Priest, the Woman & the Confessional. 2007. 180p. 25.96 *(978-1-4218-3852-6(4)*, 1st World Library - Literary Society) 1st World Publishing, Inc.

—The Priest, the Woman & the Confessional. 2007. (ENG.). 108p. per. *(978-1-4068-4554-9(X))* Echo Library.

—The Priest, the Woman & the Confessional. 2007. 180p. per. 11.95 *(978-1-4218-3952-3(0)*, 1st World Library - Literary Society) 1st World Publishing, Inc.

—The Priest the Woman & the Confessional. l.t. ed. 2007. (ENG.). 164p. pap. 21.99 *(978-1-4346-3591-4(0))* BiblioBazaar.

Fresenborg, Bernard. Thirty Years in Hell: Or from Darkness to Light. 2007. (ENG.). 162p. pap. 19.99 *(978-1-4264-5087-7(7))*; 178p. pap. 21.99 *(978-1-4264-5388-5(4))* BiblioBazaar.

Lehmann, L. H. ExPriest & the Riddle of Religion. 2006. pap. 30.95 *(978-1-4286-5811-0(4))* Kessinger Publishing, LLC.

Nevins, William. Thoughts on Popery. 2010. 232p. pap. 25.75 *(978-1-149-56791-3(0))* BiblioBazaar.

—Thoughts on Popery. 2009. 126p. pap. 21.61 *(978-1-151-22572-6(X))*; 118p. pap. 19.99 *(978-1-150-10104-5(0))* General Bks. LLC.

—Thoughts on Popery. Taylor, Isaac, ed. 2009. 224p. 39.95 *(978-1-104-55463-7(1))*; pap. 24.95 *(978-1-104-51015-2(4))* Kessinger Publishing, LLC.

Puller, F. W. The Primitive Saints & the See of Rome. 2007. (ENG.). 464p. 52.95 *(978-0-548-08386-4(X))* Kessinger Publishing, LLC.

Tyndale, William. Expositions & Notes on Sundry Portions of the Holy Scriptures. 2009. 184p. pap. *(978-0-217-71656-7(3))* Books LLC.

Wilson, Art. And So Help Us God! for Every American Who Still Wants His Liberties. 2011. 64p. 36.95 ***(978-1-258-02044-6(0))*** Literary Licensing, LLC.

CATHOLIC CHURCH—CURIA ROMANA

Haye, Thomas. Päpste und Poeten: Die mittelalterliche Kurie als Objekt und Förderer panegyrischer Dichtung. 2009.Tr. of Popes & Poets. the Medieval Curia as an Object & Sponsor of Panegyric Poetry. (GER.). 326p. 168.00 *(978-3-11-021892-3(5))* De Gruyter, Walter Inc.

Koller, Alexander. Die Außenbeziehungen der römischen Kurie unter Paul V. Borghese. Koller, Alexander, ed. 2008. (Bibliothek des Deutschen Historischen Instituts in Rom Ser.).Tr. of External Relations of the Roman Curia under Paul V Borghese (1605¿¿1621). (GER., Illus.). XVI, 527p. *(978-3-484-82115-6(9))* Verlag Max Niemeyer.

CATHOLIC CHURCH—CUSTOMS AND PRACTICES

Here are entered works on devotional customs and practices other than those which make up the official public worship of the Church.

Arbogast, Joan Marie. Feast Days & Holidays. 2012. (ENG.). 160p. spiral bd. 19.95 ***(978-0-8198-2707-4(X))*** Pauline Bks. & Media.

Badger, George. The Nestorians & Their Rituals. 2010. pap. 147.20 *(978-1-61143-377-7(0))*; pap. 147.20 *(978-1-61143-376-0(2))* Gorgias Pr., LLC.

Barrera, Ambrosio. Abide in Me. 2008. 51p. pap. 16.95 *(978-1-60672-797-3(4))* PublishAmerica, Inc.

Catanoso, Justin. My Cousin the Saint: A Story of Love, Miracles, & an Italian Family Reunited. 2009. 368p. pap. 14.99 *(978-0-06-172932-4(9)*, HarperPerennial) HarperCollins Pubs.

Chaldean Cultural Center. The Chaldeans: A Contemporary Portrait of One of Civilizations's Oldest Cultures. 2008. (Illus.). 144p. lib. bdg. 50.00 *(978-0-615-24692-5(3))* Chaldean Cultural Ctr.

Costello, Charles Robert. Celebrating on the Journey: A Guide to a Catholic-Jewish Seder For 100. 2011. 116p. 21.23 ***(978-1-4567-6114-1(5))***; pap. 10.68 ***(978-1-4567-6112-7(9))*** AuthorHouse.

Donghi, Antonio. Words & Gestures in the Liturgy. 2009. pap. 18.95 *(978-0-8146-6222-9(6))* Liturgical Pr.

Forster, Marc R. Catholic Germany from the Reformation to the Enlightenment. 2007. (European History in Perspective Ser.). (ENG., Illus.). 224p. 130.00 *(978-0-333-69837-2(1))* Palgrave Macmillan.

—Catholic Germany from the Reformation to the Enlightenment. Black, Jeremy, ed. 2007. (European History in Perspective Ser.). (ENG., Illus.). 224p. pap. 39.00 *(978-0-333-69838-9(X))* Palgrave Macmillan.

Gallagher, Lowell. Redrawing the Map of Early Modern English Catholicism. 2012. (UCLA Clark Memorial Library Ser.). (ENG., Illus.). 360p. (C). ***(978-1-4426-4312-3(9))*** Univ. of Toronto Pr.

Gunning, Tom. The Little Book of Christian Rituals in the Home. 2008. (ENG.). 96p. pap. 13.95 *(978-1-84730-023-2(5))* Veritas Pubns. IRL. Dist: Dufour Editions, Inc.

Hahn, Scott. Signs of Life: 40 Catholic Customs & Their Biblical Roots. 2009. (ENG.). 288p. 23.00 *(978-0-385-51949-6(4))* Knopf Doubleday Publishing Group.

Libreria Editrice Vaticana, creator. Essentials for Christian Living. 2008. 127p. pap. 6.95 *(978-1-60137-020-4(2))* United States Conference of Catholic Bishops.

Moschella, Mary Clark. Living Devotions: Reflections on Immigration, Identity, & Religious Imagination. 2007. (Princeton Theolgoical Monograph Ser.). 244p. pap. 26.00 *(978-1-55635-288-1(3)*, Pickwick Pubns.) Wipf & Stock Pubs.

Newland, Mary Reed. The Year & Our Children: Catholic Family Celebrations for Every Season. 2007. 328p. per. 19.95 *(978-1-933184-27-2(2))* Sophia Institute Pr.

O'Malley, William J. The Wow Factor: Bringing the Catholic Faith Back to Life. 2011. 180p. pap. 16.00 *(978-1-57075-927-7(8))* Orbis Bks.

Portmann, John. Catholic Culture in the USA: In & Out of Church. 2010. (ENG.). 224p. 34.95 *(978-1-4411-8892-2(4))*; 120.00 *(978-1-4411-6359-2(X))* Continuum International Publishing Group, Ltd. GBR. Dist: National Bk. Network.

Rupp, Joyce. Your Sorrow Is My Sorrow: Hope & Strength in Times of Suffering. *(978-0-86716-528-9(6))* Franciscan Media.

Senior, John. The Death of Christian Culture. 2008. (ENG., Illus.). 192p. per. 28.95 *(978-1-932528-15-2(6))* IHS Pr.

Shamon, Albert J. Our Lady Says: Let Holy Mass Be Your Life. 72p. pap. 3.00 *(978-1-891280-19-1(8))* CMJ Marian Pubs.

—Our Lady Says: Love People. 80p. pap. 5.00 *(978-1-891280-28-3(7))* CMJ Marian Pubs.

—Our Lady Says: Pray the Creed. pap. 3.00 *(978-1-891280-11-5(2))* CMJ Marian Pubs.

Signorotto, Gianvittorio & Visceglia, Maria Antonietta, eds. Court & Politics in Papal Rome, 1492-1700. 2011. (Cambridge Studies in Italian History & Culture Ser.). (ENG.). 268p. pap. 35.99 *(978-0-521-28314-4(0))* Cambridge Univ. Pr.

Singer-Towns, Brian, et al. Catholic Quick View: Beliefs, Definitions, Prayers, Practices, Symbols, & Saints. 2nd ed. 2008. (Illus.). 73p. pap. 8.50 *(978-0-88489-738-5(9))* St. Mary's Pr.

Skudlarek, William. Demythologizing Celibacy. 2008. 120p. pap. 14.95 *(978-0-8146-2947-5(4)*, Liturgical Pr. Bks.) Liturgical Pr.

Trigilio, John, Jr. & Brighenti, Kenneth. Catholicism for Dummies. 2nd ed. 2011. (ENG.). 432p. pap. 24.99 ***(978-1-118-07778-8(4)***, For Dummies) Wiley, John & Sons, Inc.

Van Dyke, Joseph Smith. Popery, the Foe of the Church, & of the Republic by Joseph S Van Dyke. 2006. 336p. per. 23.99 *(978-1-4255-3359-5(0))* MPublishing.

CATHOLIC CHURCH—DICTIONARIES

Collinge, William J. Historical Dictionary of Catholicism. 2nd ed. 2012. E-Book ***(978-0-8108-7979-9(4))***; (ENG.). 622p. 95.00 ***(978-0-8108-5755-1(3))*** Scarecrow Pr., Inc.

Encyclopedia CD. 2006. cd-rom 29.95 *(978-1-933919-04-1(3))* Catholic Answers, Inc.

Fastiggi, Robert L. New Catholic Encyclopedia: Supplement 2010, 2.0. 3rd ed. 2010. (ENG.). 298.00 *(978-1-4144-7588-2(8))* Cengage Gale.

—New Catholic Encyclopedia Supplement 2009, 2 vols. 2nd ed. 2009. (New Catholic Encyclopedia Ser.). (ENG.). 298.00 *(978-1-4144-7526-4(8))* Thorndike Pr.

Fastiggi, Robert L., et al. New Catholic Encyclopedia: Supplement 2011, 2.0. 4th ed. 2011. (Illus.). 298.00 *(978-1-4144-7591-2(8))* Cengage Gale.

Flinn, Frank K. & Melton, J. Gordon. Encyclopedia of Catholicism. 2007. (Encyclopedia of World Religions Ser.). (Illus.). 704p. (C). (gr. 9). 85.00 *(978-0-8160-5455-8(X)*, Checkmark Bks.) Facts On File, Inc.

Ford, John T. Glossary of Theological Terms. 2006. 207p. per. 16.95 *(978-0-88489-903-7(9))* St. Mary's Pr.

Herbermann, Charles G., ed. Catholic Encyclopedia, 15 vols. reprint ed. 1875.00 *(978-0-7222-2154-9(1))* Library Reprints, Inc.

Joseph, Lionel. My Beloved: The Theological & Liturgical Understanding of the Christian Priesthood. 2011. 256p. lib. bdg. *(978-1-936320-18-9(5))* Academica Pr., LLC.

Massaro, Thomas. Living Justice: Catholic Social Teaching in Action. 2nd ed. 2011. (ENG.). 210p. pap. 21.95 *(978-1-4422-1013-4(3))* Rowman & Littlefield Publishers, Inc.

McKenzie, Janet. The Windeatt Dictionary: Pre-Vatican II Terms & Catholic Words from Mary Fabyan Windeatt's Saint Biographies. 2007. 112p. (J). per. 11.95 *(978-1-934185-16-2(7))* Biblio Resource Pubns., Inc.

CATHOLIC CHURCH—DIPLOMATIC RELATIONS

see Catholic Church—Foreign Relations

CATHOLIC CHURCH—DIPLOMATIC SERVICE

see Legates, Papal

CATHOLIC CHURCH—DIRECTORIES

Fadica, ed. The Catholic Funding Guide: A Directory of Resources for Catholic Activities. 6th ed. 2009. (ENG.). 568p. pap. 150.00 *(978-1-891646-06-5(0))* Foundations & Donors Interested in Catholic Activities, Inc.

FADICA, Inc. Staff. The Catholic Funding Guide: A Directory of Resources for Catholic Activities. 2007. 530p. per. 110.00 *(978-1-891646-05-8(2))* Foundations & Donors Interested in Catholic Activities, Inc.

Veritas, ed. Irish Catholic Directory 2010. 2010. (ENG., Illus.). 447p. 74.95 *(978-1-84730-208-3(4))* Veritas Pubns. IRL. Dist: Dufour Editions, Inc.

100 Years of Faith: A Centennial History of our Lady of the Rosary Church. 2008. 224p. pap. 15.00 *(978-0-9715211-5-5(8))* FolgerGraphics, Inc.

CATHOLIC CHURCH—DISCIPLINE

see also Casuistry; Communicatio in Sacris; Indulgences; Inquisition; Marriage (Canon Law); Penance; Penitentials

Berry, Jason & Renner, Gerald. Vows of Silence: The Abuse of Power in the Papacy of John Paul II. 2010. (ENG.). 368p. pap. 16.00 *(978-0-7432-8706-7(1)*, Free Pr.) Free Pr.

Chinnici, Joseph P. When Values Collide: The Catholic Church, Sexual Abuse & the Challenges of Leadership. 2009. 240p. pap. 25.00 *(978-1-57075-873-7(5))* Orbis Bks.

Keenan, Marie. Child Sexual Abuse & the Catholic Church: Gender, Power, & Organizational Culture. 2011. (ENG.). 400p. 59.95 ***(978-0-19-989567-0(8))*** Oxford Univ. Pr., Inc.

Lambing, A. A. Plain Sermons on Mixed Marriages. reprint ed. 150.00 *(978-0-7222-1793-1(5))* Library Reprints, Inc.

Mentzer, Raymond & Moreil, Francois, eds. Dire L'interdit: The Vocabulary of Censure & Exclusion in the Early Modern Reformed Tradition. 2010. (Brill's Ser. in Church History Ser.). (FRE & ENG., Illus.). 347p. *(978-90-04-17922-6(4))* BRILL.

Pius XI. On Christian Marriage. 2007. 88p. per. 10.95 *(978-0-9782985-6-2(X))* Catholic Authors Pr.

Ruland, Ludwig & Rattler, T. A. Foundations of Morality: God, Man, Lower Creatures. Thompson, Newton, ed. 2011. 398p. 54.95 ***(978-1-258-02401-7(2))*** Literary Licensing, LLC.

Schlabach, Gerald W. Unlearning Protestantism: Sustaining Christian Community in an Unstable Age. 2010. 272p. pap. 30.00 *(978-1-58743-111-1(4))* Brazos Pr.

Ullathorne, W. B. Instruction on Mixed Marriages. reprint ed. 150.00 *(978-0-7222-1796-2(X))* Library Reprints, Inc.

CATHOLIC CHURCH—DOCTRINAL AND CONTROVERSIAL WORKS

see Catholic Church—Controversial Literature; Catholic Church—Doctrines

CATHOLIC CHURCH—DOCTRINES

Here are entered works on that body of revealed and defined truth which a Catholic is bound to hold, and which is often extended to include those teachings which are not of faith but are generally held and acted upon.

see also Salvation Outside the Catholic Church

Acevedo Nieves, Juan Antonio. Sobrepoblacion: Pobreza o riqueza de Puerto Rico. 2010. (SPA., Illus.). 232p. pap. 16.99 *(978-1-61505-024-6(8))* Publicaciones Gaviota.

Albl, Martin C. Reason, Faith, & Tradition: Explorations in Catholic Theology. 2009. pap. 41.00 *(978-0-88489-982-2(9))* St. Mary's Pr.

Alfani, Guido. Fathers & Godfathers: Spiritual Kinship in Early-Modern Italy. 2009. (Catholic Christendom, 1300-1700 Ser.). (Illus.). 288p. 124.95 *(978-0-7546-6737-7(5))* Ashgate Publishing Co.

Alison, James. Broken Hearts & New Creations: Intimations of a Great Reversal. 2010. (ENG.). 224p. pap. 24.95 *(978-1-4411-0711-4(8))* Continuum International Publishing Group, Ltd. GBR. Dist: National Bk. Network.

Allen, John L. The Future Church: How Ten Trends Are Revolutionizing the Catholic Church. 2012. (ENG.). 480p. pap. 16.00 ***(978-0-385-52039-3(5)***, Image) Doubleday Religious Publishing Group, The.

Allen, John L., Jr. The Future Church: How Ten Trends Are Revolutionizing the Catholic Church. 2009. (ENG.). 480p. 28.00 *(978-0-385-52038-6(7))* Knopf Doubleday Publishing Group.

—10 Things Pope Benedict XVI Wants You to Know. 2007. 45p. per. 2.95 *(978-0-7648-1672-7(1))* Liguori Pubns.

Allen, Paul L. & Hess, Peter M. J. Catholicism & Science, 1 vol. 2008. (Greenwood Guides to Science & Religion). (Illus.). 272p. 65.00 *(978-0-313-33190-9(1)*, GR3190, Greenwood Pr.) Greenwood Publishing Group, Inc.

Almen, Lowell G. & Sklba, Richard J. The Hope of Eternal Life: Lutherans & Catholics in Dialogue XI. 2011. (ENG.). 212p. pap. 22.00 ***(978-1-932688-63-4(3)***, Lutheran Univ. Pr.) Kirk Hse. Pubs.

Amadi-Azuogu, Adolphus. The Politics of Power & the Ordination of Women. 2007. 436p. per. 21.99 *(978-1-60266-602-3(4))* Xulon Pr., Inc.

Ambrose, Glenn P. The Theology of Louis-Marie Chauvet: Overcoming Onto-Theology in the Sacramental Tradition. 2012. (Illus.). 224p. 89.95 ***(978-1-4094-3339-2(0))*** Ashgate Publishing Co.

Amodei, Michael. Send Out Your Spirit: A Confirmation Candidate's Handbook for Faith. rev. ed. 2010. 256p. pap. 11.95 *(978-1-59471-225-8(5))* Ave Maria Pr.

—Send Out Your Spirit: Preparing Teens for Confirmation (Leader's Manual) rev. ed. 2010. 192p. pap. 22.95 *(978-1-59471-246-3(8))* Ave Maria Pr.

—Send Out Your Spirit: Sponsor's Handbook. rev. ed. 2010. 48p. pap. 3.95 *(978-1-59471-247-0(6))* Ave Maria Pr.

Anderson, Carl. A Civilization of Love: What Every Catholic Can Do to Transform the World. 2009. (ENG.). 240p. pap. 13.99 *(978-0-06-133532-7(0)*, HarperOne) HarperCollins Pubs.

—Civilization of Love: What Every Catholic Can Do to Transform the World. 2008. 224p. 19.95 *(978-0-06-133531-0(2)*, HarperOne) HarperCollins Pubs.

Angelus Press Staff, contrib. by. The Best of Questions & Answers. 2nd ed. 2009. *(978-1-892331-68-7(3))* Angelus Pr.

Anscombe, G. E. M. Faith in a Hard Ground: Essays on Religion, Philosophy & Ethics. Geach, Mary & Gormally, Luke, eds. 2008. (St Andrews Studies in Philosophy & Public Affairs Ser.). (ENG.). 250p. 80.00 *(978-1-84540-143-6(3))* Imprint Academic GBR. Dist: Ingram Pub. Services.

Aquilina, Mike. Roots of the Faith: From the Church Fathers to You. 2010. pap. *(978-0-86716-938-6(9)*, Servant Bks.) Franciscan Media.

Aquinas, Thomas. Action & Contemplation: 2a2ae. 179-182. Aumann, Jordan, ed. 2006. (LAT & ENG.). 156p. per. 46.00 *(978-0-521-02954-4(6))* Cambridge Univ. Pr.
—Angels: Ia. 50-64. Foster, Kenelm, ed. 2006. (LAT & ENG.). 372p. per. 46.00 *(978-0-521-02917-9(1))* Cambridge Univ. Pr.
—Baptism & Confirmation: 3a. 66-72. Cunningham, James J., ed. 2006. (LAT & ENG.). 276p. per. 46.00 *(978-0-521-02965-0(1))* Cambridge Univ. Pr.
—Charity: 2a2ae. 23-33. 2006. (LAT & ENG.). 348p. per. 46.00 *(978-0-521-02942-1(2))* Cambridge Univ. Pr.
—The Childhood of Christ: 3a. 31-37. Potter, Roland, ed. 2006. (LAT & ENG.). 196p. per. 46.00 *(978-0-521-02960-5(0))* Cambridge Univ. Pr.
—Christian Theology: 1a. 1. Gilby, Thomas, ed. 2006. (LAT & ENG.). 192p. per. 46.00 *(978-0-521-02909-4(0))* Cambridge Univ. Pr.
—Consequences of Charity: 2a2ae. 34-46. Heath, Thomas R., ed. 2006. (LAT & ENG.). 240p. per. 46.00 *(978-0-521-02943-8(0))* Cambridge Univ. Pr.
—Consequences of Faith: 2a2ae. 8-16. Gilby, Thomas, ed. 2006. (LAT & ENG.). 184p. per. 46.00 *(978-0-521-02940-7(6))* Cambridge Univ. Pr.
—Cosmogony: Ia. 65-74. Wallace, William A., ed. 2006. (LAT & ENG.). 280p. per. 46.00 *(978-0-521-02918-6(X))* Cambridge Univ. Pr.
—Courage: 2a2ae. 123-40. Ross, Anthony, ed. 2006. (LAT & ENG.). 280p. per. 46.00 *(978-0-521-02950-6(3))* Cambridge Univ. Pr.
—Creation, Variety & Evil: Ia. 44-49. Gilby, Thomas, ed. 2006. (LAT & ENG.). 208p. per. 46.00 *(978-0-521-02916-2(3))* Cambridge Univ. Pr.
—Dispositions for Human Acts: 1a2ae. 49-54. Kenny, Anthony, ed. 2006. (LAT & ENG.). 180p. per. 46.00 *(978-0-521-02930-8(9))* Cambridge Univ. Pr.
—Divine Government: Ia2ae. 103-9. 2006. (LAT & ENG.). 244p. per. 46.00 *(978-0-521-02922-3(8))* Cambridge Univ. Pr.
—Effects of Sin, Stain & Guilt: Ia2ae 86-89. 2006. (LAT & ENG.). 176p. per. 46.00 *(978-0-521-02935-3(X))* Cambridge Univ. Pr.
—The Emotions: Ia2ae. 22-30. 2006. (LAT & ENG.). 180p. per. 46.00 *(978-0-521-02927-8(9))* Cambridge Univ. Pr.
—The Eucharistic Presence: 3a. 73-78. Barden, William, ed. 2006. (LAT & ENG.). 244p. per. 46.00 *(978-0-521-02966-7(X))* Cambridge Univ. Pr.
—Existence & Nature of God: Ia. 2-11. McDermott, Timothy, ed. 2006. (LAT & ENG.). 268p. per. 46.00 *(978-0-521-02910-0(4))* Cambridge Univ. Pr.
—Faith: 2a2ae. 1-7. 2006. (LAT & ENG.). 276p. per. 46.00 *(978-0-521-02939-1(2))* Cambridge Univ. Pr.
—Father, Son & Holy Ghost: Ia. 33-43. 2006. (LAT & ENG.). 328p. per. 46.00 *(978-0-521-02915-5(5))* Cambridge Univ. Pr.
—Fear & Anger: Ia2ae. 40-48. Reid, John Patrick, ed. 2006. (LAT & ENG.). 220p. per. 46.00 *(978-0-521-02929-2(5))* Cambridge Univ. Pr.
—General Index. 2006. (LAT & ENG.). 404p. per. 46.00 *(978-0-521-02908-7(2))* Cambridge Univ. Pr.
—The Gifts of the Spirit: Ia2ae 68-70. 2006. (LAT & ENG.). 188p. per. 46.00 *(978-0-521-02932-2(5))* Cambridge Univ. Pr.
—God's Will & Providence: Ia. 19-26. Gilby, Thomas, ed. 2006. (LAT & ENG.). 232p. per. 46.00 *(978-0-521-02913-1(9))* Cambridge Univ. Pr.
—The Gospel of Grace: Ia2ae. 106-114. Ernst, Cornelius, ed. 2006. (LAT & ENG.). 288p. per. 46.00 *(978-0-521-02938-4(4))* Cambridge Univ. Pr.
—The Grace of Christ: 3a. 7-15. Walsh, Liam G., ed. 2006. (LAT & ENG.). 268p. per. 46.00 *(978-0-521-02957-5(0))* Cambridge Univ. Pr.
—Holy Communion: 3a. 79-83. Gilby, Thomas, ed. 2006. (LAT & ENG.). 216p. per. 46.00 *(978-0-521-02967-4(8))* Cambridge Univ. Pr.
—Hope: 2a2ae. 17-22. 2006. (LAT & ENG.). 228p. per. 46.00 *(978-0-521-02941-4(4))* Cambridge Univ. Pr.
—Human Intelligence. Durbin, Paul T., ed. 2006. (LAT & ENG.). 228p. per. 46.00 *(978-0-521-02920-9(1))* Cambridge Univ. Pr.
—The Incarnate Word: 3a. 1-6. 2006. (LAT & ENG.). 228p. per. 46.00 *(978-0-521-02956-8(2))* Cambridge Univ. Pr.
—Injustice: 2a2ae. 63-79. Lefebure, Marcus, ed. 2006. (LAT & ENG.). 320p. per. 46.00 *(978-0-521-02946-9(5))* Cambridge Univ. Pr.
—Justice: 2a2ae. 57-62. Gilby, Thomas, ed. 2006. (LAT & ENG.). 156p. per. 46.00 *(978-0-521-02945-2(7))* Cambridge Univ. Pr.
—Knowing & Naming God: Ia. 12-13. McCabe, Herbert, ed. 2006. (LAT & ENG.). 160p. per. 46.00 *(978-0-521-02911-7(2))* Cambridge Univ. Pr.
—Knowledge in God: Ia. 14-18. Gornall, Thomas, ed. 2006. (LAT & ENG.). 168p. per. 46.00 *(978-0-521-02912-4(0))* Cambridge Univ. Pr.
—Law & Political Theory: 1a2ae. 90-97. Gilby, Thomas, ed. 2006. (LAT & ENG.). 232p. per. 46.00 *(978-0-521-02936-0(8))* Cambridge Univ. Pr.
—The Life of Christ: 3a. 38-45. Parsons, Samuel & Pinheiro, Albert, eds. 2006. (LAT & ENG.). 244p. per. 46.00 *(978-0-521-02961-2(9))* Cambridge Univ. Pr.
—Man: Ia. 75-83. Suttor, Timothy, ed. 2006. (LAT & ENG.). 308p. per. 46.00 *(978-0-521-02919-3(8))* Cambridge Univ. Pr.
—Man Made to God's Image: Ia. 90-102. Hill, Edmund, ed. 2006. (LAT & ENG., Illus.). 260p. per. 46.00 *(978-0-521-02921-6(X))* Cambridge Univ. Pr.
—Nature & Grace: Selections from the Summa Theologica of Thomas Aquinas. Fairweather, A. M., ed. 2011. 384p. 53.95 ***(978-1-258-00631-0(6))*** Literary Licensing, LLC.
—The Old Law. Bourke, David & Littledale, Arthur, eds. 2006. (LAT & ENG.). 352p. per. 46.00 *(978-0-521-02937-7(6))* Cambridge Univ. Pr.
—On Love & Charity: Readings from the Commentary on the Sentences of Peter Lombard. 2008. (Thomas Aquinas in Translation Ser.). 448p. (C). pap. 39.95 *(978-0-8132-1525-9(0))* Catholic Univ. of America Pr.
—The One Mediator: 3a. 16-26. O'Neill, Colman E., ed. 2006. (LAT & ENG.). 300p. per. 46.00 *(978-0-521-02958-2(9))* Cambridge Univ. Pr.
—Original Sin: Ia2ae 81-85. 2006. (LAT & ENG.). 204p. per. 46.00 *(978-0-521-02934-6(1))* Cambridge Univ. Pr.
—The Passion of Christ: 3a. 46-52. Murphy, Richard T. A., ed. 2006. (LAT & ENG.). 256p. per. 46.00 *(978-0-521-02962-9(7))* Cambridge Univ. Pr.
—The Pastoral & Religious Lives: 2a2ae. 183-189. Aumann, Jordan, ed. 2006. (LAT & ENG.). 312p. per. 46.00 *(978-0-521-02955-1(4))* Cambridge Univ. Pr.
—Penance: 3a. 84-90. Masterton, Reginald, ed. 2006. (LAT & ENG.). 244p. per. 46.00 *(978-0-521-02968-1(6))* Cambridge Univ. Pr.
—Pleasure: Ia2ae. 31-39. 2006. (LAT & ENG.). 204p. per. 46.00 *(978-0-521-02928-5(7))* Cambridge Univ. Pr.
—Principles of Morality: 1a2ae. 18-21. Gilby, Thomas, ed. 2006. (LAT & ENG.). 232p. per. 46.00 *(978-0-521-02926-1(0))* Cambridge Univ. Pr.
—Prophecy & Other Charisms: 2a2ae. 171-178. Potter, Roland, ed. 2006. (LAT & ENG.). 196p. per. 46.00 *(978-0-521-02953-7(8))* Cambridge Univ. Pr.
—Prudence: 2a2ae. 47-56. Gilby, Thomas, ed. 2006. (LAT & ENG.). 216p. per. 46.00 *(978-0-521-02944-5(9))* Cambridge Univ. Pr.
—Psychology of Human Acts: Ia2ae. 6-17. Gilby, Thomas, ed. 2006. (LAT & ENG.). 256p. per. 46.00 *(978-0-521-02925-4(2))* Cambridge Univ. Pr.
—Purpose & Happiness: 1a2ae. 1-5. Gilby, Thomas, ed. 2006. (LAT & ENG.). 192p. per. 46.00 *(978-0-521-02924-7(4))* Cambridge Univ. Pr.
—Religion & Worship: 2a2ae. 80-91. 2006. (LAT & ENG.). 308p. per. 46.00 *(978-0-521-02947-6(3))* Cambridge Univ. Pr.
—The Resurrection of the Lord: 3a. 53-59. Moore, C. Thomas, ed. 2006. (LAT & ENG.). 168p. per. 46.00 *(978-0-521-02963-6(5))* Cambridge Univ. Pr.
—The Sacraments: 3a. 60-5. Bourke, David, ed. 2006. (LAT & ENG.). 196p. per. 46.00 *(978-0-521-02964-3(3))* Cambridge Univ. Pr.
—Sin: Ia2ae 71-80. Fearon, John, ed. 2006. (LAT & ENG.). 288p. per. 46.00 *(978-0-521-02933-9(3))* Cambridge Univ. Pr.
—St. Thomas Aquinas & the Mendicant Controversies: Three Translations. Proctor, John, tr. from LAT. rev. ed. 2007. 570p. 65.00 *(978-1-934182-00-0(1))* Alethes Pr.
—Summa Theologiae: Volume 51. Heath, Thomas R., ed. 2006. (LAT & ENG.). 148p. per. 46.00 *(978-0-521-02959-9(7))* Cambridge Univ. Pr.
—Summa Theologica. 2007. (ENG.). 656p. 35.95 *(978-1-60206-560-4(8))*; (ENG.). 636p. 35.95 *(978-1-60206-562-8(4))*; (ENG.). 592p. 34.95 *(978-1-60206-554-3(3))*; (ENG.). 592p. 34.95 *(978-1-60206-556-7(X))*; (ENG.). 640p. 34.95 *(978-1-60206-558-1(6))*; (ENG.). 636p. per. 24.95 *(978-1-60206-561-1(6))*; 592p. per. 23.95 *(978-1-60206-553-6(5))*; (ENG.). 592p. per. 23.95 *(978-1-60206-555-0(1))*; (ENG.). 640p. per. 23.95 *(978-1-60206-557-4(8))*; (ENG.). 652p. per. 24.95 *(978-1-60206-559-8(4))* Cosimo, Inc.
—Summa Theologica Tertia Pars. 2011. 1030p. ***(978-1-84902-414-3(6))*** Benediction Classics.
—Superstition & Irreverence: 2a2ae. 92-100. 2006. (LAT & ENG.). 196p. per. 46.00 *(978-0-521-02948-3(1))* Cambridge Univ. Pr.
—Temperance: 2a2ae. 141-154. Gilby, Thomas, ed. 2006. (LAT & ENG.). 296p. per. 46.00 *(978-0-521-02951-3(1))* Cambridge Univ. Pr.
—Treatise on Human Nature: Summa Theologiae 1a, QQ 75-89. Freddoso, Alfred J., tr. from LAT. 2010. (ENG.). 368p. (C). pap. 20.00 *(978-1-58731-881-8(4))* St. Augustine's Pr., Inc.
—The Trinity, Vol. 6. Velecky, Ceslaus, ed. 2006. (LAT & ENG.). 196p. per. 46.00 *(978-0-521-02914-8(7))* Cambridge Univ. Pr.
—Virtue: Ia2ae. 55-67. 2006. (LAT & ENG.). 284p. per. 46.00 *(978-0-521-02931-5(7))* Cambridge Univ. Pr.
—Virtues of Justice in the Human Community: 2a2ae. 101-22. 2006. (LAT & ENG.). 368p. per. 46.00 *(978-0-521-02949-0(X))* Cambridge Univ. Pr.
—Well-Tempered Passion: 2a2ae. 155-170. Gilby, Thomas, ed. 2006. (LAT & ENG.). 280p. per. 46.00 *(978-0-521-02952-0(X))* Cambridge Univ. Pr.
—The World Order: 1a. 110-119. 2006. (LAT & ENG.). 212p. per. 46.00 *(978-0-521-02923-0(6))* Cambridge Univ. Pr.
Aquini, Maria Pilar & Rosado-Nunes, Maria Jose, eds. Feminist Intercultural Theology: Latina Explorations for a Just World. 2007. (Studies in Latino/A Catholicism). 270p. per. 35.00 *(978-1-57075-741-9(0))* Orbis Bks.
ARCIC II Staff. Mary: Grace & Hope in Christ. Bolen, Donald & Cameron, Gregory, eds. rev. exp. ed. 2006. (ENG., Illus.). 288p. 22.95 *(978-0-8264-8155-9(8))* Continuum International Publishing Group, Ltd. GBR. Dist: National Bk. Network.
Armstrong, Dave. Bible Proofs for Catholic Truths: A Source Book for Apologists & Inquirers. 2009. xiv, 445p. pap. 15.95 *(978-1-933184-57-9(4))* Sophia Institute Pr.
—Development of Catholic Doctrine: Evolution, Revolution, or an Organic Process? 2007. 204p. per. 16.95 *(978-1-4303-2106-4(7))* Lulu Enterprises Inc.
—Family Matters: Catholic Theology of the Family. 2007. 164p. per. 15.95 *(978-1-4303-2110-1(5))* Lulu Enterprises Inc.
—More Biblical Evidence for Catholicism. 2007. 188p. per. 15.95 *(978-1-4303-2243-6(8))* Lulu Enterprises Inc.
—Pensées on Catholic Traditionalism. 2007. 172p. per. 15.95 *(978-1-4303-2114-9(8))* Lulu Enterprises Inc.
Arnauld, Antoine. The Necessity of Faith in Jesus Christ to Obtain Salvation. 2011. 322p. pap. 19.99 ***(978-1-4628-6351-8(5))*** Xlibris Corp.
Artigas, Mariano, et al. Negotiating Darwin: The Vatican Confronts Evolution, 1877-1902. 2006. (Medicine, Science, & Religion in Historical Context Ser.). (ENG., Illus.). 336p. (gr. 17). 53.00 *(978-0-8018-8389-7(X))* Johns Hopkins Univ. Pr.
Ashker, Patricia O'Malley. On Becoming Beloved. 2009. *(978-0-8189-1282-5(0),* St. Pauls) St Pauls/Alba Hse. Pubs.
Ashley, Benedict M. & Deely, John N. How Science Enriches Theology. 2011. ***(978-1-58731-364-6(2))*** St. Augustine's Pr., Inc.
Ashley, O.P., Benedict M & Deely, John. How Science Enriches Theology. 2012. (ENG.). 243p. 32.00 ***(978-1-58731-363-9(4))*** St. Augustine's Pr., Inc.
Bachiochi, Erika. Women, Sex & the Church: A Case for Catholic Teaching. 2010. pap. 19.95 *(978-0-8198-8320-9(4))* Pauline Bks. & Media.
Baker, S.J., Kenneth. Doctrinal Sermons on the Catechism of the Catholic Church. 2012. (ENG.). 272p. pap. 22.00 ***(978-1-58731-189-5(5))*** St. Augustine's Pr., Inc.
Balmes, Jaime Luciano. European Civilization: Protestantism & Catholicity Compared... by Rev. J. Balmes. 2006. 512p. per. 29.99 *(978-1-4255-5716-4(3))* MPublishing.
Balthasar, Hans Urs Von. The Office of Peter & the Structure of the Church. 2nd ed. 2007. (Illus.). xxv, 434p. pap. *(978-1-58617-228-2(X))* Ignatius Pr.
Baron d'Holbach, Paul-Henri Thiry, et al. Superstition in all Ages. 2010. 348p. pap. 24.95 *(978-0-557-35875-5(2))* Lulu Enterprises Inc.
Barron, Robert. Catholicism: A Journey to the Heart of the Faith. 2011. (ENG., Illus.). 304p. 27.99 *(978-0-307-72051-1(9),* Doubleday Religion) Doubleday Religious Publishing Group, The.
—The Priority of Christ: Toward a Postliberal Catholicism. 2007. 352p. (C). pap. 32.00 *(978-1-58743-198-2(X))* Brazos Pr.
—Thomas Aquinas: Spiritual Master. 2nd ed. 2008. (ENG.). 192p. pap. 19.95 *(978-0-8245-2496-8(9))* Crossroad Publishing Co., The.
—Word on Fire: Proclaiming the Power of Christ. 2008. (ENG., Illus.). 240p. pap. 19.95 *(978-0-8245-2453-1(5))* Crossroad Publishing Co., The.
Bastos, Fernando. Pequena Enciclopedia De La Doctrina Social De La Iglesia. 672p. 18.95 *(978-958-607-737-8(3))* Sociedad de San Pablo COL. Dist: St Pauls/Alba Hse. Pubs.
Bauer, Judith, ed. The Illustrated 365 Day Catholic Childrens Bible. 2011. (ENG., Illus.). 445p. (J). (gr. -1-3). 24.96 ***(978-0-88271-274-1(8))*** Regina Pr., Malhame & Co.
Baum G Staff. '73 Concilium Sexual Revolution con. 2010. pap. ***(978-0-567-30053-9(6),*** SCM Pr.) Hymns Ancient & Modern Ltd.
Bausch, William J. Touching the Heart: Tales for the Human Journey. 2007. 264p. per. 24.95 *(978-1-58595-617-3(1))* Twenty-Third Pubns./Bayard.
Beeck, Frans Jozef van. Driven under the Influence: Selected Essays in Theology, 1974-2004. 2006. *(978-1-888112-14-6(X))* Sacred Heart Univ. Pr.
Behr, Thomas. Summa Theologica by Thomas Aquinas. 2nd ed. 2008. (ENG.). (C). pap. 57.80 *(978-0-558-12384-0(8))* Pearson Learning Solutions.
Belcher, Kimberly Hope. Efficacious Engagement: Sacramental Participation in the Trinitarian Mystery. 2011. E-Book ***(978-0-8146-8041-4(0))*** Liturgical Pr.
Benedict, Joseph Ratzinger in Communio the Unity of the Church, Vol. 1. 2010. 212p. pap. 24.99 *(978-0-8028-6416-1(3))* Eerdmans, William B. Publishing Co.
Benedict XVI, pseud. La Caridad en la Verdad: Caritas in Veritate. 2009. (Carta Enciclica Ser.). (SPA.). 94p. pap. 6.95 *(978-1-60137-806-4(8))* United States Conference of Catholic Bishops.
—Charity in Truth: Caritas in Veritate: Encyclical Letter. 2009. 93p. pap. 6.95 *(978-1-60137-049-5(0))* United States Conference of Catholic Bishops.
—Meeting Saint Paul with the Pope: Wednesday Audiences During the Pauline Jubilee Year. 2009. 144p. pap. 10.95 *(978-0-8091-4664-2(9))* Paulist Pr.
—On Christian Hope: Spe Salvi. 2007. 58p. per. 6.95 *(978-1-60137-039-6(3))* United States Conference of Catholic Bishops.
—On Conscience. 2007. (Bioethics & Culture Ser.). 82p. 14.95 *(978-1-58617-160-5(7))* Ignatius Pr.
—Papa Benedicto XVI: Caridad en la Verdad. Estenger, Vilma G., tr. 2009. (SPA.). 1p. 14.95 *(978-1-59276-458-7(4))* Our Sunday Visitor, Publishing Div.
—Pope Benedict XVI: Charity in Truth. 2009. 1p. 14.95 *(978-1-59276-457-0(6))* Our Sunday Visitor, Publishing Div.
—Questions & Answers. 2008. 175p. 14.95 *(978-1-59276-439-6(8))* Our Sunday Visitor, Publishing Div.
—Saint Paul the Apostle. 2009. 122p. pap. 8.95 *(978-1-59276-615-4(3))* Our Sunday Visitor, Publishing Div.
Benestad, J. Brian. Church, State, & Society. 2011. 456p. 54.95 *(978-0-8132-1800-7(4))* Catholic Univ. of America Pr.
—Church, State, & Society: An Introduction to Catholic Social Doctrine. 2011. 456p. pap. 34.95 *(978-0-8132-1801-4(2))* Catholic Univ. of America Pr.
Benson, Pius. The Church in the Theological Writings of Avery Dulles: Impulses for African Ecclesiology. (European University Studies: Vol. 852). 341p. pap. 68.95 *(978-3-631-56492-9(9))* Lang, Peter GmbH, Europaischer Verlag der Wissenschaften DEU. Dist: Lang, Peter Publishing, Inc.
Benson, Robert Hugh. Paradoxes of Catholicism. 2007. (ENG.). 96p. per. *(978-1-4065-4847-1(2))* Dodo Pr.
Beozzo Oscar Staff. 2001/3: The Ecumenical Constitution of Churches Concilium June. 2011. pap. ***(978-0-334-03064-5(1),*** SCM Pr.) Hymns Ancient & Modern Ltd.
Bergant, Dianne. Scripture: History & Interpretation. 2008. (Engaging Theology: Catholic Perspectives Ser.). 174p. pap. 19.95 *(978-0-8146-5995-3(0),* Liturgical Pr. Bks.) Liturgical Pr.
Bergin, Liam, ed. According to Your Word: Proceedings of a Conference Held on Saturday 4 March 2006 at the Pontifical College Rome to Honour Desmond Cardinal Connell on His Eightieth Birthday. 2007. 168p. (C). 55.00 *(978-1-84682-083-0(9))* Four Courts Pr. IRL. Dist: International Specialized Bk. Services.
Berry, E. Sylvester. The Church of Christ: An Apologetic & Dogmatic Treatise. 2009. 344p. pap. 38.00 *(978-1-60608-802-9(5),* Wipf and Stock) Wipf & Stock Pubs.
Berry, Lewis & Newman, John Henry. John Henry Cardinal Newman: In My Own Words. 2010. 128p. *(978-0-7648-1910-0(0))* Liguori Pubns.
Bevans, Stephen B. An Introduction to Theology in Global Perspective. 2009. 400p. pap. 30.00 *(978-1-57075-852-2(2))* Orbis Bks.
Bevans, Stephen B. & Gross, Jeffrey. Evangelization & Religious Freedom: Ad gentes, Dignitatis Humanae. 2008. (Rediscovering Vatican II Ser.). 272p. pap. 21.95 *(978-0-8091-4202-6(3))* Paulist Pr.
Billy, Dennis J. Cssr & Billy, Dennis Joseph. Living in the Gap: Religious Life & the Call to Communion. 2011. pap. ***(978-1-56548-392-7(8))*** New City Community Pr.
Binz, Stephen J. Introduction to the Bible: A Catholic Guide to Studying Scripture. 2007. 90p. per. 8.95 *(978-0-8146-1700-7(X))* Liturgical Pr.
Blackwell, Richard J. Behind the Scenes at Galileo's Trial: Including the First English Translation of Melchior Inchofer's Tractatus Syllepticus. 2008. (ENG.). 264p. pap. 28.00 *(978-0-268-02210-5(0))* Univ. of Notre Dame Pr.
Blaise, Pascal. Pensees. (FRE.). pap. 19.95 *(978-2-253-16069-4(5))* Librairie Generale Francaise, LGF FRA. Dist: Distribooks, Inc.
Bleichner, Howard P. In the Circle of Mysteries: The Coherence of Catholic Belief. 2008. (ENG.). 344p. pap. 34.95 *(978-0-8245-2447-0(0))* Crossroad Publishing Co., The.
Bloch, Tamara. Die Stellungnahmen der römisch-katholischen Amtskirche zur Frage der Menschenrechte Seit 1215: Eine historische Untersuchung unter besonderer Berücksichtigung der Gewährleistungen im CIC/1983. 2008. (Schriften zum Staatskirchenrecht Ser.). 276p. pap. 74.95 *(978-3-631-56494-3(5))* Lang, Peter GmbH, Europaischer Verlag der Wissenschaften DEU. Dist: Lang, Peter.
Blumenthal, Uta-Renate, et al, eds. Canon Law, Religion, & Politics: Liber Amicorum Robert Somerville. 2012. (ENG.). 344p. 69.95 ***(978-0-8132-1975-2(2))*** Catholic Univ. of America Pr.
Boguslawski, O.P., RevStephen & Fastiggi, Robert, eds. Called to Holiness & Communion: Vatican II on the Church. 2009. 300p. pap. 25.00 *(978-1-58966-158-5(3))* Univ. of Scranton Pr.
Bonaventure, St. The Works of Bonaventure: Mystical Opuscula. De Vinck, Jose, tr. 2011. 282p. 47.95 ***(978-1-258-05502-8(3))*** Literary Licensing, LLC.
Bondi, Michele Elena. Your Teen Apostolate: Accepting & Sharing the Love of God. 2009. *(978-1-935356-06-6(2))* Wilderness Adventure Bks.
Bosco, Antoinette. Growing in Faith When a Catholic Marriage Fails: For Divorced or Separated Catholics & Those Who Minister with Them. 2006. (Illus.). 125p. per. *(978-1-933066-04-2(0),* Resurrection Pr.) Catholic Bk. Publishing Corp.
Bourmaud, Dominique. One Hundred Years of Modernism: A Genealogy of the Principles of the Second Vatican Council. 2006. 356p. 24.95 *(978-1-892331-43-4(8))* Angelus Pr.
Bowman, Wayne B. Hidden in Plain Sight: Catechism versus the Bible. 2009. (J). pap. 15.99 *(978-1-60799-779-5(7))* Tate Publishing & Enterprises, LLC.
Bowring, Kelly & Black, Tank. The Secrets, Chastisement, & Triumph of the Two Hearts of Jesus & Mary: And What Heaven Is Calling Us to Do. 2009. 286p. pap. 19.95 *(978-0-9802292-1-9(9))* Two Hearts Pr., LLC.
Braaten, Carl E. That All May Believe: A Theology of the Gospel & the Mission of the Church. 2008. 168p. pap. 20.00 *(978-0-8028-6239-6(X))* Eerdmans, William B. Publishing Co.
Bransfield, J. Brian. The Human Person: According to John Paul II. 2010. pap. *(978-0-8198-3394-5(0))* Pauline Bks. & Media.
Brière, Emile. I Believe: Living the Apostles' Creed. 136p. *(978-0-921440-79-6(0))* Madonna Hse. Pubns.
Brunk, Timothy M. A Critical Assessment of Sacrament & Ethics in the Thought of Louis-Marie Chauvet. 2007. (American University Studies: Vol. 254). xiv, 262p. (C). 74.95 *(978-0-8204-8689-5(2))* Lang, Peter Publishing, Inc.
Bullivant, Stephen. The Salvation of Atheists & Catholic Dogmatic Theology. 2012. (ENG.). 240p. 125.00 ***(978-0-19-965256-3(2))*** Oxford Univ. Pr., Inc.
Burgaleta, Claudio. Manual de la Teología para los Católicos de Hoy. 2009. (SPA.). 96p. pap. 6.95 *(978-0-7648-1789-2(2),* Liguori) Liguori Pubns.
Burgaleta, Claudio M. Manual de la Eclesiología para Los Católicos de Hoy. 2012. (SPA.). ***(978-0-7648-2038-0(9))*** Liguori Pubns.
Burke, Sullivan Eileen, ed. Ignatian Tradition. 2009. 168p. pap. 15.95 *(978-0-8146-1913-1(4),* Liturgical Pr. Bks.) Liturgical Pr.
Burns, Robert A. Catholic Spirituality & Prayer in the Secular City. 2008. (ENG.). 130p. 56.99 *(978-0-7618-4127-2(X))*; pap. 27.50 *(978-0-7618-4128-9(8))* Univ. Pr. of America, Inc.
Burns Senseman, Rita. Anointed in the Spirit Candidate Handbook: A Middle School Confirmation Program. 2010. pap. 11.95 *(978-0-88489-814-6(8))* St. Mary's Pr.
—Anointed in the Spirit Catechist Guide: A Middle School Confirmation Program. 2010. spiral bd. 27.95 *(978-0-88489-876-4(8))* St. Mary's Pr.
—Anointed in the Spirit Program Director Manual: A Middle School Confirmation Program. 2010. pap. 39.95 *(978-1-59982-028-6(5))* St. Mary's Pr.
Butler, Basil Christopher. The Catholic Church & the Bible. 2011 *(978-1-933184-79-1(5))* Sophia Institute Pr.
Byron, William J. One Faith, Many Faithful: Short Takes on Contemporary Catholic Concerns. 2012. ***(978-1-61643-135-8(0))***; 144p. pap. 15.95 ***(978-0-8091-4759-5(9))*** Paulist Pr.
Cafardi, Nicholas P. Voting & Holiness: Catholic Perspectives on Political Participation. 2012. 265p. ***(978-1-61643-140-2(7))*** Paulist Pr.

C

Cafardi, Nicholas P., ed. Voting & Holiness: Catholic Perspectives on Political Participation. 2012. 272p. pap. 24.95 (978-0-8091-4767-0(X)) Paulist Pr.

Caldecott, Leonie. What Do Catholics Believe? 2008. (What Do We Believe? Ser.). (ENG.). 100p. pap. 13.95 (978-1-84708-003-5(0)) Granta Bks. GBR. Dist: Independent Pubs. Group.

Campbell, Jane. Equality: A New Perspective. 2008. (Illus.). 88p. pap. (978-1-84748-219-8(8)) Athena Pr.

Capucao, Dave Dean. Religion & Ethnocentrism: An Empirical-Theological Study. 320p. (978-90-04-18470-1(8)) BRILL.

Caramuel Lobkowitz, Juan & Sabaino, Daniele. Il Tractatus Expendens Propositiones Damnatas Ab Alexandro VII Di Juan Caramuel Lobkowitz: Studio Introduttivo Ed Edizione Critica. 2010. (LAT, ITA & ENG.). 139.95 (978-0-7734-3608-4(1)) Mellen, Edwin Pr., The.

Carroll, James. Practicing Catholic. (ENG.). 400p. 2010. pap. 16.95 (978-0-547-33626-8(8), Mariner Bks.) 2009. 28.00 (978-0-618-67018-5(1)) Houghton Mifflin Harcourt Trade & Reference Pubs.

Catholic Church, United States Conference of Catholic Bishops Committee on Evangelization and Catechesis Staff, contrib. by. Catechetical Formation in Chaste Living: Guidelines for Curriculum Design & Publication. 2008. 27p. pap. (978-1-60137-043-3(1)) United States Conference of Catholic Bishops.

—Doctrinal Elements of a Curriculum Framework for the Development of Catechetical Materials for Young People of High School Age. 2008. iv, 53p. pap. (978-1-60137-042-6(3)) United States Conference of Catholic Bishops.

Catholic Church, United States Conference of Catholic Bishops Staff, contrib. by. Life-Giving Love in an Age of Technology. 2009. (Illus.). 20p. (978-1-60137-094-5(6)) United States Conference of Catholic Bishops.

—On Embryonic Stem Cell Research: A Statement of the United States Conference of Catholic Bishops. 2008. (978-1-60137-044-0(X)) United States Conference of Catholic Bishops.

The Catholic Home. 2008. (ENG.). 128p. reprint ed. pap. 12.95 (978-0-9818158-0-0(4)) Workingman's Publishing Hse.

Catoir, John T. The Dilemma of Divorced Catholics: Where Do You Stand with the Church? What Is the Internal Forum? 2007. 106p. per. 8.95 (978-1-933066-06-6(7), Resurrection Pr.) Catholic Bk. Publishing Corp.

Cebollada, Pascual & Valero Agúndez, Urbano. Experiencia y Misterio de Dios: Congreso Internacional en el 25 Aniversario Del Instituto Universitario de Espiritualidad de la Universidad Pontificia Comillas (Madrid, 24-27 de Octubre de 2007) 2009. (SPA.). 323p. (978-84-8468-269-1(2)) Universidad Pontificia Comillas de Madrid.

Chadwick, Owen. The Reformation... A Short Introduction. 2010. (ENG.). 112p. pap. 14.95 (978-0-19-960040-3(6)) Oxford Univ. Pr., Inc.

Champlin, Joseph M. What It Means to Be Catholic. 2007. (Illus.). 67p. pap. 5.95 (978-0-86716-490-9(5)) Franciscan Media.

Charleston, Philip. Shattering the Christian Looking Glass. 2009. 204p. pap. 17.14 (978-1-4251-8395-0(6)) Trafford Publishing.

Chatton, Walter. Lectura Super Sententias: Liber 1, Distinctiones 8-17, 3 vols. 2009. (Studies & Texts). (ENG.). 90.00 (978-0-88844-164-5(9)) Pontifical Institute of Mediaeval Studies, Dept. of Pubns. CAN. Dist: Univ. of Toronto Pr.

Chatton, Walter, et al. Lectura Super Sententias. (Studies & Texts). (ENG.). 2008. 89.95 (978-0-88844-158-4(4)) 2007. 94.95 (978-0-88844-156-0(8)) Pontifical Institute of Mediaeval Studies, Dept. of Pubns. CAN. Dist: Univ. of Toronto Pr.

Chiniquy. The Priest the Woman & the Confessional. 2008. 168p. 25.99 (978-0-554-27610-6(0)) 2008. 168p. 22.99 (978-0-554-36913-6(3)) 2007. 152p. pap. 19.99 (978-1-4346-3590-7(2)) BiblioBazaar.

—The Priest the Woman & the Confessional. 140p. 2009. pap. 10.95 (978-1-4385-1911-1(7)) 2008. (ENG.). pap. 13.95 (978-1-4385-1203-7(1)) Standard Pubns., Inc. (Book Jungle).

—The Priest, the Woman & the Confessional. 2007. 180p. 25.96 (978-1-4218-3852-6(4), 1st World Library - Literary Society) 1st World Publishing, Inc.

—The Priest, the Woman & the Confessional. 2007. (ENG.). 108p. per. (978-1-4068-4554-9(X)) Echo Library.

—The Priest, the Woman & the Confessional. 2007. 180p. per. 11.95 (978-1-4218-3952-3(0), 1st World Library - Literary Society) 1st World Publishing, Inc.

—The Priest the Woman & the Confessional. l.t. ed. 2007. (ENG.). 164p. pap. 21.99 (978-1-4346-3591-4(0)) BiblioBazaar.

Chiola, Richard. Catholicism for the Non-Catholic: A Brief Introduction to Catholicism. 2006. 192p. pap. 14.95 (978-0-87243-269-7(6)) Templegate Pubs.

Chittister, Joan & Kownacki, Mary Lou. In My Own Words. 2008. 14.99 (978-0-7648-1753-3(1)) Liguori Pubns.

Clark, Edward William. Five Great Catholic Ideas. 2nd ed. 2012. (ENG.). 192p. pap. 16.95 (978-0-8245-2596-5(5)) Crossroad Publishing Co., The.

Classen, Joseph F. The Essentials of Catholic Spirituality: Living & Breathing Our Faith! 2011. (978-0-8189-1329-7(0), St. Pauls) St Pauls/Alba Hse. Pubs.

Clermont, Betty. The Neo-Catholics: Implementing Christian Nationalism in America. 2009. 252p. pap. 19.95 (978-0-932863-63-8(9)) Clarity Pr., Inc.

Cloutier, David, ed. Leaving & Coming Home. 2010. (Illus.). 282p. pap. 31.00 (978-1-60899-091-7(5), Cascade Bks.) Wipf & Stock Pubs.

Cloutier, David & Zalot, Jozef D. Love, Reason, & God's Story: An Introduction to Catholic Sexual Ethics. 2008. pap. 26.25 (978-0-88489-945-7(4)) St. Mary's Pr.

Coffey, Kathy. Mary. 2009. 125p. pap. 14.00 (978-1-57075-724-2(0)) Orbis Bks.

Collins, Chuck & Wright, Mary. The Moral Measure of the Economy. 2007. (Illus.). 222p. per. 20.00 (978-1-57075-693-1(7)) Orbis Bks.

Collins, James B. The Mass As Sacrifice: Theological Reflections on the Sacrificial Elements Contained in the Roman Canon. 2008. (978-0-8189-1258-0(8)) St Pauls.

Collins, Mary Ann. Catholic Concerns: Where Does the Road to Rome Lead? 2008. 272p. pap. 20.95 (978-1-4401-1007-8(7)) iUniverse, Inc.

Collins, Pat. Basic Evangelisation: Guidelines for Catholics. 2010. (ENG.). 288p. pap. 27.95 (978-1-85607-696-8(2)) Columba Pr. IRL. Dist: Dufour Editions, Inc.

Columba Press, ed. The Columba Lectionary for the Masses with Children. 2009. (ENG.). 192p. pap. 34.95 (978-1-85607-648-7(2)) Columba Pr. IRL. Dist: Dufour Editions, Inc.

Congar, Yves. Yves Congar: Essential Writings. 2010. 176p. pap. 20.00 (978-1-57075-787-7(9)) Orbis Bks.

Connell, Francis J. Father Connell Answers Moral Questions. Weitzel, Eugene J., ed. 2011. 224p. 44.95 (978-1-258-02213-6(3)) Literary Licensing, LLC.

Connor, Charles P. The Spiritual Legacy of Archbishop Fulton J. Sheen. 2009. (978-0-8189-1311-2(8), St. Pauls) St Pauls/Alba Hse. Pubs.

Connors, Russell B., Jr. & Connors, Russell B. La Moral Cristiana: En el Aliento Divino. Walters, Thomas P., ed. 2009. (Fundamentos de la Fe Catolica Ser.). (SPA., Illus.). 128p. per. 7.95 (978-0-8294-2373-0(7)) Loyola Pr.

Conway, Daniel. Stewards of Joy: Taking Care of & Sharing the Gift of Faith. 2007. 62p. pap. (978-0-9762284-8-6(3)) St. Catherine of Siena Pr.

Cook, Michael L. Trinitarian Christology: Power That Sets Us Free. 2010. (Illus.). 128p. pap. 15.95 (978-0-8091-4657-4(6)) Paulist Pr.

Cordes, Paul Josef Cardinal, ed. Where are the Helpers? Charity & Spirituality. 2010. (ENG.). 192p. pap. 20.00 (978-0-268-02369-0(7)) Univ. of Notre Dame Pr.

Coren, Michael. Why Catholics Are Right. (ENG.). 240p. 2012. pap. 17.95 (978-0-7710-2322-4(7)) 2011. 26.99 (978-0-7710-2321-7(9)) McClelland & Stewart CAN. (McClelland & Stewart). Dist: Random Hse., Inc.

Coriden, James A. The Rights of Catholics in the Church. 2007. 145p. per. 14.95 (978-0-8091-4433-4(6), 4433-4) Paulist Pr.

Corkery, Padraig. Companion to the Compendium of the Social Doctrine of the Church. 2008. (ENG.). 124p. pap. 16.95 (978-1-85390-959-7(9)) Veritas Pubns. IRL. Dist: Dufour Editions, Inc.

Costa, Anne. Lord, I Hurt! The Grace of Forgiveness & the Road to Healing. 2012. 11.95 (978-1-59325-200-7(5)) Word Among Us Pr.

Craig-Snell, Shannon Nichole. Silence, Love, & Death: Saying "Yes" to God in the Theology of Karl Rahner. 2008. pap. (978-0-87462-733-6(8)) Marquette Univ. Pr.

Croissant, Jo. The Priesthood of the Heart: Woman's Unique Vocation. 2007. 152p. (C). pap. (978-0-8189-1251-1(0), St. Pauls) St Pauls/Alba Hse. Pubs.

Cunningham, Lawrence S. An Introduction to Catholicism. 2009. (Introduction to Religion Ser.). (ENG., Illus.). (C). 294p. 90.00 (978-0-521-84607-3(2)); 296p. pap. 30.00 (978-0-521-60855-8(4)) Cambridge Univ. Pr.

—Things Seen & Unseen: A Catholic Theologian's Notebook. 2010. 256p. 20.00 (978-1-933495-25-5(1), Sorin Bks.) Ave Maria Pr.

Curran, Charles E. & Rubio, Julie Hanlon, eds. Marriage: Readings in Moral Theology No. 15. 2009. (Readings in Moral Theology Ser.). 480p. pap. 34.95 (978-0-8091-4575-1(8)) Paulist Pr.

Daley, Michael J., ed. Why Do Catholics...? Teens Respond to Questions about the Faith. 2007. 120p. per. 14.75 (978-0-88489-915-0(2)) St. Mary's Pr.

Daniel, David Mills. Aquinas Summa Theologica: God, Part II. 2006. (Scm Briefly Ser.). 87p. per. (978-0-334-04090-3(6)) Hymns Ancient & Modern Ltd.

David Mills Daniel Staff. Briefly: Incorrect Entry - See 0334040906, Vol. 2. 2006. 12.99 (978-0-334-04065-1(5), SCM Pr.) Hymns Ancient & Modern Ltd GBR. Dist: Westminster John Knox Pr.

De Mello, Anthony. Seek God Everywhere: Reflections on the Spiritual Exercises of St. Ignatius. 2010. (ENG.). 224p. pap. 14.00 (978-0-385-53176-4(1), Image) Doubleday Religious Publishing Group, The.

—Walking on Water. Berryman, Phillip, tr. 2008. (ENG.). 208p. 14.95 (978-0-8245-2492-0(6), Crossroad 8 Avenue) Crossroad Publishing Co., The.

de Witte, Pieter. Doctrine, Dynamic & Difference: To the Heart of the Lutheran-Roman Catholic 'Differentiated Consensus' on Justification. 2012. (ENG.). 272p. 120.00 (978-0-567-23665-4(X), T&T Clark Int'l) Continuum International Publishing Group, Ltd. GBR. Dist: National Bk. Network.

Dear, John. Put down Your Sword: Answering the Gospel Call to Creative Nonviolence. 2008. 184p. pap. 16.00 (978-0-8028-6357-7(4)) Eerdmans, William B. Publishing Co.

DeVille, Adam A. J. Orthodoxy & the Roman Papacy: Ut Unum Sint & the Prospects of East-West Unity. 2011. (ENG.). 280p. pap. 38.00 (978-0-268-02607-3(6)) Univ. of Notre Dame Pr.

deWaal, Esther. On Retreat with Thomas Merton: A Seven Day Programme. 3rd ed. 2011. (Illus.). 112p. pap. 19.99 (978-1-84825-066-6(5), Canterbury Pr. Norwich) Hymns Ancient & Modern Ltd GBR. Dist: Westminster John Knox Pr.

Dietzen, John J. Catholic Q & A: Answers to the Most Common Questions about Catholicism. 2009. (ENG.). 592p. pap. 19.95 (978-0-8245-2600-9(7)) Crossroad Publishing Co., The.

Dimkpa, Anthony. The Self-Consciousness of Jesus Christ: An Analysis of Its Main Christological Trends. 2010. 404p. pap. 22.99 (978-1-4141-1635-8(7)) Pleasant Word.

Doherty, Catherine. Bogoroditza: She Who Gave Birth to God. 2nd exp. ed. (Madonna House Classics Ser.). 145p. pap. (978-0-921440-48-2(0)) Madonna Hse. Pubns.

—Urodivoi: Holy Fools. 3rd ed. (Madonna House Classics Ser.). 96p. pap. (978-0-921440-34-5(0)) Madonna Hse. Pubns.

Doherty, Tony. So You're Working for the Catholic Church: A Friendly Guide to the Catholic Tradition. 2011. 64p. pap. 12.95 (978-0-8091-4654-3(1)) Paulist Pr.

Donnelly, D., et al, eds. The Belgian Contribution to the Second Vatican Council: International Research Conference at Mechelen, Leuven & Louvain-la-Neuve (September 12-16, 2005) 2008. (Bibliotheca Ephemeridum Theologicarum Lovaniensium Ser.). (ENG.). 728p. (C). pap. 124.00 (978-90-429-2101-6(3)) Peeters Pubs. & Booksellers BEL. Dist: Brown, David Bk. Co., The.

Donovan, Jean. The Seven Virtues: An Introduction to Catholic Life. 2007. (ENG.). 160p. pap. 19.95 (978-0-8245-2452-4(7), Herder & Herder) Crossroad Publishing Co., The.

Dougherty, Joseph. From Altar-Throne to Table: The Campaign for Frequent Holy Communion in the Catholic Church. 2010. (ATLA Monograph Ser.). (ENG.). 262p. 84.00 (978-0-8108-7164-9(5)) Scarecrow Pr., Inc.

Doyle, Karen. Theology of the Body: Some Thoughts & Reflections. 2009. (Illus.). 96p. pap. 10.95 (978-0-8198-7427-6(2)) Pauline Bks. & Media.

Duffy, Regis A. An American Emmaus. 2010. 192p. pap. 21.00 (978-1-60899-534-9(8), Wipf and Stock) Wipf & Stock Pubs.

Dulles, Avery Robert. Church & Society: The Laurence J. Mcginley Lectures, 1988-2007. 3rd ed. 2008. (ENG.). 546p. 45.00 (978-0-8232-2862-1(2)) Fordham Univ. Pr.

Ederer, Rupert. Pope Pius Xii on the Economic. 2011. (Catholic Social Thought Ser.). (ENG.). 292p. (gr. 17). 50.00 (978-0-8108-7797-9(X)) Scarecrow Pr., Inc.

Egan, Philip A. Philosophy & Catholic Theology: A Primer. 2009. 192p. pap. 21.95 (978-0-8146-5661-7(7)) Liturgical Pr.

Elizondo, Virgilio P. Virgilio Elizondo: Spiritual Writings. 2010. 192p. pap. (978-1-57075-865-2(4)) Orbis Bks.

Elliott, Peter J. What God Has Joined: The Sacramentality of Marriage. 2010. 324p. pap. 36.00 (978-1-60899-373-4(6), Wipf and Stock) Wipf & Stock Pubs.

Ellis, Marc H. Peter Maurin. 2010. (Catholic Worker Reprint Ser.). (Illus.). 204p. pap. 23.00 (978-1-60899-060-3(5), Wipf and Stock) Wipf & Stock Pubs.

Emery, Gilles. The Trinity: An Introduction to Catholic Doctrine & the Triune God. Levering, Matthew, tr. from FRE. 2010. 248p. pap. 24.95 (978-0-8132-1864-9(0)) Catholic Univ. of America Pr.

England, John, abr. The Works of the Right Reverend John England. 2009. (Amer Philosophy, Religion Ser.). (ENG.). 524p. pap. 30.95 (978-1-4290-1847-0(X)); Vol. 2. 568p. pap. 33.95 (978-1-4290-1911-8(5)); Vol. 4. 516p. pap. 30.95 (978-1-4290-1910-1(7)); Vol. 5. 528p. pap. 31.95 (978-1-4290-1834-0(8)); Vol. 6. 500p. pap. 29.95 (978-1-4290-1909-5(3)); Vol. 7. 532p. pap. 31.95 (978-1-4290-1849-4(6)) Applewood Bks.

Eno, S. S., Robert B. The Rise of the Papacy. 2008. 184p. pap. 21.00 (978-1-60608-170-9(5), Wipf and Stock) Wipf & Stock Pubs.

Eric Borgman Staff. Concilium 2005/4: A Forgotten Future - Vatican 2. 2010. 157p. pap. (978-0-334-03085-0(4), SCM Pr.) Hymns Ancient & Modern Ltd.

Evans, Bernard F. Lazarus at the Table: Catholic & Social Justice. 2006. (Michael Glazier Bks.). 125p. per. 15.95 (978-0-8146-5114-8(3)) Liturgical Pr.

—Vote Catholic? Beyond the Political Din. 2008. 98p. per. 9.95 (978-0-8146-2946-8(6), Liturgical Pr. Bks.) Liturgical Pr.

Evert, Jason. Theology of His Body/Theology of Her Body: Discovering the Strength & Mission of Masculinity/Discovering the Beauty & Mystery of Femininity. 2009. (Illus.). 102p. pap. 11.99 (978-1-934217-59-7(X)) Ascension Pr.

Farkasfalvy, Denis. Inspiration & Interpretation: A Theological Introduction to Sacred Scripture. 2010. 309p. pap. 34.95 (978-0-8132-1746-8(6)) Catholic Univ. of America Pr.

fastiggi, robert. What the church teaches about Sex: God's plan for human Happiness. 2008. per. 19.95 (978-1-59276-212-5(3)) Our Sunday Visitor, Publishing Div.

Faulk, Edward. 101 Questions & Answers on Eastern Catholic Churches. 2007. (Responses to 101 Questions... Ser.). 115p. per. 12.95 (978-0-8091-4441-9(7), 4441-9) Paulist Pr.

Feduccia, Robert, Jr. & Hagarty, Maura Thompson. Who Is Jesus Christ? A Primary Source Reader. 2011. (ENG.). 191p. (gr. 9-12). pap. 14.50 (978-1-59982-126-9(5)) St. Mary's Pr.

Finley, Mitch. The Seeker's Guide to Being Catholic. 2010. (Illus.). 204p. pap. 23.00 (978-1-60899-264-5(0), Wipf and Stock) Wipf & Stock Pubs.

Fiorenza, Francis Schussler & Galvin, John P., eds. Systematic Theology: Roman Catholic Perspectives. 2nd rev. ed. 2011. 704p. (C). pap. 49.00 (978-0-8006-6291-2(1), Fortress Pr.) Augsburg Fortress, Pubs.

Fireside Catholic Publishing, creator. The New Catholic Answer Bible RCIA Program: A Scripture-Based Question & Answer Approach to Rite of Christian Initiation for Adults. 2008. 64p. pap. 19.95 (978-1-55665-034-5(5)) Fireside Catholic Bibles.

Fishberg, Sarah & Jacob, Isaac ben. The Rise: Saunière's Magical Workings & the Penitential Movement in Europe. 2008. (ENG.). 272p. pap. 17.95 (978-1-931882-87-3(8)) Adventures Unlimited Pr.

Fisher, Anthony. Catholic Bioethics for a New Millennium. 2011. (ENG.). 346p. 90.00 (978-1-107-00958-5(8)); pap. 29.99 (978-0-521-25324-6(1)) Cambridge Univ. Pr.

Flader, John. Question Time: 150 Questions & Answers on the Catholic Faith. 2010. (ENG.). 328p. pap. 16.95 (978-1-58979-593-8(8)); 16.95 (978-1-58979-594-5(6)) Taylor Trade Publishing.

Flint, Thomas P. Divine Providence: The Molinist Account. 2006. (Illus.). 272p. pap. 27.95 (978-0-8014-7336-4(5), ILR Pr.) Cornell Univ. Pr.

Flynn, Gabriel & Murray, Paul D. Ressourcement: A Movement for Renewal in Twentieth-Century Catholic Theology. 2012. (ENG.). 592p. 125.00 (978-0-19-955287-0(8)) Oxford Univ. Pr., Inc.

Foley, Leonard. Believing in Jesus: A Popular Overview of the Catholic Faith. 6th ed. 2009. pap. (978-0-86716-939-3(7)) Franciscan Media.

Ford, John T. Glossary of Theological Terms. 2006. 207p. per. 16.95 (978-0-88489-903-7(9)) St. Mary's Pr.

Ford, John T., ed. John Henry Newman: Spiritual Writings. 2012. (ENG.). 192p. pap. 22.00 (978-1-57075-954-3(5)) Orbis Bks.

Fortea, Jose Antonio & Fortea, Padre. Memorias De Un Exorcista. 2009. (SPA.). 352p. pap. 19.95 (978-84-270-3483-9(0)) Editorial Planeta, S. A. ESP. Dist: Perseus Distribution.

Fortescue, Adrian. Early Papacy. 2008. 130p. pap. 12.95 (978-1-58617-176-6(3)) Ignatius Pr.

Fourre, Connie & Bachand, Sarah Caffrey. Leader's Guide for Primary Source Readings in Catholic Social Justice. 2007. 86p. per. 16.75 (978-0-88489-969-3(1)) St. Mary's Pr.

Fragomeni, Richard N. The Eucharist. 2009. 96p. pap. 6.95 (978-0-7648-1699-4(3), Liguori) Liguori Pubns.

Frick, Peter, et al. Aelred of Rievaulx: Spiritual Friendship. 2010. (978-0-87907-970-3(3)) Cistercian Pubns., Inc.

Fuentes, Carlos Miguel. He Made Them Male & Female. 2007. 178p. pap. 14.95 (978-1-933871-25-7(3)) IVE Pr.

Fussell, Edwin Sill. The Catholic Side of Henry James. 2009. (Cambridge Studies in American Literature & Culture Ser.). (ENG.). 192p. pap. 33.00 (978-0-521-10058-8(5)) Cambridge Univ. Pr.

Gaillardetz, Richard R. The Church in the Making: Lumen Gentium, Christus Dominus, Orientalium Ecclesiarum. 2006. (Rediscovering Vatican II Ser.). 220p. per. 19.95 (978-0-8091-4276-7(7), 4276-7) Paulist Pr.

—A Daring Promise: A Spirituality of Christian Marriage. 2007. 130p. per. 14.95 (978-0-7648-1559-1(8), Liguori/Triumph) Liguori Pubns.

—Ecclesiology for a Global Church: A People Called & Sent. 2008. (Theology in Global Perspective Ser.). 312p. pap. 30.00 (978-1-57075-769-3(0)) Orbis Bks.

Gaillardetz, Richard R. & Clifford, Catherine E. Keys to the Council: Unlocking the Teaching of Vatican II. 2012. (978-0-8146-3368-7(4)); E-Book (978-0-8146-3424-0(9)) Liturgical Pr.

Gallagher, Lowell. Redrawing the Map of Early Modern English Catholicism. 2012. (UCLA Clark Memorial Library Ser.). (ENG., Illus.). 360p. (C). (978-1-4426-4312-3(9)) Univ. of Toronto Pr.

Galusha, David. Religion Coordinator Manual: School Edition. 2010. pap. 24.95 (978-1-59982-055-2(2)) St. Mary's Pr.

Gan, Eugene. Infinite Bandwidth: Encountering Christ in the Media. 2010. 148p. pap. 11.95 (978-1-931018-67-8(7)) Emmaus Road Publishing.

Garascia, Anthony. Before I Do: Preparing for the Sacrament of Marriage. rev. ed. 2007. (Illus.). 127p. pap. 8.95 (978-1-59471-141-1(0)) Ave Maria Pr.

—Combined Leader's Guide for Before I Do & Catholic Remarriage. rev. ed. 2007. 126p. per. 15.95 (978-1-59471-142-8(9)) Ave Maria Pr.

Garvey, John, et al. Sexuality & the U. S. Catholic Church: Crisis & Renewal. Cahill, Lisa Sowle & Garvey, John, eds. Kennedy, T. Frank, ed. 2006. (Boston College Church in the 21st Century Ser.). (ENG., Illus.). 240p. pap. 24.95 (978-0-8245-2408-1(X)) Crossroad Publishing Co., The.

Garvin, Joseph N. & Corbett, James A. The Summa Contra Haereticos: Ascribed to Praepositinus of Cremona. Moore, Philip S., ed. 2011. 358p. 51.95 (978-1-258-08935-1(1)) Literary Licensing, LLC.

Geisler, Norman L., et al. Is Rome the True Church A Consideration of the Roman Catholic Claim. 2008. 240p. pap. 17.99 (978-1-4335-0231-6(3)) Crossway.

Gendron, Mike. Two Ways to Eternity: Divine Accomplishment or Human Achievement? 2011. (978-0-9826155-7-7(4)) Northampton Pr., The.

George, Francis. The Difference God Makes: A Catholic Vision of Faith, Communion, & Culture. 2009. (ENG.). 368p. 26.95 (978-0-8245-2582-8(5)) Crossroad Publishing Co., The.

—God in Action: How Faith in God Can Address the Challenges of the World. 2011. 240p. 22.99 (978-0-307-59026-8(7), Doubleday Religion) Doubleday Religious Publishing Group, The.

George, Francis Cardinal. The Difference God Makes: A Catholic Vision of Faith, Communion, & Culture. 2011. (ENG.). 384p. pap. 19.95 (978-0-8245-2627-6(9)) Crossroad Publishing Co., The.

Gilbey, A.N. We Believe. 2011. 264p. pap. (978-0-85244-770-3(1)) Gracewing, Ltd.

Gilsdorf, Richard W. The Signs of the Times: Understanding the Church since Vatican II. Beno, Patrick F., ed. 2008. (Illus.). 542p. pap. 19.95 (978-0-615-18489-0(8)) Star of the Bay Pr.

Glavich, Mary Kathleen. The Catholic Companion to Mary. 2007. (Illus.). 176p. per. 9.95 (978-0-87946-330-4(9)) ACTA Pubns.

Gohdes, C. B. Does the Modern Papacy Require a New Evaluation? 2011. 264p. 47.95 (978-1-258-02117-7(X)) Literary Licensing, LLC.

Goizueta, Roberto S. Christ Our Companion: A Liberation Theological Aesthetic. 2009. 160p. pap. 30.00 (978-1-57075-853-9(0)) Orbis Bks.

Gorman, Robert. Toward the Common Good: A Catholic Critique of the Discipline of Political Science. 2011. (Catholic Social Thought Ser.). (ENG.). 194p. (gr. 17). 65.00 (978-0-8108-7796-2(1)) Scarecrow Pr., Inc.

Graham, Donald. From Eastertide to Ecclesia: John Henry Newman, the Holy Spirit & the Church. 2011. pap. (978-0-87462-795-4(8)) Marquette Univ. Pr.

Graham, William. Here Comes Everybody: Catholic Studies in American Higher Education. 2008. (ENG.). 204p. pap. 35.99 (978-0-7618-4432-7(5)) Univ. Pr. of America, Inc.

—Here Comes Everybody: Catholics Studies in American Higher Education. 2008. (ENG.). 204p. 68.50 (978-0-7618-4431-0(7)) Univ. Pr. of America, Inc.
Graham, William C. A Catholic Handbook on Sex: Essentials for the 21st Century: Explanations, Definitions, Prompts, Prayers, & Examples. 2011. 136p. pap. 10.95 **(978-0-8091-4737-3(8))** Paulist Pr.
Grebens, George. Evolution, Creation, Intelligent Design & Hybrids: Which Ones Are Scientific? 2010. (ENG.). 296p. pap. 22.00 (978-1-58982-601-4(9), American Univ. & College Pr.) American Bk. Publishing Group.
Gresham, John L. & Gresham, John Leroy. Holy Spirit 101: Present among Us. 2011. 143p. pap. **(978-0-7648-1985-8(2))** Liguori Pubns.
Gresham, John Leroy. Jesus 101: God & Man. 2010. (978-0-7648-1931-5(3)) Liguori Pubns.
Gribble, Richard. The Everything Guide to Catholicism: A complete introduction to the beliefs, traditions, & tenets of the Catholic Church from past to Present. 2010. (ENG.). 288p. pap. 15.95 (978-1-4405-0409-9(1)) Adams Media Corp.
Groeschel, Benedict J. After This Life: What Catholics Believe about What Happens Next. 2009. 128p. pap. 12.95 (978-1-59276-442-6(8)) Our Sunday Visitor, Publishing Div.
—The Journey of Faith: How to Deepen Your Faith in God, Christ, & the Church. 2010. 141p. pap. (978-1-59276-323-8(5)) Our Sunday Visitor, Publishing Div.
Groody, Daniel G. Globalization, Spirituality, & Justice: Navigating the Path to Peace. 2007. (Theology in Global Perspective Ser.). (Illus.). 280p. per. 28.00 (978-1-57075-696-2(1)) Orbis Bks.
Gros, Joye. Reflexion Teologica: Vincula la Fe con la Vida. Walters, Thomas P., ed. 2009. (Fundamentos de la Fe Catolica Ser.). (SPA., Illus.). 128p. per. 7.95 (978-0-8294-2376-1(1)) Loyola Pr.
Grumett, David & Grumett. De Lubac. 2007. (Guides for the Perplexed Ser.). (ENG.). 200p. 29.95 (978-0-8264-9315-6(7), T&T Clark Int'l) Continuum International Publishing Group, Ltd. GBR. Dist: National Bk. Network.
—De Lubac: A Guide for the Perplexed. 2007. (Guides for the Perplexed Ser.). (ENG.). 200p. 130.00 (978-0-8264-9314-9(9), T&T Clark Int'l) Continuum International Publishing Group, Ltd. GBR. Dist: National Bk. Network.
Guerrini, Luigi. Cosmologie in Lotta: Le Origini Del Processo Di Galileo. 2010. (ITA.). 312p. (C). pap. 30.00 (978-88-596-0792-2(2)) Polistampa ITA. Dist: Brown, David Bk. Co., The.
Guimaraes, Atila Sinke. In the Murky Waters of Vatican II, 11 Vols., Vol. 1. 3rd ed. 2008. (ENG.). 396p. pap. 20.00 (978-0-9726516-7-7(5)) Tradition in Action, Inc.
Haffner, Paul. El Misterio Sacramental. 2007. pap. (978-0-85244-687-4(X)) Gracewing, Ltd.
—Mystery of the Church. 2007. 332p. per. (978-0-85244-133-6(9)) Gracewing, Ltd.
Hahn, Kimberly. Beloved & Blessed: Biblical Wisdom for Family Life. 2010. 240p. pap. 14.99 (978-0-86716-945-4(1), Servant Bks.) Franciscan Media.
Hahn, Scott. First Comes Love: Finding Your Family in the Church & the Trinity. 2006. (ENG.). 224p. per. 12.99 (978-0-385-49662-9(1), Image) Doubleday Religious Publishing Group, The.
—Scott Hahn's Study Guide for the Lamb's Supper. 2010. (ENG.). 112p. pap. 9.99 (978-0-307-58905-7(6), Doubleday Religion) Doubleday Religious Publishing Group, The.
—Signs of Life: 40 Catholic Customs & Their Biblical Roots. 2009. (ENG.). 288p. 23.00 (978-0-385-51949-6(4)) Knopf Doubleday Publishing Group.
Hahn, Scott, compiled by. Spirit & Life: Essays on Interpreting the Bible in Ordinary Time. 2009. 162p. mass mkt. 15.95 (978-1-931018-53-1(7)) Emmaus Road Publishing.
Hahn, Scott, ed. Catholic Bible Dictionary. 2009. (ENG., Illus.). 1008p. 45.00 (978-0-385-51229-9(5)) Knopf Doubleday Publishing Group.
Hahn, Scott & Flaherty, Regis J., eds. Catholic for a Reason IV: Scripture & the Mystery of Marriage & Family Life. 2007. (Catholic for a Reason Ser.). 199p. per. 15.95 (978-1-931018-44-9(8)) Emmaus Road Publishing.
Hahn, Scott & Socias, James. Faith & Revelation: Knowing God Through Sacred Scripture. 2009. (978-1-936045-01-3(X)) Midwest Theological Forum.
Hahn, Scott W. Covenant & Communion: The Biblical Theology of Pope Benedict XVI. 2009. 160p. (C). 14.99 (978-1-58743-269-9(2)) Brazos Pr.
Hahnenberg, Edward J. Purgatory: An historical & Contemporary Analysis. 2008. 168p. pap. 13.95 (978-1-59594-235-7(1)) WingSpan Publishing.
Hahnenberg, Edward P. Awakening Vocation: A Theology of Christian Call. 2010. 29.95 (978-0-8146-5389-0(8)); E-Book 19.95 (978-0-8146-5733-1(8)) Liturgical Pr.
—A Concise Guide to the Documents of Vatican II. 2007. 178p. per. 19.95 (978-0-86716-552-4(9)) Franciscan Media.
Haight, Roger & Haight. The Future of Christology. 2007. (ENG.). 224p. pap. 29.95 (978-0-8264-2927-8(0)) Continuum International Publishing Group, Ltd. GBR. Dist: National Bk. Network.
Hailer, Gretchen & Pacatte, Rose. Media Mindfulness: Educating Teens about Faith & Media. 2007. (Illus.). 150p. spiral bd. 27.25 (978-0-88489-905-1(5)) St. Mary's Pr.
Hain, Randy. The Catholic Briefcase: Practical Tools for Integrating Faith & Work. 2011. **(978-0-7648-2052-6(4))** Liguori Pubns.
Haldane, John. The Church & the World. 2008. 228p. pap. (978-0-85244-588-4(1)) Gracewing, Ltd.
Hannon, Patrick. The Geography of God's Mercy: Stories of Compassion & Forgiveness. 2007. 159p. 17.95 (978-0-87946-332-6(5)); per. 12.95 (978-0-87946-333-5(3)) ACTA Pubns.
—The Long Yearning's End: Stories of Sacrament & Incarnation. 2009. 128p. 17.95 (978-0-87946-402-8(X)); pap. 12.95 (978-0-87946-403-5(8)) ACTA Pubns.
Hart, Mark. Ask the Bible Geek 2: More Answers to Questions from Catholic Teens. 2007. 180p. per. 12.99 (978-0-86716-766-5(1), Servant Bks.) Franciscan Media.
Hart, Mark & Lemieux, Todd. 100 Things Every Catholic Teen Should Know. 2007. 276p. (YA). per. 9.99 (978-0-9802362-0-0(7)) Life Teen.
Hartley, Edmund. Roman Catholic Church. 2009. (Simple Guides). (ENG., Illus.). 144p. pap. 10.95 (978-1-85733-441-8(8), Simple Guides) Kuperard Pubs. GBR. Dist: Random Hse., Inc.
Hartline, David J. The Tide Is Turning Toward Catholicism. 2006. (Illus.). 309p. per. 15.99 (978-0-9790732-0-5(0)) Catholic Report.
Healey, Charles J. The Ignatian Way: Key Aspects of Jesuit Spirituality. 2009. 176p. pap. 16.95 (978-0-8091-4616-1(9)) Paulist Pr.
Healy, Nicholas J. & Schindler, D. C. Being Holy in the World: Theology & Culture in the Thought of David L. Schindler. 2011. pap. 34.00 (978-0-8028-6554-0(2)) Eerdmans, William B. Publishing Co.
Helman, Ivy A. Women & the Vatican: An Exploration of Official Documents. 2012. x, 262p. pap. 35.00 **(978-1-57075-967-3(7))** Orbis Bks.
Herrick, Anne, et al. The Church: Christ in the World Today, Teacher Guide. 2011. (Living in Christ Ser.). (ENG.). (gr. 9-12). spiral bd. 39.95 (978-1-59982-061-3(7)) St. Mary's Pr.
Herron, Fred. Tuning the Rig: Catholic Schools for a Learning Church. 2010. (ENG.). 260p. pap. 35.75 (978-0-7618-5205-6(0)) Univ. Pr. of America, Inc.
Higgins, Gregory C. Christianity 101: A Textbook of Catholic Theology. annot. ed. 2007. 485p. per. 24.95 (978-0-8091-4208-8(2), 4208-2) Paulist Pr.
Hill, Brennan. The Ongoing Renewal of Catholicism. 2008. pap. 35.00 (978-0-88489-954-9(3)) St. Mary's Pr.
Hillier, John G. Anecdotes & Scripture Notes for All Occasions. 2007. 253p. per. 24.95 (978-1-58595-570-1(1)) Twenty-Third Pubns./Bayard.
Hilsman, Gordon J. Intimate Spirituality: The Catholic Way of Love & Sex. Hilsman, Gordon J., ed. 2007. (ENG.). 208p. 19.95 (978-1-58051-211-4(9), Sheed & Ward) Rowman & Littlefield Publishers, Inc.
Hindman, Ross Thomas. The Great Divide. 2008. 200p. pap. 15.99 (978-1-60647-601-7(7)) Xulon Pr., Inc.
Hoang, Linh. Rebuilding Religious Experience- Vietnamese Refugees in America. 2008. 292p. per. (978-3-8364-2221-5(2)) VDM Verlag Dr. Mueller e.K.
Hofstadter, Dan. The Earth Moves: Galileo & the Roman Inquisition. 2010. (Great Discoveries Ser.). (ENG., Illus.). 240p. pap. 14.95 (978-0-393-33820-1(7), 33820) Norton, W. W. & Co., Inc.
Holloway, Carson. The Way of Life: John Paul II & the Challenge of Liberal Modernity. 2008. (ENG.). 205p. pap. 29.95 (978-1-932792-96-6(1)) Baylor Univ. Pr.
Hornsby-Smith, Michael P. An Introduction to Catholic Social Thought. 2006 (Introduction to Religion Ser.). (ENG., Illus.). (C). 402p. 104.00 (978-0-521-86339-1(2)); 400p. per. 40.00 (978-0-521-68199-5(5)) Cambridge Univ. Pr.
Howard, Thomas. The Night Is Far Spent. 2007. 200p. pap. 14.95 (978-1-58617-132-2(1)) Ignatius Pr.
Hudale, Martin. The Matrix of Mysticism: An in-depth ExposT Of. 2008. 476p. pap. 24.99 (978-1-60647-657-4(2)) Xulon Pr., Inc.
Huebsch, Bill. The Council: Vatican II in Plain English. 2007. (Vatican II in Plain English Ser.: Vol. #1). 224p. per. 15.95 (978-1-59471-105-3(4)) Ave Maria Pr.
Human Nature in Its Wholeness: A Roman Catholic Perspective. annot. ed. 2006. 325p. 74.95 (978-0-8132-1440-5(8)) Catholic Univ. of America Pr.
Hütter, Reinhard, ed. Ressourcement Thomism: Sacred Doctrine, the Sacraments, & the Moral Life. Levering, Matthew, tr. 2010. (ENG.). 432p. 64.95 (978-0-8132-1785-7(7)) Catholic Univ. of America Pr.
Iber, Simeon Tsetim. The Principle of Subsidiarity in Catholic Social Thought Implications for Social Justice & Civil Society in Nigeria. 2010. (American University Studies VII: Theology & Religion Ser.). 262p. (C). pap. 42.95 (978-1-4331-1254-6(X)) Lang, Peter Publishing, Inc.
—A Study of the Principle of Subsidiarity in Catholic Social Thought: Implications for Social Justice & Civil Society in Nigeria. 2010. xix, 242p. (978-1-4331-1011-5(3)) Lang, Peter GmbH, Europaischer Verlag der Wissenschaften.
Imbelli, Robert P., ed. Handing on the Faith: The Church's Mission & Challenge. annot. ed. 2006. (Church in the 21st Century Ser.). (ENG.). 264p. pap. 24.95 (978-0-8245-2409-8(8)) Crossroad Publishing Co., The.
I.T.C. International Theological Commission, Vol II. 2009. 473p. pap. 29.95 (978-1-58617-226-8(3)) Ignatius Pr.
James & Dyson, R. W. De Regimine Christiano: A Critical Edition & Translation. 2009. (978-90-04-17597-6(0)) BRILL.
James, Theodore E. The Heart of Catholicism: Essential Writings of the Church from St. Paul to St. John Paul II. cd-rom 49.95 (978-0-87973-293-6(8)) Our Sunday Visitor, Publishing Div.
Jegen. Transformed by the Trinity. 2008. (ENG.). 128p. pap. 12.95 (978-0-8294-2612-0(4)) Loyola Pr.
John Paul II, pseud. The John Paul II Lifeguide: Words to Live By. Rice, Ellen, ed. 2006. 124p. per. 6.00 (978-1-58731-396-7(0)) St. Augustine's Pr., Inc.
—Man & Woman He Created Them: A Theology of the Body. Waldstein, Michael, tr. 2006. 768p. pap. 29.95 (978-0-8198-7421-4(3)) Pauline Bks. & Media.
—The Mercy of God: Dives in Misericordia. 53p. pap. 2.95 (978-0-8198-4745-4(3), 332-194) Pauline Bks. & Media.
—The Mother of the Redeemer.Tr. of Redemptoris Mater. 79p. pap. 3.50 (978-0-8198-4744-7(5)) Pauline Bks. & Media.
—On the Holy Spirit in the Life of the Church & the World: Dominum et Vivificantem. (Illus.). 144p. pap. 4.95 (978-0-8198-3349-5(5), 332-114) Pauline Bks. & Media.
Johnson, Keith L. Karl Barth & the Analogia Entis. 2011. (T&T Clark Studies in Systematic Theology Ser.). (ENG.). 256p. pap. 44.95 **(978-0-567-34463-2(0)**, T&T Clark Int'l) Continuum International Publishing Group, Ltd. GBR. Dist: National Bk. Network.
Kane, Brian M. The Blessing of Life: An Introduction to Catholic Bioethics. 2011. (ENG.). 172p. 60.00 (978-0-7391-2200-6(2)) Lexington Bks.
Kappeler, Warren Anthony. Communication Habits for the Pilgrim Church: Vatican Teaching on Media & Social Communication. 2009. (American University Studies VII: Theology & Religion Ser.). (ENG.). 266p. (C). 76.95 (978-1-4331-0543-2(8)) Lang, Peter Publishing, Inc.
Kardas, Dorothy K. Voice of Thunder: Footsteps to Light. 2008. 452p. pap. 20.49 (978-1-4343-9072-1(1)) AuthorHouse.
Kardas, Psy. D. Th. D. Voice of Thunder: Footsteps to Light. 2008. 452p. 30.99 (978-1-4343-9073-8(X)) AuthorHouse.
Kasiri, Hamid. Mit den Augen des Anderen: Zur Entwicklung des Umgangs mit der Hl. Schrift im Katholizismus des 20. Jahrhunderts. 2009. (Europäische Hochschulschriften. Reihe 23: Theologie Ser.). (GER.). 202p. pap. 57.95 (978-3-631-59174-1(8)) Lang, Peter GmbH, Europaischer Verlag der Wissenschaften DEU. Dist: Lang, Peter.
Keating, Thomas. The Heart of the World: An Introduction to Contemplative Christianity. 2008. (ENG.). 100p. pap. 14.95 (978-0-8245-2495-1(0)) Crossroad Publishing Co., The.
Keenan, James F., ed. Catholic Theological Ethics, Past, Present, & Future: The Trento Conference. 2012. 304p. pap. 40.00 (978-1-57075-941-3(3)) Orbis Bks.
Keenan, James F. & Keenan. A History of Catholic Moral Theology in the Twentieth Century: From Confessing Sins to Liberating Consciences. 2010. (ENG.). 256p. 85.00 (978-0-8264-2928-5(9)); pap. 29.95 (978-0-8264-2929-2(7)) Continuum International Publishing Group, Ltd. GBR. Dist: National Bk. Network.
Keller, Paul Jerome. 101 Questions & Answers on the Sacraments of Healing: Penance & Anointing of the Sick. 2010. 176p. pap. 15.95 (978-0-8091-4660-4(6)) Paulist Pr.
Kelly, Elizabeth M. Heaven in You & You in Heaven: Unveiling Eternity on Earth. 2008. 172p. pap. 12.95 (978-1-59325-119-2(X)) Word Among Us Pr.
Kendall, Daniel & Labelle, Jeffrey, eds. Pope John Paul II: A Reader. 2007. 262p. (Orig.). per. 19.95 (978-0-8091-4479-2(4), 4479-2) Paulist Pr.
Kendzia, Mary Carol. Catholic Update Guide to Baptism. 2011. x, 53p. **(978-1-61636-063-4(1))** Franciscan Media.
—Catholic Update Guide to Communion. 2011. (Catholic Update Guides). (ENG.). 55p. pap. 5.99 **(978-1-61636-240-9(5))** Franciscan Media.
—Catholic Update Guide to Confirmation. 2012. (Catholic Update Guides). (ENG.). 53p. pap. 5.99 **(978-1-61636-239-3(1))** Franciscan Media.
—Catholic Update Guide to Marriage. 2011. **(978-1-61636-062-7(3))** Franciscan Media.
—Las 5 Preguntas de Nuestra Fe Católica: à Quién, Qué, Dónde, Cuándo, For Qué — Y Cómo Entenderla. 2011. (SPA.). (978-0-7648-1992-6(5), Libros Liguori) Liguori Pubns.
—The 5 W's of Our Catholic Faith: Who, What, When, Where, Why ... & How We Live It. 2011. (978-0-7648-1986-5(0)) Liguori Pubns.
—The 5 W's of Our Catholic Faith: Who, What, Where, When, Why ... & How We Live It: Participant. 2011. (978-0-7648-1987-2(9)) Liguori Pubns.
Ker, I. T. & Merrigan, T., eds. Newman & Truth. 2008. (Louvain Theological & Pastoral Monographs). (ENG.). 289p. (C). pap. 41.00 (978-90-429-2140-5(4)) Peeters Pubs. & Booksellers BEL. Dist: Brown, David Bk. Co., The.
Ker, Ian. Mere Catholicism. 2007. 196p. per. 14.95 (978-1-931018-39-5(1)) Emmaus Road Publishing.
Kerr, Fergus. Twentieth-Century Catholic Theologians. (ENG.). 240p. 2007. per. 37.95 (978-1-4051-2084-5(3)) 2006. 99.95 (978-1-4051-2083-8(5)) Wiley, John & Sons, Inc. (Wiley-Blackwell).
Kerrigan, Michael. The Illustrated Encyclopedia of Catholicism: A Complete Guide to the History, Philosophy & Practice of Catholic Christianity, Illustrated with More Than 500 Beautiful Illustrations. 2009. (ENG., Illus.). 256p. 35.00 (978-0-7548-1956-1(6)) Anness Publishing GBR. Dist: National Bk. Network.
Kerrigan, Michael & Frances Budzik, Mary. An Illustrated History of Catholicism: An Authoritative Chronicle of the Development of Catholic Christianity & Its Doctrine with More Than 300 Photographs & Fine-Art Illustrations. 2012. (ENG., Illus.). 160p. pap. 18.99 (978-1-84476-985-8(2)) Anness Publishing GBR. Dist: National Bk. Network.
Kerwin, Donald & Gerschutz, J. R. And You Welcomed Me: Migration & Catholic Social Teaching. 2009. (ENG.). 192p. 68.50 (978-0-7391-4099-4(X)); pap. 28.50 (978-0-7391-4100-7(7)) Lexington Bks.
Kessler, Mathew, et al. Con Corazones Llenos de Gozo: Siguiendo a Cristo el Redentor. 2010. (SPA.). 64p. (978-0-7648-1912-4(7)) Liguori Pubns.
Kessler, Mathew J. & Medina, Jose Antonio. With Hearts Full of Joy: Following Christ the Redeemer. 2010. (978-0-7648-1911-7(9)) Liguori Pubns.
Koenig-Bricker, Woodeene, compiled by. A Study Guide to Living Charity in Truth: Pope Benedict's Encyclical on Social & Economic Justice. 2009. 64p. pap. 9.95 (978-1-59276-578-2(5)) Our Sunday Visitor, Publishing Div.
Krason, Stephen M. The Public Order & the Sacred Order: Contemporary Issues, Catholic Social Thought, & the Western & American Traditions, 2 vols. 2009. (Catholic Social Thought Ser.: 2 Volumes). (ENG.). 1144p. (gr. 17). 210.00 (978-0-8108-6396-5(0)) Scarecrow Pr., Inc.
Kreeft, Peter. The Philosophy of Jesus. 2007. 168p. 17.00 (978-1-58731-635-7(8)) St. Augustine's Pr., Inc.
Krier, Mich. The Challenge & Spirituality of Catholic Social Teaching: Revised Edition. 2011. 272p. pap. 22.00 (978-1-57075-945-1(6)) Orbis Bks.
Kubicki, Judith M. Presence of Christ in the Gathered Assembly. 2006. (ENG.). 192p. pap. 29.95 (978-0-8264-1901-9(1)) Continuum International Publishing Group, Ltd. GBR. Dist: National Bk. Network.
Kubicki, Judith Marie & Kubicki, Judith M. The Presence of Christ in the Gathered Assembly. 2006. (ENG.). 192p. 110.00 (978-0-8264-1900-2(3)) Continuum International Publishing Group, Ltd. GBR. Dist: National Bk. Network.
Kuhn, Johannes. Faithfully Seeking Understanding. Kaplan, Grant, tr. from GER. 2009. 312p. 74.95 (978-0-8132-1675-1(3)) Catholic Univ. of America Pr.
Lacey, Michael J. & Oakley, Francis. The Crisis of Authority in Catholic Modernity. 1 vol. 2011. (ENG., Illus.). 392p. pap. 35.00 (978-0-19-977878-2(7)) Oxford Univ. Pr., Inc.
Lakeland, Paul. Church: Living Communion. 2009. pap. 19.95 (978-0-8146-5993-9(4)) Liturgical Pr.
Lamb, Matthew L. Eternity, Time, & the Life of Wisdom. 2007. xx, 161p. pap. (978-1-932589-41-2(4)) Ave Maria Univ.
Lamb, Matthew L. & Levering, Matthew, eds. Vatican II: Renewal within Tradition. 2008. (ENG.). 480p. pap. 29.95 (978-0-19-533267-4(9)) Oxford Univ. Pr., Inc.
Lamb, Matthew L., et al. Wisdom & Holiness, Science & Scholarship: Essays in Honor of Matthew L. Lamb. 2007. xi, 428p. pap. (978-1-932589-42-9(2), Sapientia Pr.) Ave Maria Univ.
Lamoureux, Patricia & Wadell, Paul J. The Christian Moral Life: Faithful Discipleship for a Global Society. 2010. 328p. pap. 30.00 (978-1-57075-881-2(6)) Orbis Bks.
Lash, Nicholas. Theology for Pilgrims. 2008. (ENG.). 200p. pap. 25.00 (978-0-268-03409-2(5)) Univ. of Notre Dame Pr.
Leckey, Dolores, ed. Monika K Hellwig. 2010. 144p. pap. 19.95 (978-0-8146-5696-9(X)) Liturgical Pr.
Lefebvre, Marcel. The Mass of All Time: The Hidden Treasure. Troadec, Patrick, ed. 2007. 325p. pap. 25.00 (978-1-892331-46-5(2)) Angelus Pr.
Lefebvre, Marcel. Spiritual Journey: According to St. Thomas Aquinas in His Summa Theologiæ: Revised Translation. 2011. **(978-0-935952-17-9(9))** Angelus Pr.
Lehmann, L. H. ExPriest & the Riddle of Religion. 2006. pap. 30.95 (978-1-4286-5811-0(4)) Kessinger Publishing, LLC.
Lejeune, Marcel & LeJeune, Marcel. Set Free to Love: Lives Changed by the Theology of the Body. 2010. pap. (978-0-86716-940-9(0), Servant Bks.) Franciscan Media.
Leone, Massimo. Saints & Signs: A Semiotic Reading of Conversion in Early Modern Catholicism. 2010. (Religion & Society Ser.). (ENG., Illus.). XI, 652p. 196.00 **(978-3-11-022951-6(X))** De Gruyter, Walter Inc.
Levering. Catholic Theology. 2012. (Doing Theology) Ser.). (ENG.). 176p. 120.00 (978-0-567-03438-0(0)); pap. 29.95 (978-0-567-03439-7(9)) Continuum International Publishing Group, Ltd. GBR. (T&T Clark Int'l). Dist: National Bk. Network.
Levering, Matthew. The Feminine Genius of Catholic Theology. 2012. (ENG.). 160p. 90.00 **(978-0-567-63306-4(3))**; pap. 27.95 **(978-0-567-19686-6(0))** Continuum International Publishing Group, Ltd. GBR. (T&T Clark Int'l). Dist: National Bk. Network.
—Jesus & the Demise of Death: Resurrection, Afterlife, & the Fate of the Christian. 2012. (ENG.). 240p. pap. 29.95 **(978-1-60258-447-1(8))** Baylor Univ. Pr.
Levering, Matthew. Participatory Biblical Exegesis: A Theology of Biblical Interpretation. 2008. (Reading the Scriptures Ser.). (ENG.). 344p. pap. 25.00 (978-0-268-03408-5(7)) Univ. of Notre Dame Pr.
Levering, Matthew & Dauphinais, Michael. Rediscovering Aquinas & the Sacraments: Studies in Sacramental Theology. 2009. xiv, 143p. pap. (978-1-59525-032-2(8)) Hillenbrand Bks.
Libreria Editrice Vaticana, creator. Essentials for Christian Living. 2008. 127p. pap. 6.95 (978-1-60137-020-4(2)) United States Conference of Catholic Bishops.
Lindquist, Paul. Blessed among Women. 2006. pap. 9.99 (978-1-60034-627-9(8)) Xulon Pr., Inc.
Link, Mark. Path Through Catholicism. 2006. (Illus.). 320p. (Orig.). per. 20.75 (978-0-7829-0971-5(X)) RCL Benziger Publishing.
Lombard, Peter. Sentences Book 4: on the Doctrine of Signs, 4 vols. 2010. (Mediaeval Sources of Translation Ser.). (ENG.). 370p. pap. 39.95 (978-0-88844-296-3(3)) Pontifical Institute of Mediaeval Studies, Dept. of Pubns. CAN. Dist: Univ. of Toronto Pr.
Lombard, Peter & Silano, Giulio. On the Incarnation of the Word, 4 vols., Bk. 3. 2008. (Mediaeval Sources in Translation Ser.). (ENG.). pap. 34.95 (978-0-88844-295-6(5)) Pontifical Institute of Mediaeval Studies, Dept. of Pubns. CAN. Dist: Univ. of Toronto Pr.
—The Sentences, 4 vols., Bk. 2. 2008. (Mediaeval Sources in Translation Ser.). (ENG.). pap. 39.95 (978-0-88844-293-2(9)) Pontifical Institute of Mediaeval Studies, Dept. of Pubns. CAN. Dist: Univ. of Toronto Pr.
Lombardi, Josephine. The Universal Salvific Will of God in Official Documents of the Roman Catholic Church. 2007. 240p. 109.95 (978-0-7734-5246-6(X)) Mellen, Edwin Pr., The.
—What Are They Saying about the Universal Salvific Will of God? 2008. 144p. pap. 14.95 (978-0-8091-4562-1(6)) Paulist Pr.
Lonergan, Bernard. Shorter Papers. Croken, Robert C. et al, eds. 2007. (Collected Works of Bernard Lonergan Ser.). (ENG.). 368p. pap. (978-0-8020-9517-6(8)) Univ. of Toronto Pr.

C

Lonergan, Bernard J. F. & Lonergan, Bernard. Shorter Papers. Croken, Robert C. et al, eds. 2007. (Collected Works of Bernard Lonergan Ser.). (ENG.). 368p. *(978-0-8020-9753-8(7))* Univ. of Toronto Pr.

Lord of St. Aldegonde, Philip of Marnix. The Beehive of the Romish Church. 2008. 428p. pap. 44.96 *(978-1-4357-0870-9(9))* Lulu Enterprises Inc.

Lubac, Henri Cardinal de. Corpus Mysticum: The Eucharist & the Church in the Middle Ages. Stephens, Christopher et al, trs. from FRE. 2007. (ND Faith in Reason Ser.). (ENG.). 368p. pap. 35.00 *(978-0-268-02593-9(2))* Univ. of Notre Dame Pr.

Lubac, Henri De. Splendor of the Church. Mason, Michael, tr. from FRE. 384p. 17.95 *(978-0-89870-742-7(0))* Ignatius Pr.

Lunardini, Rosemary. The Mass in My Life: Cries of the Heart in the Prayers of the Mass. 2008. 132p. pap. 13.95 *(978-1-4401-0979-9(6))* iUniverse, Inc.

Lux, Richard C. The Jewish People, the Holy Land, & the State of Israel: A Catholic View. 2010. 192p. pap. 19.95 *(978-0-8091-4632-1(0))* Paulist Pr.

Lyddon, Eileen. Mysticism for Beginners: John of the Cross Made Easy. 2006. 165p. per. 13.95 *(978-1-56548-243-2(3))* New City Pr.

MacDonald, Sebastian Killoran. The Sacramental Roots of Human Freedom: A Catholic Basis for Morality. 2008. 212p. 109.95 *(978-0-7734-4986-2(8))* Mellen, Edwin Pr., The.

MacKendrick, Karmen. Fragmentation & Memory: Meditations on Christian Doctrine. 2008. (ENG.). 192p. 75.00 *(978-0-8232-2949-9(1))*; 3rd ed. pap. 28.00 *(978-0-8232-2950-5(5))* Fordham Univ. Pr.

Madrid, Patrick. A Pocket Guide to Purgatory. 2007. (Pocket Guide To Ser.). 63p. pap. 6.95 *(978-1-59276-294-1(8))* Our Sunday Visitor, Publishing Div.

—150 Bible Verses Every Catholic Should Know. 2008. pap. *(978-0-86716-902-7(8),* Servant Bks.) Franciscan Media.

Maffeo, Richard. We Believe: Forty Meditations on the Nicene Creed. 2007. 156p. per. 13.99 *(978-1-60266-205-6(3))* Xulon Pr., Inc.

Malloy, Richard G. A Faith That Frees: Catholic Matters for the 21st Century. 2007. 230p. pap. 22.00 *(978-1-57075-734-1(8))* Orbis Bks.

Manimala, Varghese. Faith, Reason, Science: Philosophical Reflections with Special Reference to Fides et Ratio. 2008. pap. *(978-1-56518-255-4(3))* Council for Research in Values & Philosophy.

Mannion, Gerard. Ecclesiology & Postmodernity: Questions for the Church in Our Time. 2007. 249p. per. 29.95 *(978-0-8146-5223-7(9))* Liturgical Pr.

Marchadour, Alain, et al. The Land, the Bible, & History: Toward the Land That I Will Show You. 3rd ed. 2010. (Abrahamic Dialogues Ser.). (ENG.). 232p. pap. 26.00 *(978-0-8232-2660-3(3))* Fordham Univ. Pr.

Marin, Antonio R. Elevation to the Most Blessed Trinity. Parrot, J. Edward, ed. Bolivar Plaza Staff, tr. from SPA. (Illus.). 125p. (C). pap. *(978-1-877905-29-2(1))* American Society for the Defense of Tradition, Family & Property, The (TFP).

Martin, Regis. The Suffering of Love: Christ's Descent into the Hell of Human Hopelessness. 2007. 254p. pap. 16.95 *(978-1-58617-105-6(4))* Ignatius Pr.

Massaro, Thomas J. United States Welfare Policy: A Catholic Response. 2007. (Moral Traditions Ser.). (ENG.). 272p. 59.95 *(978-1-58901-155-7(4))*; per. 19.95 *(978-1-58901-156-4(2))* Georgetown Univ. Pr.

Massingale, Bryan N. Racial Justice & the Catholic Church. 2010. 240p. pap. 26.00 *(978-1-57075-776-1(3))* Orbis Bks.

Matera, Angelo. Faith at the Edge: A New Generation of Catholic Writers Reflects on Life, Love, Sex, & Other Mysteries. Matera, Angelo, ed. 2008. 196p. per. 15.95 *(978-1-59471-140-4(2))* Ave Maria Pr.

May, William E. Catholic Bioethics & the Gift of Human Life. 2nd ed. 2007. 368p. per. 19.95 *(978-1-59276-330-6(8))* Our Sunday Visitor, Publishing Div.

—Theology of the Body in Context: Genesis & Growth. 2010. pap. *(978-0-8198-7431-3(0))* Pauline Bks. & Media.

McBrien, Richard P. The Church: The Evolution of Catholicism. 2009. (ENG.). 528p. pap. 17.99 *(978-0-06-124525-1(9),* HarperOne) HarperCollins Pubs.

McCarthy, David Matzko & Baker Publishing. The Heart of Catholic Social Teaching: Its Origin & Contemporary Significance, 1 vol. McCarthy, David Matzko, ed. 2009. 224p. pap. 26.00 *(978-1-58743-248-4(X))* Brazos Pr.

McCarthy, George E. & Rhodes, Royal W. Eclipse of Justice: Ethics, Economics, & the Lost Traditions of American Catholicism. 2008. 304p. pap. 33.00 *(978-1-60608-248-5(5))* Wipf & Stock Pubs.

McCloskey, Pat O. F. M. & McCloskey, Patrick. Ask a Franciscan: Answers to Catholic Questions. 2010. pap. *(978-0-86716-970-6(2))* Franciscan Media.

McCormack, Bruce & Dahlke, Benjamin. Karl Barth, Catholic Renewal & Vatican II. 2012. (ENG.). 208p. 110.00 ***(978-0-567-60593-1(0),*** T&T Clark Int'l) Continuum International Publishing Group, Ltd. GBR. Dist: National Bk. Network.

McCrossen, Vincent A. The Empty Room. 2011. 166p. 41.95 ***(978-1-258-07428-9(1))*** Literary Licensing, LLC.

McDermott, Michael J. Faithful Citizen, Faithful Catholic: Informing Your Conscience & Your Vote. 2007. 38p. pap. 7.25 *(978-0-88489-980-8(2))* St. Mary's Pr.

McDonagh, Enda & MacNamara, Vincent, eds. An Irish Reader in Moral Theology the Legacy of the Last Fifty Years Vol. 2: Sex, Marriage & the Family. 2011. (ENG.). 472p. pap. 49.95 ***(978-1-85607-739-2(X))*** Columba Pr. IRL. Dist: Dufour Editions, Inc.

McDonagh, Francis, ed. Dom Helder Camara: Essential Writings. 2009. 160p. pap. 16.00 *(978-1-57075-823-2(9))* Orbis Bks.

McDonald, Daniel, ed. Catholic Social Teaching in Global Perspective. 2010. 240p. pap. 26.00 *(978-1-57075-896-6(4))* Orbis Bks.

McGinnis, James. Activities for Catholic Social Teaching: A Resource Guide for Teachers & Youth Ministers. 2006. (Illus.). 219p. per. 19.95 *(978-1-59471-067-4(8))* Ave Maria Pr.

McIlvaine, Charles Pettit. Righteousness by Faith; or, the Nature & Means of Our Justification Before God; Illustrated by a Comparison of the Doctrine of the Oxford Tracts Wit. 2006. (Illus.). 500p. per. 29.99 *(978-1-4255-5582-5(9))* MPublishing.

McKenna, Briege. The Power of the Sacraments. 2010. pap. *(978-0-86716-982-9(6),* Servant Bks.) Franciscan Media.

McKenzie, John L. Did I Say That? A Theologian Confronts the Hard Questions. 2009. (John L. Mckenzie Reprints Ser.). 226p. pap. 24.00 *(978-1-60608-046-7(6))* Wipf & Stock Pubs.

McQueen, Moira. Bioethics Matters: A Catholic Perspective. 2009. (ENG.). 112p. 14.95 *(978-0-8264-3510-1(6),* Burns & Oates) Continuum International Publishing Group, Ltd. GBR. Dist: National Bk. Network.

Meconi, David, ed. Frank Sheed & Maisie Ward: Spiritual Writings. 2010. 20p. pap. 20.00 *(978-1-57075-887-4(5))* Orbis Bks.

Medina, Hector M. December Roses: Pastoral Reflections on Divorce. DuClos, Yolanda R. & Skarda, Pat, eds. 2011. 190p. pap. 22.00 *(978-1-61097-073-0(X),* Resource Pubns.) Wipf & Stock Pubs.

Medina, Nestor. Mestizaje: (Re)Mapping Race, Culture, & Faith in Latina/o Catholicism. 2009. 224p. pap. 28.00 *(978-1-57075-834-8(4))* Orbis Bks.

Melina, Livio & Anderson, Carl A., eds. The Way of Love: Reflections on Pope Benedict XVI's Encyclical Deus Caritas Est. 2006. 366p. 24.95 *(978-1-58617-167-4(4))* Ignatius Pr.

Méndez-Montoya, Angel F. The Theology of Food: Eating & the Eucharist. 2012. (ENG.). 182p. pap. 34.95 ***(978-0-470-67498-7(9),*** Wiley-Blackwell) Wiley, John & Sons, Inc.

Merrigan, Terrence & Ker, Ian. Newman & Truth. 2009. (Louvain Theological & Pastoral Monographs). 289p. pap. 50.00 *(978-0-8028-6477-2(5))* Eerdmans, William B. Publishing Co.

Meshar, Roxanne. The Political Nature of Doctrine. 2008. 232p. pap. 22.96 *(978-1-4357-1952-1(2))* Lulu Enterprises Inc.

Messer, Jim. Growing up Catholic: It Wasn't Easy. 2008. 48p. pap. 16.95 *(978-1-4241-9364-6(8))* PublishAmerica, Inc.

Michael, Sheehan. Apologetics & Catholic Doctrine: Catholic Clasics. 2009. (Illus.). 686p. pap. *(978-1-905574-45-2(2))* Baronius Pr. Ltd.

Michaels, Barry. Your Guide to Spe Salvi: Saved in Hope. 2008. 85p. pap. *(978-0-8198-8808-2(7))* Pauline Bks. & Media.

Mick, Lawrence E. Understanding the Sacraments: Anointing. 2007. (Understanding the Sacraments Ser.). (Illus.). 23p. pap. 2.00 *(978-0-8146-3193-5(2),* Liturgical Pr. Bks.) Liturgical Pr.

—Understanding the Sacraments: Eucharist. 2007. (Understanding the Sacraments Ser.) (Illus.). 26p. pap. 2.00 *(978-0-8146-3191-1(6),* Liturgical Pr. Bks.) Liturgical Pr.

—Understanding the Sacraments: Holy Orders. 2007. (Understanding the Sacraments Ser.). (Illus.). 23p. pap. 2.00 *(978-0-8146-3194-2(0),* Liturgical Pr. Bks.) Liturgical Pr.

—Understanding the Sacraments: Penance. 2007. (Understanding the Sacraments Ser.) (Illus.). 27p. pap. 2.00 *(978-0-8146-3192-8(4),* Liturgical Pr. Bks.) Liturgical Pr.

Mieth Dietmar Staff. 1999/1: Unanswered Questions (con 99) Concilium. 2011. pap. ***(978-0-334-03052-2(8),*** SCM Pr.) Hymns Ancient & Modern Ltd.

Miller, Monica Migliorino. Sexuality & Authority in the Catholic Church. 2007. 320p. per. 28.00 *(978-1-58966-128-8(1))* Univ. of Scranton Pr.

Miller, Richard W. God, Creation & Climate Change: Edited by Richard W. Miller. 2010. 160p. pap. 20.00 *(978-1-57075-889-8(1))* Orbis Bks.

Mills, David. Discovering Mary: Answers to Questions about the Mother of God. 2009. pap. *(978-0-86716-927-0(3),* Servant Bks.) Franciscan Media.

Minns, Denis. Irenaeus: An Introduction. 2010. (ENG.). 192p. 110.00 *(978-0-567-03365-9(1),* T&T Clark Int'l) Continuum International Publishing Group, Ltd. GBR. Dist: National Bk. Network.

Minns Op, Denis. Irenaeus: An Introduction. 2010. (ENG.). 192p. pap. 32.95 *(978-0-567-03366-6(X),* T&T Clark Int'l) Continuum International Publishing Group, Ltd. GBR. Dist: National Bk. Network.

Mize, Sandra Yocum. Joining the Revolution in Theology: The College Theology Society, 1954-2004. 2007. (ENG., Illus.). 336p. 41.95 *(978-0-7425-3195-6(3))* Rowman & Littlefield Publishers, Inc.

Molinier, M. Auguste. The Thoughts of Blaise Pascal. Paul, C. Kegan, tr. 2007. (ENG.). 372p. 48.95 *(978-0-548-09920-9(0))* Kessinger Publishing, LLC.

Monte Rochen, Guido of. Handbook for Curates: A Late Medieval Manual on Pastoral Ministry. 2011. (Medieval Translation Ser.). 384p. pap. 34.95 ***(978-0-8132-1869-4(1))*** Catholic Univ. of America Pr.

Montoya, Angel F. Méndez. The Theology of Food: Eating & the Eucharist. 2009. (Illuminations: Theory & Religion Ser.: 7). (ENG.). 184p. 104.95 *(978-1-4051-8967-5(3),* Wiley-Blackwell) Wiley, John & Sons, Inc.

Moore, Marvin. Challenge to the Remnant. 2008. pap. 16.99 *(978-0-8163-2273-2(2))* Pacific Pr. Publishing Assn.

Moore, Sebastian. The Contagion of Jesus: Doing Theology as If It Mattered. McCarthy, Stephen, ed. 2008. 208p. per. 24.00 *(978-1-57075-781-5(X))* Orbis Bks.

Morerod, Charles. The Church & the Human Quest for Truth. 2008. viii, 160p. pap. *(978-1-932589-43-6(0))* Ave Maria Univ.

Morwood, Michael. From Sand to Solid Ground: Questions of Faith for Modern Catholics. annot. ed. 2007. (ENG.). 256p. pap. 24.95 *(978-0-8245-2451-7(9))* Crossroad Publishing Co., The.

Mueller, J. J. Theological Foundations. alt. ed. 2008. (ENG.). 318p. pap. 31.95 *(978-1-59982-008-6(0))* St. Mary's Pr.

Mueller, SJ, J.J., JJ, ed. Theological Foundations: Alternate Edition. 2nd rev. ed. 2011. (ENG.). 288p. pap. 31.95 ***(978-1-59982-134-4(6))*** St. Mary's Pr.

—Theological Foundations: Concepts & Methods for Understanding Christian Faith. 2nd rev. ed. 2011. (ENG.). 355p. pap. 37.95 ***(978-1-59982-101-6(X))*** St. Mary's Pr.

Mulder, Jack, Jr. Kierkegaard & the Catholic Tradition: Conflict & Dialogue. 2010. (Indiana Series in the Philosophy of Religion Ser.). (ENG.). 304p. 70.00 *(978-0-253-35536-2(2),* 0253355362); pap. 24.95 *(978-0-253-22236-7(2),* 0253222362) Indiana Univ. Pr.

Müller, Michael. The Catholic Dogma: Extra Ecclesiam Nullus omnino Salvatur. 2007. 304p. per. 24.95 *(978-0-9782985-1-7(9))* Catholic Authors Pr.

Murphy, Michael P. A Theology of Criticism: Balthasar, Postmodernism, & the Catholic Imagination. 2008. (American Academy of Religion Book Ser.). (ENG.). 272p. 74.00 *(978-0-19-533352-7(7))* Oxford Univ. Pr., Inc.

Murray, Nicholas. The Difference Between Popery & Protestantism, in a Letter to an Inquiring Friend, by Kirwan. 2011. 18p. pap. 11.99 ***(978-1-4181-8958-7(8))*** MPublishing.

Murray, Nicholas. Romanism at Home: Letters to the Hon. Roger B. Taney / by Kirwan [Pseud.]. 2006. 292p. per. 23.99 *(978-1-4255-2627-6(6))* MPublishing.

Murray, Tony. Removing the Mysteries of Christianity. 2007. 104p. per. 11.95 *(978-1-59858-382-3(4))* Dog Ear Publishing, LLC.

Muto, Susan. Words of Wisdom for Our World. 2009. 80p. pap. 11.00 *(978-1-55635-619-3(6),* Wipf and Stock) Wipf & Stock Pubs.

New Advent. 2007. cd-rom 37.33 *(978-0-9743644-1-4(X))* New Advent.

Newman, Cardinal John Henry. Apologia Pro Vita Sua. 2007. 444p. per. *(978-1-4067-8832-7(5),* Pomona Pr.) Read Bks.

Newman, Henry John. Apologia Pro Vita Sua. 2007. 284p. (ENG.). 44.99 *(978-1-4280-7547-4(X))*; per. 37.99 *(978-1-4280-7535-1(6))* IndyPublish.com.

Newman, John Henry. Apologia pro Vita Sua. 2007. (ENG.). 326p. pap. 23.99 *(978-1-4346-4275-2(5))*; 362p. pap. 26.99 *(978-1-4346-4276-9(3))* BiblioBazaar.

—Essay on the Development of Christian Do. 2006. pap. 34.95 *(978-1-4286-5136-4(5))* Kessinger Publishing, LLC.

—An Essay on the Development of Christian Doctrine. 2010. (Cambridge Library Collection - Religion Ser.). 476p. pap. 34.99 *(978-1-108-02146-3(8))* Cambridge Univ. Pr.

Newman, John Henry, et al. Newman's Second Spring: And the Evangelization of Modern Culture. 2009. pap. *(978-1-933184-52-4(3))* Sophia Institute Pr.

Newman, John Henry C., ed. Apologia Pro Vita Sua & Six Sermons. 2007.Tr. of Apologia Pro Vita Sua. (ENG.). 312p. per. *(978-1-4065-4966-9(5))* Dodo Pr.

—Apologia Pro Vita Sua & Six Sermons. 2007.Tr. of Apologia Pro Vita Sua. (ENG.). pap. *(978-1-4068-3519-9(6))* Echo Library.

Newman, John Henry C. & Turner, Frank M., eds. Apologia Pro Vita Sua & Six Sermons. 2008.Tr. of Apologia Pro Vita Sua. 528p. 55.00 *(978-0-300-11507-9(5))* Yale Univ. Pr.

Nichols, Aidan. Divine Fruitfulness: A Guide to Balthasar's Theology Beyond the Trilogy. 2007. (Introduction to Hans Urs Von Balthasar Ser.). 364p. per. 39.95 *(978-0-8132-1481-8(5))* Catholic Univ. of America Pr.

Nichols, Aidan & Ratzinger, Joseph. The Thought of Pope Benedict XVI: An Introduction to the Theology of Joseph Ratzinger. 2nd ed. 2007. (ENG.). 304p. 29.95 *(978-0-86012-421-4(5),* Burns & Oates) Continuum International Publishing Group, Ltd. GBR. Dist: National Bk. Network.

Nichols, Aiden. Lovely, Like Jerusalem: The Fulfillment of the Old Testament in Christ & the Church. 2007. 279p. pap. 16.95 *(978-1-58617-168-1(2))* Ignatius Pr.

Nichols, OP, Aidan. Rome & the Eastern Churches. 2010. 350p. pap. 18.95 *(978-1-58617-282-4(4))* Ignatius Pr.

Norris, Thomas J. A Fractured Relationship: Faith & the Crisis of Culture. 2010. (ENG.). 267p. pap. 19.95 *(978-1-56548-331-6(6))* New City Pr.

—A Fractured Relationship: Faith & the Crisis of Culture. 2007. 267p. pap. 22.95 *(978-1-85390-964-1(5))* Veritas Pubns. IRL. Dist: Dufour Editions, Inc.

Nowell, Irene. 101 Questions & Answers on Angels & Devils. 2010. xii, 97p. pap. *(978-0-8091-4694-9(0))* Paulist Pr.

Nugent, Robert. Silence Speaks: Teilhard de Chardin, Yves Congar, John Courtney Murray, & Thomas Merton. 2011. 144p. pap. *(978-0-8091-4649-9(5))* Paulist Pr.

Oakland, Roger. Another Jesus? The Eucharistic Chirst & the New Evangelization. 2007. (ENG.). 224p. per. 12.95 *(978-0-9791315-2-3(9))* Lighthouse Trails Publishing Co.

Obach, Robert. The Catholic Church on Marital Intercourse: From St. Paul to Pope John Paul II. 2008. (ENG.). 236p. 73.50 *(978-0-7391-3087-2(0))* Lexington Bks.

Obbard Elizabeth Ruth. John of the Cross' Living Flame of Love: For Everyone. 2007. 71p. per. 8.95 *(978-1-56548-267-8(0))* New City Pr.

Obirek, Stanisaw. Obrzeza Katolicyzmu. 2008. (POL.). 217p. *(978-83-61053-11-8(5))* Forum Naukowe, Wydawnictwo, Holding Edukacyjny-Pietrzyk, Pawel, Spolka.

O'Brien, David J. & Shannon, Thomas A., eds. Catholic Social Thought: The Documentary Heritage. 2010. 824p. pap. 30.00 *(978-1-57075-891-1(3))* Orbis Bks.

O'Callaghan, Paul. Christ Our Hope: An Introduction to Eschatology. 2011. 384p. pap. 34.95 *(978-0-8132-1862-5(4))* Catholic Univ. of America Pr.

Ocáriz Braña, Fernando & Blanco, A. Fundamental Theology. 2009. *(978-1-890177-24-9(5))* Midwest Theological Forum.

O'Clock, Jr. Isaiah's Leper: A spiritual Odyssey. 2008. 328p. pap. 22.95 *(978-0-595-50983-6(5))* iUniverse, Inc.

O'Collins, Gerald. Believing in the Resurrection: The Meaning & Promise of the Risen Jesus. 2012. viii, 225p. ***(978-1-61643-133-4(4))***; 240p. pap. 24.95 ***(978-0-8091-4757-1(2))*** Paulist Pr.

—Catholicism. 2008. (Very Short Introductions Ser.). (ENG., Illus.). 144p. pap. 11.95 *(978-0-19-954591-9(X))* Oxford Univ. Pr., Inc.

—Pause for Thought: Making Time for Prayer, Jesus, & God. 2011. 160p. pap. *(978-0-8091-4710-6(6))* Paulist Pr.

—Rethinking Fundamental Theology. 2011. (ENG.). 400p. 65.00 *(978-0-19-960556-9(4))* Oxford Univ. Pr., Inc.

O'Connor, Thomas H., ed. Two Centuries of Faith: The Influence of Catholicism on Boston: 1808-2008. 2009. (Church in the 21st Century Ser.). (ENG.). 344p. pap. 39.95 *(978-0-8245-2531-6(0))* Crossroad Publishing Co., The.

O'Donnell, Desmond. God Is Love: A Simplified & Abridged Version of Deus Caritas Est an Encyclical Letter from Pope Benedict XVI. 2006. (ENG.). 23p. pap. 7.95 *(978-1-85607-537-4(0))* Columba Pr. IRL. Dist: Dufour Editions, Inc.

O'Donnell, Hugh. Eucharist & the Living Earth. 2008. (ENG.). 109p. per. 23.95 *(978-1-85607-573-2(7))* Columba Pr. IRL. Dist: Dufour Editions, Inc.

Oelrich, Anthony. A Church Fully Engaged: Yves Congar's Vision of Ecclesial Authority. 2011. E-Book ***(978-0-8146-8042-1(9))*** Liturgical Pr.

Okonkwo, Bartholomew. The Mystery of Humanity: An African Approach to the Theology of the Body in the Works of John Paul 11 & Benedict XVI. 2011. 264p. lib. bdg. *(978-1-936320-02-8(9))* Academica Pr., LLC.

Okoye, Most. Rev. Godfrey, et al, texts. Saving Christian Marriage. 2007. (Illus.). 128p. pap. 12.95 *(978-0-9793048-0-4(6))* Wanderer Forum Foundation.

O'Leary, Don. Roman Catholicism & Modern Science: A History. 2006. (ENG.). 376p. 80.00 *(978-0-8264-1868-5(6))* Continuum International Publishing Group, Ltd. GBR. Dist: National Bk. Network.

O'Leary, Don & O'Leary. Roman Catholicism & Modern Science: A History. 2007. (ENG.). 376p. pap. 24.95 *(978-0-8264-2926-1(2))* Continuum International Publishing Group, Ltd. GBR. Dist: National Bk. Network.

Olsen, Glenn W. On the Road to Emmaus: The Catholic Dialogue with America & Modernity. 2012. (ENG.). 320p. 69.95 ***(978-0-8132-1954-7(X))*** Catholic Univ. of America Pr.

Olson, Carl E. Catholicism Study Guide & Workbook. 2011. (ENG.). 240p. 34.95 ***(978-0-9832334-5-9(4))*** Word on Fire.

O'Mahony, T. P. Why the Catholic Church Needs Vatican III. 2011. (ENG.). 118p. pap. 22.95 *(978-1-85607-702-6(0))* Columba Pr. IRL. Dist: Dufour Editions, Inc.

O'Malley, William J. The Wow Factor: Bringing the Catholic Faith Back to Life. 2011. 180p. pap. 16.00 *(978-1-57075-927-7(8))* Orbis Bks.

O'Neill Fisher, Peggy. What Do You Know? A Catholic Identity Game for the Whole Community. 2007. (Illus.). 74p. per. 14.95 *(978-1-58595-586-2(8))* Twenty-Third Pubns./Bayard.

Onunkwo, Vincent Chijioke. Peace in the Social Teachings of Pope John Paul II: Its Relevance to the Igbo of Southeastern Nigeria, Vol. 834. 2006. (European University Studies Ser.: Vol. 23). 323p. pap. 62.95 *(978-0-8204-9900-0(5))* Lang, Peter Publishing, Inc.

O'Sullivan, Michael. How Roman Catholic Theology Can Transform Male Violence Against Women: Explaining the Role of Religion in Shaping Cultural Assumptions about Gender. 2010. (Illus.). 432p. 129.95 *(978-0-7734-1448-8(7))* Mellen, Edwin Pr., The.

Padgett, Chris. Wholly Mary, Mother of God. 2011. *(978-0-86716-977-5(X),* Servant Bks.) Franciscan Media.

Pagan, Peter, et al. The Human Person & a Culture of Freedom. 2009. 390p. *(978-0-9669226-7-7(0))* American Maritain Assn., Inc.

Palacios, Joseph M. & Palacios, Joseph Martin. The Catholic Social Imagination: Activism & the Just Society in Mexico & the United States. 2007. (Morality & Society Ser.). (Illus.). 320p. (ENG.). 70.00 *(978-0-226-64500-1(2))*; per. 30.00 *(978-0-226-64501-8(0))* Univ. of Chicago Pr.

Paprocki, Joe. The Bible Blueprint: A Catholic's Guide to Understanding & Embracing God's World. rev. ed. 2009. (ENG.). 144p. pap. 9.95 *(978-0-8294-2898-8(4))* Loyola Pr.

—The Catechist's Toolbox Leader Guide. 2008. 48p. pap. 2.95 *(978-0-8294-2724-0(4))* Loyola Pr.

—Una fe bien Construida: Guia catolic para conocer y compartir lo que Creemos. 2010. (SPA.). pap. 9.95 *(978-0-8294-3299-2(X))* Loyola Pr.

—Los Planos de la Biblia: Una Guía Católica para Entender y Acoger la Palabra de Dios. Arias, Miguel, tr. from ENG. 2009. (SPA.). 144p. pap. 9.95 *(978-0-8294-2858-2(5))* Loyola Pr.

—A Well-Built Faith: A Catholic's Guide to Knowing & Sharing What We Believe. 2008. (ENG.). 176p. pap. 9.95 *(978-0-8294-2757-8(0))* Loyola Pr.

Parigi, Paolo. The Rationalization of Miracles: How the Catholic Church Created Modern Sainthood. 2012. (ENG., Illus.). 232p. (C). 99.00 ***(978-1-107-01368-1(2))*** Cambridge Univ. Pr.

Pascal, Blaise. Thoughts on Religion & Other Subjects. 2007. (ENG.). 366p. 48.95 *(978-0-548-14983-6(6))*; 368p. per. 33.95 *(978-1-4304-4309-4(X))* Kessinger Publishing, LLC.

Payne, Craig. Why a Fetus Is a Human Person from the Moment of Conception: A Revisionist Interpretation of Thomas Aquinas's Treatise on Human Nature. 2010. 480p. 129.95 *(978-0-7734-1321-4(9))* Mellen, Edwin Pr., The.

Pekarske, Daniel T. Abstracts of Karl Rahner's Unserialized Essays. 2009. pap. *(978-0-87462-737-4(0))* Marquette Univ. Pr.

Pennock, Michael. Catholic Social Teaching: Learning & Living Justice. 2007. (Illus.). 282p. stu. ed., per. 24.95 *(978-1-59471-102-2(X))*; 290p. tchr. ed., per. *(978-1-59471-103-9(8))* Ave Maria Pr.

—Encountering Jesus in the New Testament. 2009. (Illus.). 332p. (YA). pap., stu. ed. 24.95 (978-1-59471-165-7(8)) Ave Maria Pr.

Pennock, Michael Francis. Questions from Seventh Period: Doc Pennock Answers Teens' Questions on Life, Love, & the Catholic Faith. rev. ed. 2006. Orig. Title: What we really want to Know. 286p. per. 18.95 (978-1-59471-101-5(1)) Ave Maria Pr.

Penrice, James. Living the Eucharist Through Sports: A Guide for Catholic Athletes, Coaches, & Fans. 2009. (978-0-8189-1292-4(8), St. Pauls) St Pauls/Alba Hse. Pubs.

Perszyk, Ken, ed. Molinism: The Contemporary Debate. 2012. (ENG., Illus.). 296p. 65.00 **(978-0-19-959062-9(1))** Oxford Univ. Pr., Inc.

Peter Lombard, et al. The Sentences-Book 1 the Mystery of the Trinity. 2007. (Mediaeval Sources in Translation Ser.). (ENG.). pap. 39.95 (978-0-88844-292-5(0)) Pontifical Institute of Mediaeval Studies, Dept. of Pubns. CAN. Dist: Univ. of Toronto Pr.

Petrosino, Arnold J. The Catholic Church vs. the Bible. 2008. 136p. pap. 14.99 (978-1-60647-836-3(2)) Xulon Pr., Inc.

Phillips, Charles. The Complete Illustrated Guide to the Catholic Faith: Examines the Institutions of the Church & Explores the Significance of the Sacraments, with over 180 Photographs. 2012. (ENG., Illus.). 96p. pap. 16.99 **(978-1-78019-041-9(7))** Anness Publishing GBR. Dist: National Bk. Network.

Pieper, Josef & Raskop, Heinz. What Catholics Believe. 2012. (ENG.). pap. 12.00 (978-1-58731-922-8(5)) St. Augustine's Pr., Inc.

Pigott, Frank W. The Parting of the Ways: The Teachings of the Liberal Catholic Church Compared & Contrasted with Traditional Catholic Teachings. 2010. (ENG.). 114p. (YA). 29.99 (978-0-935461-96-1(5)) St. Alban Pr., San Diego.

Pilon, Mark A. Magnum Mysterium: The Sacrament of Matrimony. 2010. (978-0-8189-1324-2(X)) St Pauls.

Pinckaers, Servais. The Pursuit of HappinessNtilde;God's Way: Living the Beatitudes. Noble, Mary Thomas, tr. 2011. 214p. pap. 24.00 **(978-1-61097-493-6(X)**, Wipf and Stock) Wipf & Stock Pubs.

Pistone, Michele R. & Hoeffner, John J. Stepping Out of the Brain Drain: Applying Catholic Social Teaching in a New ERA of Migration. 2007. (ENG.). 260p. 78.99 (978-0-7391-1504-6(9)); per. 34.99 (978-0-7391-1505-3(7)) Lexington Bks.

Pitstick, Alyssa Lyra. Light in Darkness: Hans Urs Von Balthasar & the Catholic Doctrine of Christ's Descent into Hell. 2007. (Illus.). 458p. 55.00 (978-0-8028-0755-7(0)); per. 36.00 (978-0-8028-4039-4(6)) Eerdmans, William B. Publishing Co.

Pohlhaus, Gaile, ed. Themes in Feminist Theology for the New Millennium, 36, Vol. 36. 2007. (Illus.). 147p. pap. 15.00 (978-0-87723-081-6(1)) Villanova Univ. Pr.

Ponessa, Joseph & Watson Manhardt, Laurie. Come & See: Acts & Letters. 2008. 218p. pap. 19.95 (978-1-931018-51-7(0)) Emmaus Road Publishing.

Ponesssa, Joseph L. & Manhardt, Laurie Watson. Come & See: Genesis. 2009. 220p. pap. 19.95 (978-1-931018-50-0(2)) Emmaus Road Publishing.

Pontifical Biblical Commission. The Interpretation of the Bible in the Church. 144p. pap. 5.95 (978-0-8198-3670-0(2), 332-132) Pauline Bks. & Media.

Pontifical Council For Justice Staff. Compendium of the Social Doctrine Church. 2006. pap. (978-0-86012-436-8(3)) Continuum International Publishing Group, Ltd.

Popcak, Gregory K. Holy Sex! A Catholic Guide to Toe-Curling, Mind-Blowing, Infallible Loving. 2008. (ENG.). 352p. pap. 14.95 (978-0-8245-2471-5(3), Crossroad 8 Avenue) Crossroad Publishing Co., The.

Pope Paul VI. Christian Values & Virtues. Schultz, Karl A., ed. 2007. (ENG., Illus.). 224p. pap. 19.95 (978-0-8245-2450-0(0)) Crossroad Publishing Co., The.

Poremba, Sue. 29 Things to Know about Catholicism. 2010. (Good Things to Know Ser.). (ENG.). 161p. pap. 9.99 (978-1-59652-588-7(6)) Turner Publishing Co.

Porter-Szûcs, Brian. Faith & Fatherland: Catholicism, Modernity, & Poland, 1 vol. 2011. (ENG., Illus.). 544p. 55.00 (978-0-19-539905-9(6)) Oxford Univ. Pr., Inc.

Portmann, John. A History of Sin: Its Evolution to Today & Beyond. annot. ed. 2007. (ENG.). 264p. 26.95 (978-0-7425-5813-7(4)) Rowman & Littlefield Publishers, Inc.

Possevino, Antonio. The Moscovia of Antonio Possevino, S. J. Translated with a Critical Introduction & Notes by Hugh F. Graham. Graham, Hugh F., tr. 2009. (Pitt Russian East European Ser.). (ENG.). 212p. (C). pap. 25.95 (978-0-8229-8597-6(7)) Univ. of Pittsburgh Pr.

Powell, Mark E. Papal Infallibility: A Protestant Evaluation of an Ecumenical Issue. 2009. 238p. pap. 40.00 (978-0-8028-6284-6(5)) Eerdmans, William B. Publishing Co.

Power, David Noel & Downey, Michael. Living the Justice of the Triune God. 2012. xiii, 140p. **(978-0-8146-8045-2(3))**; E-Book **(978-0-8146-3046-9(1))** Liturgical Pr.

Pozo, Candido. Theology of the Beyond. 2009. (978-0-8189-1300-6(2)) St Pauls.

Prentiss, Craig R. & Prentiss, Craig. Debating God's Economy: Social Justice in America on the Eve of Vatican II. 2008. (ENG.). 232p. (C). 55.00 (978-0-271-03341-9(X)) Pennsylvania State Univ. Pr.

Preston, Ronald H. Confusions in Christian Social Ethics: Problems for Geneva & Rome. 2011. 224p. **(978-0-334-02573-3(7)**, SCM Pr.) Hymns Ancient & Modern Ltd.

Primus, Asega. The Implication of Prevention of Conflicts for Justice & Peace: In the Light of the Pastoral Letter: Gerechter Friede. 2007. 279p. 82.95 (978-0-8204-8787-8(2)); pap. 82.95 (978-3-631-55936-9(4)) Lang, Peter Publishing, Inc.

Principles of Catholic Theology. pap. 31.95 (978-0-89870-215-6(1)) Ignatius Pr.

Pultorak, Mark. Contemporary Catholic Discipleship, 1 vol. 2009. 48p. pap. 16.95 (978-1-4489-2728-9(5)) PublishAmerica, Inc.

Radulphus & Evans, Christopher P. The Questions on the Sacraments: Speculum Universale 8.31-92. 2010. (Studies & Texts). (LAT & ENG.). 304p. 95.00 (978-0-88844-171-3(1)) Pontifical Institute of Mediaeval Studies, Dept. of Pubns. CAN. Dist: Univ. of Toronto Pr.

Ralph, Margaret Nutting. A Walk Through the New Testament: An Introduction for Catholics. 2009. 352p. pap. 19.95 (978-0-8091-4582-9(0)) Paulist Pr.

Ratzinger, Joseph. Eschatology: Death & Eternal Life. Nichols, Aidan, ed. Waldstein, Michael, tr. from GER. 2nd ed. 2007. 307p. per. 16.95 (978-0-8132-1516-7(1)) Catholic Univ. of America Pr.

—The God of Jesus Christ: Meditations on the Triune God. McNeil, Brian, tr. from GER. 2008. 113p. 19.95 (978-1-58617-184-1(4)) Ignatius Pr.

Rausch, Thomas P. Eschatology, Liturgy, & Christology: Toward Rediscovering an Eschatological Imagination. 2012. **(978-0-8146-5735-5(4))** Liturgical Pr.

Rausch, Thomas P. Pope Benedict XVI: An Introduction to His Theological Vision. 2009. viii, 195p. 22.95 (978-0-8091-0556-4(X)) Paulist Pr.

Reardon, Bernard. Liberalism & Tradition: Aspects of Catholic Thought in Nineteenth-Century France. 2010. (ENG.). 320p. pap. 25.99 (978-0-521-14305-9(5)) Cambridge Univ. Pr.

Regan, Richard J. Compendium of Theology. 2009. (ENG.). 288p. 99.00 (978-0-19-538530-4(6)); pap. 19.95 (978-0-19-538531-1(4)) Oxford Univ. Pr., Inc.

Rego, Aloysius. Suffering & Salvation: The Salvific Meaning of Suffering in the Later Theology of Edward Schillebeeckx. 2006. (Louvain Theological & Pastoral Monographs: 33). 363p. pap. 32.00 (978-0-8028-4000-4(0)) Eerdmans, William B. Publishing Co.

Rego, Aloysius & Rego, A. Suffering & Salvation: The Salvific Meaning of Suffering in the Later Theology of Edward. 2006. (Louvain Theological & Pastoral Monographs: Vol. 33). (ENG.). 380p. (C). pap. 32.00 (978-90-429-1732-3(6)) Peeters Pubs. & Booksellers BEL. Dist: Brown, David Bk. Co., The.

Reikerstorfer, Johann, ed. Vorwartserinnerungen. 625 Jahre Katholisch-Theologische Fakultat der Universitat Wien. 2009. (GER.). 418p. (C). 74.00 (978-3-89971-736-5(8)) Vandenhoeck & Ruprecht GmbH & Co. KG DEU. Dist: ISD.

Rice, Charles E. & Farnan, Theresa. Where Did I Come from? Where Am I Going? How Do I Get There? Straight Talk for Young Catholics. Rice, Ellen, ed. 2nd ed. 2009. (ENG., Illus.). 239p. pap. 13.00 (978-1-58731-929-7(2)) St. Augustine's Pr., Inc.

Rice, Ellen. Where Did I Come from? Where Am I Going? How Do I Get There? Straight Talk for Young Catholics. 2012. (ENG.). pap. 25.00 (978-1-58731-930-3(6)) St. Augustine's Pr., Inc.

Rigali, Justin. Reliving Vatican II: It's All about Jesus Christ. 2006. 151p. per. 10.95 (978-1-56854-597-4(5), REVAT) Liturgy Training Pubns.

Robinson, Geoffrey. Confronting Power & Sex in the Catholic Church: Reclaiming the Spirit of Jesus. 2008. 307p. (Orig.). pap. (978-1-920721-47-3(9)) Liturgical Pr.

Rosemann, Philipp W. Story of a Great Medieval Book: Peter Lombard's 'Sentences' 2007. (Rethinking the Middle Ages Ser.). (ENG., Illus.). 248p. pap. (978-1-55111-718-8(5)) Univ. of Toronto Pr.

Rossetti, Stephen J. Behold Your Mother: Priests Speak about Mary. 2007. (ENG.). 157p. per. 14.95 (978-1-59471-028-5(7)) Ave Maria Pr.

Rourke, Thomas. The Social & Political Thought of Benedict XVI. 2010. (ENG.). 158p. 57.99 (978-0-7391-4280-6(1)) Lexington Bks.

Rourke, Thomas R. The Social & Political Thought of Benedict XVI. 2011. (ENG.). 160p. pap. 24.95 (978-0-7391-4281-3(X)) Lexington Bks.

Rowland, Tracey. Benedict XVI. 2010. (Guides for the Perplexed Ser.). (ENG.). 216p. 24.95 (978-0-567-03437-3(2)); 80.00 (978-0-567-03436-6(4)) Continuum International Publishing Group, Ltd. GBR. (T&T Clark Int'l). Dist: National Bk. Network.

Rowland, Tracey & Pell, George. Ratzinger's Faith: The Theology of Pope Benedict XVI. 2009. (ENG.). 232p. pap. 17.95 (978-0-19-957034-8(5), Oxford Univ. Pr., Inc.

Ruiz, Jean-Pierre. Readings from the Edges: The Bible & People on the Move. 2011. 192p. pap. 28.00 (978-1-57075-944-4(8)) Orbis Bks.

Rush, Ormond. The Eyes of Faith: The Sense of the Faithful & the Church's Reception of Revelation. 2009. 344p. 79.95 (978-0-8132-1571-6(4)) Catholic Univ. of America Pr.

Sac Cong Doctrine of Faith Staff. Instr Respect for Human Life. 72p. pap. 4.95 (978-0-8198-3687-8(7), 332-140) Pauline Bks. & Media.

Saint John of the Cross. The Living Flame of Love by St John of the Cross with His Letters, Poems, & Minor Writings. 2007. 380p. (ENG.). 29.95 (978-1-60206-430-0(X)); per. 19.95 (978-1-60206-429-4(6)) Cosimo, Inc.

Salkeld, Brett. Can Catholics & Evangelicals Agree about Purgatory & the Last Judgment?and the Last Judgment. 2011. 144p. pap. 12.95 (978-0-8091-4681-9(9)) Paulist Pr.

salza, john. The biblical basis for the Eucharist. 2008. per. 14.95 (978-1-59276-336-8(7)) Our Sunday Visitor, Publishing Div.

Salzman, Todd A. & Lawler, Michael G. Catholic Sexual Ethics: An Introduction. 2012. 192p. (C). pap. 26.95 **(978-1-58901-913-3(X))** Georgetown Univ. Pr.

Salzman, Todd A. & Lawler, Michael G. The Sexual Person: Toward a Renewed Catholic Anthropology. 2008. (Moral Traditions Ser.). (ENG.). 352p. 59.95 (978-1-58901-207-3(0)); pap. 29.95 (978-1-58901-208-0(9)) Georgetown Univ. Pr.

Scarnecchia, D. Brian. Bioethics, Law, & Human Life Issues: A Catholic Perspective on Marriage, Family, Contraception, Abortion, Reproductive Technology, & Death & Dying. 2nd ed. 2010. (Catholic Social Thought Ser.). (ENG., Illus.). 460p. 63.00 (978-0-8108-7422-0(9)) Scarecrow Pr., Inc.

Schall, James V. The Regensburg Lecture. 2007. 180p. 20.00 (978-1-58731-695-1(1)) St. Augustine's Pr., Inc.

Schelkens, Karim. Catholic Theology of Revelation on the Eve of Vatican II: A Redaction History of the Schema de fontibus Revelationis (1960-1962) 2009. (Brill's Ser. in Church History Ser.). (978-90-04-18105-2(9)) BRILL.

Schemenauer, Kevin. Conjugal Love & Procreation: Dietrich von Hildebrand's Superabundant Integration. 2011. (ENG.). 146p. 60.00 (978-0-7391-4706-1(4)) Lexington Bks.

Schindler, David L., ed. Love Alone Is Credible. 2008. 326p. (C). pap. 40.00 (978-0-8028-6247-1(0)) Eerdmans, William B. Publishing Co.

Schloesser, Stephen, et al. Vatican II: Did Anything Happen? Schultenover, David G., ed. 2007. (ENG.). 192p. pap. 19.95 (978-0-8264-2890-5(8)) Continuum International Publishing Group, Ltd. GBR. Dist: National Bk. Network.

Schmitz, Kenneth L. The Texture of Being: Essays in First Philosophy. 2007. (Studies in Philosophy & the History of Philosophy: Vol. 46). 327p. 64.95 (978-0-8132-1468-9(8)) Catholic Univ. of America Pr.

Schoof, Ted Mark. The Schillebeeckx Case: Official exchange of letter & documents in the investigation of Fr. Edward Schillebeeckx, O. P. by the Sacred Congregation for the Doctrine of the Faith, 1976-1980. 2011. 164p. pap. 20.00 **(978-1-55635-816-6(4)**, Wipf and Stock) Wipf & Stock Pubs.

Schoof, Ted Mark. A Survey of Catholic Theology, 1800-1970. Smith, N.D., tr. 2008. 292p. pap. 31.00 (978-1-55635-817-3(2), Wipf and Stock) Wipf & Stock Pubs.

Schreck, Alan. Your Life in the Holy Spirit: What Every Catholic Nees to Know & Experience. 2007. 231p. per. 12.95 (978-1-59325-105-5(X)) Word Among Us Pr.

Schreiter, Robert R., et al, eds. Peacebuilding: Catholic Theology, Ethics, & Praxis. 2010. (Illus.). 480p. pap. 30.00 (978-1-57075-893-5(X)) Orbis Bks.

Schwanke, Johannes. John Henry Newmans Konversion: Sein Weg zur katholischen Kirche aus protestantischer Perspektive. (Theologische Bibliothek Töpelmann Ser.).Tr. of John Henry Newmanâ€(tm)s Conversion. His Way to the Catholic Church Viewed from a Protestant Perspective. 2011 (GER.). XIV, 339p. 196.00 **(978-3-11-174461-2(2))** 2010. 340p. 126.00 (978-3-11-022894-6(7)) De Gruyter, Walter Inc.

Scott, Kieran & Horell, Harold Daly. Human Sexuality in the Catholic Tradition. Scott, Kieran & Horell, Harold, eds. 2007. (ENG.). 242p. per. 29.95 (978-0-7425-5241-8(1)); 79.00 (978-0-7425-5240-1(3)) Rowman & Littlefield Publishers, Inc.

Scott, Margaret. The Eucharist & Social Justice. 2009. 156p. pap. 16.95 (978-0-8091-4566-9(9)) Paulist Pr.

Seasoltz, R. Kevin & Seasoltz. God's Gift Giving: In Christ & Through the Spirit. 2007. (ENG.). 256p. 115.00 (978-0-8264-2815-8(0)); pap. 34.95 (978-0-8264-2816-5(9)) Continuum International Publishing Group, Ltd. GBR. Dist: National Bk. Network.

Shadle, Matthew A. The Origins of War: A Catholic Perspective. 2011. (Moral Traditions Ser.). (ENG.). 256p. pap. 29.95 (978-1-58901-735-1(8)) Georgetown Univ. Pr.

Shahin, Gloria. Catholic Connections Student Activity Booklet. 2010. pap. 59.95 (978-1-59982-043-9(9)) St. Mary's Pr.

—Catholic Connections Test Booklet. 2010. spiral bd. 49.95 (978-1-59982-045-3(5)) St. Mary's Pr.

—Christian Morality & Justice. 2010. tchr. ed., spiral bd. 26.25 (978-1-59982-052-1(8)) St. Mary's Pr.

Shuster, Eric. Catholic Roots, Mormon Harvest. 2009. pap. 17.99 (978-1-59955-257-6(4)) Cedar Fort, Inc./CFI Distribution.

Singer-Towns, Brian, ed. Personal Journey Bible: New Testament & Psalms. 2009. lthr. 19.95 (978-0-88489-974-7(8)) St. Mary's Pr.

Singer-Towns, Brian, et al. Catholic Quick View: Beliefs, Definitions, Prayers, Practices, Symbols, & Saints. 2nd ed. 2008. (Illus.). 73p. pap. 8.50 (978-0-88489-738-5(9)) St. Mary's Pr.

Slattery, Joseph A. Companion on the Journey. 2011. pap. **(978-0-89390-708-2(1))** Resource Pubns., Inc.

Smith, Culling Eardley, intro. The encyclical letter of Our Lord Pope Gregory XVI. 2010. (LAT & ITA.). 85.76 (978-1-61719-001-8(2)) Gorgias Pr., LLC.

Smith SGS, Bro. Fenelon's Finest: French Enlightement Series. 2009. 258p. pap. 18.95 (978-0-9841731-3-6(7)) Revelation Insight Publishing Co.

Soames, Henry. The Latin Church During Anglo Saxon Times. 2007. (ENG.). 528p. 55.95 (978-0-548-04761-3(8)) Kessinger Publishing, LLC.

Sobrino & Sobrino, Jon. Fuera de Los Pobres No Hay Salvación: Pequeños Ensayos Utópico-Proféticos. (SPA.). 164p. (978-84-8164-918-5(X), Trotta Editorial S.A.

Sobrino, Jon. No Salvation Outside the Poor: Prophetic-Utopian Essays. 2008. 147p. pap. 22.00 (978-1-57075-752-5(6)) Orbis Bks.

Socias, James. The Blessed Trinity & Our Christian Vocation. 2009. pap. (978-1-936045-04-4(4)) Midwest Theological Forum.

—The Sacraments: Source of Our Life in Christ. 2009. (978-1-890177-92-8(X)) Midwest Theological Forum.

Sosa, Juan J. La Cuaresma: Oraciones, Ayuno y Ofrendas. 2011. (SPA.). (978-0-7648-1996-4(8)) Liguori Pubns.

Spaemann, Robert. Love & the Dignity of Human Life: Issues Concerning Nature & Natural Law in the Present Cultural Situation. 2011. pap. 12.00 **(978-0-8028-6693-6(X))** Eerdmans, William B. Publishing Co.

Spinello, Richard A. The Genius of Pope John Paul II: The Great Pope's Moral Wisdom. 2006. (ENG.). 224p. 22.95 (978-1-58051-206-0(2), Sheed & Ward) Rowman & Littlefield Publishers, Inc.

Spiteri, Laurence John. The Ten Commandments: A Positive Approach Toward Catholic Morality, Lifestyle, & Attitude. 2007. 60p. pap. (978-0-8189-1230-6(8), St. Pauls) St Pauls/Alba Hse. Pubs.

Sri, Edward. Men, Women & the Mystery of Love: Practical Insights from John Paul II's Love & Responsibility. 2007. 165p. per. (978-0-86716-840-2(4)) Franciscan Media.

St. John of the Cross. Counsels of Light & Love of St. John of the Cross. 2007. 96p. pap. 12.00 (978-1-58768-045-8(9), 045-8, HiddenSpring) Paulist Pr.

—Dark Night of the Soul. Zimmerman, Benedict, ed. Lewis, David, tr. 2008. (ENG.). 192p. pap. (978-0-9770091-4-5(9)) St. Benedict Pr., LLC.

St John of the Cross. Dark Night of the Soul. 2007. (Authentic Original Classic Ser.). 247p. per. 14.99 (978-0-7684-2456-0(9)) Destiny Image Pubs.

St. John of the Cross Staff. The Dark Night of the Soul. 2007. 240p. per. 9.85 (978-1-60206-279-5(X)) Cosimo, Inc.

—The Dark Night of the Soul. Backhouse, Halcyon, ed. 2010. (Hodder Classics Ser.). (ENG.). 160p. pap. 12.95 (978-0-340-98013-2(3), Hodder & Stoughton) Hodder General Publishing Div. GBR. Dist: Independent Pubs. Group.

Stackpole, Robert A. Divine Mercy: A Guide from Genesis to Benedict XVI. 2008. 257p. per. 14.95 (978-1-59614-185-8(9)) Marian Pr.

Stanford, Peter. Opening Up: Speaking Out in the Church. 192p. (978-0-232-52624-0(9)) Darton, Longman & Todd, Ltd.

Steffon, Jeffrey J. Spiritual Warfare for Catholics. 2007. 214p. pap. 24.00 (978-1-55635-212-6(3), Wipf and Stock) Wipf & Stock Pubs.

Stegman, Thomas D. Second Corinthians, 1 vol. 2009. (Catholic Commentary on Sacred Scripture Ser.). (ENG.). 336p. (C). pap. 19.99 (978-0-8010-3583-8(X)) Baker Academic.

Stewart, Jon. Kierkegaards Influence on Theology Tome Stewart, Jon, ed. 2012. (Kierkegaard Research: Sources, Reception & Resources Ser.). 146p. 124.95 **(978-1-4094-4480-0(5))** Ashgate Publishing Co.

Stoltz, Eric & Tomkovicz, Vince. Ascend: The Catholic Faith for a New Generation. 2009. (Illus.). 256p. pap. 24.95 (978-0-8091-4621-5(5)) Paulist Pr.

Stringfellow, William & Towne, Anthony. Suspect Tenderness: The Ethics of the Berrigan Witness. 2006. (Dissent Trilogy: Ser.). 192p. pap. 22.00 (978-1-59752-477-3(8), Wipf and Stock) Wipf & Stock Pubs.

Sullins, David & Blasi, Anthony J., eds. Catholic Social Thought: American Reflections on the Compendium. 2008. (ENG.). 218p. 68.50 (978-0-7391-2311-9(4)) Lexington Bks.

Takeuchi, S. J. Osamu & Takeuchi, S. J. Conscience & Culture. 2010. 228p. pap. (978-3-8383-5782-9(5)) Lambert Academic Publishing.

Talley, Alan J. & Holzknecht, Scott. Everyday Justice: 365 Reflections. 2009. (ENG.). 384p. (YA). pap. 14.75 (978-0-88489-858-0(X)) St. Mary's Pr.

Tanner, Norman. Vatican II: The Essential Texts. 2012. (ENG.). 416p. pap. 16.00 **(978-0-307-95280-6(0)**, Image) Doubleday Religious Publishing Group, The.

Thieman, John E. A Religious History of the Old Testament. 2008. (Illus.). iii, 211p. pap. (978-0-615-26261-1(9)) DaCapo Foundation.

Thomas à Kempis. The Imitation of Christ. 2007.Tr. of Imitatio Christi. (ENG.). 258p. pap. 21.99 (978-1-4346-1047-8(0)); 270p. pap. 23.99 (978-1-4346-1146-8(9)) BiblioBazaar.

—The Imitation of Christ. 2007.Tr. of Imitatio Christi. (ENG.). 156p. per. 9.95 (978-1-60206-102-6(5)) Cosimo, Inc.

—The Imitation of Christ. Benham, William, tr. 2007.Tr. of Imitatio Christi. 204p. per. (978-1-4065-1891-7(3)) Dodo Pr.

—The Imitation of Christ. de Rossett, Rosalie A., ed. 2007. (Moody Classics Ser.).Tr. of Imitatio Christi. (ENG.). 384p. per. 8.99 (978-0-8024-5653-3(7)) Moody Pubs.

—The Imitation of Christ.Tr. of Imitatio Christi. 2.00 (978-0-8358-0050-1(4)) Upper Room Bks.

Thomas à Kempis, et al. The Imitation of Christ. 2008. (Paraclete Essentials Ser.).Tr. of Imitatio Christi. (ENG.). 260p. (gr. 12). pap. 15.99 (978-1-55725-608-9(X)) Paraclete Pr., Inc.

Thomas, David M. Christian Marriage: The New Challenge. 2nd ed. 2007. (Michael Glazier Bks.). 128p. per. 14.95 (978-0-8146-5224-4(7)) Liturgical Pr.

Thompson, J. Milburn. Introducing Catholic Social Thought. 2010. 208p. pap. 22.00 (978-1-57075-862-1(X)) Orbis Bks.

Thompson, Phillip M. Between Science & Religion: The Engagement of Catholic Intellectuals with Science & Technology in the Twentieth Century. 2009. (ENG.). 298p. 78.99 (978-0-7391-3080-3(3)) Lexington Bks.

Thurston, Herbert. The Church & Spiritualism. 2007. (ENG.). 412p. 49.95 (978-0-548-14342-1(0)) Kessinger Publishing, LLC.

—Church & Spiritualism. 2006. pap. 34.95 (978-1-4286-5581-2(6)) Kessinger Publishing, LLC.

Tilley, Terrence W. Inventing Catholic Tradition. 2011. 208p. pap. 23.00 **(978-1-60899-749-7(9)**, Wipf and Stock) Wipf & Stock Pubs.

Tingle, Elizabeth C. Purgatory & Piety in Brittany 1480-1720. 2012. (Catholic Christendom, 1300ndash;1700 Ser.). (Illus.). 254p. 124.95 **(978-1-4094-3824-3(4))**; 310p. 124.95 **(978-1-4094-3823-6(6))** Ashgate Publishing Co.

Titus, Craig Steven. The Person & the Polis: Faith & Values Within the Secular State. 2007. (John Henry Cardinal Newman Lectures: Vol. 1). 187p. per. 29.95 (978-0-9773103-0-2(2)) Institute for the Psychological Science Pr., The.

Torrell, Jean-Pierre. Christ & Spirituality in St. Thomas Aquinas. Blankenhorn, Bernhard, tr. from FRE. 2011. 240p. pap. 24.95 **(978-0-8132-1878-6(0))** Catholic Univ. of America Pr.

Traub, George W., ed. An Ignatian Spirituality Reader. 2008. pap. 18.95 (978-0-8294-2723-3(6)) Loyola Pr.

C

Trouvé, Marianne Lorraine, compiled by. Angels: Help from on High. 2010. pap. (978-0-8198-0790-8(7)) Pauline Bks. & Media.

Tyrrell, SJ, George. Lex Credendi: A Sequel to Lex Orandi. 2009. 274p. pap. 24.00 (978-1-60608-390-1(2), Wipf and Stock) Wipf & Stock Pubs.

—Lex Orandi: Or, Prayer & Creed. 2009. 240p. pap. 21.00 (978-1-60608-388-8(0), Wipf and Stock) Wipf & Stock Pubs.

University of St. Thomas Staff, et al. The Christian Theological Tradition. 3rd ed. 2008. (ENG.). 544p. (C). pap. 90.80 (978-0-13-602832-1(2), Prentice Hall) Prentice Hall PTR.

Vaghi, Peter J. The Faith We Profess: A Catholic Guide to the Apostles' Creed. 2008. 160p. pap. 13.95 (978-1-59471-177-0(1)) Ave Maria Pr.

Vaghi, Peter J. The Prayer We Offer: A Catholic Guide to Communion with God. 2012. 160p. pap. 12.95 **(978-1-59471-294-4(8))** Ave Maria Pr.

van Ruysbroeck, Jan. The Adornment of the Spiritual Marriage. Dom, C. A. Wynschenk, tr. 2007. 176p. per. 12.95 (978-1-60206-424-9(5)) Cosimo, Inc.

—The Adornment of the Spiritual Marriage: The Sparkling Stone & the Book of Supreme Truth. Dom, C. A. Wynschenk, tr. 2007. 260p. per. 16.50 (978-1-60206-425-6(3)) Cosimo, Inc.

Vost, Kevin. Memorize the Faith! (and Most Anything Else) Using the Methods of the Great Catholic Medieval Memory Masters. 2006. (Illus.). 249p. per. 17.95 (978-1-933184-17-3(5)) Sophia Institute Pr.

Waiss, John R. Born to Love: Gay-Lesbian Identity, Relationships, & Marriage: Homosexuality, the Bible, & the Battle for Chaste Love. 2009. 318p. pap. 19.95 (978-1-4327-4242-3(6)) Outskirts Pr., Inc.

Walther, Andrew T. & Korten, Patrick. The Knights of Columbus. 2009. 248p. pap. 21.95 (978-0-7570-0224-3(2)); (Illus.). 28.95 (978-0-7570-0308-0(7)) Square One Pubs.

Watkins, ed. The Imitation of Christ: The Inspirational Teachings of Thomas A. Kempis. MacKenna, Stephen, tr. 2006. (Sacred Wisdom Ser.). (ENG., Illus.). 328p. 7.95 (978-1-84293-125-7(3), Watkins Publishing) Duncan Baird Pubs. GBR. Dist: Sterling Publishing Co., Inc.

Watton, Victor W. Catholic Christianity. 3rd rev. ed. 2010. 136p. pap. 20.00 (978-0-340-97555-8(5)) Hodder Education GBR. Dist: Trans-Atlantic Pubns., Inc.

Weigel, George. Against the Grain: Christianity & Democracy, War & Peace. 2008. (ENG.). 352p. 24.95 (978-0-8245-2448-7(9), Crossroad 8 Avenue) Crossroad Publishing Co., The.

Weinandy, O.F.M., Cap., Thomas. Sacrament of Mercy: A Spiritual & Practical Guide to Confession. 2010. 228p. pap. 25.00 (978-1-60899-345-1(0), Wipf and Stock) Wipf & Stock Pubs.

West, Christopher. Buena Neueva Sobre Sexo y Matrimoio: Respuestas A Tus Preguntas Honestas Sobre la Doctrina Catolica. 2008. 200p. per. 11.99 (978-1-932927-96-2(4)) Ascension Pr.

—Theology of the Body Explained: A Commentary on John Paul II's Man & Woman He Created Them. 2nd rev. ed. 2007. pap. 29.95 (978-0-8198-7425-2(6)) Pauline Bks. & Media.

Westcott, Frank N. Catholic Principles. 2009. 412p. pap. 45.00 (978-1-60899-115-0(6), Wipf and Stock) Wipf & Stock Pubs.

Wheatley, Leonard A. The Story of the Imitatio Christi. 2007. (ENG.). 252p. 41.95 (978-0-548-14913-3(5)); 256p. per. 26.95 (978-1-4304-4217-2(4)) Kessinger Publishing, LLC.

White, Thomas Joseph. The Analogy of Being: Invention of the Antichrist or the Wisdom of God? 2010. 448p. pap. 48.00 (978-0-8028-6533-5(X)) Eerdmans, William B. Publishing Co.

Whitehead, K. D. Affirming Religious Freedom: How Vatican Council II Developed the Church's Teaching to Meet Today's Needs. 2010. (978-0-8189-1313-6(4), St. Pauls) St Pauls/Alba Hse. Pubs.

Wicks, Jared. Doing Theology. 2009. 304p. pap. 24.95 (978-0-8091-4564-5(2)) Paulist Pr.

Williamson, Peter S. Ephesians, 1 vol. 2009. (Catholic Commentary on Sacred Scripture Ser.). (ENG.). 208p. (C). pap. 19.99 (978-0-8010-3584-5(8)) Baker Academic.

Windley-Daoust, Jerry. Primary Source Readings in Catholic Social Justice. 2007. (Illus.). 232p. per. 13.75 (978-0-88489-968-6(3)) St. Mary's Pr.

Windley-Daoust, Jerry & Kilmartin, Lorraine. Living Justice & Peace 2008: Catholic Social Teaching in Practice. 2nd ed. 2008. (Illus.). 336p. pap. 26.25 (978-0-88489-985-3(3)) St. Mary's Pr.

Wise, F. S., ed. Pearls from the Seat of Wisdom: An Invitation to Virtue. 2nd rev. ed. 2008. per. 12.95 (978-0-9768791-1-4(5)) Light of Patriarchs Pubs.

Witczak, Michael G. The Sacrament of Baptism. 2011. E-Book **(978-0-8146-3946-7(1))** Liturgical Pr.

Witherup, Ronald D. Scripture: Dei Verbum. 2006. (Rediscovering Vatican II Ser.). 160p. per. 15.95 (978-0-8091-4428-0(X), 4428-X) Paulist Pr.

Witte, John, Jr. & Alexander, Frank S., eds. The Teachings of Modern Roman Catholicism: On Law, Politics, & Human Nature. 2007. (ENG.). 536p. (gr. 17). pap. 35.00 (978-0-231-14261-8(7)) Columbia Univ. Pr.

—The Teachings of Modern Roman Catholicism on Law, Politics, & Human Nature. 2007. (ENG., Illus.). 536p. (gr. 17). 105.00 (978-0-231-14260-1(9)) Columbia Univ. Pr.

Woods, Thomas E. Beyond Distributism. 2008. 79p. pap. (978-1-880595-29-9(X)) Acton Institute for the Study of Religion & Liberty.

Woznicki, Andrew. The Transcendent Mystery of Man: A Global Approach to Ecumenism. 2006. (Illus.). 414p. lib. bdg. 79.95 (978-1-933146-15-7(X)) Academica Pr., LLC.

Wright, Wendy M. The Essential Spirituality Handbook. 2009. 14.99 (978-0-7648-1786-1(8)) Liguori Pubns.

Zagano, Phyllis. Women & Catholicism: Gender, Communion, & Authority. 2011. (ENG.). 220p. 85.00 (978-0-230-11163-9(7)); pap. 28.00 (978-0-230-11164-6(5)) Palgrave Macmillan.

Zanotto, Luigi. Profundizando y Madurando Nuestra Fe: Para la Formacion de Catequistas y Agentes de Pastoral. 2006. (SPA.). 184p. pap. 19.95 (978-1-58595-618-0(X)) Twenty-Third Pubns./Bayard.

CATHOLIC CHURCH—DOCTRINES, POPULAR

DeSiano, Frank P. Reactivating Our Catholic Faith: Reflections to Get Real about Faith. 2009. 80p. pap. 7.95 (978-0-8091-4597-3(9)) Paulist Pr.

CATHOLIC CHURCH—EDUCATION

see also Catholic Church—United States—Education; Catholic Universities and Colleges

Barr, Colin. The European Culture Wars in Ireland: The Callan Schools Affair, 1868-81. 2011. (ENG.). 320p. 89.95 (978-1-906359-53-9(9)) Univ. College Dublin Pr. IRL. Dist: Dufour Editions, Inc.

Basile, Alex. The Gentle Road to Jesus: Teaching Christ in Every Parish, School, & Home. 2010. (978-0-8189-1301-3(0)) St Pauls/Alba Hse. Pubs.

becker, ellen c. & barnes, mary t. Advent in the Home: Activities for Families. 2008. (Illus.). 120p. pap. 14.95 (978-1-59276-430-3(4)) Our Sunday Visitor, Publishing Div.

Bergman, Roger. Catholic Social Learning: Educating the Faith That Does Justice. 2011. (ENG., Illus.). 160p. pap. 24.00 (978-0-8232-3329-8(4)); 3rd ed. 75.00 (978-0-8232-3328-1(6)) Fordham Univ. Pr.

Broadley, Martin John, ed. Bishop Herbert Vaughan & the Jesuits: Education & Authority. 2010. (Catholic Record Society: Records Ser.: Volume 82). (Illus.). 286p. 80.00 (978-0-902832-25-1(5)) Catholic Record Society GBR. Dist: Boydell & Brewer, Inc.

Brown, Sfo. Lamp unto My Feet. 2008. 412p. pap. 29.95 (978-1-4241-6887-3(2)) PublishAmerica, Inc.

Carter, Karen. Creating Catholics: Catechism & Primary Education in Early Modern France. 2011. (ENG., Illus.). 328p. pap. 40.00 (978-0-268-02304-1(2)) Univ. of Notre Dame Pr.

Chlachula, Roxane Kadrlik & Shrader, Mary. Exploring Liturgical Seasons with Young Adolescents. 2008. (Illus.). 103p. pap. 29.50 (978-0-88489-729-3(X)) St. Mary's Pr.

Cushing, Richard. The Mission of the Teacher. 2011. 162p. 41.95 **(978-1-258-05263-8(6))** Literary Licensing, LLC.

Daley, Michael J. Our Catholic Symbols: A Rich Spiritual Heritage. 2009. 120p. pap. 12.95 (978-1-58595-753-8(4)) Twenty-Third Pubns./Bayard.

Deferrari, Roy J., ed. Essays on Catholic Education in the United States. (Essay Index Reprint Ser.). 566p. reprint ed. lib. bdg. 35.00 (978-0-8290-0814-2(4)) Irvington Pubs.

Donlevy, James Kent. The Ten Dimensions of Inclusion: Non-Catholic Students in Catholic Schools. 2009. 160p. pap. (978-90-8790-805-8(9)) Sense Pubs.

Elias, John L. & Nolan, Lucinda A. Educators in the Catholic Intellectual Tradition. 2009. (978-1-888112-18-4(2)) Sacred Heart Univ. Pr.

Fanning, Tim. The Fethard-on-Sea Boycott. 2010. (ENG., Illus.). 240p. pap. 26.95 (978-1-84889-032-9(X)) Collins Pr., The IRL. Dist: Dufour Editions, Inc.

Fox, Mary. Journals of the Catechesis of the Good Shepherd, 2003-2008. 2009. (Illus.). 198p. pap. (978-1-56854-274-4(7)) Good Shepherd Pubns.

Frabutt, James M., et al. No Greater Work: Meditations on Church Documents for Educators. 2010. pap. (978-1-935788-01-0(9)) Alliance for Catholic Education Pr.

Galipeau, Jerry. Apprenticed to Christ: Activities for Practicing the Catholic Way of Life. 2007. (Illus.). 112p. per. 12.95 (978-1-58459-327-0(X)) World Library Pubns.

Geltner, G. William of Saint-Amour: De periculis novissimorum Temporum. 2008. (Dallas Medieval Texts & Translations Ser.). 157p. (C). pap. 54.00 (978-90-429-2010-1(6)) Peeters Pubs. & Booksellers BEL. Dist: Brown, David Bk. Co., The.

George, Milton. Catholic Education in the Dutch Caribbean. 2010. 68p. pap. (978-3-8383-4123-1(6)) Lambert Academic Publishing.

Glavich, Mary Kathleen. Prayer First: A New Agenda for Catholic Schools. 2008. 144p. pap. (978-1-58595-703-3(8)) Twenty-Third Pubns./Bayard.

Grace, Gerald R. & O'Keefe, Joseph, eds. International Handbook of Catholic Education: Challenges for School Systems in the 21st Century. 2007. (International Handbooks of Religion & Education Ser.: Vol. 2). XXXVI, 912p. 629.00 (978-1-4020-4804-3(1), 1402048041) Springer.

Guilday, Peter K. The English Catholic Refugees on the Continent, 1558-1795. reprint ed. 55.00 (978-0-404-19900-5(3)) AMS Pr., Inc.

Haller, Gretchen & Pacatte, Rose. Our Media World: Teaching Kids K-8 about Faith & Media. 2010. (978-0-8198-5441-4(7)) Pauline Bks. & Media.

Hellinckx, Bart & Simon, Frank. The Forgotten Contribution of the Teaching Sisters: A Historiographical Essay on the Educational Work of Catholic Women Religious in the 19th & 20th Centuries. 2010. (Studia Paedagogica Ser.). 126p. pap. 34.50 (978-90-5867-765-5(6)) Leuven Univ. Pr. BEL. Dist: Cornell Univ. Pr.

Herron, Fred. Tuning the Rig: Catholic Schools for a Learning Church. 2010. (ENG.). 260p. pap. 35.75 (978-0-7618-5205-6(0)) Univ. Pr. of America, Inc.

Hoffmann, Mary Byrne. Catechesis in a Multi-Media World: Connecting to Today's Students. 2011. pap. (978-0-8091-4708-3(4)) Paulist Pr.

Huebsch, Bill & Anslinger, Leisa. Great Expectations: A Pastoral Guide for Partnering with Parents: For Catechists & Teachers, Pastors, Principals, & Parish Catechetical Leaders. 2010. (Illus.). 58p. pap. (978-1-58595-752-1(6)) Twenty-Third Pubns./Bayard.

Hughes, Monica. Planning Your Teaching Year: A Catechist's Guide to Developing Effective Goals. 2009. (Catechists Guide Ser.). 80p. pap. 8.95 (978-0-8091-4569-0(3)) Paulist Pr.

Infantino, Ginger. Handbook for Today's Catechist: The Role of the Catechist: Planning Effective Lessons, Sharing the Faith. 2009. 5.99 (978-0-7648-1846-2(5)) Liguori Pubns.

—Manual para el Catequista de Hoy: El Papel Del Catequista Planificar Lecciones Eficaces Compartir la Fe. 2010.Tr. of Handbook for Today's Catechist: Role of the Catechist: Planning Effective Lessons, Sharing the Faith. (SPA.). 5.99 (978-0-7648-1871-4(6), Libros Liguori) Liguori Pubns.

Kendzia, Mary Carol. Las Cinco Preguntas de Nuestra Fe Católica: à Quién, Qué, Dónde, Cuándo, Por Qué? — y Cómo Entendería: Maestro. 2011. (SPA.). (978-0-7648-1991-9(7)) Liguori Pubns.

Leckey, Dolores R. The Laity & Christian Education: Apostolicam Actuositatem, Gravissimum Educationis. 2007. (Rediscovering Vatican II Ser.). 113p. per. 14.95 (978-0-8091-4220-0(1), 4220-1) Paulist Pr.

Lind, Christopher. Priestly Studies in Modern Papal Teachin. 2006. pap. 19.95 (978-1-4286-6131-8(X)) Kessinger Publishing, LLC.

Lucas, Miguel. Religioso Educador En La Escuela Catolica. 80p. 3.95 (978-958-607-584-8(2)) Sociedad de San Pablo COL. Dist: St Pauls/Alba Hse. Pubs.

Macalintal, Diana. The Eucharist. 2009. (Illus.). 136p. spiral bd., instr.'s gde. ed. 26.25 (978-0-88489-765-1(6)) St. Mary's Pr.

Martineau, Mariette, et al. Intergenerational Faith Formation: All Ages Learning Together. 2008. (Illus.). 160p. pap. 19.95 (978-1-58595-653-1(8)) Twenty-Third Pubns./Bayard.

McInally, Thomas. The Sixth Scottish University: The Scots Colleges abroad: 1575 To 1799. 2011. (History of Science & Medicine Library). (Illus.). 256p. **(978-90-04-21426-2(7))** BRILL.

McKenzie, Janet. Communion with the Saints: A Family Preparation Program for First Communion & Beyond in the Spirit of St. Therese. 2007. 152p. (J). per. 27.95 (978-1-934185-18-6(3)) Biblio Resource Pubns., Inc.

—The Windeatt Dictionary: Pre-Vatican II Terms & Catholic Words from Mary Fabyan Windeatt's Saint Biographies. 2007. 112p. (J). per. 11.95 (978-1-934185-16-2(7)) Biblio Resource Pubns., Inc.

Mensing, Cyprian. Activity Analysis of the Four Cardinal V. 2006. pap. 21.95 (978-1-4286-6345-9(2)) Kessinger Publishing, LLC.

Mercadante, Fred T. Senior High Ministry That Works: A Parish-Based Initiation Model. 2008. 160p. pap. (978-1-58595-704-0(6)) Twenty-Third Pubns./Bayard.

Miller, Michael J., tr. from FRE. Handing on the Faith in an Age of Disbelief. 2006. 169p. 19.95 (978-1-58617-143-8(7)) Ignatius Pr.

Mize, Sandra Yocum. Joining the Revolution in Theology: The College Theology Society, 1954-2004. 2007. (ENG., Illus.). 336p. 41.95 (978-0-7425-3195-6(3)) Rowman & Littlefield Publishers, Inc.

Murphy, Doris. Learning Centers for First Reconciliation, First Eucharist, & the Whole Community. 2007. (Illus.). 91p. per. 14.95 (978-1-58595-564-0(7)) Twenty-Third Pubns./Bayard.

Neuberger, Anne E. A Circle of Saints: Stories & Activities for Children. 2009. pap. 16.95 (978-1-58595-750-7(X)) Twenty-Third Pubns./Bayard.

Newland, Mary Reed. How to Raise Good Catholic Children. 2006. Orig. Title: We & Our Children (Garden City, New York: Image Books, 1961). 336p. per. 15.95 (978-1-928832-86-7(5)) Sophia Institute Pr.

Nuttall, Mary. National Curriculum Developments. 2010. 316p. pap. (978-3-8383-6780-4(4)) Lambert Academic Publishing.

Nuzzi, Ronald James & Hunt, Thomas C. At the Heart of the Church: Selected Documents of Catholic Education. 2011. 39.99 **(978-1-935788-08-9(6))** Alliance for Catholic Education Pr.

Paprocki, Joe. The Catechist's Toolbox: How to Thrive as a Religious Education Teacher. 2007. (ENG., Illus.). 152p. per. 9.95 (978-0-8294-2451-5(2)) Loyola Pr.

Paul, Thayer. The Impact of Church Closings on Catholic Adolescents - Implications for Clergy, Church Leaders, & Parents. 2008. 104p. pap. (978-3-639-06287-8(6)) VDM Verlag Dr. Mueller e.K.

Peterfy, Ida. Catechist Companion: Ready-To-Use Lesson Plans: Creed, Sacraments, Commandments, & Saints. 2009. (Illus.). vii, 226p. pap. (978-1-56854-797-8(8)) Liturgy Training Pubns.

Pioneer Mentoring in Teacher Preparation. (978-0-87839-154-7(1)) North Star Pr. of St. Cloud.

Praying My Faith. 2008. (J). pap. 7.95 (978-0-8294-2853-7(4)) Loyola Pr.

Praying with Scripture. 2008. (J). pap. 7.95 (978-0-8294-2852-0(6)) Loyola Pr.

Preyat, Fabrice. Le Petit Concile de Bossuet et la Christianisation des Murs et des Pratiques Littéraires Sous Louis XIV. (FRE.). 570p. (978-3-8258-8716-2(2), Adlard Coles) Lit Verlag.

Rupert, Jane. John Henry Newman on the Nature of the Mind: Reason in Religion, Science, & the Humanities. 2010. (978-0-7391-4049-9(3)) Lexington Bks.

Sander, William. Catholic Schools: Private & Social Effects. 2010. (ENG.). 160p. pap. 129.00 (978-1-4419-4867-0(8), 1441948678) Springer.

Stuart, Janet Erskine. The Education of Catholic Girls. 2009. 264p. 24.99 (978-1-103-58859-6(1)) 2009. 264p. pap. 18.99 (978-1-103-58856-5(7)) 2008. 208p. 27.99 (978-0-554-25458-6(1)) 2008. 208p. 24.99 (978-0-554-34761-5(X)) 2007. (ENG.). 188p. pap. 19.99 (978-1-4264-9093-4(3)) 2007. (ENG.). 206p. pap. 22.99 (978-1-4264-9147-4(6)) BiblioBazaar.

—The Education of Catholic Girls. 2009. 264p. 42.95 (978-1-104-56023-2(2)); pap. 27.95 (978-1-104-48978-6(3)) Kessinger Publishing, LLC.

Sullivan, J. Catholic Education: Distinctive & Inclusive: Distinctive & Inclusive. 2010. 248p. pap. 195.00 (978-90-481-5839-3(7), 9048158397) Springer.

Talley, Alan J. Christian Morality & Justice. 2009. (Illus.). 122p. spiral bd., instr.'s gde. ed. 26.25 (978-0-88489-766-8(4)) St. Mary's Pr.

Tenbus, Eric G. English Catholics & the Education of the Poor, 1847-1902, 1 vol. 2010. (Perspectives in Economic & Social History Ser.). (ENG.). 224p. 99.00 (978-1-84893-038-4(0)) Pickering & Chatto Pubs., Ltd. GBR. Dist: Ashgate Publishing Co.

Tolman, Ashley Barker & Forsyth, Evie, eds. The Journal of Inquiry: Student Cross-Cultural Field Research. 2007. (C). pap. (978-0-8425-2679-1(X), Brigham Young Univ. Pr.) Brigham Young Univ.

Tomberg, Markus. Religionsunterricht Als Praxis der Freiheit: Überlegungen Zu Einer Religionsdidaktisch Orientierten Theorie Gläubigen Handelns. 2010. (Praktische Theologie im Wissenschaftsdiskurs Ser.).Tr. of Religious Instruction as Exercise of Freedom. Considerations on a religious didactically oriented theory of action based on Faith. (GER.). XIII, 402p. 140.00 (978-3-11-022197-8(7)) De Gruyter, Walter Inc.

Vankat, Jenni. Exploring Saints & Feast Days with Young Adolescents. 2007. 104p. per. 26.25 (978-0-88489-949-5(7)) St. Mary's Pr.

Wezeman, Phyllis Vos. 50 Interactive Bible Stories for Children Ages 5-8. 2009. 80p. (J). pap. 16.95 (978-1-58595-701-9(1)) Twenty-Third Pubns./Bayard.

Whitehead, Kenneth, ed. The Idea of the Catholic University: Proceedings from the 30th Annual Conference of the Fellowship of Catholic Scholars. 2010. (University of Scranton Press - Fellowship of Catholic Scholars Ser.). 180p. pap. 20.00 (978-1-58966-219-3(9)) Univ. of Scranton Pr.

CATHOLIC CHURCH—ENCYCLOPEDIAS

see Catholic Church—Dictionaries

CATHOLIC CHURCH—FASTS AND FEASTS

see Fasts and Feasts—Catholic Church

CATHOLIC CHURCH—FINANCE

see also Benefices, Ecclesiastical

Berry, Jason. Render unto Rome: The Secret Life of Money in the Catholic Church. 2011. (ENG.). 432p. 25.00 (978-0-385-53132-0(X), Doubleday Religion) Doubleday Religious Publishing Group, The.

Clements, C. Justin. Time, Talent, & Treasure: Reflections on the U. S. Bishops' Model for Parish Stewardship. 2006. 112p. per. 14.95 (978-0-7648-1500-3(8)) Liguori Pubns.

Conway, Daniel. Advancing the Mission of the Church: Best Practices in Stewardship & Development for Catholic Organizations. 2009. 83p. pap. (978-0-9800284-1-6(8)) St. Catherine of Siena Pr.

Costeloe, Michael P. Church Wealth in Mexico: A Study of the 'Juzgado de Capellanias' in the Archbishopric of Mexico 1800-1856. 2008. (Cambridge Latin American Studies). (ENG.). 156p. pap. 33.99 (978-0-521-08347-8(8)) Cambridge Univ. Pr.

Mazin Gómez, Oscar. Gestores de la Real Justicia: Procuradores y Agentes de Las Catedrales Hispanas Nuevas en la Corte de Madrid. 2007. (Estudios Históricos Ser.). (Illus.). 394p. pap. 46.99 (978-968-12-1266-7(5)) El Colegio de México, A.C., Biblioteca Miguel Cosío Villegas MEX. Dist: Fondo de Cultura Economica USA.

Pollard, John F. Money & the Rise of the Modern Papacy: Financing the Vatican, 1850-1950. 2008. (ENG., Illus.). 288p. pap. 38.99 (978-0-521-09211-1(6)) Cambridge Univ. Pr.

Yallop, David. In God's Name: An Investigation into the Murder of Pope John Paul I. 2007. (ENG., Illus.). 400p. per. 18.00 (978-0-7867-1984-6(2)) Basic Bks.

CATHOLIC CHURCH—FOREIGN RELATIONS

Araujo, Robert John & Lucal, John A. Papal Diplomacy & the Quest for Peace. 2010. (978-0-916101-64-0(9)) St. Joseph's Univ. Pr.

Aubert, Roger, et al. La Papauté Contemporaine (XIXe-XXe Siècles) Hommage Au Chanoine Roger Aubert, Professeur émérite à L'Université Catholique de Louvain, Pour Ses 95 Ans = il Papato Contemporaneo (Secoli XIX-XX): Omaggio Al Canonico Roger Aubert, Professore Emerito All'Università Cattolica Di Lovanio, per I 95 Anni. 2009. (ITA, FRE & ENG., Illus.). vii, 729p. pap. (978-88-85042-61-2(9)) Universiteit van Amsterdam, Universiteitsbibliotheek.

Brady, Joseph H. Rome & the Neapolitan Revolution of 18. 2006. pap. 24.95 (978-1-4286-6119-6(0)) Kessinger Publishing, LLC.

Byrnes, Timothy A. Reverse Mission: Transnational Religious Communities & the Making of U. S. Foreign Policy. 2011. (Religion & Politics Ser.). 216p. pap. 26.95 (978-1-58901-768-9(4)) Georgetown Univ. Pr.

—Reverse Mission: Transnational Religious Communities & the Making of US Foreign Policy. 2011. (Religion & Politics Ser.). 216p. 44.95 (978-1-58901-775-7(7)) Georgetown Univ. Pr.

Chick, H., ed. & tr. A Chronicle of the Carmelites in Persia: The Safavids & the Papal Mission of the 17th & 18th Centuries. 2012. (ENG.). 1424p. 349.00 **(978-1-84885-768-1(3))** I. B. Tauris & Co., Ltd. GBR. Dist: Macmillan.

Fletcher, Catherine. The Divorce of Henry VIII: The Untold Story from Inside the Vatican. 2012. (ENG.). 288p. 28.00 **(978-0-230-34151-7(9))** Palgrave Macmillan.

Fonnesberg-Schmidt, Iben. The Popes & the Baltic Crusades 1147-1254. 2006. (Northern World Ser.: Vol. 26). (Illus.). 287p. (978-90-04-15502-2(3)) BRILL.

Gallagher, Charles R. Vatican Secret Diplomacy: Joseph P. Hurley & Pope Pius XII. 2008. (ENG., Illus.). 304p. 40.00 (978-0-300-12134-6(2)) Yale Univ. Pr.

Johrendt, Jochen & Müller, Harald, eds. Römisches Zentrum und kirchliche Peripherie: Das universale Papsttum als Bezugspunkt der Kirchen von den Reformpäpsten bis zu Innozenz III. 2008. (Abhandlungen der Akademie der Wissenschaften zu Göttingen. Neue Folge Ser.). (GER., Illus.). X, 356p. 91.00 *(978-3-11-020223-6(9))* De Gruyter, Walter Inc.

Jolicoeur, Nicolas. La politique française envers les états pontificaux sous la monarchie de Juillet et la Seconde République (1830-1851) 2008. (Diplomatie et Histoire Ser.). (FRE., Illus.). 394p. pap. 46.95 *(978-90-5201-388-6(8))* PIE - Peter Lang BEL. Dist: Lang, Peter.

Koehler, John. Spies in the Vatican: The Soviet Union's Cold War Against the Catholic Church. 2011. (ENG., Illus.). 304p. pap. 15.95 *(978-1-60598-140-6(0),* 605140) Pegasus Bks.

—Spies in the Vatican: The Soviet Union's War Against the Catholic Church. 2009. (ENG., Illus.). 352p. 26.95 *(978-1-60598-050-8(1),* 605050) Pegasus Bks.

Koller, Alexander. Die Außenbeziehungen der römischen Kurie unter Paul V. Borghese. Koller, Alexander, ed. 2008. (Bibliothek des Deutschen Historischen Instituts in Rom Ser.).Tr. of External Relations of the Roman Curia under Paul V Borghese (1605â¿¿1621). (GER., Illus.). XVI, 527p. *(978-3-484-82115-6(9))* Verlag Max Niemeyer.

Kurzman, Dan. A Special Mission: Hitler's Secret Plot to Seize the Vatican & Kidnap Pope Pius XII. 2008. (ENG., Illus.). 320p. pap. 15.00 *(978-0-306-81617-8(2))* Da Capo Pr., Inc.

Leung, Beatrice. Sino-Vatican Relations: Problems in Conflicting Authority, 1976-1986. 2009. (LSE Monographs in International Studies). (ENG.). 440p. pap. 57.00 *(978-0-521-12256-6(2))* Cambridge Univ. Pr.

Lunt, William E. Financial Relations of the Papacy with England, To 1327. 2011. 776p. 72.95 ***(978-1-258-02912-8(X))*** Literary Licensing, LLC.

McCabe, Joseph. The Totalitarian Church of Rome: Its Fuehrer, Its Gauleiter, Its Gestabo, & Its Money-Box. Haldeman-Julius, E., ed. 2011. 34p. 35.95 ***(978-1-258-05584-4(8))*** Literary Licensing, LLC.

Melnyk, Roman/A. Vatican Diplomacy at the United Nations: A History of Catholic Global Engagement. 2009. vi, 269p. *(978-0-7734-3881-1(5))* Mellen, Edwin Pr., The.

Minà, Gianni. El Papa y Fidel.Tr. of Pope & Fidel. (SPA., Illus.). 367p. 16.98 *(978-970-05-1050-7(6))* Grijalbo, Editorial MEX. Dist: Continental Bk. Co., Inc.

Noel, Gerard. Pius XII: The Hound of Hitler. (ENG., Illus.). 232p. 2009. 27.95 *(978-1-4411-3629-9(0))* 2008. 29.95 *(978-1-84706-355-7(1))* Continuum International Publishing Group, Ltd. GBR. Dist: National Bk. Network.

Petersohn, Jürgen. Capitolium Conscendimus. 2009. (Wissenschaftliche Gesellschaft an der Johann Wolfgang Goethe-Universitat Frankfurt am Main - Sitzungsberichte (WGF-S) Ser.). (GER.). 36p. (C). pap. 24.00 *(978-3-515-09301-9(X))* Steiner, Franz Verlag Wiesbaden GmbH DEU. Dist: Brown, David Bk. Co., The.

Possevino, Antonio. The Moscovia of Antonio Possevino, S. J. Translated with a Critical Introduction & Notes by Hugh F. Graham. Graham, Hugh F., tr. 2009. (Pitt Russian East European Ser.). (ENG.). 212p. (C). pap. 25.95 *(978-0-8229-8597-6(7))* Univ. of Pittsburgh Pr.

Pyta, Wolfram, et al, eds. Die Herausforderung Der Diktaturen: Katholizismus in Deutschland und Italien 1918-1943/45. 2009. (Reihe der Villa Vigoni Ser.). (GER & ITA.). VI, 300p. pap. *(978-3-484-67021-1(5))* Verlag Max Niemeyer.

Sayers, Jane E. Papal Government & England during the Pontificate of Honorius III (1216-1227) 2008. (Cambridge Studies in Medieval Life & Thought: Third Ser.). (ENG.). 312p. pap. 42.00 *(978-0-521-07331-8(6))* Cambridge Univ. Pr.

Scherbaum, Bettina. Die bayerische Gesandtschaft in Rom in der frühen Neuzeit. 2008. (Bibliothek des Deutschen Historischen Instituts in Rom Ser.).Tr. of Bavarian Legation in Rome in the Early Modern Age. (GER., Illus.). VII, 448p. *(978-3-484-82116-3(7))* Verlag Max Niemeyer.

Signorotto, Gianvittorio & Visceglia, Maria Antonietta, eds. Court & Politics in Papal Rome, 1492-1700. 2011. (Cambridge Studies in Italian History & Culture Ser.). (ENG.). 268p. pap. 35.99 *(978-0-521-28314-4(0))* Cambridge Univ. Pr.

Walsh, Henry H. Concordat of 1801. (Columbia University, Studies in the Social Sciences: No. 387). reprint ed. 31.50 *(978-0-404-51387-0(5))* AMS Pr., Inc.

Wilkie, William E. The Cardinal Protectors of England: Rome & the Tudors before the Reformation. 2008. (ENG.). 276p. pap. 37.99 *(978-0-521-08764-3(3))* Cambridge Univ. Pr.

Wolf, Hubert & Kronenberg, Kenneth. Pope & Devil: The Vatican's Archives & the Third Reich. 2012. Orig. Title: Papst und Teufel: Die Archive des Vatikan und das Dritte Reich. (ENG., Illus.). 336p. pap. 19.95 ***(978-0-674-06426-3(7),*** Belknap Pr.) Harvard Univ. Pr.

Woolner, David B. & Kurial, Richard G., eds. FDR, the Vatican, & the Roman Catholic Church in America, 1933-1945. 2010. (World of the Roosevelts Ser.). (ENG.). 314p. pap. 29.00 *(978-0-230-62351-4(4))* Palgrave Macmillan.

CATHOLIC CHURCH—GOVERNMENT

see also Bishops; Cardinals; Dioceses; Investiture; Papacy; Popes; Vicars-General

Baima, Thomas A. & Hennessey, Lawrence. What Is a Parish? Canonical, Pastoral, & Theological Perspectives. 2011. xv, 207p. ***(978-1-59525-033-9(6))*** Hillenbrand Bks.

Cahoy, William John. In the Name of the Church: Vocation & Authorization of Lay Ecclesial Ministry. 2012. ***(978-0-8146-3423-3(0))*** Liturgical Pr.

Fischer, Mark F. Making Parish Councils Pastoral. 2010. 208p. pap. *(978-0-8091-4676-5(2))* Paulist Pr.

Levering, Matthew. Christ & the Catholic Priesthood: Ecclesial Hierarchy & the Pattern of the Trinity. 2010. x, 340p. *(978-1-59525-029-2(8))* Hillenbrand Bks.

McClory, Robert. As It Was in the Beginning: The Coming Democratization of the Catholic Church. 2007. (ENG.). 240p. pap. 19.95 *(978-0-8245-2419-7(5))* Crossroad Publishing Co., The.

McKenna, Kevin E. The Battle for Rights in the United States Catholic Church. 2007. 195p. per. 19.95 *(978-0-8091-4493-8(X),* 4493-8) Paulist Pr.

Signorotto, Gianvittorio & Visceglia, Maria Antonietta, eds. Court & Politics in Papal Rome, 1492-1700. 2011. (Cambridge Studies in Italian History & Culture Ser.). (ENG.). 268p. pap. 35.99 *(978-0-521-28314-4(0))* Cambridge Univ. Pr.

Swidler, Leonard. Making the Church Our Own: How We Can Reform the Catholic Church from the Ground Up. Swidler, Leonard, ed. 2007. (ENG.). 176p. pap. 14.95 *(978-1-58051-215-2(1),* Sheed & Ward) Rowman & Littlefield Publishers, Inc.

Tkacik, Michael J. & McGonigle, Thomas C. Pneumatic Correctives: What Is the Spirit Saying to the Church of the 21st Century? 2006. (ENG.). 228p. per. 39.99 *(978-0-7618-3569-1(5))* Univ. Pr. of America, Inc.

Vincentian Center for Church and Society Staff. Concise Guide to Catholic Church Management. 2010. (Illus.). 256p. pap. 18.95 *(978-1-59471-227-2(1))* Ave Maria Pr.

Zech, Charles. Best Practices in Catholic Church Ministry Performance Management. 2010. (ENG.). 130p. 57.99 *(978-0-7391-4523-4(1))* Lexington Bks.

CATHOLIC CHURCH—HISTORY

see also Catholic Church—United States—History; Councils and Synods; Counter-Reformation; Schism—Eastern and Western Church; Schism, The Great Western, 1378-1417

also names of specific councils of the Catholic Church

Aguilar, Mario I. A Social History of the Catholic Church in Chile: The Second Period of the Pinochet Government 1980-1990. 2006. 282p. (C). 109.95 *(978-0-7734-5653-2(8))* Mellen, Edwin Pr., The.

Alvarez, Manuel Díaz. Antonio de Padua, San.Tr. of St. Anthony of Padua. (SPA.). 136p. pap. 5.95 *(978-980-350-253-9(0))* Sociedad de San Pablo VEN. Dist: St Pauls/Alba Hse. Pubs.

Anderson, C. Colt. The Great Catholic Reformers: From Gregory the Great to Dorothy Day. 2007. 262p. pap. 29.95 *(978-0-8091-0579-3(9),* 0579-3) Paulist Pr.

Anonymous. Against Ratzinger. Shugaar, Antony, tr. from ITA. 2008. (ENG.). 176p. pap. 14.95 *(978-1-58322-766-4(0))* Seven Stories Pr.

Aquilina, Mike. The Fathers of the Church: An Introduction to the First Christian Teachers. exp. ed. 2006. 287p. per. 13.95 *(978-1-59276-245-3(X))* Our Sunday Visitor, Publishing Div.

—The Resilient Church: The Glory, the Shame, & the Hope for Tomorrow. 2007. 176p. per. 11.95 *(978-1-59325-104-8(1))* Word Among Us Pr.

Armenio, Peter V. & Socías, James. The History of the Church. 2010. *(978-1-936045-15-0(X))* Midwest Theological Forum.

Barbiche, Bernard. Bulla, Legatus, Nuntius: Etudes de diplomatique et de diplomatie pontificales (XIIIe-XVIIe Siecle) 2007. (Memoires et documents de l'ecole des Chartes Ser.). (FRE.). 576p. (C). pap. 99.00 *(978-2-900791-95-0(2))* Ecole des chartes FRA. Dist: Brown, David Bk. Co., The.

Bedouelle, Guy. An Illustrated History of the Church: The Great Challenges. 2007. (Illus.). 271p. 90.00 *(978-1-56854-516-5(9))* Liturgy Training Pubns.

Bedouelle, Guy & Farge, James K. The Reform of Catholicism, 1480-1620. 2008. (Studies & Texts). (ENG.). xii, 172p. pap. 24.95 *(978-0-88844-161-4(4),* Pontifical Institute of Mediaeval Studies, Dept. of Pubns. CAN. Dist: Univ. of Toronto Pr.

Bellitto, Christopher M. The Living Church: Old Treasures, New Discoveries. 2011. ***(978-0-7648-2039-7(7))*** Liguori Pubns.

Benson, Pius. The Church in the Theological Writings of Avery Dulles: Impulses for African Ecclesiology. (European University Studies: Vol. 852). 341p. pap. 68.95 *(978-3-631-56492-9(9))* Lang, Peter GmbH, Europaischer Verlag der Wissenschaften DEU. Dist: Lang, Peter Publishing, Inc.

Betances, Emelio. The Catholic Church & Power Politics in Latin America: The Dominican Case in Comparative Perspective. 2007. (Critical Currents in Latin American Perspective Ser.). (ENG., Illus.). 192p. 89.00 *(978-0-7425-5504-4(6))*; per. 37.95 *(978-0-7425-5505-1(4))* Rowman & Littlefield Publishers, Inc.

Boguslawski, Steven & Martin, Ralph. The New Evangelization: Overcoming the Obstacles. 2008. (Illus.). 176p. pap. 16.95 *(978-0-8091-4532-4(4))* Paulist Pr.

Bonmariage, C., et al, eds. Lulle et la Condamnation De 1277: La Declaration de Raymond ecrite sous forme de Dialogue. 2006. (Philosophes Medievaux Ser.). (ENG.). 196p. (C). pap. 109.00 *(978-90-429-1592-3(7))* Peeters Pubs. & Booksellers BEL. Dist: Brown, David Bk. Co., The.

Brooke, Zachary N. The English Church & the Papacy, from the Conquest to the Reign of John. reprint ed. 42.00 *(978-0-404-18756-9(0))* AMS Pr., Inc.

Bruce, Tricia Colleen. Faithful Revolution: How Voice of the Faithful Is Charging the Church. 2011. (ENG., Illus.). 240p. 49.95 *(978-0-19-538584-7(5))* Oxford Univ. Pr., Inc.

Bulman, Jan K. The Court Book of Mende & the Secular Lordship of the Bishop: Recollecting the Past in Thirteenth-Century Gévaudan. 2008. (ENG., Illus.). 176p. *(978-0-8020-9337-0(X))* Univ. of Toronto Pr.

Butler, Matthew, ed. Faith & Impiety in Revolutionary Mexico. 2007. (Studies of the Americas Ser.). (ENG.). 304p. 100.00 *(978-1-4039-8381-7(X))* Palgrave Macmillan.

Buzalka, Juraj & Buzalka. Nation & Religion: The Politics of Commemorations in South-East Poland. 2008. (ENG., Illus.). 256p. pap. 49.95 *(978-3-8258-9907-3(1))* Lit Verlag DEU. Dist: Transaction Pubs.

Cadorette, Curt. Catholicism in Social & Historical Contexts: An Introduction. 2010. 288p. pap. 20.00 *(978-1-57075-872-0(7))* Orbis Bks.

Carl, Carolina. A Bishopric Between Three Kingdoms: Calahorra, 1045-1190. 2011. (Illus.). XII, 292p. ***(978-90-04-18012-3(5))*** BRILL.

Carroll, James. Practicing Catholic. 2010. (ENG.). 400p. pap. 16.95 *(978-0-547-33626-6(8),* Mariner Bks.) Houghton Mifflin Harcourt Trade & Reference Pubs.

Carty, Francis X. Hold Firm: John Charles Mcquaid & the Second Vatican Council. 2008. (ENG.). 181p. pap. 23.95 *(978-1-85607-585-5(0))* Columba Pr. IRL. Dist: Dufour Editions, Inc.

Catholic Treasures. Letter to My Non Catholic Friend. 2007. 63p. pap. 3.00 *(978-1-885692-13-9(7))* Catholic Treasures.

Cayen, Daniel Theo. The Holy Bible: Great Truths/ Many Lies. 2008. 172p. pap. 12.95 *(978-0-7414-4547-6(6))* Infinity Publishing.

Chadwick, Owen. Catholicism & History: The Opening of the Vatican Archives. 2009. (ENG.). 184p. pap. 31.99 *(978-0-521-09330-9(9))* Cambridge Univ. Pr.

Chan, Adrian. Orientalism in Sinology. 2009. 264p. lib. bdg. *(978-1-933146-61-4(3))* Academica Pr., LLC.

Chesterton, G. K., et al. The Catholic Mind, V31: January 8, 1933 to December 22 1933. 2011. 484p. 58.95 ***(978-1-258-04466-4(8))*** Literary Licensing, LLC.

Chevalier, Jaima. La Conquistadora: Unveiling the History of Santa Fe's Six Hundred Year Old Religious Icon. 2011. pap. *(978-0-86534-789-2(1))* Sunstone Pr.

Chiola, Richard. Catholicism for the Non-Catholic: A Brief Introduction to Catholicism. 2006. 192p. pap. 14.95 *(978-0-87243-269-7(6))* Templegate Pubs.

Ciravegna, Giovanni. Iglesia Igual Amor (Church Equal Love) (SPA.). 128p. pap. 4.95 *(978-958-607-544-2(3))* Sociedad de San Pablo COL. Dist: St Pauls/Alba Hse. Pubs.

Clark, Christopher & Kaiser, Wolfram, eds. Culture Wars: Secular-Catholic Conflict in Nineteenth-Century Europe. 2009. (ENG., Illus.). 380p. pap. 51.00 *(978-0-521-10845-4(4))* Cambridge Univ. Pr.

Cleary, Edward L. The Rise of Charismatic Catholicism in Latin America. 2011. (ENG., Illus.). 256p. 74.95 *(978-0-8130-3608-3(9))* Univ. Pr. of Florida.

Cloud, David W. Call No Man Father: The Roman Catholic Church: Past, Present, Future. Date not set. pap. *(978-1-58318-055-6(9),* WOLFather) Way of Life Literature.

Collins Publishers Staff. God's New Man. 2006. 256p. *(978-0-8264-8274-7(0))* Continuum International Publishing Group, Ltd.

Colman, M. E. Sometimes a Star. 2008. 374p. per. 22.00 *(978-0-9787113-2-0(7),* Ithaca Pr.) Authors & Artists Publishers of New York, Inc.

Coppa, Frank J. The Policies & Politics of Pope Pius Xii: Between Diplomacy & Morality. 2011. (C). pap. 36.95 ***(978-1-4331-0521-0(7))*** Lang, Peter Publishing, Inc.

Coren, Michael. Why Catholics Are Right. (ENG.). 240p. 2012. pap. 17.95 ***(978-0-7710-2322-4(7))*** 2011. 26.99 *(978-0-7710-2321-7(9))* McClelland & Stewart CAN. (McClelland & Stewart). Dist: Random Hse., Inc.

Corr, Rachel. Ritual & Remembrance in the Ecuadorian Andes. 2010. (ENG., Illus.). 200p. 45.00 *(978-0-8165-2830-1(6))* Univ. of Arizona Pr.

Corthell, Ronald, et al, eds. Catholic Culture in Early Modern England. 2007. (ENG., Illus.). 336p. pap. 40.00 *(978-0-268-02294-5(1))* Univ. of Notre Dame Pr.

Creighton, Mandell. History of the Papacy from the Great Schism to the Sack of Rome, 6 vols. rev. ed. reprint ed. 165.00 *(978-0-404-01870-2(X))* AMS Pr., Inc.

Cristaudo, Wayne. The Church in China. Rule, Paul, ed. 2010. (Interface: A Forum for Theology in the World Ser.). (ENG.). 131p. pap. 19.95 *(978-1-921511-74-5(5))* ATF Pr. AUS. Dist: Brown, David Bk. Co., The.

Crosby, Michael H. Repair My House: Becoming a Kindom Catholic. 2012. (ENG.). 192p. pap. 22.00 ***(978-1-57075-953-6(7))*** Orbis Bks.

Curran, Robert Emmett. Shaping American Catholicism: Maryland & New York, 1805-1915. 2012. (ENG.). 320p. 69.95 ***(978-0-8132-1967-7(1))*** Catholic Univ. of America Pr.

Daughton, J. P. An Empire Divided: Religion, Republicanism, & the Making of French Colonialism, 1880-1914. 2006. (ENG., Illus.). 344p. 74.00 *(978-0-19-530530-2(2))* Oxford Univ. Pr., Inc.

Davidson, James D., et al. Catholics Laity: The Faith & Their Church. Davidson, James D. et al, eds. 2007. (ENG., Illus.). 214p. 73.00 *(978-0-7425-5214-2(4))* Rowman & Littlefield Publishers, Inc.

—Catholics Laity: Their Faith & Their Church. Davidson, James D. et al, eds. 2007. (ENG., Illus.). 214p. per. 28.95 *(978-0-7425-5215-9(2))* Rowman & Littlefield Publishers, Inc.

Decker, Rainer. Witchcraft & the Papacy: An Account Drawing on the Formerly Secret Records of the Roman Inquisition. Midelfort, H. C. Erik, tr. 2010. (Studies in Early Modern German History Ser.). (ENG., Illus.). 280p. (C). (gr. 13-17). pap. 22.50 *(978-0-8139-2748-0(X))* Univ. Pr. of Virginia.

D'Elia, Donald J. & Foley, Patrick, eds. The Catholic As Historian. 2006. 256p. pap. 24.95 *(978-1-932589-27-6(9))* Ave Maria Univ.

Dimond, Bro. Michael & Dimond, Bro. Peter. The Truth about What Really Happened to the Catholic Church. 2007. 611p. per. 7.00 *(978-0-9755514-1-7(8))* Most Holy Family Monastery.

Dougill, John. In Search of Japan's Hidden Christians: A Story of Suppression, Secrecy & Survival. 2012. (ENG., Illus.). 272p. 22.95 ***(978-4-8053-1147-9(9))*** Tuttle Publishing.

Dulles, Avery Robert. Church & Society: The Laurence J. Mcginley Lectures, 1988-2007. 3rd ed. 2008. (ENG.). 546p. 45.00 *(978-0-8232-2862-1(2))* Fordham Univ. Pr.

Duquesne, Jacques & Lebrette, Francois. The History of the Church through 100 Masterpieces. Borges, M. Cristina, tr. from FRE. 2011. (Illus.). 225p. pap. 29.95 *(978-0-8207-0437-1(7))* Duquesne Univ. Pr.

Ederer, Rupert. Pope Pius XII on the Economic. 2011. (Catholic Social Thought Ser.). (ENG.). 292p. (gr. 17). 50.00 *(978-0-8108-7797-9(X))* Scarecrow Pr., Inc.

Edwards, John. Inquisition. 2009. (ENG., Illus.). 240p. pap. 19.95 *(978-0-7524-5058-2(1))* History Pr. Ltd.,The GBR. Dist: Independent Pubs. Group.

Fantoli, Annibale. The Case of Galileo: A Closed Question? 2012. (ENG.). 280p. pap. 28.00 ***(978-0-268-02891-6(5))*** Univ. of Notre Dame Pr.

Fleckenstein, Gisela & Klöcker, Michael, eds. Kirchengeschichte. Alte und neue Wege: Festschrift für Christoph Weber. 2008. 1020p. 141.95 *(978-3-631-57712-7(5))* Lang, Peter GmbH, Europaischer Verlag der Wissenschaften DEU. Dist: Lang, Peter.

Fox, Matthew. The Pope's War: Why Ratzinger's Secret Crusade Has Imperiled the Church & How It Can Be Saved. 2011. (ENG.). 304p. 22.95 *(978-1-4027-8629-7(8))* Sterling Publishing Co., Inc.

Furey, Constance M. Erasmus, Contarini, & the Religious Republic of Letters. 2008. (ENG., Illus.). 272p. (C). pap. 40.00 *(978-0-521-10343-5(6))* Cambridge Univ. Pr.

Gaillardetz, Richard R. The Church in the Making: Lumen Gentium, Christus Dominus, Orientalium Ecclesiarum. 2006. (Rediscovering Vatican II Ser.). 220p. per. 19.95 *(978-0-8091-4276-7(7),* 4276-7) Paulist Pr.

Gauvreau, Michael. The Catholic Origins of Quebec's Quiet Revolution, 1931-1970. 2007. (McGill-Queen's Studies in the History of Religion Ser.). (ENG.). 522p. (C). per. *(978-0-7735-3371-4(0))* McGill-Queen's Univ. Pr.

Gibert, P. & Theobald, C., eds. Theologies & Truth: The Challenges of History. 2010. (ENG.). 372p. (C). pap. 55.00 *(978-90-429-2359-1(8))* Peeters Pubs. & Booksellers BEL. Dist: Brown, David Bk. Co., The.

Gilsdorf, Richard W. The Signs of the Times: Understanding the Church since Vatican II. Beno, Patrick F., ed. 2008. (Illus.). 542p. pap. 19.95 *(978-0-615-18489-0(8))* Star of the Bay Pr.

Golaszewski, Marcin. Clemens August Graf von Galen: Ein Politischer Prediger im Nationalsozialismus. 2010. (Gießener Arbeiten zur neueren deutschen Literatur und Literaturwissenschaft Ser.). (GER.). 292p. 72.95 *(978-3-631-61228-6(1))* Lang, Peter GmbH, Europaischer Verlag der Wissenschaften DEU. Dist: Lang, Peter.

Golightly Marshall, Brian Leonard. 2012 Mayan Calendar & the Great Pyramid Predicts Paradise begins in Australia. 2008. 688p. pap. 47.95 *(978-1-4092-2039-8(7))* Lulu Enterprises Inc.

—2012 Mayan Calendar & the Great Pyramid Predicts the Earth Will Enter Paradise after It Crosses the Milky Way Equator In 2013. 2008. 496p. pap. 38.95 *(978-1-4092-2041-1(9))* Lulu Enterprises Inc.

—2012 Mayan Calendar Found in the Great Pyramid & Christ Return. 2008. 694p. pap. 28.95 *(978-1-4092-1992-7(5))* Lulu Enterprises Inc.

Green, Maia. Priests, Witches & Power: Popular Christianity after Mission in Southern Tanzania. 2007. (Cambridge Studies in Social & Cultural Anthropology Ser.). (ENG., Illus.). 200p. (C). pap. 38.99 *(978-0-521-04027-3(2))* Cambridge Univ. Pr.

Guilday, Peter K. The English Catholic Refugees on the Continent, 1558-1795. reprint ed. 55.00 *(978-0-404-19900-5(3))* AMS Pr., Inc.

Halík, Tomas. Night of the Confessor: Christian Faith in an Age of Uncertainty. 2012. (ENG.). 240p. pap. 13.00 ***(978-0-385-52452-0(8),*** Image) Doubleday Religious Publishing Group, The.

Hanh, Etienne vo Duc. La Place du Catholicisme dans les Relations Entre la France et le Viet-Nam de 1887 a 1903. (Publications Universitaires Europeennes). (FRE.). *(978-3-906765-21-1(0))* Lang, Peter.

Harline, Craig. Miracles at the Jesus Oak: Histories of the Supernatural in Reformation Europe. 2011. (ENG., Illus.). 336p. pap. 22.00 *(978-0-300-16702-3(4))* Yale Univ. Pr.

Hartline, David J. The Tide Is Turning Toward Catholicism. 2006. (Illus.). 309p. per. 15.99 *(978-0-9790732-0-5(0))* Catholic Report.

Haverkamp, Paul. Rückkehr Zu Den Jesuanischen Quellen: Momentaufnahmen Zur Katholischen Kirche Am Beginn des 3. Jahrtausends. 2008. (GER.). 239p. *(978-3-86557-175-5(1))* Nora Verlagsgemeinschaft Dyck and Westerheide.

Hill, Brennan R. Unlikely Spiritual Heroes. 2010. 176p. pap. 14.95 *(978-0-86716-924-9(9))* Franciscan Media.

Himawan, Agustinus Surianto. Imam Diosesan: Akar Tunggang Gereja Katolik Indonesia: Refleksi 25 Tahun Unio Indonesia. 2008. (IND., Illus.). xxiii, 232p. *(978-979-565-483-4(7))* Obor.

Hunting, Penelope. The Saint & the Disciple: John Henry,Cardinal Newman, the Reverend George Dudley Ryder & the Catholic Revival in Nineteenth Century Britain. 2011. (Illus.). 280p. lib. bdg. *(978-1-936320-01-1(0))* Academica Pr., LLC.

Introduccion Al Catecismo De La Iglesia Catolica. 176p. 6.95 *(978-958-607-751-4(9))* Sociedad de San Pablo COL. Dist: St Pauls/Alba Hse. Pubs.

Johnson, Angela S. & Rezek, Antoine Ivan. Set History of the Diocese of Marquette, 3 vols. 2006. (Illus.). 27.00 *(978-0-9786970-3-7(0))* Roman Catholic Diocese of Marquette.

C

Kaiser, Robert Blair. A Church in Search of Itself: Benedict XVI & the Battle for the Future. 2007. (Vintage Ser.). (ENG., Illus.). 304p. pap. 13.95 *(978-0-307-27814-2(X)*, Vintage) Knopf Doubleday Publishing Group.

Keenan, James F. & Keenan. A History of Catholic Moral Theology in the Twentieth Century: From Confessing Sins to Liberating Consciences. 2010. (ENG.). 256p. 85.00 *(978-0-8264-2928-5(9))*; pap. 29.95 *(978-0-8264-2929-2(7))* Continuum International Publishing Group, Ltd. GBR. Dist: National Bk. Network.

Kennedy, Thomas Frank. Inculturation & the Church in North America. Kennedy, T. Frank, ed. 2007. (Boston College Church in the 21st Century Ser.). (ENG., Illus.). 256p. pap. 24.95 *(978-0-8245-2438-8(1)*, Herder & Herder) Crossroad Publishing Co., The.

Kerrigan, Michael & Frances Budzik, Mary. An Illustrated History of Catholicism: An Authoritative Chronicle of the Development of Catholic Christianity & Its Doctrine with More Than 300 Photographs & Fine-Art Illustrations. 2012. (ENG., Illus.). 160p. pap. 18.99 *(978-1-84476-985-8(2))* Anness Publishing GBR. Dist: National Bk. Network.

Knibbs, Eric. Ansgar Rimbert & the Forged Foundations of Hamburg-Bremen. 2011. (Church, Faith & Culture in the Medieval West Ser.). 270p. 124.95 ***(978-1-4094-2882-4(6))*** Ashgate Publishing Co.

Krischke, Paulo Jose. Populism & the Catholic Church: Political Crisis in Brazil 1964. 2010. (Religion & Spirituality Ser.). 129.00 *(978-1-61728-296-6(0))* Nova Science Pubs., Inc.

Kugelmann, Robert. Psychology & Catholicism: Contested Boundaries. 2011. (ENG.). 500p. 125.00 *(978-1-107-00608-9(2))* Cambridge Univ. Pr.

Kurth, Godfrey. The Church at the Turning Points of History. 2008. (ENG., Illus.). 160p. per. 22.95 *(978-1-932528-09-1(1))* IHS Pr.

—The Church at the Turning Points of History. 2008. 202p. 39.95 *(978-1-4365-1141-4(0))* 2007. (ENG.). 204p. per. 24.95 *(978-0-548-69805-1(8))* Kessinger Publishing, LLC.

Lakeland, Paul & Lakeland. Catholicism at the Crossroads: How the Laity Can Save the Church. 2007. (ENG.). 176p. pap. 22.95 *(978-0-8264-2810-3(X))* Continuum International Publishing Group, Ltd. GBR. Dist: National Bk. Network.

Larrúa Guedes, Salvador. Historia de Nuestra Señora la Virgen de la Caridad Del Cobre: Reina, Madre y Patrona de la Isla de Cuba, 2 vols. 2011. (SPA., Illus.). ***(978-1-59388-219-8(X))***; ***(978-1-59388-218-1(1))*** Ediciones Universal.

Leone, Massimo. Saints & Signs: A Semiotic Reading of Conversion in Early Modern Catholicism. 2010. (Religion & Society Ser.). (ENG., Illus.). XI, 652p. 196.00 ***(978-3-11-022951-6(X))*** De Gruyter, Walter Inc.

Linden, Ian. Global Catholicism: Diversity & Change since Vatican II. 2009. (Columbia/Hurst Ser.). (ENG.). 288p. (gr. 17). 29.50 *(978-0-231-15416-1(X))* Columbia Univ. Pr.

Lonely, Paul. Suicide Dictionary: The History of Rainbow Abbey. 2007. (ENG.). 128p. per. 16.95 *(978-1-84694-061-3(3))* Hunt, John Publishing Ltd. GBR. Dist: National Bk. Network.

Lyons, Barry J. Remembering the Hacienda: Religion, Authority, & Social Change in Highland Ecuador. 2006. (Joe R. & Teresa Lozano Long Series in Latin American & Latino Art & Culture). (ENG., Illus.). 362p. mass mkt. 24.95 *(978-0-292-71439-7(4))* Univ. of Texas Pr.

MacCuarta, Brian. Catholic Revival in the North of Ireland 1603-41. 2007. 282p. (C). 70.00 *(978-1-84682-051-9(0))* Four Courts Pr. IRL. Dist: International Specialized Bk. Services.

MacIntyre, Alasdair. God, Philosophy, Universities: A Selective History of the Catholic Philosophical Tradition. 2009. (ENG.). 200p. 29.95 *(978-0-7425-4429-1(X))* Rowman & Littlefield Publishers, Inc.

Maguire, Daniel C. Whose Church? A Concise Guide to Progressive Catholicism. 2008. (Whose Religion? Ser.). (ENG.). 178p. 23.95 *(978-1-59558-335-2(1))* New Pr., The.

Mangion, Carmen M. Contested Identities: Catholic Women Religious in Nineteenth-Century England & Wales. 2008. (ENG., Illus.). 296p. 89.00 *(978-0-7190-7627-5(7))* Manchester Univ. Pr. GBR. Dist: Macmillan.

McBride, Alfred. Story of the Church. 2009. 224p. pap. 16.95 *(978-0-86716-876-1(5))* Franciscan Media.

McGee, Martin. Christian Martyrs for a Muslim People. 2008. 224p. pap. 18.95 *(978-0-8091-4539-3(1))* Paulist Pr.

McNeill, John Thomas. The Celtic Penitentials & Their Influence on Continental Christianity. 2008. 216p. pap. 20.00 *(978-1-59740-384-9(9))* ACLS Humanities E-Book.

—The Celtic Penitentials & Their Influence on Continental Christianity. 2009. 210p. 28.99 *(978-1-113-64618-7(7))*; pap. 24.75 *(978-1-113-64617-0(9))*; pap. 23.75 *(978-1-113-64615-6(2))* BiblioBazaar.

Michael, Robert. A History of Catholic Antisemitism: The Dark Side of the Church. 2008. (ENG.). 292p. 100.00 *(978-0-230-60388-2(2))* Palgrave Macmillan.

Milman, Henry H. History of Latin Christianity, 9 vols. reprint ed. lib. bdg. 425.00 *(978-0-404-04360-5(7))* AMS Pr., Inc.

Milman, Henry Hart. History of Latin Christianity: Including That of the Popes to the Pontificate of Nicolas V V1. 2007. 468p. 52.95 *(978-0-548-09468-6(3))* Kessinger Publishing, LLC.

—History of Latin Christianity: Including That of the Popes to the Pontificate of Nicolas V V2. 2007. 456p. 52.95 *(978-0-548-09469-3(1))* Kessinger Publishing, LLC.

—History of Latin Christianity: Including That of the Popes to the Pontificate of Nicolas V V3. 2007. 500p. 53.95 *(978-0-548-09470-9(5))* Kessinger Publishing, LLC.

—History of Latin Christianity: Including That of the Popes to the Pontificate of Nicolas V V4. 2007. 440p. 51.95 *(978-0-548-09471-6(3))* Kessinger Publishing, LLC.

—History of Latin Christianity: Including That of the Popes to the Pontificate of Nicolas V V5. 2007. 480p. 53.95 *(978-0-548-09472-3(1))* Kessinger Publishing, LLC.

—History of Latin Christianity: Including That of the Popes to the Pontificate of Nicolas V V6. 2007. 484p. 53.95 *(978-0-548-09473-0(X))* Kessinger Publishing, LLC.

—History of Latin Christianity: Including That of the Popes to the Pontificate of Nicolas V V7. 2007. 520p. 55.95 *(978-0-548-09474-7(8))* Kessinger Publishing, LLC.

—History of Latin Christianity: Including That of the Popes to the Pontificate of Nicolas V V8. 2007. 492p. 53.95 *(978-0-548-09475-4(6))* Kessinger Publishing, LLC.

—History of Latin Christianity: Including That of the Popes to the Pontificate of Nicolas V V9. 2007. 480p. 53.95 *(978-0-548-09476-1(4))* Kessinger Publishing, LLC.

—History of Latin Christianity; Including That of the Popes to the Pontificate of Nicolas V by Henry Hart Milman + 2006. 552p. pap. 32.99 *(978-1-4255-6090-4(3))*; 556p. per. 32.99 *(978-1-4255-6105-5(5))* MPublishing.

Minnich, Nelson H. Councils of the Catholic Reformation: Pisa I(1409)to Trent(1545-63) 2008. (Variorum Collected Studies). (Illus.). 362p. 170.00 *(978-0-7546-5951-8(8))* Ashgate Publishing Co.

Moczar, Diane. What Every Catholic Wants to Know: Catholic History: From the Catacombs to the Reformation. 2006. 171p. per. 9.95 *(978-1-59276-302-3(2))* Our Sunday Visitor, Publishing Div.

Moral Roncal, Antonio M. & Moral Roncal, Antonio Manuel. La Cuestión Religiosa en la Segunda República Española: Iglesia y Carlismo. 2009. (SPA., Illus.). 263p. *(978-84-9742-905-4(2))* Biblioteca Nueva, Editorial, S.L.

Mourret, Fernand. Histoire Generale de L'Eglise, 9 vols. reprint ed. 1125.00 *(978-0-7222-2161-7(4))* Library Reprints, Inc.

Naaman, Paul. The Maronites: The Origins of an Antiochene Church: A Historical & Geographical Study of the Fifth to Seventh Centuries. 2011. pap. 24.95 *(978-0-87907-243-8(1))* Cistercian Pubns., Inc.

Nalle, Sara T. God in la Mancha: Religious Reform & the People of Cuenca, 1500-1650. 2008. (Johns Hopkins University Studies in Historical & Political Science Ser.: 110). (ENG., Illus.). 328p. (gr. 17). pap. 32.00 *(978-0-8018-8854-0(9))* Johns Hopkins Univ. Pr.

Nnoruka, Sylvanus. Thy Kingdom Come: The Advent, Growth & Role of the Catholic Church in Nigeria 1913-2007. 2007. 276p. pap. 29.95 *(978-3-88939-895-6(2))* IKO Verlag fur Interkulturelle Kommunikation DEU. Dist: Transaction Pubs.

Norman, Edward. The Roman Catholic Church: An Illustrated History. 2007. (Illus.). 192p. 40.00 *(978-0-520-25251-6(9))* Univ. of California Pr.

Oakley, Francis. The Conciliarist Tradition: Constitutionalism in the Catholic Church 1300-1870. 2008. (ENG.). 320p. pap. 50.00 *(978-0-19-954124-9(8))* Oxford Univ. Pr., Inc.

O'Brien, George Dennis. Finding the Voice of the Church. 2007. (ENG.). 264p. 25.00 *(978-0-268-03727-7(2))* Univ. of Notre Dame Pr.

O'Collins, Gerald. Catholicism. 2008. (Very Short Introductions Ser.). (ENG., Illus.). 144p. pap. 11.95 *(978-0-19-954591-9(X))* Oxford Univ. Pr., Inc.

Okuma, Peter Chidi. The Vatican II: The Laity & Today's Challenges. 2011. 204p. 61.95 ***(978-3-631-61864-6(6))*** Lang, Peter GmbH, Europaischer Verlag der Wissenschaften DEU. Dist: Lang, Peter.

Old Catholic Church, North American. Eucharist (SACRAMENTARY, Color) 2009. 284p. pap. 99.99 *(978-0-557-21932-2(9))* Lulu Enterprises Inc.

Old Catholic Church, North American. Eucharist (SACRAMENTARY, B&w) 2009. 282p. pap. 29.99 *(978-0-557-21970-4(1))* Lulu Enterprises Inc.

Orsy, Ladislas. Receiving the Council. 2009. 176p. pap. 29.95 *(978-0-8146-5377-7(4)*, Liturgical Pr. Bks.) Liturgical Pr.

Park, Hendrick. The Roman Catholic Church - a Critical Appraisal. 2008. 456p. 35.99 *(978-1-60477-783-3(4))* Xulon Pr., Inc.

—The Roman Catholic Church - A Critical Appraisal. 2008. 456p. pap. 23.99 *(978-1-60477-782-6(6))* Xulon Pr., Inc.

Paul, Tessa. The Illustrated History of Catholicism & the Catholic Saints: A comprehensive account of the history, philosophy & practice of Catholic Christianity & a guide to the most significant Saints. 2011. (ENG., Illus.). 512p. 35.00 *(978-0-7548-2360-5(1))* Anness Publishing GBR. Dist: National Bk. Network.

Pennock, Michael. This Is Our Church: A History of Catholicism. 2007. 300p. tchr. ed., per. 26.95 *(978-1-59471-159-6(3))* Ave Maria Pr.

Peter, Val J. Seven Secular Challenges Facing 21st-Century Catholics. 2009. 208p. pap. 17.95 *(978-0-8091-4570-6(7))* Paulist Pr.

Pierre & Williman, Daniel. The Letters of Pierre de Cros, Chamberlain to Pope Gregory XI, 1371-1378. 2008. *(978-0-86698-404-1(6))* Arizona State Univ., Arizona Ctr. for Medieval & Renaissance Studies.

Pollard, John F. Money & the Rise of the Modern Papacy: Financing the Vatican, 1850-1950. 2008. (ENG., Illus.). 288p. pap. 38.99 *(978-0-521-09211-1(6))* Cambridge Univ. Pr.

Poole, Stafford. Pedro Moya de Contreras: Catholic Reform & Royal Power in New Spain, 1571-1591. 2nd ed. 2011. (ENG., Illus.). 352p. (C). pap. 45.00 *(978-0-8061-4171-8(9))* Univ. of Oklahoma Pr.

Pritchard, Arnold. Catholic Loyalism in Elizabethan England. 2011. (ENG.). 256p. pap. 40.00 ***(978-0-8078-9755-3(8))*** Univ. of North Carolina Pr.

Privilege, John. Michael Logue & the Catholic Church in Ireland, 1879-1925. 2009. (ENG.). 224p. 89.00 *(978-0-7190-7735-7(4))* Manchester Univ. Pr. GBR. Dist: Macmillan.

Prouty, Marco G. César Chávez, the Catholic Bishops, & the Farmworkers' Struggle for Social Justice. Prouty, Marco G. 2008. (ENG., Illus.). 208p. pap. 19.95 *(978-0-8165-2731-1(8))* Univ. of Arizona Pr.

Ranan, David. Double Cross: The Code of the Catholic Church. 2007. 436p. pap. *(978-0-9554133-0-8(3))* Theo Pr. Ltd.

Reikerstorfer, Johann, ed. Vorwartserinnerungen. 625 Jahre Katholisch-Theologische Fakultat der Universitat Wien. 2009. (GER.). 418p. (C). 74.00 *(978-3-89971-736-5(8))* Vandenhoeck & Ruprecht GmbH & Co. KG DEU. Dist: ISD.

Renan, Ernest. Lectures on the Influence of the Institutions: Thought & Culture in Rome, on Christianity & the Development of the Catholic Church. Beard, Charles, tr. 2006. (Hibbert Lectures). 222p. pap. 24.00 *(978-1-59752-706-4(8)*, Wipf and Stock) Wipf & Stock Pubs.

Rezek, Antoine Ivan. History of the Diocese of Sault Ste. Marie & Marquette, 2 vols. 2006. (Illus.). reprint ed. Vol. 1. 393p. 9.00 *(978-0-9786970-1-3(4))* Vol. 2. (ENG., 401p. 9.00 *(978-0-9786970-2-0(2))* Roman Catholic Diocese of Marquette.

Rigali, Justin. Reliving Vatican II: It's All about Jesus Christ. 2006. 151p. per. 10.95 *(978-1-56854-597-4(5)*, REVAT) Liturgy Training Pubns.

Rosswurm, Steve. The FBI & the Catholic Church, 1935-1962. 2009. 352p. 39.95 net. *(978-1-55849-729-0(3))* Univ. of Massachusetts Pr.

Royal, Robert. The Catholic Martyrs of the Twentieth Century: A Comprehensive World History. 2006. (ENG., Illus.). 448p. pap. 19.95 *(978-0-8245-2414-2(4)*, Crossroad) Crossroad Publishing Co., The.

Ruether, Rosemary Radford. Catholic Does Not Equal the Vatican: A Vision for Progressive Catholicism. 2008. (Does Not Equal Ser.). (ENG.). 150p. 23.95 *(978-1-59558-406-9(4))* New Pr., The.

Russo, Anthony. In Silent Prayer: A History of Ministry with the Deaf in the Archdiocese of Philadelphia, 1846-2008. 2008. (ENG.). 196p. pap. *(978-0-7570-0238-0(2))* Square One Pubs.

Salonen, Kirsi & Schmugge, Ludwig. A Sip from the "Well of Grace" Medieval Texts from the Apostolic Penitentiary. 2008. (Illus.). 224p. pap. 29.95 *(978-0-8132-1535-8(8))* Catholic Univ. of America Pr.

Scheepsma, W. The Limburg Sermons: Preaching in the Medieval Low Countries at the Turn of the Fourteenth Century. 2008. (Brill's Ser. in Church History Ser.). (Illus.). 480p. *(978-90-04-16969-2(5))* BRILL.

Schoof, Ted Mark. A Survey of Catholic Theology, 1800-1970. Smith, N.D., tr. 2008. 292p. pap. 31.00 *(978-1-55635-817-3(2)*, Wipf and Stock) Wipf & Stock Pubs.

Schreck, Alan. The Compact History of the Catholic Church. 2009. pap. 12.99 *(978-0-86716-879-2(X))* Franciscan Media.

Selley, W. T. Sixtus V: The Hermit of Villa Montalto. 2011. 448p. pap. ***(978-0-85244-750-5(7))*** Gracewing, Ltd.

Simon, Maurice & Simon, M. La celebration du mystere chretien dans le catechisme de Jean-Paul II. 2006. (Bibliotheca Ephemeridum Theologicarum Lovaniensium Ser.). (FRE & ENG.). 638p. (C). pap. 124.00 *(978-90-429-1734-7(2))* Peeters Pubs. & Booksellers BEL. Dist: Brown, David Bk. Co., The.

Spannenberger, Norbert. Die Katholische Kirche in Ungarn 1918-1939: Positionierung Im Politischen System und "Katholische Renaissance" 2006. (HUN & GER., Illus.). 211p. (C). 52.00 *(978-3-515-08668-4(4))* Steiner, Franz Verlag Wiesbaden GmbH DEU. Dist: Brown, David Bk. Co., The.

Spinello, Richard A. The Genius of Pope John Paul II: The Great Pope's Moral Wisdom. 2006. (ENG.). 224p. 22.95 *(978-1-58051-206-0(2)*, Sheed & Ward) Rowman & Littlefield Publishers, Inc.

Stackpole, Robert A. Saint Peter Lives in Rome: Explaining the Misunderstood Ministry of the Pope. 2006. (ENG.). per. 13.95 *(978-1-59614-165-0(4))* Marian Pr.

Stewart, Cynthia. The Catholic Church: A Brief Popular History. 2008. pap. 30.45 *(978-0-88489-967-9(5))* St. Mary's Pr.

Sullivan, Maureen. The Road to Vatican II: Key Changes in Theology. 2007. 161p. per. 17.95 *(978-0-8091-4277-4(5)*, 4277-4) Paulist Pr.

Sweeney, Jon M. Almost Catholic: An Appreciation of the History, Practice, & Mystery of Ancient Faith. 2008. (ENG.). 240p. 19.95 *(978-0-7879-9470-9(7)*, Jossey-Bass) Wiley, John & Sons, Inc.

Tanner, Norman. New Short History of the Catholic Church. 2011. (ENG., Illus.). 280p. 22.95 *(978-0-86012-455-9(X)*, Burns & Oates) Continuum International Publishing Group, Ltd. GBR. Dist: National Bk. Network.

Thomsett, Michael C. Heresy in the Roman Catholic Church: A History. 2011. (ENG., Illus.). 280p. pap. 45.00 *(978-0-7864-4448-9(7))* McFarland & Co., Inc. Pubs.

Trigilio, John, Jr. & Brighenti, Kenneth. Catholicism for Dummies. 2nd ed. 2011. (ENG.). 432p. pap. 22.99 ***(978-1-118-07778-8(4)***, For Dummies) Wiley, John & Sons, Inc.

Tutino, Stefania. Law & Conscience: Catholicism in Early Modern England 1570-1625. 2007. (Catholic Christendom, 1300-1700 Ser.). 268p. 124.95 *(978-0-7546-5771-2(X))* Ashgate Publishing Co.

Vincelette, Alan Roy. Recent Catholic Philosophy: The Nineteenth Century. 2008. pap. *(978-0-87462-756-5(7))* Marquette Univ. Pr.

Walsh, Michael J. The Cardinals: Thirteen Centuries of the Men Behind the Papal Throne. 2011. 256p. pap. 23.00 *(978-0-8028-2941-2(4))* Eerdmans, William B. Publishing Co.

Weber, Christoph. Episcopus et Princeps: Italienische Bischöfe als Fürsten, Grafen und Barone vom 17. bis zum 20. Jahrhundert. 2010. (Beiträge zur Kirchen- und Kulturgeschichte Ser.). (GER.). 218p. 64.95 *(978-3-631-60242-3(1))* Lang, Peter GmbH, Europaischer Verlag der Wissenschaften DEU. Dist: Lang, Peter.

Wild, Robert A. Comrades Stumbling Along: The Friendship of Catherine de Hueck Doherty & Dorothy Day As Revealed Through Their Letters. 2009. 14.95 *(978-0-8189-1286-3(3)*, St. Pauls) St Pauls/Alba Hse. Pubs.

Wiltgen, Ralph M. The Founding of the Roman Catholic Church in Melanesia & Micronesia, 1850-1875. 2008. (Princeton Theological Monographs). (Illus.). 596p. pap. 66.00 *(978-1-55635-209-6(3)*, Pickwick Pubns.) Wipf & Stock Pubs.

—The Founding of the Roman Catholic Church in Oceania, 1825 To 1850. 2010. (Princeton Theological Monographs). (Illus.). 638p. pap. 64.00 *(978-1-60899-536-3(4)*, Pickwick Pubns.) Wipf & Stock Pubs.

Winter, Michael M. Whatever Happened to Vatican II? 221p. pap. *(978-0-7220-9720-5(4)*, Burns & Oates) Continuum International Publishing Group, Ltd.

Witherup, Ronald D. Scripture: Dei Verbum. 2006. (Rediscovering Vatican II Ser.). 160p. per. 15.95 *(978-0-8091-4428-0(X)*, 4428-X) Paulist Pr.

Woods, James M. A History of the Catholic Church in the American South, 1513-1900. 2011. (ENG., Illus.). 512p. 69.95 *(978-0-8130-3532-1(5))* Univ. Pr. of Florida.

Wright-Rios, Edward. Revolutions in Mexican Catholicism: Reform & Revelation in Oaxaca, 1887-1934. 2009. (ENG., Illus.). 376p. 94.95 *(978-0-8223-4357-8(6))*; pap. 25.95 *(978-0-8223-4379-0(7))* Duke Univ. Pr.

CATHOLIC CHURCH—HISTORY—SOURCES

Bennett, N. H., ed. The Register of Richard Fleming, Bishop of Lincoln, 1420-143, No. 2. 2009. (Canterbury & York Society Ser.: Volume 99). (LAT & ENG.). 218p. 45.00 *(978-0-907239-71-0(4))* Canterbury & York Society GBR. Dist: Boydell & Brewer, Inc.

Bruchhold, Ulrich. Deutschsprachige Beichten im 13. und 14. Jahrhundert: Editionen und Typologien zur ßberlieferungs-, Text- und Gebrauchsgeschichte vor dem Hintergrund der älteren Tradition. 2010. (Manchener Texte und Untersuchungen zur deutschen Literatur des Mittelalters Ser.). (GER.). 704p. 168.00 *(978-3-11-023462-6(9))* De Gruyter, Walter Inc.

Kehr, Paulus F., contrib. by. Regesta Pontificum Romanorum Ivbente Regai Societate Gottingensi Congessit Pavlvs Fridolinvs Kehr Vol. III: Etruria. (ITA.). 492p. *(978-3-296-20903-6(4))* Weidmann DEU. Dist: Lubrecht & Cramer, Ltd.

Loomis, Louise Ropes. Book of the Popes Liber Pontificalis. 2006. pap. 22.95 *(978-1-4286-5548-5(4))* Kessinger Publishing, LLC.

Loomis, Louise Ropes, tr. The Book of the Popes (Liber Pontificalis) To the Pontificate of Gregory I. 2006. (Christian Roman Empire Ser.: No. 3). 204p. pap. 19.95 *(978-1-889758-86-2(8)*, Evolution Publishing & Manufacturing) Arx Publishing.

Murphy, Dennis J., ed. The Church & the Bible: Official Documents of the Catholic Church. 2nd enl. ed. 2007. xcvi, 1048p. 24.95 *(978-0-8189-1250-4(2)*, St. Pauls) St Pauls/Alba Hse. Pubs.

Redworth, Glyn, ed. The Letters of Luisa de Carvajal y Mendoza, 2 vols. 2012. (ENG.). 800p. 335.00 ***(978-1-84893-218-0(9))*** Pickering & Chatto Pubs., Ltd. GBR. Dist: Ashgate Publishing Co.

Robinson, David, ed. The Register of William Melton, Archbishop of York, 1317-1340, VI. 2011. (Canterbury & York Society Ser.: Volume 101). (LAT & ENG.). 292p. 45.00 *(978-0-907239-73-4(0))* Canterbury & York Society GBR. Dist: Boydell & Brewer, Inc.

Shinners, John Raymond. Medieval Popular Religion, 1000-1500: A Reader. 2nd rev. ed. 2007. (Readings in Medieval Civilizations & Cultures Ser.: Vol. 2). (Illus.). 555p. pap. *(978-1-55111-698-3(7))* Broadview Pr.

Sot, Michel & Lobrichon, Guy. Les Gestes des évêques D'Auxerre. 2006. (LAT & FRE., Illus.). 374p. (C). pap. 62.00 ***(978-2-251-34054-8(8))*** Societe d'edition Les Belles lettres FRA. Dist: ISD.

Vandenhoeck & Ruprecht, ed. Bohemia-Moravia Pontificia: Germania Pontificia. Vol. V/3: Provincia Maguntinensis, Pars VII. 2011. (Regesta Pontificum Romanorum iubente Academia Gottingensi. Gallia Pontificia Ser.). (GER.). 229p. (C). 116.00 *(978-3-525-36038-5(X))* Vandenhoeck & Ruprecht GmbH & Co. KG DEU. Dist: ISD.

CATHOLIC CHURCH—HISTORY—MIDDLE AGES, 600-1500

Decker, Rainer. Witchcraft & the Papacy: An Account Drawing on the Formerly Secret Records of the Roman Inquisition. Midelfort, H. C. Erik, tr. from GER. 2008. (Studies in Early Modern German History Ser.). (ENG., Illus.). 280p. (gr. 17). 45.00 *(978-0-8139-2747-3(1))* Univ. Pr. of Virginia.

Horst, Ulrich. The Dominicans & the Pope: Papal Teaching Authority in the Medieval & Early Modern Thomist Tradition. Mixson, James D., tr. from GER. annot. ed. 2006. (Conway Lectures in Medieval Studies). 168p. per. 28.00 *(978-0-268-03077-3(4))* Univ. of Notre Dame Pr.

Koman, Alan J. A Who's Who of Your Ancestral Saints. 2010. 458p. pap. 34.95 *(978-0-8063-1824-0(4))* Genealogical Publishing Co., Inc.

Mingroot, Erik van. Sapientiae Immarcessibilis. vi, 329p. pap. 73.00 *(978-90-6186-620-6(0))* Leuven Univ. Pr. BEL. Dist: Cornell Univ. Pr.

Reynolds, Roger E. Studies on Medieval Liturgical & Legal Manuscripts from Spain & Southern Italy. 2009. (Variorum Collected Studies). (Illus.). 330p. 154.95 *(978-0-7546-5997-6(6))* Ashgate Publishing Co.

Tierney, Brian. Foundations of the Conciliar Theory: The Contribution of the Medieval Canonists from Gratian to the Great Schism. 2010. (ENG.). 294p. pap. 23.99 *(978-0-521-14368-4(3))* Cambridge Univ. Pr.

CATHOLIC CHURCH—HISTORY—MODERN PERIOD, 1500-

Carroll, James. Practicing Catholic. 2009. (ENG.). 400p. 28.00 *(978-0-618-67018-5(1))* Houghton Mifflin Harcourt Trade & Reference Pubs.

First, Debra. Founded in Faith: Cleveland's Lost Catholic Legacy. 2010. (Illus.). 144p. pap. 19.95 *(978-0-936760-28-5(1))* Cleveland Landmarks Pr., Inc.

Flint, Thomas P. Divine Providence: The Molinist Account. 2006. (Illus.). 272p. pap. 27.95 *(978-0-8014-7336-4(5),* ILR Pr.) Cornell Univ. Pr.

MacCaffrey, James. History of the Catholic Church: From the Renaissance to the French Revolution. reprint ed. Vol. I. 419p. lib. bdg. 28.50 *(978-0-8290-0463-2(7))* Vol. II. 470p. lib. bdg. 25.50 *(978-0-8290-0464-9(5))* Irvington Pubs.

—History of the Catholic Church from the Renaissance to the French Revolution. 2008. 408p. 32.99 *(978-0-554-26820-0(5))* 2008. 408p. 30.99 *(978-0-554-36123-9(X))* 1. 2007. (ENG.). 406p. pap. 28.99 *(978-1-4346-1946-4(X))* BiblioBazaar.

—History of the Catholic Church from the Renaissance to the French Revolution. 2007. (ENG.). 352p. per. *(978-1-4065-2980-7(X))*; per. *(978-1-4065-2981-4(8))* Dodo Pr.

—History of the Catholic Church from the Renaissance to the French Revolution Volume 1. lt. ed. 2007. (ENG.). 362p. pap. 25.99 *(978-1-4346-1777-4(7))* BiblioBazaar.

Merton, Thomas. The Waters of Siloe. 2011. 446p. pap. 36.75 ***(978-1-179-63628-3(7))*** BiblioBazaar.

Miola, Robert S., ed. Early Modern Catholicism: An Anthology of Primary Sources. 2007. (Illus.). 608p. 199.00 *(978-0-19-925985-4(2))* Oxford Univ. Pr., Inc.

Mitchell, Nathan. The Mystery of the Rosary: Marian Devotion & the Reinvention of Catholicism. (ENG.). 336p. 2012. pap. 24.00 ***(978-0-8147-6343-8(X))*** 2009. 25.00 *(978-0-8147-9591-0(9))* New York Univ. Pr.

Roberts, Tom. The Emerging Catholic Church: A Community's Search for Itself. 2011. 224p. pap. 24.00 *(978-1-57075-946-8(4))* Orbis Bks.

CATHOLIC CHURCH—HYMNS

Anon. Hymnarium Sarisburiense, Cum Rubricis et Notis Musicis Hymni et Rubricae. 2009. 156p. pap. *(978-1-906857-72-1(5))* Travis & Emery Music Bookshop.

Hildenbrand, Udo. Das Einheitsgesangbuch Gotteslob: Eine theologische Analyse der Lied- und Gesangtexte in ekklesiologischer Perspektive. 2009. (Übergänge. Studien zur Evangelischen und Katholischen Theologie/Religionspädagogik Ser.). (GER.). 1160p. pap. 188.95 *(978-3-631-58176-6(9))* Lang, Peter GmbH, Europaischer Verlag der Wissenschaften DEU. Dist: Lang, Peter.

Messenger, Ruth E. Ethical Teachings in the Latin Hymns of Medieval England. (Columbia University, Studies in the Social Sciences: No. 321). reprint ed. 20.00 *(978-0-404-51321-4(2))* AMS Pr., Inc.

Milfull, Inge B. The Hymns of the Anglo-Saxon Church: A Study & Edition of the 'Durham Hymnal' 2007. (Cambridge Studies in Anglo-Saxon England Ser.). (ENG.). 512p. pap. 84.00 *(978-0-521-03081-6(1))* Cambridge Univ. Pr.

The Seven Great Hymns of the Medieval Church. 2006. 144p. per. 16.99 *(978-1-4255-1082-4(5))* MPublishing.

CATHOLIC CHURCH—INFALLIBILITY

see also Popes—Infallibility

Harley, Thomas. Matthew Poole: His Life, His Times, His Contributions along with His Argument against the Infallibility of the Roman Catholic Church. 2009. 232p. 28.95 *(978-1-4401-1607-0(5))* iUniverse, Inc.

O'Connor, James T. The Gift of Infallibility. 2008. 225p. pap. 14.95 *(978-1-58617-174-2(7))* Ignatius Pr.

Powell, Mark E. Papal Infallibility: A Protestant Evaluation of an Ecumenical Issue. 2009. 238p. pap. 40.00 *(978-0-8028-6284-6(5))* Eerdmans, William B. Publishing Co.

Rush, Ormond. The Eyes of Faith: The Sense of the Faithful & the Church's Reception of Revelation. 2009. 344p. 79.95 *(978-0-8132-1571-6(4))* Catholic Univ. of America Pr.

Salmon, George. La Infalibilidad de la Iglesia: The Infallibility of the Church. (SPA.). 560p. *(978-84-7228-948-2(6),* 223071) Clie, Editorial.

CATHOLIC CHURCH—LITURGICAL MOVEMENT

see Liturgical Movement—Catholic Church

CATHOLIC CHURCH—LITURGY

see also Church Music—Catholic Church; Gregorian Chants; Liturgical Movement—Catholic Church; Sequences (Liturgy); Stations of the Cross

Allen, Celine M., ed. The Paulist Liturgy Planning Guide: For the Readings of Sundays & Major Feast Days, Year C. 2006. 271p. per 18.95 *(978-0-8091-4414-3(X),* 4414-x) Paulist Pr.

Andrew Burnham Staff. Heaven & Earth in Little Space: The Re-Enchantment of Liturgy. 2010. (ENG., Illus.). 224p. pap. 30.00 *(978-1-84825-005-5(3),* Canterbury Pr. Norwich) Hymns Ancient & Modern Ltd GBR. Dist: Westminster John Knox Pr.

Annual Guide for Liturgy of the Hours. 1.75 *(978-0-89942-443-9(0))* Catholic Bk. Publishing Corp.

Barren Earth to New Growth. 2007. per. 5.95 *(978-0-9719921-8-4(5))* Tau Publishing.

Barsom, Murad & Samuel, Mor Athanasius Yeshue, trs. The Order of the Burial of the Dead. 2011. (SYR.). 127.00 *(978-1-61143-960-1(4,)* Gorgias Pr., LLC.

Baumstark, Anton. On the Historical Development of Liturgy. 2011. 229p. pap. 34.95 ***(978-0-8146-6096-6(7))*** Liturgical Pr.

Bedjan, Paul, ed. Chaldean Breviary. 2010. (SYR.). 614.76 *(978-1-60724-816-3(6))*; 614.76 *(978-1-60724-818-7(2))*; 614.76 *(978-1-60724-817-0(4))* Gorgias Pr., LLC.

Bell, Thomas J. Peter Abelard after Marriage: The Spiritual Direction of Heloise & Her Nuns Through Liturgical Song. 2008. (Cistercian Studies). 346p. per. 39.95 *(978-0-87907-311-4(X),* CS211P) Cistercian Pubns., Inc.

Berry, Paul. The Bobbio Missal, A. D. 700. 2010. (Illus.). 284p. *(978-0-7734-1351-1(0))* Mellen, Edwin Pr., The.

Bone, David L. & Scifres, Mary J. The United Methodist Music & Worship Planner 2008-2009. 2008. pap. 21.00 *(978-0-687-64546-6(8))* Abingdon Pr.

The Book of the Gospels: The Saint John's Bible Edition. 2007. 526p. lthr. 695.00 *(978-0-8146-9064-2(5))*; (ENG.). 595.00 *(978-0-8146-9097-0(1))* Liturgical Pr. (Liturgical Pr. Bks.).

Bradshaw, Lee. A Guide to the Celebration of Low Mass. 2007. 65p. pap. 19.95 *(978-1-84799-921-4(2))* Lulu Enterprises Inc.

Braulik, Georg & Lohfink, Norbert. Osternacht und Altes Testament - Ergänzungsband: Vertonung des Vigilvorschlags durch Godehard Joppich. 2008. (Osterreichische Biblische Studien Ser.). (GER., Illus.). 172p. 56.95 *(978-3-631-56994-8(7))* Lang, Peter GmbH, Europaischer Verlag der Wissenschaften DEU. Dist: Lang, Peter.

Brennan, Robert Edward. Pange Lingu: Reflections on the Liturgy. 2011. 166p. 41.95 ***(978-1-258-03559-4(6))*** Literary Licensing, LLC.

Brown, Joseph A. Sweet, Sweet Spirit: Prayer Services from the Black Catholic Church. 2006. 100p. per. 9.95 *(978-0-86716-626-2(6))* Franciscan Media.

Brown, Michelle P. The Lindisfarne Gospels & the Early Medieval World. 2010. (Illus.). 160p. 45.00 *(978-0-7123-5801-9(3))* British Library, The GBR. Dist: Chicago Distribution Ctr.

Bruner, George A. Cathedral of the Sacred Heart 1906-2006: Celebrating 100 Years A Journey of Fa. 1500th ed. 2006. 29.95 *(978-0-9773153-1-4(2))* Dementi Milestone Publishing.

Byzantine Catholic Church. The Order of Baptism & Confirmation According to the Byzantine Rite of the Catholic Church. 2011. 32p. 35.95 ***(978-1-258-05197-6(4))*** Literary Licensing, LLC.

Cantalamessa, Raniero. Jesus Began to Preach: The Mystery of God's Word. 2010. (ENG.). 112p. pap. 7.95 *(978-0-8146-3304-5(8))* Liturgical Pr.

Carstens, Christopher & Martis, Douglas. Mystical Body, Mystical Voice: Encountering Christ in the Words of the Mass. 2011. (ENG.). 272p. pap. 16.95 *(978-1-56854-932-3(6))* Liturgy Training Pubns.

Catholic Book Publishing Co, creator. New St. Joseph Sunday Missal Prayerbook & Hymnal. 2007. (Illus.). 671p. per. 2.75 *(978-0-89942-628-0(X))* Catholic Bk. Publishing Corp.

—Saint Joseph Guide for Christian Prayer. lt. ed. 2006. 47p. pap. 2.75 *(978-0-89942-459-0(7))* Catholic Bk. Publishing Corp.

—Saint Joseph Guide for Christian Prayer (the Liturgy of the Hours) 2008. (Illus.). 47p. pap. 2.75 *(978-0-89942-595-5(X))* Catholic Bk. Publishing Corp.

—Saint Joseph Guide for the Liturgy of the Hours. 47p. 2008. pap. 2.75 *(978-0-89942-591-7(7))* 2007. pap. 2.75 *(978-0-89942-477-4(5))* Catholic Bk. Publishing Corp.

—Saint Joseph Guide for the Liturgy of the Hours: For 2009. 2008. 47p. pap. 2.00 *(978-0-89942-589-4(5))* Catholic Bk. Publishing Corp.

—St. Joseph Sunday Missal & Hymnal: The Complete Masses for Sundays, Holydays, & the Easter Triduum. 2008. (Illus.). 671p. pap. 2.78 *(978-0-89942-633-4(6))* Catholic Bk. Publishing Corp.

Catholic Church Liturgy Holy week office. The Complete Office of Holy Week According to the Roman Missal & Breviary, in Latin & English. 2006. 560p. per. 32.99 *(978-1-4255-6165-9(9))* MPublishing.

Cavalletti, Sofia. Living Liturgy: Elementary Reflections. 2010. 96p. pap. 15.95 *(978-1-56854-241-6(0),* Catechesis of the Good Shepherd) Liturgy Training Pubns.

Chupungco, Anscar J. What, Then, Is Liturgy? Musings & Memoir. 2010. xviii, 251p. 29.95 *(978-0-8146-6239-7(0))* Liturgical Pr.

Çiçek, Julius Yeshu. The Liturgy of the Sacrament of Penance. 2010. (SYR.). 86.96 *(978-1-61143-203-9(0))* Gorgias Pr., LLC.

Cleveland, Richard A. Vision for Ministry: Seeing more clearly the potential & process of forming Catholic Disciples. 2007. per. 6.95 *(978-0-9765242-2-7(5))* Emmaus Journey.

Clynes, Raphael. Liturgy & Christian Life. 2011. 440p. 56.95 ***(978-1-258-09315-0(4))*** Literary Licensing, LLC.

Collegeville Composers Group. We Will Follow You, Lord: Accompaniment BK. 2006. 80p. pap. 11.95 *(978-0-8146-3075-4(8),* Liturgical Pr. Bks.) Liturgical Pr.

Collegeville Composers Group, contrib. by. Psallite: Sacred Song for Liturgy & Life: Year A. 2007. 350p. pap. 24.95 *(978-0-8146-3064-8(2))* Liturgical Pr.

Collins, Gregory. Meeting Christ in His Mysteries: A Benedictine Vision of the Spiritual Life. 2011. (ENG., Illus.). 381p. pap. 26.95 *(978-1-85607-682-1(2))* Columba Pr. IRL. Dist: Dufour Editions, Inc.

Congar, Yves & Philibert, Paul J. At the Heart of Christian Worship: Liturgical Essays of Yves Congar: Translated & Edited by Paul Philibert. 2010. 24.95 *(978-0-8146-6229-8(3))* Liturgical Pr.

Connell, Martin. Church & Worship in Fifth-Century Rome. 2009. 88.00 *(978-1-60724-401-1(2))* Gorgias Pr., LLC.

Cullen-Skowronski, Fiona. Charismatic Liturgy of the Word with Children. 2009 112p. pap. *(978-1-84923-796-3(4))* YouWriteOn.

—The Spirit-Filled Liturgy of the World. 2008. 72p. pap. *(978-1-84923-055-1(2))* YouWriteOn.

Cullinan, Edmond Gerard. The Story of the Liturgy in Ireland. 2010. (ENG.). 128p. pap. 22.95 *(978-1-85607-684-5(9))* Columba Pr. IRL. Dist: Dufour Editions, Inc.

de Blas, Alonso. Barren Earth to New Growth. 2007. *(978-0-9719921-9-1(3))* Tau Publishing.

DeGrocco, Joseph. Take & Eat: Living Eucharistically. 2010. 109p. pap. ***(978-1-933066-12-7(1),*** Resurrection Pr.) Catholic Bk. Publishing Corp.

Diamond, Wilfrid. Dictionary of Liturgical Latin. 2008. 156p. pap. 13.00 *(978-1-60608-190-7(X),* Wipf and Stock) Wipf & Stock Pubs.

Dobszay, Laszlo & Hemming, Laurence Paul. The Restoration & Organic Development of the Roman Rite. 2010. (T&T Clark Studies in Fundamental Liturgy Ser.). (ENG., Illus.). 304p. 49.95 *(978-0-567-03386-4(4),* T&T Clark Int'l) Continuum International Publishing Group, Ltd. GBR. Dist: National Bk. Network.

Dobszay, Laszlo, et al. The Restoration & Organic Development of the Roman Rite. 2010. (T&T Clark Studies in Fundamental Liturgy Ser.). (ENG., Illus.). 304p. 140.00 *(978-0-567-03385-7(6),* T&T Clark Int'l) Continuum International Publishing Group, Ltd. GBR. Dist: National Bk. Network.

Doherty, Catherine. Season of Mercy: Lent & Easter. 160p. pap. *(978-0-921440-43-7(X))* Madonna Hse. Pubns.

Donghi, Antonio. Words & Gestures in the Liturgy. 2009. pap. 18.95 *(978-0-8146-6222-9(6))* Liturgical Pr.

Duffy, Regis A. An American Emmaus. 2010. 192p. pap. 21.00 *(978-1-60899-534-9(8),* Wipf and Stock) Wipf & Stock Pubs.

Dunlap, John. An Answer Key to a Primer of Ecclesiastical Latin: A Supplement to the Text. 2006. 168p. per. 19.95 *(978-0-8132-1469-6(6))* Catholic Univ. of America Pr.

Durandus, Gulielmus. The Rationale Divinorum Officiorum: The Foundational Symbolism of the Early Church, Its Structure, Decoration, Sacraments, & Vestments. 2007. (ENG., Illus.). 400p. pap. 39.95 *(978-1-887752-92-3(7))* Fons Vitae of Kentucky, Inc.

Ferrone, Rita. Liturgy: Sacrosanctum Concilium. 2007. (Rediscovering Vatican II Ser.). 134p. per. 15.95 *(978-0-8091-4472-3(7),* 4472-3) Paulist Pr.

Foley, Edward, et al, eds. A Commentary on the General Instruction of the Roman Missal: Developed under the Auspices of the Catholic Academy of Liturgy & Cosponsored by the Fereation of Diocesan Liturgical Commissions. 2008. (Pueblo Bks.). 502p. 59.95 *(978-0-8146-6017-1(7),* Liturgical Pr. Bks.) Liturgical Pr.

Foley, Edward, et al. A Commentary on the Order of Mass of the Roman Missal: A New English Translation Developed under the Auspices of the Catholic Academy of Liturgy: General Editor, Edward Foley: Associate Editors, John F. Baldovin, Mary Collins, Joanne M. Pierce: Foreword by Roger Mahony. 2011. E-Book ***(978-0-8146-6256-4(0))*** Liturgical Pr.

Fortescue, Adrian, et al. Ceremonies of the Roman Rite Described. 15th ed. 2009. (ENG., Illus.). 504p. 70.00 *(978-0-86012-462-7(2),* Burns & Oates) Continuum International Publishing Group, Ltd. GBR. Dist: National Bk. Network.

Frere, W. H. Studies in Early Roman Liturgy: I. the Kalendar. 2011. 160p. pap. 14.00 *(978-1-61097-004-4(7),* Wipf and Stock) Wipf & Stock Pubs.

—Studies in Early Roman Liturgy: II. the Roman Lectionary. 2011. 256p. pap. 22.00 *(978-1-61097-168-3(X),* Wipf and Stock) Wipf & Stock Pubs.

—Studies in Early Roman Liturgy: III. the Roman Epistle - Lectionary. 2011. 122p. pap. 11.00 *(978-1-61097-171-3(X),* Wipf and Stock) Wipf & Stock Pubs.

Gill, Gerald Dennis. Music in Catholic Liturgy: A Pastoral & Theological Companion to Sing to the Lord. 2009. 140p. 19.00 *(978-1-59525-028-5(X))* Hillenbrand Bks.

Giocondo, Maureen & Manno, John D. Countdown to Confirmation: A Resource Guide for Immediate Preparation. 2007. (Illus.). 55p. per. 15.95 *(978-1-58595-610-4(4))* Twenty-Third Pubns./Bayard.

Greisen, Thomas A., et al. Living Liturgy: Spirituality, Celebration, & Catechesis for Sundays & Solemnities - Year A 2008. 2007. (Illus.). 320p. per. 16.95 *(978-0-8146-2745-7(5),* Liturgical Pr. Bks.) Liturgical Pr.

Haas, David. Increase Our Faith: Year C: Parish Prayer Services for Whole Community Catechesis. 2006. 220p. per. 24.95 *(978-1-58595-569-5(8))* Twenty-Third Pubns./Bayard.

Hahn, Scott W. & Scott, David, eds. Letter & Spirit, Volume 4: Temple & Contemplation: God's Presence in the Cosmos, Church, & Human Heart. 2008. (Letter & Spirit Ser.). 336p. pap. 15.95 *(978-1-931018-52-4(9))* Emmaus Road Publishing.

Hani, Jean. The Divine Liturgy: Insights into Its Mystery. 2008. *(978-1-59731-076-5(X))*; pap. *(978-1-59731-075-8(1))* Perennis, Sophia.

Hans, Molly K. & Graham, William C. The Catholic Wedding Book: A Complete Guidebook. rev. ed. 2007. (Illus.). 245p. per. 14.95 *(978-0-8091-4462-4(X),* 4462-4) Paulist Pr.

Hemming, Laurence Paul & Hemming. Worship as a Revelation: The Past, Present & Future of Catholic Liturgy. 2008. (ENG.). 208p. 27.95 *(978-0-86012-460-3(6),* Burns & Oates) Continuum International Publishing Group, Ltd. GBR. Dist: National Bk. Network.

Hen, Yitzhak & Meens, Rob, eds. The Bobbio Missal: Liturgy & Religious Culture in Merovingian Gaul. 2009. (Cambridge Studies in Palaeography & Codicology Ser.). (ENG.). 248p. pap. 36.99 *(978-0-521-12691-5(6))* Cambridge Univ. Pr.

Henning, Meredith. Mondays with Mary A Celebration of Marian Feasts Throughout the Year. 2009. 176p. pap. 14.95 *(978-0-557-05951-5(8))* Lulu Enterprises Inc.

Hickman, Hoyt L. Worshiping with United Methodists: A Guide for Pastors & Church Leaders. rev. ed. 2007. (Illus.). 135p. per. 17.00 *(978-0-687-33526-8(4))* Abingdon Pr.

Holy See Staff. Layman's Missal: Sundays, Principal Feasts & Liturgy of the Sacraments. 2009. (ENG & LAT., Illus.). 1512p. 27.95 *(978-0-8264-4228-4(5),* Burns & Oates) Continuum International Publishing Group, Ltd. GBR. Dist National Bk. Network.

Holy See, The. Layman's Missal: Sundays, Principal Feasts & Liturgy of the Sacraments. 2009. (ENG.). 1512p. *(978-0-86012-442-9(8),* Burns & Oates) Continuum International Publishing Group, Ltd.

Hornby, Emma. Medieval Liturgical Chant & Patristic Exegesis: Words & Music in the Second-Mode Tracts. 2009. (Studies in Medieval & Renaissance Music Ser.: Volume 9). (Illus.). 344p. 95.00 *(978-1-84383-471-7(5),* Boydell Press) Boydell & Brewer, Ltd. GBR. Dist: Boydell & Brewer, Inc.

Hull, Geoffrey. The Banished Heart: Origins of Heteropraxis in the Catholic Church. 2010. (T&T Clark Studies in Fundamental Liturgy Ser.). (ENG.). 400p. 34.95 *(978-0-567-44220-8(9))*; 150.00 *(978-0-567-23798-9(2))* Continuum International Publishing Group, Ltd. GBR. (T&T Clark Int'l). Dist: National Bk. Network.

Icel, et al, compiled by. The Roman Missal [Third Typical Edition, Chapel Edition]. 2011. (Illus.). 1520p. 95.00 ***(978-1-56854-990-3(3))*** Liturgy Training Pubns.

—The Roman Missal [Third Typical Edition, Ritual Edition]. 2011. (Illus.). 1520p. 175.00 ***(978-1-56854-991-0(1))*** Liturgy Training Pubns.

Inaestimabile, Donum. Instr Concern Worship Euch. 16p. pap. 1.95 *(978-0-8198-3641-0(9),* 332-125) Pauline Bks. & Media.

Iwas, Ignatius Zakka I., intro. Liturgy of the Hours. 2010. (SYR.). 129.80 *(978-1-61143-240-4(5))* Gorgias Pr., LLC.

Janowiak, Paul. Standing Together in the Community of God: Liturgical Spirituality & the Presence of Christ. 2011. E-Book ***(978-0-8146-6257-1(9))*** Liturgical Pr.

Johner, Dominic. The Chants of the Vatican Gradual. Monks Of St. John's Abbey, tr. 2011. 516p. 60.95 ***(978-1-258-04436-7(6))*** Literary Licensing, LLC.

Johnson, Maxwell E. Issues in Eucharistic Praying in East & West: Essays in Liturgical & Theological Analysis. 2011. xvi, 395p. 49.95 *(978-0-8146-6227-4(7))*; E-Book *(978-0-8146-6248-9(X))* Liturgical Pr.

Jungmann, Joseph A. Liturgical Worship. 2007. (ENG.). 144p. 35.95 *(978-0-548-14062-8(6))* 2006. pap. 20.95 *(978-1-4286-5261-3(2))* Kessinger Publishing, LLC.

Kelly, Maureen. Sacraments Source Book. 2007. ***(978-0-15-901641-1(X))*** Harcourt Religion Pubs.

Kelly, Thomas Forrest & Mugmon, Matthew, eds. Ambrosiana at Harvard: New Sources of Milanese Chant. 2010. (Houghton Library Studies: 3). (Illus.). 172p. pap. 35.00 *(978-0-9818858-0-3(2))* Harvard Univ. Pr.

Kinkel, R. John. Letters to Pope Benedict: College Students Speak Out. 2011. 124p. 22.33 ***(978-1-4269-7432-8(9))***; pap. 12.33 ***(978-1-4269-7431-1(0))*** Trafford Publishing.

Kocik, Thomas. Living & Loving the Mass. 2007. 86p. per. *(978-0-9725981-8-7(9))* Zaccheus Pr.

Kubicki, Judith M. Presence of Christ in the Gathered Assembly. 2006. (ENG.) 192p. pap. 29.95 *(978-0-8264-1901-9(1))* Continuum International Publishing Group, Ltd. GBR. Dist: National Bk. Network.

Kubicki, Judith Marie & Kubicki, Judith M. The Presence of Christ in the Gathered Assembly. 2006. (ENG.). 192p. 110.00 *(978-0-8264-1900-2(3))* Continuum International Publishing Group, Ltd. GBR. Dist: National Bk. Network.

Kwatera, Michael. The Collegeville Prayer of the Faithful Annual: Cycle A, with CD-ROM. 2007. 160p. pap. 9.95 incl. cd-rom *(978-0-8146-3052-5(9),* Liturgical Pr. Bks.) Liturgical Pr.

Latin-English Sunday Missal. 2007. (Illus.). 163p. pap. 8.95 *(978-1-929291-92-2(2))* Roman Catholic Bks.

Latkovich, Sallie. Mining the Meaning of the Bible: Beyond the Literal Word. 2011. 64p. *(978-0-7648-1982-7(8))* Liguori Pubns.

Lawrence, Emeric A. Each Month with Christ: Insights into the Liturgy of the Months. 2011. 124p. 40.95 ***(978-1-258-02337-9(7))*** Literary Licensing, LLC.

—The Week with Christ: Liturgy for the Apostolate. 2011. 340p. 51.95 ***(978-1-258-10187-9(4))*** Literary Licensing, LLC.

Leachman, O.S.B., James G, ed. The Liturgical Subject: Subject, Subjectivity, & the Human Person in Contemporary Liturgical Discussion & Critique. 2009. (ND Faith in Reason Ser.). (ENG.). 288p. pap. 38.00 *(978-0-268-03410-8(9))* Univ. of Notre Dame Pr.

Lefebvre, Gaspar. Catholic Liturgy: Its Fundamental Principles. 2011. 300p. 48.95 ***(978-1-258-09915-2(2))*** Literary Licensing, LLC.

Lefebvre, Gaspar. How to Understand the Mass. 2006. 128p. per. 16.95 *(978-0-9789432-6-4(0))* Catholic Authors Pr.

Likoudis, James & Whitehead, Kenneth D. The Pope, the Council, & the Mass: Answers to Questions the Traditionalists Have Asked. 3rd ed. 2006. 374p. per. 16.95 *(978-1-931018-34-0(0))* Emmaus Road Publishing.

Lional, Joseph. Continuity in Liturgical Renewal: A Critical Analysis of the Prefaces for the Sunday's of Lent in the Editions of Missale Romanum 1570 And 2002. 2012. (ENG.). lib. bdg. ***(978-1-936320-44-8(4))*** Academica Pr., LLC.

Living Liturgy Sunday Missal 2012. 2011. 408p. pap. 9.95 ***(978-0-8146-3336-6(6))*** Liturgical Pr.

Longon, Jean, et al. The Très Riches Heures of Jean, Duke of Berry. 2008. (Illus.). 224p. 125.00 *(978-0-8076-1596-6(X))* Braziller, George Inc.

Lucatero, Heliodoro. The Living Mass: Changes to the Roman Missal & How We Worship. 2011. pap. *(978-0-7648-2007-6(9))* Liguori Pubns.

—Una Tradición Siempre Nueva, Siempre Viva: Los Cambios Recientes de la Misa. 2011.Tr. of Living Mass: Changes to the Roman Missal & How We Worship. (SPA.). *(978-0-7648-2008-3(7))* Liguori Pubns.
Magsam, Charles M. The Inner Life of Worship. 2011. 334p. 50.95 *(978-1-258-09587-1(4))* Literary Licensing, LLC.
Maines, David R. & McCallion, Michael J. Transforming Catholicism: Liturgical Change in the Vatican II Church. 2007. (ENG.). 164p. 73.50 *(978-0-7391-1802-3(1))*; per. 28.50 *(978-0-7391-1803-0(X))* Lexington Bks.
Martin, Kenneth J. Forgotten Instruction: The Roman Liturgy, Inculturation, & Legitimate Adaptations. 2007. pap. *(978-1-56854-505-9(3)*, FORINS) Liturgy Training Pubns.
McCarthy, Padraig. Wedding of Your Own. 4th rev. ed. 2007. (ENG.). 294p. pap. 20.95 *(978-1-85390-678-7(6))* Veritas Pubns. IRL. Dist: Dufour Editions, Inc.
McManus, Frederick R. The Rites of Holy Week: Ceremonies, Preparations, Music, Commentary. 2011. 158p. 41.95 ***(978-1-258-05282-9(2))*** Literary Licensing, LLC.
Mcrae-Mcmahon. Liturgies for the Young in Years. 2007. pap. *(978-0-281-05789-4(3))* SPCK Publishing.
Merton, Thomas. Seasons of Celebration: Meditations on the Cycle of Liturgical Feasts. 2009. 224p. pap. 17.95 *(978-1-59471-170-1(4))* Ave Maria Pr.
Messenger, E. C. The Liturgy of the Mass. 2011. 26p. 35.95 ***(978-1-258-04790-0(X))*** Literary Licensing, LLC.
Mick, Lawrence E. How We Worship: The Eucharist, the Sacraments, & the Hours. 2009. 14.99 *(978-0-7648-1936-0(4))* Liguori Pubns.
Miller, Michael J. Musica Sacra: Music at Mass, a Liturgical & Pastoral Challenge: Papers from the Second Study Day on the Anniversary of Sacrosanctum Concilium, Vatican City, December 5, 2005. 2010. 181p. ***(978-1-58617-301-2(4))*** Ignatius Pr.
Morgan, T. T. Lucius. The Teaching of the Temple or the Pictor. 2006. pap. 28.95 *(978-1-4286-4863-0(1))* Kessinger Publishing, LLC.
Morneau, Robert. Not by Bread Alone. 2011. 104p. pap. 2.00 ***(978-0-8146-3310-6(2))*** Liturgical Pr.
—Not by Bread Alone Large Print. 2011. 104p. pap. 5.95 ***(978-0-8146-3356-4(0))*** Liturgical Pr.
Moroney, James P. The Mass Explained. 2008. (Illus.). 128p. pap. 7.95 *(978-0-89942-104-9(0))* Catholic Bk. Publishing Corp.
Morrill, Bruce. Divine Worship & Human Healing. 2009. 280p. pap. 34.95 *(978-0-8146-6217-5(X)*, Liturgical Pr. Bks.) Liturgical Pr.
Mullins, Pat. The Mass: Understanding What's What. 2010. (ENG., Illus.). 92p. pap. 9.95 *(978-1-84730-201-4(7))* Veritas Pubns. IRL. Dist: Dufour Editions, Inc.
National Catholic Welfare Conference. On Renewing the Holy Week Liturgy: A General Decree & Instruction of the Sacred Congregation of Rites by Which the Holy Week Liturgy Is Renewed. 2011. 16p. pap. 35.95 ***(978-1-258-03633-1(9))*** Literary Licensing, LLC.
O'Loughlin, Thomas. Liturgical Resources for Matthew's Year: Sundays in Ordinary Time in Year A. 2007. (ENG.). 332p. pap. 26.95 *(978-1-85607-593-0(1))* Columba Pr. IRL. Dist: Dufour Editions, Inc.
Paprocki, Joe. The Catechist's Toolbox Leader Guide. 2008. 48p. pap. 2.95 *(978-0-8294-2724-0(4))* Loyola Pr.
Parys, Johan Van & Van Parys, Johan. Symbols That Surround Us: Faithful Reflections. 2011. ***(978-0-7648-2070-0(2))*** Liguori Pubns.
Pius XII, pseud. The Sacred Liturgy: Mediator Dei. 80p. pap. 2.50 *(978-0-8198-6924-1(4))* Pauline Bks. & Media.
Plassmann, Thomas. From Sunday to Sunday: An Interpretation of the Proper of the Mass That Seeks to Place the Venerable Liturgy in Modern Focus. 2011. 416p. 54.95 ***(978-1-258-08014-3(1))*** Literary Licensing, LLC.
Power, David, notes. Irenaeus of Lyons on Baptism & Eucharist. 2009. 88.00 *(978-1-60724-372-4(5))* Gorgias Pr., LLC.
Psallite: Sacred Song for Liturgy & Life (Years A, B, C), 3 vols. 2006. 59.95 *(978-0-8146-3060-0(X))* Liturgical Pr.
Raya, Joseph M. Liturgy: The Divine & Holy Liturgy of Our Father among the Saints, John Chrysostom. 96p. *(978-0-911726-64-0(0))* Madonna Hse. Pubns.
Repp, Debbie M. 30 Ten-Minute Prayer Celebrations for Young Children. 2009. 72p. pap. 16.95 *(978-1-58595-754-5(2))* Twenty-Third Pubns./Bayard.
Rowland, Thomas. God Acts - We React: An Approach to Liturgical Prayer. 2nd ed. 154p. pap. *(978-0-921440-51-2(0))* Madonna Hse. Pubns.
Roy, Neil & Rutherford, Janet, eds. Benedict XVI & the Sacred Liturgy. 2010. 210p. 45.00 *(978-1-84682-254-4(8))* Four Courts Pr. IRL. Dist: International Specialized Bk. Services.
Rudnik, Chrys, compiled by. Saint Joseph Missal Guide: Jan. 1 to Dec. 31 2007. 2006. (Saint Joseph Weekday Missal Ser.). 46p. pap. 2.00 *(978-0-89942-946-5(7))* Catholic Bk. Publishing Corp.
Rupp, Joyce. Your Sorrow Is My Sorrow: Hope & Strength in Times of Suffering. *(978-0-86716-528-9(6))* Franciscan Media.
Ryan, G. Thomas & Laughlin, Corinna. The Sacristy Manual, Second Edition. 2011. 272p. pap. 29.95 ***(978-1-61671-042-2(X))*** Liturgy Training Pubns.
Salvucci, Claudio R. The Roman Rite in the Algonquian & Iroquoian Missions: From the Colonial Period to the Second Vatican Council. 2008. *(978-1-889758-89-3(2)*, Evolution Publishing & Manufacturing) Arx Publishing.
Simon, Maurice & Simon, M. La celebration du mystere chretien dans le catechisme de Jean-Paul II. 2006. (Bibliotheca Ephemeridum Theologicarum Lovaniensium Ser.). (FRE & ENG.). 638p. (C). pap. 124.00 *(978-90-429-1734-7(2))* Peeters Pubs. & Booksellers BEL. Dist: Brown, David Bk. Co., The.
Simple Guide to the Daily Mass Readings 2007. 2006. 3.00 *(978-1-56854-583-7(5)*, READ07) Liturgy Training Pubns.
Socías, James. The Sacraments: Source of Our Life in Christ. 2009. *(978-1-890177-92-8(X))* Midwest Theological Forum.
St. Joseph Guide for the Liturgy of the Hours 2007Hi. l.t. ed. 2007. pap. 2.75 *(978-0-89942-720-1(0))* Catholic Bk. Publishing Corp.
St. Joseph Sunday Missal & Hymnal 2007. 2006. pap. 1.90 *(978-0-89942-626-6(3))* Catholic Bk. Publishing Corp.
Stahl, Harvey. Picturing Kingship: History & Painting in the Psalter of Saint Louis. 2008. (ENG., Illus.). 472p. 85.00 *(978-0-271-02863-7(7))* Pennsylvania State Univ. Pr.
Sternbeck, Michael. The Order of Mass According to the Extraordinary Form of the Roman Rite: The Missal of Blessed John XXIII. 2008. (LAT., Illus.). v, 89p. pap. *(978-1-58617-243-5(3))* Ignatius Pr.
Storey, William G. A Prayer Book for Eucharistic Adoration. 2010. (ENG.). 320p. 9.95 *(978-0-8294-2906-0(9))* Loyola Pr.
Stravinskas, Peter M. Rubrics of the Mass. pap. *(978-0-87973-168-7(0))* Our Sunday Visitor, Publishing Div.
The Word Among Us, ed. Abide in My Word 2010: Mass Readings at Your Fingertips. 2009. 584p. pap. 16.50 *(978-1-59325-157-4(2))* Word Among Us Pr.
The Word Among Us Press Staff. Abide in My Word 2009: Mass Readings at Your Fingertips. 2008. 568p. pap. 16.50 *(978-1-59325-137-6(8))* Word Among Us Pr.
The Word Among Us Press Staff, ed. Abide in My Word 2012: Mass Readings at Your Fingertips. 2011. 600p. pap. 16.50 *(978-1-59325-187-1(4))* Word Among Us Pr.
Thompson, Katie. Footprints in Faith: Lectionary Activities for Kids (ages 7-12) for Every Sunday of the Three-Year Cycle. 2010. (Illus.). 376p. (J). (gr. 2-7). pap. 39.95 *(978-0-89622-986-0(6))* Twenty-Third Pubns./Bayard.
—Liturgy of the Word with Children: A Complete Three-Year Program following the Lectionary. 2008. (Illus.). 393p. (J). pap. *(978-1-58595-700-2(3))* Twenty-Third Pubns./Bayard.
Tkacz, Catherine Brown. The Ruthenian Liturgy: An Historical-Theological Explication. 2012. (ENG.). 180p. 109.95 ***(978-0-7734-2555-2(1))*** Mellen, Edwin Pr., The.
Torevell, David. Liturgy & the Beauty of the Unknown: Another Place. 2007. 212p. 99.95 *(978-0-7546-3303-7(9))* Ashgate Publishing Co.
Turner, Paul. Celebrating Initiation: A Guide for Priests. Galipeau, Jerry, ed. 2008. 172p. per. 24.95 *(978-1-58459-341-6(5))* World Library Pubns.
Turner, Paul. Glory in the Cross: Holy Week in the Third Edition of the Roman Missal. 2011. E-Book ***(978-0-8146-6258-8(7))*** Liturgical Pr.
Turner, Paul & Prendergast, Michael. Guide for Liturgy Committees. 2009. (Illus.). ix, 95p. pap. *(978-1-56854-799-2(4))* Liturgy Training Pubns.
Twomey, Vincent. Benedict XVI & Beauty in Sacred Art & Architecture. Rutherford, Janet, ed. 2011. (Illus.). 224p. ***(978-1-84682-309-1(9))*** Four Courts Pr. IRL. Dist: International Specialized Bk. Services.
Usccb. Sunday Celebration in the Absence of a Priest. 2006. 49.95 *(978-1-57455-711-4(4))* United States Conference of Catholic Bishops.
Usher, Anton. Replenishing Ritual: Rediscovering the Place of Rituals in Western Christian Liturgy. 2010. pap. *(978-0-87462-784-8(2))* Marquette Univ. Pr.
Varghese, Baby. The Syriac Version of the Liturgy of St James. 2009. 88.00 *(978-1-60724-398-4(9))* Gorgias Pr., LLC.
Veritas, ed. The Funeral Mass: Readings, Prayers & Reflections. 2011. (ENG.). 64p. pap. 6.95 ***(978-1-84730-275-5(0))*** Veritas Pubns. IRL. Dist: Dufour Editions, Inc.
Vincie, Catherine. Celebrating the Divine Mystery: A Primer in Liturgical Theology. 2009. 216p. pap. 24.95 *(978-0-8146-5375-3(8))* Liturgical Pr.
Wagner, Wynn. The Complete Liturgy for Independent, Mystical & Liberal Catholics. 2010. 414p. 49.99 *(978-0-557-69959-9(2))* Lulu Enterprises Inc.
Warren, Frederick & O'Donoghue, Neil. The Liturgy & Ritual of the Celtic Church. 2009. 140.00 *(978-1-60724-100-3(5))* Gorgias Pr., LLC.
Waugh, Evelyn, et al. A Bitter Trial: Evelyn Waugh & John Carmel Cardinal Heenan on the Liturgical Changes. 2011. 123p. ***(978-1-58617-522-1(X))*** Ignatius Pr.
Whitehead, Kenneth D., ed. Sacrosanctum Concilium & the Reform of the Liturgy: Proceedings from the 29th Annual Convention of the Fellowship of Catholic Scholars. 2009. (Illus.). 210p. pap. 22.00 *(978-1-58966-171-4(0))* Univ. of Scranton Pr.
Williamson, D. Todd. Sourcebook for Sundays & Seasons 2007. 2006. pap. 15.00 *(978-1-56854-570-7(3)*, SSS07) Liturgy Training Pubns.
Woods, Thomas E., Jr. Sacred Then & Sacred Now: The Return of the Old Latin Mass. 100p. 15.95 *(978-970-49-0273-5(5))*; 2008. 124p. pap. 15.95 *(978-0-9793540-2-1(1))* Roman Catholic Bks.
World Among Us Press, creator. Abide in My Word: Mass Readings at Your Fingertips. 2006. 610p. per. 15.50 *(978-1-59325-078-2(9))* Word Among Us Pr.
Wright, Craig. Music & Ceremony at Notre Dame of Paris, 500-1550. 2008. (Cambridge Studies in Music Ser.). (ENG., Illus.). 420p. pap. 53.00 *(978-0-521-08834-3(8))* Cambridge Univ. Pr.
Zimmerman, Joyce. Living Liturgy. 2011. 328p. pap. 16.95 ***(978-0-8146-3337-3(4))*** Liturgical Pr.
—Living Liturgy for Extraordinary Ministers of Holy Communion. Harmon, Kathleen, ed. 2011. 128p. pap. 9.95 ***(978-0-8146-3334-2(X))*** Liturgical Pr.
Zimmerman, Joyce, ed. Living Liturgy for Extraordinary Ministers Year C 2010. 2009. 136p. pap. 6.95 *(978-0-8146-3005-1(7)*, Liturgical Pr. Bks.) Liturgical Pr.
—Living Liturgy Year C 2010. 2009. 336p. pap. 16.95 *(978-0-8146-2747-1(1)*, Liturgical Pr. Bks.) Liturgical Pr.
Zimmerman, Joyce Ann, et al, eds. Living Liturgy for Extraordinary Ministers of Holy Communion: Year A 2008. 2007. (Illus.). 135p. per. 6.95 *(978-0-8146-3084-6(7)*, Liturgical Pr. Bks.) Liturgical Pr.
Zimmerman, Joyce Ann, et al. Living Liturgy: Spirituality, Celebration, & Catechesis for Sundays & Solemnities (Year C) 2006. (Illus.). 317p. per. 15.95 *(978-0-8146-2744-0(7)*, Liturgical Pr. Bks.) Liturgical Pr.

CATHOLIC CHURCH—LITURGY—BIBLIOGRAPHY

Hughes, Andrew. Cataloguing Discrepancies: The Printed York Breviary of 1493. 2011. *(978-1-4426-4197-6(5))* Univ. of Toronto Pr.

CATHOLIC CHURCH—LITURGY—BREVIARY

see Breviaries

CATHOLIC CHURCH—LITURGY—HISTORY

Baldovin, John F. Reforming the Liturgy: A Response to the Critics. 2009. 192p. pap. 29.95 *(978-0-8146-6219-9(6))* Liturgical Pr.
Bisaro, Xavier. Une Nation de Fidèles: L'Église et la Liturgie Parisienne Au XVIIIe Siècle. 2006. (FRE., Illus.). 480p. (C). pap. 153.00 ***(978-2-503-52343-9(9))*** Brepols Pubs. BEL. Dist: ISD.
Collins, Paul, ed. Renewal & Resistance: Catholic Church Music from the 1850s to Vatican II. 2010. (ENG.). 283p. pap. 61.95 *(978-3-03911-381-1(X))* Lang, Peter AG GBR. Dist: Lang, Peter.
Giampietro, Nicola. The Development of the Liturgical Reform:: As Seen by Cardinal Ferdinando Antonelli from 1948 to 1970. 2010. 348p. pap. 33.75 *(978-1-934888-12-4(5))* Roman Catholic Bks.
Gribbin, Anselm J. Pope Benedict Xvi & the Liturgy. 2011. 252p. pap. ***(978-0-85244-755-0(8))*** Gracewing, Ltd.
Grillo, Andrea & Meyer-Blanck, Michael. Einführung in Die Liturgische Theologie: Zur Theorie des Gottesdienstes und der Christlichen Sakramente. 2006. (Arbeiten zur Pastoraltheologie Liturgik und Hymnologie Ser.). (GER.). 252p. (C). pap. 70.00 ***(978-3-525-62393-0(3))*** Vandenhoeck & Ruprecht GmbH & Co. KG DEU. Dist: ISD.
Klauser, Theodor. A Brief History of Liturgy. 2011. 36p. 35.95 ***(978-1-258-01415-5(7))*** Literary Licensing, LLC.
Lionel, S. Joseph. New Missal, Same Mass: Understanding the New Roman Missal & Its English Translation. 2011. 264p. ***(978-1-936320-19-6(3)***, Academic Pr.) Elsevier Science & Technology Bks.
Marini, Piero. Challenging Reform: Realizing the Vision of the Liturgical Renewal, 1963-1975. 2007. 205p. per. 15.95 *(978-0-8146-3035-8(9))* Liturgical Pr.
McGann, Mary E. Let It Shine! The Emergence of African American Catholic Worship. 4th ed. 2008. (ENG.). 200p. pap. 25.00 *(978-0-8232-2992-5(0))* Fordham Univ. Pr.
McGann, Mary E. & Harbor, Ronald D. Let It Shine! The Emergence of African American Catholic Worship. 4th ed. 2008. (ENG.). 200p. 70.00 *(978-0-8232-2991-8(2))* Fordham Univ. Pr.
Reynolds, Roger E. Studies on Medieval Liturgical & Legal Manuscripts from Spain & Southern Italy. 2009. (Variorum Collected Studies). (Illus.). 330p. 154.95 *(978-0-7546-5997-6(6))* Ashgate Publishing Co.
Smith, William Frank. Bread & Wine Blessed & Shared. 2011. 164p. pap. 16.95 ***(978-1-4575-0206-4(2))*** Dog Ear Publishing, LLC.
Tuzik, Robert L. Reynold Hillenbrand: The Reform of the Catholic Liturgy & the Call to Social Action. 2010. (Illus.). xi, 226p. pap. *(978-1-59525-030-8(1))* Hillenbrand Bks.
Whitehead, Kenneth D. Mass Misunderstandings: The Mixed Legacy of the Vatican II liturgical Reforms. 2009. (ENG., Illus.). 260p. pap. 20.00 *(978-1-58731-496-4(7))* St. Augustine's Pr., Inc.
Zeeden, Ernst Walter (Translator) & Zeeden, Ernst Walter. Faith & ACT: Medieval & Lutheran Practices Compared. 2012. ***(978-0-7586-2701-8(7))*** Concordia Publishing Hse.

CATHOLIC CHURCH—LITURGY—MISSAL

see Catholic Church—Missal

CATHOLIC CHURCH—LITURGY—STUDY AND TEACHING

Cecchetto-Capani, Marina. Dios con Nosotros para el Ano Liturgico B: Recursos para una Catequesis para Toda la Comunidad. 2006. 339.00 *(978-1-58595-581-7(7))* Twenty-Third Pubns./Bayard.
Duffy, Regis A. The Liturgy in the Catechism: Celebrating God's Wisdom & Love. 2010. 104p. pap. 14.00 *(978-1-60899-612-4(3)*, Wipf and Stock) Wipf & Stock Pubs.
Miller, Janet I., et al. Forming Ministers for Whole Community Faith Formation. 2006. 100p. *(978-0-89390-647-4(6))* Resource Pubns., Inc.
Miller, Michael J., tr. from FRE. Handing on the Faith in an Age of Disbelief. 2006. 169p. 19.95 *(978-1-58617-143-8(7))* Ignatius Pr.
Shahin, Gloria. Christian Morality & Justice. 2010. tchr. ed., spiral bd. 26.25 *(978-1-59982-052-1(8))* St. Mary's Pr.
Turner, Paul & Kerr Breedlove, Jennifer. Guide for Music Ministers, Second Edition. 2010. (Liturgical Ministry Ser.). 112p. 6.95 *(978-1-56854-916-3(4))* Liturgy Training Pubns.

CATHOLIC CHURCH—LITURGY AND RITUAL

see Catholic Church—Liturgy

CATHOLIC CHURCH—LITURGY OF THE HOURS

see also Books of Hours

Nugent, Madeline Pecora. The Divine Office for Dodos: A Step-by-Step Guide to Praying the Liturgy of the Hours. 2008. 272p. pap. 8.95 *(978-0-89942-482-8(1))* Catholic Bk. Publishing Corp.
Scotto, Dominic F. Lord, Teach Us How to Pray: A Companion to the Liturgy of the Hours. 2007. 32p. pap. *(978-0-8189-1256-6(1)*, St. Pauls) St Pauls/Alba Hse. Pubs.
Tickle, Phyllis. The Night Offices: Prayers for the Hours from Sunset to Sunrise. 2006. (ENG.). 480p. (C). 28.00 *(978-0-19-530671-2(6))* Oxford Univ. Pr., Inc.
Weber, Samuel F. The Office of Compline in Latin & English. 2010. (Illus.). xiii, 133p. ***(978-1-58617-455-2(X))*** Ignatius Pr.

CATHOLIC CHURCH—MALANKAR RITE

Vysanethu, Philip. Musicality makes the Malankara Liturgy Mystical. 2010. 111.68 *(978-1-61143-571-9(4))* Gorgias Pr., LLC.

CATHOLIC CHURCH—MARRIAGE

see Marriage—Religious Aspects—Catholic Church

CATHOLIC CHURCH—MIDDLE AGES

Scholz, Sebastian. Politik - Selbstverständnis - Selbstdarstellung: Die Päpste in Karolingischer und Ottonischer Zeit. 2006. (Historische Forschungen Ser.). (GER., Illus.). 514p. (C). 87.00 *(978-3-515-08933-3(0))* Steiner, Franz Verlag Wiesbaden GmbH DEU. Dist: Brown, David Bk. Co., The.

CATHOLIC CHURCH—MISSAL

Carstens, Christopher & Martis, Douglas. Mystical Body, Mystical Voice: Encountering Christ in the Words of the Mass. 2011. (ENG.). 272p. pap. 16.95 *(978-1-56854-932-3(6))* Liturgy Training Pubns.
Catholic Book Publishing Co, creator. Saint Joseph Missal Guide. 2008. 47p. pap. 2.00 *(978-0-89942-592-4(5))* 2007. 46p. per. 2.00 *(978-0-89942-478-1(3))* Catholic Bk. Publishing Corp.
Challoner, Richard. Daily Missal 1962: Ordinary of the Mass. 2009.Tr. of Latin with English Translation. (LAT & ENG., Illus.). 2248p. lthr. *(978-0-9545631-2-7(3))* Baronius Pr. Ltd.
Challoner, Richard, tr. Daily Missal 1962: Ordinary of the Mass. 2009.Tr. of Latin with English Translation. (ENG & LAT., Illus.). 2248p. lthr. *(978-1-905574-41-4(X))*; lthr. *(978-1-905574-05-6(3))* Baronius Pr. Ltd.
Foley, Edward. Commentary on the Order of Mass. 2011. 650p. 59.95 ***(978-0-8146-6247-2(1))*** Liturgical Pr.
Foley, Edward, et al. A Commentary on the Order of Mass of the Roman Missal: A New English Translation Developed under the Auspices of the Catholic Academy of Liturgy: General Editor, Edward Foley: Associate Editors, John F. Baldovin, Mary Collins, Joanne M. Pierce: Foreword by Roger Mahony. 2011. E-Book ***(978-0-8146-6256-4(0))*** Liturgical Pr.
Lawrence, Emeric A. The Week with Christ: Liturgy for the Apostolate. 2011. 340p. 51.95 ***(978-1-258-10187-9(4))*** Literary Licensing, LLC.
Libersat, Henry. Mass. (How to Talk to Your Children About . . . Ser.). 30p. pap. 1.50 *(978-0-87973-677-4(1))* Our Sunday Visitor, Publishing Div.
Lionel, Joseph. Continuity in Liturgical Renewal: A Critical Analysis of the Prefaces for the Sunday's of Lent in the Editions of Missale Romanum 1570 And 2002. 2012. (ENG.). lib. bdg. ***(978-1-936320-44-8(4))*** Academica Pr., LLC.
Moore, Gerard. Understanding the General Instruction of the Roman Missal. 2007. 121p. per. 14.95 *(978-0-8091-4452-5(2)*, 4452-5) Paulist Pr.
Turner, Paul. Glory in the Cross. 2011. 192p. pap. 24.95 ***(978-0-8146-6242-7(0))*** Liturgical Pr.
—Glory in the Cross: Holy Week in the Third Edition of the Roman Missal. 2011. E-Book ***(978-0-8146-6258-8(7))*** Liturgical Pr.

CATHOLIC CHURCH—MISSIONS

see also Chinese Rites

Anagnostou, Sabine. Missionspharmazie: Konzepte, Praxis, Organisation und wissenschaftliche Ausstrahlung. 2011. (Sudhoffs Archiv Ser.: 60). (GER., Illus.). 465p. (C). pap. 99.00 ***(978-3-515-09910-3(7))*** Steiner, Franz Verlag Wiesbaden GmbH DEU. Dist: Brown, David Bk. Co., The.
Bevans, Stephen B. & Gross, Jeffrey. Evangelization & Religious Freedom: Ad gentes, Dignitatis Humanae. 2008. (Rediscovering Vatican II Ser.). 272p. pap. 21.95 *(978-0-8091-4202-6(3))* Paulist Pr.
Bevans, Stephen B. & Schroeder, Roger P. Prophetic Dialogue: Reflections on Christian Mission Today. 2011. 208p. 35.00 *(978-1-57075-911-6(1))* Orbis Bks.
Bevans, Stephen B. & Tahaafe-Williams, Katalina, eds. Contextual Theology for the Twenty-First Century. 2011. (Missional Church, Public Theology, World Christianity: Ser.). 154p. pap. 18.00 ***(978-1-60899-960-6(2)***, Pickwick Pubns.) Wipf & Stock Pubs.
Bigandet, Paul Ambroise. The Catholic Burmese Mission: From the Year 1720 To 1887, Vol. 1. 2006. (Bibliotheca Orientalis Ser.). (ENG., Illus.). pap. 16.00 *(978-974-8299-75-4(9))* Orchid Pr. THA. Dist: National Bk. Network.
Boguslawski, Steven & Martin, Ralph. The New Evangelization: Overcoming the Obstacles. 2008. (Illus.). 176p. pap. 16.95 *(978-0-8091-4532-4(4))* Paulist Pr.
Braden, Charles S. Religious Aspects of the Conquest of Mexico. reprint ed. 54.50 *(978-0-404-00925-0(5))* AMS Pr., Inc.
Brugge, David M. Navajos in the Catholic Church Records of New Mexico, 1694-1875. 3rd ed. 2010. (Illus.). xxiv, 183p. *(978-1-934691-39-7(9))* School for Advanced Research Pr./SAR Pr.
Burrows, William R., ed. Redemption & Dialogue. 2009. 256p. pap. 26.00 *(978-1-60899-116-7(4)*, Wipf and Stock) Wipf & Stock Pubs.
Byerley, Timothy E. The Great Commission: Models of Evangelization in American Catholicism. 2008. 176p. pap. 18.95 *(978-0-8091-4558-4(8))* Paulist Pr.

Cabeen, Jerome. Memoirs of a Reluctant Servant: Two Years of Triumph & Sorrow in Liberia, Africa. 2011. 132p. 24.25 ***(978-1-4269-6575-3(3))***; pap. 14.25 ***(978-1-4251-5273-4(2))*** Trafford Publishing.

Chant, Elsie Ruth. The Padre of Isleta. 2009. 143p. pap. 25.00 *(978-0-86534-714-4(X))* Sunstone Pr.

Chick, H., ed. & tr. A Chronicle of the Carmelites in Persia: The Safavids & the Papal Mission of the 17th & 18th Centuries. 2012. (ENG.). 1424p. 349.00 ***(978-1-84885-768-1(3))*** I. B. Tauris & Co., Ltd. GBR. Dist: Macmillan.

Clarke, Richard F. Cardinal Lavigerie & the African Slave Trade. 2008. 414p. 49.95 *(978-1-4365-3873-2(4))* 2007. (ENG.). 416p. per. 34.95 *(978-0-548-71912-1(8))* Kessinger Publishing, LLC.

Clarke, Richard F., ed. Cardinal Lavigerie & the African Slave Trade. 2010. (Cambridge Library Collection - Religion Ser.). (ENG.). 396p. pap. 31.99 *(978-1-108-00833-4(X))* Cambridge Univ. Pr.

Clatterbuck, Mark Stephen. Demons, Saints & Patriots: Catholic Visions of Native America Through the Indian Sentinel, 1902-1962. 2009. 288p. pap. *(978-0-87462-746-6(X))* Marquette Univ. Pr.

Considine, John Joseph. When the Sorghum Was High. 2011. 186p. 42.95 ***(978-1-258-09725-5(X))*** Literary Licensing, LLC.

Courtens, Ien. Restoring the Balance: Performing Healing in West Papua. 2010. (Illus.). 264p. pap. 44.00 *(978-90-6718-278-2(8))* KITLV Pr. NLD. Dist: Univ. of Hawaii Pr.

Daughton, J. P. An Empire Divided: Religion, Republicanism, & the Making of French Colonialism, 1880-1914. (ENG., Illus.). 2008. 352p. pap. 24.95 *(978-0-19-537401-8(0))* 2006. 344p. 74.00 *(978-0-19-530530-2(2))* Oxford Univ. Pr., Inc.

De Coccola, Raymond. Ayorama: That's the Way It Is. 2007. (Illus.). 469p. per. *(978-2-89507-899-9(8))* Novalis Publishing.

Diaz, Vicente M. Repositioning the Missionary: Rewriting the Histories of Colonialism, Native Catholicism, & Indigeneity in Guam. 2010. 264p. 60.00 *(978-0-8248-3434-0(8))*; pap. 24.00 *(978-0-8248-3435-7(6))* Univ. of Hawaii Pr.

Dougherty, Dennis. Annals of the Holy Childhood V36, No 1, January 1940. 2011. 34p. 35.95 ***(978-1-258-01177-2(8))*** Literary Licensing, LLC.

Dowd, Christopher. Rome in Australia: The Papacy & Conflict in the Australian Catholic Missions, 1834-1884, 2 vols. 2008. (Studies in the History of Christian Traditions: Vol. 140). (Illus.). xxv, 653p. (C). *(978-90-04-16529-8(0))* BRILL.

Dulles, Avery. Evangelization for the Third Millennium. 2009. viii, 129p. pap. 15.95 *(978-0-8091-4622-2(3))* Paulist Pr.

Durston, Alan. Pastoral Quechua: The History of Christian Translation in Colonial Peru, 1550-1650. 2007. (History Lang & Cult Spanish Portuguese Ser.). (ENG.). 416p. per. 42.00 *(978-0-268-02591-5(6))* Univ. of Notre Dame Pr.

Early, John D. The Maya & Catholicism: An Encounter of Worldviews, 311 vols. 2006. (ENG., Illus.). 320p. 59.95 *(978-0-8130-3025-8(0))* Univ. Pr. of Florida.

Ebelebe, Charles A. Africa & the New Face of Mission: A Critical Assessment of the Legacy of the Irish Spiritans among the Igbo of Southeastern Nigeria. 2009. (Illus.). xviii, 242p. E-Book *(978-0-7618-4597-3(6))* Univ. Pr. of America, Inc.

Endres, David J. American Crusade: Catholic Youth in the World Mission Movement from World War I Through Vatican II. 2010. (American Society of Missiology Monograph Ser.). 212p. pap. 23.00 *(978-1-60899-071-9(0))*, Pickwick Pubns.) Wipf & Stock Pubs.

Eze, Damian Onwuegbuchulam. The Eucharist as Oikonso: A Study in Eucharistic Ecclesiology from an Igbo Perspective. 2008. (Europäische Hochschulschriften. Reihe 23: Theologie Ser.). 312p. pap. 74.95 *(978-3-631-57883-4(0))* Lang, Peter GmbH, Europaischer Verlag der Wissenschaften DEU. Dist: Lang, Peter.

Fisher, James T. On the Irish Waterfront: The Crusader, the Movie, & the Soul of the Port of New York. (Cushwa Center Studies of Catholicism in Twentieth-Century America). (Illus.). 392p. 2010. pap. 17.95 *(978-0-8014-7684-6(4))* 2009. 29.95 *(978-0-8014-4804-1(2))* Cornell Univ. Pr.

John Paul II, pseud. Mission of the Redeemer.Tr. of Redemptoris Missio. 128p. pap. 5.95 *(978-0-8198-4746-1(1)*, 332-195) Pauline Bks. & Media.

Lara, Jaime. Christian Texts for Aztecs: Art & Liturgy in Colonial Mexico. 2008. (ENG., Illus.). 336p. 75.00 *(978-0-268-03379-8(X))* Univ. of Notre Dame Pr.

Le Breton, Binka. The Greatest Gift: The Courageous Life & Martyrdom of Sister Dorothy Stang. l.t. ed. 2008. (Thorndike Biography Ser.). (Illus.). 333p. 30.95 *(978-1-4104-0652-1(0))* Thorndike Pr.

Lovi, Dauson. Holy Shit: A Brief Look at Christianity's Problem. 2009. 108p. 22.50 *(978-1-60693-897-3(6))*, Eloquent Bks.) AEG Literary Publishing Services, Inc.

MacMillan Publisher. Maryknoll Mission Letters, Chin: Extracts from the Letters & Diaries of the Pioneer Missioners. 2011. 926p. 78.95 ***(978-1-258-02789-6(5))*** Literary Licensing, LLC.

Manna, Paolo. Apostolic Virtues. 2009. pap. 14.95 *(978-1-933871-37-0(7))* IVE Pr.

Martin, Kathleen J. Indigenous Symbols & Practices in the Catholic Church: Visual Culture Missionization & Appropriation. 2010. (Vitality of Indigenous Religions Ser.). (Illus.). 300p. 99.95 *(978-0-7546-6631-8(X))* Ashgate Publishing Co.

McLaughlin, David J. & Mendoza, Ruben. The California Missions Source Book: Key Information, Dramatic Images, & Fascinating Anecdotes Covering All 21 Missions. 2010. (ENG., Illus.). 68p. pap. 24.95 *(978-0-9825047-0-3(5))* Pentacle Pr.

Michaud, Jean. 'Incidental' Ethnographers: French Catholic Missions on the Tonkin-Yunnan Frontier, 1880-1930. 2007. (Studies in Christian Mission Ser.). 260p. *(978-90-04-13996-1(6))*, BRILL.

Mwenhari Musings: '1964 Southern Rhodesia to Zimbabwe 1999' 2007. (Illus.). 216p. per. *(978-1-84401-804-9(0))* Athena Pr.

Newman, John Henry, et al. Newman's Second Spring: And the Evangelization of Modern Culture. 2009. pap. *(978-1-933184-52-4(3))* Sophia Institute Pr.

Okwu, Augustine S. O. Igbo Culture & the Christian Missions, 1857-1957: Conversion in Theory & Practice. 2009. (ENG., Illus.). 348p. 73.50 *(978-0-7618-4884-4(3))*; pap. 41.99 *(978-0-7618-4885-1(1))* Univ. Pr. of America, Inc.

Pasquier, Michael. Fathers on the Frontier: French Missionaries & the Roman Catholic Priesthood in the United States, 1789-1870, 1 vol. 2010. (Religion in America Ser.). (ENG., Illus.). 312p. 74.00 *(978-0-19-537233-5(6))* Oxford Univ. Pr., Inc.

Pritchett, John Perry. Black Robe & Buckskin: The Story of Catholic Pioneering in Northern North America. 2011. 130p. 40.95 ***(973-1-258-07045-8(6))*** Literary Licensing, LLC.

Ramsay, Jacob. Mandarins & Martyrs: The Church & the Nguyen Dynasty in Early Nineteenth-Century Vietnam. 2008. (ENG., Illus.). 224p. 50.00 *(978-0-8047-5651-8(1))* Stanford Univ. Pr.

Robins, Nicholas A. Priest-Indian Conflict in Upper Peru: A Generation of Rebellion, 1750-1780. 2007. (Religion & Politics Ser.). 272p. (C). 54.95 *(978-0-8156-3118-7(9))* Syracuse Univ. Pr.

—Priest-Indian Conflict in Upper Peru: The Generation of Rebellion, 1750-1780. 2007. (Religion & Politics Ser.). 315p. per. 29.95 *(978-0-8156-3142-2(1))* Syracuse Univ. Pr.

Salvucci, Claudio R. The Roman Rite in the Algonquian & Iroquoian Missions: From the Colonial Period to the Second Vatican Council. 2008. *(978-1-889758-89-3(2)*, Evolution Publishing & Manufacturing) Arx Publishing.

Savage, Alma H. The Forty-Ninth Star: Alaska. 2011. 188p. 42.95 ***(978-1-258-09607-6(2))*** Literary Licensing, LLC.

Schroeder, Roger P. What Is the Mission of the Church? A Guide for Catholics. 2008. (Illus.). 176p. pap. 16.00 *(978-1-57075-810-2(7))* Orbis Bks.

Second Vatican Council Staff. Decree on the Mission Activity of the Church. 54p. pap. 0.30 *(978-0-8198-1840-9(2)*, 332-059) Pauline Bks. & Media.

Shea, John. History of the Catholic Missions among the Indian tribes of the United States. 2010. (Native American Ser.). 542p. pap. 32.95 *(978-1-4290-2260-6(4))* Applewood Bks.

Shea, John D. History of the Catholic Missions among the Indian Tribes of the United States, 1529-1854. reprint ed. 59.50 *(978-0-404-07176-9(7))* AMS Pr., Inc.

Tomko, Cardinal Jozef. On Missionary Roads. Strecok, Lubomir J. et al, trs. from SLO. 2007. (Illus.). 390p. pap. 19.95 *(978-1-58617-165-0(8))* Ignatius Pr.

Tosti, Mario. La Chiesa Sul Fiume: La Missione Dei Cappuccini Dell'Umbria in Amazzonia, 1909-2009. 2010. (ITA., Illus.). 363p. *(978-88-88001-68-5(9))* Ist. Storico dei Cappuccini.

Venn, Henry. The Missionary Life & Labours of Francis Xavier Taken from his own Correspondence: With a Sketch of the General Results of Roman Catholic Missions among the Heathen. 2010. (Cambridge Library Collection - Religion Ser.). (Illus.). 344p. pap. 28.99 *(978-1-108-01182-2(9))* Cambridge Univ. Pr.

Wiltgen, Ralph M. The Founding of the Roman Catholic Church in Oceania, 1825 To 1850. 2010. (Princeton Theological Monographs). (Illus.). 638p. pap. 64.00 *(978-1-60899-536-3(4)*, Pickwick Pubns.) Wipf & Stock Pubs.

Yai-Chow, Teresa Wong, et al. The Cosmos in Becoming. 2009. 250p. pap. 18.00 *(978-1-920691-94-3(4))* ATF Pr. AUS. Dist: International Publishers Marketing.

CATHOLIC CHURCH—MISSIONS—CENTRAL AMERICA

Brett, Edward T. The New Orleans Sisters of the Holy Family: African American Missionaries to the Garifuna of Belize. 2012. (ENG., Illus.). 224p. pap. 30.00 ***(978-0-268-02230-3(5))*** Univ. of Notre Dame Pr.

Early, John D. Maya & Catholic Cultures in Crisis. 2012. (ENG., Illus.). 416p. 74.95 ***(978-0-8130-4013-4(2))*** Univ. Pr. of Florida.

Sullivan-Gonzalez D. Piety, Power, & Politics: Religion & Nation Formation in Guatemala 1821-1871. 2008. (Pitt Latin American Studies). (ENG.). 200p. (C). pap. 24.95 *(978-0-8229-6022-5(2))* Univ. of Pittsburgh Pr.

CATHOLIC CHURCH—MISSIONS—NORTH AMERICA

Daughton, J. P. An Empire Divided: Religion, Republicanism, & the Making of French Colonialism, 1880-1914. 2008. (ENG., Illus.). 352p. pap. 24.95 *(978-0-19-537401-8(0))* Oxford Univ. Pr., Inc.

Milliken, Randall. Native Americans of Mission San Jose. 2008. (Ballena Press Anthropological Papers: No. 49). (ENG.). pap. *(978-0-87919-148-1(1))* Malki-Ballena Pr.

Reyes, Bárbara O. Private Women, Public Lives: Gender & the Missions of the Californias. 2010. (ENG., Illus.). 245p. pap. 25.00 *(978-0-292-72347-4(4))* Univ. of Texas Pr.

CATHOLIC CHURCH—MODERNISM

see Modernism (Christian Theology)—Catholic Church

CATHOLIC CHURCH—MUSIC

see Church Music—Catholic Church

CATHOLIC CHURCH—MYSTICISM

see Mysticism—Catholic Church

CATHOLIC CHURCH—ORIENTAL RITES

Nichols, OP, Aidan. Rome & the Eastern Churches. 2010. 350p. pap. 18.95 *(978-1-58617-282-4(4))* Ignatius Pr.

CATHOLIC CHURCH—PASTORAL LETTERS AND CHARGES

Catholic Treasures. Letter to a Fallen Away Catholic. 2007. 109p. pap. 5.00 *(978-1-885692-12-2(9))* Catholic Treasures.

Cushing, Richard. Moral Values & the American Society: Pastoral Letter. 2011. 42p. 35.95 ***(978-1-258-03068-1(3))*** Literary Licensing, LLC.

CATHOLIC CHURCH—PASTORAL THEOLOGY

see Pastoral Theology—Catholic Church

CATHOLIC CHURCH—PERIODICALS

1969-1970, Vol. 2. 13.50 Arden Assocs. Corp.

1971-1972, Vol. 4. 13.50 Arden Assocs. Corp.

1975-1976, 2 Vols., 2. pap. 30.00 *(978-92-5-100001-4(8)*, F296) Bernan Assocs.

1977-1978. pap. 19.00 United Nations Pubns.

Catholic Biblical Quarterly: Washington D.C. 1939-1968, Vols. 1-30. lib. bdg. 1350.00 *(978-0-404-19567-0(9))* AMS Pr., Inc.

Clatterbuck, Mark Stephen. Demons, Saints & Patriots: Catholic Visions of Native America Through the Indian Sentinel, 1902-1962. 2009. 288p. pap. *(978-0-87462-746-6(X))* Marquette Univ. Pr.

Living Liturgy Sunday Missal 2012. 2011. 408p. pap. 9.95 ***(978-0-8146-3336-6(6))*** Liturgical Pr.

New Advent. 2007. cd-rom 37.33 *(978-0-9743644-1-4(X))* New Advent.

Pearson, T. Mms 6 Catholic Supplement Ontario. 2007. (ENG.). (C). pap. *(978-0-321-31282-2(1))* Pearson Education Canada.

Unsworth, Tim. Tim Unsworth: Articles from the National Catholic Reporter. 2008. 164p. pap. 14.95 *(978-0-87946-356-3(X))* ACTA Pubns.

CATHOLIC CHURCH—PERIODICALS—HISTORY

Baumgartner, Apollinaris W. Catholic Journalism. (BCL Ser. I). reprint ed. 21.50 *(978-0-404-00693-8(0))* AMS Pr., Inc.

Popowski, Mark D. The Rise & Fall of Triumph: The History of a Radical Roman Catholic Magazine, 1966-1976. 2011. (ENG.). 282p. (gr. 17). 75.00 ***(978-0-7391-6981-0(5))*** Lexington Bks.

CATHOLIC CHURCH—PICTORIAL WORKS

Franciscan Fathers. A Picture Story: St. Peter's New Church & Friary, Madison at Clark Street, Chicago, Illinois. 2011. 20p. pap. 35.95 ***(978-1-258-00936-6(6))*** Literary Licensing, LLC.

McKenna, Marian. Pictorial History of Catholicism. 2011. 318p. 50.95 ***(978-1-258-08270-3(5))*** Literary Licensing, LLC.

CATHOLIC CHURCH—PRAYERS AND DEVOTIONS

see also Books of Hours; Novenas

Amato, Lucas J. Scriptural Meditations: For the Divine Mercy Chaplet, Franciscan Crown, Seven Sorrows & Rosary. 2008. 79p. pap. 6.95 *(978-0-87946-388-5(0))* ACTA Pubns.

Anders, Isabel. Blessings & Prayers for Married Couples: A Faith Full Love. 2011. *(978-0-7648-1933-9(X))* Liguori Pubns.

Anderson, Christopher, et al. A Prayer Book for Catholic Families. 2007. (Illus.). 173p. per. 9.95 *(978-0-8294-2717-2(1))* Loyola Pr.

Angelus Press Staff, contrib. by. Prayer Crusade for Priests. 2009. (Illus.). 87p. pap. *(978-1-892331-75-5(6))* Angelus Pr.

Angelus Press Staff, contrib. by. The Way of the Cross: A Treasury of Stations. 2011. (Illus.). xv, 360p. ***(978-1-892331-87-8(X))*** Angelus Pr.

Aquilina, Mike & Stubna, Kris D. Take Five: Meditations with Pope Benedict XVI. 2009. 176p. pap. 9.95 *(978-1-59276-554-6(8))* Our Sunday Visitor, Publishing Div.

Benedict. Lent & Easter Wisdom from St. Benedict. 2010. *(978-0-7648-1968-1(2))* Liguori Pubns.

Benedict XVI, pseud & Benedict. The Eucharist. 2009. x, 109p. pap. *(978-1-60137-084-6(9))* United States Conference of Catholic Bishops.

—Family. 2009. xi, 93p. pap. *(978-1-60137-075-4(X))* United States Conference of Catholic Bishops.

Benedict XVI, pseud & Benedict. Lent with Pope Benedict XVI: Meditations for Every Day. 2012. 11.95 ***(978-1-59325-198-7(X))*** Word Among Us Pr.

Benedict XVI, pseud, et al. Breakfast with Benedict: Daily Readings. 2009. (Illus.). 205p. *(978-1-59276-576-8(9))* Our Sunday Visitor, Publishing Div.

Bergant, Dianne. The Word for Every Season: Reflections on the Lectionary Readings (Cycle A) 2010. 208p. pap. 19.95 *(978-0-8091-4673-4(8))* Paulist Pr.

—The Word for Every Season: Reflections on the Lectionary Readings (Cycle C) 2009. 208p. pap. 16.95 *(978-0-8091-4607-9(X))* Paulist Pr.

Berstein C.S.J., Eleanor, ed. Praying Our Lives: A Woman's Treasury of Catholic Prayer. 2012. 288p. pap. 17.95 ***(978-1-59471-270-8(0))*** Ave Maria Pr.

Bertanzetti, Eileen Dunn. Praying with Padre Pio. 2007. (Companions for the Journey Ser.). 166p. per. 12.95 *(978-1-59325-091-1(6))* Word Among Us Pr.

Binz, Steve. Conversing with God in Lent: Praying the Sunday Mass Readings with Lectio Divina. 2010. 112p. pap. 9.95 *(978-1-59325-165-9(3))* Word Among Us Pr.

Bondi, Michele Elena, compiled by. God Moments II. 2011. ***(978-1-935356-19-6(4))*** Wilderness Adventure Bks.

Bonniwell, W. R. & McDermott, T. S. The Martyrology of the Sacred Order of Friars Preachers. 2011. 302p. 48.95 ***(978-1-258-00803-1(3))*** Literary Licensing, LLC.

Boyer, Mark G. Take up Your Cross & Follow: Daily Lenten Reflections. 2009. *(978-0-8189-1294-8(4)*, St. Pauls) St Pauls/Alba Hse. Pubns.

Boyle, Elizabeth Michael. Science as Sacred Metaphor: An Evolving Revelation. 2006. 138p. per. 14.95 *(978-0-8146-2404-3(9))* Liturgical Pr.

Bratton, Heidi. Homegrown Faith: Nurturing Your Catholic Family. 2011. ***(978-1-61636-134-1(4)***, Servant Bks.) Franciscan Media.

Brown, Joseph A. Sweet, Sweet Spirit: Prayer Services from the Black Catholic Church. 2006. 100p. per. 9.95 *(978-0-86716-626-2(6))* Franciscan Media.

Bruchhold, Ulrich. Deutschsprachige Beichten im 13. und 14. Jahrhundert: Editionen und Typologien zur Überlieferungs-, Text- und Gebrauchsgeschichte vor dem Hintergrund der älteren Tradition. 2010. (Manchener Texte und Untersuchungen zur deutschen Literatur des Mittelalters Ser.). (GER.). 704p. 168.00 *(978-3-11-023462-6(9))* De Gruyter, Walter Inc.

Buckley, Michael. The Catholic Prayer Book. Castle, Tony, ed. l.t. ed. 2010. (ENG.). 354p. pap. *(978-0-86716-958-4(3)*, Servant Bks.) Franciscan Media.

Camille, Alice. 2010: A Book of Grace-Filled Days. 2009. (ENG.). 408p. pap. 11.95 *(978-0-8294-2525-3(X))* Loyola Pr.

Canadian Conference of Catholic Bishops. Blessings & Prayers for Home & Family. 2008. 284p. pap. 19.95 *(978-0-87946-380-9(5))* ACTA Pubns.

Carroll, Norm. Miracles, Messages, & Metaphors: Unlocking the Wisdom of the Bible. 2010. 400p. pap. 16.95 *(978-0-9823140-1-2(9))* Synergy Bks.

Catholic Book Publishing Co, creator. Saint Joseph Guide for Christian Prayer. l.t. ed. 2006. 47p. pap. 2.75 *(978-0-89942-459-0(7))* Catholic Bk. Publishing Corp.

Catholic Household Blessings & Prayers: Revised Edition. 2008. 528p. 34.95 *(978-0-8146-1857-8(X)*, Liturgical Pr. Bks.) Liturgical Pr.

Cavnar, Cynthia, ed. Spiritual Treasures from St. Therese of Lisieux: A Book of Reflections & Prayers. 2007. 191p. per. 10.95 *(978-1-59325-110-9(6))* Word Among Us Pr.

Cazabonne, Emma. A Light to Enlighten the Darkness: Daily Readings for Meditation During the Winter Season. 2008. (Cistercian Studies). pap. *(978-0-87907-227-8(X))* Cistercian Pubns., Inc.

Celano, Peter, compiled by. Lent & Easter with the Holy Fathers. 2010. (ENG.). 164p. (gr. 13). 17.99 *(978-1-55725-692-8(6))* Paraclete Pr., Inc.

Celano, Peter, ed. Christmas with the Holy Fathers. 2008. (ENG.). 121p. (gr. 13). 19.95 *(978-1-55725-603-4(9))* Paraclete Pr., Inc.

Christ, Jennifer. Journeying with Matthew: Five Minute Preparation for each Sunday Liturgy. 2007. (Illus.). 80p. pap. 7.95 *(978-0-8091-4477-8(8)*, 4477-8) Paulist Pr.

The Church. 2009. 104p. lib. bdg. 6.99 *(978-0-89814-092-7(7))* Grace Pubns., Inc.

Church Literature Associa Staff. The English Office Book. 2006. 368p. 29.99 *(978-1-85311-698-8(X))* Norwich Bks. & Music GBR. Dist: Westminster John Knox Pr.

Claudel, Paul. A Poet Before the Cross. 2nd ed. 2007. 340p. 55.00 *(978-1-934182-09-3(5))* Alethes Pr.

Constance, Anita M., ed. Living the Days of Lent 2009: Insights from the Gospels. 2008. (Illus.). 64p. pap. 4.95 *(978-0-8091-4553-9(7))* Paulist Pr.

Craghan, John F. Precious Gifts: Biblical Reflections on the Eucharist. 2011. ***(978-0-7648-2026-7(5))*** Liguori Pubns.

Dateno, Maria Grace & Trouvé, Marianne Lorraine. Easter Grace: Daily Gospel Reflections. 2011. pap. *(978-0-8198-2362-5(7))* Pauline Bks. & Media.

—Ordinary Grace Weeks 1-17: Daily Gospel Reflections. 2011. pap. *(978-0-8198-5442-1(5))* Pauline Bks. & Media.

Daughters of St. Paul Staff. Lenten Grace: Daily Gospel Reflections. 2008. v, 147p. pap. *(978-0-8198-4525-2(6))* Pauline Bks. & Media.

De Sales, Francis. Set Your Heart Free. Kirvan, John, ed. 2008. 120p. pap. 9.95 *(978-1-59471-153-4(4))* Ave Maria Pr.

De Schryver, Antione & Kren, Thomas. The Prayer Book of Charles the Bold: A Study of a Flemish Masterpiece from the Burgundian Court. 2008. (ENG., Illus.). 312p. 60.00 *(978-0-89236-943-0(4))* Oxford Univ. Pr., Inc.

Deeley, Mary & Deeley, Mary Katharine. Mothers, Lovers, Priests, Prophets, & Kings. 2010. xiii, 120p. pap. *(978-0-7648-1938-4(0))* Liguori Pubns.

DeLeon, Roy. Praying with the Body: Bringing the Psalms to Life. 2009. (Active Prayer Ser.). (ENG.). 150p. (gr. 13). pap. 18.99 *(978-1-55725-589-1(X))* Paraclete Pr., Inc.

Diele, Joseph, compiled by. A Day-To-Day Journey with Blessed Charles de Foucauld. 2006. *(978-0-8189-1236-8(7))* St Pauls/Alba Hse. Pubns.

Doherty, Catherine. Donkey Bells: Advent & Christmas. 156p. pap. *(978-0-921440-38-3(3))* Madonna Hse. Pubns.

—Grace in Every Season: Through the Year with Catherine Doherty. 2nd rev. ed. 320p. pap. *(978-0-921440-31-4(6))* Madonna Hse. Pubns.

—Moments of Grace. 370p. spiral bd. *(978-0-921440-56-7(1))* Madonna Hse. Pubns.

Doherty, Catherine de Hueck. Soul of My Soul: Coming to the Heart of Prayer. 2nd ed. 134p. *(978-0-921440-97-0(9))* Madonna Hse. Pubns.

Dubruiel, Michael. The Church's Most Powerful Novenas. 2006. (Illus.). 367p. per. 14.95 *(978-1-59276-097-8(X)*, Our Sunday Visitor, Publishing Div.

—A Pocket Guide to the Mass. 2007. (Pocket Guide To Ser.). 79p. per. 6.95 *(978-1-59276-293-4(X))* Our Sunday Visitor, Publishing Div.

Dumm, Demetrius. So We Do Not Lose Heart: Biblical Wisdom for All Our Days. 2006. 272p. pap. *(978-0-9773909-1-5(8))* St. Vincent Archabbey Pubns.

Edmisten, Karen. The Rosary: Keeping Company with Jesus & Mary. 2009. 96p. pap. 8.99 *(978-0-86716-875-4(7)*, Servant Bks.) Franciscan Media.

—Through the Year with Mary: 365 Meditations. 2010. ix, 133p. pap. *(978-0-86716-937-9(0)*, Servant Bks.) Franciscan Media.

Fahey, Denis. The Social Rights of Our Divine Lord, Jesus Christ, The King. unabr. ed. 204p. reprint ed. pap. 12.00 *(978-0-945001-49-2(5))* GSG & Assocs.

Finley, Mitch. Season of Promises: Praying Through Advent with Julian of Norwich, Thomas ç Kempis, Caryll Houselander, Thomas Merton, Brother Lawrence, Max Picard. 2010. 64p. pap. 9.00 *(978-1-60899-263-8(2)*, Wipf and Stock) Wipf & Stock Pubs

Foley, Marc. The Path of Merciful Love: 99 Sayings by Therese of Lisieux. 2006. 105p. 14.95 *(978-1-56548-245-6(X))* New City Pr.

Forest, Jim. Praying with Icons. 2008. (ENG., Illus.). 218p. (Orig.). pap. 22.00 *(978-1-57075-758-7(5))* Orbis Bks.

Fournier, Catherine & Fournier, Peter. Marian Devotion in the Domestic Church. 2007. (Illus.). 96p. spiral bd. 15.95 *(978-1-58617-074-5(0))* Ignatius Pr.

Frabutt, James M., et al. No Greater Work: Meditations on Church Documents for Educators. 2010. pap. *(978-1-935788-01-0(9))* Alliance for Catholic Education Pr.

Francis. Advent & Christmas Wisdom from Saint Francis of Assisi: Daily Scripture & Prayers Together with Saint Francis of Assisi's Own Words. 2008. 10.99 *(978-0-7648-1756-4(6))* Liguori Pubns.

Franco, Ronald A. Isaac Hecker for Every Day: Daily Thought from the Founder of the Paulists. 2009. 176p. pap. 8.95 *(978-0-8091-4625-3(8))* Paulist Pr.

Franklin, Barbara Jean. Through Another Lens: Reflections on the Gospels, Year A. 2010. vi, 137p. pap. *(978-0-7648-1908-7(9))* Liguori Pubns.

—Through Another Lens: Reflections on the Gospels, Year B. 2011. ***(978-0-7648-1989-6(5))*** Liguori Pubns.

Franklin, Barbara Jean. Through Another Lens: Reflections on the Gospels, Year C. 2009. 144p. pap. 14.95 *(978-0-7648-1773-1(6)*, Liguori) Liguori Pubns.

Friedman, Greg. Advent with the Saints: Daily Reflections. 2011. (Illus.). x, 70p. ***(978-1-61636-132-7(8))*** Franciscan Media.

—Lent with the Saints: Daily Reflections. 2011. (ENG.). 96p. pap. 3.99 ***(978-1-61636-131-0(X))*** Franciscan Media.

FSP Staff. Saint Dymphna Novena. 40p. pap. 1.50 *(978-0-8198-7073-5(0)*, 332-369) Pauline Bks. & Media.

Gallagher, Timothy M. The Examen Prayer: Ignatian Wisdom for Our Lives Today. annot. ed. 2006. (ENG.). 192p. pap. 16.95 *(978-0-8245-2367-1(9)*, Crossroad) Crossroad Publishing Co., The.

Gawrych, Andrew, ed. The Gift of the Cross: Lenten Reflections in the Holy Cross Tradition. 2009. 3.50 *(978-1-59471-202-9(6))* Ave Maria Pr.

Giallanza, Joel. Praying from Heart of Holy Cross Spirituality: A 30-Day Retreat with Basil Moreau. 2010. (Illus.). 128p. pap. 10.95 *(978-1-59471-232-6(8))* Ave Maria Pr.

Gozier, Andre. 15 Days of Prayer with Thomas Merton. 2010. (ENG.). 136p. pap. 12.95 *(978-1-56548-330-9(8))* New City Pr.

Grey, Mary. Praying with Saint Francis. xvii, 78p. pap. 9.95 *(978-0-281-04313-2(2))* International Publishers Marketing.

Gribble, Richard. Praying the Stations with Faith & Courage. 2011. ***(978-1-58595-865-8(4))*** Twenty-Third Pubns./Bayard.

Groeschel, Benedict. Experiencing the Mystery of Christ: Praying with the Creed. 2008. per. 14.95 *(978-1-59276-404-4(5))* Our Sunday Visitor, Publishing Div.

Groeschel, Benedict J. Praying with the Creed: Meditations from the Oratory. 2007. (Illus.). 192p. pap. 14.95 *(978-1-59276-321-4(9))* Our Sunday Visitor, Publishing Div.

Groeschel, Benedict J., et al. Life in Christ: Meditations from the Oratory of Divine Love. 2009. (Illus.). 239p. 14.95 *(978-1-59276-546-1(7))* Our Sunday Visitor, Publishing Div.

Haapala, Christine. Follow Me: A Stations of the Cross Book. 2006. (Illus.). 48p. pap. 10.00 *(978-0-9703996-9-4(3))* Suffering Servant Scriptorium.

Halfmann, Elizabeth. Ups & Downs: Prayers by & 4 Teens: Prayers. 2010. *(978-0-7648-1882-0(1))* Liguori Pubns.

Harcourt Religion Publishers Staff, creator. The Catholic Source Book. 2006. (Illus.). 508p. per. 26.50 *(978-0-15-901883-5(8))* Harcourt Religion Pubns.

Harrington, Donal. Eucharist: Enhancing the Prayer: Including Prayer of the Faithful for the Three Ye. 2007. (ENG.). 368p. pap. 36.95 *(978-1-85607-571-8(0))* Columba Pr. IRL. Dist: Dufour Editions, Inc.

Heinch, Beverly Coney, compiled by. Mornings with Fulton Sheen: 120 Holy Hour Readings. 2007. 120p. per. 10.99 *(978-0-86716-842-6(0)*, Servant Bks.) Franciscan Media.

Hendey, Lisa M. A Book of Saints for Catholic Moms: 52 Companions for Your Heart, Mind, Body, & Soul. 2011. (Illus.). 352p. pap. 16.95 ***(978-1-59471-273-9(5))*** Ave Maria Pr.

Herbeck, Debra. Safely Through the Storm: 120 Reflections on Hope. 2010. pap. *(978-0-86716-941-6(9)*, Servant Bks.) Franciscan Media.

Hoagland, Victor, ed. The Book of Catholic Prayers. 2008. (Illus.). 220p. vinyl bd. 9.95 *(978-0-88271-124-9(5))* Regina Pr., Malhame & Co.

—A Catholic Child's First Prayer Book. 2008. (Illus.). 37p. (J). (gr. -1-2). 9.95 *(978-0-88271-148-5(2))* Regina Pr., Malhame & Co.

Holy See Staff. Layman's Missal: Sundays, Principal Feasts & Liturgy of the Sacraments. 2009. (ENG & LAT., Illus.). 1512p. 27.95 *(978-0-8264-4228-4(5)*, Burns & Oates) Continuum International Publishing Group, Ltd. GBR. Dist: National Bk. Network.

Houselander, Caryll. The Risen Christ: The Forty Days after the Resurrection. 2007. 92p. pap. ***(978-1-59417-056-0(8))*** Scepter Pubs., Inc.

Icel & Collins Educational Staff. Divine Office, 3 vols., Vol. 2. 2006. (ENG.). 1920p. 90.00 *(978-0-00-721090-9(6))* HarperCollins Pubs. Ltd. GBR. Dist: Independent Pubs. Group.

Icel & Collins UK Staff. Divine Office, 3 vols., Vol. 1. 2006. (ENG.). 1984p. 90.00 *(978-0-00-721089-3(2))* HarperCollins Pubs. Ltd. GBR. Dist: Independent Pubs. Group.

Ignatius. Lent & Easter Wisdom from Saint Ignatius of Loyola. 2009. 10.99 *(978-0-7648-1821-9(X))* Liguori Pubns.

John Paul II, pseud. Advent & Christmas Wisdom from Pope John Paul II: Daily Scripture & Prayers Together with Pope John Paul II's Own Words, 1 vol. 2006. (Advent & Christmas Wisdom Ser.). (Illus.). 112p. per. 9.95 *(978-0-7648-1510-2(5))* Liguori Pubns.

Kavanaugh, Kieran, ed. Saint Teresa of Avila for Every Day: Reflections from the Interior Castle. 2006. 92p. per. 6.95 *(978-0-8091-4417-4(4)*, 4417-4) Paulist Pr.

Kelly, Francis D. Through the Church Year: Reflections for Feasts & Seasons. 2009. 192p. pap. 13.95 *(978-1-59471-174-9(7))* Ave Maria Pr.

Kelly, Matthew. Rediscover Advent. 2011. ***(978-1-61636-164-8(6))*** Franciscan Media.

—Rediscover Lent. 2011. (ENG.). 146p. pap. 9.99 ***(978-1-61636-237-9(5))*** Franciscan Media.

Kennedy, Michael E. Jesus, el Prisionero Resucitado: Una invitación para vivir en Libertad. 2011. 264p. pap. *(978-0-8091-4702-1(5))* Paulist Pr.

—Jesus, the Risen Prisoner: An Invitation to Freedom. 2008. 256p. pap. 18.95 *(978-0-8091-4572-0(3))* Paulist Pr.

Ker, Ian, ed. John Henry Newman: Meditations & Devotions. 2010. 120p. 16.95 *(978-0-8091-0598-4(5))* Paulist Pr.

Knight, David. Immersed in Christ Invitation 3: Prophet. 2010. 4.95 *(978-0-87029-433-4(4))* Abbey Pr.

—Immersed in Christ Promise 5. 2010. 1.95 *(978-0-87029-438-9(5))* Abbey Pr.

—Immersed in Christ Reflections 5. 2010. 0.95 *(978-0-87029-437-2(7))* Abbey Pr.

—Immersed in Christ Through Immersion in the Mass: Lectionary Reflections for Each Day of Lent 2011. 2011. 5.95 *(978-0-87029-456-3(3))* Abbey Pr.

Knight, David M. Experiencing the Mass — Five Moments of Mystery: Daily Reflections for Lent 2011. 2010. 4.95 *(978-0-87029-452-5(0))* Abbey Pr.

Knight, David M. Immersed in Christ: Faith Formation Series. 2009. ***(978-0-87029-435-8(0))*** Abbey Pr.

Komprobst, Roswitha. Praying with Mother Teresa. 2011. 64p. pap. *(978-0-8091-4526-3(X))* Paulist Pr.

Kosicki, George W., contrib. by. Mercy Minutes with Jesus: Praying Daily on Jesus's Words from the Diary of St. Faustina. 2008. (ENG., Illus.). 475p. pap. 12.95 *(978-1-59614-193-3(X))* Marian Pr.

Kwatera, Michael. The Collegeville Prayer of the Faithful Annual: Cycle A, with CD-ROM. 2007. 160p. pap. 9.95 incl. cd-rom *(978-0-8146-3052-5(9)*, Liturgical Pr. Bks.) Liturgical Pr.

Larkin, Jean, ed. Prayers & Guidelines for Catholics. 2007. (Illus.). 30p. pap. 2.25 *(978-1-933178-76-9(0))* Pflaum Publishing Group.

Libreria Editrice Vaticana, creator. Essentials for Christian Living. 2008. 127p. pap. 6.95 *(978-1-60137-020-4(2))* United States Conference of Catholic Bishops.

Liguori, Alfonso Maria de'. Advent & Christmas Wisdom from Saint Alphonsus Liguori: Daily Scripture & Prayers Together with Saint Alphonsus Liguori's Own Words. 2011. *(978-0-7648-1909-4(7))* Liguori Pubns.

—Lent & Easter Wisdom from Saint Alphonsus Liguori: Daily Scripture & Prayers Together with St. Alphonsus' Own Words. 2011. ***(978-0-7648-1988-9(7))*** Liguori Pubns.

Liguori, Alfonso Maria de'. The Mission Book: A Manual of instructions & Prayers Adapted to Preserve the Fruits of the Mission. Drawn Chiefly from the Works of St. Alphonsus Li. 2006. 508p. per. 29.99 *(978-1-4255-5670-9(1))* MPublishing.

Link, Mark. Praying the Way Jesus Prayed: Breaking Through the Barriers That Keep Us from Connecting with God. 2008. pap. 11.95 *(978-0-8294-2725-7(2))* Loyola Pr.

The Little Office of the Blessed Virgin Mary. 2010. (ARA.). 101.84 *(978-1-61719-761-1(0))* Gorgias Pr., LLC.

Lubich, Chiara. God's Word to Us: Short Reflections on Living the Word. 2011. pap. ***(978-1-56548-425-2(8))*** New City Community Pr.

Mangiaracina, George. A Lenten Journey with Jesus Christ & St. John of the Cross. 2009. 280p. pap. 14.95 *(978-0-9841707-2-2(3))* Christus Publishing, LLC.

Manuppella, A. Novena to St John Vianney. 13p. pap. *(978-0-8198-5121-5(3)*, 332-232) Pauline Bks. & Media.

Martin, George. Meeting Jesus in the Gospels. 2009. 149p. pap. 13.99 *(978-0-86716-900-3(1)*, Servant Bks.) Franciscan Media.

Mathson, Patricia L. Live Advent at Home: Daily Prayers & Activities for Families. 2011. *(978-0-7648-2035-9(4))* Liguori Pubns.

McBride, Alfred. The Challenge of the Cross: Praying the Stations. 2011. (ENG.). 72p. pap. 3.99 ***(978-1-61636-303-1(7))*** Franciscan Media.

McCann, Deborah. Lift up Your Hearts! 50 Blessings & Prayers for Parish Meetings & Ministries. 2007. 129p. per. 19.95 *(978-1-58595-652-4(X))* Twenty-Third Pubns./Bayard.

McCartin, James P. Prayers of the Faithful: The Shifting Spiritual Life of American Catholics. 2010. 240p. 25.95 *(978-0-674-04913-0(6))* Harvard Univ. Pr.

McDonnell, Rea. From Glory to Glory: Spirit & Sacrament in the Writings of Paul & John. 2011. pap. *(978-1-56548-368-2(5))* New City Community Pr.

McGinlay, Hugh. Prayers of the Faithful: For Sundays, Feasts, & Seasons. 2006. 140p. per. 16.95 *(978-0-8091-4426-6(3)*, 4426-3) Paulist Pr.

McKenna, Megan. Advent, Christmas & Epiphany: Stories & Reflections on the Sunday & Daily Readings. 2008. 512p. pap. 39.90 *(978-1-56548-302-6(2))* New City Pr.

—Advent, Christmas, & Epiphany: Stories & Reflections on the Sunday Readings. 2008. 256p. pap. 19.95 *(978-1-56548-300-2(6))* New City Pr.

—Mother to All, Mother Forever: Four Weeks with Mary of Nazareth. 2009. (7 x 4 A Meditation a Day for Four Weeks Ser.). (ENG.). 72p. pap. 8.95 *(978-1-56548-316-3(2))* New City Pr.

Melchiorre, Jim. Novena in Time of War: Soul-Searching Prayers & Meditations. 2008. (Illus.). 95p. per. 14.00 *(978-0-8358-9940-6(3))* Upper Room Bks.

Merton Foundation Staff. Lent & Holy Week. Montaldo, Jonathan & Toth, Robert G., eds. 2009. (Illus.). 64p. 5.95 *(978-1-59471-204-3(2))* Ave Maria Pr.

Merton Institute for Contemplative Living Staff. Advent & Christmas. Montaldo, Jonathan & Toth, Robert G., eds. 2010. (Illus.). 64p. 5.95 *(978-1-59471-195-4(X))* Ave Maria Pr.

Merton, Thomas. Lent & Easter Wisdom from Thomas Merton: Daily Scripture & Prayers Together with Thomas Merton's Own Words. 2007. per. 9.95 *(978-0-7648-1558-4(X))* Liguori Pubns.

Mickler, Jeffrey. Apóstol de Amor: Novena a San Pablo. 2008. (SPA.). *(978-0-8189-1284-9(7)*, St. Pauls) St Pauls/Alba Hse. Pubs.

—Novena to St. Paul, the Apostle of Love. 2008. *(978-0-8189-1280-1(4)*, St. Pauls) St Pauls/Alba Hse. Pubs.

Moore, Cecilia A., et al, eds. Songs of Our Hearts, Meditations of Our Souls: Prayers for Black Catholics. 2007. (Illus.). 103p. per. 9.95 *(978-0-86716-694-1(0))* Franciscan Media.

Morneau, Robert F. Lent with Bishop Morneau. 2008. 112p. pap. 12.95 *(978-0-8146-1870-7(7))* Liturgical Pr.

Murdy, Kay. A Closer Walk with Jesus: Reading & Praying the Daily Gospels for Lent. 2009. pap. *(978-0-89390-688-7(3))* Resource Pubns., Inc.

Neff, LaVonne. 2008: A Book of Grace-Filled Days. 2007. 400p. per. 10.95 *(978-0-8294-1874-3(1))* Loyola Pr.

Newman, John Henry. Heart to Heart: A Cardinal Newman Prayer Book. O'Connell, Daniel M., ed. 2011. 328p. 50.95 ***(978-1-258-02487-1(X))*** Literary Licensing, LLC.

Nouwen, Henri J. M. Heart Speaks to Heart: Three Gospel Meditations on Jesus. rev. ed. 2007. (Illus.). 61p. per. 7.95 *(978-1-59471-116-9(X))* Ave Maria Pr.

O'Boyle, Donna-Marie Cooper. Catholic Saints Prayer Book: Moments of Inspiration from Your Favorite Saints. 2008. (Illus.). 80p. 7.95 *(978-1-59276-285-9(9))* Our Sunday Visitor, Publishing Div.

O'Loughlin, Thomas. Liturgical Resources for Advent & Christmastide: Years A, B & C. 2007. (ENG.). 273p. per. 35.95 *(978-1-85607-554-1(0))* Columba Pr. IRL. Dist: Dufour Editions, Inc.

—Liturgical Resources for Luke's Year. 2007. (ENG.). 306p. pap. 27.95 *(978-1-85607-559-6(1))* Columba Pr. IRL. Dist: Dufour Editions, Inc.

Ortiz, Gloria. Delighting in the Feminine Divine: Feminine Images of God in the Bible & Christian Tradition. 2007. (Illus.). 142p. pap. 20.00 *(978-0-9793767-9-5(3))* SOFIA.

Ortiz, Michael. God & Country: Reflections for Catholics in the Military. 2007. 60p. per. 2.95 *(978-0-86716-577-7(4))* Franciscan Media.

Pasquale, Gianluigi & Francis. Day by Day with Saint Francis: 365 Meditations. 2011. pap. ***(978-1-56548-394-1(4))*** New City Community Pr.

Pasquini, John. Medicine of Immortality: Prayers & Meditations for Mass & Eucharistic Adoration. 2007. 96p. per. 10.00 *(978-1-934222-22-5(4))* Shepherds of Christ Ministries Inc.

Pat, Fosarelli. Paths to Prayer. 2010. 128p. pap. 11.95 *(978-1-59471-218-0(2))* Ave Maria Pr.

Pennington, M. Basil. Praying the Rosary. pap. 0.01 *(978-0-87973-146-5(X))* Our Sunday Visitor, Publishing Div.

Pio. Lenten Meditations with Saint Pio of Pietrelcina. 2008. 48p. *(978-0-7648-1797-7(3))* Liguori.

Powell, Philip Neri. Treasures Holy & Mystical: A Devotional Journey for Today's Catholics. 2010. 168p. 15.99 *(978-0-7648-1913-1(5))* Liguori Pubns.

—Treasures Old & New: Traditional Prayers for Today's Catholics. 2009. 15.99 *(978-0-7648-1840-0(6))* Liguori Pubns.

Praying My Faith. 2008. (J). pap. 7.95 *(978-0-8294-2853-7(4))* Loyola Pr.

Praying with Scripture. 2008. (J). pap. 7.95 *(978-0-8294-2852-0(6))* Loyola Pr.

Promises of God Daybrightners: Catholic Edition. Date not set. 7.95 *(978-0-88271-576-6(3)*, 10320) Regina Pr., Malhame & Co.

Reid, Barbara E. Abiding Word: Sunday Reflections for Year B. 2011. 18.95 *(978-0-8146-3312-0(9))* Liturgical Pr.

Reinhard, Sarah. Welcome Risen Jesus: Lent & Easter Reflections for Families. 2012. ***(978-0-7648-2074-8(5))*** Liguori Pubns.

Riccardi, Andrea & Community of Sant'Egidio Staff. Sant Egidio Bk of Prayer. 2009. 224p. pap. 14.95 *(978-1-59471-206-7(9))* Ave Maria Pr.

Rohr, Richard. Preparándose para Navidad con P. Richard Rohr, O.F.M: Reflexiones Diarias para Adviento. 2008. (SPA.). pap. *(978-0-86716-903-4(6))* Franciscan Media.

—Wondrous Encounters: Scripture for Lent. 2011. 143p. pap. 8.99 *(978-0-86716-987-4(7))* Franciscan Media.

Ruggeri, Peppino. Prigheri e Canzuneddi Divoti Da Sicilia: Prayers & Devotional Songs of Sicily. 2008. pap. *(978-1-881901-65-5(3))* LEGAS.

Rupp, Joyce. God's Enduring Presence: Strength for the Spiritual Journey. 2008. 136p. pap. 12.95 *(978-1-58595-720-0(8))* Twenty-Third Pubns./Bayard.

Ryan, Tom. Comfort My People: Prayers & Reflections Inspired by the Venerable Matt Talbot. 2008. (ENG.). 94p. pap. 13.95 *(978-1-84730-030-0(8))* Veritas Pubns. IRL. Dist: Dufour Editions, Inc.

Santa, Thomas M. Desert Graces: Meditations Inspired by the Sonoran Desert. 2010. vi, 78p. *(978-1-893757-63-9(3)*, E T Nedder) Paulist Pr.

Savage, Warren J. & McSweeny, Mary Ann. Mindful Meditations for Every Day of Lent & Easter: Years a, B, & C. 2011. *(978-0-7648-1969-8(0))* Liguori Pubns.

Schneider, M. Valerie. 26 Creative Celebrations for All Generations: Interactive Prayers, Gospel Reflections, & Activities for the Liturgical Year. 2008. pap. *(978-1-58595-702-6(X))* Twenty-Third Pubns./Bayard.

Schultz, Karl A. How to Pray with the Bible: The Ancient Prayer Form of Lectio Divina Made Simple. 2007. 157p. per. 9.95 *(978-1-59276-216-3(6))* Our Sunday Visitor, Publishing Div.

Schwenker, Gretchen & Schwenker, Gretchen L. Every Tear Will Be Wiped Away: Prayers for Comfort in Times of Grief. 2011. ***(978-0-7648-2037-3(0))*** Liguori Pubns.

Septién, Pia. Las Mujeres Del Antiguo Testamento: Sus Vidas Son Nuestra Esperanza. 2011. (SPA.). ***(978-0-7648-2054-0(0))*** Liguori Pubns.

—The Women of the Old Testament: Their Lives Are Our Hope. 2012. ***(978-0-7648-2204-9(7))*** Liguori Pubns.

Shamon, Albert J. Our Lady Teaches about Prayer at Medjugorje. pap. 3.00 *(978-1-891280-20-7(1))* CMJ Marian Pubs.

Shields, Ann. To Be Like Jesus: Inspiration from the Gospel of Luke. 2010. 128p. pap. 11.99 *(978-0-86716-951-5(6)*, Servant Bks.) Franciscan Media.

Silf, Margaret. 2012: A Book of Grace-Filled Days. 2011. (ENG.). 408p. pap. 11.95 *(978-0-8294-2912-1(3))* Loyola Pr.

Smith, Peter Andrew. All Things Are Ready: Communion Prayers for the Church Year & Pastoral Occasions. 2007. 92p. per. *(978-0-7880-2487-0(6))* CSS Publishing Co.

Socias, James. Oraciones y Devociones. (SPA.). 622p. 14.95 *(978-0-87973-859-4(6))* Our Sunday Visitor, Publishing Div.

A St Francis Prayer Book. 2.00 *(978-0-687-86195-8(0))* Abingdon Pr.

Stokes, Bernward. How to Make Your House a Home: Family Liturgy & Religious Practices. 2011. 54p. 36.95 ***(978-1-258-02996-8(0))*** Literary Licensing, LLC.

Storey, William. A Book of Marian Prayers. 2011. (ENG.). 392p. 9.95 *(978-0-8294-3574-0(3))* Loyola Pr.

—A Catholic Book of Hours & Other Devotions. 2007. pap. 9.95 *(978-0-8294-2584-0(5))* Loyola Pr.

Storey, William & McNally, Thomas. Lord Hear Our Prayer. rev. ed. 2009. 416p. pap. 15.95 *(978-1-59471-042-1(2))* Ave Maria Pr.

Storey, William G. A Beginner's Book of Prayer: An Introduction to Traditional Catholic Prayers. 2009. (ENG.). 192p. 9.95 *(978-0-8294-2792-9(9))* Loyola Pr.

—Prayers of Christian Consolation. 2008. pap. 9.95 *(978-0-8294-2585-7(3))* Loyola Pr.

Sutera, Judith & Benedict. Advent & Christmas Wisdom from Saint Benedict: Daily Scripture & Prayers Together with Saint Benedict's Own Words. 2010. pap. *(978-0-7648-1883-7(X))* Liguori Pubns.

Syrup Bergan, Jacqueline. Forgiveness: A Guide for Prayer. 2nd ed. 2011. (ENG.). 192p. pap. 12.95 *(978-0-8294-3612-9(X))* Loyola Pr.

—Love: A Guide for Prayer. 2nd ed. 2011. (ENG.). 192p. pap. 12.95 *(978-0-8294-3611-2(1))* Loyola Pr.

Tan Books, creator. St. Michael the Archangel. 2006. 60p. pap. 3.00 *(978-0-89555-844-2(0)*, 2173, TAN Bks.) St. Benedict Pr., LLC.

Teresa & Bangley, Bernard. A Little Daily Wisdom: Through the Year with St. Teresa of Avila. 2011. *(978-1-55725-865-6(1))* Paraclete Pr., Inc.

Therese of Lisieux. The Path of Merciful Love: 99 Sayings. Foley, Marc, ed. 2007. 99p. per. 9.95 *(978-1-56548-246-3(8))* New City Pr.

thigpen, paul. My daily catholic bible;new Testament. 2008. per. 12.95 *(978-1-59276-447-1(9))* Our Sunday Visitor, Publishing Div.

Tilby, Angela. Everyday Catholic Prayer. 2006. (ENG.). 136p. (gr. 13). 14.95 *(978-1-55725-510-5(5))* Paraclete Pr., Inc.

Timmerman, John. Woman, Why Are You Weeping? Daily Meditations for Lent. 2007. 135p. per. 10.95 *(978-0-7648-1560-7(1))* Liguori Pubns.

Trouvé, Lorraine. Praying the Rosary for Priests. 2009. (Illus.). 32p. 2.25 *(978-0-8198-5962-4(1))* Pauline Bks. & Media.

Trouvé, Marianne Lorraine, compiled by. Angels: Help from on High. 2010. pap. *(978-0-8198-0790-8(7))* Pauline Bks. & Media.

Trouve, Marrianne. Novena St Thomas Aquinas. 21p. pap. 1.25 *(978-0-8198-5136-9(1)*, 332-236) Pauline Bks. & Media.

Ui Bhraonáin, Donla. Paidreacha Na Gaeilge: Prayers in Irish. 2009. (ENG., Illus.). 190p. pap. 22.95 *(978-1-901176-88-9(6))* Syracuse Univ. Pr.

Ulterino, Gloria. Walking with Wisdom's Daughters: Twelve Celebrations & Stories of Women of Passion & Faith. 2006. (Illus.). 219p. per. 19.95 *(978-1-59471-063-6(5))* Ave Maria Pr.

U.S. Catholic Bishops. Catholic Household Blessings & Prayers. 2012. (ENG.). 480p. mass mkt. 9.99 ***(978-0-307-98652-8(7)**, Image)* Doubleday Religious Publishing Group, The.

Valentine Publishing House LLC, compiled by. Catholic Revival Prayers. 2007. 32p. 1.00 *(978-0-9796331-7-1(6))* Valentine Publishing Hse. LLC.

Vitek, John. My Dear Young Friends: Blessed Pope John Paul II Commemorative Edition. 2011. (ENG.). (gr. 9-12). pap. 9.95 *(978-0-88489-816-0(4))* St. Mary's Pr.

Waldron, Robert. Thomas Merton: Master of Attention: An Exploration of Prayer. 2008. 101p. per. 16.95 *(978-0-8091-4521-8(9))* Paulist Pr.

Way of the Holy Cross. 2007. *(978-0-9778570-3-6(4))* MOS, Inc.

Weible, Wayne. The Medjugorje Prayer Book: Powerful Prayers from the Apparitions of the Blessed Virgin Mary in Medjugorje. 2007. (ENG.). 162p. (gr. 13). per. 14.95 *(978-1-55725-530-3(X))* Paraclete Pr., Inc.

Welborn, Amy. Prayerful Pauses: Finding God's Presence in Daily Life. 2011. 128p. pap. 12.95 *(978-1-58595-782-8(8))* Twenty-Third Pubns./Bayard.

White, E. G. Power of Prayer. 2011. (ENG.). 168p. per. 16.95 *(978-1-57258-002-2(X)*, 945-5876) TEACH Services, Inc.

Wickenhiser, Mary. Saint Anthony Novena. 48p. pap. 1.50 *(978-0-8198-7072-8(2)*, 332-368) Pauline Bks. & Media.

Wiederkehr, Macrina. Abide: Keeping Vigil with the Word of God. 2011. E-Book ***(978-0-8146-3958-0(5))*** Liturgical Pr.

Wintz, Jack. Friar Jacks Favorite Prayers. 2011. 128p. pap. 12.99 *(978-0-86716-991-1(5))* Franciscan Media.

Word Among Us Press, compiled by. The Compact Catholic Prayer Book. 2008. 200p. pap. 12.95 *(978-1-59325-127-7(0))* Word Among Us Pr.

Wright, Allan F. Jesus in the House: Gospel Reflections on Christ's Presence in the Home. 2007. 190p. per. 14.95 *(978-0-85716-791-7(2))* Franciscan Media.

Wright, Vinita Hampton. The St. Therese of Lisieux Prayer Book. 2008. (ENG.). 166p. (gr. 13). pap. 15.99 *(978-1-55725-573-5(4))* Paraclete Pr., Inc.

Zyromski, Page McKean. How to Pray with the Bible. 2010. (ENG.). 128p. pap. 14.99 *(978-1-55725-691-1(8))* Paraclete Pr., Inc.

CATHOLIC CHURCH—RELATION TO THE STATE

see Church and State—Catholic Church

CATHOLIC CHURCH—RELATIONS

ARCIC II Staff. Mary: Grace & Hope in Christ. Bolen, Donald & Cameron, Gregory, eds. rev. exp. ed. 2006. (ENG., Illus.). 288p. 22.95 *(978-0-8264-8155-9(8))* Continuum International Publishing Group, Ltd. GBR. Dist: National Bk. Network.

Aveling, J. C., et al. Rome & the Anglicans: Historical & Doctrinal Aspects of Anglican-Roman Catholic Relations. Haase, Wolfgang, ed. (ENG.). IV, 301p. 225.00 ***(978-3-11-176503-7(2))*** De Gruyter, Walter Inc.

Becker, Karl Joseph, et al, eds. Catholic Engagement with World Religions: A Comprehensive Study. 2009. 500p. pap. 45.00 *(978-1-57075-828-7(X))* Orbis Bks.

Beckwith, Francis J. Return to Rome: Confessions of an Evangelical Catholic. 2009. 144p. pap. 14.99 *(978-1-58743-247-7(1))* Brazos Pr.

Béthune, Pierre-François de. Interreligious Hospitality: The Fulfillment of Dialogue. 2010. 21.95 *(978-0-8146-3305-2(6))* Liturgical Pr.

Biebinger, Frank. Auf der Suche nach Gottes Angesicht: Candomble & Katholizismus im Dialog: Eine Fallstudie. (GER., Illus.). xiv, 348p. *(978-3-496-02701-0(0))* Reimer, Dietrich.

Blée, Fabrice, et al. The Third Desert: The Story of Monastic Interreligious Dialogue. 2011. 24.95 *(978-0-8146-3357-1(9))*; E-Book *(978-0-8146-3949-8(6))* Liturgical Pr.

Bliss, Frederick M. Catholic & Ecumenical: History. 2nd ed. 2007. (ENG.). 208p. pap. 28.95 *(978-0-7425-5257-9(8))* Rowman & Littlefield Publishers, Inc.

—Catholic & Ecumenical: History & Hope: Why the Catholic Church Is Ecumenical & What She Is Doing about It. 2nd ed. 2007. (Sheed & Ward Book Ser.). (ENG.). 208p. 88.00 *(978-0-7425-5256-2(X))* Rowman & Littlefield Publishers, Inc.

Braaten, Carl E. That All May Believe: A Theology of the Gospel & the Mission of the Church. 2008. 168p. pap. 20.00 *(978-0-8028-6239-6(X))* Eerdmans, William B. Publishing Co.

Champlin, Joseph M. A Catholic Perspective on the Purpose Driven Life. 2006. 108p. per. 7.95 *(978-0-89942-132-2(6))* Catholic Bk. Publishing Corp.

D'Costa, Gavin. The Catholic Church & the World Religions: A Theological & Phenomenological Account. D'Costa, Gavin, ed. 2011. (ENG.). 240p. 120.00 *(978-0-567-21230-1(7))*; pap. 34.95 *(978-0-567-46697-6(3))* Continuum International Publishing Group, Ltd. GBR. (T&T Clark Int'l). Dist: National Bk. Network.

Del Colle, Ralph. Talking with Evangelicals: A Guide for Catholics. 2012. 104p. pap. 10.95 ***(978-0-8091-4742-7(4))*** Paulist Pr.

Echeverria, Eduardo J. Dialogue of Love. 2009. 280p. pap. 31.00 *(978-1-60608-176-1(4)*, Wipf and Stock) Wipf & Stock Pubs.

Feldmeier,, Peter, Peter. Encounters in Faith: Christianity in Interreligious Dialogue. 2011. (ENG.). 326p. (C). pap. 31.95 *(978-1-59982-031-6(5))* St. Mary's Pr.

Garrigan, Siobhan. The Real Peace Process: Worship, Politics, & the End of Sectarianism. 2010. (Religion & Violence Ser.). (ENG.). 240p. (C). 99.95 *(978-1-84553-693-0(2))*; pap. 34.95 *(978-1-84553-694-7(0))* Equinox Publishing Ltd. GBR. Dist: ISD.

Gioia, Francesco, ed. Interreligious Dialogue: The Official Teaching of the Catholic Church from the Second Vatican Council to John Paul II, 1963-2005. 2006. 1248p. *(978-0-8198-3693-9(1))* Pauline Bks. & Media.

Gorski, Eugene F. Theology of Religions: A Sourcebook for Interreligious Study. 2008. 336p. pap. 24.95 *(978-0-8091-4533-1(2))* Paulist Pr.

Heft, James. Catholicism & Interreligious Dialogue, 1 vol. 2011. (ENG.). 240p. 99.00 *(978-0-19-982787-9(7))*; pap. 29.95 *(978-0-19-982789-3(3))* Oxford Univ. Pr., Inc.

Heft, James, et al. Learned Ignorance: Intellectual Humility among Jews, Christians, & Muslims. 2011. E-Book *(978-0-19-977306-0(8))* Oxford Univ. Pr., Inc.

Heft, James L., et al, eds. Learned Ignorance: Intellectual Humility among Jews, Christians, & Muslims, 1 vol. 2011. 360p. pap. 39.95 *(978-0-19-976931-5(1))* Oxford Univ. Pr., Inc.

Hillman, Eugene. Many Paths: A Catholic Approach to Religious Pluralism. 2008. 108p. (Orig.). pap. 13.00 *(978-1-55635-993-4(4)*, Wipf and Stock) Wipf & Stock Pubs.

Iarccum. Anglican-Roman Catholic Dialogue. 2007. 64p. pap. *(978-0-281-05939-3(X))* SPCK Publishing.

Kuntz, Marion Leathers. Colloquium of the Seven about Secrets of the Sublime. 2008. (ENG., Illus.). 590p. (C). pap. 45.00 *(978-0-271-03435-5(1))* Pennsylvania State Univ. Pr.

Leahy, Brendan. Inter-Church Relations: Developments & Perspectives. Leahy, Brendan, ed. 2009. (ENG.). 203p. pap. 25.95 *(978-1-84730-095-9(2))* Veritas Pubns. IRL. Dist: Dufour Editions, Inc.

Lombardi, Josephine. The Universal Salvific Will of God in Official Documents of the Roman Catholic Church. 2007. 240p. 109.95 *(978-0-7734-5246-6(X))* Mellen, Edwin Pr., The.

—What Are They Saying about the Universal Salvific Will of God? 2008. 144p. pap. 14.95 *(978-0-8091-4562-1(6))* Paulist Pr.

Montalban, Manuel Vazquez. Y Dios Entro en la Habana. (SPA., Illus.). 716p. 29.95 *(978-84-03-59494-4(1))* Aguilar, S. A. de Ediciones-Grupo Santillana ESP. Dist: Santillana USA Publishing Co., Inc.

Noll, Mark A. & Nystrom, Carolyn. Is the Reformation Over? An Evangelical Assessment of Contemporary Roman Catholicism. 2008. 272p. (C). pap. 25.00 *(978-0-8010-3575-3(9))* Baker Academic.

Noll, Mark A. & Turner, James. The Future of Christian Learning: An Evangelical & Catholic Dialogue. Howard, Thomas Alberted. & Howard, Thomas Albert, eds. 2008. 144p. (C). pap. 18.00 *(978-1-58743-213-2(7))* Brazos Pr.

Nunez, E. A. & Taylor, W. D. Crisis & Hope in Latin America: An Evangelical Perspective. (Illus.). xvi, 528p. pap. *(978-1-900890-01-4(1))* WEF GBR. Dist: O. M. Literature.

ón-Emeric, Edgardo A. Wesley, Aquinas, & Christian Perfection: An Ecumenical Dialogue. 2009. (ENG.). 330p. 49.95 *(978-1-60258-211-8(4))* Baylor Univ. Pr.

Radano, John A. Celebrating a Century of Ecumenism: Exploring the Achievements of International Dialogue: In Commemoration of the Centenary of the 1910 Edinburgh World Missionary Conference. 2012. pap. ***(978-0-8028-6705-6(7))*** Eerdmans, William B. Publishing Co.

Ratzinger, Joseph. New Outpourings of the Spirit: Movements in the Church. 2007. 133p. 14.95 *(978-1-58617-181-0(X))* Ignatius Pr.

Reath, Mary. Rome & Canterbury: The Elusive Search for Unity. spiral bd. *(978-0-7425-5279-1(9))*; 2007. (ENG., Illus.). 160p. 21.95 *(978-0-7425-5278-4(0))* Rowman & Littlefield Publishers, Inc.

Roberts, Michelle. Dualities: A Theology of Difference. 2010. (ENG.). 256p. pap. 35.00 *(978-0-664-23449-2(6))* Westminster John Knox Pr.

Rountree, Kathryn. Crafting Contemporary Pagan Identities in a Catholic Society. 2010. (Illus.). 206p. 99.95 *(978-0-7546-6973-9(4))* Ashgate Publishing Co.

Semple, Pat. The Rector Who Wouldn't Pray for Rain: A Memoir. 2008. (ENG.). 224p. per. 24.95 *(978-1-85635-560-5(8))* Mercier Pr., Ltd., The IRL. Dist: Dufour Editions, Inc.

Skudlarek, William. The Attentive Voice: Reflections on the Meaning & Practice of Interreligious Dialogue. 2011. ***(978-1-59056-309-0(3))***; E-Book ***(978-1-59056-310-6(7))*** Lantern Bks.

Smith, Christian. How to Go from Being a Good Evangelical to a Committed Catholic in Ninety-Five Difficult Steps. 2011. 214p. pap. 24.00 ***(978-1-61097-033-4(0)***, Cascade Bks.) Wipf & Stock Pubs.

Steinkerchner, Scott. Beyond Agreement: Interreligious Dialogue amid Persistent Differences. 2010. (ENG.). 206p. (gr. 17). 55.00 *(978-1-4422-0642-7(X))* Rowman & Littlefield Publishers, Inc.

—Beyond Agreement: Interreligious Dialogue amid Perspective Differences. 2010. *(978-1-4422-0644-1(6))* Rowman & Littlefield Publishers, Inc.

Taraqji, Marcel & Ibrahim, Gregorios, trs. The Vienna Dialogue. 2009. (ARA.). 100.00 *(978-1-60724-268-0(0))*; 95.00 *(978-1-60724-267-3(2))* Gorgias Pr., LLC.

Taraqji, Maurice & Ibrahim, Gregorios, trs. Wort und Wahrheit. 2009. (ARA.). 127.00 *(978-1-60724-261-1(3))* Gorgias Pr., LLC.

Timmis, Mike & Fickett, Harold. Between Two Worlds: The Spiritual Journey of an Evangelical Catholic. 2008. (Living the Letters Ser.). (ENG.). 256p. pap. 14.99 *(978-1-60006-248-3(2))* NavPress Publishing Group.

Walker, Carlos. Missionary Pope. 2009. pap. 24.95 *(978-1-933871-10-3(5))* IVE Pr.

Whitehead, K. D. The New Ecumenism: How the Catholic Church after Vatican II Took over the Leadership of the World Ecumenical Movement. 2009. *(978-0-8189-1283-2(9)*, St. Pauls) St Pauls/Alba Hse. Pubs.

Wills, Garry. Bush's Fringe Government. 2006. (ENG.). 56p. pap. 7.95 *(978-1-59017-210-0(8))* New York Review of Bks., Inc., The.

Yelton, Michael. Anglican Papalism: A History: 1900-1960. 2008. (Illus.). 266p. pap. 39.99 *(978-1-85311-861-6(3))* Canterbury Pr.

Zachman, Randall C., ed. John Calvin & Roman Catholicism: Critique & Engagement, Then & Now. 2008. 224p. (C). pap. 27.00 *(978-0-8010-3597-5(X))* Baker Academic.

CATHOLIC CHURCH—RELATIONS—BUDDHISM

Habito, Ruben L. F. Total Liberation: Zen Spirituality & the Social Dimension. 2006. (Illus.). 128p. pap. 17.00 *(978-1-59752-899-3(4)*, Wipf and Stock) Wipf & Stock Pubs.

Mitchell, Donald & Skudlarek, William. Green Monasticism: A Buddhist-Catholic Response to an Environmental Calamity. 2010. *(978-1-59056-167-6(8))* Lantern Bks.

Mitchell, Donald W. & Wiseman, James A., eds. The Spiritual Life: A Dialogue of Buddhist & Christian Monastics. 2010. (Gethsemani Encounters Ser.). 305p. pap. *(978-1-59056-173-7(2))* Lantern Bks.

Soko, Keith. A Mounting East-West Tension: Buddhist-Christian Dialogue on Human Rights, Social Justice & a Global Ethic. 2009. pap. *(978-0-87462-743-5(5))* Marquette Univ. Pr.

Suzuki, Daisetz Teitaro & Anshen, Ruth Nanda. Mysticism: Christian & Buddhist. 2011. 234p. 46.95 ***(978-1-258-00662-4(6))*** Literary Licensing, LLC.

CATHOLIC CHURCH—RELATIONS—HINDUISM

Clooney, Francis X. Comparative Theology: Deep Learning Across Religious Borders. 2010. (ENG.). 200p. 99.95 *(978-1-4051-7973-7(2))*; pap. 32.95 *(978-1-4051-7974-4(0))* Wiley, John & Sons, Inc. (Wiley-Blackwell).

Clooney, Francis Xavier. Beyond Compare: St. Francis de Sales & Sri Vedanta Desika on Loving Surrender to God. 2008. (ENG.). 288p. pap. 34.95 *(978-1-58901-211-0(9))* Georgetown Univ. Pr.

Clooney, S. J. New Comparative Theology: Interreligious Insights from the Next Generation. Francis X, ed. 2010. (ENG.). 232p. pap. 29.95 *(978-0-567-14137-8(3)*, T&T Clark Int'l) Continuum International Publishing Group, Ltd. GBR. Dist: National Bk. Network.

Clooney, S. J. & Francis X, eds. New Comparative Theology: Interreligious Insights from the Next Generation. 2010. (ENG.). 232p. 100.00 *(978-0-567-31048-4(5)*, T&T Clark Int'l) Continuum International Publishing Group, Ltd. GBR. Dist: National Bk. Network.

Skudlarek, William. God's Harp String: The Life & Legacy of the Benedictine Monk Swami Abhishiktananda. 2010. *(978-1-59056-181-2(3))* Lantern Bks.

CATHOLIC CHURCH—RELATIONS—ISLAM

Baum, Gregory. The Theology of Tariq Ramadan: A Catholic Perspective. 2009. (ENG.). 184p. pap. 25.00 *(978-0-268-02214-3(3))* Univ. of Notre Dame Pr.

Bowe, Peter. Catholics in Interreligious Dialogue. 2006. 272p. per. *(978-0-85244-640-9(3))* Gracewing, Ltd.

Dalai Lama XIV, et al. Sophia: The Journal of Traditional Studies, 13. 2007. 200p. pap. 17.95 *(978-0-9798429-0-0(5))* Foundation for Traditional Studies.

CATHOLIC CHURCH—RELATIONS—JUDAISM

Ben-Dror, Graciela. Argentina, 1933-1945. 2009. (Studies in Antisemitism Ser.). (ENG.). 278p. 55.00 *(978-0-8032-1889-5(3))* Univ. of Nebraska Pr.

—La Iglesia Católica Ante el Holocausto: España y América Latina 1933-1945. (SPA., Illus.). 336p. 39.30 *(978-84-206-4164-5(2))* Alianza Editorial, S. A. ESP. Dist: Libros in Spanish, LLC.

Benedict XVI, pseud. Pope Benedict XVI in the Holy Land. 2011. 176p. pap. *(978-0-8091-4672-7(X))* Paulist Pr.

Blaschke, Olaf. Offenders or Victims? German Jews & the Causes of Modern Catholic Antisemitism. 2009. (Studies in Antisemitism Ser.). (ENG.). 232p. 50.00 *(978-0-8032-2522-0(9))* Univ. of Nebraska Pr.

Cernera, Anthony J. Examining Nostra Aetate after 40 Years: Catholic-Jewish Relations in Our Time. 2007. *(978-1-888112-15-3(8))* Sacred Heart Univ. Pr.

Connelly, John. From Enemy to Brother: The Revolution in Catholic Teaching on the Jews, 1933-1965. 2012. (ENG.). 384p. 35.00 ***(978-0-674-05782-1(1))*** Harvard Univ. Pr.

Coppa, Frank J. The Papacy, the Jews, & the Holocaust. 2008. 373p. pap. 34.95 *(978-0-8132-1547-1(1))* Catholic Univ. of America Pr.

Cornwell, John. Hitler's Pope: The Secret History of Pius XII. rev. ed. 2008. (ENG., Illus.). 464p. (gr. 12-18). 17.00 *(978-0-14-311400-0(X)*, Penguin (Non-Classics)) Penguin Group (USA) Inc.

Crane, Richard Francis. Passion of Israel: Jacques Maritain, Catholic Conscience, & the Holocaust. 2010. (ENG.). 180p. pap. 25.00 *(978-1-58966-193-6(1))* Univ. of Scranton Pr.

Cymet, David. History vs. Apologetics: The Holocaust, the Third Reich, & the Catholic Church. 2010. (ENG., Illus.). 510p. 94.50 *(978-0-7391-3293-7(8))* Lexington Bks.

—History vs Apologetics: The Holocaust, the Third Reich, & the Catholic Church. 2011. (ENG.). 510p. pap. 39.95 *(978-0-7391-3294-4(6))* Lexington Bks.

Dalin, David G. & Levering, Matthew, eds. John Paul II & the Jewish People: A Jewish-Christian Dialogue. 2007. (ENG.). 208p. 80.00 *(978-0-7425-5998-1(X))*; per. 24.95 *(978-0-7425-5999-8(8))* Rowman & Littlefield Publishers, Inc.

Debono-De-Laurentis, M. The Forgotten Roots. 2008. 316p. 30.95 *(978-1-4251-7167-4(2))* Trafford Publishing.

Dietrich, Donald J. & Dietrich, Donald. Human Rights & the Catholic Tradition. 2007. (ENG.). 234p. (gr. 11). 59.95 *(978-0-7658-0378-8(X))* Transaction Pubs.

Feldman, Egal. Catholics & Jews in Twentieth-Century America. 2006. 344p. per. 21.00 *(978-0-252-07385-4(1))* Univ. of Illinois Pr.

Goldstein, David. Letters, Hebrew-Catholic, to Mr Isaacs. 2011. 314p. 50.95 ***(978-1-258-09141-5(0))*** Literary Licensing, LLC.

Hoff, Gregor Maria & Langer, Gerhard, eds. Der Ort des Jüdischen in der christlichen Theologie. 2009. (GER., Illus.). 333p. (C). 84.00 *(978-3-525-69103-8(3))* Vandenhoeck & Ruprecht GmbH & Co. KG DEU. Dist: ISD.

Johnson, Nita (LaFond). Where Was God? 2008. (Illus.). 127p. *(978-0-9656528-7-2(4))* Graham, Robert J. Desktop Publishing.

Keller, Zsolt. Der Blutruf: Eine schweizerische Wirkungsgeschichte 1900-1950. 2006. (GER.). 200p. (C). pap. 36.00 *(978-3-525-55328-2(5))* Vandenhoeck & Ruprecht GmbH & Co. KG DEU. Dist: ISD.

Kinzer, Mark S. Israel's Messiah & the People of God: A Vision for Messianic Jewish Covenant Fidelity. Rosner, Jennifer, ed. 2011. 250p. pap. 28.00 *(978-1-60608-883-8(1)*, Cascade Bks.) Wipf & Stock Pubs.

Lawler, Justus George. Were the Popes Against the Jews? Tracking the Myths, Confronting the Truths. 2011. pap. 35.00 ***(978-0-8028-6629-5(8))*** Eerdmans, William B. Publishing Co.

Lustiger, Jean-Marie & Duchesne, Jean. Cardinal Jean-Marie Lustiger on Christians & Jews. 2010. (Stimulus Bks.). 192p. pap. 16.95 *(978-0-8091-4353-5(4))* Paulist Pr.

Marchione, Margherita. Did Pope Pius XII Help the Jews? 2007. 112p. pap. 5.95 *(978-0-8091-4476-1(X)*, 4476-1) Paulist Pr.

Michael, Jones E. Jewish Revolutionary Spirit. 2008. (ENG.). 1200p. 48.00 *(978-0-929891-07-1(4))* Fidelity Pr.

Michael, Robert. A History of Catholic Antisemitism: The Dark Side of the Church. (ENG.). 292p. 2011. pap. 28.00 *(978-0-230-11131-8(9))* 2008. 100.00 *(978-0-230-60388-2(2))* Palgrave Macmillan.

O'Reilly, Charles T. The Jews of Italy, 1938-1945: An Analysis of Revisionist Histories. 2007. (ENG.). 229p. per. 39.95 *(978-0-7864-3002-4(8))* McFarland & Co., Inc. Pubs.

O'Shea, Paul. A Cross Too Heavy: Pope Pius XII & the Jews of Europe. 2011. (ENG.). 288p. 105.00 *(978-0-230-11079-3(7))*; pap. 28.00 *(978-0-230-11080-9(0))* Palgrave Macmillan.

Paschel, Dietmar. Vatikan und Shoa: Die Haltung des Heiligen Stuhls zu den Juden. (GER.). 150p. pap. 40.95 *(978-3-631-56828-6(2))* Lang, Peter GmbH, Europaischer Verlag der Wissenschaften DEU. Dist: Lang, Peter Publishing, Inc.

Poliakov, Leon. Jewish Bankers & the Holy See, Volume 28. 2012. (ENG.). 296p. 115.00 ***(978-0-415-52327-1(3))*** Routledge.

Raz-Krakotzkin, Amnon. The Censor, the Editor, & the Text: The Catholic Church & the Shaping of the Jewish Canon in the Sixteenth Century. Feldman, Jackie, tr. from HEB. 2007. (Jewish Culture & Contexts Ser.). (ENG.). 328p. (C). 69.95 *(978-0-8122-4011-5(1))* Univ. of Pennsylvania Pr.

Riegner, Gerhart M. Never Despair: Sixty Years in the Service of the Jewish People & of Human Rights. 2006. (ENG., Illus.). 480p. 35.00 *(978-1-56663-696-4(5))* Dee, Ivan R. Pub.

Rudin, A. James. Cushing, Spellman, O'Connor: The Surprising Story of How Three American Cardinals Transformed Catholic-Jewish Relations. 2011. pap. ***(978-0-8028-6567-0(4))*** Eerdmans, William B. Publishing Co.

Stow, Kenneth. Jewish Life in Early Modern Rome: Papal Challenge Conversion & Private Life. 2007. (Variorum Collected Studies Series: CS879 Ser.). (ITA & ENG., Illus.). 352p. 165.00 *(978-0-7546-5916-7(X))* Ashgate Publishing Co.

—Popes, Church, & Jews in the Middle Ages: Confrontation & Response. 2007. (Variorum Collected Studies). (Illus.). 352p. 165.00 *(978-0-7546-5915-0(1))* Ashgate Publishing Co.

Weisbord, Robert G. & Sillanpoa, Wallace P. Chief Rabbi, the Pope, & the Holocaust: An Era in Vatican-Jewish Relations. 2008. (ENG., Illus.). 240p. pap. 29.95 *(978-1-4128-0791-3(3))* Transaction Pubs.

CATHOLIC CHURCH—RELATIONS—LUTHERAN CHURCH

Almen, Lowell G. & Skiba, Richard J. The Hope of Eternal Life: Lutherans & Catholics in Dialogue XI. 2011. (ENG.). 212p. pap. 22.00 ***(978-1-932688-63-4(3)***, Lutheran Univ. Pr.) Kirk Hse. Pubs.

de Witte, Pieter. Doctrine, Dynamic & Difference: To the Heart of the Lutheran-Roman Catholic 'Differentiated Consensus' on Justification. 2012. (ENG.). 272p. 120.00 ***(978-0-567-23665-4(X)***, T&T Clark Int'l) Continuum International Publishing Group, Ltd. GBR. Dist: National Bk. Network.

Hequet, Suzanne. The 1541 Colloquy at Regensburg. 2009. 176p. pap. *(978-3-639-18512-6(9))* VDM Verlag Dr. Mueller e.K.

Luther, Martin. The Smalcald Articles. Bente, F. & Dau, W. H. T., trs. 2009. 48p. pap. *(978-1-4065-7007-5(9))* Dodo Pr.

Radano, John A. Lutheran & Catholic Reconciliation on Justification: A Chronology of the Holy See's Contributions 1961-1999 to a New Relationship Between Lutherans & Catholics & to Steps Leading to the Joint Declaration on the Doctrine of Justification. 2009. (ENG., Illus.). xxvii, 217p. pap. 29.00 *(978-0-8028-4860-4(5))* Eerdmans, William B. Publishing Co.

CATHOLIC CHURCH—RELATIONS—ORTHODOX EASTERN CHURCH

see also Schism—Eastern and Western Church

Cleenewerck, Laurent. His Broken Body: Understanding & Healing the Schism between the Roman Catholic & Eastern Orthodox Churches. 2008. 448p. pap. 33.50 *(978-0-615-18361-9(1))* Euclid Univ. Pr.

DeVille, Adam A. J. Orthodoxy & the Roman Papacy: Ut Unum Sint & the Prospects of East-West Unity. 2011. (ENG.). 280p. pap. 38.00 *(978-0-268-02607-3(6))* Univ. of Notre Dame Pr.

Dvornik. The Photian Schism: History & Legend. 2008. (ENG.). 524p. pap. 61.00 *(978-0-521-10176-9(X))* Cambridge Univ. Pr.

Hinterberger, M. & Schabel, C., eds. Greeks, Latins, & Intellectual History 1204-1500. 2011. (Recherches de Theologie et Philosophie Medievales - Bibliotheca Ser.). (ENG.). 463p. (C). pap. 100.00 *(978-90-429-2440-6(3))* Peeters Pubs. & Booksellers BEL. Dist: Brown, David Bk. Co., The.

Kolbaba, Tia M. Inventing Latin Heretics: Byzantines & the Filioque in the Ninth Century. 2008. 40.00 *(978-1-58044-133-9(5))* Medieval Institute Pubns.

Papas, Athanasios. Rome & Constantinople: Pope Paul VI & Metropolitan Meliton of Chalcedon. 2006. 60p. per. 7.95 *(978-1-933275-11-6(1)*, Orthodox Research Institute) Cocheco Falls Publishing.

Rogers, Francis M. The Quest for Eastern Christians: Travels & Rumor in the Age of Discovery. 2009. (ENG.). 240p. pap. 50.00 *(978-0-8166-5861-9(7))* Univ. of Minnesota Pr.

Rowe, Bede. Synodality. 2010. 107p. pap. 21.50 *(978-1-4452-2795-5(9))* Lulu Enterprises Inc.

Schabel, Christopher D. Greeks Latins & the Church in Early Frankish Cyprus. 2010. (Variorum Collected Studies). (Illus.). 346p. 165.00 *(978-1-4094-0092-9(1))* Ashgate Publishing Co.

CATHOLIC CHURCH—RELATIONS—PROTESTANT CHURCHES

Armstrong, Dave. Bible Conversations: Catholic-Protestant Dialogues on the Bible, Tradition, & Salvation. 2007. 224p. per. 16.95 *(978-1-4303-2104-0(0))* Lulu Enterprises Inc.

—The One-Minute Apologist: Essential Catholic Replies to over Sixty Common Protestant Claims. 2007. 143p. per. 14.95 *(978-1-933184-23-4(X))* Sophia Institute Pr.

Cavanaugh, Stephen E., ed. Anglicans & the Roman Catholic Church: Reflections on Recent Developments. 2011. 255p. pap. 18.95 ***(978-1-58617-499-6(1))*** Ignatius Pr.

C

Chmielewski, Laura M. The Spice of Popery: Converging Christianities on an Early American Frontier. 2011. (ENG., Illus.). 352p. pap. 38.00 **(978-0-268-02307-2(7))** Univ. of Notre Dame Pr.

Clifford, Catherine E. For the Communion of the Churches: The Contribution of the Groupe des Dombes. 2010. 232p. pap. 30.00 *(978-0-8028-6532-8(1))* Eerdmans, William B. Publishing Co.

Gandolfo, Lucian. Soul Baptism. 2006. (ENG.). 21.99 *(978-1-60034-931-7(5))*; pap. 13.99 *(978-1-60034-930-0(7))* Xulon Pr., Inc.

Gjerde, Jon. Catholicism & the Shaping of 19th Century America. Kang, S. Deborah, ed. (ENG., Illus.). 2012. 292p. pap. 32.99 *(978-0-521-27966-6(6))* 2011. 304p. 99.00 *(978-1-107-01024-6(1))* Cambridge Univ. Pr.

Hill, Christopher. Anglicans & Roman Catholics Search for Unity. vii, 344p. *(978-0-281-04745-1(6))* SPCK Publishing.

Lane, Anthony N. S. Justification by Faith in Catholic-Protestant Dialogue: An Evangelical Assessment. 2006. (Scholars' Editions in Theology Ser.). (ENG.). 284p. 70.00 *(978-0-567-04004-6(6)*, T&T Clark Int'l) Continuum International Publishing Group, Ltd. GBR. Dist: National Bk. Network.

Lehner, Ulrich, ed. Beda Mayr, Vertheidigung der katholischen Religion (1789) Sammt einem Anhange von der Möglichkeit einer Vereinigung zwischen unserer, und der Evangelisch-Lutherischen Kirche. 2009. (Brill's Studies in Intellectual History). (GER & ENG.). 434p. *(978-90-04-17318-7(8))* BRILL.

Poole, Matthew & Kistler, Don. A Discussion Between a Catholic Priest & a Protestant: Wherein the Principal Points & Arguments of Both Religions Are Truly Proposed & Fully Examined. 2010. *(978-0-9826155-3-9(1))* Northampton Pr., The.

Power, Maria. From Ecumenism to Community Relations: Inter-Church Relationships in Northern Ireland 1980-1999. 2007. 262p. (C). 75.00 *(978-0-7165-3379-5(0))*; pap. 32.50 *(978-0-7165-3380-1(4))* Irish Academic Pr. IRL. Dist: International Specialized Bk. Services.

Rials, Kerby. The Protestant's Guide to Catholicism & Eastern Orthodoxy: How to answer the tough Questions. 3rd exp. ed. 2006. Orig. Title: The Three Great Churches: Comparing the beliefs of Catholics, Protestants & Orthodox. (ENG & RUS., Illus.). 183p. per. 9.99 *(978-0-9786918-0-6(6))* Delta Mills Bks.

Roussel, Napoleon. Catholic & Protestant Nations Compared, in Their Threefold Relations to Wealth, Knowledge, & Morality by Rev Napoleon Roussell [!] with an In. 2006. 648p. per. 34.99 *(978-1-4255-6678-4(2))* MPublishing.

Walsh, Pat. The Curious Case of the Mayo Librarian. 2009. (ENG., Illus.). 223p. pap. 19.95 *(978-1-85635-615-2(9))* Mercier Pr., Ltd., The IRL. Dist: Dufour Editions, Inc.

Wheeler, Michael. The Old Enemies: Catholic & Protestant in Nineteenth-Century English Culture. 2011. (ENG.). 370p. pap. 45.00 *(978-0-521-29281-8(6))* Cambridge Univ. Pr.

CATHOLIC CHURCH—RELATIONS (DIPLOMAITC)

see Catholic Church—Foreign Relations

CATHOLIC CHURCH—RELATIONS (ECCLESIASTICAL)

see Catholic Church—Relations

CATHOLIC CHURCH—SACRAMENTS

see Sacraments—Catholic Church

CATHOLIC CHURCH—SERMONS

Alfaro, Juan. Homilías Sobre Los Evangelios de Domingos. 2011. (SPA.). 160p. pap. 16.95 **(978-0-8146-3359-5(5))** Liturgical Pr.

Alfaro, Juan I. Homilías Sobre Los Evangelios de Domingos. 2011. (SPA.). **(978-0-8146-3962-7(3))**; (SPA.). 16.95 *(978-0-8146-3358-8(7))*; E-Book *(978-0-8146-3947-4(X))* Liturgical Pr.

Augustine, Saint, et al. Essential Sermons. 2007. pap. 29.95 *(978-1-56548-276-0(X))* New City Pr.

Baker, Kenneth. Preach the Word: Homilies on the Sundays & Feasts of the Extraordinary Form of the Roman Rite. 2010. *(978-0-8189-1314-3(2))* St Pauls/Alba Hse. Pubs.

Baker, S.J., Kenneth. Doctrinal Sermons on the Catechism of the Catholic Church. 2012. (ENG.). 272p. pap. 22.00 **(978-1-58731-189-5(5))** St. Augustine's Pr., Inc.

Benedict. Pope Benedict in America: The Full Texts of Papal Talks Given During His Apostolic Visit to the United States. 2008. 130p. 14.95 *(978-1-58617-293-0(X))* Ignatius Pr.

Benedict XVI, pseud. Christ Our Hope: The Papal Addresses of the Apostolic Journey to the United States. 2008. (Illus.). 160p. 14.95 *(978-0-8091-0561-8(6)*, 0561-6) Paulist Pr.

Bossuet, Jacques Benigne & Truchet, Jacques. Oraisons Funèbres. (FRE., Illus.). lvi, 463p. *(978-2-84431-002-6(8))* Garnier.

Burghardt, Walter. Short Sermons for Preachers on the Run. 2009. 144p. pap. 18.00 *(978-1-57075-848-5(4))* Orbis Bks.

Chilcott-Monk, Julien, ed. In the Name of the Father: Homilies for the Extraordinary Rite. 2010. (ENG.). 254p. pap. 26.99 *(978-1-84825-027-7(4)*, Canterbury Pr. Norwich) Hymns Ancient & Modern Ltd GBR. Dist: Westminster John Knox Pr.

Deiss, Lucien. God's Word Is Our Joy: Advent, Christmas, Lent & Easter, Cycle A. Date not set. pap. 14.95 *(978-0-937690-27-7(9))* World Library Pubns.

—God's Word Is Our Joy: Advent, Christmas, Lent, Easter, Cycle B. Date not set. pap. 14.95 *(978-0-937690-29-1(5))* World Library Pubns.

—God's Word Is Our Joy: Advent, Christmas, Lent, Easter, Cycle C. Date not set. pap. 14.95 *(978-0-937690-31-4(7))* World Library Pubns.

—God's Word Is Our Joy: Sundays 2-34 of the Year, Cycle A. Date not set. pap. 17.95 *(978-0-937690-28-4(7))* World Library Pubns.

—God's Word Is Our Joy: Sundays 2-34 of the Year, Cycle C. Date not set. pap. 17.95 *(978-0-937690-32-1(5))* World Library Pubns.

Escrivá de Balaguer, José María. In Love with the Church. 2007. 107p. pap. *(978-1-59417-058-4(4))* Scepter Pubs., Inc.

Fernandez, Tiburtius. Homilies for the Year C. 2006. (ENG.). 328p. per. 19.95 *(978-1-59526-629-3(1))* Aeon Publishing Inc.

GutiZcaron;rrez, Gustavo. Sharing the Word through the Liturgical Year. 2009. 304p. pap. 35.00 *(978-1-60608-544-8(1)*, Wipf and Stock) Wipf & Stock Pubs.

Hayes, Michael T. Homilies for the Whole Community: Wisdom from a Pastor's Heart; Year C. 2006. (Illus.). 246p. per. 24.95 *(978-1-58595-568-8(X))* Twenty-Third Pubns./Bayard.

Hogan, Martin. Weekday Homilies. 2014. (ENG.). 256p. pap. 18.95 *(978-1-85607-667-8(9))* Columba Pr. IRL. Dist: Dufour Editions, Inc.

Holloman, Russ. And Now, A Word from Our Creator. 2011. 296p. pap. 22.95 **(978-1-4497-2643-0(7)**, WestBow Pr.) Author Solutions, Inc.

Hopkins, Jasper, tr. from LAT. Nicholas of Cusa's Didactic Sermons: A Selection. 2008. 504p. 40.00 *(978-0-938060-53-6(8))* Banning, Arthur J. Pr.

Hurd, Richard. An Introduction to the Study of the Prophecies Concerning the Christian Church, And In Particular, Concerning the Church of Papal Rome. 2006. pap. 31.95 *(978-1-4286-4696-4(5))* Kessinger Publishing, LLC.

Kelty, Matthew. Gethsemani Homilies. 2010. E-Book *(978-0-87907-927-7(4))* Cistercian Pubns., Inc.

—Singing for the Kingdom: The Last of the Homilies. Paulsell, William O., ed. 2008. (Monastic Wisdom Ser.). 127p. pap. 13.95 *(978-0-87907-015-1(3))* Cistercian Pubns., Inc.

Kienzle, Beverly, tr. from LAT. Hildegard of Bingen. 2011. 228p. pap. 29.95 **(978-0-87907-241-4(5))** Cistercian Pubns., Inc.

Kinn, James W. Teach, Delight, Persuade: Scriptural Homilies for Years a, B, & C. 2009. vii, 368p. *(978-1-59525-026-1(3))* Hillenbrand Bks.

Knox, Ronald & Knox, Richard. Creed in Slow Motion. 2009. 256p. pap. 14.95 *(978-0-87061-250-3(6)*, Christian Classic) Ave Maria Pr.

Krempa, S. Joseph. Captured Fire: The New Daily Homilies. 2008. *(978-0-8189-1289-4(8))* St Pauls/Alba Hse. Pubs.

—Captured Fire: The New Daily Homilies, Year One. 2008. *(978-0-8189-1288-7(X))* St Pauls/Alba Hse. Pubs.

—Captured Fire 2 Volume Set: New Daily Homilies, Year One/Seasonal & Sanctoral Cycle, Year One. 2009. pap. 29.95 *(978-0-8189-1290-0(1))* St Pauls/Alba Hse. Pubs.

Lacordaire, Henri. Life Conferences Delivered at Toulouse. 2007. 236p. per. 22.95 *(978-0-9783198-5-4(0))* Catholic Authors Pr.

Leinenweber, John, ed. Bernard of Clairvaux: Sermons for Advent & the Christmas Season. Edmonds, Irene et al, trs. from LAT. 2007. (Cistercian Fathers Ser.). 202p. per. 24.95 *(978-0-87907-451-7(5)*, CF051P) Cistercian Pubns., Inc.

Letellier, Robert. Sunday & Feastday Sermons: Cycles a, B, & C. 2011. **(978-0-8189-1331-0(2)**, St. Pauls) St Pauls/Alba Hse. Pubs.

Matera, Frank J. Preaching Romans: Proclaiming God's Saving Grace. 2010. 14.95 *(978-0-8146-3318-2(8))* Liturgical Pr.

McGuire, Brendan. Seeds for the Soul: Sunday Homilies for Cycle A. 2007. (ENG.). 144p. per. 19.95 *(978-1-85607-569-3(3))* Columba Pr. IRL. Dist: Dufour Editions, Inc.

McKenna, Megan. Lent: Sunday Readings. 2008. (ENG.). 201p. pap. 22.95 *(978-1-84730-099-7(5))* Veritas Pubns. IRL. Dist: Dufour Editions, Inc.

Mengelle, Ervens. El Camino del Espiritu. 2007.Tr. of Path of the Spirit. (SPA.). 376p. pap. 19.95 *(978-1-933871-04-2(0))* IVE Pr.

Mengelle, Ervens Dario. Jesucristo, Misterio y Mysteria. 2009. (SPA.). 411p. 19.95 *(978-1-933871-09-7(1))* IVE Pr.

—El Padre y su Reino: Homilías Dominicales y Festivas para el ciclo A siguiendo el Catecismo de la Iglesia Catolica. 2007. (SPA.). 391p. pap. 19.95 *(978-1-933871-46-2(6))* IVE Pr.

Merton, Thomas & Guerric. The Christmas Sermons of Blessed Guerric of Igny. Sister Rose Of Lima, tr. 2011. 66p. 36.95 **(978-1-258-04469-5(2))** Literary Licensing, LLC.

Newman, John Henry, et al. John Henry Newman Sermons, 1824-1843 Vol. 4: The Church & Miscellaneous Sermons at St Mary's & Littlemore. 2011. (ENG., Illus.). 416p. 199.00 *(978-0-19-920091-7(2))* Oxford Univ. Pr., Inc.

Papineau, Andre. Homilies to Transform Hearts & Minds. 2010. pap. *(978-0-89390-690-0(5))* Resource Pubns., Inc.

Przywara, Erich. The Heart of Newman. 2010. 425p. pap. 17.95 *(978-1-58617-498-9(3))* Ignatius Pr.

Ratzinger, Joseph. The God of Jesus Christ: Meditations on the Triune God. McNeil, Brian, tr. from GER. 2008. 113p. 19.95 *(978-1-58617-184-1(4))* Ignatius Pr.

Samaniego, Eduardo & Keating, Helen. If You Preach It They Will Come. 2006. vi, 112p. *(978-0-89390-646-7(8))* Resource Pubns., Inc.

Scheepsma, W. The Limburg Sermons: Preaching in the Medieval Low Countries at the Turn of the Fourteenth Century. 2008. (Brill's Ser. in Church History Ser.). (Illus.). 480p. *(978-90-04-16969-2(5))* BRILL.

Sherwood, Timothy. The Preaching of Archbishop Fulton J. Sheen: The Gospel Meets the Cold War. 2010. (ENG.). 168p. 62.99 *(978-0-7391-4261-5(5))* Lexington Bks.

Sherwood, Timothy H. The Preaching of Archbishop Fulton J. Sheen: The Gospel Meets the Cold War. 2011. (ENG.). 168p. pap. 26.99 **(978-0-7391-4262-2(3))** 2010. *(978-0-7391-4263-9(1))* Lexington Bks.

St. Meinrad's Abbey. The Lessons of the Temporal Cycle & the Principal Feasts of the Sanctoral Cycle According to the Monastic Breviary. 2011. 532p. 60.95 **(978-1-258-04759-7(4))** Literary Licensing, LLC.

Talafous, Don. Homilies for Weekdays: Year 1. 2006. 219p. per. 16.95 *(978-0-8146-3031-0(6))* Liturgical Pr.

—Homilies for Weekdays Solemnities Feasts Memorials. 2009. 88p. pap. 16.95 *(978-0-8146-1871-4(5)*, Liturgical Pr. Bks.) Liturgical Pr.

—Homilies for Weekdays Threeet. 2009. pap. 45.00 *(978-0-8146-3303-8(X)*, Liturgical Pr. Bks.) Liturgical Pr.

Tolhurst, James, intro. Sermons Preached on Various Occasions. 2008. (ND Works of Cardinal Newman Ser.). (ENG.). 368p. 40.00 *(978-0-268-03662-1(4))* Univ. of Notre Dame Pr.

Trần, Bình Trong. Hàng Tuần Chúa Nói Vi Ta - Ta áp Tra Li Chúa: ê Cùng Chiêm Niem, Câu Nguyên, Diên Giang, T Dân àng Thiêng Liêng, Làm Giâu I Sông Tâm Linh Da Theo Li Hang Sông: Chúa Nhat, Lê Trong, Lê Kính, Lê Ac Biêt, Chu Ky Phuc Vu, Nam B. 2008. (Illus.). xvi, 329p. *(978-1-932708-23-3(5))* Tuoi Hoa Publishing.

Vieira, Antonio. The Sermon of Saint Anthony to the Fish & Other Texts. Rabassa, Gregory, tr. from POR. 2009. (Adamastor Ser.). 112p. pap. 19.95 *(978-1-933227-30-6(3))* Tagus Pr.

Ward, Louis B. & Coughlin, Charles E. Father Charles E Coughlin: An Authorized Biography. 2011. 380p. 53.95 **(978-1-258-00259-6(0))** Literary Licensing, LLC.

William & Kraebel, A. B. The Sermons of William of Newburgh: Edited from Oxford, Bodleian Library, MS Rawlinson C.31, London, Lambeth Palace Library, MS 73, & London, British Library, MS Stowe 62. 2010. (Toronto Medieval Latin Texts). (LAT & ENG.). 128p. pap. 12.95 **(978-0-88844-481-3(8))** Pontifical Institute of Mediaeval Studies, Dept. of Pubns. CAN. Dist: Univ. of Toronto Pr.

Zajac, Richard. Life Injections III: Additional Connections of Scripture to the Human Experience. 2007. 180p. per. 24.95 *(978-1-4241-7488-1(0))* PublishAmerica, Inc.

CATHOLIC CHURCH—SOCIETIES, ETC.

see also Confraternities; Monasticism and Religious Orders; Monasticism and Religious Orders for Women

Giussani, Luigi. The Journey to Truth Is an Experience. Zucchi, John, tr. from ITA. 2006. (ENG.). 160p. (C). *(978-0-7735-3147-5(5))* McGill-Queen's Univ. Pr.

Giussani, Luigi & Stevenson, Patrick. The Journey to Truth Is an Experience. Zucchi, John, tr. from ITA. 2006. (ENG.). 160p. (C). pap. *(978-0-7735-3148-2(3))* McGill-Queen's Univ. Pr.

Leahy, Brendan & Leahy, Breandan. Ecclesial Movements & Communities: Origins, Significance, & Issues. 2011. pap. 14.95 **(978-1-56548-396-5(0))** New City Pr.

CATHOLIC CHURCH—TRADITIONALIST MOVEMENT

see Catholic Traditionalist Movement

CATHOLIC CHURCH—YEARBOOKS

see Catholic Church—Periodicals

CATHOLIC CHURCH—AFRICA

Abba, Joe-Barth C. Special Pastoral Formation for Youths in Africa in the 21st Century: The Nigerian Perspective. 2009. 408p. pap. 99.95 *(978-3-631-58434-7(2))* Lang, Peter GmbH, Europaischer Verlag der Wissenschaften DEU. Dist: Lang, Peter.

Benson, Pius. The Church in the Theological Writings of Avery Dulles: Impulses for African Ecclesiology. (European University Studies: Vol. 852). 341p. pap. 68.95 *(978-3-631-56492-9(9))* Lang, Peter GmbH, Europaischer Verlag der Wissenschaften DEU. Dist: Lang, Peter Publishing, Inc.

Chukwu, Donatus Oluwa. The Church As the Extended Family of God. 2011. 214p. 29.99 **(978-1-4568-0511-1(8))**; pap. 19.99 **(978-1-4568-0510-4(X))** Xlibris Corp.

Creary, Nicholas M. Domesticating a Religious Import: The Jesuits & the Inculturation of the Catholic Church in Zimbabwe, 1879-1980. 2nd ed. 2011. (ENG., Illus.). 280p. 48.00 *(978-0-8232-3334-2(0))* Fordham Univ. Pr.

Eisentraut, Christoph. The Ministry of Permanent Deacons. 2010. 116p. pap. *(978-3-639-22186-2(9))* VDM Verlag Dr. Mueller e.K.

Eze, Damian Onwuegbuchulam. The Eucharist as Orikonso: A Study in Eucharistic Ecclesiology from an Igbo Perspective. 2008. (Europäische Hochschulschriften. Reihe 23: Theologie Ser.). 312p. pap. 74.95 *(978-3-631-57883-4(0))* Lang, Peter GmbH, Europaischer Verlag der Wissenschaften DEU. Dist: Lang, Peter.

Gribble, Richard. The Implementation of Vatican II in Eastern Africa: The Contribution of Bishop Vincent Mccauley, CSC. 2009. 312p. 119.95 *(978-0-7734-4701-1(6))* Mellen, Edwin Pr., The.

Ilibagiza, Immaculée & Erwin, Steve. Our Lady of Kibeho: Mary Speaks to the World from the Heart of Africa. 2010. (ENG.). 240p. pap. 13.95 *(978-1-4019-2743-1(2))* Hay Hse., Inc.

Jean, Yanick. Ahobobo: On the Sacramental Imagination in West Africa, Bénin, 2006-2008. 2010. (ENG.). 132p. pap. 22.00 *(978-0-7618-5365-7(0))* Univ. Pr. of America, Inc.

Jenkins, John P. The Lost History of Christianity: The Thousand-Year Golden Age of the Church in the Middle East, Africa, & Asia — And How It Died. 2008. (ENG.). 336p. 26.95 *(978-0-06-147280-0(8)*, HarperOne) HarperCollins Pubs.

Kasomo, Daniel W. Personal Ordinariate & Personal Prelature. 2011. 440p. pap. **(978-3-8443-0712-2(5))** Lambert Academic Publishing.

Martin, Phyllis M. Catholic Women of Congo-Brazzaville: Mothers & Sisters in Troubled Times. 2009. (ENG., Illus.). 280p. pap. 24.95 *(978-0-253-22055-4(6)*, 0253220556) Indiana Univ. Pr.

—Catholic Women of Congo-Brazzaville: Mothers & Sisters in Troubled Times. 2009. (ENG., Illus.). 280p. 65.00 *(978-0-253-35281-1(9)*, 0253352819) Indiana Univ. Pr.

Mbano, Dunstan M. Ecclesiological Trends in the Catholic & Protestant Churches & Their Significance for the Church in Africa: A Study of Selected Texts. 2008. (Europäische Hochschulschriften. Reihe 23: Theologie Ser.). 324p. pap. 81.95 *(978-3-631-58497-2(0))* Lang, Peter GmbH, Europaischer Verlag der Wissenschaften DEU. Dist: Lang, Peter.

McGee, Martin. Christian Martyrs for a Muslim People. 2008. 224p. pap. 18.95 *(978-0-8091-4539-3(1))* Paulist Pr.

Moerschbacher, M. Volk Gottes in Afrika: Die Rolle der Laien in der pastoralen Erneuerung von Kardinal Malula, Kinshasa. 2007. (Annua Nuntia Lovaniensia Ser.). (GER.). 375p. (C). pap. 95.00 *(978-90-429-1965-5(5))* Peeters Pubs. & Booksellers BEL. Dist: Brown, David Bk. Co., The.

Mwerihari Musings: '1964 Southern Rhodesia to Zimbabwe 1999' 2007. (Illus.). 216p. per. *(978-1-84401-804-8(0))* Athena Pr.

Naaeke, Anthony Y. Kaleidoscope Catechesis: Missionary Catechesis in Africa, Particularly in the Diocese of Wa in Ghana. 2006. 174p. (C). 62.95 *(978-0-8204-8685-7(X))* Lang, Peter Publishing, Inc.

Obodoechina, Uchechukwu. The Imperative of Self-Reliance for the Churches in Africa: A Study in Christian Social Ethics, Vol. 873. 2006. (European University Studies Ser.: Vol. 23). xx,354p. pap. 62.95 *(978-0-8204-8730-4(9))* Lang, Peter Publishing, Inc.

Okorie, George Maduakolam. The Integral Salvation of the Human Person in Ecclesia in Africa: A case study of the theological implications among the Igbo in Nigeria. 2008. (Europäische Hochschulschriften. Reihe 23: Theologie Ser.). 482p. pap. 107.95 *(978-3-631-57647-2(1))* Lang, Peter GmbH, Europaischer Verlag der Wissenschaften DEU. Dist: Lang, Peter.

Okuma, Peter Chidi. Empowerment of the Catholic Laity in the Nigerian Political Situation: An Hermeneutical Reading of Apostolicam Actuositatem (the Decree on the Apostolate of the Laity) of Vatican II & its Application to Concrete Situations. 2008. 262p. pap. 65.95 *(978-3-631-58182-7(3))* Lang, Peter GmbH, Europaischer Verlag der Wissenschaften DEU. Dist: Lang, Peter.

Onunkwo, Vincent Chijioke. Peace in the Social Teachings of Pope John Paul II: Its Relevance to the Igbo of Southeastern Nigeria, Vol. 834. 2006. (European University Studies Ser.: Vol. 23). 323p. pap. 62.95 *(978-0-8204-9900-0(5))* Lang, Peter Publishing, Inc.

Orobator, Agbonkhianmeghe E. Reconciliation, Justice, & Peace: The Second African Synod. 2011. 304p. pap. 40.00 *(978-1-57075-916-1(2))* Orbis Bks.

Rupp, Joyce. Your Sorrow Is My Sorrow: Hope & Strength in Times of Suffering. *(978-0-86716-528-9(6))* Franciscan Media.

Settimba, Henry. Testing Times: Globalisation & Investing Theology in East Africa. 2009. 312p. pap. 15.49 *(978-1-4389-4798-3(4))* AuthorHouse.

Six-Means, Horace E. Augustine Catholic Christianization: The Catholicization of Roman Africa, 391-408. 2011. **(978-1-4331-0804-4(6))** Lang, Peter GmbH, Europaischer Verlag der Wissenschaften.

Smith, Gary N. They Come Back Singing: Finding God with the Refugees. 2008. (ENG., Illus.). 248p. per. 14.95 *(978-0-8294-2701-1(5))* Loyola Pr.

UNAIDS. A Faith-based Response to HIV in Southern Africa: The Choose to Care Inititative. 2006. (UNAIDS Publication). (ENG.). 75p. pap. 18.00 *(978-92-9173-546-4(9))* World Health Organization.

Uzukwu, Elochukwu E. A Listening Church: Autonomy & Communion in African Churches. 2006. 192p. pap. 22.00 *(978-1-59752-898-6(6)*, Wipf and Stock) Wipf & Stock Pubs.

CATHOLIC CHURCH—AMERICA

Ben-Dror, Graciela. La Iglesia Católica Ante el Holocausto: España y América Latina 1933-1945. (SPA., Illus.). 336p. 39.30 *(978-84-206-4164-5(2))* Alianza Editorial, S. A. ESP. Dist: Libros in Spanish, LLC.

Garcia, Mary. The Sufferings, Assassinations, & Martyrdom of the Missionary CHurch in Olancho, Hondouras (1963-1982) The History of a Church That Lived Its Commitment to the Poor. Whelan, Winifred, tr. from SPA. 2011. (Illus.). 360p. 139.95 **(978-0-7734-3952-8(8))** Mellen, Edwin Pr., The.

Lyons, Barry J. Remembering the Hacienda: Religion, Authority, & Social Change in Highland Ecuador. 2006. (Joe R. & Teresa Lozano Long Series in Latin American & Latino Art & Culture). (ENG., Illus.). 362p. mass mkt. 24.95 *(978-0-292-71439-7(4))* Univ. of Texas Pr.

McNeil, Lou F. Recovering American Catholic Inculturation: John England's Jacksonian Populism & Romanticist Adaptation. 2008. (ENG.). 270p. 68.50 *(978-0-7391-2453-6(6))* Lexington Bks.

O'Shaughnessy, Hugh. The Priest of Paraguay: Fernando Lugo & the Making of a Nation. 2009. (ENG., Illus.). 176p. pap. 29.95 *(978-1-84813-313-6(8))*; 119.95 *(978-1-84813-312-9(X))* Zed Bks., Ltd. GBR. Dist: Macmillan.

Wright, Scott. Oscar Romero & the Communion of Saints: A Biography. 2009. (Illus.). 160p. pap. 20.00 *(978-1-57075-839-3(5))* Orbis Bks.

CATHOLIC CHURCH—ARGENTINA

Ben-Dror, Graciela. Argentina, 1933-1945. 2009. (Studies in Antisemitism Ser.). (ENG.). 278p. 55.00 *(978-0-8032-1889-5(3))* Univ. of Nebraska Pr.

Finchelstein, Federico. Transatlantic Fascism: Ideology, Violence, & the Sacred in Argentina & Italy, 1919-1945. 2010. (ENG.). 344p. pap. 25.95 *(978-0-8223-4612-8(5))*; (Illus.). 94.95 *(978-0-8223-4594-7(3))* Duke Univ. Pr.

CATHOLIC CHURCH—ASIA

Hanh, Etienne vo Duc. La Place du Catholicisme dans les Relations Entre la France et le Viet-Nam de 1887 a 1903. (Publications Universitaires Europeennes). (FRE.). *(978-3-906765-21-1(0))* Lang, Peter.

Jenkins, John P. The Lost History of Christianity: The Thousand-Year Golden Age of the Church in the Middle East, Africa, & Asia — And How It Died. 2008. (ENG.). 336p. 26.95 *(978-0-06-147280-0(8)*, HarperOne) HarperCollins Pubs.

Kadaliyil, Abraham. Toward a Relational Spirit Ecclesiology in Asi. 2009. 224p. pap. *(978-3-639-13498-8(2))* VDM Verlag Dr. Mueller e.K.

Koten, Philipus Panda. Potret Komunitas Basis Gerejani Kita: Laporan Riset Candraditya, 2004-2007. 2009. (IND., Illus.). xv, 218p. *(978-979-9447-72-2(0))* Lembaga Pembentukan Berlanjut Arnold Janssen, LPBAJ.

Sabbah, Patriarch Michel. Faithful Witness: On Reconciliation & Peace in the Holy Land. Christiansen, S.J., Drew, Drew, ed. 2009. 208p. pap. 24.95 *(978-1-56548-307-1(3))* New City Pr.

Schneider, A. M. & Power, P. St. Peter in Gallicantu. 2010. pap. 21.16 *(978-1-60724-929-0(4))* Gorgias Pr., LLC.

Steenbrink, Karel. Catholics in Indonesia, 1808-1942, Vol. 2. 2010. (Verhandelingen Van Het Koninklijk Instituut Voor Taal-, Land Ser.). (Illus.). 648p. pap. 60.00 *(978-90-6718-260-7(5))* KITLV Pr. NLD. Dist: Univ. of Hawaii Pr.

CATHOLIC CHURCH—AUSTRALIA

Cleary, Maureen. Management Dilemmas in Catholic Human Service: Health Care, Welfare, & Education. 2007. (Illus.). 304p. *(978-0-7734-5462-0(4))* Mellen, Edwin Pr., The.

Dowd, Christopher. Rome in Australia: The Papacy & Conflict in the Australian Catholic Missions, 1834-1884, 2 vols. 2008. (Studies in the History of Christian Traditions: Vol. 140). (Illus.). xxv, 658p. (C). *(978-90-04-16529-8(0))* BRILL.

Foster, Chrissie. Hell on the Way to Heaven: An Australian Mother's Love - The Power of the Catholic Church, & a Fight for Justice over Child Sexual Abuse. 2010. (ENG., Illus.). 391p. 27.95 *(978-1-74166-952-7(9))* Random Hse. Australia AUS. Dist: Independent Pubs. Group.

Giurgola, Romaldo. Luminous Simplicity: The Architecture & Art of St. Patrick's Cathedral, Parramatta. rev. ed. 2006. (Illus.). 192p. (C). 99.00 *(978-1-876832-83-4(5))* Macmillan Art Publishing AUS. Dist: Brown, David Bk. Co., The.

Williams, Sue. World Beyond Tears: The Ongoing Story of Father Chris Riley. 2007. 304p. (Orig.). *(978-0-7322-8265-3(9))* HarperCollins Pubs. Australia.

Wiltgen, Ralph M. The Founding of the Roman Catholic Church in Melanesia & Micronesia, 1850-1875. 2008. (Princeton Theological Monographs). (Illus.). 596p. pap. 66.00 *(978-1-55635-209-6(3))*, Pickwick Pubns.) Wipf & Stock Pubs.

CATHOLIC CHURCH—AUSTRIA

Burton, Katherine. One Thing Needful: The Biography of Mother Franziska Lechner, Foundress of the Daughters of Divine Charity. 2011. 224p. 44.95 *(978-1-258-06245-3(3))* Literary Licensing, LLC.

Fulton, Elaine. Catholic Belief & Survival in Late Sixteenth-Century Vienna: The Case of Georg Eder (1523-1587) 2007. (St. Andrews Studies in Reformation History). (Illus.). 216p. 124.95 *(978-0-7546-5652-4(7))* Ashgate Publishing Co.

Thaler, Manfred Josef. Das Salzburger Domkapitel in der Frühen Neuzeit (1514 Bis 1806) Verfassung und Zusammensetzung. 2011. (Wissenschaft und Religion Ser.). (GER.). 638p. 115.95 *(978-3-631-60601-8(X))* Lang, Peter GmbH, Europaischer Verlag der Wissenschaften DEU. Dist: Lang, Peter.

CATHOLIC CHURCH—BELGIUM

Donnelly, D., et al, eds. The Belgian Contribution to the Second Vatican Council: International Research Conference at Mechelen, Leuven & Louvain-la-Neuve (September 12-16, 2005) 2008. (Bibliotheca Ephemeridum Theologicarum Lovaniensium Ser.). (ENG.). 728p. (C). pap. 124.00 *(978-90-429-2101-6(3))* Peeters Pubs. & Booksellers BEL. Dist: Brown, David Bk. Co., The.

CATHOLIC CHURCH—BRAZIL

Berryman, Philip. Religion in the Megacity: Catholic & Protestant Portraits from Latin America. 2006. 216p. pap. 24.00 *(978-1-59752-903-7(6)*, Wipf and Stock) Wipf & Stock Pubs.

Krischke, Paulo Jose. Populism & the Catholic Church: Political Crisis in Brazil 1964. 2010. (Religion & Spirituality Ser.). 129.00 *(978-1-61728-296-6(0))* Nova Science Pubs., Inc.

Le Breton, Binka. The Greatest Gift: The Courageous Life & Martyrdom of Sister Dorothy Stang. Lt. ed. 2008. (Thorndike Biography Ser.). (Illus.). 333p. 30.95 *(978-1-4104-0652-1(0))* Thorndike Pr.

Ottmann, Goetz Frank. Lost for Words? Brazilian Liberationism in The 1990s. 2009. (Pitt Latin American Studies). (ENG.). 256p. (C). pap. 27.95 *(978-0-8229-8596-9(9))* Univ. of Pittsburgh Pr.

Tosti, Mario. La Chiesa Sul Fiume: La Missione Dei Cappuccini Dell'Umbria in Amazzonia, 1909-2009. 2010. (ITA., Illus.). 363p. *(978-88-88001-68-5(9))* Ist. Storico dei Cappuccini.

CATHOLIC CHURCH—CANADA

Attridge, Michael, et al, eds. Vatican II: Experiences Canadiennes - Canadian Experiences. 2011. (Religion & Beliefs Ser.). (ENG & FRE.). 580p. pap. *(978-2-7603-0763-6(8))* Univ. of Ottawa Pr./Presses de l'Universite d'Ottawa.

Briere, Emile-Marie. Under Mary's Mantle: Our Lady's Love for Canada. 227p. *(978-0-921440-52-9(9))* Madonna Hse. Pubns.

Cameron, Derek. A Journey to the Retreat Centers of British Columbia: Illustrated with Photographs. 2009. (Illus.). 124p. pap. 10.95 *(978-0-9800817-5-6(0))* Eremitical Pr.

Comiskey, John P. In My Heart's Best Wishes for You: A biography of Archbishop John Walsh. 2012. (McGill-Queen's Studies in the History of Religion Ser.). (ENG., Illus.). 304p. (C). *(978-0-7735-4013-2(X))* McGill-Queen's Univ. Pr.

Daly, George Thomas. Catholic Problems in Western Canada. 2008. 264p. 28.99 *(978-0-554-23946-0(9))* 2006. 236p. pap. 20.99 *(978-1-4264-5182-9(2))* 2007. (ENG.). 262p. pap. 23.99 *(978-1-4264-5483-7(X))* BiblioBazaar.

—Catholic Problems in Western Canada. 2009. 224p. pap. *(978-1-4065-6088-6(X))* Dodo Pr.

—Catholic Problems in Western Canada. 2007. 172p. per. *(978-1-4068-1839-3(0))* Echo Library.

—Catholic Problems in Western Canada. 2008. 352p. 46.95 *(978-1-4365-3165-5(7))* 2007. (ENG.). 356p. per. 31.95 *(978-0-548-71722-6(2))* Kessinger Publishing, LLC.

Gottlieb, Laurence. The Catholic Church & Economic Growth in Quebec from 1919 to 1929. 2007. (Illus.). 147p. *(978-0-7734-5321-0(3))* Mellen, Edwin Pr., The.

Higgins, Michael W. & Kavanagh, Peter. Suffer the Children unto Me: An Enquiry into Canada's Clerical Abuse Scandal. 2010. 256p. *(978-2-89646-233-9(3))* Novalis Publishing.

McGowan, Mark G. Michael Power: The Struggle to Build the Catholic Church on the Canadian Frontier. 2007. (McGill-Queen's Studies in the History of Religion Ser.). (ENG., Illus.). 392p. (C). per. *(978-0-7735-3248-9(X))* McGill-Queen's Univ. Pr.

Murphy, Isaac. In Season, Out of Season. 2009. 144p. pap. *(978-3-639-17317-8(1))* VDM Verlag Dr. Mueller e.K.

Sellar, Robert. The Tragedy of Quebec. 2009. (ENG.). 321p. 36.99 *(978-1-117-32395-4(1))*; pap. 29.75 *(978-1-117-32396-1(X))*; pap. 23.99 *(978-1-117-32397-8(8)*, BiblioLife) BiblioBazaar.

Tentler, Leslie Woodcock. The Church Confronts Modernity: Catholicism since 1950 in the United States, Ireland, & Quebec. 2007. 302p. per. 34.95 *(978-0-8132-1494-8(7))* Catholic Univ. of America Pr.

Trepanier, Claire. A Woman of Valour: The Biography of Marie-Louise Bouchard Labelle. 2010. 240p. pap. 24.95 *(978-1-897425-84-8(8))* Univ. of Washington Pr.

CATHOLIC CHURCH—CHINA

Butcher, Beverly J. Chinese & Chinese American Ancestor Veneration in the Catholic Church, 635 A.D. to the Present. 2010. (CHI & ENG., Illus.). viii, 447p. 129.95 *(978-0-7734-3624-4(3))* Mellen, Edwin Pr., The.

Chan, Adrian. Orientalism in Sinology. 2009. 264p. lib. bdg. *(978-1-933146-61-4(3))* Academica Pr., LLC.

Chu, Cindy Yik-Yi. The Diaries of the Maryknoll Sisters in Hong Kong, 1921-1966. 2007. (ENG., Illus.). 256p. 89.00 *(978-1-4039-7668-0(6))* Palgrave Macmillan.

Clark, Anthony E. Chinas Saints: Catholic Martyrdom During the Qing (1644-1911) 2011. (Studies in Missionaries & Christianity in China Ser.). (ENG.). 288p. 75.00 *(978-1-61146-016-2(6))* Fairleigh Dickinson Univ. Pr.

Cristaudo, Wayne. The Church in China Rule, Paul, ed. 2010. (Interface: A Forum for Theology in the World Ser.). (ENG.). 131p. pap. 19.95 *(978-1-921511-74-5(5))* ATF Pr. AUS. Dist: Brown, David Bk. Co., The.

Mariani, Paul P. Church Militant: Bishop Kung & Catholic Resistance in Communist Shanghai. 2011. (ENG., Illus.). 310p. 39.95 *(978-0-674-06153-8(5))* Harvard Univ. Pr.

Rule, Paul, ed. The Church in China. 2010. (Interface Ser.). (ENG.). 123p. (C). pap. 20.00 ***(978-1-921511-96-7(6))*** ATF Theology AUS. Dist: Brown, David Bk. Co., The.

CATHOLIC CHURCH—CUBA

Rodríguez, Fidel. Félix Varela: Profundidad Manifiesta. 2007. (SPA., Illus.). pap. 24.95 *(978-1-59388-074-3(X))* Ediciones Universal.

Rodríguez, P. Fidel. Felix Varela: Profundidad Manifiesta Vol. 1: Primeros Anos de la Vida del Padre Felix Varela y Morales. Infancia, Adolescencia y Juventud (1785-1821), 3 vols. 2007. (Coleccion Felix Varela Ser.: Vol. 28). (Illus.). 347p. pap. 24.95 *(978-1-59388-075-0(8))* Ediciones Universal.

CATHOLIC CHURCH—DEVELOPING COUNTRIES

O'Halloran, James. Living Cells: Vision & Practicalities of Small Christian Communities & Groups. 2010. (ENG., Illus.). 312p. pap. 29.95 *(978-1-85607-699-9(7))* Columba Pr. IRL. Dist: Dufour Editions, Inc.

CATHOLIC CHURCH—EUROPE

Alisauskiene, Milda. Religious Diversity in Post-Soviet Society: Ethnographies of Catholic Hegemony & the New Pluralism in Lithuania. Schroeder, Ingo W., ed. 2011. (Illus.). 224p. 99.95 ***(978-1-4094-0912-0(0))*** Ashgate Publishing Co.

Altermatt, Urs. Konfession, Nation und Rom: Essays zur Kulturgeschichte der Schweiz im 19. und 20. Jahrhundert. 2009. (GER.). 442p. *(978-3-7193-1457-6(X))* Huber & Co., AG, Verlag.

Belloc, Hilaire. Europe & the Faith. 2009. 290p. 30.99 *(978-1-110-35327-9(8))* 2009. 290p. pap. 27.75 *(978-1-110-35322-4(7))* 2009. 292p. 24.99 *(978-1-103-06246-1(8))* 2009. 292p. pap. 18.99 *(978-1-103-06243-0(3))* 2008. 200p. 25.99 *(978-0-554-22751-1(7))* 2008. 200p. 22.99 *(978-0-554-32054-0(1))* BiblioBazaar.

—Europe & the Faith. 2007. (ENG.). 188p. per. 11.95 *(978-1-60206-878-0(X))* Cosimo, Inc.

—Europe & the Faith. 2007. (ENG.). 180p. per. *(978-1-4065-4762-7(X))* Dodo Pr.

—Europe & the Faith. 2008. 188p. pap. 12.95 *(978-1-60096-615-6(2))*; pap. 12.95 *(978-1-60096-065-9(0))* Editorium, The.

—Europe & the Faith. 2007. (ENG.). 288p. 43.95 *(978-0-548-24666-5(1))*; per. 28.95 *(978-1-4326-4886-2(1))* Kessinger Publishing, LLC.

—Europe & the Faith. 2008. (ENG.). 288p. per. *(978-1-4086-6327-1(9))* Read Bks.

Bennett, Jeffrey S. When the Sun Danced: Myth, Miracles, & Modernity in Early Twentieth-Century Portugal. 2012. E-Book ***(978-0-8139-3250-7(5))***; (ENG., Illus.). 256p. (C). (gr. 13-17). pap. 24.50 ***(978-0-8139-3249-1(1))***; (ENG., Illus.). 256p. (gr. 17). 55.00 ***(978-0-8139-3248-4(3))*** Univ. Pr. of Virginia.

Bethencourt, Francisco. The Inquisition: A Global History, 1478-1834. Birrell, Jean, tr. from POR. 2009. (Past & Present Publications). (ENG., Illus.). 504p. pap. 43.00 *(978-0-521-74823-0(2))* Cambridge Univ. Pr.

Bethencourt, Francisco & Birrell, Jean. The Inquisition: A Global History, 1478-1834. 2009. (Past & Present Publications). (ENG., Illus.). 504p. 120.00 *(978-0-521-84793-3(1))* Cambridge Univ. Pr.

Bjork, James. Neither German nor Pole: Catholicism & National Indifference in a Central European Borderland. 2008. (Social History, Popular Culture & Politics in Germany Ser.). (ENG., Illus.). 304p. (C). 85.00 *(978-0-472-11646-1(0))* Univ. of Michigan Pr.

Bobic, Pavlina. War & Faith: The Catholic Church in Slovenia, 1914-1918. 2012. (Illus.). xvii, 261p. ***(978-90-04-20219-1(6))*** BRILL.

Byzantine-Slavonic Rite. Liturgical Catechism: A Catechism on the Divine Liturgy of the Byzantine-Slavonic Rite. 2011. 112p. 39.95 ***(978-1-258-10136-7(X))*** Literary Licensing, LLC.

Callahan, William J. & Higgs, David. Church & Society in Catholic Europe of the Eighteenth Century. 2008. (ENG.). 180p. pap. 31.99 *(978-0-521-09077-3(6))* Cambridge Univ. Pr.

Cerman, Ivo, et al, eds. The Enlightenment in Bohemia: Religion, morality & Multiculturalism. 2011. (Illus.). 352p. pap. ***(978-0-7294-1014-4(5))*** Voltaire Foundation GBR. Dist: Marston Bk. Services, Ltd.

Clark, Christopher & Kaiser, Wolfram, eds. Culture Wars: Secular-Catholic Conflict in Nineteenth-Century Europe. 2009. (ENG., Illus.). 380p. pap. 51.00 *(978-0-521-10845-4(4))* Cambridge Univ. Pr.

Cotts, John D. The Clerical Dilemma: Peter of Blois & Literate Culture in the Twelfth Century. 2009. 336p. pap. 74.95 *(978-0-8132-1676-8(1))* Catholic Univ. of America Pr.

Gottsmann, Andreas. Rom und die nationalen Katholizismen in der Donaumonarchie: Romischer Universalismus, habsburgische Reichspolitik und nationale Identitaten 1878-1914. 2010. (Publikationen des Historischen Instituts beim Osterreichischen Kulturforum in Rom, II. Abteilung, Quellen, 1. Reihe, Band 10 Ser.). (GER.). 408p. (C). pap. 110.00 *(978-3-7001-6596-5(X))* Austrian Academy of Sciences Press AUT. Dist: Brown, David Bk. Co., The.

Isaac Assor. The Lost Throne. 2009. 480p. pap. 25.95 *(978-1-4401-7711-8(2))* iUniverse, Inc.

Korczak, Grzegorz M. Szkoa Jeuness-Lumière O. Daniela-Ange: Próba Syntezy Duchowosci. 2009. (POL.). 309p. *(978-83-7363-830-3(X))* Katolicki Uniwersytet Lubelski, Wydawnictwo.

Kruppa, Nathalie & Zygner, Leszek. Pfarreien im Mittelalter: Deutschland, Polen, Tschechien und Ungarn im Vergleich. Veröffentlichungen des Max-Planck-Instituts für Geschichte. 2008. (Veröffentlichungen des Max-Planck-Instituts Für Geschichte Ser.). (GER & ENG., Illus.). 635p. (C). 119.00 *(978-3-525-35892-4(X))* Vandenhoeck & Ruprecht GmbH & Co. KG DEU. Dist: ISD.

Lehner, Ulrich L. & Printy, Michael O'Neill, eds. A Companion to the Catholic Enlightenment in Europe. 466p. *(978-90-04-18351-3(5))* BRILL.

Louthan, Howard. Converting Bohemia: Force & Persuasion in the Catholic Reformation. 2011. (New Studies in European History Ser.). (ENG.). 368p. pap. 45.00 ***(978-1-107-40355-0(3))*** Cambridge Univ. Pr.

Pilipkó, Erzsébet. Identitás és Hit: A Kárpátaljai Magyar Görög Katolikusok Identifikációs Útjai. 2007. (HUN., Illus.). *(978-963-9814-12-7(1))* Intermix Amerikai- Ukran Ipari Kereskedelmi es Szolgaltato Kft.

Rollo-Koster, Joëlle. Raiding Saint Peter: Empty Sees, Violence, & the Initiation of the Great Western Schism (1378) 2008. (Brill's Ser.). 288p. *(978-90-04-16560-1(6))* BRILL.

Scholz, Sebastian. Politik - Selbstverständnis - Selbstdarstellung: Die Päpste in Karolingischer und Ottonischer Zeit. 2006. (Historische Forschungen Ser.). (GER., Illus.). 514p. (C). 87.00 *(978-3-515-08933-3(0))* Steiner, Franz Verlag Wiesbaden GmbH DEU. Dist: Brown, David Bk. Co., The.

Shinners, John Raymond. Medieval Popular Religion, 1000-1500: A Reader. 2nd rev. ed. 2007. (Readings in Medieval Civilizations & Cultures Ser.: Vol. 2). (Illus.). 555p. pap. *(978-1-55111-698-3(7))* Broadview Pr.

Sullivan, Karen. The Inner Lives of Medieval Inquisitors. 2011. (ENG.). 312p. 45.00 *(978-0-226-78167-9(4))* Univ. of Chicago Pr.

Uí Bhraonáin, Donla. Paidreacha Na Gaeilge: Prayers in Irish. 2009. (ENG., Illus.). 190p. pap. 22.95 *(978-1-901176-88-9(6))* Syracuse Univ. Pr.

Wolff, Richard, ed. Catholics, the State & the European Radical Right, 1919-1945. (Atlantic Studies: No. 50). *(978-0-88033-101-2(1))* Brooklyn College Pr.

CATHOLIC CHURCH—FRANCE

see also Americanism (Catholic Controversy)

Bergin, Joseph. Church, Society & Religious Change in France, 1580-1730. 2009. (ENG., Illus.). 506p. 55.00 *(978-0-300-15098-8(9))* Yale Univ. Pr.

Berry, Jason. Render unto Rome: The Secret Life of Money in the Catholic Church. 2012. (ENG.). 320p. pap. 16.00 ***(978-0-385-53134-4(6))*** Broadway Bks.

Bisaro, Xavier. Une Nation de Fidèles: L'Église et la Liturgie Parisienne Au XVII e Siècle. 2006. (FRE., Illus.). 480p. (C). pap. 153.00 ***(978-2-503-52343-9(9))*** Brepols Pubs. BEL. Dist: ISD.

Burson, Jeffrey D. The Rise & Fall of Theological Enlightenment: Jean-Martin de Prades & Ideological Polarization in Eighteenth-Century France. 2010. (ENG.). 616p. 55.00 *(978-0-268-02220-4(8))* Univ. of Notre Dame Pr.

Dalarun, J., et al. The Two Lives of Robert of Arbrissel, Founder of Fontevraud: Legends, Writings & Testimonies. 2007. (Disciplina Monastica Ser.). (ENG., FRE & LAT., Illus.). 772p. (C). pap. 218.00 *(978-2-503-52419-1(2))* Brepols Pubs. BEL. Dist: ISD.

Daughton, J. P. An Empire Divided: Religion, Republicanism, & the Making of French Colonialism, 1880-1914. 2006. (ENG., Illus.). 344p. 74.00 *(978-0-19-530530-2(2))* Oxford Univ. Pr., Inc.

De Mullenheim, Sophie. John Mary Vianney: The Holy Cure of Ars. 2010. 36p. 14.99 *(978-1-58617-509-2(2))* Ignatius Pr.

Gay, Jean-Pascal. Jesuit Civil Wars: Theology, Politics & Government in the Society of Jesus under Tirso González, 1687-1705. 2012. (Catholic Christendom, 1300-1700 Ser.). (Illus.). 303p. 134.95 ***(978-1-4094-3852-6(X))*** Ashgate Publishing Co.

Gerbert. The Letters of Gerbert: With His Papal Privileges As Sylvester II. Lattin, Harriet Pratt, tr. 2011. 426p. 56.95 ***(978-1-258-04873-0(5))*** Literary Licensing, LLC.

Gibson, W. The Abbe de Lamennais & the Liberal Catholic Movement in France. 2007. (ENG.). 350p. 46.95 *(978-0-548-15850-0(9))*; pap. 31.95 *(978-1-4304-5354-3(0))* Kessinger Publishing, LLC.

Grumett, David & Grumett. De Lubac. 2007. (Guides for the Perplexed Ser.). (ENG.). 200p. pap. 29.95 *(978-0-8264-9315-6(7)*, T&T Clark Int'l) Continuum International Publishing Group, Ltd. GBR. Dist: National Bk. Network.

Hill, Harvey, et al. By Those Who Knew Them: French Modernists Left, Right, & Center. 2008. 200p. (C). 59.95 *(978-0-8132-1537-2(4))* Catholic Univ. of America Pr.

Hoffmann, Michael. Die französischen Konservativen in der katholischen Provinz: Parteigenese und politische Kultur im Doubs (1900-1930) 2008. (Moderne Geschichte und Politik Ser.). (GER., Illus.). 196p. pap. 56.95 *(978-3-631-58166-7(1))* Lang, Peter GmbH, Europaischer Verlag der Wissenschaften DEU. Dist: Lang, Peter.

Kullmann, Dorothea. The Church & Vernacular Literature in Medieval France. 2009. (Studies & Texts). (FRE & ENG., Illus.). vi, 296p. 75.00 *(978-0-88844-165-2(7))* Pontifical Institute of Mediaeval Studies, Dept. of Pubns. CAN. Dist: Univ. of Toronto Pr.

Langlois, Claude & Sorrel, Christian. Le Temps des Congrès Catholiques: Bibliographie Raisonnée des Actes de Congrès Tenus en France de 1870 à Nos Jours. 2010. (FRE.). 437p. *(978-2-503-53183-0(0))* Brepols Pubs.

Madignier, Jacques & Labarthe, Hugues. Diocèse D'Autun. 2010. (Fasti Ecclesiae Gallicanae Ser.: Vol. 12). (FRE., Illus.). viii, 477p. *(978-2-503-53571-5(2))* Brepols Pubs.

Mitchell, Allan. Victors & Vanquished: The German Influence on Army & Church in France After 1870. 2011. (ENG.). 183p. pap. 30.00 *(978-0-8078-9729-4(9))* Univ. of North Carolina Pr.

Oudart, Hervé. Robert D'Arbrissel Ermite et Prédicateur. 2010. (FRE.). xxxiii, 501p. *(978-88-7988-423-5(9))* Fondazione CISAM.

Preyat, Fabrice. Le Petit Concile de Bossuet et la Christianisation des Murs et des Pratiques Littéraires Sous Louis XIV. (FRE.). 570p. *(978-3-8258-8716-2(2)*, Adlard Coles) Lit Verlag.

Reardon, Bernard. Liberalism & Tradition: Aspects of Catholic Thought in Nineteenth-Century France. 2010. (ENG.). 320p. pap. 25.99 *(978-0-521-14305-9(5))* Cambridge Univ. Pr.

Rollo-Koster, Joelle. The People of Curialavignon: A Critical Edition of the Liber Divisionis & the Matriculae of Notre Dame la Majour. 2009. (Illus.). 468p. 129.95 *(978-0-7734-4680-9(X))* Mellen, Edwin Pr., The.

Tingle, Elizabeth C. Purgatory & Piety in Brittany 1480-1720. 2012. (Catholic Christendom, 1300ndash;1700 Ser.). (Illus.). 254p. 124.95 ***(978-1-4094-3824-3(4))***; 310p. 124.95 ***(978-1-4094-3823-6(6))*** Ashgate Publishing Co.

Walsh, Henry H. Concordat of 1801. (Columbia University, Studies in the Social Sciences: No. 387). reprint ed. 31.50 *(978-0-404-51387-0(5))* AMS Pr., Inc.

Wright, Anthony. The Divisions of French Catholicism, 1629-1645: The Parting of the Ways. 2011. (Catholic Christendom, 1300-1700 Ser.). 226p. 124.95 *(978-1-4094-2084-2(1))* Ashgate Publishing Co.

CATHOLIC CHURCH—GERMANY

Adenbauer, Herbert, et al. 70 Jahre Verfolgung und Vertreibung Von Bischof Joannes Baptista Sproll. 2009. (GER., Illus.). 144p. *(978-3-7966-1448-4(5))* Schwabenverlag Aktiengesellschaft.

Baudry. A Warrior Bishop of the Twelfth Century: The Deeds of Albero of Trier. Pavlac, Brian A., tr. from LAT. 2008. (Mediaeval Sources in Translation Ser.). (ENG.). pap. 15.95 *(978-0-88844-294-9(7))* Pontifical Institute of Mediaeval Studies, Dept. of Pubns. CAN. Dist: Univ. of Toronto Pr.

Bennette, Rebecca Ayako. Fighting for the Soul of Germany: The Catholic Struggle for Inclusion after Unification. 2012. (Harvard Historical Studies: 178). (ENG., Illus.). 380p. 49.95 ***(978-0-674-06563-5(8))*** Harvard Univ. Pr.

Besier, Gerhard & Piombo, Francesca. The Holy See & Hitler's Germany. 2007. (ENG.). 272p. 46.00 *(978-1-4039-8831-7(5))* Palgrave Macmillan.

Forster, Marc R. Catholic Germany from the Reformation to the Enlightenment. 2007. (European History in Perspective Ser.). (ENG., Illus.). 224p. 130.00 *(978-0-333-69837-2(1))* Palgrave Macmillan.

—Catholic Germany from the Reformation to the Enlightenment. Black, Jeremy, ed. 2007. (European History in Perspective Ser.). (ENG., Illus.). 224p. pap. 39.00 *(978-0-333-69838-9(X))* Palgrave Macmillan.

—Catholic Revival in the Age of the Baroque: Religious Identity in Southwest Germany, 1550-1750. 2007. (New Studies in European History Ser.). (ENG., Illus.). 284p. pap. 60.00 *(978-0-521-03692-4(5))* Cambridge Univ. Pr.

Godman, Peter. Hitler & the Vatican: Inside the Secret Archives That Reveal the New Story of the Nazis & the Church. 2007. (ENG.). 352p. pap. 20.95 *(978-0-7432-4598-2(9)*, Free Pr.) Free Pr.

C

Golaszewski, Marcin. Clemens August Graf von Galen: Ein Politischer Prediger im Nationalsozialismus. 2010. (Gießener Arbeiten zur neueren deutschen Literatur und Literaturwissenschaft Ser.). (GER.). 292p. 72.95 *(978-3-631-61228-6(1))* Lang, Peter GmbH, Europaischer Verlag der Wissenschaften DEU. Dist: Lang, Peter.

Hastings, Derek. Catholicism & the Roots of Nazism: Religious Identity & National Socialism, 1 vol. (ENG., Illus.). 2011. 312p. pap. 21.95 ***(978-0-19-984345-9(7))*** 2009. 320p. 29.95 *(978-0-19-539024-7(5))* Oxford Univ. Pr., Inc.

Lehner, Ulrich L. Enlightened Monks: The German Benedictines, 1740-1803. 2011. (ENG., Illus.). 356p. 99.00 *(978-0-19-959512-9(7))* Oxford Univ. Pr., Inc.

Plummer, Marjorie Elizabeth. From Priest's Whore to Pastir's Wife: Clerical Marriage & the Process of Reform in the Early German Reformation. 2012. (St Andrews Studies in Reformation History Ser.). (Illus.). 269p. 119.95 ***(978-1-4094-4155-7(5))*** Ashgate Publishing Co.

—From Priest's Whore to Pastor's Wife: Clerical Marriage & the Process of Reform in the Early German Reformation. 2012. (St Andrews Studies in Reformation History Ser.). (Illus.). 268p. 119.95 ***(978-1-4094-4154-0(7))*** Ashgate Publishing Co.

Primus, Asega. The Implication of Prevention of Conflicts for Justice & Peace: In the Light of the Pastoral Letter: Gerechter Friede. 2007. 279p. 82.95 *(978-0-8204-8787-8(2))*; pap. 82.95 *(978-3-631-55936-9(4))* Lang, Peter Publishing, Inc.

Printy, Michael. Enlightenment & the Creation of German Catholicism. (ENG.). 254p. 2011. pap. 26.99 *(978-0-521-18151-8(8))* 2009. 104.00 *(978-0-521-47839-7(1))* Cambridge Univ. Pr.

Pyta, Wolfram, et al, eds. Die Herausforderung Der Diktaturen: Katholizismus in Deutschland und Italien 1918-1943/45. 2009. (Reihe der Villa Vigoni Ser.). (GER & ITA.). VI, 300p. pap. *(978-3-484-67021-1(5))* Verlag Max Niemeyer.

Spicer, Kevin P. Hitler's Priests: Catholic Clergy & National Socialism. 2008. (Illus.). 385p. 34.95 *(978-0-87580-384-5(9))* Northern Illinois Univ. Pr.

Thorak, Thomas. Wilhelm Weskamm: Diasporaseelsorger in der SBZ/DDR. 2009. (GER., Illus.). xliii, 359p. *(978-3-429-03086-5(2))* Echter Wuerzburg.

Vandenhoeck & Ruprecht, ed. Bohemia-Moravia Pontificia: Germania Pontificia. Vol. V/3: Provincia Maguntinensis, Pars VII. 2011. (Regesta Pontificum Romanorum iubente Academia Gottingensi. Gallia Pontificia Ser.). (GER.). 229p. (C). 116.00 *(978-3-525-36038-5(X))* Vandenhoeck & Ruprecht GmbH & Co. KG DEU. Dist: ISD.

Wolf, Hubert. Pope & Devil: The Vatican's Archives & the Third Reich. Kronenberg, Kenneth, tr. from GER. 2010. Orig. Title: Papst und Teufel: Die Archive des Vatikan und das Dritte Reich. (Illus.). 336p. 29.95 *(978-0-674-05081-5(9)*, Belknap Pr.) Harvard Univ. Pr.

Wolf, Hubert & Kronenberg, Kenneth. Pope & Devil: The Vatican's Archives & the Third Reich. 2012. Orig. Title: Papst und Teufel: Die Archive des Vatikan und das Dritte Reich. (ENG., Illus.). 336p. pap. 19.95 ***(978-0-674-06426-3(7)***, Belknap Pr.) Harvard Univ. Pr.

Ziemann, Benjamin. Katholische Kirche und Sozialwissenschaften 1945-1975. 2007. (Kritische Studien Zur Geschichtswissenschaft Ser.). (GER.). 396p. (C). pap. 63.00 *(978-3-525-35156-7(9))* Vandenhoeck & Ruprecht GmbH & Co. KG DEU. Dist: ISD.

CATHOLIC CHURCH—GREAT BRITAIN

Almond, Kenneth Alfred. Saint John Almond & the Society of his Time. 2008. (Illus.). 96p. pap. *(978-1-84748-366-9(6))* Athena Pr.

Biographiq. John Wycliffe - the Morning Star of the Reformation (Biography) 2008. 60p. pap. 9.99 *(978-1-59986-075-6(9)*, Biographiq) Filiquarian Publishing, LLC.

Brett, Martin, et al, eds. Facsimiles of English Episcopal Acta, 1085-1305. 2012. (Check Info & Delete This Occurrence: c EEA v Supplementary Volume 1 t English Episcopal Acta Ser.: Vol. Supplementary Volume 1). (ENG & LAT., Illus.). 230p. 199.00 *(978-0-19-726456-0(5))* Oxford Univ. Pr., Inc.

Broadley, Martin John, ed. Bishop Herbert Vaughan & the Jesuits: Education & Authority. 2010. (Catholic Record Society: Records Ser.: Volume 82). (Illus.). 286p. 80.00 *(978-0-902832-25-1(5))* Catholic Record Society GBR. Dist: Boydell & Brewer, Inc.

Browne, Right Rev G. F. Alcuin of York. 2008. 380p. *(978-1-4437-2301-5(0))* 2006. 376p. per. *(978-1-4067-1835-5(1))* Read Bks. (Hesperides Pr.).

Cheney, Mary, et al, eds. English Episcopal Acta 34, Worcester 1186-1218. 2009. (English Episcopal Acta Ser.). (LAT & ENG., Illus.). 184p. 75.00 *(978-0-19-726430-0(1))* Oxford Univ. Pr., Inc.

Corthell, Ronald, et al, eds. Catholic Culture in Early Modern England. 2007. (ENG., Illus.). 336p. pap. 40.00 *(978-0-268-02294-5(1))* Univ. of Notre Dame Pr.

Coulton, G. G. Medieval Panorama 2 Part Set: The English Scene from Conquest to Reformation, 2 vols. 2010. (Cambridge Library Collection - History Ser.). (ENG., Illus.). 834p. pap. 53.00 *(978-1-108-01053-5(9))* Cambridge Univ. Pr.

Daly, Edward & Devlin, Kieran, eds. The Clergy of the Diocese of Derry - An Index. 2nd ed. 2009. (Illus.). 244p. 70.00 *(978-1-84682-168-4(1))* Four Courts Pr. IRL. Dist: International Specialized Bk. Services.

Daugherty, Leo. The Assassination of Shakespeare's Patron: Investigating the Death of the Fifth Earl of Derby. 2011. *(978-1-60497-737-0(X))* Cambria Pr.

Dawson, Christopher & Kollar, Rene. The Movement Towards Christian Unity in the Nineteenth Century. 2006. pap. *(978-0-9773909-0-8(X))* St. Vincent Archabbey Pubns.

Doorly, Moyra & Nichols, Aidan. The Council in Question. 2011. 108p. pap. ***(978-0-85244-765-9(5))*** Gracewing, Ltd.

Drennen, D. A. A Privilege of Intellect: Conscience & Wisdom in Newman's Narrative. 2011. (ENG.). 400p. pap. 35.00 *(978-1-58966-210-0(5))* Univ. of Scranton Pr.

Duffy, Eamon. Fires of Faith: Catholic England under Mary Tudor. (ENG., Illus.). 280p. 2010. pap. 18.00 *(978-0-300-16889-1(6))* 2009. 28.50 *(978-0-300-15216-6(7))* Yale Univ. Pr.

Erler, Mary, ed. Ecclesiastical London. 2008. (Records of Early English Drama Ser.). (ENG.). 504p. *(978-0-8020-9858-0(4))* Univ. of Toronto Pr.

Fea, Allan. Secret Chambers & Hiding Places. 2008. 160p. 25.99 *(978-0-554-24811-0(5))*; 160p. 22.99 *(978-0-554-34114-9(X))*; 392p. pap. 21.75 *(978-1-4375-4033-8(3))*; 392p. pap. 27.75 *(978-1-4375-4042-0(2))* BiblioBazaar.

—Secret Chambers & Hiding Places. 2008. (Illus.). 148p. pap. *(978-1-4099-4193-4(0))* Dodo Pr.

—Secret Chambers & Hiding Places. 2008. 72p. pap. *(978-1-4068-7542-3(2))* Echo Library.

—Secret Chambers & Hiding Places: Historic, Romantic, & Legendary Stories & Traditio. 2006. (ENG.). 144p. pap. 18.99 *(978-1-4264-7451-4(2))*; 158p. pap. 21.99 *(978-1-4264-7528-3(4))* BiblioBazaar.

—Secret Chambers & Hiding Places: Historic, Romantic, & Legendary Stories & Traditions about Hiding Holes, Secret Chambers, Etc. 2007. 324p. 45.95 *(978-0-548-11855-9(8))* Kessinger Publishing, LLC.

—Secret Chambers & Hiding-Places; the Historic, Romantic. 2009. 148p. pap. *(978-1-150-70411-6(X))* Books LLC.

Gallagher, Lowell. Redrawing the Map of Early Modern English Catholicism. 2012. (UCLA Clark Memorial Library Ser.). (ENG., Illus.). 360p. (C). ***(978-1-4426-4312-3(9))*** Univ. of Toronto Pr.

Harley, Thomas. Matthew Poole: His Life, His Times, His Contributions along with His Argument against the Infallibility of the Roman Catholic Church. 2009. 232p. pap. 18.95 *(978-0-595-52502-7(4))* iUniverse, Inc.

Harper-Bill, Christopher. English Episcopal Acta, Volume 40: Norwich 1266-1288. 2012. (English Episcopal Acta Ser.). (ENG & LAT., Illus.). 278p. 99.00 ***(978-0-19-726516-1(2))*** Oxford Univ. Pr., Inc.

—English Episcopal Acta, Volume 41: Norwich 1289-1299. 2012. (English Episcopal Acta Ser.). (ENG & LAT., Illus.). 194p. 85.00 ***(978-0-19-726517-8(0))*** Oxford Univ. Pr., Inc.

Hornsby-Smith, Michael P. Roman Catholics in England: Studies in Social Structure since the Second World War. 2008. (ENG.). 268p. pap. 37.99 *(978-0-521-09006-3(7))* Cambridge Univ. Pr.

Hoskin, Philippa M. English Episcopal Acta - London 1280-1303. 2011. (LAT & ENG., Illus.). 314p. 110.00 ***(978-0-19-726486-7(7))*** Oxford Univ. Pr., Inc.

—English Episcopal Acta, London 1280-1303. 2011. (LAT & ENG., Illus.). 276p. 99.00 ***(978-0-19-726485-0(9))*** Oxford Univ. Pr., Inc.

Hunting, Penelope. The Saint & the Disciple: John Henry,Cardinal Newman, the Reverend George Dudley Ryder & the Catholic Revival in Nineteenth Century Britain. 2011. (Illus.). 280p. lib. bdg. *(978-1-936320-01-1(0))* Academica Pr., LLC.

Jolliffe, John, ed. English Catholic Heroes. 2008. (Illus.). 252p. pap. *(978-0-85244-604-1(7))* Gracewing, Ltd.

Kaplan, Benjamin, et al, eds. Catholic Communities in Protestant States: Britain & the Netherlands C., 1570-1720. 2009. (Studies in Early Modern European History Ser.). (ENG., Illus.). 288p. 100.00 *(978-0-7190-7906-1(3))* Manchester Univ. Pr. GBR. Dist: Macmillan.

Kemp, B. R., ed. English Episcopal Acta 36, Salisbury 1229-1262, 2 vols. 2011. (ENG & LAT., Illus.). 340p. 99.00 *(978-0-19-726463-8(8))* Oxford Univ. Pr., Inc.

—English Episcopal Acta 37, Salisbury 1263-1297, 2 vols. 2011. (ENG & LAT., Illus.). 340p. 99.00 *(978-0-19-726464-5(6))* Oxford Univ. Pr., Inc.

Kesselring, K. J. The Northern Rebellion Of 1569: Faith, Politics & Protest in Elizabethan England. 2010. (ENG., Illus.). 248p. pap. 33.00 *(978-0-230-24889-2(6))* Palgrave Macmillan.

Leland, John, et al. De Viris Illustribus: Of Famous Men. 2010. (Studies & Texts). (LAT & ENG.). 498p. 95.00 ***(978-0-88844-170-6(3))*** Pontifical Institute of Mediaeval Studies, Dept. of Pubns. CAN. Dist: Univ. of Toronto Pr.

Loades, David. The Religious Culture of Marian England, 1 vol. 2010. (Religious Cultures in the Early Modern World Ser.). (ENG.). 224p. 99.00 *(978-1-85196-921-0(7))* Pickering & Chatto Pubs., Ltd. GBR. Dist: Ashgate Publishing Co.

MacCuarta, Brian. Catholic Revival in the North of Ireland 1603-41. 2007. 282p. (C). 70.00 *(978-1-84682-051-9(0))* Four Courts Pr. IRL. Dist: International Specialized Bk. Services.

Mann, Stephanie A. Supremacy & Survival: How Catholics Endured the English Reformation. 2009. (Illus.). 167p. 12.95 *(978-1-59417-079-9(7))* Scepter Pubs., Inc.

McGrath, Francis J., ed. The Letters & Diaries of John Henry Newman Volume XXXII: Supplement. 2009. (Newman Letters & Diaries). (ENG., Illus.). 600p. 199.00 *(978-0-19-953270-4(2))* Oxford Univ. Pr., Inc.

Messenger, Ruth E. Ethical Teachings in the Latin Hymns of Medieval England. (Columbia University, Studies in the Social Sciences: No. 321). reprint ed. 20.00 *(978-0-404-51321-4(2))* AMS Pr., Inc.

Miller, John. Popery & Politics in England 1660-1688. 2008. (ENG.). 304p. pap. 42.00 *(978-0-521-07742-2(7))* Cambridge Univ. Pr.

Newman, John Henry. John Henry Newman: Selected Writings To 1845. Radcliffe, Albert, ed. 2006. (Fyfield Bks.). (ENG.). 206p. per. 19.95 *(978-1-85754-545-6(1))* Carcanet Pr., Ltd. GBR. Dist: Independent Pubs. Group.

—Lectures on the Present Position of Catholics in England: Addressed to the Brothers of the Oratory in the Summer Of 1851 (1908) 2008. 454p. 52.95 *(978-1-4365-9471-4(5))* 2007. 456p. per. 37.95 *(978-0-548-79152-3(X))* Kessinger Publishing, LLC.

Questier, Michael C. Catholicism & Community in Early Modern England: Politics, Aristocratic Patronage & Religion, C. 1550-1640. 2008. (Cambridge Studies in Early Modern British History Ser.). (ENG., Illus.). 588p. pap. 74.00 *(978-0-521-06880-2(0))* Cambridge Univ. Pr.

Redworth, Glyn, ed. The Letters of Luisa de Carvajal y Mendoza, 2 vols. 2012. (ENG.). 800p. 335.00 ***(978-1-84893-218-0(9))*** Pickering & Chatto Pubs., Ltd. GBR. Dist: Ashgate Publishing Co.

Saward, John, et al. Firmly I Believe & Truly: The Spiritual Tradition of Catholic England. 2011. (ENG., Illus.). 832p. 65.00 *(978-0-19-929122-9(5))* Oxford Univ. Pr., Inc.

Shagan, Ethan H., ed. Catholics & the 'Protestant Nation' Religious Politics & Identity in Early Modern England. 2009. (Politics, Culture & Society in Early Modern Britain Ser.). (ENG.). 224p. pap. 36.00 *(978-0-7190-8052-4(5))* Manchester Univ. Pr. GBR. Dist: Macmillan.

Stacey, John. John Wycliff & Reform. 2009. 170p. pap. 20.00 *(978-1-60608-761-9(4)*, Wipf and Stock) Wipf & Stock Pubs.

Stanford, Peter. Opening Up: Speaking Out in the Church. 192p. *(978-0-232-52624-0(9))* Darton, Longman & Todd, Ltd.

Stebbing, George. The Church in England. 2010. 628p. pap. 54.00 *(978-1-60899-802-9(9)*, Wipf and Stock) Wipf & Stock Pubs.

Taylor, P. J. Called to Serve: A Review of the Work of a Permanent Deacon over a Period of Thirty Years. 2007. (Illus.). 156p. per. *(978-1-84401-904-5(7))* Athena Pr.

Tenbus, Eric G. English Catholics & the Education of the Poor, 1847-1902, 1 vol. 2010. (Perspectives in Economic & Social History Ser.). (ENG.). 224p. 99.00 *(978-1-84893-038-4(0))* Pickering & Chatto Pubs., Ltd. GBR. Dist: Ashgate Publishing Co.

Tutino, Stefania. Law & Conscience: Catholicism in Early Modern England 1570-1625. 2007. (Catholic Christendom, 1300-1700 Ser.). 268p. 124.95 *(978-0-7546-5771-2(X))* Ashgate Publishing Co.

Walker, Peter. James II & the Three Questions: Religious Toleration & the Landed Classes, 1687-1688. 2010. 337p. pap. 72.95 *(978-3-03911-927-1(3))* Lang, Peter AG GBR. Dist: Lang, Peter.

Wilkie, William E. The Cardinal Protectors of England: Rome & the Tudors before the Reformation. 2008. (ENG.). 276p. pap. 37.99 *(978-0-521-08764-3(3))* Cambridge Univ. Pr.

Wilmer, Graham. Conspiracy of Faith: Fighting for Justice after Child Abuse. 2007. (ENG.). 160p. per. 28.00 *(978-0-7188-3058-8(X))* Lutherworth Pr., The GBR. Dist: Brown, David Bk. Co., The.

Winter, Michael M. Whatever Happened to Vatican II? 221p. pap. *(978-0-7220-9720-5(4)*, Burns & Oates) Continuum International Publishing Group, Ltd.

CATHOLIC CHURCH—GREAT BRITAIN—BIBLIOGRAPHY

Bloom, Frans, et al, eds. The Correspondence of James Peter Coghlan (1731-1800) 2007. (Catholic Record Society: Records Ser.: Volume 80). (Illus.). 514p. 80.00 *(978-0-902832-23-7(9))* Catholic Record Society GBR. Dist: Boydell & Brewer, Inc.

CATHOLIC CHURCH—INDIA

Mahieu-De Praetere, Marthe. Kurisumala: Francis Mahieu Acharya, Pioneer in Christian Monasticism in India. Van Winkle, Susan, tr. from FRE. 2008. (Cistercian Father Ser.). (Illus.). 394p. per. 79.95 *(978-0-87907-614-6(3))* Cistercian Pubns., Inc.

Subramanian, Ajantha. Shorelines: Space & Rights in South India. 2009. (ENG., Illus.). 320p. 35.00 *(978-0-8047-6146-8(9))* Stanford Univ. Pr.

Vysanethu, Philip. Musicality makes the Malankara Liturgy Mystical. 2010. 111.68 *(978-1-61143-571-9(4))* Gorgias Pr., LLC.

CATHOLIC CHURCH—INDIA—GOA (STATE)

Dalrymple, William. Edge of Faith. 2009. (Illus.). 140p. 29.00 *(978-1-906497-31-6(1))* Seagull Bks. London Ltd. GBR. Dist: Chicago Distribution Ctr.

CATHOLIC CHURCH—IRELAND

Barr, Colin. The European Culture Wars in Ireland: The Callan Schools Affair, 1868-81. 2011. (ENG.). 320p. 89.95 *(978-1-906359-53-9(9))* Univ. College Dublin Pr. IRL. Dist: Dufour Editions, Inc.

Carty, Francis X. Hold Firm: John Charles Mcquaid & the Second Vatican Council. 2008. (ENG.). 181p. pap. 23.95 *(978-1-85607-585-5(0))* Columba Pr. IRL. Dist: Dufour Editions, Inc.

Carty, Francis Xavier. The Impact of the Second Vatican Council on the Archdiocese of Dublin. 2010. 564p. pap. *(978-3-8383-4433-1(2))* Lambert Academic Publishing.

Chambers, Catherine Bourke. Just a Boy from Home: With songs, stories & Recipes. 2008. 336p. 28.49 *(978-1-4343-6790-7(8))*; pap. 17.99 *(978-1-4343-6789-1(4))* AuthorHouse.

Cullinan, Edmond Gerard. The Story of the Liturgy in Ireland. 2010. (ENG.). 128p. pap. 22.95 *(978-1-85607-684-5(9))* Columba Pr. IRL. Dist: Dufour Editions, Inc.

Curtis, Maurice. Challenge to Democracy: Militant Catholicism in Modern Ireland. 2010. (ENG., Illus.). 256p. pap. 24.95 ***(978-1-84588-969-2(X))*** History Pr. Ltd.,The GBR. Dist: Independent Pubs. Group.

Dill, Edward Marcus. The Mystery Solved: Or, Ireland's Miseries; the Grand Cause & Cure. by the Rev. Edward Marcus Dill ... 2006. 356p. per. 26.99 *(978-1-4255-3647-3(6))* MPublishing.

Duffy, Eugene, ed. Parishes in Transition. 2011. (ENG., Illus.). 240p. pap. 26.95 *(978-1-85607-706-4(3))* Columba Pr. IRL. Dist: Dufour Editions, Inc.

Dullea, Gearoid, ed. Deacons: Ministers of Christ & of God's Mysteries. 2010. (ENG.). 101p. pap. 15.95 *(978-1-84730-217-5(3))* Veritas Pubns. IRL. Dist: Dufour Editions, Inc.

Egan, Kevin. Remaining a Catholic after the Murphy Report. 2011. (ENG.). 168p. pap. 25.95 ***(978-1-85607-740-8(3))*** Columba Pr. IRL. Dist: Dufour Editions, Inc.

Egger, Sabine & McDonagh, John. Polish-Irish Encounters in the Old & New Europe. 2011. (Reimagining Ireland Ser.). (ENG.). 304p. pap. 68.95 ***(978-3-0343-0253-1(3))*** Lang, Peter AG GBR. Dist: Lang, Peter.

Elliott, Marianne. When God Took Sides: Religion & Identity in Irish History. 2009. (ENG., Illus.). 304p. 34.95 *(978-0-19-920693-3(7))* Oxford Univ. Pr., Inc.

Fanning, Tim. The Fethard-on-Sea Boycott. 2010. (ENG., Illus.). 240p. pap. 26.95 *(978-1-84889-032-9(X))* Collins Pr., The IRL. Dist: Dufour Editions, Inc.

Flannery, Tony. Fragments of Reality: Collected Writings. 2009. (ENG.). 137p. pap. 22.95 *(978-1-85607-624-1(5))* Columba Pr. IRL. Dist: Dufour Editions, Inc.

Fuller, Louise, et al, eds. Irish & Catholic? Towards an Understanding of Identity. 2007. (ENG.). 256p. per. 30.95 *(978-1-85607-538-1(9))* Columba Pr. IRL. Dist: Dufour Editions, Inc.

Hederman, Mark Patrick. Underground Cathedrals. 2010. (ENG.). 194p. pap. 26.95 *(978-1-85607-695-1(4))* Columba Pr. IRL. Dist: Dufour Editions, Inc.

Hurley, Michael. Parish Cell Communities as Agents of Renewal in the Catholic Church in Ireland: A Sociological Analysis. 2011. (ENG.). 516p. 149.95 ***(978-0-7734-2558-3(6))*** Mellen, Edwin Pr., The.

Kenny, Mary. Crown & Shamrock: Love & Hate Between Ireland & the British Monarchy. 2010. (ENG., Illus.). 410p. pap. 34.95 *(978-1-905494-98-9(X))* New Island Books IRL. Dist: Dufour Editions, Inc.

Keogh, Dermot & McCarthy, Andrew. The Making of the Irish Constitution 1937: Bunreacht Na Heireann. 2008. (ENG., Illus.). 511p. 54.95 *(978-1-85635-561-2(6))* Mercier Pr., Ltd., The IRL. Dist: Dufour Editions, Inc.

Larkin, Emmet. The Roman Catholic Church & the Home Rule Movement in Ireland, 1870-1874. 2011. (ENG.). 440p. pap. 50.00 *(978-0-8078-6560-6(5))* Univ. of North Carolina Pr.

—The Roman Catholic Church in Ireland & the Fall of Parnell, 1888-1891. 2011. (ENG.). 337p. pap. 40.00 *(978-0-8078-9705-8(1))* Univ. of North Carolina Pr.

Larkin, Emmett J. The Roman Catholic Hierarchy & the Fall of Parnell. 2011. 26p. 35.95 ***(978-1-258-09723-3(0))*** Literary Licensing, LLC.

Leahy, Brendan. Inter-Church Relations: Developments & Perspectives. Leahy, Brendan, ed. 2009. (ENG.). 203p. pap. 25.95 *(978-1-84730-095-9(2))* Veritas Pubns. IRL. Dist: Dufour Editions, Inc.

MacCuarta, Brian. Catholic Revival in the North of Ireland 1603-41. 2007. 282p. (C). 70.00 *(978-1-84682-051-9(0))* Four Courts Pr. IRL. Dist: International Specialized Bk. Services.

Maguire, James G. Ireland & the Pope. 2007. (ENG.). 118p. 34.95 *(978-0-548-03923-6(2))* Kessinger Publishing, LLC.

Maguire, Moira J. Precarious Childhood in Post-Independence Ireland. 2012. (ENG.). 272p. pap. 28.95 ***(978-0-7190-8774-5(0))*** Manchester Univ. Pr. GBR. Dist: Macmillan.

Maher, Eamon. Contemporary Catholicism in Ireland: A Critical Appraisal. Maher, Eamon & Littleton, John, eds. 2008. (ENG.). 279p. pap. 32.95 *(978-1-85607-616-6(4))* Columba Pr. IRL. Dist: Dufour Editions, Inc.

Maher, Eamon & Littleton, John, eds. The Dublin/Murphy Report: A Watershed for Irish Catholicism? 2010. (ENG.). 174p. pap. 24.95 *(978-1-85607-697-5(0))* Columba Pr. IRL. Dist: Dufour Editions, Inc.

Maher, Eamon & O'Brien, Eugene. Breaking the Mould: Literary Representations of Irish Catholicism. 2010. 280p. pap. *(978-3-0343-0232-6(0))* Lang, Peter Publishing, Inc.

McDonagh, Enda. Immersed in Mystery: En Route to Theology. 2008. (ENG.). 232p. pap. 16.95 *(978-1-85390-969-6(6))* Veritas Pubns. IRL. Dist: Dufour Editions, Inc.

McManus, Sean. Seán McManus: My American Struggle for Justice in Northern Ireland 1972-2009. 2011. (ENG., Illus.). 290p. pap. 26.95 *(978-1-84889-098-5(2))* Collins Pr., The IRL. Dist: Dufour Editions, Inc.

McNeill, John Thomas. The Celtic Penitentials & Their Influence on Continental Christianity. 2008. 216p. pap. 20.00 *(978-1-59740-384-9(9))* ACLS Humanities E-Book.

—The Celtic Penitentials & Their Influence on Continental Christianity. 2009. 210p. 28.99 *(978-1-113-64618-7(7))*; pap. 23.75 *(978-1-113-64615-6(2))*; pap. 24.75 *(978-1-113-64617-0(9))* BiblioBazaar.

Mooney, Tom. All the Bishops' Men: Clerical Abuse in an Irish Diocese. 2011. (ENG., Illus.). 288p. pap. 23.95 *(978-1-84889-099-2(0))* Collins Pr., The IRL. Dist: Dufour Editions, Inc.

Ó Corráin, Daithí. Rendering to God & Caesar: The Irish Churches & the Two States in Ireland, 1949-73. 2008. (ENG., Illus.). 288p. pap. 28.00 *(978-0-7190-7347-2(2))* Manchester Univ. Pr. GBR. Dist: Macmillan.

O'Hanlon, Gerry. A New Vision for the Catholic Church: A View from Ireland. 2011. (ENG.). 120p. pap. 17.95 *(978-1-85607-729-3(2))* Columba Pr. IRL. Dist: Dufour Editions, Inc.

—Theology in the Irish Public Square. 2010. (ENG.). 231p. pap. 27.95 *(978-1-85607-685-2(7))* Columba Pr. IRL. Dist: Dufour Editions, Inc.

Power, Maria. From Ecumenism to Community Relations: Inter-Church Relationships in Northern Ireland 1980-1999. 2007. 262p. (C). 75.00 *(978-0-7165-3379-5(0))*; pap. 32.50 *(978-0-7165-3380-1(4))* Irish Academic Pr. IRL. Dist: International Specialized Bk. Services.

Privilege, John. Michael Logue & the Catholic Church in Ireland, 1879-1925. 2009. (ENG.). 224p. 89.00 *(978-0-7190-7735-7(4))* Manchester Univ. Pr. GBR. Dist: Macmillan.

Putti, Joseph, ed. Time [to] Change: Connecting the Good News with Contemporary Living. 2006. (ENG.). 262p. pap. 20.95 *(978-1-85390-927-6(0))* Veritas Pubns. IRL. Dist: Dufour Editions, Inc.

Rafferty, Oliver. The Catholic Church & the Protestant State: Nineteenth-Century Irish Realities. 2008. 221p. (C). 75.00 *(978-1-84682-084-7(7))* Four Courts Pr. IRL. Dist: International Specialized Bk. Services.

Scott, Brendan. Religion & Reform in the Diocese of Meath, 1536-1622. 2006. (Illus.). 174p. (C). 65.00 *(978-1-85182-995-8(4))* Four Courts Pr. IRL. Dist: International Specialized Bk. Services.

Smith, Sydney. Peter Plymley's Letters & Selected Ess. 2006. pap. *(978-1-84702-486-2(6))* Echo Library.

Snoddy, Debra, et al. Parish Pastoral Councils: A Formation Manual. 2011. (ENG., Illus.). 214p. pap. 29.95 *(978-1-84730-241-0(6))* Veritas Pubns. IRL. Dist: Dufour Editions, Inc.

Tentler, Leslie Woodcock. The Church Confronts Modernity: Catholicism since 1950 in the United States, Ireland, & Quebec. 2007. 302p. per. 34.95 *(978-0-8132-1494-8(7))* Catholic Univ. of America Pr.

Tierney, Martin. New Wine Old Wineskins: The Catholic Church & Change in Ireland Today. 2008. (ENG.). 139p. pap. 16.95 *(978-1-84730-059-1(6))* Veritas Pubns. IRL. Dist: Dufour Editions, Inc.

Veritas, ed. Irish Catholic Directory 2010. 2010. (ENG., Illus.). 447p. 74.95 *(978-1-84730-208-3(4))*, Veritas Pubns. IRL. Dist: Dufour Editions, Inc.

CATHOLIC CHURCH—ITALY

Broers. Politics & Religion in Napoleonic Italy. 2007. 256p. 34.00 *(978-0-415-44394-4(6))*, Routledge.

Brundin, Abigail & Treherne, Matthew. Forms of Faith in Sixteenth-Century Italy. 2009. (Catholic Christendom, 1300-1700 Ser.). (Illus.). 274p. 124.95 *(978-0-7546-6555-7(0))* Ashgate Publishing Co.

Comerford, Kathleen M. Reforming Priests & Parishes: Tuscan Dioceses in the First Century of Seminary Education. 2006. (Education & Society in the Middle Ages & Renaissance Ser.: Vol. 27). (Illus.). 162p. *(978-90-04-15357-8(8))* BRILL.

Finchelstein, Federico. Transatlantic Fascism: Ideology, Violence, & the Sacred in Argentina & Italy, 1919-1945. 2010. (ENG.). 344p. pap. 25.95 *(978-0-8223-4612-8(5))*; (Illus.). 94.95 *(978-0-8223-4594-7(3))* Duke Univ. Pr.

Fragnito, Gigliola, ed. Church, Censorship & Culture in Early Modern Italy. Belton, Adrian, tr. from ITA. 2011. (Cambridge Studies in Italian History & Culture Ser.). (ENG.). 280p. pap. 55.00 *(978-0-521-20232-9(9))* Cambridge Univ. Pr.

Garelli, Franco. Catholicism in Italy in the Age of Pluralism. 2010. (ENG.). 150p. 57.99 *(978-0-7391-4111-3(2))* Lexington Bks.

Hallett, Paul H. Catholic Reformer: The Life of St. Cajetan of Thiene. 2011. 234p. 46.95 ***(978-1-258-06898-1(2))*** Literary Licensing, LLC.

Hofstadter, Dan. The Earth Moves: Galileo & the Roman Inquisition. 2010. (Great Discoveries Ser.). (ENG., Illus.). 240p. pap. 14.95 *(978-0-393-33820-1(7), 33820)* Norton, W. W. & Co., Inc.

McCabe, Joseph. The Totalitarian Church of Rome: Its Fuehrer, Its Gauleiter, Its Gestabo, & Its Money-Box. Haldeman-Julius, E., ed. 2011. 34p. 35.95 ***(978-1-258-05584-4(8))*** Literary Licensing, LLC.

Pio, Padre. Words of Light: Inspiration from the Letters of Padre Pio. 2009. (ENG.). 206p. (gr. 13). pap. 14.99 *(978-1-55725-643-0(8))* Paraclete Pr., Inc.

Pullan, Brian. Rich & Poor in Renaissance Venice: The Social Institutions of a Catholic State, To 1620. 2008. 728p. pap. 72.00 *(978-1-59740-375-7(X))* ACLS Humanities E-Book.

Raz-Krakotzkin, Amnon. The Censor, the Editor, & the Text: The Catholic Church & the Shaping of the Jewish Canon in the Sixteenth Century. Feldman, Jackie, tr. from HEB. 2007. (Jewish Culture & Contexts Ser.). (ENG.). 328p. (C). 69.95 *(978-0-8122-4011-5(1))* Univ. of Pennsylvania Pr.

Robinson, Adam Patrick. Reforming Bishop Papal Diplomat Suspect Heretic & Presiding Legate at the Council of Trent: A Reassessment of the Career of Cardinal Giovanni Morone (1509-1580) 2012. (Illus.). 248p. 124.95 ***(978-1-4094-1783-5(2))*** Ashgate Publishing Co.

Secretaries of the American and Foreign Staff. The Story of the Madiai: With Notices of Efforts Made, in Europe & America in Their Behalf. 2007. pap. 28.95 *(978-1-4304-4214-1(X))* Kessinger Publishing, LLC.

Silanos, Pietro. Gerardo Bianchi Da Parma (1302) La Biografia Di un Cardinale-Legato Duecentesco. 2010. xxxvi, 512p. *(978-88-89670-51-4(7))* Herder, Editorial S.A.

Treece, Patricia, compiled by. Quiet Moments with Padre Pio: 120 Daily Readings. 2007. 123p. per. 10.99 *(978-0-86716-841-9(2)*, Servant Bks.) Franciscan Media.

Tylenda, Joseph N. The Pilgrim's Guide to Rome's Principal Churches. 2010. (Illus.). xvi, 425p. *(978-1-892331-78-6(0))* Angelus Pr.

Weber, Christoph. Episcopus et Princeps: Italienische Bischöfe als Fürsten, Grafen und Barone vom 17. bis zum 20. Jahrhundert. 2010. (Beiträge zur Kirchen- und Kulturgeschichte Ser.). (GER.). 218p. 64.95 *(978-3-631-60242-3(1))* Lang, Peter GmbH, Europaischer Verlag der Wissenschaften DEU. Dist: Lang, Peter.

Zaccaria, Francesco. International Law, Conflict & Development - The Emergence of a Holistic Approach in International Affairs. Kolb, Robert et al, eds. 2010. (FRE & ENG.). 666p. *(978-90-04-17858-8(9))* BRILL.

CATHOLIC CHURCH—JAPAN

Dougill, John. In Search of Japan's Hidden Christians: A Story of Suppression, Secrecy & Survival. 2012. (ENG., Illus.). 272p. 22.95 ***(978-4-8053-1147-9(9))*** Tuttle Publishing.

CATHOLIC CHURCH—KOREA

Martin, Luther & Bach, Eugene. Back to the Jerusalem of Th East: The Underground House Church of North Korea. 2011. mass mkt. 17.99 *(978-1-936533-10-7(3))* Fifth Estate, Inc.

CATHOLIC CHURCH—LATIN AMERICA

Aquini, Maria Pilar & Rosado-Nunes, Maria Jose, eds. Feminist Intercultural Theology: Latina Explorations for a Just World. 2007. (Studies in Latino/A Catholicism). 270p. per. 35.00 *(978-1-57075-741-9(0))* Orbis Bks.

Byrnes, Timothy A. Reverse Mission: Transnational Religious Communities & the Making of U. S. Foreign Policy. 2011. (Religion & Politics Ser.). 216p. pap. 26.95 *(978-1-58901-768-9(4))* Georgetown Univ. Pr.

—Reverse Mission: Transnational Religious Communities & the Making of US Foreign Policy. 2011. (Religion & Politics Ser.). 216p. 44.95 *(978-1-58901-775-7(7))* Georgetown Univ. Pr.

Cleary, Edward L. How Latin America Saved the Soul of the Catholic Church. 2010. (Illus.). 224p. pap. 22.95 *(978-0-8091-4629-1(0))* Paulist Pr.

—The Rise of Charismatic Catholicism in Latin America. 2011. (ENG., Illus.). 256p. 74.95 *(978-0-8130-3608-3(9))* Univ. Pr. of Florida.

Early, John D. The Maya & Catholicism: An Encounter of Worldviews, 311 vols. 2006. (ENG., Illus.). 320p. 59.95 *(978-0-8130-3025-8(0))* Univ. Pr. of Florida.

Edwards, Lisa Marie. Roman Virtues: The Education of Latin American Clergy in Rome, 1858-1962. 2011. (Latin America: Interdisciplinary Studies). 150p. (C). 68.95 ***(978-1-4331-1306-2(6))*** Lang, Peter Publishing, Inc.

Goldman, Francisco. Art of Political Murder: Who Killed the Bishop? 2008. (ENG.). 416p. pap. 15.00 *(978-0-8021-4385-3(7)*, Grove Pr.) Grove/Atlantic, Inc.

Hagopian, Frances, ed. Religious Pluralism, Democracy, & the Catholic Church in Latin America. 2009. (ND Kellogg Inst Int'l Studies). (ENG., Illus.). 536p. pap. 45.00 *(978-0-268-03087-2(1))* Univ. of Notre Dame Pr.

Irarrázaval, Diego. Inculturation: New Dawn of the Church in Latin America. Berryman, Phillip, tr. 2008.Tr. of Inculturacion: Amanecer Eclesial en America Latina. 146p. pap. 18.00 *(978-1-55635-831-9(8))* Wipf & Stock Pubs.

Nunez, E. A. & Taylor, W. D. Crisis & Hope in Latin America: An Evangelical Perspective. (Illus.). xvi, 528p. pap. *(978-1-900890-01-4(1))* WEF GBR. Dist: O. M. Literature.

Pelton, Robert S., ed. Aparecida: Quo Vadis? 2009. (Illus.). 248p. pap. 25.00 *(978-1-58966-143-1(5))* Univ. of Scranton Pr.

Richardson, Miles. Being-in-Christ & Putting Death in Its Place: An Anthropologist's Account of Christian Performance in Spanish America & the American South. 2006. (Illus.). 414p. per. 19.95 *(978-0-8071-3204-3(7))* Louisiana State Univ. Pr.

Schwaller, John F. History of the Catholic Church in Latin America: From Conquest to Revolution & Beyond. 2011. (ENG.). 328p. 35.00 *(978-0-8147-4003-3(0))* New York Univ. Pr.

Torres y Vargas, Canon Diego. Report on the Island & Diocese of Puerto Rico (1647) Vidal, Jaime R., tr. from SPA. 2010. (ENG., Illus.). 200p. pap. 25.00 *(978-1-58966-189-9(3))* Univ. of Scranton Pr.

Turner, Frederick C. Catholicism & Political Development in Latin America. 2011. (ENG.). 288p. pap. 40.00 *(978-0-8078-9799-7(X))* Univ. of North Carolina Pr.

Vasquez, Manuel A. The Brazilian Popular Church & the Crisis of Modernity. 2008. (Cambridge Studies in Ideology & Religion Ser.). (ENG.). 320p. pap. 44.00 *(978-0-521-09086-5(5))* Cambridge Univ. Pr.

Williams, Philip. The Catholic Church & Politics in Nicaragua & Costa Rica. 2009. (Pitt Latin American Studies). (ENG.). 244p. pap. 25.95 *(978-0-8229-8370-5(2))* Univ. of Pittsburgh Pr.

Zaballa Beascoechea, Ana de, ed. Los Indios, el Derecho Canónico y la Justicia Eclesiástica en la América Virreinal. 2011. (Tiempo Emulado. Historia de América y España Ser.). pap. 29.80 ***(978-84-8489-519-0(X))*** Iberoamericana Vervuert Publishing Corp.

CATHOLIC CHURCH—MEXICO

Austin, Ron. Peregrino: A Pilgrim Journey into Catholic Mexico. 2010. (Illus.). 234p. pap. 19.99 *(978-0-8028-6584-7(4))* Eerdmans, William B. Publishing Co.

Braden, Charles S. Religious Aspects of the Conquest of Mexico. reprint ed. 54.50 *(978-0-404-00925-0(5))* AMS Pr., Inc.

Butler, Matthew, ed. Faith & Impiety in Revolutionary Mexico. 2007. (Studies of the Americas Ser.). (ENG.). 304p. 100.00 *(978-1-4039-8381-7(X))* Palgrave Macmillan.

Chavez, Angelico. Our Lady of the Conquest. 2010. 128p. pap. 19.95 *(978-0-86534-747-2(6))* Sunstone Pr.

Connaughton, Brian F. & Lira González, Andrés. Las Fuentes Eclesiásticas para la Historia Social de México. 2009. (Otras Publicaciones Ser.). (SPA., Illus.). 420p. pap. 19.99 *(978-970-620-833-0(X))* El Colegio de México, A.C., Biblioteca Miguel Cosio Villegas MEX. Dist: Fondo de Cultura Economica USA.

Costeloe, Michael P. Church Wealth in Mexico: A Study of the 'Juzgado de Capellanias' in the Archbishopric of Mexico 1800-1856. 2008. (Cambridge Latin American Studies). (ENG.). 156p. pap. 33.99 *(978-0-521-08347-8(8))* Cambridge Univ. Pr.

Cruz, Joel Morales. The Mexican Reformation: Catholic Pluralism, Enlightenment Religion, & the Iglesia de Jesus Movement in Benito JuarezOs Mexico (1859D72) 2011. 236p. pap. 26.00 ***(978-1-61097-201-7(5)***, Pickwick Pubns.) Wipf & Stock Pubs.

Díaz, Mónica. Indigenous Writings from the Convent: Negotiating Ethnic Autonomy in Colonial Mexico. 2010. (First Peoples: New Directions in Indigenous Studies). (ENG., Illus.). 248p. 50.00 *(978-0-8165-2853-0(5))* Univ. of Arizona Pr.

Fernandez, Eduardo C. Mexican-American Catholics. 2007. (Pastoral Spirituality Ser.). 208p. pap. 18.95 *(978-0-8091-4266-8(X)*, 4266-8) Paulist Pr.

Hughes, Jennifer Scheper. Biography of a Mexican Crucifix: Lived Religion & Local Faith from the Conquest to the Present, 1 vol. 2010. (ENG., Illus.). 328p. 99.00 *(978-0-19-536706-5(5))*; pap. 29.95 *(978-0-19-536707-2(3))* Oxford Univ. Pr., Inc.

Larkin, Brian. The Very Nature of God: Baroque Catholicism & Religious Reform in Bourbon Mexico City. 2010. (ENG., Illus.). 326p. (C). pap. 27.95 *(978-0-8263-4834-0(3))* Univ. of New Mexico Pr.

Lundberg, Magnus. Church Life between the Metropolitan & the Local: Parishes, Parishioners & Parish PRiests in Seventeenth-Century Mexico. 2011. (Illus.). 278p. pap. *(978-1-936353-03-3(2))* Iberoamericana Vervuert Publishing Corp.

—Church Life Between the Metropolitan & the Local Parishes, Parishioners, & Parish Priests in Seventeenth-Century Mexico. 2011. (Illus.). 277p. pap. 39.80 *(978-84-8489-558-9(0))* Iberoamericana Vervuert Publishing Corp.

Mazín Gómez, Oscar. Gestores de la Real Justicia: Procuradores y Agentes de Las Catedrales Hispanas Nuevas en la Corte de Madrid. 2007. (Estudios Históricos Ser.). (Illus.). 394p. pap. 46.99 *(978-968-12-1266-7(5))* El Colegio de México, A.C., Biblioteca Miguel Cosio Villegas MEX. Dist: Fondo de Cultura Economica USA.

Melvin, Karen. Building Colonial Cities of God: Mendicant Orders & Urban Culture in New Spain. 2012. (ENG.). 384p. 65.00 *(978-0-8047-7486-4(2))* Stanford Univ. Pr.

Meyer, Jean A. The Cristero Rebellion: The Mexican People Between Church & State, 1926-1929. 2008. (Cambridge Latin American Studies). (ENG.). 276p. pap. 37.99 *(978-0-521-10205-6(7))* Cambridge Univ. Pr.

O'Hara, Matthew D. A Flock Divided: Race, Religion, & Politics in Mexico, 1749-1857. 2009. (ENG., Illus.). 336p. 89.95 *(978-0-8223-4627-2(3))*; pap. 24.95 *(978-0-8223-4639-5(7))* Duke Univ. Pr.

Pardo, Osvaldo F. The Origins of Mexican Catholicism: Nahua Rituals & Christian Sacraments in Sixteenth-Century Mexico. 2006. (History, Languages & Cultures of the Spanish & Portuguese Worlds Ser.). (ENG., Illus.). 288p. pap. 27.00 *(978-0-472-03184-9(8))* Univ. of Michigan Pr.

Poole, Stafford. Pedro Moya de Contreras: Catholic Reform & Royal Power in New Spain, 1571-1591. 2nd ed. 2011. (ENG., Illus.). 352p. (C). pap. 45.00 *(978-0-8061-4171-8(9))* Univ. of Oklahoma Pr.

Tavárez, David. The Invisible War: Indigenous Devotions, Discipline, & Dissent in Colonial Mexico. 2011. (ENG., Illus.). 400p. 65.00 *(978-0-8047-7328-7(9))*, Stanford Univ. Pr.

Taylor, William. Shrines & Miraculous Images: Religious Life in Mexico Before the Reforma. 2011. (Religions of the Americas Ser.). (ENG., Illus.). 304p. (C). 37.95 *(978-0-8263-4853-1(X))* Univ. of New Mexico Pr.

Terry, Edward D., et al, eds. Peripheral Visions: Politics, Society, & the Challenges of Modernity in Yucatan. 2010. (ENG., Illus.). 320p. 48.50 *(978-0-8173-1680-8(9))*; pap. 25.00 *(978-0-8173-5564-7(2))* Univ. of Alabama Pr.

Torre, Renée de la. La Ecclesia Nostra: El Catolicismo Desde la Perspectiva de Los Laicos: El Caso de Guadalajara. 2006. (Sociología Ser.). (SPA.). 439p. pap. *(978-968-16-8310-8(2))* Fondo de Cultura Economica.

Wright-Rios, Edward. Revolutions in Mexican Catholicism: Reform & Revelation in Oaxaca, 1887-1934. 2009. (ENG., Illus.). 376p. 94.95 *(978-0-8223-4357-8(6))*; pap. 25.95 *(978-0-8223-4379-0(7))* Duke Univ. Pr.

CATHOLIC CHURCH—NETHERLANDS

Berger, Andreas. Windesheimer Klosterkultur Um 1500: Vita, Werk und Lebenswelt des Rutger Sycamber. (Frahe Neuzeit Ser.).Tr. of Monastery Culture in Windesheim around 1500. the biography, works, & life-world of Rutger Sycamber. (GER.). XI, 371p. 180.00 ***(978-3-11-187175-2(4))*** De Gruyter, Walter Inc.

Capucao, Dave Dean. Religion & Ethnocentrism: An Empirical-Theological Study. 320p. *(978-90-04-18470-1(8))* BRILL.

Eck, Xander van & Van Eck, Xander. Clandestine Splendor: Paintings for the Catholic Church in the Dutch Republic. 2008. (ENG., Illus.). 368p. 100.00 *(978-90-400-8468-3(8))* Waanders B.V., Uitgeverij NLD. Dist: National Bk. Network.

Kaplan, Benjamin, et al, eds. Catholic Communities in Protestant States: Britain & the Netherlands C., 1570-1720. 2009. (Studies in Early Modern European History Ser.). (ENG., Illus.). 288p. 100.00 *(978-0-7190-7906-1(3))* Manchester Univ. Pr. GBR. Dist: Macmillan.

Parker, Charles H. Faith on the Margins: Catholics & Catholicism in the Dutch Golden Age. 2008. (Illus.). 346p. 57.50 *(978-0-674-02662-9(4))* Harvard Univ. Pr.

Pollmann, Judith. Catholic Identity & the Revolt of the Netherlands, 1520-1635 2011. (ENG., Illus.). 272p. 99.00 *(978-0-19-960991-8(6))* Oxford Univ. Pr., Inc.

van Nierop, Henk. Treason in the Northern Quarter: War, Terror, & the Rule of Law in the Dutch Revolt. Grayson, J. C., tr. from DUT. 2009. (ENG., Illus.). 326p. (C). 42.00 *(978-0-691-13564-9(9))* Princeton Univ. Pr.

CATHOLIC CHURCH—PHILIPPINES

Anonymous. Doctrina Christiana: The first book printed in the Philippines, Manila, 1593. A Facsimile of the copy in the Lessing J. Rosenwald Collection, Library. 2007. (ENG.). 154p. pap. 21.99 *(978-1-4264-2470-0(1))* BiblioBazaar.

Claver, Francisco F. The Making of a Local Church. 2008. (Illus.). 208p. *(978-1-57075-786-0(0))* Orbis Bks.

Doctrina Christiana: The first book printed in the Philippines, Manila, 1593. A Facsimile of the copy in the Lessing J. Rosenwald Collection, Library. Lt. ed. 2006. 148p. pap. 18.99 *(978-1-4264-2427-4(2))* BiblioBazaar.

Santiago, Luciano P. R. To Love & to Suffer: The Development of the Religious Congregations for Women in the Spanish Philippines, 1565-1898. 2008. (Illus.). 275p. pap. *(978-971-550-478-2(7))* Ateneo de Manila Univ. Pr.

Schumacher, John N. Growth & Decline: Essays on Philippine Church History. 2010. 302p. pap. 43.00 *(978-971-550-588-8(0))* Univ. of the Philippines Pr. PHL. Dist: Univ. of Hawaii Pr.

CATHOLIC CHURCH—POLAND

Beyer, Gerald J. Recovering Solidarity: Lessons from Poland's Unfinished Revolution. 2010. (Catholic social Thou Ser.). (ENG.). 384p. pap. 40.00 *(978-0-268-02216-7(X))* Univ. of Notre Dame Pr.

Buzalka, Juraj & Buzalka. Nation & Religion: The Politics of Commemorations in South-East Poland. 2008. (ENG., Illus.). 256p. pap. 49.95 *(978-3-8258-9907-3(1))* Lit Verlag DEU. Dist: Transaction Pubs.

Egger, Sabine & McDonagh, John. Polish-Irish Encounters in the Old & New Europe. 2011. (Reimagining Ireland Ser.). (ENG.). 304p. pap. 68.95 ***(978-3-0343-0253-1(3))*** Lang, Peter AG GBR. Dist: Lang, Peter.

Hlond, August. Persecution of the Catholic Church in German Occupied Poland. 2011. 150p. 41.95 ***(978-1-258-03476-4(X))*** Literary Licensing, LLC.

Majdanski, Kazimierz. You Shall Be My Witnesses. 2008. (ENG.). 194p. pap. *(978-0-7570-0223-6(4))* Square One Pubs.

Mazgaj, Marian S. Church & State in Communist Poland: A History, 1944-1989. 2010. (ENG., Illus.). 203p. pap. 55.00 *(978-0-7864-5904-9(2))* McFarland & Co., Inc. Pubs.

Obirek, Stanisaw. Obrzeza Katolicyzmu. 2008. (POL.). 217p. *(978-83-61053-11-8(5))* Forum Naukowe, Wydawnictwo, Holding Edukacyjny-Pietrzyk, Pawel, Spolka.

Porter-Szűcs, Brian. Faith & Fatherland: Catholicism, Modernity, & Poland, 1 vol. 2011. (ENG., Illus.). 544p. 55.00 *(978-0-19-539905-9(6))* Oxford Univ. Pr., Inc.

CATHOLIC CHURCH—SCOTLAND

Dobson, David. Scottish Catholics at Home & Abroad, 1680-1780. 2010. 168p. pap. 19.50 *(978-0-8063-5492-7(5))* Clearfield Co.

Kehoe, S. Karly. Creating a Scottish Church: Catholicism, Gender & Ethnicity in Nineteenth-Century Scotland. 2010. (ENG., Illus.). 208p. 89.95 *(978-0-7190-8078-4(9))* Manchester Univ. Pr. GBR. Dist: Macmillan.

McInally, Thomas. The Sixth Scottish University: The Scots Colleges abroad. 1575 To 1799. 2011. (History of Science & Medicine Library). (Illus.). 256p. ***(978-90-04-21426-2(7))*** BRILL.

Robertson, Joseph, ed. Concilia Scotiae, 2 vols. (Bannatyne Club, Edinburgh Publications: No. 113). reprint ed. 65.00 *(978-0-404-52866-9(X))* AMS Pr., Inc.

CATHOLIC CHURCH—SPAIN

Ben-Dror, Graciela. La Iglesia Católica Ante el Holocausto: España y América Latina 1933-1945. (SPA., Illus.). 336p. 39.30 *(978-84-206-4164-5(2))* Alianza Editorial, S. A. ESP. Dist: Libros in Spanish, LLC.

Cohen, Yehuda. The Spanish: Shadows of Embarrassment. 2012. 252p. 74.95 *(978-1-84519-392-8(X))* Sussex Academic Pr. GBR. Dist: International Specialized Bk. Services.

Eastman, Scott. Preaching Spanish Nationalism across the Hispanic Atlantic, 1759-1823. 2012. 264p. 42.50 ***(978-0-8071-3957-8(2))*** Louisiana State Univ. Pr.

López Villaverde, Angel Luis. Historia de la Iglesia en Castilla-La Mancha. 2010. (Biblioteca Añil Ser.: Vol. 21). (SPA.). 439p. *(978-84-937890-4-6(6))* Almud, Ediciones de Castilla-La Mancha.

Magnier, Grace. Pedro de Valencia & the Catholic Apologists of the Expulsion of the Moriscos: Visions of Christianity & Kingship. 2010. (Illus.). 436p. *(978-90-04-18288-2(6))* BRILL.

Nalle, Sara T. God in la Mancha: Religious Reform & the People of Cuenca, 1500-1650. 2008. (Johns Hopkins University Studies in Historical & Political Science Ser.: 110). (ENG., Illus.). 328p. (gr. 17). pap. 32.00 *(978-0-8018-8854-0(9))* Johns Hopkins Univ. Pr.

Ram-Mer. Del Rio Rojo. 2007. *(978-1-59835-057-9(9))* Cambridge BrickHouse, Inc.

Rubio, Juan. Una Voz, Diez Miradas: Cincuenta Años en la Vida de la Iglesia en España. 2009. (SPA.). 253p. *(978-84-288-2128-5(3))* Promoción Popular Cristiana.

Urbano, Pilar. The Man of Villa Tevere: St. Josemaría Escrivá: His Years in Rome. 2011. (Illus.). 397p. ***(978-1-59417-142-0(4))*** Scepter Pubs., Inc.

CATHOLIC CHURCH—UNITED STATES

see also Americanism (Catholic Controversy)

The American Catholic Heritage: Reflections on the Growth & Influence of the Catholic Church in the United States. 131p. *(978-1-55586-544-3(5))* United States Conference of Catholic Bishops.

American-French Genealogical Society Staff. Baptisms of Blessed Sacrament Catholic Church, Fall River, MA (1892 - 1995) 2007. 378p. spiral bd. 45.00 *(978-1-60305-018-0(3))* American French Genealogical Society.

Avella, Steven M. Sacramento & the Catholic Church: Shaping a Capital City. 2008. (Urban West Ser.). (ENG., Illus.). 384p. 39.95 *(978-0-87417-760-2(X))* Univ. of Nevada Pr.

Baggett, Jerome P. Sense of the Faithful: How American Catholics Live Their Faith, 1 vol. 2011. (ENG.). 320p. pap. 19.95 *(978-0-19-982608-7(0))* Oxford Univ. Pr., Inc.

Beagle, Donald Robert. Poet of the Lost Cause: A Life of Father Ryan. 2008. (ENG., Illus.). 48.95 *(978-1-57233-606-3(4))* Univ. of Tennessee Pr.

Beecher, Lyman. A Plea for the West. 2009. 58p. pap. 14.14 *(978-1-151-70883-0(6))* General Bks. LLC.

Beecher, Lyman, abr. A Plea for the West. 2009. (Amer Philosophy, Religion Ser.). (ENG.). 196p. pap. 14.95 *(978-1-4290-1837-1(2))* Applewood Bks.

Benedict. Pope Benedict in America: The Full Texts of Papal Talks Given During His Apostolic Visit to the United States. 2008. 130p. 14.95 *(978-1-58617-293-0(X))* Ignatius Pr.

The Book of the Gospels: The Saint John's Bible Edition. 2007. 526p. lthr. 695.00 *(978-0-8146-9064-2(5))*; (ENG.). 595.00 *(978-0-8146-9097-0(1))* Liturgical Pr. (Liturgical Pr. Bks.).

Bovee, David S. The Church & the Land: The National Catholic Rural Life Conference & American Society, 1923-2007. 2010. (Illus.). 418p. 79.95 *(978-0-8132-1720-8(2))* Catholic Univ. of America Pr.

Brennan, Dermot R. Your Parish Priest: A Man of Mystery. 2009. *(978-0-8189-1293-1(6)*, St. Pauls) St Pauls/Alba Hse. Pubs.

Brinkley, Douglas & Fenster, Julie. Parish Priest: Father Michael McGivney & American Catholicism. 2007. (ENG., Illus.). 272p. pap. 13.99 *(978-0-06-077685-5(4)*, HarperPerennial) HarperCollins Pubs.

Brooks, Erastus. Brooksiana; or, the Controversy Between Senator Brooks & Archbishop Hughes: Growing Out of the Recently Enacted Church Property Bill / with an Int. 2006. 220p. per. 20.99 *(978-1-4255-1824-0(9))* MPublishing.

Brown, Beth Dotson. Yes! I Am Catholic: How Faith Plays a Role in My Life. 2007. (Illus.). 190p. per. 17.75 *(978-0-88489-964-8(0))* St. Mary's Pr.

Byerley, Timothy E. The Great Commission: Models of Evangelization in American Catholicism. 2008. 176p. pap. 18.95 *(978-0-8091-4558-4(8))* Paulist Pr.

Cafardi, Nicholas P. Before Dallas: The U. S. Bishops' Response to Clergy Sexual Abuse of Children. 2008. 255p. 27.95 *(978-0-8091-0580-9(2)*, 0580-9) Paulist Pr.

Cafardi, Nicholas P. Voting & Holiness: Catholic Perspectives on Political Participation. 2012. 265p. ***(978-1-61643-140-2(7))*** Paulist Pr.

Cafardi, Nicholas P., ed. Voting & Holiness: Catholic Perspectives on Political Participation. 2012. 272p. pap. 24.95 ***(978-0-8091-4767-0(X))*** Paulist Pr.

Chaput, Charles J. Render unto Caesar: Serving the Nation by Living Our Catholic Beliefs in Political Life. 2009. (ENG.). 272p. pap. 14.00 *(978-0-385-52229-8(0)*, Image) Doubleday Religious Publishing Group, The.

—Render unto Caesar: Serving the Nation by Living Our Catholic Beliefs in Political Life. 2008. (ENG.). 272p. 21.95 *(978-0-385-52228-1(2))* Knopf Doubleday Publishing Group.

Conway, Daniel. Advancing the Mission of the Church: Best Practices in Stewardship & Development for Catholic Organizations. 2009. 83p. pap. *(978-0-9800284-1-6(8))* St. Catherine of Siena Pr.

Daly, Michael. The Book of Mychal: The Surprising Life & Heroic Death of Father Mychal Judge. 2009. (ENG., Illus.). 416p. pap. 17.99 *(978-0-312-58744-4(9)*, St. Martin's Griffin) St. Martin's Pr.

Davis, Kenneth G., ed. Misa, Mesa, y Musa, Volume 2: Liturgy in the U. S. Hispanic Church. 2008. 162p. per. 14.95 *(978-1-58459-376-8(8))* World Library Pubns.

Dear, John. A Persistent Peace: One Man's Struggle for a Nonviolent World. 2008. (ENG.). 456p. 22.95 *(978-0-8294-2720-2(1))* Loyola Pr.

Delozier, Alan Bernard. Roman Catholic Archdiocese of Newark. 2011. (Images of America Ser.). (Illus.). 128p. pap. 21.99 ***(978-0-7385-7640-4(9))*** Arcadia Publishing.

Dolan, Jay P., ed. Puerto Rican & Cuban Catholics in the U. S. , 1900-1965. 2010. (History of Hispanic Catholics in U. S. Ser.). (ENG.). 268p. pap. 32.00 *(978-0-268-02606-6(8))* Univ. of Notre Dame Pr.

Dolan, Michael Francis. Where Have All the Catholics Gone? 2010. 160p. 24.95 *(978-1-4502-6118-0(3))*; pap. 14.95 *(978-1-4502-6120-3(5))* iUniverse, Inc.

Douthat, Ross. Bad Religion: How We Became a Nation of Heretics. 2012. (ENG.). 352p. 26.00 ***(978-1-4391-7830-0(5)***, Free Pr.) Free Pr.

Duffy, Regis A. An American Emmaus. 2010. 192p. pap. 21.00 *(978-1-60899-534-9(8)*, Wipf and Stock) Wipf & Stock Pubs.

Dyrness, William A. Senses of the Soul: Art & the Visual in Christian Worship. 2008. (Art for Faith's Sake: Ser.). 198p. pap. 23.00 *(978-1-55635-864-7(4)*, Cascade Bks.) Wipf & Stock Pubs.

Endres, David J. American Crusade: Catholic Youth in the World Mission Movement from World War I. Through Vatican II. 2010. (American Society of Missiology Monograph Ser.). 212p. pap. 23.00 *(978-1-60899-071-9(0)*, Pickwick Pubns.) Wipf & Stock Pubs.

Eschenauer, Donna & Horell, Harold, eds. Reflection & Renewal. 2011. 216p. pap. 19.95 ***(978-0-8146-8016-2(X))*** Liturgical Pr.

Eschenauer, Donna & Horell, Harold Daly. Reflections on Renewal: Lay Ecclesial Ministry & the Church. 2011. E-Book ***(978-0-8146-8018-6(6))*** Liturgical Pr.

Evans, Bernard F. Lazarus at the Table: Catholic & Social Justice. 2006. (Michael Glazier Bks.). 125p. per. 15.95 *(978-0-8146-5114-8(3))* Liturgical Pr.

Fox, Zeni. Lay Ecclesial Ministry: Pathways Toward the Future. 2010. (ENG.). 242p. 69.00 *(978-1-4422-0184-2(3))*; pap. 29.95 *(978-1-4422-0185-9(1))* Rowman & Littlefield Publishers, Inc.

Galipeau, Jerry, ed. The Impact of the RCIA: Stories, Reflections, Challenges. 2008. (Fountain of Life Ser.). 133p. pap. 24.95 *(978-1-58459-407-9(1))* World Library Pubns.

Goldner, Virginia & Frawley-O'Dea, Mary G., eds. Predatory Priests, Silenced Victims: The Sexual Abuse Crisis & the Catholic Church. 2007. (ENG.). 259p. 44.50 *(978-0-88163-424-2(7))* Routledge.

Greeley, Andrew M. Chicago Catholics & the Struggles Within Their Church. 2010. (ENG.). 218p. 49.95 *(978-1-4128-1479-9(0))* Transaction Pubs.

Gribble, Richard, ed. Apostolic Religious Life in America Today: A Response to the Crisis. 2011. 192p. pap. 19.95 *(978-0-8132-1865-6(9))* Catholic Univ. of America Pr.

Groeschel, Benedict & Groeschel, Benedict J. Travelers along the Way: The Men & Women Who Shaped My Life. 2010. pap. *(978-0-86716-984-3(2)*, Servant Bks.) Franciscan Media.

Groome, Thomas H. & Daley, Michael J. Reclaiming Catholicism: Treasures Old & New. 2010. 272p. pap. 22.00 *(978-1-57075-863-8(8))* Orbis Bks.

Hehir, J. Bryan. Catholic Charities USA: 100 Years at the Intersection of Charity & Justice. 2010. E-Book 9.95 *(978-0-8146-3930-6(5))*; 19.95 *(978-0-8146-3339-7(0))* Liturgical Pr.

Hemesath, Sister Caroline. From Slave to Priest: The Inspirational Story of Fr. Augustine Tolton. 2010. 255p. pap. 16.95 *(978-1-58617-524-5(6))* Ignatius Pr.

Heyer, Kristin E., et al. Catholics & Politics: The Dynamic Tension Between Faith & Power. Heyer, Kristin E. et al, eds. 2008. (Religion & Politics Ser.). (ENG., Illus.). 248p. 44.95 *(978-1-58901-216-5(X))*; pap. 29.95 *(978-1-58901-215-8(1))* Georgetown Univ. Pr.

Hoffmann, M. M. The Church Founders of the Northwest. 387p. reprint ed. lib. bdg. 98.00 *(978-0-7222-0439-9(6))* Library Reprints, Inc.

Hogan, John J. On the Mission in Missouri, 1857-1868. (Illus.). 205p. reprint ed. lib. bdg. 98.00 *(978-0-7222-0707-9(7))* Library Reprints, Inc.

Hogan, John Joseph. On the Mission in Missouri & Fifty Years Ago: Two Irish-American Classics by Father John Joseph Hogan. Payton, Crystal, ed. 2009. (ENG., Illus.). 224p. pap. 24.95 *(978-0-9673925-5-4(1))* Lens & Pen Pr.

Hoge, Dean & Jewell, Marti. The Next Generation of Pastoral Leaders: What the Church Needs to Know. 2010. (ENG.). 208p. pap. 11.95 *(978-0-8294-2650-2(7))* Loyola Pr.

Houser, Sue. La Conquistadora: The Story of the Oldest Statue of the Virgin Mary in the United States. 2011. (SPA & ENG.). 94p. pap. 30.00 ***(978-0-86534-830-1(8))*** Sunstone Pr.

Jaimes, Rene S. The Roman Catholic Churches of Manhattan: Their History, Architecture & Decoration. 2007. (Illus.). 268p. 50.00 *(978-0-615-15726-9(2))* Jaimes, Rene Assocs., Publishing Consultants.

John, Roscoe & Robert. Legacies of Faith. 2009. 320p. pap. 19.95 *(978-0-87839-314-5(5))* North Star Pr. of St. Cloud.

Johnson, R. Kevin. Lenten Lessons: Preparing for Worship in Lent Year A. 2008. xiv, 101p. pap. *(978-0-9800621-0-6(1))* Micah Publishing.

Kammer, Fred. Faith. Works. Wonders: An Insider's Guide to Catholic Charities. 2009. 220p. pap. 24.00 *(978-1-60608-927-9(7)*, Pickwick Pubns.) Wipf & Stock Pubs.

Kautzer, Kathleen. The Underground Church: Nonviolent Resistance to the Vatican Empire. 2012. (Studies in Critical Research on Religion / Studies in Critical Social Sciences: Vol. 40/2). (ENG., Illus.). 320p. ***(978-90-04-21938-0(2))*** BRILL.

Kelly, Matthew. The One Thing. 2011. (Illus.). 60p. 13.95 ***(978-0-9841318-8-4(4))*** Beacon Publishing.

Kelly, Timothy. The Transformation of American Catholicism: The Pittsburgh Laity & the Second Vatican Council, 1950-1972. 2009. (ENG.). 456p. 45.00 *(978-0-268-03319-4(6))* Univ. of Notre Dame Pr.

Kennedy, Kerry. Being Catholic Now: Prominent Americans Talk about Change in the Church & the Quest for Meaning. 2009. (ENG., Illus.). 288p. pap. 15.00 *(978-0-307-34685-8(4)*, Three Rivers Pr.) Crown Publishing Group.

Krentz, Roger F. Polish Catholic Churches in Wisconsin In 1905. 2010. 180p. pap. 68.50 *(978-0-557-59538-9(X))* Lulu Enterprises Inc.

—St. John the Baptist Catholic Church Princeton, Wisconsin. 2010. 112p. pap. 47.96 *(978-0-557-40886-3(5))* Lulu Enterprises Inc.

Lawler, Philip F. The Faithful Departed: The Collapse of Boston's Catholic Culture. (ENG.). 2010. 288p. pap. 15.95 *(978-1-59403-374-2(9))* 2008. 280p. 25.95 *(978-1-59403-211-0(4))* Encounter Bks.

Lenhart, John M. Catholics & the American Declaration of Independence, 1774-1776. 2011. 72p. 36.95 ***(978-1-258-01989-1(2))*** Literary Licensing, LLC.

Lord, Robert H., et al. The History of the Archdiocese of Boston V1: In the Various Stages of Its Development, 1604-1943. 2011. 848p. 76.95 ***(978-1-258-04637-8(7))*** Literary Licensing, LLC.

—The History of the Archdiocese of Boston V2: In the Various Stages of Its Development, 1604-1943. 2011. 790p. 74.95 ***(978-1-258-04644-6(X))*** Literary Licensing, LLC.

—The History of the Archdiocese of Boston V3: In the Various Stages of Its Development, 1604-1943. 2011. 832p. 75.95 ***(978-1-258-04645-3(8))*** Literary Licensing, LLC.

Maguire, Connell. Foibles of Father Joe. 2008. per. 14.95 *(978-0-9727330-3-8(5))* Chi Chi Pr.

Markey, Greg J. Discovering the Camino de Santiago: A Priest's Journey to the Tomb of St. James. 2011. 74p. pap. 9.95 ***(978-1-934888-20-9(6))*** Roman Catholic Bks.

Marotti, Frank. The Cana Sanctuary: History, Diplomacy, & Black Catholic Marriage in Antebellum St. Augustine, Florida. 2012. (ENG.). 240p. 39.95 ***(978-0-8173-1747-8(3))*** Univ. of Alabama Pr.

McBride, O., Alfred. How to Make Homilies Better, Briefer, & Bolder: Tips from a Master Homilist. 2007. 158p. per. 15.95 *(978-1-59276-198-2(4))* Our Sunday Visitor, Publishing Div.

McCarrick, Theodore. Thinking of You: The Weekly Columns from the Catholic Standard. 2011. 512p. pap. 22.00 *(978-1-59471-129-9(1))* Ave Maria Pr.

McCartin, James P. Prayers of the Faithful: The Shifting Spiritual Life of American Catholics. 2010. 240p. 25.95 *(978-0-674-04913-0(6))* Harvard Univ. Pr.

McGrath, Elsie Hainz, et al, eds. Women Find a Way: The Movement & Stories of Roman Catholic Womenpriests. 2008. 160p. pap. 19.95 *(978-1-60264-223-2(0))* Virtualbookworm.com Publishing, Inc.

McGuinness, Margaret M. & Fisher, James T., eds. The Catholic Studies Reader. 2011. (Catholic Practice in North America Ser.). (ENG.). 350p. pap. 32.00 *(978-0-8232-3411-0(8))* Fordham Univ. Pr.

—The Catholic Studies Reader. 2011. (Catholic Practice in North America Ser.). (ENG.). 350p. 105.00 *(978-0-8232-3410-3(X))* Fordham Univ. Pr.

Meme, Kevin & Guhin, Jeffrey Joseph, eds. Young & Catholic in America. 2010. 144p. pap. *(978-0-8091-4548-5(0))* Paulist Pr.

Merton, Thomas, et al. A Meeting of Angels: The Correspondence of Thomas Merton with Edward Deming & Faith Andrews. 2008. (Illus.). 118p. 25.00 *(978-0-9721144-9-3(1))* Broadstone Media LLC.

Miller, Richard W., ed. We Hold These Truths: Catholicism & American Political Life. 2008. 137p. per. 14.95 *(978-0-7648-1720-5(5))* Liguori Pubns.

Morse, Samuel Finley Breese. Imminent Dangers to the Free Institutions of the United States Through Foreign Immigration, & the Present State of the Naturalization Laws. 2011. 34p. 35.95 ***(978-1-258-08152-2(0))*** Literary Licensing, LLC.

Muldoon, Tim. Seeds of Hope: Young Adults & the Catholic Church in the United States. 2008. 225p. per. 24.95 *(978-0-8091-4514-0(6))* Paulist Pr.

Nuzzi, Ronald James, et al. Faith, Finances, & the Future: The Notre Dame Study of U. S. Pastors. 2008. (ENG.). 88p. pap. 10.00 *(978-0-9788793-5-8(X))* Alliance for Catholic Education Pr.

O'Brien, David J. & Shannon, Thomas A., eds. Catholic Social Thought: The Documentary Heritage. 2010. 824p. pap. 30.00 *(978-1-57075-891-1(3))* Orbis Bks.

O'Connell, David. Furl That Banner: The Life of Abram J. Ryan, Poet-Priest of the South. 2006. (Illus.). 251p. 35.00 *(978-0-88146-035-3(4))* Mercer Univ. Pr.

Of Preachers Of The United States Of Am, et al. Vocation in Black & White: Dominican Contemplative Nuns tell how God called Them. 2009. 136p. 23.95 *(978-1-4401-2747-2(6))* iUniverse, Inc.

Old Catholic Church, North American. Canons of the North American Old Catholic Church. 2009. 66p. pap. 9.99 *(978-0-557-21972-8(8))* Lulu Enterprises Inc.

Oldfield, John. Bishop of the Barrio: The Life of Bishop Alphonse Gallegos, OAR. 2007. (AFA., Illus.). 93p. per. 12.95 *(978-0-8091-4430-3(1)*, 4430-1) Paulist Pr.

Orsi, Robert A. Between Heaven & Earth: The Religious Worlds People Make & the Scholars Who Study Them. 2006. (ENG., Illus.). 264p. (C). per. 24.95 *(978-0-691-12776-7(X))* Princeton Univ. Pr.

Owen, Olin Marvin. Rum, Rags, & Religion or, in Darkest America & the Way Out. 2007. (ENG.). 128p. 35.95 *(978-0-548-14995-9(X))*; per. 20.95 *(978-1-4304-4321-6(9))* Kessinger Publishing, LLC.

Piderit, John J. & Morey, Melanie M. Teaching the Tradition: Catholic Themes in Academic Disciplines, 1 vol. 2012. (ENG., Illus.). 504p. 99.00 ***(978-0-19-979530-7(4))***; pap. 45.00 ***(978-0-19-979531-4(2))*** Oxford Univ. Pr., Inc.

Plante, Ph.D., Thomas G & McChesney, Kathleen L., eds. Sexual Abuse in the Catholic Church: A Decade of Crisis, 2002-2012, 1 vol. 2011. (Abnormal Psychology Ser.). 270p. 48.00 ***(978-0-313-39387-7(7)***, A3405C) Greenwood Publishing Group, Inc.

Plante, Thomas G. & McChesney, Kathleen. Sexual Abuse in the Catholic Church: A Decade of Crisis, 2002-2012. 2011. E-Book ***(978-0-313-39388-4(5)***, Praeger Pubs.) Greenwood Publishing Group, Inc.

Portmann, John. Catholic Culture in the USA: In & Out of Church. 2010. (ENG.). 224p. 34.95 *(978-1-4411-8892-2(4))*; 120.00 *(978-1-4411-6359-2(X))* Continuum International Publishing Group, Ltd. GBR. Dist: National Bk. Network.

Ramey, David & Jewell, Marti. The Changing Face of the Church: Emerging Models of Parish Leadership. 2010. (ENG.). 176p. pap. 11.95 *(978-0-8294-2647-2(7))* Loyola Pr.

Ronan, Marian. Tracing the Sign of the Cross: Sexuality, Mourning, & the Future of American Catholicism. 2009. (Gender, Theory, & Religion Ser.). (ENG., Illus.). 216p. (gr. 17). 40.00 *(978-0-231-14702-6(3))* Columbia Univ. Pr.

Rosebaugh, Lorenzo & Pino, Kateri Hellman. To Wisdom Through Failure: A Journey of Compassion & Resistance. 2006. *(978-0-918346-37-7(1))* EPICA.

Ryan, Patrick. Archbishop Patrick John Ryan His Life & Times: Ireland - St. Louis - Philadelphia 1831-1911. 2010. (Illus.). 372p. pap. 17.99 *(978-1-4389-9822-0(8))* AuthorHouse.

Ryan, Robin. Catholics on Call: Discerning a Life of Service in the Church. 2010. 19.95 *(978-0-8146-3270-3(X))* Liturgical Pr.

Salpointe, J. B. Soldiers of the Cross. 2010. (Illus.). 356p. pap. 32.75 *(978-1-117-89330-3(8))* BiblioBazaar.

Schneiders, Sandra M. Prophets in their Own Country. 2011. 128p. pap. 20.00 *(978-1-57075-933-8(2))* Orbis Bks.

Shea, John. History of the Catholic Missions among the Indian tribes of the United States. 2010. (Native American Ser.). 542p. pap. 32.95 *(978-1-4290-2260-6(4))* Applewood Bks.

Smith, Gregory Allen. Politics in the Parish: The Political Influence of Catholic Priests. 2nd rev. ed. 2008. (Religion & Politics Ser.). (ENG.). 272p. pap. 26.95 *(978-1-58901-193-9(7))* Georgetown Univ. Pr.

Sullins, David & Blasi, Anthony J., eds. Catholic Social Thought: American Reflections on the Compendium. 2008. (ENG.). 218p. 68.50 *(978-0-7391-2311-9(4))* Lexington Bks.

Sullivan, Thomas K. One Happy Old Priest. 2010. 526p. 34.99 *(978-1-4500-3472-2(1))*; pap. 23.99 *(978-1-4500-3471-5(3))* Xlibris Corp.

Sweetser, Thomas P. & Forster, Patricia M. Transforming the Parish: Models for the Future. 2011. 250p. (Orig.). pap. 28.00 ***(978-1-61097-494-3(8)***, Wipf and Stock) Wipf & Stock Pubs.

Webb, B. J. Centenary of Catholicity in Kentucky. 594p. reprint ed. lib. bdg. 98.00 *(978-0-7222-4923-9(3))* Library Reprints, Inc.

Whitney, Thomas Richard. A Defence of the American Policy, As Opposed to the Encroachments of Foreign Influence, & Especially to the Interference of the Papacy in the Politi. 2006. 376p. per. 26.99 *(978-1-4255-3910-8(6))* MPublishing.

Wolfteich, Claire E. American Catholics Through the Twentieth Century: Spirituality, Lay Experience & Public Life. 2011. 212p. pap. 19.95 ***(978-0-8245-2637-5(6))*** Crossroad Publishing Co., The.

Wright, Wendy M. Mary & the Catholic Imagination: Le Point Vierge. 2011. 96p. pap. *(978-0-8091-4707-6(6))* Paulist Pr.

CATHOLIC CHURCH—UNITED STATES—BIBLIOGRAPHY

Weber, Francis J. Select Guide to California Catholic History. 22.00 *(978-0-87026-001-8(4))* Westernlore Pubns.

CATHOLIC CHURCH—UNITED STATES—EDUCATION

Andres, Suzie. A Little Way of Homeschooling: Thirteen Families Discover Catholic Unschooling. 2011. pap. 14.95 *(978-0-9831800-0-5(8))* Hillside Education.

Ashley, Benedict M. The Arts of Learning & Communication. 2009. 632p. pap. 65.00 *(978-1-60608-931-6(5)*, Wipf and Stock) Wipf & Stock Pubs.

Budzichowski, Laura. The Spirit of ACE: Celebrating 15 Years. 2008. 234p. pap. 10.00 *(978-0-9788793-4-1(1))* Alliance for Catholic Education Pr.

Caruso, Michael J. When the Sisters Said Farewell: The Transition of Leadership in Catholic Elementary Schools. 2012. (ENG.). 170p. 60.00 ***(978-1-61048-652-1(8))*** Rowman & Littlefield Education.

Caruso, Michael P. When the Sisters Said Farewell: The Transition of Leadership in Catholic Elementary Schools. 2012. (ENG.). 170p. pap. 24.95 ***(978-1-61048-653-8(6))*** Rowman & Littlefield Education.

Colwell, Stephen. The Position of Christianity in the United States, in Its Relations with Our Political Institutions,and Specially with Reference to Religious Instruct. 2006. 180p. per. 18.99 *(978-1-4255-1393-1(X))* MPublishing.

Graham, William. Here Comes Everybody: Catholic Studies in American Higher Education. 2008. (ENG.). 204p. pap. 35.99 *(978-0-7618-4432-7(5))* Univ. Pr. of America, Inc.

—Here Comes Everybody: Catholics Studies in American Higher Education. 2008. (ENG.). 204p. 68.50 *(978-0-7618-4431-0(7))* Univ. Pr. of America, Inc.

Grey, Shannon, et al. Catholic High School Entrance Exams. 2nd ed. 2010. (Catholic High School Entrance Test Prep Ser.). (ENG.). 656p. (gr. 8-8). pap. 19.95 *(978-0-7386-0667-5(7))* Research & Education Assn.

Hendershott, Anne & Hendershott, Anne B. Status Envy: The Politics of Catholic Higher Education. 2009. (ENG.). 256p. 39.95 *(978-1-4128-0817-0(0))* Transaction Pubs.

Holter, Anthony C. & Frabutt, James M. Action Research in Catholic Schools: A Step-By-Step Guide for Practitioners. 2009. pap. *(978-0-9788793-8-9(4))* Alliance for Catholic Education Pr.

Holter, Anthony C. & Frabutt, James M. Action Research in Catholic Schools: Step-By-Step Guide for Practitioners. 2nd ed. 2011. pap. ***(978-1-935788-07-2(8))*** Alliance for Catholic Education Pr.

Mayotte, Gail. Let Your Light Shine: A Guide for Preparing to Teach in a Catholic School. 2010. pap. *(978-1-935788-00-3(0))* Alliance for Catholic Education Pr.

McGucken, S.J., Ph.D, William J. The Jesuits & Education: The Society's Teaching Principles & Practice, Especially in Secondary Education in the United States. 2008. 378p. pap. 32.00 *(978-1-60608-183-9(7))*, Wipf and Stock) Wipf & Stock Pubs.

Morey, Melanie & Piderit, John. Catholic Higher Education: A Culture in Crisis, 1 vol. 2010. (ENG.). 472p. pap. 29.95 *(978-0-19-973904-2(8))* Oxford Univ. Pr., Inc.

Rausch, Thomas P. Educating for Faith & Justice: Catholic Higher Education Today. 2010. xiv, 165p. 19.95 *(978-0-8146-5459-0(2))* Liturgical Pr.

Religious Identity & Behavior of College Faculty, Vol. 2. 2007. (Profiles of the American University Ser.). pap. 12.95 *(978-1-893671-03-4(8))* Institute for Jewish & Community Research.

Ruane, John Bernard. Parish the Thought: An Inspirational Memoir of Growing up Catholic in the 1960s. 2008. (ENG., Illus.). 288p. pap. 16.00 *(978-1-4165-8949-5(X))* Gallery Pr., The IRL. Dist: Simon & Schuster, Inc.

—Parish the Thought: An Inspirational Memoir of Growing up Catholic in The 1960s. 2007. 279p. 19.60 *(978-0-9792344-0-8(9))* Roswell Pr.

Staud, John J., ed. The Carnegie Conversation on Catholic Education. 2008. (ENG.). 92p. pap. 15.00 *(978-0-9788793-3-4(3))* Alliance for Catholic Education Pr.

Wirth, Eileen. They Made All the Difference: Life-Changing Stories from Jesuit High Schools. 2007. (ENG.). 240p. 19.95 *(978-0-8294-2168-2(8))* Loyola Pr.

CATHOLIC CHURCH—UNITED STATES—HISTORY

Ball, Ann. A Century of Faith & Service: All Saints Catholic Church 1908-2008. 2008. (Illus.). 106p. pap. 20.00 *(978-0-615-19092-1(8))* All Saints Catholic Church.

Blanchard, Charles. History of the Catholic Church in Indiana Set, 2 vols. reprint ed. lib. bdg. 250.00 *(978-0-7222-0802-1(2))* Library Reprints, Inc.

Bonner, Jeremy. The Road to Renewal: Victor Joseph Reed & Oklahoma Catholicism, 1905-1971. 2007. (Illus.). 425p. 34.95 *(978-0-8132-1507-5(2))* Catholic Univ. of America Pr.
Bottum, Joseph. The Catholic Awakening: How Catholicism Replaced Protestant Christianity as America's National Church. 2013. (ENG.). 304p. 24.95 *(978-0-385-51881-9(1),* Doubleday) Doubleday Religious Publishing Group, The.
Burns, Jeffrey M., et al, eds. Keeping Faith: European & Asian Catholic Immigrants. 2006. (Illus.). 348p. pap. 33.00 *(978-1-59752-908-2(7),* Wipf and Stock) Wipf & Stock Pubs.
Carey, Patrick W. Catholics in America: A History. 2008. (ENG.). 320p. per. 29.95 *(978-0-7425-6233-2(6))* Rowman & Littlefield Publishers, Inc.
Chang, Raymond. Beyond the Magic Bullet: The Anti-Cancer Cocktail: A New Approach to Beating Cancer. 2011. (ENG.). 208p. pap. 16.95 *(978-0-7570-0232-8(3))* Square One Pubs.
Crosby, S. J. Donald & Crosby, Donald, SJ, Donald. God, Church, & Flag: Senator Joseph R. Mccarthy & the Catholic Church, 1950-1957. 2011. (ENG.). 322p. pap. 40.00 ***(978-0-8078-9642-6(X))*** Univ. of North Carolina Pr.
Cummings, Kathleen Sprows. New Women of the Old Faith: Gender & American Catholicism in the Progressive Era. 2010. (ENG., Illus.). 296p. pap. 22.95 *(978-0-8078-7152-2(4))* Univ. of North Carolina Pr.
—New Women of the Old Faith: Gender & American Catholicism in the Progressive ERA. 2009. (ENG., Illus.). 288p. 47.50 *(978-0-8078-3249-3(9))* Univ. of North Carolina Pr.
Curran, Charles E. The Social Mission of the U. S. Catholic Church: A Theological Perspective. 2010. (Moral Traditions Ser.). (ENG.). 208p. pap. 29.95 *(978-1-58901-743-6(9))* Georgetown Univ. Pr.
Curran, Charles E. The Social Mission of the U.S. Catholic Church: A Theological Perspective. 2011. xi, 196p. ***(978-1-58901-717-7(X))*** Georgetown Univ. Pr.
Curran, Robert Emmett. Shaping American Catholicism: Maryland & New York, 1805-1915. 2012. (ENG.). 320p. 69.95 ***(978-0-8132-1967-7(1))*** Catholic Univ. of America Pr.
Cushing, Richard. Pope Pius XII. 2011. 184p. 42.95 ***(978-1-258-03905-9(2))*** Literary Licensing, LLC.
Dichtl, John R. Frontiers of Faith: Bringing Catholicism to the West in the Early Republic. 2008. (ENG.). 250p. 50.00 *(978-0-8131-2486-5(7))* Univ. Pr. of Kentucky.
Donning Company Publishers Staff, contrib. by. Ascension Centennial, 1907/2007. 2007. *(978-1-57864-460-5(7))* Donning Co. Pubs.
Dávila, Carlos E. The Mustard Seed in Morttan. 2008. 344p. pap. *(978-3-8364-6451-2(9))* VDM Verlag Dr. Mueller e.K.
Ellis, John Tracy. Catholics in Colonial Americ: The American Ecclesiastical Review, V136, January Through May 1957. 2011. 82p. 37.95 ***(978-1-258-09262-7(X))*** Literary Licensing, LLC.
Farrelly, Maura Jane. Papist Patriots: The Making of an American Catholic Identity. 2012. (ENG., Illus.). 304p. 35.00 ***(978-0-19-975771-8(2))*** Oxford Univ. Pr., Inc.
Fisher, James Terence. Communion of Immigrants: A History of Catholics in America. rev. ed. 2007. (Religion Life Ser.). (ENG., Illus.). 176p. per. 12.95 *(978-0-19-533330-5(6))* Oxford Univ. Pr., Inc.
Flint-Hamilton, Kimberly. St. Hubert of the Forest - Astor, Florida: Birth of a Mission Against All Odds. 2007. (Illus.). 185p. per. 24.95 *(978-0-9789635-7-6(1))* Fortuity Pr., LLC.
Gautier, Mary, et al. Same Call, Different Men: The Evolution of the Priesthood since Vatican II. 2012. ***(978-0-8146-3429-5(X))*** Liturgical Pr.
Gjerde, Jon. Catholicism & the Shaping of 19th Century America. Kang, S. Deborah, ed. (ENG., Illus.). 2012. 292p. pap. 32.99 *(978-0-521-27966-6(6))* 2011. 304p. 99.00 *(978-1-107-01024-6(1))* Cambridge Univ. Pr.
Hanley, Boniface. Paulist Father Isaac Hecker: An American Saint. 2008. (Illus.). 48p. pap. 6.95 *(978-0-8091-5232-2(0))* Paulist Pr.
Hayes, Patrick. Pope Pius XI. 2011. 20p. pap. 35.95 ***(978-1-258-03759-8(9))*** Literary Licensing, LLC.
Heming, Harry H. The Catholic Church in Wisconsin, 2 vols., Set. 1181p. reprint ed. lib. bdg. 250.00 *(978-0-7222-0312-5(8))* Library Reprints, Inc.
Holy Rosary Parish: A Century of Community, 1908-2008. 2008. (Illus.). 153p. *(978-1-4363-6674-8(7))* Xlibris Corp.
Issel, William. For Both Cross & Flag: Catholic Action, Anti-Catholicism, & National Security Politics in World War II San Francisco. 2009. (Urban Life, Landscape & Policy Ser.). (ENG., Illus.). 216p. 42.00 *(978-1-4399-0028-4(0))* Temple Univ. Pr.
Jansen Parrent, Mary. Germantown. 2011. (Images of America Ser.). (Illus.). 128p. pap. 21.99 *(978-0-7385-8298-6(0))* Arcadia Publishing.
Johnson, William Bruce. Miracles & Sacrilege: Roberto Rossellini, the Church, & Film Censorship in Hollywood. 2008. (ENG., Illus.). 448p. *(978-0-8020-9307-3(8))*; pap. *(978-0-8020-9493-3(7))* Univ. of Toronto Pr.
Kauffman, Christopher J., ed. US Catholic Historian V 24 3. 2006. 184p. pap. 15.00 *(978-0-268-09467-6(5))* Univ. of Notre Dame Pr.
Kempker, John F. History of the Catholic Church in Iowa. reprint ed. lib. bdg. 98.00 *(978-0-7222-4779-2(6))* Library Reprints, Inc.
Knochel, Mary Ann. Roman Catholic Diocese of Pittsburgh. 2007. (Images of America Ser.). (ENG., Illus.). 128p. per. 21.99 *(978-0-7385-4963-7(0))* Arcadia Publishing.
LaVor, Marty. The Basilica of the Assumption. 2007. per. 34.95 *(978-0-9632680-4-4(X))* LaVor Group.
Lennon, Nancy. St. Ignatius Parish, Chicago: The First Century. 2007. *(978-1-57864-462-9(3))* Donning Co. Pubs.
Maes, Camillus P. The Life of Rev. Charles Nerinckx: With. 2006. pap. 48.95 *(978-1-4286-5864-6(5))* Kessinger Publishing, LLC.
Malloy, Edward A. Monk's Tale: The Pilgrimage Begins, 1941-1975. 2009. (ENG., Illus.). 256p. 25.00 *(978-0-268-03516-7(4))* Univ. of Notre Dame Pr.
Malloy, Edward A. Monk's Tale: Way Stations on the Journey. 2011. (Illus.). 280p. 25.00 ***(978-0-268-03522-8(9))*** Univ. of Notre Dame Pr.
Massa, Mark, ed. American Catholic History: A Documentary Reader. 2008. (ENG., Illus.). 320p. 75.00 *(978-0-8147-5745-1(6))*; pap. 25.00 *(978-0-8147-5746-8(4))* New York Univ. Pr.
Massa, Mark Stephen. The American Catholic Revolution: How the Sixties Changed the Church Forever. 1 vol. 2010. (ENG., Illus.). 224p. 27.95 *(978-0-19-973412-2(7))* Oxford Univ. Pr., Inc.
Matovina, Timothy. Latino Catholicism - Transformation in America#8242;s Largest Church. 2011. (ENG.). 328p. (C). 29.95 ***(978-0-691-13979-1(2))*** Princeton Univ. Pr.
Maurer, Susan A. Spirit of Enthusiasm: A History of the Catholic Charismatic Renewal, 1967-200. 2010. (ENG.). 96p. pap. 18.99 *(978-0-7618-5193-6(3))* Univ. Pr. of America, Inc.
McAvoy, Thomas T. Catholic Church in Indiana, 1789-1834. (Columbia University, Studies in the Social Sciences: No. 471). reprint ed. 27.50 *(978-0-404-51471-6(5))* AMS Pr., Inc.
McDannell, Colleen. The Spirit of Vatican II: A History of Catholic Reform in America. 2011. (ENG.). 304p. (gr. 9). 26.99 *(978-0-465-04480-1(8))* Basic Bks.
McGann, Mary E. Let It Shine! The Emergence of African American Catholic Worship. 4th ed. 2008. (ENG.). 200p. pap. 25.00 *(978-0-8232-2992-5(0))* Fordham Univ. Pr.
McGann, Mary E. & Harbor, Ronald D. Let It Shine! The Emergence of African American Catholic Worship. 4th ed. 2008. (ENG.). 200p. 70.00 *(978-0-8232-2991-8(2),* Fordham Univ. Pr.
McGregor, Alexander. The Catholic Church & Hollywood: Censorship & Morality in 1930s Cinema. 2012. (International Library of Cultural Studies: No. 20). (ENG.). 256p. 92.50 ***(978-1-84885-653-0(9))*** I. B. Tauris & Co., Ltd. GBR. Dist: Macmillan.
McKenna, Kevin E. The Battle for Rights in the United States Catholic Church. 2007. 195p. per. 19.95 *(978-0-8091-4493-8(X),* 4493-8) Paulist Pr.
Metzger, Charles H. Catholics & the American Revolution: A Study in Religious Climate. 2011. 316p. 50.95 ***(978-1-258-06899-8(0))*** Literary Licensing, LLC.
Mooney, Bernice Maher & Fitzgerald, J. Terrence. Salt of the Earth: The History of the Catholic Church in Utah, 1776-2007. 3rd ed. 2008. (ENG., Illus.). 413p. (gr. 13). 29.95 *(978-0-87480-881-0(2))* Univ. of Utah Pr.
Moore, Andrew S. The South's Tolerable Alien: Roman Catholics in Alabama & Georgia, 1945-1970. 2007. 210p. 35.00 *(978-0-8071-3212-8(8))* Louisiana State Univ. Pr.
Nativity Catholic Church: Our Golden Jubilee, 2010-2011: A Roman Catholic Church of the Diocese of St. Petersburg, Florida, 705 E. Brandon Boulevard, Brandon, Florida 33511. 2011. ***(978-1-57864-689-0(8))*** Donning Co. Pubs.
O'Connell, Jeremiah J. Catholicity in the Carolinas & Georgia: Leaves of Its History, A. D. 1820 - A. D. 1878. 647p. reprint ed. lib. bdg. 128.00 *(978-0-7222-0864-9(2))* Library Reprints, Inc.
—Catholicity in the Carolinas & Georgia: Leaves of Its History, A. D. 1820-1878. 647p. reprint ed. lib. bdg. 128.00 *(978-0-7222-4999-4(3))* Library Reprints, Inc.
O'Toole, James M. The Faithful: A History of Catholics in America. 2010. 384p. pap. 19.00 *(978-0-674-03488-4(0),* Belknap Pr.) Harvard Univ. Pr.
Page, Freda. St Patrick's Church Centennial Memory Book. 2011. 160p. 29.99 ***(978-1-4628-7022-6(8))***; pap. 19.99 ***(978-1-4628-7021-9(X))*** Xlibris Corp.
Pasquier, Michael. Fathers on the Frontier: French Missionaries & the Roman Catholic Priesthood in the United States, 1789-1870, 1 vol. 2010. (Religion in America Ser.). (ENG., Illus.). 312p. 74.00 *(978-0-19-537233-5(6))* Oxford Univ. Pr., Inc.
Peters, Shawn Francis. The Catonsville Nine: A Story of Faith & Resistance in the Vietnam Era. 2012. E-Book ***(978-0-19-982786-2(9))***; (ENG.). 400p. 34.95 ***(978-0-19-932785-5(0))*** Oxford Univ. Pr., Inc.
Piehl, Mel. Breaking Bread: The Catholic Worker & the Origin of Catholic Radicalism in America. 2006. (Religion & American Culture Ser.). (Illus.). 316p. pap. 29.95 *(978-0-8173-5327-8(5))* Univ. of Alabama Pr.
Plumer, Eric A. The Catholic Church & American Culture: Why the Claims of Dan Brown Strike a Chord. 2009. 340p. pap. 25.00 *(978-1-58966-135-6(4))* Univ. of Scranton Pr.
Prouty, Marco G. César Chávez, the Catholic Bishops, & the Farmworkers' Struggle for Social Justice. Prouty, Marco G. 2008. (ENG., Illus.). 208p. pap. 19.95 *(978-0-8165-2731-1(8))* Univ. of Arizona Pr.
—Cesar Chavez, the Catholic Bishops, & the Farmworkers' Struggle for Social Justice. 2006. (ENG., Illus.). 208p. 40.00 *(978-0-8165-2555-3(2))* Univ. of Arizona Pr.
Rossi, Joseph S. Uncharted Territory: The American Catholic Church at the United Nations, 1946-1972. 2006. (Illus.). 288p. 79.95 *(978-0-8132-1456-6(4))* Catholic Univ. of America Pr.
Rudin, A. James. Cushing, Spellman, O'Connor: The Surprising Story of How Three American Cardinals Transformed Catholic-Jewish Relations. 2011. pap. ***(978-0-8028-6567-0(4))*** Eerdmans, William B. Publishing Co.
Schultz, Nancy. Mrs. Mattingly's Miracle: The Prince, the Widow, & the Cure That Shocked Washington City. 2011. (ENG., Illus.). 288p. 30.00 *(978-0-300-11846-9(5))* Yale Univ. Pr.
Slaughter, Shirley Harris. Our Lady of Victory: The Saga of an African-American Catholic Community. 2007. 224p. (ENG.). 28.95 *(978-0-595-89668-4(5))*; per. 18.95 *(978-0-595-43482-4(7))* iUniverse, Inc.
Slawson, Douglas J. Ambition & Arrogance: Cardinal William O'Connell of Boston & the American Catholic Church. 2007. (ENG.). 248p. per. *(978-0-9787855-0-5(9))* Cobalt Productions.
St. Boniface Catholic Church. A Journey of Faith Continues. 2006. (Illus.). xix, 298p. *(978-1-57579-341-2(5))* Pine Hill Pr., Inc.
St. Joseph Catholic Church, Princeton, Indiana: History: Book I, 1855-1950. 2007. (Illus.). 96p. lib. bdg. *(978-1-932439-73-1(0))* M.T. Publishing Co., Inc.
Sterne, Evelyn Savidge. Ballots & Bibles: Ethnic Politics & the Catholic Church in Providence. 2008. (Cushwa Center Studies of Catholicism in Twentieth-Century America). 320p. pap. 22.95 *(978-0-8014-7497-2(3))* Cornell Univ. Pr.
Taylor, Mary C. A History of the Foundations of Catholicism in Northern New York. (Monographs: No. 32). (Illus.). 13.50 *(978-0-930060-12-1(1))* U. S. Catholic Historical Society.
Tentler, Leslie Woodcock. The Church Confronts Modernity: Catholicism since 1950 in the United States, Ireland, & Quebec. 2007. 302p. per. 34.95 *(978-0-8132-1494-8(7))* Catholic Univ. of America Pr.
Trevino, Roberto R. & Francaviglia, Richard V., eds. Catholicism in the American West: A Rosary of Hidden Voices. 2007. (Walter Prescott Webb Memorial Lectures). (Illus.). 184p. 29.95 *(978-1-58544-621-6(1))* Texas A&M Univ. Pr.
Wallace, W. Jason. Catholics Slaveholders & Dilem. 2010. (ENG.). 208p. pap. 30.00 *(978-0-268-04421-3(X))* Univ. of Notre Dame Pr.
White, Joseph M. Worthy of the Gospel of Christ: A History of the Catholic Diocese of Fort Wayne-South Bend. 2007. (Illus.). 609p. per. 29.95 *(978-1-59276-229-3(8))* Our Sunday Visitor, Publishing Div.
Wilson, Jacqueline E. Charting New Paths: History/National Assn of Black Catholic Administrators. 2007. (Illus.). 119p. pap. 20.00 net. *(978-0-9747324-1-1(9))* Wilson, Jacqueline E.
Woods, Thomas E., Jr. & Woods, Jr., Thomas E., Thomas E. The Church Confronts Modernity: Catholic Intellectuals & the Progressive Era. 2006. (Religion & American Culture Ser.). (ENG.). 304p. (gr. 17). pap. 27.00 *(978-0-231-13187-2(9))* Columbia Univ. Pr.
Woolner, David B. & Kurial, Richard G., eds. FDR, the Vatican, & the Roman Catholic Church in America, 1933-1945. 2010. (World of the Roosevelts Ser.). (ENG.). 314p. pap. 29.00 *(978-0-230-62351-4(4))* Palgrave Macmillan.

CATHOLIC CHURCH—UNITED STATES—HISTORY—SOURCES

Brugge, David M. Navajos in the Catholic Church Records of New Mexico, 1694-1875. 3rd ed. 2010. (Illus.). xxiv, 183p. *(978-1-934691-39-7(9))* School for Advanced Research Pr./SAR P.
Weber, Francis J. Readings in California Catholic History. 22.00 *(978-0-87026-000-1(6))* Westernlore Pubns.

CATHOLIC CHURCH—VENEZUELA

Berryman, Phillip. Religion in the Megacity: Catholic & Protestant Portraits from Latin America. 2006. 216p. pap. 24.00 *(978-1-59752-903-7(6),* Wipf and Stock) Wipf & Stock Pubs.
Donis Rios, Manuel Alberto & Straka, Tomás. Historia de la Iglesia Católica en Venezuela: Documentos para Su Estudio. 2010. (SPA.). 402p. *(978-980-244-617-9(3))* Universidad Catolica Andres Bello.
Harricharan, John T. Church & Society in Trinidad 1864-1900, Part III. 2008. 168p. pap. 17.99 *(978-1-4343-3758-0(8),* AuthorHouse.

CATHOLIC CHURCH—VIETNAM

Ramsay, Jacob. Mandarins & Martyrs: The Church & the Nguyen Dynasty in Early Nineteenth-Century Vietnam. 2008. (ENG., Illus.). 224p. 50.00 *(978-0-8047-5651-8(1))* Stanford Univ. Pr.
Schmitt, Oskar. Ein würdiger Verwalter im Weinberg unseres Herrn Jesus Christus: Bischof Pierre Martin Ngo-dinh-Thuc. 2006. 206p. pap. 17.90 *(978-3-8334-5385-4(0))* Bks. on Demand.

CATHOLIC CHURCH AND LABOR

see Church and Labor

CATHOLIC CHURCH AND SALVATION

see Salvation Outside the Catholic Church

CATHOLIC CHURCH AND SOCIAL PROBLEMS

see Church and Social Problems—Catholic Church

CATHOLIC CHURCH AND SOCIALISM

see Socialism and Catholic Church

CATHOLIC CHURCH AND STATE

see Church and State—Catholic Church

CATHOLIC CHURCH AND ZIONISM

Falk, Gerhard. The Restoration of Israel: Christian Zionism in Religion, Literature, & Politics. 2006. (American University Studies: Vol. 257). 236p. (C). 70.95 *(978-0-8204-8862-2(3))* Lang, Peter Publishing, Inc.

CATHOLIC CHURCH MUSIC

see Church Music—Catholic Church

CATHOLIC CONVERTS

Adams, Pauline. English Catholic Converts & the Oxford Movement in Mid 19th Century England. 2010. 204p. lib. bdg. ***(978-1-933146-84-3(2))*** Academica Pr., LLC.
Anderson, Emma. The Betrayal of Faith: The Tragic Journey of a Colonial Native Convert. 2007. (Harvard Historical Studies: 160). (Illus.). 318p. 51.50 *(978-0-674-02608-7(X))* Harvard Univ. Pr.
Beaumont, John. Roads to Rome: A Guide to Notable Converts from Britain & Ireland from the Reformation to The. 2010. (ENG.). 480p. 55.00 *(978-1-58731-720-0(6))* St. Augustine's Pr., Inc.
—Roads to Rome: A Guide to Notable Converts from Britain & Ireland from the Reformation to the Present Day. 2010. *(978-1-58731-721-7(4))* St. Augustine's Pr., Inc.
Beckwith, Francis J. Return to Rome: Confessions of an Evangelical Catholic. 2009. 144p. pap. 14.99 *(978-1-58743-247-7(1))* Brazos Pr.
Benson, Robert Hugh. Confessions of a Convert. 2009. 208p. 28.99 *(978-1-110-83677-2(5))*; pap. 23.75 *(978-1-110-83674-1(0))* BiblioBazaar.
—Confessions of a Convert. 2009. 82p. pap. *(978-0-217-19489-1(3))* Books LLC.
—Confessions of a Convert. 2008. 104p. pap. 9.95 *(978-1-60104-019-0(9))* Bridegroom Pr.
—Confessions of a Convert. 2008. 100p. pap. *(978-1-4099-5179-7(0))* Dodo Pr.
Caffiero, Marina. Forced Baptisms: Histories of Jews, Christians, & Converts in Papal Rome. Cochrane, Lydia, tr. from ITA. 2011. (ENG.). 312p. 60.00 *(978-0-520-25451-0(1))* Univ. of California Pr.
Choy, Leona. My Journey to the Land of More. 2010. pap. 12.95 *(978-0-9800066-6-7(X))* CHResources.
Conn, Walter E. Conscience & Conversion in Newman: A Developmental Study of Self in John Henry Newman. 2010. pap. *(978-0-87462-777-0(X))* Marquette Univ. Pr.
Day, Dorothy. From Union Square to Rome. 2006. 177p. per. 15.00 *(978-1-57075-667-2(8))* Orbis Bks.
Griffiths, Bede. The Golden String: The Autobiography of Bede Griffiths, Benedictine of Prinknash. 2011. 168p. 41.95 ***(978-1-258-04783-2(7))*** Literary Licensing, LLC.
Grodi, Marcus. Thoughts for the Journey Home. 2010. pap. 11.95 *(978-0-9800066-9-8(4))* CHResources.
Hahn, Scott. Ordinary Work, Extraordinary Grace: My Spiritual Journey in Opus Dei. 2006. (ENG.). 176p. 21.95 *(978-0-385-51924-3(9),* Doubleday Religion) Doubleday Religious Publishing Group, The.
—Ordinary Work, Extraordinary Grace: My Spiritual Journey in Opus Dei. 2008. 155p. *(978-0-385-51948-9(6))* Knopf Doubleday Publishing Group.
Hanley, Boniface. Paulist Father Isaac Hecker: An American Saint. 2008. (Illus.). 48p. pap. 6.95 *(978-0-8091-5232-2(0))* Paulist Pr.
Harline, Craig. Conversions: Two Family Stories from the Reformation & Modern America. 2011. (New Directions in Narrative History Ser.). (ENG., Illus.). 320p. 27.50 *(978-0-300-16701-6(6))* Yale Univ. Pr.
Huntington, Joshua. Gropings after Truth: A Life Journey from New England Congnogationalism to the One Catholic & Apostolic Church. by Joshua Huntington. 2006. 172p. per. 18.99 *(978-1-4255-1322-1(0))* MPublishing.
Ives, Levi. The Trials of a Mind in Its Progress to Catholicism. 2009. (Amer Philosophy, Religion Ser.). (ENG.). 236p. pap. 16.95 *(978-1-4290-1925-5(5))* Applewood Bks.
Jones, W. Paul. A Different Kind of Cell: The Story of a Murderer Who Became a Monk. 2011. 134p. pap. 14.00 ***(978-0-8028-6651-6(4))*** Eerdmans, William B. Publishing Co.
Kast, Maggie. The Crack between the Worlds. 2009. 230p. pap. 25.00 *(978-1-60608-777-0(0),* Resource Pubns.) Wipf & Stock Pubs.
Kugler, Ed. Through the Darkness Comes the Light. 2007. 272p. pap. 19.50 *(978-1-4303-0147-9(3))* Lulu Enterprises Inc.
Lang, Ariella. Converting a Nation: A Modern Inquisition & the Unification of Italy. 2008. (Studies in European Culture & History Ser.). (ENG.). 248p. 95.00 *(978-0-230-60672-2(5))* Palgrave Macmillan.
McPhee, Rosalie. Seekers of Truth: Finding the Faith. 64p. *(978-0-921440-81-9(2))* Madonna Hse. Pubns.
Osburn, Charlie & Osburn, Jeanne. Love Walks by Faith: You Got to Give It All to Jesus. 2007. pap. 14.00 *(978-0-929375-29-8(7))* Whitney, Harvey Bks. Co.
Pereiro, James. Cardinal Manning: From Anglican Archdeacon to Council Father at Vatican I. 2008. 376p. pap. *(978-0-85244-405-4(2))* Gracewing, Ltd.
Schoeman, Roy H., compiled by. Honey from the Rock: Sixteen Jews Find the Sweetness of Christ. 2007. (Illus.). 289p. pap. 16.95 *(978-1-58617-115-5(1))* Ignatius Pr.
Schwartz, Adam. The Third Spring: G. K. Chesterton, Graham Greene, Christopher Dawson, & David Jones. 2012. (ENG.). 432p. pap. 34.95 ***(978-0-8132-1982-0(5))*** Catholic Univ. of America Pr.
Stonor Saunders, Frances. The Woman Who Shot Mussolini. 2010. (ENG., Illus.). 400p. 30.00 *(978-0-8050-9121-2(1),* Metropolitan Bks.) Holt, Henry & Co.
—The Woman Who Shot Mussolini. 2011. (ENG., Illus.). 400p. pap. 19.00 *(978-0-312-68112-8(7))* Picador.
Turner, Paul. When Other Christians Become Catholic. 2007. (Illus.). 172p. per. 23.95 *(978-0-8146-6216-8(1))* Liturgical Pr.
Watkins, Christine. Full of Grace: Miraculous Stories of Healing & Conversion through Mary's Intercession. 2010. 224p. pap. 14.95 *(978-1-59471-226-5(3))* Ave Maria Pr.
Zolli, Eugenio. Before the Dawn: Autobiographical Reflections. 2008. 225p. pap. 15.95 *(978-1-58617-287-9(5))* Ignatius Pr.

CATHOLIC EMANCIPATION

see also Gordon Riots, 1780

Ó Corráin, Donnchadh & O'Riordan, Tomás. Ireland, 1815-70: Emancipation, Famine & Religion. 2011. (Illus.). 302p. pap. 30.00 *(978-1-84682-232-2(7))* Four Courts Pr. IRL. Dist: International Specialized Bk. Services.
Smith, Sydney. Peter Plymley's Letters & Selected Ess. 2006. pap. *(978-1-84702-486-2(6))* Echo Library.

C

CATHOLIC EX-PRIESTS

see Ex-Priests, Catholic

CATHOLIC FOREIGN MISSION SOCIETY OF AMERICA

Chu, Cindy Yik-Yi. The Maryknoll Sisters in Hong Kong, 1921-1969: In Love with the Chinese. 2007. (ENG., Illus.). 224p. pap. 30.00 *(978-0-230-60231-1(2))* Palgrave Macmillan.

Heim, Joseph A. What the Taught Us: How Maryknoll Missioners Were Evangelized by the Poor. 2009. (Illus.). 128p. pap. 15.00 *(978-1-57075-818-8(2))* Orbis Bks.

Veneroso, Joseph R. Mirrors of Grace: The Spirit & Spiritualities of the Maryknoll Fathers & Brothers. 2011. (Illus.). 136p. 20.00 *(978-1-57075-928-4(6))* Orbis Bks.

CATHOLIC HEALTH FACILITIES

Burns, Elizabeth Mary. Beyond Measure: A Legacy of Mercy, 1879-1976. 2009. *(978-1-886769-33-5(8))* Gold Leaf Pr.

Courtens, Ien. Restoring the Balance: Performing Healing in West Papua. 2010. (Illus.). 264p. pap. 44.00 *(978-90-6718-278-2(8))* KITLV Pr. NLD. Dist: Univ. of Hawaii Pr.

Furton, Edward J. & Cataldo, Peter J., eds. Catholic Health Care Ethics: A Manual for Ethics Committees. 2009. (ENG.). pap. 59.95 *(978-0-935372-54-0(7))* National Catholic Bioethics Ctr., The.

Nccb. Ethical & Religious Directives for Catholic Health Care Services. 5th ed. 2009. 40p. *(978-1-60137-101-0(2))* United States Conference of Catholic Bishops.

Nelson, Leonard J., III. Diagnosis Critical: The Urgent Threats Confronting Catholic Health Care. 2009. 350p. 29.95 *(978-1-59276-070-1(8))* Our Sunday Visitor, Publishing Div.

Preston, Margaret H. A Journey of Faith, a Destination of Excellence: Avera McKennan Hospital's First Century of Caring. 2010. *(978-1-57864-660-9(X))*; *(978-1-57864-661-6(8))* Donning Co. Pubs.

Reich, Adam D. With God on Our Side: The Struggle for Workers' Rights in a Catholic Hospital. 2012. (Culture & Politics of Health Care Work Ser.). (ENG.). 208p. 26.00 ***(978-0-8014-5066-2(7))*** Cornell Univ. Pr.

Ryan, Mary Jean. The Challenge to Be Great: On Becoming Exceptional: SSM Health Care's Journey to Baldrige & Beyond. 2007. 29.00 *(978-0-87389-715-0(3))* ASQ Quality Pr.

Wall, Barbra Mann. American Catholic Hospitals: A Century of Changing Markets & Missions. 2011. (Critical Issues in Health & Medicine Ser.). (ENG., Illus.). 260p. 45.95 *(978-0-8135-4940-8(X))* Rutgers Univ. Pr.

CATHOLIC HOSPITALS

see Catholic Health Facilities

CATHOLIC JOURNALISM

see Journalism, Religious

CATHOLIC LEARNING AND SCHOLARSHIP

Furey, Constance M. Erasmus, Contarini, & the Religious Republic of Letters. 2008. (ENG., Illus.). 272p. (C). pap. 40.00 *(978-0-521-10343-5(6))* Cambridge Univ. Pr.

Graham, William. Here Comes Everybody: Catholic Studies in American Higher Education. 2008. (ENG.). 204p. pap. 35.99 *(978-0-7618-4432-7(5))* Univ. Pr. of America, Inc.

—Here Comes Everybody: Catholics Studies in American Higher Education. 2008. (ENG.). 204p. 68.50 *(978-0-7618-4431-0(7))* Univ. Pr. of America, Inc.

Sloane, Andrew. On Being a Christian in the Academy: Nicholas Wolterstorff & the Practice of Christian Scholarship. 2007. (Paternoster Theological Monographs: Ser.). 306p. pap. 31.00 *(978-1-59752-771-2(8)*, Wipf and Stock) Wipf & Stock Pubs.

Thompson, Phillip M. Between Science & Religion: The Engagement of Catholic Intellectuals with Science & Technology in the Twentieth Century. 2009. (ENG.). 298p. 78.99 *(978-0-7391-3080-3(3))* Lexington Bks.

Whitehead, Kenneth, ed. The Idea of the Catholic University: Proceedings from the 30th Annual Conference of the Fellowship of Catholic Scholars. 2010. (University of Scranton Press - Fellowship of Catholic Scholars Ser.). 180p. pap. 20.00 *(978-1-58966-219-3(9))* Univ. of Scranton Pr.

CATHOLIC LITERATURE

see also Catholic Authors

Brophy, Donald. One Hundred Great Catholic Books: From the Early Centuries to the Present. 2007. (ENG.). 240p. per. 16.00 *(978-1-933346-08-3(6))* BlueBridge.

Highley, Christopher. Catholics Writing the Nation in Early Modern Britain & Ireland. 2008. (ENG., Illus.). 240p. 110.00 *(978-0-19-953340-4(7))* Oxford Univ. Pr., Inc.

John Paul II, pseud. Buoi Diem Chu Dao Huong Ve Ngan Nam Thu 3. Vietnamese Dominican Fathers Staff, ed. & tr. by. from LAT. (VIE.). 239p. pap. 5.00 *(978-1-885550-09-5(X))* Du-Sinh Saint Joseph Pub.

Manney, Jim, ed. The Best Catholic Writing. 2007. (Best Catholic Writing Ser.). 241p. per. 14.95 *(978-0-8294-2611-3(6))* Loyola Pr.

Summitt, Margaret. Catholic Literature: An Introduction. 2007. 252p. pap. 12.95 *(978-0-9791600-3-5(0))* Tumblar Hse.

Tuan, J. B. Gioi Luat Yeu Thuong. 149p. pap. 4.00 *(978-1-885550-10-1(3))* Du-Sinh Saint Joseph Pub.

Von Habsburg, Maximilian. Catholic & Protestant Translations of the Imitatio Christi: From Late Medieval Classic to Early Modern Bestseller. 2011. (St Andrews Studies in Reformation History Ser.). 376p. 134.95 ***(978-0-7546-6765-0(0))*** Ashgate Publishing Co.

Windley-Daoust, Jerry. Touching the Hearts of Teens: Saint Mary's Press 1943-2001. 2009. *(978-1-59982-057-6(9))* St. Mary's Pr.

—Touching the Hearts of Teens: Saint Mary's Press from 1943-2001. 2009. pap. *(978-0-88489-825-2(3))* St. Mary's Pr.

CATHOLIC LITERATURE (COLLECTIONS)

Catholic National Reader. 14.00 *(978-1-931555-07-4(9))*;Bk. 2. 12.00 *(978-1-931555-05-0(2))*;Bk. 3. 12.00 *(978-1-931555-06-7(0))*;Bk. 5. 14.00 *(978-1-931555-08-1(7))*;Bk. 6. 14.00 *(978-1-931555-09-8(5))* Our Lady of Victory Schl.

CATHOLIC LITERATURE—BIBLIOGRAPHY

Finotti, Joseph Maria. Bibliographia Catholica Americana: A List of Works Written by Catholic Authors, 2006. 324p. per. 23.99 *(978-1-4255-3207-9(1))* MPublishing.

CATHOLIC LITERATURE—HISTORY AND CRITICISM

Dau, W. H. T. Luther Examined & Reexamined: A Review of Catholic Criticism & a Plea for Revaluation. 2007. 176p. per. *(978-1-4068-1841-3(0))* Echo Library.

Erler, H. Raphael. Winds of Change: Saint Mary's Press from 1957-1974. 2010. pap. *(978-1-59982-023-1(4))* St. Mary's Pr.

Garvey, J. J. Guide Sur l'Opus Dei a l'Usage des Parents. (FRE.). 58p. (Orig.). pap. *(978-0-9628502-1-9(7))* Sicut Dixit Pr.

—The Prelature's Reaction: The Official Response from Opus Dei to "Parents' Guide to Opus Dei" annot. ed. 64p. (Orig.). pap. *(978-0-9628502-2-6(5))* Sicut Dixit Pr.

Reichardt, Mary R., ed. Between Human & Divine: The Catholic Vision in Contemporary Literature. 2010. (ENG.). 304p. 69.95 *(978-0-8132-1739-0(3))* Catholic Univ. of America Pr.

Shell, Alison. Oral Culture & Catholicism in Early Modern England. 2007. (ENG., Illus.). 258p. 95.00 *(978-0-521-88395-5(4))* Cambridge Univ. Pr.

Sudlow. Catholic Literature & Secularisation in France & England, 1880-1914. 2011. (ENG.). 256p. 90.00 *(978-0-7190-8311-2(7))* Manchester Univ. Pr. GBR. Dist: Macmillan.

Vaught, Carl G. Encounters with God in Augustine's Confessions: Books VII-IX. 2007. 175p. per. 24.95 *(978-0-7914-6108-2(4))* State Univ. of New York Pr.

Weyand, Norman, ed. The Catholic Renascence in a Disintegrating World. 2011. 204p. 44.95 ***(978-1-258-08308-3(5))*** Literary Licensing, LLC.

CATHOLIC MOVEMENT (ANGLICAN COMMUNION)

see Anglo-Catholicism

CATHOLIC PERIODICALS

see Catholic Church—Periodicals

CATHOLIC SCHOOLS

Barr, Colin. The European Culture Wars in Ireland: The Callan Schools Affair, 1868-81. 2011. (ENG.). 320p. 89.95 *(978-1-906359-53-9(9))* Univ. College Dublin Pr. IRL. Dist: Dufour Editions, Inc.

Bollen, David. Up on the Hill: A History of St. Patrick's College, Goulburn. 2008. (ENG.). 640p. pap. 53.95 *(978-0-86840-967-2(7)*, UNSW Press) NewSouth Publishing AUS. Dist: Independent Pubs. Group.

Callaghan, Tonya. That's So Gay!- Homophobia in Canadian Catholic Schools. 2007. 260p. per. *(978-3-8364-2497-4(5))* VDM Verlag Dr. Mueller e.K.

Davison, Liam. Going down for the Good Turf. 2008. 140p. pap. *(978-3-8364-3933-6(6))* VDM Verlag Dr. Mueller e.K.

Dienno-Demarest, Julie. Living the Vision: A Pastoral Guide to Service Learning in Catholic High Schools. 2009. 122p. pap. 17.95 *(978-0-557-03097-2(8))* Lulu Enterprises Inc.

Donlan, Andrew. Type of High School Attended & Student Behavior. 2010. 144p. pap. *(978-3-8383-7079-8(1))* Lambert Academic Publishing.

Donlevy, James Kent. The Ten Dimensions of Inclusion: Non-Catholic Students in Catholic Schools. 2009. 160p. *(978-90-8790-806-5(7))*; pap. *(978-90-8790-805-8(9))* Sense Pubs.

Edward, Inyanwachi. The Practice of Inculturation in the Nigerian Church: The Role of Catholic Schools & Universities. 2011. 172p. pap. ***(978-3-639-31747-3(5))*** VDM Verlag Dr. Mueller e.K.

Herron, Fred. Combing the Tradition: Catholic Schools in the Era of Baptismal Consciousness. 2007. (ENG.). 214p. 68.50 *(978-0-7618-3798-5(1))*; per. 39.99 *(978-0-7618-3799-2(X))* Univ. Pr. of America, Inc.

—Tuning the Rig: Catholic Schools for a Learning Church. 2010. (ENG.). 260p. pap. 35.75 *(978-0-7618-5205-6(0))* Univ. Pr. of America, Inc.

Holter, Anthony C. & Frabutt, James M. Action Research in Catholic Schools: Step-By-Step Guide for Practitioners. 2nd ed. 2011. pap. ***(978-1-935788-07-2(8))*** Alliance for Catholic Education Pr.

Kaplan Publishing Staff, ed. Kaplan Catholic High School Entrance Exams: COOP - HSPT - TACHS. 6th ed. 2010. (ENG.). 600p. pap. 18.95 *(978-1-4195-5361-5(5))* Kaplan Publishing.

Lawoyin, Oyeronke Alake. Idi-Ab. 2007. 328p. per. 17.99 *(978-1-60477-072-8(4))* Xulon Pr., Inc.

Lei, Christine. The History of a Catholic Girls Day & Boarding School, 1865-1970: The Religious & Educational Achievement of the Loretto Sisters. 2010. 268p. 109.95 *(978-0-7734-3861-3(0))* Mellen, Edwin Pr., The.

Malizia, G. & Cicatelli, Sergio. The Catholic School under Scrutiny: Ten Years of Research in Italy (1998-2008) 2011. 247p. pap. ***(978-3-0343-0558-7(3))*** Lang, Peter.

Nuzzi, Ronald James & Hunt, Thomas C. At the Heart of the Church: Selected Documents of Catholic Education. 2011. 39.99 ***(978-1-935788-08-9(6))*** Alliance for Catholic Education Pr.

Sander, William. Catholic Schools: Private & Social Effects. 2010. (ENG.). 160p. pap. 129.00 *(978-1-4419-4867-0(8)*, 1441948678) Springer.

Scanlan, Martin K. All Are Welcome: Inclusive Service Delivery in Catholic Schools. 2009. pap. *(978-0-9819501-4-3(0))* Alliance for Catholic Education Pr.

Skaar, Dr. Susan & Skaar, Susan. Profile of a Collaborative Elementary Catholic School Principal. 2010. 184p. pap. *(978-3-8383-1987-2(7))* Lambert Academic Publishing.

Sullivan, J. Catholic Education: Distinctive & Inclusive: Distinctive & Inclusive. 2010. 248p. pap. 195.00 *(978-90-481-5839-3(7)*, 9048158397) Springer.

CATHOLIC SCHOOLS—GREAT BRITAIN

Fincham, David. Pshce in Catholic Secondary Schools. 2010. 264p. pap. *(978-3-8383-3560-5(0))* Lambert Academic Publishing.

CATHOLIC SCHOOLS—UNITED STATES

Abrams, Paula. Cross Purposes: Pierce V. Society of Sisters & the Struggle over Compulsory Public Education. 2009. (ENG., Illus.). 296p. (C). 70.00 *(978-0-472-11700-0(9))* Univ. of Michigan Pr.

Antonelli, Candida. Catholic Lay Leadership Enhancing Faculty Morale. 2010. 160p. pap. *(978-3-8383-8142-8(4))* Lambert Academic Publishing.

Arbour, Linda Marie. Tales Out of School: A Challenge to Catholic Educators. 2011. 260p. pap. 19.95 ***(978-1-4502-8909-2(6))*** iUniverse, Inc.

Bloom, Marc. God on the Starting Line: The Triumph of a Catholic School Running Team & Its Jewish Coach. 2007. (ENG.). 240p. per. 14.00 *(978-1-891369-74-2(1))* Breakaway Bks.

Caruso, Michael J. When the Sisters Said Farewell: The Transition of Leadership in Catholic Elementary Schools. 2012. (ENG.). 170p. 60.00 ***(978-1-61048-652-1(8))*** Rowman & Littlefield Education.

Caruso, Michael P. When the Sisters Said Farewell: The Transition of Leadership in Catholic Elementary Schools. 2012. (ENG.). 170p. pap. 24.95 ***(978-1-61048-653-8(6))*** Rowman & Littlefield Education.

Consumer Dummies Staff, et al. Catholic High School Entrance Exams for Dummies. 2010. (ENG., Illus.). 528p. pap. 17.99 *(978-0-470-54873-8(8)*, For Dummies) Wiley, John & Sons, Inc.

Creating Safe Environments for LGBT Students: A Catholic Schools Perspective. 2007. (ENG., Illus.). 172p. per. 50.50 *(978-1-56023-606-1(X))* Routledge.

Earl, Patricia Helene. Faith Formation of the Laity in Catholic Schools: The Influence of Virtues & Spirituality Seminars. 2008. *(978-1-59311-715-3(9))*; pap. *(978-1-59311-714-6(0))* Information Age Publishing, Inc.

Frabutt, James M., et al. Research, Action, & Change: Leaders Reshaping Catholic Schools. 2008. 304p. (ENG.). 20.00 *(978-0-9788793-7-2(6))*; pap. 15.00 *(978-0-9788793-6-5(8))* Alliance for Catholic Education Pr.

Heft, James L. Catholic High Schools: Facing the New Realities, 1 vol. 2011. 272p. 24.95 *(978-0-19-979665-6(3))* Oxford Univ. Pr., Inc.

Holscher, Kathleen A. Religious Lessons: Catholic Sisters & the Captured Schools Crisis in New Mexico. 2012. (ENG., Illus.). 304p. 55.00 ***(978-0-19-978173-7(7))*** Oxford Univ. Pr., Inc.

Holter, Anthony C. & Frabutt, James M. Action Research in Catholic Schools: A Step-By-Step Guide for Practitioners. 2009. pap. *(978-0-9788793-8-9(4))* Alliance for Catholic Education Pr.

Hudson, Marilyn A., et al. One Nightclub & a Mule Barn. 2006. (Illus.). 128p. per. 11.99 *(978-1-59886-906-4(X))* Tate Publishing & Enterprises, LLC.

Hunt, Thomas C. & Walch, Timothy. Urban Catholic Education: Tales of Twelve American Cities. 2010. *(978-0-9819501-9-8(1))*; pap. *(978-0-9819501-8-1(3))* Alliance for Catholic Education Pr.

Mayotte, Gail. Let Your Light Shine: A Guide for Preparing to Teach in a Catholic School. 2010. pap. *(978-1-935788-00-3(0))* Alliance for Catholic Education Pr.

McCloskey, Patrick. The Street Stops Here: A Year at a Catholic High School in Harlem. 2010. (ENG., Illus.). 480p. pap. 18.95 *(978-0-520-26797-8(4))* Univ. of California Pr.

McCloskey, Patrick J. & McCloskey, Patrick. The Street Stops Here: A Year at a Catholic High School in Harlem. 2009. (ENG., Illus.). 480p. 50.00 *(978-0-520-25517-3(8))* Univ. of California Pr.

Moran, Michael J. Proudly We Speak Your Name: Forty-Four Years at Little Rock Catholic High School. 2009. (Illus.). 144p. 24.95 *(978-1-935106-07-4(4))* Butler Ctr. for Arkansas Studies.

Nuzzi, Ronald James, et al. Faith, Finances, & the Future: The Notre Dame Study of U. S. Pastors. 2008. (ENG.). 88p. pap. 10.00 *(978-0-9788793-5-8(X))* Alliance for Catholic Education Pr.

Peterson's. Master the Catholic High School Entrance Exams 2012. 17th ed. 2011. (ENG.). 656p. (YA). pap. 18.95 *(978-0-7689-3141-9(X))* Peterson's.

Ruane, John Bernard. Parish the Thought: An Inspirational Memoir of Growing up Catholic in the 1960s. 2008. (ENG., Illus.). 288p. pap. 16.00 *(978-1-4165-8949-5(X))* Gallery Pr., The IRL. Dist: Simon & Schuster, Inc.

Staggenborg, Rob. CBC Then & Now. 2007. 40.00 *(978-1-933370-10-1(6))* Reedy Pr.

Stanko, Bernard. The Evolution of Catholic Schools in the Diocese of Grand Rapids. 2008. 248p. pap. *(978-3-639-01058-9(2))* VDM Verlag Dr. Mueller e.K.

Stewart, Mark & Unrein, Judy. McGraw-Hill's Catholic High School Entrance Exams, 3rd Edition. 3rd ed. 2012. (ENG., Illus.). 576p. (C). pap. 17.00 ***(978-0-07-177830-5(6)***, 0071778306) McGraw-Hill Cos., The.

Young, Ethel E. & Wilson, Jerome. African American Children & Missionary Nuns & Priests in Mississippi: Achievement against Jim Crow Odds. 2010. 132p. 22.95 *(978-1-4520-2278-9(X))*; (ENG.). pap. 12.99 *(978-1-4520-2279-6(8))* AuthorHouse.

CATHOLIC SOCIETIES

see Catholic Church—Societies, etc.

CATHOLIC THEOLOGY

see Catholic Church—Doctrines

CATHOLIC THEOLOGICAL SEMINARIES

Congregation for Catholic Education. Directives Concerning the Preparation of Seminary Educators. 60p. pap. 1.75 *(978-0-8198-1871-3(2))* Pauline Bks. & Media.

Edwards, Lisa Marie. Roman Virtues: The Education of Latin American Clergy in Rome, 1858-1962. 2011. (Latin America: Interdisciplinary Studies). 150p. (C). 68.95 ***(978-1-4331-1306-2(6))*** Lang, Peter Publishing, Inc.

Englert, Jonathan. The Collar: A Year Inside a Catholic Seminary. 2007. (ENG.). 320p. pap. 14.95 *(978-0-618-87214-5(0))* Houghton Mifflin Harcourt Trade & Reference Pubs.

Gautier, Mary L., ed. CARA Catholic Ministry Formation Directory 2007. 2007. 425p. 75.00 *(978-0-9672218-4-7(6))* Ctr. for Applied Research in the Apostolate.

McInally, Thomas. The Sixth Scottish University: The Scots Colleges abroad: 1575 To 1799. 2011. (History of Science & Medicine Library). (Illus.). 256p. ***(978-90-04-21426-2(7))*** BRILL.

Murphy, Charles M. Models of Priestly Formation: Past, Present & Future. 2006. (Crossroad Faith & Formation Book Ser.). (ENG.). 96p. pap. 14.95 *(978-0-8245-2402-9(0)*, Herder & Herder) Crossroad Publishing Co., The.

O'Connell, Patricia. The Irish College at Santiago de Compostela, 1605-1769. 2007. 158p. 55.00 *(978-1-84682-032-8(4))* Four Courts Pr. IRL. Dist: International Specialized Bk. Services.

Oswald, Roy M. Crossing the Boundary Between Seminary & Parish. pap. 10.50 *(978-1-56699-182-7(X)*, OD122) Alban Institute, Inc.

Rosa, Malaki. Seminary Secrets: Experiences in a Roman Catholic Seminary, 1 vol. 2009. 111p. pap. 19.95 *(978-1-60813-464-9(4))* PublishAmerica, Inc.

CATHOLIC TRADITIONALIST MOVEMENT

Gaudron, Matthias. The Catechism of the Crisis in the Church. 2010. *(978-1-892331-79-3(9))* Angelus Pr.

Larson, Anne M. Love in the Ruins: Modern Catholics in Search of the Ancient Faith. 2009. 181p. *(978-1-892331-66-3(7))* Angelus Pr.

Lefebvre, Marcel. Spiritual Journey: According to St. Thomas Aquinas in His Summa Theologiæ: Revised Translation. 2011. ***(978-0-935952-17-9(9))*** Angelus Pr.

Likoudis, James & Whitehead, Kenneth D. The Pope, the Council, & the Mass: Answers to Questions the Traditionalists Have Asked. 3rd ed. 2006. 374p. per. 16.95 *(978-1-931018-34-0(0))* Emmaus Road Publishing.

Popowski, Mark D. The Rise & Fall of Triumph: The History of a Radical Roman Catholic Magazine, 1966-1976. 2011. (ENG.). 282p. (gr. 17). 75.00 ***(978-0-7391-6981-0(5))*** Lexington Bks.

—Roman Catholic Crusaders in the Age of Aquarius. 2011. ***(978-0-7391-6982-7(3))*** Lexington Bks.

Quinteros, Juan. El Caso Lefevre: The Lefevre Case. (SPA.). 96p. *(978-84-7228-334-3(8)*, 220147) Clie, Editorial.

CATHOLIC UNIVERSITIES AND COLLEGES

Barry, Edwarda. Georgian Court University. 2007. (Campus History Ser.). (ENG., Illus.). 128p. per. 19.99 *(978-0-7385-4962-0(2))* Arcadia Publishing.

Brosens, I. A. The Challenge of Reproductive Medicine at Catholic Universities: Time to Leave the Catacombs. Brosens, I., ed. 2006. (Illus.). 263p. (C). pap. 57.00 *(978-90-429-1762-0(8))* Peeters Pubs. & Booksellers BEL. Dist: Brown, David Bk. Co., The.

Dosen, Anthony J. Issues of Governance & Identity in Catholic Higher Education During the 1960s: Case Histories. 2009. *(978-1-931576-31-4(9))* Information Age Publishing, Inc.

—Issues of Governance & Identity in Catholic Higher Education During the 1960's: Case Histories. 2009. pap. *(978-1-931576-30-7(0))* Information Age Publishing, Inc.

Dowe, Christopher. Auch Bildungsbürger: Katholische Studierende und Akademiker Im Kaiserreich. 2006. (Kritische Studien Zur Geschichtswissenschaft Ser.). (GER.). 384p. (C). pap. 63.00 *(978-3-525-35152-9(6))* Vandenhoeck & Ruprecht GmbH & Co. KG DEU. Dist: ISD.

Esposito, Joseph A., ed. The Newman Guide to Choosing a Catholic College: What to Look for & Where to Find It. 2007. (Illus.). 245p. (J). per. 19.95 *(978-0-9786502-1-6(2))* Union Street Pr.

Estanek, Sandra M. Reading the Signs: Using Case Studies to Discuss Student Life Issues at Catholic Colleges & Universities in the United States. 2008. (Illus.). 140p. pap. *(978-1-59311-918-8(6))*; *(978-1-59311-919-5(4))* Information Age Publishing, Inc.

Graham, William. Here Comes Everybody: Catholic Studies in American Higher Education. 2008. (ENG.). 204p. pap. 35.99 *(978-0-7618-4432-7(5))* Univ. Pr. of America, Inc.

—Here Comes Everybody: Catholics Studies in American Higher Education. 2008. (ENG.). 204p. 68.50 *(978-0-7618-4431-0(7))* Univ. Pr. of America, Inc.

Haughey, John C. Where Is Knowing Going? The Horizons of the Knowing Subject. 2009. (ENG.). 192p. 34.95 *(978-1-58901-486-2(3))* Georgetown Univ. Pr.

Hayes, Giles. Unto Another Generation, St. Mary's Abbey/Delbarton, 1836-1900: A History. 2006. 39.95 net. *(978-0-9664459-6-1(1))* Newark Abbey Pr.

Hendershott, Anne & Hendershott, Anne B. Status Envy: The Politics of Catholic Higher Education. 2009. (ENG.). 256p. 39.95 (978-1-4128-0817-0(0)) Transaction Pubs.

Labelle, Jeffrey & Kendall, Daniel. Catholic Colleges in the 21st Century: A Road Map for Campus Ministry. 2011. 112p. pap. 9.95 (978-0-8091-4733-5(5)) Paulist Pr.

MacIntyre, Alasdair. God, Philosophy, Universities: A Selective History of the Catholic Philosophical Tradition. 2011. (ENG.). 200p. pap. 18.95 (978-0-7425-4430-7(3), Sheed & Ward) Rowman & Littlefield Publishers, Inc.

MacIntyre, Alasdair. God, Philosophy, Universities: A Selective History of the Catholic Philosophical Tradition. 2009. (ENG.). 200p. 29.95 (978-0-7425-4429-1(X)) Rowman & Littlefield Publishers, Inc.

Malesky, Robert P. The Catholic University of America. 2010. (Campus History Ser.). (ENG., Illus.). 128p. pap. 21.99 (978-0-7385-8552-9(1)) Arcadia Publishing.

Malloy, Edward A. Monk's Tale: The Pilgrimage Begins, 1941-1975. 2009. (ENG., Illus.). 256p. 25.00 (978-0-268-03516-7(4)) Univ. of Notre Dame Pr.

Malloy, Edward A. Monk's Tale: Way Stations on the Journey. 2011. (Illus.). 280p. 25.00 (978-0-268-03522-8(9)) Univ. of Notre Dame Pr.

Masson, Catherine. La Catho: Un Siècle D'histoire de L'Université Catholique de Lille, 1877-1977. 2011. (FRE., Illus.). 559p. pap. (978-2-7574-0166-8(1)) Presses Universitaires du Septentrion.

McDonagh, Enda. Immersed in Mystery: En Route to Theology. 2008. (ENG.). 232p. pap. 16.95 (978-1-85390-969-6(6)) Veritas Pubns. IRL. Dist: Dufour Editions, Inc.

Mize, Sandra Yocum. Joining the Revolution in Theology: The College Theology Society, 1954-2004. 2007. (ENG., Illus.). 336p. 41.95 (978-0-7425-3195-6(3)) Rowman & Littlefield Publishers, Inc.

Morey, Melanie & Piderit, John. Catholic Higher Education: A Culture in Crisis. 1 vol. 2010. (ENG.). 472p. pap. 29.95 (978-0-19-973904-2(8)) Oxford Univ. Pr., Inc.

Piderit, John J. & Morey, Melanie M. Teaching the Tradition: Catholic Themes in Academic Disciplines. 1 vol. 2012. (ENG., Illus.). 504p. 99.00 (978-0-19-979530-7(4)); pap. 45.00 (978-0-19-979531-4(2)) Oxford Univ. Pr., Inc.

Rausch, Thomas P. Educating for Faith & Justice: Catholic Higher Education Today. 2010. xiv, 165p. 19.95 (978-0-8146-5459-0(2)) Liturgical Pr.

Religious Identity & Behavior of College Faculty, Vol. 2. 2007. (Profiles of the American University Ser.). pap. 12.95 (978-1-893671-03-4(8)) Institute for Jewish & Community Research.

Rice, Charles E. What Happened to Notre Dame? 2009. (ENG.). 224p. pap. 15.00 (978-1-58731-920-4(9)) St. Augustine's Pr., Inc.

Wagner, Lavern. The True History of Quincy College. 2009. pap. (978-1-61584-478-4(3)) Independent Pub.

Whitehead, Kenneth, ed. The Idea of the Catholic University: Proceedings from the 30th Annual Conference of the Fellowship of Catholic Scholars. 2010. (University of Scranton Press - Fellowship of Catholic Scholars Ser.). 180p. pap. 20.00 (978-1-58966-219-3(9)) Univ. of Scranton Pr.

Wills, Brian S. Gone with the Glory: The Civil War in Cinema. 2011. (ENG.). 252p. pap. 17.95 (978-0-7425-4526-7(1)) Rowman & Littlefield Publishers, Inc.

Zimmerman, Joe. A Story of Quincy University: Catholic, Franciscan, Beginning Again. 2009. (978-1-57864-572-5(7)) Donning Co. Pubs.

CATHOLIC UNIVERSITY OF AMERICA

Collins, Peter M. Twentieth Century Collision: American Intellectual Culture & Pope John Paul II's Idea of a University. 2010. (ENG.). 64p. pap. 19.95 (978-0-7618-4627-7(1)) Univ. Pr. of America, Inc.

Deferrari, Roy J. Memoirs of the Catholic University of America, 1918-1960. 2011. 452p. 57.95 (978-1-258-09329-7(4)) Literary Licensing, LLC.

Malesky, Robert P. The Catholic University of America. 2010. (Campus History Ser.). (ENG., Illus.). 128p. pap. 21.99 (978-0-7385-8552-9(1)) Arcadia Publishing.

CATHOLIC WOMEN

A Carthusian. First Initiation into Carthusian Life. 2010. 120p. pap. (978-0-85244-147-3(9)) Gracewing, Ltd.

Arroyo, Raymond. The Prayers & Personal Devotions of Mother Angelica. 2010. 208p. 17.00 (978-0-307-58825-8(4), Doubleday Religion) Doubleday Religious Publishing Group, The.

Baburek, Alice. My House Filled with Many Tails. 2011. 72p. pap. 19.95 (978-1-4560-8280-2(9)) PublishAmerica, Inc.

Bean, Danielle. Mom to Mom, Day to Day: Advice & Support for Catholic Living. 2007. 155p. per. 15.95 (978-0-8198-4855-0(7)) Pauline Bks. & Media.

Bean, Danielle & Foss, Elizabeth. Small Steps for Catholic Moms: Think, Pray, ACT, Every Day. 2010. (978-1-933271-38-5(8)) Circle Pr.

Bernstein, Eleanor. Called to Holiness: Prayers for Catholic Women. 2010. 128p. pap. 9.95 (978-0-86716-955-3(9)) Franciscan Media.

Berstein C.S.J., Eleanor, ed. Praying Our Lives: A Woman's Treasury of Catholic Prayer. 2012. 288p. pap. 17.95 (978-1-59471-270-8(0)) Ave Maria Pr.

Biedenbach, Lisa A. & Curran-Hackett, Mary. Good Words: Inspiration for Catholic Women. 2010. (978-0-86716-956-0(7)) Franciscan Media.

Bucar, Elizabeth M. Creative Conformity: The Feminist Politics of U. S. Catholic & Iranian Shi'l Women. 2011. (Moral Traditions Ser.). (ENG.). 228p. pap. 39.95 (978-1-58901-739-9(0)) Georgetown Univ. Pr.

Callahan, Sidney. Creating New Life, Nurturing Families: A Woman's Perspective. 2009. 112p. pap. 11.95 (978-0-86716-893-8(5)) Franciscan Media.

Chameski, Roberta M. & McElroy, Sylvia Rauzi. A Catholic Approach to Widowhood: A Journey with Mary. 2009. (978-0-8189-1296-2(0), St. Pauls) St Pauls/Alba Hse. Pubs.

Craven, Florence E. V. A Comparison of the Social, Religious, & Gender Role Attitudes of Catholic & Protestant Women in the Republic of Ireland: Twenty-First Century Ireland from a Woman's Perspective. 2010. 354p. 119.95 (978-0-7734-3787-6(8)) Mellen, Edwin Pr., The.

Cummings, Dorothy. The Closet's All Mine! From a Seraphic Single. 2010. (978-0-7648-1961-2(5)) Liguori Pubns.

—Seraphic Singles: How I Learned to Stop Worrying & Love the Single Life. 2010. 221p. (978-2-89646-215-5(5)) Novalis Publishing.

Dickow, Cheryl. Our Jewish Roots: A Catholic Woman's Guide to Fulfillment Today by Connecting with her Past. 2010. 204p. pap. 14.99 (978-0-9823388-8-9(0)) Bezalel Bks.

Doyle, Karen. The Genius of Womanhood. 2009. (Illus.). 96p. pap. 10.95 (978-0-8198-3109-5(3)) Pauline Bks. & Media.

Dreyer, Elizabeth A. Making Sense of God: A Woman's Perspective. 2008. (Called to Holiness). 128p. pap. 11.95 (978-0-86716-884-6(5)) Franciscan Media.

Drogus, Carol Ann & Stewart-Gambino, Hannah. Activist Faith: Grassroots Women in Democratic Brazil & Chile. 2008. (ENG.). 272p. pap. 30.00 (978-0-271-02550-6(6)) Pennsylvania State Univ. Pr.

Dugan, Kate & Owens, Jen. From the Pews in the Back: Young Women & Catholicism. 2009. pap. 19.95 (978-0-8146-3258-1(0)) Liturgical Pr.

Evevard, Tammy. Becoming: The Woman God Made You to Be. 2011. (978-0-86716-998-0(2), Servant Bks.) Franciscan Media.

Fenelon, Marge. When's God Gonna Show Up? Daily Discoveries of the Divine. 2009. 176p. pap. (978-0-7648-1832-5(5), Liguori) Liguori Pubns.

Ferrara, Jennifer & Sodano Ireland, Patricia. Women in Search of the Truth: Converts to Catholism Tell Their Stories. 2009. 299p. pap. 14.95 (978-1-59276-523-2(8)) Our Sunday Visitor, Publishing Div.

Foster, William Henry. The Captors' Narrative: Catholic Women & Their Puritan Men on the Early American Frontier. 2011. (Illus.). 224p. pap. 24.95 (978-0-8014-7712-6(3)) Cornell Univ. Pr.

Glowaski, D. K. Back the Truck. 2009. 328p. 42.00 (978-1-4389-7444-6(2)); pap. 22.00 (978-1-4389-7443-9(4)) AuthorHouse.

Gonzalez, Michelle A. Embracing Latina Spirituality: A Woman's Perspective. 2009. 112p. pap. 11.95 (978-0-86716-886-0(2)) Franciscan Media.

Guyon, Jeanne. Autobiography of Madame Guyon. 2009. 212p. 32.99 (978-1-59547-532-9(X)) NuVision Pubns., LLC.

Hathaway, Patricia Cooney. Weaving Faith & Experience: A Woman's Perspective. 2010. 112p. pap., pap. 11.95 (978-0-86716-904-1(4)) Franciscan Media.

Henold, Mary J. Catholic & Feminist: The Surprising History of the American Catholic Feminist Movement. 2008. (ENG., Illus.). 304p. 36.00 (978-0-8078-3224-0(3)) Univ. of North Carolina Pr.

Hill, Joan, et al. The Miracle Chase: Three Women, Three Miracles, & a Ten Year Journey of Discovery & Friendship. 2010. (ENG.). 240p. 17.95 (978-1-4027-7765-3(5)) Sterling Publishing Co., Inc.

Hinsdale, Mary Ann. Women Shaping Theology. 2006. (Madeleva Lecture in Spirituality: Vol. 2004). (AFR.). 149p. per. 12.95 (978-0-8091-4310-8(0), 4310-0) Paulist Pr.

Iozzio, Mary Jo, et al. Calling for Justice Throughout the World: Catholic Women Theologians on the HIV/AIDS Pandemic. Roche, Mary M. Doyle, ed. 2009. (ENG.). 288p. 90.00 (978-0-8264-2863-9(0)); pap. 34.95 (978-0-8264-2864-6(9)) Continuum International Publishing Group, Ltd. GBR. Dist: National Bk. Network.

Kenworthy-Browne CJ, Christina, ed. Mary Ward (1585-1645) 'A Briefe Relation', with Autobiographical Fragments & a Selection of Letters. 2008. (Catholic Record Society Ser.). (Illus.). 90.00 (978-91-0-011194-6(5)) Catholic Record Society GBR. Dist: Boydell & Brewer, Inc.

Kichline, Kathleen MacInnis. Sisters in Scripture: Exploring the Relationships of Biblical Women. 2009. 128p. pap. 16.95 (978-0-8091-4580-5(4)) Paulist Pr.

Knobbe, Beth M. Finding My Voice: A Young Adult Woman's Perspective. 2009. 112p. pap. 11.95 (978-0-86716-894-5(3)) Franciscan Media.

Lapomarda, Vincent A. Portraits of One Hundred Catholic Women of Maine. 2011. 156p. 109.95 (978-0-7734-3914-6(5)) Mellen, Edwin Pr., The.

Leckey, Dolores R. Grieving with Grace: A Woman's Perspective. 2008. (Called to Holiness). 112p. pap. 11.95 (978-0-86716-888-4(9)) Franciscan Media.

Lipien, Ted. Wojtyla's Women: How They Shaped the Life of Pope John Paul II & Changed the Catholic Church. 2008. (ENG., Illus.). 360p. pap. 29.95 (978-1-84694-110-8(5)) Hunt, John Publishing Ltd. GBR. Dist: National Bk. Network.

Loehr, Gina. Real Women, Real Saints: Friends for Your Spiritual Journey. 2008. 165p. pap. (978-0-86716-858-7(7)) Franciscan Media.

Lux-Sterritt, Laurence. Gender, Catholicism & Spirituality: Women & the Roman Catholic Church in Britain & Europe, 1200-1900. Mangion, Carmen M. & Lux-Sterritt, Laurence, eds. 2010. (Gender & History Ser.). (ENG., Illus.). 224p. 88.00 (978-0-230-57760-2(1)); pap. 30.00 (978-0-230-57761-9(X)) Palgrave Macmillan.

MacDonald, Francis. Star of the Mohawk: Kateri Tekakwitha. 2011. 188p. 42.95 (978-1-258-09842-1(3)) Literary Licensing, LLC.

Martin, Phyllis M. Catholic Women of Congo-Brazzaville: Mothers & Sisters in Troubled Times. 2009. (ENG., Illus.). 280p. pap. 24.95 (978-0-253-22055-4(6), 0253220556) Indiana Univ. Pr.

—Catholic Women of Congo-Brazzaville: Mothers & Sisters in Troubled Times. 2009. (ENG., Illus.). 280p. 65.00 (978-0-253-35281-1(9), 0253352819) Indiana Univ. Pr.

McGuire, Kristen West. The Essential Woman: Reflections on Edith Stein's Essays on Woman. 2008. 62p. pap. 5.95 (978-0-9795376-0-8(6)) Secretum Meum Mihi Pr.

Middleton, Thomas. The Ghost of Lucrece. reprint ed. 29.00 (978-0-403-07246-0(8)) Somerset Pubs., Inc.

Miller, Richard W., et al. Women & the Shaping of Catholicism: Women Through the Ages. 2009. 128p. pap. 14.95 (978-0-7648-1770-0(1), Liguori) Liguori Pubns.

Mitchell, Patricia. Living as a Confident Daughter of God: A Faith-Sharing Guide for Catholic Women. 2008. 119p. per. 10.95 (978-1-59325-112-3(2)) Word Among Us Pr.

Morcillo, Aurora G. True Catholic Womanhood. 2008. 224p. pap. 24.00 (978-0-87580-997-7(9)) Northern Illinois Univ. Pr.

Motherhood & Family. 2008. (978-1-892331-63-2(2)) Angelus Pr.

Moyer, Ginny / Kubitz. Mary & Me: Catholic Women Reflect on the Mother of God. 2008. 120p. per. 13.95 (978-0-86716-831-0(5)) Franciscan Media.

Mueller, Joan. Living a Spirituality of Action: A Woman's Perspective. 2008. (Called to Holiness). 112p. pap. 11.95 (978-0-86716-885-3(4)) Franciscan Media.

O'Boyle, Donna-Marie Cooper. A Catholic Woman's Book of Prayers. 2010. 80p. (978-1-59276-793-9(1)) Our Sunday Visitor, Publishing Div.

O'Boyle, Donna-Marie Cooper. The Domestic Church: Room by Room: A Study Guide for Mothers. 2008. 254p. pap. 18.95 (978-1-933271-20-0(5)) Circle Pr.

Patrick, Anne E. Women, Conscience, & the Creative Process. 2011. (Madeleva Lecture in Spirituality Ser.). 96p. pap. 9.95 (978-0-8091-4706-9(8)) Paulist Pr.

Redworth, Glyn. The She-Apostle: The Extraordinary Life & Death of Luisa de Carvajal. 2011. (ENG., Illus.). 288p. pap. 19.95 (978-0-19-957122-2(8)) Oxford Univ. Pr., Inc.

Redworth, Glyn, ed. The Letters of Luisa de Carvajal y Mendoza, 2 vols. 2012. (ENG.). 800p. 335.00 (978-1-84893-218-0(9)) Pickering & Chatto Pubs., Ltd. GBR. Dist: Ashgate Publishing Co.

Redworth, Glyn & British Hispanic Foundation Staff. The She-Apostle: The Extraordinary Life & Death of Luisa de Carvajal. 2008. (ENG., Illus.). 288p. 39.95 (978-0-19-953353-4(9)) Oxford Univ. Pr., Inc.

Reynolds, Suzanne & Delgado, Alvaro. Born with A Veil: Tragedy to Triumph. 2010. pap. 15.99 (978-1-61579-776-9(9)) Xulon Pr., Inc.

Taylor, Sarah McFarland. Green Sisters: A Spiritual Ecology. (Illus.). 384p. 2009. pap. 20.00 (978-0-674-03495-2(3)) 2007. 29.95 (978-0-674-02440-3(0)) Harvard Univ. Pr.

Tighe, S. P. Arch, Steeples, & Dome: Religious Symbols on a Journey of Faith. 2009. 140p. pap. 15.49 (978-1-4389-9601-1(2)) AuthorHouse.

Tomeo, Teresa. Newsflash! My Surprising Journey from Secular Anchor to Media Evangelist. 2008. 172p. pap. 14.99 (978-0-9800483-9-1(7)) Bezalel Bks.

Turpin, Joanne. Women in Church History: 21 Stories for 21 Centuries. 2007. 232p. per. 14.95 (978-0-86716-776-4(9)) Franciscan Media.

Ulterino, Gloria. Walking with Wisdom's Daughters: Twelve Celebrations & Stories of Women of Passion & Faith. 2006. (Illus.). 219p. per. 19.95 (978-1-59471-063-6(5)) Ave Maria Pr.

Wagner, Clare. Awakening to Prayer: A Woman's Perspective. 2009. 112p. pap. 11.95 (978-0-86716-892-1(7)) Franciscan Media.

Wicker, Kate. Weightless: Making Peace with Your Body. 2011. (978-0-86716-971-3(0), Servant Bks.) Franciscan Media.

Wright, Vinita Hampton. Days of Deepening Friendship: For the Woman Who Wants Authentic Life with God. 2009. (ENG.). 408p. pap. 13.95 (978-0-8294-2811-7(9)) Loyola Pr.

Zeno, Katrina. When Life Doesn't Go Your Way: Hope for Catholic Women Facing Disappointment & Pain. 2009. 144p. pap. 11.95 (978-1-59325-152-9(1)) Word Among Us Pr.

Zeno, Katrina J. Discovering the Feminine Genius: Every Woman's Journey. 2010. pap. (978-0-8198-1884-3(4)) Pauline Bks. & Media.

CATHOLIC WORKER MOVEMENT

Baker, Kimball. Go to the Worker: America's Labor Apostles. 2010. pap. (978-0-87462-749-7(4)) Marquette Univ. Pr.

Day, et al. All the Way to Heaven: The Selected Letters of Dorothy Day. 2011. (978-0-87462-061-0(9), Ohio Univ. Ctr. for International Studies) Marquette Univ. Pr.

Day, Dorothy. All the Way to Heaven: The Selected Letters of Dorothy Day. Ellsberg, Robert, ed. 2012. (ENG.). 624p. pap. 16.00 (978-0-7679-3281-3(1), Image) Doubleday Religious Publishing Group, The.

Forest, Jim. All Is Grace: A Biography of Dorothy Day. 2011. (Illus.). 352p. pap. 27.00 (978-1-57075-921-5(9)) Orbis Bks.

Holben, Lawrence. All the Way to Heaven. 2010. (Catholic Worker Reprint Ser.). (Illus.). 164p. pap. 19.00 (978-1-60899-050-4(8), Wipf and Stock) Wipf & Stock Pubs.

McKanan, Dan. The Catholic Worker after Dorothy: Practicing the Works of Mercy in a New Generation. 2008. 236p. per. 19.95 (978-0-8146-3187-4(8), Liturgical Pr. Bks.) Liturgical Pr.

Riegle, Rosalie G. Dorothy Day: Portraits by Those Who Knew Her. 2006. (Illus.). 212p. per. 20.00 (978-1-57075-664-1(3)) Orbis Bks.

Rosebaugh, Lorenzo & Pino, Kateri Hellman. To Wisdom Through Failure: A Journey of Compassion & Resistance. 2006. (978-0-918346-37-7(1)) EPICA.

York, Tripp. Living on Hope While Living in Babylon: The Christian Anarchists of the 20th Century. 2009. 138p. pap. 17.00 (978-1-55635-685-8(4), Wipf and Stock) Wipf & Stock Pubs.

CATHOLICISM

see Catholicity

CATHOLICITY

see also Ecumenical Movement

Adam, Karl. The Spirit of Catholicism. McCann, Justin, tr. 248p. 2008. 41.95 (978-1-4366-8526-9(5)) 2007. (ENG.). per. 26.95 (978-1-4325-6705-7(5)) Kessinger Publishing, LLC.

La Alegria de Ser Catequista. (SPA.). (978-950-861-400-1(5)) Catholic Bk. Publishing Corp.

Anderson, Bill. Words & the Word. 2010. 240p. pap. (978-0-85244-745-1(0)) Gracewing, Ltd.

Baker, Kenneth S. Fundamentals of Catholicism, Vols. 1-3, Set. pap. 36.95 (978-0-89870-223-1(2)) Ignatius Pr.

Balducci, Lodovico, frwd. Enzo: The Adventure of a Friendship. 2011. 84p. 55.00 (978-0-7618-5649-8(8)) Hamilton Bks.

Balducci/Bonicelli. Enzo: The Adventure of a Friendship. 2011. 84p. pap. 22.95 (978-0-7618-5650-4(1)) Hamilton Bks.

Berger, Alison, contrib. by. Into the Fields: Teaching Specific Catholic Topics, Year 3: Catechist & Teacher Formation for the Whole Community. 2007. (Into the Fields Ser.). (Illus.). 121p. pap. 24.95 incl. audio compact disk (978-1-58595-592-3(2)) Twenty-Third Pubns./Bayard.

Bravo, Ernesto. Catolicismo y Protestantismo. (SPA.). 208p. 9.95 (978-958-607-845-0(0)) Sociedad de San Pablo COL. Dist: St Pauls/Alba Hse. Pubs.

Brighenti, Kenneth & Trigilio, John. The Catholicism Answer Book: The 300 Most Frequently Asked Questions. 2007. (ENG.). 320p. pap. 15.99 (978-1-4022-0806-5(5)) Sourcebooks, Inc.

Buckley, James J., et al, eds. The Blackwell Companion to Catholicism. 2007. (Wiley-Blackwell Companions to Religion Ser.). (ENG.). 544p. 209.95 (978-1-4051-1224-6(7), Wiley-Blackwell) Wiley, John & Sons, Inc.

Bunson, D.Min., Matthew E, ed. Our Sunday Visitor's Catholic Almanac 2006. (Our Sunday Visitor's Catholic Almanac Ser.). 640p. per. 24.95 (978-1-59276-230-9(1)) Our Sunday Visitor, Publishing Div.

Bupanda, Leonard C. The Tithing Dilemma & the Triumphs of Love. 2011. 312p. pap. 19.95 (978-1-4670-0807-5(9)) AuthorHouse.

Burns, Elizabeth Mary. Beyond Measure: A Legacy of Mercy, 1879-1976. 2009. (978-1-886769-33-5(8)) Gold Leaf Pr.

Butterworth, Robert. Catholicism Revisited: On Re-imagining God. 2007. 224p. per. (978-0-85244-142-8(8)) Gracewing, Ltd.

By What Authority. 17.00 (978-1-931555-12-8(5)) Our Lady of Victory Schl.

Byron, William J. Individuarian Observations: Essays in Catholic Social Reflection. 2007. 180p. per. 20.00 (978-1-58966-131-8(1)) Univ. of Scranton Pr.

C D Stampley Enterprises, creator. Los Misterios del Rosario. 2007. (Illus.). 56p. pap. 4.95 (978-1-58087-123-5(2)) Stampley, C. D. Enterprises, Inc.

Campbell, Anthony. Totality Beliefs & the Religious Imagination. 2008. 200p. pap. 19.95 (978-1-4092-0314-8(X)) Lulu Enterprises Inc.

Canfield, Jack L., et al. Chicken Soup for the Soul: Living Catholic Faith: 101 Stories to Offer Hope, Deepen Faith, & Spread Love. 2008. (Chicken Soup for the Soul Ser.). (ENG.). 380p. pap. 14.95 (978-1-935096-23-8(0)) Chicken Soup for the Soul Publishing, LLC.

Catholic Medical Association Staff & National Catholic Bioethics Center Staff, contrib. by. A Catholic Guide to Ethical Clinical Research. 2009. (ENG.). 68p. pap. 9.95 (978-0-935372-53-3(9)) National Catholic Bioethics Ctr., The.

Catholicism - Car & Kitchen Table Edition Vol. I: The new, unique way to generate dialogue about our Faith. 2007. (J). 14.95 (978-0-9795813-1-1(1), 80,000) Trinity's Factotum, LLC.

Champlin, Joseph M. What It Means to Be Catholic. 2007. (Illus.). 67p. pap. 5.95 (978-0-86716-490-9(5)) Franciscan Media.

Charles, William, ed. Basil Hume: Ten Years On. 2009. (ENG., Illus.). 232p. 22.95 (978-0-8264-3941-3(1), Burns & Oates) Continuum International Publishing Group, Ltd. GBR. Dist: National Bk. Network.

Christian Prayer. instr.'s gde. ed. 1.75 (978-0-89942-444-6(9)) Catholic Bk. Publishing Corp.

Cleaveland, Raymond. Faith Charts: Catholicism at a Glance. 2006. per. 7.95 (978-1-59276-223-1(9)) Our Sunday Visitor, Publishing Div.

Coffey, Kathy. The Art of Faith: 40 Steps Toward Living Artfully. 2007. (Illus.). 151p. per. 14.95 (978-1-58595-603-6(1)) Twenty-Third Pubns./Bayard.

Collins, Paul. Believers: Does Australian Catholicism Have a Future? 2008. (ENG.). 224p. pap. 31.95 (978-0-86840-831-6(X), UNSW Press) NewSouth Publishing AUS. Dist: Independent Pubs. Group.

Congr Inst Consecrated Ife Staff. Instr Contemplative Life. 56p. pap. 3.95 (978-0-8198-3679-3(6), 332-134) Pauline Bks. & Media.

Congreation for Cath Educatio Staff. Consecrated Persons & Mission. 72p. pap. 4.95 (978-0-8198-1553-7(2), 332-046) Pauline Bks. & Media.

Congregation Catholic Ed Staff. Cath Sch Threshold 3rd Millenn. 22p. pap. 2.50 (978-0-8198-1552-1(7), 332-040) Pauline Bks. & Media.

Corrance, Henry C. Points of Contact Between Catholicism an. 2006. pap. 15.95 (978-1-4286-4042-9(8)) Kessinger Publishing, LLC.

Cummings, Owen F. Prophets, Guardians, & Saints: Shapers of Modern Catholic History. annot. ed. 2007. 197p. per. 19.95 (978-0-8091-4446-4(8), 4446-4) Paulist Pr.

Depoortere, Frederiek, et al, eds. Edward Schillebeeckx & Contemporary Theology. 2010. (ENG., Illus.). 336p. 120.00 (978-0-567-18160-2(X), T&T Clark Int'l) Continuum International Publishing Group, Ltd. GBR. Dist: National Bk. Network.

Durand, Casimir F. The Old Catholic Church & Other Writings. Serge, A. Theriault, ed. 2011. 192p. pap. 16.95 (978-1-937002-16-9(0)) Apocryphile Pr.

C

Echema, Austin. Anointing of the Sick & the Healing Ministry: The Nigerian Pastoral Experience. 2006. 212p. (gr. 11). pap. 32.95 *(978-3-88939-831-4(6))* IKO Verlag fur Interkulturelle Kommunikation DEU. Dist: Transaction Pubs.
Emissary. A Faraway Ancient Country. 2007. 213p. pap. 24.94 *(978-0-615-15801-3(3))* Karitas Publishing.
Evans, Alvin. Examine My Catholic Tradition in this modifiable Book. 2009. pap. *(978-1-61584-290-2(X))* Independent Pub.
Faulkner, Mary & O'Gorman, Bob. Understanding Catholicism - The Complete Idiot's Guide. 3rd rev. ed. 2006. (Complete Idiot's Guide Ser.). (ENG., Illus.). 432p. (gr. 12-18). 18.95 *(978-1-59257-535-0(8)*, Alpha Bks.) Penguin Group (USA) Inc.
Fernández, D. A Los Catolicos Que Aman la Verdad. (Serie Realidades - Realities Ser.).Tr. of To the Catholic That Loves the Truth. (SPA.). 1.99 *(978-0-7899-0325-9(3)*, 498372) Editorial Unilit.
Fireside Catholic Publishing, creator. Thematic Plans & Activities for Catholic Youth: A Guide for Catholic Youth Ministers. 2007. 47p. pap. 19.95 *(978-1-55665-051-2(5))* Fireside Catholic Bibles.
Flavius, Susanna Magdalene. Devotions to Our Lady, the Blessed Virgin Mary. 2009. 87p. pap. 13.95 *(978-0-557-06781-7(2))* Lulu Enterprises Inc.
For Know-It-Alls Staff. Catholicism for Know-It-Alls. 2008. pap. 9.99 *(978-1-59986-238-5(7)*, For Know-It-Alls) Filiquarian Publishing, LLC.
Foster, John. Then & Now: The Historic Church & the Younger Churches. 2007. 188p. per. *(978-1-4067-8861-7(9)*, Pomona Pr.) Read Bks.
Furton, Edward James. Urged on by Christ: Catholic Health Care in Tension with Contemporary Culture. 2009. (SPA & ENG.). pap. 19.95 *(978-0-935372-52-6(0))* National Catholic Bioethics Ctr., The.
Galipeau, Jerry. Apprenticed to Christ: Activities for Practicing the Catholic Way of Life. 2007. (Illus.). 112p. per. 12.95 *(978-1-58459-327-0(X))* World Library Pubns.
Girzone, Joseph F. My Struggle with Faith. 2007. (ENG.). 256p. pap. 12.95 *(978-0-385-51713-3(0)*, Image) Doubleday Religious Publishing Group, The.
Gottfried, Roy K. & Knowles, Sebastian D. G. Joyce's Misbelief. 2008. (Florida James Joyce Ser.). (ENG.). 160p. 59.95 *(978-0-8130-3167-5(2))* Univ. Pr. of Florida.
Graña, Mari. Charity's Sister: The Story of Sister Mary Joaquin Bitler, SC. 2010. pap. *(978-0-86534-777-9(8))* Sunstone Pr.
Greiler, Alois, ed. Catholic Beginnings in Oceania: Marist Missionary Perspectives. 2009. (Marist Ser.). (ENG.). 262p. (C). pap. 18.00 *(978-1-921511-54-7(0))* ATF Pr. AUS. Dist: Brown, David Bk. Co., The.
Guthrie, Julian. The Grace of Everyday Saints: How a Band of Believers Lost Their Church & Found Their Faith. 2011. (ENG., Illus.). 288p. 25.00 *(978-0-547-13304-1(9))* Houghton Mifflin Harcourt Trade & Reference Pubs.
Haldane, John. The Church & the World. 2008. 228p. pap. *(978-0-85244-588-4(1))* Gracewing, Ltd.
Hamel, Ron, ed. Making Health Care Decisions: A Catholic Guide. 2006. 138p. per. 14.95 *(978-0-7648-1402-0(8))* Liguori Pubns.
Hampsch, John H. Mary, Our Tainted Nature's Solitary Boast. 24p. pap. 1.25 *(978-1-57918-087-4(6)*, 7172) Queenship Publishing Co.
Heynickx, Rajesh & De Maeyer, Jan, eds. The Maritain Factor: Taking Religion into Interward Modernism. 2009. (KADOC Studies on Religion, Culture & Society). 240p. pap. 42.50 *(978-90-5867-714-3(1))* Leuven Univ. Pr. BEL. Dist: Cornell Univ. Pr.
Heywood. Catholicism & Children's Lit: Catholicism & Children's Literature in France. 2012. (Studies in Modern French History Ser.). (ENG., Illus.). 240p. 95.00 ***(978-0-7190-8466-9(0))*** Manchester Univ. Pr. GBR. Dist: Macmillan.
Ives, Levi. The Trials of a Mind in Its Progress to Catholicism. 2009. (Amer Philosophy, Religion Ser.). (ENG.). 236p. pap. 16.95 *(978-1-4290-1925-5(5))* Applewood Bks.
Jaramillo, Horacio. Dialogos con Jesus el Galileo.Tr. of Dialogues with Jesus from Galileah. (SPA.). 19.48 *(978-970-05-1249-5(5))* Grijalbo, Editorial MEX. Dist: Continental Bk. Co., Inc.
Jay, Les. Catholics are NOT Christians. 2007. 140p. pap. 14.99 *(978-0-9785571-0-2(7))* Witty Publishing.
John, Jeffrey. Living the Mystery: Affirming Catholicism & the Future of Anglicanism. 144p. pap. *(978-0-232-52071-2(2))* South Asia Bks.
John Paul II, pseud. Ad Tuendam Fidem. 32p. pap. 1.95 *(978-0-8198-5913-6(3)*, 332-273) Pauline Bks. & Media.
—Cert Aspect Celebr Sac Penance. 16p. pap. 1.95 *(978-0-8198-4821-5(2)*, 332-212) Pauline Bks. & Media.
—Dies Domini. 96p. pap. 4.95 *(978-0-8198-4486-6(1)*, 332-168) Pauline Bks. & Media.
—Memory & Reconciliation. 96p. pap. 3.95 *(978-0-8198-4809-3(3)*, 332-209) Pauline Bks. & Media.
—Novo Millennio Ineunte. 80p. pap. 3.95 *(978-0-8198-5152-9(3)*, 332-250) Pauline Bks. & Media.
—Reserv Priestly Ordinat. 8p. pap. 1.75 *(978-0-8198-5433-9(6)*, 332-264) Pauline Bks. & Media.
Judge, Mark. A Tremor of Bliss: Sex, Catholicism, & Rock 'n' Roll. 2010. (ENG.). 208p. pap. 14.00 *(978-0-385-51920-5(6)*, Doubleday Religion) Doubleday Religious Publishing Group, The.
Kaffer, Bishop Roger L. Common Sense Catholicism. 2008. pap. 14.99 *(978-1-60791-214-9(7))* Xulon Pr., Inc.
Kelly, David F. Medical Care at the End of Life: A Catholic Perspective. 2006. (ENG.). 192p. pap. 19.95 *(978-1-58901-112-0(0))* Georgetown Univ. Pr.
Kerrigan, Michael. The Illustrated Encyclopedia of Catholicism: A Complete Guide to the History, Philosophy & Practice of Catholic Christianity, Illustrated with More Than 500 Beautiful Illustrations. 2009. (ENG., Illus.). 256p. 35.00 *(978-0-7548-1956-1(6))* Anness Publishing GBR. Dist: National Bk. Network.
Koncel, Ed. Views from the Pew, Pulpit & Women Religious. 2010. 166p. 29.99 *(978-1-4535-3691-9(4))*; pap. 19.99 *(978-1-4535-3690-2(6))* Xlibris Corp.
Lacueva, Francisco. Catolicismo Romano: Roman Catholicism, 1 vol. 2008.Tr. of Roman Catholicism. (SPA.). 248p. pap. 10.99 *(978-84-7228-001-4(2)*, 220146) Clie, Editorial ESP. Dist: Zondervan.
Lane, Edmund C., ed. Through the Mysteries of Light with Giotto & Fra Angelico. 32p. pap. 3.95 *(978-0-8189-0950-4(1))* St Pauls/Alba Hse. Pubs.
Lang, Ariella. Converting a Nation: A Modern Inquisition & the Unification of Italy. 2008. (Studies in European Culture & History Ser.). (ENG.). 248p. 95.00 *(978-0-230-60672-2(5))* Palgrave Macmillan.
Langenbrunner, Norm. Reflexiones Diarias para Cuaresma. 2008. (SPA.). 78p. pap. 2.95 *(978-0-86716-920-1(6))* Franciscan Media.
Leies, John A., et al. Handbook on Critical Life Issues. 3rd ed. 2010. 279p. pap. 24.95 *(978-0-935372-58-8(X))* National Catholic Bioethics Ctr., The.
Link, Mark. Path Through Catholicism. 2006. (Illus.). 320p. (Orig.). per. 20.75 *(978-0-7829-0971-5(X))* RCL Benziger Publishing.
Louthan, Howard. Converting Bohemia: Force & Persuasion in the Catholic Reformation. 2009. (New Studies in European History Ser.). (ENG., Illus.). 368p. 116.00 *(978-0-521-88929-2(4))* Cambridge Univ. Pr.
Lozano, Elizabeth B. On Call to Holiness. 2011. 126p. 29.99 ***(978-1-4568-5354-9(6))***; pap. 19.99 ***(978-1-4568-5353-2(8))*** Xlibris Corp.
Martin, Andrew. Forbidden Revolutions - P. 96p. 14.95 *(978-0-281-04999-8(8))* International Publishers Marketing.
—Low Fat Christianity. 2007. 100p. pap. 14.00 *(978-1-4303-2891-9(6))* Lulu Enterprises Inc.
Martín-Sánchez Juliá, Fernando. Discursos a la Asamblea: Intervenciones en la Asociación Católica de Propagandistas (1935-1959) Sánchez Garrido, Pablo, ed. 2009. (SPA.). 285p. *(978-84-92456-93-2(0))* Fundación Universitaria San Pablo.
Matovina, Timothy. Latino Catholicism - Transformation in America#8242;s Largest Church. 2011. (ENG.). 328p. (C). 29.95 ***(978-0-691-13979-1(2))*** Princeton Univ. Pr.
McDonough, Mary J. Can a Health Care Market Be Moral? A Catholic Vision. 2007. (ENG., Illus.). 272p. per. 29.95 *(978-1-58901-157-1(0))* Georgetown Univ. Pr.
Merton, T. Amar y Vivir. (Viaje Interior Ser.). (SPA.). 216p. 8.20 *(978-84-89920-08-8(7)*, 86902) Ediciones Oniro S.A. ESP. Dist: Lectorum Pubns., Inc.
—Dos Semanas en Alaska. (SPA.). 242p. 9.50 *(978-84-89920-88-0(5)*, 86922) Ediciones Oniro S.A. ESP. Dist: Lectorum Pubns., Inc.
Mi Pequeno Libro de Oraciones. (SPA.). 64p. 0.85 *(978-0-89942-033-2(8)*, 31/S, Resurrection Pr.) Catholic Bk. Publishing Corp.
Minnich, Nelson H. Councils of the Catholic Reformation: Pisa I(1409)to Trent(1545-63) 2008. (Variorum Collected Studies). (Illus.). 362p. 170.00 *(978-0-7546-5951-8(8))* Ashgate Publishing Co.
Morrissey, Thomas. Where Two Traditions Meet: John Sullivan SJ 1861 - 1933. 2009. (ENG.). 128p. pap. 22.95 *(978-1-85607-644-9(X))* Columba Pr. IRL. Dist: Dufour Editions, Inc.
Mulderink, Kathryn. The Way of the Cross for Children. 2008. 40p. pap. 8.95 *(978-0-9800483-7-7(0))* Bezalel Bks.
Murphy, Bill. Basic Help to Confess. 32p. pap. 1.25 *(978-0-8198-1156-1(4)*, 332-021) Pauline Bks. & Media.
Neuhaus, Richard John. Catholic Matters: Confusion, Controversy, & the Splendor of Truth. 2007. (ENG.). 272p. per. 15.95 *(978-0-465-04936-3(2))* Basic Bks.
Noble, James. The Truth Encounters the Catholic Church. 2008. 125p. pap. 19.95 *(978-1-4241-7342-6(6))* PublishAmerica, Inc.
O'Malley, Patrick R. Catholicism, Sexual Deviance, & Victorian Gothic Culture. 2006. (Cambridge Studies in Nineteenth-Century Literature & Culture Ser.: Vol. 51). (Illus.). 296p. 116.00 *(978-0-521-86398-8(8))* Cambridge Univ. Pr.
Parker, Charles H. Faith on the Margins: Catholics & Catholicism in the Dutch Golden Age. 2008. (Illus.). 346p. 57.50 *(978-0-674-02662-9(4))* Harvard Univ. Pr.
Parsons, Evelyn C. How the Catholic Prays: The Difference. 2008. 340p. pap. 19.99 *(978-1-4343-9587-0(1))* AuthorHouse.
Patrick, Anne E. Conscience in Context: Vocation, Virtue & History. 2013. (ENG.). 160p. 24.95 *(978-1-4411-4452-2(8))* Continuum International Publishing Group, Ltd. GBR. Dist: National Bk. Network.
Paul, VI. Apost Ltr Mixed Marriage. 32p. pap. *(978-0-8198-4742-3(9)*, 332-193) Pauline Bks. & Media.
—Credo the People of God. 16p. pap. *(978-0-8198-1495-1(4)*, 332-038) Pauline Bks. & Media.
Pennock, Michael. This Is Our Church: A History of Catholicism. 2007. (Illus.). 352p. stu. ed., per. 19.95 *(978-1-59471-075-9(9))*; 416p. pap., stu. ed. 19.95 *(978-1-59471-169-5(0))* Ave Maria Pr.
Pilarczyk, Daniel E. Why Do We Receive Communion? *(978-0-87973-383-4(7))* Our Sunday Visitor, Publishing Div.
Pollard. Catholicism in Modern Italy: Religion, Society & Politics, 1861 to the Present. 2007. (Christianity & Society in the Modern World Ser.). (Illus.). 208p. 148.00 *(978-0-415-23835-9(8))* Routledge.
Pontif Council for Culture Staff. Past Approach to Culture. 80p. pap. 4.50 *(978-0-8198-7402-3(7)*, 332-391) Pauline Bks. & Media.
Pontif Council for Family Staff. Past Care Divor/Vademecum. 34p. pap. 2.50 *(978-0-8198-5908-2(7)*, 332-272) Pauline Bks. & Media.
Pontifical Council for the Laity. Dignity of Older People. 63p. pap. 2.95 *(978-0-8198-1877-5(1)*, 332-072) Pauline Bks. & Media.
Reid, David P. The Grace of the Rosary: Scripture, Contemplation, & the Claim of the Kingdom of God. 2006. 199p. per. 14.95 *(978-0-8091-4427-3(1)*, 4427-1) Paulist Pr.
Resende, Madalena. Catholicism & Nationalism: Transforming Party Politics in Europe. 2013. (Extremism & Democracy Ser.). (ENG.). 208p. (C). 125.00 ***(978-0-415-67007-4(1))*** Routledge.
Rials, Kerby. The Protestant's Guide to Catholicism & Eastern Orthodoxy: How to answer the tough Questions. 3rd exp. ed. 2006. Orig. Title: The Three Great Churches: Comparing the beliefs of Catholics, Protestants & Orthodox. (ENG & RUS., Illus.). 183p. per. 9.99 *(978-0-9786918-0-6(6))* Delta Mills Bks.
Rist, John M. What Is Truth? From the Academy to the Vatican. 2008. (ENG.). 376p. 86.00 *(978-0-521-88901-8(4))*; pap. 35.99 *(978-0-521-71775-5(2))* Cambridge Univ. Pr.
Rothman, Joel. Super Quiz of Catholicism. 2008. pap. 7.95 *(978-1-934872-23-9(7))* JR Pubns.
Sanchez, Pastor Margarita I. Experience the Presence of Jesus. 2008. 48p. pap. 16.95 *(978-1-60474-848-2(6))* PublishAmerica, Inc.
Schaaf, Danielle & Prendergast, Michael. Don't Chew Jesus! A Collection of Memorable Nun Stories. 2006. (ENG.). 225p. 20.00 *(978-1-932100-82-2(2))* BenBella Bks.
Sconborn, Cardinal Christoph. Purpose or Chance? Creation, Evolution & a Rational Faith. 2007. 170p. 19.95 *(978-1-58617-212-1(3))* Ignatius Pr.
Soderini, Edward. Socialism & Catholicism. 2007. (ENG.). 354p. 46.95 *(978-0-548-05290-7(5))* Kessinger Publishing, LLC.
Stagnaro, Angelo. The Christian Book of the Dead. 2010. (ENG.). 104p. 14.95 *(978-0-8245-2614-6(7))* Crossroad Publishing Co., The.
Sterritt, Lynne J. Discovering the Treasures of the Mass: 28 Puzzles That Teach Its Rites & Rituals. 2007. (Illus.). 73p. per. 15.95 *(978-1-58595-626-5(0))* Twenty-Third Pubns./Bayard.
Stevens, Robert Joseph. Defending the Faith Series: Catholicism vs. Fundamentalist Christianity. 2009. 100p. pap. 15.49 *(978-1-4389-3561-4(7))* AuthorHouse.
Stravinskas, Peter M. A Catholic Understanding of the Gospel. 40p. pap. 1.50 *(978-0-87973-175-5(3))* Our Sunday Visitor, Publishing Div.
Sullivan, Bruce. Christ in His Fullness. 2007. (Illus.). 222p. per. 12.95 *(978-0-9702621-7-2(5))* CHResources.
Sulmasy, Daniel P. A Balm for Gilead: Meditations on Spirituality & the Healing Arts. 2006. (ENG.). 176p. pap. 21.95 *(978-1-58901-122-9(8))* Georgetown Univ. Pr.
Szews, George R. Catholic & College Bound: 5 Challenges & 5 Opportunities. 2008. (Illus.). 64p. pap. 5.95 *(978-0-87946-361-8(9))* ACTA Pubns.
Tollefsen, Christopher, ed. Bioethics with Liberty & Justice: Themes in the Work of Joseph M. Boyle. 2010. (Philosophy & Medicine Ser.). x, 190p. 139.00 *(978-90-481-9790-3(2)*, 9048197902) Springer.
Twomey, Vincent. Moral Theology after Humanae Vitae - Fundamental Issues in Moral Theology & Sexual Ethics. 2010. 226p. 45.00 *(978-1-84682-201-8(7))* Four Courts Pr. IRL. Dist: International Specialized Bk. Services.
Underhill, Evelyn. The Path of Eternal Wisdom: A Mystical Commentary on the Way of the Cross 1911. 2007. (ENG.). 150p. 36.95 *(978-0-548-05467-3(3))* Kessinger Publishing, LLC.
Wemhoff, David. Just be Catholic. 2011. 176p. pap. 11.95 *(978-1-4567-1817-6(7))* AuthorHouse.
Wilde, Melissa J. Vatican II: A Sociological Analysis of Religious Change. 2007. (ENG., Illus.). 224p. (C). 42.00 *(978-0-691-11829-1(9))* Princeton Univ. Pr.
Winters, Michael Sean. Left at the Altar: How the Democrats Lost the Catholics & How the Catholics Can Save the Democrats. 2008. (ENG.). 256p. 26.00 *(978-0-465-09166-9(0))* Basic Bks.
Wood, Regina Beauvais. A Reply to Once a Catholic. 2007. 100p. per. 10.00 *(978-1-4257-4124-2(X))* Xlibris Corp.
Zezinho, Padre. Al Dios de Mi Juventud. (SPA.). 128p. 4.95 *(978-958-607-296-0(7))* Sociedad de San Pablo COL. Dist: St Pauls/Alba Hse. Pubs.
Zieba, Maciej. Papal Economics: The Catholic Church on Democratic Capitalism, from Rerum Novarum to Caritas in Veritate. 2012. (Culture of Enterprise Ser.). (ENG.). 26.95 *(978-1-933859-97-2(0))* ISI Bks.

CATHOLICS

see also Catholic Converts

Alcott, Nan. Early Literacy for Young Catholics. 2011. (J). pap. 20.00 ***(978-1-60704-094-1(8))*** Seton Pr.
Aune, David E., ed. Rereading Paul Together: Protestant & Catholic Perspectives on Justification. 2006. 272p. (C). per. 28.00 *(978-0-8010-2840-3(X))* Baker Academic.
Brown, Joseph A. To Stand on the Rock: Meditations on Black Catholic Identity. 2011. 222p. pap. 24.00 ***(978-1-61097-568-1(5)***, Wipf and Stock) Wipf & Stock Pubs.
Carroll, James. Practicing Catholic. 2009. (ENG.). 400p. 28.00 *(978-0-618-67018-5(1))* Houghton Mifflin Harcourt Trade & Reference Pubs.
Castaldo, Chris. Holy Ground: Walking with Jesus As a Former Catholic, 1 vol. 2009. (ENG.). 224p. pap. 12.99 *(978-0-310-29232-6(8))* Zondervan.
Catalano, Dominic. Questions for Catholics. 2nd ed. 2010. 243p. pap. *(978-1-58459-472-7(1))* World Library Pubns.
The Catholic Diary 1995. (Illus.). 160p. *(978-0-9643146-0-3(6))* DESIGNZEIT.
Champlin, Joseph M. What It Means to Be Catholic. 2007. (Illus.). 67p. pap. 5.95 *(978-0-86716-490-9(5))* Franciscan Media.
Chopra, Elma. Born Again Catholic. 2010. 460p. pap. 24.99 *(978-1-60957-367-6(6))* Xulon Pr., Inc.
Deshon, George. Guide for Catholic Young Women. 2009. 204p. pap. *(978-0-217-48281-3(3))* Books LLC.
Devine, Tm Edite. Scotland's Shame. (Illus.). 281p. pap. 19.95 *(978-1-84018-330-6(6))* Mainstream Publishing Co., Ltd. GBR. Dist: Trafalgar Square Publishing.
Dodds, Monica. A Catholic Guide to Caring for Your Aging Parent. 2006. (ENG.). 360p. per. 14.95 *(978-0-8294-1872-9(5))* Loyola Pr.
Doherty, Catherine. Fragments of My Life: A Memoir. (Illus.). 206p. pap. *(978-0-921440-41-3(3))* Madonna Hse. Pubns.
Evans, Bernard F. Vote Catholic? Beyond the Political Din. 2008. 98p. per. 9.95 *(978-0-8146-2946-8(6)*, Liturgical Pr. Bks.) Liturgical Pr.
Fatica, Justin. Win It All: The Way to Heaven for Catholic Teens. 2010. (Illus.). 160p. (YA). pap. 11.95 *(978-1-59471-249-4(2))* Ave Maria Pr.
Fehrenbach, Paul K. Soul & Self: Parallels Between Spiritual & Psychological Growth. 2006. 107p. per. 14.95 *(978-0-8091-4423-5(9)*, 4423-9) Paulist Pr.
Fernandez, Eduardo C. Mexican-American Catholics. 2007. (Pastoral Spirituality Ser.). 208p. pap. 18.95 *(978-0-8091-4266-8(X)*, 4266-8) Paulist Pr.
Furey, Constance M. Erasmus, Contarini, & the Religious Republic of Letters. 2008. (ENG., Illus.). 272p. (C). pap. 40.00 *(978-0-521-10343-5(6))* Cambridge Univ. Pr.
Gildiner, Catherine. After the Falls: Coming of Age in the Sixties. 2011. (ENG.). 384p. (gr. 12). 16.00 *(978-0-14-311985-2(0)*, Penguin (Non-Classics)) Penguin Group (USA) Inc.
Goska, Danusha V. Save Send Delete. 2012. (ENG.). 299p. pap. 18.95 ***(978-1-84694-986-9(6))*** Hunt, John Publishing Ltd. GBR. Dist: National Bk. Network.
Graham, Elizabeth. Maya Christians & Their Churches in Sixteenth-Century Belize. 2011. (Maya Studies). (ENG., Illus.). 416p. 79.95 *(978-0-8130-3666-3(6))* Univ. Pr. of Florida.
Hahn, Scott, frwd. I Choose God: Stories from Young Catholics. annot. ed. 2007. 130p. per. *(978-0-86716-773-3(4)*, Servant Bks.) Franciscan Media.
Hart, Mark. Blessed Are the Bored in Spirit: A Young Catholic's Search for Meaning. 2006. 129p. per. 11.99 *(978-0-86716-677-4(0))* Franciscan Media.
Haughey, John C., ed. In Search of the Whole: Twelve Essays on Faith & Academic Life. 2011. (Illus.). 232p. pap. 29.95 *(978-1-58901-781-8(1))* Georgetown Univ. Pr.
Ilibagiza, Immaculée & Erwin, Steve. Sobrevivir para Contarlo: Como Descubri a Dios en Medio del Holocausto en Rwanda. Minino, Adriana, tr. 2007. (SPA & ENG., Illus.). 215p. per. 15.95 *(978-1-4019-1202-4(8))* Hay Hse., Inc.
King, Heather. Redeemed: Stumbling Toward God, Sanity, & the Peace That Passes All Understanding. 2009. (ENG.). 256p. (gr. 12-18). 16.00 *(978-0-14-311506-9(5)*, Penguin (Non-Classics)) Penguin Group (USA) Inc.
Klausing, Patrice & Young, Kimberly. Breaking Free of the Web: Catholics & Internet Addiction. 2007. 167p. per. *(978-0-86716-804-4(8))* Franciscan Media.
Knecht, Sharon. Oblate Sisters of Providence: A Pictorial History. 2007. *(978-1-57864-411-7(9))* Donning Co. Pubs.
Kocik, Thomas. Living & Loving the Mass. 2007. 86p. per. *(978-0-9725981-8-7(9))* Zaccheus Pr.
Kooi, Christine. Calvinists & Catholics during Holland's Golden Age: Heretics & Idolaters. 2012. (ENG.). 256p. 99.00 ***(978-1-107-02324-6(6))*** Cambridge Univ. Pr.
Kreeft, Peter. Being Catholic. (How to Talk to Your Children About . . . Ser.). 30p. pap. 1.50 *(978-0-87973-682-8(8))* Our Sunday Visitor, Publishing Div.
Lakeland, Paul & Lakeland. Catholicism at the Crossroads: How the Laity Can Save the Church. 2007. (ENG.). 176p. pap. 22.95 *(978-0-8264-2810-3(X))* Continuum International Publishing Group, Ltd. GBR. Dist: National Bk. Network.
March, Kenneth. Is God Calling His People to Leave the un-Holy Roman Catholic Church. 2010. 116p. pap. 11.99 *(978-1-60957-417-8(6))* Xulon Pr., Inc.
Marlin, George J. Narcissist Nation: Reflections of a Blue-State Conservative. 2011. 208p. 30.00 *(978-1-58731-565-7(3))*; pap. 18.00 *(978-1-58731-566-4(1))* St. Augustine's Pr., Inc.
McCoy-Thompson, Steven & Haykin, Randy M. Fuel: Catholic Men, Living the Faith - A Small Group Guide. 2008. 160p. pap. 12.95 *(978-1-59471-180-0(1))* Ave Maria Pr.
McGann, Mary E. Let It Shine! The Emergence of African American Catholic Worship. 4th ed. 2008. (ENG.). 200p. pap. 25.00 *(978-0-8232-2992-5(0))* Fordham Univ. Pr.
McGann, Mary E. & Harbor, Ronald D. Let It Shine! The Emergence of African American Catholic Worship. 4th ed. 2008. (ENG.). 200p. 70.00 *(978-0-8232-2991-8(2))* Fordham Univ. Pr.
McKenna, Kevin E. A Concise Guide to Your Rights in the Catholic Church. 2006. (Concise Guide Ser.). 127p. per. 12.95 *(978-1-59471-079-7(1))* Ave Maria Pr.
McKenzie, Janet P., compiled by. I Talk with God: The Art of Prayer & Meditation for Catholic Children. 2011. 140p. (J). pap. 14.95 ***(978-1-934185-40-7(X))*** Biblio Resource Pubns., Inc.
Medina, Jose Antonio. Temas Calientes para Los Jovenes Cristianos/Controversial Topics for Young Christians: El Aborto, la Eutanasia, la Pena de Muerte, en Defensa de la Vida/ Abortion, Euthanasia, Death Penalty, in Defense of Life. 2007. (Illus.). 63p. pap. 3.95 *(978-0-7648-1527-0(X)*, Libros Liguori) Liguori Pubns.
Mews, Sally L. Catholics Continuing the Journey: A Faith-Sharing Program for Small Groups. 2006. (Illus.). 31p. pap. 5.95 *(978-0-7648-1503-4(2))* Liguori Pubns.

Muldoon, Tim. Catholic Identity & the Laity. College Theology Society Annual Vol. 54 2008. Muldoon, Tim, ed. 2009. 272p. pap. 30.00 *(978-1-57075-821-8(2))* Orbis Bks.
Pable, Martin. Catholics & Fundamentalists: Understanding & Response. 3rd rev. ed. 2008. 96p. pap. 9.95 *(978-0-87945-167-6(5)*, 263) ACTA Pubns.
Pacer, Mike. Prayers for Catholic Men. 2008. 96p. pap. 12.99 *(978-0-86716-881-5(1)*, Franciscan Media.
Pollmann, Judith. Catholic Identity & the Revolt of the Netherlands, 1520-1635. 2011. (ENG., Illus.). 272p. 99.00 *(978-0-19-960991-8(8))* Oxford Univ. Pr., Inc.
Rice, Charles E. What Happened to Notre Dame? 2009. (ENG.). 224p. pap. 15.00 *(978-1-58731-920-4(9))* St. Augustine's Pr., Inc.
Robert J. (Bob) Burton. Christian Catholic & Praising Jesus! 2009. 304p. pap. 15.49 *(978-1-4389-8854-2(0))* AuthorHouse.
Rohr, Richard. On the Threshold of Transformation: Daily Meditations for Men. 2010. (ENG.). 400p. pap. 14.95 *(978-0-8294-3302-9(3))* Loyola Pr.
Schorn, Joel. God's Doorkeepers: Padre Pio, Solanus Casey & Andre Bessette. 2006. 162p. per. 12.99 *(978-0-86716-699-6(1)*, Servant Bks.) Franciscan Media.
Steinkamp, Mary. Maria- A True Story of Faith & Forgiveness. 2008. (Illus.). 64p. per. *(978-1-55452-243-9(9)*, Guardian Bks.) Essence Publishing.
Summers, Andrea. Born of Sin: The Natasha Moore Story. 2010. 86p. pap. 19.99 *(978-1-4500-2471-6(8))* Xlibris Corp.
Thigpen, Paul. Last Words: Final Thoughts of Catholic Saints & Sinners. 2006. 219p. per. 14.99 *(978-0-86716-724-5(5)*, Servant Bks.) Franciscan Media.
Thompson, Phillip M. Between Science & Religion: The Engagement of Catholic Intellectuals with Science & Technology in the Twentieth Century. 2009. (ENG.). 298p. 78.99 *(978-0-7391-3080-3(3))* Lexington Bks.
Trainor, Michael. Epaphras: Paul's Educator at Colossae. 2008. (Illus.). 712p. (C). pap. 12.95 *(978-0-8146-5230-5(1))* Liturgical Pr.
Vidler, Alec R. A Variety of Catholic Modernists. 2009. (ENG.). 256p. pap. 34.99 *(978-0-521-10027-4(5))* Cambridge Univ. Pr.
Wagner, Abp Wynn. A Pilgrims Guide to the Old Catholic Church. 2009. 124p. pap. 14.99 *(978-0-557-21617-8(6))* Lulu Enterprises Inc.
Walsh, James. Catholic Churchmen in Science: Sketches of the Lives of Catholic Ecclesiastics Who Were among the Great Founders in Science. 2007. 244p. per. 19.95 *(978-1-60206-981-7(6))* Cosimo, Inc.
Weldon, Tim. Be Filled with Wonder: The Franciscan Intellectual Tradition. 2007. (C). per. 22.50 *(978-1-58152-499-4(4)*, Copley Publishing Group) Copley Custom Textbooks.
Wild, Robert, ed. Compassionate Fire. 2009. (Illus.). 160p. pap. 14.95 *(978-1-59471-216-6(6))* Ave Maria Pr.
Will, Julianne M. The Twelve Days of Christmas: Celebrating the Season as Catholics. 2009. 1p. 14.95 *(978-1-59276-717-5(6))* Our Sunday Visitor, Publishing Div.

CATHOLICS—BIOGRAPHY

Agee, Gary B. A Cry for Justice: Daniel Rudd & His Life in Black Catholicism, Journalism, & Activism, 1854 -1933. 2011. 256p. 39.95 ***(978-1-55728-975-9(1))*** Univ. of Arkansas Pr.
Baker, Kimball. Go to the Worker: America's Labor Apostles. 2010. pap. *(978-0-87462-749-7(4))* Marquette Univ. Pr.
Berettari, Sebastiano, et al. The Lives of Father Joseph Anchieta, of the Society of Jesus: the Ven. Alvera von Virmundt, Religious of the Order of the Holy Sepulchre, & the Ven. John Berchmans, of the Society of Jesus. 2011. (Cambridge Library Collection - Religion Ser.). (ENG., Illus.). 432p. pap. 32.99 ***(978-1-108-03376-3(8))*** Cambridge Univ. Pr.
Blanchard, Mary Bergan. Eulc Gy - 2011. 354p. pap. 19.95 ***(978-1-61434-216-8(4))*** Booklocker.com, Inc.
Campbell, Bernadette. Jock Dalrymple: And the Path to Holiness. 2013. (ENG.). 224p. pap. 19.95 *(978-0-86012-441-2(X)*, Burns & Oates) Continuum International Publishing Group, Ltd. GBR. Dist: National Bk. Network.
Carroll, James. Practicing Catholic. 2010. (ENG.). 400p. pap. 16.95 *(978-0-547-33625-8(8)*, Mariner Bks.) Houghton Mifflin Harcourt Trade & Reference Pubs.
Catoir, John T. Encounters with Holiness: My Interviews with Mother Teresa of Calcutta, Dorothy Day, Archbishop Fulton J. Sheen, Catherine de Hueck Doherty, Fr. Walter Ciszek, SJ, Leon-Josef Cardinal Suenens, John Cardinal O'Connor, Mother Angelica & Many Others. 2007. 176p. per. *(978-0-8189-1237-5(5)*, St. Pauls) St Pauls/Alba Hse. Pubs.
Choy, Leona. My Journey to the Land of More. 2010. pap. 12.95 *(978-0-9800066-6-7(X))* CHResources.
Clemmer, Edward Joseph. Gospel (on the Road to) Emmaus, 2 vols. 2011. 656p. 46.66 *(978-1-4567-7429-5(8))*; 712p. 46.66 *(978-1-4567-7379-3(8))*; 656p. pap. 31.68 *(978-1-4567-7430-1(1))* AuthorHouse.
Day, Dorothy. The Duty of Delight: The Diaries of Dorothy Day. 2011. (ENG.). 752p. pap. 18.00 *(978-0-7679-3280-6(3)*, Doubleday Religion) Doubleday Religious Publishing Group, The.
Deats, Richard. Marked for Life: The Life of Hildegard GossMayr. 2009. (Leaders & Witnesses Ser.). 152p. pap. 13.95 *(978-1-56548-309-5(X))* New City Pr.
Duszak, Malgorzata. Odyssey of an Airhead: Ultimate Truth, Here I Come! 2010. 260p. (ENG.). 27.99 *(978-1-4520-2400-4(6))*; pap. 17.99 *(978-1-4520-2399-1(9))* AuthorHouse.
Ellis, Marc H. Peter Maurin. 2010. (Catholic Worker Reprint Ser.). (Illus.). 204p. pap. 23.00 *(978-1-60899-060-3(5)*, Wipf and Stock) Wipf & Stock Pubs.
Fink, John F. Future American Saints? Men & Women Whose Causes for Canonization Are Being Considered. 2009. *(978-0-8189-1291-7(X))* St Pauls/Alba Hse. Pubs.
Forest, Jim. All Is Grace: A Biography of Dorothy Day. 2011. (Illus.). 352p. pap. 27.00 *(978-1-57075-921-5(9))* Orbis Bks.
Franco, Angelo. The Heroic Fidelity of Venerable Michael Rua: Disciple of & Successor to St. John Bosco, 1837-1910. 2011. 396p. 54.95 ***(978-1-258-04571-5(0))*** Literary Licensing, LLC.
Gateley, Edwina. In God's Womb. 2009. (Illus.). 192p. pap. 20.00 *(978-1-57075-847-8(6))* Orbis Bks.
Gervais, Marty. Afternoons with the Devil: Growing up Catholic in a Border Town. 2010. (ENG., Illus.). 150p. pap. 15.00 *(978-0-88962-919-6(6))* Mosaic Pr.
Ghezzi, Bert. Saints at Heart: How Fault-Filled, ProblemProne, Imperfect People Like Us Can Be Holy. 2011. (ENG.). 176p. pap. 12.95 *(978-0-8294-3544-3(1))* Loyola Pr.
Grodi, Marcus, ed. Journeys Home. 3rd rev. ed. 2011. pap. 12.95 ***(978-0-9830829-1-0(X))*** CHResources.
Gudge, Patricia. Memoirs of an East End Girl. 2009. (Illus.). 100p. pap. *(978-1-84748-552-6(9))* Athena Pr.
Guenin-Lelle, Dianne & Mourad, Ronney. Jeanne Guyon: Selected Writings. 2012. (Classics of Western Spirituality Ser.). 400p. 39.92 ***(978-0-8091-0595-3(0))***; 368p. pap. 29.95 ***(978-0-8091-4718-2(1))*** Paulist Pr.
Guyon, Jeanne-Marie Bouvier de la Motte, et al. The Prison Narratives of Jeanne Guyon, 1 vol. 2011. (AAR Religions in Translation Ser.). (ENG.). 168p. 55.00 ***(978-0-19-984112-7(8))*** Oxford Univ. Pr., Inc.
Hennacy, Ammon. The Book of Ammon. 2010. (Catholic Worker Reprint Ser.). (Illus.). 512p. (Orig.). pap. 55.00 *(978-1-60899-053-5(2)*, Wipf and Stock) Wipf & Stock Pubs.
Hill, Brennan R. Unlikely Spiritual Heroes. 2010. 176p. pap., pap. 14.95 *(978-0-86716-924-9(9))* Franciscan Media.
Hines, J. The Nine of Us: A Lighthearted Memoir. 2009. 244p. pap. 14.99 *(978-1-4490-0256-5(0))* AuthorHouse.
Ilibagiza, Immaculée. Led by Faith: Rising from the Ashes of the Rwandan Genocide. 2009. (ENG., Illus.). 256p. pap. 14.95 *(978-1-4019-1888-0(3))* Hay Hse., Inc.
Ilibagiza, Immaculée & Erwin, Steve. Left to Tell: Discovering God Amidst the Rwandan Holocaust. 2007. (ENG., Illus.). 215p. pap. 14.95 *(978-1-4019-0897-3(7))* Hay Hse., Inc.
—Left to Tell: One Woman's Story of Surviving the Rwandan Holocaust. 2007. (Illus.). xx, 277p. pap. *(978-1-4019-1538-4(8)*, 457) Hay Hse. UK, Ltd. GBR. Dist: Grantham Bk. Services.
Johansen, Pauline A. G. Objects in Mirror Are Closer than They Appear: A Memoir. 2011. 152p. 24.95 *(978-1-4502-7307-7(6))*; pap. 14.95 *(978-1-4502-7305-3(X))* iUniverse, Inc.
Kennedy, Finola. Frank Duff: A Life Story. 2011. (ENG., Illus.). 304p. pap. 19.95 *(978-1-4411-6747-7(1)*, Burns & Oates) Continuum International Publishing Group, Ltd. GBR. Dist: National Bk. Network.
Kresta, Al & Thomm, Nick. Moments of Grace: Inspiring Stories from Well-Known Catholics. 2008. 224p. pap. 14.99 *(978-0-86716-862-4(5))* Franciscan Media.
Langa, Beki P. Living & Working with Cancer. 2010. (Illus.). 54p. pap. *(978-1-84748-713-1(0))* Athena Pr.
Levoy, Hughie Boy. Chicago Kid: From Whence I Came. 2011. 282p. pap. 19.99 ***(978-1-4653-4086-3(6))***; 29.99 ***(978-1-4628-5341-0(2))*** Xlibris Corp.
Mackey, Noreen. The Crystal Fountain: The Story of an Inner Journey. 2007. (ENG.). 152p. pap. 21.95 *(978-1-85607-567-1(2))* Columba Pr. IRL. Dist: Dufour Editions, Inc.
Marshall, Peter & Scott, Geoffrey. Catholic Gentry in English Society: The Throckmortons of Coughton from Reformation to Emancipation. 2009. (Catholic Christendom, 1300-1700 Ser.). (Illus.). 300p. 134.95 *(978-0-7546-6432-1(5))* Ashgate Publishing Co.
McGartland, Martin. Fifty Dead Men Walking. 2009. (ENG., Illus.). 288p. pap. 14.95 *(978-1-84454-751-7(5))* Blake, John Publishing, Ltd. GBR. Dist: Independent Pubs. Group.
Murray, Paul. I Loved Jesus in the Night: Teresa of Calcutta - A Secret Revealed. 2008. (ENG.). 120p. (gr. 13). 18.95 *(978-1-55725-579-2(2))* Paraclete Pr., Inc.
Neuhaus, Roger. (Mostly) True Confessions of A Recovering Catholic. 2011. 204p. 24.95 ***(978-1-4620-3491-8(8))***; pap. 14.95 ***(978-1-4620-3489-5(6))*** iUniverse, Inc.
Nichols, Aiden. The Latin Clerk: The Life, Work & Travels of Adrian Fortescue. 2011. (ENG.). 308p. pap. 50.00 ***(978-0-7188-9274-6(7))*** Lutherworth Pr., The GBR. Dist: Brown, David Bk. Co., The.
O'Donnell, Tim. A View from the Back Pew: God, Religion & Our Personal Quest for Truth. 2011. (ENG.). 280p. pap. 15.95 *(978-0-9845344-1-8(5))* Linchpin Publishing, LLC.
Paponetti, Giovanna, illus. Kateri, Native American Saint: The Life & Miracles of Kateri Tekakwitha. 2010. *(978-1-57416-098-7(2))* Clear Light Pubs.
Penaskovic, Richard & Penaskovic, Robert. Bobby Brown & Richie Blue: A Spiritual Memoir. 2009. (ENG.). 130p. pap. 24.99 *(978-0-7618-4909-4(2))* Hamilton Bks.
Rega, Frank M. The Greatest Catholic President: Garcia Moreno of Ecuador 1821-1875. 2009. *(978-1-892331-69-4(1))* Angelus Pr.
Rice, Anne. Called Out of Darkness: A Spiritual Confession. 2010. (ENG.). 256p. pap. 15.95 *(978-0-307-38848-3(4)*, Anchor) Knopf Doubleday Publishing Group.
Rodriguez, J. L. Random Reflections of A Recycled Catholic. 2009. 104p. pap. 12.95 *(978-1-4327-4918-7(8))* Outskirts Pr., Inc.
Rulli, Lino. Sinner: The Catholic Guys Funny, Feeble Attempts to Be a Faithful Catholic. 2011. (ENG.). 181p. pap. 18.99 ***(978-1-61636-039-9(9)***, Servant Bks.) Franciscan Media.
Smith, Charlene & Feister, John. Thea's Song: The Life of Thea Bowman. 2010. (Illus.). 352p. 28.00 *(978-1-57075-858-3(9))* Orbis Bks.
Stulberg, Miriam. God Calls Me Miriam: The Spiritual Journey of a Jewish-Christian: The Struggle with a Crippling Disease: A Life Changing Bonding with Gulag Survivors in Post-Soviet Russia. 299p. *(978-1-897145-07-4(1))* Madonna Hse. Pubns.
Sullivan, John J., ed. Divine Masterpieces: Sketches of Some Heroic Lovers of God. 2011. 222p. 44.95 ***(978-1-258-00239-8(6))*** Literary Licensing, LLC.
Tighe, S. P. Arch, Steeples, & Dome: Religious Symbols on a Journey of Faith. 2009. 140p. pap. 15.49 *(978-1-4389-9601-1(2))* AuthorHouse.
Torres, Andrés. Signing in Puerto Rican: A Hearing Son & His Deaf Family. 2009. (ENG., Illus.). 200p. pap. 34.95 *(978-1-56368-417-3(9))* Gallaudet Univ. Pr.
Van Kaam, Adrian L. The Life Journey of A Joyful Man of God: The Autobiographical Memoirs of Adrian Van Kaam. Muto, Susan, ed. 2010. 456p. pap. 50.00 *(978-1-60899-481-6(3)*, Resource Pubns.) Wipf & Stock Pubs.
Walsh, Michael J. & Walsh. The Westminster Cardinals: The Past & the Future. 2009. (ENG., Illus.). 264p. 34.95 *(978-0-86012-459-7(2)*, Burns & Oates) Continuum International Publishing Group, Ltd. GBR. Dist: National Bk. Network.
Watkins, Christine. Full of Grace: Miraculous Stories of Healing & Conversion through Mary's Intercession. 2010. 224p. pap. 14.95 *(978-1-59471-226-5(3))* Ave Maria Pr.
Wefing, John B. The Life & Times of Richard J. Hughes: The Politics of Civility. 2009. (ENG., Illus.). 352p. 32.50 *(978-0-8135-4641-4(9))* Rutgers Univ. Pr.
Wilkes, Paul. In Due Season: A Catholic Life. 2009. (ENG., Illus.). 320p. 24.95 *(978-0-470-42333-2(1)*, Jossey-Bass) Wiley, John & Sons, Inc.

CATHOLICS—LEARNING AND SCHOLARSHIP

see Catholic Learning and Scholarship

CATHOLICS—SOCIETIES, ETC.

see Catholic Church—Societies, etc.

CATHOLICS—AFRICA

Ilibagiza, Immaculée. Led by Faith: Rising from the Ashes of the Rwandan Genocide. 2009. (ENG., Illus.). 256p. pap. 14.95 *(978-1-4019-1888-0(3))* Hay Hse., Inc.
Ilibagiza, Immaculée & Erwin, Steve. Left to Tell: Discovering God Amidst the Rwandan Holocaust. 2007. (ENG., Illus.). 215p. pap. 14.95 *(978-1-4019-0897-3(7))* Hay Hse., Inc.
—Left to Tell: One Woman's Story of Surviving the Rwandan Holocaust. 2007. (Illus.). xx, 277p. pap. *(978-1-4019-1538-4(8)*, 457) Hay Hse. UK, Ltd. GBR. Dist: Grantham Bk. Services.

CATHOLICS—ASIA

Steenbrink, Karel. Catholics in Indonesia, 1808-1942, Vol. 2. 2010. (Verhandelingen Van Het Koninklijk Instituut Voor Taal-, Land Ser.). (Illus.). 648p. pap. 60.00 *(978-90-6718-260-7(5))* KITLV Pr. NLD. Dist: Univ. of Hawaii Pr.

CATHOLICS—AUSTRIA

Jägerstätter, Franz. Letters & Writings from Prison. Putz, Erna, ed. Krieg, Robert Anthony, tr. from GER. 2009. (Illus.). 260p. pap. 25.00 *(978-1-57075-826-3(3))* Orbis Bks.

CATHOLICS—CANADA

Bigart, Robert J., ed. Crossroad of Cultures: Sacramental Records at St. John the Baptist Catholic Church, Frenchtown, Montana, 1866-1899. Scott, Anita O. & Scott, James M., trs. from LAT. 2009. (Illus.). 240p. pap. 12.95 *(978-1-934594-05-6(9))* Salish Kootenia College Pr.
Doherty, Eddie. Gall & Honey: The Story of a Newspaperman. 2nd ed. (Illus.). 305p. pap. *(978-0-921440-13-0(8))* Madonna Hse. Pubns.
Pritchett, John Perry. Black Robe & Buckskin: The Story of Catholic Pioneering in Northern North America. 2011. 130p. 40.95 ***(978-1-258-07045-8(6))*** Literary Licensing, LLC.

CATHOLICS—ENGLAND

Baker, Geoff. Reading & Politics in Early Modern England: The Mental World of a Seventeenth-Century Catholic Gentleman. 2010. (Politics, Culture & Society in Early Modern Britain Ser.). (ENG.). 272p. 89.95 *(978-0-7190-8024-1(X))* Manchester Univ. Pr. GBR. Dist: Macmillan.
Bastow, Sarah L. The Catholic Gentry of Yorkshire, 1536-1642: Resistance & Accommodation. 2007. (Illus.). 288p. 109.95 *(978-0-7734-5325-8(3))* Mellen, Edwin Pr., The.
Bosworth, Jose, et al, eds. The Middleton Papers: The Financial Problems of a Yorkshire Recusant Family in the Sixteenth & Seventeenth Centuries. 2010. (Yorkshire Archaeological Soc Record Ser.: Volume 161). (Illus.). 220p. 90.00 *(978-1-903564-31-8(X))* Yorkshire Archaeological Society GBR. Dist: Boydell & Brewer, Inc.
Conn, Walter E. Conscience & Conversion in Newman: A Developmental Study of Self in John Henry Newman. 2010. pap. *(978-0-87462-777-0(X))* Marquette Univ. Pr.
Corthell, Ronald, et al, eds. Catholic Culture in Early Modern England. 2007. (ENG., Illus.). 336p. pap. 40.00 *(978-0-268-02294-5(1))* Univ. of Notre Dame Pr.
Guilday, Peter K. The English Catholic Refugees on the Continent, 1558-1795. reprint ed. 55.00 *(978-0-404-19900-5(3))* AMS Pr., Inc.
Hibbard, Caroline M. Charles I & the Popish Plot. 2011. (ENG.). 351p. pap. 30.00 *(978-0-8078-9684-6(5))* Univ. of North Carolina Pr.
Hodgson, Aileen M. & Hodgetts, Michael, eds. Little Malvern Letters: I: 1482-1737. 2011. (Catholic Record Society: Records Ser.: Volume 83). (Illus.). 296p. 80.00 *(978-0-902832-26-8(3))* Catholic Record Society GBR. Dist: Boydell & Brewer, Inc.
Holmes, Peter. Resistance & Compromise: The Political Thought of the Elizabethan Catholics. 2009. (Cambridge Studies in the History & Theory of Politics Ser.). (ENG.). 288p. pap. 38.99 *(978-0-521-10953-6(1))* Cambridge Univ. Pr.
Hopkins, Gerard Manley. Gerard Manley Hopkins: The Major Works. Phillips, Catherine, ed. & intro. by. 2009. (Oxford World's Classics Ser.). (ENG.). 480p. pap. 15.95 *(978-0-19-953885-0(9))* Oxford Univ. Pr., Inc.
Hornsby-Smith, Michael P. Roman Catholic Beliefs in England: Customary Catholicism & Transformations of Religious Authority. 2009. (ENG.). 284p. pap. 41.00 *(978-0-521-09327-9(9))* Cambridge Univ. Pr.
—Roman Catholics in England: Studies in Social Structure since the Second World War. 2008. (ENG.). 268p. pap. 37.99 *(978-0-521-09006-3(7))* Cambridge Univ. Pr.
Jolliffe, John, ed. English Catholic Heroes. 2008. (Illus.). 252p. pap. *(978-0-85244-604-1(7))* Gracewing, Ltd.
Klause, John. Shakespeare, the Earl, & the Jesuit. 2008. (Illus.). 344p. 72.50 *(978-0-8386-4137-8(7))* Fairleigh Dickinson Univ. Pr.
Lothian, James R. The Making & Unmaking of the English Catholic Intellectual Community, 1910-1950. 2009. (ENG.). 496p. 60.00 *(978-0-268-03382-8(X))* Univ. of Notre Dame Pr.
Mann, Stephanie A. Supremacy & Survival: How Catholics Endured the English Reformation. 2009. (Illus.). 167p. 12.95 *(978-1-59417-079-9(7))* Scepter Pubs., Inc.
Mariani, Paul. Gerard Manley Hopkins: A Life. 2008. (ENG.). 496p. (gr. 12-18). 34.95 *(978-0-670-02031-7(1)*, Viking Adult) Penguin Group (USA) Inc.
Mayer, Jean-Christophe. Shakespeare's Hybrid Faith: History, Religion & the Stage. 2006. (Early Modern Literature in History Ser.). (ENG., Illus.). 248p. 84.00 *(978-0-230-00525-9(X))* Palgrave Macmillan.
McAloon, Francis. The Language of Prayer As a Form of Prayer: The Theo-Poetic Aesthetics of Gerard Manley Hopkins. 2008. 260p. 109.95 *(978-0-7734-5022-6(X))* Mellen, Edwin Pr., The.
Newman, John Henry. Lectures on the Present Position of Catholics in England: Addressed to the Brothers of the Oratory in the Summer Of 1851 (1908) 2008. 454p. 52.95 *(978-1-4365-9471-4(5))* 2007. 456p. per. 37.95 *(978-0-548-79152-3(X))* Kessinger Publishing, LLC.
Pritchard, Arnold. Catholic Loyalism in Elizabethan England. 2011. (ENG.). 256p. pap. 40.00 ***(978-0-8078-9755-3(8))*** Univ. of North Carolina Pr.
Rose, Elliot. Cases of Conscience: Alternatives open to Recusants & Puritans under Elizabeth 1 & James 1. 2008. (ENG.). 280p. pap. 37.99 *(978-0-521-08114-6(9))* Cambridge Univ. Pr.
Saward, John, et al. Firmly I Believe & Truly: The Spiritual Tradition of Catholic England. 2011. (ENG., Illus.). 832p. 65.00 *(978-0-19-929122-9(5))* Oxford Univ. Pr., Inc.
Shagan, Ethan H., ed. Catholics & the 'Protestant Nation' Religious Politics & Identity in Early Modern England. 2009. (Politics, Culture & Society in Early Modern Britain Ser.). (ENG.). 224p. pap. 36.00 *(978-0-7190-8052-4(5))* Manchester Univ. Pr. GBR. Dist: Macmillan.
Shell, Alison. Oral Culture & Catholicism in Early Modern England. 2009. (ENG.). 260p. pap. 38.99 *(978-0-521-12686-1(X))* Cambridge Univ. Pr.
Southwell, Robert. An Humble Supplication to her Maiestie. Bald, R. C., ed. 2011. (ENG.). 106p. pap. 19.99 *(978-1-107-66833-1(6))* Cambridge Univ. Pr.
Tumbleson, Raymond D. Catholicism in the English Protestant Imagination: Nationalism, Religion, & Literature, 1660-1745. 2009. (ENG.). 268p. pap. 38.00 *(978-0-521-10089-2(5))* Cambridge Univ. Pr.
Walsh, Michael J. & Walsh. The Westminster Cardinals: The Past & the Future. 2009. (ENG., Illus.). 264p. 34.95 *(978-0-86012-459-7(2)*, Burns & Oates) Continuum International Publishing Group, Ltd. GBR. Dist: National Bk. Network.
Wilkie, William E. The Cardinal Protectors of England: Rome & the Tudors before the Reformation. 2008. (ENG.). 276p. pap. 37.99 *(978-0-521-08764-3(3))* Cambridge Univ. Pr.

CATHOLICS—FRANCE

Burton, Katherine. The Stars Beyond the Storms: Father Etienne Pernet, Founder of the Congregation of the Little Sisters of the Assumption. 2011. 224p. 44.95 ***(978-1-258-09578-9(5))*** Literary Licensing, LLC.
de La Motte, Jeanne-Marie Bouvier. Autobiography of Madame Guyon. 2007. (Authentic Original Classic Ser.). 447p. per. 15.99 *(978-0-7684-2529-1(8))* Destiny Image Pubs.
Gibbons, Katy. English Catholic Exiles in Late Sixteenth-Century Paris. 2011. (Royal Historical Society Studies in History New Ser.: Volume 79). 216p. 90.00 *(978-0-86193-313-6(3))* Royal Historical Society GBR. Dist: Boydell & Brewer, Inc.
Guenin-Lelle, Dianne & Mourad, Ronney. Jeanne Guyon: Selected Writings. 2012. (Classics of Western Spirituality Ser.). 400p. 39.92 ***(978-0-8091-0595-3(0))***; 368p. pap. 29.95 ***(978-0-8091-4718-2(1))*** Paulist Pr.
Guyon, Jeanne. Autobiography of Madame Guyon. 212p. 2009. 32.99 *(978-1-59547-532-9(X))* 2007. per. 12.99 *(978-1-59547-926-6(0))* NuVision Pubns., LLC.
—Autobiography of Madame Guyon. 2007. 144p. per. 8.99 *(978-1-4245-0790-0(1))* Treasures Media Inc.

C

Mahon, Joseph. Simone de Beauvoir & Her Catholicism: An Essay on Her Ethical & Religious Meditations. 2007. 216p. pap. 29.95 *(978-1-903631-27-0(0))* Arlen Hse. IRL. Dist: Syracuse Univ. Pr.

Preyat, Fabrice. Le Petit Concile de Bossuet et la Christianisation des Murs et des Pratiques Littéraires Sous Louis XIV. (FRE.). 570p. pap. *(978-3-8258-8716-2(2),* Adlard Coles) Lit Verlag.

CATHOLICS—GERMANY

Bennette, Rebecca Ayako. Fighting for the Soul of Germany: The Catholic Struggle for Inclusion after Unification. 2012. (Harvard Historical Studies: 178). (ENG., Illus.). 380p. 49.95 ***(978-0-674-06563-5(8))*** Harvard Univ. Pr.

Forster, Marc R. Catholic Germany from the Reformation to the Enlightenment. 2007. (European History in Perspective Ser.). (ENG., Illus.). 224p. 130.00 *(978-0-333-69837-2(1))* Palgrave Macmillan.

—Catholic Germany from the Reformation to the Enlightenment. Black, Jeremy, ed. 2007. (European History in Perspective Ser.). (ENG., Illus.). 224p. pap. 39.00 *(978-0-333-69838-9(X))* Palgrave Macmillan.

Ristau, Harold. Understanding Martin Luther's Demonological Rhetoric in His Treatise Against the Heavenly Prophets (1525) How What Luther Speaks Is Essential to What Luther Says. 2010. vii, 545p. 139.95 *(978-0-7734-3724-1(X))* Mellen, Edwin Pr., The.

Windell, George G. The Catholics & German Unity, 1866-1871. 2009. (ENG.). 324p. pap. 60.00 *(978-0-8166-5891-6(9))* Univ. of Minnesota Pr.

CATHOLICS—IRELAND

Butler, David. South Tipperary 1570-1841: Religion, Land & Rivalry. 2008. (Illus.). 336p. pap. 39.95 *(978-1-84682-091-5(X))* Four Courts Pr. IRL. Dist: International Specialized Bk. Services.

Craig, Patricia. Asking for Trouble: The Story of an Escapade with Disproportionate Consequences. 2008. (ENG., Illus.). 240p. pap. 22.95 *(978-0-85640-808-3(5))* Blackstaff Pr., Ltd. GBR. Dist: Dufour Editions, Inc.

Crawford, Heather K. Outside the Glow: Protestants & Irishness in Independent Ireland. 2010. (ENG., Illus.). 252p. pap. 49.95 *(978-1-906359-44-7(X))* Univ. College Dublin Pr. IRL. Dist: Dufour Editions, Inc.

Doherty, Eddie. Matt Talbot. Huston, Rob, ed. 2nd rev. ed. 240p. pap. *(978-0-921440-67-3(7))* Madonna Hse. Pubns.

Gibbons, Luke & O'Conor, Kieran, eds. Charles O'Conor of Ballinagare: Essays on His Life & Works. 2012. 240p. 70.00 *(978-1-84682-111-0(8))* Four Courts Pr. IRL. Dist: International Specialized Bk. Services.

Gibney, John. Ireland & the Popish Plot. 2009. (ENG.). 240p. 84.00 *(978-0-230-20365-5(5))* Palgrave Macmillan.

Hepburn, A. C. Catholic Belfast & Nationalist Ireland in the Era of Joe Devlin, 1871-1934. 2008. (ENG., Illus.). 320p. 125.00 *(978-0-19-929884-6(X))* Oxford Univ. Pr., Inc.

Hynes, Eugene. Knock: The Virgin's Apparition in Nineteenth-Century Ireland. 390p. 2009. pap. 39.95 *(978-1-85918-463-9(4))* 2008. (Illus.). 65.00 *(978-1-85918-440-0(5))* Cork Univ. Pr. IRL. Dist: Stylus Publishing, LLC.

Kennedy, Finola. Frank Duff: A Life Story. 2011. (ENG., Illus.). 304p. pap. 19.95 *(978-1-4411-6747-7(1),* Burns & Oates) Continuum International Publishing Group, Ltd. GBR. Dist: National Bk. Network.

Mackey, Noreen. The Crystal Fountain: The Story of an Inner Journey. 2007. (ENG.). 152p. pap. 21.95 *(978-1-85607-567-1(2))* Columba Pr. IRL. Dist: Dufour Editions, Inc.

Madden, Kyla. Forkhill Protestants & Forkhill Catholics, 1787-1858. 2007. (McGill-Queen's Studies in the History of Religion Ser.). (ENG., Illus.). 264p. (C). per. *(978-0-7735-3060-7(6))* McGill-Queen's Univ. Pr.

Maher, Eamon, ed. What Being Catholic Means to Me. 2010. (ENG.). 176p. pap. 27.95 *(978-1-85607-675-3(X))* Columba Pr. IRL. Dist: Dufour Editions, Inc.

McGartland, Martin. Fifty Dead Men Walking. 2009. (ENG., Illus.). 288p. pap. 14.95 *(978-1-84454-751-7(5))* Blake, John Publishing, Ltd. GBR. Dist: Independent Pubs. Group.

Whelan, Kevin. The Tree of Liberty: Radicalism, Catholicism & the Construction of Irish Identity 1760-1830. 236p. pap. *(978-1-85918-060-0(4))* Cork Univ. Pr.

CATHOLICS—ITALY

Franco, Angelo. The Heroic Fidelity of Venerable Michael Ru: Disciple of & Successor to St. John Bosco, 1837-1910. 2011. 396p. 54.95 ***(978-1-258-04571-5(0))*** Literary Licensing, LLC.

Frassati, Pier Giorgio, et al. Letters to His Friends & Family. 2009. *(978-0-8189-1305-1(3))* St Pauls/Alba Hse. Pubs.

La Pira, Giorgio & Giovannoni, Marco Pietro. Il Grande Lago Di Tiberiade: Lettere Di Giorgio la Pira per la Pace Nel Mediterraneo: 1954-1977. 2006. (I libri della Badia Ser.). (ITA., Illus.). 345p. (C). 26.50 *(978-88-596-0062-6(6))* Edizioni Polistampa ITA. Dist: Brown, David Bk. Co., The.

Lubich, Chiara. Early Letters: At the Origins of a New Spirituality. 2012. pap. ***(978-1-56548-432-0(0))*** New City Community Pr.

CATHOLICS—POLAND

Auerbacher, Inge & Urbanowicz Gilbride, Bozenna. Children of Terror. 2009. 120p. pap. 12.95 *(978-1-4401-7809-2(7))* iUniverse, Inc.

Ostling, Michael. Between the Devil & the Host: Imagining Witchcraft in Early Modern Poland. 2012. (ENG., Illus.). 296p. 110.00 ***(978-0-19-958790-2(6))*** Oxford Univ. Pr., Inc.

Paprocka, Elzbieta. Tolerowani, Nielubiani: Katolicy W Elblagu W Drugiej Poowie XVII I XVIII Wieku: Studium Z Dziejów Codziennego Wspólstnienia Wyznan. 2009. (POL., Illus.). 245p. *(978-83-7543-079-0(X))* Neriton, Wydawnictwo.

van Rahden, Till. Jews & Other Germans: Civil Society, Religious Diversity, & Urban Politics in Breslau, 1860-1925. Brainard, Marcus, tr. from GER. 2008. (George L. Mosse Ser.). (ENG., Illus.). 486p. pap. 29.95 *(978-0-299-22694-7(8))* Univ. of Wisconsin Pr.

CATHOLICS—SPAIN

Redworth, Glyn. The She-Apostle: The Extraordinary Life & Death of Luisa de Carvajal. 2011. (ENG., Illus.). 288p. pap. 19.95 *(978-0-19-957122-2(8))* Oxford Univ. Pr., Inc.

CATHOLICS—UNITED STATES

see also Nativism

American-French Genealogical Society Staff. Baptisms of Blessed Sacrament Catholic Church, Fall River, MA (1892 - 1995) 2007. 378p. spiral bd. 45.00 *(978-1-60305-018-0(3))* American French Genealogical Society.

—Baptisms of St. Paul Catholic Church, Blackstone, MA (1852 - 1991), 2 vols. 2008. 805p. spiral bd. 70.00 *(978-1-60305-020-3(5))* American French Genealogical Society.

Anderson, R. Bentley. Black, White, & Catholic: New Orleans Interracialism, 1947-1956. 2008. (ENG., Illus.). 320p. (C). pap. 29.95 *(978-0-8265-1484-4(7))* Vanderbilt Univ. Pr.

Arias, David. The First Catholics of the United States. 2009. 273p. pap. 15.87 *(978-0-557-07527-0(0))* Lulu Enterprises Inc.

Baggett, Jerome P. Sense of the Faithful: How American Catholics Live Their Faith, 1 vol. 2011. (ENG.). 320p. pap. 19.95 *(978-0-19-982608-7(0))* Oxford Univ. Pr., Inc.

Baker, Kimball. Go to the Worker: America's Labor Apostles. 2010. pap. *(978-0-87462-749-7(4))* Marquette Univ. Pr.

Berrigan, Daniel. Portraits of Those I Love. 2007. (Daniel Berrigan Reprint Ser.). (Illus.). 164p. pap. 18.00 *(978-1-55635-472-4(X))* Wipf & Stock Pubs.

—To Dwell in Peace: An Autobiography. 2007. (Daniel Berrigan Reprint Ser.). 364p. pap. 40.00 *(978-1-55635-473-1(8))* Wipf & Stock Pubs.

Brown, Joseph A. Sweet, Sweet Spirit: Prayer Services from the Black Catholic Church. 2006. 100p. per. 9.95 *(978-0-86716-626-2(6))* Franciscan Media.

Bruce, Susannah Ural. The Harp & the Eagle: Irish-American Volunteers & the Union Army, 1861-1865. 2006. (ENG., Illus.). 320p. 75.00 *(978-0-8147-9939-0(6))* New York Univ. Pr.

Cafardi, Nicholas P. Voting & Holiness: Catholic Perspectives on Political Participation. 2012. 265p. ***(978-1-61643-140-2(7))*** Paulist Pr.

Cafardi, Nicholas P., ed. Voting & Holiness: Catholic Perspectives on Political Participation. 2012. 272p. pap. 24.95 ***(978-0-8091-4767-0(X))*** Paulist Pr.

Carey, Patrick W. Catholics in America: A History. 2008. (ENG.). 320p. per. 29.95 *(978-0-7425-6233-2(6))* Rowman & Littlefield Publishers, Inc.

Carroll, Michael P. American Catholics in the Protestant Imagination: Rethinking the Academic Study of Religion. 2007. (ENG., Illus.). 240p. (gr. 17). 53.00 *(978-0-8018-8683-6(X))* Johns Hopkins Univ. Pr.

Carty, Thomas J. A Catholic in the White House? Religion, Politics, & John F. Kennedy's Presidential Campaign. 2008. (ENG.). 224p. pap. 32.00 *(978-1-4039-6253-9(7))* Palgrave Macmillan.

Casey, Shaun. The Making of a Catholic President: Kennedy vs. Nixon 1960. 2009. (ENG.). 304p. 27.95 *(978-0-19-537448-3(7))* Oxford Univ. Pr., Inc.

Catholic Cemetery Preservation Society, compiled by. Savannah's Catholic Cemetery: Magnolia & Palmetto Sections, 2 vols., Volume 2. 2008. (Illus.). 400p. 25.00 *(978-0-9774261-1-9(4))* Catholic Cemetery Preservation Society.

Choy, Leona. My Journey to the Land of More. 2010. pap. 12.95 *(978-0-9800066-6-7(X))* CHResources.

Cooley, Richard & Boreson, Ann. Searching Through My Prayer List: A Memoir about Family, Career, & a Meaningful Retirement. 2010. (Illus.). 256p. 24.95 *(978-1-933245-19-5(0))* Documentary Media LLC.

Copeland, M. Shawn, et al, eds. Uncommon Faithfulness: The Black Catholic Experience. 2009. 240p. pap. 26.00 *(978-1-57075-819-5(0))* Orbis Bks.

Coughlin, John J. Canon Law: A Comparative Study with Anglo-American Legal Theory, 1 vol. 2010. (ENG.). 252p. 75.00 *(978-0-19-537297-7(2))* Oxford Univ. Pr., Inc.

Coughlin, John J. Law, Person, & Community: Philosophical, Theological, & Comparative Perspectives on Canon Law, 1 vol. 2012. (ENG.). 288p. (C). 85.00 ***(978-0-19-975677-3(5))*** Oxford Univ. Pr., Inc.

Davis, Cyprian, et al. The Journal of the Black Catholic Theological Symposium, Volume 1. Flint-Hamilton, Kimberly, ed. 2007. 125p. per. 29.99 *(978-0-9789635-6-9(3))* Fortuity Pr., LLC.

Davis, George Lynn-Lachlan. The Day-Star of American Freedom; or, the Birth & Early Growth of Toleration in the Province of Maryland by George Lynn-Lachlan Davis. 2006. 292p. per. 23.99 *(978-1-4255-2724-2(8))* MPublishing.

Day, et al. All the Way to Heaven: The Selected Letters of Dorothy Day. 2011. *(978-0-87462-061-0(9),* Ohio Univ. Ctr. for International Studies) Marquette Univ. Pr.

Day, Dorothy. All the Way to Heaven: The Selected Letters of Dorothy Day. Ellsberg, Robert, ed. 2012. (ENG.). 624p. pap. 16.00 ***(978-0-7679-3281-3(1),*** Image) Doubleday Religious Publishing Group, The.

Day, Dorothy. The Duty of Delight: The Diaries of Dorothy Day. 2011. (ENG.). 752p. pap. 18.00 *(978-0-7679-3280-6(3),* Doubleday Religion) Doubleday Religious Publishing Group, The.

Day, Dorothy & Ellsberg, Robert. The Duty of Delight: The Diaries of Dorothy Day. 2008. 669p. *(978-0-87462-023-8(6))* Marquette Univ. Pr.

Dolan, Jay P., ed. The American Catholic Tradition. 1893.00 *(978-0-405-10810-5(9))* Ayer Co. Pubs., Inc.

—Puerto Rican & Cuban Catholics in the U. S. , 1900-1965. 2010. (History of Hispanic Catholics in U. S. Ser.). (ENG.). 268p. pap. 32.00 *(978-0-268-02606-6(8))* Univ. of Notre Dame Pr.

Elias, John L. & Nolan, Lucinda A. Educators in the Catholic Intellectual Tradition. 2009. *(978-1-888112-18-4(2))* Sacred Heart Univ. Pr.

Ellis, Marc H. Peter Maurin. 2010. (Catholic Worker Reprint Ser.). (Illus.). 204p. pap. 23.00 *(978-1-60899-060-3(5),* Wipf and Stock) Wipf & Stock Pubs.

Elza, Betty. The Cemeteries of Immaculate Conception Parish, Brookville, PA. 2009. (Illus.). 99p. pap. 20.00 *(978-0-615-32926-0(8))* Elderfield.

Emmons, David M. Beyond the American Pale: The Irish in the West, 1845-1910. 2010. (ENG.). 480p. 34.95 *(978-0-8061-4128-2(X))* Univ. of Oklahoma Pr.

Empereur, James L. & Fernández, Eduardo. La Vida Sacra: Contemporary Hispanic Sacramental Theology. 2006. (Celebrating Faith Ser.). (ENG.). 344p. per. 33.95 *(978-0-7425-5157-2(1))* Rowman & Littlefield Publishers, Inc.

Fatica, Justin. Hard as Nails: A Mission to Awaken Youth to the Power of God's Love. 2009. (ENG.). 208p. pap. 14.00 *(978-0-385-52717-0(9),* Image) Doubleday Religious Publishing Group, The.

Fernandez, Eduardo & Empereur, James. La Vida Sacra: Contemporary Hispanic Sacramental Theology. Fernandez, Eduardo & Empereur, James, eds. 2006. (Celebrating Faith Ser.). (ENG.). 344p. 81.00 *(978-0-7425-5156-5(3))* Rowman & Littlefield Publishers, Inc.

Fink, John F. Future American Saints? Men & Women Whose Causes for Canonization Are Being Considered. 2009. *(978-0-8189-1291-7(X))* St Pauls/Alba Hse. Pubs.

Forest, Jim. All Is Grace: A Biography of Dorothy Day. 2011. (Illus.). 352p. pap. 27.00 *(978-1-57075-921-5(9))* Orbis Bks.

Garibaldi, Rayna & Hooper, Bernadette C. Catholics of San Francisco. 2008. (Images of America Ser.). (ENG., Illus.). 128p. pap. 19.99 *(978-0-7385-5948-3(2))* Arcadia Publishing.

Gateley, Edwina. In God's Womb. 2009. (Illus.). 192p. pap. 20.00 *(978-1-57075-847-8(6))* Orbis Bks.

Giannone, Richard. Flannery O'Connor, Hermit Novelist: With a New Preface by the Author. 2010. 312p. pap. 29.95 *(978-1-57003-910-2(0))* Univ. of South Carolina Pr.

Gildiner, Catherine. After the Falls: Coming of Age in the Sixties. 2010. (ENG., Illus.). 368p. (gr. 12). 25.95 *(978-0-670-02205-2(5),* Viking Adult) Penguin Group (USA) Inc.

Giles, Paul. American Catholic Arts & Fictions: Culture, Ideology, Aesthetics. 2008. (Cambridge Studies in American Literature & Culture Ser.). (ENG.). 564p. pap. 74.00 *(978-0-521-05773-8(6))* Cambridge Univ. Pr.

Golway, Terry, ed. Catholics in New York: Society, Culture, & Politics, 1808-1946. 2008. (ENG., Illus.). 224p. 40.00 *(978-0-8232-2904-8(1))* Fordham Univ. Pr.

Greeley, Andrew M. Chicago Catholics & the Struggles Within Their Church. 2010. (ENG.). 218p. 49.95 *(978-1-4128-1479-9(0))* Transaction Pubs.

Gribble, Richard. Living as an American Catholic in the 21st Century: A Short, Self-Guided Retreat. 2011. 104p. pap. ***(978-0-8091-4731-1(9))*** Paulist Pr.

Griffin, Martin I.J. Catholics & the American Revolution V1. 2007. (ENG.). 376p. 48.95 *(978-0-548-11929-7(5))* Kessinger Publishing, LLC.

—Catholics & the American Revolution V2. 2007. (ENG.). 412p. 49.95 *(978-0-548-11928-0(7))* Kessinger Publishing, LLC.

—Catholics & the American Revolution V3. 2007. (ENG.). 436p. 51.95 *(978-0-548-11927-3(9))* Kessinger Publishing, LLC.

Groody, Daniel G. Border of Death, Valley of Life: An Immigrant Journey of Heart & Spirit. 2007. (Celebrating Faith: Explorations in Latino Spirituality & Theology Ser.). (ENG.). 212p. per. 22.95 *(978-0-7425-5890-8(8))* Rowman & Littlefield Publishers, Inc.

Hayes, Patrick J. A Catholic Brain Trust: The History of the Catholic Commission on Intellectual & Cultural Affairs, 1945-1965. 2011. (ENG.). 488p. 75.00 *(978-0-268-03109-1(6))* Univ. of Notre Dame Pr.

Hennacy, Ammon. The Book of Ammon. 2010. (Catholic Worker Reprint Ser.). (Illus.). 512p. (Orig.). pap. 55.00 *(978-1-60899-053-5(2),* Wipf and Stock) Wipf & Stock Pubs.

Henrich, Natalie & Henrich, Joseph. Why Humans Cooperate: A Cultural & Evolutionary Explanation. 2007. (Evolution & Cognition Ser.). (ENG., Illus.). 272p. per. 50.00 *(978-0-19-531423-6(9))* Oxford Univ. Pr., Inc.

Hoang, Linh. Rebuilding Religious Experience- Vietnamese Refugees in America. 2008. 292p. per. *(978-3-8364-2221-5(2))* VDM Verlag Dr. Mueller e.K.

Hoffman, Ronald. The Carroll Family of Maryland. 2008. *(978-1-929545-52-0(5))* American Antiquarian Society.

Hoge, Dean & Jewell, Marti. The Next Generation of Pastoral Leaders: What the Church Needs to Know. 2010. (ENG.). 208p. pap. 11.95 *(978-0-8294-2650-2(7))* Loyola Pr.

Hudson, Deal W. Onward, Christian Soldiers: The Growing Political Power of Catholics & Evangelicals in the United States. 2010. (ENG.). 352p. pap. 21.99 *(978-1-4165-2446-5(0),* Threshold Editions) Threshold Editions.

Kelley, Alexia & Korzen, Chris. A Nation for All: How the Catholic Vision of the Common Good Can Save America from the Politics of Division. 2008. (ENG.). 176p. 24.95 *(978-0-470-25862-0(4),* Jossey-Bass) Wiley, John & Sons, Inc.

Kelly, George Anthony. Catholics & the Practice of the Faith: A Census Study of the Diocese of St. Augustine. 2011. 232p. 46.95 ***(978-1-258-01990-7(6))*** Literary Licensing, LLC.

Kennedy, Kerry. Being Catholic Now: Prominent Americans Talk about Change in the Church & the Quest for Meaning. 2009. (ENG., Illus.). 288p. pap. 15.00 *(978-0-307-34685-8(4),* Three Rivers Pr.) Crown Publishing Group.

Knecht, Sharon C. Oblate Sisters of Providence: A Pictorial History. 2007. *(978-1-57864-437-7(2))* Donning Co. Pubs.

Knight, Thomas C. The Knights of Columbus. 2007. per. 18.95 *(978-1-4209-2935-5(6))* Digireads.com.

Knox, Andrew. Blazing an African-American Trail. 2008. (ENG.). 108p. pap. 11.95 *(978-1-934937-04-4(5))* Mill City Pr., Inc.

Krentz, Roger F. St. John the Baptist Catholic Church Princeton, Wisconsin. 2010. 112p. pap. 47.96 *(978-0-557-40886-3(5))* Lulu Enterprises Inc.

Kresta, Al & Thomm, Nick. Moments of Grace: Inspiring Stories from Well-Known Catholics. 2008. 224p. pap. 14.99 *(978-0-86716-862-4(5))* Franciscan Media.

Larsen, Deborah. The Tulip & the Pope: A Nun's Story. annot. ed. 2006. (Vintage Ser.). (ENG.). 288p. pap. 14.00 *(978-0-375-71290-6(9),* Vintage) Knopf Doubleday Publishing Group.

Lenhart, John M. Catholics & the American Declaration of Independence, 1774-1776. 2011. 72p. 36.95 ***(978-1-258-01989-1(2))*** Literary Licensing, LLC.

Lezcano, Reynier. Beggars No More. 2007. 92p. pap. 11.50 *(978-0-615-13578-6(1))* SMARTdollar Pr.

Lickona, Matthew. Swimming with Scapulars: True Confessions of a Young Catholic. 2007. (ENG.). 288p. pap. 12.95 *(978-0-8294-2471-3(7))* Loyola Pr.

Mairs, Nancy. A Dynamic God: Living an Unconventional Catholic Faith. 2008. (ENG.). 160p. pap. 15.00 *(978-0-8070-7733-7(X))* Beacon Pr.

Marlin, George J. The American Catholic Voter: 200 Years of Political Impact. 2006. (Illus.). 426p. per. 19.00 *(978-1-58731-029-4(5))* St. Augustine's Pr., Inc.

McAvoy, Thomas T. Catholic Church in Indiana, 1789-1834. (Columbia University, Studies in the Social Sciences: No. 471). reprint ed. 27.50 *(978-0-404-51471-6(5))* AMS Pr., Inc.

McDannell, Colleen. The Spirit of Vatican II: A History of Catholic Reform in America. 2011. (ENG.). 304p. (gr. 9). 26.99 *(978-0-465-04480-1(8))* Basic Bks.

McGuinness, Margaret M. & Fisher, James T., eds. The Catholic Studies Reader. 2011. (Catholic Practice in North America Ser.). (ENG.). 350p. pap. 32.00 *(978-0-8232-3411-0(8))* Fordham Univ. Pr.

—The Catholic Studies Reader. 2011. (Catholic Practice in North America Ser.). (ENG.). 350p. 105.00 *(978-0-8232-3410-3(X))* Fordham Univ. Pr.

Metzger, Charles H. Catholics & the American Revolution: A Study in Religious Climate. 2011. 316p. 50.95 ***(978-1-258-06899-8(0))*** Literary Licensing, LLC.

Moore, Cecilia A., et al, eds. Songs of Our Hearts, Meditations of Our Souls: Prayers for Black Catholics. 2007. (Illus.). 103p. per. 9.95 *(978-0-86716-694-1(0))* Franciscan Media.

Muldoon, Tim. Seeds of Hope: Young Adults & the Catholic Church in the United States. 2008. 225p. per. 24.95 *(978-0-8091-4514-0(6))* Paulist Pr.

Nilson, Jon. Hearing Past the Pain: Why White Catholic Theologians Need Black Theology. 2007. 120p. per. 16.95 *(978-0-8091-4508-9(1),* 4508-9) Paulist Pr.

O'Beirne, Kate, et al. The Catholic Vote in America. Hudson, Deal W., ed. 100p. pap. *(978-0-9660597-8-6(6))* Morley Bks.

Orsi, Robert A. Between Heaven & Earth: The Religious Worlds People Make & the Scholars Who Study Them. 2006. (ENG., Illus.). 264p. (C). per. 24.95 *(978-0-691-12776-7(X))* Princeton Univ. Pr.

O'Toole, James M. The Faithful: A History of Catholics in America. 2010. 384p. pap. 19.00 *(978-0-674-03488-4(0),* Belknap Pr.) Harvard Univ. Pr.

Payton, Leland & Payton, Crystal. Mystery of the Irish Wilderness: Land & Legend of Father John Joseph Hogan's Lost Irish Colony in the Ozark Wilderness. 2008. (Illus.). 128p. pap. 18.95 *(978-0-9673925-4-7(3))* Lens & Pen Pr.

Plummer, John & Mabry, John. Who Are the Independent Catholics? 2006. pap. 5.95 *(978-1-933993-00-3(6))* Apocryphile Pr.

Portmann, John. Catholic Culture in the USA: In & Out of Church. 2010. (ENG.). 224p. 34.95 *(978-1-4411-8892-2(4));* 120.00 *(978-1-4411-6359-2(X))* Continuum International Publishing Group, Ltd. GBR. Dist: National Bk. Network.

Poyo, Gerald E. Cuban Catholics in the United States, 1960-1980: Exile & Integration. 2007. (Latino Perspectives Ser.). (ENG.). 424p. 65.00 *(978-0-268-03832-8(5));* per. 32.00 *(978-0-268-03833-5(3))* Univ. of Notre Dame Pr.

Quinn, Peter. Looking for Jimmy: A Search for Irish America. (ENG., (gr. 12). 2008. Illus.). 288p. per. 14.95 *(978-1-59020-023-0(3))* 2007. 320p. 26.95 *(978-1-58567-870-9(8))* Overlook Pr., The.

Rice, Anne. Called Out of Darkness: A Spiritual Confession. 2010. (ENG.). 256p. pap. 15.95 *(978-0-307-38848-3(4),* Anchor) Knopf Doubleday Publishing Group.

Riegle, Rosalie G. Dorothy Day: Portraits by Those Who Knew Her. 2006. (Illus.). 212p. per. 20.00 *(978-1-57075-664-1(3))* Orbis Bks.

Ruane, John Bernard. Parish the Thought: An Inspirational Memoir of Growing up Catholic in The 1960s. 2007. 279p. 19.60 *(978-0-9792344-0-8(9))* Roswell Pr.

Rulli, Lino. Sinner: The Catholic Guys Funny, Feeble Attempts to Be a Faithful Catholic. 2011. (ENG.). 181p. pap. 18.99 ***(978-1-61636-039-9(9),*** Servant Bks.) Franciscan Media.

Rutkowski, Ryan. Catholic West Virginia. 2010. (Images of America Ser.). (Illus.). 128p. pap. 21.99 *(978-0-7385-8639-7(0))* Arcadia Publishing.

Scally, Mary Anthony. Negro Catholic Writers 1900 - 1943: A Bio-Bibliography. 2006. pap. 21.95 *(978-1-4286-5451-8(8))* Kessinger Publishing, LLC.

Schuyler, Joseph B. Northern Parish: A Sociological & Pastoral Study. 2011. 404p. 54.95 ***(978-1-258-08913-9(0))*** Literary Licensing, LLC.

Slaughter, Shirley Harris. Our Lady of Victory: The Saga of an African-American Catholic Community. 2007. 224p. (ENG.). 28.95 *(978-0-595-89668-4(5));* per. 18.95 *(978-0-595-43482-4(7))* iUniverse, Inc.

Smith, Anthony Burke. The Look of Catholics: Portrayals in Popular Culture from the Great Depression to the Cold War. 2010. (Illus.). 280p. 34.95 *(978-0-7006-1716-6(7))* Univ. Pr. of Kansas.

Sterne, Evelyn Savidge. Ballots & Bibles: Ethnic Politics & the Catholic Church in Providence. 2008. (Cushwa Center Studies of Catholicism in

Twentieth-Century America). 320p. pap. 22.95 *(978-0-8014-7497-2(3))* Cornell Univ. Pr.
Tentler, Leslie Woodcock. Catholics & Contraception: An American History. 2008. (Cushwa Center Studies of Catholicism in Twentieth-Century America). (Illus.). 352p. pap. 21.95 *(978-0-8014-7494-1(9))* Cornell Univ. Pr.
Terrar, Edward Toby. Liberation Theology along the Potomac: Labor's Golden Rule in Early American Catholicism. 2011. (Illus.). 220p. pap. 19.00 *(978-0-9764168-4-5(0))* CWPublisher.
Torres, Andrés. Signing in Puerto Rican: A Hearing Son & His Deaf Family. 2009. (ENG., Illus.). 200p. pap. 34.95 *(978-1-56368-417-3(9))* Gallaudet Univ. Pr.
Vinemount-Leopold, Missouri: The First 100 Years. 2010. (Illus.). 287p. ***(978-1-935001-41-6(8))*** Acclaim Pr., Inc.
Weber, Francis J. Catholic Heroes of Southern California. 2007. (Illus.). 192p. 29.95 *(978-2-7468-1290-1(8))* Editions du Signe FRA. Dist: Gem Guides Bk. Co.
Welsh, Thomas G. Closing Chapters: Urban Change, Religious Reform, & the Decline of Youngstown's Catholic Elementary Schools, 1960-2006. 2011. E-Book ***(978-0-7391-6596-6(8))***; (ENG.). 340p. 80.00 ***(978-0-7391-6594-2(1))*** Lexington Bks.
Wilkes, Paul. In Due Season: A Catholic Life. 2009. (ENG., Illus.). 320p. 24.95 *(978-0-470-42333-2(1),* Jossey-Bass) Wiley, John & Sons, Inc.
Wolfteich, Claire E. American Catholics Through the Twentieth Century: Spirituality, Lay Experience & Public Life. 2011. 212p. pap. 19.95 ***(978-0-8245-2637-5(6))*** Crossroad Publishing Co., The.
Yealy, Francis J. Sainte Genevieve: The Story of Missouri's Oldest Settlement. (Illus.). 150p. reprint ed. lib. bdg. 88.00 *(978-0-7222-0643-0(7))* Library Reprints, Inc.
Zanca, Kenneth J. Catholics & Mrs. Mary Surratt: How They Responded to the Trial & Execution of the Lincoln Conspirator. 2008. (ENG.). pap. 35.99 *(978-0-7618-4023-7(0))* Univ. Pr. of America, Inc.
Zeitz, Joshua M. White Ethnic New York: Jews, Catholics, & the Shaping of Postwar Politics. 2007. (ENG., Illus.). 296p. per. 27.95 *(978-0-8078-5798-4(X))* Univ. of North Carolina Pr.
100 Years of Faith: A Centennial History of our Lady of the Rosary Church. 2008. 224p. pap. 15.00 *(978-0-9715211-5-5(8))* FolgerGraphics, Inc.

CATHOLICS—UNITED STATES—BIBLIOGRAPHY
Finotti, Joseph Maria. Bibliographia Catholica Americana: A List of Works Written by Catholic Authors, 2006. 324p. per. 23.99 *(978-1-4255-3207-9(1))* MPublishing.

CATHOLICS—WALES
Hickey, John. Urban Catholics: The Irish Settlement in Cardiff, 1811-2000. 2006. 256p. 13.95 *(978-0-7083-1845-4(2))* Univ. of Wales Pr. GBR. Dist: Chicago Distribution Ctr.

CATHOLICS IN LITERATURE
Crowe, Marian E. Aiming at Heaven, Getting the Earth: The English Catholic Novel Today. 2007. (ENG.). 420p. 120.99 *(978-0-7391-1640-1(1))*; per. 40.99 *(978-0-7391-1641-8(X))* Lexington Bks.
Finotti, Joseph Maria. Bibliographia Catholica Americana: A List of Works Written by Catholic Authors, 2006. 324p. per. 23.99 *(978-1-4255-3207-9(1))* MPublishing.
Griffin, Susan M. Anti-Catholicism & Nineteenth-Century Fiction. 2009. (Cambridge Studies in American Literature & Culture Ser.). (ENG., Illus.). 296p. pap. 38.99 *(978-0-521-09352-1(X))* Cambridge Univ. Pr.
Nisly, Lamar. Wingless Chickens, Bayou Catholics, & Pilgrim Wayfarers: Constructions of Audience & Tone in O'Connor, Percy, & Gautreaux. 2011. (Flannery O'Connor Ser.). (Illus.). 256p. 35.00 *(978-0-88146-214-2(4))* Mercer Univ. Pr.
Reichardt, Mary R., ed. Between Human & Divine: The Catholic Vision in Contemporary Literature. 2010. (ENG.). 304p. 69.95 *(978-0-8132-1739-0(3))* Catholic Univ. of America Pr.
Scally, Mary Anthony. Negro Catholic Writers 1900 - 1943: A Bio-Bibliography. 2006. pap. 21.95 *(978-1-4286-5451-8(8))* Kessinger Publishing, LLC.
Shell, Alison. Catholicism, Controversy & the English Literary Imagination, 1558-1660. 2006. (ENG.). 324p. pap. 63.00 *(978-0-521-03214-8(8))* Cambridge Univ. Pr.
—Oral Culture & Catholicism in Early Modern England. 2009. (ENG.). 260p. pap. 38.99 *(978-0-521-12686-1(X))* Cambridge Univ. Pr.
Tomko, Michael. British Romanticism & the Catholic Question: Religion, History & National Identity, 1778-1829. 2010. (ENG., Illus.). 240p. 84.00 *(978-0-230-27951-3(1))* Palgrave Macmillan.

CATILINA, LUCIUS SERGIUS, 108-62 B.C.
Beesly, Edward Spencer. Catiline, Clodius & Tiberius. 2007. (ENG.). 174p. 37.95 *(978-0-548-03602-0(0))* Kessinger Publishing, LLC.
Hollingsworth, Anthony, reader. Cicero's First Catilinarian Oration: A Digital Tutor. 2008. (ENG & LAT.). cd-rom 32.00 *(978-0-86516-644-8(7))* Bolchazy-Carducci Pubs.
McGushin, Patrick. Sallust: Bellum Catilinae. 2010. (Latin Texts Ser.). (LAT & ENG.). 208p. pap. 19.95 *(978-0-905515-19-8(X))* Bristol Classical Pr. GBR. Dist: International Publishers Marketing.
Odahl, Charles M. Cicero & the Catilinarian Conspiracy. 2010. (Routledge Monographs in Classical Studies). (ENG., Illus.). 118p. (C). 125.00 *(978-0-415-87472-4(6))* Routledge.
Ramsey, J. T., ed. Sallust's Bellum Catilinae. 2nd ed. 2007. (American Philological Association Classical Texts with Commentary Ser.). (LAT & ENG., Illus.). 280p. pap. 25.00 *(978-0-19-532085-5(9))* Oxford Univ. Pr., Inc.
Sallust. Conspiracy of Catiline & the Jurgurthine War. Rev. John Selby Watson, M. A., tr. 2007. (ENG.). 206p. pap. 20.99 *(978-1-4264-2699-5(2))* BiblioBazaar.

CATIONIC POLYMERIZATION
see Addition Polymerization

CATIONS
Laali, Kenneth K. Recent Developments in Carbocation & Onium Ion Chemistry. 2007. (ACS Symposium Ser.). (ENG., Illus.). 544p. 175.00 *(978-0-8412-7414-3(2))* American Chemical Society.
Nies, Dietrich H. & Silver, S. Molecular Microbiology of Heavy Metals. 2007. (Microbiology Monographs). (Illus.). viii, 460p. 259.00 *(978-3-540-69770-1(5),* 3540697705) Springer.
Water & Metal Cations. 93.50 *(978-0-89955-335-1(4))* Business Ctr. for Academic Societies JPN. Dist: International Specialized Bk. Services.

CATLIN, GEORGE, 1796-1872
Hausdoerffer, John. Catlin's Lament: Indians, Manifest Destiny, & the Ethics of Nature. 2009. (Illus.). 208p. 34.95 *(978-0-7006-1631-2(4))* Univ. Pr. of Kansas.

CATNACH, JAMES, 1792-1841
Hindley, Charles. History of the Catnach Press: At Berwick-upon-Tweed, Alnwick & Newcastle-upon-Tyne, in Northumberland, & Seven Dials, London. 2010. (Cambridge Library Collection - Printing & Publishing History Ser.). (Illus.). 360p. pap. 29.99 *(978-1-108-00909-6(3))* Cambridge Univ. Pr.
Hindley, Charles. The Life & Times of James Catnach, (Late of Seven Dials), Ballad Monger. 2011. (Cambridge Library Collection - Literary Studies). (ENG., Illus.). 456p. pap. 34.99 ***(978-1-108-03942-0(1))*** Cambridge Univ. Pr.

CATO, MARCUS PORCIUS, 234-149 B.C.
Sciarrino, Enrica. Cato the Censor & the Beginnings of Latin Prose: From Poetic Translation to Elite Transcription. 2011. 248p. 44.95 *(978-0-8142-1165-6(8))*; cd-rom 14.95 ***(978-0-8142-9266-2(6))*** Ohio State Univ. Pr.
Wulfram, Hartmut. Ex uno Plures: Drei Studien Zum Postumen Persönlichkeitsbild des Alten Cato. 2009. (GER., Illus.). 143p. (C). 53.00 ***(978-3-938032-30-5(8))*** Antike, Verlag, e.K. DEU. Dist: ISD.

CATO STREET CONSPIRACY, 1820
Gardner, John E. Poetry & Popular Protest: Peterloo, Cato Street & the Queen Caroline Controversy. 2011. (Palgrave Studies in the Enlightenment, Romanticism & the Cultures of Print Ser.). (ENG., Illus.). 264p. 85.00 *(978-0-230-28071-7(4))* Palgrave Macmillan.

CATONIS DISTICHA
Baldzuhn, Michael. Schulbacher im Trivium des Mittelalters und der Frahen Neuzeit: Die Verschriftlichung von Unterricht in der Text- und Äceberlieferungsgeschichte der Fabulae Avians und der deutschen Disticha Catonis. 2009. (Quellen und Forschungen zur Literatur- und Kulturgeschichte Ser.).Tr. of Schoolbooks in the Medieval & Early Modern Trivium. (GER.). XXII, 1128p. 307.00 ***(978-3-11-173886-4(8))*** De Gruyter, Walter Inc.
Baldzuhn, Michael. Schulbücher im Trivium des Mittelalters und der Frühen Neuzeit: Die Verschriftlichung von Unterricht in der Text- und Überlieferungsgeschichte der 'Fabulae' Avians und der deutschen 'Disticha Catonis'. 2 Bände. 2009. (Quellen und Forschungen zur Literatur- und Kulturgeschichte Ser.).Tr. of Schoolbooks in the Medieval & Early Modern Trivium. (GER., Illus.). XXII, 1123p. 207.00 *(978-3-11-019351-0(5))* De Gruyter, Walter Inc.

CATOPTROMANCY
see Crystal Gazing

CATS
Here are entered works on domestic breeds of cats. Works on the family of cats are entered under Felidae.
see also Felidae; Siamese Cat
Alderton, David. Top Cats: Top Breeds in Detail. 2007. (Illus.). 254p. 29.99 *(978-0-7858-1927-1(4),* Chartwell) Book Sales, Inc.
Arden, Darlene. The Complete Cat's Meow: Everything You Need to Know about Caring for Your Cat. 2011. (ENG., Illus.). 256p. pap. 19.99 *(978-0-470-64167-5(3),* Howell Bk. Hse.) Wiley, John & Sons, Inc.
Artist Collection. The Cat: Love Cat, Love People, Love Life. 2011. (ENG., Illus.). 128p. 15.95 *(978-1-84732-590-7(4))* Carlton Bks., Ltd. GBR. Dist: Independent Pubs. Group.
Atlantic Publishing Group. How to Listen to Your Cat: the Complete Guide to Communicating with Your Feline Friend. 2012. (ENG.). 288p. pap. 24.95 *(978-1-60138-597-0(8))* Atlantic Publishing Co.
Barnes, Ronald A. Cat IQ Test: Fun for You, Fun for Your Pet How Smart Is Your CAT? 2006. (Illus.). 24p. per. 19.95 *(978-0-9785609-3-5(0))* New Global Publishing.
Becker, Marty. Your Cat: The Owner's Manual - Hundreds of Secrets, Surprises, & Solutions for Raising a Happy, Healthy Cat. 2012. (ENG., Illus.). 320p. 25.99 ***(978-0-446-57136-4(9))*** Grand Central Publishing.
Becker, Mikkel, et al. The Ultimate Cat Lover: The Best Experts' Advice for a Happy, Healthy Cat with Stories & Photos of Fabulous Felines. 2008. (ULTIMATE Ser.). (ENG., Illus.). 328p. pap. 14.95 *(978-0-7573-0751-5(5))* Health Communications, Inc.
Becker, Suzy. All I Need to Know I Learned from My Cat: (And Then Some) 2nd collector's ed. 2007. (ENG., Illus.). 144p. 8.95 *(978-0-7611-4766-4(7),* 0761147667) Workman Publishing Co., Inc.
Bell, K. M. Spot the Difference: Are Cheetahs Really Just Big Cats? 2010. (ENG., Illus.). 200p. pap. 66.00 *(978-1-904761-60-0(7))* Nottingham Univ. Pr. GBR. Dist: Independent Pubs. Group.
Bessant, Claire. The Cat Manual: The Complete Step-by-Step Guide to Understanding & Caring for Your Cat. 2010. (ENG., Illus.). 176p. 32.95 *(978-1-84425-675-4(8),* 1844256758) Haynes Publishing PLC GBR. Dist: MBI Distribution Services/Quayside Distribution.
Best Friends Animal Society Staff & Somerville, Bob. The Cats of Kittyville: New Lives for Rescued Felines. 2008. (Illus.). 80p. 16.95 *(978-1-4162-0527-2(6))* Sellers Publishing, Inc.
Bistline, Lesley F. Hairballs in the Morning: Real help for ALL cat Owners. 2010. 116p. pap. 12.95 *(978-1-60844-527-1(5))* Dog Ear Publishing, LLC.
Bleiman, Andrew & Eastland, Chris. ZooBorns Cats! The Newest, Cutest Kittens & Cubs from the World's Zoos. 2011. (ZooBorns Ser.). (ENG., Illus.). 160p. 11.99 *(978-1-4516-5190-4(2))* Simon & Schuster.
Boileau, Jean. Chasing the Wind. 2008. 168p. pap. 16.95 *(978-1-4357-3083-0(6))* Lulu Enterprises Inc.
Boneham, Sheila Webster. Senior Cats, 1 vol. 2007. (Animal Planet Pet Care Library). (ENG., Illus.). 112p. 11.95 *(978-0-7938-3781-6(2))* TFH Pubns., Inc.
Bordon Books, creator. For the Love of Cats: A Delightful Photo Celebration of Life with the Feline Kind. 2006. (Illus.). 125p. 12.99 *(978-1-59379-083-7(X))* White Stone Bks.
Borzendowski, Janice. Caring for Your Aging Cat: A Quality-of-Life Guide for Your Cat's Senior Years. 2007. (ENG., Illus.). 224p. pap. 12.95 *(978-1-4027-2613-2(9),* 1262475) Sterling Publishing Co., Inc.
Brown, Pam. Utterly Gorgeous Cats. 2007. (ENG., Illus.). 144p. 16.95 *(978-1-84634-094-9(2))* Exley, Helen Giftbooks GBR. Dist: National Bk. Network.
Buchan, Vivian. Vivian's Original Cat Astrology. 2007. (Illus.). 120p. pap. 12.95 *(978-1-932043-42-6(X))* Penfield Bks.
Buford, Martha. The Brown's Family , One. 2008. 20p. pap. 6.95 *(978-1-934940-56-3(9))* Mountain Valley Publishing, LLC.
Canfield, Jack L., et al. Chicken Soup for the Soul: Loving Our Cats: Heartwarming & Humorous Stories about our Feline Family Members. 2008. (Chicken Soup for the Soul Ser.). (ENG.). 380p. pap. 14.95 *(978-1-935096-08-5(7))* Chicken Soup for the Soul Publishing, LLC.
Chambers, Jane. Quotable Cat. (Illus.). 80p. 9.95 *(978-1-85479-728-5(X))* O'Mara, Michael Bks., Ltd. GBR. Dist: Trans-Atlantic Pubns., Inc.
Choron, Sandra, et al. Planet Cat: A Cat-Alog. 2007. (ENG., Illus.). 424p. pap. 15.95 *(978-0-618-81259-2(8))* Houghton Mifflin Harcourt Publishing Co.
Clark, Nan. Magnificat Puns: 50 Brain Teasers for Cat Lovers & Others. 2009. 116p. pap. 12.95 *(978-0-595-52903-2(8))* iUniverse, Inc.
Cooper, Gwen. Homer's Odyssey: A Fearless Feline Tale, or How I Learned about Love & Life with a Blind Wonder Cat. 2010. (ENG., Illus.). 320p. pap. 15.00 *(978-0-385-34398-5(1))* Random House Publishing Group.
—Homer's Odyssey: A Fearless Feline Tale, or How I Learned about Love & Life with a Blind Wonder Cat. Lt. ed. 2010. (ENG.). 452p. pap. 16.99 *(978-1-59413-407-4(3),* Large Print Pr.) 2009. 440p. 31.95 *(978-1-4104-2089-3(2))* Thorndike Pr.
Cutts, Paddy. The Complete Cat Book. (Illus.). 256p. *(978-1-84309-089-2(9))* Anness Publishing, Inc.
Daffron, Susan. Happy Tabby: Develop a Great Relationship with Your Adopted Cat or Kitten. 2007. 168p. per. 19.99 *(978-0-9749245-3-3(9))* Logical Expressions, Inc.
Daly, Carol Himsel & Davis, Karen Leigh. Maine Coon Cats: Everything about Purchase, Care, Nutrition, Health, & Behavior. 2nd ed. 2006. (Complete Pet Owner's Manual Ser.). (ENG., Illus.). 96p. pap. 8.99 *(978-0-7641-3402-9(7))* Barron's Educational Series, Inc.
Davis, Caroline. Cat Basics: The Essential Guide to Caring for Your Cat. 2006. (ENG., Illus.). 176p. pap. 9.95 *(978-0-600-61470-8(0),* Hamlyn) Octopus Publishing Group GBR. Dist: Hachette Bk. Group.
Davis, Karen Leigh. The Cat Handbook. 2nd rev. ed. 2010. (Barron's Pet Handbooks Ser.). (ENG., Illus.). 200p. pap. 12.99 *(978-0-7641-4317-5(4))* Barron's Educational Series, Inc.
Day, Michael. Clinical Immunology of the Dog & Cat. 2nd rev. ed. 2008. (ENG., Illus.). 464p. 190.00 *(978-1-84076-098-9(2))* Manson Publishing, Ltd. GBR. Dist: Thieme Medical Pubs., Inc.
Day, Michael J. Clinical Immunology of the Dog & Cat. 2nd rev. ed. 2012. (ENG., Illus.). 464p. pap. 89.95 ***(978-1-84076-171-9(7))*** Manson Publishing, Ltd. GBR. Dist: Thieme Medical Pubs., Inc.
Devereux, Eve. Cats Facts, Figures & Fun. 2006. (Illus.). 96p. 5.95 *(978-1-904332-51-0(X))* AAPPL Artists & Photographers Pr., Ltd. GBR. Dist: Sterling Publishing Co., Inc.
Dosa, David. Making Rounds with Oscar: The Extraordinary Gift of an Ordinary Cat. (ENG.). 2011. 256p. pap. 13.99 *(978-1-4013-1043-1(5))* 2010. 240p. 23.99 *(978-1-4013-2323-3(5))* Hyperion Pr.
—Making Rounds with Oscar: The Extraordinary Gift of an Ordinary Cat. l.t. ed. 2011. 304p. pap. 16.99 *(978-1-59413-462-3(6),* Large Print Pr.) 2010. (ENG.). 290p. 31.95 *(978-1-4104-2547-8(9))* Thorndike Pr.
Drobatz, Kenneth J., et al, eds. Manual of Trauma Management in the Dog & Cat. 2011. (ENG., Illus.). 392p. pap. 84.99 *(978-0-470-95831-5(6),* Wiley-Blackwell) Wiley, John & Sons, Inc.
Duno, Steve. Be the Cat! Secrets of the Natural Cat Owner. 2008. (ENG., Illus.). 160p. pap. 14.95 *(978-1-4027-5278-0(4))* Sterling Publishing Co., Inc.
Edwards, Alan. Ultimate Encyclopedia of Cats, Cat Breeds & Cat Care. 2007. *(978-1-57215-121-5(8),* JG Pr.) World Pubns. Group, Inc.
Edwards, Alan. The Ultimate Encyclopedia of Cats, Cat Breeds & Cat Care. 2012. (ENG., Illus.). 256p. pap. 18.99 ***(978-1-78019-125-6(1))*** Anness Publishing GBR. Dist: National Bk. Network.
Edwards, Alan & Turner, Trevor. The Ultimate Encyclopedia of Cats, Cat Breeds & Cat Care. 2010. (ENG., Illus.). 264p. 20.99 *(978-1-84476-897-4(X))* Anness Publishing GBR. Dist: National Bk. Network.
Ehrmann, Max. Desiderata for Cat Lovers: A Guide to Life & Happiness. 2007. (ENG., Illus.). 72p. 7.95 *(978-1-4027-4217-0(7))* Sterling Publishing Co., Inc.
Eilert-Overbeck, Brigitte. Cats. 2009. (Complete Pet Owner's Manual Ser.). (ENG., Illus.). 96p. pap. 8.99 *(978-0-7641-4284-0(4))* Barron's Educational Series, Inc.
Ellen Hasenecz Calvert. Pilgrim: Tales of a Traveling Cat. 2009. 68p. pap. 13.95 *(978-1-4389-3000-8(3))* AuthorHouse.
Elliott, Charles. The Cat Fanatic: Quirky Quotes on Frisky Felines. 2006. (Quotable Ser.). (ENG., Illus.). 456p. per. 12.95 *(978-1-59228-502-0(3),* Lyons Pr.) Globe Pequot Pr., The.
Encyclopedia of Cats. 2008. 384p. *(978-1-4075-2437-5(2))* Parragon, Inc.
Eppes, Margaret. A Tale of Two Kitties. 2008. 40p. pap. 16.99 *(978-1-4389-0496-2(7))* AuthorHouse.
Evans, J. M. & White, Kay. Catlopaedia: A Complete Guide to Cat Care. (Illus.). 212p. pap. 14.95 *(978-1-86054-018-9(X),* INT012) Ringpress Bks., Ltd. GBR. Dist: TFH Pubns., Inc.
Farameh, Patrice. Luxury for Cats. 2008. (Illus.). 220p. 49.95 *(978-3-8327-9224-4(4))* teNeues Publishing Co.
Fiedler, Susan. Birds, Mice, & Apple Pie. 2006. (Illus.). 148p. per. 11.95 *(978-0-9778580-1-9(4))* Spotted Cat Designs.
Fogle, Bruce. Complete Cat Care: What Every Cat Owner Needs to Know. 2011. (ENG., Illus.). 192p. 22.50 *(978-1-84533-544-1(9),* Mitchell Beazley) Octopus Publishing Group GBR. Dist: Hachette Bk. Group.
For the love of a Cat. 2007. per. *(978-1-934345-46-7(6))* SouthWest Pubns.
Foster, Leigh. Reference Guide to Using Essential Oils in the Animal Kingdom-Black & White Version. 2008. 128p. pap. 20.62 *(978-1-4357-4706-7(2))* Lulu Enterprises Inc.
Fraser, Mark, ed. Big Cats in Britain Yearbook 2007. 2007. 292p. per. *(978-1-905723-09-6(1))* CFZ Pr.
—Big Cats in Britain Yearbook 2008. 2008. 264p. per. *(978-1-905723-23-2(7))* CFZ Pr.
Frayling, Christopher. Horace Walpole's Cat. 2009. (ENG., Illus.). 96p. 29.95 *(978-0-500-51491-7(7),* 551491) Thames & Hudson.
Frazier, Anitra & Eckroate, Norma. The Natural Cat: The Comprehensive Guide to Optimum Care. rev. ed. 2008. (ENG.). 528p. (gr. 12-18). pap. 22.00 *(978-0-452-28975-8(0),* Plume) Penguin Group (USA) Inc.
Garza, Mario. Wet Cats. 2008. (ENG.). 20p. 14.95 *(978-0-8118-6496-1(0))* Chronicle Bks. LLC.
Getting to Know the Bengal Cat. 3rd ed. 2007. per. 22.00 *(978-0-9794984-0-4(6))* Ducote, Gene.
Green, Fiona. Mewsings: Exploring the Feline Mystique. 2008. (ENG., Illus.). 96p. *(978-1-59543-809-6(2))* Willow Creek Pr., Inc.
Greive, Bradley Trevor & Hale, Rachael. Why Dogs Are Better Than Cats. 2009. (ENG., Illus.). 224p. 19.99 *(978-0-7407-8513-9(3))* Andrews McMeel Publishing.
Gromis Di Trana, Caterina. Cats. 2010. (MiniCube Ser.). (ENG., Illus.). 768p. 6.95 *(978-88-544-0200-3(1))* White Star ITA. Dist: Sterling Publishing Co., Inc.
Haddon, Celia. The Joy of Cats. 2009. (ENG., Illus.). 320p. 16.95 *(978-0-340-95459-1(0),* Hodder & Stoughton) Hodder General Publishing Div. GBR. Dist: Independent Pubs. Group.
Haddon, Celia, ed. The Joy of Cats. 2009. (ENG., Illus.). 320p. 12.95 *(978-0-340-95464-5(7),* Hodder & Stoughton) Hodder General Publishing Div. GBR. Dist: Independent Pubs. Group.
Halligan, Karen. Doc Halligan's What Every Pet Owner Should Know: Prescriptions for Happy, Healthy Cats & Dogs. 2008. (ENG., Illus.). 336p. pap. 15.95 *(978-0-06-089860-1(7),* HarperPerennial) HarperCollins Pubs.
Halls, Vicky. The Complete Cat. 2010. (ENG., Illus.). 384p. pap. 17.95 *(978-0-553-81976-2(3))* Transworld Publishers Ltd. GBR. Dist: Independent Pubs. Group.
Hampshire, Kristen, et al. Cat Lover's Daily Companion: 365 Days of Insight & Guidance for Living a Joyful Life with Your Cat. 2011. (ENG., Illus.). 320p. pap. 15.99 *(978-1-59253-749-5(9),* 1592537499) Quayside.
Harris, Georgina. I Love My Cat. 2011. (ENG., Illus.). 64p. 9.95 *(978-1-907563-85-0(7))* CICO Bks. GBR. Dist: Ryland Peters & Small.
Harris, Helen. Tabitha: The Story of a Much-Travelled Cat. 2011. (Illus.). 38p. 19.95 ***(978-1-84624-544-2(3))*** Book Guild, Ltd. GBR. Dist: Trans-Atlantic Pubns., Inc.
Hawkins, Lorrie Bell. Jolicure Cats. 2009. (ENG., Illus.). 76p. 19.95 *(978-0-920187-09-8(9))* Percheron Pr. Pubs. CAN. Dist: Univ. of Toronto Pr.
Hayward, Janet. Living Proof: That Cats Do Have Nine Lives. 2nd ed. 2010. (ENG.). 152p. pap. 12.95 *(978-1-921497-85-8(8))* Exisle Publishing Ltd. NZL. Dist: BookMasters Distribution Services (BDS).
Haywood, Steve. Too Narrow to Swing A Cat. 2011. (ENG., Illus.). 320p. pap. 13.95 ***(978-1-84953-065-1(3))*** Summerdale Pubs. GBR. Dist: Independent Pubs. Group.
Helgren, J. Anne. Himalayan Cats. 2nd ed. 2006. (Complete Pet Owner's Manual Ser.). (ENG., Illus.). 96p. pap. 8.99 *(978-0-7641-3403-6(5))* Barron's Educational Series, Inc.
Henriksen, Sr. Tom's Journey: The Cat That God Sent to Look after Me. 2009. 98p. pap. 26.50 *(978-1-60860-221-6(4),* Eloquent Bks.) AEG Literary Publishing Services, Inc.

C

Hestad, Dolores. This Is My Kitty Life. 2011. 36p. pap. 19.95 (978-1-4567-2059-9(7)) AuthorHouse.

Holloway, C. Robert. Charlie, the Wonder Cat: A children's novel for Adults. 2011. 96p. pap. 15.99 (978-1-4653-5780-9(7)) Xlibris Corp.

Horton-Bussey, Claire. Living with a Rescued Cat. 2006. (Illus.). 141p. 12.95 (978-1-86054-254-1(9)) Ringpress Bks., Ltd. GBR. Dist: TFH Pubns., Inc.

Hotchner, Tracie. The Cat Bible: Everything Your Cat Expects You to Know. 2007. (ENG.). 416p. (gr. 12-18). 22.00 (978-1-59240-325-7(5), Gotham) Penguin Group (USA) Inc.

House, C. A. Cats: Show & Pet - Their Varieties, Br. 2006. 160p. per. (978-1-4067-9596-7(8), Hesperides Pr.) Read Bks.

How to Raise Your New Kitten in a Dog Family: The Complete Guide to a Happy Pet-Filled Home. 2012. 288p. pap. 24.95 (978-1-60138-400-3(9)) Atlantic Publishing Co.

Hubbs, Ginger. The Adventures of Maggie the Cat: Maggie Finds A Home. 2011. 20p. pap. (978-1-4269-9348-0(X)) Trafford Publishing (UK) Ltd.

Hunt, Aaron. My Cat's Record Book. 2008. (ENG., Illus.). 144p. (978-1-84597-760-3(2)) Ryland Peters & Small.

Jacobson, Steven & Miller, Jean. Walk Your Cat: The Complete Guide. 2008. (Illus.). 134p. pap. 12.99 (978-0-615-21641-6(2)) Spiraka.

Katzen: Geliebt, Gehasst, Verehrt - und Raetselhaft. (978-3-411-08331-2(X)) Bibliographisches Institut & F. A. Brockhaus AG DEU. Dist: i. b. d., Ltd.

Kemp, Gillian. The Good Cat Spell Book. 2008. (ENG., Illus.). 128p. 15.95 (978-1-58091-188-7(9), Crossing Pr.) Ten Speed Pr.

Knapp, Rene. Milo's Journey. 2011. 108p. pap. 19.95 (978-1-4626-3243-5(2)) PublishAmerica, Inc.

Kolb, Janice Gray. Cherishing: Poetry for Pilgrims Journeying On. 2007. (ENG., Illus.). 368p. pap. 19.95 (978-1-57733-205-3(9)) Blue Dolphin Publishing, Inc.

Lederer, Richard. A Treasury for Cat Lovers: Wit & Wisdom, Information & Inspiration about Our Feline Friends. 2009. (ENG., Illus.). 128p. 13.99 (978-1-4391-0321-0(6), Howard Bks.) Howard Books.

Lee, Justine A. It's a Cat's World... You Just Live in It: Everything You Ever Wanted to Know about Your Furry Feline. 2008. (ENG.). 272p. 13.95 (978-0-307-39350-0(X), Three Rivers Pr.) Crown Publishing Group.

Linford, Jenny. Cat Names. 2006. (ENG., Illus.). 64p. (978-1-84597-274-5(0)) Ryland Peters & Small.

Lualdi, Silvia, photos by. Cats! 2010. (Gotta Love ... Bks.). (ENG.). 144p. 9.99 (978-0-7641-6331-9(0)) Barron's Educational Series, Inc.

MacLeod, Diana. Bathroom Book of Cat Trivia. 2007. (Bathroom Book Of... Ser.). (ENG., Illus.). 224p. per. (978-1-897278-26-0(8)) Blue Bike Bks.

Malkin, Nina. An Unlikely Cat Lady: Feral Adventures in the Backyard Jungle. 2007. (ENG.). 192p. per. 14.95 (978-1-59228-972-1(X), Lyons Pr.) Globe Pequot Pr., The.

Marieb, Elaine N. & Mitchell, Susan J. Human Anatomy Laboratory Manual with Cat Dissections. 6th ed. 2010. (ENG., Illus.). 592p. (C). spiral bd. 112.93 (978-0-321-66706-9(9)) Benjamin-Cummings Publishing Co.

Matthews, Marcus. Big Cats Loose in Britain. 2007. 384p. per. (978-1-905723-12-6(1)) CFZ Pr.

McBeth, Nadine. Empty Window: The Story of Whiffle. 2008. 24p. pap. 13.99 (978-1-4389-0098-8(8)) AuthorHouse.

McDonald, Rita. The Cat in the No-Pet Family: A Feline Biography. 2010. 112p. pap. 11.95 (978-0-533-16308-3(0)) Vantage Pr., Inc.

McHugh, Andrea. How to Have a Happy Cat. 2007. (ENG., Illus.). 128p. pap. 14.95 (978-0-600-61658-0(4), Hamlyn) Octopus Publishing Group GBR. Dist: Hachette Bk. Group.

McKay, D. Catherine. My 85yrs with Dogs & Cats. 2010. 40p. pap. 16.99 (978-1-4490-8594-0(6)) AuthorHouse.

McKenna, Rachael Hale, et al, photos by. Meow: I Love Cats. 2011. (ENG.). 84p. 14.95 (978-1-4521-0169-9(8)) Chronicle Bks. LLC.

McMorris, Megan, ed. Cat Women: Female Writers on Their Feline Friends. 2008. (ENG.). 270p. pap. 15.00 (978-1-4379-5125-7(2)) DIANE Publishing Co.

McMorris, Megan, ed. & intro. Cat Women: Female Writers on Their Feline Friends. 2007. (ENG.). 272p. pap. 14.95 (978-1-58005-203-0(7)) Seal Pr.

Meyer, Sandy. Kittens: A Guide to Caring for Your Kitten. 2006. (Complete Care Made Easy Ser.). (ENG., Illus.). 159p. per. 9.95 (978-1-931993-77-7(7)) BowTie Pr.

Michelle, Debra. My Cat Went to Heaven. 2011. 12p. pap. 7.95 (978-1-4497-2027-8(7), WestBow Pr.) Author Solutions, Inc.

Mielke, Rita, ed. The Love of Cats. 2006. (Love Of Ser.). (Illus.). 64p. 14.95 (978-3-89985-068-0(8)) Feierabend Verlag OHG DEU. Dist: Perseus-PGW.

Milford, Francine. Tuning Fork Therapy(r) using tuning forks on Cat's Chakras. 2008. 82p. pap. 15.00 (978-1-4357-3392-3(4)) Lulu Enterprises Inc.

Mohr, Linda A. Tatiann: Tales & Teachings of My Feline Friend. 2007. 136p. (ENG.). 23.95 (978-0-595-68130-3(1)); per. 13.95 (978-0-595-42677-5(8)) iUniverse, Inc.

Moore, Arden. Happy Cat, Happy You: Quick Tips for Building a Bond with Your Feline Friend. 2008. (ENG., Illus.). 304p. pap. 10.95 (978-1-60342-033-4(9), 1603420339) Storey Publishing, LLC.

Morgan, Diane. Good Catkeeping: A Comprehensive Guide to All Things Feline, 1 vol. 2007. (ENG., Illus.). 288p. pap. 18.95 (978-0-7938-0613-3(5)) TFH Pubns., Inc.

Mugnolo-Williams, Barbara. Hooked on a Feline: Basic Cat Care from a Different PURR-spective. 2006. per. 19.95 (978-0-9777297-9-1(6), WME Bks.) Windsor Media Enterprises, Inc.

Myers, Nancy Clopton. Never kiss a Turtle: The Joys & Sorrows of Pet Ownership. 2010. 160p. pap. 14.95 (978-1-4502-4838-9(1)) iUniverse, Inc.

Myron, Vicki. Dewey: The Small-Town Library Cat Who Touched the World. l.t. ed. 2008. (ENG.). 480p. 24.99 (978-0-446-54119-0(2)) Grand Central Publishing.

Myron, Vicki & Witter, Bret. Dewey: The Small-Town Library Cat Who Touched the World. 2010. (ENG.). 304p. pap. 13.99 (978-0-446-40742-7(9)) Grand Central Publishing.

—Dewey: The Small-Town Library Cat Who Touched the World. 2009. (SPA.). 288p. pap. 19.99 (978-1-60396-648-1(X), Aguilar) Santillana USA Publishing Co., Inc.

Myron, Vicki, et al. Dewey: The Small-Town Library Cat Who Touched the World. 2008. (ENG., Illus.). 288p. 19.99 (978-0-446-40741-0(0)) Grand Central Publishing.

Naples, Virginia L., et al, eds. The Other Saber-Tooths: Scimitar-Tooth Cats of the Western Hemisphere. 2011. (ENG., Illus.). 252p. (gr. 17). 110.00 (978-0-8018-9664-4(9)) Johns Hopkins Univ. Pr.

Newnam, Dulcie. Cat Curious. 2006. pap. (978-0-7552-0246-1(5)) Authors OnLine, Ltd.

North Light Books Staff, contrib. by. Painter's Quick Reference: Cats & Dogs. 2007. (Illus.). 128p. (978-1-58180-859-9(3), North Light Bks.) F&W Media, Inc.

O'Sullivan, Joanne. Calling All Cats! Purrfect Names for Your Fabulous Feline. 2008. (ENG., Illus.). 128p. pap. 7.95 (978-1-60059-265-2(1)) Lark Bks.

Page, Jake. Do Cats Hear with Their Feet? Where Cats Come from, What We Know about Them, & What They Think about Us. 2008. (ENG., Illus.). 224p. 24.95 (978-0-06-145648-0(9)) Smithsonian Institution Pr.

Palika, Liz. Natural Health for Dogs & Cats - The Complete Idiot's Guide. 2011. (Complete Idiot's Guide Ser.). (ENG.). 384p. (gr. 12). 16.95 (978-1-61564-120-8(3), Alpha Bks.) Penguin Group (USA) Inc.

Pendleton, Richard. The Reduced History of Cats: The Story of Our Feline Companion in 101 Caterwauling Episodes. 2008. (Reduced History Ser.). (ENG., Illus.). 128p. 14.95 (978-0-233-00196-8(4)) Andre Deutsch GBR. Dist: Independent Pubs. Group.

Phillips, Marie. Dadcat University: The Story of the Feral Cats at Umass-Amherst. 2011. 296p. 25.74 (978-1-4634-4116-6(9)); pap. 17.09 (978-1-4634-4117-3(7)) AuthorHouse.

Rainbolt, Dusty. Cat Wrangling Made Easy: Maintaining Peace & Sanity in Your Multicat Home. 2007. (ENG., Illus.). 288p. pap. 14.95 (978-1-59921-224-1(2), Lyons Pr.) Globe Pequot Pr., The.

Roberts, Andy. Cat Flaps! Northern Mystery Cats. 2007. 80p. per. (978-1-905723-11-9(3)) CFZ Pr.

Rochlitz, Irene. The Welfare of Cats. 2007. (Animal Welfare Ser.). (ENG., Illus.). 308p. per. 79.95 (978-1-4020-6143-1(9)) Springer.

Rogers, Katharine M. Cat. 2006. (Reaktion Books - Animal Ser.). (ENG., Illus.). 208p. pap. 19.95 (978-1-86189-292-8(6)) Reaktion Bks., Ltd. GBR. Dist: Chicago Distribution Ctr.

Ross, Mark. Animal Shelter Portraits. 2012. (ENG., Illus.). 96p. 16.95 (978-1-935613-34-3(0)) Batty, Mark Pub., LLC.

Sadek, Tammy. Feline Geriatrics in Practice. 2007. (Illus.). 400p. 99.99 (978-0-8138-2117-7(7), Wiley-Blackwell) Wiley, John & Sons, Inc.

Sell, Colleen. Cat Lovers: Stories That Celebrate Our Feline Friends. 2008. (ENG.). 336p. pap. 9.95 (978-1-59869-654-7(8)) Adams Media Corp.

Sellers Publishing Inc. Editors & Kelly, Kevin. Entertaining Your Indoor Cat: 50 Fun & Inventive Amusements for Your Cat. 2008. (Illus.). 128p. pap. 12.95 (978-1-4162-0517-3(9)) Sellers Publishing, Inc.

Sheeran, Martha Sliter. The Tale of the Tailless Cat. 2010. 48p. pap. 10.49 (978-1-4520-2537-7(1)) AuthorHouse.

Shiebler, Gary. The Power of Purrs: Reflections on a Life with Cats. 2008. (ENG., Illus.). 160p. pap. 12.95 (978-1-59921-310-1(9), Lyons Pr.) Globe Pequot Pr., The.

Sigl, Stefanie & Dbaly, Helena. Playtime for Cats: Activities & Games for Felines. 2010. (ENG., Illus.). 112p. pap. 24.95 (978-3-86127-970-9(3)) Cadmos Verlag GmbH DEU. Dist: Independent Pubs. Group.

Silver, Burton & Busch, Heather. Why Paint Cats: The Ethics of Feline Aesthetics. 2006. (ENG., Illus.). 144p. 9.95 (978-1-58008-801-5(5)) Ten Speed Pr.

Smith, Jan. Why You Little ... A Guide for Cat People. 2011. 52p. pap. 10.03 (978-1-4269-9532-3(6)) Trafford Publishing.

Society of the U.S. Humane Staff. The H. S. of the U. S. Guide to Cat Care. Date not set. (Illus.). (978-0-312-27717-8(2)) St. Martin's Pr.

Sommerville, Louisa. Cats. 2009. (Flexi cover Ser.). (ENG., Illus.). 256p. pap. 14.99 (978-0-7858-2522-7(3), 0785825223, Chartwell) Book Sales, Inc.

Sorensen, Vanessa. Zen Kitty: A Cat's Guide to Enlightenment. 2007. (ENG., Illus.). 64p. 8.95 (978-1-4022-0855-3(3), Sourcebooks Hysteria) Sourcebooks, Inc.

Sourcebooks, Inc. Test Your Cat's Personality. 2008. (ENG.). 48p. pap. 5.95 (978-1-4022-1853-8(2)) Sourcebooks, Inc.

Sparks, Bev, photos by. The Life & Times of a Cat Lover. 2009. 64p. 9.99 (978-0-7369-2604-1(6)) Harvest Hse. Pubs.

Spencer, Neal. The Gayer-Anderson Cat. 2007. (British Museum Objects in Focus Ser.). (Illus.). 64p. pap. 12.50 (978-0-7141-1973-1(3)) British Museum Pr. GBR. Dist: Brown, David Bk. Co., The.

Stroud, Jon. The DVD Book of Cats. 2009. (DVDBook Ser.). (ENG., Illus.). 128p. 17.99 (978-1-905828-82-1(9), 1905828829) G2 Entertainment Ltd. GBR. Dist: MBI Distribution Services/Quayside Distribution.

Stroud, Jon & Groome, Clive. Cats. 2011. (Little Book Of Ser.). (ENG., Illus.). 128p. 11.99 (978-1-907803-21-5(1)) G2 Entertainment Ltd. GBR. Dist: BookMasters Distribution Services (BDS).

Suehsdorf, Adie. The Complete Book of Cats. 2011. 130p. 40.95 (978-1-258-09483-6(5)) Literary Licensing, LLC.

Suera, Vincenzo. Character Styling - The Cat, Vol. 1. 2010. (ENG., Illus.). 72p. 75.00 incl. DVD (978-88-88766-09-6(X)) Arkivia Bks. ITA. Dist: National Bk. Network.

Sullivan, Skip & Fisher, David. Why Don't Cats Go Bald? The Questions You've Always Wanted to Ask Your Vet. 2008. (ENG., Illus.). 256p. pap. 14.95 (978-1-59921-233-3(1), Lyons Pr.) Globe Pequot Pr., The.

Surman, Richard. Cathedral Cats. 2007. (ENG., Illus.). 96p. 8.95 (978-0-00-723563-6(1)) HarperCollins Pubs. Ltd. GBR. Dist: Independent Pubs. Group.

—Country House Cats. 2008. (ENG., Illus.). 96p. 19.95 (978-0-00-725917-5(4)) HarperCollins Pubs. Ltd. GBR. Dist: Independent Pubs. Group.

Sutherland Millmann, Anita. Fluffly, My Yellow Dog: A Unlikely Care Giver. 2010. 40p. pap. 16.99 (978-1-4490-6215-6(6)) AuthorHouse.

Sweetwater Press, creator. Strange but True Cats. (Illus.). 200p. 2008. pap. 9.95 (978-1-60261-047-7(9)) 2006. pap. 9.95 (978-1-58173-619-9(3)) Sweetwater Pr.

Szabo, Julia & Szabo. Pretty Pet-Friendly: Easy Ways to Keep Spot's Digs Stylish & Spotless. 2009. (ENG., Illus.). 224p. pap. 16.99 (978-0-470-37728-4(3), Howell Bk. Hse.) Wiley, John & Sons, Inc.

Taber, Gladys. Amber, A Very Personal Cat. 18.95 (978-0-8488-1185-3(2)) Amereon LTD.

Taylor, David. Cat Breeds: Facts, Figures, & Profiles of Over 80 Breeds 2010. (ENG., Illus.). 208p. pap. 9.99 (978-0-600-62094-5(8), Hamlyn) Octopus Publishing Group GBR. Dist: Hachette Bk. Group.

Thistle. 2009. (ENG., Illus.). 128p. (YA). pap. (978-0-9771136-8-2(X)) Old Gypsum Printer, Inc., The.

Thomas, David St John. For the Love of a Cat: A Publisher's Story. rev. ed. 2010. (ENG., Illus.). 248p. pap. 12.95 (978-1-921497-36-0(X)) Exisle Publishing Ltd. NZL. Dist: BookMasters Distribution Services (BDS).

Todd, Jackie. Dog Days in Andalucía: Tails from Spain. 2010. (ENG., Illus.). 256p. pap. 14.95 (978-1-84596-613-3(9)) Mainstream Publishing Co., Ltd. GBR. Dist: Independent Pubs. Group.

Trachtenberg, Peter. Another Insane Devotion: On Cats, Love, & Marriage [tent.]. 2012. (ENG., Illus.). 272p. 24.00 (978-0-7382-1526-6(0)) Da Capo Pr., Inc.

Understanding Your Cat. Date not set. 176p. 9.98 (978-1-4054-0732-8(8)) Parragon, Inc.

Van Vechten, Carl. The Tiger in the House. 2010. 442p. 41.56 (978-1-163-21421-3(3)) Kessinger Publishing, LLC.

—The Tiger in the House. (Illus.). reprint ed. lib. bdg. (978-0-7222-3085-5(0)) Library Reprints, Inc.

—The Tiger in the House: A Cultural History of the Cat. 2007. (ENG., Illus.). 452p. 22.95 (978-1-59017-223-0(X), NYRB Classics) New York Review of Bks., Inc., The.

Walker, Bob. The Cats' House. 2009. (ENG.). 92p. pap. 14.99 (978-0-7407-7861-2(7)) Andrews McMeel Publishing.

Waring, Rob. Night Hunt (US) 2008. (ENG.). 32p. (C). pap. 10.95 (978-1-4240-4430-6(8)) Cengage Heinle.

Warner, Trevor. Cat Body Language Phrasebook: 100 Ways to Read Their Signals. 2007. (ENG., Illus.). 208p. 12.95 (978-1-59223-710-4(X), Thunder Bay Pr.) Advantage Pubs. Group.

Watson, Rebecca & Hessayon, D. G. The Cat Expert: The Only Cat Book You Will Ever Need. 2010. (Expert Ser.). (ENG., Illus.). 128p. pap. 14.95 (978-0-903505-68-0(1), Expert) Transworld Publishers Ltd. GBR. Dist: Sterling Publishing Co., Inc.

Webster Boneham, Sheila. Multiple-Cat Family, 1 vol. 2008. (ENG.). 112p. pap. 10.95 (978-0-7938-3798-4(7)) TFH Pubns., Inc.

Whisler, Karen, ed. We Are the Kitties: Read This or I'll Bite You. 2007. (Illus.). 176p. per. 12.95 (978-1-932461-13-8(2)) Inkblot Bks.

Wilkins, Kelli A. Cats. 2007. (Animal Planet Pet Care Library). (Illus.). 111p. 11.95 (978-0-7938-3771-7(5)) TFH Pubns., Inc.

Williams, Lany. Wilbur's Story. 2008. 68p. pap. 9.95 (978-0-595-49847-5(7)) iUniverse, Inc.

Willow Creek Press, creator. Dump Him, Marry the Cat! Why a Cat Is a Better Match Than a Man. 2007. (ENG., Illus.). 96p. 15.95 (978-1-59543-598-9(0)) Willow Creek Pr., Inc.

Winslow, Helen M. Concerning Cats: My Own & Some Others. 2007. (ENG.). 144p. pap. 18.99 (978-1-4264-3574-4(6)) 2006. 158p. pap. 19.99 (978-1-4264-3625-3(4)) BiblioBazaar.

Wood, Michael G. Laboratory Manual for Anatomy & Physiology Featuring Martini Art. 5th rev. ed. 2012. (ENG., Illus.). 864p. (C). spiral bd. 114.73 (978-0-321-80765-6(0)) Benjamin-Cummings Publishing Co.

—Laboratory Manual for Anatomy & Physiology featuring Martini Art, Cat Version. 5th rev. ed. 2011. (ENG., Illus.). 864p. (C). spiral bd. 114.73 (978-0-321-80365-8(5)) Benjamin-Cummings Publishing Co.

Wood, Michael G. Laboratory Manual for Human Anatomy with CAT Dissections. 2008. (ENG., Illus.). 512p. (C). spiral bd. 112.93 (978-0-8053-7375-2(6)) Benjamin-Cummings Publishing Co.

Yang, Hongying. Diary of a Smiling Cat. 2009. 128p. pap. 3.99 (978-0-06-173096-2(3)) HarperCollins Pubs.

CATS—ANATOMY

Allen, Connie & Harper, Valerie. Cat Dissection. 3rd ed. 2013. (ENG.). (C). pap. 29.95 (978-0-470-13799-4(1), Wiley) Wiley, John & Sons, Inc.

Coulson, Arlene. An Atlas of Interpretative Radiographic Anatomy of the Dog & Cat. 2nd rev. ed. 2008. (ENG., Illus.). 664p. 264.99 (978-1-4051-3899-4(8), Wiley-Blackwell) Wiley, John & Sons, Inc.

Donnersberger, Anne B. A Laboratory Textbook of Anatomy & Physiology: Cat Version. 9th rev. ed. 2009. 544p. spiral bd. 139.95 (978-0-7637-5550-8(8)) Jones & Bartlett Learning, LLC.

DuPont, Gregg A. & DeBowes, Linda J. Atlas of Dental Radiography in Dogs & Cats. 2008. (ENG., Illus.). 288p. 112.00 (978-1-4160-3386-8(6), Saunders) Elsevier - Health Sciences Div.

Evans, Susan A., et al. Color Atlas of Veterinary Anatomy, Volume 3, the Dog & Cat, Vol. 3. 2nd ed. 2009. (ENG., Illus.). 540p. pap. 160.00 (978-0-7234-3415-3(8), Mosby) Elsevier - Health Sciences Div.

McCracken, Thomas O. & Kainer, Robert A. Small Animal Anatomy. rev. ed. 2009. (ENG., Illus.). 160p. pap. 72.99 (978-0-8138-1608-1(4), Wiley-Blackwell) Wiley, John & Sons, Inc.

Walker, Warren F. & Homberger, Dominique G. A Study of the Cat: With Reference to Human Beings. 5th ed. 2007. pap. 12.95 (978-1-4288-1880-4(4)) Cram101 Inc.

Wood, Michael G. Laboratory Manual for Anatomy & Physiology, Cat Version. 4th ed. 2009. (ENG.). 888p. (C). spiral bd. 114.73 (978-0-321-57180-9(0)) Benjamin-Cummings Publishing Co.

—Laboratory Manual for Anatomy & Physiology, Main Version. 4th ed. 2009. (ENG., Illus.). 792p. (C). spiral bd. 114.73 (978-0-321-57227-1(0)) Benjamin-Cummings Publishing Co.

CATS—ANECDOTES

Aadland, Tippy. Tippy the Boat Cat. 2009. 41p. pap. 19.50 (978-0-557-04497-9(9)) Lulu Enterprises Inc.

Adlon, Jeanne & Logan, Susan. Cat Calls: Wonderful Stories & Practical Advice from a Veteran Cat Sitter. 2011. (ENG., Illus.). 160p. pap. 14.95 (978-0-7570-0344-8(3)) Square One Pubs.

Anderson, Niki. Whiskers, Wit, & Wisdom: True Cat Tales & the Lessons They Teach. 2009. (ENG., Illus.). 192p. 15.99 (978-1-4165-9068-2(4), Howard Bks.) Howard Books.

Becker, Marty & Spadafori, Gina. Meowwow! Curiously Compelling Facts, True Tales, & Trivia Even Your Cat Won't Know. 2007. (ENG., Illus.). 224p. pap. 14.95 (978-0-7573-0622-8(5)) Health Communications, Inc.

Bicket, Tammy L., et al. Hugs for Cat Lovers: Stories, Sayings, & Scriptures to Encourage & Inspire. 2008. (Hugs Ser.). (ENG., Illus.). 128p. 11.99 (978-1-4165-5705-0(9), Howard Bks.) Howard Books.

Brown, Helen. Cleo: The Cat Who Mended a Family. 2010. (ENG.). 272p. pap. 15.95 (978-0-8065-3303-2(X), Citadel Pr.) Kensington Publishing Corp.

Canfield, Jack, et al. Chicken Soup for the Soul: My Cat's Life: 101 Stories about All the Ages & Stages of Our Feline Family Members. 2011. (ENG.). 400p. pap. 14.95 (978-1-935096-66-5(4)) Chicken Soup for the Soul Publishing, LLC.

Canfield, Jack L., et al. What I Learned from the Cat: 101 Stories about Life, Love & Lessons. 2009. (Chicken Soup for the Soul Ser.). (ENG.). 400p. pap. 14.95 (978-1-935096-37-5(0)) Chicken Soup for the Soul Publishing, LLC.

Carli, Joseph Charles. Twenty-Eight Paws Before Me. 2009. 56p. pap. 17.26 (978-1-4269-1123-1(8)) Trafford Publishing.

Catscapades: True Cat Tales. 2010. (Illus.). 136p. pap. 12.95 (978-0-9773576-6-6(X)) Matilija Pr.

Chemerka, William R. C.C. & the Alamo Cats. 2012. (978-0-9819904-2-2(8)) Bright Sky Pr.

Clark, Carol. My Name Is Missy. 2011. 32p. pap. 12.80 (978-1-4567-4620-9(0)) AuthorHouse.

Danielle, Anna, illus. Give a Cat a Home: True Tales of Courage & Survival. 2008. (ENG.). 96p. 13.95 (978-1-906388-20-1(2)) National Trust, Aylesbury GBR. Dist: Independent Pubs. Group.

Day, Christopher. Natural Cat Care. 2010. (ENG., Illus.). 96p. 9.95 (978-1-60710-097-3(5), Thunder Bay Pr.) Advantage Pubs. Group.

Dodman, Nicholas H. If Only They Could Speak: Understanding the Powerful Bond Between Dogs & Their Owners. 2008. (ENG., Illus.). 288p. pap. 15.95 (978-0-393-33424-1(4), 33424) Norton, W. W. & Co., Inc.

Feeney, Rik. Kitten Lover's Journal. 2008. 108p. pap. 19.95 (978-0-9637991-5-9(0)) Richardson Publishing, Inc.

Gill, Robin D. The Cat Who Thought Too Much - an Essay into Felinity. 2010. 312p. pap. 25.00 (978-0-9840923-2-1(3)) Paraverse Pr.

Hales, Steven D., ed. What Philosophy Can Tell You about Your Cat. 2008. (ENG., Illus.). 288p. pap. 14.95 (978-0-8126-9652-3(2)) Open Court Publishing Co.

A Happy Ending for Rescued Cats. 2008. pap. 19.95 (978-3-8327-9279-4(1)) teNeues Publishing Co.

Hertweck, E. Romayne. Bob the Preschool Cat: A Biography of an Urban Manx Cat. 2009. 73p. pap. 12.95 (978-1-4327-3555-5(1)) Outskirts Pr., Inc.

Hickman, B. Jo. Boo Finds a Home. 2011. 24p. pap. 15.99 (978-1-4653-3612-5(5)) Xlibris Corp.

Hite, Barbara Allan. Letters from Jane: The Adventures of an Abandoned Kitten. 2011. 280p. pap. 14.50 (978-1-4269-4884-8(0)) Trafford Publishing.

Holland, Barbara. Secrets of the Cat: Its Lore, Legend, & Lives. 2010. (ENG.). 228p. pap. 13.99 (978-0-06-197804-3(3), William Morrow Paperbacks) HarperCollins Pubs.

Iness, Camille. Pongo, the Brave River Cat Pongo, el Gato Valiente Del Río: A True Story una Historia Verdadera. 2011. 32p. pap. 15.39 (978-1-4634-3657-5(2)) AuthorHouse.

Jackson, Julie. Glamourpuss: The Enchanting World of Kitty Wigs. 2009. (ENG., Illus.). 96p. 14.95 (978-0-8118-6704-7(8)) Chronicle Bks. LLC.

Jones, Liz. Fur Babies: Why We Love Cats. 2008. (ENG., Illus.). 1p. pap. 14.95 *(978-1-84400-583-3(6))* Quadrille Publishing, Ltd. GBR. Dist: Ingram Pub. Services.

Korda, Michael & Korda, Margaret. Cat People. 2006. (Illus.). 176p. per. 12.95 *(978-0-06-075664-2(0),* HarperPerennial) HarperCollins Pubs.

Lantzy, Chloe. Cat Eyes: True Stories of Eleven Rescued Cats. 2011. pap. 11.99 ***(978-1-61346-360-4(X))*** Tate Publishing & Enterprises, LLC.

Leigh, Diane & Geyer, Marilee. One at a Time: A Week in an American Animal Shelter. 2007. (ENG., Illus.). 146p. pap. 16.95 *(978-0-9728387-0-2(8))* No Voice Unheard.

Lessing, Doris. On Cats. 2008. (ENG.). 256p. 14.95 *(978-0-06-167224-8(6))* HarperCollins Pubs.

Lombardi, Gail. Shadow & Friends. 2009. 52p. pap. 17.00 *(978-1-60860-554-5(X),* Strategic Bk. Publishing) AEG Literary Publishing Services, Inc.

Longden, Deric. Enough to Make a Cat Laugh. 2008. (ENG.). 288p. pap. 16.95 *(978-0-552-15620-2(5))* Transworld Publishers Ltd. GBR. Dist: Independent Pubs. Group.

MacMillan, Brigitta. The Cat Who Sang & Other Stories of Rescued Animals. 2009. *(978-0-9813528-0-0(4))* Insomniac Pr.

Meikle, Kathleen Walker. Medieval Cats. 2011. (Illus.). 89p. 14.95 *(978-0-7123-5818-7(8))* British Library, The GBR. Dist: Chicago Distribution Ctr.

Moore, Patrick. Miaow! Cats Really Are Nicer Than People. 2012. (ENG., Illus.). 64p. pap. 14.95 ***(978-1-84584-435-6(1),*** 1845844351, Hubble & Hattie) Veloce Publishing Ltd. GBR. Dist: MBI Distribution Services/Quayside Distribution.

Mouallem, Omar. Amazing Cats: Stories About... 2008. (ENG., Illus.). 272p. pap. *(978-1-894864-73-2(5))* Folklore Publishing CAN. Dist: Lone Pine Publishing.

Myron, Vicki. Dewey's Nine Lives: The Legacy of the Small-Town Library Cat Who Inspired Millions. 2010. (ENG.). 320p. (gr. 12). 19.95 *(978-0-525-95186-5(5),* Dutton Adult) Penguin Group (USA) Inc.

—Dewey's Nine Lives: The Legacy of the Small-Town Library Cat Who Inspired Millions. lt. ed. 2010. 32.99 *(978-1-4104-2875-2(3))* Thorndike Pr.

Myron, Vicki & Witter, Bret. Dewey's Nine Lives: The Legacy of the Small-Town Library Cat Who Inspired Millions. 2011. (ENG.). 320p. (gr. 12). 15.00 *(978-0-451-23466-7(9),* N A L Trade) Penguin Group (USA) Inc.

—Dewey's Nine Lives: The Legacy of the Small-Town Library Cat Who Inspired Millions. lt. ed. 2011. (ENG.). 488p. pap. 17.99 *(978-1-59413-472-2(3),* Large Print Pr.) Thorndike Pr.

Nash, Audrey. My Second-Hand Cats. 2008. (Illus.). 144p. pap. 11.99 *(978-1-4389-1400-8(8))* AuthorHouse.

Nevin, Jean. My Name is Amber. 2011. (Illus.). 32p. pap. 7.50 ***(978-0-9828961-2-9(3))*** Dryad Studio.

Newsome, James. Tabby Tails: Adventures of Alvin O' Malley. 2009. 102p. pap. 16.65 *(978-0-557-06557-8(7))* Lulu Enterprises Inc.

O'Connor, Denis. Paw Prints in the Moonlight: The Heartwarming True Story of One Man & his Cat. 2012. (ENG., Illus.). 256p. 19.99 ***(978-0-312-66829-7(5),*** Dunne, Thomas Bks.) St. Martin's Pr.

O'Mara, Lesley. Cats Miscellany: Everything You Always Wanted to Know about Our Feline Friends. 2011. (Books of Miscellany Ser.). (ENG., Illus.). 192p. 14.95 *(978-1-61608-356-4(5),* 608356) Skyhorse Publishing Co., Inc.

Poe, Don. Samson's Rock. 2009. 56p. pap. 9.99 *(978-1-935361-21-3(X))* Comfort Publishing Services, LLC.

Poltamees, Welleran, compiled by. Hooray for Cats. 2009. (Hooray! Ser.). (ENG., Illus.). 68p. pap. 15.95 *(978-1-59583-357-0(9))* Laughing Elephant.

Rainbolt, Dusty. Ghost Cats: Human Encounters with Feline Spirits. 2007. (ENG., Illus.). 224p. per. 14.95 *(978-1-59921-004-9(5),* Lyons Pr.) Globe Pequot Pr., The.

Romp, Julia. The Cat Who Came Back for Christmas: How a Cat Brought a Family the Gift of Love. 2012. (ENG.). 288p. (gr. 12). pap. 15.00 ***(978-0-452-29878-1(4),*** Plume) Penguin Group (USA) Inc.

Ross, Marvin. The Original Reigning Cats & Dogs: A Lighthearted Look at Pets & Their Owners. 2009. 112p. pap. 12.95 *(978-0-9810037-6-4(1))* Bridgeross Communications Inc. CAN. Dist: AtlasBooks Distribution.

Rude, Bob And Kathy. The Best Little Cat House in Maryland: The True & Mostly Accurate Story of How Rude Ranch Animal Rescue Came to Be. 2009. 256p. 24.99 *(978-1-4490-0884-0(4));* pap. 14.95 *(978-1-4490-0883-3(6))* AuthorHouse.

Russell, Michelle. Sabrina: The Autobiography of A Cat. 2008. (ENG., Illus.). 179p. per. 14.99 *(978-0-9800542-0-9(1))* Catsong Publishing.

Sacco, Nick L. In Heaven Kittens Play: The Blue Angel & Her Garden of Pets. 2010. (ENG., Illus.). 118p. pap. *(978-1-926918-15-0(0),* CCB Publishing) CCB Publishing.

Sargeant. The Artist Proposes: An inner Revolution. 2011. 100p. pap. 51.99 ***(978-1-4568-8134-4(5))*** Xlibris Corp.

Schaffer, Clair. Cats in the Parsonage: Book 1. 2009. 192p. pap. 13.99 *(978-1-58169-324-9(9),* Evergreen Pr.) Genesis Communications, Inc.

Sloan, Henry Hall. Meow about: the Carolina's Coast: A Cat's View for Travelers. 2009. pap. *(978-1-61584-477-7(5))* Independent Pub.

Smith, Janet Ellen. Butch the Gentle Giant, 1 vol. 2009. 83p. pap. 16.95 *(978-1-60836-466-4(6))* PublishAmerica, Inc.

Steadman, Ralph. The Ralph Steadman Book of Cats. 2012. (ENG., Illus.). 96p. 24.00 ***(978-0-547-59400-2(3))*** Houghton Mifflin Harcourt Trade & Reference Pubs.

Steiger, Brad & Steiger, Sherry Hansen. Cat Miracles: Inspirational True Stories of Remarkable Felines. 2008. (ENG.). 272p. pap. 12.95 *(978-1-60550-016-4(X))* Adams Media Corp.

Sutherland Millmann, Anita. Checky the Feral Cat. 2009. 32p. pap. 12.99 *(978-1-4389-5719-7(X))* AuthorHouse.

Tarte, Bob. Kitty Cornered: How Frannie & Five Other Incorrigible Cats Seized Control of Our House & Made It Their Home. 2012. (ENG.). 304p. pap. 13.95 ***(978-1-56512-999-3(7),*** 1565129997) Algonquin Bks. of Chapel Hill.

Tovey, Doreen. A Comfort of Cats. 2008. (ENG.). 192p. pap. 12.95 ***(978-1-84024-655-1(3))*** Summersdale Pubs. GBR. Dist: Independent Pubs. Group.

—Donkey Work. 2009. (ENG.). 160p. pap. 12.95 ***(978-1-84024-719-0(3))*** Summersdale Pubs. GBR. Dist: Independent Pubs. Group.

Tweedy, Bonnie. Grandma Bonnie's Cats: A Sad Time. 2009. 24p. pap. 12.98 *(978-1-4389-6740-0(3))* AuthorHouse.

What Now Mama? or Feral Cat Goes Domestic. 7.95 *(978-0-9785446-0-7(9))* Hedwig Pr.

Ziolkowska-Boehm, Aleksandra. On the Road with Suzy: From Cat to Companion. 2010. (ENG.). 180p. pap. 16.95 *(978-1-55753-554-2(X))* Purdue Univ. Pr.

CATS—BEHAVIOR

Animal, Rescue L. Animal Rescue League for Love of Cats. 2011. 128p. pap. 21.95 ***(978-1-935726-13-5(7))*** Landauer Publishing, LLC.

Appleby, David, ed. The Apbc Book of Companion Animal Behaviour. 2nd ed. 2011. (ENG., Illus.). 320p. pap. 24.95 *(978-0-285-63887-7(4))* Souvenir Pr. Ltd. GBR. Dist: Independent Pubs. Group.

Becker, Marty. Your Cat: The Owner's Manual - Hundreds of Secrets, Surprises, & Solutions for Raising a Happy, Healthy Cat. 2012. (ENG., Illus.). 320p. 25.99 ***(978-0-446-57136-4(9))*** Grand Central Publishing.

Becker, Marty & Spadafori, Gina. Why Do Cats Always Land on Their Feet? 101 of the Most Perplexing Questions Answered about Feline Unfathomables, Medical Mysteries & Befuddling Behaviors. 2006. (ENG.). 224p. pap. 12.95 *(978-0-7573-0573-3(3))* Health Communications, Inc.

Berger, Roman. Und Katzen Sprechen Doch. (GER.). *(978-3-612-20635-0(4))* Econ-Verlag GmbH DEU. Dist: International Bk. Import Service, Inc.

Bonham, Margaret H. The Cat Owner's Problem Solver: How to Manage Common Behavior Problems by Thinking Like Your Cat, 1 vol. 2008. (ENG., Illus.). 176p. pap. 15.95 *(978-0-7938-0650-8(X))* TFH Pubns., Inc.

Bonham, Margaret H. & Coile, D. Caroline. Why Do Cats Bury Their Poop? More Than 200 Feline Facts, Fallacies, & Foibles Revealed. 2008. (ENG., Illus.). 160p. pap. 12.95 *(978-1-4027-5040-3(4))* Sterling Publishing Co., Inc.

Bower, John & Bower, Caroline. The Cat Owner's Veterinary. 2010. (ENG., Illus.). 192p. instr.'s hndbk. ed. 44.95 *(978-1-84797-128-9(8))* Crowood Pr., Ltd. GBR. Dist: Independent Pubs. Group.

Braun, Martina. Chat to Your Cat: Lessons in Cat Conversation. 2009. (ENG.). 80p. pap. 19.95 *(978-3-86127-966-2(5))* Cadmos Verlag GmbH DEU. Dist: Independent Pubs. Group.

Burton, Jane & Warren Photographic, photos by. A Cat's Life. 2008. (ENG., Illus.). 208p. 35.00 *(978-88-544-0392-5(X))* White Star ITA. Dist: Random Hse., Inc.

Dodman, Nicholas H. If Only They Could Speak: Understanding the Powerful Bond Between Dogs & Their Owners. 2008. (ENG., Illus.). 288p. pap. 15.95 *(978-0-393-33424-1(4),* 33424) Norton, W. W. & Co., Inc.

Fox, Michael W. Cat Body, Cat Mind: Exploring Your Cat's Consciousness & Total Well-Being. 2007. (ENG., Illus.). 256p. 24.95 *(978-1-59921-062-9(2),* Lyons Pr.) Globe Pequot Pr., The.

Halls, Vicky. The Secret Life of Your Cat: Unlock the Mysteries of Your Pet's Behavior. 2010. (ENG., Illus.). 208p. pap. 19.95 *(978-1-55407-735-9(4))* Firefly Bks., Ltd.

A Happy Ending for Rescued Cats. 2008. pap. 19.95 *(978-3-8327-9279-4(1))* teNeues Publishing Co.

Horwitz, Debra & Mills, Daniel S., eds. BSAVA Manual of Canine & Feline Behavioural Medicine. 2nd ed. 2010. (BSAVA British Small Animal Veterinary Association Ser.). (ENG., Illus.). 336p. pap. 132.99 *(978-1-905319-15-2(0))* British Small Animal Veterinary Assn. (BSAVA) GBR. Dist: Wiley, John & Sons, Inc.

How to Raise Your New Puppy in a Cat Family: The Complete Guide to a Happy Pet-Filled Home. 2011. (ENG.). pap. 24.95 *(978-1-60138-401-0(7))* Atlantic Publishing Co.

Janik, Carolyn. Smart Guide to Understanding Your Cat. 2012. (Smart Guide Ser.). (ENG.). 272p. pap. 18.95 ***(978-0-9834421-8-9(5))*** Smart Guide Pubns., Inc.

Johnson-Bennett, Pam. Psycho Kitty: Tips for Solving Your Cat's Crazy Behavior. 2nd rev. ed. 2008. (ENG., Illus.). 128p. pap. 12.95 *(978-1-58761-323-4(9),* Celestial Arts) Ten Speed Pr.

—Starting from Scratch: How to Correct Behavior Problems in Your Adult Cat. 2007. (ENG., Illus.). 400p. (gr. 12-18). 15.00 *(978-0-14-311250-1(3),* Penguin (Non-Classics)) Penguin Group (USA) Inc.

—Think Like a Cat: How to Raise a Well-Adjusted Cat — Not a Sour Puss. rev. ed. 2011. (ENG.). 432p. (gr. 12). 18.00 *(978-0-14-311979-1(6),* Penguin (Non-Classics)) Penguin Group (USA) Inc.

Martyn, Elizabeth. Everything Cats Expect You to Know. 2008. 256p. 17.95 *(978-1-56148-625-0(6))* Good Bks.

Moore, Arden. The Cat Behavior Answer Book: Practical Insights & Proven Solutions for Your Feline Questions. 2007. (ENG., Illus.). 336p. pap. 14.95 *(978-1-58017-674-3(7),* 1580176747) Storey Publishing, LLC.

—A Cat Health & Behavior Guide. 2009. pap. *(978-1-61584-054-0(0))* Independent Pub.

Moustaki, Nikki. Boredom Busters for Cats: 40 Whisker-Twitching Games & Adventures. 2010. (ENG.). 64p. (gr. 6). pap. 6.95 *(978-1-935484-18-9(4))* BowTie Pr.

Nagelschneider, Mieshelle. The Cat Whisperer: Why Cats Do What They Do — and How to Get Them to Do What You Want. 2013. (ENG., Illus.). 336p. 25.00 *(978-0-553-80735-1(4))* Random House Publishing Group.

Okujava, V. M. & Natishvili, T. A., eds. Cognitive Visual Memory in Cats. 2010. (Animal Science, Issues & Professions Ser.). 60p. pap. 43.00 *(978-1-61668-293-4(0))* Nova Science Pubs., Inc.

Patterson, Gary, illus. Cat Laughs. 2010. 64p. 9.99 *(978-0-7369-2657-7(7))* Harvest Hse. Pubs.

Popovich, Gregory. You Can Train Your Cat: Secrets of a Master Cat Trainer. 2009. (ENG., Illus.). 240p. pap. 14.99 *(978-0-312-56528-2(3),* St. Martin's Griffin) St. Martin's Pr.

Rakover, Sam S. To Understand a Cat: Methodology & Philosophy. 2007. (Illus.). xvii, 253p. (C). 126.00 *(978-90-272-5206-7(8))* Benjamins, John Publishing Co.

Rauth-Widmann, Brigitte. Cat Speak: Recognising & Understanding Behaviour. 2012. (ENG., Illus.). 80p. pap. 19.95 *(978-1-84584-385-4(1),* 1845843851, Hubble & Hattie) Veloce Publishing Ltd. GBR. Dist: MBI Distribution Services/Quayside Distribution.

Riccommini, Francesca. Cat Care Essentials: Hamlyn All Color. 2010. (ENG., Illus.). 208p. pap. 9.99 *(978-0-600-62092-1(1),* Hamlyn) Octopus Publishing Group GBR. Dist: Hachette Bk. Group.

Salmon, France. Psycho Sella the Kitten. 2010. 20p. 13.77 *(978-1-4269-4926-5(X))* Trafford Publishing.

Seidl, Denise. Fun & Games for Cats! 2011. (ENG., Illus.). 128p. pap. 29.95 *(978-1-84584-387-8(8),* 1845843878, Hubble & Hattie) Veloce Publishing Ltd. GBR. Dist: MBI Distribution Services/Quayside Distribution.

Silver, Burton & Busch, Heather. Why Cats Paint: The Ethics of Feline Aesthetics. 2006. (ENG., Illus.). 144p. 9.95 *(978-1-58008-793-3(0))* Ten Speed Pr.

Surovec, Yasmine. Cat Versus Human. 2011. (ENG.). 152p. pap. 9.99 *(978-1-4494-0865-7(6))* Andrews McMeel Publishing.

Tabor, Roger. Understanding Cats. (Illus.). 144p. pap. *(978-0-7153-0847-9(5))* David & Charles Pubs. GBR. Dist: David & Charles Pubs.

Tarte, Bob. Kitty Cornered: How Frannie & Five Other Incorrigible Cats Seized Control of Our House & Made It Their Home. 2012. (ENG.). 304p. pap. 13.95 ***(978-1-56512-999-3(7),*** 1565129997) Algonquin Bks. of Chapel Hill.

Taylor, David A. The Secret Life of Kittens. 2008. (ENG., Illus.). 72p. 9.95 *(978-0-00-726360-8(0))* HarperCollins Pubs. Ltd. GBR. Dist: Independent Pubs. Group.

Thornton, Kim Campbell. Why Do Cats Do That? Real Answers to the Curious Things Cats Do. 2010. 64p. pap. 6.95 *(978-1-933958-85-9(5))* BowTie Pr.

White, Linda M. First Steps with Puppies & Kittens: A Practice-Team Approach to Behavior. 2009. (ENG.). pap. 84.95 *(978-1-58326-101-9(X),* AAHA Pr.) American Animal Hospital Assn. Pr.

CATS—BREEDING

Barbazon, B. S. Justice for Cats: Caring for Your Cat & Starting a Shelter. 2008. 252p. 30.95 *(978-0-595-51227-0(5));* pap. 19.95 *(978-0-595-52480-8(X))* iUniverse, Inc.

Caney, Sarah. Caring for a Cat with Kidney Failure. 2008. (Illus.). 60p. pap. 35.95 *(978-0-9556913-0-0(3))* Cat Professional Ltd. GBR. Dist: Lulu Enterprises Inc.

Eilert-Overbeck, Brigitte. Kittens. 2008. (Complete Pet Owner's Manual Ser.). (ENG., Illus.). 64p. pap. 8.99 *(978-0-7641-3962-8(2))* Barron's Educational Series, Inc.

Kimmy. The Kimmy Diaries. 2008. (Illus.). 144p. pap. *(978-0-7552-0436-6(0))* Authors OnLine, Ltd.

Milne, Emma. Truth about Cats & Dogs. 2008. (Illus.). 216p. 33.95 *(978-1-84624-137-6(5))* Book Guild, Ltd. GBR. Dist: Trans-Atlantic Pubns., Inc.

Tobias, Phyllis. The Personal Maine Coon. 2009. 80p. pap. 24.50 *(978-1-60860-915-4(4),* Eloquent Bks.) AEG Literary Publishing Services, Inc.

Vasan, Gandee & PQ Blackwell ,Ltd. Staff. Cat Capers: Catitude for Cat Lovers. 2008. (ENG., Illus.). 160p. 24.99 *(978-0-7407-7800-1(5))* Andrews McMeel Publishing.

Vella, Carolyn & McGonagle, John. Breeding Pedigreed Cats. 2nd ed. 2006. spiral bd. 20.00 net. *(978-0-9789564-0-0(0))* Pegasus Prodns.

CATS—BREEDS

see Cat Breeds

CATS—DISEASES

American Red Cross Staff, contrib. by. Cat First Aid. 2008. (Illus.). ix, 116p. *(978-1-58480-402-4(5))* StayWell Co., The.

Australian Women's Weekly Staff, contrib. by. Caring for Dogs & Cats: With a Vet's Guide to Common Complaints. (Illus.). 128p. pap. 12.95 *(978-1-86396-201-8(8))* ACP Publishing Pty, Ltd. AUS. Dist: Graphic Arts Ctr. Publishing Co.

Barr, Frances J. & Kirberger, Robert M. BSAVA Manual of Canine & Feline Musculoskeletal Imaging. 2006. (BSAVA British Small Animal Veterinary Association Ser.). (ENG., Illus.). 294p. pap. 141.99 *(978-0-905214-86-3(2))* British Small Animal Veterinary Assn. (BSAVA) GBR. Dist: Wiley, John & Sons, Inc.

Barr, Frances J. & O'Brien, Robert, eds. BSAVA Manual of Canine & Feline Abdominal Imaging. 2009. (BSAVA British Small Animal Veterinary Association Ser.). (ENG., Illus.). 250p. pap. 157.99 *(978-1-905319-10-7(X))* British Small Animal Veterinary Assn. (BSAVA) GBR. Dist: Wiley, John & Sons, Inc.

Barr, Stephen C. & Bowman, Dwight D., eds. Blackwell′S Five-Minute Veterinary Consult Clinical Companion: Canine & Feline Infectious Diseases & Parasitology. 2nd ed. 2011. (Blackwell's Five-Minute Veterinary Consult Ser.). (ENG., Illus.). 656p. pap. 99.99 ***(978-0-8138-2012-5(X),*** Wiley-Blackwell) Wiley, John & Sons, Inc.

Battaglia, Andrea M. Small Animal Emergency & Critical Care for Veterinary Technicians. 2nd rev. ed. 2007. (ENG., Illus.). 448p. (C). per. 50.95 *(978-1-4160-2804-8(8),* Saunders) Elsevier - Health Sciences Div.

Bellows, Jan. Feline Dentistry: Oral Assessment, Treatment, & Preventative Care. 2010. (ENG., Illus.). 328p. 110.99 *(978-0-8138-1613-5(0),* Wiley-Blackwell) Wiley, John & Sons, Inc.

Boag, Amanda & King, Lesley G., eds. BSAVA Manual of Canine & Feline Emergency & Critical Care. 2nd rev. ed. 2007. (BSAVA British Small Animal Veterinary Association Ser.). (ENG.). 384p. pap. 178.99 *(978-0-905214-99-3(4))* British Small Animal Veterinary Assn. (BSAVA) GBR. Dist: Wiley, John & Sons, Inc.

Bower, John & Bower, Caroline. The Cat Owner's Veterinary. 2010. (ENG., Illus.). 192p. instr.'s hndbk. ed. 44.95 *(978-1-84797-128-9(8))* Crowood Pr., Ltd. GBR. Dist: Independent Pubs. Group.

Brearley, Malcom J. Decision Making in Small Animal Oncology. Argyle, David J. & Turek, Michelle M., eds. 2008. (ENG., Illus.). 392p. pap. 82.99 *(978-0-8138-2275-4(0),* Wiley-Blackwell) Wiley, John & Sons, Inc.

Brown, Andi. The Whole Pet Diet: Eight Weeks to Great Health for Dogs & Cats. 2006. (ENG.). 240p. pap. 16.99 *(978-1-58761-271-8(2),* Celestial Arts) Ten Speed Pr.

Caney, Sarah. Caring for a Cat with Kidney Failure. 2008. (Illus.). 60p. pap. 35.95 *(978-0-9556913-0-0(3))* Cat Professional Ltd. GBR. Dist: Lulu Enterprises Inc.

Cannon, Martha. Feline Medicine: A Practical Guide for Veterinary Nurses & Technicians. Hifte, Myra Forster-Van, ed. 2006. (ENG., Illus.). 256p. pap. 63.95 *(978-0-7506-8827-7(0),* Butterworth-Heinemann) Elsevier - Health Sciences Div.

Carlson, Delbert G., et al. Cat Owner's Home Veterinary Handbook. Adelman, Beth, ed. 3rd rev. ed. 2007. (ENG., Illus.). 656p. 34.99 *(978-0-470-09530-0(X),* Howell Bk. Hse.) Wiley, John & Sons, Inc.

Case, Linda P., et al. Canine & Feline Nutrition: A Resource for Companion Animal Professionals. 3rd ed. 2010. (ENG., Illus.). 576p. pap. 76.95 *(978-0-323-06619-8(4),* Mosby) Elsevier - Health Sciences Div.

Chandler, E. A., et al. Feline Medicine & Therapeutics. 3rd rev. ed. 2007. (ENG., Illus.). 904p. pap. 120.99 *(978-1-4051-5059-0(9),* Wiley-Blackwell) Wiley, John & Sons, Inc.

Chandler, Marjorie. Small Animal Gastroenterology. 2011. (ENG., Illus.). 256p. pap. 89.95 *(978-0-7020-2910-3(6),* Saunders) Elsevier - Health Sciences Div.

Coscia, Jennifer A. The Holistic Cat: A Complete Guide to Wellness for a Healthier, Happier Cat. 2009. (ENG., Illus.). 216p. pap. 16.95 *(978-1-55643-766-3(8))* North Atlantic Bks.

Côté, Etienne. Clinical Veterinary Advisor: Dogs & Cats. 2nd ed. 2010. (ENG., Illus.). 1784p. 99.95 *(978-0-323-06864-2(2),* Mosby) Elsevier - Health Sciences Div.

Côté, Etienne, et al. Feline Cardiology. 2011. (ENG., Illus.). 516p. 149.99 *(978-0-8138-1242-7(9),* Wiley-Blackwell) Wiley, John & Sons, Inc.

Cowell, Rick L., et al. Diagnostic Cytology & Hematology of the Dog & Cat. 3rd rev. ed. 2007. (ENG., Illus.). 496p. 138.00 *(978-0-323-03422-7(5),* Mosby) Elsevier - Health Sciences Div.

Cram101 Textbook Reviews & Cram101 Textbook Reviews. Outlines & Highlights for Common Diseases of Companion Animals by Alleice Summers. 2011. 240p. pap. 31.95 ***(978-1-61830-859-7(9))*** Cram101 Inc.

Crow, Steven E., et al. Manual of Clinical Procedures in Dogs, Cats, Rabbits & Rodents. 3rd ed. 2009. (ENG., Illus.). 408p. pap. 66.99 *(978-0-8138-1304-2(2),* Wiley-Blackwell) Wiley, John & Sons, Inc.

Deeprose, Judith, ed. BSAVA Manual of Canine & Feline Dentistry. 3rd rev. ed. 2007. (BSAVA British Small Animal Veterinary Association Ser.). (ENG., Illus.). 200p. pap. 157.99 *(978-0-905214-87-0(0))* British Small Animal Veterinary Assn. (BSAVA) GBR. Dist: Wiley, John & Sons, Inc.

Dewey, Curtis W., ed. A Practical Guide to Canine & Feline Neurology. 2nd ed. 2008. (ENG., Illus.). 720p. 167.99 *(978-0-8138-1672-2(6),* Wiley-Blackwell) Wiley, John & Sons, Inc.

DiBartola, Stephen P. Fluid, Electrolyte, & Acid-Base Disorders in Small Animal Practice. 4th ed. 2011. (ENG., Illus.). 1520p. 115.00 *(978-1-4377-0654-3(1),* Saunders) Elsevier - Health Sciences Div.

Elliott, Jonathan & Grauer, Gregory F., eds. BSAVA Manual of Canine & Feline Nephrology & Urology. 2nd rev. ed. 2007. (BSAVA British Small Animal Veterinary Association Ser.: 1). (ENG., Illus.). 312p. pap. 157.99 *(978-0-905214-93-1(5))* British Small Animal Veterinary Assn. (BSAVA) GBR. Dist: Wiley, John & Sons, Inc.

Ettinger, Stephen J. & Feldman, Edward C. Textbook of Veterinary Internal Medicine, 2 vols., Set. 7th ed. 2009. (ENG., Illus.). 2208p. (C). 289.00 *(978-1-4160-6593-7(8),* Saunders) Elsevier - Health Sciences Div.

Fairchild, L. H. & Fairchild, Helen. Cats & All about Them. 2007. (ENG.). 242p. 41.95 *(978-0-548-05918-0(7))* Kessinger Publishing, LLC.

Fuentes, Virginia Luis, et al, eds. Canine & Feline Cardiorespiratory Medicine. 2nd ed. 2010. (ENG., Illus.). 328p. pap. 157.99 *(978-1-905319-12-1(6))* British Small Animal Veterinary Assn. (BSAVA) GBR. Dist: Wiley, John & Sons, Inc.

Gaschen, Frederic. Chronic Intestinal Diseases of Dogs & Cats, an Issue of Veterinary Clinics: Small Animal Practice. 2011. (Clinics: Veterinary Medicine Ser.: 41-2). (ENG., Illus.). 232p. 84.00 (978-1-4557-0682-2(5), Saunders) Elsevier - Health Sciences Div.

Gaschen, Lorrie & Barr, Frances J., eds. BSAVA Manual of Canine & Feline Ultrasonography. 2011. (BSAVA British Small Animal Veterinary Association Ser.). (ENG., Illus.). 232p. pap. 107.99 (978-1-905319-30-5(4)) British Small Animal Veterinary Assn. (BSAVA) GBR. Dist: Wiley, John & Sons, Inc.

Gough, Alex & Thomas, Alison. Breed Predispositions to Disease in Dogs & Cats. 2nd ed. 2010. (ENG., Illus.). 352p. pap. 72.99 (978-1-4051-8078-8(1), Wiley-Blackwell) Wiley, John & Sons, Inc.

Greene, Craig E. Infectious Diseases of the Dog & Cat. 4th ed. 2011. (ENG., Illus.). 1376p. (C). 169.00 (978-1-4160-6130-4(4), Saunders) Elsevier - Health Sciences Div.

Hamilton, Don. Homeopathic Care for Cats & Dogs, Revised Edition: Small Doses for Small Animals. 2010. (ENG., Illus.). 624p. pap. 27.95 (978-1-55643-935-3(0)) North Atlantic Bks.

Harris, Viv. Natural Remedies Dogs & Cats Wish You Knew: A Holistic Care Guide. 2008. (ENG., Illus.). 272p. per. 14.95 (978-1-56975-637-9(6)) Ulysses Pr.

Hnilica, Keith A. Small Animal Dermatology: A Color Atlas & Therapeutic Guide. 3rd ed. 2010. (ENG., Illus.). 640p. (C). 129.00 (978-1-4160-5663-8(7), Saunders) Elsevier - Health Sciences Div.

Hodgkins, Elizabeth M. Your Cat: Simple New Secrets to a Longer, Stronger Life. 2008. (ENG., Illus.). 304p. pap. 16.95 (978-0-312-35802-0(4), St. Martin's Griffin) St. Martin's Pr.

Holt, Peter E. Urological Disorders of the Dog & Cat. 2012. (ENG., Illus.). 176p. pap. 49.95 (978-1-84076-176-4(8)) Manson Publishing, Ltd. GBR. Dist: Thieme Medical Pubs., Inc.

Holt, Peter E. Urological Disorders of the Dog & Cat: Investigation, Diagnosis & Treatment. 2008. (ENG., Illus.). 176p. 120.00 (978-1-84076-095-8(8)) Manson Publishing, Ltd. GBR. Dist: Thieme Medical Pubs., Inc.

Hunt, Christopher Thomas. My Life with the Scorpion Kitten. 2011. 220p. 24.99 (978-1-4567-9406-4(X)); pap. 15.99 (978-1-4567-9408-8(6)) AuthorHouse.

Jackson, Hilary & Marsella, Rosanna, eds. BSAVA Manual of Canine & Feline Dermatology. 3rd ed. 2012. (ENG.). 252p. pap. 137.99 (978-1-905319-27-5(4)) British Small Animal Veterinary Assn. (BSAVA) GBR. Dist: Wiley, John & Sons, Inc.

Johnson, Lynelle R. Clinical Canine & Feline Respiratory Medicine. 2010. (ENG., Illus.). 216p. pap. 99.99 (978-0-8138-1671-5(8), Wiley-Blackwell) Wiley, John & Sons, Inc.

Koch, Sandra N., et al. Canine & Feline Dermatology Drug Handbook. 2012. (ENG.). 464p. pap. 69.99 (978-1-4051-9896-7(6), Wiley-Blackwell) Wiley, John & Sons, Inc.

Kooistra, Hans S. & Rijnberk, Ad. Clinical Endocrinology of Dogs & Cats. 2nd ed. 2010. (ENG., Illus.). 338p. 195.00 (978-3-89993-058-0(4)) Schlutersche GmbH & Co. KG Verlag und Druckerei DEU. Dist: Thieme Medical Pubs., Inc.

Lascelles, Duncan & Dobson, Jane, eds. BSAVA Manual of Canine & Feline Oncology. 3rd ed. 2011. (ENG., Illus.). 376p. pap. 130.99 (978-1-905319-21-3(5)) British Small Animal Veterinary Assn. (BSAVA) GBR. Dist: Wiley, John & Sons, Inc.

Little, Susan. The Cat: Clinical Medicine & Management. 2011. (ENG., Illus.). 1424p. 189.00 (978-1-4377-0660-4(6), Saunders) Elsevier - Health Sciences Div.

Lorenz, Michael D., et al, eds. Small Animal Medical Diagnosis. 3rd ed. 2009. (ENG., Illus.). 504p. pap. 86.99 (978-0-8138-1338-7(7), Wiley-Blackwell) Wiley, John & Sons, Inc.

Matern, Christina. Acupuncture for Dogs & Cats: A Pocket Atlas. 2011. (ENG., Illus.). 384p. pap. 79.99 (978-3-13-154691-3(3)) Thieme Medical Pubs., Inc.

Merrill, Linda, ed. Small Animal Internal Medicine for Veterinary Technicians & Nurses. 2012. (ENG.). 608p. pap. 79.99 (978-0-8138-2164-1(9), Wiley-Blackwell) Wiley, John & Sons, Inc.

Messonnier, Shawn. Natural Health Bible for Dogs & Cats: Your A-Z Guide to over 200 Conditions, Herbs, Vitamins, & Supplements. 2008. (978-1-60529-947-1(2)) Rodale Pr., Inc.

—The Natural Vet's Guide to Preventing & Treating Arthritis in Dogs & Cats. 2nd ed. 2011. (ENG.). 240p. pap. 14.95 (978-1-57731-975-7(3)) New World Library.

Montavon, P. M., et al, eds. Feline Orthopedic Surgery & Musculoskeletal Disease. 2009. (ENG., Illus.). 582p. 149.00 (978-0-7020-2986-8(6), Saunders) Elsevier - Health Sciences Div.

Mooney, Carmel T. & Peterson, Mark, eds. BSAVA Manual of Canine & Feline Endocrinology. 4th ed. 2012. (ENG.). 252p. pap. 124.00 (978-1-905319-28-2(2)) British Small Animal Veterinary Assn. (BSAVA) GBR. Dist: Wiley, John & Sons, Inc.

Morgan, Joe P. & Wolvekamp, Pim. An Atlas of Radiology of the Traumatized Dog & Cat: The Case-Based Approach. 2nd rev. ed. 2010. (ENG., Illus.). 568p. 195.00 (978-3-89993-008-5(8)) Schlutersche GmbH & Co. KG Verlag und Druckerei DEU. Dist: Thieme Medical Pubs., Inc.

Morgan, Rhea V. Small Animal Practice Client Handouts. 2010. (ENG.). 512p. pap. 103.00 (978-1-4377-0850-9(1), Saunders) Elsevier - Health Sciences Div.

Nelson, Richard W. & Couto, C. Guillermo. Small Animal Internal Medicine. 4th ed. 2008. (ENG., Illus.). 1504p. 195.00 (978-0-323-04881-1(1), Mosby) Elsevier - Health Sciences Div.

Norsworthy, Gary D., et al, eds. The Feline Patient. 4th ed. 2010. (ENG., Illus.). 1072p. 146.99 (978-0-8138-1848-1(6), Wiley-Blackwell) Wiley, John & Sons, Inc.

North American Companion Animal Formulary, 7th Edition Revised. 2007. spiral bd. 50.00 (978-1-889750-91-0(3)) North American Compendiums, Inc.

Nuttall, Tim, et al. Skin Diseases of the Dog & Cat. 2nd ed. 2009. (ENG.). 384p. instr.'s hndbk. ed. 79.95 (978-1-84076-131-3(8)) Manson Publishing, Ltd. GBR. Dist: Thieme Medical Pubs., Inc.

Osborne, Carl A. & Lulich, Jody P. Changing Paradigms in Diagnosis & Treatment of Urolithiasis: Small Animal Practice. 2008. (Clinics: Veterinary Medicine Ser.: 39-1). (ENG.). 240p. 76.00 (978-1-4377-0560-7(X), Saunders) Elsevier - Health Sciences Div.

Patel, Anita & Forsythe, Peter J. Small Animal Dermatology. 2008. (Saunders Solutions in Veterinary Practice Ser.). (ENG., Illus.). 388p. pap. 89.95 (978-0-7020-2870-0(3), Saunders) Elsevier - Health Sciences Div.

Paterson, Sue. Manual of Skin Diseases of the Dog & Cat. 2nd rev. ed. 2008. (ENG., Illus.). 368p. pap. 115.99 (978-1-4051-6753-6(X), Wiley-Blackwell) Wiley, John & Sons, Inc.

Preston, Lisa. Natural Healing for Cats, Dogs, Horses, & Other Animals: 150 Alternative Therapies Available to Owners & Caregivers. 2012. (ENG., Illus.). 208p. pap. 14.95 (978-1-61608-461-5(8), 608461) Skyhorse Publishing Co., Inc.

Raskin, Rose E. & Meyer, Denny, eds. Canine & Feline Cytology: A Color Atlas & Interpretation Guide. 2nd ed. 2009. (ENG., Illus.). 472p. 129.00 (978-1-4160-4985-2(1), Saunders) Elsevier - Health Sciences Div.

Rhodes, Karen Helton & Werner, Alexander H., eds. Blackwell's Five-Minute Veterinary Consult Clinical Companion: Small Animal Dermatology. 2nd ed. 2011. (ENG., Illus.). 768p. pap. 99.99 (978-0-8138-1596-1(7), Wiley-Blackwell) Wiley, John & Sons, Inc.

Ridgway, Robert L. How to Treat Your Dogs & Cats with over-the-Counter Drugs. 2011. 168p. 25.95 (978-1-4502-9007-4(8)); pap. 15.95 (978-1-4502-9005-0(1)) iUniverse, Inc.

Rockett, Jody, et al. Patient Assessment, Intervention & Documentation for the Veterinary Technician: A Guide to Developing Care Plans & SOAP's. 2008. (Veterinary Technology Ser.). (ENG.). 368p. (C). spiral bd. 106.95 (978-1-4180-6749-6(0)) Delmar Cengage Learning.

Schaer, Michael, ed. Clinical Medicine of the Dog & Cat. 2nd ed. 2009. (ENG., Illus.). 760p. 150.00 (978-1-84076-111-5(3)) Manson Publishing, Ltd. GBR. Dist: Thieme Medical Pubs., Inc.

Schenck, Patricia. Home-Prepared Dog & Cat Diets. 2nd ed. 2010. (ENG.). 556p. pap. 54.99 (978-0-8138-0119-3(2), Wiley-Blackwell) Wiley, John & Sons, Inc.

Schmeltzer, Linda E. & Norsworthy, Gary D., eds. Nursing the Feline Patient. 2012. (ENG., Illus.). 240p. pap. 59.99 (978-0-470-95901-5(0), Wiley-Blackwell) Wiley, John & Sons, Inc.

Schultze, Kymythy R. Natural Nutrition for Cats: The Path to Purr-Fect Health. 2008. (ENG., Illus.). 160p. pap. 9.95 (978-1-4019-1072-3(6)) Hay Hse., Inc.

Scott, Martin J. & Mariani, Gael. Bach Flower Remedies for Cats. 2007. (ENG.). 156p. per. 15.95 (978-1-84409-112-6(0)) Findhorn Pr. GBR. Dist: Independent Pubs. Group.

Southam, Lenny & Roby, Kate. The Pill Book Guide to Medication for Your Dog & Cat. 2008. (ENG.). 624p. pap. 15.00 (978-0-553-38609-7(3)) Random House Publishing Group.

Strain, George M. Deafness in Dogs & Cats. 2011. (Illus.). 160p. 145.00 (978-1-84593-764-5(3)); pap. 70.00 (978-1-84593-937-3(9)) CABI GBR. Dist: Stylus Publishing, LLC.

Summers, Alleice. Common Diseases of Companion Animals. 2nd rev. ed. 2007. (ENG., Illus.). 800p. per. 55.95 (978-0-323-04740-1(8), Mosby) Elsevier - Health Sciences Div.

Tilley, Larry P. & Smith, Francis W. K., eds. Five-Minute Veterinary Consult: Canine & Feline. 5th ed. 2011. (Blackwell's Five-Minute Veterinary Consult Ser.: 1). (ENG., Illus.). 1600p. 99.99 (978-0-8138-0763-8(8), Wiley-Blackwell) Wiley, John & Sons, Inc.

Towell, Todd L., ed. Practical Weight Management in Dogs & Cats. 2011. (ENG., Illus.). 248p. pap. 59.99 (978-0-8138-0956-4(8), Wiley-Blackwell) Wiley, John & Sons, Inc.

Villalobos, Alice & Kaplan, Laurie. Canine & Feline Geriatric Oncology: Honoring the Human-Animal Bond. 2007. (ENG., Illus.). 381p. 104.99 (978-0-8138-0266-4(0), Wiley-Blackwell) Wiley, John & Sons, Inc.

Ware, Wendy A. Cardiovascular Disease in Small Animal Medicine. 2011. (ENG., Illus.). 240p. pap. 85.00 (978-1-84076-153-5(9)) Manson Publishing, Ltd. GBR. Dist: Thieme Medical Pubs., Inc.

Watson, Penny & Linley, Samantha, eds. BSAVA Manual of Canine & Feline Rehabilitation, Supportive & Palliative Care: Case Studies in Patient Management. 2011. (BSAVA British Small Animal Veterinary Association Ser.). (ENG., Illus.). 412p. pap. 130.00 (978-1-905319-20-6(7)) British Small Animal Veterinary Assn. (BSAVA) GBR. Dist: Wiley, John & Sons, Inc.

Willard, Michael D. & Tvedten, Harold. Small Animal Clinical Diagnosis by Laboratory Methods. 5th ed. 2011. (ENG., Illus.). 432p. pap. 83.95 (978-1-4377-0657-4(6), Saunders) Elsevier - Health Sciences Div.

Wolff, H. G. Homeopathy for Your Cat: Remedies for Common Feline Ailments. 2008. (ENG.). 136p. pap. 14.95 (978-1-55643-739-7(0)) North Atlantic Bks.

Yamall, Celeste & Hofve, Jean. The Complete Guide to Holistic Cat Care: An Illustrated Handbook. 2009. (ENG., Illus.). 192p. pap. 24.99 (978-1-59253-566-8(6), 1592535666) Quayside.

CATS—FOLKLORE

Potter, Paul B. Biography in Black: Potter Is Guilty! 2011. 104p. 39.95 (978-1-258-06849-3(4)) Literary Licensing, LLC.

CATS—FOOD

Barbazon, B. S. Justice for Cats: Caring for Your Cat & Starting a Shelter. 2008. 252p. 30.95 (978-0-595-51227-0(5)); pap. 19.95 (978-0-595-52480-8(X)) iUniverse, Inc.

Brown, Andi. The Whole Pet Diet: Eight Weeks to Great Health for Dogs & Cats. 2006. (ENG.). 240p. pap. 16.99 (978-1-58761-271-8(2), Celestial Arts) Ten Speed Pr.

Burger, I. H. & Rivers, J. P. W., eds. Nutrition of the Dog & Cat: Waltham Symposium Number 7. 2009. (ENG., Illus.). 432p. pap. 55.00 (978-0-521-10545-3(5)) Cambridge Univ. Pr.

Case, Linda P., et al. Canine & Feline Nutrition: A Resource for Companion Animal Professionals. 3rd ed. 2010. (ENG., Illus.). 576p. pap. 76.95 (978-0-323-06619-8(4), Mosby) Elsevier - Health Sciences Div.

Cousino, Amy. How to Cook for Your Pet. 2009. 76p. pap. 14.95 (978-1-60693-375-6(2), Strategic Bk. Publishing) AEG Literary Publishing Services, Inc.

Garvey, Martha. My Fat Cat: Ten Simple Steps to Help Your Pet Lose Weight for a Long & Happy Life. 2006. (ENG., Illus.). 128p. pap. 11.95 (978-1-57826-197-0(X), Hatherleigh Pr.) Hatherleigh Co., Ltd., The.

LaBaff, Lisa. My Best Friend's Pawsitively Purrfect Kitty Cookbook. Date not set. (978-0-9703970-1-0(1)) Mall Co., The.

Middle, Clare. Real Food for Dogs & Cats: A Practical Guide to Feeding Your Pet a Balanced, Natural Diet. 2008. (ENG., Illus.). 160p. pap. 14.95 (978-1-921361-35-7(2)) Fremantle Pr. AUS. Dist: Independent Pubs. Group.

Nestle, Marion & Nesheim, Malden. Feed Your Pet Right: The Authoritative Guide to Feeding Your Dog & Cat. 2010. (ENG., Illus.). 384p. pap. 16.99 (978-1-4391-6642-0(0), Free Pr.) Free Pr.

O'Grady, Patricia. Lapping It Up: The Quick & Easy Guide to Making Healthy Cat Food at Home. 2009. 108p. 21.99 (978-1-4490-2433-8(5)); pap. 12.99 (978-1-4490-2430-7(0)) AuthorHouse.

Palika, Liz. The Ultimate Cat Treat Cookbook: Homemade Goodies for Finicky Felines. 2006. (ENG., Illus.). 112p. 14.99 (978-0-471-79255-0(1), Howell Bk. Hse.) Wiley, John & Sons, Inc.

Purr-Fect Recipes for a Healthy Cat: 101 Natural Cat Food & Treat Recipes to Make Your Cat Happy. 2011. (ENG.). 288p. pap. 24.95 (978-1-60138-398-3(3)) Atlantic Publishing Co.

Rees, Wendy Nan & Schlanger, Kevin. The Natural Pet Food Cookbook: Healthful Recipes for Dogs & Cats. 2007. (ENG., Illus.). 110p. 14.99 (978-0-470-22530-1(0), Howell Bk. Hse.) Wiley, John & Sons, Inc.

Schenck, Patricia. Home-Prepared Dog & Cat Diets. 2nd ed. 2010. (ENG.). 556p. pap. 54.99 (978-0-8138-0119-3(2), Wiley-Blackwell) Wiley, John & Sons, Inc.

Schultze, Kymythy R. Natural Nutrition for Cats: The Path to Purr-Fect Health. 2008. (ENG., Illus.). 160p. pap. 9.95 (978-1-4019-1072-3(6)) Hay Hse., Inc.

Tolliver, Gabrielle. You Bake 'Em Cat Treats. 2007. (ENG., Illus.). 48p. pap. 12.95 (978-0-7624-3091-8(5), Running Pr.) Running Pr. Bk. Pubs.

Weiskopf, Joan. Pet Food Nation: The Smart, Easy, & Healthy Way to Feed Your Pet Now. 2007. (ENG., Illus.). 176p. pap. 15.95 (978-0-06-145500-1(8), William Morrow Paperbacks) HarperCollins Pubs.

Winslow, Leanne. Paws above the Rest: Homemade Catfood & Dogfood Recipes. 2007. 108p. per. 19.95 (978-1-4241-9150-5(5)) PublishAmerica, Inc.

Wortinger, Ann. Nutrition for Veterinary Technicians & Nurses. 2007. (ENG., Illus.). 256p. per. 48.99 (978-0-8138-2913-5(5), Wiley-Blackwell) Wiley, John & Sons, Inc.

CATS—JUVENILE LITERATURE

see also Cats—Legends and Stories

Cat. (ENG, FRE & GER.). 5.99 (978-3-8327-1346-1(8)) teNeues Publishing Co.

Elora, Grace. Kittens. 2011. (Cute & Cuddly: Baby Animals Ser.). (Illus.). 24p. (J). (gr. k-2). pap. 8.15 (978-1-4339-4512-0(6)) Stevens, Gareth Publishing LLLP.

Jenkins, Steve. Dogs & Cats. 2012. (ENG.). 40p. (J). (gr. -1-3). pap. 7.99 (978-0-547-85063-4(8), Sandpiper) Houghton Mifflin Harcourt Trade & Reference Pubs.

CATS—LEGENDS AND STORIES

Cats. Date not set. (Pocket Reference Ser.). 192p. 4.98 (978-1-4054-0316-0(0)) Parragon, Inc.

Cats. (ENG, FRE & GER.). 12.99 (978-3-8327-1158-0(9)); (Illus.). spiral bd. 14.99 (978-3-8327-1303-4(4)) teNeues Publishing Co.

Hammond, K. S. The Legend of Pa-Miu: Cat of Ancient Egypt. 2007. 140p. per. 14.95 (978-0-9769996-1-4(7)) Sheshata Publishing Hse.

Hertweck, E. Romayne. Bob the Preschool Cat: A Biography of an Urban Manx Cat. 2009. 73p. pap. 12.95 (978-1-4327-3555-5(1)) Outskirts Pr., Inc.

CATS—MYTHOLOGY

Hammond, K. S. The Legend of Pa-Miu: Cat of Ancient Egypt. 2007. 140p. per. 14.95 (978-0-9769996-1-4(7)) Sheshata Publishing Hse.

Morris, Desmond. Fantastic Cats: A Feast of Famed & Fabled Felines. 2007. (ENG., Illus.). 224p. 14.95 (978-1-904435-62-4(9)) Little Bks., Ltd. GBR. Dist: Independent Pubs. Group.

CATS—PICTORIAL WORKS

Bacchella, Adriano, photos by. Cats, Cats... & more Cats! 2010. (ENG., Illus.). 256p. 29.95 (978-88-544-0479-3(9)) White Star ITA. Dist: Random Hse., Inc.

Bailey, Nancy J. Abyssinian & Somali Cats in Art. 2007. (Illus.). 31p. 42.95 (978-0-9800086-1-6(1)) Bailey, Nancy.

Bartlett, Geoff & Reiss, Gudrun. Cattitude: Life as Seen Through the Eyes of the King of the Urban Jungle. 2007. (ENG., Illus.). 96p. pap. 14.95 (978-1-74110-418-9(1)) New Holland Pubs. Pty, Ltd. AUS. Dist: Tuttle Publishing.

Brown, Milly. Love Kittens. 2011. (ENG., Illus.). 96p. 8.95 (978-1-84024-688-9(X)) Summersdale Pubs. GBR. Dist: Independent Pubs. Group.

Burton, Jane & Warren Photographic, photos by. A Cat's Life. 2008. (ENG., Illus.). 208p. 35.00 (978-88-544-0392-5(X)) White Star ITA. Dist: Random Hse., Inc.

Cat Rules. cd-rom 11.99 (978-1-57223-787-2(2), 7872) Willow Creek Pr., Inc.

Cats & Kittens. 2007. (Illus.). (J). cd-rom 9.99 (978-0-9795190-1-7(2)) Color & Learn.

Cobb, Bj. Icy blue - a devon rex Cat. 2008. 35p. pap. 14.96 (978-0-557-02330-1(0)) Lulu Enterprises Inc.

Cook, Gladys Emerson & Sutton, Felix. The Big Book of Cats. 2011. 28p. pap. 35.95 (978-1-258-10410-8(5)) Literary Licensing, LLC.

Earle, Ella. The Cat. 2012. (ENG., Illus.). 96p. 9.95 (978-1-84953-142-9(0)) Summersdale Pubs. GBR. Dist: Independent Pubs. Group.

Exley, Helen. A Little Book of Crafty Cats. 2009. (ENG.). 96p. 6.95 (978-1-84634-251-6(1)) Exley, Helen Giftbooks GBR. Dist: National Bk. Network.

Feeney, Rik. Kitten Lover's Journal. 2008. 108p. pap. 19.95 (978-0-9637991-5-9(0)) Richardson Publishing, Inc.

Garry, J. W. The Princess & Storm. 2009. 40p. pap. 16.99 (978-1-4389-4959-8(6)) AuthorHouse.

Gromis di Trana, Caterina. Cube Book: Gatos. 2008. (Illus.). 736p. 19.95 (978-970-718-674-3(7), Numen) Advanced Marketing, S. de R. L. de C. V. MEX. Dist: Perseus-PGW.

Hale, Rachael. The French Cat. 2011. (ENG., Illus.). 168p. 29.95 (978-1-58479-950-4(1)) Stewart, Tabori & Chang.

—Smitten: A Kitten's Guide to Happiness. 2006. (ENG., Illus.). 160p. 21.99 (978-0-8212-5848-4(6)) Bulfinch.

Hale, Rachael, photos by. The Cat's Pajamas: 101 of the World's Cutest Cats. 2009. (ENG.). 224p. 24.99 (978-0-7407-7964-0(8)) Andrews McMeel Publishing.

Happycat Staff & Icanhascheezburger.com Staff. How to Take over Teh Wurld: A LOLcat Guide 2 Winning. 2009. (ENG.). 192p. (gr. 12-18). pap. 12.00 (978-1-59240-516-9(9), Gotham) Penguin Group (USA) Inc.

Higgs. Catapult: When Cats Fly. 2008. (ENG., Illus.). 80p. 7.95 (978-1-4027-5353-4(5), Sterling/Hollan) Sterling Publishing Co., Inc.

Ingrid Sanclement, Anna Sanclement. Taylor Bell, the Traveling Kitten: Volume One. 2010. 24p. pap. 14.93 (978-1-4269-2567-2(0)) Trafford Publishing.

Iwago, Mitsuaki & Chronicle Books Staff. Curious Cats. 2010. (ENG., Illus.). 96p. 16.95 (978-0-8118-7004-7(9)) Chronicle Bks. LLC.

Iwasa, Takako. Fashion Cats. 2011. (ENG., Illus.). 160p. pap. 12.00 (978-1-57687-557-5(1), powerHouse Bks.) powerHouse Cultural Entertainment, Inc.

Katahira, Kiki, illus. The New Yorker: A Blank Journal. 2006. 126p. reprint ed. 10.00 (978-1-4223-5256-4(0)) DIANE Publishing Co.

Klondike, Archie. Dog Trick or Cat Treat: Pets Dress up for Halloween. 2007. (ENG., Illus.). 64p. 12.95 (978-1-55022-800-7(5)) ECW Pr. CAN. Dist: Independent Pubs. Group.

Kloth, Michael. Shelter Cats. 2010. (ENG., Illus.). 128p. 22.95 (978-1-85894-523-1(2)) Merrell Pubs. Ltd. GBR. Dist: Perseus Distribution.

Leczkowski, Jennifer & Running Press Staff. Scaredy Cats. 2008. (ENG.). 128p. 4.95 (978-0-7624-3423-7(5)) Perseus Bks. Group.

Manferto De Fabianis, Valeria. Cats. 2010. (Cube Bks.). (ENG., Illus.). 736p. 14.95 (978-88-544-0076-4(9)) White Star ITA. Dist: Sterling Publishing Co., Inc.

—Cats. Lavagno, Enrico, ed. Ezrin, Amy Christine, tr. from ITA. 2007. (Supercubes Ser.). (ENG., Illus.). 736p. 39.95 (978-88-544-0297-3(4), White Star) Rizzoli International Pubns., Inc.

Morita, Yoneo. Kittens in 3-D. 2011. (ENG., Illus.). 96p. 16.99 (978-0-06-203957-6(1), Collins Design) HarperCollins Pubs.

Nelson, Ron, photos by. Blue Cats: Cats of the Greek Islands. 2007. (Illus.). 56p. pap. 17.95 (978-0-9779669-0-5(9)) Blue Cats Pr.

Nevin, Jean. My Name Is Amber. 2011. (Illus.). 32p. pap. 7.50 (978-0-9828961-2-9(3)) Dryad Studio.

Quercus. The Cat Yearbook: A Hilarious Album of Lazy, Crazy & Occasionally Purr-fect Feline Students. 2010. (ENG.). 176p. pap. 7.95 (978-1-84866-023-6(5)) Quercus GBR. Dist: Independent Pubs. Group.

Roberts, Christine & Parmelee, Meredith. Desperate Housecats. 2006. (ENG., Illus.). 124p. 4.95 (978-0-7624-2960-8(7), Running Pr. Minature Editions) Running Pr. Bk. Pubs.

Saville, Susanne. CatSpotting. 2009. 56p. pap. 24.98 (978-0-557-08809-6(7)) Lulu Enterprises Inc.

Sturgill, Susan, illus. I'm Just a Cat Mattress... 2006. 54p. pap. 14.95 (978-1-889937-10-6(X)) Crescent Hill Bks.

Vitoux, Frederic & Foucart-Walter, Elisabeth. Cats in the Louvre. 2008. (ENG., Illus.). 80p. 19.95 (978-2-08-030049-2(0)) Flammarion et Cie FRA. Dist: Random Hse., Inc.

Weller, Alan & Clip Art Staff. Cats in Art CD-ROM & Book. 2012. (Dover Electronic Clip Art Ser.). (ENG., Illus.). 48p. pap. 19.95 (978-0-486-99159-7(8)) Dover Pubns., Inc.

Zuffi, Stefano. Gatos en el Arte/The Cat in Art. Calvo, Sofia Gonzalez, tr. 2009. (SPA.). 360p. (978-84-96822-89-4(3)) 451 Editores.

CATS—POETRY

Daniel, John. The Ballad of Toby & Lark: A Cat Fantasy. 2009. 60p. pap. 10.00 (978-1-56474-481-4(7), Fithian Pr) Daniel & Daniel, Pubs., Inc.

Marquardt, Jayme, et al. The Pooku - Haiku for Pooka: Thwart Not My Feline Desires. 2007. (Illus.). 70p. (J). spiral bd. 18.75 *(978-0-615-19682-4(9))* Nipton Road Group, The.

Sir Nobby: A Cat-Ography. 2007. (Illus.). 155p. (J). (gr. 3-7). per. 20.00 *(978-1-57966-079-6(7))* River City Publishing.

CATS—SURGERY

Baines, Stephen & Hotston-Moore, Alisdair. ENT & Oral Surgery of the Dog & Cat. 2nd rev. ed. 2008. (ENG., Illus.). 240p. pap. 69.99 *(978-1-4051-1893-4(8),* Wiley-Blackwell) Wiley, John & Sons, Inc.

Busch, Sara J. & Tear, Marianne. Small Animal Surgical Nursing. 2nd ed. 2011. (ENG., Illus.). 360p. (C). pap. 57.95 *(978-0-323-07735-4(8),* Mosby) Elsevier - Health Sciences Div.

Carroll, Gwendolyn L., ed. Small Animal Anesthesia & Analgesia. 2008. (ENG., Illus.). 283p. 89.99 *(978-0-8138-0230-5(X),* Wiley-Blackwell) Wiley, John & Sons, Inc.

Cook, Jimi, et al, eds. BSAVA Manual of Canine & Feline Musculoskeletal Disorders. 2006. (BSAVA British Small Animal Veterinary Association Ser.). (ENG., Illus.). 250p. pap. 167.99 *(978-0-905214-80-1(3))* British Small Animal Veterinary Assn. (BSAVA) GBR. Dist: Wiley, John & Sons, Inc.

Cram101 Textbook Reviews. Outlines & Highlights for Small Animal Surgical Nursing by Sara J Busch. 2011. 146p. pap. 29.95 ***(978-1-61905-936-8(3))*** Cram101 Inc.

Lhermette, Philip & Sobel, David, eds. BSAVA Manual of Canine & Feline Endoscopy & Endosurgery. 2008. (BSAVA British Small Animal Veterinary Association Ser.: 10). (ENG., Illus.). 244p. pap. 157.99 *(978-1-905319-02-2(9),* British Small Animal Veterinary Assn. (BSAVA) GBR. Dist: Wiley, John & Sons, Inc.

Montavon, P. M., et al, eds. Feline Orthopedic Surgery & Musculoskeletal Disease. 2009. (ENG., Illus.). 582p. 149.00 *(978-0-7020-2986-8(6),* Saunders) Elsevier - Health Sciences Div.

Pavletic, Michael M. Atlas of Small Animal Wound Management & Reconstructive Surgery. 3rd ed. 2010. (ENG., Illus.). 696p. 178.99 *(978-0-8138-1124-6(4),* Wiley-Blackwell) Wiley, John & Sons, Inc.

Schwarz, Tobias & Johnson, Victoria, eds. BSAVA Manual of Canine & Feline Thoracic Imaging. 2008. (BSAVA British Small Animal Veterinary Association Ser.). (ENG., Illus.). 408p. pap. 146.99 *(978-0-905214-97-9(8))* British Small Animal Veterinary Assn. (BSAVA) GBR. Dist: Wiley, John & Sons, Inc.

Scott, Harry W. & McLaughlin, Ronald. Feline Orthopedics. 2006. (ENG., Illus.). 384p. 190.00 *(978-1-84076-056-9(7))* Manson Publishing, Ltd. GBR. Dist: Thieme Medical Pubs., Inc.

Thomas, John & Lerche, Phillip. Anesthesia & Analgesia for Veterinary Technicians. 4th ed. 2010. (ENG., Illus.). 432p. (C). pap. 55.95 *(978-0-323-05504-8(4),* Mosby) Elsevier - Health Sciences Div.

Verstraete, Frank J. M., et al. Oral & Maxillofacial Surgery in Dogs & Cats. 2012. (ENG., Illus.). 608p. 349.00 ***(978-0-7020-4618-6(3),*** Saunders) Elsevier - Health Sciences Div.

Williams, John M., et al. Manual of Canine & Feline Wound Management & Reconstruction. 2nd ed. 2009. (BSAVA British Small Animal Veterinary Association Ser.: 7). (ENG., Illus.). 288p. pap. 157.99 *(978-1-905319-09-1(6))* British Small Animal Veterinary Assn. (BSAVA) GBR. Dist: Wiley, John & Sons, Inc.

CATS—RELIGIOUS ASPECTS

Brokering, Herbert. More Cat Psalms: Prayers My Cats Have Taught Me. 2008. (Illus.). 64p. per. 8.99 *(978-0-8066-8035-4(0),* Augsburg Bks.) Augsburg Fortress, Pubs.

Fleishauer, Connie & Adams, Dottie P. Purr-ables from Heaven: Devotions for Cat Lovers. 2008. (Illus.). 252p. per. 11.99 *(978-0-7369-2057-5(9))* Harvest Hse. Pubs.

Grant, Callie Smith, ed. A Dickens of a Cat: And Other Stories of the Cats We Love. 2007. 192p. pap. 12.99 *(978-0-8007-5846-2(3))* Revell.

Jenkins, Hortense M. Pinches Patches & the Petchary. 2011. 46p. 21.99 ***(978-1-61215-850-1(1)**;* pap. 9.99 ***(978-1-61215-849-5(8))*** Xulon Pr., Inc.

Kampling, Rainer, ed. Eine seltsame Gefahrtin: Katzen, Religion, Theologie und Theologen. (GER., Illus.). 353p. pap. 57.95 *(978-3-631-56564-3(X))* Lang, Peter GmbH, Europaischer Verlag der Wissenschaften DEU. Dist: Lang, Peter Publishing, Inc.

Kinnear, Jasmine. Every Cat Has A Story: True Stories Exploring the Spiritual Connection of Felines with Their Beloved Owners. 2007. (Illus.). 224p. pap. *(978-0-9783893-8-3(7),* CCB Publishing) CCB Publishing.

Mitchell, Patricia. Best Friends Forever: Me & My Cat: What I've Learned about Life, Love, & Faith from My Cat. 2010. 14.99 *(978-0-7642-0774-7(1))* Bethany Hse. Pubs.

Patterson, Gary, illus. Cat Laughs. 2010. 64p. 9.99 *(978-0-7369-2657-7(7))* Harvest Hse. Pubs.

Tansey, Kat. Choosing to Be: Lessons in Living from a Feline Zen Master. 2nd ed. 2010. (ENG.). 160p. pap. 12.95 *(978-1-84409-501-8(0))* Findhorn Pr. GBR. Dist: Independent Pubs. Group.

Wells, M. R., et al. The Cat Lover's Devotional. 2011. (Illus.). 240p. pap. 12.99 *(978-0-7369-2881-6(2))* Harvest Hse. Pubs.

—Purr-ables from Heaven Gift Edition: Inspirational Stories for Cat Lovers. 2008. 32p. 12.99 *(978-0-7369-2204-3(0))* Harvest Hse. Pubs.

Wright, H. Norman. Nine Lives to Love: Celebrating the Cats We Fancy. 2009. 64p. 15.99 *(978-0-7369-2326-2(8))* Harvest Hse. Pubs.

CATS—TRAINING

Animal, Rescue L. Animal Resuce League for Love of Cats. 2011. 128p. pap. 21.95 ***(978-1-935726-13-5(7))*** Landauer Publishing, LLC.

Australian Women's Weekly Staff, contrib. by. Caring for Dogs & Cats: With a Vet's Guide to Common Complaints. (Illus.). 128p. pap. 12.95 *(978-1-86396-201-8(8))* ACP Publishing Pty, Ltd. AUS. Dist: Graphic Arts Ctr. Publishing Co.

Becker, Marty. Your Cat: The Owner's Manual - Hundreds of Secrets, Surprises, & Solutions for Raising a Happy, Healthy Cat. 2012. (ENG., Illus.). 320p. 25.99 ***(978-0-446-57136-4(9))*** Grand Central Publishing.

Braun, Martina. Clicker Training for Clever Cats: Learning Can Be Fun! 2009. (ENG.). 80p. pap. 19.95 *(978-3-86127-967-9(3))* Cadmos Verlag GmbH DEU. Dist: Independent Pubs. Group.

Braybrook, Jeanee. Who Says You Can't Train a Cat? 2011. 64p. pap. 31.99 ***(978-1-4628-6593-2(3))*** Xlibris Corp.

Case, Linda P. Canine & Feline Behavior & Training: A Complete Guide to Understanding our Two Best Friends. 2009. (Veterinary Technology Ser.). (ENG.). 352p. (C). pap. 105.95 *(978-1-4283-1053-7(3))* Delmar Cengage Learning.

Caunce, et al. Grooming Manual for the Dog & Cat. 2006. (ENG., Illus.). 272p. pap. 84.99 *(978-1-4051-1183-6(6),* Wiley-Blackwell) Wiley, John & Sons, Inc.

Fields-Babineau, Miriam. Cat Training in 10 Minutes. (Illus.). 142p. pap. 14.95 *(978-0-7938-0530-3(9),* TS340) TFH Pubns., Inc.

Hauschild, Christine. Trick Training for Cats: Smart fun with the Clicker. 2011. (ENG.). 96p. pap. 19.95 *(978-0-85788-400-8(X))* Cadmos Verlag GmbH DEU. Dist: Independent Pubs. Group.

Horton-Bussey, Claire. Teach Your Cat House Training. 2006. (Illus.). 32p. pap. 4.95 *(978-1-86054-259-6(X))* Ringpress Bks., Ltd. GBR. Dist: TFH Pubns., Inc.

How to Raise Your New Puppy in a Cat Family: The Complete Guide to a Happy Pet-Filled Home. 2011. (ENG.). pap. 24.95 *(978-1-60138-401-0(7))* Atlantic Publishing Co.

Johnson-Bennett, Pam. Think Like a Cat: How to Raise a Well-Adjusted Cat — Not a Sour Puss. rev. ed. 2011. (ENG.). 432p. (gr. 12). 18.00 *(978-0-14-311979-1(6),* Penguin (Non-Classics)) Penguin Group (USA) Inc.

Krieger, Marilyn. Naughty No More: Change Unwanted Behaviors Through Positive Reinforcement. 2011. (ENG.). 160p. (gr. 6). pap. 12.95 *(978-1-933958-92-7(8,)* BowTie Pr.

Langley, Andrew. Kitten Tips. 2007. (Little Book Ser.). (ENG.). 112p. pap. 4.95 *(978-1-904573-61-6(4,)* Absolute Pr. GBR. Dist: Independent Pubs. Group.

Menke, Trisha Yeager. Potty Talk by Toast. 2006. (Illus.). 119p. per. 12.95 *(978-0-9700766-0-1(6))* ToastNHoney Pubns.

Mironov, Yana & Helmes, Naaman. How-to: the Easiest Guide to Raising a Kitten. 2010. 37p. pap. 20.00 *(978-0-557-50225-7(X))* Lulu Enterprises Inc.

Moustaki, Nikki. Boredom Busters for Cats: 40 Whisker-Twitching Games & Adventures. 2010. (ENG.). 64p. (gr. 6). pap. 6.95 *(978-1-935484-18-9(4))* BowTie Pr.

Popovich, Gregory. You Can Train Your Cat: Secrets of a Master Cat Trainer. 2009. (ENG., Illus.). 240p. pap. 14.99 *(978-0-312-56528-2(3),* St. Martin's Griffin) St. Martin's Pr.

Raisanen, Kimberly. Learn How to Professionally Groom Cats: A Practitioners Guide, Vol. 1. 2009. (Illus.). 156p. spiral bd. 49.99 *(978-0-615-27218-4(5))* Professional Cat Groomers Assn. of America.

Robbins, Sandy. Fabulous Felines: Health & Beauty Secrets for the Pampered Cat, 1 vol. 2008. (ENG.). 192p. pap. 18.95 *(978-0-7938-0665-2(8))* TFH Pubns., Inc.

Taylor, David A. Kitten Taming: Train Your Cat's Inner Tiger. 2009. (ENG.). 192p. pap. 9.95 *(978-1-59223-986-3(2),* Thunder Bay Pr.) Advantage Pubs. Group.

White, Linda M. First Steps with Puppies & Kittens: A Practice-Team Approach to Behavior. 2009. (ENG.). pap. 84.95 *(978-1-58326-101-9(X),* AAHA Pr.) American Animal Hospital Assn. Pr.

CATS (IN RELIGION, FOLK-LORE, ETC.)

see Cats—Folklore; Cats—Mythology; Cats—Religious Aspects

CAT'S CRADLE

see String Figures

CATS IN LITERATURE

Cats. Date not set. (Pocket Reference Ser.). 192p. 4.98 *(978-1-4054-0316-0(0))* Parragon, Inc.

Cats. (ENG., FRE & GER.). 12.99 *(978-3-8327-1158-0(9));* (Illus.). spiral bd. 14.99 *(978-3-8327-1303-4(4))* teNeues Publishing Co.

Cryer, Max. In Praise of Cats. 2008. (In Praise Of... Ser.). (ENG., Illus.). 212p. pap. 12.95 *(978-1-84454-479-0(6))* Blake, John Publishing, Ltd. GBR. Dist: Independent Pubs. Group.

Milly, Brown. The Cat Lover?'s Companion. 2012. (ENG., Illus.). 192p. 15.95 ***(978-1-84953-158-0(7))*** Summerdale Pubs. GBR. Dist: Independent Pubs. Group

Tempus Publishing UK. Cats in Poetry. 2007. (ENG.). 160p. 22.95 *(978-0-7524-4432-1(8))* History Pr. Ltd.,The GBR. Dist: Independent Pubs. Group.

Zuffi, Stefano. Gatos en el Arte/The Cat in Art. Calvo, Sofia Gonzalez, tr. 2009. (SPA.). 360p. *(978-84-96822-89-4(3))* 451 Editores.

CATSKILL MOUNTAINS REGION (N.Y.)

Budrock, Helen. Summary Guide to the Terms of the Watershed Agreement. Date not set. 52p. (Orig.). pap. *(978-0-9616712-7-3(0))* Catskill Ctr. for Conservation & Development, Inc.

Burk, John S. & Kick, Peter. AMC Catskill Mountain Guide, 2nd: AMC's Comprehensive Guide to Hiking Trails in the Catskills. 2nd ed. 2009. (ENG., Illus.). 272p. pap. 23.95 *(978-1-934028-19-3(3))* Appalachian Mountain Club Bks.

Burroughs, John. In the Catskills. 2008. 176p. (Orig.). 25.99 *(978-0-554-24868-4(9));* 22.99 *(978-0-554-34171-2(9))* BiblioBazaar.

—In the Catskills. 2008. 164p. (Orig.). per. *(978-1-4065-9009-8(6))* Dodo Pr.

—In the Catskills. 2007. (ENG.). 108p. (Orig.). per. *(978-1-4068-2364-6(3))* Echo Library.

Connell, Karl, Jr. Biography of an Inventor: Dr. Karl Connell. 2008. (Illus.). ix, 195p. *(978-0-9817104-0-2(9))* Wintoon Waters.

Davis, Roy. Crest Park: A Catskill Mountain Memoir. 2009. 472p. pap. 19.95 *(978-1-4327-1238-9(1))* Outskirts Pr., Inc.

Duerden, Tim. A History of Delaware County, New York: A Catskill Land & Its People, 1791-2007. 2007. (Illus.). 142p. pap. 20.00 *(978-1-930098-84-8(7))* Purple Mountain Pr., Ltd.

Galusha, Diane. Another Day, Another Dollar: The Civilian Conservation Corps in the Catskills. 2008. (Illus.). 224p. pap. 16.95 *(978-1-883789-61-9(3))* Black Dome Pr. Corp.

Heppner, Richard R. Women of the Catskills: Stories of Struggle, Sacrifice, & Hope. 2011. (Illus.). 128p. pap. 19.99 *(978-1-60949-014-0(2))* History Pr., The.

Ingersoll, Bill. Snowshoe Routes: Adirondacks & Catskills. 2006. (Snowshoe Routes Ser.). (ENG., Illus.). 237p. pap. 16.95 *(978-1-59485-009-7(7))* Mountaineers Bks., The.

Kick, Peter. AMC's Best Day Hikes in the Catskills & Hudson Valley, 2nd: Four-Season Guide to 60 of the Best Trails from the Hudson Highlands to Albany. 2nd ed. 2011. (ENG., Illus.). 304p. pap. 18.95 *(978-1-934028-45-2(2))* Appalachian Mountain Club Bks.

Kick, Peter W. Backroad Bicycling in the Hudson Valley & Catskills. 2006. (Countryman Guide Ser.). (ENG., Illus.). 224p. per. 16.95 *(978-0-88150-578-8(1),* 150578) Countryman Pr.

Michaels, Joanne. The Hudson Valley & Catskill Mountains: Includes Saratoga Springs & Albany. 6th ed. 2007. (Explorer's Guide the Hudson Valley & Catskill Mountains Ser.). (ENG., Illus.). 432p. per. 19.95 *(978-0-88150-772-0(5))* Countryman Pr.

Michaels, Joanne & Michaels, J. The Hudson Valley & Catskill Mountains: Includes Saratoga Springs & Albany. 7th ed. 2009. (Explorer's Complete Ser.). (ENG., Illus.). 464p. pap. 21.95 *(978-0-88150-823-9(3),* 150823) Countryman Pr.

Plein Air Abstraction at the Foothills of the Catskill Mountains. 2007. (Illus.). 71p. *(978-0-9640272-6-6(7))* Maiden Lane Publishing.

Ratzer, Philip. Bungalow Kid: A Catskill Mountain Summer. 2010. (Excelsior Editions Ser.). (Illus.). 120p. pap. 14.95 *(978-1-4384-3300-4(X))* State Univ. of New York Pr.

Silverman, Francine. The Catskills Alive! 2nd ed. (Illus.). 608p. pap. 18.99 *(978-1-58843-354-1(4))* Hunter Publishing, Inc.

Steuding, Bob. The Heart of the Catskills. 2008. (Illus.). 150p. pap. 15.00 *(978-1-930098-92-3(8))* Purple Mountain Pr., Ltd.

Stradling, David. Making Mountains: New York City & the Catskills. 2007. (Weyerhaeuser Environmental Bks.). (ENG., Illus.). 336p. 35.00 *(978-0-295-98747-7(2))* Univ. of Washington Pr.

Troost, Catherine M. Catskill Mountain Memories. 2008. 172p. pap. 14.99 *(978-1-60791-071-8(3))* Xulon Pr., Inc.

Via, Alan. The Catskill 67: A Hiker's Guide to the Catskill 100 Highest Peaks Under 3500' LeBrun, Fred, ed. 2011. pap. ***(978-1-931951-08-1(X))*** Adirondack Mountain Club, Inc.

White, Carol / Stone, ed. Catskill Peak Experiences: Mountaineering Tales of Endurance, Survival, Exploration & Adventure from the Catskill 3500 Club. 2008. (Illus.). 304p. pap. 19.95 *(978-1-883789-59-6(1))* Black Dome Pr. Corp.

CATT, CARRIE CHAPMAN, 1859-1947

Peck, Mary Gray. Carrie Chapman Catt: A Biography. 2011. 512p. 60.95 ***(978-1-258-07290-2(4))*** Literary Licensing, LLC.

CATTLE

see also Beef Cattle; Calves; Cattle Breeds; Cows; Dairy Cattle; Grazing; Oxen

Alsdorf, Ludwig. The History of Vegetarianism & Cow-Veneration in India. 2012. (ENG.). 184p. (C). pap. 42.95 ***(978-0-415-53360-7(0))*** Routledge.

Alsdorf, Ludwig & Bollée, Willem B. The History of Vegetarianism & Cow-Veneration in India. Patil, Bal, tr. from GER. 2010. (Routledge Advances in Jaina Studies). (ENG.). 184p. (C). 135.00 *(978-0-415-54824-3(1),* Routledge) Taylor & Francis Group GBR. Dist: Taylor & Francis Group.

Benedict, Francis G. & Ritzman, Ernest G. The Metabolism of the Fasting Steer. 2011. 256p. 47.95 ***(978-1-258-05250-8(4))*** Literary Licensing, LLC.

Blair, Robert. Nutrition & Feeding of Organic Cattle. 2011. (Illus.). 304p. 145.00 *(978-1-84593-758-4(9))* CABI GBR. Dist: Stylus Publishing, LLC.

Budras, Klaus-Dieter, et al. Bovine Anatomy: An Illustrated Text. 2nd enl. ed. 2011. (ENG., Illus.). 138p. 160.00 ***(978-3-89993-052-8(5))*** Manson Publishing, Ltd. GBR. Dist: Thieme Medical Pubs., Inc.

Byard, Jack. Know Your Cattle. 2012. (ENG., Illus.). 96p. pap. 6.95 ***(978-1-56523-613-4(0))*** Fox Chapel Publishing Co., Inc.

Chetri, Dipesh Kumar. Transhumance Effect on Yak-Cattle Herding Management & It's Physiology. 2011. 112p. pap. ***(978-3-8443-2820-2(3))*** Lambert Academic Publishing.

Collier, R. J. & Collier, J. L., eds. Environmental Physiology of Livestock. 2012. (ENG.). 368p. 199.95 ***(978-0-8138-1176-5(7),*** Wiley-Blackwell) Wiley, John & Sons, Inc.

The Complete Guide to Grass-Fed Cattle How to Raise Your Cattle on Natural Grass for Fun & Profit. 2011. (ENG.). 288p. pap. 24.95 *(978-1-60138-380-8(0))* Atlantic Publishing Co.

Dale, Nancy. Wild Florida the Way It Was: As told by the pioneer cow hunters & huntresses who lived It. 2008. 212p. 27.95 *(978-0-595-51747-3(1));* pap. 17.95 *(978-0-595-51104-4(X))* iUniverse, Inc.

De Passillé, Anne Maria, ed. The Welfare of Cattle. 2007. (Animal Welfare Ser.). (Illus.). 310p. 199.00 *(978-1-4020-6557-6(4))* Springer.

Egginton, Joyce. The Poisoning of Michigan. 2nd ed. 2009. (ENG.). 368p. pap. 19.95 *(978-0-87013-867-6(7))* Michigan State Univ. Pr.

Flagg, Oscar H. Review of the Cattle Business in Johnson County Wyoming, Since 1822, & the Causes That Led to the Recent Invasion. (Mass Violence in America Ser.). reprint ed. 27.95 *(978-0-405-01309-6(4))* Ayer Co. Pubs., Inc.

Graves, Robert Edwin. Penn State Housing Plans for Calves & Heifers. 2007. *(978-1-933395-17-3(6))* Natural Resource, Agricultural, & Engineering Service.

Hasheider, Philip. How to Raise Cattle: Everything You Need to Know. rev. ed. 2007. (ENG., Illus.). 192p. pap. 19.95 *(978-0-7603-2802-6(1),* 0760328021, Voyageur Pr) MBI Publishing Co. LLC.

Mngomezulu, Simphiwe. Formal Marketing of Cattle by Communal Farmers in South Afric. 2011. 120p. pap. ***(978-3-8443-8991-3(1))*** Lambert Academic Publishing.

Nation, Allan. Land Livestock & Life: A grazier's guide to Finance. 2007. 224p. per. 25.00 *(978-0-9721597-2-2(X))* Green Park Pr.

Petridis, Constantine. The Art of Daily Life: Portable Objects from Southern Africa. 2011. (ENG., Illus.). 112p. pap. 30.00 *(978-88-7439-578-1(7))* 5 Continents ITA. Dist: Hachette Bk. Group.

Richthofen, Walter Von. Cattle-Raising on the Plains of North America. 2008. 112p. 34.95 *(978-1-4368-8706-9(2))* pap. 19.95 *(978-1-4368-0105-8(2))* Kessinger Publishing, LLC.

Rimas, Andrew & Fraser, Evan. Beef: The Untold Story of How Milk, Meat, & Muscle Shaped the World. 2009. (ENG.). 256p. pap. 14.99 *(978-0-06-135385-7(X),* Harper Paperbacks) HarperCollins Pubs.

—Beef: The Untold Story of How Milk, Meat & Muscle Shaped the World. 2008. (Illus.). 256p. pap. 19.95 *(978-0-06-171879-3(3),* Morrow, William & Co.) HarperCollins Pubs.

Rushen, Jeffrey, et al. The Welfare of Cattle. 2010. (Animal Welfare Ser.). x, 310p. pap. 199.00 *(978-90-481-7669-4(7),* 9048176697) Springer.

Thomas, Heather Smith. The Cattle Health: Preventative Care, Disease Treatments & Emergency Procedures. 2009. (ENG., Illus.). 384p. instr.'s hndbk. ed. 34.95 *(978-1-60342-095-2(9),* 1603420959); 372p. pap. 24.95 *(978-1-60342-090-7(8),* 1603420908) Storey Publishing, LLC.

TWD & Phillips, C. J. C. Principles of Cattle Production. 2nd ed. 2010. (Modular Texts). (Illus.). 256p. pap., pap. 70.00 *(978-1-84593-397-5(4))* CABI GBR. Dist: Stylus Publishing, LLC.

Tyler, Daniel. WD Farr: Cowboy in the Boardroom. 2011. (ENG., Illus.). 312p. 29.95 *(978-0-8061-4193-0(X))* Univ. of Oklahoma Pr.

Velten, Hannah. Cow. 2007. (Reaktion Books - Animal Ser.). (ENG., Illus.). 224p. pap. 19.95 *(978-1-86189-326-0(4))* Reaktion Bks., Ltd. GBR. Dist: Chicago Distribution Ctr.

Womack, James, ed. Bovine Genomics. 2012. (ENG.). 284p. 199.95 ***(978-0-8138-2122-1(3),*** Wiley-Blackwell) Wiley, John & Sons, Inc.

CATTLE—BREEDING

Beyea, Orville. Against the Current. 2009. (Illus.). 368p. pap. *(978-1-57579-394-8(6))* Pine Hill Pr., Inc.

Chandrahasan, C. Follicular Oocytes in Buffaloes. 2011. 96p. pap. ***(978-3-8454-0962-7(2))*** Lambert Academic Publishing.

Elwes, Henry. Guide to the Primitive Breeds of Sheep & Their Crosses on Exhibition at the Royal Agricultural Society's Show, Bristol 1913 - with Notes on the Man. 2010. 86p. pap. 26.45 *(978-1-4455-0336-3(0))* Audubon Pr. & Christian Bk. Service.

Gupta, Lokesh & Murdia, P. C. Improvement of Roughages by Urea & Sulphur Supplementation. 2011. 144p. pap. ***(978-3-8443-2829-5(7))*** Lambert Academic Publishing.

Hayes, Margo. Small Cattle for Small Farms. 2008. (Landlinks Press Ser.). (Illus.). 168p. pap. 39.95 *(978-0-643-09428-4(8))* CSIRO Publishing AUS. Dist: Stylus Publishing, LLC.

Khan, Sohail Ahmad, et al. Exogenous Fibrolytic Enzymes in Cattle Feed. 2010. 92p. pap. *(978-3-8383-8190-9(4))* Lambert Academic Publishing.

King, Peter. An Introduction to Keeping Cattle. 2009. (ENG., Illus.). 272p. pap. 29.95 *(978-1-904871-39-2(9),* 1904871399) Good Life Pr., The GBR. Dist: MBI Distribution Services/Quayside Distribution.

Klopcic, Marija, et al, eds. Breeding for robustness in Cattle. 2009. (Illus.). 270p. 129.00 *(978-90-8686-084-5(2))* Wageningen Academic Publishers NLD. Dist: Enfield Publishing & Distribution Co., Inc.

Masike, Sennye. Modeling the Impacts of Climate Change on Cattle Water Demand & Supply in Botswana - System Dynamic Modeling Approach. 2008. 336p. pap. *(978-3-639-05489-7(X),* VDM Verlag Dr. Mueller e.K.

More O'Ferrall, G. J. Beef Production from Different Dairy Breeds & Dairy Beef Crosses. 2010. (Current Topics in Veterinary Medicine Ser.). 416p. pap. 389.00 *(978-90-481-8275-6(1),* 9048182751) Springer.

Nanci, Gabriella & Millman, Stefani. Dexter Cattle: A Breeders' Notebook. 2009. (Illus.). 108p. pap. 37.49 *(978-1-4389-8341-7(7))* AuthorHouse.

C

Oppenheimer, Harold L. Cowboy Arithmetic: Cattle As an Investment. 2011. 208p. 44.95 (978-1-258-09827-8(X)) Literary Licensing, LLC.

Rickard, J. A. Early Cattle Ranching on the Texas South Plains. ltd. ed. 2008. 148p. 42.95 (978-0-9767799-9-5(4)) Copano Bay Pr.

Thomas, Heather Smith. Essential Guide to Calving: Giving Your Beef or Dairy Herd a Healthy Start. 2008. (ENG., Illus.). 325p. pap. 24.95 (978-1-58017-706-1(9), 1580177069) Storey Publishing, LLC.

CATTLE—BREEDS
see Cattle Breeds

CATTLE—DISEASES
see also Bovine Spongiform Encephalopathy; Brucellosis in Cattle; Foot-And-Mouth Disease

Andrews, A. H. Differential Diagnosis in Cattle. 2nd rev. ed. 2009. (ENG., Illus.). 240p. pap. (978-0-632-04239-5(7), Wiley-Blackwell) Wiley, John & Sons, Ltd.

Blowey, Roger & Edmondson, Peter. Mastitis Control in Dairy Herds. 2nd ed. 2010. (Illus.). 270p. 75.00 (978-1-84593-550-4(0)) CABI GBR. Dist: Stylus Publishing, LLC.

Cooper, Vickie L. & Brodersen, Bruce W. Bovine Respiratory Disease, an Issue of Veterinary Clinics: Food Animal Practice. 2010. (Clinics: Veterinary Medicine Ser.: 26-2). (ENG., Illus.). xiv, 192p. 105.00 (978-1-4377-2504-9(X), Saunders) Elsevier - Health Sciences Div.

Dadd, Geo. H. Dadd on the Nature & Treatment of the Diseases of Cattle with Descriptions & Illustrations. 2008. 404p. pap. 31.45 (978-1-4437-6669-2(0)) Harrison House Pubs.

Divers, Thomas J. & Peek, Simon F. Rebhun's Diseases of Dairy Cattle. 2nd rev. ed. 2007. (ENG., Illus.). 704p. 150.00 (978-1-4160-3137-6(5), Saunders) Elsevier - Health Sciences Div.

Gashaw Kebede, Abebaw. Dynamics of Ticks & Its Control on Cattle Southwestern Ethiopi. 2010. 148p. pap. (978-3-639-24753-4(1)) VDM Verlag Dr. Mueller e.K.

Hendrickson, Dean A. & Turner, A. Simon. Techniques in Large Animal Surgery. 3rd rev. ed. 2007. (ENG., Illus.). 328p. 115.99 (978-0-7817-8255-5(4), Wiley-Blackwell) Wiley, John & Sons, Inc.

Kapil, Sanjay & McVey, David. Emerging, Reemerging, & Persistent Infectious Diseases of Cattle, an Issue of Veterinary Clinics: Food Animal Practice. 2010. (Clinics: Veterinary Medicine Ser.: 26-1). (ENG., Illus.). xiv, 190p. 105.00 (978-1-4377-1885-0(X), Saunders) Elsevier - Health Sciences Div.

Lam, T. J. G. M., ed. Mastitis Control: From science to Practice. 2008. (Illus.). 456p. 132.00 (978-90-8686-085-2(0)) Wageningen Academic Publishers NLD. Dist: Enfield Publishing & Distribution Co., Inc.

Mayhew, Joe. Large Animal Neurology. 2nd ed. 2009. (ENG., Illus.). 464p. 175.99 (978-1-4051-5493-2(4), Wiley-Blackwell) Wiley, John & Sons, Inc.

Nicholas, R., et al. Mycoplasma Diseases of Ruminants. 2008. (Illus.). 256p. 145.00 (978-0-85199-012-5(6)) CABI GBR. Dist: Stylus Publishing, LLC.

Pope, George W. & Jennings, Robert. Determining the Age of Cattle by the Teeth, & Cattle & Their Diseases. 2011. 250p. (978-1-84902-336-8(0)) Benediction Classics.

Scott, Ian & Sutherland, Ian. Gastrointestinal Nematodes of Sheep & Cattle: Biology & Control. 2009. (ENG., Illus.). 256p. 120.99 (978-1-4051-8582-0(1), Wiley-Blackwell) Wiley, John & Sons, Inc.

Scott, Philip, et al. Cattle Medicine. 2011. (ENG., Illus.). 288p. 160.00 (978-1-84076-127-6(X)) Manson Publishing, Ltd. GBR. Dist: Thieme Medical Pubs., Inc.

Setiyaningsih, Surachmi. Jembrana Disease Virus Transactivator. 2008. 132p. pap. (978-3-639-03504-9(6)) VDM Verlag Dr. Mueller e.K.

Shearer, Jan & Van Amstel, Sarel. Manual for Treatment & Control of Lameness in Cattle. 2006. (ENG., Illus.). 212p. 94.99 (978-0-8138-1418-6(9), Wiley-Blackwell) Wiley, John & Sons, Inc.

Smith, Geof W. Bovine Neonatology: Veterinary Clinics of North America - Food Animal Practice. 2009. (Clinics: Veterinary Medicine Ser.: 25-1). (ENG., Illus.). 240p. 99.00 (978-1-4377-0559-1(6), Saunders) Elsevier - Health Sciences Div.

Weaver, A. David & Blowey, Roger. Color Atlas of Diseases & Disorders of Cattle. 3rd ed. 2011. (ENG., Illus.). 280p. 155.00 (978-0-7234-3602-7(9), Mosby) Elsevier - Health Sciences Div.

CATTLE—AUSTRALIA

Hayes, Margo. Small Cattle for Small Farms. 2008. (Landlinks Press Ser.). (Illus.). 168p. pap. 39.95 (978-0-643-09428-4(8)) CSIRO Publishing AUS. Dist: Stylus Publishing, LLC.

CATTLE—CANADA

Craig, John R. Ranching with Lords & Commons, 1 vol. 2010. (ENG., Illus.). 224p. per. (978-1-894974-05-9(X)) Heritage Hse.

CATTLE—INDIA

Chandrahasan, C. Follicular Oocytes in Buffaloes. 2011. 96p. pap. (978-3-8454-0962-7(2)) Lambert Academic Publishing.

Yadav, Chouth Mal & Chaudhary, Jagdish Lal. Feeding of Protected Protein on Lactating Crossbred Cows & Heifers. 2011. 156p. pap. (978-3-8443-8808-4(7)) Lambert Academic Publishing.

CATTLE, BEEF
see Beef Cattle

CATTLE BRANDS

MacMichael, H. A. Brands Used by the Chief Camel-owning Tribes of Kordofán: A Supplement to the Tribes of Northern & Central Kordofán. 2012. (ENG., Illus.). 133p. pap. 34.00 (978-1-107-65862-2(4)) Cambridge Univ. Pr.

CATTLE BREEDING
see Cattle—Breeding

CATTLE BREEDS
see also names of specific breeds

Byard, Jack. Know Your Cattle. 2012. (ENG., Illus.). 96p. pap. 6.95 (978-1-56523-613-4(0)) Fox Chapel Publishing Co., Inc.

Felius, Marleen. Cattle Breeds: An Encyclopedia. 2007. (ENG.). 800p. 100.00 (978-90-5439-017-6(4)) Trafalgar Square Publishing.

Forabosco, Flavio & Mantovani, Roberto. European & Indigenous Cattle Breeds in Italy. 2011. 208p. pap. (978-1-84903-074-8(X)) Schiel & Denver Publishing Ltd.

King, Peter. An Introduction to Keeping Cattle. 2009. (ENG., Illus.). 272p. pap. 29.95 (978-1-904871-39-2(9), 1904871399) Good Life Pr., The GBR. Dist: MBI Distribution Services/Quayside Distribution.

Porter, Val. British Cattle. 2010. (Shire Library). (ENG., Illus.). 56p. pap. 12.95 (978-0-7478-0764-3(7)) Shire Pubns., Ltd. GBR. Dist: Random Hse., Inc.

—Cattle: A Handbook to the Breeds of the World. 2007. (ENG., Illus.). 400p. 119.95 (978-1-86126-934-8(X)) Crowood Pr., Ltd. GBR. Dist: Independent Pubs. Group.

Swaminathan, Marimuthu. Conservation Priorities & Livelihood Functions of Cattle Resources. 2011. 92p. pap. (978-3-8443-0624-8(2)) Lambert Academic Publishing.

CATTLE RANCHES
see Ranches

CATTLE—REPRODUCTION

Squires, E. James. Applied Animal Endocrinology. 2nd ed. 2011. (Modular Texts). (Illus.). 304p. 160.00 (978-1-84593-755-3(4)) CABI GBR. Dist: Stylus Publishing, LLC.

CATTLE TRADE
see also Cowboys

Bell, Young. Forty Years in the Cow Business in Texas, New Mexico & Arizon. 2011. 92p. 38.95 (978-1-258-09762-2(1)) Literary Licensing, LLC.

Benton, Frank. Cowboy Life on the Sidetrack. 2009. 212p. 23.99 (978-1-103-37044-3(8)); pap. 17.99 (978-1-103-37040-5(5)) BiblioBazaar.

Buckley, Ciaran & Ward, Chris. Strong Farmer: The Memoirs of Joe Ward. 2008. (ENG., Illus.). 192p. pap. 27.95 (978-1-905483-24-2(4)) Liberties Pr. IRL. Dist: Dufour Editions, Inc.

Cairns, Barbara. Cracker Cow: A Narrative of Florida History. 2007. (Illus.). 104p. pap. (978-0-9792885-0-0(9)) IRC Bks.

Caldwell, Clifford R. John Simpson Chisum: Cattle King of the Pecos Revisited. 2010. 226p. pap. 22.95 (978-0-86534-756-4(5)) Sunstone Pr.

Casement, Dan Dillon. Random Recollections: The Life & Times & Something on the Personal Philosophy of A Twentieth Century Cowman, an Autobiographical Account. Orndulf, Don R., ed. 2011. 110p. 39.95 (978-1-258-03695-9(9)) Literary Licensing, LLC.

Coburn, Walt. Pioneer Cattleman in Montana: The Story of the Circle C Ranch. 2011. (ENG., Illus.). 352p. (C). pap. 26.95 (978-0-8061-4208-1(1)) Univ. of Oklahoma Pr.

Cox, James. Historical & Biographical Record of the Cattle Industry & Cattlemen of Texas & Adjacent Territory. 2011. 778p. 72.95 (978-1-258-10295-1(1)) Literary Licensing, LLC.

Dale, Edward Everett. The Range Cattle Industry. 2011. 216p. 44.95 (978-1-258-05076-4(5)) Literary Licensing, LLC.

Dale, Nancy. The Legacy of the Florida Pioneer Cow Hunters: In Their Own Words. 2011. 196p. 26.95 (978-1-4502-8790-6(5)); pap. 16.95 (978-1-4502-8789-0(1)) iUniverse, Inc.

Davis, John W. Wyoming Range War: The Infamous Invasion of Johnson County. 2010. (ENG.). 384p. 29.95 (978-0-8061-4106-0(9)) Univ. of Oklahoma Pr.

Edwards, Philip Leget. The Diary of Philip Leget Edwards: The Great Cattle Drive from California to Oregon In 1837. 2011. 54p. 36.95 (978-1-258-00458-3(5)) Literary Licensing, LLC.

Emmett, Chris. Shanghai Pierce: A Fair Likeness. 2011. 358p. 51.95 (978-1-258-04537-1(0)) Literary Licensing, LLC.

Flagg, Oscar H. Review of the Cattle Business in Johnson County Wyoming, Since 1822, & the Causes That Led to the Recent Invasion. (Mass Violence in America Ser.). reprint ed. 27.95 (978-0-405-01309-6(4)) Ayer Co. Pubs., Inc.

Gibson, Rob. Highland Cowboys: From the Hills of Scotland to the American Wild West. 2009. (ENG., Illus.). 192p. pap. 14.95 (978-1-906307-28-8(8)) Luath Pr. Ltd. GBR. Dist: Ingram Pub. Services.

Haldane, A. R. B. The Drove Roads of Scotland. 2008. (ENG., Illus.). 266p. pap. 17.95 (978-1-84158-695-3(1)) Birlinn, Ltd. GBR. Dist: Interlink Publishing Group, Inc.

The Importation of Canadian Beef That Comes from Animals Older Than 30 Months of Age: Field Hearing Before the Subcommittee on Interstate Commerce, Trade, & Tourism of the Committee on Commerce, Science, & Transportation, United States Senate, One Hundred Tenth Congress, First Session, February 21, 2007. 2007. (Illus.). iii, 48p. (978-0-16-079375-2(0), 552-070-36405-6) United States Government Printing Office.

Kastner, Justin & Tenhouse, Blair. 150 Years of Kansas Beef. 2011. (978-1-57864-685-2(5)) Donning Co. Pubs.

Little, Peter D. & McPeak, John G. Pastoral Livestock Marketing in Eastern Africa: Research & Policy Challenges. Little, Peter D. & McPeak, John G., eds. 2006. (ENG., Illus.). 288p. per. 35.95 (978-1-85339-631-1(1)) Intermediate Technology Development Group of North America.

Lunsford, Terry. Characteristics of Beef Cattle That Determine the Price Difference Between Traditional & Cph Sales. 2008. (Illus.). 68p. pap. (978-3-8364-9366-6(7)) VDM Verlag Dr. Mueller e.K.

McCoy, Joseph G. Historic Sketches of the Cattle Trade of the West & Southwest. 2009. 316p. pap. (978-1-4099-7139-9(2)) Dodo Pr.

—Historic Sketches of the Cattle Trade of the West & Southwest. (Illus.). 427p. reprint ed. lib. bdg. 98.00 (978-0-7222-4872-0(5)) Library Reprints, Inc.

McInerney, Jeremy. Cattle of the Sun: Cows & Culture in the World of the Ancient Greeks. 2010. (ENG., Illus.). 360p. (C). 46.95 (978-0-691-14007-0(3)) Princeton Univ. Pr.

Mercer, Asa Shinn. The Banditti of the Plains: Or the Cattlemen's Invasion of Wyoming In 1892. 2011. 152p. 41.95 (978-1-258-05352-9(7)) Literary Licensing, LLC.

Nicol, D. L. Bill Kitt. 2009. 29.50 (978-0-615-28626-6(7)) Nicol, Donovan L.

Oppenheimer, Harold L. Cowboy Arithmetic: Cattle As an Investment. 2011. 208p. 44.95 (978-1-258-09827-8(X)) Literary Licensing, LLC.

Osgood, Ernest Staples. The Day of the Cattleman. 2009. (ENG.). 296p. pap. 50.00 (978-0-8166-5841-1(2)) Univ. of Minnesota Pr.

Peters, K. J., et al, eds. The cattle sector in Central & Eastern Europe: Developments & opportunities in a time of Transition. 2009. (Illus.). 180p. pap. 61.00 (978-90-8686-104-0(0)) Wageningen Academic Publishers NLD. Dist: Enfield Publishing & Distribution Co., Inc.

Ponting, Tom Candy. Life of Tom Candy Ponting: An Autobiography. 2011. 158p. 41.95 (978-1-258-08894-1(0)) Literary Licensing, LLC.

Puripunpinyoo, Anucha. High-Plains States. 2008. 168p. pap. (978-3-639-05394-4(X)) VDM Verlag Dr. Mueller e.K.

Richthofen, Walter Von. Cattle-Raising on the Plains of North America. 2008. 112p. 34.95 (978-1-4368-8706-9(2)); pap. 19.95 (978-1-4368-0105-8(2)) Kessinger Publishing, LLC.

Rockwell, Wilson, ed. Memoirs of a Lawman. 2011. 380p. 53.95 (978-1-258-09004-3(X)) Literary Licensing, LLC.

Ruskowsky, Nancy Heyl. Two Dot Ranch: A Biography of Place. 2007. (978-0-931271-86-1(X)); pap. (978-0-931271-87-8(8)) High Plains Pr.

—Two Dot Ranch: A Biography of Place. 2009. (ENG., Illus.). 400p. 37.95 (978-1-932636-48-2(X)) 2009. (Illus.). pap. 22.95 (978-1-932636-47-5(1)) 2008. (978-1-932636-46-8(3)) Pronghorn Pr.

Sandoz, Mari. The Cattlemen: From the Rio Grande Across the Far Marias. 2nd ed. 2010. (ENG.). 552p. pap. 19.95 (978-0-8032-2983-9(6), Bison Bks.) Univ. of Nebraska Pr.

Toulson, Shirley. The Drovers. 2nd ed. 2008. (Shire Library). (ENG., Illus.). 40p. pap. 12.95 (978-0-7478-0630-1(6)) Shire Pubns., Ltd. GBR. Dist: Random Hse., Inc.

Verckler, Stewart P. Cowtown Abilene: The Story of Abilene, Kansas, 1867-1875. 2011. 84p. 37.95 (978-1-258-06622-2(X)) Literary Licensing, LLC.

Woods, Lawrence M. Alex Swan & the Swan Companies. 2006. (Western Lands & Waters Ser.: Vol. 22). (ENG., Illus.). 296p. (C). 34.95 (978-0-87062-346-2(X), Clark, Arthur H. Co., The) Univ. of Oklahoma Pr.

CATTLE TRADE—LAW AND LEGISLATION
see Animal Industry—Law and Legislation

CATTLE TRADE—AUSTRALIA

Bowen, Jill. Kidman the Forgotten King. 2007. (978-0-7322-8610-1(7), Fourth Estate) HarperCollins Pubs. Australia.

CATULLUS, GAIUS VALERIUS

Barbaud, T. Catulle: Une poétique de L'indicible. 2006. (Bibliothèque D'études Classiques Ser.). (FRE & ENG.). 280p. (C). pap. 66.00 (978-90-429-1693-7(1)) Peeters Pubs. & Booksellers BEL. Dist: Brown, David Bk. Co., The.

Burl, Aubrey. Catullus: A Poet in the Rome of Julius Caesar. 2009. (Illus.). 224p. pap. 24.95 (978-1-84868-391-4(X)) Amberley Publishing GBR. Dist: Casemate Pubs. & Bk. Distributors, LLC.

Cairns, Francis. Roman Lyric: Collected papers on Catullus & Horace. 2012. (Beiträge zur Altertumskunde Ser.). (ENG.). X, 525p. (gr. 17). 182.00 (978-3-11-026627-6(X)) De Gruyter, Walter Inc.

Eisenhauer, Robert G. Catullan Mediations & Other Essays. 2011. (Illus.). xvi, 252p. 78.95 (978-1-4331-1349-9(X)) Lang, Peter Publishing, Inc.

Ellis, Robinson. A Commentary on Catullus. 2010. (ENG.). 468p. pap. 37.75 (978-1-149-48949-9(9)); (ENG.). 600p. pap. 44.75 (978-1-177-57612-3(0)); (ENG.). 602p. pap. 45.75 (978-1-176-52553-5(0)); 596p. pap. 44.75 (978-1-146-75980-9(0)) BiblioBazaar.

—A Commentary on Catullus. 2010. (Cambridge Library Collection - Classics Ser.). 472p. pap. 34.99 (978-1-108-01274-4(4)) Cambridge Univ. Pr.

—A Commentary on Catullus. 2009. 570p. pap. 20.11 (978-1-151-40710-8(0)) General Bks. LLC.

—A Commentary on Catullus. 2007. (ENG.). 586p. 58.95 (978-0-548-18421-9(6)); 588p. per. 43.95 (978-1-4304-8658-9(9)) Kessinger Publishing, LLC.

Gaisser, Julia Haig. Catullus. 2009. (Blackwell Introductions to the Classical World Ser.: 14). (ENG., Illus.). 256p. 110.95 (978-1-4051-1889-7(X), Wiley-Blackwell) Wiley, John & Sons, Inc.

Gaisser, Julia Haig, ed. Catullus. 2007. (Oxford Readings in Classical Studies). (LAT & ENG.). 616p. 225.00 (978-0-19-928034-6(7)); pap. 95.00 (978-0-19-928035-3(5)) Oxford Univ. Pr., Inc.

Greene, Ellen. Erotics of Domination: Male Desire & the Mistress in Latin Love Poetry. 2010. (Oklahoma Series in Classical Culture Ser.). (ENG.). 162p. pap. 19.95 (978-0-8061-4050-6(X)) Univ. of Oklahoma Pr.

Hartz, Cornelius. Catulls Epigramme Im Kontext Hellenistischer Dichtung. 2007. (Beiträge Zur Altertumskunde Ser.). (GER., Illus.). 241p. 140.00 (978-3-11-019466-1(X)) De Gruyter, Walter Inc.

Hejduk, Julia Dyson. Clodia: A Sourcebook. 2008. (Oklahoma Ser. in Classical Culture Ser.). (ENG.). 288p. (C). pap. 24.95 (978-0-8061-3907-4(2)) Univ. of Oklahoma Pr.

Putnam, Michael C. J. Poetic Interplay: Catullus & Horace. annot. ed. 2006. (Martin Classical Lectures). (ENG.). 184p. (C). 49.95 (978-0-691-12537-4(6)) Princeton Univ. Pr.

Quinn, Kenneth, ed. The Catullan Revolution. 2nd ed. 2009. 132p. pap. 24.95 (978-1-85399-600-9(9)) Bristol Classical Pr. GBR. Dist: International Publishers Marketing.

Skinner, Marilyn B., ed. A Companion to Catullus. 2007. (Blackwell Companions to the Ancient World Ser.: 30). (ENG., Illus.). 616p. 209.95 (978-1-4051-3533-7(6), Wiley-Blackwell) Wiley, John & Sons, Inc.

Smith, Sean. Teacher's Guide: Catullus: A Legamus Transitional Reader. 2010. pap. (978-0-86516-671-4(4)) Bolchazy-Carducci Pubs.

Stroup, Sarah Culpepper. Catullus, Cicero, & a Society of Patrons: The Generation of the Text. 2010. (ENG.). 322p. 104.00 (978-0-521-51390-6(1)) Cambridge Univ. Pr.

Trappes-Lomax, John M. Catullus: A Textual Reappraisal. 2007. (LAT & ENG.). 315p. 69.50 (978-1-905125-15-9(1)) Classical Pr. of Wales, The GBR. Dist: Brown, David Bk. Co., The.

CATULLUS, GAIUS VALERIUS—IN LITERATURE

Skinner, Marilyn B., ed. A Companion to Catullus. 2010. (Blackwell Companions to the Ancient World Ser.: 76). (ENG.). 616p. pap. 49.95 (978-1-4443-3925-3(7), Wiley-Blackwell) Wiley, John & Sons, Inc.

CATV
see Cable Television

CAUCASIAN LANGUAGES
see also Georgian Language

Fähnrich, Heinz. Kartwelisches Etymologisches Wörterbuch. 2007. (Handbook of Oriental Studies). 880p. (978-90-04-16109-2(0)) BRILL.

—Kartwelsprachen: Altgeorgisch, Neugeorgisch, Mingrelisch, Lasisch, Swanisch. 2008. (GER., Illus.). 344p. pap. (978-3-89500-653-1(X)) Reichert, Ludwig Dr.

Guentchéva, Zlatka & Landaburu, Jon. L'énonciation Médiatisée II le Traitement âépistémologique de L'information: Illustrations Amérindiennes et Caucasiennes. 2007. viii, 433p. (978-2-87723-960-8(8)) Peeters Pubs. & Booksellers.

—L'énonciation Médiatisée II le Traitement âépistémologique de L'information: Illustrations Amérindiennes et Caucasiennes. 2007. (Bibliothèque de l'Information Grammaticale Ser.). (ENG.). 433p. (C). pap. 66.00 (978-90-429-1864-1(0)) Peeters Pubs. & Booksellers BEL. Dist: Brown, David Bk. Co., The.

Khalidov, A. I. Chechenskii Iazyk: Morfemika, Slovoobrazovanie. 2010. (RUS.). 766p. (978-5-98896-139-0(8)) Kniznoe izdatel'stvo.

Nichols, Johanna. Ingush Grammar. 2010. (UC Publications in Linguistics Ser.). (Illus.). 740p. pap. 70.00 (978-0-520-09877-0(3)) Univ. of California Pr.

Saraliev, Sh IU. Chechenskii Arkhiv: [sbornik Materialov Po Istorii Chechenskogo Naroda. 2008. (RUS., Illus.). (978-5-98896-094-2(4)) Kniznoe izdatel'stvo.

Saraliev, Sh IU & Muzaev, M. N. Chechenskii Arkhiv: [sbornik Materialov Po Istorii Chechenskogo Naroda. 2008. (RUS., Illus.). (978-5-94587-433-6(7)) Kniznoe izdatel'stvo.

Starostin, S. A. & Nikolayev, Sergei L. A North Caucasian Etymological Dictionary. 2007. (Anatolian & Caucasian Studies). (978-0-88206-117-7(8)) Caravan Bks.

CAUCASIAN RACE

Here are entered works of an anthropological nature focusing on the physical features that characterize Caucasians and distinguish them from other races of mankind. Works of a sociological nature that discuss white people as an element in the population, especially in countries where they are a minority, are entered under Whites.

see also Indo-Europeans; Semites; Teutonic Race; Whites

Allen, Dion. Road to Domination. 2011. 64p. pap. 9.95 (978-1-4502-8691-6(7)) iUniverse, Inc.

Baum, Bruce. The Rise & Fall of the Caucasian Race: A Political History of Racial Identity. 2008. (ENG., Illus.). 352p. pap. 24.00 (978-0-8147-9893-5(4)) New York Univ. Pr.

D'Olivet, Fabre. Concerning Property in the Inequality of Conditions: Their Origin. 2006. pap. 9.95 (978-1-4286-8240-5(6)) Kessinger Publishing, LLC.

Freie, Carrie. Class Construction: White Working-Class Student Identity in the New Millennium. 2008. (ENG.). 140p. pap. 20.99 (978-0-7391-1548-0(0)) Lexington Bks.

Meyer, Armin. Alternative Werbung mit Mixed-Reality-Technologie: Konzepte mit Mehrwert für die Kommunikationspolitikdurch den Einsatz von Mixed-Reality-Technologie. 2008. 96p. pap. (978-3-639-02123-3(1)) VDM Verlag Dr. Mueller e.K.

Rolland, John. The Valorous: Caucasian Manifesto. 2009. 683p. pap. 32.95 (978-1-4327-3534-0(9)) Outskirts Pr., Inc.

Stewart, Marsha. The 8% Epitaph Disappearance of the Caucasian Race. 2007. (C). pap. 12.00 (978-0-56411-484-6(8), YBBG#0474, KHA BK. Pubs. Unltd.) UBUS Communications Systems.

—The 8% Epitaph Dissapearance of the Caucasian Race. 2007. 128p. pap. 12.00 (978-0-56411-483-9(X), YBBG#0473) UBUS Communications Systems.

Vinson, Irmin & Johnson, Greg. Some Thoughts on Hitler & Other Essays. 2012. 35.00 (978-1-935965-25-1(5)); pap. 20.00 (978-1-935965-26-8(3)) Counter Currents Publishing, Ltd. (Orbit Books).

Yasuba, Yasukichi. Birth Rates of the White Population in the United States, 1800-1860: An Economic Study. (Johns Hopkins University. Studies in the Social Sciences, Thirtieth Ser.: 2). reprint ed. 37.50 *(978-0-404-61341-9(1))* AMS Pr., Inc.

CAUCASUS

Allen, William Edward David & Muratoff, Paul. Caucasian Battlefields: A History of the Wars on the Turco-Caucasian Border 1828-1921. 2010. (Cambridge Library Collection - History Ser.). (Illus.). 716p. pap. 48.00 *(978-1-108-01335-2(X))* Cambridge Univ. Pr.

Berman, Michael. Shamanic Journeys Through Daghestan. 2010. (ENG.). 196p. pap. 29.95 *(978-1-84694-225-9(X))* Hunt, John Publishing Ltd. GBR. Dist: National Bk. Network.

—Shamanic Journeys Through the Caucasus. 2009. (ENG.). 240p. pap. 29.95 *(978-1-84694-253-2(5))* Hunt, John Publishing Ltd. GBR. Dist: National Bk. Network.

Bradley C. Ryan. The Caucasus Region: Economic & Political Developments. 2011. (Series: Caucasus Region Political, Economic, & Security Issues Ser.). 309p. 129.00 *(978-1-61122-557-0(4))* Nova Science Pubs., Inc.

Breyfogle, Nicholas B. Heretics & Colonizers: Forging Russia's Empire in the South Caucasus. 2011. (Illus.). 376p. pap. 29.95 ***(978-0-8014-7746-1(8))*** Cornell Univ. Pr.

Bullough, Oliver. Let Our Fame Be Great: Journeys among the Defiant People of the Caucasus. (ENG.). 528p. (gr. 9). 2012. pap. 19.99 ***(978-0-465-02904-4(3))*** 2010. 28.95 *(978-0-465-02184-0(0))* Basic Bks.

Çaglayan, Kaya Tuncer. British Policy towards Transcaucasia, 1917-1921. 2010. 111.32 *(978-1-61719-128-2(0))* Gorgias Pr., LLC.

Coene, Frederik. The Caucasus - an Introduction. 2009. (Routledge Contemporary Russia & Eastern Europe Ser.). (ENG., Illus.). 256p. 145.00 *(978-0-415-48660-6(2))* Routledge.

De Waal, Thomas. The Caucasus: An Introduction, 1 vol. 2010. (ENG., Illus.). 288p. pap. 18.95 *(978-0-19-539977-6(3))* Oxford Univ. Pr., Inc.

Dworzak, Thomas. Kavkas. 2010. (RUS & ENG., Illus.). 216p. 100.00 *(978-90-5330-699-4(4))* Mets en Schilt Uitgevers NLD. Dist: Ingram Pub. Services.

Evliya Çelebi, et al. Travels in Iran & the Caucasus in 1647 & 1654. 2009. *(978-1-933823-36-2(4))* Mage Pubs., Inc.

Gordin, IA A. & Lisitsyna, G. G. General A.P. Ermolov I Rossiisko-Kavkazskie Otnosheniia V XIX-Nachale XX Veka. 2009. (RUS.). 125p. *(978-5-7439-0148-7(1))* Zvezda, AO, zurnal.

Grant, B. Prisoners of the Caucasus. 2009. (Culture & Society after Socialism Ser.). (Illus.). 200p. 69.95 *(978-0-8014-4304-6(0))* Cornell Univ. Pr.

Grant, Bruce. The Captive & the Gift: Cultural Histories of Sovereignty in Russia & the Caucasus. 2009. (Culture & Society after Socialism Ser.). (Illus.). 200p. pap. 21.95 *(978-0-8014-7541-2(4))* Cornell Univ. Pr.

Grant, Bruce & Yalçin-Heckmann, Lale, eds. Caucasus Paradigms: Anthropologies, Histories, & the Making of a World Area. 2008. (ENG., Illus.). 328p. pap. 49.95 *(978-3-8258-9906-6(3))* Lit Verlag DEU. Dist: Transaction Pubs.

Griffin, Nicholas. Caucasus: In the Wake of Warriors. Date not set. pap. *(978-0-312-30854-4(X)*, St. Martin's Griffin); mass mkt. *(978-0-312-98657-5(2)*, St. Martin's Paperbacks) St. Martin's Pr.

Haro, Fran W. Georgia & the Caucasus Region. 2009. pap. 69.00 *(978-1-60692-436-5(2))* Nova Science Pubs., Inc.

Hermann, Werner & Linn, Johannes. Central Asia & the Caucasus: At the Crossroads of Eurasia in the 21st Century. 2011. (Illus.). 262p. (C). 40.00 ***(978-81-321-0743-9(8)***, B07439C) SAGE Pubns., Inc.

Jakubowski, E., et al. 10 Health Questions about the Caucasus & Central Asia. 2009. (WPRO Publication). 200p. pap. 48.00 *(978-92-890-4169-0(2))* World Health Organization.

Kapidze, Aleksandro I. Caucasus Region: Geopolitical Nexus? 2008. (Illus.). (C). 150.00 *(978-1-60021-964-1(0))* Nova Science Pubs., Inc.

King, Charles. The Ghost of Freedom: A History of the Caucasus. (ENG., Illus.). 2009. 336p. pap. 19.95 *(978-0-19-539239-5(6))* 2008. 320p. 29.95 *(978-0-19-517775-6(4))* Oxford Univ. Pr., Inc.

Kolesnikova, M. E., et al. Stavropolskaia Gubernskaia Uchenaia Arkhivnaia Komissiia: Stranitsy Istorii Arkhivnogo Dela Severnogo Kavkaza. 2007. (RUS., Illus.). 169p. *(978-5-85714-054-3(4))* Vestnik Kavkaza, Redakcija gazety.

Kotliarov, Viktor Nikolaevich. Kavkaz. 2010. (RUS.). 303p. *(978-5-93680-376-5(7))*; 315p. *(978-5-93680-389-5(9))* Poligrafservis i T.

Kurtynova-D'Herlugnan, Liubov. The Tsar's Abolitionists: The Slave Trade in the Caucasus & Its Suppression. 2010. (Illus.). ccc 30p. *(978-90-04-18344-5(2))* BRILL.

Laine, Arthur T. Economic, Political & Social Issues of the Caucasus Region. 2011. (Series: Caucasus Region Political, Economic, & Security Issues Ser.). 129.00 *(978-1-61122-553-2(1))* Nova Science Pubs., Inc.

Leskov, Aleksandr Mikhailovich. The Maikop Treasure. 2008. (Illus.). 304p. (C). 75.00 *(978-1-934536-04-9(0))*, Univ. of Pennsylvania Museum of Archaeology & Anthropology) Univ. Museum Pubns.

Lordkipanidze, Vazha, ed. The Population of the Caucasus. 2010. (Caucasus Region Political, Economic, & Security Issues Ser.). 294p. 59.00 *(978-1-60876-016-9(2))* Nova Science Pubs., Inc.

Mackie, J. Milton (John Milton). Life of Schamyl: And, Narrative of the Circassian War of independence Against Russia / by J. Milton Mackie. 2006. 312p. per. 23.99 *(978-1-4255-2996-3(8))* MPublishing.

Marshall, Alex. The Caucasus under Soviet Rule. (ENG., Illus.). 2012. 400p. (C). pap. 44.95 ***(978-0-415-62542-5(4))*** 2009. 256p. 165.00 *(978-0-415-41012-0(6))* Routledge.

Nieling, Jens. Die Einfuhrung der Eisentechnologie in Sudkaukasien und Ostanatolien wahrend der Spatbronze- und Fruheisenzeit. 2009. (Black Sea Studies). (GER., Illus.). 363p. (C). 50.00 *(978-87-7934-444-0(5))* Aarhus Universitetsforlag DNK. Dist: ISD.

Nove, Alec. The Soviet Middle East (Routledge Revivals) 2012. (Routledge Revivals Ser.). (ENG.). 164p. 110.00 ***(978-0-415-68241-1(X))*** Routledge.

Ordubadi, Mammad. Years of Blood: A History of the Armenian-Muslim Clashes in the Caucasus, 1905-1906. 2011. 205p. pap. 34.95 *(978-0-86372-390-2(X)*, Ithaca Pr.) Garnet Publishing, Ltd. GBR. Dist: International Specialized Bk. Services.

Papava, V. G. Central Caucasus: Problems of Geopolitical Economy. Ismailov, Eldar, ed. 2008. xii, 131p. (C). 98.00 *(978-1-60456-606-2(X))* Nova Science Pubs., Inc.

Roudik, Peter L. & Roudik, Peter. Culture & Customs of the Caucasus, 1 vol. 2008. (Culture & Customs of Europe Ser.). (Illus.). 228p. 49.95 *(978-0-313-34885-3(5)*, GR4885, Greenwood Pr.) Greenwood Publishing Group, Inc.

Rubinson, Karen S. & Sagona, A., eds. Ceramics in Transitions: Chalcolithic Through Iron Age in the Highlands of the Southern Caucasus & Anatolia. 2008. (Ancient near Eastern Studies Supplement Ser.). (ENG.). 368p. (C). 131.00 *(978-90-429-1998-3(1))* Peeters Pubs. & Booksellers BEL. Dist: Brown, David Bk. Co., The.

Sahni, Kalpana. Crucifying the Orient: Russian Orientalism & the Colonization of Caucasus & Central Asia. 2006. (Institute for Comparative Research in Human Culture Ser.). (ENG., Illus.). 39.00 *(978-974-8299-50-1(3))* Orchid Pr. THA. Dist: National Bk. Network.

Sanders, Thomas, et al. Russian-Muslim Confrontation in the Caucasus. 2010. (Illus.). x, 264p. pap. 39.95 ***(978-0-415-47879-3(0))*** Routledge.

Souleimanov, Emil. Endless War: The Russian-Chechen Conflict in Perspective. 366p. pap. 44.95 *(978-3-631-56040-2(0))* Lang, Peter Publishing, Inc.

Tsitsishvili, Nino. Cultural Paradigms & Political Change in the Caucasus. 2010. 316p. pap. *(978-3-8383-8856-4(9))* Lambert Academic Publishing.

Villari, Luigi. Fire & Sword in the Caucasus. 2009. 218p. pap. *(978-0-217-47608-9(2))* Books LLC.

Ware, Robert Bruce, et al. Dagestan: Russian Hegemony & Islamic Resistance in the North Caucasus. 2009. (ENG., Illus.). 272p. 99.95 *(978-0-7656-2028-6(6))* Sharpe, M.E. Inc.

Wheeler, James Talboys. Journey of a Voyage up the Irrawaddy to Mandalay & Bhamo. 2006. (Itineraria Asiatica: Burma Ser.). (ENG., Illus.). pap. 16.00 *(978-974-3299-67-9(8)*, Orchid Pr. THA. Dist: National Bk. Network.

Wooden, Amanda E. & Stefes, Christoph H., eds. The Politics of Transition in Central Asia & the Caucasus: Enduring Legacies & Emerging Challenges. 2012. (ENG., Illus.). 288p. (C). pap. 44.95 ***(978-0-415-62539-5(4))*** Routledge.

Yavuz, M. Hakan, ed. War & Diplomacy: The Russo-Turkish War of 1877-1878 & the Treaty of Berlin. 2011. (ENG., Illus.). 616p. (gr. 12). 40.00 ***(978-1-60781-150-3(2))*** Univ. of Utah Pr.

Zurcher, Christoph. The Post-Soviet Wars: Rebellion, Ethnic Conflict, & Nationhood in the Caucasus. 2009. (ENG., Illus.). 304p. pap. 24.00 *(978-0-8147-9724-2(5))* New York Univ. Pr.

CAUCHY, AUGUSTIN LOUIS, BARON, 1789-1857

Bradley, Robert E. & Sandifer, C. Edward. Cauchy's Cours d'analyse: An Annotated Translation. 2009. (Sources & Studies in the History of Mathematics & Physical Sciences Ser.). (Illus.). xx, 412p. 159.00 *(978-1-4419-0548-2(0)*, 1441905480) Springer.

Smithies, Frank. Cauchy & the Creation of Complex Function Theory. 2008. (ENG., Illus.). 228p. (C). pap. 48.00 *(978-0-521-06887-1(8))* Cambridge Univ. Pr.

CAUGHNAWAGA INDIANS

see Indians of North America—Canada

CAULFIELD, HOLDEN (FICTITIOUS CHARACTER)

Beidler, Peter G. A Reader's Companion to J. D. Salinger's the Catcher in the Rye. 2nd rev. ed. 2011. 290p. pap. 25.95 *(978-1-60381-037-1(4)*, Coffeetown Pr.) Coffeetown Enterprises, Inc.

Graham, Sarah. J. D. Salinger's the Catcher in the Rye: A Routledge Guide. 2007. (Routledge Guides to Literature Ser.). 128p. 95.00 *(978-0-415-34452-4(2))*; per. 23.95 *(978-0-415-34453-1(0))* Routledge.

CAUSALITY

see Causality (Physics); Causation

CAUSALITY (PHYSICS)

Baruk#269;#263;, Ilija. Causality I. A theory of energy, time & Space. 2008. 552p. pap. 70.00 *(978-1-4092-2952-0(1))* Lulu Enterprises Inc.

—Causality II. A theory of energy, time & Space. 2008. 320p. pap. 50.00 *(978-1-4092-2954-4(8))* Lulu Enterprises Inc.

Berzuini, Carlo, et al, eds. Causality: Statistical Perspectives & Applications. 2012. (Wiley Series in Probability & Statistics Ser.). (ENG.). 384p. 90.00 ***(978-0-470-66556-5(4)***, Wiley) Wiley, John & Sons, Inc.

Borchers, Hans Jargen & Sen, Rathindra Nath. Mathematical Implications of Einstein-Weyl Causality. 2010. (Lecture Notes in Physics Ser.). (Illus.). xii, 191p. pap. 99.00 *(978-3-642-07233-8(X)*, 364207233X) Springer.

Dowe, Phil. Physical Causation. 2007. (Cambridge Studies in Probability, Induction & Decision Theory Ser.). (ENG., Illus.). 236p. per. 53.00 *(978-0-521-03975-8(4))* Cambridge Univ. Pr.

Eells, Ellery. Probabilistic Causality. 2008. (Cambridge Studies in Probability, Induction & Decision Theory Ser.). (ENG., Illus.). 428p. pap. 58.00 *(978-0-521-06132-2(6))* Cambridge Univ. Pr.

Hendricks, Vincent F., et al, eds. Interactions: Mathematics, Physics & Philosophy, 1860-1930. 2010. (Boston Studies in the Philosophy of Science Ser.). xiv, 338p. pap. 189.00 *(978-90-481-7306-8(X)*, 904817306X) Springer.

Hunter, G., et al, eds. Causality & Locality in Modern Physics. 2010. (Fundamental Theories of Physics Ser.). 508p. pap. 359.00 *(978-90-481-5092-2(2)*, 9048150922) Springer.

Majer, Ulrich, et al, eds. David Hilbert's Lectures on the Foundations of Physics 1915-1927: Relativity, Quantum Theory & Epistemology. 2009. (GER & ENG., Illus.). xi, 690p. 139.00 *(978-3-540-20606-4(X)*, 354020606X) Springer.

McGuinness, B. F., ed. Friedrich Waismann - Causality & Logical Positivism. 2011. (Vienna Circle Institute Yearbook Ser.). (Illus.). viii, 400p. 189.00 *(978-94-007-1750-3(4)*, 9400717504) Springer.

Poli, Roberto, ed. Causality & Motivation. 2010. 235p. 109.95 *(978-3-86838-068-2(X))* Ontos Verlag DEU. Dist: Transaction Pubs.

Riggs, Peter J. Quantum Causality: Conceptual Issues in the Causal Theory of Quantum Mechanics. 2009. (Studies in History & Philosophy of Science Ser.). (ENG., Illus.). xii, 232p. 159.00 *(978-90-481-2402-2(6)*, 9048124026) Springer.

Sheehan, Daniel P. Frontiers of Time: Retrocausation - Experiment & Theory, San Diego, California, 20-22 June 2006. 2006. (AIP Conference Proceedings Ser.). (Illus.). 361p. 147.00 *(978-0-7354-0361-1(9)*, 0735403619) American Institute of Physics.

Sheehan, Daniel P., ed. Quantum Retrocausation: Theory & Experiment: Theory & Experiment. 2012. (AIP Conference Proceedings Ser.). (ENG.). 318p. pap. 154.00 ***(978-0-7354-0981-1(1)***, 0735409811, AIP Pr.) Springer.

CAUSATION

see also Necessity (Philosophy); Sufficient Reason; Teleology

Allen, Keith & Stoneham, Tom, eds. Causation & Modern Philosophy. 2010. (Routledge Advances in the History of Philosophy Ser.). (ENG.). 282p. (C). 125.00 *(978-0-415-88355-9(5))* Routledge.

Altman, Matthew C. A Companion to Kant's Critique of Pure Reason. rev. ed. 2007. (ENG.). 256p. pap. 33.00 *(978-0-8133-4383-9(6))* Westview Pr.

Bedi, Sonu. Political Contingency: Studying the Unexpected, the Accidental, & the Unforeseen. Shapiro, Ian, ed. 2007. (ENG.). 304p. 65.00 *(978-0-8147-4044-6(8))* New York Univ. Pr.

—Political Contingency: Studying the Unexpected, the Accidental, & the Unforeseen. Shapiro, Ian, ed. 2009. (ENG., Illus.). 304p. pap. 24.00 *(978-0-8147-4096-5(0))* New York Univ. Pr.

Beebee, Helen, et al, eds. The Oxford Handbook of Causation. (Oxford Handbooks Ser.). (ENG., Illus.). 2012. 806p. pap. 50.00 ***(978-0-19-964258-8(3))*** 2010. 624p. 150.00 *(978-0-19-927973-9(X))* Oxford Univ. Pr., Inc.

Berger, Sebastian. The Foundations of Non-Equilibrium Economics: The principle of circular & cumulative Causation. 2009. (Routledge Advances in Heterodox Economics Ser.). (ENG., Illus.). 224p. 135.00 *(978-0-415-77780-3(1))* Routledge.

Berzuini, Carlo, et al, eds. Causality: Statistical Perspectives & Applications. 2012. (Wiley Series in Probability & Statistics Ser.). (ENG.). 384p. 90.00 ***(978-0-470-66556-5(4)***, Wiley) Wiley, John & Sons, Inc.

Bishop, John. Natural Agency: An Essay on the Causal Theory of Action. 2008. (Cambridge Studies in Philosophy Ser.). (ENG.). 224p. pap. 46.00 *(978-0-521-06397-5(3))* Cambridge Univ. Pr.

Bracken, Joseph A. Does God Play Dice? Divine Providence for a World in the Making. 2012. ***(978-0-8146-8052-0(6))***; E-Book ***(978-0-8146-8053-7(4))*** Liturgical Pr.

Broad, C. D. Induction, Probability, & Causation: Selected Papers. 2010. (Synthese Library). 312p. pap. 289.00 *(978-90-481-8317-3(0)*, 9048183170) Springer.

Brown, Jason W. Time, Will & Mental Process. 2010. (Cognition & Language: A Series in Psycholinguistics Ser.). 276p. pap. 99.00 *(978-1-4419-3252-5(6)*, 1441932526) Springer.

Brown, Thomas. Inquiry into the Relation of Cause & Effect. 2011. (Cambridge Library Collection - Philosophy Ser.). (ENG.). 588p. pap. 43.00 ***(978-1-108-04079-2(9))*** Cambridge Univ. Pr.

—Inquiry into the Relation of Cause & Effect. 2009. 164p. pap. 19.99 *(978-0-217-49046-7(8))* General Bks. LLC.

—Inquiry into the Relation of Cause & Effect. 2008. 476p. 52.95 *(978-0-548-94164-5(5))* 2007. (ENG.). 480p. per. 37.95 *(978-0-548-60970-5(5))* Kessinger Publishing, LLC.

Bunge, Mario. Causality & Modern Science. 4th rev. ed. 2008. (ENG., Illus.). 424p. pap. 29.95 *(978-1-4128-0824-8(3))* Transaction Pubs.

Burnham, Douglas. Kant's Critique of Pure Reason. 2008. (ENG.). 224p. 50.00 *(978-0-253-35263-7(0)*, 0253352630); pap. 19.95 *(978-0-253-22035-6(1)*, 0253220351) Indiana Univ. Pr.

Campbell, Joseph Keim, et al, eds. Causation & Explanation. 2007. (Topics in Contemporary Philosophy Ser.). (ENG., Illus.). 336p. (gr. 17). 85.00 *(978-0-262-03363-3(1))*; pap. 36.00 *(978-0-262-53290-7(5))* MIT Pr.

Campbell, Neil. Mental Causation: A Nonreductive Approach. 2008. 124p. (C). 58.95 *(978-1-4331-0374-2(5))* Lang, Peter Publishing, Inc.

Carroll, John W. Laws of Nature. 2008. (Cambridge Studies in Philosophy Ser.). (ENG.). 216p. pap. 46.00 *(978-0-521-06413-2(9))* Cambridge Univ. Pr.

Casti, John L. The Temper of the Times: How Today's Social Mood Foreshadows Tomorrow's Headlines. 2010. (Illus.). xvi, 210p. 27.50 *(978-3-642-04834-0(X)*, 364204834X) Springer.

Causal Inference. 2011. 49.95 *(978-1-4200-7617-2(5)*, CRC Press) Taylor & Francis Group GBR. Dist: Taylor & Francis Group.

Cheyne, C. Knowledge, Cause, & Abstract Objects: Causal Objections to Platonism. 2010. (Western Ontario Series in Philosophy of Science Ser.). 252p. pap. 139.00 *(978-90-481-5836-2(2)*, 9048158362) Springer.

Cooper, Barry, et al. Challenging the Qualitative-Quantitative Divide: Explorations in Case-focused Causal Analysis. 2012. (ENG., Illus.). 288p. pap. 44.95 *(978-1-4411-1439-6(4))* Continuum International Publishing Group, Ltd. GBR. Dist: National Bk. Network.

—Challenging the Qualitative-Quantitative Divide: Explorations in Case-Focused Causal Analysis. 2012. (Illus.). 240p. E-Book ***(978-1-4411-4220-7(7))***; E-Book ***(978-1-4411-0063-4(6))*** Continuum International Publishing Group, Ltd.

—Challenging the Qualitative-Quantitative Divide: Explorations in Case-Focused Causal Analysis. 2012. (ENG.). 288p. 140.00 *(978-1-4411-7144-3(4))* Continuum International Publishing Group, Ltd. GBR. Dist: National Bk. Network.

Coventry, Angela M. & Coventry. Hume's Theory of Causation: A Quasi-Realist Interpretation. 2006. (Continuum Studies in British Philosophy). (ENG.). 192p. 120.00 *(978-0-8264-8635-6(5))* Continuum International Publishing Group, Ltd. GBR. Dist: National Bk. Network.

Dardis, Anthony. Mental Causation: The Mind-Body Problem. 2008. (ENG., Illus.). 216p. (gr. 17). 80.00 *(978-0-231-14416-2(4))*; pap. 26.50 *(978-0-231-14417-9(2))* Columbia Univ. Pr.

de Muijnck, Wim. Dependencies, Connections, & Other Relations: A Theory of Mental Causation. 2010. (Philosophical Studies Ser.). 320p. pap. 219.00 *(978-90-481-6326-7(9)*, 9048163269) Springer.

Dechter, Rina, et al, eds. Heuristics, Probability & Causality a Tribute to Judea Pearl. 2010. (Illus.). 580p. *(978-1-904987-66-6(4))*; pap. *(978-1-904987-65-9(6))* College Pubns.

Dekker, Sidney. Drift into Failure: From Hunting Broken Components to Understanding Complex Systems. 2011. (Illus.). 234p. 124.95 *(978-1-4094-2222-8(4))*; pap. 29.95 *(978-1-4094-2221-1(6))* Ashgate Publishing Co.

Dembski, William A. No Free Lunch: Why Specified Complexity Cannot Be Purchased Without Intelligence. Dembski, William A., ed. 2nd ed. 2007. (ENG., Illus.). 432p. pap. 28.95 *(978-0-7425-5810-6(X))* Rowman & Littlefield Publishers, Inc.

Denkel, Arda. Object & Property. 2007. (Cambridge Studies in Philosophy Ser.). (ENG.). 276p. pap. 58.00 *(978-0-521-04209-3(7))* Cambridge Univ. Pr.

Dodds, Michael J. Unlocking Divine Action: Contemporary Science & Thomas Aquinas. 2012. ***(978-0-8132-1989-9(2))*** Catholic Univ. of America Pr.

Eells, Ellery. Rational Decision & Causality. 2009. (Cambridge Studies in Philosophy Ser.). (ENG.). 248p. (C). pap. 36.00 *(978-0-521-11011-2(4))* Cambridge Univ. Pr.

Eilan, Naomi, et al, eds. Perception, Causation, & Objectivity. 2011. (ENG.). 360p. 110.00 *(978-0-19-969204-0(1))* Oxford Univ. Pr., Inc.

Estimating Causal Effects Using Experimental & Observational Designs. 2007. per. *(978-0-935302-34-9(4))* American Educational Research Assn.

Ewing, A. C. Kant's Treatment of Causality (Routledge Revivals), Volume 1. 2012. (Routledge Revivals Ser.). (ENG.). 258p. 120.00 ***(978-0-415-52661-6(2))*** Routledge.

Exadaktylos, Theofanis & Radaelli, Claudio M., eds. Research Design in European Studies: Establishing Causality in Europeanization. 2012. (ENG., Illus.). 296p. 95.00 ***(978-0-230-28531-6(7))*** Palgrave Macmillan.

Fales, Evan. Divine Intervention: Metaphysical & Epistemological Puzzles. 2009. (Routledge Studies in the Philosophy of Religion Ser.). (ENG., Illus.). 204p. (C). 125.00 *(978-0-415-87590-5(0))* Routledge.

Freedman, David A. Statistical Models & Causal Inference: A Dialogue with the Social Sciences. Collier, David et al, eds. 2009. (ENG., Illus.). 416p. pap. 30.99 *(978-0-521-12390-7(9))*; 93.00 *(978-0-521-19500-3(4))* Cambridge Univ. Pr.

Gladwell, Malcolm. The Tipping Point. 2009. 14.42 *(978-0-7848-1841-1(X)*, Everbind) Marco Bk. Co.

Goldberg, Richard, ed. Perspectives on Causation, 0 vols. 2011. (ENG.). 478p. 150.00 *(978-1-84946-086-6(8))* Hart Publishing Ltd. GBR. Dist: International Specialized Bk. Services.

Gopnik, Alison & Schulz, Laura, eds. Causal Learning: Psychology, Philosophy, & Computation. 2007. (ENG., Illus.). 384p. 49.95 *(978-0-19-517680-3(4))* Oxford Univ. Pr., Inc.

Groff, Ruth. Critical Realism, Post-Positivism & the Possibility of Knowledg. 2007. 256p. 39.95 *(978-0-415-46435-2(8))* Routledge.

—Revitalizing Causality: Realism about Causality in Philosophy & Social Science. 2009. 268p. pap. 39.95 *(978-0-415-56871-5(4))* Routledge.

Groff, Ruth, ed. Revitalizing Causality: Realism about Causality in Philosophy & Social Science. 2008. (Routledge Studies in Critical Realism Ser.). 265p. 160.00 *(978-0-415-37218-3(6))* Routledge.

Hall, Bryan. The Arguments of Kant's Critique of Pure Reason. 2010. (ENG., Illus.). 242p. 75.00 *(978-0-7391-4165-6(1))*; pap. 29.95 *(978-0-7391-4166-3(X))* Lexington Bks.

Handfield, Toby, ed. Dispositions & Causes. 2009. (Mind Association Occasional Ser.). (ENG., Illus.). 304p. 99.00 *(978-0-19-955893-3(0))* Oxford Univ. Pr., Inc.

Hanna, Robert & Maiese, Michelle. Embodied Minds in Action. 2009. (ENG., Illus.). 280p. 75.00 *(978-0-19-923031-0(5))* Oxford Univ. Pr., Inc.

C

Harbecke, Jens. Mental Causation: Investigating the Mind's Powers in a Natural World. 2009. (ENG.). 434p. 162.00 *(978-3-938793-94-7(5))* Ontos Verlag DEU. Dist: Transaction Pubs.

Hart, W. D. The Engines of the Soul. 2009. (Cambridge Studies in Philosophy Ser.). (ENG.). 204p. pap. 31.99 *(978-0-521-10769-3(5))* Cambridge Univ. Pr.

Hattab, Helen. Descartes on Forms & Mechanisms. 2009. (ENG., Illus.). 246p. 93.00 *(978-0-521-51892-5(X))* Cambridge Univ. Pr.

Hausman, Daniel M. Causal Asymmetries. 2008. (Cambridge Studies in Probability, Induction & Decision Theory Ser.). (ENG.). 320p. pap. 61.00 *(978-0-521-05242-9(4))* Cambridge Univ. Pr.

Hodgson, Douglas. The Law of Intervening Causation. 2008. 292p. 124.95 *(978-0-7546-7366-8(9))* Ashgate Publishing Co.

Hoerl, Christoph, et al, eds. Understanding Counterfactuals, Understanding Causation: Issues in Philosophy & Psychology. 2012. (ENG., Illus.). 256p. 99.00 *(978-0-19-959069-8(9))*; 272p. pap. 45.00 *(978-0-19-969513-3(X))* Oxford Univ. Pr., Inc.

Höffe, Otfried. Kant's Critique of Pure Reason: The Foundation of Modern Philosophy. 2010. (Studies in German Idealism Ser.). Orig. Title: Kants Kritik der reinen Vernunft. Die Grundlegung der modernen Philosophie. â€Translator: Nicholas Walker. (ENG., Illus.). xvii, 340p. 189.00 *(978-90-481-2721-4(1)*, 9048127211) Springer.

Illari, Phyllis McKay, et al, eds. Causality in the Sciences. 2011. (ENG., Illus.). 952p. 170.00 *(978-0-19-957413-1(8))* Oxford Univ. Pr., Inc.

Illetterati, Luca & Michelini, Francesca, eds. Purposiveness: Teleology Between Nature & Mind. 2009. (ENG., Illus.). 219p. 39.95 *(978-3-938793-72-5(4))* Ontos Verlag DEU. Dist: Transaction Pubs.

Jung, C. G. Synchronicity - an Acausal Connecting Principle. 2010. (Jung Extracts Ser.). (ENG., Illus.). 152p. pap. 9.95 *(978-0-691-15050-5(8)*, Bollingen) Princeton Univ. Pr.

Kant, Immanuel. Critique of Pure Reason. 2010. 650p. pap. 46.75 *(978-1-143-56896-1(6))* BiblioBazaar.

—Critique of Pure Reason. 2009. 408p. pap. *(978-1-4590-7523-8(4))* Books LLC.

—Critique of Pure Reason. 2007. (ENG.). 564p. 57.95 *(978-0-548-00341-1(6))* Kessinger Publishing, LLC.

—Critique of Pure Reason. 2007. (ENG.). 516p. (gr. 12). 49.95 *(978-1-4344-8629-5(X))*; per. 29.95 *(978-1-4344-8628-8(1))* Wildside Pr., LLC.

—The Critique of Pure Reason. 2009. 628p. 38.99 *(978-0-559-07890-3(0))*; 31.99 *(978-0-559-07906-1(0))*; pap. 45.75 *(978-0-559-07896-5(X))*; pap. 44.75 *(978-0-559-07903-0(6))* BiblioBazaar.

—The Critique of Pure Reason. Meiklejohn, J. M. D., tr. 2007. 540p. per. *(978-1-4065-1854-2(9))* Dodo Pr.

—The Critique of Pure Reason. l.t. ed. 2006. pap. *(978-1-4068-3407-9(6))* Echo Library.

—The Critique of Pure Reason. Meiklejohn, J. M. D., tr. 2007. 372p. per. 19.95 *(978-1-934255-07-0(6))* El Paso Norte Pr.

—The Critique of Pure Reason. 2008. 384p. 24.95 *(978-1-60459-275-7(3))*; pap. 9.99 *(978-1-60459-274-0(5))* Wilder Pubns., Ltd.

—Critique of Pure Reason. Smith, Norman Kemp, tr. from GER. 2nd ed. 2007. (ENG.). 768p. 110.00 *(978-0-230-01337-7(6))* Palgrave Macmillan.

—Critique of Pure Reason. Muller, Max & Weigelt, Marcus, trs. from GER. rev. ed. 2008. (ENG., Illus.). 784p. (gr. 12-18). 20.00 *(978-0-14-044747-7(4)*, Penguin Classics) Penguin Group (USA) Inc.

Kant, Immanuel & Banham, Gary. Critique of Pure Reason. Kemp Smith, Norman, tr. from GER. 2nd ed. 2007. (ENG.). 768p. pap. 34.00 *(978-0-230-01338-4(4))* Palgrave Macmillan.

Kant, Immanuel & Meiklejohn, J. M. D. Critique of Pure Reason. 2010. 542p. pap. 40.75 *(978-1-142-61043-2(8))* BiblioBazaar.

Kant, Immanuel & Meiklejohn, John Miller Dow. Critique of Pure Reason. 2010. 592p. pap. 44.75 *(978-1-145-80510-1(8))*; 580p. pap. 43.75 *(978-1-143-09404-0(2))* BiblioBazaar.

Kern, Stephen. A Cultural History of Causality: Science, Murder Novels, & Systems of Thought. 2006. (ENG.). 448p. (C). per. 28.95 *(978-0-691-12768-2(9))* Princeton Univ. Pr.

Kistler, Max. Causation & Laws of Nature. 2006. (Routledge Studies in Contemporary Philosophy: Vol. 2). (Illus.). 264p. 153.00 *(978-0-415-39859-6(2))* Routledge.

Kistler, Max & Gnassounou, Bruno, eds. Dispositions & Causal Powers. 2007. (Illus.). 316p. 134.95 *(978-0-7546-5425-4(7))* Ashgate Publishing Co.

Kordela, A. Kiarina. Surplus: Spinoza, Lacan. (Suny Series, Insinuations: Philosophy, Psychoanalysis, Liter Ser.). 195p. 2008. per. 19.95 *(978-0-7914-7020-6(2))* 2007. 65.00 *(978-0-7914-7019-0(9))* State Univ. of New York Pr.

Kramer, Matthew H., et al, eds. The Legacy of H. L. A. Hart: Legal, Political, & Moral Philosophy. 2008. (ENG.). 380p. 143.00 *(978-0-19-954289-5(9))* Oxford Univ. Pr., Inc.

Lewis, Neil & Wood, Rega, eds. Richard Rufus of Cornwall: in Aristotelis de Generatione et Corruptione. 2011. (Auctores Britannici Medii Aevi Ser.). 350p. 135.00 ***(978-0-19-726499-7(9))*** Oxford Univ. Pr., Inc.

Lindahl, B. I. B. On Causal Attribution. 2009. (Stockholm Studies in Philosophy Ser.). (Illus.). 360p. pap. 147.50 *(978-91-86071-18-9(1))* Stockholms Universitet SWE. Dist: Coronet Bks.

Losee, John. Theories of Causality: From Antiquity to the Present. 2011. (ENG., Illus.). 218p. 59.95 *(978-1-4128-1832-2(X))* Transaction Pubs.

Machamer, Peter & Wolters, Gereon, eds. Thinking about Causes: From Greek Philosophy to Modern Physics. 2007. (Pitt Konstanz Phil Hist Scienc Ser.). (Illus.). 384p. 75.00 *(978-0-8229-4309-9(3))* Univ. of Pittsburgh Pr.

Manuel, Michael. Maritime Risk & Organizational Learning. 2011. (Illus.). 356p. 134.95 *(978-1-4094-1963-1(0))* Ashgate Publishing Co.

Marcus, Eric. Rational Causation. 2012. (ENG., Illus.). 280p. 45.00 ***(978-0-674-05990-0(5))*** Harvard Univ. Pr.

McCormack, Teresa, et al. Tool Use & Causal Cognition. 2011. (ENG., Illus.). 272p. 65.00 ***(978-0-19-957115-4(5))*** Oxford Univ. Pr., Inc.

McCosh, James. Energy Efficient & Final Cause. 2006. pap. 16.95 *(978-1-4286-4210-2(2))* Kessinger Publishing, LLC.

Medlow, Sharon. The 'Paradox' of Mental Causation. 2008. 152p. pap. *(978-3-639-08642-3(2))* VDM Verlag Dr. Mueller e.K.

Meurk, Carla. Causally Appropriate Graphical Modelling of Time Series. 2008. 108p. pap. *(978-3-639-02195-0(9))* VDM Verlag Dr. Mueller e.K.

Meyer, Susan Sauvé. Aristotle on Moral Responsibility: Character & Cause. 2012. (ENG.). 240p. 75.00 *(978-0-19-969742-7(6))*; 216p. pap. 35.00 *(978-0-19-969743-4(4))* Oxford Univ. Pr., Inc.

Moore, Michael S. Causation & Responsibility: An Essay in Law, Morals, & Metaphysics. 2010. (ENG., Illus.). 640p. pap. 55.00 *(978-0-19-959951-6(3))* Oxford Univ. Pr., Inc.

Morgan, Stephen L. & Winship, Christopher. Counterfactuals & Causal Inference: Methods & Principles for Social Research. 2007. (Analytical Methods for Social Research Ser.). (ENG.). 334p. 98.00 *(978-0-521-85615-7(9))*; 328p. pap. 29.99 *(978-0-521-67193-4(0))* Cambridge Univ. Pr.

Morrison, Keith. Causation in Educational Research. 2009. (ENG., Illus.). 238p. 130.00 *(978-0-415-49648-3(9))*; pap. 37.95 *(978-0-415-49649-0(7))* Routledge.

Mosser, Kurt. Necessity & Possibility: The Logical Strategy of Kant's Critique of Pure Reason. 2008. 256p. 74.95 *(978-0-8132-1532-7(3))* Catholic Univ. of America Pr.

Mumford, Stephen & Anjum, Rani Lill. Getting Causes from Powers. 2011. (ENG., Illus.). 256p. 65.00 *(978-0-19-969561-4(X))* Oxford Univ. Pr., Inc.

Newman, Andrew. The Physical Basis of Predication. 2007. (Cambridge Studies in Philosophy Ser.). (ENG.). 288p. (C). pap. 45.00 *(978-0-521-03761-7(1))* Cambridge Univ. Pr.

Ott, Walter. Causation & Laws of Nature in Early Modern Philosophy. 2009. (ENG.). 272p. 85.00 *(978-0-19-957043-0(4))* Oxford Univ. Pr., Inc.

Owens, David. Causes & Coincidences. 2007. (Cambridge Studies in Philosophy Ser.). (ENG.). 204p. pap. 39.99 *(978-0-521-04448-6(0))* Cambridge Univ. Pr.

Pearl, Judea. Causality. 2nd ed. 2008. (ENG., Illus.). 484p. (C). 50.00 *(978-0-521-89560-6(X))* Cambridge Univ. Pr.

Planck, Max & Einstein, Albert. Where Is Science Going? Murphy, James, tr. 2011. 220p. 44.95 ***(978-1-258-09749-3(4))*** Literary Licensing, LLC.

Roessler, Johannes, et al, eds. Perception, Causation, & Objectivity. 2011. (ENG.). 360p. pap. 45.00 ***(978-0-19-969205-7(X))*** Oxford Univ. Pr., Inc.

Russo, F., et al. Causality & Probability in the Sciences. 2007. (Illus.). vii, 543p. pap. *(978-1-904987-35-2(4))* College Pubns.

Russo, Federica. Causality & Causal Modelling in the Social Sciences. 2008. (Methodos Ser.). 252p. (C). 139.00 *(978-1-4020-8816-2(7))* Springer.

Ruth Groff Staff. Revitalising Causality. 2007. 240p. 120.00 *(978-0-415-37214-5(3))* Routledge.

Sancinetti, Marcelo A. & Müller, M. L. Causalidad, Riesgo e Imputación: 100 Años de Contribuciones Críticas Sobre Imputación Objetiva y Subjetiva. 2009. (SPA.). 693p. *(978-950-741-414-5(2))*; *(978-950-741-415-2(0))* Hammurabi S.R.L., Editorial.

Sanders, Ted & Sweetser, Eve, eds. Causal Categories in Discourse & Cognition. 2009. (Cognitive Linguistics Research [CLR] Ser.). (ENG., X, 249p. Illus.). 140.00 *(978-3-11-022441-2(0))*; 210.00 ***(978-3-11-173959-5(7))*** De Gruyter, Mouton DEU. Dist: de Gruyter, Walter GmbH & Co. KG.

Sankey, H., ed. Causation & Laws of Nature. 2010. (Studies in History & Philosophy of Science Ser.). (Illus.). 384p. pap. 279.00 *(978-90-481-5303-9(4)*, 9048153034) Springer.

Sassen, Brigitte. Kant's Early Critics: The Empiricist Critique of the Theoretical Philosophy. 2007. (ENG.). 344p. pap. 44.00 *(978-0-521-03764-8(6))* Cambridge Univ. Pr.

Schliemann, Oliver. Die Axiome der Anschauung in Kants 'Kritik der reinen Vernunft' 2010. (Kantstudien-Ergänzungshefte Ser.). (GER.). 154p. 112.00 ***(978-3-11-022842-7(4))*** De Gruyter, Walter Inc.

Schmaltz, Tad M. Descartes on Causation. 2007. (ENG.). 256p. 85.00 *(978-0-19-532794-6(2))* Oxford Univ. Pr., Inc.

Schnepf, Robert. Die Frage Nach der Ursache: Systematische und Problemgeschichtliche Untersuchungen Zum Kausalitäts- und Zum Schöpfungsbegriff. 2006. (GER.). 535p. (C). 111.00 *(978-3-525-30157-9(X))* Vandenhoeck & Ruprecht GmbH & Co. KG DEU. Dist: ISD.

Sheehan, Daniel P. Frontiers of Time: Retrocausation - Experiment & Theory, San Diego, California, 20-22 June 2006. 2006. (AIP Conference Proceedings Ser.). (Illus.). 361p. 147.00 *(978-0-7354-0361-1(9)*, 0735403619) American Institute of Physics.

Shoemaker, Sydney. Physical Realization. (ENG.). 2009. 168p. pap. 24.00 *(978-0-19-957155-0(4))* 2007. 160p. 45.00 *(978-0-19-921439-6(5))* Oxford Univ. Pr., Inc.

Sorensen, Roy. Seeing Dark Things: The Philosophy of Shadows, 1 vol. 2011. (ENG.). 328p. pap. 24.95 *(978-0-19-979713-4(7))* Oxford Univ. Pr., Inc.

Sorensen, Roy A. Seeing Dark Things: The Philosophy of Shadows. 2008. (ENG., Illus.). 328p. 45.00 *(978-0-19-532657-4(1))* Oxford Univ. Pr., Inc.

Spohn, Wolfgang. Causation, Coherence & Concepts: A Collection of Essays. 2008. (Boston Studies in the Philosophy of Science Ser.). (Illus.). 410p. 239.00 *(978-1-4020-5473-0(4))* Springer.

Spohn, Wolfgang. The Laws of Belief: Ranking Theory & Its Philosophical Applications. 2012. (ENG.). 625p. 125.00 ***(978-0-19-969750-2(7))*** Oxford Univ. Pr., Inc.

Stapleford, Scott & Stapleford. Kant's Transcendental Arguments: Disciplining Pure Reason. 2008. (Continuum Studies in Philosophy Ser.). (ENG.). 160p. 130.00 *(978-0-8264-9928-8(7))* Continuum International Publishing Group, Ltd. GBR. Dist: National Bk. Network.

Steward, Helen. A Metaphysics for Freedom. 2012. (ENG.). 256p. 60.00 ***(978-0-19-955205-4(3))*** Oxford Univ. Pr., Inc.

Storr, Vernon F. Development & Divine Purpose. 2007. (ENG.). 300p. 43.95 *(978-0-548-09742-7(9))* Kessinger Publishing, LLC.

Strevens, Michael. Depth: An Account of Scientific Explanation. (Illus.). 536p. 2011. (ENG.). pap. 29.95 *(978-0-674-06257-3(4))* 2009. 65.50 *(978-0-674-03183-8(0))* Harvard Univ. Pr.

Stroud, Barry. Engagement & Metaphysical Dissatisfaction: Modality & Value. 2011. (ENG.). 208p. 49.95 *(978-0-19-976496-9(4))* Oxford Univ. Pr., Inc.

Suárez, Mauricio, ed. Probabilities, Causes & Propensities in Physics. 2010. (Synthese Library). (Illus.). ix, 264p. 139.00 *(978-1-4020-9903-8(7)*, 1402099037) Springer.

Taborsky, Paul. The Logic of Cultures: Three Structures of Philosophical Thought. 2010. (Illus.). 274p. pap. *(978-3-0343-0378-1(5))* Lang, Peter.

Taube, Mortimer. Causation Freedom & Determinism. 2006. 260p. per. *(978-1-4067-3195-8(1)*, Hesperides Pr.) Read Bks.

Tilly, Charles. Why? 2008. (ENG., Illus.). 224p. (C). pap. 19.95 *(978-0-691-13648-6(3))* Princeton Univ. Pr.

Turner, Stephen P., ed. Causality, 4 vols. 2010. (SAGE Benchmarks in Social Research Methods Ser.). (Illus.). 1704p. 995.00 *(978-1-84787-933-2(0)*, B79332C) SAGE Pubns., Ltd. GBR. Dist: SAGE Pubns., Inc.

van Inwagen, P., ed. Time & Cause: Essays presented to Richard Taylor. 2010. (Philosophical Studies Ser.). 332p. pap. 289.00 *(978-90-481-8358-6(8)*, 9048183588) Springer.

Vayda, Andrew. Causal Explanation for Social Scientists: A Reader. 2011. (ENG.). 336p. 85.00 *(978-0-7591-1325-1(4))*; (Illus.). pap. 39.95 *(978-0-7591-1326-8(2))* AltaMira Pr.

Viljanen, Valtteri. Spinoza's Geometry of Power. 2011. (ENG., Illus.). 208p. 90.00 *(978-1-107-00780-2(1))* Cambridge Univ. Pr.

Vollmer, F. Agent Causality. 2010. (Synthese Library). 176p. pap. 109.00 *(978-90-481-5272-8(0)*, 9048152720) Springer.

Williams, Glenys O. Intention & Causation in Medical Non-Killing: The Impact of Criminal Law Concepts on Euthanasia & Assisted Suicide. 2007. (Biomedical Law & Ethics Library). (ENG.). 248p. (C). per. 59.95 *(978-0-415-42302-1(3)*, Routledge Cavendish) Taylor & Francis Group GBR. Dist: Taylor & Francis Group.

Winiger, Bénédict, et al, eds. Essential Cases on Natural Causation. 2007. (Digest of European Tort Law Ser.). xxi, 632p. 229.00 *(978-3-211-36957-9(0)*, 3211369570) Springer.

Young, Gerald, et al. Causality of Psychological Injury: Presenting Evidence in Court. 2010. (ENG., Illus.). xii, 648p. pap. 109.00 *(978-1-4419-4214-2(9)*, 1441942149) Springer.

CAUSE AND EFFECT

see Causation

CAVA (PLANT)

see Kava Plant

CAVAFY, CONSTANTINE, 1863-1963

The Adventures of Constantine Cavafy. 2007. (Illus.). 112p. *(978-1-931885-54-6(0))* Twin Palms Pubs.

Albee, Edward. Shades of Love: Photographs Inspired by the Poems of C. P. Cavafy. Connolly, David, tr. from GRE. 2011. (ENG., Illus.). 168p. 75.00 *(978-1-60887-013-4(8))* Palace Pr. International.

Cavafy, Constantine. Cavafy: 166 Poems. Boegehold, Alan, tr. from GRE. & intro. by. 2009. (ENG.). 240p. 18.00 *(978-1-60419-005-2(1))* Axios Pr.

Coleman, Kathleen M., et al. Imagination & Logos - Essays on C. P. Cavafy. 2010. (Cultural Politics, Socioaesthetics, Beginnings Ser.: 1). (ENG.). 250p. 55.00 *(978-0-674-05339-7(7))* Harvard Univ. Pr.

McKinsey, Martin. Hellenism & the Postcolonial Imagination: Yeats, Cavafy, Walcott. 2010. (Illus.). 223p. 55.00 *(978-0-8386-4201-6(2))* Fairleigh Dickinson Univ. Pr.

CAVALIER KING CHARLES SPANIEL

Coile, D. Caroline. Cavalier King Charles Spaniels. 2nd rev. ed. 2008. (Complete Pet Owner's Manual Ser.). (ENG., Illus.). 96p. pap. 8.99 *(978-0-7641-3771-6(9))* Barron's Educational Series, Inc.

Dog Fancy Magazine, compiled by. Cavalier King Charles Spaniel. 2011. (Smart Owner's Guide Ser.). (ENG., Illus.). 176p. 17.95 *(978-1-59378-753-0(7))* Kennel Club Bks.

Dog Fancy Magazine, ed. Cavalier King Charles Spaniel. 2011. (Smart Owner's Guide Ser.). (ENG.). 176p. pap. 15.95 *(978-1-59378-788-2(X))* Kennel Club Bks.

Ewing, Susan M. Cavalier King Charles Spaniels, 1 vol. 2007. (ENG., Illus.). 112p. 11.95 *(978-0-7938-3784-7(7))* TFH Pubns., Inc.

Garnett-Wilson, Barbara. The Cavalier King Charles Spaniel, in Fact & Fancy. Wilson, Roy A., ed. 2007. (Illus.). 297p. 59.95 *(978-0-9662985-1-2(9))* Cascade Pubns.

Garnett-Wilson, Barbara & Wilson, Roy A. The Cavalier King Charles Spaniel, a Tribute in Art. 2007. (ENG., Illus.). 194p. 59.95 *(978-0-9662985-2-9(7))* Cascade Pubns.

Lang, Laura. Cavalier King Charles Spaniel, 1 vol. 2011. (ENG., Illus.). 144p. 15.95 *(978-0-7938-3715-1(4))* TFH Pubns., Inc.

Linzy, Jan & Pata, Sharae. Cavalier King Charles Spaniel Champions, 2002-2005. 2006. (Illus.). 149p. spiral bd. 46.95 *(978-1-55893-203-6(8))* Camino E.E. & Bk. Co.

Savant-Harris, Myra. The Cavalier King Charles Spaniel, 1 vol. 2009. (ENG.). 208p. *(978-0-7938-3679-6(4))* TFH Pubns., Inc.

Smith, Sheila. Cavalier King Charles Spaniels Today. (Illus.). 96p. tchr. ed. 24.95 *(978-1-86054-025-7(2)*, INT050) Ringpress Bks., Ltd. GBR. Dist: TFH Pubns., Inc.

Spiotta-DiMare, Loren. Cavalier King Charles Spaniel, 1 vol. 2011. (DogLife Ser.). (ENG., Illus.). 224p. 19.95 *(978-0-7938-3604-8(2))* TFH Pubns., Inc.

Summers, Judith. My Life with George: Surviving Life with the King of the Canines. 2009. (ENG.). 288p. pap. 13.99 *(978-1-4013-4085-8(7))* Hyperion Pr.

—My Life with George: What I Learned about Joy from One Neurotic (And Very Expensive) Dog. l.t. ed. 2008. (Wheeler Hardcover Ser.). 357p. 30.50 *(978-1-59722-711-7(0)*, Wheeler Publishing, Inc.) Cengage Gale.

CAVALRY

Brnardic, Vladimir. Imperial Armies of the Thirty Years' War (2) Cavalry, 2 vols. 2010. (Men-at-Arms Ser.). (ENG., Illus.). 48p. pap. 17.95 *(978-1-84603-997-3(5))* Osprey Publishing, Ltd. GBR. Dist: Random Hse., Inc.

Clark, Cath & Helbock, Richard W., eds. Frontier Cavalryman: Lt. William Carey Brown's Letters from Fort Klamath, Oregon, 1878-1880. 2007. (Illus.). pap. 14.00 *(978-1-930111-65-3(7))* Bear Creek Pr.

Cruso, John. Militarie Instructions for the Cavallrie. 2007. (ENG., Illus.). 176p. 34.95 *(978-1-85367-638-3(1))* Greenhill Bks./Lionel Leventhal, Ltd. GBR. Dist: MBI Distribution Services/Quayside Distribution.

Curry, W. L. First Ohio Cavalry. reprint ed. 150.00 *(978-0-7222-8161-1(7))* Library Reprints, Inc.

Dallal, Henry. Horse Warriors: India's 61st Cavalry. 2009. (ENG., Illus.). 224p. 126.00 *(978-0-9544083-1-2(4))* I. B. Tauris & Co., Ltd. GBR. Dist: Macmillan.

Denison, George T. A History of Cavalry from the Earliest Times: With Lessons for the Future. 2007. (ENG.). 502p. 53.95 *(978-0-548-18391-5(0))*; 504p. per. 38.95 *(978-1-4304-8613-8(9))* Kessinger Publishing, LLC.

Doty, Ralph E., tr. from GEC. A Translation from Ancient Greek into English of Xenophon's Manual on the Duties of a Cavalry Commander: Including an Introduction by Ralph E. Doty. 2011. (GRE & ENG.). 96p. ***(978-0-7734-1599-7(8))*** Mellen, Edwin Pr., The.

Drews, Robert. Early Riders: The Beginnings of Mounted Warfare in Asia & Europe. 2008. 232p. 39.95 *(978-0-415-48680-4(7))* Routledge.

Elliott, G. H. The Armament of Cavalry. 2009. 56p. pap. *(978-1-84734-852-4(1))* Naval & Military Pr., The.

Fields, Nic. Tarentine Horseman of Magna Graecia: 430-190 BC. 2008. (Warrior Ser.). (Illus.). 64p. pap. 18.95 *(978-1-84603-279-0(2))* Osprey Publishing, Ltd. GBR. Dist: Random Hse., Inc.

Fries, Carsten H. Riding into the Twilight: Organization, Uniforms, Insignia, & Equipment of the German Army's Last Cavalrymen 1920-1945. 2011. Orig. Title: 2011. (Illus.). 448p. 99.95 *(978-0-9819295-1-4(6))* Tiger III Books.

Gould, W. J. Three Cheers for the Queen-Lancers Charge! the Experiences of a Sergeant of 16th Queen's Lancers in Afghanistan, the Gwalior War, the First Sikh War. 2010. 124p. pap. *(978-0-85706-173-7(9))* Leonaur Ltd.

Hill, P. R. & Watkinson, J. M. Major Sanderson's War: Diary of a Parliamentary Cavalry Officer. 2009. (ENG., Illus.). 160p. pap. 39.95 *(978-1-86227-468-6(1))* History Pr. Ltd., The GBR. Dist: Independent Pubs. Group.

Hunt, Eric & Light Dragoons Staff. The Light Dragoons: A Regimental History, 1715-2009. 2011. (General Military Ser.). (ENG., Illus.). 80p. pap. 18.95 *(978-1-84908-325-6(8))* Osprey Publishing, Ltd. GBR. Dist: Random Hse., Inc.

Jarymowycz, Roman. Cavalry from Hoof to Track, 1 vol. 2007. (War, Technology, & History Ser.). (Illus.). 316p. 49.95 *(978-0-275-98726-8(4)*, C8726, Praeger Security International) Greenwood Publishing Group, Inc.

—Cavalry from Hoof to Track. 2009. (Military History Ser.). (ENG., Illus.). 320p. pap. 21.95 *(978-0-8117-3577-3(X))* Stackpole Bks.

Johnson, David. Napoleon's Cavalry & Its Leaders. 2007. (ENG., Illus.). 192p. 29.95 *(978-1-86227-378-8(2)*, Spellmount, Limited Pubs.) History Pr. Ltd., The GBR. Dist: Independent Pubs. Group.

Lapray, Olivier. A Dictionary of the Cuirassier Officers of the First Empire, 1804-1815. 2007. (Illus.). 144p. 65.00 *(978-2-35250-026-1(5))* Histoire et Collections FRA. Dist: Casemate Pubs. & Bk. Distributors, LLC.

Larson, Mike. Heroes: A Year in Vietnam with the First Air Cavalry Division. 2008. 272p. 30.95 *(978-0-595-51267-6(4))*; pap. 20.95 *(978-0-595-52521-8(0))* iUniverse, Inc.

Leslie, Lt. Charles. Treatise on the Employment of Light Troops on Actual Service ,1843. 2007. 244p. per. *(978-1-84574-375-8(X))* Naval & Military Pr., The.

MacLean, French L. Custer's Best: The Story of Company M, 7th Cavalry at the Little Bighorn. 2011. (Illus.). 272p. 69.99 *(978-0-7643-3757-4(2))* Schiffer Publishing, Ltd.

Maydon, J. G. French's Cavalry Campaign: A Special Correspondent's View of British Army Mounted troops During the Boer War. 2009. 120p. pap. *(978-1-84677-751-6(8))* Leonaur Ltd.

McConnell, H. H. Five Years a Cavalryman. 2009. 124p. pap. *(978-0-217-47742-0(9))*; pap. *(978-0-217-83460-5(4))* Books LLC.

Mulford, Ami Frank. Fighting Indians in the 7th United States Cavalry: The Recollections of a Bugler of the Campaign Against the Nez Perce Indians

1876-77. 2010. 164p. *(978-1-84677-960-2(X))*; pap. *(978-1-84677-959-6(6))* Leonaur Ltd.
Nash, John Tulloch & Henry, Metcalfe. Men of the Mutiny: Two Accounts of the Great Indian Mutiny Of 1857. 2009. 192p. *(978-1-84677-624-3(4))* Leonaur Ltd.
Nicolle, David. European Medieval Tactics: The Fall & Rise of Cavalry, 450-1260. 2011. (Elite Ser.). (ENG., Illus.). 64p. pap. 18.95 *(978-1-84908-503-8(X))* Osprey Publishing, Ltd. GBR. Dist: Random Hse., Inc.
Nolan, Keith W. Search & Destroy: The Story of an Armored Cavalry Squadron in Vietnam - 1-1 Cav, 1967-1968. 2010. (ENG., Illus.). 448p. 30.00 *(978-0-7603-3312-9(2)*, 0760333122, Zenith Pr.) MBI Publishing Co. LLC.
Robinson, Gavin. Horses People & Parliaments in the English Civil War: Extracting Resources & Constructing Allegiance. 2012. 262p. 124.95 ***(978-1-4094-2093-4(0))*** Ashgate Publishing Co.
Shoffner, Thomas. Napoleon's Cavalry: A Key Element to Decisive Victory. 2010. 114p. pap. 19.05 *(978-1-60888-043-0(5))* Nimble Bks. LLC.
Sinclair, Andrew. Man & Horse: Four Thousand Years of the Mounted Warrior. 2009. (ENG., Illus.). 288p. 39.95 *(978-0-7509-5034-3(X))* History Pr. Ltd.,The GBR. Dist: Independent Pubs. Group.
Smith, Digby. Charge! Great Cavalry Charges of the Napoleonic Wars. rev. ed. 2007. (ENG., Illus.). 304p. per. 24.95 *(978-1-85367-722-9(1)*, 1853677221) Greenhill Bks./Lionel Leventhal, Ltd. GBR. Dist: MBI Distribution Services/Quaysice Distribution.
Smith, Gene & Smith. Mounted Warriors: From Alexander the Great & Cromwell to Stuart, Sheridan, & Custer. 2009. (ENG., Illus.). 336p. 27.95 *(978-0-471-78332-9(3)*, Wiley) Wiley, John & Sons, Inc.
Tillios, Angelos. Die Funktion und Bedeutung der Reiter-und Pferdeführerdarstellungen auf attischen Grab- und Weihreliefs des 5. und 4. Jhs. v. Chr. 2010. (Bar S Ser.). (ENG., Illus.). 170p. (C). pap. 90.00 *(978-1-4073-0679-0(2))* British Archaeological Reports Ltd. GBR. Dist: Brown, David Bk. Co., The.
Wilson, Marcus. The Good Steed: The Experience of New Zealand's Military Horse During the Anglo-Boer War & World War One. 2008. (Illus.). 216p. pap. *(978-3-8364-9857-9(X))* VDM Verlag Dr. Mueller e.K.
Wood, Evelyn. Cavalry at Waterloo: British Mounted Troops During the Campaign Of 1815. 2009. 144p. *(978-1-84677-730-1(5))*; pap. *(978-1-84677-729-5(1))* Leonaur Ltd.

CAVAN (IRELAND: COUNTY)
Scott, Brendan. Cavan, 1609-1653: Plantation, War & Religion. 2007. (Illus.). 63p. (C). pap. 14.95 *(978-1-84682-062-5(6))* Four Courts Pr. IRL. Dist: International Specialized Bk. Services.
Scott, Brendan, ed. Culture & Society in Early Modern Breifne/Cavan. 2009. (Illus.). 241p. 70.00 *(978-1-84682-184-4(3))* Four Courts Pr. IRL. Dist: International Specialized Bk. Services.

CAVE ANIMALS
Culver, David C. & Pipan, Tanja. The Biology of Caves & Other Subterranean Habitats. 2009. (Biology of Habitats Ser.). (ENG., Illus.). 256p. 135.00 *(978-0-19-921992-6(3))*; pap. 60.00 *(978-0-19-921993-3(1))* Oxford Univ. Pr., Inc.
Fong, Daniel W., et al. The invertebrate cave fauna of west virginia, second Edition: Bulletin 16. 2007. 163p. per. 50.00 *(978-0-9620336-3-6(4))*; (ENG.). per. 50.00 *(978-0-9620636-3-3(0))* West Virginia Speleological Survey.
Graening, G. O., et al. Cave Life of Oklahoma & Arkansas: Exploration & Conservation of Subterranean Biodiversity. 2012. (Animal Natural History Ser.). (ENG., Illus.). 248p. 59.95 ***(978-0-8061-4223-4(5))*** Univ. of Oklahoma Pr.

CAVE CHURCHES
see also Cave Temples
Mercier, Jacques & Lepage, Claude. Lalibela: Christian Art of Ethiopia, the Monolithic Churches & Their Treasures. 2012. (ENG., Illus.). 320p. (C). 60.00 *(978-1-907372-19-3(9))* Holberton, Paul Publishing GBR. Dist: Univ. of Washington Pr.

CAVE-DRAWINGS
see Cave Paintings

CAVE DWELLERS
Jordan, Paul. Life in a Cave. 2008. (ENG.). 96p. (YA). (gr. 7). pap. 11.95 *(978-0-7509-4641-4(5))* History Pr. Ltd.,The GBR. Dist: Independent Pubs. Group.
Shang, Hong & Trinkaus, Erik. The Early Modern Human from Tianyuan Cave, China. 2010. (Texas A&M University Anthropology Ser.). (ENG., Illus.). 272p. 45.00 *(978-1-60344-177-3(8))* Texas A&M Univ. Pr.

CAVE DWELLINGS
Baring-Gould, Sabine. Cliff Castles & Cave Dwellings of Europe. 2008. 292p. 28.99 *(978-0-554-22899-0(8))* 2008. 292p. 25.99 *(978-0-554-32202-5(1))* 2007. (ENG.). 262p. pap. 21.99 *(978-1-4264-3286-6(0))* BiblioBazaar.

CAVE FAUNA
see Cave Animals

CAVE PAINTINGS
Aczel, Amir D. The Cave & the Cathedral: How a Real-Life Indiana Jones & a Renegade Scholar Decoded the Ancient Art of Man. 2009. (ENG., Illus.). 264p. 25.95 *(978-0-470-37353-8(9)*, Wiley) Wiley, John & Sons, Inc.
Agnew, Neville, ed. Ancient Sites on the Silk Road: Proceedings of the Second International Conference on the Conservation of Grotto Sites, Mogao Grottoes, Dunhuang, People's Republic of China, June 28-July 3, 2004. 2010. (ENG., Illus.). pap. 89.00 *(978-1-60606-013-1(9)*, Getty Conservation Institute, The) Getty Pubns.
Bahn, Paul. An Enquiring Mind: Studies in Honor of Alexander Marshack. 2009. (American school of prehistoric research Monograph Ser.). (ENG., Illus.). 352p. (C). 35.00 *(978-1-84217-383-1(9))* Oxbow Bks., Ltd. GBR. Dist: Brown, David Bk. Co., The.
Bahn, Paul G. Cave Art: A Guide to the Decorated Ice Age Caves of Europe. 2012. (ENG., Illus.). 248p. pap. 24.95 ***(978-0-7112-3257-0(1))*** Lincoln, Frances Ltd. GBR. Dist: Perseus-PGW.
Bahn, Paul G. Prehistoric Rock Art: Polemics & Progress. 2010. (ENG., Illus.). 238p. (C). 90.00 *(978-0-521-19278-1(1))*; pap. 27.99 *(978-0-521-14087-4(0))* Cambridge Univ. Pr.
Bevan, Lynne. Worshippers & Warriors: Reconstructing Gender & Gender Relations in the Prehistoric Rock Art of Naquane National Park, Valcamonica, Brescia, Northern Italy. 2006. (BAR International Ser.: Vol. 1485). (ENG., Illus.). 192p. (C). pap. 85.00 *(978-1-84171-920-7(X))* British Archaeological Reports Ltd. GBR. Dist: Brown, David Bk. Co., The.
Clottes, Jean. Cave Art. 2010. (ENG., Illus.). 336p. pap. 39.95 *(978-0-7148-5723-7(9))* Phaidon Pr., Inc.
Curtis, Gregory. The Cave Painters: Probing the Mysteries of the World's First Artists. 2007. (ENG., Illus.). 288p. pap. 15.95 *(978-1-4000-7887-5(3)*, Anchor) Knopf Doubleday Publishing Group.
Desdemaines-Hugon, Christine. Stepping-Stones: A Journey through the Ice Age Caves of the Dordogne. 2010. (Illus.). 272p. 30.00 *(978-0-300-15266-1(3))* Yale Univ. Pr.
Farthing, Stephen, ed. Art: From Cave Art to Street Art - 40,000 Years of Creativity. 2010. (ENG., Illus.). 576p. 35.00 *(978-0-7893-1833-6(4))* Universe Publishing.
Groenen, Marc, et al, eds. Session C74: Methods of Art History Tested against Prehistory; Session C81: Spirals & Circular Forms: the Most Commom Rock Art in the World? Session C85: European Cave Art; Session S02: Euro-Mediterranean Rock Art Studies; Session S07: Global State of the Art; Session WS37: Current State of North American Rock Art, Vol. 35. 2010. (Bar S Ser.). (POR, FRE & ENG., Illus.). 177p. (C). pap. 92.50 *(978-1-4073-0649-0(9))* British Archaeological Reports Ltd. GBR. Dist: Brown, David Bk. Co., The.
Lawson, Andrew J. Painted Caves: Palaeolithic Rock Art in Western Europe. 2012. (ENG., Illus.). 456p. 180.00 ***(978-0-19-969822-6(8))*** Oxford Univ. Pr., Inc.
Lewis-Williams, J. David. San Rock Art. 2011. (Pocket History Guides). (Illus.). 160p. pap. 12.95 ***(978-1-4314-0100-0(5))*** Jacana Media ZAF. Dist: Independent Pubs. Group.
Ripoll, Roger. Palaeolithic Cave Art at Creswell Crags in European Context. Pettitt, Paul et al, eds. 2007. (ENG., Illus.). 312p. 140.00 *(978-0-19-929917-1(X))* Oxford Univ. Pr., Inc.
Stone, Andrea J. Images from the Underworld: Naj Tunich & the Tradition of Maya Cave Painting. 2011. (ENG., Illus.). 304p. pap. 35.00 *(978-0-292-72652-9(X))* Univ. of Texas Pr.
Whitley, David S. Cave Paintings & the Human Spirit: The Origin of Creativity & Belief. 2008. (ENG., Illus.). 250p. 25.98 *(978-1-59102-636-5(9))* Prometheus Bks. Pubs.

CAVE TEMPLES
see also Cave Churches
Agnew, Neville, ed. Ancient Sites on the Silk Road: Proceedings of the Second International Conference on the Conservation of Grotto Sites, Mogao Grottoes, Dunhuang, People's Republic of China, June 28-July 3, 2004. 2010. (ENG., Illus.). pap. 89.00 *(978-1-60606-013-1(9)*, Getty Conservation Institute, The) Getty Pubns.
Brancaccio, Pia. The Caves at Aurangabad: Buddhist Art in Transformation. 2010. (Brill's Indological Library: Vol. 34). (Illus.). 300p. *(978-90-04-18525-8(9))* BRILL.
Fergusson, James & Burgess, James. The Cave Temples of India. 2010. 766p. 54.36 *(978-1-169-82568-0(0))* 2010. 766p. 67.95 *(978-1-161-97406-5(7))* 2009. 738p. pap. 52.95 *(978-1-104-48278-7(9))* Kessinger Publishing, LLC.
Owen, Lisa N. Carving Devotion in the Jain Caves at Ellora. 2012. ***(978-90-04-20629-8(9))*** BRILL.
Qureshi, Dulari. The Rock-Cut Temples of Western India. 2010. (Illus.). xxxii, 409p. *(978-81-8090-202-4(1)*, Library of Congress — New Delhi Overseas Office) Bhartiya Kala Prakashan.
Wauchope, Robert S. Buddhist Cave Temples of India. reprint ed. 41.50 *(978-0-404-17409-5(4))* AMS Pr., Inc.

CAVELL, EDITH LOUISA, 1865-1915
Beck, James M. The Case of Edith Cavell: A Study of the Rights of Non-Combatants. 2007. 48p. per. *(978-1-4065-3712-3(8))* Dodo Pr.
Hill, William Thomson & Van Til, Jacqueline. Nurse Edith Cavell: Two Accounts of a Notable British Nurse of the First World War — the Martyrdom of Nurse Cavell by William Thomson Hill & with Edit. 2011. 144p. ***(978-0-85706-507-0(6))***; pap. ***(978-0-85706-508-7(4))*** Leonaur Ltd.
Pickles, Katie. Transnational Outrage: The Death & Commemoration of Edith Cavell. 2007. (ENG., Illus.). 256p. 95.00 *(978-1-4039-8607-8(X))* Palgrave Macmillan.
Souhami, Diana. Edith Cavell. 2010. (Illus.). 432p. *(978-1-84916-359-0(6)*, Quercus) Quercus.

CAVENDISH LABORATORY (CAMBRIDGE, ENGLAND)
Dong-Won Kim. Leadership & Creativity: A History of the Cavendish Laboratory, 1871-1919. 2010. (Archimedes Ser.). 248p. pap. 139.00 *(978-90-481-5956-7(3)*, 9048159563) Springer.
Thomson, Joseph John. Recollections & Reflections. 2011. (Cambridge Library Collection - Physical Sciences Ser.). (ENG., Illus.). 482p. pap. 35.99 ***(978-1-108-03792-1(5))*** Cambridge Univ. Pr.

CAVES
see also Hiding Places; Speleology
also names of caves, e.g. Lascaux Cave
Aikens, C. Melvin. Hogup Cave. (Utah Anthropological Papers: No. 93). reprint ed. 24.00 *(978-0-404-60693-0(8))* AMS Pr., Inc.
Beamon, Sylvia. Royston Cave: Used by Saints or Sinners? 2011. (ENG., Illus.). 316p. pap. 33.00 ***(978-0-9557400-0-8(2))*** Temple Pubns., The GBR. Dist: SCB Distributors.
Bergsvik, Knut Andreas & Skeates, Robin, eds. Caves in Context: The Cultural Significance of Caves & Rockshelters in Europe. 2012. (ENG., Illus.). 304p. (C). 90.00 ***(978-1-84217-474-6(6))*** Oxbow Bks., Ltd. GBR. Dist: Brown, David Bk. Co., The.
Brady, James E. & Prufer, Keith M., eds. In the Maw of the Earth Monster: Studies of Mesoamerican Ritual Cave Use. 2010. (ENG., Illus.). 448p. pap. 37.50 *(978-0-292-72596-6(5))* Univ. of Texas Pr.
Brick, Greg. Subterranean Twin Cities. 2009. (ENG., Illus.). 256p. pap. 18.95 *(978-0-8166-4597-6(3))* Univ. of Minnesota Pr.
Browne, George Forrest. Ice-Caves of France & Switzerland. 2008. 296p. 28.99 *(978-0-554-24840-0(9))* 2008. 296p. 25.99 *(978-0-554-34143-9(3))* 2006. (ENG.). 256p. pap. 21.99 *(978-1-4264-7480-4(6))* 2007. 292p. pap. 23.99 *(978-1-4264-7557-3(8))* BiblioBazaar.
Burney, David A. Back to the Future in the Caves of Kaua'i: A Scientist's Adventures in the Dark. (Illus.). 216p. 2011. pap. 18.00 *(978-0-300-17209-6(5))* 2010. (ENG., 28.00 *(978-0-300-15094-0(6))* Yale Univ. Pr.
Chladek, Stanislav. Exploring Maya Ritual Caves: Dark Secrets from the Maya Underworld. 2011. (ENG., Illus.). 240p. 49.95 *(978-0-7591-1987-1(2))* AltaMira Pr.
Corrigan, Don. Show Me ... Natural Wonders. 2007. 224p. pap. *(978-1-933370-13-2(0))* Reedy Pr.
Dye, David H., ed. Cave Archaeology of the Eastern Woodlands: Papers in Honor of Patty Jo Watson. 2008. (ENG., Illus.). 278p. 42.95 *(978-1-57233-608-7(0))* Univ. of Tennessee Pr.
Fabri, Nadia. Ghar Dalam: the Cave, Museum & Garden. 2007. (ENG.). 40p. (C). pap. 9.95 *(978-99932-7-144-4(6))* Midsea Bks. Ltd. MLT. Dist: Brown, David Bk. Co., The.
Fairchild, Ian J. & Baker, Andy. Speleothem Science: From Process to Past Environments. 2012. (Blackwell Quaternary Geoscience Ser.). (ENG.). 450p. 119.95 ***(978-1-4051-9620-8(3)***, Wiley-Blackwell) Wiley, John & Sons, Inc.
Ford, Trevor D., ed. Limestones & Caves of Wales. 2011. (ENG.). 267p. pap. 35.99 *(978-0-521-15913-4(5))* Cambridge Univ. Pr.
Frushour, Samuel S. A Guide to Caves & Karst of Indiana. 2012. (Indiana Natural Science Ser.). (ENG., Illus.). 152p. pap. 22.00 ***(978-0-253-00096-5(3)***, 0253000963) Indiana Univ. Pr.
Hartwig, G. (Georg). The Subterranean World. 2006. 568p. per. 32.99 *(978-1-4255-6245-8(0))* MPublishing.
Hurd, Barbara. Entering the Stone: On Caves & Feeling Through the Dark. 2008. (ENG.). 184p. pap. 17.95 *(978-0-8203-3153-9(8))* Univ. of Georgia Pr.
Jennings, Jesse D. Danger Cave. (Utah Anthropological Papers: No. 27). reprint ed. 24.50 *(978-0-404-60627-5(X))* AMS Pr., Inc.
Jennings, Jesse David & Rudy, Sara Sue. Danger Cave: Memoirs of the Society for American Archaeology, No. 14, Supplement to American Antiquity, V23, No. 2, Part 2, October 1957. Woodbury, Richard B., ed. 2011. 354p. 51.95 ***(978-1-258-10271-5(4))*** Literary Licensing, LLC.
Klimchouk, Alexander. Hypogene Speleogenesis: Hydrogeological & Morphogenetic Perspective, Special Paper No.1. 2007. (Illus.). 106p. per. 35.00 *(978-0-9795422-0-6(0))* National Cave & Karst Research Institute.
Kornfeld, Marcel. On Shelter's Ledge: Histories, Theories & Methods of Rockshelter Research. 2007. (Bar S Ser.). (FRE & ENG., Illus.). 199p. (C). pap. 87.50 *(978-1-4073-0091-7(1))* British Archaeological Reports Ltd. GBR. Dist: Brown, David Bk. Co., The.
Latham, Sean. Caves. 2009. (Illus.). 272p. pap. 37.95 *(978-0-415-43833-9(0))* Routledge.
Lera, Thomas. Cave Post Offices. 2011. pap. *(978-0-939748-76-1(2))* Cave Bks.
Love, Judy L. Jewel Cave National Monument. 2008. (Images of America Ser.). (ENG., Illus.). 128p. pap. 21.99 *(978-0-7385-6198-1(3))* Arcadia Publishing.
Mark, Stephen R. Domain of the Caveman: A Historic Resource Study of Oregon Caves National Monument. 2006. (ENG., Illus.). 252p. per. 26.50 *(978-0-16-077093-7(9))* National Park Service Div. of Pubns.
Matthews, Larry E. Caves of Chattanooga. 2007. (Illus.). 192p. pap. *(978-1-879961-27-2(X))* National Speleological Society, Inc.
—Caves of Knoxville & the Great Smoky Mountains. 2008. (Illus.). 296p. pap. *(978-1-879961-30-2(X))* National Speleological Society, Inc.
Owen, Luella Agnes. Cave Regions of the Ozarks & Black Hills. 2008. 172p. 22.99 *(978-0-554-35613-6(9))* 2008. 172p. 25.99 *(978-0-554-26310-6(6))* 2007. (ENG.). 156p. pap. 19.99 *(978-1-4346-0844-4(1))* 2007. (ENG.). 170p. pap. 21.99 *(978-1-4346-0918-2(9))* BiblioBazaar.
—Cave Regions of the Ozarks & Black Hills. 2009. (Illus.). 160p. pap. *(978-1-4099-6036-2(6))* Dodo Pr.
Palmer, Arthur N. Cave Geology. 2007. *(978-0-939748-66-2(5))* Cave Bks.
Perera, Halawathage Nimal. Prehistoric Sri Lanka: Late Pleistocene Rockshelters & an Open-Air Site. 2010. (Bar S Ser.). (ENG., Illus.). 268p. (C). pap. 130.00 *(978-1-4073-0683-4(9))* British Archaeological Reports Ltd. GBR. Dist: Brown, David Bk. Co., The.
Prufer, Olaf H., et al, eds. Caves & Culture: 10,000 Years of Ohio History. 2006. (Illus.). 463p. 45.00 *(978-0-87338-865-8(8))* Kent State Univ. Pr.
Rhinehart, Richard. Cave of the Winds Then & Now. 2011. (Illus.). 112p. pap. 17.95 ***(978-1-56579-650-8(0))*** Westcliffe Pubs.
Robison, Mabel Otis. Mystic Wonderlands. 2011. 96p. 38.95 ***(978-1-258-03439-9(5))*** Literary Licensing, LLC.
Sasowsky, Ira D. & Mylroie, John, eds. Studies of Cave Sediments: Physical & Chemical Records of Paleoclimate. 2nd ed. 2007. (ENG., Illus.). x, 329p. 219.00 *(978-1-4020-5326-9(6)*, 1402053266) Springer.
Shick, Harry. Understanding Lava Tubes & Lava Caves. 2009. 130p. pap. 15.00 *(978-1-4251-8985-3(7))* Trafford Publishing.
Shoemaker, Henry. Penn's Grandest Cavern: The History, Legends & Description of Penn's Cave in Centre County. 2007. (ENG.). 108p. pap. 12.00 *(978-0-271-02266-6(3))* Pennsylvania State Univ. Pr.
Sidisunthorn, Pindar, et al. Caves of Northern Thailand. 2007. (ENG., Illus.). 392p. 35.00 *(978-974-9863-13-8(5))* River Bks. THA. Dist: Antique Collectors' Club.
Spink, Walter. Ajanta: History & Development: Volume 5: Cave by Cave. 2006. (Handbook of Oriental Studies. India Ser.). (Illus.). 396p. *(978-90-04-15644-9(5))* BRILL.
Stafford, Kevin W. & Majkowski, Lisa. The Mystery of Black Water Cave. 2007. (Illus.). 52p. (J). *(978-0-9795422-2-0(7))* National Cave & Karst Research Institute.
Steele, C. William. Huautla: Thirty Years in One of the World's Deepest Caves. 2009. *(978-0-939748-70-9(3))* Cave Bks.
Stermer, Esther. We Fight to Survive. 2009. 140p. lib. bdg. *(978-0-9799963-9-9(2))* IGI Pr.
Ustinova, Yulia. Caves & the Ancient Greek Mind: Descending Underground in the Search for Ultimate Truth. 2009. (ENG.). 328p. 110.00 *(978-0-19-954856-9(0))* Oxford Univ. Pr., Inc.
Veth, Peter Marius. The Archaeology of Montebello Islands, North-West Australia: Late Quaternary Foragers on an Arid Coastline. 2007. (Bar S Ser.). (ENG., Illus.). 84p. (C). pap. 62.50 *(978-1-4073-0103-7(9))* British Archaeological Reports Ltd. GBR. Dist: Brown, David Bk. Co., The.
Waltham, Tony. Great Caves of the World. 2008. (ENG., Illus.). 112p. 29.95 *(978-1-55407-413-6(4))* Firefly Bks. Ltd.
Weaver, H. Dwight. Missouri Caves in History & Legend. 2008. (Missouri Heritage Readers Ser.). (ENG., Illus.). 176p. (gr. 9). per. 16.95 *(978-0-8262-1778-3(8))* Univ. of Missouri Pr.
White, William B. & Culver, David C., eds. Encyclopedia of Caves. 2nd ed. 2012. (ENG., Illus.). 966p. 130.00 ***(978-0-12-383832-2(0)***, Academic Pr.) Elsevier Science & Technology Bks.
Wilkinson, Ernest. Snow Caves for Fun & Survival. 2007. *(978-0-9795590-0-6(6))* Adobe Village Pr.

CAVES—JUVENILE LITERATURE
Hutmacher, Kimberly M. Caves. 2010. (Natural Wonders Ser.). (ENG.). 24p. (gr. k-1). pap. 41.70 *(978-1-4296-5589-7(5)*, Pebble Plus) Capstone Pr., Inc.

CAVETT, DICK, 1936-
Cavett, Dick. Talk Show: Confrontations, Pointed Commentary, & off-Screen Secrets. 2010. (ENG.). 304p. 25.00 *(978-0-8050-9195-3(5)*, Times Bks.) Holt, Henry & Co.
—Talk Show: Confrontations, Pointed Commentary, & off-Screen Secrets. 2011. (ENG.). 304p. pap. 14.99 *(978-0-312-61052-4(1)*, St. Martin's Griffin) St. Martin's Pr.

CAVIAR
Carey, Richard Adams. The Philosopher Fish: Sturgeon, Caviar & the Geography of Desire. 2007. 333p. 26.00 *(978-1-4223-6708-7(8))* DIANE Publishing Co.
Fletcher, Nichola. Caviar: A Global History. 2010. (Reaktion Books - Edible Ser.). (ENG., Illus.). 144p. 15.95 *(978-1-86189-650-6(6))* Reaktion Bks., Ltd. GBR. Dist: Chicago Distribution Ctr.
Swengel, Andrea Lynn. Discovering Caviar. 2008. pap. *(978-0-9771489-7-4(1))* Campbell & Lewis Pubs.

CAVITATION
American Society of Mechanical Engineers Staff, ed. Cavitation. (Illus.). 326p. 232.00 *(978-0-85298-804-6(4))* Professional Engineering Publishing GBR. Dist: SAE Intl.
Brujan, Emil. Cavitation in Non-Newtonian Fluids: With Biomedical & Bioengineering Applications. 2010. (ENG., Illus.). xi, 269p. 179.00 *(978-3-642-15342-6(9)*, 3642153429) Springer.
D'Agostino, Luca. Fluid Dynamics of Cavitation & Cavitating Turbopumps. 2008. (CISM International Centre for Mechanical Sciences Ser.). 189.00 *(978-3-211-76668-2(5))* Springer.
d'Agostino, Luca & Salvetti, Maria Vittoria, eds. Fluid Dynamics of Cavitation & Cavitating Turbopumps. 2010. (CISM International Centre for Mechanical Sciences Ser.). (Illus.). vii, 351p. pap. 189.00 *(978-3-211-99920-2(5)*, 3211999205) Springer.
Encyclopaedia Britannica, Inc., compiled by. Cavitation. 2009. 49.00 *(978-1-60835-050-6(9))* Encyclopaedia Britannica, Inc.
Franc, Jean-Pierre & Michel, Jean-Marie. Fundamentals of Cavitation. 2010. (Fluid Mechanics & Its Applications Ser.). (ENG.). xxii, 306p. pap. 189.00 *(978-90-481-6618-3(7)*, 9048166187) Springer.

C

Ozonek, Janusz. Application of Hydrodynamic Cavitation in Environmental Engineering. 2012. (ENG., Illus.). 144p. 109.00 *(978-0-415-61626-3(3)*, CRC Press) Taylor & Francis Group GBR. Dist: Taylor & Francis Group.

Peshkovsky, Alexey S. & Peshkovsky, Sergei L. Acoustic Cavitation Theory & Equipment Design Principles for Industrial Applications of High-Intensity Ultrasound. 2010. (Illus.). 60p. pap. 49.00 *(978-1-61761-093-6(3))* Nova Science Pubs., Inc.

CAVOUR, CAMILLO BENSO, CONTE DI, 1810-1861

Botta, Vincenzo. A Discourse on the Life, Character, & Policy of Count Cavour, Delivered in the Hall of the New York Historical Society, February 20, 1862 by Vincen. 2006. 112p. per. 16.99 *(978-1-4255-0740-4(9))* MPublishing.

De Mazade, Charles. The Life of Count Cavour. 2007. (ENG.). 366p. 48.95 *(978-0-548-04618-0(2))* Kessinger Publishing, LLC.

Martinengo-Cesaresco, Countess Evelyn. Cavour. 2008. 192p. 22.99 *(978-0-554-33627-5(8))* 2008. 192p. 25.99 *(978-0-554-24324-5(5))* 2006. (ENG.). 168p. pap. 19.99 *(978-1-4264-6189-7(5))* BiblioBazaar.

Orsi, Pietro. Cavour & the Making of Modern Italy. (Heroes of the Nations Ser.). reprint ed. 30.00 *(978-0-404-58279-1(6))* AMS Pr., Inc.

Thayer, William Roscoe. The Life & Times of Cavour. 2007. Vol. 1. 628p. 60.95 *(978-0-548-01764-7(6))* Vol. 2. 582p. 58.95 *(978-0-548-01205-5(9))* Kessinger Publishing, LLC.

Villari, Pasquale. Studies, Historical & Critical. 2010. (ENG.). 364p. pap. 32.75 *(978-1-171-70476-8(3))* 2010. 364p. pap. 32.75 *(978-1-146-43475-1(8))* 2010. 366p. pap. 32.75 *(978-1-142-36414-4(3))* 2009. (ENG.). 342p. pap. 24.99 *(978-1-116-22019-3(9)*, BiblioLife) 2009. (ENG.). 342p. pap. 23.99 *(978-1-116-22020-9(2)*, BiblioLife) BiblioBazaar.

—Studies, Historical & Critical. 2009. 162p. pap. 19.99 *(978-1-150-28964-4(3))* General Bks. LLC.

Weber, Camilla. Camillo Cavour in den Schulbüchern des liberalen Italien: Nationale Selbstdarstellung im Geschichtsunterricht zwischen Risorgimento und Faschismus. 2010. (Italien in Geschichte und Gegenwart Ser.). (GER.). 430p. 101.95 *(978-3-631-58792-8(9))* Lang, Peter GmbH, Europaischer Verlag der Wissenschaften DEU. Dist: Lang, Peter.

White, Andrew Dickson. Seven Great Statesmen in the Warfare of Humanity with Unreason. 2009. 338p. pap. 25.23 *(978-1-4589-7315-3(8))* General Bks. LLC.

—Seven Great Statesmen in the Warfare of Humanity with Unreason. 2007. (ENG.). 562p. 58.95 *(978-0-548-01978-8(9))* Kessinger Publishing, LLC.

Whyte, Arthur J. The Early Life & Letters of Cavour, 1810-1848. reprint ed. 32.50 *(978-0-404-15356-4(9))* AMS Pr., Inc.

CAXTON, WILLIAM, CA. 1422-1491

Aurner, Nellie Slayton. Caxton Mirror of Fifteenth Century Lette. 2006. pap. 31.95 *(978-1-4286-3581-4(5))* Kessinger Publishing, LLC.

Blades, William. The Biography & Typography of William Caxton. 2008. 436p. 30.99 *(978-0-559-83843-9(3))*; pap. 34.75 *(978-0-559-83840-8(9))* BiblioBazaar.

—The Biography & Typography of William Caxton: England's First Printer. 2010. 374p. pap. 32.75 *(978-1-142-28180-9(9))* BiblioBazaar.

—The Biography & Typography of William Caxton: England's first Printer. 2010. (ENG.). 434p. pap. 35.75 *(978-1-177-39633-2(5))* BiblioBazaar.

—The biography & typography of William Caxton: England's first Printer. (ENG.). VIII, 383p. 225.00 ***(978-3-11-200116-5(8))***; 147.00 ***(978-3-11-130132-7(X))*** De Gruyter, Walter Inc.

Blades, William. The Biography & Typography of William Caxton, England's First Printer. 2010. 438p. pap. 35.75 *(978-1-146-42187-4(7))* BiblioBazaar.

—The Biography & Typography of William Caxton, England's First Printer. 2010. 214p. pap. *(978-1-151-92171-0(8))* 2009. 264p. pap. *(978-0-217-29135-4(X))* Books LLC.

Blades, William & Blades, East & Blades. bkp CU-BANC. The Biography & Typography of William Caxton, England's First Printer. 2010. (ENG.). 436p. pap. 35.75 *(978-1-177-57564-5(7))* BiblioBazaar.

Hellinga, Lotte. William Caxton & Early Printing in England. 2010. (ENG., Illus.). 212p. 45.00 *(978-0-7123-5088-4(8))* British Library, The GBR. Dist: Chicago Distribution Ctr.

Knight, Charles. The Old Printer & the Modern Press. 2010. (Cambridge Library Collection - Printing & Publishing History Ser.). (Illus.). 332p. pap. 28.99 *(978-1-108-00922-5(0))* Cambridge Univ. Pr.

—William Caxton: The First English Printer. 2010. 240p. pap. 26.75 *(978-1-143-06545-3(X))* BiblioBazaar.

Marshall, David. Printing: an Account of Its Invention & of William Caxton, the First. 2007. (ENG.). 92p. per. 18.95 *(978-1-4304-4525-8(4))* Kessinger Publishing, LLC.

CAXTON FAMILY

Bulwer-Lytton, Edward. The Caxtons: A Family Picture. 2009. 384p. 26.99 *(978-0-559-90156-0(9))*; pap. 20.99 *(978-0-559-90153-9(4))* BiblioBazaar.

CAYAKS

see Kayaks

CAYCE, EDGAR, 1877-1945

Auken, John Van. Edgar Cayce's Tales of Egypt. 2011. 200p. pap. 16.95 ***(978-0-87604-623-4(5))*** A.R.E. Pr.

Auken, John Van. From Karma to Grace. 2010. 144p. pap. 15.95 *(978-0-87604-495-7(X))* A.R.E. Pr.

Bro, Harmon. Edgar Cayce on Religion Spirituality. 2008. 200p. pap. 15.95 *(978-0-87604-545-9(X))* A.R.E. Pr.

Cayce, Edgar. The Christmas Story. Carter, Mary Ellen & Gammon, Margaret, eds. 2011. 26p. 35.95 ***(978-1-258-00795-9(9))*** Literary Licensing, LLC.

Cayce, Edgar. Spiritual Healing for Personal Prosperity. 2011. 160p. pap. 15.95 *(978-0-87604-609-8(X))* A.R.E. Pr.

Cayce, Edgar & Van Auken, John. Toward a Deeper Meditation: Rejuvenating the Body Illuminating the Mind Experiencing the Spirit. 2007. 232p. per. *(978-0-87604-527-5(1))* A.R.E. Pr.

Cayce, Edgar Evans, et al. Mysteries of Atlantis. 2007. (Illus.). 210p. per. 14.95 *(978-0-87604-574-9(3))* A.R.E. Pr.

Cerminara, Gina. Many Mansions Part II: Healing the Karma Within You. 2006. 187p. per. 14.95 *(978-0-87604-522-0(0))* A.R.E. Pr.

Fazekas, Istvan. Edgar Cayce & the Yoga Sutras. 2008. 200p. pap. 15.95 *(978-0-87604-530-5(1))* A.R.E. Pr.

Gabbay, Simone. Edgar Cayce's Diet Plan for Optimal Health & Weight Loss. 2007. (Illus.). 160p. pap. 14.95 *(978-0-87604-564-0(6))* A.R.E. Pr.

Grant, Robert J. Angeles, Arcangeles y Fuerzas Invisibles. 2007. (SPA., Illus.). 251p. per. *(978-0-87604-537-4(9)*, Libros Iluminados) A.R.E. Pr.

Gray, Lydia J. Schrader. Children of the New Age. 2011. 52p. 36.95 ***(978-1-258-00141-4(1))*** Literary Licensing, LLC.

Hartzell Bro, Harmon. Edgar Cayce: A Seer Out of Season: The Life of History's Greatest Psychic. 2011. 512p. pap. 8.95 *(978-0-87604-604-3(9))* A.R.E. Pr.

Hruska, Elaine. Your Key to Good Health. 2008. pap. 15.95 *(978-0-87604-570-1(0))* A.R.E. Pr.

Jaffin, Ann M. Past Lives & Present Karma. 2008. xvii, 206p. pap. *(978-0-87604-532-9(8))* A.R.E. Pr.

Kukor, David. Miracle Oil. 2008. 200p. pap. 15.95 *(978-0-87604-572-5(7))* A.R.E. Pr.

L&L Publishing Co., creator. Ye Are the Light. 2008. (Illus.). 70p. per. 20.00 *(978-0-9799833-4-4(7))* L & L Publishing Co.

Millard, Joseph. Edgar Cayce Hombre de los Milagros. 2008. (SPA., Illus.). 292p. pap. 16.95 *(978-0-87604-538-1(7)*, Libros Iluminados) A.R.E. Pr.

—Edgar Cayce: Mystery Man of Miracles. 2007. 207p. per. *(978-0-87604-528-2(X))* A.R.E. Pr.

Mullaney, James. Edgar Cayce & the Cosmos. 2007. (Illus.). 136p. per. *(978-0-87604-566-4(2))* A.R.E. Pr.

My Life as a Seer. Date not set. pap. *(978-0-312-28409-1(8)*, St. Martin's Griffin) St. Martin's Pr.

Pagano, John O. A. One Cause — Many Ailments: The Leaky Gut Syndrome: What It Is & How It May Be Affecting Your Health. 2008. pap. *(978-0-87604-573-2(5))* A.R.E. Pr.

Reed, Henry & Cayce, Charles Thomas. Edgar Cayce on Channeling Your Higher Self. 2007. (Illus.). 308p. pap. *(978-0-87604-531-2(X))* A.R.E. Pr.

Sherbenou, Judith. Edgar Cayce & a Course in Miracles. 2006. (Illus.). 55p. per. *(978-0-87604-568-8(9))* A.R.E. Pr.

Stearn, Jess. Edgar Cayce: The Sleeping Prophet. Date not set. 350p. 25.95 *(978-0-8488-2397-9(4))* Amereon LTD.

Thomas, Jeanette M. The Edgar Cayce Plant Encyclopedi: Volume One. 2009. (Illus.). 288p. pap. 69.99 *(978-1-4389-7881-9(2))* AuthorHouse.

Todeschi, Kevin J. Edgar Cayce on Vibrations: Spirit in Motion. 2007. 119p. per. *(978-0-87604-567-1(0))* A.R.E. Pr.

Turner, William T. & Gilkey, Chris. Edgar Cayce's Hometown: Hopkinsville, Kentucky. 2010. (Illus.). 128p. pap. 21.95 *(978-1-934898-08-6(2))* McClanahan Publishing Hse., Inc.

CAYMAN ISLANDS

Frink, Stephen, et al. The Cayman Islands: White Star Guides Diving. 2006. (White Star Guides Ser.). (ENG., Illus.). 192p. pap. 18.95 *(978-88-544-0112-9(9)*, White Star) Rizzoli International Pubns., Inc.

Philpott, Don & Landmarks Staff. Cayman Islands. 3rd rev. ed. 2008. (Illus.). 144p. 14.99 *(978-1-84306-370-4(0))* Landmark Publishing Ltd. GBR. Dist: Hunter Publishing, Inc.

Rock, Tim & Lonely Planet Staff. Diving & Snorkeling Cayman Islands. 2nd rev. ed. 2007. (Lonely Planet Diving & Snorkeling Guides). (ENG., Illus.). 144p. pap. 24.99 *(978-1-74059-897-2(0))* Lonely Planet Pubns.

CAYMAN ISLANDS—DESCRIPTION AND TRAVEL

Bodden, Jackie. A Cayman Childhood Remembered. 2007. 288p. im. lthr. 24.95 *(978-0-9785936-4-3(2))* Bodden, Jackie.

Fodor's Travel Publications, Inc. Staff. Cayman Islands. 2nd ed. 2010. (In Focus-Color Ser.). (ENG., Illus.). 268p. pap. 11.99 *(978-1-4000-0478-2(0)*, Fodor's) Fodor's Travel Pubns.

Hayne, Tricia. Cayman Islands: The Bradt Travel Guide. 3rd ed. 2008. (Bradt Travel Guide Ser.). (ENG., Illus.). 240p. pap. 22.99 *(978-1-84162-214-9(1))* Bradt Travel Guides GBR. Dist: Globe Pequot Pr., The.

Locken, E. Travel Journal Cayman Islands. 2009. 192p. pap. 20.95 *(978-0-557-07793-9(1))* Lulu Enterprises Inc.

Palmer, Jenny. The Cayman Islands: Island Portrait. 2nd ed. 2011. (Illus.). 256p. *(978-1-4050-7724-8(7))* Macmillan Caribbean.

Permenter, Paris. Cayman Islands Adventure Guide. Bigley, John, ed. 3rd rev. ed. 2008. (Illus.). 340p. pap. 9.99 *(978-1-58843-640-5(3))* Hunter Publishing, Inc.

Porter, Darwin & Prince, Danforth. Frommer's Portable Cayman Islands. 5th ed. 2011. (Frommer's Portable Ser.: 271). (ENG., Illus.). 216p. pap. 12.99 *(978-1-118-00429-6(9)*, Frommers) Wiley, John & Sons, Inc.

Wood, Lawson. Dive the Cayman Islands. Hanna, Nick, ed. 2007. (Dive Ser.). (ENG., Illus.). 176p. pap. 20.00 *(978-1-56656-706-0(8))* Interlink Publishing Group, Inc.

CAYMAN ISLANDS—ECONOMIC CONDITIONS

Icon Group International, Inc. Staff, compiled by. The 2006 Economic & Product Market Databook for George Town, Cayman Islands. 2006. 618p. ring bd. 95.00 *(978-0-497-80588-3(X))* Icon Group International, Inc.

—The 2006 Economic & Product Market Databook for Savannah, Cayman Islands. 2006. 618p. ring bd. 95.00 *(978-0-497-81481-6(1))* Icon Group International, Inc.

—The 2006 Economic & Product Market Databook for West Bay, Cayman Islands. 2006. 618p. ring bd. 95.00 *(978-0-497-81819-7(1))* Icon Group International, Inc.

CAYMAN ISLANDS—HISTORY

Bodden, Jackie. A Cayman Childhood Remembered. 2007. 288p. im. lthr. 24.95 *(978-0-9785936-4-3(2))* Bodden, Jackie.

CBA (EDUCATIONAL TEST)

see Curriculum-Based Assessment

CBR WARFARE

see Biological Warfare; Chemical Warfare; Nuclear Warfare

CD-I TECHNOLOGY

Dulaney, Emmett, et al. CompTIA Security+ Exam SYO-201. 4th ed. 2008. (ENG., Illus.). 600p. pap., pupil's gde. ed. 49.99 *(978-0-470-37297-5(4)*, Sybex) Wiley, John & Sons, Inc.

CD PLAYERS

see Compact Disc Players

CD-ROMS

Davis, Robert L., et al. Entrevistas. 2nd ed. (SPA & ENG., Illus.). cd-rom *(978-0-07-296417-2(0))* McGraw-Hill Cos., The.

Monaco, James. How to Read a Film: Movies, Media, & Beyond. 4th ed. 2009. (ENG., Illus.). 688p. pap. 29.95 *(978-0-19-532105-0(7))* Oxford Univ. Pr., Inc.

Nosrati, Farhad D. & Ghalili, Jesse. What the Heck Is Internet. Date not set. (What the Heck Is . . . Ser.). pap. 4.99 incl. audio compact disk *(978-0-9660787-3-2(X))* Crystal Media Publishing.

Stan, Sorin G. The CD-ROM Drive: A Brief System Description. 2010. (ENG.). 160p. pap. 169.00 *(978-1-4419-5039-0(7)*, 1441950397) Springer.

CDI TECHNOLOGY

see CD-I Technology

CDMA

see Code Division Multiple Access

CDS (COMPACT DISCS)

see Compact Discs

CEAUSESCU, NICOLAI, 1918-1991

Biographiq. Nicolae Ceausescu - the Genius of the Carpathians (Biography) 2008. 60p. pap. 9.99 *(978-1-59986-380-1(4)*, Biographiq) Filiquarian Publishing, LLC.

Büchel, Christoph & Carmine, Giovanni. Ceau, 1 vol. 2009. (ENG., Illus.). 352p. pap. 45.00 *(978-3-86521-600-7(5))* Steidl, Gerhard Druckerei und Verlag DEU. Dist: Innovative Logistics.

Popovici, Teodor. Exiled by Romanian Oppression: Legs Without Freedom: Memoir of Teodor Popovici. 2008. pap. 24.95 *(978-1-60563-137-0(X))* PublishAmerica, Inc.

CEBU DIALECT

see Cebuano Language

CEBUANO LANGUAGE

Icon Group International, Inc. Staff, compiled by. Webster's Cebuano - English Thesaurus Dictionary. 2008. 700p. ring bd. 28.95 incl. audio compact disk *(978-0-497-83464-7(2))* Icon Group International, Inc.

Paragoso, Liberacion Tecson. The Origin & Semantics of Some Cebuano Words. 2009. 204p. 29.99 *(978-1-4363-9615-8(8))*; pap. 19.99 *(978-1-4363-9614-1(X))* Xlibris Corp.

CECIDOLOGY

see Galls (Botany)

CECIL FAMILY

Bateman, Katherine & Bateman, Katherine R. Kentucky Clay: Eleven Generations of a Southern Dynasty. 2008. (ENG., Illus.). 256p. 24.95 *(978-1-55652-795-1(0))* Chicago Review Pr., Inc.

CECIL COUNTY (MD.)

ADC, the Map People Staff, creator. Cecil County Maryland Street Atlas. 2007. (Illus.). 40p. 12.95 *(978-0-87530-880-7(5))* ADC The Map People.

Diggins, Milt. Cecil County. 2008. (Images of America Ser.). (ENG., Illus.). 128p. pap. 21.99 *(978-0-7385-5366-5(2))* Arcadia Publishing.

Maryland Historical Markers Cecil County. 2008. (ENG.). per. 49.95 *(978-0-9742554-7-7(5))* Blackpool, Stephen Inc.

CEDAR

Betteridge, Margaret, et al. Red Cedar in Australia. 2008. (ENG., Illus.). 128p. pap. 49.95 *(978-1-876991-19-7(4))* Historic Houses Trust of New South Wales AUS. Dist: National Bk. Network.

Lerner, Robert E. The Powers of Prophecy: The Cedar of Lebanon Vision from the Mongol Onslaught to the Dawn of the Enlightenment. 2009. 264p. pap. 25.95 *(978-0-8014-7537-5(6))* Cornell Univ. Pr.

Wade, Roger & Skinner, Tina. Cedar Style: A Look at Lovely Log Homes. 2008. (Illus.). 192p. 39.95 *(978-0-7643-2951-7(0))* Schiffer Publishing, Ltd.

CEDAR MOUNTAIN, BATTLE OF, VA., 1862

Sheppard, Eric William. The Campaign in Virginia & Maryland, June 26th to Sept. 20th, 1862, Cedar Run, Manassas, & Sharpsburg. (Special Campaign Ser.). 306p. reprint ed. 98.00 *(978-0-7222-8038-6(6))*; 98.00 *(978-0-7222-8042-3(4))* Library Reprints, Inc.

CEDAR RAPIDS (IOWA)

Collins, Brian C. Cedar Falls Iowa: Iowa. 2006. (Images of America Ser.). (ENG., Illus.). 128p. pap. 21.99 *(978-0-7385-4582-0(1))* Arcadia Publishing.

Reilly, Donna Grant. An American Proceeding: Building the Grant House with Frank Lloyd Wright. 2010. (Illus.). 196p. pap. 22.95 *(978-1-58465-978-5(5))* Univ. Pr. of New England.

CEILINGS

see also Mural Painting and Decoration

Barrett, Neal. Architectural Ceiling Treatments. 2008. (Home Improvement Ser.). (ENG., Illus.). 192p. (gr. 5). pap. 19.95 *(978-1-58011-414-1(8))* Creative Homeowner.

Bauer, Hermann, et al. Corpus der Barocken Deckenmalerei 13. Bayern Landkreis Eichstätt. 2009. (GER., Illus.). (C). 168.00 *(978-3-7774-9690-0(1))* Hirmer Verlag GmbH DEU. Dist: Brown, David Bk. Co., The.

Cameron, Bob. Illumination & Decoration of Flat Surfaces. 6th ed. 2009. (Illus.). 40p. pap. 21.95 *(978-0-643-09490-1(3))* CSIRO Publishing AUS. Dist: Stylus Publishing, LLC.

Designer Books Staff, ed. Ceiling Design. 2009. (ENG., Illus.). 295p. 80.00 *(978-4-903233-37-6(5))* Azur Corp. JPN. Dist: Antique Collectors' Club.

Dover. Renaissance & Baroque Ceiling Masterpieces. 2008. (Dover Pictorial Archive Ser.). (ENG., Illus.). 80p. pap. 17.95 *(978-0-486-46529-6(2))* Dover Pubns., Inc.

Kosonen, Risto. Performance of Ventilated Ceilings in Commercial Kitchens. 2008. 144p. pap. *(978-3-639-08873-1(5))* VDM Verlag Dr. Mueller e.K.

Robinson, Cynthia. Courting the Alhambra: Cross-Disciplinary Approaches to the Hall of Justice Ceilings. Pinet, Simone, ed. 2008. 293p. pap. *(978-90-04-17342-2(0))* BRILL.

CELA, CAMILO JOSE, 1916-2002

Cela, Camilo José. Boxwood. Haugaard, Patricia, tr. 2008. (ENG., Illus.). 224p. pap. 14.95 *(978-0-8112-1751-4(5))* New Directions Publishing Corp.

—Nuevo Viaje a la Alcarria. (SPA., Illus.). 251p. *(978-84-01-38088-4(X))* Plaza & Janes Editories, S.A. ESP. Dist: AIMS International Bks., Inc.

Choi, Myung. Employing the Grotesque as a Communication Strategy: The History of an Artistic Style. 2009. ii, 120p. *(978-0-7734-3844-6(0))* Mellen, Edwin Pr., The.

Porrua, Enrique J. El discurso postmodernista en la trilogia gallega de Camilo Jose Cela. 2007. (SPA & ENG.). 268p. 109.95 *(978-0-7734-5256-5(7))* Mellen, Edwin Pr., The.

Rodiek, Christoph. Del Cuento Al Relato Hibrido: En Torno a la Narrativa Breve de Camilo José Cela. 2008. (SPA., Illus.). 171p. pap. 24.80 *(978-84-8489-420-9(7))* Iberoamericana Vervuert Publishing Corp.

CELEBES (INDONESIA)

Harvey, Barbara S. Permesta: Half a Rebellion. 2010. 264p. pap. 29.95 *(978-602-8397-38-4(5))* Equinox Publishing IDN. Dist: Univ. of Hawaii Pr.

Kaudern, Walter A. Ethnographical Studies in Celebes: Results of the Author's Expedition to Celebes, 1917-1920, 6 vols., Set. reprint ed. 275.00 *(978-0-404-16740-0(3))* AMS Pr., Inc.

CELEBRITIES

AA, W. Double Life. 2011. (ENG., Illus.). 108p. pap. 75.00 *(978-88-370-7528-6(6)*, Mondadori Electa (Acc)) Antique Collectors' Club GBR. Dist: National Bk. Network.

Aarons, Slim & Getty Images, Inc Staff, photos by. Poolside with Slim Aarons. 2007. (ENG., Illus.). 240p. 85.00 *(978-0-8109-9407-2(0))* Abrams.

Abanes, Richard. Religions of the Stars: What Hollywood Believes & How It Affects You. 2009. 224p. pap. 13.99 *(978-0-7642-0648-1(6))* Bethany Hse. Pubs.

Abrahams, Mark, photos by. Mark Abrahams. 2011. (ENG., Illus.). 300p. 70.00 *(978-88-6208-138-2(3))* Damiani ITA. Dist: D.A.P./Distributed Art Pubs.

Adams, Jan Thatcher. Football Wife: Coming of Age with the NFL as Mrs. Karl Kassulke. 2011. (ENG., Illus.). 288p. pap. 16.95 *(978-1-936487-04-2(7)*, 1936487047) Franklin Green Publishing.

Addamo, Vince. My Silent Heroes: Guide in selecting role Models. 2010. 108p. pap. 10.99 *(978-1-4490-5386-4(6))* AuthorHouse.

Alam, Mohammed Badrul. Jackie Kennedy: Images & Reality. 2011. (Presidential Wives Ser.). pap. 43.00 *(978-1-61761-840-6(3)*, Nova Novinka) Nova Science Pubs., Inc.

Alden, Vernon R. Presidents, Kings, Astronauts, & Ball Players: Fascinating People I have Known. 2009. (ENG.). 163p. 25.00 *(978-0-533-16021-1(9))* Vantage Pr., Inc.

Allison, Jay. This I Believe: The Personal Philosophies of Remarkable Men & Women. Allison, Jay & Gediman, Dan, eds. 2007. (ENG., Illus.). 320p. pap. 15.00 *(978-0-8050-8658-4(7)*, Holt Paperback) Holt, Henry & Co.

—This I Believe: The Personal Philosophies of Remarkable Men & Women. Allison, Jay & Gediman, Dan, eds. 2006. (ENG., Illus.). 304p. 25.00 *(978-0-8050-8087-2(2))* Holt, Henry & Co.

Allison, Jay & Gediman, Dan. This I Believe II: More Personal Philosophies of Remarkable Men & Women. Gregory, John et al, eds. 2008. (ENG.). 288p. 23.00 *(978-0-8050-8768-0(0))* Holt, Henry & Co.

—This I Believe II: The Personal Philosophies of Remarkable Men & Women. 2009. (ENG.). 288p. pap. 15.00 *(978-0-8050-9089-5(4)*, Holt Paperback) Holt, Henry & Co.

Alm, Sara & McDevitt, Hannah. Famous Frocks: Patterns & Instructions for Recreating Fabulous Iconic Dresses - 10 Patterns for 20 Dresses in All! 2011. (ENG.). 156p. 29.95 *(978-0-8118-7791-6(4))* Chronicle Bks. LLC.

Almanac of Famous People. 10th ed. 2011. 267.00 *(978-1-4144-4548-9(2))* Cengage Gale.

Altman, Robert. The Sixties: Photographs by Robert Altman. 2007. (ENG., Illus.). 192p. 39.95 *(978-1-59580-024-4(7))* Santa Monica Pr.

Anderson, Mark Lynn. Twilight of the Idols: Hollywood & the Human Sciences in 1920s America. 2011. (ENG., Illus.). 224p. 60.00 *(978-0-520-23711-7(0))*; pap. 24.95 *(978-0-520-26708-4(7))* Univ. of California Pr.

Anthony, George. Starring Brian Linehan: A Life Behind the Scenes. 2008. (ENG., Illus.). 360p. pap. 19.99 *(978-0-7710-0758-3(2)*, Emblem Edns) McClelland & Stewart CAN. Dist: Random Hse., Inc.

Arender, Shea. Shea Arender Illusions of the King: A Magical Journey-Life as Elvis Presley. Edcings, Pam, ed. 2010. (Illus.). 128p. pap. 13.99 *(978-0-9826531-1-5(4))* JEC Publishing Co.

Aspen, Nelson. Hollywood Insider Exposed! Secrets, Stars & Showbiz. 2009. (ENG., Illus.). 256p. pap. 19.95 *(978-1-74110-698-5(2))* New Holland Pubs. Pty, Ltd. AUS. Dist: Tuttle Publishing.

Aspinall, Julie. Victoria Beckham: Queen of America. 2008. (ENG., Illus.). 288p. 24.95 *(978-1-84454-465-3(6))* Blake, John Publishing, Ltd. GBR. Dist: Independent Pubs. Group.

Aspinall, Julie & Herbert, Emily. Katie & Peter - Too Much in Love: The Inside Story of Their Break-Up. 2010. (ENG., Illus.). 250p. pap. 13.95 *(978-1-84454-868-2(6))* Blake, John Publishing, Ltd. GBR. Dist: Independent Pubs. Group.

Associated Media Company, creator. V. I. P. Address Book. 2007. (V. I. P. Address Book Ser.). 673p. 119.75 *(978-0-938731-51-1(3))* Associated Media Cos., Ltd.

Assouline, creator. The Proust Questionnaire. 2009. *(978-2-7594-0216-8(9))* Assouline.

Atteu, Pol & Simpson, Patrik. Anna Nicole Smith: Portrait of an Icon. 2008. 122p. pap. 24.95 *(978-0-9815353-0-2(5))* Kings Road Publishing.

Barnes, Robin D. Outrageous Invasions: Celebrities' Private Lives, Media, & the Law. 2010. (ENG., Illus.). 324p. 65.00 *(978-0-19-539276-0(0))* Oxford Univ. Pr., Inc.

Barnes, Scott. About Face: Amazing Transformations Using the Secrets of the Top Celebrity Makeup Artist. 2010. (ENG., Illus.). 240p. 24.99 *(978-1-59233-399-8(0)*, 1592333990) Quayside.

Barone, Arturo. The Italian Achievement: A-Z over 1000 'Firsts' Achieved by Italians in Almost Every Aspect of Life over the Last 1000 Years. 2008. 364p. 29.95 *(978-1-898823-55-1(3))* Renaissance Bks. Ltd. GBR. Dist: Midpoint Trade Bks., Inc.

Barry, Michael Thomas. Final Resting Places: Orange County's Dead & Famous. 2010. (Illus.). 224p. pap. 16.99 *(978-0-7643-3421-4(2))* Schiffer Publishing, Ltd.

Bayley, Stephen. La Dolce Vita: The Golden Age of Italian Style & Celebrity, 1 vol. 2011. (ENG, ITA & GER., Illus.). 256p. 59.95 *(978-1-906863-57-9(1))* FIELL Pubng. Ltd. GBR. Dist: D.A.P./Distributed Art Pubs.

Bego, Mark & Jones, Randy. Macho Man: The Disco Era & Gay America's Coming Out, 1 vol. 2008. (Illus.). 232p. 39.95 *(978-0-275-99962-9(9)*, C9962, Praeger Pubs.) Greenwood Publishing Group, Inc.

Benoit, Tod. Where Are They Buried? How Did They Die? Fitting Ends & Final Resting Places of the Famous, Infamous, & Noteworthy. rev. ed. 2009. (ENG., Illus.). 560p. pap. 14.95 *(978-1-57912-822-7(X)*, 157912822X) Black Dog & Leventhal Pubs., Inc.

Berger, Raqota. High-Profile Celebrity Court Cases: A Look into Audience Needs & Motivations. 2009. 242p. pap. 30.00 *(978-0-557-05415-2(X))* Lulu Enterprises Inc.

Blitz, Michael & Krasniewicz, Louise. Arnold Schwarzenegger: A Biography, 1 vol. 2006. (Greenwood Biographies Ser.). (Illus.). 192p. 29.95 *(978-0-313-33810-6(8)*, GR3810, Greenwood Pr.) Greenwood Publishing Group, Inc.

Blow, Detmar & Sykes, Tom. Blow by Blow: The Story of Isabella Blow. 2010. (ENG.). 304p. 30.00 *(978-0-06-202087-1(0))* HarperCollins Pubs.

Bowles, Hamish. Vogue Living: Houses, Gardens, People. 2007. (ENG., Illus.). 400p. 85.00 *(978-0-307-26622-4(2)*, Knopf) Knopf Doubleday Publishing Group.

Boyer Rumbaugh, Gina. X-Chromosomes Within the X-Files. 2008. 128p. pap. *(978-3-639-07196-2(4))* VDM Verlag Dr. Mueller e.K.

Brett, Bill, photos by. Boston: An Extended Family. 2007. (ENG., Illus.). 136p. 27.95 *(978-1-933212-38-8(1))* Commonwealth Editions.

Brewin, Belinda. Trouble Brewin: A True Story of Sex, Murder, Love & Betrayal. 2007. (ENG., Illus.). 288p. per. 15.95 *(978-1-84358-168-0(X))* Blake, John Publishing, Ltd. GBR. Dist: Independent Pubs. Group.

Brighthaupt, Moe & Jasper, Kenji. Baby Girl: My Life with Anna Nicole Smith. 2007. 256p. 24.95 *(978-0-06-145073-0(1)*, Harper Entertainment) HarperCollins Pubs.

Brockington, Dan. Celebrity & the Environment: Frame, Wealth & Power in Conservation. 2009. (ENG.). 224p. 107.95 *(978-1-84277-973-6(7))*; pap. 26.95 *(978-1-84277-974-3(5))* Zed Bks., Ltd. GBR. Dist: Macmillan.

Browne, Sylvia. Afterlives of the Rich & Famous. 2011. (ENG.). 256p. pap. 14.99 *(978-0-06-196680-4(0)*, HarperOne) HarperCollins Pubs.

Browne, Sylvia. Afterlives of the Rich & Famous: Reconnect with the Celebrities You Have Loved & Lost Reconnect with the Celebrities You Have Loved & Lost. 2011. (ENG.). 256p. 25.99 *(978-0-06-196679-8(7)*, HarperOne); 410p. pap. 25.99 *(978-0-06-201798-7(5)*, HarperLuxe) HarperCollins Pubs.

Bruns, Roger. Icons of Latino America: Latino Contributions to American Culture, 2 vols. 2008. (Greenwood Icons Ser.). (Illus.). 648p. 175.00 *(978-0-313-34086-4(2)*, GR4086, Greenwood Pr.) Greenwood Publishing Group, Inc.

Buell, Bebe. Wild at Heart. mass mkt. *(978-0-312-98039-9(6)*, St. Martin's Paperbacks) St. Martin's Pr.

Bui, Doan & Monnin, Isabelle. Ils Sont Devenus Français: Dans le Secret des Archives. 2010. (FRE., Illus.). 303p. *(978-2-7096-3552-3(6))* Lattes, Jean-Claude Editions.

Burbank, Jeff. Las Vegas Babylon: The True Tales of Glitter, Glamour, & Greed. 2008. (ENG., Illus.). 322p. pap. 16.95 *(978-1-59077-136-5(2))* Evans, M. & Co., Inc.

Burke, Brooke. The Naked Mom: A Modern Mom's Fearless Revelations, Savvy Advice, & Soulful Reflections. 2012. (ENG.). 320p. (gr. 12). 15.00 *(978-0-451-23507-7(X)*, N A L Trade) Penguin Group (USA) Inc.

Burman, Sanjay. Reading People: The Body Language of Your Favorite Stars. 2011. (ENG.). 152p. pap. 14.95 *(978-1-897404-32-4(8))* Burman Books, Inc. CAN. Dist: Innovative Logistics.

Burton, David Henry. Animating History: The Biographical Pulse. 2007. (ENG.). 45.00 *(978-0-916101-75-6(4))* St. Joseph's Univ. Pr.

Butler, F. Patrick. Cavorting with Strangers: Great Ideas & Their Champions-Paris. 2006. 576p. pap. 19.95 *(978-1-879384-71-2(X))* Cypress Hse.

—Cavorting with Strangers: Great Ideas & Their Champions: Paris. 2007. 564p. 29.95 *(978-1-879384-72-9(8))* Cypress Hse.

Buttolph, Angela. Kate Moss: Style. 2008. (ENG., Illus.). 208p. 29.95 *(978-1-84605-430-3(3))* Random Hse. GBR. Dist: Independent Pubs. Group.

—Style. 2009. (ENG., Illus.). 208p. 35.00 *(978-1-84605-429-7(X))* Random Hse. GBR. Dist: Independent Pubs. Group.

Buttrose, Larry. Dead Famous: Deaths of the Famous & Famous Deaths. 2007. (ENG., Illus.). 304p. pap. 19.95 *(978-1-74110-564-3(1))* New Holland Pubs. Pty, Ltd. AUS. Dist: Tuttle Publishing.

Carter, Graydon, ed. Vanity Fair's Proust Questionnaire: 101 Luminaries Ponder Love, Death, Happiness, & the Meaning of Life. 2009. (ENG., Illus.). 224p. 23.99 *(978-1-60529-595-4(7))* Rodale Pr., Inc.

Carter, Graydon & Friend, David. Vanity Fair: The Portraits - A Century of Iconic Images. 2008. (ENG., Illus.). 384p. 65.00 *(978-0-8109-7298-8(0))* Abrams.

Cashmore, Ellis. Celebrity Culture. 2006. 311p. 170.00 *(978-0-415-37310-4(7))* Routledge.

—Celebrity/Culture. 2006. (ENG.). 320p. per. 51.95 *(978-0-415-37311-1(5))* Routledge.

Cassidi, Deborah, compiled by. Favourite Heroes & Holy People: Chosen by People from All Walks of Life. 2008. (ENG., Illus.). 280p. 19.95 *(978-1-84706-329-8(2))* Continuum International Publishing Group, Ltd. GBR. Dist: National Bk. Network.

Chandler, Harry Brant. Dreamers in Dream City. 2009. *(978-1-883318-84-0(X))* Angel City Pr.

Charles, C. H. Love Letters of Great Men & Women: From the Eighteenth Century to the Present Day. 2010. (Illus.). 354p. pap. 10.95 *(978-1-57898-882-2(9))* Martino Publishing.

Chris Beetles Gallery. Terry O'Neill: The Art of Photography. 2007. (ENG., Illus.). 80p. pap. *(978-1-871136-95-1(4))* Beetles, Chris Ltd.

Christoforou, Christina. Whose Hair? 2011. (ENG., Illus.). 128p. pap. 12.95 *(978-1-85669-715-6(0))* King, Laurence Publishing GBR. Dist: Hachette Bk. Group.

Chronicle Books Staff & Eyal, Irad. Sex Degrees of Separation: The Ultimate Guide to Celebrity Relationships. 2010. (ENG., Illus.). 160p. pap. 14.95 *(978-0-8118-7180-8(0))* Chronicle Bks. LLC.

Church Gibson, Pamela. Fashion & Celebrity Culture. 2012. (ENG., Illus.). 256p. 99.95 *(978-1-84788-385-8(0))*; pap. 29.95 *(978-1-84788-386-5(9))* Berg Pubs. GBR. Dist: Macmillan.

Churchward, Charles. Herb Ritts: The Golden Hour - A Photographer's Life & His World. 2010. (ENG., Illus.). 320p. 65.00 *(978-0-8478-3472-3(7))* Rizzoli International Pubns., Inc.

Cipriani, Arrigo. Harry's Bar: The Life & Times of the Legendary Venice Landmark. 2nd ed. 2011. (ENG., Illus.). 192p. 24.95 *(978-1-61145-320-1(8)*, 611320, Arcade Publishing) Skyhorse Publishing Co., Inc.

Clarke, Norm. Vegas Confidential: Sinsational Celebrity Tales. Weatherford, Mike, ed. 2008. 272p. pap. 15.95 *(978-1-932173-77-2(3))* Stephens Pr. LLC.

Clarke, Victoria Mary. Why Did God Make Gucci If Not for Me? 2007. (ENG., Illus.). 344p. pap. 23.95 *(978-1-905172-35-1(4))* Collins Pr., The IRL. Dist: Dufour Editions, Inc.

Collins, Ace. I Saw Him in Your Eyes: Everyday People Making Extraordinary Impact in the Lives of Karen Kingsbury, Terri Blackstock, Bobby Bowden, Charlie Daniels, S. Truett Cathy, & More. Lt. ed. 2006. (Thorndike Inspirational Ser.). 245p. 27.95 *(978-0-7862-8857-1(4))* Thorndike Pr.

Conservation Heroes. 2011. (Conservation Heroes Ser.). (gr. 6-12). 350.00 *(978-0-7910-9964-3(4)*, Chelsea Hse.) Facts On File, Inc.

Corbijn, Anton, photos by. Inwards & Onwards: Inwards & Onwards. 2011. (ENG & GER., Illus.). 80p. 39.95 *(978-3-8296-0558-8(7))* Schirmer/Mosel Verlag GmbH DEU. Dist: Prestel Publishing.

Corkery, Richard. Star Shot: Thirty Years of New York Celebs, Icons, & Perennial Beauties. 2008. 256p. 29.95 *(978-0-06-111635-3(1)*, Harper Entertainment) HarperCollins Pubs.

Corzine, Chaz. Dear Baby: A Very Special Welcom to Life. 2009. (ENG.). 192p. pap. 14.95 *(978-1-4391-6844-8(X)*, Howard Bks.) Howard Books.

Cosby, Rita. Blonde Ambition: The Untold Story Behind Anna Nicole Smith's Death. 2008. 336p. mass mkt. 7.99 *(978-0-446-40612-3(0))* Grand Central Publishing.

Cottrell, Robert C. Icons of American Popular Culture: From P. T. Barnum to Jennifer Lopez. 2009. (ENG.). 280p. 74.95 *(978-0-7656-2298-3(X))*; pap. 32.95 *(978-0-7656-2299-0(8))* Sharpe, M.E. Inc.

Cowell, Tony. Is It Just Me or Is Everyone Famous? From A-List to Z-List & How to Make It Yourself. 2006. (ENG., Illus.). 288p. 17.95 *(978-1-84454-316-8(1))* Blake, John Publishing, Ltd. GBR. Dist: Independent Pubs. Group.

Cox, Caroline. How to Be Adored: A Girl's Guide to Hollywood Glamour. 2010. (ENG.). 256p. 19.99 *(978-0-06-199291-9(7)*, Collins Design) HarperCollins Pubs.

Cox, Julian. Robert Weingarten: The Portrait Unbound. 2010. (ENG., Illus.). 120p. 35.00 *(978-1-932543-33-9(3))* High Museum of Art.

D'Agostino, Ryan. Esquire the Meaning of Life: Wisdom, Humor, & Damn Good Advice from 64 Extraordinary Lives. 2009. (ENG., Illus.). 160p. 22.95 *(978-1-58816-646-3(5))* Hearst Communications, Inc.

Davis, Patti. The Lives Our Mothers Leave Us: Prominent Women Discuss the Complex, Humorous, & Ultimately Loving Relationships They Have with Their Mothers. 2009. (ENG.). 264p. pap. 14.95 *(978-1-4019-2162-0(0))* Hay Hse., Inc.

De Baeck, Philippe. Mini Celebrity Bible, 1 vol. 2011. (ENG, DUT & FRE., Illus.). 384p. 24.95 *(978-90-79761-83-8(4))* Tectum B.V.B.A. BEL. Dist: Innovative Logistics.

de Lafayette, Maximillien. Music, Showbiz & Entertainment. 2007. per. *(978-1-59916-152-5(4))* Printing Systems.

DeCaro, Frank. The Dead Celebrity Cookbook: A Resurrection of Recipes from More Than 145 Stars of Stage & Screen. 2011. (ENG.). 384p. pap. 19.95 *(978-0-7573-1596-1(8))* Health Communications, Inc.

Demarchelier, Patrick, photos by. Patrick Demarchelier, 1 vol. 2nd ed. 2009. (ENG., Illus.). 408p. 70.00 *(978-3-86521-736-3(2))* Steidl, Gerhard Druckerei und Verlag DEU. Dist: Innovative Logistics.

Derrick, Robin & Muir, Robin, eds. Vogue Covers: On Fashion's Front Page. 2010. (ENG., Illus.). 256p. pap. 28.95 *(978-1-4087-0213-0(4))* Little, Brown Bk. Group Ltd. GBR. Dist: Independent Pubs. Group.

—Vogue Covers: On Fashion's Front Page. 2008. (ENG., Illus.). 240p. 65.00 *(978-0-316-02785-4(5))* Little, Brown Bk. Group Ltd. GBR. Dist: Independent Pubs. Group.

Dershowitz, Alan M. What Israel Means to Me: By 80 Prominent Writers, Performers, Scholars, Politicians, & Journalists. 2007. (ENG.). 368p. per. 15.95 *(978-0-470-16914-8(1)*, Wiley) Wiley, John & Sons, Inc.

Dillon, Brian. The Hypochondriacs: Nine Tormented Lives. 2011. (ENG., Illus.). 288p. pap. 15.00 *(978-0-86547-946-3(1))* Faber & Faber, Inc.

Dillon-Malone, A. Half Wit: The Silliest Things People Wish They'd Never Said. 2008. (ENG., Illus.). 208p. 14.95 *(978-1-84024-693-3(6))* Summersdale Pubs. GBR. Dist: Independent Pubs. Group.

Diman, Paz. CELEBRITIES, 1 vol. 2009. (DUT, FRE, GER & ENG., Illus.). 476p. pap. 14.95 *(978-94-6065-003-1(1))* booQs Publishers bvba BEL. Dist: Innovative Logistics.

Dimant, Elyssa. The Style Mentors: Women Who Define the Art of Dressing Today. 2012. (ENG., Illus.). 192p. 30.00 *(978-0-06-199218-6(6)*, Collins Design) HarperCollins Pubs.

Dravis, Betty & Von, Chase. Dream Reachers II. 2011. 838p. pap. 24.95 *(978-0-9823464-7-1(6))* VonChase Publishing.

Dubin, Eric. The Star Chamber: How Celebrities Go Free & Their Lawyers Become Famous. 2007. (Illus.). 214p. 25.95 *(978-1-59777-553-3(3))* Phoenix Bks., Inc.

Dunn, Jancee. But Enough about Me: How a Small-Town Girl Went from Shag Carpet to the Red Carpet. 2007. (ENG.). 288p. per. 13.95 *(978-0-06-084365-6(9))* HarperCollins Pubs.

Dunton-Downer, Leslie. The English Is Coming! How One Language Is Sweeping the World. 2010. (ENG., Illus.). 352p. 24.00 *(978-1-4391-7665-8(5)*, Touchstone) Touchstone.

Ebert, John David. Dead Celebrities, Living Icons: Tragedy & Fame in the Age of the Multimedia Superstar, 1 vol. 2010. 230p. 44.95 *(978-0-313-37764-8(2)*, C37764, Praeger Pubs.) Greenwood Publishing Group, Inc.

Edelman, Abra. Celebrity Scarves. 2008. (ENG.). 120p. pap. 18.00 *(978-1-4379-5140-0(6))* DIANE Publishing Co.

Edwards, Jane. Interiors London. Taschen, Angelika, ed. 25th ed. 2009. (Interiors (Taschen) Ser.). (FRE, GER & ENG., Illus.). 277p. 19.99 *(978-3-8365-0997-8(0))* TASCHEN DEU. Dist: Ingram Pub. Services.

Edwards, Louise & Jeffreys, Elaine. Celebrity in China. 2010. (Illus.). 300p. *(978-988-220-667-0(0))* Hong Kong Univ. Pr.

Edwards, Louise & Jeffreys, Elaine, eds. Celebrity in China. 2010. (ENG.). 300p. (gr. 17). 55.00 *(978-962-209-087-3(7))*; pap. 28.00 *(978-962-209-088-0(5))* Hong Kong Univ. Pr. HKG. Dist: Columbia Univ. Pr.

Elle Magazine Staff & Bullock, Maggie. The Elements of Personal Style: 25 Modern Fashion Icons on How to Dress, Shop, & Live. Zee, Joe, ed. 2010. (ENG.). 256p. (gr. 12). 30.00 *(978-1-59240-557-1(3)*, Gotham) Penguin Group (USA) Inc.

Ellenberger, Allan R. Celebrities in the 1930 Census: Household Data of 2,265 U. S. Actors, Musicians, Scientists, Athletes, Writers, Politicians & Other Public Figures. 2008. (ENG., Illus.). 288p. per. 49.95 *(978-0-7864-3411-4(2))* McFarland & Co., Inc. Pubs.

Ellis, Lee, ed. The Celebrity Address Directory & Autograph Collector's Guide. 3rd ed. 2007. per. 39.95 *(978-0-9759569-2-2(2))* Americana Group Publishing.

Engel, Laura. Fashioning Celebrity: Eighteenth-Century British Actresses & Strategies for Image Making. 2011. 216p. 44.95 *(978-0-8142-1148-9(8))*; cd-rom 14.95 *(978-0-8142-9247-1(X))* Ohio State Univ. Pr.

Epstein, Barbara. The Company They Kept: Writers on Unforgettable Friendships. 2006. 298p. pap. *(978-1-59017-204-9(3))* New York Review of Bks., Inc., The.

Epstein, Barbara & Silvers, Robert B., eds. The Company They Kept: Writers on Unforgettable Friendships. 2006. (ENG.). 316p. 24.95 *(978-1-59017-203-2(5))* New York Review of Bks., Inc., The.

Erskine, John. The Memory of Certain Persons. 2007. (ENG.). 433p. 51.95 *(978-0-548-07025-3(3))* Kessinger Publishing, LLC.

—The Memory of Certain Persons. 2007. (ENG.). 440p. per. *(978-1-4067-3583-3(3))* Read Bks.

Evans, Chris. It's Not What You Think. 2010. (ENG.). 352p. pap. 22.95 *(978-0-00-732722-5(6))* HarperCollins Pubs. Ltd. GBR. Dist: Independent Pubs. Group.

Evergreen, ed. Mediterranean Living (EV) 2007. (ENG., Illus.). 192p. pap. 14.99 *(978-3-8228-4051-1(3))* TASCHEN DEU. Dist: Ingram Pub. Services.

Falkner, Leonard. Painted Lady, Eliza Jumel: Her Life & Times. 2011. 252p. 46.95 *(978-1-258-09180-4(1))* Literary Licensing, LLC.

Ferris, Kerry O. & Harris, Scott R. Stargazing: Celebrity, Fame, & Social Interaction. 2010. (Contemporary Sociological Perspectives Ser.). (ENG., Illus.). 176p. 135.00 *(978-0-415-88427-3(6))*; pap. 25.95 *(978-0-415-88428-0(4))* Routledge.

Fink, Mitchell. The Last Days of Dead Celebrities. 2007. (Illus.). 352p. per. 14.95 *(978-1-4013-6025-2(4))* Miramax Bks.

Finnigan, Michael. Impossible to Inevitable: The Catalyst for Positive Change. 2010. 192p. pap. 15.99 *(978-1-4490-4426-8(3))* AuthorHouse.

Fitzgerald, Michael. Attention Deficit Hyperactivity Disorder: Creativity, Novelty Seeking & Risk. 2008. 189p. 79.00 *(978-1-60456-855-4(0))* Nova Science Pubs., Inc.

Fitzgerald, Terence J. Celebrity Culture in the United States. 2008. *(978-0-8242-1078-6(6))* Wilson, H.W.

Fitzpatrick, Richard. Where Clare Leads, Ireland Follows. 2009. (ENG., Illus.). 255p. 38.95 *(978-1-85635-606-0(X))* Mercier Pr., Ltd., The IRL. Dist: Dufour Editions, Inc.

Fleming, E. J., compiled by. The Movieland Directory: Nearly 30,000 Addresses of Celebrity Homes, Film Locations & Historical Sites in the Los Angeles Area, 1900-Present. alt. ed. 2010. (ENG., Illus.). 528p. pap. 95.00 *(978-0-7864-4337-6(5))* McFarland & Co., Inc. Pubs.

Fogelman, Bea. Copy Cats. 2008. 248p. pap. 19.99 *(978-1-4363-2285-0(5))* Xlibris Corp.

Fowler, Bridget. The Obituary as Collective Memory. 2009. 300p. 39.95 *(978-0-415-87130-3(1))* Routledge.

Frank, Liza. My Celebrity Boyfriend. 2007. (ENG., Illus.). 1p. 15.00 *(978-0-7475-8158-1(4))* Bloomsbury Publishing Plc GBR. Dist: Independent Pubs. Group.

Frasier, David K. Show Business Homicides: An Encyclopedia, 1908-2009. 2010. (ENG., Illus.). 420p. 75.00 *(978-0-7864-4422-9(3))* McFarland & Co., Inc. Pubs.

Frescobaldi, Fiametta d'Aremberg & Gabriel, Jean Pierre. The Art of Living in Brussels. 2012. (ENG., Illus.). 208p. 60.00 *(978-90-209-2653-8(5))* Lannoo Pubs./Racine.

Friedman, Drew. Too Soon? Celebrity Portraits. 2010. (ENG., Illus.). 204p. 29.99 *(978-1-60699-357-6(7)*, 699357) Fantagraphics Bks.

Friedman, Kinky. Celebrity Pet Files. 2009. (ENG., Illus.). 224p. 24.95 *(978-1-4165-9278-5(4))* Simon & Schuster.

Gaffney & Holmes, eds. Stardom in Postwar France. 2011. (Polygons Ser.). (Illus.). 248p. 29.95 *(978-0-85745-160-6(X))* Berghahn Bks., Inc.

Gaines, Steven. Fool's Paradise: Players, Poseurs, & the Culture of Excess in South Beach. 2009. (ENG., Illus.). 288p. pap. 15.00 *(978-0-307-34628-5(5)*, Three Rivers Pr.) Crown Publishing Group.

Gale Editor, ed. Encyclopedia of World Biography. 2nd ed. 2011. lib. bdg. 195.00 *(978-1-4144-5906-6(8))* Cengage Gale.

Galella, Ron, photos by. Viva L'Italia. 2009. (ENG., Illus.). 200p. 55.00 *(978-0-615-28678-5(X)*, powerHouse Bks.) powerHouse Cultural Entertainment, Inc.

Galow, Timothy W. Writing Celebrity: Stein, Fitzgerald, & the Modern(ist) Art of Self-Fashioning. 2011. (American Literature Readings in the Twenty-First Century Ser.). (ENG.). 252p. 85.00 *(978-0-230-11271-1(4))* Palgrave Macmillan.

Gardner, Gerald & Bellows, Jim. 80: From Ben Bradlee to Lena Horne to Carl Reiner, Our Most Famous Eighty Year Olds, Reveal Why They Never Felt So Young. 2007. (ENG., Illus.). 320p. 29.99 *(978-1-4022-0840-9(5))* Sourcebooks, Inc.

Gargia, Massimo. Le Guide du Millionnaire: Codes, Toquades, Tendances et Adresses. 2007. (FRE.). 265p. *(978-2-8289-0952-9(2))* Favre SA, Editions.

Garland, Robert. Celebrity in Antiquity: From Media Tarts to Tabloid Queens. 2007. (Classical Inter/Faces Ser.). 144p. (C). pap. 27.95 *(978-0-7156-3448-6(8))* Duckworth Publishers GBR. Dist: International Publishers Marketing.

Ghosh, Bishnupriya. Global Icons: Apertures to the Popular. 2011. (ENG., Illus.). 400p. 94.95 *(978-0-8223-5004-0(1))*; pap. 25.95 *(978-0-8223-5016-3(5))* Duke Univ. Pr.

Glick, Thomas F. What about Darwin? All Species of Opinion from Scientists, Sages, Friends, & Enemies Who Met, Read, & Discussed the Naturalist Who Changed the World. 2010. (ENG.). 552p. pap. 29.95 *(978-0-8018-9462-6(X))* Johns Hopkins Univ. Pr.

Goldengirl. Sex & Celebrities: The Truth, the Whole Truth, the Naked Truth. Jackson, Kathleen, ed. 2007. 83p. per. 14.95 *(978-0-9798860-0-3(7))* Black Barbee, Inc.

Goldman, Jonathan. Modernism Is the Literature of Celebrity. (ENG., Illus.). 2012. 216p. pap. 25.00 ***(978-0-292-74404-2(8))*** 2011. 220p. 55.00 *(978-0-292-72339-9(3))* Univ. of Texas Pr.

Goldstein Crowe, Lauren. Isabella Blow: A Life in Fashion. 2010. (ENG., Illus.). 304p. 27.99 *(978-0-312-59294-3(9)*, Dunne, Thomas Bks.) St. Martin's Pr.

Goldstein, Steve. LA's Graveside Companion: Where the V. I. P.'s. R. I. P. 2009. 192p. pap. 19.99 *(978-0-7643-3154-1(X))* Schiffer Publishing, Ltd.

Goodman, Len. Better Late Than Never: From Barrow Boy to Ballroom. 2009. (ENG., Illus.). 336p. pap. 15.95 *(978-0-09-192803-2(6))* Ebury Publishing GBR. Dist: Independent Pubs. Group.

—Better Late Than Never: My Story. 2008. (ENG., Illus.). 320p. 29.95 *(978-0-09-192802-5(8))* Ebury Publishing GBR. Dist: Independent Pubs. Group.

Gorman, Greg, photos by & text. Greg Gorman: Framed: For L. A. Eyeworks. 2012. (ENG., Illus.). 192p. 50.00 ***(978-88-6208-203-7(7))*** Damiani ITA. Dist: D.A.P./Distributed Art Pubs.

Goscilo, Helena & Strukov, Vlad, eds. Celebrity & Glamour in Contemporary Russia: Shocking Chic. 2012. (ENG., Illus.). 320p. (C). pap. 44.95 ***(978-0-415-62543-2(2))*** Routledge.

Goscilo, Helena & Strukov, Vlad, eds. The Culture of Celebrity & Glamour in Contemporary Russia. 2010. (BASEES/Routledge Series on Russian & East European Studies). (ENG., Illus.). 320p. (C). 155.00 *(978-0-415-58765-5(4))* Routledge.

Grauel & Heine, Olaf. Leaving the Comfort Zone. 2008. (FRE, GER & ENG., Illus.). 208p. 60.00 *(978-3-7757-2218-6(1))* Hatje Cantz Verlag GmbH & Co KG DEU. Dist: D.A.P./Distributed Art Pubs.

Grecco, Michael. Lighting & the Dramatic Portrait: The Art of Celebrity & Editorial Photography. 2006. (ENG., Illus.). 192p. pap. 29.95 *(978-0-8174-4227-9(8)*, Amphoto Bks.) Watson-Guptill Pubns., Inc.

Green, Joey. How They Met: Fateful Encounters of Famous Lovers, Rivals, Partners, & Other Strange Bedfellows. 2007. (Illus.). 320p. 25.00 *(978-1-4223-6673-8(1))* DIANE Publishing Co.

Griffin, Maggie. Tip It! The World According to Maggie. 2010. (ENG.). 256p. 23.99 *(978-1-4013-2404-9(5))* Hyperion Pr.

Guler, Ara, photos by. Ara Guler - Creating the 20th Century: 100 Artists, Writers & Thinkers. 2011. (ENG., Illus.). 240p. 49.95 *(978-981-4260-46-6(0)*, Didier Millet,Csi) Continental Sales, Inc.

Gundle, Stephen. Glamour: A History. 2008. (ENG., Illus.). 320p. 45.00 *(978-0-19-921098-5(5))* Oxford Univ. Pr., Inc.

Gurvis, Sandra. Paris Hilton: A Biography, 1 vol. 2011. (Greenwood Biographies Ser.). (Illus.). 149p. 35.00 *(978-0-313-37940-6(8)*, GR7940) Greenwood Publishing Group, Inc.

Gygax, Raphael & Munder, Heike, eds. Dawn Mellor. 2009. (ENG & GER., Illus.). 64p. 35.00 *(978-3-905829-98-3(3))* JRP Ringier Kunstverlag AG CHE. Dist: D.A.P./Distributed Art Pubs.

Haber, Mel. Palm Springs á la Carte: The Colorful World of the Caviar Crowd at Their Favorite Desert Hideaway. 2008. 256p. 23.95 *(978-1-56980-353-0(6))* Barricade Bks., Inc.

Hack, Jefferson, ed. Another Portrait Book, 1 vol. 2010. (ENG., Illus.). 272p. 85.00 *(978-3-86521-842-1(3))* Steidl, Gerhard Druckerei und Verlag DEU. Dist: Innovative Logistics.

Haden-Guest, Anthony. The Last Party: Studio 54, Disco, & the Culture of the Night. 2009. (ENG.). 464p. pap. 14.99 *(978-0-06-172374-2(6))* HarperCollins Pubs.

Hall, Andy. A Sense of Belonging to Scotland: The Complete Collection. 2008. (Illus.). 224p. pap. 35.00 *(978-1-84183-107-7(7))* Birlinn, Ltd. GBR. Dist: Interlink Publishing Group, Inc.

Hallenbeck-Huber, Marjorie. Celebrities' Most Wanted: The Top 10 Book of Lavish Lifestyles, Tabloid Tidbits, & Other Superstar Oddities. 2010. (Most Wantedâ„¢ Ser.). (Illus.). 360p. pap. 14.95 *(978-1-59797-510-0(9))* Potomac Bks., Inc.

Halperin, Ian. Brangelina: The Untold Story of Brad Pitt & Angelina Jolie. 2009. (ENG.). 271p. 25.00 *(978-0-9812396-6-8(8))* Transit Publishing (Transit Editeur Inc.) CAN. Dist: Midpoint Trade Bks., Inc.

Halpern, Jake. Fame Junkies: The Hidden Truths Behind America's Favorite Addiction. (ENG.). 256p. 2008. pap. 13.95 *(978-0-618-91871-3(X)*, Mariner Bks.) 2006. 23.00 *(978-0-618-45369-6(5))* Houghton Mifflin Harcourt Trade & Reference Pubs.

Hanks, Mark. The Book of Celebrity Useless Information. 2009. (ENG.). 250p. 14.95 *(978-1-84454-651-0(9))* Blake, John Publishing, Ltd. GBR. Dist: Independent Pubs. Group.

Hanson, Eric. A Book of Ages: An Eccentric Miscellany of Great & Offbeat Moments in the Lives of the Famous & Infamous, Ages 1 To 100. (ENG.). 320p. 2010. pap. 13.00 *(978-0-307-40902-7(3)*, Three Rivers Pr.) 2008. (Illus.). 19.95 *(978-0-307-40894-5(9)*, Harmony) Crown Publishing Group.

Hayes, Steve. Googies, Coffee Shop to the Stars. 2008. 232p. pap. 19.95 *(978-1-59393-307-4(X))*; 296p. pap. 24.95 *(978-1-59393-306-7(1))* BearManor Media.

Haymes, Gary. People Who Have Changed History. 2010. 55p. pap. 8.98 *(978-0-557-45553-9(7))* Lulu Enterprises Inc.

Hazard, Sharon. Long Branch in the Golden Age: Tales of Fascinating & Famous People. 2007. (Illus.). 126p. pap., per. 19.99 *(978-1-59629-216-1(4))* History Pr., The.

Heard, Christopher. Britney Spears: Little Girl Lost. 2010. (ENG.). 312p. pap. 16.95 ***(978-1-926745-02-2(7))*** Transit Publishing (Transit Editeur Inc.) CAN. Dist: Midpoint Trade Bks., Inc.

Heard, Christopher. The Suite Life: The Magic & Mystery of Hotel Living. 2011. (ENG., Illus.). 264p. pap. 24.99 *(978-1-55488-862-7(X)*, Dundurn Pr.) Dundurn CAN. Dist: Ingram Pub. Services.

Heine, Achim, ed. Oliver Mark. 2010. (ENG., Illus.). 192p. 60.00 *(978-3-7757-2484-5(2))* Hatje Cantz Verlag GmbH & Co KG DEU. Dist: D.A.P./Distributed Art Pubs.

Heine, Olaf. Olaf Heine: I Love You but I've Chosen Rock. 2011. (ENG., Illus.). 304p. 75.00 *(978-3-7757-2662-7(4))* Hatje Cantz Verlag GmbH & Co KG DEU. Dist: D.A.P./Distributed Art Pubs.

Herbert, Emily. Peter & Katie - Moving On. 2010. (ENG., Illus.). 250p. pap. 12.95 *(978-1-84454-972-6(0))* Blake, John Publishing, Ltd. GBR. Dist: Independent Pubs. Group.

Herwitz, Daniel Alan. The Star as Icon: Celebrity in the Age of Mass Consumption. 2008. (ENG., Illus.). 176p. (gr. 17). 27.50 *(978-0-231-14540-4(3))* Columbia Univ. Pr.

Herzig, Helene. Legendary Long Islanders: Interviews with Famous Residents from the Hamptons to New York. 2008. (Illus.). 288p. pap. 24.95 *(978-0-9800669-0-6(5))* Mixed Media Memoirs LLC.

Heymann, C. David. Bobby & Jackie: A Love Story. 2010. (ENG., Illus.). 240p. pap. 15.00 *(978-1-4165-5629-9(X)*, Beyond Words/Atria Bks.) Atria Bks.

Higham, Charles. In & Out of Hollywood: A Biographer's Memoir. 2009. (ENG., Illus.). 300p. 29.95 *(978-0-299-23340-2(5))* Univ. of Wisconsin Pr.

Hirst, Damien. 8 Minutes, 1 vol. 2009. (ENG., Illus.). 264p. 68.00 *(978-3-86521-864-3(4))* Steidl, Gerhard Druckerei und Verlag DEU. Dist: Innovative Logistics.

Hixson, Walter L. Murder, Culture, & Injustice: Four Sensational Cases in American History. 2008. (ENG., Illus.). 274p. pap. 19.95 *(978-1-931968-54-6(3))* Univ. of Akron Pr., The.

Hofler, Robert. Camp Hollywood. Date not set. *(978-0-312-28577-7(9))* St. Martin's Pr.

Hogan, Dave. Hogan's Heroes. 2009. (ENG., Illus.). 160p. 32.00 *(978-1-906229-97-9(X)*, 190622997X) G2 Entertainment Ltd. GBR. Dist: MBI Distribution Services/Quayside Distribution.

Hogan, Linda. Wrestling the Hulk: My Life Against the Ropes. 2011. (ENG.). 256p. 25.99 *(978-0-06-203020-7(5)*, Morrow, William & Co.) HarperCollins Pubs.

Holmes, Su & Redmond, Sean. Framing Celebrity: New Directions in Celebrity Culture. 2006. (Illus.). (ENG.). 384p. (C). 140.00 *(978-0-415-37709-6(9))*; 369p. per. 39.95 *(978-0-415-37710-2(2))* Routledge.

Hopkinson, Frank. My Guy: The Photostories. 2007. (ENG., Illus.). 192p. pap. 24.95 *(978-1-906032-17-3(3))* Anova Bks. GBR. Dist: Independent Pubs. Group.

—My Guy Vol. 1: The Best of the Photostories. 2006. (ENG., Illus.). 144p. 24.95 *(978-1-86105-979-6(5))* Anova Bks. GBR. Dist: Independent Pubs. Group.

Hoppel, Joe. People I've Met, Things I've Done: 50 Years in Country Music Radio. 2010. (Illus.). 235p. pap. ***(978-0-9827582-0-5(0))*** BFreedia.

House, Silas & Howard, Jason. Something's Rising: Appalachians Fighting Mountaintop Removal. (ENG., Illus.). 320p. 2011. pap. 19.95 *(978-0-8131-3383-6(1))* 2009. 27.95 *(978-0-8131-2546-6(4))* Univ. Pr. of Kentucky.

Howell, Brian, photos by. Fame Us: Celebrity Impersonators & the Cult(ure) of Fame. 2007. (ENG., Illus.). 196p. pap. 18.95 *(978-1-55152-228-9(4))* Arsenal Pulp Pr. CAN. Dist: Consortium Bk. Sales & Distribution.

Howell, Vickie. Vickie Howell's Pop Goes Crochet! 36 Projects Inspired by Icons of Popular Culture. 2009. (ENG., Illus.). 144p. pap. 19.95 *(978-1-60059-466-3(2))* Lark Bks.

Huxley-Parlour, Giles. John Swannell: Photographs. 2013. (ENG., Illus.). 80p. pap. *(978-1-905738-06-9(4))* Beetles, Chris Ltd.

Huxley-Parlour, Giles & Lichfield, Patrick. Lichfield. 2013. (ENG., Illus.). 80p. pap. *(978-1-905738-09-0(9))* Beetles, Chris Ltd.

Idols + Believers. 2006. (Illus.). 219p. *(978-2-916355-00-9(6))* Editions Intervalles.

Inglis, Fred. A Short History of Celebrity. 2010. (ENG., Illus.). 322p. 29.95 *(978-0-691-13562-5(2))* Princeton Univ. Pr.

Jackson, Alison. Exposed! 2011: The Pictures the Celebs Didn't Want You to See! 2012. (ENG., Illus.). 128p. 17.95 ***(978-0-85786-350-8(9))*** Canongate UK.

Jackson, Dan & Smith, David B. God's Christmas Cards. 2011. pap. ***(978-0-8163-2624-2(X))*** Pacific Pr. Publishing Assn.

Jackson, Stanley. Get Me a Celebrity! 2011. 256p. ***(978-1-907722-47-9(5))*** Ecademy Pr. Ltd.

Jaffe, Aaron. Modernism & the Culture of Celebrity. 2009. (ENG., Illus.). 264p. pap. 38.99 *(978-0-521-12379-2(8))* Cambridge Univ. Pr.

Jeans, J. Stephen. Western Worthies: A Gallery of Biographical & Critical Sketches of West of Scotland Celebrities. 2007. 164p. per. *(978-1-4065-2710-0(6))* Dodo Pr.

Jeans, Stephen James. Western Worthies: A Gallery of Biographical & Critical Sketches of West of Scotland Celebrities. 2007. (ENG.). 174p. pap. 19.99 *(978-1-4346-3162-6(1))*; 194p. pap. 21.99 *(978-1-4346-3163-3(X))* BiblioBazaar.

Jenkins, Peter Watson, compiled by. Talking with Leaders of the Past: A book of spiritual Interviews. 2008. 266p. pap. 17.95 *(978-0-9798917-2-4(8))* Celestial Voices, Inc.

Jensen, Todd Aaron. On Gratitude. 2010. E-Book *(978-1-4405-0892-9(5))* Adams Media Corp.

Johnson, Veronica Dye. Giants: Legends of the Oil & Gas Industry. 2008. (Illus.). 160p. 75.00 *(978-0-9817695-0-9(0))* Ha! Publishing.

Jones, Jeremy L. C. & Teter, Betsy Wakefield. Stars Fell on Spartanburg: Hub City's Celebrity Encounters. 2008. *(978-1-891885-62-4(6))*; pap. *(978-1-891885-61-7(8))* Hub City Writers Project.

Jones, Sam. The Here & Now: The Photography of Sam Jones. 2007. (ENG., Illus.). 128p. 39.95 *(978-0-06-134812-9(0))* HarperCollins Pubs.

Kardashian, Kim, et al. Kardashian Konfidential: New! Inside Kim's Wedding with Never-Seen Pix, Plus a New Chapter! 2nd ed. 2011. (ENG., Illus.). 272p. 25.99 ***(978-1-250-00606-6(6))*** St. Martin's Pr.

Karl, Michele. What Celebrities Collect!, 1 vol. 2006. (ENG., Illus.). 96p. pap. 19.95 *(978-1-58980-142-4(3))* Pelican Publishing Co., Inc.

Kasher, Steven. Max's Kansas City: Art, Glamour, Rock & Roll. 2010. (ENG., Illus.). 160p. 24.95 *(978-0-8109-9597-0(2)*, Abrams Image) Abrams.

Katona, Kerry. Survive the Worst & Aim for the Best: How to Get Your Life Back on Track. 2007. 128p. pap. 5.00 *(978-0-09-191754-8(9))* Random Hse. GBR. Dist: Independent Pubs. Group.

Kearney, Mark & Ray, Randy. Whatever Happened To ... ? Catching up with Canadian Icons. 2006. (ENG., Illus.). 264p. pap. 21.99 *(978-1-55002-654-2(2)*, Hounslow Pr.) Dundurn CAN. Dist: Ingram Pub. Services.

Keel, Howard & Radke, Linda F., compiled by. Legends in the Kitchen: Celebrity Recipes for a Cause. 2010. (ENG.). 148p. 17.95 *(978-1-58985-054-5(8))* Five Star Pubns., Inc.

Keller, Christopher J., ed. The Other Journal: The Celebrity Issue. 2011. (ENG.). 186p. pap. 18.75 ***(978-1-61097-333-5(X)***, Cascade Bks.) Wipf & Stock Pubs.

Kerr, Gordon & Kerr, Gordon. Goners: The Final Hours of the Notable & Notorious. 2009. (ENG.). 256p. 21.95 *(978-0-8109-8364-9(8)*, Abrams Image) Abrams.

King, Larry. Taking on Heart Disease: Peggy Fleming, Brian Littrell, Mike Ditka, Walter Cronkite, Joyce Carol Oates, Eddie Griffin, Mike Wallace, Kate Jackson, Ed Bradley, Tommy Lasorda, Regis Philbin, & Others... Reveal How They Triumphed over the Nation's #1 Killer & How You Can Too. 2007. (Illus.). 287p. reprint ed. 24.00 *(978-1-4223-6793-3(2))* DIANE Publishing Co.

—Truth Be Told: Off the Record about Favorite Guests, Memorable Moments, Funniest Jokes, & a Half Century of Asking Questions. 2011. (ENG., Illus.). 248p. 25.00 *(978-1-60286-130-5(7))* Perseus Bks. Group.

Kingston, Kenny. The Moment: By Legendary Celebrity Psychic Kenny Kingston as told to Valerie Porter. 2011. 116p. pap. 14.95 ***(978-1-59393-629-7(X))*** BearManor Media.

Kipnis, Laura. How to Become a Scandal: Adventures in Bad Behavior. 2010. (ENG., Illus.). 224p. 24.00 *(978-0-8050-8979-0(9)*, Metropolitan Bks.) Holt, Henry & Co.

—How to Become a Scandal: Adventures in Bad Behavior. 2011. (ENG., Illus.). 224p. pap. 15.00 *(978-0-312-61057-9(2))* Picador.

Kniffel, Leonard. Reading with the Stars: Why They Love Libraries. 2010. 160p. pap. *(978-0-8389-3598-9(2))* American Library Assn.

Kniffel, Leonard, ed. Reading with the Stars: A Celebration of Books & Libraries. 2011. (ENG., Illus.). 160p. 17.95 *(978-1-61608-277-2(1)*, 608277) Skyhorse Publishing Co., Inc.

Koblar, Stanislav. Cetrta Stran Trikotnika: Znameniti Slovenci in Slovenska Druztva V Bosni in Hercegovini, 1878-2000. 2008. (SLV., Illus.). 465p. *(978-961-01-0377-6(4))* Mladinska Knjiga Zalozba, d.d.

Kobrin, Bill. Bill Kobrin's Stars & Celebrities. 2008. (Illus.). *(978-0-9727572-6-3(0))* Desert Springs Publishing.

Kost, Jeremy, photos by. It's Always Darkest Before Dawn. 2011. (ENG., Illus.). 80p. 49.95 *(978-1-57687-568-1(7))* powerHouse Cultural Entertainment, Inc.

Koster, Heinz. Heinz Köster. 'Stern Spezial Fotografie 59' Berlinale 1954-1967 . 2010. (ENG., Illus.). 96p. 45.00 *(978-3-570-19899-5(5))* teNeues Publishing Co.

Kramer, Jill Ed. What They Know about... Parenting. 2007. 176p. *(978-1-4019-1576-6(0)*, 489) Hay Hse. UK, Ltd. GBR. Dist: Grantham Bk. Services.

Kratochvil, Antonin, ed. Inside: The Chelsea Hotel. 2007. (ENG., Illus.). 208p. 49.95 *(978-1-57687-406-6(0))* powerHouse Cultural Entertainment, Inc.

Krols, Birgit. Bad Boys: A photographic Tribute, 1 vol. 2012. (ENG, FRE & DUT., Illus.). 192p. 49.95 ***(978-94-6158-031-3(2))*** Tectum B.V.B.A. BEL. Dist: Innovative Logistics.

—Bimbos & Machos: A Photographical View on a 20th Century Phenomenon, 1 vol. 2011. (ENG., Illus.). 192p. 29.95 *(978-90-79761-71-5(0))* Tectum B.V.B.A. BEL. Dist: Innovative Logistics.

—Too Young to Die: 20th Century Icons That Moved Generations, 1 vol. 2010. (ENG, DUT & FRE., Illus.). 224p. 39.95 *(978-90-79761-31-9(1))* Tectum B.V.B.A. BEL. Dist: Innovative Logistics.

Labash, Matt. Fly Fishing with Darth Vader: And Other Adventures with Evangelical Wrestlers, Political Hitmen, & Jewish Cowboys. (ENG.). 336p. 2011. pap. 16.00 *(978-1-4391-5998-9(X))* 2010. 25.99 *(978-1-4391-5997-2(1))* Simon & Schuster.

LaChapelle, David. Heaven to Hell - GOLDEN BOOK. 2010. (Go Ser.). (ENG., Illus.). 344p. 39.99 *(978-3-8365-2284-7(5))* TASCHEN DEU. Dist: Ingram Pub. Services.

LaChapelle, David, photos by. LaChapelle Land. 2nd deluxe ed. 2006. (ENG., Illus.). 160p. 60.00 *(978-0-9766708-0-3(1))* Channel Photographics.

Laddage, Reialdo. Tres vidas secretas/ Three Secret Lives. 2008. (SPA.). 155p. pap. *(978-987-1156-81-8(2))* Hidalgo, Adriana Editora S.A.

Langella, Frank. Dropped Names: Famous Men & Women as I Knew Them. 2012. (ENG., Illus.). 374p. 25.99 ***(978-0-06-209447-6(5))*** HarperCollins Pubs.

Largo, Michael. The Portable Obituary: How the Famous, Rich, & Powerful Really Died. 2007. (ENG., Illus.). 304p. pap. 14.95 *(978-0-06-123166-7(5)*, William Morrow Paperbacks) HarperCollins Pubs.

Lawrence, Cooper. The Cult of Celebrity: What Our Fascination with the Stars Reveals about Us. 2009. (ENG.). 256p. pap. 14.95 *(978-1-59921-335-4(4)*, skirt!) Globe Pequot Pr., The.

Lawrence, Sue. Taste Ye Back: Great Scots & the Food That Made Them. 2010. (ENG., Illus.). 224p. 34.95 *(978-0-7553-1863-6(3))* Headline Bk. Publishing GBR. Dist: Independent Pubs. Group.

Lee, Jason. Celebrity, Pedophilia, & Ideology in American Culture. 2009. 464p. 29.99 *(978-1-60497-599-4(7))* Cambria Pr.

Lee, Lois, pref. You'll Never Make Love in This Town Again. 2006. (Illus.). 251p. per. 16.95 *(978-1-59777-542-7(8))* Phoenix Bks., Inc.

Leibovitz, Annie. Pilgrimage: Pilgerreisen zu den Kultorten der Welt. 2011. (ENG., Illus.). 246p. 50.00 *(978-0-375-50508-9(3)*, Random House) Random House Publishing Group.

Lentz, Harris M., III. Obituaries in the Performing Arts, 2007: Film, Television, Radio, Theatre, Dance, Music, Cartoons & Pop Culture. 2008. (Lentz's Performing Arts Obituaries Ser.). (ENG.). 436p. pap. 49.95 *(978-0-7864-3481-7(3))* McFarland & Co., Inc. Pubs.

Lentz, Harris M. Obituaries in the Performing Arts 2008: Film, Television, Radio, Theatre, Dance, Music, Cartoons & Pop Culture. 2009. (Lentz's Performing Arts Obituaries Ser.). (ENG., Illus.). 482p. pap. 49.95 *(978-0-7864-3482-4(1))* McFarland & Co., Inc. Pubs.

—Obituaries in the Performing Arts 2009: Film, Television, Radio, Theatre, Dance, Music, Cartoons & Pop Culture. 2010. (Lentz's Performing Arts Obituaries Ser.). (ENG., Illus.). 600p. pap. 49.95 *(978-0-7864-4174-7(7))* McFarland & Co., Inc. Pubs.

—Obituaries in the Performing Arts 2010. 2011. (Lentz's Performing Arts Obituaries Ser.). (ENG., Illus.). 480p. pap. 49.95 *(978-0-7864-4175-4(5))* McFarland & Co., Inc. Pubs.

Lentz, Harris M., 3rd & Lentz, Harris M., III. Obituaries in the Performing Arts 2006: Film, Television, Radio, Theatre, Dance, Music, Cartoons & Pop Culture. 2007. (Obituaries in the Performing Arts Ser.). (ENG., Illus.). 428p. per. 49.95 *(978-0-7864-2933-2(X))* McFarland & Co., Inc. Pubs.

Lerner, Barron H. When Illness Goes Public: Celebrity Patients & How We Look at Medicine. (ENG., Illus.). 352p. 2009. pap. 19.95 *(978-0-8018-9227-1(9))* 2006. 29.00 *(978-0-8018-8462-7(4))* Johns Hopkins Univ. Pr.

Leslie, Larry Z. Celebrity in the 21st Century: A Reference Handbook, 1 vol. 2011. (Contemporary World Issues Ser.). 272p. 55.00 *(978-1-59884-484-9(9)*, A2974C) ABC-CLIO, LLC.

Lester, David. Exit Weeping: Understanding Suicide through the Study of Famous Suicides. 2008. x, 203p. 59.00 *(978-1-60456-573-7(X))* Nova Science Pubs., Inc.

Lewis, Edward. Celebrity Almanac. 2006. per. 24.95 *(978-0-9759569-1-5(4))* Americana Group Publishing.

Life Magazine Editors. Remembering Jackie. 2009. (ENG., Illus.). 128p. 17.95 *(978-1-60320-078-3(9))* Time Home Entertainment, Inc.

Life Publishers Staff. Gone Too Soon: Their Lives Were Not Long but Mattered. 2010. (ENG., Illus.). 128p. 32.95 *(978-1-60320-143-8(2))* Time Home Entertainment, Inc.

Liguori, Ann. A Passion for Golf: Celebrity Musings about the Game. 2nd rev. ed. 2007. (ENG., Illus.). 304p. 22.95 *(978-1-58979-304-0(8))* Taylor Trade Publishing.

Lip, Tony & Prigge, Steven. Shut up & Eat! Mangia with Family Recipes & Stories from Your Favorite Italian-American Stars. 2006. (ENG., Illus.). 320p. (gr. 12-18). 17.00 *(978-0-425-21177-9(0)*, Berkley Trade) Penguin Group (USA) Inc.

Lloyd, Suzanne, ed. Harold Lloyd's Hollywood Nudes In 3-D! 2011. (ENG., Illus.). 160p. pap. 19.95 *(978-1-57912-882-1(3)*, 1579128823) Black Dog & Leventhal Pubs., Inc.

Lofton, Kathryn. Oprah: The Gospel of an Icon. 2011. 304p. 55.00 *(978-0-520-25927-0(0))*; pap. 22.95 *(978-0-520-26752-7(4))* Univ. of California Pr.

Ludwig, Amber, et al. Thomas Gainsborough & the Modern Woman. Leca, Benedict, ed. & contrib. by by. 2010. (ENG., Illus.). 196p. 49.95 *(978-1-904832-85-0(7))* Giles, D. Ltd. GBR. Dist: Antique Collectors' Club.

Lynch, Christopher. When Hollywood Landed at Chicago's Midway Airport: The Photos & Stories of Mike Rotunno. 2012. 160p. pap. 19.99 ***(978-1-60949-592-3(6))*** History Pr., The.

Lynch, Jack. Don't Quit Your Day Job: What the Famous Did That Wasn't. 2010. *(978-1-929154-40-1(2))* Levenger Pr.

Lyons, Jeffrey. Stories My Father Told Me: Notes from the Lyons Den. 2011. (ENG., Illus.). 400p. 35.00 *(978-0-7892-1102-6(5))* Abbeville Pr., Inc.

MacPherson, Andrew. Two Million Miles. 2007. (Illus.). 240p. 85.00 *(978-3-8327-9160-5(4))* teNeues Publishing Co.

Macpherson, Andrew, photos by. Two Million Miles Collector's Edition. 2007. 300.00 *(978-3-8327-9164-3(7))* teNeues Publishing Co.

Mahmood, Mazher. Confessions of a Fake Sheik: The King of the Sting Reveals All. 2008. (ENG., Illus.). 310p. 27.95 *(978-0-00-728809-0(3))* HarperCollins Pubs. Ltd. GBR. Dist: Independent Pubs. Group.

Majoli, Alex. One Jump! 2008. (Illus.). 148p. pap. *(978-1-904563-77-8(5))* Trolley.

Mancinelli, Antonio. Fashion Box. 2011. (ENG.). 480p. 29.95 (978-0-8109-9754-7(1)) Abrams.

Mansbridge, Peter. Peter Mansbridge One on One: Favourite Conversations & the Stories Behind Them. 2010. (ENG., Illus.). 352p. pap. 19.50 (978-0-307-35785-4(6), Vintage Canada) Random Hse. of Canada, Ltd. CAN. Dist: Random Hse., Inc.

Marshall, P. David. The Celebrity Culture Reader. 2006. (ENG.). 872p. (C). 150.00 (978-0-415-33791-5(7), RU42305); per. 52.95 (978-0-415-33792-2(5), RU42306) Routledge.

Martinez-Lewi, Linda. Freeing Yourself from the Narcissist in Your Life. 2008. (ENG.). 256p. (gr. 12-18). 23.95 (978-1-58542-624-9(5), Tarcher) Penguin Group (USA) Inc.

Massenet, Ariane, et al. Frères & Soeurs: Ce Que Je Voudrais Te Dire- 2010. (FRE., Illus.). 226p. (978-2-7324-4279-2(8)) Editions de la Martiniere.

McAuley, Jordan, ed. The Celebrity Black Book: Over 55,000 Accurate Celebrity Addresses. 17th ed. 2007. (Celebrity Black Book Ser.). 768p. per. 75.00 (978-0-9707095-8-5(7)) Mega Niche Media, LLC.

McCartney, Mary. Mary McCartney: From Where I Stand. 2010. (ENG., Illus.). 192p. 35.00 (978-0-8109-9654-0(5)) Abrams.

McGregor, Jackie, ed. They Can't Take That Away from Me. 2011. (ENG.). 208p. pap. 21.95 (978-1-907726-96-5(9)) Accent Pr. Ltd. GBR. Dist: SCB Distributors.

Mcmillan, Tracy. I Love You & I'm Leaving You Anyway: A Memoir. 2011. (ENG.). 352p. pap. 14.99 (978-0-06-172459-6(9)) HarperCollins Pubs.

Meloy, J. Reid, et al. Stalking, Threatening, & Attacking Public Figures: A Psychological & Behavioral Analysis. 2008. (ENG., Illus.). 496p. (C). 65.00 (978-0-19-532638-3(5)) Oxford Univ. Pr., Inc.

Merrell, creator. Portrait of a Nation: Men & Women Who Have Shaped America. 2006. (ENG., Illus.). 286p. 22.95 (978-1-85894-345-9(0)) Merrell Pubs. Ltd. GBR. Dist: Perseus Distribution.

Meserve, F. H. Historical Portraits & Lincolniana, 28 vol., set. reprint ed. 3500.00 (978-0-7222-8421-6(7)) Library Reprints, Inc.

Milano, Sally. Backstage at Ruth Eckerd Hall: Meet & Greet & Eat with the Stars. 2011. 112p. pap. 35.49 (978-1-4567-3976-8(X)) AuthorHouse.

Moore, David R. The Celebrity Address Directory & Guide to Writing Fundraising Letters. 2007. per. 39.95 (978-0-9759569-3-9(0)) Americana Group Publishing.

Moore, Edwin. Brief Encounters: Meetings Between (Mostly)Remarkable People. 2008. (ENG.). 168p. pap. 15.95 (978-0-550-10350-5(3)) Chambers Harrap Pubs., Ltd. GBR. Dist: Houghton Mifflin Harcourt Trade & Reference Pubs.

Morehouse, Ward & Morehouse III, Ward. Broadway after Dark. 2007. 376p. per. 24.95 (978-1-59393-081-3(X)) BearManor Media.

Morgan, John, des. Mario Testino: Obsessed by You. 2008. pap. 60.00 (978-0-9792277-3-8(9)) de Pury, Phillips & Co.

Morris, David. Motostars: Celebrities & Motorcycles. 2008. (ENG.). 160p. 50.00 (978-0-9796891-4-7(7), Parker Hse. Publishing Inc.,Csi) Continental Sales, Inc.

Moss, Marie & Leiner Grant, Barri. Jersey Girls: The Fierce & the Fabulous. 2011. (ENG.). 208p. 20.00 (978-0-7624-4131-0(3)) Running Pr. Bk. Pubs.

Moulton, Donelee. Celebrity Court Cases: Trials of the Rich & Famous. 2006. (Late Breaking Amazing Stories Ser.). (Illus.). 172p. per. (978-1-55265-321-0(8)) Altitude Publishing Canada Ltd.

Murphy, Myatt & Pasternak, Harley. The 5-Factor Diet. 2009. (ENG.). 256p. pap. 15.00 (978-0-345-51349-6(5), Ballantine Bks.) Random House Publishing Group.

The Music Book. 2008. 160p. 75.00 (978-3-8327-9258-9(9)) teNeues Publishing Co.

Nagler, Richard, photos by. Word on the Street. 2010. (978-1-59714-141-3(0)); pap. (978-1-59714-140-6(2)) Heyday.

Nayar, Pramod K. Seeing Stars: Spectacle, Society & Celebrity Culture. 2009. (Illus.). 220p. (C). pap. 26.00 (978-81-7829-907-5(0), B99075P) SAGE Pubns., Inc.

Newkey-Burden, Chas. Paris Hilton: Life on the Edge The Biography. 2008. (ENG., Illus.). 288p. per. 14.95 (978-1-84454-457-8(5)) Blake, John Publishing, Ltd. GBR. Dist: Independent Pubs. Group.

Newsmakers. 2011. 272.00 (978-1-4144-4755-1(8)) Cengage Gale.

Newsmakers 2008, 8 vols. 2008th rev. ed. 2007. (Newsmakers Ser.). (ENG.). 272.00 (978-0-7876-9620-7(X)) Cengage Gale.

Newsmakers 2009 Ed, 4 vols. 2009th rev. ed. 2008. (Newsmakers Ser.). (ENG.). 272.00 (978-1-4144-0682-4(7)) Cengage Gale.

Newsmakers 2011, 4 vols. 2011th ed. 2010. (ENG.). 272.00 (978-1-4144-4164-1(9)) Cengage Gale.

Newton, Michael. Celebrities & Crime. 2008. (Criminal Investigations Ser.). (Illus.). 112p. (C). (gr. 9-12). 35.00 (978-0-7910-9402-0(2), Chelsea Hse.) Facts On File, Inc.

Nicotext, creator. Bla Bla Celebs: Something to Gossip about When You Have Nothing Else to Say! 2006. 188p. per. 9.95 (978-91-85449-12-5(1)) Nicotext, Ltd. SWE. Dist: SCB Distributors.

Norton, Jim. Happy Endings: The Tales of a Meaty-Breasted Zilch. 2008. (ENG., Illus.). 288p. pap. 14.95 (978-1-4169-6105-5(4)) Gallery Pr., The IRL. Dist: Simon & Schuster, Inc.

Nourmand, Tony. Stars & Cars. 2009. (ENG., Illus.). 192p. 52.50 (978-0-7522-2645-3(2), Boxtree) Pan Macmillan GBR. Dist: Trans-Atlantic Pubns., Inc.

Ogden, Tom. Hollywood: Spooky Stories of the Stars. 2009. (Haunted Ser.). (ENG.). 288p. pap. 14.95 (978-0-7627-5078-8(2)) Globe Pequot Pr., The.

Olbermann, Keith. Pitchforks & Torches: The Worst of the Worst, from Beck, Bill, & Bush to Palin & Other Posturing Republicans. 2010. (ENG.). 272p. 24.95 (978-0-470-61447-1(1), Wiley) Wiley, John & Sons, Inc.

Oldham, Mike. Movie Stars' Homes. 2008. (Illus.). 96p. pap. 12.95 (978-0-7643-2902-9(2)) Schiffer Publishing, Ltd.

Olivia, et al. Hooking Up: You'll Never Make Love in This Town Again Again. 2006. 202p. per. 24.95 (978-1-59777-504-5(5)) Phoenix Bks., Inc.

Orr, Lyndon. Famous Affinities of History the Romance of Devotion. 2007. (ENG.). 692p. 64.95 (978-0-548-03337-1(4)) Kessinger Publishing, LLC.

Otto, Lucas. Greatest Modern Heroes. 2007. (50 Plus One Ser.). (ENG.). 211p. pap. (978-1-933766-13-3(1)) Encouragement Pr., 2nd Edition, LLC.

Parker, Adele. Famous People Don't Get Fat. 2008. (ENG.). 352p. pap. 13.95 (978-1-84454-494-3(X)) Blake, John Publishing, Ltd. GBR. Dist: Independent Pubs. Group.

Parr, Rob & House, Laurel. Star Quality: The Red Carpet Workout for the Celebrity Body of Your Dreams. 2008. (ENG., Illus.). 264p. 24.95 (978-0-470-18400-4(0), Wiley) Wiley, John & Sons, Inc.

Parry, Nigel. Blunt. 2006. (ENG., Illus.). 180p. 60.00 (978-1-57687-326-7(9)) powerHouse Cultural Entertainment, Inc.

Payne, Tom. Fame: What the Classics Tell Us about Our Cult of Celebrity. 2010. (ENG.). 288p. pap. 16.00 (978-0-312-42993-5(2)) Picador.

Pearson, Lynn F. Discovering Famous Graves. 2nd ed. 2008. (Shire Discovering Ser.). (ENG., Illus.). 152p. per. 17.95 (978-0-7478-0619-6(5)) Shire Pubns., Ltd. GBR. Dist: Random Hse., Inc.

Pellicer, Raynal. Mug Shots: An Archive of the Famous, Infamous, & Most Wanted. 2010. (ENG., Illus.). 288p. pap. 19.95 (978-0-8109-9612-0(X)) Abrams.

Penfold-Mounce, Ruth. Celebrity Culture & Crime: The Joy of Transgression. Penfold-Mounce, Ruth, ed. 2010. (Cultural Criminology Ser.). (ENG.). 224p. 89.00 (978-0-230-22468-1(7)) Palgrave Macmillan.

People Magazine Editors. The Best & Worst of the Year 2008. Durkee, Cutler, ed. 2008. (ENG., Illus.). 144p. 29.95 (978-1-933821-16-0(7), People Bks.) Time Home Entertainment, Inc.

—People Before They Were Stars: What Your Favorite Celebrities Were Like Before They Became Famous. 2012. (ENG., Illus.). 144p. 33.95 (978-1-60320-225-1(0), People Bks.) Time Home Entertainment, Inc.

—People Book of Celebrity Scandals. 2009. (ENG., Illus.). 128p. 33.95 (978-1-60320-099-8(1), People Bks.) Time Home Entertainment, Inc.

—The People Celebrity Puzzler, Set. 2011. (ENG.). 384p. (gr. 11-17). pap. 29.95 (978-1-60320-397-5(4), People Bks.) Time Home Entertainment, Inc.

—People Celebrity Puzzler Classics! 2011. (ENG., Illus.). 128p. (gr. 11-17). pap. 11.99 (978-1-60320-894-9(1), People Bks.) Time Home Entertainment, Inc.

—The People Celebrity Puzzler Extra! 2008. (ENG.). 144p. (YA). (gr. 8-17). pap. 11.99 (978-1-60320-794-2(5)) Time Home Entertainment, Inc.

—People Celebrity Puzzler Holiday Superbook! 2011. (ENG., Illus.). 128p. (gr. 11-17). pap. 11.99 (978-1-60320-909-0(3), People Bks.) Time Home Entertainment, Inc.

—People Celebrity Puzzler TV Madness! 2011. (ENG., Illus.). 128p. pap. 11.99 (978-1-60320-886-4(0), People Bks.) Time Home Entertainment, Inc.

—People Celebrity Transformations. 2009. (ENG., Illus.). 144p. 33.95 (978-1-60320-066-0(5), People Bks.) Time Home Entertainment, Inc.

—People Great Lives Remembered: 55 Stars, Heroes & Icons America Loved. 2010. (ENG., Illus.). 144p. 33.95 (978-1-60320-135-3(1), People Bks.) Time Home Entertainment, Inc.

—The People Puzzler Book: Jumbo Edition. 2008. (ENG.). 144p. (YA). (gr. 8-17). pap. 10.99 (978-1-60320-771-3(6), People Bks.) Time Home Entertainment, Inc.

—PEOPLE Yearbook 2011. 2011. (ENG., Illus.). 144p. 33.95 (978-1-60320-145-2(9), People Bks.) Time Home Entertainment, Inc.

People Magazine Editors, ed. Celebrate the 80's. 2008. (ENG., Illus.). 144p. 29.95 (978-1-60320-026-4(6)) Time Home Entertainment, Inc.

—The People Puzzler, Set. 2008. (ENG.). 144p. (YA). (gr. 8-17). pap. 24.95 (978-1-60320-278-7(1)) Time Home Entertainment, Inc.

—People Yearbook 2009. 2009. (ENG.). 144p. 29.95 (978-1-60320-048-6(7)) Time Home Entertainment, Inc.

Petrucelli, Alan W. Morbid Curiosity: The Disturbing Demises of the Famous & Infamous. 2009. (ENG., Illus.). 240p. (gr. 12-18). 13.95 (978-0-399-53527-7(6), Perigee Trade) Penguin Group (USA) Inc.

Pinsky, Drew & Young, S. Mark. The Mirror Effect: How Celebrity Narcissism Is Endangering Our Families — And How to Save Them. 2010. 288p. pap. 14.99 (978-0-06-158234-9(4), Harper Paperbacks) HarperCollins Pubs.

—The Mirror Effect: How Celebrity Narcissism Is Seducing America. 2009. (ENG.). 368p. 26.99 (978-0-06-158233-2(6)) HarperCollins Pubs.

Porter, Darwin. Howard Hughes: Hell's Angel. 2nd ed. 2010. (ENG., Illus.). 814p. 32.95 (978-1-936003-13-6(9)) Blood Moon Productions, Ltd.

Powell, Michael. Celebrity Insults. 2010. (ENG.). 256p. 16.95 (978-1-85375-705-1(5)) Prion GBR. Dist: Independent Pubs. Group.

Pratt, A. T. Camden, ed. People of the Period: A Collection of the Biographies of Upwards. 2007. 1100p. 825.00 (978-4-901481-85-4(1)) Synapse, Edition JPN. Dist: Taylor & Francis Group.

Quinn, John. The Curious Mind: 25 Years of John Quinn Radio Programmes. 2010. (ENG.). 355p. pap. 21.95 (978-1-84730-200-7(9)) Veritas Pubns. IRL. Dist: Dufour Editions, Inc.

Raab, Scott. Real Hollywood Stories: Inside the Minds of 22 Celebrities, with One A-List Writer. 2008. (ENG.). 196p. per. 16.00 (978-0-9776142-5-7(5)) Tatra Pr.

Rachline, Sonia. Paris Vogue, 1920-2009. 2010. (ENG., Illus.). 208p. 45.00 (978-0-500-51513-6(1), 551513) Thames & Hudson.

Rafiq, Fiaz. Bruce Lee: Conversations. 2010. (Illus.). 352p. 24.95 (978-0-9552648-9-4(8)) Health 'n' Life Publishing GBR. Dist: Midpoint Trade Bks., Inc.

—Bruce Lee: Conversations. 2011. 352p. pap. 19.95 (978-0-9562586-3-2(8)) Health 'n' Life Publishing GBR. Dist: Midpoint Trade Bks., Inc.

—Muhammad Ali: Conversations. 2011. 352p. 24.95 (978-0-9562586-4-9(6)) Health 'n' Life Publishing GBR. Dist: Midpoint Trade Bks., Inc.

Randall, Stephen. Larger Than Life. Playboy Magazine Editors, ed. 2006. (Politics, Culture & Society Ser.). 400p. 22.95 (978-1-59582-045-7(0)) M Pr.

Rankin & Youth, Music, eds. Destroy/Rankin. 2010. (Illus.). 172p. 69.00 (978-3-89955-280-5(6)) Die Gestalten Verlag DEU. Dist: Prestel Publishing.

Rappaport, Jill. Mazel Tov: Celebrities' Bar & Bat Mitzvah Memories. 2007. (ENG., Illus.). 176p. 25.00 (978-0-7432-8787-6(8)) Simon & Schuster.

Reaves, Wendy Wick. Ballyhoo: Posters as Portraits. 2008. (ENG., Illus.). 160p. pap. 19.95 (978-0-295-98862-7(2)) Univ. of Washington Pr.

Redding, Eric & Redding, D'Eva. Great Big Beautiful Doll: The Anna Nicole Smith Story. 2007. (Illus.). 219p. per. 16.95 (978-1-56980-328-8(5)) Barricade Bks., Inc.

Redfern, Nick. Celebrity Secrets: Official Government Files on the Rich & Famous. 2007. (ENG., Illus.). 272p. per. 17.99 (978-1-4165-2866-1(0)) Pocket Books.

Redmond, Sean & Holmes, Su, eds. Stardom & Celebrity: A Reader. 2007. (Illus.). 400p. (C). 135.00 (978-1-4129-2320-0(4), B23204C); pap. 60.00 (978-1-4129-2321-7(2), B23204P) SAGE Pubns., Ltd. GBR. Dist: SAGE Pubns., Inc.

Richardson, Nan. Dressed to Kill: What to Wear When Fashion Makes History. 2011. (ENG.). 104p. 18.99 (978-1-884167-72-0(1)) Umbrage Editions.

Riley, Sam, ed. Star Struck: An Encyclopedia of Celebrity Culture, 1 vol. 2010. (Illus.). 358p. 85.00 (978-0-313-35812-8(5), GR5812) Greenwood Publishing Group, Inc.

Ripley, Jacqui. Celebrity Style Secrets: An Insider's Guide to Looking A-List. 2007. (Illus.). 230p. pap. 11.95 (978-0-7499-2465-2(9)) Piatkus Bks. GBR. Dist: National Bk. Network.

Robinson, Craig. Minipops: Famous People Drewn Really Small. 2006. (Mitchell Beazley Book Ser.). (ENG., Illus.). 128p. (978-1-84533-029-3(3), Mitchell Beazley) Octopus Publishing Group GBR. Dist: Sterling Publishing Co., Inc.

Rogers, Byron. On the Trail of the Last Human Cannonball: And Other Small Journeys in Search of Great Men. 2007. (ENG.). 272p. pap. 15.95 (978-1-84513-187-6(8)) Aurum Pr., Ltd. GBR. Dist: Independent Pubs. Group.

Rojek, Chris. Fame Attack: The Inflation of Celebrity & Its Consequences. 2012. (ENG.). 208p. 120.00 (978-1-84966-072-3(7)); pap. 32.95 (978-1-84966-071-6(9)) Bloomsbury Publishing.

—Rojek: Celebrity, Vol. I: Celebrity, Vol. I, 4 vols. 2009. (Illus.). (978-0-415-49467-0(2)) Routledge.

—Rojek: Celebrity, Vol. II: Celebrity, Vol. II, 4 vols. 2009. (Illus.). (978-0-415-49468-7(0)) Routledge.

—Rojek: Celebrity, Vol. III: Celebrity, Vol. III, 4 vols. 2009. (Illus.). (978-0-415-49469-4(9)) Routledge.

—Rojek: Celebrity, Vol. IV: Celebrity, Vol. IV, 4 vols. 2009. (Illus.). (978-0-415-49470-0(2)) Routledge.

Rojek, Chris, ed. Celebrity, 4 vols., Set. 2010. (Critical Concepts in Sociology Ser.). (ENG., Illus.). 1768p. (C). 1430.00 (978-0-415-49466-3(4)) Routledge.

Rolston, Matthew. BeautyLIGHT: Matthew Rolston. 2007. (Illus.). 192p. 75.00 (978-0-06-136730-4(3)); 288p. 2500.00 (978-0-06-136923-0(3)) HarperCollins Pubs. (Collins Design).

Romaine, Susan Steffensen. Readers & Leaders, 1 vol. 2007. (Illus.). 160p. per. 35.00 (978-1-59158-516-9(3), LU5163) Libraries Unlimited, Inc.

Rose, George. Hollywood, Beverly Hills, & Other Perversities: Pop Culture of the 1970s & 1980s. 2008. (ENG., Illus.). 192p. 30.00 (978-1-58008-924-1(0)) Ten Speed Pr.

Rosenberg, Oliver Halsman, ed. Unknown Halsman. 2008. (ENG., Illus.). 144p. 75.00 (978-1-933045-87-0(6)) D.A.P./Distributed Art Pubs.

Rusche, Ed. Barely Private, 1997-2008. 2009. (ENG.). 300p. pap. 39.99 (978-3-8365-1460-6(5)) TASCHEN DEU. Dist: Ingram Pub. Services.

Ryersson, Scot D. & Yaccarino, Michael Orlando. The Marchesa Casati: Portraits of a Muse. 2009. (ENG., Illus.). 240p. 50.00 (978-0-8109-4815-0(X)) Abrams.

Sack, Adriano & Niermann, Ingo. The Curious World of Drugs & Their Friends: A Very Trippy Miscellany. 2008. (ENG.). 192p. (gr. 12-18). 14.00 (978-0-452-28991-8(2), Plume) Penguin Group (USA) Inc.

Saks, Diane. Overcoming Celebrity Obsession. 2011. 484p. pap. 29.95 (978-1-4502-2847-3(X)) iUniverse, Inc.

Salem Press Staff, contrib. by. American Heroes, 3 vols. 2008. (Magill's Choice Ser.). (Illus.). 73.00 (978-1-58765-459-6(8)); 73.00 (978-1-58765-458-9(X)); 73.00 (978-1-58765-460-2(1)); 960p. 217.00 (978-1-58765-457-2(1)) Salem Pr., Inc.

Samuels, Allison. Off the Record: A Reporter Unveils the Celebrity Worlds of Hollywood, Hip-Hop, & Sports. 2008. 208p. per. 13.95 (978-0-06-137435-7(0), Harper Paperbacks) HarperCollins Pubs.

Sandvoss, Cornel, et al. Bodies of Discourse: Sports Stardom & Celebrity in the Global Public Sphere. 2012. (978-1-4331-1173-0(X)); E-Book (978-1-4539-0211-0(2)) Lang, Peter GmbH, Europaischer Verlag der Wissenschaften.

Sante, Luc & Carter, Ash, texts. The Vanities: Hollywood Parties 2000-2009. 2011. (ENG & GER., Illus.). 120p. (978-3-8296-0526-7(9)) Schirmer/Mosel Verlag GmbH.

Scarfe, Gerald. Heroes & Villains. 2006. (Illus.). 40.00 (978-1-85514-338-8(0)) National Portrait Gallery Pubns. GBR. Dist: Antique Collectors' Club.

Schmitt, Anne-Florence. Karl Lagerfeld: Trait par Trait, 1 vol. 2011. (ENG., Illus.) 144p. pap. 25.00 (978-3-86521-552-9(1)) Steidl, Gerhard Druckerei und Verlag DEU. Dist: Innovative Logistics.

Schnakenberg, Robert E. Distory: A Treasury of Historical Insults. Date not set. mass mkt. (978-0-312-99576-8(8), St. Martin's Paperbacks) St. Martin's Pr.

Schoeller, Martin, photos by. Martin Schoeller. 2009. (ENG.). 45.00 (978-3-570-19775-2(1)) teNeues Publishing Co.

Schwarz, Ted. Cleveland Curiosities: Eliot Ness & His Blundering Raid, a Busker's Promise, the Richest Heiress Who Never Lived & More. 2010. (ENG., Illus.). 128p. pap. 19.99 (978-1-59629-919-1(3)) History Pr., The.

Seal, Mark. Celebrated Weekends: The Stars' Guide to the Most Exciting Destinations in the World, 0 vols. 2007. (Illus.). 304p. per. 24.99 (978-1-4016-0243-7(6)) Nelson, Thomas Inc.

Selby, Todd & Arfin, Lesley. The Selby Is in Your Place. 2010. (ENG., Illus.). 256p. 35.00 (978-0-8109-8486-8(5)) Abrams.

Sellers, Robert. An A-Z of Hellraisers: A Comprehensive Compendium of Outrageous Insobriety. (ENG., Illus.). 2012. 420p. pap. 14.95 (978-1-84809-246-4(6)) 2010. 432p. 36.95 (978-1-84809-244-0(X)) 2010. 416p. pap. 25.95 (978-1-84809-245-7(8)) Random Hse. GBR. Dist: Independent Pubs. Group.

Shampine, David & Watertown Daily Times Staff. Colorful Characters of Northern New York: Northern Lights. 2010. (American Chronicles Ser.). (ENG., Illus.). 160p. pap. 19.99 (978-1-59629-821-7(9)) History Pr., The.

Shampo, Marc A., et al. Famous Personalities Honored on Stamps: Links to Medicine. 2011. 280p. pap. 22.95 (978-0-533-16361-8(7)) Vantage Pr., Inc.

Sheehy, Colleen J. Seed Queen: The Story of Crop Art & the Amazing Lillian Colton. 2007. (ENG., Illus.). 128p. 24.95 (978-0-87351-592-4(7)) Minnesota Historical Society Pr.

Sherrill, Jamie. Nurse Jamie's Botox Diaries: Real Stories from A Fake World. 2007. 188p. per. 17.95 (978-0-9797286-0-0(6)) Red Carpet Pr., The.

Showbiz, Pioneers, Beat Singers, Entertainers, & Musicians from 1606 to Present: Vol. 4 of the World's Who's Who in Jazz, Cabaret, Music, & Entertainment. 2007. per. (978-1-59916-240-9(7)) Printing Systems.

Silvers, Robert B. & Epstein, Barbara, eds. The Company They Kept: Writers on Unforgettable Friendships. 2009. (ENG.). 316p. pap. 19.95 (978-1-59017-334-3(1)) New York Review of Bks., Inc., The.

Sischy, Ingrid. Andy Warhol's Interview Vol. 1, 1 vol. 2008. (ENG., Illus.). 996p. 1000.00 (978-3-86521-023-4(0)) Steidl, Gerhard Druckerei und Verlag DEU. Dist: Innovative Logistics.

Sizer, Mona. Outrageous Texans: Tales of the Rich & Infamous. 2008. (ENG.). 272p. pap. 16.95 (978-1-58979-338-5(2)) Taylor Trade Publishing.

Smith, Ronald L. Horror Stars on Radio: The Broadcast Histories of 29 Chilling Hollywood Voices. 2010. (ENG., Illus.). 260p. pap. 45.00 (978-0-7864-4525-7(4)) McFarland & Co., Inc. Pubs.

Smith, Sean. Cheryl, Bk. 2. 2010. (ENG., Illus.). 240p. pap. 13.95 (978-1-84739-317-3(9)) Simon & Schuster, Ltd. GBR. Dist: Independent Pubs. Group.

Snodgrass, Mary Ellen. Beating the Odds: A Teen Guide to 75 Superstars Who Overcame Adversity, 1 vol. 2008. 368p. 75.00 (978-0-313-34564-7(3), GR4564, Greenwood Pr.) Greenwood Publishing Group, Inc.

Solomon, Juliet, compiled by. The Book of Regrets: Thoughts, Memories & Revelations from a Celebrated Cast. 2008. (ENG.). 208p. 24.95 (978-1-906217-10-5(6)) Aurum Pr., Ltd. GBR. Dist: Independent Pubs. Group.

Southwell, David. Mysterious Deaths & Disappearances. 2009. (Mysteries & Conspiracies Ser.). 80p. (gr. 10-10). 61.20 (978-1-61514-744-1(6)) Rosen Publishing Group, Inc., The.

Southwell, David & Twist, Sean. Mysterious Deaths & Disappearances. 2007. (Mysteries & Conspiracies Ser.). (Illus.). 80p. (YA). (gr. 9-12). lib. bdg. 30.50 (978-1-4042-1081-3(4)) Rosen Publishing Group, Inc., The.

—Unsolved Celebrity Mysteries. 2007. (Mysteries & Conspiracies Ser.). (Illus.). 80p. (YA). (gr. 9-12). lib. bdg. 30.50 (978-1-4042-1082-0(2)) Rosen Publishing Group, Inc., The.

Spragins, Ellyn. If I'd Known Then: Women in Their 20s & 30s Write Letters to Their Younger Selves. 2008. ((What I Know Now Series)). (ENG., Illus.). 192p. 18.00 (978-0-7382-1120-6(6)) Da Capo Pr., Inc.

—What I Know Now: Letters to My Younger Self. 2008. (ENG., Illus.). 208p. pap. 13.99 (978-0-7679-1790-2(1)) Broadway Bks.

Spragins, Ellyn, ed. What I Know Now about Success: Letters from Extraordinary Women to Their Younger Selves. 2011. (ENG.). 208p. pap. 13.00 (978-0-7382-1471-9(X)) Da Capo Pr., Inc.

Steen, M. F. Celebrity Death Certificates 3. 2010. (ENG., Illus.). 267p. pap. 39.95 (978-0-7864-5935-3(2)) McFarland & Co., Inc. Pubs.

Stern Fotografie Portfolio 48. Mark Seliger. 2007. (Illus.). 94p. per. 22.95 (978-3-570-19734-9(4)) teNeues Publishing Co.

Stern, Howard. Miss America. 2010. (ENG.). 496p. pap. 16.99 (978-0-06-188555-6(X)) HarperCollins Pubs.

Sternheimer, Karen. Celebrity Culture & the American Dream: Stardom & Social Mobility in the United States. 2011. (ENG., Illus.). 304p. 144.00 (978-0-415-88678-9(3)); pap. 29.95 (978-0-415-88679-6(1)) Routledge.

Stevens, Alan & Nicholas, Jeremy. MediaMasters: Insider Secrets from the Big Names of Broadcast, Print & Social Media. 2009. (Illus.). 192p. pap. (978-1-905430-61-1(2)) Lean Marketing Pr.

C

Stevens, Norma, et al. Performance. 2008. (ENG., Illus.). 304p. 100.00 *(978-0-8109-7288-9(3))* Abrams.

Stewart, Alana. My Journey with Farrah: A Story of Life, Love, & Friendship. 2010. (ENG.). 288p. pap. 14.99 *(978-0-06-196059-8(4)*, Harper Paperbacks) 2009. 288p. 23.99 *(978-0-06-196058-1(6)*, Morrow, William & Co.) 2009. 338p. pap. 23.99 *(978-0-06-196636-1(3)*, HarperLuxe) HarperCollins Pubs.

Strasser, Naomi, ed. Love Letters to the South: Messages of Hope & Healing from the World's Best Loved Celebrities, 0 vols. 2006. (Illus.). 144p. 24.99 *(978-1-59555-857-2(8))* Nelson, Thomas Inc.

Strauss, Alix. Death Becomes Them: Unearthing the Suicides of the Brilliant, the Famous, & the Notorious. 2009. (Illus.). 288p. pap. 14.99 *(978-0-06-172856-3(X)*, Harper Paperbacks) HarperCollins Pubs.

Strauss, Neil. Everyone Loves You When You're Dead: Journeys into Fame & Madness. 2011. (ENG., Illus.). 304p. pap. 16.99 *(978-0-06-154367-8(5))* HarperCollins Pubs.

Strauss-Peyton: Celebrity & Glamour. 2006. 49.95 *(978-0-9768804-4-8(X))* Sunswetpt Pr.

Street Howe, Zoe. How's Your Dad: Living in the Shadow of a Rock Star Parent. 2010. (ENG., Illus.). 272p. pap. 24.95 *(978-1-84938-074-4(0))* Omnibus Pr.

Strickland, Melissa R & Rycroft, Melissa. My Reality. 2012. (ENG., Illus.). 304p. 25.00 *(978-1-4516-3163-0(4))* Gallery Pr., The IRL. Dist: Simon & Schuster, Inc.

Strodder, Chris. The Encyclopedia of Sixties Cool: A Celebration of the Grooviest People, Events, & Artifacts of The 1960s. 2007. (ENG., Illus.). 336p. pap. 24.95 *(978-1-59580-017-6(4))* Santa Monica Pr.

Stromberg, Gary & Merrill, Jane. The Harder They Fall: Celebrities Tell Their Real-Life Stories of Addiction & Recovery. l.t. ed. 2007. (ENG., Illus.). 368p. pap. 13.95 *(978-1-59285-476-9(1))* Hazelden Publishing & Educational Services.

Sumner, Cassie. Loving It. 2008. (ENG., Illus.). 288p. 34.95 *(978-1-84454-554-4(7))* Blake, John Publishing, Ltd. GBR. Dist: Independent Pubs. Group.

Sun, Zhen. Celebrities, Products, & Presentation Styles. 2010. 176p. pap. *(978-3-8383-9673-6(1))* Lambert Academic Publishing.

Tagliaferri, Mariarosaria. Cars & Stars: 50 Years of Dreams, 1 vol. 2009. (ENG, DUT & FRE., Illus.). 208p. pap. 55.00 *(978-90-76886-00-8(8))* Tectum B.V.B.A. BEL. Dist: Innovative Logistics.

Tannenbaum, Allen. New York in The 70s. 2009. (ENG., Illus.). 272p. (gr. 12-18). 45.00 *(978-1-59020-172-5(8))* Overlook Pr., The.

Taylor, Brent D. The Creative Edge: 17 Biographies of Cultural Icons. 2008. (ENG.). 392p. pap. 29.95 *(978-0-7314-0847-4(0)*, Wrightbooks) Wiley, John & Sons Australia, Ltd. AUS. Dist: Wiley, John & Sons, Inc.

Taylor, John A. Prince William, the Internet, & the Tabloids: Contemporary Celebrity & the Monarchy. 2010. *(978-0-7734-1381-8(2))* Mellen, Edwin Pr., The.

Teller, Juergen. Marc Jacobs Vol. 1: Advertising 1997-2008, 1 vol. 2009. (ENG., Illus.). 576p. 120.00 *(978-3-86521-715-8(X))* Steidl, Gerhard Druckerei und Verlag DEU. Dist: Innovative Logistics.

Tester, Keith. Humanitarianism & Modern Culture. 2010. (ENG.). 160p. 60.00 *(978-0-271-03735-6(0))*; 24.95 *(978-0-271-03678-6(8))* Pennsylvania State Univ. Pr.

Testino, Mario, photos by. Let Me In! 2007. (Illus.). 306p. 700.00 *(978-90-00-01845-1(5))* TASCHEN DEU. Dist: Ingram Pub. Services.

Thomas, Mario, et al. The Right Words at the Right Time Vol. 2: Your Turn! 2007. (ENG.). 432p. pap. 16.00 *(978-0-7434-9744-2(9)*, Beyond Words/Atria Bks.) Atria Bks.

Thomas, Robert McG. 52 Mcgs: The Best Obituaries from Legendary New York Times Reporter Robert McG. Thomas. Calhoun, Chris, ed. 2008. (ENG.). 192p. pap. 14.95 *(978-1-4165-9827-5(8)*, Scribner) Scribner.

Thomson Gale Staff. Newsmakers, 4 vols. 2007th ed. 2006. (Newsmakers Ser.). (ENG.). 272.00 *(978-0-7876-8087-9(7))* Cengage Gale.

Tiegel, Eliot. Overexposed: The Price of Fame - The Troubles of Britney, Lindsay, Paris & Nicole. 2008. (ENG.). 288p. 19.95 *(978-1-59777-599-1(1))* Phoenix Bks., Inc.

Time-Life Books Staff. True Crime: Death of Celebrity. (Illus.). 192p. 20.00 *(978-1-84447-105-8(5))* Time Life Value GBR. Dist: Mercury Bks. Ltd.

Tom, Munro, photos by. Tom Munro, 1 vol. 2010. (ENG.). 240p. 75.00 *(978-88-6208-125-2(1))* Damiani ITA. Dist: D.A.P./Distributed Art Pubs.

Tomlinson, Ricky. Celebrities My Arse! The Funniest Book of Celebrity Anecdotes You'll Ever Read. 2007. (ENG., Illus.). 256p. 19.00 *(978-0-316-02990-2(4))* Little Bks., Ltd. GBR. Dist: Independent Pubs. Group.

—Celebrities My Arse! The Funniest Book of Celebrity Anecdotes You'll Ever Read. 2008. (ENG., Illus.). 256p. pap. 12.95 *(978-0-7515-3919-6(8))* Little, Brown Bk. Group Ltd. GBR. Dist: Independent Pubs. Group.

Trehan, Madhu. Tehelka As Metaphor: Prism Me a Lie, Tell Me a Truth. 2010. (Roli Bks.) (ENG.). 587p. 24.95 *(978-81-7436-580-4(X))* Roli Bks. Private, Ltd. IND. Dist: Ingram Pub. Services.

Trimble, Patrick. Media & the Creation of Babe Ruth. 2012. (Studies in American Popular History & Culture Ser.). (ENG.). 240p. 125.00 *(978-0-415-99407-1(1))* Routledge.

Ullman, Dana. The Homeopathic Revolution: Why Famous People & Cultural Heroes Choose Homeopathy. 2007. (ENG.). 408p. pap. 19.95 *(978-1-55643-671-0(8))* North Atlantic Bks.

Unger, Steven P. Before the Paparazzi: 50 Years of Extraordinary Photographs. Strozier, M. Stefan, ed. 2011. 232p. pap. 29.00 ***(978-1-935444-39-8(5))*** World Audience Pubs.

Uruburu, Paula. American Eve: Evelyn Nesbit, Stanford White, the Birth of the It Girl, & the Crime of the Century. 2009. (ENG., Illus.). 400p. (gr. 12-18). 17.00 *(978-1-59448-369-1(8)*, Riverhead Trade (Paperbacks)) Penguin Group (USA) Inc.

van Heerikhuizen, Annemarie, et al, eds. Tweede Levens: Over personen en personages in de geschiedschrijving en de Literatuur. 2010. (DUT., Illus.). 268p. pap. *(978-90-5629-643-8(4)*, Vossiupers UvA) Amsterdam Univ. Pr.

van Krieken, Robert. Celebrity Society. 2012. (ENG., Illus.). 200p. 160.00 *(978-0-415-58149-3(4))*; pap. 44.95 *(978-0-415-58150-9(8))* Routledge.

Van Sant, Gus. One Step Big Shot. 2010. (Illus.). 29p. ***(978-1-59005-287-7(0))*** Nazraeli Pr.

Vanderbilt, Gloria. It Seemed Important at the Time: A Romance Memoir. 2009. (ENG., Illus.). 176p. pap. 12.99 *(978-1-4391-8982-5(X))* Simon & Schuster.

Vanity Fair Editors. Vintage Postcards from Vanity Fair: One Hundred Classic Covers. 2011. (ENG.). 100p. (gr. 12). 25.00 *(978-1-84614-467-7(1)*, Penguin (Non-Classics)) Penguin Group (USA) Inc.

Vargas Llosa, Alvaro. Cuando Hablaba Dormido.Tr. of When I Talked Asleep. (SPA.). 360p. 17.98 *(978-970-05-1125-2(1))* Grijalbo, Editorial MEX. Dist: Continental Bk. Co., Inc.

Vonnegut, Mark. Just Like Someone Without Mental Illness Only More So: A Memoir. 2010. (Illus.). 224p. 24.00 *(978-0-385-34379-4(5)*, Delacorte Pr) Random House Publishing Group.

Wahl, Grant. The Beckham Experiment: How the World's Most Famous Athlete Tried to Conquer America. 2010. (ENG., Illus.). 320p. pap. 15.00 *(978-0-307-40859-4(0)*, Three Rivers Pr.) Crown Publishing Group.

Walker, Diana. The Bigger Picture: Thirty Years of Portraits. 2007. (ENG., Illus.). 200p. 40.00 *(978-1-4262-0129-5(X)*, National Geographic) National Geographic Society.

Wan, Gok. Through Thick & Thin: My Autobiography. 2011. (ENG., Illus.). 360p. pap. 12.95 ***(978-0-09-193838-3(4))*** Ebury Publishing GBR. Dist: Independent Pubs. Group.

Wang, Luxiang. Wo Men de Chuan Tong: Wang Luxiang Wen Hua Fang Tan Lu. 2009. (CHI., Illus.). 222p. *(978-7-5057-2603-1(X))* China Friendship Publishing Hse.

Ward, Pete. Gods Behaving Badly: Media, Religion, & Celebrity Culture. 2011. (ENG.). 160p. pap. 24.95 *(978-1-60258-150-0(9))* Baylor Univ. Pr.

Wasef, Basem. Legendary Motorcycles: The Stories & Bikes Made Famous by Elvis, Peter Fonda, Kenny Roberts & Other Motorcycling Greats. rev. ed. 2007. (ENG., Illus.). 176p. 34.95 *(978-0-7603-3070-8(0)*, 0760330700, Motorbooks) MBI Publishing Co. LLC.

Watts, Ben. Lickshot: A Photo Scrapbook. 2009. (ENG., Illus.). 208p. 50.00 *(978-1-56898-838-2(9))* Princeton Architectural Pr.

Weber, Uli, photos by. Uli Weber: Portraits. 2011. (ENG., Illus.). 168p. 60.00 *(978-88-572-0703-2(X))* Skira Editore ITA. Dist: Random Hse., Inc.

Welkowitz, David S. & Ochoa, Tyler T. Celebrity Rights: Rights of Publicity & Related Rights in the United States & Abroad. 2010. 640p. 70.00 *(978-1-59460-657-1(9))* Carolina Academic Pr.

Wendt, Jana. A Matter of Principle: New Meetings with the Good, the Great & the Formidable. 2008. (ENG.). 304p. pap. 24.95 *(978-0-522-85525-8(3))* Melbourne Univ. Publishing AUS. Dist: Independent Pubs. Group.

Werle, Simone. Fashionista: A Century of Style Icons. 2009. (Illus.). 176p. 29.95 *(978-3-7913-3936-8(2))* Prestel Publishing.

—Fashionisto: A Century of Style Icons. 2010. (Illus.). 176p. 29.99 *(978-3-7913-4476-8(5))* Prestel Publishing.

Who's Who in Italy S. R. L. Who's Who in Italy 2010, 3 Vols. 2010. (Who's Who red Ser.). 3100p. *(978-88-85246-68-3(0))* Who's Who in Italy ITA. Dist: Independent Pubs. Group.

Williams, Anne. Infamous Scandals. 2008. 512p. 9.99 *(978-0-7088-0365-3(2))* Little, Brown Bk. Group Ltd. GBR. Dist: Book Sales, Inc.

Wills, David, ed. & text. Ara Gallant. 2010. (ENG., Illus.). 220p. 60.00 *(978-88-6208-120-7(0))* Damiani ITA. Dist: D.A.P./Distributed Art Pubs.

Wilson, Scott. Resting Place: The Burial Sites of over 10,000 Famous Persons, 2 vols. 2nd rev. ed. 2007. (ENG.). 936p. per. 95.00 *(978-0-7864-2896-0(1))* McFarland & Co., Inc. Pubs.

Winslet, Kate & Ericsdottir, Margret. The Golden Hat: Talking Back to Autism. 2012. (ENG., Illus.). 256p. 29.95 *(978-1-4516-4543-9(0))* Simon & Schuster.

Wright, Michele & Wright, Michele R. Dear Success Seeker: Wisdom from Outstanding Women. 2009. (ENG.). 240p. pap. 15.99 *(978-1-4165-7079-0(9)*, Beyond Words/Atria Bks.) Atria Bks.

Xavier, Waterkeyn. Celebrity Crimes: The Dark Side of the Limelight. 2008. (ENG.). 256p. pap. 19.95 *(978-1-74110-565-0(X))* New Holland Pubs. Pty, Ltd. AUS. Dist: Tuttle Publishing.

Yamada, Michiko. A Lucrative Double-Standard on Pop Culture. 2010. 208p. pap. *(978-3-639-24332-1(3))* VDM Verlag Dr. Mueller e.K.

Zabel, Jackie & Most, Morgan. The Hollywood Cookbook: Cooking for Causes; Award Winning Edition. 2008. (Illus.). 271p. 39.95 *(978-0-615-22134-2(3))* Good Looking Cooking.

Zastoupil, Lynn. Rammohun Roy & the Making of Victorian Britain. 2010. (Palgrave Studies in Cultural & Intellectual History Ser.). (ENG., Illus.). 276p. 84.00 *(978-0-230-61680-6(1))* Palgrave Macmillan.

Zeitz, Joshua. Flapper: A Madcap Story of Sex, Style, Celebrity, & the Women Who Made America Modern. 2007. (ENG., Illus.). 352p. pap. 15.00 *(978-1-4000-8054-0(1)*, Three Rivers Pr.) Crown Publishing Group.

Zheng, Hongtai, et al. Grand Old Man of Hong Kong: Sir Shouson Chow. 2010. (Illus.). 332p. pap. ***(978-962-8269-52-5(6))*** Hong Kong Univ. Pr.

Zim, Steve & Laska, Mark. 6 Weeks to a Hollywood Body: Look Fit & Feel Fabulous with the Secrets of the Stars. 2007. (ENG., Illus.). 240p. per. 14.95 *(978-0-470-09822-6(8)*, Wiley) Wiley, John & Sons, Inc.

Zim, Steve & Steinberg, Steve. The 30-Minute Celebrity Makeover Miracle: Achieve the Body You've Always Wanted. 2008. (ENG., Illus.). 264p. 24.95 *(978-0-470-17403-6(X)*, Wiley) Wiley, John & Sons, Inc.

Zorich, Louis & Hal Leonard Corporation Staff. What Have You Done? The Inside Stories of Auditioning, from the Ridiculous to the Sublime, 1 vol. Zorich, Louis, ed. 2009. (ENG., Illus.). 320p. pap. 14.99 *(978-0-87910-365-1(5)*, 0879103655, Limelight Editions) Leonard, Hal Corp.

Zuckerman, Andrew. Wisdom. 2011. (Illus.). 216p. ***(978-0-8109-9800-1(9))*** Abrams.

Zuckerman, Andrew. Wisdom - Ideas: The Greatest Gift One Generation Can Give to Another. 2009. (ENG., Illus.). 160p. pap. 16.95 *(978-0-8109-8438-7(5))* Abrams.

CELEBRITIES—POLITICAL ACTIVITY

Cooper, Andrew F. Celebrity Diplomacy. 2007. (International Studies Intensives Ser.). (Illus.). 176p. 125.00 *(978-1-59451-478-4(X))*; per. 33.95 *(978-1-59451-479-1(8))* Paradigm Pubs.

Critchlow, Donald T. Hollywood & Politics: A Sourcebook. Raymond, Emilie, ed. 2009. (ENG., Illus.). 342p. 130.00 *(978-0-415-96535-4(7))* Routledge.

Espejo, Roman. Can Celebrities Change the World? 2008. (At Issue Ser.). (ENG., Illus.). 80-128p. (gr. 10-12). 22.50 *(978-0-7377-4089-9(2))*; pap. 31.80 *(978-0-7377-4088-2(4))* Cengage Gale. (Greenhaven Pr., Inc.).

Mattera, Jason. Hollywood Hypocrites: The Devastating Truth about Obama's Biggest Backer. 2012. (Illus.). ix, 256p. pap. ***(978-1-4516-2562-2(6)***, Threshold Editions) Threshold Editions.

—Hollywood Hypocrites: The Devastating Truth about Obama's Biggest Backers. 2012. (ENG., Illus.). 272p. 25.00 ***(978-1-4516-2561-5(8)***, Threshold Editions) Threshold Editions.

Negra, Diane & Holmes, Su. In the Limelight & under the Microscope: Forms & Functions of Female Celebrity. Negra, Diane & Holmes, Su, eds. 2011. (ENG., Illus.). 352p. 120.00 *(978-1-4411-5495-8(7))*; pap. 34.95 *(978-0-8264-3855-3(5))* Continuum International Publishing Group, Ltd. GBR. Dist: National Bk. Network.

Peyser, Andrea. Celebutards. (ENG.). 256p. 2010. pap. 14.95 *(978-0-8065-3110-6(X))* 2009. 22.95 *(978-0-8065-3109-0(6))* Kensington Publishing Corp. (Citadel Pr.).

Richey, Lisa Ann & Ponte, Stefano. Brand Aid: Shopping Well to Save the World. 2011. (Illus.). 288p. 57.00 *(978-0-8166-6545-7(1))*; pap. 18.95 *(978-0-8166-6546-4(X))* Univ. of Minnesota Pr.

Tsaliki, Liza, et al, eds. Transnational Celebrity Activism in Global Politics: Changing the World? 2011. 317p. pap. 40.00 *(978-1-84150-349-3(5))* Intellect, Ltd. GBR. Dist: Chicago Distribution Ctr.

CELEBRITY

see Fame

CELESTIAL MECHANICS

see also Kepler's Equation; Lunar Theory; Perturbation (Astronomy); Planetary Theory

Aarseth, Sverre J. Gravitational N-Body Simulations: Tools & Algorithms. 2009. (Cambridge Monographs on Mathematical Physics Ser.). (ENG., Illus.). 432p. (C). pap. 86.00 *(978-0-521-12153-8(1))* Cambridge Univ. Pr.

Andersen, Johannes, et al. The Galaxy Disk in Cosmological Context. Andersen, Johannes et al, eds. 2009. (Proceedings of the International Astronomical Union Symposia & Colloquia Ser.). (ENG., Illus.). 532p. 118.00 *(978-0-521-88985-8(5))* Cambridge Univ. Pr.

Arnold, Vladimir I. Vladimir I. Arnold - Collected Works: Representations of Functions, Celestial Mechanics, & KAM Theory 1957-1965, 8 vols. Givental, Alexander et al, eds. 2009. (Vladimir I. Arnold - Collected Works). (ENG., Illus.). xiv, 487p. 149.00 *(978-3-642-01741-4(X)*, 364201741X) Springer.

Arnold, Vladimir I., et al. Mathematical Aspects of Classical & Celestial Mechanics. Khukhro, E., tr. 3rd ed. 2010. (Encyclopaedia of Mathematical Sciences Ser.). Orig. Title: Matematicheskie Aspekty Klassicheskoj i Nebesnoj Mekhaniki. (Illus.). xiii, 518p. pap. 155.00 *(978-3-642-06647-4(X)*, 364206647X) Springer.

—Mathematical Aspects of Classical & Celestial Mechanics. Khukhro, Evgeny & Khukhro, E., trs. from RUS. 3rd rev. ed. 2007. (Encyclopaedia of Mathematical Sciences Ser.: Vol. 3). Orig. Title: Matematicheskie Aspekty Klassicheskoj i Nebesnoj Mekhaniki. (Illus.). 518p. 155.00 *(978-3-540-28246-4(7)*, 3540282467) Springer.

Böhringer, Hans, et al, eds. Heating versus Cooling in Galaxies & Clusters of Galaxies: Proceedings of the MPA/ESO/MPE/USM Joint Astronomy Conference held in Garching, Germany, 6-11 August 2006. 2010. (ESO Astrophysics Symposia Ser.). (Illus.). xxiv, 446p. pap. 139.00 *(978-3-642-09257-2(8)*, 3642092578) Springer.

Belbruno, Edward. Fly Me to the Moon: An Insider's Guide to the New Science of Space Travel. 2007. (ENG., Illus.). 176p. (C). 19.95 *(978-0-691-12822-1(7))* Princeton Univ. Pr.

Benest, D., et al, eds. Topics in Gravitational Dynamics: Solar, Extra-Solar & Galactic Systems. 2008. (Lecture Notes in Physics Ser.). (Illus.). 413p. 129.00 *(978-3-540-72983-9(6))* Springer.

Benest, Daniel, et al, eds. Topics in Gravitational Dynamics: Solar, Extra-Solar & Galactic Systems. 2010. (Lecture Notes in Physics Ser.). (Illus.). x, 414p. pap. 129.00 *(978-3-642-09207-7(1)*, 3642092071) Springer.

Benest, Daniel & Froeschle, Claude, eds. Singularities in Gravitational Systems: Applications to Chaotic Transport in the Solar System. 2010. (Lecture Notes in Physics Ser.). xi, 215p. pap. 69.95 *(978-3-642-07844-6(3)*, 3642078443) Springer.

Beutler, Gerhard. Methods of Celestial Mechanics: Volume I: Physical, Mathematical, & Numerical Principles. 2010. (Astronomy & Astrophysics Library). (Illus.). xvi, 464p. pap. 89.95 *(978-3-642-14857-6(3)*, 3642148573); 129.00 *(978-3-642-10529-6(7)*, 3642105297) Springer.

Binney, James & Tremaine, Scott. Galactic Dynamics. 2nd ed. 2008. (Princeton Series in Astrophysics). (Illus.). (ENG.). 920p. (C). per. 85.00 *(978-0-691-13027-9(2))*; 885p. 120.00 *(978-0-691-13026-2(4))* Princeton Univ. Pr.

Blilie, Charles. The Promise & Limits of Computer Modeling. 2007. (Illus.). 276p. 121.00 *(978-981-270-795-6(6))* World Scientific Publishing Co., Inc.

Bodo, Gianluigi. Jets from Young Stars III: Numerical MHD & Instabilities. 2008. (Lecture Notes in Physics Ser.). (Illus.). 188p. 79.95 *(978-3-540-76966-8(8))* Springer.

Bois, Eric. L' Univers Sans Repos ou L'essence Premiere du Mouvement. (Philosophia Naturalis et Geometricalis Ser.: Vol. 1). (FRE., Illus.). 237p. 38.95 *(978-3-906767-19-2(1))* Lang, Peter CHE. Dist: Lang, Peter Publishing, Inc.

Burstein, Joseph. Precise Numerical Analysis for Nonlinear Dynamics: Basic Problem of Exterior Ballistics & Primary Problem of Celestial Mechanics. 2007. (Illus.). v, 94p. *(978-0-9765949-4-9(3))* Metrics Pr.

Carignan, Claude, et al, eds. Tracing the Ancestry of Galaxies (IAU S277) 2012. (Proceedings of the International Astronomical Union Symposia & Colloquia Ser.). (ENG., Illus.). 368p. 125.00 ***(978-0-521-76602-9(8))*** Cambridge Univ. Pr.

Celletti, Alessandra. Stability & Chaos in Celestial Mechanics. 2009. (Springer Praxis Books / Astronomy & Planetary Sciences Ser.). (ENG., Illus.). xvi, 264p. 139.00 *(978-3-540-85145-5(3)*, 3540851453) Springer.

Celletti, Alessandra, et al, eds. Modern Celestial Mechanics: from Theory to Applications: From Theory to Applications. 2010. (Illus.). 488p. pap. 179.00 *(978-90-481-6078-5(2)*, 9048160782) Springer.

Celletti, Alessandra & Chierchia, Luigi. KAM Stability & Celestial Mechanics. 2007. (Memoirs of the American Mathematical Society Ser.). 134p. pap. 66.00 *(978-0-8218-4169-3(6))* American Mathematical Society.

Celletti, Alessandra & Ferraz-Mello, Sylvio, eds. Periodic, Quasi-Periodic & Chaotic Motions in Celestial Mechanics: Theory & Applications: Theory & Applications. 2010. (ENG.). viii, 440p. pap. 199.00 *(978-90-481-7340-2(X)*, 904817340X) Springer.

Celletti, Alessandra & Ferraz-Mello, Sylvio S., eds. Periodic, Quasi-Periodic & Chaotic Motions in Celestial Mechanics: Theory & Applications. 2006. (ENG., Illus.). viii, 440p. 199.00 *(978-1-4020-5324-5(X)*, 140205324X) Springer.

Celletti, Alessandra & Perozzi, Ettore. Celestial Mechanics: The Waltz of the Planets. 2006. (Springer-Praxis Books in Popular Astronomy). (Illus.). 245p. per. 32.95 *(978-0-387-30777-0(X)*, 038730777X) Springer.

Colombo, Giovanni. Modern Questions of Celestial Mechanics: Lectures given at the Centro Internazionale Matematico Estivo (C. I. M. E.) held in Bressanone (Bolzano), Italy, May 22-31 1967. 2010. (CIME Summer Schools Ser.). 241p. pap. 49.95 *(978-3-642-11053-5(3)*, 3642110533) Springer.

Contopoulos, George. Order & Chaos in Dynamical Astronomy. 2010. (Astronomy & Astrophysics Library). (Illus.). xiv, 624p. pap. 169.00 *(978-3-642-07770-8(6)*, 3642077706) Springer.

Corbett, Ian F., ed. Proceedings of the Twenty Seventh General Assembly Rio de Janeiro 2009: Transactions of the International Astronomical Union XXVIIB. 2010. (Proceedings of the International Astronomical Union Symposia & Colloquia Ser.). (Illus.). 538p. 125.00 *(978-0-521-76831-3(4))* Cambridge Univ. Pr.

Darwin, George Howard. The Scientific Papers of Sir George Darwin: Figures of Equilibrium of Rotating Liquid & Geophysical Investigations. 2009. (Cambridge Library Collection - Physical Sciences Ser.). (ENG., Illus.). 548p. pap. 39.99 *(978-1-108-00445-9(8))* Cambridge Univ. Pr.

—The Scientific Papers of Sir George Darwin: Oceanic Tides & Lunar Disturbance of Gravity. 2009. (Cambridge Library Collection - Physical Sciences Ser.). (ENG., Illus.). 488p. pap. 35.99 *(978-1-108-00442-8(3))* Cambridge Univ. Pr.

—The Scientific Papers of Sir George Darwin: Periodic Orbits & Miscellaneous Papers. 2009. (Cambridge Library Collection - Physical Sciences Ser.). (ENG., Illus.). 628p. pap. 43.00 *(978-1-108-00447-3(4))* Cambridge Univ. Pr.

—The Scientific Papers of Sir George Darwin: Supplementary Volume. Stratton, F. J. M. & Jackson, J., eds. 2009. (Cambridge Library Collection - Physical Sciences Ser.). (ENG., Illus.). 148p. pap. 19.99 *(978-1-108-00448-0(2))* Cambridge Univ. Pr.

—The Scientific Papers of Sir George Darwin: Tidal Friction & Cosmogony. 2009. (Cambridge Library Collection - Physical Sciences Ser.). (ENG., Illus.). 540p. pap. 39.99 *(978-1-108-00443-5(1))* Cambridge Univ. Pr.

de Jong, R. S. Island Universes: Structure & Evolution of Disk Galaxies. 2006. (Astrophysics & Space Science Proceedings Ser.: Vol. 3). (Illus.). xxiv, 584p. 219.00 *(978-1-4020-5572-0(2)*, 1402055722) Springer.

Dobrzycki, J., ed. The Reception of Copernicus' Heliocentric Theory. 2010. 376p. pap. 264.00 *(978-90-481-8340-1(5)*, 9048183405) Springer.

Esposito, Larry W. Planetary Rings. 2006. (Cambridge Planetary Science Ser.). (ENG., Illus.). 214p. 171.00 *(978-0-521-36222-1(9))* Cambridge Univ. Pr.

Ferraz-Mello, Sylvio. Canonical Perturbation Theories: Degenerate Systems & Resonance. 2007. (Astrophysics & Space Science Library). (Illus.). 341p. 159.00 *(978-0-387-38900-4(8)*, 0387389008) Springer.

Fitzpatrick, Richard. An Introduction to Celestial Mechanics. 2012. (ENG., Illus.). 288p. (C). 65.00 ***(978-1-107-02381-9(5))*** Cambridge Univ. Pr.

Fridman, Alexei M. & Gorkavyi, Nikolai N. Physics of Planetary Rings: Celestial Mechanics of Continuous Media. Haar, D. ter, tr. 2010. (Astronomy & Astrophysics Library). (Illus.). xxi, 436p. pap. 149.00 (978-3-642-08437-9(0), 3642084370) Springer.

Gal, Ofer. Meanest Foundations & Nobler Superstructures: Hooke, Newton & the Compounding of the Celestiall Motions of the Planetts. 2010. (Boston Studies in the Philosophy of Science Ser.). 256p. pap. 119.00 (978-90-481-6067-9(7), 9048160677) Springer.

Gracia, Jose, et al, eds. Jets from Young Stars V: High Performance Computing & Applications. 2009. (Lecture Notes in Physics Ser.). (Illus.). xi, 227p. 89.95 (978-3-642-03365-8(5), 3642033695) Springer.

I Estrada, Sergi Simon. On the Non-Integrability of Some Problems in Celestial Mechanics. 2008. 132p. pap. (978-3-639-05015-8(0)) VDM Verlag Dr. Mueller e.K.

Isaaco Newtono, Newtono, et al. Philosophiæ Naturalis Principia Mathematica. 2010. 568p. pap. 11.95 (978-1-60386-379-7(6), Watchmaker Publishing) Wexford College Pr.

Jardetzky, Wenceslas S. Theories of Figures of Celestial Bodies. 2011. 198p. 42.95 **(978-1-258-05833-3(2))** Literary Licensing, LLC.

Jeans, James. Problems of Cosmology & Stellar Dynamics. 2009. (Cambridge Library Collection - Physical Sciences Ser.). (ENG.). 316p. pap. 31.99 (978-1-108-00568-5(3)) Cambridge Univ. Pr.

Jong, R. S. de. Island Universes: Structure & Evolution of Disk Galaxies. 2010. (Astrophysics & Space Science Proceedings Ser.). xxiv, 584p. pap. 219.00 (978-90-481-7398-3(1), 9048173981) Springer.

Koon, Wang Sang & Lo, Lo. Dynamical Systems, the Three-Body Problem & Space Mission Design. 2007. 336p. 89.95 (978-0-387-49515-6(0)) Springer.

Kopeikin, Sergei, et al. Relativistic Celestial Mechanics of the Solar System. 2011. (ENG., Illus.). 892p. 220.00 (978-3-527-40856-6(8), Wiley-VCH) Wiley, John & Sons, Inc.

Kushvah, Badam Singh. The Celestial Mechanics: Study of Stability. 2009. 152p. pap. (978-3-639-19743-3(7)) VDM Verlag Dr. Mueller e.K.

Lang-Wescott, Martha, ed. Asteroid Mechanics, 1925-2006, 2 vols., Vol. II. (Asteroid Ephemerides Ser.). 80p. 15.95 (978-0-9619852-4-0(0)) Treehouse Mountain.

Laplace, Pierre Simon. Mechanism of the Heavens. Somerville, Mary, tr. 2009. (Cambridge Library Collection - Life Sciences Ser.). 700p. pap. 48.00 (978-1-108-00157-1(2)) Cambridge Univ. Pr.

Mann, Ingrid, et al. Small Bodies in Planetary Systems. 2008. (Lecture Notes in Physics Ser.). (Illus.). 300p. 89.95 (978-3-540-76934-7(X)) Springer.

Massaglia, Silvano, et al, eds. Jets from Young Stars III: Numerical MHD & Instabilities. 2010. (Lecture Notes in Physics Ser.). (Illus.). viii, 178p. pap. 79.95 (978-3-642-09567-2(4), 3642095674) Springer.

Mazer, Arthur. Shifting the Earth: The Mathematical Quest to Understand the Motion of the Universe. 2011. (ENG., Illus.). 328p. pap. 59.95 **(978-1-118-02427-0(3)**, Wiley) Wiley, John & Sons, Inc.

Milani, Andrea & Gronchi, Giovanni. Theory of Orbit Determination. 2009. (ENG., Illus.). 392p. 75.00 (978-0-521-87389-5(4)) Cambridge Univ. Pr.

Mioc, Vasile. Exploring the Solar System & the Universe. Mioc, Vasile et al, eds. 2008. (AIP Conference Proceedings / Astronomy & Astrophysics Ser.). 452p. 229.00 (978-0-7354-0571-4(9)) American Institute of Physics.

Misra, Ram Bilas. Influence of Celestial Bodies on Human Lives. 2011. 60p. pap. **(978-3-8383-2259-9(2))** Lambert Academic Publishing.

Perozzi, Ettore & Ferraz-Mello, Sylvio S., eds. Space Manifold Dynamics: Novel Spaceways for Science & Exploration. 2010. (Space Technology Proceedings Ser.). (ENG., Illus.). xvi, 258p. 189.00 (978-1-4419-0347-1(X), 144190347X) Springer.

Pretka-Ziomek, Halina, et al, eds. Dynamics of Natural & Artificial Celestial Bodies. 2012. (ENG., Illus.). 460p. pap. 209.00 (978-90-481-5865-2(6), 9048158656) Springer.

Ryabov, Y. An Elementary Survey of Celestial Mechanics. Yankovsky, G., tr. 2011. 166p. 41.95 **(978-1-258-01594-7(3))** Literary Licensing, LLC.

Schaub, Hanspeter & Junkins, John L. Analytical Mechanics of Space Systems. 2nd ed. 2009. 104.95 (978-1-60086-721-7(9)) American Institute of Aeronautics & Astronautics.

Sharma, Ishan, et al. Dynamics of Deformable Bodies: An approximate approach, with applications to solar system Bodies. 2010. (Advances in Geophysical & Environmental Mechanics & Mathematics Ser.). (Illus.). 300p. 199.00 (978-3-642-12075-6(X), 364212075X) Springer.

Smith, Beverly J. Galaxy Wars: Stellar Populations & Star Formation in Interacting Galaxies: Proceedings of a Conference Held at East Tennessee State University, Johnson City, Tennessee, USA, 19-22 July 2009. 2010. (Illus.). xvi, 376p. (978-1-58381-727-8(1)); (978-1-58381-726-1(3)) Astronomical Society of the Pacific, The.

Souchay, Jean J., ed. Dynamics of Extended Celestial Bodies & Rings. 2010. (Lecture Notes in Physics Ser.). xii, 207p. pap. 99.00 (978-3-642-06630-6(5), 3642066305) Springer.

Sterne, Theodore E. An Introduction to Celestial Mechanics. 2011. 218p. 44.95 **(978-1-258-01830-6(6))** Literary Licensing, LLC.

Turakulov, Zafar. Selected Problems of Celestial Mechanics & Astrophysics. 2011. 92p. pap. **(978-3-8443-9491-7(5))** Lambert Academic Publishing.

Verdes-Montenegro, Lourdes, et al. Galaxies in Isolation: Exploring Nature Versus Nurture: Proceedings of a Conference Held at Granada, Spain 12-15 May 2009. 2010. (Illus.). xxii, 302p. (978-1-58381-722-3(0)) Astronomical Society of the Pacific, The.

Villard, Ray, ed. Changes Within Physical Systems and/or Conservation of Energy & Momentum: An Anthology of Current Thought. 2009. (Contemporary Discourse in the Field of Physics Ser.). 220p. (gr. 10-12). 63.90 (978-1-61511-915-8(9)) Rosen Publishing Group, Inc., The.

Vozmischeva, T. G. Integrable Problems of Celestial Mechanics in Spaces of Constant Curvature. 2010. (Astrophysics & Space Science Library). 196p. pap. 149.00 (978-90-481-6382-3(X), 904816382X) Springer.

Weiland, Claus. Computational Space Flight Mechanics. 2010. 310p. 179.00 (978-3-642-13582-8(X), 364213582X) Springer.

CELESTIAL NAVIGATION

see Nautical Astronomy

CELIAC DISEASE

see also Gluten-Free Diet

Ahern, Shauna James. Gluten-Free Girl: How I Found the Food That Loves Me Back... And How You Can Too. 2009. (ENG., Illus.). 288p. pap. 14.95 (978-0-470-41164-3(3), Wiley) Wiley, John & Sons, Inc.

Anca, Alexandra & Santandrea-Cull, Theresa. Complete Gluten-Free Diet & Nutrition Guide: With 30-Day Meal Plan & over 100 Recipes. 2010. (ENG., Illus.). 272p. pap. 24.95 (978-0-7788-0252-5(3)) Rose, Robert Inc. CAN. Dist: Firefly Bks., Ltd.

Arendt, Elke & Dal Bello, Fabio. The Science of Gluten-Free Foods & Beverages: Proceedings of the First International Conference of Gluten-Free Cereal Products & Beverages. 2009. (Illus.). iv, 165p. **(978-1-891127-67-0(5))** AACC International.

Bauer, Eydi. Life after Bread: How to Get off Gluten & Reclaim Your Health. 2009. 128p. pap. 14.95 (978-1-879384-77-4(9)) Cypress Hse.

Blumer, Ian & Crowe, Sheila. Celiac Disease for Dummies. 2010. (ENG., Illus.). 384p. pap. 19.99 (978-0-470-16036-7(5), For Dummies) Wiley, John & Sons, Inc.

Borg, Joseph, et al. The Genetics of Coeliac Disease in Malt. 2010. 112p. pap. (978-3-8383-6742-2(1)) Lambert Academic Publishing.

Bower, Sylvia Llewelyn. Celiac Disease: A Guide to Living with Gluten Intolerance. 2006. (American Academy of Neurology Ser.). (ENG., Illus.). 151p. pap. 16.95 (978-1-932603-25-5(5)) Demos Medical Publishing, LLC.

—What Nurses Know... Gluten-Free Lifestyle. 2011. (What Nurses Know... Ser.). (ENG.). 192p. pap. 16.95 (978-1-936303-07-5(8)) Demos Medical Publishing, LLC.

Brown, Marlisa. Gluten-Free, Hassle Free: A Simple, Sane, Dietitian-Approved Program for Eating Your Way Back to Health. 2009. (ENG.). 378p. pap. 19.95 (978-1-932603-79-8(4)) Demos Medical Publishing, LLC.

Brown, Ruby M. Gluten-Free Cooking: More Than 150 Gluten-Free Recipes, 1 vol. 2007. (Illus.). 304p. pap. 18.95 (978-1-59120-202-8(7)) Basic Health Pubns., Inc.

Brownstein, David & Shenefelt, Sheryl. The Guide to a Gluten-Free Diet. 2nd ed. 2009. 195p. **(978-0-9660882-8-1(X)**, Healthy Living) Book Publishing Co.

Burns, David L. 100 Questions & Answers about Celiac Disease & Sprue: A Lahey Clinic Guide. 2007. (Illus.). 226p. per. 22.95 (978-0-7637-4502-8(2)) Jones & Bartlett Learning, LLC.

Coping with Coeliac Disease. (978-0-85969-903-7(X), Sheldon Press) SPCK Publishing.

Cummings, Dede. Cooking Well: IBS: Over 100 Easy Recipes for Irritable Bowel Syndrome Plus Other Digestive Diseases Including Crohn's, Celiac, & Colitis. Krusinski, Anna, ed. 2011. (Cooking Well Ser.). (ENG., Illus.). 176p. pap. 12.50 (978-1-57826-388-2(3)) Hatherleigh Co., Ltd., The.

Dennis, Melinda & Leffler, D. Real Life with Celiac Disease. 2010. 370p. pap. 18.95 (978-1-60356-008-5(4)) AGA Institute Pr.

Edwards, Matthew A., ed. Celiac Disease: Etiology, Diagnosis, & Treatment. 2009. (Illus.). xiii, 273p. 150.00 (978-1-60692-633-8(0)) Nova Science Pubs., Inc.

Fasano, Alessio, et al. Frontiers in Celiac Disease. 2008. (Pediatric & Adolescent Medicine Ser.). (Illus.). 230p. (C). (978-3-8055-8526-2(8)) Karger, S. AG.

Figg, Deborah. My Tummy Hurt for A Hundred Years. 2010. 18p. 19.50 (978-0-557-28315-6(9)) Lulu Enterprises Inc.

Green, Peter H. R. & Jones, Rory. Celiac Disease: A Hidden Epidemic. 2008. 304p. pap. 16.99 (978-0-06-076694-8(8)) 2010. (ENG.). 352p. 25.99 (978-0-06-172816-7(0), Morrow, William & Co.) HarperCollins Pubs.

Griffiths, Helen. Coeliac Disease: Nursing Care & Management. 2008. (Wiley Series in Nursing Ser.: 18). (ENG., Illus.). 214p. pap. 58.99 (978-0-470-51260-9(1), Wiley) Wiley, John & Sons, Inc.

Guidelines for A Gluten-Free Lifestyle. 4th ed. 2006. 10.00 (978-0-9789141-0-3(4)) Celiac Disease Foundation.

Haas, Sidney Valentine & Haas, Merrill Patterson. Management of Celiac Disease. 2011. 206p. 44.95 **(978-1-258-09153-8(4))** Literary Licensing LLC.

Hasselbeck, Elisabeth. The G-Free Diet: A Gluten-Free Survival Guide. (Gluten-Free Survival Guide Ser.). (ENG.). 256p. 2011. pap. 14.99 (978-1-59995-189-8(4)) 2009. 24.99 (978-1-59995-188-1(6)) Center St.

Hernell, Olle & Schmitz, J., eds. Feeding During Late Infancy & Early Childhood Vol. 56: Impact on Health. (Nestle Nutrition Workshop Ser.: Vol. 56). (Illus.). (978-3-8055-7906-3(3)) Karger, S. AG.

Holmes, Geoffrey, et al. Fast Facts: Fast Facts. 2nd rev. ed. 2009. (Illus.). 128p. pap. 25.00 **(978-1-905832-56-9(7))** Health Pr., Ltd. GBR. Dist: BookMasters Distribution Services (BDS).

Howdle, Peter. Your Guide to Coeliac Disease. 2007. (Royal Society of Medicine Ser.). (ENG., Illus.). 160p. pap. 19.95 (978-0-340-92885-1(9)) Hodder Arnold Pubs.

Korn, Danna. Gluten-Free Kids: Raising Happy, Healthy Children with Celiac Disease, Autism & Other Conditions. 2010. 280p. pap. (978-1-60613-006-3(4)) Woodbine Hse.

Lewey, Scot. The Food Doc's Guide to Understanding Celiac & Gluten Sensitivity. 2007. 14.95 (978-0-9798254-1-5(5)) Food Doc LLC, The.

Libonati, Cleo J. Recognizing Celiac Disease: Signs, Symptoms, Associated Disorders & Complications. 2007. (Illus.). 320p. per. 34.95 (978-0-9788626-4-0(3)) Gluten Free Works Publishing.

Lieberman, Shari. The Gluten Connection: How Gluten Sensitivity May Be Sabotaging Your Weight & Your Health-And What You Can Do to Take Control Now. 2006. xxii, 281p. (978-1-59486-386-8(5)) Rodale Pr., Inc.

Marsh, Michael N., ed. Celiac Disease: Methods & Protocols. 2010. (Methods in Molecular Medicine Ser.). 304p. pap. 149.00 (978-1-61737-115-8(7), 1617371157) Humana Pr.

McKenna, Erin. Babycakes: Vegan, Gluten-Free, & (Mostly) Sugar-Free Recipes from New York's Most Talked-About Bakery. 2009. (ENG., Illus.). 144p. 24.00 (978-0-307-40883-9(3), Clarkson Potter) Crown Publishing Group.

Mearin, M. L. & Mulder, Chr. J, eds. Coeliac Disease: 40 Years Gluten-Free. 2010. (Developments in Gastroenterology Ser.). (ENG.). 228p. pap. 269.00 (978-90-481-4087-9(0), 9048140870) Springer.

Myrsky, Essi. Vascular Biology in Coeliac Disease. 2010. (Acta Universitatis Tamperensis Ser.). (Illus.). 144p. pap. 82.50 (978-951-44-8116-1(X)) Tampere Univ. Pr. FIN. Dist: Coronet Bks.

Rancourt, Giselle C., ed. Proteomics: Methods, Applications & Limitations. 2010. (Protein Biochemistry, Synthesis, Structure & Cellular Functions Ser.). (Illus.). xi, 194p. 69.00 (978-1-61668-691-8(X)) Nova Science Pubs., Inc.

Shepard, Jules E. Dowler. Celiac Disease & Living Gluten-Free: An Essential Guide for the Newly Diagnosed. 2008. (ENG.). 304p. pap. 16.95 (978-0-7382-1227-2(X)) Perseus Bks. Group.

Smith, Terry L. Celiac Disease. 2007. (Frequently Asked Questions Ser.). (Illus.). 64p. (YA). (gr. 7-12). lib. bdg. 27.95 (978-1-4042-0962-6(X)) Rosen Publishing Group, Inc., The.

Snow, Trent & Snow, Michelle. Gluten Free Food Storage. 2010. pap. 14.99 (978-1-59955-489-1(5)) Cedar Fort, Inc./CFI Distribution.

Stenman, Saturnarja. Coeliac Disease-Inducing Gluten: In Vitro Harmfulness & Detoxification by Germinating Cereal Enzymes. 2011. (Acta Universitatis Tamperensis Ser.). (Illus.). 126p. pap. 87.50 (978-951-44-8318-9(9)) Tampere Univ. Pr. FIN. Dist: Coronet Bks.

The Editors of Good Housekeeping. Good Housekeeping Easy Gluten-Free! Healthy & Delicious Recipes for Every Meal. 2012. (ENG., Illus.). 176p. spiral bd. 14.95 **(978-1-58816-870-2(0))** Hearst Communications, Inc.

Thompson, Tricia. ADA Pocket Guide to Gluten-Free Strategies for Clients with Multiple Diet Restrictions. 2011. **(978-0-88091-451-2(3))** Academy of Nutrition & Dietetics.

Thompson, Tricia. The Gluten-Free Nutrition Guide. 2008. (ENG.). 288p. pap. 16.95 (978-0-07-154541-9(7), 0071545417) McGraw-Hill Cos., The.

Wangen, Stephen. Healthier Without Wheat: A New Understanding of Wheat Allergies, Celiac Disease, & Non-Celiac Gluten Intolerance. 2009. (Illus.). 285p. pap. 19.95 (978-0-9768537-9-4(5)) Innate Health Publishing.

Wedman-St. Louis, Betty. Living Gluten-Free: Meal Plans, Recipes, & Consumer Tips. 2007. 186p. spiral bd. 28.95 (978-0-398-07790-7(8)) Thomas, Charles C. Pub., Ltd.

CELIBACY

Here are entered works on the renunciation of marriage because of a religious vow or commitment. Works on the virtue that moderates and regulates the sexual appetite in human beings are entered under Chastity.

see also Patarines; Virginity; Vows

Apostoli, Andrew. When God Asks for an Undivided Heart: Choosing Celibacy in Love & Freedom. 2007. 203p. per. 12.95 (978-1-930314-10-8(8)) Basilica Pr.

Blastares, Matthew & Viscuso, Patrick. Sexuality, Marriage, & Celibacy in Byzantine Law: Selections from a Fourteenth-Century Encyclopedia of Canon Law & Theology: The Alphabetical Collection of Matthew Blastares. 2008 (978-1-935317-00-5(8)) Holy Cross Orthodox Pr.

Bordisso, Lou A. Sex, Celibacy, & Priesthood: A Bishop's Provocative Inquisition. 2011. 108p. 22.95 **(978-1-4620-3843-5(3))**; pap. 12.95 **(978-1-4620-3841-1(7))** iUniverse, Inc.

Butler, Brian, et al. Theology of the Body for Teens: Discovering God's Plan for Love & Life. 2006. (Illus.). 209p. per. 29.95 (978-1-932927-87-0(5)) Ascension Pr.

Cabrera, Juan B. Celibato Forzoso Del Clero: The Forced Celibacy of the Clero. (SPA.). (978-84-7645-398-8(1), 223433) Clie, Editorial.

Celebrating Celibacy. 2006. pap. 13.99 (978-1-59781-872-8(0)) Xulon Pr., Inc.

Cochini, Christian. Apostolic Origins of Priestly Celibacy. 470p. pap. 29.95 (978-0-89870-951-3(2)) Ignatius Pr.

Colón, Christine & Field, Bonnie. Singled Out: Why Celibacy Must Be Reinvented in Today's Church. 2009. 256p. pap. 19.00 (978-1-58743-237-8(4)) Brazos Pr.

Coney, Jean & Conley, Mike. Celibate Lovers: Confessions of a wayward Priest & a Good Girl Gone Bad. 2009. 138p. pap. 13.95 (978-1-60594-320-6(7), Llumina Pr.) Aeon Publishing Inc.

—Celibrate Lovers: Confessions of a wayward Priest & a Good Girl Gone Bad 2009. 138p. 23.95 (978-1-60594-321-3(5), Llumina Pr.) Aeon Publishing Inc.

Cozzens, Donald B. Freeing Celibacy. 2006. 115p. 15.95 (978-0-8146-3160-7(6)) Liturgical Pr.

Cutie, Albert. Dilemma: A Priest's Struggle with Faith & Love. 2011. (ENG.). 336p. (gr. 12). 25.95 (978-0-451-23201-4(1)) Penguin Group (USA) Inc.

Cutie, Padre Alberto. Dilema: La Lucha de un Sacerdote Entre Su Fe y el Amor. Ochoa, Santiago, tr. from ENG. 2011. (SPA.). 368p. (gr. 12). 25.95 (978-0-451-23202-1(X)) Penguin Group (USA) Inc.

Danylak, Barry. Redeeming Singleness: How the Storyline of Scripture Affirms the Single Life. 2010. 256p. pap. 16.99 (978-1-4335-0588-1(6)) Crossway.

Eberley, Ronald N. The Unnatural Law of Celibacy: One Married Man's Struggle to Become a Catholic Priest. 2006. 204p. reprint ed. 23.00 (978-1-4223-5340-0(0)) DIANE Publishing Co.

Fulton, Justin D. Why Priests Should Wed. 2010. pap. 64.60 (978-1-61719-322-4(4)) Gorgias Pr., LLC.

Gallier, Laura. Choosing to Wait: A Guide to Inspiring Abstinence. 2009. pap. 16.99 (978-0-7684-2740-0(1)) Destiny Image Pubs.

Hunter, David G. Marriage, Celibacy, & Heresy in Ancient Christianity: The Jovinianist Controversy. (Oxford Early Christian Studies). (ENG.). 336p. 2009. pap. 50.00 (978-0-19-956553-5(8)) 2007. (Illus.). 95.00 (978-0-19-927978-4(0)) Oxford Univ. Pr., Inc.

Kaschno, Daniel W. Arguments for Priestly Celibacy. 2011. 316p. pap. **(978-3-8443-9230-2(0))** Lambert Academic Publishing.

—Towards Optional Celibacy. 2011. 268p. pap. **(978-3-8443-3441-8(6))** Lambert Academic Publishing.

Launderville, Dale. Celibacy in the Ancient World: Its Ideal & Practice in Pre-Hellenistic Israel, Mesopotamia, & Greece. 2010. E-Book 49.95 (978-0-8146-5734-8(6)); (ENG.). 576p. pap. 69.95 (978-0-8146-5697-6(8), Liturgical Pr. Bks.) Liturgical Pr.

Lea, Henry Charles. An Historical Sketch of Sacerdotal Celibacy in the Christian Church. 2006. 612p. per. 34.99 (978-1-4255-6505-3(0)) MPublishing.

Nevins, Shawn. The Celibate Seeker: An Exploration of Celibacy As a Modern Spiritual Practice. 2009. 56p. pap. **(978-0-9799630-3-2(6))** TAT Foundation.

Olson, Carl, ed. Celibacy & Religious Traditions. 2007. (ENG.). 368p. per. 25.00 (978-0-19-530632-3(5)) Oxford Univ. Pr., Inc.

Parish, Helen. Clerical Celibacy & Clerical Marriage in the West, 1100-1700. 2010. (Catholic Christendom, 1300-1700 Ser.). 294p. 124.95 (978-0-7546-3949-7(5)) Ashgate Publishing Co.

Sipe, A. W. Richard. The Serpent & the Dove: Celibacy in Literature & Life, 1 vol. 2007. (Psychology, Religion, & Spirituality Ser.). 288p. 49.95 (978-0-313-34725-2(5), C34725, Praeger Pubs.) Greenwood Publishing Group, Inc.

Skudlarek, William. Demythologizing Celibacy. 2008. 120p. pap. 14.95 (978-0-8146-2947-5(4), Liturgical Pr. Bks.) Liturgical Pr.

Suchon, Gabrielle. A Woman Who Defends All the Persons of Her Sex: Selected Philosophical & Moral Writings. Stanton, Domna C. & Wilkin, Rebecca M., trs. from FRE. 2010. (Other Voice in Early Modern Europe Ser.). (ENG., Illus.). 448p. 95.00 (978-0-226-77920-1(3)); pap. 35.00 (978-0-226-77921-8(1)) Univ. of Chicago Pr.

Taylor, Isaac. Ancient Christianity & the Doctrines O. 2006. pap. 43.95 (978-1-4286-4276-8(5)); pap. 42.95 (978-1-4286-4275-1(7)) Kessinger Publishing, LLC.

CELINE, LOUIS-FERDINAND, 1894-1961

Hindus, Milton. The Crippled Giant: A Bizarre Adventure in Contemporary Letters. 2011. 158p. 41.95 **(978-1-258-09427-0(4))** Literary Licensing, LLC.

Stasková, Alice. Nächte der Aufklärung: Studien zur Ästhetik, Ethik und Erkenntnistheorie in 'Voyage au bot de la nuit' von Louis Ferdinand Céline und 'Die Schlafwandler' von Hermann Broch. 2007. (Communicatio Ser.). (GER.). X, 342p. pap. (978-3-484-63039-0(6)) Verlag Max Niemeyer.

CELIOSCOPY

see Laparoscopy

CELL, VOLTAIC

see Electric Batteries

CELL ADHESION

Baèáková, L. Cell Colonization Control by Physical & Chemical Modification of Materials. 2008. pap. 29.00 (978-1-60456-887-5(9)) Nova Science Pubs., Inc.

Behrens, Jargen & Nelson, Warren James. Cell Adhesion. 2010. (Handbook of Experimental Pharmacology Ser.). (Illus.). x, 481p. pap. 589.00 (978-3-642-05893-6(0), 3642058930) Springer.

Bhatia Sujata K. & Bhatia, Sujata K. Selectin-mediated Leukocyte Adhesion During the Immune Response: Experimental & computational studies of white blood cell recruitment to the vascular wall. 2008. 220p. pap. (978-3-639-09454-1(9)) VDM Verlag Dr. Mueller e.K.

Carré, Alain & Mittal, K. L. Surface & Interfacial Aspects of Cell Adhesion. 2011. (ENG., Illus.). 544p. 260.00 **(978-90-04-19078-8(3)**, CRC Press) Taylor & Francis Group GBR. Dist: Taylor & Francis Group.

Cheresh, David A. Integrins, Vol. 426. 2007. (Methods in Enzymology Ser.). (ENG., Illus.). 616p. 187.00 (978-0-12-373924-7(1), Academic Pr.) Elsevier Science & Technology Bks.

Coutts, Amanda S. Adhesion Protein Protocols. Coutts, Amanda S., ed. 2nd ed. 2007. (Methods in Molecular Biology Ser.: Vol. 370). (Illus.). X, 234p. 149.00 (978-1-58829-533-0(8), 1588295338) Humana Pr.

Coutts, Amanda S., ed. Adhesion Protein Protocols. 2nd ed. 2010. (Methods in Molecular Biology Ser.). (Illus.). x, 234p. pap. 149.00 (978-1-61737-625-2(6), 1617376256) Humana Pr.

Cress, Anne E. & Nagle, Raymond B., eds. Cell Adhesion & Cytoskeletal Molecules in Metastasis. 2010. (Cancer Metastasis - Biology & Treatment Ser.). xii, 198p. pap. 189.00 (978-90-481-7290-0(X), 904817290X) Springer.

Denker, H. W., ed. Molecular Approaches to Cell-Cell Adhesion: From Leukocyte Extravasation to Embryo Implantation: Cells Tissues Organs, Vol. 172. (Cells Tissues Organs Ser.). (Illus.). 108p. (978-3-8055-7532-4(7)) Karger, S. AG.

Gock, Hilton. Small Animal Models of Gal-Mediated & Xenograft Rejection. 2008. 200p. pap. (978-3-639-03057-0(5)) VDM Verlag Dr. Mueller e.K.

Hortsch, Michael & Umemori, Hisashi, eds. The Sticky Synapse: Cell Adhesion Molecules & Their Role in Synapse Formation & Maintenance. 2009. (ENG., Illus.). xii, 456p. 217.00 *(978-0-387-92707-7(7),* 0387927077) Springer.

Ley, Klaus, ed. Adhesion Molecules: Function & Inhibition. 2007. (Progress in Inflammation Research Ser.). (Illus.). 309p. 219.00 *(978-3-7643-7974-2(X))* Birkhauser Verlag AG CHE. Dist: Springer.

—Leucocyte Adhesion. 2009. (Current Topics in Membranes Ser.: 64). (ENG., Illus.). 300p. 193.00 *(978-0-12-374909-3(3),* Academic Pr.) Elsevier Science & Technology Bks.

Nott, Patrick & Temple, Matthew, eds. New Cell Adhesion Research. 2009. 129.00 *(978-1-60692-378-8(1))* Nova Science Pubs., Inc.

Preedy, Victor R. Adhesion Molecules. 2010. (ENG., Illus.). 520p. 149.95 *(978-1-57808-671-9(X))* BIOS Scientific Publishers Ltd. GBR. Dist: Taylor & Francis Group.

Shimaoka, Motomu, ed. Integrin & Cell Adhesion Molecules: Methods & Protocols. 2011. (Methods in Molecular Biology Ser.). (ENG., Illus.). xvi, 529p. 159.00 *(978-1-61779-165-9(2),* 1617791652) Humana Pr.

Smith, Andrew M. & Callow, James A., eds. Biological Adhesives. 2010. (ENG., Illus.). xvii, 284p. pap. 249.00 *(978-3-642-06821-8(9),* 3642068219) Springer.

Yona, Simon & Stacey, Martin, eds. Adhesion-GPCRs: Structure to Function. 2011. (Advances in Experimental Medicine & Biology Ser.). (ENG., Illus.). xxii, 200p. 189.00 *(978-1-4419-7912-4(3),* 1441979123) Springer.

CELL BIOLOGY

see Cytology

CELL-CELL INTERACTION

see Cell Interaction

CELL COMMUNICATION

see Cell Interaction

CELL CULTURE

Aschner, Michael, et al, eds. Cell Culture Techniques. 2011. (Neuromethods Ser.). (ENG., Illus.). xiv, 497p. 139.00 *(978-1-61779-076-8(1),* 1617790761) Humana Pr.

Bánfalvi, Gáspár. Cell Cycle Synchronization: Methods & Protocols. 2011. xii, 295p. E-Book ***(978-1-61779-182-6(2))*** Humana Pr.

Berry, M. N. & Edwards, Anthony M., eds. The Hepatocyte Review. 2010. 624p. pap. 369.00 *(978-90-481-5402-9(2),* 9048154022) Springer.

Butler, Michael, ed. Cell Culture & Upstream Processing. 2007. (ENG., Illus.). 250p. (C). per. 125.00 *(978-0-415-39969-2(6),* Taylor & Francis) Taylor & Francis Group GBR. Dist: Taylor & Francis Group.

Chang, Robert & Sun, Wei. Biofabrication of 3d Liver Tissue Constructs As Drug Metabolism Models. 2010. 140p. pap. *(978-3-8383-2150-9(2))* Lambert Academic Publishing.

Cram101 Textbook Reviews & Cram101 Textbook Reviews. Outlines & Highlights for Culture of Human Stem Cells by R Freshney. 2011. 224p. pap. 30.95 ***(978-1-61830-591-6(3))*** Cram101 Inc.

Davey, Michael R. & Anthony, Paul. Plant Cell Culture: Essential Methods. 2010. (ENG., Illus.). 358p. 104.00 *(978-0-470-68648-5(0),* Wiley) Wiley, John & Sons, Inc.

Davis, John & Davis, John M., eds. Animal Cell Culture: Essential Methods. 2011. (Essential Methods Ser.: 1). (ENG., Illus.). 374p. pap. 64.95 *(978-0-470-66658-6(7),* Wiley) Wiley, John & Sons, Inc.

Davis, John & Stacey, Glyn N., eds. Medicines from Animal Cell Culture. 2007. (ENG.). 696p. 335.00 *(978-0-470-85094-7(9),* Wiley) Wiley, John & Sons, Inc.

Duong Tan Nhut, et al, eds. Thin Cell Layer Culture System: Regeneration & Transformation Applications: Regeneration & Transformation Applications. 2010. 530p. pap. 299.00 *(978-90-481-6259-8(9),* 9048162599) Springer.

Freshney, R. Ian, et al. Culture of Human Stem Cells. 2007. (Culture of Specialized Cells Ser.: 12). (ENG., Illus.). 351p. 169.95 *(978-0-470-05246-4(5),* Wiley-Liss) Wiley, John & Sons, Inc.

Gimble, Jeffrey M. & Bunnell, Bruce A., eds. Adipose-Derived Stem Cells: Methods & Protocols. 2010. (Methods in Molecular Biology Ser.). (ENG., Illus.). xv, 473p. 139.00 *(978-1-61737-959-8(X),* 161737959X) Humana Pr.

Green, Howard. Therapy with Cultured Cells. 2010. (ENG., Illus.). 88p. pap. 79.95 *(978-981-4267-70-0(8))* Pan Stanford Publishing SGP. Dist: Taylor & Francis Group.

Guisán, José M., ed. Immobilization of Enzymes & Cells. 2nd ed. 2010. (Methods in Biotechnology Ser.). (Illus.). 464p. pap. 199.00 *(978-1-61737-473-9(3),* 1617374733) Humana Pr.

Gurav, Shailendra, et al. Plant Cell Culture. 2011. 224p. pap. ***(978-3-8433-8739-2(7))*** Lambert Academic Publishing.

Haycock, John W., ed. 3D Cell Culture: Methods & Protocols. 2010. (Methods in Molecular Biology Ser.). (Illus.). xi, 343p. 139.00 *(978-1-60761-983-3(0),* 1607619830) Humana Pr.

Heiser, William C., ed. Gene Delivery to Mammalian Cells: Volume 1: Nonviral Gene Transfer Techniques. 2010. (Methods in Molecular Biology Ser.). (Illus.). 320p. pap. 119.00 *(978-1-61737-349-7(4),* 1617373494) Humana Pr.

—Gene Delivery to Mammalian Cells: Volume 2: Viral Gene Transfer Techniques. 2010. (Methods in Molecular Biology Ser.). (Illus.). 592p. pap. 189.00 *(978-1-61737-353-4(2),* 1617373532) Humana Pr.

Helfrich, Miep H. & Ralston, Stuart H., eds. Bone Research Protocols. 2010. (Methods in Molecular Medicine Ser.). (Illus.). 468p. pap. 159.00 *(978-1-61737-321-3(4),* 1617373214) Humana Pr.

Hu, Wei-Shu. Cell Culture Engineering. (Advances in Biochemical Engineering Biotechnology Ser.). xii, 168p. 2010. pap. 279.00 *(978-3-642-07051-8(5),* 3642070515) 2006. (Illus.). 279.00 *(978-3-540-34006-5(8),* 3540340068) Springer.

Kamihira, Masamichi, et al, eds. Animal Cell Technology: Basic & Applied Aspects: Proceedings of the 21st Annual & International Meeting of the Japanese Association for Animal Cell Technology (JAACT), Fukuoka, Japan, November 24-27 2008. 2010. (ENG.). 464p. 189.00 *(978-90-481-3582-0(6),* 9048135826) Springer.

Koller, F., et al, eds. Human Cell Culture: Volume IV: Primary Hematopoietic Cells. 2010. (Human Cell Culture Ser.). 352p. pap. 359.00 *(978-90-481-5264-3(X),* 904815264X) Springer.

—Human Cell Culture: Volume V: Primary Mesenchymal Cells. 2010. (Human Cell Culture Ser.). (Illus.). 256p. pap. 239.00 *(978-90-481-5633-7(5),* 9048156335) Springer.

Landecker, Hannah. Culturing Life: How Cells Became Technologies. 2010. (Illus.). 288p. pap. 20.00 *(978-0-674-03476-1(7))* Harvard Univ. Pr.

Loyola-Vargas, Víctor M. & Vázquez-Flota, Felipe, eds. Plant Cell Culture Protocols. 2010. (Methods in Molecular Biology Ser.). (Illus.). 416p. pap. 144.00 *(978-1-61737-634-4(5),* 1617376345) Humana Pr.

Marx, Uwe & Sandig, Volker, eds. Drug Testing in Vitro: Breakthroughs & Trends in Cell Culture Technology. 2007. (ENG., Illus.). 318p. 195.00 *(978-3-527-31488-1(1),* Wiley-VCH) Wiley, John & Sons, Inc.

Masters, John & Palsson, Bernhard, eds. Human Cell Culture: Volume II: Cancer Cell Lines Part 2. 2010. (Human Cell Culture Ser.). (Illus.). 400p. pap. 329.00 *(978-90-481-5286-5(0),* 9048152860) Springer.

Masters, John R. & Palsson, Bernhard, eds. Human Adult Stem Cells. 2009. (Human Cell Culture Ser.). (ENG., Illus.). xii, 212p. 189.00 *(978-90-481-2268-4(6))* Springer.

Mitry, Ragai R. & Hughes, Robin D., eds. Human Cell Culture Protocols. 3rd ed. 2011. (Methods in Molecular Biology Ser.). (ENG., Illus.). xiv, 435p. 139.00 ***(978-1-61779-366-0(3),*** 1617793663) Humana Pr.

Nahmias, Yaakov. Methods in Bioengineering: Microdevices in Biology & Medicine. Nahmias, Yaakov & Bhatia, Sangeeta, eds. 2009. (Illus.). 274p. 129.00 *(978-1-59693-404-7(2))* Artech Hse., Inc.

Nasir, Idrees Ahmad. Regeneration Response of Gladiolus. 2009. 132p. pap. *(978-3-639-14906-7(8))* VDM Verlag Dr. Mueller e.K.

Nedovic, Viktor & Willaert, Ronnie, eds. Fundamentals of Cell Immobilisation Biotechnology. 2010. (Focus on Biotechnology Ser.). 550p. pap. 319.00 *(978-90-481-6534-6(2),* 9048165342) Springer.

Ng, Kee Woei & Schantz, Jan-Thorsten. Manual for Primary Human Cell Culture, Vol. 1. 2nd ed. 2010. 212p. pap. 48.00 *(978-981-283-477-5(X))* World Scientific Publishing Co., Inc.

Noll, Thomas, ed. Proceedings of the 20th ESACT Meeting, Dresden, Germany, June 17-20,2007. 2009. (ESACT Proceedings Ser.). (ENG., Illus.). 800p. 349.00 *(978-90-481-3418-2(8),* 9048134188) Springer.

Nolta, Jan A., ed. Genetic Engineering of Mesenchymal Stem Cells. 2010. (ENG.). vi, 169p. pap. 169.00 *(978-90-481-6999-3(2),* 9048169992) Springer.

Palsson, Bernhard & Masters, John, eds. Human Cell Culture: Volume III: Cancer Cell Lines Part 3 Leukemias & Lymphomas. 2010. (Human Cell Culture Ser.). (Illus.). 384p. pap. 379.00 *(978-90-481-5420-3(0),* 9048154200) Springer.

Pardee, Joel D. Mechanisms of Cell & Tissue Aging: Why We Get Old. 2011. (Colloquium Series on the Cell Biology of Medicine Ser.). 100p. pap. 35.00 *(978-1-61504-297-5(0))* Morgan & Claypool Life Science Publishers.

Picot, Joanna, ed. Human Cell Culture Protocols. 2nd ed. 2010. (Methods in Molecular Medicine Ser.). (Illus.). 376p. pap. 199.00 *(978-1-61737-431-9(8),* 1617374318) Humana Pr.

Pörtner, Ralf, ed. Animal Cell Biotechnology: Methods & Protocols. 2nd ed. 2007. (Methods in Biotechnology Ser.). (Illus.). 512p. 229.00 *(978-1-58829-660-3(1),* 1588296601) Humana Pr.

Prockop, Darwin J., et al, eds. Mesenchymal Stem Cells: Methods & Protocols. 2010. (Methods in Molecular Biology Ser.). (Illus.). xvi, 192p. pap. 129.00 *(978-1-61737-767-9(8),* 1617377678) Humana Pr.

R, Freshney & Freshney, R. Ian. Culture of Animal Cells: A Manual of Basic Technique & Specialized Applications. 6th ed. 2010. (ENG., Illus.). 796p. 99.95 *(978-0-470-52812-9(5),* Wiley-Blackwell) Wiley, John & Sons, Inc.

Rauthan, Swati. Cell Culture Techniques. 2011. 64p. pap. ***(978-3-8443-8653-0(X))*** Lambert Academic Publishing.

Riegler, Johannes. Comparative Optimisation of Perfusion Based Bioprocesses. 2010. 64p. pap. *(978-3-639-22947-9(9))* VDM Verlag Dr. Mueller e.K.

Shea, et al. Cell Culture Laboratory Exercises. rev. ed. 2010. (ENG.). 56p. spiral bd. 28.88 *(978-1-933005-83-6(1))* Kendall Hunt Publishing Co.

Shirahata, Sanetaka, et al, eds. Animal Cell Technology: Basic & Applied Aspects: Proceedings of the 19th Annual Meeting of the Japanese Association for Animal Cell Technology (JAACT), Kyoto, Japan, September 25-28 2006. 2009. (Animal Cell Technology: Basic & Applied Aspects Ser.). (ENG., Illus.). xv, 357p. 269.00 *(978-1-4020-9645-7(3),* 1402096453) Springer.

Sigurdsson, Einar M., ed. Amyloid Proteins. 2010. (Methods in Molecular Biology Ser.). (Illus.). 408p. pap. 134.00 *(978-1-61737-502-6(0),* 1617375020) Humana Pr.

Skloot, Rebecca. The Immortal Life of Henrietta Lacks. (ENG., Illus.). 2011. 400p. pap. 16.00 *(978-1-4000-5218-9(1),* Three Rivers Pr.) 2010. 384p. 26.00 *(978-1-4000-5217-2(3),* Crown) Crown Publishing Group.

—The Immortal Life of Henrietta Lacks. l.t. ed. 604p. 2011. (ENG.). pap. 16.99 *(978-1-59413-432-6(4),* Large Print Pr.) 2010. 31.99 *(978-1-4104-2792-2(7))* Thorndike Pr.

Smith, Rodney, ed. Cell Technology for Cell Products: Proceedings of the 19th ESACT Meeting, Harrogate, UK, June 5-8 2005. 2007. (ESACT Proceedings Ser.). (Illus.). LXXIX, 824p. 549.00 *(978-1-4020-5475-4(0),* 1402054750) Springer.

Stacey, G., et al, eds. Cell Culture Methods for in vitro Toxicology. 2010. 162p. pap. 149.00 *(978-90-481-5936-9(9),* 9048159369) Springer.

Stettler, Matthieu. Bioreactor Processes Based on Disposable Materials. 2009. 152p. pap. *(978-3-639-15028-5(7))* VDM Verlag Dr. Mueller e.K.

Tampion, J. & Tampion, M. D. Immobilized Cells: Principles & Applications. 2011. (Cambridge Studies in Biotechnology Ser.). (ENG.). 264p. pap. 35.99 *(978-0-521-29253-5(0))* Cambridge Univ. Pr.

Thorpe, Trevor A. & Yeung, Edward C., eds. Plant Embryo Culture: Methods & Protocols. 2011. (Methods in Molecular Biology Ser.). (Illus.). xii, 380p. 139.00 *(978-1-61737-987-1(5),* 1617379875) Humana Pr.

Varga, John, et al, eds. Fibrosis Research: Methods & Protocols. 2010. (Methods in Molecular Medicine Ser.). (Illus.). 408p. pap. 149.00 *(978-1-61737-592-7(6),* 1617375926) Humana Pr.

Vinci, Victor A. & Parekh, Sarad R., eds. Handbook of Industrial Cell Culture: Mammalian, Microbial, & Plant Cells. 2010. (Illus.). 546p. pap. 239.00 *(978-1-61737-315-2(X),* 161737315X) Humana Pr.

Ward, Andrew & Tosh, David. Mouse Cell Culture. 2010. (Methods in Molecular Biology Ser.). (Illus.). 256p. 139.00 *(978-1-58829-772-3(1))* Humana Pr.

Wilson, Duncan. Tissue Culture in Science & Society: The Public Life of a Biological Technique in Twentieth Century Britain. 2011. (ENG., Illus.). 196p. 80.00 *(978-0-230-28427-2(2))* Palgrave Macmillan.

Wise, Clare, ed. Epithelial Cell Culture Protocols. 2010. (Methods in Molecular Biology Ser.). (Illus.). 424p. pap. 179.00 *(978-1-61737-241-4(2),* 1617372412) Humana Pr.

Wong Davila, Jorge Luis. Synthesis of Cyclic Peptides through Plant Cell Culture: Production of Cell Cultures from Viola Tricolor Plants & Induction of Cyclic Peptides Synthesis by Cell Redifferentiation Processes. 2008. 92p. pap. *(978-3-8364-8203-5(7))* VDM Verlag Dr. Mueller e.K.

CELL DEATH

see also Apoptosis

Curran, Thomas & Christen, Yves, eds. Two Faces of Evil: Cancer & Neurodegeneration: Cancer & Neurodegeneration. 2011. (Research & Perspectives in Alzheimer's Disease Ser.). (ENG., Illus.). xiii, 163p. 189.00 *(978-3-642-16601-3(6),* 3642166016) Springer.

Fujikawa, Denson G. Acute Neuronal Injury: The Role of Excitotoxic Programmed Cell Death Mechanisms. Fujikawa, Denson G., ed. 2009. (ENG., Illus.). xii, 306p. 189.00 *(978-0-387-73225-1(X),* 038773225X) Springer.

Green, Douglas R. Apoptosis: Physiology & Pathology. Reed, John C., ed. 2011. (ENG., Illus.). 472p. 125.00 *(978-0-521-88656-7(2))* Cambridge Univ. Pr.

—Means to an End: Apoptosis & Other Cell Death Mechanisms. 2010. (Illus.). 250p. 81.00 *(978-0-87969-887-4(X));* pap. 46.00 *(978-0-87969-888-1(8))* Cold Spring Harbor Laboratory Pr.

Khosravi-Far, Roya & White, Eileen, eds. Programmed Cell Death in Cancer Progression & Therapy. (Advances in Experimental Medicine & Biology Ser.). 2010. xiv, 356p. pap. 219.00 *(978-90-481-7668-7(9),* 9048176689) 2008. 480p. 219.00 *(978-1-4020-6553-8(1))* Springer.

Klionsky, Daniel. Autophagy Pt. A: Lower Eukaryotes & Non-Mammalian Systems, 3 vols. 2008. (ENG., Illus.). 808p. 187.00 *(978-0-12-374548-4(9),* Academic Pr.) Elsevier Science & Technology Bks.

Klionsky, Daniel J. Autophagy in Disease & Clinical Applications: Part C, 3 vols., Pt. C. Klionsky, Daniel, ed. 2009. (ENG., Illus.). 536p. 187.00 *(978-0-12-374936-9(0),* Academic Pr.) Elsevier Science & Technology Bks.

Konoplyannikov, Anatoly, et al, eds. Adult Stem Cell Survival. 2010. (Stem Cells - Laboratory & Clinical Research Ser.). xii, 56p. pap. 43.00 *(978-1-61668-035-0(0))* Nova Science Pubs., Inc.

Krysko, Dmitri V. & Vandenabeele, Peter. Phagocytosis of Dying Cells: From Molecular Mechanisms to Human Diseases. 2009. (ENG., Illus.). x, 454p. 189.00 *(978-1-4020-9292-3(X))* Springer.

Melino, Gerry & Vaux, David, eds. Cell Death. 2010. (ENG., Illus.). 316p. 149.95 *(978-0-470-71573-4(1),* Wiley) Wiley, John & Sons, Inc.

Mevorach, Dror, ed. Clearance of Dying Cells in a Healthy & Diseased Immune System. 2010. (Annals of the New York Academy of Sciences Ser.: 65). (ENG., Illus.). 252p. pap. 130.00 *(978-1-57331-797-9(7),* Wiley-Blackwell) Wiley, John & Sons, Inc.

Rubinsky, Boris, ed. Irreversible Electroporation. 2009. (Series in Biomedical Engineering Ser.). (ENG., Illus.). xiv, 314p. 169.00 *(978-3-642-05419-8(6),* 3642054196) Springer.

Savabieasfahani, Mozhgan. Pollution & Reproductive Damage. 2009. 192p. pap. *(978-3-639-13583-1(0))* VDM Verlag Dr. Mueller e.K.

Schacht, Jochen, et al, eds. Auditory Trauma, Protection, & Repair. 2008. (Springer Handbook of Auditory Research Ser.). (Illus.). 350p. 149.00 *(978-0-387-72560-4(1))* Springer.

Schacht, Jochen & Fay, Richard R., eds. Auditory Trauma, Protection, & Repair. 2010. (Springer Handbook of Auditory Research Ser.). (Illus.). xvi, 352p. pap. 149.00 *(978-1-4419-4443-6(5),* 1441944435) Springer.

Shokolenko, Inna. Modulation of Cell Survival by Altering Mtdna Damage & Repair. 2009. 68p. pap. *(978-3-639-17823-4(8))* VDM Verlag Dr. Mueller e.K.

Stillman, Bruce, et al, eds. Evolution: The Molecular Landscape, Vol. LXXIV. 2010. (ENG., Illus.). 512p. 310.00 *(978-0-87969-870-6(5))* Cold Spring Harbor Laboratory Pr.

Stoddart, Martin J. Mammalian Cell Viability: Methods & Protocols. 2011. (Illus.). xi, 240p. E-Book ***(978-1-61779-108-6(3))*** Humana Pr.

Stoddart, Martin J., ed. Mammalian Cell Viability: Methods & Protocols. 2011. (Methods in Molecular Biology Ser.). (Illus.). xi, 240p. 119.00 *(978-1-61779-107-9(5),* 1617791075) Humana Pr.

Vázquez-Nin, Gerardo H., et al. Cell Death in Mammalian Ovary. 2011. (ENG., Illus.). vi, 235p. 139.00 *(978-94-007-1133-4(6),* 9400711336) Springer.

Wallach, David, et al, eds. Advances in TNF Family Research: Proceedings of the 12th International TNF Conference 2009. 2010. (Advances in Experimental Medicine & Biology Ser.). (Illus.). xxxvi, 424p. 209.00 *(978-1-4419-6611-7(0),* 1441966110) Springer.

Wei, Yau-Huei, et al, eds. The Role of the Mitochondria in Human Aging & Disease: From Genes to Cell Signaling. 2006. (Annals of the New York Academy of Sciences Ser.: Vol. 1042). (ENG., Illus.). 540p. pap. 139.95 *(978-1-57331-542-5(7),* Wiley-Blackwell) Wiley, John & Sons, Inc.

CELL DIFFERENTIATION

Abreu, T. & Silva, G. Cell Movement: New Research Trends. 2008. (Illus.). xiii, 383p. 129.00 *(978-1-60692-570-6(9))* Nova Science Pubs., Inc.

Adult Stem Cells. 2010. (Illus.). 360p. pap. 179.00 *(978-1-61737-392-3(3),* 1617373923) Humana Pr.

Brown, Geoffrey & Ceredig, Rodri. Cell Determination during Hematopoiesis. 2009. (Cell Biology Research Progress Ser.). 89.00 *(978-1-60741-733-0(2))* Nova Science Pubs., Inc.

Cancro, Michael P., ed. BLyS Ligands & Receptors. 2009. (Contemporary Immunology Ser.). (ENG., Illus.). 300p. 189.00 *(978-1-60327-012-0(4))* Humana Pr.

Davis, Cyndy D. & Sanberg, Paul R., eds. Cell Therapy, Stem Cells & Brain Repair. 2010. (Contemporary Neuroscience Ser.). (Illus.). 408p. pap. 179.00 *(978-1-61737-604-7(3),* 1617376043) Humana Pr.

Deldicque, Louise & Francaux, Marc. Regulation of Muscle Cell Differentiation & Growth by Nutrients & Exercise. 2008. 264p. pap. *(978-3-8364-9235-5(0))* VDM Verlag Dr. Mueller e.K.

Dijke, Peter & Heldin, Carl-Henrik, eds. Smad Signal Transduction: Smads in Proliferation, Differentiation & Disease. 2010. (Proteins & Cell Regulation Ser.). xiii, 473p. pap. 249.00 *(978-90-481-7145-3(8),* 9048171458) Springer.

Freudenrich, Craig, ed. The Growth & Development of Specialized Cells, Tissues, & Organs: An Anthology of Current Thought. 2009. (Contemporary Discourse in the Field of Biology Ser.). 224p. (gr. 10-12). 63.90 *(978-1-61511-913-4(2))* Rosen Publishing Group, Inc., The.

Gerecht, Sharon, ed. Biophysical Regulation of Vascular Differentiation & Assembly. 2011. (Biological & Medical Physics, Biomedical Engineering Ser.). (ENG., Illus.). xiii, 232p. 129.00 *(978-1-4419-7834-9(8),* 1441978348) Springer.

Hauser, Jannek. Regulation of B Cell Development by Antigen Receptors. 2011. 64p. pap. ***(978-3-8443-2501-0(8))*** Lambert Academic Publishing.

Hitomi, Ayane & Katoaka, Masuyo, eds. Daughter Cells: Properties, Characteristics & Stem Cells. 2010. (Cell Biology Research Progress Ser.). 343p. 145.00 *(978-1-60876-790-8(6),* Nova Biomedical Bks.) Nova Science Pubs., Inc.

Ivanova, Laura B., ed. Cell Differentiation Research Developments. 2008. 129.00 *(978-1-60021-939-9(X),* Nova Biomedical Bks.) 2007. (Illus.). 276p. 185.00 *(978-1-60021-938-2(1))* Nova Science Pubs., Inc.

Kawakami, Toshiyuki. Cell Differentiation of Neoplastic Cells Originating in the Oral & Craniofacial Regions. 2008. pap. 29.00 *(978-1-60456-932-2(8))* Nova Science Pubs., Inc.

Klimanskaya, Irina & Lanza, Robert. Adult Stem Cells. 2006. (ENG., Illus.). 576p. 187.00 *(978-0-12-373650-5(1),* Academic Pr.) Elsevier Science & Technology Bks.

Kopan, Raphael. Notch Signalling. 2010. (ENG., Illus.). 548p. 198.00 *(978-0-12-380914-8(2),* Academic Pr.) Elsevier Science & Technology Bks.

Macieira-Coelho, Alvaro. Asymmetric Cell Division. 2010. (Progress in Molecular & Subcellular Biology Ser.). (Illus.). xii, 248p. pap. 209.00 *(978-3-642-08865-0(1),* 3642088651) Springer.

—Asymmetric Cell Division. 2007. (Progress in Molecular & Subcellular Biology Ser.). (Illus.). 247p. 209.00 *(978-3-540-69160-0(X),* 354069160X) Springer.

Madhani, Hiten D. From A to Alpha: Yeast as a Model for Cellular Differentiation. 2006. (ENG., Illus.). 115p. rev. ed. 65.00 *(978-0-87969-737-2(7))* 2nd ed. pap. 45.00 *(978-0-87969-738-9(5))* Cold Spring Harbor Laboratory Pr.

Maquat, Lynne E. & Kiledjian, Megerditch, eds. RNA Turnover in Eukaryotes Vol. 448: Nucleases, Pathways & Analysis of mRNA Decay. 2008. (ENG., Illus.). 656p. 187.00 *(978-0-12-374378-7(8),* Academic Pr.) Elsevier Science & Technology Bks.

Marchal, Juan Antonio, et al. Therapeutic Potential of Differentiation in Cancer & Normal Stem Cells. 2008. pap. 37.00 *(978-1-60692-917-9(8))* Nova Science Pubs., Inc.

Marelli-Berg, Federica M. & Nourshargh, S., eds. T-Cell Trafficking. 2010. (Methods in Molecular Biology Ser.). (ENG., Illus.). x, 246p. 119.00 *(978-1-60761-460-9(X),* 160761460X) Humana Pr.

Martin, Keith. Mechanisms of Retinal Ganglion Cell Death in Glaucom. 2009. 104p. pap. *(978-3-639-16165-6(3))* VDM Verlag Dr. Mueller e.K.

Masters, John R., et al, eds. Embryonic Stem Cells. 2010. (Human Cell Culture Ser.). viii, 288p. pap. 259.00 *(978-90-481-7495-9(3),* 9048174953) Springer.

Morioka, K. Hair Follicle: Differentiation under the Electron Microscope - an Atlas. 2010. (Illus.). xiii, 152p. pap. 229.00 *(978-4-431-99805-1(5),* 4431998055) Springer.

Nicholas, Harry. Single-Cell Gene-Expression Analysis. 2010. 232p. pap. *(978-3-639-18560-7(9))* VDM Verlag Dr. Mueller e.K.

Ghetie, Joseph. Fixed-Mobile Wireless Networks Convergence: Technologies, Solutions, Services. 2008. (ENG., Illus.). 464p. 109.00 *(978-0-521-51356-2(1))* Cambridge Univ. Pr.

Ghosh, Arunabha, et al. Fundamentals of LTE. 2010. (Prentice Hall Communications Engineering & Emerging Technologies Ser.). (ENG., Illus.). 464p. 79.99 *(978-0-13-703311-9(7))* Prentice Hall PTR.

Giang, Triet. Efficient Admission Control Schemes in Cellular Ip Networks. 2009. 128p. pap. *(978-3-639-21968-5(6))* VDM Verlag Dr. Mueller e.K.

Gibbons, Thomas. Regulating Audiovisual Services. 2009. (Library of Essays in Media Law Ser.). 622p. 350.00 *(978-0-7546-2798-2(5))* Ashgate Publishing Co.

Goggin, Gerard. Mobile Phone Cultures. 2007. ix, 190p. pap. 40.00 *(978-0-415-49499-1(0))* Routledge.

Harper, Alvin C. & Buress, Raymond V. Mobile Telephones: Networks, Applications & Performance. 2008. (Illus.). 290p. (C). 137.00 *(978-1-60456-436-5(9))* Nova Science Pubs., Inc.

Harrison, Richard & Shackman, Mark, eds. Symbian OS C++ for Mobile Phones, Vol. 3. 2007. (Symbian Press Ser.). (ENG., Illus.). 834p. per. 85.00 *(978-0-470-06641-6(5),* Wiley) Wiley, John & Sons, Inc.

Harte, Lawrence. Introduction to Mobile Telephone Systems, 2nd Edition, 1G, 2G, 2. 5G, & 3G Technologies & Services. 2nd ed. 2006. (ENG., Illus.). 96p. per. 19.99 *(978-1-932813-93-7(4))* Althos.

Harte, Lawrence, et al. Introduction to Gsm: Physical Channels, Logical Channels, Network Functions, & Operation. 2011. 112p. pap. 19.99 ***(978-1-932813-85-2(3))*** Althos.

Hossain, Ekram, et al, eds. Cooperative Cellular Wireless Networks. 2011. (ENG., Illus.). 542p. 130.00 *(978-0-521-76712-5(1))* Cambridge Univ. Pr.

Issott, Adrian. Common Design Patterns for Symbian OS: The Foundations of Smartphone Software. 2008. (Symbian Press Ser.). (ENG., Illus.). 444p. pap. 65.00 *(978-0-470-51635-5(6),* Wiley) Wiley, John & Sons, Inc.

Jenabi, Mahsa. Selexels- Adapting User Interfaces to Mobile Input Devices. 2007. 116p. per. *(978-3-8364-4706-5(1))* VDM Verlag Dr. Mueller e.K.

Jipping, Michael J., et al. Smartphone Operating System Concepts with Symbian OS: A Tutorial Guide. 2007. (Symbian Press Ser.: 15). (ENG., Illus.). 354p. per. 69.99 *(978-0-470-03449-1(1),* Wiley) Wiley, John & Sons, Inc.

Johnson, Chris. Radio Access Networks for UMTS: Principles & Practice. 2008. (ENG., Illus.). 626p. 150.00 *(978-0-470-72405-7(6),* Wiley) Wiley, John & Sons, Inc.

Ketola, Pekka. Usability, Concurrent Engineering & Mobile Phone Development. 2010. 184p. pap. *(978-3-8383-0211-9(7))* Lambert Academic Publishing.

Klemens, Guy. The Cellphone: The History & Technology of the Gadget That Changed the World. 2010. (ENG., Illus.). 222p. pap. 35.00 *(978-0-7864-5867-7(4))* McFarland & Co., Inc. Pubs.

Krum, Cindy. Mobile Marketing: Finding Your Customers No Matter Where They Are. 2010. (Que Biz-Tech Ser.). (ENG., Illus.). 360p. pap. 24.99 *(978-0-7897-3976-6(3))* Que.

Lozano, Angel. Dynamic Channel Assignment. 2010. 152p. pap. *(978-3-8383-2060-1(3))* Lambert Academic Publishing.

Martinez-Ramon, Manel, ed. Kernel Methods in Bioengineering, Signal & Image Processing. 2006. (Illus.). 415p. 99.95 *(978-1-59904-042-4(5))* IGI Global.

Miller, Charles, et al. Cracking iPhone Security. 2009. (ENG.). 408p. pap. 49.99 *(978-0-470-50252-5(5),* Wiley) Wiley, John & Sons, Inc.

Mishra, Ajay R. Cellular Technologies for Emerging Markets: 2G, 3G & Beyond. 2010. (ENG., Illus.). 326p. 115.00 *(978-0-470-77947-7(0),* Wiley) Wiley, John & Sons, Inc.

Muhammad, Faris A. An Introduction to UMTS Technology: Testing, Specifications, & Standard Bodies for Engineers & Managers. 2008. 344p. 119.95 *(978-1-59942-446-0(0),* Brown Walker Pr.) Universal Pubs.

National Research Council (U.S.)., Committee on Identification of Research Needs Relating to Potential Biological or Adverse Health Effects of Wireless Communications Devices Staff, contrib. by. Identification of Research Needs Relating to Potential Biological or Adverse Health Effects of Wireless Communication. 2008. (ENG.). 78p. pap. 21.00 *(978-0-309-11294-9(X))* National Academies Pr.

Ni, Lionel M., et al. Professional Microsoft Smartphone Programming. 2007. (ENG., Illus.). 494p. pap. 49.99 *(978-0-471-76293-5(8),* Wrox) Wiley, John & Sons, Inc.

Noldus, Rogier. Camel: Intelligent Networks for GSM, GPRS & UMTS Network. 22nd ed. 2008. 480p. 140.00 *(978-0-470-51773-4(5),* Wiley) Wiley, John & Sons, Inc.

Oggier, Frdtrique, et al. Cyclic Division Algebras: A Tool for Space-Time Coding. 2007. 108p. pap. 80.00 *(978-1-60198-050-2(7))* Now Pubs.

Park, Yongwan & Adachi, Fumiyuki, eds. Enhanced Radio Access Technologies for Next Generation Mobile Communication. 2010. vi, 280p. pap. 135.00 *(978-90-481-7386-0(8),* 9048173868) Springer.

Perez, Andrea. Mobile Networks Architecture. 2012. (Iste Ser.: 599). (ENG., Illus.). xii, 275p. 125.00 ***(978-1-84821-333-3(6),*** Wiley-ISTE) Wiley, John & Sons, Inc.

Perez-Neira, Ana I. & Realp Campalans, Marc. Cross-Layer Resource Allocation in Wireless Communications: Techniques & Models from PHY & MAC Layer Interaction. 2008. (ENG., Illus.). 192p. 109.00 *(978-0-12-374141-7(6),* Academic Pr.) Elsevier Science & Technology Bks.

Rothenberg, Christian Esteve. Fixed-Mobile Convergence in Tispan/3gpp Ims. 2008. 144p. pap. *(978-3-639-05359-3(1))* VDM Verlag Dr. Mueller e.K.

Saeed, Rashid A., et al. Femtocell Communications & Technologies: Business Opportunities & Deployment Challenges. 2012. ***(978-1-4666-0092-8(6)); (978-1-4666-0094-2(2));*** E-Book ***(978-1-4666-0093-5(4))*** IGI Global.

Saeed, Rashid Abdelhaleem & Shellhammer, Stephen J., eds. Tv White Spaces (Tvws) Spectrum Technologies. 2011. (ENG., Illus.). 509p. 119.95 *(978-1-4398-4879-1(3),* CRC Press) Taylor & Francis Group GBR. Dist: Taylor & Francis Group.

Sarkar, Subir Kumar, et al. Ad Hoc Mobile Wireless Networks: Principles, Protocols, & Applications. 2007. (ENG., Illus.). 336p. 149.95 *(978-1-4200-6221-2(2))* Auerbach Pubs., Inc.

Saunders, Simon, et al. Femtocells: Opportunities & Challenges for Business & Technology. 2009. (Telecoms Explained Ser.). (ENG., Illus.). 252p. pap. 69.95 *(978-0-470-74816-9(8),* Wiley) Wiley, John & Sons, Inc.

Sesia, Stefania, et al. LTE: The UMTS Long Term Evolution - From Theory to Practice. 2nd ed. 2011. (ENG., Illus.). 792p. 120.00 *(978-0-470-66025-6(2),* Wiley) Wiley, John & Sons, Inc.

Shapira, Joseph & Miller, Shmuel. CDMA Radio with Repeaters. 2007. (Information Technology — Transmission, Processing, & Storage Ser.). (Illus.). 424p. 159.00 *(978-0-387-26329-8(2),* 0387263292) Springer.

Shneyderman, Alex & Casati, Alessio. Fixed Mobile Convergence: Voice over Wi-Fi, IMS, UMA & Other FMC Enablers. 2008. (ENG., Illus.). 272p. 79.95 *(978-0-07-148606-4(2),* 0071486062) McGraw-Hill Osborne.

Song, Lingyang & Shen, Jia, eds. Evolved Cellular Network Planning & Optimization for UMTS & LTE. 2010. (ENG., Illus.). 630p. 99.95 *(978-1-4398-0649-4(7),* CRC Press) Taylor & Francis Group GBR. Dist: Taylor & Francis Group.

Stasiak, Maciej, et al. Modelling & Dimensioning of Mobile Wireless Networks: From GSM to LTE. 2011. (ENG., Illus.). 340p. 105.00 *(978-0-470-66586-2(6),* Wiley) Wiley, John & Sons, Inc.

Stetz, Penelope J. The Cell Phone Handbook: Everything You Wanted to Know about Wireless Telephony (but Didn't Know Who or What to Ask) 2nd ed. 2006. per. 22.95 *(978-0-9787637-0-1(X))* FindTech Ltd.

Stichbury, Jo, et al. Games on Symbian OS: A Handbook for Mobile Development. 2008. (Symbian Press Ser.: 24). (ENG., Illus.). 400p. pap. 50.00 *(978-0-470-99804-5(0),* Wiley) Wiley, John & Sons, Inc.

Takagi, Hideaki & Walke, Bernhard H., eds. Spectrum Requirement Planning in Wireless Communications: Model & Methodology for IMT-Advanced. 2008. (Wireless Communications & Mobile Computing Ser.: 10). (ENG., Illus.). 266p. 140.00 *(978-0-470-98647-9(6),* Wiley) Wiley, John & Sons, Inc.

Toftegaard Nielsen, Thomas & Wigard, Jeroen. Performance Enhancements in a Frequency Hopping GSM Network. 2010. (ENG.). 352p. pap. 129.00 *(978-1-4419-4976-9(3),* 1441949763) Springer.

Tripathi, Nishith D. & Reed, Jeffrey H. Cellular Communications: A Comprehensive & Practical Guide. 2009. (Illus.). 820p. 99.00 *(978-0-387-89000-5(9))* Springer.

Varche, Kanchan. Cooperative Diversity for the Cellular Uplink. 2008. 100p. pap. *(978-3-639-11367-9(5))* VDM Verlag Dr. Mueller e.K.

Venkataraman, Hrishikesh & Muntean, Gabriel-Miro, eds. Cognitive Radio & its Application for Next Generation Cellular & Wireless Networks. 2012. (Lecture Notes in Electrical Engineering Ser.). (ENG., Illus.). xi, 409p. 179.00 ***(978-94-007-1826-5(8),*** 9400718268) Springer.

Wireless Innovation & Consumer Protection: Hearing Before the Subcommittee on Telecommunications & the Internet of the Committee on Energy & Commerce, House of Representatives, One Hundred Tenth Congress, First Session, July 11, 2007. 2008. vi, 160p. *(978-0-16-081928-5(8),* 552-070-38101-5) United States Government Printing Office.

Zhang, Yan, et al, eds. Resource, Mobility, & Security Management in Wireless Networks & Mobile Communications. 2006. (Wireless Networks & Mobile Communications Ser.). (ENG., Illus.). 618p. 124.95 *(978-0-8493-8036-5(7))* Auerbach Pubs., Inc.

CELL PHONES

see also iPhone (Smartphone)

Ahmed, Ishfaq & Fiaz Qazi, Tehmina. Mobile Phone Adoption a Habit or Necessity. 2011. 72p. pap. ***(978-3-8443-8175-7(9))*** Lambert Academic Publishing.

Ahson, Syed A. Mobile Web 2. 0: Developing & Delivering Services to Mobile Phones. 2010. (ENG., Illus.). 617p. 119.95 *(978-1-4398-0082-9(0))* Auerbach Pubs., Inc.

Al-Hakim, Latif. Web Mobile-Based Applications for Healthcare Management. 2007. (Illus.). xxvi, 421p. pap. 94.95 *(978-1-59140-659-4(5));* 450p. 94.95 *(978-1-59140-658-7(7))* IGI Global. (IRM Pr.).

Al-Mously, Salah. Cell Phones. 2009. 180p. pap. *(978-3-639-21871-8(X))* VDM Verlag Dr. Mueller e.K.

Ali, Maher. iPhone SDK Programming: Developing Mobile Applications for Apple iPhone & iPod Touch. 2009. (ENG., Illus.). 396p. pap. 44.99 *(978-0-470-74282-2(8),* Wiley) Wiley, John & Sons, Inc.

Allen, Sarah, et al. Pro Smartphone Cross-Platform Development: iPhone, Blackberry, Windows Mobile & Android Development & Distribution. 2010. (ENG.). 288p. pap. 49.99 *(978-1-4302-2868-4(7))* Apress L. P.

Ames, Patrick. Now You Know Palm Centro. 2008. (One-off Ser.). (Illus.). 160p. pap. 19.99 *(978-0-321-57902-7(X))* Peachpit Pr.

Antoniac, Peter Mihai. New User Interfaces for Mobile Devices UsingAugmented Reality: Expanding the Interaction by Intuitive GestureRecognition. 2008. 196p. pap. *(978-3-639-01050-3(7))* VDM Verlag Dr. Mueller e.K.

Aqeel, Javaid Chouhdary. Viability of Nokia & Siemens Merger: Nokia, Siemens Plan Telecom Networks Merger. 2011. 132p. pap. ***(978-3-639-30243-1(5))*** VDM Verlag Dr. Mueller e.K.

Asante, Rabiu. Mobile Phone Usage Patterns. 2011. 120p. pap. ***(978-3-8454-1004-3(3))*** Lambert Academic Publishing.

Ayers, Rick. Cell Phone Forensic Tools: An Overview & Analysis. 2007. (Illus.). 176p. (C). reprint ed. pap. 35.00 *(978-1-4223-1296-4(8))* DIANE Publishing Co.

—Cell Phone Forensic Tools: An Overview & Analysis Updat. 2007. (Illus.). 176p. (C). pap. 40.00 *(978-1-4223-1295-7(X))* DIANE Publishing Co.

Baig, Ed. Palm Pre. 2009. (Missing Manual Ser.). (ENG., Illus.). 288p. pap. 24.99 *(978-0-596-80370-4(2),* Pogue Pr.) O'Reilly Media, Inc.

Baig, Edward C. & LeVitus, Bob. iPhone 4S for Dummies. 5th ed. 2011. (ENG., Illus.). 400p. pap. 24.99 *(978-1-118-03671-6(9),* For Dummies) Wiley, John & Sons, Inc.

Bellew, Joli. Blackberry Storm. 2010. (How to Do Everything Ser.). (ENG., Illus.). 256p. pap. 24.99 *(978-0-07-170332-1(2),* 0071703322) McGraw-Hill Osborne.

Bamberg, Matthew, et al. Killer Photos with Your iPhone. 2010. (ENG.). 280p. pap. 24.99 *(978-1-4354-5689-1(0))* Course Technology.

Baniuszewicz, Olivia & Goldstein, Debra. Flirtexting: How to Text Your Way to His Heart. 2009. (ENG.). 192p. pap. 12.95 *(978-1-60239-367-7(2),* 239367) Skyhorse Publishing Co., Inc.

Batchelor, Simon, et al. M-Banking: An African Financial Revolution. 2010. (ENG.). 130p. pap. 29.95 *(978-90-5727-063-5(3))* International Bks. NLD. Dist: Independent Pubs. Group.

Baym, Nancy. Personal Connections in the Digital Age. 2010. (DMS - Digital Media & Society Ser.). (ENG., Illus.). 196p. pap. 19.95 *(978-0-7456-4332-8(9))* Polity Pr. GBR. Dist: Wiley, John & Sons, Inc.

—Personal Connections in the Digital Age. 2010. (DMS - Digital Media & Society Ser.). (ENG., Illus.). 196p. 64.95 *(978-0-7456-4331-1(0))* Polity Pr. GBR. Dist: Wiley, John & Sons, Inc.

Begun, Daniel A. Amazing Android Apps for Dummies. 2011. (ENG., Illus.). 256p. pap. 18.99 *(978-0-470-93629-0(0),* For Dummies) Wiley, John & Sons, Inc.

Bernardi, Daniel & Cheong, Pauline Hope. Introduction to New Media. 2009. (ENG.). (C). pap. 114.80 *(978-0-558-24630-3(3))* Pearson Learning Solutions.

Bertossi, Robert. Automation of Mobile Network Management. 2010. 100p. pap. *(978-3-639-27491-2(1))* VDM Verlag Dr. Mueller e.K.

Bhowmik, Achintya K., et al, eds. Mobile Displays: Technology & Applications. 2008. (Wiley Series in Display Technology Ser.: 16). (ENG., Illus.). 650p. 180.00 *(978-0-470-72374-6(2),* Wiley) Wiley, John & Sons, Inc.

Bove, Tony. iPod Touch for Dummies. 3rd ed. 2011. (ENG., Illus.). 288p. pap. 24.99 ***(978-1-118-12960-9(1),*** For Dummies) Wiley, John & Sons, Inc.

Braddock. The Ultimate Guide to Phone & Text Game. 2010. 166p. pap. 117.00 *(978-0-557-28817-5(7))* Lulu Enterprises Inc.

Breen, Christopher. The iPhone. (Pocket Guide Ser.). (ENG., Illus.). 2nd ed. 2007. 272p. per. 9.99 *(978-0-321-54494-0(3))* 3rd ed. 2008. 288p. pap. 9.99 *(978-0-321-56403-0(0))* Peachpit Pr.

—The iPhone Pocket Guide: All the Secrets of the iPhone, Pocket Sized. 2007. (Pocket Guide Ser.). (Illus.). 262p. per. 14.99 *(978-0-321-51008-2(9))* Peachpit Pr.

Burgess, Adam. The Contemporary Emergence of Health Concerns Related to Mobile Phones. 2010. 268p. pap. *(978-3-639-22621-8(6))* VDM Verlag Dr. Mueller e.K.

Burnette, Ed. Hello, Android: Introducing Google's Mobile Development Platform. 3rd ed. 2010. (ENG., Illus.). 300p. pap. 34.95 *(978-1-934356-56-2(5),* Pragmatic Bookshelf, The) Pragmatic Programmers, LLC, The.

Butow, Eric & Ballew, Joli. Droid Companion. 2011. (ENG.). 304p. pap. 19.99 ***(978-1-118-17764-8(9),*** Wiley) Wiley, John & Sons, Inc.

Cabrera, P. J., et al. Beginning iPhone Games Development. 2010. (ENG., Illus.). 728p. pap. 39.99 *(978-1-4302-2599-7(8))* Apress L. P.

—iPhone Games Projects. 2009. (ENG., Illus.). 280p. pap. 39.99 *(978-1-4302-1968-2(8))* Apress L. P.

Cameron, Rob. Pro Windows Phone App Development. 2nd ed. 2011. (ENG., Illus.). 664p. pap. 44.99 ***(978-1-4302-3936-9(0))*** Apress L. P.

Campbell, Duncan. iPhone SDK 3: Visual QuickStart Guide. 2009. (Visual QuickStart Guide Ser.). (Illus.). 336p. pap. 34.99 *(978-0-321-66953-7(3))* Peachpit Pr.

Carlo, George L., ed. Wireless Phones & Health II: State of the Science. 2010. (ENG.). 304p. pap. 239.00 *(978-1-4419-5007-9(9),* 1441950079) Springer.

Caronia, Letizia & Caron, Andre H. Moving Cultures: Mobile Communication in Everyday Life. 2007. (ENG., Illus.). 276p. (C). per. *(978-0-7735-3230-4(7))* McGill-Queen's Univ. Pr.

Cartman, Joseph & Ting, Richard. Strategic Mobile Design: Creating Engaging Experiences. 2008. (Voices That Matter Ser.). (ENG., Illus.). 224p. pap. 34.99 *(978-0-321-58007-8(9))* New Riders Publishing.

Celik, Burce. Technology & National Identity in Turkey: Mobile Communications & the Evolution of a Post-Ottoman Nation. 2011. (International Library of Cultural Studies). (ENG., Illus.). 288p. 96.00 *(978-1-84885-429-1(3),* Tauris Academic Studies) I. B. Tauris & Co., Ltd. GBR. Dist: Macmillan.

Cell Phone Decoder Ring: Discover how to make the right choice when selecting a device & explore different options when it comes to Services. 2007. per. 16.95 *(978-0-9792692-0-2(2))* Voice Of Wireless, Inc.

Cell Tax Fairness ACT of 2008: Hearing Before the Subcommittee on Commercial & Administrative Law of the Committee on the Judiciary, House of Representatives, One Hundred Tenth Congress, Second Session, on H.R. 5793, September 18, 2008. 2009. iv, 78p. *(978-0-16-082697-9(7),* 552-070-38714-5) United States Government Printing Office.

Chalamalasetty, Kalyani. Architecture for Ims Security to Mobile. 2010. 60p. pap. *(978-3-8383-8245-6(5))* Lambert Academic Publishing.

Chambers, David. Femtocell Primer (2nd Edition) 2010. 268p. pap. 63.50 *(978-1-4457-4434-6(1))* Lulu Enterprises Inc.

Chen, Jason & Pash, Adam. How to Do Everything with Your iPhone. 2007. (ENG., Illus.). 296p. per. 24.99 *(978-0-07-149790-9(0),* 0071497900) McGraw-Hill Osborne.

Clare, Andrew. The Rough Guide to Android Phones & Tablets. 2nd ed. 2012. (Rough Guide To... Ser.). (ENG., Illus.). 272p. 13.99 ***(978-1-4093-5806-0(2))*** Rough Guides, Ltd. GBR. Dist: Dorling Kindersley Publishing, Inc.

Codacci, Lorenzo. Mobile 4 All - il Mobile alla portata di Tutti. 2010. (ITA.). 191p. pap. 23.95 *(978-1-4457-2784-4(6))* Lulu Enterprises Inc.

Cohen, Akiba A., et al. The Wonder Phone in the Land of Miracles: Mobile Telephony in Israel. 2008. (C). *(978-1-57273-855-3(3)); (978-1-57273-854-6(5))* Hampton Pr., Inc.

Conrad, Jan. Flexible User Interface - Flusi: An architecture for a context-aware user interface. 2007. 96p. per. *(978-3-86550-914-7(2))* VDM Verlag Dr. Mueller e.K.

The Consumer Wireless Experience: Hearing Before the Committee on Commerce, Science, & Transportation, United States Senate, One Hundred Eleventh Congress, First Session, June 17, 2009. 2010. (Illus.). iii, 87p. *(978-0-16-085931-1(X),* 552-070-41127-5) United States Government Printing Office.

Contraband Cell Phones in Correctional Facilities: Public Safety Impact & the Potential Implications of Jamming Technologies: Hearing Before the Committee on Commerce, Science, & Transportation, United States Senate, One Hundred Eleventh Congress, First Session, July 15, 2009. 2010. iv, 52p. *(978-0-16-086362-2(7),* 552-070-41441-0) United States Government Printing Office.

Craft, Chris & McElveen, Jamey. iPhone Game Development. 2009. (Developer Reference Ser.: 4). (ENG., Illus.). 512p. pap. 49.99 *(978-0-470-49666-4(5),* Wiley) Wiley, John & Sons, Inc.

Crofton, Kerry. Radiation Rescue. 2009. 432p. pap. 19.95 *(978-0-9864735-0-0(2))* West.

Cross, Brian. Get Mobile: The Essential Guide to Building Your Own Mobile Real Estate Office. 2006. (Illus.). 56p. per. 19.95 *(978-1-4251-0383-5(9))* Trafford Publishing.

Crystal, David. Txtng: The Gr8 Db8. 2009. (ENG., Illus.). 256p. pap. 12.95 *(978-0-19-957133-8(3))* Oxford Univ. Pr., Inc.

Das, Sajal K. Mobile Handset Design. 2010. (ENG., Illus.). 672p. 150.00 *(978-0-470-82467-2(0),* Wiley) Wiley, John & Sons, Inc.

Davis, Devra. Disconnect: The Truth about Cell Phone Radiation, What the Industry Is Doing to Hide It, & How to Protect Your Family. 2011. (ENG., Illus.). 304p. (gr. 12). 16.00 *(978-0-452-29744-9(3),* Plume) Penguin Group (USA) Inc.

Dawes, Adam. Windows Mobile Game Development: Building Games for the Windows Phone & Other Mobile Devices. 2010. (ENG.). 464p. pap. 49.99 *(978-1-4302-2928-5(4))* Apress L. P.

Dawson, Di. E-Guidelines 12 Handheld Technologies for Mobile Learning. 2007. (Illus.). 67p. pap. *(978-1-86201-320-9(9))* National Institute of Adult Continuing Education.

De Bruijn, Mirjam, et al, eds. Mobile Phones: the New Talking Drums of Everyday Africa: The New Talking Drums of Everyday Africa. 2009. 184p. pap. *(978-9956-558-53-7(2))* Langaa Research & Publishing Common Initiative Group CMR. Dist: Michigan State Univ. Pr.

De Ruiter, Peter. Take Better Photos with Your Phone. 2008. (ENG., Illus.). 120p. per. 7.95 *(978-1-84773-002-2(7))* New Holland Pubs., Ltd. GBR. Dist: Sterling Publishing Co., Inc.

Dushinski, Kim. The Mobile Marketing Handbook: A Step-by-Step Guide to Creating Dynamic Mobile Marketing Campaigns. 2nd ed. 2012. (ENG.). 264p. pap. 29.95 ***(978-0-910965-90-3(0))*** Information Today, Inc.

Dwivedi, Himanshu, et al. Mobile Application Security. 2010. (ENG., Illus.). 432p. pap. 49.99 *(978-0-07-163356-7(1),* 0071633561) McGraw-Hill Osborne.

Eagle, Nathan & Ekine, Sokari. SMS Uprising: Mobile Phone Activism in Africa. 2010. (Illus.). 172p. pap. 20.95 *(978-1-906387-35-8(4))* Pambuzuka Pr. GBR. Dist: Independent Pubs. Group.

Ebert, Sven. EMF Risk Assessment: Exposure Systems for Large-Scale Laboratory & Experimental Provocation Studies. 2010. (ENG & GER., Illus.). xv, 192p. pap. *(978-3-86628-331-2(8))* Hartung-Gorre, Wolfgang, Wissenschaftliche Publikationen.

ECPA Reform & the Revolution in Location Based Technologies & Services: Hearing Before the Subcommittee on the Constitution, Civil Rights, & Civil Liberties of the Committee on the Judiciary, House of Representatives, One Hundred Eleventh Congress, Second Session, June 24, 2010. 2010. (Illus.). ii, 156p. *(978-0-16-086970-9(6),* 552-070-41836-9) United States Government Printing Office.

Eddy, Patricia DiGiacomo & Eddy, John. Google on the Go: Using an Android-Powered Mobile Phone. 2009. (ENG., Illus.). 216p. pap. 19.99 *(978-0-7897-3953-7(4))* Que.

Eissa, Eiman & Amin, Hussein. Media Convergence: Effects on the Egyptian Mobile Phone Users. 2010. 208p. pap. *(978-3-8383-3468-4(X))* Lambert Academic Publishing.

Engdahl, Sylvia, ed. Electronic Devices. 2012. (Teen Rights & Freedoms Ser.). (ENG., Illus.). 176p. (gr. 10-12). lib. bdg. 37.10 ***(978-0-7377-5825-2(2),*** Greenhaven Pr., Inc.) Cengage Gale.

C

Estevez, Daniel J. & Gutierrez, Isobel M. Contraband Cell Phones in Prisons: Technology Solutions & Perspectives. 2011. (Media & Communications - Technologies, Policies & Challenges Ser.). (Illus.). 183p. 185.00 (978-1-61324-563-7(7)) Nova Science Pubs., Inc.

Farkas, Bart G. The Motorola Xoom. rev. ed. 2011. (Visual QuickStart Guide Ser.). (ENG., Illus.). 208p. pap. 24.95 **(978-0-321-79263-1(7))** Peachpit Pr.

Farrell, Austin. Impress Your Cat: Know about mobile phones & their Safety. 2011. 114p. pap. 24.95 **(978-1-4466-6398-1(1))** Lulu Enterprises Inc.

Ferracchiati, Fabio Claudio & Garofalo, Emanuele. Windows Phone Recipes: A Problem Solution Approach. 2nd ed. 2011. (ENG.). 492p. pap. 39.99 **(978-1-4302-4137-9(3))** Apress L. P.

Fitzek, Frank H. P. & Reichert, Frank, eds. Mobile Phone Programming: And Its Application to Wireless Networking. 2007. (Illus.). 473p. 129.00 (978-1-4020-5968-1(X)) Springer.

Fogie, Seth & Dunham, Ken. Mobile Malware Attacks & Defense. 2008. (ENG., Illus.). 440p. pap. 59.95 (978-1-59749-298-0(1), Syngress Press) Elsevier Science & Technology Bks.

Ford, Rob. The App & Mobile Case Study Book. Wiedemann, Julius, ed. 2011. (ENG., Illus.). 384p. 39.99 **(978-3-8365-2880-1(0))** TASCHEN DEU. Dist: Ingram Pub. Services.

Frederick, Gail & Lal, Rajesh. Smartphone Web Development: Building JavaScript, CSS, HTML & Ajax-Based Applications for iPhone, Android, Palm Pre, BlackBerry, Windows Mobile & Nokia S60. 2010. (ENG., Illus.). 368p. pap. 39.99 (978-1-4302-2620-8(X)) Apress L. P.

Goggin, Gerard. Cell Phone Culture: Mobile Technology in Everyday Life. 2006. (Illus.). 251p. 120.00 (978-0-415-36743-1(3)); per. 29.95 (978-0-415-36744-8(1)) Routledge.

Goggin, Gerard & Gough, Richard, eds. Mobile Phone Culture. 2008. (ENG.). 208p. 140.00 (978-0-415-42530-8(1), 0415425301) Routledge.

Goggin, Gerard & Hjorth, Larissa, eds. Mobile Technologies. 2009. 298p. pap. 39.95 (978-0-415-87843-2(8)) Routledge.

Goldstein, Neal & Bove, Tony. iPhone Application Development All-In-One for Dummies. 2010. (ENG., Illus.). 888p. pap. 39.99 (978-0-470-54293-4(4), For Dummies) Wiley, John & Sons, Inc.

Gookin, Dan. Android Phones for Dummies. 2012. (ENG., Illus.). 352p. pap. 24.99 **(978-1-118-16952-0(2)**, For Dummies) Wiley, John & Sons, Inc.

—Droid 2 for Dummies. 2010. (ENG., Illus.). 384p. pap. 24.99 (978-1-118-00286-5(5), For Dummies) Wiley, John & Sons, Inc.

—Droid 3 for Dummies. 2011. (ENG.). 368p. pap. 24.99 **(978-1-118-15721-3(4)**, For Dummies) Wiley, John & Sons, Inc.

—Droid X for Dummies. 2010. (ENG., Illus.). 352p. pap. 24.99 (978-0-470-90319-3(8), For Dummies) Wiley, John & Sons, Inc.

—HTC ThunderBolt for Dummies. 2011. (ENG., Illus.). 416p. pap. 24.99 (978-1-118-07601-9(X), For Dummies) Wiley, John & Sons, Inc.

Gralla, Preston. Galaxy S II: the Missing Manual. 2011. (ENG.). 436p. pap. 19.99 **(978-1-4493-9681-7(X)**, Pogue Pr.) O'Reilly Media, Inc.

Habib, Usman. Secure Mobile Authentication for Linux Workstation Log On. 2011. 120p. pap. **(978-3-8454-0289-5(X))** Lambert Academic Publishing.

Haddon, Leslie & Green, Nicola. Mobile Communications: An Introduction to New Media. 2009. (Berg New Media Ser.). (ENG., Illus.). 1p. 99.95 (978-1-84520-813-4(7)); pap. 29.95 (978-1-84520-814-1(5)) Berg Pubs. GBR. Dist: Macmillan.

Hanson, Jarice. 24/7: How Cell Phones & the Internet Change the Way We Live, Work, & Play, 1 vol. 2007. (Illus.). 176p. 44.95 (978-0-275-99333-7(7), C9333, Praeger Pubs.) Greenwood Publishing Group, Inc.

Harte, Lawrence. Introduction to Mobile Telephone Systems, 2nd Edition, 1G, 2G, 2. 5G, & 3G Technologies & Services. 2nd ed. 2006. (ENG., Illus.). 96p. per. 19.99 (978-1-932813-93-7(4)) Althos.

Harty, Julian. A Practical Guide to Testing Wireless Smartphone Applications. Satyanarayanan, Mahadev, ed. 2009. (Synthesis Lectures on Mobile & Pervasive Computing Ser.). 99p. pap. 35.00 (978-1-60845-253-8(0)) Morgan & Claypool Pubs.

Hayun, Roy Ben. Java ME on Symbian OS: Inside the Smartphone Model. 2009. (Symbian Press Ser.). (ENG., Illus.). 482p. pap. 60.00 (978-0-470-74318-8(2), Wiley) Wiley, John & Sons, Inc.

Hjorth, Larissa. Mobile Media in the Asia-Pacific: Gender & the Art of Being Mobile. 2008. (Asia's Transformations/Asia. com Ser.). (Illus.). 320p. 150.00 (978-0-415-43809-4(8)) Routledge.

Hoffman, Daniel V. Blackjacking: Security Threats to BlackBerry Devices, PDAs, & Cell Phones in the Enterprise. 2007. (ENG., Illus.). 312p. per. 39.99 (978-0-470-12754-4(6), Wiley) Wiley, John & Sons, Inc.

Horst, Heather & Miller, Daniel. The Cell Phone: An Anthropology of Communication. annot. ed. 2006. (ENG.). 1p. 120.95 (978-1-84520-400-6(X)) Berg Pubs. GBR. Dist: Macmillan.

Huddleston, Rob. Android Fully Loaded. 2nd ed. 2012. (ENG., Illus.). 256p. pap. 24.99 **(978-1-118-17302-2(3)**, Wiley) Wiley, John & Sons, Inc.

Hughes, Bill. Samsung Galaxy S for Dummies. 2011. (ENG., Illus.). 320p. pap. 24.99 (978-1-118-02447-8(8), For Dummies) Wiley, John & Sons, Inc.

Ibrahim, Dogan. GSM MOBILE PHONES IN FORENSIC INVESTIGATIONS: GSM MOBILE PHONES. 2008. 76p. pap. (978-3-639-11233-7(4)) VDM Verlag Dr. Mueller e.K.

Ihnatko, Andy. iPhone Fully Loaded. 3rd ed. 2009. (ENG., Illus.). 288p. pap. 19.99 (978-0-470-54213-2(6), Wiley) Wiley, John & Sons, Inc.

Ikezue, Emeka Clement. Theft of Mobile Phones. 2011. 92p. pap. **(978-3-8443-8822-0(2))** Lambert Academic Publishing.

Imtiaz Bin Hamid, Nafiz, et al. Some Vital Aspects of Mobile Wimax. 2010. 72p. pap. (978-3-639-24922-4(4)) VDM Verlag Dr. Mueller e.K.

Issott, Adrian. Common Design Patterns for Symbian OS: The Foundations of Smartphone Software. 2008. (Symbian Press Ser.). (ENG., Illus.). 444p. pap. 65.00 (978-0-470-51635-5(6), Wiley) Wiley, John & Sons, Inc.

Jhangiani, Ira. A Comparison of Cell Phone User Interface Design Preferences. 2008. 180p. pap. (978-3-8364-9053-5(6)) VDM Verlag Dr. Mueller e.K.

Johnston, Craig James. My Samsung Galaxy Nexus. 2012. (My... Ser.). (ENG., Illus.). 400p. pap. 24.99 **(978-0-7897-4946-8(7))** Que.

Jones, Bradley L. & Miller, Matthew. Windows Phone 7 Companion. 2010. (ENG., Illus.). 288p. pap. 19.99 (978-0-470-93856-0(0), Wiley) Wiley, John & Sons, Inc.

Kao, Robert & Sarigumba, Dante. Blackberry Pearl 3G for Dummies. 2010. (ENG., Illus.). 360p. pap. 24.99 (978-0-470-96472-9(3), For Dummies) Wiley, John & Sons, Inc.

Kao, Robert, et al. BlackBerry Storm for Dummies. 2nd ed. 2010. (ENG., Illus.). 360p. pap. 24.99 (978-0-470-56531-5(4), For Dummies) Wiley, John & Sons, Inc.

Karimi, Hassan A. Universal Navigation on Smartphones. 2011. (ENG., Illus.). x, 157p. 99.00 (978-1-4419-7740-3(6), 1441977406) Springer.

Katz, James, ed. Mobile Communication: Dimensions of Social Policy. 2011. (ENG., Illus.). 338p. 49.95 **(978-1-4128-1468-3(5))** Transaction Pubs.

Katz, James E., ed. Handbook of Mobile Communication Studies. 2008. (ENG., Illus.). 488p. (gr. 17). 49.00 (978-0-262-11312-0(0)) MIT Pr.

Kelby, Scott & White, Terry. The IPhone Book: How to Do the Things You Want to Do with Your IPhone. 2007. (ENG., Illus.). 240p. pap. 24.99 (978-0-321-53410-1(7)) Peachpit Pr.

—The iPhone Book: How to Do the Things You Want to Do with Your iPhone. 3rd ed. 2009. (ENG., Illus.). 312p. pap. 19.99 (978-0-321-64723-8(8)) Peachpit Pr.

King, Chris. Advanced BlackBerry Development. 2009. (ENG.). 350p. pap. 39.99 (978-1-4302-2656-7(0)) Apress L. P.

Kolb, Liz. Cell Phones in the Classroom: A Practical Guide for the K-12 Educator. 2011. pap. **(978-1-56484-299-2(1))** International Society for Technology in Education.

Kolb, Liz. Toys to Tools: Connecting Student Cell Phones to Education. 2008. 230p. pap. 34.95 (978-1-56484-247-3(9)) International Society for Technology in Education.

Koskinen, Ilpo. Mobile Multimedia in Action. 2010. (ENG., Illus.). 224p. pap. 24.95 (978-1-4128-1820-9(6)) Transaction Pubs.

Lahde, Sven. Dynamic Network Selection for Optimized Use of Mobile Internet. 2011. 310p. pap. (978-3-8325-2767-9(2)) Logos Verlag Berlin.

Laitinen, Saila. S60 Smartphone Quality Assurance: A Guide for Mobile Engineers & Developers. 2007. (ENG., Illus.). 218p. pap. 90.00 (978-0-470-05685-1(1), Wiley) Wiley, John & Sons, Inc.

Lapp, Cristopher. Instant Gratification: 21st Century Art & the Mobile Phone Camera. 2011. 144p. 39.95 (978-0-615-40959-7(8)) West Hollywood Bks.

Levinson, Paul. Cell Phone: The Story of the World's Most Mobile Medium & How It Has Transformed Everything! 2006. (Illus.). 221p. reprint ed. 30.00 (978-1-4223-5280-9(3)) DIANE Publishing Co.

Ling, Rich. New Tech, New Ties: How Mobile Communication Is Reshaping Social Cohesion. 2010. (ENG., Illus.). 240p. (gr. 17). pap. 13.95 (978-0-262-51504-7(0)) MIT Pr.

Ling, Richard. New Tech, New Ties: How Mobile Communication Is Reshaping Social Cohesion. 2008. (ENG., Illus.). 240p. (gr. 17). 26.95 (978-0-262-12297-9(9)) MIT Pr.

Loguidice, Bill & Gookin, Dan. Motorola ATRIX for Dummies. 2011. (ENG.). 352p. pap. 24.99 (978-1-118-10737-9(3), For Dummies) Wiley, John & Sons, Inc.

Madanda, Aramanzan. Gender Relations & Adoption of Ict in Ugand. 2011. 208p. pap. **(978-3-8443-3074-8(7))** Lambert Academic Publishing.

Making Money in Cellular Phone Audety. Date not set. pap. (978-1-884350-70-2(4)) Alpha Publishing, Inc.

Mark, Dave. More iPhone 3 Development: Tackling iPhone SDK 3. 2009. 450p. pap. 39.99 (978-1-4302-2742-7(7)) Apress L. P.

Mark, Dave & LaMarche, Jeff. More iPhone 3 Development: Tackling iPhone SDK 3. 2010. (ENG., Illus.). 552p. pap. 39.99 (978-1-4302-2505-8(X)) Apress L. P.

Mark, Dave, et al. Beginning iPhone 4 Development: Exploring the IOS SDK. 2011. (Illus.). xvi, 657p. E-Book **(978-1-4302-3025-0(8))** Apress L. P.

Mark, David & LaMarche, Jeff. Beginning iPhone 3 Development: Exploring the iPhone SDK. 2009. (ENG., Illus.). 584p. pap. 39.99 (978-1-4302-2459-4(2)) Apress L. P.

Matsuda, Misa, et al, eds. Personal, Portable, Pedestrian: Mobile Phones in Japanese Life. 2006. (ENG., Illus.). 368p. (gr. 17). per. 22.95 (978-0-262-59025-9(5)) MIT Pr.

Maynard, Richard & Litovski, Ivan. Inside Symbian SQL: A Mobile Developer's Guide to SQLite. 2010. (ENG., Illus.). 432p. pap. 55.00 (978-0-470-74402-4(2), Wiley) Wiley, John & Sons, Inc.

Mazo, Gary, et al. Droids Made Simple: For the Droid, Droid X, Droid 2, & Droid 2 Global. 2010. (ENG.). 616p. pap. 24.99 (978-1-4302-3279-7(X)) Apress L. P.

McFedries, Paul. iPhone 4. 2nd ed. 2010. (Portable Genius Ser.: 34). (ENG., Illus.). 336p. pap. 25.00 (978-0-470-64205-4(X), Wiley) Wiley, John & Sons, Inc.

McFedries, Paul & Mcfedries. iPhone 3GS: Portable Genius. 2nd ed. 2009. (Portable Genius Ser.: 17). (ENG., Illus.). 320p. pap. 25.00 (978-0-470-52422-0(7), Wiley) Wiley, John & Sons, Inc.

McIntosh, Frank J. & Childs, G. W. Making Music with Mobile Devices. 2010. (ENG.). 192p. pap. 29.99 (978-1-4354-5533-7(9)) Course Technology.

Melchioly, Simon. Icts & Development. 2009. 132p. pap. (978-3-639-10450-9(1)) VDM Verlag Dr. Mueller e.K.

Meng, Liqiu, et al. Map-Based Mobile Services: Interactivity & Usability. 2007. (Lecture Notes in Geoinformation & Cartography Ser.). (Illus.). 260p. 239.00 (978-3-540-37109-0(5)) Springer.

Mercer, David. The Telephone: The Life Story of a Technology, 1 vol. 2006. (Greenwood Technographies Ser.). (Illus.). 176p. 45.00 (978-0-313-33207-4(X), GR3207, Greenwood Pr.) Greenwood Publishing Group, Inc.

Miller, Daniel & Horst, Heather A. The Cell Phone: An Anthropology of Communication. 2006. (ENG.). 224p. pap. 32.95 (978-1-84520-401-3(8)) Berg Pubs. GBR. Dist: Macmillan.

Miller, Kokeita K. Putting the Care in Customer Service: Cause a Revolution in Your Business. 2011. 52p. pap. 10.03 **(978-1-4269-9227-8(0))** Trafford Publishing.

Minoli, Daniel, et al. Newnes Wireless Telephony Ebook Collection. 2008. (Newnes Ultimate CDs Ser.). (ENG.). cd-rom 225.00 (978-1-85617-599-9(5), Newnes) Elsevier Science & Technology Bks.

Mohr, Werner, et al, eds. Radio Technologies & Concepts for IMT-Advanced. 2009. (ENG., Illus.). 624p. 165.00 (978-0-470-74763-6(3), Wiley) Wiley, John & Sons, Inc.

Morris, Ben. The Symbian OS Architecture Sourcebook: Design & Evolution of a Mobile Phone OS. 2007. (Symbian Press Ser.: 11). (ENG., Illus.). 630p. per. 75.00 (978-0-470-01846-0(1), Wiley) Wiley, John & Sons, Inc.

Morris, Ben, et al. An Introduction to Bada: A Developer's Guide. 2010. (ENG., Illus.). 504p. pap., instr.'s gde. ed. 55.00 (978-0-470-97401-8(X), Wiley) Wiley, John & Sons, Inc.

Muk, Alexander. Acceptance of SMS Advertising: A Cross-Cultural Study of Young American & Taiwanese Consumers. 2008. 60p. pap. (978-3-639-09025-3(X)) VDM Verlag Dr. Mueller e.K.

Mullins, Chris. Monkey Business for Today's Phone Weary Office. 2010. pap. (978-1-61623-677-9(9)) Independent Pub.

Munusamy, Jayaraman, et al. The Determinants of Consumer Buying Behaviour in Mobile Phone Industry. 2010. 64p. pap. (978-3-8383-8885-4(2)) Lambert Academic Publishing.

Nathan, Adam. 101 Windows Phone 7 Apps, Volume I: Developing Apps 1-50. rev. ed. 2011. (ENG., Illus.). 1152p. pap. 59.99 (978-0-672-33552-5(2)) Sams.

—101 Windows Phone 7 Apps, Volume II: Developing Apps 51-101. rev. ed. 2012. (ENG., Illus.). 700p. pap. 59.99 (978-0-672-33560-0(3)) Sams.

Nest, Michael. Coltan. 2011. (PRS - Polity Resources Ser.: 4). (ENG., Illus.). 200p. pap. 19.95 (978-0-7456-4932-0(7)); 49.95 (978-0-7456-4931-3(9)) Polity Pr. GBR. Dist: Wiley, John & Sons, Inc.

Nielsen, Lisa & Webb, Willyn. Teaching Generation Text: Using Cell Phones to Enhance Learning. 2011. (ENG.). 304p. pap. 22.95 (978-1-118-07687-3(7), Jossey-Bass) Wiley, John & Sons, Inc.

Noar, Seth M. & Harrington, Nancy, eds. EHealth Applications: Promising Strategies for Health Behavior Change. 2012. (Routledge Communication Ser.). (ENG., Illus.). 336p. (C). pap. 49.95 (978-0-415-88818-9(2)) Routledge.

—Interactive Health Communication Applications: Promising Strategies for Health Behavior Change. 2012. (Routledge Communication Ser.). (ENG., Illus.). 336p. (C). 150.00 (978-0-415-88817-2(4)) Routledge.

O'Grady, Jason D. The Droid. 2010. (Pocket Guide Ser.). (ENG., Illus.). 240p. pap. 14.99 (978-0-321-71193-9(9)) Peachpit Pr.

—The Droid Pocket Guide. 2nd rev. ed. 2011. (Pocket Guide Ser.). (ENG., Illus.). 240p. pap. 14.99 (978-0-321-74742-6(9)) Peachpit Pr.

—The Google Phone. 2009. (Pocket Guide Ser.). (ENG., Illus.). 168p. pap. 14.99 (978-0-321-62059-0(3)) Peachpit Pr.

Öqvist Seimyr, Gustaf. Evaluating Readability on Mobile Devices. 2010. 84p. pap. (978-3-639-20564-0(2)) VDM Verlag Dr. Mueller e.K.

Pace, Eugenio, et al. Windows Phone 7 Developer Guide: Building Connected Mobile Applications with Microsoft Silverlight. 2011. (ENG., Illus.). 336p. pap. 34.99 (978-0-7356-5609-3(6)) Microsoft Pr.

Pearson, Andrew. The Mobile Revolution - 2011. 212p. pap. 18.99 **(978-1-4583-8456-0(X))** Lulu Enterprises Inc.

Penttinen, Jyrki T. J., ed. The LTE / SAE Deployment Handbook. 2012. (ENG., Illus.). 448p. 110.00 **(978-0-470-97726-2(4)**, Wiley) Wiley, John & Sons, Inc.

Posey, Brien. My Windows Phone 7. 2011. (My... Ser.). (ENG., Illus.). 448p. pap. 24.99 (978-0-7897-4825-6(8)) Que.

Pousttchi, Key & Wiedemann, Dietmar G., eds. Handbook of Research on Mobile Marketing Management. 2009. (Illus.). 598p. 295.00 (978-1-60566-074-5(4)) IGI Global.

Prima Games Staff, et al. The iPhone App Book 2009 Vol. 1: The Essential Directory of iPhone & iPod Touch Applications. 2009. (ENG., Illus.). 240p. pap. 12.99 (978-0-7615-6285-6(0), Prima Games) Random Hse. Information Group.

Quintyne, Vasco. A Novel Fair Channel Access Algorithm for Cellular Networks. 2011. 128p. pap. **(978-3-8443-3290-2(1))** Lambert Academic Publishing.

Rathbone, Andy. Motorola Xoom for Dummies. 2011. (ENG., Illus.). 336p. pap. 24.99 (978-1-118-08835-7(2), For Dummies) Wiley, John & Sons, Inc.

Reed, Jeffrey H., et al. Cellular Communications: A Comprehensive & Practical Guide. 2012. (ENG., Illus.). 800p. pap. 110.00 (978-0-470-47207-1(3), Wiley-IEEE Pr.) Wiley, John & Sons, Inc.

Rizk, Anthony, et al. Beginning BlackBerry 7 Development. 2nd ed. 2011. (ENG., Illus.). 280p. pap. 39.99 (978-1-4302-3015-1(0)) Apress L. P.

Sadun, Erica. Taking Your iPhone to the Max. 2007. (ENG.). 182p. pap. 24.99 (978-1-59059-926-6(8)) Apress L. P.

Sadun, Erica, et al. Taking Your iPhone 4S to the Max: For iPhone 4S & Other iOS 5-Enabled iPhones. 2011. (ENG.). 524p. pap. 24.99 **(978-1-4302-3581-1(0))** Apress L. P.

Schulz, Trenton. Mobile Phones & the Keystroke-Level Model. 2010. 172p. pap. (978-3-8383-5556-6(3)) Lambert Academic Publishing.

Schwartz, Steve. My Samsung Galaxy S II. 2012. (My... Ser.). (ENG., Illus.). 432p. pap. 24.99 **(978-0-7897-4963-5(7))** Que.

Scott, Allen W. & Frobenius, Rex. RF Measurements for Cellular Phones & Wireless Data Systems. 2008. (ENG., Illus.). 504p. 136.00 (978-0-470-12948-7(4), Wiley-IEEE Pr.) Wiley, John & Sons, Inc.

Shapira, Joseph & Miller, Samuel. CDMA Radio with Repeaters. 2010. (Information Technology: Transmission, Processing & Storage Ser.). (Illus.). xxiv, 425p. pap. 159.00 (978-1-4419-3884-8(2), 1441938842) Springer.

Shing Chyi, Chua. A Robotic Pool Prototype. 2009. 188p. pap. (978-3-639-14054-5(0)) VDM Verlag Dr. Mueller e.K.

Shoup, Kate. Iphone Visual Quick Tips. 2008. (Visual Quick Tips Ser.: 2). (ENG., Illus.). 197p. per. 12.99 (978-0-470-17371-8(8), Visual) Wiley, John & Sons, Inc.

Slack, Sally E. & Ballew, Joli. Motorola Xoom Companion. 2011. (ENG., Illus.). 304p. pap. 19.99 (978-1-118-01377-9(8), Wiley) Wiley, John & Sons, Inc.

Smith, C. B., photos by. Phonebook. 2011. (ENG.). 184p. 50.00 **(978-88-88493-75-6(1))** Drago Arts & Communication ITA. Dist: SCB Distributors.

Stetz, Penelope J. The Cell Phone Handbook: Everything You Wanted to Know about Wireless Telephony (but Didn't Know Who or What to Ask) 2nd ed. 2006. per. 22.95 (978-0-9787637-0-1(X)) FindTech Ltd.

Stolarz, Damien, et al. iPhone Hacks: Pushing the iPhone & iPod Touch Beyond Their Limits. 2009. (Hacks Ser.). (ENG., Illus.). 480p. pap. 34.99 (978-0-596-51664-2(9)) O'Reilly Media, Inc.

szumski, bonnie & karson, jill. Are cell phones Dangerous? 2011. (In Controversy Ser.). (YA). (gr. 7-12). lib. bdg. 37.27 **(978-1-60152-232-0(0))** ReferencePoint Pr., Inc.

Tallon, Loc. Digital Technologies & the Museum Experience: Handheld Guides & Other Media. 2008. (ENG., Illus.). 264p. 80.00 (978-0-7591-1119-6(7)); pap. 30.95 (978-0-7591-1121-9(9)) AltaMira Pr.

Tan, Joseph K. H. Mobile Health Solutions for Biomedical Applications. Olla, Phillip, ed. 2009. (Advances in Healthcare Information Systems & Informatics (AHISI) Book Ser.). (Illus.). 366p. 225.00 (978-1-60566-332-6(8)) IGI Global.

Telli Yamamoto, Gonca. Mobilized Marketing & the Consumer: Technological Developments & Challenges. 2009. 398p. 180.00 (978-1-60566-916-8(4)) IGI Global.

Thomas, J. Dennis. Capturing Better Photos & Video with Your iPhone. 2011. (ENG., Illus.). 208p. pap. 19.99 (978-0-470-63802-6(8), Wiley) Wiley, John & Sons, Inc.

Tripathi, Nishith D., et al. Radio Resource Management in Cellular Systems. 2010. (Springer International Series in Engineering & Computer Science Ser.). 248p. pap. 209.00 (978-1-4419-4897-7(X), 144194897X) Springer.

Tumors & Cell Phone Use: What the Science Says: Hearing Before the Subcommittee on Domestic Policy of the Committee on Oversight & Government Reform, House of Representatives, One Hundred Tenth Congress, Second Session, September 25, 2008. 2009. (Illus.). iii, 226p. (978-0-16-083848-4(7), 552-070-39545-8) United States Government Printing Office.

Unmehopa, Musa & Brenner, Michael. The Open Mobile Alliance: Delivering Service Enablers for Next-Generation Applications. 2008. (ENG., Illus.). 530p. 135.00 (978-0-470-51918-9(5), Wiley) Wiley, John & Sons, Inc.

Varral, Geoff & Auslander, Edgar, eds. Camera Phone Design. 2007. (Illus.). 416p. 120.00 (978-0-470-02722-6(3)) Wiley, John & Sons, Inc.

Wagner, Marcel, et al. 3g Performance & Security. 2010. 144p. pap. (978-3-639-23235-6(6)) VDM Verlag Dr. Mueller e.K.

Wagner, Richard. IPhone & iPod Touch Programming: Handling Touch Interactions & Events for Mobile Safari. 2007. (Wrox Briefs Ser.). 26p. 6.99 (978-0-470-26022-7(X), Wrox) Wiley, John & Sons, Inc.

Watson, Lonzell. My HTC Evo 3D. 2011. (My... Ser.). (ENG., Illus.). 336p. pap. 24.99 **(978-0-7897-4909-3(2))** Que.

Westfall, Jon. Windows Phone 7 Made Simple. 2011. (ENG.). 472p. pap. 29.99 (978-1-4302-3312-1(5)) Apress L. P.

Whitechapel, Andrew. Windows Phone 7 Development Internals: Covers versions 7. 0 Through 7. 5. 2012. (ENG.). 750p. pap. 59.99 **(978-0-7356-6325-1(4))** Microsoft Pr.

Whitman, Robert. Robert Whitman Local Report. Martin, Julie, ed. 2007. (Illus.). per. 27.50 (978-0-931286-09-4(3)) Experiments in Art & Technology.

Wiley, et al. BlackBerry Application Development for Dummies. 2010. (ENG., Illus.). 408p. pap. 29.99 (978-0-470-46711-4(8), For Dummies) Wiley, John & Sons, Inc.

Williams, Sara. Cellspace & Teen Culture. 2010. 64p. pap. (978-3-8383-7069-9(4)) Lambert Academic Publishing.

Wireless Tax Fairness ACT of 2011: Hearing Before the Subcommittee on Courts, Commercial & Administrative Law of the Committee on the Judiciary, House of Representatives, One Hundred Twelfth Congress, on H.R. 1002, March 15, 2011. 2011. (Illus.). iii, 72p. **(978-0-16-088790-1(9)**, 552-070-42930-1) United States Government Printing Office.

Zammetti, Frank. Practical Palm Pre WebOS Projects. 2009. (ENG., Illus.). 400p. pap. 39.99 (978-1-4302-2674-1(9)) Apress L. P.

Zdziarski, Jonathan. iPhone SDK Application Development: Building Applications for the AppStore. 2009. (ENG., Illus.). 400p. pap. 34.99 (978-0-596-15405-9(4)) O'Reilly Media, Inc.

Ziaja, Paulina Gabriele. Adoption of Mobile Route Planning Applications for Backpackers Enroute: Usefulness & Ease of Use of Digital Maps. 2011. 84p. pap. (978-3-639-32064-0(6)) VDM Verlag Dr. Mueller e.K.

Ziegler, Chris. Palm Pre for Dummies. 2009. (ENG., Illus.). 336p. pap. 24.99 (978-0-470-52689-7(0), For Dummies) Wiley, John & Sons, Inc.

CELL PHYSIOLOGY

Aguda, Baltazar & Friedman, Avner. Models of Cellular Regulation. 2008. (Oxford Graduate Texts). (ENG., Illus.). 200p. 99.00 (978-0-19-857091-2(0)) Oxford Univ. Pr., Inc.

Al. Textbook of Structural Biology. 2008. 136.00 (978-981-277-207-7(3)); (Illus.). viii, 572p. pap. 88.00 (978-981-277-208-4(1)) World Scientific Publishing Co., Inc.

Al-Rubeai, Mohamed & Fussenegger, Martin, eds. Systems Biology. (Cell Engineering Ser.). viii, 425p. 2010. pap. 279.00 (978-90-481-7322-8(1), 9048173221) 2007. (Illus.). 279.00 (978-1-4020-5251-4(0), 1402052510) Springer.

Anderson, Alexander R. A. & Rejniak, Katarzyna A., eds. Single-Cell-Based Models in Biology & Medicine. 2007. (Mathematics & Biosciences in Interaction Ser.). (Illus.). 349p. 249.00 (978-3-7643-8101-1(9)) Birkhauser Verlag AG CHE. Dist: Springer.

Bamba, Shigeki & Rotto, William. Gut Stem Cells: Multipotent, Clonogenic, & the Origin of Gastrointestinal Cancer. 2008. pap. 29.00 (978-1-60456-968-1(9)) Nova Science Pubs., Inc.

Bechtel, William. Discovering Cell Mechanisms: The Creation of Modern Cell Biology. 2008. (Cambridge Studies in Philosophy & Biology Ser.). (ENG.). 336p. pap. 30.99 (978-0-521-72944-4(0)) Cambridge Univ. Pr.

Booss, Bernhelm. BetaSys: Systems Biology of Regulated Exocytosis in Pancreatic [Beta]-Cells. 2011. (Illus.). xviii, 558p. (978-1-4419-6956-9(X)) Springer.

Boron, Walter F. & Boulpaep, Emile L. Medical Physiology: A Cellular & Molecular Approach. 2nd ed. 2009. (Illus.). xii, 1337p. (978-0-8089-2360-2(9), Saunders) Elsevier - Health Sciences Div.

Braggina, Josse R. Stem Cell Research Trends. 2007. 225.00 (978-1-60021-622-0(6)) Nova Science Pubs., Inc.

Cai, Haijiang. The Role of Complexin in Regulated Exocytosis: A Study Shows that the SNARE-binding Protein Complexin is a Positive Regulator of Vesicle Priming in Fast, Calcium-triggered Exocytosis. 2008. 132p. pap. (978-3-639-01439-6(1)) VDM Verlag Dr. Mueller e.K.

Chauviere, Arnaud & Claude, Verdier. Cell Mechanics: From Single Scale-Based Models to Multiscale Modeling. Preziosi, Luigi & Verdier, Claude, eds. 2010. (Chapman & Hall/CRC Mathematical & Computational Biology Ser.). (ENG., Illus.). 482p. 119.95 (978-1-4200-9454-1(8), Chapman & Hall/CRC) CRC Pr. LLC.

Conn, P. Michael. The Unfolded Protein Response & Cellular Stress, Part C, 3 vols. 2011. (ENG., Illus.). 464p. 187.00 (978-0-12-385928-0(X), Academic Pr.) Elsevier Science & Technology Bks.

Conn, P. Michael, ed. The Unfolded Protein Response & Cellular Stress, Part A, 3 vols. 2011. (ENG., Illus.). 432p. 187.00 (978-0-12-385116-1(5), Academic Pr.) Elsevier Science & Technology Bks.

—The Unfolded Protein Response & Cellular Stress, Part B, 3 vols. 2011. (ENG., Illus.). 432p. 187.00 (978-0-12-385114-7(9), Academic Pr.) Elsevier Science & Technology Bks.

Cram101 Textbook Reviews. Outlines & Highlights for Netters Essential Physiology by Susan Mulroney. 2011. 466p. pap. 36.95 (978-1-61905-821-7(9)) Cram101 Inc.

Csermely, Peter & Vigh, László, eds. Molecular Aspects of the Stress Response: Chaperones, Membranes & Networks: Chaperones, Membranes & Networks. 2010. (Advances in Experimental Medicine & Biology Ser.). (Illus.). xviii, 201p. pap. 189.00 (978-1-4419-2297-7(0), 1441922970) Springer.

De La Barrera, Erick & Smith, William K. Perspectives in Biophysical Plant Ecophysiology: A Tribute to Park S. Nobel. 2009. (Illus.). 440p. (978-0-578-00421-1(6)) Universidad Nacional Autónoma de México.

Di Silvio, L., ed. Cellular response to Biomaterials. 2009. (ENG., Illus.). 500p. 289.95 (978-1-4200-9373-5(8)) CRC Pr. LLC.

Dikic, Ivan. Endosomes. 2006. (Illus.). 157p. (978-1-58706-060-1(4)) Landes Bioscience.

Dikic, Ivan, ed. Endosomes. (Molecular Biology Intelligence Unit Ser.). (Illus.). 2010. xi, 157p. pap. 199.00 (978-1-4419-2292-2(X), 144192292X) 2006. 157p. 199.00 (978-0-387-39950-8(X), 038739950X) Springer.

Frank, Joachim, ed. Molecular Machines in Biology: Workshop of the Cell. 2011. (ENG., Illus.). 272p. 125.00 (978-0-521-19428-0(8)) Cambridge Univ. Pr.

Grimm, Dirk. Cellular RNA Interference Mechanisms. 2011. (ENG.). 261p. 161.00 (978-0-12-415795-8(5), Academic Pr.) Elsevier Science & Technology Bks.

Henzler, H. J., et al. Influence of Stress on Cell Growth & Product Formation. 2010. (Advances in Biochemical Engineering Biotechnology Ser.). (Illus.). ix, 190p. pap. 269.00 (978-3-642-08594-9(6), 3642085946) Springer.

Iglesias, Pablo A. & Ingalls, Brian P., eds. Control Theory & Systems Biology. 2009. (ENG., Illus.). 358p. (gr. 17). 45.00 (978-0-262-01334-5(7)) MIT Pr.

Ivanov, Andrei I., ed. Exocytosis & Endocytosis. (Methods in Molecular Biology Ser.). (Illus.). 2010. (ENG.). xv, 412p. pap. 129.00 (978-1-61737-813-3(5), 1617378135) 2007. 412p. 129.00 (978-1-58829-865-2(5), 1588298655) Humana Pr.

Khan, Wasim S. & Hardingham, Timothy E., eds. Stem Cells & Cartilage Tissue Engineering Approaches to Orthopaedic Surgery. 2010. (Surgery - Procedures, Complications, & Results Ser.). 53p. pap. 43.00 (978-1-60876-864-6(3), Nova Biomedical Bks.) Nova Science Pubs., Inc.

Koleske, Anthony J. Abl Family Kinases in Development & Disease. 2007. (Molecular Biology Intelligence Unit Ser.). (Illus.). 125p. 159.00 (978-0-387-36640-1(7), 0387366407) Springer.

Kudlicki, Wieslaw A., et al, eds. Cell-Free Protein Expression. 2007. (978-1-58706-123-3(6)) Landes Bioscience.

Kuriyan, et al. Structural Biology. 2012. (ENG., Illus.). 1032p. pap. 145.00 (978-0-8153-4188-8(1), Garland Science) Taylor & Francis Group.

Laurent, Brehon. Chromatin Dynamics in Cellular Function. 2006. (Results & Problems in Cell Differentiation Ser.: Vol. 41). (Illus.). viii, 151p. 109.00 (978-3-540-33685-3(0), 3540336850) Springer.

Lejeune, Thomas & Delvaux, Pascal. Human Spermatozoa: Maturation, Capacitation & Abnormalities. 2010. (Human Reproductive System - Anatomy, Roles & Disorders Ser.). 568p. 245.00 (978-1-60876-401-3(X), Nova Biomedical Bks.) Nova Science Pubs., Inc.

Lewin. Itk- Lewin's Cells 2E Instructor's Toolkit. 2nd rev. ed. 2010. cd-rom 124.95 (978-0-7637-9506-1(2)) Jones & Bartlett Learning, LLC.

Macagnano, Antonella, et al. Advanced Topics in Cell Model Systems. 2009. 89.00 (978-1-60692-906-3(2)) Nova Science Pubs., Inc.

Mayer, R. John, et al, eds. Protein Degradation, 4 vols., Set. 2008. (Protein Degradation Ser.: 6). (ENG., Illus.). 1203p. 835.00 (978-3-527-31878-0(X), Wiley-VCH) Wiley, John & Sons, Inc.

Mulroney, Susan & Myers, Adam. Netter's Essential Physiology: With STUDENT CONSULT Online Access. 2008. (Netter Basic Science Ser.). (ENG., Illus.). 408p. 64.95 (978-1-4160-4196-2(6), Saunders) Elsevier - Health Sciences Div.

—Netter's Physiology Flash Cards. 2009. (Netter Basic Science Ser.). (ENG., Illus.). 420p. 37.95 (978-1-4160-4628-8(3), Saunders) Elsevier - Health Sciences Div.

Murgatroyd, Chris, ed. The Power of the Gene: the Origin & Impact of Genetic Disorders. 2010. (Genetics - Research & Issues Ser.). 89.00 (978-1-60876-949-0(6), Nova Biomedical Bks.) Nova Science Pubs., Inc.

Nabi, Ivan R. Cellular Domains. 2011. (ENG., Illus.). 504p. 129.95 (978-0-470-59544-2(2), Wiley-Blackwell) Wiley, John & Sons, Inc.

Pociot, Flemming. BetaSys: Systems Biology of Regulated Exocytosis in Pancreatic ß-Cells. Pociot, Flemming et al, eds. 2011. (Systems Biology Ser.). (ENG., Illus.). xviii, 558p. 209.00 (978-1-4419-6955-2(1), 1441969551) Springer.

Pollack, Gerald H., et al, eds. Water & the Cell. 2010. (ENG & ABK.). ix, 354p. pap. 89.95 (978-90-481-7228-3(4), 9048172284) Springer.

Posas, Francesc & Nebreda, Angel R., eds. Stress-Activated Protein Kinases. 2008. (Topics in Current Genetics Ser.). (Illus.). 312p. 249.00 (978-3-540-75568-5(3)) Springer.

Regazzi, Romano, ed. Molecular Mechanisms of Exocytosis. 2010. (Molecular Biology Intelligence Unit Ser.). (Illus.). ix, 178p. pap. 179.00 (978-1-4419-2295-3(4), 1441922954) Springer.

Rogers, Kara, ed. The Chemical Reactions of Life: From Metabolism to Photosynthesis. 2011. (Biochemistry, Cells, & Life Ser.). (Illus.). 280p. (YA). 80.00 (978-1-61530-432-5(0)) Rosen Publishing Group, Inc., The.

Schleifenbaum, Andreas. Kinase C Probes. 2008. 156p. pap. (978-3-639-03651-0(4)) VDM Verlag Dr. Mueller e.K.

Segev, Nava, ed. Trafficking Inside Cells: Pathways, Mechanisms & Regulation. 2009. (Molecular Biology Intelligence Unit Ser.). (ENG., Illus.). 465p. 209.00 (978-0-387-93876-9(1), 0387938761) Springer.

Sopjani, Mentor. The Ampk in the Regulation of Eryptosis & Na+ Coupled Transporters. 2010. 124p. pap. (978-3-639-25829-5(0)) VDM Verlag Dr. Mueller e.K.

Sperelakis, Nicholas, ed. Cell Physiology Source Book: Essentials of Membrane Biophysics. 4th ed. 2011. (ENG., Illus.). 996p. 149.95 (978-0-12-387738-3(5), Academic Pr.) Elsevier Science & Technology Bks.

Stoddart, Martin J. Mammalian Cell Viability: Methods & Protocols. 2011. (Illus.). xi, 240p. E-Book (978-1-61779-108-6(3)) Humana Pr.

Stoddart, Martin J., ed. Mammalian Cell Viability: Methods & Protocols. 2011. (Methods in Molecular Biology Ser.). (Illus.). xi, 240p. 119.00 (978-1-61779-107-9(5), 1617791075) Humana Pr.

Süchof, Thomas C. & Starke, Klaus. Pharmacology of Neurotransmitter Release. 2010. (Handbook of Experimental Pharmacology Ser.). (Illus.). xiv, 582p. pap. 549.00 (978-3-642-09424-8(4), 3642094244) Springer.

Szallasi, Zoltan. System Modeling in Cellular Biology: From Concepts to Nuts & Bolts. Stelling, Jorg & Periwal, Vipul, eds. 2010. (ENG.). 464p. (gr. 17). pap. 28.00 (978-0-262-51422-4(2)) MIT Pr.

Upledger, John. Cell Talk: Transmitting Mind into DNA. 2010. (ENG.). 544p. pap. 29.95 (978-1-55643-913-1(X)) North Atlantic Bks.

Villas-Boas, Silas G., et al. Metabolome Analysis: An Introduction. 2007. (Wiley - Interscience Series on Mass Spectrometry Ser.: 24). (ENG., Illus.). 319p. 99.95 (978-0-471-74344-6(5), Wiley-Interscience) Wiley, John & Sons, Inc.

Wada. Biomechanics at Micro- Nanoscale... (V3) 2007. 84.00 (978-981-270-814-4(6)) World Scientific Publishing Co., Inc.

Wada, Hiroshi, ed. Biomechanics at Micro- & Nanoscale Levels: Volume IV. 2007. (Biomechanics at Micro- & Nanoscale Levels Ser.). (Illus.). 172p. 104.00 (978-981-277-131-5(X)) World Scientific Publishing Co., Inc.

Wang, Jian-Ying, ed. Polyamine Cell Signaling: Physiology, Pharmacology, & Cancer Research. 2010. (Illus.). 504p. pap. 165.00 (978-1-61737-679-5(5), 1617376795) Humana Pr.

Wittrup, K. Dane & Tidor, Bruce. Biomolecular Kinetics & Cellular Dynamics. 2008. 550p. 95.00 (978-0-8153-4139-0(3), Garland Science) Taylor & Francis Group.

CELL RECEPTORS

see also Drug Receptors; Hormone Receptors

Bačáková, L. Cell Colonization Control by Physical & Chemical Modification of Materials. 2008. pap. 29.00 (978-1-60456-887-5(9)) Nova Science Pubs., Inc.

Bauer, Stefan & Hartmann, Gunther. Toll-Like Receptors (TLRs) & Innate Immunity. 2010. (Handbook of Experimental Pharmacology Ser.). (Illus.). xii, 240p. pap. 399.00 (978-3-642-09133-9(4), 3642091334) Springer.

Bauer, Stefan & Hartmann, Gunther, eds. Toll-Like Receptors (TLRs) & Innate Immunity. 2008. (Handbook of Experimental Pharmacology Ser.). (Illus.). 240p. 399.00 (978-3-540-72166-6(5)) Springer.

Bunce, Chris & Campbell, Moray J., eds. Nuclear Receptors: Current Concepts & Future Challenges. 2010. (Proteins & Cell Regulation Ser.). (ENG.). 365p. 239.00 (978-90-481-3302-4(5), 9048133025) Springer.

Cancro, Michael P., ed. BLyS Ligands & Receptors. 2009. (Contemporary Immunology Ser.). (ENG., Illus.). 300p. 189.00 (978-1-60327-012-3(4)) Humana Pr.

Davenport, Anthony P., ed. Receptor Binding Techniques. (Methods in Molecular Biology Ser.). (Illus.). 2nd ed. 2010. 256p. pap. 139.00 (978-1-61737-556-9(X), 161737556X) 3rd ed. 2012. (ENG., xxiv, 324p. 119.00 (978-1-61779-908-2(4), 1617799084) Humana Pr.

Di Giovanni, Giuseppe. 5-HT2C Receptors in the Pathophysiology of CNS Disease. Di Giovanni, Giuseppe et al, eds. 2010. (Receptors Ser.). (ENG., Illus.). xi, 557p. 239.00 (978-1-60761-940-6(7), 1607619407) Humana Pr.

Dickson, Robert C. & Mendenhall, Michael D., eds. Signal Transduction Protocols. 2nd ed. 2010. (Methods in Molecular Biology Ser.). (Illus.). 327p. pap. 115.00 (978-1-61737-448-7(2), 1617374482) Humana Pr.

El-Deiry, Wafik S., ed. Death Receptors in Cancer Therapy. 2010. (Cancer Drug Discovery & Development Ser.). (Illus.). 384p. pap. 209.00 (978-1-61737-401-2(6), 1617374016) Humana Pr.

Enna, S. J. Pharmacology of g protein coupled Receptors. 2011. (ENG., Illus.). 408p. 241.00 (978-0-12-385952-5(2), Academic Pr.) Elsevier Science & Technology Bks.

Froment, Pascal, ed. Ars & Rxrs in Male & Female Fertility & Reproduction. 2007. 128p. pap. 20.00 (978-977-454-020-2(4)) Hindawi Publishing Corp.

Giraldo, Jesus & Pin, Jean-Philippe, eds. G Protein-Coupled Receptors: From Structure to Function. 2011. (ENG., Illus.). 548p. 272.00 (978-1-84973-183-6(7)) Royal Society of Chemistry, The GBR. Dist: Ingram Pub. Services.

Goetzl, Edward J., ed. Neural Signaling: Opportunities for Novel Diagnostic Approaches & Therapies. 2008. (Annals of the New York Academy of Sciences Ser.). (ENG., Illus.). 360p. pap. 139.95 (978-1-57331-704-7(7), Wiley-Blackwell) Wiley, John & Sons, Inc.

Harrison, Jeffrey K. & Lukacs, Nicholas W. The Chemokine Receptors. 2007. (Receptors Ser.). (Illus.). 403p. 229.00 (978-1-58829-773-0(X)) Humana Pr.

Harrison, Jeffrey K. & Lukacs, Nicholas W., eds. The Chemokine Receptors. 2010. (Receptors Ser.). (Illus.). xiii, 403p. pap. 229.00 (978-1-61737-768-6(6), 1617377686) Humana Pr.

Kielian, Tammy. Toll-like Receptors: Roles in Infection & Neuropathology: Roles in Infection & Neuropathology. Kielian, Tammy, ed. 2009. (Current Topics in Microbiology & Immunology Ser.). (ENG., Illus.). xi, 191p. 219.00 (978-3-642-00548-0(9), 3642005489) Springer.

Konat, Gregory W Staff & Konat, Gregory W. Signaling by Toll-Like Receptors. 2008. (Methods in Signal Transduction Ser.). (ENG., Illus.). 224p. 162.95 (978-1-4200-4318-1(8), CRC Press) Taylor & Francis Group GBR. Dist: Taylor & Francis Group.

Lansing, Sébastien & Rousseau, Tristan, eds. Cytoskeleton: Cell Movement, Cytokinesis & Organelles Organization. 2010. (Cell Biology Research Progress Ser.). 129.00 (978-1-60876-559-1(8), Nova Biomedical Bks.) Nova Science Pubs., Inc.

Li, Jonathan J., ed. Hormonal Carcinogenesis 5. 2008. (Advances in Experimental Medicine & Biology Ser.: Vol. 617). (Illus.). 600p. 199.00 (978-0-387-69078-0(6)) Springer.

Limbird, Lee E. Cell Surface Receptors: A Short Course on Theory & Methods. 3rd ed. 2010. (ENG., Illus.). xii, 219p. pap. 129.00 (978-1-4419-3571-7(1), 1441935711) Springer.

Luttrell, Louis M. & Ferguson, Stephen S. G., eds. Signal Transduction Protocols. 3rd ed. 2011. (Methods in Molecular Biology Ser.). (ENG., Illus.). xiv, 430p. 139.00 (978-1-61779-159-8(8), 1617791598) Humana Pr.

McCoy, Claire E. & O'Neill, Luke A. J. Toll-Like Receptors: Methods & Protocols. 2009. (Methods in Molecular Biology Ser.). (Illus.). (ENG.). 400p. 129.00 (978-1-934115-72-5(X)); xiv, 447p. (978-1-59745-541-1(5)) Humana Pr.

McEwan, I. J. The Nuclear Receptor Superfamily: Methods & Protocols. 2009. (Methods in Molecular Biology Ser.). (Illus.). 240p. 119.00 (978-1-60327-574-3(6)) Humana Pr.

Pasterkamp, Gera, ed. Semaphorins. 2007. (Advances in Experimental Medicine & Biology Ser.). (Illus.). XIV, 147p. 179.00 (978-0-387-70955-0(X), 038770955X) Springer.

Pasterkamp, Gerard, ed. Semaphorins: Receptor & Intracellular Signaling Mechanisms: Receptor & Intracellular Signaling Mechanisms. 2010. (Advances in Experimental Medicine & Biology Ser.). (Illus.). xiv, 147p. pap. 179.00 (978-1-4419-2427-8(2), 1441924272) Springer.

Pohjanvirta, Raimo. The AH Receptor in Biology & Toxicology. 2011. (ENG., Illus.). 560p. 149.95 (978-0-470-60182-2(5), Wiley) Wiley, John & Sons, Inc.

Poyner, David & Wheatley, Mark, eds. G Protein-Coupled Receptors: Essential Methods. 2010. (ENG., Illus.). 310p. 109.95 (978-0-470-74914-2(8), Wiley) Wiley, John & Sons, Inc.

Rast, Jonathan P. & Booth, James W. D., eds. Immune Receptors: Methods & Protocols. 2011. (Methods in Molecular Biology Ser.). (Illus.). xi, 301p. 119.00 (978-1-61779-138-3(5), 1617791385) Humana Pr.

Rast, Jonathan Patrick & Booth, James W. D. Immune Receptors: Methods & Protocols. 2011. (Illus.). xi, 301p. E-Book (978-1-61779-139-0(3)) Humana Pr.

Rich, Tina. Toll & Toll-Like Receptors: An Immunologic Perspective. 2010. (Molecular Biology Intelligence Unit Ser.). (Illus.). x, 218p. pap. 199.00 (978-1-4419-3438-3(3), 1441934383) Springer.

Samelson, Lawrence E. & Shaw, Andrey, eds. Immunoreceptor Signaling. 2010. (ENG., Illus.). 350p. 135.00 (978-0-87969-896-6(9)) Cold Spring Harbor Laboratory Pr.

Schrader, Thomas. Creative Chemical Sensor Systems. (Topics in Current Chemistry Ser.). (Illus.). xiv, 303p. 2010. pap. 389.00 (978-3-642-09075-2(3), 3642090753) 2007. 389.00 (978-3-540-71546-7(0), 3540715460) Springer.

Schwabe, John & Nagy, Laszlo, eds. Handbook of Nuclear Receptors: Part I: Receptor Families - Part II: Receptor Concepts. 2010. 1200p. 575.00 (978-3-527-31697-7(3), Wiley-VCH) Wiley, John & Sons, Inc.

Shakibaei, Mehdi. Diverse Roles of Integrin Receptors in Articular Cartilage. 2008. (Advances in Anatomy, Embryology & Cell Biology Ser.). (Illus.). 85p. pap. 139.00 (978-3-540-78770-9(4), 3540787704) Springer.

Sigalov, Alexander, ed. Multichain Immune Recognition Receptor Signaling: From Spatiotemporal Organization to Human Disease. 2010. (Advances in Experimental Medicine & Biology Ser.). (Illus.). xxvii, 357p. pap. 199.00 (978-1-4419-1887-1(6), 1441918876) Springer.

Sigalov, Alexander B. Multichain Immune Recognition Receptor Signaling: From Spatiotemporal Organization to Human Disease. 2008. (Advances in Experimental Medicine & Biology Ser.: Vol. 640). (Illus.). 386p. 199.00 (978-0-387-09788-6(0), 0387097880) Springer.

Spiro, Stephen & Dixon, Ray, eds. Sensory Mechanisms in Bacteria: Molecular Aspects of Signal Recognition. 2010. (Illus.). 287p. 319.00 (978-1-904455-69-1(7)) Caister Academic Pr. GBR. Dist: International Specialized Bk. Services.

Vauquelin, Georges & Mentzer, Bengt von. G Protein-coupled Receptors: Molecular Pharmacology. 2008. (ENG., Illus.). 264p. 179.95 (978-0-470-51647-8(X), Wiley) Wiley, John & Sons, Inc.

Willars, Gary B. & Challiss, R. A. John, eds. Receptor Signal Transduction Protocols. 2nd ed. 2010. (Methods in Molecular Biology Ser.). (Illus.). xiii, 418p. pap. 99.50 (978-1-61737-498-2(9), 1617374989) Humana Pr.

—Receptor Signal Transduction Protocols: Third Edition. 3rd ed. 2011. (Methods in Molecular Biology Ser.). (Illus.). xi, 479p. 139.00 (978-1-61779-125-3(3), 1617791253) Humana Pr.

Yona, Simon & Stacey, Martin, eds. Adhesion-GPCRs: Structure to Function. 2011. (Advances in Experimental Medicine & Biology Ser.). (ENG., Illus.). xxii, 200p. 189.00 (978-1-4419-7912-4(3), 1441979123) Springer.

Yuan, Jason X. -J & Ward, Jeremy P. T., eds. Membrane Receptors, Channels & Transporters in Pulmonary Circulation. 2010. (Advances in Experimental Medicine & Biology Ser.). (Illus.). xv, 966p. 399.00 (978-1-60761-499-9(5), 1607614995) Humana Pr.

Zourob, Mohammed, et al, eds. Recognition Receptors in Biosensors. 2010. (ENG., Illus.). xiv, 849p. 209.00 (978-1-4419-0918-3(4), 1441909184) Springer.

CELL REGULATION

see Cellular Control Mechanisms

CELL SEPARATION

Chalmers, Jeffrey J. & Zborowski, Maciej. Magnetic Cell Separation. 2007. (Laboratory Techniques in Biochemistry & Molecular Biology Ser.: 32). (ENG., Illus.). 486p. 107.00 (978-0-444-52754-7(0), Elsevier Science) Elsevier Science & Technology Bks.

Katz, Nevin. Classifying Cells: Middle & High School. 2007. (Dr. Birdley Teaches Science Ser.). (Illus.). 93p. per. 12.99 (978-0-86530-539-7(0)) Incentive Pubns., Inc.

Kumar, Ashok, et al. Cell Separation: Fundamenals, Analytical & Preparative Methods. 2007. (Advances in Biochemical Engineering Biotechnology Ser.). (Illus.). xii, 180p. 239.00 (978-3-540-75262-2(5), 3540752625) Springer.

Macey, Marion G., ed. Flow Cytometry: Principles & Applications. 2007. (Illus.). 290p. 124.00 (978-1-58829-691-7(1), 1588296911) Humana Pr.

Roberts, Jeremy A. & Gonzalez-Carranza, Zinnia, eds. Plant Cell Separation & Adhesion, Volume 25. 2007. (Annual Plant Reviews Ser.: 29). (ENG., Illus.). 232p. 245.00 (978-1-4051-3892-5(0), Wiley-Blackwell) Wiley, John & Sons, Inc.

CELL SKELETON

see Cytoskeleton

CELL STORAGE DISORDERS

see Lysosomal Storage Diseases

CELL SURFACES

see Cell Membranes

CELL-WALL-DEFICIENT BACTERIA

see L-Form Bacteria

CELL WALLS, BACTERIAL

see Bacterial Cell Walls

C

CELLARS
see Basements

CELLINI, BENVENUTO, 1500-1571
Cellini, Benvenuto. The Autobiography of Benvenuto Cellini. 2010. 404p. pap. 34.75 *(978-1-142-57590-8(X))* BiblioBazaar.
—The Autobiography of Benvenuto Cellini. Symonds, John Addington, tr. 2007. (ENG.). 608p. per. 31.99 *(978-1-4346-7254-4(9))* BiblioBazaar.
—The Autobiography of Benvenuto Cellini. 2009. 428p. pap. *(978-0-217-28934-4(7))* Books LLC.
—The Autobiography of Benvenuto Cellini. Symonds, John Addington, tr. 2009. 574p. pap. *(978-1-4099-8301-9(3))* Dodo Pr.
—The Autobiography of Benvenuto Cellini. 2007. (ENG.). 328p. per. *(978-1-4068-4450-4(0))* Echo Library.
—The Autobiography of Benvenuto Cellini. 2008. 572p. pap. 26.99 *(978-1-4378-0847-6(6))* IndyPublish.com.
—The Autobiography of Benvenuto Cellini. Symonds, J. Addington, tr. 2009. 410p. 49.95 *(978-1-104-83458-6(8))* 2007. (ENG.). 408p. per. 34.95 *(978-1-4325-7806-0(5))* Kessinger Publishing, LLC.
—The Autobiography of Benvenuto Cellini. 2010. 540p. (J). ***(978-1-84159-328-9(1))*** Knopf, Alfred A. Inc.
—The Autobiography of Benvenuto Cellini. 2007. (ENG.). 412p. 32.95 *(978-1-4344-9283-8(4))*; per. 19.95 *(978-1-4344-9282-1(6))* Wildside Pr., LLC.
—The Autobiography of Benvenuto Cellini. 2010. (ENG.). 504p. 28.00 *(978-0-307-59274-3(X)*, Everyman's Library) Knopf Doubleday Publishing Group.
—The Autobiography of Benvenuto Cellini. Symonds, John Addington, tr. l.t. ed. 2007. (ENG.). 668p. per. 34.99 *(978-1-4346-7255-1(7))* BiblioBazaar.
—My Life. Bondanella, Julia Conaway & Bondanella, Peter, trs. from ITA. 2009. (Oxford World's Classics Ser.). (ENG.). 512p. (Orig.). 13.95 *(978-0-19-955531-4(1))* Oxford Univ. Pr., Inc.
Finger, Charles J. Autobiography of Benvenuto Cellini. 2007. (ENG.). 108p. 33.95 *(978-0-548-09419-8(5))* Kessinger Publishing, LLC.
Hubbard, Elbert. Little Journeys to the Homes of Eminent Artists. 2009. 40p. pap. 12.99 *(978-1-110-79401-0(0))* BiblioBazaar.
—Little Journeys to the Homes of Eminent Artists. 2009. 48p. pap. *(978-0-217-50806-3(5))* Books LLC.

CELLO
see Violoncello

CELLPHONES
see Cell Phones

CELLS
see also Astrocytes; Blood Cells; Cancer Cells; Cell Death; Chromatin; Chromatophores; Cilia and Ciliary Motion; Contractility (Biology); Cytology; Embryology; Epithelium; Eukaryotic Cells; Fertilization (Biology); Histology; Karyokinesis; Macrophages; Membranes (Biology); Osmosis; Pathology, Cellular; Phagocytes; Plant Cells and Tissues; Protozoa; Regeneration (Biology); Stem Cells; Tissue Culture; Ultrastructure (Biology)
Abramoff. Cell Structure. Date not set. 1.20 *(978-0-7167-9017-4(3))* Freeman, W. H. & Co.
Al. Textbook of Structural Biology. 2008. 136.00 *(978-981-277-207-7(3))*; (Illus.). viii, 572p. pap. 88.00 *(978-981-277-208-4(1))* World Scientific Publishing Co., Inc.
Allen, Terence & Cowling, Graham. The Cell: A Very Short Introduction. 2011. (Very Short Introductions Ser.). (ENG., Illus.). 152p. pap. 11.95 *(978-0-19-957875-7(3))* Oxford Univ. Pr., Inc.
Banfalvi, Gaspar, ed. Cellular Effects of Heavy Metals. 2011. (ENG., Illus.). xiv, 348p. 209.00 *(978-94-007-0427-5(5)*, 9400704275) Springer.
Barrett, Sondra. Secrets of Your Cells: Engaging the Healing Wisdom of Your Body's Natural Intelligence. 2012. 304p. pap. 17.95 ***(978-1-60407-626-4(7)***, 1604076267) Sounds True, Inc.
Becker, Wayne M. The World of the Cell. 7th ed. 2009. (Illus.). xxviii, 791p. *(978-0-321-52748-6(8))* Benjamin-Cummings Publishing Co.
Becker, Wayne M., et al. The World of the Cell. 7th ed. 2008. (ENG., Illus.). 912p. (C). 173.20 *(978-0-8053-9393-4(5))* Benjamin-Cummings Publishing Co.
Bedau, Mark A. & Parke, Emily C., eds. The Ethics of Protocells: Moral & Social Implications of Creating Life in the Laboratory. 2009. (Basic Bioethics Ser.). (ENG., Illus.). 384p. (gr. 17). 55.00 *(978-0-262-01262-1(6))*; pap. 29.00 *(978-0-262-51269-5(6))* MIT Pr.
Belkin, Shimshon & Gu, Man Bock, eds. Whole Cell Sensing System II: Applications, 2 vols. 2010. (Advances in Biochemical Engineering Biotechnology Ser.). (Illus.). xii, 220p. 299.00 *(978-3-642-12852-3(1)*, 3642128521) Springer.
Beyar, Rafael & Landesberg, Amir, eds. Analysis of Cardiac Development: From Embryo to Old Age. 2010. (Annals of the New York Academy of Sciences Ser.: 44). (ENG., Illus.). 352p. pap. 130.00 *(978-1-57331-747-4(0)*, Wiley-Blackwell) Wiley, John & Sons, Inc.
Bittles, A. H. & Collins, K. J. The Biology of Human Ageing. 2009. (Society for the Study of Human Biology Symposium Ser.). (ENG., Illus.). 292p. pap. 42.00 *(978-0-521-11261-1(3))* Cambridge Univ. Pr.
Boal, David. Mechanics of the Cell. 2nd ed. 2012. (ENG., Illus.). 622p. (C). 150.00 ***(978-0-521-11376-2(8))***; pap. 80.00 ***(978-0-521-13069-1(7))*** Cambridge Univ. Pr.
Campton, John. Biology: Molecules & Cells. 2010. (Illus.). 110p. (gr. 10-12). pap. 27.50 *(978-0-340-99193-0(3))* Hodder Education GBR. Dist: Trans-Atlantic Pubns., Inc.
Carolina Biological Staff, compiled by. Energizing Cells. 2009. (Inquiries in Science Biology Ser.). *(978-1-4350-0346-0(2))* Carolina Biological Supply Co.
Cassimeris. Lewin's Cells 2E International Edition. 2nd rev. ed. 2010. (Illus.). xxiv, 1053p. pap. 145.95 *(978-0-7637-8266-5(1))* Jones & Bartlett Learning, LLC.
Chandra, Ravi. Writing Cells with Dn. 2008. 96p. pap. *(978-3-639-07745-2(8))* VDM Verlag Dr. Mueller e.K.
Chang, Thomas Ming Swi. Artificial Cells: Biotechnology, Nanomedicine, Regenerative Medicine, Blood Substitutes, Bioencapsulation, & Cell/Stem Cell Therapy. 2007. (Regenerative Medicine, Artificial Cells & Nanomedicine Ser.: Vol. 1). (Illus.). 455p. pap. 98.00 *(978-981-270-778-9(6))* World Scientific Publishing Co., Inc.
—Artificial Cells: Biotechnology, Nanomedicine, Regenerative Medicine, Blood Substitutes, Bioencapsulation, Cell/Stem Cell Therapy. 2007. (Regenerative Medicine, Artificial Cells & Nanomedicine Ser.: Vol. 1). (Illus.). 455p. 197.00 *(978-981-270-576-1(7))* World Scientific Publishing Co., Inc.
Conn, P. Michael. Imaging & Spectroscopic Analysis of Living Cells: Imaging Live Cells in Health & Disease. 2012. (ENG.). 544p. 187.00 ***(978-0-12-391856-7(1)***, Academic Pr.) Elsevier Science & Technology Bks.
—Imaging & spectroscopic analysis of living Cells: Live cell imaging of cellular elements & Functions. 2012. (ENG.). 576p. 187.00 ***(978-0-12-388448-0(9)***, Academic Pr.) Elsevier Science & Technology Bks.
—Imaging & Spectroscopic Analysis of Living Cells: Optical & Spectroscopic Techniques. 2012. (ENG.). 560p. 182.00 ***(978-0-12-391857-4(X)***, Academic Pr.) Elsevier Science & Technology Bks.
Cooper, Geoffrey M. The Cell: A Molecular Approach. 3rd ed. (Illus.). 739p. incl. cd-rom *(978-0-87893-215-3(1))* Sinauer Assocs., Inc.
Curran, Thomas & Christen, Yves, eds. Two Faces of Evil: Cancer & Neurodegeneration: Cancer & Neurodegeneration. 2011. (Research & Perspectives in Alzheimer's Disease Ser.). (ENG., Illus.). xiii, 163p. 189.00 *(978-3-642-16601-3(6)*, 3642166016) Springer.
Dhawan, Anil & Hughes, Robin D., eds. Hepatocyte Transplantation: Methods & Protocols. 2009. (Methods in Molecular Biology Ser.). (Illus.). xvii, 231p. 79.95 *(978-1-58829-883-6(3))* Humana Pr.
Diaspro, Alberto, ed. Optical Fluorescence Microscopy: From the Spectral to the Nano Dimension. 2010. (ENG., Illus.). xii, 244p. 209.00 *(978-3-642-15174-3(4)*, 3642151744) Springer.
Farkas, Daniel, et al. Imaging, Manipulation, & Analysis of Biomolecules, Cells, & Tissues IX. 2011. (Proceedings of SPIE Ser.). 450p. pap. 140.00 ***(978-0-8194-8439-0(3))*** SPIE.
—Imaging, Manipulation, & Analysis of Biomolecules, Cells, & Tissues VI. 2008. (Proceedings of SPIE Ser.). 448p. pap. 130.00 ***(978-0-8194-7034-8(1))*** SPIE.
Farkas, Daniel L., et al. Imaging, Manipulation, & Analysis of Biomolecules, Cells, & Tissues VII: 26-28 January 2009, San Jose, California, United States. 2009. (Proceedings of SPIE Ser.). (Illus.). 450p. pap. 130.00 *(978-0-8194-7428-5(2))* SPIE.
Farkas, Daniel L., et al. Imaging, Manipulation, & Analysis of Biomolecules, Cells, & Tissues VIII: 23-25 January 2010, San Francisco, California, United States. 2010. (Proceedings of SPIE Ser.). (Illus.). 460p. pap. 140.00 ***(978-0-8194-7964-8(0))*** SPIE.
Fischman, Donald. Skeletal Muscle & Muscular Dystrophy: A Visual Approach. 2009. (Colloquium Series on the Cell Biology of Medicine Ser.). 56p. pap. 30.00 *(978-1-61504-003-2(X))* Morgan & Claypool Life Science Publishers.
Fm, Prof Bilqees, et al. Root Tissue Damage in Ber Ziziphus Mauritiana Associated with Nematode. 2010. 168p. pap. *(978-3-639-28859-9(9))* VDM Verlag Dr. Mueller e.K.
Frank, Joachim, ed. Electron Tomography: Methods for Three-Dimensional Visualization of Structures in the Cell. 2nd rev. ed. 2006. (ENG., Illus.). xiv, 455p. 179.00 *(978-0-387-31234-7(X)*, 038731234X) Springer.
Garvey, Reginald B. New Research on Cell Aging. 2006. 186p. 225.00 *(978-1-60021-401-1(0))* Nova Science Pubs., Inc.
Gefen, Amit, ed. Cellular & Biomolecular Mechanics & Mechanobiology. 2011. (Studies in Mechanobiology, Tissue Engineering & Biomaterials Ser.). ix, 560p. 179.00 *(978-3-642-14217-8(6)*, 3642142176) Springer.
Goldman, Robert. Live Cell Imaging. Swedlow, Jason & Spector, David, eds. 2nd ed. 2009. (ENG., Illus.). 752p. pap., lab manual ed. 169.00 *(978-0-87969-893-5(4))*; lab manual ed. 246.00 *(978-0-87969-892-8(6))* Cold Spring Harbor Laboratory Pr.
Goodsell, David S. The Machinery of Life. 2nd ed. 2010. (ENG., Illus.). x, 167p. 25.00 *(978-0-387-84924-9(6)*, 0387849246) Springer.
Hancock, John. Cell Signalling. 3rd ed. 2010. (ENG., Illus.). 352p. pap. 84.95 *(978-0-19-923210-9(5))* Oxford Univ. Pr., Inc.
Hayashi, Takumi, ed. Progress in Cell Growth Process Research. 2008. 129.00 *(978-1-60456-325-2(7))* Nova Science Pubs., Inc.
Hill, Andrew F. Protein Folding, Misfolding, & Disease: Methods & Protocols. 2011. (Illus.). x, 249p. E-Book ***(978-1-60327-223-0(2))*** Humana Pr.
Ide-Ektessabi, Ari. Applications of Synchrotron Radiation: Micro Beams in Cell Micro Biology & Medicine. 2010. (Biological & Medical Physics, Biomedical Engineering Ser.). (Illus.). xiv, 218p. pap. 209.00 *(978-3-642-07979-5(2)*, 3642079792) Springer.
Jékely, Gáspár, ed. Eukaryotic Membranes & Cytoskeleton: Origins & Evolution. 2010. (Advances in Experimental Medicine & Biology Ser.). xv, 146p. pap. 189.00 *(978-1-4419-2541-1(4)*, 1441925414) Springer.
Ji, Sungchul. Molecular Theory of the Living Cell: Concepts, Molecular Mechanisms, & Biomedical Applications. 2012. (ENG., Illus.). xxi, 748p. 219.00 ***(978-1-4614-2151-1(9)***, 1461421519) Springer.
Kamkin, Andre & Kiseleva, Irina, eds. Mechanosensitivity & Mechanotransduction. 2010. (Mechanosensitivity in Cells & Tissues Ser.). (Illus.). xxiv, 371p. 189.00 *(978-90-481-9880-1(1)*, 9048198801) Springer.
Kamm, Roger & Kaazempur-Mofrad, Mohammad, eds. Cytoskeletal Mechanics: Models & Measurements. 2006. (Cambridge Texts in Biomedical Engineering Ser.). (ENG., Illus.). 252p. (C). 85.00 *(978-0-521-84637-0(4))* Cambridge Univ. Pr.
Kardami, Elissavet, et al, eds. Cardiac Cell Biology. 2010. (Developments in Molecular & Cellular Biochemistry Ser.). 204p. pap. 269.00 *(978-1-4419-5324-7(8)*, 1441953248) Springer.
Kaul, S. & Wadwha, Renu, eds. Aging of Cells in & Outside the Body. 2010. (Biology of Aging & its Modulation Ser.). 288p. pap. 189.00 *(978-90-481-6314-4(5)*, 9048163145) Springer.
Kimura, Daiki. Cell Growth Processes: New Research. 2008. (C). 129.00 *(978-1-60456-132-6(7))* Nova Science Pubs., Inc.
Kitamura, Daisuke, ed. How the Immune System Recognizes Self & Nonself: Immunoreceptors & Their Signaling. 2007. (ENG., Illus.). xviii, 251p. 149.00 *(978-4-431-73883-1(5)*, 4431738835) Springer.
Komuro, Terumasa. Atlas of Interstitial Cells of Cajal in the Gastrointestinal Tract. 2012. (ENG., Illus.). xii, 134p. 189.00 ***(978-94-007-2916-2(2)***, 9400729162) Springer.
Kovalchuk, Igor & Kovalchuk, Olga. Epigenetics in Health & Disease. 2012. (FT Press Science Ser.). (ENG.). 592p. 99.99 ***(978-0-13-259708-1(X))*** FT Press.
Kuriyan, et al. Structural Biology. 2012. (ENG., Illus.). 1032p. pap. 145.00 *(978-0-8153-4188-8(1)*, Garland Science) Taylor & Francis Group.
Labouesse, Michel. Forces & Tension in Development. 2011. (ENG., Illus.). 328p. 198.00 *(978-0-12-385065-2(7)*, Academic Pr.) Elsevier Science & Technology Bks.
Lakshmipathy, Uma & Thyagarajan, Bhaskar. Primary & Stem Cells: Gene Transfer Technologies & Applications. 2011. (ENG., Illus.). 304p. 110.00 ***(978-0-470-61074-9(3)***, Wiley) Wiley, John & Sons, Inc.
Lew, Kristi. How Scientists Research Cells. 2011. (Cells: the Building Blocks of Life Ser.). 116p. (gr. 6-12). 37.50 *(978-1-61753-007-4(7)*, Chelsea Hse.) Facts On File, Inc.
Lewin. Itk- Lewin's Cells 2E Instructor's Toolkit. 2nd rev. ed. 2010. cd-rom 124.95 *(978-0-7637-9506-1(2))* Jones & Bartlett Learning, LLC.
Loughna, P. T. & Pell, J. M. Molecular Physiology of Growth. Loughna, P. T. & Pell, J. M., eds. 2009. (Society for Experimental Biology Seminar Ser.). (ENG., Illus.). 184p. pap. 46.00 *(978-0-521-11453-0(5))* Cambridge Univ. Pr.
Luisi, Pier Luigi & Stano, Pasquale, eds. The Minimal Cell: The Biophysics of Cell Compartment & the Origin of Cell Functionality. 2010. (ENG., Illus.). x, 298p. 189.00 *(978-90-481-9943-3(3)*, 9048199433) Springer.
Macagnano, Antonella, et al. Advanced Topics in Cell Model Systems. 2009. 89.00 *(978-1-60692-906-3(2))* Nova Science Pubs., Inc.
Materials Research Society ( ) Staff, compiled by. Biosurfaces & Biointerfaces. 2007. (Materials Research Society Symposium Proceedings Ser.). 240p. pap. 115.00 *(978-1-60423-406-0(7))* Curran Assocs., Inc.
Mofrad, Mohammad & Kamm, Roger, eds. Cellular Mechanotransduction: Diverse Perspectives from Molecules to Tissues. 2009. (ENG., Illus.). 478p. 135.00 *(978-0-521-89523-1(5))* Cambridge Univ. Pr.
Moll, Pamela. Identification of Vitamin D Target Genes in Human Keratinocytes. 2008. 112p. pap. *(978-3-639-00492-2(2))* VDM Verlag Dr. Mueller e.K.
Nelson, James W. & Fuchs, Elaine, eds. Cell-Cell Junctions. 2010. (ENG., Illus.). 456p. 135.00 *(978-0-87969-884-3(5))* Cold Spring Harbor Laboratory Pr.
Newman, Michael E. & Sprague, Ingrid Schaefer. Cells & Human Health. 2012. (Cells: the Building Blocks of Life Ser.). 136p. (gr. 6-12). 37.50 *(978-1-61753-008-1(5)*, Chelsea Hse.) Facts On File, Inc.
Nomura, Taishin & Asai, Yoshiyuki. Harnessing Biological Complexity: An Introduction to Computational Physiology. 2010. (First Course in â€œIn Silico Medicineâ€ Ser.). x, 190p. pap. 89.95 *(978-4-431-53879-0(8)*, 4431538798) Springer.
Ockleford, C. & Whyte, A. Coated Vesicles. 2009. (ENG., Illus.). 404p. pap. 53.00 *(978-0-521-10574-3(9))* Cambridge Univ. Pr.
Papkovsky, Dmitri B. Live Cell Imaging: Methods & Protocols. 2009. (Methods in Molecular Biology Ser.). (ENG., Illus.). xi, 367p. 110.00 *(978-1-60761-403-6(0)*, 1607614030) Humana Pr.
Peckham, Michelle. Histology at a Glance. 2011. (At a Glance Ser.: 40). (ENG., Illus.). 112p. pap. 40.95 *(978-1-4443-3332-9(1)*, Wiley-Blackwell) Wiley, John & Sons, Inc.
Pena, Antonio. Como Funciona una Celula? (Ciencia para Todos Ser.). (SPA.). pap. 6.99 *(978-968-16-4365-2(8))* Fondo de Cultura Economica USA.
Perloft, Jack W. & Wong, Alexander H., eds. Cell Aging. 2011. (Series: Cell Biology Research Progress Ser.). 140.00 *(978-1-61324-369-5(3))* Nova Science Pubs., Inc.
PH Inc. Staff. Physical Science Cells. 2nd ed. tchr. ed. *(978-0-13-225293-5(7))* Prentice Hall (Schl. Div.).
Pollack, Gerald H., et al, eds. Water & the Cell. 2006. (ENG., Illus.). ix, 354p. 89.95 *(978-1-4020-4926-2(9)*, 1402049269) Springer.
Pozrikidis, Constantine, ed. Computational Hydrodynamics of Capsules & Biological Cells. 2010. (Chapman & Hall/CRC Mathematical & Computational Biology Ser.). (ENG., Illus.). 327p. 135.95 *(978-1-4398-2005-6(8)*, CRC Press) Taylor & Francis Group GBR. Dist: Taylor & Francis Group.
P.R., Sanjaya, et al. Cell Cycle. 2011. 68p. pap. ***(978-3-8383-4942-8(3))*** Lambert Academic Publishing.
Prentice-Hall Staff. Cells. 2nd ed. tchr. ed. *(978-0-13-400474-7(4))*; stu. ed. *(978-0-13-400466-2(3))*; pap., act. bk. ed. *(978-0-13-400482-2(5))* Prentice Hall (Schl. Div.).
—Physical Science Cells Building Blocks. stu. ed., lab manual ed. *(978-0-13-985979-3(9))* Prentice Hall (Schl. Div.).
Rasmussen, Steen, et al, eds. Protocells: Bridging Nonliving & Living Matter. 2008. (ENG., Illus.). 712p. (gr. 17). 75.00 *(978-0-262-18268-3(8))* MIT Pr.
Rogers, Kara. The Cell. 2011. (Biochemistry, Cells, & Life Ser.). (ENG.). 240p. (YA). lib. bdg. 40.00 *(978-1-61530-314-4(6))* Rosen Publishing Group, Inc., The.
Rogers, Kara, ed. The Cell. 2011. (Biochemistry, Cells, & Life Ser.). (Illus.). 240p. (YA). 80.00 *(978-1-61530-431-8(2))* Rosen Publishing Group, Inc., The.
—Fungi, Algae, & Protists. 2011. (Biochemistry, Cells, & Life Ser.). (Illus.). 232p. (YA). 80.00 *(978-1-61530-464-6(9))* Rosen Publishing Group, Inc., The.
Rudolph, K. Lenhard. Molecular Mechanisms of Adult Stem Cell Aging. 2010. (Illus.). viii, 107p. *(978-3-8055-9244-4(2))* Karger, S. AG.
Sadava, et al. Life, Volume 1: The Cell & Heredity: the Science of Biology. 8th ed. 2010. pap. 23.95 *(978-1-4292-7429-6(8))* Freeman, W. H. & Co.
Schekman, Randy, et al, eds. Annual Review of Cell & Developmental Biology. 2007. 731p. 215.00 *(978-0-8243-3123-8(0))* Annual Reviews, Inc.
Shestopaloff, Yuri K. Growth & replication of cells & other living Organisms: Fundamental physical mechanisms that govern nature's Evolvement. 2nd ed. 2009. (ENG., Illus.). 80p. pap. 39.95 *(978-0-9809667-3-2(6))* AKVY Pr. CAN. Dist: Lightning Source, Inc.
—Physics of Growth & Replication: Physical & Geometrical Perspectives on Living Organisms' Development. 2010. (Illus.). 172p. 57.95 *(978-0-9809667-5-6(2))* AKVY Pr. CAN. Dist: Lightning Source, Inc.
Smith, Terry L. The Evolution of Cells. 2012. (Cells: the Building Blocks of Life Ser.). (gr. 6-12). 37.50 *(978-1-61753-006-7(9)*, Chelsea Hse.) Facts On File, Inc.
Solomon, Lewis D. Synthetic Biology: Science, Business, & Policy. 2011. (ENG.). 174p. 39.95 ***(978-1-4128-1856-8(7))*** Transaction Pubs.
Spaan, J. A. E, et al, eds. Biopacemaking. 2010. (Series in Biomedical Engineering Ser.). viii, 182p. pap. 159.00 *(978-3-642-09127-8(X)*, 364209127X) Springer.
Sprague, Ingrid Schaefer. Cells: The Building Blocks of Life. 2012. (Cells: the Building Blocks of Life Ser.). (gr. 6-12). 225.00 ***(978-0-7910-9989-6(X)***, Chelsea Hse.) Facts On File, Inc.
Taatjes, Douglas J. & Mossman, Brooke T., eds. Cell Imaging Techniques. 2010. (Methods in Molecular Biology Ser.). (Illus.). 512p. pap. 199.00 *(978-1-61737-394-7(X)*, 161737394X) Humana Pr.
Tachezy, Jan. Hydrogenosomes & Mitosomes. 2008. (Microbiology Monographs). 279.00 *(978-3-540-76732-9(0)*, 3540767320) Springer.
Tapia, Ricardo. Las Celulas de la Mente. (Ciencia para Todos Ser.). (SPA.). pap. 6.99 *(978-968-16-2545-0(5))* Fondo de Cultura Economica USA.
Tavernarakis, Nektarios. Protein Metabolism & Homeostasis in Aging. 2010. (Advances in Experimental Medicine & Biology Ser.). (ENG., Illus.). xxii, 248p. 189.00 *(978-1-4419-7001-5(0)*, 1441970010) Springer.
Wada. Biomechanics at Micro- Nanoscale. . Vii. (Illus.). 107.00 *(978-981-256-746-8(1))* World Scientific Publishing Co., Inc.
Wolpert, Lewis. How We Live & Why We Die: The Secret Lives of Cells. 2011. (ENG.). 240p. pap. 15.95 *(978-0-393-33938-3(6)*, 33938) Norton, W. W. & Co., Inc.
Yon-Kahn, Jeannine & Hervé, G. Molecular & Cellular Enzymology, 2 vols. 2010. (ENG., Illus.). xliv, 783p. 299.00 *(978-3-642-01227-3(2)*, 3642012272) Springer.
Zaikowski, Lori & Friedrich, Jon M. Chemical Evolution Across Space & Time: From Big Bang to Prebiotic Chemistry. Zaikowski, Lori & Friedrich, Jon, eds. 2008. (ACS Symposium Ser.). (ENG., Illus.). 300p. (C). 145.00 *(978-0-8412-7431-0(2))* American Chemical Society.

CELLS—EFFECT OF DRUGS ON
Papageorgiou, Anna-Pia. Expression & Function of a Serotoninergic System in the Rat Anterior Pituitary. 2006. (Acta Biomedical Lovaniensia: 379). (Illus.). 144p. (Orig.). pap. 97.50 *(978-90-5867-582-8(3))* Leuven Univ. Pr. BEL. Dist: Cornell Univ. Pr.
Scatena, Roberto, et al, eds. Advances in Mitochondrial Medicine. 2012. (Advances in Experimental Medicine & Biology Ser.). (ENG., Illus.). xii, 461p. 209.00 ***(978-94-007-2868-4(9)***, 9400728689) Springer.

CELLS—JUVENILE LITERATURE
Cregan, Elizabeth R. All about Mitosis & Meiosis. 2010. (Mission: Science Ser.). (ENG.). 40p. (gr. 5-6). lib. bdg. 27.99 *(978-0-7565-4067-8(4)*, Exploring Science) Compass Point Bks.

CELLS—METABOLISM
see Cell Metabolism

CELLS—MOTILITY
Abreu, T. & Silva, G. Cell Movement: New Research Trends. 2008. (Illus.). xiii, 383p. 129.00 *(978-1-60692-570-6(9))* Nova Science Pubs., Inc.
Carlier, Marie-France, ed. Actin-based Motility: Cellular, Molecular & Physical Aspects. 2010. (ENG.). xii, 300p. 209.00 *(978-90-481-9300-4(1)*, 9048193001) Springer.
Douglas, Mark. Retrograde Cellular Transport of Herpes Simplex Virus. 2008. 180p. pap. *(978-3-639-02865-2(1))* VDM Verlag Dr. Mueller e.K.
Hu, Jiancheng. Regulation of B Cell Migration & Antigen Receptor Signaling by Lsc. 2010. 136p. pap. *(978-3-639-27472-1(5))* VDM Verlag Dr. Mueller e.K.
Inoue. The Collected Works of Shinya Inoue. 2008. 237.00 *(978-981-270-388-0(8))* World Scientific Publishing Co., Inc.

Lenz, Peter, ed. Cell Motility. 2007. (Biological & Medical Physics, Biomedical Engineering Ser.). (Illus.). 248p. 209.00 *(978-0-387-73049-3(4))* Springer.

Marelli-Berg, Federica M. & Nourshargh, S., eds. T-Cell Trafficking. 2010. (Methods in Molecular Biology Ser.). (ENG., Illus.). x, 246p. 119.00 *(978-1-60761-460-9(X)*, 160761460X) Humana Pr.

Pardee, Joel. The Actin Cytoskeleton in Cell Motility, Cancer, & Infection. Pardee, Joel, ed. 2010. (Colloquium Series on Cell Biology of Medicine Ser.). 57p. (C). pap., pap. 30.00 *(978-1-61504-006-3(4))* Morgan & Claypool Life Science Publishers.

Segev, Nava, ed. Trafficking Inside Cells: Pathways, Mechanisms & Regulation. 2009. (Molecular Biology Intelligence Unit Ser.). (ENG., Illus.). 465p. 209.00 *(978-0-387-93876-9(1)*, 0387938761) Springer.

Witman, George, ed. The Chlamydomonas Sourcebook - Cell Motility & Behavior, 3 vols., Vol. 3. 2nd ed. 2008. (The Chlamydomonas Sourcebook). (ENG., Illus.). 512p. 87.95 *(978-0-12-370876-2(1)*, Academic Pr.) Elsevier Science & Technology Bks.

CELLS—PERMEABILITY

Baluska, Frantisek, ed. Cell-Cell Channels. 2006. (Illus.). xviii, 321p. 185.00 *(978-0-387-36058-4(1)*, 0387360581) Springer.

CELLS, EFFECT OF DRUGS ON

see Cells—Effect of Drugs on

CELLS, KILLER

see Killer Cells

CELLS, SOLAR

see Solar Cells

CELLULAR AUTOMATA

Adamatzky, Andrew, ed. Game of Life Cellular Automata. 2010. (ENG., Illus.). xvi, 621p. 159.00 *(978-1-84996-216-2(2)*, 1849962162) Springer.

Aladjev, V. Z. Classical Cellular Automata Homogeneous Structures. 2010. 480p. pap. 25.99 *(978-1-59682-222-1(8))* Fultus Corp.

Alonso-Sanz, Ramon. Cellular Automata with Memory. 2008. (Illus.). iii, 245p. ***(978-2-914610-80-3(7))*** Editions des Archives.

Altmann, Jö, et al, eds. Advances in Collective Intelligence 2011. 2012. (Advances in Intelligent & Soft Computing Ser.). (ENG., Illus.). x, 170p. pap. 199.00 ***(978-3-642-25320-1(2)***, 3642253202) Springer.

Bandini, Stefania, et al, eds. Cellular Automata: 9th International Conference on Cellular Automata for Research & Industry, ACRI 2010, Ascoli Piceno, Italy, September 21-24, 2010, Proceedings. 2010. (Lecture Notes in Computer Science / Theoretical Computer Science & General Issues Ser.). xvi, 672p. pap. 119.00 *(978-3-642-15978-7(8)*, 3642159788) Springer.

Bastiaens, Theo, et al, eds. On Collective Intelligence. 2010. (Advances in Intelligent & Soft Computing Ser.). 170p. pap. 199.00 *(978-3-642-14480-6(2)*, 3642144802) Springer.

Bilotta, Eleonora & Pantano, Pietro. Cellular Automata & Complex Systems: Methods for Modeling Biological Phenomena. 2010. (Illus.). 361p. 245.00 *(978-1-61520-787-9(2))* IGI Global.

Blum, Christian & Merkle, Daniel. Swarm Intelligence: Introduction & Applications. 2008. (Natural Computing Ser.). (Illus.). 285p. 99.00 *(978-3-540-74088-9(0)*, 3540740880) Springer.

Bonchev, Danail D. & Rouvray, Dennis, eds. Complexity in Chemistry, Biology, & Ecology. 2010. (Mathematical & Computational Chemistry Ser.). xx, 344p. pap. 129.00 *(978-1-4419-3592-2(4)*, 1441935924) Springer.

Ceccherini-Silberstein, Tullio & Ccornaert, Michel. Cellular Automata & Groups. 2010. (Springer Monographs in Mathematics Ser.). xix, 439p. 124.00 *(978-3-642-14033-4(5)*, 3642140335) Springer.

Cellular Automata with Memory. 2008. pap. 90.00 *(978-1-933153-07-0(5)*, OCP Science) Old City Publishing, Inc.

Chen, Ching-Yi. Pso-Based Evolutionary Learning. 2011. 156p. pap. ***(978-3-8443-3153-0(0))*** Lambert Academic Publishing.

Chua, Leon O. Nonlinear Dynamics Perspective of Wolfram's New Kind of Science. 2009. (World Scientific Series on Nonlinear Science). (Illus.). 360p. 130.00 *(978-981-283-793-6(0))* World Scientific Publishing Co., Inc.

—A Nonlinear Dynamics Perspective of Wolfram's New Kind of Science: Volume 2, 2 vols. 2007. (World Scientific Series on Nonlinear Science, Series A Ser.: Vol. 57). (Illus.). 947p. 375.00 *(978-981-256-642-3(2))* World Scientific Publishing Co., Inc.

Chua, Leon O. Nonlinear Dynamics Perspective of Wolfram's New Kind of Science, A (Volume V) 2012. 352p. 158.00 ***(978-981-4390-51-4(8))*** World Scientific Publishing Co., Inc.

Chua, Leon O. & Wolfram, Stephen. Nonlinear Dynamics Perspective of Wolfram's New Kind of Science, A (Volume Iv) 2010. (World Scientific Series on Nonlinear Science). (Illus.). 400p. 178.00 *(978-981-4317-30-6(6))* World Scientific Publishing Co., Inc.

Coello Coello, Carlos A., et al, eds. Swarm Intelligence for Multi-objective Problems in Data Mining. 2009. (Studies in Computational Intelligence Ser.). (ENG., Illus.). xiv, 288p. 159.00 *(978-3-642-03624-8(4)*, 3642036244) Springer.

Delorme, M. & Mazoyer, J, eds. Cellular Automata: A Parallel Model. 2010. (Mathematics & Its Applications Ser.). 388p. pap. 279.00 *(978-90-481-5143-1(0)*, 9048151430) Springer.

Dorigo, Marco. Ant Colony Optimization & Swarm Intelligence. 2008. (Lecture Notes in Computer Science / Theoretical Computer Science & General Issues Ser.). (Illus.). xv, 416p. 89.95 *(978-3-540-87526-0(3))* Springer.

Durand-Lose, Jerome, ed. Machines, Computations, & Universality: 5th International Conference, MCU 2007 Orleans, France, September 10-13, 2007 Proceedings. 2007. (Lecture Notes in Computer Science Ser.). (Illus.). 324p. per. 79.95 *(978-3-540-74592-1(0))* Springer.

El-Gallad, Ahmed. Multiple Criteria Decision Making for Swarm Optimization. 2008. (Illus.). 200p. pap. *(978-3-639-06416-2(X))* VDM Verlag Dr. Mueller e.K.

El Yacoubi, Samira, et al, eds. Cellular Automata: 7th International Conference on Cellular Automata for Research & Industry, ACRI 2006 Perpignan, France, September 20-23, 2006 Proceedings. 2007. (Lecture Notes in Computer Science Ser.). (Illus.). 735p. per. 139.00 *(978-3-540-40929-8(7)*, 3540409297) Springer.

Fadaei, Amir Hosein & Setayeshi, Saeed. CA Upgrading for Extending the Optimization Problem Solving Ability. 2011. (Series: Computational Mathematics & Analysis Ser.). pap. 43.00 *(978-1-61122-743-7(7)*, Nova Novinka) Nova Science Pubs., Inc.

Fisher, Len. The Perfect Swarm: The Science of Complexity in Everyday Life. 2011. (ENG.). 288p. (gr. 9). pap. 14.99 *(978-0-465-02024-9(0))* Basic Bks.

Fleischer, Frank (German Institute for Economic Research. Analysis & Fitting of Random Tessellation Models. 2008. 220p. pap. *(978-3-8364-8743-6(8))* VDM Verlag Dr. Mueller e.K.

Frisco, Pierluigi. Computing with Cells: Advances in Membrane Computing. 2009. (ENG., Illus.). 330p. (C). 110.00 *(978-0-19-954286-4(4))* Oxford Univ. Pr., Inc.

Goles, E. & Martinez, Servet, eds. Cellular Automata & Complex Systems. 2010. (Nonlinear Phenomena & Complex Systems Ser.). 196p. pap. 189.00 *(978-90-481-5154-7(6)*, 9048151546) Springer.

—Cellular Automata, Dynamical Systems & Neural Networks. 2010. (Mathematics & Its Applications Ser.). 204p. pap. 189.00 *(978-90-481-4382-5(9)*, 9048143829) Springer.

—Dynamics of Complex Interacting Systems. 2010. (Nonlinear Phenomena & Complex Systems Ser.). 186p. pap. 189.00 *(978-90-481-4734-2(4)*, 9048147344) Springer.

Guldogan, Mehmet Burak. Multipath Channel Identification. 2011. 184p. pap. ***(978-3-8443-9712-3(4))*** Lambert Academic Publishing.

Jakimovski, Bojan. Biologically Inspired Approaches for Locomotion, Anomaly Detection & Reconfiguration for Walking Robots. 2011. (Cognitive Systems Monographs). (ENG., Illus.). x, 206p. 109.00 ***(978-3-642-22504-8(7)***, 3642225047) Springer.

Kholosha, Alexander. Investigations in the Design & Analysis of Key-Stream Generators. 2008. 120p. pap. *(978-3-639-10716-6(0))* VDM Verlag Dr. Mueller e.K.

Kroc, Jiri, et al, eds. Simulating Complex Systems by Cellular Automata. 2010. (Understanding Complex Systems Ser.). (ENG., Illus.). xxi, 384p. 169.00 *(978-3-642-12202-6(7)*, 3642122027) Springer.

Li, Thomas M. Cellular Automata. 2011. (Mathematics Research Developments Ser.). (Illus.). xii, 295p. 195.00 *(978-1-61761-592-4(7))* Nova Science Pubs., Inc.

Lim, Chee Peng, et al, eds. Innovations in Swarm Intelligence. 2009. (Studies in Computational Intelligence Ser.). (Illus.). viii, 256p. 159.00 *(978-3-642-04224-9(4)*, 3642042244) Springer.

Liu, Yan. Modelling Urban Development with Geographical Information Systems & Cellular Automata. 2008. (ENG., Illus.). 186p. 129.95 *(978-1-4200-5989-2(0)*, CRC Press) Taylor & Francis Group GBR. Dist: Taylor & Francis Group.

MacLennan, Bruce, ed. Theoretical & Technological Advancements in Nanotechnology & Molecular Computation: Interdisciplinary Gains. 2010. (Illus.). 350p. 245.00 *(978-1-60960-186-7(6)*, Information Science Reference) IGI Global.

Mainzer, Klaus & Chua, Leon O. The Universe as Automaton: From Simplicity & Symmetry to Complexity. 2011. (SpringerBriefs in Complexity Ser.). (ENG., Illus.). viii, 108p. pap. 49.95 ***(978-3-642-23476-7(3)***, 3642234763) Springer.

Margenstern, Maurice. Cellular Automata in Hyperbolic Spaces - Volume 1. 2007. per. 80.00 *(978-1-933153-04-9(0)*, OCP Science) Old City Publishing, Inc.

Mazzola, Guerino B. & Cherlin, Paul B. Flow, Gesture, & Spaces in Free Jazz: Towards a Theory of Collaboration. 2009. (Computational Music Science Ser.). (ENG., Illus.). xiv, 141p. 79.95 *(978-3-540-92194-3(X))* Springer.

Nedjah, Nadia, et al, eds. Multi-Objective Swarm Intelligent Systems: Theory & Experiences. 2009. (Studies in Computational Intelligence Ser.). (Illus.). xxii, 218p. 159.00 *(978-3-642-05164-7(2)*, 3642051642) Springer.

Olsson, Andrea E., ed. Particle Swarm Optimization: Theory, Techniques & Applications. 2010. (Mathematics Research Developments Ser.). (Illus.). xi, 305p. 129.00 *(978-1-61668-527-0(1))* Nova Science Pubs., Inc.

Panigrahi, Bijaya Ketan, et al, eds. Handbook of Swarm Intelligence: Concepts, Principles & Applications. 2011. (Adaptation, Learning, & Optimization Ser.). (ENG.). 542p. pap. 24.95 ***(978-3-642-17391-2(8))*** Springer.

—Swarm, Evolutionary, & Memetic Computing: Second International Conference, SEMCCO 2011, Visakhapatnam, India, December 19-21, 2011, Proceedings, Part I, 2 vols. 2011. (Lecture Notes in Computer Science / Theoretical Computer Science & General Issues Ser.). (ENG., Illus.). xxii, 754p. pap. 131.00 ***(978-3-642-27171-7(5)***, 3642271715) Springer.

Panigraphi, Bijata Ketan, et al, eds. Swarm, Evolutionary, & Memetic Computing, Part II: Second International Conference, SEMCCO 2011, Visakhapatnam, India, December 19-21, 2011, Proceedings, Part II, 2 vols. 2011. (Lecture Notes in Computer Science / Theoretical Computer Science & General Issues Ser.). (ENG., Illus.). xxii, 332p. pap. 83.00 ***(978-3-642-27241-7(X)***, 364227241X) Springer.

Parikka, Jussi. Insect Media: An Archaeology of Animals & Technology. 2010. (Posthumanities Ser.). (ENG., Illus.). 320p. 75.00 *(978-0-8166-6739-0(X))*; pap. 25.00 *(978-0-8166-6740-6(3))* Univ. of Minnesota Pr.

Parsopoulos, Konstantinos E. & Vrahatis, Michael N. Particle Swarm Optimization & Intelligence: Advances & Applications. 2010. 378p. 180.00 *(978-1-61520-666-7(3)*, Information Science Reference) IGI Global.

Sahin, Erol, et al, eds. Swarm Robotics: Second SAB 2006 International Workshop, Rome, Italy, September 30-October 1, 2006 Revised Selected Papers. 2008. (Lecture Notes in Computer Science Ser.). xii, 221p. pap. 69.95 *(978-3-540-71540-5(1))* Springer.

Sasaki, Hideyasu. Intelligent & Knowledge-Based Computing for Business & Organizational Advancements. 2012. ***(978-1-4666-1579-3(6))*** IGI Global.

Sasaki, Hideyasu, et al, eds. Intelligent & Knowledge-Based Computing for Business & Organizational Advancements. 2012. ***(978-1-4666-1577-9(X))*** IGI Global.

Schiff, Joel L. Cellular Automata: A Discrete View of the World. 2007. (Wiley Series in Discrete Mathematics & Optimization Ser.: 45). (ENG., Illus.). 280p. 139.00 *(978-0-470-16879-0(X)*, Wiley-Interscience) Wiley, John & Sons, Inc.

Solnon, Christine. Ant Colony Optimization & Constraint Programming. 2010. (Iste Ser.: 410). (ENG., Illus.). 320p. 142.00 *(978-1-84821-130-8(9)*, Wiley-ISTE) Wiley, John & Sons, Inc.

Spears, William M. & Spears, Diana F., eds. Physicomimetics: Physics-Based Swarm Intelligence. 2012. (ENG., Illus.). xxx, 643p. 159.00 ***(978-3-642-22803-2(8)***, 3642228038) Springer.

Sun, Jun, et al. Particle Swarm Optimisation. 2011. (Chapman & Hall/CRC Numerical Analysis & Scientific Computation Ser.). (ENG., Illus.). 419p. 89.95 *(978-1-4398-3576-0(4)*, CRC Press) Taylor & Francis Group GBR. Dist: Taylor & Francis Group.

Tan, Ying, et al, eds. Advances in Swarm Intelligence: First International Conference, ICSI 2010, Beijing, China, June 12-15, 2010, Proceedings, Part I. 2010. (Lecture Notes in Computer Science / Theoretical Computer Science & General Issues Ser.). xxvi, 746p. pap. 139.00 *(978-3-642-13494-4(7)*, 3642134947) Springer.

—Advances in Swarm Intelligence: First International Conference, ICSI 2010, Beijing, China, June 12-15, 2010, Proceedings, Part II. 2010. (Lecture Notes in Computer Science / Theoretical Computer Science & General Issues Ser.). 772p. pap. 139.00 *(978-3-642-13497-5(1)*, 3642134971) Springer.

—Advances in Swarm Intelligence: Second International Conference, Icsi 2011, Chongqing, China, June 12-15, 2011, 2 vols. 2011. (Lecture Notes in Computer Science / Theoretical Computer Science & General Issues Ser.). (Illus.). xxvi, 587p. pap. 119.00 ***(978-3-642-21523-0(8)***, 3642215238) Springer.

—Advances in Swarm Intelligence, Part I: Second International Conference, ICSI 2011, Chongqing, China, June 12-15, 2011, Proceedings, Part I, 2 vols. 2011. (Lecture Notes in Computer Science / Theoretical Computer Science & General Issues Ser.). (Illus.). xxvi, 639p. pap. 119.00 ***(978-3-642-21514-8(9)***, 3642215149) Springer.

Trianni, Vito. Evolutionary Swarm Robotics: Evolving Self-Organising Behaviours in Groups of Autonomous Robots. 2010. (Studies in Computational Intelligence Ser.). (Illus.). xvi, 190p. pap. 179.00 *(978-3-642-09635-8(2)*, 3642096352) Springer.

Umeo, Hiroshi. Cellular Automata. 2008. (Lecture Notes in Computer Science / Theoretical Computer Science & General Issues Ser.). spiral bd. 99.00 *(978-3-540-79991-7(5))* Springer.

Walters, Louis P., ed. Applications of Swarm Intelligence. 2010. (Engineering Tools, Techniques & Tables Ser.). 99.00 *(978-1-61728-602-5(8))* Nova Science Pubs., Inc.

Zahiri, Seyed-Hamid. Swarm Intelligence & Fuzzy Systems. 2010. pap. 49.00 *(978-1-61729-975-0(2))* Nova Science Pubs., Inc.

CELLULAR BIOLOGY

see Cytology

CELLULAR CONTROL MECHANISMS

Here are entered works on the various mechanisms of cellular control such as structural control, biochemical control, cell differentiation, etc. Works on the control of the type and rate of cellular processes by regulation of the activity of specific genes controlling individual biochemical reactions are entered under Genetic Regulation.

see also Cell Interaction; Cell Metabolism; Genetic Regulation

Aguda, Baltazar & Friedman, Avner. Models of Cellular Regulation. (ENG., Illus.). 200p. 2012. pap. 64.99 ***(978-0-19-965750-6(5))*** 2008. 99.00 *(978-0-19-857091-2(0))* Oxford Univ. Pr., Inc.

Buchanan, Mark, et al, eds. Networks in Cell Biology. 2010. (ENG., Illus.). 280p. 75.00 *(978-0-521-88273-6(7))* Cambridge Univ. Pr.

Carré, Alain & Mittal, K. L. Surface & Interfacial Aspects of Cell Adhesion. 2011. (ENG., Illus.). 544p. 260.00 ***(978-90-04-19078-8(3)***, CRC Press) Taylor & Francis Group GBR. Dist: Taylor & Francis Group.

Conn, P. Michael. The Unfolded Protein Response & Cellular Stress, Part C, 3 vols. 2011. (ENG., Illus.). 464p. 187.00 *(978-0-12-385928-0(X)*, Academic Pr.) Elsevier Science & Technology Bks.

Conn, P. Michael, ed. The Unfolded Protein Response & Cellular Stress, Part A, 3 vols. 2011. (ENG., Illus.). 432p. 187.00 *(978-0-12-385116-1(5)*, Academic Pr.) Elsevier Science & Technology Bks.

—The Unfolded Protein Response & Cellular Stress, Part B, 3 vols. 2011. (ENG., Illus.). 432p. 187.00 *(978-0-12-385114-7(9)*, Academic Pr.) Elsevier Science & Technology Bks.

Dai, Wei, ed. Checkpoint Responses in Cancer Therapy. 2008. (Cancer Drug Discovery & Development Ser.). (Illus.). 300p. 219.00 *(978-1-58829-930-7(9))* Humana Pr.

Fahmy Mohamed, Inas. New Discoveries on Begomovirus-Vector Interaction Through Their Vector. 2011. 184p. pap. ***(978-3-8443-0459-6(2))*** Lambert Academic Publishing.

Giordano, Antonio & Galderisi, Umberto, eds. Cell Cycle Regulation & Differentiation in Cardiovascular & Neural Systems. 2009. (Illus.). 300p. 189.00 *(978-1-60327-152-3(X))* Humana Pr.

Henzler, H. J., et al. Influence of Stress on Cell Growth & Product Formation. 2010. (Advances in Biochemical Engineering Biotechnology Ser.). (Illus.). ix, 190p. pap. 269.00 *(978-3-642-08594-9(6)*, 3642085946) Springer.

Inzé, Dirk, ed. Annual Plant Reviews, Cell Cycle Control & Plant Development, Volume 32. 2007. (Annual Plant Reviews Ser.: 34). (ENG., Illus.). 384p. 239.95 *(978-1-4051-5043-9(2)*, Wiley-Blackwell) Wiley, John & Sons, Inc.

Jentsch, Stefan & Haendler, Bernhard. The Ubiquitin System in Health & Disease. (Ernst Schering Foundation Symposium Proceedings Ser.). (Illus.). xvi, 191p. 2010. (ENG.). pap. 99.00 *(978-3-642-09880-2(0)*, 3642098800) 2008. 99.00 *(978-3-540-85106-6(2))* Springer.

Jiang, Shuiping, ed. Regulatory T Cells & Clinical Application. (ENG., Illus.). xviii, 588p. 2010. pap. 169.00 *(978-1-4419-2670-8(4)*, 1441926704) 2008. 169.00 *(978-0-387-77908-9(6)*, 0387779086) Springer.

Jones, Phill. Cell Structure, Processes, & Reproduction. 2011. (Cells: the Building Blocks of Life Ser.). 124p. (gr. 6-12). 37.50 *(978-1-61753-004-3(2)*, Chelsea Hse.) Facts On File, Inc.

Kaldis, Philipp, ed. Cell Cycle Regulation. (Results & Problems in Cell Differentiation Ser.). (Illus.). xii, 374p. 2010. pap. 269.00 *(978-3-642-07093-8(0)*, 3642070930) 2006. 269.00 *(978-3-540-34552-7(3)*, 3540345523) Springer.

Keränen, Sirkka & Jäntti, Jussi, eds. Regulatory Mechanisms of Intracellular Membrane Transport. 2010. (Topics in Current Genetics Ser.). (Illus.). x, 214p. pap. 169.00 *(978-3-642-06095-3(1)*, 3642060951) Springer.

Klionsky, Daniel J. Autophagy in Mammalian Systems, 3 vols., Pt. B. Klionsky, Daniel, ed. 2009. (ENG., Illus.). 560p. 187.00 *(978-0-12-374547-7(0)*, Academic Pr.) Elsevier Science & Technology Bks.

Lang, Florian. Mechanisms & Significance of Cell Volume Regulation. (Contributions to Nephrology Ser.: Vol. 152). (Illus.). vi, 275p. *(978-3-8055-8174-5(2))* Karger, S. AG.

Leroy, Nathan H. & Fournier, Noah T. Cell Cycle Control: New Research. 2008. (Illus.). 496p. (C). 129.00 *(978-1-60456-796-0(1))* Nova Science Pubs., Inc.

Liu, Weijiu. Introduction to Modeling Biological Cellular Control Systems. 2011. (Ms&a Ser.). (ENG., Illus.). x, 290p. 69.95 ***(978-88-470-2489-2(7)***, 8847024897) Springer.

Mallick, Bibekanand & Ghosh, Zhumur, eds. Regulatory RNAs: Basics, Methods & Applications. 2012. (ENG., Illus.). ix, 552p. 209.00 ***(978-3-642-22516-1(0)***, 3642225160) Springer.

Mancuso, Stefano & Shabala, Sergey, eds. Rhythms in Plants: Phenomenology, Mechanisms, & Adaptive Significance. 2010. (ENG., Illus.). xx, 362p. pap. 289.00 *(978-3-642-08774-5(4)*, 3642087744) Springer.

Monette, F. Cell Cycle Biology. (Illus.). 352p. pap. 44.95 *(978-0-632-04297-5(4)*, Wiley-Blackwell) Wiley, John & Sons, Inc.

Quinn, Peter J., ed. Membrane Dynamics & Domains. 2010. (Subcellular Biochemistry Ser.). 516p. pap. 199.00 *(978-1-4419-3447-5(2)*, 1441934472) Springer.

Radtke, Freddy, ed. Notch Regulation of the Immune System. 2012. (Current Topics in Microbiology & Immunology Ser.). (ENG., Illus.). x, 200p. 189.00 ***(978-3-642-24293-9(6)***, 3642242936) Springer.

Rudensky, Alexander & Sakaguchi, Shimon. Regulatory T-Cells. 2011. (Advances in Immunology Ser.: 112). (ENG., Illus.). 240p. 182.00 ***(978-0-12-387827-4(6)***, Academic Pr.) Elsevier Science & Technology Bks.

Schönthal, Axel H., ed. Checkpoint Controls & Cancer: Volume 1: Reviews & Model Systems. 2010. (Methods in Molecular Biology Ser.). (Illus.). xvi, 318p. pap. 119.00 *(978-1-61737-426-5(1)*, 1617374261) Humana Pr.

—Checkpoint Controls & Cancer: Volume 2: Activation & Regulation Protocols. 2010. (Methods in Molecular Biology Ser.). (Illus.). 348p. pap. 139.00 *(978-1-61737-603-0(5)*, 1617376035) Humana Pr.

Segev, Nava, ed. Trafficking Inside Cells: Pathways, Mechanisms & Regulation. 2009. (Molecular Biology Intelligence Unit Ser.). (ENG., Illus.). 465p. 209.00 *(978-0-387-93876-9(1)*, 0387938761) Springer.

Shultz, Lawrence B. Cell Apoptosis: Regulation & Environmental Factors. 2007. 211p. 129.00 *(978-1-60021-508-7(4))* Nova Science Pubs., Inc.

Silberberg, Yaron. Cellular Mechanics & Intracellular Organization. 2010. 168p. pap. *(978-3-639-22122-0(2))* VDM Verlag Dr. Mueller e.K.

Terzer, Marco. Large Scale Methods to Enumerate Extreme Rays & Elementary Modes (b/w Print) 2009. 168p. pap. 12.40 *(978-1-4452-4877-6(8))* Lulu Enterprises Inc.

—Large Scale Methods to Enumerate Extreme Rays & Elementary Modes (color Print) 2009. 168p. pap. 54.40 *(978-1-4452-4879-0(4))* Lulu Enterprises Inc.

Thiriet, Marc. Control of Cell Fate in the Circulatory & Ventilatory Systems. 2011. (Biomathematical & Biomechanical Modeling of the Circulatory & Ventilatory Systems Ser.). (ENG., Illus.). x, 536p. 199.00 *(978-1-4614-0328-9(6)*, 1461403286) Springer.

Wilusz, Jeffrey. Post-Transcriptional Gene Regulation. 2008. (Methods in Molecular Biology Ser.). 129.00 *(978-1-58829-783-9(7))* Humana Pr.

Wilusz, Jeffrey, ed. Post-Transcriptional Gene Regulation. 2010. (Methods in Molecular Biology Ser.). (Illus.). xviii, 318p. pap. 129.00 *(978-1-61737-776-1(7)*, 1617377767) Humana Pr.

C

CELLULAR GROWTH FACTORS
see Growth Factors

CELLULAR IMMUNITY
see also Cytokines

Abbas, Abul K., et al. Cellular & Molecular Immunology. 7th ed. 2012. (Illus.). x, 545p. ***(978-0-8089-2425-8(7)***, Saunders) Elsevier - Health Sciences Div.

Abbas, Abul K., et al. Cellular & Molecular Immunology: With STUDENT CONSULT Online Access. 7th ed. 2011. (ENG., Illus.). 560p. (C). pap. 84.95 *(978-1-4377-1528-6(1)*, Saunders) Elsevier - Health Sciences Div.

Cellular Immunology. pap. *(978-0-412-24380-6(6))* CENGAGE Learning.

Fiorino, S., et al. Hepatitis B Virus & Immune Response. 2008. vi, 99p. (C). pap. 50.00 *(978-1-60456-450-1(4))* Nova Science Pubs., Inc.

Gundelfinger, Eckart D., et al. Cell Communication in Nervous & Immune System. 2010. (Results & Problems in Cell Differentiation Ser.). (Illus.). xiv, 313p. pap. 239.00 *(978-3-642-07192-8(9)*, 3642071929) Springer.

Kassiotis, George & Liston, Adrian, eds. Regulatory T Cells: Methods & Protocols. 2011. (Methods in Molecular Biology Ser.). (Illus.). xi, 282p. 119.00 *(978-1-61737-978-9(6)*, 1617379786) Humana Pr.

McCoy, Claire E. & O'Neill, Luke A. J. Toll-Like Receptors: Methods & Protocols. 2009. (Methods in Molecular Biology Ser.). (Illus.). (ENG.). 400p. 129.00 *(978-1-934115-72-5(X))*; xiv, 447p. *(978-1-59745-541-1(5))* Humana Pr.

Nagorsen, Dirk & Marincola, Francesco M., eds. Analyzing T Cell Responses: How to analyze cellular immune responses against tumor associated Antigens. 2010. (ENG., Illus.). xii, 313p. pap. 169.00 *(978-90-481-6911-5(9)*, 9048169119) Springer.

Rast, Jonathan P. & Booth, James W. D., eds. Immune Receptors: Methods & Protocols. 2011. (Methods in Molecular Biology Ser.). (Illus.). xi, 301p. 119.00 *(978-1-61779-138-3(5)*, 1617791385) Humana Pr.

Salt, George. The Cellular Defence Reactions of Insects. 2009. (Cambridge Monographs in Experimental Biology Ser.). (ENG.). 132p. pap. 31.99 *(978-0-521-10425-8(4))* Cambridge Univ. Pr.

Welles, Lorraine C., ed. Dendritic Cells: Types, Life Cycles & Biological Functions. 2010. (Cell Biology Research Progress Ser.). 160.00 *(978-1-61668-954-4(4))* Nova Science Pubs., Inc.

CELLULAR IMMUNOLOGY
see Cellular Immunity

CELLULAR INTERACTION
see Cell Interaction

CELLULAR PATHOLOGY
see Pathology, Cellular

CELLULAR PHARMACOLOGY
see Cells—Effect of Drugs on

CELLULAR PHONES
see Cell Phones

CELLULAR PLASTICS
see Plastic Foams

CELLULAR RADIO
see Cell Phone Services Industry; Cell Phone Systems; Cell Phones

CELLULAR RADIO EQUIPMENT INDUSTRY
see Cell Phone Equipment Industry

CELLULAR RADIOTELOPHONE SYSTEMS
see Cell Phone Systems

CELLULAR REGULATION

Manser, Edward J., ed. Rho Family GTPases. 2010. (Proteins & Cell Regulation Ser.). (Illus.). xiii, 296p. pap. 199.00 *(978-90-481-6873-6(2)*, 9048168732) Springer.

CELLULAR SERVICES INDUSTRY
see Cell Phone Services Industry

CELLULAR SIGNAL TRANSDUCTION

Agostinis, Patrizia & Afshin, Samali, eds. Endoplasmic Reticulum Stress in Health & Disease. 2012. (ENG., Illus.). i, 349p. 209.00 ***(978-94-007-4350-2(5)***, 9400743505) Springer.

Ali, Hydar & Bodduluri, Haribabu, eds. Transmembrane Signaling Protocols. 2nd ed. 2010. (Methods in Molecular Biology Ser.). (Illus.). 376p. pap. 139.00 *(978-1-61737-633-7(7)*, 1617376337) Humana Pr.

Altmann, A. & Theofilopoulos, Argyrios N., eds. Signal Transduction Pathways in Autoimmunity, Vol. 5. (Current Directions in Autoimmunity Ser.: Vol. 5). (Illus.). *(978-3-8055-7308-5(1))* Karger, S. AG.

Armati, Patricia, ed. The Biology of Schwann Cells: Development, Differentiation & Immunomodulation. 2007. (ENG., Illus.). 264p. 171.00 *(978-0-521-85020-9(7))* Cambridge Univ. Pr.

Aspenstrom, Pontus, ed. The Pombe Cdc 15 Homology Proteins. 2009. (Molecular Biology Intelligence Unit Ser.). *(978-1-58706-313-8(1))* Landes Bioscience.

Baier, Gottfried, et al. Sparking Signals: Kinases as Molecular Signaltransducers & Pharmacological Drug Targets in Inflammation. 2010. (Ernst Schering Foundation Symposium Proceedings Ser.). (Illus.). xiv, 187p. pap. 159.00 *(978-3-642-09262-6(4)*, 3642092624) Springer.

Baier, Gottfried, et al, eds. Sparking Signals: Kinases as Molecular Signaltransducers & Pharmacological Drug Targets in Inflammation. 2008. (Ernst Schering Foundation Symposium Proceedings Ser.). (Illus.). 185p. 99.00 *(978-3-540-73500-7(3))* Springer.

Balaban, Naomi, ed. Control of Biofilm Infections by Signal Manipulation. (Springer Series on Biofilms Ser.). (Illus.). 2010. xvi, 175p. pap. 159.00 *(978-3-642-09309-8(4)*, 3642093094) 2008. 175p. 159.00 *(978-3-540-73852-7(5))* Springer.

Baluka, Frantiek, et al, eds. Communication in Plants: Neuronal Aspects of Plant Life. 2010. (ENG., Illus.). xxx, 438p. pap. 289.00 *(978-3-642-06672-6(0)*, 3642066720) Springer.

Baluska, F. & Mancuso, Stefano. Signaling in Plants. 2008. (Signaling & Communication in Plants Ser.). (Illus.). 320p. 239.00 *(978-3-540-89227-4(3))* Springer.

Becchetti, Andrea & Arcangeli, Annarosa, eds. Integrins & Ion Channels: Molecular Complexes & Signaling. 2010. (Advances in Experimental Medicine & Biology Ser.). (ENG., Illus.). xx, 124p. 159.00 *(978-1-4419-6065-8(1)*, 1441960651) Springer.

Beckerman, Martin. Cellular Signaling in Health & Disease. 2009. (Biological & Medical Physics, Biomedical Engineering Ser.). (ENG., Illus.). x, 488p. 189.00 *(978-0-387-98172-7(1))* Springer.

—Molecular & Cellular Signaling. 2010. (Biological & Medical Physics, Biomedical Engineering Ser.). (Illus.). xxxiv, 582p. pap. 149.00 *(978-1-4419-1966-3(X)*, 144191966X) Springer.

Bhattacharya, Jahar, ed. Cell Signaling in Vascular Inflammation. 2010. (ENG., Illus.). 240p. pap. 135.00 *(978-1-61737-619-1(1)*, 1617376191) Humana Pr.

Bianchi, Michele. Multiscale Fabrication of Functional Materials for Regenerative Medicine. 2011. (Springer Theses Ser.). (ENG., Illus.). xv, 92p. 129.00 ***(978-3-642-22880-3(1)***, 3642228801) Springer.

Bins, Adriaan. Induction & Analysis Antigen-Specific. 2007. (LUP Dissertaties Ser.). 152p. pap. *(978-90-8728-011-6(4)*, Leiden Univ. Pr.) Amsterdam Univ. Pr.

Boelsterli, Urs A. Mechanistic Toxicology: The Molecular Basis of How Chemicals Disrupt Biological Targets. 2nd rev. ed. 2007. (ENG., Illus.). 416p. pap. 100.00 *(978-0-8493-7272-8(0))* CRC Pr. LLC.

Bootman, Martin D. Calcium Signaling. 2011. 135.00 ***(978-0-87969-903-1(5))*** Cold Spring Harbor Laboratory Pr.

Borsello, Tiziana, ed. Neuroprotection Methods & Protocols. (Methods in Molecular Biology Ser.). (Illus.). 2010. xii, 239p. pap. 129.00 *(978-1-61737-707-5(4)*, 1617377074) 2007. 239p. 129.00 *(978-1-58829-666-5(0)*, 1588296660) Humana Pr.

Bradshaw, Ralph A. & Dennis, Edward A., eds. Functioning of Transmembrane Receptors in Signaling Mechanisms: Cell Signaling Collection. 2011. (ENG., Illus.). 456p. pap. 79.95 *(978-0-12-382211-6(4)*, Academic Pr.) Elsevier Science & Technology Bks.

—Handbook of Cell Signaling, 3 vols., Set. 2nd ed. 2009. (Cell Biology Ser.). (ENG.). 3048p. 515.00 *(978-0-12-374145-5(9)*, Academic Pr.) Elsevier Science & Technology Bks.

—Regulation of Organelle & Cell Compartment Signaling: Cell Signaling Collection. 2011. (ENG., Illus.). 550p. pap. 79.95 *(978-0-12-382213-0(0)*, Academic Pr.) Elsevier Science & Technology Bks.

Brembilla, Nicolò Costantino. Profiling of Signal Transduction in Human Memory T Cells: A Reverse Phase Protein Array Approach. 2011. 116p. pap. ***(978-3-639-32656-7(3))*** VDM Verlag Dr. Mueller e.K.

Britsch, Stefan. The Neuregulin-I/ErbB Signaling System in Development & Disease. 2007. (Advances in Anatomy, Embryology & Cell Biology Ser.). (Illus.). xii, 70p. pap. 159.00 *(978-3-540-37105-2(2)*, 3540371052) Springer.

Buytaert, Esther. Molecular Signaling in Photodynamic Therapy: Cell Death Mechanisms & Gene Expression Analysis. 2007. (Illus.). 144p. (Orig.). pap. 97.50 *(978-90-5867-588-0(2))* Leuven Univ. Pr. BEL. Dist: Cornell Univ. Pr.

Cadenas, Enrique & Packer, Lester. Thiol Redox Transitions in Cell Signaling, Part B, 2 vols. 2010. (ENG., Illus.). 392p. 187.00 *(978-0-12-381003-8(5)*, Academic Pr.) Elsevier Science & Technology Bks.

Canepari, Marco & Zecevic, Dejan. Membrane Potential Imaging in the Nervous System: Methods & Applications. 2010. (Illus.). (ENG.). x, 170p. 139.00 *(978-1-4419-6557-8(2)*, 1441965572); x, 168p. E-Book ***(978-1-4419-6558-5(0))*** Springer.

Chalfant, Charles & Del Poeta, Maurizio. Sphingolipids As Signaling & Regulatory Molecules. 2010. (Advances in Experimental Medicine & Biology Ser.). (ENG., Illus.). xxvi, 287p. 239.00 *(978-1-4419-6740-4(0)*, 1441967400) Springer.

Choi, Sangdun, ed. Systems Biology of Signaling Networks. 2010. (Systems Biology Ser.). (ENG., Illus.). xvi, 890p. 279.00 *(978-1-4419-5796-2(0)*, 1441957960) Springer.

Ciruela, Franciso & Lujan, Rafael, eds. Molecular Aspects of G Protein-Coupled Receptors: Interacting Proteins & Function. 2008. (C). 89.00 *(978-1-60021-915-3(2)*, Nova Biomedical Bks.) Nova Science Pubs., Inc.

Civera, Javier, et al. Structure from Motion using the Extended Kalman Filter. 2011. (Springer Tracts in Advanced Robotics Ser.). (ENG., Illus.). xvi, 172p. 109.00 ***(978-3-642-24833-7(0)***, 3642248330) Springer.

Collin, M. & Schuch, R., eds. Bacterial Sensing & Signaling. 2009. (Contributions to Microbiology Ser.). (ENG., Illus.). 230p. *(978-3-8055-9132-4(2))* Karger, S. AG.

Conn, P. Michael & Means, Anthony R., eds. Principles of Molecular Regulation. 2010. (Illus.). 476p. pap. 140.00 *(978-1-61737-104-2(1)*, 1617371041) Humana Pr.

Crane, Brian R., et al. Two-Component Signaling Systems, 2 vols., Pt. A, Vol. 422. 2007. (Methods in Enzymology Ser.). (ENG., Illus.). 592p. 187.00 *(978-0-12-373851-6(2)*, Academic Pr.) Elsevier Science & Technology Bks.

—Two-Component Signaling Systems, Part B, 2 vols. 2007. (Methods in Enzymology Ser.). (ENG., Illus.). 648p. 187.00 *(978-0-12-373852-3(0)*, Academic Pr.) Elsevier Science & Technology Bks.

Damjanovich, Sándor, ed. Biophysical Aspects of Transmembrane Signaling. 2010. (Springer Series in Biophysics Ser.). (Illus.). xviii, 321p. pap. 269.00 *(978-3-642-06411-1(6)*, 3642064116) Springer.

Das, Dipak Kumar. Methods in Redox Signaling. 2009. (ENG., Illus.). 264p. 249.00 *(978-1-934854-06-8(9))* Liebert, Mary Ann Inc.

Datta, Aniruddha & Dougherty, Edward R. Introduction to Genomic Signal Processing with Control. 2006. (ENG., Illus.). 288p. 124.95 *(978-0-8493-7198-1(8)*, CRC Press) Taylor & Francis Group GBR. Dist: Taylor & Francis Group.

Decker, Thomas & Müller, Mathias, eds. Jak-Stat Signaling: from Basics to Disease: From Basics to Disease. 2012. (ENG., Illus.). xiii, 441p. 209.00 ***(978-3-7091-0890-1(X)***, 370910890X) Springer.

Demasi, Alex R., ed. Cellular Signaling & Apoptosis Research. 2007. (C). 129.00 *(978-1-60021-565-0(3))* Nova Science Pubs., Inc.

Dennis, Edward A. & Bradshaw, Ralph A., eds. Transduction Mechanisms in Cellular Signaling. 2011. (ENG., Illus.). 610p. pap. 79.95 *(978-0-12-383862-9(2)*, Academic Pr.) Elsevier Science & Technology Bks.

Dickson, Robert C. & Mendenhall, Michael D., eds. Signal Transduction Protocols. 2nd ed. 2010. (Methods in Molecular Biology Ser.). (Illus.). 327p. pap. 115.00 *(978-1-61737-448-7(2)*, 1617374482) Humana Pr.

Diederich, Marc, ed. Natural Compounds & Their Role in Apoptotic Cell Signaling Pathways. 2009. (Annals of the New York Academy of Sciences Ser.: 29). (ENG., Illus.). 400p. pap. 154.95 *(978-1-57331-737-5(3)*, Wiley-Blackwell) Wiley, John & Sons, Inc.

—Signal Transduction Pathways Pt. A: Apoptotic & Extracellular Signaling, 4 vols. 2007. (Annals of the New York Academy of Sciences Ser.: 11). (ENG., Illus.). 400p. pap. 159.95 *(978-1-57331-645-3(8)*, Wiley-Blackwell) Wiley, John & Sons, Inc.

—Signal Transduction Pathways Pt. B: Stress Signaling & Transcriptional Control, 4 vols. 2007. (Annals of the New York Academy of Sciences Ser.: 12). (ENG., Illus.). 400p. pap. 159.95 *(978-1-57331-647-7(4)*, Wiley-Blackwell) Wiley, John & Sons, Inc.

—Signal Transduction Pathways, Part C: Cell Signaling in Health & Disease. 2007. (Annals of the New York Academy of Sciences Ser.: 13). (ENG., Illus.). 592p. per. 169.95 *(978-1-57331-695-8(4)*, Wiley-Blackwell) Wiley, John & Sons, Inc.

—Signal Transduction Pathways, Part D: Inflammatory Signaling Pathways & Neuropathology. 2007. (Annals of the New York Academy of Sciences Ser.: 14). (ENG., Illus.). 288p. per. 149.95 *(978-1-57331-697-2(0)*, Wiley-Blackwell) Wiley, John & Sons, Inc.

Dijke, Peter & Heldin, Carl-Henrik, eds. Smad Signal Transduction: Smads in Proliferation, Differentiation & Disease. 2010. (Proteins & Cell Regulation Ser.). xiii, 473p. pap. 249.00 *(978-90-481-7145-3(8)*, 9048171458) Springer.

Dijke, Peter ten & Heldin, Carl-Henrik, eds. Smad Signal Transduction: Smads in Proliferation, Differentiation & Disease. 2006. (Proteins & Cell Regulation Ser.). xiii, 473p. 249.00 *(978-1-4020-4542-4(5)*, 1402045425) Springer.

Ding, Sheng, ed. Cellular Programming & Reprogramming: Methods & Protocols. 2010. (Methods in Molecular Biology Ser.). (ENG., Illus.). xii, 336p. 159.00 *(978-1-60761-690-0(4)*, 1607616904) Humana Pr.

Dougherty, Edward, et al, eds. Genetic Regulatory Networks. 2007. 120p. per. 19.00 *(978-977-5945-93-8(3))* Hindawi Publishing Corp.

Dufour, Jean-Francois & Clavien, Pierre-Alain, eds. Signaling Pathways in Liver Diseases. 2nd ed. 2009. (ENG., Illus.). viii, 578p. 239.00 *(978-3-642-00149-9(1)*, 3642001491) Springer.

El-Deiry, Wafik S., ed. Death Receptors in Cancer Therapy. 2010. (Cancer Drug Discovery & Development Ser.). (Illus.). 384p. pap. 209.00 *(978-1-61737-401-2(6)*, 1617374016) Humana Pr.

Elkouby, Yaniv & Frank, Dale. Role of Canonical Wnt-Signaling in Anterior-Posterior Patterning of Developing Vertebrate. Kessler, Daniel, ed. 2010. (Colloquium Series on Developmental Biology Ser.). 79p. pap. 40.00 *(978-1-61504-054-4(4))* Morgan & Claypool Life Science Publishers.

Entschladen, F. & Zaenker, K. S., eds. Cell Migration: Signalling & Mechanisms. 2009. (Translational Research in Biomedicine Ser.). (Illus.). 176p. *(978-3-8055-9321-2(X))* Karger, S. AG.

Falcke, Martin & Malchow, Dieter, eds. Understanding Calcium Dynamics: Experiments & Theory. 2010. (Lecture Notes in Physics Ser.). xii, 300p. pap. 139.00 *(978-3-642-07302-1(6)*, 3642073026) Springer.

Farrar, William L., ed. Cancer Stem Cells. 2009. (ENG., Illus.). 182p. 95.00 *(978-0-521-89628-3(2))* Cambridge Univ. Pr.

Fields, R. Douglas, ed. Beyond the Synapse: Cell-Cell Signaling in Synaptic Plasticity. 2008. (ENG., Illus.). 320p. 120.00 *(978-0-521-86914-0(5))* Cambridge Univ. Pr.

Fliesler, Steven J. & Kisselev, Oleg G., eds. Signal Transduction in the Retina. 2007. (Methods in Signal Transduction Ser.). (ENG., Illus.). 408p. 185.95 *(978-0-8493-7315-2(8)*, CRC Press) Taylor & Francis Group GBR. Dist: Taylor & Francis Group.

Flockerzi, Veit M. & Nilius, Bernd. Transient Receptor Potential (TRP) Channels. 2007. (Handbook of Experimental Pharmacology Ser.). (Illus.). X, 622p. 609.00 *(978-3-540-34889-4(1)*, 3540348891) Springer.

Forman, H. J., et al, eds. Signal Transduction by Reactive Oxygen & Nitrogen Species: Pathways & Chemical Principles: Pathways & Chemical Principles. 2011. 436p. pap. 189.00 *(978-90-481-6216-1(5)*, 9048162165) Springer.

Franciscis, Vittorio de. Signalling Molecules as Targets in Cancer Therapy. 2006. 240p. 89.00 *(978-1-60021-243-7(3)*, Nova Biomedical Bks.) Nova Science Pubs., Inc.

Frank, David, ed. Signaling Pathways in Cancer Pathogenesis & Therapy. 2011. (ENG., Illus.). viii, 148p. 139.00 ***(978-1-4614-1215-1(3)***, 1461412153) Springer.

Frank, Philippe G., et al, eds. Caveolins & Caveolae: Roles in Signaling & Disease Mechanisms. 2012. (Advances in Experimental Medicine & Biology Ser.). (ENG., Illus.). xx, 184p. 189.00 ***(978-1-4614-1221-2(8)***, 1461412218) Springer.

Geisler, Markus & Venema, Kees, eds. Transporters & Pumps in Plant Signaling. 2010. (Signaling & Communication in Plants Ser.). (Illus.). x, 378p. 209.00 *(978-3-642-14368-7(7)*, 3642143687) Springer.

Gomperts, Bastien D., et al. Signal Transduction. 2nd ed. 2009. (ENG., Illus.). 576p. 92.95 *(978-0-12-369441-6(8)*, Academic Pr.) Elsevier Science & Technology Bks.

Grachevsky, Nickolas O. Signal Transduction Research Trends. 2007. 129.00 *(978-1-60021-487-5(8))* Nova Science Pubs., Inc.

Groner, B. Targeted Interference with Signal Transduction Events. 2007. (Recent Results in Cancer Research Ser.). (Illus.). x, 188p. 139.00 *(978-3-540-31208-6(0)*, 3540312080) Springer.

Hancock, John T. Redox-Mediated Signal Transduction: Methods & Protocols. Hancock, John T., ed. 2008. (Methods in Molecular Biology Ser.). (Illus.). 220p. 89.95 *(978-1-58829-842-3(6))* Humana Pr.

Hancock, John T., ed. Redox-Mediated Signal Transduction: Methods & Protocols. 2010. (Methods in Molecular Biology Ser.). (Illus.). x, 234p. pap. 89.95 *(978-1-61737-802-7(X)*, 161737802X) Humana Pr.

Hartung, Anke. Localization of Bmp Receptors in Specific Plasma Membrane Microdomains. 2008. 156p. pap. *(978-3-639-05562-7(4))* VDM Verlag Dr. Mueller e.K.

Hedden, Peter & Napier, Richard. Intracellular Signaling in Plants, Volume 33. Yang, Zhenbiao, ed. 2008. (Annual Plant Reviews Ser.: 22). (ENG., Illus.). 448p. 259.95 *(978-1-4051-6002-5(0)*, Wiley-Blackwell) Wiley, John & Sons, Inc.

Heller, Stefan, told to. TRP Ion Channel Function in Sensory Transduction & Cellular Signaling Cascades. 2006. (Frontiers in Neuroscience Ser.). (ENG., Illus.). 467p. 172.95 *(978-0-8493-4048-2(9)*, 4048, CRC Press) Taylor & Francis Group GBR. Dist: Taylor & Francis Group.

Henderson, Brian & Pockley, A. Graham, eds. Molecular Chaperones & Cell Signalling. 2011. (ENG., Illus.). 346p. pap. 60.00 *(978-0-521-17747-4(2))* Cambridge Univ. Pr.

Horabin, Jamila I., ed. Hedgehog Signaling Protocols. (Methods in Molecular Biology Ser.). (Illus.). 2010. xvii, 256p. pap. 149.00 *(978-1-61737-721-1(X)*, 161737721X) 2007. 256p. 149.00 *(978-1-58829-692-4(X)*, 158829692X) Humana Pr.

Howie, Sarah & Fisher, Carolyn Elaine, eds. Shh & gli Signalling in Development. 2010. (Molecular Biology Intelligence Unit Ser.). (Illus.). xi, 158p. pap. 159.00 *(978-1-4419-2294-6(6)*, 1441922946) Springer.

—Shh & gli Signalling in Development. 2006. (Molecular Biology Intelligence Unit Ser.). (Illus.). 158p. 159.00 *(978-0-387-39956-0(9)*, 0387399569) Springer.

Intracellular Traffic & Neurodegenerative Disorders. 2008. (Research & Perspectives in Alzheimer's Disease Ser.). (Illus.). 205p. 159.00 *(978-3-540-87940-4(4))* Springer.

Islam, Shahidul, ed. Calcium Signaling. 2012. (Advances in Experimental Medicine & Biology Ser.: 740). (ENG., Illus.). xiii, 1267p. 279.00 ***(978-94-007-2887-5(5)***, 9400728875) Springer.

Kahn, Richard A., ed. ARF Family GTPases. 2010. (Proteins & Cell Regulation Ser.). 384p. pap. 229.00 *(978-90-481-6469-1(9)*, 9048164699) Springer.

Kalyuzhny, Alexander E., ed. Signal Transduction Immunohistochemistry: Methods & Protocols. 2011. (Methods in Molecular Biology Ser.). (ENG., Illus.). xiii, 302p. 119.00 *(978-1-61779-023-2(0)*, 1617790230) Humana Pr.

Kandel, Eric R. In Search of Memory: The Emergence of a New Science of Mind. 2007. (ENG., Illus.). 528p. per. 19.95 *(978-0-393-32937-7(2)*, 32937) Norton, W. W. & Co., Inc.

Kawakami, Toshiyuki. Cell Differentiation of Neoplastic Cells Originating in the Oral & Craniofacial Regions. 2008. pap. 29.00 *(978-1-60456-932-2(8))* Nova Science Pubs., Inc.

Kazanietz, Marcelo G., ed. Protein Kinase C in Cancer Signaling & Therapy. 2010. (Current Cancer Research Ser.). (ENG., Illus.). xiv, 494p. 239.00 *(978-1-60761-542-2(8)*, 1607615428) Humana Pr.

Keyse, Stephen M., ed. Stress Response: Methods & Protocols. 2010. (Methods in Molecular Biology Ser.). (Illus.). 505p. 139.00 *(978-1-61737-097-7(5)*, 1617370975) Humana Pr.

Kim, Sang Geon, et al, eds. AMPK-S6K1 Signaling Pathway as a Target for Treating Hepatic Insulin Resistance. 2010. (Hepatology Research & Clinical Developments Ser.). pap. 43.00 *(978-1-60876-693-2(4))* Nova Science Pubs., Inc.

Kitamura, Daisuke, ed. How the Immune System Recognizes Self & Nonself: Immunoreceptors & Their Signaling. (ENG., Illus.). xviii, 251p. 2010. pap. 149.00 *(978-4-431-99831-0(4)*, 4431998314) 2007. 149.00 *(978-4-431-73883-1(5)*, 4431738835) Springer.

Köfalvi, Attila, ed. Cannabinoids & the Brain. 2010. (ENG., Illus.). xvi, 584p. pap. 179.00 *(978-1-4419-4493-1(1)*, 1441944931) Springer.

—Cannabinoids & the Brain. 2008. (ENG., Illus.). xvi, 584p. 179.00 *(978-0-387-74348-6(0)*, 0387743480) Springer.

Konat Gregory W Staff & Konat, Gregory W. Signaling by Toll-Like Receptors. 2008. (Methods in Signal Transduction Ser.). (ENG., Illus.). 224p. 162.95

(978-1-4200-4318-1(8), CRC Press) Taylor & Francis Group GBR. Dist: Taylor & Francis Group.
Kopan, Raphael. Notch Signalling. 2010. (ENG., Illus.). 548p. 198.00 (978-0-12-380914-8(2), Academic Pr.) Elsevier Science & Technology Bks.
Krämer, Reinhard & Jung, Kirsten, eds. Bacterial Signaling. 2010. (ENG., Illus.). 513p. 169.95 (978-3-527-32365-4(1), Wiley-VCH) Wiley, John & Sons, Inc.
Krauss, Gerhard. Biochemistry of Signal Transduction & Regulation. 4th ed. 2008. (ENG.). 646p. pap. 160.00 (978-3-527-31397-6(4), Wiley-VCH) Wiley, John & Sons, Inc.
Kühl, Michael, ed. Wnt Signaling in Development. 2010. (Molecular Biology Intelligence Unit Ser.). 280p. pap. 209.00 (978-1-4419-3409-3(X), 144193409X) Springer.
Lambert, David G., ed. Calcium Signaling Protocols. 2nd ed. 2010. (Methods in Molecular Biology Ser.). (Illus.). 376p. pap. 134.00 (978-1-61737-573-6(X), 161737573X) Humana Pr.
Lang, Florian. Mechanisms & Significance of Cell Volume Regulation. (Contributions to Nephrology Ser.: Vol. 152). (Illus.). vi, 275p. (978-3-8055-8174-5(2)) Karger, S. AG.
Larijani, Banafshe, et al. Lipid Signaling Protocols. Larijani, Banafshe, ed. 2008. (Methods in Molecular Biology Ser.). (Illus.). 532p. 139.00 (978-1-58829-727-3(6)) Humana Pr.
Linden, Joel & Jacobson, Kenneth A. Pharmacology of Purine & Pyrimidine Receptors. 2011. (ENG., Illus.). 558p. 241.00 (978-0-12-385526-8(8), Academic Pr.) Elsevier Science & Technology Bks.
Liu, X. Johné, ed. Xenopus Protocols: Cell Biology & Signal Transduction. 2010. (Methods in Molecular Biology Ser.). (Illus.). 512p. pap. 159.00 (978-1-61737-520-0(9), 1617375209) Humana Pr.
Luan, Sheng, ed. Coding & Decoding of Calcium Signals in Plants. 2011. (Signaling & Communication in Plants Ser.). (ENG., Illus.). viii, 265p. 189.00 (978-3-642-20828-7(2), 3642208282) Springer.
Luo, Z. David, ed. Pain Research: Methods & Protocols. 2010. (Methods in Molecular Medicine Ser.). (Illus.). 320p. pap. 129.00 (978-1-61737-358-9(3), 1617373583) Humana Pr.
Luttrell, Louis M. & Ferguson, Stephen S. G., eds. Signal Transduction Protocols. 3rd ed. 2011. (Methods in Molecular Biology Ser.). (ENG., Illus.). xiv, 430p. 139.00 (**978-1-61779-159-8(8)**, 1617791598) Humana Pr.
Madshus, Inger Helene, ed. Signalling from Internalised Growth Factor Receptors. 2011. (Current Topics in Microbiology & Immunology Ser.). (ENG., Illus.). ix, 187p. pap. 179.00 (978-3-642-05912-4(0), 3642059120) Springer.
Mancuso, Stefano & Shabala, Sergey, eds. Waterlogging Signalling & Tolerance in Plants. 2010. (ENG., Illus.). xx, 290p. 199.00 (978-3-642-10304-9(9), 3642103049) Springer.
Mansour, Ahmed. Heat Stress Signal Transduction in Plant Cells. 2008. 112p. pap. (978-3-639-00420-5(5)) VDM Verlag Dr. Mueller e.K.
Marín-García, José. Signaling in the Heart. 2011. (Illus.). xx, 507p. 169.00 (978-1-4419-9460-8(2), 1441994602) Springer.
Marks, Friedrich, et al. Cellular Signal Processing: An Introduction to the Molecular Mechanisms of Signal Transduction. 2008. (ENG., Illus.). 656p. 125.00 (978-0-8153-4215-1(2), Garland Science) Taylor & Francis Group.
Maroto, Miguel & Monk, Nick, eds. Cellular Oscillatory Mechanisms. 2010. (Advances in Experimental Medicine & Biology Ser.). (Illus.). viii, 153p. pap. 199.00 (978-1-4419-1888-8(4), 1441918884) Springer.
Marx, Andreas & Seitz, Oliver, eds. Molecular Beacons: Signalling Nucleic Acid Probes, Methods, & Protocols. 2008. (Methods in Molecular Biology Ser.). (Illus.). 265p. 129.00 (978-1-58829-700-6(4)) Humana Pr.
—Molecular Beacons: Signalling Nucleic Acid Probes, Methods, & Protocols: Signalling Nucleic Acid Probes, Methods, & Protocols. 2010. (Methods in Molecular Biology Ser.). (Illus.). xii, 266p. pap. 129.00 (978-1-61737-726-6(0), 1617377260) Humana Pr.
Mattson, Mark P., ed. Membrane Microdomain Signaling: Lipid Rafts in Biology & Medicine. 2010. (Illus.). x, 214p. pap. 115.00 (978-1-61737-515-6(2), 1617375152) Humana Pr.
McAlpine, Gavin. Focus on Signal Transduction Research. 2006. 240p. 225.00 (978-1-60021-376-2(6)) Nova Science Pubs., Inc.
Merchant PhD, Kendra, et al. Novel Molecular Targets for Genistein in Prostate Cancer Cells. 2010. 100p. pap. (978-3-8383-3884-2(7)) Lambert Academic Publishing.
Meridith, Alan T. Handbook of Prostate Cancer Cell Research: Growth, Signalling & Survival. 2009. (Cancer Etiology, Diagnosis & Treatments Ser.). 129.00 (978-1-60741-954-9(8), Nova Biomedical Bks.) Nova Science Pubs., Inc.
Meyers, Jennifer N. Trends in Signal Transduction Research. 2006. (Illus.). 254p. 225.00 (978-1-60021-375-5(8)) Nova Science Pubs., Inc.
Munnik, Teun, ed. Lipid Signaling in Plants. 2009. (Plant Cell Monographs). (Illus.). xviii, 330p. 239.00 (978-3-642-03872-3(7), 3642038727) Springer.
Murphy, Eric J. & Rosenberger, Thad A. Lipid-Mediated Signaling. 2010. (Methods in Signal Transduction Ser.). (ENG., Illus.). 452p. 159.95 (978-0-8493-8141-6(X), CRC Press) Taylor & Francis Group GBR. Dist: Taylor & Francis Group.
Nott, Patrick & Temple, Matthew, eds. New Cell Adhesion Research. 2009. 129.00 (978-1-60692-378-8(1)) Nova Science Pubs., Inc.
Ockner, Robert K. Integration of Metabolism, Energetics, & Signal Transduction. 2011. (ENG.). 406p. pap. 275.00 (978-1-4419-3450-5(2), 1441934502) Springer.
Oleskin, Alexander V., et al. Symbiotic Biofilms & Brain Neurochemistry. 2010. (Illus.). viii, 57p. pap. 49.00 (978-1-61761-005-9(4)) Nova Science Pubs., Inc.
Osborne, Daphne J. & McManus, Michael T. Hormones, Signals & Target Cells in Plant Development. 2011. (Developmental & Cell Biology Ser.). (ENG., Illus.). 268p. pap. 50.00 (978-0-521-17745-0(5)) Cambridge Univ. Pr.
Pandey, Akhilesh. Signal Transduction: A Systems Biology Approach. 2008. 350p. 125.00 (978-1-58829-487-6(0), 1588294870) Humana Pr.
Pasterkamp, Gera, ed. Semaphorins. 2007. (Advances in Experimental Medicine & Biology Ser.). (Illus.). XIV, 147p. 179.00 (978-0-387-70955-0(X), 038770955X) Springer.
Pasterkamp, Gerard, ed. Semaphorins: Receptor & Intracellular Signaling Mechanisms: Receptor & Intracellular Signaling Mechanisms. 2010. (Advances in Experimental Medicine & Biology Ser.). (Illus.). xiv, 147p. pap. 179.00 (978-1-4419-2427-8(2), 1441924272) Springer.
Pestell, Richard G. & Nevalainen, Marja T., eds. Prostate Cancer: Signaling Networks, Genetics, & New Treatment Strategies. 2008. (Current Clinical Oncology Ser.). (Illus.). 455p. 189.00 (978-1-58829-741-9(1)) Humana Pr.
Pfannschmidt, Thomas. Plant Signal Transduction: Methods & Protocols. (Illus.). 2009. xi, 357p. (978-1-59745-289-2(0)) 2008. 320p. 129.00 (978-1-58829-943-7(0)) Humana Pr.
Pickens, Charles O. Cell Apoptotic Signaling Pathways. 2007. 222p. 129.00 (978-1-60021-507-0(6)) Nova Science Pubs., Inc.
Plessevaux, Julie. SOCS Proteins & Cytokine Signalling: The many Faces of the SOCS Box: Regulation of SOCS Proteins. 2008. 212p. pap. (978-3-639-10792-0(6)) VDM Verlag Dr. Mueller e.K.
Polunovsky, Vitaly & Houghton, Peter J. MTOR Pathway & mTOR Inhibitors in Cancer Therapy. 2010. (Cancer Drug Discovery & Development Ser.). (ENG., Illus.). 235p. 239.00 (978-1-60327-270-4(4)) Humana Pr.
Quinn, Peter J., ed. Membrane Dynamics & Domains. 2010. (Subcellular Biochemistry Ser.). 516p. pap. 199.00 (978-1-4419-3447-5(2), 1441934472) Springer.
Raizada, Mohan K., et al, eds. Cardiovascular Genomics. 2010. (Contemporary Cardiology Ser.). (Illus.). 376p. pap. 189.00 (978-1-61737-542-2(X), 161737542X) Humana Pr.
Rameseder, Jonathan & Martens, Lennart. Computational Methods for Fragment Spectrum Interpretation. 2010. 56p. pap. (978-3-639-22858-8(8)) VDM Verlag Dr. Mueller e.K.
Regazzi, Romano, ed. Molecular Mechanisms of Exocytosis. 2006. (Molecular Biology Intelligence Unit Ser.). (Illus.). 178p. 179.00 (978-0-387-39960-7(7), 0387399607) Springer.
Reichrath, Jörg & Reichrath, Sandra, eds. Notch Signaling in Embryology & Cancer. 2012. (Advances in Experimental Medicine & Biology Ser.). (ENG., Illus.). xxii, 322p. 209.00 (**978-1-4614-0898-7(9)**, 1461408989) Springer.
Rhoads, Robert E., ed. Signaling Pathways for Translation: Stress, Calcium, & Rapamycin. 2010. (Progress in Molecular & Subcellular Biology Ser.). (Illus.). x, 176p. pap. 149.00 (978-3-642-07505-6(3), 3642075053) Springer.
Robubi, Armin. RAF Kinases: Pathway, Modulation & Modeling: New — Potentially Irreversible — Kinase Inhibitors, Computational Modeling of the Signaling Cascade, & the Effect of DiRas3 on RAF Signaling. 2008. 96p. pap. (978-3-639-05665-5(5)) VDM Verlag Dr. Mueller e.K.
Rodriguez-Moreno, Antonio & Sihra, Talvinder S., eds. Kainate Receptors: Novel Signaling Insights. 2011. (Advances in Experimental Medicine & Biology Ser.). (ENG., Illus.). xx, 128p. 139.00 (978-1-4419-9556-8(0), 1441995560) Springer.
Royal Society of Chemistry Staff. Extracellular & Intracellular Signaling. Adams, James D. & Parker, Keith, eds. 2011. (RSC Drug Discovery Ser.). (ENG., Illus.). 318p. 213.00 (978-1-84973-160-7(8)) Royal Society of Chemistry, The GBR. Dist: Ingram Pub. Services.
Rumbaugh, Kendra P., ed. Quorum Sensing: Methods & Protocols. 2010. (Methods in Molecular Biology Ser.). (Illus.). xvi, 310p. 139.00 (978-1-60761-970-3(9), 1607619709) Humana Pr.
Sako, Yasushi & Ueda, Masahiro, eds. Cell Signaling Reactions: Single-Molecular Kinetic Analysis. 2010. (ENG.). x, 300p. 209.00 (978-90-481-9863-4(1), 9048198631) Springer.
Samelson, Lawrence E. & Shaw, Andrey, eds. Immunoreceptor Signaling. 2010. (ENG., Illus.). 350p. 135.00 (978-0-87969-896-6(9)) Cold Spring Harbor Laboratory Pr.
Schönthal, Axel H., ed. Checkpoint Controls & Cancer: Volume 1: Reviews & Model Systems. 2010. (Methods in Molecular Biology Ser.). (Illus.). xvi, 318p. pap. 119.00 (978-1-61737-426-5(1), 1617374261) Humana Pr.
—Checkpoint Controls & Cancer: Volume 2: Activation & Regulation Protocols. 2010. (Methods in Molecular Biology Ser.). (Illus.). 348p. pap. 139.00 (978-1-61737-603-0(5), 1617376035) Humana Pr.
Seger, Rony, ed. MAP Kinase Signaling Protocols. 2nd ed. 2010. (Methods in Molecular Biology Ser.). (Illus.). xiv, 529p. 159.00 (978-1-60761-794-5(3), 1607617943) Humana Pr.
Sehgal, P., et al, eds. Signal Transducers & Activators of Transcription (STATs) Activation & Biology. 2010. 775p. pap. 375.00 (978-90-481-6421-9(4), 9048164214) Springer.
Sigalov, Alexander, ed. Multichain Immune Recognition Receptor Signaling: From Spatiotemporal Organization to Human Disease. 2010. (Advances in Experimental Medicine & Biology Ser.). (Illus.). xxvii, 357p. pap. 199.00 (978-1-4419-1887-1(6), 1441918876) Springer.
Sigalov, Alexander B. Multichain Immune Recognition Receptor Signaling: From Spatiotemporal Organization to Human Disease. 2008. (Advances in Experimental Medicine & Biology Ser.: Vol. 640). (Illus.). 386p. 199.00 (978-0-387-09788-6(0), 0387097880) Springer.
Signal Transduction: New Research. 2008. 129.00 (978-1-60456-338-2(9)) Nova Science Pubs., Inc.
Simon, Melvin I., et al. Two-Component Signaling Systems, Part C. 2010. (ENG., Illus.). 496p. 187.00 (978-0-12-381347-3(6), Academic Pr.) Elsevier Science & Technology Bks.
Singh, Shree Ram & Mishra, Manoj K. Signaling, Gene Regulation, & Cancer. 2012. (**978-1-61942-088-5(0)**) Nova Science Pubs., Inc.
Sitaramayya, Ari, ed. Signal Transduction: Pathways, Mechanisms & Diseases: Pathways, Mechanisms & Diseases. 2009. (ENG., Illus.). xi, 436p. 229.00 (978-3-642-02111-4(5), 3642021115) Springer.
Smrcka, Alan V., ed. G Protein Signaling: Methods & Protocols. 2010. (Methods in Molecular Biology Ser.). (Illus.). 264p. pap. 119.00 (978-1-61737-381-7(8), 1617373818) Humana Pr.
Sokol, Sergei Y., ed. WNT Signaling in Embryonic Development. 2007. (Advances in Developmental Biology Ser.). (ENG., Illus.). 264p. 133.00 (978-0-444-52874-2(1), Elsevier Science) Elsevier Science & Technology Bks.
Spiro, Stephen & Dixon, Ray, eds. Sensory Mechanisms in Bacteria: Molecular Aspects of Signal Recognition. 2010. (Illus.). 287p. 319.00 (978-1-904455-69-1(7)) Caister Academic Pr. GBR. Dist: International Specialized Bk. Services.
Srivastava, Rakesh. Apoptosis, Cell Signaling, & Human Diseases: Molecular Mechanisms, 2 vols., Vol. 2. 2007. (ENG., Illus.). 384p. 159.00 (978-1-58829-677-1(6), 1588296776) Humana Pr.
Srivastava, Rakesh, ed. Apoptosis, Cell Signaling, & Human Diseases. 2010. (ENG., Illus.). 384p. pap. 159.00 (978-1-61737-713-6(9), 1617377139) Humana Pr.
—Apoptosis, Cell Signaling, & Human Diseases: Molecular Mechanisms, Volume 2. (ENG., Illus.). xvi, 402p. 2010. pap. 179.00 (978-1-61737-823-2(2), 1617378232) Vol. 2. 2007. 179.00 (978-1-58829-882-9(5), 1588298825) Humana Pr.
Stephanou, Anastasis, ed. JAK-STAT Pathway in Disease. 2009. (Medical Intelligence Unit Ser.). (978-1-58706-315-2(8)) Landes Bioscience.
Surh, Young-Joon. Dietary Modulation of Cell Signaling Pathways. Dong, Zigang et al, eds. Cadenas, Enrique et al, eds. 2008. (Oxidative Stress & Disease Ser.). (ENG., Illus.). 504p. 162.95 (978-0-8493-8148-5(7), CRC Press) Taylor & Francis Group GBR. Dist: Taylor & Francis Group.
Tax, Frans & Kemmerling, Birgit, eds. Receptor-like Kinases in Plants: From Development to Defense. 2012. (Signaling & Communication in Plants Ser.). (ENG., Illus.). viii, 313p. 209.00 (**978-3-642-23043-1(1)**, 3642230431) Springer.
Terrian, David M., ed. Cancer Cell Signaling: Methods & Protocols. 2010. (Methods in Molecular Biology Ser.). (Illus.). 352p. pap. 139.00 (978-1-61737-341-1(9), 1617373419) Humana Pr.
Thiriet, Marc. Signaling at the Cell Surface in the Circulatory & Ventilatory Systems. 2011. (Biomathematical & Biomechanical Modeling of the Circulatory & Ventilatory Systems Ser.). (Illus.). xv, 982p. 219.00 (**978-1-4614-1990-7(5)**, 1461419905) Springer.
Tombran-Tink, Joyce & Barnstable, Colin J., eds. The Visual Transduction Cascade. 2008. (Ophthalmology Research Ser.). (Illus.). 435p. 229.00 (978-1-58829-957-4(0)) Humana Pr.
Tsaneva-Atanasova, Krasimira. A Mathematical Study of Calcium Oscillations & Waves. 2009. 176p. pap. (978-3-639-13651-7(9)) VDM Verlag Dr. Mueller e.K.
Ulrich, Henning, ed. Perspectives of Stem Cells: From tools for studying mechanisms of neuronal differentiation towards Therapy. 2009. (ENG., Illus.). xiv, 285p. 199.00 (978-90-481-3374-1(2), 9048133742) Springer.
Utsumi, Ryutaro, ed. Bacterial Signal Transduction: Networks & Drug Targets. 2008. (Advances in Experimental Medicine & Biology Ser.: Vol. 631). (Illus.). XVII, 242p. 209.00 (978-0-387-78884-5(0), 0387788840) Springer.
—Bacterial Signal Transduction: Networks & Drug Targets: Networks & Drug Targets. 2010. (Advances in Experimental Medicine & Biology Ser.). (Illus.). xvii, 242p. pap. 209.00 (978-1-4419-2703-3(4), 1441927034) Springer.
Verkhratsky, Alexei & Petersen, Ole H., eds. Calcium Measurement Methods. 2009. (Neuromethods Ser.). (ENG., Illus.). xii, 256p. 189.00 (978-1-60761-475-3(8), 1607614758) Humana Pr.
Vincan, Elizabeth. Wnt Signaling, 2 vols. 2008. (Methods in Molecular Biology Ser.). (Illus.). 467p. 99.50 (978-1-58829-912-3(0)); 419p. 119.00 (978-1-60327-468-5(5)) Humana Pr.
Vincan, Elizabeth, ed. Wnt Signaling: Volume 1: Pathway Methods & Mammalian Models. 2010. (Methods in Molecular Biology Ser.). (Illus.). xvi, 336p. pap. 99.50 (978-1-61737-841-6(0), 1617378410) Humana Pr.
—Wnt Signaling: Volume 2, Pathway Models. 2010. (Methods in Molecular Biology Ser.). (Illus.). xiv, 498p. pap. 119.00 (978-1-61737-899-7(2), 1617378992) Humana Pr.
Vladimirov, Nikita, et al. Multiscale Modeling of Bacterial Chemotaxis. 2010. 132p. pap. (978-3-8383-4246-7(1)) Lambert Academic Publishing.
Volk, Talila, ed. Post-Transcriptional Regulation by Star Proteins: Control of RNA Metabolism in Development & Disease. 2010. (Advances in Experimental Medicine & Biology Ser.). (ENG., Illus.). xviii, 162p. 219.00 (978-1-4419-7004-6(5), 1441970045) Springer.
Wajant, Harald, ed. Fas Signaling. 2010. (Medical Intelligence Unit Ser.). (Illus.). viii, 160p. pap. 189.00 (978-1-4419-4074-2(X), 144194074X) Springer.
Wang, Jian-Ying, ed. Polyamine Cell Signaling: Physiology, Pharmacology, & Cancer Research. 2010. (Illus.). 504p. pap. 165.00 (978-1-61737-679-5(5), 1617376795) Humana Pr.
Wang, Ping, et al. Cell-Based Biosensors: Principles & Applications. 2009. (Illus.). 310p. 129.00 (978-1-59693-439-9(5)) Artech Hse., Inc.
Wang-Rosenke, Yingrui. Nitric Oxide-Cgmp Signal Transduction. 2008. 120p. pap. (978-3-8364-9390-1(X)) VDM Verlag Dr. Mueller e.K.
Wang, Rui, ed. Signal Transduction & the Gasotransmitters: NO, CO, & H2S in Biology & Medicine. 2010. (Illus.). 392p. pap. 155.00 (978-1-61737-512-5(8), 1617375128) Humana Pr.
Willars, Gary B. & Challiss, R. A. J. Receptor Signal Transduction Protocols. 3rd ed. 2011. (Illus.). xi, 479p. E-Book (**978-1-61779-126-0(1)**) Springer.
Willars, Gary B. & Challiss, R. A. John, eds. Receptor Signal Transduction Protocols. 2nd ed. 2010. (Methods in Molecular Biology Ser.). (Illus.). xiii, 418p. pap. 99.50 (978-1-61737-498-2(9), 1617374989) Humana Pr.
—Receptor Signal Transduction Protocols: Third Edition. 3rd ed. 2011. (Methods in Molecular Biology Ser.). (Illus.). xi, 479p. 139.00 (978-1-61779-125-3(3), 1617791253) Humana Pr.
Winans, Stephen C. & Bassler, Bonnie L., eds. Chemical Communication among Bacteria. 2008. (Illus.). 483p. 170.00 (978-1-55581-404-5(2)) ASM Pr.
Winyard, Paul G. Redox Signaling & Regulation in Biology & Medicine. Jacob, Claus & Winyard, Paul G., eds. 2009. (ENG., Illus.). 514p. 135.00 (978-3-527-31925-1(5), Wiley-VCH) Wiley, John & Sons, Inc.
Witzany, Günther, ed. Biocommunication of Fungi. 2012. (ENG., Illus.). xi, 344p. 189.00 (**978-94-007-4263-5(0)**, 9400742630) Springer.
Wong, Y. H., ed. G Protein Signaling. 2009. (ENG., Illus.). 110p. pap. (978-3-8055-9053-2(9)) Karger, S. AG.
Wu, Hao, ed. TNF Receptor Associated Factors. 2007. (Advances in Experimental Medicine & Biology Ser.: Vol. 597). (Illus.). 206p. 179.00 (978-0-387-70629-0(1), 0387706291) Springer.
—TNF Receptor Associated Factors (TRAFs) 2010. (Advances in Experimental Medicine & Biology Ser.). (Illus.). xix, 206p. pap. 179.00 (978-1-4419-2420-9(5), 1441924205) Springer.
Wu, Wen-Sheng. Signal Transduction in Cancer Metastasis. Wu, Wen-Sheng & Hu, Chi-Tan, eds. 2010. (Cancer Metastasis - Biology & Treatment Ser.). (Illus.). xi, 285p. 209.00 (978-90-481-9521-3(7), 9048195217) Springer.
Xie, Jingwu, ed. Hedgehog signaling activation in human cancer & its clinical Implications. 2011. (ENG., Illus.). ix, 217p. 189.00 (978-1-4419-8434-0(8), 1441984348) Springer.
Yalovsky, Shaul, et al, eds. Integrated G Proteins Signaling in Plants. 2009. (Signaling & Communication in Plants Ser.). (ENG., Illus.). x, 336p. 239.00 (978-3-642-03523-4(X), 364203523X) Springer.
Yamaguchi, Masayoshi. Calcium Signaling. 2012. (Series: Protein Biochemistry, Synthesis, Structure & Cellular Functions Ser.). (Illus.). 245p. 140.00 (978-1-61324-313-8(8)) Nova Science Pubs., Inc.
Yanson, Bruce R. New Research on Signal Transduction. 2006. 250p. 225.00 (978-1-60021-379-3(0)) Nova Science Pubs., Inc.
Yoshioka, Keiko. Signal Crosstalk in Plant Stress Responses. Shinozaki, Kazuo, ed. 2009. (ENG.). 224p. 229.95 (978-0-8138-1963-1(6), Wiley-Blackwell) Wiley, John & Sons, Inc.
2007 IEEE International Workshop on Genomic Signal Processing & Statistics. 2007. pap. 234.00 (978-1-4244-0998-3(5), 07EX1700) IEEE.

CELLULAR SYSTEMS (TELECOMMUNICATION)

see Cell Phone Systems

CELLULAR TELEPHONE EQUIPMENT INDUSTRY

see Cell Phone Equipment Industry

CELLULAR TELEPHONE SERVICES INDUSTRY

see Cell Phone Services Industry

CELLULAR TELEPHONE SYSTEMS

see Cell Phone Systems

CELLULAR TELEPHONES

see Cell Phones

CELLULAR THERAPY

American Association of Blood Banks Staff, contrib. by. Standards for Cellular Therapy Product Services. 3rd ed. 2008. (978-1-56395-273-9(4), AABB Pr.) American Assn. of Blood Banks.
Areman, Ellen M. & Loper, Kathy. Cellular Therapy: Principles, Methods, & Regulations. 2009. (978-1-56395-296-8(3), AABB Pr.) American Assn. of Blood Banks.
Ashford, Paul, ed. ISBT 128 for Cellular Therapy an Intoduction. 2006. (978-1-933243-02-3(3)) ICCBBA Inc.
Athiraman, Hemanthkumar. Quantitative Determination of Labeled Cell Concentration Using Mri. 2010. 112p. pap. (978-3-8383-0339-0(3)) Lambert Academic Publishing.
Baharvand, Hossein, ed. Trends in Stem Cell Biology & Technology. 2009. (ENG., Illus.). xvii, 402p. 169.00 (978-1-60327-904-8(0)) Humana Pr.
Berliner, Nancy. Immunodeficiency, Infection, & Stem Cell Transplantation, an Issue of Hematology/Oncology Clinics of North America. 2011. (Clinics: Internal Medicine Ser.: 25-1). (ENG., Illus.). 256p. 104.00 (978-1-4557-0633-4(7), Saunders) Elsevier - Health Sciences Div.
Davis, Cyndy D. & Sanberg, Paul R., eds. Cell Therapy, Stem Cells & Brain Repair. 2010. (Contemporary Neuroscience Ser.). (Illus.). 408p. pap. 179.00 (978-1-61737-604-7(3), 1617376043) Humana Pr.
Ding, Sheng, ed. Cellular Programming & Reprogramming: Methods & Protocols. 2010. (Methods in Molecular Biology Ser.). (ENG., Illus.). xii, 336p. 159.00 (978-1-60761-690-0(4), 1607616904) Humana Pr.

C

Ebert, Allison D. & Svendsen, Clive. Encyclopedia of Stem Cell Research, 2 vols. Svendsen, Clive Niels & Ebert, Allison D., eds. 2008. (Illus.). 952p. 265.00 *(978-1-4129-5908-7(X)*, B59087C) SAGE Pubns., Inc.

Efrat, Shimon, ed. Stem Cell Therapy for Diabetes. 2009. (Stem Cell Biology & Regenerative Medicine Ser.). (ENG., Illus.). xi, 291p. 189.00 *(978-1-60761-365-7(4)*, 1607613654) Humana Pr.

Gee, Adrian, ed. Cell Therapy: CGMP Facilities & Manufacturing. 2009. (ENG., Illus.). xx, 256p. 159.00 *(978-0-387-89583-3(3)*, 0387895833) Springer.

Gerald & Kadereit, Suzanne. Umbilical Cord Blood: A Future for Regenerative Medicine. 2010. 400p. 85.00 *(978-981-283-329-7(3))* World Scientific Publishing Co., Inc.

Green, Howard. Therapy with Cultured Cells. 2010. (ENG., Illus.). 88p. pap. 79.95 *(978-981-4267-70-0(8))* Pan Stanford Publishing SGP. Dist: Taylor & Francis Group.

Heine, Vivi M. Induced Pluripotent Stem Cells in Brain Diseases: Understanding the Methods, Epigenetic Basis, & Applications for Regenerative Medicine. 2011. (SpringerBriefs in Neuroscience Ser.). (Illus.). xv, 59p. pap. 49.95 ***(978-94-007-2815-8(8)***, 9400728158) Springer.

Kraitchman, Dara L. & Wu, Joseph, eds. Stem Cell Labeling for Delivery & Tracking Using Non-Invasive Imaging. 2011. (Series in Medical Physics & Biomedical Engineering Ser.). (ENG., Illus.). 489p. 129.95 *(978-1-4398-0751-4(5)*, CRC Press) Taylor & Francis Group GBR. Dist: Taylor & Francis Group.

Law, Peter K., et al. Pioneering Human Myoblast Genome Therapy. 2008. pap. 37.00 *(978-1-60692-817-2(1))* Nova Science Pubs., Inc.

Lindroos, Bettina. Characterization & Optimization of in Vitro Culture Conditions of Adult Stem Cells for Clinical Cell Therapy. 2009. (Acta Universitatis Tamperensis Ser.). 172p. pap. 82.50 *(978-951-44-7914-4(9))* Tampere Univ. Pr. FIN. Dist: Coronet Bks.

Ludewig, Burkhard & Hoffmann, Matthias W., eds. Adoptive Immunotherapy: Methods & Protocols. 2010. (Methods in Molecular Medicine Ser.). (Illus.). 520p. pap. 169.00 *(978-1-61737-546-0(2)*, 1617375462) Humana Pr.

Perin, Emerson C., et al, eds. An Essential Guide to Cardiac Cell Therapy. 2006. (ENG., Illus.). 222p. 190.00 *(978-1-84184-471-8(3))* Taylor & Francis Group.

Prokop, Ale, ed. Intracellular Delivery: Fundamentals & Applications. 2011. (Fundamental Biomedical Technologies Ser.). (ENG., Illus.). xix, 867p. 209.00 *(978-94-007-1247-8(2)*, 9400712472) Springer.

Sanberg, Paul R. & Davis, Cyndy D., eds. Cell Therapy, Stem Cells & Brain Repair. 2006. (Contemporary Neuroscience Ser.). (Illus.). 408p. 179.00 *(978-1-58829-502-6(8)*, 1588295028) Humana Pr.

Stowell, Christopher P. & Sazama, Kathleen. Informed Consent in Blood Transfusion & Cellular Therapies: Patients, Donors, & Research Subjects. 2007. *(978-1-56395-254-8(8)*, AABB Pr.) American Assn. of Blood Banks.

Taupin, Philippe. Stem Cells & Regenerative Medicine: Volume I: Adult Neurogenesis & Neural Stem Cells, 3 vols. 2008. (Illus.). 164p. 98.00 *(978-1-60456-472-3(5))* Nova Science Pubs., Inc.

Taupin, Philippe. Stem Cells & Regenerative Medicine: Volume III: Pharmacology & Therapy, 3 vols. 2008. (Illus.). 133p. 98.00 *(978-1-60456-474-7(1))* Nova Science Pubs., Inc.

Templeton, Nancy Smyth. Gene & Cell Therapy: Therapeutic Mechanisms & Strategies. Templeton, Nancy Smyth, ed. 3rd rev. ed. 2008. (ENG., Illus.). 1120p. 259.95 *(978-0-8493-8768-5(X)*, CRC Press) Taylor & Francis Group GBR. Dist: Taylor & Francis Group.

Walters, Lisa M. & Badley, Jacquelyn K. Carpenter. S3: Simple Six Sigma for Blood Banking, Transfusion, & Cellular Therapy. 2007. *(978-1-56395-249-4(1)*, AABB Pr.) American Assn. of Blood Banks.

Wiwanitkit, Viroj, ed. Cell, Gene, & Molecular Therapy: New Concepts. 2009. 187p. 98.00 *(978-1-60692-532-4(6))* Nova Science Pubs., Inc.

Zigova, Tanja, ed. Neural Stem Cells for Brain & Spinal Cord Repair. 2010. (Contemporary Neuroscience Ser.). (Illus.). 456p. pap. 189.00 *(978-1-61737-298-8(6)*, 1617372986) Humana Pr.

CELLULASE

Gilbert, Harry. Cellulases. 2012. (ENG.). 554p. 187.00 ***(978-0-12-415931-0(1)***, Academic Pr.) Elsevier Science & Technology Bks.

Golan, Adam E. Cellulase: Types & Action, Mechanism, & Uses. 2011. (Series: Biotechnology in Agriculture, Industry & Medicine Ser.). 129.00 *(978-1-61761-983-0(3))* Nova Science Pubs., Inc.

CELLULITE

Bissoon, Lionel. The Cellulite Cure. 2006. (Illus.). 232p. 29.95 *(978-0-9764821-0-9(X))* Meso Pr.

Burke, Karen. Thin Thighs: Exercises & Recipes for Trim, Toned Thighs. 2010. (ENG., Illus.). 128p. pap. 9.95 *(978-0-600-61911-6(7)*, Hamlyn) Octopus Publishing Group GBR. Dist: Hachette Bk. Group.

CELLULOSE

see also Lignocellulose; Polysaccharides; Wood—Chemistry

Álvarez, Jesús Miguel, et al. Cellulose Biosynthesis Inhibitors as Tools for Research of Cell Wall Structural Plasticity. 2011. (Cell Biology Research Progress Ser.). 230p. pap. 47.00 ***(978-1-61470-946-6(7))*** Nova Science Pubs., Inc.

American Society of Mechanical Engineers Staff, ed. Mechanics of Cellulosic Materials. 184p. 80.00 *(978-0-7918-1613-4(3))* ASME Pr.

Beg, Mohammad Dalour Hossen & Pickering, Kim. Wood Plastic Composites. 2010. 176p. pap. *(978-3-639-20351-6(8))* VDM Verlag Dr. Mueller e.K.

Brown, R. Malcolm, Jr. & Saxena, Inder M., eds. Cellulose: Molecular & Structural Biology: Selected Articles on the Synthesis, Structure, & Applications of Cellulose. 2007. (ENG., Illus.). xvi, 379p. 219.00 *(978-1-4020-5332-0(0)*, 1402053320) Springer.

Brown, R. Malcolm Jr. & Saxena, Inder M., eds. Cellulose: Molecular & Structural Biology: Selected Articles on the Synthesis, Structure, & Applications of Cellulose. 2010. (ENG., Illus.). xvi, 379p. pap. 219.00 *(978-90-481-7344-0(2)*, 9048173442) Springer.

Buckeridge, Marcos Silveira & Goldman, Gustavo H., eds. Routes to Cellulosic Ethanol. 2011. 284p. ***(978-0-387-92739-8(5))*** Springer London, Ltd.

Burkheisser, Ernest V. Biological Barriers to Cellulosic Ethanol. 2009. pap. 37.00 *(978-1-60692-203-3(3))* Nova Science Pubs., Inc.

Ciolacu, Diana & Popa, Valentin I., eds. Cellulose Allomorphs: Structure, Accessibility & Reactivity. 2010. (Polymer Science & Technology Ser.). (Illus.). x, 69p. pap. 43.00 *(978-1-61668-323-8(6))* Nova Science Pubs., Inc.

Follain, Nadege, ed. Amidation of Cellulose Materials. 2010. (Materials Science & Technologies Ser.). 76p. pap. 43.00 *(978-1-61668-196-8(9))* Nova Science Pubs., Inc.

Heinze, Thomas. Polysaccharides I: Structure, Characterisation & Use. 2010. (Advances in Polymer Science Ser.). xii, 281p. pap. 309.00 *(978-3-642-06553-8(8)*, 3642065538) Springer.

Klemm, Dieter. Polysaccharides II. 2010. (Advances in Polymer Science Ser.). xii, 300p. pap. 389.00 *(978-3-642-07203-1(8)*, 3642072038) Springer.

Klemm, Dieter, et al. Comprehensive Cellulose Chemistry, 2 vols. 2nd ed. 2009. (ENG.). 700p. 435.00 *(978-3-527-31534-5(9)*, Wiley-VCH) Wiley, John & Sons, Inc.

Lawoko, Martin. Lignin Carbohydrate Complexes in Softwood & Chemical Pulps: Characterisation, Structure & Reactivity. 2008. 68p. pap. *(978-3-639-10239-0(8))* VDM Verlag Dr. Mueller e.K.

Lejeune, Arnaud & Deprez, Thibaut, eds. Cellulose: Structure & Properties, Derivatives & Industrial Uses. 2010. (Biotechnology in Agriculture, Industry & Medicine Ser.). 145.00 *(978-1-60876-388-7(9)*, Nova Biomedical Bks.) Nova Science Pubs., Inc.

Matamá, Teresa. Surface Functionalization of Acrylic & Cellulose Acetate Fibres. 2009. 140p. pap. *(978-3-639-20376-9(3))* VDM Verlag Dr. Mueller e.K.

The Next Generation of Biofuels: Cellulosic Ethanol & the 2007 Farm Bill: Hearing Before the Subcommittee on Energy, Science, & Technology of the Committee on Agriculture, Nutrition, & Forestry, United States Senate, One Hundred Tenth Congress, First Session, April 4, 2007. 2007. (Illus.). iii, 123p. *(978-0-16-079621-0(0)*, 552-070-36578-8) United States Government Printing Office.

Roman, Maren, ed. Model Cellulosic Surfaces, 1 vol. 2010. (ACS Symposium Ser.). (ENG., Illus.). 328p. 150.00 *(978-0-8412-6965-1(3))* American Chemical Society.

Simon?i?, Barbara, et al, eds. Biodegradation of Cellulose Fibers. 2010. (Bacteriology Research Developments Ser.). pap. 43.00 *(978-1-61668-154-8(3))* Nova Science Pubs., Inc.

Tsao, G. T. Recent Progress in Bioconversion of Lignocellulosics. 2010. (Advances in Biochemical Engineering Biotechnology Ser.). (Illus.). xii, 292p. pap. 499.00 *(978-3-642-08488-1(5)*, 3642084885) Springer.

Voronova, M. I., et al, eds. Interactions of Aqueous-Organic Mixtures with Cellulose. 2009. (Chemistry Research & Applications Ser.). pap. 38.70 *(978-1-61668-766-3(5)*, Nova Novinka) Nova Science Pubs., Inc.

Zugenmaier, Peter. Crystalline Cellulose & Derivatives: Characterization & Structures. (Springer Series in Wood Science Ser.). (Illus.). 2010. x, 286p. pap. 249.00 *(978-3-642-09319-7(1)*, 3642093191) 2007. 285p. 249.00 *(978-3-540-73933-3(5))* Springer.

CELSUS, PLATONIC PHILOSOPHER, FL. 180

Selwyn, William, ed. Origen's Contra Celsum, Bk. 1-4. 2007. 385p. pap. 35.00 *(978-1-55635-065-8(1)*, Wipf and Stock) Wipf & Stock Pubs.

CELTIBERI

see also Basques; Berbers

Curchin, Leonard A. The Romanization of Central Spain. 2011. (ENG., Illus.). 312p. pap. 42.95 ***(978-0-415-62007-9(4))*** Routledge.

CELTIC ART

see Art, Celtic

CELTIC CHURCH

Adam. Rhythm of Life, the Gift Ed. 2007. *(978-0-281-05865-5(2))* SPCK Publishing.

Balzer, Tracy. Thin Places: An Evangelical Journey into Celtic Christianity. 2007. 173p. per. 12.99 *(978-0-89112-513-6(2)*, Leafwood Pubs.) Abilene Christian Univ. Pr.

Bradley, Ian. The Celtic Way. 144p. pap. *(978-0-232-52001-9(1))* South Asia Bks.

Bradley, Ian C. The Celtic Way. 2nd ed. 152p. *(978-0-232-52495-6(5))* Darton, Longman & Todd, Ltd.

Child, Jenny. Celtic Prayers & Reflections. 2008. 112p. (ENG.). pap. 15.95 *(978-1-85607-592-3(3))*; pap. 15.95 *(978-1-85607-606-7(7))* Columba Pr. IRL. Dist: Dufour Editions, Inc.

Denham, Joyce. Circle of Prayer: Prayers & Psalms in the Celtic Tradition. (Illus.). 96p. pap. 14.95 *(978-0-7459-4782-2(4)*, Lion) Lion Hudson PLC GBR. Dist: Trafalgar Square Publishing.

Dowling, Maelruain & Dowling, Elizabeth. Lorrha-Stowe Missal & the Hours of Bangor. 2008. 463p. pap. 30.00 *(978-0-557-00229-0(X))* Lulu Enterprises Inc.

Earle, Mary C., anno. Celtic Christian Spirituality: Essential Writings — Annotated & Explained. 2011. (CEL & ENG.). 176p. pap. 16.99 *(978-1-59473-302-4(3))* SkyLight Paths Publishing.

Edwards, Nancy. He BArchaeology of the Early Medieval Celtic Churches. 2009. (Society for medieval archaeology Monographs). (ENG., Illus.). 424p. (C). 95.00 *(978-1-906540-61-6(6))* Maney Publishing GBR. Dist: Brown, David Bk. Co., The.

Grey, Mary. Celtic Heart. 144p. pap. 6.99 *(978-0-281-05028-4(7))* International Publishers Marketing.

—On Eagles Wings. (Illus.). 128p. 9.00 *(978-0-281-05216-5(6))* SPCK Publishing GBR. Dist: Pilgrim Pr., The/United Church Pr.

Hanna, James Arthur MacClannahan. A History of the Celtic Church from Its Inception To 1153. 2011. 124p. 40.95 ***(978-1-258-01287-8(1))*** Literary Licensing, LLC.

Hughes, Kathleen. The Church in Early Irish Society. 2008. 340p. pap. 33.00 *(978-1-59740-542-3(6))* ACLS Humanities E-Book.

Hunter, George G. Iii. The Celtic Way of Evangelism, How Christianity Can Reach the West ... Again. 10th anniv. ed. 2010. 144p. pap. 17.00 *(978-1-4267-1137-4(9))* Abingdon Pr.

McIntosh, Kenneth. Water from an Ancient Well: Celtic Spirituality for Modern Life. 2011. pap. 24.95 ***(978-1-933630-98-4(1)***, Anamchara Bks.) Harding Hse. Publishing Sebice Inc.

McMaster, Johnston. A Passion for Justice: Social Ethics in the Celtic Tradition. 2008. (Illus.). 242p. pap. 26.50 *(978-1-906716-04-2(8))* Dunedin Academic Pr. GBR. Dist: International Specialized Bk. Services.

Neilson, Kurt. Urban Iona: Celtic Hospitality in the City. 2007. 192p. per. 15.00 *(978-0-8192-2234-3(8))* Church Publishing, Inc.

O'Malley, Brendan. Lord of Creation: A Resource for Creative Celtic Spirituality. 2008. 320p. per. 28.00 *(978-0-8192-2295-4(X))* Church Publishing, Inc.

Praying with Celtic Holy Women. 2007. 20.00 *(978-0-9793767-2-6(6))* SOFIA.

Sampson, Fay. Visions & Voyages: The Story of Celtic Spirituality. 2009. (ENG., Illus.). 192p. pap. 16.95 *(978-0-7459-5235-2(6))* Lion Hudson PLC GBR. Dist: Independent Pubs. Group.

Sanna, Ellyn. The Wings of God: Wild Goose to Pelican, Phoenix to Dove. 2011. pap. 12.95 ***(978-1-937211-14-1(2)***, Anamchara Bks.) Harding Hse. Publishing Sebice Inc.

Taylor, Daniel. In Search of Sacred Places: Looking for Wisdom on Celtic Holy Lands. 2011. (Illus.). 168p. pap. 10.95 ***(978-0-9706511-4-3(7))*** Bog Walk Pr.

To the Isles Afar Off. 2009. (Illus.). 320p. 24.95 *(978-0-9627659-1-9(0))* Four Directions Pr.

Wallace, Martin. Celtic Resource Book. 2nd ed. 2009. (ENG., Illus.). 208p. pap. 40.00 *(978-0-7151-4186-1(4))* Church Hse. Publishing GBR. Dist: Westminster John Knox Pr.

Ward, Tess. The Celtic Wheel of the Year: Celtic & Christian Seasonal Prayers. 2007. (ENG., Illus.). 272p. per. 21.95 *(978-1-905047-95-6(9))* Hunt, John Publishing Ltd. GBR. Dist: National Bk. Network.

Warren, F. E. The Liturgy & Ritual of the Celtic Church. 2008. 318p. pap. 27.00 *(978-1-60608-247-8(7)*, Wipf and Stock) Wipf & Stock Pubs.

Warren, Frederick & O'Donoghue, Neil. The Liturgy & Ritual of the Celtic Church. 2009. 140.00 *(978-1-60724-100-3(5))* Gorgias Pr., LLC.

CELTIC CIVILIZATION

see Civilization, Celtic

CELTIC FOLKLORE

see Celts—Folklore

CELTIC LANGUAGES

see also Breton Language; Cornish Language; Gaulish Language; Irish Language; Manx Language; Scottish Gaelic Language; Welsh Language

Albu, Marius. Celtic Names in Western & Eastern European Languages: Evidence for Cultural Diffusion. 2010. i, 170p. *(978-0-7734-1408-2(8))* Mellen, Edwin Pr., The.

Filppula, Markku, et al, eds. English & Celtic in Contact. 2008. (Routledge Studies in Germanic Linguistics). (Illus.). CCLVIp. 141.00 *(978-0-415-26602-4(5))* Routledge.

Hamnett, Keith. The Plight of Three Celtic Languages - Welsh, Irish, & Gaelic: What Can Be Done to Rescue Them? 2011. 268p. 129.95 *(978-0-7734-3639-8(1))* Mellen, Edwin Pr., The.

Hogan, Edmund, ed. Cath Ruis na Rig for Boinn. (Royal Irish Academy, Todd Lecture Ser.: Vol. 4). reprint ed. 27.50 *(978-0-404-60564-3(8))* AMS Pr., Inc.

KORTLANDT, Frederik. Italo-Celtic Origins & Prehistoric Development of the Irish Language. 2007. (Leiden Studies in Indo-European: 14). 228p. 60.00 *(978-90-420-2177-8(2))* Rodopi.

Lhuyd, Edward, et al. Archaeologia Britannica: Texts & Translations. Evans, Dewi W. & Roberts, Brynley F., eds. 2007. (Celtic Studies Publications Ser.). (COR, WEL & ENG., Illus.). 320p. 39.95 *(978-1-891271-14-4(8))* Celtic Studies Pubns.

MacAulay, Donald, ed. The Celtic Languages. 2008. (Cambridge Language Surveys Ser.). (ENG., Illus.). 488p. pap. 61.00 *(978-0-521-08891-6(7))* Cambridge Univ. Pr.

Matasović, Ranko. Etymological Dictionary of Proto-Celtic. 2008. (Leiden Indo-European Etymological Dictionary Ser.). 576p. *(978-90-04-17336-1(6))* BRILL.

Schmidt, Uwe Friedrich. Praeromanica der Italoromania auf der Grundlage des LEI (A und B) 2009. (Europäische Hochschulschriften. Reihe 9: Italienische Sprache und Literatur Ser.). 510p. pap. 115.95 *(978-3-631-58770-6(8))* Lang, Peter GmbH, Europäischer Verlag der Wissenschaften DEU. Dist: Lang, Peter.

Sims-Williams, Patrick. Ancient Celtic Place-Names in Europe & Asia Minor. 2006. (Publications of the Philological Society Ser.: 1). (ENG., Illus.). 420p. per. 39.95 *(978-1-4051-4570-1(6)*, Wiley-Blackwell) Wiley, John & Sons, Inc.

Stokes, Whitley & Strachan, John. Thesaurus Palaeohibernicus. 2009. 466p. 42.99 *(978-1-115-81078-4(2))*; (LAT.). 465p. pap. 28.99 *(978-1-115-81083-8(9)*, BiblioLife) BiblioBazaar.

Stokes, Whitley & Strachan, John, eds. Thesaurus Palaeohibernicus, 3 vols. (Celtic Language & Literature Ser.: Goidelic & Brythonic). reprint ed. 150.00 *(978-0-404-17593-1(7))* AMS Pr., Inc.

University of Louisiana at Lafayette, Graduate School Staff. The Celtic Languages. Muller, Nicole & Ball, Martin, eds. 2nd rev. ed. 2009. (Routledge Language Family Ser.). (ENG., Illus.). 816p. 315.00 *(978-0-415-42279-6(5))* Routledge.

Vendryes, Joseph. Grammaire du Vieil Irlandais. (Celtic Language & Literature Ser.: Goidelic & Brythonic). reprint ed. 32.00 *(978-0-404-17604-4(6))* AMS Pr., Inc.

Virgil. Auraicept Na N-Eces. Calder, George, ed. (Celtic Language & Literature Ser.: Goidelic & Brythonic). reprint ed. 47.50 *(978-0-404-17538-2(4))* AMS Pr., Inc.

CELTIC LEGENDS

see Celts—Folklore; Legends—Great Britain; Legends—Ireland

CELTIC LITERATURE

see also Irish Literature; Scottish Gaelic Literature; Scottish Literature

Ogle, M. B. The Stag-Messenger Episode. 2010. 83.60 *(978-1-61143-143-8(3))* Gorgias Pr., LLC.

Otto Simms, George. Exploring the Book of Kells. 2nd rev. ed. 2008. (ENG., Illus.). 72p. pap. 15.95 ***(978-1-84717-077-4(3))*** O'Brien Pr., Ltd., The IRL. Dist: Dufour Editions, Inc.

Smith, Gregg A. The Function of the Living Dead in Medieval Norse & Celtic Literature: Death & Desire. 2008. (Illus.). 160p. *(978-0-7734-5353-1(9))* Mellen, Edwin Pr., The.

Stokes, Whitley & Strachan, John. Thesaurus Palaeohibernicus. 2009. 466p. 42.99 *(978-1-115-81078-4(2))*; (LAT.). 465p. pap. 28.99 *(978-1-115-81083-8(9)*, BiblioLife) BiblioBazaar.

Stokes, Whitley & Strachan, John, eds. Thesaurus Palaeohibernicus, 3 vols. (Celtic Language & Literature Ser.: Goidelic & Brythonic). reprint ed. 150.00 *(978-0-404-17593-1(7))* AMS Pr., Inc.

Van de Weyer, Robert. Celtic Parables: Stories, Poems & Prayers. 2009. 144p. pap. 16.95 *(978-0-281-06174-7(2))* SPCK Publishing GBR. Dist: Westminster John Knox Pr.

CELTIC LITERATURE—HISTORY AND CRITICISM

Arnold, Matthew. Celtic Literature. 2008. 124p. 21.99 *(978-0-554-37202-0(9))* 2008. 124p. 24.99 *(978-0-554-27899-5(5))* 2007. (ENG.). 112p. per. 18.99 *(978-1-4346-4269-1(0))* 2007. (ENG.). 120p. per. 19.99 *(978-1-4346-4270-7(4))* BiblioBazaar.

—Celtic Literature. 2006. pap. *(978-1-4065-1028-7(9))* Dodo Pr.

—On the Study of Celtic Literature. 2009. 208p. 23.99 *(978-1-103-63678-5(2))* 2009. 208p. pap. 17.99 *(978-1-103-63675-4(8))* 2008. 124p. 21.99 *(978-0-554-39369-8(7))* 2008. 124p. 24.99 *(978-0-554-30066-5(4))* 2007. (ENG.). 120p. per. 19.99 *(978-1-4346-9097-5(0))* 2007. (ENG.). 108p. per. 18.99 *(978-1-4346-9096-8(2))* BiblioBazaar.

—On the Study of Celtic Literature. 2009. 92p. pap. *(978-0-217-52228-1(9))*; 106p. pap. *(978-0-217-26741-0(6))* Books LLC.

—On the Study of Celtic Literature. reprint ed. lib. bdg. 98.00 *(978-0-7426-2164-0(2))* Classic Bks.

—On the Study of Celtic Literature. 2008. 92p. pap. 10.99 *(978-1-59547-735-4(7))* NuVision Pubns., LLC.

—On Translating Homer: Three Lectures Given at Oxford. reprint ed. lib. bdg. 98.00 *(978-0-7426-2159-6(6))* Classic Bks.

Bernhardt-House, Phillip / A. Werewolves, Magical Hounds, & Dog-Headed Men in Celtic Literature: A Typological Study of Shape-Shifting. 2010. xiv, 498p. *(978-0-7734-3714-2(2))* Mellen, Edwin Pr., The.

Boon, Erin, et al, eds. Proceedings of the Harvard Celtic Colloquium 2010, 30. 2011. (ENG., Illus.). 322p. 32.95 *(978-0-674-06242-9(6))* Harvard Univ. Pr.

Chadbourne, Kathryn, et al, eds. Proceedings of the Harvard Celtic Colloquium, 1995, 15. 2006. (Proceedings of the Harvard Celtic Colloquium Ser.). (Illus.). 256p. 32.50 *(978-0-9642446-9-6(1)*, PHCC15) Harvard Univ. Pr.

Chance, Christina, et al, eds. Proceedings of the Harvard Celtic Colloquium 2006, 26/27. 2010. (Proceedings of the Harvard Celtic Colloquium Ser.). (Illus.). 418p. 32.95 *(978-0-674-05343-4(5))* Harvard Univ. Pr.

Conley, Kassandra, et al. Proceedings of the Harvard Celtic Colloquium, 29: 2009, 29. Boon, Erin et al, eds. 2011. (ENG.). 272p. 32.95 *(978-0-674-05595-7(0))* Harvard Univ. Pr.

Davies, Morgan Thomas. Proceedings of the Celtic Studies Association of North America Annual Meeting 2008. 2011. pap. *(978-0-19-256823-6(X))* Colgate Univ. Pr.

Davies, Morgan Thomas, ed. Proceedings of the Celtic Studies Association of North America Annual Meeting 2008: CSANA Yearbook 10. 2011. (Illus.). viii, 154p. pap. 27.50 *(978-0-912568-24-9(0))* Colgate Univ. Pr.

Eska, Joseph F. Law, Literature & Society: CSANA Yearbook, Volume 7. Eska, Joseph, ed. 2008. (Illus.). 133p. (C). 74.50 *(978-1-84682-099-1(5))* Four Courts Pr. IRL. Dist: International Specialized Bk. Services.

Ferguson, Frank & Holmes, Andrew, eds. Revising Robert Burns & Ulster: Literature, Religion & Politics, C. 1770-1920. 2009. 198p. 65.00 *(978-1-84682-197-4(5))* Four Courts Pr. IRL. Dist: International Specialized Bk. Services.

Heinz, Sabine. Celtic Literatures - Discoveries. 2007. (Polish Studies in English Language & Literature Ser.: Vol. 20). 160p. pap. 40.95 *(978-0-8204-8754-0(6))* Lang, Peter Publishing, Inc.
Jackson, Kenneth. Studies in Early Celtic Nature Poetry. 2011. 216p. pap. 22.99 *(978-1-107-60018-8(9))* Cambridge Univ. Pr.
Kimpton, Bettina. Proceedings of the Harvard Celtic Colloquium 2003, 23. Knight, Matthew, ed. 2009. (Proceedings of the Harvard Celtic Colloquium Ser.). (Illus.). 350p. 32.95 *(978-0-674-03139-5(3))* Harvard Univ. Pr.
Krappe, Alexander Hagg. Balor with the Evil Eye Studies in Celti. 2006. pap. 26.95 *(978-1-4286-5232-3(9))* Kessinger Publishing, LLC.
Krappe, Alexander Haggerty. Balor with the Evil Eye: Studies in Celtic & French Literature. 2007. (ENG.). 240p. 41.95 *(978-0-548-14035-2(9))* Kessinger Publishing, LLC.
Murray, K. Sarah-Jane. From Plato to Lancelot: A Preface to Chrétien de Troyes. 2008. (C). 26.95 *(978-0-8156-3160-6(X))* Syracuse Univ. Pr.
Nagy, Joseph Falaky, ed. Memory & the Modern in Celtic Literatures 5: CSANA Yearbook. 2006. 168p. 70.00 *(978-1-85182-982-8(2))* Four Courts Pr. IRL. Dist: International Specialized Bk. Services.
—Myth in Celtic Literatures: CSANA Yearbook., Vol. 6. 2007. 166p. 70.00 *(978-1-84682-046-5(4))* Four Courts Pr. IRL. Dist: International Specialized Bk. Services.
Pittock, Murray. Poetry & Jacobite Politics in Eighteenth-Century Britain & Ireland. 2006. (Cambridge Studies in Eighteenth-Century English Literature & Thought Ser.). (ENG.). 272p. pap. 53.00 *(978-0-521-03027-4(7))* Cambridge Univ. Pr.
Rolleston, T. W. Myths & Legends of the Celtic Race. 2008. 360p. pap. 18.95 *(978-1-60096-400-8(1))* Editorium, The.
Rolleston, Thomas. Myths & Legends of the Celtic Race. 2009. 368p. 29.99 *(978-0-559-11169-3(X))*; 31.99 *(978-0-559-11152-5(5))*; pap. 32.75 *(978-0-559-11156-3(8))*; pap. 31.75 *(978-0-559-11164-8(9))* BiblioBazaar.
Thurneysen, Rudolf. Die Irische Helden-und Konigssage bis zum Siebzehnten Jahrhundert. (Celtic Language & Literature Ser.: Goidelic & Brythonic). reprint ed. 49.50 *(978-0-404-17599-3(6))* AMS Pr., Inc.

CELTIC LITERATURE—TRANSLATIONS INTO ENGLISH

Jackson, Kenneth. Studies in Early Celtic Nature Poetry. 2011. 216p. pap. 22.99 *(978-1-107-60018-8(9))* Cambridge Univ. Pr.
Jackson, Kenneth Hurlstone, tr. A Celtic Miscellany: Translations from the Celtic Literatures. 2011. 358p. 51.95 ***(978-1-258-01179-6(4))*** Literary Licensing, LLC.
MacLeod, Sharon Paice. Celtic Myth & Religion: A Study of Traditional Belief, with Newly Translated Prayers, Poems & Songs. 2011. (ENG.). 243p. pap. 35.00 *(978-0-7864-6476-0(3))* McFarland & Co., Inc. Pubs.

CELTIC MYTHOLOGY

see Mythology, Celtic

CELTIC PHILOLOGY

see also Celtic Languages

Boon, Erin, et al, eds. Proceedings of the Harvard Celtic Colloquium 2010, 30. 2011. (ENG., Illus.). 322p. 32.95 *(978-0-674-06242-9(6))* Harvard Univ. Pr.
Chadbourne, Kathryn, et al. Proceedings of the Harvard Celtic Colloquium, 1996 & 1997, 16/17. Larson, Heather et al, eds. 2006. (Proceedings of the Harvard Celtic Colloquium Ser.). (Illus.). 250p. 29.50 *(978-1-891271-08-3(3))* Harvard Univ. Pr.
Chance, Christina, et al, eds. Proceedings of the Harvard Celtic Colloquium 2006, 26/27. 2010. (Proceedings of the Harvard Celtic Colloquium Ser.). (Illus.). 418p. 32.95 *(978-0-674-05343-4(5))* Harvard Univ. Pr.
Conley, Kassandra, et al. Proceedings of the Harvard Celtic Colloquium, 29: 2009, 29. Boon, Erin et al, eds. 2011. (ENG.). 272p. 32.95 *(978-0-674-05595-7(0))* Harvard Univ. Pr.
Delfosse, Heinrich P., et al. Reimregister zu Nikolaus Lenaus Versepen. (Indices zur deutschen Literatur Ser.). (GER., Illus.). XX, 180p. 210.00 ***(978-3-11-186341-2(7))*** De Gruyter, Walter Inc.
Fogarty, Hugh, et al, eds. Proceedings of the Harvard Celtic Colloquium 2000 & 2001, 20/21. 2007. (Proceedings of the Harvard Celtic Colloquium Ser.). (Illus.). 370p. 32.95 *(978-0-674-02383-3(8))* Harvard Univ. Pr.
Izzo, Kathryn & Olson, Katharine, eds. Proceedings of the Harvard Celtic Colloquium, 22. 2008. (Proceedings of the Harvard Celtic Colloquium Ser.). (Illus.). 250p. 32.95 *(978-0-674-03134-0(2))* Harvard Univ. Pr.
Jones, Samuel. Proceedings of the Harvard Celtic Colloquium, 24/25, 2004 & 2005, 24/25. Jones, Aled & Knight, Jennifer Dukes, eds. 2009. (Proceedings of the Harvard Celtic Colloquium Ser.). 200p. 32.95 *(978-0-674-03528-7(3))* Harvard Univ. Pr.
Kimpton, Bettina. Proceedings of the Harvard Celtic Colloquium 2003, 23. Knight, Matthew, ed. 2009. (Proceedings of the Harvard Celtic Colloquium Ser.). (Illus.). 350p. 32.95 *(978-0-674-03139-5(3))* Harvard Univ. Pr.
Linkletter, Michael. Proceedings of the Harvard Celtic Colloquium, 18/19. Luft, Diana et al, eds. 2007. (Proceedings of the Harvard Celtic Colloquium Ser.). (Illus.). 460p. 29.95 *(978-0-674-02384-0(6))* Harvard Univ. Pr.
Malone, Christopher. Proceedings of the Harvard Celtic Colloquium, 28: 2008, 28. Conley, Kassandra et al, eds. 2011. (ENG., Illus.). 240p. 32.95 *(978-0-674-05596-4(9))* Harvard Univ. Pr.
McMahon, Timothy G. Grand Opportunity: The Gaelic Revival & Irish Society, 1893-1910. 2008. 45.00 *(978-0-8156-3158-3(8))*; (Illus.). 342p. pap. 22.95 *(978-0-8156-3184-2(7))* Syracuse Univ. Pr.
Ó Croinín, Dáibhí. Whitley Stokes (1830-1909) The Lost Celtic Notebooks Rediscovered. 2011. 166p. 55.00 *(978-1-84682-174-5(6))* Four Courts Pr. IRL. Dist: International Specialized Bk. Services.
Rockel, Martin & Zimmer, Stefan, eds. Akten des ersten Symposiums deutschsprachiger Keltologen: (Gosen bei Berlin, 8.-10. April 1992) (Buchreihe der Zeitschrift für celtische Philologie Ser.). (GER.). X, 395p. 210.00 ***(978-3-11-183584-6(7))*** De Gruyter, Walter Inc.
Spindler, Konrad, et al. Kelten-Einfälle an der Donau: Akten des Vierten Symposiums Deutschsprachiger Keltologinnen und Keltologen: Philologische, Historische, Archäologische Evidenzen: Konrad Spindler, 1939-2005 Zum Gedenken: Linz/Donau, 17.-21. Juli 2005. 2007. (Denkschriften der Phil. -Hist. Klasse Ser.). (GER., Illus.). 678p. (C). 203.00 *(978-3-7001-3670-5(6))* Austrian Academy of Sciences Press AUT. Dist: Brown, David Bk. Co., The.

CELTS

see also Britons; Druids and Druidism; Picts; Welsh

Adams, Geoff W. Power & Religious Acculturation in Romano-Celtic Society: An Examination of Archaeological Sites in Gloucestershire. 2009. (Bar Ser.). (Illus.). 290p. (C). 112.50 *(978-1-4073-0387-1(2))* British Archaeological Reports Ltd. GBR. Dist: Brown, David Bk. Co., The.
Arnold, Matthew. On the Study of Celtic Literature. 2009. 208p. 23.99 *(978-1-103-63678-5(2))* 2009. 208p. pap. 17.99 *(978-1-103-63675-4(8))* 2008. 124p. 24.99 *(978-0-554-30066-5(4))* 2008. 124p. 21.99 *(978-0-554-39369-8(7))* 2007. (ENG.). 108p. per. 18.99 *(978-1-4346-9096-8(2))* 2007. (ENG.). 120p. per. 19.99 *(978-1-4346-9097-5(0))* BiblioBazaar.
—On the Study of Celtic Literature. 2009. 106p. pap. *(978-0-217-26741-0(6))*; 92p. pap. *(978-0-217-52228-1(9))* Books LLC.
—On the Study of Celtic Literature. reprint ed. lib. bdg. 98.00 *(978-0-7426-2164-0(2))* Classic Bks.
—On the Study of Celtic Literature. 2008. 92p. pap. 10.99 *(978-1-59547-735-4(7))* NuVision Pubns., LLC.
—On Translating Homer: Three Lectures Given at Oxford. reprint ed. lib. bdg. 98.00 *(978-0-7426-2159-6(6))* Classic Bks.
Balzer, Tracy. Thin Places: An Evangelical Journey into Celtic Christianity. 2007. 173p. per. 12.99 *(978-0-89112-513-6(2),* Leafwood Pubs.) Abilene Christian Univ. Pr.
Breeze, Andrew. The Mary of the Celts. 2008. 192p. pap. *(978-0-85244-682-9(9))* Gracewing, Ltd.
Carruthers, Gerard & Rawes, Alan, eds. English Romanticism & the Celtic World. 2010. (ENG.). 280p. pap. 30.99 *(978-0-521-13666-2(0))* Cambridge Univ. Pr.
Cunliffe, Barry. Britain Begins. 2012. (ENG., Illus.). 400p. 45.00 ***(978-0-19-960933-8(0))*** Oxford Univ. Pr., Inc.
Freeman, Philip. War, Women, & Druids: Eyewitness Reports & Early Accounts of the Ancient Celts. 2008. (ENG., Illus.). 112p. pap. 19.95 *(978-0-292-71836-4(5))* Univ. of Texas Pr.
Hal Leonard Corporation Staff, creator. Favorite Celtic Songs for Easy Piano, 1 vol. 2009. (ENG.). 90p. pap. 12.99 *(978-1-60378-097-1(1),* 1603780971) Cherry Lane Music Co.
Haywood, John. The Historical Atlas of the Celtic World. 2009. (ENG., Illus.). 144p. pap. 24.95 *(978-0-500-28831-3(3),* 528831) Thames & Hudson.
Heaven, Ross. Plant Spirit Wisdom: Celtic Healing & the Power of Nature. 2008. (ENG.). 224p. pap. 19.95 *(978-1-84694-123-8(7))* Hunt, John Publishing Ltd. GBR. Dist: National Bk. Network.
Heinz, Sabine. Celtic Symbols. 2008. (ENG., Illus.). 304p. per. 12.95 *(978-1-4027-4624-6(5))* Sterling Publishing Co., Inc.
Howarth, Nicki. Cartimandua: Queen of the Brigantes. 2009. (ENG., Illus.). 224p. pap. 34.95 *(978-0-7524-4705-6(X))* History Pr. Ltd.,The GBR. Dist: Independent Pubs. Group.
Jerome. Early Celts in Americ. 2011. 50p. 36.95 ***(978-1-258-01821-4(7))*** Literary Licensing, LLC.
Kaiser, Marlene Sophia. Das Keltisch-Römische Gräberfeld von Wederath-Belginum: Die Aschengruben und Aschenfl ächen - Ausgegraben 1954-1985. 2006. (GER., Illus.). 216p. 112.00 *(978-3-8053-3666-6(7))* Zabern, Philipp von Verlag, GmbH DEU. Dist: Brown, David Bk. Co., The.
Karl & Stifter. Celtic World: Critical Concepts in Historical Studies Vol1, 4 vols. 2007. (Illus.). *(978-0-415-35712-8(8))* Routledge.
—Celtic World: Critical Concepts in Historical Studies Vol2, 4 vols. 2007. (Illus.). *(978-0-415-35713-5(6))* Routledge.
—Celtic World: Critical Concepts in Historical Studies Vol3, 4 vols. 2007. (Illus.). *(978-0-415-35714-2(4))* Routledge.
—Celtic World: Critical Concepts in Historical Studies Vol4, 4 vols. 2007. (Illus.). *(978-0-415-35715-9(2))* Routledge.
Karl, Raimund. Altkeltische Sozialstrukturen. 2006. (Main Ser.). (GER., Illus.). 609p. (C). 106.00 *(978-963-8046-69-7(4))* Archaeolingua Alapitvany HUN. Dist: Brown, David Bk. Co., The.
Kistler, Erich. Funktionalisierte Keltenbilder: Die Indienstnahme der Kelten Zur Vermittlung Von Normen und Werten in der Hellenistischen Welt. 2010. (GER., Illus.). 432p. (C). 120.00 ***(978-3-938032-36-7(7))*** Antike, Verlag, e.K. DEU. Dist: ISD.
Koch, John T. Tartessian 2: The Inscription of Mesas do Castelinho ro & the Verbal Complex. Preliminaries to Historical Phonology. 2011. (ENG., Illus.). 198p. (C). pap. 29.95 ***(978-1-907029-07-3(9))*** Celtic Studies Pubns.
Koch, John Thomas & Minard, Antone. The Celts: History, Life, & Culture, 2 vols. 2012. (Illus.). 962p. 189.00 ***(978-1-59884-964-6(6),*** A3636C) ABC-CLIO, LLC.
Logan, James. The Scottish Gael: Or, Celtic Manners As Preserved among the Highlanders, 2 vols., Set. reprint ed. 59.50 *(978-0-404-16560-4(5))* AMS Pr., Inc.
MacCulloch, J. A. The Religion of the Ancient Celts. l.t. ed. 2007. 376p. pap. 26.99 *(978-1-4264-8210-6(8))*; (ENG.). 328p. pap. 23.99 *(978-1-4264-8138-3(1))* BiblioBazaar.
—The Religion of the Ancient Celts. 2007. (ENG.). 352p. per. *(978-1-4065-2983-8(4))* Dodo Pr.
Marsden, John. Somerled: And the Emergence of Gaelic Scotland. 2010. (ENG., Illus.). 180p. pap. 35.00 *(978-1-904607-80-9(2),* Tuckwell Pr.) Birlinn, Ltd. GBR. Dist: Independent Pubs. Group.
Martin, Neill. The Form & Function of Ritual Dialogue in the Marriage Traditions of Celtic-Language Cultures. 2007. (Illus.). 424p. 129.95 *(978-0-7734-5328-9(8))* Mellen, Edwin Pr., The.
Matthews, Caitlin. Bookinabox: Celtic Wisdom. 2010. (Book-in-A-Box Ser.). (ENG., Illus.). 224p. 14.95 *(978-1-85906-261-6(X))* Connections Bk. Publishing, Ltd. GBR. Dist: Red Wheel/Weiser.
McCabe, Ebe Chandler. Celtic Warrior Descendants: A Genetic & Cultural History of a Rural American Family. 2011. 144p. pap. 19.95 *(978-1-4502-9364-8(6))* iUniverse, Inc.
McCormick, Marlene Deborah, et al. Horses & the Mystical Path: The Celtic Way of Expanding the Human Soul. 2006. (ENG.). 208p. per. 16.95 *(978-1-57731-556-8(1))* New World Library.
Miller, Calvin. Celtic Devotions: A Guide to Morning & Evening Prayer. 2008. (ENG.). 131p. 15.00 *(978-0-8308-3505-8(9),* IVP Bks.) InterVarsity Pr.
—The Path of Celtic Prayer: An Ancient Way to Everyday Joy. 2007. (ENG.). 170p. 18.00 *(978-0-8308-3504-1(0),* IVP Bks.) InterVarsity Pr.
Moffat, Alistair. The Sea Kingdoms: The History of Celtic Britain & Ireland. 2008. (ENG., Illus.). 316p. pap. 20.00 *(978-1-84158-717-2(6))* Birlinn, Ltd. GBR. Dist: Interlink Publishing Group, Inc.
Muldoon, James. The North Atlantic Frontier: Vikings & Celts. 2009. (Expansion of Latin Europe, 1000-1500 Ser.). (Illus.). 434p. 190.00 *(978-0-7546-5958-7(5))* Ashgate Publishing Co.
Neville, Cynthia J. Land, Law & People in Medieval Scotland. 2010. (ENG., Illus.). 240p. (gr. 17). 105.00 *(978-0-7486-3958-8(6))* Edinburgh Univ. Pr. GBR. Dist: Columbia Univ. Pr.
Ó Hógáin, Dáithí. The Celts: A History. 2007. (Illus.). 248p. pap. 29.95 *(978-0-85115-923-2(0),* Boydell Press) Boydell & Brewer, Ltd. GBR. Dist: Boydell & Brewer, Inc.
Paine, Angela. The Healing Power of Celtic Plants. 2006. (ENG., Illus.). 240p. per. 29.95 *(978-1-905047-62-8(2))* Hunt, John Publishing Ltd. GBR. Dist: National Bk. Network.
Rhys, John. Celtic Britain. 2009. 360p. 33.99 *(978-1-110-03866-4(6))*; 344p. 32.99 *(978-1-110-23762-3(6))*; 360p. pap. 31.75 *(978-1-110-03864-0(X))*; 344p. pap. 31.75 *(978-1-110-23758-6(8))* BiblioBazaar.
—Celtic Britain. 2009. 264p. pap. *(978-0-217-69468-1(3))*; 238p. pap. *(978-0-217-18847-0(8))*; 266p. pap. *(978-0-217-18844-9(3))* Books LLC.
Robert Harvey. 1,000 More Celtic, Quotes, Notes & Anecdotes. 2009. 208p. pap. 17.00 *(978-1-4269-1989-3(1))* Trafford Publishing.
Robertson, John MacKinnon. The Saxon & the Celt - a Study in Sociology. 2009. 372p. pap. 30.95 *(978-1-4446-2027-6(4),* Kent Pr.) Kent Communications, Ltd.
Spindler, Konrad, et al. Kelten-Einfälle an der Donau: Akten des Vierten Symposiums Deutschsprachiger Keltologinnen und Keltologen: Philologische, Historische, Archäologische Evidenzen: Konrad Spindler, 1939-2005 Zum Gedenken: Linz/Donau, 17.-21. Juli 2005. 2007. (Denkschriften der Phil. -Hist. Klasse Ser.). (GER., Illus.). 678p. (C). 203.00 *(978-3-7001-3670-5(6))* Austrian Academy of Sciences Press AUT. Dist: Brown, David Bk. Co., The.
Telwyn. The Confluence. 2010. (Illus.). 224p. pap. 14.49 *(978-1-4490-7125-7(2))* AuthorHouse.
Thompson, Christopher. Highland Martial Culture: The Fighting Heritage of Scotland. 2009. (Illus.). 124p. pap. 13.00 *(978-1-58160-692-8(3))* Paladin Pr.
Verlag Philipp von Zabern, ed. Kelten Am Rhein: Akten des Dreizehnten Internationalen Keltologiekongresses = Proceedings of the Thirteenth International Congress of Celtic Studies: 23. Bis 27. Juli 2007 in Bonn, 2 vols. 2010. (Beihefte der Bonner Jahrbucher Ser.). (GER., Illus.). 628p. (C). 192.00 *(978-3-8053-4102-8(4))* Zabern, Philipp von Verlag, GmbH DEU. Dist: Brown, David Bk. Co., The.
Villa, Silvia Alfaye. Santuarios y Rituales en la Hispania Celtica. 2009. (ENG & SPA., Illus.). 583p. (C). pap. 195.00 *(978-1-4073-0446-5(1))* British Archaeological Reports Ltd. GBR. Dist: Brown, David Bk. Co., The.
Vitali, Daniele. The Celts: History & Treasures of an Ancient Civilization. 2008. (ENG., Illus.). 208p. 35.00 *(978-88-544-0321-5(0))* White Star ITA. Dist: Random Hse., Inc.
Wallace, Martin. Celtic Resource Book. 2nd ed. 2009. (ENG., Illus.). 208p. pap. 40.00 *(978-0-7151-4186-1(4))* Church Hse. Publishing GBR. Dist: Westminster John Knox Pr.
Watkins, Bill. The Once & Future Celt. 2008. (ENG.). 340p. pap. 16.95 *(978-0-9765201-9-1(2))* Scarletta Pr.
Welch & Babbs, Liz. Celtic Treasure: Unearthing the Riches of Celtic Spirituality. 2009. (ENG., Illus.). 80p. 9.95 *(978-0-7459-5355-7(7))* Lion Hudson PLC GBR. Dist: Independent Pubs. Group.
Wright, Thomas. The Celt, the Roman & the Saxon: A History of the Early Inhabitants of Britain 1861. 2007. (ENG.). 542p. 57.95 *(978-0-548-05396-6(0))* Kessinger Publishing, LLC.

CELTS—FOLKLORE

Akins, Steven L. The Lebor Feasa Rund: A Druidic Grammar of Celtic Lore & Magic. 2008. 180p. 26.95 *(978-1-4401-0282-0(1))*; pap. 16.95 *(978-1-4401-0280-6(5))* iUniverse, Inc.
Campbell, J. F. & Campbell, J. F. The Celtic Dragon Myth with the Geste of Fraoch. Henderson, George, tr. 2009. (Illus.). 184p. pap. 12.99 *(978-1-61534-000-2(9))* EZreads Pubns., LLC.
Curran, Bob. Mysterious Celtic Mythology in American Folklore, 1 vol. 2010. (ENG.). 296p. 25.00 *(978-1-58980-743-3(X))* Pelican Publishing Co., Inc.
de Waal, Esther. God under My Roof: Celtic Songs & Blessings. 2006. (Illus.). 72p. 14.95 *(978-1-55725-516-7(4))* Paraclete Pr., Inc.
Evans-Wentz, W. The Fairy Faith in Celtic Countries: The Classic Study of Leprechauns, Pixies, & Other Fairy Spirits. 2007. 404p. per. 23.99 *(978-1-59547-878-8(7))* NuVision Pubns., LLC.
Evans-Wentz, W. Y. The Fairy-Faith in Celtic Countries. 2008. (ENG.). 574p. per. 43.75 *(978-1-4375-3178-7(4))*; 498p. per. 37.75 *(978-1-4375-3067-4(2))*; 498p. pap. 37.75 *(978-1-4375-1933-4(4))* BiblioBazaar.
—The Fairy Faith in Celtic Countries. 2008. 564p. pap. 24.95 *(978-1-60096-756-6(6))*; 560p. pap. 24.95 *(978-1-60096-335-3(8))* Editorium, The.
—The Fairy-Faith in Celtic Countries. l.t. ed. 2008. (ENG.). 574p. pap. 43.75 *(978-1-4375-1934-1(2))* BiblioBazaar.
—The Fairy Faith in Celtic Countries: The Classic Study of Leprechauns, Pixies, & Other Fairy Spirits. 2009. 404p. 42.99 *(978-1-59547-529-9(X))* NuVision Pubns., LLC.
Evans-Wentz, Walter Yeeling. The Fairy-Faith in Celtic Countries. 2009. 386p. pap. *(978-0-217-38495-7(1))* Books LLC.
Henderson, George. Survivals in Belief among the Celts. 2009. 284p. 28.99 *(978-0-559-13531-6(9))*; 25.99 *(978-0-559-13543-9(2))*; pap. 23.99 *(978-0-559-13535-4(1))*; pap. 18.99 *(978-0-559-13540-8(8))* BiblioBazaar.
Jacobs, Joseph. Celtic Fairy Tales. rev. ed. 2006. 314p. 29.95 *(978-1-4218-1783-5(7))*; pap. 14.95 *(978-1-4218-1883-2(3))* 1st World Publishing, Inc. (1st World Library - Literary Society).
—Celtic Fairy Tales. 2008. 232p. 27.99 *(978-0-554-28818-5(4))* 2008. 232p. 24.99 *(978-0-554-38121-3(4))* 2007. (ENG.). 210p. pap. 20.99 *(978-1-4346-6340-5(X))* 2007. 228p. pap. 22.99 *(978-1-4346-6341-2(8))* BiblioBazaar.
—Celtic Fairy Tales. 2007. (ENG.). 212p. per. *(978-1-4065-1814-6(X))* Dodo Pr.
—Celtic Fairy Tales. 304p. 2008. 29.95 *(978-1-4344-6905-2(0))* 2008. pap. 19.95 *(978-1-4344-6904-5(2))* 2007. (ENG.). 29.95 *(978-1-4344-9578-5(7))* 2007. (ENG.). per. 19.95 *(978-1-4344-9577-8(9))* Wildside Pr., LLC.
Jacobs, Joseph, ed. Celtic Fairy Tales. 23.95 *(978-0-89190-078-8(0))* Amereon LTD.
—More Celtic Fairy Tales. 22.95 *(978-0-89190-079-5(9))* Amereon LTD.
MacDougall, James. Folk & Hero Tales. 2010. 196p. pap. 15.37 *(978-1-152-46495-7(7))* General Bks. LLC.
Mees, Bernard. Celtic Curses. 2009. (Illus.). 238p. 99.00 *(978-1-84383-457-1(X),* Boydell Press) Boydell & Brewer, Ltd. GBR. Dist: Boydell & Brewer, Inc.
Monaghan, Patricia. The Encyclopedia of Celtic Mythology & Folklore. 2008. 528p. (C). (gr. 9). per. 21.95 *(978-0-8160-7556-0(5),* Checkmark Bks.) Facts On File, Inc.
Rhys, John. Celtic Folklore Welsh & Manx V1. 2006. pap. 37.95 *(978-1-4286-3714-6(1))* Kessinger Publishing, LLC.
—Celtic Folklore Welsh & Manx V2. 2006. pap. 30.95 *(978-1-4286-3712-2(5))* Kessinger Publishing, LLC.
Speranza Wilde, Lady Francesca. Ancient Legends, Mystic Charms, & Superstitions of Ireland. 2008. 286p. pap. 16.95 *(978-1-4357-3146-2(8))* Lulu Enterprises Inc.
Squire, Charles. Celtic Myth & Legend. 2009. 392p. 31.99 *(978-0-559-11644-5(6))*; 29.99 *(978-0-559-11657-5(8))*; pap. 26.99 *(978-0-559-11646-9(2))*; pap. 32.75 *(978-0-559-11655-1(1))* BiblioBazaar.
—Celtic Myth & Legend Poetry & Romanc. 2006. (Illus.). pap. 38.95 *(978-1-4286-4400-7(8))* Kessinger Publishing, LLC.
—Celtic Myth & Legend, Poetry & Romance. 2010. 512p. *(978-1-4446-5728-9(3))*; pap. *(978-1-4446-5640-4(6))* Read Bks. (Obscure Pr.).
Suckling, Nigel. Faeries of the Celtic Lands. 2007. (ENG., Illus.). 224p. 19.95 *(978-1-904332-74-9(9))* AAPPL Artists & Photographers Pr., Ltd. GBR. Dist: Sterling Publishing Co., Inc.
Taylor, Ken & Taylor, Joules. Celts (Lost Worlds) 2009. (Lost Worlds Ser.). (ENG.). 144p. 19.95 *(978-1-4027-5469-2(8))* Sterling Publishing Co., Inc.
Thomson, Cindy. Celtic Wisdom: Treasures from Ireland. 2009. (ENG., Illus.). 96p. 12.95 *(978-0-7459-5325-0(5))* Lion Hudson PLC GBR. Dist: Independent Pubs. Group.
Wentz, W. Y. Evans. The Fairy-Faith in Celtic Countries. 2009. 554p. 44.99 *(978-1-117-07067-4(0))*; (ENG.). 553p. pap. 30.99 *(978-1-117-07069-8(7),* BiblioLife); (ENG.). 553p. pap. 41.75 *(978-1-117-07068-1(9))* BiblioBazaar.
Young, Ella. Celtic Wonder Tales. 2008. 120p. per. 19.75 *(978-1-4375-2483-3(4))*; (ENG.). 130p. per. 20.75 *(978-1-4375-2619-6(5))* BiblioBazaar.
—Celtic Wonder Tales. 2009. (Illus.). 148p. pap. *(978-1-4099-3567-4(1))* Dodo Pr.
—Celtic Wonder Tales. 212p. 2008. 39.95 *(978-1-4366-7403-4(4))* 2007. per. 24.95 *(978-1-4325-9028-4(6))* Kessinger Publishing, LLC.

CELTS—RELIGION

Alcock, Joan P. Daily Life of the Pagan Celts, 1 vol. 2009. (Daily Life Ser.). (Illus.). 224p. 49.95 *(978-1-84645-021-1(7),* GWP021) Greenwood Publishing Group, Inc.
Anwyl, Edward. Celtic Religion in Pre-Christian Times. 2008. 48p. per. *(978-1-4065-7005-2(2))* Dodo Pr.

C

—Celtic Religion in Pre-Christian Times. 2009. 48p. pap. 9.99 (978-1-4344-5822-3(9)) Wildside Pr., LLC.

Emick, Jennifer. The Everything Celtic Wisdom Book: Find Inspiration Through Ancient Traditions, Rituals, & Spirituality. 2009. (ENG., Illus.). 304p. pap. 15.95 (978-1-59869-540-3(1)) Adams Media Corp.

Evans-Wentz, W. The Fairy Faith in Celtic Countries: The Classic Study of Leprechauns, Pixies, & Other Fairy Spirits. 2007. 404p. per. 23.99 (978-1-59547-878-8(7)) NuVision Pubns., LLC.

Evans-Wentz, W. Y. The Fairy-Faith in Celtic Countries. 2008. (ENG.). 574p. per. 43.75 (978-1-4375-3178-7(4)); 498p. per. 37.75 (978-1-4375-3067-4(2)); 498p. pap. 37.75 (978-1-4375-1933-4(4)) BiblioBazaar.

—The Fairy Faith in Celtic Countries. 2008. 560p. pap. 24.95 (978-1-60096-335-3(8)); 564p. pap. 24.95 (978-1-60096-756-6(6)) Editorium, The.

—The Fairy-Faith in Celtic Countries. l.t. ed. 2008. (ENG.). 574p. pap. 43.75 (978-1-4375-1934-1(2)) BiblioBazaar.

—The Fairy Faith in Celtic Countries: The Classic Study of Leprechauns, Pixies, & Other Fairy Spirits. 2009. 404p. 42.99 (978-1-59547-529-9(X)) NuVision Pubns., LLC.

Evans-Wentz, Walter Yeeling. The Fairy-Faith in Celtic Countries. 2009. 386p. pap. (978-0-217-38495-7(1)) Books LLC.

Haeussler, Ralph & King, A., eds. Continuity & innovation in religion in the roman west, Volume 2, Vol. 2. 2008. (ENG, FRE, GER & ITA., Illus.). 238p. 89.00 (978-1-887829-96-0(2)) Journal of Roman Archaeology, LLC.

Henderson, George. Survivals in Belief among the Celts. 2009. 284p. 25.99 (978-0-559-13543-9(2)); 28.99 (978-0-559-13531-6(9)); pap. 18.99 (978-0-559-13540-8(8)); pap. 23.99 (978-0-559-13535-4(1)) BiblioBazaar.

Hofeneder, Andreas. Die Religion der Kelten in den antiken literarischen Zeugnissen: Sammlung, Übersetzung und Kommentierung Band II: Von Cicero bis Florus. 2008. (Mitteilungen der Prahistorischen Kommission Ser.). 680p. (C). pap. 120.00 (978-3-7001-3931-7(4)) Austrian Academy of Sciences Press AUT. Dist: Brown, David Bk. Co., The.

Lee-Evans, Nancy. Deep Relations. 2010. 108p. pap. (978-3-8383-4373-0(5)) Lambert Academic Publishing.

MacCulloch, J. A. The Religion of the Ancient Celts. 2008. 380p. 31.99 (978-0-554-25086-1(1)); 29.99 (978-0-554-34389-1(4)) BiblioBazaar.

Matthews, Caitlin. Celtic Visions: Omens, Dreams & Spirits of the Otherworld. 2012. (ENG.). 256p. 14.95 **(978-1-78028-111-7(0)**, Watkins Publishing) Duncan Baird Pubs. GBR. Dist: Sterling Publishing Co., Inc.

NicDhàna, Kathryn Price, et al. The CR FAQ: An Introduction to Celtic Reconstructionist Paganism. 2007. 204p. pap. 19.99 (978-0-615-15800-6(5)) River Hse. Publishing.

O'Donoghue, Neil Xavier. The Eucharist in Pre-Norman Ireland. 2011. (ENG., Illus.). 384p. pap. 48.00 (978-0-268-03732-1(9)) Univ. of Notre Dame Pr.

Power, Rosemary. The Celtic Quest: A Contemporary Spirituality. 2011. (ENG.). 189p. pap. 25.95 (978-1-85607-698-2(9)) Columba Pr. IRL. Dist: Dufour Editions, Inc.

Rolleston, T. W. Myths & Legends of the Celtic Race. 2008. 360p. pap. 18.95 (978-1-60096-400-8(1)) Editorium, The.

Rolleston, Thomas. Myths & Legends of the Celtic Race. 2009. 368p. 29.99 (978-0-559-11169-3(X)); 31.99 (978-0-559-11152-5(5)); pap. 32.75 (978-0-559-11156-3(8)); pap. 31.75 (978-0-559-11164-8(9)) BiblioBazaar.

Thomson, Cindy. Celtic Wisdom: Treasures from Ireland. 2009. (ENG., Illus.). 96p. 12.95 (978-0-7459-5325-0(5)) Lion Hudson PLC GBR. Dist: Independent Pubs. Group.

Wentz, W. Y. Evans. The Fairy-Faith in Celtic Countries. 2009. 554p. 44.99 (978-1-117-07067-4(0)); (ENG.). 553p. pap. 30.99 (978-1-117-07069-8(7), BiblioLife); (ENG.). 553p. pap. 41.75 (978-1-117-07068-1(9)) BiblioBazaar.

CEMBALO

see Dulcimer; Harpsichord

CEMENT

see also Adhesives; Concrete; Pavements; Portland Cement

Alhaj Hussein, Mohammed. Corrosion Behavior & Durability of Various Cements & Pozzolans. 2010. 168p. pap. (978-3-8383-3835-4(9)) Lambert Academic Publishing.

Asphalt Institute, creator. Calibration Factors for Polymer-Modified Asphalts Using M-E Based Design Methods. 2008. (Engineering Reports). (Illus.). 28p. pap. 30.00 (978-1-934154-55-7(5)) Asphalt Institute.

Bapat, Jayant Dattatraya. Mineral Admixtures in Cement & Concrete. 2012. (ENG., Illus.). 320p. 129.95 **(978-1-4398-1792-6(8)**, CRC Press) Taylor & Francis Group GBR. Dist: Taylor & Francis Group.

Bart, Florence, et al, eds. Cement-Based Materials for Nuclear Waste Storage. 2012. (ENG., Illus.). v, 261p. 129.00 **(978-1-4614-3444-3(0)**, 1461434440) Springer.

Bassir, Mouhamadou. Low Temperature Processes. 2011. (Energy Science, Engineering & Technology Ser.). 75.00 **(978-1-62100-038-9(9))** Nova Science Pubs., Inc.

Bissonnette, Benoit & Fowler, David. Bonded Cement-Based Material Overlays for the Repair, the Linking or the Strengthening of Slabs or Pavements: State-of-the-Art Report of the RILEM Technical Committee 193-RLS. Courard, Luc & Granju, Jean-Louis, eds. 2011. (RILEM State-of-the-Art Reports). (Illus.). xiii, 185p. 129.00 (978-94-007-1238-6(3), 9400712383) Springer.

Boshoff, Billy. Advances in Cement-Based Materials: Proc. Int. Conf. Advanced Concrete Materials, 17-19 Nov. 2009, Stellenbosch, South Africa. Van Zijl, Gideon P. A. G., ed. 2009. (ENG.). 300p. (C). 144.95 (978-0-415-87637-7(0), CRC Press) Taylor & Francis Group GBR. Dist: Taylor & Francis Group.

Brandt, Andrzej M. Cement-Based Composites: Materials, Mechanical Properties & Performance. 2nd rev. ed. 2009. (ENG., Illus.). 544p. 200.00 (978-0-415-40909-4(8), CRC Press) Taylor & Francis Group GBR. Dist: Taylor & Francis Group.

Dardeery, Samyha Sayed Ahmed, et al. Spectrophotometric Studies of Strontium Oxide in Portland Cement. 2011. 216p. pap. **(978-3-8454-0165-2(6))** Lambert Academic Publishing.

Elhelece, Wael. Like Cement Material for Water Treatment. 2011. 92p. pap. **(978-3-8443-0425-1(8))** Lambert Academic Publishing.

Gab-Allah, Diaa. Cement Neurotoxicity. 2011. 140p. pap. **(978-3-8443-1894-4(1))** Lambert Academic Publishing.

Ghorab, Hanaa Youssef, et al. The Compatibility Between the Superplasticizers & Portland Cements. 2011. 120p. pap. **(978-3-8433-7016-5(8))** Lambert Academic Publishing.

Gillmore, Quincy. Limes Hydraulic Cements & Mortars - 2006. 336p. 49.95 (978-1-933998-24-4(5), Merchant Bks.) Rough Draft Printing.

Hossain, Zakaria. Environment-Friendly Cement Composite (EFFC) for Soil Reinforcement & Earth Slope Protection. 2009. (Environmental Remediation Technologies, Regulations & Safety Ser.). 79.00 (978-1-60741-956-3(4)) Nova Science Pubs., Inc.

Hötzl, Manuela & Ringli, Kornel, eds. NiVo: Journal for Architecture & Cement Composite. 2012. (ENG., Illus.). 114p. pap. 39.95 **(978-3-7091-1196-3(X)**, 370911196X) Springer.

International Cement Microscopy Association (ICMA) Staff, compiled by. 29th International Conference on Cement Microscopy 2007. 2007. 527p. pap. 81.00 (978-1-60423-215-8(3)) Curran Assocs., Inc.

Konsta-Gdoutos, Maria S., ed. Measuring, Monitoring & Modeling Concrete Properties. 2006. (ENG.). xix, 786p. 269.00 (978-1-4020-5103-6(4), 1402051034) Springer.

Neville, A. M. & Brooks, J. J. Concrete Technology. 2nd rev. ed. 2010. (ENG., Illus.). 464p. pap. 147.50 (978-0-273-73219-8(6)) Prentice Hall PTR.

Page, C. L. Durability of Concrete & Cement Composites. 2007. (Illus.). 416p. (978-1-85573-940-6(2)) Woodhead Publishing Ltd.

Provis, J. L. Geopolymers: Structures, processing, properties & industrial Applications. 2009. (ENG., Illus.). xiv, 454p. 229.95 (978-1-4398-0970-9(4), CRC Press) Taylor & Francis Group GBR. Dist: Taylor & Francis Group.

Provis, J. L. & van Deventer, J. S. J., eds. Geopolymers: Structures, Processing, Properties & Industrial Applications. 2009. (Illus.). 464p. (978-1-84569-449-4(X)) Woodhead Publishing Ltd.

Safiuddin, et al. High Performance Mortar with Carbon Fibers. 2010. 208p. pap. (978-3-8383-0623-0(6)) Lambert Academic Publishing.

Scrivener, Karen & Young, Francis. Introduction to the Chemistry of Inorganic Cements. 2010. 320p. pap. 59.95 (978-0-415-54801-4(2), Taylor & Francis) Taylor & Francis Group GBR. Dist: Taylor & Francis Group.

Siddique, Rafat & Khan, Mohammad Iqbal. Supplementary Cementing Materials. 2011. (Engineering Materials Ser.). (ENG., Illus.). xv, 350p. 179.00 (978-3-642-17865-8(0), 3642178650) Springer.

Thaha, Wafiq. Development of Controlled Low Strength Materials Using Ckd. 2008. 164p. pap. (978-3-639-06322-6(8)) VDM Verlag Dr. Mueller e.K.

Vincenzini, P. & Leonelli, Cristina. Geopolymers & Geocements: Low Environmentally Impact Ceramic Materials: 12th International Ceramics Congress, Part H. 2011. (Illus.). 208p. pap. (978-3-908158-52-3(4)) Trans Tech Pubns., Ltd.

Xiaojun, Wang. Microstructure of Hydrating Cementitious Materials: Experimental Investigation Based on Poroelasticity. 2011. 168p. pap. **(978-3-639-33255-1(5))** VDM Verlag Dr. Mueller e.K.

CEMENT GUN

see also Gunite

Rodriguez, Louis. From Elephants to Swimming Pools: Carl Akeley, Samuel W. Traylor, & the Development of the Cement Gun. 2006. (Illus.). 160p. per. 15.95 (978-0-930973-39-1(9), Canal History & Technology Pr.) Moore, Hugh Historical Park & Museums, Inc.

CEMENT INDUSTRIES

Baby, V. Kurien. Globalisation & Market Outcomes: Strategic Evidences. 2009. (Illus.). 173p. 35.00 (978-81-316-0259-1(1)) Rawat Pubns. IND. Dist: International Specialized Bk. Services.

Biniam Taddele, Maru. Technical, Economical & Environmental. 2010. 196p. pap. (978-3-639-16048-2(7)) VDM Verlag Dr. Mueller e.K.

Deolalkar, S. P. Nomograms for Design & Operation of Cement Plants. 2011. (ENG.). 180p. 149.95 (978-0-415-66577-3(9), CRC Press) Taylor & Francis Group GBR. Dist: Taylor & Francis Group.

Ghebrab, Tewodros. Structure-Property Relationships for Cement-Based Materials. 2009. 164p. pap. (978-3-639-11930-5(4)) VDM Verlag Dr. Mueller e.K.

Prahalad, C. K., et al. Madras Cement, Ltd. 2010. (C). pap. 20.00 (978-1-61674-251-5(8)); pap. 20.00 (978-1-61674-249-2(6)) Davidson, William Institute At The Univ. of Michigan, The.

Recommended Guidelines for Solid fuel handling preparation & Firing Systems in Cement Plants. 2007. (978-0-89312-254-6(8)) Portland Cement Assn.

Silverman, Miriam D. Stopping the Plant: The St. Lawrence Cement Controversy & the Battle for Quality of Life in the Hudson Valley. 2006. (American Region Ser.). (Illus.). 176p. per. 24.95 (978-0-7914-6962-0(X)) State Univ. of New York Pr.

—Stopping the Plant: The St. Lawrence Cement Controversy & the Battle for Quality of Life in the Hudson Valley. Wermuth, Thomas S., ed. 2006. (American Region Ser.). (Illus.). 176p. 44.50 (978-0-7914-6961-3(1)) State Univ. of New York Pr.

2007 IEEE Cement Industry Technical Conference Record. 2007. pap. 188.00 (978-1-4244-1195-5(5), 07CH37902) IEEE.

CEMENT SUBSTANCE (ANATOMY)

see Extracellular Matrix

CEMETERIES

see also Burial Laws; Catacombs; Epitaphs; National Cemeteries—United States; Tombs

Ackerman, Herbert S. & Goff, Arthur J. Thirty-Seven Cemetries in New Jersey. 143p. reprint ed. 33.00 (978-0-9726864-3-3(6)) Bergen Historic Bks., Inc.

Adams, Josephine & Colls, Kevin. 'Out of Darkness, Cometh Light' Life & Death in 19th-Century Wolverhampton. 2007. (Bar Bs Ser.). (ENG., Illus.). 102p. (C). pap. 70.00 (978-1-4073-0123-5(3)) British Archaeological Reports Ltd. GBR. Dist: Brown, David Bk. Co., The.

Anderson Reisinger, Kris. Cemeteries of Tacoma. 2011. (Images of America Ser.). (Illus.). 128p. pap. 21.99 (978-0-7385-7531-5(3)) Arcadia Publishing.

Anderson, Sue. A Medieval Cemetery at Mill Lane, Ormesby St Margaret, Norfolk. 2009. (East anglian archaeology Monograph Ser.). (ENG., Illus.). 50p. (C). pap. 18.00 (978-0-905594-49-1(5)) East Anglian Archaeology GBR. Dist: Brown, David Bk. Co., The.

Anderson, Trevor & Parfitt, Keith. Buckland Anglo-Saxon Cemetery, Dover. Excavations 1994. 2012. (Archaeology of Canterbury Ser.). (ENG.). (C). 70.00 **(978-1-870545-23-5(0))** Canterbury Archaeological Trust, Ltd. GBR. Dist: Brown, David Bk. Co., The.

Annable, F. K. & Eagles, Bruce N. The Anglo-Saxon Cemetery at Blacknall Field, Pewsey, Wiltshire. 2010. (ENG., Illus.). 336p. (C). 80.00 (978-0-947723-14-9(5)) Wiltshire Archaeological & Natural History Society GBR. Dist: Brown, David Bk. Co., The.

Anon. A Guide Through Glasnevin Cemetery with Plan & Illustrations. 2010. 140p. pap. 27.45 (978-1-4455-5423-5(2)) Barclay Pr., Inc.

Ansah, Hassan. Life, Death, & Community in Cairo's City of the Dead. 2010. 108p. pap. 12.95 (978-1-4502-6700-7(9)) iUniverse, Inc.

Ashley, Linda Ramsey, ed. Marshfield Cemetery Records to 1950. viii, 223p. (978-0-9665564-2-1(9)) Meadow Geese Pr.

Baker, Shane A. At Rest in Zion: The Archaeology of Salt Lake City's First Pioneer Cemetery. 2011. (BYU Occasional Papers). (ENG., Illus.). 146p. (gr. 13). pap. 25.00 (978-0-9753945-5-7(X)) Univ. of Utah Pr.

Ballard, Jack Stokes & Logan, Friends of Historic Fort. Fort Logan. 2011. (Images of America Ser.). (ENG., Illus.). 128p. pap. 21.99 **(978-0-7385-7582-7(8))** Arcadia Publishing.

Barry, Michael Thomas. Final Resting Places: Orange County's Dead & Famous. 2010. (Illus.). 224p. pap. 16.99 (978-0-7643-3421-4(2)) Schiffer Publishing, Ltd.

Beach, Darren. London's Cemeteries. 2011. (ENG., Illus.). 256p. pap. 14.95 (978-1-902910-40-6(0)) Metro Pubns. GBR. Dist: Independent Pubs. Group.

Bekvalac, Jelena, et al. Late 17th- to 19th-Century Burial & Earlier Occupation at All Saints, Chelsea Old Church, Royal Borough of Kensington & Chelsea. 2007. (MoLAS Archaeology Studies). (Illus.). 67p. (C). pap. 18.00 (978-1-901992-73-1(X)) Museum of London Archaeology Service GBR. Dist: Brown, David Bk. Co., The.

Bennett, Gordon, ed. Cemeteries of Northwest Cherokee County, Texas, 5. 2nd ed. 2006. (Cemeteries of Cherokee County, Texas Ser.: 1). (Illus.). 92p. 10.00 net. (978-1-931167-46-8(X)) Cherokee County Genealogical Society.

—Cemeteries of Southern Cherokee County, Texas, 5, 5. 2nd ed. 2006. (Cemeteries of Cherokee County, Texas Ser.: 5). (Illus.). 67p. 8.00 net. (978-1-931167-44-4(3)) Cherokee County Genealogical Society.

Benoit, Tod. Where Are They Buried? How Did They Die? Fitting Ends & Final Resting Places of the Famous, Infamous, & Noteworthy. rev. ed. 2009. (ENG., Illus.). 560p. pap. 14.95 (978-1-57912-822-7(X), 157912822X) Black Dog & Leventhal Pubs., Inc.

Betts, Paul, et al, eds. Between Mass Death & Individual Loss: The Place of the Dead in Twentieth-Century Germany. 2008. (Studies in German History). (Illus.). 344p. (C). 100.00 (978-1-84545-397-8(2)) Berghahn Bks., Inc.

Blakey, Michael L. & Rankin-Hill, Leslie M., eds. The New York African Burial Ground: Skeletal Biology of the New York African Burial Ground, Part I, 6 vols., Vol. 1. 2009. pap. (978-0-88258-252-8(6)) Howard Univ. Pr.

—The New York African Burial Ground: Skeletal Biology of the New York African Burial Ground, Part II: Appendices, 6 vols., Vol. 1. 2009. pap. (978-0-88258-253-5(4)) Howard Univ. Pr.

Blesi, Sue. Where Dead Men Still Fight: A history of Stanton, Missouri. 2008. (ENG., Illus.). pap. (978-0-9797654-3-8(9)) Missouri Kid Pr.

Bowley, Steve. Bethesda Cemetery: Maryborough Township, Wellington County, 8398 Wellington Road #8, Concession 10, Lot 9. 3rd ed. 2008. (Illus.). 74p. pap. **(978-0-7779-3903-1(7))** Ontario Genealogical Society.

—McDougall Cemetery: East Luther Township, Dufferin County, near 174275 County Road 25, Concession 6, Lot 31. 2nd ed. 2008. pap. **(978-0-7779-3883-6(9))** Ontario Genealogical Society.

—Victoria Cemetery: Peel Township, Wellington County, 7289 Wellington Road 11, East of Drayton. 3rd ed. 2008. (Illus.). 100p. pap. **(978-0-7779-3907-9(X))** Ontario Genealogical Society.

Bowley, Steve & Pletch, Pat. Huxley Cemetery: Erin Township, Wellington County, 5982 Well. Road 24 at Sideroad 27, Concession 7, Lot 28. 2nd ed. 2008. (Illus.). 92p. pap. **(978-0-7779-3889-8(8))** Ontario Genealogical Society.

—Rockwood Cemetery (Including St. John's) Eramosa Township, Wellington County, 501 Main St. S., Rockwood, Concession 4, Lot 3. 3rd ed. 2008. (Illus.). 70p. pap. **(978-0-7779-3906-2(1))** Ontario Genealogical Society.

Boyle, Angela, et al. The Anglo-Saxon Cemetery at Butler's Field, Lechlade, Gloucestershire Vol. 2: Discussion & Synthesis, 2 vols. 2011. (Thames Valley Landscapes Ser.: 33). (ENG., Illus.). 197p. (C). pap. 40.00 **(978-1-905905-19-5(X))** Oxford Archaeological Unit GBR. Dist: Brown, David Bk. Co., The.

Boylston, Anthea, et al, eds. "Lepers Outside the Gate" Excavations at the Cemetery of the Hospital of St James & St Mary Magdalene, Chichester, 1986-87 & 1993. 2008. (CBA Research Report). (ENG., Illus.). 317p. (C). pap. 80.00 (978-1-902771-74-8(5)) Council for British Archaeology GBR. Dist: Brown, David Bk. Co., The.

Bracken, Robert D. The Ins & Outs of Life in a Dying Industry. 2007. 128p. per. 19.95 (978-1-4241-8758-4(3)) PublishAmerica, Inc.

Branigan, Keith & Vasilakis, Andonis. Moni Odigitria: A Prepalatial Cemetery & Its Environs in the Asterousia, Southern Crete. 2010. (Prehistory Monographs). (ENG., Illus.). 530p. (C). 80.00 (978-1-931534-58-1(6)) Institute for Aegean Prehistory Pr.

Brassard, Sr., et al. Scott County Cemeteries. 2011. (Illus.). 128p. pap. 21.99 **(978-0-7385-8315-0(4))** Arcadia Publishing.

Brooks, Patricia & Brooks, Jonathan. Laid to Rest in California: A Guide to the Cemeteries & Grave Sites of the Rich & Famous. 2006. (Insiders' Guide Ser.). (ENG., Illus.). 352p. per. 15.95 (978-0-7627-4101-4(5)) Globe Pequot Pr., The.

Brorsson, Torbjorn. The Pottery from the Early Medieval Trading Site & Cemetery at Gross Stromkendorf, Lkr. Nordwestmecklenburg: Forschungen zu Gross Stromkendorf III. 2010. (Fruhmittelalterliche Archaologie zwischen Ostsee und Mittelmeer Ser.). (ENG., Illus.). 157p. (C). 50.00 (978-3-89500-751-4(X)) Reichert, Ludwig Dr. DEU. Dist: Brown, David Bk. Co., The.

Broughton, Dawn. Four Cemeteries of Emestown Township, Lennox & Addington County, Ontario. 2009. (Illus.). 40p. pap. **(978-0-7779-2708-3(X))** Ontario Genealogical Society.

C-Span Staff. Who's Buried in Grant's Tomb? A Tour of Presidential Gravesites. 2010. (ENG., Illus.). 288p. pap. 16.95 (978-1-58648-869-7(4)) PublicAffairs.

Carroll County Genealogical Society. Carroll County, Maryland Cemeteries, Volume 2: East-Central. 2007. pap. 22.00 (978-0-7884-4056-4(X)) Heritage Bks.

Castro, Vanessa de. Das Igrejas Ao Cemitério: Políticas Públicas Sobre a Morte No Recife Do Século XIX. 2007. (POR., Illus.). 312p. (978-85-7044-176-8(2)) Fundacao De Cultura cidade do Recife.

Cataldi, Nancy & Ballenas, Carl. Maple Grove Cemetery. 2006. (Images of America Ser.). (ENG., Illus.). 128p. per. 19.99 (978-0-7385-4914-9(2)) Arcadia Publishing.

Caterino, David M. & Mallios, Seth. Cemeteries of San Diego County. 2008. (Images of America Ser.). (ENG., Illus.). 128p. pap. 19.99 (978-0-7385-5821-9(4)) Arcadia Publishing.

Chaparro, Martina Will de. Death & Dying in New Mexico. 2007. (ENG., Illus.). 285p. 34.95 (978-0-8263-4163-1(2)) Univ. of New Mexico Pr.

Chapman, Marcia, compiled by. Columbia County, Arkansas Cemeteries. 2008. 60.00 (978-0-9816451-0-0(0)) Arkansas Genealogical Society, Inc.

Cimperman, John D. Erie Street Cemetery. 2011. (Images of America Ser.). (Illus.). 128p. pap. 21.99 (978-0-7385-8342-6(1)) Arcadia Publishing.

Clark, Bob. Enfield Connecticut: Stories Carved in Stone. 2006. (Illus.). 272p. per. 17.95 (978-0-9755362-5-4(7)) Dog Pond Pr.

—Westfield Massachusetts: Stories Carved in Stone. 2008. (Illus.). 196p. pap. 15.95 (978-0-9755362-3-0(0)) Dog Pond Pr.

Cockburn, Perry A. Everton Cemetery: Eramosa Township, Wellington County, 5381 Wellington Road #49, Concession 7, Lots 12 & 13. 3rd ed. 2008. (Illus.). 66p. pap. **(978-0-7779-3905-5(3))** Ontario Genealogical Society.

Collins, Herbert Ridgeway. Cemeteries of Caroline County, Virginia: Volume 1, PUBLIC CEMETERIES. 2009. 209p. per. 21.00 (978-1-58549-362-3(7)) Heritage Bks.

Communication Works. Marengo Township Cemeteries, Calhoun County, Michigan: Johnson, Marengo Memorial, Marengo Village, Samson & Townsend Cemeteries, Recorded 2008. 2010. (ENG., Illus.). 130p. spiral bd. 16.00 net. **(978-0-9726491-0-0(7))** Calhoun County Genealogical Society.

Confino, et al, eds. Between Mass Death & Individual Loss: The Place of the Dead in the Twentieth-Century Germany. 2011. (SGH Ser.). (ENG.). 344p. pap. 37.95 (978-0-85745-169-9(3)) Berghahn Bks., Inc.

Connell, Brian & Miles, Adrian. The City Bunhill Burial Ground, Golden Lane, London: Excavations at South Islington Schools 2006. 2010. (MoLAS Archaeology Studies Ser.: 21). (ENG., Illus.). 74p. (C). pap. 18.00 (978-1-901992-91-5(8)) Museum of London Archaeology Service GBR. Dist: Brown, David Bk. Co., The.

Cygielman, Shmuel Arthur. Jews of Poland & Lithuania. (HEB & ENG., Illus.). 38p. 44.99 (978-965-90187-1-0(1)) Cygielman Pubs. ISR. Dist: Feldheim Pubs.

Douillette, Jean Anne. Lakeville, Massachusetts Gravestone Inscriptions 1711-2003: A Complete Collection of Epitaphs from the Thirty-One Known Cemeteries in the Town of Lakeville. 2007. 463p. pap. 39.95 (978-0-9796644-0-3(3)) Um & Willow Publishing.

—Photographs of Lakeville, Massachusetts Gravestones 1711-2003: A pictorial companion to the book Lakeville, Massachusetts Gravestone Inscriptions 1711-2003. 2008. 19.95 (978-0-9796644-1-0(1)) Um & Willow Publishing.

Duer, Stephen C. & Smith, Allan B. Cypress Hills Cemetery. 2010. (Images of America Ser.). (Illus.). 128p. pap. 21.99 (978-0-7385-7343-4(4)) Arcadia Publishing.

Eggener, Keith. Cemeteries. 2010. (Library of Congress Visual Sourcebooks Ser.). (ENG., Illus.). 320p. 75.00 (978-0-393-73169-9(3), 73169) Norton, W. W. & Co., Inc.

Elliott, Donald R., compiled by. Cemeteries of Colorado: A Guide to Locating Colorado Burial Sites & Publications about Their Residents. 2007. cd-rom 10.00 (978-0-9796751-4-0(6)) Colorado Research Pubns.

—Colorado Cemetery Index: 84,000 Individuals Interred in Small Colorado Burial Sites. 2007. cd-rom 15.00 (978-0-9796751-5-7(4)) Colorado Research Pubns.

Elliott, Donald R. & Elliott, Doris S., compiled by. Colorado Cemetery Index II: Individuals Interred in Small Colorado Burial Sites. 2007. 456p. lib. bdg. 60.00 (978-0-9796751-2-6(X)) Colorado Research Pubns.

—Colorado Cemetery Index III: Individuals Interred in Small Colorado Burial Sites. 2007. 480p. lib. bdg. 60.00 (978-0-9796751-3-3(8)) Colorado Research Pubns.

Elza, Betty. Seceder Cemetery: A Transcription with Photographs. 2011. 45p. (J). pap. 18.95 (978-1-4327-6804-1(2)) Outskirts Pr., Inc.

Emery, P. A., et al. St Pancras Burial Ground: Excavations for St Pancras International, the London Terminus of High Speed 1 2002-3. 2011. (Gifford Monographs). (ENG., Illus.). 231p. (C). 56.00 (978-0-9569406-0-5(9)) Gifford, John Ltd. GBR. Dist: Brown, David Bk. Co., The.

Ennis, Trevor. An Early Saxon Cemetery at Rayleigh, Essex: Excavations at the Former Park School. 2009. (ENG., Illus.). viii, 62p. (C). pap. 25.00 (978-1-84194-086-1(0)) East Anglian Archaeology GBR. Dist: Brown, David Bk. Co., The.

Enquez, Christina. Our History in Stone: the New England Cemetery Dictionary. 2010. 185p. pap. 17.95 (978-0-557-24169-9(3)) Lulu Enterprises Inc.

Eshelman, Ralph E., et al. The War of 1812 in the Chesapeake: A Reference Guide to Historic Sites in Maryland, Virginia, & the District of Columbia. 2010. (Johns Hopkins Books on the War Of 1812 Ser.). (ENG., Illus.). 424p. (gr. 17). 67.00 (978-0-8018-9235-6(X)) Johns Hopkins Univ. Pr.

Feldman, Dianne Weiner & Stark, Nancy. The Tents of Baltimore: Ohelim in the Jewish Cemeteries. 2011. 94p. pap. 14.50 (978-0-7884-5291-8(6)) Heritage Bks.

Flammer, Joseph & Hill, Diane. Long Island's Most Haunted Cemeteries. 2010. (Illus.). 160p. pap. 24.99 (978-0-7643-3589-1(8)) Schiffer Publishing, Ltd.

Fogle, Patricia A. Frederick County, Maryland, Church & Cemetery Records, Volume 4. 2008. 260p. per. 24.00 (978-1-58549-639-6(1)) Heritage Bks.

Forest, Christopher. Boston's Haunted History: Exploring the Ghosts & Graves of Beantown. 2008. (Illus.). 128p. pap. 12.95 (978-0-7643-2874-9(3)) Schiffer Publishing, Ltd.

Frankel, David & Webb, Jennifer M. Bronze Age Cemeteries at Deneia in Cyprus. 2007. (Studies in Mediterranean Archeology Ser.). (Illus.). 266p. 250.00 (978-91-7081-235-4(7)) Astroms, Paul Forlag SWE. Dist: Coronet Bks.

Garfield, John. The Fallen: A Photographic Journey Through the War Cemeteries & Memorials of the Great War, 1914-18. 2008. (ENG.). 192p. 46.95 (978-1-86227-481-5(9)) History Pr. Ltd., The GBR. Dist: Independent Pubs. Group.

Garfield, John & Fletcher, Ian. In Hell Before Daylight: The Siege & Storming of the Fortress of Badajoz 1812. 2008. (ENG., Illus.). 192p. pap. 27.95 (978-1-86227-480-8(0)) History Pr. Ltd., The GBR. Dist: Independent Pubs. Group.

Garfinkel, Yosef & Cohen, Susan, eds. The Middle Bronze Age IIA Cemetery at Gesher: Final Report. 2007. (Annual of ASOR Ser.). (ENG., Illus.). 168p. (C). 74.95 (978-0-89757-075-6(8)) American Schls. of Oriental Research.

George, Harold. DEAD Soldiers at Gettysburg. 2007. (ENG., Illus.). 60p. 5.95 (978-0-9728183-3-9(2)) George, H. Publishing.

Gliddon, Gerald & Skelton, Timothy John. Lutyens & the Great War. 2009. (ENG., Illus.). 224p. 60.00 (978-0-7112-2878-8(7)) Lincoln, Frances Ltd. GBR. Dist: Perseus-PGW.

Goldstein, Steve. LA's Graveside Companion: Where the V. I. P.'s R. I. P. 2009. 192p. pap. 19.99 (978-0-7643-3154-1(X)) Schiffer Publishing, Ltd.

Goodwyn, Melba. Chasing Graveyard Ghosts: Investigations of Haunted & Hallowed Ground. 2011. (ENG.). 312p. pap. 16.95 (978-0-7387-2126-2(3)) Llewellyn Pubns.

Grant, Robert N. Wright Family: Patent Deeds & Land Grants, 1761-1900, Deed Records, 1761-1903, Chancery Court Files, 1804-1900, Death Records, 1853-1920, Cemetery Records by Cemetery & Probate Records, 1761-1900 in Amherst County, Virginia. 2009. (978-0-7884-8163-5(0)); pap. 23.50 (978-0-7884-4646-7(0)) Heritage Bks.

Gustin, Sandy, ed. & text. Montgomery County Ohio Cemetery Inscriptions: Butler Township, 12, Vol. VII. 2009. 518p. spiral bd. 40.00 (978-1-887665-27-8(7)) Montgomery County Chapter, Ohio Genealogical Society.

Hadley Historical Commission (Hadley, Mass.) Staff & Hadley 350th Committee (Hadley, Mass.) Staff, contrib. by. The Town Cemeteries & Gravestones of Hadley, Massachusetts. 2010. (978-1-935052-24-1(1)) White River Pr.

Haile, John J., Jr., compiled by. Saint Edward's Roman Catholic Cemetery - Coal Township, Northumberland County, Pennsylvania: Record of Interments 1870-2005. 2006. (Illus.). 856p. lib. bdg. (978-0-9711236-2-5(4)) Firenze Pr.

Halsall, Guy. Cemeteries & Society in Merovingian Gaul: Selected Studies in History & Archaeology, 1992-2009. 2009. (978-90-04-17999-8(2)) BRILL.

Hamilton County Chapter of the Ohio Genealogical Society. Hamilton County, Ohio, Burial Records: Volume 7: Springfield Township Cemeteries. 2008. pap. 54.50 (978-0-7884-0081-0(9)) Heritage Bks.

Hamilton, R. Keith. Those Grey Rebels at Upper Black Creek Church: Bulloch County, Georgia. 2008. 25.99 (978-1-60647-004-6(3)); pap. 15.99 (978-1-60647-003-9(5)) Xulon Pr., Inc.

Harmony Grove Cemetery. 2006. 148p. per. 16.99 (978-1-4255-1098-5(1)) MPublishing.

Harris, Mark. Grave Matters: A Journey Through the Modern Funeral Industry to a Natural Way of Burial. 2008. (ENG.). 224p. pap. 15.00 (978-1-4165-6404-1(7), Scribner) Scribner.

Haskins, Lola. Fifteen Florida Cemeteries: Strange Tales Unearthed. 2011. (ENG., Illus.). 208p. pap. 22.50 (978-0-8130-3572-7(4)) Univ. Pr. of Florida.

Hawkes, Sonia Chadwick. The Anglo-Saxon Cemetery at Finglesham, Kent. 2006. (Oxford University School of Archaeology Monograph Ser.). (ENG., Illus.). 436p. (C). 52.00 (978-0-9549627-1-5(0)) Oxford Univ. Schl. of Archaeology GBR. Dist: Brown, David Bk. Co., The.

Herbert, Jeffrey G. Hamilton County, Ohio Burial Records: Volume 20, St. John German Cemetery, 1849-1879. 2010. (Illus.). 562p. pap. 55.00 (978-1-932250-79-4(4)) Little Miami Publishing Co.

Hershenzon, Gail D. Detroit's Woodmere Cemetery. 2006. (Images of America Ser.). (ENG., Illus.). 128p. per. 21.99 (978-0-7385-4120-4(6)) Arcadia Publishing.

—Michigan Memorial Park. 2007. (Images of America Ser.). (ENG., Illus.). 128p. per. 19.99 (978-0-7385-5159-3(7)) Arcadia Publishing.

Hettinga, Kathy T. Grave Images: San Luis Valley. 2009. (ENG., Illus.). 180p. (978-0-89013-561-7(4)) Museum of New Mexico Pr.

Historic Buckingham Inc. Buckingham Burials, A Survey of Cemeteries in Buckingham County, Virginia, Volume 3. 2007. pap. 50.00 (978-0-7884-4087-8(X)) Heritage Bks.

Horn, Zachary. Cemeteries & the Control of Bodies: A Study of Cemeteries in the City of Hamilton, Canada. 2008. 112p. pap. (978-3-8364-6997-5(9)) VDM Verlag Dr. Mueller e.K.

Hudnall, Ken & Hudnall, Sharon. Spirits of the Border: Restless Spirits. 2007. 320p. per. 19.95 (978-1-933951-09-6(5)) Omega Pr.

Huffman, Dennis, et al. Mount Pleasant & Oliver Cemeteries: Richmond Township, Lennox & Addington County, Ontario. 2009. (978-0-7779-2685-7(7)) Ontario Genealogical Society.

Ingalls, Anita M., et al, compiled by. Guide to Madison County Cemeteries. 2009. (Illus.). 229p. pap. 19.99 (978-0-9801076-2-3(8)) Ingalls Publishing.

Integrity Burial Boxes Ltd. The Abc's of Building & Marketing A Columbarium Wall. 2011. 80p. pap. 27.08 (978-1-4567-5087-9(9)) AuthorHouse.

Irwin, Jane. Old Canadian Cemeteries: Places of Memory. 2007. (ENG., Illus.). 320p. 75.00 (978-1-55407-146-3(1)) Firefly Bks., Ltd.

Jabbour, Alan & Jabbour, Karen. Decoration Day in the Mountains: Traditions of Cemetery Decoration in the Southern Appalachians. 2010. (ENG., Illus.). 256p. 35.00 (978-0-8078-3397-1(5)) Univ. of North Carolina Pr.

Jacobs, Joachim. Houses of Life: Jewish Cemeteries of Europe. 2008. (ENG., Illus.). 208p. 65.00 (978-0-7112-2648-7(2)) Lincoln, Frances Ltd. GBR. Dist: Perseus-PGW.

Jacobson, Kimberly R. & Greene County Historical Society, The. Greene County & Mesopotamia Cemetery. 2007. (Images of America Ser.). (ENG., Illus.). 128p. per. 19.99 (978-0-7385-5277-4(1)) Arcadia Publishing.

James, June. Nin[e]th Line Cemetery: Lot 15, con 9, Cavan Township, Peterborough County (Formerly Durham County) 2007. 19p. pap. (978-0-7779-3319-0(5)) Ontario Genealogical Society.

James, June & Head, Diane. Fairview Cemetery: Lot 19, con 1, Haldimand Township, Northumberland County. 2007. (Illus.). 64p. pap. (978-0-7779-3321-3(7)) Ontario Genealogical Society.

Jensen, Cecile Wendt. Detroit's Mount Elliott Cemetery. 2006. (Images of America Ser.). (ENG., Illus.). 128p. per. 19.99 (978-0-7385-4093-1(5)) Arcadia Publishing.

—Detroit's Mount Olivet Cemetery. 2006. (Images of America Ser.). (ENG., Illus.). 128p. per. 19.99 (978-0-7385-4092-4(7)) Arcadia Publishing.

The Jewish Cemeteries of New Hampshire. 2010. (Illus.). 270p. pap. 19.95 net. (978-0-9764057-5-7(X)) Jewish Cemetery Pubns., LLC.

Johansen, Lynn. White Bronze. 2008. 48p. pap. 22.95 (978-1-4357-1702-2(3)) Lulu Enterprises Inc.

Johnson, Greg. Sacred Claims: Repatriation & Living Tradition. 2007. (Studies in Religion & Culture Ser.). (ENG.). 224p. (gr. 17). 55.00 (978-0-8139-2661-2(0)); pap. 19.50 (978-0-8139-2662-9(9)) Univ. Pr. of Virginia.

Johnson, Kristina Dunn. No Holier Spot of Ground: Confederate Monuments & Cemeteries of South Carolina. 2009. (ENG., Illus.). 160p. pap. 19.99 (978-1-59629-397-7(7)) History Pr., The.

Kacharava, Darejan & Kvirkvelia, Guram. Wine, Worship, & Sacrifice. Chi, Jennifer Y., ed. 2008. (Illus.). 216p. (C). 40.00 (978-0-691-13856-5(7)) Princeton Univ. Pr.

Kaemmerlen, Cathy J. Historic Oakland Cemetery of Atlanta. 2007. 128p. pap. 19.99 (978-1-59629-330-4(6)) History Pr., The.

Kath, Laura. Forest Lawn: The First 100 Years. 2007. (Illus.). 136p. 29.95 (978-0-9665801-5-0(X)); per. 15.95 (978-0-9665801-3-6(3)) Tropico Pr.

—100 Years in the Life of Forest Lawn. 2007. (Illus.). 214p. 59.95 (978-0-9665801-1-2(7)) Tropico Pr.

Kath, Laura & Frank, Eric, intros. 100 Years in the Life of Forest Lawn. 2007. (Illus.). 214p. per. 39.95 (978-0-9665801-0-5(9)) Tropico Pr.

Keister, Douglas. Stories in Stone New York: A Field Guide to New York City Area Cemeteries & Their Residents, 1 vol. 2011. (ENG., Illus.). 256p. 24.99 (978-1-4236-2102-7(6)) Gibbs Smith, Publisher.

Keister, Douglas, photos by. Forever Dixie: A Field Guide to Southern Cemeteries & Their Residents, 1 vol. 2008. (ENG., Illus.). 256p. pap. 19.99 (978-1-4236-0314-6(1)) Gibbs Smith, Publisher.

—Forever L. A. A Field Guide to Los Angeles Area Cemeteries & Their Residents. 2010. (ENG., Illus.). 256p. pap. 19.99 (978-1-4236-0522-5(5)) Gibbs Smith, Publisher.

Kennedy, Royce. Arlington National Cemetery Became My Classroom. 2011. 134p. pap. 24.95 (978-1-4560-3661-4(0)) PublishAmerica, Inc.

Kessler, Katrin. The Buildings of the Jewish Community in Schwedt/Oder. 2008. (ENG.). 64p. pap. 14.95 (978-3-86568-314-4(2)) Imhof, Michael Verlag GmbH & Co. KG DEU. Dist: Independent Pubs. Group.

Ketover, Karen S. Westbrook Maine Cemeteries: Plus Surrounding Towns of Cumberland, Falmouth, Gorham, Portland & Windham. 2009. (Illus.). 460p. pap. 37.50 (978-0-7884-0401-6(6), K175) Heritage Bks.

Kinsley, Maxine. Roots in Dakota Soil: Prairie Cemeteries of Bon Homme County, South Dakota. 2007. (Illus.). 88p. pap. (978-1-57579-347-4(4)) Pine Hill Pr., Inc.

Kissling, Barbara. Cemeteries: Alive with Learning. 2010. (978-1-56090-238-6(8)) National Middle Schl. Assn.

Kloner, Amos, et al. The Necropolis of Jerusalem in the Second Temple Period. 2007. (Interdisciplinary Studies in Ancient Culture & Religion: Vol. 8). (ENG., Illus.). 820p. (C). pap. 152.00 (978-90-429-1792-7(X)) Peeters Pubs. & Booksellers BEL. Dist: Brown, David Bk. Co., The.

Kraynek, Sharon L. D., compiled by. Allegheny County, PA Cemetery Records, 13 vols., Vol. 1. 51p. pap. 9.00 (978-1-55856-005-5(X), 436) Closson Pr.

Kulakov, V.I. Dollkeim-Kovrovo, Kaliningrad Region, Russia. 2009. (ENG., Illus.). 333p. (C). pap. 137.50 (978-1-4073-0433-5(X)) British Archaeological Reports Ltd. GBR. Dist: Brown, David Bk. Co., The.

Kunstamt & Heimatmuseum Reinickendorf, eds. Leben mit den Toten: Manifestationen gegenwärtiger Bestattungskultur. 2009. (GER.). 172p. pap. 46.95 (978-3-631-59124-6(1)) Lang, Peter GmbH, Europaischer Verlag der Wissenschaften DEU. Dist: Lang, Peter.

Lamb, Brian & C-SPAN. Who's Buried in Grant's Tomb? A Tour of Presidential Gravesites. 2010. (ENG.). 272p. pap. 16.95 (978-1-58648-870-3(8)) PublicAffairs.

Lanna, Simone. Lo Stato Egiziano nelle Fonti Scritte del Periodo Tinita. 2008. (Bar S Ser.). (ITA., Illus.). 194p. (C). pap. 92.50 (978-1-4073-0322-2(8)) British Archaeological Reports Ltd. GBR. Dist: Brown, David Bk. Co., The.

Leahy, Kevin. "Interrupting the Pots" The Excavation of Cleatham Anglo-Saxon Cemetery, North Lincolnshire. 2007. (CBA Research Report). (Illus.). 278p. (C). pap. 60.00 (978-1-902771-71-7(0)) Council for British Archaeology GBR. Dist: Brown, David Bk. Co., The.

Lees, Hilary. Exploring English Churchyard Memorials. (ENG., Illus.). 176p. pap. 29.95 (978-0-7524-2525-2(0)) History Pr. Ltd., The GBR. Dist: Trafalgar Square Publishing.

Lefebvre, Scott. Spooky Creepy Long Island. 2008. 128p. pap. 12.95 (978-0-7643-2814-5(X)) Schiffer Publishing, Ltd.

Lennox and Addington Historical Society Staff & Ontario Genealogical Society, Kingston Branch Staff, contrib. by. Nine Camden East Township Cemeteries: Lennox & Addington County, Ontario. 2009. (Illus.). 72p. pap. (978-0-7779-2696-3(2)) Ontario Genealogical Society.

—Roblin Cemetery, Richmond Township, Lennox & Addington County, Ontario. 2009. (Illus.). 29p. pap. (978-0-7779-2703-8(9)) Ontario Genealogical Society.

Lim, Patricia. Forgotten Souls: A Social History of the Hong Kong Cemetery. 2011. (Royal Asiatic Society Hong Kong Studies). (CHI., Illus.). 624p. (978-988-220-771-4(5)); (978-988-8053-74-2(4)) Hong Kong Univ. Pr.

—Forgotten Souls: A Social History of the Hong Kong Cemetery. 2011. (Royal Asiatic Society Hong Kong Studies Ser.). (ENG., Illus.). 624p. (gr. 17). 55.00 (978-962-209-990-6(4)) Hong Kong Univ. Pr. HKG. Dist: Columbia Univ. Pr.

Lincoln, Abraham. Gettysburg Address. 2010. (Little Books of Wisdom Ser.). (ENG.). 32p. 9.95 (978-1-55709-073-7(4)) Applewood Bks.

Linden, Blanche M. G. Silent City on a Hill: Picturesque Landscapes of Memory & Boston's Mount Auburn Cemetery. 2007. (Illus.). 373p. per. 39.95 (978-1-55849-571-5(1)) Univ. of Massachusetts Pr.

Loe, Louise, et al. Life & Death in a Roman City: Excavation of a Roman cemetery with a mass grave at 120-122 London Road, Gloucester. 2008. (Oxford Archaeology Monographs). (Illus.). 182p. (C). pap. 40.00 (978-0-904220-49-0(4)) Oxford Archaeological Unit GBR. Dist: Brown, David Bk. Co., The.

Lohwasser, Angelika. The Kushite Cemetery of Sanam: A Non-Royal Burial Ground of the Nubian Capital, Ca 800-600BC. 2010. (ENG., Illus.). 158p. (C). pap. 39.95 (978-1-906137-16-8(1)) Golden Hse. Pubns. GBR. Dist: Brown, David Bk. Co., The.

Lucy, Sam, et al. The Anglo-Saxon Settlement & Cemetery at Bloodmoor Hill, Carlton Colville, Suffolk. 2010. (East anglian archaeology Monograph Ser.). (Illus.). 476p. (C). pap. 80.00 (978-0-9544824-6-6(3)) East Anglian Archaeology GBR. Dist: Brown, David Bk. Co., The.

Mainfort, Robert C. Two Historic Cemeteries in Crawford County, Arkansas. 2006. viii, 261p. (978-1-56349-101-6(X)) Arkansas Archeological Survey.

Mallios, Seth & David M. Caterino and the San Diego County Gravestone Project. Cemeteries of San Diego. 2007. (Images of America Ser.). (ENG., Illus.). 128p. pap. 19.99 (978-0-7385-4714-5(X)) Arcadia Publishing.

Martin, Edward C., III. The Peaceable Kingdom in Hartsdale - America's First Pet Cemetery. 2010. 112p. pap. 14.95 (978-0-557-46610-2(8)) Lulu Enterprises Inc.

Matthews, Bruce. Elmwood Cemetery: Stories of Kansas City. Canfield, Anne, ed. 2010. 240p. pap. 29.95 (978-1-935362-67-8(4)) Kansas City Star Bks.

May, Roger. Civil War Veterans Buried in Stevens County, Washington. 2007. (Illus.). 220p. per. 24.95 (978-0-9705654-4-0(5)) Northeast Washington Genealogical Society.

McCann, Dennis. Badger Boneyards: The Eternal Rest of the Story. 2010. (ENG., Illus.). 176p. pap. 16.95 (978-0-87020-451-7(3)) Wisconsin Historical Society.

McGlashan, Zena Beth. Buried in Butte. 2010. (Illus.). 460p. pap. 24.95 (978-1-891057-21-2(9)) Wordz & Ink Publishing.

McKinley, Jacqueline I. The 13th Century Baptist Church & Burial Ground at West Butts Street, Poole, Dorset. 2008. (Illus.). xiii, 168p. (C). 19.95 (978-1-874350-45-3(0)) Trust for Wessex Archaeology Ltd. GBR. Dist: Brown, David Bk. Co., The.

Medford, Edna Greene, ed. The New York African Burial Ground: Historical Perspectives of the Burial Ground: New York Blacks & the Diaspora, 6 vols., Vol. 3. 2009. 166p. pap. (978-0-88258-257-3(7)) Howard Univ. Pr.

Meller, Hugh & Parsons, Brian. London Cemeteries: An Illustrated Guide & Gazetteer. 4th ed. (ENG., Illus.). 2011. 448p. pap. 34.95 (978-0-7524-6183-0(4)) 2008. 418p. 58.95 (978-0-7509-4622-3(9)) History Pr. Ltd., The GBR. Dist: Independent Pubs. Group.

Melugin, Ron. Heroes, Scoundrels, & Angels: Fairview Cemetery of Gainesville, Texas. 2010. 256p. pap. 19.99 (978-1-60949-033-1(9)) History Pr., The.

Melzer, Richard. Buried Treasures: Famous & Unusual Gravesites in New Mexico History. 2007. (ENG.). 476p. per. 45.00 (978-0-86534-531-7(7)) Sunstone Pr.

Menachemson, Nolan. A Practical Guide to the Jewish Cemeteries. 2007. 256p. 39.00 (978-1-886223-29-5(7)) Avotaynu, Inc.

Migliniene, Skirmante, et al. Sv. Kazimiero Lietuviu Kapinems 100 Metu. 2007. (LIT & ENG., Illus.). 195p. (978-0-929700-58-8(9)) Lithuanian Research & Studies Ctr.

Milano, Kenneth W. Historic Cemeteries of Kensington & Fishtown: Palmer, Hanover & West Street Burial Grounds. 2011. 128p. pap. 19.99 (978-1-60949-242-7(0)) History Pr., The.

Miles, Adrian, et al. Burial at the Site of the Parish Church of St Benet Sherehog Before & after the Great Fire: Excavations at 1 Poultry, City of London. 2008. (MoLAS Monograph Ser.). (Illus.). 112p. (C). 26.00 (978-1-901992-75-5(6)) Museum of London Archaeology Service GBR. Dist: Brown, David Bk. Co., The.

—St Marylebone Church & Burial Ground in the 18th to19th Centuries: Excavations at St Marylebone School, 1992 & 2004-6. 2008. (MoLAS Monograph Ser.). (ENG., Illus.). 170p. (C). 38.00 (978-1-901992-79-3(9)) Museum of London Archaeology Service GBR. Dist: Brown, David Bk. Co., The.

Miles, Barry W. Cemeteries of the City of Hampton, Virginia, Formerly Elizabeth City County. 2007. pap. 36.00 (978-0-7884-4462-3(X)) Heritage Bks.

Miles, Barry W. & Stead, Gertrude. Cemeteries of the City of Newport News, Formerly Warwick County, Virginia. 2007. pap. 27.00 (978-0-7884-4396-1(8)) Heritage Bks.

Miller, C. L. Mt. Calvary Cemetery. 2008. (Images of America Ser.). (ENG., Illus.). 128p. pap. 19.99 (978-0-7385-5205-7(4)) Arcadia Publishing.

Moffett, Garret. Haunted Macomb. 2010. (Haunted America Ser.). 112p. pap. 19.99 (978-1-59629-097-6(8)) History Pr., The.

Mondelli, Teresa, compiled by. Calvary Catholic Cemetery, Lexington, Kentucky: Transcribed, Plus Some Obits, A-Z. 2010. 205p. (978-0-7884-8586-2(5)); pap. (978-0-7884-5268-0(1)) Heritage Bks.

Moore, Carol. Greensboro's First Presbyterian Church Cemetery. 2006. (Images of America Ser.). (ENG., Illus.). 128p. per. 19.99 (978-0-7385-4310-9(1)) Arcadia Publishing.

Morgan, Yvonne L. Blair, compiled by. Alphabetical Listing, Flatwoods Cemetery Record: Franklin Twp., Fayette County, PA. 2009. (Illus.). 58p. (978-1-55856-510-4(8)) Closson Pr.

Mosca, Alexandra Kathryn & Scanlon, Karen. Green-Wood Cemetery. 2008. (Images of America Ser.). (ENG., Illus.). 128p. pap. 21.99 (978-0-7385-5650-5(5)) Arcadia Publishing.

Nava, Margaret M., photos by. Remembering: A Guide to Cemeteries & Monuments in New Mexico. 2006. (Illus.). 228p. pap. 22.95 (978-0-86534-486-0(8)) Sunstone Pr.

Nedoroscik, Jeffrey A. Walking in the City of the Dead: A Visitor's Guide. 2010. 144p. pap. 13.14 (978-1-4269-3685-2(0)) Trafford Publishing.

Nichols, Jeremy D. Potter's Field: The Chanate Historical Cemetery in Santa Rosa, California. 2009. 174p. pap. 26.00 (978-0-7884-5010-5(7)) Heritage Bks.

Nichols, Jeremy Dwight. Potter's Field: The Chanate Historic Cemetery in Santa Rosa, California: A History of the Old Sonoma County Cemetery: Plus a Biographical Record of Burials, 1381-1944. 2009. (Illus.). xxxiv, 139p. (978-0-7884-8202-1(5)) Heritage Bks.

Nicolson, Ken. The Happy Valley: A History & Tour of the Hong Kong Cemetery. 2010. (Illus.). 144p. (978-988-220-756-1(1)) Hong Kong Univ. Pr.

—The Happy Valley: A History & Tour of the Hong Kong Cemetery. 2010. (ENG., Illus.). 144p. (gr. 17). pap. 22.00 (978-988-8028-10-8(3)) Hong Kong Univ. Pr. HKG. Dist: Columbia Univ. Pr.

Nocturnum, Corvis. Cemetery Gates: Death & Mourning Through the Ages. 2011. (Illus.). 144p. (978-0-7643-3787-1(4), Schiffer Publishing Ltd) Schiffer Publishing, Ltd.

Oakdale / Union Hill Cemetery, Salisbury, North Carolina: A Study of A Twentieth Cenrury African American Cemetery. 2007. 69.95 (978-0-9777389-0-8(6)) Brown, Reginald.

C

Olen, Catherine. The Final Curtain: Celebrity Deaths. 2010. (Illus.). 160p. pap. 14.99 (978-0-7643-3472-6(7)) Schiffer Publishing, Ltd.

Ontario Genealogical Society, Kawartha Branch Staff, contrib. by. Kirkfield Roman Catholic Cemetery: Lot 43, con 8, Eldon Township, Victoria County. 2010. (Illus.). 12p. pap. (978-0-7779-3333-6(0)) Ontario Genealogical Society.

Ontario Genealogical Society, Oxford County Branch Staff, contrib. by. Cemetery Transcription of African Methodist Episcopal Cemetery: Concession VIII, Lot 12, South Norwich Township, Now Known As 732695 Pick Line, Norwich Township. 2008. (Illus.). 7p. pap. (978-0-7779-3520-0(1)) Ontario Genealogical Society.

—Cemetery Transcription of Canning Cemetery: Concession II, Lot 4, Blenheim Township, Now Known As 955207 Canning Road, Blandford-Blenheim Township. 2007. (Illus.). 15p. pap. (978-0-7779-2344-3(0)) Ontario Genealogical Society.

—Cemetery Transcription of Innerkip Cemetery: Concession XVII, Lot 10, East Zorra Township, Now Known As Main Street, Innerkip, East Zorra-Tavistock Township. 2007. (Illus.). 146p. pap. (978-0-7779-3498-2(1)) Ontario Genealogical Society.

—Cemetery Transcription of Newark Community Cemetery: Concession V, Lot 22, North Norwich Township, Now Known As 593189 Oxford Road 13, Norwich Township. 2007. (Illus.). 8p. pap. (978-0-7779-3509-5(0)) Ontario Genealogical Society.

—Cemetery Transcription of Norwich Gore Cemetery: Concession IV, Lot 1, North Norwich Township, Now Known As 813303 Base Line, Norwich Township. 2007. (Illus.). 39p. pap. (978-0-7779-3510-1(4)) Ontario Genealogical Society.

—Cemetery Transcription of Pine Street Burying Ground (Also Known As the Friend's Cemetery) Concession IX, Lot 13, South Norwich Township, Now Known As 356 Main Street W, Otterville, Norwich Township. 2008. (Illus.). 17p. pap. (978-0-7779-3519-4(8)) Ontario Genealogical Society.

—Cemetery Transcription of Rosanna Cemetery: Concession XI, Lot 18, South Norwich Township, Now Known As 145199 Potters Road, Norwich Township. 2008. (Illus.). 19p. pap. (978-0-7779-3522-4(8)) Ontario Genealogical Society.

Orep Editions, creator. Gardens of Remembrance: The Men & Their Destiny. 2007. (Illus.). 47p. pap. 16.95 (978-2-912925-15-2(0)) OREP Edition & Communication FRA. Dist: Casemate Pubs. & Bk. Distributors, LLC.

Osler, Michael T. Westfall Cemetery: Copley Township, Knox County, Illinois, 2 vols. 2009. (Illus.). (978-0-7884-8191-8(6)); (978-0-7884-8192-5(4)) Heritage Bks.

—Westfall Cemetery, Copley Township, Knox County, Illinois: Cemetery History. 2009. 320p. pap. 29.00 (978-0-7884-5004-4(2)) Heritage Bks.

—Westfall Cemetery, Copley Township, Knox County, Illinois: Cemetery Layout. 2009. 72p. pap. 13.00 (978-0-7884-5003-7(4)) Heritage Bks.

Pace, Sherry. Historic Churches of Mississippi. 2007. (ENG., Illus.). 178p. 40.00 (978-1-57806-940-8(8)) Univ. Pr. of Mississippi.

Papadopoulos, Constantinos. Death Management & Virtual Pursuits: A Virtual Reconstruction of the Minoan Cemetery at Phourni, Archanes. 2010. (Bar S Ser.). (ENG., Illus.). 156p. (C). pap. 115.00 (978-1-4073-0558-5(1)) British Archaeological Reports Ltd. GBR. Dist: Brown, David Bk. Co., The.

Penn, Kenneth. The Anglo-Saxon Cemetery at Shrubland Hall Quarry, Coddenham, Suffolk. 2011. (East Anglian Archaeology Monograph Ser.: 139). (ENG., Illus.). 146p. (C). pap. 30.00 (978-0-9568747-0-2(3)) East Anglian Archaeology GBR. Dist: Brown, David Bk. Co., The.

Perry, Warren R., et al, eds. The New York African Burial Ground: The Archaeology of the New York African Burial Ground, Part I, 6 vols., Vol. 2. 2009. pap. (978-0-88258-254-2(2)) Howard Univ. Pr.

—The New York African Burial Ground: The Archaeology of the New York African Burial Ground, Part II: Descriptions of Burials, 6 vols., Vol. 2. 2009. pap. (978-0-88258-255-9(0)) Howard Univ. Pr.

—The New York African Burial Ground: The Archaeology of the New York African Burial Ground, Part III: Appendices, 6 vols., Vol. 2. 2009. pap. (978-0-88258-256-6(9)) Howard Univ. Pr.

Petrie, W. M. Flinders. Medum. 2009. 90.00 (978-1-57898-730-6(X)) Martino Publishing.

Petterchak, Janice A., ed. In Lincoln's Shadow: Oak Ridge Cemetery Chronicles. 2007. (Illus.). 171p. pap. 15.00 (978-0-9792326-0-2(0)) Sangamon County Historical Society.

Philibert-Ortega, Gena. Cemeteries of the Eastern Sierra. 2007. (Images of America Ser.). (ENG., Illus.). 128p. per. 21.99 (978-0-7385-4786-2(7)) Arcadia Publishing.

Phillips, Faye. Baton Rouge Cemeteries. 2012. (Images of America Ser.). (ENG., Illus.). 128p. pap. 21.99 (978-0-7385-9184-1(X)) Arcadia Publishing.

Pierret, P. Memoires, Mentalites Religieuses, Art Funeraire: La Partie Juive du Cimitiere de Dieweg a Bruxelles, XIXe-XXe Siecles. 2006. (Collection de la Revue des Etudes Juives Ser.). (ENG & FRE.). 334p. (C). pap. 99.00 (978-90-429-1632-6(X)) Peeters Pubs. & Booksellers BEL. Dist: Brown, David Bk. Co., The.

Pippenger, Wesley E. Tombstone Inscriptions of Alexandria. 2008. 248p. per. 21.00 (978-1-58549-495-8(X)); 228p. per. 22.00 (978-1-58549-248-0(5)) Heritage Bks.

Poisson, Sara. Silent Voices from the Past: A Chronicle of the Almshouse of Sullivan County. 2010. 116p. pap. 12.95 (978-1-4502-5907-1(3)) iUniverse, Inc.

Powers-Douglas, Minda. Chippiannock Cemetery. 2010. (Images of America Ser.). (ENG., Illus.). 128p. pap. 21.99 (978-0-7385-7741-8(3)) Arcadia Publishing.

Propst, Matthew. Savannah Cemeteries. 2009. (Illus.). 80p. 19.99 (978-0-7643-3308-8(9)) Schiffer Publishing, Ltd.

Rabideau, Clyde M. Obituary information, A-k: 50 Years, 1955-2004, Clinton, Franklin & Essex County, New York. 2007. 635p. 30.00 (978-0-9793974-0-0(5)) Rabideau, Clyde M.

—Obituary Information, L-Z: 50 Years, 1955,2004, Clinton, Franklin & Essex County, New York. 2007. 633p. 45.00 net. (978-0-9793974-1-7(3)) Heartnut Publishing Company.

Rebman, Kimberly P. Haunted Florid: A Guide to the Departed Soul. 2008. 164p. pap. 13.50 (978-1-4389-0915-8(2)) AuthorHouse.

Reyher, Ken. Through the Valley of the Shadow of Death: Death & Dying in Early Western Colorado. 2009. pap. 14.95 (978-1-932738-59-9(2)) Western Reflections Publishing Co.

Rousmaniere, John. The Evergreens: The Story of Brooklyn Cemetery, 1850-2007. 2009. (ENG.). 240p. 50.00 (978-0-9786899-4-0(1)) Smith/Kerr Assoc.

Rutherford, Sarah. The Victorian Cemetery. 2009. (Shire Library). (ENG., Illus.). 64p. pap. 12.95 (978-0-7478-0701-8(9)) Osprey Publishing, Ltd. GBR. Dist: Random Hse., Inc.

Salvatori, Sandro & Usai, Donatella. A Neolithic Cemetery in the Northern Dongola Reach: Excavations at Site R12. 2008. (Bar S Ser.). (Illus.). xxiii, 358p. (C). 125.00 (978-1-4073-0300-0(7)) British Archaeological Reports Ltd. GBR. Dist: Brown, David Bk. Co., The.

Santa Rosa Rural Cemetery Preservation Committee Staff, contrib. by. Santa Rosa Rural Cemetery, 1854-2007: A Listing of Burials in Fulkerson, Moke, Rural, & Stanley Cemeteries, Now Known Collectively As Santa Rosa Rural Cemetery. 2007. (Illus.). 224p. pap. 43.50 (978-0-7884-4181-3(7)) Heritage Bks.

Schneider, Stuart. Ghosts in the Cemetery II: Farther Afield. 2010. (Illus.). 128p. 24.99 (978-0-7643-3590-7(1)) Schiffer Publishing, Ltd.

Schneider, Sturart L. Ghosts in the Cemetery: A Pictorial Study. 2008. (Illus.). 128p. pap. 19.99 (978-0-7643-2988-3(X)) Schiffer Publishing, Ltd.

Schrijvers, Peter. The Margraten Boys: How a European Village Kept America's Liberators Alive. 2012. (ENG., Illus.). 344p. 105.00 (978-0-230-34663-5(4)); pap. 30.00 (978-0-230-34664-2(2)) Palgrave Macmillan.

Segal, Joshua L. The Old Jewish Cemetery of Newport: A History of North Ameica's Oldest Extant Jewish Cemetery. 2007. per. 29.95 (978-0-9764057-2-6(5)) Jewish Cemetery Pubns., LLC.

—A Self-Guided Tour of Monuments of Jews Buried in the Mount Auburn Cemetery Cambridge, MA. 2007. pap. 14.95 (978-0-9764057-3-3(3)) Jewish Cemetery Pubns., LLC.

Seng, Charles F. Lehigh County Tombstone Abstracts of Persons Born Prior to 1800:: From 64 Cemeteries Within the Limits of Lehigh County, Pennsylvania. 2007. ii, 124p. pap. (978-1-55856-486-2(1)) Closson Pr.

Shannon, Robin. Cemeteries of Seattle. 2008. (Images of America Ser.). (ENG., Illus.). 128p. per. 19.99 (978-0-7385-4813-5(8)) Arcadia Publishing.

Shepley, Carol Ferring. Movers & Shakers, Scalawags & Suffragettes: Tales from Bellefontaine Cemetery, 1849-2006. 2009. (ENG., Illus.). 384p. (gr. 9). 29.95 (978-1-883982-65-2(0)) Missouri Historical Society Pr.

Shull, Marie. Jericho Cemetery: Lot 1, Concession 5 (#1258 Forestry Farm Road), Charlotteville Township, Norfolk County. 2nd ed. 2007. (Illus.). 11p. pap. (978-0-7779-2925-4(2)) Ontario Genealogical Society.

—Marston Cemetery: Concession 10, Lot 2-3 (#163 10th Concession Road), North Walsingham Township, Norfolk County. 2nd ed. 2007. (Illus.). 13p. pap. (978-0-7779-2927-8(9)) Ontario Genealogical Society.

—St. John's Anglican Cemetery: Con. 3, Lot 1, 857 Norfolk St. S. (Hwy. 24 S), Simcoe, on, Woodhouse Township, Norfolk County. 2007. (Illus.). 64p. pap. (978-0-7779-3918-5(5)) Ontario Genealogical Society.

—Wyecombe United Church Cemetery: Con. 13, Lot 9 (2376 East 1/4 Line Rd), North Walsingham Township, Norfolk County. 2nd ed. 2007. (Illus.). 11p. pap. (978-0-7779-2929-2(5)) Ontario Genealogical Society.

Sluby, Paul E. Bury Me Deep, Burial Places Past & Present in & Nearby Washington, DC: A Historical Review & Reference Manual. 2009. pap. (978-1-61584-107-3(5)) Independent Pub.

South Suburban Genealogical and Historical Society. CD: Cemetery Census Series, New Lenox Township, Will County, Illinois: Maple Wood Cemetery, Marshall Cemetery. 2008. cd-rom 15.95 (978-0-7884-4521-7(9)) Heritage Bks.

—CD: Cemetery Census Series, Will Township, Will County, Illinois: Peotone Cemetery, Will Presbyterian Cemetery. 2008. cd-rom 15.95 (978-0-7884-4529-3(4)) Heritage Bks.

Southerland, Cindy. Cemeteries of Carson City & Carson Valley. 2010. (Images of America Ser.). (Illus.). 128p. pap. 21.99 (978-0-7385-8106-4(2)) Arcadia Publishing.

Sterling, John Eylers. Newport, Rhode Island Colonial Burial Grounds. Bamberg, Cherry Fletcher, ed. 2009. (Illus.). 576p. lib. bdg. 35.00 (978-0-9604144-9-9(5)) Rhode Island Genealogical Society.

Stirland, Ann. Criminals & Paupers: The Graveyard of St Margaret Fyebriggate in combusto, Norwich. 2009. (East anglian archaeology Monograph Ser.). (ENG., Illus.). 54p. (C). pap. 18.00 (978-0-905594-47-7(9)) Norfolk Museums Service, Archaeology & Environment Div. GBR. Dist: Brown, David Bk. Co., The.

Stott, Annette. Pioneer Cemeteries: Sculpture Gardens of the Old West. 2008. (ENG., Illus.). 408p. (C). 36.95 (978-0-8032-1608-2(4)) Univ. of Nebraska Pr.

Sullivan, Steven Edward & Welsch, Robert Louis. Cemetery Inscriptions & Burial Sites of St. George, Maine & the Nearby Islands. 2009. (Illus.). lxvi, 539p. (978-0-89725-854-8(1), Penobscot Pr.) Picton Pr.

Sullivan, Winnifred Fallers. The Impossibility of Religious Freedom. 2007. (ENG., Illus.). 320p. (C). per. 25.95 (978-0-691-13058-3(2)) Princeton Univ. Pr.

Summers, Julie. Remembered: The History of the Commonwealth War Graves Commission. 2007. (ENG., Illus.). 191p. 59.95 (978-1-85894-374-9(4)) Merrell Pubs. Ltd. GBR. Dist: Perseus Distribution.

Sutherlin, Peggy, compiled by. Martinburg Cemetery Centenial Celebration, Camp County, Texas. 2008. 60p. pap. 15.00 (978-1-57088-160-2(X)) J&W Enterprises.

Teknari. Père Lachaise. 2011. 88p. pap. 49.99 (978-0-557-72810-7(X)) Lulu Enterprises Inc.

Thompson, H. Lloyd. Revolutionary War Vets: Westmoreland County, PA: From the Research Files of H. Lloyd Thompson. 2009. 25p. pap. (978-1-55856-509-8(4)) Closson Pr.

Torre, J. D., ed. Epitaphs: 243 Gravestone Inscriptions. 2008. 96p. per. 12.95 (978-1-4327-1642-4(5)) Outskirts Pr., Inc.

Trere, Cristina Chiaramonte. La Necropoli di Campovalano, 2 vols. 2010. (Bar S Ser.). (ITA., Illus.). 428p. (C). pap. 165.00 (978-1-4073-0718-3(5)) British Archaeological Reports Ltd. GBR. Dist: Brown, David Bk. Co., The.

Trinkley, Michael & Hacker, Debi. A Small Sample of Burials at Randolph Cemetery: What Their Stories Tell Us about the Cemetery & African American Life in Columbia. 2007. (Illus.). 70p. per. 25.00 (978-1-58317-069-4(3)) Chicora Foundation, Inc.

Turpin, John. The Magnificent Seven. 2011. (Illus.). 160p. pap. 22.95 (978-1-4456-0038-3(2)) Amberley Publishing GBR. Dist: Casemate Pubs. & Bk. Distributors, LLC.

Veit, Richard Francis. New Jersey Cemeteries & Tombstones: History in the Landscape. 2008. (ENG.). 320p. pap. 23.95 (978-0-8135-4236-2(7)); (Illus.). 70.00 (978-0-8135-4235-5(9)) Rutgers Univ. Pr.

Venango County Historical Society Staff, contrib. by. VENANGO COUNTY, PENNSYLVANIA Cemetery Records & Early Church Histories. 2011. (Illus.). (978-1-55856-542-5(6)) Closson Pr.

Vernon, Christopher. Graceland Cemetery: A Design History. 2011. (Illus.). 208p. 39.95 (978-1-55849-926-3(1)) Univ. of Massachusetts Pr.

Vigil, Vicki Blum. Cemeteries of Northeast Ohio: Stones, Symbols & Stories. 2007. (ENG., Illus.). 350p. per. 15.95 (978-1-59851-025-6(8)) Gray and Company, Publishers.

Walker, Jason & Erwin, Will. Texas State Cemetery. 2011. (ENG., Illus.). 224p. 39.95 (978-0-292-72672-7(4)) Univ. of Texas Pr.

Webster, Don & James, June. Hillside Cemetery: Lot 19, con 7, Douro Township, Peterborough County. 2007. (Illus.). 65p. pap. (978-0-7779-3323-7(3)) Ontario Genealogical Society.

West Florida Genealogical Society Staff & Jernigan, Richard E. Santa Rosa Cemeteries: Index & Introduction. (Illus.). 128p. pap. (978-0-9646616-1-5(6)) Beyreuth Enterprises.

—Santa Rosa Cemeteries Vol. 1: Allen-Howell Cemeteries. (Illus.). 248p. pap. (978-0-9646616-2-2(4)) Beyreuth Enterprises.

—Santa Rosa Cemeteries Vol. 2: Jay-Williams Cemeteries. (Illus.). 293p. pap. (978-0-9646616-3-9(2)) Beyreuth Enterprises.

White, Sarah L. Somewhere Special. 2008. 28p. pap. 13.50 (978-1-4343-8123-1(4)) AuthorHouse.

Whitney, Frederic Augustus. An Address Delivered at the Consecration of Evergreen Cemetry, Brighton, Wednesday, August 7 1850. 2011. 28p. pap. 11.99 (978-1-4181-9257-0(0)) MPublishing.

Wilkins, Charles. In the Land of Long Fingernails: A Gravedigger in the Age of Aquarius. 2009. (ENG.). 240p. 24.95 (978-1-60239-709-5(0), 239709) Skyhorse Publishing Co., Inc.

Williams, Kenneth P. Residents of Graveyard Lane. 2008. 178p. pap. 23.20 (978-1-4251-7756-0(5)) Trafford Publishing.

Williamson, Tom. Sutton Hoo & Its Landscape: The Contexts of Monuments. 2008. (Illus.). 220p. (C). pap. 40.00 (978-1-905119-25-7(9)) Windgather Pr. GBR. Dist: Brown, David Bk. Co., The.

Willsher, Betty. Understanding Scottish Graveyards. 2006. (ENG., Illus.). 96p. per. 16.95 (978-1-901663-96-9(5)) NMS Enterprises Ltd. - Publishing GBR. Dist: National Bk. Network.

Wright, John F. St. Thomas Anglican Cemetery (Allenwood Anglican Cemetery) (Thor Churchyard) Conc 10, Lot 13, Flos Township, Now 1910 Flos Road Ten West, Springwater Township. 2008. (Illus.). pap. (978-0-7779-3570-5(8)) Ontario Genealogical Society.

—Waverley Gospel Hall Cemetery: 17017 County Road 27, Tay Township, Ontario, Conc 1 WPR, Lot 75, Flos Township. 2008. (Illus.). pap. (978-0-7779-3578-1(3)) Ontario Genealogical Society.

Yalom, Marilyn. The American Resting Place: Four Hundred Years of History Through Our Cemeteries & Burial Grounds. 2008. (ENG., Illus.). 352p. 30.00 (978-0-618-62427-0(9)) Houghton Mifflin Harcourt Trade & Reference Pubs.

Ziino, Bart. A Distant Grief: Australians, War Graves & the Great War. 2007. (Illus.). 243p. (Orig.). pap. 31.00 (978-1-920694-89-0(7)) UWA Publishing AUS. Dist: International Specialized Bk. Services.

CENA, ULTIMA

see Lord's Supper

CENCI, BEATRICE, 1577-1599—DRAMA

Shelley, Percy Bysshe. The Cenci. 2007. (ENG.). 108p. 33.95 (978-0-548-07821-1(1)) Kessinger Publishing, LLC.

—The Cenci. 2007. (ENG.). 200p. per. 10.45 (978-1-60424-160-0(8), Book Jungle) Standard Pubns., Inc.

CENCI FAMILY

Dumas, Alexandre. The Cenci (from Celebrated Crimes) 2008. 48p. per. 5.99 (978-1-60450-124-7(3)) Arc Manor.

CENOZOIC PERIOD

see Geology, Stratigraphic—Cenozoic

CENSORSHIP

see also Expurgated Books; Freedom of the Press; Prohibited Books also subdivision Censorship under specific subjects, e.g. Motion Pictures—Censorship

Abdulla, Rasha A. The Internet in the Arab World: Egypt & Beyond. 175p. (C). 65.95 (978-0-8204-8673-4(6)); 2007. (Illus.). xxi, 175p. pap. (978-0-8204-8674-1(4)) Lang, Peter Publishing, Inc.

Adams, Helen R. Ensuring Intellectual Freedom & Access to Information in the School Library Media Program, 1 vol. 2008. (Illus.). 276p. pap. 40.00 (978-1-59158-539-8(2), LU8539) Libraries Unlimited, Inc.

Al-Obaidi, Jabbar Audah. Media Censorship in the Middle East. 2007. 144p. 99.95 (978-0-7734-5286-2(9)) Mellen, Edwin Pr., The.

Alford, Lacey. The Great Firewall of Chin. 2010. 88p. pap. (978-3-639-23537-1(1)) VDM Verlag Dr. Mueller e.K.

Arrington, Lauren. W. B. Yeats, the Abbey Theatre, Censorship, & the Irish State: Adding the Half-pence to the Pence. 2010. (ENG.). 252p. 110.00 (978-0-19-959057-5(5)) Oxford Univ. Pr., Inc.

Baez, Fernando. A Universal History of the Destruction of Books: From Ancient Sumer to Modern-Day Iraq. MacAdam, Alfred, tr. from SPA. 2008. (ENG., Illus.). 1p. 25.00 (978-1-934633-01-4(1)) Atlas & Co.

—A Universal History of the Destruction of Books: From Ancient Sumer to Modern Iraq. MacAdam, Alfred, tr. from SPA. 2010. (ENG., Illus.). 372p. pap. 15.00 (978-1-934633-24-3(0), 934624) Atlas & Co.

Bald, Margaret. Literature Suppressed on Religious Grounds. 3rd rev. ed. 2011. (Banned Bks.). (Illus.). 544p. (C). (gr. 9). 60.00 (978-0-8160-8230-8(8)) Facts On File, Inc.

Banned Books. 2011. (Banned Bks.). (C). (gr. 9). 240.00 (978-0-8160-8417-3(3)) Facts On File, Inc.

Barbierato, Federico. The Inquisitor in the Hat Shop: Inquisition, Forbidden Books & Unbelief in Early Modern Venice. 2012. 430p. 124.95 (978-1-4094-3547-1(4)) Ashgate Publishing Co.

Bauder, Julia. Censorship. 2007. (Current Controversies Ser.). (ENG.). 275p. (gr. 10-12). 27.50 (978-0-7377-3278-8(4), Greenhaven Pr., Inc.); (Illus.). (YA). (gr. 9-12). pap. 39.70 (978-0-7377-3277-1(6)) Cengage Gale.

Beattie, Scott. Regulatory Communities & the Spaces of Online Censorship. 2009. 284p. 124.95 (978-0-7546-7308-8(1)) Ashgate Publishing Co.

Berlatsky, Noah, ed. Are Textbooks Biased? 2011. (At Issue Ser.). 128p. (ENG.). pap. 22.50 (978-0-7377-5551-0(2), Greenhaven Pr., Inc.); (YA). (gr. 9-12). 31.80 (978-0-7377-5550-3(4)) Cengage Gale.

Billiani, Francesca. Modes of Censorship & Translation: National Contexts & Diverse Media. 2006. 328p. (978-1-900650-94-6(0)) St. Jerome Publishing.

Bim, Raymond. Royal Censorship of Books in Eighteenth-Century France. 2012. (ENG.). 216p. 60.00 (978-0-8047-6359-2(3)) Stanford Univ. Pr.

Bonsaver, Guido. Censorship & Literature in Fascist Italy. 2007. (Toronto Italian Studies). (Illus.). 384p. (ENG.). (978-0-8020-9301-1(9)); pap. (978-0-8020-9496-4(1)) Univ. of Toronto Pr.

Buchanan, Robert W. On Descending into Hell A Letter Address. 2006. pap. 15.95 (978-1-4286-3726-9(5)) Kessinger Publishing, LLC.

Bulla, David W. Lincoln's Censor: Milo Hascall & Freedom of the Press in Civil War Indiana. 2008. 300p. (C). (978-1-55753-473-6(X)) Purdue Univ. Pr.

Burns, Kate, ed. Censorship. 2006. (History of Issues Ser.). (ENG., Illus.). 261p. (J). (gr. 7-18). lib. bdg. 39.70 (978-0-7377-2009-9(3), Greenhaven Pr., Inc.) Cengage Gale.

Cane, James. Fourth Enemy: Journalism & Power in the Making of Peronist Argentina, 1930-1955. 2011. (ENG.). 328p. 74.95 (978-0-271-04876-5(X)) Pennsylvania State Univ. Pr.

Caravale, Giorgio. Ecclesiastical Censorship & Devotional Literature in Early Modern Italy. 2012. (Catholic Christendom, 1300ndash;1700 Ser.). 308p. 114.95 (978-1-4094-2988-3(1)) Ashgate Publishing Co.

Chvojka, Michal. Josef Graf Sedlnitzky als Präsident der Polizei- und Zensurhofstelle in Wien (1817-1848) Ein Beitrag zur Geschichte der Staatspolizei in der Habsburgermonarchie. 2010. (Schriftenreihe der Internationalen Forschungsstelle Demokratische Bewegungen in Mitteleuropa 1770 - 1850 Ser.). (GER.). 420p. 72.95 (978-3-631-59584-8(0)) Lang, Peter GmbH, Europaischer Verlag der Wissenschaften DEU. Dist: Lang, Peter.

Clegg, Cyndia Susan. Press Censorship in Caroline England. 2008. (ENG., Illus.). 298p. 104.00 (978-0-521-87668-1(0)) Cambridge Univ. Pr.

Committee to Protect Journalists, creator. Attacks on the Press In 2006: A Worldwide Survey by the Committee to Protect Journalists. 2007. (ENG., Illus.). 325p. per. 30.00 (978-0-944823-26-2(2)) Committee to Protect Journalists.

Deibert, Ronald J., et al, eds. Access Controlled: The Shaping of Power, Rights, & Rule in Cyberspace. 2010. (Information Revolution & Global Politics Ser.). (ENG., Illus.). 640p. (gr. 17). pap. 27.00 (978-0-262-51435-4(4)) MIT Pr.

Dosenrode, SoRen, ed. The Press under Strain: Freedom of the Press, Censorship, Self-Censorship & Press Ethics. 2010. 203p. pap., pap. 43.00 (978-3-8329-5184-9(9)) Nomos Verlagsgesellschaft DEU. Dist: International Specialized Bk. Services.

Doyle, Robert P. Banned Books Resource Guide. 2007. (Banned Books Resource Guide Ser.). (Illus.). 282p. pap. 39.00 (978-0-8389-8425-3(8)) American Library Assn.

Egan, Kate. Trash or Treasure? Censorship & the Changing Meanings of the Video Nasties. 2008. (Inside Popular Film Ser.). (ENG., Illus.). 224p. 79.00 *(978-0-7190-7232-1(8))* Manchester Univ. Pr. GBR. Dist: Macmillan.

Farrer, James Anson. Books Condemned to Be Burnt. 2009. 220p. 28.99 *(978-1-110-62935-4(3))*; pap. 23.75 *(978-1-110-62933-0(7))* BiblioBazaar.

—Books Condemned to Be Burnt. 2009. 94p. pap. *(978-0-217-68802-4(0))* Books LLC.

Favoretto, Mara. Alegoría e Ironía Bajo Censura en la Argentina Del Proceso (1976-1983) 2010. (SPA.). 129.95 *(978-0-7734-1292-7(1))* Mellen, Edwin Pr., The.

Fishburn, Matthew. Burning Books. 2008. (ENG., Illus.). 240p. 42.00 *(978-0-230-55328-6(1))* Palgrave Macmillan.

Fisher, Paul. Radio Redux: Freedom on the Airways. Glanville, Jo & Index on Censorship (Organization) Staff, eds. 2010. (Index on Censorship Ser.). (Illus.). 192p. pap. 12.95 *(978-1-85702-155-4(X)*, B2155XP) SAGE Pubns., Ltd. GBR. Dist: SAGE Pubns., Inc.

Fragnito, Gigliola, ed. Church, Censorship & Culture in Early Modern Italy. Belton, Adrian, tr. from ITA. 2011. (Cambridge Studies in Italian History & Culture Ser.). (ENG.). 280p. pap. 55.00 *(978-0-521-20232-9(9))* Cambridge Univ. Pr.

Fraser, Jay. The American Publisher: Paying the Cost of Corporatism & Censorship for Writing the Truth about Cuba, Russia, & the War on Terror. 2010. (Illus.). 256p. 28.00 *(978-1-879915-22-0(7))* Signal Peak Pr. LLC.

Freshwater, Helen. Theatre Censorship in Britain: Silencing, Censure & Suppression. 2009. (ENG., Illus.). 240p. 95.00 *(978-0-230-22378-3(8))* Palgrave Macmillan.

Garry, Patrick. Rediscovering a Lost Freedom: The First Amendment Right to Censor Unwanted Speech. 2009. (ENG.). 175p. pap. 22.95 *(978-1-4128-0860-6(X))* Transaction Pubs.

Glanville, Jo, ed. The Net Effect: The Limits of Digital Freedom. 2011. (Index on Censorship Ser.). 192p. pap. 13.00 ***(978-1-4462-0321-7(2)**,* B03217P) SAGE Pubns., Ltd. GBR. Dist: SAGE Pubns., Inc.

Glanville, Jo & Index on Censorship (Organization) Staff, eds. Smashed Hits 2. 0: Music under Pressure. 2010. (Index on Censorship Ser.). 192p. pap. 13.00 *(978-0-85702-531-9(7)*, B25319P) SAGE Pubns., Ltd. GBR. Dist: SAGE Pubns., Inc.

Goldstein, Robert Justin. The Frightful Stage: Political Censorship of the Theater in Nineteenth-Century Europe. 2009. 322p. 90.00 *(978-1-84545-459-3(6))* Berghahn Bks., Inc.

Goldstein, Robert Justin, ed. The Frightful Stage: Political Censorship of the Theater in Nineteenth-Century Europe. 2011. (ENG.). 322p. 34.95 *(978-0-85745-171-2(5))* Berghahn Bks., Inc.

Google & Internet Control in China: A Nexus Between Human Rights & Trade?: Hearing Before the Congressional-Executive Commission on China, One Hundred Eleventh Congress, Second Session, March 24, 2010. 2010. (Illus.). iii, 79p. *(978-0-16-086205-9(X)*, 552-070-41304-9) United States Government Printing Office.

Graves, Robert. Lars Porsena: On the Future of Swearing. 2009. (Oneworld Classics Ser.). (ENG.). 150p. 14.95 *(978-1-84749-068-1(9))* Alma Classics GBR. Dist: Independent Pubs. Group.

He, Qing Lian. The Fog of Censorship: Media Control in China. 2007. pap. 13.95 *(978-0-9717356-2-0(X))* Human Rights In China.

Heins, Marjorie. Not in Front of the Children: Indecency, Censorship, & the Innocence of Youth. 2007. (ENG., Illus.). 442p. per. 23.95 *(978-0-8135-4221-8(9))* Rutgers Univ. Pr.

Herrero-Olaizola, Alejandro. The Censorship Files: Latin American Writers & Franco's Spain. 2008. (SUNY Series in Latin American & Iberian Thought & Culture). (SPA & ENG., Illus.). 233p. per. 29.95 *(978-0-7914-6986-6(7))* State Univ. of New York Pr.

Höchli, Marc. The Invisible Scissors: Media Freedom & Censorship in Switzerland. 2010. (Illus.). 359p. pap. *(978-3-0343-0385-7(0))* Lang, Peter.

Huff, Mickey & Project Censored, eds. Censored 2012: The Top Censored Stories & Media Analysis of 2010-11. 2011. (ENG., Illus.). 496p. pap. 19.95 *(978-1-60980-347-6(7))* Seven Stories Pr.

Jennings, Brian. Censorship: The Threat to Silence Talk Radio. 2010. (ENG.). 320p. pap. 16.00 *(978-1-4391-7289-6(7)*, Threshold Editions) Threshold Editions.

Jin, Xingyao. Qing Dai Bi Huo L. 2010. (CHI.). pap. *(978-7-80047-919-9(6))* Forbidden City Publishing Hse.

Jones, Sara. Complicity, Censorship & Criticism: Negotiating Space in the GDR Literary Sphere. 2011. (Interdisciplinary German Cultural Studies). (ENG., Illus.). IX, 221p. 196.00 ***(978-3-11-219141-5(2))*** De Gruyter, Walter Inc.

Jostock, Ingeborg. La Censure Négociée: Le Contrôle du Livre a Genève, 1560-1625. 2007. (Travaux d'Humanisme et Renaissance Ser.). (FRE.). 440p. (C). 150.00 *(978-2-600-01115-0(3))* Droz, Librairie CHE. Dist: Brown, David Bk. Co., The.

Jütte, Bettina. Verlagslizenzierungen in der Sowjetischen Besatzungszone (1945-1949) 2010. (Archiv für Geschichte des Buchwesens. Studien Ser.).Tr. of Publishing Licences in the Soviet Occupation Zone of Germany (1945-1949). (GER., Illus.). 390p. 168.00 *(978-3-11-023011-6(9))* De Gruyter, Walter Inc.

Karolides, Nicholas J. Literature Suppressed on Political Grounds. 3rd rev. ed. 2011. (Banned Bks.). 724p. (C). (gr. 9). 60.00 *(978-0-8160-8231-5(6))* Facts On File, Inc.

Karolides, Nicholas J., et al. 120 Banned Books. 3rd rev. ed. 2011. 568p. pap. 19.95 *(978-0-8160-8232-2(4)*, Checkmark Bks.) Facts On File, Inc.

Kaur, Raminder, et al, eds. Censorship in South Asia: Cultural Regulation from Sedition to Seduction. 2009. (ENG., Illus.). 256p. 65.00 *(978-0-253-35335-1(1)*, 0253353351); pap. 24.95 *(978-0-253-22093-6(9)*, 0253220939) Indiana Univ. Pr.

Kemp, Geoffrey & McElligott, Jason. Censorship & the Press, 1580-1720, 4 vols. 2009. (ENG.). 1984p. 625.00 *(978-1-85196-993-7(4))* Pickering & Chatto Pubs., Ltd. GBR. Dist: Ashgate Publishing Co.

Kerby-Fulton, Kathryn. Books under Suspicion: Censorship & tolerance of Revelatory Writing in Late Medieval England. 2011. (ENG., Illus.). 616p. pap. 35.00 ***(978-0-268-03323-1(4))*** Univ. of Notre Dame Pr.

Kermode, Mark, et al. Censoring the Moving Image. 2008. (Manifestos for the 21st Century Ser.). (ENG., Illus.). 128p. 20.00 *(978-1-905422-55-5(5))* Seagull Bks. GBR. Dist: Chicago Distribution Ctr.

Kolbert, Kathryn & Mettger, Zak. Censoring the Web: Leading Advocates Debate Today's Most Controversial Issues. Kolbert, Kathryn & Mettger, Zak, eds. 2006. 171p. reprint ed. pap. 25.00 *(978-1-4223-5816-0(X))* DIANE Publishing Co.

Ladenson, Elisabeth. Dirt for Art's Sake: Books on Trial from Madame Bovary to Lolita. 2007. 272p. per. 19.95 *(978-0-8014-7410-1(8))* 2006. 304p. 57.50 *(978-0-8014-4168-4(4))* Cornell Univ. Pr.

Laing, Heidi. The Right to Read the Handmaid's Tale in School. 2010. 128p. pap. *(978-3-8383-5718-8(3))* Lambert Academic Publishing.

Lange, Dorothea. Impounded: Dorothea Lange & the Censored Images of Japanese American Internment. Gordon, Linda & Okihiro, Gary Y., eds. (ENG., Illus.). 224p. 2008. per. 18.95 *(978-0-393-33090-8(7)*, 33090) 2006. 29.95 *(978-0-393-06073-7(X)*, 6073) Norton, W. W. & Co., Inc.

Larke, Mogens. The Use of Censorship in the Enlightenment. 2009. x, 203p. *(978-90-04-17558-7(X))* BRILL.

Levinson, Nan. Outspoken: Free Speech Stories. 2006. 359p. per. 21.95 *(978-0-520-24997-4(6))* Univ. of California Pr.

Lorenz, Matthias N. & N Lorenz, Matthias. Literatur und Zensur in der Demokratie: Die Bundesrepublik und die Freiheit der Kunst. 2009. (GER.). 214p. (C). pap. 23.00 ***(978-3-8252-3266-5(2))*** Vandenhoeck & Ruprecht GmbH & Co. KG DEU. Dist: ISD.

Mander, Mary S. Pen & Sword: American War Correspondents, 1898-1975. 2010. (ENG.). 208p. 45.00 *(978-0-252-03556-2(9))* Univ. of Illinois Pr.

Manning, Patricia. Voicing Dissent in Seventeenth-Century Spain: Inquisition, Social Criticism & Theology in the Case of el Criticón. 2009. (Medieval & Early Modern Iberian World Ser.). 340p. *(978-90-04-17851-9(1))* BRILL.

Marshall, Paul & Shea, Nina. Silenced: How Apostasy & Blasphemy Codes Are Choking Freedom Worldwide. 2011. (ENG., Illus.). 544p. pap. 35.00 *(978-0-19-981228-8(4))* Oxford Univ. Pr., Inc.

Marshik, Celia. British Modernism & Censorship. (ENG., Illus.). 272p. 2009. pap. 36.99 *(978-0-521-10128-8(X))* 2006. 109.00 *(978-0-521-85966-0(2))* Cambridge Univ. Pr.

McCormick, John, et al, eds. Versions of Censorship. 2006. (ENG.). 392p. (gr. 11). pap. 32.95 *(978-0-202-30875-3(8))* Aldine Transaction.

McCormick, John & MacInnes, Mairi, eds. Versions of Censorship: An Anthology. 2011. 396p. 54.95 ***(978-1-258-01089-8(5))*** Literary Licensing, LLC.

McDonald, Peter D. The Literature Police: Apartheid Censorship & Its Cultural Consequences. (Illus.). 2010. 432p. pap. 27.95 *(978-0-19-959111-4(3))* 2009. (ENG., 448p. 55.00 *(978-0-19-928334-7(6))* Oxford Univ. Pr., Inc.

McLeod, Jane. Licensing Loyalty: Printers, Patrons, & the State in Early Modern France. 2011. (Penn State Studies in the History of the Bk Ser.). (ENG.). 280p. 74.95 *(978-0-271-03768-4(7))* Pennsylvania State Univ. Pr.

McNicol, Sarah. Forbidden Fruit: The Censorship of Literature & Information for Young People - Conference Proceedings. 2008. 128p. pap. 25.95 *(978-1-59942-480-4(0)*, Brown Walker Pr.) Universal Pubs.

Mertelsmann, Olaf, ed. Central & Eastern European Media under Dictatorial Rule & in the Early Cold War. 2011. (Tartu Historical Studies). 234p. 64.95 *(978-3-631-61103-6(X))* Lang, Peter GmbH, Europäischer Verlag der Wissenschaften DEU. Dist: Lang, Peter.

Miller, Neil. Banned in Boston: The Watch & Ward Society's Crusade Against Books, Burlesque, & the Social Evil. 2010. (ENG.). 240p. 26.95 *(978-0-8070-5112-2(8))* Beacon Pr.

—Banned in Boston: The Watch & Ward Society's Crusade against Books, Burlesque, & the Social Evil. 2011. (ENG.). 224p. pap. 16.00 *(978-0-8070-5111-5(X))* Beacon Pr.

Mooney, Susan. The Artistic Censoring of Sexuality: Fantasy & Judgment in the Twentieth Century Novel. 2008. (ENG.). 384p. 89.95 *(978-0-8142-1082-6(1))*; xviii, 321p. cd-rom 14.95 *(978-0-8142-9161-0(9))* Ohio State Univ. Pr.

Morgan, Bill & Peters, Nancy J., eds. Howl on Trial: The Battle for Free Expression. 2006. (ENG., Illus.). 224p. per. 14.95 *(978-0-87286-479-5(0))* City Lights Bks.

Morozov, Evgeny. The Net Delusion: The Dark Side of Internet Freedom. 2011. (ENG., Illus.). 432p. 27.95 *(978-1-58648-874-1(0))* PublicAffairs.

Morrison, Toni. Burn This Book: PEN Writers on the Power of Language. 2012. (ENG.). 208p. pap. 12.99 ***(978-0-06-177401-0(4)**,* Harper Paperbacks) HarperCollins Pubs.

Mullin, Katherine. James Joyce, Sexuality & Social Purity. 2007. (ENG., Illus.). 240p. pap. 53.00 *(978-0-521-03596-5(1))* Cambridge Univ. Pr.

Murche-Kikut, Angela & Universität Bremen, Forschungsstelle Osteuropa Staff. Monographien Im Polnischen Zweiten Umlauf, 1976-1990. 2008. (POL & GER.). 510p. *(978-3-89821-883-2(X))* ibidem-Verlag.

Nesvig, Martin Austin. Ideology & Inquisition: The World of the Censors in Early Mexico. 2009. (ENG., Illus.). 384p. pap. 60.00 *(978-0-300-14040-8(1))* Yale Univ. Pr.

Ní Chuilleanáin, Eiléan, et al, eds. Translation & Censorship: Patterns of Communication & Interference. 2009. 256p. 75.00 *(978-1-84682-143-1(6))* Four Courts Pr. IRL. Dist: International Specialized Bk. Services.

Nicholson, Steve. Censorship of British Drama, 1900-1968, 4 vols., Vol. 3. 2011. (University of Exeter Press - Exeter Performance Studies). 272p. 95.00 *(978-0-85989-750-1(8))* Univ. of Exeter Pr. GBR. Dist: Chicago Distribution Ctr.

Nishio, Kanji. GHQ Funsho Tosho Kaifu. 2008. (JPN., Illus.). *(978-4-19-862516-0(6))*; *(978-4-19-862636-5(7))* Tokuma Shoten.

Nock, Marjorie. Uncensored: Adventures in the US Office of Censorship. 2008. 112p. pap. 9.95 *(978-1-60594-164-6(6)*, Llumina Pr.) Aeon Publishing Inc.

O'Leary, Brad. Shut up, America! The End of Free Speech. 2009. 208p. 25.95 *(978-1-935071-09-9(2))* WND Bks, Inc.

Pariser, Eli. The Filter Bubble: What the Internet Is Hiding from You. 2011. (ENG.). 304p. (gr. 12). 25.95 *(978-1-59420-300-8(8)*, Penguin Pr. HC, The) Penguin Group (USA) Inc.

Paxton, Mark. Censorship, 1 vol. 2008. (Historical Guides to Controversial Issues in America). 172p. 49.95 *(978-0-313-33751-2(9)*, GR3751, Greenwood Pr.) Greenwood Publishing Group, Inc.

Pelizaeus, Ludolf & Pelgen, Franz Stephan, eds. Kontrolle und Nutzung - Medien in Geistlichen Gebieten Europas 1680-1800. 2011. (Mainzer Studien zur Neueren Geschichte Ser.). (GER.). 290p. 72.95 *(978-3-631-61140-1(4))* Lang, Peter GmbH, Europäischer Verlag der Wissenschaften DEU. Dist: Lang, Peter.

Pennel-Stevens, June. Protecting Intellectual Freedom in Your Public Library: Scenarios from the Front Lines. 2011. pap. 50.00 *(978-0-8389-3583-5(4))* American Library Assn.

Petley, Julian. Censoring the Word. 2007. (Manifestos for the 21st Century Ser.). (ENG., Illus.). 128p. 20.00 *(978-1-905422-54-8(7))* Seagull Bks. GBR. Dist: Chicago Distribution Ctr.

—Censorship. 2009. (Beginners Guide (Oneworld) Ser.). (ENG.). 224p. pap. 14.95 *(978-1-85168-674-2(6))* Oneworld Pubns. GBR. Dist: National Bk. Network.

—Media & Censorship. 2008. pap. 80.00 *(978-0-415-25123-5(0))*; pap. 26.95 *(978-0-415-25124-2(9))* Routledge.

Polastron, Lucien X. Books on Fire: The Destruction of Libraries Throughout History. Graham, Jon E., tr. from FRE. 2007. (ENG.). 1p. 24.95 *(978-1-59477-167-5(7))* Inner Traditions International, Ltd.

Press Freedom in the Americas: Hearing Before the Subcommittee on the Western Hemisphere of the Committee on Foreign Affairs, House of Representatives, One Hundred Eleventh Congress, Second Session, June 16, 2010. 2010. iii, 55p. *(978-0-16-086528-2(X)*, 552-070-41526-2) United States Government Printing Office.

Project Censored, et al, eds. Censored 2009: The Top 25 Censored Stories of 2007-08. 2008. 416p. pap. 19.95 *(978-1-58322-852-4(7))* Seven Stories Pr.

Raz-Krakotzkin, Amnon. The Censor, the Editor, & the Text: The Catholic Church & the Shaping of the Jewish Canon in the Sixteenth Century. Feldman, Jackie, tr. from HEB. 2007. (Jewish Culture & Contexts Ser.). (ENG.). 328p. (C). 69.95 *(978-0-8122-4011-5(1))* Univ. of Pennsylvania Pr.

Ringmar, Erik. A Blogger's Manifesto: Free Speech & Censorship in a Digital World. 2007. (Anthem Politics & IR Ser.). (ENG., Illus.). 160p. per. 14.99 *(978-1-84331-288-8(3))* Anthem Pr. GBR. Dist: Books International, Inc.

Robertson, Randy. Censorship & Conflict in Seventeenth-Century England: The Subtle Art of Division. 2009. (Penn State Studies in the History of the Bk Ser.). (ENG.). 264p. 75.00 *(978-0-271-03466-9(1))* Pennsylvania State Univ. Pr.

Robinson, Kerry. Innocence, Knowledge & the Construction of Childhood: The Contradictory Nature of Sexuality & Censorship in Children's Contemporary Lives. 2012. (ENG.). 160p. (C). 130.00 *(978-0-415-60967-8(4))*; pap. 39.95 *(978-0-415-60763-6(9))* Routledge.

Rose, Jonathan, ed. The Holocaust & the Book: Destruction & Preservation. 2008. (Studies in Print Culture & the History of the Book). (ENG., Illus.). 314p. pap. 29.95 *(978-1-55849-643-9(2))* Univ. of Massachusetts Pr.

Ruud, Charles A. Fighting Words: Imperial Censorship & the Russian Press, 1804-1906. 2009. 330p. pap. *(978-1-4426-1024-8(7))* Univ. of Toronto Pr.

Scales, Pat. Protecting Intellectual Freedom in Your School Library: Scenarios from the Front Lines. 2009. 256p. 55.00 *(978-0-8389-3581-1(8))* American Library Assn.

Schroeder, Theodore Albert. Free Press Anthology. 2009. 278p. 30.99 *(978-1-110-97194-7(X))* 2009. 278p. pap. 26.75 *(978-1-110-97191-6(5))* 2008. 280p. 25.99 *(978-0-554-45649-2(4))* 2008. 280p. 28.99 *(978-0-554-45637-9(0))* 2008. 280p. pap. 27.75 *(978-0-554-45640-9(0))* 2008. 280p. pap. 26.75 *(978-0-554-45646-1(X))* BiblioBazaar.

Schroeder, Theodore Albert, ed. Free Press Anthology. 2008. 282p. 43.95 *(978-1-4366-4138-8(1))*; 284p. pap. 28.95 *(978-0-548-89544-3(9))* Kessinger Publishing, LLC.

Schwartz, Lowell H. & Helmus, Todd C. Barriers to the Broad Dissemination of Creative Works in the Arab World. 2009. 58p. pap. 23.00 *(978-0-8330-4730-4(2)*, MG-879) RAND Corp., The.

Semonche, John E. Censoring Sex: A Historical Journey Through American Media. 2007. (ENG., Illus.). 310p. 80.00 *(978-0-7425-5131-2(8))*; per. 30.95 *(978-0-7425-5132-9(6))* Rowman & Littlefield Publishers, Inc.

Shamir, Avner. Christian Conceptions of Jewish Books: The Pfefferkorn Affair. 2011. 130p. pap. 25.00 *(978-87-635-0772-1(2))* Museum Tusculanum Pr. DNK. Dist: Chicago Distribution Ctr.

Shariff, S. & Johnny, L. Censorship! or Selection? 2007. 152p. per. *(978-90-8790-074-8(0))* Sense Pubs.

Silver, Derigan Almond. National Security in the Courts: The Need for Secrecy vs. the Requirement of Transparency. 2010. *(978-1-59332-420-9(0))* LFB Scholarly Publishing LLC.

Sova, Dawn B. Literature Suppressed on Social Grounds. 3rd rev. ed. 2011. (Banned Bks.). 492p. (C). (gr. 9). 60.00 *(978-0-8160-8228-5(6))* Facts On File, Inc.

Stark, Gary D. Banned in Berlin: Literary Censorship in Imperial Germany, 1871-1918. 2009. (Illus.). 342p. 95.00 *(978-1-84545-570-5(3))* Berghahn Bks., Inc.

Sweeney, Michael S. The Military & the Press: An Uneasy Truce. 2006. (Visions of the American Press Ser.). (ENG.). 302p. per. 24.95 *(978-0-8101-2299-4(5))* Northwestern Univ. Pr.

Talbot, George. Censorship in Fascist Italy, 1922-43: Policies, Procedures & Protagonists. 2007. (ENG., Illus.). 264p. 100.00 *(978-0-230-54308-9(1))* Palgrave Macmillan.

Thacker, Toby. Music after Hitler, 1945-1955. 2007. (Illus.). 292p. 114.95 *(978-0-7546-5346-2(3))* Ashgate Publishing Co.

That Which Is Not Obligatory Is Prohibited: Censorship & Incitement in the Arab World: Hearing Before the Subcommittee on the Middle East & South Asia of the Committee on Foreign Affairs, House of Representatives, One Hundred Tenth Congress, Second Session, January 22, 2008. 2008. iii, 43p. *(978-0-16-080858-6(8)*, 552-070-37411-6) United States Government Printing Office.

Trombetta, Jim. The Horror! The Horror! Comic Books the Government Didn't Want You to Read! 2010. (ENG., Illus.). 304p. pap. 29.95 *(978-0-8109-5595-0(4))* Abrams.

Turner, Frederick. Renegade: Henry Miller & the Making of Tropic of Cancer. 2012. (Icons of America Ser.). (ENG.). 256p. 24.95 *(978-0-300-14949-4(2))* Yale Univ. Pr.

van Rooyen, Kobus. A South African Censor's Tale. 2012. (Illus.). 140p. pap. 30.00 ***(978-1-86919-415-4(2))*** International Publishers Marketing.

Walton, Charles. Policing Public Opinion in the French Revolution: The Culture of Calumny & the Problem of Free Speech. 2009. (ENG., Illus.). 352p. 49.95 *(978-0-19-536775-1(8))* Oxford Univ. Pr., Inc.

Werner, Thomas. Den Irrtum liquidieren: Bücherverbrennungen im Mittelalter. Veröffentlichungen des Max-Planck-Instituts für Geschichte. 2007. (Veröffentlichungen des Max-Planck-Instituts Für Geschichte Ser.). (GER., Illus.). 853p. (C). 165.00 *(978-3-525-35880-1(6))* Vandenhoeck & Ruprecht GmbH & Co. KG DEU. Dist: ISD.

White, Amy E. Virtually Obscene: The Case for an Uncensored Internet. 2006. (ENG.). 188p. per. 35.00 *(978-0-7864-2801-4(5))* McFarland & Co., Inc. Pubs.

Wiegand, Shirley A. & Wiegand, Wayne A. Books on Trial: Red Scare in the Heartland. 2007. (ENG., Illus.). 280p. 24.95 *(978-0-8061-3868-8(8))* Univ. of Oklahoma Pr.

Worrall, David. Theatric Revolution: Drama, Censorship, & Romantic Period Subcultures 1773-1832. 2008. (ENG.). 416p. pap. 60.00 *(978-0-19-923913-9(4))* Oxford Univ. Pr., Inc.

Yahoo! Inc.'s Provision of False Information to Congress: Hearing Before the Committee on Foreign Affairs, House of Representatives, One Hundred Tenth Congress, First Session, November 6, 2007. 2008. iii, 62p. *(978-0-16-080164-8(8)*, 552-070-36901-5) United States Government Printing Office.

Yeats, W. B. & Witt, Marion. Great Art Beaten Down: Yeats on Censorship. 2011. 16p. pap. 35.95 ***(978-1-258-01978-5(7))*** Literary Licensing, LLC.

Yonas, Nebiyu. Self-Censorship in Ethiopian Government Medi. 2009. 60p. pap. *(978-3-639-17484-7(4))* VDM Verlag Dr. Mueller e.K.

Zittrain, Jonathan. Access Contested: Security, Identity, & Resistance in Asian Cyberspace. Deibert, Ronald et al, eds. 2011. (Information Revolution & Global Politics Ser.). (ENG., Illus.). 432p. (gr. 17). 48.00 ***(978-0-262-01678-0(8))***; pap. 24.00 ***(978-0-262-51680-8(2))*** MIT Pr.

CENSORSHIP—BIBLIOGRAPHY

Nsouli, Mona A. & Meho, Lokman I. Censorship in the Arab World: An Annotated Bibliography. annot. ed. 2006. (ENG & MUL.). 192p. per. 60.00 *(978-0-8108-5869-5(X))* Scarecrow Pr., Inc.

CENSORSHIP OF THE PRESS

see Freedom of the Press; Press Law; Prohibited Books

CENSUS

see also Household Surveys

also subdivision Census under names of countries, cities, etc. e.g. United States—Census

De La Roque, Sieur. Journal & Census of the Royale. reprint ed. 150.00 *(978-0-7222-6735-6(5))* Library Reprints, Inc.

Design of the 2010 Census Program of Evaluations Staff & National Research Council Staff. Envisioning the 2020 Census. Brown, Lawrence D. et al, eds. 2010. (ENG.). 362p. pap. 72.25 *(978-0-309-15115-3(5))* National Academies Pr.

Levitan, Kathrin. A Cultural History of the British Census: Envisioning the Multitude in the Nineteenth Century. 2011. (Palgrave Studies in Cultural & Intellectual History Ser.). (ENG., Illus.). 288p. 85.00 *(978-0-230-11937-6(9))* Palgrave Macmillan.

Prewitt, Kenneth, ed. The Federal Statistical System: Its Vulnerability Matters More Than You Think: Its Vulnerability Matters More Than You Think. 2010. (ANNALS of the American Academy of Political & Social Science Ser.: 631). 240p. (C). 47.00 *(978-1-4129-9257-2(5)*, 295631C); pap. 34.00 *(978-1-4129-9258-9(3)*, 295631P) SAGE Pubns., Inc.

Qi, Haodong. Population under Harsh Time. 2010. 76p. pap. *(978-3-8383-1441-9(7))* Lambert Academic Publishing.

Saenz, Rogelio, et al, eds. The International Handbook of the Demography of Race & Ethnicity. 2010. (International Handbooks of Population Ser.). 15p. 369.00 *(978-90-481-8890-1(3)*, 9048188903) Springer.

United Nations Publications Staff. Principles & Recommendations for Population & Housing Censuses. 2008. (Statistical Papers (Ser. M) Ser.). (ENG.). 440p. pap. 75.00 *(978-92-1-161505-0(4))* United Nations Pubns.

United Nations, Statistical Division Staff, contrib. by. Handbook on Population & Housing Census Editing: Revision 1. 2010. (ENG.). 196p. 52.00 *(978-92-1-161530-2(5))* United Nations Pubns.

United Nations: Department of Economic and Social Affairs. Measuring the Economically Active in Population Censuses: A Handbook. 2010. (ENG., Illus.). 352p. pap. 56.00 ***(978-92-1-161526-5(7))*** United Nations Pubns.

United Nations.Department Of Economic And Social Affairs.Statistics Division Staff. Handbook on Geospatial Infrastructure in Support of Census Activities. 2009. (ENG., Illus.). 270p. pap. 55.00 *(978-92-1-161527-2(5))* United Nations Pubns.

CENTENARIANS

Cooper, Ann Nixon. A Century & Some Change: My Life Before the President Called My Name. 2010. (ENG., Illus.). 224p. 19.99 *(978-1-4391-5887-6(8)*, Beyond Words/Atria Bks.) Atria Bks.

Cooper, Ann Nixon & Bates, Karen Grigsby. A Century & Some Change: My Life Before the President Called My Name. 2010. pap. *(978-1-4391-5888-3(6)*, Beyond Words/Atria Bks.) Atria Bks.

Johnson, Ella Mae Cheeks & Mulcahy, Patricia. It Is Well with My Soul: The Extraordinary Life of a 106-Year-Old Woman. 2010. (ENG.). 224p. (gr. 12). 14.00 *(978-0-14-311744-5(0)*, Penguin (Non-Classics)) Penguin Group (USA) Inc.

Maier, Heiner, et al, eds. Supercentenarians. 2010. (Demographic Research Monographs). (ENG., Illus.). xv, 323p. 159.00 *(978-3-642-11519-6(5)*, 3642115195) Springer.

Poon, Leonard W. & Perls, Thomas T., eds. Biopsychosocial Approaches to Longevity. 2008. (Annual Review of Gerontology & Geriatrics Ser.). (Illus.). 273p. 58.00 *(978-0-8261-1537-9(3))* Springer Publishing Co., Inc.

Robbins, John. Healthy At 100: The Scientifically Proven Secrets of the World's Healthiest & Longest-Lived Peoples. l.t. ed. 2007. (Thorndike Health, Home & Learning Ser.). 671p. 29.95 *(978-0-7862-9900-3(2))* Thorndike Pr.

Steele-Perkins, Chris. Fading Light: Portraits of Centenarians. 2012. (ENG.). 104p. 39.95 ***(978-0-85716-032-4(X))*** Northumbria University Press GBR. Dist: Independent Pubs. Group.

Taylor, Henry. From Lead Mines to Gold Fields: Memories of an Incredibly Long Life. Parman, Donald L., ed. 2006. (ENG., Illus.). 230p. pap. 24.95 *(978-0-8032-9461-5(1))* Univ. of Nebraska Pr.

CENTER PARTIES

Boyarsky, Bill. Big Daddy: Jesse Unruh & the Art of Power Politics. 2007. (Illus.). 265p. 37.95 *(978-0-520-21967-0(8))* Univ. of California Pr.

CENTER-PERIPHERY RELATIONS

see Dependency

CENTERS FOR THE PERFORMING ARTS

see also Auditoriums; Music-Halls; Theaters

Appleton, Ian. Buildings for the Performing Arts: A Design & Development Guide. 2nd rev. ed. 2008. (ENG., Illus.). 296p. pap. 67.95 *(978-0-7506-6835-4(0))* Routledge.

Jaffe, Lee & Jaffe, J. Christopher. The Acoustics of Performance Halls Spaces for Music from Carnegie Hall to the Hollywood Bowl. 2010. (ENG., Illus.). 208p. 50.00 *(978-0-393-73255-9(X)*, 73255) Norton, W. W. & Co., Inc.

Serafin, Steven, ed. BAM: The Collected Works. 2011. (ENG., Illus.). 384p. 95.00 *(978-1-59372-046-9(7)*, 372046) Quantuck Lane Pr. & The Mill Road Collaborative, The.

Watt, Daniel. A Performance Cosmology: Testimony from the Future, Evidence of the Past. 2006. (Illus.). 321p. pap. 57.00 *(978-0-415-37258-9(5))* Routledge.

CENTIPEDES

Chao, Jui Lung. Scolopendromorpha of Taiwan. 2008. 100p. pap. *(978-3-639-00301-7(2))* VDM Verlag Dr. Mueller e.K.

Lewis, J. G. E. The Biology of Centipedes. 2007. (ENG.). 488p. pap. 95.00 *(978-0-521-03411-1(6))* Cambridge Univ. Pr.

CENTLIVRE, SUSANNA, 1667-1723

Centlivre, Susanna. Dramatic Works of the Celebrated Mrs. Centlivre, 3 vols. reprint ed. 230.00 *(978-0-404-01480-3(1))* AMS Pr., Inc.

CENTRAL AFRICA

see Africa, Central

CENTRAL AFRICAN REPUBLIC

Icon Group International, Inc. Staff, compiled by. The 2006 Economic & Product Market Databook for Bouar, Central African Republic. 2006. 618p. ring bd. 95.00 *(978-0-497-80230-1(9))* Icon Group International, Inc.

Vinck, Patrick & Pham, Phuong. Building Peace, Seeking Justice: A Population-Based Survey on Attitudes about Accountability & Social Reconstruction in the Central African Republic. 2010. (ENG., Illus.). 41p. pap. 19.95 *(978-0-9826323-0-7(4))* Human Rights Ctr., Univ. of California, Berkeley, The.

Woodfork, Jacqueline. Culture & Customs of the Central African Republic, 1 vol. 2006. (Culture & Customs of Africa Ser.). (Illus.). 232p. 49.95 *(978-0-313-33203-6(7)*, GR3203, Greenwood Pr.) Greenwood Publishing Group, Inc.

CENTRAL AMERICA

Here are entered works on Central America as a whole. For information about specific countries see names of countries, e. g. Panama.

Koebel, William Henry. Central America. (South American Ser.). 382p. reprint ed. 98.00 *(978-0-7222-9481-9(6))* Library Reprints, Inc.

Palmer, Frederick. Central America & Its Problems. 2009. 168p. pap. 19.99 *(978-1-150-43352-8(3))* General Bks. LLC.

Routledge Staff, creator. South America, Central America & the Caribbean. 15th rev. ed. 2006. (South America, Central America & the Caribbean Ser.). (Illus.). 1076p. 615.00 *(978-1-85743-392-0(0))* Routledge.

Shepherd, William Robert. Central & South America. 256p. reprint ed. 98.00 *(978-0-7222-9527-4(8))*; 98.00 *(978-0-7222-9484-0(0))* Library Reprints, Inc.

CENTRAL AMERICA—ANTIQUITIES

Bowditch, Charles P. Mexican & Central American Antiquities, Calendar Systems, & History. 682p. reprint ed. 128.00 *(978-0-7222-9682-0(7))* Library Reprints, Inc.

Braswell, Geoffrey, et al, eds. The Technology of Maya Civilization: Political Economy & Beyond in Lithic Studies. 2011. (Approaches to Anthropological Archaeology Ser.). (ENG., Illus.). 210p. (C). 115.00 *(978-1-84553-508-7(1))* Equinox Publishing Ltd. GBR. Dist: ISD.

Childress, David Hatcher. The Mystery of the Olmecs. 2007. (Illus.). 262p. per. 20.00 *(978-1-931882-71-2(1))* Adventures Unlimited Pr.

Chladek, Stanislav. Exploring Maya Ritual Caves: Dark Secrets from the Maya Underworld. 2011. (ENG., Illus.). 240p. 49.95 *(978-0-7591-1987-1(2))* AltaMira Pr.

Coe, Michael D. Breaking the Maya Code. 3rd rev. ed. 2012. (ENG., Illus.). 304p. pap. 19.95 ***(978-0-500-28955-6(7)***, 528955) Thames & Hudson.

Duverger, Christian. El Primer Mestizaje: La Clave para Entender el Pasado Mesoamericano. 2007. (ESP., Illus.). 740p. per. 54.99 *(978-970-770-856-3(5))* Santillana, S.A. de C.V., Editorial MEX. Dist: Santillana USA Publishing Co., Inc.

Evans, Susan Toby. Ancient Mexico & Central America: Archaeology & Culture History. 2nd ed. 2008. (ENG., Illus.). 608p. pap. 65.00 net. *(978-0-500-28714-9(7)*, 528714) Thames & Hudson.

Evans, Susan Toby & Webster, David L. Archaeology of Ancient Mexico & Central America. 2009. (ENG., Illus.). 992p. pap. 59.95 *(978-0-415-87399-4(1))* Routledge.

Finamore, Daniel & Houston, Stephen D. Fiery Pool: The Maya & the Mythic Sea. 2010. (Illus.). 328p. pap. *(978-0-87577-219-6(6))* Peabody Essex Museum.

Garber, James F., ed. The Ancient Maya of the Belize Valley: Half a Century of Archaeological Research. 2011. (Maya Studies). (ENG., Illus.). 448p. pap. 39.95 *(978-0-8130-3979-4(7))* Univ. Pr. of Florida.

Graham, Ian. The Road to Ruins. 2010. (ENG., Illus.). 546p. 39.95 *(978-0-8263-4754-1(1))* Univ. of New Mexico Pr.

Guderjan, Thomas H. Ancient Maya Traders of Ambergris Caye. 2nd ed. 2007. (Caribbean Archaeology & Ethnohistory Ser.). (ENG., Illus.). 48p. per. 9.95 *(978-0-8173-5463-3(8))* Univ. of Alabama Pr.

Helferich, Gerard. Stone of Kings: In Search of the Lost Jade of the Maya. 2011. (ENG., Illus.). 304p. 24.95 *(978-0-7627-6351-1(5)*, Lyons Pr.) Globe Pequot Pr., The.

Hirth, Kenneth G., ed. Archeological Papers of the American Anthropological Association, Housework: Craft Production & Domestic Economy in Ancient Mesoamerica, Number 19. 2010. (APAZ - Archaeological Papers of the American Anthropological Association Ser.). (ENG., Illus.). 252p. pap. 33.95 *(978-1-4443-3669-6(X)*, Wiley-Blackwell) Wiley, John & Sons, Inc.

Hunt, Norman Bancroft. Historical Atlas of Ancient America. 2009. (Illus.). 192p. 25.00 *(978-1-904668-11-4(9))* Mercury Bks. Ltd. GBR. Dist: International Publishers Marketing.

Kaehr, Shelley. Crystal Skull Consciousness. Armstrong, Linnea M., ed. 2007. 96p. per. 14.95 *(978-0-9648209-4-4(3))* An Out of this World Production.

LeCount, Lisa J. & Yaeger, Jason, eds. Classic Maya Provincial Politics: Xunantunich & Its Hinterlands. 2010. (ENG., Illus.). 464p. 72.50 *(978-0-8165-2884-4(5))* Univ. of Arizona Pr.

Lucero, Lisa J. Precolumbian Water Management: Ideology, Ritual, & Power. 2006. (ENG., Illus.). 296p. 55.00 *(978-0-8165-2314-6(2))* Univ. of Arizona Pr.

Maudslay, Anne Cary & Maudslay, Alfred Percival. A Glimpse at Guatemala, & Some Notes on the Ancient Monuments of Central America. 2010. (Cambridge Library Collection - Archaeology Ser.). (Illus.). 512p. pap. 34.99 *(978-1-108-01704-6(5))* Cambridge Univ. Pr.

McAnany, Patricia A. Ancestral Maya Economies in Archaeological Perspective. 2010. (ENG., Illus.). 392p. 90.00 *(978-0-521-89518-7(9))* Cambridge Univ. Pr.

McEwan, Colin. Ancient American Art in Detail. 2009. (Art in Detail Ser.). Orig. Title: Ancient American Art in Detail. (Illus.). 144p. 21.95 *(978-0-674-03315-3(9))* Harvard Univ. Pr.

McKillop, Heather. The Ancient Maya: New Perspectives. 2006. (ENG., Illus.). 480p. per. 22.95 *(978-0-393-32890-5(2)*, 32890) Norton, W. W. & Co., Inc.

Morehart, Christopher T. Food, Fire & Fragrance: A Paleoethnobotanical Perspective on Classic Maya Cave Rituals. 2011. (Bar S Ser.). (Illus.). 177p. (C). pap. 92.50 *(978-1-4073-0741-1(X))* British Archaeological Reports Ltd. GBR. Dist: Brown, David Bk. Co., The.

Palka, Joel W. The A to Z of Ancient Mesoamerica. 2010. (A to Z Guide Ser.). (ENG.). 236p. pap. 34.45 *(978-0-8108-7566-1(7))* Scarecrow Pr., Inc.

Pendergast, David M. & Andrews, Anthony P. Reconstructing the Past: Studies in Mesoamerican & Central American Prehistory. 2006. (BAR International Ser.: Vol. 1529). (ENG., Illus.). 158p. (C). pap. 100.00 *(978-1-84171-751-7(7))* British Archaeological Reports Ltd. GBR. Dist: Brown, David Bk. Co., The.

Pool, Christopher A. Pottery Economics in Mesoamerica. 2008. (ENG.). 336p. 55.00 *(978-0-8165-2577-5(3))* Univ. of Arizona Pr.

Sitchin, Zecharia. The Lost Realms. 2007. (Earth Chronicles Ser.: Bk. 4). (ENG., Illus.). 320p. mass mkt. 7.99 *(978-0-06-137925-3(5))* HarperCollins Pubs.

Spinden, Herbert Joseph. Ancient Civilizations of Mexico & Central America. 2009. 244p. 41.95 *(978-1-104-03061-2(6))*; pap. 26.95 *(978-1-104-02061-3(0))* Kessinger Publishing, LLC.

Stephens, John Lloyd. Incidents of Travel in Central America, Chiapas, & Yucatan. 2010. (Cambridge Library Collection - Archaeology Ser.). (ENG.). 550p. pap. 39.99 *(978-1-108-01729-9(0))*; (Illus.). 472p. pap. 34.99 *(978-1-108-01728-2(2))* Cambridge Univ. Pr.

Turner, B. L. & Harrison, Peter D., eds. Pulltrouser Swamp: Ancient Maya Habitat, Agriculture, & Settlement in Northern Belize. 2012. (ENG., Illus.). 310p. pap. 30.00 ***(978-0-292-74194-2(4))*** Univ. of Texas Pr.

Uriarte, María Teresa, ed. Pre-Columbian Architecture in Mesoamerica. 2010. (ENG., Illus.). 336p. 125.00 *(978-0-7892-1045-6(2))* Abbeville Pr., Inc.

Weeks, John M. The Carnegie Maya III: Carnegie Institution of Washington Notes on Middle American Archaeology & Ethnology, 1940-1957. 2011. E-Book *(978-1-60732-061-6(4))* Univ. Pr. of Colorado.

Weeks, John M., ed. The Carnegie Maya IV. 2012. (ENG., Illus.). 112p. 200.00 ***(978-1-60732-158-3(0))*** Univ. Pr. of Colorado.

Whittington, Stephen L. & Reed, David M., eds. Bones of the Maya: Studies of Ancient Skeletons. 2006. (Illus.). 312p. per. 34.95 *(978-0-8173-5376-6(3))* Univ. of Alabama Pr.

Wilson, Samuel Meredith, et al, contrib. by. The Prehistory of Nevis, a Small Island in the Lesser Antilles. 2010. (Yale University Publications in Anthropology Ser.). (Illus.). 248p. pap. 49.50 *(978-0-913516-23-2(6))* Yale Univ. Pubns. in Anthropology.

Young-Sánchez, Margaret. Nature & Spirit: Ancient Costa Rican Treasures in the Mayer Collection at the Denver Art Museum. 2011. (ENG.). 192p. (C). 49.95 *(978-0-914738-68-8(2))* Denver Art Museum.

CENTRAL AMERICA—BIOGRAPHY

Aguilar, Sonia Elizabeth. Realidades Lejos Del Mundo Feliz: Penas de la Comunidad Salvadore+ a. 2008. 144p. pap. 12.99 *(978-1-4389-0614-0(5))* AuthorHouse.

Argueta, Manlio. Once upon a Time (Bomb) Craft, Linda J., tr. from SPA. 2007. (ENG.). 260p. 74.99 *(978-0-7618-3786-2(8))* Univ. Pr. of America, Inc.

Argueta, Manlio & Argueta, Manlio. Once upon a Time (Bomb) Craft, Linda J., tr. from SPA. 2007. (ENG.). 260p. pap. 41.99 *(978-0-7618-3787-9(6))* Univ. Pr. of America, Inc.

Bubenik, Jenifer. Thoughts from the Chicken Bus. 2009. 220p. pap. 15.00 *(978-1-60844-052-8(4))* Dog Ear Publishing, LLC.

Carrera, Margarita. Sumario Del Recuerdo: Memorias (1929-1981) 2006. (Colección Escritores Centroamericanos Ser.). (SPA., Illus.). 244p. pap. *(978-99922-48-51-5(3))* Fondo de Cultura Economica.

Connor, Guillermina. Memories & Hope: The Road I Traveled. 2007. 126p. pap. 12.95 *(978-1-57258-489-1(0))* TEACH Services, Inc.

Doyle, Edwina Ann. Midlife Monkeyla!: Escape to & from a Tropical Paradise. 2011. 244p. pap. 15.95 ***(978-1-60594-674-0(5)***, Llumina Pr.) Aeon Publishing Inc.

Duszak, Malgorzata. Odyssey of an Airhead: Ultimate Truth, Here I Come! 2010. 260p. (ENG.). 27.99 *(978-1-4520-2400-4(6))*; pap. 17.99 *(978-1-4520-2399-1(9))* AuthorHouse.

Edwards, Leland & Williams, Ron. Chasing the Vision. 2006. (ENG., Illus.). 176p. pap. 11.99 *(978-1-59979-019-0(X)*, Creation Hse.) Charisma Media.

Els, Jane. Journey to the Kingdom of God. 2009. pap. *(978-0-9765337-7-1(4))* Bottom-Up Media.

Giudice, Christian. Hands of Stone: The Life & Legend of Roberto Duran. 2009. (ENG., Illus.). 384p. pap. 14.95 *(978-1-903854-75-4(X))* Milo Bks. GBR. Dist: Consortium Bk. Sales & Distribution.

Gonzalez Palma, Luis, photos by. Luis Gonzalez Palma: PHotoBolsillo. 2011. (ENG & SPA., Illus.). 112p. pap. 20.00 *(978-84-92841-65-3(6))* La Fabrica ESP. Dist: D.A.P./Distributed Art Pubs.

Koons, David. Gringo on a Chicken Bus. 2009. 320p. pap. 22.95 *(978-0-595-53292-6(6))* iUniverse, Inc.

Mendoza, Sonia Noelia. America Is My Home: A Guatemalan Emigrant's Story. 2007. 88p. pap. 13.00 *(978-0-8059-7467-6(9))* Dorrance Publishing Co., Inc.

Montgomery, Kenneth E. A Backward Look: God was There Through it All. 2009. 136p. 23.95 *(978-1-4401-3970-3(9))*; pap. 13.95 *(978-1-4401-3971-0(7))* iUniverse, Inc.

Oliver, Beverly, ed. & compiled by. Seven Days in Usha Village: A Conversation with Dr. Sebi. 2008. 132p. per. 19.95 *(978-0-615-18681-8(5))* Dr. Sebi's Office, LLC.

Peham, Helga. Escaping the Rat Race - Freedom in Paradise. Ward, Matthew & Strozier, M. Stefan, eds. 2010. 342p. pap. 49.00 *(978-1-935444-13-8(1))* World Audience Pubs.

—Escaping the Rat Race - Freedom in Paradise. Ward, Matthew, ed. 2007. 344p. per. 17.99 *(978-1-934209-93-6(7))* World Audience Pubs.

R.H. Velasquez Staff. Don Chente. 2009. 292p. pap. 15.99 *(978-1-4389-6851-3(5))* AuthorHouse.

Rosebaugh, Lorenzo & Pino, Kateri Hellman. To Wisdom Through Failure: A Journey of Compassion & Resistance. 2006. *(978-0-918346-37-7(1))* EPICA.

Rushton, Jack L. Arise & Shine Forth: Heeding the Call to Serve. 2008. 182p. pap. 14.99 *(978-1-59955-118-0(7))* Cedar Fort, Inc./CFI Distribution.

Saint-Germain, Michelle A. & Metoyer, Cynthia Chavez. Women Legislators in Central America: Politics, Democracy, & Policy. 2008. (ENG., Illus.). 356p. pap. 30.00 *(978-0-292-71717-6(2))* Univ. of Texas Pr.

Shepard, Lucius. With Christmas in Honduras: Men, Myths, & Miscreants in Modern Central America. 2013. (ENG.). 272p. 24.95 *(978-1-56025-679-3(6))* Westview Pr.

CENTRAL AMERICA—DESCRIPTION AND TRAVEL

Baldy, François, ed. Conquerants et Chroniqueurs espagnols en pays Maya (1515-1697) Livre 2: Conquetes. 2011. (roue a Livres Ser.). (FRE., Illus.). 720p. (C). pap. 68.00 ***(978-2-251-33959-7(0))*** Societe d'edition Les Belles lettres FRA. Dist: ISD.

Bubenik, Jenifer. Thoughts from the Chicken Bus. 2009. 220p. pap. 15.00 *(978-1-60844-052-8(4))* Dog Ear Publishing, LLC.

Carpenter, Rhys. The Land Beyond Mexico. 2009. 198p. 26.99 *(978-1-110-68319-2(7))*; 198p. pap. 22.75 *(978-1-110-68316-1(2))*; 200p. 22.99 *(978-1-103-50817-4(2))*; 200p. pap. 16.99 *(978-1-103-50814-3(8))*; 200p. 22.99 *(978-0-559-89970-6(X))*; 200p. pap. 16.99 *(978-0-559-89966-9(1))* BiblioBazaar.

—The Land Beyond Mexico. 2009. 76p. pap. 14.14 *(978-0-217-49434-2(X))* General Bks. LLC.

—The Land Beyond Mexico. 2008. 198p. 39.95 *(978-1-4372-0392-9(2))*; pap. 24.95 *(978-1-4370-7406-2(5))* Kessinger Publishing, LLC.

—The Land Beyond Mexico. 181p. reprint ed. 88.00 *(978-0-7222-9479-6(4))* Library Reprints, Inc.

Edwards, Robert F. Antarctica: My Journey North from Antarctica. 2010. 23.65 *(978-1-4269-2075-2(X))* Trafford Publishing.

Glassman, Steve. On the Trail of the Maya Explorer: Tracing the Epic Journey of John Lloyd Stephens. 2nd ed. 2007. (Alabama Fire Ant Ser.). (Illus.). 304p. per. 22.00 *(978-0-8173-5442-8(5))* Univ. of Alabama Pr.

Greene, Donald. Americas Overland - the Driving Handbook. 2008. 368p. pap. 29.95 *(978-0-557-00712-7(7))* Lulu Enterprises Inc.

Heggstad, Glen. Two Wheels Through Terror: Diary of a South American Motorcycle Odyssey. 2010. (ENG., Illus.). 380p. pap. 16.95 *(978-1-55022-922-6(2))* ECW Pr. CAN. Dist: Independent Pubs. Group.

Leguineche, M. Sobre el Volcan (Over the Volcano) (SPA., Illus.). 288p. 8.95 *(978-84-01-33268-5(0))* Plaza & Janes Editories, S.A. ESP. Dist: AIMS International Bks., Inc.

Martin, Bruce T., photos by. Look Close, See Far: A Cultural Portrait of the Maya. 2007. (Illus.). 147p. 34.95 *(978-0-8076-1589-8(7))* Braziller, George Inc.

Penland, Paige R. Granada, San Juan del Sur & Southwest Nicaragua. 2010. (Great Destinations Ser.). (ENG., Illus.). 288p. pap. 19.95 *(978-1-58157-113-4(5)*, 157113) Countryman Pr.

Putnam, George Palmer. The Southland of North America, Rambles & Observations in Central America During the Year 1912. 2010. 152p. pap. *(978-1-153-17112-0(0))* Books LLC.

—The Southland of North America, Rambles & Observations in Central America During the Year 1912. 425p. reprint ed. 98.00 *(978-0-7222-9483-3(2))* Library Reprints, Inc.

Sangster, Rob & Leffel, Tim. Mexico & Central America: Everything You Need to Know to Eat Well, Stay Healthy, Travel Safely, Save Money, & Have a Ball! 2008. (Traveler's Tool Kit Ser.). (ENG., Illus.). 554p. pap. 22.95 *(978-0-89732-984-2(8))* Menasha Ridge Pr., Inc.

Stephens, John Lloyd. Incidents of Travel in Central America, Chiapas, & Yucatan. 2010. (Cambridge Library Collection - Archaeology Ser.). (ENG.). 550p. pap. 39.99 *(978-1-108-01729-9(0))*; (Illus.). 472p. pap. 34.99 *(978-1-108-01728-2(2))* Cambridge Univ. Pr.

A Traveller in Mexico - a Collection of Historical Articles Containing Travelling Experiences in Central Americ. 2011. 254p. pap. 28.95 ***(978-1-4474-0980-9(9))*** Audubon Pr. & Christian Bk. Service.

Tschiffely, A. F. Tschiffely's Ride: Ten Thousand Miles in the Saddle from Southern Cross to Pole Star. 2011. 386p. 53.95 ***(978-1-258-09895-7(4))*** Literary Licensing, LLC.

Unferth, Deb Olin. Revolution: The Year I Fell in Love & Went to Join the War. 2011. (ENG.). 224p. 24.00 *(978-0-8050-9323-0(0))* Holt, Henry & Co.

Wallace, David Rains. The Monkey's Bridge: Mysteries of Evolution in Central America. 2007. (ENG., Illus.). 280p. per. 18.95 *(978-1-59534-040-5(8))* Trinity Univ. Pr.

Whitman, Edmund S. Those Wild West Indies. 2006. 304p. per. *(978-1-4067-2456-1(4)*, Hesperides Pr.) Read Bks.

Wiatt, Thomas T. Just Tell Me What Happened: My Adventures in Central America, 1 vol. 2010. 63p. pap. 16.95 *(978-1-4489-5721-7(4))* PublishAmerica, Inc.

Williams, Ken. Cruising under Power - Pacific Coasts of Mexico & Central America. 2008. 234p. pap. 25.95 *(978-1-4357-1901-9(8))* Lulu Enterprises Inc.

Winker, Kevin, ed. Moments of Discovery: Natural History Narratives from Mexico & Central America. 2010. (ENG., Illus.). 384p. 75.00 *(978-0-8130-3417-1(5))* Univ. Pr. of Florida.

CENTRAL AMERICA—DISCOVERY AND EXPLORATION

see America—Discovery and Exploration

CENTRAL AMERICA—ECONOMIC CONDITIONS

Bacon, Christopher M., et al, eds. Confronting the Coffee Crisis: Fair Trade, Sustainable Livelihoods & Ecosystems in Mexico & Central America. 2008. (Food, Health, & the Environment Ser.). (ENG., Illus.). 408p. (gr. 17). 67.00 *(978-0-262-02633-8(3))*; per. 30.00 *(978-0-262-52480-3(5))* MIT Pr.

Berger, Erica M. South & Central America: Economic, Political & Social Issues. 2011. (Series: Latin American Political, Economic, & Security Issues Ser.). 195.00 *(978-1-61122-551-8(5))* Nova Science Pubs., Inc.

Carey Jones, N. S. The Pattern of a Dependent Economy: The National Income of British Honduras. 2011. (ENG.). 178p. pap. 19.99 ***(978-0-521-24201-1(0))*** Cambridge Univ. Pr.

Central America: Business Financing Handbook. (Illus.). 70p. (Orig.). pap. 295.00 *(978-0-7605-1183-1(7))* Rector Pr., Ltd.

Cucinotta, Vincenzo, ed. Politics & Economics of South & Central America. 2011. (Latin American Political, Economic, & Security Issues Ser.). 185.00 ***(978-1-61470-446-1(5))*** Nova Science Pubs., Inc.

Dym, Jordana & Belaubre, Christophe, eds. Politics, Economy, & Society in Bourbon Central America, 1759-1821. 2007. (ENG., Illus.). 310p. 65.00 *(978-0-87081-844-3(9))* Univ. Pr. of Colorado.

Endo, Isaku, et al. The U. S.-Honduras Remittance Corridor: Acting on Opportunities to Increase Financial Inclusion & Foster Development of a Transnational Economy. 2010. (World Bank Working Papers: 177). (ENG., Illus.). 96p. pap. 20.00 *(978-0-8213-8139-7(3))*, 9780821381397) World Bank Pubns.

Europa Publications, ed. South America Central America & the Caribbean 2012. 20th rev. ed. 2011. (ENG.). 1148p. 880.00 *(978-1-85743-619-8(9))* Routledge.

Icon Group International, Inc. Staff, compiled by. The 2006 Economic & Product Market Databook for Belize City, Belize. 2006. 618p. ring bd. 95.00 *(978-0-497-80176-2(0))* Icon Group International, Inc.

—The 2006 Economic & Product Market Databook for Belmopan, Belize. 2006. 618p. ring bd. 95.00 *(978-0-497-80177-9(9))* Icon Group International, Inc.

—The 2006 Economic & Product Market Databook for Dangriga, Belize. 2006. 618p. ring bd. 95.00 *(978-0-497-80442-8(5))* Icon Group International, Inc.

—The 2006 Economic & Product Market Databook for Orange Walk, Belize. 2006. 618p. ring bd. 95.00 *(978-0-497-81164-8(2))* Icon Group International, Inc.

—The 2006 Economic & Product Market Databook for Siguatepeque, Honduras. 2006. 618p. ring bd. 95.00 *(978-0-497-81535-3(2))* Icon Group International, Inc.

—The 2006 Economic & Product Market Databook for Sonsonate, el Salvador. 2006. 618p. ring bd. 95.00 *(978-0-497-81557-8(5))* Icon Group International, Inc.

Lehoucq, Fabrice. The Politics of Modern Central America: Civil War, Democratization, & Underdevelopment. 2012. (ENG., Illus.). 250p. (C). 90.00 ***(978-0-521-51506-1(8))***; pap. 27.99 ***(978-0-521-73079-2(1))*** Cambridge Univ. Pr.

Lewis, Colin, et al. South America, Central America & the Caribbean 2010. 18th rev. ed. 2009. (ENG.). 1136p. 810.00 *(978-1-85743-525-2(7))* Routledge.

Lucero, Lisa J. Water & Ritual: The Rise & Fall of Classic Maya Rulers. 2010. (ENG., Illus.). 269p. pap. 25.00 *(978-0-292-72611-6(2))* Univ. of Texas Pr.

MacLeod, Murdo J. Spanish Central America: A Socioeconomic History, 1520-1720. 2nd rev. ed. 2007. (ILAS Special Publication Ser.). (ENG., Illus.). 616p. pap. 40.00 *(978-0-292-71761-9(X))* Univ. of Texas Pr.

Morazzoni, Monica. Geopolitica Dell'America Centrale: Le Inquietudini, L'eredità, il Futuro. 2010. (ITA., Illus.). 222p. *(978-88-89891-42-1(4))* Archetipo Libri.

Munro, Dana Gardner. The Five Republics of Central America: Their Political & Economic Development & Their Relation with the United States. (Carnegie Endowment for International Peace Ser.). 332p. reprint ed. 98.00 *(978-0-7222-9482-6(4))* Library Reprints, Inc.

Nicholls, Jane A., ed. Economics & Politics of South & Central America. 2011. (Politics & Economics of Latin America Ser.). 162p. 89.00 *(978-1-61209-780-0(4))* Nova Science Pubs., Inc.

The Pending Free Trade Agreements with Colombia, Panama, & South Korea & the Creation of U.S. Jobs: Hearing Before the Committee on Ways & Means, U.S. House of Representatives, One Hundred Twelfth Congress, First Session, January 25, 2011. 2011. (Illus.). ii, 226p. ***(978-0-16-089384-1(4)***, 552-070-43368-6) United States Government Printing Office.

Roessingh, Carel & Plasil, Tanja, eds. Between Horse & Buggy & Four-Wheel Drive: Change & Diversity among Mennonite Settlements in Belize, Central America. 2009. (ENG.). 222p. pap. 39.95 *(978-90-8659-332-3(1))* VU Univ. Pr. NLD. Dist: Independent Pubs. Group.

Sànchez, Rafael A. & Sánchez Sánchez, Rafael A. The Politics of Central American Integration. 2008. (ENG., Illus.). 248p. 125.00 *(978-0-415-99615-0(5))* Routledge.

Sánchez Sánchez, Rafael A. The Politics of Central American Integration. 2012. (ENG., Illus.). 248p. pap. 42.95 ***(978-0-415-62159-5(3))*** Routledge.

South America Central America & the Caribbean 2011. 19th rev. ed. 2010. (ENG.). 1152p. 835.00 *(978-1-85743-562-7(1))* Routledge.

Trejo, Jose. Valuing a Marine Protected Area in Belize. 2009. 72p. pap. *(978-3-639-19660-3(0))* VDM Verlag Dr. Mueller e.K.

United Nations Conference on Trade and Development. Investment Policy Review: El Salvador. 2010. (ENG., Illus.). 132p. pap. 29.00 ***(978-92-1-112797-3(1))*** United Nations Pubns.

United Nations Staff. Social Panorama of Latin America 2008 (Includes CD-ROM) 2010. (ENG.). 256p. pap. 35.00 incl. cd-rom *(978-92-1-121580-6(X))* United Nations Pubns

Waite, Marilyn. Sustainable Water Resources in the Built Environment. 2010. (Illus.). 248p. (C). pap. *(978-1-84339-323-8(9))* IWA Publishing.

CENTRAL AMERICA—EMIGRATION AND IMMIGRATION

Aspatore Books Staff, compiled by. Immigration Law Client Strategies in Central & South America: Leading Lawyers on Understanding Local Laws, Interacting with Government Agencies, & Developing a Comprehensive Immigration Strategy (Inside the Minds) 2010. 264p. pap. 100.00 *(978-0-314-26715-3(8))* Aspatore Bks.

Johnson, Paul Christopher. Diaspora Conversions: Black Carib Religion & the Recovery of Africa. 2007. (Illus.). 330p. 65.00 *(978-0-520-24969-1(0))*; per. 28.95 *(978-0-520-24970-7(4))* Univ. of California Pr.

Palos, Mauricio, photos by. Mauricio Palos: My Perro Rano. 2011. (ENG., Illus.). 112p. pap. 29.95 *(978-84-92480-94-4(7))* RM Verlag S.L. ESP. Dist: D.A.P./Distributed Art Pubs.

Roessingh, Carel & Plasil, Tanja, eds. Between Horse & Buggy & Four-Wheel Drive: Change & Diversity among Mennonite Settlements in Belize, Central America. 2009. (ENG.). 222p. pap. 39.95 *(978-90-8659-332-3(1))* VU Univ. Pr. NLD. Dist: Independent Pubs. Group.

Sandoval-García, Carlos. Shattering Myths on Immigration & Emigration in Costa Rica. 2010. (ENG., Illus.). 366p. 85.00 *(978-0-7391-4467-1(7))* Lexington Bks.

Sandoval García, Carlos. Shattering Myths on Immigration & Emigration in Costa Rica. 2010. *(978-0-7391-4469-5(3))* Lexington Bks.

CENTRAL AMERICA—FOREIGN RELATIONS

Calvert, Peter, ed. The Central American Security System: North-South or East-West? 2008. (ENG.). 224p. pap. 31.00 *(978-0-521-05668-7(3))* Cambridge Univ. Pr.

Inama. Eu-Cariforum Economic Partnership Agreement Central American Free. 2010. (Illus.). xxiii, 264p. *(978-90-411-3284-0(8))* Kluwer Law International.

Lopez, J. Humberto & Shankar, Rashmi. Getting the Most Out of Free Trade Agreements in Central America. 2011. 448p. ***(978-0-8213-8713-9(8))*** World Bank Pubns.

Lopez, J. Humberto & Shankar, Rashmi, eds. Getting the Most Out of Free Trade Agreements in Central America. 2011. (Directions in Development Ser.). (ENG., Illus.). 456p. pap. 39.95 *(978-0-8213-8712-2(X)*, 9780821387122) World Bank Pubns.

Matthew, Laura E. Memories of Conquest: Becoming Mexicano in Colonial Guatemala. 2012. (ENG., Illus.). 320p. 45.00 ***(978-0-8078-3537-1(4))*** Univ. of North Carolina Pr.

Meacham, Carl Elliott. Losing Jobs & Alienating Friends: The Consequences of Falling Behind on Free Trade with Colombia & Panama: A Report to the Members of the Committee on Foreign Relations, United States Senate, One Hundred Twelfth Congress, First Session, February 8, 2011. 2011. (Illus.). vi, 18p. ***(978-0-16-087987-6(6)***, 552-070-42397-4) United States Government Printing Office.

Ojeda Gómez, Mario. Retrospección de Contadora: Los Esfuerzos de México para la Paz en Centroamérica (1983-1985) 2007. (Estudios Internacionales Ser.). (SPA.). 159p. pap. 25.99 *(978-968-12-1297-1(5))* El Colegio de México, A.C., Biblioteca Miguel Cosio Villegas MEX. Dist: Fondo de Cultura Economica USA.

Shoman, Assad. Belize's Independence & Decolonization in Latin America: Guatemala, Britain, & the UN. 2010. (Studies of the Americas Ser.). (ENG., Illus.). 272p. 89.00 *(978-0-230-62066-7(3))* Palgrave Macmillan.

CENTRAL AMERICA—FOREIGN RELATIONS—UNITED STATES

Blakeslee, George Hubbard. Mexico & the Caribbean. 2009. 256p. pap. *(978-0-217-23651-5(0))* Books LLC.

—Mexico & the Caribbean. (Clark University Addresses Ser.). 363p. reprint ed. 98.00 *(978-0-7222-9498-7(0))*; 98.00 *(978-0-7222-9454-3(9))* Library Reprints, Inc.

Blakeslee, George Hubbard, ed. Mexico & the Caribbean. 2008. 376p. pap. 33.95 *(978-1-4371-3201-4(4))* Kessinger Publishing, LLC.

Colby, Jason M. The Business of Empire: United Fruit, Race, & U. S. Expansion in Central America. 2011. (United States in the World Ser.). (Illus.). 264p. 45.00 ***(978-0-8014-4915-4(4))*** Cornell Univ. Pr.

Durham, Brian J., ed. Central America: Profiles & U. S. Relations. 2011. (Series Latin American Political, Economic, & Security Issues Ser.). 206p. 125.00 ***(978-1-61470-122-4(9))*** Nova Science Pubs., Inc.

Greentree, Todd. Crossroads of Intervention: Insurgency & Counterinsurgency Lessons from Central America, 1 vol. 2008. (Praeger Security International Ser.). (Illus.). 220p. 49.95 *(978-0-275-99215-6(2)*, C9215, Praeger Security International) Greenwood Publishing Group, Inc.

Lynch, Edward. The Cold War's Last Battlefield: Reagan, the Soviets, & Central America. 2011. 356p. 85.00 ***(978-1-4384-3949-5(0)***, Suny Pr.) State Univ. of New York Pr.

Munro, Dana Gardner. The Five Republics of Central America: Their Political & Economic Development & Their Relation with the United States. (Carnegie Endowment for International Peace Ser.). 332p. reprint ed. 98.00 *(978-0-7222-9482-6(4))* Library Reprints, Inc.

Rosenberg, Mark, et al. The United States & Central America: Geopolitical Realities & Regional Fragility. 2007. (Illus.). 128p. 143.00 *(978-0-415-95834-9(2))* Routledge.

Solis, Luis G., et al. The United States & Central America: Geopolitical Realities & Regional Fragility. 2007. (ENG., Illus.). 152p. per. 43.95 *(978-0-415-95835-6(0))* Routledge.

CENTRAL AMERICA—GUIDEBOOKS

Arghiris, Richard. Central America Footprint Handbook. 19th ed. 2012. (Footprint - Handbooks Ser.). (ENG., Illus.). 1040p. 27.95 *(978-1-907263-47-7(0))* Footprint Handbooks GBR. Dist: Globe Pequot Pr., The.

Argueta, Al. Guatemala's Western Highlands: Including Chichicastenango & Lake Atitlan. 2009. (Moon Spotlight Ser.). (ENG.). 80p. pap. 7.95 *(978-1-59880-266-5(6))* Avalon Travel Publishing.

Butler, G. Paul & Butler, Erica. Butlers' Caribbean & Central America & the Bahamas & Bermud. 2011. 460p. 57.95 ***(978-1-258-06801-1(X))*** Literary Licensing, LLC.

Central America. (Cartographia International Road Map Ser.). *(978-963-352-932-4(8)*, 6933) Cartographia Kft.

Central America. pap. 11.95 *(978-3-8283-0096-5(0))* Hallwag Verlag GmbH DEU Dist: Rand McNally.

Colas, Antony & Sutherland, Bruce. Central America & the Caribbean. 2010. (ENG., Illus.). 120p. pap. 19.95 *(978-0-9562455-0-2(1))* Wilderness Pr.

Fodor's Travel Publications, Inc. Staff. Central America. Taplin, Adam et al, eds. 3rd rev. ed. 2008. (Fodor's Gold Guides). (ENG., Illus.). 640p. pap. 22.95 *(978-1-4000-1908-3(7))* Fodor's Travel Pubns.

Greenspan, Eliot, et al. Frommer's Central America. 2nd ed. 2011. (Frommer's Complete Guides: 927). (ENG., Illus.). 768p. pap. 25.99 *(978-0-470-90346-9(5)*, Frommers) Wiley, John & Sons, Inc.

Harvard Student Agencies Inc. Staff. Let's Go Central America: The Student Travel Guide. 2009. (Let's Go Ser.). (ENG., Illus.). 656p. pap. 21.95 *(978-1-59880-296-2(8)*, Let's Go) Avalon Travel Publishing.

Insight Gd. Belize. 4th rev. ed. 2008. (Insight Guides). (ENG.). 341p. pap. 23.95 *(978-981-258-995-8(3))* APA Publications Services SGP. Dist: Ingram Pub. Services.

Lonely Planet Staff. Central & South America. 2nd rev. ed. 2008. (Healthy Travel Ser.). (ENG., Illus.). 456p. pap. 8.99 *(978-1-74059-146-1(1))* Lonely Planet Pubns.

Lonely Planet Staff, et al. Central America on a Shoestring. 7th rev. ed. 2010. (Shoestring Ser.). (ENG., Illus.). 776p. pap. 25.99 *(978-1-74179-147-1(2))* Lonely Planet Pubns.

Lougheed, Vivien. Adventure Guide: Belize. 6th ed. 2007. (Adventure Guide to Belize Ser.). (Illus.). 576p. pap. 22.99 *(978-1-58843-590-3(3))* Hunter Publishing, Inc.

Rough, Guides. The Rough Guide to Central America on a Budget. 2nd ed. 2011. (ENG., Illus.). 704p. 26.99 *(978-1-4053-8227-4(9))* Rough Guides, Ltd. GBR. Dist: Dorling Kindersley Publishing, Inc.

Streeter, Michael. Central America & the Treaty of Versailles: The Peace Conferences of 1919-23 & Their Aftermath. 2011. (Makers of the Modern World Ser.). (ENG., Illus.). 220p. 19.95 *(978-1-906598-25-9(8))* Haus Publishing GBR. Dist: Consortium Bk. Sales & Distribution.

Tips for Travelers to Central & South America. 24p. pap. *(978-0-16-061923-6(8)*, State Dept.) United States Government Printing Office.

CENTRAL AMERICA—HISTORY

Argueta, Jose Maria. Enlightened Dissent: A Leadership Methodology for Peace Building. 2008. 68p. per. 11.95 *(978-1-59594-227-2(0))* WingSpan Publishing.

Bancroft, Hubert Howe. History of Central America. 2009. 678p. pap. *(978-1-150-26239-5(7))*; 522p. pap. *(978-0-217-48822-8(6))*; 568p. pap. *(978-0-217-48828-0(5))*; 632p. pap. *(978-0-217-00504-3(7))* Books LLC.

—History of the Pacific States of North America. 2009. 654p. pap. *(978-0-217-00580-7(2))*; 558p. pap. *(978-0-217-00586-9(1))*; 710p. pap. *(978-0-217-22513-7(6))*; 558p. pap. *(978-0-217-22516-8(0))*; 618p. pap. *(978-0-217-00574-6(8))*; 630p. pap. *(978-0-217-00570-8(5))*; 514p. pap. *(978-0-217-00564-7(0))*; 540p. pap. *(978-0-217-93256-1(8))*; 628p. pap. *(978-0-217-93268-4(1))*; 550p. pap. *(978-0-217-93272-1(X))*; 566p. pap. *(978-0-217-95996-4(2))*; 556p. pap. *(978-0-217-69970-9(7))* Books LLC.

—History of the Pacific States of North America. 2009. 612p. pap. 38.14 *(978-0-217-95991-9(1))* General Bks. LLC.

—History of the Pacific States of North America, 34 vol., set. reprint ed. 4250.00 *(978-0-7222-7072-1(0))* Library Reprints, Inc.

Booth, John A., et al. Understanding Central America: Global Forces, Rebellion, & Change. 5th ed. 2009. (ENG.). 360p. (C). pap. 35.00 *(978-0-8133-4421-8(2))* Westview Pr.

Chapman, Peter. Bananas: How the United Fruit Company Shaped the World. 2009. (ENG.). 240p. pap. 14.00 *(978-1-84767-194-3(2))* Canongate Bks. GBR. Dist: Perseus-PGW.

Colby, Jason M. The Business of Empire: United Fruit, Race, & U. S. Expansion in Central America. 2011. (United States in the World Ser.). (Illus.). 264p. 45.00 ***(978-0-8014-4915-4(4))*** Cornell Univ. Pr.

Cortès, Hernàn. Fifth Letter of Hernan Cortes to the Emperor Charles V: Containing an Account of his Expedition to Honduras. Gayangos, Pascual de, tr. 2010. (Cambridge Library Collection - Hakluyt First Ser.). (ENG.). 180p. pap. 19.99 *(978-1-108-01344-4(9))* Cambridge Univ. Pr.

Domville-Fife, Charles William. Guatemala & the States of Central America. 310p. reprint ed. 98.00 *(978-0-7222-9487-1(5))* Library Reprints, Inc.

Durham, Brian J., ed. Central America: Profiles & U. S. Relations. 2011. (Series Latin American Political, Economic, & Security Issues Ser.). 206p. 125.00 ***(978-1-61470-122-4(9))*** Nova Science Pubs., Inc.

Dym, Jordana & Belaubre, Christophe, eds. Politics, Economy, & Society in Bourbon Central America, 1759-1821. 2007. (ENG., Illus.). 310p. 65.00 *(978-0-87081-844-8(9))* Univ. Pr. of Colorado.

Foster, Lynn V. A Brief History of Central America. 2nd rev. ed. 2007. (Brief History Ser.). (Illus.). 352p. (C). (gr. 9). 49.50 *(978-0-8160-6671-1(X)*, Checkmark Bks.) Facts On File, Inc.

Gradwohl, Judith & Greenberg, Russell. Natural Resource Management Set. 2009. (Earthscan Library Collection). (ENG.). 4724p. 1780.00 *(978-1-84971-011-4(2))* Routledge.

Grube, Nikolai, ed. Maya: Divine Kings of the Rainforest. 2008. (Illus.). 479p. 49.95 *(978-0-8416-0095-9(3))* American Map Corp.

Harmon, Russell S., ed. The Rio Chagres, Panama: A Multidisciplinary Profile of a Tropical Watershed. 2010. (Water Science & Technology Library). xviii, 354p. pap. 195.00 *(978-90-481-6832-3(5)*, 9048168325) Springer.

Hawkins, Timothy P. Jose de Bustamante & Central American Independence: Colonial Administration in an Age of Imperial Crisis. 2011. (Atlantic Crossings Ser.). (ENG., Illus.). 312p. pap. 29.95 ***(978-0-8173-5710-8(6))*** Univ. of Alabama Pr.

James, N. Aztecs & Maya: The Origins & Legacy of Central America's Ancient Civilisations. 2010. (ENG., Illus.). 208p. pap. 24.95 *(978-0-7524-5428-3(5))* History Pr. Ltd., The GBR. Dist: Independent Pubs. Group.

King, Matthew W. Political Ecology of Mangroves in Southern Honduras. 2009. 412p. pap. *(978-3-639-20264-9(3))* VDM Verlag Dr. Mueller e.K.

Lohse, Jon C. & Valdez, Fred, Jr., eds. Ancient Maya Commoners. 2010. (ENG., Illus.). 311p. pap. 30.00 *(978-0-292-72610-9(4))* Univ. of Texas Pr.

Macpherson, Anne S. From Colony to Nation: Women Activists & the Gendering of Politics in Belize, 1912-1982. 2009. (Engendering Latin America Ser.). (ENG., Illus.). 408p. pap. 24.95 *(978-0-8032-2492-6(3))* Univ. of Nebraska Pr.

Macpherson, Anne S. & Rich, Jeremy. From Colony to Nation: Women Activists & the Gendering of Politics in Belize, 1912-1982. 2007. (Engendering Latin America Ser.). (ENG., Illus.). 408p. 24.95 *(978-0-8032-3242-6(X))* Univ. of Nebraska Pr.

Murray, Sonia, compiled by. The First Parish Register of Belize, 1794-1810, & the First Four Censuses, 1813-1826. 2010. 292p. pap. 29.50 *(978-0-8063-5482-8(8))* Clearfield Co.

Rodríguez, Ana Patricia. Dividing the Isthmus: Central American Transnational Histories, Literatures, & Cultures. (ENG., Illus.). 308p. 2010. pap. 30.00 *(978-0-292-72348-1(2))* 2009. 55.00 *(978-0-292-71909-5(4))* Univ. of Texas Pr.

Routledge, creator. South America, Central America & the Caribbean. 16th rev. ed. 2007. (Europa Regional Surveys of the World Ser.). (Illus.). 1103p. 720.00 *(978-1-85743-432-3(3))* Routledge.

Saunders, Nicholas J. Ancient Americas: Maya, Aztec, Inca & Beyond. 2006. (ENG., Illus.). 256p. per. 19.95 *(978-0-7509-3341-4(0))* History Pr. Ltd., The GBR. Dist: Independent Pubs. Group.

Shoman, Assad. Belize's Independence & Decolonization in Latin America: Guatemala, Britain, & the UN. 2010. (Studies of the Americas Ser.). (ENG., Illus.). 272p. 89.00 *(978-0-230-62066-7(3))* Palgrave Macmillan.

Stevens, Henry, ed. The New Laws of the Indies for the Good Treatment & Preservation of the Indians. (Illus.). reprint ed. 52.50 *(978-0-404-06159-3(1))* AMS Pr., Inc.

Tsouras, Peter G. Warlords of the Ancient Americas: Central America. (Illus.). 256p. pap. 17.95 *(978-1-85409-474-2(2))* Arms & Armour Pr. GBR. Dist: Sterling Publishing Co., Inc.

Vail, Gabrielle & Hernández, Christine, eds. Astronomers, Scribes, & Priests: Intellectual Interchange Between the Northern Maya Lowlands & Highland Mexico in the Late Postclassic Period. 2010. (Dumbarton Oaks Other Titles in Pre-Columbian Studies). (Illus.). 300p. 49.95 *(978-0-88402-346-3(X))* Dumbarton Oaks.

Weeks, John M. The Carnegie Maya III: Carnegie Institution of Washington Notes on Middle American Archaeology & Ethnology, 1940-1957. 2011. E-Book *(978-1-60732-061-6(4))* Univ. Pr. of Colorado.

Woodward, Ralph Lee, Jr. Rafael Carrera & the Emergence of the Republic of Guatemala, 1821-1871. 2008. (ENG., Illus.). 648p. pap. 34.95 *(978-0-8203-3065-5(5))* Univ. of Georgia Pr.

CENTRAL AMERICA—MAPS

Argueta, Al. Guatemala's Western Highlands: Including Chichicastenango & Lake Atitlan. 2009. (Moon Spotlight Ser.). (ENG.). 80p. pap. 7.95 *(978-1-59880-266-5(6))* Avalon Travel Publishing.

Hunt, Norman Bancroft. Historical Atlas of Ancient America. 2009. (Illus.). 192p. 25.00 *(978-1-904668-11-4(9))* Mercury Bks. Ltd. GBR. Dist: International Publishers Marketing.

CENTRAL AMERICA—POLITICS AND GOVERNMENT

Ajenjo, Natalia. Legislative Procedures & Lawmaking in Central Americ. 2008. 204p. pap. *(978-3-639-07270-9(7))* VDM Verlag Dr. Mueller e.K.

Argueta, Jose Maria. Enlightened Dissent: A Leadership Methodology for Peace Building. 2008. 68p. per. 11.95 *(978-1-59594-227-2(0))* WingSpan Publishing.

Baracco, Luciano, ed. National Integration & Contested Autonomy: The Caribbean Coast of Nicaragua. 2011. 252p. pap. 33.95 *(978-0-87586-823-3(1))*; pap. 23.95 *(978-0-87586-822-6(3))* Algora Publishing.

Berger, Erica M. South & Central America: Economic, Political & Social Issues. 2011. (Series: Latin American Political, Economic, & Security Issues Ser.). 195.00 *(978-1-61122-551-8(5))* Nova Science Pubs., Inc.

Bruneau, Thomas, et al. Maras: Gang Violence & Security in Central America. 2011. (ENG., Illus.). 319p. pap. 24.95 *(978-0-292-72928-5(6))* Univ. of Texas Pr.

Bruneau, Thomas C., et al. Maras: Gang Violence & Security in Central America. 2011. (Illus.). viii, 309p. E-Book ***(978-0-292-73534-7(0))*** Univ. of Texas Pr.

Central America: Peace Plan. pap. *(978-0-660-15238-7(X))* Canadian Government Publishing.

Central America Peace. pap. *(978-0-660-16762-6(X))* Canadian Government Publishing.

Colburn, Forrest D. & Cruz S., Arturo J. Varieties of Liberalism in Central America: Nation-States as Works in Progress. 2007. (ENG., Illus.). 136p. (C). 45.00 *(978-0-292-71720-6(2))*; pap. 17.95 *(978-0-292-71721-3(0))* Univ. of Texas Pr.

C

Cucinotta, Vincenzo, ed. Politics & Economics of South & Central America. 2011. (Latin American Political, Economic, & Security Issues Ser.). 185.00 (978-1-61470-446-1(5)) Nova Science Pubs., Inc.

Dym, Jordana & Belaubre, Christophe, eds. Politics, Economy, & Society in Bourbon Central America, 1759-1821. 2007. (ENG., Illus.). 310p. 65.00 (978-0-87081-844-8(9)) Univ. Pr. of Colorado.

Employment Law Client Strategies in Central & South America: Leading Lawyers on Understanding Regional Differences, Addressing Client Compliance Needs, & Responding to New Trends (Inside the Minds) 2009. 172p. pap. 90.00 (978-0-314-22933-5(7)) Aspatore Bks.

Grant, C. H. The Making of Modern Belize: Politics, Society & British Colonialism in Central America. 2008. (Cambridge Commonwealth Ser.). (ENG.). 424p. pap. 53.00 (978-0-521-10141-7(7)) Cambridge Univ. Pr.

Greentree, Todd. Crossroads of Intervention. 2009. 0224p. pap. 21.95 (978-1-59114-343-7(8)) Naval Institute Pr.

—Crossroads of Intervention: Insurgency & Counterinsurgency Lessons from Central America, 1 vol. 2008. (Praeger Security International Ser.). (Illus.). 220p. 49.95 (978-0-275-99215-6(2), C9215, Praeger Security International) Greenwood Publishing Group, Inc.

Kruijt, Dirk. Guerrillas: War & Peace in Central America. 2008. (ENG., Illus.). 192p. 99.00 (978-1-84277-738-1(6)); 272p. pap. 32.00 (978-1-84277-739-8(4)) Zed Bks., Ltd. GBR. Dist: Macmillan.

Leguineche, M. Sobre el Volcan (Over the Volcano) (SPA., Illus.). 288p. 8.95 (978-84-01-33268-5(0)) Plaza & Janes Editores, S.A. ESP. Dist: AIMS International Bks., Inc.

Lehoucq, Fabrice. The Politics of Modern Central America: Civil War, Democratization, & Underdevelopment. 2012. (ENG., Illus.). 250p. (C). 90.00 (978-0-521-51506-1(8)); pap. 27.99 (978-0-521-73079-2(1)) Cambridge Univ. Pr.

Morazzoni, Monica. Geopolitica Dell'America Centrale: Le Inquietudini, L'eredità, il Futuro. 2010. (ITA., Illus.). 222p. (978-88-89891-42-1(4)) Archetipo Libri.

Munro, Dana Gardner. The Five Republics of Central America: Their Political & Economic Development & Their Relation with the United States. (Carnegie Endowment for Internation Peace Ser.). 332p. reprint ed. 98.00 (978-0-7222-9482-6(4)) Library Reprints, Inc.

Nicholls, Jane A., ed. Economics & Politics of South & Central America. 2011. (Politics & Economics of Latin America Ser.). 162p. 89.00 (978-1-61209-780-0(4)) Nova Science Pubs., Inc.

North & Central America Business & Political Handbook. (Illus.). 600p. (Orig.). pap. 2400.00 (978-0-7605-1333-0(3)) Rector Pr., Ltd.

Pssbo, Heiko. Great Power's Dependency Policies in a Geostrategic Subregion. 2009. 124p. pap. (978-3-639-16331-5(1)) VDM Verlag Dr. Mueller e.K.

Roniger, Luis. Transnational Politics in Central America. 2011. (ENG., Illus.). 224p. 74.95 (978-0-8130-3663-2(1)) Univ. Pr. of Florida.

Saint-Germain, Michelle A. & Metoyer, Cynthia Chavez. Women Legislators in Central America: Politics, Democracy, & Policy. 2008. (ENG., Illus.). 356p. pap. 30.00 (978-0-292-71717-6(2)) Univ. of Texas Pr.

Sánchez Sánchez, Rafael A. The Politics of Central American Integration. 2012. (ENG., Illus.). 248p. pap. 42.95 (978-0-415-62159-5(3)) Routledge.

Schatan, Claudia & Rivera, Eugenio. Competition Policies in Emerging Economies: Lessons & Challenges from Central America & Mexico. 2008. (Illus.). xii, 238p. pap. 15.00 (978-0-387-78434-2(9)) Springer.

Schneider, Aaron. State-Building & Tax Regimes in Central America. 2012. (ENG., Illus.). 264p. 90.00 (978-1-107-01909-6(5)) Cambridge Univ. Pr.

Tax Law Client Strategies in Central & South America: Leading Lawyers on Navigating Regional Tax Laws, Assisting Clients with Compliance Challenges, & Understanding Recent Legal Developments (Inside the Minds) 2009. 288p. pap. 95.00 (978-0-314-22619-8(2)) Aspatore Bks.

Urrutia, Eugenio Rivera. Competition Policies in Emerging Economies: Lessons & Challenges from Central America & Mexico. Schatan, Claudia, ed. 2008. (ENG., Illus.). xii, 244p. 109.00 (978-0-387-78432-8(2), 0387784322) Springer.

Wainwright, Joel. Decolonizing Development: Colonial Power & the Maya. 2008. (Antipode Book Ser.). (ENG., Illus.). 328p. pap. 40.95 (978-1-4051-5706-3(2)); 94.95 (978-1-4051-5705-6(4)) Wiley, John & Sons, Inc. (Wiley-Blackwell).

CENTRAL AMERICA—RELIGION

Johnson, Paul Christopher. Diaspora Conversions: Black Carib Religion & the Recovery of Africa. 2007. (Illus.). 330p. 65.00 (978-0-520-24969-1(0)); per. 28.95 (978-0-520-24970-7(4)) Univ. of California Pr.

Maggiore, Jacqueline Hansen & Vint, Catherine McDermott. Vessel of Clay: The Inspirational Journey of Sister Carla. 2010. (University of Scranton Press - Peace, Justice, Human Rights, & Freedom in Lati Ser.). (Illus.). 171p. pap. 18.00 (978-1-58966-217-9(2)) Univ. of Scranton Pr.

Mexico & Central America: A Tapestry of Triumph. 2008. 88p. pap. 7.99 (978-0-8341-2348-9(7), 083-412-3487) Beacon Hill Pr. of Kansas City.

Mulligan, Joseph E. S. J. The Jesuit Martyrs of el Salvador: Celebrating the Anniversaries. 2010. (Catholic Worker Reprint Ser.). 196p. pap. 21.00 (978-1-60899-056-6(7), Wipf and Stock) Wipf & Stock Pubs.

O'Neill, Kevin. City of God: Christian Citizenship in Postwar Guatemala. 2009. (Anthropology of Christianity Ser.). (ENG.). 312p. 55.00 (978-0-520-26062-7(7)); pap. 24.95 (978-0-520-26063-4(5)) Univ. of California Pr.

Prechtel, Martin. The Unlikely Peace at Cuchumaquic: The Parallel Lives of People As Plants - Keeping the Seeds Alive. 2012. (ENG., Illus.). 476p. 24.95 (978-1-58394-360-1(9)) North Atlantic Bks.

Roessingh, Carel & Plasil, Tanja, eds. Between Horse & Buggy & Four-Wheel Drive: Change & Diversity among Mennonite Settlements in Belize, Central America. 2009. (ENG.). 222p. pap. 39.95 (978-90-8659-332-3(1)) VU Univ. Pr. NLD. Dist: Independent Pubs. Group.

Scott, Blake C. The Crossroads of Religion & Development. 2011. 96p. pap. (978-3-8443-1497-7(0)) Lambert Academic Publishing.

Smith, Calvin L. Revolution, Revival, & Religious Conflict in Sandinista Nicaragua. 2007. (Religion in the Americas Ser.). 312p. pap. (978-90-04-15645-6(3)) BRILL.

Tompkins, Ptolemy. This Tree Grows Out of Hell: Mesoamerica & the Search for the Magical Body. 2008. (Living Planet Book Ser.). (ENG.). 240p. per. 14.95 (978-1-4027-4882-0(5)) Sterling Publishing Co., Inc.

Wasson, Gordon. The Wondrous Mushroom: Sacred Mushrooms in Mexico & Mesoamerica. 2007. (Illus.). 304p. pap. 18.95 (978-0-87286-484-9(7)) City Lights Bks.

CENTRAL AMERICA—SOCIAL CONDITIONS

Alexander, Robert J. A History of Organized Labor in Panama & Central America, 1 vol. 2008. 320p. 140.00 (978-0-275-97740-5(4), C7740, Praeger Pubs.) Greenwood Publishing Group, Inc.

Anderson, Mark. Black & Indigenous: Garifuna Activism & Consumer Culture in Honduras. 2009. (ENG., Illus.). 304p. 75.00 (978-0-8166-6101-5(4)); pap. 25.00 (978-0-8166-6102-2(2)) Univ. of Minnesota Pr.

Babiadelis, Paul. Developing Institutional Options for Watershed Management - the Sixaola Binational Watershed and. 2008. 276p. pap. (978-3-8364-6312-6(1)) VDM Verlag Dr. Mueller e.K.

Berger, Erica M. South & Central America: Economic, Political & Social Issues. 2011. (Series: Latin American Political, Economic, & Security Issues Ser.). 195.00 (978-1-61122-551-8(5)) Nova Science Pubs., Inc.

Cecil, Leslie & Pugh, Timothy W., eds. Maya Worldviews at Conquest. 2009. (Mesoamerican Worlds Ser.). (ENG., Illus.). 432p. 65.00 (978-0-87081-945-2(3)) Univ. Pr. of Colorado.

Central America: Peace Plan. pap. (978-0-660-15238-7(X)) Canadian Government Publishing.

Central America Peace. pap. (978-0-660-16762-6(X)) Canadian Government Publishing.

Chambers, Glenn Anthony. Race, Nation, & West Indian Immigration to Honduras, 1890-1940. 2010. 232p. 35.00 (978-0-8071-3557-0(7)) Louisiana State Univ. Pr.

Cortez, Beatriz & Carranza, Douglas G. Introduction to Central American Studies. rev. ed. 2008. (ENG.). 324p. pap. 74.03 (978-0-7575-5538-1(1)) Kendall Hunt Publishing Co.

Davis-Salazar, Karla, ed. Mesoamerican Ritual Economy: Archaeological & Ethnological Perspectives. 2007. (Mesoamerican Worlds Ser.). (ENG., Illus.). 336p. 70.00 (978-0-87081-871-4(6)) Univ. Pr. of Colorado.

Derose, Kathryn Pitkin, et al. The Role of Faith-Based Organizations in HIV Prevention & Care in Central America. 2010. 128p. pap. 20.00 (978-0-8330-4999-5(2)) RAND Corp., The.

Duncan, Samuel B. Implications of Climate Change in Mexico, the Caribbean & Central America. 2011. (Climate Change & its Causes, Effects & Prediction Ser.). 89.00 (978-1-61122-849-6(2)) Nova Science Pubs., Inc.

Europa Publications, ed. South America Central America & the Caribbean 2012. 20th rev. ed. 2011. (ENG.). 1148p. 880.00 (978-1-85743-619-8(9)) Routledge.

Grüttner, Peter. Neue Informations- und Kommunikationstechnologien und Traditionelle Medien in Costa Rica. 2007. (Illus.). 51p. pap. (978-3-86010-949-6(9)) Martin-Luther-Universitat Halle-Wittenberg, Universitats- und Landesbibliothek Sachsen-Anhalt.

Gudmundson, Lowell & Wolfe, Justin, eds. Blacks & Blackness in Central America: Between Race & Place. 2010. (ENG., Illus.). 416p. 89.95 (978-0-8223-4787-3(3)); pap. 24.95 (978-0-8223-4803-0(9)) Duke Univ. Pr.

Horton, Lynn R. Grassroots Struggles for Sustainability in Central America. 2007. (ENG., Illus.). 215p. 60.00 (978-0-87081-872-1(4)) Univ. Pr. of Colorado.

Kepner, Charles D. Social Aspects of the Banana Industry. (Columbia University, Studies in the Social Sciences: No. 414). reprint ed. 27.50 (978-0-404-51414-3(6)) AMS Pr., Inc.

Lewis, Colin, et al. South America, Central America & the Caribbean 2010. 18th rev. ed. 2009. (ENG.). 1136p. 810.00 (978-1-85743-525-2(7)) Routledge.

MacLeod, Murdo J. Spanish Central America: A Socioeconomic History, 1520-1720. 2nd rev. ed. 2007. (ILAS Special Publication Ser.). (ENG., Illus.). 616p. pap. 40.00 (978-0-292-71761-9(X)) Univ. of Texas Pr.

Macq, Jean. The Local Health Systems & the Care for People with Tuberculosis. 2009. 192p. pap. (978-3-639-13663-0(2)) VDM Verlag Dr. Mueller e.K.

Martin, Bruce T., photos by. Look Close, See Far: A Cultural Portrait of the Maya. 2007. (Illus.). 147p. 34.95 (978-0-8076-1589-8(7)) Braziller, George Inc.

Monroe, Hochstetler, compiled by. Life & Times in Honduras: Twenty Families Struggle in Honduras. 2007. 406p. 12.95 (978-0-9797819-0-2(6)) Hochstetler Variety.

Monteith, Michele L., ed. Transnational Gangs: The MS-13 Gang & Others. 2010. (Law, Crime & Law Enforcement Ser.). (Illus.). ix, 135p. 115.00 (978-1-61728-917-0(5)) Nova Science Pubs., Inc.

Mwakikagile, Godfrey. Belize & Its People: Life in A Multicultural Society. 2010. 222p. pap. 16.95 (978-9987-9322-1-4(5)) Continental Pr.

Pine, Adrienne. Working Hard, Drinking Hard: On Violence & Survival in Honduras. 2008. (Illus.). 272p. 50.00 (978-0-520-25543-2(7)); 253p. pap. 24.95 (978-0-520-25544-9(5)) Univ. of California Pr.

Prechtel, Martin. The Unlikely Peace at Cuchumaquic: The Parallel Lives of People As Plants - Keeping the Seeds Alive. 2012. (ENG., Illus.). 476p. 24.95 (978-1-58394-360-1(9)) North Atlantic Bks.

Quesada Pacheco, Miguel Angel. El Español Hablado en América Central: Nivel Fonético. 2010. (SPA., Illus.). 214p. pap. 36.00 (978-84-8489-498-8(3)) Iberoamericana Vervuert Publishing Corp.

Roessingh, Carel & Plasil, Tanja, eds. Between Horse & Buggy & Four-Wheel Drive: Change & Diversity among Mennonite Settlements in Belize, Central America. 2009. (ENG.). 222p. pap. 39.95 (978-90-8659-332-3(1)) VU Univ. Pr. NLD. Dist: Independent Pubs. Group.

Rubio, Mauricio. Pandillas, Rumba, y Actividad Sexual: Desmitificando la Violencia Juvenil. 2006. (SPA., Illus.). 214p. pap. 18.00 (978-958-710-158-4(8)) Universidad Externado de Colombia COL. Dist: Siglo del Hombre.

Rylander, Amalia L. The Belizean Garifuna Identity. 2011. 92p. pap. (978-3-639-29738-6(5)) VDM Verlag Dr. Mueller e.K.

Seelke, Clare Ribando. Gangs in Central America. 2010. 19p. (C). pap. 15.00 (978-1-4379-2763-4(7)) DIANE Publishing Co.

Silber, Irina Carlota. Everyday Revolutionaries: Gender, Violence, & Disillusionment in Postwar el Salvador. 2010. (Genocide, Political Violence, Human Rights Ser.). (ENG., Illus.). 288p. (C). 72.00 (978-0-8135-4934-7(5)); pap. 27.95 (978-0-8135-4935-4(3)) Rutgers Univ. Pr.

South America Central America & the Caribbean 2011. 19th rev. ed. 2010. (ENG.). 1152p. 835.00 (978-1-85743-562-7(1)) Routledge.

Tiesler, Vera & Cucina, Andrea, eds. New Perspectives on Human Sacrifice & Ritual Body Treatment in Ancient Maya Society. 2007. (Interdisciplinary Contributions to Archaeology Ser.). (ENG., Illus.). x, 322p. 199.00 (978-0-387-48870-7(7), 0387488707) Springer.

Violence in Central America: Briefing & Hearing Before the Subcommittee on the Western Hemisphere of the Committee on Foreign Affairs, House of Representatives, One Hundred Tenth Congress, First Session, June 26, 2007. 2007. (Illus.). iii, 87p. (978-0-16-079256-4(8), 552-070-36336-0) United States Government Printing Office.

Wheeler, Jacob R. Between Light & Shadow: A Guatemalan Girl's Journey Through Adoption. 2011. (ENG., Illus.). 248p. 24.95 (978-0-8032-3362-1(0)) Univ. of Nebraska Pr.

Wolseth, Jon. Jesus & the Gang: Youth Violence & Christianity in Urban Honduras. 2011. (ENG., Illus.). 176p. pap. 24.95 (978-0-8165-2908-7(6)) Univ. of Arizona Pr.

CENTRAL AMERICAN LITERATURE

Here are entered collections of literature from Central America written in Spanish or in several of the languages of Central America.

Brinton, Daniel G. The Annals of the Cakchiquels. 2009. 238p. 28.99 (978-1-110-40423-0(9)); pap. 25.75 (978-1-110-40419-3(0)) BiblioBazaar.

—The Annals of the Cakchiquels. 2007. (ENG.). 236p. 41.95 (978-0-548-09235-4(4)) Kessinger Publishing, LLC.

DeGuzmán, María. Buenas Noches, American Culture: Latina/o Aesthetics of Night. 2012. (ENG., Illus.). 310p. pap. 28.00 (978-0-253-00189-4(7), 0253001897) Indiana Univ. Pr.

CENTRAL AMERICAN LITERATURE—HISTORY AND CRITICISM

Arias, Arturo. Taking Their Word: Literature & the Signs of Central America. 2007. 304p. 67.50 (978-0-8166-4848-1(4)); per. 24.50 (978-0-8166-4849-8(2)) Univ. of Minnesota Pr.

DeGuzmán, María. Buenas Noches, American Culture: Latina/o Aesthetics of Night. 2012. (ENG., Illus.). 310p. 80.00 (978-0-253-00179-5(X), 025300179X) Indiana Univ. Pr.

Litteratures Francophones d'Afrique Centrale.Tr. of Literature for French-Speaking People of Central Africa. (FRE.). pap. (978-2-09-882403-4(3)) Editions Rouge et Or.

Niblett, Michael & Oloff, Kerstin, eds. Perspectives on the 'Other America' Comparative Approaches to Caribbean & Latin American Culture. 2009. (Illus.). 272p. pap. 78.00 (978-90-420-2704-6(5)) Rodopi.

Rodríguez, Ana Patricia. Dividing the Isthmus: Central American Transnational Histories, Literatures, & Cultures. (ENG., Illus.). 308p. 2010. pap. 30.00 (978-0-292-72348-1(2)) 2009. 55.00 (978-0-292-71909-5(4)) Univ. of Texas Pr.

CENTRAL ASIA

see Asia, Central

CENTRAL ASIATIC JOURNAL

Index to the Table of Contents of the Central Asiatic Journal. (978-0-911706-02-4(X)) Mongolia Society, Inc., The.

CENTRAL ASIAN QUESTION

see Eastern Question (Central Asia)

CENTRAL BANKS

see Banks and Banking, Central

CENTRAL BUSINESS DISTRICTS

American Map Staff. Map-Philadelphia PA City Slicker. 2010. 8.99 (978-0-8416-8843-8(5)) American Map Corp.

Bronsky, Eric & Samors, Neal. Downtown Chicago in Transition. 2007. (Illus.). 256p. 39.50 (978-0-9797892-0-5(6), Chicago's Bks. Pr.) Chicago's Neighborhoods, Inc.

Cancienne, Henry, photos by. Main Streets of Louisiana. 2012. 35.00 (978-1-935754-12-1(2)) Univ. of Louisiana at Lafayette Pr.

Crabb, Guy. San Luis Obispo: 100 Years of Downtown Businesses: Higuera Street. 2007. (Illus.). 108p. pap. (978-0-9790616-0-8(1)) Crabb, Guy.

Crankshaw, Ned. Creating Vibrant Public Spaces: Streetscape Design in Commercial & Historic Districts. 2nd ed. 2008. (ENG.). 240p. pap. 35.00 (978-1-59726-483-9(0)); (Illus.). 238p. 70.00 (978-1-59726-482-2(2)) Island Pr.

Davies, Ross. Marketing Geography (RLE Retailing & Distribution) With special reference to Retailing. 2012. (Routledge Library Editions Ser.). (ENG.). 316p. 115.00 (978-0-415-54030-8(5)) Routledge.

English, D. N. Downtown Wanderings Memories & More. 2006. (Illus.). 206p. pap. 18.00 (978-0-9760414-2-9(1)) Main St Publishing, Inc.

Feit, Marvin D. Making Business Districts Work: Leadership & Management of Downtown, Main Street, Business District, & Community Development Organizations. Feehan, David, ed. 2006. (ENG., Illus.). 472p. 115.00 (978-0-7890-2390-2(3)); pap. 59.95 (978-0-7890-2391-9(1)) Routledge.

Groarke, Leo. Reinventing Brantford: A University Comes Downtown. 2009. (ENG., Illus.). 288p. pap. 30.00 (978-1-55488-459-9(4)) Dundurn CAN. Dist: Ingram Pub. Services.

Helbrecht, Ilse & Dirksmeier, Peter. New Urbanism: Life Work & Space in the New Downtown. 2012. (Design & the Built Environment Ser.). (Illus.). 190p. 99.95 (978-1-4094-3136-7(3)) Ashgate Publishing Co.

Hinshaw, Mark L. True Urbanism: Living in & near the Center. 2007. (Illus.). (ENG.). 224p. per. 53.95 (978-1-932364-27-9(7)); xiii, 225p. (978-1-932364-28-6(5)) American Planning Assn.

Kreis, Karen. Housing: Life Downtown A Strategy to Encourage Market-Rate Housing in Calgary's Downtown Core. 2008. 220p. pap. (978-3-639-07384-3(3)) VDM Verlag Dr. Mueller e.K.

Lancaster, Adelaide & Abrams, Amy. The Big Enough Company: Creating a Business That Works for You. 2011. (ENG.). 288p. (gr. 12). 25.95 (978-1-59184-421-1(5), Portfolio (Hardcover)) Penguin Group (USA) Inc.

Map Easy Staff & Other Publisher Map Staff. Map Map Easy Dallas Tx. 2011. 7.95 (978-1-929038-29-9(1)) Mapeasy, Inc.

MapEasy Inc Staff. Chicago Mini Map. 2009. 6.95 (978-1-878979-39-1(6)) Mapeasy, Inc.

—Washington Dc Mini Map. 2009. 6.95 (978-1-878979-32-2(9)) Mapeasy, Inc.

Martí, Néstor. Old Havana - La Habana Vieja: Spirit of the Living City - El Espíritu de la Ciudad Viva. 2012. (SPA & ENG.). 228p. 49.95 (978-0-8173-1762-1(7)) Univ. of Alabama Pr.

McCoy, Jerry A., et al. Downtown Silver Spring. 2010. (Then & Now Ser.). (Illus.). 96p. pap. 21.99 (978-0-7385-8631-1(5)) Arcadia Publishing.

McDonogh, Gary & Peterson, Marina, eds. Global Downtowns. 2011. (City in the Twenty-First Century Ser.). (Illus.). 368p. (C). 59.95 (978-0-8122-4384-0(6)) Univ. of Pennsylvania Pr.

Mitchell, Jerry. Business Improvement Districts & the Shape of American Cities. (SUNY Series in Urban Public Policy Ser.). 2009. 160p. pap. 24.95 (978-0-7914-7310-8(4)) 2008. 152p. 55.00 (978-0-7914-7309-2(0)) State Univ. of New York Pr.

Morcol, Goktug, et al. Business Improvement Districts: Research, Theories, & Controversies. 2008. (Public Administration & Public Policy Ser.). (ENG., Illus.). 544p. 109.95 (978-1-4200-4576-5(8)) Auerbach Pubs., Inc.

Murad, Paul. Manhattanizing Las Vegas. 2008. pap. 24.95 (978-0-9769531-3-5(7)) Lotus Pr.

Murphy, Raymond E. & Murphy, Raymond. The Central Business District: A Study in Urban Geography. 2007. (ENG., Illus.). 199p. pap. 21.95 (978-0-202-30958-3(4)) Aldine Transaction.

Oakman, Jonathan, ed. New Downtowns: The Future of Urban Centers. 2006. (ENG.). 112p. pap. 11.95 (978-0-9778531-5-1(2)) Policy Research Institute for the Region.

Robl, Marion. Das beschleunigte Verfahren für Bebauungspläne der Innenentwicklung: Ein Aspekt des Innenstadtentwicklungsgesetzes (BauGB 2007) 2010. (Regensburger Beiträge zum Staats- und Verwaltungsrecht Ser.). (GER.). 684p. 149.95 (978-3-631-60014-6(3)) Lang, Peter GmbH, Europaischer Verlag der Wissenschaften DEU. Dist: Lang, Peter.

Walking Guide of Historic Carlisle Pennsylvania. (978-0-9638923-7-9(1)) Cumberland County Historical Society.

CENTRAL CITIES

see Inner Cities

CENTRAL CITY (COLO.)

Central City Opera House Association (Central City, Colo.) Staff, contrib. by. Theatre of Dreams: Celebrating 75 Years: the Glorious Central City Opera. 2007. 65.00 (978-0-9788306-0-1(1)) Central City Opera Hse. Assn.

CENTRAL EUROPE

see Europe, Central

CENTRAL HEATING PLANTS

see Heating From Central Stations

CENTRAL-LOCAL GOVERNMENT RELATIONS

Here are entered works on the division of powers between the central government and state or provincial and local governments in non-federal systems. Works on the division of powers between central government and state or provincial and local governments in federal systems are entered under Federal Government. Works on the division of powers between the executive, legislative, and judicial branches of government are entered under Separation of Powers.

see also Decentralization in Government; Federal Government

Agranoff, Robert. Local Governments & Their Intergovernmental Networks in Federalizing Spain. 2010. 360p. (C). (ENG.). pap. *(978-0-7735-3623-4(X))*; (Illus.). *(978-0-7735-3616-6(7))* McGill-Queen's Univ. Pr.

Bache, Ian. Europeanization & Multilevel Governance. 2007. (Governance in Europe Ser.). (ENG., Illus.). 206p. per. 35.95 *(978-0-7425-4133-7(9))* Rowman & Littlefield Publishers, Inc.

—Europeanization & Multilevel Governance: Cohesion Policy in the European Union & Britain. 2007. (Governance in Europe Ser.). (ENG., Illus.). 206p. 85.00 *(978-0-7425-4132-0(0))* Rowman & Littlefield Publishers, Inc.

Bergh, Andreas & Hoijer, Rolf, eds. Institutional Competition. 2008. (New Thinking in Political Economy Ser.). (Illus.). 288p. (C). 137.00 *(978-1-84720-669-5(7))* Elgar, Edward Publishing, Inc.

Blindenbacher, Raoul & Pasma, Chandra. Dialogues on Local Government & Metropolitan Regions in Federal Countries. 2007. (Global Dialogue on Federalism Booklet Ser.). (ENG., Illus.). 80p. (C). per. *(978-0-7735-3319-6(2))* McGill-Queen's Univ. Pr.

Brancati, Dawn. Peace by Design: Managing Intrastate Conflict through Decentralization. 320p. 2011. (ENG.). pap. 35.00 *(978-0-19-958744-5(2))* 2009. (Illus.). 99.00 *(978-0-19-954900-9(1))* Oxford Univ. Pr., Inc.

Buur, Lars & Kyed, Helene Maria. State Recognition & Democratization in Sub-Saharan Africa: A New Dawn for Traditional Authorities? 2007. (Governance, Security & Development Ser.). (ENG.). 256p. 95.00 *(978-0-230-60033-1(6))* Palgrave Macmillan.

Chattopadhyay, Rupak. Dialogues on Political Parties & Civil Society in Federal Countries. 2011. (Global Dialogue on Federalism Booklet Ser.). (ENG.). 60p. (C). pap. *(978-0-7735-3740-8(6))* McGill-Queen's Univ. Pr.

Chebankova, Elena. Russia's Federal Relations. 2010. (BASEES/Routledge Series on Russian & East European Studies). (ENG., Illus.). 256p. (C). 140.00 *(978-0-415-55961-4(8))* Routledge.

Colombo, Alessandro, ed. Subsidiarity Governance: Theoretical & Empirical Models. 2012. (ENG., Illus.). 196p. 85.00 ***(978-0-230-33869-2(0))*** Palgrave Macmillan.

Crossley & Crossley, Pamela Kyle. The Wobbling Pivot, China since 1800: An Interpretive History. 2010. (Wiley Desktop Editions Ser.). (ENG., Illus.). 328p. pap. 35.95 *(978-1-4051-6080-3(2)*, Wiley-Blackwell) Wiley, John & Sons, Inc.

Crossley, Pamela Kyle. The Wobbling Pivot, China since 1800: An Interpretive History. 2010. (ENG., Illus.). 328p. 99.95 *(978-1-4051-6079-7(9)*, Wiley-Blackwell) Wiley, John & Sons, Inc.

Diamond, John, et al, eds. Managing the City. (Illus.). 208p. 2007. 175.00 *(978-0-415-38257-1(2))* 2006. per. 58.95 *(978-0-415-38258-8(0))* Routledge.

Dickovick, J. Tyler. Decentralization & Recentralization in the Developing World: Comparative Studies from Africa & Latin America. 2011. (ENG.). 232p. 64.95 *(978-0-271-03790-5(3))* Pennsylvania State Univ. Pr.

Erb, Maribeth. Regionalism in Post-Suharto Indonesia. 2009. 236p. pap. 39.95 *(978-0-415-54602-7(8))* Routledge.

Faguet, Jean-Paul. Decentralization & Popular Democracy: Governance from below in Bolivia. 2012. (ENG.). 352p. 85.00 ***(978-0-472-11819-9(6))*** Univ. of Michigan Pr.

Falleti, Tulia G. Decentralization & Subnational Politics in Latin America. 2010. (ENG., Illus.). 312p. 85.00 *(978-0-521-51679-2(X))*; pap. 26.99 *(978-0-521-73635-0(8))* Cambridge Univ. Pr.

Federally Induced Costs Affecting State & Local Governments. 53p. pap. 35.00 *(978-0-7881-1583-7(9))* DIANE Publishing Co.

Fein, Michael R. Paving the Way: New York Road Building & the American State, 1880-1956. 2008. (Illus.). 316p. *(978-0-7006-1562-9(8))* Univ. Pr. of Kansas.

Feiock, Richard C. & Scholz, John T., eds. Self-Organizing Federalism: Collaborative Mechanisms to Mitigate Institutional Collective Action Dilemmas. 2009. (ENG., Illus.). 368p. 93.00 *(978-0-521-76493-3(9))* Cambridge Univ. Pr.

Fleming, D. A. Politics & Provincial People: Sligo & Limerick, 1691-1761. 2010. (ENG., Illus.). 304p. 89.95 *(978-0-7190-8179-8(3))* Manchester Univ. Pr. GBR. Dist: Macmillan.

Frank, Jonas. Decentralization in Ecuador: Actors, Institutions, & Incentives. 2007. 328p. (C). pap. 83.00 *(978-3-8329-2708-0(5))* Nomos Verlagsgesellschaft DEU. Dist: International Specialized Bk. Services.

Froy, Francesca, et al. Breaking Out of Policy Silos: Doing More with Less. 2011. (ENG.). 142p. pap. 42.00 *(978-92-64-05680-0(7))* Organization for Economic Cooperation & Development.

Fuchs, Manfred. From Legislators to the End-User: Practical Difficulties of Implementing European Directives. 2011. (Illus.). 379p. pap. 59.95 ***(978-3-531-17787-8(7)***, 3531177877) VS Verlag fur Sozialwissenschaften GmbH DEU. Dist: Springer.

Gill, Graeme. Politics in the Russian Regions. Gill, Graeme, ed. 2007. (Studies in Central & Eastern Europe Ser.). (ENG., Illus.). 240p. 105.00 *(978-0-230-51686-1(6))* Palgrave Macmillan.

Goode, J. Paul. The Decline of Regionalism in Putin's Russia. 2011. (BASEES/Routledge Series on Russian & East European Studies). (ENG., Illus.). 240p. (C). 140.00 *(978-0-415-60807-7(4))* Routledge.

Graney, Katherine E. Of Khans & Kremlins: Tatarstan & the Future of Ethno-Federalism in Russia. 2009. (ENG., Illus.). 226p. 73.50 *(978-0-7391-2635-6(0))* Lexington Bks.

Graziano, Paolo. Europeanization & the Domestic Politics Change. 2012. (Europe & the Nation State Ser.). (ENG.). 224p. (C). 120.00 *(978-0-415-57491-4(9))* Routledge.

Hayward, Katy & Murphy, Mary C., eds. The Europeanization of Party Politics in Ireland, North & South. 2010. (ENG., Illus.). 224p. (C). 125.00 *(978-0-415-57991-2(4)*, Routledge) Taylor & Francis Group GBR. Dist: Taylor & Francis Group.

Hein, Carola & Pelletier, Philippe, eds. Cities, Autonomy, & Decentralization in Japan. 2009. 200p. pap. 39.95 *(978-0-415-54696-6(6))* Routledge.

Hess, David J. Localist Movements in a Global Economy: Sustainability, Justice, & Urban Development in the United States. 2009. (Urban & Industrial Environments Ser.). (ENG., Illus.). 336p. (gr. 17). 50.00 *(978-0-262-01264-5(2))*; pap. 27.00 *(978-0-262-51232-9(7))* MIT Pr.

Horak, Martin & Young, Robert A. Sites of Governance: Multilevel Governance & Policy Making in Canada's Big Cities. 2012. (Fields of Governance: Policy Making in Canadian Municipalities Ser.). (ENG.). 424p. (C). ***(978-0-7735-4001-9(6))***; pap. ***(978-0-7735-4002-6(4))*** McGill-Queen's Univ. Pr.

Jin, Ruizi. Guangdong Ren Shi Zheng Duo Liu Shi Nian: Zhong Yang He Di Fang de an Zhan. 2011. (CHI., Illus.). 398p. ***(978-1-935981-17-6(X))*** Mirror Bks. USA.

Kazepov, Yuri. Rescaling Social Policies Towards Multilevel Governance in Europe: Social Assistance, Activation & Care for Older People. 2010. (Public Policy & Social Welfare Ser.). (Illus.). 506p. pap. 89.95 *(978-1-4094-1021-8(8))* Ashgate Publishing Co.

Kiiver, Philipp. The Early Warning System for the Principle of Subsidiarity: Constitutional Theory & Empirical Reality. 2012. (Routledge Research in European Union Law Ser.). (ENG.). 184p. (C). 125.00 *(978-0-415-68522-1(2))* Routledge.

Kono, Koretaka. Chiho Kofuzei to Chiho Bunken: Local Grant Tax & Local Decentralization. 2010. (JPN., Illus.). 7p. *(978-4-419-05488-5(3))* Zeimu Keiri Kyokai.

Landry, Pierre. Decentralized Authoritarianism in China: The Communist Party's Control of Local Elites in the Post-Mao Era. 2008. (ENG., Illus.). 320p. 98.00 *(978-0-521-88235-4(4))* Cambridge Univ. Pr.

Lazar, Harvey & Leuprecht, Christian. Spheres of Governance: Comparative Studies of Cities in Multilevel Governance Systems. 2007. (Institute of Intergovernmental Relations Ser.). (FRE & ENG., Illus.). 320p. (C). pap. 29.95 *(978-1-55339-019-0(9))* Queen's Univ., Schl. of Policy Studies CAN. Dist: McGill-Queen's Univ. Pr.

—Spheres of Governance: Comparative Studies of Cities in Multilevel Governance Systems. 2007. (Institute of Intergovernmental Relations Ser.). (FRE & ENG., Illus.). 320p. (C). 95.00 *(978-1-55339-129-6(2))* Queens Univ., Institute of Intergovernmental Relations CAN. Dist: McGill-Queen's Univ. Pr.

Lim, Regina. Federal-State Relations in Sabah, Malaysia: The Berjaya Administration, 1976-85. 2008. (Illus.). x, 153p. *(978-981-230-812-2(1))* Institute of Southeast Asian Studies.

Lo, Shiu Hing. The Dynamics of Beijing-Hong Kong Relations: A Model for Taiwan? 2008. (ENG.). 344p. (gr. 17). 60.00 *(978-962-209-908-1(4))*; pap. 27.95 *(978-962-209-909-8(2))* Hong Kong Univ. Pr. HKG. Dist: Columbia Univ. Pr.

MacMillan, Ken. The Atlantic Imperial Constitution: Center & Periphery in the English Atlantic World. 2011. (ENG., Illus.). 256p. 85.00 *(978-0-230-11174-5(2))* Palgrave Macmillan.

Maksimov, Konstantin N. Kalmykia in Russia's Past & Present National Policies & Administrative System. 2008. (ENG.). 512p. 49.95 *(978-963-9776-17-3(3))* Central European Univ. Pr.

Meek, Jack W. & Thurmaier, Kurt. Networked Governance: The Future of Intergovernmental Management. rev. ed. 2011. 360p. pap. 49.00 ***(978-1-4522-0325-6(3))*** CQ Pr.

Miller, Michelle Ann. Rebellion & Reform in Indonesia: Jakarta's Security & Autonomy Polices in Aceh. 2009. (Routledge Contemporary Southeast Asia Ser.). (Illus.). 240p. 150.00 *(978-0-415-45467-4(0))* Routledge.

—Rebellion & Reform in Indonesia: Jakarta's security & autonomy polices in Aceh. 2010. (ENG.). 234p. pap. 39.95 *(978-0-415-59036-5(1))* Routledge.

Mullen, Rani D. Decentralization, Local Governance, & Social Wellbeing in India: Do Local Governments Matter? 2011. (Routledge Advances in South Asian Studies). (ENG., Illus.). 256p. (C). 140.00 *(978-0-415-67065-4(9))* Routledge.

Murray, Fiona. The European Union & Member State Territories: A New Legal Framework under the EU Treaties. 2012. (ENG., Illus.). xx, 285p. 139.00 ***(978-90-6704-825-5(9)***, 9067048259) T.M.C. Asser Pr. NLD. Dist: Springer.

Ongaro, Edoardo, et al, eds. Governance & Intergovernmental Relations in the European Union & the United States: Theoretical Perspectives. 2010. 224p. 112.00 *(978-1-84844-319-8(6))* Elgar, Edward Publishing, Inc.

—Policy, Performance & Management in Governance & Intergovernmental Relations: Transatlantic Perspectives. 2011. (Illus.). 392p. 150.00 *(978-1-84844-320-4(X))* Elgar, Edward Publishing, Inc.

Organisation for Economic Co-operation and Development Staff. Aspects Fondamentaux des Assurances No. 09: Assurance du Risque Terroriste Dans les Pays de L'Ocde. 2007. (Illus.). 196p. pap. 54.00 *(978-92-64-00873-1(X))* Organization for Economic Cooperation & Development.

—Linking Regions & Central Governments: (French Version) 2009. 216p. pap. 63.00 *(978-92-64-00746-8(6))* Organization for Economic Cooperation & Development.

Perry, Rick. Fed Up! Our Fight to Save America from Washington. 2010. (ENG.). 240p. 21.99 *(978-0-316-13295-4(0))*; 416p. 23.99 *(978-0-316-13346-3(9))* Little Brown & Co.

Perry, Rick. Fed Up! Our Rights, Our Constitution, Our Fight for Freedom from Big Government. 2012. (ENG.). 240p. pap. 15.99 ***(978-0-316-13296-1(9)***, Back Bay Bks.) Little Brown & Co.

Pfisterer, Petra. Kommunale Selbstverwaltung und Lokale Governance vor dem Hintergrund des europäischen Integrationsprozesses. 2009. (Speyerer Schriften zur Verwaltungswissenschaft Ser.). (GER.). 456p. 112.95 *(978-3-631-59100-0(4))* Lang, Peter GmbH, Europaischer Verlag der Wissenschaften DEU. Dist: Lang, Peter.

Polosin, A. V. Politicheskii Region: Opyt Operatsionalizatsii I Kontseptualizatsii Poniatiia. 2010. 195p. *(978-5-211-05829-3(1))* Moskovskovo Gosudarstvennogo Univ.

Potter, Matthew. The Municipal Revolution in Ireland: A Handbook of Urban Government in Ireland since 1800. 2011. (Illus.). 509p. pap. ***(978-0-7165-3149-4(6))*** Irish Academic Pr. IRL. Dist: International Specialized Bk. Services.

Qualls, Karl D. From Ruins to Reconstruction: Urban Identity in Soviet Sevastopol after World War II. 2009. (Illus.). 272p. 49.95 *(978-0-8014-4762-4(3))* Cornell Univ. Pr.

Rodin, Jonny. Rethinking Russian Federalism. 2008. 292p. pap. *(978-3-639-04568-0(8))* VDM Verlag Dr. Mueller e.K.

Ross, Cameron. Federalism & Local Politics in Russia. 2010. (ENG.). xv, 306p. pap. 39.95 *(978-0-415-59018-1(3))* Routledge.

Schmitt, Nicolas, et al. Dialogues sur la Pratique du Fédéralisme Fiscal Vol. 4: Perspectives Comparatives. 2007. (Global Dialogue on Federalism Booklet Ser.). (FRE & ENG.). 88p. (C). pap. *(978-0-7735-3305-9(2))* McGill-Queen's Univ. Pr.

Schulze Harling, Caroline. Das materielle Abweichungsrecht der Länder: Art. 72 Abs. 3 GG. 2011. (Verfassungs- und Verwaltungsrecht unter dem Grundgesetz Ser.). (GER.). 262p. 75.95 *(978-3-631-61846-2(8))* Lang, Peter GmbH, Europaischer Verlag der Wissenschaften DEU. Dist: Lang, Peter.

Seri, Andrea. Local Power in Old Babylonian Mesopotamia. 2006. (Studies in Egyptology & the Ancient near East). (ENG., Illus.). 288p. (C). 120.00 *(978-1-84553-010-5(1))* Equinox Publishing Ltd. GBR. Dist: ISD.

Singh, Pritam. Federalism, Nationalism & Development: India & the Punjab Economy. 2009. 230p. pap. 39.95 *(978-0-415-54488-7(2))* 2008. (ENG., Illus.). 256p. (C). 170.00 *(978-0-415-45666-1(5))* Routledge.

Smith, Beattie. British State & Northern Ireland: Crisis 1969 To 1973. 2011. 374p. pap. 22.50 *(978-1-60127-067-2(4))* U. S. Institute of Peace Pr. (USIP Pr.).

Smith, Benjamin T. Pistoleros & Popular Movements: The Politics of State Formation in Postrevolutionary Oaxaca. 2009. (Mexican Experience Ser.). (ENG., Illus.). 596p. pap. 35.00 *(978-0-8032-2280-9(7))* Univ. of Nebraska Pr.

Smoke, Paul, et al, eds. Decentralization in Asia & Latin America: A Comparative Interdisciplinary Perspective. 2007. (Studies in Fiscal Federalism & State-Local Finance). 400p. 173.00 *(978-1-84542-030-7(6))* Elgar, Edward Publishing, Inc.

Sommer, Frank. Kulturpolitik als Bewährungsprobe für den deutschen Föderalismus. 2008. (Studien zur Kulturpolitik Ser.). 340p. pap. 81.95 *(978-3-631-58090-5(8))* Lang, Peter GmbH, Europaischer Verlag der Wissenschaften DEU. Dist: Lang, Peter.

Stetter, Stephan. EU Foreign & Interior Policies: Cross-Pillar Politics & the Social Construction of Sovereignty. 2009. 242p. pap. 37.50 *(978-0-415-54359-0(2))* 2007. (ENG., Illus.). 272p. (C). 150.00 *(978-0-415-41491-3(1))* Routledge.

Sulakshin, S. Paket Zakonodatelnoi Initsiativy Po Probleme Vzaimodeistviia Federalnykh I Regionalnykh Organov Gosudarstvennoi Vlasti. 2010. (RUS.). 57p. *(978-5-91290-114-0(9))* Institut Zakonodatel'stva I Normativno-Pravovyh Razrabotok, ANO.

Swianiewicz, Pawel. Territorial Consolidation. 2010. (Illus.). 310p. pap. 35.00 *(978-963-9719-16-3(1))* Institute for Local Government & Public Service, Open Soc. Institute HUN. Dist: Books International, Inc.

Taylor, Paul. The End of European Integration: Anti-Europeanism Examined. 2007. (Routledge/UACES Contemporary European Studies). (Illus.). VIII, 192p. 39.95 *(978-0-415-43106-4(9))*; 150.00 *(978-0-415-43105-7(0))* Routledge.

Thurman, Robert. Why the Dalai Lama Matters: His Act of Truth as the Solution for China, Tibet, & the World. 2011. (ENG., Illus.). 256p. pap. 14.00 *(978-1-58270-221-6(7)*, Beyond Words/Atria Bks.) Atria Bks.

Thurman, Robert & Thurman, Robert A. F. Why the Dalai Lama Matters: His Act of Truth As the Solution for China, Tibet, & the World. 2008. (ENG., Illus.). 256p. 24.00 *(978-1-58270-220-9(9)*, Beyond Words/Atria Bks.) Atria Bks.

Torfing, Jacob & Marcussen, Martin, eds. Democratic Network Governance in Europe. 2007. (ENG., Illus.). 308p. 110.00 *(978-1-4039-9530-8(3))* Palgrave Macmillan.

Treisman, Daniel. The Architecture of Government: Rethinking Political Decentralization. 2007. (Cambridge Studies in Comparative Politics). (ENG., Illus.). 348p. (C). 98.00 *(978-0-521-87229-4(4))*; per. 27.99 *(978-0-521-69382-0(9))* Cambridge Univ. Pr.

University of Toronto Press. Steering from the Centre: Central Government Offices & Their Roles in Governing. 2009. *(978-1-4426-4148-8(7))*; (Illus.). vi, 279p. pap. *(978-1-4426-1069-9(7))* Univ. of Toronto Pr.

Waugh, William L. & Tierney, Kathleen J. Emergency Management: Principles & Practice for Local Government. 2nd ed. 2007. (ENG.). 360p. 92.00 *(978-0-87326-719-9(2))* International City/County Management Assn.

Witzenrath, Christoph. Cossacks & the Russian Empire, 1598-1725: Manipulation, Rebellion & Expansion into Siberia. 2009. 264p. pap. 39.95 *(978-0-415-54418-4(1))* 2007. (Illus.). 259p. 170.00 *(978-0-415-41621-4(3))* Routledge.

CENTRAL NERVOUS SYSTEM

see also Afferent Pathways; Brain; Spinal Cord

Alberstone, Cary D., et al. Anatomic Basis of Neurologic Diagnosis. 2009. (ENG., Illus.). 600p. 129.99 *(978-0-86577-976-1(7))* Thieme Medical Pubs., Inc.

Armati, Patricia, ed. The Biology of Schwann Cells: Development, Differentiation & Immunomodulation. 2007. (ENG., Illus.). 264p. 171.00 *(978-0-521-85020-9(7))* Cambridge Univ. Pr.

Baulieu, Etienne-Emile, ed. Neurosteroids: A New Regulatory Function in the Nervous System. 2010. (Contemporary Endocrinology Ser.). (Illus.). 396p. pap. 179.00 *(978-1-61737-068-7(1)*, 1617370681) Humana Pr.

Bayer, Shirley A. & Altman, Joseph. Atlas of Human Central Nervous System Development -5 Volume Set, 5 vols. 2007. (ENG.). 850.00 *(978-1-4200-6800-9(8)*, CRC Press) Taylor & Francis Group GBR. Dist: Taylor & Francis Group.

Bhatnagar, Subhash C. Neuroscience for the Study of Communicative Disorders. 4th rev. ed. 2012. (ENG., Illus.). 576p. 79.95 ***(978-1-60913-871-4(6))*** Lippincott Williams & Wilkins.

Bloom, Floyd E., et al. Introduction to Neuropsychopharmacology. 2008. (ENG., Illus.). 576p. pap. 45.00 *(978-0-19-538053-8(3))* Oxford Univ. Pr., Inc.

Borsini, Franco. Pharmacology of 5-HT6 Receptors, 2 vols., Pt. 1. 2010. (ENG., Illus.). 224p. 198.00 *(978-0-12-384976-2(4)*, Academic Pr.) Elsevier Science & Technology Bks.

C

Brodal, Per. The Central Nervous System, 1 vol. 4th ed. 2010. (ENG., Illus.). 640p. 69.50 *(978-0-19-538115-3(7))* Oxford Univ. Pr. GBR. Dist: Oxford Univ. Pr., Inc.

Calton, Robert N. Handbook on White Matter: Structure, Function & Changes. Westland, Timothy B., ed. 2009. 195.00 *(978-1-60741-034-8(6))* Nova Science Pubs., Inc.

Caplivski, Daniel & Scheld, W. Michael. Consultations in Infectious Disease: A Case Based Approach to Diagnosis & Management, 1 vol. 2012. (ENG.). 392p. pap. 65.00 *(978-0-19-973500-6(X))* Oxford Univ. Pr., Inc.

Carta, Angelico, et al. Critical Pathways to Success in CNS Drug Development. 2nd ed. 2010. (ENG., Illus.). 272p. 160.95 *(978-1-4443-3064-9(0)*, Wiley-Blackwell) Wiley, John & Sons, Inc.

Castillo, Mauricio. Neuroradiology Companion: Methods, Guidelines, & Imaging Fundamentals. 4th rev. ed. 2011. (Imaging Companion Ser.). (ENG., Illus.). 624p. pap. 92.99 *(978-1-4511-1175-0(4))* Lippincott Williams & Wilkins.

Clément, Gilles & Reschke, Millard F. Neuroscience in Space. 2008. (Illus.). 322p. pap. 54.95 *(978-0-387-78949-1(9))* Springer.

Cram101 Textbook Reviews & Cram101 Textbook Reviews. Outlines & Highlights for Brain Atlas: A Visual Guide to the Human Central Nervous System by Thomas Woolsey, ISBN. 2011. 520p. pap. 38.95 ***(978-1-61461-087-8(8))*** Cram101 Inc.

—Outlines & Highlights for Critical Pathways to Success in Cns Drug Development by Neal Cutler. 2011. 70p. pap. 27.95 ***(978-1-61830-766-8(5))*** Cram101 Inc.

Cram101 Textbook Reviews Staff. Outlines & Highlights for Human Brain: An Introduction to its Functional Anatomy by John Nolte, ISBN. 2009. 256p. pap. 31.95 *(978-1-4288-9877-6(8))* Cram101 Inc.

Crossman, Alan R. & Neary, David. Neuroanatomy: An Illustrated Colour Text. 4th ed. 2010. (Illustrated Colour Text Ser.). (ENG., Illus.). 200p. (C). pap. 64.95 *(978-0-7020-3086-4(4)*, Churchill Livingstone) Elsevier - Health Sciences Div.

Cummings, Jeffrey, ed. Progress in Neurotherapeutics & Neuropsychopharmacology: Volume 3. 2008. (ENG.). 312p. 162.00 *(978-0-521-86255-4(8))* Cambridge Univ. Pr.

Cummings, Jeffrey L., ed. Progress in Neurotherapeutics & Neuropsychopharmacology: Volume 3 2008. 2009. (ENG.). 312p. pap. 61.00 *(978-0-521-11561-2(2))* Cambridge Univ. Pr.

Di Chiara, Gaetano, ed. Dopamine in the CNS II. 2010. (Handbook of Experimental Pharmacology / Dopamine in the CNS Ser.). (Illus.). xxiv, 514p. pap. 559.00 *(978-3-642-07659-6(9)*, 3642076599) Springer.

Di Giovanni, Giuseppe. 5-HT2C Receptors in the Pathophysiology of CNS Disease. Di Giovanni, Giuseppe et al, eds. 2010. (Receptors Ser.). (ENG., Illus.). xi, 557p. 239.00 *(978-1-60761-940-6(7)*, 1607619407) Humana Pr.

Di Napoli, Mario & Wojcik, Cezary. The Ubiquitin Proteasome System in the Central Nervous System: From Physiology to Pathology - 2008 Update. 2009. (Biochemistry Research Trends Ser.). 69.00 *(978-1-60741-694-4(8)*, Nova Biomedical Bks.) Nova Science Pubs., Inc.

Dietzschold, B. & Richt, J. A., eds. Protective & Pathological Immune Responses in the CNS. 2010. (Current Topics in Microbiology & Immunology Ser.). (Illus.). ix, 277p. pap. 199.00 *(978-3-642-07655-8(6)*, 3642076556) Springer.

Edinger, Ludwig, et al. The Anatomy of the Central Nervous System of Man & of Vertebrates in General. 2010. (Illus.). 470p. pap. 37.75 *(978-1-142-97766-5(8))* BiblioBazaar.

Freed, William J. Neural Transplantation. 2009. (Cellular & Molecular Neuroscience Ser.). (ENG., Illus.). 573p. (gr. 17). pap. 38.00 *(978-0-262-51387-6(0))* MIT Pr.

Grisold, Wolfgang & Soffietti, Riccardo. Neuro-Oncology, Part II, Vol 105 HCN Series: Handbook of Clinical Neurology (Series editors: Aminoff, Boller, Swaab), 2 vols. 2012. (Handbook of Clinical Neurology Ser.: 105). (ENG., Illus.). 572p. 250.00 ***(978-0-444-53502-3(0))*** Elsevier Science & Technology Bks.

Grisold, Wolfgang & Soffietti, Riccardo, eds. Neuro-Oncology: Handbook of Clinical Neurology, 2 vols. 2012. (Handbook of Clinical Neurology Ser.: 104). (ENG., Illus.). 488p. 250.00 ***(978-0-444-52138-5(0))*** Elsevier Science & Technology Bks.

Haines. Neuroanatomy (US ED) 8th rev. ed. 2011. (ENG.). 344p. pap. 76.99 *(978-1-60547-653-7(6))* Lippincott Williams & Wilkins.

Itabashi, Hideo H., et al. Forensic Neuropathology: A Practical Review of the Fundamentals. 2007. (ENG., Illus.). 496p. 235.00 *(978-0-12-058527-4(8),* Academic Pr.) Elsevier Science & Technology Bks.

Jones, Edward G., et al. The Human Pain System: Experimental & Clinical Perspectives. 2010. (ENG., Illus.). 648p. 140.00 *(978-0-521-11452-3(7))* Cambridge Univ. Pr.

Kalali, Amir, et al, eds. Essential CNS Drug Development. 2012. (Illus.). 232p. 99.00 ***(978-0-521-76606-7(0))*** Cambridge Univ. Pr.

Keating, Robert, et al. Tumors of the Pediatric Central Nervous System. 2011. (ENG., Illus.). 544p. 109.95 *(978-1-60406-546-6(X))* Thieme Medical Pubs., Inc.

Krings, Timo, et al. Case-Based Interventional Neuroradiology. 2011. (ENG., Illus.). 464p. 99.99 *(978-1-60406-373-8(4))* Thieme Medical Pubs., Inc.

Lane, Emma L. & Dunnett, S. B. Animal Models of Movement Disorders. 2011. (Illus.). ***(978-1-61779-301-1(9))*** Humana Pr.

Lanzino, Giuseppe & Spetzler, Robert F. Cavernous Malformations of the Brain & Spinal Cord. 2007. 139.95 *(978-3-13-141891-3(5))* Thieme Medical Pubs., Inc.

Lanzino, Giuseppe & Spetzler, Robert F., eds. Cavernous Malformations of the Brain & Spinal Cord. 2007. (ENG.). 139p. pap. 149.99 *(978-1-58890-343-3(5))* Thieme Medical Pubs., Inc.

Lewellen, Gale R. & Torgerud, Steven Ray. Human Cns Structure. 7th rev. ed. 2011. (ENG.). 282p. spiral bd. 73.01 *(978-0-7575-8470-1(5))* Kendall Hunt Publishing Co.

Marcoux, Frank W. & Choi, Dennis W. CNS Neuroprotection. 2010. (Handbook of Experimental Pharmacology Ser.). (Illus.). xxii, 506p. pap. 469.00 *(978-3-642-07625-1(4),* 3642076254) Springer.

Martin, John. Neuroanatomy Text & Atlas. 4th ed. 2012. (ENG., Illus.). 528p. pap. 70.00 *(978-0-07-160396-6(4),* 0071603964) McGraw-Hill Medical Publishing Div.

Martin, Justin McCory. Brain. 2010. (Illus.). 16p. ***(978-0-545-24800-6(0))*** Scholastic, Inc.

Mayes, Rick, et al. Medicating Children: ADHD & Pediatric Mental Health. 2009. (Illus.). 360p. 44.00 *(978-0-674-03163-0(6))* Harvard Univ. Pr.

Mendoza, John & Foundas, Anne. Clinical Neuroanatomy: A Neurobehavioral Approach. 2010. (ENG., Illus.). ix, 710p. pap. 109.00 *(978-1-4419-2266-3(0),* 1441922660) Springer.

Minagar, Alireza. The Neurobiology of Multiple Sclerosis. 2007. (International Review of Neurobiology Ser.). (ENG., Illus.). 760p. 198.00 *(978-0-12-373736-6(2),* Academic Pr.) Elsevier Science & Technology Bks.

Napoli, Mario Di & Wojcik, Cezary. Ubiquitin Proteasome System in the Central Nervous System: From Physiology to Pathology. 2007. 125.00 *(978-1-60021-749-4(4))* Nova Science Pubs., Inc.

Nieuwenhuys, Rudolf, et al. The Human Central Nervous System. 4th rev. ed. 2007. (Illus.). 967p. 99.00 *(978-3-540-34684-5(8))* Springer.

Nowakowski, R.S. & Bhide, P. G., eds. Stem & Progenitor Cells in the Central Nervous System. (Illus.). 212p. *(978-3-8055-7870-7(9))* Karger, S. AG.

Nuez, A. & Malmierca, E. Corticofugal Modulation of Sensory Information. 2007. (Advances in Anatomy, Embryology & Cell Biology Ser.). (Illus.). 74p. per. 149.00 *(978-3-540-36769-7(1),* 3540367691) Springer.

Nyberg, Fred, ed. Neuropeptides in Neuroprotection & Neuroregeneration. 2012. (ENG., Illus.). 320p. 149.95 ***(978-1-4398-3062-8(2),*** CRC Press) Taylor & Francis Group GBR. Dist: Taylor & Francis Group.

Pagel, J. F. The Limits of Dream: A Scientific Exploration of the Mind/Brain Interface. 2008. (ENG., Illus.). 250p. 27.95 *(978-0-12-374215-5(3),* Academic Pr.) Elsevier Science & Technology Bks.

Pfaff, D. W. & Gunnar, M. R., eds. Development of Mechanisms Regulating Global CNS States. 2009. (Illus.). 112p. pap. *(978-3-8055-9239-0(6))* Karger, S. AG.

Pinel, John P. J. & Edwards, Maggie. A Colorful Introduction to the Anatomy of the Human Brain: A Brain & Psychology Coloring Book. 2nd ed. 2007. (ENG., Illus.). 264p. (C). per. 24.00 *(978-0-205-54874-3(1))* Allyn & Bacon, Inc.

Ribak, Charles E., et al, eds. From Development to Degeneration & Regeneration of the Nervous System. 2008. (ENG., Illus.). 408p. 89.50 *(978-0-19-536900-7(9))* Oxford Univ. Pr., Inc.

Rosenwasser, Robert H., ed. Interventional Neuroradiology. 2007. (ENG., Illus.). 440p. 330.00 *(978-0-8493-9562-8(3),* Informa Healthcare) Taylor & Francis Group GBR. Dist: Taylor & Francis Group.

Rosenwasser, Robert H. & Jabbour, Pascal M. Neuroendovascular Management: Cranial & Spinal Disorders - An Issue of Neurosurgery Clinics. 2009. (Clinics: Surgery Ser.: 20-4). (ENG.). 99.00 *(978-1-4377-1574-3(5),* Saunders) Elsevier - Health Sciences Div.

Sakas, Damianos E., et al, eds. Operative Neuromodulation: Volume 1: Functional Neuroprosthetic Surgery. an Introduction. 2007. (Acta Neurochirurgica Supplementum Ser.). (Illus.). 482p. 359.00 *(978-3-211-33078-4(X),* 321133078X) Springer.

Sakas, Damianos E. & Simpson, Brian A., eds. Operative Neuromodulation: Volume 2: Neural Networks Surgery. 2007. (Acta Neurochirurgica Supplementum Ser.). (Illus.). 590p. 319.00 *(978-3-211-33080-7(1),* 3211330801) Springer.

Seidenbecher, Constanze I., ed. Cell Communication in Nervous & Immune Systems. 2006. (Results & Problems in Cell Differentiation Ser.). (Illus.). 313p. 239.00 *(978-3-540-36828-1(0),* 3540368280) Springer.

Shoshkes Reiss, Carol, ed. Neurotropic Viral Infections. 2008. (ENG., Illus.). 484p. 174.00 *(978-0-521-86964-5(1))* Cambridge Univ. Pr.

Springhouse Publishing Company Staff & Lippincott Williams and Wilkins Staff, eds. Nursing Central Nervous System Drug Handbook 2011. 2010. (ENG.). 300p. pap. 25.99 *(978-1-4511-0312-0(3))* Lippincott Williams & Wilkins.

Stahl, Stephen M. Pharmacology: Neuroscientific Basis & Practical Applications. 3rd ed. 2008. (ENG., Illus.). 1134p. 261.00 *(978-0-521-74609-0(4))* Cambridge Univ. Pr.

Unknown. Pharmacology of 5-HT6 receptors, Part II, 2 vols. 2011. (ENG., Illus.). 242p. 198.00 *(978-0-12-385902-0(6),* Academic Pr.) Elsevier Science & Technology Bks.

Upledger, D.O., O.M.M, John E. A Brain Is Born: Exploring the Birth & Development of the Central Nervous System. 2010. (ENG., Illus.). 400p. pap. 49.95 *(978-1-58394-301-4(3))* North Atlantic Bks.

Vereczki, Viktoria & Köves, Katalin. The Centrifugal Visual System of Rat. 2008. 80p. pap. *(978-3-639-09279-0(1))* VDM Verlag Dr. Mueller e.K.

Wang, John Q., ed. Drugs of Abuse: Neurological Reviews & Protocols. 2010. (Methods in Molecular Medicine Ser.). (Illus.). 528p. pap. 169.00 *(978-1-61737-328-2(1),* 1617373281) Humana Pr.

Wilkinson, Ashley, et al. Central Nervous System Tissue Engineerng: Current Considerations & Strategies. 2011. (Synthesis Lectures on Tissue Engineering Ser.). pap. 35.00 ***(978-1-60845-786-1(9))*** Morgan & Claypool Pubs.

Woolsey, Thomas A., et al. The Brain Atlas: A Visual Guide to the Human Central Nervous System. 3rd rev. ed. 2007. (ENG., Illus.). 272p. pap. 75.95 *(978-0-470-08476-2(6),* Wiley-Liss) Wiley, John & Sons, Inc.

CENTRAL NERVOUS SYSTEM—DISEASES

see also Brain—Diseases; Creutzfeldt-Jakob Disease; Poliomyelitis; Spinal Cord—Diseases

Anschel, David, et al. Clinical Neuroimaging: Cases & Key Points. 2008. (Illus.). vii, 177p. *(978-0-07-128723-4(X))* McGraw-Hill Cos., The.

Atlas, Scott W., ed. Magnetic Resonance Imaging of the Brain & Spine, 2 vols. 4th rev. ed. 2008. (ENG., Illus.). 2000p. 459.99 *(978-0-7817-6985-3(X))* Lippincott Williams & Wilkins.

Bain, Peter, et al, eds. Deep Brain Stimulation. 2009. (ENG., Illus.). 232p. pap. 55.00 *(978-0-19-954371-7(2))* Oxford Univ. Pr., Inc.

Barkovich, A. James. Diagnostic Imaging Pediatric Neuroradiology. 2007. *(978-0-8089-2395-4(1))* Harcourt Health Sciences Group.

Barkovich, A. James & Raybaud, Charles. Pediatric Neuroimaging. 5th rev. ed. 2011. (ENG.). 1144p. 284.99 *(978-1-60547-714-5(1))* Lippincott Williams & Wilkins.

Barkovich, A. James, et al. Pediatric Neuroradiology. 2007. (ENG., Illus.). 1100p. 319.00 *(978-1-4160-4918-0(5))* Amirsys, Inc.

Beal, Eileen. Ritalin: Its Use & Abuse. 2009. (Drug Abuse Prevention Library). 64p. (gr. 5-5). 58.50 *(978-1-60853-431-9(6))* Rosen Publishing Group, Inc., The.

Brat, Daniel J. & Schniederjan, Matthew. Biopsy Interpretation of the Central Nervous System. 2011. (Biopsy Interpretation Ser.). (ENG., Illus.). 360p. 163.99 *(978-0-7817-9993-5(7))* Lippincott Williams & Wilkins.

DeAngelis, Lisa M. & Posner, Jerome B. Neurologic Complications of Cancer. 2nd ed. 2008. (Contemporary Neurology Ser.: Vol. 73). (ENG., Illus.). 656p. 135.00 *(978-0-19-536674-7(3))* Oxford Univ. Pr., Inc.

Donaghy, Michael, ed. Brain's Diseases of the Nervous System. 12th ed. 2009. (ENG., Illus.). 1376p. 395.00 *(978-0-19-856938-1(6))* Oxford Univ. Pr., Inc.

du Plessis, Adre J. Fetal Neurology, an Issue of Clinics in Perinatology. 2009. (Clinics: Internal Medicine Ser.: 36-3). (ENG.). 99.00 *(978-1-4377-1259-9(2),* Saunders) Elsevier - Health Sciences Div.

Emerich, Dwaine F., et al, eds. Central Nervous System Diseases. 2010. (Contemporary Neuroscience Ser.). 532p. pap. 179.00 *(978-1-61737-152-3(1),* 1617371521) Humana Pr.

Espinosa, Patricio S., et al. Focus on Neuroimaging. 2009. (Neurology Self-Assessment Ser.). (ENG., Illus.). 352p. pap. 99.99 *(978-0-7817-9912-6(0))* Lippincott Williams & Wilkins.

Gendelman, Howard E., et al, eds. The Neurology of AIDS, 1 vol. 3rd ed. 2011. (ENG., Illus.). 1160p. 275.00 ***(978-0-19-539934-9(X))*** Oxford Univ. Pr., Inc.

Ghazala, Shaheen, et al. Diseases of Central Nervous System: Description & Managment. 2011. 216p. pap. ***(978-3-639-34006-8(X))*** VDM Verlag Dr. Mueller e.K.

Giraldeau, Luc-Alain, ed. Ecology & the Central Nervous System: 9th Biennial Congress of the International Society for Behavioral Ecology Montreal, July 7-12, 2002. (Brain, Behavior & Evolution Ser.: Vol. 63, No. 4). (Illus.). 60p. pap. *(978-3-8055-7762-5(1))* Karger, S. AG.

Gjelsvik, Bente E. Bassoe. The Bobath Concept in Adult Neurology. 2007. (ENG., Illus.). 240p. 84.99 *(978-1-58890-621-2(3))* Thieme Medical Pubs., Inc.

Gupta, Nalin. Pediatric CNS Tumors. Banerjee, Anuradha & Haas-Kogan, Daphne, eds. 2nd ed. 2009. (Pediatric Oncology Ser.). (ENG., Illus.). xxv, 357p. 199.00 *(978-3-540-87976-3(5),* 3540879765) Springer.

Hodler, Jurg. Diseases of the Brain, Head & Neck, Spine: Diagnostic Imaging & Interventional Techniques. Schulthess, Gustav K. Von & Zollikofer, Christoph L., eds. 2008. (ENG.). xii, 288p. pap. 129.00 *(978-88-470-0839-7(5),* 8847008395) Springer.

Irani, David N. Cerebrospinal Fluid in Clinical Practice. 2008. (ENG., Illus.). 336p. 170.00 *(978-1-4160-2908-3(7),* Saunders) Elsevier - Health Sciences Div.

Jain, Kewal K., ed. Drug Delivery to the Central Nervous System. 2009. (Neuromethods Ser.). (ENG., Illus.). xii, 324p. 159.00 *(978-1-60761-528-6(2),* 1607615282) Humana Pr.

Jallo, George, et al. Neuroendoscopy of the Central Nervous System. 2008. (Illus.). 140p. 149.99 *(978-1-59756-141-9(X))* Plural Publishing, Inc.

Junien, Jean-Louis & Staels, B. Nuclear Receptors as Molecular Targets for Cardiometabolic & Central Nervous System Diseases, 8. 2008. (Illus.). ix, 117p. 126.00 *(978-1-58603-857-1(5))* IOS Pr., Inc.

Kelly, John. Principles of CNS Drug Development: From Test Tube to Patient. 2010. (ENG., Illus.). 324p. 153.00 *(978-0-470-51979-0(7),* Wiley) Wiley, John & Sons, Inc.

Ketonen, L. M., et al. Pediatric Brain & Spine: An Atlas of MRI & Spectroscopy. 2010. (Illus.). xiv, 494p. pap. 209.00 *(978-3-642-05969-8(4),* 3642059694) Springer.

Kielian, Tammy. Toll-like Receptors: Roles in Infection & Neuropathology: Roles in Infection & Neuropathology. Kielian, Tammy, ed. 2009. (Current Topics in Microbiology & Immunology Ser.). (ENG., Illus.). xi, 191p. 219.00 *(978-3-642-00548-0(9),* 3642005489) Springer.

Kordower, Jeffrey & Tuszynski, Mark H., eds. CNS Regeneration: Basic Science & Clinical Advances. 2nd ed. 2007. (ENG., Illus.). 526p. 165.00 *(978-0-12-373994-0(2),* Academic Pr.) Elsevier Science & Technology Bks.

Lane, Thomas E., et al, eds. Central Nervous System Diseases & Inflammation. (ENG., Illus.). viii, 318p. 2010. pap. 169.00 *(978-1-4419-4480-1(X),* 144194480X) 2008. 169.00 *(978-0-387-73893-2(2),* 0387738932) Springer.

LaPointe, Leonard L. Aphasia & Related Neurogenic Language Disorders. 4th ed. 2010. 64.95 *(978-1-60406-262-5(2))* Thieme Medical Pubs., Inc.

LaPointe, Leonard L., ed. Aphasia & Related Neurogenic Language Disorders. 4th ed. 2011. (ENG., Illus.). 288p. 64.99 *(978-1-60406-261-8(4))* Thieme Medical Pubs., Inc.

Laws, Edward R. & Sheehan, Jason P. Pituitary Surgery: A Modern Approach, Vol. 34. (Frontiers of Hormone Research Ser.: Vol. 34). (Illus.). 286p. *(978-3-8055-8051-9(7))* Karger, S. AG.

Levene, Malcolm I. & Chervenak, Frank A. Fetal & Neonatal Neurology & Neurosurgery. 4th ed. 2009. (ENG., Illus.). 960p. 549.00 *(978-0-443-10407-7(7),* Churchill Livingstone) Elsevier - Health Sciences Div.

Maloney, Beth Alison. Saving Sammy: A Mother's Fight to Cure Her Son's OCD. 2010. (ENG.). 272p. pap. 14.00 *(978-0-307-46184-1(X),* Three Rivers Pr.) Crown Publishing Group.

Mannock, Edward, ed. Emergency Management in Neurocritical Care. 2012. (NIP- Neurology in Practice Ser.). (ENG.). 256p. pap. 79.95 ***(978-0-470-65473-6(2),*** Wiley-Blackwell) Wiley, John & Sons, Inc.

Markman, Maurie, et al, eds. Molecular Neuro-Oncology: Glioma Methods & Protocols. (Methods in Molecular Medicine Ser.). 400p. 2008. 115.00 *(978-1-58829-393-0(9),* 1588293939) 2006. 115.00 *(978-1-59745-334-9(X))* Humana Pr.

McCandless, David W. Kernicterus. 2010. (Contemporary Clinical Neuroscience Ser.). (ENG., Illus.). xiv, 286p. 219.00 *(978-1-4419-6554-7(6),* 1441965548) Humana Pr.

Meadows, Linzi, et al, eds. Bobath Concept: Theory & Clinical Practice in Neurological Rehabilitation. 2009. (ENG., Illus.). 232p. pap. 70.99 *(978-1-4051-7041-3(7),* Wiley-Blackwell) Wiley, John & Sons, Inc.

Michael-Titus, Adina, et al. The Nervous System. 2nd ed. 2010. (Systems of the Body Ser.). (ENG., Illus.). 336p. pap. 64.95 *(978-0-7020-3373-5(1),* Churchill Livingstone) Elsevier - Health Sciences Div.

Moller, Aage R. The Malleable Brain: Benefits & Harm from Plasticity of the Brain. 2009. (Illus.). iv, 247p. 79.00 *(978-1-60692-881-3(3))* Nova Science Pubs., Inc.

Naidu, Sakkubai, et al, eds. Leukodystrophies. 2011. (International Child Neurology Association Ser.: 2). (ENG.). 252p. 125.00 ***(978-1-907655-09-8(3))*** Mac Keith Pr. GBR. Dist: Wiley, John & Sons, Inc.

Napoli, Mario Di & Wojcik, Cezary. Ubiquitin Proteasome System in the Central Nervous System: From Physiology to Pathology. 2007. 125.00 *(978-1-60021-749-4(4))* Nova Science Pubs., Inc.

Nelson, Charles A. & Luciana, Monica, eds. Developmental Cognitive Neuroscience. 2nd ed. 2008. (Developmental Cognitive Neuroscience Ser.). (ENG., Illus.). 936p. (gr. 17). instr.'s hndbk. ed. 175.00 *(978-0-262-14104-8(3))* MIT Pr.

Nestler, Eric J., et al. Molecular Neuropharmacology: A Foundation for Clinical Neuroscience. 2nd ed. 2008. (ENG., Illus.). 516p. pap. 62.00 *(978-0-07-148127-4(3),* 0071481273) McGraw-Hill Professional Publishing.

Newberg, Andrew B. & Alavi, Abass. Pet in CNS Disease: Pet Clinics. 2010. (Clinics: Radiology Ser.: 5-2). (ENG., Illus.). x, 132p. 79.00 *(978-1-4377-1942-0(2),* Saunders) Elsevier - Health Sciences Div.

Papathanasiou. Aphasia & Related Neurogenic Communication Disorders. rev. ed. 2011. 512p. pap. 79.95 *(978-0-7637-7100-3(7))* Jones & Bartlett Learning, LLC.

Porterfield, Jason. Ritalin: A Difficult Choice. 2009. (Drug Abuse & Society Ser.). 64p. (gr. 6-6). 58.50 *(978-1-61512-227-1(3))* Rosen Publishing Group, Inc., The.

Prayson, Richard & Napekoski, Karl. Frozen Section Library: Central Nervous System: Central Nervous System. 2010. (Frozen Section Library). (Illus.). xi, 230p. pap. 139.00 *(978-1-4419-7578-2(0),* 1441975780) Springer.

Qayyum Rana, Frcpc. A Synopsis of Neurological Emergencies. 2009. 194p. pap. 49.00 *(978-1-4389-2384-0(8))* AuthorHouse.

Riascos, Roy & Bonfante, Eliana, eds. Neuro Imaging. 2010. (ENG., Illus.). 224p. pap. 54.99 *(978-1-60406-189-5(8))* Thieme Medical Pubs., Inc.

Ricker, Joseph H. & Joel, E. Morgan, eds. Textbook of Clinical Neuropsychology. 2008. (Studies on Neuropsychology, Development, & Cognition). (ENG., Illus.). 1048p. 124.95 *(978-1-84169-477-1(0),* Taylor & Francis) Taylor & Francis Group GBR. Dist: Taylor & Francis Group.

Roos, Karen L. & Tunkel, Allan R., eds. Bacterial Infections of the Central Nervous System: Handbook of Clinical Neurology (Series Editors: Aminoff, Boller & Swaab) 2010. (Handbook of Clinical Neurology Ser.: 96). (ENG., Illus.). 304p. 258.00 *(978-0-444-52015-9(5))* Elsevier Science & Technology Bks.

Schantz-Feld, Mali Rebecca. Sleep Drugs. 2011. (Understanding Drugs Ser.). (Illus.). 104p. (C). (gr. 9-12). 34.95 *(978-1-60413-551-0(4))* Facts On File, Inc.

Sharma, Hari Shanker, ed. New Concepts of Psychostimulants Induced Neurotoxicity. 2009. (ENG., Illus.). xvi, 473p. 198.00 *(978-0-12-374504-0(7),* Academic Pr.) Elsevier Science & Technology Bks.

Site-Specific Cancer Series Central Nervous System Cancers. 2010. pap. *(978-1-890504-98-4(X))* Oncology Nursing Society.

Starr, Phillip A., et al, eds. Functional Neurosurgery. 2nd ed. 2008. (Neurosurgical Operative Atlas Ser.). (ENG., Illus.). 304p. 269.99 *(978-1-58890-399-0(0))* Thieme Medical Pubs., Inc.

Stippich, C., ed. Clinical Functional MRI: Presurgical Functional Neuroimaging. 2007. (Medical Radiology / Diagnostic Imaging Ser.). (Illus.). 268p. 219.00 *(978-3-540-24469-1(7),* 3540244697) Springer.

Timor-Tritsch, Ilan, et al. Ultrasonography of the Prenatal & Neonatal Brain. 3rd ed. 2012. (ENG., Illus.). 600p. 280.00 *(978-0-07-161306-4(4),* 0071613064) McGraw-Hill Professional Publishing.

Vogel, Hannes. Nervous System. 2009. (Cambridge Illustrated Surgical Pathology Ser.). (ENG., Illus.). 524p. 142.00 *(978-0-521-88161-6(7))* Cambridge Univ. Pr.

Weinges, Stefan. A Proteomic Approach on Synapse Formation. 2008. 136p. pap. *(978-3-639-00553-0(8))* VDM Verlag Dr. Mueller e.K.

Wendy Chapin Ford. To Get Back Home: A Mysterious Disease. 2010. 180p. 26.95 *(978-1-4401-9914-1(0));* pap. 16.95 *(978-1-4401-9916-5(7))* iUniverse, Inc.

Westphal, Manfred. Oncology of CNS Tumors. Tonn, Jörg-Christian & Rutka, James T., eds. 2nd ed. 2009. (Illus.). xxiii, 793p. 269.00 *(978-3-642-02873-1(X),* 364202873X) Springer.

Wheeler, Derek S., et al. The Central Nervous System in Pediatric Critical Illness & Injury. 2009. (Illus.). 152p. pap. 59.95 *(978-1-84800-992-9(5))* Springer.

Wijdicks, Eelco F. M. The Practice of Emergency & Critical Care Neurology, 1 vol. 2010. (ENG., Illus.). 832p. *(978-0-19-539402-3(0))* Oxford Univ. Pr.

Woolf, Nancy J., et al, eds. Nanoneuroscience: Novel Biomolecular Contributions to Mind. 2009. (Biological & Medical Physics, Biomedical Engineering Ser.). (ENG., Illus.). xii, 279p. 159.00 *(978-3-642-03583-8(3),* 3642035833) Springer.

Zigova, Tanja, ed. Neural Stem Cells for Brain & Spinal Cord Repair. 2010. (Contemporary Neuroscience Ser.). (Illus.). 456p. pap. 189.00 *(978-1-61737-298-8(6),* 1617372986) Humana Pr.

CENTRAL PACIFIC RAILROAD COMPANY

Derby, Elias. The Overland Route to the Pacific. 2011. 104p. pap. 9.95 *(978-1-4290-4630-5(9))* Applewood Bks.

Francaviglia, Richard V. Over the Range: A History of the Promontory Summit Route of the Pacific. 2008. (ENG.). 320p. 34.95 *(978-0-87421-705-6(9),* Utah State Univ. Pr.) Univ. Pr. of Colorado.

Rayner, Richard. The Associates: Four Capitalists Who Created California. 2009. (Enterprise Ser.). (ENG.). 224p. pap. 14.95 *(978-0-393-33361-9(2),* 33361) Atlas & Co.

CENTRAL PARK (NEW YORK, N.Y.)

Amenta, Edwin. Professor Baseball: Searching for Redemption & the Perfect Lineup on the Softball Diamonds of Central Park. 2007. (Illus.). 242p. 25.00 *(978-0-226-01666-5(8))* Univ. of Chicago Pr.

Blauner, Andrew. Central Park: An Anthology. 2012. (ENG.). 288p. pap. 16.00 ***(978-1-60819-600-5(3))*** Bloomsbury Publishing.

Cooke, Oliver D. Rethinking Municipal Privatization. (New Political Economy Ser.). (ENG., Illus.). 210p. 2012. pap. 42.95 ***(978-0-415-54311-8(8))*** 2007. 125.00 *(978-0-415-96209-4(9))* Routledge.

Heckscher, Morrison H. Creating Central Park. 2008. (Illus.). 73p. 19.95 *(978-1-58839-246-6(5))* Metropolitan Museum of Art, The.

—Creating Central Park. 2008. (ENG., Illus.). 76p. per. 19.95 *(978-0-300-13669-2(2))* Yale Univ. Pr.

Levine, Edward J. Central Park. (Then & Now Ser.). (ENG., Illus.). 2008. 96p. per. 21.99 *(978-0-7385-5507-2(X))* 2006. 128p. per. 21.99 *(978-0-7385-4627-8(5))* Arcadia Publishing.

Levy, Bob. Club George: The Diary of a Central Park Birdwatcher. pap. 12.95 *(978-0-312-34168-8(7),* St. Martin's Paperbacks) St. Martin's Pr.

McCabe, Robert A., photos by. The Ramble in Central Park: A Wilderness West of Fifth. 2011. (ENG., Illus.). 152p. 35.00 *(978-0-7892-1091-3(6))* Abbeville Pr., Inc.

Miller, Sara Cedar. Strawberry Fields: Central Park's Memorial to John Lennon. 2011. (ENG., Illus.). 96p. 16.95 *(978-0-8109-9786-8(X))* Abrams.

Miller, Sara Cedar & Miller, Sara Cedar. Seeing Central Park: The Official Guide to the World's Greatest Urban Park. 2009. (ENG., Illus.). 192p. 19.95 *(978-0-8109-9628-1(6))* Abrams.

Reisner, Fran, photos by. The Dogs of Central Park. 2011. (ENG., Illus.). 144p. 19.95 *(978-0-7893-2212-8(9))* Universe Publishing.

Reiss, Marcia. Central Park Then & Now. 2010. (Then & Now Thunder Bay Ser.). (ENG., Illus.). 144p. 19.95 *(978-1-60710-007-2(X),* Thunder Bay Pr.) Advantage Pubs. Group.

Schiff, Betsy Pinover. Windows on Central Park: The Landscape Revealed. 2011. (Illus.). 160p. 45.00 **(978-0-7643-3835-9(8)**, Schiffer Publishing Ltd) Schiffer Publishing, Ltd.

Slavicek, Louise. New York City's Central Park. 2009. (Building America Ser.). (Illus.). 120p. (gr. 5-8). 35.00 *(978-1-60413-044-7(X)*, Chelsea Hse.) Facts On File, Inc.

Spiegler, Jennifer C. & Gaykowski, Paul M. The Bridges of Central Park. 2006. (ENG., Illus.). 144p. per. 25.99 *(978-0-7385-3861-7(2))* Arcadia Publishing.

CENTRAL PLACES

see also Cities and Towns

Grimm, Oliver. Grobootshaus, Zentrum, Herrschaft. 2006. (Reallexikon der Germanischen Altertumskunde - Ergänzungsbände Ser.). (GER., Illus.). XI, 448p. 196.00 *(978-3-11-018482-2(6))* De Gruyter, Walter Inc.

Gupta, Prema Katari. Creating Great Town Centers & Urban Villages. 2008. (ENG.). 200p. 99.95 *(978-0-87420-076-8(8))* Urban Land Institute.

Mishra, R. N. & Sharma, P. K. Rural Growth Centres for Micro Level Planning. 2007. (Illus.). 151p. *(978-81-87445-22-7(X))* Ritu Pubns.

Scott, Peter & Kurtén, Björn. Geography & Retailing. 2007. (ENG., Illus.). 192p. pap. 21.95 *(978-0-202-30946-0(0))* Aldine Transaction.

CENTRAL PLANNING

Adelstein, Richard. The Rise of Planning in Industrial America 1865-1914. 2012. (Routledge Explorations in Economic History Ser.). (ENG.). 272p. (C). 140.00 **(978-0-415-58465-4(5))** Routledge.

Adelstein, Richard P. The Rise of Planning in Industrial America, 1865-1914. 2012. 256p. E-Book **(978-0-203-13771-0(X))** Routledge.

Crew, Michael A. & Parker, David, eds. International Handbook on Economic Regulation. 2008. (Elgar Original Reference Ser.). 424p. pap. 75.00 *(978-1-84844-172-9(X))* Elgar, Edward Publishing, Inc.

Devine, Pat. Democracy Adn Economic Planning. 2010. (ENG.). 320p. pap. 29.95 *(978-0-7456-3479-1(6))* Polity Pr. GBR. Dist: Wiley, John & Sons, Inc.

India, Planning Commission Staff, contrib. by. Mid-Term Appraisal: Eleventh Five Year Plan, 2007-2012. 2011. (ENG., Illus.). 500p. pap. 75.00 *(978-0-19-807205-8(8))* Oxford Univ. Pr., Inc.

Mathur, Vibha & Sury, M. India: Sixty Years of Planned Economic Development: 1950 To 2010. 2010. 470p. 98.75 *(978-81-7708-245-6(0))* New Century Publications IND. Dist: International Specialized Bk. Services.

Mises, Ludwig von. Economic Freedom & Interventionism: An Anthology of Articles & Essays by Ludwig Von Mises. 2006. (ENG.). 312p. (C). (gr. 12). 24.00 *(978-0-86597-672-6(4))*; pap. 14.50 *(978-0-86597-673-3(2))* Liberty Fund, Inc.

von Mises, Ludwig. Interventionism: An Economic Analysis. 2011. (ENG.). 122p. (C). (gr. 12). 22.00 *(978-0-86597-738-9(0))*; pap. 12.00 *(978-0-86597-739-6(9))* Liberty Fund, Inc.

Zack-Williams, Tunde ed. When the State Fails: Studies on Intervention in the Sierra Leone Civil War, 1 vol. 2012. (ENG., Illus.). 288p. 99.00 **(978-0-7453-3221-5(8))** Pluto Pr. GBR. Dist: Macmillan.

CENTRAL PLANNING—EUROPE

De Jasay, Anthony. Political Economy, Concisely: Essays on Policy That Does Not Work & Markets That Do. 2010. (Collected Papers of Anthony de Jasay Ser.). (ENG.). 360p. (C). (gr. 12). 24.00 *(978-0-86597-777-8(1))*; pap. 14.50 *(978-0-86597-778-5(X))* Liberty Fund, Inc.

Hardt, John P. & McMillan, Carl H., eds. Planned Economies: Confronting the Challenges of The 1980s. 2010. (International Council for Central & East European Studies). (ENG.). 207p. pap. 22.99 *(978-0-521-16844-1(9))* Cambridge Univ. Pr.

Smith, John. The Distorted World of Soviet-Type Economies (Routledge Revivals) 2011. (Routledge Revivals Ser.). (ENG.). 246p. 120.00 *(978-0-415-67605-2(3))* Routledge.

Steiner, André. The Plans That Failed: An Economic History of the GDR. 2010. (SGH Ser.). (Illus.). 236p. 60.00 *(978-1-84545-748-8(X))* Berghahn Bks., Inc.

CENTRAL PLANNING—SOVIET UNION

Dobb, Maurice. Soviet Economy & the War Bound with Soviet Planning & Labour. 2012. (ENG.). 224p. 115.00 **(978-0-415-52366-0(4))** Routledge.

Domar, Evsey D. Capitalism, Socialism, & Serfdom: Essays by Evsey D. Domar. 2008. (ENG.). 320p. pap. 42.00 *(978-0-521-07020-1(1))* Cambridge Univ. Pr.

Nell, Guinevere Liberty. Reinventing Fire: Basic Economic Lessons from the Soviet Experiment to Eliminate the Market. 2010. 338p. pap. 23.95 *(978-0-87586-747-2(2))*; (Illus.). 33.95 *(978-0-87586-748-9(0))* Algora Publishing.

CENTRAL UTAH RELOCATION CENTER

Suyemoto, Toyo, ed. I Call to Remembrance: Toyo Suyemoto's Years of Internment. 2007. (ENG., Illus.). 256p. per. 23.95 *(978-0-8135-4072-6(0))* Rutgers Univ. Pr.

Suyemoto, Toyo & Richardson, Susan B., eds. I Call to Remembrance: Toyo Suyemoto's Years of Internment. 2007. (ENG., Illus.). 224p. 68.00 *(978-0-8135-4071-9(2))* Rutgers Univ. Pr.

CENTRAL VALLEY PROJECT (CALIFORNIA)

Garone, Philip. The Fall & Rise of the Wetlands of California's Great Central Valley. 2011. (ENG., Illus.). 402p. 39.95 *(978-0-520-26663-6(3))* Univ. of California Pr.

Moffat, Amy. 2020: Visions for the Central Valley. 2010. pap 12.95 *(978-1-59714-133-8(X))* Heyday.

CENTRALIA (WASH.)

DeKok, David. Fire Underground: The Ongoing Tragedy of the Centralia Mine Fire. rev. ed. 2009. (ENG., Illus.). 288p. pap. 18.95 *(978-0-7627-5427-4(3))* Globe Pequot Pr., The.

Goffinet, Esther Barnett. Ripples of a Lie. 2011. 498p. 44.95 **(978-0-557-88438-4(1))** Lulu Enterprises Inc.

CENTRALIZATION IN GOVERNMENT

see Decentralization in Government

CENTRALIZATION OF SCHOOLS

see Schools—Centralization

CENTRIFUGAL COMPRESSORS

see Compressors

CENTRIFUGAL FORCE

see also Gravitation

Baker, Lawrence C., et al. Turbine Tip Clearance Measurement - Propulsion Engineering Series. 2008. 176p. pap. 65.00 *(978-1-934939-37-6(4))* Wexford College Pr.

CENTRIFUGAL PUMPS

American Society of Mechanical Engineers Staff, ed. Centrifugal Pump: Low-Flow Protection. (Illus.). 78p. 70.00 *(978-0-85298-791-9(9))* Professional Engineering Publishing GBR. Dist: SAE Intl.

—Centrifugal Pumps. 77p. 55.00 *(978-0-7918-2085-8(8))* ASME Pr.

—Shaft Sealing in Centrifugal Pumps. (Illus.). 76p. 84.00 *(978-0-85298-811-4(7))* Professional Engineering Publishing GBR. Dist: SAE Intl.

—Specificaiton for Sealless Horizontal End Suction Centrifugal Pumps for Chemical Process. 36p. 45.00 *(978-0-7918-2463-4(2))* ASME Pr.

—Specification for Horizontal End Suction Centrifugal Pumps for Chemical Process. 25p. 29.00 *(978-0-7918-2110-7(2))* ASME Pr.

—Specification for Vertical In-Line Centrifugal Pumps for Chemical Process. 25p. 29.00 *(978-0-7918-2127-5(7))* ASME Pr.

—Thermoplastic/Thermoset Polymer Material Horizontal End Suction Centrifugal Pumps Chemical Processes. 28p. 35.00 *(978-0-7918-2325-5(3))* ASME Pr

—Vibrations in Centrifugal Pumps. (Illus.). 65p. 66.00 *(978-0-85298-758-2(7))* Professional Engineering Publishing GBR. Dist: SAE Intl.

Barrios, Lissett & Prado, Mauricio. Study of Two-Phase Performance Inside an Esp. 2008. 248p. pap. *(978-3-639-00763-3(8))* VDM Verlag Dr. Mueller e.K.

Biggs, Robert E. Space Shuttle Main Engine: The First Twenty Years & Beyond, 1, 29. 2008. (ENG., Illus.). 270p. 70.00 *(978-0-87703-546-6(6))*, American Astronautical Society); pap. 50.00 *(978-0-87703-547-3(4))* Univelt, Inc.

Billy McNally's Pump & Seal Manual. pap 99.95 *(978-0-9670068-1-9(3))* McNally Institute.

D'Agostino, Luca. Fluid Dynamics of Cavitation & Cavitating Turbopumps. 2008. (CISM International Centre for Mechanical Sciences Ser.). 189.00 *(978-3-211-76668-2(5))* Springer.

d'Agostino, Luca & Salvetti, Maria Vittoria eds. Fluid Dynamics of Cavitation & Cavitating Turbopumps. 2010. (CISM International Centre for Mechanical Sciences Ser.). (Illus.). vii, 351p. pap. 189.00 *(978-3-211-99920-2(5)*, 3211999205) Springer.

Gülich, Johann Friedrich. Centrifugal Pumps. 2007. (Illus.). 960p. 279.00 *(978-3-540-73694-3(8)*, 3540736948) Springer.

—Centrifugal Pumps. 2nd ed. 2010. (ENG., Illus.). xxxiv, 966p. 279.00 *(978-3-642-12823-3(8)*, 3642128238) Springer.

Nourbakhsh, Ahmad, et al. Turbopumps & Pumping Systems. 2010. (ENG., Illus.). xxvi, 184p. pap. 139.00 *(978-3-642-06421-0(3)*, 3642064213) Springer.

Sulzer Pumps. Centrifugal Pump Handbook. 3rd ed. 2010. (ENG., Illus.). 302p. 165.00 *(978-0-7506-8612-9(X)*, Butterworth-Heinemann) Elsevier Science & Technology Bks.

Wilson, K. C., et al. Slurry Transport Using Centrifugal Pumps. 3rd ed. (ENG., Illus.). x, 432p. 2010. pap. 179.00 *(978-1-4419-3591-5(6)*, 1441935916) 2008. 179.00 *(978-0-387-23262-1(1)*, 0387232621) Springer.

CENTRIFUGAL REGULATORS

see Governors (Machinery)

CENTRIFUGES

see also Sedimentation Analysis

Depountis, Nikos. Applications of Geotechnical Centrifuge for Environmental Research. 2010. 204p. pap. *(978-3-639-24899-9(6))* VDM Verlag Dr. Mueller e.K.

Lampiao, Fanuel. Measurement of Free Radicals & Their Effects on Human Spermatozo. 2008. 84p. pap. *(978-3-639-07705-6(9))* VDM Verlag Dr. Mueller e.K.

Wandrey, Christine & Cölfen, Helmut. Analytical Ultracentrifugation VIII. 2010. (Progress in Colloid & Polymer Science Ser.). viii, 174p. pap. 259.00 *(978-3-642-06740-2(9)*, 3642067409) Springer.

CENTRISTS

see Center Parties

CENTURY CHANGE PROBLEM (COMPUTER SYSTEMS)

see Year 2000 Date Conversion (Computer Systems)

CEOS (EXECUTIVES)

see Chief Executive Officers

CEPHALOPODA

see also Ammonoidea; Nautilus; Octopuses

Flusser, Vilém. Vampyroteuthis Infernalis. Novaes, Rodrigo Maltez, tr. 2011. 160p. pap. 24.95 **(978-0-9831734-1-0(9))** Atropos Pr.

Jereb, P., ed. Cephalopods of the World: an Annotated & Illustrated Catalogue of Cephalopod Species Known to Date: Chambered Nautiluses & Sepioids (Nautilidae, Sepiidae, Sepiolidae, Sepiadariidae, Idiosepiidae & Spirulidae) Vol. 1. 2nd ed. 2006. (FAO Species Catalogue for Fishery Purposes Ser.: No. 4). (Illus.). 262p. pap. *(978-92-5-105383-6(9))* Food & Agriculture Organization of the United Nations.

Jorgensen, Elaina M. Field Guide to Squids & Octopods of the Eastern North Pacific & Bering Sea. 2011. (ENG., Illus.). 100p. pap. 25.00 *(978-1-56612-139-2(6))* Alaska Sea Grant College Program.

King, Nancy & Dunlop, Colin. Cephalopods: Octopuses & Cuttlefishes for the Home Aquarium, 1 vol. 2008. (ENG., Illus.). 240p. 39.95 *(978-0-7938-0658-4(5))* TFH Pubns., Inc.

Kroger, Bjorn. Nautiloids Before & During the Origin of Ammonoids in a Siluro-Devonian Section in the Tafilalt, Anti-Atlas, Morocco, No. 79. 2009. (Special Papers in Palaeontology Ser.). (ENG., Illus.). 112p. pap. 145.95 *(978-1-4051-8770-1(0)*, Wiley-Blackwell) Wiley, John & Sons, Inc.

Landman, Neil H., et al, eds. Cephalopods Present & Past: New Insights & Fresh Perspectives. 2007. (Illus.). 400p. 259.00 *(978-1-4020-6461-6(6)*, 1402064616) Springer.

Lee, Henry. Sea Monsters Unmasked. 2007. per. 11.95 *(978-1-930585-37-9(3))* Coachwhip Pubns.

CERAMBYCIDAE

Lingafelter, Steven. Illustrated Key to the Longhorned Woodboring Beetles of the Eastern United States. 2007. (Illus.). 206p. spiral bd. 65.00 *(978-0-9726087-7-0(X))* Coleopterists Society, The.

CERAMIC ART

see Pottery

CERAMIC COATING

see also Enamel and Enameling

Acers Staff. Advanced Ceramic Coatings & Interfaces V, Vol. 31. Lin, Hua-Tay & Zhu, Dongming, eds. 2010. (Ceramic Engineering & Science Proceedings Ser.: 527). (ENG., Illus.). 204p. 89.95 *(978-0-470-59468-1(3)*, Wiley-American Ceramic Society) Wiley, John & Sons, Inc.

American Ceramic Society Staff, ed. & contrib. by. Progress in Thermal Barrier Coatings. 2009. (Progress in Ceramic Technology Ser.: 2). (ENG., Illus.). 628p. 205.00 *(978-0-470-40838-4(3)*, Wiley-American Ceramic Society) Wiley, John & Sons, Inc.

Jiménez-Piqué, E. & Hvizdos, P. Layered, Functional Gradient Ceramics, & Thermal Barrier Coatings. Anlada, Marc, ed. (Key Engineering Materials Ser.: Vol. 333). (Illus.). 304p. pap. *(978-0-87849-424-8(3))* Trans Tech Pubns., Ltd.

Lin, Hua-Tay & Zhu, Dongming, eds. Advanced Ceramic Coatings & Interfaces III. 2008. (Ceramic Engineering & Science Proceedings Ser.: 46). (ENG., Illus.). 182p. 89.95 *(978-0-470-34495-8(4)*, Wiley-American Ceramic Society) Wiley, John & Sons, Inc.

Schulz, Uwe. Advanced Ceramic Coatings & Interfaces II. Lin, Hua-Tay, ed. 2007. (Ceramic Engineering & Science Proceedings Ser.). (ENG., Illus.). 266p. 111.00 *(978-0-470-19634-2(3)*, Wiley-American Ceramic Society) Wiley, John & Sons, Inc.

Shin, Dong-Il. Development of Metal Based Thermal Barrier Coatings Thermal Barrier Coatings for Internal Combustion/Diesel Engines. 2008. 144p. pap. *(978-3-639-00726-8(3))* VDM Verlag Dr. Mueller e.K.

Soltani, Reza. Thermo-Mechanical Behavior of Plasma Sprayed Zirconia Coatings. 2008. 240p. pap. *(978-3-639-04186-6(0))* VDM Verlag Dr. Mueller e.K.

Technology Research Editors, ed. Ceramic Based Cutting Tools, 2007 Ed. 2007. pap. 118.50 *(978-1-60030-293-0(9)*, Search-In-Print) CSA Journal Division.

—Microstructure of Thermal Spray Coatings, 2007 Ed. 2007. pap. 128.50 *(978-1-60030-351-7(X)*, Search-In-Print) CSA Journal Division.

—Thermal Spray Ceramic Coatings, 2007 Ed. 2007. pap. 118.50 *(978-1-60030-358-6(7)*, Search-In-Print) CSA Journal Division.

Vincenzini, P. & Montavon, Ghislain. Ceramic Thin Films & Coatings for Protective, Tribological & Multifunctional Applications: 12th International Ceramics Congress, Part E. 2011. (Illus.). 178p. pap. *(978-3-908158-49-3(4))* Trans Tech Pubns., Ltd.

Widjaja, Sujanto, et al. Advanced Ceramic Coatings & Materials for Extreme Environments: Ceramic Engineering & Science Proceedings. Zhu, Dongming et al, eds. 2011. (Ceramic Engineering & Science Proceedings Ser.: 545). (ENG., Illus.). 208p. 79.95 *(978-1-118-05988-3(3)*, Wiley-American Ceramic Society) Wiley, John & Sons, Inc.

Zhu, Dongming & Lin, Hua-Tay, eds. Advanced Ceramic Coatings & Interfaces IV. 2009. (Ceramic Engineering & Science Proceedings Ser.: 507). (ENG., Illus.). 136p. 94.95 *(978-0-470-45753-5(8)*, Wiley-American Ceramic Society) Wiley, John & Sons, Inc.

CERAMIC INDUSTRIES

BCC Research Staff. Technical & Advanced Structural Ceramics. 2008. pap. 4850.00 *(978-1-59623-424-6(5))* BCC Research.

Blair, Munroe. Bathroom Ceramics. 2008. (Shire Library). (ENG., Illus.). 40p. pap. 11.95 *(978-0-7478-0513-7(X))* Shire Pubns., Ltd. GBR. Dist: Random Hse., Inc.

Finlay, Robert. The Pilgrim Art: Cultures of Porcelain in World History. 2010. (California World History Library). (ENG., Illus.). 441p. 36.95 *(978-0-520-24468-9(0))* Univ. of California Pr.

Goldscheider, Filipp, et al. Goldscheider - Weltmarke der Keramik: Firmengeschichte und Werkverzeichnis. 2008. (GER, ENG & MUL., Illus.). 640p. 225.00 *(978-3-89790-216-9(8))* Arnoldsche Art Pubs. DEU. Dist: Antique Collectors' Club.

Guadagnin, Remy. Fosses, Vallee de l'Ysieux. Mille ans de production ceramique en Ile-de-France: Volume 2: Catalogue typochronologique des Productions, 2 vols. 2007. (Publications du Centre de Recherches Archéologiques et Historiques Médiévales Ser.). (FRE., Illus.). 735p. (C). 96.00 *(978-2-902685-41-7(6))* Brepols Pubs. BEL. Dist: Brown, David Bk. Co., The.

High Tech Ceramics Industry Review 2005. 2006. per. 1950.00 *(978-1-59623-214-3(5))* BCC Research.

Lin, Hua-Tay, et al, eds. Developments in Strategic Materials: Ceramic Engineering & Science Proceedings. 2008. (Ceramic Engineering & Science Proceedings Ser.: 58). (ENG., Illus.). 310p. 89.95 *(978-0-470-34500-9(4)*, Wiley-American Ceramic Society) Wiley, John & Sons, Inc.

Sinton, Christopher W., ed. Pathways to Sustainable Ceramic & Glass Manufacturing. 2013. (ENG.). 300p. 99.95 *(978-0-470-46002-3(4)*, Wiley-American Ceramic Society) Wiley, John & Sons, Inc.

CERAMIC MATERIALS

see also Ceramic Metals

ACerS. Advances in Solid Oxide Fuel Cells, Vol. VI. 2010. (Ceramic Engineering & Science Proceedings Ser.: 528). (ENG., Illus.). 174p. 89.95 *(978-0-470-59469-8(1)*, Wiley-American Ceramic Society) Wiley, John & Sons, Inc.

ACerS, null. Advances in Electroceramic Materials II, Vol. 221. Nair, K. M. & Priya, Shashank, eds. 2010. (Ceramic Transactions Ser.: 106). (ENG., Illus.). 276p. 132.00 *(978-0-470-92716-8(X)*, Wiley-American Ceramic Society) Wiley, John & Sons, Inc.

Acers Staff. Advanced Materials for Sustainable Developments, Vol. 31. An, Linan et al, eds. 2010. (Ceramic Engineering & Science Proceedings Ser.: 533). (ENG., Illus.). 150p. 89.95 *(978-0-470-59474-2(8)*, Wiley-American Ceramic Society) Wiley, John & Sons, Inc.

—Ceramic Engineering & Science Proceedings 2008, Set. 2008. (Ceramic Engineering & Science Proceedings Ser.). 2800p. 485.00 *(978-0-470-22401-4(0)*, Wiley-American Ceramic Society) Wiley, John & Sons, Inc.

—Characterization & Control of Interfaces for High Quality Advanced Materials III, Vol. 219. Ewsuk, Kevin G. et al, eds. 2010. (Ceramic Transactions Ser.: 104). (ENG., Illus.). 418p. 132.00 *(978-0-470-90917-1(X)*, Wiley-American Ceramic Society) Wiley, John & Sons, Inc.

Acers Staff, et al, eds. Advances in Materials Science for Environmental & Nuclear Technology II: Ceramic Transactions. 2011. (Ceramic Transactions Ser.). (ENG., Illus.). 348p. 125.00 *(978-1-118-06000-1(8)*, Wiley-American Ceramic Society) Wiley, John & Sons, Inc.

Advanced Ceramics & Nano Ceramic Powders. 2006. per. 4250.00 *(978-1-59623-254-9(4))* BCC Research.

Aegerter, Michel A. & Mennig, M., eds. Sol-Gel Technologies for Glass Producers & Users. 2011. (ENG.). xx, 493p. pap. 259.00 *(978-1-4419-5455-8(4)*, 1441954554) Springer.

Al. Crystalline Materials for Actinide Immobilisation. 2010. (Illus.). xvi, 197p. 66.00 *(978-1-84816-418-5(1))* World Scientific Publishing Co., Inc.

Aldinger, Fritz & Weberruß, Volker A. Advanced Ceramics & Future Materials: An Introduction to Structures, Properties, Technologies, Methods. 2010. (ENG., Illus.). 520p. 130.00 *(978-3-527-32157-5(8)*, Wiley-VCH) Wiley, John & Sons, Inc.

An, Linan, et al. Developments in Strategic Materials & Computational Design II: Ceramic Engineering & Science Proceedings. Gyekenyesi, Andrew et al, eds. 2011. (Ceramic Engineering & Science Proceedings Ser.: 552). (ENG., Illus.). 260p. 79.95 *(978-1-118-05995-1(6)*, Wiley-American Ceramic Society) Wiley, John & Sons, Inc.

Bansal, Narottam P. Advances in Solid Oxide Fuel Cells III: Ceramic Engineering & Science Proceedings. Salem, Jonathan & Zhu, Dongming, eds. 2007. (Ceramic Engineering & Science Proceedings Ser.: 52). (ENG., Illus.). 437p. 111.00 *(978-0-470-19635-9(1)*, Wiley-American Ceramic Society) Wiley, John & Sons, Inc.

—Handbook of Ceramic Composites. 2010. (Illus.). x, 558p. pap. 399.00 *(978-1-4419-5482-4(1)*, 1441954821) Springer.

Bansal, Narottam P. & Boccaccini, Aldo R., eds. Ceramics & Composites Processing Methods. 2012. (ENG.). 596p. 175.00 **(978-0-470-55344-2(8)**, Wiley-American Ceramic Society) Wiley, John & Sons, Inc.

Bansal, Narottam P. & Singh, Prabhakar, eds. Advances in Solid Oxide Fuel Cells V. 2009. (Ceramic Engineering & Science Proceedings Ser.: 508). (ENG., Illus.). 274p. 94.95 *(978-0-470-45754-2(6)*, Wiley-American Ceramic Society) Wiley, John & Sons, Inc.

Bansal, Narottam P., et al. Processing & Properties of Advanced Ceramics & Composites, Vol 207. 2009. (Ceramic Transactions Ser.: 83). (ENG., Illus.). 266p. 153.00 *(978-0-470-40845-2(6)*, Wiley-American Ceramic Society) Wiley, John & Sons, Inc.

—Processing & Properties of Advanced Ceramics & Composites II: Ceramic Transactions, Vol. 220. 2010. (Ceramic Transactions Ser.: 105). (ENG., Illus.). 322p. 132.00 *(978-0-470-92715-1(1)*, Wiley-American Ceramic Society) Wiley, John & Sons, Inc.

Basu, Bikramjit & Balani, Kantesh. Advanced Structural Ceramics. 2011. (ENG., Illus.). 512p. 165.00 *(978-0-470-49711-1(4)*, Wiley-American Ceramic Society) Wiley, John & Sons, Inc.

Basu, Bikramjit & Kalin, Mitjan. Tribology of Ceramics & Composites: Materials Science Perspective. 2011. (ENG.). 550p. 165.00 *(978-0-470-52263-9(1)*, Wiley-American Ceramic Society) Wiley, John & Sons, Inc.

BCC Research Staff. Technical & Advanced Structural Ceramics. 2008. pap. 4850.00 *(978-1-59623-424-6(5))* BCC Research.

C

Bellosi, Alida, et al, eds. Interfacial Science in Ceramic Joining. 2010. (NATO Science Partnership Sub-Series: 3: Ser.). 496p. pap. 299.00 *(978-90-481-5086-1(8)*, 9048150868) Springer.

Bellucci, Stefano, ed. Physical Properties of Ceramic & Carbon Nanoscale Structures: The INFN Lectures, Vol. II. 2011. (Lecture Notes in Nanoscale Science & Technology Ser.). (ENG., Illus.). xiv, 280p. 129.00 *(978-3-642-15777-6(7)*, 3642157777) Springer.

Bengisu, M. Engineering Ceramics. 2010. (Engineering Materials Ser.). (ENG., Illus.). xxi, 620p. pap. 219.00 *(978-3-642-08719-6(1)*, 3642087191) Springer.

Bernard, Samuel. Design, Processing & Properties of Ceramic Materials from Preceramic Precursors. 2011. (Series: Materials Science & Technologies Ser.). (Illus.). 246p. 75.00 *(978-1-61209-995-8(5))* Nova Science Pubs., Inc.

Bioactive Glasses, Ceramics, Composites, Other Advanced Materials. 2006. per. 4250.00 *(978-1-59623-235-8(8))* BCC Research.

Boch, Philippe & Niépce, Jean-Claude, eds. Ceramic Materials: Processes, Properties & Applications. 2007. (Iste Ser.: 632). (ENG., Illus.). 573p. 289.00 *(978-1-905209-23-1(1)*, Wiley-ISTE) Wiley, John & Sons, Inc.

Bosworth, Joy. Ceramics with Mixed Media. 2006. (Ceramics Handbooks Ser.). (Illus.). 112p. pap. 26.50 *(978-0-8122-1962-3(7))* Univ. of Pennsylvania Pr.

Bradt, R. C., et al, eds. Fracture Mechanics of Ceramics: Active Materials, Nanoscale Materials, Composites, Glass, & Fundamentals. 2010. (Fracture Mechanics of Ceramics Ser.). (Illus.). x, 636p. pap. 349.00 *(978-1-4419-3692-9(0)*, 1441936920) Springer.

—Fracture Mechanics of Ceramics, Volume 13: Crack-Microstructure Interaction, R-Curve Behavior, Environmental Effects in Fracture, & Standardization. 2010. (ENG.). 538p. pap. 225.00 *(978-1-4419-3370-6(0)*, 1441933700) Springer.

Brito, Manuel E. Developments in Porous, Biological & Geopolymer Ceramics. Case, Eldon et al, eds. 2007. (Ceramic Engineering & Science Proceedings Ser.: 520). (ENG., Illus.). 384p. 111.00 *(978-0-470-19640-3(8)*, Wiley-American Ceramic Society) Wiley, John & Sons, Inc.

Brorsson, Torbjorn. The Pottery from the Early Medieval Trading Site & Cemetery at Gross Stromkendorf, Lkr. Nordwestmecklenburg: Forschungen zu Gross Stromkendorf III. 2010. (Fruhmittelalterliche Archaologie zwischen Ostsee und Mittelmeer Ser.). (ENG., Illus.). 157p. (C). 50.00 *(978-3-89500-751-4(X))* Reichert, Ludwig Dr. DEU. Dist: Brown, David Bk. Co., The.

Carter, C. Barry & Norton, M. Grant. Ceramic Materials: Science & Engineering. 2007. (Illus.). 716p. 124.00 *(978-0-387-46270-7(8)*, 0387462708) Springer.

Caruntu, Daniela. Nanocrystalline Transition Metal Ferrites. 2008. 136p. pap. *(978-3-639-06866-5(1))* VDM Verlag Dr. Mueller e.K.

Caurant, D., et al. Ceramics, Glass-Ceramics & Glasses for Immobilization of High-Level Nuclear Wastes. 2008. (Illus.). xii, 359p. pap. 69.00 *(978-1-60456-174-6(2))* Nova Science Pubs., Inc.

Ceramic Powders Characterization, Results of a International Laboratory Study. per. *(978-0-16-060854-4(6))* United States Government Printing Office.

Chen, Dong. Ultrasonic Control of Ceramic Membrane Fouling. 2009. 160p. pap. *(978-3-639-20905-1(2))* VDM Verlag Dr. Mueller e.K.

Choi, Sung R., et al, eds. Processing & Properties of Advanced Ceramics & Composites III. 2011. (Ceramic Transactions Ser.: 112). (ENG., Illus.). 218p. 125.00 *(978-1-118-05998-2(0)*, Wiley-American Ceramic Society) Wiley, John & Sons, Inc.

Cobb, Justin P. Modern Trends in THA Bearings: Material & Clinical Performance. Cobb, Justin P., ed. 2010. (Ceramics in Orthopaedics Ser.). (Illus.). 300p. 109.00 *(978-3-642-13988-8(4)*, 3642139884) Springer.

Cozzi, et al. Ceramic Materials & Components for Energy & Environmental Applications, Vol. 210. 2010. (Ceramic Transactions Ser.: 80). (ENG.). 678p. 158.00 *(978-0-470-40842-1(1)*, Wiley-American Ceramic Society) Wiley, John & Sons, Inc.

Dimitriou, Eros & Petralia, Marco, eds. Ceramic & Polymer Matrix Composites: Properties, Performance & Applications. 2010. (Polymer Science & Technology Ser.). 145.00 *(978-1-60741-896-2(7))* Nova Science Pubs., Inc.

Dogan, Faith. Environmental Issues & Waste Management Technologies in the Materials & Nuclear Industries XII, Vol. 210. Cozzi, Alex & Ohji, Tatsuki, eds. 2009. (Ceramic Transactions Ser.: 86). (ENG., Illus.). 320p. 153.00 *(978-0-470-40848-3(0)*, Wiley-American Ceramic Society) Wiley, John & Sons, Inc.

Dogan, Fatih, et al, eds. Ceramics for Environmental & Energy Applications. 2010. (Ceramic Transactions Ser.: 102). (ENG., Illus.). 186p. 105.00 *(978-0-470-90547-0(6)*, Wiley-American Ceramic Society) Wiley, John & Sons, Inc.

Esquivias, Luis, ed. Progress in Sol-Gel Production. 2009. 194p. pap. *(978-0-87849-365-4(4))* Trans Tech Pubns., Ltd.

Ewsuk, Kevin. Characterization & Control of Interfaces for High Quality Advanced Materials II. Nogi, Kiyoshi et al, eds. 2007. (Ceramic Transactions Ser.: 72). (ENG., Illus.). 490p. 156.00 *(978-0-470-18414-1(0)*, Wiley-American Ceramic Society) Wiley, John & Sons, Inc.

Fisher, David, ed. Defects & Diffusion in Ceramics XII: An Annual Retrospective XII. 2011. 308p. pap. ***(978-3-03785-153-1(8))*** Trans Tech Pubns., Ltd.

Fox, Kevin, et al. Advances in Materials Science for Environmental & Nuclear Technology, Vol. 222. 2010. (Ceramic Transactions Ser.: 107). (ENG., Illus.). 312p. 132.00 *(978-0-470-92729-8(1)*, Wiley-American Ceramic Society) Wiley, John & Sons, Inc.

Franks, L. Advances in Ceramic Armor III: Ceramic Engineering & Science Proceedings. Salem, Jonathan & Zhu, Dongming, eds. 2007. (Ceramic Engineering & Science Proceedings Ser.). (ENG., Illus.). 224p. 111.00 *(978-0-470-19636-6(X)*, Wiley-American Ceramic Society) Wiley, John & Sons, Inc.

Franks, Lisa Prokurat, ed. Advances in Ceramic Armor IV: Ceramic Engineering & Science Proceedings. 2008. (Ceramic Engineering & Science Proceedings Ser.: 50). (ENG., Illus.). 242p. 89.95 *(978-0-470-34497-2(0)*, Wiley-American Ceramic Society) Wiley, John & Sons, Inc.

Fujihara, Shinobu & Takenaka, Tadashi, eds. Electroceramics in Japan XIII: Selected, Peer Reviewed Papers from the 9th Electronics Division Meeting of the Ceramic Society of Japan, Tokyo, Japan, Oct. 23-24, 2009, Vol. 445. 2010. (Key Engineering Materials Ser.). 256p. pap. *(978-0-87849-264-0(X))* Trans Tech Pubns., Ltd.

Gubinyi, Zoltan. Electrical Properties of Pzt Piezoelectric Ceramics at High Temperatures. 2008. 116p. pap. *(978-3-639-02304-6(8))* VDM Verlag Dr. Mueller e.K.

Hinklin, T., et al. Advances in Energy Materials, Vol. 205. 2009. (Ceramic Transactions Ser.: 81). (ENG., Illus.). 168p. 111.00 *(978-0-470-40843-8(X)*, Wiley-American Ceramic Society) Wiley, John & Sons, Inc.

Hu. Ceramic Nanomaterials & Nanotechnology. 2007. (Ceramic Transactions Ser.). pap. 115.00 *(978-0-470-29226-6(1)*, Wiley-American Ceramic Society) Wiley, John & Sons, Inc.

Ianculescu, Adelina & Mitoseriu, Liliana, eds. Ba(Ti,Zr)O3 - Functional Materials: from Nanopowders to Bulk Ceramics. 2010. (Nanotechnology Science & Technology Ser.). 113p. pap. 43.00 *(978-1-61668-752-6(5)*, Nova Novinka) Nova Science Pubs., Inc.

Igata, N. & Takeuchi, Shin. High Damping Materials II: Proceedings of the 2nd International Symposium on High Damping Materials Held in Kyoto, September 9-10, 2005. 2006. (Key Engineering Materials Ser.: Vol. 319). (Illus.). x, 244p. pap. *(978-0-87849-406-4(5))* Trans Tech Pubns., Ltd.

International Microelectronics and Packaging Society (IMAPS) Staff, compiled by. 2nd International Conference & Exhibition on Ceramic Interconnect & Ceramic Microsystems Technologies (CICMT2006) 2007. 504p. pap. 250.00 *(978-1-60423-620-0(5))* Curran Assocs., Inc.

Jansen, M., ed. High Performance Non-Oxide Ceramics II. 2011. (Structure & Bonding Ser.). (ENG., Illus.). x, 188p. pap. 249.00 *(978-3-642-07724-1(2)*, 3642077242) Springer.

Jansen, M. & contrib. by. High Performance Non-Oxide Ceramics I. 2011. (Structure & Bonding Ser.). (ENG., Illus.). xiv, 216p. pap. 259.00 *(978-3-642-07723-4(4)*, 3642077234) Springer.

Katayama, K., et al, eds. Electroceramics in Japan X: Proceedings of the 26th Electonics Division Meeting of the Ceramic Society of Japan, Tokyo, Japan, October 26-27, 2006. 2007. 251p. pap. *(978-0-87849-449-1(9))* Trans Tech Pubns., Ltd.

Kato, Kazumitsu, et al, eds. Electroceramics in Japan XI. 2009. (Key Engineering Materials Ser.). 322p. pap. *(978-0-87849-359-3(X))* Trans Tech Pubns., Ltd.

Komeya, Katsutoshi, et al, eds. Innovation in Ceramic Science & Engineering: Publications of the Ceramic Society of Japan. 2007. 330p. pap. *(978-0-87849-454-5(5))* Trans Tech Pubns., Ltd.

Konsowski, J. & Lower, L. Advanced Ceramic Materials & Processes for Electronic Applications. Date not set. *(978-0-8247-9583-2(0))* Dekker, Marcel Inc.

Kriven, Waltraud M., et al. Strategic Materials & Computational Design. 2010. (Ceramic Engineering & Science Proceedings Ser.: 538). (ENG.). 204p. 89.95 *(978-0-470-92191-3(9)*, Wiley-American Ceramic Society) Wiley, John & Sons, Inc.

Lara-Curzio, Edgar. Mechanical Properties & Performance of Engineering Ceramics & Composites III. Salem, Jonathan & Zhu, Dongming, eds. 2007. (Ceramic Engineering & Science Proceedings Ser.: 49). (ENG., Illus.). 530p. 111.00 *(978-0-470-19633-5(5)*, Wiley-American Ceramic Society) Wiley, John & Sons, Inc.

Leventis, Nicholas & Aegerter, Michel A., eds. Aerogels Handbook. 2011. (Advances in Sol-Gel Derived Materials & Technologies Ser.). (ENG., Illus.). xxxi, 932p. 349.00 *(978-1-4419-7477-8(6)*, 1441974776) Springer.

Li, Kang. Ceramic Membranes for Separation & Reaction. 2007. (ENG., Illus.). 316p. 215.00 *(978-0-470-01440-0(7)*, Wiley) Wiley, John & Sons, Inc.

Lin, Hua-Tay, et al, eds. Corrosion, Wear, Fatigue, & Reliability of Ceramics, Vol. 29. 2008. (Ceramic Engineering & Science Proceedings Ser.: 347). (ENG., Illus.). 214p. 89.95 *(978-0-470-34493-4(8)*, Wiley-American Ceramic Society) Wiley, John & Sons, Inc.

—Developments in Strategic Materials: Ceramic Engineering & Science Proceedings. 2008. (Ceramic Engineering & Science Proceedings Ser.: 58). (ENG., Illus.). 310p. 89.95 *(978-0-470-34500-9(4)*, Wiley-American Ceramic Society) Wiley, John & Sons, Inc.

Lin, Hua-Tay & Zhu, Dongming, eds. Advanced Ceramic Coatings & Interfaces III. 2008. (Ceramic Engineering & Science Proceedings Ser.: 46). (ENG., Illus.). 182p. 89.95 *(978-0-470-34495-8(4)*, Wiley-American Ceramic Society) Wiley, John & Sons, Inc.

Lin, Paul B. Ceramic Materials Research Trends. 2007. 129.00 *(978-1-60021-769-2(9))* Nova Science Pubs., Inc.

Löhe, Detlef & Haußelt, Jürgen, eds. Microengineering of Metals & Ceramics Set, Pts. 1&2: Design, Tooling, & Injection Molding - Special Replication Techniques, Automation, & Properties. 2008. (Advanced Micro & Nanosystems Ser.). (ENG.). 698p. 389.00 *(978-3-527-32378-4(3)*, Wiley-VCH) Wiley, John & Sons, Inc.

Mahajan, Yashwant & Sekhar, J. A., eds. Progress in High Temperature Ceramics. 2009. (Key Engineering Materials Ser.). 242p. pap. *(978-0-87849-361-6(1))* Trans Tech Pubns., Ltd.

Mallick, Sudhanshu. High Temperature Piezoelectric Ceramics. 2009. 152p. pap. *(978-3-639-12935-9(0))* VDM Verlag Dr. Mueller e.K.

Marinescu, Ioan D., ed. Handbook of Advanced Ceramics Machining. 2006. (ENG., Illus.). 384p. 179.95 *(978-0-8493-3837-3(9)*, CRC Press) Taylor & Francis Group GBR. Dist: Taylor & Francis Group.

Mathur, Sanjay. Proceedings of the 35th International Conference on Advanced Ceramics & Composites. 2012. (ENG.). 395.00 ***(978-1-118-15582-0(3)***, Wiley-American Ceramic Society) Wiley, John & Sons, Inc.

Mathur, Sanjay, et al, eds. Nanostructured Materials & Nanotechnology. 2007. (Ceramic Engineering & Science Proceedings Ser.). (ENG., Illus.). 196p. 111.00 *(978-0-470-19637-3(8)*, Wiley-American Ceramic Society) Wiley, John & Sons, Inc.

Mathur, Sanjay & Singh, Mrityunjay, eds. Nanostructured Materials & Nanotechnology II. 2008. (Ceramic Engineering & Science Proceedings Ser.: 54). (ENG., Illus.). 266p. 89.95 *(978-0-470-34498-9(9)*, Wiley-American Ceramic Society) Wiley, John & Sons, Inc.

Mathur, Sanjay, et al. Nanostructured Materials & Systems. 2010. (Ceramic Transactions Ser.: 99). (ENG., Illus.). 168p. 105.00 *(978-0-470-88128-6(3)*, Wiley-American Ceramic Society) Wiley, John & Sons, Inc.

Mizutani, N., et al, eds. Electroceramics in Japan I. (Key Engineering Materials Ser.: Vol. 157-158). (Illus.). 324p. (C). 142.00 *(978-0-87849-813-0(3))* Trans Tech Pubns., Ltd. CHE. Dist: Enfield Publishing & Distribution Co., Inc.

Mohamed, Adel, et al. Piezoelectric Ceramic Materials. 2011. 116p. pap. ***(978-3-8433-8768-2(0))*** Lambert Academic Publishing.

Munir, Zuhair A., et al. Innovative Processing & Manufacturing of Advanced Ceramics & Composites, Vol. 212. 2010. (Ceramic Transactions Ser.: 97). (ENG., Illus.). 250p. 105.00 *(978-0-470-87646-6(8)*, Wiley-American Ceramic Society) Wiley, John & Sons, Inc.

—Pulse Electric Current Synthesis & Processing of Materials. 2011. (Ceramic Transactions Ser.). (ENG.). 450p. 156.00 *(978-0-470-08275-1(5)*, Wiley-American Ceramic Society) Wiley, John & Sons, Inc.

—Pulse Electric Current Synthesis & Processing of Materials: Ceramic Transactions. 2006. (Ceramic Transactions Ser.: 63). (ENG., Illus.). 314p. per. 156.00 *(978-0-470-08156-3(2)*, Wiley-American Ceramic Society) Wiley, John & Sons, Inc.

Murphy, Matthew. The Use of Ion Implantation for Biomedical Applications. 2010. 348p. pap. *(978-3-8383-7895-4(4))* Lambert Academic Publishing.

Narayan, Roger, et al, eds. Biomaterials Science: Processing, Properties, & Applications. 2011. (Ceramic Transactions Ser.: 118). (ENG.). 204p. 125.00 *(978-1-118-06001-8(6)*, Wiley-American Ceramic Society) Wiley, John & Sons, Inc.

Narayan, Roger & Colombo, Paolo, eds. Advances in Bioceramics & Porous Ceramics. 2009. (Ceramic Engineering & Science Proceedings Ser.: 510). (ENG., Illus.). 344p. 94.95 *(978-0-470-45756-6(2)*, Wiley-American Ceramic Society) Wiley, John & Sons, Inc.

—Advances in Bioceramics & Porous Ceramics III, Vol. 31. 2010. (Ceramic Engineering & Science Proceedings Ser.: 530). (ENG., Illus.). 188p. 89.95 *(978-0-470-59471-1(3)*, Wiley-American Ceramic Society) Wiley, John & Sons, Inc.

Narayan, Roger, et al. Advances in Bioceramics & Biotechnologies. 2010. (Ceramic Transactions Ser.: 103). (ENG., Illus.). 244p. 105.00 *(978-0-470-90548-7(4)*, Wiley-American Ceramic Society) Wiley, John & Sons, Inc.

Ohji, T., et al, eds. The Science of Engineering Ceramics. 2006. (Key Engineering Materials Ser.: Vol. 318). (Illus.). 950p. (C). 343.00 *(978-0-87849-401-9(4))* Trans Tech Pubns., Ltd. CHE. Dist: Enfield Publishing & Distribution Co., Inc.

Ohji, Tatsuki. Proceedings of the 32nd International Conference on Advanced Ceramics & Composites. 2008. (ENG.). 4p. 384.00 *(978-0-470-40833-9(2)*, Wiley-American Ceramic Society) Wiley, John & Sons, Inc.

Ohji, Tatsuki & Singh, Mrityunjay, eds. Advanced Processing & Manufacturing Technologies for Structural & Multifunctional Materials, Vol. 2. 2008. (Ceramic Engineering & Science Proceedings Ser.: 56). (ENG., Illus.). 236p. 89.95 *(978-0-470-34499-6(7)*, Wiley-American Ceramic Society) Wiley, John & Sons, Inc.

—Advanced Processing & Manufacturing Technologies for Structural & Multifunctional Materials III. 2009. (Ceramic Engineering & Science Proceedings Ser.: 512). (ENG., Illus.). 246p. 94.95 *(978-0-470-45758-0(9)*, Wiley-American Ceramic Society) Wiley, John & Sons, Inc.

Pabst, Willi & Gregorova, Eva. Phase Mixture Models for the Properties of Nanoceramics. 2010. (Nanotechnology Science & Technology Ser.). (Illus.). xiv, 74p. pap. 43.00 *(978-1-61668-673-4(1))* Nova Science Pubs., Inc.

Priya, Shashank, et al, eds. Advances in Electronic Ceramics II. 2009. (Ceramic Engineering & Science Proceedings Ser.: 513). (ENG., Illus.). 164p. 94.95 *(978-0-470-45759-7(7)*, Wiley-American Ceramic Society) Wiley, John & Sons, Inc.

Rahaman Mohamed N Staff. Solutions Manual for Ceramic Processing. 2006. (Illus.). 57p. (C). *(978-1-4200-4362-4(5))* CRC Pr. LLC.

Rossiere, Dena. Developments in Ceramic Materials Research. 2007. 185.00 *(978-1-60021-770-8(2))* Nova Science Pubs., Inc.

Sakka, Sumio, ed. Handbook of Sol-Gel Science & Technology: Processing, Characterization & Applications. 2007. (Illus.). LX, 1980p. 1875.00 *(978-0-387-33554-4(4)*, 0387335544) Springer.

—Sol-Gel Science & Technology Vol. 1: Topics in Fundamental Research & Applications, 4 vols. 2011. (ENG.). 1700p. pap. 599.00 *(978-1-4419-5323-0(X)*, 144195323X) Springer.

Salem, Jonathan, et al, eds. Mechanical Properties & Processing of Ceramic Binary, Ternary, & Composite Systems. 2008. (Ceramic Engineering & Science Proceedings Ser.: 346). (ENG., Illus.). 200p. 89.95 *(978-0-470-34492-7(X)*, Wiley-American Ceramic Society) Wiley, John & Sons, Inc.

Schneider, Gerold A. & Petzow, G., eds. Thermal Shock & Thermal Fatigue Behavior of Advanced Ceramics. 2010. (NATO Science Series E: (closed) Ser.). (Illus.). 612p. pap. 589.00 *(978-90-481-4291-0(1)*, 9048142911) Springer.

Shackelford, James F. & Doremus, Robert H., eds. Ceramic & Glass Materials: Structure, Properties & Processing. (ENG., Illus.). xii, 201p. 2010. pap. 149.00 *(978-1-4419-4460-3(5)*, 1441944605) 2008. 149.00 *(978-0-387-73361-6(2)*, 0387733612) Springer.

Singh, D. & Kriven, Waltraud M., eds. Mechanical Properties & Performance of Engineering Ceramics & Composites IV. 2009. (Ceramic Engineering & Science Proceedings Ser.: 506). (ENG., Illus.). 348p. 94.95 *(978-0-470-45752-8(X)*, Wiley-American Ceramic Society) Wiley, John & Sons, Inc.

Singh, Dileep & Salem, Jonathan, eds. Mechanical Properties & Performance of Engineering Ceramics & Composites, Vol. 5. 2010. (Ceramic Engineering & Science Proceedings Ser.: 526). (ENG., Illus.). 386p. 89.95 *(978-0-470-59467-4(5)*, Wiley-American Ceramic Society) Wiley, John & Sons, Inc.

Singh, Dileep, et al. Design, Development, & Applications of Engineering Ceramics & Composites Vol. 215: Ceramic Transactions. 2010. (Ceramic Transactions Ser.: 100). (ENG., Illus.). 350p. 105.00 *(978-0-470-88936-7(5)*, Wiley-American Ceramic Society) Wiley, John & Sons, Inc.

Singh, J. P. & Hinklin. Processing of Nanoparticle Structures & Composites, Vol. 208. Hinklin, Tom & Lu, Kathy, eds. 2009. (Ceramic Transactions Ser.: 84). (ENG., Illus.). 148p. 111.00 *(978-0-470-40846-9(4)*, Wiley-American Ceramic Society) Wiley, John & Sons, Inc.

Singh, Mrityunjay, et al, eds. Ceramic Integration & Joining Technologies: From Macro to Nanoscale. 2011. (ENG., Illus.). 830p. 175.00 *(978-0-470-39122-8(7)*, Wiley-American Ceramic Society) Wiley, John & Sons, Inc.

Singh, Mrityunjay & Ohji, Tatsuki, eds. Advanced Processing & Manufacturing Technologies for Structural & Multifunctional Material, Vol. IV. 2010. (Ceramic Engineering & Science Proceedings Ser.: 532). (ENG., Illus.). 260p. 89.95 *(978-0-470-59473-5(X)*, Wiley-American Ceramic Society) Wiley, John & Sons, Inc.

Singh, Prabhakar & Bansal, Narottam P., eds. Advances in Solid Oxide Fuel Cells IV, Vol. 29. 2008. (Ceramic Engineering & Science Proceedings Ser.: 48). (ENG., Illus.). 296p. 89.95 *(978-0-470-34496-5(2)*, Wiley-American Ceramic Society) Wiley, John & Sons, Inc.

Swab, Jeffrey J., ed. Advances in Ceramic Armor VI, Vol. 31. 2010. (Ceramic Engineering & Science Proceedings Ser.: 529). (ENG., Illus.). 274p. 89.95 *(978-0-470-59470-4(5)*, Wiley-American Ceramic Society) Wiley, John & Sons, Inc.

Swab, Jeffrey J. & Franks, Lisa, eds. Advances in Ceramic Armor V. 2009. (Ceramic Engineering & Science Proceedings Ser.: 509). (ENG., Illus.). 246p. 94.95 *(978-0-470-45755-9(4)*, Wiley-American Ceramic Society) Wiley, John & Sons, Inc.

Takenaka, Tadashi, et al, eds. Asian Ceramic Science for Electronics III & Electroceramics in Japan XII. 2010. (Key Engineering Materials Ser.: Vol. 422). (Illus.). 584p. pap. *(978-0-87849-306-7(9))* Trans Tech Pubns., Ltd.

Technology Research Editors, ed. Aluminum Nitride Substrates, 2007 Ed. 2007. pap. 128.50 *(978-1-60030-292-3(0)*, Search-In-Print) CSA Journal Division.

—Ceramic Based Cutting Tools, 2007 Ed. 2007. pap. 118.50 *(978-1-60030-293-0(9)*, Search-In-Print) CSA Journal Division.

—Ceramic Materials in Fuel Cells, 2007 Ed. 2007. pap. 118.50 *(978-1-60030-297-8(1)*, Search-In-Print) CSA Journal Division.

—Ceramic to Ceramic Joining, 2007 Ed. 2007. pap. 118.50 *(978-1-60030-298-5(X)*, Search-In-Print) CSA Journal Division.

—Ceramics in Engine Components, 2007 Ed. 2007. pap. 118.50 *(978-1-60030-240-4(8)*, Search-In-Print) CSA Journal Division.

—Chemical Analysis of Ceramic Materials, 2007 Ed. 2007. pap. 118.50 *(978-1-60030-302-9(1)*, Search-In-Print) CSA Journal Division.

—Fabrication & Applications of Functionally Gradient Materials, 2007 Ed. 2007. pap. 128.50 *(978-1-60030-366-1(8)*, Search-In-Print) CSA Journal Division.

—Fabrication of Ceramic Composites by Infiltration, 2007 Ed. 2007. pap. 118.50 *(978-1-60030-285-5(8)*, Search-In-Print) CSA Journal Division.

—Fracture Toughness of Monolithic Silicon Based Ceramics, 2007 Ed. 2007. pap. 118.50 *(978-1-60030-310-4(2)*, Search-In-Print) CSA Journal Division.

—Fracture Toughness of Whisker-Reinforced Ceramic Composites, 2007 Ed. 2007. pap. 118.50 *(978-1-60030-311-1(0)*, Search-In-Print) CSA Journal Division.

—Fracture Toughness of Zirconia Ceramics, 2007 Ed. 2007. pap. 118.50 *(978-1-60030-312-8(9)*, Search-In-Print) CSA Journal Division.

—Functionally Gradient Materials, 2007 Ed. 2007. pap. 128.50 *(978-1-60030-547-4(4)*, Search-In-Print) CSA Journal Division.

—Impact Response of Armor Incorporating Polymer or Ceramic Based Materials, 2007 Ed. 2007. pap. 118.50 *(978-1-60030-314-2(5)*, Search-In-Print) CSA Journal Division.

—Machining Ceramic Materials Components, 2007 Ed. 2007. pap. 118.50 *(978-1-60030-315-9(3)*, Search-In-Print) CSA Journal Division.

—Microstructure & Properties of Sialon, 2007 Ed. 2007. pap. 128.50 *(978-1-60030-318-0(8)*, Search-In-Print) CSA Journal Division.

—Modeling & Simulation of Fracture in Polymer & Ceramic Matrix Composites, 2007 Ed. 2007. pap. 128.50 *(978-1-60030-560-3(1)*, Search-In-Print) CSA Journa Division.

—Polymer- & Ceramic-Based Materials for Nuclear Reactor Components, 2007 Ed. 2007. pap. 118.50 *(978-1-60030-225-1(4)*, Search-In-Print) CSA Journal Division.

Vallet-Regí, María, ed. Progress in Bioceramics. 2008. (Key Engineering Materials Ser.: Vol. 377). 284p. pap. *(978-0-87849-395-1(6))* Trans Tech Pubns., Ltd.

Vincenzini, P. Advances in Electrical & Magnetic Ceramics: 12th International Ceramics Congress, Part F. 2011. (Illus.). 228p. pap. *(978-3-908158-50-9(8))* Trans Tech Pubns., Ltd.

—Novel Routes for Ceramics Synthesis & Processing: 12th International Ceramics Congress, Part B. 2011. (Illus.). 440p. pap. *(978-3-908158-46-2(X))* Trans Tech Pubns., Ltd.

Vincenzini, P. & Baumard, Jean-François. Ceramic Powders: Synthesis, Processing & Sintering: 12th International Ceramics Congress, Part A. 2011. (Illus.). 250p. pap. *(978-3-908158-45-5(1))* Trans Tech Pubns., Ltd.

Vincenzini, P. & Leonelli, Cristina. Geopolymers & Geocements: Low Environmentally Impact Ceramic Materials: 12th International Ceramics Congress, Part H. 2011. (Illus.). 208p. pap. *(978-3-908158-52-3(4))* Trans Tech Pubns., Ltd.

Vincenzini, Pietro, ed. Complete Set of Congress of Cimtec 2010. 2011. 2400p. pap. *(978-3-908158-60-8(5))* Trans Tech Pubns., Ltd.

—Complete Set of Forum of Cimtec 2010. 2011. 1500p. pap. *(978-3-908158-44-8(3))* Trans Tech Pubns., Ltd.

Wachtman, John B., Jr., et al. Mechanical Properties of Ceramics. 2nd ed. 2009. (ENG., Illus.). 479p. 146.00 *(978-0-471-73581-6(7)*, Wiley) Wiley, John & Sons, Inc.

Walkosz, Weronika. Atomic Scale Characterization & First-Principles Studies of Si3N4 Interfaces. 2011. (Springer Theses Ser.). (ENG., Illus.). xiii, 108p. 129.00 *(978-1-4419-7816-5(X)*, 144197816X) Springer.

Wereszczak, Andrew, et al, eds. Advances in Solid Oxide Fuel Cells II, Ceramic Engineering & Science Proceedings, Cocoa Beach. 2006. (Ceramic Engineering & Science Proceedings Ser.: 40). (ENG.). 437p. pap. 111.00 *(978-0-470-08054-2(X)*, Wiley-American Ceramic Society) Wiley, John & Sons, Inc.

Wereszczak, Andrew & Lara-Curzio, Edgar. Proceedings of the 30th International Conference on Advanced Ceramics & Composites. 2006. (ENG.). 227.00 *(978-0-470-11702-6(8)*, Wiley-American Ceramic Society) Wiley, John & Sons, Inc.

Widjaja, Sujanto & Acers Staff. Mechanical Properties & Performance of Engineering Ceramics & Composites VI: Ceramic Engineering & Science Proceedings. Singh, Dileep & Salem, Jonathan, eds. 2011. (Ceramic Engineering & Science Proceedings Ser.: 544). (ENG., Illus.). 328p. 79.95 *(978-1-118-05987-6(5)*, Wiley-American Ceramic Society) Wiley, John & Sons, Inc.

Widjaja, Sujanto, et al. Advances in Solid Oxide Fuel Cells VII Vol. 32: Ceramic Engineering & Science Proceedings. Bansal, Narottam P. & Singh, Prabhakar, eds. 2011. (Ceramic Engineering & Science Proceedings Ser.: 546). (ENG., Illus.). 224p. 79.95 *(978-1-118-05989-0(1)*, Wiley-American Ceramic Society) Wiley, John & Sons, Inc.

—Ceramic Materials for Energy Applications: Ceramic Engineering & Science Proceedings. Lin, Hua-Tay et al, eds. 2011. (Ceramic Engineering & Science Proceedings Ser.: 551). (ENG., Illus.). 216p. 79.95 *(978-1-118-05994-4(8)*, Wiley-American Ceramic Society) Wiley, John & Sons, Inc.

Woo, Hee-Gweon & Li, Hong, eds. Advanced Functional Materials. 2011. (ENG., Illus.). 350p. 219.00 *(978-3-642-19076-6(6)*, 3642190766) Springer.

Xiao, Ping & Ralph, Brian, eds. Advances in Ceramic Materials. 2009. (Materials Science Forum Ser.). 160p. pap. *(978-0-87849-350-0(6))* Trans Tech Pubns., Ltd.

Yin, Qingrui, et al. Microstructure, Property & Processing of Functional Ceramics. 2009. (ENG., Illus.). 400p. 279.00 *(978-3-642-01693-6(6)*, 3642016936) Springer.

Zaghib, K., ed. Intercalation Compounds for Batteries & Hybrid Supercapacitors. 2008. (ECS Transactions Ser.). 232p. pap. 100.00 *(978-1-60423-912-6(3))* Curran Assocs., Inc.

CERAMIC METALS

Bergmann, Carlos P. & Vicenzi, Juliane. Proctection Against Erosive Wear Using Thermal Sprayed Cermet: A Review. 2011. (Illus.). viii, 84p. 129.00 ***(978-3-642-21986-3(1)**, 3642219861)* Springer.

Kimeya, Katsutoshi, et al, eds. SiAlONs & Non-oxides. 2009. (Key Engineering Material Ser.: Vol. 403). 280p. pap. *(978-0-87849-345-6(X))* Trans Tech Pubns., Ltd.

Lal Gupta, Kanhaiya. Bond Strength of Porcelain to Metal under Different Firing Atmospheres. 2011. 96p. pap. ***(978-3-8443-1480-9(6))*** Lambert Academic Publishing.

Pastor, Henri. Tungsten Carbide - Cobalt Cermets. 2012. 512p. 170.00 *(978-1-85617-428-2(X)*, Elsevier Science) Elsevier Science & Technology Bks.

Technology Research Editors, ed. Cermets, 2007 Ed. 2007. pap. 128.50 *(978-1-60030-301-2(3)*, Search-In-Print) CSA Journal Division.

Widjaja, Sujanto, et al. Advances in Bioceramics & Porous Ceramics No. 4: Ceramic Engineering & Science Proceedings, Vol. IV. Narayan, Roger & Colombo, Paolo, eds. 2011. (Ceramic Engineering & Science Proceedings Ser.: 548). (ENG., Illus.). 224p. 79.95 *(978-1-118-05991-3(3)*, Wiley-American Ceramic Society) Wiley, John & Sons, Inc.

—Advances in Ceramic Armor No. 7. Swab, Jeffrey J., ed. 2011. (Ceramic Engineering & Science Proceedings Ser.: 547). (ENG., Illus.). 286p. 79.95 *(978-1-118-05990-6(5)*, Wiley-American Ceramic Society) Wiley, John & Sons, Inc.

Zhou, Yanchun & Low, It-Meng. Max Phases: Microstructure, Properties & Applications. 2012. (Series: Materials Science & Technologies Ser.). 294p. 140.00 *(978-1-61324-182-0(8))* Nova Science Pubs., Inc.

CERAMIC SCULPTURE

Abadie, D. Dubuffet As Architect. 2011. (ENG., Illus.). 168p. pap. ***(978-2-7541-0543-9(3))*** Yale Univ. Pr.

Abadie, Daniel. Dubuffet As Architect. 2011. (Illus.). 192p. pap. 40.00 *(978-0-300-17661-2(9))* Yale Univ. Pr.

Bertoni, Franco, ed. Bertozzi & Casoni: Opere/Works 1980-2010. 2012. (ENG & ITA., Illus.). 272p. 97.00 ***(978-88-422-1936-1(3))*** Allemandi, Umberto & Co. GBR. Dist: National Bk. Network.

Bonansinga, Kate. Full & Spare: Ceramics in the 21st Century. 2008. (Illus.). 64p. *(978-1-889282-20-6(0))* Florida State Univ., Museum of Fine Arts.

Bovier, Lionel & Caratsch, Andrea, eds. Milan Kunc: Sculpture. 2010. (ENG., Illus.). 96p. 35.00 *(978-3-03764-062-3(6))* JRP Ringier Kunstverlag AG CHE. Dist: D.A.P./Distributed Art Pubs.

Cooksey, Susan, et al. Resonance & Inspiration: New Works by Magdalene Odundo. 2006. 14.95 *(978-0-9762552-2-2(7))* Harn Museum of Art.

Haggerty, Michael, tr. Bertozzi & Casoni: Le Bugie Dell'arte. 2008. (ENG., Illus.). 112p. 40.00 *(978-88-6208-005-7(0))* Damiani ITA. Dist: D.A.P./Distributed Art Pubs.

Higgs, Matthew, contrib. by. Ken Price: Sculpture & Drawings, 1962-2006, 1 vol. 2008. (ENG., Illus.). 148p. 45.00 *(978-3-86521-315-0(4))* Steidl, Gerhard Druckerei und Verlag DEU. Dist: Innovative Logistics.

Ise-Neuman, Ursula & Kardon, Janet. Conversations in Clay. 2008. (Illus.). 45p. *(978-0-915171-76-7(7))* Katonah Gallery.

Lark Books. Lark Studio Series: Ceramic Sculptures. 2011. (ENG., Illus.). 204p. 12.95 *(978-1-4547-0084-5(X))* Lark Bks.

Lark Books Staff & Tourtillott, Suzanne J. E. 500 Ceramic Sculptures: Contemporary Practice, Singular Works. 2009. (500 Ser.). (ENG., Illus.). 420p. pap. 24.95 *(978-1-60059-247-8(3))* Lark Bks.

Lark Crafts. The Best of 500 Ceramics: Celebrating a Decade in Clay. 2012. (500 Ser.). (ENG., Illus.). 420p. 30.00 ***(978-1-4547-0141-5(2))*** Lark Bks.

Marks, Andreas, ed. Fukami: Purity of Form. 2011. (ENG., Illus.). 172p. 50.00 *(978-0-615-41782-0(5))* Clark Ctr. for Japanese Art & Culture.

Miller, Tony & Hui, Humphrey K. F. Elegance in Relief: Carved Porcelain from Jingdezhen of the 19th to early 20th Centuries. (CHI & ENG., Illus.). 358p. 55.00 *(978-962-7101-75-8(3))* Art Media Resources, Inc.

Nel, Hylton. Hylton Nel: A Curious World. 2011. (ENG.). 144p. pap. 64.95 *(978-1-4314-0076-8(9))* Jacana Media ZAF. Dist: Independent Pubs. Group.

Piepenburg, Robert. The Spirit of Ceramic Design: Cultivating Creativity with Clay. 2008. (Illus.). 253p. pap. 34.95 *(978-0-9628481-7-9(4))* Pebble Pr., Inc.

Pietsch, Ulrich. Die figuerliche Porzellanplastik von Gottlieb Kirchner und Johann Joachim Kaendler. 2006. (Bestandskataloge der Staatlichen Kunstsammlungen Dresden Ser.). (GER., Illus.). 208p. (C). pap. 120.00 *(978-3-7774-3265-6(2))* Hirmer Verlag GmbH DEU. Dist: Brown, David Bk. Co., The.

Snyder, Jeffrey B., ed. Ceramics Today. 2010. 50.00 *(978-0-7643-3465-8(4))* Schiffer Publishing, Ltd.

Tourtillott, Suzanne J. E. & Lark Books Staff. The Figure in Clay: Contemporary Sculpting Techniques by Master Artists. 2007. (Lark Ceramics Book Ser.). (ENG., Illus.). 176p. per. 17.95 *(978-1-57990-961-1(2))* Lark Bks.

Weekly Nancy, et al. Anne Currier: Sculptures. 2006. (GER & ENG., Illus.). 112p. 45.00 *(978-3-89790-243-5(5))* Arnoldsche Art Pubs. DEU. Dist: Antique Collectors' Club.

CERAMIC TO METAL BONDING

Easter, Greg, ed. Ceramic-to-Metal Joints & Seals. 2008. 296p. per. 89.95 *(978-1-934939-09-3(9))* Wexford College Pr.

Technology Research Editors, ed. Ceramic to Metal Joining, 2007 Ed. 2007. pap. 118.50 *(978-1-60030-299-2(8)*, Search-In-Print) CSA Journal Division.

CERAMICS

Here are entered general works on the technology of fired earth products, or clay products intended for industrial and technical use. Works on earthenware, chinaware, and art objects are entered under Pottery or Pottery Craft. Particular objects and types are entered under their specific names, e.g. Bricks; Refractory Materials; Tiles; Vases.

see also Abrasives; Glass; Glazes; Pottery; Pottery Craft; Tiles

ACerS & Zhou, Yanchun. PACRIM Proceedings Bundle. 2010. (Ceramic Transactions Ser.: 109). (ENG.). 1536p. 519.95 *(978-0-470-93918-5(4)*, Wiley-American Ceramic Society) Wiley, John & Sons, Inc.

Acers Staff. Ceramic Engineering & Science Proceedings 2008. 2008. (Ceramic Engineering & Science Proceedings Ser.). Set. 2800p. 485.00 *(978-0-470-22401-4(0))* Vol. 29. 2nd ed. (ENG.). 560.00 *(978-0-470-38107-6(8))* Wiley, John & Sons, Inc. (Wiley-American Ceramic Society).

—CESP 2010, Set. 2010. (Ceramic Engineering & Science Proceedings Ser.: 522). (ENG.). 1000p. 625.00 *(978-0-470-59463-6(2))*; 665.00 *(978-0-470-59465-0(9))* Wiley, John & Sons, Inc. (Wiley-American Ceramic Society).

—70th Conference on Glass Problems. Drummond, Charles H., ed. 2010. (Ceramic Engineering & Science Proceedings Ser.: 525). (ENG.). 232p. 89.95 *(978-0-470-59466-7(7)*, Wiley-American Ceramic Society) Wiley, John & Sons, Inc.

Akedo, Jun, et al. Advances in Multifunctional Materials & Systems. 2010. (Ceramic Transactions Ser.: 101). (ENG., Illus.). 188p. 105.00 *(978-0-470-89058-5(4)*, Wiley-American Ceramic Society) Wiley, John & Sons, Inc.

American Ceramic Society Staff. Ceramic Transactions Bundle. 2008. (Ceramic Transactions Ser.). (ENG.). 3220p. 940.00 *(978-0-470-47425-9(4)*, Wiley-American Ceramic Society) Wiley, John & Sons, Inc.

—Proceedings of the 6th Pacific Rim Conference on Ceramic & Glass Technology. 2006. (ENG.). 4p. 389.00 *(978-0-470-08995-8(4)*, Wiley-American Ceramic Society) Wiley, John & Sons, Inc.

American Ceramic Society Staff, ed. CESP 2009, Set. 2009. (Ceramic Engineering & Science Proceedings Ser.: 515). (ENG.). 2800p. 595.00 *(978-0-470-45777-1(5)*, Wiley-American Ceramic Society) Wiley, John & Sons, Inc.

American Ceramic Society Staff & Acers Staff. CESP Set 2009 for Prepaid International. 2009. (Ceramic Engineering & Science Proceedings Ser.). 540.00 *(978-0-470-52469-5(3)*, Wiley-American Ceramic Society) Wiley, John & Sons, Inc.

American Society of Mechanical Engineers Staff, ed. Applications of Engineering Ceramics. 20.00 *(978-0-85298-612-7(2))* Professional Engineering Publishing GBR. Dist: SAE Intl.

Bansal, Narottam P. Handbook of Ceramic Composites. 2010. (Illus.). x, 558p. pap. 399.00 *(978-1-4419-5482-4(1)*, 1441954821) Springer.

Bansal, Narottam P., et al. Processing & Properties of Advanced Ceramics & Composites, Vol. 207. 2009. (Ceramic Transactions Ser.: 83). (ENG., Illus.). 266p. 153.00 *(978-0-470-40845-2(6)*, Wiley-American Ceramic Society) Wiley, John & Sons, Inc.

Benazzo, Francesco, et al, eds. Bioceramics & Alternative Bearings in Joint Arthroplasty: 11th BIOLOX Symposium. Proceedings. 2007. (Ceramics in Orthopaedics Ser.). (Illus.). xvii, 321p. pap. 89.95 *(978-3-7985-1634-2(0)*, 3798516340) Steinkopff, Dietrich DEU. Dist: Springer.

Betancourt, Philip P. The Bronze Age Begins: The Ceramics Revolution of Early Minoan I & the New Forms of Wealth That Transformed Prehistoric Society. 2009. (ENG., Illus.). 156p. (C). pap. 36.00 *(978-1-931534-52-9(7))* Institute for Aegean Prehistory Pr.

Bimson, Mavis & Freestone, Ian. Early Vitreous Materials. (Illus.). 72p. pap. 18.00 *(978-0-86159-056-8(2))* British Museum Pr. GBR. Dist: Brown, David Bk. Co., The.

Brown, Roxanna Maude. Ming Gap & Shipwreck Ceramics in Southeast Asia: Towards a Chronology of Thai Trade Ware. 2009. (ENG., Illus.). 206p. 50.00 *(978-974-9863-77-0(1))* River Bks. THA. Dist: Antique Collectors' Club.

Ceramic Society of Japan Staff. Advanced Ceramic Technologies & Products. Imanaka, Yoshihiko, ed. 2012. Orig. Title: Ceramic Archives. (ENG., Illus.). xxx, 770p. 209.00 *(978-4-431-53913-1(1)*, 4431539131) Springer.

Chung, M. P., ed. Handbook on Borates: Chemistry, Production & Applications. 2009. (Materials Science & Technologies Ser.). 195.00 *(978-1-60741-822-1(3))* Nova Science Pubs., Inc.

Colombo, Paolo, et al. Advances in Polymer Derived Ceramics & Composites. 2010. (Ceramic Transactions Ser.: 98). (ENG., Illus.). 150p. 105.00 *(978-0-470-87800-2(2)*, Wiley-American Ceramic Society) Wiley, John & Sons, Inc.

Connell, Jo. Coloring Clay. 2007. (Ceramics Handbooks Ser.). (Illus.). 96p. pap. 26.50 *(978-0-8122-2011-7(0))* Univ. of Pennsylvania Pr.

Crick, Monique. Chinese Trade Ceramics for Southeast Asia, I-XVII Centuries: Collection of Ambassador & Mrs. Charles Muller. 2010. (ENG., Illus.). 416p. 150.00 *(978-88-7439-463-0(2))* 5 Continents ITA. Dist: Hachette Bk. Group.

DAAB Media Staff, creator. Ceramic Design, 1 vol. 2008. (ENG., Illus.). 384p. 37.95 *(978-3-86654-004-0(3))* DAAB Media Gmbh DEU. Dist: Innovative Logistics.

Dai, Xiangming. Pottery Production, Settlement Patterns & Development of Social Complexity in the Yuanqu Basin, North Central China. 2006. (Bar S Ser.). (Illus.). viii,129p. (C). 75.00 *(978-1-84171-939-9(0))* British Archaeological Reports Ltd. GBR. Dist: Brown, David Bk. Co., The.

Dogan, Fatih, et al, eds. Ceramics for Environmental & Energy Applications. 2010. (Ceramic Transactions Ser.: 102). (ENG., Illus.). 186p. 105.00 *(978-0-470-90547-0(6)*, Wiley-American Ceramic Society) Wiley, John & Sons, Inc.

Donthu, Suresh. Nanopatterning of Functional Oxide Ceramics. 2009. 268p. pap. *(978-3-639-16013-0(4))* VDM Verlag Dr. Mueller e.K.

Dusza, J., et al, eds. Fractography of Advanced Ceramics III. 2009. (Key Engineering Materials Ser.: Vol. 409). 428p. pap. *(978-0-87849-332-6(8))* Trans Tech Pubns., Ltd.

Edirisinghe. Introduction to Structural Engineering Ceramics. pap. 50.00 *(978-0-901716-57-6(X))* Institute of Management Consultants.

Faust, William D. 68th Porcelain Enamel Institute Technical Forum: A Collection of Papers Presented at the 68th Porcelain Enamel Institute Technical Forum, May 15-18, 2006, Nashville, Tennessee. 2007. (Ceramic Engineering & Science Proceedings Ser.: 40). (ENG.). 219p. pap. 111.00 *(978-0-470-09735-9(3)*, Wiley-American Ceramic Society) Wiley, John & Sons, Inc.

—69th Porcelain Enamel Institute Technical Forum Vol. 28: Ceramic Engineering & Science Proceedings. 2008. (Ceramic Engineering & Science Proceedings Ser.: 338). (ENG., Illus.). 104p. 111.00 *(978-0-470-19641-0(6)*, Wiley-American Ceramic Society) Wiley, John & Sons, Inc.

Fisher, D. J., ed. Defects & Diffusion in Ceramics: An Annual Retrospective IX. 2007. 253p. pap. 166.00 *(978-3-908451-47-1(7))* Trans Tech Pubns., Ltd. CHE. Dist: Enfield Publishing & Distribution Co., Inc.

—Defects & Diffusion in Ceramics X. 2008. (Defect & Diffusion Forum Ser.). 410p. pap. *(978-3-908451-62-4(0))* Trans Tech Pubns., Ltd.

Freiman, Stephen, et al. Proceedings of the 1st International Congress on Ceramics: A Global Roadmap. 2006. (ENG.). 4p. cd-rom 84.95 *(978-0-470-11656-2(0)*, Wiley-American Ceramic Society) Wiley, John & Sons, Inc.

Gai, Guosheng. Powder Technology & Application: Selected, Peer Reviewed Papers from International Forum on Powder Technology & Application, Tsinghua University Beijing, 1-2 April 2008. Gai, Guosheng, ed. 2009. (Advanced Materials Research Ser.). (Illus.). 244p. pap. *(978-0-87849-352-4(2))* Trans Tech Pubns., Ltd.

Gaume, Romain, ed. Handbook of Optical Ceramics. 2010. 350p. 99.95 *(978-1-4200-8737-6(1))* CRC Pr. LLC.

Gonzalez, Mark. Solid-Colored Dinnerware: Depression to Mid-Century. 2008. (Schiffer Book for Collectors Ser.). (Illus.). 160p. pap. 29.95 *(978-0-7643-2646-6(8))* Schiffer Publishing, Ltd.

Gopal, Madan. Dynamic Performance of High Temperature Ceramic Check Valves. 2008. 156p. pap. *(978-3-639-09098-8(X))* VDM Verlag Dr. Mueller e.K.

Goralczyk, Vicky. Cells in Ceramics: Finding out about Getting In. 2011. 144p. pap. ***(978-3-8381-2413-1(8))*** Südwestdeutscher Verlag für Hochschulschriften AG & Co. KG.

Handle, Frank, ed. Extrusion in Ceramics. 2007. (Engineering Materials & Processes Ser.). (Illus.). 470p. 179.00 *(978-3-540-27100-0(7)*, 3540271007) Springer.

Händle, Frank, ed. Extrusion in Ceramics. 2010. (Engineering Materials & Processes Ser.). (Illus.). xi, 413p. pap. 179.00 *(978-3-642-06601-6(1)*, 3642066011) Springer.

Heimann, Robert B. Classic & Advanced Ceramics: From Fundamentals to Applications. 2010. (ENG., Illus.). 573p. 205.00 *(978-3-527-32517-7(4)*, Wiley-VCH) Wiley, John & Sons, Inc.

Heiremans, Marc & Heiremans, Mark. Art Ceramics: Pioneers in Flanders, 1938-1978. 2006. (ENG., Illus.). 192p. 60.00 *(978-3-89790-240-4(0))* Arnoldsche Art Pubs. DEU. Dist: Antique Collectors' Club.

Held, Peter, ed. Eden Revisited: The Ceramic Art of Kurt Weiser. 2007. (ENG.). 96p. ***(978-0-9777624-5-3(9))*** Arizona State Univ. Art Museum.

Henrywood, R. K. Jugs. 2009. (Shire Library) (ENG., Illus.). 56p. pap. 12.95 *(978-0-7478-0734-6(5))* Shire Pubns., Ltd. GBR. Dist: Random Hse., Inc.

Hill, Simona. Painting Ceramics: 30 Step-by-Step Decorative Projects. Hill, Simona, ed. 2008. (ENG.). 96p. pap. 9.99 *(978-1-84476-593-5(8))* Anness Publishing GBR. Dist: National Bk. Network.

Holand, Wolfram & Beall, George H. Glass Ceramic Technology. 2nd ed. 2012. (ENG.). 440p. 159.95 *(978-0-470-48787-7(9)*, Wiley-American Ceramic Society) Wiley, John & Sons, Inc.

Hong, Cheng-Shong. Investigating the Effects of the Mno Additives & Process Conditions on the Relaxor Ferroelectric Ceramics - by Using the Diffuse Phase Transition Mo. 2008. 184p. pap. *(978-3-639-00076-4(5))* VDM Verlag Dr. Mueller e.K.

Hunter, Robert, ed. Ceramics in America 2006. 2006. (Ceramics in America Annual Ser.). (Illus.). 356p. pap. 60.00 *(978-0-9724353-7-6(9))* Chipstone Foundation.

—Ceramics in America 2011. 2011. (Ceramics in America Annual Ser.). (Illus.). 232p. 65.00 *(978-0-9767344-8-2(6))* Chipstone Foundation.

Huntley, Deborah L. Ancestral Zuni Glaze-Decorated Pottery: Viewing Pueblo IV Regional Organization Through Ceramic Production & Exchange. 2008. (Anthropology Papers). (ENG., Illus.). 112p. pap. 17.95 *(978-0-8165-2564-5(1))* Univ. of Arizona Pr.

Husfloen, Kyle. Antique Trader Pottery & Porcelain Ceramics. 6th ed. 2009. (ENG., Illus.). 768p. pap. 25.99 *(978-0-89689-933-9(0))* Krause Pubns.

Jansen, M., ed. High Performance Non-Oxide Ceramics II. 2011. (Structure & Bonding Ser.). (ENG., Illus.). x, 188p. pap. 249.00 *(978-3-642-07724-1(2)*, 3642077242) Springer.

Jansen, M. & contrib. by. High Performance Non-Oxide Ceramics I. 2011. (Structure & Bonding Ser.). (ENG., Illus.). xv, 216p. pap. 259.00 *(978-3-642-07723-4(4)*, 3642077234) Springer.

Jernegan, Jeremy. Dry Glazes. 2009. (Ceramics Handbooks Ser.). (Illus.). 128p. pap. 27.50 *(978-0-8122-2097-1(8))* Univ. of Pennsylvania Pr.

Jiménez-Piqué, E. & Hvizdos, P. Layered, Functional Gradient Ceramics, & Thermal Barrier Coatings. Anlada, Marc, ed. (Key Engineering Materials Ser.: Vol. 333). (Illus.). 304p. pap. *(978-0-87849-424-8(3))* Trans Tech Pubns., Ltd.

Jones, Bill, ed. Raku Firing: Advanced Techniques. 2009. (Ceramic Arts Handbook Ser.). (Illus.). 136p. pap. 29.95 *(978-1-57498-301-2(6)*, CA77) American Ceramic Society, The.

Jones, David. Firing: Philosophies Within Contemporary Ceramic Practice. 2007. (ENG., Illus.). 160p. 60.00 *(978-1-86126-935-5(8))* Crowood Pr., Ltd. GBR. Dist: Independent Pubs. Group.

Jordan, Peter & Zvelebil, Marek, eds. Ceramics Before Farming: The Dispersal of Pottery among Prehistoric Eurasian Hunter-Gatherers. 2010. (University College London Institute of Archaeology Publications). (ENG., Illus.). 589p. (C). lib. bdg. 99.00 *(978-1-59874-245-9(0))* Left Coast Pr., Inc.

C

Kamel, Talal. Poling & Switching of Pzt Ceramics. 2010. 156p. pap. (978-3-639-27249-9(8)) VDM Verlag Dr. Mueller e.K.

Kokubo, T., ed. Bioceramics & Their Clinical Applications. 2008. (Illus.). 354.95 (978-1-4200-7207-5(2)) CRC Pr. LLC.

Kreiter, Attila. Technological Choices & Material Meanings in Early & Middle Bronze Age Hungary: Understanding the Active Role of Material Culture Through Ceramic Analysis. 2007. (Bar S Ser.). (Illus.). xiii, 251p. pap. 92.50 (978-1-4073-0021-4(0)) Archaeopress GBR. Dist: Brown, David Bk. Co., The.

Krenkel, Walter & Krenkel, Walter, eds. Ceramic Matrix Composites: Fiber Reinforced Ceramics & their Applications. 2008. (ENG., Illus.). 440p. 235.00 (978-3-527-31361-7(3), Wiley-VCH) Wiley, John & Sons, Inc.

Lara-Curzio, Edgar. Mechanical Properties & Performance of Engineering Ceramics & Composites III. Salem, Jonathan & Zhu, Dongming, eds. 2007. (Ceramic Engineering & Science Proceedings Ser.: 49). (ENG., Illus.). 530p. 111.00 (978-0-470-19633-5(5), Wiley-American Ceramic Society) Wiley, John & Sons, Inc.

Li, Qiang. Sha Hai Xie Ying. 2009. (CHI., Illus.). 188p. (978-7-5601-4590-7(6)) Jilin Univ. Pr.

Marc, Jacques. Pacific Coast Ship China, 1 vol. 2009. (ENG.). 192p. 75.00 (978-0-7726-5979-8(6)) UBC Pr. CAN. Dist: Univ. of Washington Pr.

McColm, I. J. Ceramic Hardness. 2010. (ENG.). 336p. pap. 229.00 (978-1-4419-3213-6(5), 1441932135) Springer.

McColm, Ian John. Dictionary of Ceramic Science & Engineering. 3rd ed. 2012. (ENG.). 400p. 189.00 (**978-94-007-0915-7(3)**, 9400709153) Springer.

McHale, Anna E. Phase Diagrams & Ceramic Processes. 2010. (ENG., Illus.). 232p. pap. 169.00 (978-1-4419-4726-0(4), 1441947264) Springer.

Messing, Gary L., et al. Proceeding of the 9th International Ceramic Processing Science Symposium. 2006. (ENG.). 4p. 144.00 (978-0-470-10889-5(4), Wiley-American Ceramic Society) Wiley, John & Sons, Inc.

Mills, Maureen. Surface Design for Ceramics. (Lark Ceramics Book Ser.). (ENG., Illus.). 144p. 2011. pap. 21.95 (978-1-60059-782-4(3)) 2008. 29.95 (978-1-57990-844-7(6)) Lark Bks.

Mistler, Richard E. & Twiname, Eric R., eds. Tape Casting: Theory & Practice. 2nd ed. 2010. (ENG.). 330p. 110.00 (978-0-470-31288-9(2), Wiley-American Ceramic Society) Wiley, John & Sons, Inc.

Nair, K. M., et al, eds. Advances & Applications in Electroceramics. 2011. (Ceramic Transactions Ser.: 114). (ENG.). 270p. 125.00 (978-1-118-05999-9(9), Wiley-American Ceramic Society) Wiley, John & Sons, Inc.

Narayan, Roger, et al. Advances in Bioceramics & Biotechnologies. 2010. (Ceramic Transactions Ser.: 103). (ENG., Illus.). 244p. 105.00 (978-0-470-90548-7(4), Wiley-American Ceramic Society) Wiley, John & Sons, Inc.

Ohji, Tatsuki & Mathur, Sanjay, eds. CESP 2010, Set. 2010. (Ceramic Engineering & Science Proceedings Ser.: 523). (ENG.). 1000p. 625.00 (978-0-470-59464-3(0), Wiley-American Ceramic Society) Wiley, John & Sons, Inc.

Ohji, Tatsuki & Singh, Mrityunjay, eds. Advanced Processing & Manufacturing Technologies for Structural & Multifunctional Materials, Vol. 28. 2007. (Ceramic Engineering & Science Proceedings Ser.: 387). (ENG., Illus.). 204p. 111.00 (978-0-470-19638-0(6), Wiley-American Ceramic Society) Wiley, John & Sons, Inc.

O'Rorke, Margaret. Clay, Light, & Water. 2010. (Ceramics Handbooks Ser.). (Illus.). 128p. pap. 28.95 (978-0-8122-2099-5(4)) Univ. of Pennsylvania Pr.

Pan, Wei & Gong, Jianghong. Chinese Ceramics Communications: Selected, Peer Reviewed Papers from the Sixth China International Conference on High-Performance Ceramics (CICC-6), Harbin, China, August 16-19, 2009, 2 vols., Vol. 105-106. 2010. (Advanced Materials Research Ser.). (Illus.). 910p. (978-0-87849-275-6(5)) Trans Tech Pubns., Ltd.

—High-Performance Ceramics V. 2008. (Key Engineering Materials Ser.: Vols. 368-372). 2000p. pap. (978-0-87849-473-6(1)) Trans Tech Pubns., Ltd.

Pan, Wei & Gong, Jianghong, eds. High Performance Ceramics IV, 3 vols. 2007. (Key Engineering Materials Ser.: Vols. 336-338). (Illus.). 2800p. (978-0-87849-410-1(3)) Trans Tech Pubns., Ltd.

Paul, Shiladitya. Ceramic Thermal Barrier Coatings. 2011. 232p. pap. (**978-3-8443-1593-6(4)**) Lambert Academic Publishing.

Perryman, Jane. Smoke Firing: Contemporary Artists & Approaches. 2008. (Illus.). 176p. 49.95 (978-0-8122-4089-4(8)) Univ. of Pennsylvania Pr.

Peterson, Sarah E. Thin-Section Petrography of Ceramic Materials. 2009. (Instap archaeological excavation Manual Ser.). (ENG.). 27p. (C). pap. 9.95 (978-1-931534-55-0(1)) Institute for Aegean Prehistory Pr.

Petrie, Kevin. Ceramic Transfers. 2011. (Ceramic Arts Handbook Ser.). (Illus.). 128p. pap. 26.95 (978-1-57498-310-4(5), CA113) American Ceramic Society, The.

Quinn, Anthony. Ceramic Design Course: Principles, Practice, & Techniques: A Complete Course for Ceramicists. 2007. (ENG., Illus.). 144p. per. 21.99 (978-0-7641-3733-4(6)) Barron's Educational Series, Inc.

Quinn, George D., et al. Fractography of Glasses & Ceramics V. 2007. (Ceramic Transactions Ser.: 75). (ENG., Illus.). 484p. 163.00 (978-0-470-09737-3(X), Wiley-American Ceramic Society) Wiley, John & Sons, Inc.

Quinn, Patrick Sean, ed. Interpreting Silent Artefacts: Petrographic Approaches to Archaeological Ceramics. 2009. (ENG., Illus.). 303p. (C). pap. 50.00 (978-1-905739-29-5(X)) Archaeopress GBR. Dist: Brown, David Bk. Co., The.

Rahaman, Mohamed N. Ceramic Processing. 2006. (ENG., Illus.). 473p. (C). 115.95 (978-0-8493-7285-8(2), CRC Press) Taylor & Francis Group GBR. Dist: Taylor & Francis Group.

—Sintering of Ceramics. 2007. (ENG., Illus.). 388p. (C). 92.95 (978-0-8493-7286-5(0), CRC Press) Taylor & Francis Group GBR. Dist: Taylor & Francis Group.

Rahaman Mohamed N Staff. Solutions Manual for Ceramic Processing. 2006. (Illus.). 57p. (C). (978-1-4200-4362-4(5)) CRC Pr. LLC.

Reedy, Chandra L. Thin-Section Petrography of Stone & Ceramic Cultural Materials. 2008. (ENG., Illus.). 260p. pap. 160.00 (978-1-904982-33-3(6)) Archetype Pubns. GBR. Dist: National Bk. Network.

Richerson, David W. The Magic of Ceramics. 2nd ed. 2012. (ENG.). 320p. 59.95 (**978-0-470-63805-7(2)**, Wiley-American Ceramic Society) Wiley, John & Sons, Inc.

Riedel, Ralf & Chen, I-Wei, eds. Ceramics Science & Technology Vol. 1: Structures, Volume 1. 2008. (Ceramics Science & Technology (VCH) Ser.: 3). (ENG., Illus.). 612p. 399.00 (978-3-527-31155-2(6), Wiley-VCH) Wiley, John & Sons, Inc.

—Ceramics Science & Technology Vol. 2: Materials & Properties, Volume 2. 2010. (Ceramics Science & Technology (VCH) Ser.: 1). (ENG., Illus.). 888p. 360.00 (978-3-527-31156-9(4), Wiley-VCH) Wiley, John & Sons, Inc.

—Ceramics Science & Technology Vol. 3: Synthesis & Processing, Volume 3. 2012. (Ceramics Science & Technology (VCH) Ser.: 2). (ENG., Illus.). 554p. 360.00 (978-3-527-31157-6(2), Wiley-VCH) Wiley, John & Sons, Inc.

Riley, Frank & Riley, F. L. Structural Ceramics: Fundamentals & Case Studies. 2009. (ENG., Illus.). 418p. 90.00 (978-0-521-84586-1(6)) Cambridge Univ. Pr.

Rincon, Jesus Ma & Romero, Maximina, eds. Characterization Techniques of Glasses & Ceramics. 2010. (ENG., Illus.). xii, 239p. pap. 215.00 (978-3-642-08348-8(X), 364208348X) Springer.

Roberts, Susan Stokes, ed. Michael Simon: Evolution. 2011. (ENG., Illus.). 140p. 45.00 (978-0-8078-7214-7(8)) Univ. of North Carolina Pr.

Roesler, Joachim, et al. Mechanical Behaviour of Engineering Materials: Metals, Ceramics, Polymers, & Composites. 2010. (ENG., Illus.). xvi, 536p. pap. 109.00 (978-3-642-09252-7(7), 3642092527) Springer.

Rollett, A. D. Ceramic Transactions Volumes 200 & 201 Set, 2 vols., Vols. 200 & 201, Set. 2008. (Ceramic Transactions Ser.: 94). (ENG., Illus.). 1648p. 295.00 (978-0-470-47418-1(1), Wiley-American Ceramic Society) Wiley, John & Sons, Inc.

Salazar, Jaime, text. Rhythms, Cycles, Performances: Ceramics in Architecture. 2010. (ENG.). 160p. pap. 39.95 (978-84-613-9405-0(4)) Ico López-Rienda ESP. Dist: Actar Birkhauser Distribution.

Salem, J. Proceedings of the 31st International Conference on Advanced Ceramics & Composites. Zhu, Dongming, ed. 2007. (ENG.). 4p. 343.00 (978-0-470-24679-5(0), Wiley-American Ceramic Society) Wiley, John & Sons, Inc.

Schaffner, Ingrid, et al, texts. Dirt on Delight: Impulses That Form Clay. 2009. (ENG., Illus.). 112p. pap. 35.00 (978-0-88454-117-2(7)) Univ. of Pennsylvania, Institute of Contemporary Art.

Schenck, Tine. Why Were They Pots? 2010. 108p. pap. (978-3-8383-5591-7(1)) Lambert Academic Publishing.

Sekunda, Nicholas, ed. Ergasteria: Works Presented to John Ellis Jones on His 80th Birthday. 2011. (ENG., Illus.). 188p. (C). 50.00 (978-83-929798-0-7(X)) Akanthina POL. Dist: Brown, David Bk. Co., The.

Singh, D. & Kriven, Waltraud M., eds. Mechanical Properties & Performance of Engineering Ceramics & Composites IV. 2009. (Ceramic Engineering & Science Proceedings Ser.: 506). (ENG., Illus.). 348p. 94.95 (978-0-470-45752-8(X), Wiley-American Ceramic Society) Wiley, John & Sons, Inc.

Singh, Dileep, et al. Design, Development, & Applications of Engineering Ceramics & Composites Vol. 215: Ceramic Transactions. 2010. (Ceramic Transactions Ser.: 100). (ENG., Illus.). 350p. 105.00 (978-0-470-88936-7(5), Wiley-American Ceramic Society) Wiley, John & Sons, Inc.

Singh, Mrityunjay. 6th International Conference on High Temperature Ceramic Matrix Composites. 2008. (Ceramic Transactions Ser.). 500p. 125.00 (978-0-470-23056-5(8), Wiley-American Ceramic Society) Wiley, John & Sons, Inc.

Singh, Mrityunjay, et al, eds. Ceramic Integration & Joining Technologies: From Macro to Nanoscale. 2011. (ENG., Illus.). 830p. 175.00 (978-0-470-39122-8(7), Wiley-American Ceramic Society) Wiley, John & Sons, Inc.

Singh, Mrityunjay, et al. Global Roadmap for Ceramic & Glass Technology. Freiman, Stephen, ed. 2007. (ENG.). 951p. 335.00 (978-0-470-10491-0(0), Wiley-American Ceramic Society) Wiley, John & Sons, Inc.

Somiya, Shigeyuki. Handbook of Advanced Ceramics: Materials, Applications, Processing & Properties. 2nd ed. 2012. (ENG., Illus.). 525.00 (978-0-12-385469-8(5), Academic Pr.) Elsevier Science & Technology Bks.

Somiya, Shigeyuki & Inomata, Yoshizo, eds. Silicon Carbide Ceramics, 2 vols., Vol. 2. 2007. (Illus.). 324p. 499.00 (978-1-85166-561-7(7)) Springer.

Stark, Miriam T., et al, eds. Cultural Transmission & Material Culture: Breaking down Boundaries. 2008. (ENG., Illus.). 320p. 49.95 (978-0-8165-2675-8(3)) Univ. of Arizona Pr.

Strongman, Jay. Tiki Mugs: Cult Artifacts of Polynesian Pop. 2008. (ENG., Illus.). 176p. 39.95 (978-0-9553398-1-3(2)) Korero Books LLP GBR. Dist: Independent Pubs. Group.

Taylor, Louisa. The Ceramics Bible: The Complete Guide to Materials & Techniques. 2011. (ENG.). 288p. 40.00 (978-1-4521-0162-0(0)) Chronicle Bks. LLC.

Technology Research Editors, ed. Ceramic Binder Removal, 2007 Ed. 2007. pap. 118.50 (978-1-60030-294-7(7), Search-In-Print) CSA Journal Division.

—Ceramic Honeycomb Structures, 2007 Ed. 2007. pap. 118.50 (978-1-60030-295-4(5), Search-In-Print) CSA Journal Division.

—Ceramic Preforms, 2007 Ed. 2007. pap. 118.50 (978-1-60030-296-1(3), Search-In-Print) CSA Journal Division.

—Extrusion of Glass & Ceramics, 2007 Ed. 2007. pap. 118.50 (978-1-60030-305-0(6), Search-In-Print) CSA Journal Division.

—Fracture Toughness of Alumina Ceramics, 2007 Ed. 2007. pap. 118.50 (978-1-60030-308-1(0), Search-In-Print) CSA Journal Division.

—Friction & Lubrication of Ceramics, 2007 Ed. 2007. pap. 118.50 (978-1-60030-313-5(7), Search-In-Print) CSA Journal Division.

—Microwave Sintering of Ceramics, 2007 Ed. 2007. pap. 118.50 (978-1-60030-319-7(6), Search-In-Print) CSA Journal Division.

—Multilayer Ceramic Capacitors, 2007 Ed. 2007. pap. 128.50 (978-1-60030-320-3(X), Search-In-Print) CSA Journal Division.

—Nondestructive Testing of Ceramics, 2007 Ed. 2007. pap. 118.50 (978-1-60030-321-0(8), Search-In-Print) CSA Journal Division.

—Plasma Spraying of Ceramics, 2007 Ed. 2007. pap. 118.50 (978-1-60030-323-4(4), Search-In-Print) CSA Journal Division.

—Processing Ceramic-Ceramic Composites, 2007 Ed. 2007. pap. 118.50 (978-1-60030-378-4(1), Search-In-Print) CSA Journal Division.

—Processing of PZT Ceramics, 2007 Ed. 2007. pap. 118.50 (978-1-60030-326-5(9), Search-In-Print) CSA Journal Division.

—Processing of Sialon, 2007 Ed. 2007. pap. 128.50 (978-1-60030-327-2(7), Search-In-Print) CSA Journal Division.

—Properties of PZT Ceramics, 2007 Ed. 2007. pap. 118.50 (978-1-60030-328-9(5), Search-In-Print) CSA Journal Division.

—Sintering Mechanisms for Ceramics, 2007 Ed. 2007. pap. 118.50 (978-1-60030-333-3(1), Search-In-Print) CSA Journal Division.

—Sintering of Silicone Nitride & Sialons, 2007 Ed. 2007. pap. 128.50 (978-1-60030-332-6(3), Search-In-Print) CSA Journal Division.

—Surface Finishing of Ceramics, 2007 Ed. 2007. pap. 118.50 (978-1-60030-335-7(8), Search-In-Print) CSA Journal Division.

—Suspension Forming of Ceramics, 2007 Ed. 2007. pap. 118.50 (978-1-60030-336-4(6), Search-In-Print) CSA Journal Division.

—Testing of Ceramics & Polymer Matrix Composites for Aerospace Applications, 2007 Ed. 2007. pap. 118.50 (978-1-60030-156-8(8), Search-In-Print) CSA Journal Division.

Turner, Anderson, ed. Ceramic Art: Innovative Techniques. 2009. (Ceramic Arts Handbook Ser.). (Illus.). 136p. pap. 29.95 (978-1-57498-299-2(0), CA74) American Ceramic Society, The.

—Electric Firing: Creative Techniques. 2008. (Ceramic Arts Handbook Ser.). (Illus.). 144p. pap. (978-1-57498-294-7(X), CA67) American Ceramic Society, The.

—Glazes & Glazing: Finishing Techniques. 2008. (Ceramic Arts Handbook Ser.). (Illus.). 144p. pap. (978-1-57498-295-4(8), CA68) American Ceramic Society, The.

Ueda, Ken-Ichi, et al. Modern Laser Ceramics: First 10 years research & Applications. 2009. (ENG.). 300p. 190.00 (978-3-527-40692-0(1), Wiley-VCH) Wiley, John & Sons, Inc.

Vetter, Ingrid. Moderne Keramik des 20. Jahrhunderts: Bestandskatalog der Sammlung Hinder/Reimers des Landes Rheinland-Pfalz. 2008. (ENG & GER., Illus.). 304p. 110.00 (978-3-89790-275-6(3)) Arnoldsche Art Pubs. DEU. Dist: Antique Collectors' Club.

Vincenzini, P. Medical Applications of Novel Biomaterials & Nano-Biotechnology: 5th Forum on New Materials Part E. 2011. (Illus.). 280p. pap. (978-3-908158-59-2(1)) Trans Tech Pubns., Ltd.

Vincenzini, P. & Dondi, Michele. Advances in Silicate Ceramics: 12th International Ceramics Congress, Part G. 2011. (Illus.). 228p. pap. (978-3-908158-51-6(6)) Trans Tech Pubns., Ltd.

Vincenzini, P., et al. Ceramics & Composites in Extreme Environments & for Chemical & Electrochemical Applications: 12th International Ceramics Congress Part D. 2011. (Illus.). 284p. pap. (978-3-908158-48-6(6)) Trans Tech Pubns., Ltd.

—Ceramics Surfaces for Tribology & Corrosion & Ceramic Joining Science & Technology: 12th International Ceramics Congress Part C. 2011. (Illus.). 166p. pap. (978-3-908158-47-9(8)) Trans Tech Pubns., Ltd.

Waksman, S. Y. Archaeometric & Archaeological Approaches to Ceramics: Papers Presented at EMAC '05, 8th European Meeting on Ancient Ceramics, Lyon 2005. 2007. (Bar S Ser.). (Illus.). 204p. (C). pap. 87.50 (978-1-4073-0129-7(2)) British Archaeological Reports Ltd. GBR. Dist: Brown, David Bk. Co., The.

Wang, Ziyi. Zhong Ri Tao Ci Cha Qi Wen Hua Bi Jiao Yan Jiu: Comparative Study of Ceramic Tea Ware Culture in China & Japan. 2010. (CHI., Illus.). (978-7-01-008507-4(2)) People's Publishing Hse., The.

Warner, Ian & Posegay, Mike. Figurines & Miniatures. 2011. 392p. 49.99 (978-0-7643-3628-7(2)) Schiffer Publishing, Ltd.

Watkins, James C. & Wandless, Paul Andrew. Alternative Kilns & Firing Techniques: Raku * Saggar * Pit * Barrel. 2006. (Lark Ceramics Book Ser.). (ENG., Illus.). 128p. pap. 14.95 (978-1-57990-952-9(3)) Lark Bks.

Whincop, Matthew R. Pots, People, & Politics: A Reconsideration of the Role of Ceramics in Reconstructions of the Iron Age Northern Levant. 2009. (Bar S Ser.). (ENG., Illus.). 408p. (C). pap. 175.00 (978-1-4073-0384-0(8)) British Archaeological Reports Ltd. GBR. Dist: Brown, David Bk. Co., The.

Widjaja, Sujanto, et al. Advanced Processing & Manufacturing Technologies for Structural & Multifunctional Materials V: Ceramic Engineering & Science Proceedings. Ohji, Tatsuki & Singh, Mrityunjay, eds. 2011. (Ceramic Engineering & Science Proceedings Ser.: 550). (ENG., Illus.). 200p. 79.95 (978-1-118-05993-7(X), Wiley-American Ceramic Society) Wiley, John & Sons, Inc.

CERAMICS—DICTIONARIES

McColm, I. J. Dictionary of Ceramic Science & Engineering. 2nd ed. 2010. (ENG.). 396p. pap. 179.00 (978-1-4419-3235-8(6), 1441932356) Springer.

CERAMICS—MATERIALS

see Ceramic Materials

CERAMICS (ART)

see Pottery

CERAMICS, DENTAL

see Dentistry—Ceramics

CERAMICS, ELECTRONIC

see Electronic Ceramics

CERAMICS IN MEDICINE

Barinov, Sergey & Komlev, Vladimir, eds. Calcium Phosphate Based Bioceramics for Bone Tissue Engineering. 2008. (Materials Science Foundations Ser.: Vol. 48). 170p. pap. (978-0-87849-380-7(8)) Trans Tech Pubns., Ltd.

Benazzo, Francesco, et al, eds. Bioceramics & Alternative Bearings in Joint Arthroplasty: 11th BIOLOX Symposium. Proceedings. 2007. (Ceramics in Orthopaedics Ser.). (Illus.). xvii, 321p. pap. 89.95 (978-3-7985-1634-2(0), 3798516340) Steinkopff, Dietrich DEU. Dist: Springer.

Boccaccini, A. & Gough, J. Tissue Engineering Using Ceramics & Polymers. 2007. (Illus.). 624p. (978-1-84569-176-9(8)) Woodhead Publishing Ltd.

Chang, Jun-Dong & Billau, Karl, eds. Bioceramics & Alternative Bearings in Joint Arthroplasty: 12th Biolox Symposium Seoul, Republic of Korea September 7-8, 2007 Proceedings. 2007. (Ceramics in Orthopaedics Ser.). (Illus.). 343p. per. 119.00 (978-3-7985-1782-0(7)) Steinkopff, Dietrich DEU. Dist: Springer.

Cobb, Justin P., ed. Bioceramics & Alternative Bearings in Joint Arthroplasty: 13th BIOLOX Symposium Edingburgh, United KingdomSeptember 4 - 5, 2009, Proceedings. 2010. (Ceramics in Orthopaedics Ser.). (Illus.). 300p. 89.95 (978-3-7985-1921-3(8), 3798519218) Steinkopff, Dietrich DEU. Dist: Springer.

El-Meliegy, Emad & Noort, Richard van. Glasses & Glass Ceramics for Medical Applications. 2011. (ENG., Illus.). xxiv, 244p. 129.00 (**978-1-4614-1227-4(7)**, 1461412277) Springer.

Kokubo, T., ed. Bioceramics & their Clinical Applications. 2008. (Illus.). 784p. (978-1-84569-204-9(7)) Woodhead Publishing Ltd.

—Bioceramics & Their Clinical Applications. 2008. (Illus.). 354.95 (978-1-4200-7207-5(2)) CRC Pr. LLC.

Kossler, Wolffe & Fuchs, Jacob. Bioceramics: Properties, Preparation & Applications. 2009. 98.00 (978-1-60741-056-0(7)) Nova Science Pubs., Inc.

Li, Panjian, et al, eds. Bioceramics for Orthopaedic & Dental Applications. 2008. 500p. 175.00 (978-0-471-78764-8(7), Wiley-Interscience) Wiley, John & Sons, Inc.

Narayan, Roger & Colombo, Paolo, eds. Advances in Bioceramics & Porous Ceramics. 2009. (Ceramic Engineering & Science Proceedings Ser.: 510). (ENG., Illus.). 344p. 94.95 (978-0-470-45756-6(2), Wiley-American Ceramic Society) Wiley, John & Sons, Inc.

—Advances in Bioceramics & Porous Ceramics: Ceramic Engineering & Science Proceedings. 2008. (Ceramic Engineering & Science Proceedings Ser.: 52). (ENG., Illus.). 372p. 89.95 (978-0-470-34494-1(6), Wiley-American Ceramic Society) Wiley, John & Sons, Inc.

Narayan, Roger, et al. Advances in Bioceramics & Biotechnologies. 2010. (Ceramic Transactions Ser.: 103). (ENG., Illus.). 244p. 105.00 (978-0-470-90548-7(4), Wiley-American Ceramic Society) Wiley, John & Sons, Inc.

Prado, Marcelo & Zavaglia, Cecília. Bioceramics 21: Selected Papers from the 21st International Symposium on Ceramics in Medicine, the Annual Meeting of the International Society for Ceramics in Medicine (ISCM), Búzios, Brazil, 21-24 October 2008. Prado, Marcelo & Zavaglia, Cecília, eds. 2009. (Key Engineering Materials Ser.). (Illus.). 758p. (978-0-87849-353-1(0)) Trans Tech Pubns., Ltd.

Vallet-Regí, M. & Vila, M., eds. Advanced Bioceramics in Nanomedicine & Tissue Engineering: Special Topic Volume with Invited Peer Reviewed Papers Only, Vol.441. 2010. (Key Engineering Materials Ser.). (Illus.). 392p. pap. (978-0-87849-270-1(4)) Trans Tech Pubns., Ltd.

Vallet-Regí, Maria, ed. Progress in Bioceramics. 2008. (Key Engineering Materials Ser.: Vol. 377). 284p. pap. (978-0-87849-395-1(6)) Trans Tech Pubns., Ltd.

Vallet-Regí, Maria & Navarrete, Daniel Arcos. Biomimetic Nanoceramics in Clinical Use: From Materials to Applications. 2008. (RSC Nanoscience & Nanotechnology Ser.). (ENG., Illus.). 192p. (C). 195.00 (**978-0-85404-142-8(7)**) Royal Society of Chemistry, The GBR. Dist: Ingram Pub. Services.

Zhang, Xingdong, et al, eds. Bioceramics 19, 2 vols. (Illus.). 1512p. (978-0-87849-422-4(7)) Trans Tech Pubns., Ltd.

CEREAL PRODUCTS

see also Flour

Awika, Joseph M., et al. Advances in Cereal Science: Implications to Food Processing & Health Promotion. 2nd ed. 2012. (ACS Symposium Ser.). (ENG.). 224p. 150.00 (**978-0-8412-2636-4(9)**) American Chemical Society.

Breakfast Cereals International Market: Companies-Products-Services. (Orig.). pap. (978-0-7605-2201-1(4)) Rector Pr., Ltd.

Cauvain, Stanley, ed. The ICC Handbook of Cereals, Flour, Dough & Product Testing: Methods & Applications. 2009. (Illus.). 504p. lib. bdg. 179.50 (978-1-932078-99-2(1)) DEStech Pubns., Inc.
Crosbie, Graham B. & Ross, Andrew S., eds. The RVA Handbook. 2nd ed. 2007. (Illus.). 152p. pap. 139.00 (978-1-891127-54-0(3)) American Phytopathological Society, The.
Dal Bello, Fabio & Arendt, Elke K., eds. Gluten-Free Cereal Products & Beverages. 2008. (Food Science & Technology Ser.). (ENG., Illus.). 464p. 141.00 (978-0-12-373739-7(7), Academic Pr.) Elsevier Science & Technology Bks.
Delcour, Jan A. & Hoseney, R. Carl. Principles of Cereal Science & Technology. 3rd ed. 2010. (Illus.). vii, 270p. (978-1-891127-63-2(2)) AACC International.
Elkins MH, Rita. Red Yeast Rice. 3rd ed. 2011. (Woodland Health Ser.). 36p. pap. 4.95 (978-1-58054-200-5(X)) Woodland Publishing, Inc.
Hamaker, B. R., ed. Technology of Functional Cereal Products. 2007. 568p. (978-1-84569-177-6(6)) Woodhead Publishing Ltd.
Hamaker, Bruce R., ed. Technology of Functional Cereal Products. 2007. (Illus.). 548p. 279.95 (978-1-4200-6673-9(0)) CRC Pr. LLC.
Introduction to Cereal Grains. 2011. 99.00 (978-1-4398-1561-8(5), CRC Press) Taylor & Francis Group GBR. Dist: Taylor & Francis Group.
Mears, Catherine & Young, Helen. Acceptability & Use of Cereal-Based Foods in Refugee Camps: Case Studies from Nepal, Ethiopia & Tanzania. (Oxfam Working Papers Ser.). (ENG., Illus.). 136p. pap. 23.95 (978-0-85598-402-1(3)) Oxfam Publishing GBR. Dist: Stylus Publishing, LLC.
Murray, Guillermo. Poder Curative de los Cereales.Tr. of Power of Cereals. (SPA.). 8.98 (978-970-643-146-2(2)) Selector, S.A. de C.V. MEX. Dist: AIMS International Bks., Inc.
Prentice-Hall Staff. Cereal. 6.47 (978-0-13-800442-2(0)) Prentice Hall (Schl. Div.).
Rovinski, Rachel M. Rachel's Recipes for Success, 1 vol. 2009. 73p. pap. 16.95 (978-1-60749-129-3(X)) PublishAmerica, Inc.
Wale, Melaku. Ecological & Biological Management of Cereal Stemborers. 2011. 148p. pap. (978-3-8443-8387-4(5)) Lambert Academic Publishing.
Weegels, Peter L. Consumer Driven Cereal Innovation: Where Science Meets Industry. 2008. (Illus.). x, 190p. pap. (978-1-891127-61-8(6)) AACC International.

CEREALS
see Grain

CEREALS AS FOOD
see also Cooking (Cereals)

Barrett, Sharon Kebschull. Morning Glories: Breakfast, Brunch & Light Fare from an Herb Garden. Date not set. pap. (978-0-312-28570-8(1), St. Martin's Griffin) St. Martin's Pr.
Breakfast Foods Market: Companies-Products-Services. 100p. (Orig.). pap. (978-0-7505-2199-1(9)) Rector Pr., Ltd.
Cao, Rong. Cereals & Pulses: Nutraceutical Properties & Health Benefits. Shahidi, Fereidoon et al, eds. 2012. (ENG., Illus.). 328p. 199.95 (978-0-8138-1839-9(7), Wiley-Blackwell) Wiley, John & Sons, Inc.
Concepts in Cereal Chemistry. 2011. 69.95 (978-1-4398-3583-8(7), CRC Press) Taylor & Francis Group GBR. Dist: Taylor & Francis Group.
Delcour, Jan A. & Hoseney, R. Carl. Principles of Cereal Science & Technology. 3rd ed. 2010. (Illus.). vii, 270p. (978-1-891127-63-2(2)) AACC International.
Gitlin, Marty, et al. The Great American Cereal Book: How Breakfast Got Its Crunch. 2012. (ENG., Illus.). 368p. 19.95 (978-0-8109-9799-8(1), Abrams Image) Abrams.
Macritchie, Finlay. Concepts in Cereal Chemistry. 2010. (ENG., Illus.). 197p. 72.95 (978-1-4398-3582-1(9), CRC Press) Taylor & Francis Group GBR. Dist: Taylor & Francis Group.
Milward, Randi Lynn. 50 Eggcellent Egg-Free Breakfast Recipes: Because People with Egg Allergies Deserve a Good Breakfast, Too! 2009. 90p. pap. 16.95 (978-1-60749-988-6(6)) PublishAmerica, Inc.
Orton, Mildred Ellen. Cooking with Wholegrains: The Basic Wholegrain Cookbook. 2010. (ENG., Illus.). 80p. pap. 12.00 (978-0-374-53261-1(3)) Farrar, Straus & Giroux.
Publications International Staff, ed. 4 Books in1 Recipes for Kids: Breakfast, Lunch, Snacks, Dinner. 2011. 320p. spiral bd. 17.98 (978-1-4508-1098-2(5)) Publications International, Ltd.
Serna-Saldivar, Sergio O. Cereal Grains: Properties, Processing & Nutritional Attributes. 2010. (Food Preservation Technology Ser.). (ENG., Illus.). 752p. 99.00 (978-1-4398-1560-1(7), CRC Press) Taylor & Francis Group GBR. Dist: Taylor & Francis Group.
Spendley, Juli. A Study of Factors Influencing Students' Breakfast Routines. 2010. 112p. pap. (978-3-8383-2122-6(7)) Lambert Academic Publishing.
Wrigley, C., et al, eds. Cereal Grains. 2010. (Illus.). 560p. 249.95 (978-1-4398-3095-6(9), CRC Press) Taylor & Francis Group GBR. Dist: Taylor & Francis Group.

CEREBELLUM

Bambakidis, Nicholas C., et al. Surgery of the Cerebellopontine Angle. 2009. (Illus.). 310p. 149.00 (978-1-60795-001-1(4)) PMPH-USA, Ltd.
Boltshauser, Eugen & Schmahmann, Jeremy D., eds. Cerebellar Disorders in Children. 2012. (Clinics in Developmental Medicine Ser.: 189). (ENG., Illus.). 456p. 200.00 (978-1-907655-01-2(8)) Mac Keith Pr. GBR. Dist: Wiley, John & Sons, Inc.
Cram101 Textbook Reviews. Outlines & Highlights for Cerebellar Disorders: A Practical Approach to Diagnosis & Management by Edited by Mario Ubaldo Manto, ISBN. 2011. 62p. pap. 27.95 (978-1-61461-474-6(1)) Cram101 Inc.
Cram101 Textbook Reviews & Cram101 Textbook Reviews. Outlines & Highlights for Subcortical Structures & Cognition: Implications for Neuropsychological Assessment by Leonard F. Koziol. 2011. 62p. pap. 27.95 (978-1-61830-426-1(7)) Cram101 Inc.
Dow, Robert S. & Moruzzi, Guiseppe. The Physiology & Pathology of the Cerebellum. 2009. (ENG.). 692p. pap. 60.00 (978-0-8166-5749-0(1)) Univ. of Minnesota Pr.
Ito, Masao. Cerebellum: The Brain for an Implicit Self. rev. ed. 2011. (FT Press Science Ser.). (ENG., Illus.). 320p. 79.99 (978-0-13-705068-0(2)) FT Press.
Koziol, Leonard F. & Budding, Deborah Ely. Subcortical Structures & Cognition: Implications for Neuropsychological Assessment. 2009. (ENG., Illus.). xiii, 405p. 148.00 (978-0-387-84866-2(5), 0387848665) Springer.
Larsell, Olof. The Comparative Anatomy & Histology of the Cerebellum: From Monotremes Through Apes. Jansen, Jan, ed. 2009. (ENG.). 280p. pap. 50.00 (978-0-8166-5809-1(9)) Univ. of Minnesota Pr.
Levin, Fred M. Emotion & the Psychodynamics of the Cerebellum: A Neuro-Psychoanalytic Analysis & Synthesis. 2009. (Illus.). 270p. pap. 48.95 (978-1-85575-577-2(7)) Karnac Bks. GBR. Dist: Stylus Publishing, LLC.
Manto, Mario, et al, eds. Handbook of the Cerebellum & Cerebellar Disorders, 2 vols. 2012. (ENG., Illus.). 1200p. 679.00 (978-94-007-1332-1(0), 9400713320); 849.00 (978-94-007-1404-5(1), 9400714041) Springer.
McArthur, Sara. Ataxia: How I Had to Cope with an Untreatable, Incurable Neurodegenerative Cerebellum Disease, 1 vol. 2010. 240p. pap. 24.95 (978-1-60672-271-8(9)) PublishAmerica, Inc.
Naidich, Thomas P., et al. Duvernoy's Atlas of the Human Brain Stem & Cerebellum: High-Field MRI, Surface Anatomy, Internal Structure, Vascularization & 3 D Sectional Anatomy. 2008. (Illus.). 500p. 459.00 (978-3-211-73970-9(X)) Springer.
Paquier, P., ed. The Cerebellum & Language. 2007. (Illus.). 60p. pap. (978-3-8055-8329-9(X)) Karger, S. AG.
Pombano, Laura J. & Evans, Daniel M., eds. Cerebellum: Anatomy, Functions & Disorders. 2012. (Neuroscience Research Progress Ser.). 190p. 140.00 (978-1-61324-547-7(5)) Nova Science Pubs., Inc.
Rademaker, G. G. J. The Physiology of Standing (das Stehen: Postural Reactions & Equilibrium with Special References to the Behavior of Decerebellate Animals. 2009. (ENG.). 682p. pap. 60.00 (978-0-8166-6053-7(0)) Univ. of Minnesota Pr.
Thomas, Andr & Thomas, Andre. Cerebellar Functions. 2010. 634p. pap. 45.75 (978-1-148-58436-2(6)) BiblioBazaar.
Thomas, Andre. Cerebellar Functions. 2010. 240p. pap. 26.75 (978-1-177-13873-4(5)) 2010. 234p. pap. 25.75 (978-1-146-59378-6(3)) 2009. (ENG.). 230p. pap. 22.99 (978-1-110-27042-2(9), BiblioLife) 2009. (ENG.). 230p. pap. 20.99 (978-1-110-27039-2(9), BiblioLife) BiblioBazaar.
—Cerebellar Functions. 2010. 306p. pap. 29.69 (978-1-150-95130-5(3)) General Bks. LLC.

CEREBRAL CORTEX
see also Hippocampus (Brain)

Balleine, Bernard, et al, eds. Reward & Decision Making in Corticobasal Ganglia Networks. 2007. (Annals of the New York Academy of Sciences Ser.: Vol. 1105). (ENG., Illus.). 300p. pap. 159.95 (978-1-57331-674-3(1), Wiley-Blackwell) Wiley, John & Sons, Inc.
Bendor, Daniel. Temporal Processing in Primate Auditory Cortex. 2011. 184p. pap. (978-3-8443-2481-5(X)) Lambert Academic Publishing.
Binshtok, Alexander. Neurons at the Gate. 2010. 192p. pap. (978-3-8383-6130-7(X)) Lambert Academic Publishing.
Brodmann, K. Brodmann's: Localisation in the Cerebral Cortex. Garey, Laurence J., tr. from GER. 2010. (ENG., Illus.). xv, 298p. pap. 79.95 (978-1-4419-3895-4(8), 1441938958) Springer.
Chalupa, Leo M., et al, eds. Cerebral Plasticity: New Perspectives. 2011. (ENG., Illus.). 432p. (gr. 17). 60.00 (978-0-262-01523-3(4)) MIT Pr.
Cram101 Textbook Reviews & Cram101 Textbook Reviews. Outlines & Highlights for Subcortical Structures & Cognition: Implications for Neuropsychological Assessment by Leonard F. Koziol. 2011. 62p. pap. 27.95 (978-1-61830-426-1(7)) Cram101 Inc.
Eggermont, Jos J. & Lomber, Stephen G., eds. Reprogramming the Cerebral Cortex: Plasticity Following Central & Peripheral Lesions. 2006. (ENG., Illus.). 456p. 185.00 (978-0-19-852899-9(X)) Oxford Univ. Pr., Inc.
Elhilali, Mounya. Auditory Cortex: Anatomy, Functions, & Disorders. 2012. (978-1-62100-685-5(9)) Nova Science Pubs., Inc.
Erzurumlu, Reha, et al, eds. Development & Plasticity in Sensory Thalamus & Cortex. 2010. (ENG., Illus.). xiv, 322p. pap. 135.00 (978-1-4419-4068-1(5), 1441940685) Springer.
Falk, Dean & Gibson, Kathleen R., eds. Evolutionary Anatomy of the Primate Cerebral Cortex. 2008. (ENG., Illus.). 364p. pap. 69.00 (978-0-521-08995-1(6)) Cambridge Univ. Pr.
Fallani, Fabrizio De Vico & Babiloni, Fabio. The Graph Theoretical Approach in Brain Functional Networks: Theory & Applications. 2010. (Synthesis Lectures on Biomedical Engineering Ser.). 92p. pap. 35.00 (978-1-60845-449-5(5)) Morgan & Claypool Pubs.
Fox, Kevin. Barrel Cortex. 2008. (ENG., Illus.). 318p. 140.00 (978-0-521-85217-3(X)) Cambridge Univ. Pr.
Graziano, Michael S. A. The Intelligent Movement Machine: An Ethological Perspective on the Primate Motor System. 2008. (ENG., Illus.). 240p. 79.95 (978-0-19-532670-3(9)) Oxford Univ. Pr., Inc.
Hecht-Nielsen, Robert. Confabulation Theory: The Mechanism of Thought. 2007. (ENG., Illus.). x, 245p. 109.00 (978-3-540-49603-8(3), 3540496033) Springer.
Hung, George K. & Ciuffreda, Kenneth C., eds. Models of the Visual System. 2010. (Topics in Biomedical Engineering Ser.). 798p. pap. 239.00 (978-1-4419-3377-5(8), 1441933778) Springer.
Johnsen, Niels & Agerskov, Rolf, eds. Somatosensory Cortex: Roles, Interventions & Traumas. 2009. (Neurology - Laboratory & Clinical Research Developments Ser.). 129.00 (978-1-60741-876-4(2), Nova Biomedical Bks.) Nova Science Pubs., Inc.
Klingberg, Torkel. The Overflowing Brain: Information Overload & the Limits of Working Memory. 2008. (ENG., Illus.). 224p. 21.95 (978-0-19-537288-5(3)) Oxford Univ. Pr., Inc.
Koziol, Leonard F. & Budding, Deborah Ely. Subcortical Structures & Cognition: Implications for Neuropsychological Assessment. 2010. (ENG., Illus.). xiii, 405p. pap. 79.95 (978-0-387-84867-9(3), 0387848673) Springer.
Nasir, Nazim & Aljaz Ahmed Khan, Prof. Depression & Hippocampus. 2011. 80p. pap. (978-3-8443-0414-5(2)) Lambert Academic Publishing.
Nelissen, Koen. Functional Anatomy of Visual Processing in the Cerebral Cortex of the Macaque. 2006. (Acta Biomedica Lovaniensia Ser.: Vol. 362). (Illus.). pap. 165.00 (978-90-5867-541-5(6)) Leuven Univ. Pr. BEL. Dist: Cornell Univ. Pr.
Nuez, A. & Malmierca, E. Corticofugal Modulation of Sensory Information. 2007. (Advances in Anatomy, Embryology & Cell Biology Ser.). (Illus.). 74p. per. 149.00 (978-3-540-36769-7(1), 3540367691) Springer.
Petrides, Michael. The Human Cerebral Cortex: An MRI Atlas of the Sulci & Gyri in MNI Stereotaxic Space. 2011. (ENG., Illus.). 168p. 200.00 (978-0-12-386938-8(2), Academic Pr.) Elsevier Science & Technology Bks.
Poeppel, David, et al, eds. The Human Auditory Cortex. 2012. (Springer Handbook of Auditory Research Ser.: 43). (ENG., Illus.). xiv, 396p. 139.00 (978-1-4614-2313-3(9), 1461423139) Springer.
Schmahmann, Jeremy D. & Pandya, Deepak N. Fiber Pathways of the Brain. 2009. (ENG.). 654p. pap. 99.99 (978-0-19-538826-8(7)) Oxford Univ. Pr., Inc.
Sherman, S. Murray, et al. Exploring the Thalamus & Its Role in Cortical Function. 2nd ed. 2009. (ENG., Illus.). 512p. (gr. 17). pap. 36.00 (978-0-262-51344-9(7)) MIT Pr.
Traub, Roger D. & Whittington, Miles A. Cortical Oscillations in Health & Disease, 1 vol. 2010. (ENG., Illus.). 464p. 74.95 (978-0-19-534279-6(8)) Oxford Univ. Pr., Inc.
Tseng, Kuei-Yuan & Atzori, Marco, eds. Monoaminergic Modulation of Cortical Excitability. 2007. (ENG., Illus.). x, 329p. 179.00 (978-0-387-72254-2(8), 0387722548) Springer.
von Economo, C. Cellular Structure of the Human Cerebral Cortex. Triarhou, L. C., ed. 2009. (ENG., Illus.). 246p. (978-3-8055-9061-7(X)) Karger, S. AG.
von Economo, C. & Koskinas, G. N. Atlas of Cytoarchitectonics of the Adult Human Cerebral Cortex. Triarhou, L. C., ed. 2007. (Illus.). 182p. (978-3-8055-8289-6(7)) Karger, S. AG.
Weber, Cornelius. Maximum a Posteriori Models for Cortical Modeling. 2008. 112p. pap. (978-3-8364-9698-8(4)) VDM Verlag Dr. Mueller e.K.

CEREBRAL DEATH
see Brain Death

CEREBRAL DOMINANCE
see also Laterality

Band, Guido P. H. & Jolicoeur, Pierre, eds. Integrative Views on Dual-Task Costs. 2006. (Special Issues of the European Journal of Cognitive Psychology Ser.). (ENG.). 192p. 64.50 (978-1-84169-808-3(3), Psychology Press) Taylor & Francis Group GBR. Dist: Taylor & Francis Group.
Decostérd, Mary Lou. Right Brain - Left Brain President: Barack Obama's Uncommon Leadership Ability, & How We Can Each Develop It. 2010. (Contemporary Psychology Ser.). (Illus.). 169p. 34.95 (978-0-313-38072-3(4), A2225C, Praeger Pubs.) Greenwood Publishing Group, Inc.
Decosterd, Mary Lou. Right Brain/Left Brain Leadership: Shifting Style for Maximum Impact, 1 vol. 2008. (Contemporary Psychology Ser.). (Illus.). 208p. 44.95 (978-0-275-99934-6(3), C9934, Praeger Pubs.) Greenwood Publishing Group, Inc.
Edwards, Betty. Drawing on the Right Side of the Brain: The Definitive, 4th Edition. 4th ed. 2012. (ENG.). 320p. (gr. 12). 32.95 (978-1-58542-919-6(8), Tarcher) Penguin Group (USA) Inc.
Hugdahl, Kenneth. The Two Halves of the Brain: Information Processing in the Cerebral Hemispheres. Westerhausen, Rene, ed. 2010. (ENG., Illus.). 704p. (gr. 17). 75.00 (978-0-262-01413-7(0)) MIT Pr.
Malashichev, Yegor B. & Deckel, A. Wallace. Behavioral & Morphological Asymmetries in Vertebrates. 2006. 139.00 (978-1-58706-105-9(8)) Landes Bioscience.
McGilchrist, Iain. The Master & His Emissary: The Divided Brain & the Making of the Western World. 2010. (Illus.). 544p. pap. 25.00 (978-0-300-16892-1(6)) Yale Univ. Pr.
Olson, James. The Whole-Brain Path to Peace: The Role of Left-And Right-Brain Dominance in the Polarization & Reunification of America. 2011. (Illus.). 335p. 21.95 (978-1-57983-055-7(2)) Origin Pr.
Phillips, Charles. Left Brain Right Brain. 2011. (50 Puzzles to Change the Way You Think Ser.). (Illus.). 144p. pap. (978-1-85906-320-0(9)) Connections Bk. Publishing, Ltd.

CEREBRAL EDEMA

Czernicki, Zbigniew. Brain Edema XIV. Czernicki, Zbigniew et al, eds. 2009. (Acta Neurochirurgica Supplementum Ser.). (ENG., Illus.). xiii, 403p. 319.00 (978-3-211-98758-2(4), 3211987584) Springer.
Hoff, Julian T., et al, eds. Brain Edema XIII. 2010. (Acta Neurochirurgica Supplementum Ser.). (Illus.). xv, 460p. pap. 309.00 (978-3-211-99882-3(9), 3211998829) Springer.

CEREBRAL HEMISPHERES
see also Cerebral Dominance

Nikolaeva, Elena & Leutin, Vitali. Functional Brain Asymmetry: Myth & Reality. 2011. 352p. pap. (978-3-8433-8289-2(1)) Lambert Academic Publishing.
Rä, et al. Cerebral Haemodynamic Impairment. 2010. 72p. pap. (978-3-8383-0679-7(1)) Lambert Academic Publishing.

CEREBRAL HEMORRHAGE
see Brain—Hemorrhage

CEREBRAL ISCHEMIA

Äänismaa, Riikka. Human Embryonic Stem Cell-Derived Neural & Neuronal Cells in Vitro & in Vivo: Treatment of Experimental Cerebral Ischemia. 2010. (Acta Universitatis Tamperensis Ser.). 109p. pap. 77.50 (978-951-44-7973-1(4)) Tampere Univ. Pr. FIN. Dist: Coronet Bks.
Annunziato, Lucio, ed. New Strategies in Stroke Intervention: Ionic Transporters, Pumps & New Channels. 2009. (Contemporary Neuroscience Ser.). (Illus.). 490p. 189.00 (978-1-4419-0356-3(9)) Springer.
Bendok, Bernard R., et al, eds. Hemorrhagic & Ischemic Stroke: Medical, Imaging, Surgical & Interventional Approaches. 2011. (ENG., Illus.). 584p. 199.99 (978-1-60406-234-2(7)) Thieme Medical Pubs., Inc.
Di Napoli, Mario & Francesca, P. Neuroinflammation: An Important Role in the Pathogenic Pathways of Cerebral Ischemia. 2008. pap. 35.00 (978-1-60692-030-5(8)) Nova Science Pubs., Inc.
Díez-Tejedor, E., ed. Ischemic Stroke: Knowledge & Research, Challenges & Goals:5th International Workshop, Madrid, April 2008. 2009. (Illus.). 216p. pap. (978-3-8055-9051-8(2)) Karger, S. AG.
Eisert, Wolfgang, et al, eds. Innate Inflammation & Stroke. 2010. (Annals of the New York Academy of Sciences Ser. 61). (ENG., Illus.). 300p. pap. 150.00 (978-1-57331-813-6(2), Wiley-Blackwell) Wiley, John & Sons, Inc.
Gean, Alisa & Schaefer, Pamela W. Stroke Imaging, an Issue of Neuroimaging Clinics. 2011. (Clinics: Radiology Ser.: 21-2). (ENG., Illus.). 248p. 105.00 (978-1-4377-2693-0(3), Saunders) Elsevier - Health Sciences Div.
González, R. Gilberto, et al, eds. Acute Ischemic Stroke: Imaging & Intervention. 2nd ed. 2010. (ENG., Illus.). xiii, 297p. 169.00 (978-3-642-12750-2(9), 3642127509) Springer.
Greer, David M., ed. Acute Ischemic Stroke: An Evidence-Based Approach. 2007. (ENG., Illus.). 248p. 154.95 (978-0-470-06807-6(8), Wiley-Liss) Wiley, John & Sons, Inc.
Haddad, Gabriel G. & Yu, Shan Ping. Brain Hypoxia & Ischemia. 2009. (Contemporary Clinical Neuroscience Ser.). (ENG., Illus.). xii, 268p. 189.00 (978-1-60327-578-1(9)) Humana Pr.
Hämäläinen, Eetu. New Trends in Brain Hypoxia Ischemia Research. 2008. (Illus.). 315p. (C). 129.00 (978-1-60456-140-1(8)) Nova Science Pubs., Inc.
Kaste, Markku & Castillo, José, eds. Neuroprotection in Brain Ischemia: An Update. (Cerebrovascular Diseases Ser.). (Illus.). 134p. pap. (978-3-8055-8122-6(X)) Karger, S. AG.
Lajtha, Abel & Chan, Pak H. Acute Ischemic Injury & Repair in the Nervous System. 3rd ed. 2009. (Illus.). xi, 291p. 4550.00 (978-0-387-35478-1(6), 0387354786) Springer.
—Acute Ischemic Injury & Repair in the Nervous System. Chan, Pak, ed. 3rd rev. ed. 2006. (Springer Reference Ser.). (Illus.). 291p. 249.00 (978-0-387-30352-9(9), 0387303529) Springer.
Lees, Kennedy R., ed. Optimizing the Treatment of Acute Ischemic Stroke - a STAIR-Way to Success? Satellite Symposium at the 14th European Stroke Conference Bologna, Italy, May 25-28, 2005, Vol. 22. (Cerebrovascular Diseases Ser.). (Illus.). pap. (978-3-8055-8149-3(1)) Karger, S. AG.
Liebeskind, David S. Therapeutic Strategies in Cerebral Ischemia. 2011. 152p. pap. (978-1-84692-045-5(0)) Clinical Publishing Services.
Liebeskind, David S., ed. Diagnostic Strategies in Cerebral Ischemia. 2011. (Illus.). 127p. (978-1-84692-085-1(X)) Clinical Publishing Services.
Maier, Carolina M. & Steinberg, Gary K., eds. Hypothermia & Cerebral Ischemia: Mechanisms & Clinical Applications. 2010. (Illus.). 200p. pap. 125.00 (978-1-61737-120-2(3), 1617371203) Humana Pr.
Mishra, Om P. Mechanisms of Hypoxic Brain Injury in the Newborn & Potential Strategies for Neuroprotection. 2007. (Illus.). 218p. (978-81-7895-263-5(7)) Transworld Research Network.
Padovani, Alessandro & Pezzini, Alessandro. Cerebral Ischemia in Young Adults: Pathogenic & Clinical Perspectives. 2009. (Neurology - Laboratory & Clinical Research Developments Ser.). pap. 89.00 (978-1-60741-627-2(1), Nova Biomedical Bks.) Nova Science Pubs., Inc.
Pluta, Ryszard. Ischemia-Reperfusion Pathways in Alzheimer's Disease. 2007. 89.00 (978-1-60021-744-9(3)) Nova Science Pubs., Inc.
Ronco, C. & Diez-Tejedor, E., eds. Atherothrombotic Disease & Cerebral Ischemia: 3rd International Workshop, Madrid, June 2005, Vol. 20. (Contributions to Nephrology Ser.). (Illus.). 180p. pap. (978-3-8055-8066-3(5)) Karger, S. AG.
Roux, Océane M. Brain Hypoxia-Ischemia Research Progress. 2008. (C). 129.00 (978-1-60456-139-5(4)) Nova Science Pubs., Inc.
Savitz, Sean I. & Rosenbaum, Daniel M., eds. Stroke Recovery with Cellular Therapies. 2007. (Current Clinical Neurology Ser.). (Illus.). 166p. 119.00 (978-1-58829-732-7(2)) Humana Pr.
Schaller, Bernhard J. Endogenous Neuroprotection. 2008. (Illus.). 100p. 89.00 (978-1-60456-228-6(5), Nova Biomedical Bks.) Nova Science Pubs., Inc.

C

Tonchev, Anton B., et al. Distribution & Phenotype of Proliferating Cells in the Forebrain of Adult Macaque Monkeys after Transient Global Cerebral Ischemia. 2007. (Advances in Anatomy, Embryology & Cell Biology Ser.). (Illus.). x, 108p. pap. 159.00 *(978-3-540-39613-0(6)*, 3540396136) Springer.
Zaidat, Osama O. Endovascular Ischemic Stroke Therapy. 2009. 300p. 125.00 *(978-1-58829-810-2(8))* Humana Pr.

CEREBRAL LATERALITY
see Cerebral Dominance

CEREBRAL LOCALIZATION
see Brain—Localization of Functions

CEREBRAL PALSIED CHILDREN

Cram101 Textbook Reviews & Cram101 Textbook Reviews. Outlines & Highlights for Finnies Handling the Young Child with Cerebral Palsy at Home by Eva Bower, Isbn: 9780750688109. 2011. 252p. pap. 31.95 ***(978-1-61461-063-2(0))*** Cram101 Inc.
Eliasson, Ann-Christin & Burtner, Patricia. Improving Hand Function in Children with Cerebral Palsy. 2008. (Clinics in Developmental Medicine Ser.). (ENG., Illus.). 480p. 158.00 *(978-1-898683-53-7(0))* Mac Keith Pr. GBR. Dist: Wiley, John & Sons, Inc.
Ferrari, Adriano & Cioni, Giovanni. The Spastic Forms of Cerebral Palsy: A Guide to the Assessment of Adaptive Functions. 2009. (ENG., Illus.). xx, 360p. 79.95 *(978-88-470-1477-0(8)*, 8847014778) Springer.
Finnie, Nancie R. Finnie's Handling the Young Child with Cerebral Palsy at Home. Bower, Eva, ed. 4th rev. ed. 2008. (ENG., Illus.). 396p. pap. 60.95 *(978-0-7506-8810-9(6)*, Butterworth-Heinemann) Elsevier - Health Sciences Div.
Getchman, Jean. Can Do! 2011. 56p. 24.99 ***(978-1-4568-3851-5(2))***; pap. 15.99 ***(978-1-4568-3850-8(4))*** Xlibris Corp.
Harry, Beth. Melanie, Bird with a Broken Wing: A Mother's Story. 2010. (Illus.). 232p. pap. 24.95 *(978-1-59857-113-4(3))* Brookes, Paul H. Publishing Co.
Hewett, Sheila, et al. The Family & the Handicapped Child: A Study of Cerebral Palsied Children in Their Homes. 2007. (ENG., Illus.). 240p. pap. 22.95 *(978-0-202-30951-4(7))* Aldine Transaction.
Hinchcliffe, Archie. Children with Cerebral Palsy: A Manual for Therapists, Parents & Community Workers. 2nd ed. 2007. (Illus.). 259p. (C). per. 36.00 *(978-0-7619-3560-5(6)*, B35606P) SAGE Pubns., Inc.
Horstmann, Helen Meeks & Bleck, Eugene. Orthopaedic Management in Cerebral Palsy. 2nd ed. 2007. (Clinics in Developmental Medicine Ser.: 7). (ENG., Illus.). 412p. 232.00 *(978-1-898683-52-0(2))* Mac Keith Pr. GBR. Dist: Wiley, John & Sons, Inc.
Leone, Marianne. Knowing Jesse: A Mother's Story of Grief, Grace, & Everyday Bliss. 2010. (ENG., Illus.). 272p. 25.00 *(978-1-4391-8392-2(9))* Simon & Schuster.
Levitt, Sophie. Treatment of Cerebral Palsy & Motor Delay. 5th ed. 2010. (ENG., Illus.). 368p. pap. 66.99 *(978-1-4051-7616-3(4)*, Wiley-Blackwell) Wiley, John & Sons, Inc.
Miller, Frederic P., et al, eds. Cerebral Palsy. 2010. 104p. pap. ***(978-613-0-72913-4(8))*** VDM Verlag Dr. Mueller e.K.
Osler, William. The Cerebral Palsies of Children: A Clinical Study from the Infirmary for Nervous Diseases, Philadelphia. 2007. (ENG.). 110p. 34.95 *(978-0-548-15659-9(X))* Kessinger Publishing, LLC.
—The Cerebral Palsies of Children: a Clinical Study from the Infirmary. 2007. pap. 19.95 *(978-1-4304-5124-2(6))* Kessinger Publishing, LLC.
Philps, Alan & Lahutsky, John. The Boy from Baby House 10: From the Nightmare of a Russian Orphanage to a New Life in America. 2011. (ENG., Illus.). 312p. pap. 14.99 *(978-0-312-65648-5(3)*, St. Martin's Griffin) St. Martin's Pr.
Russell, Dianne J., et al. Gross Motor Function Measure (GMFM-66 & GMFM-88) User's Manual. 2007. (Clinics in Developmental Medicine Ser.: No. 159). (ENG., Illus.). 244p. 112.95 *(978-1-898683-29-2(8))* Mac Keith Pr. GBR. Dist: Wiley, John & Sons, Inc.
Stamer, Marcia Hornbrook. Posture & Movement of the Child with Cerebral Palsy. 2006. pap. 55.00 *(978-1-4164-0311-1(6))* PRO-ED, Inc.
StewartJones, Mark. Daughter. 2009. (Illus.). 244p. pap. 26.50 *(978-1-84624-293-9(2))* Book Guild, Ltd. GBR. Dist: Trans-Atlantic Pubns., Inc.
Thomson, Donna. The Four Walls of My Freedom. 2012. (ENG., Illus.). 262p. pap. 18.95 ***(978-1-55278-986-5(1))*** McArthur & Co. CAN. Dist: National Bk. Network.

CEREBRAL PALSY

Boyer, Patrick, et al. Solitary Courage: Mona Winberg & the Triumph over Disability. 2010. (ENG.). 383p. pap. 22.95 ***(978-0-9781600-5-0(3))*** Dundurn CAN. Dist: Ingram Pub. Services.
Chambers, Hank. Orthopedic Management of Cerebral Palsy, an Issue of Orthopedic Clinics. 2010. (Clinics: Orthopedics Ser.: 41-4). (ENG., Illus.). x, 442p. 105.00 *(978-1-4377-2475-2(2)*, Saunders) Elsevier - Health Sciences Div.
Cram101 Textbook Reviews & Cram101 Textbook Reviews. Outlines & Highlights for Finnies Handling the Young Child with Cerebral Palsy at Home by Eva Bower, Isbn: 9780750688109. 2011. 252p. pap. 31.95 ***(978-1-61461-063-2(0))*** Cram101 Inc.
Dodd, Karen J., et al, eds. Physiotherapy & Occupational Therapy for People with Cerebral Palsy: A Problem-Based Approach to Assessment & Management. 2010. (PGMKP - a Practical Guide from MKP Ser.). (ENG., Illus.). 256p. pap. 41.99 *(978-1-898683-68-1(9))* Mac Keith Pr. GBR. Dist: Wiley, John & Sons, Inc.
Ferrari, Adriano & Cioni, Giovanni. The Spastic Forms of Cerebral Palsy: A Guide to the Assessment of Adaptive Functions. 2009. (ENG., Illus.). xx, 360p. 79.95 *(978-88-470-1477-0(8)*, 8847014778) Springer.
Gage, James R. Gait Analysis in Cerebral Palsy. (Illus.). xv, 206p. (C). *(978-0-901260-90-1(8))* Mac Keith Pr. GBR. Dist: Cambridge Univ. Pr.
Gage, James R., et al, eds. The Identification & Treatment of Gait Problems in Cerebral Palsy. 2nd ed. 2009. (Clinics in Developmental Medicine Ser.: 4). (ENG., Illus.). 660p. 209.00 *(978-1-898683-65-0(4))* Mac Keith Pr. GBR. Dist: Wiley, John & Sons, Inc.
Gregory, D. J. & Eubanks, Steve. Walking with Friends: An Inspirational Year on the PGA Tour. 2010. (ENG., Illus.). 224p. pap. 15.00 *(978-1-4391-5403-8(1)*, Simon Spotlight Entertainment) Simon & Schuster.
Higgins, Jim. Head Boy: The SHAKING Trilogy. 2009. 296p. pap. 15.49 *(978-1-4490-0112-4(2))* AuthorHouse.
Jewell, Geri & Nichelson, Ted. I'm Walking as Straight as I Can: Transcending Disability in Hollywood & Beyond. 2011. (ENG., Illus.). 264p. pap. 19.95 *(978-1-55022-883-0(8))* ECW Pr. CAN. Dist: Independent Pubs. Group.
Kimaro, Marine. Cerebral Palsy: Case control study of risk factors (ohangwena Namibia) 2011. 60p. pap. ***(978-3-8383-7642-4(0))*** Lambert Academic Publishing.
Maloney, Stuart. 26: A Behind-the-Scenes Tour of Life with Cerebral Palsy. 2011. 236p. pap. 17.09 ***(978-1-4670-0788-7(9))*** AuthorHouse.
Michaud, Linda J. Cerebral Palsy, an Issue of Physical Medicine & Rehabilitation Clinics. 2009. (Clinics: Orthopedics Ser.: 20-3). (ENG.). 99.00 *(978-1-4377-1262-9(2)*, Saunders) Elsevier - Health Sciences Div.
Miller, Frederic P., et al, eds. Cerebral Palsy. 2010. 104p. pap. ***(978-613-0-72913-4(8))*** VDM Verlag Dr. Mueller e.K.
Miller, Freeman, ed. Physical Therapy of Cerebral Palsy. 2007. (Illus.). x, 416p. 69.95 *(978-0-387-38303-3(4)*, 0387383034) Springer.
Naidoo, Pravani. The Experiences of Children with Disabilities in Therapeutic Riding. 2010. 308p. pap. *(978-3-8383-6474-2(0))* Lambert Academic Publishing.
Pirils, Silja & van der Meere, Jaap. The Meaning of Functional Motor Limitations in Childhood - a Monograph. 2008. 52p. pap. *(978-3-639-09406-0(9))* VDM Verlag Dr. Mueller e.K.
Segalman, Bob. Against the Current. 2009. 159p. spiral bd. 19.00 *(978-1-57861-675-6(1))* Attainment Co., Inc.

CEREBRAL PALSY—JUVENILE LITERATURE

Marilyn Maple, Ph. D. & Marilyn Maple. I Can't Hear the Walls. 2010. 52p. pap. *(978-1-4269-2892-5(0))* Trafford Publishing (UK) Ltd.

CEREBRAL PALSY—PATIENTS

Clare, Eli. Exile & Pride (Classics Edition) Disability, Queerness, & Liberation. 2009. (ENG.). 192p. pap. 18.00 *(978-0-89608-788-0(3))* South End Pr.
Reagan, Marianne. Different Cousins. 2011. 24p. pap. 11.32 ***(978-1-4670-2508-9(9))*** AuthorHouse.
Slate, Gayle. Dana's Legacy: From Heartbreak to Healing. 2009. (ENG.). pap. 17.95 *(978-1-60037-537-8(5))* Morgan James Publishing.
Vasseghi, Sourena. Love Your Life & It Will Love You Back: 10 Lessons for Using the Power of Love to Succeed in Life. 2007. 19.95 *(978-0-9791369-0-0(3))* Vasseghi, Sourena.

CEREBRAL PALSY—PATIENTS—BIOGRAPHY

Anderson, Ben D. IQ of 63 - So What! Going Beyond Everybody Else's Expectations. 2007. (Illus.). 144p. per. 16.95 *(978-0-615-15257-8(0))* Break Through, Inc.
Brimmer, Gaby & Poniatowska, Elena. Gaby Brimmer: An Autobiography in Three Voices. 2009. (HBI Series on Jewish Women Ser.). (ENG.). 232p. pap. 26.00 *(978-1-58465-758-3(8)*, Brandeis University Press) Univ. Pr. of New England.
Burianek, Helen C. Father's Gypsy Child. 2010. 296p. pap. 21.00 *(978-0-557-42330-9(9))* Lulu Enterprises Inc.
Davis, Kevin. Power of Persistence. 2006. 134p. pap. 20.86 *(978-0-615-13520-5(X))* Williamson, Lisa A.
Elwood, Lynne Marie. Rollingaround. 2008. 184p. pap. 14.99 *(978-1-60647-758-8(7))* Xulon Pr., Inc.
Enck Mph, Becki. Walking Hand in Hand with Cameron, Together We Can! One Family's Journey with Cerebral Palsy. 2008. 216p. pap. 17.95 *(978-0-595-49005-9(0))* iUniverse, Inc.
Grimm, James. The Heart's Alphabet: Daring to Live with Cerebral Palsy. 2007. (Illus.). 120p. per. 12.95 *(978-0-9789946-7-9(1))* Tasora Bks.
Hambleton, Georgina Louise. Christy Brown: The Life That Inspired My Left Foot. 2012. (ENG., Illus.). 288p. pap. 14.95 *(978-1-84596-318-7(0))* Mainstream Publishing Co., Ltd. GBR. Dist: Independent Pubs. Group.
Hambleton, Georgina Louise & Brown, Christy. Christy Brown: The Life That Inspired My Left Foot. 2007. (ENG., Illus.). 240p. 29.95 *(978-1-84596-280-7(X))* Mainstream Publishing Co., Ltd. GBR. Dist: Independent Pubs. Group.
Harry, Beth. Melanie, Bird with a Broken Wing: A Mother's Story. 2010. (Illus.). 232p. pap. 24.95 *(978-1-59857-113-4(3))* Brookes, Paul H. Publishing Co.
Higgins, Jim. Shaking. 2008. 224p. pap. 14.49 *(978-1-4343-8994-7(4))* AuthorHouse.
—Still Shaking: The Shaking Trilogy: Book Three. 2010. 216p. pap. 15.99 *(978-1-4520-4131-5(8))* AuthorHouse.
Hocutt, Elizabeth C. Living with Cerebral Palsy. 2007. 48p. per. 16.95 *(978-1-4241-9202-1(1))* PublishAmerica, Inc.
Komoroski-McConnell, Christine. Only You Christine, Only You! One Woman's Journey Through Life with Cerebral Palsy. 2009. 164p. 25.95 *(978-1-4401-3094-6(9))*; pap. 15.95 *(978-1-4401-3092-2(2))* iUniverse, Inc.
Leone, Marianne. Jesse: A Mother's Story. 2011. (ENG.). 288p. pap. 15.00 *(978-1-4391-8432-5(1))* Simon & Schuster.
Longo, A. R. Life's Waiting to Begin. 2011. 114p. pap. 11.95 ***(978-1-4327-7580-3(4))*** Outskirts Pr., Inc.
Peterson, Bonnie. We Climbed Every Mountain: The Life Story of Don & Bonnie Peterson. 2011. 252p. pap. 15.99 ***(978-1-4634-0806-0(4))*** AuthorHouse.
Philps, Alan & Lahutsky, John. The Boy from Baby House 10: From the Nightmare of a Russian Orphanage to a New Life in America. 2009. (ENG., Illus.). 304p. 24.99 *(978-0-312-57697-4(8))* St. Martin's Pr.
Shulman, Alix Kates. To Love What Is: A Marriage Transformed. 2009. (ENG., Illus.). 192p. pap. 14.00 *(978-0-374-53205-5(2))* Farrar, Straus & Giroux.
Smart, J M. I'LI Never Walk Alone. 2007. (Illus.). 227p. pap. *(978-0-9525654-4-4(7))* Wren Pubns.
StewartJones, Mark. Daughter. 2009. (Illus.). 244p. pap. 26.50 *(978-1-84624-293-9(2))* Book Guild, Ltd. GBR. Dist: Trans-Atlantic Pubns., Inc.
Thomson, Donna. The Four Walls of My Freedom. 2010. (ENG., Illus.). 200p. 29.95 *(978-1-55278-890-5(3))* McArthur & Co. CAN. Dist: National Bk. Network.
Wambach, Tim. How We Roll: 2 Men, 1 Wheelchair & a lifetime of lessons in Perseverance. 2010. (ENG.). 122p. pap. 11.99 *(978-1-59932-159-2(9))* Advantage Media Group.
Wiggins, Bishop Christopher. The Book of Hope. 2011. 76p. pap. 15.99 ***(978-1-4568-5249-8(3))*** Xlibris Corp.

CEREBROSPINAL FLUID
see also Blood-Brain Barrier; Spine—Puncture

Abbott, Ira Richmond, et al, eds. Cerebrospinal Fluid Disorders. 2009. (ENG., Illus.). 640p. 350.00 *(978-0-8247-2833-5(5)*, Informa Healthcare) Taylor & Francis Group GBR. Dist: Taylor & Francis Group.
Ali, Syed Z. & Cibas, Edmund S. Serous Cavity Fluid & Cerebrospinal Fluid Cytopathology. 2012. (Essentials in Cytopathology Ser.). (ENG., Illus.). ix, 287p. pap. 79.95 ***(978-1-4614-1775-0(9)***, 1461417759) Springer.
Cold, Georg E. & Juul, Niels, eds. Monitoring of Cerebral & Spinal Hemodynamic During Neurosurgery. 2008. (ENG., Illus.). xx, 332p. 149.00 *(978-3-540-77872-1(1)*, 354077872l) Springer.
Helio, Tomas R., ed. The Blood Brain Barrier. 2008. 129.00 *(978-1-60456-894-3(1))* Nova Science Pubs., Inc.
Irani, David N. Cerebrospinal Fluid in Clinical Practice. 2008. (ENG., Illus.). 336p. 170.00 *(978-1-4160-2908-3(7)*, Saunders) Elsevier - Health Sciences Div.
Kluge, Harald. Atlas of CSF Cytology. 2006. (Illus.). xii, 139p. 149.95 *(978-3-13-143161-5(X))* Thieme Medical Pubs., Inc.
Kluge, Harald, et al. Atlas of CSF Cytology. 2006. (ENG., Illus.). 151p. 149.99 *(978-1-58890-546-8(2))* Thieme Medical Pubs., Inc.
Peirsman, Etienne & Peirsman, Neeto. Craniosacral Therapy for Babies & Small Children. 2006. (ENG., Illus.). 120p. pap. 24.95 *(978-1-55643-597-3(5))* North Atlantic Bks.
Ridley, Charles. Stillness: Biodynamic Cranial Practice & the Evolution of Consciousness. 2006. (ENG.). 264p. pap. 19.95 *(978-1-55643-592-8(4))* North Atlantic Bks.
Rosenberg, Gary A. Molecular Physiology & Metabolism of the Nervous System: A Clinical Perspective. 2012. (Contemporary Neurology Ser.: 82). (ENG.). 240p. 99.99 ***(978-0-19-539427-6(5))*** Oxford Univ. Pr., Inc.
Torzewski, Michael, et al. Integrated Cytology of Cerebrospinal Fluid. (ENG., Illus.). viii, 94p. 2010. pap. 69.95 *(978-3-642-09502-3(X)*, 364209502X) 2008. 69.95 *(978-3-540-75884-6(4)*, 3540758844) Springer.

CEREBROVASCULAR DISEASE
see also Brain—Hemorrhage; Cerebral Ischemia; Sinus Thrombosis

Abdulrauf, Saleem I. Cerebral Revascularization: Techniques in Extracranial-to-Intracranial Bypass Surgery. 2010. (ENG., Illus.). 424p. 274.00 *(978-1-4377-1785-3(3)*, Saunders) Elsevier - Health Sciences Div.
Aburahma, Ali & Bergan, John J., eds. Noninvasive Cerebrovascular Diagnosis. 2010. (ENG., Illus.). 150p. pap. 39.95 *(978-1-84882-956-5(6)*, 1848829566) Springer.
Adams, Harold P., Jr. Principles of Cerebrovascular Disease. 2006. (ENG., Illus.). 564p. 214.00 *(978-0-07-141653-5(6)*, 0071416536) McGraw-Hill Professional Publishing.
Aiyagari, Venkatesh & Gorelick, Philip B., eds. Hypertension & Stroke: Pathophysiology & Treatment. 2009. (Clinical Hypertension & Vascular Diseases Ser.). (Illus.). 300p. 189.00 *(978-1-60761-009-0(4))* Humana Pr.
Alexandrov, Andrei V., ed. Cerebrovascular Ultrasound in Stroke Prevention & Treatment. 2nd ed. 2011. (ENG., Illus.). 296p. 209.95 *(978-1-4051-9576-8(2)*, Wiley-Blackwell) Wiley, John & Sons, Inc.
Alway, David & Cole, John Walden. Stroke Essentials for Primary Care: A Practical Guide. 2008. (Current Clinical Practice Ser.). (Illus.). 232p. 79.95 *(978-1-934115-01-5(0))* Humana Pr.
Amarenco, Pierre, ed. Cardiovascular Risk Factor Management in the Prevention of Stroke Vol. 16: Satellite Symposium Held on the Occasion of the 11th European Stroke Conference, Geneva, Switzerland, May 31, 2002: Proceedings. (Cerebrovascular Diseases Ser.: Vol. 16, Suppl. 3). (Illus.). *(978-3-8055-7587-4(4))* Karger, S. AG.
Anand, Vijaya & KALAVATHY, S. Clinical Utility of High Sensitivity C-Reactive Protein. 2011. 224p. pap. ***(978-3-8443-9715-4(9))*** Lambert Academic Publishing.
Annunziato, Lucio. New Strategies in Stroke Intervention: Ionic Transporters, Pumps, & New Channels. 2009. (Contemporary Neuroscience Ser.). (ENG., Illus.). xv, 254p. 219.00 *(978-1-60761-279-7(8)*, 1607612798) Humana Pr.
Annunziato, Lucio, ed. New Strategies in Stroke Intervention: Ionic Transporters, Pumps & New Channels. 2009. (Contemporary Neuroscience Ser.). (Illus.). 490p. 189.00 *(978-1-4419-0356-3(9))* Springer.
Baker, Daryl M. Stroke Prevention in Clinical Practice. 2007. (Illus.). 131p. per. 39.95 *(978-1-85233-964-7(0)*, 1852339640) Springer.
Baltgaile, G., et al, eds. European Society of Neurosonology & Cerebral Hemodynamics: 14th Meeting, Riga, May 2009: Abstracts. 2009. 44p. pap. *(978-3-8055-9157-7(8))* Karger, S. AG.
Barker, Peter, et al. Clinical MR Spectroscopy: Techniques & Applications. 2009. (ENG., Illus.). 274p. 125.00 *(978-0-521-86898-3(X))* Cambridge Univ. Pr.
Bartels, E., et al, eds. European Society of Neurosonology & Cerebral Hemodynamics: 16th Meeting, Munich, May 2011: Abstracts. Supplement Issue:'Cerebrovascular Diseases 2011, Vol. 31, Suppl. 1' 2011. (ENG.). 74p. pap. ***(978-3-8055-9775-3(4))*** Karger, S. AG.
Baumgartner, R. W. Handbook on Neurovascular Ultrasound, Vol. 21. (Frontiers of Neurology & Neuroscience Ser.: Vol. 21). (Illus.). 250p. *(978-3-8055-8022-9(3))* Karger, S. AG.
Becker, Richard C. & Spencer, Fredrick A. Antithrombotic Therapy in Prevention of Ischemic Stroke. 2010. (Oxford American Pocket Notes Ser.). (ENG., Illus.). 56p. pap. 14.95 *(978-0-19-539432-0(1))* Oxford Univ. Pr., Inc.
Bendok, Bernard R., et al, eds. Hemorrhagic & Ischemic Stroke: Medical, Imaging, Surgical & Interventional Approaches. 2011. (ENG., Illus.). 584p. 199.99 ***(978-1-60406-234-2(7))*** Thieme Medical Pubs., Inc.
Bhardwaj, Anish & Mirski, Marek A., eds. Handbook of Neurocritical Care: Second Edition. 2nd ed. 2010. (ENG., Illus.). xix, 625p. pap. 79.95 *(978-1-4419-6841-8(5)*, 1441968415) Springer.
Bhatt, Deepak L., ed. Peripheral & Cerebrovascular Intervention. 2011. (Contemporary Cardiology Ser.). (ENG.). 350p. 189.00 *(978-1-60327-964-2(4)*, 1603279644) Humana Pr.
Biller, Jose. Stroke in Children & Young Adults. 2nd ed. 2009. (ENG., Illus.). 368p. 142.00 *(978-0-7506-7418-8(0)*, Saunders) Elsevier - Health Sciences Div.
Biller, Jose & Ferro, José M. Evidence-Based Management of Stroke. 2010. (Illus.). 350p. *(978-1-903378-76-2(1))* TFM Publishing Ltd.
Birkett, D. Peter. The Psychiatry of Stroke. 2nd ed. 2007. (Illus.). 408p. 175.00 *(978-0-7890-3179-2(5))*; per. 69.95 *(978-0-7890-3180-8(9))* Routledge.
Bogousslavsky, Julien, ed. Stroke Management in Patients with Diabetes Mellitus or Metabolic Syndromes: Plenary Symposium at the 14th European Stroke Conference, Bologna, May 26 2005, Vol. 20. (Illus.). *(978-3-8055-8037-3(1))* Karger, S. AG.
—Stroke Prevention by the Practitioner, Vol. 15. 2nd rev. ed. (Cerebrovascular Diseases Ser.: Vol. 15, Suppl. 2). (Illus.). *(978-3-8055-7569-0(6))* Karger, S. AG.
Bogousslavsky, Julien & Bousser, Marie-Germaine, eds. Advances in Stroke Prevention: Plenary Symposium at the 11th European Stroke Conference, Geneva, May 29-June 1, 2002, Vol. 16. (Illus.). *(978-3-8055-7583-6(1))* Karger, S. AG.
Bogousslavsky, Julien & Hacke, Werner, eds. Thrombolytic & Antithrombotic Therapy for Stroke. 2006. (ENG., Illus.). 272p. 200.00 *(978-1-84184-203-5(6)*, CRC Press) Taylor & Francis Group GBR. Dist: Taylor & Francis Group.
Bogousslavsky, Julien, et al. Stroke: Selected Topics. 2006. (World Federation of Neurology Seminars in Clinical Neurology Ser.: Vol. 4). (Illus.). 65p. 39.95 *(978-1-933864-01-3(X))* Demos Medical Publishing, LLC.
Bornstein, N. M., ed. Stroke: Practical Guide for Clinicians. 2009. (Illus.). 204p. *(978-3-8055-9099-0(7))* Karger, S. AG.
Bradley, T. Douglas. Sleep Apnea: Implications in Cardiovascular & Cerebrovascular Disease. 2nd rev. ed. 2008. (ENG., Illus.). 416p. 300.00 *(978-0-8493-4150-2(7))* Taylor & Francis Group.
Brainin, Michael & Heiss, Wolf-Dieter, eds. Textbook of Stroke Medicine. 2009. (ENG., Illus.). 336p. 109.00 *(978-0-521-51826-0(1))* Cambridge Univ. Pr.
Burkman, Kip. The Stroke Recovery Book: A Guide for Patients & Families. 2nd ed. 2010. (ENG.). 152p. pap. 19.95 *(978-1-886039-98-8(4))* Addicus Bks.
Butler, Paul, ed. Endovascular Neurosurgery: A Multidisciplinary Approach. 2010. (ENG.). x, 160p. pap. 259.00 *(978-1-84996-890-4(X)*, 184996890X) Springer.
Canavero, Sergio. Textbook of Therapeutic Cortical Stimulation. 2009. (Illus.). xiv, 450p. 79.00 *(978-1-60692-537-9(7))* Nova Science Pubs., Inc.
Candolotti, Jean T. & Burnside, Jason E., eds. Women & Strokes Research. 2008. (Illus.). (C). 129.00 *(978-1-60456-374-0(5))* Nova Science Pubs., Inc.
Caplan, Louis. Caplan's Stroke: A Clinical Approach. 4th ed. 2009. (ENG., Illus.). 688p. 174.00 *(978-1-4160-4721-6(2)*, Saunders) Elsevier - Health Sciences Div.
Caplan, Louis R. Stroke, 1 vol. 2010. (What Do I Do Now Ser.). (ENG., Illus.). 176p. pap. 34.00 *(978-0-19-973914-1(5))* Oxford Univ. Pr., Inc.
Caplan, Louis R. & Bogousslavsky, Julien, eds. Uncommon Causes of Stroke. 2nd ed. 2008. (ENG., Illus.). 576p. 220.00 *(978-0-521-87437-3(8))* Cambridge Univ. Pr.
Carey, Leeanne M., ed. Stroke Rehabilitation: Insights from Neuroscience & Imaging. 2012. (ENG.). 280p. 135.00 ***(978-0-19-979788-2(9))*** Oxford Univ. Pr., Inc.
Castellani, S., ed. Stroke in the Real World: 17th National Congress of the Italian Interdisciplinary Neurovascular Society (SINV), Montecatini Terme, December 2008: Abstracts. 2008. 30p. pap. *(978-3-8055-9067-9(9))* Karger, S. AG.
Chan, Pak H., ed. Cerebrovascular Disease: 22nd Princeton Conference. 2011. (ENG.). 488p. pap. 85.00 *(978-0-521-18753-4(2))* Cambridge Univ. Pr.

Cohen, Ronald & Gunstad, John. Neuropsychology & Cardiovascular Disease. 2009. (ENG., Illus.). 432p. 85.00 *(978-0-19-534118-8(X))* Oxford Univ. Pr., Inc.
Cram101 Textbook Reviews & Cram101 Textbook Reviews. Outlines & Highlights for Caplans Stroke: A Clinical Approach by Louis Caplan, ISBN. 2011. 298p. pap. 30.95 ***(978-1-61461-188-2(2))*** Cram101 Inc.
Crawford, James G. A Stroke Was My Teacher. 2011. 248p. 35.95 ***(978-1-4525-3569-2(8))***; pap. 19.95 ***(978-1-4525-3567-8(1))*** Get Published.
Daffertshofer, Michael, et al. Case Studies in Stroke: Common & Uncommon Presentations. 2006. (Case Studies in Neurology Ser.). (ENG., Illus.). 290p. per. 86.00 *(978-0-521-67367-9(4))* Cambridge Univ. Pr.
Daneski, Katharine. A Sociohistory of Cerebrovascular Disease & the Development of Modern Stroke Medicine: A Foucauldian Analysis. 2010. iv, 290p. 119.95 *(978-0-7734-3659-6(6))* Mellen, Edwin Pr., The.
David, Ferro. Stroke. 2008. E-Book 14.50 incl. cd-rom *(978-0-9789242-3-2(1))* White Cat Bks.
De Georgia, Michael. Struck by the Hand of God: The Collision of Stroke & World History. 2008. (ENG.). pap. 14.95 *(978-1-59624-078-0(4))* Cleveland Clinic Pr.
Dearle, Luschka. Long after the Stroke. 2011. 112p. pap. ***(978-3-8443-3233-9(2))*** Lambert Academic Publishing.
Del Sette, M., et al, eds. European Society of Neurosonology & Cerebral Hemodynamics / Italian Society of Neurosonology & Cerebral Hemodynamics: 13th Meeting of the European Society of Neurosonology & Cerebral Hemodynamics / 5th National Congress of the Italian Society of Neurosonology & Cerebral Hemodynamics, Genova, May 2008: Abstracts. 2008. 72p. pap. *(978-3-8055-8586-6(1))* Karger, S. AG.
Di Napoli, Mario & Francesca, P. Neuroinflammation: An Important Role in the Pathogenic Pathways of Cerebral Ischemia. 2008. pap. 35.00 *(978-1-60692-030-5(8))* Nova Science Pubs., Inc.
Diez-Tejedor, E., ed. Ischemic Stroke: Knowledge & Research, Challenges & Goals:5th International Workshop, Madrid, April 2008. 2009. (Illus.). 216p. pap. *(978-3-8055-9051-8(2))* Karger, S. AG.
—Ischemic Stroke: Improving the Knowledge for the Best Treatment & Prevention [Bibliography & Price not Definite.]: 4th International Workshop, Madrid, June 2006: Supplement Issue: Cerebrovascular Diseases 2007, Vol. 24, Suppl. 1. 2007. (Illus.). 196p. pap. *(978-3-8055-8402-9(4))* Karger, S. AG.
Dirnagl, Ulrich. Rodent Models of Stroke. 2010. (Neuromethods Ser.). (ENG., Illus.). xii, 285p. 139.00 *(978-1-60761-749-5(8)*, 1607617498) Humana Pr.
Dolezsar, Cynthia. Determinants of Social Participation. 2010. 68p. pap. *(978-3-639-27258-1(7))* VDM Verlag Dr. Mueller e.K.
Edlow, Jonathan A. Stroke. 1 vol. 2008. (Biographies of Disease Ser.). (Illus.). 184p. 45.00 *(978-0-313-34241-7(5)*, GR4241, Greenwood Pr.) Greenwood Publishing Group, Inc.
Eisert, Wolfgang, et al, eds. Innate Inflammation & Stroke. 2010. (Annals of the New York Academy of Sciences Ser.: 61). (ENG., Illus.). 300p. pap. 150.00 *(978-1-57331-813-6(2)*, Wiley-Blackwell) Wiley, John & Sons, Inc.
Erkinjuntti, Timo & Steinmetz, Helmuth, eds. Small Vessel Diseases, White Matter Lesions & Vascular Cognitive Impairment. (Illus.). *(978-3-8055-7390-0(1))* Karger, S. AG.
European Stroke Conference: 12th Conference, Valencia, Spain, May 21-24, 2003: Abstracts, Vol. 16. (Cerebrovascular Diseases Ser.). incl. cd-rom *(978-3-8055-7592-8(0))* Karger, S. AG.
European Stroke Conference: 17th Conference, Nice, May 2008: AbstractsIncluding 2nd Stroke Meeting for Nurses, Physiotherapists, Speech & Occupational Therapists, Study/Monitoring Assistants. 2008. 204p. pap. *(978-3-8055-8588-0(8))* Karger, S. AG.
European Stroke Conference: 18th Conference, Stockholm, May 2009: AbstractsIncluding 3rd Stroke Meeting for Nurses, Physiotherapists, Speech & Occupational Therapists, Study/Monitoring Assistants. 2009. 256p. pap. *(978-3-8055-9159-1(4))* Karger, S. AG.
European Stroke Conference: 19th Conference, Barcelona, May 2010: AbstractsIncluding 4th Stroke Meeting for Nurses, Physiotherapists, Speech & Occupational Therapists, Study/Monitoring Assistants. 2010. cd-rom *(978-3-8055-9482-0(8))* Karger, S. AG.
European Stroke Conference: 20th Conference, Hamburg, May 2011: AbstractsIncluding 5th Stroke Meeting for Nurses, Physiotherapists, Speech & Occupational Therapists, Study/Monitoring Assistants. Supplement Issue:'Cerebrovascular Diseases 2011, Vol. 31, Suppl. 2' 2011. (ENG.). cd-rom ***(978-3-8055-9777-7(0))*** Karger, S. AG.
Fiebach, Jochen & Schellinger, Pet. Stroke Mri. 2006. 130p. 119.00 *(978-3-7985-1579-6(4))* Springer.
Fisher, Marc, ed. Stroke Pt. 1: Basic & Epidemiological Aspects - Handbook of Clinical Neurology, 3 vols. 2008. (Handbook of Clinical Neurology Ser.: 92). (ENG., Illus.). 464p. 275.00 *(978-0-444-52003-6(1))* Elsevier Science & Technology Bks.
—Stroke Pt. 2: Clinical Manifestations & Pathogenesis, 3 vols. 2008. (Handbook of Clinical Neurology Ser.: 93). (ENG., Illus.). 592p. 275.00 *(978-0-444-52004-3(X))* Elsevier Science & Technology Bks.
—Stroke Pt. 3: Investigation & Management, 3 vols. 2008. (Handbook of Clinical Neurology Ser.: 94). (ENG., Illus.). 416p. 275.00 *(978-0-444-52005-0(8))* Elsevier Science & Technology Bks.
Futrell, Nancy & Jamieson, Dara G. Vascular Neurology: Questions & Answers. 2007. (Illus.). 311p. 75.00 *(978-1-933864-24-2(9))* Demos Medical Publishing, LLC.
Gan, Robert N. & Ramani, N. Venketasubramanian, eds. The Stroke Clinician's Handbook: A Practical Guide to the Care of Stroke Patients. 2008. (Illus.). 247p. 70.00 *(978-981-277-879-6(9))* World Scientific Publishing Co., Inc.
Gillard, Jonathan H., et al, eds. Clinical MR Neuroimaging: Physiological & Functional Techniques. 2nd ed. 2009. (ENG., Illus.). 916p. 295.00 *(978-0-521-51563-4(7))* Cambridge Univ. Pr.
Godefroy, Olivier & Bogousslavsky, Julien, eds. The Behavioral & Cognitive Neurology of Stroke. 2009. (ENG., Illus.). 668p. pap. 116.00 *(978-0-521-10695-5(8))* Cambridge Univ. Pr.
Goldstein, Larry B., ed. A Primer on Stroke Prevention & Treatment: An Overview Based on AHA/ASA Guidelines. 2009. (ENG., Illus.). 280p. instr.'s hndbk. ed. 104.95 *(978-1-4051-8651-3(8)*, Wiley-Blackwell) Wiley, John & Sons, Inc.
Goldszmidt, Adrian J. & Caplan, Louis R. Stroke Essentials 2010. 2nd rev. ed. 2009. 198p. pap. 28.95 *(978-0-7637-7789-0(7))* Jones & Bartlett Learning, LLC.
Gomez, Camilo R. & Geyer, James D. Stroke: A Practical Approach. 2008. (ENG., Illus.). 384p. 170.00 *(978-0-7817-6614-2(1))* Lippincott Williams & Wilkins.
Greer, David M., ed. Acute Ischemic Stroke: An Evidence-Based Approach. 2007. (ENG., Illus.). 248p. 154.95 *(978-0-470-06807-6(8)*, Wiley-Liss) Wiley, John & Sons, Inc.
Grunwald, Iris Q., et al. How to set up an Acute Stroke Service. 2012. (ENG., Illus.). xxii, 198p. pap. 49.95 *(978-3-642-21404-2(5)*, 3642214045) Springer.
Guidelines, American College of Chest Physicians. Ischemic Stroke GUIDELINES Pocketcard (2010) Antithrombotic & Thrombolytic Therapy. 2010. 10p. 9.95 *(978-0-9843604-4-4(1))* International Guidelines Ctr., Inc.
Guillot, Aymeric & Collet, Christian, eds. The neurophysiological foundations of mental & motor imagery. 2010. (ENG., Illus.). 318p. 110.00 *(978-0-19-954625-1(8))* Oxford Univ. Pr., Inc.
Hankey, Graeme. Stroke Treatment & Prevention: An Evidence-based Approach. 2009. (ENG., Illus.). 536p. pap. 95.00 *(978-0-521-10158-4(9))* Cambridge Univ. Pr.
Hankey, Graeme J. Stroke: Your Questions Answered. 2nd rev. ed. 2007. (Your Questions Answered Ser.). (ENG., Illus.). 408p. (C). per. 54.95 *(978-0-443-10322-3(4)*, Churchill Livingstone) Elsevier - Health Sciences Div.
Harrar, Sari & Berner, Mark. Conquering Heart Attacks & Strokes: A Simple 10-Step Plan for Lifetime Cardiac Health. 2012. (ENG.). 256p. (gr. 12). 16.99 ***(978-1-60652-361-2(9))*** Reader's Digest Assn., Inc., The.
Hennerici, M. G., ed. European Stroke Conference: 11th Conference, Geneva, May - June 2002. (Cerebrovascular Diseases Ser.). (Illus.). *(978-3-8055-7417-4(7))* Karger, S. AG.
—European Stroke Conference: 16th Conference, Glasgow, May-June 2007: Abstracts: Supplement Issue: Cerebrovascular Diseases 2007, Vol. 23, Supp. 2. 2007. (Illus.). 158p. pap. *(978-3-8055-8308-4(7))* Karger, S. AG.
—A New Concept in Stroke Prevention: Satellite Symposium Held at the 18th European Stroke Conference, Stockholm, May 2009. 2009. (ENG., Illus.). 32p. pap. *(978-3-8055-9153-9(5))* Karger, S. AG.
Himmelreich, Uwe, et al, eds. In vivo Imaging of Animal Models: Stroke: Stroke. 2012. (ENG., Illus.). 300p. 189.00 *(978-94-007-1547-9(1)*, 9400715471) Springer.
Hreib, Kinan K. 100 Questions & Answers about Stroke: A Lahey Clinic Guide. 2008. (ENG., Illus.). 185p. pap. 22.95 *(978-0-7637-5070-1(0))* Jones & Bartlett Learning, LLC.
Hurst, Robert W. & Rosenwasser, Robert H., eds. Neurointerventional Management, Second Edition: Diagnosis & Treatment. 2nd rev. ed. 2012. (ENG., Illus.). 656p. ***(978-1-84184-806-8(9))*** Informa Pharmaceuticals & Healthcare.
Icon Health Publications Staff. Stroke A Medical Dictionary Bibliograph. 2006. 336p. per. 28.95 *(978-0-497-11182-3(9))* Icon Group International, Inc.
Kalimo, Hannu, ed. Cerebrovascular Diseases. 2006. (ENG., Illus.). 352p. pap. 123.95 *(978-3-9522313-4-0(7)*, Wiley-Blackwell) Wiley, John & Sons, Inc.
Kiris, Talat. Cerebral Vasospasm: New Strategies in Research & Treatment. Kiris, Talat & Zhang, John H., eds. 2008. (Acta Neurochirurgica Supplementum Ser.). xii, 450p. 319.00 *(978-3-211-75717-8(1))* Springer.
Kleiman, Berenice. Lessons Learned: Stroke Recovery from a Caregiver's Prospective. 2007. (ENG.). 126p. per. 9.95 *(978-1-59624-007-0(5))* Cleveland Clinic Pr.
Kummer, Rudiger von & Back, Tobias. Magnetic Resonance Imaging in Ischemic Stroke. 2010. (Medical Radiology / Diagnostic Imaging Ser.). (Illus.). xii, 308p. pap. 279.00 *(978-3-642-05654-3(7)*, 3642056547) Springer.
Laakso, Aki, et al. Surgical Management of Cerebrovascular Disease & Stroke. 2009. (Acta Neurochirurgica Supplementum Ser.). (ENG., Illus.). viii, 122p. 219.00 *(978-3-211-99372-9(X)*, 321199372X) Springer.
Laine, E. E. Praise God for Tattered Dreams. 2009. 208p. pap. 19.57 *(978-0-578-03375-4(5))* Laine, E.E.
Langhammer, Birgitta. Physiotherapy after Stroke. 2008. 88p. pap. *(978-3-639-07133-7(6))* VDM Verlag Dr. Mueller e.K.
Lapchak, Paul A. & Zhang, John H., eds. Translational Stroke Research: From Target Selection to Clinical Trials. 2012. (Springer Series in Translational Stroke Research Ser.). (ENG., Illus.). xxx, 974p. 209.00 *(978-1-4419-9529-2(3)*, 1441995293) Springer.
Lee, Vivien H., ed. Handbook of Stroke & Neurocritical Care. 2011. (Series: Neurology - Neurology - Laboratory & Clinical Research Developments Ser.). 95.00 *(978-1-61324-786-0(9)*, Nova Biomedical Bks.) Nova Science Pubs., Inc.
Lees, Kennedy R., ed. Optimizing the Treatment of Acute Ischemic Stroke - a STAIR-Way to Success? Satellite Symposium at the 14th European Stroke Conference Bologna, Italy, May 25-28, 2005, Vol. 22. (Cerebrovascular Diseases Ser.). (Illus.). pap. *(978-3-8055-8149-3(1))* Karger, S. AG.
Lincoln, Nadina B., et al. Psychological Management of Stroke. 2012. (ENG., Illus.). 638p. pap. 65.00 ***(978-0-470-68426-9(7))***; 115.00 ***(978-0-470-68427-6(5))*** Wiley, John & Sons, Inc. (Wiley).
Lindley, Richard I. Stroke. 2008. (Facts Ser.). (ENG., Illus.). 120p. per. 19.95 *(978-0-19-921272-9(4))* Oxford Univ. Pr., Inc.
Lyden, Patrick D., ed. Thrombolytic Therapy for Acute Stroke. 2nd ed. 2010. (Current Clinical Neurology Ser.). (Illus.). 392p. pap. 139.00 *(978-1-61737-540-8(3)*, 1617375403) Humana Pr.
Madajka, Maria. Nitroxidative Stress in Intracerebral Hemorrhage Stroke. 2009. 184p. pap. *(978-3-639-17117-4(9))* VDM Verlag Dr. Mueller e.K.
Manley, Geoffrey, et al, eds. Intracranial Pressure & Brain Monitoring XIII: Mechanisms & Treatment. (Acta Neurochirurgica Supplementum Ser.). (Illus.). x, 448p. 2010. (ENG.). pap. 359.00 *(978-3-211-99942-4(6)*, 3211999426) 2009. 359.00 *(978-3-211-85577-5(7))* Springer.
Mant, Jonathan & Walker, Marion F., eds. ABC of Stroke. 2011. (ABC Ser.: 155). (ENG., Illus.). 72p. pap. 32.95 *(978-1-4051-6790-1(4))* Wiley, John & Sons, Inc.
Manto, Mario-Ubaldo, ed. Cerebellar Disorders: A Practical Approach to Diagnosis & Management. 2010. (ENG., Illus.). 312p. 99.00 *(978-0-521-87813-5(6))* Cambridge Univ. Pr.
Mao, Ying. Early Brain Injury or Cerebral Vasospasm: Vol 2: Clinical Management. Mao, Ying et al, eds. 2010. (Acta Neurochirurgica Supplementum Ser.). (Illus.) xii, 264p. 249.00 *(978-3-7091-0355-5(X)*, 370910355X) Springer.
Markus, Hugh, et al. Stroke Medicine. 2010. (Oxford Specialist Handbooks in Neurology Ser.). (ENG., Illus.). 600p. pap. 79.95 *(978-0-19-921877-6(3))* Oxford Univ. Pr., Inc.
Marler, John. Ischemic Stroke: Pathways to Treatment. Zoppo, Gregory Del, ed. 2007. (Illus.). 368p. 115.00 *(978-1-4051-0367-1(1)*, Wiley-Blackwell) Wiley, John & Sons, Inc.
Masaryk, Thomas J., et al, eds. Endovascular Techniques in the Management of Cerebrovascular Disease. 2008. (ENG., Illus.). 216p. 200.00 *(978-1-84184-607-1(4)*, Informa Healthcare) Taylor & Francis Group GBR. Dist: Taylor & Francis Group.
Matias-Guiu, J., et al, eds. European Society of Neurosonology & Cerebral Hemodynamics: 8th Meeting, Alicante, Spain, May 18-21, 2003: Abstracts, Vol. 16. (Cerebrovascular Diseases Ser.). *(978-3-8055-7608-6(0))* Karger, S. AG.
Maxwell, Roger. Taking Charge of Your Stroke Recovery: A Personal Recovery Workbook. 2008. 336p. pap. 29.95 *(978-0-615-24916-2(7))* Taking Charge Bks., Inc.
Meairs, S., ed. Bubbles, Ultrasound & Cerebrovascular Diseases. 2009. (Illus.). 76p. pap. *(978-3-8055-9091-4(1))* Karger, S. AG.
Mehrholz, Jan. Physical Therapy for the Stroke Patient. 2012. (ENG., Illus.). 208p. 79.99 ***(978-3-13-154721-7(9))*** Thieme Medical Pubs., Inc.
Meyer, Maria M. & Derr, Paula. The Comfort of Home for Stroke: A Guide for Caregivers. 2007. (Comfort of Home Ser.). (ENG., Illus.). 342p. per. 24.95 *(978-0-9664767-8-1(6))* CareTrust Pubns., LLC.
Mohr, J. P., et al. Stroke: Pathophysiology, Diagnosis, & Management. 5th ed. 2011. (ENG., Illus.). 1520p. 349.00 *(978-1-4160-5478-8(2)*, Saunders) Elsevier - Health Sciences Div.
Mok, V. Poststroke Dementia & Imaging. 2009. pap. 37.00 *(978-1-60692-247-7(5))* Nova Science Pubs., Inc.
Moratinos, Cristina & Cárdenas, Bruno. Hypertension, Heredity & Stroke. 2009. (Cerebrovascular Research & Disorders Ser.). 129.00 *(978-1-60741-496-4(1)*, Nova Biomedical Bks.) Nova Science Pubs., Inc.
Morris, P. Pearse. Practical Neuroangiography. 2nd rev. ed. 2006. (Illus.). 560p. 225.99 *(978-0-7817-6515-2(3))* Lippincott Williams & Wilkins.
Morris, Pearse. Interventional & Endovascular Therapy of the Nervous System: A Practical Guide. 2010. (ENG., Illus.). xv, 318p. pap. 295.00 *(978-1-4419-2903-7(7)*, 1441929037) Springer.
Moulin, T. & Audebert, H., eds. Telestroke: the Use of Telemedicine in Stroke Care. 2009. (Illus.). 40p. pap. *(978-3-8055-9155-3(1))* Karger, S. AG.
Nosko, Herwig. Alpha Neurofeedback Training in the Rehabilitation Process of Stroke Patients. 2008. (Illus.). 132p. pap. *(978-3-8364-8046-8(8))* VDM Verlag Dr. Mueller e.K.
Nowinski, Wieslaw L., et al. The Cerefy Atlas of Cerebral Vasculature. 2009. (ENG.). cd-rom 209.99 *(978-1-60406-090-4(5))* Thieme Medical Pubs., Inc.
Nussbaum, Eric & Mocco, J., eds. Cerebral Revascularization: Microsurgical & Endovascular Techniques. 2011. (ENG., Illus.). 272p. 149.99 *(978-1-60406-263-2(0))* Thieme Medical Pubs., Inc.
Nyquist, Paul, et al. Aneurysmal Subarachnoid Hemorrhage, an Issue of Neurosurgery Clinics. 2010. (Clinics: Surgery Ser.: 21-2). (ENG., Illus.). xiv, 222p. 105.00 *(978-1-4377-1928-4(7)*, Saunders) Elsevier - Health Sciences Div.
Paciaroni, M., et al, eds. Manifestations of Stroke. 2012. (Frontiers of Neurology & Neuroscience Ser.). (ENG., Illus.). 206p. ***(978-3-8055-9910-8(2))*** Karger, S. AG.
Peery, Shelley. Neuropsychological Recovery after Subarachnoid Hemorrhage. 2009. 136p. pap. *(978-3-639-13841-2(4))* VDM Verlag Dr. Mueller e.K.
Pendlebury, Sarah T., et al. Oxford Case Histories in Stroke. 2012. (ENG., Illus.). 312p. pap. 79.95 ***(978-0-19-953934-5(0))*** Oxford Univ. Pr., Inc.
Pendlebury, Sarah T., et al. Transient Ischemic Attack & Stroke: Diagnosis, Investigation & Management. 2009. (ENG., Illus.). 404p. pap. 74.00 *(978-0-521-73512-4(2))* Cambridge Univ. Pr.
Poon, Wai S., et al, eds. Intracranial Pressure & Brain Monitoring XII. 2010. (Acta Neurochirurgica Supplementum Ser.). xiv, 484p. pap. 224.00 *(978-3-211-99878-6(0)*, 3211998780) Springer.
Primozich, Jean & Strandness, D. E. Techniques of Cerebrovascular Sonography. Date not set. *(978-0-941022-30-9(7))* Davies Publishing, Inc.
Qureshi, Adnan. Atlas of Interventional Neurology. 2008. (Illus.). 248p. 175.00 *(978-1-933864-31-0(1))* Demos Medical Publishing, LLC.
Qureshi, Adnan I., ed. Textbook of Interventional Neurology. 2011. (ENG., Illus.). 506p. 140.00 *(978-0-521-87639-1(7))* Cambridge Univ. Pr.
Rabinstein, Alejandro, et al. Practical Neuroimaging in Stroke: A Case-Based Approach. 2009. (ENG., Illus.). 416p. 199.00 *(978-0-7506-7537-6(3)*, Saunders) Elsevier - Health Sciences Div.
Read, Simon J. & Virley, David, eds. Stroke Genomics: Methods & Reviews. 2010. (Methods in Molecular Medicine Ser.). (Illus.). x, 351p. pap. 159.00 *(978-1-61737-500-2(4)*, 1617375004) Humana Pr.
Recommendations for Stroke Management, Vol. 17. (Illus.). *(978-3-8055-7689-5(7))* Karger, S. AG.
Roach, E. Steve, et al. Toole's Cerebrovascular Disorders. 6th rev. ed. 2007. (ENG., Illus.). 422p. 165.00 *(978-0-521-86622-4(7))* Cambridge Univ. Pr.
Ronco, C., ed. 14th European Stroke Conference: Bologna, Italy, May 25-28, 2005: Abstracts, Vol. 19. *(978-3-8055-7963-6(2))* Karger, S. AG.
Rosenberg, Gary A. Molecular Physiology & Metabolism of the Nervous System: A Clinical Perspective. 2012. (Contemporary Neurology Ser.: 82). (ENG.). 240p. 99.99 ***(978-0-19-539427-6(5))*** Oxford Univ. Pr., Inc.
Ruper, Garret D. New Developments in Stroke Research. 2006. (Illus.). 160p. (C). 129.00 *(978-1-60021-295-6(6))* Nova Science Pubs., Inc.
Savitz, Sean I. & Rosenbaum, Daniel M., eds. Stroke Recovery with Cellular Therapies. 2007. (Current Clinical Neurology Ser.). (Illus.). 166p. 119.00 *(978-1-58829-732-7(2))* Humana Pr.
Schaller, Bernhard. State-Of-The-Art Imaging in Stroke. 2007. 378p. pap. 149.00 *(978-1-60021-500-1(9))* Nova Science Pubs., Inc.
Schaller, Bernhard, ed. Imaging of Carotid Artery Stenosis. 2006. (Illus.). 272p. 259.00 *(978-3-211-32332-8(5)*, 3211323325) Springer.
Shih, Andy Yi-An. Nrf2 As a Therapeutic Target for Stroke & Neurodegeneration. 2009. 240p. pap. *(978-3-639-14226-6(8))* VDM Verlag Dr. Mueller e.K.
Siebler, M., et al, eds. 11th Meeting of the European Society of Neurosonology & Cerebral Hemodynamics. (Illus.). pap. *(978-3-8055-8142-4(4))* Karger, S. AG.
Silverman, Isaac E. & Rymer, Marilyn M. Hemorrhagic Stroke: An Atlas of Investigation & Treatment. 2010. (Illus.). 140p. *(978-1-84692-039-4(6))* Clinical Publishing Services.
Silverman, Jonathan, ed. Stroke: Complete Handbook. 2011. 132p. pap. 14.95 ***(978-1-937354-04-6(0))*** Rapid Publishing LLC.
Smith, Tom. Coping with Strokes. 2nd ed. (Illus.). 95p. *(978-0-85969-842-9(4)*, Sheldon Press) SPCK Publishing.
Smith, William. Exercises for Stroke: The Complete Program for Rehabilitation Through Movement, Balance, & Coordination. 2010. (Exercises For Ser.). (ENG.). 128p. pap. 15.00 *(978-1-57826-317-2(4))* Hatherleigh Co., Ltd., The.
Spence, J. David. How to Prevent Your Stroke. 2006. (ENG., Illus.). 200p. per. 19.95 *(978-0-8265-1537-7(1))* Vanderbilt Univ. Pr.
—How to Prevent Your Stroke. 2006. (ENG., Illus.). 200p. 39.95 *(978-0-8265-1536-0(3))* Vanderbilt Univ. Pr.
State-of-the-Art Imaging in Stroke, Volume 2. 2007. 149.00 *(978-1-60021-499-8(1))* Nova Science Pubs., Inc.
Stroke. *(978-0-340-57719-6(3)*, Hodder Arnold) Hodder Education.
Sutton, Amy L. Stroke Sourcebook: Basic Consumer Health Information about Stroke, Including Ischemic, Hemorrhagic, & Mini Strokes, As Well As Risk Factors, Prevention Guidelines, Diagnostic Tests, Medications & Surgical Treatments, & Complications of Stroke: Along with Rehabilitation Techniques & Innovations, Tips on Staying Healthy & Maintaining Independence after Stroke, a Glossary of Related Terms, & a Directory of. 2nd ed. 2008. 620p. 87.00 *(978-0-7808-1035-8(X))* Omnigraphics, Inc.
Torbey, Michel T. & Selim, Magdy H. The Stroke Book. 2007. (ENG., Illus.). 348p. per. 52.00 *(978-0-521-67160-6(4))* Cambridge Univ. Pr.
Turner, Glenn O. & Rosin, Mark Bruce. Recognizing & Surviving Heart Attacks & Strokes: Lifesaving Advice You Need Now. 2008. (ENG., Illus.). 296p. (gr. 9). pap. 22.95 *(978-0-8262-1794-3(X))* Univ. of Missouri Pr.
Uchino, Ken, et al. Acute Stroke Care. 2nd ed. 2011. (Cambridge Pocket Clinicians Ser.). (ENG., Illus.). 234p. mass mkt. 49.99 *(978-0-521-18484-7(3))* Cambridge Univ. Pr.
Valdueza, José M., et al. Neurosonology & Neuroimaging of Stroke. 2008. (ENG., Illus.). 399p. 199.99 *(978-3-13-141871-5(0))* Thieme Medical Pubs., Inc.
Veloso, Felix. Stroke Prevention Naturally: Proven Non-Pharmaceutical Stroke Avoidance Strategies. 2010. (Illus.). 192p. pap. *(978-1-894431-57-6(X))* Your Nickel's Worth Publishing.
Verbeek, M. M., et al, eds. Cerebral Amyloid Angiopathy in Alzheimer's Disease & Related Disorders. 2010. 384p. pap. 182.00 *(978-90-481-5480-7(4)*, 9048154804) Springer.
Wahlund, Lars-Olof, et al. Vascular Cognitive Impairment in Clinical Practice. Wahlund, Lars-Olof et al, eds. 2009. (ENG., Illus.). 254p. 142.00 *(978-0-521-87537-0(4))* Cambridge Univ. Pr.
Wakhloo, Ajay K. Thrombus & Stroke. Gounis, Matthew J. et al, eds. 2008. (ENG., Illus.). 232p. 150.00 *(978-0-8493-4136-0(5)*, Informa Healthcare) Taylor & Francis Group GBR. Dist: Taylor & Francis Group.
Wang-Fischer, Yanlin. Manual of Stroke Models in Rats. 2008. (ENG., Illus.). 332p. pap. 109.95 *(978-0-8493-9578-9(X)*, CRC Press) Taylor & Francis Group GBR. Dist: Taylor & Francis Group.

Warlow, Charles, et al. Stroke: Practical Mangement. 3rd rev. ed. 2008. (ENG., Illus.). 1008p. 370.95 *(978-1-4051-2766-0(X)*, Wiley-Blackwell) Wiley, John & Sons, Inc.

Werring, David, ed. Cerebral Microbleeds: Pathophysiology to Clinical Practice. 2011. (ENG., Illus.). 198p. 99.00 *(978-0-521-19845-5(3))* Cambridge Univ. Pr.

Williams, Jane, et al, eds. Acute Stroke Nursing. 2010. (ENG., Illus.). 368p. pap. 57.99 *(978-1-4051-6104-6(3)*, Wiley-Blackwell) Wiley, John & Sons, Inc.

Wong, K. S. Lawrence. Intracranial Atherosclerosis. Kim, Jong S. & Caplan, Louis R., eds. 2008. (ENG., Illus.). 272p. 162.95 *(978-1-4051-7822-8(1)*, Wiley-Blackwell) Wiley, John & Sons, Inc.

Yao. Contemporary Vascular Surgery. 2011. (Illus.). 600p. ***(978-1-60795-166-7(5))*** PMPH-USA. Ltd.

Yonekawa, Yasuhiro, et al, eds. Changing Aspects in Stroke Surgery: Aneurysms, Dissection, Moyamoya Angiopathy & EC-IC Bypass. 2008. (ACTA Neurochirurgica Supplementum Ser.). (Illus.). 137p. 239.00 *(978-3-211-76588-3(3)*, 3211765883) Springer.

—Changing Aspects in Stroke Surgery: Aneurysms, Dissection, Moyamoya angiopathy & EC-IC Bypass: Aneurysms, Dissection, Moyamoya angiopathy & EC-IC Bypass. 2010. (Acta Neurochirurgica Supplementum Ser.). viii, 141p. pap. 239.00 *(978-3-211-99918-9(3)*, 3211999183) Springer.

—New Trends of Surgery for Cerebral Stroke & its Perioperative Management. 2010. (Acta Neurochirurgica Supplementum Ser.). ix, 187p. pap. 179.00 *(978-3-211-99879-3(9)*, 3211998799) Springer.

Zaidat, Osama O. Endovascular Ischemic Stroke Therapy. 2009. 300p. 125.00 *(978-1-58829-810-2(8))* Humana Pr.

Zivin, Justin A. & Simmons, John Galbraith. TPA for Stroke: The Story of a Controversial Drug, 1 vol. 2010. (ENG.). 224p. 27.95 *(978-0-19-539392-7(9))* Oxford Univ. Pr., Inc.

Zoltan, Barbara. Vision, Perception, & Cognition: A Manual for the Evaluation & Treatment of the Adult with Acquired Brain Injury. 4th ed. 2007. (ENG., Illus.). 368p. (C). 52.95 *(978-1-55642-738-1(7))* SLACK, Inc.

15th European Stroke Conference: Brussels, Belgium, May16-19, 2006, Vol. 21. (Cerebrovascular Diseases Ser.). pap. *(978-3-8055-8146-2(7))* Karger, S. AG.

CEREBROVASCULAR DISEASE—PATIENTS

Anderson, Robert. The Aftermath of Stroke: The Experience of Patients & their Families. 2006. (ENG., Illus.). 276p. pap. 56.00 *(978-0-521-02982-7(1))* Cambridge Univ. Pr.

Barnes, Michael P., et al. Recovery after Stroke. Barnes, Michael P. et al, eds. 2009. (ENG., Illus.). 672p. pap. 116.00 *(978-0-521-10514-9(5))* Cambridge Univ. Pr.

Campeau, John D. Stroke My Ego. 2009. 184p. pap. 24.99 *(978-1-4490-0166-7(1))*; pap. 15.95 *(978-1-4490-0165-0(3))* AuthorHouse.

Edmans, Judi. Occupational Therapy & Stroke. 2nd ed. 2010. (ENG., Illus.). 264p. pap. 51.99 *(978-1-4051-9266-8(6)*, Wiley-Blackwell) Wiley, John & Sons, Inc.

Ficko, Alenka. Art Therapy in Retirement Home. 2010. 156p. pap. *(978-3-639-22284-5(9))* VDM Verlag Dr. Mueller e.K.

Gillen, Glen. Stroke Rehabilitation: A Function-Based Approach. 3rd ed. 2010. (ENG., Illus.). 800p. (C). 92.95 *(978-0-323-05911-4(2)*, Mosby) Elsevier - Health Sciences Div.

Harkema, Susan, et al. Locomotor Training: Principles & Practice, 1 vol. 2011. (ENG., Illus.). 224p. 59.95 *(978-0-19-534208-6(9))* Oxford Univ. Pr., Inc.

Harwood, Rowan H., et al. Stroke Care: A practical Manual. 2nd ed. 2011. (ENG., Illus.). 368p. pap. 45.00 *(978-0-19-955831-5(0))* Oxford Univ. Pr., Inc.

Hillman, Anne. Occupational Role Performance in the Presence of Disability - a Qualitative Study of the Perceptions of a Group of Men over Sixty. 2007. 296p. per. *(978-3-8364-2781-4(8))* VDM Verlag Dr. Mueller e.K.

Kalra, Lalit. A Practical Guide to Comprehensive Stroke Care: Meeting Population Needs. 2010. (Illus.). 420p. 139.00 *(978-981-4299-51-0(0))* World Scientific Publishing Co., Inc.

Kleiman, Berenice. Lessons Learned: Stroke Recovery from a Caregiver's Prospective. 2007. (ENG.). 126p. per. 9.95 *(978-1-59624-007-0(5))* Cleveland Clinic Pr.

Maxwell, Grace. Falling & Laughing: The Restoration of Edwyn Collins. (ENG., Illus.). 2010. 288p. pap. 16.95 *(978-0-09-193000-4(6))* 2009. 310p. 32.95 *(978-0-09-192999-2(7))* Ebury Publishing GBR. Dist: Independent Pubs. Group.

McKenna, David Loren & Seraydarian, Patricia McKenna. A Stroke of Grace. 2008. 116p. pap. 11.99 *(978-1-60647-795-3(1))* Xulon Pr., Inc.

McNeal, Franne. Stroke of Luck & the Power of the T. 2007. 160p. pap. 21.95 *(978-0-9791643-2-3(X))* Significant Business Results LLC.

Palmer, Sara & Palmer, Jeffrey B. When Your Spouse Has a Stroke: Caring for Your Partner, Yourself, & Your Relationship. 2011. (Johns Hopkins Press Health Book Ser.). (ENG.). 224p. pap. 19.95 *(978-0-8018-9887-7(0))*; (gr. 17). 45.00 *(978-0-8018-9886-0(2))* Johns Hopkins Univ. Pr.

Parenté, Rick & Herrmann, Douglas J. Retraining Cognition: Techniques & Applications. 3rd ed. 2010. 70.00 *(978-1-4164-0438-5(4))* PRO-ED, Inc.

Prowe, Garry. Successfully Surviving a Brain Injury: From the Emergency Room to Selecting a Rehabilitation Facility. 2010. 246p. pap. 17.95 *(978-0-9841974-3-9(5))* Brain Injury Success Bks.

Radmer, Jochen. Depth Data based Determination of Gait Parameters of Subjects after Stroke for the Use in Clinical Gait Rehabilitation. Fraunhofer IPK, Berlin & Krüger, Jörg, eds. 2011. (ENG., Illus.). 152p. pap. 32.24 ***(978-3-8396-0332-1(3))*** Fraunhofer IRB Verlag DEU. Dist: Silvermine International Bks., LLC.

Sabari, Joyce S. & Lieberman, Deborah. Occupational Therapy Practice Guidelines for Adults with Stroke. 2008. (Aota Practice Guidelines Ser.). (Illus.). 158p. pap. 126.50 *(978-1-56900-263-6(0))* American Occupational Therapy Assn., Inc.

Siles, Madonna. Eureka! Memories & Motivations: A Strategy for Creating a Healing Home for the Stroke / Brain Injury Patient & Caregiver. 2010. (ENG., Illus.). 216p. pap. 17.95 *(978-0-9825518-0-6(0))* Third Step Pr.

Snell, Jim. At the Precipice: My Three-Year Journey from Stroke to Good Health with Type 2 Diabetes. 2011. 92p. pap. 9.95 ***(978-1-4620-3456-7(X))*** iUniverse, Inc.

Sokol, Jennifer. Six Years of Grace: Caregiving Episodes with My Mother. 2006. 160p. per. 12.99 *(978-1-59886-624-7(9))* Tate Publishing & Enterprises, LLC.

Spence, David & Barnett, Henry J. M. Preventing Stroke A Guide for Physicians & Patients. 2012. (ENG., Illus.). 400p. pap. 55.00 ***(978-0-07-176235-9(3)***, 0071762353) McGraw-Hill Professional Publishing.

Stein, Joel, ed. Stroke Recovery & Rehabilitation. 2008. (Illus.). 992p. 175.00 *(978-1-933864-12-9(5))* Demos Medical Publishing, LLC.

Tanner, Dennis C. The Family Guide to Surviving Stroke & Communication Disorders. 2nd rev. ed. 2007. (Illus.). 295p. per. 60.95 *(978-0-7637-5105-0(7))* Jones & Bartlett Learning, LLC.

Tubbs. Heart Recovery Book. 2007. (Illus.). 128p. pap. 13.95 *(978-0-85969-955-6(2)*, Sheldon Press) SPCK Publishing GBR. Dist: Westminster John Knox Pr.

Williams, Olajide. Stroke Diaries: A Guide for Survivors & their Families. 2010. (ENG., Illus.). 176p. pap. 19.95 *(978-0-19-974026-0(7))* Oxford Univ. Pr., Inc.

CEREBROVASCULAR DISEASE—PATIENTS—BIOGRAPHY

Ackerman, Diane. One Hundred Names for Love: A Stroke, A Marriage, & the Language of Healing. 2011. (ENG.). 322p. 26.95 *(978-0-393-07241-9(X)*, 7241) Norton, W. W. & Co., Inc.

—One Hundred Names for Love: A Stroke, A Marriage, & the Language of Healing. l.t. ed. 2011. 515p. 32.99 *(978-1-4104-3648-1(9))* Thorndike Pr.

Antu-Urias, Mickey. The Other Side of the Rainbow: Memoirs of a Brain Aneurysm Survivor. 2011. pap. 10.99 *(978-1-61739-929-9(9))* Tate Publishing & Enterprises, LLC.

Barnes, Joanna. Life after My Stroke. 2011. (Illus.). 104p. pap. 17.24 ***(978-1-4567-8168-2(5))*** AuthorHouse.

Berger Morse, Margaret. Laugh a Lot Cry a Lot: When Tragedy Strikes - A journey through stroke/s & Healing. 2009. 264p. 24.99 *(978-1-4389-7301-2(2))*; pap. 14.49 *(978-1-4389-7300-5(4))* AuthorHouse.

Bolzan, Scott, et al. My Life, Deleted: A Memoir. 2012. (ENG.). 256p. pap. 14.99 ***(978-0-06-202548-7(1)***, HarperOne) HarperCollins Pubs.

Boudreaux, Charles J. Escaping the Silent Killer. 2009. 64p. pap. 15.25 *(978-1-4389-5305-2(4))* AuthorHouse.

Bredow, Hasso Von. In the Blink of an Eye. l.t. ed. 2010. 320p. 35.50 *(978-0-7531-9572-7(0))* Isis Publishing Ltd. GBR. Dist: Ulverscroft Large Print Bks., Ltd.

Brewster, Mike. Wheels for Sale: The Diary & Memoirs of a Stroke Survivor's Husband. 2011. (Illus.). 204p. pap. 18.50 *(978-1-4567-7382-3(8))* AuthorHouse.

Bruschi, Tedy. Never Give Up: My Stroke, My Recovery, & My Return to the NFL. 2008. (ENG., Illus.). 304p. pap. 16.95 *(978-0-470-37354-5(7)*, Wiley) Wiley, John & Sons, Inc.

Burns, Richard L. Live or Die - A Stroke of Good Luck. 2012. (ENG.). 165p. pap. 14.95 ***(978-0-615-52036-0(7))*** D & N Bks.

Caza, J. Euclide. The Lights of Lancaster: Letters to Rome. Caza, A. Margaret, tr. (Illus.). 160p. pap. *(978-0-9698752-7-7(4))* Shoreline.

Edsall, Susan. Into the Blue: A Father's Flight & a Daughter's Return. Date not set. mass mkt. *(978-0-312-99329-0(3)*, St. Martin's Paperbacks) St. Martin's Pr.

Everhart, Fred F. Death's Door Denied: The Man That Should Have Died, Would Have Died, but Could Not Die. 2011. 80p. pap. 9.99 *(978-1-4567-3664-4(7))* AuthorHouse.

Gay, Kim A. Hiding an Elephant: Living with Adult ADHD. 2010. pap. 9.99 *(978-1-61663-433-9(2))* Tate Publishing & Enterprises, LLC.

Gosling, Geo. TBI Purgatory: Comes after Being in TBI Hell. 2010. 159p. pap. 12.95 *(978-1-4327-5845-5(4))* Outskirts Pr., Inc.

Greene, Valerie. Conquering Stroke: How I Fought My Way Back & How You Can Too. 2008. (ENG., Illus.). 272p. 24.95 *(978-0-470-13792-5(4)*, Wiley) Wiley, John & Sons, Inc.

Hale, Sheila. The Man Who Lost His Language: A Case of Aphasia. 2007. (ENG., Illus.). 256p. per. *(978-1-84310-564-0(0))* Kingsley, Jessica Ltd.

Hepburn, Stuart. A Most Curious Detour. 2010. 154p. pap. 14.95 *(978-1-4457-8896-8(9))* Lulu Enterprises Inc.

Housley, Kathleen L. Keys to the Kingdom: Reflections on Music & the Mind. 2010. 81p. pap. 14.00 *(978-0-9827262-0-4(1))* Wising Up Pr.

Kagan, Jeff. Life after Stroke: On the Road to Recovery. 2011. 92p. pap. 14.95 ***(978-1-60746-818-9(2))*** FastPrncil, Inc.

Kutty, V. K. Madhavan. No Curtains Yet. 2007. (ENG.). 280p. pap. *(978-81-87943-83-9(1))* India Research Pr. IND. Dist: Independent Pubs. Group.

Mason, Timothy. Best That I Can Be. 2006. 196p. per. *(978-1-84667-024-4(1))* Derwent Pr., The.

McEwen, Mark & Paisner, Daniel. After the Stroke: My Journey Back to Life. 2009. (ENG.). 256p. (gr. 12-18). 15.00 *(978-1-59240-460-5(X)*, Gotham) Penguin Group (USA) Inc.

McGregor, John C. My Hidden Self: A Plastic Surgeon's Diary of a Stroke. 2009. (Illus.). 176p. pap. *(978-1-84748-518-2(9))* Athena Pr.

Nutt, Amy E. Shadows Bright as Glass: The Remarkable Story of One Man's Journey from Brain Trauma to Artistic Triumph. 2011. (ENG., Illus.). 288p. 26.00 *(978-1-4391-4310-0(2)*, Free Pr.) Free Pr.

Nutt, Amy Ellis. Shadows Bright as Glass: An Accidental Artist & the Search for the Soul. 2011. pap. *(978-1-4391-4311-7(0)*, Free Pr.) Free Pr.

Parsons, Dale. Dementia. 2006. 17.00 *(978-0-8059-8813-0(0))* Dorrance Publishing Co., Inc.

Pritchard, Kathleen M. Worthy in His Eyes: Looking Beyond the Reflection in the Mirror. 2012. 256p. pap. ***(978-1-77069-441-5(2))*** Word Alive Pr.

Rudnick, Eileen. The Glass Between Us. 2011. (Illus.). ix, 193p. pap. ***(978-1-934074-64-0(0))*** Apprentice Hse.

Smith, Robert F. After the Stroke of Midnight: 20 Years after a Brain Attack. 2011. 188p. pap. 20.00 ***(978-1-4567-5847-9(0))*** AuthorHouse.

Sorbo, Kevin. True Strength: My Journey from Hercules to Mere Mortal — and How Nearly Dying Saved My Life. 2012. (ENG., Illus.). 296p. pap. 16.00 ***(978-0-7382-1602-7(X))*** Da Capo Pr., Inc.

Sussler, Robert. A Brain's Battle Against a Stroke: Refocusing My Memory on Earlier Medicine. 2007. (Illus.). 152p. 23.99 *(978-1-4259-9784-7(8))*; per. 12.99 *(978-1-4259-9785-4(6))* AuthorHouse.

Taylor, Jill Bolte. My Stroke of Insight: A Brain Scientist's Personal Journey. 2009. (CHI., Illus.). 293p. pap. *(978-986-216-284-2(8))* Commonwealth Publishing Co., Ltd.

—My Stroke of Insight: A Brain Scientist's Personal Journey. 2009. (ENG.). 224p. (gr. 12-18). 15.00 *(978-0-452-29554-4(8)*, Plume) Penguin Group (USA) Inc.

—My Stroke of Insight: A Brain Scientist's Personal Journey. l.t. ed. 2009. 292p. pap. 16.95 *(978-1-59413-337-4(9)*, Large Print Pr.) 2008. 342p. 31.95 *(978-1-4104-1049-8(8))* Thorndike Pr.

von Bredow, Hasso & von Bredow, Catherine. In the Blink of an Eye: An Inspiring & True Story of Enduring Love. 2010. (ENG., Illus.). 288p. 14.95 *(978-0-7528-8401-1(8))* Orion Publishing Group, Ltd. GBR. Dist: Independent Pubs. Group.

Wenmouth, Richard. Life goes On. 2010. 147p. pap. 16.95 *(978-1-4457-6716-1(3))* Lulu Enterprises Inc.

Wines, Renee. My Stroke a Will to Recover. 2007. 88p. per. 10.95 *(978-0-595-47923-9(0))* iUniverse, Inc.

Wisbey, Nick. 'What Are You Thinking of, Dad?' 2011. (ENG., Illus.). 224p. pap. ***(978-1-84876-481-1(2))*** Troubadour Publishing Ltd.

CEREBRUM

see Brain

CEREMONIAL PURITY

see Purity, Ritual

CEREMONIES

see Etiquette; Manners and Customs; Rites and Ceremonies

CERMAK, ANTON JOSEPH, 1873-1933

Barnard, H. K. Anton the Martyr. 2011. 94p. 38.95 ***(978-1-258-01748-4(2))*** Literary Licensing, LLC.

CERMETS

see Ceramic Metals

CERNUDA, LUIS, 1902-1963

Edelman, Olivia Maciel. Surrealismo en la poesia de Xavier Villaurrutia, Octavio Paz, y Luis Cernuda. Mexico (1926-1963) 2008. (SPA.). 220p. 109.95 *(978-0-7734-4946-6(9))* Mellen, Edwin Pr., The.

Rivero Taravillo, Antonio & Rivero, Antonio. Luis Cernuda. Los Años Del Exilio (1938-1963) años de exilio, 1938-1963. 2011. (SPA., Illus.). 408p. pap. 26.95 ***(978-84-8383-321-6(2))*** Tusquets Editores ESP. Dist: Ediciones Urano S. A.

CERNY, JAROSLAV, PALEOGRAPHER

Ruzova, J. The Scribner in the Place of Truth: The Biography of Egyptologist Jaroslav Cerny. 2010. (CZE & ENG., Illus.). 311p. (C). 42.00 *(978-80-7277-465-4(4))* Czech Institute of Egyptology CZE. Dist: Brown, David Bk. Co., The.

CEROPLASTIC

see Wax Modeling

CERTAINTY

Barris, Jeremy. The Crane's Walk: Plato, Pluralism, & the Inconstancy of Truth. 3rd ed. 2009. (ENG.). 300p. 70.00 *(978-0-8232-2913-0(0))* Fordham Univ. Pr.

Berger, Peter & Zijderveld, Anton. In Praise of Doubt: How to Have Convictions Without Becoming a Fanatic. 2010. (ENG.). 192p. pap. 13.99 *(978-0-06-177817-9(6)*, HarperOne) HarperCollins Pubs.

Berger, Peter & Zijderveld, Anton C. In Praise of Doubt: How to Have Convictions Without Becoming a Fanatic. 2009. 192p. 23.99 *(978-0-06-177816-2(8)*, HarperOne) HarperCollins Pubs.

Brenner, William & Moyal-Sharrock, Danièle, eds. Readings of Wittgenstein's on Certainty. 2007. (ENG.). 352p. pap. 39.00 *(978-0-230-53552-7(6))* Palgrave Macmillan.

Burton, Robert A. & Burton, Robert. On Being Certain: Believing You Are Right Even When You're Not. 2009. (ENG.). 272p. pap. 14.95 *(978-0-312-54152-1(X)*, St. Martin's Griffin) St. Martin's Pr.

Coliva, Annalisa. Moore & Wittgenstein: Scepticism, Certainty & Common Sense. 2010. (History of Analytic Philosophy Ser.). (ENG.). 288p. 89.00 *(978-0-230-58063-3(7))* Palgrave Macmillan.

Hamilton, Andy. Wittgenstein & on Certainty. 2008. (Routledge Philosophy GuideBooks Ser.). (ENG.). 240p. (C). 27.95 *(978-0-415-45076-8(4))* Routledge.

Loewen, G. V. Three Apodeictic Dialogues: Examples of Conceptual Mirrors in Religion, Psychology, & Social Organization. 2010. (ENG.). 172p. pap. 26.50 *(978-0-7618-5411-1(8))* Univ. Pr. of America, Inc.

Moyal-Sharrock, Daniele & Moyal-sharrock, Danile. Understanding Wittgenstein's on Certainty. 2007. (ENG.). 264p. pap. 39.00 *(978-0-230-53553-4(4))* Palgrave Macmillan.

Schiemann, Gregor. Hermann Von Helmholtz's Mechanism: The Loss of Certainty: A Study on the Transition from Classical to Modern Philosophy of Nature. 2008. (Archimedes Ser.). (ENG.). 300p. 159.00 *(978-1-4020-5629-1(X)*, 140205629X) Springer.

Schreiner, Susan. Are You Alone Wise? The Search for Certainty in the Early Modern Era. 2010. (Oxford Studies in Historical Theology Ser.). (ENG.). 352p. 74.00 *(978-0-19-531342-0(9))* Oxford Univ. Pr., Inc.

Stenholm, Stig. The Quest for Reality: Bohr & Wittgenstein - Two Complementary Views. 2011. 296p. 62.95 *(978-0-19-960358-9(8))* Oxford Univ. Pr., Inc.

CERTIFICATION OF LIBRARIANS

see Librarians—Certification

CERTIFICATION OF SCHOOL SUPERINTENDENTS AND PRINCIPALS

see School Superintendents and Principals

CERTIFICATION OF TEACHERS

see Teachers—Certification

CERTIFIED PUBLIC ACCOUNTANTS

see Accountants

CERVANTES SAAVEDRA, MIGUEL DE, 1547-1616

Allen, John Jay. Don Quixote: Hero or Fool? Remixed. 2008. (Documentacion Cervantina Ser.: 30). 212p. pap. 22.95 *(978-1-58871-131-1(5)*, Juan de la Cuesta-Hispanic Monographs) LinguaText, Ltd.

—Don Quixote: Hero or Fool? Remixed (Hardback) 2008. (Documentacion Cervantina Ser.: 30). 212p. 29.95 *(978-1-58871-147-2(1)*, Juan de la Cuesta-Hispanic Monographs) LinguaText, Ltd.

Babayan, Kathryn & Najmabadi, Afsaneh. Islamicate Sexualities: Translations Across Temporal Geographies of Desire. 2008. (Harvard Middle Eastern Monographs: 39). 384p. pap. 19.95 *(978-0-674-03204-0(7))* Harvard Univ., Ctr. for Middle Eastern Studies.

Bagno, V. E. "Don Kikhot" V Rossii I Russkoe Donkikhotstvo. 2009. (Illus.). 226p. *(978-5-02-025270-7(0))* NBD - Biblion B.V.

—"Don Kikhot" V Rossii I Russkoe Donkikhotstvo. 2009. (RUS., Illus.). 226p. *(978-5-02-027020-6(2))* Nauka.

Bandera, Cesareo. The Humble Story of Don Quixote: Reflections on the Birth of the Modern Novel. 2006. 318p. 79.95 *(978-0-8132-1452-8(1))* Catholic Univ. of America Pr.

Bloom, Harold. Don Quixote - Miguel de Cervantes. 2nd rev. ed. 2010. (Bloom's Modern Critical Interpretations Ser.). 194p. (C). (gr. 9-18). 45.00 *(978-1-60413-821-4(1)*, Chelsea Hse.) Facts On File, Inc.

Builes, Ruben. The Emergence of Europe in the Work of Miguel de Cervantes. 2009. 176p. pap. *(978-3-639-18172-2(7))* VDM Verlag Dr. Mueller e.K.

Burke, Ulick Ralph. Sancho Panza's Proverbs. 2007. 140p. (ENG.). 24.95 *(978-1-4344-9265-4(6))*; per. 14.95 *(978-1-4344-9264-7(8))* Wildside Pr., LLC.

Burningham, Bruce R. Tilting Cervantes: Baroque Reflections on Postmodern Culture. 2008. (ENG., Illus.). 228p. pap. 29.95 *(978-0-8265-1603-9(3))*; lib. bdg. 69.95 *(978-0-8265-1602-2(5))* Vanderbilt Univ. Pr.

Camacho, Gabriel. El concepto de la frontera en Cervantes: Un análisis desde el punto de vista chicano. 2008. 84p. pap. *(978-3-639-10156-0(1))* VDM Verlag Dr. Mueller e.K.

Carrión, Gabriela. Staging Marriage in Early Modern Spain: Conjugal Doctrine in Lope, Cervantes, & Calderón. 2011. (ENG.). 166p. 60.00 *(978-1-61148-052-8(3))* Bucknell Univ. Pr.

Cascardi, Anthony J. Cervantes, Literature & the Discourse of Politics. 2011. (Totonto Iberic Ser.). (ENG.). 352p. ***(978-1-4426-4371-0(4))*** Univ. of Toronto Pr.

—Cervantes, Literature, & the Discourse of Politics. 2011. (Totonto Iberic Ser.). (ENG.). 352p. pap. ***(978-1-4426-1223-5(1))*** Univ. of Toronto Pr.

Cervantes Saavedra, Miguel de. Espanola Inglesa. (SPA.). pap. 20.95 incl. audio compact disk *(978-88-7754-898-6(3))* Cideb ITA. Dist: Distribooks, Inc.

—Novelas Ejemplares. 2011. (SPA.). 470p. 32.00 *(978-84-9816-979-9(8))*; per. 26.95 *(978-84-96428-80-5(X))* Linkgua Ediciones, S.L. ESP. Dist: AtlasBooks Distribution.

—Rinconete y Cortadillo. 2008. (Leer en Espanol: Level 2 Ser.). (Illus.). 64p. pap. incl. audio compact disk *(978-84-9713-062-2(6))* Español Santillana Universidad de Salamanca.

—Rinconete y Cortadillo. 2011. (SPA.). 46p. (gr. 7-12). per. 4.00 *(978-84-96290-71-6(9))* Linkgua Ediciones, S.L. ESP. Dist: AtlasBooks Distribution.

Cervantes Saavedra, Miguel de & Cervantes, Miguel de. Rinconete y Cortadillo. annot. ed. (SPA., Illus.). 131p. 13.95 *(978-84-207-2632-8(X)*, ANY006) Grupo Anaya, S.A. ESP. Dist: Continental Bk. Co., Inc.

Close, Anthony. The Romantic Approach to 'Don Quixote' A Critical History of the Romantic Tradition in 'Quixote' Criticism. 2010. (ENG.). 300p. pap. 24.99 *(978-0-521-14258-8(X))* Cambridge Univ. Pr.

de Armas, Frederick A. Cervantes, Raphael & the Classics. 2010. (Cambridge Studies in Latin American & Iberian Literature Ser.). 256p. pap. 36.99 *(978-0-521-15277-8(1))* Cambridge Univ. Pr.

De Armas, Frederick A. Don Quixote among the Saracens. 2011. ***(978-1-4426-4345-1(5))*** Univ. of Toronto Pr.

De Armas, Frederick A. Quixotic Frescoes: Cervantes & Italian Renaissance Art. 2009. (ENG., Illus.). 344p. pap. (978-1-4426-1031-6(X)) Univ. of Toronto Pr.
Dunn, Peter N. & Jehenson, Yvonne. The Utopian Nexus in Don Quixote. 2006. (ENG.). 216p. 59.95 (978-0-8265-1517-9(7)) Vanderbilt Univ. Pr.
Durr, Susanne. Die Öffnung der Welt: Sujetbildung und Sujetbefragung in Cervantes' Novelas ejemplares. 2010. (Text und Kontext Ser.). (GER.). 303p. (C). pap. 72.00 (978-3-515-09272-2(2)) Steiner, Franz Verlag Wiesbaden GmbH DEU. Dist: Brown, David Bk. Co., The.
Endress, Heinz-Peter. Don Quijotes Ideale im Umbruch der Werte vom Mittelalter bis zum Barock. (Mimesis Ser.). (GER.). V, 124p. 210.00 **(978-3-11-182409-3(8))** De Gruyter, Walter Inc.
Ertler, Klaus-Dieter & Rodríguez Díaz, Alejandro. El Quijote Hoy: La Riqueza de Su Recepción. 2007. (SPA.). 290p. pap. 29.80 (978-84-8489-300-4(6)) Iberoamericana Vervuert Publishing Corp.
Fitzmaurice-Kelly, James. Cervantes in England. 2010. 24p. pap. 14.75 (978-1-149-97503-9(2)) BiblioBazaar.
Fox, Soledad. Flaubert & Don Quijote: The Influence of Cervantes on Madame Bovary. (ENG., Illus.). 2010. 210p. pap. 35.00 (978-1-84519-397-3(0)) 2008. 200p. 69.50 (978-1-84519-257-0(5)) Sussex Academic Pr. GBR. Dist: International Specialized Bk. Services.
Friedman, Edward. Cervantes in the Middle: Realism & Rea. 2006. (C). pap. 24.95 (978-1-58871-091-8(2), Juan de la Cuesta-Hispanic Monographs) LinguaText, Ltd.
Gonzalez Echevarría, Roberto. Love & the Law in Cervantes. 2012. (ENG.). 320p. pap. 25.00 (978-0-300-17784-8(4)) Yale Univ. Pr.
Gonzalez, Jose Manuel & Bellis, Clive A., eds. Shakespeare, Cervantes, & Rabelais: New Interpretations & Comparative Studies. 2011. 220p. 119.95 (978-0-7734-3663-3(4)) Mellen, Edwin Pr., The.
Gordon, Scott Paul. The Practice of Quixotism: Postmodern Theory & Eighteenth-Century Women's Writing. 2006. (ENG.). 256p. 84.00 (978-1-4039-7444-0(6)) Palgrave Macmillan.
Graf, E. C. Cervantes & Modernity: Four Essays on Don Quijote. 2007. (ENG.). 48.50 (978-1-61148-261-4(5)); (Illus.). (C). (978-0-8387-5655-3(7)) Bucknell Univ. Pr.
Jehenson, Yvonne & Dunn, Peter N. The Utopian Nexus in Don Quixote. 2006. (ENG.). 216p. (C). per. 29.95 (978-0-8265-1518-6(5)) Vanderbilt Univ. Pr.
Ji, Meng. Phraseology in Corpus-Based Translation Studies. 2010. (ENG.). 251p. pap. 60.95 (978-3-03911-550-1(2)) Lang, Peter AG GBR. Dist: Lang, Peter.
Kahn, Aaron M. The Ambivalence of Imperial Discourse: Cervantes' la Numancia within the 'Lost Generation' of Spanish Drama (1570-90) 2008. (Hispanic Studies: Culture & Ideas Ser.). 243p. pap. 66.95 (978-3-03911-098-8(5)) Lang, Peter AG GBR. Dist: Lang, Peter.
Laguna, Ana María G. Cervantes & the Pictorial Imagination: A Study on the Power of Images & Images of Power in Works by Cervantes. 2009. (ENG.). 175p. 35.00 (978-1-61148-322-2(0)) 2008. (Illus.). 176p. 35.00 (978-0-8387-5727-7(8)) Bucknell Univ. Pr.
Luteran, Paula. Six French & English Translations of Don Quixote Compared: A Study in the History of Translation Theory. 2010. v, 115p. 99.95 (978-0-7734-3803-3(3)) Mellen, Edwin Pr., The.
Martinez Mata, Emilio. Cervantes on Don Quixote. 2010. 204p. pap. (978-3-0343-0352-1(1)) Lang, Peter.
Marx, Walter. Transfer des Sakralen: Die Säkularisierung christlicher Denkformen, Motive und Gebräuche in Cervantes' Don Quijote. 2008. (Europäische Hochschulschriften. Reihe 24: Ibero-Romanische Sprachen und Literaturen Ser.). 314p. pap. 74.95 (978-3-631-58155-1(6)) Lang, Peter GmbH, Europaischer Verlag der Wissenschaften DEU. Dist: Lang, Peter.
McCrory, Donald P. No Ordinary Man: The Life & Times of Miguel de Cervantes. 2006. (ENG., Illus.). 352p. per. 14.95 (978-0-486-45361-3(8)) Dover Pubns., Inc.
Miñana, Rogelio. Monstruos Que Hablan: El Discurso de la Monstruosidad en Cervantes. 2007. (SPA.). 256p. pap. 41.95 (978-0-8078-9294-7(7)) Univ. of North Carolina Pr.
Morey, Tracy Crowe. Between History & Fiction: The Early Modern Spanish Siege Play. 2010. (Illus.). 176p. pap. (978-3-0343-0303-3(3)) Lang, Peter.
Pace, Donald & Pace, Donald Gene. Unfettering Confession: Ritualized Performance in Spanish Narrative & Drama. 2009. (ENG.). 100p. pap. 19.99 (978-0-7618-4510-2(0)) Univ. Pr. of America, Inc.
Paul, Kong Kim Por. The Raiders & Writers of Cervantes' Archive: Borges, Puig, & Marquez. 2009. 154p. 99.95 (978-0-7546-6533-5(X)) Ashgate Publishing Co.
Percy, Thomas & Bowle. Cervantine Correspondence. Eisenberg, ed. Date not set. (Hispanic Text Ser.: No. 40). (SPA.). 97p. pap. 17.95 (978-0-85989-288-9(3)) Univ. of Exeter Pr. GBR. Dist: Brown, David Bk. Co., The.
Puig, Idoya. Tradition & Modernity: Cervantes's Presence in Spanish Contemporary Literature. 2009. (Hispanic Studies: Culture & Ideas Ser.). 221p. 46.95 (978-3-03911-526-6(X)) Lang, Peter AG GBR. Dist: Lang, Peter.
Randall, Dale B. J. & Boswell, Jackson C. Cervantes in Seventeenth-Century England: The Tapestry Turned. 2009. (ENG., Illus.). 640p. 175.00 (978-0-19-953952-9(9)) Oxford Univ. Pr., Inc.
Reyes, Alfonso, et al. Alfonso Reyes Lee el Quijote: Artículos, Ensayos, un Poema y Fragmentos Sobre el Quijote, Seguidos de una Relación de Las Obras de Cervantes Existentes en la Capilla Alfonsina. 2008. (Estudios Lingüísticos y Literarios Ser.). (SPA.). 215p. pap. 42.99 (978-968-12-1339-8(4)) El Colegio de México, A.C., Biblioteca Miguel Cosio Villegas MEX. Dist: Fondo de Cultura Economica USA.
Ricapito, Joseph V. Consciousness & Truth in Don Quijote & Connected Essays. 2007. (Documentacion Cervantina Ser.: 28). 172p. pap. 18.95 (978-1-58871-112-0(9), RICAPITO-DQ, Juan de la Cuesta-Hispanic Monographs) LinguaText, Ltd.
Roy, Gregor. Monarch Notes on Cervantes' Don Quixote. (C). 3.95 (978-0-671-00553-5(7), Arco) Peterson's.
Salomon, Roger B. Desperate Storytelling: Post-Romantic Elaborations of the Mock-Heroic Mode. 2008. (ENG.). 312p. pap. 24.95 (978-0-8203-3262-8(3)) Univ. of Georgia Pr.
Schevill, Rudolph. Cervantes. 2009. 238p. pap. 19.99 (978-1-4588-1707-5(5)) General Bks. LLC.
Schmidt, Rachel. Forms of Modernity: Don Quixote & Modern Theories of the Novel. 2011. (University of Toronto Romance Ser.). **(978-1-4426-4251-5(3))** Univ. of Toronto Pr.
Seris, Homero. Ediciones de Don Quijote. 2006. (Documentacion Cervantina Ser.: 27). (SPA.). 156p. pap. 18.95 (978-1-58871-107-6(2), SERIS, Juan de la Cuesta-Hispanic Monographs) LinguaText, Ltd.
Shuger, Dale. Don Quixote in the Archives: Madness & Literature in Early Modern Spain. 2012. (Edinburgh Critical Studies in Renaissance Culture Ser.). (ENG.). 272p. (gr. 17). 105.00 **(978-0-7486-4463-6(6))** Edinburgh Univ. Pr. GBR. Dist: Columbia Univ. Pr.
Smith, Robinson. The Life of Cervantes. 2008. 132p. 21.99 (978-0-559-81438-9(0)); pap. 19.75 (978-0-559-81433-4(X)) BiblioBazaar.
—The Life of Cervantes. 2009. 132p. 35.95 (978-1-104-42079-6(1)); pap. 20.95 (978-1-104-39597-1(5)) Kessinger Publishing, LLC.
—The Life of Cervantes. 2008. 128p. pap. (978-1-4437-0384-0(2)) Read Bks.
Sullivan, Henry W. Grotesque Purgatory: A Study of Cervantes's Don Quixote, Part II. 2008. 236p. per. 26.95 (978-0-271-02806-4(8)) Pennsylvania State Univ. Pr.
Velasco, Sherry. Tradition & Innovation in Early Modern Spanish Studies. Essays in Memory of Carroll B. Johnson. 2008. (Juan de la Cuesta Hispanic Monographs). 356p. (C). pap. 26.95 (978-1-58871-134-2(X), Juan de la Cuesta-Hispanic Monographs) LinguaText, Ltd.
Weiger, John G. The Substance of Cervantes. 2010. (ENG.). 306p. pap. 24.99 (978-0-521-16834-2(1)) Cambridge Univ. Pr.

CERVICAL VERTEBRAE
see Vertebrae, Cervical

CERVIX UTERI
see Uterus

CESAIRE, AIME, 1913-
Bouvier, Pierre. Aimé Césaire, Frantz Fanon: Portraits de Décolonisés. 2010. (FRE., Illus.). 288p. (C). pap. 41.00 **(978-2-251-90003-2(9))** Societe d'edition Les Belles lettres FRA. Dist: ISD.
Davis, Gregson. Aim_C_saire. 2008. (Cambridge Studies in African & Caribbean Literature). (ENG.). 228p. pap. 31.00 (978-0-521-05542-0(3)) Cambridge Univ. Pr.
Ojo-Ade, Femi. Aimé Césaire's African Theater: Of Poets, Prophets, & Politicians. 2010 (978-1-59221-738-0(9)) Africa World Pr.
—Aimé Césaire's African Theatre: Of Poets, Prophets & Politicians. 2010. 320p. pap. (978-1-59221-739-7(7)) Africa World Pr.
Parker, Gabrielle. Aimé Césaire. 2010. (Inspirations Ser.). (ENG.). 100p. pap. 10.95 (978-1-906413-24-8(X)) Arcadia Bks. Ltd. GBR. Dist: Independent Pubs. Group.
Thebia-Melsan, Annick & Alker, Pierre. Aimé Césaire, le Legs: "Nous Sommes de Ceux Qui Disent Non à L'ombre" 2009. (FRE., Illus.). 474p. (978-2-915978-52-0(2)) Argol Editions.
Widgen, Quirin. Aimé Césaire Zwischen Poesie und Politik: Identität und Gesellschaft Auf Martinique. 2010. (GER.). 120p. (978-3-631-60185-3(9)) Lang, Peter Publishing, Inc.

CESAREAN SECTION
Bhattacharjee, Somen & CHHARI, Vivek. Outcome of Cesarean Sections-an Ongoing Challenge. 2011. 136p. pap. **(978-3-8443-0413-8(4))** Lambert Academic Publishing.
Hoy, Angela J. DON't CUT ME AGAIN! True Stories about Vaginal Birth after Cesarean (VBAC) 2007. 236p. pap. 15.95 (978-1-59113-994-2(5)) Booklocker.com, Inc.
Jukelevics, Nicette. Understanding the Dangers of Cesarean Birth: Making Informed Decisions, 1 vol. 2008. (Praeger Series on Contemporary Health & Living Ser.). (Illus.). 304p. 49.95 (978-0-275-99906-3(8), C9906, Praeger Pubs.) Greenwood Publishing Group, Inc.
Knight, Mary Beth & Rosenthal, James. Strategies for the C-Section Mom: A Complete Fitness, Nutrition, & Lifestyle Guide. 2010. (ENG., Illus.). 240p. pap. 15.95 (978-1-4405-0202-6(1)) Adams Media Corp.
Kroelinger, Charlan. Biological & Psychosocial Determinants of Problematic Birth Outcomes. 2008. 252p. pap. (978-3-639-03158-4(X)) VDM Verlag Dr. Mueller e.K.
Mandala, Vincenzo, ed. The Role of Laparoscopy in Emergency Abdominal Surgery. 2011. (Updates in Surgery Ser.). (ENG.). 208p. 189.00 **(978-88-470-2326-0(2)**, 8847023262) Springer.
Mander, Rosemary. Caesarean: Just Another Way of Birth? 2007. (Illus.). 208p. 150.00 (978-0-415-40135-7(6)); per. 47.95 (978-0-415-40136-4(4)) Routledge.
Murphy, Magnus & Hull, Pauline McDonagh. Choosing Cesarean: A Natural Birth Plan. 2012. (ENG.). 375p. pap. 21.00 **(978-1-61614-511-8(0))** Prometheus Bks., Pubs.
Mwachaka, Philip, et al. The Human Rectus Sheath. 2010. 84p. pap. (978-3-8383-7686-8(2)) Lambert Academic Publishing.
Oregon Health & Science University, Evidence-Based Practice Center Staff, contrib. by. Vaginal Birth after Cesarean: New Insights. 2010. (Illus.). xi, 170p. (978-1-58763-391-1(4)) Agency for Healthcare Research & Quality.
Rosen, Michael J. Atlas of Abdominal Wall Reconstruction. 2011. (ENG., Illus.). 352p. 225.00 **(978-1-4377-2751-7(4)**, Saunders) Elsevier - Health Sciences Div.
Vadeboncoeur, Helene. Birthing Normally after a Cesarean or Two (American Ed) A guide for pregnant women - exploring reasons & practicalities for VBAC. 2011.Tr. of autre cesarienne ou un accouchement Naturel? (Illus.). 336p. pap. 50.00 **(978-1-906619-20-6(4))** Fresh Heart Publishing GBR. Dist: Lightning Source, Inc.

CESIUM
Gilli, Gastone & Gilli, Paola. The Nature of the Hydrogen Bond: Outline of a Comprehensive Hydrogen Bond Theory. 2009. (International Union of Crystallography Monographs on Crystallography Ser.). (ENG., Illus.). 304p. 130.00 (978-0-19-955896-4(5)) Oxford Univ. Pr., Inc.

CESIUM—ISOTOPES
National Council on Radiation Protection and Measurements Staff, contrib. by. Cesium-137 in the Environment: Radioecology & Approaches to Assessment & Management. 2007. (NCRP Reports). (978-0-929600-91-8(6)) National Council on Radiation Protection & Measurements.
Zhu, Qi. Statistical Modeling for the Analysis of Maldi-Tof Mass Spectrometry. 2011. 360p. pap. **(978-3-8433-9446-8(6))** Lambert Academic Publishing.

CESSIO BONORUM
see Assignments; Bankruptcy

CESSNA (AIRPLANES)
Bruckert, Danielle. Cessna 152 Training Manual. 2009. 79p. pap. 20.00 (978-0-557-02280-9(0)) Lulu Enterprises Inc.
Bruckert, Danielle & Roud, Oleg. Cessna 172 Training Manual. 2009. 99p. pap. 20.01 (978-0-557-01472-9(7)) Lulu Enterprises Inc.
Rodengen, Jeffrey L. The Legend of Cessna. Fernandez, Elizabeth & Lieber, Alex, eds. 3rd ed. 2007. (Illus.). 336p. 39.95 (978-1-932022-26-1(0)) Write Stuff Enterprises, Inc.
Roud, Oleg & Bruckert, Danielle. C182 Training Manual. 2009. 113p. pap. 20.00 (978-0-557-04524-2(X)) Lulu Enterprises Inc.
Shiel, Walt, et al. T-41 Mescalero: The Military Cessna 172. 2006. (Cessna Warbirds Ser.: 1). (Illus.). 216p. pap. 39.95 (978-0-9746553-3-8(3)) Slipdown Mountain Pubns. LLC.
Smith, Ron. Cessna 172 A Pocket History. 2010. (Illus.). 128p. pap. 16.95 **(978-1-4456-0086-4(2))** Amberley Publishing GBR. Dist: Casemate Pubs. & Bk. Distributors, LLC.

CESTODA
Smyth, J. D. & McManus, D. P. The Physiology & Biochemistry of Cestodes. 2007. (ENG., Illus.). 412p. pap. 79.00 (978-0-521-03995-9(2)) Cambridge Univ. Pr.
Wardle, Robert A. & McLeod, James A. The Zoology of Tapeworms. 2009. (ENG.). 810p. pap. 60.00 (978-0-8166-5996-8(6)) Univ. of Minnesota Pr.

CETACEAE
see also Dolphins; Whales
Among Whales. (978-0-02-063500-0(1)) ScottForesman CAN. Dist: HarperCollins Canada, Ltd.
Brakes, Philippa & Simmonds, Mark, eds. Whales & Dolphins: Cognition, Culture, Conservation & Human Perceptions. 2011. (ENG., Illus.). 256p. 140.00 (978-1-84971-224-8(7)); pap. 39.95 (978-1-84971-225-5(5)) Routledge.
Day, Trevor. Whale Watcher: A Global Guide to Watching Whales, Dolphins, & Porpoises in the Wild. 2006. (ENG., Illus.). 160p. pap. 19.95 (978-1-55407-200-2(X)) Firefly Bks., Ltd.
Ellis, Richard. The Great Sperm Whale: A Natural History of the Ocean's Most Magnificent & Mysterious Creature. 2011. (Illus.). 432p. 34.95 (978-0-7006-1772-2(8)) Univ. Pr. of Kansas.
Groc, Isabelle. Gentle Giants: An Emotional Face to Face with Dolphins & Whales. 2011. (ENG., Illus.). 272p. 29.95 (978-88-544-0581-3(7)) White Star ITA. Dist: Sterling Publishing Co., Inc.
Hoyt, Erich. Marine Protected Areas for Whales, Dolphins & Porpoises: A World Handbook for Cetacean Habitat Conservation & Planning. 2nd rev. ed. 2011. (ENG., Illus.). 492p. 160.00 (978-1-84407-762-5(4)); pap. 69.95 (978-1-84407-763-2(2)) Routledge.
Hughes, Chris B. The Porpoise-Given Life: Inspiration from the Cetacean Nation. 2008. 160p. pap. 14.95 (978-1-57736-413-9(9)) Providence Hse Pubs.
Jamieson, Barrie G.M., ed. Reproductive Biology & Phylogeny of Cetacea: Whales, Dolphins, & Porpoises. 2007. (ENG.). 450p. 139.95 (978-1-57808-360-2(5)) BIOS Scientific Publishers Ltd. GBR. Dist: Taylor & Francis Group.
Murray, Craig A., ed. Whales & Dolphins: Behavior, Biology & Distribution. 2010. (Animal Science, Issues & Professions Ser.). 59.00 (978-1-61668-693-2(6)) Nova Science Pubs., Inc.
Walker, Dylan, et al. Whales & Dolphins of the European Atlantic: The Bay of Biscay, English Channel, Celtic Sea & Coastal SW Ireland. 2nd ed. 2008. (Illus.). 88p. pap. 30.00 (978-1-903657-31-7(8)) Trans-Atlantic Pubns., Inc.
Zimmer, Walter. Passive Acoustic Monitoring of Cetaceans. 2011. (ENG., Illus.). 366p. 105.00 **(978-0-521-19342-9(7))** Cambridge Univ. Pr.

CEVENNES MOUNTAINS (FRANCE)
Castle, Alan. The Robert Louis Stevenson Trail: A Walking Tour in the Velay & Cevennes, Southern France. 2nd rev. ed. 2010. (Illus.). 192p. pap. 22.95 (978-1-85284-511-7(2)) Cicerone Pr. GBR. Dist: Midpoint Trade Bks., Inc.
Stevenson, Robert. Travels with a Donkey in the Cevennes. 2009. (Stanfords Travel Classics Ser.). 104p. pap. 9.95 (978-1-906780-07-4(2)) Beaufoy, John Publishing GBR. Dist: Midpoint Trade Bks., Inc.
Stevenson, Robert Louis. Travels with a Donkey. 2010. (Atlas Pocket Classics Ser.). (ENG.). 200p. 12.00 (978-1-934633-98-4(4), 934698) Atlas & Co.
—Travels with a Donkey in the Cevennes. 2007. (ENG.). 88p. per. (978-1-4065-8226-0(3)) Dodo Pr.
—Travels with a Donkey in the Cevennes. Lt. ed. 2007. 196p. (978-1-4068-2235-9(3)) Echo Library.
—Travels with a Donkey in the Cevennes. 2008. (ENG.). 100p. pap. 8.95 (978-1-4385-0268-7(0), Book Jungle) Standard Pubns., Inc.

CEWA DIALECT
see Chewa Dialect

CEYLON
see Sri Lanka

CEZANNE, PAUL, 1839-1906
Bardazzi, Francesca, et al. Cézanne in Florence: Two Collectors & the 1910 Exhibition of Impressionism. 2007. (Illus.). 272p. pap. (978-88-370-4971-3(4)) Electa.
Becks-Malorny, Ulrike. Cezanne. 2011. (25 Ser.). (ENG., Illus.). 96p. 14.99 **(978-3-8365-3110-8(0))** TASCHEN DEU. Dist: Ingram Pub. Services.
Berman, Ronald. Translating Modernism: Fitzgerald & Hemingway. 2nd ed. 2009. (ENG.). 202p. 29.75 (978-0-8173-1647-1(7)) Univ. of Alabama Pr.
Buck, Stephanie, et al. The Courtauld Cézannes. 2008. (ENG., Illus.). 160p. pap. 45.00 (978-1-903470-84-8(6)) Holberton, Paul Publishing GBR. Dist: Casemate Pubs. & Bk. Distributors, LLC.
Carolyn, Lanchner. Paul Cézanne. 2011. (ENG., Illus.). 48p. pap. 9.95 (978-0-87070-789-6(2)) Museum of Modern Art.
Cezanne. 2009. (978-3-8365-1767-6(1), TASCHEN.
Cezanne: Art in Focus. 2008. 5.95 (978-0-8416-0395-0(2)) American Map Corp.
Cezanne, Paul. Cezanne. Suarez-Rojas, Alberto, tr. 2006. (Illus.). 80p. 9.95 (978-970-718-373-5(X), Numen) Advanced Marketing, S. de R. L. de C. V. MEX. Dist: Perseus-PGW.
—Color Your Own Cezanne Paintings. 2006. (Dover Art Coloring Book Ser.). (ENG., Illus.). 32p. (J). 3.95 (978-0-486-45166-4(6)) Dover Pubns., Inc.
—Paul Cezanne, Letters. Rewald, John, ed. (Illus.). reprint ed. 49.50 (978-0-404-20053-4(2)) AMS Pr., Inc.
Cézanne, Paul, et al. Cezanne & American Modernism. 2009. pap. (978-0-9824716-0-9(2)) Montclair Art Museum.
Danchev, Alex. Cezanne: A Biography. 2012. (ENG., Illus.). 544p. 40.00 **(978-0-307-37707-4(5)**, Pantheon) Knopf Doubleday Publishing Group.
D'Souza, Aruna. Cezanne's Bathers: Biography & the Erotics of Paint. 2008. (Refiguring Modernism Ser.). (ENG., Illus.). 184p. pap. 50.00 (978-0-271-03214-6(6)) Pennsylvania State Univ. Pr.
Duchting, Hajo & Dchting, Hajo. Cézanne. 25th ed. 2009. (ENG., Illus.). 224p. 14.99 (978-3-8365-1012-7(X)) TASCHEN DEU. Dist: Ingram Pub. Services.
Hodge, Susie. Cezanne: His life & works in 500 Images: An illustrated exploration of the artist, his life & context, with a gallery of 300 of his finest Paintings. 2011. (ENG., Illus.). 256p. 35.00 (978-0-7548-2313-1(X)) Anness Publishing GBR. Dist: National Bk. Network.
Machotka, Pavel. Cézanne: The Eye & the Mind. 2009. (ENG.). 544p. pap. 69.00 (978-2-7537-0047-5(8)) Editions Crès FRA. Dist: Independent Pubs. Group.
—On Site with P. Cezanne in Provence. 2008. 144p. (978-2-7537-0043-7(5)) Editions Crès.
Parkstone Press Staff. Cézanne. 2010. (Mega Square Ser.). (ENG., Illus.). 256p. 12.95 (978-1-84484-933-8(3)) Parkstone Pr. USA, Ltd.
Pissarro, Joachim. Cézanne/Pissarro, Johns/Rauschenberg: Comparative Studies on Intersubjectivity in Modern Art. 2006. (ENG., Illus.). 330p. 124.00 (978-0-521-83640-1(9)) Cambridge Univ. Pr.
—Pioneering Modern Painting: Cezanne & Pissarro, 1865-1885, 1 vol. 2007. (ENG., Illus.). 256p. pap. 40.00 (978-0-87070-185-6(1)) Museum of Modern Art.
Rishel, Joseph J., et al. Cézanne & Beyond. 2009. (Illus.). xiii, 585p. (978-0-87633-208-5(4)); pap. (978-0-87633-209-2(2)) Philadelphia Museum of Art.
Robbins, Anne. Cézanne in Britain. 2006. (ENG., Illus.). 96p. pap. 30.00 (978-1-85709-351-3(8)) Yale Univ. Pr.
Sanders, Michael. Cezanne: In Acrylics. 2011. (Ready to Paint the Masters Ser.). (ENG., Illus.). 88p. pap. 19.95 (978-1-84448-575-8(7)) Search Pr., Ltd. GBR. Dist: Independent Pubs. Group.
Sidlauskas, Susan. Cézanne's Other: The Portraits of Hortense. 2009. (ENG., Illus.). 368p. 49.95 (978-0-520-25745-0(6)) Univ. of California Pr.
Simms, Matthew Thomas & Cézanne, Paul. Cezanne's Watercolors: Between Drawing & Painting. 2008. (ENG., Illus.). 256p. 60.00 (978-0-300-14066-8(5)) Yale Univ. Pr.
Spence, David. Cezanne. 2009. (Ticktock Essential Artists Ser.). (ENG.). 32p. (J). (gr. 4-7). pap. 6.95 (978-1-84696-970-6(0)) TickTock Bks. GBR. Dist: Independent Pubs. Group.
Stavitsky, Gail & Rothkopf, Katherine. Cezanne & American Modernism. 2009. (ENG., Illus.). 376p. 65.00 (978-0-300-14715-5(5)) Yale Univ. Pr.
Taschen Staff. Cezanne. Date not set. (SPA.). pap. 4.99 (978-3-8228-8785-1(4)) TASCHEN DEU. Dist: Digital Manga Publishing.

C

Tojner, Poul & Baumann, Felix, eds. Cezanne & Giacometti: Paths of Doubt. 2008. (ENG., Illus.). 360p. 60.00 *(978-3-7757-2089-2(8))* Hatje Cantz Verlag GmbH & Co KG DEU. Dist: D.A.P./Distributed Art Pubs.

VV Staff. Cézanne. (Colección Art Book). (SPA., Illus.). 144p. *(978-84-8156-199-9(1))* Sociedad Editorial Electa Espana ESP. Dist: Lectorum Pubns., Inc.

CF (DISEASE)
see Cystic Fibrosis

CFCS (CHEMICALS)
see Chlorofluorocarbons

CGI (COMPUTER NETWORK PROTOCOL)

Forsythe, Kevin & Ubelhor, Laura. HTML for the Business Programmer: With JavaServer Pages, PHP, ASP.NET, CGI, & JavaScript. 2008. (Business Developers Ser.). (ENG., Illus.). 350p. pap. 49.95 *(978-1-58347-079-4(4))* MC Pr., LLC.

CHA-NO-YU
see Japanese Tea Ceremony

CHACO CANYON (N.M.)

Cameron, Catherine M. Chaco & after in the Northern San Juan: Excavations at the Bluff Great House. 2008. (ENG., Illus.). 280p. 75.00 *(978-0-8165-2681-9(8))* Univ. of Arizona Pr.

Campbell, John Martin. The Great Houses of Chaco. 2007. (ENG., Illus.). 168p. 29.95 *(978-0-8263-4248-5(5))* Univ. of New Mexico Pr.

Lekson, Stephen H. The Architecture of Chaco Canyon, New Mexico. 2007. (Chaco Canyon Ser.). (ENG.). 296p. pap. 29.95 *(978-0-87480-948-0(7))* Univ. of Utah Pr.

—Great Pueblo Architecture of Chaco Canyon, New Mexico. 2007. (Foundations of Archaeology). (Illus.). 325p. pap. *(978-0-9752738-7-6(6),* Percheron Pr.) Werner, Eliot Pubns., Inc.

Noble, David Grant. In Search of Chaco: New Approaches to an Archaeological Enigma. (Illus.). 168p. pap. 24.95 *(978-1-930618-42-8(5))* School for Advanced Research Pr./SAR Pr.

CHACO WAR, 1932-1935

English, Adrian J. The Green Hell: A Concise History of the Chaco War Between Bolivia & Paraguay, 1932-35. 2008. (Spellmount Military Studies). (ENG., Illus.). 224p. pap. 32.95 *(978-1-86227-445-7(2))* History Pr. Ltd.,The GBR. Dist: Independent Pubs. Group.

Estigarribia, Jose Felix & Estigarribia, José Félix. The Epic of the Chaco: Marshal Estigarribia's Memoirs of the Chaco War, 1932-1935. Ynsfran, Pablo Max, ed. 2011. 340p. 51.95 ***(978-1-258-04917-1(1))*** Literary Licensing, LLC.

John, S. Sándor. Bolivia's Radical Tradition: Permanent Revolution in the Andes. 2009. (ENG., Illus.). 320p. 55.00 *(978-0-8165-2764-9(4))* Univ. of Arizona Pr.

Quesada, Alejandro. The Chaco War 1932-35: South America's Greatest War. 2011. (Men-at-Arms Ser.). (ENG., Illus.). 48p. pap. 17.95 *(978-1-84908-416-1(5))* Osprey Publishing, Ltd. GBR. Dist: Random Hse., Inc.

CHAD

Icon Group International, Inc. Staff, compiled by. The 2006 Economic & Product Market Databook for Kelo, Chad. 2006. 618p. ring bd. 95.00 *(978-0-497-81986-6(4))* Icon Group International, Inc.

Locken, E. Travel Journal Chad. 2009. 192p. pap. 20.95 *(978-0-557-07979-7(9))* Lulu Enterprises Inc.

Seid, Joseph Brahim. Told by Starlight in Chad. 2007. *(978-1-59221-047-3(3))*; 84p. pap. *(978-1-59221-048-0(1))* Africa World Pr.

CHAD—FOREIGN RELATIONS

Chad & the Central African Republic: The Regional Impact of the Darfur Crisis: Hearing Before the Subcommittee on African Affairs of the Committee on Foreign Relations, United States Senate, One Hundred Tenth Congress, First Session, March 20, 2007. 2008. iii, 42p. *(978-0-16-080151-8(6),* 552-070-36888-4) United States Government Printing Office.

CHAD—HISTORY

Burr, J. Millard & Collins, Robert O. Darfur: The Long Road to Disaster. exp. ed. (Illus.). 2006. 400p. 89.95 *(978-1-55876-404-0(6))* 2008. 390p. 89.95 *(978-1-55876-469-9(0))* 2007. 390p. per. 28.95 *(978-1-55876-470-5(4))* Wiener, Markus Pubs., Inc.

CHADWICK, LYNN

Collins, Joan. Lynn Chadwick. 2006. (ENG.). 176p. 65.00 *(978-1-932646-19-1(1))* Ruder-Finn Pr.

CHAFFEE, ADNA ROMANZA, 1884-1941

Carter, William Harding. The Life of Lieutenant General Chaffee. 2009. 198p. pap. *(978-0-217-54674-4(9))* Books LLC.

—The Life of Lieutenant General Chaffee. 2008. 332p. 45.95 *(978-0-548-98646-2(0))* 2007. (ENG.). 336p. per. 30.95 *(978-0-548-66072-0(7))* Kessinger Publishing, LLC.

—The Life of Lieutenant General Chaffee. 296p. reprint ed. 98.00 *(978-0-7222-9275-4(9))* Library Reprints, Inc.

CHAFING DISH COOKERY
see Chafing Dish Cooking

CHAFING DISH COOKING
see also Fondue

Southworth, May E. Midnight Feasts: Two Hundred & Two Salads & Chafing-Dish Recipes. 2008. (Cooking in America Ser.). (ENG.). 156p. pap. 12.95 *(978-1-4290-1077-1(0))* Applewood Bks.

CHAGA (AFRICAN PEOPLE)

Raum, Otto F. Chaga Childhood: A Description of Indigenous Education in an East African Tribe. reprint ed. 39.50 *(978-0-404-15966-5(4))* AMS Pr., Inc.

CHAGALL, MARC, 1887-1985

Baal-Teshuva, Jacob. Marc Chagall: 1887-1985. 25th ed. 2008. (ENG., Illus.). 279p. 14.99 *(978-3-8228-3128-1(X))* TASCHEN DEU. Dist: Ingram Pub. Services.

Chagall: In neuem Licht. 14.95 *(978-3-8238-6133-1(6))* teNeues Publishing Co.

Chagall, Marc. My Life: Marc Chagall. 2011. (Peter Owen Modern Classic Ser.). (ENG.). 200p. pap. 15.95 *(978-0-7206-1356-8(6))* Owen, Peter Ltd. GBR. Dist: Independent Pubs. Group.

Chagall, Marc & Tériade, E. Chagall et Tériade: L'empreinte D'un Peintre. 2008. (ENG., Illus.). 224p. pap. 60.00 *(978-2-35340-012-6(4))* Gourcuff Gradenigo FRA. Dist: National Bk. Network.

Chagall, Marc, et al. Marc Chagall: Ceramics. 2006. (ENG & DUT., Illus.). 144p. 40.00 *(978-90-400-9081-3(5))* Waanders B.V., Uitgeverij NLD. Dist: National Bk. Network.

—Marc Chagall: Der Maler Am Fenster. 2009. (GER., Illus.). 167p. (C). 45.00 *(978-3-7774-6025-3(7))* Hirmer Verlag GmbH DEU. Dist: Brown, David Bk. Co., The.

Dorot, Ruth. The Art of Time, the Art of Place: Isaac Bashevis Singer & Marc Chagall - A Dialogue. 2011. (ENG., Illus.). 150p. 59.95 *(978-1-84519-409-3(8))* Sussex Academic Pr. GBR. Dist: International Specialized Bk. Services.

Doschka, Roland, ed. Marc Chagall: Origins & Paths. 2010. (Illus.). 232p. pap. 19.95 *(978-3-7913-4395-2(5))* Prestel Publishing.

Goodman, Susan Tumarkin & Gitelman, Zvi Y. Chagall & the Artists of the Russian Jewish Theater. 2008. (Illus.). xiii, 226p. pap. *(978-0-87334-202-5(X))* Yale Univ. Pr.

Goodman, Susan Tumarkin, et al. Chagall & the Artists of the Russian Jewish Theater. 2008. (ENG., Illus.). 256p. 65.00 *(978-0-300-11155-2(X))* Yale Univ. Pr.

Guerman, Mikhail, et al. Chagall: Vitebsk-Paris-Nueva York. Suarez, Daniel, tr. 2007. (Illus.). 287p. 19.95 *(978-970-718-425-1(6),* Numen) Advanced Marketing, S. de R. L. de C. V. MEX. Dist: Perseus-PGW.

Kloomok, Isaac. Marc Chagall: His Life & Work. 2011. 188p. 42.95 ***(978-1-258-03728-4(9))*** Literary Licensing, LLC.

Rainer M & Walther I. T25 kr Chagall. 2012. (25 Ser.). (ENG., Illus.). 96p. 14.99 ***(978-3-8365-3114-6(3))*** TASCHEN DEU. Dist: Ingram Pub. Services.

Taylor, Michael & Chagall, Marc. Paris Through the Window: Marc Chagall & His Circle. 2010. *(978-0-87633-230-6(0))* Philadelphia Museum of Art.

Westheider, Ortrud & Philipp, Michael. Marc Chagall: Lebenslinien. Westheider, Ortrud & Philipp, Michael, eds. 2010. (ENG., Illus.). 232p. (C). 49.00 *(978-3-7774-2961-8(9))* Hirmer Verlag GmbH DEU. Dist: Brown, David Bk. Co., The.

Wilson, Jonathan. Marc Chagall. 2007. (Jewish Encounters Ser.). (ENG., Illus.). 224p. 19.95 *(978-0-8052-4201-0(5),* Schocken) Knopf Doubleday Publishing Group.

Wullschlager, Jackie. Chagall: A Biography. 2008. (ENG., Illus.). 608p. 40.00 *(978-0-375-41455-8(X),* Knopf) Knopf Doubleday Publishing Group.

CHAGGA (AFRICAN PEOPLE)
see Chaga (African People)

CHAIN REACTION, POLYMERASE
see Polymerase Chain Reaction

CHAIN REACTION PILES
see Nuclear Reactors

CHAIN RESTAURANTS

Douglas, Ron. America's Most Wanted Recipes: Delicious Recipes from Your Family's Favorite Restaurants. 2009. (ENG., Illus.). 304p. pap. 16.00 *(978-1-4391-4706-1(X),* Beyond Words/Atria Bks.) Atria Bks.

—More of America's Most Wanted Recipes: More Than 200 Simple & Delicious Secret Restaurant Recipes — All for $10 or Less! 2010. (ENG.). 352p. pap. 16.00 *(978-1-4391-4826-6(0),* Beyond Words/Atria Bks.) Atria Bks.

Wilbur, Todd. Top Secret Restaurant Recipes 2: More Amazing Clones of Famous Dishes from America's Favorite Restaurant Chains. 2006. (ENG., Illus.). 416p. (gr. 12-18). 16.00 *(978-0-452-28800-3(2),* Plume) Penguin Group (USA) Inc.

—Top Secret Restaurant Recipes 3: The Secret Formulas for Duplicating Your Favorite Restaurant Dishes at Home. 2010. (ENG., Illus.). 448p. (gr. 12). 16.00 *(978-0-452-29645-9(5),* Plume) Penguin Group (USA) Inc.

CHAIN STORES
see also Department Stores

Bevan, Judi. The Rise & Fall of Marks & Spencer: And How It Rose Again. rev. ed. 2007. (Illus.). 336p. per. 17.00 *(978-1-86197-898-1(7))* Profile Bks. Ltd. GBR. Dist: Independent Pubs. Group.

Edwards, Jonathan & Griffiths, Ian. The Ice Man Cometh. 2007. (ENG.). 288p. 34.95 *(978-1-84454-484-4(2))* Blake, John, Publishing, Ltd. GBR. Dist: Independent Pubs. Group.

Hicks, Michael J. The Local Economic Impact of Wal-Mart. 2007. (ENG.). 372p. 114.95 *(978-1-934043-38-7(9))* Cambria Pr.

Mitchell, Stacy. Big-Box Swindle: The True Cost of Mega-Retailers & the Fight for America's Independent Businesses. 2007. (ENG.). 344p. per. 15.00 *(978-0-8070-3501-6(7))* Beacon Pr.

Randall, Geoffrey & Seth, Andrew. The Grocers: The Rise & Rise of Supermarket Chains. 3rd ed. 2011. (ENG., Illus.). 208p. pap. 24.95 *(978-0-7494-6104-1(7))* Kogan Page, Ltd. GBR. Dist: Ingram Pub. Services.

Rawal, Radhakishan. The Taxation of Permanent Establishments: An International Perspective. 2006. 551p. (C). pap. 135.00 *(978-1-904905-45-5(5))* Spiramus Pr. GBR. Dist: International Specialized Bk. Services.

Salerno, Humberto & Gay Zaragoza, Andrea. The Mango Story. 2011. (ENG., Illus.). 160p. pap. 24.99 ***(978-1-907794-11-7(5))*** LID Publishing GBR. Dist: AtlasBooks Distribution.

CHAINED BOOKS

Blades, William. Books in Chains & Other Bibliographical Papers. 2007. (ENG.). 268p. 42.95 *(978-0-548-17913-0(1))*; 272p. per. 27.95 *(978-1-4304-7958-1(2))* Kessinger Publishing, LLC.

Streeter, Burnett Hillman. The Chained Library: A Survey of Four Centuries in the Evolution of the English Library. 2011. (Cambridge Library Collection - Printing & Publishing History Ser.). (Illus.). 396p. pap. 31.99 *(978-1-108-02789-2(X))* Cambridge Univ. Pr.

CHAIR CANING

Kelsey, John. Chair Seats of Cane, Rush, & Tape: Repairing Favorite Chairs for More Years of Use. 2012. 48p. pap. 12.99 ***(978-1-57421-412-3(8))*** Design Originals.

CHAIRS
see also Chair Caning; Wheelchairs

Abbott, Mike. Going with the Grain: Making Chairs in the 21st Century. 2011. (ENG., Illus.). 192p. pap. 29.95 ***(978-0-9542345-5-3(3))*** Living Wood Bks. GBR. Dist: Chelsea Green Publishing.

Aktion Plagiarius Staff, contrib. by. Kreuzschwinger(r): Dynamisches Sitzen/Dynamic Seating. 2009. (GER & ENG., Illus.). 176p. 45.00 *(978-3-7861-2570-9(8),* Art Stock Bks. Ltd/Csi) Continental Sales, Inc.

Bryan, Melinda. Pilates Chairs Personal Studio Guide. 2011. (Illus.). pap. 14.99 ***(978-0-9834374-1-3(6))*** Performing Arts Physical Therapy of Los Angeles.

—Pilates Chairs Training Manual. 2011. (Illus.). pap. 24.99 ***(978-0-9841492-9-2(5))*** Performing Arts Physical Therapy of Los Angeles.

Chairmaking & Repairing. 2010. *(978-1-56523-501-4(0))* Fox Chapel Publishing Co., Inc.

Design Museum Staff. Fifty Chairs That Changed the World. 2010. (ENG., Illus.). 110p. 20.00 *(978-1-84091-540-2(4),* Conran Octopus) Octopus Publishing Group GBR. Dist: Hachette Bk. Group.

—How to Design a Chair. 2010. (ENG., Illus.). 112p. 20.00 *(978-1-84091-546-4(3),* Conran Octopus) Octopus Publishing Group GBR. Dist: Hachette Bk. Group.

Evans, Jeffrey S. Come in & Have a Seat: Vernacular Chairs of the Shenandoah Valley. 2010. (Illus.). pap. 24.95 *(978-0-9844624-0-7(6))* Museum of the Shenandoah Valley.

Fine Woodworking Magazine Editors, ed. Designing & Building Chairs. 2006. (New Best of Fine Woodworking Ser.). (ENG., Illus.). 155p. per. 17.95 *(978-1-56158-857-2(1),* Taunton) Taunton Pr., Inc.

Fischer, Volker & von der Schulenburg, Stephan. Sit in China: Ein Streifzug durch 500 Jahre Kultur des Sitzens / An Excursion through 500 Years of the Culture of Sitting. 2010. (GER & ENG., Illus.). 96p. 59.00 *(978-3-936681-36-9(8))* Edition Axel Menges GmbH DEU. Dist: National Bk. Network.

Harding-Hill, Michael. The Windsor Chair: An Illustrated Celebration. 2007. (ENG., Illus.). 208p. *(978-1-85149-429-3(4),* Antique Collectors Club Dist) Antique Collectors' Club.

Hemachandra, Ray. Lark Studio Series: Chairs. 2010. (ENG., Illus.). 204p. 12.95 *(978-1-60059-683-4(5))* Lark Bks.

Hemachandra, Ray & Nutt, Craig. 500 Chairs: Celebrating Traditional & Innovative Designs. 2008. (500 Ser.). (ENG., Illus.). 408p. pap. 24.95 *(978-1-57990-872-0(1))* Lark Bks.

Kooler Desing Studio, des. Painted Chairs for Tiny Tots. 2007. 52p. 11.95 *(978-1-60140-427-5(1))* Leisure Arts, Inc.

Kuper, Marijke, text. Rietveld's Chair: DVD & Book. 2011. (DUT & ENG., Illus.). 160p. 25.00 *(978-90-5662-778-2(3))* NAi Uitgevers / Publishers Stichting NLD. Dist: D.A.P./Distributed Art Pubs.

Mack, Daniel. The Adirondack Chair: A Celebration of a Summer Classic. 2008. (ENG., Illus.). 128p. 19.95 *(978-1-58479-568-1(9))* Stewart, Tabori & Chang.

Miller, Jeff. Chairmaking & Design. 2nd ed. 2007. (ENG., Illus.). 199p. pap. 22.95 *(978-1-933502-06-9(1))* Linden Publishing Co., Inc.

Miller, Judith. Chairs. 2009. (ENG., Illus.). 336p. 65.00 *(978-1-84091-523-5(4),* Conran Octopus) Octopus Publishing Group GBR. Dist: Hachette Bk. Group.

Mursell, James. Windsor Chairmaking. 2010. (ENG., Illus.). 176p. 49.95 *(978-1-84797-154-8(7))* Crowood Pr., Ltd. GBR. Dist: Independent Pubs. Group.

Opsvik, Peter & Opsvik. Rethinking Sitting. 2009. (ENG., Illus.). 208p. pap. 39.95 *(978-0-393-73288-7(6),* 73288) Norton, W. W. & Co., Inc.

Ospina, Alison. Green Wood Chairs: Chairs & Chairmakers of Ireland. 2009. (ENG., Illus.). 150p. pap. 35.00 *(978-0-85442-151-0(3))* Stobart Davies, Ltd. GBR. Dist: Brown, David Bk. Co., The.

Pallot, Bill G.B. L'art du Siège Au XVIIIe Siècle en France. 2007. (World's Images Ser.). (FRE & ENG., Illus.). 332p. 165.00 *(978-2-86770-023-1(X))* ACR Edition FRA. Dist: Antique Collectors' Club.

Pierce, Kerry. Chairmaking Simplified: 24 Projects Using Shop-Made Jigs. 2008. (ENG., Illus.). 192p. 26.99 *(978-1-55870-827-3(8),* Popular Woodworking Bks.) F&W Media, Inc.

Richardson, Carole. ... Good & Bad Chair Days... 2010. (Illus.). 100p. pap. 28.99 *(978-1-4490-3803-8(4))* AuthorHouse.

Roe, Fred. Ancient Church Chests & Chairs. 2007. 144p. per. *(978-1-905217-80-9(3))* Mills, Jeremy Publishing.

Tables, Desks & Chairs. (Custom Woodworking Ser.). (Illus.). 127p. *(978-0-8487-2681-2(2))* Oxmoor Hse., Inc.

Woodworker's Journal Editors. Benches, Chairs & Beds: Practical Projects from Shaker to Contemporary. 2007. (Best of Woodworker's Journal Ser.). (ENG.). 151p. pap. 19.95 *(978-1-56523-343-0(3))* Fox Chapel Publishing Co., Inc.

CHAKA, ZULU CHIEF, 1787-1828

Mabana, Kahiudi Claver. Des Transpositions Francophones du Mythe de Chaka. (FRE.). 190p. 33.95 *(978-3-906769-40-0(2))* Lang, Peter CHE. Dist: Lang, Peter Publishing, Inc.

CHAKRAS

Andrews, Synthia. The Path of Energy: Awaken Your Personal Power & Expand Your Consciousness. 2011. E-Book *(978-1-60163-654-6(7))*; (ENG.). 1p. pap. 16.99 *(978-1-60163-172-5(3))* Career Pr., Inc. (New Page Bks.).

Arewa, Caroline Shola. Energy 4 Life. 2010. (ENG., Illus.). 200p. pap. 19.95 *(978-1-84694-312-6(4))* Hunt, John Publishing Ltd. GBR. Dist: National Bk. Network.

Arian, Artimia. Cosmic Reawakening. 2007. 296p. per. 21.95 *(978-0-595-44240-9(4))* iUniverse, Inc.

Ashcroft-Nowicki, Dolores. Body of Light. 2006. 216p. pap. 17.95 *(978-0-7387-0320-6(6))* Llewellyn Pubns.

Ashley-Farrand, Thomas. Chakra Mantras: Liberate Your Spiritual Genius Through Chanting. 2006. (ENG.). 1p. per. 18.95 *(978-1-57863-367-8(2),* Weiser Bks.) Red Wheel/Weiser.

Barnett, Larkin. Practical Centering: Exercises to Energize Your Chakras for Relaxation, Vitality, & Health. 2012. (ENG.). 168p. pap. 15.95 ***(978-0-8356-0903-6(0),*** Quest Bks.) Theosophical Publishing Hse.

Bhatnagar, Sri Shyamji & Isaacs, David. Microchakras: Innertuning for Psychological Well-Being. 2009. (ENG.). 1p. 24.95 *(978-1-59477-213-9(4))* Inner Traditions International, Ltd.

Chandler, Sue. Just Ask. 2010. 136p. pap. 13.99 *(978-1-4490-7398-5(0))* AuthorHouse.

Christensen, Katherine. Journey Through Willowseyez BOOK ONE. 2008. 478p. pap. 49.95 *(978-0-615-15623-1(1))* Christensen, Katherine M.

Cross, John. Healing with the Chakra Energy System: Acupressure, Bodywork, & Reflexology for Total Health. 2006. (ENG., Illus.). 332p. pap. 22.95 *(978-1-55643-625-3(4))* North Atlantic Bks.

Cross, John R. Acupuncture & the Chakra Energy System: Treating the Cause of Disease. 2008. (ENG., Illus.). 208p. pap. 19.95 *(978-1-55643-721-2(8))* North Atlantic Bks.

Crow, Cinnamon. The Chakra Zodiac Oracle. 2011. 150p. 17.00 *(978-1-886940-19-2(3))* Ozark Mountain Publishing, Inc.

Cumes, Carol. Chakra Gardens: Opening the Senses of the Soul. 2008. *(978-0-9654003-9-8(5))* Mitra Pubns.

Curnivan, Jude. The 8th Chakra: What It Is & How It Can Transform Your Life. 2007. (ENG.). 288p. per. 14.95 *(978-1-4019-1695-4(3))* Hay Hse., Inc.

Dale, Cyndi. The Complete Book of Chakra Healing: Activate the Transformative Power of Your Energy Centers. 2nd rev. ed. 2009. (ENG., Illus.). 456p. pap. 24.95 *(978-0-7387-1502-5(6))* Llewellyn Pubns.

—Illuminating the Afterlife: Your Soul's Journey: Through the Worlds Beyond. 2008. 313p. 21.95 *(978-1-59179-944-3(9))* Sounds True, Inc.

—The Subtle Body: An Encyclopedia of Your Energetic Anatomy. 2009. (Illus.). 500p. pap. 39.95 *(978-1-59179-671-8(7))* Sounds True, Inc.

D'Angelo, James. Seed Sounds for Tuning the Chakras: Vowels, Consonants, & Syllables for Spiritual Transformation. 2012. pap. ***(978-1-59477-460-7(9),*** Destiny Bks.) Inner Traditions International, Ltd.

Day, Lorraine. Put Attraction into Action & Balance Your Chakras. 2011. 160p. pap. 20.33 ***(978-1-4567-8698-4(9))*** AuthorHouse.

De Rosa, Wendy. Energy Healing Through the Chakras: A Guide to Self-Healing: A Guide to Self-Healing with CD. 2011. pap. 29.95 ***(978-0-7414-6444-6(6))*** Infinity Publishing.

D'Este, Sorita. Avalonias Book of Chakras A Practical M. 2006. pap. *(978-1-905297-08-5(4))* Avalonia.

Fiennes, Maya. Yoga for Real Life. 2011. (ENG., Illus.). 208p. pap. 19.95 *(978-1-84354-937-6(9))* Atlantic Bks., Ltd. GBR. Dist: Independent Pubs. Group.

Fiennes, Maya & Garratt, Sheryl. Yoga for Real Life: The Kundalini Method. 2012. (ENG., Illus.). 208p. pap. 15.95 ***(978-0-85789-577-6(X))*** Atlantic Bks., Ltd. GBR. Dist: Independent Pubs. Group.

Fraser, Kim. Ignite Your Spirit. 2007. (ENG., Illus.). 234p. per. 18.95 *(978-1-84409-106-5(6))* Findhorn Pr. GBR. Dist: Independent Pubs. Group.

Goodson Parker, D. & Bressler, K. W. Yoga para el Bebe. (SPA.). 192p. *(978-84-95456-34-2(6),* 86607) Ediciones Oniro S.A.

Greszczyszyn, Andrew. The Complete Chakra System. 2010. 270p. pap. *(978-1-926582-74-0(8))* Insomniac Pr.

Hale, Gill, et al. Crystals, Colour & Chakra: Learn to harness the transforming power of natural energies with practical New Age techniques & over 1000 stunning photographs & Artworks. 2012. (ENG., Illus.). 512p. pap. 18.99 ***(978-1-78019-068-6(9))*** Anness Publishing GBR. Dist: National Bk. Network.

Hodder & Ozaniec, Naomi. Chakras for Beginners. 2nd ed. (Illus.). xx, 90p. pap. 11.95 *(978-0-340-74244-0(5),* Hodder & Stoughton) Hodder General Publishing Div. GBR. Dist: Trafalgar Square Publishing.

Ison, David. The Chakra Sound System: Activate Your Fullest Potential Through the Essential Power of Music. 2012. 80p. pap. 99.00 ***(978-1-60407-625-7(9))*** Sounds True, Inc.
Jolly, Karen. Chakra Heart. unabr. ed. *(978-0-9701207-3-1(7))* Age of Awareness.
Kett, Kendra. The Pinwheel Girl Takes Flight: Everywoman's Journey Through Seven Stages of Transformation. 2006. (Illus.). 268p. pap. 24.95 *(978-0-9642823-3-9(X))* Key Answer Products, Inc.
Kul, Djwal. Activar los Chakras.Tr. of Activating the Chakras. (SPA.). 192p. 19.98 *(978-84-95513-01-4(3))* Porcia Publishing Corp.
Kynes, Sandra. Change at Hand: Balancing Your Energy Through Palmistry, Chakras & Mudras. 2009. (ENG., Illus.). 240p. pap. 17.95 *(978-0-7387-1570-4(0))* Llewellyn Pubns.
Landwehr, Joe. Tracking the Soul with an Astrology of Consciousness. 2007. (Illus.). xxviii, 470p. per. *(978-0-9747626-1-6(X))* Ancient Tower Pr.
Lee, Ilchi. Healing Chakras: Awaken Your Body's Energy System for Complete Health, Happiness & Peace. 2009. (Illus.). 144p. pap. 21.95 *(978-1-935127-04-8(7))* BEST Life Media.
Lembo, Margaret Ann. Chakra Awakening: Transform Your Reality Using Crystals, Color, Aromatherapy & the Power of Positive Thought. 2011. (ENG., Illus.). 264p. pap. 19.95 *(978-0-7387-1485-1(2))* Llewellyn Pubns.
Lilly, Simon & Lilly, Sue. Crystal, Color & Chakra Healing: How to harness the transforming powers of crystals, colour & your body's own subtle energies to increase health & Well-being. 2010. (ENG., Illus.). 256p. pap. 24.99 *(978-1-84476-920-9(8))* Anness Publishing GBR. Dist: National Bk. Network.
Lipstick & Love: Six soul memoirs from a modern day Mystic. 2009. 144p. pap. *(978-0-9812399-1-0(9))* Arias Pr.
Lockhart, Maureen. The Subtle Energy Body. 2010. (ENG.). 1p. pap. 29.95 *(978-1-59477-339-6(4))* Inner Traditions International, Ltd.
Logan, Jean. Unlocking the Power of Glyphs. 2009. 224p. spiral bd. *(978-1-60530-170-9(1))* Independent Pub.
Manuchehri, Marie. Intuitive Self-Healing: Achieve Balance & Wellness Through the Body's Energy Centers. 2012. 220p. pap. 16.95 ***(978-1-60407-627-1(5))*** Sounds True, Inc.
May, Nadine. The Language of Light. 2009. 274p. pap. *(978-0-9814278-5-0(5))* Kima Global Pubs.
Mercier, Patricia. The Chakra Bible: The Definitive Guide to Chakra Energy. 2007. (ENG., Illus.). 400p. pap. 14.95 *(978-1-4027-5224-7(5))* Sterling Publishing Co., Inc.
Milford, Francine. Tuning Fork Therapy(r) on Dogs Chakras. 2008. 80p. pap. 20.00 *(978-1-4357-2321-4(X))* Lulu Enterprises Inc.
—Tuning Fork Therapy(r) using tuning forks on Cat's Chakras. 2008. 82p. pap. 15.00 *(978-1-4357-3392-3(4))* Lulu Enterprises Inc.
Milovidov, Grigoril. Energiia Zhizni V Tvoikh Rukakh: Ezotericheskaia Anatomiia I Fiziologiia Cheloveka, Znakomstvo S Ezotericheskoi Astrologiei I Khirologiei Mudry. 2008. (RUS., Illus.). v, 315p. pap. *(978-0-9791791-9-8(X))* Seagul Pr.
Minich, Deanna M. Chakra Foods for Optimum Health: A Guide to the Foods That Can Improve Your Energy, Inspire Creative Changes, Open Your Heart, & Heal Body, Mind, & Spirit. 2009. (ENG., Illus.). 288p. pap. 18.95 *(978-1-57324-373-5(6))* Conari Pr.) Red Wheel/Weiser.
—Quantum Supplements: A Complete Guide to the Energy Healing Properties of Vitamins, Minerals, Herbs, & Supplements. 2010. (Conari Wellness Ser.). (ENG., Illus.). 192p. pap. 14.95 *(978-1-57324-420-6(1))* Red Wheel/Weiser.
O'Connell-Miller, Cathleen. Living the Spiral. N/a. 2007. (Illus.). 238p. per. 18.00 *(978-0-9800058-0-6(9))* Miller, Cathleen.
Petty, April. Kundalini Rising: Exploring the Chakra/Asanas Connection. 2007. (Illus.). 166p. per. 14.00 *(978-0-9792703-0-0(6))* Kitsune Bks.
Rados, Ivan. Health: It's All about Consciousness. 2010. (ENG.). 192p. pap. 16.95 *(978-1-897238-43-1(6))* Namaste Publishing, Inc. CAN. Dist: Perseus-PGW.
Redmond, Layne. Chakra Meditation: Transformation Through the Seven Energy Centers of the Body. unabr. ed. 2010. (Illus.). 112p. pap. 15.95 *(978-1-59179-780-7(2))* Sounds True, Inc.
Rippentrop, Betsy & Adamson, Eve. The Complete Idiot's Guide to Chakras. 2009. (Complete Idiot's Guide Ser.). (ENG.). 352p. (gr. 12-18). pap. 17.95 *(978-1-59257-898-6(5),* Alpha Bks.) Penguin Group (USA) Inc.
Ritberger, Carol. What Color Is Your Personality: Red, Orange, Yellow, Green... 2009. (ENG.). 150p. pap. 12.95 *(978-1-4019-2414-0(X))* Hay Hse., Inc.
Rocher, Olivier. Mandalas to Heal Your Chakras: 20 Mandalas to Colour. 2009. 43p. pap. *(978-0-9810260-3-9(6))* Essenia Bks. Publishing.
Salmon, Philip. Dr Bachs Flower Remedies & the Chakras. 3rd ed. 2006. pap. *(978-1-905367-04-7(X))* North Atlantic Bks.
Salmon, Philip & Jeoffroy, Anne. Dr. Bach's Flower Remedies: Tapping into the Positive Emotional Qualities of the Chakras. 3rd ed. 2007. (ENG., Illus.). 128p. pap. 22.95 *(978-1-55643-640-6(6))* North Atlantic Bks.
Saradananda, Swami. Chakra Meditation: Discover Energy, Creativity, Focus, Love, Communication, Wisdom, & Spirit. 2008. (ENG., Illus.). 160p. per. 14.95 *(978-1-84483-495-2(6))* Duncan Baird Pubs. GBR. Dist: Sterling Publishing Co., Inc.
—Chakra Meditations: Meditations, Visualizations & Exercises to Help You Find Energy & Balance. 2010. (ENG., Illus.). 17.95 *(978-1-907486-34-0(8),* Watkins Publishing) Duncan Baird Pubs. GBR. Dist: Sterling Publishing Co., Inc.
—The Essential Guide to Chakras: Discover the Healing Power of Chakras for Mind, Body & Spirit. 2011. (ENG., Illus.). 288p. pap. 14.95 *(978-1-78028-004-2(1),* Watkins Publishing) Duncan Baird Pubs. GBR. Dist: Sterling Publishing Co., Inc.
SashaFenton. Simply Chakras. 2009. (Illus.). 134p. pap. 9.95 *(978-1-903065-62-4(3),* 1297147, Sterling/Zambezi) Sterling Publishing Co., Inc.
Schulz, Mona Lisa. The Intuitive Advisor: A Psychic Doctor Teaches You How to Solve Your Most Pressing Health Problems. 2009. (ENG.). 288p. 25.95 *(978-1-4019-2393-8(3))* Hay Hse., Inc.
Selby, Anna. Total Chakra Energy Plan: The Practical 7-Step Program to Balance & Revitalize. 2009. (ENG., Illus.). 144p. pap. 14.95 *(978-1-84483-855-4(2))* Duncan Baird Pubs. GBR. Dist: Sterling Publishing Co., Inc.
Shephard, Adolphina. Yatuvay the Manual: How to Perform Miraculous Healing Through Energy Medicine. 2009. (Illus.). xiii, 121p. ***(978-1-4401-3874-4(5))***; E-Book ***(978-1-4401-3873-7(7))*** iUniverse, Inc.
Sherwood, Keith. Sex & Transcendence: Enhance Your Relationships Through Meditations, Chakra & Energy Work. 2011. (ENG., Illus.). 336p. pap. 18.95 *(978-0-7387-1340-3(6))* Llewellyn Pubns.
Shurtleff, Mary. Reconnecting Your Spirit: Seeing the Possibilities, 3 bks., Bk.2. 2008. per. 19.95 *(978-0-9770424-8-7(0),* Juniper Pr.
Tadd, Ellen. The Wisdom of the Chakras: Tools for Navigating the Complexity of Life. 2010. *(978-1-59056-175-1(9))* Lantern Bks.
Wauters, Ambika. The Complete Guide to Chakras, Vintage Edition: Unleash the Positive Power Within. 2010. (ENG.). 144p. 16.99 *(978-0-7641-6313-5(2))* Barron's Educational Series, Inc.
—The Healing Power of Angels: How They Guide & Protect Us. 2011. (ENG.). 256p. pap. 14.95 *(978-1-907486-42-5(9),* Watkins Publishing) Duncan Baird Pubs. GBR. Dist: Sterling Publishing Co., Inc.
—Homeopathic Color & Sound Remedies, Rev. 2007. (ENG.). 192p. pap. 14.95 *(978-1-58091-183-2(8))* Ten Speed Pr.
Weteling, Cees. Chakra Cards: Spiritual Guides Towards Inner Harmony. 2009. (ENG.). 1p. 22.95 *(978-90-78302-25-4(9))* Binkey Kok NLD. Dist: Red Wheel/Weiser.
Wright, Susan. Los Chakras en la Practica Chamanica. 2009. (SPA & ENG.). 1p. pap. 16.95 *(978-1-59477-279-5(7))* Inner Traditions International, Ltd.
Wright, Susan J. The Chakras in Shamanic Practice: Eight Stages of Healing & Transformation. 2007. (ENG., Illus.). 1p. per. 18.95 *(978-1-59477-184-2(7),* Destiny Bks.) Inner Traditions International, Ltd.

CHALCEDON, COUNCIL OF, 451

Meinhardt, Birgitta. Fanatiker Oder Heilige? Frühchristliche Mönche und das Konzil Zu Chalkedon. 2011. (Europäische Hochschulschriften. Reihe 23: Theologie Ser.). (GER.). 370p. pap. 90.95 *(978-3-631-59935-8(8))* Lang, Peter GmbH, Europäischer Verlag der Wissenschaften DEU. Dist: Lang, Peter.
Price, Richard & Whitby, Mary, eds. Chalcedon in Context: Church Councils 400-700. 2011. (Liverpool University Press - Translated Texts for Historians Ser.). (ENG.). 256p. pap. 34.95 *(978-1-84631-648-7(0))* Liverpool Univ. Pr. GBR. Dist: Chicago Distribution Ctr.
Sarkissian, Karekin. The Council of Chalcedon & the Armenian Church: With Maps. (Orthodoxies & Heresies in the Early Church Ser.). (Illus.). reprint ed. 41.50 *(978-0-404-62393-7(X))* AMS Pr., Inc.

CHALCOGENIDES

Bouroushian, Mirtat. Electrochemistry of Metal Chalcogenides. 2010. (Monographs in Electrochemistry Ser.). (ENG., Illus.). xii, 358p. 199.00 *(978-3-642-03966-9(9),* 3642039669) Springer.
Capper, Peter & Garland, James, eds. Mercury Cadmium Telluride: Growth, Properties & Applications. 11th ed. 2010. (Wiley Series in Materials for Electronic & Optoelectronic Applications Ser.: 33). (ENG., Illus.). 590p. 260.00 *(978-0-470-69706-1(7),* Wiley) Wiley, John & Sons, Inc.
Devillanova, F. A. Handbook of Chalcogen Chemistry: New Perspectives in Sulfur, Selenium & Tellurium. 2006. (ENG., Illus.). 894p. 480.00 *(978-0-85404-366-8(7))* Royal Society of Chemistry, The GBR. Dist: Ingram Pub. Services.
Hilton, A. Ray. Chalcogenide Glasses for Infrared Optics. 2009. (ENG., Illus.). 304p. 150.00 *(978-0-07-159697-8(6),* 0071596976) McGraw-Hill Professional Publishing.
Kato, Shinzi. Chalcogenocarboxylic Acid Derivatives. 2010. (Topics in Current Chemistry Ser.). (Illus.). x, 280p. pap. 349.00 *(978-3-642-06193-6(1),* 3642061931) Springer.
Kolobov, Alexander V. & Tominaga, Junji. Chalcogenides: Metastability & Phase Change Phenomena. 2012. (Springer Series in Materials Science Ser.: 164). (ENG., Illus.). xvi, 284p. 129.00 ***(978-3-642-28704-6(2),*** 3642287042) Springer.
Mikla, Victor I. & Mikla, Victor V. Amorphous Chalcogenides: The Past, Present & Future. 2011. (ENG.). 172p. 140.00 ***(978-0-12-388429-9(2))*** Elsevier Science & Technology Bks.
Mikla, Victor I. & Mikla, Victor V. Metastable States in Amorphous Chalcogenide Semiconductors. 2009. (Springer Series in Materials Science Ser.). (ENG., Illus.). xii, 122p. 129.00 *(978-3-642-02744-4(X),* 364202744X) Springer.
Tanaka, Keiji & Shimakawa, Koichi. Amorphous Chalcogenide Semiconductors & Related Materials. 2011. (ENG., Illus.). xv, 242p. 129.00 *(978-1-4419-9509-4(9),* 1441995099) Springer.
Zakery, A. & Elliott, S. R. Optical Nonlinearities in Chalcogenide Glasses & Their Applications. 2007. (Springer Series in Optical Sciences Ser.). (Illus.). 199p. 189.00 *(978-3-540-71066-0(3))* Springer.
—Optical Nonlinearities in Chalcogenide Glasses & their Applications. 2010. (Springer Series in Optical Sciences Ser.). (Illus.). x, 202p. pap. 189.00 *(978-3-642-09013-4(3),* 3642090133) Springer.

CHALDEAN CHURCH

see Nestorian Church

CHALDEAN LANGUAGE

see Aramaic Language

CHALIAPIN, FEODOR IVANOVICH, 1873-1893

Darsky, Joseph. Tsar Feodor: Chaliapin in America. 2012. ***(978-1-62100-413-4(9))*** Nova Science Pubs., Inc.

CHALICES

see also Grail

Grutz, Robert. Late Bronze & Iron Age Chalices in Canaan & Ancient Israel. 2007. (Bar S Ser.). (ENG., Illus.). 240p. (C). pap. 90.00 *(978-1-4073-0106-8(3))* British Archaeological Reports Ltd. GBR. Dist: Brown, David Bk. Co., The.
Silver, Vernon. The Lost Chalice: The Real-Life Chase for One of the World's Rarest Masterpieces - A Priceless 2,500-Year-Old Artifact Depicting the Fall of Troy. 352p. 2010. (ENG.). pap. 14.99 *(978-0-06-155829-0(X),* Harper Paperbacks) 2009. 26.99 *(978-0-06-155828-3(1),* Morrow, William & Co.) HarperCollins Pubs.

CHALICOSIS

see Lungs—Dust Diseases

CHALK FIGURES

see Hill Figures

CHALK-TALKS

Griswold, B. J. Crayon & Character: Truth Made Clear Through Eye & Ear or Ten-Minute Walks with Colored Chalks. 2007. (ENG.). 244p. pap. 20.99 *(978-1-4346-0012-7(2))*; 278p. pap. 23.99 *(978-1-4346-0097-4(1))* BiblioBazaar.

CHALLENGER (SPACECRAFT)

Evans, Ben. Space Shuttle Challenger: Ten Journeys into the Unknown. 2007. (Springer Praxis Books / Space Exploration Ser.). (Illus.). 290p. per. 39.95 *(978-0-387-46355-1(0),* 0387463550) Springer.
Mahler, Julianne G., et al. Organizational Learning at NASA: The Challenger & the Columbia Accidents. 2009. (Public Management & Change Ser.). (ENG., Illus.). 256p. pap. 29.95 *(978-1-58901-266-0(6))* Georgetown Univ. Pr.
McDonald, Allan J. & Hansen, James R. Truth, Lies, & O-Rings: Inside the Space Shuttle Challenger Disaster. 2009. (ENG., Illus.). 576p. 39.95 *(978-0-8130-3326-6(8))* Univ. Pr. of Florida.

CHALLENGER AUTOMOBILE

Grist, Peter. Dodge Challenger Plymouth Barracuda: Chrysler's Potent Pony Cars. 2009. (ENG., Illus.). 196p. 59.95 *(978-1-84584-105-8(0),* 1845841050) Veloce Publishing Ltd. GBR. Dist: MBI Distribution Services/Quayside Distribution.
Schild, Jim. Challenger & Barracuda, 1970-74. 2010. (Collector's Originality Guide Ser.). (ENG., Illus.). 128p. pap. 24.99 *(978-0-7603-3788-2(8),* 0760337888, Motorbooks) MBI Publishing Co. LLC.

CHAMBER MUSIC

see also Ensemble Playing

Alfred Publishing, ed. Expanding Horizons: The Suzuki-Trained Violinist Grows Up. 2008. (ENG.). 152p. pap. 19.95 *(978-0-7390-5109-2(1))* Alfred Publishing Co., Inc.
Bashford, Christina. The Pursuit of High Culture: John Ella & Chamber Music in Victorian London. 2007. (Music in Britain, 1600-1900 Ser.: Volume 3). (Illus.). 424p. 90.00 *(978-1-84383-298-0(4),* Boydell Press) Boydell & Brewer, Ltd. GBR. Dist: Boydell & Brewer, Inc.
Carter, Elliott. Clarinet Quintet: For Clarinet in B-Flat & String Quartet Score & Parts. 2009. (ENG.). 108p. pap. 40.00 *(978-1-4234-8430-1(4),* 1423484304) Boosey & Hawkes, Inc.
Christensen, James. Chamber Music. 2008. (ENG.). 288p. per. 24.95 *(978-0-8126-9627-1(1))* Open Court Publishing Co.
Clementi, Muzio. Sonata for Fortepiano, Violin & Cello, Op. 27, Op. 27, No. 1. Brendler, Charlene, ed. (Classical Music Ser.: Vol. 2). ii, 39p. pap. *(978-1-56571-157-0(2),* CL002) PRB Productions.
Cobbett, Walter Willson. Cobbett's Cyclopedic Survey of Chamber Music, 2 vols. 2009. (Illus.). 612p. pap. *(978-1-906857-82-0(2))*; 660p. pap. *(978-1-906857-84-4(9))* Travis & Emery Music Bookshop.
Crookshank, Suzanne. Chamber Music of Eric Mandat. 2008. 80p. pap. *(978-3-639-04003-6(1))* VDM Verlag Dr. Mueller e.K.
Cyr, Mary. Essays on the Performance of Baroque Music: Opera & Chamber Music in France & England. 2008. (Variorum Collected Studies). (Illus.). 344p. 165.00 *(978-0-7546-5926-6(7))* Ashgate Publishing Co.
Ferguson, Donald N. Image & Structure in Chamber Music. 2009. (ENG.). 350p. pap. 60.00 *(978-0-8166-6045-2(X))* Univ. of Minnesota Pr.
Frescobaldi, Girolamo. D'Arie Musicali per Cantarsi Primo Libro & Secondo Libro [Facsimiles of the 1630 Editions] 2009. 92p. pap. *(978-1-904331-96-4(3))* Travis & Emery Music Bookshop.
Hal Leonard Corp., creator. Horn Chamber Music: The Ultimate Collection. 2011. (ENG.). 8p. pap. 19.95 ***(978-1-4584-1415-1(9),*** 1458414159) Leonard, Hal Corp.
Harlow, Martin. Mozart's Chamber Music with Keyboard. 2012. (ENG., Illus.). 300p. 99.00 ***(978-1-107-00248-7(6))*** Cambridge Univ. Pr.
Kammermusik No. 2 Op. 36 No. 1 (Chamber Music No. 1) Eulenburg Study Score. 2010. 98p. pap. 21.95 *(978-3-7957-7195-9(1),* 3795771951) Schott Musik International GmbH & Co. KG DEU. Dist: Leonard, Hal Corp.
Keller, James M. Chamber Music: A Listener's Guide, 1 vol. 2010. (ENG.). 576p. 39.95 *(978-0-19-538253-2(6))* Oxford Univ. Pr., Inc.
Kreuzer, Gundula, ed. & intro. Chamber Music. 2011. (Works of Giuseppe Verdi, Series V: Chamber Music Ser.). (ENG., Illus.). 120p. 115.00 *(978-0-226-85301-7(2))* Univ. of Chicago Pr.
Lederer, Victor. Beethoven's Chamber Music: Unlocking the Masters Series. 2012. (ENG.). 180p. pap. 22.99 incl. audio compact disk ***(978-1-57467-203-9(7),*** 1574672037, Amadeus Press) Leonard, Hal Corp.
Mirka, Danuta. Metric Manipulations in Haydn & Mozart: Chamber Music for Strings, 1787-1791. 2009. (Oxford Studies in Music Theory Ser.). (ENG., Illus.). 352p. 55.00 *(978-0-19-538492-5(X))* Oxford Univ. Pr., Inc.
Radice, Mark A. Chamber Music: An Essential History. 2012. E-Book ***(978-0-472-02811-5(1))***; (ENG.). 384p. (C). 90.00 ***(978-0-472-07165-4(3))***; (ENG.). 384p. (C). pap. 40.00 ***(978-0-472-05165-6(2))*** Univ. of Michigan Pr.
Reich, Steve. Double Sextet: Study Score. 2011. (ENG.). 232p. pap. 40.00 *(978-1-61780-724-4(9),* 1617807249) Boosey & Hawkes, Inc.
Sourek, Otakar. The Chamber Music of Antonin Dvorak. 2010. (ENG.). 192p. pap. 23.75 *(978-1-176-53897-9(7))* BiblioBazaar.
—The Chamber Music of Antonin Dvorak. 2010. 78p. pap. *(978-1-151-96143-3(4))* Books LLC.
Watson, Angus. Beethoven's Chamber Music in Context. 2012. (Illus.). 318p. pap. 29.95 ***(978-1-84383-716-9(1),*** Boydell Press) Boydell & Brewer, Ltd. GBR. Dist: Boydell & Brewer, Inc.
Wright, James K. & Gillmor, Alan M., eds. Schoenberg's Chamber Music, Schoenberg's World. 2009. (ENG.). 272p. pap. 54.00 *(978-1-57647-130-2(6))* Pendragon Pr.
Zajicek, Daniel. A Rhetorical Guide to Ebb. 2010. 56p. pap. *(978-3-639-19121-9(8))* VDM Verlag Dr. Mueller e.K.

CHAMBER MUSIC—BIBLIOGRAPHY

Ashbee, Andrew, et al. The Viola Da Gamba Society Index of Manuscripts Containing Consort Music, Vol. 2. 2008. (Illus.). 436p. 144.95 *(978-0-7546-5866-5(X))* Ashgate Publishing Co.
Baron, John H. Chamber Music. 3rd ed. 2010. 784p. 150.00 *(978-0-415-99418-7(7))* Routledge.
Meyer, Dirk. Chamber Orchestra & Ensemble Repertoire: A Catalog of Modern Music. 2011. (Music Finders Ser.). (ENG.). 444p. 75.00 *(978-0-8108-7731-3(7))* Scarecrow Pr., Inc.

CHAMBERED NAUTILUS

see Nautilus

CHAMBERLAIN, DANIEL HENRY, 1835-1907

West, Jerry L. The Bloody South Carolina Election Of 1876: Wade Hampton III, the Red Shirt Campaign for Governor & the End of Reconstruction. 2010. (ENG., Illus.). 222p. pap. 35.00 *(978-0-7864-4889-0(X))* McFarland & Co., Inc. Pubs.

CHAMBERLAIN, JOHN, 1927-

Stockebrand, Marianne, ed. John Chamberlain: The Foam Sculptures, 1 vol. 2008. (ENG., Illus.). 200p. 35.00 *(978-1-60461-370-4(X))* Chinati Foundation, The.

CHAMBERLAIN, JOSEPH, 1836-1914

Crosby, Travis L. Joseph Chamberlain: A Most Radical Imperialist. 2011. (ENG., Illus.). 336p. 99.00 *(978-1-84885-753-7(5))* I. B. Tauris & Co., Ltd. GBR. Dist: Macmillan.
Drake, Peter. Birmingham & the Chamberlains. 2007. (Images of England Ser.). (ENG.). 128p. pap. 29.95 *(978-0-7524-4492-5(1))* History Pr. Ltd., The GBR. Dist: Independent Pubs. Group.
Marsh, Peter T. The Chamberlain Litany: Letters Within a Governing Family from Empire to Appeasement. 2010. (ENG., Illus.). 350p. 30.00 *(978-1-906598-63-1(0))* Haus Publishing GBR. Dist: Consortium Bk. Sales & Distribution.

CHAMBERLAIN, JOSHUA LAWRENCE, 1828-1914

Chamberlain Corp. Staff. A Sketch, the Original 1905 Biography of Joshua Lawerence Chamberlain. Date not set. (Illus.). 70p. *(978-0-9649433-1-5(X))* NPS.
Chamberlain, Joshua Lawrence. The Passing of the Armies: An Account of the Final Campaign of the Army of the Potomac. 392p. reprint ed. 98.00 *(978-0-7222-8178-9(1))* Library Reprints, Inc.
Desjardin, Thomas & National Civil War Museum Staff. Joshua Chamberlain: The Life in Letters of a Great Leader of the American Civil War. 2012. (ENG., Illus.). 336p. 25.95 ***(978-1-84908-559-5(5))*** Osprey Publishing, Ltd. GBR. Dist: Random Hse., Inc.
Nesbitt, Mark. Through Blood & Fire: Selected Civil War Papers of Major General Joshua Chamberlain. 2011. (ENG., Illus.). 240p. pap. 16.95 ***(978-0-8117-3129-4(4))*** Stackpole Bks.

CHAMBERLAIN, NEVILLE, 1869-1940

James, Michael F. Neville Chamberlain's Domestic Policies: Social Reform, Tariffs & Financial Orthodoxy. 2010. (Illus.). xxiv, 259p. 119.95 *(978-0-7734-3642-8(1))* Mellen, Edwin Pr., The.
Macklin, Graham. Chamberlain. 2006. (British Prime Ministers of the 20th Century Ser.). (ENG., Illus.). 176p. pap. 16.95 *(978-1-904950-62-2(0))* Haus Publishing GBR. Dist: Consortium Bk. Sales & Distribution.
Olson, Lynne. Troublesome Young Men: The Rebels Who Brought Churchill to Power & Helped Save England. 2008. (ENG., Illus.). 448p. pap. 17.00 *(978-0-374-53133-1(1))* Farrar, Straus & Giroux.
Smart, Nick. Neville Chamberlain. 2009. (Routledge Historical Biographies Ser.). (ENG., Illus.). 328p. 90.00 *(978-0-415-36797-4(2))* Routledge.

C

Smart, Nick & Smart, Nick D. Neville Chamberlain. 2009. (Routledge Historical Biographies Ser.). (ENG., Illus.). 314p. pap. 27.95 *(978-0-415-45865-8(X))* Routledge.

Stedman, Andrew David. Alternatives to Appeasement: Neville Chamberlain & Hitler's Germany. 2011. (International Library of Twentieth Century History Ser.). (ENG.). 320p. 99.00 *(978-1-84885-377-5(7),* Tauris Academic Studies) I. B. Tauris & Co., Ltd. GBR. Dist: Macmillan.

CHAMBERLAIN, WILT, 1936-1999

Lynch, Wayne. Season of the 76ers: The Story of Wilt Chamberlain & the 1967 NBA Champion Philadelphia 76ers. Date not set. pap. *(978-0-312-30309-9(2),* St. Martin's Griffin) St. Martin's Pr.

Pomerantz, Gary M. Wilt 1962: The Night of 100 Points & the Dawn of a New Era. 2008. (ENG.). 267p. 25.00 *(978-1-4379-5129-5(5))* DIANE Publishing Co.

Taylor, John. The Rivalry: Bill Russell, Wilt Chamberlain, & the Golden Age of Basketball. annot. ed. 2006. (ENG.). 432p. pap. 17.00 *(978-0-8129-7030-2(6),* Ballantine Bks.) Random House Publishing Group.

CHAMBERLAIN FAMILY

Chamberlain, Dennis D. Run Chamberlain, Run! Solving the 200-year-old Mystery of Runaway Pond. 2010. pap. 12.95 *(978-0-578-05615-9(1))* Mount Olympus Publishing Co.

Gross, Philip H. Trains, Plains, & Pioneers: A Personalized History of Migration to the Great Plains During America's Railroad ERA. 2009. (Illus.). vii, 563p. pap. *(978-983-43084-1-4(8))* AP Publications.

Marsh, Peter T. The Chamberlain Litany: Letters Within a Governing Family from Empire to Appeasement. 2010. (ENG., Illus.). 350p. 30.00 *(978-1-906598-63-1(0))* Haus Publishing GBR. Dist: Consortium Bk. Sales & Distribution.

CHAMBERS, OSWALD, 1874-1917

Ann, Froelichm Mary & Chambers, Oswald. Hope: A Holy Promise. 2009. (ENG.). 176p. 12.99 *(978-1-57293-308-8(9))* Discovery Hse. Pubs.

Braddock, Thomas. A Study Guide for Oswald Chambers' My Utmost for His Highest. 2006. 544p. per. 31.99 *(978-1-4141-0527-7(4))* Pleasant Word.

Christian, Martha. Searching for Mrs. Oswald Chambers: One Woman's Quest to Uncover the Truth about the Woman Behind the Most Celebrated Devotional of All Time. 2008. (ENG.). 184p. pap. 12.99 *(978-1-4143-2332-9(8))* Tyndale Hse. Pubs.

McCasland, David & Chambers, Oswald. The Quotable Oswald Chambers. 2008. (ENG., Illus.). 352p. 19.99 *(978-1-57293-194-7(9))* Discovery Hse. Pubs.

Robinson, Haddon W. & Chambers, Oswald. My Utmost for His Highest. 2008. (Oswald chambers Library). (ENG.). 416p. pap. 14.99 *(978-1-57293-310-1(0))* Discovery Hse. Pubs.

CHAMBERS, ROBERT, 1802-1871

Clyne, Norval. The Romantic Scottish Ballads & the Lady Wardlaw Heresy. 2009. 52p. pap. 15.75 *(978-1-116-88881-2(5));* pap. 16.75 *(978-1-116-88880-5(7))* BiblioBazaar.

—The Romantic Scottish Ballads & the Lady Wardlaw Heresy. 2009. 54p. pap. 9.19 *(978-0-217-72789-1(1))* General Bks. LLC.

—The Romantic Scottish Ballads & the Lady Wardlaw Heresy. 2009. 48p. pap. 15.95 *(978-1-104-32691-3(4))* Kessinger Publishing, LLC.

Fyfe, Aileen. Steam-Powered Knowledge: William Chambers & the Business of Publishing, 1820-1860. 2012. (ENG., Illus.). 336p. 50.00 ***(978-0-226-27651-9(1))*** Univ. of Chicago Pr.

Walker, James Barr. The God Revealed in the Process of Creation, & by the Manifestation of Jesus Christ; Including an Examination of the Development Theory Contained In. 2006. 296p. per. 23.99 *(978-1-4255-2744-0(2))* MPublishing.

CHAMBERS, WHITTAKER, 1901-1961

Cook, Fred J. The Unfinished Story of Alger Hiss. 2011. 192p. 42.95 *(978-1-258-10590-7(X))* Literary Licensing, LLC.

Kimmage, Michael & Kimmage, M. The Conservative Turn: Lionel Trilling, Whittaker Chambers, & the Lessons of Anti-Communism. 2009. (Harvard Historical Studies: 165). 440p. 47.50 *(978-0-674-03258-3(6))* Harvard Univ. Pr.

Reinsch, Richard M., II. Whittaker Chambers: The Spirit of a Counterrevolutionary. 2010. (Library Modern Thinkers Ser.). (ENG.). 224p. 24.95 *(978-1-935191-52-0(7))* ISI Bks.

CHAMBERS COUNTY (TEX.)

Ladd, Kevin. Monroe City- the Town Oil Built. 2011. (Illus.). 336p. 30.00 ***(978-0-9822899-7-6(9))*** Kemp & Co.

CHAMBERS OF COMMERCE

see Boards of Trade

CHAMBORD, HENRI CHARLES FERDINAND MARIE DIEUDONNE D'ARTOIS, COMTE DE, 1820-1883

Sala, George Augustus. The Story of the Comte de Chambord: a Trilogy. 2007. (ENG.). 112p. per. 19.95 *(978-1-4304-4227-1(1))* Kessinger Publishing, LLC.

CHAMBORD (CHATEAU)

Chateau of Chambord. 48p. pap. *(978-88-7009-966-9(0))* Casa Editrice Bonechi.

CHAMELEONS

Ferguson, Gary, et al. Chameleons: Care & Breeding of Jackson's, Panther, Veiled, & Parson's. 2007. (Herpetocultural Library). (ENG., Illus.). 148p. per. 12.95 *(978-1-882770-95-3(1))* BowTie Pr.

LeBerre, Jacques, et al. The Chameleon Handbook. 3rd rev. ed. 2009. (Barron's Pet Handbooks Ser.). (ENG., Illus.). 168p. pap. 12.99 *(978-0-7641-4142-3(2))* Barron's Educational Series, Inc.

Lovein, Mary L. Chameleons in the Garden: Being Jackson's, Doing What Jackson's Do. 2007. 112p. 34.95 *(978-0-615-16926-2(0))* Lovein Corp.

Mattison, Christopher & Garbutt, Nick. Chameleons. 2012. (ENG., Illus.). 112p. 29.95 ***(978-1-77085-121-4(6))*** Firefly Bks., Ltd.

Tolley, Krystal & Burger, Marius. Chameleons of Southern Africa. 2007. (Illus.). 100p. pap. 18.95 *(978-1-77007-375-3(2))* Struik Pubs. ZAF. Dist: International Publishers Marketing.

CHAMORRO (MICRONESIAN PEOPLE)

Aguon, Julian. Fire This Time Essays on Life under Us O. 2006. 128p. per. *(978-4-902837-11-7(0))* Aoishima Kenkyusha.

Camacho, Keith L. Cultures of Commemoration: The Politics of War, Memory, & History in the Mariana Islands. 2011. 52.00 *(978-0-8248-3546-0(8))* Univ. of Hawaii Pr.

Diaz, Vicente M. Repositioning the Missionary: Rewriting the Histories of Colonialism, Native Catholicism, & Indigeneity in Guam. 2010. 264p. 60.00 *(978-0-8248-3434-0(8));* pap. 24.00 *(978-0-8248-3435-7(6))* Univ. of Hawaii Pr.

Goetzfridt, Nicholas J. Guahan: A Bibliographic History. 2011. (Illus.). xix, 617p. 55.00 *(978-0-8248-3481-4(X))* Univ. of Hawaii Pr.

CHAMORRO LANGUAGE

Icon Group International, Inc. Staff, compiled by. Webster's Chamorro - English Thesaurus Dictionary. 2008. 166p. ring bd. 28.95 incl. audio compact disk *(978-0-497-83465-4(0))* Icon Group International, Inc.

CHAMORROS

see Chamorro (Micronesian People)

CHAMPAGNE (WINE)

Brown, Jared McDaniel & Miller, Anistatia Renard. Champagne Cocktails. 2010. 136p. pap. *(978-1-907434-16-7(X))* Mixellany, Ltd.

Bull, Donald A. & Paradi, Joseph C. Champagne Collectibles. 2011. (Illus.). 336p. *(978-0-7643-3721-5(1))* Schiffer Publishing, Ltd.

Charters, Steve, ed. The Contemporary Business of Champagne. 2011. (Routledge Studies of Gastronomy, Food & Drink Ser.). (ENG., Illus.). 240p. (C). 135.00 *(978-0-415-59440-0(5))* Routledge.

Edwards, Michael. The Finest Wines of Champagne: A Guide to the Best Cuvées, Houses, & Growers. 2009. (World's Finest Wines Ser.). (Illus.). 320p. pap. 39.95 *(978-0-520-25940-9(8))* Univ. of California Pr.

Epstein, Becky Sue. Champagne: A Global History. 2011. (Reaktion Books - Edible Ser.). (Illus.). 136p. 17.00 *(978-1-86189-857-9(6))* Reaktion Bks., Ltd. GBR. Dist: Chicago Distribution Ctr.

Guy, Kolleen M. When Champagne Became French: Wine & the Making of a National Identity. 2007. (Johns Hopkins University Studies in Historical & Political Science Ser.: 121). (ENG., Illus.). 280p. (gr. 17). per. 28.00 *(978-0-8018-8747-5(X))* Johns Hopkins Univ. Pr.

Haasarud, Kim. 101 Champagne Cocktails. 2008. (ENG., Illus.). 128p. 16.95 *(978-0-470-16942-1(7),* Wiley) Wiley, John & Sons, Inc.

Juhlin, Richard. Champagne Guide. 2008. (ENG.). 460p. pap. 39.95 *(978-91-633-3191-6(8))* Wine Appreciation Guild, Ltd.

Kladstrup, Don & Kladstrup, Petie. Champagne: How the World's Most Glamorous Wine Triumphed over War & Hard Times. 2006. (ENG., Illus.). 320p. pap. 13.99 *(978-0-06-073793-1(X),* HarperPerennial) HarperCollins Pubs.

Mazzeo, Tilar. The Widow Clicquot: The Story of a Champagne Empire & the Woman Who Ruled It. (ENG.). 288p. 2009. pap. 15.99 *(978-0-06-128858-6(6))* 2008. 25.99 *(978-0-06-128856-2(X))* HarperCollins Pubs. (Collins).

Steidl, Gerhard, ed. I'M Drinking Stars: Dom Pérignon - A History of Champagne, 1 vol. 2009. (ENG., Illus.). 140p. 34.00 *(978-3-86521-750-9(8))* Steidl, Gerhard Druckerei und Verlag DEU. Dist: Innovative Logistics.

Sutcliffe, Serena, et al. The Art of Vintage: An Aesthetic Odyssey Through 20 Vintage Perrier-Jouët Champagnes. 2009. (ENG., Illus.). 400p. 75.00 *(978-1-906417-34-5(2))* Aurum Pr., Ltd. GBR. Dist: Independent Pubs. Group.

Vedrenne, Elisabeth. Veuve Clicquot: Yellow. 2007. (ENG., Illus.). 63p. 25.00 *(978-2-7594-0253-3(3))* Assouline FRA. Dist: Perseus Distribution.

CHAMPIGNONS

see Mushrooms

CHAMPLAIN, SAMUEL DE, 1567-1635

Champlain, Samuel de. Samuel de Champlain: Founder of New France: A Brief History with Documents. Brunelle, Gayle, ed. 2012. (ENG.). 160p. (C). pap. 15.95 ***(978-0-312-59263-9(9))*** Bedford/Saint Martin's.

—The Voyages & Explorations of Samuel de Champlain, 1604-1616: Narrated by Himself, 2 vol., set. (Trail Makers Ser.). reprint ed. 250.00 *(978-0-7222-6430-0(5))* Library Reprints, Inc.

—Voyages of Samuel de Champlain. 2008. 212p. 24.99 *(978-0-554-33085-3(7));* 300p. 25.99 *(978-0-554-33034-1(2));* 300p. 28.99 *(978-0-554-23731-2(8));* 212p. 27.99 *(978-0-554-23782-4(2))* BiblioBazaar.

—Voyages of Samuel de Champlain. 2009. 160p. pap. *(978-0-217-30358-3(7))* Books LLC.

—Voyages of Samuel de Champlain, Volume 1. 2007. 254p. pap. 21.99 *(978-1-4264-4964-2(X));* (ENG.). 298p. pap. 23.99 *(978-1-4264-5265-9(9))* BiblioBazaar.

—Voyages of Samuel de Champlain, Volume 2. 2006. (ENG.). 238p. pap. 20.99 *(978-1-4264-4989-5(5));* 276p. pap. 23.99 *(978-1-4264-5290-1(X))* BiblioBazaar.

—Voyages of Samuel de Champlain, Volume 3. 2007. (ENG.). 182p. pap. 19.99 *(978-1-4264-5015-0(X));* 208p. pap. 22.99 *(978-1-4264-5316-8(7))* BiblioBazaar.

Champlain, Samuel de & Otis, Charles P. Voyages of Samuel de Champlain. 2008. 280p. 28.99 *(978-0-554-23756-5(3));* 25.99 *(978-0-554-33059-4(8))* BiblioBazaar.

Colby, Charles Willia. Founder of New France A Chronicle of Cha. 2007. pap. *(978-1-4065-1350-9(4))* Dodo Pr.

Colby, Charles William. The Founder of New France: A Chronicle of Champlain. (Chronicles of Canada Ser.). 158p. reprint ed. 88.00 *(978-0-7222-6764-6(9));* 88.00 *(978-0-7222-6432-4(1))* Library Reprints, Inc.

Dionne, Narcisse-Eutrope. Champlain. 2009. 316p. 32.99 *(978-1-115-24084-0(6));* 36.99 *(978-1-115-24085-7(4));* pap. 30.75 *(978-1-115-24082-6(X))* BiblioBazaar.

—Champlain. 2009. 198p. pap. *(978-0-217-45641-8(3))* Books LLC.

—Champlain. (Makers of Canada Ser.). 299p. reprint ed. 98.00 *(978-0-7222-6433-1(X));* 98.00 *(978-0-7222-6901-5(3))* Library Reprints, Inc.

Dix, Edwin Asa. Champlain: The Founder of New France. (Appleton's Historic Lives Ser.). 246p. reprint ed. 98.00 *(978-0-7222-6434-8(8))* Library Reprints, Inc.

—Champlain the Founder of New France. 2009. 272p. 30.99 *(978-1-113-64777-1(9));* 34.99 *(978-1-113-64779-5(5));* pap. 27.75 *(978-1-113-64776-4(0));* pap. 26.75 *(978-1-113-64774-0(4))* BiblioBazaar.

—Champlain the Founder of New France. 2007. (ENG.). 268p. 42.95 *(978-0-548-02176-7(7))* Kessinger Publishing, LLC.

Fischer, David Hackett. Champlain's Dream. 2009. (ENG., Illus.). 848p. pap. 18.99 *(978-1-4165-9333-1(0))* Simon & Schuster.

Ganong, William F. Champlain's Island: An Expanded Edition of Ste. Croix (Dochet) Island. exp. ed. (Illus.). 172p. pap. 16.95 *(978-0-919326-57-6(9))* New Brunswick Museum CAN. Dist: Goose Lane Editions.

Heidenreich, Conrad. Samuel de Champlain Before 1604: Des Sauvages & other Documents Related to the Period. Ritch, K. Janet, ed. 2010. (FRE & ENG.). 526p. (C). *(978-0-7735-3757-6(0))* McGill-Queen's Univ. Pr.

Larson, Denise. Companions of Champlain: Founding Families of Quebec, 1608-1635. 2008. pap. 22.95 *(978-0-8063-5367-8(8))* Clearfield Co.

Parkman, Francis. Pioneers of France in the New World. (France & England in North America Ser.: Pt. 1). 2010. 520p. pap. 39.75 *(978-1-146-36349-5(4))* 2010. 512p. reprint ed. pap. 39.75 *(978-1-146-70038-2(5))* 2010. 516p. reprint ed. pap. 39.75 *(978-1-145-39682-1(8))* 2010. 470p. reprint ed. pap. 37.75 *(978-1-142-25680-7(4))* 2010. 472p. reprint ed. pap. 37.75 *(978-1-142-39877-4(3))* 2010. 532p. reprint ed. pap. 40.75 *(978-1-141-97657-7(9))* 2010. 508p. reprint ed. pap. 39.75 *(978-1-142-79714-0(7))* 2010. 518p. reprint ed. pap. 39.75 *(978-1-143-10500-5(1))* 2010. 466p. reprint ed. pap. 37.75 *(978-1-142-42483-1(9))* 2010. 516p. reprint ed. pap. 39.75 *(978-1-142-64233-4(X))* 2009. 504p. reprint ed. 43.99 *(978-1-115-61653-9(6))* 2009. 504p. reprint ed. pap. 38.75 *(978-1-115-61654-6(4))* 2009. 502p. reprint ed. pap. 30.99 *(978-1-115-61655-3(2),* BiblioLife) 2009. 502p. reprint ed. pap. 31.99 *(978-1-116-49360-3(8),* BiblioLife) 2009. 502p. reprint ed. pap. 30.99 *(978-1-116-49361-0(6),* BiblioLife) BiblioBazaar.

—Pioneers of France in the New World. 2010. (France & England in North America: Pt. 1). 240p. reprint ed. pap. *(978-1-151-78292-2(0))* Books LLC.

—Pioneers of France in the New World. 2008. (France & England in North America Ser.: Pt. 1). 200p. reprint ed. pap. *(978-1-4068-6539-4(7))* Echo Library.

—Pioneers of France in the New World. (France & England in North America Ser.: Pt. 1). reprint ed. 2010. (Illus.). 176p. pap. 26.16 *(978-1-153-67771-4(7))* 2010. 158p. pap. 26.16 *(978-1-153-08880-0(0))* 2010. 116p. pap. 26.16 *(978-1-153-08877-0(0))* 2009. 254p. pap. 33.49 *(978-1-151-09344-8(0))* General Bks. LLC.

—Pioneers of France in the New World. (France & England in North America Ser.: Pt. 1). reprint ed. 2009. 460p. pap. 37.95 *(978-1-120-33674-3(0))* 2007. 536p. 57.95 *(978-0-548-10298-5(8))* Kessinger Publishing, LLC.

—Pioneers of France in the New World (Webster's French Thesaurus Edition) 2008. (France & England in North America Ser.: Pt. 1). 349p. pap. 28.95 *(978-0-497-96611-9(5))* Icon Group International, Inc.

—Pioneers of France in the New World (Webster's Korean Thesaurus Edition) 2008. (France & England in North America Ser.: Pt. 1). (KOR & ENG.). 351p. pap. 28.95 *(978-0-546-54072-7(4))* Icon Group International, Inc.

—Pioneers of France in the New World (Webster's Spanish Thesaurus Edition) 2008. (France & England in North America Ser.: Pt. 1). (SPA & ENG.). 354p. pap. 28.95 *(978-0-497-99856-1(4))* Icon Group International, Inc.

Thompson, Don & Thompson, Carol. Seeking the Northwest Passage: The Explorations & Discoveries of Champlain & Hudson. 2008. (Illus.). 88p. (J). pap. 8.50 *(978-1-930098-90-9(1))* Purple Mountain Pr., Ltd.

CHAMPLAIN, LAKE

Bartholomew, Robert E. The Untold Story of Champ: A Social History of America's Loch Ness Monster. 2012. (Excelsior Editions Ser.). (ENG.). 256p. pap. 24.95 ***(978-1-4384-4484-0(2))*** State Univ. of New York Pr.

Disturnell, John. A Trip Through the Lakes of North America; 2006. 396p. per. 26.99 *(978-1-4255-4257-3(3))* MPublishing.

Foulke, Patricia & Foulke, Robert. Adventure Guide to the Champlain & Hudson River Valleys. (Illus.). 360p. pap. 17.99 *(978-1-58843-345-9(5))* Hunter Publishing, Inc.

Frank, Catherine & Holden, Margaret. A Kayaker's Guide to Lake Champlain: Exploring the New York, Vermont & Quebec Shores. 2009. (Illus.). 320p. pap. 17.95 *(978-1-883789-65-7(6))* Black Dome Pr. Corp.

Lamay, Kimberly J. & Paquette, Celine Racine. Champlain. 2006. (Images of America Ser.). (ENG., Illus.). 128p. pr. 21.99 *(978-0-7385-4547-9(3))* Arcadia Publishing.

Laramie, Michael G. The European Invasion of North America: Colonial Conflict along the Hudson - Champlain Corridor, 1609-1760, 1 vol. 2012. (Illus.). 567p. 58.00 ***(978-0-313-39737-0(6),*** A3558C) Greenwood Publishing Group, Inc.

Manley, Tom, et al. Lake Champlain: Partnerships & Research in the New Millennium. 2010. ix, 411p. pap. 179.00 *(978-1-4419-3449-9(9),* 1441934499) Springer.

Parkman, Francis. Historic Handbook of the Northern Tour: Lakes George & Champlain; Niagara; Montreal; Quebec. 2010. 86p. pap. 20.00 *(978-1-152-29425-7(3))* 2009. 102p. pap. 14.14 *(978-1-151-35189-0(X))* General Bks. LLC.

—Historic Handbook of the Northern Tour: Lakes George & Champlain; Niagara; Montreal; Quebec. 2008. 204p. 39.95 *(978-0-548-97622-7(8))* 2007. 208p. per. 24.95 *(978-0-548-67158-0(3))* Kessinger Publishing, LLC.

Van de Water, Frederic. Lake Champlain & Lake George. (American Lakes Ser.). lib. bdg. 26.95 *(978-0-8488-2038-1(X))* Amereon LTD.

Winslow, Mike. Lake Champlain: A Natural History. 2008. (Illus.). 160p. pap. 18.95 *(978-1-884592-51-5(1))* Images from the Past, Inc.

CHAMPOLLION, JEAN FRANCOIS, 1790-1832

Robinson, Andrew. Cracking the Egyptian Code: The Revolutionary Life of Jean-Francois Champollion. 2012. (ENG., Illus.). 272p. 29.95 ***(978-0-19-991499-9(0))*** Oxford Univ. Pr., Inc.

CHAMSON, ANDRE, 1900-1993

Tame, Peter D. Andre Chamson, 1900-1983 Book 1: The Life of a French Novelist, 2 vols. 2006. 332p. *(978-0-7734-5681-5(3))* Mellen, Edwin Pr., The.

—Andre Chamson, 1900-1983 Book 2: The Life of a French Novelist, 2 vols. 2006. 392p. *(978-0-7734-5683-9(X))* Mellen, Edwin Pr., The.

CHANCE

see also Coincidence; Combinations; Games of Chance (Mathematics); Necessity (Philosophy); Probabilities; Serendipity

Allen, J. Edward. Winning Craps for the Serious Player. 2010. (ENG.). 288p. pap. 16.95 *(978-1-58042-267-3(5))* Cardoza Publishing.

Atlan, Henri. Sparks of Randomness Vol. 1: Spermatic Knowledge. Schramm, Lenn, tr. from FRE. 2010. (Cultural Memory in the Present Ser.). (ENG & HEB.). 352p. 65.00 *(978-0-8047-7357-7(2));* pap. 24.95 *(978-0-8047-6027-0(6))* Stanford Univ. Pr.

Belo, Catarina. Chance & Determinism in Avicenna & Averroes. 2007. 252p. *(978-90-04-15587-9(2))* BRILL.

Bentley, Peter J. Why Sh*t Happens: The Science of a Really Bad Day. 2009. (ENG.). 320p. 16.95 *(978-1-59486-956-3(1))* Rodale Pr., Inc.

Brill, John. The Chance Character of Human Existence. 2011. 158p. 41.95 ***(978-1-258-07008-3(1))*** Literary Licensing, LLC.

Carr, Albert H. Z. How to Attract Good Luck & Make the Most of It in Your Daily Life. 2011. 252p. 46.95 ***(978-1-258-02895-4(6))*** Literary Licensing, LLC.

Cioffari, Vincent. Fortune & Fate from Democritus to St Thomas Aquinas. 2011. 140p. 40.95 ***(978-1-258-03261-6(9))*** Literary Licensing, LLC.

Dudley, John. Aristotle's Concept of Chance: Accidents, Cause, Necessity, & Determinism. 2012. (SUNY series in Ancient Greek Philosophy Ser.). (Illus.). 416p. 95.00 *(978-1-4384-3227-4(5))* State Univ. of New York Pr.

Durschmied, Erik. The Hinge Factor: How Chance & Stupidity Have Changed History. 2011. (ENG.). 416p. pap. 16.95 *(978-1-61145-321-8(6),* 611321, Arcade Publishing) Skyhorse Publishing Co., Inc.

Enzensberger, Hans Magnus. Fatal Numbers: Why Count on Chance. Leeder, Karen, tr. from GER. 2011. (Illus.). 52p. pap. 13.95 *(978-1-935830-01-6(5))* Upper West Side Philosophers, Inc.

Gandy, Oscar. Coming to Terms with Chance: Engaging Rational Discrimination & Cumulative Disadvantage. 2009. 248p. 114.95 *(978-0-7546-7961-5(6))* Ashgate Publishing Co.

Handfield, Toby. A Philosophical Guide to Chance: Physical Probability. 2012. (ENG., Illus.). 264p. 90.00 ***(978-1-107-01378-0(X));*** pap. 29.99 ***(978-1-107-60735-4(3))*** Cambridge Univ. Pr.

Krumboltz, John D. & Levin, Al S. Luck Is No Accident: Making the Most of happenstance in Your Life & Career. 2nd ed. 2010. (Illus.). 176p. pap. 18.95 *(978-1-886230-03-3(X))* Impact Pubs., Inc.

Lurie, Alan J. & Lurie, Alan. Five Minutes on Mondays: Finding Unexpected Purpose, Peace, & Fulfillment at Work. 2009. (ENG.). 288p. 21.99 *(978-0-13-700778-3(7))* FT Press.

Lustig, Richard. Learn How to Increase Your Chances of Winning the Lottery. 2010. 40p. pap. 40.00 *(978-1-4520-7746-8(0))* AuthorHouse.

Makridakis, Spyros, et al. Dance with Chance: Harnessing the Power of Luck. 2009. (ENG.). 336p. 22.95 *(978-1-85168-679-7(7))* Oneworld Pubns. GBR. Dist: National Bk. Network.

Marques de Sa, Joaquim P. Chance: The Life of Games & the Game of Life. 2008. (Illus.). 224p. pap. 29.95 *(978-3-540-74416-0(9),* 3540744169) Springer.

Mele, Alfred R. Free Will & Luck. 2008. (ENG.). 240p. pap. 19.95 *(978-0-19-537439-1(8))* Oxford Univ. Pr., Inc.

Mlodinow, Leonard. The Drunkard's Walk: How Randomness Rules Our Lives. (Vintage Ser.). (ENG., Illus.). 272p. 2009. pap. 15.00 *(978-0-307-27517-2(5),*

Vintage) 2008. 24.95 *(978-0-375-42404-5(0),* Pantheon) Knopf Doubleday Publishing Group.

Ohsawa, Yukio & McBurney, Peter, eds. Chance Discovery. 2010. (Advanced Information Processing Ser.). (Illus.). xvi, 400p. pap. 149.00 *(978-3-642-05609-3(1),* 3642056091) Springer.

Pavé, Alain. On the Origins & Dynamics of Biodiversity: the role of Chance: The role of Chance. 2010. (ENG., Illus.). xviii, 178p. 129.00 *(978-1-4419-6243-0(3),* 1441962433) Springer.

Sampson, Carl. Killer Roulette. 2008. (ENG.). 208p. pap. 19.95 *(978-1-904468-38-7(1))* D & B Publishing GBR. Dist: Globe Pequot Pr., The.

Skyrms, Brian. Choice & Chance. Date not set. (Philosophy Ser.). pap. 4.00 net. *(978-0-8221-6775-4(1))* Wadsworth.

Sternstein, Malynne M. The Will to Chance: Necessity & Arbitrariness in the Czech Avant-Garde from Poetism to Surrealism. 2007. (ENG.). 226p. pap. *(978-0-89357-323-2(X))* Slavica Pubs.

Surprise, Kirby. Synchronicity: The Art of Coincidence, Choice, & Unlocking Your Mind. 2011. E-Book ***(978-1-60163-643-0(1),*** New Page Bks.) Career Pr., Inc.

Taleb, Nassim Nicholas. Fooled by Randomness: The Hidden Role of Chance in Life & in the Markets. 2nd ed. 2008. (ENG.). 368p. 28.00 *(978-1-4000-6793-0(6),* Random House) Random House Publishing Group.

Venn, John. Logic of Chance. 2006. (ENG.). pap. 42.95 *(978-1-4286-6361-9(4))* Kessinger Publishing, LLC.

—The Logic of Chance. 2009. 318p. pap. *(978-0-217-59793-7(9));* 184p. pap. *(978-0-217-62980-5(6))* Books LLC.

—The Logic of Chance. 2006. (Dover Books on Mathematics Ser.). (ENG., Illus.). 544p. per. 34.95 *(978-0-486-45055-1(4))* Dover Pubns., Inc.

—The Logic of Chance. 2009. 318p. pap. 24.02 *(978-1-4589-2857-3(8))* General Bks. LLC.

—The Logic of Chance. 2007. (ENG.). 540p. 57.95 *(978-0-548-14854-9(6))* Kessinger Publishing, LLC.

Wernik, Uri. Chance Action & Therapy: The Playful Way of Changing. 2011. (Health & Human Development (Joav Merrick - Ser. Editor - National Institute of Child Health & Human Development, Ministry of Social Affairs, Jerusalem) Ser.). pap. 43.00 *(978-1-61122-987-5(1))* Nova Science Pubs., Inc.

Wernik, Uri, ed. Chance Action Therapy. the Playful Way of Changing. 2010. (Health & Human Development (Joav Merrick - Series Editor - National Institute of Child Health & Human Development, Ministry of Social Affairs, Jerusalem Ser.). 89.00 *(978-1-60876-393-1(5))* Nova Science Pubs., Inc.

CHANCELLOR, RICHARD, D. 1556

Hakluyt, Richard. The Discovery of Muscovy. 2007. 104p. per. *(978-1-4065-1565-7(5))* Dodo Pr.

—Discovery of Muscovy etc. 2006. pap. *(978-1-84702-508-1(0))* Echo Library.

CHANCELLORSVILLE, BATTLE OF, CHANCELLORSVILLE, VA., 1863

Allan, William & Hotchkiss, Jed. Chancellorsville. (Illus.). 152p. reprint ed. lib. bdg. 88.00 *(978-0-7222-0930-1(4))* Library Reprints, Inc.

Bigelow, John. The Campaign of Chancellorsville: A Strategic & Tactical Study. 2009. 554p. 44.99 *(978-1-115-49274-4(8));* 37.99 *(978-1-115-49275-1(6));* pap. 42.75 *(978-1-115-49276-8(4));* pap. 41.75 *(978-1-115-49277-5(2))* BiblioBazaar.

—The Campaign of Chancellorsville: A Strategic & Tactical Study. 528p. reprint ed. 98.00 *(978-0-7222-8047-8(5))* Library Reprints, Inc.

Bryant, James K. The Chancellorsville Campaign: The Nation's High Water Mark. 2009. (Civil War Sesquicentennial Ser.). (ENG., Illus.). 160p. pap. 19.99 *(978-1-59629-594-0(5))* History Pr., The.

Dalbiac, Philip Hugh. The American War of Secession 1863. reprint ed. 150.00 *(978-0-7222-8026-3(2))* Library Reprints, Inc.

Dodge, Theodore A. The Campaign of Chancellorsville. l.t. ed. 2007. (ENG.). 210p. pap. 22.99 *(978-1-4264-2082-5(X))* BiblioBazaar.

—The Campaign of Chancellorsville: An Overwhelming Confederate Victory that Won the Accolade, 'Lee's Perfect Battle' 2009. 208p. *(978-1-84677-868-1(9));* pap. *(978-1-84677-867-4(0))* Leonaur Ltd.

Doubleday, Abner. Chancellorsville & Gettysburg. 2009. 232p. 23.99 *(978-0-559-09744-7(1));* 27.99 *(978-0-559-09733-1(6));* pap. 25.75 *(978-0-559-09736-2(0));* pap. 24.75 *(978-0-559-09741-6(7))* BiblioBazaar.

—Chancellorsville & Gettysburg. 2007. (ENG.). 272p. 42.95 *(978-0-548-21112-0(4));* per. 27.95 *(978-1-4325-2994-9(3))* Kessinger Publishing, LLC.

—Chancellorsville & Gettysburg. (Campaigns of the Civil War Ser.). 243p. reprint ed. 98.00 *(978-0-7222-8027-0(0))* Library Reprints, Inc.

—Chancellorsville & Gettysburg. 2008. (ENG.). 268p. per. *(978-1-4086-5343-2(5))* Read Bks.

—Chancellorsville & Gettysburg: A View of the Campaign by the Commander of the Washington Defences. 2009. 196p. *(978-1-84677-870-4(0));* pap. *(978-1-84677-869-8(7))* Leonaur Ltd.

—Chancellorsville & Gettysburg: An Eyewitness Account of the Pivotal Battles of the Civil War. 2009. 232p. pap. *(978-1-934941-69-0(7))* Red & Black Pubs.

Gallagher, Gary W., ed. Chancellorsville: The Battle & Its Aftermath. 2009. (Civil War America Ser.). (ENG., Illus.). 288p. pap. 20.95 *(978-0-8078-5970-4(2))* Univ. of North Carolina Pr.

Gordon, George Henry. History of the Second Mass Regiment of Infantry: Second paper. Delivered at the annual meeting of the Second Mass. Infantry Assoc. , on May 11 1874. 2011. 72p. pap. 14.99 ***(978-1-4255-0172-3(9))*** MPublishing.

Keller, Christian. Chancellorsville & the Germans: Nativism, Ethnicity, & Civil War Memory. 4th ed. 2010. (North's Civil War Ser.). (ENG.). 244p. pap. 28.00 *(978-0-8232-2651-1(4))* Fordham Univ. Pr.

Keller, Christian B. Chancellorsville & the Germans: Nativism, Ethnicity, & Civil War Memory. 4th ed. 2007. (North's Civil War Ser.). (ENG., Illus.). 244p. 65.00 *(978-0-8232-2650-4(6))* Fordham Univ. Pr.

Military Historical Society of Massachusetts Staff. Petersburg, Chancellorsville, Gettysburg. (Papers of the Military Historical Society of Massachusetts Ser.). 442p. reprint ed. 98.00 *(978-0-7222-8033-1(5))* Library Reprints, Inc.

Nesbitt, Mark. Fredericksburg & Chancellorsville: The Ghost Hunter's Field Guide to Civil War Battlefields. 2007. 128p. per. 10.95 *(978-0-9752836-3-9(4))* Second Chance Pubns.

Richardson, Charles. The Chancellorsville Campaign. 2009. (ENG.). 125p. 28.99 *(978-1-117-53376-6(X));* pap. 19.75 *(978-1-117-53377-3(8))* BiblioBazaar.

—The Chancellorsville Campaign. 124p. reprint ed. 88.00 *(978-0-7222-8049-2(1))* Library Reprints, Inc.

—The Chancellorsville Campaign: Fredericksburg to Salem Church (1907) 2008. 128p. 35.95 *(978-1-4373-7012-6(8));* pap. 20.95 *(978-1-4371-7126-6(5))* Kessinger Publishing, LLC.

Sutherland, Daniel E. Fredericksburg & Chancellorsville: The Dare Mark Campaign. 2010. (Great Campaigns of the Civil War Ser.). (ENG.). 264p. pap. 24.95 *(978-0-8032-3282-2(9))* Univ. of Nebraska Pr.

Wheeler, Richard. Lee's Terrible Swift Sword: From Antietam to Chancellorsville: an Eyewitness History. 2008. (ENG., Illus.). 430p. 9.99 *(978-0-7858-1712-3(3),* 0785817123) Book Sales, Inc.

CHANCERY

see Equity; Equity Pleading and Procedure

CHANCERY COURTS

see Courts—Great Britain

CHANDLER, RAYMOND, 1888-1959

Athanasourelis, John Paul. Raymond Chandler's Philip Marlowe: The Hard-Boiled Detective Transformed. 2011. (ENG.). 208p. pap. 40.00 ***(978-0-7864-4215-7(8))*** McFarland & Co., Inc. Pubs.

Freeman, Judith. The Long Embrace: Raymond Chandler & the Woman He Loved. 2008. (Vintage Ser.). (ENG., Illus.). 368p. pap. 14.95 *(978-1-4000-9517-9(4),* Vintage) Knopf Doubleday Publishing Group.

Gale, Robert L. Characters & Plots in the Fiction of Raymond Chandler. 2010. (ENG., Illus.). 232p. pap. 55.00 *(978-0-7864-4772-5(9))* McFarland & Co., Inc. Pubs.

Guerrero, Raul. Raul Guerrero: The Whaling Bar: la Jolla. 2007. (Illus.). 10.00 *(978-0-9744804-7-3(9),* Athenaeum Music & Arts Library) Library Assn. of La Jolla.

Rhodes, Chip. Politics, Desire, & the Hollywood Novel. 2008. (ENG.). 198p. 34.95 *(978-1-58729-629-1(2))* Univ. of Iowa Pr.

CHANDLER, ZACHARIAH, 1813-1879

Porter, Fitz-John. Gen'l Fitz John Porter's Reply to Hon Z Chandler's Speech in the U S Senate, Feb 21 1870. 2011. 24p. pap. 11.99 ***(978-1-4181-9214-3(7))*** MPublishing.

CHANDOS, JAMES BRYDGES, DUKE OF, 1674-1744

Jenkins, Susan. Portrait of a Patron. 2007. (Illus.). 232p. 124.95 *(978-0-7546-4156-8(2))* Ashgate Publishing Co.

CHANEL, COCO, 1883-1971

Bott, Danièle. Chanel: Collections & Creations. 2007. (ENG., Illus.). 208p. 40.00 *(978-0-500-51360-6(0),* 551360) Thames & Hudson.

Chaney, Lisa. Coco Chanel: An Intimate Life. (ENG.). 464p. (gr. 12). 2012. Illus.). pap. 17.00 ***(978-0-14-312212-8(6),*** Penguin (Non-Classics)) 2011. 27.95 *(978-0-670-02309-7(4),* Viking Adult) Penguin Group (USA) Inc.

de la Haye, Amy. Chanel: Couture & Industry. 2011. (ENG., Illus.). 128p. pap. 30.00 *(978-1-85177-643-6(5))* V & A Pubns. GBR. Dist: Hachette Bk. Group.

Fiemeyer, Isabelle. Intimate Chanel. 2011. (ENG., Illus.). 208p. 60.00 *(978-2-08-030162-8(4))* Flammarion et Cie FRA. Dist: Random Hse., Inc.

Froment, Jean-Louis & Prodhon, Françoise Claire. Culture Chanel. 2012. (ENG., Illus.). 440p. 250.00 ***(978-1-4197-0332-4(3))*** Abrams.

Helleu, Jacques. Jacques Helleu & Chanel. Pickford, Susan, tr. from FRE. 2006. (ENG., Illus.). 280p. 125.00 *(978-0-8109-4312-4(3))* Abrams.

Karbo, Karen. The Gospel According to Coco Chanel: Life Lessons from the World's Most Elegant Woman. 2009. (ENG., Illus.). 240p. 19.95 *(978-1-59921-523-5(3),* skirt!) Globe Pequot Pr., The.

Kirkland, Douglas. Coco Chanel: Three Weeks/1962. 2008. (ENG., 144p. Illus.). 50.00 *(978-0-9801557-1-6(1));* 500.00 *(978-0-9801557-5-4(4))* Glitterati, Inc.

Kirkland, Douglas, photos by. Madamoiselle - Coco Chanel / Summer 62, 1 vol. 2009. (ENG., Illus.). 104p. 45.00 *(978-3-86521-865-0(2))* Steidl, Gerhard Druckerei und Verlag DEU. Dist: Innovative Logistics.

Leymarie, Jean. Eternal Chanel. 2011. (ENG., Illus.). 266p. 45.00 *(978-0-8109-9694-6(4))* Abrams.

Mazzeo, Tilar J. The Secret of Chanel No. 5: The Intimate History of the World's Most Famous Perfume. 2011. (P. S. Ser.). (ENG., Illus.). 304p. pap. 15.99 *(978-0-06-179103-1(2),* HarperPerennial) HarperCollins Pubs.

—The Secret of Chanel No. 5: The Intimate History of the World's Most Famous Perfume. 2010. (ENG., Illus.). 304p. 25.99 *(978-0-06-179101-7(6))* HarperCollins Pubs.

Morand, Paul. Allure of Chanel. 2008. (ENG., Illus.). 224p. pap. 29.95 *(978-1-906548-10-0(2))* Pushkin Pr., Ltd. GBR. Dist: Consortium Bk. Sales & Distribution.

—The Allure of Chanel. Cameron, Euan, tr. from FRE. 2008. (ENG.). 180p. pap. 19.95 *(978-1-901285-98-7(7))* Pushkin Pr., Ltd. GBR. Dist: Consortium Bk. Sales & Distribution.

PICARDIE, Justine. Chanel - Her Life, 1 vol. 2011. 400p. 58.00 ***(978-978-38693-0-1(2))*** Steidl, Gerhard Druckerei und Verlag DEU. Dist: Innovative Logistics.

Picardie, Justine. Chanel - Her Life, 1 vol. 2011. (ENG., Illus.). 400p. 58.00 ***(978-3-86930-262-1(3))*** Steidl, Gerhard Druckerei und Verlag DEU. Dist: Innovative Logistics.

Picardie, Justine. Coco Chanel: The Legend & the Life. 2011. (ENG.). 352p. pap. 20.00 *(978-0-06-207417-1(2))* 2010. (ENG., Illus.). 352p. 40.00 *(978-0-06-196385-8(2))* 2009. (Illus.). 336p. *(978-0-00-731761-5(1))* HarperCollins Pubs.

Simon, Linda. Coco Chanel. 2011. (Reaktion Books - Critical Lives Ser.). (Illus.). 207p. pap. 16.95 *(978-1-86189-859-3(2))* Reaktion Bks., Ltd. GBR. Dist: Chicago Distribution Ctr.

Taylor-Wood, Sam. Third Floor, 1 vol. 2012. (ENG., Illus.). 80p. 145.00 ***(978-3-86930-264-5(X))*** Steidl, Gerhard Druckerei und Verlag DEU. Dist: Innovative Logistics.

Vaughan, Hal. Sleeping with the Enemy: Coco Chanel's Secret War. (Vintage Ser.). (ENG., Illus.). 2012. 368p. pap. 16.95 ***(978-0-307-47591-6(3),*** Vintage) 2011. 304p. 27.95 ***(978-0-307-59263-7(4),*** Knopf) Knopf Doubleday Publishing Group.

CHANEY, JAMES EARL, 1943-1964

Scheppler, Bill. The Mississippi Burning Trial: A Primary Source Account. 2009. (Great Trials of the Twentieth Century Ser.). 64p. (gr. 5-8). 58.50 *(978-1-61513-215-7(5))* Rosen Publishing Group, Inc., The.

CHANEY, LON, 1883-1930

Gargiulo, Suzanne. Lon Chaney's Shadow - John Jeske & the Chaney Mystique. 2009. 184p. pap. 19.00 *(978-1-59393-330-2(4))* BearManor Media.

CHANGE

Bandy, Thomas G. Spirited Leadership: Empowering People to Do What Matters. 2008. (Illus.). 170p. per. 19.99 *(978-0-8272-3468-0(6))* Chalice Pr.

Becking, Bob. Orthodoxy, Liberalism, & Acaptation: Essays on Ways of Worldmaking in Times of Change from Biblical, Historical, & Systematic Perspectives. 2011. (Illus.). 230p. ***(978-90-04-20869-8(0))*** BRILL.

Bernal Trujillo, Marta Ines & Gutierrez, Jaime Lopera. La Culpa Es de la Vaca: Anecdotas, Parabolas, Fabulas y Reflexiones Sobre el Liderazgo. 2008. (SPA.). 252p. pap. 12.95 *(978-958-8227-05-4(4))* Circulo de Lectores S.A. COL. Dist: Random Hse., Inc.

Bohnet, Iris. Exploring Landscape Character. 2011. 512p. pap. ***(978-3-8443-1166-2(1))*** Lambert Academic Publishing.

Borysenko, Joan Z. & Borysenko, Joan. It's Not the End of the World: Developing Resilience in Times of Change. 2009. (ENG.). 176p. 14.95 *(978-1-4019-2532-8(0),* 1125) Hay Hse., Inc.

Braddy, Judi. True North: Staying on Course Through Life's Changing Circumstances. 2007. (ENG.). 192p. per. 14.99 *(978-0-8341-2341-0(X),* 083-412-341X) Beacon Hill Pr. of Kansas City.

Brubaker, David. Promise & Peril: Understanding & Managing Change & Conflict in Congregations. 2009. *(978-1-56699-382-1(2))* Alban Institute, Inc.

Bucker, Andreas, et al, eds. Resonances: Historical Essays on Continuity & Change. 2011. (Ritus et Artes Ser.). (ENG., Illus.). 266p. (C). 116.00 *(978-2-503-53493-0(7))* Brepols Pubs. BEL. Dist: ISD.

Building Capacity for Change Sourcebook. unabr. ed. 135p. ring bd. 295.00 *(978-0-9700321-0-2(2))* Maurer & Assocs.

Chalke, Steve. Change Agents: 25 Hard-Learned Lessons in the Art of Getting Things Done, 1 vol. 2007. (ENG., Illus.). 160p. pap. 10.99 *(978-0-310-27549-7(0))* Zondervan.

Clay, James. Just One Thing. 2011. 152p. pap. 14.95 ***(978-1-257-06089-4(9))*** Lulu Enterprises Inc.

Davison, Annie. Time to Change: A Guide to Life after Greed. 2011. (ENG.). 127p. pap. 14.95 ***(978-1-84694-939-5(4))*** Hunt, John Publishing Ltd. GBR. Dist: National Bk. Network.

De Cauter, Lieven & Dehaene, Michiel, eds. Heterotopia & the City: Public Space in a Postcivil Society. 2008. (ENG., Illus.). 360p. (C). 130.00 *(978-0-415-42288-8(4))* Routledge.

Dorschel, Andreas. Verwandlung: Mythologische Ansichten, technologische Absichten. 2009. (Neue Studien zur Philosophie Ser.). (GER.). 200p. (C). 51.00 *(978-3-89971-751-8(1))* Vandenhoeck & Ruprecht GmbH & Co. KG DEU. Dist: ISD.

Fligstein, Neil & McAdam, Doug. A Theory of Fields, 1 vol. 2012. (ENG., Illus.). 256p. 29.95 ***(978-0-19-985994-8(9))*** Oxford Univ. Pr., Inc.

Furseth, Inger. From Quest for Truth to Being Oneself: Religious Change in Life Stories. 2006. (Illus.). 325p. pap. *(978-0-8204-9944-4(7))* Lang, Peter AG.

Gallagher, Carol J. Reweaving the Sacred: A Practical Guide to Change & Growth for Challenged Congregations. 2008. 144p. pap. 16.00 *(978-0-89869-588-5(0))* Church Publishing, Inc.

Galloway, Dale E. & Bird, Warren. Innovative Transitions: How Change Can Take Your Church to the Next Level. 2007. (ENG.). 160p. per. 14.99 *(978-0-8341-2339-7(8),* 083-412-3398) Beacon Hill Pr. of Kansas City.

Grainger, Roger. The Uses of Chaos. 2010. (ENG.). 139p. pap. 51.95 *(978-3-0343-0131-2(6))* Lang, Peter AG GBR. Dist: Lang, Peter.

Griffiths, Ken. Oh God, Change This Scene! Changing the Situation. 2008. 300p. pap. 21.95 *(978-1-4327-2896-0(2))* Outskirts Pr., Inc.

Grin, John, et al. Transitions to Sustainable Development: New Directions in the Study of Long Term Transformative Change. 2010. (Routledge Studies in Sustainability Transitions Ser.). (ENG., Illus.). 418p. 50.00 *(978-0-415-87675-9(3),* Routledge) Taylor & Francis Group GBR. Dist: Taylor & Francis Group.

Hammett, Edward H., et al. Making Shifts Without Making W. 2009. 144p. pap. 19.99 *(978-0-8272-2337-0(4))* Chalice Pr.

Hamish, James A. Simple Rules for Money: John Wesley on Earning, Saving, & Giving. 2010. 79p. pap. 10.00 *(978-0-687-46616-0(4))* Abingdon Pr.

Harrelson, Angie. Changes. 2007. (ENG.). 288p. (gr. 2-2). pap. 79.95 *(978-1-59363-299-1(1))* Prufrock Pr.

Haslanger, Sally & Kurtz, Roxane Marie, eds. Persistence: Contemporary Readings. 2006. (MIT Readers in Contemporary Philosophy Ser.). (ENG., Illus.). 496p. (gr. 17). 80.00 *(978-0-262-08350-8(7));* per. 38.00 *(978-0-262-58268-1(6))* MIT Pr.

Healy, Deirdre. The Dynamics of Desistance: Charting Pathways Through Change. 2010. (International Series on Desistance & Rehabilitation Ser.). (ENG., Illus.). 240p. 69.95 *(978-1-84392-783-9(7))* Willan Publishing GBR. Dist: Taylor & Francis Group.

Hettling, Manfred & Müller, Michael G. Menschenformung in Religiösen Kontexten: Visionen Von der Veränderbarkeit des Menschen Vom Mittelalter Bis Zur Gegenwart. 2007. (GER.). 209p. (C). 53.00 *(978-3-89971-361-9(3))* Vandenhoeck & Ruprecht GmbH & Co. KG DEU. Dist: ISD.

Hillman, Os. Change Agent. 2011. E-Book ***(978-1-61638-567-5(7),*** Charisma Hse.) Charisma Media.

Honnefelder, Ludger, et al, eds. Unity & Time in Metaphysics. 2009. (ENG.). VIII, 254p. 98.00 *(978-3-11-021234-1(X));* 154.00 ***(978-3-11-174055-3(2))*** De Gruyter, Walter Inc.

Jespersen, Lori. From This Day On: Preserving Newfound Insight, Change & Growth in the Real-World. 2010. 216p. pap. 14.95 *(978-0-87516-847-0(7),* Devorss Pubns.) DeVorss & Co.

Kallestad, Walt & Cole, Shawn-Marie. Reign Down: Change Your Life Through the Gift of Repentance. 2008. (ENG.). 272p. 18.99 *(978-1-4165-6271-9(0),* Howard Bks.) Howard Books.

Koob, Joseph E. Leaders Managing Change. 2007. 193p. pap. 13.95 *(978-0-7414-4256-7(6))* Infinity Publishing.

Laszlo, Ervin. Worldshift 2012: Making Green Business, New Politics & Higher Consciousness Work Together. 2009. 128p. pap. 14.95 *(978-1-59477-328-0(9))* Inner Traditions International, Ltd.

Lillies, Philip. Case Study of a Knowledge-Based Organization. 2011. 124p. pap. ***(978-3-8454-0263-5(6))*** Lambert Academic Publishing.

Linamen, Karen. Only Nuns Change Habits Overnight: Fifty-Two Amazing Ways to Master the Art of Personal Change. 2008. (ENG., Illus.). 208p. pap. 13.99 *(978-1-4000-7400-6(2),* WaterBrook Pr.) Doubleday Religious Publishing Group, The.

MacDonald, Gordon. Who Stole My Church: What to Do When the Church You Love Tries to Enter the 21st Century, 0 vols. 2010. 272p. pap. 15.99 *(978-0-7852-3049-6(1))* Nelson, Thomas Inc.

Mansfield, John. The Nature of Change or the Law of Unintended Consequences: An Introductory Text to Designing Complex Systems & Managing Change. 2010. (Illus.). 212p. 51.00 *(978-1-84816-540-3(4))* Imperial College Pr. GBR. Dist: World Scientific Publishing Co., Inc.

Matthews, Leah. Facing Change. 2010. (Insights: Bible Studies for Growing Faith Ser.). 48p. pap. 7.00 *(978-1-60899-222-5(5),* Wipf and Stock) Wipf & Stock Pubs.

Mattox, Mickey Leland & Roeber, A. G. Changing Churches: An Orthodox, Catholic, & Lutheran Theological Conversation. 2012. pap. ***(978-0-8028-6694-3(8))*** Eerdmans, William B. Publishing Co.

McIntosh, Gary. Here Today, There Tomorrow: Unleashing Your Church's Potential. 2010. *(978-0-89827-422-6(2))* Wesleyan Publishing Hse.

Mosser, David N., ed. Transitions: Leading Churches through Change. 2011. (ENG.). 256p. pap. 20.00 *(978-0-664-23543-7(3))* Westminster John Knox Pr.

Munroe, Myles. Keys for Change. 2009. 157p. pap. 5.99 *(978-1-60374-151-4(8))* Whitaker Hse.

—Los Principios y Beneficios del Cambio: Cumpliendo tu propósito en medio de tiempos Inciertos. 2009.Tr. of Principles & Benefits of Change: Fulfilling Your Purpose in Unsettled Times. (SPA.). pap. 11.99 *(978-1-60374-159-0(3))* Whitaker Hse.

—The Principles & Benefits of Change: Fulfilling Your Purpose in Unsettled Times. 2009. 208p. 19.99 *(978-1-60374-097-5(X),* 770975) Whitaker Hse.

Oswald, Lowell K. & Waterbury, John. Becometh As a Child: A Guide to Healing Emotionally, Growing Spiritually, & Experiencing a Change of Heart. 2009. 14.99 *(978-1-59955-331-3(7))* Cedar Fort, Inc./CFI Distribution.

Pazmany, Peter, et al. Driving Complex Change: Mastering the Process of Change. 2007. 200p. 21.95 *(978-0-9774669-1-7(4))* Asil, Inc.

Pensak, David & Licorish, Elizabeth. Innovation for Underdogs: How to Make the Leap from What If to Now What. 2008. (ENG.). 1p. 19.99 *(978-1-60163-035-3(2))* Career Pr., Inc.

Peterson, Grethe B., ed. The Tanner Lectures Vol 28. 2009. (Tanner Lectures on Human Values Ser.). (ENG., Illus.). 264p. (gr. 13). 35.00 *(978-0-87480-967-1(3))* Univ. of Utah Pr.

Pusca, Anca M., ed. Walter Benjamin & the Aesthetics of Change. 2010. (ENG., Illus.). 240p. 89.00 *(978-0-230-58086-2(6))* Palgrave Macmillan.

Reid, J. M. & Gallagher, Maureen. The Art of Change: Faith, Vision, & Prophetic Planning. 2010. (Illus.). xii, 116p. 12.99 *(978-0-7648-1867-7(8))* Liguori Pubns.

Rescher, Nicholas. Process Philosophical Deliberations. 2007. (ENG.). 195p. (gr. 11). 69.95 *(978-3-938793-37-4(6))* Ontos Verlag DEU. Dist: Transaction Pubs.

C

Robertson, C. K. A Dangerous Dozen: Twelve Christians Who Threatened the Status Quo but Taught Us to Live Like Jesus. 2011. 160p. pap. 16.99 *(978-1-59473-298-0(1))* SkyLight Paths Publishing.

Rowdon, Harold, ed. 10 Changing Churches. 2006. (ENG.). pap. 10.99 *(978-0-900128-21-9(6)*, Paternoster) Authentic Media.

Roxburgh, Alan. Missional Map-Making: Skills for Leading in Times of Transition. 2010. (Jossey-Bass Leadership Network Ser.: 43). (ENG., Illus.). 224p. 24.95 *(978-0-470-48672-6(4)*, Jossey-Bass) Wiley, John & Sons, Inc.

Scott, Katherine Tyler. Transforming Leadership. 2010. (Transformations Ser.). 144p. pap. 16.00 *(978-0-89869-599-1(6))* Church Publishing, Inc.

Seim, Turid Karlsen & Økland, Jorunn, eds. Metamorphoses: Resurrection, Body & Transformative Practices in Early Christianity. 2009. (Ekstasis: Religious Experience from Antiquity to the Middle Ages Ser.). (ENG.). VI, 401p. 196.00 ***(978-3-11-916748-2(7))*** De Gruyter, Walter Inc.

Seim, Turid Karlsen & Økland, Jorunn. Metamorphoses: Resurrection, Body, & Transformative Practices in Early Christianity. 2009. (Ekstasis: Religious Experience from Antiquity to the Middle Ages Ser.). (ENG.). VI, 401p. 123.00 ***(978-3-11-020298-4(0))*** De Gruyter, Walter Inc.

Skafish, Malabou. The Heidegger Change: On the Fantastic in Philosophy. 2011. 224p. 75.00 ***(978-1-4384-3955-6(5)***, Suny Pr.) State Univ. of New York Pr.

Smith, Kathleen S. Stilling the Storm: Worship in Difficult Times. 2006. xxv, 229p. *(978-1-56699-327-2(X))* Alban Institute, Inc.

Sorrell, Eric. Expressions for Change. 2007. 78p. pap. 16.95 *(978-1-4241-8901-4(2))* PublishAmerica, Inc.

Stanley, Charles F. Stuck in Reverse: How to Let God Change Your Direction, 0 vols. 2008. 160p. per. 7.99 *(978-1-4002-0094-8(6))* Nelson, Thomas Inc.

Swedish, Margaret. Living Beyond the End of the World: A Spirituality of Hope. 2008. 222p. pap. 20.00 *(978-1-57075-767-9(4))* Orbis Bks.

Tapp, Billie. God's Timed Zone. 2008. 124p. pap. 19.95 *(978-1-60703-688-3(6))* PublishAmerica, Inc.

Thompson, Beverly & Thompson, George B. Grace for the Journey: Practices & Possibilities for In-Between Times. 2011. ***(978-1-56699-420-0(9))*** Alban Institute, Inc.

Trent, John. The 2-Degree Difference: How Little Things Can Change Everything. 2006. (Illus.). 243p. 19.99 *(978-0-8054-3064-6(4))* B&H Publishing Group.

Wells, Rosemary. Helping Children Cope with Change & Loss. 128p. *(978-0-85969-891-7(2)*, Sheldon Press) SPCK Publishing.

Wilkins, Gary Nelson. The Personification of Change. 2008. 64p. pap. 15.99 *(978-1-4363-0701-7(5))* Xlibris Corp.

Williams, M. & Rott, Hans, eds. Frontiers in Belief Revision. 2010. (Applied Logic Ser.). 460p. pap. 249.00 *(978-90-481-5720-4(X)*, 904815720X) Springer.

Wilson, Scott. Steering Through Chaos: Mapping a Clear Direction for Your Church in the Midst of Transition & Change, 1 vol. 2010. (ENG.). 224p. pap. 18.99 *(978-0-310-32463-8(7))* Zondervan.

CHANGE (PSYCHOLOGY)

see also Neurolinguistic Programming

Adams, Marilee G. Change Your Questions, Change Your Life: 10 Powerful Tools for Life & Work. 2nd ed. 2009. (BK Life Ser.). (ENG.). 240p. pap. 18.95 *(978-1-57675-600-3(9))* Berrett-Koehler Pubs., Inc.

Ahrens, Justin. Life Kerning: Creative Ways to Fine Tune Your Perspective on Career & Life. 2011. (ENG., Illus.). 176p. pap. 22.95 *(978-1-118-06782-6(7)*, Wiley) Wiley, John & Sons, Inc.

Alexander, Angela. Subject to Change: I'm Open to You. 2009. 244p. 29.95 *(978-0-595-69673-4(2))*; pap. 19.95 *(978-0-595-45765-6(7))* iUniverse, Inc.

Allen, Dianne. Contributing to Learning to Change. 2008. (Illus.). 180p. pap. *(978-3-639-06165-9(9))* VDM Verlag Dr. Mueller e.K.

Allen, Roger K. The Hero's Choice: Living from the Inside Out. 2009. 270p. pap. 16.95 *(978-0-9797831-2-8(7))* Leadership Pr.

Anderson, Susan. Taming Your Outer Child: A Revolutionary Program to Overcome Self-Defeating Patterns. 2011. 304p. 25.00 *(978-0-345-51448-6(3)*, Ballantine Bks.) Random House Publishing Group.

Arnell, Peter. Shift: How to Reinvent Your Business, Your Career, & Your Personal Brand. 2010. (ENG., Illus.). 208p. 23.00 *(978-0-385-52627-2(X)*, Broadway Business) Knopf Doubleday Publishing Group.

Austin, Andrew T. The Rainbow Machine: Tales from a Neurolinguist's Journal. 2007. 220p. per. 16.50 *(978-0-911226-44-7(3))* Real People Pr.

Ballard, Elise. Epiphany: True Stories of Sudden Insight. 2011. *(978-0-307-71611-8(2)*, Harmony) Crown Publishing Group.

Ballard, Elise, ed. Epiphany: True Stories of Sudden Insight to Inspire, Encourage, & Transform. 2011. 320p. 22.99 *(978-0-307-71610-1(4)*, Harmony) Crown Publishing Group.

Bandler, Richard. Get the Life You Want: The Secrets to Quick & Lasting Life Change with Neuro-Linguistic Programming. 2008. (ENG.). 264p. 19.95 *(978-0-7573-0776-8(0))* Health Communications, Inc.

Barranger, Jack. Knowing When to Quit. 2011. 200p. (Orig.). pap. 18.95 ***(978-1-58509-138-6(3))*** Book Tree, The.

Basu, Rintu. Persuasion Skills Black Book: Practical NLP Language Patterns for Getting the Response You Want. 2009. (Illus.). 188p. pap. *(978-1-905430-54-3(X))* Lean Marketing Pr.

Beattie, Melody. The Grief Club: The Secret to Getting Through All Kinds of Change. 2006. (ENG.). 368p. pap. 14.95 *(978-1-59285-349-6(8))* Hazelden Publishing & Educational Services.

—Make Miracles in Forty Days: Turning What You Have into What You Want. 2010. (ENG.). 192p. 23.00 *(978-1-4391-0215-2(5))* Simon & Schuster.

The Beauty of Mentoring: Growing Through Change. (Christian Women's Bible Study Ser.). pap. 8.99 *(978-0-570-06852-5(5)*, 20-3042) Concordia Publishing Hse.

Bergner, Raymond M. Status Dynamics: Creating New Paths to Therapeutic Change. 2007. 141p. 24.95 *(978-0-9772286-1-4(4))* Burns Park Pubs.

Bijou, Jude. Attitude Reconstruction: A Blueprint for Building a Better Life. 2011. 376p. 24.95 *(978-0-9843879-0-8(0))* Synergy Bks.

Bittner, John Lee. Change. 2009. 28p. pap. 21.99 *(978-1-4415-0692-4(6))* Xlibris Corp.

Blumenthal, Noah. Be the Hero: Three Powerful Ways to Overcome Challenges in Work & Life. (ENG.). 2012. 168p. pap. 15.95 ***(978-1-60994-082-9(2))*** 2009. 144p. 19.95 *(978-1-60509-000-9(X))* Berrett-Koehler Pubs., Inc.

Blumenthal, Noah. You're Addicted to You: Why It's So Hard to Change - & What You Can Do about It. 2007. (ENG.). 163p. per. 15.95 *(978-1-57675-427-6(8))* Berrett-Koehler Pubs., Inc.

Bolsta, Phil. Sixty Seconds: One Moment Changes Everything. 2008. (ENG.). 240p. 18.95 *(978-1-58270-193-6(8)*, Beyond Words/Atria Bks.) Atria Bks.

Borden, Paul. Direct Hit: Aiming Real Leaders at the Mission Field. 2006. (Convergence eBook Ser.). 159p. per. 20.00 *(978-0-687-33194-9(3))* Abingdon Pr.

Borg, James. Mind Power: Change Your Thinking, Change Your Life. 2010. (ENG., Illus.). 288p. (C). pap. 19.99 ***(978-0-273-73007-1(X))*** FT Press.

Bower, D. William. Revising the Person-Centered Approach: Pushing on the Envelope, but Not Very Hard. 2011. 216p. pap. 17.95 *(978-1-4502-9270-2(4))* iUniverse, Inc.

Britten, Rhonda. Fearless Living: Live Without Excuses & Love Without Regret. 2011. (ENG.). 304p. (gr. 12). 14.95 *(978-0-399-53678-6(7)*, Perigee Trade) Penguin Group (USA) Inc.

Brown, William H. Unleashing the Power of God: Words of Empowerment. 2008. 103p. pap. 16.95 *(978-1-60563-203-2(1))* PublishAmerica, Inc.

Bushnell, Laura. Life Magic: The Reknowned Psychic Healer Shares Her 7 Keys to Finding Your Power & Living Your Purpose. 2007. 272p. pap. 13.95 *(978-1-4013-6014-6(9))* Miramax Bks.

Buzan, Tony & Buzan, Barry. Embracing Change: Essential Steps to Make Your Future Today. 2006. (ENG., Illus.). 288p. (C). pap. *(978-1-4066-1023-9(2))* Pearson Education Canada.

Camins, Benjamin Franklin & Reynoso, Patricia D. The Best Team to Inspire Change: As Illustrated By. 2008. 132p. pap. 13.95 *(978-0-595-48634-2(7))* iUniverse, Inc.

Cannon, Steven. Checklist for Change Journal - Second Edition. 2008. 158p. pap. 9.95 *(978-0-557-01722-5(X))* Lulu Enterprises Inc.

Cartwright, Talula & Center for Creative Leadership Staff. Changing Yourself & Your Reputation. 2009. (J-B CCL (Center for Creative Leadership) Ser.). (ENG.). 28p. pap. 12.95 *(978-1-60491-069-8(0)*, Pfeiffer) Wiley, John & Sons, Inc.

Cherry, Scott. A Critical Study of Self-Help & Self-Improvement Practices: Textual, Discursive, & Ethnographic Perspectives. 2011. (Illus.). 404p. 169.95 *(978-0-7734-1576-8(9))* Mellen, Edwin Pr., The.

Chester, Tim. You Can Change: God's Transforming Power for Our Sinful Behavior & Negative Emotions. 2010. 192p. pap. 15.99 *(978-1-4335-1231-5(9))* Crossway.

Christmas, Jane. The Pelee Project: One Woman's Escape from Urban Madness. (Illus.). 250p. pap. 18.95 *(978-1-55022-547-1(2))* ECW Pr. CAN. Dist: Independent Pubs. Group.

Clerc, Olivier. Invaluable Lessons from a Frog: Seven Life-Enhancing Metaphors. Marcelin-Rice, Louis, tr. 2009. (ENG.). 112p. pap. 14.95 *(978-0-9797908-3-6(2))* Dreamriver Pr.

Cohen, Patricia. Applied Data Analytic Techniques for Turning Points Research. Cohen, Patricia, ed. 2008. (Multivariate Applications Ser.). (ENG., Illus.). 256p. 125.00 *(978-0-8058-5451-0(7))*; pap. 44.95 *(978-0-8058-5452-7(5))* Routledge.

Conroy, Mervyn. Ethical Approach to Leading Change: An Alternative & Sustainable Application. 2010. (ENG., Illus.). 256p. 100.00 *(978-0-230-23847-3(5))* Palgrave Macmillan.

Cooke, Phil. IE: Jolt! Get the Jump on a World That's Constantly Changing. 2011. 240p. pap. 15.99 ***(978-1-59554-773-6(8))*** Nelson, Thomas Inc.

Cornelius, Bil. I Dare You to Change! Discover the Difference Between Dreaming of a Better Life & Living It. 2011. 224p. pap. 14.99 *(978-0-8249-4914-3(5)*, GuidepostsBooks) Ideals Pubns.

Cornelius, Bill. I Dare You to Change: Discover the Difference Between Dreaming a Better Life & Living It. 2010. 212p. pap. 19.99 *(978-0-8249-4818-4(1)*, GuidepostsBooks) Ideals Pubns.

Cornell, Karen, et al. The Pocketbook of Transformation & Transcendence. 2008. 72p. pap. 9.95 *(978-0-9797906-2-1(X))* Triple Eight Publishing.

Daniels, Myra Janco. Secrets of a Rutbuster: Breaking Rules & Selling Dreams. 2009. (ENG.). 96p. 15.95 *(978-1-932646-49-8(3))* Ruder-Finn Pr.

Davidson, Richard J. & Begley, Sharon. The Emotional Life of Your Brain: How Its Unique Patterns Affect the Way You Think, Feel, & Live - & How You Can Change Them. 2012. (ENG.). 304p. (gr. 12). 25.95 ***(978-1-59463-089-7(5)***, Hudson Street Pr.) Penguin Group (USA) Inc.

Davison, Annie. Time to Change: A Guide to Life after Greed. 2011. (ENG.). 127p. pap. 14.95 ***(978-1-84694-939-5(4))*** Hunt, John Publishing Ltd. GBR. Dist: National Bk. Network.

Day, Laura. The Circle: How the Power of a Single Wish Can Change Your Life. 2009. (ENG.). 192p. pap. 15.00 *(978-1-4391-1821-4(3)*, Beyond Words/Atria Bks.) Atria Bks.

—The Circle: How the Power of a Single Wish Can Change Your Life. 2007. (ENG.). 160p. (gr. 12-18). 14.95 *(978-1-58542-598-3(2)*, Tarcher) Penguin Group (USA) Inc.

De Bonvoisin, Ariane. The First 30 Days: Your Guide to Making Any Change Easier. 2009. (ENG.). 240p. pap. 14.99 *(978-0-06-147282-4(4)*, HarperOne) HarperCollins Pubs.

—Los Primeros 30 Días: Tu Guía para Enfrentar Cualquier Cambio. 2008. (Adelante Ser.). (SPA.). 256p. pap. 12.99 *(978-0-06-171040-7(7)*, Rayo) HarperCollins Pubs.

Degraff, Jeff & Lichtenberg, Greg. Innovation You: Four Steps to Becoming New & Improved. 2011. 256p. 25.00 *(978-0-345-53069-1(1)*, Ballantine Bks.) Random House Publishing Group.

DeLong, Thomas J. Flying Without a Net: Turn Fear of Change into Fuel for Success. 2011. (ENG., Illus.). 288p. 29.95 *(978-1-4221-6229-3(X))* Harvard Business Review Pr.

Demetre, Danna. Change Your Habits, Change Your Life: A Proven Plan for Healthy Living. 2009. 352p. pap. 15.99 *(978-0-8007-3331-5(2))* Revell.

Dickinson, David. Changing the Course of AIDS: Peer Education in South Africa & Its Lessons for the Global Crisis. 2009. (Culture & Politics of Health Care Work Ser.). (Illus.). 248p. 39.95 *(978-0-8014-4831-7(X)*, ILR Pr.) Cornell Univ. Pr.

Dickson, Amanda. Change It Up: Looking Differently at the Change You Want, & the Change You Don't. 2009. 18.99 *(978-1-60641-202-2(7)*, Shadow Mountain) Deseret Bk. Co.

Dispenza, Joe. Breaking the Habit of Being Yourself: How to Lose Your Mind & Create a New One. 2012. (ENG.). 25.95 ***(978-1-4019-3808-6(6))*** Hay Hse., Inc.

Dokoupil, Jarda. The Invitation. 2010. 104p. pap. 31.50 *(978-1-4461-6887-5(5))* Lulu Enterprises Inc.

Dool, Richard. Enervative Change- the Impact of Change Initiatives on Employee Job Satisfaction. 2007. 176p. per. *(978-3-8364-1801-0(0))* VDM Verlag Dr. Mueller e.K.

Dooley, Mike. Manifesting Change: It Couldn't Be Easier. (ENG., Illus.). 224p. 2011. pap. 14.00 *(978-1-58270-276-6(4))* 2010. 21.99 *(978-1-58270-275-9(6))* Atria Bks. (Beyond Words/Atria Bks.).

Downton, James. Today I Will... Words to Inspire Positive Life Changes. 2009. (ENG.). 96p. 13.95 *(978-1-59842-424-9(6))* Blue Mountain Arts Inc.

Doyle, Bruce I., III. How to Think Your Way to the Life You Want: A Guide to Understanding How Your Thoughts & Beliefs Create Your Life. 2011. 160p. pap. 14.95 *(978-1-57174-640-5(4))* Hampton Roads Publishing Co., Inc.

Duhigg, Charles. The Power of Habit: Why We Do What We Do in Life & Business. 2012. (ENG., Illus.). 400p. 28.00 ***(978-1-4000-6928-6(9)***, Random House) Random House Publishing Group.

Duquin, Lorene Hanley. Living Through Change in Your Parish. 2009. 1p. 14.95 *(978-1-59276-699-4(4))* Our Sunday Visitor, Publishing Div.

—Viviendo A Traves de Cambios en Su Parroquia. Estenger, Vilma G., tr. 2009. (SPA.). 1p. 14.95 *(978-1-59276-700-7(1))* Our Sunday Visitor, Publishing Div.

Dutra-St. John, Rich & St. John-Dutra, Yvonne. Be the Hero: You've Been Waiting For. 2009. 343p. pap. 23.95 *(978-1-935253-00-6(X))* Challenge Assocs.

Dyer, Wayne W. Excuses Begone! How to Change Lifelong, Self-Defeating Thinking Habits. 2009. (KOR.). 285p. pap. *(978-89-509-2121-7(9))* 21st C. Bks. Sae Nal.

—Excuses Begone! How to Change Lifelong, Self-Defeating Thinking Habits. (ENG.). 2011. 288p. pap. 14.95 *(978-1-4019-2294-8(5))* 2009. 256p. 24.95 *(978-1-4019-2173-6(6))* Hay Hse., Inc.

Edgecombe, Linda. Shift or Get off the Pot: 26 Simple Truths about Getting a Life. 2009. (ENG., Illus.). 256p. pap. *(978-1-897178-65-2(4))* Insomniac Pr.

Edwards, Jacqueline M. The Consultant as an Instrument of Change. 2008. 104p. pap. 29.50 *(978-1-4357-0803-7(2))* Lulu Enterprises Inc.

Elwins, Dannie. How to End All of Your Negative Bad Habits Forever. 2009. 36p. pap. 16.99 *(978-0-557-15441-8(3))* Lulu Enterprises Inc.

Flanagan, Eileen. The Wisdom to Know the Difference: When to Make a Change-And When to Let Go. 2010. (ENG.). 288p. (gr. 12). 15.95 *(978-1-58542-829-8(9)*, Tarcher) Penguin Group (USA) Inc.

Fraser, J. Scott & Solovey, Andrew. Second-Order Change in Psychotherapy: The Golden Thread That Unifies Effective Treatments. 2006. (Illus.). 320p. 49.95 *(978-1-59147-436-4(1))* American Psychological Assn.

Frenn, Jason. Power to Reinvent Yourself: How to Break the Destructive Patterns in Your Life. 2010. (ENG.). 288p. 19.99 *(978-0-446-54622-5(4))* FaithWords.

Gagnon, Alfred. Eternal: For Those Who Know They Are. 2010. 55p. pap. 8.95 *(978-0-533-16233-8(5))* Vantage Pr., Inc.

Galardi, Toni. The LifeQuake Phenomenon: How to Thrive (Not Just Survive) in Times of Personal & Global Upheaval. 2009. 204p. 39.95 *(978-1-60494-222-4(3))* Wheatmark.

Gallagher, Winifred. New: Understanding Our Need for Novelty & Change. 2011. (ENG.). 272p. (gr. 12). 25.95 ***(978-1-59420-320-6(2)***, Penguin Pr. HC, The) Penguin Group (USA) Inc.

Gardner, Howard. Changing Minds: The Art & Science of Changing Our Own & Other People's Minds. 2006. (Center for Public Leadership Ser.). (ENG., Illus.). 272p. per. 18.00 *(978-1-4221-0329-6(3))* Harvard Business Review Pr.

Garner, Lesley. Everything I'Ve Ever Learned Chan. 2006. 288p. *(978-1-4019-1104-1(8)*, 396) Hay Hse. UK, Ltd. GBR. Dist: Grantham Bk. Services.

Gerlach, Peter K. Msw. Who's Really Running Your Life? 2011. 390p. 29.99 ***(978-1-4568-7505-3(1))***; pap. 19.99 ***(978-1-4568-7504-6(3))*** Xlibris Corp.

Gilardi, Toni. The LifeQuake Phenomenon: How to Thrive (Not Just Survive) in Times of Personal & Global Upheaval. 2010. pap. 16.95 *(978-1-60494-445-7(5))* Wheatmark.

Gill, Libby. You Unstuck: Mastering the New Rules of Risk-Taking in Work & Life. 2009. (ENG., Illus.). 252p. pap. 16.95 *(978-1-932361-68-1(5))* Travelers' Tales, Inc.

Gilligan, Steven, et al. The Hero's Journey: A Voyage of Self Discovery. 2009. (Illus.). 288p. *(978-1-84590-286-5(6))* Crown Hse. Publishing.

Gitomer, Jeffrey. Little Gold Book of YES! Attitude: How to Find, Build & Keep a YES! Attitude for a Lifetime of Success. 2006. (Gitomer Ser.). (ENG., Illus.). 208p. 19.99 *(978-0-13-198647-3(3))* FT Press.

Goi, James. How to Attract Money Using Mind Power. 2011. 15.95 ***(978-0-7414-6630-3(9))*** Infinity Publishing.

Gold, Stuart Avery. Ping. 2007. (ENG., Illus.). 90p. pap. 6.99 *(978-1-55704-756-4(1))* Newmarket Pr.

—The Way of Ping: Journey to the Great Ocean. 2009. (ENG., Illus.). 96p. 15.00 *(978-1-55704-820-2(7))* Newmarket Pr.

Golemon, Larry A. Finding Our Story: Narrative Leadership & Congregational Change. 2009. *(978-1-56699-376-0(8))* Alban Institute, Inc.

Greaves, Suzy. Making the Big Leap: Coach Yourself to Create the Life You Really Want. 2008. (ENG.). 176p. pap. *(978-1-84537-899-8(7))* New Holland Pubs., Ltd. GBR. Dist: Sterling Publishing Co., Inc.

Grinnan, Edward. The Promise of Hope: How True Stories of Hope & Inspiration Saved My Life & How They Can Transform Yours. 2011. 288p. 19.99 *(978-0-8249-4815-3(7)*, GuidepostsBooks) Ideals Pubns.

Gutmann, David. From Transformation to Transformaction: Methods & Practices. 2009. (Illus.). 328p. pap. 43.95 *(978-1-85575-615-1(3))* Karnac Bks. GBR. Dist: Stylus Publishing, LLC.

Guttman, Howard M. Coach Yourself to Win: 7 Steps to Breakthrough Performance on the Job... & in Your Life. 2010. (Illus.). 272p. 25.00 *(978-0-07-164034-3(7)*, 0071640347) McGraw-Hill Cos., The.

Hafley, George A. Your Way Is Not God's Way: No Subtitle. 2008. 288p. pap. 15.99 *(978-1-60647-180-7(5))* Xulon Pr., Inc.

Hales, Dianne & Christian, Kenneth E. An Invitation to Personal Change. 2008. (ENG., Illus.). 160p. (C). pap. 16.95 *(978-0-495-39017-6(8))* Wadsworth.

Hall, Bertie. Hurry, Hurry! Urgent Actions! Suggestions to Make the World A Better Place. 2010. 116p. 22.95 *(978-1-4502-1356-1(1))*; pap. 12.95 *(978-1-4502-1358-5(8))* iUniverse, Inc.

Harra, Carmen. Wholeliness: Embracing the Sacred Unity That Heals Our World. 2011. (ENG.). pap. 15.95 *(978-1-4019-3144-5(8))* Hay Hse., Inc.

Harvey, Eric & Sedas, Michelle. The Power Of 10% How Small Changes Can Make A BIG Difference. 2008. (Illus.). 116p. pap. 12.95 *(978-1-885228-71-0(6))* WalkTheTalk.com.

Hay, Louise L. You Can Heal Your Life, Set. 2009. (ENG.). 19.95 *(978-1-4019-2652-6(5)*, 1145) Hay Hse., Inc.

Healy, Deirdre. The Dynamics of Desistance: Charting Pathways Through Change. 2012. (ENG.). 240p. pap. 42.95 ***(978-0-415-62805-1(9))*** Routledge.

Heath, Chip. Switch: How to Change Things When Change Is Hard. l.t. ed. 2011. (ENG.). 486p. 32.99 *(978-1-4104-3313-8(7))* Thorndike Pr.

Heath, Chip & Heath, Dan. Switch: How to Change Things When Change Is Hard. 2010. (ENG.). 320p. 26.00 *(978-0-385-52875-7(2)*, Broadway Business) Knopf Doubleday Publishing Group.

—Switch: How to Change Things When Change Is Hard. 2010. (CHI.). 327p. pap. ***(978-986-213-199-2(3))*** Locus Publishing Co.

Heath, Dan & Heath, Chip. Switch: Cómo cambiar las cosas cuando cambiar es Difícil. 2011. (Vintage Espanol Ser.). (SPA.). 368p. pap. 15.95 *(978-0-307-74235-3(0)*, Vintage) Knopf Doubleday Publishing Group.

Henry, Dale. Ten Cans: Are You an Opener? 2007. (Illus.). 127p. pap. 17.99 *(978-0-8127-0473-0(8))* Review & Herald Publishing Assn.

Hoeche, Daniela. From New York City to the World - Lets remind Ourselves. 2010. 162p. pap. 20.95 *(978-1-4457-5565-6(3))* Lulu Enterprises Inc.

Holman, Peggy. Engaging Emergence: Turning Upheaval into Opportunity. 2010. (ENG., Illus.). 192p. pap. 24.95 *(978-1-60509-521-9(4))* Berrett-Koehler Pubs., Inc.

Holmes, Ernest. Reader on Change. 5.95 *(978-0-917849-21-3(3))* Science of Mind Publishing.

Huber, Cheri. Making a Change for Good: A Guide to Compassionate Self-Discipline. 2007. (ENG., Illus.). 144p. per. 14.95 *(978-1-59030-208-8(7))* Shambhala Pubns., Inc.

Hull, Jeffrey W. & Baldi, Malaga. Shift: Let Go of Fear & Get Your Life in Gear. 2010. (ENG.). 304p. pap. 16.95 *(978-0-7627-5662-9(4)*, Lyons Pr.) Globe Pequot Pr., The.

Hunt, Helen W. A Change Did Come, 1 vol. 2009. 48p. pap. 16.95 *(978-1-4489-2094-5(9))* PublishAmerica, Inc.

Hutegger, Thomas. You Are the Change: Find Your Own Spirituality - Make Your Life Count. 2010. (ENG.). 128p. pap. 12.95 *(978-1-84409-196-6(1))* Findhorn Pr. GBR. Dist: Independent Pubs. Group.

In., Emmanuel. Divinely Structured Mind. 2008. 164p. pap. 16.99 *(978-1-4343-9319-7(4))* AuthorHouse.

Jacobs. Take-Charge Living: How to Recast Your Role in Life... One Scene at A Time. 2008. 176p. pap. 15.95 *(978-1-60528-014-1(3)*, iUniverse Star) iUniverse, Inc.

Jara Rocha, Pamela Alejandra. Cambia el Concepto Que Tienes de Ti Mismo. 2008. 84p. pap. 27.45 *(978-1-59754-406-1(X))* Editorial Libros en Red.

Jeary, Tony. Strategic Acceleration: Succeed at the Speed of Life. 2010. (ENG.). 304p. pap. 15.95 *(978-1-59315-564-3(6))* Vanguard Pr.

—Strategic Acceleration: Succeed at the Speed of Life. 2009. (ENG.). 304p. 25.95 *(978-1-59315-501-8(8))* Westview Pr.

Johnson, Spencer. Qui a Pique Mon Fromage?Tr. of Who Moved My Cheese? 48p. pap. 18.95 incl. audio compact disk *(978-2-89558-006-5(5))* Coffragants CAN. Dist: Penton Overseas, Inc.

Judy, Dwight H. Discerning Life Transitions: Listening Together in Spiritual Direction. 2010. (Spiritual Directors International Ser.) (Illus.). 192p. pap. 24.00 *(978-0-8192-2407-1(3),* Morehouse Publishing) Church Publishing, Inc.

Kahn, Wallace J. The A-B-C's of Human Experience: An Integrative Model, Instructor's Manual with Text Items. tchr. ed. *(978-0-534-35982-9(5))* Wadsworth.

Katz, Orly. Women: Decode the Law of Attraction. 2008. (Illus.). 247p. per. 15.95 *(978-0-9779131-9-0(8),* Creative Bk. Pubs. International) Communication Projects International, Ltd.

Kumar, Anil. Good-Bye, Mr Patel. 2010. (Illus.). 236p. pap. 15.99 *(978-1-4520-1458-6(2))* AuthorHouse.

Lake, Danielle. Institutions & Process. 2008. 72p. pap. *(978-3-639-00841-8(3))* VDM Verlag Dr. Mueller e.K.

Lamm, Brad. How to Help the One You Love: A New Way to Intervene & Stop Someone from Self-Destructing. 2010. (ENG.). 304p. pap. 14.99 *(978-0-312-66276-9(9),* St. Martin's Griffin) St. Martin's Pr.

Lawana Rene' Lofton. Psychological Précipice: The Psychological Pursuit to Find the Best in You. 2009. 232p. 28.95 ***(978-1-4401-3059-5(0))*** iUniverse, Inc.

Lawson, Carol. Imagine That! Breaking Through to Other Worlds. Lawson, Robert F., ed. 2007. (Chrysalis Readers Ser.). (ENG., Illus.). 192p. pap. 15.95 *(978-0-87785-238-4(3))* Swedenborg Foundation, Inc.

Liedtka, Jeanne. The Catalyst: How You Can Become an Extraordinary Growth Leader. 2011. (ENG.). 260p. 27.50 ***(978-1-933199-36-8(9))*** Racom Communications.

Liggett, Tony. The Mental Diet. 2011. 124p. pap. 18.95 ***(978-0-89334-889-2(9))*** Humanics Publishing Group.

Lincoln, Michael J. What Is Happening to ME!!?? 2007. spiral bd. 34.00 *(978-0-9772069-4-0(7))* Talking Hearts.

Little, Tony. There's Always a Way, Set. 2009. 24.95 *(978-0-470-60183-9(3),* Wiley) Wiley, John & Sons, Inc.

—There's Always a Way: How to Develop a Positive Mindset & Succeed in Life & Business. 2009. (ENG., Illus.). 272p. 24.95 *(978-0-470-55841-6(5),* Wiley) Wiley, John & Sons, Inc.

Liv, Sean. The Ticket: Unite Your Body, Mind & Spirit for a Powerful Life. 2010. 9.99 ***(978-0-9813986-0-0(X),*** 9780981398600) Liv Publishing CAN. Dist: BookBaby.

Loehr, Jim. The Power of Story: Change Your Story, Change Your Destiny in Business & in Life. 2008. (ENG., Illus.). 288p. pap. 15.00 *(978-0-7432-9468-3(8),* Free Pr.) Free Pr.

Lofton, Lawana Rene'. Psychological Précipice: The Psychological Pursuit to Find the Best in You. 2009. 232p. pap. 18.95 *(978-1-4401-3057-1(4))* iUniverse, Inc.

Lucas, Bill. rEvolution: How to Thrive in Crazy Times. 2009. (Illus.). 256p. pap. *(978-1-84590-129-5(0))* Crown Hse. Publishing.

Macina, Gina. The Handbook to Happiness: A Ten-step Challenge to Change, Achieve & Move Forward to a Happier Life!, 1 vol. 2009. 88p. pap. 16.95 *(978-1-60836-351-3(1))* PublishAmerica, Inc.

Malhotra, Deepak. I Moved Your Cheese: For Those Who Refuse to Live as Mice in Someone Else's Maze. 2011. (Bk Business Ser.). (ENG., Illus.). 120p. 19.95 *(978-1-60994-065-2(2))* Berrett-Koehler Pubs., Inc.

Mancini, Jay A. & Roberto, Karen A. Pathways of Human Development: Explorations of Change. 2009. (ENG., Illus.). 410p. 83.99 *(978-0-7391-3686-7(0))* Lexington Bks.

Mandell, Fred & Jordan, Kathleen. Becoming a Life Change Artist: 7 Creative Skills to Reinvent Yourself at Any Stage of Life. 2010. (ENG.). 320p. (gr. 12). 18.00 *(978-1-58333-404-1(1),* Avery) Penguin Group (USA) Inc.

May, James A. & May, Dianne. Why Did I Do That? Freeing Your God-Given Emotions. 2007. 186p. per. 16.95 *(978-0-8091-4483-9(2,* 4483-9) Paulist Pr.

Mayeux, Patty. Beautiful Women: Like you & Me. 2007. 39.95 *(978-1-888237-69-6(4))* Baxter Pr.

McGhee, Carol Y. Human Enough 2 Change. 2007. 169p. pap. 24.95 *(978-1-4241-9646-3(9))* PublishAmerica, Inc.

McGrail, John. The Synthesis Effect: Your Direct Path to Personal Power & Transformation. 2012. (Illus.). 236p. E-Book ***(978-1-60163-612-6(1));*** (ENG., 224p. pap. 15.99 ***(978-1-60163-205-0(3))*** Career Pr., Inc.

McKinnon, Margie. It's Your Choice! Decisions That Will Change Your Life. 2011. *(978-1-61599-045-0(3));* 200p. pap. *(978-1-61599-044-3(5))* Loving Healing Pr., Inc.

Michels, Barry & Stutz, Phil. The Tools: Transform Your Problems into Courage, Confidence, & Creativity. 2012. (ENG., Illus.). 288p. 25.00 ***(978-0-679-64444-6(X))*** Spiegel & Grau.

—The Tools: Wie Sie wirklich Selbstvertrauen, Lebensfreude, Gelassenheit und innere Stärke gewinnen. 2012. (ENG.). 288p. E-Book ***(978-0-679-64445-3(8))*** Spiegel & Grau.

Molden, David & Hutchinson, Pat. Brilliant NLP: What the Most Successful People Know, Do & Say. 2nd rev. ed. 2010. (ENG., Illus.). 232p. (C). pap. 19.99 *(978-0-273-73255-6(2))* FT Press.

Morgan, Ralph A. Simple Truth: The Whole Is Greater Than the Sum of Its' Parts. 2009. 52p. pap. 9.95 *(978-1-4401-4653-4(5))* iUniverse, Inc.

Moseley, Dan. Lose, Love, Live: The Spiritual Gifts of Loss & Change. 2011. *(978-0-8358-1043-2(7))* Upper Room Bks.

Neenan, Michael & Dryden, Windy. Working with Resistance in REBT. 2011. (ENG.). 240p. (C). 99.00 *(978-0-415-66479-0(9));* pap. 36.95 *(978-0-415-66750-0(X))* Routledge.

Nichols, Bob & Laura. Issues a Guide to Heart Health. 2007. 228p. (ENG.). 24.99 *(978-1-60477-041-4(4));* per. 14.99 *(978-1-60477-040-7(6))* Xulon Pr., Inc.

Nodine, Jon. Window Three: You Always Have A Choice. 2009. 196p. pap. 14.99 *(978-1-59858-998-6(9))* Dog Ear Publishing, LLC.

Noel, Brook. Make Today Matter Makeover: The 26 Best Ways to Recapture Daily Magic, Kickstart High-Energy Living, & Get the Most Out of Life. 2009. (ENG.). 320p. pap. 14.99 *(978-1-4022-1223-9(2))* Sourcebooks, Inc.

O'Brien, Michael J. & Shook, Larry. Profit from Experience: A Guide to Knowing Yourself & Influencing Others. 2009. 192p. pap. 15.95 *(978-1-934738-26-9(3))* Printed Word Inc., The.

O'Connell, Liam. The Fire Philosophy: Cope Positively with Change & Live a Happy Life. 2012. (ENG., Illus.). 96p. pap. 8.95 ***(978-1-908086-91-4(2))*** Accent Pr. Ltd. GBR. Dist: SCB Distributors.

—My Fire's Gone Out! 2010. (ENG., Illus.). 84p. pap. 9.95 ***(978-1-907016-51-6(1))*** Accent Pr. Ltd. GBR. Dist: SCB Distributors.

O'Hanlon, Bill. Change 101: A Practical Guide to Creating Change in Life or Therapy. 2006. (ENG., Illus.). 184p. 23.95 *(978-0-393-70496-9(3),* 70496) Norton, W. W. & Co., Inc.

O'Hanlon, Bill. The Change Your Life Book. 2012. (ENG.). 144p. pap. 9.95 ***(978-0-7573-1631-9(X))*** Health Communications, Inc.

Olsen, Kaedrich. Runes for Transformation: Using Ancient Symbols to Change Your Life. 2008. (ENG., Illus.). 1p. pap. 16.95 *(978-1-57863-425-5(3),* Weiser Bks.) Red Wheel/Weiser.

Oz, Lisa. Us: Transforming Ourselves & the Relationships That Matter Most. (ENG.). 224p. 2011. pap. 14.00 *(978-1-4391-2394-2(2))* 2010. 26.00 *(978-1-4391-2392-8(6))* Free Pr. (Free Pr.).

Palmer. Life Transitions & Generational C. 2010. (Essential Coaching Skills & Knowledge Ser.). (ENG., Illus.). 240p. (C). 84.95 *(978-0-415-47359-0(4));* pap. 30.95 *(978-0-415-47360-6(8))* Routledge.

Pantalon, Michael. Instant Influence: How to Get Anyone to Do Anything — Fast. 2011. (ENG.). 256p. 25.99 *(978-0-316-08334-8(8))* Little Brown & Co.

Pate, Jennifer & Machen, Barbara. The Mothers of Reinvention: Reclaim Your Identity, Unleash Your Potential, Love Your Life. 2012. (ENG.). 256p. pap. 15.99 *(978-1-59315-683-1(9))* Vanguard Pr.

Patterson, Kerry, et al. Change Anything: The New Science of Personal Success. (ENG.). 288p. 2012. pap. 17.99 ***(978-0-446-57390-0(6))*** 2011. 26.99 *(978-0-446-57391-7(4))* Grand Central Publishing. (Business Plus).

Peitler, Erica. Open Up & Say Aaah! Discover... Who you are Now. Shape... Who you are Becoming. Create...What you Want to Experience. 2008. 219p. pap. 29.95 *(978-0-9815124-0-2(2))* Circle Takes The Square.

Pelzer, Dave. Moving Forward: Taking the Lead in Your Life. 2009. (ENG.). 224p. pap. 14.99 *(978-1-59995-066-2(9))* Center St.

Peterson, Andrew. The Next Ten Minutes: 51 Absurdly Simple Ways to Seize the Moment. 2010. pap. *(978-1-58270-277-3(2));* E-Book *(978-1-4391-9523-9(4));* (ENG.). 320p. 17.99 *(978-1-58270-274-2(8))* Atria Bks. (Beyond Words/Atria Bks.).

Porto, Patti. You Can't Change the Outside until You Change What's Inside. 2008. 80p. pap. 16.95 *(978-1-60441-427-1(8))* PublishAmerica, Inc.

Posen, David. Staying Afloat When the Water Gets Rough: How to Manage Your Life in a Rapidly Changing World. 2009. (ENG.). 232p. pap. 14.95 *(978-1-55470-224-4(0))* Key Porter Bks. CAN. Dist: Perseus-PGW.

Posen, David B. Always Change a Losing Game: Winning Strategies for Work, for Home & for Your Health. 2010. (ENG., Illus.). 270p. (J). pap. 14.95 *(978-1-55470-225-1(9))* Key Porter Bks. CAN. Dist: Perseus-PGW.

Preston, Teresa. My Devotion, My Heart: Spiritual Encouragement from My Heart to Yours. 2010. pap. 27.99 *(978-1-61566-460-3(2))* Tate Publishing & Enterprises, LLC.

Raelin, Jonathan D. Resistance to Change. 2008. 212p. pap. *(978-3-639-05542-9(X))* VDM Verlag Dr. Mueller e.K.

Rathgeber, Holger, et al. Our Iceberg Is Melting: Changing & Succeeding under Any Conditions. 2006. (ENG., Illus.). 160p. 19.99 *(978-0-312-36198-3(X))* St. Martin's Pr.

Reeves, Douglas B. & Allison, Elle. Renewal Coaching Workbook. 2010. (ENG.). 304p. pap. 35.00 *(978-0-470-41497-2(9),* Jossey-Bass) Wiley, John & Sons, Inc.

Reeves, Douglas B., et al. Renewal Coaching: Sustainable Change for Individuals & Organizations. 2009. (ENG., Illus.). 336p. 29.95 *(978-0-470-41496-5(0),* Jossey-Bass) Wiley, John & Sons, Inc.

Reid, Greg S. Everything Is Subject to Change: Finding Success When Life Shifts. 2010. (ENG.). 178p. pap. 19.95 *(978-0-9829850-0-7(2))* Sherpa Pr.

Robbins, Mel. Stop Saying You're Fine: Discover a More Powerful You. 2011. (ENG.). 272p. 24.00 *(978-0-307-71672-9(4),* Crown Archetype) Crown Publishing Group.

Robbins, Mel. Stop Saying You're Fine: The No-BS Guide to Getting What You Want. 2012. (ENG.). 272p. pap. 15.00 ***(978-0-307-71673-6(2),*** Three Rivers Pr.) Crown Publishing Group.

Romaner, Kim Marcille. The Science of Making Things Happen: Turn Any Possibility into Reality. 2010. (ENG.). 304p. pap. 14.95 *(978-1-57731-853-8(6))* New World Library.

Rosenthal, Robert S. From Plagues to Miracles: The Transformational Journey of Exodus, from the Slavery of Ego to the Promised Land of Spirit. 2012. (ENG.). 256p. pap. 15.95 ***(978-1-4019-3130-8(8))*** Hay Hse., Inc.

Rufus, Anneli. Stuck: Why We Can't (Or Won't) Move On. 2009. audio compact disk 29.95 *(978-1-59316-174-3(3))* Listen & Live Audio, Inc.

—Stuck: Why We Can't (Or Won't) Move On. 2009. (ENG.). 336p. (gr. 12-18). 15.95 *(978-1-58542-776-5(4),* Tarcher) Penguin Group (USA) Inc.

Ruti, Mari. The Case for Falling in Love: Why We Can't Master the Madness of Love — And Why That's the Best Part. 2011. (ENG.). 304p. 21.99 *(978-1-4022-5080-4(0),* Sourcebooks Casablanca) Sourcebooks, Inc.

Ruti, Mari. How to Look for Love: A Refreshing New Take on Men, Women, & Romance. 2012. (ENG.). 304p. pap. 14.99 ***(978-1-4022-6462-7(3),*** Sourcebooks Casablanca) Sourcebooks, Inc.

Saarinen, Risto. Weakness of Will in Renaissance & Reformation Thought. 2011. (ENG.). 256p. 75.00 *(978-0-19-960681-8(1))* Oxford Univ. Pr., Inc.

Salerno, Ann & Brock, Lillie. The Change Cycle: How People Can Survive & Thrive in Organizational Change. 2008. (Bk Business Ser.). (ENG., Illus.). 199p. pap. 19.95 *(978-1-57675-498-6(7))* Berrett-Koehler Pubs., Inc.

Salmansohn, Karen. How to Change Your Entire Life by Doing Absolutely: 10 Do-Nothing Relaxation Exercises to Calm You Dow. 2011. (ENG.). 112p. pap. 9.99 ***(978-1-4516-7704-1(9))*** Simon & Schuster.

Sandford, John Loren & Sandford, Paula. God's Power to Change: Healing the Wounded Spirit. 2007. (Transformation Ser.). (ENG., Illus.). 288p. pap. 14.99 *(978-1-59979-068-8(8),* Charisma Hse.) Charisma Media.

Schlossberg, Nancy K. Overwhelmed: Coping with Life's Ups & Downs. 2nd rev. ed. 2007. (ENG., Illus.). 216p. per. 14.95 *(978-1-59077-126-6(5))* Evans, M. & Co., Inc.

Schwartz, Jeffrey & Gladding, Rebecca. You Are Not Your Brain: The 4-Step Solution for Changing Bad Habits, Ending Unhealthy Thinking, & Taking Control of Your Life. 2011. (ENG.). 368p. (gr. 12). 26.00 *(978-1-58333-426-3(2),* Avery) Penguin Group (USA) Inc.

Seale, Alan. Create a World That Works: Tools for Personal & Global Transformation. 2011. (ENG.). 1p. pap. 17.95 *(978-1-57863-497-2(0),* Weiser Bks.) Red Wheel/Weiser.

Seasons of Change: A Journey of Self-Discovery. 2006. spiral bd. 19.95 *(978-0-9789183-0-9(4))* Foster Your Dreams, LLC.

Segalove, Ilene. 40 Days & 40 Nights: Taking Time Out for Self-Discovery. 2009. (ENG.). 272p. 14.99 *(978-0-7407-7995-4(8))* Andrews McMeel Publishing.

Seinz, Crystal. I Ching To Go. 2008. 146p. pap. 12.95 *(978-1-4199-8045-9(9))* Ellora's Cave Publishing, Inc.

Seligman, Martin E. What You Can Change & What You Can't: The Complete Guide to Successful Self-Improvement. 2007. (Vintage Ser.). (ENG.). 336p. pap. 15.00 *(978-1-4000-7840-0(7),* Vintage) Knopf Doubleday Publishing Group.

Smith, Judy. Good Self, Bad Self: Transforming Your Worst Qualities into Your Biggest Assets. 2012. (ENG.). 272p. 26.00 *(978-1-4516-4999-4(1),* Free Pr.) Free Pr.

Smith, Molly Dale. Transitional Ministry: A Time of Opportunity. 2009. 208p. pap. 20.00 *(978-0-89869-622-6(4))* Church Publishing, Inc.

Smith, Ward. Who Me? Choosing Radiance, A Better Way of Being. 2011. 140p. 29.99 ***(978-1-4628-5038-9(3));*** pap. 19.99 ***(978-1-4628-5037-2(5))*** Xlibris Corp.

St. Clair, Michael. So Much, So Fast, So Little Time: Coming to Terms with Rapid Change & Its Consequences, 1 vol. 2011. 235p. 44.95 *(978-0-313-39275-7(7,* A3294C); xi, 235p. E-Book *(978-0-313-39276-4(5),* Praeger Pubs.) Greenwood Publishing Group, Inc.

Stanley, Verdree B. Closed, yet in My Right Mind. 2009. 96p. pap. 19.95 *(978-1-4389-8614-2(9))* AuthorHouse.

Stivers, Jan. A Teacher's Guide to Change: Understanding, Navigating, & Leading the Process. Cramer, Sharon F., ed. 2009. (Illus.). 176p. 76.95 *(978-1-4129-6446-3(6),* B64463C); pap. 33.95 *(978-1-4129-6447-0(4),* B64463P) Corwin Pr.

Tiggelaar, Ben. Can Do! How to Achieve Real Personal Change & Growth. 2007. (ENG., Illus.). 302p. per. 26.95 *(978-1-904879-73-2(X))* Cyan Communications GBR. Dist: Independent Pubs. Group.

—Can Do! (New Edition) 2010. (Illus.). 288p. pap. *(978-0-462-09938-5(5))* Marshall Cavendish.

Tipton, Robert. Jump! - Get Unstuck: Extraordinary Life Breakthroughs Through Innovative Change. 2010. 280p. 24.95 *(978-0-9825900-0-3(8))* Alden Swain Pr.

Tirabassi, Becky. Keep the Change: Breaking Through to Permanent Transformation, 0 vols. 2008. 224p. per. 12.99 *(978-1-59145-122-8(1))* Nelson, Thomas Inc.

Tisdale, Stacey & Kennedy, Paula Boyer. The True Cost of Happiness: The Real Story Behind Managing Your Money. (ENG., Illus.). 288p. 2009. pap. 16.95 *(978-0-470-49657-2(6))* 2007. 24.95 *(978-0-470-13906-6(4))* Wiley, John & Sons, Inc. (Wiley).

Vaszily, Brian. The 9 Intense Experiences: An Action Plan to Change Your Life Forever. 2011. (ENG.). 288p. 24.95 *(978-0-470-59635-7(X),* Wiley) Wiley, John & Sons, Inc.

Viars, Stephen. Putting Your Past in Its Place: Moving Forward in Freedom & Forgiveness. 2011. 256p. pap. 12.99 *(978-0-7369-2739-0(5))* Harvest Hse. Pubs.

Watson, Irene & Volkman, Victor R., eds. The Story That Must Be Told: True Tales of Transformation. 2007. (ENG., Illus.). 204p. per. *(978-1-932690-35-5(7))* Loving Healing Pr., Inc.

Watzlawick, Paul, et al. Change: Principles of Problem Formulation & Problem Resolution. 2011. (ENG., Illus.). 200p. pap. 19.95 *(978-0-393-70706-9(7),* 70706) Norton, W. W. & Co., Inc.

Webster, Darryl K. Small Change: Great Impact! 2008. 96p. pap. 10.99 *(978-1-60647-865-3(6))* Xulon Pr., Inc.

Wehlander, Keri. Creating Change: The Arts as Catalyst for Spiritual Transformation. 2008. (ENG., Illus.). 160p. pap. 29.95 *(978-1-55145-568-6(4),* Copperhouse) Wood Lake Publishing, Inc. CAN. Dist: Westminster John Knox Pr.

Weil, Zoe. Most Good, Least Harm: A Simple Principle for a Better World & Meaningful Life. 2009. (ENG.). 224p. pap. 15.00 *(978-1-58270-206-3(3),* Beyond Words/Atria Bks.) Atria Bks.

Weiss, Avrum Geurin. Change Happens: When to Try Harder & When to Stop Trying So Hard. 2011. (ENG.). 188p. 32.95 ***(978-1-4422-1149-0(0))*** Rowman & Littlefield Publishers, Inc.

—Change Happens: When to Try Harder & When to Stop Trying So Hard. 2011. ***(978-1-4422-1151-3(2))*** Rowman & Littlefield Publishers, Inc.

What's My Purpose: A Journey of Personal & Professional Growth. 2007. 25.00 *(978-0-9795216-0-7(2))* JL White International, Inc.

White, Paula. Move on, Move Up: Turn Yesterday's Trials into Today's Triumphs. Lt. ed. 2008. (ENG.). 400p. pap. 21.99 *(978-0-446-54133-6(8))* FaithWords.

Whitney, George. A Time for Action. 2007. 112p. per. 11.95 *(978-0-595-45790-8(8))* iUniverse, Inc.

Womack, Jason W. Your Best Just Got Better: Work Smarter, Think Bigger, Make More. 2012. (ENG.). 272p. 24.95 ***(978-1-118-12198-6(8),*** Wiley) Wiley, John & Sons, Inc.

Wood, Elaine & Harrison, Elaine. Today Is the Day You Change Your Life. rev. ed. 2011. (ENG.). 184p. pap. 36.50 ***(978-0-273-75040-6(2))*** Pearson Education, Ltd. GBR. Dist: Trans-Atlantic Pubns., Inc.

Wynhausen, Elisabeth. On Resilience. 2010. (Little Books on Big Themes Ser.) (ENG.). 96p. 15.95 *(978-0-522-85663-7(2))* Melbourne Univ. Publishing AUS. Dist: Independent Pubs. Group.

You Can Only Hope to Contain Me: It is impossible to stop a person who won't Quit. 2008. 150p. pap. *(978-0-9662689-3-5(8))* Coloring Outside The Lines.

Your Best You: Discovering & Developing the Strengths God Gave You. 2009. (ENG.). 192p. pap. 14.99 *(978-0-8341-2439-4(4),* 9780834124394) Beacon Hill Pr. of Kansas City.

Zeff, Joel. Make the Right Choice: Creating a Positive, Innovative, & Productive Work Life. 2007. (ENG.). 176p. 21.95 *(978-0-470-05699-2(1),* Wiley) Wiley, John & Sons, Inc.

CHANGE, EDUCATIONAL

see Educational Change

CHANGE, LINGUISTIC

see Linguistic Change

CHANGE, SOCIAL

see Social Change

CHANGE IN PERSONALITY

see Personality Change

CHANGE OF ATTITUDE

see Attitude Change

CHANGE OF LIFE IN MEN

see Climacteric

CHANGE OF LIFE IN WOMEN

see Climacteric; Menopause

CHANGE OF SEX

see Sex Change

CHANGE OF STATE (PHYSICS)

American Society of Mechanical Engineers Staff, contrib. by. Proceedings of the 6th International Conference on Nanochannels, Microchannels & Minichannels, 2008: Presented at 6th International Conference on Nanochannels, Microchannels & Minichannels, June 23-25, 2008, Darmstadt, Germany: Sponsored by ASME, 2 vols. 2008. (Illus.). xxxiii, 1948p. pap. *(978-0-7918-4834-0(5))* American Society of Mechanical Engineers, The.

Carey, Van P. Liquid-Vapor Phase-Change Phenomena: An Introduction to the Thermophysics of Vaporization & Condensation Processes in Heat Transfer Equipment. 2nd rev. ed. 2007. (ENG., Illus.). 600p. (C). 125.95 *(978-1-59169-035-1(8),* Taylor & Francis) Taylor & Francis Group GBR. Dist: Taylor & Francis Group.

Cram101 Textbook Reviews & Cram101 Textbook Reviews. Outlines & Highlights for Liquid Vapor Phase Change Phenomena by Van P Carey, Isbn: 9781591690351 1591690358. 2011. 144p. pap. 28.95 ***(978-1-61490-070-2(1))*** Cram101 Inc.

Fortov, Vladimir E. Extreme States of Matter: On Earth & in the Cosmos. 2011. (Frontiers Collection). Orig. Title: Extreme States of Matter. (ENG., Illus.). xii, 333p. 99.00 *(978-3-642-16463-7(3),* 3642164633) Springer.

Kaviany, Massoud. Heat Transfer Physics. 2008. (ENG., Illus.). 688p. 139.00 *(978-0-521-89897-3(8))* Cambridge Univ. Pr.

Smirnov, Henry. Vaporization Heat Mass Transfer: In Capillaries & Porous Structures. 2009. (ENG., Illus.). 400p. 185.95 *(978-1-4200-6203-8(4),* CRC Press) Taylor & Francis Group GBR. Dist: Taylor & Francis Group.

CHANGE OF VOICE

see Voice, Change Of

CHANGE, LANDSCAPE

see Landscape Changes

CHANGING CAREERS

see Career Changes

C

CHANNEL ISLANDS
see also Guernsey (Channel Islands); Jersey (Channel Islands)
Backhurst, Marie-Louise. Tracing Your Channel Islands Ancestors. 2011. (Illus.). 224p. pap. 24.95 ***(978-1-84884-372-1(0))*** Pen & Sword Bks. Ltd. GBR. Dist: Casemate Pubs. & Bk. Distributors, LLC.
Pinnegar, Edward. Aviation in Alderney. 2011. (Illus.). 96p. pap. 19.95 *(978-1-84868-981-7(0))* Amberley Publishing GBR. Dist: Casemate Pubs. & Bk. Distributors, LLC.
Thin, Edmond. Channel Islands & Cotentin P. 2008. 128p. pap. 59.95 *(978-2-915762-66-2(X))* OREP Edition & Communication FRA. Dist: Casemate Pubs. & Bk. Distributors, LLC.

CHANNEL ISLANDS (CALIF.)
see also Santa Catalina Island (Calif.)
Fagan, Brian M., et al. Life on the Dunes. 2007. (ENG.). 200p. pap. 30.00 *(978-1-879442-96-2(5))* Statistical Res.
Hauf, Tim. Channel Islands National Park & National Marine Sanctuary. 2008. (Illus.). 159p. ***(978-0-9788219-2-0(0))***; pap. ***(978-0-9788219-3-7(9))*** Hauf, Tim Photography.

CHANNEL TUNNEL (ENGLAND AND FRANCE)
Cordner, Ken. Tunnel Vision. 2009. (ENG., Illus.). 96p. pap. 27.95 *(978-0-7110-3342-9(0))* Allan, Ian Publishing GBR. Dist: BookMasters Distribution Services (BDS).
Gourvish, Terry. The Official History of Britain & the Channel Tunnel. 2006. (Whitehall Histories: Government Official History Ser.). (ENG., Illus.). 544p. 120.00 *(978-0-415-39183-2(0))* Routledge.

CHANNEL ISLANDS—DESCRIPTION AND TRAVEL
Cecil Smith. Birds of Guernsey: And the Neighbouring Islands: Alderney Sark Jeth. l.t. ed. 2007. (ENG.). 166p. pap. 21.99 *(978-1-4264-8075-1(X))* BiblioBazaar.
Cumberlidge, Peter. North Brittany & Channel Islands Cruising Companion. 2nd ed. 2008. (ENG., Illus.). 288p. 49.95 *(978-0-470-98829-9(0)*, Wiley) Wiley, John & Sons, Inc.
Daniel, Geoff. Landscapes of Jersey: A Countryside Guide. 3rd rev. ed. (Illus.). 72p. pap. 9.95 *(978-1-85691-207-5(8))* Sunflower Bks. (UK) GBR. Dist: Hunter Publishing, Inc.
Daniel, Geoff & Earl, Tim. Landscapes of Guernsey: With Alderney, Sark & Herm: A Countryside Guide. 3rd ed. (Illus.). 72p. pap. 9.95 *(978-1-85691-227-3(2))* Hunter Publishing, Inc.
Daniel, Geoff & Sunflower Publishing Co. Staff. Guernsey: With Alderney, Sark & Herm. 4th rev. ed. 2008. (Illus.). 72p. pap. 9.99 *(978-1-85691-344-7(9))* Hunter Publishing, Inc.
McAlpine, Ken. Islands Apart: A Year on the Edge of Civilization. 2009. (ENG.). 272p. pap. 16.95 *(978-1-59030-530-0(2)*, Trumpeter) Shambhala Pubns., Inc.
Rothwell, Catherine. Around the Channel Islands. 2008. (ENG.). 128p. pap. 30.95 *(978-0-7509-4958-3(9))* History Pr. Ltd.,The GBR. Dist: Independent Pubs. Group.
Suffling, Ernest R. Jethou: Or Crusoe Life in the Channel Isles. 2007. 200p. pap. 19.99 *(978-1-4346-1182-6(5))*; (ENG.). 222p. pap. 22.99 *(978-1-4346-1253-3(8))* BiblioBazaar.

CHANNELING (SPIRITUALISM)
Alex & Wedel, Michelle. Lesson Book II. Wedel, Paul, ed. 2007. 260p. pap. 14.95 *(978-0-9745434-9-9(7)*, Sweetgrass Pr.) Sweetgrass Pr., L.L.C.
Banducci, Sandra. Conversations with Raine: Guidance in the New Millennium. 2007. 158p. pap. 13.00 *(978-0-9792700-2-4(2))* Kitsune Bks.
Bolduc, Henry Leo. The Journey Within: Past-Life Regression & Channeling. 2010. 304p. pap. 19.95 *(978-1-929661-38-1(X))* Transpersonal Publishing.
Browne, Sylvia. Past Lives of the Rich & Famous. 2012. (ENG.). 256p. 25.99 ***(978-0-06-196681-1(9)***, HarperOne) HarperCollins Pubs.
—Past Lives of the Rich & Famous LP. l.t. ed. 2012. (ENG.). 256p. pap. 25.99 ***(978-0-06-220159-1(X)***, HarperLuxe) HarperCollins Pubs.
Choquette, Sonia. Soul Lessons & Soul Purpose: A Channeled Guide to Why You Are Here. 2008. (ENG.). 256p. pap. 14.95 *(978-1-4019-0789-1(X))* 2007. 229p. 24.95 *(978-1-4019-0788-4(1))* Hay Hse., Inc.
Devereau, Sherri Lee. Shadows on My Shift: Real-Life Stories of a Psychic EMT. 2006. (Illus.). 120p. per. 14.95 *(978-1-891724-08-4(8))* New River Pr.
Dewey, Linda Alice. Aaron's Crossing: An Inspiring True Ghost Story. 2006. (ENG.). 232p. per. 16.95 *(978-1-57174-512-5(2))* Hampton Roads Publishing Co., Inc.
DuBois, Allison. We Are Their Heaven: Why the Dead Never Leave Us. 2007. (ENG.). 240p. pap. 14.00 *(978-0-7432-9113-2(1)*, Touchstone) Touchstone.
Emery, Kevin Ross & Hensel, Thomas A. Good Settles Greatness Soars: The Journey from Great to Greatness. 2011. pap. 14.95 *(978-1-890405-07-6(8))* Lightlines Publishing Co.
Ezekiah & Wedel, Michelle. Channeling: A Comprehensive & Instructional Guide. Wedel, Paul, ed. 2007. 272p. pap. 14.95 *(978-0-9745434-5-1(4))* Sweetgrass Pr., L.L.C.
Farley, B. When Horses Run You Will Know the Meaning of the Times. 2006. (ENG.). 88p. per. 10.00 *(978-1-4257-5001-5(X))* Xlibris Corp.
Galvan, Jill Nicole. The Sympathetic Medium: Feminine Channeling, the Occult, & Communication Technologies, 1859-1919. 2010. (Illus.). 224p. 45.00 *(978-0-8014-4801-0(8))* Cornell Univ. Pr.
Graviet, Xandra A. Angel in Disguise. 2006. pap. *(978-1-928806-15-8(5))* Lightworker Pubns.
Holland, Eileen. The Wicca Handbook. 2nd rev. ed. 2008. (ENG.). 1p. pap. 16.95 *(978-1-57863-438-5(5)*, Weiser Bks.) Red Wheel/Weiser.
Knight-Jadczyk, Laura. Soul Hackers: The Hidden Hands Behind the New Age Movement, 8 vols., Vol. 2. 3rd ed. 2010. (Illus.). 364p. pap. *(978-1-897244-51-7(7))* Red Pill Pr.
Mallasz, Gitta. Talking with Angels. 4th ed. 2006. (ENG.). 473p. per. 29.00 *(978-3-85630-704-2(4)*, 255-088) Daimon Verlag CHE. Dist: AtlasBooks Distribution.
Marston, Moriah. Soul Searching with Djwahl Khul, the Tibetan. 2006. 248p. per. 19.95 *(978-1-60002-220-3(0)*, 4122) Mountain Valley Publishing, LLC.
Messenger, Gloria. A Mirroring Discovery... with Angelic Visitation! 2011. 320p. 37.95 ***(978-1-4525-4008-5(X))***; pap. 20.99 ***(978-1-4525-4009-2(8))*** Balboa Pr.
Missett, Bill. Awakening the Soul: The Trilogy. 2008. 732p. pap. 25.99 *(978-1-4343-7122-5(0))* AuthorHouse.
Morel, John Henry. Great Whale. 2009. 180p. 29.99 *(978-1-935436-53-9(8))* Rodaian Pr.
Mountain, Blue. Awakening. 2008. 140p. per. *(978-1-84748-055-2(1))* Athena Pr.
Parsons, Dh. The Strong Witch Society. 2011. 206p. pap. 16.99 ***(978-0-9846297-3-2(4))*** All Things That Matter Pr.
Paul, Sarah. Spiritual Culture: A Channeled Galaxy Teacher Book. 2012. (ENG.). 158p. pap. 14.00 ***(978-1-4679-0962-4(9))*** CreateSpace.
Reed, Henry & Cayce, Charles Thomas. Edgar Cayce on Channeling Your Higher Self. 2007. (Illus.). 308p. pap. *(978-0-87604-531-2(X))* A.R.E. Pr.
Ripley, Frances. Visions Unseen: Aspects of the Natural Realm. 2007. (ENG., Illus.). 96p. pap. 27.95 *(978-1-84409-093-8(0))* Findhorn Pr. GBR. Dist: Independent Pubs. Group.
Roman, Sanaya & Packer, Duane. Creating Money: Attracting Abundance. 2nd rev. ed. 2007. (Roman, Sanaya Ser.). (ENG.). 288p. per. 13.95 *(978-1-932073-22-5(1))* Kramer, H.J. Inc.
Rosen, Rebecca & Rose, Samantha. Spirited: Connect to the Guides All Around You. 2010. 272p. 24.99 *(978-0-06-176624-4(0))* HarperCollins Pubs.
—Spirited: Unlock Your Psychic Self & Change Your Life. 2011. (ENG.). 272p. pap. 13.99 *(978-0-06-176625-1(9)*, HarperPerennial) HarperCollins Pubs.
Scott, Grace J. Beyond Cell Memory: Messages from Creator on Origin, Purpose, & Use of Dna & Cell Memory. 2011. 240p. 29.95 ***(978-1-4620-3713-1(5))***; pap. 19.95 ***(978-1-4620-3714-8(3))*** iUniverse, Inc.
Scott, Grace J. Heroes Without Halos. 2008. 432p. pap. 26.95 *(978-0-595-52061-9(8))* iUniverse, Inc.
Simpson, Jean. The Meaning Behind the Meeting. 2006. (ENG.). 132p. per. 24.95 *(978-1-4241-3405-2(6))* PublishAmerica, Inc.
St. Germain, Adamus, et al. Live Your Divinity: Inspiration for New Consciousness. 2012. (ENG.). 1p. pap. 16.95 ***(978-1-57863-524-5(1)***, Weiser Bks.) Red Wheel/Weiser.
Stevens, Ramon. Conscious Life: Creating Your Reality. 2nd rev. ed. 2009. (ENG.). 298p. pap. 15.95 *(978-0-9639413-2-9(1))* Pepperwood Pr.
Straughan, Roger. A Study in Survival: Conan Doyle Solves the Final Problem. 2009. (ENG.). 224p. pap. 24.95 *(978-1-84694-240-2(3))* Hunt, John Publishing Ltd. GBR. Dist: National Bk. Network.
Strub, Sherry. Ghosts of Madison, Wisconsin. 2008. (Illus.). 224p. pap. 14.99 *(978-0-7643-3072-8(1))* Schiffer Publishing, Ltd.
Taylor, Barbara J. Concordance to the Michael Teachings. 2009. 156p. pap. 21.90 *(978-0-557-08067-0(3))* Lulu Enterprises Inc.
Wiseman, Sara. Writing the Divine: How to Use Channeling for Soul Growth & Healing. 2009. (ENG.). 312p. pap. 16.95 *(978-0-7387-1581-0(6))* Llewellyn Pubns.
Woodward, Bob. Spirit Communications. 2007. 168p. per. *(978-1-84401-959-5(4))* Athena Pr.
Worth, Patience. The Patience Worth Record: Volume I. 2008. 348p. pap. 16.80 *(978-1-4357-1237-9(4))* Lulu Enterprises Inc.

CHANNELS (HYDRAULIC ENGINEERING)
see also Aqueducts; Canals; Harbors; Lakes; Waterways
Barkdoll, Brian D., et al. Countermeasures to Protect Bridge Abutments from Scour. 2007. (Illus.). 220p. 53.00 *(978-0-309-09895-3(5))* Transportation Research Board.
Barr, D. I. & Wallingford, H. R. Additional Tables for the Hydraulic Design of Pipes, Sewers & Channels. (Illus.). 224p. 79.00 *(978-0-7277-1667-5(0))* Telford, Thomas Ltd. GBR. Dist: Routledge, Chapman & Hall, Inc.
Biron, Pascale, et al, eds. Gravel Bed Rivers: Processes, Tools, Environments. 2nd ed. 2012. (ENG., Illus.). 580p. 129.95 ***(978-0-470-68890-8(4)***, Wiley-Blackwell) Wiley, John & Sons, Inc.
Chaudhry, M. Hanif. Open-Channel Flow. 2nd rev. ed. 2007. (ENG., Illus.). xvi, 523p. 109.00 *(978-0-387-30174-7(7)*, 0387301747) Springer.
Cram101 Textbook Reviews & Cram101 Textbook Reviews. Outlines & Highlights for Open Channel Hydraulics by Terry W Sturm. 2011. 118p. pap. 28.95 ***(978-1-61830-791-0(6))*** Cram101 Inc.
Dingman, S. Lawrence. Fluvial Hydraulics: An Introduction to Fluvial Hydraulics & Hydrology. 2009. (ENG., Illus.). 416p. 95.00 *(978-0-19-517286-7(8))* Oxford Univ. Pr., Inc.
Hunt, Beatrice E. Monitoring Scour Critical Bridges. 2009. (Illus.). 158p. *(978-0-309-09834-2(3))* Transportation Research Board.
Jeppson, Roland. Open Channel Flow: Numerical Methods & Computer Applications. 2010. (ENG., Illus.). 1258p. 189.95 *(978-1-4398-3975-1(1)*, CRC Press) Taylor & Francis Group GBR. Dist: Taylor & Francis Group.
Knight, Donald W., et al. Practical Channel Hydraulics: Roughness, Conveyance & Afflux. 2009. (ENG., Illus.). 470p. (C). 124.95 *(978-0-415-54974-5(4)*, CRC Press) Taylor & Francis Group GBR. Dist: Taylor & Francis Group.
Lagasse, Peter F. Countermeasures to Protect Bridge Piers from Scour. 2007. (Illus.). 60.00 *(978-0-309-09909-7(9))* Transportation Research Board.
Lewis, Jason M. Estimation of Annual Suspended-Sediment Fluxes, 1931-95, & Evaluation of Geomorphic Changes, 1950-2010, in the Arkansas River near Tulsa, Oklahoma. 2011. (Illus.). v, 22p. ***(978-1-4113-3165-5(6))*** United States Geological Survey.
McAnally, William H. Navigation Engineering Practice & Ethical Standards. 2008. (Illus.). 120p. 79.00 *(978-0-7844-0992-3(7))* American Society of Civil Engineers.
Molina, Daniel A. River Channels: Types, Dynamics & Changes. 2012. (Earth Sciences in the 21st Century Ser.). 210p. 95.00 ***(978-1-61324-148-6(8))*** Nova Science Pubs., Inc.
Srivastava, Rajesh. Flow Through Open Channels. 2008. (ENG., Illus.). 432p. 38.00 *(978-0-19-569038-5(9))* Oxford Univ. Pr., Inc.
Sturm, Terry W. Open Channel Hydraulics. 2nd ed. 2009. (ENG., Illus.). 576p. (C). 204.00 *(978-0-07-339787-0(3)*, 0073397873, McGraw-Hill Science, Engineering & Mathematics) McGraw-Hill Higher Education.
Szymkiewicz, Romuald. Open Channel Flow Modelling. 2010. (Water Science & Technology Library). (ENG.). x, 370p. 199.00 *(978-90-481-3673-5(3)*, 9048136733) Springer.

CHANNING, WILLIAM ELLERY, 1780-1842
Addison, Daniel Dulany. Clergy in American Life & Letters. 2006. pap. 34.95 *(978-1-4286-3782-5(6))* Kessinger Publishing, LLC.
Brown, Arthur W. Always Young for Liberty: A Biography of William Ellery Channing. 2011. 280p. 47.95 ***(978-1-258-01281-6(2))*** Literary Licensing, LLC.
Chadwick, John White. William Ellery Channing: Minister of Religion. 2007. (ENG.). 488p. 53.95 *(978-0-548-08988-0(4))* Kessinger Publishing, LLC.
Channing, William E. The Works of William Ellery Channing, 6 Vols. reprint ed. 750.00 *(978-0-7222-9713-1(0))* Library Reprints, Inc.
Channing, William Ellery. Memoir of William Ellery Channing V1 Wit. 2006. pap. 36.95 *(978-1-4286-4058-0(4))* Kessinger Publishing, LLC.
—Memoir of William Ellery Channing V2 Wit. 2006. pap. 37.95 *(978-1-4286-4059-7(2))* Kessinger Publishing, LLC.
Eliot, Charles William. Four American Leaders. 2007. (ENG.). 48p. per. *(978-1-4065-1796-5(8))* Dodo Pr.
—Four American Leaders. 2008. (ENG.). 136p. per. *(978-1-4086-6480-3(1))* Read Bks.
Guiducci, James V. Natural Religion against Slavery: William Ellery Channing on Slavery. 2007. pap. 10.00 *(978-0-8059-7185-9(8))* Dorrance Publishing Co., Inc.

CHANSON DE ROLAND
Burland, Margaret Jewett. Strange Words: Retelling & Reception in the Medieval Roland Textual Tradition. 2007. (ENG.). 376p. per. 37.00 *(978-0-268-02203-7(8))* Univ. of Notre Dame Pr.
Kibler, William W. & Morgan, Leslie Zarker, eds. The Song of Roland. 2006. (Approaches to Teaching World Literature Ser.: Vol. 92). (Illus.). 317p. 37.50 incl. audio compact disk *(978-0-87352-998-3(7))* Modern Language Assn. of America.
Morgan, Leslie Zarker & Kibler, William, eds. The Song of Roland. 2006. (Approaches to Teaching World Literature Ser.: Vol. 92). (Illus.). 317p. pap. 19.75 incl. audio compact disk *(978-0-87352-999-0(5))* Modern Language Assn. of America.
Pei, Mario A. French Precursors of the Chanson De Roland. reprint ed. 20.00 *(978-0-404-04967-6(2))* AMS Pr., Inc.

CHANSONS DE GESTE
see also Byliny
Hartman, A. Richard & Malicote, Sandra, eds. Elye of Saint-Gilles: A Chanson de Geste. Hartman, A. Richard & Malicote, Sandra, trs. from FEM. 2010. (ENG & FRO., Illus.). 266p. 30.00 *(978-1-59910-191-0(2))*; pap. 15.00 *(978-1-59910-192-7(0))* Italica Pr.
James, G. P. R. The History of Charlemagne: with a Sketch of the State & History. 2007. (ENG.). 532p. per. 40.95 *(978-1-4304-4361-2(8))* Kessinger Publishing, LLC.

CHANSONS DE GESTE—HISTORY AND CRITICISM
Gaffney, Phyllis. Constructions of Youth in Old French Narrative: Writing the Medieval Child. 2011. 244p. 99.95 *(978-0-7546-6920-3(3))* Ashgate Publishing Co.
Leverage, Paula. Reception & Memory: A Cognitive Approach to the Chansons de Geste. 2010. (ENG., Illus.). 338p. pap. 88.00 *(978-90-420-3042-8(9))* Rodopi.
Malicote, Sandra. Image & Imagination: Picturing the Old French Epic. 2009. (ENG., Illus.). 220p. pap. 31.50 *(978-0-7618-4832-5(0))* Univ. Pr. of America, Inc.
Ribémont, Bernard. Crimes et Châtiments Dans la Chanson de Geste. 2008. (FRE.). 364p. (C). pap. 44.00 ***(978-2-252-03669-3(9))*** Klincksieck, Editions FRA. Dist: ISD.
Sinclair, Keith V. Tristan de Nanteuil: Thematic infrastructure & literary Creation. (Beihefte zur Zeitschrift fur romanische Philologie Ser.). (ENG.). XVII, 167p. 210.00 ***(978-3-11-192886-9(1))*** De Gruyter, Mouton DEU. Dist: de Gruyter, Walter GmbH & Co. KG.

CHANTEYS
see Sea Songs

CHANTS
see also Buddhist Chants; Byzantine Chants; Gregorian Chants; Hindu Chants; Jewish Chants
Bourgeault, Cynthia. Chanting the Psalms: A Practical Guide with Instructional CD. 2006. (Illus.). 240p. pap. 24.95 *(978-1-59030-257-6(5)*, New Seeds Bks.) Shambhala Pubns., Inc.
Kelly, Thomas Forrest & Mugmon, Matthew, eds. Ambrosiana at Harvard: New Sources of Milanese Chant. 2010. (Houghton Library Studies: 3). (Illus.). 172p. pap. 35.00 *(978-0-9818858-0-3(2))* Harvard Univ. Pr.
Levitt, Jo Ann & Norian, Todd, eds. Sounds of the Sacred: Chants of Love & Prayer. (Illus.). 158p. (Orig.). pap. 14.95 *(978-0-940258-23-5(4))* Kripalu Pubns.
Sha, Zhi Gang. Divine Soul Songs: Sacred Practical Treasures to Heal, Rejuvenate, & Transform You, Humanity, Mother Earth, & All Universes. 2010. (ENG., Illus.). 384p. pap. 16.00 *(978-1-4391-2974-6(6))*, Beyond Words/Atria Bks.) Atria Bks.
Sha, Zhi Gang. Tao Song & Tao Dance: Sacred Sound, Movement, & Power from the Source for Healing, Rejuvenation, Longevity, & Transformation of All Life. 2011. (ENG., Illus.). 416p. 29.95 ***(978-1-4516-7312-8(4)***, Beyond Words/Atria Bks.) Atria Bks.

CHANTRIES
Luxford, Julian & McNeill, John, eds. The Medieval Chantry in England & Wales. 2012. (Journal of the British Archaeological Association Ser.). (ENG.). 368p. (C). 88.00 *(978-1-907975-16-5(0))* Maney Publishing GBR. Dist: Brown, David Bk. Co., The.
Roffey, Simon. Chantry Chapels: And Medieval Strategies for the Afterlife. 2008. (ENG., Illus.). 208p. pap. 42.95 *(978-0-7524-4571-7(5))* History Pr. Ltd.,The GBR. Dist: Independent Pubs. Group.
Rousseau, Marie-Helene. Saving the Souls of Medieval London: Perpetual Chantries at St Paul's Cathedral C., 1200-1548. 2011. (Church, Faith & Culture in the Medieval West Ser.). (Illus.). 256p. 124.95 *(978-1-4094-0581-8(8))* Ashgate Publishing Co.
Wood-Legh, K. L. Perpetual Chantries in Britain. 2008. (ENG.). 376p. pap. 48.00 *(978-0-521-08957-9(3))* Cambridge Univ. Pr.

CHANTS (BUDDHIST)
see Buddhist Chants

CHANTS (BYZANTINE)
see Byzantine Chants

CHANTS (HINDU)
see Hindu Chants

CHANTS (JEWISH)
see Jewish Chants

CHANTS (PLAIN, GREGORIAN, ETC.)
see Gregorian Chants

CHANTYS
see Sea Songs

CHANUKAH
see Hanukkah

CHAOS THEORY
see Chaotic Behavior in Systems

CHAOTIC BEHAVIOR IN SYSTEMS
Adeli, Hojjat & Jiang, Xiaomo. Intelligent Infrastructure: Neural Networks, Wavelets, & Chaos Theory for Intelligent Transportation Systems & Smart Structures. 2008. (ENG., Illus.). 440p. 179.95 *(978-1-4200-8536-5(0)*, CRC Press) Taylor & Francis Group GBR. Dist: Taylor & Francis Group.
Al. Advanced Topics on Cellular Self-Orga... 2008. (Illus.). xvi, 191p. 87.00 *(978-981-281-404-3(3))* World Scientific Publishing Co., Inc.
—Topics on Chaotic Systems. 2009. 124.00 *(978-981-4271-33-2(0))* World Scientific Publishing Co., Inc.
Anishchenko, Vadim S., et al. Nonlinear Dynamics of Chaotic & Stochastic Systems: Tutorial & Modern Developments. 2nd rev. ed. 2007. (Springer Series in Synergetics Ser.). (Illus.). XVI, 450p. 129.00 *(978-3-540-38164-8(3)*, 3540381643) Springer.
Anosov, D. V., ed. Dynamical Systems IX: Dynamical Systems with Hyperbolic Behaviour. Gould, G. G., tr. from RUS. 2010. (Encyclopaedia of Mathematical Sciences Ser.). (Illus.). vii, 235p. pap. 169.00 *(978-3-642-08168-2(1)*, 3642081681) Springer.
Ausloos, Marcel & Dirickx, Michel, eds. The Logistic Map & the Route to Chaos: From the Beginnings to Modern Applications. 2010. (Understanding Complex Systems Ser.). (Illus.). xx, 413p. pap. 169.00 *(978-3-642-06657-3(7)*, 3642066577) Springer.
Awrejcewicz, Jan & Krys'ko, Vadim Anatolevich. Chaos in Structural Mechanics. 2010. (Understanding Complex Systems Ser.). (Illus.). xiii, 424p. pap. 189.00 *(978-3-642-09645-7(X)*, 364209645X) Springer.
Awrejcewicz, Jan & Krysko, Vadim Anatolevich. Chaos in Structural Mechanics. 2008. (Understanding Complex Systems Ser.). (Illus.). 424p. 189.00 *(978-3-540-77675-8(3))* Springer.
Bakunin, Oleg G. Chaotic Flows: Correlation Effects, Transport, & Structures. 2011. (Springer Series in Synergetics Ser.). (ENG., Illus.). xx, 351p. 99.00 *(978-3-642-20349-7(3)*, 3642203493) Springer.
Ball, Philip. Branches: Nature's Patterns, 3 vols. 2011. (ENG., Illus.). 240p. pap. 18.95 *(978-0-19-960488-3(6))* Oxford Univ. Pr., Inc.
—Branches: Nature's Patterns - A Tapestry in Three Parts, 3 vols. 2009. (ENG., Illus.). 272p. 29.95 *(978-0-19-923798-2(0))* Oxford Univ. Pr., Inc.
—Flow: Nature's Patterns - A Tapestry in Three Parts, 3 vols. (ENG., Illus.). 2011. 208p. pap. 18.95 *(978-0-19-960487-6(8))* 2009. 272p. 29.95 *(978-0-19-923797-5(2))* Oxford Univ. Pr., Inc.

—Shape - Nature's Patterns: A Tapestry in Three Parts, 3 vols. 2009. (ENG., Illus.). 320p. 29.95 (978-0-19-923796-8(4)) Oxford Univ. Pr., Inc.

—Shapes: Nature's Patterns - A Tapestry in Three Parts, 3 vols. 2011. (ENG., Illus.). 320p. pap. 18.95 (978-0-19-960486-9(X)) Oxford Univ. Pr., Inc.

Banerjee, Santo. Chaos Synchronization & Cryptography for Secure Communications: Applications for Encryption. 2010. (Illus.). 350p. 180.00 (978-1-61520-737-4(6)) IGI Global.

Baofu. The Future of Complexity. 2007. (C). 124.00 (978-981-270-898-4(7)) World Scientific Publishing Co., Inc.

Becerra Alonso, David. Deterministic Chaos in Malkus' Waterwheel. 2010. 152p. pap. (978-3-8383-5864-2(3)) Lambert Academic Publishing.

Bejan, Adrian & Zane, J. Peder. Design in Nature: How the Constructal Law Governs Evolution in Biology, Physics, Technology, & Social Organization. 2012. (ENG., Illus.). 304p. 27.95 **(978-0-385-53461-1(2)**, Doubleday) Knopf Doubleday Publishing Group.

Belbruno, Edward. Fly Me to the Moon: An Insider's Guide to the New Science of Space Travel. 2007. (ENG., Illus.). 176p. (C). 19.95 (978-0-691-12822-1(7)) Princeton Univ. Pr.

Benest, Daniel & Froeschle, Claude, eds. Singularities in Gravitational Systems: Applications to Chaotic Transport in the Solar System. 2010. (Lecture Notes in Physics Ser.). xi, 215p. pap. 69.95 (978-3-642-07844-6(3), 3642078443) Springer.

Bezruchko, Boris & Smirnov, Dmitry. Extracting Knowledge from Time Series: An Introduction to Nonlinear Empirical Modeling. 2010. (Springer Series in Synergetics Ser.). (ENG., Illus.). 124.00 (978-3-642-12600-0(6), 3642126006) Springer.

Blumel, Reinhold. Advanced Quantum Mechanics. 2010. (Illus.). 430p. 104.95 (978-1-934015-52-0(0)) Jones & Bartlett Learning, LLC.

Bolotin, Yurii, et al. Chaos: Concepts, Control & Constructive Use. 2009. (Illus.). viii, 198p. **(978-3-642-00937-2(9))** Springer.

Bolotin, Yurii, et al. Chaos: Concepts, Control & Constructive Use: Concepts, Control & Constructive Use. 2009. (Understanding Complex Systems Ser.). (ENG., Illus.). viii, 198p. 159.00 (978-3-642-00936-5(0), 3642009360) Springer.

Bolotnov, A. V. Verbalizatsiia Kontsepta Khaos V Poeticheskom Diskurse Serebrianogo Veka: Na Materiale Tvorchestva M.I. TSvetaevoi, M.A. Voloshina, O.E. Mandelshtama Monografiia. 2010. (RUS., Illus.). 286p. (978-5-89428-492-7(9)) Tomskij Gosudarstvennyj Pedagogiceskij Universitet.

Bossomaier, Terry R. J. & Green, David G., eds. Complex Systems. 2007. (ENG., Illus.). 420p. (C). pap. 83.00 (978-0-521-04371-7(9)) Cambridge Univ. Pr.

Brady, Bernadette. Astrology a Place in Chaos. 2006. pap. (978-1-902405-21-6(8)) Wessex Astrologer Ltd., The.

Braun, Eliezer. Caos, Fractales y Cosas Raras. 2nd ed. (Ciencia para Todos Ser.). (SPA., Illus.). 154p. pap. 6.99 (978-968-16-5070-4(0)) Fondo de Cultura Economica USA.

Breban, Romulus. Progress in Low-Dimensional Chaos. 2011. 104p. pap. **(978-3-8433-7107-0(5))** Lambert Academic Publishing.

Broer, Henk & Takens, Floris. Dynamical Systems & Chaos. 2010. (Applied Mathematical Sciences Ser.). (Illus.). xvi, 313p. 74.95 (978-1-4419-6869-2(5), 1441968695) Springer.

Cahill, Kevin M., ed. Even in Chaos: Education in Times of Emergency. 3rd ed. 2010. (International Humanitarian Affairs Ser.). (ENG.). 330p. 70.00 (978-0-8232-3196-6(8)) Fordham Univ. Pr.

—Even in Chaos: Education in Times of Emergency. 3rd ed. 2010. (International Humanitarian Affairs Ser.). (ENG.). 330p. pap. 28.00 (978-0-8232-3197-3(6)) Fordham Univ. Pr.

Callebaut, Werner & Rasskin-Gutman, Diego, eds. Modularity: Understanding the Development & Evolution of Natural Complex Systems. 2009. (Vienna Series in Theoretical Biology Ser.). (ENG., Illus.). 472p. (gr. 17). pap. 29.00 (978-0-262-51326-5(9)) MIT Pr.

Caragata, Daniel, et al. Development of Some Encryption Algorithms Using Chaotic Functions. 2011. 88p. pap. **(978-3-8454-0172-0(9))** Lambert Academic Publishing.

Casati, Giulio & Chirikov, Boris, eds. Quantum Chaos: Between Order & Disorder. 2006. (ENG., Illus.) 700p. pap. 130.00 (978-0-521-03166-0(4)) Cambridge Univ. Pr.

Castiglione, Patrizia, et al. Chaos & Coarse Graining in Statistical Mechanics. 2008. (ENG., Illus.). 280p. 120.00 (978-0-521-89593-4(6)) Cambridge Univ. Pr.

Celletti, Alessandra. Stability & Chaos in Celestial Mechanics. 2009. (Springer Praxis Books / Astronomy & Planetary Sciences Ser.). (ENG., Illus.). xvi, 264p. 139.00 (978-3-540-85145-5(3), 3540851453) Springer.

Celletti, Alessandra & Ferraz-Mello, Sylvio, eds. Periodic, Quasi-Periodic & Chaotic Motions in Celestial Mechanics: Theory & Applications: Theory & Applications. 2010. (ENG.). viii, 440p. pap. 199.00 (978-90-481-7340-2(X), 904817340X) Springer.

Cels. Recent Progress in Controlling Chaos. 2010. 450p. 135.00 (978-981-4291-69-9(2)) World Scientific Publishing Co., Inc.

Cencini & Vulpiani, Angelo. Chaos: From Simple Models to Complex Systems. 2009. (Illus.). 480p. 99.00 (978-981-4277-65-5(7)) World Scientific Publishing Co., Inc.

Chandre, Cristel, et al, eds. Chaos, Complexity & Transport: Theory & Applications. 2008. (Illus.). 364p. 124.00 (978-981-281-879-9(0)) World Scientific Publishing Co., Inc.

Charpentier, Eric, et al, eds. The Scientific Legacy of Poincare. 2010. (History of Mathematics Ser.). (FRE., Illus.). 391p. 89.00 (978-0-8218-4718-3(X)) American Mathematical Society.

Chau, K. T. & Wang, Zheng. Chaos in Electric Drive Systems: Analysis, Control & Application. 2011. (ENG., Illus.). 288p. 149.95 (978-0-470-82633-1(9), Wiley) Wiley, John & Sons, Inc.

Chen, Goong & Huang, Yu. Dynamical Systems & Chaos. 2011. (Synthesis Lectures on Mathematics & Statistics Ser.). 100p. pap. 35.00 (978-1-59829-914-4(X)) Morgan & Claypool Pubs.

Chernov, Nikolai & Markarian, Roberto. Chaotic Billiards. 2006. (Mathematical Surveys & Monographs Ser.). (Illus.). 316p. (C). 88.00 (978-0-8218-4096-2(7)) American Mathematical Society.

Coles, Peter. From Cosmos to Chaos: The Science of Unpredictability. 2006. (ENG., Illus.). 224p. 60.00 (978-0-19-856762-2(6)) Oxford Univ. Pr., Inc.

—From Cosmos to Chaos: The Science of Unpredictability. 2010. (ENG., Illus.). 224p. pap. 26.95 (978-0-19-958814-5(7)) Oxford Univ. Pr., Inc.

Colinet, Pierre & Nepomnyashchy, Alexander. Pattern Formation at Interfaces. 2010. (CISM International Centre for Mechanical Sciences Ser.). (Illus.). viii, 304p. 209.00 (978-3-7091-0124-7(7), 3709101247) Springer.

Contopoulos, George. Order & Chaos in Dynamical Astronomy. 2010. (Astronomy & Astrophysics Library). (Illus.). xiv, 624p. pap. 169.00 (978-3-642-07770-8(6), 3642077706) Springer.

Contopoulos, George & Patsis, Peter. Chaos in Astronomy: Conference 2007. 2008. (Astrophysics & Space Science Proceedings Ser.). (Illus.). 480p. 219.00 (978-3-540-75825-9(9)) Springer.

Coronado, Gabriela, et al. Chaos Theory & the Larrikin Principle. 2010. (Illus.). 243p. pap. 32.00 (978-87-630-0235-6(3)) Copenhagen Business Schl. Pr. DNK. Dist: International Specialized Bk. Services.

Cram101 Textbook Reviews Staff. Outlines & Highlights for Differential Equations, Dynamical Systems, & an Introduction to Chaos by Morris W Hirsch, Stephen Smale, Robert Devaney. 2009. 98p. pap. 27.95 (978-1-4288-7465-7(8)) Cram101 Inc.

Cvitanovic, P., et al, eds. Quantum Chaos - Quantum Measurement. 2010. (NATO Science Series C: (closed) Ser.). 348p. pap. 359.00 (978-90-481-4120-3(6), 9048141206) Springer.

Denz, Cornelia, et al. Transverse-Pattern Formation in Photorefractive Optics. 2010. (Springer Tracts in Modern Physics Ser.). (Illus.). xviii, 332p. pap. 299.00 (978-3-642-05693-2(8), 3642056938) Springer.

Diacu, Florin. Megadisasters: The Science of Predicting the Next Catastrophe. 2009. (ENG., Illus.). 216p. 24.95 (978-0-691-13350-8(6)) Princeton Univ. Pr.

Driebe, Dean J. Fully Chaotic Maps & Broken Time Symmetry. 2010. (Nonlinear Phenomena & Complex Systems Ser.). (Illus.). 174p. pap. 135.00 (978-90-481-5168-4(6), 9048151686) Springer.

Dmner, Dietrich. Between Chaos & Sclerosis. 2008. 312p. pap. (978-3-639-07992-0(2)) VDM Verlag Dr. Mueller e.K.

Elhadj, Zeraoulia. Frontiers in the Study of Chaotic Dynamical Systems with Open Problems. 2011. 268p. 98.00 (978-981-4340-69-4(3)) World Scientific Publishing Co., Inc.

Fabricand, Burton P. American History Through the Eyes of Modern Chaos Theory. 2009. 342p. pap. 29.95 (978-0-557-15668-9(8)) Lulu Enterprises Inc.

Femat, Ricardo & Solis-Perales, Gualberto. Robust Synchronization of Chaotic Systems Via Feedback. 2008. (Lecture Notes in Control & Information Sciences Ser.). (Illus.). 198p. pap. 109.00 (978-3-540-69306-2(8)) Springer.

Fortuna, Luigi. Chua's Circuit Implementations: Yesterday, Today & Tomorrow. 2009. (Illus.). 224p. 81.00 (978-981-283-924-4(0)) World Scientific Publishing Co., Inc.

Franco F. Orsucci (University College, London) Nicoletta Sala (L'Università della Svizzera Italiana), ed. Chaos & Complexity Research Progress. 2008. 69.00 (978-1-60456-166-1(1)) Nova Science Pubs., Inc.

Gallavotti, Giovanni, ed. The Fermi-Pasta-Ulam Problem: A Status Report. (Lecture Notes in Physics Ser.). (Illus.). 2010. viii, 302p. pap. 139.00 (978-3-642-09209-1(8), 3642092098) 2007. 301p. 139.00 (978-3-540-72994-5(1)) Springer.

Gericke, Wolf-Dieter. Tokyo: A Metropolis as a Self Organizing System. 2009. (ENG., Illus.). 60p. 49.00 (978-3-936681-27-7(9)) Edition Axel Menges GmbH DEU. Dist: National Bk. Network.

Gharajedaghi, Jamshid. Systems Thinking: Managing Chaos & Complexity - A Platform for Designing Business Architecture. 3rd ed. 2011. (ENG., Illus.). 376p. pap. 39.95 **(978-0-12-385915-0(8)**, Morgan Kaufmann) Elsevier Science & Technology Bks.

Gilmore, Robert & Lefranc, Marc. The Topology of Chaos: Alice in Stretch & Squeezeland. 2nd ed. 2012. (ENG & GER., Illus.). 618p. 135.00 **(978-3-527-41067-5(8)**, Wiley-VCH) Wiley, John & Sons, Inc.

Gitterman, Moshe. The Chaotic Pendulum. 2010. 156p. 68.00 (978-981-4322-00-3(8)) World Scientific Publishing Co., Inc.

Gleick, James. Chaos: Making a New Science. rev. ed. 2008. (ENG.). 384p. (gr. 12-18). 20.00 (978-0-14-311345-4(3), Penguin (Non-Classics)) Penguin Group (USA) Inc.

Goertzel, Ben. Chaotic Logic: Language, Thought, & Reality from the Perspective of Complex Systems Science. 2010. (IFSR International Series on Systems Science & Engineering Ser.). 296p. pap. 199.00 (978-1-4419-3238-9(0), 1441932380) Springer.

Grosse-Erdmann, Karl & Manguillot, Alfred Peris. Linear Chaos. 2011. (Universitext Ser.). (ENG., Illus.). xii, 388p. pap. 69.95 **(978-1-4471-2169-5(4)**, 1447121694) Springer.

Guastello, Stephen J., et al, eds. Chaos & Complexity in Psychology: The Theory of Nonlinear Dynamical Systems. 2011. (ENG., Illus.). 552p. pap. 39.99 **(978-1-107-68026-5(3))** Cambridge Univ. Pr.

Guastello, Stephen J., et al. Chaos & Complexity in Psychology: The Theory of Nonlinear Dynamical Systems. Guastello, Stephen J. et al, eds. 2008. (ENG., Illus.). 552p. 116.00 (978-0-521-88726-7(7)) Cambridge Univ. Pr.

Hartmann, T., told to. Chaos: A Program Collection for the PC. 3rd ed. 2008. (Illus.). 341p. 109.00 incl. cd-rom (978-3-540-74866-3(0)) Springer.

Henderson, Harry. Edward Lorenz. 2012. (Trailblazers in Science & Technology Ser.). 35.00 (978-1-60413-677-7(4), Chelsea Hse.) Facts On File, Inc.

Heylighen, Francis, et al, eds. The Evolution of Complexity: The Violet Book of 'Einstein Meets Magritte' 2010. (Einstein Meets Magritte: an Interdisciplinary Reflection on Science, Nature, Art, Human Action & Society Ser.). (Illus.). 392p. pap. 269.00 (978-90-481-5244-5(5), 9048152445) Springer.

Hirsch, Morris W., et al. Differential Equations, Dynamical Systems, & an Introduction to Chaos. 3rd ed. 2012. (ENG.). 432p. (C). 99.95 **(978-0-12-382010-5(3)**, Academic Pr.) Elsevier Science & Technology Bks.

Hughes, B. & Ninham, B., eds. The Mathematics & Physics of Disordered Media: Percolation, Random Walk, Modeling,and Simulation. Proceedings of a Workshop held at the IMA, University of Minnesota, Minneapolis, February 13-19, 1983. 2008. (Lecture Notes in Mathematics Ser.). pap. 59.00 (978-3-540-12707-9(0)) Springer.

Hunt, Brian R., et al, eds. The Theory of Chaotic Attractors. 2012. (ENG.). vi, 514p. pap. 89.95 (978-1-4419-2330-1(6), 1441923306) Springer.

Hurt, N. E. Quantum Chaos & Mesoscopic Systems: Mathematical Methods in the Quantum Signatures of Chaos. 2010. (Mathematics & Its Applications Ser.). 356p. pap. 339.00 (978-90-481-4811-0(1), 9048148111) Springer.

Iordache, Octavian. Polystochastic Models for Complexity. 2010. (Understanding Complex Systems Ser.). (ENG., Illus.). 298p. 219.00 (978-3-642-10653-8(6), 3642106536) Springer.

Ivancevic, Vladimir G. & Ivancevic, Tijana T. Complex Dynamics: Advanced System Dynamics in Complex Variables. 2007. (Intelligent Systems, Control & Automation: Science & Engineering Ser.). 822p. 209.00 **(978-1-4020-6411-1(X)**, 140206411X) Springer.

—Computational Mind: A Complex Dynamics Perspective. 2007. (Studies in Computational Intelligence Ser.). (Illus.). 691p. 259.00 (978-3-540-71465-1(0)) Springer.

—Computational Mind: A Complex Dynamics Perspective: A Complex Dynamics Perspective. 2010. (Studies in Computational Intelligence Ser.). (Illus.). xii, 692p. pap. 259.00 (978-3-642-09068-4(0), 3642090680) Springer.

—Handbook of Nonlinearity, Chaos, & Complexity Methods for Scientists & Engineers. 2011. (978-1-61209-937-8(8)) Nova Science Pubs., Inc.

—High-Dimensional Chaotic & Attractor Systems: A Comprehensive Introduction. 2007. (International Series on Intelligent Systems, Control & Automation — Science & Engineering: Vol. 32). (Illus.). xvi, 704p. (C). 219.00 (978-1-4020-5455-6(6), 1402054556) Springer.

Johnson, Neil. Simpy Complexity. 2009. (ENG., Illus.). 256p. pap. 15.95 (978-1-85168-630-8(4)) Oneworld Pubns. GBR. Dist: National Bk. Network.

Jovic, Branislav. Synchronization Techniques for Chaotic Communication Systems. 2011. (Signals & Communication Technology Ser.). (ENG., Illus.). xvi, 348p. 129.00 **(978-3-642-21848-4(2)**, 3642218482) Springer.

Kautz, Richard. Chaos: The Science of Predictable Random Motion. 2010. (ENG., Illus.). 384p. 98.50 (978-0-19-959457-3(0)); pap. 44.95 (978-0-19-959458-0(9)) Oxford Univ. Pr., Inc.

Kellert, Stephen H. Borrowed Knowledge: Chaos Theory & the Challange of Learning Across Desciplines. 2008. 288p. 35.00 (978-0-226-42978-6(4)) Univ. of Chicago Pr.

Keppeler, Stefan. Spinning Particles - Semiclassics & Spectral Statistics. 2010. (Springer Tracts in Modern Physics Ser.). (Illus.). x, 190p. pap. 239.00 (978-3-642-05678-9(4), 3642056784) Springer.

Kilic. Studying Chua's Circuits. 2010. (Illus.). xiii, 204p. 81.00 (978-981-4291-13-2(7)) World Scientific Publishing Co., Inc.

Kocarev, Ljupco, et al, eds. Intelligent Computing Based on Chaos. 2009. (Studies in Computational Intelligence Ser.). (Illus.). x, 382p. 159.00 (978-3-540-95971-7(8)) Springer.

Kocarev, Ljupco & Lian, Shiguo, eds. Chaos-based Cryptography: Theory, Algorithms & Applications. 2011. (Studies in Computational Intelligence Ser.). (Illus.). x, 390p. 179.00 (978-3-642-20541-5(0), 3642205410) Springer.

Kong. Reconstruction of Chaotic Signals with. . 2008. (Illus.). xiv, 218p. 82.00 (978-981-277-113-1(1)) World Scientific Publishing Co., Inc.

Lai, Ying-Cheng & Tél, Tamás. Transient Chaos: Complex Dynamics in Finite Time Scales. 2011. (Applied Mathematical Sciences Ser.) (ENG., Illus.). xiv, 497p. 89.95 (978-1-4419-6986-6(1), 1441969861) Springer.

Landsman, Alexandra. Nonlinear Dynamics & Chaos Inside the Frc. 2009. 152p. pap. (978-3-639-15711-6(7)) VDM Verlag Dr. Mueller e.K.

Larson, Lawrence E., et al, eds. Digital Communications Using Chaos & Nonlinear Dynamics. 2010. (Institute for Nonlinear Science Ser.). (Illus.). xiv, 382p. pap. 189.00 (978-1-4419-2130-7(3), 1441921303) Springer.

Lau, Francis C. M. & Tse, Chi K. Chaos-Based Digital Communication Systems: Operating Principles, Analysis Methods, & Performance Evaluation. 2011. (Signals & Communication Technology Ser.). (ENG., Illus.). xii, 228p. pap. 119.00 (978-3-642-05616-1(4), 3642056164) Springer.

Lee, Thomas H. & Mongan, James J. Chaos & Organization in Health Care. (ENG., Illus.). 296p. (gr. 17). 2012. pap. 13.95 **(978-0-262-51762-1(0))** 2009. 29.95 (978-0-262-01353-6(3)) MIT Pr.

Li, Zhong. Fuzzy Chaotic Systems: Modeling, Control, & Applications. 2010. (Studies in Fuzziness & Soft Computing Ser.). (Illus.). xii, 299p. pap. 179.00 (978-3-642-06979-6(7), 3642069797) Springer.

Li, Zhong & Chen, Guanrong, eds. Integration of Fuzzy Logic & Chaos Theory. 2010. (Studies in Fuzziness & Soft Computing Ser.). (Illus.). viii, 625p. pap. 169.00 (978-3-642-06594-1(5), 3642065945) Springer.

Ling, Bingo Wing-Kuen, et al, eds. Control of Chaos in Nonlinear Circuits & Systems. 2008. (Illus.). 250p. 104.00 (978-981-279-056-9(X)) World Scientific Publishing Co., Inc.

Lovett, Teems. Polynomial Chaos Simulation of Analog & ed-Signal Systems. 2010. 104p. pap. (978-3-8383-5385-2(4)) Lambert Academic Publishing.

Luo, Albert C. J. Global Transversality, Resonance & Chaotic Dynamics. 2008. (Illus.). (C). 188.00 (978-981-277-111-7(5)) World Scientific Publishing Co., Inc.

Luo, Albert C. J. Regularity & Complexity in Dynamical Systems. 2011. (ENG., Illus.). xi, 493p. 179.00 **(978-1-4614-1523-7(3)**, 1461415233) Springer.

Mahmoud, Emad & Mahmoud, Gamal. Chaotic & Hyperchaotic Nonlinear Systems. 2011. 176p. pap. **(978-3-8433-8222-9(0))** Lambert Academic Publishing.

Majumdar, Mukul, et al. Optimization & Chaos. 2010. (Studies in Economic Theory Ser.). (Illus.). x, 454p. pap. 189.00 (978-3-642-08636-6(5), 3642086365) Springer.

Makarov & Prants, Sergey V. Ray & Wave Chaos in Ocean Acoustics. 2009. 412p. 122.00 (978-981-4273-17-6(1)) World Scientific Publishing Co., Inc.

Manneville. Instabilities, Chaos & Turbulence: An Introduction to Nonlinear Dynamics & Complex Systems. 2nd ed. 2010. (Illus.). xv, 439p. pap. 73.00 (978-1-84816-393-5(2)) World Scientific Publishing Co., Inc.

Manneville, Paul. Instabilities, Chaos & Turbulence: An Introduction to Nonlinear Dynamics & Complex Systems. 2nd rev. ed. 2010. (Illus.). 456p. 118.00 (978-1-84816-392-8(4)) World Scientific Publishing Co., Inc.

Mariusz. Smooth & Nonsmooth High Dimensional. . V60. 2007. (World Scientific Series on Nonlinear Science, Series A Ser.). (Illus.). 121.00 (978-981-270-909-7(6)) World Scientific Publishing Co., Inc.

McGlade, James. Time, Process & Structured Transformation in Archaeology. 2010. 504p. pap. 39.95 (978-0-415-58909-3(6)) Routledge.

Morrison, Foster. The Art of Modeling Dynamic Systems: Forecasting for Chaos, Randomness & Determinism. 2008. (Dover Books on Computer Science Ser.). (ENG., Illus.). 416p. per. 22.95 (978-0-486-46295-0(1), Dover Pubns., Inc.

Nadykto, Alexey B., et al, eds. Mathematical Models of Non-linear Phenomena, Processes & Systems: from Molecular Scale to Planetary Atmosphere. 2010. (Mathematics Research Developments Ser.). 125.00 (978-1-60876-994-0(1)) Nova Science Pubs., Inc.

Nakamura, K. Quantum versus Chaos: Questions Emerging from Mesoscopic Cosmos. 2010. (Fundamental Theories of Physics Ser.). 224p. pap. 139.00 (978-90-481-4850-9(2), 9048148502) Springer.

Northeastern University, China Staff, et al, contrib. by. 2010 International Workshop on Chaos-Fractals Theories & Applications: Proceedings, Kunming, Yunnan, China, 29-31 October 2010. 2010. (Illus.). xv, 500p. pap. **(978-0-7695-4247-8(6))** IEEE Computer Society Pr.

Northrop, Robert B. Introduction to Complexity & Complex Systems. 2010. (ENG., Illus.). 551p. 83.95 (978-1-4398-3901-0(8), CRC Press) Taylor & Francis Group GBR. Dist: Taylor & Francis Group.

Ohtsubo, Junji. Semiconductor Lasers: Stability, Instability & Chaos. 2nd ed. 2010. (Springer Series in Optical Sciences Ser.). (Illus.). xviii, 475p. pap. 219.00 (978-3-642-09170-4(9), 3642091709) Springer.

Orsucci, Franco & Sala, Nicoletta. Chaos & Complexity Research Compendium. 2008. 115.00 (978-1-60456-787-8(2)) Nova Science Pubs., Inc.

Orsucci, Franco F., ed. Developments in Chaos & Complexity Research. 2008. (Illus.). 264p. 69.00 (978-1-60456-340-5(0)) Nova Science Pubs., Inc.

Orsucci, Franco F. & Sala, Nicoletta. New Research on Chaos & Complexity. 2006. (Illus.). (C). 175.00 (978-1-60021-275-8(1)) Nova Science Pubs., Inc.

Orsucci, Franco F. & Sala, Nicoletta, eds. Chaos & Complexity: New Research. 2008. 95.00 (978-1-60456-841-7(0)) Nova Science Pubs., Inc.

—Progress in Chaos Complexity Research. 2008. (Illus.). x, 221p. 69.00 (978-1-60456-375-7(3), Nova Biomedical Bks.) Nova Science Pubs., Inc.

Otsuka, Kenju. Nonlinear Dynamics in Optical Complex Systems. 2010. (Advances in Opto-Electronics Ser.). 308p. pap. 189.00 (978-90-481-5383-1(2), 9048153832) Springer.

Parker, Jo Alyson. Narrative Form & Chaos Theory in Sterne, Proust, Woolf & Faulkner. 2007. (ENG.). 208p. 89.00 (978-1-4039-8384-8(4)) Palgrave Macmillan.

Peccati, Giovanni & Taqqu, Murad S. Wiener Chaos: Moments, Cumulants & Diagrams: A survey with Computer Implementation. 2010. (Bocconi & Springer Ser.). (Illus.). 200p. 99.00 (978-88-470-1678-1(9), 8847016789) Springer.

Perlidze, Tomas B. New Nonlinear Phenomena Research. 2008. (Illus.). ix, 421p. 69.00 (978-1-60021-996-2(9)) Nova Science Pubs., Inc.

Pietro. A Gallery of Chua Attractors(with Cd-Rom. 2008. (Illus.). lxxii, 533p. 196.00 (978-981-279-062-0(4)) World Scientific Publishing Co., Inc.

Podshivalov, G. K. Metodologicheskie Osnovy, Metodika I Instrumentarii Dlia Izmereniia Khaosa: Monografiia. 2010. (RUS., Illus.). 121p. (978-5-98079-601-3(0)) Goskovskaja Gumanitarno-Social'naja Akademija.

Poet, Ron. Chaos Theory: Bullet Guides. 2012. (Bullet Guides). (ENG.). 120p. pap. 6.95 **(978-1-4441-4439-0(1)**, Hodder & Stoughton) Hodder General Publishing Div. GBR. Dist: Independent Pubs. Group.

Pryor, Robert. The Chaos Theory of Careers. 2011. (ENG., Illus.). 256p. (C). 160.00 (978-0-415-55188-5(9)) Routledge.

C

Pryor, Robert & Bright, Jim. The Chaos Theory of Careers: A New Perspective on Working in the Twenty-First Century. 2011. (ENG., Illus.). 256p. (C). pap. 49.95 *(978-0-415-80634-3(8))* Routledge.
Puu, Tonu. Attractors, Bifurcations, & Chaos: Nonlinear Phenomena in Economics. 2nd ed. 2010. (ENG., Illus.). xii, 549p. pap. 239.00 *(978-3-642-07296-3(8)*, 3642072968) Springer.
Rao, Aditya. Inducing Robust Chaos in Electronic Circuits. 2010. 128p. pap. *(978-3-8383-5317-3(X))* Lambert Academic Publishing.
Reichl, Linda E. The Transition to Chaos: Conservative Classical Systems & Quantum Manifestations. 2nd ed. 2011. (Institute for Nonlinear Science Ser.). (ENG., Illus.). xviii, 675p. pap. 134.00 *(978-1-4419-3163-4(5)*, 1441931635) Springer.
Robertson, Robin. Indra's Net: Alchemy & Chaos Theory as Models for Transformation. 2009. (ENG., Illus.). 224p. pap. 16.95 *(978-0-8356-0862-6(X)*, Quest Bks.) Theosophical Publishing Hse.
Robnik, Marko & Romanovski, Valery, eds. Let's Face Chaos Through Nonlinear Dynamics: Proceedings of Let's Face Chaos Through Nonlinear Dynamics 7th International Summer School & Conference. 2008. (AIP Conference Proceedings Ser.). 328p. pap. 169.00 *(978-0-7354-0607-0(3))* American Institute of Physics.
Rodriguez, Enric, et al. Chaos in Switching Converters for Power Management: Designing for Prediction & Control. 2012. (ENG., Illus.). 250p. 129.00 ***(978-1-4614-2127-6(6)***, 1461421276) Springer.
Roetzheim, William. Why Things Are: How Complexity Theory Answers Life's Toughest Questions. 2007. (Illus.). 240p. 24.95 *(978-1-933769-26-4(2))* Level 4 Press, Inc.
Sanders, T. Irene. Strategic Thinking & the New Science: Planning in the Midst of Chaos Complexity & Chan. 2010. (ENG.). 192p. pap. 13.99 *(978-1-4516-2428-1(X)*, Free Pr.) Free Pr.
Schuster, Heinz Georg & Schöll, Eckehard, eds. Handbook of Chaos Control. 2nd ed. 2007. (ENG., Illus.). 849p. 320.00 *(978-3-527-40605-0(0)*, Wiley-VCH) Wiley, John & Sons, Inc.
Scott, Alwyn C. The Nonlinear Universe: Chaos, Emergence, Life. (Frontiers Collection). (Illus.). 2010. xiv, 364p. pap. 89.95 *(978-3-642-07057-0(4)*, 3642070574) 2007. 364p. 89.95 *(978-3-540-34152-9(8))* Springer.
Sengupta, Ashok & Nashed, M. Zuhair, eds. Chaos, Nonlinearity, Complexity: The Dynamical Paradigm of Nature. 2006. (Studies in Fuzziness & Soft Computing: Vol. 206). (Illus.). xvi, 358p. 169.00 *(978-3-540-31756-2(2)*, 3540317562) Springer.
Shivamoggi, B.K. Nonlinear Dynamics & Chaotic Phenomena: An Introduction. 2011. (Fluid Mechanics & Its Applications Ser.). 420p. pap. 109.00 *(978-90-481-4926-1(6)*, 9048149266) Springer.
Simiu, Emil. Chaotic Transitions in Deterministic & Stochastic Dynamical Systems: Applications of Melnikov Processes in Engineering, Physics, & Neuroscience. 2009. (Princeton Series in Applied Mathematics Ser.). (ENG., Illus.). 246p. (C). pap. 39.95 *(978-0-691-14434-4(6))* Princeton Univ. Pr.
Skiadas, Christos H. Modeling, Simulation & Application - Proceedings of the 3rd Chaotic Modeling & Simulation International Conference (Chaos2010) Dimotikalis, Ioannis & Skiadas, Charilaos, eds. 2011. 440p. 142.00 *(978-981-4350-33-4(8))* World Scientific Publishing Co., Inc.
Skiadas, Christos H. & Dimotikalis, Ioannis, eds. Chaotic Systems: Theory & Applications. 2010. (Illus.). 396p. 144.00 *(978-981-4299-71-8(5))* World Scientific Publishing Co., Inc.
Skiadas, Christos H. & Skiadas, Charilaos. Chaotic Modeling & Simulation: Analysis of Chaotic Models, Attractors & Forms. 2008. (ENG., Illus.). 364p. 97.95 *(978-1-4200-7900-5(X)*, Chapman & Hall/CRC) CRC Pr. LLC.
Skjeltorp, Arne T. & Belushkin, Alexander V., eds. Dynamics of Complex Interconnected Systems: Networks & Bioprocesses: Networks & Bioprocesses. 2006. (NATO Science Ser.: Vol. 232). (Illus.). xv, 211p. 169.00 *(978-1-4020-5028-2(3)*, 1402050283) Springer.
Smith, Leonard A. Chaos: A Very Short Introduction. 2007. (Very Short Introductions Ser.). (ENG., Illus.). 176p. per. 11.95 *(978-0-19-285378-3(3))* Oxford Univ. Pr., Inc.
Smith, Richard G. Qualitative Complexity. 2007. (Illus.). VI, 314p. pap. 41.95 *(978-0-415-43967-1(1))* Routledge.
Sprott. Elegant Chaos: Algebraically Simple Chaotic Flows. 2010. (Illus.). 300p. 88.00 *(978-981-283-881-0(3))* World Scientific Publishing Co., Inc.
Steeb, Willi-Hans. The Nonlinear Workbook: Chaos, Fractals, Cellular Automata, Genetic Algorithms, Gene Expression Programming, Support Vector Machine, Wavelets, Hidden Markov Models, Fuzzy Logic with C++, Java & Symbolicc++ Programs. 5th rev. ed. 2011. (Illus.). 644p. 128.00 *(978-981-4335-77-5(0))*; pap. 62.00 *(978-981-4335-78-2(9))* World Scientific Publishing Co., Inc.
Strogatz, Steven. The Calculus of Friendship - What a Teacher & a Student Learned about Life while Corresponding about Math. 2011. (ENG., Illus.). 184p. pap. 14.95 *(978-0-691-15038-3(9))* Princeton Univ. Pr.
Strogatz, Steven H. & Joffray, Don. The Calculus of Friendship: What a Teacher & a Student Learned about Life While Corresponding about Math. 2009. (ENG., Illus.). 184p. (C). 19.95 *(978-0-691-13493-2(6))* Princeton Univ. Pr.
Tam, Wai M., et al. Digital Communications with Chaos: Multiple Access Techniques & Performance. 2006. (ENG., Illus.). 256p. 205.00 *(978-0-08-045151-0(9)*, Elsevier Science) Elsevier Science & Technology Bks.
Tel, Tamas & Gruiz, Marton. Chaotic Dynamics: An Introduction Based on Classical Mechanics. Kulacsy, Katalin, tr. from HUN. 2006. (ENG., Illus.). 412p. per. 75.00 *(978-0-521-54783-3(0))* Cambridge Univ. Pr.
Thiel, Marco, et al, eds. Nonlinear Dynamics & Chaos: Advances & Perspectives. 2010. (Understanding Complex Systems Ser.). (Illus.). xvi, 320p. 159.00 *(978-3-642-04628-5(2)*, 3642046282) Springer.
Thirugnanasambandan, Thelvasanthi & SIVADEVI, S. Chaos, Bifurcations & Simple Dynamical Models. 2010. 80p. pap. *(978-3-8383-8431-3(8))* Lambert Academic Publishing.
Tsimring, L. S. Digital Communications Using Chaos & Nonlinear Dynamics. Larson, Lawrence E. & Liu, Jia-Ming, eds. 2006. (Institute for Nonlinear Science Ser.). (ENG., Illus.). xiv, 382p. 189.00 *(978-0-387-29787-3(1)*, 0387297871) Springer.
Uchida, Atsushi. Optical Communication with Chaotic Lasers: Applications of Nonlinear Dynamics & Synchronization. 2012. (ENG., Illus.). 664p. 220.00 ***(978-3-527-40869-6(X)***, Wiley-VCH) Wiley, John & Sons, Inc.
van Wyk, M. A. & Steeb, W. -H. Chaos in Electronics. 2010. (Mathematical Modelling: Theory & Applications Ser.). 496p. pap. 349.00 *(978-90-481-4857-8(X)*, 904814857X) Springer.
Walker, Ricki. Chaotic Semiconductor Lasers: A Dynamical Analysis. 2009. 236p. pap. *(978-3-639-14000-2(1))* VDM Verlag Dr. Mueller e.K.
Wang, Charles W. Nonlinear Phenomena Research Perspectives. 2007. 454p. 129.00 *(978-1-60021-520-9(3))* Nova Science Pubs., Inc.
Whittle, Peter. Neural Nets & Chaotic Carriers. 2nd rev. ed. 2010. (Illus.). 250p. 85.00 *(978-1-84816-590-8(0))* Imperial College Pr. GBR. Dist: World Scientific Publishing Co., Inc.
Wiggins, Stephen. Introduction to Applied Nonlinear Dynamical Systems & Chaos. 2nd ed. 2010. (Texts in Applied Mathematics Ser.). (Illus.). 808p. pap. 109.00 *(978-1-4419-1807-9(8)*, 1441918078) Springer.
Yoshida, Zensho. Nonlinear Science: Challenge to Complex Systems. 2010. Orig. Title: Nonlinear Science. (ENG., Illus.). xii, 205p. 129.00 *(978-3-642-03405-3(5)*, 3642034055) Springer.
Zaslavsky, George M. Hamiltonian Chaos & Fractional Dynamics. 2008. (ENG., Illus.). 336p. pap. 65.00 *(978-0-19-953548-4(5))* Oxford Univ. Pr., Inc.
—The Physics of Chaos in Hamiltonian Systems. 2nd ed. 2007. (Illus.). 315p. 108.00 *(978-1-86094-795-7(6))* World Scientific Publishing Co., Inc.
Zelinka, Ivan, et al, eds. Evolutionary Algorithms & Chaotic Systems. 2010. (Studies in Computational Intelligence Ser.). 560p. 209.00 *(978-3-642-10706-1(0)*, 3642107060) Springer.
Zeraoulia, Elhadj. Models & Applications of Chaos Theory in Modern Sciences. 2011. (ENG.). 742p. 199.95 ***(978-1-57808-722-8(8))*** BIOS Scientific Publishers Ltd. GBR. Dist: Taylor & Francis Group.
Zhang, Huaguang, et al. Controlling Chaos: Suppression, Synchronization & Chaotification. 2009. (Communications & Control Engineering Ser.). (ENG., Illus.). xx, 344p. 189.00 *(978-1-84882-522-2(6)*, 1848825226) Springer.

CHAOTIC MOTION IN SYSTEMS

see Chaotic Behavior in Systems

CHAPARRAL COCK

see Roadrunner

CHAPBOOKS

see also Booksellers and Bookselling—Colportage, Subscription Trade, etc.
Ashton, John. Chap-Books of the Eighteenth Century. 2010. 538p. pap. 40.75 *(978-1-177-15718-6(7))*; 518p. pap. 39.75 *(978-1-149-30416-7(2))*; 510p. pap. 39.75 *(978-1-143-66066-5(8))*; 508p. pap. 39.75 *(978-1-144-78883-2(8))* BiblioBazaar.
—Chap-Books of the Eighteenth Century. 2010. 220p. pap. *(978-1-151-96097-9(7))* Books LLC.
Bawden, Charles R. A Tract for the Buryats. Walravens, Hartmut, ed. 2009. (Abhandlungen Für Die Kunde des Morgenlandes Ser.). (ENG., Illus.). 105p. (C). pap. 51.00 *(978-3-447-05990-9(7))* Harrassowitz, Otto Verlag DEU. Dist: ISD.
Haffner, Stephen Haffner, ed. Bonus Chapbook. 2011. 110.00 net. *(978-1-893887-56-5(1))* Haffner Pr.
Hindley, Charles, compiled by. Curiosities of Street Literature: Comprising 'Cocks,' Or 'Catchpennies' 2011. (Cambridge Library Collection - Literary Studies). (ENG., Illus.). 266p. pap. 42.00 ***(978-1-108-03867-6(0))*** Cambridge Univ. Pr.
Meriton, John, ed. Small Books for the Common Man: A Descriptive Bibliography. 2010. (Illus.). 1008p. 115.00 *(978-1-58456-254-2(4))* Oak Knoll Pr.
Sepúlveda Llanos, Fidel. El Canto a lo Poeta, a lo Divino y a lo Humano: Análisis Estético Antropológico y Antología Fundamental. Cornejo D, Nicolás & Gallardo M, Sebastián, eds. 2009. (SPA., Illus.). 581p. *(978-956-14-1009-1(5))* Pontificia Universidad Catolica de Chile.
Shelley, Mary Wollstonecraft. Mounseer Nongtongpaw: Or, the Discoveries of John Bull in a Trip to Paris. reprint ed. lib. bdg. 98.00 *(978-0-7426-2098-8(0))* Classic Bks.

CHAPBOOKS—BIBLIOGRAPHY

American Tract Society Staff, compiled by. The Publications of the American Tract Society: Volume I. 2007. 400p. per. 30.00 *(978-1-59925-078-6(0))* Solid Ground Christian Bks.
—The Publications of the American Tract Society: Volume II. 2007. 408p. per. 30.00 *(978-1-59925-099-1(3))* Solid Ground Christian Bks.
—The Publications of the American Tract Society: Volume III. 2007. 416p. per. 30.00 *(978-1-59925-106-6(X))* Solid Ground Christian Bks.
—The Publications of the American Tract Society: Volume IV. 2007. 412p. per. 30.00 *(978-1-59925-107-3(8))* Solid Ground Christian Bks.
—The Publications of the American Tract Society: Volume V. 2007. 408p. per. 30.00 *(978-1-59925-110-3(8))* Solid Ground Christian Bks.
—The Publications of the American Tract Society: Volume VI. 2007. 412p. per. 30.00 *(978-1-59925-115-8(9))* Solid Ground Christian Bks.
Chap Book, 10 vols., Set, Vol. 1-9. reprint ed. lib. bdg. 495.00 *(978-0-404-19508-3(3))* AMS Pr., Inc.
Hindley, Charles. The Life & Times of James Catnach, (Late of Seven Dials), Ballad Monger. 2011. (Cambridge Library Collection - Literary Studies). (ENG., Illus.). 456p. pap. 34.99 ***(978-1-108-03942-0(1))*** Cambridge Univ. Pr.

CHAPEL GARDENS

see Church Gardens

CHAPEL HILL (N.C.)

ADC, the Map People Staff, creator. Raleigh, Durham & Chapel Hill, North Carolina Street Atlas. 2007. (Illus.). 180p. 21.95 *(978-0-87530-884-5(8))* ADC The Map People.
de Hart, Allen. Trails of the Triangle: Over 400 Trails in the Raleigh/Durham/Chapel Hill Area. 2nd ed. 2007. (Illus.). 298p. per. 13.95 *(978-0-89587-349-1(4))* Blair, John F. Pub.
Little, M. Ruth. The Town & Gown Architecture of Chapel Hill, North Carolina, 1795-1975. 2006. (Distributed for the Preservation Society of Chapel Hill Ser.). (ENG., Illus.). 320p. 27.95 *(978-0-8078-3072-7(0))* Univ. of North Carolina Pr.
Morgan, Ed, photos by. Raleigh, Durham, Chapel Hill: A Photographic Portrait. 2006. (Photographic Portrait Ser.). (ENG., Illus.). 128p. 26.95 *(978-1-885435-67-5(3))* Twin Lights Pubs., Inc.
Schwartz, Valarie. Remembering Chapel Hill: The Twentieth Century As We Lived It. 2009. (American Chronicles Ser.). (ENG., Illus.). 128p. pap. 21.99 *(978-1-59629-704-3(2))* History Pr., The.

CHAPELS

see also Chantries
also subdivision Churches under names of cities, e.g. New York (N.Y.)—Churches
Bellinato, Claudio. Giotto, the Scrovegni Chapel (boxed set W/CD) 2006. (ENG.). 90.00 incl. lp *(978-88-7200-248-3(6))* Vianello Libri ITA. Dist: National Bk. Network.
Hopkins, Susan M., et al. My Dura-Europos: The Letters of Susan M. Hopkins, 1927-1935. 2011. 39.95 *(978-0-8143-3588-8(8))* Wayne State Univ. Pr.
Huneck, Stephen. Even Bad Dogs Go to Heaven: More from the Dog Chapel. 2010. (ENG., Illus.). 80p. 19.95 *(978-0-8109-9629-8(4))* Abrams.
La Rivière, Dominique de. La Chapelle de Passy-Buzenval: 1955-1960. 2010. (FRE., Illus.). 191p. *(978-2-35039-093-2(4))* Chaudun, Nicolas Editions.
Lurson, Benoît. Osiris, Ramses, Thot et le Nil: Les Chapelles Secondaires des Temples de Derr et Ouadi Es-Seboua. 2007. (Orientalia Lovaniensia Analecta Ser.). (ENG., Illus.). 234p. (C). 109.00 *(978-90-429-1891-7(8))* Peeters Pubs. & Booksellers BEL. Dist: Brown, David Bk. Co., The.
McKasey, John. Ancient Chapels & Churches in Wales. 2007. (ENG., Illus.). 72p. pap. 11.95 *(978-0-86243-665-0(6)*, Virago Press) Y Lolfa GBR. Dist: Dufour Editions, Inc.
Owen, D. Huw. Welsh Chapels. 2012. (ENG., Illus.). 288p. pap. 25.95 ***(978-1-85411-554-6(5))*** Seren Bks. GBR. Dist: Independent Pubs. Group.
Roffey, Simon. The Medieval Chantry Chapel: An Archaeology. 2007. (Studies in the History of Medieval Religion Ser.: Volume 34). (Illus.). 206p. 90.00 *(978-1-84383-334-5(4)*, Boydell Press) Boydell & Brewer, Ltd. GBR. Dist: Boydell & Brewer, Inc.
Settis, Salvatore & Brenk, Beat. La Capella Palatina a Palermo, 3 vols. 2011. (ITA & ENG., Illus.). 1300p. 1325.00 *(978-88-248-0351-9(2))* Panini Franco Cosimo ITA. Dist: National Bk. Network.
Williams, Ned. Black Country Chapels: A Third Selection. 2008. (ENG., Illus.). 128p. pap. 29.95 *(978-0-7509-4665-0(2))* History Pr. Ltd., The GBR. Dist: Independent Pubs. Group.
Wooding, Jonathan. The Churches & Chapels of Wales. Yates, Nigel, ed. 2011. (ENG., Illus.). 228p. pap. 25.00 *(978-0-7083-2118-8(6))* Univ. of Wales Pr. GBR. Dist: Chicago Distribution Ctr.

CHAPELS (MUSIC)

see also Choirs (Music)
Ahrens, Christian. 'Zu Gotha ist eine gute Kapelle...' Aus dem Innenleben einer thüringischen Hofkapelle des 18. Jahrhunderts. 2009. (Friedenstein-Forschungen Ser.). (GER., Illus.). 374p. (C). 97.00 *(978-3-515-09236-4(6))* Steiner, Franz Verlag Wiesbaden GmbH DEU. Dist: Brown, David Bk. Co., The.

CHAPLAINS

Adams, Carl L. Wanted: Lost Souls. 2011. 360p. 22.99 ***(978-1-4568-8221-1(X))***; pap. 15.99 ***(978-1-4568-8220-4(1))*** Xlibris Corp.
Anderson, Rick. God's Feet are in My Sandbox: Faith Chronicles of a Texas Death Row Chaplain. 2011. pap. 17.99 *(978-1-61739-810-0(1))* Tate Publishing & Enterprises, LLC.
Autry, Jerry. Gun-Totin' Chaplain. 2006. 301p. pap. 14.00 *(978-0-934145-11-4(3))* Airborne Pr.
Barnett, Beverly James. For God & Country: Memoirs of a military Chaplain. 2008. 380p. pap. 19.99 *(978-1-60477-891-5(1))* Xulon Pr., Inc.
Beazley, Frank. The Gap in Catholic Healthcare Chaplaincy. 2011. 80p. pap. ***(978-3-8443-9560-0(1))*** Lambert Academic Publishing.
Best, Steve. Stories of the Street. 2008. 176p. pap. 12.95 *(978-1-60693-353-4(1)*, Strategic Bk. Publishing) AEG Literary Publishing Services, Inc.
Black, Barry C. From the Hood to the Hill: A Story of Overcoming, 0 vols. 2006. 240p. 22.99 *(978-0-7852-1881-4(5))* Nelson, Thomas Inc.
Brendle, Franz & Schindling, Anton. Geistliche Im Krieg. 2009. (GER., Illus.). 445p. pap. *(978-3-402-12790-2(3))* Aschendorff Verlag GmbH & Co. KG.
Caskie, Donald. The Tartan Pimpernel. 2006. (ENG., Illus.). 272p. per. 14.95 *(978-1-84341-035-5(4))* Birlinn, Ltd. GBR. Dist: Casemate Pubs. & Bk. Distributors, LLC.
The Complete Corporate Chaplain's Handbook. rev. ed. 2006. 69.95 *(978-0-9762151-9-6(5))* Lanphier Pr.
Cortino, Becky. A Heart 4 Clowning: How to Establish a Hospital Clown or Creative Ministry Guide. 2007. 110p. spiral bd. 22.00 *(978-0-9799093-0-6(9))* Heart 4 Clowning Pr., A.
Cress, Mark, et al. The Complete Community Chaplain's Handbook. 2006. (ENG.). 512p. pap. 99.99 *(978-0-9786039-0-8(7))* Lanphier Pr.
Dept. of Defense. Religious Support. 2009. per. 14.95 *(978-1-60170-034-6(2))* Pentagon Publishing.
Dorsett, Lyle W. For God & Country: United States Military Chanplains in World War II. 2012. (ENG.). 304p. (gr. 12). 25.95 ***(978-0-425-24786-0(4)***, Berkley Hardcover) Penguin Group (USA) Inc.
Emerson, W. Eric & Stokes, Karen, eds. Faith, Valor, & Devotion: The Civil War Letters of William Porcher Dubose. 2010. (ENG.). 392p. 49.95 *(978-1-57003-912-6(7))* Univ. of South Carolina Pr.
Font, Pedro. With Anza to California, 1775-1776: The Journal of Pedro Font, O. F. M. Brown, Alan K., tr. 2011. (Early California Commentaries Ser.). (ENG.). 472p. (C). 55.00 *(978-0-87062-375-2(3)*, Clark, Arthur H. Co., The) Univ. of Oklahoma Pr.
Freedman, Shalom. Rabbi Shlomo Goren: Torah Sage & General. 2006. 221p. 23.95 *(978-965-7108-81-9(0))* Urim Pubns. ISR. Dist: Coronet Bks.
Gache, Pere Louis-Hippolyte. Frenchman, Chaplain, Rebel: The Civil War Letters of Pere Louis-Hippolyte Gache, S. J. , 10th Louisiana Infantry. Buckley, Cornelius M., ed. & tr. by. 2007. 288p. per. 35.00 *(978-0-8173-5443-5(3))* Univ. of Alabama Pr.
Goodman, Cecily. The Survivors: The Story of the Belsen Remnant. 2009. (Illus.). 113p. pap. 16.95 *(978-0-85303-821-4(X))* Vallentine Mitchell Pubs. GBR. Dist: International Specialized Bk. Services.
—The Survivors: The Story of the Belsen Remnant. 2009. (Illus.). 113p. 39.95 *(978-0-85303-831-3(7))* Vallentine Mitchell Pubs. GBR. Dist: International Specialized Bk. Services.
Graves, Joel. Leadership Paradigms in Chaplaincy. 2007. 232p. per. 25.95 *(978-1-58112-372-2(8)*, Dissertation.com) Universal Pubs.
Hopkins, Samuel W., Jr. A Chaplain Remembers Vietnam. Rast, Franklin D., ed. 2nd ed. 2007. (Illus.). 292p. pap. 19.95 *(978-0-615-15828-0(5))* SamPat Pr.
Itokazu, Kiyo. A Chaplain's Pilgrimage: An Autobiography. 2007. 156p. per. 14.95 *(978-0-595-47321-2(0))* iUniverse, Inc.
Jibben, Ken. Emerge: Leaders to Continue a Life of Vision & Purpose. 2009. 198p. pap. 13.95 *(978-1-4327-3951-5(4))* Outskirts Pr., Inc.
Kaspar, Donald. On Duty. 2006. pap. 12.99 *(978-1-60034-441-1(0))* Xulon Pr., Inc.
Kennedy, Nancy B. Miracles & Moments of Grace: Inspiring Stories from Military Chaplains. 2011. 240p. pap. 14.99 *(978-0-89112-269-2(9)*, Leafwood Pubs.) Abilene Christian Univ. Pr.
Lawson, Kenneth E. Reliable & Religious: U. S. Army Chaplains & the War of 1812. Office of the Chief of Chaplains (U.S. Army), ed. 2011. (ENG., Illus.). 314p. pap. 47.00 ***(978-0-16-089615-6(0)***, Dept. of the Army) United States Government Printing Office.
Leonard, Pat. The Fighting Padre: Pat Leonard's Letters from the Trenches 1915-1918. Leonard, John & Leonard-Johnson, Philip, eds. 2010. (Illus.). 256p. 39.95 *(978-1-84884-159-8(0))* Pen & Sword Bks. Ltd. GBR. Dist: Casemate Pubs. & Bk. Distributors, LLC.
Lerner Jaccarino, Pamela, ed. Honor: Uriah P. Levy Center & Jewish Chapel. 2008. (ENG., Illus.). 148p. 49.95 *(978-0-9764713-9-4(6))* Sandow Media.
Madigan, Edward. Faith under Fire: Anglican Army Chaplains & the Great War. 2011. (ENG., Illus.). 332p. 85.00 *(978-0-230-23745-2(2))* Palgrave Macmillan.
Maguire, Connell. Foibles of Father Joe. 2008. per. 14.95 *(978-0-9727330-3-8(5))* Chi Chi Pr.
Maryniak, Benedict R. & Brinsfield, John Wesley, Jr., eds. The Spirit Divided: Memoirs of Civil War Chaplains: the Union. 2007. (Illus.). 269p. 35.00 *(978-0-86554-996-8(6))* Mercer Univ. Pr.
McDonnell, Thomas. The Priest Goes to War. 2006. 128p. per. 19.95 *(978-0-9789432-2-6(8))* Catholic Authors Pr.
McWilliams, Tennant S. The Chaplain's Conflict: Good & Evil in a War Hospital, 1943-1945. 2012. (Williams-Ford Texas A&M University Military History Ser.). 144p. 35.00 ***(978-1-60344-470-5(X))*** Texas A&M Univ. Pr.
Moczynski, Walter, et al, eds. Medical Ethics in Health Care Chaplaincy. 2011. (ENG.). 336p. pap. 39.95 *(978-3-8258-1550-9(1))* Lit Verlag DEU. Dist: Transaction Pubs.
O'Connor, Brian P., et al. The Role of the Minister in Caring for the Dying Patient & the Bereaved. 19.95 *(978-0-405-12504-1(6))* Ayer Co. Pubs., Inc.
O'Connor, Daniel. The Chaplains of the East India Company, 1601-1858. 2012. (ENG.). 176p. *(978-1-4411-7534-2(2))* Continuum International Publishing Group, Ltd.
Parker, Linda. The Whole Armour of God: Anglican Army Chaplains in the Great War. 2009. (Illus.). 112p. 59.95 *(978-1-906033-32-3(3))* Helion & Co., Ltd. GBR. Dist: Casemate Pubs. & Bk. Distributors, LLC.
Pickett, Carroll & Stowers, Carlton. Within These Walls: Memoirs of a Death House Chaplain. 2009. (ENG.). 256p. pap. 16.95 *(978-1-904132-74-5(X))* Vision Paperbacks GBR. Dist: Independent Pubs. Group.
Rennick, Joanne. Religion in the Ranks: Belief & Religious Experience in the Canadian Forces. 2011. (Illus.). 224p. ***(978-1-4426-4287-4(4))*** Univ. of Toronto Pr.

Swift, Christopher. Hospital Chaplaincy in the Twenty-First Century: The Crisis of Spiritual Care on the NHS. 2009. (Explorations in Practical, Pastoral & Empirical Theology Ser.). (Illus.). 212p. 99.95 *(978-0-7546-6416-1(3))* Ashgate Publishing Co.
Vella, Charles G. Ethics in the Service of the Sick: Reflections & Experiences of Life at the San Raffaele Hospital. 2009. (ENG.). 200p. pap. 35.95 *(978-1-84730-165-6(5))* Veritas Pubns. IRL. Dist: Dufour Editions, Inc.
Whitehead, Alfred North. Religion in the Making. 2011. (ENG.). 156p. pap. 19.99 *(978-1-107-64799-2(1))* Cambridge Univ. Pr.
Williamson, Chaplain Don. Bringing Courage to the Courageous. 2010. 170p. pap. 14.99 *(978-1-60957-687-5(X))* Xulon Pr., Inc.

CHAPLIN, CHARLIE, 1889-1977

Bengtson, John. Silent Traces: Discovering Early Hollywood Through the Films of Charlie Chaplin. 2006. (ENG., Illus.). 304p. per. 24.95 ***(978-1-59580-014-5(X))*** Santa Monica Pr.
Bowman, W. Dodgson. Charlie Chaplin: His Life & Art. 152p. 2010. pap. 17.56 *(978-1-163-19492-8(1))* 2008. 36.95 *(978-1-4366-8816-1(7))* 2007. (ENG.). per. 21.95 *(978-1-4325-9777-1(9))* Kessinger Publishing, LLC.
Coates, Peter & Niklaus, Thelma. The Little Fellow. *(978-0-8022-0307-6(8))* Philosophical Library, Inc.
Duncan, Paul (Ed) & Robinson, David. MOVIE ICONS - Charlie Chaplin. 2006. (Movie Icons Ser.). (FRE, GER & ENG., Illus.). 192p. pap. 9.99 *(978-3-8228-2005-6(9))* TASCHEN DEU. Dist: Ingram Pub. Services.
Flom, Eric L. Chaplin in the Sound Era: An Analysis of the Seven Talkies. alt. ed. 2008. (ENG.). 336p. pap. 39.95 *(978-0-7864-4052-8(X))* McFarland & Co., Inc. Pubs.
Harness, Kyp. The Art of Charlie Chaplin: A Film-by-Film Analysis. 2007. (ENG.). 228p. per. 39.95 *(978-0-7864-3193-9(8))* McFarland & Co., Inc. Pubs.
Kamin, Dan. The Comedy of Charlie Chaplin: Artistry in Motion. 2011. (ENG.). 244p. pap. 35.00 *(978-0-8108-7780-1(5))* Scarecrow Pr., Inc.
Larcher, Jérôme. Masters of Cinema: Charlie Chaplin. 2011. (ENG., Illus.). 104p. pap. 9.95 *(978-2-86642-606-4(1))* Phaidon Pr., Inc.
Maland, Charles J. City Lights. 2007. (BFI Film Classics Ser.). (ENG., Illus.). 272p. pap. 14.95 *(978-1-84457-175-8(0))* BFI Publishing GBR. Dist: Macmillan.
Neibaur, James L. Chaplin at Essanay: A Film Artist in Transition, 1915-1916. 2008. (ENG., Illus.). 220p. pap. 39.95 *(978-0-7864-3512-8(7))* McFarland & Co., Inc. Pubs.
Neibaur, James L. Early Charlie Chaplin: The Artist As Apprentice at Keystone Studios. 2012. E-Book ***(978-0-8108-8243-0(4))*** Scarecrow Pr., Inc.
Nysenholc, Adolphe, ed. Charlie Chaplin: His Reflection in Modern Times. (Approaches to Semiotics [AS] Ser.). (ENG.). XVI, 412p. 196.00 ***(978-3-11-178773-2(7))*** De Gruyter, Mouton DEU. Dist: de Gruyter, Walter GmbH & Co. KG.
Payne, Robert. The Great God Pan: A Biography of the Tramp Played by Charles Chaplin. 2011. 338p. 51.95 ***(978-1-258-08778-4(2))*** Literary Licensing, LLC.
Scheide, Frank, et al, eds. Chaplin's Limelight & the Music Hall Tradition. 2006. (ENG., Illus.). 228p. per. 49.95 *(978-0-7864-2425-2(7))* McFarland & Co., Inc. Pubs.
Shklovsky, Viktor. Literature & Cinematography. Masinovsky, Irina, tr. from RUS. 2008. (Russian Literature Ser.).Tr. of Literatura i Kinematograf. (ENG & RUS.). 74p. pap. 14.95 *(978-1-56478-482-7(7))* Dalkey Archive Pr.
Smith, Stephen P. The Charlie Chaplin Walk. 2010. (ENG., Illus.). 192p. pap. 20.00 *(978-1-85058-852-8(X)*, Sigma Pr.) Stobart Davies, Ltd. GBR. Dist: Brown, David Bk. Co., The.
Tomo, Grandes de, ed. Los Grandes - Charles Chiplin. 2007. 136p. pap. 5.95 *(978-970-666-732-8(6))* Grupo Editorial Tomo, S.A. de C.V. MEX. Dist: Giron Bks.
Wada, Linda. The Sea Gull A Woman of the Sea: The Chaplin's Studio Lost Film starring Edna Purviance. 3rd rev. ed. 2010. (Illus.). 132p. pap. 39.95 *(978-0-9826332-0-5(3))* Leading Ladies.
Weissman, Stephen M. Chaplin: A Life. 2011. (ENG.). 320p. pap. 14.95 *(978-1-61145-040-8(3)*, 611040, Arcade Publishing) Skyhorse Publishing Co., Inc.

CHAPLIN, HENRY CHAPLIN, VISCOUNT, 1841-1923

Londonderry, The Marchioness Of. Henry Chaplin: A Memoir. 428p. 2008. 51.95 *(978-1-4366-7824-7(2))* 2007. per. 36.95 *(978-1-4325-8194-7(5))* Kessinger Publishing, LLC.

CHAPMAN, GEORGE, 1559?-1634

Chapman, George. Bussy DAmbois & the Revenge of Bussy D. 2006. pap. 34.95 *(978-1-4286-3512-8(2))* Kessinger Publishing, LLC.
Swinburne, Algernon Charles. George Chapman: A Critical Essay. 2007. (ENG.). 192p. 37.95 *(978-0-548-11724-8(1))*; 190p. 37.95 *(978-0-548-24073-1(6))*; 192p. per. 22.95 *(978-1-4326-4232-7(4))* Kessinger Publishing, LLC.

CHAPMAN, JOHN, 1774-1845

see Appleseed, Johnny, 1774-1845

CHAR, RENE, 1907-1988

Baker, Robert. In Dark Again in Wonder: The Poetry of Rene Char & George Oppen. 2012. (ENG.). 248p. pap. 36.00 ***(978-0-268-02229-7(1))*** Univ. of Notre Dame Pr.
Char, Rene & Carlson, Nancy Naomi. Stone Lyre: Poems of Rene Char. 2010. (FRE.). 124p. pap. 16.95 *(978-1-932195-78-1(5))* Tupelo Pr., Inc.

CHARACTER

see also Conduct of Life; Temperament; Virtue and Virtues

Alark, Betty. What Type of Character Are You Hanging Out With? 2011. 48p. 24.99 ***(978-1-4535-9980-8(0))***; pap. 15.99 ***(978-1-4535-9979-2(7))*** Xlibris Corp.
Alexander, Bennie Ray. A. R. T: Guide Booklet for at Risk Teens. Alexander, Bennie Ray, ed. 2007. 30p. (YA). (gr. 6-12). pap. 10.00 *(978-0-9764609-2-3(0))* Circle of Friends Bks.
Allen, James. Cause & Effect in Human Conduct. 2006. pap. 12.95 *(978-1-4286-6576-7(5))* Kessinger Publishing, LLC.
—The Mastery of Destiny. 2011. 64p. pap. 7.99 ***(978-1-61203-128-6(5))*** Bottom of the Hill Publishing.
—The Selected Teachings of James Allen: Eight Pillars of Prosperity, Foundation Stones to Happiness & Success, the Shining Gateway, James All. 2008. 288p. pap. 14.95 *(978-1-60459-599-4(X))* Wilder Pubns., Ltd.
—The Wisdom of James Allen. 2008. pap. 7.99 ***(978-956-291-622-6(7))*** Meirovich, Igal.
—The Wisdom of James Allen. 2009. 296p. pap. 14.95 *(978-1-60459-607-6(4))* 2008. 192p. pap. 14.95 *(978-1-60459-605-2(8))* Wilder Pubns., Ltd.
Allen, Roger K. The Hero's Choice: Living from the Inside Out. 2009. 270p. pap. 16.95 *(978-0-9797831-2-8(7))* Leadership Pr.
Atkinson, William Walker. How to Read Human Nature Its Inner State. 2006. pap. 24.95 *(978-1-4286-5513-3(1))* Kessinger Publishing, LLC.
Beauboeuf-Lafontant, Tamara. Behind the Mask of the Strong Black Woman: Voice & the Embodiment of a Costly Performance. 2009. (ENG.). 194p. 66.50 *(978-1-59213-667-4(2))*; pap. 24.95 *(978-1-59213-668-1(0))* Temple Univ. Pr.
Bell, James Stuart. The One Year Men of the Bible: 365 Meditations on Men of Character. 2008. (ENG.). 384p. pap. 14.99 *(978-1-4143-1607-9(0))* Tyndale Hse. Pubs.
Berthel, Tom & Fry, Hayden. Beyond Xs & Os: What I Learned about Friendship & Success from a Football Legend. 2010. (ENG., Illus.). 256p. 24.95 *(978-1-61608-113-3(9)*, 608113) Skyhorse Publishing Co., Inc.
Bland, Dave & Fleer, David. Preaching Character: Reclaiming Wisdom's Paradigmatic Imagination for Transformation. 2010. 256p. pap. 18.99 *(978-0-89112-544-0(2)*, ACU Pr.) Abilene Christian Univ. Pr.
Brawley, Robert L. Character Ethics & the New Testament: Moral Dimensions of Scripture. 2007. (ENG.). 269p. per. 30.00 *(978-0-664-23066-1(0))* Westminster John Knox Pr.
Brazelton, Katie, et al. Character Makeover: 40 Days with a Life Coach to Create the Best You. 1 vol. 2007. (ENG., Illus.). 336p. (gr. 13). pap. 14.99 *(978-0-310-25653-3(4))* Zondervan.
A Bridge to Nowhere: Memories, Morals, Martinis, & the Myth of the Promiscuous Man. 2006. 240p. 23.95 *(978-0-9789983-0-1(8))* Three Angels Publishing.
Brooks, David. The Social Animal: The Hidden Sources of Love, Character, & Achievement. (ENG.). 2012. 448p. pap. 16.00 *(978-0-8129-7937-4(C)*, Random Hse. Trade Paperbacks) 2011. 448p. 27.00 *(978-1-4000-6760-2(X)*, Random House) 2011. xviii, 424p. E-Book *(978-0-679-60393-1(X)*, Random House) Random House Publishing Group.
Brower, Robert & Keller, Amy. Empowering Students: Seven Strategies for a Smart Start in School & Life. 2006. (ENG.). 164p. 55.00 *(978-1-57886-491-1(7))*; per. 27.95 *(978-1-57886-492-8(5))* Rowman & Littlefield Education.
Canfield, Jack L., et al. Chicken Soup for the Woman's Soul. 2008. (Chicken Soup Ser.). (ENG.). 120p. 4.95 *(978-0-7573-0716-4(7))* Health Communications, Inc.
Carlisle, Janice. John Stuart Mill & the Writing of Character. 2010. (ENG.). 352p. pap. 24.95 *(978-0-8203-3790-6(0))* Univ. of Georgia Pr.
Carroll, M. Daniel & Lapsley, Jacqueline E., eds. Character Ethics & the Old Testament: Moral Dimensions of Scripture. 2007. (ENG., Illus.). 260p. per. 30.00 *(978-0-664-22936-8(0))* Westminster John Knox Pr.
Carter, Samuel Casey. On Purpose: How Great School Cultures Form Strong Character. 2010. (Illus.). 208p. pap. 31.95 *(978-1-4129-8672-4(9)*, B83724P) Corwin Pr.
Chandler, Mary G. The Elements of Character. 2008. 160p. 22.99 *(978-0-554-33601-5(4))* 2008. 160p. 25.99 *(978-0-554-24298-9(2))* 2007. 158p. 21.99 *(978-1-4264-6218-4(2))* BiblioBazaar.
—The Elements of Character. 2009. 94p. pap. *(978-0-217-94818-0(9))* Books LLC.
—The Elements of Character. 2009. 146p. pap. *(978-1-4099-9021-5(4))* Dodo Pr.
—The Elements of Character. 2007. 100p. per. *(978-1-4068-4505-1(1))* Echo Library.
—The Elements of Character: The Elements of Character. 2007. (ENG.). 142p. pap. 18.99 *(978-1-4264-6163-7(1))* BiblioBazaar.
Chassell, Clara Frances. Relation Between Morality & Intellect. 2006. pap. 43.95 *(978-1-4286-5174-6(8))* Kessinger Publishing, LLC.
Cloud, Henry. Integrity: The Courage to Meet the Demands of Reality. 2009. (ENG.). 304p. pap. 16.99 *(978-0-06-084969-6(X)*, Collins) HarperCollins Pubs.
Cram101 Textbook Reviews Staff. Outlines & Highlights for Building Character: Strengthening the Heart of Good Leadership by Klann, ISBN. 2009. 80p. pap. 10.95 *(978-1-4288-6599-0(3))* Cram101 Inc.
Cullen, Jim. Imperfect Presidents: Tales of Misadventure & Triumph. 2008. (ENG., Illus.). 256p. pap. 14.95 *(978-0-230-60578-7(8))* Palgrave Macmillan.
Danforth, William. Wisdom of William H Danforth James Alle. 2006. 116p. per. *(978-956-291-322-5(8))* Editorial Benei Noaj.
Danforth, William H. I Dare You. 2009. (ENG., Illus.). 144p. pap. 15.00 *(978-1-933715-82-7(0))* Executive Bks.
De Bower, Edward W. Business Mans Book of Proverbs Fundament. 2006. pap. 24.95 *(978-1-4286-5277-4(9))* Kessinger Publishing, LLC.
DeMotte, John B. How Long May You Be a Master? 2006. pap. 9.95 *(978-1-4286-8455-3(7))* Kessinger Publishing, LLC.
DeSteno, David & Valdesolo, Piercarlo. Out of Character: Surprising Truths about the Liar, Cheat, Sinner (and Saint) Lurking in All of Us. 2011. (ENG.). 272p. 25.00 *(978-0-307-71775-7(5)*, Crown Archetype) Crown Publishing Group.
DeVitis, Joseph L. & Yu, Tianlong. Character & Moral Education: A Reader. 2011. xiii, 419p. ***(978-1-4331-1100-6(4))***; pap. ***(978-1-4331-1099-3(7))***; E-Book ***(978-1-4539-0140-3(X))*** Lang, Peter GmbH, Europaischer Verlag der Wissenschaften.
Dougherty. Underground Springs. 2007. (ENG., Illus.). 312p. (C). 39.95 *(978-0-415-40300-9(6))* Routledge.
Dougherty, Nancy J. & West, Jacqueline J. Underground Springs. 2007. (ENG., Illus.). 312p. (C). 110.00 *(978-0-415-40301-6(4))* Routledge.
Eliot, William Greenleaf. Lectures to Young Men by William G Eliot, Jr. 2006. 192p. per. 18.99 *(978-1-4255-1532-4(0))* MPublishing.
Engel, Susan. Red Flags or Red Herrings? Predicting Who Your Child Will Become. 2011. (ENG.). 288p. 24.00 *(978-1-4391-5011-5(7)*, Beyond Words/Atria Bks.) Atria Bks.
Evans, Amy. The Journey to Excellence, Year 2. Lamb, Judy, ed. 2008. (Journey to Moral & Social Excellence: 2). 192p. pap. 19.95 *(978-1-892056-51-1(8))* Character Development Group, Inc.
Fiske, Lewis Ransom. Man Building: A Treatise on Human Life & Its Forces. 2007. (ENG.). 334p. 45.95 *(978-0-548-03847-5(3))* Kessinger Publishing, LLC.
Foster, John. Essays in a Series of Letters. 2007. (ENG.). 336p. 45.95 *(978-0-548-06034-6(7))* Kessinger Publishing, LLC.
Fuller, Thomas. The Holy & Profane States by Thomas Fuller with Some Account of the Author & His Writings. 2006. 336p. per. 23.99 *(978-1-4255-3357-1(4))* MPublishing.
Garcia, Marcelino. Discover Your Character, 35. 2008. (Félix Varela Ser.). (Illus.). 123p. pap. 16.00 *(978-1-59388-126-3(2)*, 128-2) Ediciones Universal.
George, Elizabeth. Jueces/Rut Cultiva una Vida de Integridad, 1 vol. 2010. (mujer conforme al coraz#xF3;n de Dios Ser.). Orig. Title: Judges/Ruth, Cultivating a Life of Character. (SPA.). 160p. pap. 8.99 *(978-0-8254-1256-1(0)*, Editorial Portavoz) Kregel Pubns.
Gerwig, George W. Perseverance: An Element in the Character of A Good American. 2011. 96p. 38.95 ***(978-1-258-03564-8(2))*** Literary Licensing, LLC.
Goodart, Clarence. A Course in Morals & Manners. 2011. 66p. 36.95 ***(978-1-258-01063-8(1))*** Literary Licensing, LLC.
Gottlieb, Paula. The Virtue of Aristotle's Ethics. (ENG.). 2011. 261p. pap. 50.00 *(978-0-521-36999-2(1))* 2009. (Illus.). 262p. (C). 92.00 *(978-0-521-76176-5(X))* Cambridge Univ. Pr.
Handley, Rod. Character That Counts - Who's Counting Yours? Growing Through Accountability. 2007. mass mkt. 16.99 *(978-1-929478-76-7(3))* Cross Training Publishing.
Haner, Jean. The Wisdom of Your Child's Face: Discover Your Child's True Nature with Chinese Face Reading. 2010. (ENG., Illus.). 336p. pap. 15.95 *(978-1-4019-2534-5(0))* Hay Hse., Inc.
Hannemann, Charles & Potter, Rosemary. What Are You Saying? Thinking Adventures in Character Education. 2nd rev. ed. 2009. 29p. (J). spiral bd. 31.95 *(978-0-9788193-2-3(2))* Rose & Lee Pr.
Hartsock, Chad. Sight & Blindness in Luke-Acts: The Use of Physical Features in Characterization. 2008. (Biblical Interpretation Ser.). 232p. *(978-90-04-16535-9(5))* BRILL.
Hillis, Newell Dwight. The Contagion of Character: Studies in Culture & Success. 2007. (ENG.). 336p. 45.95 *(978-0-548-12542-7(2))* 2006. pap. 30.95 *(978-1-4286-3514-2(9))* Kessinger Publishing, LLC.
Hooberman, Robert. Forgiving, Forgetting, & Moving On: Living a Less-Conflicted Life. 2010. (ENG.). 170p. 55.00 *(978-0-7657-0667-6(9)*, Aronson, Jason) Rowman & Littlefield Publishers, Inc.
Hooberman, Robert E. Forgiving, Forgetting, & Moving On: Living a Less-Conflicted Life. 2010. x, 159p. *(978-0-7657-0669-0(5)*, Aronson, Jason) Rowman & Littlefield Publishers, Inc.
Indigo, True Blue. A Personal Aristocracy: Cultivating the Power of Spiritual Nobility. 2010. (ENG.). 328p. pap. 17.95 *(978-1-55643-866-0(4))* North Atlantic Bks.
Isete, Salvador. Caracter y Personalidad: Character & Personality. (SPA.). 96p. *(978-84-7228-405-0(0)*, 220138) Clie, Editorial.
Jastrow, Joseph. Character & Temperament. 2009. 618p. 38.99 *(978-1-113-64838-9(4))*; 45.99 *(978-1-113-64839-6(2))*; pap. 45.75 *(978-1-113-64836-5(8))*; pap. 44.75 *(978-1-113-64834-1(1))* BiblioBazaar.
—Character & Temperament. 2009. 378p. pap. *(978-0-217-34339-8(2))*; 384p. pap. *(978-1-4588-1748-8(2))*; 380p. pap. *(978-1-4590-6345-7(7))* Books LLC.
—Character & Temperament. 2008. 614p. 59.95 *(978-1-4365-9868-2(0))* 2007. (ENG.). 616p. per. 44.95 *(978-0-548-80245-8(9))* Kessinger Publishing, LLC.
Johnson, Rick. The Power of a Man: Using Your Influence as a Man of Character. 2009. 208p. pap. 13.99 *(978-0-8007-3249-3(9))* Revell.
Kennedy, Judith. Self-Esteem & Character Building: For Individual Students in Grades 4-8. 2007. (ENG.). 96p. pap. *(978-1-930572-49-2(2))* Educational Media Corp.
Kerrigan, Michael J. Politics with Principle: Ten Characters with Character. 2010. (Illus.). 290p. 46.95 *(978-1-60494-448-8(X))*; pap. 21.95 *(978-1-60494-447-1(1))* Wheatmark.
Kershnar, Stephen. Desert & Virtue: A Theory of Intrinsic Value. 2009. (ENG., Illus.). 168p. 62.99 *(978-0-7391-3936-3(3))* Lexington Bks.
Ketterman, Diana Chavez, et al. Songs & Stories from Character Island, Vol. 1. 2012. pap. ***(978-0-9850722-6-1(1))*** Character Champions Foundation.
Knowles, Liz & Smith, Martha. Character Builders: Books & Activities for Character Education, 1 vol. annot. ed. 2006. (Through Children's Literature Ser.). 156p. per. 40.00 *(978-1-59158-370-7(5)*, LU3705) Libraries Unlimited, Inc.
Kolencik, Patricia Lotta & Bernadowski, Carianne. Teaching with Books That Heal: Authentic Literature & Literacy Strategies to Help Children Cope with Everyday Problems, 1 vol. 2007. (Illus.). 184p. per. 36.95 *(978-1-58683-220-9(4)*, A2463P) Linworth Publishing, Inc.
Lee, Witness. Caracter. 2008.Tr. of Character. (SPA.). pap. 5.75 *(978-0-7363-3754-0(7))* Living Stream Ministry.
Ligon, Ernest M. Dimensions of Character. 2011. 526p. 60.95 ***(978-1-258-08402-8(3))*** Literary Licensing, LLC.
Lonberger, Rosemary & Harrison, Jane. Links to Literature: Teaching Tools to Enhance Literacy, Character, & Social Skills. 2008. (Illus.). 108p. pap. 26.00 *(978-0-942349-24-5(5))* Educators for Social Responsibility.
Lowen, Alexander. The Language of the Body: Physical Dynamics of Character Structure. 2006. Orig. Title: Physical Dynamics of Character Structure. (Illus.). 358p. per. 24.95 *(978-0-9743737-9-9(6))* Bioenergetics Pr.
Lukacs, John. George Kennan: A Study of Character. 2009. (ENG., Illus.) 224p. pap. 15.00 *(978-0-300-14306-5(0))* Yale Univ. Pr.
Malikow, Max, ed. Profiles in Character: Twenty-Six Stories That Will Instruct & Inspire Teenagers. 2007. (ENG.). 109p. 52.50 *(978-0-7618-3686-5(1))*; per. 28.50 *(978-0-7618-3687-2(X))* Univ. Pr. of America, Inc.
March, Kathrym, et al. My Grandmother Is Praying for Me: Daily Prayers & Proverbs for Character Development in Grandchildren. 2011. (ENG.). 382p. 18.00 ***(978-1-59638-400-2(X))*** P & R Publishing.
Marchiano, Bruce. The Character of a Man: Reflecting the Image of Jesus. 2010. (ENG.). 224p. pap. 15.99 *(978-1-4516-2379-6(8)*, Howard Bks.) Howard Books.
McCain, John & Salter, Mark. Character Is Destiny: Inspiring Stories Every Young Person Should Know & Every Adult Should Remember. 2007. (Modern Library Classics Ser.). (ENG., Illus.). 336p. per. 17.00 *(978-0-8129-7445-4(X)*, Random Hse. Trade Paperbacks) Random House Publishing Group.
McDowell, Stephen. Apostle of Liberty: The World-Changing Leadership of George Washington. 2007. (Leaders in Action Ser.). (ENG.). 320p. 16.95 *(978-1-58182-584-8(6))* Turner Publishing Co.
Meyer, Susan Sauve. Aristotle on Moral Responsibility: Character & Cause. 2012. (ENG.). 240p. 75.00 *(978-0-19-969742-7(6))*; 216p. pap. 35.00 *(978-0-19-969743-4(4))* Oxford Univ. Pr., Inc.
Miller, J. R. The Building of Character. 2011. 132p. pap. 14.99 ***(978-1-61203-157-5(6))*** Bottom of the Hill Publishing.
—The Building of Character. 2010. (Illus.). 88p. pap. 20.00 *(978-1-154-65093-8(6))* General Bks. LLC.
—The Building of Character. 2010. 282p. pap. 22.36 *(978-1-163-90281-3(0))* 2008. 280p. 42.95 *(978-0-548-92587-4(9))* 2007. (ENG.). 280p. per. 27.95 *(978-0-548-60824-1(5))* Kessinger Publishing, LLC.
Musschenga, A. W., et al, eds. Personal & Moral Identity. 2010. (Library of Ethics & Applied Philosophy Ser.). 336p. pap. 179.00 *(978-90-481-6080-8(4)*, 9048160804) Springer.
Myers, R. E. Character Matters. 2008. pap. 15.95 *(978-1-59647-264-8(2))* Good Year Bks.
Newbrough, Jennie. At the Core: Character Determines Destiny. 2008. 140p. pap. 12.95 *(978-0-9792739-0-2(0))* Ajoyin Publishing, Inc.
Norwood, Andy. 30 Life Lessons My Boys Learned from Baseball. 1 vol. 2010. (ENG., Illus.). 136p. 14.95 *(978-1-58980-794-5(4))* Pelican Publishing Co., Inc.
O'Neill, Rob. Digital Character Development: Theory & Practice. 2008. (ENG., Illus.). 352p. (C). 69.95 *(978-0-12-372561-5(5)*, Morgan Kaufmann) Elsevier Science & Technology Bks.
Owens, Jeff. The One Thing Money Can't Buy - The One Thing You Can't Afford to Be Without! Character. Date not set. *(978-0-9649393-0-1(4))* Owens Pubns.
Parlette, Ralph. The University of Hard Knocks: The School that Completes Our Education. 2006. (ENG.). 122p. pap. 18.99 *(978-1-4264-0339-2(9))* BiblioBazaar.
Phillips, Ellen. Kick the Clutter: Clear Out Excess Stuff Without Losing What You Love. 2008. pap. 14.50 *(978-1-60529-916-7(2))* Rodale Pr., Inc.
Pierce, Edgar. The Philosophy of Character. 2007. (ENG.). 450p. 52.95 *(978-0-548-02660-1(2))* Kessinger Publishing, LLC.
Riach, Steve. True Heroes of Sports: Discovering the Heart of a Champion, 0 vols. 2009. 160p. 15.99 *(978-1-4041-8699-6(9))* Nelson, Thomas Inc.
Rizzo, Margaret & Brown, Joyce. Building Character Through Community Service: Strategies to Implement the Missing Element in Education. 2006. (ENG.). 208p. pap. 35.95 *(978-1-57886-366-2(X))* Rowman & Littlefield Education.
Roback, A. A. Psychology of Character with A Survey of. 2006. pap. 45.95 *(978-1-4286-4927-9(1))* Kessinger Publishing, LLC.
Salls, Holly Shepard. Character Education: Transforming Values into Virtue. 2006. (ENG.). 170p. pap. 33.99 *(978-0-7618-3612-4(8))* Univ. Pr. of America, Inc.
Sandbrook. Christian Meat for Christian Muscles: Part 2 - Self Esteem, Prayer, Character, Wisdom & God's Promises. 2011. 352p. pap. 23.03 ***(978-1-4567-9742-3(5))*** AuthorHouse.
Schwartz, Merle. Effective Character Education: A Guidebook for Future Educators. 2007. (ENG., Illus.). 184p. (C). pap. 51.33 *(978-0-07-340378-6(4)*, 0073403784) McGraw-Hill Higher Education.
Smiles, Samuel. Character. 2009. 254p. pap. 8.99 *(978-1-60450-704-1(7)*, Serenity Pubs.) Arc Manor.

—Character. 2008. (ENG.). 296p. pap. 27.75 *(978-1-4375-0128-5(1))*; 338p. pap. 31.75 *(978-1-4375-0129-2(X))* BiblioBazaar.
—Character. 2009. 228p. pap. *(978-0-217-34337-4(6))* Books LLC.
—Character. 2008. 296p. pap. *(978-1-4065-7571-2(2))* Dodo Pr.
—Character. 2006. (ENG.). pap. *(978-1-4068-0579-6(3))* Echo Library.
—Character. 2008. 320p. pap. 16.95 *(978-1-60096-387-2(0))*; 360p. pap. 18.95 *(978-1-60096-900-3(3))* Editorium, The.
—Character. 2008. 400p. 49.95 *(978-1-4369-9229-9(X))*; pap. 34.95 *(978-1-4368-0240-6(7))* Kessinger Publishing, LLC.
—Character. 2008. 408p. *(978-1-4437-3690-9(2)*, Hesperides Pr.) Read Bks.
Soulsby, Lucy H. M. Stray Thoughts for Girls. 2008. 152p. 24.99 *(978-0-554-27097-5(8))* 2008. 152p. 21.99 *(978-0-554-36400-1(X))* 2007. (ENG.). 136p. pap. 18.99 *(978-1-4346-2497-0(8))* 2007. 148p. pap. 19.99 *(978-1-4346-2539-7(7))* BiblioBazaar.
Spring, Gardiner & Kistler, Don. The Distinguishing Traits of Christian Character. 2009. *(978-0-9798579-8-0(8))* Northampton Pr., The.
Titus, Craig Steven, ed. The Psychology of Character & Virtue. 2009. (John Henry Cardinal Newman Lecture Ser.). 152p. pap. 24.95 *(978-0-9773103-4-0(5))* Institute for the Psychological Science Pr., The.
Trine, Ralph. Character-Building Thought Power. 2006. pap. 12.95 *(978-1-59605-981-8(8)*, Cosimo Classics) Cosimo, Inc.
—What All the World's A-Seeking: Or, the Vital Law of True Life, True Greatness Power & Happiness. 2007. 96p. per. 8.99 *(978-1-60459-039-5(4))* Wilder Pubns., Ltd.
—What All the World's A-Seeking: the Vital Law of True Life, True. 2006. pap. 19.95 *(978-1-59605-974-0(5)*, Cosimo Classics) Cosimo, Inc.
Trine, Ralph Waldo. What All the World's A-Seeking. 2008. 196p. 22.99 *(978-0-559-54907-6(5))*; 196p. pap. 22.75 *(978-0-559-54906-9(7))*; 265p. 24.99 *(978-0-554-90049-0(1))*; 213p. 27.99 *(978-0-554-90040-7(8))*; 265p. pap. 24.75 *(978-0-554-90046-9(7))*; 159p. pap. 25.75 *(978-0-554-90042-1(4))* BiblioBazaar.
—What All the World's A-Seeking. 2009. 84p. pap. *(978-1-151-72473-1(4))* Books LLC.
—What All the World's A-Seeking. 2009. 120p. pap. *(978-1-4065-3933-2(3))* Dodo Pr.
—What All the World's A-Seeking. 2006. (ENG.). pap. *(978-1-4068-1083-7(5))* Echo Library.
Turner, J. B. Seventh Anniversary Address Before the Platonian Literary Society of M'Kendree College by J B Turner, April 21 1856. 2011. 18p. pap. 11.99 ***(978-1-4181-9052-1(7))*** MPublishing.
Ulrich, Wendy. Weakness Is Not Sin: The Liberating Distinction That Awakens Our Strengths. 2009. 15.95 *(978-1-60641-139-1(X))* Deseret Bk. Co.
Upton, Candace L. Situational Traits of Character: Dispositional Foundations & Implications for Moral Psychology & Friendship. 2009. (ENG.). 120p. 57.99 *(978-0-7391-3249-5(9))* Lexington Bks.
Walsh, David. No: Why Kids — of All Ages — Need to Hear It & Ways Parents Can Say It. 2007. (ENG.). 336p. pap. 15.00 *(978-0-7432-8920-7(X)*, Free Pr.) Free Pr.
Wangaard, David B. The Golden Compass for Chracter - Based Decision Making: A Skill for Students & Educators. 2006. 106p. pap. 16.95 *(978-1-892056-47-4(X))* Character Development Group, Inc,.
Ware, Henry. Formation of the Christian Character. 2009. 98p. pap. 14.14 *(978-0-217-92929-5(X))* General Bks. LLC.
—Formation of the Christian Character. 2006. 280p. per. 23.99 *(978-1-4255-2495-1(8))* MPublishing.
Washington, Booker T. Character Building. 2012. ***(978-1-4128-4732-2(X))*** Transaction Pubs.
Weininger, Otto. Sex & Character.Tr. of Geschlecht & Charakter. 2010. 392p. pap. 33.75 *(978-1-148-96375-4(8))* 2009. (ENG.). 381p. 38.99 *(978-1-117-36588-6(3))* 2009. (ENG.). 381p. pap. 25.99 *(978-1-117-36590-9(5)*, BiblioLife) 2009. (ENG.). 381p. pap. 32.75 *(978-1-117-36589-3(1))* BiblioBazaar.
—Sex & Character. 2010.Tr. of Geschlecht & Charakter. 216p. pap. *(978-1-153-15118-4(9))* Books LLC.
—Sex & Character. 2010.Tr. of Geschlecht & Charakter. 382p. pap. 27.16 *(978-1-162-93506-5(5))* Kessinger Publishing, LLC.
—Sex & Character.Tr. of Geschlecht & Charakter. 356p. reprint ed. 98.00 *(978-0-7222-1629-3(7))* Library Reprints, Inc.
Whipple, Edwin P. Character & Characteristic Men. 2007. (ENG.). 330p. 45.95 *(978-0-548-04838-2(X))* Kessinger Publishing, LLC.
Wilburn, Brad. Moral Cultivation: Essays on the Development of Character & Virtue. 2010. (ENG.). 170p. pap. 24.95 *(978-0-7391-4668-2(8))* Lexington Bks.
Wilburn, Brad, ed. Moral Cultivation: Essays on the Development of Character & Virtue. 2007. (ENG.). 170p. 62.99 *(978-0-7391-1220-5(1))* Lexington Bks.
Williams, Frank J. Judging Lincoln. 2007. (ENG., Illus.). 232p. per. 17.95 *(978-0-8093-2759-1(7))* Southern Illinois Univ. Pr.
Wright, N. T. After You Believe: Why Christian Character Matters. 2010. (ENG.). 304p. 24.99 *(978-0-06-173055-9(6)*, HarperOne) HarperCollins Pubs.

CHARACTER EDUCATION
see Moral Education

CHARACTER RECOGNITION SYSTEMS
see Perceptrons

CHARACTER SKETCHES—HISTORY AND CRITICISM
see Characters and Characteristics in Literature

CHARACTERISTIC FUNCTIONS
see also Distribution (Probability Theory)

Geramita, Anthony V., et al. The Hilbert Function of a Level Algebra. 2007. (Memoirs of the American Mathematical Society Ser.: No. 872). (Illus.). 139p. pap. 66.00 *(978-0-8218-3940-9(3))* American Mathematical Society.
Rossi, Maria Evelina & Valla, Giuseppe. Hilbert Functions of Filtered Modules. 2010. (Lecture Notes of the Unione Matematica Italiana Ser.). xviii, 100p. pap. 49.95 *(978-3-642-14239-0(7)*, 3642142397) Springer.

CHARACTERS AND CHARACTERISTICS
see also Eccentrics and Eccentricities; National Characteristics; Physiognomy; Polarity (Psychology); Typology (Psychology)

Adler, Alfred. Understanding Human Nature: Alfred Adler on the Psychology of Personality. Brett, Colin, ed. & tr. by. from GER. 2009. (ENG.). 240p. pap. 29.95 *(978-1-85168-667-4(3))* Oneworld Pubns. GBR. Dist: National Bk. Network.
Andrews, Lauren. Manga University Presents: the Cosplayer's Handbook: The Cosplayer's Handbook. 2012. (Illus.). 160p. (YA). pap. 14.95 *(978-4-921205-29-4(9))* Japanime Co., Ltd. JPN. Dist: Diamond Bk. Distributors.
Bergner, Heinz [Ed.], ed. English Character-Writing. (English Texts). (ENG.). X, 126p. 210.00 ***(978-3-11-189981-7(0))*** De Gruyter, Mouton DEU. Dist: de Gruyter, Walter GmbH & Co. KG.
Bigbrosworkshop, prod. I Love U Baby: Characters Collection Book. 2007. (Illus.). 486p. 35.00 *(978-1-58423-274-2(9))* Gingko Pr., Inc.
Blackford, Katherine M. H. Analyzing Character. 2008. (Illus.). 480p. pap. *(978-1-4065-6841-7(4))* Dodo Pr.
Blackford, Katherine M. H. & Arthur Newcomb. Analyzing Character. 2006. (ENG.). 438p. pap. 26.99 *(978-1-4264-6204-7(2))* 2007. 496p. pap. 30.99 *(978-1-4264-6259-7(X))* BiblioBazaar.
Blackford, Katherine M. H. & Newcomb, Arthur. Analyzing Character. 2008. 500p. 31.99 *(978-0-554-33641-1(3))*; 33.99 *(978-0-554-24338-2(5))* BiblioBazaar.
Blondell, Ruby. The Play of Character in Plato's Dialogues. 2006. (ENG.). 468p. pap. 63.00 *(978-0-521-03142-4(7))* Cambridge Univ. Pr.
Christiansen, Jeff & Fichera, Mike. Official Handbook of the Marvel Universe A to Z, 14 vols., Vol. 13. 2010. (ENG., Illus.). 240p. (YA). (gr. 8-17). 24.99 *(978-0-7851-4178-5(2))* Marvel Worldwide, Inc.
Crafton, Donald. Shadow of a Mouse: Performance, Belief, & World-Making in Animation. 2012. (ENG.). 443p. 75.00 ***(978-0-520-26103-7(8))***; pap. 34.95 ***(978-0-520-26104-4(6))*** Univ. of California Pr.
Delicatessen, compiled by. Mascotte 2. 2006. (Mascotte Ser.). (Illus.). 191p. pap. 49.95 *(978-88-86416-67-2(9))* Happy Bks. ITA. Dist: Gingko Pr., Inc.
Disney Storybook Artists Staff, contrib. by. Learn to Draw The Fairies of Pixie Hollow. 2010. (Learn to Draw Favorite Characters Ser.). 32p. (J). (gr. k-3). 28.50 *(978-1-936309-05-4(X))* Foster, Walter Publishing, Inc.
Disney Storybook Artists Staff & Pixar (Firm) Staff, contrib. by. Learn to Draw Disney/Pixar WALL-E. 2010. (Learn to Draw Favorite Characters Ser.). 32p. (J). (gr. k-3). 28.50 *(978-1-936309-04-7(1))* Foster, Walter Publishing, Inc.
Elsam, Paul. Acting Characters: 16 Simple Steps from Rehearsal to Performance. 2011. (ENG., Illus.). 192p. pap. 19.95 *(978-0-7136-7586-3(1)*, Methuen Drama) A & C Black GBR. Dist: Macmillan.
Emigh, John. Prepare for Pictopia, 1 vol. Thaler, Peter, ed. 2010. (ENG., Illus.). 228p. 39.95 *(978-3-9810458-6-4(6))* Pictoplasma Publishing DEU. Dist: Innovative Logistics.
Eury, Michael. Captain Action: The Original Super-Hero Action Figure. 2009. 176p. 39.95 *(978-1-60549-017-5(2))* TwoMorrows Publishing.
Genu, Madame. Knee Reading 101. 2008. 152p. pap. 14.95 *(978-1-4357-1188-4(2))* Lulu Enterprises Inc.
Graphic-Sha. How to Cosplay Volume 2. 2011. (Illus.). 144p. (YA). pap. 24.99 *(978-4-7661-1961-9(4))* Graphic-Sha JPN. Dist: Diamond Bk. Distributors.
—How to Cosplay Volume 7: Props Edition: Props Edition. 2010. (Illus.). 144p. (YA). pap. 24.99 *(978-4-7661-2005-9(1))* Graphic-Sha JPN. Dist: Diamond Bk. Distributors.
Hall, Manly Palmer. Studies in Character Analysis. 2011. 90p. 38.95 ***(978-1-258-00870-3(X))*** Literary Licensing, LLC.
Harrison, John & Harrison, Edward. Idle Idol: The Japanese Mascot. 2010. (ENG., Illus.). 144p. 16.95 *(978-0-9841906-1-4(9))* Batty, Mark Pub., LLC.
Hart, Christopher. Superheroes & Beyond: How to Draw the Leading & Supporting Characters of Today's Comics. 2009. (ENG., Illus.). 160p. pap. 21.99 *(978-0-8230-3305-8(8))* Watson-Guptill Pubns., Inc.
Kingslien, Ryan. ZBrush Studio Projects: Realistic Game Characters. 2011. (ENG., Illus.). 320p. pap. 49.99 *(978-0-470-87256-7(X)*, Sybex) Wiley, John & Sons, Inc.
Packer, Sharon. Superheroes & Superegos: Analyzing the Minds Behind the Masks, 1 vol. 2009. 275p. 54.95 *(978-0-313-35536-3(3)*, C35536, Praeger Pubs.) Greenwood Publishing Group, Inc.
Payany, Esterelle. Recipe for Murder: Frightfully Good Food Inspired by Fiction. 2010. (ENG., Illus.). 144p. 24.95 *(978-2-08-030164-2(0))* Flammarion et Cie FRA. Dist: Random Hse., Inc.
Razo, Rebecca J. Learn to Draw Tinker Bell. 2010. (Learn to Draw Favorite Characters Ser.). 32p. (J). (gr. k-3). 28.50 *(978-1-936309-03-0(3))* Foster, Walter Publishing, Inc.
Roye, Jocelyn. La Figure du Pedant de Montaigne A Moliere. 2008. (Travaux du Grand Siecle Ser.). 235p. (C). pap. 85.00 *(978-2-600-01147-1(1))* Droz, Librairie CHE. Dist: Brown, David Bk. Co., The.
Scivally, Bruce. Superman on Film, Television, Radio & Broadway. 2007. (ENG., Illus.). 248p. 49.95 *(978-0-7864-3166-3(0))* McFarland & Co., Inc. Pubs.
Shaftesbury, Anthony Ashley Cooper. Characteristicks of Men, Manners, Opinions, Times. 2009. 280p. pap. *(978-0-217-34340-4(6))*; 54p. pap. *(978-1-4588-1749-5(0))*; 272p. pap. *(978-0-217-80891-0(3))* Books LLC.
—Characteristicks of Men, Manners, Opinions, Times. 2008. 300p. pap. *(978-1-4097-9277-2(3))* Read Bks.
Singer, Mark. Character Studies: Encounters with the Curiously Obsessed. 2006. (ENG.). 272p. pap. 15.95 *(978-0-618-77363-3(0)*, Mariner Bks.) Houghton Mifflin Harcourt Trade & Reference Pubs.
Sizer, Mona. Outrageous Texans: Tales of the Rich & Infamous. 2008. (ENG.). 272p. pap. 16.95 *(978-1-58979-338-5(2))* Taylor Trade Publishing.
Terrace, Vincent. Television Characters: 1,485 Profiles, 1947-2004. alt. ed. 2011. (ENG.). 448p. pap. 55.00 *(978-0-7864-6631-3(6))* McFarland & Co., Inc. Pubs.
UDON. UDON's Art of Capcom 2. 2010. (Illus.). 284p. (YA). pap. 39.99 *(978-1-926778-05-1(7))* URON Entertainment Corp. CAN. Dist: Diamond Bk. Distributors.
Ussher, R. G. & Theophrastus. Theophrastus: Characters. 2008. (GEC.). 328p. pap. 32.95 *(978-1-85399-188-2(0))* Bristol Classical Pr. GBR. Dist: International Publishers Marketing.
Uyeda, Laura & Razo, Rebecca J. Learn to Draw Disney's The Princess & the Frog. 2010. (Learn to Draw Favorite Characters Ser.). 32p. (J). (gr. k-3). 28.50 *(978-1-936309-01-6(7))* Foster, Walter Publishing, Inc.
Vick, Erik Henry. Emotion Notions: Modeling Personality in Game Character AI. 2009. (ENG.). 624p. pap. 49.99 *(978-1-59863-527-0(1))* Course Technology.
Waggoner, Herman A. Von. How to Read Character at a Glance: A Practical System of Understanding People. 2011. 66p. 36.95 ***(978-1-258-02366-9(0))*** Literary Licensing, LLC.

CHARACTERS AND CHARACTERISTICS IN LITERATURE
see also subdivision Characters under names of individual authors, e.g. Shakespeare, William, 1564-1616—Characters; also subdivision In Literature under names of individual persons, e.g. Shelley, Percy Bysshe, 1792-1822—In Literature; and headings for individual characteristics and classes of persons in literature, e.g. Children in Literature; Honor in Literature

Adams, Jennifer. Y Is for Yorick: A Slightly Irreverent Shakespearean ABC Book for Grown-Ups, 1 vol. 2011. (ENG., Illus.). 128p. 14.99 *(978-1-4236-0754-0(6))* Gibbs Smith, Publisher.
Alsup, Janet, ed. Young Adult Literature & Adolescent Identity Across Cultures & Classrooms: Contexts for the Literary Lives of Teens. 2010. (ENG., Illus.). 240p. pap. 39.95 *(978-0-415-87699-5(0)*, Routledge) Taylor & Francis Group GBR. Dist: Taylor & Francis Group.
Ansari, Asloob Ahmad. The Existential Dramaturgy of William Shakespeare: Character Created Through Crisis. 2010. 260p. 109.95 *(978-0-7734-3603-9(0))* Mellen, Edwin Pr., The.
Anthony, David. Paper Money Men: Commerce, Manhood, & the Sensational Public Sphere in Antebellum America. 2009. (ENG.). 288p. 53.95 *(978-0-8142-1110-6(0))*; cd-rom 14.95 *(978-0-8142-9207-5(0))* Ohio State Univ. Pr.
Ballon, Rachel. Breathing Life into Your Characters. 2nd ed. 2009. (ENG.). 256p. pap. 16.99 *(978-1-58297-597-9(3)*, Writer's Digest Bks.) F&W Media, Inc.
Barnett, Colleen. Mystery Women: an Encyclopedia of Leading Women Characters in Mystery Fiction: Volume Two: (1980-1989) rev. ed. 2008. (ENG.). 492p. per. 16.95 *(978-1-59058-226-8(8))* Poisoned Pen Pr.
—Mystery Women: an Encyclopedia of Leading Women Characters in Mystery Fiction: Volume Three (1990-1999) (Revised) Volume Three (1990-1999) (Revised) 2010. 700p. pap. 39.95 *(978-1-59058-422-4(8))* Poisoned Pen Pr.
Bates, Blanchard W. Literary Portraiture in the Historical Narrative of the French Renaissance. 2011. 176p. 42.95 ***(978-1-258-08991-7(2))*** Literary Licensing, LLC.
Beerbohm, Max. Seven Men. 2010. 234p. pap. 25.75 *(978-1-141-70205-3(3))* 2009. (ENG.). 226p. 32.99 *(978-1-117-48931-5(0))* 2009. (ENG.). 226p. pap. 24.75 *(978-1-117-48932-2(9))* 2009. (ENG.). 226p. pap. 20.99 *(978-1-117-48933-9(7)*, BiblioLife) 2009. 244p. 23.99 *(978-1-103-96390-4(2))* 2009. 244p. pap. 17.99 *(978-1-103-96385-0(6))* BiblioBazaar.
—Seven Men. 2009. 102p. pap. *(978-0-217-25308-6(3))* Books LLC.
—Seven Men. 2007. (ENG.). 96p. per. *(978-1-4065-3724-6(1))* Dodo Pr.
—Seven Men. 2010. 236p. pap. 26.75 *(978-1-178-34428-8(2))*; 232p. pap. 25.75 *(978-1-178-34427-1(4))*; 238p. pap. 26.75 *(978-1-178-06101-7(9))*; 236p. pap. 26.75 *(978-1-177-20148-3(8))* BiblioBazaar.
—Seven Men. 2010. (Illus.). 70p. pap. 20.00 *(978-1-153-68698-3(8))* General Bks. LLC.
—Seven Men. 2010. 100p. pap. 15.16 *(978-1-162-68357-7(0))*; 27.16 ***(978-1-169-23973-9(0))***; 33.95 *(978-1-161-45222-8(2))* Kessinger Publishing, LLC.
Berger, Thomas L., et al. An Index of Characters in Early Modern English Drama: Printed Plays, 1500-1660. 2006. (ENG.). 180p. pap. 44.00 *(978-0-521-03150-9(8))* Cambridge Univ. Pr.
Black, Brian. The Character of the Self in Ancient India: Priests, Kings, & Women in the Early Upanisads. 2007. (SUNY Series in Hindu Studies). 224p. 65.00 *(978-0-7914-7013-8(X))* State Univ. of New York Pr.
Bloom, Harold. Bloom's Literary Themes: The Sublime. 2010. (Bloom's Literary Themes Ser.). 314p. (C). (gr. 9-18). 45.00 *(978-1-60413-443-8(7)*, Chelsea Hse.) Facts On File, Inc.
—Shakespeare: La Invencion de lo Humano. Segovia, Tomas, tr. abr. ed. 2008. (Verticales de Bolsillo Ser.). 909p. pap. *(978-958-45-1157-7(2))* Grupo Editorial Norma.
Bo, Hongjun & Yao, Dongxia. Tu Shuo Hong Lou Meng. 2009. (CHI., Illus.). *(978-7-80211-798-3(4))* Cetial Compilation & Fanslation Pr.
Boehrer, Bruce Thomas. Animal Characters: Nonhuman Beings in Early Modern Literature. 2010. (Haney Foundation Ser.). (Illus.). 256p. (C). 49.95 *(978-0-8122-4249-2(1))* Univ. of Pennsylvania Pr.
Boldrini, Lucia. Autobiographies of Others. 2012. (Routledge Studies in Twentieth-Century Literature Ser.). (ENG., Illus.). 244p. (C). 125.00 ***(978-0-415-50737-0(5))*** Routledge.
Bóta, Judit. Tennessee Williams' Maggie, the Cat. 2009. 64p. pap. *(978-3-639-12513-9(4))* VDM Verlag Dr. Mueller e.K.
Bradbury, Jim. Robin Hood. 2010. (ENG., Illus.). 224p. pap. 29.95 *(978-1-84868-185-9(2))* Amberley Publishing GBR. Dist: Casemate Pubs. & Bk. Distributors, LLC.
Brown, Anthony Gary. The Patrick O'Brian Muster Book: Persons, Animals, Ships & Cannon in the Aubrey-Maturin Sea Novels. 2nd annot. ed. 2006. (ENG., Illus.). 407p. 49.95 *(978-0-7864-2482-5(6))* McFarland & Co., Inc. Pubs.
Brustein, Robert. The Tainted Muse: Prejudice & Presumption in Shakespeare's Works & Times. 2009. (ENG.). 288p. 26.00 *(978-0-300-11576-5(8))* Yale Univ. Pr.
Byrne, James P., et al. Affecting Irishness: Negotiating Cultural Identity Within & Beyond the Nation. 2008. (Reimagining Ireland Ser.). (Illus.). xvii, 314p. 55.95 *(978-3-03911-830-4(7))* Lang, Peter AG GBR. Dist: Lang, Peter.
Card, Orson Scott. Elements of Fiction Writing - Characters & Viewpoint: Proven advice & timeless techniques for creating compelling characters by an award-winning Author. 2nd ed. 2011. (ENG.). 240p. pap. 14.99 *(978-1-59963-212-4(8)*, Writer's Digest Bks.) F&W Media, Inc.
Carr, Nick. America's Secret Service Ace: The Operator 5 Story. 2007. (ENG.). 64p. per. 14.95 *(978-1-4344-9048-3(3)*, Borgo Pr.) Wildside Pr., LLC.
Carroll, Joseph, et al. Graphing Jane Austen: The Evolutionary Basis of Literary Meaning. 2012. (Cognitive Studies in Literature & Performance Ser.). (ENG., Illus.). 318p. 90.00 ***(978-1-137-00240-2(9))*** Palgrave Macmillan.
Chesterton, G. K. Twelve Types. 2008. (ENG.). 72p. per. *(978-1-4065-9095-1(9))* Dodo Pr.
—Twelve Types. 2008. 56p. pap. *(978-1-4068-9023-5(5))* Echo Library.
—Twelve Types. 208p. 2008. 39.95 *(978-1-4365-1224-4(7))* 2007. (ENG.). per. 24.95 *(978-0-548-72389-0(3))* Kessinger Publishing, LLC.
Christiansen, Jeff & Fichera, Mike. Official Handbook of the Marvel Universe A to Z, 12 vols., Vol. 7. 2009. (ENG., Illus.). 240p. (YA). (gr. 8-17). 24.99 *(978-0-7851-3104-5(3))* Marvel Worldwide, Inc.
Clamp Staff. Tsubasa Character Guide. Flanagan, William, tr. from JPN. 2006. (ENG., Illus.). 240p. pap. 12.95 *(978-0-345-49484-9(9)*, Del Rey) Random House Publishing Group.
—Tsubasa Character Guide 2. 2009. (ENG., Illus.). 240p. pap. 17.99 *(978-0-345-51001-3(1)*, Ballantine Bks.) Random House Publishing Group.
Cox, Roger L. Shakespeare's Comic Changes: The Time-Lapse Metaphor As Plot Device. 2011. (ENG.). 224p. pap. 24.95 ***(978-0-8203-3847-7(8))*** Univ. of Georgia Pr.
Crockett, Laura. Creating Personas. 2007. 96p. pap. 16.00 *(978-0-615-16921-7(X))* Historical Resources.
Davidson, Adele. Shakespeare in Shorthand: The Textual Mystery of King Lear. 2009. (Illus.). 328p. 65.00 *(978-0-87413-047-8(6))* Univ. of Delaware Pr.
Davis, Lindsey. Falco: The Official Companion. 2012. (ENG., Illus.). 256p. pap. 15.95 *(978-0-09-954253-7(6))* Random Hse. GBR. Dist: Independent Pubs. Group.
De Haven, Tom. Our Hero: Superman on Earth. (Icons of America Ser.). (ENG., Illus.). 240p. 2011. pap. 16.00 *(978-0-300-17124-2(2))* 2010. 24.00 *(978-0-300-11817-9(1))* Yale Univ. Pr.
de Mourgues, Odette. Two French Moralists: La Rochefoucauld & la Bruyère. 2010. (Major European Authors Ser.). (ENG.). 192p. pap. 19.99 *(978-0-521-14244-1(X))* Cambridge Univ. Pr.
DiBattista, Maria. Novel Characters: A Genealogy. 2010. (ENG.). 208p. 94.95 *(978-1-4051-5951-7(0)*, Wiley-Blackwell) Wiley, John & Sons, Inc.
Dickin, Margaret. A Vehicle for Performance: Acting the Messenger in Greek Tragedy. 2008. (ENG., Illus.). 218p. pap. 38.99 *(978-0-7618-4355-9(8))* Univ. Pr. of America, Inc.
DiGangi, Mario. Sexual Types: Embodiment, Agency, & Dramatic Character from Shakespeare to Shirley. 2011. (Illus.). 304p. (C). 65.00 ***(978-0-8122-4361-1(7))*** Univ. of Pennsylvania Pr.
Dizer, John T. Readings in American Juvenile Literature: The Collected Essays of John T. Dizer. Terryberry, Karl J., ed. 2006. (Illus.). 320p. *(978-0-7734-5601-3(5))* Mellen, Edwin Pr., The.
Drew, Bernard A. Literary Afterlife: Posthumous Continuations of 325 Authors' Fictional Characters. 2009. (ENG., Illus.). 420p. pap. 45.00 *(978-0-7864-4179-2(8))* McFarland & Co., Inc. Pubs.
Edelstein, Linda. Writer's Guide to Character Traits: Includes Profiles of Human Behaviors & Personality Types. 2nd ed. 2006. (ENG., Illus.). 384p. per. 16.99 *(978-1-58297-390-6(3)*, 11013) F&W Media, Inc.
Engber, Martha. Growing Great Characters from the Ground Up: A Thorough Primer for Writers of Fiction & Nonfiction. 2007. 223p. per. 13.95 *(978-0-9715344-8-3(9))* Central Ave. Pr.
Ephron, Hallie. The Bibliophile's Devotional: 365 Days of Literary Classics. 2009. (ENG.). 400p. 16.95 *(978-1-60550-105-5(0))* Adams Media Corp.

Fein, Eric. The Creation of the Fantastic Four. 2006. (Story Behind the Creation of Action Heroes Ser.). (Illus.). 48p. lib. bdg. 21.95 *(978-1-4042-0765-3(1))* Rosen Publishing Group, Inc., The.
Fernandes, Ana Raquel Lourenço. What about the Rogue? Survival & Metamorphosis in Contemporary British Literature & Culture. 2011. *(978-90-5201-733-4(6))* Lang, Peter Publishing, Inc.
Fielding, Henry. The History of the Life of the Late Mr. Jonathan Wild the Great. 2008. 196p. pap. *(978-1-4065-9642-7(6))* Dodo Pr.
Fiske, Horace Spencer. Provincial Types in American Fiction. 2008. 288p. pap. 25.99 *(978-0-559-53395-2(0))*; pap. 27.75 *(978-0-559-53391-4(8))* BiblioBazaar.
—Provincial Types in American Fiction. 2009. 144p. pap. *(978-0-217-74622-9(5))* Books LLC.
—Provincial Types in American Fiction. 2009. 144p. pap. 19.99 *(978-1-4588-4508-5(7))* General Bks. LLC.
—Provincial Types in American Fiction. 2007. (ENG.). 282p. 43.95 *(978-0-548-03063-9(4))* Kessinger Publishing, LLC.
Francke, Kuno. Personality in German Literature Before Luther. 2009. (ENG.). 240p. 32.99 *(978-1-117-38895-3(6))*; pap. 25.75 *(978-1-117-38896-0(4))* BiblioBazaar.
—Personality in German Literature Before Luther. 2009. 96p. pap. 14.14 *(978-0-217-44036-3(3))* General Bks. LLC.
Frantz, Sarah. Women Constructing Men: Female Novelists & Their Male Characters, 1750Ð2000. 2011. (ENG.). 280p. pap. 32.95 *(978-0-7391-3366-8(7))* Lexington Bks.
Frantz, Sarah & Rennhak, Katharina. Women Constructing Men: Female Novelists & Their Male Characters, 1750-2000. 2009. (ENG.). 280p. 73.50 *(978-0-7391-3365-1(9))* Lexington Bks.
Fulda, Daniel, et al, eds. 'Kann man denn auch nicht lachend sehr ernsthaft sein?' Sprachen und Spiele des Lachens in der Literatur. 20^0.Tr. of Languages & Games of Laughter in Literature. (GER.). XIV, 263p. 126.00 *(978-3-11-023229-5(4))* De Gruyter, Walter Inc.
Fyfe, Thomas Alexander. Who's Who in Dickens: A Complete Dickens Repertory in Dickens' Own Words. 2009. 356p. 26.99 *(978-1-103-82494-6(5))*; pap. 20.99 *(978-1-103-82487-8(2))* BiblioBazaar.
Gregson, Ian. Character & Satire in Post War Fiction. 2008. (Continuum Literary Studies). (ENG.). 192p. 39.95 *(978-1-84706-265-9(2))* Continuum International Publishing Group, Ltd. GBR. Dist: National Bk. Network.
Gruber, William E. Missing Persons: Essays on Character & Characterization in Modern Drama. 2011. (ENG.). 240p. pap. 24.95 ***(978-0-8203-3852-1(4))*** Univ. of Georgia Pr.
Hilfer, Anthony Channell. The Ethics of Intensity in American Fiction. 2011. (ENG.). 224p. pap. 25.00 ***(978-0-292-74113-3(8))*** Univ. of Texas Pr.
Hovis, George. Vale of Humility: Plain Folk in Contemporary North Carolina Fiction. 2007. 325p. *(978-1-57003-696-5(9))* Univ. of South Carolina Pr.
Hunter, Cheryl A. Myths & Archetypes in the Lord of the Rings & Harry Potter. 2011. 96p. pap. ***(978-3-8443-0074-1(0))*** Lambert Academic Publishing.
Huntley, H. Robert & Huntley, H. Robert. The Alien Protagonist of Ford Madox Ford. 2011. (ENG.). 208p. pap. 40.00 ***(978-0-8078-9690-7(X))*** Univ. of North Carolina Pr.
Hurley, Patrick J. Pynchon Character Names: A Dictionary. 2008. (ENG.). 207p. per. 45.00 *(978-0-7864-3458-9(9))* McFarland & Co., Inc. Pubs.
Hyers, Conrad. The Spirituality of Comedy: Comic Heroism in a Tragic World. 2008. (ENG.). 288p. pap. 29.95 *(978-1-4128-0781-4(6))* Transaction Pubs.
Jaffee, Max. The Parabolic Masqueraders. 2007. (Illus.). 107p. per. 12.95 *(978-0-9789837-0-3(X))* ParaMasq Pr.
Jarosova, Pavla. Women in the Novels of Fay Weldon. 2011. 64p. pap. ***(978-3-8443-0169-4(0))*** Lambert Academic Publishing.
Kahan, Gerald. George Alexander Stevens & the Lecture on Heads. 2008. (ENG.). 232p. pap. 22.95 *(978-0-8203-3264-2(X))* Univ. of Georgia Pr.
Kwa, Shiamin & Idema, Wilt L., trs. from CHI. Mulan: Five Versions of a Classic Chinese Legend with Related Texts. 2010. 192p. (C). 39.95 *(978-1-60384-197-9(0))*; pap. 12.95 *(978-1-60384-196-2(2))* Hackett Publishing Co., Inc.
Kyriakou, Poulheria. The Past in Aeschylus & Sophocles. 2011. (Trends in Classics - Supplementary Volumes Ser.). (ENG.). IX, 606p. 154.00 *(978-3-11-025752-6(1))*; (Illus.). 238.00 ***(978-3-11-218869-9(1))*** De Gruyter, Walter Inc.
Lanters, Jose. The 'Tinkers' in Irish Literature: Unsettled Subjects & the Construction of Difference. 2008. 248p. 65.00 *(978-0-7156-2959-0(9))* Irish Academic Pr. IRL. Dist: International Specialized Bk. Services.
Laqua, Carten. Mickey Mouse, Hitler, & Nazi Germany: How Disney's Characters Conquered the Third Reich: How Disney's Characters Conquered the Third Reich. 2012. 224p. pap. 39.99 *(978-1-932563-34-4(2))* Hermes Pr.
Leisure Arts. Storybook Dolls to Knit. 2011. (ENG.). 80p. pap. 19.95 *(978-1-60900-099-8(4))* Leisure Arts, Inc.
Levin, Carole & Watkins, John. Shakespeare's Foreign Worlds: National & Transnational Identites in the Elizabethan Age. 2009. 216p. 45.00 *(978-0-8014-4741-9(0))* Cornell Univ. Pr.
Lucy Pollard-Gott. The Fictional 100: Ranking the Most Influential Characters in World Literature & Legend. 2010. 496p. pap. 25.95 *(978-1-4401-5439-3(2))* iUniverse, Inc.
Ludwig, Elizabeth. American Stand-up & Sketch Comedy. 2008. 96p. pap. *(978-3-8364-9426-7(4))* VDM Verlag Dr. Mueller e.K.
Lyons, Paddy & O'Malley-Younger, Alison, eds. No Country for Old Men: Fresh Perspectives on Irish Literature. 2008. (Reimagining Ireland Ser.). 289p. pap. 61.95 *(978-3-03911-841-0(2))* Lang, Peter AG GBR. Dist: Lang, Peter.
Madrid, Mike. The Supergirls: Fashion, Feminism, Fantasy, & the History of Comic Book Heroines. 2009. (ENG.). 334p. pap. 16.95 *(978-1-935259-03-9(2))* Exterminating Angel Pr.
Mancini, Candice. Censorship in Ray Bradbury's Fahrenheit 451. 2011. (Social Issues in Literature Ser.). 224p. lib. bdg. 38.45 *(978-0-7377-5288-5(2))*; (ENG., Illus.). pap. 26.50 *(978-0-7377-5289-2(0))* Cengage Gale. (Greenhaven Pr., Inc.).
Markell, Kathryn A. & Markell, Marc A. The Children Who Lived: Using Harry Potter & Other Fictional Characters to Help Grieving Children & Adolescents. 2008. (ENG., Illus.). 208p. 39.95 *(978-0-415-95765-6(6))* Routledge.
Markovits, Stefanie. The Crisis of Action in Nineteenth-Century English Literature. 2006. 258p. 54.95 *(978-0-8142-1040-6(6))*; ix, 258p. cd-rom 9.95 *(978-0-8142-9118-4(X))* Ohio State Univ. Pr.
Mccormack. Dissolute Characters: Irish literary history through Balzac, Sheridan le Fanu, Yeats & Bowen. 2011. (ENG.). 265p. pap. 29.95 *(978-0-7190-8563-5(2))* Manchester Univ. Pr. GBR. Dist: Macmillan.
McGirr, Elaine. Eighteenth-Century Characters: A Guide to the Literature of the Age. 2007. (ENG., Illus.). 224p. 120.00 *(978-1-4039-8557-6(X))* Palgrave Macmillan.
Mcgirr, Elaine. Eighteenth-Century Characters: A Guide to the Literature of the Age. 2007. (ENG., Illus.). 226p. pap. 39.00 *(978-1-4039-8558-3(8))* Palgrave Macmillan.
Missotten, G. Don Juan Diabolus in Scriptura: Roman, autobiographie, Thanatographie (1800-2000) 2009. (Republique des Lettres Ser.). 498p. (C). pap. 79.00 *(978-90-429-2008-8(4))* Peeters Pubs. & Booksellers BEL. Dist: Brown, David Bk. Co., The.
Morley, Henry, LLD. Character Writings of the 17th Century. 2007. (ENG.). 412p. pap. 26.99 *(978-1-4264-4287-2(4))*; 468p. pap. 30.99 *(978-1-4264-4351-0(X))* BiblioBazaar.
Morrell, Jessica & Morrell, Jessica Page. Bullies, Bastards & Bitches: How to Write the Bad Guys of Fiction. 2008. (ENG., Illus.). 304p. pap. 16.99 *(978-1-58297-484-2(5))*, Writer's Digest Bks.) F&W Media, Inc.
Nichols, James R. The Stronger Sex: The Fictional Women of Lawrence Durrell. 2011. 165p. *(978-0-8386-4247-4(0))*; (ENG.). 168p. 60.00 *(978-1-61147-066-6(8))* Fairleigh Dickinson Univ. Pr.
Nilsen, Alleen Pace & Nilsen, Don L. F. Names & Naming in Young Adult Literature. 2007. (Scarecrow Studies in Young Adult Literature). (ENG.). 192p. 55.00 *(978-0-8108-5808-4(8))* Scarecrow Pr., Inc.
Odhiambo, Elizabeth. The Female Character in Cyprian Ekwensi's Children's Literature. 2011. 112p. pap. ***(978-3-8443-9117-6(7))*** Lambert Academic Publishing.
Ormsby-Lennon, Hugh. Hey Presto! Swift & the Quacks. 412p. 2011. (ENG.). 85.00 *(978-1-61149-012-1(X))* 2010. *(978-0-87413-087-4(5))* Univ. of Delaware Pr.
Pack, Robert. Willing to Choose: Volition & Storytelling in Shakespeare's Major Plays. 2011. (ENG.). 200p. pap. 18.00 *(978-0-9762114-4-0(0))* Lost Horse Pr.
Paris, Bernard. Bargains with Fate: Psychological Crisis & Conflicts in Shakespeare & His Plays. 2009. (ENG.). 339p. pap. 29.95 *(978-1-4128-0873-6(1))* Transaction Pubs.
Paris, Bernard J. Heaven & Its Discontents: Milton's Characters in Paradise Lost. 2010. (ENG.). 145p. 39.95 *(978-1-4128-1091-3(4))* Transaction Pubs.
Patterson, J. G. Zola Dictionary. 2006. pap. *(978-1-4068-0151-4(8))* Echo Library.
—A Zola Dictionary: The Characters of the Rougon-Macquart Novels of Emile Zola; 2006. (ENG.). 276p. pap. 21.99 *(978-1-4264-1214-1(2))*; 260p. pap. 23.99 *(978-1-4264-1257-8(6))* BiblioBazaar.
Penzler, Otto, ed. The Lineup: The World's Greatest Crime Writers Tell the Inside Story of Their Greatest Detectives. 2010. (ENG.). 416p. pap. 15.99 *(978-0-316-03194-3(1)*, Back Bay Bks.) Little Brown & Co.
Penzler, Otto, et al. Detectionary. Date not set. lib. bdg. 23.95 *(978-0-8488-2155-5(6))* Amereon LTD.
Philips, Edith. The Good Quaker in French Legend. 2011. 262p. 47.95 ***(978-1-258-04617-0(2))*** Literary Licensing, LLC.
Potts, Willard. Joyce & the Two Irelands. 2010. (Literary Modernism Ser.). (ENG.). 232p. pap. 25.00 *(978-0-292-71885-2(3))* Univ. of Texas Pr.
Premat, Julio. Héroes Sin Atributos: Figuras de Autor en la Literatura Argentina. 2009. (Tierra Firme Ser.). (SPA.). 276p. pap. 25.99 *(978-950-557-778-1(8))* Fondo de Cultura Económica.
Price, Anthony. Ill-Weaved Ambition. 2011. 108p. pap. ***(978-3-8443-9211-1(4))*** Lambert Academic Publishing.
Price, Martin. Forms of Life: Character & Moral Imagination in the Novel. 2011. (ENG.). 374p. pap. 39.00 ***(978-0-300-18020-6(9))*** Yale Univ. Pr.
Propp, Vladimir J., et al. On the Comic & Laughter. 2009. (Toronto Studies in Semiotics & Communication Ser.). 224p. *(978-0-8020-9926-6(2))* Univ. of Toronto Pr.
Pulitano, Elvira, ed. Transatlantic Voices: Interpretations of Native North American Literatures. 2007. (ENG.). 336p. pap. 26.95 *(978-0-8032-6034-4(2))* Univ. of Nebraska Pr.
Robertson, Jame Cox. An Uncommon Heroine. 2010. E-Book ***(978-1-4405-0878-3(X))*** Adams Media Corp.
Roche, Isabel. Character & Meaning in the Novels of Victor Hugo. 2006. (Purdue Studies in Romance Literatures Ser.). (ENG.). 220p. per. 43.95 *(978-1-55753-438-5(1))* Purdue Univ. Pr.
Rochford, Philip Guy. Glimpses of Greatness: Autobiography of Philip Guy Rochford, HBM. 2009. 180p. 26.95 *(978-0-595-51921-7(0))*; pap. 16.95 *(978-0-595-53163-9(6))* iUniverse, Inc.
Rokotnitz, Naomi. Trusting Performance: A Cognitive Approach to Embodiment in Drama. 2011. (Cognitive Studies in Literature & Performance Ser.). (ENG., Illus.). 208p. 80.00 *(978-0-230-33737-4(6))* Palgrave Macmillan.
Rosa, Don, et al. Walt Disney Treasures - Donald Duck: 75 Unlucky Years: 75 Unlucky Years. 2009. 168p. pap. 16.99 *(978-1-60360-098-9(1))* Gemstone Publishing, Inc.
Salazar, James. Bodies of Reform: The Rhetoric of Character in Gilded Age America. 2010. (ENG., Illus.). 304p. 75.00 *(978-0-8147-4130-6(4))*; pap. 25.00 *(978-0-8147-4131-3(2))* New York Univ. Pr.
Schmidt, Victoria. 45 Master Characters. 2nd ed. 2007. (ENG., Illus.). 304p. per. 14.99 *(978-1-58297-522-1(1))* F&W Media, Inc.
Scott, Shelley. The Violent Woman as a New Theatrical Character Type: Cases from Canadian Drama. 2007. (Illus.). 136p. *(978-0-7734-5445-3(4))* Mellen, Edwin Pr., The.
Sharp, Jolly. Between the House & the Chicken Yard: The Masks of Flannery O Connor. 2011. 192p. 35.00 *(978-0-88146-263-0(2))* Mercer Univ. Pr.
Skulsky, Harold. Spirits Finely Touched: The Testing of Value & Integrity in Four Shakespearean Plays. 2011. (ENG.). 298p. pap. 24.95 ***(978-0-8203-3859-0(1))*** Univ. of Georgia Pr.
Smellie, William. Literary & Characteristic Lives: To Which Are Added a Dissertation on Public Spirit; & Three Essays. reprint ed. 67.50 *(978-0-404-17203-9(2))* AMS Pr., Inc.
Snow, Jack. Who's Who in Oz: The Happiest Who's Who Ever Written. 2010. (ENG.). 292p. (J). pap. 28.95 *(978-1-59583-425-6(7)*, Green Tiger Pr.) Laughing Elephant.
Sollars, Michael D. Dictionary of Literary Characters, 5 vols., Set. 2010. (Dictionary of Literary Characters Ser.). 2576p. (C). (gr. 9). 400.00 *(978-0-8160-7379-5(1))* Facts On File, Inc.
Stabler, Jane. Byron, Poetics & History. 2009. (Cambridge Studies in Romanticism Ser.). (ENG.). 272p. pap. 38.99 *(978-0-521-11165-0(4))* Cambridge Univ. Pr.
Stokes, Francis Griffin. Who's Who in Shakespeare: A Dictionary of Characters & Proper Names. 2007. (Dover Books on Literature & Drama Ser.). (ENG., Illus.). 384p. per. 14.95 *(978-0-486-45458-0(4))* Dover Pubns., Inc.
Swain, Dwight V. Creating Characters: How to Build Story People. 2008. (ENG.). 208p. per. 19.95 *(978-0-8061-3918-0(8))* Univ. of Oklahoma Pr.
Tatira, Liveson. The Portrayal of White Characters As Stereotypes in the Shona Novels. 2011. 58p. pap. ***(978-3-8443-1578-3(0))*** Lambert Academic Publishing.
Theophrastus. The Characters of Theophrastus. 2007. (Cambridge Classical Texts & Commentaries). (ENG.). 612p. pap. 77.00 *(978-0-521-04576-6(2))* Cambridge Univ. Pr.
—The Characters of Theophrastus. Howell, Francis, tr. 2010. 344p. 37.56 ***(978-1-165-22081-6(4))***; pap. 25.56 ***(978-1-165-11651-5(0))*** Kessinger Publishing, LLC.
Theophrastus. The Characters of Theophrastus. 2009. 96p. pap. *(978-1-4588-6630-1(0))* Books LLC.
—The Characters of Theophrastus. Howell, Francis, tr. 2008. 344p. 46.95 *(978-1-4374-0498-2(7))*; pap. 31.95 *(978-1-4373-1765-7(0))* Kessinger Publishing, LLC.
Thévenet, Lucie. Le Personnage: Du Mythe Au Théâtre: La Question de L'identité Dans la Tragédie Grecque. 2009. (FRE.). 268p. (C). pap. 53.00 ***(978-2-251-32456-2(9))*** Societe d'edition Les Belles lettres FRA. Dist: ISD.
Thompson, Dave. Eclectic Gypsy: An Unauthorised Biography of Doctor Who. 2008. (ENG., Illus.). 200p. pap. 19.95 *(978-1-894959-89-6(2))* Collector's Guide Publishing, Inc. CAN. Dist: Independent Pubs. Group.
van Alphen, Ernst, et al, eds. The Rhetoric of Sincerity. 2008. (Cultural Memory in the Present Ser.). (ENG., Illus.). 352p. 70.00 *(978-0-8047-5827-7(1))* Stanford Univ. Pr.
van Heerikhuizen, Annemarie, et al, eds. Tweede Levens: Over personen en personages in de geschiedschrijving en de Literatuur. 2010. (DUT., Illus.). 268p. pap. *(978-90-5629-643-8(4))*, Vossiupers UvA) Amsterdam Univ. Pr.
Vermeule, Blakey. Why Do We Care about Literary Characters? (ENG., Illus.). 296p. (gr. 17). 2011. pap. 30.00 ***(978-1-4214-0400-4(1))*** 2009. 62.00 *(978-0-8018-9360-5(7))* Johns Hopkins Univ. Pr.
Viders, Sue, et al. Ten Steps to Creating Memorable Characters: Forms, Checklists & Exercises. rev. ed. 2006. (ENG., Illus.). 180p. pap. 17.95 *(978-1-58065-068-7(6)*, Lone Eagle Publishing Company, LLC) Watson-Guptill Pubns., Inc.
Voltolini, Alberto. How Ficta Follow Fiction: A Syncretistic Account of Fictional Entities. 2010. (Philosophical Studies Ser.). xxiv, 273p. pap. 189.00 *(978-90-481-7295-5(0)*, 9048172950) Springer.
Warner, Penny. The Official Nancy Drew Handbook: Skills, Tips, & Life Lessons from Everyone's Favourite Girl Detective. 2007. (ENG., Illus.). 176p. 16.95 *(978-1-59474-194-4(8))* Quirk Bks.
Westlake, H. D. Individuals in Thucydides. 2010. (ENG.). 336p. pap. 28.99 *(978-0-521-14753-8(0))* Cambridge Univ. Pr.
Whyte, Alexander. Bunyan Characters. 2008. 196p. 22.99 *(978-0-554-30875-3(4))*; 25.99 *(978-0-554-21572-3(1))* BiblioBazaar.
—Bunyan Characters. 2009. 164p. pap. *(978-0-217-72915-4(C))* Books LLC.
Wright, Sarah. Tales of Seduction: The Figure of Don Juan in Spanish Culture. (ENG., Illus.). 2012. 304p. pap. 28.00 ***(978-1-84885-975-3(9))*** 2007. 272p. 89.00 *(978-1-84511-477-0(9)*, Tauris Academic Studies) I. B. Tauris & Co., Ltd. GBR. Dist: Macmillan.
Yachnin, Paul, et al, eds. Shakespeare & Character: Theory, History, Performance & Theatrical Persons. 2009. (Palgrave Shakespeare Studies). (ENG.). 264p. 100.00 *(978-0-230-57262-1(6))* Palgrave Macmillan.
Zunshine, Lisa. Introduction to Cognitive Cultural Studies. Zunshine, Lisa, ed. 2010. (ENG., Illus.). 400p. (C). (gr. 13-17). pap. 35.00 *(978-0-8018-9488-6(3))* Johns Hopkins Univ. Pr.
Zunshine, Lisa, ed. Introduction to Cognitive Cultural Studies. 2010. (ENG., Illus.). 400p. (C). (gr. 13-17). 70.00 *(978-0-8018-9487-9(5))* Johns Hopkins Univ. Pr.

CHARACTERS AND CHARACTERISTICS IN LITERATURE—BIBLIOGRAPHY

Bowker Staff, ed. Bowker's Guide to Characters in Fiction 2008-2009, 2 vols. 2008. Set. 299.00 ***(978-0-8352-4975-1(1))*** Vol. 1. ***(978-0-8352-5030-6(X))*** Vol. 2. ***(978-0-8352-5029-0(6))*** Bowker LLC, R. R.
Walbridge, Earle. Literary Characters Drawn from Life. 2007. (ENG., Illus.). 204p. per. *(978-1-4067-3142-2(0))* Read Bks.

CHARADES

see also Riddles

Ballard, Harlan H. Open Sesame: One Hundred Answers in Rhyme to William Bellamy's Century of Charades. 2007. (ENG.). 112p. 34.95 *(978-0-548-06487-0(3))* Kessinger Publishing, LLC.
Bellamy, William. A Second Century of Charades. 2009. 114p. 28.99 *(978-1-117-03C15-9(6))* BiblioBazaar.
—A Second Century of Charades. 2008. 112p. 34.95 *(978-1-4368-8755-7(0))*; pap. 19.95 *(978-1-4367-4841-4(0))* Kessinger Publishing, LLC.
Dirty Charades: The Book, the Game, the Fun. 2012. (ENG.). 200p. pap. 9.95 ***(978-91-86283-72-8(3))*** Nicotext, Ltd. SWE. Dist: SCB Distributors.

CHARCOAL

see also Carbon, Activated

Bruges, James. The Biochar Debate: Charcoal's Potential to Reverse Climate Change & Build Soil Fertility. 2010. (ENG.). 128p. pap. 14.95 *(978-1-60358-255-1(X))* Chelsea Green Publishing.
Deckers, K. Holocene Landscapes Through Time in the Fertile Crescent. 2011. (Subartu Ser.). (ENG., Illus.). 184p. (C). pap. 102.00 ***(978-2-503-54106-8(2))*** Brepols Pubs. BEL. Dist: ISD.
Emrich, Walter. Handbook of Charcoal Making: The Traditional & Industrial Methods. 2010. (Solar Energy R&D in the Ec Series E: Ser.). 300p. pap. 339.00 *(978-90-481-8411-8(8)*, 9048184118) Springer.
Fiorentino, Girolamo & Magri, Donatella, eds. Charcoals from the Past: Cultural & Palaeoenvironmental Implications. 2008. (Bar S Ser.). (Illus.). 318p. (C). 120.00 *(978-1-4073-0294-2(9))* British Archaeological Reports Ltd. GBR. Dist: Brown, David Bk. Co., The.
Kelley, D. W. Charcoal & Charcoal Burning. 2008. (Album Ser.: No. 159). (ENG., Illus.). 32p. pap. 11.95 *(978-0-85263-731-9(4))* Shire Pubns., Ltd. GBR. Dist: Random Hse., Inc.
Lehmann, Johannes & Joseph, Stephen, eds. Biochar for Environmental Management: Science & Technology. 2009. (Illus.). 448p. 79.95 *(978-1-84407-658-1(X))* Routledge.

CHARCOAL DRAWING

Gold, E. J. Charcoal Nudes. 2009. (ENG.). 128p. pap. 24.95 *(978-0-89556-255-5(3))* Gateways Bks. & Tapes.
Grunbein, Durs, et al, texts. KH Hödicke: Charcoal Drawings 1975 â#8364; 1982. 2009. (ENG., Illus.). 212p. 65.00 *(978-3-86678-135-1(0))* Kerber Verlag DEU. Dist: D.A.P./Distributed Art Pubs.
Landy, Michael. Michael Landy: H2ny. 2007. (Illus.). 93p. *(978-1-905464-07-4(X))* Ridinghouse.
Woodring, Jim. Seeing Things. 2007. (ENG., Illus.). 104p. pap. 16.95 *(978-1-56097-803-4(2)*, 56808) Fantagraphics Bks.

CHARCOT, J. M. (JEAN MARTIN), 1825-1893

Bogousslavsky, J., ed. & contrib. by. Following Charcot: A Forgotten History of Neurology & Psychiatry. 2010. (Frontiers of Neurology & Neuroscience Ser.). (Illus.). 208p. *(978-3-8055-9556-8(5))* Karger, S. AG.
Hustvedt, Asti. Medical Muses: Hysteria in Nineteenth-Century Paris. 2011. (ENG., Illus.). 372p. 26.95 *(978-0-393-02560-6(8)*, 2560) Norton, W. W. & Co., Inc.

CHARCOT JOINTS

Frykberg, Robert G. The Diabetic Charcot Foot: Principles & Management. 2010. *(978-1-57400-130-3(2))* Data Trace Publishing, Co.

CHARDIN, JEAN BAPTISTE SIMEON, 1699-1779

Dulau, Anne. Boucher & Chardin: Masters of Modern Manners. 2008. (Illus.). 128p. pap. 50.00 ***(978-1-903470-75-6(7))*** Holberton, Paul Publishing GBR. Dist: Casemate Pubs. & Bk. Distributors, LLC.
Lajer-Burcharth, Ewa. Chardin Material. Birnbaum, Daniel & Graw, Isabelle, eds. 2011. (ENG., Illus.). 69p. pap. 19.95 ***(978-1-934105-47-4(3))*** Sternberg Pr.

CHARGE COUPLED DEVICES

Amico, P. & Beletic, James W., eds. Scientific Detectors for Astronomy: The Beginning of a New Era. 2010. (Astrophysics & Space Science Library). 668p. pap. 439.00 *(978-90-481-6506-3(7)*, 9048165067) Springer.
Blouke, Morley M. Sensors, Cameras, & Systems for Scientific/Industrial Applications VIII: 30 January-1 February, 2007, San Jose, California, USA. 2007. (Proceedings of SPIE Ser.). (Illus.). 310p. pap. 80.00 *(978-0-8194-6614-3(X))* SPIE.
Blouke, Morley M. & Bodegom, Erik. Sensors, Cameras, & Systems for Industrial/Scientific Applications IX: 29-31 January 2008, San Jose, California, USA. 2008. (Proceedings of SPIE Ser.). (Illus.). 240p. pap. 70.00 *(978-0-8194-6988-5(2))* SPIE.
Holst, Gerald C. & Lomheim, Terrence S. CMOS/CCD Sensors & Camera Systems. 2007. 90.00 net. *(978-0-9707749-3-4(1))* JCD Publishing.
—CMOS/CCD Sensors & Camera Systems. 2nd rev. ed. 2011. (Press Monographs). 408p. 96.00 *(978-0-8194-8653-0(1))* SPIE.

C

Saravanan, Ramachandran. Experimental Charge Density - Semiconductors, Oxides & Fluorides. 2010. 216p. pap. *(978-3-8383-8816-8(X))* Lambert Academic Publishing.

Theuwissen, A. J. Solid-State Imaging with Charge-Coupled Devices. 2010. (Solid-State Science & Technology Library). (Illus.). 420p. pap. 529.00 *(978-90-481-4543-0(0)*, 9048145430) Springer.

Trishenkov, M. A. Detection of Low-Level Optical Signals: Photodetectors, Focal Plane Arrays & Systems. 2010. (Solid-State Science & Technology Library). 484p. pap. 379.00 *(978-90-481-4892-9(8)*, 9048148928) Springer.

Widenhorn, Ralf. Charge-Coupled Devices - Performance & Dark Noise Characteristics. 2008. 156p. pap. *(978-3-639-01018-3(3))* VDM Verlag Dr. Mueller e.K.

CHARGE OF THE LIGHT BRIGADE, BALAKLAVA, UKRAINE, 1854
see Balaklava, Battle of, Balaklava, Ukraine, 1854

CHARGED PARTICLE ACCELERATORS
see Particle Accelerators

CHARIBBS
see Carib Indians

CHARISMA (PERSONALITY TRAIT)

Baehr, Peter. Caesarism, Charisma, & Fate: Historical Sources & Modern Resonances in the Work of Max Weber. 2008. (ENG., Illus.). 254p. 44.95 *(978-1-4128-0813-2(8))* Transaction Pubs.

Bhargava, Rohit. Likeonomics: The Unexpected Truth Behind Earning Trust, Influencing Behavior, & Inspiring Action. 2012. (ENG.). 224p. 24.95 ***(978-1-118-13753-6(1)***, Wiley) Wiley, John & Sons, Inc.

Burton, Darren G. Dating & Mating: Attract the Opposite Sex. 2009. 88p. pap. 11.95 *(978-1-4092-8326-3(7))* Lulu Enterprises Inc.

Cabane, Olivia Fox. The Charisma Myth: How Anyone Can Master the Art & Science of Personal Magnetism. 2012. (ENG.). 256p. (gr. 12). 25.95 ***(978-1-59184-456-3(8)***, Portfolio (Hardcover)) Penguin Group (USA) Inc.

Dumont, Theron Q. Personal Magnetism & Charism: The Essence & Practice of It. 2009. 152p. pap. 25.95 *(978-1-60444-022-5(8))* IndoEuropeanPublishing.com.

Falco, Raphael. Charisma & Myth. 2011. (ENG.). 222p. pap. 44.95 ***(978-1-4411-1255-2(3))*** Continuum International Publishing Group, Ltd. GBR. Dist: National Bk. Network.

Falco, Raphael & Falco. Charisma & Myth. 2010. (ENG.). 224p. 120.00 *(978-0-8264-3365-7(0))* Continuum International Publishing Group, Ltd. GBR. Dist: National Bk. Network.

Gebhardt, Winfried, et al, eds. Charisma: Theorie - Religion - Politik. (Materiale Soziologie / TB Ser.). (GER.). VIII, 267p. 90.00 ***(978-3-11-180531-3(X))*** De Gruyter, Walter Inc.

Gillespie, David & Warren, Mark. Teach Yourself the Clinton Factor: Communicating with Charisma. 2008. (Teach Yourself: Business Ser.). (ENG.). 240p. pap. 12.95 *(978-0-07-158189-9(8)*, 0071581898) McGraw-Hill Cos., The.

Heath, John. Behind the Legends: The Cult of Personality & Self-Presentation in the Literary Works of Stefan Heym. 2008. 179p. pap. 57.95 *(978-3-03911-419-1(0))* Lang, Peter AG GBR. Dist: Lang, Peter.

Hodgson, David. The Little Book of Charisma. Gilbert, Ian, ed. 2010. (Illus.). 144p. *(978-1-84590-293-3(9))* Crown Hse. Publishing.

Kwok-bun, Chan & Hava, Dayan. Charismatic Leadership in Singapore: Three Extraordinary People. 2012. (ENG.). xii, 250p. 129.00 ***(978-1-4614-1450-6(4)***, 1461414504) Springer.

Leigh, Andrew. Charisma: The Secrets of Making a Lasting Impression. 2nd ed. 2011. (ENG.). 256p. pap. 22.99 ***(978-0-273-76158-7(7))*** FT Press.

Mortensen, Kurt. The Laws of Charisma: How to Captivate, Inspire, & Influence for Maximum Succes, 1 vol. 2010. (ENG.). 208p. 21.95 *(978-0-8144-1591-7(1))* Amacom.

Olsson, Peter Alan. The Cult of Osama: Psychoanalyzing Bin Laden & His Magnetism for Muslim Youths, 1 vol. 2007. (Praeger Security International Ser.). 184p. 44.95 *(978-0-275-99989-6(0)*, C9989, Praeger Security International) Greenwood Publishing Group, Inc.

Potts, John. A History of Charisma. 2009. (ENG., Illus.). 256p. 39.00 *(978-0-230-55153-4(X))* Palgrave Macmillan.

Rieff, Philip. Charisma: The Gift of Grace, & How It Has Been Taken Away from Us. 2008. (Vintage Ser.). (ENG.). 288p. pap. 15.95 *(978-0-307-27753-4(4)*, Vintage) Knopf Doubleday Publishing Group.

Smith, Mitzi J. The Literary Construction of the Other in the Acts of the Apostles: Charismatics, the Jews, & Women. 2012. (ENG.). 186p. pap. 30.00 ***(978-0-227-68022-3(7))*** Clarke, James Co., Ltd. GBR. Dist: Brown, David Bk. Co., The.

—The Literary Construction of the Other in the Acts of the Apostles: Charismatics, the Jews, & Women. 2010. (Princeton Theological Monographs). 186p. pap. 21.00 *(978-1-60899-384-0(1)*, Pickwick Pubns.) Wipf & Stock Pubs.

Stutje, Jan Willem. Reason & Charisma: Love at Last Sight. 2012. E-Book ***(978-0-85745-330-3(0))*** Berghahn Bks., Inc.

Stutje, Jan Willem, ed. Charismatic Leadership & Social Movements: The Revolutionary Power of Ordinary Men & Women. 2012. (ENG.). 200p. 70.00 ***(978-0-85745-329-7(7))*** Berghahn Bks., Inc.

Takim, Liyakat N. & Takim, Liyakatali. The Heirs of the Prophet: Charisma & Religious Authority in Shi'ite Islam. 2007. 236p. per. 29.95 *(978-0-7914-6738-1(4))* State Univ. of New York Pr.

Triantis, Georgios. Moral & Reptilian Charism. 2009. 120p. pap. *(978-3-639-15488-7(6))* VDM Verlag Dr. Mueller e.K.

CHARISMATA
see Gifts, Spiritual

CHARISMATIC MOVEMENT
see Pentecostalism

CHARITABLE BEQUESTS
see also Charitable Uses, Trusts and Foundations

Hallett, Anna. Almshouses. 2008. (Shire Library). (ENG., Illus.). 64p. pap. 12.95 *(978-0-7478-0583-0(0))* Shire Pubns., Ltd. GBR. Dist: Random Hse., Inc.

Shenkman, Martin M. Funding the Cure: Helping Your Loved One While Making a Charitable Donation. 2007. pap. *(978-1-932603-48-4(4))* Demos Medical Publishing, LLC.

Valinsky, David & Boyd, Melanie. Raising Money through Bequests: How Your Organization Can Profit from the Biggest Intergenerational Transfer of Wealth in History. 2007. per. 24.95 *(978-1-889102-29-0(6))* Emerson & Church, Pubs.

CHARITABLE CONTRIBUTIONS, INCOME TAX DEDUCTIONS FOR
see Income Tax Deductions for Charitable Contributions

CHARITABLE INSTITUTIONS
see Almshouses; Asylums; Charities; Institutional Care

CHARITABLE USES, TRUSTS AND FOUNDATIONS
Here are entered works on the legal aspects of the subject. General works on endowed institutions, endowment funds and donations to such funds are entered under the heading Endowments.
see also Endowments; Mortmain

Alterman, Jon B. & Von Hippel, Karin. Understanding Islamic Charities. 2007. 200p. pap. 21.95 net. *(978-0-89206-513-4(3))* Ctr. for Strategic & International Studies.

Anheier, Helmut K. & Daly, Siobhan, eds. The Politics of Foundations: A Comparative Analysis. 2008. 368p. 41.95 *(978-0-415-47984-4(3))* Routledge.

Association of Governing Boards of Universities and Colleges, text. Effective Foundation Boards. 2011. pap. 35.00 ***(978-0-926508-10-1(5))*** Assn. of Governing Boards of Universities & Colleges.

Blattmachr, Jonathan. Blattmachr on Income Taxation of Estates & Trusts. 15th ed. 2007. (ENG.). 953p. ring bd. 295.00 *(978-1-4024-0976-9(1))* Practising Law Institute.

Braxator, Irena. Fundamental Principles of Panamanian Foundations. 2011. (Bochumer Studien zum Stiftungswesen Ser.). 264p. 61.95 *(978-3-631-61332-0(6))* Lang, Peter GmbH, Europaischer Verlag der Wissenschaften DEU. Dist: Lang, Peter.

—Grundlagen der Panama-Stiftung. 2009. (Bochumer Studien zum Stiftungswesen Ser.). (GER.). 248p. 61.95 *(978-3-631-58841-3(0))* Lang, Peter GmbH, Europaischer Verlag der Wissenschaften DEU. Dist: Lang, Peter.

Cafardi, Nicholas P. & Cherry, Jaclyn Fabean. Tax Exempt Organizations: Cases & Materials. 2nd ed. 2008. *(978-1-4224-1754-6(9))* LexisNexis Matthew Bender.

Cafardi, Nicholas P. & Cherry, Jaclyn Fabean. Understanding Nonprofit & Tax Exempt Organizations. 2nd ed. 2012. ***(978-1-4224-9757-9(7))*** LexisNexis Matthew Bender.

Clark, David L., ed. National Directory of Corporate Giving. 12th ed. 2006. (National Directory of Corporate Giving Ser.). 1527p. per. 195.00 *(978-1-59542-098-5(3))* Foundation Ctr., The.

Commitee on Nonprofit Corporations & Nonprofit Corp. Guide to Representing Religious Organizations. 2009. (ENG.). 250p. pap. 89.95 *(978-1-59031-400-5(X))* American Bar Assn.

Crutchfield, Leslie R., et al. Do More Than Give: The Six Practices of Donors Who Change the World. 2011. (ENG., Illus.). 272p. 29.95 *(978-0-470-89144-5(0)*, Jossey-Bass) Wiley, John & Sons, Inc.

District 5950 Rotary International. Rotary International: Almost a Century 1910-2007. 2009. 264p. pap. 29.95 *(978-1-4389-0584-6(X))* AuthorHouse.

Dogan, Mattei, et al, eds. The Legitimacy of Philanthropic Foundations: United States & European Perspectives. 2006. (Illus.). 294p. 45.00 *(978-0-87154-696-8(5))* Russell Sage Foundation.

Fishman, James J. The Faithless Fiduciary & the Elusive Quest for Charitable Accountability, 1200-2005. 2006. 100.00 *(978-0-89089-496-5(5))* Carolina Academic Pr.

Fishman, Stephen, abr. Every Nonprofit's Tax Guide: How to Keep Your Tax-Exempt Status & Avoid IRS Problems. 2nd rev. ed. 2011. (ENG.). 460p. pap. 34.99 *(978-1-4133-1637-7(9))* NOLO.

Foundation Center Staff, ed. Foundation 1000: 2001/2002 Edition. Date not set. per. 295.00 *(978-0-87954-971-8(8))* Foundation Ctr., The.

Foundation Reporter 1991. Date not set. 327.00 *(978-0-914756-64-4(8)*, 00009422) Taft Group, The.

Gantenbrink, Matthias. Die Hoheitliche Beendigung der Stiftung Durch Die Stiftungsbehörde: Zur Aufhebung und ZusammenfüHrung Von Stiftungen. 2011. (Bochumer Studien zum Stiftungswesen Ser.). (GER.). 358p. 93.95 ***(978-3-631-61111-1(0))*** Lang, Peter GmbH, Europaischer Verlag der Wissenschaften DEU. Dist: Lang, Peter.

Garcia Sanjuan, Alejandro. Till God Inherits the Earth: Islamic Pious Endowments in Al-Andalus (9-15th Centuries) 2006. (Medieval & Early Modern Iberian World Ser.: Vol. 31). (Illus.). 545p. *(978-90-04-15358-5(6))* BRILL.

Gazaleh, Pascale. Held in Trust: Waqf in the Islamic World. Gazaleh, Pascale, ed. 2011. (Illus.). 272p. 29.50 ***(978-977-416-393-7(1))*** American Univ. in Cairo Pr. EGY. Dist: Oxford Univ. Pr., Inc.

Goldberg, Alison & Pittelman, Karen. Creating Change Through Family Philanthropy: The Next Generation. 2007. *(978-1-891053-03-0(5))* Garrett County Pr.

Goldberg, Alison, et al. Creating Change Through Family Philanthropy: The Next Generation. 2007. (ENG.). 192p. per. 24.95 *(978-1-933368-09-2(8))* Counterpoint LLC.

Hoffmann, Jakob. Zusammenlegung und Zulegung Rechtsfähiger Stiftungen des Bürgerlichen Rechts. 2011. (Zivilrechtliche Schriften. Beiträge zum Wirtschafts-, Bank- und Arbeitsrecht Ser.). (GER.). 286p. 79.95 *(978-3-631-61717-5(8))* Lang, Peter GmbH, Europaischer Verlag der Wissenschaften DEU. Dist: Lang, Peter.

Hopkins, Bruce R. Fundraising Law Made Easy. 2009. (ENG.). 362p. 45.00 *(978-0-470-50378-2(5)*, Wiley) Wiley, John & Sons, Inc.

—The Law of Fundraising: 2007 Cumulative Supplement. 3rd rev. ed. 2007. 240p. pap. 85.00 *(978-0-471-79725-8(1)*, Wiley) Wiley, John & Sons, Inc.

—Legal Responsibilities of Nonprofit Boards. 2nd ed. 2008. (BoardSource Governance Ser.: Bk. 2). vi, 86p. *(978-1-58686-107-0(7))* National Ctr. for Nonprofit Boards.

—Planning Guide for the Law of Tax-Exempt Organizations: Strategies & Commentaries. 2007. (Wiley Nonprofit Law, Finance & Management Ser.: 224). (ENG., Illus.). 436p. per., instr.'s planning gde. ed. 80.00 *(978-0-470-14917-1(5)*, Wiley) Wiley, John & Sons, Inc.

—Private Foundation Law Made Easy. 2008. (ENG.). 302p. 49.95 *(978-0-470-40123-1(0)*, Wiley) Wiley, John & Sons, Inc.

Hopkins, Bruce R. & Blazek, Jody. Private Foundations: Tax Law & Compliance. 3rd ed. 2008. (Wiley Nonprofit Law, Finance & Management Ser.: 230). (ENG., Illus.). 768p. 252.50 *(978-0-470-32242-0(X)*, Wiley) Wiley, John & Sons, Inc.

Hopkins, Bruce R. & Hopkins. The Law of Fundraising. 4th ed. 2009. (ENG.). 680p. 252.50 *(978-0-470-39794-7(2)*, Wiley) Wiley, John & Sons, Inc.

Hsieh, Jasper. Strategic Orientation in the Nonprofit Arts - a Stakeholder Approach. 2008. 116p. pap. *(978-3-639-05621-1(3))* VDM Verlag Dr. Mueller e.K.

Information Today Inc, creator. Annual Register of Grant Support: A Directory of Funding Sources. 40th ed. 2006. (Directories Ser.). 1402p. 249.00 *(978-1-57387-251-5(2))* Information Today, Inc.

Jacobs, David G., ed. The Foundation Directory. 29th ed. 2007. (Foundation Directory Ser.). 2734p. 215.00 *(978-1-59542-124-1(6))* Foundation Ctr., The.

—The Foundation Directory, Part 2. 16th ed. 2007. (Foundation Directory Part 2 Ser.). 2197p. per. 185.00 *(978-1-59542-125-8(4))* Foundation Ctr., The.

Jankowski, Katherine. The Directory of Corporate & Foundation Givers, 1995: A National Listing of the 8,000 Major Funding Sources for Nonprofits. pap. *(978-1-56995-258-0(2))* Taft Group, The.

Jewell, George. Charitable Trusts. 2008. 1162p. pap. 255.00 *(978-0-8080-9166-0(2))* 2009th ed. 2009. 1100p. pap. 290.00 incl. cd-rom *(978-0-8080-2128-5(1))* Toolkit Media Group.

—Charitable Trusts: 2006. 2006. 1234p. pap. 200.00 *(978-0-8080-9036-6(4))* Toolkit Media Group.

Jones, Gareth. History of the Law of Charity, 1532-1827. 2008. (Cambridge Studies in English Legal History Ser.). (ENG.). 296p. pap. 38.99 *(978-0-521-07392-9(8))* Cambridge Univ. Pr.

Knost, Stefan. Die Organisation des Religiösen Raums in Aleppo: Die Rolle der Islamischen Religiösen Stiftungen (Auqaf) in der Gesellschaft Einer Provinzhauptstadt des Osmanischen Reiches an der Wende Zum 19. Jahrhundert. 2009. (GER., Illus.). 350p. *(978-3-89913-735-4(3))* Orient-Institut.

Ko, Sang-Hyun. Errichtung einer Stiftung nach deutschem und koreanischem Recht. 2009. (Bochumer Studien zum Stiftungswesen Ser.). (GER.). 164p. 57.95 *(978-3-631-59778-1(9))* Lang, Peter GmbH, Europaischer Verlag der Wissenschaften DEU. Dist: Lang, Peter.

Kozlowski, Gregory C. Muslim Endowments & Society in British India. 2008. (Cambridge South Asian Studies). (ENG.). 228p. pap. 32.99 *(978-0-521-08867-1(4))* Cambridge Univ. Pr.

Krotz, Joanna L. The Guide to Intelligent Giving: Make a Difference in the World — And in Your Own Life. 2009. (ENG.). 256p. 19.95 *(978-1-58816-761-3(5)*, 1297173) Hearst Communications, Inc.

Luxton, Peter & Hill, Judith. The Law of Charities. 2nd ed. 2012. 1104p. 375.00 *(978-0-19-921480-8(8))* Oxford Univ. Pr., Inc.

Makkreel, Rudolf A. Dilthey Foundation. 49.50 *(978-0-691-07309-5(0))* Princeton Univ. Pr.

Maxwell, Ryan A. Charitable Giving & Taxes: Benefits, Changes & Proposals. 2012. ***(978-1-62100-696-1(4))*** Nova Science Pubs., Inc.

McCoy JD, Jerry & Miree JD, Kathryn. Family Foundation Handbook (2012) 2011. 940p. pap. 302.00 ***(978-0-8080-2836-9(7))*** Toolkit Media Group.

McCoy, Jerry J. & Miree, Kathryn W. Family Foundation Handbook. 2007th rev. ed. 2006. (Illus.). 940p. pap. 205.00 *(978-0-8080-9051-9(8)*, CCH) Wolters Kluwer Tax & Accounting.

McKinnon, Harvey. The 11 Questions Every Donor Asks & the Answers All Donors Crave: How You Can Inspire Someone to Give Generously. 2008. pap. 24.95 *(978-1-889102-37-5(7))* Emerson & Church, Pubs.

Moore, Jonathon R. A Practical Guide to International Philanthropy. 2009. (ENG., Illus.). 380p. 80.00 *(978-0-521-11641-1(4))* Cambridge Univ. Pr.

Nigito, Daniel G. The Power of Leveraging the Charitable Remainder Trust: Your Secret Weapon Against the War on Wealth. 2009. (ENG., Illus.). 285p. 29.95 *(978-0-470-54112-8(1)*, Wiley) Wiley, John & Sons, Inc.

O'Halloran, Kerry. The Profits of Charity. 2012. (ENG.). 608p. 125.00 ***(978-0-19-976771-7(8))*** Oxford Univ. Pr., Inc.

O'Halloran, Kerry, et al. Charity Law & Social Policy: National & International Perspectives on the Functions of the Law Relating to Charities. 2010. (Library of Public Policy & Public Administration Ser.). xxxi, 616p. pap. 169.00 *(978-90-481-7874-2(6)*, 9048178746) Springer.

Oppenheimer, Danny & Olivola, Christopher, eds. The Science of Giving: Experimental Approaches to the Study of Charity. 2010. (Society for Judgment & Decision Making Ser.). (ENG., Illus.). 274p. 79.95 *(978-1-84872-885-1(9)*, Psychology Press) Taylor & Francis Group GBR. Dist: Taylor & Francis Group.

Owino, Alfred O. & Oyugi, Joseph O. Directory of Conservation Funding Sources for Developing Countries: Conservation Biology, Education & Training, Fellowships & Scholarships. 2009. 79.00 *(978-1-60741-367-7(1))* Nova Science Pubs., Inc.

Ramutsindela, Maano, et al. Sponsoring Nature: Environmental Philanthropy for Conservation. 2011. (ENG., Illus.). 224p. 99.95 *(978-1-84407-904-9(X))* Routledge.

Said, Ew, et al. Private Foundations: Tax Law & Compliance 2012. 3rd ed. 2011. (Wiley Nonprofit Law, Finance & Management Ser.: 240). (ENG.). 256p. pap., suppl. ed. 95.00 ***(978-1-118-03747-8(2)***, Wiley) Wiley, John & Sons, Inc.

Schuck, Frank. Die Doppelstiftung: Instrument zur Gestaltung der Unternehmensnachfolge. 2009. (Bochumer Studien zum Stiftungswesen Ser.). (GER.). 330p. 86.95 *(978-3-631-59332-5(5))* Lang, Peter GmbH, Europaischer Verlag der Wissenschaften DEU. Dist: Lang, Peter.

Shipp Simone, Kelly. Top 10 Ways Private Foundations Can Influence Public Policy. 2006. *(978-1-932677-45-4(3))* Council on Foundations, Inc.

Silk, Roger D., et al. Managing Foundations & Charitable Trusts: Essential Knowledge, Tools, & Techniques for Donors & Advisors. 2nd ed. 2011. (Bloomberg Financial Ser.: 145). (ENG., Illus.). 288p. 60.00 *(978-1-118-03826-0(6)*, Bloomberg Pr.) Wiley, John & Sons, Inc.

Steiner, Matthias Günter. Die Klöster und ihr Wirken - eine der Wurzeln des Stiftungswesens? 2009. (Rechtshistorische Reihe Ser.). (GER.). 430p. 108.95 *(978-3-631-58578-8(0))* Lang, Peter GmbH, Europaischer Verlag der Wissenschaften DEU. Dist: Lang, Peter.

Tax-Exempt Charitable Organizations: Hearing Before the Subcommittee on Oversight of the Committee on Ways & Means, U.S. House of Representatives, One Hundred Tenth Congress, First Session, July 24, 2007. 2007. (Illus.). iv, 262p. *(978-0-16-079611-1(3)*, 552-070-36567-2) United States Government Printing Office.

Taylor, Scott. Tax-Exempt Organizations in a Nutshell. 2011. 359p. pap. 38.00 ***(978-0-314-26234-9(2)***, West Legalworks) West.

Thurman, Eric & Smith, Philip. A Billion Bootstraps: Microcredit, Barefoot Banking, & the Business Solution for Ending Poverty. 2007. (ENG., Illus.). 224p. 24.95 *(978-0-07-148997-3(5)*, 0071489975) McGraw-Hill Cos., The.

van Laarhoven, Elise & Van Laarhoven, Elise. Diversity in Corporate Giving. 2011. 80p. pap. ***(978-3-8443-2013-8(X))*** Lambert Academic Publishing.

Wooster, Martin Morse. The Great Philanthropists & the Problem of "Donor Intent" 2007. pap. *(978-1-892934-12-3(4))* Capital Research Ctr.

World Guide to Foundations. (ENG.). ***(978-3-11-184465-7(X))*** Saur, K. G. Verlag GmbH & Co.

Wyszomierski, Sara, ed. Guide to Funding for International & Foreign Programs. 9th ed. 2008. (Guide to Funding for International & Foreign Programs Ser.). 791p. pap. 173.75 *(978-1-59542-182-1(3))* Foundation Ctr., The.

CHARITIES
Here are entered works on privately supported welfare activities. Works on tax-supported welfare activities are entered under Public Welfare. Works on the methods employed in social work, public or private, are entered under Social Service. Works that discuss collectively the various policies, programs, services, and facilities to meet basic human needs relating to the quality of life, such as education, health, welfare, etc. are entered under Human Services.
see also Almshouses; Asylums; Charitable Uses, Trusts and Foundations; Charity Laws and Legislation; Charity Organizations; Charity-Schools; Child Welfare; Church Charities; Community Organization; Corporations—Charitable Contributions; Endowments; Food Relief; Friendly Societies; Humanitarianism; Institutional Care; International Relief; Monasteries; Old Age Homes; Sisterhoods; Sisters of Charity of St. Vincent de Paul; Social Settlements; Social Workers
also subdivision Charities under names of ethnic groups and names of corporate bodies; and subdivision Civilian Relief under names of wars, e.g. World War, 1939-1945—Civilian Relief

Aarts, Leon. Feeding People. 2010. 198p. pap. *(978-1-905823-86-4(X))* Ecademy Pr. Ltd.

Adams, Herbert B. & Adams, Herbert Baxter. Notes on the Literature of Charities. 2009. 50p. pap. 15.75 *(978-1-113-56087-2(8))*; pap. 16.75 *(978-1-113-60146-9(9))* BiblioBazaar.

Alterman, Jon B. & Von Hippel, Karin. Understanding Islamic Charities. 2007. 200p. pap. 21.95 net. *(978-0-89206-513-4(3))* Ctr. for Strategic & International Studies.

Anheier, Helmut K., et al, eds. Innovation in Strategic Philanthropy: Local & Global Perspectives. 2010. (Nonprofit & Civil Society Studies). (Illus.). xvi, 240p. pap. 129.00 *(978-1-4419-4172-5(X)*, 144194172X) Springer.

Arrillaga-Andreessen, Laura. Giving 2.0: Transform Your Giving & Our World. 2011. (ENG., Illus.). 320p. 25.95 *(978-1-118-11940-2(1)*, Jossey-Bass) Wiley, John & Sons, Inc.

Axelrod, Terry. Beyond the Ask Event: Fully Integrating the Benevon Model. 2007 (Illus.). ix, 212p. *(978-0-9700455-7-7(3))* Benevon Pubns.
Axelrod, Terry. Missionizing Your Special Events: How to Build a System of Events That Engages Donors Who Will Stay with You for Life. 2008. (Illus.). ix, 159p. *(978-0-9700455-9-1(X))* Benevon Pubns.
Baylouny, Anne Marie. Privatizing Welfare in the Middle East: Kin Mutual Aid Associations in Jordan & Lebanon. 2010. (Indiana Series in Middle East Studies). (ENG., Illus.). 316p. 70.00 *(978-0-253-35472-3(2),* 0253354722); pap. 26.95 *(978-0-253-22195-7(1),* 0253221951) Indiana Univ. Pr.
Benthall, Jonathan & Bellion-Jourdan, Jerome. Charitable Crescent: Politics of Aid in the Muslim World. 2nd rev. ed. 2009. (ENG.). 256p. pap. 31.00 *(978-1-84511-899-0(5))* I. B. Tauris & Co., Ltd. GBR. Dist: Macmillan.
Brest, Paul & Harvey, Hal. Money Well Spent: A Strategic Plan for Smart Philanthropy. 2008. (Bloomberg Ser.: 14). (ENG., Illus.). 288p. 27.95 *(978-1-57660-312-3(1),* Bloomberg Pr.) Wiley, John & Sons, Inc.
Bronfman, Charles, et al. The Art of Giving: Where the Soul Meets a Business Plan. 2009. (ENG., Illus.). 288p. 29.95 *(978-0-470-50146-7(4),* Jossey-Bass) Wiley, John & Sons, Inc.
Christensen, Jan. Liberalernas Stad: Fattigvård Och Kulturdonationer I Artonhundratalets Göteborg. 2009. (SWE., Illus.). 339p. *(978-91-7173-292-7(6))* Daidalos, Bokforlaget, AB.
Coleman, Mary, ed. Best-Sellers for Fairs & Fetes. (Australian Women's Weekly Craft Library). (Illus.). 120p. pap. *(978-1-86396-184-4(4),* Australian Women's Weekly) ACP Publishing Pty, Ltd.
Crutchfield, Leslie R., et al. Do More Than Give: The Six Practices of Donors Who Change the World. 2011. (ENG., Illus.). 272p. 29.95 *(978-0-470-89144-5(0),* Jossey-Bass) Wiley, John & Sons, Inc.
Davis, Philip. The Field of Social Service. 2009. 120p. pap. 19.99 *(978-1-150-18230-3(X))* General Bks. LLC.
Dayton, Kenneth. The Stages of Giving. Date not set. (Conversations with Leaders Ser.). 6p. pap. 9.00 *(978-0-929556-21-5(6))* Independent Sector.
Dietlin, Lisa M. Transformational Philanthropy: Entrepreneurs & Nonprofits. 2009. 330p. 62.95 *(978-0-7637-6678-8(X))* Jones & Bartlett Learning, LLC.
Duschinsky, Jon & Duschinsky. Philanthropy in a Flat World: Inspiration Through Globalization. 2009. (AFP/Wiley Fund Development Ser.: 185). (ENG.). 220p. 27.95 *(978-0-470-45801-3(1),* Wiley) Wiley, John & Sons, Inc.
Dusenbery, Verne A. & Tatla, Darshan S., eds. Sikh Diaspora Philanthropy in Punjab: Global Giving for Local Good. 2009. (ENG., Illus.). 336p. 27.95 *(978-0-19-806102-1(1))* Oxford Univ. Pr., Inc.
Gary, Tracy. Inspired Philanthropy: Your Step-by-Step Guide to Creating a Giving Plan & Leaving a Legacy. 3rd rev. ed. 2007. (Kim Klein's Fundraising Ser.: 23). (ENG., Illus.). 336p. pap. 29.95 *(978-0-7879-9652-9(1),* Jossey-Bass) Wiley, John & Sons, Inc.
Gaudiani, Claire. Generosity Unbound: How American Philanthropy Can Strengthen the Economy & Expand the Middle Class. 2010. 272p. 25.00 *(978-1-931764-18-6(2),* Broadway Pubns.) Institute for American Values.
Gemelli, Giuliana. Religions & Philanthropy: Global Issues in Historical Perspective. 2007. (Illus.). 361p. *(978-88-8000-508-7(1))* Baskerville (Centro Studi sulla Comunicazione).
Genn, Adina. The Everything Guide to Fundraising Book: From Grassroots Campaigns to Corporate Sponsorships — All You Need to Support Your Cause - Capital Campaigns/ Online Fundraising / Cause Marketing / Special Events. 2009. (ENG.). 320p. pap. 15.95 *(978-1-59869-823-7(0))* Adams Media Corp.
Giles, Colum. Building a Better Society: Liverpool's Historic Institutional Buildings. 2008. (Informed Conservation Ser.). (ENG., Illus.). 96p. pap. 16.00 *(978-1-873592-90-8(6))* English Heritage GBR. Dist: Brown, David Bk. Co., The.
Goldberg, Steven H. & Goldberg. Billions of Drops in Millions of Buckets: Why Philanthropy Doesn't Advance Social Progress. 2009. (ENG., Illus.). 302p. 39.95 *(978-0-470-45467-1(9),* Wiley) Wiley, John & Sons, Inc.
Gorgens-Albino, Marelize, et al. Programme Plurinational de Lutte Contre le Sida en Afrique, 2000-2006: Bilan des Interventions de la Banque Mondiale Face a une Crise de Developpement. 2007. (FRE., Illus.). 208p. per. 15.00 *(978-0-8213-7109-1(6),* 9780821371091) World Bank Pubns.
Granier, Camille. Essai de Bibliographie Charitable. 2010. 472p. pap. 37.75 *(978-1-142-65018-6(9))* BiblioBazaar.
Gunewardena, Nan. Capitalizing on Catastrophe: Neoliberal Strategies in Disaster Reconstruction. Schuller, Mark, ed. 2008. (Globalization & the Environment Ser.). (ENG., Illus.). 288p. pap. 35.95 *(978-0-7591-1103-5(0))* AltaMira Pr.
Gunewardena, Nandini & Schuller, Mark, eds. Capitalizing on Catastrophe: The Globalization of Disaster Assistance. 2008. (Globalization & the Environment Ser.). (ENG., Illus.). 288p. 90.00 *(978-0-7591-1102-8(2))* AltaMira Pr.
Hamid, Minister Michael. The Power in Giving: (Practical Guidelines for Tithing & Giving of Offerings) 2008. 48p. pap. 9.99 *(978-1-60647-660-4(2))* Xulon Pr., Inc.
Hammack, David C. & Heydemann, Steven, eds. Globalization, Philanthropy, & Civil Society: Projecting Institutional Logics Abroad. 2009. (Philanthropic & Nonprofit Studies). (ENG.). 320p. 45.00 *(978-0-253-35303-0(3),* 0253353033) Indiana Univ. Pr.
Harmsen, Egbert. Islam, Civil Society & Social Work. 2008. (ISIM Dissertations Ser.). pap. *(978-90-5356-995-5(2),* Leiden Univ. Pr.) Amsterdam Univ. Pr.
Hewa, Soma & Stapleton, Darwin, eds. Globalization, Philanthropy, & Civil Society: Toward a New Political Culture in the Twenty-First Century. 2010. (Nonprofit & Civil Society Studies). (Illus.). xvi, 236p. pap. 139.00 *(978-1-4419-3670-1(2),* 1441938702) Springer.
Jackson, Rodney. A Philanthropic Covenant with Black America. 2009. (ENG.). 238p. 29.95 *(978-0-470-39792-3(6),* Wiley) Wiley, John & Sons, Inc.
Karoff, Peter. The World We Want: New Dimensions in Philanthropy & Social Change. (ENG., Illus.) 280p. 2007. 82.00 *(978-0-7591-1047-2(6))* 2006. per. 26.95 *(978-0-7591-1048-9(4),* AltaMira Pr.
Kass, Amy A., ed. Giving Well, Doing Good: Readings for Thoughtful Philanthropists. 2008. (Philanthropic & Nonprofit Studies). (ENG.). 520p. pap. 19.95 *(978-0-253-21955-8(8),* 0253219558) Indiana Univ. Pr.
Keller, Gray. Everyone Wants Your Money: Helping You Navigate Through Philanthropy. 2010. 212p. 24.99 *(978-1-4520-3753-0(1));* pap. 15.95 *(978-1-4520-3754-7(X))* AuthorHouse.
Kennedy, Finola. Frank Duff: A Life Story. 2011. (ENG., Illus.). 304p. pap. 19.95 *(978-1-4411-6747-7(1),* Burns & Oates) Continuum International Publishing Group, Ltd. GBR. Dist: National Bk. Network.
Kihlstedt, Andrea. How to Raise a Million Dollars (or More!) in 10 Bite-Sized Steps: A Failproof Guide for Board Members, Volunteers, & Staff. 2010. pap. 24.95 *(978-1-889102-41-2(5))* Emerson & Church, Pubs.
Klein, Peter & Berrie, Angelica. A Passion for Giving: Tools & Inspiration for Creating a Charitable Foundation. 2012. (ENG.). 293p. 45.00 ***(978-1-118-02387-7(0),*** Wiley) Wiley, John & Sons, Inc.
Korten, Alicia Epstein, et al. Change Philanthropy: Candid Stories of Foundations Maximizing Results Through Social Justice. 2009. (Kim Klein's Fundraising Ser.: 29). (ENG., Illus.). 320p. 34.95 *(978-0-470-43516-8(X),* Jossey-Bass) Wiley, John & Sons, Inc.
Layton, Michael & Moreno, Alejandro. Filantropía y Sociedad Civil en México: Análisis de la ENAFI 2005-2008. 2010. (Illus.). 231p. *(978-607-401-345-0(4))* ITAM.
Lord, Susan. Wealth & Social Responsibility. 2008. 208p. pap. *(978-3-639-07180-1(8))* VDM Verlag Dr. Mueller e.K.
Macci, Joy & Hilton, Alexandria. Enjoy: Luxury of Life: Your Secret Keys to Global Giving & World Wealth. 2009. (ENG.). 199p. 69.95 *(978-1-59930-249-2(7))* LifeSuccess Publishing.
Macwan, Martin, et al. Social Justice Philanthropy: Approaches & Strategies of Funding Organisations. 2009. 303p. 50.00 *(978-81-316-0204-1(4))* Rawat Pubns. IND. Dist: International Specialized Bk. Services.
McKinnon, Harvey. The 11 Questions Every Donor Asks & the Answers All Donors Crave: How You Can Inspire Someone to Give Generously. 2008. pap. 24.95 *(978-1-889102-37-5(7))* Emerson & Church, Pubs.
National Directory of Children Youth & Families Services, creator. The National Directory of Children, Youth, & Families Services: The Professionals' Reference. 2007. (National Directory of Children, Youth & Families Services Ser.). 1438p. per. 179.00 *(978-1-885461-18-6(6))* National Directory CYF.
Nober, Jane C. Donor Initiated Fundraising: Issues & Guidelines for Community Foundations. 2nd ed. 2006. *(978-1-932677-44-7(5))* Council on Foundations, Inc.
Novogratz, Jacqueline. The Blue Sweater: Bridging the Gap Between Rich & Poor in an Interconnected World. 2010. (ENG.). 320p. pap. 15.99 *(978-1-60529-476-6(4))* 2009. 20.50 *(978-1-60529-670-8(8))* Rodale Pr., Inc.
O'Halloran, Kerry. The Politics of Charity. 2011. (Routledge Research in Comparative Politics Ser.). (ENG.). 280p. 138.00 *(978-0-415-45299-1(6))* Routledge.
Orosz, Joel J. Effective Foundation Management: 14 Challenges of Philanthropic Leadership-and How to Outfox Them. 2007. (ENG.). 194p. 65.00 *(978-0-7591-0986-5(9))* AltaMira Pr.
—Effective Foundation Management: 14 Challenges of Philanthropic Leadership-And How to Outfox Them. 2007. (ENG.). 194p. per. 24.95 *(978-0-7591-0987-2(7))* AltaMira Pr.
Ottinger, Randall J. Beyond Success: Building a Personal, Financial, & Philanthropic Legacy. 2007. (ENG.). 320p. 27.95 *(978-0-07-149676-6(9),* 0071496769) McGraw-Hill Cos., The.
Paprocki, Steve L. & Bothwell, Robert O. Answering the Call? The Telecommunication Industry's Grant Making for Racial/Ethnic Communities. Date not set. (Corporate Grant Making to Racial/Ethnic Populations Ser.: 2 vol.). spiral bd. 25.00 *(978-1-891465-09-3(0))* National Committee for Responsive Philanthropy.
Payton, Robert L. & Moody, Michael P. Understanding Philanthropy: Its Meaning & Mission. 2008. (Philanthropic & Nonprofit Studies). (ENG., Illus.). 224p. 26.95 *(978-0-253-35049-7(2),* 0253350492) Indiana Univ. Pr.
Perkey, Angela. Change the World, Change Your Life: Discover Your Life Purpose Through Service. 2010. (ENG.). 224p. pap. 15.95 *(978-1-57324-463-3(5),* Conari Pr.) Red Wheel/Weiser.
Peter Hochstein. Cigars & Other Passions: The Biography of Edgar M. Cullman. 2010. 404p. 31.96 *(978-1-4269-2370-8(8));* pap. 21.96 *(978-1-4269-2369-2(4))* Trafford Publishing.
Rebecca, Leet. Message Matters: Succeeding at the Crossroads of Mission & Market. 2007. (ENG.). 160p. per. 26.95 *(978-0-940069-63-3(6),* Fieldstone Alliance) Turner Publishing Co.
Robinson, Andy. How to Raise $500 to $5,000 from Almost Anyone: A 1-Hour Guide for Board Members, Volunteers, & Staff. 2011. 109p. pap. 24.95 ***(978-1-889102-46-7(6))*** Emerson & Church, Pubs.
Rumford, Benjamin. Essays: Political, Economical & Philosophical. Volume 1. 2007. 248p. per. *(978-1-4068-4069-8(6))* Echo Library.
—Essays Political, Economical & Philosophical, Vol. 1. 2006. (ENG.). 344p. pap. 23.99 *(978-1-4264-0054-4(3));* 336p. pap. 24.99 *(978-1-4264-0183-1(3))* BiblioBazaar.
Sabra, Adam. Poverty & Charity in Medieval Islam: Mamluk Egypt, 1250-1517. 2006. (Cambridge Studies in Islamic Civilization Ser.). (ENG., Illus.). 208p. pap. 52.00 *(978-0-521-03474-6(4))* Cambridge Univ. Pr.
Sacha, Schets. Meet Charities Online: How Can Charities Utilize Social Media As a Promotional Tool? 2011. 96p. pap. ***(978-3-639-33737-2(9))*** VDM Verlag Dr. Mueller e.K.
Salim, Arskal. The Shift in Zakat Practice in Indonesia: From Piety to an Islamic Socio-Political-Economic System. 2008. (ENG., Illus.). 111p. (C). pap. 16.95 ***(978-974-9511-08-4(5))*** Silkworm Bks. THA. Dist: Univ. of Washington Pr.
Scanlan, Lawrence. A Year of Living Generously: Dispatches from the Frontlines of Philanthropy. 1 vol. 2011. (ENG.). 368p. pap. 16.95 *(978-1-55365-841-2(8))* D&M Pubs. Inc. CAN. Dist: Perseus-PGW.
Seddon, Nicholas. Who Cares? How State Funding & Political Activism Change Charity. 2007. 200p. (C). pap. 23.50 *(978-1-903386-56-9(X))* Civitas:Institute for the Study of Civil Society GBR. Dist: Coronet Bks.
Sherwin, Michael S. By Knowledge & by Love: Charity & Knowledge in the Moral Theology of St. Thomas Aquinas. 2011. (Illus.). 269p. pap. 35.00 ***(978-0-8132-1871-7(3))*** Catholic Univ. of America Pr.
Singer, Amy. Charity in Islamic Societies. 2008. (Themes in Islamic History Ser.). (ENG., Illus.). 264p. (C). 95.00 *(978-0-521-82164-3(9));* pap. 29.99 *(978-0-521-52912-9(3))* Cambridge Univ. Pr.
Small, Pamela J. Justin Grows His Hair. 2010. 44p. pap. 16.99 *(978-1-4520-6331-7(1))* AuthorHouse.
Smith, David Horton, et al. A Dictionary of Nonprofit Terms & Concepts. 2006. (Philanthropic & Nonprofit Studies). (ENG.). 360p. 35.00 *(978-0-253-34783-1(1),* 0253347831) Indiana Univ. Pr.
Snyder, Gary. Silence the Impending Threat to the Charitable Sector: The Impending Threat to the Charitable Sector. 2011. 240p. 29.99 ***(978-1-4628-7539-9(4));*** pap. 19.99 ***(978-1-4628-7538-2(6))*** Xlibris Corp.
Stout, Chris E. The New Humanitarians: Inspiration, Innovations, & Blueprints for Visionaries, 3 vols. 2008. (Social & Psychological Issues: Challenges & Solutions Ser.). (Illus.). 1000p. 300.00 *(978-0-275-99768-7(5),* C9768, Praeger Pubs.) Greenwood Publishing Group, Inc.
Templeton, Beth Lindsay. Loving Our Neighbor: A Thoughtful Approach to Helping People in Poverty. 2008. 208p. 27.95 *(978-0-595-71712-5(8));* pap. 17.95 *(978-0-595-48276-4(7))* iUniverse, Inc.
Usera, Abe. God's Work. 2010. 112p. (ENG.). 21.49 *(978-1-4520-1037-3(4));* pap. 10.99 *(978-1-4520-1035-9(8))* AuthorHouse.
Van Nguyen-Marshall. In Search of Moral Authority: The Discourse on Poverty, Poor Relief, & Charity in French Colonial Vietnam. 2008. (Illus.). 190p. (C). 67.95 *(978-1-4331-0215-8(3))* Lang, Peter Publishing, Inc.
Von Zitzewitz, Vanessa. Slaughterhouse Angels. 2008. (Illus.). 180p. 95.00 *(978-3-8327-9246-6(5))* teNeues Publishing Co.
Wenar, Leif, et al, eds. Giving Well: The Ethics of Philanthropy, 1 vol. 2011. (ENG., Illus.). 320p. 45.00 *(978-0-19-973907-3(2))* Oxford Univ. Pr., Inc.
Williamson, Arbutas. The Making of Me & Help from the Sanctuary, Inc: A Charitable Organization. 2010. 132p. pap. 25.95 *(978-1-4327-5890-5(X))* Outskirts Pr., Inc.
Wilson, Roger. Authority, Leadership & Concern. 2007. 92p. per. *(978-0-901689-85-6(8))* Quaker Books.
Wolcott, Robert C. Dreams for Kids: Changing the World One Person at a Time. 2010. (Illus.). 256p. 14.95 *(978-0-615-36818-4(2))* Dream Vision Publishing.
World Bank Staff. O Programa Multinacional de Africa Contra a Sida 2000-2006: Resultados Da Resposta Do Banco Mundial a Uma Crise de Desenvolvimento. 2007. (POR., Illus.). 180p. per. 15.00 *(978-0-8213-7229-6(7),* 9780821372296) World Bank Pubns.
World Champions: 25 Charities That Make Our Home a Better Place to Live. ltd. ed. 2007. im. lthr. 29.95 *(978-0-9774544-1-9(X))* Window View Pubns.
Zastrow, Charles H. Introduction to Social Welfare Institutions. 3rd ed. Date not set. (Social Work Ser.). pap. *(978-0-534-10898-4(9))* Brooks/Cole.

CHARITIES—ACCOUNTING

Buzzacotts LLP Charity Team & Buzzacotts LLP Charity Team. Charity Accounting & Taxation. 5th ed. 2010. (ENG., Illus.). 462p. pap. 145.00 *(978-1-84766-267-5(6),* Bloomsbury Professional) Bloomsbury Publishing Plc GBR. Dist: International Specialized Bk. Services.
Dawes, Greyham, et al. Charity Accounts: A Practical Guide to the Charities SORP. 4th rev. ed. 2009. (ENG.). 736p. pap. incl. cd-rom *(978-1-84661-154-4(7))* Jordan Publishing, Ltd.
Fishman, James J. The Faithless Fiduciary & the Elusive Quest for Charitable Accountability, 1200-2005. 2006. 100.00 *(978-0-89089-496-5(5))* Carolina Academic Pr.
Vincent. Vincent Charity Accounting Handbook. 5th rev. ed. 2008. pap. 108.00 *(978-1-84592-229-0(8),* Bloomsbury Professional) Bloomsbury Publishing Plc GBR. Dist: International Specialized Bk. Services.

CHARITIES—HISTORY

Adam, Thomas. Buying Respectability: Philanthropy & Urban Society in Transnational Perspective, 1840s to 1930s. 2009. (Philanthropic & Nonprofit Studies). (ENG., Illus.). 256p. 39.95 *(978-0-253-35274-3(6),* 0253352746) Indiana Univ. Pr.
Bridgen, Paul & Harris, Bernard. Charity & Mutual Aid in Europe & North America since 1800. 2007. (Routledge Studies in Modern History Ser.). (ENG., Illus.). 258p. (C). 149.00 *(978-0-415-36559-8(7))* Routledge.
Buxton, null. Patronizing the Public: American Philanthropy's Transformation of Culture, Communication, & the Humanities. 2009. (Critical Media Studies). (ENG.). 362p. 99.99 *(978-0-7391-2305-8(X))* Lexington Bks.
Buxton, William Jose. Patronizing the Public: American Philanthropy's Transformation of Culture, Communication, & the Humanities. 2009. (Critical Media Studies). (ENG.). 362p. pap. 41.99 *(978-0-7391-2306-5(8))* Lexington Bks.
Chastel, Tienne Louis. The Charity of the Primitive Churches. 2006. 364p. per. 26.99 *(978-1-4255-3787-6(1))* MPublishing.
Crocker, Ruth. Mrs. Russell Sage: Women's Activism & Philanthropy in Gilded Age & Progressive Era America. 2008. (Philanthropic & Nonprofit Studies). (ENG., Illus.). 552p. pap. 24.95 *(978-0-253-22045-5(9),* 0253220459) Indiana Univ. Pr.
Harris, Bernard & Bridgen, Paul, eds. Charity & Mutual Aid in Europe & North America Since 1800. 2012. (Routledge Studies in Modern History Ser.). (ENG., Illus.). 258p. (C). pap. 42.95 ***(978-0-415-54105-3(0))*** Routledge.
Hathaway, Esse V. Partners in Progress. 2007. (ENG.). 316p. per. *(978-1-4067-4375-3(5))* Read Bks.
Kiger, Joseph. Philanthropists & Foundation Globalization. 2007. (ENG.). 188p. (gr. 11). 49.95 *(978-1-4128-0673-2(9))* Transaction Pubs.
Marland, Hilary. Medicine & Society in Wakefield & Huddersfield, 1780-1870. 2008. (Cambridge Studies in the History of Medicine Ser.). (ENG., Illus.). 528p. pap. 69.00 *(978-0-521-08928-9(X))* Cambridge Univ. Pr.
Moore, Sarah E. Ribbon Culture: Charity, Compassion & Public Awareness. 2010. (ENG.). 200p. pap. 26.00 *(978-0-230-24789-5(X))* Palgrave Macmillan.
Schmidt, Sebastian & Aspelmeier, Jens. Norm und Praxis der Armenfürsorge in Spätmittelalter und Früher Neuzeit. 2006. (Vierteljahrschrift fur Sozial- und Wirtschaftsgeschichte - Beihefte (VSWG-B) Ser.). (GER., Illus.). 233p. (C). 60.00 *(978-3-515-08874-9(1))* Steiner, Franz Verlag Wiesbaden GmbH DEU. Dist: Brown, David Bk. Co., The.
Smith, Joanna Handlin. The Art of Doing Good: Charity in Late Ming China. 2009. (ENG., Illus.). 424p. 40.00 *(978-0-520-25363-6(9))* Univ. of California Pr.
Tomkins, Alannah. The Experience of Urban Poverty, 1723-82: Parish, Charity & Credit. 2007. (ENG., Illus.). 304p. 94.00 *(978-0-7190-7504-9(1))* Manchester Univ. Pr. GBR. Dist: Macmillan.
Weaver, Alain Epp, ed. A Table of Sharing: Mennonite Central Committee & the Expanding Networks of Mennonite Identity. 2011. 432p. pap. 29.95 *(978-1-931038-78-2(3))* Cascadia Publishing Hse., LLC.
Williams, Ian. The Alms Trade: Charities, Past, Present & Future. 2007. 236p. per 15.95 *(978-1-60206-753-0(6))* Cosimo, Inc.

CHARITIES—LAW AND LEGISLATION

see Charity Laws and Legislation

CHARITIES—TAXATION

see also Church Property—Taxation

Jewell, George. Charitable Trusts. 2008. 1162p. pap. 255.00 *(978-0-8080-9166-0(2))* 2009th ed. 2009. 1100p. pap. 290.00 incl. cd-rom *(978-0-8080-2128-5(1))* Toolkit Media Group.
—Charitable Trusts: 2006. 2006. 1234p. pap. 200.00 *(978-0-8080-9036-6(4))* Toolkit Media Group.
—Charitable Trusts: 2008 Edition. 2007. pap. 218.50 *(978-0-8080-9203-2(0))* Toolkit Media Group.
O'Halloran, Kerry. The Profits of Charity. 2012. (ENG.). 608p. 125.00 ***(978-0-19-976771-7(8))*** Oxford Univ. Pr., Inc.
Vincent. Vincent Charity Accounting Handbook. 5th rev. ed. 2008. pap. 108.00 *(978-1-84592-229-0(8),* Bloomsbury Professional) Bloomsbury Publishing Plc GBR. Dist: International Specialized Bk. Services.

CHARITIES—CANADA

Kelly, Elaine Ricker. Give Smart: How to Make a Dramatic Difference with Your Donation Dollar. 2008. (ENG., Illus.). 240p. per. 19.95 *(978-1-55022-802-1(1))* ECW Pr. CAN. Dist: Independent Pubs. Group.

CHARITIES—CHINA

Smith, Joanna Handlin. The Art of Doing Good: Charity in Late Ming China. 2009. (ENG., Illus.). 424p. 40.00 *(978-0-520-25363-6(9))* Univ. of California Pr.

CHARITIES—EUROPE

Anheier, Helmut K. & Daly, Siobhan, eds. The Politics of Foundations: A Comparative Analysis. 2008. 368p. 41.95 *(978-0-415-47984-4(3),* Routledge.
Brodman, James. Charity & Religion in Medieval Europe. 2009. 328p. 59.95 *(978-0-8132-1580-8(3),* Catholic Univ. of America Pr.
Frohman, Larry. Poor Relief & Welfare in Germany from the Reformation to World War I. (ENG., Illus.). 2011. 268p. pap. 35.99 *(978-0-521-18885-2(7))* 2008. 272p. 95.00 *(978-0-521-50603-8(4))* Cambridge Univ. Pr.
Martz, Linda. Poverty & Welfare in Habsburg Spain. 2009. (Cambridge Iberian & Latin American Studies). 288p. pap. 42.00 *(978-0-521-12248-1(1))* Cambridge Univ. Pr.
Steiner, Matthias Günter. Die Klöster und ihr Wirken - eine der Wurzeln des Stiftungswesens? 2009. (Rechtshistorische Reihe Ser.). (GER.). 430p. 108.95 *(978-3-631-58578-8(0))* Lang, Peter GmbH, Europaischer Verlag der Wissenschaften DEU. Dist: Lang, Peter.
Wiepking, Pamala, ed. The State of Giving Research in Europe: Household Donations to Charitable Organizations in Twelve European Countries. 2010. 80p. pap. *(978-90-8555-009-9(2),* Pallas Publications) Amsterdam Univ. Pr.

CHARITIES—FRANCE

Gavitt, Philip. Gender, Honor, & Charity in Late Renaissance Florence. 2011. (ENG., Illus.). 308p. 90.00 *(978-1-107-00294-4(X))* Cambridge Univ. Pr.
[Lawrence, William Richards]. Charities of France In 1866. 2006. 220p. per. 20.99 *(978-1-4255-1822-6(2))* MPublishing.
Ticktin, Miriam I. Casualties of Care: Immigration & the Politics of Humanitarianism in France. 2011. (ENG., Illus.). 275p. 65.00 *(978-0-520-26904-0(7));* pap. 26.95 *(978-0-520-26905-7(5))* Univ. of California Pr.

C

CHARITIES—GREAT BRITAIN

Bawtree, Don & Kirkland, Kate. Charity Administration Handbook. 4th rev. ed. 2008. (Illus.). 716p. pap. 125.00 *(978-1-84592-239-9(5))*, Bloomsbury Professional) Bloomsbury Publishing Plc GBR. Dist: International Specialized Bk. Services.

Ben-Amos, Ilana Krausman. The Culture of Giving: Informal Support & Gift-Exchange in Early Modern England. 2011. (Cambridge Social & Cultural Histories Ser.). (ENG.). 440p. pap. 39.99 *(978-0-521-17413-8(9))* Cambridge Univ. Pr.

Burdett-Coutts, Angela G. The Woman's Mission: A Series of Congress Papers on the Philanthropic Work of Women. 485p. reprint ed. 98.00 *(978-0-7222-1657-6(2))* Library Reprints, Inc.

Chew, Celine. Strategic Positioning in Voluntary & Charitable Organizations. 2009. (Routledge Studies in the Management of Voluntary & Non-Profit Organizations Ser.). (ENG., Illus.). XVIII, 260p. 166.00 *(978-0-415-45304-2(6))* Routledge.

Clay, Rotha Mary. The Medieval Hospitals of England. 2007. (ENG.). 500p. 53.95 *(978-0-548-11842-9(6))* Kessinger Publishing, LLC.

Croucher, Matt & The Royal British Legion. The Royal British Legion: 90 Years of Heroes. 2011. (ENG., Illus.). 256p. 32.95 ***(978-0-00-744153-2(3))*** HarperCollins Pubs. Ltd. GBR. Dist: Independent Pubs. Group.

Dawes, Greyham, et al. Charity Accounts: A Practical Guide to the Charities SORP. 4th rev. ed. 2009. (ENG.). 736p. pap. incl. cd-rom *(978-1-84661-154-4(7))* Jordan Publishing, Ltd.

Eden, Frederick Morton. The State of the Poor: Or, an History of the Labouring Classes in England, from the Conquest to the Present Period. 2011. (Cambridge Library Collection - History Ser.). (ENG.). 706p. pap. 57.00 ***(978-1-108-03688-7(0))***; 678p. pap. 57.00 ***(978-1-108-03687-0(2))***; 674p. pap. 54.00 ***(978-1-108-03689-4(9))*** Cambridge Univ. Pr.

Fowler, Simon. Workhouse: People Places Life Behind Door. 2008. (Illus.). 288p. pap. 19.95 *(978-1-905615-28-5(0))* National Archives (PRO), The GBR. Dist: International Publishers Marketing.

Gawthorpe, Ann. Successful Grant Applications: Bullet Guides. 2012. (Bullet Guides). (ENG.). 128p. pap. 6.95 ***(978-1-4441-6358-2(2))***, Hodder & Stoughton) Hodder General Publishing Div. GBR. Dist: Independent Pubs. Group.

Gray, Benjamin Kirkman. The A History of English Philanthropy: from the Dissolution Of. 2007. (ENG.). 320p. per. 30.95 *(978-1-4304-5141-9(6))* Kessinger Publishing, LLC.

Hampson, Ethel Mary. Treatment of Poverty in Cambridgeshire, 1597-1834. 2009. (Cambridge Library Collection - Cambridge Ser.). (Illus.). 356p. pap. 29.99 *(978-1-108-00234-9(X))* Cambridge Univ. Pr.

Hilton, Matthew, et al. A History of NGOs in Britain: Charities, Civil Society & the Voluntary Sector Since 1945. 2012. (ENG., Illus.). 400p. 125.00 ***(978-0-230-30444-4(3))*** Palgrave Macmillan.

Jordan, W. K. Philanthropy in England. 2006. (Illus.). 463p. 400.00 *(978-0-415-40193-7(3))* Routledge.

Koven, Seth. Slumming: Sexual & Social Politics in Victorian London. 2006. (ENG., Illus.). 424p. (C). per. 28.95 *(978-0-691-12800-9(6))* Princeton Univ. Pr.

Lloyd, Sarah. Charity & Poverty in England, C. 1680-1820: Wild & Visionary Schemes. 2010. (ENG., Illus.). 352p. 95.00 *(978-0-7190-7883-5(0))* Manchester Univ. Pr. GBR. Dist: Macmillan.

Maclennan, Alison. Running a Charity. 3rd rev. ed. 2008. (ENG.). 178p. pap. *(978-1-84661-093-6(1))* Jordan Publishing, Ltd.

Marland, Hilary. Medicine & Society in Wakefield & Huddersfield, 1780-1870. 2008. (Cambridge Studies in the History of Medicine Ser.). (ENG., Illus.). 528p. pap. 69.00 *(978-0-521-08928-9(X))* Cambridge Univ. Pr.

Mayhew, Henry. London Labour & the London Poor. 2009. 514p. pap. 39.75 *(978-1-115-90409-4(4))* BiblioBazaar.

Porter, Stephen. London Charterhouse. 2009. (ENG., Illus.). 176p. pap. 24.95 *(978-1-84868-090-6(2))* Amberley Publishing GBR. Dist: Casemate Pubs. & Bk. Distributors, LLC.

Reed, Andrew. Memoirs of the Life & Philanthropic Labours of Andrew Reed, D. D. With Selections from his Journals. 2011. (Cambridge Library Collection - History Ser.). (ENG., Illus.). 592p. pap. 43.00 ***(978-1-108-03621-4(X))*** Cambridge Univ. Pr.

Rosenthal, Joel T. The Purchase of Pardise. 2006. 192p. 180.00 *(978-0-415-41302-2(8))* Routledge.

Rossi, Paul. Fighting Cancer with More Than Medicine: A History of Macmillan Cancer Support. 2009. (ENG., Illus.). 320p. 39.95 *(978-0-7524-4844-2(7))* History Pr. Ltd., The GBR. Dist: Independent Pubs. Group.

Smith, Sally Dixon. Historic Royal Palaces: Curator's Choice. 2011. (Illus.). 80p. pap. 14.95 *(978-1-85759-677-9(3))* Scala, Editions FRA. Dist: National Bk. Network.

Trebilcox, Dorothy. The Red Cross Letters: A Real Life Account 1944-1946. 2010. 616p. pap. 29.99 *(978-1-4490-7291-9(7))* AuthorHouse.

Vincent. Vincent Charity Accounting Handbook. 5th rev. ed. 2008. pap. 108.00 *(978-1-84592-229-0(8))*, Bloomsbury Professional) Bloomsbury Publishing Plc GBR. Dist: International Specialized Bk. Services.

Weinbren, Daniel. The Oddfellows, 1810 - 2010: Two Hundred Years of Making Friends & Helping People. 2012. (Illus.). 384p. 38.95 ***(978-1-85936-207-5(9))*** International Publishers Marketing.

Williams, Ian. The Alms Trade: Charities, Past, Present & Future. 2007. 236p. per. 15.95 *(978-1-60206-753-0(8))* Cosimo, Inc.

CHARITIES—UNITED STATES

Allen, Lee, des. The Charity Letters of Joann Cayce. 2008. 236p. pap. 15.00 *(978-0-9801231-0-4(0))* Bright Cloud Pr.

Alt, Jeff. A Walk for Sunshine: A 2,160 Mile Expedition for Charity on the Appalachian Trail. 2nd ed. 2007. 288p. per. 15.95 *(978-0-9679482-2-5(3))* 3rd rev. ed. 2009. 304p. pap. 15.95 *(978-0-9679482-3-2(1))* Dreams Shared Pubns., LLC.

Baldwin, William Delavan. How to Meet Hard Times: a Program for the Prevention & Relief. 2007. pap. 20.95 *(978-1-4304-5040-5(1))* Kessinger Publishing, LLC.

Brooks, Arthur C. Who Really Cares: The Surprising Truth about Compassionate Conservatism — America's Charity Divide — Who Gives, Who Doesn't, & Why It Matters. 2007. (ENG.). 272p. per. 16.95 *(978-0-465-00823-0(2))* Basic Bks.

Brown, Melissa S., ed. Giving USA 2007: The Annual Report on Philanthropy for the Year 2006. 2007. (Illus.). 256p. pap. 75.00 *(978-0-9786199-2-3(7))* Giving USA Foundation.

Buxton, null. Patronizing the Public: American Philanthropy's Transformation of Culture, Communication, & the Humanities. 2009. (Critical Media Studies). (ENG.). 362p. 99.99 *(978-0-7391-2305-8(X))* Lexington Bks.

Buxton, William Jose. Patronizing the Public: American Philanthropy's Transformation of Culture, Communication, & the Humanities. 2009. (Critical Media Studies). (ENG.). 362p. pap. 41.99 *(978-0-7391-2306-5(8))* Lexington Bks.

Cambron, Jeff, et al, eds. Grant Funding for Elderly Health Services. 6th ed. 2008. (Illus.). 170p. pap. 189.00 *(978-1-882364-84-8(8))* Health Resources Publishing.

Chambers, Clarke A. Seedtime of Reform: American Social Service & Social Action, 1918-1933. 2009. (ENG.). 348p. pap. 60.00 *(978-0-8166-5722-3(X))* Univ. of Minnesota Pr.

Chehade, Mohamad & Jassemm, Khalil. Guarding a Sacred Trust: Muslim Nonprofit Management for Post-911 World. 2010. 520p. 47.99 *(978-1-4490-9256-6(X))*; (ENG.). pap. 37.95 *(978-1-4490-9257-3(8))* AuthorHouse.

Chmidling, Catherine. History of the Kansas Orphans' Home, 1887-1962: The Professionalization of Charity. 2010. (ENG., Illus.). 324p. 119.95 *(978-0-7734-3667-1(7))* Mellen, Edwin Pr., The.

Clemens, Elisabeth Stephanie & Guthrie, Doug, eds. Politics & Partnerships: The Role of Voluntary Associations in America's Political Past & Present. 2011. (ENG., Illus.). 352p. 55.00 *(978-0-226-10996-1(8))* Univ. of Chicago Pr.

Crandell, Steven Scott. Silver Tongue — Secrets of Mr. Santa Barbara: The Larry Crandell Story. 2007. (Illus.). 24.95 *(978-0-9789358-0-1(2))*; per. 14.95 *(978-0-9789358-1-8(0))* Quinn, Rose, Elliot & Ellery Pubs.

Crocker, Ruth. Mrs. Russell Sage: Women's Activism & Philanthropy in Gilded Age & Progressive Era America. 2008. (Philanthropic & Nonprofit Studies). (ENG., Illus.). 552p. pap. 24.95 *(978-0-253-22045-5(9))*, 0253220459) Indiana Univ. Pr.

Dashefsky, Arnold & Lazerwitz, Bernard Melvin. Time to Give. 2009. (ENG., Illus.). 172p. 68.50 *(978-0-7391-0987-8(1))* Lexington Bks.

Ealy, Lenore T., ed. Conversations on Philanthropy: The Legacy of Kenneth Boulding, 10, Vol. IV. 2007. 54p. pap. 0.00 *(978-0-9761904-3-1(5))* Philanthropic Enterprise, LLC, The.

Eikenberry, Angela M. Giving Circles: Philanthropy, Voluntary Association, & Democracy. 2009. (Philanthropic & Nonprofit Studies). (ENG., Illus.). 192p. 55.00 *(978-0-253-35319-1(X))*, 025335319X); pap. 21.95 *(978-0-253-22085-1(8))*, 0253220858) Indiana Univ. Pr.

Fishman, James J. The Faithless Fiduciary & the Elusive Quest for Charitable Accountability, 1200-2005. 2006. 100.00 *(978-0-89089-496-5(5))* Carolina Academic Pr.

Fleishman, Joel, et al. Casebook for the Foundation: A Great American Secret. 2007. (ENG.). 354p. pap. 30.00 *(978-1-58648-488-0(5))* PublicAffairs.

Fleishman, Joel L. The Foundation: A Great American Secret; How Private Wealth Is Changing the World. 2009. (ENG., Illus.). 464p. pap. 19.95 *(978-1-58648-702-7(7))* PublicAffairs.

Foundation Center Staff, contrib. by. Foundations & Public Policy: Leveraging Philanthropic Dollars, Knowledge, & Networks for Greater Impact. 2009. (Illus.). vii, 308p. *(978-1-59542-218-7(8))* Foundation Ctr., The.

Frumkin, Peter. Strategic Giving: The Art & Science of Philanthropy. 2006. (ENG., Illus.). 448p. 47.50 *(978-0-226-26626-8(5))* Univ. of Chicago Pr.

Gillin, John L. History of Poor Relief Legislation in Iowa. reprint ed. lib. bdg. 98.00 *(978-0-7222-4805-8(9))* Library Reprints, Inc.

Guthrie, Doug & Clemens, Elisabeth S., eds. Politics & Partnerships: The Role of Voluntary Associations in America's Political Past & Present. 2011. (ENG., Illus.). 352p. pap. 19.00 *(978-0-226-10997-8(6))* Univ. of Chicago Pr.

Jackson, William L. The Wisdom of Generosity: A Reader in American Philanthropy. 2008. (ENG., Illus.). 480p. pap. 49.95 *(978-1-60258-059-6(6))* Baylor Univ. Pr.

Kiger, Joseph. Philanthropists & Foundation Globalization. 2007. (ENG.). 188p. (gr. 11). 49.95 *(978-1-4128-0673-2(9))* Transaction Pubs.

Kroll, Judith A. 2006 Grantmakers Salary & Benefits Report. 2007. *(978-1-932677-46-1(1))* Council on Foundations, Inc.

Lockley, Timothy James. Welfare & Charity in the Antebellum South. 2009. (New Perspectives on the History of the South Ser.). (ENG., Illus.). 304p. pap. 29.95 *(978-0-8130-3446-1(9))* Univ. Pr. of Florida.

Lupton, Robert D. Toxic Charity: How Churches & Charities Hurt Those They Help (And How to Reverse It) 2011. (ENG.). 208p. 22.99 *(978-0-06-207620-5(5))*, HarperOne) HarperCollins Pubs.

Mark I. Rosen. Mission, Meaning, & Money. 2010. 204p. pap. 17.95 *(978-1-4401-6741-6(9))* iUniverse, Inc.

Mason, Philip P. Tracy W. Mcgregor: Humanitarian, Philanthropist, & Detroit Civic Leader. 2008. (Great Lakes Bks.). (Illus.). 266p. 49.95 *(978-0-8143-3376-1(1))* Wayne State Univ. Pr.

Menkhaus, Ken. Philanthropy & the Nonprofit Sector: An Introduction. 2013. 256p. 75.00 *(978-1-56549-304-9(4))*; pap. 24.95 *(978-1-56549-303-2(6))* Stylus Publishing, LLC.

Moore, Jonathon R. A Practical Guide to International Philanthropy. 2009. (ENG., Illus.). 380p. 80.00 *(978-0-521-11641-1(4))* Cambridge Univ. Pr.

National Directory of Nonprofit Organizations, 3 vols.; set. 21st rev. ed. 2008. 780.00 *(978-1-56995-501-7(8))* Taft Group, The.

Naufits, Mitchell F. Philanthropy in the 21st Century: The Foundation Center's 50th Anniversary Interviews. 2007. pap. *(978-1-59542-163-0(7))* Foundation Ctr., The.

Olasky, Marvin. The Tragedy of American Compassion. 2008. 320p. pap. 27.00 *(978-1-4335-0110-4(4))* Crossway.

Peirce, Bradford Kinney. A Half Century with Juvenile Delinquents; 2006. 412p. per. 26.99 *(978-1-4255-4408-9(8))* MPublishing.

Roberts, Jonathan & Durant, Thomas J., Jr. A History of the Charity Hospitals of Louisiana: A Study of Poverty, Politics, Public Health, & the Public Interest. 2009. 340p. 119.95 *(978-0-7734-3886-6(6))* Mellen, Edwin Pr., The.

Ruppel, Warren. Not-for-Profit Organization Audits with Single Audits. 2006th rev. ed. 2006. (Illus.). 957p. pap. 189.00 incl. cd-rom *(978-0-8080-9025-0(9))* Toolkit Media Group.

Salamon, Lester M. America's Nonprofit Sector: A Primer. 3rd ed. 2011. pap. ***(978-1-59542-360-3(5))*** Foundation Ctr., The.

Solomon, Lewis. Tech Billionaires: Reshaping Philanthropy in a Quest for a Better World. 2009. (ENG.). 158p. 34.95 *(978-1-4128-0847-7(2))* Transaction Pubs.

Spiller, Harry. Support Programs for Ex-Offenders: A State-by-State Directory. 2011. (ENG., Illus.). 230p. pap. 40.00 *(978-0-7864-4868-5(7))* McFarland & Co., Inc. Pubs.

Tierney, Thomas J. & Fleishman, Joel L. Give Smart: Philanthropy That Gets Results. 2011. (ENG., Illus.). 272p. 23.99 *(978-1-58648-895-6(3))* PublicAffairs.

To Examine Whether Charitable Organizations Serve the Needs of Diverse Communities: Hearing Before the Subcommittee on Oversight of the Committee on Ways & Means, U.S. House of Representatives, One Hundred Tenth Congress, First Session, September 25, 2007. 2009. (Illus.). iii, 80p. *(978-0-16-083296-3(9))*, 552-070-39124-0) United States Government Printing Office.

Tuohy, Tom. Kiss of a Dolphin. 2006. per. 14.95 *(978-0-9787788-8-0(X))* LUMEN-US Pubns.

Van Til, Jon. Growing Civil Society: From Nonprofit Sector to Third Space. 2008. (Philanthropic & Nonprofit Studies). (ENG., Illus.). 264p. pap. 24.95 *(978-0-253-22047-9(5))*, 0253220475) Indiana Univ. Pr.

Verducci, Susan & Damon, William V. B., eds. Taking Philanthropy Seriously: Beyond Noble Intentions to Responsible Giving. 2006. (Philanthropic & Nonprofit Studies). (ENG., Illus.). 272p. pap. 27.95 *(978-0-253-21860-5(8))*, 0253218608) Indiana Univ. Pr.

Wooster, Martin Morse. Great Philanthropic Mistakes. 2nd ed. 2010. *(978-1-55813-161-3(2))* Hudson Institute Pr.

—The Great Philanthropists & the Problem of "Donor Intent" 2007. pap. *(978-1-892934-12-3(4))* Capital Research Ctr.

Zunz, Olivier. Philanthropy in America: A History. 2011. (Politics & Society in Twentieth Century America Ser.). (ENG.). 396p. 29.95 ***(978-0-691-12836-8(7))*** Princeton Univ. Pr.

CHARITIES, MEDICAL

see also Hospitals; Medical Social Work; Older People—Medical Care; Psychiatric Hospitals; Voluntary Health Agencies

Bowman, Edwin A. Cesarean Hysterectomy: An Analysis of One Thousand Consecutive Operations From Charity Hospital of Louisiana at New Orleans, & the Early History of the Operaton. 2009. 61p. 29.95 *(978-0-615-31788-5(X))* Bowman, Edwin A. Jr., M.D.

Meyers, Marilyn. Through Fire & Sea: Adventures on the Mercy Ship: A Family's Journey to the World's Forgotten Poor. 2007. *(978-1-897213-33-9(6))* BayRidge Bks.

Rossi, Paul. Fighting Cancer with More Than Medicine: A History of Macmillan Cancer Support. 2009. (ENG., Illus.). 320p. 39.95 *(978-0-7524-4844-2(7))* History Pr. Ltd., The GBR. Dist: Independent Pubs. Group.

Shaffer, Alice. The Indiana Poor Law: Its Development & Administration with Special Reference to the Provision of State Care for the Sick Poor. 378p. reprint ed. lib. bdg. 98.00 *(978-0-7222-0509-9(0))* Library Reprints, Inc.

CHARITON

Smith, Steven D. Greek Identity & the Athenian Past in Chariton: The Romance of Empire. 2007. (Ancient Narrative Supplementum Ser.). (ENG.). 282p. (C). 116.00 ***(978-90-77922-28-6(8))*** Barkhuis Publishing NLD. Dist: Brown, David Bk. Co., The.

Tilg, Stefan. Chariton of Aphrodisias & the Invention of the Greek Love Novel. 2010. (ENG.). 360p. 99.00 *(978-0-19-957694-4(7))* Oxford Univ. Pr., Inc.

CHARITY

see also Altruism; Benevolence; Humanity; Kindness; Women in Charitable Work

Allen, S. C. Drought Amidst the Flood. 2010. 132p. pap. 16.00 *(978-1-58982-767-7(8))*, Millennial Mind Publishing) American Bk. Publishing Group.

Arnold, Marilyn. From the Heart: Charity in the Book of Mormon. 2011. pap. 13.99 *(978-1-59955-485-3(2))* Cedar Fort, Inc./CFI Distribution.

Barber, Nicola. Fighting Poverty. 2012. (Charities in Action Ser.). (ENG.). 64p. (gr. 6-10). pap. 9.99 ***(978-1-4329-6392-7(9))***; lib. bdg. 35.00 ***(978-1-4329-6385-9(6))*** Heinemann-Raintree. (NA-h).

Beatrice, Dennis F. Health Care Conversions & Philanthropy: Important Issues for Practice & Research. 2007. (ENG.). 60p. pap. 7.00 *(978-0-89843-267-1(7))* Aspen Institute, The.

Ben-Amos, Ilana Krausman. The Culture of Giving: Informal Support & Gift-Exchange in Early Modern England. 2008. (Cambridge Social & Cultural Histories Ser.). (ENG., Illus.). 454p. 99.00 *(978-0-521-86723-8(1))* Cambridge Univ. Pr.

Benedict XVI, pseud. Papa Benedicto XVI: Caridad en la Verdad. Estenger, Vilma G., tr. 2009. (SPA.). 1p. 14.95 *(978-1-59276-458-7(4))* Our Sunday Visitor, Publishing Div.

—Pope Benedict XVI: Charity in Truth. 2009. 1p. 14.95 *(978-1-59276-457-0(6))* Our Sunday Visitor, Publishing Div.

Bornstein, Erica. Disquieting Gifts: Humanitarianism in New Delhi. 2012. (Stanford Studies in Human Rights Ser.). (ENG.). 232p. 70.00 ***(978-0-8047-7001-9(8))***; pap. 22.95 ***(978-0-8047-7002-6(6))*** Stanford Univ. Pr.

Christiansen, Betty. Knitting for Peace: Make the World a Better Place One Stitch at a Time. 2006. (ENG., Illus.). 132p. 19.95 *(978-1-58479-533-9(6))* Stewart, Tabori & Chang.

Colwell, Stephen. New Themes for the Protestant Clergy. 2009. (Illus.). 198p. pap. 19.99 *(978-1-150-36469-3(6))* General Bks. LLC.

—New Themes for the Protestant Clergy: Creeds Without Charity, theology Without Humanity, & Protestantism Without Christianity ... 2006. 420p. per. 26.99 *(978-1-4255-4498-0(3))* MPublishing.

Colwell, Stephen, abr. New Themes for the Protestant Clergy. 2009. (Amer Philosophy, Religion Ser.). (ENG.). 420p. pap. 25.95 *(978-1-4290-1843-2(7))* Applewood Bks.

Conyngton, Mary. How to Help: A Manual of Practical Charity. 2007. (ENG.). 376p. 48.95 *(978-0-548-10504-7(9))* Kessinger Publishing, LLC.

Cooke, Parsons. The Divine Law of Beneficence. 2009. 358p. pap. 31.75 *(978-1-116-09507-4(6))*; pap. 32.75 *(978-1-116-09506-7(8))* BiblioBazaar.

—The Divine Law of Beneficence. 2008. 364p. 46.95 *(978-0-548-96249-7(9))* 2007. (ENG.). 368p. per. 31.95 *(978-0-548-63792-0(X))* Kessinger Publishing, LLC.

—The Divine Law of Beneficence. 2006. 364p. per. 26.99 *(978-1-4255-3709-8(X))* MPublishing.

Davis, Tom. Fields of the Fatherless: Discover the Joy of Compassionate Living. 2008. (ENG.). 192p. pap. 14.99 *(978-0-7814-4847-5(6))* Cook, David C.

Dobson, Austin. A Paladin of Philanthropy & Other Papers. 2007. 380p. 48.95 *(978-0-548-33166-8(9))*; (ENG.). per. 33.95 *(978-1-4326-9046-5(9))* Kessinger Publishing, LLC.

Dutton, June & Perl, Susan. Faith, Hope & Charity. (Illus.). 5.95 *(978-0-915696-46-8(0))* Determined Productions, Inc.

Elizondo, Virgilio P. Charity. 2008. 144p. pap. 14.00 *(978-1-57075-720-4(8))* Orbis Bks.

Fraser, Ede & Spizman, Robyn Freedman. Do Your Giving While You Are Living: Inspirational Lessons on What You Can Do Today to Make a Difference Tomorrow. 2009. (ENG.). pap. 14.95 *(978-1-60037-452-4(2))* Morgan James Publishing.

Frenkel, Miriam. Giving in Monotheistic Religions. 2009. (Studien zur Geschichte und Kultur des islamischen Orients Ser.). (ENG.). XVI, 413p. 140.00 *(978-3-11-020946-4(2))* De Gruyter, Walter Inc.

Gilmore, Alec. Aid Matters. 160p. 17.00 *(978-0-334-02717-1(9))* Hymns Ancient & Modern Ltd GBR. Dist: Morehouse Publishing.

Goldin, Barbara Diamond. Creating Angels: Stories of Tzedakah. 2006. (ENG.). 160p. per. 22.95 *(978-0-7425-5284-5(5))* Rowman & Littlefield Publishers, Inc.

Goose, Nigel & Moden, Leanne. History of Doughty's Hospital, Norwich, 1687-2009. 2010. (ENG., Illus.). 288p. pap. 19.95 *(978-1-905313-93-8(4))* Univ. of Hertfordshire Pr. GBR. Dist: Independent Pubs. Group.

Gregory, Bradley. Like an Everlasting Signet Ring: Generosity in the Book of Sirach. 2010. (Deuterocanonical & Cognate Literature Studies). (ENG.). XVII, 378p. 196.00 ***(978-3-11-174054-6(4))*** De Gruyter, Walter Inc.

Gregory, Bradley C. Like an Everlasting Signet Ring: Generosity in the Book of Sirach. 2010. (Deuterocanonical & Cognate Literature Studies). (ENG.). XVII, 378p. 126.00 *(978-3-11-022366-8(X))* De Gruyter, Walter Inc.

Haavik, Kristof. The Socialist Christian. 2007. 184p. per. 24.95 *(978-1-4241-9764-4(3))* PublishAmerica, Inc.

Havers, Grant N. Lincoln & the Politics of Christian Love. 2009. (ENG.). 224p. (C). 44.95 *(978-0-8262-1857-5(1))* Univ. of Missouri Pr.

Hawkins, Jim. 1001 Fundraising Ideas & Strategies: For Charity & Other Not-for-Profit Groups in Canada, 1 vol. (ENG.). 378p. pap. *(978-1-55041-280-2(9))* Fitzhenry & Whiteside, Ltd.

Hedrick, Elizabeth. Charity & Philanthropy: Readings in English Literature. rev. ed. 2010. (ENG.). 312p. ring bd. 107.34 *(978-0-7575-7858-8(6))* Kendall Hunt Publishing Co.

Hill, Octavia. Our Common Land: And Other Short Essays. 2011. (Cambridge Library Collection - History Ser.). (ENG.). 220p. pap. 22.99 *(978-1-108-02458-7(0))* Cambridge Univ. Pr.

Holland, Matthew S. Bonds of Affection: Civic Charity & the Making of America - Winthrop, Jefferson, & Lincoln. 2007. (Religion & Politics Ser.). (ENG., Illus.). 336p. pap. 29.95 *(978-1-58901-183-0(X))* Georgetown Univ. Pr.
Jamal, Azim & McKinnon, Harvey. The Power of Giving: How Giving Back Enriches Us All. 2009. (ENG.). 256p. (gr. 12-18). 13.95 *(978-1-58542-751-2(9)*, Tarcher) Penguin Group (USA) Inc.
Kakuru Luhunde, Vincent-B & Luhunde, Vincent-B Kakuru. The Applicability of the Branding Theory to Giving in Charity Mergers: The Case of Clicsargent. 2011. 100p. pap. ***(978-3-639-32506-5(0))*** VDM Verlag Dr. Mueller e.K.
Kass, Amy A., ed. Giving Well, Doing Good: Readings for Thoughtful Philanthropists. 2008. (Philanthropic & Nonprofit Studies). (ENG.). 520p. pap. 19.95 *(978-0-253-21955-8(8)*, 0253219558) Indiana Univ. Pr.
Knuth, Jane. Thrift Store Graces: Finding God's Gifts in the Midst of the Mess. 2012. (ENG.). 144p. pap. 13.95 ***(978-0-8294-3692-1(8))*** Loyola Pr.
Koenig-Bricker, Woodeene, compiled by. A Study Guide to Living Charity in Truth: Pope Benedict's Encyclical on Social & Economic Justice. 2009. 64p. pap. 9.95 *(978-1-59276-578-2(5))* Our Sunday Visitor, Publishing Div.
Kolm, Serge-Christophe, et al, eds. Handbook of the Economics of Giving, Altruism & Reciprocity: Foundations, 2 vols., Vol. 1. 2006. (Handbooks in Economics Ser.). (ENG., Illus.). 948p. 150.00 *(978-0-444-50697-9(7)*, North Holland) Elsevier Science & Technology Bks.
Kosso, Cynthia & Scott, Anne. Poverty & Prosperity in the Middle Ages & the Renaissance. 2012. (ENG., Illus.). 336p. (C). 102.00 ***(978-2-503-53032-1(X)***, Brepols Pubs. BEL. Dist: ISD.
Kramer, Bill. Unexpected Grace: Stories of Faith, Science, & Altruism. 2007. (Illus.). 256p. pap. 22.95 *(978-1-59947-112-9(4))* Templeton Pr.
Levering, Matthew. The Betrayal of Charity: The Sins That Sabotage Divine Love. 2011. pap. *(978-1-60258-354-2(4))* Baylor Univ. Pr.
—The Betrayal of Charity: The Sins that Sabotage Divine Love. 2011. 229p. pap. 24.95 *(978-1-60258-356-6(0))* Baylor Univ. Pr.
Lupton, Robert D. Toxic Charity: How Churches & Charities Hurt Those They Help (and How to Reverse It) 2012. (ENG.). 208p. pap. 14.99 ***(978-0-06-207621-2(3)***, HarperOne) HarperCollins Pubs.
Moore, Sarah E. H. & Moore, Sarah. Ribbon Culture: Charity, Compassion & Public Awareness. 2008. (ENG.). 240p. 89.00 *(978-0-230-54921-0(7))* Palgrave Macmillan.
Morneau, Robert F. Pathways to God: Four Weeks on Faith, Hope & Charity. 2008. (7 X 4 Ser.). 72p. per. 8.95 *(978-1-56548-286-9(7))* New City Pr.
Oppenheimer, Danny & Olivola, Christopher, eds. The Science of Giving: Experimental Approaches to the Study of Charity. 2010. (Society for Judgment & Decision Making Ser.). (ENG., Illus.). 274p. 79.95 *(978-1-84872-885-1(9)*, Psychology Press) Taylor & Francis Group GBR. Dist: Taylor & Francis Group.
Payton, Robert L. & Moody, Michael P. Understanding Philanthropy: Its Meaning & Mission. 2008. (Philanthropic & Nonprofit Studies). (ENG., Illus.). 224p. 26.95 *(978-0-253-35049-7(2)*, 0253350492) Indiana Univ. Pr.
Richards, Marty. Caresharing: A Reciprocal Approach to Caregiving & Care Receiving in the Complexities of Aging, Illness or Disability. 2010. 256p. pap. 16.99 *(978-1-59473-286-7(8))* 2008. 250p. 24.99 *(978-1-59473-247-8(7))* SkyLight Paths Publishing.
Rockefeller, John Davison. Random Reminiscences of Men & Events. 2009. 200p. 22.99 *(978-1-103-97423-8(8))* 2009. 200p. pap. 16.99 *(978-1-103-97416-0(5))* 2008. 120p. 21.99 *(978-0-554-37205-1(3))* 2008. 120p. 24.99 *(978-0-554-27902-2(9))* 2007. 108p. pap. 18.99 *(978-1-4346-4279-0(8))* 2007. (ENG.). 118p. pap. 19.99 *(978-1-4346-4280-6(1))* BiblioBazaar.
—Random Reminiscences of Men & Events. 2009. 204p. 39.95 *(978-1-104-42982-9(9))*; pap. 24.95 *(978-1-104-37112-8(X))* Kessinger Publishing, LLC.
Shipman, Brian. Burn, 0 vols. 2008. 196p. pap. 12.99 *(978-0-7852-9686-7(7))* Nelson, Thomas Inc.
Singer, Peter. The Life You Can Save: How to Do Your Part to End World Poverty. 2010. (ENG., Illus.). 240p. pap. 15.00 *(978-0-8129-8156-8(1)*, Random Hse. Trade Paperbacks) Random House Publishing Group.
Smith, David H. Religious Giving: For Love of God. 2010. (Philanthropic & Nonprofit Studies). (ENG., Illus.). 220p. 65.00 *(978-0-253-35459-4(5)*, 0253354595); pap. 24.95 *(978-0-253-22188-9(9)*, 0253221889) Indiana Univ. Pr.
Smith, Robert. Biblical Charity. 29p. pap. 2.99 *(978-0-9652883-2-3(3))* Audubon Pr. & Christian Bk. Service.
The Zakat Foundation Of America. The Zakat Handbook: A Practical Guide for Muslims in the West. 2008. 136p. pap. 10.99 *(978-1-4389-0213-5(1))* AuthorHouse.
West, Matthew. Give This Christmas Away: 101 Simple & Thoughtful Ways To. 2009. (ENG.). 112p. 9.99 *(978-1-4143-3644-2(6))* Tyndale Hse. Pubs.
Wilkinson, Bruce. The God Pocket: He Owns It - You Carry It - Suddenly, Everything Changes. 2011. 144p. 12.99 *(978-1-60142-185-2(0)*, Multnomah) Doubleday Religious Publishing Group, The.
Wilkinson, Bruce & Kopp, David. The God Pocket: He Owns It, You Carry It: Suddenly, Everything Changes. 2011. ***(978-1-60142-413-6(2))***; ***(978-0-307-71384-1(9))*** Doubleday Religious Publishing Group, The. (Multnomah).

CHARITY, SISTERS OF
see Sisters of Charity of St. Vincent de Paul

CHARITY LAWS AND LEGISLATION
see also Charitable Uses, Trusts and Foundations; Poor Laws

Breen, Oonagh & Smith, Philip. Law of Charities in Ireland. 2013. 500p. pap. 168.00 *(978-1-84766-325-2(7)*, Bloomsbury Professional) Bloomsbury Publishing Plc GBR. Dist: International Specialized Bk. Services.
Bryson, Ellen, et al. Top Ten Ways Family Foundations Get into Trouble. 3rd ed. 2007. *(978-1-932677-51-5(8))* Council on Foundations, Inc.
Dunn, Alison. Charity, Law & Politics: Radicals, Conservatives or Subversives. 2012. (ENG.). 256p. 100.00 *(978-1-84113-416-1(3))* Hart Publishing Ltd. GBR. Dist: International Specialized Bk. Services.
Fishman, James J. The Faithless Fiduciary & the Elusive Quest for Charitable Accountability, 1200-2005. 2006. 100.00 *(978-0-89089-496-5(5))* Carolina Academic Pr.
Fishman, Stephen, abr. Nonprofit Fundraising Registration: The 50 State Guide. 2010. (ENG.). 368p. pap. 39.99 *(978-1-4133-1273-7(X))* NOLO.
Jones, Darryl K. The Tax Law of Charities & Other Exempt Organizations: Cases, Materials, Questions & Activities. 2nd ed. 2007. lv, 924p. pap. *(978-0-314-18417-7(1))* West Publishing Co., College & Schl. Div.
Kelly, Elaine Ricker. Give Smart: How to Make a Dramatic Difference with Your Donation Dollar. 2008. (ENG., Illus.). 240p. per. 19.95 *(978-1-55022-802-1(1))* ECW Pr. CAN. Dist: Independent Pubs. Group.
King, Michael & Phillips, Ann. Charities Act 2006: A Guide to the New Law. 2007. (Legislation Guides Ser.). 400p. pap. *(978-1-85328-913-2(2))* Law Society.
Lockley, Timothy James. Welfare & Charity in the Antebellum South. 2007. (New Perspectives on the History of the South Ser.). (ENG., Illus.). 304p. 59.95 *(978-0-8130-3173-6(7))* Univ. Pr. of Florida.
McGregor-Lowndes, Myles & O'Halloran, Kerry, eds. Modernising Charity Law: Recent Developments & Future Directions. 2010. 296p. 139.00 *(978-1-84980-250-5(5))* Elgar, Edward Publishing, Inc.
O'Halloran, Kerry. Charity Law & Social Inclusion: An International Study. 2006. 437p. 180.00 *(978-0-415-34722-8(X))*; per. 44.95 *(978-0-415-34723-5(8))* Routledge.
O'Halloran, Kerry. The Profits of Charity. 2012. (ENG.). 608p. 125.00 ***(978-0-19-976771-7(8))*** Oxford Univ. Pr., Inc.
O'Halloran, Kerry, et al. Charity Law & Social Policy: National & International Perspectives on the Functions of the Law Relating to Charities. 2008. (Library of Public Policy & Public Administration Ser.). XXVIII, 616p. (C). 169.00 *(978-1-4020-8413-3(7)*, 1402084137) Springer.
White, Doug. Charity on Trial: What You Should Know Before You Contribute. 2006. 295p. 24.95 *(978-1-56980-301-1(3))* Barricade Bks., Inc.

CHARITY LAWS AND LEGISLATION—GREAT BRITAIN

Bawtree, Don & Kirkland, Kate. Charity Administration Handbook. 4th rev. ed. 2008. (Illus.). 716p. pap. 125.00 *(978-1-84592-239-9(5)*, Bloomsbury Professional) Bloomsbury Publishing Plc GBR. Dist: International Specialized Bk. Services.
Davies, Ann & Picarda, Hubert. Law & Practice Relating to Charities, 2 vols. 4th rev. ed. 2010. 1583p. 495.00 *(978-1-84766-074-9(6)*, Bloomsbury Professional) Bloomsbury Publishing Plc GBR. Dist: International Specialized Bk. Services.
Donald, Gillian & Eccles, Alan. Charity Law in Scotland. 2013. 500p. pap., pap. 130.00 *(978-1-84766-680-2(9)*, Bloomsbury Professional) Bloomsbury Publishing Plc GBR. Dist: International Specialized Bk. Services.
Gillard, Cecile. Charities & Not-for-Profit Entities: Law & Practice. 2010. (ENG.). 150p. pap. 51.00 *(978-0-85490-074-9(8))* Wildy, Simmonds & Hill GBR. Dist: Gaunt, Inc.
Jones, Gareth. History of the Law of Charity, 1532-1827. 2008. (Cambridge Studies in English Legal History Ser.). (ENG.). 296p. pap. 38.99 *(978-0-521-07392-9(8))* Cambridge Univ. Pr.
Lloyd, Stephen. Charities - the New Law 2006: A Practical Guide to the Charities Act. 2007. (New Law Ser.). (ENG.). 754p. pap. *(978-0-85308-971-1(X))* Jordan Publishing, Ltd.
Lloyd, Stephen, et al. Charities, Trading & the Law. 2nd rev. ed. 2009. (ENG.). 356p. pap. *(978-1-84661-106-3(7))* Jordan Publishing, Ltd.
Luxton, Peter & Hill, Judith. The Law of Charities. 2nd ed. 2012. 1104p. 375.00 *(978-0-19-921480-8(8))* Oxford Univ. Pr., Inc.
Maclennan, Alison. Blackstone's Guide to the Charities Act 2006. Quint, Francesca, ed. 2007. (Blackstone's Guide Ser.). 400p. pap. 120.00 *(978-0-19-921479-2(4)*, Blackstone Pr.) Oxford Univ. Pr. GBR. Dist: Oxford Univ. Pr., Inc.
Meakin, Robert. The Law of Charitable Status: Maintenance & Removal. 2008. (Law Practitioner Ser.). (ENG.). 240p. 158.00 *(978-0-521-51603-7(X))* Cambridge Univ. Pr.
O'Halloran, Kerry, et al. Charity Law & Social Policy: National & International Perspectives on the Functions of the Law Relating to Charities. 2010. (Library of Public Policy & Public Administration Ser.). xxxi, 616p. pap. 169.00 *(978-90-481-7874-2(6)*, 9048178746) Springer.
Williams, Ian. The Alms Trade: Charities, Past, Present & Future. 2007. 236p. per. 15.95 *(978-1-60206-753-0(8))* Cosimo, Inc.

CHARITY ORGANIZATIONS
see also Charities

Atwater, Pierce. Problems of Administration in Social Work. 2009. (ENG.). 331p. pap. 60.00 *(978-0-8166-5932-6(X))* Univ. of Minnesota Pr.
Dietlin, Lisa M. Transformational Philanthropy: Entrepreneurs & Nonprofits. 2009. 330p. 62.95 *(978-0-7637-6678-8(X))* Jones & Bartlett Learning, LLC.
Frumkin, Peter. The Essence of Strategic Giving: A Practical Guide for Donors & Fundraisers. 2010. (ENG., Illus.). 192p. pap. 15.00 *(978-0-226-26627-5(3))* Univ. of Chicago Pr.
Jordan, W. K. Philanthropy in England. 2006. (Illus.). 463p. 400.00 *(978-0-415-40193-7(3))* Routledge.
Langley, Andrew. Saving the Environment. 2012. (Charities in Action Ser.). (ENG.). 64p. (gr. 6-10). pap. 9.99 ***(978-1-4329-6396-5(1))***; lib. bdg. 35.00 ***(978-1-4329-6389-7(9))*** Heinemann-Raintree. (NA-h).
Lee, Ji Hoon. Heeding the Call. 2011. 128p. pap. ***(978-3-8443-2598-0(0))*** Lambert Academic Publishing.
Lord, Susan. Wealth & Social Responsibility. 2008. 208p. pap. *(978-3-639-07180-1(8))* VDM Verlag Dr. Mueller e.K.
Maclennan, Alison. Running a Charity. 3rd rev. ed. 2008. (ENG.). 178p. pap. *(978-1-84661-093-6(1))* Jordan Publishing, Ltd.
Milano, Kenneth W. The History of the Kensington Soup Society. 2009. 19.99 *(978-1-59629-624-4(0))* History Pr., The.
Ogilvy, Julia. Turning Points: Stories to Change Your Life. 2009. (ENG., Illus.). 256p. pap. 15.95 *(978-0-7459-5380-9(8))* Lion Hudson PLC GBR. Dist: Independent Pubs. Group.
Pallotta, Dan. Uncharitable: How Restraints on Nonprofits Undermine Their Potential. 2010. (Civil Society: Historical & Contemporary Perspectives Ser.). (ENG., Illus.). 336p. pap. 24.95 *(978-1-58465-955-6(6)*, Tufts University Press) Univ. Pr. of New England.
Portocarrero, Felipe. Wealth & Philanthropy: The economic elite in Peru 1916-1960. 2010. 384p. pap. *(978-3-639-21891-6(4))* VDM Verlag Dr. Mueller e.K.
Smith, Joanna Handlin. The Art of Doing Good: Charity in Late Ming China. 2009. (ENG., Illus.). 424p. 40.00 *(978-0-520-25363-6(9))* Univ. of California Pr.
Williams, Jennifer. How to Start & Run a Rescue. 2007. *(978-1-929164-36-3(X))* Primedia Enthusiast Pubns.
Wood, John & Wood, John. Leaving Microsoft to Change the World: An Entrepreneur's Odyssey to Educate the World's Children. (ENG., Illus.). 2007. 304p. pap. 16.99 *(978-0-06-112108-1(8))* 2006. 272p. 25.95 *(978-0-06-112107-4(X))* HarperCollins Pubs. (Collins).

CHARITY-SCHOOLS

Lima, Emanoel Marcos. Disclosure in Philantropic Institutions of Higher Education in Brazil. 2010. 136p. pap. *(978-3-639-27760-9(0))* VDM Verlag Dr. Mueller e.K.
Mandeville, Bernard. The Fable of the Bees. 2009. 410p. pap. 15.32 *(978-1-150-18216-7(4))* General Bks. LLC.
Mandeville, Bernard & Tonson, Jacob. The Fable of the Bees. 2010. 370p. pap. 32.75 *(978-1-142-05222-5(2))* BiblioBazaar.
Trimmer, Sarah. Reflections upon the Education of Children in Charity Schools: With the Outlines of a Plan of Appropriate Instruction for the Children of the Poor. 2010. (Cambridge Library Collection - Women's Writing Ser.). 62p. pap. 19.99 *(978-1-108-01886-9(6))* Cambridge Univ. Pr.

CHARITY SHOPS
see Thrift Shops

CHARLATANS
see Impostors and Imposture; Quacks and Quackery

CHARLEMAGNE, EMPEROR, 742-814

Billings, Anna Hunt. A Guide to the Middle English Metrical Romances, Dealing with English & Germanic Legends, & with the Cycles of Charlemagne & of Arthur. 2008. 264p. 42.95 *(978-1-4369-4426-7(0))*; pap. 27.95 *(978-1-4367-3052-5(X))* Kessinger Publishing, LLC.
Bobrick, Benson. The Caliph's Splendor: Islam & the West in the Golden Age of Baghdad. 2012. (ENG., Illus.). 288p. 28.00 ***(978-1-4165-6762-2(3))*** Simon & Schuster.
Bulfinch, Thomas. Legends of Charlemagne. 2009. 250p. 32.99 *(978-1-115-27856-0(9))* 2009. 250p. 28.99 *(978-1-115-27855-3(X))* 2009. 250p. pap. 26.75 *(978-1-115-27854-6(1))* 2008. 312p. 29.99 *(978-0-554-28533-7(9))* 2008. 312p. 28.99 *(978-0-554-37836-7(1))* 2007. 276p. pap. 21.99 *(978-1-4346-5651-3(9))* BiblioBazaar.
—Legends of Charlemagne. 2009. 164p. pap. *(978-1-151-13736-4(7))*; 174p. pap. *(978-0-217-23019-3(9))*; 174p. pap. *(978-0-217-23017-9(2))* Books LLC.
—Legends of Charlemagne. 2008. 288p. pap. *(978-1-4099-2393-0(2))* Dodo Pr.
—Legends of Charlemagne. 2006. 408p. per. 26.99 *(978-1-4255-4410-2(X))* MPublishing.
—Legends of Charlemagne. Lt. ed. 2007. (ENG.). 308p. pap. 24.99 *(978-1-4346-5652-0(7))* BiblioBazaar.
Gabriele, Matthew. An Empire of Memory: The Legend of Charlemagne, the Franks, & Jerusalem before the First Crusade. 2011. (ENG., Illus.). 256p. 99.00 *(978-0-19-959144-2(X))* Oxford Univ. Pr., Inc.
Hodgkin, Thomas. Charles the Great. 2010. 276p. pap. 27.75 *(978-1-172-27330-0(3))* 2010. 260p. pap. 26.75 *(978-1-145-76342-5(1))* 2009. 266p. 30.99 *(978-1-110-21974-2(1))* 2009. 266p. pap. 26.75 *(978-1-110-21972-8(5))* 2009. (ENG.). 264p. pap. 23.99 *(978-1-110-21971-1(7)*, BiblioLife) 2009. (ENG.). 264p. pap. 21.99 *(978-1-110-21968-1(7)*, BiblioLife) BiblioBazaar.
—Charles the Great. 2009. 122p. pap. *(978-1-4588-1780-8(5))* Books LLC.
James, G. P. R. The History of Charlemagne: with a Sketch of the State & History. 2007. (ENG.). 532p. per. 40.95 *(978-1-4304-4361-2(8))* Kessinger Publishing, LLC.
Komornicka, Jolanta. Shadowing the Other. 2009. 132p. pap. *(978-3-639-01835-6(4))* VDM Verlag Dr. Mueller e.K.
McCormick, Michael. Charlemagne's Survey of the Holy Land: Wealth, Personnel, & Buildings of a Mediterranean Church Between Antiquity & the Middle Ages. 2011. (Dumbarton Oaks Medieval Humanities Ser.). (ENG., Illus.). 310p. 39.95 *(978-0-88402-363-0(X))* Dumbarton Oaks.
McKitterick, Rosamond. Charlemagne: The Formation of a European Identity. 2008. (ENG., Illus.). 478p. (C). pap. 29.99 *(978-0-521-71645-1(4))* Cambridge Univ. Pr. GBR. Dist: Cambridge Univ. Pr.
Mitchell, John. Out of the Dark Ages. 2008. (Illus.). 192p. pap. 27.00 *(978-0-7156-3685-5(5))* Duckworth Publishers GBR. Dist: International Publishers Marketing.
Moffitt, John F. The Enthroned Corpse of Charlemagne: The Lord-in-Majesty Theme in Early Medieval Art & Life. 2006. (ENG., Illus.). 239p. per. 39.95 *(978-0-7864-2767-3(1))* McFarland & Co., Inc. Pubs.
Morgan, Leslie Zarker, intro. & notes. La Geste Francor: Chansons de Geste of Ms. Marc. Fr. XIII (=256) 2008. *(978-0-86698-396-9(1))* Arizona State Univ., Arizona Ctr. for Medieval & Renaissance Studies.
Newth, Michael A. H. Fierabras & Floripas: A French Epic Allegory First Modern English Translation. 2010. (ENG., Illus.). 292p. pap. 20.00 *(978-1-59910-157-6(2))* Italica Pr.
Noble, Thomas F. X. Charlemagne & Louis the Pious: Lives by Einhard, Notker, Ermoldus, Thegan, & the Astronomer. 2009. (ENG., Illus.). 312p. 84.00 *(978-0-271-03573-4(0))* Pennsylvania State Univ. Pr.
Noble, Thomas F. X., tr. from LAT. Charlemagne & Louis the Pious: Lives by Einhard, Notker, Ermoldus, Thegan, & the Astronomer. 2009. (Illus.). 318p. pap. 27.95 ***(978-0-271-03715-8(6))*** Pennsylvania State Univ. Pr.
Romig, Andrew J. Charlemagne's Book on Images. 2010. (ENG.). pap. *(978-1-4426-0164-2(7))*; *(978-1-4426-0163-5(9))* Univ. of Toronto Pr.
Schwam-Baird, Shira I. Valentin et Orson: An Edition & Translation of the Fifteenth- Century Romance Epic. 2011. (FEM & ENG.). *(978-0-86698-420-1(8))* Arizona State Univ., Arizona Ctr. for Medieval & Renaissance Studies.
Sypeck, Jeff. Becoming Charlemagne: Europe, Baghdad, & the Empires of A. D. 800. 2006. (ENG., Illus.). 256p. 25.95 *(978-0-06-079706-5(1)*, Ecco) HarperCollins Pubs.
Williams, Hywel. Emperor of the West: Charlemagne & the Carolingian Empire. 2011. (ENG., Illus.). 448p. 17.95 ***(978-0-85738-162-0(8))*** Quercus GBR. Dist: Independent Pubs. Group.
Wilson, Derek. Charlemagne: Barbarian & Emperor. 2007. (Vintage Ser.). (ENG., Illus.). 256p. pap. 16.00 *(978-0-307-27480-9(2)*, Vintage) Knopf Doubleday Publishing Group.

CHARLES I, EMPEROR OF AUSTRIA, 1887-1922

Balassa, Imre. Death of an Empire. 316p. 2008. 45.95 *(978-1-4366-9637-1(2))* 2007. per. 30.95 *(978-1-4325-9681-1(0))* Kessinger Publishing, LLC.
Harding, Bertita. Imperial Twilight - the Story of Karl & Zita of Hungary. 2007. 388p. per. *(978-1-4067-1135-6(7))* Read Bks.
Uderzo, Marcel & Bourgne, Marc. Karl 1: The Emperor of Peace. 2011.Tr. of Charles 1. 56p. (YA). pap. 9.95 ***(978-1-936260-34-8(4))*** Magnificat USA LLC.

CHARLES I, KING OF ENGLAND 1600-1649

Abbott, Jacob. Charles I. 2009. 104p. pap. *(978-1-151-56027-8(8))* Books LLC.
—Charles I. 2008. (Illus.). 152p. pap. *(978-1-4099-0984-2(0))* Dodo Pr.
—Charles I. 288p. 2008. pap. *(978-1-4097-9615-2(9))* 2007. (ENG.). per. *(978-1-4067-3283-2(4))* Read Bks.
Atherton, Ian & Sanders, Julie, eds. The 1630s: Interdisciplinary Essays on Culture & Politics in the Caroline Era. 2006. (Politics, Culture, & Society in Early Modern Britain Ser.). (ENG., Illus.). 256p. 94.00 *(978-0-7190-7158-4(5))* Manchester Univ. Pr. GBR. Dist: Macmillan.
Coit, Charles Wheele. Life of Charles the First the Royal Mart. 2006. pap. 37.95 *(978-1-4286-5667-3(7))* Kessinger Publishing, LLC.
Corns, Thomas N., ed. The Royal Image: Representations of Charles I. 2009. (ENG.). 336p. pap. 42.00 *(978-0-521-11870-5(0))* Cambridge Univ. Pr.
Cust, Richard. Charles I: A Political Life. 2007. (ENG., Illus.). 512p. pap. 33.95 *(978-1-4058-5903-5(2))* Longman Publishing Group.
De Jesus, Francisco. Narrative of the Spanish Marriage Treaty. Gardiner, Samuel Rawson, tr. (Camden Society, London, Publications, First Ser.: No. 101). reprint ed. 82.50 *(978-0-404-50201-0(6))* AMS Pr., Inc.
Fox, John. The King's Smuggler: Jane Whorwood, Secret Agent to Charles I. 2010. (ENG., Illus.). 224p. 44.95 *(978-0-7524-5001-8(8))* History Pr. Ltd., The GBR. Dist: Independent Pubs. Group.
Hibbard, Caroline M. Charles I & the Popish Plot. 2011. (ENG.). 351p. pap. 30.00 *(978-0-8078-9584-6(5))* Univ. of North Carolina Pr.
Hibbert, Christopher. Charles I: A Life of Religion, War & Treason. 2nd ed. 2007. (ENG., Illus.). 304p. pap. 18.95 *(978-1-4039-8378-7(X))* Palgrave Macmillan.
Holmes, Clive. Why Was Charles I Executed? 2006. (ENG., Illus.). 264p. 65.00 *(978-1-85285-282-5(8)*, Hambledon Continuum) Continuum International Publishing Group, Ltd. GBR. Dist: National Bk. Network.
Holmes, Clive & Holmes. Why Was Charles I Executed? 2007. (ENG., Illus.). 262p. 29.95 *(978-1-84725-024-7(6)*, Hambledon Continuum) Continuum International Publishing Group, Ltd. GBR. Dist: National Bk. Network.
Knoppers, Laura Lunger. Politicizing Domesticity from Henrietta Maria to Milton's Eve. 2011. (ENG., Illus.). 240p. 95.00 ***(978-1-107-00788-3(7))*** Cambridge Univ. Pr.
Pakenham, Pansy. King Charles I. 2006. 320p. per. *(978-1-4067-2040-2(2)*, Hesperides Pr.) Read Bks.
Potter, Lois. Secret Rites & Secret Writing: Royalist Literature, 1641-1660. 2009. (ENG.). 260p. pap. 36.99 *(978-0-521-10796-9(2))* Cambridge Univ. Pr.

C

Smith, Charles Anthony. The Rise & Fall of War Crimes Trials: From Charles I to Bush II. 2012. (ENG.). 336p. 99.00 **(978-1-107-02354-3(8))** Cambridge Univ. Pr.

Wedgwood, C. V. A King Condemned: The Trial & Execution of Charles I. 2011. (ENG.). 264p. pap. 16.00 *(978-1-84885-688-2(1),* Tauris Parke Paperbacks) I. B. Tauris & Co., Ltd. GBR. Dist: Macmillan.

Whitaker, Katie. A Royal Passion: The Turbulent Marriage of King Charles I of England & Henrietta Maria of France. 2010. (ENG., Illus.). 352p. 26.95 *(978-0-393-06079-9(9),* 6079) Norton, W. W. & Co., Inc.

CHARLES II, KING OF ENGLAND, 1630-1685

Abbott, Jacob. History of King Charles II of England. 2009. 148p. pap. 7.99 *(978-1-60450-681-5(4),* Serenity Pubs.) Arc Manor.

—History of King Charles the Second: Makers of History. 2009. (ENG.). 306p. pap. 19.95 *(978-1-60520-770-4(5),* Cosimo Classics) Cosimo, Inc.

Airy, Osmund. Charles II. 2010. (ENG.). 434p. pap. 35.75 *(978-1-176-40598-1(5));* 472p. pap. 37.75 *(978-1-146-80512-4(8));* 472p. pap. 37.75 *(978-1-145-44931-2(X))* BiblioBazaar.

—Charles II. 2009. 200p. pap. *(978-0-217-80935-1(9))* Books LLC.

—Charles II. 432p. 2010. pap. 29.56 *(978-1-162-96786-8(2))* 2007. (ENG.). 51.95 *(978-0-548-11835-1(3))* Kessinger Publishing, LLC.

—Charles II. 2007. (ENG.). 428p. per. *(978-1-4067-8106-9(1))* Read Bks.

Beauclerk, Charles. Nell Gwyn: Mistress to a King. 2006. (ENG., Illus.). 448p. per. 18.00 *(978-0-8021-4274-0(5),* Grove Pr.) Grove/Atlantic, Inc.

Cunningham, Peter. The Story of Nell Gwyn & the Sayings of Charles II. 2009. 222p. 28.99 *(978-1-110-53562-0(7));* pap. 23.75 *(978-1-110-53559-0(7))* BiblioBazaar.

Falkus, Christopher. The Life & Times of Charles II. l.t. ed. 176p. 24.95 *(978-1-85695-073-2(5))* ISIS Large Print Bks. GBR. Dist: Transaction Pubs.

Jameson, Anna Brownell. Memoirs of Beauties of the Court of Charles II. reprint ed. 150.00 *(978-0-7222-1880-8(X))* Library Reprints, Inc.

Jesse, John Heneage. Charles the Second. 2006. pap. 30.95 *(978-1-4286-5977-3(3))* Kessinger Publishing, LLC.

Keay, Anna. The Magnificent Monarch: Charles II & the Ceremonies of Power. 2008. (ENG., Illus.). 336p. 39.95 *(978-1-84725-225-8(7),* Hambledon Continuum) Continuum International Publishing Group, Ltd. GBR. Dist: National Bk. Network.

Loth, David. Royal Charles Ruler & Rake. 2006. 364p. per. *(978-1-4067-3598-7(1),* Hesperides Pr.) Read Bks.

MacLeod, Catharine & Alexander, Julia Marciari, eds. Politics, Transgression, & Representation at the Court of Charles II. 2008. (Studies in British Art). (ENG., Illus.). 288p. 65.00 *(978-0-300-11656-4(X))* Yale Ctr. for British Art.

Molloy, Joseph Fitzgerald. Royalty Restored: Or London under Charles II. l.t. ed. 2007. (ENG.). 348p. pap. 24.99 *(978-1-4346-1824-5(2));* 314p. pap. 23.99 *(978-1-4346-1655-5(X))* BiblioBazaar.

Patterson, Annabel. The Long Parliament of Charles II. 2008. (ENG., Illus.). 304p. 45.00 *(978-0-300-13708-8(7))* Yale Univ. Pr.

Smith, H. F. Russell. The Theory of Religious Liberty in the Reigns of Charles II & James II. 2007. (ENG.). 150p. 36.95 *(978-0-548-04757-6(X))* Kessinger Publishing, LLC.

CHARLES V, HOLY ROMAN EMPEROR, 1500-1558

Armstrong, Edward. The Emperor Charles V. 2009. 338p. pap. *(978-0-217-07616-6(5))* Books LLC.

Armstrong, Edward A. The Emperor Charles V, 2 vols., Set. reprint ed. 155.00 *(978-0-404-19800-8(7))* AMS Pr., Inc.

Espinosa, Aurelio. The Empire of the Cities: Emperor Charles V, the Comunero Revolt, & the Transformation of the Spanish System. 2008. (Studies in Medieval & Reformation Traditions: History, Culture, Religion, Ideas). (Illus.). 368p. (C). *(978-90-04-17136-7(3))* BRILL.

Ferer, Mary Tiffany. Music & Ceremony at the Court of Charles V: The Capilla Flamenca & the Art of Political Promotion. 2012. (Studies in Medieval & Renaissance Music Ser.: Volume 12). (Illus.). 320p. 99.00 **(978-1-84383-699-5(8),** Boydell Press) Boydell & Brewer, Ltd. GBR. Dist: Boydell & Brewer, Inc.

Frieder, Braden. Chivalry & the Perfect Prince: Tournaments, Art, & Armor at the Spanish Habsburg Court. 2008. (Sixteenth Century Essays & Studies). (Illus.). 256p. 65.00 *(978-1-931112-69-7(X))* Truman State Univ. Pr.

Headley, John M. The Emperor & His Chancellor: A Study of the Imperial Chancellery under Gattinara. 2008. (Cambridge Studies in Early Modern History Ser.). (ENG.). 204p. pap. 31.99 *(978-0-521-09019-3(9))* Cambridge Univ. Pr.

McElwee, William L. The Reign of Charles V, 1516-1558. reprint ed. 36.00 *(978-0-404-19807-7(4))* AMS Pr., Inc.

Perrone, Sean T. Charles V & the Castilian Assembly of the Clergy: Negotiations for the Ecclesiastical Subsidy. 2008. (Illus.). 288p. (C). *(978-90-04-17116-9(9))* BRILL.

Reston, James, Jr. Defenders of the Faith: Christianity & Islam Battle for the Soul of Europe, 1520-1536. 2010. (ENG.). 448p. (gr. 12). 17.00 *(978-0-14-311759-9(9),* Penguin (Non-Classics)) Penguin Group (USA) Inc.

Robertson, William. The History of the Reign of the Emperor Charles the Fifth. 2006. 648p. per. 34.99 *(978-1-4255-6668-5(5))* MPublishing.

—The History of the Reign of the Emperor Charles V - with a View of the Progress of Society in Europe, from the Subversion of the Roman Empire, To. 2010. 502p. pap. 34.95 *(978-1-4460-2419-5(9))* Harrison House Pubs.

Rodriguez-Salgado, M. J. The Changing Face of Empire: Charles V, Philip II & Habsburg Authority, 1551-1559. 2008. (Cambridge Studies in Early Modern History Ser.). (ENG., Illus.). 396p. pap. 53.00 *(978-0-521-08567-0(5))* Cambridge Univ. Pr.

Rodriguez-Salgado, Mia. The Global Policy of Charles V. 2008. (ENG., Illus.). 448p. 35.00 *(978-0-300-11228-3(9))* Yale Univ. Pr.

Saen de Casas, Maria / del Carmen. La imagen literaria de Carlos V en sus cronicas Castellanas. 2009. (SPA.). ix, 289p. *(978-0-7734-3821-7(1))* Mellen, Edwin Pr., The.

Stirling Maxwell, William. Das Klosterleben Kaiser Karls des Funften. Kaiser, A., tr. from ENG. 2010.Tr. of Cloister Life of the Emperor Charles the Fifth. (GER.). 368p. pap. 33.95 *(978-1-160-36734-9(5))* Kessinger Publishing, LLC.

Stirling Maxwell, William & Kaiser, A. Das Klosterleben Kaiser Karls des Funften. 2010.Tr. of Cloister Life of the Emperor Charles the Fifth. 368p. 48.95 *(978-1-160-62462-6(3))* Kessinger Publishing, LLC.

Thomas, Hugh. The Golden Empire: Spain, Charles V, & the Creation of America. 2011. (ENG., Illus.). 672p. 35.00 *(978-1-4000-6125-9(3))* Random Hse., Inc.

Tracy, James D. Emperor Charles V, Impresario of War: Campaign Strategy, International Finance, & Domestic Politics. 2010. (ENG., Illus.). 362p. pap. 36.99 *(978-0-521-14766-8(2))* Cambridge Univ. Pr.

von Arnim, Achim. Isabella Von Gypten Kaiser Karl des Fün. 2006. (GER.). pap. *(978-1-4068-3211-2(1))* Echo Library.

Zara, Louis. Against This Rock. 2007. (ENG.). 638p. 60.95 *(978-0-548-05756-8(7))* Kessinger Publishing, LLC.

CHARLES V, KING OF FRANCE, 1338-1380

Christine, et al. Le Livre des Faits et Bonnes Murs du Roi Charles V le Sage. (FRE.). 370p. *(978-2-234-02377-2(7))* Stock, Editions.

CHARLES VI, KING OF FRANCE, 1368-1422

Adams, Tracy. The Life & Afterlife of Isabeau of Bavaria. 2010. (Rethinking Theory Ser.). (ENG., Illus.). 368p. (gr. 17). 55.00 *(978-0-8018-9625-5(8))* Johns Hopkins Univ. Pr.

CHARLES VII, KING OF FRANCE, 1403-1461

Barker, Juliet. Conquest: The English Kingdom of France 1417-1450. 2012. (Illus.). 512p. 29.95 **(978-0-674-06560-4(3))** Harvard Univ. Pr.

CHARLES X, KING OF FRANCE, 1757-1836

Hall, John Richard. The Bourbon Restoration. 2009. 466p. pap. *(978-0-217-06653-2(4))* Books LLC.

CHARLES XII, KING OF SWEDEN, 1682-1718

Adlerfelt, G., tr. The Life of Charles Xii, King of Sweden. 2007. (ENG.). 144p. 35.95 *(978-0-548-20891-5(3));* 148p. per. 20.95 *(978-1-4325-2733-4(9))* Kessinger Publishing, LLC.

Bain, R. Nisbet. Charles Xii. 2008. 404p. *(978-1-4437-2471-5(8))* 2006. 400p. per. *(978-1-4067-3116-3(1))* Read Bks. (Hesperides Pr.).

Browning, Oscar. Charles Xii of Sweden. 2008. 380p. pap. *(978-1-4097-9650-3(7))* Read Bks.

Voltaire. The Life of Charles Xii, King of Sweden: Including Memoirs of Several of the Crowned Heads of Europe (1815) 2009. 268p. 42.95 *(978-1-104-43765-7(1));* pap. 27.95 *(978-1-104-39598-8(3))* Kessinger Publishing, LLC.

CHARLES XIV JOHN, KING OF SWEDEN AND NORWAY, 1763-1844

Barton, Dunbar Plunket. Bernadotte: The First Phase, 1763-1799 (1914) 2008. 600p. 59.95 *(978-1-4366-7066-1(7));* pap. 44.95 *(978-0-548-89524-5(4))* Kessinger Publishing, LLC.

Pingaud, Léonce. Bernadotte: Napoleon et les Bourbons 1797-1844 (1901) 2009. 464p. 52.95 *(978-1-104-07425-8(7));* pap. 37.95 *(978-1-104-03962-2(1))* Kessinger Publishing, LLC.

Schefer, Christian. Bernadotte: Roi 1810-1818-1844 (1899) 2009. 304p. 43.95 *(978-1-104-07026-7(X));* pap. 28.95 *(978-1-104-03963-9(X))* Kessinger Publishing, LLC.

CHARLES, COUNT OF FLANDERS, D. 1127

Galbert Of Bruges. The Murder of Charles the Good, Count of Flanders: Records of Civilization, Sources & Studies, No. 61. Barzun, Jacques, ed. Ross, James Bruce, tr. 2011. 368p. 53.95 **(978-1-258-08643-5(3))** Literary Licensing, LLC.

Rider, Jeff & Murray, Alan V., eds. Galbert of Bruges & the Historiography of Medieval Flanders. 2009. (Illus.). 312p. (C). pap. 37.95 *(978-0-8132-1719-2(9))* Catholic Univ. of America Pr.

CHARLES, D'ORLEANS, 1394-1465

Charles, et al. Poetry of Charles D'Orléans & His Circle: A Critical Edition of BnF MS. Fr. 25458, Charles D'Orléans's Personal Manuscript. 2010. (FEM & ENG.). lxiii, 957p. *(978-0-86698-431-7(3))* MRTS.

CHARLES, DUKE OF BURGUNDY, 1433-1477

Kirk, John Foster. History of Charles the Bold, Duke of Burgundy by John Foster Kirk. 2006. 628p. pap. 34.99 *(978-1-4255-6605-0(7));* 568p. per. 32.99 *(978-1-4255-6212-0(4))* MPublishing.

Marti, Susan. Splendour of the Burgundian Court: Charles the Bold (1433-1477) Borchert, Till-Holger & Keck, Gabriele, eds. 2009. (Illus.). 384p. 80.00 *(978-0-8014-4853-9(0))* Cornell Univ. Pr.

Putnam, Ruth. Charles the Bold. 2008. 400p. 29.99 *(978-0-554-34330-3(4));* 31.99 *(978-0-554-25027-4(6))* BiblioBazaar.

—Charles the Bold. 2008. (ENG.). 392p. per. *(978-1-4065-6828-8(7))* Dodo Pr.

—Charles the Bold: Last Duke of Burgundy 1433-1477. 2007. (ENG.). 348p. pap. 23.99 *(978-1-4264-8026-3(1));* 396p. pap. 26.99 *(978-1-4264-8083-6(0))* BiblioBazaar.

Weightman, Christine. Margaret of York Diabolical Duchess. 2009. (Illus.). 208p. pap. 24.95 *(978-1-84868-099-9(6))* Amberley Publishing GBR. Dist: Casemate Pubs. & Bk. Distributors, LLC.

CHARLES, PRINCE OF WALES, 1948-

Andersen, Christopher. After Diana: William, Harry, Charles, & the Royal House of Windsor. (ENG., 352p. 2008. Illus.). mass mkt. 7.99 *(978-0-7868-9124-5(6))* 2007. 25.95 *(978-1-4013-0360-0(9))* Hyperion Pr.

Brandreth, Gyles Daubeney & Brandreth, Gyles. Charles & Camilla: Portrait of a Love Affair. 2007. (ENG., Illus.). 368p. pap. 14.95 *(978-0-09-949087-6(0),* Arrow Bks., Ltd.) Random Hse. GBR. Dist: Independent Pubs. Group.

Clayton, Martin & Leonardo. Charles, Prince of Wales: A Birthday Souvenir Album. 2008. (Illus.). 120p. *(978-1-905686-09-4(9))* Royal Collection Enterprises Ltd.

Hodgson, Howard. The King & Di: The True Story. 2009. (Illus.). 716p. pap. *(978-1-84747-674-6(0))* Chipmunkapublishing.

Roberts, Jane & Wong, Rhian. Charles Prince of Wales: A Birthday Souvenir Album. 2010. (Illus.). 120p. 15.00 *(978-1-905686-04-9(8))* Royal Collection Enterprises Ltd. GBR. Dist: Chicago Distribution Ctr.

CHARLES, RAY, 1930-2004

Evans, Mike. Ray Charles: The Birth of Soul. 2007. (ENG., Illus.). 362p. per. 17.95 *(978-1-84609-341-8(4),* OP51348) Omnibus Pr.

Mathis, Sharon Bell. Ray Charles. de La Vega, Eida, tr. from ENG. 2006. (SPA., Illus.). 40p. (J). (gr. -1-3). pap. 7.95 *(978-1-58430-281-0(X))* Lee & Low Bks., Inc.

CHARLES, THE GOOD, COUNT OF FLANDERS, D. 1127

see Charles, Count of Flanders, d. 1127

CHARLES BORROMEO, SAINT, 1538-1584

Kenny, Louise M. Stacpoole. Saint Charles Borromeo. 2009. 154p. pap. *(978-0-217-04340-3(2))* Books LLC.

Louise M. Stacpoole (Louise Mary Stacp. Saint Charles Borromeo: A Sketch of the Reforming Cardinal. 2009. 288p. 30.99 *(978-1-110-36436-7(9));* pap. 27.75 *(978-1-110-36429-9(6))* BiblioBazaar.

Stacpoole-Kenny, Louise M. Saint Charles Borromeo: A Sketch of the Reforming Cardinal (1911) 2008. 290p. 43.95 *(978-1-4365-8430-2(2))* 2007. 288p. per. 28.95 *(978-0-548-80001-0(4))* Kessinger Publishing, LLC.

CHARLES EDWARD, PRINCE, GRANDSON OF JAMES II, KING OF ENGLAND, 1720-1788

Cooke, Charlie & Knight, Martin. The Bonnie Prince: Charlie Cooke - My Football Life. 2007. (ENG., Illus.). 331p. pap. 15.95 *(978-1-84596-227-2(3))* Mainstream Publishing Co., Ltd. GBR. Dist: Independent Pubs. Group.

Crummy, Andrew. The Prestonpans Tapestry. 2010. (Illus.). 272p. 50.00 *(978-0-85011-121-7(8));* pap. 34.95 *(978-0-85011-122-4(6))* Burke's Peerage & Gentry (UK) Ltd. GBR. Dist: Boydell & Brewer, Inc.

De La Tremoille, Duc. Royalist Family Irish & French 1689178. 2006. pap. 20.95 *(978-1-4286-6341-1(X))* Kessinger Publishing, LLC.

Duffy, Christopher. The '45: Bonnie Prince Charlie & the Untold Story of the Jacobite Rising. 2007. (Illus.). 639p. per. 22.95 *(978-0-7538-2262-3(8),* Phoenix) Orion Publishing Group, Ltd. GBR. Dist: Sterling Publishing Co., Inc.

Jesse, John Heneage. Memoirs of the Pretenders & Their Adherents. 2009. 422p. 34.99 *(978-1-115-95322-1(2));* 41.99 *(978-1-115-95321-4(4));* pap. 35.75 *(978-1-115-95323-8(0));* pap. 34.75 *(978-1-115-95324-5(9))* BiblioBazaar.

—Memoirs of the Pretenders & Their Adherents. 2009. 144p. pap. *(978-0-217-73187-4(2))* Books LLC.

Lang, Andrew. Pickle the Spy. 2009. 380p. 33.99 *(978-1-115-35080-8(3))* 2009. 380p. 38.99 *(978-1-115-35081-5(1))* 2009. 380p. pap. 33.75 *(978-1-115-35077-8(3))* 2008. 260p. 25.99 *(978-0-554-33077-8(6))* 2008. 260p. 28.99 *(978-0-554-23774-9(1))* BiblioBazaar.

—Pickle the Spy. 2009. 244p. pap. *(978-1-4588-4189-6(8))* Books LLC.

—Pickle the Spy. 2009. (CAM.). 212p. pap. 14.95 *(978-1-4385-7389-2(8),* Book Jungle) Standard Pubns., Inc.

—Pickle the Spy... 2009. 379p. (ENG.). pap. 26.99 *(978-1-115-35073-0(0));* pap. 25.99 *(978-1-115-35071-6(4))* BiblioBazaar. (BiblioLife).

—Pickle the Spy. 2010. 214p. pap. 19.96 *(978-1-162-67972-3(7));* 39.95 *(978-1-161-44837-5(3))* Kessinger Publishing, LLC.

—Pickle the Spy: Or, the Incognito of Prince Charles. 2007. 230p. pap. 20.99 *(978-1-4264-5007-5(9))* BiblioBazaar.

—Pickle the Spy: Or, the Incognito of Prince Charles. 2010. 164p. pap. *(978-1-151-78164-2(9))* Books LLC.

—Pickle the Spy: Or, the Incognito of Prince Charles. 2007. 216p. per. *(978-1-4065-2638-7(X))* Dodo Pr.

—Pickle the Spy: Or, the Incognito of Prince Charles. 2009. 208p. pap. 25.57 *(978-1-150-99409-8(6))* General Bks. LLC.

—Pickle the Spy: Or, the Incognito of Prince Charles. 2008. 384p. 48.95 *(978-1-4372-5982-7(0));* 380p. pap. 33.95 *(978-1-4371-3290-8(1))* Kessinger Publishing, LLC.

—Pickle the Spy: Or, the Incognito of Prince Charles. 2008. 380p. pap. *(978-1-4086-9096-3(9))* Read Bks.

—Pickle the Spy: Or, the Incognito of Prince Charles. 2010. 386p. pap. 33.75 *(978-1-146-54282-1(8))* BiblioBazaar.

—Pickle the Spy: Or, the Incognito of Prince Charles. 2010. (ENG.). 408p. pap. 34.75 *(978-1-178-02824-9(0))* BiblioBazaar.

—Pickle the Spy: Or, the Incognito of Prince Charles. l.t. ed. 2007. 256p. pap. 23.99 *(978-1-4264-5308-3(6))* BiblioBazaar.

—Pickle the Spy or the Incognito of Prince Charles. 2010. 394p. pap. 33.75 *(978-1-146-04738-8(X))* BiblioBazaar.

—Pickle the Spy; or, the Incognito of Prince Charles. 2010. 388p. pap. 33.75 *(978-1-144-13000-6(X));* 406p. pap. 34.75 *(978-1-141-88639-5(1));* 394p. pap. 33.75 *(978-1-142-84428-8(5))* BiblioBazaar.

—Pickle the Spy; or, the Incognito of Prince Charles. 2010. (Illus.). 144p. pap. 23.19 *(978-1-153-67751-6(2))* General Bks. LLC.

—Pickle the Spy, or, the Incognito of Prince Charles. 2010. 390p. pap. 33.75 *(978-1-177-81249-8(5))* BiblioBazaar.

—Prince Charles Edward Stuart: The Young Chevalier. reprint ed. 105.00 *(978-0-404-03855-7(7))* AMS Pr., Inc.

Pininski, Peter. Heigham Through Time. 2010. (ENG., Illus.). 256p. 34.95 *(978-1-84868-194-1(1))* Amberley Publishing GBR. Dist: Casemate Pubs. & Bk. Distributors, LLC.

Schuchard, Marsha Keith. Emanuel Swedenborg, Secret Agent on Earth & in Heaven: Jacobites, Jews & Freemasons in Early Modern Sweden. 2011. (Northern World Ser.). (Illus.). 832p. **(978-90-04-18312-4(4))** BRILL.

CHARLES EDWARD, THE YOUNG PRETENDER, 1720-1788

see Charles Edward, Prince, Grandson of James II, King of England, 1720-1788

CHARLES LE BON, COUNT OF FLANDERS, D. 1127

see Charles, Count of Flanders, d. 1127

CHARLES LE TEMERAIRE, DUKE OF BURGUNDY, 1433-1477

see Charles, Duke of Burgundy, 1433-1477

CHARLES SCRIBNER'S SONS

Trogdon, Robert W. The Lousy Racket: Hemingway, Scribners, & the Business of Literature. 2007. 307p. 39.95 *(978-0-87338-904-4(2))* Kent State Univ. Pr.

CHARLES UNIVERSITY

see Univerzita Karlova

CHARLESTON (S.C.)

American Map. Charleston: South Carolina. 2008. 160p. 16.95 *(978-0-8416-1065-1(7))* American Map Corp.

Rubin Jr., Louis D. Uptown/Downtown in Old Charleston: Sketches & Stories. 2010. 128p. 29.95 *(978-1-57003-909-6(7))* Univ. of South Carolina Pr.

Worthington, Curtis, ed. Literary Charleston & the Lowcountry. 2nd ed. 2012. (Literary Cities Ser.). (ENG.). 352p. pap. 16.95 *(978-1-59534-079-5(3))* Trinity Univ. Pr.

CHARLESTON (S.C.)—DESCRIPTION AND TRAVEL

Baldwin, William P. Charleston Impressions. 2011. 112p. 23.95 **(978-0-933101-27-2(9))** Legacy Pubns.

Baldwin, William P., ed. Ornamental Ironwork of Charleston. 2007. (Illus.). 191p. pap., per. 14.99 *(978-1-59629-367-0(5))* History Pr., The.

Becker, Ida A. Charleston Icons: 50 Symbols of the Holy City. 2009. (Icons Ser.). (ENG., Illus.). 112p. 16.95 *(978-0-7627-4799-3(4))* Globe Pequot Pr., The.

A Charleston Christmas: Low Country Traditions. (Orig.). pap. *(978-1-56944-057-5(3))* Terrell Creative.

Coker, Mike. Charleston Curiosities: Stories of the Tragic, Heroic, & Bizarre. 2008. pap. 17.99 *(978-1-59629-511-7(2))* History Pr., The.

Herrick, Holly. Food Lovers' Guide to Charleston & Savannah: Best Local Specialties, Markets, Recipes, Restaurants, Events & More. 2011. (Food Lovers' Ser.). (ENG.). 264p. pap. 14.95 *(978-0-7627-6012-1(5))* Globe Pequot Pr., The.

Historic Homes of Charleston. *(978-1-56944-008-7(5))* Terrell Creative.

McEaddy, T. Hunter & McEaddy, Catherine P. Historic Charleston Gardens. 2007. (Images of America Ser.). (ENG., Illus.). 128p. per. 19.99 *(978-0-7385-5278-1(X))* Arcadia Publishing.

Salater, Michelle. Charleston, South Carolina: A Photographic Portrait. 2008. (ENG., Illus.). 128p. 26.95 *(978-1-885435-94-1(0))* Twin Lights Pubs., Inc.

Smith, Alice R. Huger. The Dwelling Houses of Charleston, South Carolina. 2007. 256p. pap. 24.99 *(978-1-59629-261-1(X))* History Pr., The.

Station 18: Sailing on & around Charleston Harbour. 2007. 9.95 net. *(978-0-9786170-0-4(2))* Baker, Robert S.

Wooten, Bayard & Stoney, Samuel G. Charleston: Azaleas & Old Bricks. (Illus.). 147p. reprint ed. lib. bdg. 88.00 *(978-0-7222-0561-7(9))* Library Reprints, Inc.

CHARLESTON (S.C.)—GUIDEBOOKS

Cannon, Gwen, et al. Must Sees Charleston Savannah Sc Coast Michelin. 2009. (Must Sees Ser.). (ENG., Illus.). 192p. pap. 11.99 *(978-1-906261-66-5(0))* Michelin Travel & Lifestyle.

Dodge, Jeff. Photographing Charleston, Savannah & the Coastal Islands: Where to Find Perfect Shots & How to Take Them. 2011. (Photographer's Guide Ser.). (ENG., Illus.). 112p. pap. 16.95 *(978-0-88150-921-2(3),* 150921) Countryman Pr.

Fodor's Travel Publications, Inc. Staff. Charleston: With Hilton Head & the Lowcountry. 2nd ed. 2011. (In Focus Ser.). (ENG., Illus.). 240p. pap. 10.99 *(978-1-4000-0527-7(2),* Fodor's) Fodor's Travel Pubns.

Herrick, Holly. The Charleston Chef's Table: Extraordinary Recipes from the Heart of the Old South. 2009. (ENG., Illus.). 208p. 24.95 *(978-0-7627-5010-8(3))* Three Forks Pr.

Historic Homes of Charleston. pap. *(978-1-56944-007-0(7))* Terrell Creative.

Mazyck, Arthur. Guide to Charleston Illustrated. 2006. (Illus.). 244p. per. 20.99 *(978-1-4255-2033-5(2))* MPublishing.

McMillan, Cecily. Charleston, Savannah & the Coastal Islands - An Explorer's Guide: A Great Destination. 7th ed. 2011. (Explorer's Guides). (ENG., Illus.). 216p. pap. 19.95 *(978-1-58157-130-1(5),* 157130) Countryman Pr.

Middleton, Mary. Go Local Charleston: The Parent's Guide for Children's Activities in Charleston, SC. 2010th ed. 2010. pap. 14.95 *(978-0-615-33687-9(6))* Backroads Publishing, LLC.

Moore, Margaret. Complete Charleston: A Guide to the Architecture, History, Gardens & Food of Charleston, 1. 4th ed. 2007. (Illus.). 324p. (YA). per. *(978-0-9660144-3-3(X))* TM Photography, Inc.

Morekis, Jim. Moon Charleston & Savannah. (Moon Handbooks Ser.). (ENG.). 2012. 400p. pap. 17.99 *(978-1-61238-344-6(0))* 2010. (Illus.). 404p. pap. 17.95 *(978-1-59880-641-0(6))* Avalon Travel Publishing.
Morekis, Jim. Moon Spotlight Charleston & the South Carolina Lowcountry. 2010. (Moon Spotlight Ser.). (ENG.). 184p. pap. 9.95 *(978-1-59880-680-9(7))* Avalon Travel Publishing.
Phillips, Ted Ashton, Jr. & Brown, Thomas J. City of the Silent: The Charlestonians of Magnolia Cemetery. 2010. 216p. 39.95 *(978-1-57003-872-3(4))* Univ. of South Carolina Pr.
Porter, Darwin & Prince, Danforth. Frommer's Portable Charleston. 5th ed. 2011. (Frommer's Portable Ser.: 265). (ENG., Illus.). 192p. pap. 12.99 *(978-0-470-88731-8(1),* Frommers) Wiley, John & Sons, Inc.
Rand McNally, creator. Rand Mcnally Greater Charleston Street Guide. 3rd ed. 2008. (Rand Mcnally Greater Charleston Street Guide Ser.). (Illus.). pap. 16.95 *(978-0-528-87056-9(4))* Rand McNally.
Rocz, Ron A. Seeing Charleston: A Field Guide to Photographing a World-Class City. 2007. (Illus.). 142p. per. 19.95 *(978-0-9753498-4-7(8))* Joggling Board Pr.

CHARLESTON (S.C.)—HISTORY

Borick, Carl P. Relieve Us of This Burthen: American Prisoners of War in the Revolutionary South, 1780-1782. 2012. (ENG.). 192p. 29.95 *(978-1-61117-039-9(7))* Univ. of South Carolina Pr.
Calhoun, Joanne. The Circular Church: Three Centuries of Charleston History. 2008. (Illus.). 191p. pap. 21.99 *(978-1-59629-359-5(4))* History Pr., The.
Carroon, Robert G., ed. Provost Marshal of Charleston: The Letter Book of Colonel Alexander Haskell Brown, Provost Marshal of Charleston. 2007. cd-rom 15.00 *(978-0-9791000-3-1(8))* Between the Lakes Group, LLC.
Coker, Mike. Charleston Curiosities: Stories of the Tragic, Heroic, & Bizarre. 2008. pap. 17.99 *(978-1-59629-511-7(2))* History Pr., The.
Crooks, Daniel J. Charleston Is Burning! Two Decades of Fire & Flames. 2009. (Disasters Ser.). (ENG., Illus.). 128p. pap. 19.99 *(978-1-59629-635-0(6))* History Pr., The.
Eastman, Margaret, et al. Hidden History of Old Charleston. 2010. (Hidden Histories Ser.). 128p. pap. 19.99 *(978-1-59629-843-9(X))* History Pr., The.
Eastman, Margaret M. R. Remembering Old Charleston: A Peek Behind Parlor Doors. 2008. pap. 17.99 *(978-1-59629-559-9(7))* History Pr., The.
Eastman, Margaret Rivers. Old Charleston Originals: From Celebrities to Scoundrels. 2011. (Illus.). 160p. pap. 19.99 ***(978-1-60949-252-6(8))*** History Pr., The.
Greene, Harlan, et al. Slave Badges & the Slave-Hire System in Charleston, South Carolina, 1783-1865. alt. ed. 2008. (ENG.). 208p. pap. 35.00 *(978-0-7864-4090-0(2))* McFarland & Co., Inc. Pubs.
Hart, Emma. Building Charleston: Town & Society in the Eighteenth-Century British Atlantic World. 2009. (ENG., Illus.). 288p. (gr. 17). 45.00 *(978-0-8139-2867-8(2))* Univ. Pr. of Virginia.
Hendrix, M. Patrick. Down & Dirty: Archaeology of the South Carolina Lowcountry. 2007. (Illus.). 168p. pap., per. 24.99 *(978-1-59629-092-1(7))* History Pr., The.
Iorio, Richard, 2nd. Colonial Gothic: The Grimoire. Carroll, Sean, ed. 2011. (Illus.). 120p. pap. 10.99 ***(978-0-9826598-5-4(7))*** Rogue Games, Inc.
Kean, Virginia, ed. Noisette Roses: Nineteenth-Century Charleston's Gift to the World. 2010. (Distributed for the Charleston Horticultural Society Ser.). pap. 17.00 *(978-0-615-25111-0(0))* Univ. of South Carolina Pr.
McCray, Jack. Charleston Jazz. 2007. (ENG., Illus.). 128p. per. 19.99 *(978-0-7385-4350-5(0))* Arcadia Publishing.
Mcqueeney, E. Thomas. The Rise of Charleston: Conversations with Visionaries, Luminaries & Emissaries of the Holy City. 2011. (Illus.). 320p. 24.99 ***(978-1-60949-479-7(2))*** History Pr., The.
Moore, Margaret. Complete Charleston: A Guide to the Architecture, History, Gardens & Food of Charleston. 1. 4th ed. 2007. (Illus.). 324p. (YA). per. *(978-0-9660144-3-3(X))* TM Photography, Inc.
Orr, Bruce. Six Miles to Charleston: The True Story of John & Lavinia Fisher. 2010. (ENG., Illus.). 128p. pap. 19.99 *(978-1-60949-117-8(3))* History Pr., The.
Ragan, Mark K. The Hunley. 2006. (ENG., Illus.). 360p. per. *(978-0-87844-177-8(8))* Sandlapper Publishing Co., Inc.
Ryan, William R. The World of Thomas Jeremiah: Charles Town on the Eve of the American Revolution. 1 vol. 2012. (ENG., Illus.). 282p. pap. 24.95 ***(978-0-19-992287-1(X))*** Oxford Univ. Pr., Inc.
Ryan, William Randolph. The World of Thomas Jeremiah: Charles Town on the Eve of the American Revolution. 1 vol. 2010. (ENG., Illus.). 280p. 49.95 *(978-0-19-538728-5(7))* Oxford Univ. Pr., Inc.
Scott, Robie, ed. Our Charleston: Lowcountry Photos, People & Places, Vol. 1. 2007. (Illus.). 168p. 35.95 *(978-1-929647-10-1(7))* Evening Post Publishing Co.
Scott, Robie & Evening Post Publishing Company Staff, eds. Our Charleston: Lowcountry Photos, People & Places, Vol. 2. 2008. (Illus.). 168p. 29.95 *(978-0-615-25271-1(0))* Evening Post Publishing Co.
Smith, Daniel M., Jr., text. African-Americans & Charleston: Histories Intertwined. 2010. (Illus.). ix, 113p. ***(978-0-615-36805-4(0))*** Independent Pub.
Trouche, Michael. The Charm of Charleston: Stories of the South Carolina Lowcountry. 2007.Tr. of Charm of Charleston. 96p. 39.95 *(978-0-9777138-6-8(5))*; 26.95 *(978-0-9777138-4-4(9))*; pap. 16.95 *(978-0-9777138-5-1(7))* Charleston Postcard Co., Inc.
Williams, Susan Millar & Hoffius, Stephen G. Upheaval in Charleston: Earthquake & Murder on the Eve of Jim Crow. 2011. (ENG., Illus.). 392p. 29.95 *(978-0-8203-3715-9(3))* Univ. of Georgia Pr.

CHARLESTON (S.C.)—HISTORY—CIVIL WAR, 1861-1865

Bostick, Douglas W. Charleston under Siege: The Impregnable City. 2010. (Civil War Sesquicentennial Ser.). (ENG., Illus.). 160p. pap. 19.99 *(978-1-59629-757-9(3))* History Pr., The.
Doubleday, Abner. Reminiscences of Forts Sumter & Moultrie in 1860-'61, by Abner Doubleday. 2006. 196p. per. 18.99 *(978-1-4255-1589-8(4))* MPublishing.
Emerson, W. Eric. Sons of Privilege. 2011. (ENG.). 208p. pap. 19.95 *(978-1-61117-010-8(9))* Univ. of South Carolina Pr.
[French, Justus Clement]. The Trip of the Steamer Oceanus to Fort Sumter & Charleston, S C. 2006. 188p. per. 18.99 *(978-1-4255-1508-9(8))* MPublishing.
Mehrländer, Andrea. The Germans of Charleston, Richmond & New Orleans During the Civil War Period, 1850-1870: A Study & Research Compendium. 2011. (ENG., Illus.). XIV, 442p. 182.00 ***(978-3-11-023688-0(5))*** De Gruyter, Walter Inc.
Rosen, Robert N. Confederate Charleston. 2011. 180p. pap. 24.95 *(978-1-61117-009-2(5))* Univ. of South Carolina Pr.
Rosen, Robert N. & Hatcher III, Richard W. The First Shot. 2011. (Images of America Ser.). (Illus.). 128p. pap. 24.99 *(978-0-7385-8242-9(5))* Arcadia Publishing.

CHARLESTOWN (BOSTON, MASS.)—HISTORY

Adams, Jim. The Immortal Tavern. 2008. 216p. pap. 12.95 *(978-1-4327-1943-2(2))* Outskirts Pr., Inc.

CHARLOTTE, CONSORT OF GEORGE III, KING OF GREAT BRITAIN, 1744-1818

Delany. Autobiography & Correspondence of Mary Granville -, Vol. 1. 2007. 632p. per. *(978-1-4067-5344-8(0))* Read Bks.
Granville, Mar. The Autobiography & Correspondence of Mary Granville. 2008. 596p. 33.99 *(978-0-559-87541-0(X))*; pap. 43.75 *(978-0-559-87539-7(8))* BiblioBazaar.
Granville, Mary. Autobiography & Correspondence of Mary Granville V1. Llanover, Lady, ed. 2008. 634p. 60.95 *(978-1-4365-9888-0(5))* 2007. (ENG.). 636p. per. 45.95 *(978-0-548-80294-6(7))* Kessinger Publishing, LLC.
Llanover, Lady, ed. The Autobiography & Correspondence of Mary Granville, Mrs Delany V2: With Interesting Reminiscences of King George the Third & Queen Charlotte. 2007. 640p. 60.95 *(978-0-548-33523-9(0))*; (ENG.). per. 45.95 *(978-1-4326-9429-6(4))* Kessinger Publishing, LLC.
Oulton, Walley Chamberlain. Authentic & Impartial Memoirs of Her Late Majesty, Charlotte: Queen of Great Britain & Ireland (1819) 2008. 492p. 53.95 *(978-1-4370-0766-4(X))*; pap. 38.95 *(978-1-4367-8379-8(8))* Kessinger Publishing, LLC.
Papendiek. Court & Private Life in the Time of Queen Charlotte V2: Being the Journals of Mrs. Papendiek, Assistant Keeper of the Wardrobe & Reader to Her Maj. Broughton, Vernon Delves, ed. 2008. 344p. 46.95 *(978-1-4369-7641-1(3))*; pap. 31.95 *(978-1-4368-1534-5(7))* Kessinger Publishing, LLC.

CHARLOTTE, CONSORT OF MAXIMILIAN, EMPEROR OF MEXICO, 1840-1927

see Carlota, Empress, Consort of Maximilian, Emperor of Mexico, 1840-1927

CHARLOTTE, OF WALES, PRINCESS OF GREAT BRITAIN, 1796-1817

see Charlotte Augusta, Princess Of Great Britain, 1796-1817

CHARLOTTE, PRINCESS OF WALES, 1796-1817

see Charlotte Augusta, Princess Of Great Britain, 1796-1817

CHARLOTTE (N.C.)

ADC. Atlas Charlotte Greater Nc Atlas. 2007. 300p. 39.95 *(978-0-87530-820-3(1))* ADC The Map People.
ADC, the Map People Staff, creator. ADC Charlotte Mecklenburg County North Carolina Street Atlas. 6th ed. 2007. (Illus.). 108p. 12.95 *(978-0-87530-908-8(9))* ADC The Map People.
Claiborne, Jack. Of Pleasures & Power: The Story of the Charlotte City Club. 2007. (Illus.). vi, 158p. *(978-1-4243-2822-2(5))* Survival in College Pr.
Davis, Jennifer. Best Hikes near Charlotte. 2011. (Best Hikes near Ser.). (ENG., Illus.). 256p. pap. 18.95 *(978-0-7627-7148-6(8),* Falcon Guides) Globe Pequot Pr., The.
Flono, Fannie. Thriving in the Shadows: The Black Experience in Charlotte & Mecklenburg County. 2007. (Illus.). 152p. *(978-0-9760963-8-2(2))* Novello Festival Pr.
Greenawalt, Greg. Destination Charlotte: The Book. Rindoks, Leslie, ed. 2010. (Illus.). 268p. 29.95 *(978-0-9826171-5-1(1))* Lorimer Pr.
Helmer, Jodi. Charlotte: Including Nascar Country. 2010. (Moon Handbooks Ser.). (ENG., Illus.). 256p. pap. 16.95 *(978-1-59880-366-2(2))* Avalon Travel Publishing.
Hoffman, James L. Day Trips from Charlotte: Getaway Ideas for the Local Traveler. 2011. (Day Trips Ser.). (ENG.). 256p. pap. 14.95 *(978-0-7627-7306-0(5))* Globe Pequot Pr., The.
Moore, David. Charlotte: Murder, Mystery & Mayhem. 2008. pap. 19.99 *(978-1-59629-490-5(6))* History Pr., The.
Penry, Jerry. Down in Charlotte: The Plane, the Train, & the Burning Broom. 2008. (Illus.). 68p. per. 9.95 net. *(978-0-9679041-2-2(9))* Blue Mound Pr.
Pressley Clinard, Leigh & Distl, Craig. Charlotte. 11th ed. 2010. (Insiders' Guide Ser.). (ENG., Illus.). 320p. pap. 18.95 *(978-0-7627-5312-3(9),* Insiders' Guide) Globe Pequot Pr., The.
Rindoks, Leslie Rindoks, ed. Destination Charlotte: The Book. 2010. (Illus.). 268p. pap. 19.95 *(978-0-9826171-3-7(X))* Lorimer Pr.
Sumner, Ryan. Historic Photos of Charlotte. 2006. (Historic Photos Ser.). (ENG., Illus.). 205p. 39.95 *(978-1-59652-282-4(8))* Turner Publishing Co.
Williams, Stephanie Burt. Wicked Charlotte: The Sordid Side of the Queen City. 2006. (Wicked Ser.). (ENG., Illus.). 96p. pap. 19.99 *(978-1-59629-160-7(5))* History Pr., The.

CHARLOTTE AUGUSTA, PRINCESS OF GREAT BRITAIN, 1796-1817

Anonymous & Anonymous. Autobiography of Miss Cornelia Knight, Lady Companion to the Princess Charlotte of Wales, with Extracts from Her Journals & Anecdote Books. 2010. 362p. 38.99 *(978-1-140-18261-0(7))*; pap. 32.75 *(978-1-140-18262-7(5))* BiblioBazaar.
Chambers, James. Charlotte & Leopold: The True Story of the Original People's Princess. 2008. (ENG., Illus.). 256p. 24.95 *(978-1-905847-23-5(8))* Old Street Publishing GBR. Dist: Consortium Bk. Sales & Distribution.
Green, Thomas. Memoirs of Her Late Royal Highness Charlotte-Augusta of Wales, & of Saxe-Coburg to Which Is Prefixed, a Concise History of the Illustrious. 2010. 312p. pap. 38.88 *(978-1-152-40989-7(1))* General Bks. LLC.
—Memoirs of Her Late Royal Highness Charlotte-Augusta of Wales, & of Saxe-Coburg to Which Is Prefixed, a Concise History of the Illustrious House. 2010. 610p. pap. 45.75 *(978-1-171-84932-2(X))* BiblioBazaar.
Huish, Robert. Memoirs of Her Late Royal Highness Charlotte Augusta, Princess of Wales; 2010. (Illus.). 456p. pap. 29.69 *(978-1-151-00231-0(3))* General Bks. LLC.
—Memoirs of Her Late Royal Highness Charlotte Augusta, Princess of Wales: And etc. (from Infancy to... Her... Death, Funeral Rites, & etc. & etc.) & of H. 2010. 886p. pap. 59.75 *(978-1-174-63338-6(7))* BiblioBazaar.
—Memoirs of Her Late Royal Highness Charlotte Augusta, Princess of Wales, Etc: From Infancy to the Period of Her Much Lamented Death, Funeral Rites, E. 2008. 728p. 65.95 *(978-1-4372-8195-8(8))*; pap. 50.95 *(978-1-4371-5758-1(0))* Kessinger Publishing, LLC.
Huish, Robert, ed. A Sacred Memorial of Her Late Royal Highness Charlotte Augusta, Princess of Wales, & of Saxe-Coburg Saalfeld. 2008. 144p. 35.95 *(978-1-4371-8577-5(0))*; pap. 20.95 *(978-1-4370-5456-9(0))* Kessinger Publishing, LLC.
Jones, C. Rachel. The Princess Charlotte of Wales. 2009. 96p. pap. *(978-0-217-60430-7(7))* Books LLC.
—The Princess Charlotte of Wales: An Illustrated Monograph. 2010. 240p. pap. 26.75 *(978-1-144-51631-2(5))* BiblioBazaar.
Knight, Cornelia. Autobiography of Miss Cornelia Knight, Lady Companion to the Princess Charlotte of Wales, with Extracts from Her Journals & Anecdote Books. 2010. 160p. pap. *(978-1-152-81450-9(8))* Books LLC.
—Autobiography of Miss Cornelia Knight, Lady Companion to the Princess Charlotte of Wales, with Extracts from Her Journals & Anecdote Books. 2010. 174p. pap. 26.06 *(978-1-152-81452-3(4))* General Bks. LLC.
Knight, Ellis Cornelia. Autobiography of Miss Cornelia Knight: Lady Companion to the Princess Charlotte of Wales, with Extracts from Her Journals & Anecdote Books ... 2010. 398p. pap. 33.75 *(978-1-147-16398-8(7))*; 368p. pap. 32.75 *(978-1-144-01570-9(7))* BiblioBazaar.
—Autobiography of Miss Cornelia Knight, Lady Companion to the Princess Charlotte of Wales. 2008. 360p. 29.99 *(978-0-559-40191-6(4))*; pap. 31.75 *(978-0-559-40187-9(6))* BiblioBazaar.
—Autobiography of Miss Cornelia Knight, Lady Companion to the Princess Charlotte of Wales. 2009. 178p. pap. 19.99 *(978-1-150-10671-2(9))* General Bks. LLC.
—Autobiography of Miss Cornelia Knight, Lady Companion to the Princess Charlotte of Wales: With Extra. 2009. 364p. 33.99 *(978-1-110-02505-3(X))*; pap. 31.75 *(978-1-110-02502-2(5))* BiblioBazaar.
—Autobiography of Miss Cornelia Knight, Lady Companion to the Princess Charlotte of Wales: with Extra. 2009. 362p. pap. 25.99 *(978-1-110-02499-5(1))* (ENG.). pap. 26.99 *(978-1-110-02500-8(9))* BiblioBazaar. (BiblioLife).
—Autobiography of Miss Cornelia Knight, Lady Companion to the Princess Charlotte of Wales, with Extracts from Her Journals And. 2010. 168p. pap. 20.65 *(978-1-154-19663-4(1))* General Bks. LLC.
—Autobiography of Miss Cornelia Knight; Lady Companion to the Princess Charlotte of Wales, with Extracts from Her Journals And. 2010. (Illus.). 166p. pap. 19.99 *(978-1-154-30540-1(6))* General Bks. LLC.
—Autobiography of Miss Cornelia Knight; Lady Companion to the Princess Charlotte of Wales, with Extracts from Her Journals & Anecdote Books. 2009. 186p. pap. *(978-1-150-06096-0(4))* Books LLC.
—Autobiography of Miss Cornelia Knight V2: Lady Companion to the Princess Charlotte of Wales, with Extracts from Her Journals & Anecdote Books (1861) 2008. 392p. 48.95 *(978-1-4369-9089-9(0))*; pap. 33.95 *(978-1-4367-8405-4(0))* Kessinger Publishing, LLC.
Memoirs of Her Late Royal Highness Charlotte-Augusta of Wales, & of Saxe-Cobourg. 2009. (Illus.). 332p. pap. *(978-1-150-46049-4(0))* Books LLC.
Pearce, Charles E. The Beloved Princess, Princess Charlotte of Wales. 2010. 228p. pap. *(978-1-151-91305-0(7))* Books LLC.
Williams, Kate. Becoming Queen Victoria: The Tragic Death of Princess Charlotte & the Unexpected Rise of Britain's Greatest Monarch. 2010. (ENG., Illus.). 464p. 30.00 *(978-0-345-46195-7(9),* Ballantine Bks.) Random House Publishing Group.

CHARLOTTESVILLE (VA.)

Brennan, Eryn S. & Maliszewski, Margaret. Charlottesville. 2011. (Images of America Ser.). (Illus.). 128p. pap. 21.99 *(978-0-7385-8228-3(X))* Arcadia Publishing.
Butterfield, Katherine Walker. Teach Them Diligently: A Centennial History of St. Anne's-Belfield School, Charlottesville, Virginia. 2010. *(978-1-57864-617-3(0))* Donning Co. Pubs.
Cooper, Jean L. A Guide to Historic Charlottesville & Albemarle County, Virginia. 2007. pap. 19.99 *(978-1-59629-173-7(7))* History Pr., The.

CHARM

Ascroft, Eileen. The Magic Key to Charm: Instructions for a Delightful Life. 2009. (ENG., Illus.). 138p. 23.95 *(978-0-09-951823-5(6))* Random Hse. GBR. Dist: Independent Pubs. Group.
Christy, Jordan. How to Be a Hepburn in a Hilton World: The Art of Living with Style, Class, & Grace. 2009. (ENG.). 208p. 16.99 *(978-1-59995-183-6(5))* Center St.
de Lesseps, Countess LuAnn. Class with the Countess: How to Live with Elegance & Flair. 2009. (ENG.). 272p. (gr. 12-18). 15.00 *(978-1-59240-520-6(7),* Gotham) Penguin Group (USA) Inc.
Del Nevo, Matthew. The Work of Enchantment. 2011. (ENG.). 178p. 34.95 *(978-1-4128-1860-5(5))* Transaction Pubs.
Karolyi, Julia. C. H. A. R. m: How to Make Your World a More Beautiful Place. 2010. (ENG., Illus.). 191p. pap. 14.95 *(978-0-9822583-1-6(3))* Continental Shelf Publishing.

CHARMS

see also Amulets; Birthstones; Talismans

Alexander, Skye. Everything Spells & Charms Book: Cast Incantations That Will Bring You Love, Success, & Good Health. 2nd ed. 2008. (ENG., Illus.). 320p. per. 15.95 *(978-1-59869-386-7(7))* Adams Media Corp.
—Good Spells for Bad Days: Broken Hearts, Bounced Checks, & Bitchy Co-Workers - Simple Magick to Fix Any Misfortune. 2009. (ENG.). 240p. pap. 9.95 *(978-1-60550-131-4(X))* Adams Media Corp.
Beth, Rae. Spellcraft for Hedge Witches: A Guide to Healing Our Lives. 2009. (ENG., Illus.). 176p. pap. 12.95 *(978-0-7090-8618-5(0))* Hale, Robert Ltd. GBR. Dist: Independent Pubs. Group.
Bratley, George H. The Power of Gems & Charms. 2009. 110p. pap. 14.14 *(978-1-150-30189-6(9))* General Bks. LLC.
—The Power of Gems & Charms. 2009. 212p. 39.95 *(978-1-104-34081-0(X))*; pap. 24.95 *(978-1-104-32269-4(2))* Kessinger Publishing, LLC.
Bruce, Marie. The Witch's Almanac 2007: Practical Magic & Spells for Every Season. 2006. (ENG., Illus.). 224p. per. *(978-0-572-03272-2(2))* Foulsham, W. Co., Ltd.
—The Witch's Almanac 2010: Practical Magic & Spells for Every Season. 2009. (ENG., Illus.). 224p. pap. 19.95 *(978-0-572-03524-2(1))* Foulsham, W. Co., Ltd. GBR. Dist: APG Sales & Distribution Services.
Daimler, Morgan. Selected Charms from the Carmina Gadelica. 2010. (ENG.). 108p. pap. 12.50 *(978-0-557-37762-6(5))* Lulu Enterprises Inc.
Davies, Owen. Grimoires: A History of Magic Books. 2010. (ENG., Illus.). 384p. pap. 27.95 *(978-0-19-959004-9(4))* Oxford Univ. Pr., Inc.
Dugan, Ellen. Book of Witchery: Spells, Charms & Correspondences for Every Day of the Week. 2009. (ENG.). 360p. pap. 19.95 *(978-0-7387-1584-1(0))* Llewellyn Pubns.
Hardie, Titania. Health & Happiness: Titania's Spell Cards. 16.95 *(978-1-55285-289-7(X))* Whitecap Bks., Ltd. CAN. Dist: Graphic Arts Ctr. Publishing Co.
—Hocus Pocus: Titania's Book of Spells. (Illus.). 120p. 19.95 *(978-1-55285-136-4(2))* Whitecap Bks., Ltd. CAN. Dist: Graphic Arts Ctr. Publishing Co.
—Love. (Illus.). 64p. 12.95 *(978-1-902757-08-7(4))* Quadrille Publishing, Ltd. GBR. Dist: Graphic Arts Ctr. Publishing Co.
—Love & Success: Titania's Spell Cards. 16.95 *(978-1-55285-290-3(3))* Whitecap Bks., Ltd. CAN. Dist: Graphic Arts Ctr. Publishing Co.
—Love Potions: Titania's Book of Romantic Elixirs. (Illus.). 92p. 19.95 *(978-1-55285-305-4(5))* Whitecap Bks., Ltd. CAN. Dist: Graphic Arts Ctr. Publishing Co.
—White Magic: Highlights of Titania's Spells. (Illus.). 160p. 29.95 *(978-1-55285-248-4(2))* Whitecap Bks., Ltd. CAN. Dist: Graphic Arts Ctr. Publishing Co.
Hoffman, Devorah Mystic. DeVorah's Little Book of Spells. 2008. 88p. pap. 16.95 *(978-1-60474-988-5(1))* PublishAmerica, Inc.
Illes, Judika. Magic When You Need It: 150 Spells You Can't Live Without. 2008. (ENG.). 192p. pap. 16.95 *(978-1-57863-419-4(9),* Weiser Bks.) Red Wheel/Weiser.
Johnstone, Michael. The Book of Spells: Positive Enchantments to Enhance Your Life. 2009. (ENG.). 386p. spiral bd. 9.99 *(978-0-7858-2123-6(6),* 0785821236, Chartwell) Book Sales, Inc.
Kemp, Gillian. Good Witch, Bad Witch: Sweet Spells & Dark Charms. 2006. (Illus.). 64p. reprint ed. pap. 18.00 *(978-1-4223-5271-7(4))* DIANE Publishing Co.
Lark Books. Simply Charms: 20 Beading Projects. 2011. (Simply Pamphlet Ser.). (ENG., Illus.). 64p. 9.95 *(978-1-4547-0025-8(4))* Lark Bks.
MAGNUS, Albertus. Forbidden Knowledge of Ancient Philosophers. 2008. 270p. pap. 26.30 *(978-1-4357-4433-2(0))* Lulu Enterprises Inc.
Marie, Bruce. The Witch's Almanac: Practical Magic Spells for Every Season. 2007. (ENG., Illus.). 224p. pap. 18.95 *(978-0-572-03337-8(Q))* Foulsham, W. Co., Ltd. GBR. Dist: APG Sales & Distribution Services.

C

Mees, Bernard. Celtic Curses. 2009. (Illus.). 238p. 99.00 (978-1-84383-457-1(X), Boydell Press) Boydell & Brewer, Ltd. GBR. Dist: Boydell & Brewer, Inc.
Mickaharic, Draja. Magic Spells of All Kinds. 2008. 77p. pap. 16.95 (978-1-4357-3408-1(4)) Lulu Enterprises Inc.
Morrison, Dorothy. Utterly Wicked: Curses, Hexes, & Other Unsavory Notions. 2007. 194p. pap. 14.95 (978-0-9794533-1-1(3), WillowTree Pr. Bks.) WillowTree Pr., L.L.C.
Murphy-Hiscock, Arin. The Way of the Hedge Witch: Rituals & Spells for Hearth & Home. 2009. (ENG.). 256p. pap. 12.95 (978-1-59869-974-6(1), Provenance Pr.) Adams Media Corp.
Nock, Judy Ann. The Provenance Press Guide to the Wiccan Year: Spells, Rituals, Holiday Celebrations. 2007. (ENG., Illus.). 272p. per. 12.95 (978-1-59869-125-2(2)) Adams Media Corp.
Orn, Mya. The un-Spell Book: Energy Essentials for Mastering Magick. 2011. (ENG.). 192p. pap. 14.95 (978-0-7387-2338-9(X)) Llewellyn Pubns.
Oribello, William A. Godspells: Written Spells, Spoken Spells & Spell Enhancers. 2nd ed. (Illus.). 66p. pap. 15.00 (978-0-938294-49-8(0)) Inner Light - Global Communications.
Pollington, Stephen, ed. Leechcraft: Early English Charms, Plant Lore, & Healing. 2nd ed. 2008. (ENG., Illus.). 539p. (C). pap. 39.95 (978-1-898281-47-4(5)) Anglo-Saxon Bks. GBR. Dist: Brown, David Bk. Co., The.
Rankine, David. The Grimoire of Arthur Gauntlet. 2011. 334p. **(978-1-905297-54-2(8))**; pap. **(978-1-905297-38-2(6))** Avalonia.
Roper, Jonathan. Charms, Charmers & Charming: International Research on Verbal Magic. 2008. (ENG., Illus.). 272p. 100.00 (978-0-230-55184-8(X)) Palgrave Macmillan.
Routier, Martine. 80 Original Charms. 2008. (ENG., Illus.). 64p. pap. 17.95 (978-1-84448-279-5(0)) Search Pr., Ltd. GBR. Dist: Independent Pubs. Group.
Silja. The Green Wiccan Book of Shadows. 2011. (ENG., Illus.). 160p. pap. 19.95 (978-1-907563-64-5(4)) CICO Bks. GBR. Dist: Ryland Peters & Small.
Snelling, Kelly & Rae, Ruth. A Charming Exchange: 25 Jewelry Projects to Create & Share. 2008. (ENG., Illus.). 128p. pap. 22.99 (978-1-60061-051-6(X), North Light Bks.) F&W Media, Inc.
Stewart, Christy Leigh. Satan Is the New Cupid. 2009. 84p. pap. 8.27 (978-0-557-09556-8(5)) Lulu Enterprises Inc.
Varner, Gary R. The History & Use of Amulets, Charms & Talismans. 2008. 192p. 28.50 (978-0-557-00891-9(3)); pap. 15.95 (978-1-4357-1988-0(3)) Lulu Enterprises Inc.
Whitehurst, Tess. Magical Housekeeping: Simple Charms & Practical Tips for Creating a Harmonious Home. 2010. (ENG.). 240p. pap. 16.95 (978-0-7387-1985-6(4)) Llewellyn Pubns.

CHARRIERE, ISABELLE DE, 1740-1805

Bostic, Heidi. The Fiction of Enlightenment: Women of Reason in the French Eighteenth Century. 2010. 270p. 59.50 (978-0-87413-074-4(3)) Univ. of Delaware Pr.
Strien, C. D. van. Isabelle de Charriere (Belle de Zuylen) Early Writings: New Materials from Dutch Archives. 2006. (Republique des Lettres Ser.). (ENG.). 338p. (C). pap. 66.00 (978-90-429-1646-3(X)) Peeters Pubs. & Booksellers BEL. Dist: Brown, David Bk. Co., The.

CHARTER-PARTIES

Cooke, Julian, et al. Voyage Charters. 3rd rev. ed. 2007. 1254p. 846.00 (978-1-84311-537-3(9)) Informa Professional GBR. Dist: International Specialized Bk. Services.
Gorton, Lars, et al. Shipbroking & Chartering Practice. 7th rev. ed. 2009. (Illus.). 409p. 414.00 (978-1-84311-806-0(8)) Informa Professional GBR. Dist: International Specialized Bk. Services.
Thomas, D. R. Legal Issues Relating to Time Charterparties. Thomas, D. Rhidian, ed. 2008. (Maritime & Transport Law Library Ser.). 378p. 468.00 (978-1-84311-745-2(2)) Informa Professional GBR. Dist: International Specialized Bk. Services.
Thomas, D. Rhidian, ed. The Evolving Law & Practice of Voyage Charterparties. 2009. 432p. 495.00 (978-1-84311-808-4(4)) Informa Professional GBR. Dist: International Specialized Bk. Services.
Wilson, John. Carriage of Goods by Sea, 1 vol. 6th rev. ed. 2008. 584p. pap. 96.50 (978-1-4058-4669-1(0)) Pearson Education.

CHARTER SCHOOLS

Here are entered works on legislatively authorized, independent, innovative, outcome-based, public schools that operate under the authority of a charter.
see also Privatization in Education

Arrastia, Lisa & Hoffman, Marvin. Starting Up: Critical Lessons from 10 New Schools. 2012. (ENG.). 192p. 64.00 **(978-0-8077-5308-8(4))**; pap. 29.95 **(978-0-8077-5307-1(6))** Teachers College Pr., Teachers College, Columbia Univ.
Batie, Michael. Charter Schools & Market Segmentation. 2010. 152p. pap. (978-3-8383-6365-3(5)) Lambert Academic Publishing.
Berends, Mark, et al, eds. Charter School Outcomes. 2007. (ENG., Illus.). 328p. (C). 150.00 (978-0-8058-6221-8(8)); per. 94.95 (978-0-8058-6222-5(6)) Routledge.
Betts, Julian R. & Hill, Paul T. Taking Measure of Charter Schools. 2010. (New Frontiers in Education Ser.). (ENG., Illus.). 216p. 90.00 (978-1-60709-358-9(8)) Rowman & Littlefield Education.
—Taking Measure of Charter Schools: Better Assessments, Better Policymaking, Better Schools. 2010. (New Frontiers in Education Ser.). (ENG., Illus.). 216p. pap. 34.95 (978-1-60709-359-6(6)) Rowman & Littlefield Education.
Bloch, Thomas M. Stand for the Best: What I Learned after Leaving My Job As CEO of H & R Block to Become a Teacher & Founder of an Inner-City Charter School. 2008. (ENG., Illus.). 256p. 24.95 (978-0-470-18896-5(0), Jossey-Bass) Wiley, John & Sons, Inc.
Buckley, Jack & Schneider, Mark. Charter Schools: Hope or Hype? 2009. (ENG., Illus.). 376p. (C). pap. 25.95 (978-0-691-14319-4(6)) Princeton Univ. Pr.
Building on What Works at Charter Schools: Hearing Before the Committee on Education & Labor, U.S. House of Representatives, One Hundred Eleventh Congress, First Session, Hearing Held in Washington, DC, June 4, 2009. 2009. (Illus.). iii, 57p. (978-0-16-084447-8(9), 552-070-39974-7) United States Government Printing Office.
Camilleri, Lucas A., ed. District of Columbia Schools: Reform Progress. 2011. (Education in a Competitive & Globalizing World Ser.). 168p. 95.00 **(978-1-61324-649-8(8))** Nova Science Pubs., Inc.
Carpenter, Brian L. Charter School Board University. 2006. spiral bd. 29.95 (978-0-9788573-0-1(5)) National Charter Schls. Institute.
—The Seven Outs: Strategic Planning Made Easy for Charter Schools. 2008. 184p. 29.95 (978-0-9788573-2-5(1)) National Charter Schls. Institute.
Castanza, Gordon. Alaska's Charter Schools. 49.95 (978-1-888125-57-3(8)) Publication Consultants.
Chakrabarti, Rajashri & Peterson, Paul E., eds. School Choice International: Exploring Public-Private Partnerships. 2008. (ENG., Illus.). 280p. (gr. 17). 38.00 (978-0-262-03376-3(3)) MIT Pr.
Chubb, John E. & Finn, Chester E., Jr., contrib. by. Charter Schools Against the Odds. 2006. (Hoover Inst Press Publication). (Illus.). 219p. per. 15.00 (978-0-8179-4762-0(0)) Hoover Institution Pr.
Corwin, Ronald G. & Schneider, E. Joseph. The School Choice Hoax: Fixing America's Schools. 2007. (ENG.). 256p. per. 21.95 (978-1-57886-586-4(7)) Rowman & Littlefield Education.
Fabricant, Michael & Fine, Michelle. Charter Schools & the Corporate Makeover of Public Education: What's at Stake? 2012. (ENG., Illus.). 176p. pap. 25.95 **(978-0-8077-5285-2(1))** Teachers College Pr., Teachers College, Columbia Univ.
Farnsworth, Kent A. Grassroots School Reform: A Community Guide to Developing Globally Competitive Students. 2010. (ENG.). 224p. 84.00 (978-0-230-10832-5(6)); pap. 29.00 (978-0-230-10833-2(4)) Palgrave Macmillan.
Finn, Chester E., Jr., et al. Charter Schools in Action: What Have We Learned? 5.00 (978-1-55813-083-8(7)) Hudson Institute.
Henig, Jeffrey R. Spin Cycle: How Research Is Used in Policy Debates: the Case of Charter Schools. 2008. (Illus.). 297p. 32.50 (978-0-87154-339-4(7)) Russell Sage Foundation.
H.R. 4330: The All Students Achieving Through Reform ACT of 2009: Hearing Before the Committee on Education & Labor, U.S. House of Representatives, One Hundred Eleventh Congress, Second Session, Hearing Held in Washington, DC, February 24, 2010. 2010. (Illus.). iii, 71p. (978-0-16-086857-3(2), 552-070-41769-9) United States Government Printing Office.
Jossey-Bass Publishers. The Jossey-Bass Reader on Charter Schools. 2013. (ENG.). 400p. pap. 35.00 (978-0-470-89156-8(4), Jossey-Bass) Wiley, John & Sons, Inc.
Klein, Carol. Virtual Charter Schools & Home Schooling. 2006. (Illus.). 74.95 (978-1-934043-21-9(4)) Cambria Pr.
Kolderie, Ted. Creating the Capacity for Change: How & Why Governors & Legislatures Are Opening a New-Schools Sector in Public Education. 2007. pap. 14.95 (978-0-9674795-6-9(8)) Editorial Projects in Education.
—Creating the Capacity for Change: How & Why Governors & Legislatures Are Opening A New-Schools Sector in Public Education. 2008. 190p. pap. 14.95 (978-0-9674795-7-6(6), EdWeek Pr.) Editorial Projects in Education.
Lin, Margaret. Making the Mission Matter: A Guidebook for Developing Rigorous Educational Goals & Measures. 2009. 64p. (C). pap. (978-0-9841765-0-2(0)) Ctr. for Charter Schls, The.
Loveless, Tom. The 2010 Brown Center Report on American Education: How Well Are American Students Learning? With Sections on International Tests, Who's Winning the Real Race to the Top, & Naep & the Common Core State Standards. 2011. (ENG.). 32p. pap. 12.95 **(978-0-8157-2232-8(X))** Brookings Institution Pr.
Lubienski, Christopher & Weitzel, Peter C. The Charter School Experiment: Expectations, Evidence, & Implications. 2010. xi, 292p. lib. bdg. **(978-1-934742-67-9(8)**, Harvard Education Pr.) Harvard Education Publishing Group (HEPG).
Lubienski, Christopher A. & Weitzel, Peter C., eds. The Charter School Experiment: Expectations, Evidence, & Implications. 2010. (Illus.). 304p. pap. 29.95 (978-1-934742-66-2(X), Harvard Education Pr.) Harvard Education Publishing Group (HEPG).
Maloney, Arthur, et al. Blurring the Lines: Charter, Public, Private & Religious Schools Coming Together. 2010. (978-1-61735-145-7(8)); pap. (978-1-61735-144-0(X)); E-Book (978-1-61735-146-4(6)) Information Age Publishing, Inc.
Merseth, Katherine K., et al. Inside Urban Charter Schools: Promising Practices & Strategies in Five High-Performing Schools. 2009. 275p. pap. 29.95 (978-1-934742-10-5(4)); lib. bdg. 54.95 (978-1-934742-11-2(2)) Harvard Education Publishing Group (HEPG). (Harvard Education Pr.).
Powers, Jeanne M. Charter Schools: From Reform Imagery to Reform Reality. 2009. (Palgrave Studies in Urban Education Ser.). (ENG.). 260p. 105.00 (978-0-230-60627-2(X)) Palgrave Macmillan.
Prisser, Oliver M., ed. Charter Schools: Impact & Grant Challenges. 2011. (Education in a Competitive & Globalizing World Ser.). 301p. 215.00 **(978-1-61324-662-7(5))** Nova Science Pubs., Inc.
A Review & Assessment of the Use, Impact, & Accomplishments of Federal Appropriations Provided to Improve the Education of Children in the District of Columbia: Hearings Before a Subcommittee of the Committee on Appropriations, United States Senate, One Hundred Eleventh Congress, First Session: Special Hearings, September 16, 2009, Washington, DC: September 29, 2009, Washington, DC. 2010. (Illus.). iv, 167p. **(978-0-16-085918-2(2)**, 552-070-41114-3) United States Government Printing Office.
Schneider, Mark & Buckley, Jack. Charter Schools: Hope or Hype? 2007. (ENG., Illus.). 376p. (C). 52.50 (978-0-691-12985-3(1)) Princeton Univ. Pr.
Shon, Jim. A Charter School Story: Hawaii's Experience in Creating A Charter School System. 2008. 153p. pap. 14.49 (978-1-4357-0889-1(X)) Lulu Enterprises Inc.
Tryjankowski, Anne Marie. Charter School Primer. 2012. **(978-1-4331-1189-1(6))** Lang, Peter GmbH, Europaischer Verlag der Wissenschaften.
—Charter School Primer. 2011. (C). pap. 18.95 **(978-1-4331-1188-4(8))** Lang, Peter Publishing, Inc.
Weil, Danny, ed. Charter School Movement: History, Politics, Policies, Economics & Effectiveness. 2nd rev. ed. 2009. (gr. 4-6). 145.00 (978-1-59237-289-8(9)) Grey Hse. Publishing.
Weinberg, Lawrence D. Religious Charter Schools: Legalities & Practicalities. 2007. (ENG.). 188p. (C). (978-1-59311-759-7(0)); per. (978-1-59311-758-0(2)) Information Age Publishing, Inc.
Williams, Joe. Charter Schools Today: Stories of Inspiration, Struggle & Success. 2007. (978-0-9646028-3-0(0)) Ctr. for Education Reform, The.
Zimmer, Ron, et al. Charter Schools in Eight States: Effects on Achievement, Attainment, Integration, & Competition. 2009. 144p. pap. 25.00 (978-0-8330-4693-2(4), mg-869) RAND Corp., The.

CHARTERING OF SHIPS

see Charter-Parties

CHARTERS

see also Archives; Manuscripts; Municipal Charters

Barnwell, P. S. Medieval Legal Process: Physical, Spoken & Written Performance in the Middle Ages. Mostert, Marco, ed. 2011. (Utrecht Studies in Medieval Literacy Ser.). (ENG., Illus.). 299p. (C). 123.00 **(978-2-503-54174-7(7))** Brepols Pubs. BEL. Dist: ISD.
Brett, Martin, et al, eds. Facsimiles of English Episcopal Acta, 1085-1305. 2012. (Check Info & Delete This Occurrence: c EEA v Supplementary Volume 1 t English Episcopal Acta Ser.: Vol. Supplementary Volume 1). (ENG & LAT., Illus.). 230p. 199.00 (978-0-19-726456-0(5)) Oxford Univ. Pr., Inc.
City Club Of New York. Calendar of the New York City Charter, Giving All Times Fixed by the Charter at or Within Which the Municipal Officers Are to Perform Certain Duties. 2011. 60p. pap. 14.99 **(978-1-4181-8679-1(1))** MPublishing.
MacDonald, William. Select Charters & Other Documents Illustrative of American History, 1606-1775. 2010. (ENG.). 416p. pap. 34.75 (978-1-177-56384-0(3)); 420p. pap. 34.75 (978-1-177-19113-5(X)); 420p. pap. 34.75 (978-1-146-74192-7(8)); 424p. pap. 34.75 (978-1-145-31884-7(3)) BiblioBazaar.
—Select Charters & Other Documents Illustrative of American History, 1606-1775. 2010. (Illus.). 276p. pap. 24.21 (978-1-154-28301-3(1)) 2009. 300p. pap. 24.49 (978-1-150-15980-0(4)) General Bks. LLC.
—Select Charters & Other Documents Illustrative of American History, 1606-1775. 2010. 416p. pap. 27.96 (978-1-163-95174-3(9)) 2008. 414p. 49.95 (978-0-548-96478-1(5)) 2007. (ENG.). 416p. per. 34.95 (978-0-548-64026-5(2)) Kessinger Publishing, LLC.
Mercantile Library Of Philadelphia. Charter, Bylaws & Library Rules of the Mercantile Library Company of Philadelphia. 2011. 18p. pap. 11.99 **(978-1-4181-9046-0(2))** MPublishing.
Woodman, David, ed. Charters of Northern Houses. 2012. (Anglo-Saxon Charters Ser.). (ENG., Illus.). 450p. 185.00 **(978-0-19-726529-1(4))** Oxford Univ. Pr., Inc.

CHARTISM

Chase, Malcolm. Chartism: A New History. 2007. (ENG.). 432p. 89.00 (978-0-7190-6086-1(9)); pap. 33.00 (978-0-7190-6087-8(7)) Manchester Univ. Pr. GBR. Dist: Macmillan.
Cole, George D. Chartist Portraits. reprint ed. 39.50 (978-0-404-58490-0(X)) AMS Pr., Inc.
Faulkner, Harold U. Chartism & the Churches. (Columbia University, Studies in the Social Sciences: No. 173). reprint ed. 30.00 (978-0-404-51173-9(2)) AMS Pr., Inc.
Fraser, W. Hamish. Chartism in Scotland. 2010. (ENG., Illus.). 296p. pap. 35.00 (978-0-85036-666-2(6)) Merlin Pr. Ltd. GBR. Dist: Independent Pubs. Group.
Hall, Robert G. Voices of the People: Democracy & Chartist Political Identity, 1830-1870. 2007. (Chartist Studies Ser.). (Illus.). 240p. 85.00 (978-0-85036-564-1(3)); pap. 32.95 (978-0-85036-557-3(0)) Merlin Pr. Ltd. GBR. Dist: Independent Pubs. Group.
Hovell, Mark. The Chartist Movement. 2010. 376p. pap. 33.75 (978-1-149-04152-9(8)); pap. 32.75 (978-1-142-07931-4(7)) BiblioBazaar.
—The Chartist Movement. 2010. (Illus.). 268p. pap. 23.00 (978-1-150-83936-8(8)) General Bks. LLC.
—The Chartist Movement. Tout, T. F., ed. 2008. 366p. 48.95 (978-1-4365-6501-1(4)) 2007. (ENG.). 368p. per. 33.95 (978-0-548-77304-8(1)) Kessinger Publishing, LLC.
Hovell, Mark & Tout, T. F. The Chartist Movement. 2010. (ENG.). 376p. pap. 33.75 (978-1-171-71623-5(0)) BiblioBazaar.
Paz, Denis. Dickens & Barnaby Rudge: Anti-Catholicism & Chartism. 2007. 256p. 50.00 (978-0-85036-575-7(9)) Merlin Pr. Ltd. GBR. Dist: Independent Pubs. Group.
Pickering, Paul A. Feargus O'Connor. 2008. (ENG., Illus.). 240p. pap. 29.95 (978-0-85036-561-0(9)) Merlin Pr. Ltd. GBR. Dist: Independent Pubs. Group.
Roberts, Stephen. The Chartist Prisoners: The Radical Lives of Thomas Cooper (1805-1892) & Arthur O'Neill (1819-1896) 2008. (Illus.). 198p. pap. 57.95 (978-3-03911-388-0(7)) Lang, Peter AG GBR. Dist: Lang, Peter.
Schnepf, Ariane. Our Original Rights As a People: Representations of the Chartist Encyclopaedic Network & Political, Social & Cultural Change in Early Nineteenth Century Britain. 2006. 324p. pap. 84.95 (978-3-03910-968-5(5)); pap. 61.95 (978-0-8204-8049-7(5)) Lang, Peter Publishing, Inc.

CHARTRES (FRANCE)

Burckhardt, Titus. Chartres & the Birth of the Cathedral. 2010. (ENG., Illus.), 160p. pap. 24.95 (978-1-933316-77-2(2)) World Wisdom, Inc.

CHARTRES (FRANCE)—CATHEDRAL

see Cathedrale de Chartres

CHARTREUX, ORDRE DE

see Carthusians

CHARTS

see also Maps

BarCharts Inc., Staff, creator. American History. 2006. (Quickstudy Bks.). (ENG.). 144p. pap. 6.95 (978-1-4232-0258-5(9)) Barcharts, Inc.
Brooks, Randy & BarCharts Inc., Staff. Biology. 2006. (Quickstudy Bks.). (ENG., Illus.). 144p. pap. 6.95 (978-1-4232-0256-1(2)) Barcharts, Inc.
Federal Aviation Administration Staff. Aeronautical Chart User's Guide. 2008. (FAA Handbooks Ser.). (ENG.). 85p. pap. 14.95 (978-1-56027-730-9(0)) Aviation Supplies & Academics, Inc.
Gauguin, Jan. Designing Diagrams: Making Information accessible through Design. 2011. (ENG., Illus.). 192p. 49.00 **(978-90-6369-228-5(5))** Bis B.V., Uitgeverij(BIS Publishers) NLD. Dist: Consortium Bk. Sales & Distribution.
Tables, Graphs & Charts Mastery. (Illus.). wbk. ed. 9.99 (978-1-58523-013-6(8)) Systems Impact, Inc.
Walkenbach, John. Excel 2007 Charts. 2007. (Mr. Spreadsheet's Bookshelf Ser.: 1). (ENG., Illus.). 555p. pap. 44.99 (978-0-470-04400-1(4), Wiley) Wiley, John & Sons, Inc.
Warnock, Christopher. Warnock's Horary Case Book 2nd Edition. 2009. 111p. pap. 19.95 (978-0-557-20286-7(8)) Lulu Enterprises Inc.

CHARTS, NAUTICAL

see Nautical Charts

CHARTULARIES

see Cartularies

CHASDAI BEN ABRAHAM CRESCAS, 1340-1410

Waxman, Meyer. Philosophy of Don Hasdai Crescas. (Columbia University, Oriental Studies: No. 17). reprint ed. 29.50 (978-0-404-50507-3(4)) AMS Pr., Inc.

CHASE, MARY ELLEN, 1887-1973

Chase, Mary E. A Goodly Fellowship. reprint ed. 29.50 (978-0-404-20057-2(5)) AMS Pr., Inc.

CHASE, SALMON P. (SALMON PORTLAND), 1808-1873

Evarts, William Maxwell. Eulogy on Chief-Justice Chase. 2009. 36p. pap. 15.75 (978-1-113-39461-3(7)) BiblioBazaar.
—Eulogy on Chief-Justice Chase. 2007. 48p. per. (978-1-4065-3380-4(7)) Dodo Pr.
Hart, Albert Bushnell. Salmon Portland Chase. 2008. 476p. 31.99 (978-0-559-45031-0(1)); pap. 36.75 (978-0-559-45028-0(1)) BiblioBazaar.
—Salmon Portland Chase. 2009. 208p. pap. 21.05 (978-1-150-48068-3(8)); 210p. pap. 21.05 (978-1-150-37765-5(8)) General Bks. LLC.
—Salmon Portland Chase. 2007. 480p. 52.95 (978-0-548-55832-4(9)); (ENG.). per. 37.95 (978-0-548-50105-4(X)) Kessinger Publishing, LLC.
—Salmon Portland Chase. 465p. reprint ed. 98.00 (978-0-7222-8485-8(3)); 98.00 (978-0-7222-9032-3(2)) Library Reprints, Inc.
McClure, James P., et al, eds. Spur up Your Pegasus: Family Letters of Salmon, Kate, & Nettie Chase, 1844-1873. 2009. (Illus.). 544p. 70.00 (978-0-87338-988-4(3)) Kent State Univ. Pr.
Piatt, Donn. Memories of the Men Who Saved the Union. 2009. 320p. 25.99 (978-1-103-15708-2(6)); pap. 19.99 (978-1-103-15707-5(8)) BiblioBazaar.
—Memories of the Men Who Saved the Union. 2007. 320p. 45.95 (978-0-548-11183-3(9)) Kessinger Publishing, LLC.
Rothschild, Alonzo. Lincoln, Master of Men: A Study in Character. 2009. 436p. pap. 35.75 (978-1-116-48156-3(1)) 2009. 436p. 41.99 (978-1-116-48154-9(5)) 2009. 436p. 34.99 (978-1-116-48155-6(3)) 2009. 542p. 43.99 (978-1-115-83581-7(5)) 2009. 436p. pap. 34.75 (978-1-116-48157-0(X)) 2008. 544p. 32.99 (978-0-559-49001-9(1)) 2008. 544p. pap. 40.75 (978-0-559-48998-3(6)) BiblioBazaar.
—Lincoln, Master of Men: A Study in Character. 2007. (ENG.). 552p. 57.95 (978-0-548-04723-1(5)) Kessinger Publishing, LLC.
—Lincoln, Master of Men: A Study in Character. 531p. reprint ed. 98.00 (978-0-7222-8806-1(9)) Library Reprints, Inc.

—Lincoln, Master of Men: A Study in Character. 2008. 432p. pap. *(978-1-4086-8449-8(7))* Read Bks.

Schuckers, Jacob. The Life & Public Services of Salmon Portland Chase. 2009. (Civil War Ser.). (ENG.). 700p. pap. 39.95 *(978-1-4290-1965-1(4))* Applewood Bks.

Schuckers, Jacob William. The Life & Public Services of Salmon Portland Chase, United States Senator & Governor of Ohio. 669p. reprint ed. 128.00 *(978-0-7222-9033-0(0))* Library Reprints, Inc.

CHASE, WILLIAM MERRITT, 1849-1916

Pisano, Ronald G. William Merritt Chase: Landscapes in Oil, 4 vols. 2009. (ENG., Illus.). 192p. 65.00 *(978-0-300-11020-3(0))* Yale Univ. Pr.

—William Merritt Chase Vol. 4: Still Lifes, Interiors, Figures, Copies of Old Masters, & Drawings, 4 vols. 2010. (Illus.). 240p. 65.00 *(978-0-300-11019-7(7))* Yale Univ. Pr.

Pisano, Ronald G., et al. William Merritt Chase: Portraits in Oil, 4 vols. 2007. (ENG., Illus.). 312p. 75.00 *(978-0-300-11021-0(9))* Yale Univ. Pr.

CHASIDIM

see Hasidim

CHASIDISM

see Hasidism

CHASSIS-MOUNTED COACHES

see Truck Campers

CHASTITY

Here are entered works on the virtue that moderates and regulates the sexual appetite in human beings. Works on the renunciation of marriage because of a religious vow or commitment are entered under Celibacy.

Anderson, Neil T. Winning the Battle Within: Realistic Steps to Overcoming Sexual Strongholds. 2008. 225p. pap. 12.99 *(978-0-7369-2422-1(1))* Harvest Hse. Pubs.

Arterburn, Stephen & Ethridge, Shannon. Every Young Woman's Battle: Guarding Your Mind, Heart, & Body in a Sex-Saturated World. 2009. (Every Man Ser.). (ENG.). 304p. pap. 15.99 *(978-0-307-45800-1(8),* WaterBrook Pr.) Doubleday Religious Publishing Group, The.

Butler, Brian, et al. Theology of the Body for Teens: Discovering God's Plan for Love & Life. 2006. (Illus.). 209p. per. 29.95 *(978-1-932927-87-0(5))* Ascension Pr.

Catholic Church, United States Conference of Catholic Bishops Committee on Evangelization and Catechesis Staff, contrib. by. Catechetical Formation in Chaste Living: Guidelines for Curriculum Design & Publication. 2008. 27p. pap. *(978-1-60137-043-3(1))* United States Conference of Catholic Bishops.

Classen, Albercht & Classen, Albrecht. The Medieval Chastity Belt: The Myth-Making Process. 2007. (New Middle Ages Ser.). (ENG., Illus.). 232p. 89.00 *(978-1-4039-7558-4(2))* Palgrave Macmillan.

Ethridge, Shannon. Every Woman's Battle: Discovering God's Plan for Sexual & Emotional Fulfillment. 2009. (Every Man Ser.). (ENG.). 288p. pap. 14.99 *(978-0-307-45798-1(2),* WaterBrook Pr.) Doubleday Religious Publishing Group, The.

Graham, Janice Barrett. Chased by an Elephant: The Gospel Truth about Today's Stampeding Sexuality. 2010. (Illus.). 142p. pap. *(978-0-9724770-5-5(5))* Tidal Wave Bks.

Launderville, Dale. Celibacy in the Ancient World: Its Ideal & Practice in Pre-Hellenistic Israel, Mesopotamia, & Greece. 2010. E-Book 49.95 *(978-0-8146-5734-8(6));* (ENG.). 576p. pap. 69.95 *(978-0-8146-5697-6(8),* Liturgical Pr. Bks.) Liturgical Pr.

St James, Rebecca. Wait for Me: Rediscovering the Joy of Purity in Romance, 0 vols. 2008. (Illus.). 208p. (YA). (gr. 8-13). pap. 14.99 *(978-1-4003-1287-0(6))* Nelson, Thomas Inc.

Stieglitz, Gil. Mission Possible: Winning the Battle over Temptation: Helping Individuals, Families, & Organizations. 2007. (Illus.). 242p. *(978-1-59684-289-2(X))* Pathway Pr.

Stoeker, Fred & Arterburn, Stephen. Every Young Man's Battle: Strategies for Victory in the Real World of Sexual Temptation. 2009. (Every Man Ser.). (ENG.). 336p. (YA). pap. 15.99 *(978-0-307-45799-8(0),* WaterBrook Pr.) Doubleday Religious Publishing Group, The.

Taylor, Jenny & Taylor. Wild Constraint: The Case for Chastity. 2009. (ENG.). 176p. 24.95 *(978-0-8264-8712-4(2))* Continuum International Publishing Group, Ltd. GBR. Dist: National Bk. Network.

van Deusen, Nancy, ed. Chastity: A Study in Perception, Ideals, Opposition. 2008. (Presenting the Past Ser.). (Illus.). 211p. *(978-90-04-16671-4(8))* BRILL.

Van Vliet, C. J. Conquest of the Serpent: A Way to Solve the Sex Problem. 2011. 154p. 41.95 ***(978-1-258-00175-9(6))*** Literary Licensing, LLC.

Webb, Geoffrey & Walker, Adrian, trs. from LAT. Letter to My Sister. 2nd ed. 64p. pap. *(978-1-901157-52-9(0))* St. Austin Pr.

Winner, Lauren F. Real Sex: The Naked Truth about Chastity. annot. ed. 2006. 192p. reprint ed. pap. 14.99 *(978-1-58743-197-5(1))* Brazos Pr.

CHAT GROUPS, ONLINE

see Online Chat Groups

CHAT ROOMS, ONLINE

see Online Chat Groups

CHAT SERVICES, ONLINE

see Online Chat Groups

CHATEAU DE VERSAILLES (VERSAILLES, FRANCE)

see also Parc de Versailles (Versailles, France)

Bajou, Valerie. Versailles. 2012. (ENG., Illus.). 480p. 40.00 *(978-1-4197-0067-5(7))* Abrams.

Bajou, Valerie & Picon, Guillaume. Versailles: A Private Invitation. 2011. (ENG., Illus.). 320p. 95.00 *(978-2-08-020076-1(3))* Flammarion et Cie FRA. Dist: Random Hse., Inc.

Martinez, Frédéric & Targat, Gilles. Versailles, Palais des Rois. (FRE., Illus.). 253p. *(978-2-8123-0200-8(3))* Editions du Chene.

Payne, Francis Loring. The Story of Versailles. 2009. 236p. pap. 23.99 *(978-1-103-63512-2(3))* 2009. 236p. pap. 17.99 *(978-1-103-63511-5(5))* 2008. 120p. 21.99 *(978-0-554-37218-1(5))* 2008. 120p. 24.99 *(978-0-554-27915-2(0))* 2007. (ENG.). 106p. pap. 18.99 *(978-1-4346-4309-4(3))* 2007. (ENG.). 116p. pap. 19.99 *(978-1-4346-4310-0(7))* BiblioBazaar.

—The Story of Versailles. 2008. (ENG., Illus.). 112p. per. *(978-1-4065-7008-3(7))* Dodo Pr.

—The Story of Versailles. 2007. (ENG.). 236p. per. *(978-1-4067-7198-5(8))* Read Bks.

Spawforth, Tony. Versailles: A Biography of a Palace. 2010. (ENG., Illus.). 320p. pap. 19.99 *(978-0-312-60346-5(0),* St. Martin's Griffin) St. Martin's Pr.

CHATEAUX

see Castles

CHATHAM, WILLIAM PITT, EARL OF, 1708-1778

see Pitt, William, Earl of Chatham, 1708-1778

CHATTANOOGA (TENN.)

Arnold, Dean W. Old Money, New South: The Spirit of Chattanooga. 2009. (ENG.). 515p. pap. 29.95 *(978-0-9749076-2-8(6))* 2nd ed. 2006. reprint ed. pap. 29.95 *(978-0-9749076-4-2(2))* Chattanooga Historical Foundation Co.

Carroll, David. Chattanooga Radio & Television. 2011. (Images of America Ser.). (ENG., Illus.). 128p. pap. 21.99 *(978-0-7385-8685-4(4))* Arcadia Publishing.

Chambliss, Jac. Columns Left: Essayettes of a 20th Century Man. 2007. 288p. per. 18.95 *(978-0-9779189-6-6(3))* Waldenhouse Pubs., Inc.

Chattanooga Tn Atlas. 2008. 136p. 16.95 *(978-0-8416-1075-0(4))* American Map Corp.

Clark, Alexandra Walker. Hidden History of Chattanooga. 2008. pap. 19.99 *(978-1-59629-473-8(6))* History Pr., The.

Henighan Potter, Susanna. Moon Spotlight Chattanooga & Knoxville. 2010. (Moon Spotlight Ser.). (ENG.). 76p. pap. 7.95 *(978-1-59880-560-4(6))* Avalon Travel Publishing.

Hollis, Tim. See Rock City: The History of Rock City Gardens. 2008. *(978-1-59629-577-3(5))* History Pr., The.

Hull, William F. Chattanooga. 2008. (Then & Now Ser.). (ENG., Illus.). 96p. per. 21.99 *(978-0-7385-5316-0(6))* Arcadia Publishing.

Matthews, Larry E. Caves of Chattanooga. 2007. (Illus.). 192p. pap. *(978-1-879961-27-2(X))* National Speleological Society, Inc.

Moore, Gay Morgan. Chattanooga's Forest Hills Cemetery. 2011. (Images of America Ser.). (Illus.). 128p. pap. 21.99 *(978-0-7385-8694-6(3))* Arcadia Publishing.

Stevens, Philip G. Chattanooga: The Renaissance of a City. 2008. 49.95 *(978-1-882933-86-0(9))* Cherbo Publishing Group, Inc.

The Junior League of Chattanooga Inc. Seasoned to Taste: Savoring the Scenic City. 2011. (Illus.). 190p. 29.95 ***(978-0-9611806-1-4(7))*** Junior League of Chattanooga, Inc.

CHATTANOOGA, BATTLE OF, CHATTANOOGA, TENN., 1863

Boynton, Henry V. The Battles of Chickamauga & Chattanooga & the Organizations Engaged. 2010. (ENG.). 34.95 *(978-1-57233-694-0(3))* Univ. of Tennessee Pr.

Hurst, Jack. Born to Battle: Grant & Forrest-Shiloh, Vicksburg, & Chattanooga: The Campaigns That Doomed the Confederacy. 2012. (ENG.). 512p. (gr. 9). 32.00 ***(978-0-465-02018-8(6))*** Basic Bks.

Woodworth, Steven E. & Grear, Charles D. The Chattanooga Campaign. 2012. E-Book ***(978-0-8093-3120-8(9))*** Southern Illinois Univ. Pr.

Woodworth, Steven E. & Grear, Charles D., eds. The Chattanooga Campaign. 2012. (Illus.). 280p. 29.95 ***(978-0-8093-3119-2(5))*** Southern Illinois Univ. Pr.

CHATTANOOGA RAILROAD EXPEDITION, 1862

Bonds, Russell S. Stealing the General: The Great Locomotive Chase & the First Medal of Honor. (Illus.). 464p. 2008. (ENG.). pap. 18.95 *(978-1-59416-078-3(3))* 2006. 29.95 *(978-1-59416-033-2(3))* Westholme Publishing.

Cable, G. W. Famous Adventures & Prison Escapes of the Civil War. 2010. 350p. 36.99 *(978-1-117-92704-6(0));* pap. 32.75 *(978-1-117-92705-3(9))* BiblioBazaar.

Cable, George W. Famous Adventures & Prison Escapes of the Civil War. 2007. (ENG.). 242p. pap. 20.99 *(978-1-4264-9437-6(8));* 274p. pap. 23.99 *(978-1-4264-9818-3(7))* BiblioBazaar.

—Famous Adventures & Prison Escapes of the Civil War. 2006. pap. *(978-1-4065-1208-3(7))* Dodo Pr.

Cable, George Washington. Famous Adventures & Prison Escapes of the Civil War. 2010. 360p. pap. 32.75 *(978-1-175-14240-5(9))* 2008. 276p. 25.99 *(978-0-554-35009-7(2))* 2008. 276p. 28.99 *(978-0-554-25706-8(8))* BiblioBazaar.

—Famous Adventures & Prison Escapes of the Civil War. 2009. 60p. pap. *(978-0-217-21119-2(4))* Books LLC.

—Famous Adventures & Prison Escapes of the Civil War. 2010. (Illus.). 152p. pap. 23.93 *(978-1-153-60597-7(X))* General Bks. LLC.

Cable, George Washington, et al. Famous Adventures & Prison Escapes of the Civil War. 2011. 352p. pap. 32.75 ***(978-1-178-61664-4(9))*** BiblioBazaar.

Famous Adventures & Prison Escapes of the Civil War. 338p. reprint ed. 98.00 *(978-0-7222-8118-5(8))* Library Reprints, Inc.

Pittenger, William. Capturing a Locomotive: A History of Secret Service in the Late War. 2007. (ENG.). 338p. 46.95 *(978-0-548-16896-7(2));* 340p. per. 31.95 *(978-1-4304-6625-3(1))* Kessinger Publishing, LLC.

—Daring & Suffering. 2009. 192p. 25.99 *(978-0-559-07067-9(5))* 2009. 192p. 22.99 *(978-0-559-07082-2(9))* 2009. 192p. pap. 22.75 *(978-0-559-07072-3(1))* 2009. 192p. pap. 21.75 *(978-0-559-07078-5(0))* 2008. 248p. 25.99 *(978-0-554-86633-8(1))* 2008. 180p. 28.99 *(978-0-554-86623-9(4))* 2008. 180p. pap. 28.75 *(978-0-554-86627-7(7))* 2008. 180p. pap. 27.75 *(978-0-554-86631-4(5))* BiblioBazaar.

—Daring & Suffering. 2009. 420p. pap. *(978-1-4590-6587-1(5))* Books LLC.

—Daring & Suffering. 2006. 296p. per. 23.99 *(978-1-4255-2769-3(8))* MPublishing.

—Daring & Suffering: A History of the Andrews Railroad Raid into Georgia in 1862. 2007. 476p. per. *(978-1-4086-0100-6(1))* Read Bks.

—Daring & Suffering: A History of the Great Railroad Adventure. 2010. 306p. pap. 29.75 *(978-1-146-89925-3(4))* BiblioBazaar.

—Daring & Suffering: A History of the Great Railroad Adventure. 2009. (Illus.). 188p. pap. *(978-1-4099-6710-1(7))* Dodo Pr.

—Daring & Suffering: A History of the Great Railroad Adventure. 2008. 120p. pap. *(978-1-4068-6658-2(X))* Echo Library.

—Daring & Suffering: A History of the Great Railroad Adventure. 2010. 298p. 35.16 *(978-1-163-34847-5(3))* 2010. 298p. pap. 23.16 *(978-1-162-77343-8(X))* 2007. 296p. 43.95 *(978-0-548-03720-1(5))* Kessinger Publishing, LLC.

—Daring & Suffering: A History of the Great Railroad Adventure. 2012. 182p. pap. ***(978-3-8472-3474-6(9))*** Tredition GmbH.

—Daring & Suffering: A history of the great railroad Adventure. 2010. (ENG.). 308p. pap. 29.75 *(978-1-175-51284-0(2));* pap. 29.75 *(978-1-175-51285-7(0))* BiblioBazaar.

—Daring & Suffering a History of the Great Railroad Adventure. 2009. 298p. pap. 28.75 *(978-1-115-69430-8(8));* 25.99 *(978-1-115-69428-5(6))* BiblioBazaar.

—Daring & Suffering a History of the Great Railroad Adventure. 288p. reprint ed. 98.00 *(978-0-7222-8283-0(4))* Library Reprints, Inc.

—Daring & Suffering a History of the Great Railroad Adventure. 2007. (ENG.). 296p. per. *(978-1-4086-0101-3(X))* Read Bks.

Pittenger, William & Clark, A. Daring & Suffering: A history of the great railroad Adventure. 2010. 306p. pap. 29.75 *(978-1-178-13405-6(9))* BiblioBazaar.

Rottman, Gordon. The Great Locomotive Chase: The Andrews Raid 1862. 2009. (Raid Ser.). (ENG., Illus.). 64p. pap. 18.95 *(978-1-84603-400-8(0))* Osprey Publishing, Ltd. GBR. Dist: Random Hse., Inc.

CHATTEL MORTGAGES

see also Liens; Pledges (Law); Sales, Conditional; Ship Mortgages

Brook. Secured Transactions: Examples & Explanations. 5th ed. 2010. (Illus.). xix, 468p. pap., stu. ed. *(978-0-7355-8854-7(6))* Wolters Kluwer Law & Business.

Brook, James. Secured Transactions. 5th ed. 2011. (Examples & Explanations Ser.). (ENG.). 430p. pap. 56.95 ***(978-1-4548-0563-2(3),*** Aspen Pubs.) Wolters Kluwer Law & Business.

Smith, Edwin E. Taking & Enforcing Security Interests in Personal Property. 2007. pap. 125.00 *(978-1-57589-465-2(3))* Massachusetts Continuing Legal Education, Inc.

CHATTELS

see Personal Property

CHATTERTON, THOMAS, 1752-1770

Ingram, John H. Chatterton & His Poetry. 2009. (ENG.). 150p. 28.99 *(978-1-117-53373-5(5));* pap. 20.75 *(978-1-117-53374-2(3))* BiblioBazaar.

—Chatterton & His Poetry. 2010. 152p. pap. 17.56 *(978-1-163-89056-1(1))* 2008. 150p. 36.95 *(978-0-548-91364-2(1))* 2007. (ENG.). 152p. per. 21.95 *(978-0-548-60337-6(5))* Kessinger Publishing, LLC.

Maitland, Samuel Roffey. Chatterton: An Essay. 2008. 263p. 21.99 *(978-0-554-88200-0(0));* 119p. pap. 19.75 *(978-0-554-88199-7(3));* 152p. 24.99 *(978-0-554-88193-5(4));* 119p. pap. 19.75 *(978-0-554-88194-2(2))* BiblioBazaar.

Masson, David. Chatterton: A Biography. 2007. (ENG.). 324p. 45.95 *(978-0-548-14949-2(6))* Kessinger Publishing, LLC.

—Chatterton: A Biography. 2008. 328p. pap. *(978-1-4097-9479-0(2))* Read Bks.

—Chatterton: A Story of the Year 1770. 2009. 296p. pap. 24.99 *(978-1-103-38806-6(1));* pap. 18.99 *(978-1-103-38803-5(7))* BiblioBazaar.

—Chatterton: a Biography. 2007. (ENG.). 328p. per. 30.95 *(978-1-4304-4265-3(4))* Kessinger Publishing, LLC.

Richter, Helene. Thomas Chatterton. 2010. 282p. pap. 27.75 *(978-1-141-31917-6(9))* BiblioBazaar.

CHATTI

see Hittites

CHATWIN, BRUCE, 1940-1989

Chatwin, Bruce. Under the Sun: The Letters of Bruce Chatwin. Shakespeare, Nicholas & Chatwin, Elizabeth, eds. (ENG., Illus.). 560p. (gr. 12). 2012. 20.00 ***(978-0-14-312038-4(7),*** Penguin (Non-Classics)) 2011. 35.00 *(978-0-670-02246-5(2),* Viking Adult) Penguin Group (USA) Inc.

Featherstone, Kerry. Bruce Chatwin. 2012. (Writers & Their Work Ser.). (ENG.). 128p. (C). 80.00 *(978-0-7463-1045-8(5));* pap. 26.00 *(978-0-7463-1050-2(1))* Northcote Hse. Publishers, Ltd. GBR. Dist: Brown, David Bk. Co., The.

Shakespeare, Nicholas, et al. Under the Sun: The Letters of Bruce Chatwin. 2010. (Illus.). 560p. *(978-0-224-08989-0(7),* Jonathan Cape) Random Hse.

CHAUCER, GEOFFREY, D. 1400

Alexander, Michael. Geoffrey Chaucer. 2012. (ENG., Illus.). 40p. pap. 9.99 ***(978-1-85759-748-6(6))*** Scala, Editions FRA. Dist: National Bk. Network.

Anderson, Judith H. Reading the Allegorical Intertext: Chaucer, Spenser, Shakespeare, Milton. 3rd ed. 2008. (ENG.). 320p. 70.00 *(978-0-8232-2847-8(9))* Fordham Univ. Pr.

Andrew, Malcolm. The Palgrave Literary Dictionary of Chaucer. 2009. (Palgrave Literary Dictionaries Ser.). (ENG.). 288p. pap. 35.00 *(978-0-230-23148-1(9))* Palgrave Macmillan.

Ashton. Chaucer's the Canterbury Tales. 2007. (Reader's Guides). (ENG.). 128p. 100.00 *(978-0-8264-8935-7(4))* Continuum International Publishing Group, Ltd. GBR. Dist: National Bk. Network.

Ashton, Gail. Geoffrey Chaucer. 2011. (Brief Lives Ser.). (ENG., Illus.). 120p. pap. 12.95 *(978-1-84391-918-6(4))* Hesperus Pr. GBR. Dist: Independent Pubs. Group.

Ashton, Gail & Ashton. Chaucer's the Canterbury Tales. 2007. (Reader's Guides (Continuum Paperback) Ser.). (ENG.). 128p. 19.95 *(978-0-8264-8936-4(2))* Continuum International Publishing Group, Ltd. GBR. Dist: National Bk. Network.

Bloom, Harold, ed. The Canterbury Tales. annot. ed. 2008. (Bloom's Guides). 120p. (C). (gr. 9). 30.00 *(978-0-7910-9792-2(7),* Chelsea Hse.) Facts On File, Inc.

—Geoffrey Chaucer. 2nd rev. ed. 2007. (Modern Critical Views Ser.). 272p. (C). (gr. 9). 45.00 *(978-0-7910-9438-9(3),* Chelsea Hse.) Facts On File, Inc.

—Geoffrey Chaucer's the Canterbury Tales. 2nd ed. 2008. (Modern Critical Interpretations Ser.). 296p. (C). (gr. 9). 45.00 *(978-0-7910-9518-5(1),* Chelsea Hse.) Facts On File, Inc.

Bowers, John M. Chaucer & Langland: The Antagonistic Tradition. 2007. 488p. per. 45.00 *(978-0-268-02202-0(X))* Univ. of Notre Dame Pr.

Brewer, Derek. Geoffrey Chaucer Vol. 2: The Critical Heritage, 1837-1933. 2009. 520p. pap. 45.00 *(978-0-415-56888-3(9))* Routledge.

Brinkman, Baba. The Rap Canterbury Tales. 2006. (ENG., Illus.). 352p. per. 24.95 *(978-0-88922-548-0(6))* Talonbooks, Ltd. CAN. Dist: Consortium Bk. Sales & Distribution.

Brown, Peter. Chaucer & the Making of Optical Space. 2007. (Illus.). 378p. pap. 85.95 *(978-3-03911-340-8(2))* Lang, Peter Publishing, Inc.

Browne, Matthew. Chaucer's England. 2009. 340p. 25.99 *(978-1-103-66736-9(X));* pap. 19.99 *(978-1-103-66734-5(3))* BiblioBazaar.

—Chaucer's England. 2009. 182p. pap. *(978-0-217-81007-4(1));* pap. *(978-0-217-19195-1(9))* Books LLC.

Butterfield, Ardis. The Familiar Enemy: Chaucer, Language, & Nation in the Hundred Years War. 2010. (ENG., Illus.). 432p. 99.00 *(978-0-19-957486-5(3))* Oxford Univ. Pr., Inc.

Carlson, David R. Chaucer's Jobs. 2008. (New Middle Ages Ser.). (ENG.). 180p. pap. 30.00 *(978-0-230-60243-4(6))* Palgrave Macmillan.

Chaganti, Seeta. The Medieval Poetics of the Reliquary: Enshrinement, Inscription, Performance. 2008. (New Middle Ages Ser.). (ENG., Illus.). 268p. 100.00 *(978-0-230-60466-7(8))* Palgrave Macmillan.

Chaucer, Geoffrey. General Prologue to the Canterbury Tales. 2009. (ENG., Illus.). 192p. (YA). pap. 15.95 *(978-0-19-832876-6(1))* Oxford Univ. Pr., Inc.

—The Minor Poems. 2009. 462p. pap. *(978-1-150-51772-3(7))* Books LLC.

—Pardoner's Prologue. Date not set. (Longman Critical Essays Ser.). (Illus.). 136p. pap. 83.00 *(978-0-582-06049-4(4))* Addison-Wesley Longman, Ltd. GBR. Dist: Trans-Atlantic Pubns., Inc.

Chaucer, Geoffrey & Winstanley, Lilian. The Prioress's Tale, the Tale of Sir Thopas. 2011. (ENG.). 120p. pap. 19.99 ***(978-0-521-23296-8(1))*** Cambridge Univ. Pr.

Clermont-Ferrand, Meredith, ed. Jean D'Angouleme's Copy of the Canterbury Tales: An Annotated Edition of Bibliotheque Nationale's Fond Anglais 39 (Paris) 2007. (ENM & ENG.). 488p. 129.95 *(978-0-7734-5327-2(X))* Mellen, Edwin Pr., The.

Cole, Andrew. Literature & Heresy in the Age of Chaucer. 2008. (Cambridge Studies in Medieval Literature Ser.). (ENG.). 324p. 98.00 *(978-0-521-88791-5(7))* Cambridge Univ. Pr.

Condren, Edward I. Chaucer from Prentice to Poet: The Metaphor of Love in Dream Visions & Troilus & Criseyde. 2008. (ENG., Illus.). 240p. 59.95 *(978-0-8130-3241-2(5))* Univ. Pr. of Florida.

Coulton, G. G. Chaucer & His England. (ENG.). 416p. 2007. 49.95 *(978-0-548-13186-2(4))* 2006. per. 34.95 *(978-1-4286-4247-8(1))* Kessinger Publishing, LLC.

—Chaucer & His England. 2008. (ENG.). 372p. per. *(978-1-4086-4312-9(X))* Read Bks.

Crocker, Holly A. & Crocker, Holly. Chaucer's Visions of Manhood. 2007. (New Middle Ages Ser.). (ENG.). 264p. 89.00 *(978-1-4039-7571-3(X))* Palgrave Macmillan.

Croft, Steven, ed. Geoffrey Chaucer: The Pardoner's Tale. 2nd rev. ed. 2008. (Oxford Student Texts). (ENG., Illus.). 144p. (YA). 15.50 *(978-0-19-832549-9(5))* Oxford Univ. Pr., Inc.

—Wife of Bath's Tale. 2nd rev. ed. 2008. (Oxford Student Texts). (ENG.). 224p. (YA). 15.95 *(978-0-19-832572-7(X))* Oxford Univ. Pr., Inc.

Cullen, Dolores. Ensnared by His Words: My Chaucer Obsession. 2008. (Illus.). 176p. pap. 12.95 *(978-1-56474-472-2(8),* Fithian Pr) Daniel & Daniel, Pubs., Inc.

Curtis, Carl C., III. Chaucer's the Knight's Tale & the Limits of Human Order in the Pagan World. 2008. 276p. 109.95 (978-0-7734-5059-2(9)) Mellen, Edwin Pr., The.

Davidson, Mary Catherine. Medievalism, Multilingualism, & Chaucer. 2009. (New Middle Ages Ser.). (ENG.). 224p. 100.00 (978-0-230-60297-7(5)) Palgrave Macmillan.

Dempsey, James, tr. from ENM. & compiled by. The Court Poetry of Chaucer: A Facing-Page Translation in Modern English. 2007. (ENM & ENG.). 204p. 99.95 (978-0-7734-5434-7(9)) Mellen, Edwin Pr., The.

Donaldson, E. Talbot. Speaking of Chaucer. Date not set. 187p. pap. (978-0-485-12021-9(6)) Continuum International Publishing Group, Ltd.

Dryden, John. Essays of John Dryden. 2009. 244p. 23.99 (978-1-103-61393-9(6)); pap. 17.99 (978-1-103-61390-8(1)) BiblioBazaar.

—Essays of John Dryden. Yonge, Charles Duke, ed. 2007. (ENG.). 240p. 41.95 (978-0-548-11067-6(0)) Kessinger Publishing, LLC.

—Essays of John Dryden. 2008. (ENG.). 404p. per. (978-1-4086-6181-9(0)) Read Bks.

Edmondson, George. The Neighboring Text: Chaucer, Boccaccio, Henryson. 2011. (ENG.). 296p. pap. 40.00 (978-0-268-02775-9(7)) Univ. of Notre Dame Pr.

Edmunds, Edward William. Chaucer & His Poetry. 2009. 224p. 24.99 (978-0-554-40020-4(0)); pap. 24.75 (978-0-554-40019-8(7)) BiblioBazaar.

Ferster, Judith. Chaucer on Interpretation. 2009. (ENG.). 208p. pap. 33.99 (978-0-521-11093-8(9)) Cambridge Univ. Pr.

Fleay, Frederick Gard. Guide to Chaucer & Spenser. 2008. 126p. 24.99 (978-0-554-74699-9(9)); 126p. 21.99 (978-0-554-74708-8(1)); 262p. pap. 19.75 (978-0-554-74705-7(7)); 262p. pap. 20.75 (978-0-554-74700-2(6)) BiblioBazaar.

Forgeng, Jeffrey L. & McLean, Will. Daily Life in Chaucer's England. 2nd rev. ed. 2008. (Greenwood Press Daily Life Through History Ser.). (Illus.). 328p. 49.95 (978-0-313-35951-4(2), GR5951, Greenwood Pr.) Greenwood Publishing Group, Inc.

Foster, Michael. Chaucer's Narrators & the Rhetoric of Self-Representation. 2008. 196p. pap. 57.95 (978-3-03911-121-3(3)) Lang, Peter AG GBR. Dist: Lang, Peter.

French, Robert D. A Chaucer Handbook. 2nd ed. reprint ed. 35.00 (978-0-404-20100-5(8)) AMS Pr., Inc.

Fyler, John M. Language & the Declining World in Chaucer, Dante, & Jean de Meun. (Cambridge Studies in Medieval Literature Ser.). (ENG.). 2010. 322p. pap. 39.99 (978-0-521-14771-2(9)) 2007. 380p. 127.00 (978-0-521-87215-7(4)) Cambridge Univ. Pr.

Gardner, John E. The Poetry of Chaucer. 2006. 408p. reprint ed. pap. 22.00 (978-1-4223-5314-1(1)) DIANE Publishing Co.

Giancarlo, Matthew. Parliament & Literature in Late Medieval England. 2007. (Cambridge Studies in Medieval Literature Ser.). (ENG., Illus.). 306p. 115.99 (978-0-521-87539-4(0)) Cambridge Univ. Pr.

Goodall, Peter. Chaucer's Monk's Tale & Nun's Priest's Tale: Bibliography. annot. ed. 2009. (Chaucer Bibliographies Ser.). 530p. (978-0-8020-9320-2(5)) Univ. of Toronto Pr.

Goth, Maik. From Chaucer's Pardoner to Shakespeare's Iago: Aspects of Intermediality in the History of the Vice. 2009. (Studien zur englischen und amerikanischen Literatur Ser.). 150p. pap. 49.95 (978-3-631-56465-3(1)) Lang, Peter GmbH, Europaischer Verlag der Wissenschaften DEU. Dist: Lang, Peter.

Grady, Frank, ed. Studies in the Age of Chaucer, Volume 29. 2007. (ND Studies Age Chaucer Ser.). (ENG.). 720p. 60.00 (978-0-933784-31-4(7)) New Chaucer Society, The.

Gust, Geoffrey & Gust, Geoffrey W. Constructing Chaucer: Author & Autofiction in the Critical Tradition. 2009. (New Middle Ages Ser.). (ENG.). 300p. 105.00 (978-1-4039-7643-7(0)) Palgrave Macmillan.

Hadow, Grace E. Chaucer & His Times. 2010. 256p. pap. 22.36 (978-1-162-72951-0(1)) Kessinger Publishing, LLC.

—Chaucer & His Times. 2008. 272p. (978-1-4437-2369-5(X)) 2006. (ENG.). 268p. per. (978-1-4067-2384-7(3)) Read Bks. (Hesperides Pr.).

Hamaguchi, Keiko. Non-European Women in Chaucer: A Postcolonial Study. Vol. 14. 2006. (Studies in English Medieval Language & Literature Ser.). ix,194p. pap. (978-0-8204-9875-1(0)) Lang, Peter AG.

Hammond, Eleanor P. Chaucer: A Bibliographical Manual. 579p. reprint ed. lib. bdg. 67.00 (978-0-8328-3129-4(8)) Higginson Bk. Co.

Haskell, Ann S. Essays on Chaucer's Saints. (Studies in English Literature Ser.). (ENG.). VI, 84p. 210.00 (978-3-11-174393-6(4)) De Gruyter, Mouton DEU. Dist: de Gruyter, Walter GmbH & Co. KG.

Heinrichs, Katherine. The Myths of Love: Classical Lovers in Medieval Literature. 2008. (ENG.). 284p. per. 23.95 (978-0-271-02826-2(2)) Pennsylvania State Univ. Pr.

Helmbold, Anita. Understanding the Manuscript Frontispiece to Corpus Christi College Cambridge MS 61: The Political Lanuage of a Lancastrian Portrait. 2009. 464p. 129.95 (978-0-7734-4691-5(5)) Mellen, Edwin Pr., The.

Hill, Thomas. She, this in Blak: Vision, Truth, & Will in Geoffrey Chaucer's Troilus & Criseyde. 2008. 144p. 39.95 (978-0-415-99357-9(1)) Routledge.

Holley, Linda Tarte. Reason & Imagination in Chaucer, the Perle-Poet, & the Cloud-Author: Seeing from the Center. 2011. (New Middle Ages Ser.). (ENG., Illus.). 208p. 80.00 (978-0-230-10510-2(6)) Palgrave Macmillan.

Holton, Amanda. The Sources of Chaucer's Poetics. 2008. 178p. 99.95 (978-0-7546-6394-2(9)) Ashgate Publishing Co.

Hulbert, James R. 1884-1969. Chaucer's Official Life. 2010. 84p. pap. 18.75 (978-1-174-82115-6(9)) BiblioBazaar.

Hulbert, James Root. Chaucer's Official Life. 2010. 86p. pap. 18.75 (978-1-148-65854-4(8)) 2010. 84p. pap. 18.75 (978-1-147-56858-5(8)) 2009. 84p. pap. 18.75 (978-1-116-91364-4(X)) 2009. 84p. pap. 18.75 (978-1-116-91365-1(8)) BiblioBazaar.

—Chaucer's Official Life. 2009. 74p. pap. (978-1-4588-1799-0(7)) Books LLC.

—Chaucer's Official Life. 2008. 88p. pap. (978-1-4099-1486-0(0)) Dodo Pr.

—Chaucer's Official Life. 2010. (Illus.). 60p. pap. 20.00 (978-1-153-59519-3(2)) General Bks. LLC.

—Chaucer's Official Life. 84p. 2010. 26.36 (978-1-168-94754-3(5)) 2010. 32.95 (978-1-161-74868-0(7)) 2008. pap. 17.95 (978-0-548-86505-7(1)) Kessinger Publishing, LLC.

—Chaucer's Official Life. 2008. 84p. pap. (978-1-4097-9701-2(5)) Read Bks.

—Chaucer's Official Life . . 2009. 82p. pap. 16.99 (978-1-116-91367-5(4)); (ENG.). pap. 18.99 (978-1-116-91366-8(6)) BiblioBazaar. (BiblioLife).

Kane, George. Chaucer & Langland. 312p. pap. (978-0-485-11325-9(2)) Continuum International Publishing Group, Ltd.

Kittredge, George Lyman. Chaucer & Some of His Friends. 2009. 24p. pap. 15.95 (978-1-120-17454-3(6)) Kessinger Publishing, LLC.

Knapp, Peggy. Chaucer & the Social Contest. 2011. (Routledge Revivals Ser.). (ENG.). 174p. 95.00 (978-0-415-61603-4(4)) Routledge.

Knapp, Peggy A. Chaucerian Aesthetics. 2008. (New Middle Ages Ser.). (ENG.). 252p. 95.00 (978-0-230-60668-5(7)) Palgrave Macmillan.

Kolve, V. A. Chaucer & the Imagery of Narrative: The First Five Canterbury Tales. 2011. (ENG., Illus.). 568p. reprint ed. pap. 37.95 (978-0-8047-1349-8(9)) Stanford Univ. Pr.

—Telling Images: Chaucer & the Imagery of Narrative II. (ENG., Illus.). 408p. 2010. pap. 24.95 (978-0-8047-7658-5(X)) 2009. 65.00 (978-0-8047-5583-2(3)) Stanford Univ. Pr.

Lerer, S. The Yale Companion to Chaucer. 2007. (ENG., Illus.). 432p. per. 20.00 (978-0-300-12597-9(6)) Yale Univ. Pr.

Lerer, Seth. Courtly Letters in the Age of Henry VIII: Literary Culture & the Arts of Deceit. 2006. (Cambridge Studies in Renaissance Literature & Culture Ser.). (ENG.). 272p. pap. 55.00 (978-0-521-03527-9(9)) Cambridge Univ. Pr.

Lindeboom, B. W. Venus¿ Owne Clerk: Chaucer¿s Debt to the Confessio Amantis. 2007. (Costerus New Ser.: 167). 484p. 130.00 (978-90-420-2150-1(0)) Rodopi.

Linden, Stanton J. Darke Hieroglyphicks: Alchemy in English Literature from Chaucer to the Restoration. 2008. (Studies in the English Renaissance Ser.). (ENG., Illus.). 384p. pap. 30.00 (978-0-8131-9212-3(9)) Univ. Pr. of Kentucky.

Lounsbury, Thomas R. Studies in Chaucer V1 His Life & Writi. 2006. pap. 42.95 (978-1-4286-3958-4(6)) Kessinger Publishing, LLC.

—Studies in Chaucer V2 His Life & Writi. 2006. pap. 42.95 (978-1-4286-3959-1(4)) Kessinger Publishing, LLC.

—Studies in Chaucer V3 His Life & Writi. 2006. pap. 40.95 (978-1-4286-3960-7(8)) Kessinger Publishing, LLC.

Lounsbury, Thomas RaynesFord. Studies in Chaucer. 2009. 340p. pap. (978-0-217-87763-3(X)) Books LLC.

—Studies in Chaucer. 2009. 394p. pap. 21.70 (978-0-217-56185-3(3)) General Bks. LLC.

Lowell, James Russell. My Study Windows by James Russell Lowell. 2006. 448p. per. 26.99 (978-1-4255-4921-3(7)) MPublishing.

Lowes, John L. Geoffrey Chaucer. reprint ed. 26.00 (978-0-404-20161-6(X)) AMS Pr., Inc.

Mack, Peter & Wilson, Chris, eds. Geoffrey Chaucer. 2nd rev. ed. 2008. (Oxford Student Texts). (ENG.). 208p. (YA). 15.95 (978-0-19-832577-2(0)) Oxford Univ. Pr., Inc.

Mack, Peter, et al. The Nun's Priest's Tale. Mack, Peter et al, eds. 2nd rev. ed. 2008. (Oxford Student Texts). (ENG., Illus.). 176p. (YA). 15.95 (978-0-19-832548-2(7)) Oxford Univ. Pr., Inc.

Madeleva, M. Grace. Chaucer's Nuns & Other Essays. reprint ed. 39.00 (978-0-403-04008-7(6)) Somerset Pubs., Inc.

Marshall, Simone Celine. The Anonymous Text: The 500-Year History of the Assembly of Ladies. 2010. 219p. 55.95 (978-3-03911-953-0(2)) Lang, Peter Publishing, Inc.

Masciandaro, Nicola. The Voice of the Hammer: The Meaning of Work in Middle English Literature. 2006. 208p. per. 25.00 (978-0-268-03498-6(2)) Univ. of Notre Dame Pr.

Matthews, David, ed. Studies in the Age of Chaucer, Volume 32. 2011. (ND Studies Age Chaucer Ser.). (ENG.). 560p. 60.00 (978-0-933784-34-5(1)) New Chaucer Society, The.

McCormack, Frances. Chaucer & the Culture of Dissent. 2007. 252p. (C). 70.00 (978-1-84682-049-6(9)) Four Courts Pr. IRL. Dist: International Specialized Bk. Services.

Miller, Mark. Philosophical Chaucer: Love, Sex, & Agency in the Canterbury Tales. 2009. (Cambridge Studies in Medieval Literature Ser.). (ENG.). 304p. pap. 39.99 (978-0-521-10066-3(6)) Cambridge Univ. Pr.

Minnis, Alastair. Fallible Authors: Chaucer's Pardoner & Wife of Bath. 2007. (Middle Ages Ser.). 528p. (C). 69.95 (978-0-8122-4030-6(8)) Univ. of Pennsylvania Pr.

Mitchell, J. Allan. Ethics & Eventfulness in Middle English Literature. 2009. (New Middle Ages Ser.). (ENG.). 204p. 95.00 (978-1-4039-7442-6(X)) Palgrave Macmillan.

Morrison, Susan Signe. Excrement in the Late Middle Ages: Sacred Filth & Chaucer's Fecopoetics. 2008. (New Middle Ages Ser.). (ENG.). 288p. 105.00 (978-1-4039-8488-3(3)) Palgrave Macmillan.

Morse, Ruth & Windeatt, Barry, eds. Chaucer Traditions: Studies in Honour of Derek Brewer. 2006. (ENG., Illus.). 292p. (C). pap. 58.00 (978-0-521-03149-3(4)) Cambridge Univ. Pr.

Mosser, Daniel W. A Digital Catalogue of the pre-1500 Manuscripts & Incunables of the Canterbury Tales. 2011. cd-rom 90.00 (978-1-904628-14-9(1)); cd-rom 210.00 (978-1-904628-13-2(3)) Scholarly Digital Editions GBR. Dist: Boydell & Brewer, Inc.

Passmore, S. Elizabeth & Carter, Susan. The English "Loathly Lady" Tales: Boundaries, Traditions, Motifs. 2008. (Studies in Medieval Culture). 40.00 (978-1-58044-123-0(8)); pap. 20.00 (978-1-58044-124-7(6)) Medieval Institute Pubns.

Patterson, Lee. Temporal Circumstances: Form & History in the Canterbury Tales. 2006. (New Middle Ages Ser.). (ENG.). 288p. 89.00 (978-1-4039-7481-5(0)) Palgrave Macmillan.

Phillips, Susan E. Transforming Talk: The Problem with Gossip in Late Medieval England. 2007. (ENG., Illus.). 192p. 45.00 (978-0-271-02994-8(3)) Pennsylvania State Univ. Pr.

Pugh, Tison & Weisl, Angela Jane, eds. Chaucer's Troilus & Criseyde & the Shorter Poems. 2006. (Approaches to Teaching World Literature Ser.: Vol. 91). (Illus.). 217p. 37.50 (978-0-87352-996-9(0)); per. 19.75 (978-0-87352-997-6(9)) Modern Language Assn. of America.

Quinn, Esther Casier. Geoffrey Chaucer & the Poetics of Disguise. 2008. (ENG.). 274p. pap. 44.50 (978-0-7618-4010-7(9)) Univ. Pr. of America, Inc.

Rigby, S. H. Wisdom & Chivalry: Chaucer's Knight's Tale & Medieval Political Theory. 2009. (Medieval & Renaissance Authors & Texts Ser.). 345p. (978-90-04-17624-9(1)) BRILL.

Rogers, Shannon L., ed. All Things Chaucer: An Encyclopedia of Chaucer's World, 2 vols. 2006. (Illus.). 584p. 149.95 (978-0-313-33252-4(5), GR3252, Greenwood Pr.) Greenwood Publishing Group, Inc.

Scanlon, Larry. Narrative, Authority & Power: The Medieval Exemplum & the Chaucerian Tradition. 2007. (Cambridge Studies in Medieval Literature Ser.). (ENG.). 392p. pap. 79.00 (978-0-521-04425-7(1)) Cambridge Univ. Pr.

Tobler, Alfred. Geoffrey Chaucer's Influence on English Literature. 2009. 138p. 24.99 (978-1-116-44265-6(5)); pap. 19.75 (978-1-116-44267-0(1)); pap. 20.75 (978-1-116-44266-3(3)) BiblioBazaar.

—Geoffrey Chaucer's Influence on English Literature. 2009. 134p. 35.95 (978-1-104-79133-9(1)); pap. 20.95 (978-1-104-75368-9(5)) Kessinger Publishing, LLC.

Tuckwell, William. Chaucer. 2008. 111p. 21.99 (978-0-554-97208-4(5)); 24.99 (978-0-554-97194-0(1)); pap. 19.75 (978-0-554-97206-0(9)); pap. 19.75 (978-0-554-97196-4(8)) BiblioBazaar.

—Chaucer. 2009. 70p. pap. (978-0-217-19187-6(8)) Books LLC.

—Chaucer. 2008. 124p. pap. (978-1-4097-9699-2(X)) Read Bks.

Turner, Marion. Chaucerian Conflict: Languages of Antagonism in Late Fourteenth-Century London. 2007. (Oxford English Monographs). 224p. 125.00 (978-0-19-920789-3(5)) Oxford Univ. Pr., Inc.

Urban, Malte. Fragments: Past & Present in Chaucer & Gower. 2008. 248p. pap. 66.95 (978-3-03911-376-7(3)) Lang, Peter AG GBR. Dist: Lang, Peter.

Vazquez, Nila. The Tale of Gamelyn of the Canterbury Tales: An Annotated Edition with Introduction, Translation, Commentary, & Glossary by Nila Vazquez. 2009. vi, 466p. (978-0-7734-3852-1(1)) Mellen, Edwin Pr., The.

Ward, Adolphus Willi & Ward, Adolphus William. Chaucer. 2010. 214p. pap. 24.75 (978-1-148-58153-8(7)) BiblioBazaar.

Ward, Adolphus William. Chaucer. 2011. 222p. pap. 25.75 (978-1-175-18826-7(3)) 2011. 222p. pap. 24.75 (978-1-175-18700-0(3)) 2010. 558p. pap. 42.75 (978-1-178-45067-5(8)) 2010. 218p. pap. 24.75 (978-1-177-85182-4(2)) 2010. (ENG.). 224p. pap. 25.75 (978-1-176-25400-8(6)) 2010. 218p. pap. 24.75 (978-1-148-59828-4(6)) 2010. 214p. pap. 24.75 (978-1-147-86369-7(5)) 2010. 220p. pap. 24.75 (978-1-146-75264-0(4)) 2010. 608p. pap. 45.75 (978-1-143-64210-4(4)) 2010. 216p. pap. 24.75 (978-1-145-53094-2(X)) 2010. 224p. pap. 24.75 (978-1-145-68010-4(0)) 2010. 214p. pap. 24.75 (978-1-145-66352-7(4)) 2010. 226p. pap. 25.75 (978-1-141-56213-8(8)) 2009. (ENG.). 216p. pap. 20.99 (978-1-110-54698-5(X), BiblioLife) 2009. (ENG.). 216p. pap. 22.99 (978-1-110-54700-5(5), BiblioLife) BiblioBazaar.

—Chaucer. 2011. (Cambridge Library Collection - English Men of Letters Ser.). (ENG.). 212p. pap. 22.99 (978-1-108-03464-7(0)) Cambridge Univ. Pr.

—Chaucer. 2010. (Illus.). 108p. pap. 19.94 (978-1-153-59518-6(4)) General Bks. LLC.

—Chaucer. 2010. 154p. pap. 17.56 (978-1-162-65769-1(3)); 29.56 (978-1-169-26593-6(6)); 36.95 (978-1-161-42634-2(5)) Kessinger Publishing, LLC.

Ward, Adolphus William, creator. Chaucer. 2011. 148p. pap. 21.75 (978-1-246-47513-5(8)) BiblioBazaar.

Williams, David. Language Redeemed: Chaucer's Mature Poetry. 2007. 133p. pap. (978-1-932589-35-1(X)) Ave Maria Univ.

Williams, Deanne. The French Fetish from Chaucer to Shakespeare. 2007. (Cambridge Studies in Renaissance Literature & Culture Ser.). (ENG., Illus.). 304p. pap. 62.00 (978-0-521-03738-9(7)) Cambridge Univ. Pr.

Wimsatt, James I. Chaucer & the Poems of "Ch" 2008. (FRO & ENG.). pap. 13.00 (978-1-58044-132-2(7)) Medieval Institute Pubns.

Woods, William F. Chaucerian Spaces: Spatial Poetics in Chaucer's Opening Tales. 2008. (SUNY Series in Medieval Studies). xi, 203p. pap. 21.95 (978-0-7914-7488-4(7)); 60.00 (978-0-7914-7487-7(9)) State Univ. of New York Pr.

CHAUCER, GEOFFREY, D. 1400—BIBLIOGRAPHY

Martin, Willard E., Jr. Chaucer Bibliography, 1925-1933. reprint ed. 31.50 (978-0-404-04195-3(7)) AMS Pr., Inc.

Peterson, William S., et al. The Kelmscott Chaucer: A Census. 2011. (978-1-58456-289-4(7)) Oak Knoll Pr.

CHAUCER, GEOFFREY, D. 1400—CONTEMPORARY ENGLAND

Hadow, Grace E. Chaucer & His Times. 2010. 256p. pap. 22.36 (978-1-162-72951-0(1)) Kessinger Publishing, LLC.

—Chaucer & His Times. 2008. 272p. (978-1-4437-2369-5(X)) 2006. (ENG.). 268p. per. (978-1-4067-2384-7(3)) Read Bks. (Hesperides Pr.).

Hughes, Dorothy. Illustrations of Chaucer's England. 2009. 176p. pap. (978-0-217-49217-1(7)) Books LLC.

—Illustrations of Chaucer's England. 2008. 314p. 45.95 (978-1-4365-8591-0(0)) 2007. (ENG.). 316p. per. 30.95 (978-0-548-80060-7(X)) Kessinger Publishing, LLC.

Hughes, Dorothy, ed. Illustrations of Chaucer's England. 2009. 318p. 45.95 (978-1-120-82002-0(2)); pap. 30.95 (978-1-120-62973-9(X)) Kessinger Publishing, LLC.

Jenks, Tudor. In the Days of Chaucer. 2009. 326p. 32.99 (978-1-116-53001-8(5)) 2009. 326p. 36.99 (978-1-116-53000-1(7)) 2009. 326p. pap. 29.75 (978-1-116-53003-2(1)) 2009. 326p. pap. 30.75 (978-1-116-53002-5(3)) 2008. 324p. 28.99 (978-0-559-45121-8(0)) 2008. 324p. pap. 29.75 (978-0-559-45117-1(2)) BiblioBazaar.

—In the Days of Chaucer. 2008. 318p. 45.95 (978-1-4372-4219-5(7)); pap. 30.95 (978-1-4371-1430-0(X)) Kessinger Publishing, LLC.

CHAUCER, GEOFFREY, D. 1400—CRITICISM AND INTERPRETATION

Anderson, Judith H. Reading the Allegorical Intertext: Chaucer, Spenser, Shakespeare, Milton. 3rd ed. 2010. (ENG.). 320p. pap. 30.00 (978-0-8232-2848-5(7)) Fordham Univ. Pr.

Baranski, Zygmunt & Cachey Jr, Theodore J., Jr., eds. Petrarch & Dante: Anti-Dantism, Metaphysics, Tradition. 2009. (ND Devers Series in Dante Studies). (ENG.). 496p. pap. 50.00 (978-0-268-02211-2(9)) Univ. of Notre Dame Pr.

Barr, Jessica. Willing to Know God: Dreamers & Visionaries in the Later Middle Ages. 2010. 49.95 (978-0-8142-1127-4(5)); cd-rom 14.95 (978-0-8142-9226-6(7)) Ohio State Univ. Pr.

Beidler, Peter G. Chaucer's Canterbury Comedies: Origins & Originality. 2011. 328p. pap. 18.95 (978-1-60381-075-3(7), Coffeetown Pr.) Coffeetown Enterprises, Inc.

Brewer, Derek. Geoffrey Chaucer Vol. 1: The Critical Heritage, 1385-1837. 2009. 342p. pap. 45.00 (978-0-415-56887-6(0)) Routledge.

Brown, Peter. Geoffrey Chaucer. 2011. (Oxford World's Classics Ser.). (ENG., Illus.). 266p. pap. 13.95 (978-0-19-280429-7(4)) Oxford Univ. Pr., Inc.

Bryant, Brantley L. Geoffrey Chaucer Hath a Blog: Medieval Studies & New Media. 2010. (New Middle Ages Ser.). (ENG.). 212p. 89.00 (978-0-230-10506-5(8)); pap. 26.00 (978-0-230-10507-2(6)) Palgrave Macmillan.

Burrow, John A. English Poets in the Late Middle Ages: Chaucer Langland & Others. 2012. (Variorum Collected Studies). 356p. 165.00 (978-1-4094-4455-8(4)) Ashgate Publishing Co.

Cawsey, Kathy. Twentieth-Century Chaucer Criticism: Reading Audiences. 2011. 198p. 99.95 (978-1-4094-0478-1(1)) Ashgate Publishing Co.

Chaucer, Geoffrey. The Wife of Bath. Swan, Richard, ed. 2010. 94p. pap. 24.95 (978-1-4441-1984-8(2)) Hodder Education GBR. Dist: Trans-Atlantic Pubns., Inc.

Chaucer, Geoffrey & Trahern, Joseph B. The Wife of Bath's Prologue & Tale. Allen, Mark & Fisher, John H., eds. 2012. (Variorum Chaucer Ser.). (ENG., Illus.). 776p. 90.00 (978-0-8061-4224-1(3)) Univ. of Oklahoma Pr.

Clarke, K. P. Chaucer & Italian Textuality. 2011. 256p. 110.00 (978-0-19-960777-8(X)) Oxford Univ. Pr., Inc.

Fein, Susanna & Raybin, David, eds. Chaucer: Contemporary Approaches. 2009. (ENG., Illus.). 280p. pap. 29.95 (978-0-271-03568-0(4)) Pennsylvania State Univ. Pr.

Fumo, Jamie. The Legacy of Apollo: Antiquity, Authority & Chaucerian Poetics. 2010. (ENG., Illus.). 344p. (978-1-4426-4170-9(3)) Univ. of Toronto Pr.

Hanning, Robert W. Serious Play: Desire & Authority in the Poetry of Ovid, Chaucer, & Ariosto. 2010. (Leonard Hastings Schoff Lectures). (ENG.). 312p. (gr. 17). 45.00 (978-0-231-15210-5(8)) Columbia Univ. Pr.

Jack, Adolphus Alfred. A Commentary on the Poetry of Chaucer & Spenser. 2008. 380p. 48.95 (978-1-4365-3515-1(8)) 2007. (ENG.). 384p. per. 33.95 (978-0-548-72194-0(7)) Kessinger Publishing, LLC.

Kelly, Henry Ansgar. Law & Religion in Chaucer's England. 2010. (Variorum Collected Studies). (Illus.). 416p. 165.00 (978-1-4094-0751-5(9)) Ashgate Publishing Co.

Kordecki, Lesley. Ecofeminist Subjectivities: Chaucer's Talking Birds. 2011. (New Middle Ages Ser.). (ENG., Illus.). 224p. 85.00 (978-0-230-11527-9(6)) Palgrave Macmillan.

Matthews, David, ed. Studies in the Age of Chaucer, Volume 31. 2010. (ND Studies Age Chaucer Ser.). (ENG.). 60.00 (978-0-933784-33-8(3)) New Chaucer Society, The.

McTaggart, Anne. Shame & Guilt in Chaucer. 2012. (New Middle Ages Ser.). (ENG.). 208p. 80.00 (978-0-230-33738-1(4)) Palgrave Macmillan.

Raybin, David. Chaucer: Contemporary Approaches. 2009. (ENG., Illus.). 216p. 65.00 (978-0-271-03567-3(6)) Pennsylvania State Univ. Pr.

Rossiter, William T. Chaucer & Petrarch. 2010. (Chaucer Studies: Volume 41). 250p. 90.00 (978-1-84384-215-6(7), D. S. Brewer) Boydell & Brewer, Ltd. GBR. Dist: Boydell & Brewer, Inc.

Sauer, Michelle M. Bloom's How to Write about Geoffrey Chaucer. 2009. (Bloom's How to Write about Literature Ser.). 240p. (C). (gr. 9-18). 45.00 (978-1-60413-330-1(9), Chelsea Hse.) Facts On File, Inc.

Schibanoff, Susan. Chaucer's Queer Poetics: Rereading the Dream Trio. 2006. (ENG.). 460p. (978-0-8020-9035-5(4)) Univ. of Toronto Pr.

Stewart Jr, George R. & Stewart Jr., George R. The Moral Chaucer: Essays in Criticism. Durham, W. H. & Flaherty, M. J., eds. 2011. 22p. 35.95 **(978-1-258-05489-2(2))** Literary Licensing, LLC.

Tatlock, John Strong Perry. The Mind & Art of Chaucer. 2011. 126p. 40.95 **(978-1-258-05441-0(8))** Literary Licensing, LLC.

Travis, Peter W. Disseminal Chaucer: Rereading the NUN's PRIEST's TALE. 2009. (ENG.). 432p. pap. 40.00 (978-0-268-04235-6(7)) Univ. of Notre Dame Pr.

CHAUCER, GEOFFREY, D. 1400—LANGUAGE

Ashton, Gail. Teaching Chaucer. Ashton, Gail & Sylvester, Louise, eds. annot. ed 2007. (Teaching the New English Ser.). (ENG., Illus.). 192p. pap. 33.00 (978-1-4039-8827-0(7)) Palgrave Macmillan.

Brink, Bernard Ten. The Language & Metre of Chaucer. Kluge, Friedrich, ed. Smith, M. Bentinck, tr. 2011. 320p. 45.95 **(978-1-169-91827-6(1))** Kessinger Publishing, LLC.

—The Language & Metre of Chaucer. Kluge, Friedrich, ed. 2010. 320p. 36.76 (978-1-163-42778-1(0)) Kessinger Publishing, LLC.

—The Language & Metre of Chaucer. Kluge, Friedrich, ed. Smith, M. Bentinck, tr. 2010. 320p. pap. 24.76 (978-1-162-96735-6(8)) Kessinger Publishing, LLC.

—The Language & Metre of Chaucer. Kluge, Friedrich, ed. 2007. (ENG.). 320p. 45.95 (978-0-548-12055-2(2)) Kessinger Publishing, LLC.

Brink, Bernhard Aegidius Konrad ten. The Language & Metre of Chaucer. 2010. 328p. pap. 31.75 (978-1-146-44944-1(5)) BiblioBazaar.

—The Language & Metre of Chaucer. 2009. 168p. pap. 14.14 (978-1-150-60833-9(1)) General Bks. LLC.

—The Language & Metre of Chaucer 2d Ed , Rev by Friedrich Kluge; Translated by M Bentinck Smith. 2011. 326p. pap. 30.75 **(978-1-179-79997-1(6))** 2009. 318p. 36.99 (978-1-116-78777-1(6)) 2009. 318p. 32.99 (978-1-116-78778-8(4)) 2009. 318p. pap. 29.75 (978-1-116-78780-1(6)) 2009. 318p. pap. 30.75 (978-1-116-78779-5(2)) BiblioBazaar.

—The language & metre of Chaucer. 2d ed. , rev. by Friedrich Kluge; translated by M. Bentinck Smith. 2009. (ENG.). 320p. pap. 23.99 (978-1-116-78782-5(2)); pap. 24.99 (978-1-116-78781-8(4)) BiblioBazaar. (BiblioLife).

—The Language & Metre of Chaucer Set Forth by Bernhard Ten Brink. 2009. 166p. pap. 19.99 (978-1-151-19867-9(6)) General Bks. LLC.

Brink, Bernhard Aegidius Konrad ten, et al. The Language & Metre of Chaucer Set Forth by Bernhard Ten Brink. 2010. 328p. pap. 31.75 (978-1-171-85155-4(3)) BiblioBazaar.

Hempl, George. Chaucer's Pronunciation & the Spelling of the Ellesmere Ms. 2009. 44p. pap. 12.99 (978-1-110-80173-2(4)) BiblioBazaar.

Horobin, Simon. Chaucer's Language. 2007. (ENG.). 224p. 95.00 (978-1-4039-9355-7(6)); pap. 31.00 (978-1-4039-9356-4(4)) Palgrave Macmillan.

Sylvester, Louise & Ashton, Gail, eds. Teaching Chaucer. 2007. (Teaching the New English Ser.). (ENG., Illus.). 192p. 116.00 (978-1-4039-8826-3(9)) Palgrave Macmillan.

CHAUCER, GEOFFREY, D. 1400—SOURCES

Correale, Robert M. & Hamel, Mary, eds. Sources & Analogues of the Canterbury Tales, 2 vols., Vol. 2. 2009. (Chaucer Studies: Volume 35). (MUL & ENG.). 840p. pap. 50.00 (978-1-84384-190-6(8), D. S. Brewer) Boydell & Brewer, Ltd. GBR. Dist: Boydell & Brewer, Inc.

—Sources & Analogues of the Canterbury Tales (pb Set) 2009. (Chaucer Studies). pap. 90.00 (978-1-84384-191-3(6), D. S. Brewer) Boydell & Brewer, Ltd. GBR. Dist: Boydell & Brewer, Inc.

CHAUCER, GEOFFREY, D. 1400—STUDY AND TEACHING

Ashton, Gail. Teaching Chaucer. Ashton, Gail & Sylvester, Louise, eds. annot. ed. 2007. (Teaching the New English Ser.). (ENG., Illus.). 192p. pap. 33.00 (978-1-4039-8827-0(7)) Palgrave Macmillan.

Grennen, Joseph. Monarch Notes on Chaucer's Canterbury Tales. (C). 3.95 (978-0-671-00511-5(1), Arco) Peterson's.

Matthews, David, ed. Studies in the Age of Chaucer, Volume 30. 2009. (ND Studies Age Chaucer Ser.). (ENG.). 60.00 (978-0-933784-32-1(5)) New Chaucer Society, The.

Sylvester, Louise & Ashton, Gail, eds. Teaching Chaucer. 2007. (Teaching the New English Ser.). (ENG., Illus.). 192p. 116.00 (978-1-4039-8826-3(9)) Palgrave Macmillan.

CHAUNCEY, CHARLES, 1705-1787

Corrigan, John. The Hidden Balance: Religion & the Social Theories of Charles Chauncy & Jonathan Mayhew. 2006. (ENG.). 176p. pap. 38.99 (978-0-521-02671-0(7)) Cambridge Univ. Pr.

Griffin, Edward M. Old Brick: Charles Chauncy of Boston, 1705-1787. 2009. (ENG.). 264p. pap. 50.00 (978-0-8166-5777-3(7)) Univ. of Minnesota Pr.

CHAUTAUQUA COUNTY (N.Y.)

Houck, Douglas. Historic Chautauqua County: A Bicentennial History. 2010. (Illus.). 72p. (978-1-935377-20-7(5)) Historical Publishing Network.

CHAUTAUQUAS

Canning, Charlotte M. The Most American Thing in America: Circuit Chautauqua as Performance. 2007. (Studies Theatre Hist & Culture Ser.). (Illus.). 280p. per. 19.95 (978-1-58729-585-0(7)) Univ. of Iowa Pr.

Miller, Darrel. Lincoln Park Chautauqua: Every Man's University. 2007. (Illus.). 176p. pap. (978-0-9793763-0-6(0)) Miller Publishing.

Robertson, James. Hedding among the Pines. 2008. (Illus.). 400p. per. 34.95 (978-1-933002-65-1(4)) PublishingWorks.

Tapia, John E. Circuit Chautauqua: From Rural Education to Popular Entertainment in Early Twentieth Century America. alt. ed. 2008. (ENG., Illus.). 240p. pap. 35.00 (978-0-7864-4084-9(8)) McFarland & Co., Inc. Pubs.

Thornton, Harrison John. Chautauqua in Iow. 2011. 30p. 35.95 **(978-1-258-00515-3(8))** Literary Licensing, LLC.

CHAUVINISM AND JINGOISM

see also Imperialism; Militarism

Aczel, Amir D. The Cave & the Cathedral: How a Real-Life Indiana Jones & a Renegade Scholar Decoded the Ancient Art of Man. 2009. (ENG., Illus.). 264p. 25.95 (978-0-470-37353-8(9), Wiley) Wiley, John & Sons, Inc.

Causton, E. E. N. Militarism & Foreign Policy in Japan. 2010. (ENG.). 224p. 115.00 (978-0-415-58532-3(5), Routledge) Taylor & Francis Group GBR. Dist: Taylor & Francis Group.

Hvithamar & Warburg, M., eds. Holy Nations & Global Identities: Civil Religion, Nationalism, & Globalisation. 2009. (International Studies in Religion & Society). (Illus.). 281p. (978-90-04-17828-1(7)) BRILL.

Nechtman, Tillman W. Nabobs: Empire & Identity in Eighteenth-Century Britain. 2010. (ENG., Illus.). 280p. 104.00 (978-0-521-76353-0(3)) Cambridge Univ. Pr.

CHAVEZ, CESAR, 1927-1993

Bender, Steven W. One Night in America: Robert Kennedy, César Chávez, & the Dream of Dignity. (Illus.). 264p. 2008. per. 33.95 (978-1-59451-429-6(1)) 2007. 125.00 (978-1-59451-428-9(3)) Paradigm Pubs.

Bruns, Roger A. Cesar Chavez & the United Farm Workers Movement. 2011. E-Book (978-0-313-38651-0(X), Greenwood Pr.) Greenwood Publishing Group, Inc.

Bruns, Roger A. & Bruns, Roger. Cesar Chavez & the United Farm Workers Movement, 1 vol. 2011. (Landmarks of the American Mosaic Ser.). (Illus.). 186p. 35.00 (978-0-313-38650-3(1), A3092C) Greenwood Publishing Group, Inc.

Byte Me! Electronically Created Books. Celebrating Cesar Chavez with Songs & Marches. 2007. Tr. of Celebrar a Cesar Chavez con marchas y Canciones. (SPA., Illus.). 36p. per. 5.99 (978-0-9798611-6-1(0)) Byte Me! Inc.

Chavez, Denise. A Taco Testimony: Meditations on Family, Food & Culture. 2006. (Illus.). 207p. per. 16.95 (978-1-887896-94-8(5)) Rio Nuevo Pubs.

Dunne, John Gregory. Delano: The Story of the California Grape Strike. 2007. (Illus.). 202p. per. 24.95 (978-0-520-25433-6(3)) Univ. of California Pr.

Ferriss, Susan & Sandoval, Ricardo. The Fight in the Fields: Cesar Chavez & the Farmworkers Movement. 2009. 15.13 (978-0-7848-2311-8(1), Everbind) Marco Bk. Co.

Garcia, Mario T., ed. & intro. The Gospel of Cesar Chavez: My Faith in Action. 2007. (Celebrating Faith Ser.). (ENG., Illus.). 140p. per. 16.95 (978-1-58051-223-7(2), Sheed & Ward) Rowman & Littlefield Publishers, Inc.

Hedrick, Georgia. Journey to Justice. 2007. 84p. pap. 29.98 (978-0-615-14953-0(7)) Byte Me! Inc.

—WORKBOOK on JOURNEY to JUSTICE_Memories_Where Were You? When Farmworkers Fought for Justice. Hedrick, Georgia, ed. Tmka, Marina et al, trs. 2007. Tr. of Libro de Trabajo_Viaje a la justicia_Cuando Peones agrícolas Luchados por Justicia. (ENG & SPA., Illus.). 92p. (J). per. 8.00 (978-0-9798611-4-7(4)) Byte Me! Inc.

Levy, Jacques E. & Chavez, Cesar. Cesar Chavez: Autobiography of la Causa. 2007. (Illus.). 600p. per. 19.95 (978-0-8166-5049-1(7)) Univ. of Minnesota Pr.

Orosco, José-Antonio. Cesar Chavez & the Common Sense of Nonviolence. 2008. (ENG.). 151p. 24.95 (978-0-8263-4375-8(9)) Univ. of New Mexico Pr.

Pawel, Miriam. The Union of Their Dreams: Power, Hope, & Struggle in Cesar Chavez's Farm Worker Movement. (ENG., Illus.). 384p. 2010. pap. 18.00 (978-1-60819-099-7(4)) 2009. 28.00 (978-1-59691-460-5(2)) Bloomsbury Publishing.

Pitti, Stephen. Cesar Chavez. 2007. (ENG.). 320p. 30.00 (978-0-300-10080-3(9)) Yale Univ. Pr.

Pitti, Stephen J. Cesar Chavez & the Mexican Mexican Revolution. Date not set. (978-0-8090-3390-4(9), Hill & Wang) Farrar, Straus & Giroux.

Prouty, Marco G. César Chávez, the Catholic Bishops, & the Farmworkers' Struggle for Social Justice. Prouty, Marco G. 2008. (ENG., Illus.). 208p. pap. 19.95 (978-0-8165-2731-1(8)) Univ. of Arizona Pr.

—Cesar Chavez, the Catholic Bishops, & the Farmworkers' Struggle for Social Justice. 2006. (ENG., Illus.). 208p. 40.00 (978-0-8165-2555-3(2)) Univ. of Arizona Pr.

Shaw, Randy. Beyond the Fields: Cesar Chavez, the UFW, & the Struggle for Justice in the 21st Century. (Illus.). 368p. 2010. (ENG.). pap. 17.95 (978-0-520-26804-3(0)) 2008. 45.00 (978-0-520-25107-6(5)) Univ. of California Pr.

Stavans, Ilan. César Chávez. 2010. (ENG., Illus.). 96p. pap. 13.95 (978-1-933693-22-4(3)) Cinco Puntos Pr.

—César Chávez, 1 vol. 2009. (Ilan Stavans Library of Latino Civilization Ser.). 160p. 55.00 (978-0-313-36488-4(5), GR6488) Greenwood Publishing Group, Inc.

Watt, Alan J. Farm Workers & the Churches: The Movement in California & Texas. 2010. (Fronteras Series, sponsored by Texas A&M International University Ser.). (ENG., Illus.). 264p. 48.00 (978-1-60344-174-2(3)); pap. 24.00 (978-1-60344-193-3(X)) Texas A&M Univ. Pr.

CHAVEZ, CESAR, 1927-1993—JUVENILE LITERATURE

Wadsworth, Ginger. Cesar Chavez. (J). 16.20 **(978-0-7569-6865-6(8))** Perfection Learning Corp.

CHAZARS

see Khazars

CHEADLE, WALTER BUTLER, 1835-1910

Cheadle, Walter. Cheadle's Journal of Trip Across Canada:Of Trip Across Canada, 1862-1863, 1 vol. 2010. (ENG., Illus.). 312p. pap. (978-1-926741-07-9(2)) TouchWood Editions.

CHEAP COOKING

see Low Budget Cooking

CHEATING AT CARDS

see Cardsharping

CHEATING IN SPORTS

see Sports—Corrupt Practices

CHEBYSHEV POLYNOMIALS

Kotovshchikova, Marina. Pseudospectral Simulations of 2d Flow Past a Dimpled Cylinder - Numerical Simulations of 2d Flow Past a Dimpled Cylinder Using Fourier-Chebyshev Pseud. 2008. 80p. pap. (978-3-8364-8853-2(1)) VDM Verlag Dr. Mueller e.K.

CHEBYSHEV SYSTEMS

see also Approximation Theory; Chebyshev Polynomials

Kitahara, K. Spaces of Approximating Functions with Haar-like Conditions. 2008. (Lecture Notes in Mathematics Ser.). 120p. pap. 26.00 (978-3-540-57974-8(5)) Springer.

Zielke, R. Discontinuous Cebysev Systems. 2008. (Lecture Notes in Mathematics Ser.). 124p. pap. 26.00 (978-3-540-09125-7(4)) Springer.

CHECHNIA (RUSSIA)—HISTORY

Akhmadov, Ilyas & Lanskoy, Miriam. The Chechen Struggle: Independence Won & Lost. 2010. (ENG., Illus.). 288p. 37.00 (978-0-230-10534-8(3)) Palgrave Macmillan.

Jagielski, Wojciech. Towers of Stone: The Battle of Wills in Chechnya. Gauger, Soren, tr. 2009. 352p. pap. 19.95 (978-1-58322-864-7(0)) Seven Stories Pr.

Moore, Cerwyn. Contemporary Violence: Post-Modern War in Kosovo & Chechnya. 2011. (ENG.). 192p. 95.00 (978-0-7190-7599-5(8)) Manchester Univ. Pr. GBR. Dist: Macmillan.

Saraliev, Sh IU. Chechenskii Arkhiv: [sbornik Materialov Po Istorii Chechenskogo Naroda. 2008. (RUS., Illus.). (978-5-98896-094-2(4)) Kniznoe izdatel'stvo.

Saraliev, Sh IU & Muzaev, M. N. Chechenskii Arkhiv: [sbornik Materialov Po Istorii Chechenskogo Naroda. 2008. (RUS., Illus.). (978-5-94587-433-6(7)) Kniznoe Izdatel'stvo.

Wood, Tony. Chechnya: The Case for Independence. 2007. (ENG., Illus.). 160p. per. 22.95 (978-1-84467-114-4(3), 844114) Verso Bks. GBR. Dist: Norton, W. W. & Co., Inc.

CHECHNIA (RUSSIA)—HISTORY—CIVIL WAR, 1994-

Babchenko, Arkady. One Soldier's War. Allen, Nick, tr. 2009. (ENG.). 416p. pap. 15.00 (978-0-8021-4403-4(9), Grove Pr.) Grove/Atlantic, Inc.

Eichler, Maya. Militarizing Men: Gender, Conscription, & War in Post-Soviet Russia. 2011. (ENG.). 256p. 80.00 **(978-0-8047-7619-6(9))**; pap. 24.95 **(978-0-8047-7620-2(2))** Stanford Univ. Pr.

Gilligan, Emma. Terror in Chechnya: Russia & the Tragedy of Civilians in War. 2009. (Human Rights & Crimes against Humanity Ser.). (ENG., Illus.). 288p. (C). 37.50 (978-0-691-13079-8(5)) Princeton Univ. Pr.

Hughes, James. Chechnya: From Nationalism to Jihad. 2008. (National & Ethnic Conflict in the 21st Century Ser.). (Illus.). 296p. (C). pap. 26.50 (978-0-8122-2030-8(7)) Univ. of Pennsylvania Pr.

Hughes, James H. Chechnya: From Nationalism to Jihad. 2007. (National & Ethnic Conflict in the 21st Century Ser.). (ENG., Illus.). 296p. (C). 55.00 (978-0-8122-4013-9(8)) Univ. of Pennsylvania Pr.

Jagielski, Wojciech. Towers of Stone: The Battle of Wills in Chechnya. Gauger, Soren A., tr. from POL. 2009. (ENG.). 336p. pap. 19.95 (978-1-58322-900-2(0)) Seven Stories Pr.

Orlov, O. P. & Cherkasov, Aleksandr. Rossiia — Chechnia: Tsep Oshibok I Prestuplenii, 1994-1996. 2010. (RUS., Illus.). 446p. (978-5-7712-0420-8(X)) Prava Celoveka, Izdatel'stvo.

Russell, Bertrand. Chechnya. 2007. (Illus.). 272p. 150.00 (978-0-415-38064-5(2)) Routledge.

Souleimanov, Emil. Endless War: The Russian-Chechen Conflict in Perspective. 366p. pap. 44.95 (978-3-631-56040-2(0)) Lang, Peter Publishing, Inc.

Toler, George S. Chechnya Still Boiling. 2009. (Russian Political, Economic & Security Issues Ser.). 43.00 (978-1-60692-577-5(6)) Nova Science Pubs., Inc.

Wood, Tony. Chechnya: The Case for Independence. 2007. (ENG., Illus.). 160p. per. 22.95 (978-1-84467-114-4(3), 844114) Verso Bks. GBR. Dist: Norton, W. W. & Co., Inc.

CHECK FRAUD

Cross, Richard F. & Gillette, Clayton P. Self-Paced Security & Fraud Training for Banks. (978-1-55827-385-3(7)) Sheshunoff Information Services.

Schaeffer, Mary S. New Payment World: A Manager's Guide to Creating an Efficient Payment Process. 2007. (ENG., Illus.). 208p. 57.95 (978-0-470-12054-5(1), Wiley) Wiley, John & Sons, Inc.

Singh, Dr Jasvinder, et al. Hand Book on Dishonour of Cheque Part- 2011. 330p. pap. **(978-3-8443-1838-8(0))** Lambert Academic Publishing.

—Hand Book on Dishonour of Cheque Part-B,C. 2011. 628p. pap. **(978-3-8443-2045-9(8))** Lambert Academic Publishing.

CHECKERS

Clarke, R. M. Checker Automobiles. 2010. (Road Test Portfolio Ser.). (ENG., Illus.). 140p. pap. 36.95 (978-1-85520-898-8(9), 1855208989) Brooklands Bks. GBR. Dist: MBI Distribution Services/Quayside Distribution.

Denvir, John T. Three Move Guide to Checkers. 2011. 162p. pap. 11.95 **(978-1-61646-102-7(0))** Coachwhip Pubns.

Ryan, William F. Tricks, Traps & Shots of the Checkerboard. 2011. 164p. pap. 11.95 **(978-1-61646-078-5(4))** Coachwhip Pubns.

Schaeffer, Jonathan. One Jump Ahead: Computer Perfection at Checkers. 2nd ed. 2008. (ENG., Illus.). XX, 585p. pap. 49.95 (978-0-387-76575-4(1), 0387765751) Springer.

Schneider, Harold. Realistically Starting Board Game Tournaments for the Fun, Profit, & Professionalism of the Public. 2006. 9.00 (978-0-8059-7325-9(7)) Dorrance Publishing Co., Inc.

CHECKS

see also Clearinghouses

Brook. Payment Systems. 4th ed. 2009. pap., stu. ed. 46.95 (978-0-7355-8853-0(8)) Wolters Kluwer Law & Business.

Cheatham, Anne J. Guide to Check 21 Implementation & Operations. (978-1-55827-950-6(4)) Alex eSolutions, Inc.

Ezon. E-Z Rules for Negotiable Instruments & Bank Deposits. 2008. xvii, 329p. pap., stu. ed. 31.95 (978-0-7355-7199-0(6)) Wolters Kluwer Law & Business.

Hoffman, E. E. Billion Dollar Check Racket. 2011. 134p. 40.95 **(978-1-258-07043-4(X))** Literary Licensing, LLC.

Jones, Thatcher C. Clearings & Collections: Foreign & Domestic. (Columbia University, Studies in the Social Sciences: No. 347). reprint ed. 29.50 (978-0-404-51347-4(6)) AMS Pr., Inc.

McJohn, Stephen M. Glannon Guide to Commercial Paper & Payment Systems: Learning Commercial Paper & Payment Systems Through Multiple-Choice Questions & Analysis. 2009. xi, 361p. pap., stu. ed. 38.95 (978-0-7355-7802-9(8)) Wolters Kluwer Law & Business.

McJohn, Stephen M. The Glannon Guide to Commercial Paper & Payment Systems: Learning Commercial Paper & Payment Systems Through Multiple-Choice Questions & Analysis. 2nd ed. 2011. **(978-1-4548-0405-5(X))** Kluwer Law International.

Miller, Frederick H. The Lawyer's Guide to Modern Payment Methods: ACH, Credit, Debit, & More. 2007. (ENG., Illus.). 199p. pap. 59.95 incl. cd-rom (978-1-59031-819-5(6)) American Bar Assn.

Schaeffer, Mary S. New Payment World: A Manager's Guide to Creating an Efficient Payment Process. 2007. (ENG., Illus.). 208p. 57.95 (978-0-470-12054-5(1), Wiley) Wiley, John & Sons, Inc.

Spengler, Mark. Die Entstehung des Scheckgesetzes vom 11. März 1908. 2008. (Rechtshistorische Reihe Ser.). (GER.). 422p. pap. 99.95 (978-3-631-57092-0(9)) Lang, Peter GmbH, Europaischer Verlag der Wissenschaften DEU. Dist: Lang, Peter.

Toussaint, Guido. Das Recht des Zahlungsverkehrs im Überblick: Praxishandbuch. 2009. (De Gruyter Handbuch Ser.). Tr. of Payment Law. (GER.). XXIII, 254p. 70.00 (978-3-89949-532-4(2)) De Gruyter, Walter Inc.

Toussaint, Guido. Das Recht des Zahlungsverkehrs Im Aceberblick. 2009. (De Gruyter Handbuch Ser.). Tr. of Payment Law. (GER.). XXIII, 254p. 112.00 **(978-3-11-173447-7(1))** De Gruyter, Walter Inc.

CHEERFULNESS

see also Happiness; Optimism

Hubbard, Sara A. Catch Words of Cheer. 2009. 116p. 24.99 (978-1-110-65038-5(8)); pap. 19.75 (978-1-110-65036-1(1)) BiblioBazaar.

—Catch Words of Cheer. 2007. (ENG.). 118p. 34.95 (978-0-548-05915-9(2)) Kessinger Publishing, LLC.

Meberg, Marilyn. I'd Rather Be Laughing, 0 vols. 2008. 176p. pap. 12.99 (978-1-4002-7798-8(1)) Nelson, Thomas Inc.

Miller, J. R. The Blessing of Cheerfulness. 2011. 32p. pap. 7.99 **(978-1-61203-153-8(6))** Bottom of the Hill Publishing.

CHEERLEADERS

see Cheerleading

CHEERLEADING

American Sport Education Program Staff. Coaching Youth Cheerleading. 2009. (ENG., Illus.). 152p. pap. 16.95 (978-0-7360-7444-5(9)) Human Kinetics Pubs.

Appenzeller, Herb, et al. Cheerleading & the Law: Risk Management Strategies. 2008. (Illus.). 232p. per. 22.00 (978-1-59460-342-6(1)) Carolina Academic Pr.

Farina, Christine & Clark, Courtney A. Complete Guide to Cheerleading: All the Tips, Tricks, & Inspiration. 2011. (ENG., Illus.). 192p. 24.99 (978-0-7603-3849-0(3), 0760338493, MVP Bks.) MBI Publishing Co. LLC.

Headridge, Pam. 101 School Spirit Ideas. 2008. (Illus.). 141p. per. 19.95 (978-1-58518-058-5(0)) Coaches Choice.

Inside Cheerleading Magazine Editors. Cheerleading: From Tryouts to Championships. 2007. (ENG., Illus.). 144p. pap. 14.95 (978-0-7893-1565-6(3)) Universe Publishing.

C

Lovett, O. Rufus. Kilgore Rangerettes. 2008. (Clifton & Shirley Caldwell Texas Heritage Ser.). (ENG., Illus.). 192p. 50.00 (978-0-292-71673-5(7)) Univ. of Texas Pr.

Murray, Tinker D., et al. 101 Cheerleading Facts, Tips, & Drills. 2007. (Illus.). 163p. per. 17.95 (978-1-58518-003-5(3)) Coaches Choice.

Nichols, Sandra & Nichols, Chase. College Cheerleading Guide. 2nd ed. Date not set. pap. 12.00 (978-0-9656179-1-8(2)) College Cheerleading Guide.

Porterfield, Jason. Band Front: Color Guard, Drum Majors, & Majorettes. 2006. (Team Spirit! (Rosen) Ser.). (Illus.). 64p. (YA). (gr. 8-12). lib. bdg. 26.50 (978-1-4042-0729-5(5)) Rosen Publishing Group, Inc., The.

Torgovnick, Kate. Cheer! Inside the Secret World of College Cheerleaders. 2009. (ENG., Illus.). 384p. pap. 15.00 (978-1-4165-3597-3(7), Touchstone) Touchstone.

Vikmanis, Laura & Sohn, Amy. It's Not about the Pom-Poms: How a 40-Year-Old Mom Became the NFL's Oldest Cheerleader- And Found Hope, Joy, & Inspiration along the Way. 2012. (ENG., Illus.). 304p. 25.00 **(978-0-345-53290-9(2)**, Ballantine Bks.) Random Hse. of Canada, Ltd. CAN. Dist: Random Hse., Inc.

CHEESE

see also Cooking (Cheese)

Anderson, Glynn & McLaughlin, John. Farmhouse Cheeses of Ireland: A Celebration. 2011. (ENG., Illus.). 392p. 44.95 **(978-1-84889-121-0(0))** Collins Pr., The IRL. Dist: Dufour Editions, Inc.

Ash, Rita. Cheese Making: Self-Sufficiency. 2010. (Self-Sufficiency Ser.). (ENG., Illus.). 128p. 12.95 (978-1-60239-960-0(3), 239960) Skyhorse Publishing Co., Inc.

Beckett, Fiona. Fiona Beckett's Cheese Course. 2009. (Illus.). 160p. (978-1-84597-917-1(6)) Ryland Peters & Small.

Boisard, Pierre. Camembert: A National Myth. Miller, Richard, tr. 2006. 254p. reprint ed. 27.00 (978-1-4223-5620-3(5)) DIANE Publishing Co.

Caldwell, Gianaclis. Farmstead Creamery Advisor: The Complete Guide to Building & Running a Small, Farm-Based Cheese Business. 2010. (ENG., Illus.). 256p. pap. 29.95 (978-1-60358-221-6(5)) Chelsea Green Publishing.

Culture Magazine Staff, et al. Cheese for Dummies. 18th ed. 2012. (ENG., Illus.). 408p. pap. 19.99 **(978-1-118-09939-1(7)**, For Dummies) Wiley, John & Sons, Inc.

Dalby, Andrew. Cheese: A Global History. 2009. (Reaktion Books - Edible Ser.). (ENG., Illus.). 128p. 15.95 (978-1-86189-523-3(2)) Reaktion Bks., Ltd. GBR. Dist: Chicago Distribution Ctr.

Davies, Sasha. The Guide to West Coast Cheese: More Than 300 Cheeses Handcrafted in California, Oregon, & Washington. 2010. (ENG.). 225p. pap. 18.95 (978-1-60469-090-3(9), 1604690909) Timber Pr., Inc.

Farnham, Jody & Druart, Marc. The Joy of Cheesemaking. 2011. (ENG., Illus.). 256p. pap. 14.95 (978-1-61608-060-0(4), 608060) Skyhorse Publishing Co., Inc.

Fletcher, Janet Kessel. Cheese & Wine: Perfect Pairings for Entertaining & Everyday. 2007. (978-0-8118-5713-0(1)) Chronicle Bks. LLC.

Foster, Richard D., ed. Cheese: Types, Nutrition & Consumption. 2011. (Nutrition & Diet Research Progress Ser.). (Illus.). xv, 320p. 129.00 (978-1-61209-828-9(2)) Nova Science Pubs., Inc.

Gibbons, David & McCalman, Max. Mastering Cheese: Lessons for Connoisseurship from a Maître Fromager. 2009. (ENG., Illus.). 384p. 40.00 (978-0-307-40648-4(2), Clarkson Potter) Crown Publishing Group.

Green, Henrietta. A Green Guide to Country Foods. 2011. (ENG., Illus.). 192p. 24.95 (978-1-907563-28-7(8)) CICO Bks. GBR. Dist: Ryland Peters & Small.

Greet, Andrew. Beating Unusual Chess Defences: 1 E. 2011. (ENG.). 192p. pap. 27.95 **(978-1-85744-621-0(6))** Everyman Chess GBR. Dist: Globe Pequot Pr., The.

Harbutt, Juliet & Walton, Stuart. Wine & Cheese: A Complete Guide to the World of Wine & Cheese in Two Illustrated Encyclopedias with 900 Photographs, 2 vols. 2010. (ENG., Illus.). 528p. 30.00 (978-0-7548-2016-1(5)) Anness Publishing GBR. Dist: National Bk. Network.

Herbst, Ron, et al. The Cheese Lover's Companion: The Ultimate A-to-Z Cheese Guide with More Than 1,000 Listings for Cheeses & Cheese-Related Terms. 2007. (ENG.). 512p. pap. 16.99 (978-0-06-053704-3(3), Morrow, William Cookbooks) HarperCollins Pubs.

Hurst, Janet. Homemade Cheese: Recipes for 50 Cheeses from Artisan Cheesemakers. 2011. (ENG., Illus.). 160p. pap. 19.99 (978-0-7603-3848-3(5), 0760338485, Voyageur Pr) MBI Publishing Co. LLC.

Hurt, Jeanette. The Cheeses of California: A Culinary Travel Guide. 2009. (ENG., Illus.). 208p. pap. 19.95 (978-0-88150-812-3(8), 150812) Countryman Pr.

—The Cheeses of Wisconsin: A Culinary Travel Guide. 2008. (ENG., Illus.). 192p. pap. 19.95 (978-0-88150-784-3(9)) Countryman Pr.

Kessler, Brad. Goat Song: A Seasonal Life, a Short History of Herding, & the Art of Making Cheese. (ENG.). 2010. 272p. pap. 15.00 (978-1-4165-6100-2(5)) 2009. (Illus.). 256p. 24.00 (978-1-4165-6099-9(8)) Scribner. (Scribner).

Kindstedt, Paul. Cheese & Culture: A History of Cheese & Its Place in Western Civilization. 2012. **(978-1-60358-412-8(9))**; (ENG.). 256p. 24.95 **(978-1-60358-411-1(0))** Chelsea Green Publishing.

Law, Barry A. & Tamime, Adnan, eds. Technology of Cheesemaking. 2nd ed. 2010. (Society of Dairy Technology Ser.: 11). (ENG., Illus.). 512p. 19.95 (978-1-4051-8298-0(9), Wiley-Blackwell) Wiley, John & Sons, Inc.

Long, James & Benson, John. Cheese & Cheese-Making. 2007. (Cooking in America Ser.). (ENG.). 164p. per. 12.95 (978-1-4290-1062-7(2)) Applewood Bks.

McSweeney, P. L. H., ed. Cheese Problems Solved. 2007. (ENG., Illus.). 402p. 269.95 (978-1-4200-4394-5(3), CRC Press) Taylor & Francis Group GBR. Dist: Taylor & Francis Group.

McSweeney, Paul. Cheese Problems Solved. 2007. (Woodhead Publishing Series in Food Science, Technology & Nutrition Ser.). (ENG., Illus.). 424p. 245.00 (978-1-84569-060-1(5)) Woodhead Publishing Ltd. GBR. Dist: Ingram Pub. Services.

Michelson, Patricia. The Cheese Room. 2008. (ENG., Illus.). 224p. (gr. 12-18). 20.00 (978-0-14-029543-6(7), Penguin Global) Penguin Group (USA) Inc.

Norton, James & Dilley, Becca. The Master Cheesemakers of Wisconsin. 2009. (ENG., Illus.). 204p. pap. 24.95 (978-0-299-23434-8(7)) Univ. of Wisconsin Pr.

Parr, Tami & Parr, T. Artisan Cheese of the Pacific Northwest: A Discovery Guide. 2009. (ENG., Illus.). 208p. pap. 19.95 (978-0-88150-834-5(9), 150834) Countryman Pr.

Peacock, Paul. The Cheesemaking Book. 2007. (ENG., Illus.). 152p. 15.95 (978-1-904871-24-8(0), 1904871240) Good Life Pr., The GBR. Dist: MBI Distribution Services/Quayside Distribution.

Ray, Norm & Ray, Barbara. Wine & Cheese Pairing Guide: Your Exciting Search for Wow! Combinations. 2007. 224p. per. 15.95 (978-1-877810-00-8(2)) Rayve Productions, Inc.

Roberts, Jeffrey P. The Atlas of American Artisan Cheese. 2007. (ENG., Illus.). 400p. pap. 35.00 (978-1-933392-34-9(7)) Chelsea Green Publishing.

Robinson, R. K. & Tamime, A. Y., eds. Feta & Related Cheeses. 272p. (978-1-85573-278-0(5)) Woodhead Publishing Ltd.

Steinka, Izabela. Lactic Acid Cheese Safety. 2008. (Illus.). vi, 114p. pap. 39.00 (978-1-60456-244-6(7)) Nova Science Pubs., Inc.

Tamime, Adnan. Processed Cheese & Analogues. 2011. (Society of Dairy Technology Ser.: 5). (ENG., Illus.). 368p. 199.99 (978-1-4051-8642-1(9), Wiley-Blackwell) Wiley, John & Sons, Inc.

Tamime, Adnan, ed. Brined Cheeses. 2006. (Society of Dairy Technology Ser.: 6). (ENG., Illus.). 344p. 239.95 (978-1-4051-2460-7(1), Wiley-Blackwell) Wiley, John & Sons, Inc.

Taye, Bezaye & Admassu, Eng. Shimelis. Evaluation of Cheddar & Cottage Cheese Production from Doe & Ewe. 2011. 108p. pap. **(978-3-8443-9508-2(3))** Lambert Academic Publishing.

Thom, Charles. The Book of Cheese. 2009. 252p. pap. (978-1-4589-1058-5(X)) Books LLC.

Thom, Charles & Fisk, Walter. The Book of Cheese. 2007. (Cooking in America Ser.). (ENG.). 420p. per. 25.95 (978-1-4290-1074-0(6)) Applewood Bks.

Thom, Charles & Fisk, Walter Warner. The Book of Cheese. 2008. 416p. 49.95 (978-1-4372-6630-6(4)); 414p. pap. 34.95 (978-1-4371-3986-0(8)) Kessinger Publishing, LLC.

Thorpe, Liz. The Cheese Chronicles: A Journey Through the Making & Selling of Cheese in America, from Field to Farm to Table. 2009. (ENG.). 384p. pap. 15.99 (978-0-06-145116-4(9), Ecco) HarperCollins Pubs.

Thorpe, Liz & Kaufelt, Rob. The Murray's Cheese Handbook: A Guide to More Than 300 of the World's Best Cheeses. 2006. (ENG., Illus.). 240p. pap. 14.00 (978-0-7679-2130-5(5), Broadway) Broadway Bks.

Tyrisevs, Anna-Maria. Options for Selecting Dairy Cattle for MilkCoagulation Ability. 2008. 84p. pap. (978-3-639-08785-7(2)) VDM Verlag Dr. Mueller e.K.

Weimer, B., ed. Improving the Flavour of Cheese. 2007. 600p. (978-1-84569-007-6(9)) Woodhead Publishing Ltd.

Weimer B Staff. Improving the Flavour of Cheese. 2007. 580p. 299.95 (978-0-8493-9158-3(X)) CRC Pr. LLC.

Weinstein, Bruce & Scarbrough, Mark. Goat: Meat, Milk, Cheese. 2011. (ENG., Illus.). 256p. 29.95 (978-1-58479-905-4(6)) Stewart, Tabori & Chang.

CHEESE—BACTERIOLOGY

see Cheese—Microbiology

CHEESE—MICROBIOLOGY

Okpala, Charles. High Pressure Processing. 2010. 104p. pap. (978-3-8383-7735-3(4)) Lambert Academic Publishing.

CHEESE CAKE

see Cheesecake

CHEESECAKE

Australian Women's Weekly Staff, contrib. by. Cheesecakes, Pavlovas & Trifles. (Illus.). 64p. pap. 5.95 (978-1-86396-305-3(7)) ACP Publishing Pty, Ltd. AUS. Dist: Graphic Arts Ctr. Publishing Co.

Blake, Susannah. 500 Cakes: The Only Cake Compendium You'll Ever Need. 2009. (Illus.). 288p. 16.95 (978-1-4162-0534-0(9)) Sellers Publishing, Inc.

Draper, Selena M. 50+ Cheesecakes. 2008. 73p. pap. 16.95 (978-1-60610-012-7(2)) PublishAmerica, Inc.

Eulo, Annamaria. Sweet Elegance: A Cheesecake Cookbook. 2008. 58p. pap. 16.95 (978-1-60672-354-8(5)) PublishAmerica, Inc.

G & R Publishing Company. Brownie Babies & Cheesecake Pops: Fun & easy bite-sized Delights. 2010. 60p. spiral bd. 12.00 (978-1-56383-364-9(6)) G & R Publishing.

Geary, George. The Cheesecake Bible: Includes 200 Recipes. 2008. (ENG., Illus.). 320p. pap. 24.95 (978-0-7788-0192-4(6)) Rose, Robert Inc. CAN. Dist: Firefly Bks., Ltd.

Heatter, Maida. Maida Heatter's Cakes. 2011. (ENG.). 368p. pap. 19.99 (978-1-4494-0114-6(7)) Andrews McMeel Publishing.

Publications International Staff, ed. Philadelphia. 2009. 256p. 14.98 (978-1-4127-7877-0(8), PIL Kids) Publications International, Ltd.

—3 Books in 1 Jell-O & CoolWhip Favorite Desserts/Philadelphia Cheesecakes & More/Baker's Desserts for Chocolate Lovers. 2008. (3 Books In 1 Ser.). (Illus.). 288p. 12.98 (978-1-4127-7611-0(2)) Publications International, Ltd.

Rosen, Alan & Allen, Beth. Junior's Cheesecake Cookbook: 50 to-Die-for Recipes for New York-Style Cheesecake. 2007. (ENG., Illus.). 170p. 24.95 (978-1-56158-880-0(6), Taunton) Taunton Pr., Inc.

CHEETAH

Bell, K. M. Spot the Difference: Are Cheetahs Really Just Big Cats? 2010. (ENG., Illus.). 200p. pap. 66.00 (978-1-904761-60-0(7)) Nottingham Univ. Pr. GBR. Dist: Independent Pubs. Group.

Divyabhanusinh. The Cheetah in India. 3rd ed. 2007. (ENG., Illus.). 302p. 75.00 (978-0-19-568697-5(7)) Oxford Univ. Pr., Inc.

Hunter, Luke. Cheetah. 2007. (Illus.). 144p. 34.95 (978-1-86872-719-3(X)) New Holland Publishing SA (Pty.), Ltd. ZAF. Dist: Continental Enterprises Group, Inc. (CEG).

CHEETAHS

see Cheetah

CHEEVER, JOHN, 1912-1982

Bailey, Blake. Cheever: A Life. 2010. (Vintage Ser.). (ENG.). 816p. pap. 16.95 (978-1-4000-7968-1(3), Vintage) Knopf Doubleday Publishing Group.

Cheever, John. The Journals of John Cheever. Gottlieb, Robert, ed. 2008. (Vintage International Ser.). (ENG.). 416p. pap. 16.95 (978-0-307-38725-7(9), Vintage) Knopf Doubleday Publishing Group.

—The Letters of John Cheever. Cheever, Benjamin, ed. 2009. (ENG., Illus.). 400p. pap. 18.00 (978-1-4391-6464-8(9)) Simon & Schuster.

Miller, Anita. Uncollecting Cheever. 2009. (ENG.). 363p. pap. 18.95 (978-0-89733-593-5(7)) Academy Chicago Pubs., Ltd.

Morace, Robert A. John Cheever. 2011. **(978-1-58765-827-3(5))** Salem Pr., Inc.

CHEFS

see Cooks

CHEIROMANCY

see Palmistry

CHEIROPTERA

see Bats

CHEKHOV, ANTON PAVLOVICH, 1860-1904

Bunin, Ivan. About Chekhov: The Unfinished Symphony. Marullo, Thomas Gaiton, tr. from RUS. 2007. (Studies in Russian Literature & Theory). (ENG.). 256p. per. 27.95 (978-0-8101-2388-5(6)); 156p. 59.95 (978-0-8101-2382-3(7)) Northwestern Univ. Pr.

Chekhov, Anton. How to Write Like Chekhov: Advice & Inspiration, Straight from His Own Letters & Work. Brunello, Piero & Lencek, Lena, eds. 2008. (ENG.). 254p. pap. 15.99 (978-1-56924-259-9(3)) Da Capo Pr., Inc.

—Letters of Anton Chekhov. 2008. 356p. 29.99 (978-0-554-38801-4(4)); 31.99 (978-0-554-29498-8(2)) BiblioBazaar.

—Ten Plays. 2008. (RUS & ENG.). 336p. pap. 9.95 (978-0-486-46560-9(8)) Dover Pubns., Inc.

Chekhov, Anton & Reeve, Brian. Sakhalin Island. 2007. (Illus.). 500p. 17.00 (978-1-84749-039-1(5)) Alma Classics GBR. Dist: Independent Pubs. Group.

Chekhov, Mikhail Pavlovich. Anton Chekhov: A Brother's Memoir. Alper, Eugene, tr. from RUS. 2009. (ENG., Illus.). 256p. 25.00 (978-0-230-61883-1(9)) Palgrave Macmillan.

Gottlieb, Vera. Chekhov & the Vaudeville: A Study of Chekhov's One-Act Plays. 2010. (ENG.). 240p. pap. 27.99 (978-0-521-13698-3(9)) Cambridge Univ. Pr.

Kramer, Karl D. The Chameleon & the Dream: The Image of Reality in Cexov's Stories. (Slavistic Printings & Reprintings Ser.). (ENG.). 182p. 210.00 **(978-3-11-180484-2(4))** De Gruyter, Mouton DEU. Dist: de Gruyter, Walter GmbH & Co. KG.

Miles. Chekov & Britain. Date not set. (978-0-85496-847-3(4)) Berg Pubs.

Miles, Patrick. Anton Chekhov. 2008. (Brief Lives Ser.). (ENG.). 112p. pap. 13.95 (978-1-84391-900-1(1)) Hesperus Pr. GBR. Dist: Independent Pubs. Group.

Pritchett, V. S. Chekhov: A Biography. 2012. 256p. pap. **(978-1-4482-0092-4(X)**, 143052, Bloomsbury Reader) Bloomsbury Publishing Plc.

Sekirin, Peter. Memories of Chekhov: Accounts of the Writer from His Family, Friends & Contemporaries. 2011. (ENG., Illus.). 223p. pap. 45.00 (978-0-7864-5871-4(2)) McFarland & Co., Inc. Pubs.

Shestov, Lev. Penultimate Words, & Other Essays. 2009. (ENG.). 224p. 32.99 (978-1-117-23946-0(2)); pap. 24.75 (978-1-117-23947-7(0)) BiblioBazaar.

Simmons, Ernest J. Chekhov: A Biography. 2011. 690p. 69.95 **(978-1-258-07264-3(5))** Literary Licensing, LLC.

Speirs, Logan. Tolstoy & Chekhov. 2010. (ENG.). 248p. pap. 31.99 (978-0-521-15555-7(X)) Cambridge Univ. Pr.

Tabachnikova, Olga, ed. Anton Chekhov Through the Eyes of Russian Thinkers: Vasilii Rozanov, Dmitrii Merezhkovskii & Lev Shestov. 2010. (Anthem Series on Russian, East European & Eurasian Studies). (ENG., Illus.). 312p. 99.00 (978-1-84331-841-5(5)) Anthem Pr. GBR. Dist: Books International, Inc.

von Bruhl, Christine Grafin. Die Nonverbalen Ausdrucksmittel in Anton Cechovs Buhnenwerk. (GER.). 248p. 51.95 (978-3-631-49062-4(3)) Lang, Peter Publishing, Inc.

CHEKHOV, ANTON PAVLOVICH, 1860-1904—CRITICISM AND INTERPRETATION

Bloom, Harold, ed. & intro. Anton Chekhov. 2nd rev. ed. 2009. (Bloom's Modern Critical Views Ser.). 200p. (C). (gr. 9-18). 45.00 (978-1-60413-576-3(X), Chelsea Hse.) Facts On File, Inc.

Emeljanow, Victor. Anton Chekhov. 2009. 472p. pap. 45.00 (978-0-415-56900-2(1)) Routledge.

Finke, Michael & De Sherbinin, Julie W., eds. Chekhov the Immigrant: Translating a Cultural Icon. 2008. (ENG., Illus.). 364p. pap. (978-0-89357-340-9(X)) Slavica Pubs.

Finke, Michael C., et al. Chekhov the Immigrant: Translating a Cultural Icon. 2007. (978-0-89357-345-4(0)) Slavica Pubs.

Golomb, Harai. A New Poetics of Chekhov's Major Plays: Presence Through Absence. 2012. (ENG.). 296p. 99.50 (978-1-903900-47-5(6)) 2008. 252p. pap. 29.95 (978-1-903900-48-2(4)) Sussex Academic Pr. GBR. Dist: International Specialized Bk. Services.

Gurcinov, Milan. A. P. Cehov. 2008. (MAC., Illus.). 341p. (978-9989-49-900-5(4)) Matica Makedonska.

Loehlin, James N. The Cambridge Introduction to Chekhov. 2010. (Cambridge Introductions to Literature Ser.). (ENG.). 210p. (C). 72.00 (978-0-521-88077-0(7)); pap. 21.99 (978-0-521-70688-9(2)) Cambridge Univ. Pr.

Narayan, Kirin. Alive in the Writing: Crafting Ethnography in the Company of Chekhov. 2012. (ENG., Illus.). 168p. 50.00 **(978-0-226-56818-8(0))** Univ. of Chicago Pr.

Parts, Lyudmila. The Chekhovian Intertext: Dialogue with a Classic. 2008. (ENG.). 232p. 69.95 (978-0-8142-1083-3(X)); cd-rom 14.95 (978-0-8142-9162-7(7)) Ohio State Univ. Pr.

Pennington, Michael. Anton Chekhov's Three Sisters: A Study-Guide. 2007. (ENG.). 128p. pap. 18.95 (978-1-85459-899-8(6)) Theatre Communications Group, Inc.

Rayfield, D., ed. Chekhov's Uncle Vanya & the Wood Demon: Critical Study. 2010. (Critical Studies in Russian Literature). (Illus.). 96p. pap. 19.95 (978-1-85399-405-0(7)) Bristol Classical Pr. GBR. Dist: International Publishers Marketing.

Reid, John McKellor. The Polemical Force of Chekhovian Comedies: A Rhetorical Analysis. 2007. 216p. (978-0-7734-5388-3(1)) Mellen, Edwin Pr., The.

Steinberg-Pavlova, Viktoria. Musik in Anton Cechovs Erzählungen. 2008. (Heidelberger Publikationen zur Slavistik. B) - Literaturwissenschaftliche Reihe Ser.). 212p. pap. 56.95 (978-3-631-56813-2(4)) Lang, Peter GmbH, Europaischer Verlag der Wissenschaften DEU. Dist: Lang, Peter.

Tabachnikova, Olga & Ure, Adam. Anton Chekhov Through the Eyes of Russian Thinkers: Vasilii Rozanov, Dmitrii Merezhkovskii & Lev Shestov. 2010. (Illus.). lix, 245p. E-Book (978-0-85728-982-7(9)) Anthem Pr.

CHELATES

Ashmead, H. DeWayne. Amini Acid Chelation in Human & Animal Nutrition. 2012. (ENG., Illus.). 269p. 129.95 **(978-1-4398-9767-6(0)**, CRC Press) Taylor & Francis Group GBR. Dist: Taylor & Francis Group.

Nesterenko, Pavel, et al. High Performance Chelation Ion Chromatography. 2010. (RSC Chromatography Monographs). (ENG., Illus.). 316p. (C). 160.00 **(978-1-84973-041-9(5))** Royal Society of Chemistry, The GBR. Dist: Ingram Pub. Services.

CHELATION THERAPY

Fitzpatrick, Michael. Defeating Autism: A Damaging Delusion. 2008. (Illus.). XVIII, 166p. pap. 39.95 (978-0-415-44981-6(2)) Routledge.

Gordon, Gary & Brown, David Jay. Detox with Oral Chelation: Protecting Yourself from Lead, Mercury, & Other Environmental Toxins. 2007. (ENG.). 288p. pap. 17.95 (978-1-890572-20-4(9)) Smart Pubns.

Hawken, C. M. Chelation Therapy. 3rd ed. 2011. (Woodland Health Ser.). 32p. pap. 4.95 **(978-1-58054-198-5(4))** Woodland Publishing, Inc.

Murphree, Rodger H. Heart Disease: What Your Doctor Won't Tell You. 2008. 222p. pap. 14.95 (978-0-9728938-3-1(0)) Harrison & Hampton Publishing.

CHELONIA

see Turtles

CHELSEA HOTEL

Ambrose, Joe. Chelsea Hotel Manhattan. 2007. (Illus.). 192p. pap. 19.95 (978-1-900486-60-6(1)) Headpress GBR. Dist: SCB Distributors.

Kratochvil, Antonin, ed. Inside: The Chelsea Hotel. 2007. (ENG., Illus.). 208p. 49.95 (978-1-57687-406-6(0)) powerHouse Cultural Entertainment, Inc.

Smith, Patti. Just Kids: Die Geschichte einer Freundschaft. 2010. (ENG.). 304p. 27.00 (978-0-06-621131-2(X), Ecco) HarperCollins Pubs.

—Just Kids: Die Geschichte Einer Freundschaft. 2010. (ENG.). 224p. pap. 16.00 (978-0-06-093622-8(3), Ecco) HarperCollins Pubs.

CHELTENHAM (ENGLAND)

Brooks, Robin. A Century of Cheltenham. 2012. (ENG.). 128p. pap. 18.95 **(978-0-7524-7474-8(X))** History Pr. Ltd., The GBR. Dist: Independent Pubs. Group.

Carnegie, Maria. Fusillade from a Rifleman: The Story of John Kincaid. 2009. (ENG.). 128p. 42.95 (978-1-86227-346-7(4)) History Pr. Ltd., The GBR. Dist: Independent Pubs. Group.

Hanks, David. Cheltenham Past & Present. 2010. (ENG., Illus.). 128p. pap. 23.95 (978-0-7524-5366-8(1)) History Pr. Ltd., The GBR. Dist: Independent Pubs. Group.

Humphris, Edith & Willoughby, E. C. Georgian Cheltenham. 2008. (ENG.). 256p. pap. 34.95 (978-1-84588-606-6(2)) History Pr. Ltd., The GBR. Dist: Independent Pubs. Group.

White, Diz. Haunted Cheltenham. 2010. (Haunted Ser.). (ENG., Illus.). 96p. pap. 18.95 (978-0-7524-5427-6(7)) History Pr. Ltd., The GBR. Dist: Independent Pubs. Group.

CHEMICAL ADDITIVES IN FOOD

see Food Additives

CHEMICAL AFFINITY

see also Chemical Kinetics; Valence (Theoretical Chemistry)

Faraday, Michael. The Forces of Matter. 2010. (Dover Books on Engineering Ser.). (ENG.). 96p. pap. 5.95 *(978-0-486-47482-3(8))* Dover Pubns., Inc.
—The Forces of Matter. 2007. (ENG.). 108p. 33.95 *(978-0-548-07828-0(9))* Kessinger Publishing, LLC.
—The Forces of Matter. 2010. 90p. 27.16 *(978-1-169-00409-2(1))*; pap. 15.16 *(978-1-162-90707-9(X))*; 33.95 *(978-1-161-59586-4(4))* Kessinger Publishing, LLC.
Kim, Mi Gyung. Affinity, That Elusive Dream: A Genealogy of the Chemical Revolution. 2008. (Transformations: Studies in the History of Science & Technology Ser.). (ENG., Illus.). 613p. (gr. 17). per. 29.00 *(978-0-262-61223-4(2))* MIT Pr.

CHEMICAL ANALYSIS
see Chemistry, Analytic

CHEMICAL APPARATUS
see also Centrifuges; Chemistry—Manipulation; Glass Blowing and Working
Brodd, R. J., ed. Electrochemical Capacitors 2006. 2008. (ECS Transactions Ser.). 67p. pap. 60.00 *(978-1-60423-913-3(1))* Curran Assocs., Inc.
Goodwin, Harold. Laboratory Autoclaves, High Pressure & Hydrogenation Apparatus - Design & Construction. 2008. 164p. 59.95 *(978-1-4276-1406-3(7))* Wexford College Pr.
Lackner, Maximilian, ed. Lasers in Chemistry: Probing & Influencing Matter, 2 vols. 2008. (ENG., Illus.). 1554p. 555.00 *(978-3-527-31997-8(2)*, Wiley-VCH) Wiley, John & Sons, Inc.
Luyben, William L. & Yu, Cheng-Ching. Reactive Distillation Design & Control. 2008. (ENG., Illus.). 574p. 142.00 *(978-0-470-22612-4(9))* American Institute of Chemical Engineers.
Vincenzini, P., et al. Ceramics & Composites in Extreme Environments & for Chemical & Electrochemical Applications: 12th International Ceramics Congress Part D. 2011. (Illus.). 284p. pap. *(978-3-908158-48-6(6))* Trans Tech Pubns., Ltd.

CHEMICAL BONDS
see also Molecular Orbitals
Al-Hafez Sayda, Hikmat S. Hilaland Abed. Introductory Course on Group Theory & Chemical Applications. 2011. (Chemistry Research & Applications Ser.). 43.00 *(978-1-61761-923-6(X))* Nova Science Pubs., Inc.
Cotton, Simon. Every Molecule Tells A Story. 2011. (ENG., Illus.). 280p. 59.95 ***(978-1-4398-0773-6(6)***, Chapman & Hall/CRC) CRC Pr. LLC.
Cram101 Textbook Reviews & Cram101 Textbook Reviews. Outlines & Highlights for Molecular Physics & Elements of Quantum Chemistry by Hermann Haken. 2011. 272p. pap. 32.95 ***(978-1-61830-104-8(7))*** Cram101 Inc.
Cram101 Textbook Reviews Staff. Outlines & Highlights for Chemical Structure & Bonding by Dekock Isbn: 093570261x. 2007. 112p. pap. 11.95 *(978-1-4286-3072-1(3))* Cram101 Inc.
Danheiser, Rick L. & Organic Syntheses Inc. Staff. Palladium, Nickel, & Iron-Catalyzed Reactions Vol. 1. 2010. (Thematic Collections of Organic Syntheses Ser.). (ENG.). 200p. 74.95 *(978-0-470-53734-8(2)*, Wiley) Wiley, John & Sons, Inc.
Fleming, Ian. Molecular Orbitals & Organic Chemical Reactions. 2010. (ENG., Illus.). 526p. 165.00 *(978-0-470-74658-5(0)*, Wiley) Wiley, John & Sons, Inc.
Fliszar, Sandor. Atomic Charges, Bond Properties, & Molecular Energies. 2008. (ENG., Illus.). 234p. 117.00 *(978-0-470-37622-5(8)*, Wiley-Interscience) Wiley, John & Sons, Inc.
Fuchs, Philip L. Reagents for Direct Functionalization of C-H Bonds. 2006. (Hdbk of Reagents for Organic Synthesis Ser.). (ENG., Illus.). 424p. 185.00 *(978-0-470-01022-8(3)*, Wiley) Wiley, John & Sons, Inc.
Haken, Hermann & Wolf, Hans-Christoph. Molecular Physics & Elements of Quantum Chemistry: Introduction to Experiments & Theory. Brewer, William D., tr. from GER. 2nd ed. 2010. (Advanced Texts in Physics Ser.). (Illus.). xxi, 592p. pap. 139.00 *(978-3-642-07400-4(6)*, 3642074006) Springer.
Harrison, Walter. Theoretical Alchemy: Modeling Matter. 2010. (Illus.). 212p. 64.00 *(978-981-4322-13-3(X))*; pap. 28.00 *(978-981-4322-14-0(8))* World Scientific Publishing Co., Inc.
Israelachvili, Jacob N. Intermolecular & Surface Forces. 3rd rev. ed. 2011. (ENG.). 704p. 109.95 ***(978-0-12-391927-4(4)***, Academic Pr.) Elsevier Science & Technology Bks.
Kettle, Sidney F. A. Symmetry & Structure: Readable Group Theory for Chemists. 3rd ed. (ENG., Illus.). 436p. 2008. per. 79.00 *(978-0-470-06040-7(9))* 2007. 220.00 *(978-0-470-06039-1(5))* Wiley, John & Sons, Inc. (Wiley).
Luo, Yu-Ran. Comprehensive Handbook of Chemical Bond Energies. 2007. (ENG., Illus.). 1688p. 484.00 *(978-0-8493-7366-4(2)*, CRC Press) Taylor & Francis Group GBR. Dist: Taylor & Francis Group.
Magnasco, Valerio. Models for Bonding in Chemistry. 2010. (ENG., Illus.). 232p. 145.00 *(978-0-470-66702-6(8))*; pap. 59.95 *(978-0-470-66703-3(6))* Wiley, John & Sons, Inc. (Wiley).
Marder, Todd B. & Lin, Zhenyang. Contemporary Metal Boron Chemistry I: Borylenes, Boryls, Borane Sigma-Complexes, & Borohydrides. 2010. (Structure & Bonding Ser.). (Illus.). xiv, 218p. pap. 289.00 *(978-3-642-09739-3(1)*, 3642097391) Springer.
Micha, David. Molecular Interactions. 2009. 400p. 125.00 *(978-0-470-29074-3(9)*, Wiley-Interscience) Wiley, John & Sons, Inc.
Murai, Shinji, ed. Activation of Unreactive Bonds & Organic Synthesis. 2012. (Topics in Organometallic Chemistry Ser.). (ENG., Illus.). ix, 272p. pap. 319.00 *(978-3-642-08436-2(2)*, 3642084362) Springer.
Nalewajski, Roman F., ed. Information Origins of the Chemical Bond. 2010. (Chemistry Research & Applications Ser.). 196p. pap. 43.00 *(978-1-61668-305-4(8))* Nova Science Pubs., Inc.
Nilsson, Anders, et al, eds. Chemical Bonding at Surfaces & Interfaces. 2007. (ENG., Illus.). 532p. 107.00 *(978-0-444-52837-7(7)*, Elsevier Science) Elsevier Science & Technology Bks.
Ogawa, Shinichi, et al, eds. Stress-Induced Phenomena in Metallization: Ninth International Workshop on Stress-Induced Phenomena in Metallization. 2008. (AIP Conference Proceedings / Materials Physics & Applications Ser.). (Illus.). 204p. 99.00 *(978-0-7354-0459-5(3))* American Institute of Physics.
Parkin, Gerard, ed. Metal-Metal Bonding. 2010. (Structure & Bonding Ser.). (Illus.). xi, 240p. 389.00 *(978-3-642-05242-2(8)*, 3642052428) Springer.
Postigo, J. Alberto. Organic Radical Reactions in Water & Alternative Media. 2011. (Chemistry Research & Applications Ser.). (Illus.). 268p. 89.00 *(978-1-61209-648-3(4))* Nova Science Pubs., Inc.
Pullman, A., ed. Intermolecular Forces. 2010. (Jerusalem Symposia Ser.). 584p. pap. 439.00 *(978-90-481-8368-5(5)*, 9048183685) Springer.
Putz, Mihai V., ed. Quantum Frontiers of Atoms & Molecules. 2010. (Chemistry Research & Applications Ser.). 195.00 *(978-1-61668-158-6(6))* Nova Science Pubs., Inc.
Rawls, Matthew. Charge Separation in Convalently Bound & Self-Assembled Donor Chromophore Acceptor Systems. 2008. 104p. pap. *(978-3-639-01281-1(X))* VDM Verlag Dr. Mueller e.K.
Salam, Akbar. Molecular Quantum Electrodynamics: Long-Range Intermolecular Interactions. 2009. (ENG., Illus.). 399p. 134.00 *(978-0-470-25930-6(2)*, Wiley) Wiley, John & Sons, Inc.
Satoh, Akira. Introduction to Practice of Molecular Simulation: Molecular Dynamics, Monte Carlo, Brownian Dynamics, Lattice Boltzmann & Dissipative Particle Dynamics. 2010. (ENG., Illus.). 330p. 150.00 *(978-0-12-385148-2(3))* Elsevier Science & Technology Bks.
Schönherr, Thomas. Optical Spectra & Chemical Bonding in Transition Metal Complexes: Special Volume II, dedicated to Professor Jørgensen 2010. (Structure & Bonding Ser.). (Illus.). xvi, 310p. pap. 359.00 *(978-3-642-05652-9(0)*, 3642056520) Springer.
Schönherr, Thomas, ed. Optical Spectra & Chemical Bonding in Inorganic Compounds: Special Volume I, dedicated to Professor Jørgensen 2010. (Structure & Bonding Ser.). (Illus.). xvi, 263p. pap. 299.00 *(978-3-642-05651-2(2)*, 3642056512) Springer.
Shida, Tadamasa. The Chemical Bond: A Fundamental Quantum-Mechanical Picture. 2010. (Springer Series in Chemical Physics Ser.). Orig. Title: Fundamental Understanding of Chemical Bond. (Illus.). xvi, 206p. pap. 219.00 *(978-3-642-05838-7(8)*, 3642058388) Springer.
Spruell, Jason M. The Power of Click Chemistry for Molecular Machines & Surface Patterning. 2011. (Springer Theses Ser.). (Illus.). xvii, 119p. 129.00 *(978-1-4419-9646-6(X)*, 144199646X) Springer.
Turovskyi, A. A., et al, eds. Non-Valency Interaction in Organic Peroxides Homolysis Reactions. 2012. (Chemistry Research & Applications Ser.). (Illus.). 262p. 75.00 *(978-1-61324-645-0(5))* Nova Science Pubs., Inc.
Vigalok, Arkadi, ed. C-X Bond Formation. 2010. (Topics in Organometallic Chemistry Ser.). (ENG., Illus.). xi, 187p. 299.00 *(978-3-642-12072-5(5)*, 3642120725) Springer.
Wales, D. Intermolecular Forces & Clusters I. 2010. (Structure & Bonding Ser.). xvi, 206p. pap. 239.00 *(978-3-642-06644-3(5)*, 3642066445) Springer.
—Intermolecular Forces & Clusters II. 2010. (Structure & Bonding Ser.). (ABK.). xvi, 158p. pap. 219.00 *(978-3-642-06642-9(9)*, 3642066429) Springer.
Wallace, Dorothy & Belbruno, Joseph J. The Bell That Rings Light: A Primer in Quantum Mechanics & Chemical Bonding. 2006. (Mathematics Across the Curriculum Ser.). (Illus.). 137p. pap. 24.00 *(978-981-256-706-2(2))*; Vol. 1. 49.00 *(978-981-256-705-5(4))* World Scientific Publishing Co., Inc.
Weinhold, Frank. Discovering Chemistry with Natural Bond Orbitals. 2012. (ENG.). 360p. pap. 79.95 ***(978-1-118-11996-9(7)***, Wiley) Wiley, John & Sons, Inc.
Yudin, Andrei K., ed. Catalyzed Carbon-Heteroatom Bond Formation. 2010. (ENG., Illus.). 522p. 215.00 *(978-3-527-32428-6(3)*, Wiley-VCH) Wiley, John & Sons, Inc.

CHEMICAL COMPOSITION OF THE EARTH
see Geochemistry

CHEMICAL DEPENDENCY
see Substance Abuse

CHEMICAL DETECTORS
Here are entered works on apparatus used to detect the presence or absence of chemicals on a relatively gross scale in industrial processes, environmental protection, etc.
Anslyn, Eric V. & Wang, Binghe, eds. Chemosensors: Principles, Strategies, & Applications. 2011. (Wiley Series in Drug Discovery & Development Ser.: 15). (ENG., Illus.). 540p. 149.95 *(978-0-470-59206-9(0)*, Wiley) Wiley, John & Sons, Inc.
Arregui, Francisco J., et al. Optical Chemical Nanosensors. 2012. (Series in Sensors Ser.: 9). (ENG., Illus.). 664p. 129.95 *(978-1-4398-5489-1(0)*, Taylor & Francis) Taylor & Francis Group GBR. Dist: Taylor & Francis Group.
Carapezza, Edward M. Unmanned/Unattended Sensors & Sensor Networks III: 11-12 September, 2006, Stockholm, Sweden. 2006. (Proceedings of SPIE Ser.). (Illus.). 184p. pap. 80.00 *(978-0-8194-6492-7(9))* SPIE.
—Unmanned/Unattended Sensors & Sensor Networks IV: 18-20 September 2007, Florence, Italy. 2007. (Proceedings of SPIE Ser.). (Illus.). 378p. pap. 90.00 *(978-0-8194-6894-9(0))* SPIE.
—Unmanned/Unattended Sensors & Sensor Networks V: 16-18 September 2008, Cardiff, Wales, United Kingdom. 2008. (Proceedings of SPIE Ser.). (Illus.). 306p. pap. 90.00 *(978-0-8194-7344-8(8))* SPIE.
—Unmanned/Unattended Sensors & Sensor Networks VI: 1-3 September 2009, Berlin, Germany. 2009. (Proceedings of SPIE Ser.). (Illus.). 298p. pap. 90.00 *(978-0-8194-7786-6(9))* SPIE.
Carapezza, Edward M. Unmanned/Unattended Sensors & Sensor Networks VII: 20-22 September 2010, Toulouse, France. 2010. (Proceedings of SPIE Ser.). (Illus.). 256p. pap. 90.00 ***(978-0-8194-8351-5(6))*** SPIE.
Carrano, John C. & Collins, Charles J. Optically Based Biological & Chemical Detection for Defence V: 1 September 2009, Berlin, Germany. 2009. (Proceedings of SPIE Ser.). (Illus.). 172p. pap. 70.00 ***(978-0-8194-7790-3(7))*** SPIE.
Carrano, John C. & Zukauskas, Arturas. Optically Based Biological & Chemical Detection for Defence III: 11-13 September 2006, Stockholm, Sweden. 2006. (Proceedings of SPIE Ser.). (Illus.). 248p. pap. 90.00 *(978-0-8194-6496-5(1))* SPIE.
Center for Chemical Process Safety (CCPS) Staff. Continuous Monitoring for Hazardous Material Releases. 2009. (ENG., Illus.). 86p. 83.95 *(978-0-470-14890-7(X))* American Institute of Chemical Engineers.
Cha, Wansik. Electrochemical S-Nitrosothiol Sensors - Nitric Oxide Generation by Polymeric Organoselenium Catalysts. 2008. 216p. pap. *(978-3-8364-7000-1(4))* VDM Verlag Dr. Mueller e.K.
Christesen, Steven Dale. Chemical & Biological Sensors for Industrial & Environmental Monitoring II: 3-4 October, 2006, Boston, Massachusetts, USA. 2006. (Progress in Biomedical Optics & Imaging Ser.: No. 7). (Illus.). 372p. pap. 105.00 *(978-0-8194-6476-7(7))* SPIE.
Comini, Elisabetta, et al, eds. Solid State Gas Sensing. (ENG., Illus.). xx, 280p. 2010. pap. 129.00 *(978-1-4419-3507-6(X)*, 144193507X) 2008. 129.00 *(978-0-387-09664-3(7)*, 0387096647) Springer.
Dighavkar, Chandrakant. Tio2 Thick Film Gas Sensor. 2011. 284p. pap. ***(978-3-8443-8755-1(2))*** Lambert Academic Publishing.
Eliaz, Noam, ed. Applications of Electrochemistry & Nanotechnology in Biology & Medicine I, 2 vols. 2011. (Modern Aspects of Electrochemistry Ser.). (ENG., Illus.). xxiii, 425p. 189.00 *(978-1-4614-0346-3(4)*, 1461403464) Springer.
Eliaz, Noam, ed. Applications of Electrochemistry & Nanotechnology in Biology & Medicine II, 2 vols. 2011. (Modern Aspects of Electrochemistry Ser.). (ENG., Illus.). xx, 338p. 129.00 ***(978-1-4614-2136-8(5)***, 1461421365) Springer.
Ewing, Kenneth J. Chemical & Biological Sensors for Industrial & Environmental Monitoring III: 11-12 September 2007, Boston, Massachusetts, USA. 2007. (Proceedings of SPIE Ser.). (Illus.). 146p. pap. 70.00 ***(978-0-8194-6916-8(5))*** SPIE.
Fabry, Pierre & Fouletier, Jacques. Chemical & Biological Microsensors: Applications in Fluid Media. 2010. (Iste Ser.: 422). (ENG., Illus.). 320p. 158.00 *(978-1-84821-142-1(2)*, Wiley-ISTE) Wiley, John & Sons, Inc.
Fountain, Augustus & Gardner, Patrick. Chemical, Biological, Radiological, Nuclear, & Explosives (CBRNE) Sensing XII. 2011. (Proceedings of SPIE Ser.). 568p. pap. 130.00 ***(978-0-8194-8592-2(6))*** SPIE.
Fountain, Augustus W. Chemical & Biological Sensing VIII: 11-12 April 2007, Orlando, Florida, USA. 2007. (Proceedings of SPIE Ser.). (Illus.). 284p. pap. 80.00 *(978-0-8194-6676-1(X))* SPIE.
Fountain, Augustus W. & Gardner, Patrick J. Chemical, Biological, Radiological, Nuclear, & Explosives (CBRNE) Sensing IX: 18-20 March 2008, Orlando, Florida, USA. 2008. (Proceedings of SPIE Ser.). (Illus.). 354p. pap. 90.00 *(978-0-8194-7145-1(3))* SPIE.
—Chemical, Biological, Radiological, Nuclear, & Explosives (CBRNE) Sensing X: 14-16 April 2009, Orlando, Florida, United States. 2009. (Proceedings of SPIE Ser.). (Illus.). 416p. pap. 120.00 *(978-0-8194-7570-1(X))* SPIE.
Francia. Sensors & Microsystems. Di, Francia G., ed. 2008. 187.00 *(978-981-283-358-7(7))* World Scientific Publishing Co., Inc.
Gouma, Perena. Nanomaterials for Chemical Sensors & Biotechnology. 2009. (ENG., Illus.). 159p. 129.95 *(978-981-4267-11-3(2))* Pan Stanford Publishing SGP. Dist: Taylor & Francis Group.
Gouma, Perena, ed. Olfaction & Electronic Nose: Proceedings of the 14th International Symposium on Olfaction & Electronic Nose. 2012. (AIP Conference Proceedings Ser.). (ENG.). 280p. pap. 143.00 ***(978-0-7354-0920-0(X)***, 073540920X, AIP Pr.) Springer.
Grote, James G., et al. Optical Materials in Defence Systems Technology V: 15-16 September 2008, Cardiff, Wales, United Kingdom. 2008. (Proceedings of SPIE Ser.). (Illus.). 88p. pap. 70.00 *(978-0-8194-7350-9(2))* SPIE.
Grote, James Gerard, et al. Optical Materials in Defence Systems Technology III: 13-14 September 2006, Stockholm, Sweden. 2006. (Proceedings of SPIE Ser.). (Illus.). 144p. pap. 70.00 *(978-0-8194-6499-6(6))* SPIE.
—Optical Materials in Defence Systems Technology IV: 17-13 September 2007, Florence, Italy. 2007. (Proceedings of SPIE Ser.). (Illus.). 104p. pap. 70.00 ***(978-0-8194-6898-7(3))*** SPIE.
Grote, James Gerard, et al. Optical Materials in Defence Systems Technology VI: 31 August-1 September 2009, Berlin, Germany. 2009. (Proceedings of SPIE Ser.). (Illus.). 182p. pap. 70.00 *(978-0-8194-7793-4(1))* SPIE.
Grundler, Peter. Chemical Sensors: An Introduction for Scientists & Engineers. 2007. (ENG., Illus.). x, 273p. 99.00 *(978-3-540-45742-8(3)*, 3540457429) Springer.
Gründler, Peter. Chemical Sensors: An Introduction for Scientists & Engineers. 2010. (ENG., Illus.). x, 273p. pap. 99.00 *(978-3-642-07958-0(X)*, 364207958X) Springer.
Gutiérrez, Agustín & Marco, Santiago. Biologically Inspired Signal Processing for Chemical Sensing. 2009. (Illus.). xiii, 157p. E-Book *(978-3-642-00176-5(9))* Springer.
Harrison, Ronald V., ed. Chemical Sensors: Properties, Performance & Applications. 2010. (Chemistry Research & Applications Ser.). 69.00 *(978-1-60741-897-9(5))* Nova Science Pubs., Inc.
Hsu, Jui Ching. Fabrication of Single Walled Carbon Nanotube (SW-CNT) Cantilevers for Chemical Sensing: Carbon Nanotubes for Chemical Detection. 2008. 124p. pap. *(978-3-8364-7325-5(9))* VDM Verlag Dr Mueller e.K.
Hunter, G. & Hesketh, P. J., eds. Chemical Sensors 7 -and- MEMS/NEMS 7: ECS Transactions: Volume 3, Issue 10. 2006. (ECS Transactions Ser.). (Illus.). 515p. 114.00 *(978-1-56677-510-6(8)*, ECS Transactions) Electrochemical Society, The.
Jensen, Janet & Woolard, Dwight L., eds. Spectral Sensing Research for Water Monitoring Applications & Frontier Science & Technology for Chemical, Biological & Radiological Defense. 2008. (Illus.). xv, 486p. 152.00 *(978-981-283-323-5(4))* World Scientific Publishing Co., Inc.
Kamerman, Gary, et al. Electro-Optical Remote Sensing, Photonic Technologies, & Applications III. 2009. (Proceedings of SPIE Ser.). 264p. pap. 70.00 ***(978-0-8194-7788-0(5))*** SPIE.
Kamerman, Gary W. Electro-Optical Remote Sensing, Detection, & Photonic Technologies & Their Applications: 18-20 September 2007, Florence, Italy. 2007. (Proceedings of SPIE Ser.). (Illus.). 414p. pap. 105.00 *(978-0-8194-6897-0(5))* SPIE.
—Electro-Optical Remote Sensing, Photonic Technologies, & Applications II: 15-16 September 2008, Cardiff, Wales, United Kingdom. 2008. (Proceedings of SPIE Ser.). (Illus.). 206p. pap. 80.00 *(978-0-8194-7346-2(4))* SPIE.
Kamerman, Gary W. Electro-Optical Remote Sensing, Photonic Technologies, & Applications IV: 20 & 22-23 September 2010, Toulouse, France. 2010. (Proceedings of SPIE Ser.). (Illus.). 322p. pap. 80.00 ***(978-0-8194-8353-9(2))*** SPIE.
Korotcenkov, Ghenadii. Chemical Sensors Comprehensive Sensor Technologies: Volume 6 Chemical Sensors Applications. 2011. 380p. 199.95 *(978-1-60650-239-6(5))* Momentum Pr.
Korotcenkov, Ghenadii, ed. Chemical Sensors Comprehensive Sensor Technologies: Solid State Sensors. 2011. 500p. 199.95 *(978-1-60650-233-4(6))* Momentum Pr.
—Chemical Sensors Comprehensive Sensor Technologies: Volume 5 Electrochemical & Optical Sensors. 2011. 450p. 199.95 *(978-1-60650-236-5(0))* Momentum Pr.
—Chemical Sensors Fundamentals of Sensing Materials Vol. 3 Polymers & Other Materials. 2011. 350p. 109.95 *(978-1-60650-230-3(1))* Momentum Pr.
Lange, D., et al. CMOS Cantilever Sensor Systems: Atomic-Force Microscopy & Gas Sensing Applications. 2010. (Microtechnology & MEMS Ser.). (Illus.). viii, 150p. pap. 159.00 *(978-3-642-07728-9(5)*, 3642077285) Springer.
Lee, Taewoo. Thermal & Flow Measurements. 2008. (ENG., Illus.). 400p. (C). 107.95 *(978-0-8493-7970-3(9)*, CRC Press) Taylor & Francis Group GBR Dist: Taylor & Francis Group.
Lieber, Charles & Royal Society of Chemistry Staff. Nano & Microsensors for Chemical & Biological Terrorism Surveillance. Tok, Jeffrey B-H, ed. 2008. (ENG., Illus.). 224p. 160.00 ***(978-0-85404-140-4(0))*** Royal Society of Chemistry, The GBR. Dist: Ingram Pub. Services.
Liu, Tianshu & Sullivan, John P. Pressure & Temperature Sensitive Paints. 2010. (Experimental Fluid Mechanics Ser.). (Illus.). xi, 328p. pap. 179.00 *(978-3-642-06075-5(7)*, 3642060757) Springer.
M. Ibrahim, Azhar, et al. Electronic Nose for Robots. 2011. 120p. pap. ***(978-3-8443-9887-8(2))*** Lambert Academic Publishing.
Marco, Santiago & Gutiérrez, Agustí, eds. Biologically Inspired Signal Processing for Chemical Sensing. 2009. (Studies in Computational Intelligence Ser.). (ENG., Illus.). xiv, 170p. 159.00 *(978-3-642-00175-8(0))* Springer.
Mason, Elena C. & Weber, Allison P. Polypyrrole: Properties, Performance & Applications. 2011. (Materials Science & Technologies Ser.). (Illus.). 296p. 165.00 *(978-1-61209-143-3(1))* Nova Science Pubs., Inc.
Materials Research Society ( ) Staff, compiled by. Nanofunctional Materials, Nanostructures, & Novel Devices for Biological & Chemical Detection. 2007. (Materials Research Society Symposium Proceedings Ser.). 306p. pap. 115.00 *(978-1-60423-407-7(5))* Curran Assocs., Inc.
Mirsky, Vladimir M., ed. Ultrathin Electrochemical Chemo- & Biosensors: Technology & Performance. 2010. (Springer Series on Chemical Sensors & Biosensors Ser.). (Illus.). xx, 358p. pap. 199.00 *(978-3-642-05961-2(9)*, 3642059619) Springer.
Mulchandani, Ashok & Rogers, Kim, eds. Enzyme & Microbial Biosensors: Techniques & Protocols. 2010. (Methods in Biotechnology Ser.). 284p. pap 159.00 *(978-1-61737-028-1(2)*, 1617370282) Humana Pr.
Natale C., Di. Sensors & Microsystems. 2008. (Illus.). xix, 544p. 187.00 *(978-981-283-597-0(0))* World Scientific Publishing Co., Inc.
Nikolelis, Dimitrios P., ed. Portable Chemical Sensors: Weapons Against Bioterrorism. 2012. (NATO Science for Peace & Security Series A: Chemistry & Biology Ser.). (ENG., Illus.). xiii, 344p. pap. 119.00 ***(978-94-007-2874-5(3)***, 9400728743) Springer.
—Portable Chemical Sensors: Weapons Against Bioterrorism. 2012. (NATO Science for Peace & Security Series A: Chemistry & Biology Ser.). (ENG., Illus.). xiii, 344p. 229.00 ***(978-94-007-2871-4(9)***, 9400728719) Springer.
Orellana, Guillermo & Moreno-Bondi, Maria Cruz. Frontiers in Chemical Sensors: Novel Principles & Techniques. 2010. (Springer Series on Chemical Sensors & Biosensors Ser.). (Illus.). xii, 370p. pap. 269.00 *(978-3-642-06612-2(7)*, 3642066127) Springer.

Osada, Yoshihito & De Rossi, Danilo E. Polymer Sensors & Actuators. 2010. (Macromolecular Systems - Materials Approach Ser.). (Illus.). xx, 448p. pap. 489.00 *(978-3-642-08482-9(6),* 3642084826) Springer.

Pardo, Matteo & Sberveglieri, Giorgio, eds. Olfaction & Electronic Nose: Proceedings of the 13th International Symposium on Olfaction & Electronic Nose. 2009. (AIP Conference Proceedings / Materials Physics & Applications Ser.). (ENG.). 614p. pap. 299.00 *(978-0-7354-0674-2(X),* 073540674X) American Institute of Physics.

Potyrailo, Radislav A. & Mirsky, Vladimir M. Combinatorial Methods for Chemical & Biological Sensors. 2009. (Integrated Microanalytical Systems Ser.). (Illus.). xx, 494p. E-Book *(978-0-387-63713-6(3))* Springer.

Potyrailo, Radislav A. & Mirsky, Vladimir M., eds. Combinatorial Methods for Sensor Materials. 2009. (Integrated Analytical Systems Ser.). (Illus.). xx, 494p. 99.00 *(978-0-387-73712-6(X))* Springer.

Qiu, Xiaotun, ed. Gas Sensors: Developments, Efficacy & Safety. 2012. (Safety & Risk in Society Ser.). 283p. 95.00 ***(978-1-61470-829-2(0))*** Nova Science Pubs., Inc.

Rao, T. Prasada, et al. Electrochemical Sensing of Deadly Toxin-Atrazine: An Overview. 2010. (Illus.). 43p. pap. 49.00 *(978-1-61761-100-1(X))* Nova Science Pubs., Inc.

Ren, Fan & Pearton, Stephen J., eds. Semiconductor Device-Based Sensors for Gas Chemical & Bio App. 2011. (ENG., Illus.). 324p. 149.95 *(978-1-4398-1387-4(6),* CRC Press) Taylor & Francis Group GBR. Dist: Taylor & Francis Group.

Ryan, Margaret A., et al, eds. Computational Methods for Sensor Material Selection. 2009. (Integrated Analytical Systems Ser.). (ENG., Illus.). xv, 319p. 159.00 *(978-0-387-73714-0(6),* 0387737146) Springer.

Schrader, Thomas. Creative Chemical Sensor Systems. (Topics in Current Chemistry Ser.). (Illus.). xiv, 303p. 2010. pap. 389.00 *(978-3-642-09075-2(3),* 3642090753) 2007. 389.00 *(978-3-540-71546-7(0),* 3540715460) Springer.

Schubert, Hiltmar & Rimski-Korsakov, Alexander, eds. Stand-off Detection of Suicide Bombers & Mobile Subjects. 2006. (NATO Science for Peace & Security Series / NATO Science for Peace & Security Series B: Physics & Biophysics Ser.). x, 165p. 189.00 *(978-1-4020-5157-9(3),* 1402051573); pap. 99.00 *(978-1-4020-5158-6(1),* 1402051581) Springer.

Shinar, Ruth & Malliaras, George G. Organic-Based Chemical & Biological Sensors: 28 August 2007, San Diego, California, USA. 2007. (Proceedings of SPIE Ser.). (Illus.). 86p. pap. 60.00 ***(978-0-8194-6807-9(X))*** SPIE.

Siciliano, P. Sensors & Microsystems: Proceedings of the 11Th Italian Conference. 2008. 211.00 *(978-981-279-338-6(0))* World Scientific Publishing Co., Inc.

Steinem, Claudia & Janshoff, Andreas, eds. Piezoelectric Sensors. (Springer Series on Chemical Sensors & Biosensors Ser.). (Illus.). xii, 483p. 2010. pap. 379.00 *(978-3-642-07167-6(8),* 3642071678) 2007. 379.00 *(978-3-540-36567-9(2),* 3540365672) Springer.

Theriault, Jean-Marc. Spectral Sensing Research for Surface & Air Monitoring in Chemical, Biological & Radiological Defense & Security Applications, Vol. 49. 2009. (Illus.). 544p. 135.00 *(978-981-283-591-8(1))* World Scientific Publishing Co., Inc.

Tuller, H. L., et al, eds. Oxygen Ion & Mixed Conductors & their Technological Applications. 2012. (NATO Science Series E: (closed) Ser.). (ENG.). 484p. pap. 264.00 *(978-90-481-5434-0(0),* 9048154340) Springer.

Vergara Tinoco, Alexander. Improving the Performance of Micro-MacHined Metal Oxide Gas Sensors. 2009. 252p. pap. *(978-3-639-14018-7(4))* VDM Verlag Dr. Mueller e.K.

Vo-Dinh, Tuan, et al. Advanced Environmental, Chemical, & Biological Sensing Technologies IV: 1-3 October 2006, Boston, Massachusetts, USA. 2006. (Progress in Biomedical Optics & Imaging Ser.: No. 7). (Illus.). 220p. pap. 80.00 *(978-0-8194-6475-0(9))* SPIE.

—Advanced Environmental, Chemical, & Biological Sensing Technologies V: 10-11 September 2007, Boston, Massachusetts, USA. 2007. (Proceedings of SPIE Ser.). (Illus.). 156p. pap. 80.00 *(978-0-8194-6915-1(7))* SPIE.

—Advanced Environmental, Chemical, & Biological Sensing Technologies VI: 13-14 April 2009, Orlando, Florida, United States. 2009. (Proceedings of SPIE Ser.). (Illus.). 210p. pap. 80.00 *(978-0-8194-7578-7(5))* SPIE.

Vo-Dinh, Tuan, et al. Advanced Environmental, Chemical, & Biological Sensing Technologies VIII. 2011. (Proceedings of SPIE Ser.). pap. 80.00 ***(978-0-8194-8598-4(5))*** SPIE.

Zourob, Mohammed & Lakhtakia, A. Optical Guided-Wave Chemical & Biosensors, 2 vols. 2010. (Springer Series on Chemical Sensors & Biosensors Ser.). (ENG., Illus.). x, 250p. 249.00 *(978-3-540-88241-1(3),* 3540882413) Springer.

CHEMICAL ELEMENTS

see also Actinide Elements; Allotropy; Atomic Weights; Nonmetals; Periodic Law; Trace Elements; Valence (Theoretical Chemistry)

also names of elements

Acar, Selçuk. Sodium Amide - Sodium Tetrahydridoborate System. 2010. 120p. pap. *(978-3-8383-6496-4(1))* Lambert Academic Publishing.

Adair, Rick. Boron. 2009. (Understanding the Elements of the Periodic Table Ser.). 48p. (gr. 6-6). 53.00 *(978-1-60854-637-4(3),* Rosen Central) Rosen Publishing Group, Inc., The.

Aldersey-Williams, Hugh. Periodic Tales: A Cultural History of the Elements, from Arsenic to Zinc. 448p. 2012. pap. 14.99 ***(978-0-06-182473-9(9))*** 2011. 32.50 *(978-0-06-182472-2(0))* HarperCollins Pubs. (Ecco).

Angelo, Joseph A. Extreme States of Matter. 2012. (States of Matter Ser.). 272p. (C). (gr. 9). 45.00 *(978-0-8160-7606-2(5))* Facts On File, Inc.

BarCharts, Inc. Periodic Table. 2008. (ENG.). 4p. instr.'s gde. ed. 3.95 *(978-1-4232-0422-0(0))* Barcharts, Inc.

Belval, Brian. The Carbon Elements: Carbon, Silicon, Germanium, Tin, Lead. 2009. (Understanding the Elements of the Periodic Table Ser.). (ENG., Illus.). 48p. (YA). (gr. 5-9). lib. bdg. 26.50 *(978-1-4358-5334-8(2))* Rosen Publishing Group, Inc., The.

Besant, Annie. Occult Chemistry. 2007. 144p. per. 13.45 *(978-1-59462-814-6(9),* Book Jungle) Standard Pubns., Inc.

Dietl, Tomasz, et al, contrib. by. New Data & Updates for I-VII, III-V, III-VI & IV-VI Compounds. 2009. (Landolt-Börnstein: Numerical Data & Functional Relationships in Science & Technology Ser.). (ENG., Illus.). vi, 325p. 5389.00 *(978-3-540-48528-5(7))* Springer.

Emsley, John. Nature's Building Blocks: An A-Z Guide to the Elements. 2nd ed. 2011. (ENG., Illus.). 720p. pap. 24.95 *(978-0-19-960563-7(7))* Oxford Univ. Pr., Inc.

Fehlner, Thomas, et al. Molecular Clusters: A Bridge to Solid-State Chemistry. 2007. (Cambridge Molecular Science Ser.). (ENG., Illus.). 390p. 170.00 *(978-0-521-85236-4(6))* Cambridge Univ. Pr.

Fisher, David J. Diffusion in Semiconductors, Other Than Silicon: Compilation, Vol. 308. Fisher, David J., ed. 2011. (Defect & Diffusion Forum Ser.: Vol. 308). 168p. pap. ***(978-3-03785-093-0(0))*** Trans Tech Pubns., Ltd.

Gray, Theodore. The Elements: A Visual Exploration of Every Known Atom in the Universe. 2012. (ENG., Illus.). 320p. pap. 19.95 ***(978-1-57912-895-1(5))*** Black Dog & Leventhal Pubs., Inc.

—The Elements: A Visual Exploration of Every Known Atom in the Universe. 2011. 49.95 *(978-1-61535-432-0(8))* Encyclopaedia Britannica, Inc.

Guandalini, Roald. The Ninth Torino Workshop on Evolution & Nucleosynthesis in AGB Stars & the Second Perugia Workshop on Nuclear Astrophysics: Held in Perugia, Italy, 21-27 October 2007. 2008. (AIP Conference Proceedings Ser.). (Illus.). 203.00 *(978-0-7354-0520-2(4))* American Institute of Physics.

Hasan, Heather. Aluminum. 2006. 52p. pap. 26.50 *(978-1-4358-3759-1(2));* (Illus.). 48p. (YA). (gr. 5-9). lib. bdg. 26.50 *(978-1-4042-0705-9(8))* Rosen Publishing Group, Inc., The.

—The Boron Elements: Boron, Aluminum, Gallium, Indium, Thallium. 2009. (Understanding the Elements of the Periodic Table Ser.). (ENG., Illus.). 48p. (YA). (gr. 5-9). lib. bdg. 26.50 *(978-1-4358-5333-1(4))* Rosen Publishing Group, Inc., The.

—Fluorine. 2009. (Understanding the Elements of the Periodic Table Ser.). 48p. (gr. 6-6). 53.00 *(978-1-60854-649-7(7),* Rosen Central) Rosen Publishing Group, Inc., The.

—Manganese. (Understanding the Elements of the Periodic Table Ser.). 48p. 2009. (gr. 6-6). 53.00 *(978-1-60854-665-7(9),* Rosen Central) 2008. (Illus.). (YA). (gr. 5-9). lib. bdg. 26.50 *(978-1-4042-1408-8(9))* Rosen Publishing Group, Inc., The.

Jaschek, Carlos & Jaschek, Mercedes. The Behavior of Chemical Elements in Stars. 2009. (ENG., Illus.). 340p. pap. 61.00 *(978-0-521-10240-7(5))* Cambridge Univ. Pr.

Kaldor, U. & Wilson, Stephen, eds. Theoretical Chemistry & Physics of Heavy & Superheavy Elements. 2010. (Progress in Theoretical Chemistry & Physics Ser.). 584p. pap. 229.00 *(978-90-481-6313-7(7),* 9048163137) Springer.

Katz, Nevin. Elements, Compounds, & Mixtures: Middle & High School. 2007. (Dr. Birdley Teaches Science Ser.). (Illus.). 94p. per. 12.99 *(978-0-86530-536-6(6))* Incentive Pubns., Inc.

Kean, Sam. The Disappearing Spoon: And Other True Tales of Madness, Love, & the History of the World from the Periodic Table of the Elements. (ENG., Illus.). 2011. 416p. pap. 14.99 *(978-0-316-05163-7(2),* Back Bay Bks.) 2010. 400p. 24.99 *(978-0-316-05164-4(0))* Little Brown & Co.

Krebs, Robert E. The History & Use of Our Earth's Chemical Elements: A Reference Guide, 1 vol. 2nd rev. ed. 2006. (Illus.). 448p. 75.00 *(978-0-313-33438-2(2),* GR3438, Greenwood Pr.) Greenwood Publishing Group, Inc.

Leadbeater, C. W. Occult Chemistry: Clairvoyant Observations on the Chemical Elements. 2007. 132p. per. 28.95 *(978-1-60206-693-9(0))* Cosimo, Inc.

Leadbeater, C. W. & Besant, Annie. Occult Chemistry: Clairvoyant Observations on the Chemical Elements. Sinnett, A. P., ed. 2007. 152p. per. *(978-1-4065-3640-9(7))* Dodo Pr.

Lee, Vladimir Ya. & Sekiguchi, Akira. Organometallic Compounds of Low-Coordinate Si, Ge, Sn & Pb: From Phantom Species to Stable Compounds. 2010. (ENG., Illus.). 448p. 195.00 *(978-0-470-72543-6(5),* Wiley) Wiley, John & Sons, Inc.

Lew, Kristi. Lead. (Understanding the Elements of the Periodic Table Ser.). 48p. 2009. (gr. 6-6). 53.00 *(978-1-60854-660-2(8),* Rosen Central) 2008. (Illus.). (YA). (gr. 5-9). lib. bdg. 26.50 *(978-1-4042-1779-9(7))* Rosen Publishing Group, Inc., The.

—Mercury. 2008. (Understanding the Elements of the Periodic Table Ser.). (Illus.). 48p. (YA). (gr. 5-9). lib. bdg. 26.50 *(978-1-4042-1780-5(0))* Rosen Publishing Group, Inc., The.

—Radium. 2009. (Understanding the Elements of the Periodic Table Ser.). 48p. (gr. 6-6). 53.00 *(978-1-60854-679-4(9),* Rosen Central); (YA). (gr. 5-9). lib. bdg. 26.50 *(978-1-4358-5072-9(6))* Rosen Publishing Group, Inc., The.

—Zinc. (Understanding the Elements of the Periodic Table Ser.). 48p. 2009. (gr. 6-6). 53.00 *(978-1-60854-689-3(6),* Rosen Central) 2008. (Illus.). (YA). (gr. 5-9). lib. bdg. 26.50 *(978-1-4042-1407-1(0))* Rosen Publishing Group, Inc., The.

Newton, David E. & Edgar, Kathleen J. Chemical Elements. 2nd ed. 2010. *(978-1-4144-7611-7(6)); (978-1-4144-7610-0(8)); (978-1-4144-7609-4(4));* (ENG.). 225.00 *(978-1-4144-7608-7(6))* Cengage Gale. (UXL).

Penionzhkevich, Yu E. & Lukyanov, S. M., eds. International Symposium on Exotic Nuclei. 2010. (AIP Conference Proceedings / Accelerators, Beams, & Instrumentations Ser.). 638p. 344.00 *(978-0-7354-0768-8(1),* 0735407681, AIP Pr.) Springer.

Periodic Table. cd-rom 80.00 *(978-0-7932-8940-0(8))* CLEARVUE/eav, Inc.

Quadbeck-Seeger, Hans-Jürgen. The Periodic Table Through History: Who Charted the Elements? 2007. (ENG.). 2p. 30.00 *(978-3-527-32083-7(0),* Wiley-VCH) Wiley, John & Sons, Inc.

Scerri, Eric. The Periodic Table: A Very Short Introduction. 2012. (Very Short Introductions Ser.). (ENG., Illus.). 144p. 11.95 ***(978-0-19-958249-5(1))*** Oxford Univ. Pr., Inc.

Scerri, Eric. Selected Papers on the Periodic Table by Eric Scerri. 2009. (Illus.). 156p. 99.00 *(978-1-84816-425-3(4))* Imperial College Pr. GBR. Dist: World Scientific Publishing Co., Inc.

Scerri, Eric R. The Periodic Table: Its Story & Its Significance. 2006. (ENG., Illus.). 368p. 35.00 *(978-0-19-530573-9(6))* Oxford Univ. Pr., Inc.

Schweitzer, George Keene & Pesterfield, Lester L. The Aqueous Chemistry of the Elements. 2010. (ENG., Illus.). 448p. 99.00 *(978-0-19-539335-4(X))* Oxford Univ. Pr., Inc.

Scott, William C. ENERGY WAVE of the Periodic Table Definitive Periodic Law REVEALED. 2007. (Illus.). 80p. per. 24.95 *(978-0-9798235-1-0(X))* Energy Spectrum Publishing.

—QUANTUM MECHANICS of the Periodic Table PROTONS REVEALED. 2008. (Illus.). 88p. (C). per. 29.95 *(978-0-9798235-2-7(8),* Energy Spectrum) Energy Spectrum Publishing.

Smith, Mike. Chemistry: Equilibria, Energetics & Elements. 2009. 112p. pap., stu. ed. 22.50 *(978-0-340-95759-2(X))* Hodder Education GBR. Dist: Trans-Atlantic Pubns., Inc.

Sommers, Michael A. Silicon. 2007. (Understanding the Elements of the Periodic Table Ser.). (Illus.). 48p. (YA). (gr. 5-9). lib. bdg. 26.50 *(978-1-4042-1959-5(5))* Rosen Publishing Group, Inc., The.

Stwertka, Albert. A Guide to the Elements, 1 vol. 3rd ed. 2012. (Illus.). 256p. 39.95 ***(978-0-19-983251-4(X));*** (ENG., pap. 19.95 ***(978-0-19-983252-1(8))*** Oxford Univ. Pr., Inc.

Suda, Takuma. Origin of Matter & Evolution of Galaxies: The 10th International Symposium on Origin of Matter & Evolution of Galaxies: From the Dawn of Universe to the Formation of Solar System, Sapporo, Japan, 4-7 December 2007. 2008. (AIP Conference Proceedings / Astronomy & Astrophysics Ser.). (Illus.). 520p. 218.00 *(978-0-7354-0537-0(9))* American Institute of Physics.

Van der Wal, Jurjen. Decoding the Periodic Table. 2010. 200p. pap. 25.95 *(978-1-4401-8672-1(3))* iUniverse, Inc.

CHEMICAL EMBRYOLOGY

Sharpe, Paul & Mason, Ivor, eds. Molecular Embryology: Methods & Protocols. 2nd ed. 2010. (Methods in Molecular Biology Ser.). (Illus.). 400p. pap. 179.00 *(978-1-61737-565-1(9),* 1617375659) Humana Pr.

CHEMICAL ENGINEERING

see also Biochemical Engineering; Biotechnology; Chemical Plants; Chemistry, Technical; Metallurgy; Mixing; Molecular Sieves; Polymer Engineering; Protective Atmospheres

Abraham, Martin A. Innovations in Industrial & Engineering Chemistry: A Century of Achievements & Prospects for the New Millennium. Flank, William H. & Matthews, Michael A., eds. 2009. (American Chemical Society Publication). (ENG., Illus.). 480p. 175.00 *(978-0-8412-6963-7(7))* American Chemical Society.

Adidharma, Hertanto & Temyanko, Valery. Mathcad for Chemical Engineers-second Edition. 2009. 184p. pap. 50.00 *(978-1-4269-0812-5(1))* Trafford Publishing.

Al. Chemistry of Nanocrystalline Oxide Ma... 2008. 135.00 *(978-981-279-314-0(3))* World Scientific Publishing Co., Inc.

Alkire, Richard C., et al, contrib. by. Diffraction & Spectroscopic Methods in Electrochemistry. 2006. (Advances in Electrochemical Sciences & Engineering Ser.: 5). (ENG., Illus.). 445p. 250.00 *(978-3-527-31317-4(6),* Wiley-VCH) Wiley, John & Sons, Inc.

American Institute of Chemical Engineers (AIChE) Staff, compiled by. Topical Conference on Novel Technologies 2007. 2007. 79p. pap. 93.00 *(978-1-60423-361-2(3))* Curran Assocs., Inc.

—19th Ethylene Producers Conference 2007. 2007. 706p. pap. 143.00 *(978-1-60423-351-3(6))* Curran Assocs., Inc.

—41st Loss Prevention Symposium 2007. 2007. 431p. pap. 118.00 *(978-1-60423-353-7(2))* Curran Assocs., Inc.

American Society of Mechanical Engineers Staff, ed. Performance Standard Installation Procedures for Stainless Steel Drainage System Sanitary Storm Chemical Applications. 32p. 35.00 *(978-0-7918-2272-2(9))* ASME Pr.

Arie, Arenst Andreas & KEE LEE, Joong. Fullerene C60 Thin Film As a Novel Coating Material for Si Film Anodes. 2011. 100p. pap. ***(978-3-8443-0577-7(7))*** Lambert Academic Publishing.

Azbel, David. Two Phase Flows in Chemical Engineering. 2009. (ENG.). 332p. pap. 46.00 *(978-0-521-10424-1(6))* Cambridge Univ. Pr.

BCC Research Staff. Catalysts for Environmental & Energy Applications. 2007. per. 4250.00 *(978-1-59623-301-0(X))* BCC Research.

Becher, J. & Schaumburg, Kjeld, eds. Molecular Engineering for Advanced Materials. 2010. (NATO Science Series C: (closed) Ser.). 400p. pap. 389.00 *(978-90-481-4521-8(X),* 904814521X) Springer.

Benchmarking the Research Competitiveness of the U.S. in Chemical Engineering Committee. International Benchmarking of U. S. Chemical Engineering Research Competitiveness. 2007. (ENG., Illus.). 246p. per. 54.00 *(978-0-309-10537-8(4))* National Academies Pr.

Benitez, Jaime. Principles & Modern Applications of Mass Transfer Operations. 2nd ed. 2009. (ENG., Illus.). 648p. 128.00 *(978-0-470-18178-2(8),* Wiley-Interscience) Wiley, John & Sons, Inc.

Berton, Leon P. Chemical Engineering Research Trends. 2007. 395p. (C). 129.00 *(978-1-60021-486-8(X))* Nova Science Pubs., Inc.

Boyadjiev, Christo. Theoretical Chemical Engineering: Modeling & Simulation. 2010. (ENG., Illus.). xxix, 600p. 209.00 *(978-3-642-10777-1(X),* 364210777X) Springer.

Brennan, David. Sustainable Engineering: Green Concepts, Strategies, Evaluation & Implementation. 2012. (ENG.). 300p. 149.95 ***(978-981-4316-78-1(4))*** Pan Stanford Publishing SGP. Dist: Taylor & Francis Group.

Buzzi-Ferraris, Guido & Manenti, Flavio. Interpolation & Regression Models for the Chemical Engineer: Solving Numerical Problems. 2010. (ENG., Illus.). 442p. 130.00 *(978-3-527-32652-5(9),* Wiley-VCH) Wiley, John & Sons, Inc.

Byrne, Christopher Alan. The God Archetype & the Development of Faster Than Light Technology: Volume III. Advanced Concepts of Metallurgy in the Design of the UFO. 2008. 420p. pap. 20.00 *(978-1-4343-8232-0(X))* AuthorHouse.

Cao, Eduardo. Heat Transfer in Process Engineering: Calculations & Equipment Design. 2009. (ENG., Illus.). 576p. 89.95 *(978-0-07-162408-4(2),* 0071624082) McGraw-Hill Professional Publishing.

Cao, Zhong, et al, eds. Application of Chemical Engineering. 2011. (Advanced Materials Research Ser.: Vol. 236-238). 3102p. pap. ***(978-3-03785-121-0(X))*** Trans Tech Pubns., Ltd.

—Fundamental of Chemical Engineering, Proceedings. 2011. (Advanced Materials Research Ser.: Vol. 233-235). 3230p. pap. ***(978-3-03785-119-7(8))*** Trans Tech Pubns., Ltd.

Carre, Antoine. Development of Empirical Potentials for Amorphous Silic. 2008. 180p. pap. *(978-3-8364-9129-7(X))* VDM Verlag Dr. Mueller e.K.

Caruso, Denise. Intervention: Confronting the Real Risks. 2006. 270p. pap. 17.95 *(978-0-615-13553-3(6))* Hybrid Vigor Institute, The.

Center for Chemical Process Safety (CCPS) Staff. Guidelines for Risk Based Process Safety. 2007. (ENG.). 768p. 178.00 *(978-0-470-16569-0(3))* American Institute of Chemical Engineers.

Center for Chemical Process Safety Staff. Inherently Safer Chemical Processes: A Life Cycle Approach. 2nd ed. 2008. (ENG., Illus.). 412p. 105.00 *(978-0-471-77892-9(3))* American Institute of Chemical Engineers.

Center for the Advancement of Process TechnoloCARP Staff. Safety, Health & Environment. 2006. (ENG.). (C). 139.40 *(978-0-536-25843-4(0))* Pearson Learning Solutions.

Chapman, T. W., ed. Industrial & Environmental Electrochemistry. 2007. (ECS Transactions Ser.). 89p. pap. 65.00 *(978-1-60423-371-1(0))* Curran Assocs., Inc.

Cooper, Paul W. Explosives Engineering. 2nd ed. 2008. 600p. 99.95 *(978-0-471-74499-3(9),* Wiley) Wiley, John & Sons, Inc.

Coughanowr, Donald R., et al. Process Systems Analysis & Control. 3rd ed. 2008. (ENG., Illus.). 624p. (C). 225.00 *(978-0-07-339789-4(X),* 007339789X, McGraw-Hill Science, Engineering & Mathematics) McGraw-Hill Higher Education.

Cram101 Textbook Reviews. Outlines & Highlights for Chemical & Engineering Thermodynamics by Sandler, Isbn: 0471182109 9780471182108. 2011. 144p. pap. 28.95 ***(978-1-61812-608-5(3))*** Cram101 Inc.

—Outlines & Highlights for Modeling in Transport Phenomena by Ismail Tosun. 2011. 98p. pap. 27.95 ***(978-1-61905-756-2(5))*** Cram101 Inc.

Cram101 Textbook Reviews & Cram101 Textbook Reviews. Outlines & Highlights for Thermodynamic Models for Industrial Applications: From Classical & Advanced Mixing Rules to Association Theories by Georg. 2011. 464p. pap. 36.95 ***(978-1-61461-301-5(X))*** Cram101 Inc.

Cram101 Textbook Reviews Staff. Outlines & Highlights for Chemical, Biochemical, & Engineering Thermodynamics by Stanley I Sandler, Isbn: 9780471661740. 2009. 202p. pap. 30.95 *(978-1-4288-7452-7(6))* Cram101 Inc.

Cussler, E. L. & Moggridge, G. D. Chemical Product Design. 2nd ed. 2011. (Cambridge Series in Chemical Engineering Ser.). (ENG., Illus.). 452p. (C). pap. 65.00 *(978-0-521-16822-9(8))* Cambridge Univ. Pr.

Dal Pont, Jean-Pierre. Process Engineering & Industrial Management. 2012. (Iste Ser.: 592). (ENG.). 195.00 ***(978-1-84821-326-5(3),*** Wiley-ISTE) Wiley, John & Sons, Inc.

de Brito Alves, Rita Maria, et al, eds. 10th International Symposium on Process Systems Engineering - PSE2009, 2 vols., Pt. A. 2009. (Computer Aided Chemical Engineering Ser.). (Illus.). 1224p. 0.02 *(978-0-444-53435-4(0),* Elsevier Science) Elsevier Science & Technology Bks.

De Swaan Arons, Jakob, et al. Efficiency & Sustainability in the Energy & Chemical Industries: Scientific Principles & Case Studies. 2nd rev. ed. 2010. (Green Chemistry & Chemical Engineering Ser.). (ENG., Illus.). 393p. 149.95 *(978-1-4398-1470-3(8),* CRC Press) Taylor & Francis Group GBR. Dist: Taylor & Francis Group.

Deen, William M. Analysis of Transport Phenomena, 1 vol. 2nd ed. 2011. (Topics in Chemical Engineering Ser.). (ENG.). 688p. (C). 139.00 ***(978-0-19-974028-4(3))*** Oxford Univ. Pr., Inc.

Denn, Morton. Chemical Engineering: An Introduction. 2011. (Cambridge Series in Chemical Engineering Ser.). (ENG., Illus.). 280p. (C). 125.00

(978-1-107-01189-2(2)); pap. 48.00 (978-1-107-66937-6(5)) Cambridge Univ. Pr.

do Carmo Nicoletti, Maria & Jain, Lakhmi C., eds. Computational Intelligence Techniques for Bioprocess Modelling, Supervision & Control. 2009. (Studies in Computational Intelligence Ser.). (Illus.). x, 346p. 179.00 (978-3-642-01887-9(4), 3642018874) Springer.

Dobre, Tanase G. & Marcano, José G. Sanchez. Chemical Engineering: Modeling, Simulation & Similitude. 2007. (ENG., Illus.). 568p. 249.00 (978-3-527-30607-7(2), Wiley-VCH) Wiley, John & Sons, Inc.

Drieben-Holsche, B, et al. Grundriss der Chemischen Technik. 2012. (ENG.). 800p. 105.00 (978-3-527-30446-2(0), Wiley-VCH) Wiley, John & Sons, Inc.

Du, Yanan. 3d Hepatocyte Monolayer for Hepatocyte Based Applications. 2010. 172p. pap. (978-3-8383-8029-2(0)) Lambert Academic Publishing.

Elliott, J. Richard & Lira, Carl T. Introductory Chemical Engineering Thermodynamics. 2nd rev. ed. 2012. (Prentice Hall International Series in the Physical & Chemical Engineering Sciences Ser.). (ENG.). 912p. (C). 130.00 (978-0-13-606854-9(5), Prentice Hall) Prentice Hall PTR.

Ende, David J. am. Chemical Engineering in the Pharmaceutical Industry: R&D to Manufacturing. 2010. (ENG., Illus.). 887p. 199.95 (978-0-470-42669-2(1), Wiley) Wiley, John & Sons, Inc.

Engineers Australia Staff, compiled by. 32nd Australasian Chemical Engineering Conference (CHEMECA 2004) 2007. 988p. pap. 187.00 (978-1-60423-327-8(3)) Curran Assocs., Inc.

Felden, Andrew. Update on Undertaking Extractable & Leachable Testing. 2011. (iSmithers Update Ser.). (Illus.). 180p. (978-1-84735-455-6(6)) iSmithers Rapra Publishing.

Floudas, Christodoulos A., et al. Handbook of Test Problems in Local & Global Optimization. 2010. (Nonconvex Optimization & Its Applications Ser.). 484p. pap. 399.00 (978-1-4419-4812-0(0), 1441948120) Springer.

Folas, Georgios K. & Kontogeorgis, Georgios M. Thermodynamic Models for Industrial Applications: From Classical & Advanced Mixing Rules to Association Theories. 2010. (ENG., Illus.). 710p. 160.00 (978-0-470-69726-9(1), Wiley) Wiley, John & Sons, Inc.

Froment, Gilbert F., et al. Chemical Reactor Analysis & Design. 3rd ed. 2010. (ENG., Illus.). 900p. (C). 178.95 (978-0-470-56541-4(1), Wiley) Wiley, John & Sons, Inc.

Ghasem, Nayef & Henda, Redhouane. Principles of Chemical Engineering Processes. 2008. (ENG., Illus.). 400p. (C). 102.95 (978-1-4200-8013-1(X), CRC Press) Taylor & Francis Group GBR. Dist: Taylor & Francis Group.

Giordano, Francesca. A Landscape Approach for the Monitoring of Desertification. 2010. 140p. pap. (978-3-639-23608-8(4)) VDM Verlag Dr. Mueller e.K.

Glavatskiy, Kirill. Multicomponent Interfacial Transport: Described by the Square Gradient Model during Evaporation & Condensation. 2011. (Springer Theses Ser.). (ENG., Illus.). xviii, 171p. 129.00 (978-3-642-15265-8(1), 3642152651) Springer.

Global Market for Catalyst Regeneration. 2006. per. 4250.00 (978-1-59623-226-6(9)) BCC Research.

Gorban, Alexander N., et al, eds. Model Reduction & Coarse-Graining Approaches for Multiscale Phenomena. 2006. (Springer Complexity Ser.). (ENG., Illus.). xii, 560p. 249.00 (978-3-540-35885-5(4), 3540358854) Springer.

Gulshan, Samina & Ramzan, Naveed. Production of Hydrogen by Coal Gasification. 2011. 96p. pap. (978-3-8443-9854-0(6)) Lambert Academic Publishing.

Haber, Robert, et al. Predictive Control in Process Engineering: From the Basics to the Applications. 2011. (ENG., Illus.). 629p. 190.00 (978-3-527-31492-8(X), Wiley-VCH) Wiley, John & Sons, Inc.

Haghi, A. K. Modern Trends in Chemistry & Chemical Engineering. 2012. (ENG.). 167p. 99.95 (978-1-926895-00-0(2)) Apple Academic Pr., Inc. CAN. Dist: Taylor & Francis Group.

Haghi, A. K., ed. Chemistry & Chemical Engineering Research Progress. 2009. (Chemical Engineering Methods & Technology Ser.). (Illus.). vi, 238p. 116.10 (978-1-61668-502-7(6)) Nova Science Pubs., Inc.

—Handbook of Research on Chemoinformatics & Chemical Engineering. 2009. (Chemical Engineering Methods & Technology Ser.). (Illus.). 218p. 80.10 (978-1-61668-504-1(2)) Nova Science Pubs., Inc.

—Recent Progress in Chemistry & Chemical Engineering Research. 2010. (Chemical Engineering Methods & Technology Ser.). 129.00 (978-1-61728-237-9(5)) Nova Science Pubs., Inc.

Hall, Steven. Rules of Thumb for Chemical Engineers. 5th ed. 2012. (ENG., Illus.). 448p. pap. 120.00 (978-0-12-387785-7(7), Butterworth-Heinemann) Elsevier Science & Technology Bks.

Heaton, C.A. An Introduction to Industrial Chemistry. 2nd ed. 2008. 448p. pap. 69.95 (978-0-216-92919-7(9)) Springer.

Hessel, Volker, et al, eds. Micro Process Engineering Set: A Comprehensive Handbook, 3 vols. 2009. (ENG., Illus.). 1412p. 720.00 (978-3-527-31550-5(0), Wiley-VCH) Wiley, John & Sons, Inc.

Hinchliffe, A. Chemical Modelling: Applications & Theory, Vol. 4. 2006. (Specialist Periodical Reports). (ENG.). 542p. 448.00 (978-0-85404-243-2(1)) Royal Society of Chemistry, The GBR. Dist: Ingram Pub. Services.

Hua, Song. Catalytic Hydrogen Production from Bioethanol: Investigation of Reaction Network & Active Sites in Bio-Ethanol Steam Reforming over Cobalt Based Catalysts. 2011. 288p. pap. (978-3-639-34441-7(3)) VDM Verlag Dr. Mueller e.K.

Kai, Li. Chemical, Biological & Environmental Engineering: Proceedings of the International Conference on Cbee 2009. 2009. (Illus.). 548p. 212.00 (978-981-4293-46-4(6)) World Scientific Publishing Co., Inc.

Kaliyan, Nalladurai & Morey, R. Vance. Densification of Biomass. 2008. 360p. pap. (978-3-639-05185-8(8)) VDM Verlag Dr. Mueller e.K.

Kamal, Musa R., et al. Injection Molding. 2009. (978-1-56990-434-3(0)) Hanser Pubns.

Kehiaian, Henry V., ed. & contrib. by. Volumetric Properties of Mixtures & Solutions Binary Liquid Systems of Nonelectrolytes. 2009. (Landolt-Börnstein: Numerical Data & Functional Relationships in Science & Technology Ser.). x, 563p. 6739.00 (978-3-540-73583-0(6)) Springer.

Kent, James A., ed. Handbook of Industrial Chemistry & Biotechnology. 11th rev. ed. 2007. (Illus.). 1400p. 199.00 (978-0-387-27842-1(7), 0387278427) Springer.

Khasawneh, Hussam. Drying Behavior of Fractionated Fibers. 2010. 136p. pap. (978-3-8383-1591-1(X)) Lambert Academic Publishing.

Killcross, Martin. Chemical & Process Plant Commissioning Handbook: A Practical Guide to Plant System & Equipment Installation & Commissioning. 2011. (ENG., Illus.). 312p. 124.99 (978-0-08-097174-2(1), Butterworth-Heinemann) Elsevier Science & Technology Bks.

Kirk-Othmer & Kirk-Othmer. Kirk-Othmer Encyclopedia of Chemical Technology, Vol. 26, Volume 26. Wiley-Interscience Publication Staff, ed. 5th rev. ed. 2007. (Kirk 5e Print Continuation Ser.: 1). (ENG., Illus.). 1076p. 425.00 (978-0-471-48495-0(4), Wiley-Interscience) Wiley, John & Sons, Inc.

Kissinger, P. T. Electrochemical Detection in HPLC & HPCE. Date not set. (Chromatographic Science Ser.). (978-0-8247-0019-5(8)) Dekker, Marcel Inc.

Kockmann, Norbert. Transport Phenomena in Micro Process Engineering. 2008. 350p. 112.50 (978-3-527-32019-6(9)) Wiley, John & Sons, Inc.

—Transport Phenomena in Micro Process Engineering. (Heat & Mass Transfer Ser.). (Illus.). 2010. xx, 365p. pap. 179.00 (978-3-642-09406-4(6), 3642094066) 2007. 365p. 179.00 (978-3-540-74616-4(1)) Springer.

Koseoglu, Omer Refa, et al, eds. Hydrotreating/Hydrocracking Technologies: Status & Future Challenges. 2010. (ENG., Illus.). 432p. (C). 224.50 (978-0-8412-7417-4(7)) Oxford Univ. Pr., Inc.

Lasa, Hugo de, et al. Photocatalytic Reaction Engineering. 2010. (Illus.). xii, 187p. pap. 129.00 (978-1-4419-3627-1(0), 1441936270) Springer.

Lewis, Peter Rhys & Gagg, Colin, eds. Forensic Polymer Engineering. 2010. (ENG., Illus.). xxii, 476p. 249.95 (978-1-4398-3114-4(9), CRC Press) Taylor & Francis Group GBR. Dist: Taylor & Francis Group.

Li, Jinghai. Advances in Chemical Engineering: Characterization of Flow, Particles & Interfaces. 2009. (Advances in Chemical Engineering Ser.: 37). (ENG.). 231.00 (978-0-12-374738-9(4), Academic Pr.) Elsevier Science & Technology Bks.

Lloyd, Lawrie. Handbook of Industrial Catalysts. 2007. (Illus.). xxii, 490p. (978-0-387-49962-8(8)) Springer.

Loney, Norman W. Applied Mathematical Methods for Chemical Engineers. 2nd rev. ed. 2006. (ENG., Illus.). 454p. (C). 115.95 (978-0-8493-9778-3(2), CRC Press) Taylor & Francis Group GBR. Dist: Taylor & Francis Group.

—Solutions Manual - Applied Mathematical Methods for Chemical Engi 2nd ed. 2006. 80p. (C). (978-0-8493-9667-0(0)) Taylor & Francis Group.

Luyben, William L. Principles & Case Studies of Simultaneous Design. 2011. (ENG., Illus.). 344p. 149.95 (978-0-470-92708-3(9)) American Institute of Chemical Engineers.

Mahmud, Rubayat. Hierarchical Approach of Process Integration. 2009. 168p. pap. (978-3-639-17429-8(1)) VDM Verlag Dr. Mueller e.K.

Mann, Uzi. Principles of Chemical Reactor Analysis & Design: New Tools for Industrial Chemical Reactor Operations. 2nd ed. 2009. (ENG., Illus.). 473p. 99.95 (978-0-471-26180-3(7), Wiley-Interscience) Wiley, John & Sons, Inc.

Mansha, Muhammad. Natural Gas Combustion Modelling in Ic Engine. 2011. 324p. pap. (978-3-8454-0911-5(8)) Lambert Academic Publishing.

Marin, Guy B., ed. Advances in Chemical Engineering. (Advances in Chemical Engineering Ser.: 31). (ENG., Illus.). 2006. 418p. (C). 231.00 (978-0-12-008531-6(3)) Vol. 32. 2007. 338p. 231.00 (978-0-12-373699-8(7)) Elsevier Science & Technology Bks. (Academic Pr.).

Melton, Trish & Iles-Smith, Peter. Managing Project Delivery: Maintaining Control & Achieving Success. 2009. (ENG., Illus.). 312p. pap. 52.95 (978-0-7506-8515-3(8), Butterworth-Heinemann) Elsevier Science & Technology Bks.

Microbiology. Microbial Production of Industrial Chemicals [Bibliography & Price Not Definite.]. Gosset Lagarda, G., ed. 2008. (Illus.). 66p. pap. (978-3-8055-8444-9(X)) Karger, S. AG.

Molaainezhad, Khadijeh. Membrane Transport & Supercritical Carbon Dioxide. 2010. 212p. pap. (978-3-639-28707-3(X)) VDM Verlag Dr. Mueller e.K.

Mordini, Alessandro. New Methodologies & Techniques for a Sustainable Organic Chemistry. 2008. (NATO Science Series II). (Illus.). x, 337p. spiral bd. 109.00 (978-1-4020-6792-1(5)) Springer.

Mordini, Alessandro & Faigl, Ferenc. New Methodologies & Techniques for a Sustainable Organic Chemistry: Sustainable Developments in a Secure Environment (NeMeTOC): Proceedings of the NATO Advanced Study Institute on New Methodologies & Techniques in Organic Chemistry, Siena, Italy, 14-23 October 2005. 2008. (NATO Science Series II). (Illus.). xi, 365p. 289.00 (978-1-4020-6791-4(7)) Springer.

Mukhopadhyay, Subhas Chandra & Sen Gupta, Gourab, eds. Smart Sensors & Sensing Technology. 2010. (Lecture Notes in Electrical Engineering Ser.). (Illus.). xxii, 412p. pap. 179.00 (978-3-642-09652-9(5), 3642096525) Springer.

Nolan, Dennis P. Safety & Security Review for the Process Industries: Application of HAZOP, PHA, What-IF & SVA Reviews. 3rd ed. 2011. (ENG.). 174p. 149.95 (978-1-4377-3518-5(5)) William Andrew, Inc.

Norman, Peter. Process Modelling & Computer Aided Design in Chemical Engineering. 350p. 100.00 (978-0-471-93870-5(X)); pap. 39.95 (978-0-471-96761-3(0)) Wiley, John & Sons, Inc.

Nussinovitch, Amos. Polymer Macro- & Micro-Gel Beads: Fundamentals & Applications: Fundamentals & Applications. 2010. (ENG., Illus.). xxv, 303p. 209.00 (978-1-4419-6617-9(X), 144196617X) Springer.

Ogawa, Kohei. Chemical Engineering: A New Perspective. 2007. (ENG., Illus.). 190p. 101.00 (978-0-444-53096-7(7), Elsevier Science) Elsevier Science & Technology Bks.

Ooman, Colin William. Material & Energy Balances for Engineers & Environmentalists, Vol. 1. 2009. (Illus.). 300p. 80.00 (978-1-84816-368-3(1)); pap. 55.00 (978-1-84816-369-0(X)) Imperial College Pr. GBR. Dist: World Scientific Publishing Co., Inc.

Perry, Robert H. & Green, Don W. Perry's Chemical Engineers' Handbook. 8th rev. ed. 2007. (ENG., Illus.). 2400p. (C). 199.00 (978-0-07-142294-9(3), 0071422943) McGraw-Hill Professional Publishing.

Peter, et al. Linear Mathematical Models in Chemical Engineering. 2009. (Illus.). 600p. 107.00 (978-981-279-415-4(8)) World Scientific Publishing Co., Inc.

Pollak, Peter. Fine Chemicals: The Industry & the Business. 2nd ed. 2011. (ENG., Illus.). 312p. 125.00 (978-0-470-62767-9(0), Wiley) Wiley, John & Sons, Inc.

Prins, Mark Jan. Thermodynamic analysis of biomass gasification: Including torrefaction as a thermal pre-treatment. 2008. 160p. pap. (978-3-639-10006-8(9)) VDM Verlag Dr. Mueller e.K.

Qin, S. Joe. Chemical Engineering Faculty Directory: 2006-2007. 2007. (ENG.). 266p. pap. 184.00 (978-0-470-14782-5(2)) American Institute of Chemical Engineers.

Rähse, Wilfried. Produktdesign in der chemischen Industrie: Schnelle Umsetzung kundenspezifischer Lösungen. 2006. (VDI-Buch / Chemische Technik / Verfahrenstechnik Ser.). (Illus.). XII, 348p. 139.00 (978-3-540-25162-0(6), 3540251626) Springer.

Raju, K. S. N. Fluid Mechanics, Heat Transfer, & Mass Transfer: Chemical Engineering Practice. 2011. (ENG., Illus.). 768p. 158.00 (978-0-470-63774-6(9)) American Institute of Chemical Engineers.

Rangaiah, Gade Pandu, ed. Multi-Objective Optimization: Techniques & Applications in Chemical Engineering. 2008. (Advances in Process Systems Engineering Ser.). (Illus.). 450p. 142.00 (978-981-283-651-9(9)) World Scientific Publishing Co., Inc.

Realpe, Alvaro, Sr. Modeling of Wet Granulation in a High Shear Mixer: Aggregation Phenomenon. 2007. pap. 139.00 (978-0-9798015-0-1(8)) Research Publishing.

Robinson, Clark. The Recovery of Volatile Solvents in Chemical Engineering. 2006. 200p. 29.95 (978-1-933998-37-4(7), Merchant Bks.) Rough Draft Printing.

Routh, Alexander F. & Keddie, Joseph. Latex Film Formation: With Applications in Nanomaterials. 2010. (Springer Laboratory Ser.). (ENG., Illus.). iv, 246p. 179.00 (978-90-481-2844-0(7), 9048128447) Springer.

Royal Society of Chemistry Staff. Concepts of Chemical Engineering 4 Chemists. Simons, Stefaan, ed. 2007. (ENG., Illus.). 370p. (C). 64.00 (978-0-85404-951-6(7)) Royal Society of Chemistry, The GBR. Dist: Ingram Pub. Services.

Saadi Ibrahem, Ahmmed. Matlab Software for Chemical & Petroleum Engineering. 2011. 172p. pap. (978-3-8433-9444-4(X)) Lambert Academic Publishing.

Salmi, Tapio O., et al. Chemical Reaction Engineering & Reactor Technology. 2010. (Chemical Industries Ser.). (ENG., Illus.). 644p. (C). 119.95 (978-1-4200-9268-4(5), CRC Press) Taylor & Francis Group GBR. Dist: Taylor & Francis Group.

Schouten, J. C. Micro Systems & Devices for (Bio)chemical Processes. 2010. (Advances in Chemical Engineering Ser.: 38). (ENG.). 272p. 231.00 (978-0-12-374458-6(X), Academic Pr.) Elsevier Science & Technology Bks.

Schügerl, Karl & Zeng, A. P., eds. Tools & Applications of Biochemical Engineering Science. 2010. (Advances in Biochemical Engineering Biotechnology Ser.). (Illus.). xviii, 274p. pap. 349.00 (978-3-642-07598-8(3), 3642075983) Springer.

Scott, David M. Industrial Process Sensors. 2007. (ENG., Illus.). 256p. 144.95 (978-1-4200-4416-4(8), CRC Press) Taylor & Francis Group GBR. Dist: Taylor & Francis Group.

Seidle, John. Fundamentals of Coalbed Methane Reservoir Engineering. 2011. (ENG.). 470p. 149.00 (978-1-59370-001-0(6)) PennWell Corp.

Shakir, Osama. Concentration & Temperature Profiles Within a Monolith Catalyst. 2010. 100p. pap. (978-3-8383-1440-2(9)) Lambert Academic Publishing.

Silveston, P. L. & Hudgins, R. R. Periodic Operation of Chemical Reactors. 2012. (ENG.). 608p. 150.00 (978-0-12-391854-3(5), Butterworth-Heinemann) Elsevier Science & Technology Bks.

Skogestad, Sigurd. Chemical & Energy Process Engineering. 2008. (ENG., Illus.). 440p. (C). 99.95 (978-1-4200-8755-0(X), CRC Press) Taylor & Francis Group GBR. Dist: Taylor & Francis Group.

Solen, Kenneth A. & Harb, John. Introduction to Chemical Engineering: Tools for Today & Tomorrow. 5th ed. 2010. (C). pap. 18.95 (978-0-470-92810-3(7), Wiley) Wiley, John & Sons, Inc.

Sproull, Robert D. Albright's Chemical Engineering Handbook. Albright, Lyle F., ed. 2008. (ENG., Illus.). 1928p. 169.95 (978-0-8247-5362-7(3), CRC Press) Taylor & Francis Group GBR. Dist: Taylor & Francis Group.

Stanford Geothermal Program Staff, compiled by. 30th Workshop on Geothermal Reservoir Engineering 2005. 2008. (Stanford Geothermal Program Workshop Report Ser.). 521p. pap. 95.00 (978-1-60423-970-6(0)) Curran Assocs., Inc.

—32nd Workshop on Geothermal Reservoir Engineering 2007. 2008. (Stanford Geothermal Program Workshop Report Ser.). 463p. pap. 95.00 (978-1-60423-971-3(9)) Curran Assocs., Inc.

Strauss, Anselm L., et al. The Professional Scientist a Study of American Chemists. 2011. (ENG.). 296p. pap. 34.95 (978-1-4128-1658-2(3)) Aldine Transaction.

Sundmacher. Fuel Cell Engineering. 2012. (Advances in Chemical Engineering Ser.: 41). (ENG.). 480p. 231.00 (978-0-12-386874-9(2), Academic Pr.) Elsevier Science & Technology Bks.

Swinnea, J. Steven & AIChE Ammonia Plant Safety Committee Staff. Chemical Engineering Faculty Directory: 2009-2010. 2009. (ENG.). 291p. pap. 166.00 (978-0-470-57216-0(7)) American Institute of Chemical Engineers.

Theodore, Louis & Abulencia, James P. Fluid Flow for the Practicing Chemical Engineer. 2009. (Essential Engineering Calculations Ser.: 1). (ENG., Illus.). 600p. 122.00 (978-0-470-31763-1(9)) American Institute of Chemical Engineers.

Theodore, Louis, et al. Thermodynamics for the Practicing Engineer. 2009. (Essential Engineering Calculations Ser.: 2). (ENG., Illus.). 414p. 122.00 (978-0-470-44468-9(1)) American Institute of Chemical Engineers.

Thoenes, D. Chemical Reactor Development: From Laboratory Synthesis to Industrial Production. 2010. 368p. pap. 231.00 (978-90-481-4446-4(9), 9048144469) Springer.

Thoma, J. & Ould Bouamama, B. Modelling & Simulation in Thermal & Chemical Engineering: A Bond Graph Approach. 2010. (ENG., Illus.). xiv, 221p. pap. 149.00 (978-3-642-08566-6(0), 3642085660) Springer.

Tkacova, K., ed. Proceedings of 1st International Conference on Mechanochemistry, Set. pap. (978-1-898326-39-7(8)) Cambridge International Science Publishing, Ltd. GBR. Dist: Balogh International, Inc.

Tosun, Ismail. Modelling in Transport Phenomena: A Conceptual Approach. 2nd ed. 2007. (ENG., Illus.). 628p. (C). pap. 93.95 (978-0-444-53021-9(5), Elsevier Science) Elsevier Science & Technology Bks.

Towler, Gavin & Sinnott, R. K. Chemical Engineering Design: Principles, Practice & Economics of Plant & Process Design. (ENG., Illus.). 2007. 1266p. (C). 91.95 (978-0-7506-8423-1(2)) 2nd ed. 2012. 1320p. 129.95 (978-0-08-096659-5(4)) Elsevier Science & Technology Bks. (Butterworth-Heinemann).

Trimm, Harold H. & Hunter, William, 3rd, eds. Industrial Chemistry: New Applications, Processes & Systems. 2011. (ENG.). 334p. 99.95 (978-1-926692-83-8(7)) Apple Academic Pr., Inc. CAN. Dist: Taylor & Francis Group.

Turton, Richard, et al. Analysis, Synthesis & Design of Chemical Processes. 3rd ed. 2008. (Prentice Hall International Series in the Physical & Chemical Engineering Sciences Ser.). (ENG., Illus.). 1088p. 97.51 (978-0-13-512966-1(4), Prentice Hall) Prentice Hall PTR.

Vasantha Kandasamy, W. B. & Smarandache, Florentin. Methods in Industrial Biotechnology for Chemical Engineers. 2008. 125p. (978-1-59973-034-9(0)) Multimedia Large.

Walker, Derek. The Management of Chemical Process Development in the Pharmaceutical Industry. 2008. (ENG., Illus.). 416p. 128.00 (978-0-470-17156-1(1)) American Institute of Chemical Engineers.

Wankat, Phillip C. & Farmus, Cristina D. A Pictorial History of Chemical Engineering at Purdue University, 1911-2011. 2011. (ENG., Illus.). 128p. 29.95 (978-1-55753-621-1(X)) Purdue Univ. Pr.

Wankat, Phillip C. & Pappas, Nicholas A. 100 Years of Chemical Engineering at Purdue University, 1911-2011. 2011. (ENG.). 500p. pap. 75.00 (978-1-55753-622-8(8)) Purdue Univ. Pr.

Wei, James. Product Engineering: Molecular Structure & Properties. 2007. (Topics in Chemical Engineering Ser.). (ENG., Illus.). 376p. 125.00 incl. cd-rom (978-0-19-515917-2(9)) Oxford Univ. Pr., Inc.

Weinhold, Frank. Classical & Geometrical Theory of Chemical & Phase Thermodynamics. 2009. (ENG., Illus.). 490p. 150.00 (978-0-470-40236-8(9), Wiley-Interscience) Wiley, John & Sons, Inc.

West, D. H. & Yablonsky, Gregory. Advances in Chemical Engineering: Solution Thermodynamics. 2010. (Advances in Chemical Engineering Ser.: 39). (ENG.). 232p. 231.00 (978-0-12-374459-3(8), Academic Pr.) Elsevier Science & Technology Bks.

Wiley-VCH Staff, ed. Ullmann's Fibers, 2 vols. 2008. (ENG., Illus.). 899p. 480.00 (978-3-527-31772-1(4), Wiley-VCH) Wiley, John & Sons, Inc.

Wolnsky, Samuel. Economic Analysis Made Easy. 2011. 124p. pap. 18.00 (978-1-4567-2048-3(1)) AuthorHouse.

Woods, Donald R. Rules of Thumb in Engineering Practice. 2007. (ENG., Illus.). 479p. 145.00 (978-3-527-31220-7(X), Wiley-VCH) Wiley, John & Sons, Inc.

Xu, Jingyi. Microcellular Injection Molding. 2010. (Wiley Series on Polymer Engineering & Technology Ser.: 5). (ENG., Illus.). 618p. 158.00 (978-0-470-46612-4(X), Wiley) Wiley, John & Sons, Inc.

Yen. Chemistry for Engineers. 2008. (C). 108.00 (978-1-86094-774-2(3)) Imperial College Pr. GBR. Dist: World Scientific Publishing Co., Inc.

Yen, Teh Fu. Chemistry for Engineers. 2008. (Illus.). 558p. pap. 61.00 (978-1-86094-775-9(1)) Imperial College Pr. GBR. Dist: World Scientific Publishing Co., Inc.

Yunardi, Y. Conditional Moment Closure Modelling Of. 2011. 320p. pap. (978-3-8443-1677-3(9)) Lambert Academic Publishing.

Zheng, Rong, et al. Injection Molding: Integration of Theory & Modeling Methods. 2011. (ENG., Illus.). xii, 188p. 129.00 (978-3-642-21262-8(X), 364221262X) Springer.

C

CHEMICAL ENGINEERING—APPARATUS AND SUPPLIES
see Chemical Engineering—Equipment and Supplies

CHEMICAL ENGINEERING—DATA PROCESSING

Beers, Kenneth. Numerical Methods for Chemical Engineering: Applications in MATLAB. 2006. (ENG., Illus.). 486p. (C). 118.00 *(978-0-521-85971-4(9))* Cambridge Univ. Pr.

Castro, Eduardo A. & Haghi, A. K., eds. Nanoscience & Advancing Computational Methods in Chemistry: Research Progress. 2012. ***(978-1-4666-1607-3(5))*** IGI Global.

Crabtree, John. Atomic Reaction Mapping. 2008. 92p. pap. *(978-3-639-07358-4(4))* VDM Verlag Dr. Mueller e.K.

Cutlip, Michael B. & Shacham, Mordechai. Problem Solving in Chemical & Biochemical Engineering with POLYMATH, Excel, & MATLAB. 2nd rev. ed. 2007. (Prentice Hall International Series in the Physical & Chemical Engineering Sciences Ser.). (ENG., Illus.). 752p. per. 65.00 *(978-0-13-148204-3(1))*, Prentice Hall) Prentice Hall PTR.

de Brito Alves, Rita Maria, et al, eds. 10th International Symposium on Process Systems Engineering - PSE2009, 2 vols. 2009. (Computer Aided Chemical Engineering Ser.: 27). (ENG., Illus.). lvi, 2166p. 560.00 *(978-0-444-53472-9(5))* Elsevier Science & Technology Bks.

Finlayson, Bruce A. Introduction to Chemical Engineering Computing. 2nd ed. 2012. (ENG.). 416p. pap. 59.95 ***(978-0-470-93295-7(3)***, Wiley) Wiley, John & Sons, Inc.

Ghasem, Nayef. Computer Methods in Chemical Engineering. 2011. (ENG., Illus.). 523p. pap. 69.95 *(978-1-4398-4999-6(4)*, CRC Press) Taylor & Francis Group GBR. Dist: Taylor & Francis Group.

Haghi, A. K. Nanoscience & Advancing Computational Methods in Chemistry: Research Progress. Castro, Eduardo A., ed. 2012. ***(978-1-4666-1609-7(1))*** IGI Global.

Ingham, John, et al. Chemical Engineering Dynamics: An Introduction to Modelling & Computer Simulation. 3rd ed. 2007. (ENG., Illus.). 640p. 379.00 *(978-3-527-31678-6(7)*, Wiley-VCH) Wiley, John & Sons, Inc.

Kapuno, Raul. Programming for Chemical Engineers: Using C, C++, & MATLAB(r). 2008. (ENG., Illus.). 400p. 114.95 *(978-1-934015-09-4(1))* Jones & Bartlett Learning, LLC.

Keil, Frerich, et al, eds. Scientific Computing in Chemical Engineering II: Simulation, Image Processing, Optimization, & Control. 2010. (ENG., Illus.). xvii, 436p. pap. 259.00 *(978-3-642-08514-7(8)*, 3642085148) Springer.

Marquardt, Wolfgang, et al. OntoCAPE: A Re-Usable Ontology for Chemical Process Engineering. 2010. (RWTHedition Ser.). (ENG., Illus.). xvii, 481p. 199.00 *(978-3-642-04654-4(1)*, 3642046541) Springer.

Pistikopoulos, E. N., et al. 21st European Symposium on Computer Aided Process Engineering, 2 vols. 2011. (Computer Aided Chemical Engineering Ser.: 29). (ENG., Illus.). 2082p. 575.00 ***(978-0-444-53895-6(X))*** Elsevier Science & Technology Bks.

Stewart, Warren E. & Caracotsios, Michael. Computer-Aided Modeling of Reactive Systems. 2008. (ENG., Illus.). 268p. 94.95 *(978-0-470-27495-8(6))* American Institute of Chemical Engineers.

White, Ralph E. & Subramanian, Venkat R. Computational Methods in Chemical Engineering with Maple Applications. 2010. 860p. 99.00 *(978-3-642-04310-9(0)*, 3642043100) Springer.

CHEMICAL ENGINEERING—EQUIPMENT AND SUPPLIES
see also Heat Exchangers; Packed Towers; Separators (Machines)

Chandrasekaran, V. C. Tank Linings for Chemical Process Industries. 2008. (Handbook Ser.). (Illus.). x, 157p. pap. *(978-1-84735-105-0(0))* iSmithers Rapra Publishing.

Chandrasekaran, V. V. Tank Linings for the Chemical Process Industries. 2009. (Handbook Ser.). (Illus.). x, 157p. *(978-1-84735-106-7(9))* iSmithers Rapra Publishing.

Couper, James R. Chemical Process Equipment: Selection & Design. 3rd ed. 2012. (ENG.). 832p. 150.00 ***(978-0-12-396959-0(X)***, Butterworth-Heinemann) Elsevier Science & Technology Bks.

Couper, James R., et al. Chemical Process Equipment: Selection & Design. 2nd ed. 2009. (ENG., Illus.). 832p. 185.00 *(978-0-12-372506-6(2)*, Gulf Professional Publishing) Elsevier Science & Technology Bks.

Russell, T W F, et al. Mass & Heat Transfer: Analysis of Mass Contactors & Heat Exchangers. 2008. (Cambridge Series in Chemical Engineering). (ENG., Illus.). 402p. 121.00 *(978-0-521-88670-3(8))* Cambridge Univ. Pr.

Stewart, Maurice & Arnold, Ken. Emulsions & Oil Treating Equipment: Selection, Sizing & Troubleshooting. 2008. (ENG., Illus.). 304p. 134.00 *(978-0-7506-8970-0(6)*, Gulf Professional Publishing) Elsevier Science & Technology Bks.

—Gas-Liquid & Liquid-Liquid Separators. 2008. (ENG., Illus.). 240p. 134.00 *(978-0-7506-8979-3(X)*, Gulf Professional Publishing) Elsevier Science & Technology Bks.

VandenBussche, Kurt M., et al, eds. Micro Instrumentation: For High Throughput Experimentation & Process Intensification. 2007. (ENG., Illus.). 520p. 235.00 *(978-3-527-31425-6(3)*, Wiley-VCH) Wiley, John & Sons, Inc.

CHEMICAL ENGINEERING—EXAMINATIONS, QUESTIONS, ETC.

Das, Dilip K. & Prabhudesai, Rajaram K. Chemical Engineering FE/EIT Exam Prep. 3rd ed. 2007. (ENG., Illus.). 288p. pap. 36.95 *(978-1-4277-6132-3(9))* Kaplan Publishing.

—Chemical Engineering PE License Review. 3rd ed. 2007. (ENG., Illus.). 816p. pap. 109.95 *(978-1-4277-6118-7(3))* Kaplan Publishing.

Leone, Annalisa, et al. Fundamentals of Engineering Afternoon Exam for Chemical Engineering. Date not set. (Illus.). 454p. (C). pap. 60.00 *(978-1-882767-23-6(3))* ETS, Inc.

Nandagopal, N. S. Chemical Engineering Solved Problems. 2006. (ENG., Illus.). 80p. per. 104.00 *(978-1-59126-090-5(6))* Professional Pubns., Inc.

Prabhudesai, Rajaram K. Chemical Engineering PE Sample Exam. 2nd ed. 2007. (ENG., Illus.). 184p. pap. 39.95 *(978-1-4277-6121-7(3))* Kaplan Publishing.

CHEMICAL ENGINEERING—GRAPHIC METHODS

Deza, Michel & Dutour Sikiric, Mathieu. Geometry of Chemical Graphs: Polycycles & Two-faced Maps. 2008. (Encyclopedia of Mathematics & its Applications Ser.). (ENG., Illus.). 316p. 110.00 *(978-0-521-87307-9(X))* Cambridge Univ. Pr.

CHEMICAL ENGINEERING—PROBLEMS, EXERCISES, ETC.

Bonem, J. M. Problem Solving for Process Operators & Specialists. 2011. (ENG., Illus.). 344p. 84.95 *(978-0-470-62774-7(3))* American Institute of Chemical Engineers.

Cram101 Textbook Reviews Staff. Outlines & Highlights for Introduction to Chemical Engineering Thermodynamics by Smith, J M / Abbott, Michael M / Van Ness, H C , Isbn: 9780073104. 2009. 60p. pap. 26.95 *(978-1-4288-8475-5(0))* Cram101 Inc.

Cutlip, Michael B. & Shacham, Mordechai. Problem Solving in Chemical & Biochemical Engineering with POLYMATH, Excel, & MATLAB. 2nd rev. ed. 2007. (Prentice Hall International Series in the Physical & Chemical Engineering Sciences Ser.). (ENG., Illus.). 752p. per. 65.00 *(978-0-13-148204-3(1)*, Prentice Hall) Prentice Hall PTR.

Das, Dilip K. & Prabhudesai, Rajaram K. Chemical Engineering FE/EIT Exam Prep. 3rd ed. 2007. (ENG., Illus.). 288p. pap. 36.95 *(978-1-4277-6132-3(9))* Kaplan Publishing.

—Chemical Engineering PE Problems & Solutions. 3rd ed. 2007. (ENG., Illus.). 192p. pap. 44.95 *(978-1-4277-6126-2(4))* Kaplan Publishing.

Jeris, John S., et al, eds. Handbook of Chemical & Environmental Engineering Calculations. 2007. (ENG., Illus.). 968p. per. 163.00 *(978-0-470-13902-8(1)*, Wiley-Interscience) Wiley, John & Sons, Inc.

Nandagopal, N. S. Chemical Engineering Solved Problems. 2006. (ENG., Illus.). 80p. per. 104.00 *(978-1-59126-090-5(6))* Professional Pubns., Inc.

Vasquez, Marta & Zinn, Robert R. More Six-Minute Solutions for Chemical PE Exam Problems. 2006. *(978-1-59126-077-6(9))* Professional Pubns.

CHEMICAL ENGINEERING—TABLES

Himmelblau, David M. & Riggs, James B. Basic Principles & Calculations in Chemical Engineering. 8th rev. ed. 2012. (Prentice Hall International Series in the Physical & Chemical Engineering Sciences Ser.). (ENG.). 768p. (C). 144.00 ***(978-0-13-234660-3(5)***, Prentice Hall) Prentice Hall PTR.

CHEMICAL ENGINEERING—VOCATIONAL GUIDANCE

Baine, Celeste. Is There a Chemical Engineer Inside You? A Student's Guide to Exploring Careers in Chemical Engineering. 2nd ed. 2006. (YA). 7.95 *(978-0-9664763-4-7(4)*, Engineering Education Service Ctr.) Bonamy Publishing.

CHEMICAL ENGINEERS
see also Chemists

Center for the Advancement of Process TechnoloCARP Staff. Safety, Health & Environment. 2006. (ENG.). (C). 139.40 *(978-0-536-25843-4(0))* Pearson Learning Solutions.

Coutinho, Cecil. An Introduction to Mass Transfer Operations for Chemical Engineers. 2010. 156p. pap. *(978-3-8383-9234-9(5))* Lambert Academic Publishing.

Das, Dilip K. & Prabhudesai, Rajaram K. Chemical Engineering PE License Review. 3rd ed. 2007. (ENG., Illus.). 816p. pap. 109.95 *(978-1-4277-6118-7(3))* Kaplan Publishing.

Morimoto, Tom. Breaking Trail: From Canada's Northern Frontier to the Oil Fields of Dubai, 1 vol. 2007. (ENG., Illus.). 296p. per. 18.99 *(978-1-897252-17-8(X))* Fifth Hse. Pubs. CAN. Dist: Ingram Pub. Services.

Putman, Russell L. Pioneers of Progress Benefactors of Mank. 2006. pap. 15.95 *(978-1-4286-6265-0(0))* Kessinger Publishing, LLC.

Speegle, Michael. Safety, Health, & Environmental Concepts for the Process Industry. 2nd ed. 2012. (ENG., Illus.). 384p. (C). pap. 100.95 ***(978-1-133-01347-1(3))*** Delmar Cengage Learning.

Swinnea, J. Steven & AIChE Ammonia Plant Safety Committee Staff. Chemical Engineering Faculty Directory: 2009-2010. 2009. (ENG.). 291p. pap. 166.00 *(978-0-470-57216-0(7))* American Institute of Chemical Engineers.

Woinsky, Samuel. Economic Analysis Made Easy. 2011. 124p. pap. 18.00 ***(978-1-4567-2048-3(1))*** AuthorHouse.

CHEMICAL EQUATIONS

Bernstein, Matt A. & Friedman, William A. Thinking about Equations: A Practical Guide for Developing Mathematical Intuition in the Physical Sciences & Engineering. 2009. (ENG., Illus.). 258p. pap. 66.95 *(978-0-470-18620-6(8)*, Wiley) Wiley, John & Sons, Inc.

Carolina Biological Staff, compiled by. Balancing Chemical Equations. 2009. (Inquiries in Science Chemistry Ser.). *(978-1-4350-0396-5(9))*; tchr. ed., spiral bd. *(978-1-4350-0395-8(0))* Carolina Biological Supply Co.

Oriakhi, Christopher. Chemistry in Quantitative Language: Fundamentals of General Chemistry Calculations. 2009. (ENG., Illus.). 432p. 85.00 *(978-0-19-536799-7(5))* Oxford Univ. Pr., Inc.

CHEMICAL EQUILIBRIUM
see also Linear Free Energy Relationship; Phase Rule and Equilibrium

Carolina Biological Staff, compiled by. Attaining Equilibrium. 2009. (Inquiries in Science Chemistry Ser.). *(978-1-4350-0408-5(6))*; tchr. ed., spiral bd. *(978-1-4350-0407-8(8))* Carolina Biological Supply Co.

de Nevers, Noel. Physical & Chemical Equilibrium for Chemical Engineers. 2nd ed. 2012. (ENG.). 384p. 130.00 ***(978-0-470-92710-6(0)***, Wiley) Wiley, John & Sons, Inc.

Demaison, Jean, et al, eds. Equilibrium Molecular Structures. 2010. (ENG., Illus.). 302p. 135.95 *(978-1-4398-1132-0(6)*, CRC Press) Taylor & Francis Group GBR. Dist: Taylor & Francis Group.

Descalzi, Orazio, et al, eds. Localized States in Physics: Solitons & Patterns: Solitons & Patterns. 2010. (ENG., Illus.). xviii, 286p. 129.00 *(978-3-642-16548-1(6)*, 3642165486) Springer.

Hillert, Mats. Phase Equilibria, Phase Diagrams & Phase Transformations: Their Thermodynamic Basis. 2nd rev. ed. 2007. (ENG., Illus.). 524p. (C). 105.00 *(978-0-521-85351-4(6))* Cambridge Univ. Pr.

Iwunze, Maurice. Equilibrium Concept in Analytical Chemistry. 2009. 300p. 25.99 *(978-1-4389-5456-1(5))*; pap. 15.49 *(978-1-4389-5455-4(7))* AuthorHouse.

Ross, John. Thermodynamics & Fluctuations far from Equilibrium. (Springer Series in Chemical Physics Ser.). (Illus.). xii, 210p. 2010. pap. 219.00 *(978-3-642-09395-1(7)*, 3642093957) 2008. (ENG., 219.00 *(978-3-540-74554-9(8)*, 3540745548) Springer.

Runkel, Robert L. One-Dimensional Transport with Equilibrium Chemistry (OTEQ) A Reactive Transport Model for Streams & Rivers. 2010. (Illus.). vii, 101p. pap. *(978-1-4113-2665-1(2))* United States Geological Survey.

Smith, Mike. Chemistry: Equilibria, Energetics & Elements. 2009. 112p. pap., stu. ed. 22.50 *(978-0-340-95759-2(X))* Hodder Education GBR. Dist: Trans-Atlantic Pubns., Inc.

Van Zeggeren, F. & Storey, S. H. The Computation of Chemical Equilibria. 2011. (ENG.). 190p. pap. 26.99 *(978-0-521-17225-7(X))* Cambridge Univ. Pr.

Weinhold, Frank. Classical & Geometrical Theory of Chemical & Phase Thermodynamics. 2009. (ENG., Illus.). 490p. 150.00 *(978-0-470-40236-8(9)*, Wiley-Interscience) Wiley, John & Sons, Inc.

Wolfsberg, Max, et al. Isotope Effects: In the Chemical, Geological, & Bio Sciences. 2009. (ENG., Illus.). xvi, 466p. 199.00 *(978-90-481-2264-6(3)*, 9048122643) Springer.

Wright, Margaret Robson. An Introduction to Aqueous Electrolyte Solutions. 2007. (ENG., Illus.). 602p. 215.00 *(978-0-470-84293-5(8))*; per. 85.00 *(978-0-470-84294-2(6))* Wiley, John & Sons, Inc. (Wiley).

CHEMICAL EVOLUTION
see Molecular Evolution

CHEMICAL FORMULAE
see Chemistry—Notation

CHEMICAL GENETICS
see Biochemical Genetics

CHEMICAL GEOLOGY
see Geochemistry; Mineralogical Chemistry; Mineralogy, Determinative; Rocks—Analysis

CHEMICAL INDUSTRIES
see Chemical Industry

CHEMICAL INDUSTRY
Here are entered works on industries that produce chemicals or are based on chemical processes. Works on individual chemical industries are entered under specific headings, e.g. Soda Industry.
see also Nitrogen Industries

Alireza, Bahadori. Novel Predictive Tools for Oil, Gas & Chemical Industries: New & Simple-to-Use Mathematical Predictive Tools for Various Engineering Parameters in Oil, Gas & Chemical Industries. 2011. 280p. pap. ***(978-3-639-32019-0(0))*** VDM Verlag Dr. Mueller e.K.

Belgacem, Mohamed Naceur & Gandini, Alessandro, eds. Monomers, Polymers & Composites from Renewable Resources. 2008. (ENG., Illus.). 560p. 205.00 *(978-0-08-045316-3(3)*, Elsevier Science) Elsevier Science & Technology Bks.

BIA. Essential Chemical Manufacturers of Western Europe. 6th rev. ed. 2006. 400p. (J). pap. 249.00 *(978-1-4187-4272-0(4))* Business Information Agency.

—Leading Chemical Manufacturers of the USA. 6th rev. ed. 2006. 420p. (J). pap. 249.00 *(978-1-4187-4428-1(X))* Business Information Agency.

—Major Chemical Manufacturers of the World. 6th rev. ed. 2006. 400p. (J). pap. 249.00 *(978-1-4187-4270-6(8))* Business Information Agency.

—Major Chemical Wholesalers of the World. 6th rev. ed. 2006. 400p. (J). pap. 249.00 *(978-1-4187-4315-4(1))* Business Information Agency.

Bilitewski, Bernd, et al, eds. Global Risk-Based Management of Chemical Additives I: Production, Usage & Environmental Occurrence. 2012. (Handbook of Environmental Chemistry Ser.). (Illus.). xiv, 290p. 309.00 ***(978-3-642-24875-7(6)***, 3642248756) Springer.

Blaszczyk, Regina Lee. Rohm & Haas: A Century of Innovation. 2009. (Illus.). 224p. (C). 55.00 *(978-0-8122-4189-1(4))* Univ. of Pennsylvania Pr.

Boehlert, Sherwood L., ed. Green Chemistry Research & Development Act Of 2004: Congressional Report. 2006. (Illus.). 132p. (C). reprint ed. pap. 35.00 *(978-1-4223-0644-4(5))* DIANE Publishing Co.

Bucknell, Duncan. Pharmaceutical, Biotechnology & Chemical Inventions: World Protection & Exploitation, 2 vols. 2011. (ENG.). 2100p. 590.00 *(978-0-19-928901-1(8))* Oxford Univ. Pr., Inc.

Chemical Producers: Canada. 129p. (Orig.). pap. *(978-0-7605-2906-5(X))* Rector Pr., Ltd.

Chemical Producers: East Asia. 839p. (Orig.). pap. *(978-0-7605-2907-2(8))* Rector Pr., Ltd.

Chemical Producers: Mexico. 139p. (Orig.). pap. *(978-0-7605-2909-6(4))* Rector Pr., Ltd.

Chemical Producers: Middle East. 300p. (Orig.). pap. *(978-0-7605-2913-3(2))* Rector Pr., Ltd.

Chemical Producers: South America. 428p. (Orig.). pap. *(978-0-7605-2910-2(8))* Rector Pr., Ltd.

Chemical Producers: U. S. A. 1122p. (Orig.). pap. *(978-0-7605-2911-9(6))* Rector Pr., Ltd.

Chirravuri, Subbarao. Drag Reduction Using Polymer Solutions in Gravity Driven Flow Systems. 2011. 188p. pap. ***(978-3-8443-9384-2(6))*** Lambert Academic Publishing.

Chiusoli, G. P. Metal-Catalysis in Industrial Organic Processes. 2008. (ENG., Illus.). 312p. (C). pap. 72.00 *(978-0-85404-150-3(8))* Royal Society of Chemistry, The GBR. Dist: Ingram Pub. Services.

Coussens, Christine. Global Environmental Health in the 21st Century: From Governmental Regulation to Corporate Social Responsibility: Workshop Summary. 2007. (ENG., Illus.). 126p. pap. 32.00 *(978-0-309-10380-0(0))* National Academies Pr.

Cussler, E. L. & Moggridge, G. D. Chemical Product Design. 2nd ed. 2011. (Cambridge Series in Chemical Engineering Ser.). (ENG., Illus.). 452p. (C). pap. 65.00 *(978-0-521-16822-9(8))* Cambridge Univ. Pr.

Dal Pont, Jean-Pierre. Process Engineering & Industrial Management. 2012. (Iste Ser.: 592). (ENG.). 195.00 ***(978-1-84821-326-5(3)***, Wiley-ISTE) Wiley, John & Sons, Inc.

dmg World Media Ltd Staff, compiled by. Asia Pacific Coatings Conference 2007: Novel Concepts & Materials within Organic Coatings. 2007. 254p. pap. 312.00 *(978-1-60423-346-9(X))* Curran Assocs., Inc.

—Asia Pacific Coatings Show 2006: New Advances in Organic Coatings Technologies & Science. 2007. 317p. pap. 343.00 *(978-1-60423-661-3(2))* Curran Assocs., Inc.

Earnhart, Dietrich & Glicksman, Robert. Pollution Limits & Polluters' Efforts to Comply: The Role of Government Monitoring & Enforcement. 2011. (ENG., Illus.). 336p. 90.00 *(978-0-8047-6257-1(0))*; pap. 29.95 *(978-0-8047-6258-8(9))* Stanford Univ. Pr. (Stanford Economics & Finance).

Electronic Chemicals & Materials: The Global Market. 2006. per. 4250.00 *(978-1-59623-229-7(3))* BCC Research.

Engell, Sebastian, ed. Logistic Optimization of Chemical Production Processes. 2008. (ENG., Illus.). 298p. 340.00 *(978-3-527-30830-9(X)*, Wiley-VCH) Wiley, John & Sons, Inc.

Floyd, Raymond C. Liquid Lean: Lean Manufacturing in the Chemical & Process Manufacturing. 2010. (ENG., Illus.). 346p. 51.95 *(978-1-4200-8862-5(9))* Productivity Pr.

Fuel Cell Industry Review 2005. 2006. per. 1950.00 *(978-1-59623-213-6(7))* BCC Research.

Galambos, Louis, et al. The Global Chemical Industry in the Age of the Petrochemical Revolution. 2006. (ENG., Illus.). 540p. 94.00 *(978-0-521-87105-1(0))* Cambridge Univ. Pr.

Haynes, Williams. Southern Horizons. 2010. 338p. pap. 31.75 *(978-1-171-84611-6(8))* BiblioBazaar.

—Southern Horizons. 2010. 138p. pap. 22.63 *(978-1-153-55313-1(9))* General Bks. LLC.

Hofius, Hanns-Wirich. Sales-Force-Demotivation durch Standardisierung? Die Auswirkung der Commoditisierung der chemischen Industrie auf Außendienststeuerung und -organisation sowie auf Arbeitseinstellung und -verhalten der Außendienstmitarbeiter. eine neoinstitutionenökonomisch und sozialpsychologisch fundierte Untersuchung. 2010. (GER.). 362p. pap. *(978-3-8325-2430-2(4))* Logos Verlag Berlin.

Hübner, Reinhard. Strategic Supply Chain Management in Process Industries: An Application to Specialty Chemicals Production Network Design. 2007. (Lecture Notes in Economics & Mathematical Systems Ser.). (Illus.). xii, 243p. pap. 129.00 *(978-3-540-72180-2(0))* Springer.

Jakl, Thomas & Schwager, Petra, eds. Chemical Leasing Goes Global: Selling Services Instead of Barrels: A Win-Win Business Model for Environment & Industry. 2008. (Illus.). 245p. pap. 99.00 *(978-3-211-73751-4(0))* Springer Wien AUT. Dist: Springer.

Jones, Roger F. The Chemical Industry & Globalization. 2006. (ACS Symposium Ser.: Vol. 942). (ENG., Illus.). 200p. 124.50 *(978-0-8412-3977-7(0))* American Chemical Society.

Jones, Roger F., ed. The Future of the Chemical Industry, 1 vol. 2010. (ACS Symposium Ser.). (ENG., Illus.). 144p. 150.00 *(978-0-8412-0002-9(5))* American Chemical Society.

Kannegiesser, Matthias. Value Chain Management in the Chemical Industry: Global Value Chain Planning of Commodities. (Contributions to Management Science Ser.). (ENG., Illus.). xvi, 270p. 2010. pap. 139.00 *(978-3-7908-2550-3(6)*, 3790825506) 2008. 139.00 *(978-3-7908-2031-7(8)*, 3790820318) Physica-Verlag DEU. Dist: Springer.

Leimkühler, Hans-Joachim, ed. Managing CO2 Emissions in the Chemical Industry. 2010. (ENG., Illus.). 480p. 195.00 *(978-3-527-32659-4(6)*, Wiley-VCH) Wiley, John & Sons, Inc.

Macleod, Roy & Johnson, Jeffrey Allan, eds. Frontline & Factory: Comparative Perspectives on the Chemical Industry at War, 1914-1924. 2007. (Archimedes Ser.). (Illus.). xx, 280p. (C). 189.00 *(978-1-4020-5489-1(0)*, 1402054890) Springer.

Ndiaye, Pap A. Nylon & Bombs: DuPont & the March of Modern America. Forster, Elborg, tr. from FRE. 2006. (Studies in Industry & Society Ser.). (ENG., Illus.). 304p. (gr. 17). 45.00 *(978-0-8018-8444-3(6))* Johns Hopkins Univ. Pr.
Newcomb, James, et al. Genome Synthesis & Design Futures. 2007. *(978-0-9792349-2-7(1))* Bio Economic Research Assocs., LLC.
—Genome Synthesis & Design Futures: Implications for the U. S. Economy. 2007. pap. *(978-0-9792349-1-0(3))* Bio Economic Research Assocs., LLC.
Ng, Ka M., et al. Chemical Product Design: Toward a Perspective Through Case Studies. Gani, Rafiqul & Ng, Ka M., eds. Dam-Johansen, Kim, ed. 2006. (Computer Aided Chemical Engineering Ser.: 23). (ENG., Illus.). 512p. 240.00 *(978-0-444-52217-7(4),* Elsevier Science) Elsevier Science & Technology Bks.
Park, Gerlann P. & Crull, Anna W. Supercritical Fluids: Their Time Has Come. (Business Opportunity Report Ser.: Vol. 183). (Illus.). xvii, 179p. *(978-1-56965-030-1(6))* BCC Research.
Pollak, Peter. Fine Chemicals: The Industry & the Business. 2nd ed. 2011. (ENG., Illus.). 312p. 125.00 *(978-0-470-62767-9(0),* Wiley) Wiley, John & Sons, Inc.
Putman, Russell L. Pioneers of Progress Benefactors of Mank. 2006. pap. 15.95 *(978-1-4286-6265-0(0))* Kessinger Publishing, LLC.
Rähse, Wilfried. Produktdesign in der chemischen Industrie: Schnelle Umsetzung kundenspezifischer Lösungen. 2006. (VDI-Buch / Chemische Technik / Verfahrenstechnik Ser.). (Illus.). XII, 348p. 139.00 *(978-3-540-25162-0(6),* 3540251626) Springer.
Rao, C. Someswara. The Chemistry of Process Development in Fine Chemical & Pharmaceutical Industry. 2nd ed. 2007. (ENG., Illus.). 1328p. 325.00 *(978-0-470-31995-6(X),* Wiley) Wiley, John & Sons, Inc.
Ross, Benjamin & Amter, Steven. The Polluters: The Making of Our Chemically Altered Environment. 1 vol. (ENG., Illus.). 2012. 240p. pap. 19.95 ***(978-0-19-993096-8(1))*** 2010. 256p. 27.95 *(978-0-19-973995-0(1))* Oxford Univ. Pr., Inc.
Scholtissek, Stephan. Innovation Excellence: Creating Market Success in the Energy & Natural Resources Sectors. 2011. (ENG.). 224p. 55.00 *(978-0-7494-6346-5(5))* Kogan Page, Ltd. GBR. Dist: Ingram Pub. Services.
Selectos Metodos Oficiales y Practicas Recomendadas de la AOCS. 110.00 *(978-0-935315-88-2(8))* American Oil Chemists' Society.
Sieckhaus, John F. Chemicals, Human Health, & the Environment. 2009. 290p. 31.99 *(978-1-4415-0141-7(X));* pap. 21.99 *(978-1-4415-0140-0(1))* Xlibris Corp.
Singh, Balaji. Market Research & Strategic Planning for Global Chemical, Petrochemical, & Plastics Industries. 2012. (ENG.). 400p. 150.00 *(978-0-470-94813-2(2),* Wiley-Scrivener) Wiley, John & Sons, Inc.
Spellman, Frank R. Chemical Infrastructure Protection & Homeland Security. 2009. (ENG.). 224p. pap. 85.00 *(978-0-86587-182-3(5))* Government Institutes.
SRI Consulting Staff, compiled by. 2008 Directory of Chemical Producers: East Asia. 2007. 2360.00 *(978-0-9795259-2-6(6))* SRI Consulting.
Stringer, Ruth & Johnston, Paul. Chlorine & the Environment: An Overview of the Chlorine Industry. 2010. 448p. pap. 219.00 *(978-90-481-5645-0(9),* 9048156459) Springer.
Tarabanko, Nikolay & Tarabanko, Valery. Vanadium Catalysts of the Deacon Process. 2011. 104p. pap. ***(978-3-8454-1852-0(4))*** Lambert Academic Publishing.
Technology Research Editors, ed. Corrosion Prevention in Petroleum Refinery & Chemical Environments, 2007 Ed. 2007. pap. 118.50 *(978-1-60030-395-1(1),* Search-In-Print) CSA Journal Division.
Vince, Ivan. Major Accidents to the Environment: A Practical Guide to the Seveso II Directive & COMAH Regulations. 2008. (ENG., Illus.). 320p. 109.00 *(978-0-7506-8389-0(9),* Butterworth-Heinemann) Elsevier Science & Technology Bks.
2007 Directory of Chemical Producers - Canada. 2007. 880.00 *(978-0-9778175-6-6(3))* SRI Consulting.
2007 Directory of Chemical Producers - Mexico. 2007. 1010.00 *(978-0-9778175-7-3(1))* SRI Consulting.
2007 Directory of Chemical Producers - South & Central America. 2007. 1450.00 *(978-0-9778175-8-0(X))* SRI Consulting.
2007 Directory of Chemical Producers - United States. 2007. 1515.00 *(978-0-9778175-9-7(8))* SRI Consulting.
2007 Industry Applications Society Fifty-Fourth Annual Petroleum & Chemical Industry Conference. 2007. pap. 200.00 *(978-1-4244-1139-9(4),* 07CH37895) IEEE.

CHEMICAL INDUSTRY—DIRECTORIES

Dunsford, Carolina, et al, eds. Major Chemical & Petrochemical Companies of the World. 15th ed. 2011. (Major Chemical & Petrochemical Companies of the World Ser.). 1550p. pap. 1350.00 ***(978-1-86099-679-5(5),*** Graham & Whiteside) Cengage Gale.
Plunkett, Jack W. E-Book Plunkett's Chemicals, Coatings & Plastics Industry Almanac 2008: Chemicals, Coatings & Plastics Industry Market Research, Statistics, Trends & Leading Companies. annuals Plunkett, Jack W., ed. 2007. E-Book 299.99 incl. cd-rom *(978-1-59392-434-8(8))* Plunkett Research, Ltd.
—Plunkett's Chemicals, Coatings & Plastics Industry Almanac 2007: Chemicals, Coatings & Plastics Industry Market Research, Statistics, Trends & Leading Companies. Plunkett, Jack W., ed. 2006. 494p. pap. 299.99 incl. cd-rom *(978-1-59392-075-3(X))* Plunkett Research, Ltd.
—Plunkett's Chemicals, Coatings & Plastics Industry Almanac 2007 (E-Book) Chemicals, Coatings & Plastics Industry Market Research, Statistics, Trends & Leading Companies. Plunkett, Jack W., ed. 2006. 519p. E-Book 499.99 incl. cd-rom *(978-1-59392-417-1(8))* Plunkett Research, Ltd.
—Plunkett's Chemicals, Coatings & Plastics Industry Almanac 2008: Chemicals, Coatings & Plastics Industry Market Research, Statistics, Trends & Leading Companies. annuals Plunkett, Jack W., ed. 2007. pap. 299.99 incl. cd-rom *(978-1-59392-091-3(1))* Plunkett Research, Ltd.
—Plunkett's Chemicals, Coatings & Plastics Industry Trends & Statistics 2007 (Summary) A summary version of Plunkett's Chemicals, Coatings & Plastics Industry Almanac 2007. Plunkett, Jack W., ed. 2006. 28p. pap. 199.99 incl. cd-rom *(978-1-59392-736-3(3))* Plunkett Research, Ltd.
—Plunkett's Renewable, Alternative & Hydrogen Industry Almanac 2008: Renewable, Alternative & Hydrogen Energy Industry Market Research, Statistics, Trends & Leading Companies. annuals Plunkett, Jack W., ed. 2007. 399p. pap. 299.99 incl. cd-rom *(978-1-59392-100-2(4))* Plunkett Research, Ltd.
—Plunkett's Renewable, Alternative & Hydrogen Industry Almanac 2008 (E-Book) Renewable, Alternative & Hydrogen Energy Industry Market Research, Statistics, Trends & Leading Companies. annuals Plunkett, Jack W., ed. 2007. 410p. E-Book 299.99 incl. cd-rom *(978-1-59392-443-0(7))* Plunkett Research, Ltd.
SRI Consulting Staff, compiled by. 2007 Directory of Chemical Producers: Europe. 2007. 2550.00 *(978-0-9795259-1-9(8))* SRI Consulting.
—2007 Directory of Chemical Producers: Middle East. 2007. 1150.00 *(978-0-9795259-0-2(X))* SRI Consulting.
—2008 Directory of Chemical Producers: Canada. 2008. 1840.00 *(978-0-9795259-5-7(0))* SRI Consulting.
—2008 Directory of Chemical Producers: China. 2007. 1840.00 *(978-0-9795259-4-0(2))* SRI Consulting.
—2008 Directory of Chemical Producers: East Asia. 2007. 2360.00 *(978-0-9795259-2-6(6))* SRI Consulting.
—2008 Directory of Chemical Producers: India. 2007. 1910.00 *(978-0-9795259-3-3(4))* SRI Consulting.
—2008 Directory of Chemical Producers: Mexico. 2008. 1030.00 *(978-0-9795259-6-4(9))* SRI Consulting.
—2008 Directory of Chemical Producers: Middle East. 2008. 1170.00 *(978-0-9795259-9-5(3))* SRI Consulting.
—2008 Directory of Chemical Producers: South & Central America. 2008. 1490.00 *(978-0-9795259-7-1(7))* SRI Consulting.
—2008 Directory of Chemical Producers: United States. 2008. 1950.00 *(978-0-9795259-8-8(5))* SRI Consulting.
—2009 Directory of Chemical Producers: East Asia. 2008. 2490.00 *(978-0-9818856-1-2(6))* SRI Consulting.

CHEMICAL INDUSTRY—SAFETY MEASURES

Abbasi, Shahid Abbas, et al. Pool Fires in Chemical Process Industries: Concepts, Case Histories, Modeling & Control. 2013. (ENG., Illus.). 232p. 129.95 *(978-1-4398-5665-9(6),* CRC Press) Taylor & Francis Group GBR. Dist: Taylor & Francis Group.
American Institute of Chemical Engineers (AIChE) Staff, compiled by. 41st Loss Prevention Symposium 2007. 2007. 431p. pap. 118.00 *(978-1-60423-353-7(2))* Curran Assocs., Inc.
BP (Firm) Staff & Institution of Chemical Engineers (Great Britain) Staff, contrib. by. Control of Work. 2nd ed. 2007. (BP Process Safety Ser.). (Illus.). v, 86p. pap. *(978-0-85295-514-7(6))* Institution of Chemical Engineers, The.
Center for Chemical Process Safety (CCPS). A Practical Approach to Hazard Identification for Operations & Maintenance Workers. 2010. (ENG., Illus.). 295p. 127.00 *(978-0-470-63524-7(X))* American Institute of Chemical Engineers.
Center for Chemical Process Safety (CCPS) Staff, creator. Guidelines for the Management of Change for Process Safety. 2008. (ENG., Illus.). 200p. 111.00 *(978-0-470-04309-7(1))* American Institute of Chemical Engineers.
Center for Chemical Process Safety Staff. Guidelines for Auditing Process Safety Management Systems. 2nd ed. 2011. (ENG., Illus.). 900p. 158.00 *(978-0-470-28235-9(5))* American Institute of Chemical Engineers.
—Guidelines for Non-SIS Independent Protection Layers. 2012. (ENG.). 150p. 79.95 *(978-0-470-34385-2(0))* American Institute of Chemical Engineers.
—Incidents That Define Process Safety. 2008. (ENG., Illus.). 352p. 111.00 *(978-0-470-12204-4(8))* American Institute of Chemical Engineers.
Chemical Security, a Rising Concern for America: Examination of the Department's Chemical Security Regulations & Its Effect on the Public & Private Sector: Hearing Before the Subcommittee on Transportation Security & Infrastructure Protection of the Committee on Homeland Security, House of Representatives, One Hundred Tenth Congress, First Session, July 24, 2007. 2009. (Illus.). iii, 62p. *(978-0-16-084081-4(3),* 552-070-39797-7) United States Government Printing Office.
Crowl, Daniel A. & Louvar, Joseph F. Chemical Process Safety: Fundamentals with Applications. 3rd rev. ed. 2011. (Prentice Hall International Series in the Physical & Chemical Engineering Sciences Ser.). (ENG., Illus.). 752p. 150.00 *(978-0-13-138226-8(8),* Prentice Hall) Prentice Hall PTR.
Schwartz, Sheila. The Chemical Industry after Bhopal: An International Symposium Held in London, 7/8th November 1985. 2012. (Life&Times Ser.). (ENG., Illus.). 220p. pap. 14.95 ***(978-0-907822-73-8(8))*** Haus Publishing GBR. Dist: Consortium Bk. Sales & Distribution.
Simeonov, Lubomir I. & Hassanien, Mahmoud A., eds. Exposure & Risk Assessment of Chemical Pollution - Contemporary Methodology. 2009. (NATO Science for Peace & Security Series C: Environmental Security Ser.). (ENG., Illus.). xxvii, 526p. pap. 159.00 *(978-90-481-2334-6(8));* 409.00 *(978-90-481-2333-9(X))* Springer.
Spellman, Frank R. Occupational Safety & Health Simplified for the Chemical Industry. 2009. (ENG.). 204p. pap. 79.00 *(978-0-86587-186-1(8))* Government Institutes.

CHEMICAL INDUSTRY—AFRICA

Bond, Patrick, et al, eds. Climate Change, Carbon Trading & Civil Society: Negative Returns on South African Investments. 2009. 231p. pap. 38.95 *(978-1-86914-141-7(5))* Univ. of Natal Pr. ZAF. Dist: International Specialized Bk. Services.
McKinley, Catherine E. Indigo: In Search of the Color That Seduced the World. 2011. (ENG., Illus.). 256p. 27.00 *(978-1-60819-505-3(8))* Bloomsbury Publishing.

CHEMICAL INDUSTRY—CHINA

Chemical Producers: China. 224p. (Orig.). pap. *(978-0-7605-2912-6(4))* Rector Pr., Ltd.
Festel, G., et al, eds. The Chemical & Pharmaceutical Industry in China: Opportunities & Threats for Foreign Companies. 2010. (ENG., Illus.). xii, 295p. pap. 79.95 *(978-3-642-06140-0(0),* 3642061400) Springer.
SRI Consulting Staff, compiled by. 2008 Directory of Chemical Producers: China 2007. 1840.00 *(978-0-9795259-4-0(2))* SRI Consulting.
Xicoy Almirall, Borja. Exergoeconomics Applied to Thermochemical Processes. 2011. 188p. pap. ***(978-3-8443-1910-1(7))*** Lambert Academic Publishing.

CHEMICAL INDUSTRY—EUROPE

Bender, Herbert F. & Eisenbarth, Philipp. Hazardous Chemicals: Control & Regulation in the European Market. 2007. (ENG., Illus.). 409p. 170.00 *(978-3-527-31541-3(1),* Wiley-VCH) Wiley, John & Sons, Inc.
Chandler, Alfred D., Jr. Shaping the Industrial Century: The Remarkable Story of the Evolution of the Modern Chemical & Pharmaceutical Industries. 2009. (Harvard Studies in Business History Ser.: 46). (Illus.). 384p. pap. 23.50 *(978-0-674-03221-7(7))* Harvard Univ. Pr.
Chemical Producers: Europe. 1870p. (Orig.). pap. *(978-0-7605-2908-9(6))* Rector Pr., Ltd.
Hansjürgens, Bernd & Nordbeck, Ralf, eds. Chemikalienregulierung und Innovationen zum nachhaltigen Wirtschaften. (Nachhaltigkeit und Innovation Ser.). (GER., Illus.). VIII, 363p. pap. 99.00 *(978-3-7908-1597-9(7))* Physica-Verlag DEU. Dist: Springer.
Homburg, Ernst, et al, eds. The Chemical Industry in Europe, 1850-1914: Industrial Growth, Pollution & Professionalization. Industrial Growth, Pollution & Professionalization. 2011. (Chemists & Chemistry Ser.). (ENG.). 356p. pap. 229.00 *(978-90-481-4971-1(1),* 9048149711) Springer.
McDonnery, Shannon M., et al. Chemical Regulation in the EU: Introduction & Comparisons. 2012. pap. ***(978-1-62100-786-9(3))*** Nova Science Pubs., Inc.
Rijnmond Public Authority. Risk Analysis of Six Potentially Hazardous Industrial Objects in the Rijnmond Area: A Pilot Study. 2010. 820p. pap. 499.00 *(978-90-481-8371-5(5),* 9048183715) Springer.
SRI Consulting Staff, compiled by. 2007 Directory of Chemical Producers: Europe. 2007. 2550.00 *(978-0-9795259-1-9(8))* SRI Consulting.
Travis, Anthony S., et al, eds. Determinants in the Evolution of the European Chemical Industry, 1900-1939: New Technologies, Political Frameworks, Markets & Companies. 2010. (Chemists & Chemistry Ser.). 300p. pap. 349.00 *(978-90-481-4972-8(X),* 904814972X) Springer.
Tschochohei, Heinrich. Chemikalien-Governance: Chemikalienregulierung aus ökonomischer Perspektive. 2009. (GER.). 228p. 69.95 *(978-3-631-58696-9(5))* Lang, Peter GmbH, Europaischer Verlag der Wissenschaften DEU. Dist: Lang, Peter.
Zlatev, Nikolay. Third & Fourth Party Logistics As the Next Growth Pole in Rotterdam. 2011. 60p. pap. ***(978-3-8433-7773-7(1))*** Lambert Academic Publishing.

CHEMICAL INDUSTRY—GERMANY

Abelshauser, Werner, et al. German Industry & Global Enterprise: BASF: the History of a Company. 2009. (ENG., Illus.). 732p. pap. 63.00 *(978-0-521-10119-6(0))* Cambridge Univ. Pr.
Lesch, John E., ed. The German Chemical Industry in the Twentieth Century. 2010. (Chemists & Chemistry Ser.). 480p. pap. 299.00 *(978-90-481-5529-3(0),* 9048155290) Springer.
Lindner, Stephan. Inside IG Farben: Hoechst During the Third Reich. 2008. (ENG., Illus.). 424p. 61.00 *(978-0-521-86766-3(6))* Cambridge Univ. Pr.
Lindner, Stephan H. Inside IG Farben: Hoechst During the Third Reich. 2011. (ENG.). 426p. pap. 31.99 *(978-0-521-17838-9(X))* Cambridge Univ. Pr.
Perrey, Hans-Joachim. Zwischen Krieg, Wiederaufbau und Demontagen: Die BASF 1939 Bis 1952/53. 2009. (GER., Illus.). xii, 336p. *(978-3-924667-42-9(X))* Surseer Schriften, Reihe Kataloge.
Wagner-Kyora, Georg. Vom 'nationalen' zum 'sozialistischen' Selbst: Zur Erfahrungsgeschichte deutscher Chemiker und Ingenieure im 20. Jahrhundert. 2009. (Beitrage zur Unternehmensgeschichte (BZUG) Ser.). (GER., Illus.). 795p. (C). pap. 127.00 *(978-3-515-09262-3(5))* Steiner, Franz Verlag Wiesbaden GmbH DEU. Dist: Brown, David Bk. Co., The.

CHEMICAL INDUSTRY—GREAT BRITAIN

BP (Firm) Staff & Institution of Chemical Engineers (Great Britain) Staff, contrib. by. Control of Work. 2nd ed. 2007. (BP Process Safety Ser.). (Illus.). v, 86p. pap. *(978-0-85295-514-7(6))* Institution of Chemical Engineers, The.
Pettigrew, Andrew. The Awakening Giant: Continuity & Change in Ici. 2011. (Routledge Revivals Ser.). (ENG., Illus.). 562p. 150.00 *(978-0-415-61994-3(7))* Routledge.

CHEMICAL INDUSTRY—INDIA

S F, Sheeja. Research & Development & Its Impact on Firm Performance. 2011. 188p. pap. ***(978-3-8443-2653-6(7))*** Lambert Academic Publishing.
SRI Consulting Staff, compiled by. 2008 Directory of Chemical Producers: India. 2007. 1910.00 *(978-0-9795259-3-3(4))* SRI Consulting.
Xicoy Almirall, Borja. Exergoeconomics Applied to Thermochemical Processes. 2011. 188p. pap. ***(978-3-8443-1910-1(7))*** Lambert Academic Publishing.

CHEMICAL INDUSTRY—JAPAN

Kobayashi, Takeshi. Recent Progress of Biochemical & Biomedical Engineering in Japan II. 2010. (Advances in Biochemical Engineering Biotechnology Ser.). (Illus.). xii, 239p. pap. 289.00 *(978-3-642-05801-1(9),* 3642058019) Springer.

CHEMICAL INDUSTRY—SOVIET UNION

BIA. Key Chemical Manufacturers of Russia & the Former Soviet Republics. 6th rev. ed. 2006. 456p. (J). pap. 249.00 *(978-1-4187-4480-9(8))* Business Information Agency.

CHEMICAL INSTRUMENTS

see Chemical Apparatus

CHEMICAL KINETICS

see also Activity Coefficients; Pharmacokinetics

Alberty, Robert A. Enzyme Kinetics: Rapid-Equilibrium Applications of Mathematica. 2011. (Methods of Biochemical Analysis Ser.: 147). (ENG.). 456p. 158.00 *(978-0-470-63932-0(6),* Wiley) Wiley, John & Sons, Inc.
Amirov, Anvar Kh. Integral Geometry & Inverse Problems for Kinetic Equations (Inverse & Ill-Posed Problems Ser.). (ENG.). VIII, 201p. 358.00 ***(978-3-11-182979-1(0))*** De Gruyter, Walter Inc.
Amaut, Luis, et al. Chemical Kinetics: From Molecular Structure to Chemical Reactivity. 2006. (ENG., Illus.). 562p. 205.00 *(978-0-444-52186-6(0),* Elsevier Science) Elsevier Science & Technology Bks.
Bisswanger, Hans. Enzyme Kinetics: Principles & Methods. 2nd ed. 2008. (ENG., Illus.). 320p. 225.00 *(978-3-527-31957-2(3),* Wiley-VCH) Wiley, John & Sons, Inc.
Buback, Michael & van Herk, A. M., eds. Radical Polymerization: Kinetics & Mechanism. 2007. (Macromolecular Symposia Ser.: 25). (ENG., Illus.). 268p. 199.00 *(978-3-527-32056-1(3),* Wiley-VCH) Wiley, John & Sons, Inc.
Buchachenko, Antoly Leonidovich. Magnetic Isotope Effect in Chemistry & Biochemistry. 2009. (Illus.). 149p. 129.00 *(978-1-60741-363-9(9))* Nova Science Pubs., Inc.
Carolina Biological Staff, compiled by. Investigating Reaction Rates. 2009. (Inquiries in Science Chemistry Ser.). *(978-1-4350-0406-1(X))* Carolina Biological Supply Co.
—Investigating Reaction Rates. 2009. (Inquiries in Science Chemistry Ser.). tchr. ed., spiral bd. *(978-1-4350-0405-4(1))* Carolina Biological Supply Co.
Chorkendorff, I. & Niemantsverdriet, J. W. Concepts of Modern Catalysis & Kinetics. 2nd ed. 2007. (ENG.). 477p. 100.00 *(978-3-527-31672-4(8),* Wiley-VCH) Wiley, John & Sons, Inc.
Côme, Guy-Marie. Gas-Phase Thermal Reactions: Chemical Engineering Kinetics. 2010. 364p. pap. 179.00 *(978-90-481-5834-8(6),* 9048158346) Springer.
Cook, Paul F. & Cleland, W. W. Enzyme Kinetics & Mechanism. 2007. (Illus.). 416p. 81.00 *(978-0-8153-4140-6(7))* Routledge.
Cornish-Bowden, Athel. Fundamentals of Enzyme Kinetics. 4th ed. 2012. (ENG., Illus.). 510p. pap. 79.95 ***(978-3-527-33074-4(7),*** Wiley-VCH) Wiley, John & Sons, Inc.
DaCosta, Herbert. Rate Constant Estimation for Thermal Reactions: Methods & Applications. Fan, Maohong, ed. 2012. (ENG., Illus.). 360p. 135.00 ***(978-0-470-58230-5(8),*** Wiley) Wiley, John & Sons, Inc.
Feng, Jing. Abiotic Reductive Dehalogenation with Bimetallic Nano-Scale Iron. 2009. 204p. pap. *(978-3-639-20088-1(8))* VDM Verlag Dr. Mueller e.K.
Gennady, Zaikov E., et al, eds. Influence of the Solvents on Some Radical Reactions. 2010. (Chemistry Research & Applications Ser.). (Illus.). 130p. 43.00 *(978-1-60876-635-2(7))* Nova Science Pubs., Inc.
Gorban, Alexander N., et al, eds. Model Reduction & Coarse-Graining Approaches for Multiscale Phenomena. 2010. (ENG., Illus.). xi, 560p. pap. 249.00 *(978-3-642-07149-2(X),* 364207149X) Springer.
Guerrero Sánchez, Carlos. Ionic Systems in Materials Science: New Materials & Processes Based on Ionic Liquids and/or Ionic Polymerizations. 2008. 188p. pap. *(978-3-639-09201-1(5))* VDM Verlag Dr. Mueller e.K.
Hedaya, Mohsen A., ed. Basic Pharmacokinetics 2D. 2nd rev. ed. 2012. (Plant Engineering Ser.). (ENG., Illus.). 595p. 89.95 ***(978-1-4398-5073-2(9),*** CRC Press) Taylor & Francis Group GBR. Dist: Taylor & Francis Group.
House, James E. & House, James E. Principles of Chemical Kinetics. 2nd ed. 2007. (ENG., Illus.). 336p. (C). 55.95 *(978-0-12-356787-1(4),* Academic Pr.) Elsevier Science & Technology Bks.
Houston, Paul L. Chemical Kinetics & Reaction Dynamics. 2006. (Dover Books on Chemistry Ser.). (ENG., Illus.). 352p. per. 32.95 *(978-0-486-45334-7(0))* Dover Pubns., Inc.
Ikariya, Takao & Shibasaki, Masakatsu, eds. Bifunctional Molecular Catalysis. 2011. (Topics in Organometallic Chemistry Ser.). (Illus.). xii, 200p. 259.00 *(978-3-642-20730-3(8),* 3642207308) Springer.
Kamasak, Mustafa. Statistical Methods for Dynamic Positron Emission Tomography. 2010. 108p. pap. *(978-3-8383-5398-1(1))* Lambert Academic Publishing.

C

Kei, Tominaga. Heterogeneous Kinetics: Theory of Ziegler-Natta-Kaminsky Polymerization. 2011. (Springer Series in Chemical Physics Ser.). (ENG., Illus.). xiii, 264p. pap. 239.00 *(978-3-642-06186-8(9),* 3642061869) Springer.

Kimble, Michele. Femtochemistry VII: Fundamental Ultrafast Processes in Chemistry, Physics, & Biology. Castleman, Welford A., Jr., ed. 2006. (ENG., Illus.). 610p. 255.00 *(978-0-444-52821-6(0),* Elsevier Science) Elsevier Science & Technology Bks.

Kloucek, Petr, ed. Transport of Nanoparticles in Tissues. 2012. (Illus.). 350p. 149.00 *(978-981-4267-06-9(6))* Pan Stanford Publishing SGP. Dist: Independent Pubs. Group.

Korobov, Viktor & Ochkov, Valery. Chemical Kinetics with Mathcad & Maple. 2011. (ENG., Illus.). xi, 344p. 129.00 *(978-3-7091-0530-6(7),* 3709105307) Springer.

Kurzynski, Michal. The Thermodynamic Machinery of Life. 2010. (Frontiers Collection). (Illus.). xiv, 431p. pap. 99.00 *(978-3-642-06284-1(9),* 3642062849) Springer.

Lomova, T. N. & Zaikov, Gennadii Efremovich, eds. Chemical Processes with Participation of Biological & Related Compounds: Biophysical & Chemical Aspects of Porphyrins, Pigments, Drugs, Biodegradable Polymers & Nanofibers. 2008. (ENG., Illus.). 422p. 216.00 *(978-90-04-16210-5(0),* CRC Press) Taylor & Francis Group GBR. Dist: Taylor & Francis Group.

Makitra, R. G., et al. Linear Energy Relationships to Chemical Kinetics. 2009. 82p. pap. 37.00 *(978-1-60692-219-4(X))* Nova Science Pubs., Inc.

—Liquid Phase Correlation Analysis in the Chemistry of Solutions. 2007. 225.00 *(978-1-60021-895-8(4))* Nova Science Pubs., Inc.

Mansha, Muhammad. Natural Gas Combustion Modelling in Ic Engine. 2011. 324p. pap. **(978-3-8454-0911-5(8))** Lambert Academic Publishing.

Marin, Guy & Yablonsky, Gregory S. Kinetics of Chemical Reactions: Decoding Complexity. 2011. (ENG., Illus.). 446p. 105.00 *(978-3-527-31763-9(5),* Wiley-VCH) Wiley, John & Sons, Inc.

Medvedevskikh, Y. G. Organic & Physical Chemistry Using Chemical Kinetics: Prospects & Developments. 2007. 145.00 *(978-1-60021-763-0(X))* Nova Science Pubs., Inc.

Naik, Chitralkumar. Low Temperature Oxydation of Hydrocarbons. 2008. 168p. pap. *(978-3-639-08765-9(8))* VDM Verlag Dr. Mueller e.K.

Nölting, Bengt. Protein Folding Kinetics: Biophysical Methods. 2nd ed. 2010. (ENG., Illus.). xvi, 222p. pap. 139.00 *(978-3-642-06604-7(6),* 3642066046) Springer.

Pearce, Eli M. & Zaikov, Gennadii Efremovich, eds. Kinetics & Thermodynamics for Chemistry & Biochemistry, Vol. 2. 2009. 145.00 *(978-1-60692-352-8(8))* Nova Science Pubs., Inc.

Pellissier, Hélène. Chirality from Dynamic Kinetic Resolution. 2011. (ENG., Illus.). 318p. (C). 160.00 **(978-1-84973-197-3(7))** Royal Society of Chemistry, The GBR. Dist: Ingram Pub. Services.

Plonka, Andrzej. Dispersive Kinetics. 2010. 244p. pap. 109.00 *(978-90-481-5754-9(4),* 9048157544) Springer.

Prinz, Heino. Numerical Methods for the Life Scientist: Binding & Enzyme Kinetics Calculated with GNU Octave & MATLAB. 2011. (ENG., Illus.). ix, 149p. 129.00 *(978-3-642-20819-5(3),* 3642208193) Springer.

Purich, Daniel L. Enzyme Kinetics: Catalysis & Control: A Reference of Theory & Best-Practice Methods. 2010. (ENG., Illus.). 920p. 210.00 *(978-0-12-380924-7(X))* Elsevier Science & Technology Bks.

Purich, Daniel L., ed. Contemporary Enzyme Kinetics & Mechanism. 3rd ed. 2009. (Reliable Lab Solutions Ser.). (ENG.). 704p. pap. 78.95 *(978-0-12-378608-1(8),* Academic Pr.) Elsevier Science & Technology Bks.

Ramasamy, Subramanian & Cholan, Sivasankari. Chemical Kinetics. 2011. 148p. pap. **(978-3-8443-0820-4(2))** Lambert Academic Publishing.

Schmal, Martin. Chemical Reaction Engineering: Essentials, Exercises & Examples. 2012. (ENG.). 550p. (C). pap. 89.95 **(978-0-415-69538-1(4),** CRC Press) Taylor & Francis Group GBR. Dist: Taylor & Francis Group.

Shteinberg, Alexander S. Fast Reactions in Energetic Materials: High-Temperature Decomposition of Rocket Propellants & Explosives. Rusanova, Maria, tr. 2010. (ENG., Illus.). xiv, 202p. pap. 299.00 *(978-3-642-09767-6(7),* 3642097677) Springer.

—Fast Reactions in Energetic Materials: High-Temperature Decomposition of Rocket Propellants & Explosives. 2008. (ENG., Illus.). xiv, 202p. 299.00 *(978-3-540-78860-7(3),* 3540788603) Springer.

Soustelle, Michel. An Introduction to Chemical Kinetics. 2011. (Iste Ser.: 570). (ENG., Illus.). 480p. 195.00 **(978-1-84821-302-9(6),** Wiley-ISTE) Wiley, John & Sons, Inc.

Sugden, T. M. Photochemistry & Reaction Kinetics. Ashmore, P. G. & Dainton, F. S., eds. 2010. (ENG.). 404p. pap. 53.00 *(978-0-521-14747-7(6))* Cambridge Univ. Pr.

Traut, Thomas. Allosteric Regulatory Enzymes. 2007. (ENG., Illus.). xiv, 250p. 169.00 *(978-0-387-72888-9(0),* 0387728880) Springer.

Traut, Thomas W. Allosteric Regulatory Enzymes. 2010. (ENG., Illus.). xiv, 250p. pap. 169.00 *(978-1-4419-4453-5(2),* 1441944532) Springer.

Upadhyay, Santosh K. Chemical Kinetics & Reaction Dynamics. (ENG.). xv, 256p. 2010. pap. 209.00 *(978-90-481-7146-0(6),* 9048171466) 2006. (Illus.). 209.00 *(978-1-4020-4546-2(8),* 1402045468) Springer.

Van Boekel Tiny Staff. Kinetic Modelling of Reactions in Foods. 2008. (Food Science & Technology Ser.). (ENG., Illus.). 767p. 209.95 *(978-1-57444-614-2(2),* CRC Press) Taylor & Francis Group GBR. Dist: Taylor & Francis Group.

Vannice, M. Albert. Kinetics of Catalytic Reactions. 2010. (ENG., Illus.). xviii, 240p. pap. 109.00 *(978-1-4419-3758-2(7),* 1441937587) Springer.

Yates, John T., et al. Molecular Physical Chemistry for Engineers. 2007. (Illus.). 482p. 92.00 *(978-1-891389-27-6(0))* Univ. Science Bks.

Zaikov, G. E. Chemical & Biochemical Kinetics: New Perspectives. 2011. (Biochemistry Research Trends Ser.). 263p. pap. 89.00 *(978-1-61209-224-9(1))* Nova Science Pubs., Inc.

Zaikov, Gennadii Efremovich, ed. Chemical & Biochemical Physics, Kinetics & Thermodynamics: New Perspectives. 2008. (Illus.). (C). 205.00 *(978-1-60456-024-4(X))* Nova Science Pubs., Inc.

Zhang, Youxue. Geochemical Kinetics. 2008. (ENG., Illus.). 656p. (C). 75.00 *(978-0-691-12432-2(9))* Princeton Univ. Pr.

Zhang, Youxue & Cherniak, Daniele, eds. Diffusion in Minerals & Melts, vol. 72. 2010. (ENG.). 1038p. pap. 50.00 *(978-0-939950-86-7(3))* Mineralogical Society of America.

Zvara, Ivo. The Inorganic Radiochemistry of Heavy Elements: Methods for Studying Gaseous Compounds. 2010. xxviii, 228p. pap. 279.00 *(978-90-481-7679-3(4),* 9048176794) Springer.

CHEMICAL LABORATORIES

see also Nuclear Energy—Research—Laboratories

American Industrial Hygiene Association Staff, contrib. by. Clandestine Methamphetamine Laboratory Assessment & Remediation Guidance. 2007. i, 29p. *(978-1-931504-80-5(6))* American Industrial Hygiene Assn.

Ardus, Paul V., ed. Methamphetamine Laboratories. 2010. pap. 47.00 *(978-1-60692-653-6(5))* Nova Science Pubs., Inc.

Committee on Promoting Safe and Secure Chemical Management in Developing Countries & National Research Council. Promoting Chemical Laboratory Safety & Security in Developing Countries. 2010. (ENG.). 136p. pap. 33.75 *(978-0-309-15041-5(8))* National Academies Pr.

De Bièvre, Paul & Günzler, Helmut, eds. Validation in Chemical Measurement. 2010. x, 167p. pap. 219.00 *(978-3-642-05867-7(1),* 3642058671) Springer.

Doraiswamy, L. K. The Sinews of Excellence: The Big History of India's National Chemical Laboratory. 2009. 95.00 *(978-0-415-56449-6(2),* Routledge India) Taylor & Francis Group GBR. Dist: Taylor & Francis Group.

Fink, Richard C. & Lunn, George. Destruction of Hazardous Chemicals in the Laboratory. 3rd ed. 2012. (ENG.). 800p. 125.00 **(978-0-470-48755-6(0),** Wiley) Wiley, John & Sons, Inc.

Funk, Werner, et al. Quality Assurance in Analytical Chemistry: Applications in Environmental, Food & Materials Analysis, Biotechnology, & Medical Engineering. Iannelli, Eric & Iannelli, Sarah, trs. from GER. 2nd ed. 2007. (ENG., Illus.). 300p. 167.00 *(978-3-527-31114-9(9),* Wiley-VCH) Wiley, John & Sons, Inc.

Gac, Severine le, et al. Miniaturization & Mass Spectrometry. 2008. (ENG., Illus.). 332p. 213.00 **(978-0-85404-129-9(X))** Royal Society of Chemistry, The GBR. Dist: Ingram Pub. Services.

Hertzberg, Mark & Wright, Frank Lloyd. Frank Lloyd Wright's SC Johnson Research Tower. 2010. 80p. 19.95 *(978-0-7649-5609-6(4))* Pomegranate Communications, Inc.

Hill, Robert H. & Finster, David. Laboratory Safety for Chemistry Students. 2010. (ENG., Illus.). 546p. pap. 69.95 *(978-0-470-34428-6(8),* Wiley) Wiley, John & Sons, Inc.

Huber, Ludwig. Validation & Qualification in Analytical Laboratories. 2nd rev. ed. 2007. (ENG., Illus.). 288p. 250.00 *(978-0-8493-8267-3(X),* Informa Healthcare) Taylor & Francis Group GBR. Dist: Taylor & Francis Group.

Konieczka, Piotr & Namiesnik, Jacek, eds. Quality Assurance & Quality Control in the Analytical Chemical Laboratory: A Practical Approach. 2009. (Analytical Chemistry Ser.). (ENG., Illus.). 232p. 133.95 *(978-1-4200-8270-8(1),* CRC Press) Taylor & Francis Group GBR. Dist: Taylor & Francis Group.

Narayan, Mahesh, et al. General Chemistry Laboratories. 2nd rev. ed. 2011. (ENG.). 162p. spiral bd. 35.50 *(978-0-7575-7958-5(2))* Kendall Hunt Publishing Co.

Pyatt, Kevin. Simulating Lab Experiences. 2008. 168p. pap. *(978-3-639-05277-0(3))* VDM Verlag Dr. Mueller e.K.

CHEMICAL LITERATURE

see also Information Storage and Retrieval Systems—Chemistry

Barden, Sandra K. Becoming Chemically Literate: Basic Concepts in Plain Language. 2008. (Illus.). 208p. pap. 12.95 *(978-0-615-17504-1(X))* Barden, Sandra K.

Garson, Lorrin R. & Coghill, Anne M., eds. The ACS Style Guide: Effective Communication of Scientific Information. 3rd rev. ed. 2006. (ENG., Illus.). 448p. 59.50 *(978-0-8412-3999-9(1))* American Chemical Society.

Maizell, Robert E. How to Find Chemical Information: A Guide for Practicing Chemists, Educators & Students. 4th ed. 2013. (ENG.). 512p. 105.00 *(978-0-471-72071-3(2),* Wiley-Interscience) Wiley, John & Sons, Inc.

CHEMICAL MANIPULATION

see Chemistry—Manipulation

CHEMICAL MICROSCOPY

Ibanez, Jorge G., et al. Environmental Chemistry: Microscale Laboratory Experiments. 2007. (Illus.). 238p. spiral bd. 54.95 *(978-0-387-49492-0(8))* Springer.

CHEMICAL MODELS

Bindslev, Niels. Drug-Acceptor Interactions: Modeling theoretical tools to test & evaluate experimental equilibrium Effects. 2008. (Illus.). 428p. pap. *(978-91-977071-0-7(4))* Co-Action Publishing.

Bladon, Peter, et al. Molecular Modelling: Computational Chemistry Demystified. 2011. (ENG., Illus.). 310p. pap. 112.00 **(978-1-84973-352-6(X))** Royal Society of Chemistry, The GBR. Dist: Ingram Pub. Services.

Comba, Peter, et al. Molecular Modeling of Inorganic Compounds. 3rd ed. 2009. (ENG., Illus.). 344p. 220.00 *(978-3-527-31799-8(6),* Wiley-VCH) Wiley, John & Sons, Inc.

Jensen, Jan H. Molecular Modeling Basics. 2010. (ENG., Illus.). 189p. 49.95 *(978-1-4200-7526-7(8),* CRC Press) Taylor & Francis Group GBR. Dist: Taylor & Francis Group.

Kitagawa, Terutaka. Biomimetic Modeling Of Superoxide Reductase: Synthetic Insight into a Natural Process. 2008. 188p. pap. *(978-3-8364-6745-2(3))* VDM Verlag Dr. Mueller e.K.

Meunier, Marc. Industrial Applications of Molecular Simulations. 2011. (ENG., Illus.). 421p. 129.95 *(978-1-4398-6101-1(3),* CRC Press) Taylor & Francis Group GBR. Dist: Taylor & Francis Group.

Putz, Mihai V. Advances in Chemical Modeling. 2011. (Chemistry Research & Applications Ser.). 481p. 195.00 *(978-1-61209-028-3(1))* Nova Science Pubs., Inc.

Shargel, Leon, et al. Applied Biopharmaceutics & Pharmacokinetics. 6th ed. 2012. (ENG.). 811p. 75.00 **(978-0-07-160393-5(X),** 007160393X) McGraw-Hill Medical Publishing Div.

Wako, Hiroshi & Abe, Haruo. Folding/Unfolding Kinetics of Lattice Proteins by Applying a Simple Statistical Mechanical Model for Protein Folding. 2011. (Biochemistry Research Trends Ser.). (Illus.). 42p. pap. 43.00 *(978-1-61761-922-9(1),* Nova Biomedical Bks.) Nova Science Pubs., Inc.

Woolley, Adam. A Guide to Practical Toxicology: Evaluation, Prediction, & Risk. 2nd rev. ed. 2008. (ENG., Illus.). 472p. pap. 100.00 *(978-1-4200-4314-3(5))* CRC Pr. LLC.

CHEMICAL NOMENCLATURE

see Chemistry—Nomenclature

CHEMICAL OCEANOGRAPHY

see also Water Chemistry

Brightwell, Chris. Marine Chemistry: A Complete Guide to Water Chemistry in Marine Aquariums. 2007. (Illus.). 272p. 39.95 *(978-0-7938-0574-7(0))* TFH Pubns., Inc.

Cram101 Textbook Reviews. Outlines & Highlights for Introduction to Marine Biogeochemistry by Susan Libes. 2011. 88p. pap. 27.95 **(978-1-61905-851-4(0))** Cram101 Inc.

—Outlines & Highlights for Marine Biogeochemical Cycles by Open University. 2011. 102p. pap. 27.95 **(978-1-61905-574-2(0))** Cram101 Inc.

Cram101 Textbook Reviews & Cram101 Textbook Reviews. Outlines & Highlights for Chemical Oceanography & the Marine Carbon Cycle by Steven R Emerson, Isbn: 9780521833134 0521833132. 2011. 128p. pap. 28.95 **(978-1-61490-404-5(9))** Cram101 Inc.

Crompton, T. R. Analysis of Seawater: A Guide for the Analytical & Environmental Chemist. 2010. (ENG., Illus.). xxii, 510p. pap. 269.00 *(978-3-642-06593-4(7),* 3642065937) Springer.

Eisler, Ronald. Oceanic Acidification. 2011. (ENG.). 260p. 89.95 **(978-1-57808-770-9(8))** BIOS Scientific Publishers Ltd. GBR. Dist: Taylor & Francis Group.

Emelyanov, Emelyan M. The Barrier Zones in the Ocean. Akulov, L. D. et al, trs. 2010. (ENG., Illus.). xx, 632p. pap. 239.00 *(978-3-642-06479-1(5),* 3642064795) Springer.

Emerson, Steven R. & Hedges, John I. Chemical Oceanography & the Marine Carbon Cycle. 2008. (ENG., Illus.). 468p. (C). 90.00 *(978-0-521-83313-4(2))* Cambridge Univ. Pr.

Farrugia, Christina A., ed. Dispersant & Oil Monitoring in the Deepwater Horizon Spill. 2011. (Environmental Remediation Technologies, Regulations & Safety Ser.). (Illus.). 160p. 95.00 *(978-1-61324-011-3(2))* Nova Science Pubs., Inc.

Ferronsky, V. I. & Polyakov, V. A. Isotopes of the Earth's Hydrosphere. 2012. Orig. Title: Isotopes of the Earth's Hydrosphere (Isotopiya Gidrosfery Zemli). (ENG., Illus.). 644p. 229.00 **(978-94-007-2855-4(7),** 9400728557) Springer.

Gade, Martin, et al, eds. Marine Surface Films: Chemical Characteristics, Influence on Air-Sea Interactions & Remote Sensing. 2010. (ENG., Illus.). xvii, 342p. pap. 159.00 *(978-3-642-06991-8(6),* 3642069916) Springer.

Gianguzza, Antonio, et al. Chemical Processes in Marine Environments. 2010. (Environmental Science & Engineering / Environmental Science Ser.). (Illus.). xviii, 441p. pap. 329.00 *(978-3-642-08589-5(X),* 364208589X) Springer.

Gianguzza, Antonio, et al, eds. Chemistry of Marine Water & Sediments. 2012. (Environmental Science & Engineering / Environmental Science Ser.). (ENG., Illus.). xviii, 508p. pap. 349.00 *(978-3-642-07559-9(2),* 3642075592) Springer.

—Marine Chemistry: An Environmental Analytical Chemistry Approach. 2012. (Water Science & Technology Library). (ENG.). 420p. pap. 239.00 *(978-90-481-4872-1(3),* 9048148723) Springer.

Handa, N., et al, eds. Dynamics & Characterization of Marine Organic Matter. 2010. (Ocean Sciences Research Ser.). 572p. pap. 309.00 *(978-90-481-5451-7(0),* 9048154510) Springer.

Hayes, Maria, ed. Marine Bioactive Compounds: Sources, Characterization & Applications. 2011. (ENG., Illus.). xii, 229p. 209.00 **(978-1-4614-1246-5(3),** 1461412463) Springer.

Head, P. C. Practical Estuarine Chemistry: A Handbook. 2011. (ENG.). 348p. pap. 43.00 **(978-0-521-27412-8(5))** Cambridge Univ. Pr.

Jiao, Nianzhi & Zhang, Chuanlun. Microbial Processes & Carbon Cycling in the Ocean. 2008. (Illus.). 87p. (C). pap. 29.00 *(978-1-60456-779-3(1))* Nova Science Pubs., Inc.

Kim, Se-Kwon, ed. Marine Cosmeceuticals. 2011. (ENG., Illus.). 428p. 169.95 *(978-1-4398-6028-1(9),* CRC Press) Taylor & Francis Group GBR. Dist: Taylor & Francis Group.

Libes, Susan. Introduction to Marine Biogeochemistry. 2nd ed. 2009. (ENG., Illus.). 928p. (C). 82.95 *(978-0-12-088530-5(1),* Academic Pr.) Elsevier Science & Technology Bks.

Liu, Yonggang. Monitoring & Modeling the Deepwater Horizon Oil Spill: A Record-Breaking Enterprise. 2011. **(978-0-87590-485-6(8))** American Geophysical Union.

Martorino, Louis & Puopolo, Karl. New Oceanography Research Developments: Marine Chemistry, Ocean Floor Analyses & Marine Phytoplankton. 2010. (Oceanography & Ocean Engineering Ser.). 145.00 *(978-1-60876-341-2(2))* Nova Science Pubs., Inc.

Quevauviller, Philippe, et al, eds. Chemical Marine Monitoring: Policy Framework & Analytical Trends. 2011. (Water Quality Measurements Ser.: 24). (ENG., Illus.). 466p. 180.00 **(978-0-470-74765-0(X),** Wiley) Wiley, John & Sons, Inc.

Rona, Peter A. Diversity of Hydrothermal Systems on Slow Spreading Ocean Ridges. 2010. *(978-0-87590-478-8(5))* American Geophysical Union.

Ryann, Amy L. & Perkins, Nathan J. The Black Sea: Dynamics, Ecology & Conservation. 2011. (Oceanography & Ocean Engineering; Marine Biology Ser.). (Illus.). xii, 293p. 129.00 *(978-1-61122-855-7(7))* Nova Science Pubs., Inc.

Schulz, Horst D. & Zabel, Matthias, eds. Marine Geochemistry. 2nd ed. 2010. (Illus.). xx, 574p. pap. 139.00 *(978-3-642-06876-8(6),* 3642068766) Springer.

Soloviev, Alexander & Lukas, Roger. The near-Surface Layer of the Ocean: Structure, Dynamics & Applications. 2010. (Atmospheric & Oceanographic Sciences Library). xv, 572p. pap. 329.00 *(978-90-481-7025-8(7),* 9048170257) Springer.

Steele, John H., et al, eds. Marine Chemistry & Geochemistry: A Derivative of the Encyclopedia of Ocean Sciences. 2009. (ENG., Illus.). 608p. pap. 104.00 *(978-0-08-096483-6(4),* Academic Pr.) Elsevier Science & Technology Bks.

Vetrov, Alexander & Romankevich, Evgeny. Carbon Cycle in the Russian Arctic Seas. 2010. (ENG., Illus.). x, 332p. pap. 169.00 *(978-3-642-05991-9(0),* 3642059910) Springer.

Wangersky, P. J., ed. Marine Chemistry. 2011. (Handbook of Environmental Chemistry / Water Pollution Ser.). (ENG., Illus.). xiv, 230p. pap. 189.00 *(978-3-642-08531-4(8),* 3642085318) Springer.

Wiggert, Jerry D. Indian Ocean Biogeochemical Processes & Ecological Variability. 2009. (Illus.). vii, 429p. *(978-0-87590-475-7(0))* American Geophysical Union.

Williams, Richard G. & Follows, Michael J. Ocean Dynamics & the Carbon Cycle: Principles & Mechanisms. 2011. (ENG., Illus.). 416p. (C). 73.00 *(978-0-521-84369-0(3))* Cambridge Univ. Pr.

Yebra-Biurrun, M. C. Flow Injection Analysis of Marine Samples. 2009. (Illus.). x, 312p. 79.00 *(978-1-60741-506-0(2))* Nova Science Pubs., Inc.

CHEMICAL PLANTS

American Institute of Chemical Engineers (AIChE) Staff, compiled by. 9th Process Plant Safety Symposium (PPSS 2007) 2007. 394p. pap. 118.00 *(978-1-60423-352-0(4))* Curran Assocs., Inc.

—22nd Annual International Conference of the Center for Chemical Process Safety (CCPS 2007) 2007. 227p. pap. 118.00 *(978-1-60423-310-0(9))* Curran Assocs., Inc.

Attwood, Dennis, et al. Human Factors Methods for Improving Performance in the Process Industries. Crowl, Daniel A., ed. 2007. (ENG., Illus.). 248p. 128.00 *(978-0-470-11754-5(0))* American Institute of Chemical Engineers.

CCPS. Recognizing Catastrophic Incident Warning Signs in the Process Industries. 2011. (ENG., Illus.). 264p. 125.00 **(978-0-470-76774-0(X))** American Institute of Chemical Engineers.

Center for Chemical Process Safety (CCPS). Guidelines for Engineering Design for Process Safety. 2nd ed. 2012. (ENG.). 440p. 125.00 *(978-0-470-76772-6(3))* American Institute of Chemical Engineers.

—Guidelines for Pressure Relief & Effluent Handling Systems. 2nd ed. 2013. (ENG.). 608p. 149.95 *(978-0-470-76773-3(1))* American Institute of Chemical Engineers.

Center for Chemical Process Safety (CCPS) Staff. Guidelines for Mechanical Integrity Systems. 2006. (ENG., Illus.). 320p. 156.00 incl. cd-rom *(978-0-8169-0952-0(0))* American Institute of Chemical Engineers.

Center for Chemical Process Safety Staff. Guidelines for Auditing Process Safety Management Systems. 2nd ed. 2011. (ENG., Illus.). 900p. 158.00 *(978-0-470-28235-9(5))* American Institute of Chemical Engineers.

—Guidelines for Evaluating Process Plant Buildings for External Explosions, Fires, & Toxic Releases. 2nd ed. 2012. (ENG.). 232p. 115.00 *(978-0-470-64367-9(6))* American Institute of Chemical Engineers.

—Guidelines for Hazard Evaluation Procedures. 3rd ed. 2008. (ENG., Illus.). 576p. 144.00 *(978-0-471-97815-2(9))* American Institute of Chemical Engineers.

Chemical Facility Anti-Terrorism ACT of 2008: Hearing Before the Committee on Homeland Security, House of Representatives, One Hundred Tenth Congress, Second Session, February 26, 2008. 2008. iii, 62p. *(978-0-16-081748-9(X),* 552-070-37956-8) United States Government Printing Office.

Chemical Security, a Rising Concern for America: Examination of the Department's Chemical Security Regulations & Its Effect on the Public & Private Sector: Hearing Before the Subcommittee on Transportation Security & Infrastructure Protection of the Committee on Homeland Security, House of

Representatives, One Hundred Tenth Congress, First Session, July 24, 2007. 2009. (Illus.). iii, 62p. *(978-0-16-084081-4(3)*, 552-070-39797-7) United States Government Printing Office.

Coker, A. Kayode. Ludwig's Applied Process Design for Chemical & Petrochemical Plants. 4th ed. 2007. (ENG., Illus.). 1024p. 235.00 *(978-0-7506-7766-0(X)*, Gulf Professional Publishing) Elsevier Science & Technology Bks.

—Ludwig's Applied Process Design for Chemical & Petrochemical Plants Vol. 2: Distillation, Packed Towers, Petroleum Fractionation, Gas Processing & Dehydration, 2 vols. 4th ed. 2010. (ENG., Illus.). 1008p. 220.00 *(978-0-7506-8366-1(X)*, Gulf Professional Publishing) Elsevier Science & Technology Bks.

Falqi, Fahad H. Miracle of Petrochemicals: Olefins Industry. 2009. pap. 99.95 *(978-1-59942-915-1(2))* Universal Pubs.

Giles, E. F. Who's Who in Chemical Plants. 4th ed. 400p. 195.00 *(978-1-56760-104-6(9))* Platts UDI.

The Goodyear Explosion: Ensuring Our Nation Is Secure by Developing a Risk Management Framework for Homeland Security: Hearing Before the Subcommittee on Transportation Security & Infrastructure Protection of the Committee on Homeland Security, House of Representatives, One Hundred Tenth Congress, Second Session, June 25, 2008. 2008. (Illus.). iii, 69p. *(978-0-16-082108-0(8)*, 552-070-38255-1) United States Government Printing Office.

Grewer, Theodor & Rogers, Richard. Thermal Hazards of Chemical Reactions. 2nd ed. 2011. (Industrial Safety Ser.). (ENG.). 220.00 *(978-0-444-52226-9(3)*, Elsevier Science) Elsevier Science & Technology Bks.

Hearing on H.R. 5533, the Chemical Facilities ACT of 2008 & H.R. 5577, the Chemical Facility Anti-Terrorism ACT of 2008: Hearing Before the Subcommittee on Environment & Hazardous Materials of the Committee on Energy & Commerce, House of Representatives, One Hundred Tenth Congress, Second Session, June 12, 2008. 2008. (Illus.). vi, 163p. *(978-0-16-083012-9(5)*, 552-070-38910-5) United States Government Printing Office.

Helmus, Frank Peter. Process Plant Design: Project Management from Inquiry to Acceptance. Ahner, Christine, tr. 2008. (ENG., Illus.). 204p. 126.00 *(978-3-527-31313-6(3)*, Wiley-VCH) Wiley, John & Sons, Inc.

H.R: The Chemical Facility Anti-Terrorism ACT of 2008: Hearing Before the Subcommittee on Transportation Security & Infrastructure Protection of the Committee on Homeland Security, House of Representatives, One Hundred Tenth Congress, First Session, December 12, 2007. 2009. iii, 66p. *(978-0-16-084644-1(7)*, 552-070-40139-3) United States Government Printing Office.

H.R. 5695: Chemical Facility Anti-Terrorism ACT of 2006: Hearing Before the Subcommittee on Economic Security, Infrastructure Protection, & Cybersecurity of the Committee on Homeland Security, House of Representatives, One Hundred Ninth Congress, Second Session, June 29, 2006. 2007. iii, 50p. *(978-0-16-078997-7(4)*, 552-070-36112-0) United States Government Printing Office.

Kletz, Trevor. What Went Wrong? Case Histories of Process Plant Disasters & How They Could Have Been Avoided. 5th ed. 2009. (ENG., Illus.). 640p. 92.95 *(978-1-85617-531-9(6)*, Butterworth-Heinemann) Elsevier Science & Technology Bks.

Kletz, Trevor A. & Amyotte, Paul. Process Plants: A Handbook for Inherently Safer Design. 2nd rev. ed. 2010. (ENG., Illus.). 384p. (C). 99.95 *(978-1-4398-0455-1(9)*, CRC Press) Taylor & Francis Group GBR. Dist: Taylor & Francis Group.

Lieberman, Norman P. Process Engineering for a Small Planet: How to Reuse, Re-Purpose, & Retrofit Existing Process Equipment. 2010. (ENG., Illus.). 296p. 85.00 *(978-0-470-58794-2(6)*, Wiley) Wiley, John & Sons, Inc.

Lieberman, Norman P. & Lieberman, Elizabeth T. A Working Guide to Process Equipment. 3rd ed. 2008. (ENG., Illus.). 591p. 79.95 *(978-0-07-149674-2(2)*, 0071496742) McGraw-Hill Professional Publishing.

McConville, Francis X. The Pilot Plant Real Book: A Unique Handbook for the Chemical Process Industry. 2nd num. ed. 2007. (Illus.). 320p. 114.95 *(978-0-9721769-2-7(6))* FXM Engineering & Design.

Nikraz, Magid. Integration of Operational Tasks in Chemical Plants- Investigating an Agent-Based Approach. 2007. 508p. per. *(978-3-8364-2833-0(4))* VDM Verlag Dr. Mueller e.K.

Nolan, Dennis P. Handbook of Fire & Explosion Protection Engineering Principles: For Oil, Gas, Chemical & Related Facilities. 2nd ed. 2010. (ENG., Illus.). 340p. 149.00 *(978-1-4377-7857-1(7))* William Andrew, Inc.

Noureldin, Mahmoud Bahy. Pinch Technology & Beyond Pinch: New Vistas on Energy Efficiency Optimization. 2011. (Series: Energy Science, Engineering & Technology Ser.). (Illus.). 341p. 129.00 *(978-1-61122-510-5(8))* Nova Science Pubs., Inc.

Rangaiah, Gade Pandu & Kariwala, Vinay, eds. Plantwide Control: Recent Developments & Applications. 2nd ed. 2012. (ENG., Illus.). 494p. 180.00 ***(978-0-470-98014-9(1)***, Wiley) Wiley, John & Sons, Inc.

Reniers, Genserik L. L. Multi-Plant Safety & Security Management in the Chemical & Process Industries. 2010. (ENG., Illus.). 290p. 115.00 *(978-3-527-32551-1(4)*, Wiley-VCH) Wiley, John & Sons, Inc.

Ricardez-Sandoval, Luis. Simultaneous Design & Control of Chemical Plants. 2009. 284p. pap. *(978-3-639-15751-2(6))* VDM Verlag Dr. Mueller e.K.

Rijnmond Public Authority. Risk Analysis of Six Potentially Hazardous Industrial Objects in the Rijnmond Area: A Pilot Study. 2010. 820p. pap. 499.00 *(978-90-481-8371-5(5)*, 9048183715) Springer.

Smithersrapra Technology, compiled by. High Performance Elastomers & Polymers for Oil & Gas Conference Proceedings. 2010. 216p. pap. *(978-1-84735-493-8(9))* iSmithers Rapra Publishing.

Spellman, Frank R. Chemical Infrastructure Protection & Homeland Security. 2009. (ENG.). 224p. pap. 85.00 *(978-0-86587-182-3(5))* Government Institutes.

Westerberg, A. W., et al. Process Flowsheeting. 2011. (ENG.). 262p. pap. 35.99 *(978-0-521-27915-4(1))* Cambridge Univ. Pr.

Wilson, Diane. An Unreasonable Woman: A True Story of Shrimpers, Politicos, Polluters, & the Fight for Seadrift, Texas. 2006. (ENG.). 400p. pap. 18.00 *(978-1-933392-27-1(4))* Chelsea Green Publishing.

Woodward, John L. & Pitbaldo, Robin. LNG Risk Based Safety: Modeling & Consequence Analysis. 2010. (ENG., Illus.). 374p. 121.00 *(978-0-470-31764-8(7))* American Institute of Chemical Engineers.

Yang, Robert. Process Plant Lifecycle Information Management. 2009. 132p. pap. 14.95 *(978-1-4401-4757-9(4))* iUniverse, Inc.

CHEMICAL PLANTS—TABLES

Quarantelli, E. L. Chemical Disasters: Preparations & Responses at the Local Level. *(978-0-8290-1289-7(3))* Irvington Pubs.

CHEMICAL POLLUTANTS

see Pollutants

CHEMICAL PROCESS CONTROL

Bai, Shuanghua. Dynamic Data Reconciliation. 2009. 160p. pap. *(978-3-639-21779-7(9))* VDM Verlag Dr. Mueller e.K.

Bakeev, Katherine A., ed. Process Analytical Technology: Spectroscopic Tools & Implementation Strategies for the Chemical & Pharmaceutical Industries. 2nd ed. 2010. (ENG., Illus.). 576p. 200.00 *(978-0-470-72207-7(X)*, Wiley) Wiley, John & Sons, Inc.

Bogle, David & Fairweather, Michael. 22nd European Symposium on Computer Aided Process Engineering. 2012. (Computer Aided Chemical Engineering Ser.: 30). (ENG., Illus.). 1400p. 575.00 ***(978-0-444-59431-0(0))*** Elsevier Science & Technology Bks.

Braunschweig, Bertrand & Joulia, Xavier, eds. 18th European Symposium on Computer Aided Process Engineering. 2008. (Computer Aided Chemical Engineering Ser.: 25). (ENG., Illus.). 1232p. 530.00 *(978-0-444-53227-5(7)*, Elsevier Science) Elsevier Science & Technology Bks.

Cao, Zhong, et al, eds. Application of Chemical Engineering. 2011. (Advanced Materials Research Ser.: Vol. 236-238). 3102p. pap. ***(978-3-03785-121-0(X))*** Trans Tech Pubns., Ltd.

CCPS. Recognizing Catastrophic Incident Warning Signs in the Process Industries. 2011. (ENG., Illus.). 264p. 125.00 ***(978-0-470-76774-0(X))*** American Institute of Chemical Engineers.

Center for Chemical Process Safety Staff. Guidelines for Safe & Reliable Instrumented Protective Systems. 2007. (ENG., Illus.). 405p. 163.00 *(978-0-471-97940-1(6))* American Institute of Chemical Engineers.

—Incidents That Define Process Safety. 2008. (ENG., Illus.). 352p. 111.00 *(978-0-470-12204-4(8))* American Institute of Chemical Engineers.

Christofides, Panagiotis D. Control & Optimization of Multiscale Process Systems. 2008. (Control Engineering Ser.). (Illus.). 224p. 79.95 *(978-0-8176-4792-6(9))* Birkhauser Boston.

Corriou, Jean-Pierre. Process Control: Theory & Applications. 2010. (ENG., Illus.). xx, 758p. pap. 209.00 *(978-1-84996-911-6(6)*, 1849969116) Springer.

Cram101 Textbook Reviews. Outlines & Highlights for Principles & Practice of Automatic Process Control by Smith & Corripio, Isbn: 0471575887. 2011. 138p. pap. 28.95 ***(978-1-61812-582-8(6))*** Cram101 Inc.

—Outlines & Highlights for Process Dynamics, Modeling, & Control by Ogunnaike & Ray. 2011. 250p. pap. 31.95 ***(978-1-61812-892-8(2))*** Cram101 Inc.

Cram101 Textbook Reviews & Cram101 Textbook Reviews. Outlines & Highlights for Advanced Process Control: Beyond Single Loop Control by Ceci Smith, ISBN. 2011. 92p. pap. 27.95 ***(978-1-61461-390-9(7))*** Cram101 Inc.

—Outlines & Highlights for Process Technology Systems by Michael Speegle. 2011. 58p. pap. 26.95 ***(978-1-61830-905-1(6))*** Cram101 Inc.

Edgar, Thomas F., et al. Process Dynamics & Control. 3rd ed. 2010. (ENG., Illus.). 514p. (C). 190.95 *(978-0-470-12867-1(4)*, Wiley) Wiley, John & Sons, Inc.

EL-HALWAGI, Mahmoud M., et al. Design for Energy & the Environment: Proceedings of the Seventh International Conference on the Foundations of Computer-Aided Process Design. El-halwag, Mahmoud M. & Linninger, Andreas A., eds. 2009. (ENG., Illus.). 1126p. 185.95 *(978-1-4398-0912-9(7)*, CRC Press) Taylor & Francis Group GBR. Dist: Taylor & Francis Group.

Fikar, Miroslav & Mikles, Ján. Process Modelling, Identification, & Control. 2007. (ENG., Illus.). xxvi, 480p. 119.00 *(978-3-540-71969-4(5)*, 3540719695) Springer.

Georgiadis, Michael C. & Pistikopoulos, Efstratios N. Energy & Process Integration. 2006. (Illus.). xii, 199p. *(978-1-56700-228-7(5))* Begell Hse. Pubs., Inc.

Jezowski, Jacek & Thullie, Jan, eds. 19th European Symposium on Computed Aided Process Engineering - CD-ROM: ESCAPE-19: June 14-17, 2009, Cracow, Poland. 2009. (Computer Aided Chemical Engineering Ser.). (ENG., Illus.). xxvii, 1312p. cd-rom 0.02 *(978-0-444-53441-5(5)*, Elsevier Science) Elsevier Science & Technology Bks.

—19th European Symposium on Computer Aided Process Engineering: ESCAPE-19: June 14-17, 2009, Cracow, Poland, Vol. 26. 2009. (Computer Aided Chemical Engineering Ser.: 26). (ENG., Illus.). 1200p. 505.00 *(978-0-444-53433-0(4)*, Elsevier Science) Elsevier Science & Technology Bks.

Keil, Frerich Johannes & Keil, Frerich J., eds. Modeling of Process Intensification. 2007. (ENG., Illus.). 422p. 235.00 *(978-3-527-31143-9(2)*, Wiley-VCH) Wiley, John & Sons, Inc.

Killcross, Martin. Chemical & Process Plant Commissioning Handbook: A Practical Guide to Plant System & Equipment Installation & Commissioning. 2011. (ENG., Illus.). 312p. 124.99 ***(978-0-08-097174-2(1)***, Butterworth-Heinemann) Elsevier Science & Technology Bks.

King, Michael & King, Myke. Process Control: A Practical Approach. 2011. (ENG., Illus.). 416p. 140.00 *(978-0-470-97587-9(3)*, Wiley) Wiley, John & Sons, Inc.

Lauer, William, et al. Chemical Feed Field Guide for Treatment Plant Operators: Calculations & Systems. 2009. 175p. per. 72.00 *(978-1-58321-588-3(3))* American Water Works Assn.

Luyben, William L. & Yu, Cheng-Ching. Reactive Distillation Design & Control. 2008. (ENG., Illus.). 574p. 142.00 *(978-0-470-22612-4(9))* American Institute of Chemical Engineers.

Méndez-Acosta, Hugo Oscar, et al, eds. Selected Topics in Dynamics & Control of Chemical & Biological Processes. 2007. (Lecture Notes in Control & Information Sciences Ser.). x, 319p. 179.00 *(978-3-540-73187-0(3)*, 3540731873) Springer.

Mikles, Ján & Fikar, Miroslav. Process Modelling, Identification, & Control. 2010. (ENG., Illus.). xxvi, 480p. pap. 119.00 *(978-3-642-09112-4(1)*, 3642091121) Springer.

Pistikopoulos, E. N., et al, eds. 21st European Symposium on Computer Aided Process Engineering, 2 vols. 2011. (Computer Aided Chemical Engineering Ser.). (Illus.). 1136p. 570.00 *(978-0-444-53711-9(2))* Elsevier Science & Technology Bks.

Pistikopoulos, Efstratios, et al, contrib. by. Process Systems Engineering, 7 vols. Set. 2010. (Process Systems Engineering Ser.). (ENG.). 2400p. 1115.00 *(978-3-527-31684-7(1)*, Wiley-VCH) Wiley, John & Sons, Inc.

Pistikopoulos, Efstratios, et al, eds. Dynamic Process Modeling. 2010. (Process Systems Engineering Ser.). (ENG., Illus.). 628p. 190.00 *(978-3-527-31696-0(5)*, Wiley-VCH) Wiley, John & Sons, Inc.

Rangaiah, Gade Pandu & Kariwala, Vinay, eds. Plantwide Control: Recent Developments & Applications. 2nd ed. 2012. (ENG., Illus.). 494p. 180.00 ***(978-0-470-98014-9(1)***, Wiley) Wiley, John & Sons, Inc.

Rauwendaal, Chris. SPC: Statistical Process Control in Injection Molding & Extrusion. 2nd ed. 2008. (C). *(978-1-56990-427-5(8))* Hanser Pubns.

Ricardez-Sandoval, Luis. Simultaneous Design & Control of Chemical Plants. 2009. 284p. pap. *(978-3-639-15751-2(6))* VDM Verlag Dr. Mueller e.K.

Roffel, Brian & Betlem, Ben. Process Dynamics & Control: Modeling for Control & Prediction. 2007. (ENG., Illus.). 560p. 215.00 *(978-0-470-01663-3(9)*, Wiley) Wiley, John & Sons, Inc.

—Process Dynamics & Control: Modeling for Control & Prediction. 2007. (ENG., Illus.). 560p. pap. 75.00 *(978-0-470-01664-0(7)*, Wiley) Wiley, John & Sons, Inc.

Romagnoli, Jose & Palazoglu, Ahmet. Introduction to Process Control. 2nd rev. ed. 2012. (Chemical Industries Ser.). (ENG., Illus.). 643p. (C). 149.95 *(978-1-4398-5486-0(6)*, CRC Press) Taylor & Francis Group GBR. Dist: Taylor & Francis Group.

Scheffian, Ralph. Teach Yourself the Basics of Aspen Plus. 2011. (ENG., Illus.). 232p. pap. 68.95 *(978-0-470-56795-1(3))* American Institute of Chemical Engineers.

Schmidt-Traub, Henner & Gorak, Andrzej, eds. Integrated Reaction & Separation Operations: Modelling & experimental Validation. 2010. (ENG., Illus.). xii, 366p. pap. 159.00 *(978-3-642-06763-1(8)*, 3642067638) Springer.

Sieniutycz, Stanislaw & Jezowski, Jacek. Energy Optimization in Process Systems. 2009. (ENG., Illus.). 768p. 275.00 *(978-0-08-045141-1(1)*, Elsevier Science) Elsevier Science & Technology Bks.

Smith, Cecil L. Advanced Process Control: Beyond Single Loop Control. 2010. (ENG., Illus.). 450p. 105.00 *(978-0-470-38197-7(3))* American Institute of Chemical Engineers.

Speegle, Michael. Process Technology Systems. 2007. (ENG., Illus.). 336p. (C). per. 104.95 *(978-1-4180-3999-8(3))* Delmar Cengage Learning.

Thomas, Charles E. Process Technology Troubleshooting. 2008. (ENG., Illus.). 480p. (C). per. 98.95 *(978-1-4283-1100-8(9))* Delmar Cengage Learning.

Walker, Derek. The Management of Chemical Process Development in the Pharmaceutical Industry. 2008. (ENG., Illus.). 416p. 128.00 *(978-0-470-17156-1(1))* American Institute of Chemical Engineers.

Westerberg, A. W., et al. Process Flowsheeting. 2011. (ENG.). 262p. pap. 35.99 *(978-0-521-27915-4(1))* Cambridge Univ. Pr.

CHEMICAL PROCESSES

see also Chemical Reactions; Curing

Ahmad, Nadeem & Pasha, Riffat Asim. Temperature Sensitivity of Anti Armour Projectile. 2011. 64p. pap. ***(978-3-8454-1225-2(9))*** Lambert Academic Publishing.

American Institute of Chemical Engineers (AIChE) Staff, compiled by. 22nd Annual International Conference of the Center for Chemical Process Safety (CCPS 2007) 2007. 227p. pap. 118.00 *(978-1-60423-310-0(9))* Curran Assocs., Inc.

American Society of Mechanical Engineers Staff, ed. Proceedings of DETC99, 19th Computers & Information in Engineering Conference, Vol. 2 1108p. 110.00 *(978-0-7918-1972-2(8))* ASME Pr.

Anderson, Neal G. Practical Process Research & Development: A Guide for Organic Chemists. 2nd ed. 2012. (ENG.). 488p. (C). 125.00 ***(978-0-12-386537-3(9))***, Academic Pr.) Elsevier Science & Technology Bks.

Attwood, Dennis, et al. Human Factors Methods for Improving Performance in the Process Industries. Crowl, Daniel A., ed. 2007. (ENG., Illus.). 248p. 128.00 *(978-0-470-11754-5(0))* American Institute of Chemical Engineers.

Biegler, Lorenz T. Nonlinear Programming: Concepts, Algorithms, & Applications to Chemical Processes. 2010. (Illus.). 416p. *(978-0-89871-702-0(7))* Society for Industrial and Applied Mathematics.

Braish, Tamim & Gadamasetti, Kumar, eds. Process Chemistry in the Pharmaceutical Industry, Volume 2: Challenges in an Ever Changing Climate. 2nd rev. ed. 2007. (ENG., Illus.). 520p. 279.95 *(978-0-8493-9051-7(6)*, CRC Press) Taylor & Francis Group GBR. Dist: Taylor & Francis Group.

Center for Chemical Process Safety Staff. Guidelines for Safe & Reliable Instrumented Protective Systems. 2007. (ENG., Illus.). 405p. 163.00 *(978-0-471-97940-1(6))* American Institute of Chemical Engineers

Center for the Advancement of Process TechnoloCARP Staff. Safety, Health & Environment. 2006. (ENG.). (C). 139.40 *(978-0-536-25843-4(0))* Pearson Learning Solutions.

Center for the Advancement of Process Technology Staff, contrib. by. Introduction to Process Technology. 2009. (ENG.). 384p. (C). 126.00 *(978-0-13-700414-0(1)*, Prentice Hall) Prentice Hall PTR.

—Process Technology Equipment. 2009. (ENG.). 464p. (C). 112.80 *(978-0-13-700412-6(5)*, Prentice Hall) Prentice Hall PTR.

Chemical Process Monitoring Devices. 2007. per. 4250.00 *(978-1-59623-279-2(X))* BCC Research.

Chen, Hongzhang. Process Engineering in Plant-Based Products. 2009. (Environmental Science, Engineering & Technology Ser.). 89.00 *(978-1-60741-962-4(9))* Nova Science Pubs., Inc.

Christofides, Panagiotis D. Control & Optimization of Multiscale Process Systems. 2008. (Control Engineering Ser.). (Illus.). 224p. 79.95 *(978-0-8176-4792-6(9))* Birkhauser Boston.

Cinar, Ali, et al. Chemical Process Performance Evaluation. 2007. (Chemical Industries Ser.). (ENG., Illus.). 344p. 184.95 *(978-0-8493-3806-9(9)*, CRC Press) Taylor & Francis Group GBR. Dist: Taylor & Francis Group.

Coker, A. Kayode. Ludwig's Applied Process Design for Chemical & Petrochemical Plants Vol. 2: Distillation, Packed Towers, Petroleum Fractionation, Gas Processing & Dehydration, 2 vols. 4th ed. 2010. (ENG., Illus.). 1008p. 220.00 *(978-0-7506-8366-1(X)*, Gulf Professional Publishing) Elsevier Science & Technology Bks.

Comyns, Alan E. Encyclopedic Dictionary of Named Processes in Chemical Technology. 3rd rev. ed. 2007. (ENG., Illus.). 440p. 169.95 *(978-0-8493-9163-7(6)*, CRC Press) Taylor & Francis Group GBR. Dist: Taylor & Francis Group.

Corsano, Gabriela, et al. Mathematical Modeling Approaches for Optimization of Chemical Processes. 2008. pap. 29.00 *(978-1-60456-942-1(5))* Nova Science Pubs., Inc.

Couper, James R. Chemical Process Equipment: Selection & Design. 3rd ed. 2012. (ENG.). 832p. 150.00 ***(978-0-12-396959-0(X)***, Butterworth-Heinemann) Elsevier Science & Technology Bks.

Couper, James R., et al. Chemical Process Equipment: Selection & Design. 2nd ed. 2009. (ENG., Illus.). 832p. 185.00 *(978-0-12-372506-6(2)*, Gulf Professional Publishing) Elsevier Science & Technology Bks.

Cram101 Textbook Reviews. Outlines & Highlights for Analysis, Synthesis, & Design of Chemical Process by Turton et Al , Isbn: 0130647926. 2011. 214p. pap. 30.95 ***(978-1-61812-840-9(X))*** Cram101 Inc.

Cram101 Textbook Reviews & Cram101 Textbook Reviews. Outlines & Highlights for Elementary Principles of Chemical Processes: Update by Richard M. Felder, ISBN. 2011. 514p. pap. 28.95 ***(978-1-61490-827-2(3))*** Cram101 Inc

—Outlines & Highlights for Introduction to Process Technology by Capt L. 2011. 134p. pap. 28.95 ***(978-1-61830-607-4(3))*** Cram101 Inc.

—Outlines & Highlights for Process Technology Equipment & Systems by Charles Thomas. 2011. 176p. pap. 29.95 ***(978-1-61830-606-7(5))*** Cram101 Inc.

—Outlines & Highlights for Process Technology Equipment by Prentice Hall Ptr, Isbn: 9780137004126 0137004125. 2011. 86p. pap. 27.95 ***(978-1-61812-070-0(0))*** Cram101 Inc.

Crowl, Daniel A. & Louvar, Joseph F. Chemical Process Safety: Fundamentals with Applications. 3rd rev. ed. 2011. (Prentice Hall International Series in the Physical & Chemical Engineering Sciences Ser.). (ENG., Illus.). 752p. 150.00 *(978-0-13-138226-8(8)*, Prentice Hall) Prentice Hall PTR.

D'Amore, Alberto & Zaikov, Gennadii Efremovich. Monomers & Polymers: Reactions & Properties. 2006. (Illus.). 224p. 225.00 *(978-1-60021-415-8(0))* Nova Science Pubs., Inc.

Datta, Arun. Process Engineering & Design Using Visual Basic. 2007. (ENG., Illus.). 472p. 144.95 *(978-1-4200-4542-0(3)*, CRC Press) Taylor & Francis Group GBR. Dist: Taylor & Francis Group.

Davis, Mark E., et al. Fundamentals of Chemical Reaction Engineering. 2012. (Dover Civil & Mechanical Engineering Ser.). (ENG.). 384p. (C). pap. 27.95 ***(978-0-486-48855-4(1))*** Dover Pubns., Inc.

De Falco, Marcello, et al, eds. Membrane Reactors for Hydrogen Production Processes. 2011. (Illus.). xii, 235p. 179.00 *(978-0-85729-150-9(5)*, 0857291505) Springer.

Dimian, Alexandre C. & Bildea, Costin Sorin. Chemical Process Design: Computer-Aided Case Studies. 2008. (ENG., Illus.). 527p. 249.00 *(978-3-527-31403-4(2)*, Wiley-VCH) Wiley, John & Sons, Inc.

El-Halwagi, Mahmoud M. Sustainable Design Through Process Integration Fundamentals & Applications to Industrial Pollution Prevention, Resource Conservation, & Profitability Enhancement. 2011. (ENG., Illus.). 448p. 130.00 ***(973-1-85617-744-3(0)***, Butterworth-Heinemann) Elsevier Science & Technology Bks.

C

EL-HALWAGI, Mahmoud M., et al. Design for Energy & the Environment: Proceedings of the Seventh International Conference on the Foundations of Computer-Aided Process Design. El-halwagi, Mahmoud M. & Linninger, Andreas A., eds. 2009. (ENG., Illus.). 1126p. 185.95 *(978-1-4398-0912-9(7),* CRC Press) Taylor & Francis Group GBR. Dist: Taylor & Francis Group.

Foo, Dominic C. Y. Recent Advances in Sustainable Process Design & Optimization. 2010. 900p. 178.00 *(978-981-4271-95-0(0))* World Scientific Publishing Co., Inc.

Gmehling, Jürgen, et al. Chemical Thermodynamics: For Process Simulation. 2012. (ENG.). 760p. 135.00 ***(978-3-527-31277-1(3)***, Wiley-VCH) Wiley, John & Sons, Inc.

Grulke Eric Staff. Devolatilization & Purification of Polymers. 2009. 169.95 *(978-1-57444-747-7(5))* CRC Pr. LLC.

Harrington, Peter J. Pharmaceutical Process Chemistry for Synthesis: Rethinking the Routes to Scale-up. 2011. (ENG., Illus.). 376p. 132.00 *(978-0-470-57755-4(X)*, Wiley) Wiley, John & Sons, Inc.

Houson, Ian, ed. Process Understanding: For Scale-Up & Manufacture of Active Ingredients. 2011. (ENG., Illus.). 370p. 145.00 *(978-3-527-32584-9(0),* Wiley-VCH) Wiley, John & Sons, Inc.

Kelland, Malcolm. Production Chemicals for the Oil & Gas Industry. 2009. (ENG., Illus.). 400p. 139.95 *(978-1-4200-9290-5(1)*, CRC Press) Taylor & Francis Group GBR. Dist: Taylor & Francis Group.

Khanaev, Valeri M., et al. Fixed Bed Reactors with Gradient Catalysts. 2008. 103p. 29.00 *(978-1-60456-780-9(5))* Nova Science Pubs., Inc.

Kirpekar, Sujit. Turbulent Flows in Hard Disk Drives. 2008. 280p. pap. *(978-3-8364-7494-8(8))* VDM Verlag Dr. Mueller e.K.

Kiss, Anton Alexandru. Process Design & Control by Nonlinear Analysis. 2010. 164p. pap. *(978-3-8383-4242-9(9))* Lambert Academic Publishing.

Koroneos, C. & Happel, J. Chemical Process Economics. 3rd ed. Date not set. (Chemical Industries Ser.). *(978-0-8247-9967-0(4))* Dekker, Marcel Inc.

Kutz, Myer, ed. Environmentally Conscious Materials & Chemicals Processing. 2007. (Environmentally Conscious Engineering, Myer Kutz Ser.: 2). (ENG., Illus.). 480p. 140.00 *(978-0-471-73904-3(9)*, Wiley) Wiley, John & Sons, Inc.

Liu, LinShu & Zaikov, Gennadii Efremovich, eds. Chemistry as Music. 2007. 129.00 *(978-1-60021-894-1(6))* Nova Science Pubs., Inc.

Majozi, Thokozani. Batch Chemical Process Integration: Analysis, Synthesis & Optimization. 2009. (ENG., Illus.). xix, 282p. 199.00 *(978-90-481-2587-6(1),* 9048125871) Springer.

Malhotra, Girish K. Chemical Process Simplification: Improving Productivity & Sustainability. 2011. (ENG., Illus.). 282p. 94.95 *(978-0-470-48754-9(2)*, Wiley) Wiley, John & Sons, Inc.

Mannan, Sam, ed. Lees' Loss Prevention in the Process Industries: Hazard Identification, Assessment & Control. 4th ed. 2012. (ENG.). 3710p. 800.00 ***(978-0-12-397189-0(6)***, Butterworth-Heinemann) Elsevier Science & Technology Bks.

Mayer, Istvan, et al. Bond Orders & Energy Components: Extracting Chemical Information from Molecular Wave Functions. 2009. (ENG., Illus.). 250p. 129.95 *(978-1-4200-9011-6(9))* CRC Pr. LLC.

McConville, Francis X. The Pilot Plant Real Book: A Unique Handbook for the Chemical Process Industry. 2nd num. ed. 2007. (Illus.). 320p. 114.95 *(978-0-9721769-2-7(6))* FXM Engineering & Design.

Mersmann, Alfons, et al. Thermal Separation Technology: Fundamentals & Methods. 2011. (VDI-Buch / Chemische Technik / Verfahrenstechnik Ser.). (Illus.). 650p. 229.00 *(978-3-642-12524-9(7)*, 3642125247) Springer.

Mironov, Maxim A. Mcr 2009: Proceedings of the 4th International Conference on Multi-Component Reactions & Related Chemistry, Ekaterinburg, Russia. Mironov, Maxim A., ed. 2010. (Advances in Experimental Medicine & Biology Ser.). (Illus.). x, 230p. 189.00 *(978-1-4419-7269-9(2)*, 1441972692) Springer.

Mory, Mathieu. Fluid Mechanics for Chemical Engineering. 2011. (Iste Ser.: 549). (ENG., Illus.). xv, 422p. 205.00 *(978-1-84821-281-7(X)*, Wiley-ISTE) Wiley, John & Sons, Inc.

Mundschau, Michael V. & Sammells, Anthony F., eds. Nonporous Inorganic Membranes: For Chemical Processing. 2006. (ENG., Illus.). 291p. 189.00 *(978-3-527-31342-6(7)*, Wiley-VCH) Wiley, John & Sons, Inc.

Noureldin, Mahmoud Bahy. Pinch Technology & Beyond Pinch: New Vistas on Energy Efficiency Optimization. 2011. (Series: Energy Science, Engineering & Technology Ser.). (Illus.). 341p. 129.00 *(978-1-61122-510-5(8))* Nova Science Pubs., Inc.

Pensé-Lhéritier, Anne-Marie. Formulation. 2011. (ENG., Illus.). 352p. 145.00 *(978-1-84821-259-6(3)*, Wiley-ISTE) Wiley, John & Sons, Inc.

Pistikopoulos, Efstratios, et al, eds. Dynamic Process Modeling. 2010. (Process Systems Engineering Ser.). (ENG., Illus.). 628p. 190.00 *(978-3-527-31696-0(5)*, Wiley-VCH) Wiley, John & Sons, Inc.

Salmi, Tapio O., et al. Chemical Reaction Engineering & Reactor Technology. 2010. (Chemical Industries Ser.). (ENG., Illus.). 644p. (C). 119.95 *(978-1-4200-9268-4(5)*, CRC Press) Taylor & Francis Group GBR. Dist: Taylor & Francis Group.

Seider, Warren D., et al. Product & Process Design Principles: Synthesis, Analysis & Design. 3rd ed. 2008. (ENG.). 736p. (C). 208.95 *(978-0-470-04895-5(6)*, Wiley) Wiley, John & Sons, Inc.

Sharma, Sanjay Kumar & Mudhoo, Ackmez, eds. Green Chemistry for Environmental Sustainability. 2010. (Sustainability Ser.). (ENG., Illus.). 450p. 159.95 *(978-1-4398-2473-3(8)*, CRC Press) Taylor & Francis Group GBR. Dist: Taylor & Francis Group.

Shioiri, Takayuki, et al, eds. Pharmaceutical Process Chemistry. 2010. (ENG., Illus.). 526p. 210.00 *(978-3-527-32650-1(2)*, Wiley-VCH) Wiley, John & Sons, Inc.

Solen, Kenneth A. & Harb, John. Introduction to Chemical Engineering: Tools for Today & Tomorrow. 5th ed. 2010. (C). pap. 18.95 *(978-0-470-92810-3(7)*, Wiley) Wiley, John & Sons, Inc.

—Introduction to Chemical Process Fundamentals & Design. 5th ed. 2010. (ENG.). 227p. (C). pap. 53.95 *(978-0-470-88572-7(6)*, Wiley) Wiley, John & Sons, Inc.

Speegle, Michael. Safety, Health, & Environmental Concepts for the Process Industry. 2nd ed. 2012. (ENG., Illus.). 384p. (C). pap. 100.95 ***(978-1-133-01347-1(3))*** Delmar Cengage Learning.

Thomas, Charles E. Introduction to Process Technology. 3rd ed. 2009. (ENG.). 480p. (C). pap. 103.95 *(978-1-4354-5425-5(1))* Delmar Cengage Learning.

—Process Technology: Safety, Health, & Environment. 3rd ed. 2011. (ENG., Illus.). 352p. (C). pap. 111.95 *(978-1-111-03635-5(7))* Delmar Cengage Learning.

—Process Technology Equipment & Systems. 3rd ed. 2010. (ENG.). 496p. (C). pap. 119.95 *(978-1-4354-9912-6(3))* Delmar Cengage Learning.

Turton, Richard, et al. Analysis, Synthesis & Design of Chemical Processes. 4th rev. ed. 2012. (Prentice Hall International Series in the Physical & Chemical Engineering Sciences Ser.). (ENG., Illus.). 1056p. (C). 140.00 ***(978-0-13-261812-0(5)***, Prentice Hall) Prentice Hall PTR.

VandenBussche, Kurt M., et al, eds. Micro Instrumentation: For High Throughput Experimentation & Process Intensification. 2007. (ENG., Illus.). 520p. 235.00 *(978-3-527-31425-6(3)*, Wiley-VCH) Wiley, John & Sons, Inc.

van't Land, C. M. Drying in the Process Industry. 2nd ed. 2011. (ENG., Illus.). 400p. 115.00 ***(978-0-470-13117-6(9)***, Wiley) Wiley, John & Sons, Inc.

Yen, Teh Fu. Chemical Processes for Environmental Engineering. 2007. (Illus.). 549p. 121.00 *(978-1-86094-759-9(X))* Imperial College Pr. GBR. Dist: World Scientific Publishing Co., Inc.

CHEMICAL PROCESSES—MATHEMATICAL MODELS

Agachi, Paul Serban, et al. Model Based Control: Case Studies in Process Engineering. 2007. (ENG., Illus.). 290p. 165.00 *(978-3-527-31545-1(4),* Wiley-VCH) Wiley, John & Sons, Inc.

Benoudjit, Nabil. Variable selection & neural networks: Application in infrared spectroscopy & chemometrics. 2008. 168p. pap. *(978-3-8364-9504-2(X))* VDM Verlag Dr. Mueller e.K.

Bonem, J. M. Problem Solving for Process Operators & Specialists. 2011. (ENG., Illus.). 344p. 84.95 *(978-0-470-62774-7(3))* American Institute of Chemical Engineers.

Cameron, Ian & Gani, Rafiqul. Product & Process Modelling: A Case Study Approach. 2011. (ENG.). 548p. 119.00 *(978-0-444-53161-2(0))* Elsevier Science & Technology Bks.

Crabtree, John. Atomic Reaction Mapping. 2008. 92p. pap. *(978-3-639-07358-4(4))* VDM Verlag Dr. Mueller e.K.

Datta, Arun. Process Engineering & Design Using Visual Basic. 2007. (ENG., Illus.). 472p. 144.95 *(978-1-4200-4542-0(3)*, CRC Press) Taylor & Francis Group GBR. Dist: Taylor & Francis Group.

Fikar, Miroslav & Mikles, Ján. Process Modelling, Identification, & Control. 2007. (ENG., Illus.). xxvi, 480p. 119.00 *(978-3-540-71969-4(5)*, 3540719695) Springer.

Morris, Arthur E., et al. Handbook on Material & Energy Balance Calculations in Materials Processing. 3rd ed. 2011. (ENG., Illus.). 640p. 149.95 *(978-1-118-06565-5(4)*, Wiley-TMS) Wiley, John & Sons, Inc.

Peter, et al. Linear Mathematical Models in Chemical Engineering. 2009. (Illus.). 600p. 107.00 *(978-981-279-415-4(8))* World Scientific Publishing Co., Inc.

CHEMICAL REACTION, CONDITIONS AND LAWS OF

see also Linear Free Energy Relationship; Passivity (Chemistry); Reactivity (Chemistry)

Grossman, Robert B. The Art of Writing Reasonable Organic Reaction Mechanisms. 2nd ed. 2010. (ENG., Illus.). xvi, 355p. pap. 64.95 *(978-1-4419-3016-3(7)*, 1441930167) Springer.

Henriksen, Niels E. & Hansen, Flemming Y. Theories of Molecular Reaction Dynamics: The Microscopic Foundation of Chemical Kinetics. 2012. (ENG., Illus.). 392p. pap. 62.99 ***(978-0-19-965275-4(9))*** Oxford Univ. Pr., Inc.

Knipe, A. C., ed. Organic Reaction Mechanisms 2007. 2011. (Organic Reaction Mechanisms Ser.: 123). (ENG.). 550p. 530.00 *(978-0-470-71238-2(4)*, Wiley) Wiley, John & Sons, Inc.

Lasa, Hugo de, et al. Photocatalytic Reaction Engineering. 2010. (Illus.). xii, 187p. pap. 129.00 *(978-1-4419-3627-1(0)*, 1441936270) Springer.

Levine, Raphael. Molecular Reaction Dynamics. 2009. (ENG., Illus.). 568p. pap. 66.99 *(978-0-521-14071-3(4))* Cambridge Univ. Pr.

Makitra, R. G., et al. Linear Energy Relationships to Chemical Kinetics. 2009. 82p. pap. 37.00 *(978-1-60692-219-4(X))* Nova Science Pubs., Inc.

Moss, Robert A., et al, eds. Reviews of Reactive Intermediate Chemistry. 2007. (ENG., Illus.). 480p. 156.00 *(978-0-471-73166-5(8)*, Wiley-Interscience) Wiley, John & Sons, Inc.

Rich, Ronald L. Inorganic Reactions in Water. 2008. (ENG., Illus.). xxii, 521p. 279.00 *(978-3-540-73961-6(0)*, 3540739610) Springer.

Wolfsberg, Max, et al. Isotope Effects: In the Chemical, Geological, & Bio Sciences. 2009. (ENG., Illus.). xvi, 466p. 199.00 *(978-90-481-2264-6(3)*, 9048122643) Springer.

Yang, Jaemoon. Six-Membered Transition States in Organic Synthesis. 2008. (ENG., Illus.). 210p. 163.00 *(978-0-470-17883-6(3)*, Wiley-Interscience) Wiley, John & Sons, Inc.

CHEMICAL REACTION, RATE OF

see Chemical Kinetics

CHEMICAL REACTIONS

see also Activity Coefficients; Alkylation; Chemical Equations; Chemical Reactors; Friedel-Crafts Reaction; Nitroso-Compounds; Oxidation-Reduction Reaction; Phosphorylation; Polymerization; Reactivity (Chemistry); Rearrangements (Chemistry); Ring Formation (Chemistry); Substitution Reactions

Ackermann, Lutz, ed. Modern Arylation Methods. 2009. (ENG., Illus.). 561p. 230.00 *(978-3-527-31937-4(9)*, Wiley-VCH) Wiley, John & Sons, Inc.

Adamovic, Ivana & Gordon, Mark S. Solvation Methods - Theoretical Perspectives. 2008. 176p. pap. *(978-3-639-07605-9(2))* VDM Verlag Dr. Mueller e.K.

Atkins, Peter. Reactions: The Private Life of Atoms. 2011. (ENG., Illus.). 256p. 24.95 *(978-0-19-969512-6(1))* Oxford Univ. Pr., Inc.

Azzopardi, Barry, et al. Hydrodynamics of Gas-Liquid Reactors: Normal Operation & Upset Conditions. 2011. (ENG., Illus.). 344p. 195.00 *(978-0-470-74771-1(4)*, Wiley) Wiley, John & Sons, Inc.

Banks, Alton J. Chemistry & Chemical Reactivity - Student Solutions Manual. 8th ed. 2011. (ENG.). 480p. (C). pap. 95.95 *(978-1-111-42698-9(8))* Brooks/Cole.

Bart, Hans-Jörg. Reactive Extraction. 2010. (Heat & Mass Transfer Ser.). (Illus.). xviii, 209p. pap. 119.00 *(978-3-642-07430-1(8)*, 3642074308) Springer.

Baxter, Roberta. The Reactions of Metals, 1 vol. 2008. (Sci-Hi: Physical Science Ser.). (ENG., Illus.). 48p. (gr. 4-4). pap. 8.99 *(978-1-4109-3261-7(3)*, Sci-Hi) Heinemann-Raintree.

Bethke, Craig M. Geochemical & Biogeochemical Reaction Modeling. 2nd rev. ed. (ENG., Illus.). 564p. 2010. pap. 53.00 *(978-0-521-15570-0(3))* 2007. 94.00 *(978-0-521-87554-7(4))* Cambridge Univ. Pr.

Bretherick, L., et al. Bretherick's Handbook of Reactive Chemical Hazards, 2 vols. 7th ed. 2006. (Illus.). 2208p. 0.02 *(978-0-12-373945-2(4))*;Set. 472p. 0.02 *(978-0-12-373946-9(2))* Elsevier Science & Technology Bks. (Academic Pr.).

Busse, Friedrich H. & Müller, Stefan C., eds. Evolution of Spontaneous Structures in Dissipative Continuous Systems. 2012. (Lecture Notes in Physics Monographs). (ENG.). x, 583p. pap. 139.00 *(978-3-642-08455-3(9)*, 3642084559) Springer.

Carolina Biological Staff, compiled by. Balancing Chemical Equations. 2009. (Inquiries in Science Chemistry Ser.). *(978-1-4350-0396-5(9))*; tchr. ed., spiral bd. *(978-1-4350-0395-8(0))* Carolina Biological Supply Co.

Castillon, S. & Cavinato, G., contrib. by. Catalytic Carbonylation Reactions. 2006. (Topics in Organometallic Chemistry Ser.: Vol. 18). (Illus.). 283p. 259.00 *(978-3-540-33002-8(X)*, 354033002X) Springer.

Committee on the Development of an Integrated Science Strategy for Ocean Acidification Monitoring, Research, and Impacts Assessment & National Research Council. Ocean Acidification: A National Strategy to Meet the Challenges of a Changing Ocean. 2010. (ENG.). 175p. pap. 32.00 *(978-0-309-15359-1(X))* National Academies Pr.

Cordova, Armando, ed. Catalytic Asymmetric Conjugate Reactions. 2010. (ENG., Illus.). 464p. 200.00 *(978-3-527-32411-8(9)*, Wiley-VCH) Wiley, John & Sons, Inc.

Cossy, Janine, et al, eds. Metathesis in Natural Product Synthesis: Strategies, Substrates & Catalysts. 2010. (ENG., Illus.). 412p. 205.00 *(978-3-527-32440-8(2)*, Wiley-VCH) Wiley, John & Sons, Inc.

Cottilard, Sophie A., ed. Catalytic Combustion. 2011. (Series: Chemical Engineering Methods & Technology Ser.). (Illus.). 208p. 140.00 *(978-1-61324-279-7(4))* Nova Science Pubs., Inc.

Coxon, James Morriss, ed. Advances in Detailed Reaction Mechanisms, Vol. 5. Date not set. 109.50 *(978-0-7623-0061-7(2)*, JAI Pr.) Elsevier Science & Technology Bks.

Crabtree, John. Atomic Reaction Mapping. 2008. 92p. pap. *(978-3-639-07358-4(4))* VDM Verlag Dr. Mueller e.K.

Cram101 Textbook Reviews. Outlines & Highlights for Chemistry & Chemical Reactivity, Volume 2 by John C Kotz, Isbn: 9780495387121 0495387126. 2011. 568p. pap. 39.95 ***(978-1-61812-363-3(7))*** Cram101 Inc.

DaCosta, Herbert. Rate Constant Estimation for Thermal Reactions: Methods & Applications. Fan, Maohong, ed. 2012. (ENG., Illus.). 360p. 135.00 ***(978-0-470-58230-5(8)***, Wiley) Wiley, John & Sons, Inc.

D'Amore, Alberto & Zaikov, Gennadii Efremovich. Monomer & Polymers Research Frontiers: Trends in Biochemical Physics Research. 2006. (Illus.). 152p. (C). 225.00 *(978-1-60021-435-6(5))* Nova Science Pubs., Inc.

—Monomers & Polymers: Reactions & Properties. 2006. (Illus.). 224p. 225.00 *(978-1-60021-415-8(0))* Nova Science Pubs., Inc.

—New Topics in Monomer & Polymers Research. 2006. (Illus.). 184p. (C). 225.00 *(978-1-60021-436-3(3))* Nova Science Pubs., Inc.

Davies, P. R. & Roberts, M. W. Atom Resolved Surface Reactions: Nanocatalysis. 2007. (RSC Nanoscience & Nanotechnology Ser.). (ENG., Illus.). 240p. (C). 195.00 *(978-0-85404-269-2(5))* Royal Society of Chemistry, The GBR. Dist: Ingram Pub. Services.

Denmark, Scott E. Organic Reactions. (Organic Reactions Ser.: 76). (ENG.). Volume 73. 2009. 624p. 166.00 *(978-0-470-43690-5(5),* Wiley-Interscience)Volume 78. 2012. 592p. 149.95 ***(978-1-118-35636-4(5)***, Wiley) Wiley, John & Sons, Inc.

Denmark, Scott E. Organic Reactions Vol. 77, Vol. 77/a. 2012. (Organic Reactions Ser.: 86). (ENG.). 640p. 149.95 ***(978-1-118-16380-1(X)***, Wiley) Wiley, John & Sons, Inc.

Denmark, Scott E., ed. Organic Reactions. (Organic Reactions Ser.: 78). (ENG.). Volume 72. 2008. 704p. 166.00 *(978-0-470-42374-5(9)*, Wiley-Interscience)Volume 74. 2009. 705p. 156.00 *(978-0-470-53048-1(0)*, Wiley)Volume 75. 2011. 880p. 175.00 *(978-0-470-88907-7(1)*, Wiley)Volume 76. 2011. 584p. 149.95 *(978-0-470-63843-9(5)*, Wiley) Wiley, John & Sons, Inc.

Denmark, Scott E. & Overman, Larry E., eds. Organic Reactions, Vol. 71. 2008. (Organic Reactions Ser.: 75). (ENG., Illus.). 772p. 178.00 *(978-0-470-09899-8(6)*, Wiley-Interscience) Wiley, John & Sons, Inc.

Donahue, Walker S. & Brandt, Jack C. Pyrolysis: Types, Processes, & Industrial Sources & Products. 2009. 145.00 *(978-1-60741-669-2(7))* Nova Science Pubs., Inc.

Duncan, James I. & Klein, Artur B., eds. Chemical Reactions on Surfaces. 2008. 324p. 179.00 *(978-1-60456-898-1(4))* Nova Science Pubs., Inc.

Dyson, Paul J. & Geldbach, Tilmann J. Metal Catalysed Reactions in Ionic Liquids. 2010. (Catalysis by Metal Complexes Ser.). x, 246p. pap. 249.00 *(978-90-481-6996-2(8)*, 9048169968) Springer.

Eisler, Ronald. Oceanic Acidification. 2011. (ENG.). 260p. 89.95 ***(978-1-57808-770-9(8))*** BIOS Scientific Publishers Ltd. GBR. Dist: Taylor & Francis Group.

Frey, Perry A. & Hegeman, Adrian D. Enzymatic Reaction Mechanisms. 2007. (ENG., Illus.). 848p. (C). 225.00 *(978-0-19-512258-9(5))* Oxford Univ. Pr., Inc.

Froment, Gilbert F., et al. Chemical Reactor Analysis & Design. 3rd ed. 2010. (ENG., Illus.). 900p. (C). 178.95 *(978-0-470-56541-4(1)*, Wiley) Wiley, John & Sons, Inc.

Gattuso, Jean-Pierre & Hansson, Lina. Ocean Acidification. 2011. (ENG., Illus.). 408p. 135.00 ***(978-0-19-959108-4(3))*** Oxford Univ. Pr., Inc.

Gattuso, Jean-Pierre & Hansson, Lina, eds. Ocean Acidification. 2011. (ENG., Illus.). 352p. pap. 67.95 ***(978-0-19-959109-1(1))*** Oxford Univ. Pr., Inc.

Geyer, Cyril. Electrodenitrification of Water Using the Enzyme Nitrate Reductase. 2010. 92p. pap. *(978-3-8383-1951-3(6))* Lambert Academic Publishing.

Ghosh, Rajshekhar. Titanium Isopropoxide Mediated Insertion & Metathesis. 2010. 168p. pap. *(978-3-639-25338-2(8))* VDM Verlag Dr. Mueller e.K.

Green, N. J. B. & Carr, R. W., eds. Modeling of Chemical Reactions. 2007. (Comprehensive Chemical Kinetics Ser.: 42). (ENG., Illus.). 316p. 315.00 *(978-0-444-51366-3(3)*, Elsevier Science) Elsevier Science & Technology Bks.

Grzegosz, Tanislaw & Nikitin, Lev Nikolaevich. Quantitative Foundation of Chemical Reactions. Zaikov, Gennadii Efremovich, ed. 2008. (Illus.). 306p. 145.00 *(978-1-60692-707-6(8))* Nova Science Pubs., Inc.

Herman de Groot, W. Sulphonation Technology in the Detergent Industry. 2010. 312p. pap. 369.00 *(978-90-481-4088-6(9)*, 9048140889) Springer.

Hoff-Ginsberg, Erika & Hoff. Handbook of Transition Metal Polymerization Catalysts. Hoff, Ray & Mathers, Robert T., eds. 2010. (ENG., Illus.). 575p. instr.'s hndbk. ed. 157.95 *(978-0-470-13798-7(3)*, Wiley) Wiley, John & Sons, Inc.

Hoffmann, R. W. Elements of Synthesis Planning. 2009. (ENG., Illus.). x, 227p. pap. 49.95 *(978-3-540-79219-2(8)*, 3540792198) Springer.

Hofmann, Thomas F. The Maillard Reaction: Recent Advances in Food & Biomedical Sciences. Schleicher, Erwin et al, eds. 2008. (Annals of the New York Academy of Sciences Ser.: Vol. 1126). (ENG., Illus.). 500p. pap. 159.95 *(978-1-57331-719-1(5)*, Wiley-Blackwell) Wiley, John & Sons, Inc.

Houston, Paul L. Chemical Kinetics & Reaction Dynamics. 2006. (Dover Books on Chemistry Ser.). (ENG., Illus.). 352p. per. 32.95 *(978-0-486-45334-7(0))* Dover Pubns., Inc.

Hussain, Raja Rizwan, et al. Corrosion of Rc Structures under Severe Environmental Actions. 2010. 120p. pap. *(978-3-639-24113-6(4))* VDM Verlag Dr. Mueller e.K.

Ikariya, Takao & Shibasaki, Masakatsu, eds. Bifunctional Molecular Catalysis. 2011. (Topics in Organometallic Chemistry Ser.). (Illus.). xii, 200p. 259.00 *(978-3-642-20730-3(8)*, 3642207308) Springer.

Indarto, Antonius. Chemical Reactions Using Gliding Arc Plasma. 2010. 162p. pap. 19.50 *(978-0-557-48618-2(1))* Lulu Enterprises Inc.

Islamova, Regina M., et al, eds. Kinetics, Catalysis & Mechanism of Chemical Reactions. from Pure to Applied Science - Today & Tomorrow. 2012. (Chemistry Research & Applications Ser.). 324p. 140.00 ***(978-1-61470-696-0(4))*** Nova Science Pubs., Inc.

Islamova, Regina M., et al. Kinetics, Catalysis & Mechanism of Chemical Reactions: From Pure to Applied Science - Tomorrow & Perspectives. 2012. (Chemistry Research & Applications/Polymer Science & Technology Ser.). 460p. 165.00 ***(978-1-61470-712-7(X))*** Nova Science Pubs., Inc.

Katz, Nevin. Atomic Structure & Chemical Reactions: Middle & High School. 2007. (Dr. Birdley Teaches Science Ser.). (Illus.). 94p. per. 12.99 *(978-0-86530-537-3(4))* Incentive Pubns., Inc.

Köppel, Horst, et al, eds. The Jahn-Teller-Effect: Fundamentals & Implications for Physics & Chemistry. 2009. (Springer Series in Chemical Physics Ser.). (ENG., Illus.). xxi, 915p. 199.00 *(978-3-642-03431-2(4)*, 3642034314) Springer.

Knipe, A. C., ed. Organic Reaction Mechanisms, 1999-2003, 5 vols., Set. 2008. (ENG.). 3400p. 2950.00 *(978-0-470-77955-2(1)*, Wiley) Wiley, John & Sons, Inc.

Kotz, et al. Chemistry & Chemical Reactivity. 8th ed. 2011. (Textbooks Available with Cengage YouBook Ser.). (ENG.). 1296p. (C). 273.95 *(978-0-8400-4828-8(9))* Brooks/Cole.

Kotz, John C., et al. Chemistry & Chemical Reactivity. 7th ed. 2008. (Available Titles OWL Ser.). (ENG., Illus.). 1312p. (C). 273.95 *(978-0-495-38703-9(7))* Brooks/Cole.

—Chemistry & Chemical Reactivity. 7th ed. 2008. (ENG.). 432p. (C). pap. 95.95 *(978-0-495-38707-7(X))* Brooks/Cole.

—Chemistry & Chemical Reactivity, Vol. 2. 7th ed. 2008. (ENG., Illus.). 800p. (C). 179.95 *(978-0-495-38712-1(6))* Brooks/Cole.

Kotz, Zreichel & Cram101 Textbook Reviews Staff. Chemistry & Chemical Reactivity. 2007. 348p. per. 16.95 *(978-1-4288-3052-3(9))* Cram101 Inc.

Krantz, William B. Scaling Analysis in Modeling Transport & Reaction Processes: A Systematic Approach to Model Building & the Art of Approximation. 2007. (ENG.). 529p. 144.00 *(978-0-471-77261-3(5))* American Institute of Chemical Engineers.

Kroon, Maaike. Chemical Processing with Ionic Liquids & Carbon Dioxide. 2009. 276p. pap. *(978-3-639-18543-0(9))* VDM Verlag Dr. Mueller e.K.

Kyteja. Mechanism in Protein Chemistry 2nd Edition. 2nd rev. ed. 2008. 95.95 *(978-0-8153-3868-0(5))* Routledge.

Li, Chao-Jun & Chan, Tak-Hang. Comprehensive Organic Reactions in Aqueous Media. 2nd rev. ed. 2007. (ENG., Illus.). 417p. 166.00 *(978-0-471-76129-7(X),* Wiley-Interscience) Wiley, John & Sons, Inc.

Li, Jie Jack. Name Reactions: A Collection of Detailed Mechanisms & Synthetic Applications. 4th ed. 2009. (ENG., Illus.). xxii, 621p. 99.00 *(978-3-642-01052-1(0),* 3642010520) Springer.

—Name Reactions: A Collection of Detailed Reaction Mechanisms. 3rd rev. ed. 2006. (Illus.). 652p. 99.00 *(978-3-540-30030-4(9),* 3540300309) Springer.

Li, Jie Jack & Corey, E. J. Name Reactions of Functional Group Transformations. 2007. (Comprehensive Name Reactions Ser.: 1). (ENG., Illus.). 768p. 178.00 *(978-0-471-74868-7(4),* Wiley) Wiley, John & Sons, Inc.

Li, Zhengqi, ed. Corn Straw & Biomass Blends: Combustion Characteristics & NO Formation. 2010. (Energy Science, Engineering & Technology Ser.). 43.00 *(978-1-60876-578-2(4))* Nova Science Pubs., Inc.

Luis, Santiago V. & Garcia-Verdugo, Eduardo. Chemical Reactions & Processes under Flow Conditions. 2009. (RSC Green Chemistry Ser.). (ENG., Illus.). 212p. (C). 160.00 *(978-0-85404-192-3(3))* Royal Society of Chemistry, The GBR. Dist: Ingram Pub. Services.

Ma, Shengming, ed. Handbook of Cyclization Reactions, 2 vols. 2009. (ENG., Illus.). 1288p. 465.00 *(978-3-527-32088-2(1),* Wiley-VCH) Wiley, John & Sons, Inc.

Makitra, R. G., et al. Liquid Phase Correlation Analysis in the Chemistry of Solutions. 2007. 225.00 *(978-1-60021-895-8(4))* Nova Science Pubs., Inc.

Maqsood, Sajid, et al. Plant Polyphenolic Compounds. 2011. 132p. pap. ***(978-3-8443-8429-1(4))*** Lambert Academic Publishing.

Marchisio, Daniele L. & Fox, Rodney O., eds. Multiphase reacting flows: modelling & Simulation. 2007. (CISM International Centre for Mechanical Sciences Ser.). (Illus.). vii, 269p. pap. 129.00 *(978-3-211-72463-7(X))* Springer.

Marin, Guy & Yablonsky, Gregory S. Kinetics of Chemical Reactions: Decoding Complexity. 2011. (ENG., Illus.). 446p. 105.00 *(978-3-527-31763-9(5),* Wiley-VCH) Wiley, John & Sons, Inc.

Maskill, Howard, ed. The Investigation of Organic Reactions & Their Mechanisms. 2007. (ENG., Illus.). 392p. 225.00 *(978-1-4051-3142-1(X),* Wiley-Blackwell) Wiley, John & Sons, Inc.

Masterton, William L. & Hurley, Cecile N. Chemistry: Principles & Reactions. 6th ed. 2008. (Available Titles CengageNOW Ser.). (ENG., Illus.). 736p. (C). 217.95 *(978-0-495-12671-3(3))* Brooks/Cole.

Masterton, William L., et al. Chemistry: Principles & Reactions. 7th ed. 2011. (Textbooks Available with Cengage YouBook Ser.). (ENG.). 800p. (C). 217.95 *(978-1-111-42710-8(0))* Brooks/Cole.

Mironov, Maxim A. Mcr 2009. Proceedings of the 4th International Conference on Multi-Component Reactions & Related Chemistry, Ekaterinburg, Russia. Mironov, Maxim A., ed. 2010. (Advances in Experimental Medicine & Biology Ser.). (Illus.). x, 230p. 189.00 *(978-1-4419-7269-9(2),* 1441972692) Springer.

Moran, Michael J., et al. Chemistry & Chemical Reactivity - Study Guide. 8th ed. 2011. (ENG.). 464p. (C). pap. 87.95 *(978-1-111-42699-6(6))* Brooks/Cole.

Nazir, Misbah. Ozone in Our Atmosphere. 2011. 68p. pap. ***(978-3-8443-2180-7(2))*** Lambert Academic Publishing.

Oriakhi, Christopher. Chemistry in Quantitative Language: Fundamentals of General Chemistry Calculations. 2009. (ENG., Illus.). 432p. 85.00 *(978-0-19-536799-7(5))* Oxford Univ. Pr., Inc.

Orru, Romano V. A. & Ruijter, Eelco, eds. Synthesis of Heterocycles via Multicomponent Reactions I. 2010. (Topics in Heterocyclic Chemistry Ser.). (Illus.). xv, 280p. 299.00 *(978-3-642-12674-1(X),* 364212674X) Springer.

—Synthesis of Heterocycles via Multicomponent Reactions II. 2010. (Topics in Heterocyclic Chemistry Ser.). (Illus.). x, 300p. 389.00 *(978-3-642-15454-6(9),* 3642154549) Springer.

Overman, Larry E. Organic Reactions, Vol. 69. Denmark, Scott E., ed. 2007. (Organic Reactions Ser.: 71). (ENG.). 704p. 178.00 *(978-0-470-22397-0(9),* Wiley-Interscience) Wiley, John & Sons, Inc.

—Organic Reactions, Volumes 1 - 74. 2010. (Organic Reactions Ser.: 83). (ENG.). 8200.00 *(978-0-470-63218-5(6),* Wiley) Wiley, John & Sons, Inc.

Overman, Larry E., ed. Organic Reactions, Volumes 1 - 73. 2009. (Organic Reactions Ser.: 79). (ENG.). 8050.00 *(978-0-470-52304-9(2),* Wiley) Wiley, John & Sons, Inc.

Overman, Larry E., et al, eds. Organic Reactions, Vol. 70. 2008. (Organic Reactions Ser.: 72). (ENG., Illus.). 656p. 178.00 *(978-0-470-25453-0(X),* Wiley-Interscience) Wiley, John & Sons, Inc.

Perchyonok, Tamara. Radical Reactions in Aqueous Media. 2009. (RSC Green Chemistry Ser.). (ENG., Illus.). 142p. 118.00 *(978-1-84973-000-6(8))* Royal Society of Chemistry, The GBR. Dist: Ingram Pub. Services.

Pignataro, Bruno, ed. New Strategies in Chemical Synthesis & Catalysis. 2012. (ENG.). 406p. 140.00 ***(978-3-527-33090-4(9),*** Wiley-VCH) Wiley, John & Sons, Inc.

Pol, Vilas. Sonochemical Deposition of Nanoparticles on Desired Substrates. 2009. 84p. pap. *(978-3-639-16821-1(6))* VDM Verlag Dr. Mueller e.K.

Pritchard, H. O. The Quantum Theory of Unimolecular Reactions. 2009. (ENG.). 192p. pap. 39.99 *(978-0-521-10586-6(2))* Cambridge Univ. Pr.

Putz, Mihai V., ed. Advances in Chemical Modeling. 2011. (Chemistry Research & Applications Ser.). (Illus.). 479p. 295.00 *(978-1-61209-669-8(7))* Nova Science Pubs., Inc.

Raff, Lionel M. Neural Networks in Chemical Reaction Dynamics, 1 vol. 2012. (ENG., Illus.). 336p. 79.95 ***(978-0-19-976565-2(0))*** Oxford Univ. Pr., Inc.

Roberts, George W. Chemical Reactions & Chemical Reactors. 2008. (ENG., Illus.). 480p. (C). 146.95 *(978-0-471-74220-3(1),* Wiley) Wiley, John & Sons, Inc.

Rokita, Steven. Carbon-Centered Free Radicals & Radical Cations: Structure, Reactivity, & Dynamics. Forbes, Malcolm D., ed. 2010. (Wiley Series of Reactive Intermediates in Chemistry & Biology Ser.: 2). (ENG., Illus.). 370p. 139.00 *(978-0-470-39009-2(3),* Wiley) Wiley, John & Sons, Inc.

Royal Society of Chemistry Staff. Coherence & Control in Chemistry: Faraday Discussions No 153. 2011. (ENG., Illus.). 428p. (C). 240.00 ***(978-1-84973-238-3(8))*** Royal Society of Chemistry, The GBR. Dist: Ingram Pub. Services.

—The Maillard Reaction: Interface between Aging, Nutrition & Metabolism. Thomas, Merlin C. & Forbes, Josephine, eds. 2010. (Special Publication). (Illus.). 256p. 176.00 ***(978-1-84973-079-2(2))*** Royal Society of Chemistry, The GBR. Dist: Ingram Pub. Services.

—Proton-Coupled Electron Transfer: A Carrefour of Chemical Reactivity Traditions. Formosinho, Sebastiao & Barroso, Mónica, eds. 2011. (RSC Catalysis Ser.). (ENG., Illus.). 168p. 195.00 ***(978-1-84973-141-6(1))*** Royal Society of Chemistry, The GBR. Dist: Ingram Pub. Services.

Santos, Leonardo S., ed. Reactive Intermediates: MS Investigations in Solution. 2010. (ENG., Illus.). 341p. 170.00 *(978-3-527-32351-7(1),* Wiley-VCH) Wiley, John & Sons, Inc.

Sartori, Giovanni & Maggi, Raimondo. Advances in Friedel-Crafts Acylation Reactions: Catalytic & Green Processes. 2009. (ENG., Illus.). 216p. 154.95 *(978-1-4200-6792-7(3),* CRC Press) Taylor & Francis Group GBR. Dist: Taylor & Francis Group.

Schmal, Martin. Chemical Reaction Engineering: Essentials, Exercises & Examples. 2012. (ENG.). 550p. (C). pap. 89.95 ***(978-0-415-69538-1(4)*** CRC Press) Taylor & Francis Group GBR. Dist: Taylor & Francis Group.

Schmidt-Traub, Henner & Górak, Andrzej, eds. Integrated Reaction & Separation Operations: Modelling & experimental Validation. 2006. (Chemische Technik/Verfahrenstechnik Ser.). (ENG., Illus.). xii, 366p. 159.00 *(978-3-540-30148-6(8),* 3540301488) Springer.

Schmidt-Traub, Henner & Gorak, Andrzej, eds. Integrated Reaction & Separation Operations: Modelling & experimental Validation. 2010. (ENG. Illus.). xii, 366p. pap. 159.00 *(978-3-642-06763-1(8),* 3642067638) Springer.

Shi, Min, et al. The Chemistry of the Morita-Baylis-Hillman Reaction. 2011. (RSC Catalysis Ser.). (ENG., Illus.). 563p. (C). 232.00 *(978-1-84973-129-4(2))* Royal Society of Chemistry, The GBR. Dist: Ingram Pub. Services.

Singh, Jagdamba & Singh, Jaya. Photochemistry & Pericyclic Reactions. 3rd ed. 2009. (Illus.). 460p. *(978-1-906574-16-1(2))* New Age Science, Ltd.

Stacy, Angelica M. Earth Fire & Air. (C). pap. *(978-0-393-92441-1(6))* Norton, W. W. & Co., Inc.

Stoessel, Francis. Thermal Safety of Chemical Processes: Risk Assessment & Process Design. 2008. (ENG., Illus.). 393p. 170.00 *(978-3-527-31712-7(0),* Wiley-VCH) Wiley, John & Sons, Inc.

Tanji, Kenneth K. & Wallender, Wesley W., eds. Agricultural Salinity Assessment & Management. 2nd ed. 2011. (ENG.). 1124p. 180.00 ***(978-0-7844-1169-8(7))*** American Society of Civil Engineers.

Torres, Ramon Rios. The Pauson-Khand Reaction: Scope, Variations & Applications. 2012. (ENG.). 328p. 160.00 ***(978-0-470-97076-8(6),*** Wiley) Wiley, John & Sons, Inc.

Tsuge, Shin, et al. Pyrolysis - GC/MS Data Book of Synthetic Polymers: Pyrograms, Thermograms & MS of Pyrolyzates. 2011. (ENG.). 420p. 295.00 ***(978-0-444-53892-5(5))*** Elsevier Science & Technology Bks.

Turro, Nicholas J., et al. Modern Molecular Photochemistry of Organic Molecules. 2010. (Illus.). 1120p. (C). 134.50 *(978-1-891389-25-2(4))* Univ. Science Bks.

Upadhyay, Santosh K. Chemical Kinetics & Reaction Dynamics. (ENG.). xv, 256p. 2010. pap. 209.00 *(978-90-481-7146-0(6),* 9048171466) 2006. (Illus.). 209.00 *(978-1-4020-4546-2(8),* 1402045468) Springer.

Urben, Peter, ed. Bretherick's Handbook of Reactive Chemical Hazards, 2 vols., Set. 7th ed. 2006. (ENG., Illus.). 2680p. 505.00 *(978-0-12-372563-9(1),* Academic Pr.) Elsevier Science & Technology Bks.

van Eldik, Rudi & Ivanovic-Burmacovic, Ivana. Inorganic/Bioinorganic Reaction Mechanisms. 2012. (ENG.). 320p. 258.00 ***(978-0-12-396462-5(6),*** Academic Pr.) Elsevier Science & Technology Bks.

Walker, Denise. Chemical Reactions. 2006. (Core Chemistry/Evans Brothers Ser.). (Illus.). 48p. (YA). (gr. 5-9). 34.25 *(978-1-58340-820-9(7))* Black Rabbit Bks.

—Metals & Nonmetals. 2006. (Core Chemistry/Evans Brothers Ser.). (Illus.). 48p. (YA). (gr. 5-9). 34.25 *(978-1-58340-822-3(3))* Black Rabbit Bks.

Wang, Zerong. Comprehensive Organic Name Reactions & Reagents, 3 vols. 2009. (ENG., Illus.). 1368p. 198.33 ***(978-0-470-53346-8(3));*** Vol. 1. 1304p. 198.34 *(978-0-470-28662-3(8));* Vol. 2. 987p. 198.33 *(978-0-470-28663-0(6))* Wiley, John & Sons, Inc. (Wiley-Interscience).

Wang, Zerong & Wang. Comprehensive Organic Name Reactions & Reagents, 3 vols., 3 Volume Set. 2009. (ENG., Illus.). 3824p. 655.00 *(978-0-471-70450-8(4),* Wiley-Interscience) Wiley, John & Sons, Inc.

Welker-Nieuwoudt, Cathrin. Ruthenium Based Fischer-Tropsch Synthesis. 2011. 216p. pap. ***(978-3-8443-2127-2(6))*** Lambert Academic Publishing.

Zaikov, Gennadii Efremovich, ed. Progress in Chemical & Biochemical Physics, Kinetics & Thermodynamics. 2008. (C). 185.00 *(978-1-60456-079-4(7))* Nova Science Pubs., Inc.

Zarrouk, Sadiq J. Reacting Flows in Porous Media: Complex Multi-Phase,Multi-Component Simulation. 2008. 424p. pap. *(978-3-639-09985-0(0))* VDM Verlag Dr. Mueller e.K.

CHEMICAL REACTORS

see also Bioreactors

American Institute of Chemical Engineers (AIChE) Staff, compiled by. Topical Conference on Applications of Micro-Reactor Engineering 2007. 2007. 206p. pap. 118.00 *(978-1-60423-350-6(8))* Curran Assocs., Inc.

Azzopardi, Barry, et al. Hydrodynamics of Gas-Liquid Reactors: Normal Operation & Upset Conditions. 2011. (ENG., Illus.). 344p. 195.00 *(978-0-470-74771-1(4),* Wiley) Wiley, John & Sons, Inc.

Caccavale, Fabrizio, et al. Control & Monitoring of Chemical Batch Reactors. 2010. (Advances in Industrial Control Ser.). (ENG., Illus.). xvii, 186p. 129.00 *(978-0-85729-194-3(7),* 0857291947) Springer.

Chaudhari, Raghunath, et al. Trickle Bed Reactors: Reactor Engineering & Applications. 2011. (ENG.). 284p. 260.00 *(978-0-444-52738-7(9))* Elsevier Science & Technology Bks.

Cybulski, Andrzej, et al, eds. Novel Concepts in Catalysis & Chemical Reactors: Improving the Efficiency for the Future. 2010. (ENG., Illus.). 398p. 200.00 *(978-3-527-32469-9(0),* Wiley-VCH) Wiley, John & Sons, Inc.

Dietrich, T., et al. Microchemical Engineering in Practice. 2009. (ENG., Illus.). 487p. 122.00 *(978-0-470-23956-8(5))* American Institute of Chemical Engineers.

Fogler, H. Scott. Essentials of Chemical Reaction Engineering. 2010. (Prentice Hall International Series in the Physical & Chemical Engineering Sciences Ser.). (ENG., Illus.). 752p. 120.00 *(978-0-13-714612-3(4),* Prentice Hall) Prentice Hall PTR.

Froment, Gilbert F., et al. Chemical Reactor Analysis & Design. 3rd ed. 2010. (ENG., Illus.). 900p. (C). 178.95 *(978-0-470-56541-4(1),* Wiley) Wiley, John & Sons, Inc.

Geiser, Juergen. Modelling & Simulation of a Multi-Component Transport for a Chemical Reactor Based on CVD-Processes. 2008. 89.00 *(978-1-60692-325-2(0))* Nova Science Pubs., Inc.

Hartman, Eve & Meshbesher, Wendy. Chemical Reactions, 1 vol. 2008. (Sci-Hi: Physical Science Ser.). (ENG.). 48p. (gr. 4-4). pap. 8.99 *(978-1-4109-3262-4(1),* Sci-Hi) Heinemann-Raintree.

Inglezakis, Vassilis & Poulopoulos, Stavros. Adsorption, Ion Exchange & Catalysis: Design of Operations & Environmental Applications. 2006. (ENG., Illus.). 614p. 255.00 *(978-0-444-52783-7(4),* Elsevier Science) Elsevier Science & Technology Bks.

Jakobsen, Hugo A. General Reactor Technology Fundamentals: Multiphase Reactive Flows. 2007. (Illus.). 1250p. 269.00 *(978-3-540-25197-2(9),* 3540251979) Springer.

Jung, Jonghwun. Design & Understanding of Fluidized-Bed Reactors. 2009. 156p. pap. *(978-3-639-13367-7(6))* VDM Verlag Dr. Mueller e.K.

Khanaev, Valeri M., et al. Fixed Bed Reactors with Gradient Catalysts. 2008. 103p. 29.00 *(978-1-60456-780-9(5))* Nova Science Pubs., Inc.

Kumacheva, Eugenia & Garstecki, Piotr, trs. Microfluidic Reactors for Polymer Particles. 2011. (Illus.). xi, 223p. E-Book *(978-0-470-97923-5(2))* Wiley, John & Sons, Inc.

Levenspiel, Octave. Chemical Reactor Omnibook. pap. 30.00 *(978-0-88246-170-0(2))* Oregon State Univ. Bk. Stores, Inc.

Li, Jie Jack & Corey, E. J. Name Reactions Series. 2010. (Comprehensive Name Reactions Ser.). (ENG.). 3718p. 720.00 *(978-0-470-94032-7(8),* Wiley) Wiley, John & Sons, Inc.

Luyben, William L. Chemical Reactor Design & Control. 2007. (ENG., Illus.). 419p. 150.00 *(978-0-470-09770-0(1),* Wiley-Interscience) Wiley, John & Sons, Inc.

Myasnikova, Liuba, ed. Reactor Powder Morphology. 2010. (Polymer Science & Technology Ser.). (Illus.). xv, 353p. 175.00 *(978-1-61668-592-8(1))* Nova Science Pubs., Inc.

Nauman, E. Bruce. Chemical Reactor Design, Optimization, & Scaleup. 2nd ed. 2008. (ENG., Illus.). 608p. 150.00 *(978-0-470-10525-2(9))* American Institute of Chemical Engineers.

Parmon, V. M., et al. Photocatalysis: Catalysts, Kinetics & Reactors. 2012. (ENG.). 400p. 190.00 ***(978-3-527-31784-4(8),*** Wiley-VCH) Wiley, John & Sons, Inc.

Rani, K. Yamuna. Optimization & Control of Semi-Batch Reactors. 2011. 204p. pap. ***(978-3-8443-0242-4(5))*** Lambert Academic Publishing.

Roberts, George W. Chemical Reactions & Chemical Reactors. 2008. (ENG., Illus.). 480p. (C). 146.95 *(978-0-471-74220-3(1),* Wiley) Wiley, John & Sons, Inc.

Salmi, Tapio O., et al. Chemical Reaction Engineering & Reactor Technology. 2010. (Chemical Industries Ser.). (ENG., Illus.). 644p. (C). 179.95 *(978-1-4200-9268-4(5),* CRC Press) Taylor & Francis Group GBR. Dist: Taylor & Francis Group.

Schiavello, Mario, ed. Photoelectrochemistry, Photocatalysis & Photoreactors Fundamentals & Developments. 2010. (NATO Science Series C: (closed) Ser.). 660p. pap. 469.00 *(978-90-481-8414-9(2),* 9048184142) Springer.

Silveston, P. L. & Hudgins, R. R. Periodic Operation of Chemical Reactors. 2012. (ENG.). 608p. 150.00 ***(978-0-12-391854-3(5),*** Butterworth-Heinemann) Elsevier Science & Technology Bks.

Theodore, Louis. Chemical Reactor Analysis & Applications for the Practicing Engineer. 2012. (Essential Engineering Calculations Ser.: 5). (ENG.). 592p. 125.00 ***(978-0-470-91535-6(8),*** Wiley) Wiley, John & Sons, Inc.

Thoenes, D. Chemical Reactor Development: From Laboratory Synthesis to Industrial Production. 2010. 368p. pap. 281.00 *(978-90-481-4446-4(9),* 9048144469) Springer.

Vojtesek, Jiri. Modern Control Methods for Chemical Reactors. 2010. 132p. pap. *(978-3-8383-4006-7(X))* Lambert Academic Publishing.

Wiles, Charlotte & Watts, Paul. Micro Reaction Technology in Organic Chemistry. 2011. (ENG., Illus.). 453p. 139.95 *(978-1-4398-2471-9(1),* CRC Press) Taylor & Francis Group GBR. Dist: Taylor & Francis Group.

Wirth, Thomas, ed. Microreactors in Organic Synthesis & Catalysis. 2008. (ENG., Illus.). 297p. 229.00 *(978-3-527-31869-8(0),* Wiley-VCH) Wiley, John & Sons, Inc.

Zahedi, Gholamreza. Industrial Methanol Reactor Dynamic Modeling & Optimization. 2011. 108p. pap. ***(978-3-8443-8863-3(X))*** Lambert Academic Publishing.

Zaikov, Gennadii Efremovich, ed. Chemical & Biochemical Physics, Kinetics & Thermodynamics: New Perspectives. 2008. (Illus.). (C). 205.00 *(978-1-60456-024-4(X))* Nova Science Pubs., Inc.

CHEMICAL REAGENTS

see Chemical Tests and Reagents

CHEMICAL REDUCTION

see Reduction, Chemical

CHEMICAL RESEARCH

see Chemistry—Research

CHEMICAL SPILLS

Bloom, Howard S., et al. Toxic Chemical Releases. Simmons, Jeremy B., ed. 2009. pap. 79.00 *(978-1-60692-134-0(7))* Nova Science Pubs., Inc.

Lerner, Steve & Robert, M. Sacrifice Zones: The Front Lines of Toxic Chemical Exposure in the United States. 2010. (ENG.). 368p. (gr. 17). 29.95 *(978-0-262-01440-3(8))* MIT Pr.

CHEMICAL STRUCTURE

see also Chemical Bonds; Molecular Structure; Stereochemistry; Valence (Theoretical Chemistry)

Banville, Debra L. Chemical Information Mining: Facilitating Literature-Based Discovery. 2008. (ENG., Illus.). 208p. 109.95 *(978-1-4200-7649-3(3),* CRC Press) Taylor & Francis Group GBR. Dist: Taylor & Francis Group.

Cram101 Textbook Reviews Staff. Outlines & Highlights for Chemical Structure & Bonding by Dekock Isbn: 093570261x. 2007. 112p. pap. 11.95 *(978-1-4288-3072-1(3))* Cram101 Inc.

Crews, Phillip, et al. Organic Structure Analysis, 1 vol. 2nd ed. 2009. (ENG., Illus.). 655p. (C). 164.95 *(978-0-19-533604-7(6))* Oxford Univ. Pr., Inc.

John Wiley & Sons Staff. Wiley Chemical Structure Library 2005. 2011. 1000.00 *(978-0-471-72562-6(5),* Wiley) Wiley, John & Sons, Inc.

Keeler, James & Wothers, Peter. Chemical Structure & Reactivity: An Integrated Approach. 2008. (ENG., Illus.). 944p. (C). pap. 104.95 *(978-0-19-928930-1(1))* Oxford Univ. Pr., Inc.

Kettle, Sidney F. A. Symmetry & Structure: Readable Group Theory for Chemists. 3rd ed. (ENG., Illus.). 436p. 2008. per. 79.00 *(978-0-470-06040-7(9))* 2007. 220.00 *(978-0-470-06039-1(5))* Wiley, John & Sons, Inc. (Wiley).

Klein, U. ed. Tools & Modes of Representation in the Laboratory Sciences. 2010. (Boston Studies in the Philosophy of Science Ser.). 276p. pap. 149.00 *(978-90-481-5859-1(1),* 9048158591) Springer.

Koleva, Bojidarka & Kolev, Tsonko. Linearly Polarized IR Spectroscopy: Theory & Applications for Structural Analysis. 2011. (ENG., Illus.). 240p. 129.95 *(978-1-4398-2559-4(9),* CRC Press) Taylor & Francis Group GBR. Dist: Taylor & Francis Group.

Li, Wai-Kee, et al. Advanced Structural Inorganic Chemistry. 2008. (International Union of Crystallography Texts on Crystallography Ser.). (ENG., Illus.). 848p. 185.00 *(978-0-19-921694-9(0));* 688p. pap. 85.00 *(978-0-19-921695-6(9))* Oxford Univ. Pr., Inc.

Pretsch, Ernö, et al. Structure Determination of Organic Compounds: Tables of Spectral Data. 4th ed. 2009. (ENG., Illus.). xvi, 436p. pap. 69.95 *(978-3-540-93809-5(5),* 3540938095) Springer.

Putz, Mihai V., ed. Advances in Chemical Modeling. 2011. (Chemistry Research & Applications Ser.). (Illus.). 479p. 295.00 *(978-1-61209-669-8(7))* Nova Science Pubs., Inc.

Rogers, Robin D., et al. Ionic Liquids IV: Not Just Solvents Anymore. 2007. (American Chemical Society Publication). (ENG.). 434p. 155.00 *(978-0-8412-7445-7(2))* American Chemical Society.

Structural Aspects of Protein Synthesis (2nd Edition) 2010. pap. 65.00 *(978-981-4313-21-6(1))* World Scientific Publishing Co., Inc.

Wang, Liya. Analysis of Nmr Chemical Shifts in Peptide & Protein Structure Determination. 2008. 236p. per. *(978-3-8364-5773-6(3))* VDM Verlag Dr. Mueller e.K.

Wells, Alexander Frank. Structural Inorganic Chemistry. 2012. (ENG., Illus.). 1416p. pap. 99.99 ***(978-0-19-965763-6(7))*** Oxford Univ. Pr., Inc.

Zhou, Gongdu & Duan, Lianyun. Jie Gou Hua Xue Ji Chu. 4th ed. 2008. (CH., Illus.). 362p. *(978-7-301-05773-5(3))* Beijing University Pr.

CHEMICAL SYMBOLS

see Abbreviations; Chemistry—Nomenclature; Chemistry—Notation

CHEMICAL TECHNOLOGY

see Chemistry, Technical

CHEMICAL TESTS AND REAGENTS

see also Grignard Reagents; Ozone

Arshad, Nuzhat. C-P & C-C Bond Forming Reactions Based on Carbostyrils & Thioamide. 2010. 92p. pap. *(978-3-639-25660-4(3))* VDM Verlag Dr. Mueller e.K.

Bulatovic, Srdjan M. Handbook of Flotation Reagents: Chemistry, Theory & Practice: Volume 2: Flotation of Gold, PGM & Oxide Minerals. 2010. (ENG., Illus.). 230p. 310.00 *(978-0-444-53082-0(7)*, Elsevier Science) Elsevier Science & Technology Bks.

Fuchs, Philip L., ed. Reagents for Silicon-Mediated Organic Synthesis. 2011. (Hdbk of Reagents for Organic Synthesis Ser.). (ENG., Illus.). 854p. 155.00 ***(978-0-470-71023-4(3)***, Wiley) Wiley, John & Sons, Inc.

Gokden, Fritz & Lazzarotto, André. Hydroquinone: Production, Uses, & Health Effects. 2012. ***(978-1-62100-258-1(6))*** Nova Science Pubs., Inc.

Ho, Tse-Lok. Fieser & Fieser's Reagents for Organic Synthesis, 26 vols., Set. 3rd ed. 2011. (Fiesers' Reagents for Organic Synthesis Ser.: 44). (ENG.). 3700p. 3250.00 ***(978-0-470-89458-3(X)***, Wiley) Wiley, John & Sons, Inc.

Ho, Tse-Lok. Fiesers' Reagents for Organic Synthesis. (Fiesers' Reagents for Organic Synthesis Ser.: 39). (ENG., Volume 24. 2nd ed. 2008. Illus.). 524p. 184.00 *(978-0-470-22554-7(8))*Volume 25. 2009. (Illus.). 571p. 166.00 *(978-0-470-43375-1(2))*Volume 26. 2011. 744p. 149.95 *(978-0-470-58771-3(7))*Volumes 1-25, and Collective Index for Volumes 1-2. 2nd ed. 2010. (Illus.). 3000p. 3310.00 *(978-0-470-52111-3(2))* Wiley, John & Sons, Inc. (Wiley).

Ho, Tse-Lok, ed. Fieser & Fieser's Reagents for Organic Synthesis Set, Vols. 1-24, Vols. 1-24, Set. 2008. (Fiesers' Reagents for Organic Synthesis Ser.: 40). (ENG.). 2564p. 3180.00 *(978-0-470-43133-7(4)*, Wiley-Interscience) Wiley, John & Sons, Inc.

Hoenig, Steven L. Compendium of Chemical Warfare Agents. 2010. (ENG., Illus.). xii, 222p. pap. 109.00 *(978-1-4419-2239-7(3)*, 1441922393) Springer.

Houghton, Rick. Field Confirmation Testing for Suspicious Substances. 2009. (ENG., Illus.). 453p. 144.95 *(978-1-4200-8615-7(4)*, CRC Press) Taylor & Francis Group GBR. Dist: Taylor & Francis Group.

Korenev, K. D., et al. Chemicals Based on the Light Fraction of Natural Mercaptans. 2007. 212p. 145.00 *(978-1-60021-650-3(1))* Nova Science Pubs., Inc.

Lerner, Leonid. Small-Scale Laboratory Synthesis of Chemical Reagents. 2011. (ENG., Illus.). 240p. 139.95 *(978-1-4398-1312-6(4)*, CRC Press) Taylor & Francis Group GBR. Dist: Taylor & Francis Group.

Lukey, Brian J., et al, eds. Chemical Warfare Agents: Chemistry, Pharmacology, Toxicology, & Therapeutics. 2nd rev. ed. 2007. (ENG., Illus.). 752p. 210.00 *(978-1-4200-4661-8(6))* CRC Pr. LLC.

Mackowiak, Elaine D. Essentials of Nonprescription Medications & Devices. 2009. (Illus.). 240p. pap. 49.99 *(978-0-85369-861-6(9))* Pharmaceutical Pr. GBR. Dist: Smith Fulfillment Services.

Molander, Gary. Handbook of Reagents, 4 vols., Set. 2010. (Hdbk of Reagents for Organic Synthesis Ser.). (ENG.). 2870p. 500.00 *(978-0-470-66649-4(8)*, Wiley) Wiley, John & Sons, Inc.

Paquette, Leo A., ed. Fluorine-Containing Reagents. 2007. (Hdbk of Reagents for Organic Synthesis Ser.). (ENG., Illus.). 730p. 220.00 *(978-0-470-02177-4(2)*, Wiley-Interscience) Wiley, John & Sons, Inc.

Paquette, Leo A., et al. Handbook of Reagents for Organic Synthesis Set: Chiral Reagents for Asymmetric Synthesis, 4 vols. 2007. (ENG.). 2184p. 585.00 *(978-0-470-06652-2(0)*, Wiley) Wiley, John & Sons, Inc.

Perosa, Alvise & Zecchini, Fulvio. Methods & Reagents for Green Chemistry: An Introduction. Tundo, Pietro, ed. 2007. (ENG., Illus.). 336p. 134.00 *(978-0-471-75400-8(5)*, Wiley-Interscience) Wiley, John & Sons, Inc.

Rich, Ronald. Inorganic Reactions in Water. 2010. (ENG., Illus.). xxii, 521p. pap. 279.00 *(978-3-642-09324-1(8)*, 3642093248) Springer.

Rich, Ronald L. Inorganic Reactions in Water. 2008. (ENG., Illus.). xxii, 521p. 279.00 *(978-3-540-73961-6(0)*, 3540739610) Springer.

Sabnis, R. W. Handbook of Acid-Base Indicators. 2007. (ENG., Illus.). 416p. 226.95 *(978-0-8493-8218-5(1)*, CRC Press) Taylor & Francis Group GBR. Dist: Taylor & Francis Group.

Terry, Mark, ed. Quality Counts: Washington 6-2 Reports Second National Reagent Vendor Quality Survey Report. 2007. (Illus.). 68p. pap. 595.00 *(978-1-58673-254-7(4))* Institute of Management & Administration, IOMA.

Wang, Zerong. Comprehensive Organic Name Reactions & Reagents, 3 vols. 2009. (ENG., Illus.). 1368p. 198.33 ***(978-0-470-53346-8(3))***; Vol. 1. 1304p. 198.34 *(978-0-470-28662-3(8))*; Vol. 2. 987p. 198.33 *(978-0-470-28663-0(6))* Wiley, John & Sons, Inc. (Wiley-Interscience).

Wang, Zerong & Wang. Comprehensive Organic Name Reactions & Reagents, 3 vols., 3 Volume Set. 2009. (ENG., Illus.). 3824p. 655.00 *(978-0-471-70450-8(4)*, Wiley-Interscience) Wiley, John & Sons, Inc.

Wenzel, Thomas J. Discrimination of Chiral Compounds Using NMR Spectroscopy. 2007. (ENG., Illus.). 576p. 150.00 *(978-0-471-76352-9(7)*, Wiley-Interscience) Wiley, John & Sons, Inc.

World Health Organization. The Use of Malaria Rapid Diagnostics Tests. 2nd ed. 2009. (WPRO Nonserial Publication Ser.). 19p. pap. 10.00 *(978-92-9061-441-8(2))* World Health Organization.

CHEMICAL TOXICOLOGY

see Toxicological Chemistry

CHEMICAL WARFARE

see also Decontamination (from Gases, Chemicals, etc.)

also subdivision Chemical Warfare under individual wars, e.g. Vietnamese Conflict, 1961-1975—Chemcial Warfare

Balmer, Brian. Secrecy & Science: A Historical Sociology of Biological & Chemical Warfare. 2012. 180p. 99.95 ***(978-1-4094-3057-5(X))*** Ashgate Publishing Co.

Biodetection Technologies, 4th Edition: Technological Responses to Biological Threats. 2007. 529p. pap. 299.00 *(978-1-59430-126-1(3))* Knowledge Pr.

Borden Institute, Walter Reed Army Medical Center, compiled by. Medical Aspects of Chemical Warfare. 2009. (Textbooks of Military Medicine Ser.). (ENG., Illus.). 850p. 88.00 *(978-0-16-081532-4(0)*, Dept. of the Army) United States Government Printing Office.

Cashman, John R. Emergency Response Handbook for Chemical & Biologica Agents & Weapons. 2nd rev. ed. 2008. (ENG., Illus.). 528p. 115.95 *(978-1-4200-5265-7(9)*, CRC Press) Taylor & Francis Group GBR. Dist: Taylor & Francis Group.

Committee on Protecting Occupants of DOD Buildings from Chemical and Biological Release & National Research Council Staff. Protecting Building Occupants & Operations from Biological & Chemical Airborne Threats: A Framework for Decision Making. 2007. (ENG.). 152p. pap. 36.50 *(978-0-309-10955-0(8))* National Academies Pr.

Committee on Toxicologic and Radiologic Effects from Exposure to Depleted Uranium During and After Combat, et al. Review of Toxicologic & Radiologic Risks to Military Personnel from Exposure to Depleted Uranium During & after Combat. 2008. (ENG.). 172p. pap. 39.75 *(978-0-309-11036-5(X))* National Academies Pr.

Committee to Review and Assess Developmental Issues Concerning the Metal Parts Treater Design for the Blue Grass Chemical Agent Destruction Pilot Plant & National Research Council. Review & Assessment of Developmental Issues Concerning the Metal Parts Treater Design for the Blue Grass Chemical Agent Destruction Pilot Plant. 2008. (ENG.). 62p. pap. 21.00 *(978-0-309-11515-5(9))* National Academies Pr.

Coverdell, Donald. Terror in the Air. 2008. 160p. pap. 19.50 *(978-1-4357-5957-2(5))* Lulu Enterprises Inc.

Department of the Army. U. S. Army Special Forces Guide to Unconventional Warfare: Devices & Techniques for Incendiaries. 2011. (ENG., Illus.). 160p. pap. 12.95 *(978-1-61608-009-9(4)*, 608009) Skyhorse Publishing Co., Inc.

Dishovsky, Christophor & Pivovarov, Alexander, eds. Counteraction to Chemical & Biological Terrorism in East European Countries. 2009. (NATO Science for Peace & Security Series A: Chemistry & Biology Ser.). (ENG., Illus.). xxiv, 324p. 319.00 *(978-90-481-2340-7(2))*; pap. 99.00 *(978-90-481-2341-4(0))* Springer.

Ellison, D. Hank. Handbook of Chemical & Biological Warfare Agents. 2nd rev. ed. 2007. (ENG., Illus.). 800p. 149.95 *(978-0-8493-1434-6(8)*, CRC Press) Taylor & Francis Group GBR. Dist: Taylor & Francis Group.

Government Printing Office Staff. CML, Army Chemical Review. pap. 13.00 *(978-0-16-010355-1(X))* United States Government Printing Office.

Gupta, Ramesh C., ed. Handbook of Toxicology of Chemical Warfare Agents. 2009. (ENG., Illus.). 1168p. 235.00 *(978-0-12-374484-5(9)*, Academic Pr.) Elsevier Science & Technology Bks.

Haldane, Liddell Hart, et al. Callinicus: A Defence of Chemical Warfare: with Paris or the Future of War & Janus: the Conquest of War & Sinon or the Future of Politics & Typhoeus ... the Future of Socialism, 25 vols. 2008. (Illus.). IV, 524p. 215.00 *(978-0-415-46337-9(8))* Routledge.

Haru, Ere & Thakur, Ramesh Chandra, eds. The Chemical Weapons Convention: Implementation, Challenges & Opportunities. 2006. (ENG.). 200p. per. 30.00 *(978-92-808-1123-0(1))* United Nations Univ. Pr. JPN. Dist: United Nations Pubns.

Hoenig, Steven L. Compendium of Chemical Warfare Agents. 2006. (ENG., Illus.). xii, 222p. 109.00 *(978-0-387-34626-7(0)*, 0387346260) Springer.

Human Rights Watch (Organization) Staff, contrib. by. Rain of Fire: Israel's Unlawful Use of White Phosphorus in Gaza. 2009. (Illus.). 71p. pap. *(978-1-56432-458-0(3))* Human Rights Watch.

Hurst, Gary, ed. Medical Management of Chemical Casualties Handbook. 2008. (ENG.). pap. 16.00 *(978-0-16-081320-7(4)*, Dept. of the Army) United States Government Printing Office.

Kiesbye, Stefan. Biological & Chemical Weapons. 2010. (At Issue Ser.). (ENG.). 104p. 31.80 *(978-0-7377-4870-3(2))*; pap. 22.50 *(978-0-7377-4871-0(0))* Cengage Gale. (Greenhaven Pr., Inc.).

Lefebure, Victor. The Riddle of the Rhine: Chemical Strategy in Peace & War. 2009. (Illus.). 224p. pap. *(978-1-4099-8929-5(1))* Dodo Pr.

—The Riddle of the Rhine: Chemical Strategy in Peace & War. 2010. 292p. 35.16 *(978-1-163-34073-8(1))* 2010. 292p. pap. 23.16 *(978-1-162-72080-7(8))* 2007. (ENG.). 290p. 43.95 *(978-0-548-02917-6(2))* Kessinger Publishing, LLC.

—The Riddle of the Rhine, Chemical Strategy in Peace & War. 2010. 148p. pap. 22.72 *(978-1-153-24478-7(0))* General Bks. LLC.

—The Riddle of the Rhine; Chemical Strategy in Peace & War. 2010. (Illus.). 138p. pap. 22.72 *(978-1-153-71914-8(2))* General Bks. LLC.

—The Riddle of the Rhine; Chemical Strategy in Peace & War. 2010. 162p. pap. *(978-1-4076-1294-2(8))* HardPr.

Lefebure, Victor & Aberigh-Mackay, George Robert. Riddle of the Rhine. 2008. 224p. 27.99 *(978-0-554-21435-1(0))* 2008. 224p. 24.99 *(978-0-554-30738-1(3))* 2006. (ENG.). 222p. pap. 22.99 *(978-1-4264-0164-0(7))* 2006. (ENG.). 230p. pap. 20.99 *(978-1-4264-0035-3(7))* BiblioBazaar.

Lefevre, Peggy. Can International Law Achieve the Effective Disarmament of Chemical Weapons. 2008. 244p. pap. *(978-3-639-01898-1(2))* VDM Verlag Dr. Mueller e.K.

Lukey, Brian J., et al, eds. Chemical Warfare Agents: Chemistry, Pharmacology, Toxicology, & Therapeutics. 2nd rev. ed. 2007. (ENG., Illus.). 752p. 210.00 *(978-1-4200-4661-8(6))* CRC Pr. LLC.

Macleod, Roy & Johnson, Jeffrey Allan, eds. Frontline & Factory: Comparative Perspectives on the Chemical Industry at War, 1914-1924. 2007. (Archimedes Ser.). (Illus.). xx, 280p. (C). 189.00 *(978-1-4020-5489-1(0)*, 1402054890) Springer.

Marmiroli, Nelson, et al, eds. Advanced Science & Technology for Biological Decontamination of Sites Affected by Chemical & Radiological Nuclear Agents. 2006. (Nato Science Series: IV: Earth & Environmental Sciences Ser.). (Illus.). xviii, 266p. 189.00 *(978-1-4020-5518-8(8)*, 1402055188); pap. 79.95 *(978-1-4020-5519-5(6)*, 1402055196) Springer.

Mauroni, Al. Chemical & Biological Warfare: A Reference Handbook. 2nd rev. ed. 2006. (Contemporary World Issues Ser.). 319p. 55.00 *(978-1-59884-027-8(4))* ABC-CLIO, LLC.

Maynard, Robert L., et al, eds. Chemical Warfare Agents: Toxicology & Treatment. 2nd rev. ed. 2007. (ENG., Illus.). 750p. 389.95 *(978-0-470-01359-5(1)*, Wiley) Wiley, John & Sons, Inc.

Mayor, Adrienne. Greek Fire, Poison Arrows, & Scorpion Bombs: Biological & Chemical Warfare in the Ancient World. 2008. (ENG.). 336p. (gr. 12). pap. 15.95 *(978-1-59020-177-0(9))* Overlook Pr., The.

Mirzayanov, Vil S. State Secrets: An Insider's Chronicle of the Russian Chemical Weapons Program. 2008. 624p. 43.95 *(978-1-4327-1923-4(8))*; pap. 29.95 *(978-1-4327-2566-2(1))* Outskirts Pr., Inc.

National Research Council (U.S.) Staff & Review and Evaluation of International Technologies for the Destruction of Non-Stockpile Chemical Materiel Committee. Review of International Technologies for Destruction of Recovered Chemical Warfare Materiel. 2006. (ENG., Illus.). 128p. pap. 32.50 *(978-0-309-10203-2(0))* National Academies Pr.

Nuclear, Biological & Chemical Defence: Get Equipped to Meet the NBC Threat. 495.00 *(978-0-7106-2325-6(9))* Jane's Information Group, Inc.

Paige, Christopher Robin. Canada & Chemical Warfare 1939-1945. 2011. 116p. pap. ***(978-1-926635-56-9(6))*** Adlibbed, Ltd.

Parker. Killing Factory. Date not set. (Illus.). vii, 230p. *(978-1-85685-121-3(4))* Robert Smith Literary Agency.

Pearson, Alan M., et al, eds. Incapacitating Biochemical Weapons: Promise or Peril? 2007. (Toposophia: Sustainability, Dwelling, Design Ser.). (ENG., Illus.). 338p. 100.00 *(978-0-7391-1438-4(7))* Lexington Bks.

Pearson, Alan M., et al. Incapacitating Biochemical Weapons: Promise or Peril? 2007. (Toposophia: Sustainability, Dwelling, Design Ser.). (ENG., Illus.). 338p. per. 49.95 *(978-0-7391-1439-1(5))* Lexington Bks.

Schram, Martin. Avoiding Armageddon: Our Future, Our Choice. 2006. (Illus.). 356p. reprint ed. 26.00 *(978-1-4223-5459-9(8))* DIANE Publishing Co.

Stephenson, Charles. The Admiral's Secret Weapon: Lord Dundonald & the Origins of Chemical Warfare. 2006. (Illus.). 196p. 45.00 *(978-1-84383-280-5(1))* Boydell & Brewer, Inc.

Tabassi, Lisa Woolomes, compiled by. OPCW: the Legal Texts. 2nd rev. ed. 2010. (Illus.). 774p. 189.00 *(978-90-6704-318-2(4))* T.M.C. Asser Pr. NLD. Dist: Springer.

Tucker, Jonathan. War of Nerves: Chemical Warfare from World War I to Al-Qaeda. 2007. (ENG., Illus.). 496p. pap. 18.95 *(978-1-4000-3233-4(4)*, Anchor) Knopf Doubleday Publishing Group.

Wilcox, Fred A. Scorched Earth: Legacies of Chemical Warfare in Vietnam. 2011. (ENG., Illus.). 240p. 23.95 *(978-1-60980-138-0(5))* Seven Stories Pr.

CHEMICAL WEATHERING

Jamtveit, B. & Meakin, P., eds. Growth, Dissolution & Pattern Formation in Geosystems. 2010. 428p. pap. 228.00 *(978-90-481-4030-5(7)*, 9048140307) Springer.

CHEMICAL WORKS

see Chemical Plants

CHEMICALS

see also Biomass Chemicals; Cleaning Compounds; Inorganic Compounds; Monomers; Pollutants; Xenobiotics

also groups of chemicals, e.g. Acids, Alkalies, Explosives; and individual chemical substances, e.g. Antimony

Ahmad, Iqbal. Borates: Chemical, Pharmaceutical, & Pharmacological Aspects. 2011. (Materials Science & Technologies Ser.). 166p. 69.00 *(978-1-61209-573-8(9))* Nova Science Pubs., Inc.

Aircraft Icing: Hearing Before the Subcommittee on Aviation of the Committee on Transportation & Infrastructure, House of Representatives, One Hundred Eleventh Congress, Second Session, February 24, 2010. 2010. (Illus.). xv, 170p. ***(978-0-16-086345-5(7)***, 552-070-41429-1) United States Government Printing Office.

Albertov, Leo B. Polymer Degradation & Stability Research Developments. 2007. 225.00 *(978-1-60021-827-9(X))* Nova Science Pubs., Inc.

Allen, Robert, ed. Bulletproof Feathers: How Science Uses Nature's Secrets to Design Cutting-Edge Technology. 2010. (ENG., Illus.). 192p. 35.00 *(978-0-226-01470-8(3))* Univ. of Chicago Pr.

Allured, Michael, ed. McCutcheon's Functional Materials: North American & International Edition. 2007. *(978-1-933430-18-8(4))* MC Publishing Co.

Armarego, W. L. F. & Chai, Christina. Purification of Laboratory Chemicals. (ENG.). 6th ed. 2009. 760p. pap. 134.00 *(978-1-85617-567-8(7))* 7th ed. 2012. 992p. pap. 160.00 ***(978-0-12-382161-4(4))*** Elsevier Science & Technology Bks. (Butterworth-Heinemann).

Ash, Michael & Ash, Irene, eds. Specialty Chemicals Source Book. 4th ed. 2009. 3278p. 575.00 *(978-1-934764-17-6(5))* Synapse Information Resources, Inc.

Aurifeille, Jacques-Marie & Deissenberg, Christopher, eds. Bio-Mimetic Approaches in Management Science. 2010. (Advances in Computational Management Science Ser.). 224p. pap. 209.00 *(978-1-4419-4791-8(4)*, 1441947914) Springer.

Ballini, Roberto & Royal Society of Chemistry Staff. Eco-Friendly Synthesis of Fine Chemicals. Ballini, Roberto, ed. 2009. (RSC Green Chemistry Ser.). (ENG., Illus.). 312p. (C). 213.00 *(978-1-84755-908-1(5))* Royal Society of Chemistry, The GBR. Dist: Ingram Pub. Services.

Bar-Cohen, Yoseph. Biomimetics. 2011. (ENG., Illus.). 788p. 159.95 *(978-1-4398-3476-3(8)*, CRC Press) Taylor & Francis Group GBR. Dist: Taylor & Francis Group.

Bhushan, Bharat, et al, eds. Applied Scanning Probe Methods X: Biomimetics & Industrial Applications. (NanoScience & Technology Ser.). (Illus.). 2010. lx, 427p. pap. 269.00 *(978-3-642-09342-5(6)*, 3642093426) 2008. 380p. 269.00 *(978-3-540-74084-1(8))* Springer.

Birk, Yehudith. Plant Protease Inhibitors: Significance in Nutrition, Plant Protection, Cancer Prevention & Genetic Engineering. 2010. (ENG., Illus.). xi, 170p. pap. 149.00 *(978-3-642-05514-0(1)*, 3642055141) Springer.

Bosze, Zsuszanna, ed. Bioactive Components of Milk. (Advances in Experimental Medicine & Biology Ser.). (Illus.). 2010. xvi, 492p. pap. 189.00 *(978-1-4419-2545-9(7)*, 1441925457) 2007. 492p. 189.00 *(978-0-387-74086-7(4))* Springer.

Brammer, Christopher N. Fluorine-Related Nanoscience with Energy Applications, 1 vol. Nelson, Donna J., ed. 2011. (ACS Symposium Ser.). (ENG., Illus.). 182p. 150.00 ***(978-0-8412-2610-4(5))*** American Chemical Society.

Bukharov, S. V., et al, eds. Polyfunctional Stabilizers of Polymers. 2009. (Illus.). 280p. 145.00 *(978-1-60692-536-2(9))* Nova Science Pubs., Inc.

Caenn, Ryen, et al. Composition & Properties of Drilling & Completion Fluids. 6th ed. 2011. (ENG., Illus.). 720p. 169.95 *(978-0-12-383858-2(4)*, Gulf Professional Publishing) Elsevier Science & Technology Bks.

Carlomagno, Teresa. Microtubule Stabilizing & Destabilizing Agents: Synthetic, Structural & Mechanistic Insights. 2009. (Topics in Current Chemistry Ser.). (ENG., Illus.). xi, 331p. 389.00 *(978-3-540-69036-8(0))* Springer.

Carrier, Danielle Julie, et al. Biorefinery Co-Products: Phytochemicals, Primary Metabolites & Value-Added Biomass Processing. 2012. (Wiley Series in Renewable Resource Ser.). (ENG.). 382p. 140.00 ***(978-0-470-97357-8(9)***, Wiley) Wiley, John & Sons, Inc.

Chemicals: D & B Gale Industry Reference. Date not set. 99.00 *(978-0-7876-3840-5(4))* Cengage Gale.

de la Rosa, Laura A., et al, eds. Fruit & Vegetable Phytochemicals: Chemistry, Nutritional Value & Stability. 2010. (ENG., Illus.). 384p. 219.95 *(978-0-8138-0320-3(9)*, Wiley-Blackwell) Wiley, John & Sons, Inc.

De Mora, Stephen J., ed. Tributyltin: Case Study of an Environmental Contaminant. 2009. (Cambridge Environmental Chemistry Ser.). (ENG., Illus.). 320p. (C). pap. 58.00 *(978-0-521-10512-5(9))* Cambridge Univ. Pr.

Denner, Jon C. Effects of Highway Road Salting on the Water Quality of Selected Streams in Chittenden County, Vermont, November 2005-2007. 2009. (Illus.). viii, 43p. *(978-1-4113-2669-9(5))* United States Geological Survey.

Deswarte, Fabien & Clark, James H., eds. The Introduction to Chemicals from Biomass. 2008. (Wiley Series in Renewable Resource Ser.: 9). (ENG., Illus.). 198p. 95.00 *(978-0-470-05805-3(6)*, Wiley) Wiley, John & Sons, Inc.

Dolbier, W. R., et al. Guide to Fluorine NMR for Organic Chemists. 2009. (ENG., Illus.). 272p. instr.'s gde. ed., instr.'s hndbk. ed. 99.95 *(978-0-470-19341-9(7)*, Wiley) Wiley, John & Sons, Inc.

Eguchi, Shoji. Bioactive Heterocycles II. 2010. (Topics in Heterocyclic Chemistry Ser.). (Illus.). xii, 309p. pap. 319.00 *(978-3-642-09160-5(1)*, 3642091601) Springer.

Eguchi, Shoji, contrib. by. Bioactive Heterocycles II. 2007. (Topics in Heterocyclic Chemistry Ser.). (Illus.). 309p. 319.00 *(978-3-540-72591-6(1))* Springer.

Environment Canada Staff. Non-Domestic Substances List: Registry Number Index. 1760p. pap. *(978-0-660-56394-7(0))* Canadian Government Publishing.

The EPA's IRIS Program: Hearings Before the Subcommittee on Investigations & Oversight, Committee on Science & Technology, One Hundred Tenth Congress, Second Session, May 21, 2008 & June 12, 2008. 2008. (Illus.). v, 227p. *(978-0-16-082647-4(0)*, 552-070-38666-1) United States Government Printing Office.

Fell, Nicholas Francis & Swaminathan, Venkataraman S. Bio-Inspired/Biomimetic Sensor Technologies & Applications: 13-14 April 2009, Orlando, Florida, United States. 2009. (Proceedings of SPIE Ser.). (Illus.). 162p. pap. 60.00 *(978-0-8194-7587-9(4))* SPIE.

Feng, Lin & Jiang, Lei. Bioinspired Intelligent Nanostructured Interfacial Materials. 2010. (Illus.). 364p. 135.00 *(978-981-4280-31-0(3))* World Scientific Publishing Co., Inc.

Fink, Johannes. Petroleum Engineer's Guide to Oil Field Chemicals & Fluids. 2011. (ENG., Illus.). 808p. pap. 139.95 *(978-0-12-383844-5(4)*, Gulf Professional Publishing) Elsevier Science & Technology Bks.

Firn, Richard. Nature's Chemicals: The Natural Products that Shaped Our World. 2011. (ENG., Illus.). 264p. pap. 44.95 *(978-0-19-960302-2(2))* Oxford Univ. Pr., Inc.

Gang, David R., ed. The Biological Activity of Phytochemicals. 2010. (Recent Advances in Phytochemistry Ser.). (Illus.). xiii, 210p. 189.00 *(978-1-4419-6961-3(6)*, 1441969616) Springer.

Geisler, Beth. Resveratrol: Unleashing the Benefits of Red Wine. 2011. 96p. pap. 9.95 *(978-1-57067-242-2(3)*, Healthy Living) Book Publishing Co.

Grubb, Philip W. & Thomsen, Peter R. Patents for Chemicals, Pharmaceuticals & Biotechnology: Fundamentals of Global Law, Practice & Strategy. 5th ed. 2010. (ENG., Illus.). 576p. 235.00 *(978-0-19-957523-7(1))* Oxford Univ. Pr., Inc.

Gruber, Petra. Biomimetics in Architecture: Architecture of Life & Buildings. 2010. (ENG., Illus.). 280p. pap. 89.95 *(978-3-7091-0331-9(2)*, 3709103312) Springer Wien AUT. Dist: Springer.

Hasenhuettl, Gerard L. & Hartel, Richard W., eds. Food Emulsifiers & Their Applications. 2nd ed. 2010. (ENG., Illus.). xiv, 430p. pap. 89.95 *(978-1-4419-2590-9(2)*, 1441925902) Springer.

Hayes, Maria, ed. Marine Bioactive Compounds: Sources, Characterization & Applications. 2011. (ENG., Illus.). xii, 229p. 209.00 ***(978-1-4614-1246-5(3)***, 1461412463) Springer.

He, Qiang, et al. Molecular Assembly of Biomimetic Systems. 2011. (ENG., Illus.). 202p. pap. 210.00 *(978-3-527-32542-9(5)*, Wiley-VCH) Wiley, John & Sons, Inc.

Holm, Edward K. Dispersants in Oil Spills: Issues & Research. 2011. (Environmental Science, Engineering & Technology Ser.). 89.00 *(978-1-61209-241-6(1))* Nova Science Pubs., Inc.

Hou, Michael Z., et al, eds. Underground Storage of CO2 & Energy. 2010. (ENG.). 384p. 145.95 *(978-0-415-60049-1(9)*, CRC Press) Taylor & Francis Group GBR. Dist: Taylor & Francis Group.

Inuki, Shinsuke. Total Synthesis of Bioactive Natural Products by Palladium-Catalyzed Domino Cyclization of Allenes & Related Compounds. 2011. (Springer Theses Ser.). (ENG., Illus.). xvi, 106p. 129.00 ***(978-4-431-54042-7(3)***, 4431540423) Springer.

Jakl, Thomas & Schwager, Petra, eds. Chemical Leasing Goes Global: Selling Services Instead of Barrels: A Win-Win Business Model for Environment & Industry. 2008. (Illus.). 245p. pap. 99.00 *(978-3-211-73751-4(0))* Springer Wien AUT. Dist: Springer.

Khan, Ikhlas A., et al. Leung's Encyclopedia of Common Natural Ingredients: Used in Food, Drugs & Cosmetics. 3rd ed. 2009. (ENG., Illus.). 810p. 148.00 *(978-0-471-46743-4(X)*, Wiley) Wiley, John & Sons, Inc.

Khan, Mahmud Tareq Hassan. Bioactive Heterocycles V. 2010. (Topics in Heterocyclic Chemistry Ser.). (Illus.). xvi, 335p. pap. 299.00 *(978-3-642-09246-6(2)*, 3642092462) Springer.

Khan, Mahmud Tareq Hassan, ed. Bioactive Heterocycles III. 2007. (Topics in Heterocyclic Chemistry Ser.). (Illus.). 287p. 259.00 *(978-3-540-73401-7(5))* Springer.

Kisailus, D., et al, eds. Structure-Property Relationships in Biomineralized & Biomimetic Composites: Volume 1187. 2009. (MRS Proceedings Ser.). (ENG.). 195p. (C). 113.00 *(978-1-60511-160-5(0))* Cambridge Univ. Pr.

Leamon, Earl. Handbook of Chemical Magic. 2007. 48p. per. 14.95 *(978-1-4344-9651-5(1))* Wildside Pr., LLC.

Lewis, Richard J. Hawley's Condensed Chemical Dictionary. 15th rev. ed. 2007. (ENG., Illus.). 1400p. 174.00 *(978-0-471-76865-4(0)*, Wiley-Interscience) Wiley, John & Sons, Inc.

Likhtenshtein, Gertz I. New Trends in Enzyme Catalysis & Biomimetic Chemical Reactions. 2012. (ENG.). 240p. pap. 144.00 *(978-1-4419-5234-9(9)*, 1441952349) Springer.

Mahour, Dr. Kanhiya & Mahour, Kanhiya. Toxic Response Oof Mercuric Chloride on Haematology. 2011. 84p. pap. ***(978-3-8454-0581-0(3))*** Lambert Academic Publishing.

Meena, Ram Raj & Mukharjee, Subrata. Application of Pgrs & Chemicals on Guav. 2011. 120p. pap. ***(978-3-8433-8793-4(1))*** Lambert Academic Publishing.

Milner, John A. & Romagnolo, Donato F., eds. Bioactive Compounds & Cancer. 2010. (Nutrition & Health Ser.). (ENG., Illus.). xiv, 882p. 269.00 *(978-1-60761-626-9(2)*, 1607616262) Humana Pr.

Moeller, Herbert W. Progress in Polymer Degradation & Stability Research. 2007. 185.00 *(978-1-60021-828-6(8))* Nova Science Pubs., Inc.

Motohashi, Noboru. Bioactive Heterocycles VI: Flavonoids & Anthocyanins in Plants, & Latest Bioactive Heterocycles I. 2010. (Topics in Heterocyclic Chemistry Ser.). (Illus.). xiv, 283p. pap. 349.00 *(978-3-642-09809-3(6)*, 3642098096) Springer.

—Bioactive Heterocylces VII: Flavonoids & Anthocyanins in Plants, & Latest Bioactive Heterocycles II. 2009. (Topics in Heterocyclic Chemistry Ser.). (ENG., Illus.). xiv, 236p. 359.00 *(978-3-642-00335-6(4))* Springer.

Münstermann, Ernst. Ternary Systems. 2009. (Landolt-Börnstein: Numerical Data & Functional Relationships in Science & Technology - New Series / Physical Chemistry Ser.). 300p. 4489.00 *(978-3-540-88153-7(0))* Springer.

Myers, Richard L. The 100 Most Important Chemical Compounds: A Reference Guide, 1 vol. 2007. (Illus.). 352p. 85.00 *(978-0-313-33758-1(6)*, GR3758, Greenwood Pr.) Greenwood Publishing Group, Inc.

National Research Council (U.S.), Transportation Research Board Staff, et al, contrib. by. Deicing Planning Guidelines & Practices for Stormwater Management Systems. 2009. (Illus.). 40p. *(978-0-309-11778-4(X))* Transportation Research Board.

Nosonovsky, Michael & Rohatgi, Pradeep K. Biomimetics in Materials Science: Self-Healing, Self-Lubricating, & Self-Cleaning Materials. 2011. (Springer Series in Materials Science Ser.). (ENG., Illus.). xxvi, 415p. 169.00 ***(978-1-4614-0925-0(X)***, 146140925X) Springer.

O'Neil, Maryadele J., ed. The Merck Index: An Encyclopedia of Chemicals, Drugs, & Biologicals. 14th rev. ed. 2006. (ENG., Illus.). 2564p. 125.00 *(978-0-911910-00-1(X))* Merck & Co., Inc.

Paquette, Leo A., ed. Sulfur-Containing Reagents. 2010. (Hdbk of Reagents for Organic Synthesis Ser.). (ENG., Illus.). 728p. 180.00 *(978-0-470-74872-5(9)*, Wiley-Blackwell) Wiley, John & Sons, Inc.

Patnaik, Pradyot. A Comprehensive Guide to the Hazardous Properties of Chemical Substances. 3rd rev. ed. 2007. (ENG., Illus.). 1059p. 205.00 *(978-0-471-71458-3(5)*, Wiley-Interscience) Wiley, John & Sons, Inc.

Pearson, Brian, ed. Speciality Chemicals: Innovations in Industrial Synthesis & Applications. 2007. (Illus.). 636p. 399.00 *(978-1-85166-646-1(X))* Springer.

Peters, Thomas. Bioactive Conformation II, 2 vols. 2008. (Topics in Current Chemistry Ser.). (Illus.). 210p. 279.00 *(978-3-540-49079-1(5)*, 3540490795) Springer.

Pollak, Peter. Fine Chemicals: The Industry & the Business. 2nd ed. 2011. (ENG., Illus.). 312p. 125.00 *(978-0-470-62767-9(0)*, Wiley) Wiley, John & Sons, Inc.

Review of the Use of Dispersants in Response to the Deepwater Horizon Oil Spill: Hearings Before a Subcommittee of the Committee on Appropriations, United States Senate, One Hundred Eleventh Congress, Second Session, Special Hearing, July 15, 2010, Washington, DC. 2011. iii, 57p. ***(978-0-16-089124-3(8)***, 552-070-43136-5) United States Government Printing Office.

Rosenstock, Jerome. The Law of Chemical & Pharmaceutical Invention: Patent & Nonpatent Protection. 3rd ed. 2011. (Illus.). *(978-0-7355-0987-0(5)*, Aspen Pubs.) Wolters Kluwer Law & Business.

Ross, Benjamin & Amter, Steven. The Polluters: The Making of Our Chemically Altered Environment, 1 vol. 2010. (ENG., Illus.). 256p. 27.95 *(978-0-19-973995-0(1))* Oxford Univ. Pr., Inc.

Royal Society of Chemistry Staff. Gums & Stabilisers for the Food Industry 16. Williams, Peter A. & Phillips, Glyn O., eds. 2012. (Special Publication). (ENG., Illus.). 442p. 192.00 ***(978-1-84973-358-8(9))*** Royal Society of Chemistry, The GBR. Dist: Ingram Pub. Services.

Salem, Abdel-Fattah Z. M. Plant-Phytochemicals in Animal Nutrition. 2011. (Animal Science, Issues & Professions Chemistry Research & Applications Ser.). 188p. 89.00 *(978-1-61209-555-4(0))* Nova Science Pubs., Inc.

Schröder, Peter & Collins, Christopher D., eds. Organic Xenobiotics & Plants: From Mode of Action to Ecophysiology. 2010. (Plant Ecophysiology Ser.). (Illus.). viii, 311p. 209.00 *(978-90-481-9851-1(8)*, 9048198518) Springer.

Simeonov, Lubomir I. & Hassanien, Mahmoud A., eds. Exposure & Risk Assessment of Chemical Pollution - Contemporary Methodology. 2009. (NATO Science for Peace & Security Series C: Environmental Security Ser.). (ENG., Illus.). xxvii, 526p. pap. 159.00 *(978-90-481-2334-6(8))*; 409.00 *(978-90-481-2333-9(X))* Springer.

Smithersrapra Technology, compiled by. Latex & Synthetic Polymer Dispersions 2010. 2010. (Conference Proceedings Ser.). (Illus.). 172p. pap. *(978-1-84735-399-3(1))* iSmithers Rapra Publishing.

Swiegers, Gerhard. Bioinspiration & Biomimicry in Chemistry. 2012. (ENG.). 504p. 139.95 ***(978-0-470-56667-1(1)***, Wiley) Wiley, John & Sons, Inc.

Turkington, Robert & Turkington. Chemicals Used for Illegal Purposes: A Guide for First Responders to Identify Explosives, Recreational Drugs & Poisons. 2009. (ENG., Illus.). 456p. 111.00 *(978-0-470-18730-7(8)*, Wiley) Wiley, John & Sons, Inc.

United Nations. Systeme General Harmonise de Classification et d'etiquetage des Produits Chimiques (SGH) 2011. (ENG.). 622p. pap. 115.00 ***(978-92-1-216526-4(5))*** United Nations Pubns.

United States, Congress House Committee on Science and Technology (2007) Subcommittee on Investigations and Oversight Staff, contrib. by. Fixing EPA's Broken Integrated Risk Information System: Hearing Before the Subcommittee on Investigations & Oversight, Committee on Science & Technology, House of Representatives, One Hundred Eleventh Congress, First Session, June 11. 2009. 2009. (Illus.). iv, 139p. *(978-0-16-085096-7(7)*, 552-070-40452-0) United States Government Printing Office.

Vallet-Regi, Maria & Navarrete, Daniel Arcos. Biomimetic Nanoceramics in Clinical Use: From Materials to Applications. 2008. (RSC Nanoscience & Nanotechnology Ser.). (ENG., Illus.). 192p. (C). 195.00 ***(978-0-85404-142-8(7))*** Royal Society of Chemistry, The GBR. Dist: Ingram Pub. Services.

Vepa, Ranjan. Biomimetic Robotics: Mechanisms & Control. 2009. (ENG., Illus.). 360p. (C). 103.00 *(978-0-521-89594-1(4))* Cambridge Univ. Pr.

Winter, Ruth. A Consumer's Dictionary of Household, Yard & Office Chemicals: Complete Information about Harmful & Desirable Chemicals Found in Everyday Home Products, Yard Poisons, & Office Polluters. 2007. (ENG.). 368p. per. 21.95 *(978-0-595-44948-4(4)*, ASJA Pr.) iUniverse, Inc.

Wu, Chih-I. Electronic Properties of Gan & Aln Surfaces & Interfaces. 2009. 188p. pap. *(978-3-639-15631-7(5))* VDM Verlag Dr. Mueller e.K.

Wypych, George. Handbook of UV Degradation & Stabilization. 2010. (ENG., Illus.). 704p. 275.00 *(978-1-895198-46-1(1))* ChemTec Publishing CAN. Dist: Elsevier Science & Technology Bks.

—PVC Degradation & Stabilization. 2nd ed. 2008. (ENG., Illus.). 442p. 285.00 *(978-1-895198-39-3(9))* ChemTec Publishing CAN. Dist: Elsevier Science & Technology Bks.

Xu, Zhimin & Howard, Luke R. Analysis of Antioxidant-Rich Phytochemicals. 2012. (ENG.). 408p. 199.95 ***(978-0-8138-2391-1(9)***, Wiley-Blackwell) Wiley, John & Sons, Inc.

Yaws, Carl L. The Yaws Handbook of Thermodynamic Properties for Hydrocarbons & Chemicals. 2006. (Illus.). 777p. 195.00 *(978-1-933762-07-4(1))* Gulf Publishing Co.

Zhao, X., et al, eds. Bioactive Materials in Medicine: Design & Applications. 2011. (Woodhead Publishing Series in Biomaterials Ser.). (ENG., Illus.). 288p. 215.00 *(978-1-84569-624-5(7))* Woodhead Publishing Ltd. GBR. Dist: Ingram Pub. Services.

CHEMICALS—LAW AND LEGISLATION

Behrendt, Jenny. Reaching for Sustainable Development- Impact Assessment of the European Chemicals Framework. 2007. 60p. per. *(978-3-8364-2132-4(1))* VDM Verlag Dr. Mueller e.K.

Cranor, Carl F. Toxic Torts: Science, Law & the Possibility of Justice. 2008. (ENG.). 416p. pap. 34.99 *(978-0-521-72840-9(1))* Cambridge Univ. Pr.

Drohmann, Dieter & Townsend, Matthew. Reach - Regulation: The European Regulation on Registration, Evaluation, Authorisation & Restriction of Chemical Substances. 2013. (ENG.). 800p. 500.00 ***(978-1-84946-194-8(5))*** Hart Publishing Ltd. GBR. Dist: International Specialized Bk. Services.

Eriksson, Johan, et al, eds. Regulating Chemical Risks: European & Global Challenges. 2010. (ENG., Illus.). xii, 350p. 189.00 *(978-90-481-9427-8(X)*, 904819427X) Springer.

Gardiner, Frances & Garmson, Eleanor, eds. Update on Reach & Ghs - the Asian Outlook. 2010. (ISmithers Update Ser.). 114p. *(978-1-84735-394-8(0))* iSmithers Rapra Publishing.

Gold, Miriam V. & Warshaw, Jean. The Toxic Substances Control Act. 2010. (ENG., Illus.). 600p. pap. 215.00 *(978-0-19-538862-6(3))* Oxford Univ. Pr., Inc.

Kilburn, M.D., Kaye H. Brain Robber: The Poisoning of America by Rotten Egg Gas, 1 vol. 260p. 44.95 *(978-0-313-38306-9(5)*, A2705C, Praeger Pubs.) Greenwood Publishing Group, Inc.

McDonnery, Shannon M., et al. Toxic Substances Control ACT: Summary, Challenges, & Reform Proposals. 2012. ***(978-1-62100-783-8(9))*** Nova Science Pubs., Inc.

Rawson, William K. TSCA Deskbook. 2nd ed. 2012. (ENG.). 650p. pap. 119.95 *(978-1-58576-143-2(5))* Environmental Law Institute.

Smithers Rapra, compiled by. Reach Usa 2008 Conference Proceedings. 2008. (Conference Proceedings Ser.). 192p. per. *(978-1-84735-070-1(4))* iSmithers Rapra Publishing.

Smithers Rapra, compiled by. Reach Usa 2011 Conference Proceedings. 2011. (Conference Proceedings Ser.). 196p. pap. ***(978-1-84735-629-1(X))*** iSmithers Rapra Publishing.

United Nations. Consolidated List of Products whose Consumption and/or Sale Have been Banned, Withdrawn, Severely Restricted or not Approved by Governments. 2011. (ENG.). 80p. pap. 35.00 ***(978-92-1-130281-3(1))*** United Nations Pubns.

Wexler, Philip, ed. Global Cooperation on Environmental Risk Management. 2011. (ENG., Illus.). 845p. 139.95 *(978-1-4200-8469-5(0)*, CRC Press) Taylor & Francis Group GBR. Dist: Taylor & Francis Group.

CHEMICALS—MANUFACTURE AND INDUSTRY

see Chemical Industry

CHEMICALS—PHYSIOLOGICAL EFFECT

see also Pharmacology

ABBE Research Division Staff. Titanium Dioxide & Its Adverse Effects: Index & Medical Analysis of New Research Information for All Nations. 2007. (Illus.). 160p. (YA). ring bd. 74.50 *(978-0-7883-4588-3(5)*, 07883-45885) ABBE Pubs. Assn. of Washington, D.C.

—Titanium Dioxide Applications & Uses in Science & Medicine: Index & Medical Analysis of New Research Information. 2007. (Illus.). 160p. ring bd. 74.50 *(978-0-7883-4699-6(7)*, 07883-46997) ABBE Pubs. Assn. of Washington, D.C.

—Titanium Dioxide in Food, Biology & Medicine: Index & Medical Analysis of New Research Information for All Nations. 2007. (Illus.). 160p. ring bd. 74.50 *(978-0-7883-4491-6(9)*, 07883-44919) ABBE Pubs. Assn. of Washington, D.C.

Emsley, John. Better Looking, Better Living, Better Loving: How Chemistry Can Help You Achieve Life's Goals. 2007. (ENG.). 249p. 39.99 *(978-3-527-31863-6(1)*, Wiley-VCH) Wiley, John & Sons, Inc.

Gilbert, John & Senyuva, Hamide, eds. Bioactive Compounds in Foods. 2008. (ENG., Illus.). 432p. 219.95 *(978-1-4051-5875-6(1)*, Wiley-Blackwell) Wiley, John & Sons, Inc.

Gore, Andrea C. Endocrine-Disrupting Chemicals: From Basic Research to Clinical Practice. 2007. (Contemporary Endocrinology (Humana Press) Ser.). (Illus.). 361p. 199.00 *(978-1-58829-830-0(2))* Humana Pr.

Jacoby, Edgar, ed. Chemogenomics: Methods & Applications. 2009. (Methods in Molecular Biology Ser.). (ENG., Illus.). viii, 315p. 129.00 *(978-1-60761-273-5(9)*, 1607612739) Humana Pr.

Matthews, Bonnye L., ed. Defining Multiple Chemical Sensitivity. alt. ed. 2007. (ENG., Illus.). 212p. per. 35.00 *(978-0-7864-3750-4(2))* McFarland & Co., Inc. Pubs.

Ochiai, Eiichiro. Chemicals for Life & Living. 2011. (Illus.). xviii, 288p. 24.95 *(978-3-642-20272-8(1)*, 3642202721) Springer.

Robertson, John. Carbon Dioxide Feeds the World: CO2 - the Marvel Molecule. 2011. 50p. pap. 25.00 ***(978-1-60746-640-6(6))*** FastPencil, Inc.

Rodricks, Joseph V. Calculated Risks: The Toxicity & Human Health Risks of Chemicals in Our Environment. 2nd rev. ed. 2006. (ENG., Illus.). 358p. 110.00 *(978-0-521-78308-8(9))*; per. 44.00 *(978-0-521-78878-6(1))* Cambridge Univ. Pr.

Scoggan, Nita. Feel Like a Million Dollars. 2007. 76p. pap. 39.95 *(978-0-910487-62-7(6))* Royalty Publishing Co.

Steiner, Tobias, ed. Phytogenics in Animal Nutrition: Natural Concepts to Optimize Gut Health & Performance. 2010. (ENG., Illus.). 192p. pap. 57.95 *(978-1-904761-71-6(2))* Nottingham Univ. Pr. GBR. Dist: Independent Pubs. Group.

World Health Organization. Skin Sensitization in Chemical Risk Assessment: IPCS Harmonization Project Document, No. 5. 2008. (Nonserial Publication Ser.). 89p. pap. 42.00 *(978-92-4-156360-4(5))* World Health Organization.

CHEMICALS—SAFETY MEASURES

American Industrial Hygiene Association Staff, contrib. by. Clandestine Methamphetamine Laboratory Assessment & Remediation Guidance. 2007. i, 29p. *(978-1-931504-80-5(6))* American Industrial Hygiene Assn.

Bender, Herbert F. & Eisenbarth, Philipp. Hazardous Chemicals: Control & Regulation in the European Market. 2007. (ENG., Illus.). 409p. 170.00 *(978-3-527-31541-3(1)*, Wiley-VCH) Wiley, John & Sons, Inc.

Bretherick, L., et al. Bretherick's Handbook of Reactive Chemical Hazards, 2 vols. 7th ed. 2006. (Illus.). 2208p. 0.02 *(978-0-12-373945-2(4))*; Set. 472p. 0.02 *(978-0-12-373946-9(2))* Elsevier Science & Technology Bks. (Academic Pr.).

Center for Chemical Process Safety (CCPS) Staff. Guidelines for Risk Based Process Safety. 2007. (ENG.). 768p. 178.00 *(978-0-470-16569-0(3))* American Institute of Chemical Engineers.

Center for Chemical Process Safety Staff. Guidelines for Chemical Transportation Safety, Security, & Risk Management. 2nd ed. 2008. (ENG., Illus.). 166p. 150.00 *(978-0-471-78242-1(4))* American Institute of Chemical Engineers.

—Guidelines for Performing Effective Pre-Startup Safety Reviews. 2007. (ENG.). 192p. 144.00 *(978-0-470-13403-0(8)*, Wiley-Interscience) Wiley, John & Sons, Inc.

Committee on Prudent Practices in the Laboratory. Prudent Practices in the Laboratory: Handling & Management of Chemical Hazards. Natl. Research Council Staff, ed. 2nd rev. ed. 2011. (ENG.). 360p. 99.95 *(978-0-309-13864-2(7))* National Academies Pr.

Dikshith, T. S. S. Handbook of Chemicals & Safety. 2010. (ENG., Illus.). 531p. 159.95 *(978-1-4398-2060-5(0)*, CRC Press) Taylor & Francis Group GBR. Dist: Taylor & Francis Group.

—Safe Use of Chemicals: A Practical Guide. 2008. (ENG., Illus.). 312p. 109.95 *(978-1-4200-8051-3(2)*, CRC Press) Taylor & Francis Group GBR. Dist: Taylor & Francis Group.

Drohmann, Dieter & Townsend, Matthew. Reach - Regulation: The European Regulation on Registration, Evaluation, Authorisation & Restriction of Chemical Substances. 2013. (ENG.). 800p. 500.00 ***(978-1-84946-194-8(5))*** Hart Publishing Ltd. GBR. Dist: International Specialized Bk. Services.

Eisler, Ronald. Eisler's Encyclopedia of Environmentally Hazardous Priority Chemicals. 2007. (ENG., Illus.). 986p. 215.00 *(978-0-444-53105-6(X)*, Elsevier Science) Elsevier Science & Technology Bks.

Forsberg, Krister & Mansdorf, S. Z. Quick Selection Guide to Chemical Protective Clothing. 5th rev. ed. 2007. (ENG., Illus.). 216p. pap. 64.95 *(978-0-470-14681-1(8)*, Wiley) Wiley, John & Sons, Inc.

Gertz, Susan, et al. Safe Not Sorry! Chemical Safety Activity Handbook. 2007. 50p. (YA). pap. 9.95 *(978-1-883822-52-1(1))* Terrific Science Pr.

HS Safety Handbook. 2nd ed. 2008. *(978-0-88698-224-9(3))* Petroleum Extension Service (PETEX).

National Research Council (U.S.), Committee on Full-System Testing and Evaluation of Personal Protection Equipment Ensembles in Simulated Checmial-Warfare Environments Staff & National Research Council (U.S.), Board on Chemical Sciences and Technology Staff, contrib. by. Soldier Protective Clothing & Equipment: Feasibility of Chemical Testing Using a Fully Articulated Robotic Mannequin. 2008. (ENG., Illus.). 170p. pap. 41.00 *(978-0-309-10933-8(7))* National Academies Pr.

Pereira, Rohan P. Hazardous Chemicals. 2011. 76p. pap. ***(978-3-8443-2185-2(3))*** Lambert Academic Publishing.

Pohanish, Richard P., et al. Chemical Incompatibilities. 3rd ed. 2009. (ENG.). 1110p. 195.00 *(978-0-470-38763-4(7)*, Wiley) Wiley, John & Sons, Inc.

Ruggeri, Lynn Tondat & Costa, Laura. Safer for Your Baby: A Guide to Living Better with Fewer Chemicals. 3rd ed. 2008. (ENG., Illus.). 67p. per. 9.95 *(978-0-9767419-2-3(X))* SaferWorks.

Talford, Robert W., ed. Chemical Safety Board. 2009. 43.00 *(978-1-60692-586-7(5))* Nova Science Pubs., Inc.

Toxic Substances Control ACT & the Chemicals Management Program at EPA: Hearing Before the Committee on Environment & Public Works, United States Senate, One Hundred Ninth Congress, Second Session, August 2, 2006. 2009. (Illus.). iv, 270p. *(978-0-16-084964-0(0)*, 552-070-40354-0) United States Government Printing Office.

United Nations. United Nations Environment Programme Report of the Governing Council: Tenth Special Session (20-22 February 2008) 2008. (ENG.). 28p. pap. 6.00 *(978-92-1-820043-3(7))* United Nations Pubns.

Urben, Peter, ed. Bretherick's Handbook of Reactive Chemical Hazards, 2 vols., Set. 7th ed. 2006. (ENG., Illus.). 2680p. 505.00 *(978-0-12-372563-9(1)*, Academic Pr.) Elsevier Science & Technology Bks.

Wexler, Philip, ed. Global Cooperation on Environmental Risk Management. 2011. (ENG., Illus.). 845p. 139.95 *(978-1-4200-8469-6(0)*, CRC Press) Taylor & Francis Group GBR. Dist: Taylor & Francis Group.

Woodward, John L. & Pitbaldo, Robin. LNG Risk Based Safety: Modeling & Consequence Analysis. 2010. (ENG., Illus.). 374p. 121.00 *(978-0-470-31764-8(7))* American Institute of Chemical Engineers.

World Health Organization. Mono- And Disubstituted Methyltin Butyltin & Octyltin Compounds. 2006. (Concise International Chemical Assessment Document,

No 73 Ser.). (ENG.). 69p. pap. 36.00 *(978-92-4-153073-6(1))* World Health Organization.

—Uncertainty & Data Quality in Exposure Assessment: Part 1: Guidance Document on Characterizing & Communicating Uncertainty in Exposure Assessment. Part 2: Hallmarks of Data Quality in Chemical Exposure Assessmen. 2009. (Nonserial Publication Ser.). (ENG.). 171p. pap. 48.00 *(978-92-4-156376-5(1))* World Health Organization.

CHEMICULTURE

see Hydroponics

CHEMILUMINESCENCE

Iranifam, Mortaza. Flow Analysis & Chemiluminescence: An Update. 2011. 116p. pap. ***(978-3-8443-1417-5(2))*** Lambert Academic Publishing.

Roda, A. Chemiluminescence & Bioluminescence: Past, Present & Future. 2010. (ENG., Illus.). 608p. (C). 192.00 ***(978-1-84755-812-1(7))*** Royal Society of Chemistry, The GBR. Dist: Ingram Pub. Services.

Shimomura, Osamu. Bioluminescence: Chemical Principles & Methods. 2011. 500p. 120.00 ***(978-981-4366-08-3(0))*** 2006. (Illus.). 470p. 111.00 *(978-981-256-801-4(8))* World Scientific Publishing Co., Inc.

Szalay, Aladar A., et al, eds. Bioluminescence & Chemiluminescence: Chemistry, Biology & Applications: Proceedings of the 14th International Symposium. 2007. (Illus.). 283p. 124.00 *(978-981-270-816-8(2))* World Scientific Publishing Co., Inc.

CHEMISTRY

see also Acids; Agricultural Chemistry; Alchemy; Assaying; Bases (Chemistry); Biochemistry; Catalysis; Chemistry, Forensic; Chemistry, Inorganic; Chemistry, Organic; Chemistry, Physical and Theoretical; Color; Cosmochemistry; Crystallization; Dental Chemistry; Electrochemistry; Environmental Chemistry; Evaporation; Fermentation; Fire; Geochemistry; Microchemistry; Pharmaceutical Chemistry; Pharmacy; Photographic Chemistry; Plasma Chemistry; Salts; Solution (Chemistry); Stereochemistry; Toxicological Chemistry

also headings beginning with the word Chemical

Acidity & Basicity. 2010. (Molecular Sieves Ser.). (Illus.). viii, 275p. pap. 389.00 *(978-3-642-09325-8(6),* 3642093256) Springer.

Adams, Gretchen M., et al. Chemistry: The Practical Science. 2007. (ENG., Illus.). 368p. (C). per., pupil's gde. ed. 89.95 *(978-0-618-73621-8(2),* 329680) Brooks/Cole.

Aggeli, A., et al, eds. Self-Assembling Peptide Systems in Biology, Medicine & Engineering. 2010. 372p. pap. 199.00 *(978-90-481-5740-2(4),* 9048157404) Springer.

Ahlberg. Nobel Lectures in Chemistry 2001-2005. 2008. 106.00 *(978-981-279-444-4(1))* World Scientific Publishing Co., Inc.

Ahlberg, Per, ed. Chemistry 2001-2005. 2008. (Nobel Lectures in Chemistry Ser.). (Illus.). 481p. pap. 65.00 *(978-981-279-445-1(X))* World Scientific Publishing Co., Inc.

Allcock, Harry R. Introduction to Materials Chemistry. 2008. (ENG., Illus.). 460p. 99.95 *(978-0-470-29333-1(0),* Wiley) Wiley, John & Sons, Inc.

Allegra, Giuseppe. Interphases & Mesophases in Polymer Crystallization I. 2010. (Advances in Polymer Science Ser.). xiv, 220p. pap. 259.00 *(978-3-642-06466-1(3),* 3642064663) Springer.

—Interphases & Mesophases in Polymer Crystallization II. 2010. (Advances in Polymer Science Ser.). xiv, 204p. pap. 239.00 *(978-3-642-06465-4(5),* 3642064655) Springer.

Amateis, Patricia & Silberberg, Martin S. Student Solutions Manual to Accompany Chemistry: The Molecular Nature of Matter & Change. 5th ed. 2008. (ENG., Illus.). 320p. (C). pap. 80.00 *(978-0-07-304860-4(7),* 0073048607, McGraw-Hill Science, Engineering & Mathematics) McGraw-Hill Higher Education.

American Chemical Society Staff. Chemistry in the Community. 5th ed. 2006. (ENG.). (C). stu. ed. 124.95 incl. cd-rom *(978-0-7167-6961-3(1))* Freeman, W. H. & Co.

Arena, Susan & Hein, Morris. Foundations of College Chemistry. 13th alt. ed. 2010. (ENG.). 518p. (C). ring bd. 98.95 *(978-0-470-55654-2(4),* Wiley) Wiley, John & Sons, Inc.

Armstrong. General, Organic, & Biochemistry: An Applied Approach. 2011. (ENG.). 832p. pap. ***(978-0-8400-6828-6(X))*** Brooks/Cole.

Armstrong, James. General, Organic, & Biochemistry: An Applied Approach. 2011. (Textbooks Available with Cengage YouBook Ser.). (ENG.). 832p. (C). 135.95 *(978-0-534-49349-3(1))* Brooks/Cole.

—General, Organic, & Biochemistry - Lecture Notebook. 2011. (ENG.). 848p. (C). pap. 32.95 *(978-0-8400-6826-2(3))* Brooks/Cole.

Arnold, Melvin T. Essentials of General Organic & Biochemistry. tchr. ed. *(978-0-03-005649-9(7))* Saunders College Publishing.

—Essentials of General Organic Biochemistry. 100p. pap. *(978-0-03-005687-1(X))* Saunders College Publishing.

Atkins, Peter W. Oht T/A Chemical Principles 3e. 3rd ed. 218.40 *(978-0-7167-0741-7(1))* Freeman, W. H. & Co.

Atkins, P.W., et al. Chemistry: Principles & Applications. Date not set. (Illus.). 564p. pap. 11.25 *(978-0-582-35590-3(7))* Addison-Wesley Longman, Ltd. GBR. Dist: Trans-Atlantic Pubns., Inc.

Attfield, John. Chemistry, General, Medical, & Pharmaceutical. 2006. 632p. per. 34.99 *(978-1-4255-6598-5(0))* MPublishing.

Atwood, Charles H. Survival Guide for Introductory Chemistry. 2008. (ENG.). 160p. (C). pap. 46.95 *(978-0-495-82826-6(2))* Brooks/Cole.

Özben, Tomris, ed. Free Radicals, Oxidative Stress, & Antioxidants: Pathological & Physiological Significance. 2010. (Nato Science Series: A: Ser.). 406p. pap. 289.00 *(978-1-4419-3292-1(5),* 1441932925) Springer.

Badin, Mihaela Georgeta. Self-Assembled Monolayers on Gold Substrates: Structure & Characterization. 2008. 132p. pap. ***(978-3-8364-9070-2(6))*** VDM Verlag Dr. Mueller e.K.

Baird, Davis, et al, eds. Philosophy of Chemistry: Synthesis of a New Discipline. 2010. (Boston Studies in the Philosophy of Science Ser.). vii, 362p. pap. 279.00 *(978-90-481-6825-5(2),* 9048168252) Springer.

Banks, Alton J. Chemistry & Chemical Reactivity - Student Solutions Manual. 8th ed. 2011. (ENG.). 480p. (C). pap. 95.95 *(978-1-111-42698-9(8))* Brooks/Cole.

BarCharts, Inc. Chemistry Nursing. 2010. (ENG.). 6p. 5.95 *(978-1-4232-1420-5(X))* Barcharts, Inc.

Baroncini, Massimo. Design, Synthesis & Characterization of new Supramolecular Architectures. 2011. (Springer Theses Ser.). (Illus.). xiii, 90p. 99.00 *(978-3-642-19284-5(X),* 364219284X) Springer.

Bauer, Rich, et al. Accompany Introduction to Chemistry. 2nd ed. 2009. 256p. (C). pap. 61.56 *(978-0-07-322658-3(0),* 0073226580, McGraw-Hill Science, Engineering & Mathematics) McGraw-Hill Higher Education.

—Introduction to Chemistry. 2nd ed. 2009. (ENG.). (C). 172.33 *(978-0-07-727430-6(X),* 007727430X, McGraw-Hill Science, Engineering & Mathematics) McGraw-Hill Higher Education.

—Introduction to Chemistry. 2nd ed. 2009. (ENG.). (C). ring bd., ring bd. 120.67 *(978-0-07-737153-1(4),* 0077371534, McGraw-Hill Science, Engineering & Mathematics) McGraw-Hill Higher Education.

—Loose Leaf Version for Introduction to Chemistry. (ENG.). (C). 2nd ed. 2009. ring bd. 98.75 *(978-0-07-734419-1(7),* 0077344197) 3rd ed. 2012. ring bd. 120.67 ***(978-0-07-749123-9(8),*** 0077491238) McGraw-Hill Higher Education. (McGraw-Hill Science, Engineering & Mathematics).

—Student Solutions Manual for A Conceptual Introduction to Chemistry. 2nd ed. 2009. (ENG.). 256p. (C). pap. 73.67 *(978-0-07-740530-4(7),* 0077405307, McGraw-Hill Science, Engineering & Mathematics) McGraw-Hill Higher Education.

Bauer, Rich, et al. Student's Solutions Manual for Introduction to Chemistry. 3rd ed. 2012. (ENG.). 256p. (C). pap. 73.67 ***(978-0-07-737817-2(2),*** 0077378172, McGraw-Hill Science, Engineering & Mathematics) McGraw-Hill Higher Education.

Bauer, Richard C., et al. A Conceptual Introduction to Chemistry. 2nd ed. 2009. *(978-0-07-351107-8(2))* McGraw-Hill Cos., The.

Bauer, Richard C., et al. Introduction to Chemistry. 3rd ed. 2012. (ENG., Illus.). 800p. (C). 172.33 ***(978-0-07-340267-3(2),*** 0073402672, McGraw-Hill Science, Engineering & Mathematics) McGraw-Hill Higher Education.

Benedek, I., ed. Pressure-Sensitive Design & Formulation, Application, 2 vols., Vol. 2. 2006. (ENG., Illus.). 392p. 301.00 *(978-90-6764-440-2(4),* CRC Press) Taylor & Francis Group GBR. Dist: Taylor & Francis Group.

—Pressure-Sensitive Design, Theoretical Aspects, 2 vols. 2006. (ENG., Illus.). 420p. 301.00 *(978-90-6764-439-6(0),* CRC Press) Taylor & Francis Group GBR. Dist: Taylor & Francis Group.

Bensaude-Vince. Chemistry - the Impure Science. 2008. (Illus.). xii, 268p. 86.00 *(978-1-84816-225-9(1))* Imperial College Pr. GBR. Dist: World Scientific Publishing Co., Inc.

Bermingham, Shane. Novel Extraction & Separation of Chemotherapy Drugs. 2010. 96p. pap. *(978-3-8383-5863-5(5))* Lambert Academic Publishing.

Berthod, Alain, ed. Chiral Recognition in Separation Methods: Mechanisms & Applications. 2010. (ENG., Illus.). xv, 337p. 189.00 *(978-3-642-12444-0(5),* 3642124445) Springer.

Best, Leo R., et al. Introduction to General, Organic, & Biochemistry. 9th ed. 2008. (ENG., Illus.). 1184p. (C). 212.95 *(978-0-470-12925-8(5),* Wiley) Wiley, John & Sons, Inc.

Bettelheim, Frederick. Introduction to General, Organic & Biochemistry, Hybrid. 10th ed. 2012. (Cengage Learningsrquo;s New Hybrid Editions! Ser.). (ENG.). 768p. (C). pap. 165.95 ***(978-1-133-10982-2(9))*** Brooks/Cole.

Billo, E. Joseph. Excel for Chemists - A Comprehensive Guide. 3rd ed. 2011. (ENG., Illus.). 760p. pap. 59.95 *(978-0-470-38123-6(X),* Wiley) Wiley, John & Sons, Inc.

Binder, Wolfgang. Hydrogen Bonded Polymers. 2010. (Advances in Polymer Science Ser.). (Illus.). xii, 206p. pap. 279.00 *(978-3-642-08813-1(9),* 3642088139) Springer.

Binnewies, Michael, et al. Chemische Transportreaktionen.Tr. of Chemical Vapor Reactions. (GER.). 2011. XIV, 639p. 196.00 ***(978-3-11-214738-2(3))*** 2010. 543p. 126.00 *(978-3-11-024896-8(4))* De Gruyter, Walter Inc.

Bishop, Mark. Study Guide for an Introduction to Chemistry - Atoms First. 2007. 324p. (C). per. 64.95 *(978-0-9778105-7-4(7))* Chiral Publishing Co.

Blei, Ira & Odian, George. General, Organic, & Biochemistry Media Update. 2nd ed. 2008. (ENG.). 800p. (C). pap. 163.95 *(978-1-4292-0994-6(1))* Freeman, W. H. & Co.

Blondeau, Pascal. Anion Receptors Based on Ion Pairing & Hydrogen Bonding. 2011. 196p. pap. ***(978-3-8443-8424-6(3))*** Lambert Academic Publishing.

Blystone. Chemistry 101: Armchair Chemistry. 4th rev. ed. 2011. (ENG.). 176p. spiral bd. 32.95 ***(978-0-7575-9517-2(0))*** Kendall Hunt Publishing Co.

Bonamin, Leoni Villano, ed. Signals & Images: Contributions & Contradictions about High Dilution Research. 2010. (ENG.). viii, 222p. pap. 209.00 *(978-90-481-7904-6(1),* 9048179041) Springer.

Bottle, R. T. & Rowland, J. F. B., eds. Information Sources in Chemistry. 4th ed. 2012. (Guides to Information Sources Ser.). (ENG.). XVI, 340p. E-Book 238.00 ***(978-3-11-186790-8(0))*** De Gruyter, Walter Inc.

Boyce, Conal. The Chemistry Redemption. 2010. 502p. pap. 29.16 *(978-0-557-52793-9(7))* Lulu Enterprises Inc.

Boyd, Donald B., et al, eds. Reviews in Computational Chemistry, Volume 23. 2007. (Reviews in Computational Chemistry Ser.: 30). (ENG., Illus.). 484p. 198.00 *(978-0-470-08201-0(1),* Wiley-VCH) Wiley, John & Sons, Inc.

Brady & Senese. Chemistry: Matter & Its Changes. 5th ed. 2007. (ENG.). 1048p. (C). ring bd. 140.95 *(978-0-470-27983-0(4),* Wiley) Wiley, John & Sons, Inc.

Brady, James E. Chemistry: The Study of Matter & It's Changes + WileyPlus Access Card. 2006. 121.00 net. *(978-0-470-10137-7(7))* Wiley, John & Sons, Inc.

Brady, James E., et al. Chemistry: The Study of Matter & Its Changes. 5th ed. (ENG., Illus.). (C). 2008. 552p. pap., pupil's gde. ed. 62.95 *(978-0-470-18464-6(7))* 2007. 1048p. 222.95 *(978-0-470-12094-1(0))* Wiley, John & Sons, Inc. (Wiley).

Braese, Stefan. Combinatorial Chemistry on Solid Supports. 2010. (Topics in Current Chemistry Ser.). (Illus.). xii, 360p. pap. 419.00 *(978-3-642-09155-1(5),* 3642091555) Springer.

Brèchignac, Catherine, et al, eds. Nanomatérials & Nanochemistry. 2008. Orig. Title: Les Nanosciences - les Nanomatériaux. (ENG., Illus.). xxx, 747p. 219.00 *(978-3-540-72992-1(5),* 3540729925) Springer.

Brooker, Robert. Biology: Chemistry, Cell Biology & Genetics, Vol. 1. 2nd ed. 2010. (ENG.). (C). pap. 90.67 *(978-0-07-740565-6(X),* 007740565X, McGraw-Hill Science, Engineering & Mathematics) McGraw-Hill Higher Education.

Brouard, M. & Vallance, Claire. Tutorials in Molecular Reaction Dynamics. 2010. (ENG., Illus.). 508p. 80.00 ***(978-0-85404-158-9(3))*** Royal Society of Chemistry, The GBR. Dist: Ingram Pub. Services.

Brown, Kate. General, Organic, & Biochemistry. 2nd ed. Date not set. (Chemistry Ser.). tchr. ed. 1.00 *(978-0-87150-774-7(9));* stu. ed. 14.25 net. *(978-0-87150-772-3(2))* Brooks/Cole. (Brooks/Cole).

Brown, Larry & Holme, Tom. Chemistry for Engineering Students. 2nd ed. 2010. (Available Titles OWL Ser.). (ENG.). (C). 608p. 231.95 *(978-1-4390-4791-0(X));* 384p. pap., pupil's gde. ed. 105.95 *(978-1-4390-4981-5(5))* Brooks/Cole.

Brown, LeMay & Cram101 Textbook Reviews Staff. Chemistry: The Central Science. 2007. 348p. per. 16.95 *(978-1-4288-3050-9(2))* Cram101 Inc.

Brown, Theodore E. Books A la Carte for Chemistry: The Central Science. 12th ed. 2011. (ENG.). 1200p. (C). ring bd. 133.20 *(978-0-321-74145-5(5),* Prentice Hall) Prentice Hall PTR.

Brown, Theodore E. & Hill, James C. Student's Guide for Chemistry: The Central Science. 12th ed. 2011. (ENG.). 504p. (C). pap. 71.47 *(978-0-321-70458-0(4),* Prentice Hall) Prentice Hall PTR.

Brown, Theodore E. & Wilson, Roxy. Solutions to Red Exercises for Chemistry: The Central Science. 12th rev. ed. 2011. (ENG.). 360p. (C). pap. 75.13 *(978-0-321-70548-8(3),* Prentice Hall) Prentice Hall PTR.

Brown, Theodore E., et al. Chemistry: The Central Science. 12th ed. (ENG.). (C). 2011. ring bd. 143.20 *(978-0-321-78756-9(0))* 2011. 1248p. 232.00 *(978-0-321-74105-9(6))* 2011. 1200p. E-Book, E-Book 126.67 *(978-0-321-70512-9(2))* 2010. 1200p. 222.00 *(978-0-321-69672-4(7))* Prentice Hall PTR. (Prentice Hall).

—Laboratory Experiments for Chemistry: The Central Science. 12th rev. ed. 2011. (ENG.). 752p. (C). pap. 113.93 *(978-0-321-70502-0(5),* Prentice Hall) Prentice Hall PTR.

—Solutions to Black Exercises for Chemistry: The Central Science. 12th rev. ed. 2011. (ENG.). 448p. (C). pap. 75.13 *(978-0-321-70501-3(7),* Prentice Hall) Prentice Hall PTR.

Bruckner, Dietmar, et al, eds. Bionics in Materials Structure, Architecture & Information: Examples, Ideas & Case Studies. 2011. (Biological & Medical Physics, Biomedical Engineering Ser.). (Illus.). 250p. 129.00 *(978-3-642-11933-0(6),* 3642119336) Springer.

Buchmeiser, Michael R. Metathesis Polymerization. 2010. (Advances in Polymer Science Ser.). (Illus.). xi, 142p. pap. 219.00 *(978-3-642-06238-4(5),* 3642062385) Springer.

Burdge, Julia. Chemistry. (ENG., (C). 2008. Illus.). 612p. pap. 56.88 *(978-0-07-327169-9(1),* 0073271691) 2008. (Illus.). 1056p. 198.75 *(978-0-07-722132-4(X),* 007722132X) 2nd ed. 2010. 243.00 *(978-0-07-746842-2(2),* 0077468422) 2nd ed. 2010. (Illus.). 1088p. 229.67 *(978-0-07-735476-3(1),* 0077354761) McGraw-Hill Higher Education. (McGraw-Hill Science, Engineering & Mathematics).

—Chemistry: Atoms First 2011. (ENG.). (C). 238.66 *(978-0-07-746841-5(4),* 0077468414, McGraw-Hill Science, Engineering & Mathematics) McGraw-Hill Higher Education.

—Loose Leaf Chemistry. 2nd ed. 2010. (ENG.). (C). ring bd. 161.00 *(978-0-07-740173-3(5),* 0077401735, McGraw-Hill Science, Engineering & Mathematics) McGraw-Hill Higher Education.

—Student Solutions Manual to accompany Chemistry. (ENG.). (C). 2008. 608p. pap. 60.31 *(978-0-07-327170-5(5),* 0073271705) 2nd ed. 2010. 400p. pap. 70.67 *(978-0-07-729683-4(4),* 0077296834) McGraw-Hill Higher Education. (McGraw-Hill Science, Engineering & Mathematics).

—Student Study Guide to accompany Chemistry. 2nd ed. 2010. (ENG.). 512p. (C). pap. 66.67 *(978-0-07-729684-1(2),* 0077296842, McGraw-Hill Science, Engineering & Mathematics) McGraw-Hill Higher Education.

—VitalSource Access Code Card to accompany Chemistry. 2008. (ENG.). (C). 109.25 *(978-0-07-728023-9(7),* 0077280237, McGraw-Hill Science, Engineering & Mathematics) McGraw-Hill Higher Education.

Burdge, Julia & Chang, Raymond. Chemistry. 2008. 1056p. *(978-0-07-302554-4(2))* McGraw-Hill Cos., The.

Burdge, Julia & Overby, Jason. Chemistry: Atoms First. 2011. (ENG.). (C). ring bd. 161.00 *(978-0-07-743083-2(2),* 0077430832, McGraw-Hill Science, Engineering & Mathematics) McGraw-Hill Higher Education.

Burdge, Julia R. Chemistry. 2nd ed. 2010. *(978-0-07-337564-9(0))* McGraw-Hill Cos., The.

Burdge, Julia R. & Overby, Jason. Chemistry: Atoms First. 2011. (ENG., Illus.). 1128p. (C). 229.67 *(978-0-07-351116-0(1),* 0073511161, McGraw-Hill Science, Engineering & Mathematics) McGraw-Hill Higher Education.

Carlsen, Lars & Brüggemann, Rainer, eds. Partial Order in Environmental Sciences & Chemistry. 2006. (Illus.). 406p. 159.00 *(978-3-540-33968-7(X),* 354033968X) Springer.

Caroli, Sergio, ed. The Determination of Chemical Elements in Food: Applications for Atomic & Mass Spectrometry. 2007. (ENG., Illus.). 733p. 195.00 *(978-0-471-68784-9(7),* Wiley-Interscience) Wiley, John & Sons, Inc.

Carolina Biological Staff, compiled by. Chemical & Nuclear Bundle. 2009. (Inquiries in Science Chemistry Ser.). *(978-1-4350-0420-7(5))* Carolina Biological Supply Co.

—Complete Chemistry Series Bundle. 2009. (Inquiries in Science Chemistry Ser.). *(978-1-4350-0417-7(5))* Carolina Biological Supply Co.

—Expanding on the Gas Laws. 2009. (Inquiries in Science Chemistry Ser.). *(978-1-4350-0392-7(6))* Carolina Biological Supply Co.

—Finding Solutions. 2009. (Inquiries in Science Chemistry Ser.). *(978-1-4350-0402-3(7))* Carolina Biological Supply Co.

Cavendish, Henry. The Scientific Papers of the Honourable Henry Cavendish, F. R. S. Maxwell, James Clerk & Larmor, Sir Joseph, eds. 2011. (Cambridge Library Collection - Physical Sciences Ser.). (Illus.). 488p. pap. 35.99 *(978-1-108-01821-0(1))* Cambridge Univ. Pr.

—The Scientific Papers of the Honourable Henry Cavendish, F. R. S. Thorpe, Sir Edward, ed. 2011. (Cambridge Library Collection - Physical Sciences Ser.). (Illus.). 522p. pap. 39.99 *(978-1-108-01822-7(X))* Cambridge Univ. Pr.

Cenini, S. & Ragaini, F. Catalytic Reductive Carbonylation of Organic Nitro Compounds. 2010. (Catalysis by Metal Complexes Ser.). 356p. pap. 349.00 *(978-90-481-4766-3(2),* 9048147662) Springer.

Central Florida Community College Staff. Supplement for Chemistry Fundamentals Ii. rev. ed. 2010. (ENG.). 180p. spiral bd. 33.92 *(978-0-7575-6587-8(5))* Kendall Hunt Publishing Co.

Chang, Raymond. Chemistry. 10th ed. 2009. *(978-0-07-351109-2(9))* McGraw-Hill Cos., The.

—Chemistry. 9th ed. 2006. (Illus.). 1063p. 187.19 *(978-0-07-330170-9(1),* 9780073301709) 10th ed. 2009. (ENG.). (C). 238.66 *(978-0-07-738830-0(5),* 0077388305) 10th ed. 2009. (ENG., Illus.). (C). 229.67 *(978-0-07-727431-3(8),* 0077274318) McGraw-Hill Higher Education. (McGraw-Hill Science, Engineering & Mathematics).

—General Chemistry: The Essential Concepts. 5th ed. 2007. 153.44 *(978-0-07-304851-2(8))* McGraw-Hill Cos., The.

—General Chemistry: The Essential Concepts. 5th rev. ed. 2007. (ENG., Illus.). 832p. (C). 161.25 *(978-0-07-331185-2(5),* 0073311855, McGraw-Hill Science, Engineering & Mathematics) McGraw-Hill Higher Education.

—General Chemistry: The Essential Concepts with ARIS Plus Access Card. 6th ed. 2010. (ENG.). (C). 190.33 *(978-0-07-746843-9(0),* 0077468430, McGraw-Hill Science, Engineering & Mathematics) McGraw-Hill Higher Education.

—Loose Leaf Version for Chemistry. 10th ed. 2009. (ENG.). (C). ring bd. 131.25 *(978-0-07-734387-3(5),* 0077343875, McGraw-Hill Science, Engineering & Mathematics) McGraw-Hill Higher Education.

Chang, Raymond & Goldsby, Kenneth. Chemistry. 11th ed. 2012. (ENG., Illus.). 1168p. (C). 229.67 ***(978-0-07-340268-0(0),*** 0073402680, McGraw-Hill Science, Engineering & Mathematics) McGraw-Hill Higher Education.

—Loose Leaf Version for Chemistry. 11th ed. 2012. (ENG.). (C). ring bd. 161.00 ***(978-0-07-749125-3(4),*** 0077491254, McGraw-Hill Science, Engineering & Mathematics) McGraw-Hill Higher Education.

—Student Solutions Manual for Chemistry. 11th ed. 2012. (ENG.). 656p. (C). pap. 88.00 ***(978-0-07-738654-2(X),*** 007738654X, McGraw-Hill Science, Engineering & Mathematics) McGraw-Hill Higher Education.

—Student Study Guide for Chemistry. 11th ed. 2012. (ENG.). 624p. (C). pap. 83.67 ***(978-0-07-738657-3(4),*** 0077386574, McGraw-Hill Science, Engineering & Mathematics) McGraw-Hill Higher Education.

Chang, Raymond & Overby, Jason. General Chemistry: The Essential Concepts. 6th ed. 2010. (ENG., Illus.). 832p. (C). 181.33 *(978-0-07-735471-8(0),* 0077354710, McGraw-Hill Science, Engineering & Mathematics) McGraw-Hill Higher Education.

—Loose Leaf General Chemistry: the Essential Concepts. 6th ed. 2010. (ENG.). (C). ring bd. 126.00 *(978-0-07-740177-1(8),* 0077401778, McGraw-Hill Science, Engineering & Mathematics) McGraw-Hill Higher Education.

Chang, Raymond & Overby, Jason Scott. General Chemistry: The Essential Concepts. 6th ed. 2010. *(978-0-07-337563-2(2))* McGraw-Hill Cos., The.

Chatellier, Dana S. Chemistry 101 Lecture Notes. rev. ed. 2010. (ENG.). 122p. spiral bd. 33.74 *(978-0-7575-2146-1(0))* Kendall Hunt Publishing Co.

Die Chemie. (Schulerduden Ser.). (ENG & GER.). 27.95 *(978-3-411-02218-2(3),* B2218) Bibliographisches Institut & F. A. Brockhaus AG DEU. Dist: Continental Bk. Co., Inc.

Chemistry 6E Volume 2 for Southern Connecticut State University. 2011. (C). ring bd. 83.95 ***(978-1-118-12119-1(8),*** Wiley) Wiley, John & Sons, Inc.

Chemistry Quick Reference Guide. 2007. *(978-1-934529-08-9(7))* Innovative Academic Solutions.

Chemistry Workbook. 2007. *(978-1-934529-07-2(9))* Innovative Academic Solutions.

Ciarlet, Philippe G. Essential Computational Modeling in Chemistry. 2010. (ENG., Illus.). 400p. pap. 79.95 *(978-0-444-53754-6(6),* North Holland) Elsevier Science & Technology Bks.

Clemente Gallardo, Jesús, et al, eds. Large Scale Simulations of Complex Systems, Condensed Matter & Fusion Plasma: Proceedings of the BIFI2008 International Conference. 2008. (AIP Conference Proceedings / Plasma Physics Ser.). 138p. 109.00 *(978-0-7354-0602-5(2))* American Institute of Physics.

Clinton, Sandra, et al. AS Chemistry Planning & Resource Pack with Oxbox CD-ROM. 2010. 304p. (YA). 700.00 *(978-0-19-915275-9(6))* Oxford Univ. Pr., Inc.

Coastline Learning Systems Staff. Understanding Chemistry in Our World. rev. ed. 2010. (ENG.). 500p. pap. 149.95 *(978-0-7575-6017-0(2))* Kendall Hunt Publishing Co.

Colbert, Bruce J., et al. An Integrated Approach to Health Sciences: Anatomy & Physiology, Math, Chemistry & Medical Microbiology (Book Only) 2nd ed. 2011. (ENG.). 496p. (C). 161.95 *(978-1-111-31999-1(5))* Delmar Cengage Learning.

COLLEGE OF WILLIAM & MARY. Acid, Acid Everywhere: Student Pak. 2007. pap. 49.95 *(978-0-7575-3891-9(6))* Kendall Hunt Publishing Co.

Cooke, Josiah Parsons. First Principles of Chemical Philosophy. 2006. 568p. per. 32.99 *(978-1-4255-6235-9(3))* MPublishing.

Cooley, Le Roy C[lark]. A Text-Book of Chemistry a Modern & Systematic Explanation of the Elementary Principles of the Science. 2006. 232p. per. 20.99 *(978-1-4255-1998-8(9))* MPublishing.

Corwin, Charles H. Introductory Chemistry: Concepts & Critical Thinking. 6th ed. 2010. (ENG.). 800p. (C). 170.80 *(978-0-321-70621-8(8))*; E-Book 126.67 *(978-0-321-70695-9(1))*; (Illus.). 160.80 *(978-0-321-66305-4(5))* Prentice Hall PTR. (Prentice Hall).

—Prentice Hall Laboratory Manual to Introductory Chemistry: Concepts & Connections. 5th ed. 2008. (ENG.). 352p. (C). pap. 95.80 *(978-0-13-604301-0(1),* Prentice Hall) Prentice Hall PTR.

—Study Guide & Selected Solutions Manual for Introductory Chemistry: Concepts & Critical Thinking. 6th ed. 2010. (ENG.). 336p. (C). pap. 61.93 *(978-0-321-67514-9(2),* Prentice Hall) Prentice Hall PTR.

Cox, Michael, et al, eds. Combustion Residues: Current, Novel & Renewable Applications. 2008. (ENG., Illus.). 442p. 225.00 *(978-0-470-09442-6(7),* Wiley) Wiley, John & Sons, Inc.

Cracolice. Lab Manual-Liberal Arts Chemistry. 2008. (C). pap. 33.95 *(978-0-534-42277-6(2))* Brooks/Cole.

—S. G. Liberal Arts Chemistry. 2008. (C). pap. 37.95 *(978-0-534-42276-9(4))* Brooks/Cole.

Cracolice, Mark, et al. Introductory Chemistry: An Active Learning Approach, International Edition. 4th ed. 2011. (Illus.). 800p. pap. 179.95 *(978-0-495-55853-8(2))* Brooks/Cole.

Cram101 Textbook Reviews Staff. Outlines & Highlights for Fundamentals of General, Organic, & Biological Chemistry by Holum, Isbn: 0471175749. 2007. 500p. pap. 20.95 *(978-1-4288-3012-7(X))* Cram101 Inc.

—Outlines & Highlights for General Chemistry: Principles & Modern Applications by Petrucci ISBN. 2007. 588p. pap. 22.95 *(978-1-4288-3080-6(4))* Cram101 Inc.

—Outlines & Highlights for General Chemistry by Ebbing, Isbn: 0618447962. 2007. 476p. pap. 19.95 *(978-1-4288-3032-5(4))* Cram101 Inc.

—Outlines & Highlights for General, Organic, & Biochemistry by Denniston, Isbn: 0072469056. 2007. 408p. pap. 18.95 *(978-1-4288-3044-8(8))* Cram101 Inc.

—Outlines & Highlights for General, Organic, & Biological Chemistry by Timberlake, Isbn: 0805389148. 2007. 412p. pap. 18.95 *(978-1-4288-3016-5(2))* Cram101 Inc.

—Outlines & Highlights for Introductory Chemistry a Foundation by Zumdahl, Isbn: 0618304991. 2007. 248p. pap. 14.95 *(978-1-4288-3058-5(8))* Cram101 Inc.

—Outlines & Highlights for Introductory Chemistry by Cracolice, Isbn: 0534407293. 2007. 316p. pap. 16.95 *(978-1-4288-3036-3(7))* Cram101 Inc.

—Outlines & Highlights for Introductory Chemistry Concepts & Connections by Corwin, Isbn: 0131448501. 2007. 288p. pap. 15.95 *(978-1-4288-3060-8(X))* Cram101 Inc.

—Outlines & Highlights for Principles of Chemistry by Munowitz, Isbn: 0393972887. 2007. 344p. pap. 16.95 *(978-1-4288-3040-0(5))* Cram101 Inc.

Crawford, Daniel. Coupled Cluster Theory. 2013. (ENG., Illus.). 408p. 129.95 *(978-1-4200-8451-1(8),* CRC Press) Taylor & Francis Group GBR. Dist: Taylor & Francis Group.

Crowe, Jonathan & Bradshaw, Tony. Chemistry for the Biosciences: The Essential Concepts. 2nd ed. 2010. (ENG., Illus.). 512p. 59.95 *(978-0-19-957087-4(6))* Oxford Univ. Pr., Inc.

Dahm, Donald J. & Nelson, Eric A. Calculations in Chemistry — Modules 1-16. 2011. 416p. (C). pap. 19.00 net. ***(978-0-9823931-8-5(0))*** ChemReview.

Dai, Li-Xin & Hou, Xue-Long, eds. Chiral Ferrocenes in Asymmetric Catalysis: Synthesis & Applications. 2010. (ENG., Illus.). 431p. 215.00 *(978-3-527-32280-0(9),* Wiley-VCH) Wiley, John & Sons, Inc.

Dalton, John. A New System of Chemical Philosophy. 2009. 242p. pap. 28.99 *(978-1-115-44137-7(X))*; 32.99 *(978-1-115-44139-1(6))*; pap. 26.75 *(978-1-115-44135-3(3))*; pap. 25.75 *(978-1-115-44133-9(7))* BiblioBazaar.

—A New System of Chemical Philosophy. 2009. 202p. pap. *(978-1-151-75460-8(9))*; 186p. pap. *(978-0-217-15343-0(7))*; 252p. pap. *(978-0-217-43330-3(8))*; 150p. pap. *(978-1-4432-9157-6(9))* Books LLC.

—A New System of Chemical Philosophy. 2010. (Cambridge Library Collection - Physical Sciences Ser.). 376p. pap. 29.99 *(978-1-108-01968-2(4))* Cambridge Univ. Pr.

Davies, Geoffrey, et al. Chemistry: The Science in Context. 3rd ed. 2011. (ENG., Illus.). 1240p. (C). 125.00 net. *(978-0-393-93431-1(4),* 93431) Norton, W. W. & Co., Inc.

Davy, Humphry. The Collected Works of Sir Humphry Davy. 2010. 390p. pap. 33.75 *(978-1-143-66957-6(6))* BiblioBazaar.

—The Collected Works of Sir Humphry Davy. 2009. 272p. pap. *(978-0-217-88944-5(1))* Books LLC.

—The Collected Works of Sir Humphry Davy: Elements of chemical Philosophy (1840) 2009. 216p. pap. *(978-0-217-88947-6(6))* Books LLC.

—The Collected Works of Sir Humphry Davy: Discourses Delivered Before the Royal Society, & Agricultural Lectures, Pt. 2009. 204p. pap. *(978-1-150-29295-8(4))* Books LLC.

—The Collected Works of Sir Humphry Davy: Discourses Delivered Before the Royal Society Elements of Agricultural Chemistry, Pt I. 2009. 214p. pap. 19.66 *(978-1-150-09233-5(5))* General Bks. LLC.

—The Collected Works of Sir Humphry Davy, Ed by J Davy. 2009. 202p. pap. 19.99 *(978-1-150-51030-4(7))* General Bks. LLC.

De la Selva, Teresa. De la Alquimia a la Quimica. (Ciencia para Todos Ser.). (SPA.). pap. 6.99 *(978-968-16-3740-8(2))* Fondo de Cultura Economica USA.

DeCoste, Donald J. & Zumdahl, Steven S. Introductory Chemistry: A Foundation. 6th ed. 2007. (ENG., Illus.). 224p. (C). stu. ed., per. 77.95 *(978-0-618-80333-0(5),* 370845) Brooks/Cole.

Denniston, Katherine, et al. Student Study Guide/Solutions Manual to Accompany General, Organic & Biochemistry. 6th ed. 2007. (ENG., Illus.). 576p. (C). per. 65.31 *(978-0-07-322684-2(X),* 007322684X, McGraw-Hill Science, Engineering & Mathematics) McGraw-Hill Higher Education.

Denniston, Katherine J., et al. General Chemistry, Chapters 1-9 from General, Organic, & Biochemistry. 6th ed. 2007. (ENG., Illus.). 317p. (C). per. 98.67 *(978-0-07-724036-3(7),* 0077240367, McGraw-Hill Science, Engineering & Mathematics) McGraw-Hill Higher Education.

—Student Solutions Manual to Accompany Foundations of General Organic & Biochemistry. 2007. (ENG., Illus.). 460p. (C). per. 69.67 *(978-0-07-321743-7(3),* 0073217433, McGraw-Hill Science, Engineering & Mathematics) McGraw-Hill Higher Education.

Derouane, Eric G. & Roberts, Stanley M., eds. Microporous & Mesoporous Solid Catalysts, Vol. 4. 2007. (Catalysts for Fine Chemicals Synthesis Ser.: 4). (ENG., Illus.). 258p. 269.00 *(978-0-471-49054-8(7),* Wiley-Interscience) Wiley, John & Sons, Inc.

Devillanova, F. A. Handbook of Chalcogen Chemistry: New Perspectives in Sulfur, Selenium & Tellurium. 2006. (ENG., Illus.). 894p. 480.00 *(978-0-85404-366-8(7))* Royal Society of Chemistry, The GBR. Dist: Ingram Pub. Services.

DeWane, Marian & Hattori, Heather. Practice Makes Perfect Chemistry. 2011. (Practice Makes Perfect Ser.). (ENG., Illus.). 192p. (C). pap. 13.00 *(978-0-07-174549-9(1),* 0071745491) McGraw-Hill Cos., The.

Dixon, Donovan. Supplement for Chemistry Fundamentals Ii. rev. ed. 2011. (ENG.). 180p. spiral bd. 35.00 ***(978-0-7575-9692-6(4))*** Kendall Hunt Publishing Co.

Dorgan, Lonnie & Jones, Richard. Introduction to Chemistry: Sinclair Chemistry Department. rev. ed. 2012. (ENG.). 170p. spiral bd. 35.00 ***(978-0-7575-9363-5(1))*** Kendall Hunt Publishing Co.

Dorin. Physical Science Chemical Study Matter '92. lab manual ed. 9.97 *(978-0-13-127358-0(2))*; 4th ed. 20.97 *(978-0-13-127515-7(1),* Prentice Hall (Schl. Div.).

—Physical Science Chemistry Study Matter '92. 4th ed. 1727p. 38.47 *(978-0-13-127333-7(7))* Prentice Hall (Schl. Div.).

Dorn, James M. & Hopkins, Barbara M. Thanatochemistry: Survey of General, Organic, & Biochemistry for Funeral Service Professionals. 3rd ed. 2009. (ENG.). 360p. (C). pap. 149.47 *(978-0-13-602687-7(7),* Prentice Hall) Prentice Hall PTR.

Dragutan, Valerian, et al, eds. Green Metathesis Chemistry: Great Challenges in Synthesis, Catalysis & Nanotechnology. 2009. (NATO Science for Peace & Security Series A: Chemistry & Biology Ser.). (Illus.). xix, 425p. 269.00 *(978-90-481-3431-1(5),* 9048134315); (ENG., pap. 139.00 *(978-90-481-3432-8(3),* 9048134323) Springer.

Draper, Henry. A Text-Book on Chemistry: For the Use of Schools & Colleges / by Henry Draper. 2006. 512p. per. 29.99 *(978-1-4255-5819-2(4))* MPublishing.

Ebbing, Darrell & Gammon, Steven D. General Chemistry. 9th ed. 2009. (Available 2010 Titles Enhanced Web Assign Ser.). (ENG.). 1184p. (C). 250.95 *(978-1-4390-4399-8(X))* Brooks/Cole.

Echekki, Tarek & Mastorakos, Epaminondas, eds. Turbulent Combustion Modeling: Advances, New Trends & Perspectives. 2010. (Fluid Mechanics & Its Applications Ser.). (ENG., Illus.). xxi, 490p. 179.00 *(978-94-007-0411-4(9),* 9400704119) Springer.

Editorial Temis Staff. Hacia la Quimica 1 (Toward Chemistry 1), Set. (SPA.). 13.50 *(978-958-604-128-7(X))* Temis S.A., Editorial COL. Dist: AIMS International Bks., Inc.

Edwards-Buckles. Chemistry Manual. rev. ed. 2011. (ENG.). 100p. pap. 40.00 ***(978-0-7575-9313-0(5))*** Kendall Hunt Publishing Co.

Elementos Encadenados. (Serie de Quimica: No. 5). (SPA.). pap. 3.50 *(978-0-8270-6340-2(7))* Organization of American States.

Endler, P. C. & Schulte, J., eds. Ultra High Dilution: Physiology & Physics. 2010. 284p. pap. 189.00 *(978-90-481-4359-7(4),* 9048143594) Springer.

Eubanks, Lucy Pryde, et al. Chemistry in Context: Applying Chemistry to Society. 6th ed. 2008. (ENG., Illus.). 608p. (C). pap., pap. 144.38 *(978-0-07-722134-8(6),* 0077221346, McGraw-Hill Science, Engineering & Mathematics) McGraw-Hill Higher Education.

Evangelist. Mcgraw-Hill's Sat Subject Test Chemistry: 3rd Edition. 3rd rev. ed. 2011. (ENG., Illus.). 320p. (C). pap. 18.00 ***(978-0-07-176875-7(0),*** 0071768750) McGraw-Hill Cos., The.

Fabbrizzi, Luigi & Poggi, Antonio, eds. Chemistry at the Beginning of the Third Millennium: Molecular Design, Supramolecules, Nanotechnology & Beyond. 2010. (Illus.). viii, 356p. pap. 299.00 *(978-3-642-08687-8(X),* 364208687X) Springer.

Facer, George. A2 Chemistry. 2nd ed. 2009. 326p. pap. 57.50 *(978-0-340-95761-5(1))* Hodder Education GBR. Dist: Trans-Atlantic Pubns., Inc.

Faraday, Michael. The Chemical History of a Candle. 2008. 116p. 21.99 *(978-0-554-37260-0(6))*; 24.99 *(978-0-554-27957-2(6))* BiblioBazaar.

—The Chemical History of a Candle. 2008. 76p. pap. *(978-1-4068-7535-5(X))* Echo Library.

—The Chemical History of a Candle: A Course of Lectures Delivered before a Juvenile Audience at the Royal Institution. 2007. 106p. pap. 18.99 *(978-1-4346-4397-1(2))*; (ENG.). 114p. pap. 19.99 *(978-1-4346-4398-8(0))* BiblioBazaar.

—A Course of Six Lectures on the Chemical History of a Candle: To Which Is Added A Lecture on Platinum. by Michael Faraday ... Delivered Before A Juve. 2006. 228p. per. 20.99 *(978-1-4255-1974-2(1))* MPublishing.

Fay, Robert C. & McMurry, John E. Chemistry. 5th rev. ed. 2007. (ENG., Illus.). 1216p. (C). 218.67 *(978-0-13-199323-5(2),* Prentice Hall) Prentice Hall PTR.

Fay, Robert C., et al. Laboratory Manual for Chemistry. 6th rev. ed. 2011. (ENG.). 426p. (C). pap. 95.80 *(978-0-321-72720-6(7),* Prentice Hall) Prentice Hall PTR.

—Study Guide for Chemistry. 6th ed. 2011. (ENG.). 648p. (C). pap. 71.47 *(978-0-321-72724-4(X),* Prentice Hall) Prentice Hall PTR.

Field, Simon Quellen. Culinary Reactions: The Everyday Chemistry of Cooking. 2011. (ENG.). 288p. pap. 16.95 *(978-1-56976-706-1(8))* Chicago Review Pr., Inc.

—Why There's Antifreeze in Your Toothpaste: The Chemistry of Household Ingredients. 2007. (ENG.). 288p. pap. 16.95 *(978-1-55652-697-8(0))* Chicago Review Pr., Inc.

Fischer-Cripps, Anthony Craig. The Chemistry Companion. 2011. (ENG., Illus.). 195p. pap. 29.95 *(978-1-4398-3088-6(6),* CRC Press) Taylor & Francis Group GBR. Dist: Taylor & Francis Group.

Floudas, Christodoulos A. & Pardalos, Panos M., eds. Optimization in Computational Chemistry & Molecular Biology: Local & Global Approaches. 2010. (Nonconvex Optimization & Its Applications Ser.). 352p. pap. 229.00 *(978-1-4419-4826-7(0),* 1441948260) Springer.

Fownes, George. Elementary Chemistry, Theoretical & Practical. 2010. (Illus.). 566p. pap. 43.75 *(978-1-142-47312-9(0))* BiblioBazaar.

Frazer, Andrew. General Chemistry Notebook. rev. ed. 2010. (ENG.). 208p. spiral bd. 35.92 *(978-0-7575-7503-7(X))* Kendall Hunt Publishing Co.

Fried. Computational Chemistry & Molecular Simulation. 2010. (ENG.). 500p. 89.95 *(978-0-471-46244-6(6))* Wiley, John & Sons, Inc.

Frost, Laura & Deal, Todd S. Guided Inquiry Workbook for General, Organic, & Biological Chemistry: An Integrated Approach. 2011. (ENG.). 288p. (C). pap. 35.73 *(978-0-321-76569-7(9),* Prentice Hall) Prentice Hall PTR.

Frost, Laura D. Books a la Carte for General, Organic, & Biological Chemistry: An Integrated Approach. 2010. (ENG.). 496p. (C). ring bd. 100.20 *(978-0-321-75086-0(1),* Prentice Hall) Prentice Hall PTR.

Frost, Laura D. & Deal, S. Todd. General, Organic, & Biological Chemistry. 2011. (ENG.). (C). ring bd. 110.20 ***(978-0-321-79590-8(3),*** Prentice Hall) Prentice Hall PTR.

Frost, Laura D., et al. General, Organic, & Biological Chemistry. 2010. (ENG.). 512p. (C). 175.00 *(978-0-321-70619-5(6),* Prentice Hall) Prentice Hall PTR.

—General, Organic, & Biological Chemistry: An Integrated Approach. 2010. (ENG.). 496p. (C). 167.00 *(978-0-8053-8178-8(3),* Prentice Hall) Prentice Hall PTR.

Gabbay, Dov M., et al, contrib. by. Philosophy of Chemistry. 2011. (Handbook of the Philosophy of Science Ser.: 6). (ENG.). 575p. 205.00 ***(978-0-444-51675-6(1),*** North Holland) Elsevier Science & Technology Bks.

Gade, Lutz H. Dendrimer Catalysis. 2006. (Topics in Organometallic Chemistry Ser.). (Illus.). xii, 189p. 239.00 *(978-3-540-34474-2(8),* 3540344748) Springer.

Gaensslen, Robert E., ed. Journal of Forensic Comprehensive Index, 1987-1995. Date not set. 275p. 40.00 *(978-0-8031-1793-8(0),* JOFSINDX) American Society for Testing & Materials.

García-Martínez, Javier & Serrano-Torregrosa, Elena, eds. The Chemical Element: Chemistry's Contribution to Our Global Future. 2011. (ENG., Illus.). 396p. 34.50 *(978-3-527-32880-2(7),* Wiley-VCH) Wiley, John & Sons, Inc.

Gaspard, Pierre & Sauvage, J. P., eds. From Non-Convalent Assemblies to Molecular Machines. 2010. (ENG., Illus.). 506p. 205.00 *(978-3-527-32277-0(9),* Wiley-VCH) Wiley, John & Sons, Inc.

Geary, Caroline. Adventures in Chemistry. 2007. (ENG., Illus.). 272p. (C). per., pupil's gde. ed. 90.95 *(978-0-618-37663-6(1),* 337781) Brooks/Cole.

Giddings, Luther. Elementary Chemistry: Lecture Notes. rev. ed. 2011. 260p. ring bd. 31.99 ***(978-0-7575-9030-6(6))*** Kendall Hunt Publishing Co.

Gielen, M. General Chemistry. (Illus.). 276p. *(978-965-294-079-7(8))* Freund Publishing Hse., Ltd.

Gil, Antonio, et al, eds. Pillared Clays & Related Catalysts. 2010. (ENG., Illus.). xvi, 550p. 259.00 *(978-1-4419-6669-8(2),* 1441966692) Springer.

Gilbert & Brewer, Karen S. Chemistry. 3rd ed. 2011. (ENG.). 579p. (C). pap. 40.00 net. *(978-0-393-93454-0(3),* 93454) Norton, W. W. & Co., Inc.

Gilbert, Thomas. Chemistry: The Science in Context. 2nd ed. 2008. (ENG.). 305p. (C). pap., pupil's gde. ed. 20.00 net. *(978-0-393-93202-7(8),* 93202) Norton, W. W. & Co., Inc.

Gilbert, Thomas & Brewer, Karen. Chemistry: The Science in Context. 2nd ed. 2008. (ENG.). 586p. (C). pap. 40.00 net. *(978-0-393-93076-4(9),* 93076) Norton, W. W. & Co., Inc.

Gilbert, Thomas R., et al. Chemistry: The Science in Context. 2nd ed. 2008. (ENG., Illus.). 1064p. (C). 187.69 *(978-0-393-92649-1(4),* 92649) Norton, W. W. & Co., Inc.

Gilman, Michelle Rose, et al. Chemistry for Dummies. 2008. (ENG., Illus.). 360p. pap., wbk. ed. 19.99 *(978-0-470-25152-2(2),* For Dummies) Wiley, John & Sons, Inc.

Gitari, Wilson. Treatment of Acid Mine Drainage with Coal Fly Ash. 2010. 368p. pap. *(978-3-639-26433-3(9))* VDM Verlag Dr. Mueller e.K.

Glavatskiy, Kirill. Multicomponent Interfacial Transport: Described by the Square Gradient Model during Evaporation & Condensation. 2011. (Springer Theses Ser.). (ENG., Illus.). xviii, 171p. 129.00 *(978-3-642-15265-8(1),* 3642152651) Springer.

Goffer, Zvi & Winefordner, James D. Archaeological Chemistry. 2nd rev. ed. 2007. (Chemical Analysis: a Series of Monographs on Analytical Chemistry & Its Applications Ser.: 170). (ENG., Illus.). 656p. 139.00 *(978-0-471-25288-7(3),* Wiley-Interscience) Wiley, John & Sons, Inc.

Goodman, Jonathan M. Chemical Applications of Molecular Modelling. 2nd ed. 2007. (Illus.). 350p. 49.00 *(978-0-85404-641-6(0),* 0854046410) Royal Society of Chemistry, The GBR. Dist: Ingram Pub. Services.

Gottlieb, Adam. Holy Holmium! Complete General Chemistry in 150 Pages. 2007. 170p. pap. 24.95 *(978-1-4357-0081-9(3))* Lulu Enterprises Inc.

Graham, Thomas. Elements of Chemistry, Including the Applications of the Science in the Arts with Numerous Illustrations by Thomas Graham with Notes & Additions. 2006. 444p. per. 26.99 *(978-1-4255-4975-6(6))* MPublishing.

Gray, Theodore & Mann, Nicky, photos by. The Elements: A Visual Exploration of Every Known Atom in the Universe. 2009. (ENG., Illus.). 240p. (gr. 9). 29.95 *(978-1-57912-814-2(9),* 1579128149) Black Dog & Leventhal Pubs., Inc.

Gray, Theodore & Quellen Field, Simon. Elements Vault: Treasures of the Periodic Table with Removable Archival Documents, a Model Pop-Up Atom, a Poster, & Real Element Samples - Including Pure Gold. 2011. (ENG., Illus.). 128p. 39.95 *(978-1-57912-880-7(7),* 1579128807) Black Dog & Leventhal Pubs., Inc.

Greenberg, Arthur. From Alchemy to Chemistry in Picture & Story. 2007. (ENG., Illus.). 688p. 94.95 *(978-0-471-75154-0(5),* Wiley-Interscience) Wiley, John & Sons, Inc.

Gribble, Gordon W. & Joule, John A., eds. Progress in Heterocyclic Chemistry. (Progress in Heterocyclic Chemistry Ser.: 18). (ENG., Illus.). Vol. 18. 2006. 470p. 340.00 *(978-0-08-045025-4(3))* Vol. 19. 2008. 504p. 225.00 *(978-0-08-045407-8(0))* Elsevier Science & Technology Bks. (Elsevier Science).

Griep & Griep, Mark A. Lab Manual for Chem 105: Chemistry in Context. rev. ed. 2010. (ENG.). 58p. ring bd. 31.57 *(978-0-7575-6899-2(8))* Kendall Hunt Publishing Co.

Griep, Mark A. Lab Manual for Chem 105: Chemistry in Context. rev. ed. 2011. (ENG.). 59p. ring bd. 32.85 ***(978-0-7575-9415-1(8))*** Kendall Hunt Publishing Co.

Grossman, Robert B. The Art of Writing Reasonable Organic Reaction Mechanisms. 2nd rev. ed. 2008. (ENG., Illus.). xvi, 355p. 64.95 *(978-0-387-95468-4(6),* 0387954686) Springer.

Guch, Ian. The Complete Idiot's Guide to Chemistry, 3rd Edition. 2011. (Complete Idiot's Guide Ser.). (ENG.). 416p. (gr. 12). 19.95 *(978-1-61564-126-0(2),* Alpha Bks.) Penguin Group (USA) Inc.

Guinn, Denise & Brewer, Rebecca. Essentials of General, Organic, & Biochemistry. 2010. (ENG.). 640p. (C). 80.95 *(978-1-4292-6240-8(0),* Freeman, W. H. & Co.

Haghi, A. K. Modern Trends in Chemistry & Chemical Engineering. 2012. (ENG.). 187p. 99.95 ***(978-1-926895-00-0(2))*** Apple Academic Pr., Inc. CAN. Dist: Taylor & Francis Group.

Haghi, A. K., ed. Chemistry & Chemical Engineering Research Progress. 2009. (Chemical Engineering Methods & Technology Ser.). (Illus.). vi, 238p. 116.10 *(978-1-61668-502-7(6))* Nova Science Pubs., Inc.

Hall, James W. Introductory Chemistry. 7th ed. 2010. (ENG.). (C). 368p. pap., lab manual ed. 119.95 *(978-0-538-73642-8(9))*; 240p. pap. 77.95 *(978-0-538-73641-1(0))* Brooks/Cole.

Hall, James W. & DeCoste, Donald J. Introductory Chemistry. 7th ed. 2010. (ENG.). (C). 224p. pap., pupil's gde. ed. 77.95 *(978-0-538-73640-4(2))*; (Illus.). 736p. 185.95 *(978-0-538-73638-1(0))*; (Illus.). 736p. pap. 165.95 *(978-0-538-73639-8(9))* Brooks/Cole.

Hallford, Randal. STRUCTURE, SYMMETRY AND LUMINESCENCE: OF ANIONIC COPPER(I), SILVER(I), AND GOLD(I) HALIDE COMPLEXES. 2008. 372p. pap. *(978-3-639-09310-0(0))* VDM Verlag Dr. Mueller e.K.

Hanson, David. General Chemistry: Guided Explorations. 2nd ed. 2010. (ENG.). 224p. (C). pap. 81.95 *(978-1-4390-4965-5(3))* Brooks/Cole.

Hanson, James R. Chemistry in the Garden. 2007. (ENG., Illus.). 158p. 24.00 *(978-0-85404-897-7(9))* Royal Society of Chemistry, The GBR. Dist: Ingram Pub. Services.

C

Hanson, James R. Chemistry in the Kitchen Garden. 2011. (ENG., Illus.). 300p. 40.00 (978-1-84973-323-6(6)) Royal Society of Chemistry, The GBR. Dist: Ingram Pub. Services.

Harada, Akira, ed. Supramolecular Polymer Chemistry. 2012. (ENG., Illus.). 390p. 195.00 (978-3-527-32321-0(X), Wiley-VCH) Wiley, John & Sons, Inc.

Harden, Helen. Chemistry: Bullet Guides. 2012. (Bullet Guides). (ENG.). 128p. pap. 6.95 (978-1-4441-3493-3(0), Hodder & Stoughton) Hodder General Publishing Div. GBR. Dist: Independent Pubs. Group.

Hassan, Atya. Chemistry Practical Book. 2011. 64p. pap. (978-3-8443-2831-8(9)) Lambert Academic Publishing.

Hazari, Bharat R. & Hoshmand, Reza, eds. Tourism, Trade & Welfare: Theoretical & Empirical Issues. 2011. (Tourism & Hospitality Development & Management Ser.). 228p. 69.00 (978-1-61209-714-5(6)) Nova Science Pubs., Inc.

Hein. Introduction to General, Organic, & Biochemistry, Ninth Edition Binder Ready. 9th ed. 2008. (ENG.). 1184p. (C). ring bd. 123.95 (978-0-470-39224-9(X), Wiley) Wiley, John & Sons, Inc.

Hein, Morris. Foundations of College Chemistry. 11th ed. 2006. pap. 56.95 (978-0-470-07567-8(8)) 12th ed. 2007. pap. 60.95 (978-0-470-16775-5(0), Wiley) 12th ed. 2006. pap. 60.95 (978-0-470-11657-9(9)) 12th alt. ed. 2006. pap. 55.95 (978-0-470-13199-2(3)) 12th alt. ed. 2006. pap. 55.95 (978-0-470-13566-2(2), Wiley) 12th rev. ed. 2006. 92.00 net. (978-0-470-13209-8(4)) 13th alt. ed. 2010. (ENG.). 518p. (C). pap. 152.95 (978-0-470-46060-3(1), Wiley) Wiley, John & Sons, Inc.

—Foundations of College Chemistry, Alternate 12th Edition WileyPLUS Set. 12th rev. ed. 2006. pap. 84.00 net. (978-0-470-13210-4(8)) Wiley, John & Sons, Inc.

—Introduction to General, Organic, & Biochemistry. 8th ed. 2006. pap. 62.95 (978-0-470-07874-7(X)) Wiley, John & Sons, Inc.

—(WCS)Introduction to General, Organic, & Biochemistry, Custom Unbound Eighth Edition for Ohio University. 2007. ring bd. 82.95 (978-0-470-89546-7(2), Wiley) Wiley, John & Sons, Inc.

—Wiley Plus/WebCT Stand-alone to accompany Foundations of College Chemistry. 12th ed. 2006. (Wiley Plus Products Ser.). pap. 60.95 (978-0-470-13565-5(4), Wiley) Wiley, John & Sons, Inc.

Hein, Morris & Arena, Susan. Foundations of College Chemistry. (ENG., (C). 12th alt. rev. ed. 2006. Illus.). 560p. pap. 152.95 (978-0-471-77991-9(1)) 13th ed. 2010. 360p. pap. 131.95 (978-0-470-55490-6(8)) 13th ed. 2010. 216p. pap., pupil's gde. ed. 70.95 (978-0-470-53000-9(6)) Wiley, John & Sons, Inc. (Wiley).

Hein, Morris, et al. Foundations of College Chemistry. 13th ed. 2010. (ENG.). (C). 640p. 173.95 (978-0-470-46061-0(X)); 304p. pap. 79.95 (978-0-470-55492-0(4)) Wiley, John & Sons, Inc. (Wiley).

—Introduction to General, Organic, & Biochemistry. (ENG., (C). 9th ed. 2008. Illus.). 516p. pap. 77.95 (978-0-470-24765-5(7)) 10th ed. 2011. (Illus.). 1120p. 212.95 (978-0-470-59880-1(8)) 10th ed. 2011. 496p. pap. 68.95 (978-0-470-59883-2(2)) Wiley, John & Sons, Inc. (Wiley).

—Wiley Plus Stand-Alone to Accompany Introduction to General, Organic, & Biochemistry. 9th ed. 2007. pap. 59.95 (978-0-470-11729-3(X)) Wiley, John & Sons, Inc.

Hélix-Nielsen, Claus, ed. Biomimetic Membranes for Sensor & Separation Applications. 2012. (Biological & Medical Physics, Biomedical Engineering Ser.). (ENG., Illus.). xv, 284p. 169.00 (978-94-007-2183-8(8), 9400721838) Springer.

Heron, Carl, et al. Archaeological Chemistry. 2nd rev. ed. 2008. (ENG., Illus.). 456p. (C). 64.00 (978-0-85404-262-3(8)) Royal Society of Chemistry, The GBR. Dist: Ingram Pub. Services.

Hildebrand, Joel Henry. Principles of Chemistry. 2008. 328p. 28.99 (978-0-559-31877-1(4)); pap. 30.75 (978-0-559-31876-4(6)) BiblioBazaar.

—Principles of Chemistry. 2009. 214p. pap. (978-0-217-79325-4(8)) Books LLC.

Hill, James C., et al. Student's Guide for Chemistry: The Central Science. 11th ed. 2008. (ENG.). 592p. (C). pap. 70.40 (978-0-13-600264-2(1), Prentice Hall) Prentice Hall PTR.

Hill, John W. & Jones, Richard W. Study Guide for Chemistry for Changing Times. 12th ed. 2009. (ENG.). 272p. (C). pap. 58.47 (978-0-321-61243-4(4), Prentice Hall) Prentice Hall PTR.

Hill, John W. & Kolb, Doris K. Chemistry for Changing Times. 11th ed. 2007. (Illus.). 744p. pap. (978-0-13-242984-9(5)) Prentice Hall PTR.

Hill, John W., et al. Chemistry for Changing Times. 12th ed. 2009. (ENG., Illus.). 640p. (C). pap. 156.33 (978-0-13-605449-8(8), Prentice Hall) Prentice Hall PTR.

—Chemistry for Changing Times with MasteringChemistry & Reg; 13th rev. ed. 2012. (ENG.). 776p. (C). 166.33 (978-0-321-75010-5(1), Prentice Hall) Prentice Hall PTR.

—Chemistry for the Changing Times. 13th ed. 2012. (ENG.). (C). ring bd. 103.80 (978-0-321-76810-0(8), Prentice Hall) Prentice Hall PTR.

—Study Guide & Selected Solutions Manual for Chemistry for Changing Times. 13th rev. ed. 2012. (ENG.). 272p. (C). pap. 58.47 (978-0-321-76781-3(0), Prentice Hall) Prentice Hall PTR.

Ho, Tse-Lok. Fiesers' Reagents for Organic Synthesis, Fiesers' Reagents for Organic Synthesis, Volume 23. 2006. (Fiesers' Reagents for Organic Synthesis Ser.: 23). (ENG.). 533p. 184.00 (978-0-471-68243-1(8), Wiley-Interscience) Wiley, John & Sons, Inc.

Holleman, A. F. Lehrbuch der Anorganischen Chemie. 102nd ed. 2007. (GER., Illus.). XXXIX, 2149p. (C). 132.00 (978-3-11-017770-1(6)) De Gruyter, Walter Inc.

Holleman, Arnold Frederik [Begr.] & Richter, Friedrich [Bearb.], eds. Lehrbuch der anorganischen Chemie. 33rd ed. (GER.). XII, 568p. 328.00 (978-3-11-219458-4(6)); 218.00 (978-3-11-131992-6(X)) De Gruyter, Walter Inc.

Holm, Johanna. Forgotten Chemistry: A Refresher Course. 2006. (ENG., Illus.). 272p. per. 16.99 (978-0-7641-3317-6(9)) Barron's Educational Series, Inc.

Holmes, John, 3rd. Handbook of Ion Structures in the Gas Phase. 2006. (ENG., Illus.). 472p. 184.95 (978-0-8493-1950-1(1), CRC Press) Taylor & Francis Group GBR. Dist: Taylor & Francis Group.

Holt, Rinehart and Winston Staff. Holt Chemistry. 6th ed. Date not set. tchr. ed. 109.06 (978-0-03-039108-8(3)) Holt McDougal.

—Modern Chemistry: Premier Online Edition. 6th ed. Date not set. 83.93 (978-0-03-036809-7(X)) Holt McDougal.

Howard, John. Practical Chemistry. 2006. 144p. per. 16.99 (978-1-4255-1067-1(1)) MPublishing.

Howorka, Stefan. Molecular Assembly in Natural & Engineered Systems. 2011. (ENG.). 414p. 161.00 (978-0-12-415906-8(0), Academic Pr.) Elsevier Science & Technology Bks.

Hummel, Thomas. Student Solutions Manual for Zumdahl/Zumdahl's Chemistry: an Atoms First Approach. 2011. (ENG.). 432p. (C). pap. 83.95 (978-0-8400-6583-4(3)) Brooks/Cole.

Hunt. Chemistry. Date not set. (Illus.). 368p. pap. 31.50 (978-0-582-33108-2(0)) Addison-Wesley Longman, Ltd. GBR. Dist: Trans-Atlantic Pubns., Inc.

Hunt, Thomas Sterry. Chemical & Geological Essays, by Thomas Sterry Hunt. 2006. 516p. per. 29.99 (978-1-4255-5783-6(X)) MPublishing.

Imbihl, Ronald, et al. Nonlinear Dynamics in Chemistry & Biochemistry. 2006. (ENG.). 400p. 175.00 (978-3-527-30824-8(5)) Wiley, John & Sons, Inc.

Ivanyi. Weisse Wannen. 2006. 250p. pap. 55.00 (978-3-433-01786-9(7), Wiley-VCH) Wiley, John & Sons, Inc.

James E. Brady & Cram101 Textbook Reviews Staff. General Chemistry: Principles & Structure. 2007. 348p. per. 16.95 (978-1-4288-2936-7(9)) Cram101 Inc.

Jennings, Terry. Quimica Facil (Everyday Chemistry) (SPA.). 6.95 (978-84-348-2244-3(X)) SM Ediciones ESP. Dist: AIMS International Bks., Inc.

Jespersen, Neil D., et al. Chemistry: The Molecular Nature of Matter. 6th ed. 2011. (ENG.). 1152p. (C). 215.95 (978-0-470-57771-4(1), Wiley) Wiley, John & Sons, Inc.

Joesten, Melvin, et al. Chem - In Your World. 2010. (Available Titles CourseMate Ser.). (ENG., Illus.). 448p. pap. 82.95 (978-0-538-73821-7(9)) Brooks/Cole.

Joesten, Melvin D. & Hogg, John. Chem in Your World. 2011. (Illus.). 440p. (978-0-538-49428-1(X)) Brooks/Cole.

Johnston, John. A Manual of Chemistry, on the Basis of Turner's Elements of Chemistry; Containing, in a Condensed Form, All the Most Important Facts & Principles Of. 2006. 532p. per. 29.99 (978-1-4255-5894-9(1)) MPublishing.

Jones, Philip. Chemistry Matters Volume 1, 1 of 2. 2007. 80.00 (978-1-59657-120-4(9)) Teaching Point, Inc.

—Chemistry Matters Volume 2, 2 of 2. 2007. 80.00 (978-1-59657-122-8(5)) Teaching Point, Inc.

Joule, James Prescott. Joint Scientific Papers of James Prescott Joule. 2011. (Cambridge Library Collection - Physical Sciences Ser.). (ENG., Illus.). 422p. pap. 32.00 (978-1-108-02883-7(7)) Cambridge Univ. Pr.

—The Scientific Papers of James Prescott Joule. 2011. (Cambridge Library Collection - Physical Sciences Ser.). (ENG., Illus.). 714p. pap. 48.00 (978-1-108-02882-0(9)) Cambridge Univ. Pr.

Junk, Matthias. Assessing the Functional Structure of Molecular Transporters by EPR Spectroscopy. 2012. (Springer Theses Ser.). (ENG., Illus.). xvi, 212p. 129.00 (978-3-642-25134-4(X), 364225134X) Springer.

Jurs, Peter, et al. Chemistry: The Molecular Science, International Edition. 4th ed. 2011. 1280p. pap. (978-1-4390-4966-2(1)) Brooks/Cole.

Kargol, Marta. Multifunctional Shaped Aluminosilica Monoliths. 2010. 124p. pap. (978-3-8383-4348-8(4)) Lambert Academic Publishing.

Kausch, Hans-Henning. Intrinsic Molecular Mobility & Toughness of Polymers II. 2010. (Advances in Polymer Science Ser.). xii, 262p. pap. 299.00 (978-3-642-06560-6(0), 3642065600) Springer.

Kautz. Chemistry 110 Recitation Manual. 3rd rev. ed. 2011. (ENG.). 132p. spiral bd. 20.00 (978-0-7575-9578-3(2)) Kendall Hunt Publishing Co.

Kee, et al. Chemistry Within. 2007. 350p. pap. 37.50 (978-0-471-48919-1(0)) Wiley, John & Sons, Inc.

Kelley, Colleen. Visualising Chemistry for the Non-major Study Guide & Student Solutions Manual. 2008. pap. 38.95 (978-0-470-03974-8(4)) Wiley, John & Sons, Inc.

Kelter, Carr & Cram101 Textbook Reviews Staff. Chemistry: A World of Choices. 2007. 212p. per. 13.95 (978-1-4288-2930-5(X)) Cram101 Inc.

Kelter, Paul, et al. Chemistry Vol. 1: The Practical Science. 2008. (Available 2010 Titles Enhanced Web Assign Ser.). (ENG.). 1088p. (C). 282.95 (978-0-547-05393-6(2), 1036371) CENGAGE Learning.

Kelter, Paul B. Chemistry: The Practical Science. 2007. (ENG.). 304p. (C). pap. 94.95 (978-0-618-73623-2(9), 329682) Brooks/Cole.

Kelter, Paul B., et al. Chemistry: The Practical Science. 2007. (ENG., Illus.). 1088p. (C). 282.95 (978-0-618-00072-2(0), 329670) CENGAGE Learning.

—Chemistry: The Practical Science. 2008. (Illus.). xxxii, 969p. (978-0-618-82860-9(5)) Houghton Mifflin Harcourt Publishing Co.

Kerner, Nancy Konigsberg, et al. Guided Inquiry Experiments for General Chemistry: Practical Problems & Applications. 11th ed. 2007. (ENG., Illus.). 432p. (C). pap. 100.95 (978-0-471-69842-5(3), Wiley) Wiley, John & Sons, Inc.

Kiernan, Denise & D'Agnese, Joseph. Science 101: Chemistry. 2007. (Science 101 Ser.). (ENG., Illus.). 224p. (gr. 9). pap. 15.99 (978-0-06-089138-1(6), HarperPerennial) HarperCollins Pubs.

Kirkland, Kyle. Chemistry. 2010. (Frontiers of Science Ser.). (Illus.). 232p. (C). (gr. 9-18). 39.50 (978-0-8160-7440-2(2)) Facts On File, Inc.

Knipe, A. C., ed. Organic Reaction Mechanisms 2006. 2010. (Organic Reaction Mechanisms Ser.: 122). (ENG.). 602p. 540.00 (978-0-470-51905-9(3), Wiley) Wiley, John & Sons, Inc.

Koeck, Deborah. Chemistry Assistant Kit. rev. ed. 2010. (ENG.). 1p. 30.10 (978-0-7575-5678-4(7)) Kendall Hunt Publishing Co.

Kotz, John C., et al. Chemistry & Chemical Reactivity with OWL, Hybrid. 8th ed. 2011. (Cengage Learningrsquo;s New Hybrid Editions! Ser.). (ENG., Illus.). 992p. (C). pap. 154.95 (978-1-111-57498-7(7)) Brooks/Cole.

Kouadio, Kay I. General Chemistry I Lecture Templates. 2nd rev. ed. 2008. (ENG.). 260p. pap. 48.69 (978-0-7575-5589-3(6)) Kendall Hunt Publishing Co.

Kovac, Jeffrey & Weisberg, Michael, eds. Roald Hoffmann on the Philosophy, Art, & Science of Chemistry, 1 vol. 2012. (ENG., Illus.). 448p. 35.00 (978-0-19-975590-5(6)) Oxford Univ. Pr., Inc.

Kozlowski, Henryk, et al. Metallochemistry of Neurodegeneration: Biological, Chemical & Genetic. 2006. (ENG., Illus.). 294p. 213.00 (978-0-85404-360-6(8), 0854043608) Royal Society of Chemistry, The GBR. Dist: Ingram Pub. Services.

Krygowski, Tadeusz Marek & Cyranski, Michal K. Aromaticity in Heterocyclic Compounds. 2009. (Topics in Heterocyclic Chemistry Ser.). (Illus.). 370p. 439.00 (978-3-540-68329-2(1)) Springer.

Kurfürst, Ulrich, ed. Solid Sample Analysis: Direct & Slurry Sampling using GF-AAS & ETV-ICP. 2012. (ENG., Illus.). xix, 423p. pap. 329.00 (978-3-642-08290-0(4), 3642082904) Springer.

Laird, Brian. Student's Solutions Manual to accompany University Chemistry. 2008. (ENG.). (C). pap. 71.33 (978-0-07-310736-3(0), 0073107360, McGraw-Hill Science, Engineering & Mathematics) McGraw-Hill Higher Education.

—University Chemistry. 2008. (ENG., Illus.). 864p. (C). 236.67 (978-0-07-722133-1(8), 0077221338, McGraw-Hill Science, Engineering & Mathematics) McGraw-Hill Higher Education.

Larionov, Evgeny. Activity & selectivity of DMAP derivatives in acylation reactions: Experimental & Theoretical Studies. 2011. 324p. pap. (978-3-8381-2767-5(6)) Südwestdeutscher Verlag für Hochschulschriften AG & Co. KG.

Lebitz, Mina & editor - Evangelist, Thomas A. 5 Steps to a 5 500 AP Chemistry Questions to Know by Test Day. 2011. (5 Steps to a 5 on the Advanced Placement Examinations Ser.). (ENG., Illus.). 224p. (C). pap. 14.00 (978-0-07-177405-5(X), 007177405X) McGraw-Hill Cos., The.

Lehninger, Albert L., et al. Printed Test Bank. 4th ed. 100p. 204.00 (978-0-7167-5952-2(7)) Freeman, W. H. & Co.

Lichtfouse, Eric, et al, eds. Environmental Chemistry for a Sustainable World Vol. 1: Nanotechnology & Health Risk, 2 vols. 2011. (ENG., Illus.). xix, 410p. 179.00 (978-94-007-2441-9(1), 9400724411) Springer.

Liebig, Justus. Familiar Letters on Chemistry. 2009. 196p. 22.99 (978-1-103-26593-0(8)); 232p. 23.99 (978-1-103-34717-9(9)); 196p. pap. 16.99 (978-1-103-26592-3(X)); 232p. pap. 17.99 (978-1-103-34714-8(4)) BiblioBazaar.

—Familiar Letters on Chemistry. 2009. 420p. pap. (978-0-217-21090-4(2)) Books LLC.

—Familiar Letters on Chemistry. Gardner, John E., ed. 2009. 108p. pap. (978-1-4099-7079-8(5)) Dodo Pr.

Liebig, Justus Freiherr von. Familiar Letters on Chemistry: And its Relation to Commerce Physiology & Agriculture. 2007. (ENG.). 112p. per. 18.99 (978-1-4346-1828-3(5)); 122p. per. 19.99 (978-1-4346-1916-7(8)) BiblioBazaar.

Limon, Jerzy. The Chemistry of the Theatre: Performativity of Time. 2010. (ENG., Illus.). 264p. 84.00 (978-0-230-24111-4(5)) Palgrave Macmillan.

Lin, Sheng-Hsien. Wolf Prize in Chemistry: An Epitome of Chemistry in 20th Century & Beyond. 2011. 600p. 180.00 (978-981-4280-39-6(9)) World Scientific Publishing Co., Inc.

Lin, Zhiqun. Evaporative Self-Assembly of Ordered Complex Structures. 2011. 300p. 99.00 (978-981-4304-68-9(9)) World Scientific Publishing Co., Inc.

Lippy, John. Chemical Magic. 164p. pap. 4.00 (978-0-913022-32-0(2)) Angriff Pr.

Liu, LinShu & Zaikov, Gennadii Efremovich, eds. Chemistry as Music. 2007. 129.00 (978-1-60021-894-1(6)) Nova Science Pubs., Inc.

London Chemical Society Staff. Annual Reports on the Progress of Chemistry. reprint ed. lib. bdg. (978-0-7222-3058-9(3)) Library Reprints, Inc.

Long, Gary. Math Review. 3rd ed. 2008. (ENG.). 64p. (C). pap. 17.27 (978-0-13-601858-2(0), Prentice Hall) Prentice Hall PTR.

Malone & Cram101 Textbook Reviews Staff. Basic Concepts of Chemistry. 2007. 216p. per. 13.95 (978-1-4288-2968-8(7)) Cram101 Inc.

Malone, Leo J. & Dolter, Theodore. Basic Concepts of Chemistry. (ENG., Illus.). (C). 8th ed. 2008. 656p. 159.95 (978-0-471-74154-1(X)) 8th ed. 2008. 336p. pap., stu. ed., pupil's gde. ed. 71.95 (978-0-470-08769-5(2)) 9th ed. 2012. 696p. 164.95 (978-0-470-93845-4(5)) Wiley, John & Sons, Inc. (Wiley).

Marcet, Jane Haldimand. Conversations on Chemistry: In which the Elements of that Science are Familiarly Explained & Illustrated by Experiments. 2010. (Cambridge Library Collection - Physical Sciences Ser.). (Illus.). 412p. pap. 31.99 (978-1-108-01683-4(9)); (ENG., 394p. pap. 31.99 (978-1-108-01684-1(7)) Cambridge Univ. Pr.

March, Joe L., et al. Pogil Prep Chemistry Prelim. 2007. (ENG., Illus.). 160p. (C). per. 47.95 (978-0-618-85478-3(9), 344620) CENGAGE Learning.

Marks, Pamela S., et al. A Conceptual Introduction to Chemistry. 2007. (Illus.). 647p. 140.94 (978-0-07-330172-3(8), 9780073301723, McGraw-Hill Science, Engineering & Mathematics) McGraw-Hill Higher Education.

Masterton, William L. & Hurley, Cecile N. Chemistry: Principles & Reactions. 6th ed. 2008. (Available Titles CengageNOW Ser.). (ENG., Illus.). 736p. (C). 217.95 (978-0-495-12671-3(3)) Brooks/Cole.

—Chemistry - Principles & Reactions. 7th ed. 2011. (ENG.). 1p. (C). pap. 89.95 (978-1-111-57060-6(4)) Brooks/Cole.

—Chemistry: Principles & Reactions: Study Guide & Workbook. 7th ed. 2011. (ENG.). 432p. (C). spiral bd. 89.95 (978-1-111-57059-0(0)) Brooks/Cole.

Masterton, William L., et al. Chemistry: Principles & Reactions. 7th ed. 2011. (Textbooks Available with Cengage YouBook Ser.). (ENG.). 800p. (C). 217.95 (978-1-111-42710-8(0)) Brooks/Cole.

Matsumoto, Kiyoshi. Heterocyclic Supramolecules 1. 2008. (Topics in Heterocyclic Chemistry Ser.). (Illus.). 200p. 269.00 (978-3-540-68189-2(2), 3540681892) Springer.

McCreary, Terry W., et al. Chemistry for Changing Times. 13th rev. ed. 2011. (ENG., Illus.). 800p. (C). 156.33 (978-0-321-75087-7(X), Prentice Hall) Prentice Hall PTR.

Mcdougal, Owen & Steiner, Rick. General, Organic & Biological Chemistry. 2006. pap., stu. ed. 43.95 (978-0-471-69942-2(X)) Wiley, John & Sons, Inc.

McGraw-Hill-Glencoe Staff, creator. Glencoe Chemistry Standardized Test Practice: Matter & Change. 2007. (Glencoe Science Ser.). (Illus.). 48p. pap. 8.50 (978-0-07-878759-1(9)) McGraw-Hill Cos., The.

McMenamin, Mark A. S. Memoirs of Chemistry (1856) by C. J. Koene: A Facing-Page English Translation of the French Text of Memoires de Chimie. (FRE & ENG.). 284p. 109.95 (978-0-7734-5319-7(9)) Mellen, Edwin Pr., The.

McMurray & Fay & Cram101 Textbook Reviews Staff. Chemistry. 2007. 324p. per. 16.95 (978-1-4288-2928-2(8)) Cram101 Inc.

McMurry, et al. Fundamentals of General, Organic, & Biological Chemistry, Kit. 6th ed. 2010. (ENG.). 992p. (C). ring bd. 128.93 (978-0-321-73885-1(3), Prentice Hall) Prentice Hall PTR.

McMurry, John. Fundament General Organic & Biolog Chem. 6th ed. 2010. (Illus.). 976p. pap. (978-0-13-815228-4(4)) Prentice Hall PTR.

Mcmurry, John, et al. Chemistry. 5th ed. 2008. (Illus.). 1216p. pap. (978-0-13-232146-4(7)) Prentice Hall PTR.

McMurry, John, et al. Study Guide & Full Solutions Manual for Fundamentals of General, Organic, & Biological Chemistry. 6th ed. 2009. (ENG.). 544p. (C). pap. 74.33 (978-0-321-61238-0(8), Prentice Hall) Prentice Hall PTR.

—Study Guide & Selected Solutions Manual for Fundamentals of General, Organic, & Biological Chemistry. 6th ed. 2009. (ENG.). 432p. (C). pap. 69.87 (978-0-321-61239-7(6), Prentice Hall) Prentice Hall PTR.

McMurry, John C., et al. Student Solution Manual for Chemistry. 6th rev. ed. 2011. (ENG.). 432p. (C). pap. 79.60 (978-0-321-72726-8(6), Prentice Hall) Prentice Hall PTR.

McMurry, John E. & Fay, Robert C. Books a la Carte for Chemistry. 6th ed. 2011. (ENG.). 1080p. (C). ring bd. 133.20 (978-0-321-74160-8(9), Prentice Hall) Prentice Hall PTR.

—Chemistry. 6th ed. 2011. (ENG.). (C). ring bd. 143.20 (978-0-321-78757-6(9)); 1080p. 232.00 (978-0-321-74103-5(X)) Prentice Hall PTR. (Prentice Hall).

—General Chemistry: Atoms First. 2009. (ENG., Illus.). 1056p. (C). 222.00 (978-0-321-57163-2(0), Prentice Hall) Prentice Hall PTR.

McMurry, John E., et al. Full Solutions Manual for General Chemistry: Atoms First. 2009. (ENG.). 688p. (C). pap. 76.20 (978-0-321-56398-9(0), Prentice Hall) Prentice Hall PTR.

—Fundamentals of General, Organic, & Biological Chemistry. 6th ed. 2009. (ENG.). 992p. (C). 198.13 (978-0-13-605450-4(1), Prentice Hall) Prentice Hall PTR.

—Fundamentals of General, Organic, & Biological Chemistry. 7th ed. 2012. (ENG.). 992p. (C). 126.67 (978-0-321-77621-1(6), Prentice Hall) Prentice Hall PTR.

—Fundamentals of General Organic & Biological Chemistry. 7th ed. 2012. (ENG.). (C). ring bd. 127.13 (978-0-321-76725-7(X), Prentice Hall) Prentice Hall PTR.

—Fundamentals of General, Organic, & Biological Chemistry. 7th rev. ed. 2012. (ENG.). (C). 1008p. 208.13 (978-0-321-75011-2(X)); (Illus.). 992p. 198.13 (978-0-321-75083-9(7)) Prentice Hall PTR. (Prentice Hall).

—Fundamentals of General, Organic, & Biological Chemistry, Books a la Carte Edition. 7th ed. 2012. (ENG.). 992p. (C). ring bd. 118.93 (978-0-321-77612-9(7), Prentice Hall) Prentice Hall PTR.

—Selected Solutions Manual for General Chemistry: Atoms First. 2009. (ENG.). 416p. (C). pap. 72.93 (978-0-321-56025-4(6), Prentice Hall) Prentice Hall PTR.

—Study Guide & Full Solutions Manual for Fundamentals of General, Organic, & Biological Chemistry. 7th ed. 2012. (ENG.). 552p. (C). pap. 74.33 (978-0-321-77616-7(X), Prentice Hall) Prentice Hall PTR.

—Study Guide & Selected Solutions Manual for Fundamentals of General, Organic, & Biological Chemistry. 7th rev. ed. 2012. (ENG.). 432p. (C). pap. 69.87 (978-0-321-77610-5(0), Prentice Hall) Prentice Hall PTR.

McQuarrie, Carole H. Student Solutions Manual to Accompany General Chemistry. 4th ed. 2011. (Illus.). 376p. (C). pap. 40.00 (978-1-891389-73-3(4)) Royal Society of Chemistry, The GBR. Dist: Ingram Pub. Services.

Mechoulam, Raphael & Bekenstein, Jacob D. Albert Einstein Memorial Lectures. 2011. 250p. 78.00 (978-981-4329-42-2(8)); pap. 34.00 (978-981-4329-43-9(6)) World Scientific Publishing Co., Inc.

Meierhenrich, Uwe. Amino Acids & the Asymmetry of Life: Caught in the Act of Formation. 2010. (Advances in Astrobiology & Biogeophysics Ser.). (Illus.). xxii, 242p. pap. 109.00 *(978-3-642-09558-0(5)*, 3642095585) Springer.

Meinrath, Gunther & Schneider, Petra. Quality Assurance for Chemistry & Environmental Science: Metrology from pH Measurement to Nuclear Waste Disposal. 2007. (Illus.). 326p. 189.00 incl. cd-rom *(978-3-540-71271-8(2))* Springer.

Meng, Zhiyong. Self-Assembly & Chemo-Ligation of Polymeric Responsive Microgels. 2010. 172p. pap. *(978-3-8383-8710-9(4))* Lambert Academic Publishing.

Metzger, Robert M. The Physical Chemist's Toolbox. 2nd ed. 2012. (ENG.). 960p. 165.00 *(978-0-470-88925-1(X)*, Wiley) Wiley, John & Sons, Inc.

Millard, Julie T. Adventures in Chemistry. 2006. (ENG., Illus.). 672p. (C). 190.95 *(978-0-618-37662-9(3)*, 337780) CENGAGE Learning.

—Adventures in Chemistry. 2008. (Illus.). xxiii, 668p. *(978-0-618-73065-0(6))* Houghton Mifflin Harcourt Publishing Co.

Miller, William Allen. Elements of Chemistry: Theoretical & Practical. by William Allen Miller, ... Part I-[II]... . 2006. 564p. per. 32.99 *(978-1-4255-6265-6(5))* MPublishing.

Moog, Richard S. (WCS)Chemistry: A Guided Inquiry, Third Edition Selected Activities - University of South Florida. 2007. 104p. pap. 26.95 *(978-0-470-89613-6(2))* Wiley, John & Sons, Inc.

Moog, Richard S. & Farrell, John J. Chemistry: A Guided Inquiry. (ENG., Illus.). 408p. (C). 4th ed. 2008. per. 74.95 *(978-0-470-12926-5(3))* 5th ed. 2011. pap. 74.95 *(978-0-470-64790-5(6))* Wiley, John & Sons, Inc. (Wiley).

—Selected Activities from Chemistry: A Guided Inquiry. 3rd ed. 2006. (Illus.). 74p. per. 24.95 *(978-0-470-10703-4(0))* Wiley, John & Sons, Inc.

Moore, John T. Chemistry Essentials for Dummies. 2010. (ENG., Illus.). 192p. pap. 9.99 *(978-0-470-61836-3(1)*, For Dummies) Wiley, John & Sons, Inc.

—Chemistry for Dummies. 2nd ed. 2011. (ENG., Illus.). 384p. pap. 19.99 *(978-1-118-00730-3(1)*, For Dummies) Wiley, John & Sons, Inc.

Moore, John T. & Langley, Richard H. Chemistry for the Utterly Confused. 2007. (Utterly Confused Ser.). (ENG., Illus.). 304p. per. 17.95 *(978-0-07-147529-7(X)*, 007147529X) McGraw-Hill Cos., The.

Moore, John W., et al. Chemistry: The Molecular Science. 4th ed. 2010. (Available Titles OWL Ser.). (ENG.). 1264p. (C). 263.95 *(978-1-4390-4930-3(0))* Brooks/Cole.

—Chemistry Vol. 1: The Molecular Science. 3rd ed. 2007. (ENG., Illus.). 784p. (C). 151.95 *(978-0-495-11960-9(1))* Brooks/Cole.

—Chemistry, Volume II: The Molecular Science. 3rd ed. 2007. (ENG., Illus.). 736p. (C). pap. 151.95 *(978-0-495-11961-6(X))* Brooks/Cole.

—Principles of Chemistry: The Molecular Science. 2009. (ENG.). (C). 224p. pap., pupil's gde. ed. 76.95 *(978-0-495-39157-9(3))*; 848p. pap. 195.95 *(978-0-495-39079-4(8))* Brooks/Cole.

Moore, Stanitski & Cram101 Textbook Reviews Staff. Chemistry the Molecular Science. 2007. 364p. per. 17.95 *(978-1-4288-3054-7(5))* Cram101 Inc.

Moran, Bruce T. Distilling Knowledge: Alchemy, Chemistry, & the Scientific Revolution. 2006. (New Histories of Science, Technology, & Medicine Ser.). (Illus.). 224p. per. 21.00 *(978-0-674-02249-2(1))* Harvard Univ. Pr.

Morrison, Richard, et al. General, Organic, & Biochemistry: With Math Review. 2007. (ENG., Illus.). 192p. (C). per. 32.95 *(978-0-495-55469-1(3))* Wadsworth.

Myers. Chemistry. 6th ed. Date not set. cd-rom 83.93 *(978-0-03-039112-5(1))* Holt McDougal.

Nahar, Lutfun, et al. Chemistry for Pharmacy Students: General, Organic & Natural Product Chemistry. 2007. (ENG., Illus.). 396p. 178.95 *(978-0-470-01780-7(5)*, Wiley-Interscience) Wiley, John & Sons, Inc.

Narayanan, Ranga. Interfacial Processes & Molecular Aggregation of Surfactants. 2008. (Advances in Polymer Science Ser.). (Illus.). xii, 263p. 309.00 *(978-3-540-69809-8(4))* Springer.

Nathan, Harold D. & Henrickson, Charles. CliffsNotes Chemistry Quick Review. 2nd ed. 2011. (ENG.). 192p. pap. 9.99 *(978-0-470-90543-2(3)*, Cliff Notes) Wiley, John & Sons, Inc.

Nelson, Eric. Preparation for Topics in College Chemistry, Modules 1-16. 2nd ed. 2006. (C). spiral bd. *(978-0-9771087-1-8(6))* ChemReview.

—Preparation for Topics in College Chemistry, Volume II. 2006. (C). spiral bd. *(978-0-9771087-3-2(2))* ChemReview.

Neuss, Geoffrey. Chemistry for the IB Diploma: Standard & Higher Level. 2nd ed. 2007. (International Baccalaureate Course Companions Ser.). (ENG., Illus.). 224p. (YA). pap. 42.00 *(978-0-19-915142-4(3))* Oxford Univ. Pr., Inc.

Nichols, Christopher. Chemistry 370. rev. ed. 2012. (ENG.). 100p. ring bd. 35.00 ***(978-0-7575-9908-8(7))*** Kendall Hunt Publishing Co.

Nordstrom, Brian. Smart Guide to Chemistry. 2012. (Smart Guide Ser.). (ENG.). 272p. pap. 19.95 ***(978-1-937636-02-9(X))*** Smart Guide Pubns., Inc.

Norris, Helen & Martin, Jean. Science Foundations: Chemistry Class Book. 3rd ed. 2006. (Science Foundations Ser.). (ENG., Illus.). 252p. pap., stu. ed. 27.50 *(978-0-521-68675-4(X))* Cambridge Univ. Pr.

Nussinovitch, Amos. Polymer Macro- & Micro-Gel Beads: Fundamentals & Applications: Fundamentals & Applications. 2010. (ENG., Illus.). xxv, 303p. 209.00 *(978-1-4419-6617-9(X)*, 144196617X) Springer.

Nuyken, Oskar. Neodymium Based Ziegler Catalysts - Fundamental Chemistry. 2006. (Advances in Polymer Science Ser.: Vol. 204). (Illus.). xii, 287p. 349.00 *(978-3-540-34809-2(3)*, 3540348093) Springer.

Ogilvy, Guy. The Alchemist's Kitchen: Extraordinary Potions & Curious Notions. 2006. (Wooden Bks.). (ENG., Illus.). 64p. 12.00 *(978-0-8027-1540-1(0))* Walker & Co.

Okada, Tatsuhiro & Kaneko, Masao, eds. Molecular Catalysts for Energy Conversion. 2010. (Springer Series in Materials Science Ser.). (Illus.). xxiv, 434p. pap. 239.00 *(978-3-642-08965-7(8)*, 3642089658) Springer.

Olah, George A., et al. Superacid Chemistry. 2nd ed. 2009. (ENG., Illus.). 850p. 178.00 *(978-0-471-59668-4(X)*, Wiley-Interscience) Wiley, John & Sons, Inc.

Otera, Junzo & Nishikido, Joji. Esterification: Methods, Reactions, & Applications. 2nd ed. 2010. (ENG., Illus.). 386p. 215.00 *(978-3-527-32289-3(2)*, Wiley-VCH) Wiley, John & Sons, Inc.

Overton, Tina, et al. Study & Communication Skills for the Chemical Sciences. 2011. (ENG., Illus.). 272p. 34.95 *(978-0-19-953968-0(5))* Oxford Univ. Pr., Inc.

Oxtoby & Gillis, H. Pat. Principles of Modern Chemistry. 7th ed. 2010. (ENG.). 336p. (C). pap. 97.95 *(978-1-111-42724-5(0))* Brooks/Cole.

Ozment, Judy. Chemistry: The Molecular Science. 4th ed. 2010. (ENG.). 496p. (C). pap. 96.95 *(978-1-4390-4963-1(7))* Brooks/Cole.

Parashar, Amit. Monograph on Green Chemistry by Dr Amit Parashar,Ph D,Ficc,Aicce. 2011. 88p. pap. ***(978-3-8433-7046-2(X))*** Lambert Academic Publishing.

Patino, Pedro. Chemistry Fundamentals Ia. rev. ed. 2010. (ENG.). 126p. spiral bd. 30.05 *(978-0-7575-5500-8(4))* Kendall Hunt Publishing Co.

—Chemistry Fundamentals Ib. rev. ed. 2010. (ENG.). 126p. spiral bd. 31.21 *(978-0-7575-5693-7(0))* Kendall Hunt Publishing Co.

Pauling, Linus. General Chemistry. 2011. 976p. ***(978-1-60796-298-4(5))*** Editorial Benei Noaj.

Pawliszyn, Janusz & Lord, Heather L., eds. Handbook of Sample Preparation. 2010. (ENG., Illus.). 496p. 158.00 *(978-0-470-09934-6(8)*, Wiley-Blackwell) Wiley, John & Sons, Inc.

Pechenik, Jan A., et al. A Short Guide to Writing about Chemistry. 2009. (Short Guides Ser.). (ENG.). 288p. (C). pap. 49.40 *(978-0-205-55060-9(6))* Longman Publishing Group.

Peeters, Marloes. Biohybrid Nanocomposites. 2010. 120p. pap. *(978-3-8383-7873-2(3))* Lambert Academic Publishing.

Pelouze, ThTophile Jules. General Notions of Chemistry. 2006. 476p. per. 29.99 *(978-1-4255-5265-7(X))* MPublishing.

Perchyonok, Tamara, et al. Streamlining Free Radical Green Chemistry. 2011. (ENG., Illus.). 804p. (C). 107.00 ***(978-1-84973-332-8(5))*** Royal Society of Chemistry, The GBR. Dist: Ingram Pub. Services.

Peters, Edward & Cracolice, Mark. Cengage Advantage Books: Introductory Chemistry: An Active Learning Approach. 5th ed. 2012. (ENG.). 816p. (C). ring bd. 119.95 ***(978-1-133-11312-6(5))*** Brooks/Cole.

Petrucci, Ralph H., et al. Books A la Carte for Chemistry: Principles & Modern Applications. 10th ed. 2011. (ENG.). 1424p. (C). ring bd. 133.20 ***(978-0-13-509777-9(0)***, Prentice Hall) Prentice Hall PTR.

—General Chemistry: Principles & Modern Applications. 10th ed. 2010. (ENG.). (C). 75.07 *(978-0-13-703701-8(5)*, Prentice Hall) Prentice Hall PTR.

—Math Review Toolkit for General Chemistry: Principles & Modern Applications. 10th ed. 2010. (ENG.). 150p. (C). pap. 37.40 *(978-0-13-612039-1(3)*, Prentice Hall) Prentice Hall PTR.

—Study Card for General Chemistry: Principles & Modern Applications. 10th ed. 2010. (ENG., Illus.). 10p. (C). pap. 23.80 *(978-0-13-703212-9(9)*, Prentice Hall) Prentice Hall PTR.

PH Inc. Staff. Physical Science Chemical Matter. 2nd ed. tchr. ed. *(978-0-13-225426-7(3))* Prentice Hall (Schl. Div.).

Pignataro, Bruno, ed. Ideas in Chemistry & Molecular Sciences: 3 Volume Set: Advances in Synthetic Chemistry - Where Chemistry Meets Life - Advances in Nanotechnology, Materials & Devices. 2010. (ENG., Illus.). 1272p. 345.00 *(978-3-527-32875-8(0)*, Wiley-VCH) Wiley, John & Sons, Inc.

—Ideas in Chemistry & Molecular Sciences: Advances in Nanotechnology, Materials & Devices. 2010. (ENG., Illus.). 432p. 145.00 *(978-3-527-32543-6(3)*, Wiley-VCH) Wiley, John & Sons, Inc.

—Ideas in Chemistry & Molecular Sciences: Advances in Synthetic Chemistry. 2010. (ENG., Illus.). 332p. 145.00 *(978-3-527-32539-9(5)*, Wiley-VCH) Wiley, John & Sons, Inc.

Polster, Burkard, et al. Sciencia: Mathematics, Physics, Chemistry, Biology, & Astronomy for All. 2011. (Wooden Bks.). (ENG., Illus.). 416p. 20.00 *(978-0-8027-7899-4(2))* Walker & Co.

Prentice-Hall Staff. Chemical Matter. 2nd ed. tchr. ed. *(978-0-13-400672-7(0))* Prentice Hall (Schl. Div.).

—Physical Science Chemical Matter. stu. ed., lab manual ed. *(978-0-13-986373-8(7))* Prentice Hall (Schl. Div.).

Press, Roman J., et al. Introduction to Hydrogen Technology. 2008. (ENG., Illus.). 324p. 105.00 *(978-0-471-77985-8(7)*, Wiley-Interscience) Wiley, John & Sons, Inc.

Prof Bansal, Raj. Heterocyclic Chemistry. 4th ed. 2008. (Illus.). 562p. 80.00 *(978-1-84829-001-3(2))* Anshan GBR. Dist: Publishers Storage & Shipping.

Prout, William. Chemistry, Meteorology & the Function of Digestion Considered with Reference to Natural Theology. 2009. (Cambridge Library Collection - Religion Ser.). 608p. pap. 43.00 *(978-1-108-00066-6(5))* Cambridge Univ. Pr.

Putz, Mihai V., ed. Chemical Information & Computational Challenges in the 21st Century. 2011. (Chemistry Research & Applications Ser.). 145.00 *(978-1-61209-712-1(X))* Nova Science Pubs., Inc.

Ramasami, Ponnadurai, et al, eds. Chemistry for Sustainable Development. 2012. (ENG., Illus.). xvii, 486p. 189.00 ***(978-90-481-8649-5(8)***, 9048186498) Springer.

Rao, C. N. R. Understanding Chemistry. 2009. 312p. pap. 43.00 *(978-981-283-603-8(9))* World Scientific Publishing Co., Inc.

Rappaport, Zvi. The Chemistry of Function Groups, 6 vols., Set. 2008. (ENG.). 7272p. 5700.00 *(978-0-470-77952-1(7)*, Wiley) Wiley, John & Sons, Inc.

Raven, Peter, et al. Chemistry, Cell Biology, & Genetics, Volume I (COL1) 9th ed. 2010. (ENG.). (C). pap. 90.67 *(978-0-07-739750-0(9)*, 0077397509, McGraw-Hill Science, Engineering & Mathematics) McGraw-Hill Higher Education.

Raymond, Kenneth W. General Organic & Biological Chemistry. 3rd ed. 2010. (ENG., Illus.). 624p. (C). 188.95 *(978-0-470-50476-5(5)*, Wiley) Wiley, John & Sons, Inc.

Reger, Daniel, et al. Study Guide for Reger/Goode/Ball's Chemistry: Principles & Practice, 3rd. 3rd ed. 2009. (ENG.). 576p. (C). pap. 62.95 *(978-0-495-55979-5(2))* Brooks/Cole.

Rhodes, Peter. Information Sources in Chemistry. 5th rev. ed. 2007. *(978-3-598-24437-7(1))* Saur, K. G. Verlag GmbH & Co.

Riedel, Erwin. Allgemeine und Anorganische Chemie. 9th ed. 2008. (De Gruyter Lehrbuch Ser.).Tr. of General & Inorganic Chemistry. (GER., Illus.). X, 432p. (C). pap. *(978-3-11-020277-9(8))* de Gruyter, Walter GmbH & Co. KG.

Riedel, Erwin & Grimmich, Willm. Atombau, Chemische Bindung, Chemische Reaktion: Grundlagen in Aufgaben Und Lösungen. (De Gruyter Lehrbuch Ser.). (GER.). 264p. 210.00 ***(978-3-11-196693-9(3))*** De Gruyter, Walter Inc.

—Atombau, chemische Bindung, chemische Reaktion: Grundlagen in Aufgaben und Lösungen. (De Gruyter Lehrbuch Ser.). (GER.). 264p. 135.00 ***(978-3-11-006845-0(1))*** De Gruyter, Walter Inc.

—Atombau. Chemische Bindung. Chemische Reaktion: Grundlagen in Aufgaben und Lösungen. 2nd ed. (De Gruyter Lehrbuch Ser.). (GER.). 264p. (C). 196.00 ***(978-3-11-180656-3(1))*** De Gruyter, Walter Inc.

Riedel, Erwin & Meyer, Hans-Jargen. Allgemeine und Anorganische Chemie. 10th ed. 2010. (De Gruyter Studium Ser.).Tr. of General & Inorganic Chemistry. (GER., Illus.). X, 452p. (C). pap. 56.00 *(978-3-11-022781-9(9))* De Gruyter, Walter Inc.

Robinson, Marin, et al. Write Like a Chemist: A Guide & Resource. 2008. (ENG., Illus.). 1504p. pap. 49.95 *(978-0-19-530507-4(8))* Oxford Univ. Pr., Inc.

Rolfe, W. J. (William James). Handbook of Chemistry, for School & Home Use by W J Rolfe & J a Gillet. 2006. 220p. per. 20.99 *(978-1-4255-1836-3(2))* MPublishing.

Roscoe, Henry E. Lessons in Elementary Chemistry: Inorganic & organic. by Henry E. Roscoe ... 2006. 412p. per. 26.99 *(978-1-4255-4458-4(4))* MPublishing.

Ross, Frederic C. Cell Biology & Chemistry for Allied Health Science. 6th rev. ed. 2010. (ENG.). 432p. spiral bd. 79.86 *(978-0-7575-5365-3(6))* Kendall Hunt Publishing Co.

Rothstein, et al. Chemistry. 6th rev. ed. 2010. (ENG., Illus.). 1080p. (C). 222.00 *(978-0-321-70495-5(9)*, Prentice Hall) Prentice Hall PTR.

Royal Society of Chemistry Staff. Gums & Stabilisers for the Food Industry, No. 15. Williamson, Peter A. & Phillips, Glyn O., eds. 2009. (Special Publication). (ENG., Illus.). 454p. 192.00 ***(978-1-84755-199-3(8))*** Royal Society of Chemistry, The GBR. Dist: Ingram Pub. Services.

Ruland, Alfred, et al. Rechentafeln für die Chemische Analytik: Basiswissen für die Analytische Chemie. 107th ed. 2011. (De Gruyter Studium Ser.). (GER.). (C). 49.00 ***(978-3-11-022962-2(5))*** De Gruyter, Walter Inc.

Rusay. Study Guide-Chem Bytes: User Friendly Chemistry. 2007. (C). pap. 37.95 *(978-0-534-99964-3(6))* Brooks/Cole.

Russo, Steve. Introductory Chemistry. 4th ed. 2011. (ENG.). (C). 75.07 *(978-0-321-73021-3(6)*, Prentice Hall) Prentice Hall PTR.

Russo, Steve & McGuire, Saundra Y. Study Guide & Student Solutions Manual for Introductory Chemistry. 4th ed. 2010. (ENG.). 684p. (C). pap. 60.73 *(978-0-321-71935-5(2)*, Prentice Hall) Prentice Hall PTR.

Russo, Steve & Pearson Staff. Introductory Chemistry. 4th ed. 2011. (ENG.). 792p. (C). E-Book, E-Book 126.67 *(978-0-321-73022-0(4)*, Prentice Hall) Prentice Hall PTR.

Russo, Steve & Silver, Michael E. Introductory Chemistry. 4th ed. 2010. (ENG.). 792p. (C). 155.53 *(978-0-321-66301-6(2)*, Prentice Hall) Prentice Hall PTR.

—Introductory Chemistry, Books a la Carte Edition. 4th ed. 2011. (ENG.). 792p. (C). ring bd. 93.33 *(978-0-321-78797-2(8)*, Prentice Hall) Prentice Hall PTR.

Russo, Steve & Silver, Michael E. Introductory Chemistry, Books a la Carte Plus Masteringchemistry. 4th ed. 2011. (ENG.). (C). ring bd. 103.33 ***(978-0-321-80304-7(3)***, Prentice Hall) Prentice Hall PTR.

Sahai, Mahendra, et al. Fortschritte der Chemie organischer Naturstoffe / Progress in the Chemistry of Organic Natural Products, Vol. 93. Kinghorn, A. Douglas et al, eds. 2010. (Fortschritte der Chemie organischer Naturstoffe Progress in the Chemistry of Organic Natural Products Ser.). (Illus.). xv, 264p. 359.00 *(978-3-7091-0139-1(5)*, 3709101395) Springer.

Sakai, Kenichi, et al. Novel Optical Resolution Technologies. (Topics in Current Chemistry Ser.). (Illus.). xiv, 313p. 2010. pap. 319.00 *(978-3-642-07969-5(5)*, 3642079695) 2007. 319.00 *(978-3-540-46317-7(8)*, 3540463178) Springer.

Sapling Learning Staff. One Semester Chemistry Course. 2011. (ENG.). (C). pap. 29.95 ***(978-1-118-27494-1(6)***, Wiley) Wiley, John & Sons, Inc.

—Two Semester Chemistry Course. 2011. (ENG.). (C). pap. 48.95 ***(978-1-118-27495-8(4)***, Wiley) Wiley, John & Sons, Inc.

Sawai, Hidefumi, ed. Biological Functions for Information & Communication Technologies: Theory & Inspiration. 2011. (Studies in Computational Intelligence Ser.). Orig. Title: Life & ICT - Inspiring Life-like functions into ICT. (Illus.). xi, 280p. 129.00 *(978-3-642-15101-9(9)*, 3642151019) Springer.

Scerri, Eric R. Collected Papers on Philosophy of Chemistry. 2008. 248p. 121.00 *(978-1-84816-137-5(9))* World Scientific Publishing Co., Inc.

Schubert, Ulrich S., et al. Terpyridine-Based Materials: For Catalytic, Optoelectronic & Life Science Applications. 2011. (ENG., Illus.). 542p. 195.00 ***(978-3-527-33038-6(0)***, Wiley-VCH) Wiley, John & Sons, Inc.

Schummer, Joachim, et al, eds. The Public Image of Chemistry. 2008. (Illus.). 383p. 87.00 *(978-981-277-584-9(6))* World Scientific Publishing Co., Inc.

Schwarcz, Joe. Good Chemistry. 2012. (ENG.). 272p. pap. 19.50 ***(978-0-385-67159-0(8))*** Doubleday Canada, Ltd. CAN. Dist: Random Hse., Inc.

Seager, Spencer L. & Slabaugh, Michael R. Chemistry for Today: General, Organic, & Biochemistry. 7th ed. 2010. (Available Titles OWL Ser.). (ENG.). 896p. (C). 212.95 *(978-0-538-73332-8(2))* Brooks/Cole.

—Introductory Chemistry for Today. 7th ed. 2010. (ENG.). 496p. (C). pap. 184.95 *(978-0-538-73430-1(2))* Brooks/Cole.

—Organic & Biochemistry for Today. 7th ed. 2010. (ENG.). 512p. (C). pap. 193.95 *(978-0-538-73431-8(0))* Brooks/Cole.

Seitz, Harald. Analytics of Protein-DNA Interactions. 2010. (Advances in Biochemical Engineering Biotechnology Ser.). (Illus.). xii, 204p. pap. 269.00 *(978-3-642-08007-4(3)*, 3642080073) Springer.

Serra, Michael. Chemistry 1505L: General Chemistry Laboratory for the Allied Health Sciences. 2nd rev. ed. 2010. (ENG.). 186p. spiral bd. 41.17 *(978-0-7575-5322-6(2))* Kendall Hunt Publishing Co.

Sharma, Virender K. & Rokita, Steven E. Oxidation of Amino Acids, Peptides, & Proteins: Kinetics & Mechanism. 2012. (Wiley Series of Reactive Intermediates in Chemistry & Biology Ser.: 7). (ENG.). 400p. 125.00 *(978-0-470-62776-1(X)*, Wiley) Wiley, John & Sons, Inc.

Shimizu, Toshimi. Self-Assembled Nanomaterials I: Nanofibers. 2010. (Advances in Polymer Science Ser.). (Illus.). xii, 175p. pap. 229.00 *(978-3-642-09878-9(9)*, 3642098789) Springer.

—Self-Assembled Nanomaterials II: Nanotubes. 2010. (Advances in Polymer Science Ser.). (Illus.). xii, 191p. pap. 239.00 *(978-3-642-09879-6(7)*, 3642098797) Springer.

Shubert, David & Leyba, John. Chemistry & Physics for Nurse Anesthesia: A Student Centered Approach. 2009. (Illus.). xix, 423p. *(978-0-8261-1844-8(5))* Springer.

Silberberg & Cram101 Textbook Reviews Staff. Chemistry: The Molecular Nature of Matter & Change. 2007. 360p. per. 17.95 *(978-1-4288-2934-3(2))* Cram101 Inc.

Silberberg, Martin. Chemistry: The Molecular Nature of Matter & Change. 6th ed. 2011. (ENG.). (C). 480p. pap. 72.00 *(978-0-07-734017-9(5)*, 0077340175); 544p. pap. 88.00 *(978-0-07-734021-6(3)*, 0077340213) McGraw-Hill Higher Education. (McGraw-Hill Science, Engineering & Mathematics).

—Loose Leaf Version for Chemistry: The Molecular Nature of Matter & Change. 6th ed. 2011. (ENG.). (C). ring bd. 161.00 *(978-0-07-743137-2(5)*, 0077431375, McGraw-Hill Science, Engineering & Mathematics) McGraw-Hill Higher Education.

—Loose Leaf Version for Principles of General Chemistry. 3rd ed. 2012. (ENG.). (C). ring bd. 129.00 ***(978-0-07-749126-0(2)***, 0077491262, McGraw-Hill Science, Engineering & Mathematics) McGraw-Hill Higher Education.

—Principles of General Chemistry. 2nd ed. 2009. (ENG.). (C). ring bd., ring bd. 129.00 *(978-0-07-736667-4(0)*, 0077366670); 184.00 *(978-0-07-727432-0(6)*, 0077274326) McGraw-Hill Higher Education. (McGraw-Hill Science, Engineering & Mathematics).

—Principles of General Chemistry 2nd ed. 2010. (ENG.). (C). 193.00 *(978-0-07-746848-4(1)*, 0077468481, McGraw-Hill Science, Engineering & Mathematics) McGraw-Hill Higher Education.

—Student Study Guide for Principles of General Chemistry. 3rd ed. 2012. (ENG.). 448p. (C). pap. 68.33 ***(978-0-07-738648-1(5)***, 0077386485, McGraw-Hill Science, Engineering & Mathematics) McGraw-Hill Higher Education.

—Student Study Guide to accompany Chemistry: The Molecular Nature of Matter & Change. 5th ed. 2008. (ENG., Illus.). 576p. (C). pap., pupil's gde. ed. 65.31 *(978-0-07-304861-1(5)*, 0073048615, McGraw-Hill Science, Engineering & Mathematics) McGraw-Hill Higher Education.

Silberberg, Martin. Student's Solutions Manual to accompany Principles of General Chemistry. 3rd ed. 2012. (ENG., Illus.). 384p. (C). pap. 71.33 ***(978-0-07-738646-7(9)***, 0077386469, McGraw-Hill Science, Engineering & Mathematics) McGraw-Hill Higher Education.

Silberberg, Martin S. Chemistry: The Molecular Nature of Matter & Change. 6th ed. 2011. (ENG., Illus.). 1248p. (C). 229.67 *(978-0-07-340265-9(6)*, 0073402656, McGraw-Hill Science, Engineering & Mathematics) McGraw-Hill Higher Education.

—Principles of General Chemistry. 2nd ed. 2009. *(978-0-07-351108-5(0))* McGraw-Hill Cos., The.

—Principles of General Chemistry. (Illus.). 2006. 792p. 151.88 *(978-0-07-330171-6(X)*, 9780073301716) 3rd ed. 2012. (ENG., 960p. (C). 184.00 ***(978-0-07-340269-7(9)***, 0073402699) McGraw-Hill Higher Education. (McGraw-Hill Science, Engineering & Mathematics).

Slade, Roger. Cambridge Checkpoints VCE Chemistry Unit 3 2007. 2006. (Cambridge Checkpoints Ser.). pap. 15.95 *(978-0-521-69732-3(9))* Cambridge Univ. Pr.

Smith. General, Organic & Biological Chemistry. 2nd ed. 2012. (ENG., Illus.). 944p. (C). 210.33 ***(978-0-07-340278-9(8)***, 0073402788, McGraw-Hill Science, Engineering & Mathematics) McGraw-Hill Higher Education.

Smith, Alexander. Intermediate Text Book of Chemistry. 2007. 536p. per. 33.95 *(978-1-4086-2480-7(X))* Audubon Pr. & Christian Bk. Service.

—Intermediate Text Book of Chemistry. 2009. 60p. pap. *(978-0-217-49119-8(7))* Books LLC.

C

Smith, Janice. Loose Leaf Version for General Organic & Biological Chemistry. 2009. (ENG.). (C). ring bd. 115.94 *(978-0-07-734400-9(6)*, 0077344006, McGraw-Hill Science, Engineering & Mathematics) McGraw-Hill Higher Education.

—Loose Leaf Version for General Organic & Biological Chemistry. 2nd ed. 2012. (ENG.). (C). ring bd. 147.33 ***(978-0-07-749130-7(0)***, 0077491300, McGraw-Hill Science, Engineering & Mathematics) McGraw-Hill Higher Education.

—Student Study Guide/Solutions Manual to accompany General, Organic & Biological Chemistry. 2nd ed. 2012. (ENG.). 528p. (C). pap. 68.67 ***(978-0-07-733230-3(X)***, 007733230X, McGraw-Hill Science, Engineering & Mathematics) McGraw-Hill Higher Education.

Smith, Janice G. General, Organic, & Biological Chemistry. 2009. (Illus.). *(978-0-07-302657-2(3))* McGraw-Hill Cos., The.

Smith, Janice Gorzynski. General, Organic & Biological Chemistry. 2009. (ENG.). (C). 210.33 *(978-0-07-727429-0(6)*, 0077274296, McGraw-Hill Science, Engineering & Mathematics) McGraw-Hill Higher Education.

—Loose Leaf Version for Principles of General, Organic, & Biochemistry. 2011. (ENG.). (C). ring bd. 130.00 *(978-0-07-743138-9(3)*, 0077431383, McGraw-Hill Science, Engineering & Mathematics) McGraw-Hill Higher Education.

—Package: Principles of General, Organic & Biochemistry. 2011. (ENG.). (C). 194.66 *(978-0-07-746845-3(7)*, 0077468457, McGraw-Hill Science, Engineering & Mathematics) McGraw-Hill Higher Education.

—Principles of General, Organic, & Biological Chemistry. 2011. (ENG., Illus.). 736p. (C). 185.67 *(978-0-07-351115-3(3)*, 0073511153, McGraw-Hill Science, Engineering & Mathematics) McGraw-Hill Higher Education.

Smith, John Lawrence. Mineralogy & Chemistry: Original Researches by Prof. J. Lawrence Smith. 2006. 408p. per. 26.99 *(978-1-4255-4376-1(6))* MPublishing.

Smithersrapra Technology, Technology. Svhc & Clp 2010 Conference Proceedings. 2010. (Conference Proceedings Ser.). 188p. pap. *(978-1-84735-490-7(4))* iSmithers Rapra Publishing.

Snyder, Carl H. Extraordinary Chemistry 4th Edition for Middlebury College. 4th ed. 2011. 684p. (C). ring bd. 104.95 ***(978-1-118-09613-0(4)***, Wiley) Wiley, John & Sons, Inc.

Solomon, Sally, et al. Chemistry: An Everyday Approach to Chemical Investigation. 2008. (ENG.). 312p. (C). pap. 65.95 *(978-0-470-08510-3(X)*, Wiley) Wiley, John & Sons, Inc.

Solomons, T. W. Graham. Wiley Plus/Webct Stand-Alone to Accompany Organic Chemistry. 9th ed. 2007. pap. 0.01 *(978-0-470-09952-0(6)*, Wiley) Wiley, John & Sons, Inc.

Sorge, Laurie. Prep for Success in Chemistry, a Bridge Between Math & Science. 2011. 232p. pap. 24.95 ***(978-1-257-10381-2(4))*** Lulu Enterprises Inc.

Spencer, James N. Chemistry: Structure & Dynamics. 3rd rev. ed. 2006. 80.00 net. *(978-0-470-10410-1(4))* Wiley, John & Sons, Inc.

Spencer, James N., et al. Chemistry: Structure & Dynamics. 3rd ed. 2006. pap. 51.95 *(978-0-470-07962-1(2))* 3rd ed. 2006. pap. 51.95 *(978-0-470-07756-6(5))* 4th ed. 2008. (ENG., Illus.). 880p. (C). 164.95 *(978-0-470-12928-9(X)*, Wiley) 5th ed. 2010. (ENG., Illus.). 928p. (C). 164.95 *(978-0-470-58711-9(3)*, Wiley) 5th ed. 2011. (ENG.). 160p. (C). pap. 59.95 *(978-0-470-58712-6(1)*, Wiley) Wiley, John & Sons, Inc.

—Chemistry, Student Solutions Manual: Structure & Dynamics. 4th ed. 2008. (ENG.). 160p. (C). pap. 70.95 *(978-0-470-18591-9(0)*, Wiley) Wiley, John & Sons, Inc.

—Wiley Plus/WebCT Premium to Accompany Chemistry: Structure & Dynamics. 4th ed. 2007. pap. 18.95 *(978-0-470-11735-4(4))* Wiley, John & Sons, Inc.

Sreerama, Lakshmaiah, et al. Introduction to Chemistry for Health Sciences Lab Manual. rev. ed. 2011. (ENG.). 154p. spiral bd. 36.98 *(978-0-7575-7624-9(9))* Kendall Hunt Publishing Co.

Steele, Joel Dorman. Fourteen Weeks in Chemistry. 2009. 176p. pap. *(978-0-217-21525-1(4))* Books LLC.

—Fourteen Weeks in Chemistry. 2006. 312p. per. 23.99 *(978-1-4255-3003-7(6))* MPublishing.

Sterner, Olov. Chemistry, Health & Environment. 2nd ed. 2010. (ENG., Illus.). 413p. 124.95 *(978-3-527-32582-5(4)*, Wiley-VCH) Wiley, John & Sons, Inc.

Stoker, H. Stephen. General, Organic & Biological Chemistry. 4th ed. 2006. (ENG.). 432p. (C). pap., lab manual ed. 110.95 *(978-0-618-60608-5(4)*, 354232) Brooks/Cole.

—Introduction to Chemical Principles. 10th ed. 2010. (ENG.). 736p. (C). pap. 126.73 *(978-0-321-66604-8(6)*, Prentice Hall) Prentice Hall PTR.

Stoker, H. Stephen & Gardner, Nancy J. Chemical Principles. 10th ed. 2010. (ENG.). 192p. (C). pap. 67.40 *(978-0-321-67619-1(X)*, Prentice Hall) Prentice Hall PTR.

Study Guide for Atwood/Morrison's Chemistry. 2008. (C). pap. 37.95 *(978-0-495-01625-0(X))* Brooks/Cole.

Suchocki & Suchocki, John A. Books a la Carte for Conceptual Chemistry. 4th ed. 2010. (ENG.). 576p. (C). ring bd. 97.00 *(978-0-321-72699-5(5)*, Prentice Hall) Prentice Hall PTR.

Suchocki, John. Conceptual Chemistry. 3rd ed. 2006. (ENG., Illus.). 224p. (C). per. 59.20 *(978-0-8053-1789-3(9))* Benjamin-Cummings Publishing Co.

—Conceptual Chemistry: Understanding Our World of Atoms & Molecules. 4th ed. 2009. 120.00 *(978-0-13-137630-4(6))*; tchr. ed. *(978-0-321-69527-7(5))* Pearson Education.

Suchocki, John A. Conceptual Chemistry. 4th ed. (ENG.). (C). 2011. ring bd. 103.80 ***(978-0-321-80267-5(5))*** 2011. 75.07 *(978-0-321-76741-7(1))* 2010. (Illus.). 576p. pap. 156.33 *(978-0-13-605453-5(6))* 2011. 576p. pap. 161.60 *(978-0-321-63913-4(8))* Prentice Hall PTR. (Prentice Hall).

Suchocki, John A. & Pearson Staff. Conceptual Chemistry. 4th ed. 2011. (ENG.). 576p. (C). E-Book, E-Book 126.67 *(978-0-321-76722-6(5)*, Prentice Hall) Prentice Hall PTR.

Sutton, Raul, et al. Chemistry for the Life Sciences. 2nd rev. ed. 2008. (ENG., Illus.). 280p. (C). pap. 41.95 *(978-1-4200-6935-8(7)*, CRC Press) Taylor & Francis Group GBR. Dist: Taylor & Francis Group.

Tarter. Chemistry Basics. rev. ed. 2011. 42.00 ***(978-0-7575-9172-3(8))*** Kendall Hunt Publishing Co.

Taylor, D. Lansing, ed. High Content Screening. 2010. (Methods in Molecular Biology Ser.). (Illus.). 464p. pap. 209.00 *(978-1-61737-746-4(5)*, 1617377465) Humana Pr.

Taylor, James C., ed. Advances in Chemistry Research. Volume 3. 2010. (Chemistry Research & Applications Ser.). 245.00 *(978-1-60876-464-8(8))* Nova Science Pubs., Inc.

—Advances in Chemistry Research. Volume 4. 2010. (Advances in Chemistry Research Ser.). 145.00 *(978-1-61668-743-4(6))* Nova Science Pubs., Inc.

—Advances in Chemistry Research, Volume 5. 2009. (Advances in Chemistry Research Ser.). 129.00 *(978-1-61728-773-2(3))* Nova Science Pubs., Inc.

Tekade, Pradip. Investigatory Projects in Chemistry. 2011. 144p. pap. ***(978-3-8454-0554-4(6))*** Lambert Academic Publishing.

Thomson Brooks/Cole Publishing, creator. Chemistry: The Molecular Science, Volume 1. 2007. pap. 73.95 *(978-0-495-46254-5(3))* Brooks/Cole.

Timberlake, Karen. Basic Chemistry. 2nd ed. 2007. (ENG., Illus.). 250p. (C). per. 54.60 *(978-0-321-49635-5(3))* Pearson Education Canada CAN. Dist: Pearson Education.

—General, Organic, & Biological Chemistry: Structures of Life: CourseCompass Student Access Kit. 2nd ed. 2006. 31.20 *(978-0-8053-1711-4(2))* Addison-Wesley Longman, Inc.

Timberlake, Karen C. Basic Chemistry. 3rd ed. 2010. (ENG.). (C). 608p. ring bd. 96.27 *(978-0-321-72700-8(2))*; 752p. 170.40 *(978-0-321-70616-4(1))*; 744p. 160.40 *(978-0-321-66310-8(1))*; 744p. E-Book 126.67 *(978-0-321-67419-7(7))* Prentice Hall PTR. (Prentice Hall).

—Chemistry: An Introduction to General, Organic, & Biological Chemistry. (ENG., (C). 10th ed. 2008. Illus.). 744p. 181.33 *(978-0-13-601970-1(6))* 11th ed. 2011. ring bd. 120.47 *(978-0-321-78755-2(2))* 11th rev. ed. 2010. 744p. 184.07 *(978-0-321-69345-7(0))* Prentice Hall PTR. (Prentice Hall).

—Chemistry: An Introduction to General, Organic, & Biological Chemistry, Books a la Carte Edition. 11th ed. 2011. (ENG.). 744p. (C). ring bd. 110.47 *(978-0-321-74153-0(6)*, Prentice Hall) Prentice Hall PTR.

—Chemistry: An Introduction to General, Organic, & Biological Chemistry with MasteringChemistry(r). 11th rev. ed. 2011. (ENG.). 744p. (C). 194.07 *(978-0-321-74104-2(8)*, Prentice Hall) Prentice Hall PTR.

—General, Organic, & Biological Chemistry: Structures of Life. 3rd ed. 2009. (ENG., Illus.). 936p. (C). 198.13 *(978-0-13-605454-2(4)*, Prentice Hall) Prentice Hall PTR.

—General, Organic, & Biological Chemistry: Structures of Life. 4th ed. (ENG.). (C). 2012. ring bd. 128.93 ***(978-0-321-76747-9(0))*** 2011. 936p. 198.13 ***(978-0-321-75089-1(6))*** 2011. 936p. 208.13 ***(978-0-321-75012-9(8))*** Prentice Hall PTR. (Prentice Hall).

—General, Organic, & Biological Chemistry: Structures of Life, Books ala Carte Edition. 4th ed. 2012. (ENG.). 936p. (C). ring bd. 118.93 ***(978-0-321-76748-6(9)***, Prentice Hall) Prentice Hall PTR.

—Selected Solution Manual for Chemistry: An Introduction to General, Organic, & Biological Chemist. 11th ed. 2011. (ENG.). 168p. (C). pap. 82.47 *(978-0-321-76521-5(4)*, Prentice Hall) Prentice Hall PTR.

—Selected Solution Manual for General, Organic, & Biological Chemistry: Structures of Life. 4th ed. 2012. (ENG.). 216p. (C). pap. 80.00 ***(978-0-321-76703-5(9)***, Prentice Hall) Prentice Hall PTR.

—Selected Solutions Manual for General, Organic, & Biological Chemistry for General, Organic, & Biological Chemistry: Structures of Life. 3rd ed. 2009. (ENG.). 168p. (C). pap. 80.00 *(978-0-321-61663-0(4)*, Prentice Hall) Prentice Hall PTR.

—Study Guide for Basic Chemistry. 3rd ed. 2010. (ENG.). 480p. (C). pap. 58.47 *(978-0-321-67626-9(2)*, Prentice Hall) Prentice Hall PTR.

—Study Guide for Chemistry: An Introduction to General, Organic, & Biological Chemistry. 11th ed. 2011. (ENG., Illus.). 288p. (C). pap. 82.47 *(978-0-321-71942-3(5)*, Prentice Hall) Prentice Hall PTR.

—Study Guide for General, Organic & Biological Chemistry: Structures of Life. 3rd ed. 2009. (ENG.). 360p. (C). pap., pupil's gde. ed. 72.93 *(978-0-321-58755-8(3)*, Prentice Hall) Prentice Hall PTR.

Timberlake, Karen C. Study Guide for General, Organic, & Biological Chemistry: Structures of Life. 4th rev. ed. 2012. (ENG.). 360p. (C). pap. 72.93 ***(978-0-321-76702-8(0)***, Prentice Hall) Prentice Hall PTR.

Timberlake, Karen C. & Pearson Staff. Chemistry: An Introduction to General, Organic, & Biological Chemistry. 11th rev. ed. 2011. (ENG.). 744p. (C). E-Book, E-Book 126.67 *(978-0-321-72715-2(0)*, Prentice Hall) Prentice Hall PTR.

—General, Organic, & Biological Chemistry: Structures of Life. 3rd ed. 2009. (ENG.). (C). E-Book, E-Book 126.67 *(978-0-321-63355-2(5)*, Prentice Hall) Prentice Hall PTR.

Toupadakis, Andreas. Chemistry Reader 2A. rev. ed. 2009. (ENG.). 306p. spiral bd. 39.09 *(978-0-7575-6064-4(4))* Kendall Hunt Publishing Co.

—Chemistry Reader 2C. rev. ed. 2009. (ENG.). 310p. spiral bd. 53.63 *(978-0-7575-6230-3(2))* Kendall Hunt Publishing Co.

Tro & Tro, Nivaldo J. Introductory Chemistry with MasteringChemistryreg; with Math Review Kit. 4th ed. 2011. (ENG.). (C). pap. 170.40 ***(978-0-321-79849-7(X)***, Prentice Hall) Prentice Hall PTR.

Tro, Nivaldo J. Chemistry: A Molecular Approach. 2nd ed. 2010. (ENG.). 1224p. (C). 222.00 *(978-0-321-65178-5(2)*, Prentice Hall) Prentice Hall PTR.

—Introductory Chemistry. 4th ed. (ENG.). (C). 2011. ring bd. 106.27 *(978-0-321-78758-3(7))* 2011. 848p. 170.40 *(978-0-321-74102-8(1))* 2010. 832p. 160.40 *(978-0-321-68793-7(0))* Prentice Hall PTR. (Prentice Hall).

—Introductory Chemistry, Books a la Carte Edition. 4th ed. 2011. (ENG.). 848p. (C). ring bd. 96.27 *(978-0-321-74149-3(8)*, Prentice Hall) Prentice Hall PTR.

—Introductory Chemistry Essentials. 3rd ed. 2008. (ENG., Illus.). 744p. (C). 147.00 *(978-0-13-601991-6(9))* Prentice Hall Higher Education.

—Introductory Chemistry Essentials. 4th ed. 2011. (ENG., (C). Illus.). 736p. 149.27 *(978-0-321-72599-8(9))*; 752p. 159.27 *(978-0-321-76580-2(X))* Prentice Hall PTR. (Prentice Hall).

—MasteringGeneralChemistry (tm) Student Access Kit for Principles of Chemistry: A Molecular Approach. 2009. (ENG.). (C). 75.07 *(978-0-321-58657-5(3)*, Prentice Hall) Prentice Hall PTR.

Tro, Nivaldo J. Principles of Chemistry: A Molecular Approach. 2nd rev. ed. 2011. (ENG.). (C). 888p. 183.00 ***(978-0-321-75009-9(8))***; 936p. 173.00 ***(978-0-321-75090-7(X))*** Prentice Hall PTR. (Prentice Hall).

Tro, Nivaldo J. & Friedman, Donna J. Study Guide for Introductory Chemistry. 4th ed. 2011. (ENG.). 304p. (C). pap. 70.27 *(978-0-321-73010-7(0)*, Prentice Hall) Prentice Hall PTR.

Tro, Nivaldo J. & Johll, Matthew J. Student Solution Manual for Introductory Chemistry. 4th ed. 2011. (ENG.). 176p. (C). pap. 85.07 *(978-0-321-73018-3(6)*, Prentice Hall) Prentice Hall PTR.

Tro, Nivaldo J. & Pearson Staff. MasteringChemistry. 4th rev. ed. 2011. (ENG.). 848p. (C). E-Book, E-Book 126.67 *(978-0-321-73027-5(5)*, Prentice Hall) Prentice Hall PTR.

Tro, Nivaldo J., et al. Chemistry: A Molecular Approach. 2007. (ENG.). 448p. (C). pap. 74.00 *(978-0-13-615116-6(7)*, Prentice Hall) Prentice Hall PTR.

Tro, Nivaldo Jose & Shanoski, Jennifer J. Study Guide for Chemistry: A Molecular Approach. (ENG.). (C). 2008. 304p. pap. 70.40 *(978-0-321-56635-5(1))* 2nd ed. 2010. 352p. pap. 71.47 *(978-0-321-66788-5(3))* Prentice Hall PTR. (Prentice Hall).

Tro, Nivaldo Jose, et al. Selected Solutions Manual for Principles of Chemistry: A Molecular Approach. 2009. (ENG.). 350p. (C). pap. 73.53 *(978-0-321-58638-4(7)*, Prentice Hall) Prentice Hall PTR.

Trsic, Milan. A Serious Glance at Chemistry: Basic Notions Explained. 2010. (Illus.). 204p. 72.00 *(978-1-84816-530-4(7))* World Scientific Publishing Co., Inc.

Tweedie-Cullen, Ry. Quantitative Proteomics. 2010. 124p. pap. *(978-3-639-26221-6(2))* VDM Verlag Dr. Mueller e.K.

Umland, Jean B. General Chemistry. Date not set. (Chemistry). 59.50 net. *(978-0-314-10702-2(9))* Brooks/Cole.

Urbansky, Edward. Writing It Right in Chemistry - a Little Blue Book. 2008. 192p. pap. 24.98 *(978-1-4357-1347-5(8))* Lulu Enterprises Inc.

Valacchi, Giuseppe, ed. Oxidants in Biology: A Question of Balance. 2010. (ENG.). viii, 328p. pap. 189.00 *(978-90-481-7867-4(3)*, 9048178673) Springer.

Verma, Hem Raj. Atomic & Nuclear Analytical Methods: XRF, Mössbauer, XPS, NAA & Ion-Beam Spectroscopic Techniques. 2007. (ENG., Illus.). xiv, 376p. 219.00 *(978-3-540-30277-3(8)*, 3540302778) Springer.

Wachter, Helmut & Hausen, Arno. Chemie für Mediziner. (De Gruyter Lehrbuch Ser.). (GER.). XIX, 319p. 135.00 ***(978-3-11-004934-3(1))*** De Gruyter, Walter Inc.

—Chemie Für Mediziner. (De Gruyter Lehrbuch Ser.). (GER.). XIX, 319p. 210.00 ***(978-3-11-216331-3(1))*** De Gruyter, Walter Inc.

Walde, Peter. Prebiotic Chemistry: From Simple Amphiphiles to Protocell Models. 2010. (Topics in Current Chemistry Ser.). xii, 221p. pap. 249.00 *(978-3-642-06614-6(3)*, 3642066143) Springer.

Waller, Francis J. Writing Chemistry Patents & Intellectual Property: A Practical Guide. 2011. (ENG., Illus.). 256p. 79.95 *(978-0-470-49740-1(8)*, Wiley) Wiley, John & Sons, Inc.

Wang, S. J., et al, eds. Positron & Positronium Chemistry. 2009. (Material Science Forum Ser.: Vol. 607). 282p. pap. *(978-0-87849-348-7(4))* Trans Tech Pubns., Ltd.

Wegner, Patrick. Chemhelp to Accompany Catalyst for General Chemistry. 2014. (ENG.). 272p. (C). pap. 32.95 *(978-0-470-47021-3(6)*, Wiley) Wiley, John & Sons, Inc.

Wehrens, Ron. Chemometrics with R: Multivariate data analysis in the natural sciences & life Sciences. 2011. (Use R Ser.). (Illus.). xiv, 285p. pap. 59.95 *(978-3-642-17840-5(5)*, 3642178405) Springer.

Weiner. Introduction to Chemical Principles: A Laboratory Approach. 7th ed. 2009. (ENG.). 480p. (C). pap. 152.95 *(978-0-495-11479-6(0))* Brooks/Cole.

Weisblatt, Jayne & Montney, Charles B. Chemical Compounds, 3 vols. rev. ed. 2006. (ENG., Illus.). 720p. 225.00 *(978-1-4144-0150-8(7)*, UXL) Cengage Gale.

Wells, David Ames. Wells's Principles & Applications of Chemistry: For the Use of Academies, High-Schools, & Colleges. 2006. 524p. per. 29.99 *(978-1-4255-5828-4(3))* MPublishing.

—Wells's Principles & Applications of Chemistry; for the Use of Academies, High Schools, & Colleges: Introducing the Latest Results of Scientific D. 2006. 520p. per. 29.99 *(978-1-4255-5789-8(9))* MPublishing.

Werther, Meike & Seitz, Harald. Protein - Protein Interaction. 2010. (Advances in Biochemical Engineering Biotechnology Ser.). (Illus.). xiv, 272p. pap. 279.00 *(978-3-642-08838-4(4)*, 3642088384) Springer.

Werwa, Eric, et al. Glencoe Science Modules: Physical Science, Chemistry. 2007. (ENG., Illus.). 173p. (C). lib. bdg. 26.80 *(978-0-07-877834-6(4)*, 0078778344) McGraw-Hill Higher Education.

Whitten, Kenneth, et al. Study Guide for Whitten/Davis/Peck/Stanley's Chemistry, 9th. 9th ed. 2009. (ENG.). 400p. (C). pap. 101.95 *(978-0-495-39173-9(5))* Brooks/Cole.

Whitten, Kenneth W. Chemistry. 8th ed. 2007. (Illus.). xxxviii, 1066p. *(978-0-495-10594-7(5))* Brooks/Cole.

Whitten, Kenneth W., et al. Chemistry. 9th ed. 2009. (Available Titles OWL Ser.). (ENG.). 1168p. (C). 273.95 *(978-0-495-39163-0(8))* Brooks/Cole.

Wiley. Binder for Binder Ready Versions. 2008. *(978-0-470-40696-0(8)*, Wiley) Wiley, John & Sons, Inc.

Williams, Gregory M. & Olmsted, John A. Think Molecules: An Introduction to Chemistry. 2007. 544p. 84.95 *(978-0-471-09534-7(6)*, Wiley-Liss) Wiley, John & Sons, Inc.

—Think Molecules, Solutions Manual: An Introductionn to Chemistry. 2007. 544p. stu. ed. 31.95 *(978-0-471-21514-1(7)*, Wiley-Interscience) Wiley, John & Sons, Inc.

Williams, Linda. Chemistry DeMYSTiFieD. 2nd ed. 2011. (Demystified Ser.). (ENG., Illus.). 368p. pap. 20.00 *(978-0-07-175130-8(0)*, 0071751300) McGraw-Hill Professional Publishing.

Williams, Michael. The Development of New Methods Towards Guaiane Natural. 2008. 420p. pap. *(978-3-8364-9641-4(0))* VDM Verlag Dr. Mueller e.K.

Willock, David. Molecular Symmetry. 2009. (ENG., Illus.). 438p. pap. 55.00 *(978-0-470-85348-1(4)*, Wiley) Wiley, John & Sons, Inc.

Willock, David, et al. Molecular Symmetry. 2009. (ENG., Illus.). 438p. 160.00 *(978-0-470-85347-4(6)*, Wiley) Wiley, John & Sons, Inc.

Wittmann, Valentin. Glycopeptides & Glycoproteins: Synthesis, Structure, & Application. 2007. (Topics in Current Chemistry Ser.). (Illus.). XII, 265p. 295.00 *(978-3-540-36760-4(8)*, 3540367608) Springer.

Woo, Hee-Gweon & Li, Hong, eds. Advanced Functional Materials. 2011. (ENG., Illus.). 350p. 219.00 *(978-3-642-19076-6(6)*, 3642190766) Springer.

Yan, Bing. Analytical Methods in Combinatorial Chemistry, Second Edition. 2nd rev. ed. 2010. (Critical Reviews in Combinatorial Chemistry Ser.). (ENG., Illus.). 238p. 199.95 *(978-0-8493-1860-3(2)*, CRC Press) Taylor & Francis Group GBR. Dist: Taylor & Francis Group.

Youmans, Edward Livingston. A Class-Book of Chemistry. 2006. 468p. per. 29.99 *(978-1-4255-5194-0(7))* MPublishing.

Zachariah, Benjamin. Prafulla Chandra Ray: The Chemistry of a National Life. 2012. (Pathfinders Ser.). (ENG.). 175p. (C). 100.00 *(978-0-415-44612-9(0)*, Routledge India) Taylor & Francis Group GBR. Dist: Taylor & Francis Group.

Zaikov, Gennadii Efremovich, ed. Success in Chemistry & Biochemistry Vol. 4: Mind's Flight in Time & Space. 2009. 139.00 *(978-1-60692-343-6(9))* Nova Science Pubs., Inc.

Zumdahl, Steven & DeCoste, Donald J. Introductory Chemistry: A Foundation, Hybrid. 7th ed. 2010. (Cengage Learningrsquo;s New Hybrid Editions! Ser.). (ENG.). 656p. (C). pap. 134.95 *(978-0-538-75708-9(6))* Brooks/Cole.

Zumdahl, Steven S. & DeCoste, Donald J. Basic Chemistry. 7th ed. 2010. (Available 2011 Titles Enhanced Web Assign Ser.). (ENG., Illus.). 640p. (C). pap. 163.95 *(978-0-538-73637-4(2))* Brooks/Cole.

—Basic Chemistry. 6th ed. 2007. (ENG., Illus.). 624p. (C). per. 172.95 *(978-0-618-80330-9(0)*, 370843) CENGAGE Learning.

—Introductory Chemistry: A Foundation. 7th ed. 2010. (Available Titles OWL Ser.). (ENG., Illus.). 816p. (C). 191.95 *(978-1-4390-4940-2(8))* Brooks/Cole.

—Introductory Chemistry: A Foundation. 6th ed. 2007. (Available 2010 Titles Enhanced Web Assign Ser.). (ENG., Illus.). 800p. (C). 210.95 *(978-0-618-80327-9(0)*, 370840) CENGAGE Learning.

Zumdahl, Steven S. & Zumdahl, Susan A. Chemistry. 8th ed. 2012. (Illus.). xxix, 1064p. ***(978-1-111-57734-6(X))*** 2008. (ENG.). 1184p. (C). 273.95 *(978-0-547-12532-9(1))* Brooks/Cole.

—Chemistry: An Atoms First Approach. 2011. (Textbooks Available with Cengage YouBook Ser.). (ENG.). 1152p. (C). 240.95 *(978-0-8400-6532-2(9))* Brooks/Cole.

—Zumdahl Chemistry Media Enhanced Edition Seventh Edition. 7th ed. 2007. (Available 2010 Titles Enhanced Web Assign Ser.). (ENG., Illus.). 1168p. (C). 273.95 *(978-0-547-05405-6(X)*, 1036318) CENGAGE Learning.

Zumdahl, Steven S., et al. Chemistry: Instructor's Resource Guide. 7th ed. 2007. xxxv, 128p. *(978-0-618-71581-7(9))* Houghton Mifflin Harcourt Publishing Co.

CHEMISTRY—APPARATUS

see Chemical Apparatus

CHEMISTRY—BIBLIOGRAPHY

see also Chemical Literature

Neville, Roy G. The Roy G. Neville Historical Chemical Library: An Annotated Catalogue of Printed Books on Alchemy, Chemistry, Chemical Technology, & Related Subjects. 2006. 250.00 *(978-0-941901-40-6(8))* Chemical Heritage Foundation.

CHEMISTRY—DATA PROCESSING

A. Wheeler, Ralph, ed. Annual Reports in Computational Chemistry. 2011. (ENG.). 288p. pap. 241.00 ***(978-0-444-53835-2(6))*** Elsevier Science & Technology Bks.

Abdel-Azeim, Safwat. Protein Ligand Binding Interactions. 2010. 200p. pap. *(978-3-639-27790-6(2))* VDM Verlag Dr. Mueller e.K.
Amos. Recent Advances in Computational Chemistry Software, Vol. 7. 2011. 118.00 *(978-981-4289-32-0(9))* World Scientific Publishing Co., Inc.
Bender, Andreas, et al. Systems Chemical Biology: Integrating Chemistry & Biology Through Cheminformatics Approaches. 2012. (ENG.). 300p. 99.95 *(978-0-470-55447-0(9),* Wiley) Wiley, John & Sons, Inc.
Boyd, Donald B. Reviews in Computational Chemistry, Volume 26. Cundari, Thomas R. & Lipkowitz, Kenny B., eds. 2nd ed. 2008. (Reviews in Computational Chemistry Ser.: 51). (ENG.). 532p. 205.00 *(978-0-470-38839-6(0),* Wiley-VCH) Wiley, John & Sons, Inc.
Boyd, Donald B. & Lipkowitz, Kenny B. Reviews in Computational Chemistry, Vols. 1-23. Cundari, Thomas R., ed. 2007. (Reviews in Computational Chemistry Ser.: 47). (ENG.). 500p. 4735.00 *(978-0-470-13994-3(3),* Wiley-VCH) Wiley, John & Sons, Inc.
Castro, E. A. & Haghi, A. K. Advanced Methods & Applications in Chemoinformatics: Research Progress & New Applications. 2011. ***(978-1-60960-862-0(3))*** IGI Global.
Castro, Eduardo A. & Haghi, A. K., eds. Advanced Methods & Applications in Chemoinformatics: Research Progress & New Applications. 2011. (Illus.). 485p. 195.00 *(978-1-60960-860-6(7),* Engineering Science Reference) IGI Global.
Chalk, Stuart J. XML & Scientific Markup Languages for Chemists. 2010. 276p. pap. 69.95 incl. cd-rom *(978-0-470-23293-4(5),* Wiley-Interscience) Wiley, John & Sons, Inc.
Collett, Charles T. & Robson, Christopher D. Handbook of Computational Chemistry Research. 2009. 195.00 *(978-1-60741-047-8(8))* Nova Science Pubs., Inc.
Cundari, Thomas R. & Lipkowitz, Kenny B. Reviews in Computational Chemistry, Volume 25. Boyd, Donald B., ed. 2nd rev. ed. 2007. (Reviews in Computational Chemistry Ser.: 48). (ENG., Illus.). 448p. 222.00 *(978-0-470-17998-7(8),* Wiley-VCH) Wiley, John & Sons, Inc.
Cundari, Thomas R., et al. Reviews in Computational Chemistry, Volume 24. Cundari, Thomas R., ed. 2007. (Reviews in Computational Chemistry Ser.: 31). (ENG.). 517p. 227.00 *(978-0-470-11281-6(6),* Wiley-VCH) Wiley, John & Sons, Inc.
Fuller, Lawrence A. Powerpoint Slides/Notes to Accompany Chemistry for Changing Times. rev. ed. 2009. (ENG.). 162p. pap. 37.00 *(978-0-7575-1165-3(1))* Kendall Hunt Publishing Co.
Guha, Rajarshi & Bender, Andreas, eds. Computational Approaches in Cheminformatics & Bioinformatics. 2012. (ENG., Illus.). 292p. 115.00 *(978-0-470-38441-1(7),* Wiley) Wiley, John & Sons, Inc.
Halbesleben, Jonathon R. B., ed. Medical Biochemoinformatics. 2008. 249p. (C). 98.00 *(978-1-60456-501-0(2))* Nova Science Pubs., Inc.
Hanrahan, Grady. Artificial Neural Networks in Biological & Environmental Analysis. 2011. (Analytical Chemistry Ser.). (ENG., Illus.). 214p. 89.95 *(978-1-4398-1258-7(6),* CRC Press) Taylor & Francis Group GBR. Dist: Taylor & Francis Group.
Heine, Thomas, et al. Computational Chemistry. 2009. (ENG., Illus.). 250p. pap., wbk. ed. 57.00 *(978-3-527-32442-2(9),* Wiley-VCH) Wiley, John & Sons, Inc.
Jensen, Frank. Introduction to Computational Chemistry. 2nd rev. ed. 2006. (ENG., Illus.). 624p. 210.00 *(978-0-470-01186-7(6));* per. 80.00 *(978-0-470-01187-4(4))* Wiley, John & Sons, Inc. (Wiley).
Johnston, Roy L. Applications of Evolutionary Computation in Chemistry. 2010. (Structure & Bonding Ser.). (Illus.). xi, 184p. pap. 239.00 *(978-3-642-07307-6(7),* 3642073077) Springer.
Judson, Phillip. Not Counting on Computers: Knowledge-Based Expert Systems in Chemistry. 2009. (RSC Theoretical & Computational Chemistry Ser.). (ENG., Illus.). 222p. (C). 195.00 *(978-0-85404-160-2(5))* Royal Society of Chemistry, The GBR. Dist: Ingram Pub. Services.
Kazimirski, Jan. Computational Study of Hydrogen Bonded Systems. 2011. 148p. pap. ***(978-3-8454-0807-1(3))*** Lambert Academic Publishing.
Leach, Andrew R. & Gillet, Valerie J. An Introduction to Chemoinformatics. 2007. (Illus.). 255p. pap. 69.95 *(978-1-4020-6290-2(7))* Springer.
Leszczynski, Jerzy. Computational Chemistry: Reviews of Current Trends. 350p. 113.00 *(978-981-02-3752-3(9))* World Scientific Publishing Co., Inc.
Leszczynski, Jerzy, ed. Handbook of Computational Chemistry, 3 vols. 2012. (ENG., Illus.). xx, 1430p. 949.00 *(978-94-007-0710-8(X),* 940070710X); 1200.00 *(978-94-007-0712-2(6),* 9400707126) Springer.
Leszczynski, Jerzy & Shukla, Manoj K., eds. Practical Aspects of Computational Chemistry: Methods, Concepts & Applications. 2009. (ENG., Illus.). xvii, 465p. 199.00 *(978-90-481-2686-6(X),* 904812686X) Springer.
Leszczynski, Jerzy & Shukla, Manoj K., eds. Practical Aspects of Computational Chemistry II: An Overview of the Last Two Decades & Current Trends, 2 vols. 2012. (ENG., Illus.). x, 685p. 179.00 ***(978-94-007-0922-5(6),*** 9400709226) Springer.
Lewars, Errol G. Computational Chemistry: Introduction to the Theory & Applications of Molecular & Quantum Mechanics. 2nd ed. (ENG., Illus.). xvi, 664p. 2011. pap. 99.00 *(978-90-481-3861-6(2),* 9048138612) 2010. 199.00 *(978-90-481-3860-9(4),* 9048138604) Springer.
—Modeling Marvels. 2008. (Illus.). xiv, 282p. 139.00 *(978-1-4020-6972-7(3))* Springer.
Li, Fan. Developing Chemical Information Systems: An Object-Oriented Approach Using Enterprise Java. 2006. (ENG., Illus.). 216p. 247.00 *(978-0-471-75157-1(X),* Wiley) Wiley, John & Sons, Inc.
Lipkowitz. Reviews in Computational Chemistry Bundle. 2008. (Reviews in Computational Chemistry Ser.). 3580p. 1208.00 *(978-0-470-38789-4(0),* Wiley-VCH) Wiley, John & Sons, Inc.
Lipkowitz, Kenny B. Reviews in Computational Chemistry, Volume 27. 2nd ed. 2010. (Reviews in Computational Chemistry Ser.: 52). (ENG.). 481p. 205.00 *(978-0-470-58714-0(8),* Wiley) Wiley, John & Sons, Inc.
Miller, James & Miller, Jane C. Statistics & Chemometrics for Analytical Chemistry. 6th ed. 2010. (ENG., Illus.). 296p. pap. 97.50 *(978-0-273-73042-2(8),* Prentice Hall) Pearson Education, Ltd. GBR. Dist: Trans-Atlantic Pubns., Inc.
Otto, Matthias. Chemometrics: Statistics & Computer Application in Analytical Chemistry. 2nd ed. 2007. (ENG., Illus.). 343p. pap. 110.00 *(978-3-527-31418-8(0),* Wiley-VCH) Wiley, John & Sons, Inc.
Paneth, Piotr & Dybala-Defratyka, Agnieszka, eds. Kinetics & Dynamics: From Nano- to Bio-Scale. 2010. (Challenges & Advances in Computational Chemistry & Physics Ser.). (Illus.). 750p. 519.00 *(978-90-481-3033-7(6),* 9048130336) Springer.
Papadopoulos, M. G., et al, eds. Linear-Scaling Techniques in Computational Chemistry & Physics: Methods & Applications. 2010. (Challenges & Advances in Computational Chemistry & Physics Ser.). (Illus.). 400p. 309.00 *(978-90-481-2852-5(8),* 9048128528) Springer.
Rode, Bernd Michael, et al. The Basics of Theoretical & Computational Chemistry. 2007. (ENG., Illus.). 195p. 98.00 *(978-3-527-31773-8(2),* Wiley-VCH) Wiley, John & Sons, Inc.
Spellmeyer, David C., ed. Annual Reports in Computational Chemistry, Vol. 2. 2006. (Annual Reports in Computational Chemistry Ser.). (ENG.). 346p. 241.00 *(978-0-444-52822-3(9),* Elsevier Science) Elsevier Science & Technology Bks.
Spellmeyer, David C. & Wheeler, Ralph A., eds. Annual Reports in Computational Chemistry. 2007. (ENG.). 254p. 241.00 *(978-0-444-53088-2(6),* Elsevier Science) Elsevier Science & Technology Bks.
Varnek, Alexandre & Tropsha, Alex. Chemoinformatics Approaches to Virtual Screening: An Approach to Virtual Screening. 2008. (ENG., Illus.). 356p. 224.00 ***(978-0-85404-144-2(3))*** Royal Society of Chemistry, The GBR. Dist: Ingram Pub. Services.
Wei, Dong-Qing & Wang, Xi-Jun, eds. Theory & Applications of Computational Chemistry - 2008. 2009. (AIP Conference Proceedings / Mathematical & Statistical Phsyics Ser.). (ENG.). 326p. pap. 147.00 *(978-0-7354-0637-7(5))* American Institute of Physics.
Wheeler, Ralph A. & Spellmeyer, David C., eds. Annual Reports in Computational Chemistry. (ENG.). 2010. 344p. pap. 241.00 *(978-0-444-53552-8(7))* 2009. 216p. pap. 241.00 *(978-0-444-53359-3(1),* Elsevier Science) 2008. 272p. 241.00 *(978-0-444-53250-3(1),* Elsevier Science) Elsevier Science & Technology Bks.
Yamanashi, Yoshihiro. Chemoinformatics & Advanced Machine Learning Perspectives: Complex Computational Methods & Collaborative Techniques. Lodhi, Huma M., ed. 2010. (Illus.). 350p. 245.00 *(978-1-61520-911-8(5),* IGI Global.

CHEMISTRY—DICTIONARIES

Anstein, Stefanie & Kremer, Gerhard. Analysing Names of Organic Chemical Compounds. 2008. 112p. per. *(978-3-8364-5985-2(5))* VDM Verlag Dr. Mueller e.K.
Ash, Michael & Ash, Irene, eds. Specialty Chemicals Electronic Source Book. 4th ed. 2009. cd-rom 495.00 *(978-1-934764-18-3(3))* Synapse Information Resources, Inc.
Begley, Tadhg P. Chemical Biology Vol. 3, 4 vols., Vol. 3. 2009. (ENG., Illus.). 818p. 348.00 *(978-0-470-47019-0(4),* Wiley) Wiley, John & Sons, Inc.
Buckingham, John, et al, eds. Dictionary of Alkaloids. 2nd rev. ed. 2010. (ENG., Illus.). 2374p. 795.00 *(978-1-4200-7769-8(4),* CRC Press) Taylor & Francis Group GBR. Dist: Taylor & Francis Group.
Chemistry Matters! 2007. *(978-0-7172-6197-0(2)); (978-0-7172-6195-6(6)); (978-0-7172-6196-3(4)); (978-0-7172-6204-5(9)); (978-0-7172-6198-7(0)); (978-0-7172-6199-4(9)); (978-0-7172-6200-7(6)); (978-0-7172-6201-4(4)); (978-0-7172-6202-1(2)); (978-0-7172-6203-8(0))* Grolier, Ltd.
Clark & Hemsley, William. The Rosen Comprehensive Dictionary of Chemistry. John, O. E., ed. 2009. (Rosen Comprehensive Student Dictionaries Ser.). 286p. (gr. 9-9). 93.00 *(978-1-60852-505-8(8))* Rosen Publishing Group, Inc., The.
Clark, John O. E. & Hemsley, William, eds. The Rosen Comprehensive Dictionary of Chemistry. 2007. (Rosen Comprehensive Student Dictionaries Ser.). (Illus.). 285p. (YA). (gr. 9-12). lib. bdg. 46.50 *(978-1-4042-0700-4(7))* Rosen Publishing Group, Inc., The.
Daintith, John, ed. Oxford Dictionary of Chemistry. 6th ed. 2008. (Oxford Paperback Reference Ser.). (ENG., Illus.). 608p. 17.95 *(978-0-19-920463-2(2))* Oxford Univ. Pr., Inc.
The Dictionary of Chemistry. (Key to Science Ser.). 4.95 *(978-958-04-0031-8(8))* Norma S.A. COL. Dist: Distribuidora Norma, Inc.
Gewehr, Markus, ed. Japanese-English Chemical Dictionary: Including a Guide to Japanese Patents & Scientific Literature. 2007. (JPN & ENG.). 680p. 270.00 *(978-3-527-31293-1(5),* Wiley-VCH) Wiley, John & Sons, Inc.
Gross, H. W. & Hildebrand, H. Kleines Worterbuch der Chemie und Chem. Technik, Vol. 2. (ENG & GER.). 128p. 9.95 *(978-3-87144-219-3(4))* French & European Pubns., Inc.
Gross, Helmut. English-German Dictionary of Chemistry & Chemical Technology. (ENG & GER.). *(978-0-7859-9341-4(X))* French & European Pubns., Inc.
Hesperides. The Chemical Age - Chemical Dictionary - Chemical Terms. 2008. 176p. *(978-1-4437-2899-7(3))* 2007. 172p. per. *(978-1-4067-5756-3(6),* Read Bks. (Hesperides Pr.).
Hunt, Andrew. A-Z Chemistry Handbook. 4th ed. 2009. (Illus.). 416p. 22.99 *(978-0-340-99100-8(3))* Hodder Education GBR. Dist: Oxford Univ. Pr., Inc.
Kirk-Othmer & Kirk-Othmer. Kirk-Othmer Encyclopedia of Chemical Technology, Vol. 26, Volume 26. Wiley-Interscience Publication Staff, ed. 5th rev. ed. 2007. (Kirk 5e Print Continuation Ser.: 1). (ENG., Illus.). 1076p. 426.00 *(978-0-471-48495-0(4),* Wiley-Interscience) Wiley, John & Sons, Inc.
Lewis, Richard J. Hawely's Condensed Chemical Dictionary Network CD 11 + Users. 15th rev. ed. 2007. (ENG.). 450.00 *(978-0-470-12434-5(2),* Wiley-Interscience) Wiley, John & Sons, Inc.
—Hawely's Condensed Chemical Dictionary Fifteeth Edition Network CD 2-5 Users. 15th rev. ed. 2007. (ENG.). 300.00 *(978-0-470-12432-1(6),* Wiley-Interscience) Wiley, John & Sons, Inc.
—Hawley's Condensed Chemical Dictionary. 15th ed. 2007. (ENG.). 4p. 174.00 *(978-0-471-76896-8(0),* Wiley-Interscience) Wiley, John & Sons, Inc.
—Hawley's Condensed Chemical Dictionary, Book & CD-ROM Set. 15th rev. ed. 2007. (ENG.). 1380p. 310.00 *(978-0-470-12482-6(2),* Wiley-Interscience) Wiley, John & Sons, Inc.
Newmann, Gerald R. & Albertis, Andrew P. Encyclopedia of Chemistry Research. 2011. (Chemistry Research & Applications Ser.). 325.00 ***(978-1-61470-104-0(0))*** Nova Science Pubs., Inc.
Storer, Francis Humphreys. A Cyclopaedia of Quantitative Chemical Analysis by Frank H Storer. 2006. 244p. per. 20.99 *(978-1-4255-2140-0(1))* MPublishing.
Thompson, Reginald C. A Dictionary of Assyrian Chemistry & Geology. (Ancient Mesopotamian Texts & Studies). reprint ed. 37.50 *(978-0-404-18222-9(4))* AMS Pr., Inc.

CHEMISTRY—DIRECTORIES

Geddes, Chris D. Who's Who in Fluorescence 2008. 2008. 206p. pap. 19.95 ***(978-0-387-78176-1(5),*** 0387781765) Springer.

CHEMISTRY—EARLY WORKS TO 1800

International Conference on the History of Alchemy and Chymistry & Principe, Lawrence. Chymists & Chymistry: Studies in the History of Alchemy & Early Modern Chemistry. 2007. (Illus.). 287p. 45.00 *(978-0-88135-396-9(5),* Science History Pubns./USA) Watson Publishing International, LLC.
Venel, Gabriel-François, et al. Cours de Chimie. 2010. (FRE., Illus.). 450p. *(978-2-915611-64-9(5))* Editions universitaires de Dijon.

CHEMISTRY—EXAMINATIONS, QUESTIONS, ETC.

Aldridge, Claire, et al. Kaplan SAT Subject Test Chemistry 2011-2012. 2011. (Kaplan SAT Subject Test Ser.). (ENG.). 394p. pap. 18.99 *(978-1-60714-869-2(2))* Kaplan Publishing.
BarCharts, Inc. AP Chemistry. 2010. (ENG.). 6p. 5.95 *(978-1-4232-1491-5(9))* Barcharts, Inc.
Barker, Brett & Peterson's Guides Staff. Chemistry. 2nd ed. 2007. (ENG., Illus.). 640p. pap. 18.00 *(978-0-7689-2472-5(3))* Peterson's.
Beavon, Rod. Edexcel As Chemistry Student Unit Guide. 2008. pap. 22.50 *(978-0-340-95012-8(9))* Hodder Education GBR. Dist: Trans-Atlantic Pubns., Inc.
Bevan, David. Cambridge International As & A Level Chemistry Revision Guide. rev. ed. 2011. 272p. pap. 42.50 *(978-1-4441-1268-9(6))* Hodder Education GBR. Dist: Trans-Atlantic Pubns., Inc.
Bobrow Test Preparation Services & Thorpe, Gary S. CliffsAP Chemistry. 4th ed 2007. (ENG., Illus.). 480p. pap. 16.99 *(978-0-470-13500-6(X),* Cliff Notes) Wiley, John & Sons, Inc.
Bobrow Test Preparation Services Production Staff. CliffsNotes AP Chemistry. 4th ed. 2009. (ENG., Illus.). 480p. pap. 29.99 *(978-0-470-40034-0(X),* Cliff Notes) Wiley, John & Sons, Inc.
Boone, Steven R., et al. College Chemistry. Exstrom, Christopher L., ed. 2nd ed. 2007. (Collins College Outlines Ser.). (Illus.). 512p. pap. 15.95 *(978-0-06-088147-4(X))* HarperCollins Pubs.
Burrows, Andy, et al. Chemistry: Introducing Inorganic, Organic & Physical Chemistry. Holman, John & Pilling, Gwen, eds. 2009. (ENG., Illus.). 1,184p. (C). pap. 154.95 *(978-0-19-927789-6(3))* Oxford Univ. Pr., Inc.
Chang, Raymond, et al. AP Achiever. 9th ed. 2008. (ENG., Illus.). 512p. (C). per., instr.'s gde. ed. 24.00 *(978-0-07-328659-4(1),* 0073286591) McGraw-Hill Higher Education.
Cracolice, Mark S. Basics of Introductory Chemistry with Math Review. 2nd ed. 2009. (ENG.). 848p. (C). pap. 160.95 *(978-0-495-55850-7(8))* Brooks/Cole.
Cross, Margaret. Aqa As Chemistry. 2008. (Illus.). pap. 22.50 *(978-0-340-97110-9(X))* Hodder Education GBR. Dist: Trans-Atlantic Pubns., Inc.
—AQA As Chemistry: Chemistry in Action. 2009. (Illus.). 112p. pap., stu. ed., instr.'s gde. ed. 22.50 *(978-0-340-97111-6(8))* Hodder Education GBR. Dist: Trans-Atlantic Pubns., Inc.
D'Alessio, Michael. AP Chemistry Crash Course. 2010. (Advanced Placement (AP) Crash Course Ser.). (ENG.). 224p. (gr. 10-12). pap. 11.95 *(978-0-7386-0697-2(9))* Research & Education Assn.
Dingle, Adrian. SAT Chemistry Crash Course (REA) 2012. (SAT PSAT ACT (College Admission) Prep Ser.). (ENG.). 256p. (YA). (gr. 11-12). pap. 12.95 ***(978-0-7386-1034-4(8))*** Research & Education Assn.
Dobson, Philip. AQA GCSE Chemistry. 2011. (My Revision Notes Ser.). 94p. pap. 19.95 ***(978-1-4441-2082-0(4))*** Hodder Education GBR. Dist: Trans-Atlantic Pubns., Inc.
Dumas, P. E., et al. AP Chemistry. Fikar, R. M., ed. 10th ed. 2008. (Advanced Placement (AP) Test Preparation Ser.). (ENG., Illus.). 500p. (gr. 11-12). pap. 18.95 *(978-0-7386-0427-5(5))* Research & Education Assn.
Facer, George. Chemistry. 2nd ed. 2008. (Illus.). 99p. tchr. ed., spiral bd. 159.50 *(978-0-340-95762-2(X))* Hodder Education GBR. Dist: Trans-Atlantic Pubns., Inc.
—Edexcel A2 Chemistry: Transition Metals & Organic Nitrogen Chemistry. 2009. 96p. pap., stu. ed., instr.'s gde. ed. 22.50 *(978-0-340-94949-8(X))* Hodder Education GBR. Dist: Trans-Atlantic Pubns., Inc.
—Edexcel A2 Chemistry Unit 4: Rates Equilibria & Further Organic Chemistry. 2009. 112p. pap., stu. ed. 22.50 *(978-0-340-94948-1(1))* Hodder Education GBR. Dist: Trans-Atlantic Pubns., Inc.
—Edexcel AS Chemistry. 2nd ed. 2008. (Illus.). 352p. pap. 59.50 *(978-0-340-95760-8(3))* Hodder Education GBR. Dist: Trans-Atlantic Pubns., Inc.
Gava, Rita, et al. AP Chemistry All Access. 2012. (Advanced Placement (AP) All Access Ser.). (ENG.). 272p. (gr. 10-12). pap. 18.95 ***(978-0-7386-1027-6(5))*** Research & Education Assn.
Goldberg, David. McGraw-Hill's 500 College Chemistry Questions to Know by Test Day. 2012. (ENG., Illus.). 192p. (C). pap. 16.00 ***(978-0-07-179700-9(9),*** 0071797009) McGraw-Hill Cos., The.
GRE Subject Exam Secrets Test Prep Staff, ed. GRE Chemistry Test Flashcard Study System: GRE Subject Exam Practice Questions & Review for the Graduate Record Examination. 2011. (C). 62.99 *(978-1-61403-555-5(5))* Mometrix Media LLC.
Harris, Frank. OCR A2 Chemistry. 2009. 96p. pap., stu. ed. 22.50 *(978-0-340-94824-8(8))* Hodder Education GBR. Dist: Trans-Atlantic Pubns., Inc.
—OCR (Salters) AS Chemistry. 2008. pap., stu. ed., instr.'s gde. ed. 22.50 *(978-0-340-94821-7(3))* Hodder Education GBR. Dist: Trans-Atlantic Pubns., Inc.
Harwood, Richard & Lodge, Ian. Cambridge IGCSE Chemistry Coursebook with CD-ROM. 3rd rev. ed. 2010. (Cambridge International Examinations Ser.). (ENG.). 408p. pap. 33.50 incl. cd-rom *(978-0-521-15333-1(6))* Cambridge Univ. Pr.
—Cambridge IGCSE Chemistry Teacher's Resource CD-ROM. 3rd rev. ed. 2011. (Cambridge International Examinations Ser.). (ENG.). cd-rom 56.00 *(978-0-521-18387-1(1))* Cambridge Univ. Pr.
—Cambridge IGCSE Chemistry Workbook. 3rd rev. ed. 2011. (Cambridge International Examinations Ser.). (ENG.). 92p. pap. 17.00 *(978-0-521-18117-4(8))* Cambridge Univ. Pr.
Hostage, David W. & Fossett, Martin. AP Advantage Laboratory Investigations: AP Chemistry. 2006. (AP Advantage Ser.). (C). pap. 27.99 *(978-1-4138-0489-8(6))* Peoples Education.
Ibhadon, A. O. Physical Chemistry Examinations. 2009. pap. 42.00 *(978-1-60692-345-0(5))* Nova Science Pubs., Inc.
Jespersen, Neil D. Barron's AP Chemistry Flash Cards. 2008. (ENG.). 504p. 18.99 *(978-0-7641-6116-2(4))* Barron's Educational Series, Inc.
Jespersen, Neil D., et al. Chemistry: The Molecular Nature of Matter. 6th ed. 2011. (ENG.). (C). 576p. pap., pupil's gde. ed. 62.95 *(978-0-470-57772-1(X));* 264p. pap. 64.95 *(978-0-470-57773-8(8))* Wiley, John & Sons, Inc. (Wiley).
Kaplan. KTPA MCAT General Chemistry. 2010. (ENG.). 464p. pap. 45.00 *(978-1-60714-824-1(2))* Kaplan Publishing.
Kaplan Higher Education Staff. Kaplan MCAT General Chemistry Review. 2010. (ENG.). 464p. pap. 45.00 *(978-1-60714-639-1(8))* Kaplan Publishing.
King, Rob. Chemistry. 2nd ed. 2008. (Illus.). 152p. pap. 32.50 *(978-0-340-95859-9(6))* Hodder Education GBR. Dist: Trans-Atlantic Pubns., Inc.
Kirk, Frederick. UPCO's Physical Setting - CHEMISTRY. 2011. pap. 32.88 *(978-0-937323-21-2(7))* United Publishing Co., Inc.
Langley, Richard H. & Moore, John. 5 Steps to a 5 AP Chemistry 2012-2013. 4th ed. 2011. (5 Steps to a 5 on the Advanced Placement Examinations Ser.). (ENG., Illus.). 400p. (C). pap. 18.95 *(978-0-07-175168-1(8),* 0071751688) McGraw-Hill Cos., The.
Mascetta, Joseph A. & Kernion, Mark C. E-Z Chemistry. 5th rev. ed. 2009. (Barron's E-Z Ser.). (ENG., Illus.). 528p. pap. 16.99 *(978-0-7641-4128-7(7))* Barron's Educational Series, Inc.
Mascetta M.A., Joseph A. SAT Subject Test Chemistry. 10th rev. ed. 2010. (ENG.). 528p. 29.99 *(978-0-7641-9757-4(6));* pap. 16.99 *(978-0-7641-4480-6(4))* Barron's Educational Series, Inc.
McGinnis, Michael B. & LearningExpress Staff. Chemistry Success in 20 Minutes a Day. 2007. (Skill Builders Ser.). (ENG., Illus.). 160p. per. 17.00 *(978-1-57685-484-6(1))* LearningExpress, LLC.
Moore, David & Taylor, Jane. Chemistry. 2nd rev. ed. 2009. (Illus.). 104p. pap. 13.95 *(978-0-340-99228-9(X))* Hodder Education GBR. Dist: Trans-Atlantic Pubns., Inc.
Moore, John & Langley, Richard H. McGraw-Hill's 500 MCAT General Chemistry Questions to Know by Test Day. 2012. (ENG., Illus.). 208p. (C). pap. 25.00 ***(978-0-07-178311-8(3),*** 0071783113) McGraw-Hill Cos., The.
—McGraw-Hill's 500 MCAT Organic Chemistry Questions to Know by Test Day. 2012. (ENG., Illus.). 256p. (C). pap. 25.00 ***(978-0-07-178275-3(3),*** 0071782753) McGraw-Hill Cos., The.
Nelson, Eric A. Preparation for Topics in College Chemistry, Modules 1-16. 2007. (C). spiral bd. 18.95 *(978-0-9771087-2-5(4))* ChemReview.
Neuss, Geoffrey. Chemistry. 2nd ed. 2010. (ENG., Illus.). 432p. (YA). pap. 42.00 *(978-0-19-913955-2(5))* Oxford Univ. Pr., Inc.
Norris, Roger & Ryan, Lawrie. Cambridge International AS & A Level Chemistry Coursebook with CD-ROM. 2011. (Cambridge International Examinations

C

Ser.). (ENG.). 560p. pap. 56.00 incl. cd-rom *(978-0-521-12661-8(4))* Cambridge Univ. Pr.

Older, J. & Smith, M. AS OCR Chemistry. 2008. (Illus.). 272p. pap. 59.50 *(978-1-84489-434-5(7))* Hodder Education GBR. Dist: Trans-Atlantic Pubns., Inc.

—OCR A2 Chemistry. 2009. (Illus.). 280p. pap. 59.50 *(978-1-84489-435-2(5))* Hodder Education GBR. Dist: Trans-Atlantic Pubns., Inc.

ORELA Exam Secrets Test Prep Staff, ed. ORELA Chemistry Flashcard Study System: ORELA Test Practice Questions & Exam Review for the Oregon Educator Licensure Assessments. 2011. (C). 62.99 *(978-1-61403-636-4(5))* Mometrix Media LLC.

—ORELA Chemistry Secrets Study Guide: ORELA Test Review for the Oregon Educator Licensure Assessments. 2011. (C). 62.99 *(978-1-61403-635-7(7))* Mometrix Media LLC.

Owen, Steve. Chemistry for the IB Diploma Coursebook with CD-ROM. 2011. (Ib Ser.). (ENG.). 544p. pap. 69.00 incl. cd-rom *(978-0-521-18294-2(8))* Cambridge Univ. Pr.

Princeton Review. Cracking the AP Chemistry Exam, 2013 Edition. 2012. (College Test Preparation Ser.). (ENG.). 464p. pap. 18.99 ***(978-0-307-94488-7(3)***, Princeton Review) Random Hse. Information Group.

Princeton Review Staff. Cracking the AP Chemistry Exam, 2012 Edition. 2011. (College Test Preparation Ser.). (ENG.). 464p. pap. 18.99 *(978-0-375-42721-3(X)*, Princeton Review) Random Hse. Information Group.

—Cracking the SAT Chemistry Subject Test, 2011-2012 Edition. 2011. (College Test Preparation Ser.). 368p. pap. 19.99 *(978-0-375-42814-2(3)*, Princeton Review) Random Hse. Information Group.

—MCAT General Chemistry Review. 2010. (Graduate School Test Preparation Ser.). (ENG.). 320p. pap. 45.00 *(978-0-375-42794-7(5)*, Princeton Review) Random Hse. Information Group.

—MCAT Organic Chemistry Review. 2010. (Graduate School Test Preparation Ser.). (ENG.). 320p. pap. 45.00 *(978-0-375-42793-0(7)*, Princeton Review) Random Hse. Information Group.

Reel, Kevin R. The CLEP Chemistry: College-Level Examination Program. 2007. (CLEP Test Preparation Ser.). (ENG., Illus.). 224p. (C). pap. 34.95 *(978-0-7386-0319-3(8))* Research & Education Assn.

Research and Education Association Staff. SAT Subject Test: Chemistry. Reel, Kevin R., ed. 6th ed. 2006. (SAT PSAT ACT (College Admission) Prep Ser.). (ENG., Illus.). 350p. (gr. 12-12). pap. 21.95 *(978-0-7386-0273-8(6))* Research & Education Assn.

Research and Education Association Staff & Van Amum, Susan. GRE Chemistry with TestWare. 4th ed. 2010. (GRE Test Preparation Ser.). (ENG.). 480p. (C). pap. 32.95 *(978-0-7386-0658-3(8))* Research & Education Assn.

Rudman, Jack. Chemistry. Date not set. (College Board SAT II Subject Test Ser.). pap. 29.95 *(978-0-8373-6303-5(9)*, SATII-3); (Graduate Record Examination Ser.: Vol. 2). 49.95 *(978-0-8373-5252-7(5))*; (Undergraduate Program Field Tests Ser.: Vol. 4). 49.95 *(978-0-8373-6054-6(4)*, Passbooks); (Regents College Proficiency Examination Ser.: Vol. 6). (C). 49.95 *(978-0-8373-5456-9(0)*, Passbooks) National Learning Corp.

—General Chemistry. (College Level Examination Ser.: Vol. 13). (C). 49.95 *(978-0-8373-5363-0(7)*, Passbooks) National Learning Corp.

Ryan, Lawrie. Top Chemistry Grades for You GCSE Revision Guide for AQA. 2006. (ENG., Illus.). 120p. pap. 17.95 *(978-0-7487-8376-2(8))* Nelson Thornes Ltd. GBR. Dist: Trans-Atlantic Pubns., Inc.

SAT Subject Exam Secrets Test Prep Staff, ed. SAT Chemistry Subject Test Flashcard Study System: SAT Subject Exam Practice Questions & Review for the SAT Subject Test. 2011. 62.99 *(978-1-61403-724-8(8))* Mometrix Media LLC.

Slade, Roger. Cambridge Checkpoints VCE Chemistry Unit 3 2008. 2007. (Cambridge Checkpoints Ser.). pap. *(978-0-521-71647-5(0))* Cambridge Univ. Pr.

Slade, Roger & Slade, Maureen. Cambridge Checkpoints VCE Chemistry Unit 4 2009. 2008. (Cambridge Checkpoints Ser.). pap. 15.95 *(978-0-521-73988-7(8))* Cambridge Univ. Pr.

Smith, Mike. OCR (A) AS Chemistry: Chains, Energy & Resources. 2008. pap., stu. ed. 22.50 *(978-0-340-95757-8(3))* Hodder Education GBR. Dist: Trans-Atlantic Pubns., Inc.

—OCR A2 Chemistry: Rings, Polymers & Analysis. 2009. 96p. pap., stu. ed. 22.50 *(978-0-340-95758-5(1))* Hodder Education GBR. Dist: Trans-Atlantic Pubns., Inc.

—OCR(A) As Chemistry: Atoms, Bonds & Groups. 2008. (Illus.). pap. 22.50 *(978-0-340-95756-1(5))* Hodder Education GBR. Dist: Trans-Atlantic Pubns., Inc.

Talbot, Christopher. Chemistry for the IB Diploma. 2010. (Illus.). 620p. pap. 89.50 *(978-0-340-98505-2(4))* Hodder Education GBR. Dist: Trans-Atlantic Pubns., Inc.

Wheway, Ashley. OCR (Salters) AS Chemistry, Unit 2. 2008. pap., stu. ed. 22.50 *(978-0-340-94822-4(1))* Hodder Education GBR. Dist: Trans-Atlantic Pubns., Inc.

Wilson, David. Kaplan AP Chemistry 2012. 2011. (Kaplan AP Ser.). (ENG.). 396p. pap. 17.99 *(978-1-60978-062-3(0))* Kaplan Publishing.

Wynne, Sharon. FTCE Chemistry 6-12. 2008. (Xam Ftce Ser.). (ENG.). 384p. pap., pupil's gde. ed. 64.95 *(978-1-58197-046-3(3))* XAMonline, Inc.

—MTTC Chemistry 18. XAMonline, ed. 2007. (Xam Mttc Ser.). (ENG.). 380p. per. 64.95 *(978-1-58197-955-8(X))* XAMonline, Inc.

—Praxis Chemistry 20241, 20242, 20245. 2008. (Xam Praxis Ser.). (ENG., Illus.). 309p. pap. 64.95 *(978-1-58197-691-5(7))* XAMonline, Inc.

—WEST-E Chemistry 0245. 2008. (Xam West-E/Praxis II Ser.). (ENG., Illus.). 310p. pap. 64.95 *(978-1-58197-693-9(3))* XAMonline, Inc.

CHEMISTRY—EXPERIMENTS

see also Chemistry, Organic—Experiments

Chemistry in Action. Date not set. (Nuffield Advanced Science Ser.). pap. 9.95 *(978-0-582-82660-1(8))* Addison-Wesley Longman, Ltd. GBR. Dist: Trans-Atlantic Pubns., Inc.

Chemistry, Royal Society of, ed. Chemistry for Non-Specialists: Course Book. 2010. (ENG., Illus.). 262p. (C). pap. 42.00 ***(978-1-84973-112-6(8))*** Royal Society of Chemistry, The GBR. Dist: Ingram Pub. Services.

Chemistry with Vernier. 2007. spiral bd. 45.00 *(978-1-929075-41-6(3))* Vernier Software & Technology.

Dept. of Chemistry, compiled by. Laboratory Experiments in General Chemistry: Chem 110 & Chem 111. 2007. (C). spiral bd. *(978-1-60036-106-7(4))* Academx Publishing Services, Inc.

Faraday, Michael. Experimental Researches in Chemistry & Physics. 2010. 520p. pap. 39.75 *(978-1-141-96314-0(0))* BiblioBazaar.

—Experimental Researches in Chemistry & Physics. 2009. 396p. pap. *(978-1-4588-2808-8(5))* Books LLC.

Fruen. The Real World of Chemistry. 12th rev. ed. 2011. (ENG.). 150p. spiral bd. 65.00 ***(978-0-7575-9450-2(6))*** Kendall Hunt Publishing Co.

Ganguly Dhara, Mahua & Sivaram, Swaminathan. Living Anionic Polymerization of Methyl Methacrylate. 2010. 188p. pap. *(978-3-639-23174-8(0))* VDM Verlag Dr. Mueller e.K.

Griep, Mark A., et al. ReAction! Chemistry in the Movies. 2009. (ENG., Illus.). 352p. 49.95 *(978-0-19-532692-5(X))* Oxford Univ. Pr., Inc.

Heasley, Victor L., et al. Chemistry & Life in the Laboratory: Experiments. 6th rev. ed. 2011. (ENG.). 448p. (C). pap. 99.93 ***(978-0-321-75160-7(4)***, Prentice Hall) Prentice Hall PTR.

Henrickson, Charles H. Experimental Chemistry: A Laboratory for Science Majors. 3rd rev. ed. 2010. (ENG.). 410p. spiral bd. 74.97 *(978-0-7872-9589-9(2))* Kendall Hunt Publishing Co.

Holt, Rinehart and Winston Staff. Chemfile Inquiry Experiments. 6th ed. Date not set. pap., stu. ed. 15.93 *(978-0-03-036802-8(2))* Holt McDougal.

—Chemfile Microscale Experiments. 6th ed. Date not set. pap., tchr. ed. 22.60 *(978-0-03-036801-1(4))* Holt McDougal.

—Chemfile Skills Practice Experiments. 6th ed. Date not set. pap., stu. ed. 15.93 *(978-0-03-036797-7(2))* Holt McDougal.

Horton, Michael. Take-Home Chemistry: 50 Low-Cost Activities to Extend Classroom Learning. 2011. (Illus.). xxix, 244p. ***(978-1-936137-39-8(9))*** National Science Teachers Assn.

Karan, Hiroko, et al. Laboratory Experiments in Chemistry for Health Professionals. rev. ed. 2010. (ENG.). 132p. spiral bd. 46.12 *(978-0-7575-5030-0(4))* Kendall Hunt Publishing Co.

Landesberg, Joseph M. eneral, Organic, & Biochemistry - Laboratory Experiments. 2011. (ENG.). 256p. (C). pap. 69.95 *(978-1-111-42661-3(9))* Brooks/Cole.

Ridlon, Robert W., et al. Christian Kids Explore Chemistry. 2007. (Christian Kids Explore Ser.). (Illus.). 384p. pap. 29.95 *(978-1-892427-18-2(4))* Bright Ideas! Educational Resources.

Roesky, et al. Experiments in Green & Sustainable Chemistry. Roesky, Herbert W. & Kennepohl, Dietmar, eds. 2009. (ENG., Illus.). 307p. 45.00 *(978-3-527-32546-7(8)*, Wiley-VCH) Wiley, John & Sons, Inc.

Roesky, Herbert W. Spectacular Chemical Experiments. 2007. (ENG., Illus.). 240p. 45.00 *(978-3-527-31865-0(8)*, Wiley-VCH) Wiley, John & Sons, Inc.

Rutenburg, Irina, et al. Introductory College Chemistry Laboratory Experiments. 2nd rev. ed. 2011. (ENG.). 120p. spiral bd. 48.81 *(978-0-7575-2968-9(2))* Kendall Hunt Publishing Co.

Sandall, Barbara R. Chemistry: Physical & Chemical Changes in Matter. 2010. (Expanding Science Skills Ser.). (ENG., Illus.). 80p. (gr. 5). pap. 11.99 *(978-1-58037-522-1(7))* Twain, Mark Media, Inc. Pubs.

Sarquis, Mickey, et al. Chemistry with Charisma. 2010. 254p. pap. 21.95 *(978-1-883822-56-9(4))* Terrific Science Pr.

Shakhashiri, Bassam Z. Chemical Demonstrations Vol. 5: A Handbook for Teachers of Chemistry. 2011. (ENG., Illus.). 408p. 45.00 *(978-0-299-22650-3(6))* Univ. of Wisconsin Pr.

Slabaugh, Michael & Seager, Spencer. Safety Scale Lab Experiments - Chemistry for Today: General, Organic, & Biochemistry. 7th ed. 2010. (ENG.). 544p. (C). pap. 103.95 *(978-0-538-73454-7(X))* Brooks/Cole.

Stanton, Bobby, et al. Experiments in General Chemistry: Featuring MeasureNet. 2nd ed. 2009. (ENG.). 448p. (C). pap. 152.95 *(978-0-495-56179-8(7))* Brooks/Cole.

Suchocki, John A. & Paradis, Jeffrey. Explorations in Conceptual Chemistry: A Student Activity Manual. 4th ed. 2010. (ENG.). 384p. (C). pap. 61.93 *(978-0-321-68172-0(X)*, Prentice Hall) Prentice Hall PTR.

Svoronos, Paris, et al. Lab Experiments for General Chemistry. rev. ed. 2011. (ENG.). 236p. spiral bd. 48.81 *(978-0-7575-0315-3(2))* Kendall Hunt Publishing Co.

Thompson, Robert Bruce. Illustrated Guide to Home Chemistry Experiments: All Lab, No Lecture. 2008. (DIY Science Ser.). (ENG., Illus.). 432p. pap. 29.99 *(978-0-596-51492-1(1))* O'Reilly Media, Inc.

Waldmann, Herbert & Janning, Petra, eds. Chemical Biology: Learning Through Case Studies. 2009. (ENG., Illus.). 304p. pap. 60.00 *(978-3-527-32330-2(9)*, Wiley-VCH) Wiley, John & Sons, Inc.

Woollins, J. Derek, ed. Inorganic Experiments. 3rd ed. 2010. (ENG., Illus.). 482p. 80.00 *(978-3-527-32472-9(0)*, Wiley-VCH) Wiley, John & Sons, Inc.

CHEMISTRY—EXPERIMENTS—JUVENILE LITERATURE

O'Neal, Claire. A Project Guide to Chemistry. 2011. (Physical Science Projects for Kids Ser.). (Illus.). 48p. (J). (gr. 3-6). lib. bdg. 29.95 *(978-1-58415-968-1(5))* Mitchell Lane Pubs., Inc.

CHEMISTRY—HANDBOOKS, MANUALS, ETC.

Atwood, Charles H. Survival Guide for General Chemistry: With Math Review & Proficiency Questions. 2nd rev. ed. 2007. (ENG., Illus.). 216p. (C). per. 40.95 *(978-0-495-38751-0(7))* Brooks/Cole.

Brady, James E. & Senese, Fred. Chemistry: The Study of Matter & Its Changes. 5th ed. 2008. (ENG., Illus.). 240p. (C). per. 59.95 *(978-0-470-18465-3(5)*, Wiley) Wiley, John & Sons, Inc.

Carmichael, A. High School Chemistry Handbook. 2010. (Illus.). 156p. pap. 11.99 *(978-1-4490-3661-4(9))* AuthorHouse.

Chang, Raymond. Loose Leaf Chemistry. 10th ed. 2009. (ENG.). (C). ring bd., ring bd. 161.00 *(978-0-07-736669-8(7)*, 0077366697, McGraw-Hill Science, Engineering & Mathematics) McGraw-Hill Higher Education.

Driscoll, Jerry & Hubbard, Connie. Student Study Guide & Solution Manual to Introductory Chemistry. rev. ed. 2009. (ENG.). 162p. spiral bd. 57.33 *(978-0-7575-0881-3(2))* Kendall Hunt Publishing Co.

Hall, James W. & DeCoste, Donald J. Introductory Chemistry. 6th ed. 2007. (ENG.). 256p. (C). pap. 77.95 *(978-0-618-80334-7(3)*, 370847) Brooks/Cole.

Kelter, Paul, et al. Chemistry: The Practical Science. 2008. (ENG.). 320p. (C). pap. 69.95 *(978-0-547-07761-1(0)*, 1042163) CENGAGE Learning.

Khan, Aamna Saleem. A Guide to Teach Chemistry. 2011. 140p. pap. ***(978-3-8443-8790-2(0))*** Lambert Academic Publishing.

Kotz, et al. Chemistry & Chemical Reactivity. 8th ed. 2011. (Textbooks Available with Cengage YouBook Ser.). (ENG.). 1296p. (C). 273.95 *(978-0-8400-4828-8(9))* Brooks/Cole.

Kotz, John C., et al. Chemistry & Chemical Reactivity. 7th ed. 2008. (Available Titles OWL Ser.). (ENG., Illus.). 1312p. (C). 273.95 *(978-0-495-38703-9(7))* Brooks/Cole.

Oxtoby, et al. Principles of Modern Chemistry. 7th ed. 2011. (Textbooks Available with Cengage YouBook Ser.). (ENG.). 1120p. (C). 234.95 *(978-0-8400-4931-5(5))* Brooks/Cole.

Riley, Gail Blasser & BarCharts Inc., Staff. Chemistry. 2006. (ENG.). 144p. pap. 6.95 *(978-1-4232-0261-5(9))* Barcharts, Inc.

Seager, Spencer L. & Slabaugh, Michael R. Chemistry for Today. 7th ed. 2010. (ENG.). 432p. (C). pap., stu. ed. 96.95 *(978-0-538-73458-5(2))* Brooks/Cole.

Shishkina, Ludmila N., et al. Handbook of Chemistry, Biochemistry & Biology: New Frontiers. 2009. 195.00 *(978-1-60741-861-0(4))* Nova Science Pubs., Inc.

Student Solutions Manual & Quick Guide for Vining/Young/Botch/Day's Egeneral Chemistry. 2007. (C). pap. 40.95 *(978-0-534-40756-8(0))* Brooks/Cole.

Williams, Rebecca. Preparatory Chemistry Handouts. rev. ed. 2010. (ENG.). 116p. pap. 34.14 *(978-0-7575-2089-1(8)*, 0757520898) Kendall Hunt Publishing Co.

CHEMISTRY—HISTORY

see also Alchemy; Chemical Literature

Archer, Mary & Haley, Christopher D., eds. The 1702 Chair of Chemistry at Cambridge: Transformation & Change. 2007. (ENG., Illus.). 344p. pap. 69.00 *(978-0-521-03085-4(4))* Cambridge Univ. Pr.

Brock, William H. The Case of the Poisonous Socks: Tales from Chemistry. 2011. (ENG., Illus.). 362p. pap. 32.00 ***(978-1-84973-324-3(4))*** Royal Society of Chemistry, The GBR. Dist: Ingram Pub. Services.

Califano, Salvatore & Califano, S. Storia Della Chimica. 2010. (ITA.). *(978-88-339-2157-0(3))* Bollati Boringhieri.

Clericuzio, Antonio. Elements, Principles & Corpuscles: A Study of Atomism & Chemistry in the Seventeenth Century. 2010. (International Archives of the History of Ideas / archives internationales d'histoire des Idées Ser.). 240p. pap. 179.00 *(978-90-481-5640-5(8)*, 9048156408) Springer.

Coffey, Patrick. Cathedrals of Science: The Personalities & Rivalries That Made Modern Chemistry. 2008. (ENG., Illus.). 416p. 29.95 *(978-0-19-532134-0(0))* Oxford Univ. Pr., Inc.

Dalton, John. A New System of Chemical Philosophy. 2010. (Cambridge Library Collection - Physical Sciences Ser.). (Illus.). 592p. pap. 43.00 *(978-1-108-01967-5(6))* Cambridge Univ. Pr.

Duhem, Pierre. Mixture & Chemical Combination: And Related Essays. Needham, P., tr. from FRE. 2011. (Boston Studies in the Philosophy of Science Ser.). (ENG.). 352p. pap. 219.00 *(978-90-481-5924-6(5)*, 9048159245) Springer.

Faraday, Michael. Experimental Researches in Chemistry & Physics. 2010. 520p. pap. 39.75 *(978-1-141-96314-0(0))* BiblioBazaar.

—Experimental Researches in Chemistry & Physics. 2009. 396p. pap. *(978-1-4588-2808-8(5))* Books LLC.

Greenberg, Arthur. Chemistry: Decade by Decade. Cannon, William J., ed. 2007. (Twentieth-Century Science Ser.). (Illus.). 496p. (gr. 6-12). 49.50 *(978-0-8160-5531-9(9))* Facts On File, Inc.

Ibn Zakariya, Muhammad. Practical Chemistry in the Twelfth Century. Steele, Robert R., ed. Gerard Of Cremona, tr. reprint ed. 37.50 *(978-0-404-18444-5(8))* AMS Pr., Inc.

International Conference on the History of Alchemy and Chymistry & Principe, Lawrence. Chymists & Chymistry: Studies in the History of Alchemy & Early Modern Chemistry. 2007. (Illus.). 287p. 45.00 *(978-0-88135-396-9(5)*, Science History Pubns./USA) Watson Publishing International, LLC.

Kan & Lin, Sheng-Hsien. Wolf Prize in Chemistry: An Epitome of Chemistry History in 20th Century. 2011. 600p. pap. 78.00 *(978-981-4327-96-1(4))* World Scientific Publishing Co., Inc.

Kean, Sam. The Disappearing Spoon: And Other True Tales of Madness, Love, & the History of the World from the Periodic Table of the Elements. (ENG., Illus.). 2011. 416p. pap. 14.99 *(978-0-316-05163-7(2)*, Back Bay Bks.) 2010. 400p. 24.99 *(978-0-316-05164-4(0))* Little Brown & Co.

Klein, Ursula & Lefèvre, Wolfgang. Materials in Eighteenth-Century Science: A Historical Ontology. 2007. (Transformations: Studies in the History of Science & Technology Ser.). (ENG., Illus.). 350p. (gr. 17). 43.00 *(978-0-262-11306-9(6))* MIT Pr.

Knight, David. Ideas in Chemistry. (Illus.). 224p. pap. *(978-0-485-12112-4(3))* Continuum International Publishing Group, Ltd.

—Ideas in Chemistry: A History of the Science. 224p. *(978-0-485-11390-7(2))* Continuum International Publishing Group, Ltd.

Knight, David & Kragh, Helge, eds. The Making of the Chemist: The Social History of Chemistry in Europe, 1789-1914. 2008. (ENG., Illus.). 376p. pap. 48.00 *(978-0-521-09079-7(2))* Cambridge Univ. Pr.

McEvoy, John G. The Historiography of the Chemical Revolution: Patterns of Interpretation in the History of Science, 1 vol. 2010. (ENG.). 352p. 99.00 *(978-1-84893-030-8(5))* Pickering & Chatto Pubs., Ltd. GBR. Dist: Ashgate Publishing Co.

Muir, M. M. Pattison. The Alchemical Notion of the Unity & Simplicity of Nature - 2006. pap. 12.95 *(978-1-4304-1437-7(5))* Kessinger Publishing, LLC.

—The Story of Alchemy & the Beginnings of Chemistry. 2008. (Illus.). 172p. 25.99 *(978-0-554-24893-6(X))* 2008. (Illus.). 172p. 22.99 *(978-0-554-34196-5(4))* 2007. 152p. pap. 19.99 *(978-1-4264-7610-5(8))* 2007. (ENG.). 168p. pap. 21.99 *(978-1-4264-7661-7(2))* BiblioBazaar.

—The Story of Alchemy & the Beginnings of Chemistry. 2008. (Illus.). 156p. pap. *(978-1-4099-0388-8(5))* Dodo Pr.

Neville, Roy G. The Roy G. Neville Historical Chemical Library: An Annotated Catalogue of Printed Books on Alchemy, Chemistry, Chemical Technology, & Related Subjects. 2006. 250.00 *(978-0-941901-40-6(8))* Chemical Heritage Foundation.

Newcomb, Ellsworth & Kenny, Hugh. Alchemy to Atoms. 2011. 128p. 40.95 ***(978-1-258-00938-0(2))*** Literary Licensing, LLC.

Nielsen, Anita Kildebaek & Strbánová, Sona. Creating Networks in Chemistry. 2008. (Special Publication). (ENG., Illus.). 380p. 160.00 ***(978-0-85404-279-1(2))*** Royal Society of Chemistry, The GBR. Dist: Ingram Pub. Services.

Palmer, W. G. A History of the Concept of Valency To 1930. 2010. (ENG.). 188p. pap. 19.99 *(978-0-521-14814-6(6))* Cambridge Univ. Pr.

Partington, J. R. A History of Chemistry. 2009. *(978-1-57898-731-3(8))* Martino Publishing.

Powers, John C. Inventing Chemistry: Herman Boerhaave & the Reform of the Chemical Arts. 2012. (Synthesis Ser.). (ENG., Illus.). 288p. 40.00 ***(978-0-226-67760-6(5))*** Univ. of Chicago Pr.

Principe, Lawrence M., ed. New Narratives in Eighteenth-Century Chemistry: Contributions from the First Francis Bacon Workshop, 21-23 April 2005, California Institute of Technology, Pasadena, California. (Archimedes Ser.). 2010. xii, 204p. pap. 169.00 *(978-90-481-7593-2(3)*, 9048175933) 2007. (Illus.). 200p. 169.00 *(978-1-4020-6273-5(7))* Springer.

Ray, Priyadaranjian & Ray, Acharya P., eds. History of Chemistry in Ancient & Medieval India, Incorporating the History of Hindu Chemistry. reprint ed. 42.50 *(978-0-404-18483-4(9))* AMS Pr., Inc.

Russell, Colin A. & Hudson, John. Early Railway Chemistry & its Legacy. 2011. (ENG., Illus.). 208p. pap. 48.00 ***(978-1-84973-326-7(0))*** Royal Society of Chemistry, The GBR. Dist: Ingram Pub. Services.

Soliman, William. The Rise of Chemistry. 2008. 324p. pap. *(978-3-639-06973-0(0))* VDM Verlag Dr. Mueller e.K.

Thomson, Thomas. The History of Chemistry. 2009. 64p. pap. *(978-0-217-29947-3(4))* Books LLC.

Thorpe, Thomas E. Essays in Historical Chemistry. 2007. 392p. 48.95 *(978-0-548-55266-7(5))*; (ENG.). per. 33.95 *(978-0-548-47727-4(2))* Kessinger Publishing, LLC.

Tilden, William Augustus. Famous Chemists; the Men & Their Work. 2011. 380p. pap. 31.95 ***(978-1-4460-7167-0(7))*** Aslan Pr.

Walton, Michael Thomson. Genesis & the Chemical Philosophy: True Christian Science in the Sixteenth & Seventeenth Centuries. 2011. *(978-0-404-62345-6(X))* AMS Pr., Inc.

Yoshito, Takeuchi. Lectures in Japanese about Significant Events in the History of Chemistry. Daub, Edward E. & Miller, Paul K., eds. 2011. (JPN & ENG.). 104p. 24.95 *(978-0-9748952-4-6(5))* Univ. of Wisconsin Pr.

CHEMISTRY—JUVENILE LITERATURE

The Elements - Group 5, 4 bks., Set. 102.57 *(978-0-7614-1460-5(6)*, Benchmark Bks.) Marshall Cavendish Corp.

Holt, Rinehart and Winston Staff. Chemistry: Chapter Resource Package. 6th ed. Date not set. pap. 217.73 *(978-0-03-041309-4(5))* Holt McDougal.

—Holt Chemistry Chptr. 1: The Science of Chemistry. 4th ed. Date not set. pap. 11.20 *(978-0-03-066744-2(5))* Holt McDougal.

—Holt Chemistry Chptr. 2: Matter & Energy. 4th ed. Date not set. pap. 11.20 *(978-0-03-066746-6(1))* Holt McDougal.

Holtzclaw. General Chemistry Software IBM. *(978-0-669-12656-3(X))* Houghton Mifflin Harcourt School Pubs.

Myers. Chemistry: Premier Online Edition. 6th ed. Date not set. 83.93 *(978-0-03-039111-8(3))* Holt McDougal.

—Holt Chemistry: Enhanced Online Edition. 6th ed. Date not set. cd-rom 91.93 (978-0-03-040073-5(2)) Holt McDougal.

Slade, Suzanne. Elements in Living Organisms. 2006. 28p. (gr. 3-7). pap. 21.25 (978-1-4358-3822-2(X), PowerKids Pr.) Rosen Publishing Group, Inc., The.

CHEMISTRY—LABORATORIES

see Chemical Laboratories

CHEMISTRY—LABORATORY MANUALS

see also Indicators and Test-Papers

also subdivision Laboratory Manuals under specific types of chemistry, e.g Chemistry, Organic—Laboratory Manuals; Clinical Chemistry—Laboratory Manuals; etc.

Abrams, Binyomin. Quantitative General Chemistry Lab Manual. rev. ed. 2011. (ENG.). 204p. spiral bd. 60.30 (978-0-7575-8431-2(4)) Kendall Hunt Publishing Co.

Alpay, Mete H. How to Make an "A" in Freshman Chemistry Laboratory for the First-Year Student. (Illus.). 325p. (C). pap. 17.95 (978-0-9634134-0-6(6)) Home Ed Systems, Educational Publishing.

American Chemical Society. Laboratory Manual Chemistry in Context. 7th ed. 2011. (ENG.). 224p. (C). spiral bd. 72.00 (978-0-07-733448-2(5), 0077334485, McGraw-Hill Science, Engineering & Mathematics) McGraw-Hill Higher Education.

American Chemical Society Staff. Laboratory Manual to Accompany Chemistry in Context: Applying Chemistry to Society. Steehler, Gail A., ed. 6th ed. 2008. (ENG., Illus.). 224p. (C). spiral bd. 65.31 (978-0-07-304877-2(1), 0073048771, McGraw-Hill Science, Engineering & Mathematics) McGraw-Hill Higher Education.

Azab, Safwat. Chemistry in Life: Laboratory Experiments. 3rd rev. ed. 2010. (ENG.). 210p. spiral bd. 61.19 (978-0-7575-4102-5(X)) Kendall Hunt Publishing Co.

Ballinger, Jack T. & Shugar, Gershon J. Chemical Technicians' Ready Reference Handbook. 5th ed. 2011. (ENG., Illus.). 704p. 99.00 (978-0-07-174592-5(0), 0071745920) McGraw-Hill Professional Publishing.

Barth, Roger. Experimental General Chemistry. (C). 2006. spiral bd. (978-1-60036-036-7(X)) 3rd ed. 2008. pap. (978-1-60036-219-4(2)) Academx Publishing Services, Inc.

Bauer, Richard, et al. Laboratory Inquiry in Chemistry. 3rd rev. ed. 2008. (ENG.). 288p. (C). pap. 92.95 (978-0-495-11345-4(X)) Brooks/Cole.

Beatty, Alicia, et al. Chemistry II. rev. ed. 2012. (ENG.). 128p. spiral bd., lab manual ed. 46.95 (978-0-7575-9419-9(0)) Kendall Hunt Publishing Co.

Benavides, Maria. Chem 1107: General Chemistry Lab I. rev. ed. 2010. (ENG.). 194p. pap. 44.24 (978-0-7575-6009-5(1)) Kendall Hunt Publishing Co.

Beran, Jo Allan. Laboratory Manual for Principles of General Chemistry 9th Edition for CH 115L for Lake Superior State University. 9th ed. 2011. 204p. (C). pap. 38.95 (978-1-118-11193-2(1), Wiley) Wiley, John & Sons, Inc.

—Laboratory Manual for Principles of General Chemistry 9th Edition for CH 116L for Lake Superior State University. 9th ed. 2011. 208p. (C). pap. 38.95 (978-1-118-11194-9(X), Wiley) Wiley, John & Sons, Inc.

Beran, Jo Allan. Principles of General Chemistry. 9th ed. 2010. (ENG., Illus.). 464p. (C). pap., lab manual ed. 143.95 (978-0-470-64789-9(2), Wiley) Wiley, John & Sons, Inc.

Borer, Philip. General Chemistry Laboratory Manual & Notebook: Using Biochemical Tools with Website. 3rd rev. ed. 2010. (ENG.). 126p. spiral bd. 67.00 (978-0-7575-7995-0(7)) Kendall Hunt Publishing Co.

Burdge, Julia, et al. Lab Manual for Chemistry: Atoms First. 2012. (ENG., Illus.). 288p. (C). pap. 87.33 (978-0-07-743968-2(6), 0077439686, McGraw-Hill Science, Engineering & Mathematics) McGraw-Hill Higher Education.

Burnham, Weldon S. General Chemistry Laboratory Studies. 5th rev. ed. 2011. (ENG.). 432p. pap. 68.50 (978-0-7575-8296-7(6)) Kendall Hunt Publishing Co.

Byrd, Larry C., et al. General, Organic, & Biochemistry: A Laboratory Manual. 6th ed. 2007. (ENG., Illus.). 448p. (C). spiral bd. 83.75 (978-0-07-322683-5(1), 0073226831, McGraw-Hill Science, Engineering & Mathematics) McGraw-Hill Higher Education.

Chemistry 149/151 Laboratory Manual. 2006. (C). spiral bd. (978-1-60036-015-2(7)) Academx Publishing Services, Inc.

Chemistry 252 Laboratory Manual, Spring 2007. 2007. (C). spiral bd. (978-1-60036-054-1(8)) Academx Publishing Services, Inc.

Chemistry 309 Laboratory Manual. 2006. (C). spiral bd. (978-1-60036-017-6(3)) Academx Publishing Services, Inc.

Chemistry 353 Laboratory Manual. 2006. (C). spiral bd. (978-1-60036-016-9(5)) Academx Publishing Services, Inc.

Chemistry 354 Laboratory Manual: Spring 2007. 2007. (C). spiral bd. (978-1-60036-055-8(6)) Academx Publishing Services, Inc.

Chemistry 356 Laboratory Manual, Spring 2007. 2006. (C). spiral bd. (978-1-60036-056-5(4)) Academx Publishing Services, Inc.

Chemistry 391 Laboratory Manual. 2006. (C). spiral bd. (978-1-60036-018-3(1)) Academx Publishing Services, Inc.

Chemistry 392 Laboratory Manual, Spring 2007. 2006. (C). spiral bd. (978-1-60036-057-2(2)) Academx Publishing Services, Inc.

Chemistry with Vernier. 2007. spiral bd. 45.00 (978-1-929075-41-6(3)) Vernier Software & Technology.

Coker, W. Lin. Chemistry Survival Manual. 2nd rev. ed. 2011. (ENG.). 168p. pap. 54.95 (978-0-7575-7710-9(5)) Kendall Hunt Publishing Co.

Coker, W. Lin & Elmore, Kimberly A. General Chemistry Lab Manual. 2nd rev. ed. 2010. (ENG.). 256p. spiral bd. 45.27 (978-0-7575-6342-3(2)) Kendall Hunt Publishing Co.

Contis & Contis, Ellene T. Investigating Chemistry: Up 'N Atom. 2nd rev. ed. 2010. (ENG.). 142p. pap. 48.59 (978-0-7575-7430-6(0)) Kendall Hunt Publishing Co.

Cooper. Cooperative Chemistry Lab Manual. 4th ed. 2008. (ENG., Illus.). 176p. (C). spiral bd., lab manual ed. 79.38 (978-0-07-305023-2(7), 0073050237, McGraw-Hill Science, Engineering & Mathematics) McGraw-Hill Higher Education.

Cooper & Cooper, Melanie M. Cooperative Chemistry Lab Manual. 5th ed. 2011. (ENG., Illus.). 192p. (C). pap. 87.33 (978-0-07-340272-7(9), 0073402729, McGraw-Hill Science, Engineering & Mathematics) McGraw-Hill Higher Education.

Corwin, Charles H. Prentice Hall Laboratory Manual to Introductory Chemistry: Concepts & Connections. 5th ed. 2008. (ENG.). 352p. (C). pap. 95.80 (978-0-13-604301-0(1), Prentice Hall) Prentice Hall PTR.

De Luca, Nancy. Chemistry Laboratory Manual. 3rd rev. ed. (ENG.). 288p. 2012. pap. 52.87 (978-0-7575-7787-1(3)) 2010. 47.20 (978-0-7575-5289-2(7)) Kendall Hunt Publishing Co.

Dean, John, et al. Practical Skills in Chemistry. 2nd rev. ed. 2011. (ENG., Illus.). 592p. pap. 79.50 (978-0-273-73118-4(1)) Pearson Education, Ltd. GBR. Dist: Trans-Atlantic Pubns., Inc.

Donaldson, Kurt D. & Scott, Jamie M. General Chemistry I: Lecture Notes & Workbook. 2nd rev. ed. 2010. (ENG.). 538p. pap. 110.38 (978-0-7872-9077-1(7)) Kendall Hunt Publishing Co.

Dunstan, Marie. Chemistry 123 Laboratory Notebook, Fall 2011. 2011. (C). (978-1-60036-455-6(1)) Academx Publishing Services, Inc.

Experiments in General Chemistry I Laboratory (CHEM 122) 7th ed. 2006. (C). spiral bd. (978-1-932768-05-3(X)) Academx Publishing Services, Inc.

Farrant & Yau, Crystal. Chemistry 203 Laboratory Manual. 2007. (C). spiral bd. (978-1-60036-032-9(7)) Academx Publishing Services, Inc.

Gellene & Gellene-Purkiss. Experimental General Chemistry I: Chem 1105 2nd rev. ed. 2011. (ENG.). 128p. spiral bd. 49.99 (978-0-7575-9483-0(2)) Kendall Hunt Publishing Co.

Gellene, Gregory & Purkiss, Laquetta. Experimental General Chemistry II: Chem 1106. rev. ed. 2010. (ENG.). 152p. spiral bd. 60.94 (978-0-7575-6106-1(3)) Kendall Hunt Publishing Co.

Gibson, Donna & Suchocki, John. Conceptual Chemistry: Understanding Our Woird of Atoms & Molecules. 3rd ed. 2006. (ENG., Illus.). 200p. (C). per., lab manual ed. 41.00 (978-0-8053-8232-7(1)) Benjamin-Cummings Publishing Co.

Griep, Mark A. Lab Manual for Chem 105: Chemistry in Context I. rev. ed. 2008. (ENG.). 56p. ring bd. 31.57 (978-0-7575-4165-0(8)) Kendall Hunt Publishing Co.

—Lab Manual for Chem 106 Chemistry in Context. rev. ed. 2011. (ENG.). 66p. ring bd. 31.42 (978-0-7575-7293-7(6)) Kendall Hunt Publishing Co.

Guinn, Denise, et al. Essentials of General, Organic, & Biochemistry. 2009. (ENG.). 225p. (C). pap., pupil's gde. ed. 48.95 (978-1-4292-2432-1(0)) Freeman, W. H. & Co.

Gunn, Bonnie M. General Chemistry: Laboratory Interface Guide. rev. ed. 2008. (ENG.). 245p. spiral bd. 38.33 (978-0-7575-5485-8(7)) Kendall Hunt Publishing Co.

Gunn, Bonnie M. General Chemistry: Laboratory Interface Guide. rev. ed. 2012. (ENG.). 276p. spiral bd. 36.50 (978-0-7575-9344-4(5)) Kendall Hunt Publishing Co.

Heasley, Victor L., et al. Chemistry & Life in the Laboratory: Experiments. 6th rev. ed. 2011. (ENG.). 448p. (C). pap. 99.93 (978-0-321-75160-7(4), Prentice Hall) Prentice Hall PTR.

Hein, Morris, et al. Introduction to General Organic & Biochemistry. 10th ed. 2011. (ENG.). 512p. (C). pap., lab manual ed. 142.95 (978-0-470-59881-8(6), Wiley) Wiley, John & Sons, Inc.

—Introduction to General, Organic, & Biochemistry in the Laoratory. 9th ed. 2008. (ENG., Illus.). 504p. (C). pap., lab manual ed. 142.95 (978-0-470-23965-0(4), Wiley) Wiley, John & Sons, Inc.

Hill, John W., et al. Chemical Investigations for Chemistry for Changing Times. (ENG.). (C). 12th ed. 2009. 512p. pap. 72.07 (978-0-321-61245-8(0)) 13th ed. 2012. 608p. pap. 72.07 (978-0-321-76779-0(9)) Prentice Hall PTR. (Prentice Hall).

Horton, Michael. Take-Home Chemistry: 50 Low-Cost Activities to Extend Classroom Learning. 2011. (Illus.). xxix, 244p. (978-1-936137-39-8(9)) National Science Teachers Assn.

Jesperson, Neil. Laboratory Manual for General Chemistry 12th Edition for St. John's Univ-Jamaica. 2011. (Wiley Custom Select Ser.). (C). pap. 35.95 (978-1-118-12188-7(0), Wiley) Wiley, John & Sons, Inc.

Johll, Matthew. Lab Manual for Investigating Chemistry. 2nd ed. 2008. (ENG.). 220p. (C). pap. 76.95 (978-1-4292-2243-3(3)) Freeman, W. H. & Co.

Juszczak, Laura. Experiments for Core Chemistry. rev. ed. 2011. (ENG.). 184p. spiral bd. 30.89 (978-0-7575-5849-8(6)) Kendall Hunt Publishing Co.

Kelter, Paul B., et al. Chemistry. 2007. (ENG., Illus.). 528p. (C). per., lab manual ed. 140.95 (978-0-618-00092-0(5), 329671) CENGAGE Learning.

Krishnaswamy, N.R. Chemistry of Natural Products. 2012. (ENG.). 216p. 79.95 (978-1-4665-0524-7(9), CRC Press) Taylor & Francis Group GBR. Dist: Taylor & Francis Group.

Landesberg, Joseph M. eneral, Organic, & Biochemistry - Laboratory Experiments. 2011. (ENG.). 256p. (C). pap. 69.95 (978-1-111-42661-3(9)) Brooks/Cole.

Liu, Brian C. -S & Ehrlich, Joshua R., eds. Tissue Proteomics: Pathways, Biomarkers, & Drug Discovery. 2008. (Methods in Molecular Biology Ser.). (Illus.). 225p. 109.00 (978-1-58829-679-5(2)) Humana Pr.

Lowell & Zona, Thomas. Chemistry & Society: Lab & Lecture. rev. ed. 2011. (ENG.). 81.50 (978-0-7575-7799-4(7)) Kendall Hunt Publishing Co.

Macaulay, David B., et al. General, Organic & Biological Chemistry: An Integrated Approach. 2nd ed. 2009. (ENG.). 344p. (C). pap., lab manual ed. 88.95 (978-0-470-56171-3(8), Wiley) Wiley, John & Sons, Inc.

Majorski, Sharyl A. Chemistry 127 Laboratory Manual. 2nd rev. ed. 2010. (ENG.). 244p. spiral bd. 40.90 (978-0-7575-7062-9(3)) Kendall Hunt Publishing Co.

—Chemistry 131 Laboratory Manual. rev. ed. 2011. (ENG.). 116p. spiral bd. 39.79 (978-0-7575-4625-9(0)) Kendall Hunt Publishing Co.

—Chemistry 132 Laboratory Manual. rev. ed. 2010. (ENG.). 120p. spiral bd. 40.90 (978-0-7575-4673-0(0)) Kendall Hunt Publishing Co.

Mcguffey, Angela R. & Geanangel, Russell A. General Chemistry Laboratories: A Freshman Workbook. 2nd rev. ed. 2010. (ENG.). 208p. pap. 34.70 (978-0-7575-3145-3(8)) Kendall Hunt Publishing Co.

Murov, Steven & Stedjee, Brian. Experiments & Exercises in Basic Chemistry. 7th ed. 2008. (ENG.). 416p. (C). pap. 123.95 (978-0-470-42373-8(0), Wiley) Wiley, John & Sons, Inc.

Nelson, John H., et al. Laboratory Experiments for Chemistry: The Central Science. 11th ed. 2008. (ENG., Illus.). 616p. (C). pap. 112.20 (978-0-13-600285-7(4), Prentice Hall) Prentice Hall PTR.

Nicholson, Ken & Weaver, Tom. Chemistry Lab Manual. 2011. (ENG.). 90p. ring bd. 33.80 (978-0-7575-8575-3(2)) Kendall Hunt Publishing Co.

North Carolina University Staff. General Chemistry: Chemistry 101/102 Laboratory Manual. 4th rev. ed. 2011. (ENG.). 338p. spiral bd. 52.00 (978-0-7575-9258-4(9)) Kendall Hunt Publishing Co.

Odziana, Doreen. A Collection of Chemistry & Physics Labs. 2008. 264p. pap. 27.95 (978-1-4401-1305-5(X)) iUniverse, Inc.

Oregon Museum of Science and Industry. No Hassle Messy Science with a Wow: Chemistry in the K-8 Classroom. Nunez, Veronika, tr. 2007. (Illus.). 480p. ring bd. 29.00 (978-0-9799206-0-8(4)) Oregon Museum of Science & Industry.

Postma, James M., et al. Chemistry in the Laboratory. 7th rev. ed. 2009. (ENG., Illus.). 550p. (C). pap. 101.95 (978-1-4292-1954-9(8)) Freeman, W. H. & Co.

Previdi & Winter, David. Experiments in General Chemistry II Laboratory (CHEM 124), 4th Ed. 2006. (C). spiral bd. (978-1-60036-005-3(X)) Academx Publishing Services, Inc.

Roesky, et al. Experiments in Green & Sustainable Chemistry. Roesky, Herbert W. & Kennepohl, Dietmar, eds. 2009. (ENG., Illus.). 307p. 45.00 (978-3-527-32546-7(8), Wiley-VCH) Wiley, John & Sons, Inc.

Rowley, Steven. General Chemistry I: Lab Manual. 2nd rev. ed. 2011. (ENG.). 172p. spiral bd. 31.90 (978-0-7575-8942-3(1)) Kendall Hunt Publishing Co.

—General Chemistry I: Laboratory Manual. rev. ed. 2008. (ENG.). 154p. spiral bd. 35.81 (978-0-7575-2106-5(1), 0757521061) Kendall Hunt Publishing Co.

—General Chemistry Ii: Laboratory Manual. rev. ed. (ENG.). 2011. 150p. spiral bd., lab manual ed. 40.65 (978-0-7575-7156-5(5)) 2009. 148p. spiral bd., lab manual ed. 42.58 (978-0-7575-4980-9(2)) Kendall Hunt Publishing Co.

Rugg, Barry, et al. General Chemistry Ii Laboratory Manual. 2nd rev. ed. 2008. 226p. spiral bd., lab manual ed. 42.47 (978-0-7575-4920-5(9)) Kendall Hunt Publishing Co.

Rusay. Lab Manual for Liberal Arts Chemistry-Chem Bytes. 2007. (C). pap. 33.95 (978-0-534-99965-0(4)) Brooks/Cole.

Russo, Steve, et al. Laboratory Manual for Introductory Chemistry. 4th rev. ed. 2011. (ENG.). 154p. (C). pap. 95.40 (978-0-321-73025-1(9), Prentice Hall) Pearson Education Canada CAN. Dist: Pearson Education.

Sherman, Alan & Sherman, Sharon. Laboratory Experiments for Basic Chemistry. 9th rev. ed. 2011. (ENG.). 276p. pap. 45.42 (978-0-7575-8805-1(0)) Kendall Hunt Publishing Co.

—Laboratory Manual for Basic Chemistry. 8th rev. ed. 2010. (ENG.). 276p. pap. 48.03 (978-0-7575-5086-7(X)) Kendall Hunt Publishing Co.

Shultz. General Chemistry Engineers Laboratory Manual: Used with ... Shultz-Chemistry for Engineers: An Applied Approach. 2006. (YA). pap., lab manual ed. 62.36 (978-0-618-27195-5(3), 317731) CENGAGE Learning.

Siegel, Donald. Introduction to Chemistry Lab Manual. rev. ed. 2012. (ENG.). 198p. pap. 13.25 (978-0-7575-9449-6(2)) Kendall Hunt Publishing Co.

Slowinski, Emil, et al. Chemical Principles in the Laboratory. 10th ed. 2011. (ENG.). 400p. (C). spiral bd. 163.95 (978-0-8400-4834-9(3)) Brooks/Cole.

Stanitski, Conrad L. Laboratory Handbook for General Chemistry. 3rd ed. 2007. (Illus.). vi, 120p. (978-0-495-18673-1(2)) Brooks/Cole.

Steel, Bill. Chemistry 135 Laboratory Manual, Fall 2011. 2011. (C). spiral bd. (978-1-60036-467-9(5)) Academx Publishing Services, Inc.

—Chemistry 137 Laboratory Manual, Fall 2011. 2011. (C). spiral bd. (978-1-60036-468-6(3)) Academx Publishing Services, Inc.

Stevens, Dennis L. Cu in Lab General Chemistry Laboratory Manual. (ENG.). 5th rev. ed. 2010. 318p. spiral bd. 44.59 (978-0-7575-3333-4(7)) 6th rev. ed 2011. 322p. spiral bd. 46.75 (978-0-7575-8233-2(8)) Kendall Hunt Publishing Co.

Suchocki, John A. & Gibson, Donna. Laboratory Manual for Conceptual Chemistry. 4th ed. 2010. (ENG.). 160p. (C). pap. 41.80 (978-0-321-68171-3(1), Prentice Hall) Prentice Hall PTR.

Svoronos, Paris, et al. Lab Experiments for General Chemistry. rev. ed. 2011 (ENG.). 236p. spiral bd. 48.81 (978-0-7575-0315-3(2)) Kendall Hunt Publishing Co.

Thompson, Robert Bruce. Illustrated Guide to Home Chemistry Experiments: All Lab, No Lecture. 2008. (DIY Science Ser.). (ENG., Illus.). 432p. pap. 29.99 (978-0-596-51492-1(1)) O'Reilly Media, Inc.

Tro, Nivaldo Jose, et al. Laboratory Manual for Chemistry: A Molecular Approach. 2nd ed. 2010. (ENG.). 368p. (C). spiral bd. 86.40 (978-0-321-66785-4(9), Prentice Hall) Prentice Hall PTR.

Twomey, Kendra. General Chemistry Laboratory Manual. 2nd rev. ed. (ENG.). 112p. 2011. spiral bd. 27.99 (978-0-7575-8558-6(2)) 2010. spiral bd. 25.96 (978-0-7575-5360-8(5)) Kendall Hunt Publishing Co.

Unger. General Chemistry Laboratory Experiments. rev. ed. 2011. (ENG.). 498p. spiral bd. 39.99 (978-0-7575-8688-0(0)) Kendall Hunt Publishing Co.

University of North Carolina Press Staff. General Chemistry: Chemistry 101/102. 4th rev. ed. 2010. (ENG.). 334p. spiral bd., lab manual ed. 54.75 (978-0-7575-7081-0(X)) Kendall Hunt Publishing Co.

Wassell, Peter T. Chemistry Lab Manual. 2nd rev. ed. 2011. 126p. spiral bd. 34.00 (978-0-7575-9301-7(1)) Kendall Hunt Publishing Co.

Wassell, Peter T. Chemistry Lab Manual: Chem 111/113. rev. ed. 2007. (ENG.). 128p. spiral bd. 30.38 (978-0-7575-4605-1(6)) Kendall Hunt Publishing Co.

White, Gary D. Chem 1120 Laboratory Manual. 2011. (ENG.). 112p. spiral bd., lab manual ed. 35.74 (978-0-7575-2415-8(X), 075752415X) Kendall Hunt Publishing Co.

Williams, Rebecca. Preparatory Chemistry Laboratory Studies. rev. ed. 2010. (ENG.). 136p. ring bd. 47.02 (978-0-7575-1418-0(9)) Kendall Hunt Publishing Co.

Williamson, Vickie & Peck, Larry. Experiments in General Chemistry: Inquiry & Skill Building. 2008. (ENG., Illus.). 384p. (C). per. 106.95 (978-0-495-55300-7(X)) Brooks/Cole.

Wingrave, James A. Chemistry 102 General Chemistry II Workshop & Activity-Based Pre-lab Manual, Fall 2006. 2006. (C). spiral bd. (978-1-60036-013-8(0)) Academx Publishing Services, Inc.

—Chemistry 102E General Chemistry Workshop & Activity-Based Pre-lab Manual, Fall 2006. 2006. (C). spiral bd. (978-1-60036-011-4(4)) Academx Publishing Services, Inc.

Witten, Edward. General Chemistry Laboratory Manual. 2011. (ENG.). 230p. spiral bd., lab manual ed. 38.71 (978-0-7575-3220-7(9)) Kendall Hunt Publishing Co.

World Health Organization. WHO Laboratory Manual for the Examination of Human Semen & Sperm-Cervical Mucus Interaction. 5th rev. ed. 2010. (Nonserial Publications Ser.). (ENG., Illus.). 287p. pap. 60.00 (978-92-4-154778-9(2)) World Health Organization.

Yeh, Jesse. Chemistry 1406: Introduction to Chemistry I. 2010. (ENG.). 96p. pap., lab manual ed. 22.22 (978-0-7575-1678-8(5), 0757516785) Kendall Hunt Publishing Co.

—Chemistry 1411: General Chemistry I. 2010. (ENG.). 122p. pap., lab manual ed. 26.06 (978-0-7575-1679-5(3), 0757516793) Kendall Hunt Publishing Co.

York, Deanna. More Teacher Friendly Chemistry Labs & Activities. 2010. 324p. pap. 43.00 (978-1-4520-7171-8(3)) AuthorHouse.

Young, Sarah. Gourmet Lab: The Scientific Principles Behind Your Favorite Foods. 2011. (978-1-936137-08-4(9)) National Science Teachers Assn.

Zumdahl, Steven S. & DeCoste, Donald J. Introductory Chemistry: A Foundation. 6th ed. 2007. (ENG.). 384p. (C). pap., lab manual ed. 119.95 (978-0-618-80332-3(7), 370846) Brooks/Cole.

CHEMISTRY—LECTURE EXPERIMENTS

see Chemistry—Experiments

CHEMISTRY—LITERATURE

see Chemical Literature

CHEMISTRY—MANIPULATION

see also Distillation, Fractional; Electric Furnaces; Glass Blowing and Working

Faraday, Michael. Chemical Manipulation. 2009. 482p. pap. (978-0-217-81031-9(4)); 570p. pap. (978-0-217-33804-2(6)) Books LLC.

Hao, Jingcheng, ed. Self-Assembled Structures: Properties & Applications in Solution & on Surfaces. 2010. (ENG., Illus.). 248p. 139.95 (978-1-4398-4083-2(0), CRC Press) Taylor & Francis Group GBR. Dist: Taylor & Francis Group.

CHEMISTRY—MATHEMATICS

Antonov, Anton. Mathematica for Chemists & Chemical Engineers: The Program for Mathematical Methods in Chemistry. 2012. (ENG.). 300p. pap. 99.95 (978-3-527-32748-5(7), Wiley-VCH) Wiley, John & Sons, Inc.

Beddard, Godfrey. Applying Maths in the Chemical & Biomolecular Sciences: An Example-Based Approach. 2009. (ENG., Illus.). 512p. (C). 64.95 (978-0-19-923091-4(9)) Oxford Univ. Pr., Inc.

Blinder, S. M. Guide to Essential Math: A Review for Physics, Chemistry & Engineering Students. 2008. (Complementary Science Ser.). (ENG., Illus.). 312p. pap. 48.95 (978-0-12-374264-3(1), Academic Pr.) Elsevier Science & Technology Bks.

Boyd, Donald B. Reviews in Computational Chemistry, Volume 26. Cundari, Thomas R. & Lipkowitz, Kenny B., eds. 2nd ed. 2008. (Reviews in Computational Chemistry Ser.: 51). (ENG.). 532p. 205.00 (978-0-470-38839-6(0), Wiley-VCH) Wiley, John & Sons, Inc.

Boyd, Donald B. & Lipkowitz, Kenny B. Reviews in Computational Chemistry, Vols. 1-23. Cundari, Thomas R., ed. 2007. (Reviews in Computational Chemistry Ser.: 47). (ENG.). 500p. 4735.00 (978-0-470-13994-3(3), Wiley-VCH) Wiley, John & Sons, Inc.

Brereton, Richard G. Applied Chemometrics for Scientists. 2007. (ENG., Illus.). 396p. 125.00 (978-0-470-01686-2(8), Wiley) Wiley, John & Sons, Inc.

Cockett, Martin & Doggett, Graham. Maths for Chemists. 2nd ed. 2012. (Tutorial Chemistry Texts). (ENG., Illus.). 404p. (C). pap. 40.00 ***(978-1-84973-359-5(7))*** Royal Society of Chemistry, The GBR. Dist: Ingram Pub. Services.

Cracolice, Mark S. Basics of Introductory Chemistry with Math Review. 2006. 816p. (C). pap. 87.95 *(978-0-495-11964-7(4))* Brooks/Cole.

Cundari, Thomas R. & Lipkowitz, Kenny B. Reviews in Computational Chemistry, Volume 25. Boyd, Donald B., ed. 2nd rev. ed. 2007. (Reviews in Computational Chemistry Ser.: 48). (ENG., Illus.). 448p. 222.00 *(978-0-470-17998-7(8)*, Wiley-VCH) Wiley, John & Sons, Inc.

Cundari, Thomas R., et al. Reviews in Computational Chemistry, Volume 24. Cundari, Thomas R., ed. 2007. (Reviews in Computational Chemistry Ser.: 31). (ENG.). 517p. 227.00 *(978-0-470-11281-6(6)*, Wiley-VCH) Wiley, John & Sons, Inc.

Ghergu, Marius & Rdulescu, Viceniu D. Nonlinear PDEs: Mathematical Models in Biology, Chemistry & Population Genetics. 2011. (Springer Monographs in Mathematics Ser.). (ENG., Illus.). xviii, 391p. 124.00 ***(978-3-642-22663-2(9)***, 3642226639) Springer.

Hanrahan, Grady. Environmental Chemometrics: Principles & Modern Applications. 2008. (Analytical Chemistry Ser.). (ENG., Illus.). 310p. (C). pap. 94.95 *(978-1-4200-6796-5(6)*, CRC Press) Taylor & Francis Group GBR. Dist: Taylor & Francis Group.

Hargittai, I. & Hargittai, M. Symmetry Through the Eyes of a Chemist. 3rd ed. 2009. (ENG., Illus.). xii, 520p. 219.00 *(978-1-4020-5627-7(3)*, 1402056273) Springer.

Hargittai, István & Hargittai, Magdolna. Symmetry through the Eyes of a Chemist. 3rd ed. 2010. (ENG., Illus.). xii, 520p. pap. 89.95 *(978-90-481-3689-6(X)*, 904813689X) Springer.

Hong, W. I., ed. Mathematical Chemistry. 2010. (Chemistry Research & Applications Ser.). (Illus.). xii, 613p. 145.00 *(978-1-60876-894-3(5))* Nova Science Pubs., Inc.

Jensen, Frank. Introduction to Computational Chemistry. 2nd rev. ed. 2006. (ENG., Illus.). 624p. 210.00 *(978-0-470-01186-7(6))*; per. 80.00 *(978-0-470-01187-4(4))* Wiley, John & Sons, Inc. (Wiley).

Kowalski, B. R., ed. Chemometrics: Mathematics & Statistics in Chemistry. 2010. (NATO Science Series C: (closed) Ser.). 508p. pap. 449.00 *(978-90-481-8407-1(X)*, 904818407X) Springer.

Leach, Andrew R. & Gillet, Valerie J. An Introduction to Chemoinformatics. 2007. (Illus.). 255p. pap. 69.95 *(978-1-4020-6290-2(7))* Springer.

Leszczynski, Jerzy. Computational Chemistry: Reviews of Current Trends. 350p. 113.00 *(978-981-02-3752-3(9))* World Scientific Publishing Co., Inc.

Liang, Yizeng & Xu, Qing-Song. Support Vector Machines & Their Application in Chemistry & Biotechnology. 2011. (ENG., Illus.). 211p. 119.95 *(978-1-4398-2127-5(5)*, CRC Press) Taylor & Francis Group GBR. Dist: Taylor & Francis Group.

Lipkowitz, Kenny B. Reviews in Computational Chemistry, Volume 27. 2nd ed. 2010. (Reviews in Computational Chemistry Ser.: 52). (ENG.). 481p. 205.00 *(978-0-470-58714-0(8)*, Wiley) Wiley, John & Sons, Inc.

Loney, Norman W. Applied Mathematical Methods for Chemical Engineers. 2nd rev. ed. 2006. (ENG., Illus.). 454p. (C). 115.95 *(978-0-8493-9778-3(2)*, CRC Press) Taylor & Francis Group GBR. Dist: Taylor & Francis Group.

Monk, Paul & Munro, Lindsey. Maths for Chemistry: A chemist's toolkit of Calculations. 2nd ed. 2010. (ENG., Illus.). 448p. pap. 59.95 *(978-0-19-954129-4(9))* Oxford Univ. Pr., Inc.

Nelson, Eric A. Calculations in Chemistry — Modules 1-16. 2007. 336p. (C). per. *(978-0-9771087-4-9(0))* ChemReview.

—Calculations in Chemistry — Modules 17-23. 2007. 216p. (C). per. 17.99 *(978-0-9771087-5-6(9))* ChemReview.

—Calculations in Chemistry — Modules 24-27. 2007. 236p. (C). per. 17.99 *(978-0-9771087-6-3(7))* ChemReview.

—Calculations in Chemistry — Volume 1 — Modules 1-16. 2008. (ESK.). (C). pap. *(978-0-9771087-7-0(5))* ChemReview.

—Calculations in Chemistry — Volume 2 — Modules 17-24. 2008. 274p. (C). pap. *(978-0-9771087-8-7(3))* ChemReview.

—Calculations in Chemistry — Volume 3 — Modules 25-30. 2008. 274p. (C). pap. *(978-0-9771087-9-4(1))* ChemReview.

Papadopoulos, M. G., et al, eds. Linear-Scaling Techniques in Computational Chemistry & Physics: Methods & Applications. 2010. (Challenges & Advances in Computational Chemistry & Physics Ser.). (Illus.). 400p. 309.00 *(978-90-481-2852-5(8)*, 9048128528) Springer.

Papadopoulos, Manthos G., et al, eds. Non-Linear Optical Properties of Matter: From molecules to condensed Phases. 2010. (Challenges & Advances in Computational Chemistry & Physics Ser.). xvii, 676p. pap. 439.00 *(978-90-481-7211-5(X)*, 904817211X) Springer.

Pota, Gyorgy. Mathematical Problems for Chemistry Students. 2006. (ENG., Illus.). 258p. 235.00 *(978-0-444-52794-3(X)*, Elsevier Science) Elsevier Science & Technology Bks.

Spellmeyer, David C., ed. Annual Reports in Computational Chemistry, Vol. 2. 2006. (Annual Reports in Computational Chemistry Ser.). (ENG.). 346p. 241.00 *(978-0-444-52822-3(9)*, Elsevier Science) Elsevier Science & Technology Bks.

Spellmeyer, David C. & Wheeler, Ralph A., eds. Annual Reports in Computational Chemistry. 2007. (ENG.). 254p. 241.00 *(978-0-444-53088-2(6)*, Elsevier Science) Elsevier Science & Technology Bks.

Thompson, Michael. Notes on Statistics & Data Quality for Analytical Chemists. 2011. 260p. 90.00 *(978-1-84816-616-5(8))*; pap. 49.00 *(978-1-84816-617-2(6))* Imperial College Pr. GBR. Dist: World Scientific Publishing Co., Inc.

Yates, Paul. Chemical Calculations: Mathematics for Chemistry. 2nd rev. ed. 2007. (ENG., Illus.). 384p. (C). per. 45.95 *(978-0-8493-9164-4(4)*, CRC Press) Taylor & Francis Group GBR. Dist: Taylor & Francis Group.

CHEMISTRY—METHODOLOGY

Majoral, Jean-Pierre. New Aspects in Phosphorus Chemistry II. 2010. (Topics in Current Chemistry Ser.). (Illus.). x, 263p. pap. 299.00 *(978-3-642-07900-9(8)*, 3642079008) Springer.

—New Aspects in Phosphorus Chemistry III. 2010. (Topics in Current Chemistry Ser.). (Illus.). xii, 213p. pap. 269.00 *(978-3-642-05637-6(7)*, 3642056377) Springer.

—New Aspects in Phosphorus Chemistry V. 2010. (Topics in Current Chemistry Ser.). (Illus.). xiii, 275p. pap. 349.00 *(978-3-642-06136-3(2)*, 3642061362) Springer.

CHEMISTRY—MODELS

see Chemical Models

CHEMISTRY—NOMENCLATURE

Anstein, Stefanie & Kremer, Gerhard. Analysing Names of Organic Chemical Compounds. 2008. 112p. per. *(978-3-8364-6985-2(5))* VDM Verlag Dr. Mueller e.K.

Leigh, G. Jeff, ed. Principles of Chemical Nomenclature: A Guide to IUPAC Recommendations. 2011. (ENG., Illus.). 270p. (C). 40.00 ***(978-1-84973-007-5(5))*** Royal Society of Chemistry, The GBR. Dist: Ingram Pub. Services.

CHEMISTRY—NOTATION

see also Chemical Equations

Abt, Theodor. Corpus Alchemicum Arabicum Vol. 1B (CALA1 B) Book of the Explanation of the Symbols. 2010. (Corpus Alchemicum Arabicum (CALA) Ser.). 400p. 98.00 *(978-3-9522608-8-3(6))* Daimon Verlag CHE. Dist: AtlasBooks Distribution.

Klein, U, ed. Tools & Modes of Representation in the Laboratory Sciences. 2010. (Boston Studies in the Philosophy of Science Ser.). 276p. pap. 149.00 *(978-90-481-5859-1(1)*, 9048158591) Springer.

Umail, Muhammad Bin. Corpus Alchemicum Arabicum Vol 1a: Book of the Explantion of the Symbols Kitab Hall Ar-Rumuz — Psychological Commentary by Marie-Louise Von Franz. Abt, Theodor, ed. 2007. (ENG.). 241p. spiral bd. 45.00 *(978-3-9522608-3-8(5))* Daimon Verlag CHE. Dist: AtlasBooks Distribution.

CHEMISTRY—OUTLINES, SYLLABI, ETC.

Blei & Odian & Cram101 Textbook Reviews Staff. General, Organic, & Biochemistry. 2007. 284p. per. 15.95 *(978-1-4288-2932-9(6))* Cram101 Inc.

Cram101 Textbook Reviews. Outlines & Highlights for Adventures in Chemistry by Julie T Millard, Isbn: 9780618376629. 2010. 200p. pap. 30.95 *(978-1-61698-548-6(8))* Cram101 Inc.

—Outlines & Highlights for Basic Chemistry by Karen C Timberlake, William Timberlake, Isbn: 9780805344691. 2010. 218p. pap. 30.95 *(978-1-61698-576-9(3))* Cram101 Inc.

—Outlines & Highlights for Basic Chemistry by Zumdahl & Decoste. 2010. 666p. pap. 41.95 *(978-1-61698-870-8(3))* Cram101 Inc.

—Outlines & Highlights for Basic Concepts of Chemistry by Leo J Malone, Isbn: 9780471741541. 2010. 494p. pap. 37.95 *(978-1-61698-052-8(4))* Cram101 Inc.

—Outlines & Highlights for Basics of Introductory Chemistry by Mark S Cracolice. 2010. 470p. pap. 36.95 *(978-1-4288-5310-2(3))* Cram101 Inc.

—Outlines & Highlights for Biology: Chemistry, Cell Biology & Genetics. 2011. 714p. pap. 43.95 ***(978-1-61812-483-8(8))*** Cram101 Inc.

—Outlines & Highlights for Chemical Principles: A Queset for Insight by Peter Atkins, Loretta Jones, ISBN. 2010. 264p. pap. 31.95 *(978-1-61698-575-2(5))* Cram101 Inc.

—Outlines & Highlights for Chemical Principles by Steven S Zumdahl, Isbn: 9780618946907. 2010. 424p. pap. 35.95 *(978-1-61698-587-5(9))* Cram101 Inc.

—Outlines & Highlights for Chemistry: Introduction to General, Organic, & Biological Chemistry by Timberlake. 2010. 684p. pap. 42.95 *(978-1-4288-5304-1(9))* Cram101 Inc.

—Outlines & Highlights for Chemistry: Molecular Science by Moore, ISBN. 2011. 408p. pap. 35.95 ***(978-1-61490-401-4(4))*** Cram101 Inc.

—Outlines & Highlights for Chemistry: Principles & Practice by Daniel L. Reger, Edward Mercer, David W. Ball, Scott R. Goode, ISBN. 2010. 278p. pap. 32.95 *(978-1-61698-595-0(X))* Cram101 Inc.

—Outlines & Highlights for Chemistry: Principles, Patterns, & Applications by Bruce A. Averill, ISBN. 2011. 552p. pap. 38.95 ***(978-1-61490-402-1(2))*** Cram101 Inc.

—Outlines & Highlights for Chemistry: Structure & Dynamics by George M. Bodner, Lyman H. Rickard, James N. Spencer, ISBN. 2010. 184p. pap. 29.95 *(978-1-61698-584-4(4))* Cram101 Inc.

—Outlines & Highlights for Chemistry: The Molecular Science by John W. Moore, Peter C. Jurs, Conrad L. Stanitski, ISBN. 2010. 492p. pap. 37.95 *(978-1-61698-558-5(5))* Cram101 Inc.

—Outlines & Highlights for Chemistry: The Molecular Science, Volume II, Chapters 12-22 by John W. Moore, ISBN. 2011. 404p. pap. 35.95 ***(978-1-61490-400-7(6))*** Cram101 Inc.

—Outlines & Highlights for Chemistry: The Practical Science by Paul Kelter. 2011. 482p. pap. 37.95 ***(978-1-61490-998-9(9))*** Cram101 Inc.

—Outlines & Highlights for Chemistry: The Practical Science, Media Enhanced Edition by Paul Kelter, Andrew Scott, Michael Mosher, ISBN. 2010. 488p. pap. 37.95 *(978-1-61698-573-8(9))* Cram101 Inc.

—Outlines & Highlights for Chemistry: The Science in Context by Geoffrey Davies, Natalie Foster, Thomas R. Gilbert, Rein V. Kirss, ISBN. 2010. 284p. pap. 32.95 *(978-1-61698-572-1(0))* Cram101 Inc.

—Outlines & Highlights for Chemistry: The Study of Matter & Its Changes by Fred Senese, James E. Brady, ISBN. 2010. 252p. pap. 31.95 *(978-1-61698-601-8(8))* Cram101 Inc.

—Outlines & Highlights for Chemistry: The Study of Matter & Its Changes by James E. Brady, ISBN. 2011. 384p. pap. 34.95 ***(978-1-61490-399-4(9))*** Cram101 Inc.

—Outlines & Highlights for Chemistry & Chemical Reactivity, Volume 1 by John C Kotz, John Townsend, Paul M Treichel, Isbn: 9780495387114. 2010. 478p. pap. 37.95 *(978-1-61698-599-8(2))* Cram101 Inc.

—Outlines & Highlights for Chemistry & Chemical Reactivity, Volume 2 by John C Kotz, Isbn: 9780495387121 0495387126. 2011. 568p. pap. 39.95 ***(978-1-61812-363-3(7))*** Cram101 Inc.

—Outlines & Highlights for Chemistry by John Mcmurry, Robert C Fay, Isbn: 9780131993235. 2010. 390p. pap. 34.95 *(978-1-61698-594-3(1))* Cram101 Inc.

—Outlines & Highlights for Chemistry by Mcmurry, John / Fay, Robert C , Isbn: 9780131402089. 2010. 334p. pap. 33.95 *(978-1-61698-588-2(7))* Cram101 Inc.

—Outlines & Highlights for Chemistry by Steven S Zumdahl, Isbn: 9780618528448. 2010. 436p. pap. 36.95 *(978-1-61698-596-7(8))* Cram101 Inc.

—Outlines & Highlights for Chemistry by Thomas Hummel. 2010. 636p. pap. 40.95 *(978-1-4288-5313-3(8))* Cram101 Inc.

—Outlines & Highlights for Chemistry for Changing Times by John W Hill, Isbn: 9780136054498 0136054498. 2011. 440p. pap. 36.95 ***(978-1-61812-308-4(4))*** Cram101 Inc.

—Outlines & Highlights for Chemistry for Engineering Students by Larry Brown. 2010. 408p. pap. 35.95 *(978-1-4288-5307-2(3))* Cram101 Inc.

—Outlines & Highlights for Chemistry in Focus: Molecular View of Our World by Nivaldo J. Tro. 2010. 514p. pap. 37.95 *(978-1-4288-5299-0(9))* Cram101 Inc.

—Outlines & Highlights for Conceptual Chemistry by John a Suchocki, Isbn: 9780805382211. 2010. 190p. pap. 30.95 *(978-1-61698-600-1(X))* Cram101 Inc.

—Outlines & Highlights for Essentials of Chemical Biology by Andrew D Miller, Isbn: 9780470845318 0470845317. 2011. 246p. pap. 31.95 ***(978-1-61490-245-4(3))*** Cram101 Inc.

—Outlines & Highlights for Foundations of College Chemistry, Alternate Edition by Hein, Morris / Arena, Susan, Isbn: 9780471779919. 2010. 110p. pap. 28.95 *(978-1-61698-556-1(9))* Cram101 Inc.

—Outlines & Highlights for Foundations of College Chemistry by Morris Hein, Susan Arena, Isbn: 9780471741534. 2010. 130p. pap. 32.95 *(978-1-61698-597-4(6))* Cram101 Inc.

—Outlines & Highlights for General Chemistry by Darrell Ebbing, Steven D Gammon, Isbn: 9780618857487. 2010. 464p. pap. 36.95 *(978-1-61698-602-5(6))* Cram101 Inc.

—Outlines & Highlights for General, Organic, & Biological Chemistry: An Integrated Approach by Kenneth W. Raymond, ISBN. 2010. 156p. pap. 29.95 *(978-1-61698-598-1(4))* Cram101 Inc.

—Outlines & Highlights for General, Organic, & Biological Chemistry by H Stephen Stoker, Isbn: 9780547152813 0547152817. 2011. 560p. pap. 38.95 ***(978-1-61490-182-2(1))*** Cram101 Inc.

—Outlines & Highlights for General Organic & Biological Chemistry by Kenneth W Raymond, Isbn: 9780470504765 0470504765. 2011. 366p. pap. 34.95 ***(978-1-61490-185-3(6))*** Cram101 Inc.

—Outlines & Highlights for General, Organic, & Biological Chemistry by Laura D Frost, Isbn: 9780805381788 0805381783. 2011. 272p. pap. 32.95 ***(978-1-61490-181-5(3))*** Cram101 Inc.

—Outlines & Highlights for Introduction to Chemistry by Steven S Zumdahl, Isbn: 9780618803293. 2010. 274p. pap. 32.95 *(978-1-61698-578-3(X))* Cram101 Inc.

—Outlines & Highlights for Introductory Chemistry by Steve Russo, Michael E Silver, Isbn: 9780805382983. 2010. 244p. pap. 36.95 *(978-1-61698-590-5(9))* Cram101 Inc.

—Outlines & Highlights for Introductory Chemistry Essentials by Nivaldo J Tro, Isbn: 9780136019916. 2010. 166p. pap. 29.95 *(978-1-61698-557-8(7))* Cram101 Inc.

—Outlines & Highlights for Introductory Chemistry for Today by Spencer L Seager. 2010. 272p. pap. 32.95 *(978-1-4288-5267-9(0))* Cram101 Inc.

—Outlines & Highlights for Modern Chemistry by Sarquis Davis. 2011. 428p. pap. 35.95 ***(978-1-61905-784-5(0))*** Cram101 Inc.

—Outlines & Highlights for Physical Chemistry: For the Biosciences by Raymond Chang, ISBN. 2010. 120p. pap. 28.95 *(978-1-61698-552-3(6))* Cram101 Inc.

—Outlines & Highlights for Physical Chemistry by Ira N Levine, Isbn: 9780072538625. 2010. 246p. pap. 31.95 *(978-1-61698-549-3(6))* Cram101 Inc.

—Outlines & Highlights for Physical Chemistry for the Life Sciences by Peter Atkins, Julio de Paula, Isbn: 9780716786283. 2010. 136p. pap. 28.95 *(978-1-61698-551-6(8))* Cram101 Inc.

—Outlines & Highlights for Principles of Modern Chemistry by David W Oxtoby, Alan Campion, H Pat Gillis, Isbn: 9780534493660. 2010. 186p. pap. 30.95 *(978-1-61698-592-9(5))* Cram101 Inc.

—Outlines & Highlights for the Chemistry of Everything by Kimberley Waldron, Isbn: 9780130085221. 2010. 170p. pap. 29.95 *(978-1-61698-574-5(7))* Cram101 Inc.

—Outlines & Highlights for the World of Chemistry: Essentials by Melvin D. Joesten, Mary E. Castellion, John L. Hogg, ISBN. 2010. 242p. pap. 31.95 *(978-1-61698-555-4(0))* Cram101 Inc.

—Outlines & Highlights for University Chemistry by Brian Laird, Isbn: 9780077221331. 2010. 350p. pap. 40.95 *(978-1-61698-585-1(2))* Cram101 Inc.

Cram101 Textbook Reviews & Cram101 Textbook Reviews. Outlines & Highlights for Basics of Introductory Chemistry by Mark S Cracolice, Isbn: 9780495558507 0495558508. 2011. 232p. pap. 31.95 ***(978-1-61490-090-0(6))*** Cram101 Inc.

—Outlines & Highlights for Chemistry by Steven S Zumdahl & Susan a Zumdahl, Isbn: 9780547125329. 2011. 226p. pap. 30.95 ***(978-1-61461-826-3(7))*** Cram101 Inc.

—Outlines & Highlights for Chemistry, Cell Biology, & Genetics, Volume I by Peter Raven, Isbn: 9780077397500. 2011. 496p. pap. 37.95 ***(978-1-4288-1864-4(2))*** Cram101 Inc.

—Outlines & Highlights for Ebbing General Chemistry by Ebbing, Isbn: 9780547154633 0547154631. 2011. 504p. pap. 37.95 ***(978-1-61490-197-6(X))*** Cram101 Inc.

—Outlines & Highlights for Foundations of College Chemistry by Morris Hein, Isbn: 9780470460603 9780470460610 9780470554920. 2011. 184p. pap. 29.95 ***(978-1-61461-828-7(3))*** Cram101 Inc.

—Outlines & Highlights for Foundations of College Chemistry by Morris Hein, Isbn: 9780470460610. 2011. 254p. pap. 31.95 ***(978-1-61461-827-0(5))*** Cram101 Inc.

—Outlines & Highlights for Introduction to General, Organic & Biochemistry by Frederick a Bettelheim, Isbn: 9780495391128 0495391123. 2011. 308p. pap. 32.95 ***(978-1-61490-121-1(X))*** Cram101 Inc.

—Outlines & Highlights for Introductory Chemistry: An Active Learning Approach by Mark S. Cracolice, ISBN. 2011. 282p. pap. 32.95 ***(978-1-61490-807-4(9))*** Cram101 Inc.

—Outlines & Highlights for Introductory Chemistry by Charles H Corwin, Isbn: 9780321663054 0321663055. 2011. 280p. pap. 31.95 ***(978-1-61490-104-4(X))*** Cram101 Inc.

—Outlines & Highlights for Introductory Chemistry by Steven S Zumdahl, Isbn: 9781439049402 1439049408. 2011. 458p. pap. 36.95 ***(978-1-61490-042-9(6))*** Cram101 Inc.

—Outlines & Highlights for Trace Quantitative Analysis by Mass Spectrometry by Cecilia Basic, Isbn: 9780470057711 0470057718. 2011. 140p. pap. 28.95 ***(978-1-61812-057-1(3))*** Cram101 Inc.

Cram101 Textbook Reviews Staff. Outlines & Highlights for Adventures in Chemistry by Julie T Millard, Isbn: 9780618376629. 2009. 178p. pap. 29.95 *(978-1-4288-7440-4(2))* Cram101 Inc.

—Outlines & Highlights for Basic Chemistry by Karen C Timberlake, William Timberlake, Isbn: 9780805344691. 2009. 192p. pap. 30.95 *(978-1-4288-7425-1(9))* Cram101 Inc.

—Outlines & Highlights for Cengage Advantage Books: Introductory Chemistry. 2009. 228p. pap. 31.95 *(978-1-4288-9162-3(5))* Cram101 Inc.

—Outlines & Highlights for Chemical Principles: A Queset for Insight by Peter Atkins, Loretta Jones, Loretta Jones, ISBN. 2009. 232p. pap. 31.95 *(978-1-4288-7431-2(3))* Cram101 Inc.

—Outlines & Highlights for Chemical Principles: The Quest for Insight by Atkins ISBN. 2007. 440p. pap. 19.95 *(978-1-4288-3078-3(2))* Cram101 Inc.

—Outlines & Highlights for Chemical Principles by Steven S Zumdahl, Steven S Zumdahl, Isbn: 9780618946907. 2009. 372p. pap. 34.95 *(978-1-4288-7435-0(6))* Cram101 Inc.

—Outlines & Highlights for Chemical Principles by Zumdahl, Isbn: 0618372067. 2007. 420p. pap. 18.95 *(978-1-4288-3024-0(3))* Cram101 Inc.

—Outlines & Highlights for Chemical Principles, Enhanced Edition by Steven S Zumdahl, Isbn: 9781439043981. 2009. 366p. pap. 34.95 *(978-1-4288-7648-4(0))* Cram101 Inc.

—Outlines & Highlights for Chemistry. 2007. pap. 18.95 *(978-1-4288-5733-9(8))* Cram101 Inc.

—Outlines & Highlights for Chemistry: Central Science by Theodore L. Brown, ISBN. 2009. 562p. pap. 39.95 *(978-1-4288-9209-5(5))* Cram101 Inc.

—Outlines & Highlights for Chemistry: The Central Science by Theodore E. Brown, ISBN. 2009. 612p. pap. 40.95 *(978-1-4288-8722-0(9))* Cram101 Inc.

—Outlines & Highlights for Chemistry: The Molecular Nature of Matter & Change by Martin S. Silberberg, ISBN. 2009. 688p. pap. 42.95 *(978-1-4288-9573-7(6))* Cram101 Inc.

—Outlines & Highlights for Chemistry: The Molecular Science by John W. Moore, Peter C. Jurs, Conrad L. Stanitski, ISBN. 2009. 416p. pap. 35.95 *(978-1-4288-8299-7(5))* Cram101 Inc.

—Outlines & Highlights for Chemistry: The Molecular Science by Moore, ISBN. 2007. 544p. pap. 21.95 *(978-1-4288-3014-1(6))* Cram101 Inc.

—Outlines & Highlights for Chemistry: The Science in Context by Gilbert, ISBN. 2007. 364p. pap. 17.95 *(978-1-4288-3038-7(3))* Cram101 Inc.

—Outlines & Highlights for Chemistry by Chang, Isbn: 0071241655. 2007. 496p. pap. 20.95 *(978-1-4288-3028-8(6))* Cram101 Inc.

—Outlines & Highlights for Chemistry by Chang, Isbn: 0072980605. 2007. 272p. per. 14.95 *(978-1-4288-5713-1(3))* Cram101 Inc.

—Outlines & Highlights for Chemistry by John Mcmurry, Robert C Fay, Isbn: 9780131993235. 2009. 330p. pap. 33.95 *(978-1-4288-7418-3(6))* Cram101 Inc.
—Outlines & Highlights for Chemistry by Julia Burdge, Isbn: 9780077221324. 2009. 284p. pap. 32.95 *(978-1-4288-9611-6(2))* Cram101 Inc.
—Outlines & Highlights for Chemistry by Kenneth W Whitten, Isbn: 9780495391630. 2009. 226p. pap. 30.95 *(978-1-4288-8826-5(8))* Cram101 Inc.
—Outlines & Highlights for Chemistry by Olmsted, Isbn: 9780471478119. 2008. 288p. pap. 15.95 *(978-1-4288-6584-6(5))* Cram101 Inc.
—Outlines & Highlights for Chemistry by Raymond Chang, Isbn: 9780077274313. 2009. 332p. pap. 33.95 *(978-1-4288-9042-8(4))* Cram101 Inc.
—Outlines & Highlights for Chemistry by Timberlake, Isbn: 0805331328. 2007. 252p. pap. 14.95 *(978-1-4288-3018-9(9))* Cram101 Inc.
—Outlines & Highlights for Chemistry by Whitten Isbn: 0495011967. 2007. 544p. pap. 21.95 *(978-1-4288-3082-0(0))* Cram101 Inc.
—Outlines & Highlights for Chemistry by Zumdahl, Isbn: 0618610324. 2007. 448p. pap. 19.95 *(978-1-4288-3042-4(1))* Cram101 Inc.
—Outlines & Highlights for Chemistry, Cell Biology, & Genetics, Volume I by Raven Isbn: 9780073337487. 2008. 264p. pap. 14.95 *(978-1-4288-5979-1(9))* Cram101 Inc.
—Outlines & Highlights for Chemistry for Changing Times by John W Hill, Isbn: 9780132280846. 2009. 530p. pap. 38.95 *(978-1-4288-9138-8(2))* Cram101 Inc.
—Outlines & Highlights for Chemistry for the Health Sciences by Sackheim Isbn: 0137443196. 2007. 380p. pap. 17.95 *(978-1-4288-3062-2(6))* Cram101 Inc.
—Outlines & Highlights for Chemistry for Today: General, Organic, & Biochemistry by Spencer L. Seager, Michael R. Slabaugh, ISBN. 2009. 128p. pap. 28.95 *(978-1-4288-7760-3(6))* Cram101 Inc.
—Outlines & Highlights for Chemistry in Context: Applying Chemistry to Society by American Chemical Society, ISBN. 2009. 142p. pap. 28.95 *(978-1-4288-7927-0(7))* Cram101 Inc.
—Outlines & Highlights for Chemistry in Context by Lucy Pryde Eubanks, Isbn: 9780077221348. 2009. 230p. pap. 31.95 *(978-1-4288-8935-4(3))* Cram101 Inc.
—Outlines & Highlights for Chemistry in Your Life by Colin Baird, Isbn: 9780716770428. 2009. 154p. pap. 29.95 *(978-1-4288-7925-6(0))* Cram101 Inc.
—Outlines & Highlights for Chemistry of Everything by Kimberley Waldron, Isbn: 9780132284516. 2009. 282p. pap. 32.95 *(978-1-4288-8659-9(1))* Cram101 Inc.
—Outlines & Highlights for Chemistry Science of Change by Oxtoby Isbn: 0030331889. 2007. 536p. pap. 21.95 *(978-1-4288-3066-0(9))* Cram101 Inc.
—Outlines & Highlights for Conceptual Chemistry by John a Suchocki, Isbn: 9780805382211. 2009. 164p. pap. 29.95 *(978-1-4288-7412-1(7))* Cram101 Inc.
—Outlines & Highlights for Foundations of College Chemistry, Alternate Edition by Hein, Morris / Arena, Susan, Isbn: 9780471779919. 2009. 94p. pap. 27.95 *(978-1-4288-7432-9(1))* Cram101 Inc.
—Outlines & Highlights for Fundamentals of Chemistry by Burns, Isbn: 0130337196. 2007. 340p. pap. 16.95 *(978-1-4288-3064-6(2))* Cram101 Inc.
—Outlines & Highlights for Fundamentals of Chemistry by Goldberg, Isbn. 2008. 112p. pap. 11.95 *(978-1-4288-5886-2(5))* Cram101 Inc.
—Outlines & Highlights for Fundamentals of Chemistry by Goldberg, Isbn: 0072472243. 2007. 220p. pap. 13.95 *(978-1-4288-3068-4(5))* Cram101 Inc.
—Outlines & Highlights for Fundamentals of General, Organic, & Biological Chemistry by Prentice Hall, Isbn: 9780132210911. 2009. 422p. pap. 35.95 *(978-1-4288-9874-5(3))* Cram101 Inc.
—Outlines & Highlights for General Chemistry: The Essential Concepts by Chang, ISBN. 2007. 228p. per. 13.95 *(978-1-4288-5714-8(1))* Cram101 Inc.
—Outlines & Highlights for General Chemistry by Darrell Ebbing, Steven D Gammon, Isbn: 9780618857487. 2009. 404p. pap. 35.95 *(978-1-4288-7424-4(0))* Cram101 Inc.
—Outlines & Highlights for General, Organic, & Biochemistry by Denniston Isbn: 0072828471. 2007. 264p. per. 14.95 *(978-1-4288-5715-5(X))* Cram101 Inc.
—Outlines & Highlights for General, Organic & Biological Chemistry by Janice Gorzynski Smith, Isbn: 9780077274290. 2009. 264p. pap. 31.95 *(978-1-4288-7449-0(8))* Cram101 Inc.
—Outlines & Highlights for Introduction to Chemistry by Rich Bauer, Isbn: 9780077274306. 2009. 152p. pap. 29.95 *(978-1-4288-8882-1(9))* Cram101 Inc.
—Outlines & Highlights for Introduction to Chemistry by Steven S Zumdahl, Isbn: 9780618803293. 2009. 238p. pap. 31.95 *(978-1-4288-7427-5(5))* Cram101 Inc.
—Outlines & Highlights for Introduction to General, Organic & Biochemistry by Frederick a Bettelheim, Mary K Campbell, William H Brown, Shawn O F. 2009. 252p. pap. 31.95 *(978-1-4288-7413-8(5))* Cram101 Inc.
—Outlines & Highlights for Introductory Chemistry by Mark S Cracolice, Isbn: 9780495013327. 2009. 198p. pap. 30.95 *(978-1-4288-9811-0(5))* Cram101 Inc.
—Outlines & Highlights for Introductory Chemistry by Tro, Nivaldo J , Isbn: 9780136003823. 2009. 222p. pap. 30.95 *(978-1-4288-8699-5(0))* Cram101 Inc.
—Outlines & Highlights for Introductory Chemistry Essentials by Nivaldo J Tro, Isbn: 9780136019916. 2009. 146p. pap. 29.95 *(978-1-4288-7433-6(X))* Cram101 Inc.
—Outlines & Highlights for Organic Chemistry by Bruice, Isbn: 0131407481. 2007. 532p. pap. 21.95 *(978-1-4288-3026-4(X))* Cram101 Inc.
—Outlines & Highlights for Organic Chemistry by Mcmurry, Isbn: 0534389996. 2007. 500p. pap. 20.95 *(978-1-4288-3046-2(4))* Cram101 Inc.
—Outlines & Highlights for Practice of Chemistry by Donald J Wink, Sharon Fetzer-Gislason, Sheila Mcnicholas, Isbn: 9780716748717. 2009. 110p. pap. 28.95 *(978-1-4288-7416-9(X))* Cram101 Inc.
—Outlines & Highlights for Principles of Chemistry: The Molecular Science by John W. Moore, ISBN. 2009. 228p. pap. 31.95 *(978-1-4288-9148-7(X))* Cram101 Inc.
—Outlines & Highlights for Principles of General Chemistry by Martin Silberberg, Isbn: 9780077274320. 2009. 532p. pap. 38.95 *(978-1-4288-9160-9(9))* Cram101 Inc.
—Outlines & Highlights for Principles of General Chemistry by Silberberg, Isbn: 0073107204. 2007. 344p. per. 16.95 *(978-1-4288-5734-6(6))* Cram101 Inc.
—Outlines & Highlights for the Chemistry of Everything by Kimberley Waldron, Isbn: 9780130085221. 2009. 146p. pap. 29.95 *(978-1-4288-7423-7(2))* Cram101 Inc.
—Outlines & Highlights for the Extraordinary Chemistry of Ordinary Things by Snyder, Isbn: 0471415758. 2007. 264p. pap. 14.95 *(978-1-4288-3048-6(0))* Cram101 Inc.
—Outlines & Highlights for the World of Chemistry: Essentials by Melvin D. Joesten, Mary E. Castellion, John L. Hogg, ISBN. 2009. 212p. pap. 30.95 *(978-1-4288-7442-8(9))* Cram101 Inc.
—Outlines & Highlights for World of Chemistry by Steven S Zumdahl, Isbn: 0618134964. 2009. 266p. pap. 31.95 *(978-1-4288-7837-2(8))* Cram101 Inc.
—Outlines & Highlights for World of Chemistry Essentials by Joesten Isbn: 0534559093. 2007. 268p. pap. 14.95 *(978-1-4288-3070-7(7))* Cram101 Inc.

Fisher, Julie & Arnold, John. BIOS Instant Notes in Chemistry for Biologists. 3rd rev. ed. 2012. (Instant Notes Ser.). (ENG., Illus.). 320p. (C). pap. 40.00 *(978-0-415-68003-5(4)*, Taylor & Francis) Taylor & Francis Group GBR. Dist: Taylor & Francis Group.
Giddings, Luther. Elementary Chemistry: Lecture Notes. 2008. 266p. spiral bd. 31.31 *(978-0-7575-5423-0(7))* Kendall Hunt Publishing Co.
Goldberg, David. Beginning Chemistry. 3rd ed. 2009. (Schaum's Outline Ser.). (ENG., Illus.). 360p. (C). pap. 18.95 *(978-0-07-163537-0(8)*, 0071635378) McGraw-Hill Cos., The.
Goldberg, David E. Beginning Chemistry. 2nd ed. 2010. (Schaum's Outline Ser.). (ENG., Illus.). 144p. (C). pap. 11.00 *(978-0-07-174588-8(2)*, 0071745882) McGraw-Hill Cos., The.
Holt & Cram101 Textbook Reviews Staff. Chemistry: Visualizing Matter. 2007. 72p. per. 10.95 *(978-1-4288-2926-8(1))* Cram101 Inc.
Mascetta, Joseph A. & Kernion, Mark C. E-Z Chemistry. 5th rev. ed. 2009. (Barron's E-Z Ser.). (ENG., Illus.). 528p. pap. 16.99 *(978-0-7641-4128-7(7))* Barron's Educational Series, Inc.
Odian, George & Blei, Ira. General, Organic, & Biochemistry for Nursing & Allied Health. 2nd ed. 2009. (Schaum's Outline Ser.). (ENG., Illus.). 528p. (C). pap. 20.00 *(978-0-07-161165-7(7)*, 0071611657) McGraw-Hill Cos., The.
Rosenberg, Jerome, et al. College Chemistry. (Schaum's Easy Outlines Ser.). (ENG., Illus.). (C). 2nd ed. 2010. 160p. pap. 11.00 *(978-0-07-174587-1(4)*, 0071745874) 9th ed. 2009. 408p. pap. 18.95 *(978-0-07-163530-1(0)*, 0071635300) McGraw-Hill Cos., The.
Sackheim, George I. An Introduction to Chemistry for Biology Students. 9th rev. ed. 2007. (ENG., Illus.). 352p. (C). per. 41.47 *(978-0-8053-9571-6(7))* Benjamin-Cummings Publishing Co.
Whitten, Kenneth, et al. Lecture Outline for Whitten/Davis/Peck/Stanley's Chemistry, 9th. 9th ed. 2009. (ENG.). 512p. (C). pap. 68.95 *(978-0-495-39176-0(X))* Brooks/Cole.

CHEMISTRY—POPULAR WORKS

Braterman, Paul S. From Stars to Stalagmites: How Everything Connects. 2012. 250p. pap. 38.00 ***(978-981-4324-97-7(3))*** World Scientific Publishing Co., Inc.
Chemical Sciences Roundtable & National Research Council. Chemistry in Primetime & Online: Communicating Chemistry in Informal Environments. 2011. (ENG.). 102p. pap. 30.00 ***(978-0-309-18770-1(2))*** National Academies Pr.
Cobb, Cathy & Fetterolf, Monty L. Joy of Chemistry: The Amazing Science of Familiar Things. 2009. (ENG., Illus.). 393p. pap. 19.00 *(978-1-59102-771-3(3))* Prometheus Bks., Pubs.
Emsley, John. A Healthy, Wealthy, Sustainable World. 2010. (ENG., Illus.). 242p. 30.00 ***(978-1-84755-862-6(3))*** Royal Society of Chemistry, The GBR. Dist: Ingram Pub. Services.
Faraday, Michael, et al. The Chemical History of a Candle. 2011. (ENG., Ilus.). 192p. 24.95 *(978-0-19-969491-4(5))* Oxford Univ. Pr., Inc.
Nickell, Duane S. Guidebook for the Scientific Traveler: Visiting Physics & Chemistry Sites Across America. 2010. (Scientific Traveler Ser.). (ENG., Illus.). 280p. pap. 19.95 *(978-0-8135-4730-5(X))* Rutgers Univ. Pr.
Robertson, William C. Chemistry Basics: Stop Faking It! Finally Understanding Science So You Can Teach It. 2007. (Illus.). 112p. pap. 23.95 *(978-0-87355-239-4(3))* National Science Teachers Assn.
—More Chemistry Basics. 2010. 153p. 24.95 *(978-1-933531-47-2(9))* National Science Teachers Assn.
Schwarcz, Joe. Science, Sense & Nonsense. 2009. (ENG.). 256p. pap. 18.50 *(978-0-385-66604-6(7)*, Anchor Can) Doubleday Canada, Ltd. CAN. Dist: Random Hse., Inc.
—Science, Sense & Nonsense: 61 Nourishing, Healthy, Bunk-Free Commentaries on the Chemistry That Affects Us All. 2011. (ENG.). 256p. pap. 15.00 *(978-0-385-66605-3(5)*, Anchor Can) Doubleday Canada, Ltd. CAN. Dist: Random Hse., Inc.
Thompson, Robert Bruce. Illustrated Guide to Home Chemistry Experiments: All Lab, No Lecture. 2008. (DIY Science Ser.). (ENG., Illus.). 432p. pap. 29.99 *(978-0-596-51492-1(1))* O'Reilly Media, Inc.

CHEMISTRY—PROBLEMS, EXERCISES, ETC.

see also Chemical Engineering—Problems, Exercises, etc.

Atkins, Peter & Jones, Loretta. Chemical Principles. 5th ed. 2009. (ENG.). 1024p. (C). 180.95 *(978-1-4292-1955-6(6))* Freeman, W. H. & Co.
—Chemical Principles: The Quest for Insight. 5th rev. ed. 2010. (ENG.). 755p. (C). pap. 57.95 *(978-1-4292-3135-0(1))* Freeman, W. H. & Co.
Atkins, Peter W. Ism T/A Chemical Principles. 3rd ed. 100p. 36.30 *(978-0-7167-0700-4(4))* Freeman, W. H. & Co.
Atwood, Charles H. Survival Guide for General Chemistry: With Math Review & Proficiency Questions. 2nd rev. ed. 2007. (ENG., Illus.). 216p. (C). per. 40.95 *(978-0-495-38751-0(7))* Brooks/Cole.
Averill & Eldredge. Chemistry Ssm. 2007. (ENG.). 368p. (C). per. 62.60 *(978-0-8053-3813-3(6)*, Prentice Hall) Prentice Hall PTR.
Balsaraf, V. M., et al. Applied Chemistry, 2 vols. 2009. 192p. (C). pap. *(978-81-907770-9-4(2))* I.K. International Publishing House Pvt. Ltd.
BarCharts Inc., Staff. Science Fundamentals. 2009. (ENG.). 4p. 4.95 *(978-1-4232-0869-3(2))* Barcharts, Inc.
—Science Fundamentals 2. 2009. (ENG.). 4p. 4.95 *(978-1-4232-0867-9(6))* Barcharts, Inc.
—Science Fundamentals 3 Physical Science. 2009. (ENG.). 4p. 4.95 *(978-1-4232-0868-6(4))* Barcharts, Inc.
—Science Fundamentals Cells-Plants-Animals, No. 1. 2009. (ENG.). 4p. 4.95 *(978-1-4232-0866-2(8))* Barcharts, Inc.
Boikess, Robert. How to Solve General Chemistry Problems. 8th rev. ed. 2008. (ENG., Illus.). 336p. (C). pap. 50.13 *(978-0-13-154273-0(7)*, Prentice Hall) Prentice Hall PTR.
Burdge, Julia & Overby, Jason. Chemistry: Atoms First. 2011. (ENG.). 880p. (C). pap. 70.67 *(978-0-07-738576-7(4)*, 0077385764, McGraw-Hill Science, Engineering & Mathematics) McGraw-Hill Higher Education.
Chang, Raymond. Loose Leaf Chemistry. 10th ed. 2009. (ENG.). (C). ring bd., ring bd. 161.00 *(978-0-07-736669-8(7)*, 0077366697, McGraw-Hill Science, Engineering & Mathematics) McGraw-Hill Higher Education.
Chang, Raymond & Overby, Jason. Workbook with Solutions to accompany General Chemistry. 6th ed. 2010. (ENG.). 592p. (C). pap. 86.67 *(978-0-07-729611-7(7)*, 0077296117, McGraw-Hill Science, Engineering & Mathematics) McGraw-Hill Higher Education.
Corwin, Charles H. Prentice Hall Laboratory Manual to Introductory Chemistry: Concepts & Connections. 5th ed. 2008. (ENG.). 352p. (C). pap. 95.80 *(978-0-13-604301-0(1)*, Prentice Hall) Prentice Hall PTR.
Cracolice, Mark & Varma-Nelson, Pratibha. Peer-Led Team Learning, General, Organic, & Biological Chemistry. 2nd rev. ed. 2008. 326p. (C). pap. 23.20 *(978-0-13-187672-9(4)*, Prentice Hall) Prentice Hall PTR.
Cram101 Textbook Reviews. Outlines & Highlights for How to Solve General Chemistry Problems by Robert Boikess, Isbn: 9780131542730 0131542737. 2011. 58p. pap. 26.95 ***(978-1-61812-489-0(7))*** Cram101 Inc.
Curran, Greg. Homework Helpers. 2011. E-Book *(978-1-60163-663-8(6))* Career Pr., Inc.
—Homework Helpers: Chemistry. 2nd ed. 2011. (ENG.). 336p. pap. 17.99 *(978-1-60163-163-3(4))* Career Pr., Inc.
Dahm, Donald J. & Nelson, Eric A. Calculations in Chemistry - Modules 1-16. 2011. (C). pap. ***(978-0-9837097-2-5(6))*** ChemReview.
—Calculations in Chemistry - Modules 17-27. 2011. (C). ***(978-0-9837097-0-1(X))*** ChemReview.
—Calculations in Chemistry - Modules 28-39. 2011. 440p. (C). pap. ***(978-0-9823931-9-2(9))*** ChemReview.
—Introduction to Chemistry Calculations. 2011. (C). pap. ***(978-0-9837097-1-8(8))*** ChemReview.
DeWane, Marian. Easy Chemistry Step-by-Step. 2012. (Easy Step-by-Step Ser.). (ENG., Illus.). 224p. (C). pap. 14.00 ***(978-0-07-176788-0(6)***, 0071767886) McGraw-Hill Cos., The.
Driscoll, Jerry & Hubbard, Connie. Student Study Guide & Solution Manual to Introductory Chemistry. rev. ed. 2009. (ENG.). 162p. spiral bd. 57.33 *(978-0-7575-0881-3(2))* Kendall Hunt Publishing Co.
Duffy, Stephen J. & vanLoon, Gary W. Environmental Chemistry: A Global Perspective. 3rd ed. 2010. (ENG., Illus.). 530p. pap. 59.95 *(978-0-19-922886-7(8))* Oxford Univ. Pr., Inc.
Ebbing, Darrell & Gammon, Steven D. General Chemistry. 9th ed. 2010. (ENG.). 1152p. (C). 243.95 *(978-0-538-49752-7(1))* Brooks/Cole.
Fredeen, Donnajean & Fay, Robert C. Student's Study Guide. 5th ed. 2007. (ENG.). 648p. (C). pap. 70.40 *(978-0-13-199348-8(8)*, Prentice Hall) Prentice Hall PTR.
Frost, Laura D., et al. Study Guide with Selected Solutions for General, Organic, & Biological Chemistr: An Integrated Approach. 2010. (ENG.). 360p. (C). pap. 55.47 *(978-0-8053-8186-3(4)*, Prentice Hall) Prentice Hall PTR.
Glinka, Nikolai. Problems in General Chemistry. 2006. 260p. per. 29.50 *(978-1-4102-2589-4(5))* Univ. Pr. of the Pacific.
Goldberg, David. Beginning Chemistry. 3rd ed. 2009. (Schaum's Outline Ser.). (ENG., Illus.). 360p. (C). pap. 18.95 *(978-0-07-163537-0(8)*, 0071635378) McGraw-Hill Cos., The.
Goldberg, David E. Beginning Chemistry. 2nd ed. 2010. (Schaum's Outline Ser.). (ENG., Illus.). 144p. (C). pap. 11.00 *(978-0-07-174588-8(2)*, 0071745882) McGraw-Hill Cos., The.
—3,000 Solved Problems in Chemistry. 2011. (Schaum's Outline Ser.). (ENG.). 624p. (C). pap. 30.00 *(978-0-07-175500-9(4)*, 0071755004) McGraw-Hill Cos., The.
Harriss, Frank. OCR A2 Chemistry. 2009. 96p. pap., stu. ed. 22.50 *(978-0-340-94824-8(8))* Hodder Education GBR. Dist: Trans-Atlantic Pubns., Inc.
Henrickson, Charles. CliffsNotes Chemistry Practice, Pack. 2010. (ENG.). 360p. pap., wbk. ed. 18.99 *(978-0-470-49595-7(2)*, Cliff Notes) Wiley, John & Sons, Inc.
Hill, Graham & Heslop, Nigel. Aqa GCSE Chemistry. 2011. 310p. pap., stu. ed. 56.00 *(978-1-4441-2079-0(4))* Hodder Education GBR. Dist: Trans-Atlantic Pubns., Inc.
—AQA GCSE Science Chemistry Student's Book. 2007. (Illus.). 240p. pap. 47.50 *(978-0-340-92800-4(X)*, Hodder Murray) Hodder Education GBR. Dist: Trans-Atlantic Pubns., Inc.
Housecroft, Catherine & Constable, Edwin. Chemistry: An Introduction to Organic, Inorganic & Physical Chemistry. 4th ed. 2010. (Illus.). 1517p. pap. 122.50 *(978-0-273-73308-9(7)*, Prentice Hall) Pearson Education, Ltd. GBR. Dist: Trans-Atlantic Pubns., Inc.
Jespersen, Neil D., et al. Chemistry: The Molecular Nature of Matter. 6th ed. 2011. (ENG.). (C). 576p. pap., pupil's gde. ed. 62.95 *(978-0-470-57772-1(X))*; 264p. pap. 64.95 *(978-0-470-57773-8(8))* Wiley, John & Sons, Inc. (Wiley).
Johll, Matthew J. Selected Solutions Manual. 3rd ed. 2008. (ENG.). 184p. (C). pap. 83.80 *(978-0-13-601883-4(1)*, Prentice Hall) Prentice Hall PTR.
Kelter, Paul. Study Guide for Zumdahl's Chemical Principles with OWL, Enhanced Edition, 6th. 6th ed. 2010. (ENG.). 464p. (C). pap. 86.95 *(978-1-111-42629-3(5))* Brooks/Cole.
Kenkel, John. Basic Chemistry Concepts & Exercises. 2010. (ENG., Illus.). 468p. pap. 59.95 *(978-1-4398-1337-9(X)*, CRC Press) Taylor & Francis Group GBR. Dist: Taylor & Francis Group.
Kotz, John C., et al. Chemistry & Chemical Reactivity. 7th ed. 2008. (ENG.). 432p. (C). pap. 95.95 *(978-0-495-38707-7(X))* Brooks/Cole.
—Chemistry & Chemical Reactivity, Vol. 2. 7th ed. 2008. (ENG., Illus.). 800p. (C). 179.95 *(978-0-495-38712-1(6))* Brooks/Cole.
Kotz, Ztreichel & Cram101 Textbook Reviews Staff. Chemistry & Chemical Reactivity. 2007. 348p. per. 16.95 *(978-1-4288-3052-3(9))* Cram101 Inc.
Malone, Leo J. Basic Concepts of Chemistry. 9th ed. 2012. (ENG.). 336p. (C). pap., pupil's gde. ed. 69.95 ***(978-1-118-15643-8(9)***, Wiley) Wiley, John & Sons, Inc.
March, Joe & McClure, Craig P. Introductory Chemistry: A Guided Inquiry. 2011. (ENG.). 272p. (C). pap. 42.95 *(978-0-8400-6221-5(4))* Brooks/Cole.
McMurry, John E. & Fay, Robert C. Chemistry with Masteringchemistry with Student Solutions. 6th ed. 2011. (ENG.). (C). pap. 271.80 ***(978-0-321-78844-3(3)***, Prentice Hall) Prentice Hall PTR.
McQuarrie, Donald A., et al. General Chemistry. 4th rev. ed. 2011. 1116p. (C). pap. 98.50 *(978-1-891389-60-3(2))* Univ. Science Bks.
Moog, Richard S. & Farrell, John J. Chemistry: A Guided Inquiry. 5th ed. 2011. (ENG., Illus.). 408p. (C). pap. 74.95 *(978-0-470-64790-5(6)*, Wiley) Wiley, John & Sons, Inc.
Moore, John W., et al. Chemistry: The Molecular Science. 4th ed. 2010. (ENG.). 272p. (C). pap., pupil's gde. ed. 96.95 *(978-1-4390-4964-8(5))* Brooks/Cole.
Moran, Michael J., et al. Chemistry & Chemical Reactivity - Study Guide. 8th ed. 2011. (ENG.). 464p. (C). pap. 87.95 *(978-1-111-42699-6(6))* Brooks/Cole.
Older, J. & Smith, M. OCR A2 Chemistry. 2009. (Illus.). 280p. pap. 59.50 *(978-1-84489-435-2(5))* Hodder Education GBR. Dist: Trans-Atlantic Pubns., Inc.
Oriakhi, Christopher. Chemistry in Quantitative Language: Fundamentals of General Chemistry Calculations. 2009. (ENG., Illus.). 432p. 85.00 *(978-0-19-536799-7(5))* Oxford Univ. Pr., Inc.
Pankow, James F. Aquatic Chemistry Concepts. 2nd rev. ed. 2012. (ENG.). 700p. 99.95 *(978-1-4398-5440-2(8)*, CRC Press) Taylor & Francis Group GBR. Dist: Taylor & Francis Group.
Peck, Larry. Student Solutions Manual for Whitten/Davis/Peck/Stanley's Chemistry, 9th. 9th ed. 2009. (ENG.) 448p. (C). pap. 111.95 *(978-0-495-39174-6(3))* Brooks/Cole.
Petrucci, Ralph H., et al. General Chemistry: Principles & Modern Applications. 10th ed. 2010. (ENG.). (C). pap. 74.95 *(978-0-13-504293-9(3))* Pearson Education Canada CAN. Dist: Pearson Education.
—General Chemistry: Principles & Modern Applications. 10th ed. 2010. (ENG.). (C). 1424p. pap. 232.00 *(978-0-13-612149-7(7))*; pap. 60.73 *(978-0-13-504292-2(5))* Prentice Hall PTR. (Prentice Hall).
Pintauer, Tomislav. Student's Resource Manual for Fundamentals of Chemistry: Chemistry 131. rev. ed. 2008. (ENG.). 86p. spiral bd. 51.09 *(978-0-7575-5516-9(0))* Kendall Hunt Publishing Co.
Pota, Gyorgy. Mathematical Problems for Chemistry Students. 2006. (ENG., Illus.). 258p. 235.00 *(978-0-444-52794-3(X))*; pap. 83.95 *(978-0-444-52793-6(1))* Elsevier Science & Technology Bks. (Elsevier Science).
Riedel, Erwin & Janiak, Christoph. Übungsbuch Allgemeine und Anorganische Chemie. 2009.Tr. of Tutorial General & Inorganic Chemistry. (GER., Illus.). X, 266p. (C). pap. *(978-3-11-020687-6(0))* de Gruyter, Walter GmbH & Co. KG.
—Übungsbuch. Allgemeine und Anorganische Chemie: Allgemeine und Anorganische Chemie. 2nd ed. 2011 (De Gruyter Studium Ser.).Tr. of Tutorial

C

General & Inorganic Chemistry. (GER.). 285p. (C). pap. 28.00 (978-3-11-022964-6(1)) De Gruyter, Walter Inc.

Rosenberg, Jerome, et al. College Chemistry. (Schaum's Easy Outlines Ser.). (ENG., Illus.). (C). 2nd ed. 2010. 160p. pap. 11.00 (978-0-07-174587-1(4), 0071745874) 9th ed. 2009. 408p. pap. 18.95 (978-0-07-163530-1(0), 0071635300) McGraw-Hill Cos., The.

Ryan, Lawrie. New Chemistry for You. 2nd rev. ed. 2011. (ENG., Illus.). 400p. pap. 62.50 **(978-1-4085-0921-0(0))** Nelson Thornes Ltd. GBR. Dist: Trans-Atlantic Pubns., Inc.

Sasin, George S., et al. Chemistry Computations & Reactions. pap. 4.95 (978-0-914770-06-0(3)) Littoral Development Co.

Soledad Rodríguez, Beatriz Elena. Solved Problems in Chemistry Volume I. 2010. 131p. pap. 18.49 (978-0-557-76441-9(6)) Lulu Enterprises Inc.

Spencer, James N., et al. Chemistry: Structure & Dynamics. 5th ed. 2011. (ENG.). 160p. (C). pap. 59.95 (978-0-470-58712-6(1), Wiley) Wiley, John & Sons, Inc.

Thrush Shaginaw, Kathy J., et al. Selected Solutions Manual for Chemistry: A Molecular Approach. 2nd ed. 2010. (ENG.). 504p. (C). pap. 72.93 (978-0-321-66754-0(9), Prentice Hall) Prentice Hall PTR.

Timberlake, Karen C. Essential Laboratory Manual for General, Organic & Biological Chemistry. 2nd ed. 2010. (ENG.). 416p. (C). spiral bd. 54.60 (978-0-13-605547-1(8)) Pearson Education Canada CAN. Dist: Pearson Education.

Zumdahl, Steven S. Student Solutions Manual for Zumdahl's Chemical Principles with OWL, Enhanced Edition, 6th. 6th ed. 2010. (ENG.). 432p. (C). pap. 91.95 (978-1-111-42630-9(9)) Brooks/Cole.

Zumdahl, Steven S. & Zumdahl, Susan A. Zumdahl/Zumdahl's Chemistry. 8th ed. 2009. (ENG.). 464p. (C). pap. 94.95 (978-0-547-16856-2(X)) Brooks/Cole.

CHEMISTRY—PROGRAMMED INSTRUCTION

Kelley, Colleen & Weeks, Wendy. Chemistry Case Studies for Allied Health Students. 2nd ed. 2010. (ENG.). 96p. (C). pap. 23.95 (978-0-470-59138-3(2), Wiley) Wiley, John & Sons, Inc.

CHEMISTRY—RESEARCH

Bamfield, Peter. Research & Development in the Chemical & Pharmaceutical Industry. 3rd ed. 2006. (ENG., Illus.). 289p. 130.00 (978-3-527-31775-2(9), Wiley-VCH) Wiley, John & Sons, Inc.

Boehlert, Sherwood L., ed. Green Chemistry Research & Development Act Of 2004: Congressional Report. 2006. (Illus.). 132p. (C). reprint ed. pap. 35.00 (978-1-4223-0644-4(5)) DIANE Publishing Co.

Bunce, Diane M. Investigating Classroom Myths Through Research on Teaching & Learning. 2012. (ACS Symposium Ser.: 1074). (ENG.). 240p. 150.00 **(978-0-8412-2659-3(8))** American Chemical Society.

Bunce, Diane M. & Cole, Renee S., eds. Nuts & Bolts of Chemical Education Research. 2008. (American Chemical Society Publication). (ENG., Illus.). 248p. per. 80.00 (978-0-8412-6958-3(0)) American Chemical Society.

Chemical Sciences Roundtable & National Research Council. Bioinspired Chemistry for Energy: A Workshop Summary to the Chemical Sciences Roundtable. 2008. (ENG.). 68p. pap. 21.00 (978-0-309-11487-5(X)) National Academies Pr.

Chen, Liangbao, et al. Lifetimes of Fluorinated Compounds. 2008. (Illus.). 137p. pap. 39.00 (978-1-60456-206-4(4)) Nova Science Pubs., Inc.

Ghosh, Abhik, ed. Letters to a Young Chemist. 2011. (ENG., Illus.). 320p. pap. 39.95 (978-0-470-39043-6(3), Wiley-Interscience) Wiley, John & Sons, Inc.

Haghi, A. K., ed. Recent Progress in Chemistry & Chemical Engineering Research. 2010. (Chemical Engineering Methods & Technology Ser.). 129.00 (978-1-61728-237-9(5)) Nova Science Pubs., Inc.

Hemmer, Markus C. Expert Systems in Chemistry Research. 2007. (ENG., Illus.). 416p. 157.95 (978-1-4200-5323-4(X), CRC Press) Taylor & Francis Group GBR. Dist: Taylor & Francis Group.

Horvath, I. T., ed. Management of Chemical Research, Development & Innovation. (NATO-4 Science Ser.). 107.00 (978-90-5199-458-2(3)) IOS Pr., Inc.

Hüseynov, Elnur S. & Babayev, Vusal. Chemistry Research, Biographical Sketches, & Research Summaries. 2012. **(978-1-62100-771-5(5))** Nova Science Pubs., Inc.

Macleod, Roy & Johnson, Jeffrey Allan, eds. Frontline & Factory: Comparative Perspectives on the Chemical Industry at War, 1914-1924. 2007. (Archimedes Ser.). (Illus.). xx, 280p. (C). 189.00 (978-1-4020-5489-1(0), 1402054890) Springer.

Mayer, Istvan, et al. Bond Orders & Energy Components: Extracting Chemical Information from Molecular Wave Functions. 2009. (ENG., Illus.). 250p. 129.95 (978-1-4200-9011-6(9)) CRC Pr. LLC.

Mirskiy, Anton G. Thermochemistry & Advances in Chemistry Research. 2009. (Illus.). xi, 342p. pap. 149.00 (978-1-60692-376-4(5)) Nova Science Pubs., Inc.

National Research Council Staff, creator. The Future of U. S. Chemistry Research: Benchmarks & Challenges. 2007. (ENG., Illus.). 160p. per. 47.00 (978-0-309-10533-0(1)) National Academies Pr.

Newmann, Gerald R. & Albertis, Andrew P. Encyclopedia of Chemistry Research. 2011. (Chemistry Research & Applications Ser.). 325.00 **(978-1-61470-104-0(0))** Nova Science Pubs., Inc.

Peters, Thomas. Bioactive Confirmation I, 2 vols. 2007. (Topics in Current Chemistry Ser.). (Illus.). xii, 309p. 319.00 (978-3-540-49077-7(9)) Springer.

Rogers, David N. Nobel Laureate Contributions to 20th Century Chemistry. 2006. (ENG., Illus.). 668p. 160.00 (978-0-85404-356-9(X), 085404356X) Royal Society of Chemistry, The GBR. Dist: Ingram Pub. Services.

Russell, Colin A. From Atoms to Molecules: Studies in the History of Chemistry from the 19th Century. 2010. (Variorum Collected Studies). (Illus.). 342p. 165.00 (978-0-7546-6855-8(X)) Ashgate Publishing Co.

Shakya, Pawan Raj & Shova Tamrakar, Chirika. Alfred Nobel & the Nobel Laureates. 2010. 328p. pap. (978-3-639-25247-7(0)) VDM Verlag Dr. Mueller e.K.

Steinhauser, Thomas, et al. Hundert Jahre an der Schnittstelle von Chemie und Physik: Das Fritz-Haber-Institut der Max-Planck-Gesellschaft zwischen 1911 und 2011. 2011. (GER., Illus.). 340p. 84.00 **(978-3-11-023914-0(0))** De Gruyter, Walter Inc.

Taylor, James C. Advances in Chemistry Research. 2011. (Advances in Chemistry Research Ser.). 89.00 (978-1-61209-089-4(3)); 129.00 (978-1-61761-898-7(5)) Nova Science Pubs., Inc.

Taylor, James C., Jr. Advances in Chemistry Research. 2011. (Advances in Chemistry Research Ser.). 524p. 215.00 (978-1-61324-018-2(X)) Nova Science Pubs., Inc.

Taylor, James C., ed. Advances in Chemistry Research. (Advances in Chemistry Research Ser.). 2012. 305p. 140.00 **(978-1-61470-449-2(X))** 2011. 185.00 (978-1-61324-815-7(6)) Vol. 6. 2010. 129.00 (978-1-61728-982-8(5)) Nova Science Pubs., Inc.

Taylor, James C., ed. Advances in Chemistry Research. Volume 9. 2011. (Advances in Chemistry Research Ser.). 360p. 129.00 (978-1-61209-702-2(2)) Nova Science Pubs., Inc.

CHEMISTRY—STATISTICAL METHODS

Babkin, V., et al, eds. Selected Aspects of Theoretical Physics & Organic Chemistry. 2010. pap. 55.00 (978-1-61728-684-1(2)) Nova Science Pubs., Inc.

Bertrand, Dominique. Chemometrics in Food & Agricultural Sciences. 2007. (ENG., Illus.). 352p. 199.99 (978-1-4051-0868-3(1), Wiley-Blackwell) Wiley, John & Sons, Inc.

Brereton, Richard G. Applied Chemometrics for Scientists. 2007. (ENG., Illus.). 396p. 125.00 (978-0-470-01686-2(8), Wiley) Wiley, John & Sons, Inc.

Charton, Marvin. Modeling Structural Effects on Reactivities, Properties & Bioactivities by Statistical Methods. 2010. (Wiley Series in Chemical, Computational, & Systems Biology Ser.). 450p. 145.00 (978-0-470-48749-5(6), Wiley) Wiley, John & Sons, Inc.

Filzmoser, Peter & Varmuza, Kurt. Introduction to Multivariate Statistical Analysis in Chemometrics. 2009. (ENG., Illus.). 336p. 124.95 (978-1-4200-5947-2(5), CRC Press) Taylor & Francis Group GBR. Dist: Taylor & Francis Group.

Hanrahan, Grady. Environmental Chemometrics Laboratory Manual with CD-ROM. 2008. 72p. 49.95 (978-1-4200-6794-1(X)) CRC Pr. LLC.

Kowalski, B. R., ed. Chemometrics: Mathematics & Statistics in Chemistry. 2010. (NATO Science Series C: (closed) Ser.). 508p. pap. 449.00 (978-90-481-8407-1(X), 904818407X) Springer.

Lesne, Annick & Lagues, Michel, eds. Scale Invariance: From Phase Transitions to Turbulence. 2011. Orig. Title: Invariances D'échelle. (ENG., Illus.). xv, 395p. 99.00 (978-3-642-15122-4(1), 3642151221) Springer.

Otto, Matthias. Chemometrics: Statistics & Computer Application in Analytical Chemistry. 2nd ed. 2007. (ENG., Illus.). 343p. pap. 110.00 (978-3-527-31418-8(0), Wiley-VCH) Wiley, John & Sons, Inc.

CHEMISTRY—STUDY AND TEACHING

Abbas. Lectures in General Chemistry a Summary of Key Concepts for General Chemistry Students. rev. ed. 2011. (ENG.). 116p. pap. 50.00 **(978-0-7575-9497-7(2))** Kendall Hunt Publishing Co.

Acaster, David, et al. Chemistry Options Teacher Materials CD-ROM. 2007. (Cambridge Advanced Sciences Ser.). (ENG.). 160p. tchr. ed. 120.00 incl. cd-rom (978-0-521-68539-9(7)) Cambridge Univ. Pr.

ALEKS Chemistry: 52 Weeks. 2009. (C). pap. (978-0-9818739-5-4(2)) ALEKS Corp.

American Chemical Society Staff. Science in a Technical World, 6 vols. tchr. ed. 60.00 (978-0-7167-3550-2(4)) Freeman, W. H. & Co.

—Science in a Technical World: Teacher's Editions, 6 vols. tchr. ed. 60.00 (978-0-7167-3934-0(8)) Freeman, W. H. & Co.

Asirvatham, Margaret R. Clickers in Action: Increasing Student Participation in General Chemistry. 2009. (ENG.). 256p. (C). pap. 25.00 net. incl. cd-rom (978-0-393-93353-6(9), 93353) Norton, W. W. & Co., Inc.

Banerjee, Anil. Research-Based Resources to Teach Chemistry. 2011. 188p. pap. **(978-3-8443-0564-7(5))** Lambert Academic Publishing.

Barbakam LLC, compiled by. Lab Notebook Top Permanent Bound 50 Page (Copy Page Perforated) 2008. (ENG.). 50p. per. 7.50 (978-0-9785344-3-1(3)) Barbakam.

—Lab Notebook Top Permanent Bound100 Pages (Copy Page Perforated) 2008. (ENG.). 100p. per. 10.50 (978-0-9785344-5-5(X)) Barbakam.

Barke, Hans-Dieter, et al. Essentials of Chemical Education. Gerdau, Hannah, tr. from GER. 2011. (ENG., Illus.). xx, 326p. 99.00 **(978-3-642-21755-5(9)**, 3642217559) Springer.

Barke, Hans-Dieter, et al. Misconceptions in Chemistry: Addressing Perceptions in Chemical Education. 2009. (ENG., Illus.). xi, 294p. 109.00 (978-3-540-70988-6(6), 3540709886) Springer.

Basu-Dutt, Sharmistha, ed. Making Chemistry Relevant: Strategies for Including All Students in a Learner-Sensitive Classroom Environment. 2010. (ENG., Illus.). 289p. 89.95 (978-0-470-27898-7(6), Wiley) Wiley, John & Sons, Inc.

Bautista Amedo, María Mercedes. Nociones esenciales de química para ciencias de la Vida. 2007. 76p. pap. 10.50 (978-1-84753-749-2(9)) Lulu Enterprises Inc.

Bent, Henry A. Molecules & the Chemical Bond. 2011. 404p. pap. 21.14 (978-1-4269-6299-8(1)) Trafford Publishing.

Bishop, Mark. An Introduction to Chemistry - Atoms First. 2009. (Illus.). 812p. (C). 79.95 (978-0-9778105-9-8(3)) Chiral Publishing Co.

Bodner, George M. Theoretical Frameworks for Research in Chemistry/Science Education. 2007. (ENG., Illus.). 312p. (C). per. 35.33 (978-0-13-241036-6(2), Prentice Hall) Prentice Hall PTR.

Bretz, Stacey. Chemistry in the National Science Education Standards: A Reader & Resource Manual for High School Teachers. 2nd ed. 2008. (Illus.). 157p. 24.95 (978-0-8412-6991-0(2)) American Chemical Society.

Bunce, Diane M. Investigating Classroom Myths Through Research on Teaching & Learning. 2012. (ACS Symposium Ser.: 1074). (ENG.). 240p. 150.00 **(978-0-8412-2659-3(8))** American Chemical Society.

Bunce, Diane M. & Cole, Renee S., eds. Nuts & Bolts of Chemical Education Research. 2008. (American Chemical Society Publication). (ENG., Illus.). 248p. per. 80.00 (978-0-8412-6958-3(0)) American Chemical Society.

Buthelezi, Thandi, et al. Chemistry: Matter & Change. 2007. (ENG., Illus.). 1052p. (C). stu. ed. 111.96 (978-0-07-874637-6(X), 007874637X) McGraw-Hill Higher Education.

Carolina Biological Staff, compiled by. Bonding Chemicals. 2009. (Inquiries in Science Chemistry Ser.). (978-1-4350-0390-3(X)); tchr. ed., spiral bd. (978-1-4350-0389-7(6)) Carolina Biological Supply Co.

—Determining Chemical Formulas. 2009. (Inquiries in Science Chemistry Ser.). (978-1-4350-0394-1(2)); tchr. ed., spiral bd. (978-1-4350-0393-4(4)) Carolina Biological Supply Co.

—Discovering Acids & Bases. 2009. (Inquiries in Science Chemistry Ser.). tchr. ed., spiral bd. (978-1-4350-0409-2(4)) Carolina Biological Supply Co.

—Discovering Nucleic Acids. 2009. (Inquiries in Science Biology Ser.). tchr. ed., spiral bd. (978-1-4350-0347-7(0)) Carolina Biological Supply Co.

—Examining Thermochemistry. 2009. (Inquiries in Science Chemistry Ser.). tchr. ed., spiral bd. (978-1-4350-0399-6(3)) Carolina Biological Supply Co.

—Expanding on the Gas Laws. 2009. (Inquiries in Science Chemistry Ser.). tchr. ed., spiral bd. (978-1-4350-0391-0(8)) Carolina Biological Supply Co.

—Exploring the Nitrogen Cycle. 2009. (Inquiries in Science Biology Ser.). tchr. ed., spiral bd. (978-1-4350-0357-6(8)) Carolina Biological Supply Co.

—Finding Solutions. 2009. (Inquiries in Science Chemistry Ser.). tchr. ed., spiral bd. (978-1-4350-0401-6(9)) Carolina Biological Supply Co.

—Interpreting the Periodic Table. 2009. (Inquiries in Science Chemistry Ser.). tchr. ed., spiral bd. (978-1-4350-0387-3(X)) Carolina Biological Supply Co.

—Investigating Reaction Rates. 2009. (Inquiries in Science Chemistry Ser.). tchr. ed., spiral bd. (978-1-4350-0405-4(1)) Carolina Biological Supply Co.

—Modeling Hydrocarbons. 2009. (Inquiries in Science Chemistry Ser.). (978-1-4350-0416-0(7)); tchr. ed., spiral bd. (978-1-4350-0415-3(9)) Carolina Biological Supply Co.

—Observing Colligative Properties. 2009. (Inquiries in Science Chemistry Ser.). (978-1-4350-0404-7(3)); tchr. ed., spiral bd. (978-1-4350-0403-0(5)) Carolina Biological Supply Co.

—Reconstructing Atomic Theory. 2009. (Inquiries in Science Chemistry Ser.). (978-1-4350-0386-6(1)); tchr. ed., spiral bd. (978-1-4350-0385-9(3)) Carolina Biological Supply Co.

—Simulating Nuclear Transformations. 2009. (Inquiries in Science Chemistry Ser.). (978-1-4350-0414-6(0)); tchr. ed., spiral bd. (978-1-4350-0413-9(2)) Carolina Biological Supply Co.

—Understanding Properties of Matter. 2009. (Inquiries in Science Chemistry Ser.). (978-1-4350-0382-8(9)); tchr. ed., spiral bd. (978-1-4350-0381-1(0)) Carolina Biological Supply Co.

Chang, Raymond. Student Study Guide to accompany Chemistry. 10th ed. 2009. (ENG.). 624p. (C). pap. 81.33 (978-0-07-322676-7(9), 0073226769, McGraw-Hill Science, Engineering & Mathematics) McGraw-Hill Higher Education.

—Student's Solutions Manual to accompany Chemistry. 10th ed. 2009. (ENG.). 640p. (C). pap. 88.00 (978-0-07-322674-3(2), 0073226742, McGraw-Hill Science, Engineering & Mathematics) McGraw-Hill Higher Education.

Charles, Henrickson. Cliffsnotes Chemistry Bundle. 2009. pap. 24.99 (978-0-470-44537-2(8), Cliff Notes) Wiley, John & Sons, Inc.

Chatellier, Dana S. Chem 105 Lecture Notes. rev. ed. 2010. (ENG.). 168p. pap. 38.29 (978-0-7575-5177-2(7)) Kendall Hunt Publishing Co.

—Chemistry 102 Lecture Notes. rev. ed. 2010. (ENG.). 128p. pap. 33.74 (978-0-7575-1509-5(6)) Kendall Hunt Publishing Co.

Chemical Sciences Graduate School Finder, 1993-1994. 3rd ed. 702p. 49.95 (978-0-8412-2739-2(X)) American Chemical Society.

Chemical Sciences Roundtable Staff & National Research Council Canada Staff. Strengthening High School Chemistry Education Through Teacher Outreach Programs: A Workshop Summary to the Chemical Sciences Roundtable. 2009. (ENG.). 70p. pap. 21.00 (978-0-309-12859-9(5)) National Academies Pr.

Chemistry, Royal Society of, ed. Chemistry for Non-Specialists: Course Book. 2010. (ENG., Illus.). 262p. (C). pap. 42.00 **(978-1-84973-112-6(8))** Royal Society of Chemistry, The GBR. Dist: Ingram Pub. Services.

Chemistry Theme Set. 2008. (Differentiated Instruction Ser.). (J). (gr. 3-8). 585.00 (978-1-60437-666-1(X)) Benchmark Education Co.

Chen, Loris. Painless Chemistry. 2011. (Painless Ser.). (ENG., Illus.). 264p. pap. 9.99 (978-0-7641-4602-2(5)) Barron's Educational Series, Inc.

Cohen-Schmidt, Clarie. Elementary Chemistry Lecture Guide. rev. ed. 2010. (ENG.). 178p. spiral bd. 31.20 (978-0-7575-5496-4(2)) Kendall Hunt Publishing Co.

Columbia University. Addresses of the Newly-Appointed Professors of Columbia College. 2006. 216p. per. 20.99 (978-1-4255-1826-4(5)) MPublishing.

Copley, Phil, et al. Chemistry Olympiad Support Booklet. 2008. (ENG.). 56p. pap. 11.00 (978-1-84755-866-4(6)) Royal Society of Chemistry, The GBR. Dist: Ingram Pub. Services.

Cram101 Textbook Reviews. Outlines & Highlights for University Chemistry by Brian Laird, Isbn: 9780077221331. 2010. 350p. pap. 40.95 (978-1-61698-585-1(2)) Cram101 Inc.

Dadmun. Instructor's Resource Manual. 51.00 (978-0-7167-3584-7(9)) Freeman, W. H. & Co.

Danili, Eleni. Assessment Formats & Cognitive Styles - Some Factors That Might Affect Pupils' Performance at School Chemistry. 2008. 320p. pap. (978-3-639-06472-8(0)) VDM Verlag Dr. Mueller e.K.

Dobson, Philip. AQA GCSE Chemistry. 2011. (My Revision Notes Ser.). 94p. pap. 19.95 **(978-1-4441-2082-0(4))** Hodder Education GBR. Dist: Trans-Atlantic Pubns., Inc.

Driscoll, Jerry A. Introduction to College Chemistry. rev. ed. 2010. (ENG.). 386p. spiral bd. 69.54 (978-0-7575-1744-0(7)) Kendall Hunt Publishing Co.

Ebbing, Darrell D. General Chemistry. 9th ed. 2008. (ENG.). 576p. (C). pap., pupil's gde. ed. 90.95 (978-0-618-94591-7(1), 1019651) Brooks/Cole.

Ellison, Mark D. & Schoolcraft, Tracy A., eds. Advances in Teaching Physical Chemistry. 2007. (American Chemical Society Publication). (ENG.). 364p. 150.00 (978-0-8412-3998-2(3)) American Chemical Society.

Facer, George. Chemistry. 2nd ed. 2008. (Illus.). 99p. tchr. ed., spiral bd. 159.50 (978-0-340-95762-2(X)) Hodder Education GBR. Dist: Trans-Atlantic Pubns., Inc.

—Edexcel A2 Chemistry. 2nd ed. 2009. (Illus.). 123p. tchr. ed., spiral bd. 159.50 (978-0-340-95763-9(8)) Hodder Education GBR. Dist: Trans-Atlantic Pubns., Inc.

Flener Lovitt, Charity & Kelter, Paul, eds. Chemistry as a Second Language: Chemical Education in a Globalized Society, 1 vol. 2011. (ACS Symposium Ser.). (ENG., Illus.). 200p. 150.00 (978-0-8412-2590-9(7)) American Chemical Society.

Gatlin, Connie. Mystery Science: The Case of the Missing Lunch. 2010. (ENG.). 48p. (gr. 3-4). pap. 14.95 (978-1-59363-419-3(6)) Prufrock Pr.

Gilbert, John K. Multiple Representations in Chemical Education. 2009. (Models & Modeling in Science Education Ser.). (Illus.). x, 367p. 189.00 (978-1-4020-8871-1(X)) Springer.

Gilman, Michelle Rose, et al. AP Chemistry for Dummies. 2008. (ENG., Illus.). 408p. pap. 16.99 (978-0-470-38976-8(1), For Dummies) Wiley, John & Sons, Inc.

Greenberg, Arthur. Chemistry: Decade by Decade. Cannon, William J., ed. 2007. (Twentieth-Century Science Ser.). (Illus.). 496p. (gr. 6-12). 49.50 (978-0-8160-5531-9(9)) Facts On File, Inc.

Greenberg, Barbara R. & Patterson, Dianne. Art in Chemistry, Chemistry in Art, 1 vol. 2nd rev. ed. 2007. (Illus.). 412p. per. 35.00 (978-1-59158-309-7(8), LU3098, Teacher Ideas Pr.) Libraries Unlimited, Inc.

Gupta-Bhowon, Minu, et al, eds. Chemistry Education in the ICT Age. 2009. (ENG.). 460p. 219.00 (978-1-4020-9731-7(X), 140209731X) Springer.

Holt, Rinehart and Winston Staff. Holt Chemistry: Chapter Resources File Introduction Booklet. 4th ed. Date not set. pap. 4.20 (978-0-03-068737-2(3)) Holt McDougal.

—Holt Chemistry: Chapter Resources Package. 4th ed. Date not set. pap. 213.46 (978-0-03-066464-9(0)) Holt McDougal.

Horton, Michael. Take-Home Chemistry: 50 Low-Cost Activities to Extend Classroom Learning. 2011. (Illus.). xxix, 244p. **(978-1-936137-39-8(9))** National Science Teachers Assn.

Jespersen, Neil D., et al. General Chemistry Abridged for the College of St Rose. 6th ed. 2011. 1148p. (C). ring bd. 128.95 **(978-1-118-10149-0(9)**, Wiley) Wiley, John & Sons, Inc.

Jolliff, Tim & Royal Society of Chemistry Staff. Chemistry for the Gifted & Talented. 2007. (ENG., Illus.). 96p. pap. 32.00 **(978-0-85404-288-3(1))** Royal Society of Chemistry, The GBR. Dist: Ingram Pub. Services.

Katz, Nevin. Elements, Compounds, & Mixtures: Middle & High School. 2007. (Dr. Birdley Teaches Science Ser.). (Illus.). 94p. per. 12.99 (978-0-86530-536-6(6)) Incentive Pubns., Inc.

Keller, R W. Chemistry Level I Teacher's Manual. 2nd ed. 2006. (Real Science-4-Kids Ser.). (Illus.). 84p. per. 21.95 (978-0-9749149-8-5(3)) Gravitas Pubns., Inc.

Keller, Rebecca Keller. Real Science-4-Kids Chemistry Level 2 Student Text. 2007. 72.95 (978-0-9765097-5-2(X)) Gravitas Pubns., Inc.

Kinney, Cyndi. Apologia Exploring Creation with Chemistry 2nd Edition Lapbook Journal. 2010. (YA). pap. 64.99 (978-1-61625-152-9(2)); (ENG.). cd-rom 36.99 (978-1-61625-151-2(4)) Knowledge Box Central.

Klein, David R. Organic Chemistry I: Translating the Basic Concepts. 2nd rev. ed. 2007. (ENG., Illus.). 384p. (C). per. 42.95 (978-0-470-12929-6(8), Wiley) Wiley, John & Sons, Inc.

Kobrak, Mark N. Experiments in General Chemistry. 2nd rev. ed. 2011. (ENG.). 258p. spiral bd. 44.24 (978-0-7575-8042-0(4)) Kendall Hunt Publishing Co.

Kouadio, Kay I. General Chemistry II Lecture Templates. 2nd rev. ed. 2008. (ENG.). 316p. pap. 47.53 (978-0-7575-5758-3(9)) Kendall Hunt Publishing Co.

Laird, Brian B. University Chemistry. 2008. (Illus.). xxiii, 893p. (J). (978-0-07-296904-7(0)) McGraw-Hill Cos., The.

Lawrence, Debbie & Lawrence, Richard. Properties of Atoms & Molecules. (God's Design for Life Ser.). (Illus.). 2006. 134p. per. 22.99 *(978-0-9725365-7-8(4))* 3rd ed. 2009. (ENG., 143p. (J). pap. 24.99 *(978-1-60092-163-6(9))* Answers in Genesis Ministries.
—Properties of Matter. (God's Design for Life Ser.). (Illus.). 2006. 134p. per. 22.99 *(978-0-9725365-6-1(6))* 3rd ed. 2009. (ENG., 144p. (J). pap. 24.99 *(978-1-60092-162-9(0))* Answers in Genesis Ministries.
LearningExpress Staff, ed. Chemistry Review in 20 Minutes a Day. 2nd rev. ed. 2011. 176p. pap. 18.00 *(978-1-57685-799-1(9))* LearningExpress, LLC.
March, Joe & McClure, Craig P. Introductory Chemistry: A Guided Inquiry. 2011. (ENG.). 272p. (C). pap. 42.95 *(978-0-8400-6221-5(4))* Brooks/Cole.
Margolin, Michael. Hands-on Science Series ABCs of Chemistry. 2nd rev. ed. 2009. 170p. pap. 25.00 *(978-0-8251-6517-7(2))* Walch Education.
Middlecamp, Catherine & Jorgensen, Andrew D. Sustainability in the Chemistry Curriculum. 2012. (ACS Symposium Ser.: 1087). (ENG.). 240p. 150.00 ***(978-0-8412-2694-4(6))*** American Chemical Society.
Nelson, Eric A. Calculations in Chemistry — Volume 3 — Modules 25-30. 2008. 274p. (C). pap. *(978-0-9771087-9-4(1))* ChemReview
Niaz, Mansoor. Teaching General Chemistry: A History & Philosophy of Science Approach. 2008. (Illus.). 409p. 39.00 *(978-1-60456-105-0(X))* Nova Science Pubs., Inc.
Norris, Roger & Ryan, Lawrie. Cambridge International AS Level & A Level Chemistry Teacher's Resource CD-ROM. 2011. (Cambridge International Examinations Ser.). (ENG.). cd-rom 80.00 *(978-0-521-12662-5(2))* Cambridge Univ. Pr.
Oxford University Press Staff, ed. A2 Chemistry Planning & Resource Pack with Oxbox CD-ROM. 2009. (ENG., Illus.). 304p. (YA). cd-rom 900.00 *(978-0-19-915278-0(0))* Oxford Univ. Pr., Inc.
Panichas, Michael. Learning in the Laboratory. 2009. 284p. pap. *(978-3-639-15101-5(1))* VDM Verlag Dr. Mueller e.K.
Pember, Richard. Friday Afternoon Chemistry, Pack. 2010. (Illus.). 140p. 225.00 *(978-0-340-99180-0(1))* Hodder Education GBR. Dist: Trans-Atlantic Pubns., Inc.
Pienta, Norbert J., et al. Chemists' Guide to Effective Teaching, Vol. 2. 2nd ed. 2008. (Educational Innovation Ser.). (ENG.). 288p. (C). pap. 35.33 *(978-0-321-61195-6(0)*, Prentice Hall) Prentice Hall PTR.
Pintauer, Tomislav. Student's Resource Manual for Fundamentals of Chemistry: Chemistry 131. rev. ed. 2008. (ENG.). 86p. spiral bd. 51.09 *(978-0-7575-5516-9(0))* Kendall Hunt Publishing Co.
Powers, John C. Inventing Chemistry: Herman Boerhaave & the Reform of the Chemical Arts. 2012. (Synthesis Ser.). (ENG., Illus.). 288p. 40.00 ***(978-0-226-67760-6(5))*** Univ. of Chicago Pr.
Reger, Daniel L., et al. Chemistry: Principles & Practice. 3rd ed. 2009. (Available Titles OWL Ser.). (ENG.). 1120p. (C). 263.95 *(978-0-534-42012-3(5))* Brooks/Cole.
Ridlon, Robert W., et al. Christian Kids Explore Chemistry. 2007. (Christian Kids Explore Ser.). (Illus.). 384p. pap. 29.95 *(978-1-892427-18-2(4))* Bright Ideas! Educational Resources.
Roesky, et al. Experiments in Green & Sustainable Chemistry. Roesky, Herbert W. & Kennepohl, Dietmar, eds. 2009. (ENG., Illus.). 307p. 45.00 *(978-3-527-32546-7(8)*, Wiley-VCH) Wiley, John & Sons, Inc.
Rogach, Alexander, Sr., tr. Twenty First Century General Chemistry: Introductory Level Teaching Guide. 2007. 380p. lib. bdg. *(978-0-9664143-1-8(4))* Gankin, Victor Y. Institute of Theoretical Chemistry (ITC).
Royal Society of Chemistry Staff. Innovative Methods of Teaching & Learning Chemistry in Higher Education. Eilks, Ingo & Byers, Bill, eds. 2009. (ENG., Illus.). 267p. (C). pap. 32.00 *(978-1-84755-958-6(1))* Royal Society of Chemistry, The GBR. Dist: Ingram Pub. Services.
Sandall, Barbara R. Chemistry: Physical & Chemical Changes in Matter. 2010. (Expanding Science Skills Ser.). (ENG., Illus.). 80p. (gr. 5). pap. 11.99 *(978-1-58037-522-1(7))* Twain, Mark Media, Inc. Pubs.
Sarquis, Mickey, et al. Chemistry with Charisma. 2010. 254p. pap. 21.95 *(978-1-883822-56-9(4))* Terrific Science Pr.
Scott. The Art of Studying General Chemistry. rev. ed. 2011. (ENG.). 76p. spiral bd. 30.95 ***(978-0-7575-9126-6(4))*** Kendall Hunt Publishing Co.
Seager, Spencer L. & Slabaugh, Michael R. Chemistry for Today. 7th ed. 2010. (ENG.). 432p. (C). pap., stu. ed. 96.95 *(978-0-538-73458-5(2))* Brooks/Cole.
Shwartz, Yael. Chemical Literacy. 2010. 212p. pap. *(978-3-8383-0216-4(8))* Lambert Academic Publishing.
Silberberg, Martin. Chemistry: The Molecular Nature of Matter & Change. 6th ed. 2011. (ENG.). (C). 238.66 *(978-0-07-746844-6(9)*, 0077468449, McGraw-Hill Science, Engineering & Mathematics) McGraw-Hill Higher Education.
—Student Study Guide to accompany Principles of General Chemistry. 2nd ed. 2009. (ENG.). 448p. (C). pap. 68.33 *(978-0-07-336732-3(X)*, 007336732X, McGraw-Hill Science, Engineering & Mathematics) McGraw-Hill Higher Education.
—Student's Solutions Manual to accompany Principles of General Chemistry. 2nd ed. 2009. (ENG., Illus.). 368p. (C). pap. 71.33 *(978-0-07-322664-4(5)*, 0073226645, McGraw-Hill Science, Engineering & Mathematics) McGraw-Hill Higher Education.
Smith, Janice Gorzynski & Berk, Erin Smith. Student Study Guide/Solutions Manual to accompany General, Organic & Biological Chemistry. 2009. (ENG.). 528p. (C). pap. 68.67 *(978-0-07-302658-9(1)*, 0073026581, McGraw-Hill Science, Engineering & Mathematics) McGraw-Hill Higher Education.
Tofan, Daniel C. General Chemistry Workbook. 2010. 500p. pap. 45.00 *(978-0-557-53748-8(7))* Lulu Enterprises Inc.
Walch Publishing Staff. Real-Life Science: Chemistry. 2007. (gr. 9-12). pap., tchr. ed. 21.00 *(978-0-8251-6333-3(1))* Walch Education.
Williams, Robert J. P. & Royal Society of Chemistry Staff. Chemistry School at Oxford: A History from 1600 to 2005. Chapman, Allan & Rowlinson, John S., eds. 2008. (ENG., Illus.). 318p. 118.00 *(978-0-85404-139-8(7))* Royal Society of Chemistry, The GBR. Dist: Ingram Pub. Services.
Wingrave, James A. Chemistry 102 General Chemistry II Lecture Manual, Fall 2006. 2006. (C). spiral bd. *(978-1-60036-012-1(2))* Academx Publishing Services, Inc.
—Chemistry 103 General Chemistry Lecture Manaul: Winer 2007. 2006. (C). spiral bd. *(978-1-60036-078-7(5))* Academx Publishing Services, Inc.
—Chemistry 103E General Chemistry Lecture Manual, Fall 2006. 2006. (C). spiral bd. *(978-1-60036-010-7(6))* Academx Publishing Services, Inc.
—Chemistry 104 General Chemistry II Lecture Manual: Winter 2007. 2007. (C). spiral bd. *(978-1-60036-079-4(3))* Academx Publishing Services, Inc.
Wong, V. Inspirational Chemistry: Resources for Modern Curricula. 2006. (ENG., Illus.). 200p. (C). cd-rom 32.00 *(978-0-85404-399-6(3))* Royal Society of Chemistry, The GBR. Dist: Ingram Pub. Services.
Wynne, Sharon. CSET Earth & Planetary Science 122, 126. 2008. (Xam Cset Ser.). (ENG.). 164p. pap. 64.95 *(978-1-58197-399-0(3))* XAMonline, Inc.
York, Deanna. More Teacher Friendly Chemistry Labs & Activities. 2010. 324p. pap. 43.00 *(978-1-4520-7171-8(3))* AuthorHouse.

CHEMISTRY—TABLES

Bruno, Thomas J. & Svoronos, Paris D. N. Basic Tables for Chemical Analysis. 3rd ed. 2010. (ENG., Illus.). 887p. instr.'s hndbk. ed. 139.95 *(978-1-4200-8042-1(3)*, CRC Press) Taylor & Francis Group GBR. Dist: Taylor & Francis Group.
Handbook of Chemistry & Physics Set, 57 vols. (Illus.). reprint ed. lib. bdg. 7125.00 *(978-0-7222-3061-9(3))* Library Reprints, Inc.
Haynes, William M., ed. CRC Handbook of Chemistry & Physics. 92nd rev. ed. 2011. (ENG., Illus.). 2656p. 149.95 *(978-1-4398-5511-9(0)*, CRC Press) Taylor & Francis Group GBR. Dist: Taylor & Francis Group.
—Crc Handbook of Chemistry & Physics on Dvd Version 2012. 13th rev. ed. 2011. (ENG.). 169.95 *(978-1-4398-7661-9(4)*, CRC Press) Taylor & Francis Group GBR. Dist: Taylor & Francis Group.
Kaye, George William Clarkson & Laby, Thomas Howell. Tables of Physical & Chemical Constants & Some Mathematical Functions. 2008. 162p. 36.95 *(978-1-4366-0409-3(5))*; 3rd ed. (ENG.). 164p. per. 21.95 *(978-0-548-82854-0(7))* Kessinger Publishing, LLC.
Lew, Kristi. Mercury. 2008. (Understanding the Elements of the Periodic Table Ser.). (Illus.). 48p. (YA). (gr. 5-9). lib. bdg. 26.50 *(978-1-4042-1780-5(0))* Rosen Publishing Group, Inc., The.
Materials Science International Services Staff, contrib. by. Selected Systems from Co-Fe-Si to Fe-La-Si. 2008. (Landolt-Börnstein: Numerical Data & Functional Relationships in Science & Technology Ser.). (Illus.). 424p. 7279.00 *(978-3-540-74197-8(6))* Springer.
Sharples, Stephen Paschall. Chemical Tables. 2006. 200p. per. 20.99 *(978-1-4255-1679-6(3))* MPublishing.
Turova, Nataliya. Inorganic Chemistry in Tables. 2011. (ENG., Illus.). iv, 157p. pap. 49.95 *(978-3-642-20486-9(4)*, 3642204864) Springer.
Wichterle, I., et al, contrib. by. Binary Liquid Systems of Nonelectrolytes. 2007. (Landolt-Börnstein: Numerical Data & Functional Relationships in Science & Technology - New Series / Physical Chemistry Ser.). (Illus.). x, 571p. 10000.00 *(978-3-540-49314-3(X)*, 354049314X) Springer.
Yaws, Carl L. Thermophysical Properties of Chemicals & Hydrocarbons. 2008. (ENG., Illus.). 800p. 305.00 *(978-0-8155-1596-8(0))* William Andrew, Inc.

CHEMISTRY—TERMINOLOGY

BarCharts, Inc. Chemistry Terminology. 2011. (ENG.). 6p. 5.95 *(978-1-4232-1637-7(7))* Barcharts, Inc.
Senning, Alexander. Elsevier's Dictionary of Chemoetymology: The Whies & Whences of Chemical Nomenclature & Terminology. 2006. (ENG.). 442p. 160.00 *(978-0-444-52239-9(5)*, Elsevier Science) Elsevier Science & Technology Bks.

CHEMISTRY—VOCATIONAL GUIDANCE

Fetzer, John. Career Management for Chemists: A Guide to Success in a Chemistry Career. 2010. (ENG., Illus.). xi, 266p. pap. 69.95 *(978-3-642-05886-8(8)*, 3642058868) Springer.
Ghosh, Abhik, ed. Letters to a Young Chemist. 2011. (ENG., Illus.). 320p. pap. 39.95 *(978-0-470-39043-6(3)*, Wiley-Interscience) Wiley, John & Sons, Inc.
Slade, Roger. Cambridge Checkpoints VCE Chemistry Unit 3 2008. 2007. (Cambridge Checkpoints Ser.). pap. *(978-0-521-71647-5(0))* Cambridge Univ. Pr.
Strauss, Anselm L., et al. The Professional Scientist a Study of American Chemists. 2011. (ENG.). 296p. pap. 34.95 *(978-1-4128-1858-2(3))* Aldine Transaction.

CHEMISTRY, AGRICULTURAL

see Agricultural Chemistry

CHEMISTRY, ANALYTIC

see also Chromatographic Analysis; Electrolysis; Fluorimetry; Indicators and Test-Papers; Instrumental Analysis; Metallurgical Analysis; Mineralogy, Determinative; Phosphorimetry; Radiochemical Analysis; Separation (Technology); Spectrophotometry; Thermal Analysis; Trace Analysis
also subdivision Analysis under substances or chemicals for works on methods of analyzing these items or analyzing a sample to determine the presence or quantity of these items, and for works presenting the results of analyzing substances not produced naturally, e.g. Gases—Analysis; Rocks—Analysis

ABBE Scientist Research Division Staff. Analysis of Food Containing Chemicals with Index & Medical Analysis of New Clinical & Research Information for All Nations. 2008. (Illus.). 160p. 69.95 *(978-0-7883-4827-3(2))* ABBE Pubs. Assn. of Washington, D.C.
Aery, N. C. & Kshirsagar, Shruti, eds. Manual of Environmental Analysis. 2010. (ENG., Illus.). 300p. 135.95 *(978-1-4200-6915-0(2)*, CRC Press) Taylor & Francis Group GBR. Dist: Taylor & Francis Group.
Ahmadi, Latifeh & G. Marangoni, Alejandro. Physico-Chemical Properties of Non & Interesterified Oil/Fat Ture. 2010. 160p. pap. *(978-3-8383-3414-1(0))* Lambert Academic Publishing.
Ahuja, Satinder. Arsenic Contamination of Groundwater: Mechanism, Analysis, & Remediation. 2008. (ENG., Illus.). 404p. 178.00 *(978-0-470-14447-3(5)*, Wiley-Interscience) Wiley, John & Sons, Inc.
Al-Faiyz, Yasair. Hydroxamic Acid Chemistry. 2009. 216p. pap. *(978-3-639-20719-4(X))* VDM Verlag Dr. Mueller e.K.
Al-Talla, Zeyad & Howard, Maury. Analytical Chemistry. 2nd rev. ed. 2010. (ENG.). 154p. spiral bd. 57.65 *(978-0-7575-6007-1(5))* Kendall Hunt Publishing Co.
Alfassi, Zeev B. Radical Chemistry, 5 Volume Set. 2008. (ENG.). 2470p. 2400.00 *(978-0-470-77950-7(0)*, Wiley) Wiley, John & Sons, Inc.
Ambrose, Stanley H. & Katzenberg, M. Anne, eds. Biogeochemical Approaches to Paleodietary Analysis. 2010. (Advances in Archaeological & Museum Science Ser.). 286p. pap. 189.00 *(978-1-4419-3345-4(X)*, 144193345X) Springer.
Annual Reviews, Inc. Editorial Committee. Annual Review of Analytical Chemistry. 2008. 500p. 246.00 *(978-0-8243-4401-6(4))* Annual Reviews, Inc.
Bakeev, Katherine A., ed. Process Analytical Technology: Spectroscopic Tools & Implementation Strategies for the Chemical & Pharmaceutical Industries. 2nd ed. 2010. (ENG., Illus.). 576p. 200.00 *(978-0-470-72207-7(X)*, Wiley) Wiley, John & Sons, Inc.
Barnard, H. & Eerkens, Jelmer W. Theory & Practice of Archaeological Residue Analysis. 2007. (Bar S Ser.). (ENG., Illus.). 274p. (C). pap. 90.00 *(978-1-4073-0084-9(9))* British Archaeological Reports Ltd. GBR. Dist: Brown, David Bk. Co., The.
Bell, Suzanne. Forensic Chemistry. 2nd rev. ed. 2012. (ENG., Illus.). 648p. (C). 169.93 ***(978-0-321-76575-8(3)***, Prentice Hall) Prentice Hall PTR.
—Solutions Manual for Forensic Chemistry. 2nd ed. 2012. (ENG.). 144p. (C). pap. 68.40 ***(978-0-321-76607-6(5)***, Prentice Hall) Prentice Hall PTR.
Berger, Stefan & Sicker, Dieter. Classics in Spectroscopy: Isolation & Structure Elucidation of Natural Products. 2009. (ENG., Illus.). 659p. 179.00 *(978-3-527-32617-4(0)*, Wiley-VCH) Wiley, John & Sons, Inc.
Bertrand, Dominique. Chemometrics in Food & Agricultural Sciences. 2007. (ENG., Illus.). 352p. 199.99 *(978-1-4051-0868-3(1)*, Wiley-Blackwell) Wiley, John & Sons, Inc.
Boeyens, Jan C. A. & Ogilvie, J. F., eds. Models, Mysteries, & Magic of Molecules. 2010. (ENG., Illus.). xiv, 514p. pap. 219.00 *(978-90-481-7483-6(X)*, 904817483X) Springer.
Bond, A. M. Modern Voltammetric Methods in Analytic Chemistry. Date not set. *(978-0-8247-9443-9(5))* Dekker, Marcel Inc.
Bowman, John Eddowes. An Introduction to Practical Chemistry. 2006. 320p. per. 23.99 *(978-1-4255-3159-1(8))* MPublishing.
Brereton, Richard G., et al. Chemometrics for Pattern Recognition. 2009. (ENG., Illus.). 522p. 145.00 *(978-0-470-98725-4(1)*, Wiley) Wiley, John & Sons, Inc.
Brewster, Nicholas J. Laboratory Analysis Following Homeland Security Events. 2011. (Environmental Science, Engineering & Technology Terrorism, Hot Spots & Conflict-Related Issues Ser.). (Illus.). 218p. 215.00 ***(978-1-61324-692-4(7))*** Nova Science Pubs., Inc.
Brown, Steven D., et al. Comprehensive Chemometrics Set: Chemical & Biochemical Data Analysis, 4 vols. 2009. (ENG., Illus.). 2896p. 1920.00 *(978-0-444-52702-8(8)*, Elsevier Science) Elsevier Science & Technology Bks.
Bruno, Thomas J. & Svoronos, Paris D. N. Basic Tables for Chemical Analysis. 3rd ed. 2010. (ENG., Illus.). 887p. instr.'s hndbk. ed. 139.95 *(978-1-4200-8042-1(3)*, CRC Press) Taylor & Francis Group GBR. Dist: Taylor & Francis Group.
Burgot, Jean-Louis. Ionic Equilibria in Analytical Chemistry. 2012. Orig. Title: Chimie analytique et équilibres ioniques. (ENG., Illus.). xxiv, 770p. 229.00 *(978-1-4419-8381-7(3)*, 1441983813) Springer.
Capelo-Martínez, José-Luis, ed. Ultrasound in Chemistry: Analytical Applications. 2009. (ENG., Illus.). 171p. 225.00 *(978-3-527-31934-3(4)*, Wiley-VCH) Wiley, John & Sons, Inc.
Capote, F. Priego & Luque de Castro, M. D. Analytical Applications of Ultrasound. 2007. (Techniques & Instrumentation in Analytical Chemistry Ser.: 26). (ENG., Illus.). 350p. 250.00 *(978-0-444-52825-4(3)*, Elsevier Science) Elsevier Science & Technology Bks.
Cecchi, Teresa. Ion-Pair Chromatography & Related Techniques. 2009. (Analytical Chemistry Ser.). (ENG., Illus.). 215p. 133.95 *(978-1-4398-0096-6(0)*, CRC Press) Taylor & Francis Group GBR. Dist: Taylor & Francis Group.
Chan, Kim Seng & Tan, Jeanne. Understanding Advanced Organic & Analytical Chemistry: The Learner's Approach. 2011. 556p. pap. 34.00 ***(978-981-4374-98-9(9))*** World Scientific Publishing Co., Inc.
Charton, Marvin. Modeling Structural Effects on Reactivities, Properties & Bioactivities by Statistical Methods. 2010. (Wiley Series in Chemical, Computational, & Systems Biology Ser.). 450p. 145.00 *(978-0-470-48749-5(6)*, Wiley) Wiley, John & Sons, Inc.
Chateigner, Daniel. Combined Analysis. 2010. (Iste Ser.: 478). (ENG., Illus.). 496p. 205.00 *(978-1-84821-198-8(8)*, Wiley-ISTE) Wiley, John & Sons, Inc.
Ciborowski, Pawel, et al, eds. Proteomic Profiling & Analytical Chemistry: The Crossroads. 2012. (ENG.). 350p. 199.95 ***(978-0-444-59378-8(0))*** Elsevier Science & Technology Bks.
Claridge, T. D. W. High-Resolution NMR Techniques in Organic Chemistry. 2nd ed. 2008. (Tetrahedron Organic Chemistry Ser.: 27). (ENG., Illus.). 398p. 215.00 *(978-0-08-054628-5(5)*, Elsevier Science) Elsevier Science & Technology Bks.
Compton, Richard G. & Banks, Craig E. Understanding Voltammetry. 2007. (Illus.). 371p. 111.00 *(978-981-270-625-6(9))* World Scientific Publishing Co., Inc.
Cooks, R. Graham & Yeung, Edward S., eds. Annual Review of Analytical Chemistry. 2011. 478p. pap. 91.00 ***(978-0-8243-4404-7(9))*** Annual Reviews, Inc.
Cram101 Textbook Reviews. Outlines & Highlights for Fundamentals of Analytical Chemistry by Daniel C Harris, Isbn: 9780030355233. 2010. 208p. pap. 30.95 *(978-1-61654-770-7(7))* Cram101 Inc.
Cram101 Textbook Reviews Staff. Outlines & Highlights for Fundamentals of Analytical Chemistry by Daniel C Harris, Isbn: 9780030355233. 2009. 132p. pap. 30.95 *(978-1-4288-8481-6(5))* Cram101 Inc.
Danzer, Klaus. Analytical Chemistry: Theoretical & Metrological Fundamentals. (ENG., Illus.). xxxii, 315p. 2010. pap. 129.00 *(978-3-642-07152-2(X)*, 364207152X) 2006. 129.00 *(978-3-540-35988-3(5)*, 3540359885) Springer.
De Bièvre, Paul & Günzler, Helmut, eds. Validation in Chemical Measurement. 2010. x, 167p. pap. 219.00 *(978-3-642-05867-7(1)*, 3642058671) Springer.
de la Guardia, Miguel & Garrigues, Salvador. Handbook of Green Analytical Chemistry. 2012. (ENG.). 566p. 180.00 ***(978-0-470-97201-4(7)***, Wiley) Wiley, John & Sons, Inc.
Dean, John R. Extraction Techniques in Analytical Sciences. 2010. (Analytical Techniques in the Sciences (AnTs) * Ser.). (ENG., Illus.). 308p. pap. 80.00 *(978-0-470-77284-3(0))*; 200.00 *(978-0-470-77285-0(9))* Wiley, John & Sons, Inc. (Wiley).
Ellis, Andrew M. & Monks, Paul S. Proton Transfer Reaction Mass Spectrometry & Related Techniques. 2013. (ENG.). 328p. 160.00 *(978-1-4051-7668-2(7)*, Wiley) Wiley, John & Sons, Inc.
Ellison, L. R. Stephen & Farrant, Trevor J. Practical Statistics for the Analytical Scientist: A Bench Guide. 2nd rev. ed. 2009. (ENG., Illus.). 282p. pap. 48.00 ***(978-0-85404-131-2(1))*** Royal Society of Chemistry, The GBR. Dist: Ingram Pub. Services.
Forensic Applications of High Performance Liquid Chromatography. 2011. (C). 59.95 ***(978-1-4200-9192-2(1)***, CRC Press) Taylor & Francis Group GBR. Dist: Taylor & Francis Group.
Fritzsche, Wolfgang & Popp, Jürgen, eds. Optical Nano- & Microsystems for Bioanalytics. 2012. (Springer Series on Chemical Sensors & Biosensors Ser.: 10). (ENG., Illus.). xii, 329p. 409.00 ***(978-3-642-25497-0(7)***, 3642254977) Springer.
Fuhrhop, Jürgen-Hinrich & Wang, Tianyu. Metallic & Molecular Interactions in Nanometer Layers, Pores & Particles: New Findings at the Yoctolitre Level. 2009. (RSC Nanoscience & Nanotechnology Ser.). (ENG., Illus.). 422p. 224.00 *(978-0-85404-166-4(4))* Royal Society of Chemistry, The GBR. Dist: Ingram Pub. Services.
Funk, Werner, et al. Quality Assurance in Analytical Chemistry: Applications in Environmental, Food & Materials Analysis, Biotechnology, & Medical Engineering. Iannelli, Eric & Iannelli, Sarah, trs. from GER. 2nd ed. 2007. (ENG., Illus.). 300p. 167.00 *(978-3-527-31114-9(9)*, Wiley-VCH) Wiley, John & Sons, Inc.
Garg, A. N., ed. Essentials of Analytical Chemistry. 2008. 89.95 *(978-1-4200-6941-9(1))* CRC Pr. LLC.
Gault, Victor, et al. Understanding Bioanalytical Chemistry: Principles & Applications. 2009. (ENG., Illus.). 300p. 179.95 *(978-0-470-02906-0(4))*; 304p. pap. 75.00 *(978-0-470-02907-7(2))* Wiley, John & Sons, Inc. (Wiley).
Goswami, Shubhodeep. Chip Electrochromatographic Systems. 2011. 140p. pap. ***(978-3-8433-8095-9(3))*** Lambert Academic Publishing.
Guardia, Miguel de la & Armenta, Sergio. Green Analytical Chemistry: Theory & Practice. 2010. (Comprehensive Analytical Chemistry Ser.: 57). (ENG., Illus.). 268p. 255.00 *(978-0-444-53709-6(0))* Elsevier Science & Technology Bks.
Hage, David S. & Carr, James R. Analytical Chemistry & Quantitative Analysis. 2010. (ENG., Illus.). 720p. (C). 181.13 *(978-0-321-59694-9(3)*, Prentice Hall) Prentice Hall PTR.
Härdle, Wolfgang, et al, eds. Statistical Methods for Biostatistics & Related Fields. 2010. (ENG., Illus.). xvii, 370p. pap. 159.00 *(978-3-642-06921-5(5)*, 3642069215) Springer.
Harris, Daniel C. Exploring Chemical Analysis. 4th rev. ed. 2008. (ENG., Illus.). 640p. (C). pap. 137.95 *(978-1-4292-0147-6(9))* Freeman, W. H. & Co.
Harrison, Roy M. IUPAC Series on Analytical & Physical Chemistry of Environmental Systems, 6 vols., Set. 2008. (ENG.). 3524p. 2500.00 *(978-0-470-77958-3(6)*, Wiley) Wiley, John & Sons, Inc.
Hayashi, Kenta, ed. Electroanalytical Chemistry Research Trends. 2008. (Illus.). xi, 297p. 129.00 *(978-1-60456-278-1(1))* Nova Science Pubs., Inc.
He, Zhongqi. Environmental Chemistry of Animal Manure. 2011. (Environmental Science, Engineering & Technology Ser.). (Illus.). viii, 459p. 195.00 *(978-1-61209-222-5(5))* Nova Science Pubs., Inc.
Helburn, Robin & Vitha, Mark F., eds. Interfaces & Interphases in Analytical Chemistry, 1 vol. 2011. (ACS Symposium Ser.). (ENG., Illus.). 298p. 150.00 *(978-0-8412-2604-3(0))* American Chemical Society.

C

Higson, Séamus & Davis, Frank. Macrocycles: Construction, Chemistry & Nanotechnology Applications. 2011. (ENG., Illus.). 608p. 180.00 *(978-0-470-71462-1(X))*; pap. 70.00 *(978-0-470-71463-8(8))* Wiley, John & Sons, Inc. (Wiley).

Huber, Ludwig. Validation & Qualification in Analytical Laboratories. 2nd rev. ed. 2007. (ENG., Illus.). 288p. 250.00 *(978-0-8493-8267-3(X)*, Informa Healthcare) Taylor & Francis Group GBR. Dist: Taylor & Francis Group.

Introduction to Analytical Chemistry, 2 vols. (Illus.). tchr. ed. 995.00 *(978-0-87683-339-1(3))*; tchr. ed. 1600.00 *(978-0-87683-335-3(0))*; ring bd. 275.00 *(978-0-87683-336-0(9))*; 395.00 *(978-0-87683-341-4(5))*; trans. 175.00 *(978-0-87683-340-7(7))* GP Courseware.

Iwunze, Maurice. Equilibrium Concept in Analytical Chemistry. 2009. 300p. 25.99 *(978-1-4389-5456-1(5))*; pap. 15.49 *(978-1-4389-5455-4(7))* AuthorHouse.

Jin, Chunguang. Chemometrics & Microanalytical Instrumentation. 2010. 252p. pap. *(978-3-8383-8113-8(0))* Lambert Academic Publishing.

Kahn, Bernd, ed. Radioanalytical Chemistry. 2006. (ENG., Illus.). iv, 600p. 99.00 *(978-0-387-34122-4(6)*, 0387341226) Springer.

Kandasamy, Nagarajan, et al. Trends in Hyphenated Analytical Techniques. 2011. 60p. pap. ***(978-3-8443-9542-6(3))*** Lambert Academic Publishing.

Khandal, Rakesh Kumar & Aggarwal, Manjeet. Determining Residual Levels of Toxic Compounds in Complex Matrices. 2010. 280p. pap. *(978-3-8383-3874-3(X))* Lambert Academic Publishing.

Koel, Mihkel, ed. Ionic Liquids in Chemical Analysis. 2008. (Analytical Chemistry Ser.). (ENG., Illus.). 448p. 162.95 *(978-1-4200-4646-5(2)*, CRC Press) Taylor & Francis Group GBR. Dist: Taylor & Francis Group.

Koel, Mihkel & Kaljurand, Mikhkel Rikhovich. Green Analytical Chemistry. 2010. (ENG., Illus.). 332p. (C). 80.00 ***(978-1-84755-872-5(0))*** Royal Society of Chemistry, The GBR. Dist: Ingram Pub. Services.

Kokosa, John M., et al. Solvent Microextraction: Theory & Practice. 2009. (ENG., Illus.). 323p. 128.00 *(978-0-470-27859-8(5)*, Wiley) Wiley, John & Sons, Inc.

Konieczka, Piotr & Namiesnik, Jacek, eds. Quality Assurance & Quality Control in the Analytical Chemical Laboratory: A Practical Approach. 2009. (Analytical Chemistry Ser.). (ENG., Illus.). 232p. 133.95 *(978-1-4200-8270-8(1)*, CRC Press) Taylor & Francis Group GBR. Dist: Taylor & Francis Group.

Kozlov, G. V. & Zaikov, Gennadii Efremovich. Fractal Analysis & Synergetics of Catalysis in Nanosystems. 2008. (Illus.). viii, 163p. 145.00 *(978-1-60456-364-1(8))* Nova Science Pubs., Inc.

Lang, J. K. Handbook on Mass Spectrometry: Instrumentation, Data & Analysis, & Applications. 2009. (Advances in Chemistry Research Ser.). 195.00 *(978-1-60741-580-0(1))* Nova Science Pubs., Inc.

Liu, Brian & Ehrlich, Joshua R., eds. Tissue Proteomics: Pathways, Biomarkers, & Drug Discovery. 2010. (Methods in Molecular Biology Ser.). (Illus.). x, 226p. pap. 109.00 *(978-1-61737-714-3(7)*, 1617377147) Humana Pr.

Lobnik, Aleksandra. Handbook of Optical Chemical Sensors. 2010. 150.00 *(978-0-387-24139-5(6)*, 0387241396) Springer.

Majozi, Thokozani. Batch Chemical Process Integration: Analysis, Synthesis & Optimization. 2009. (ENG., Illus.). xix, 282p. 199.00 *(978-90-481-2587-6(1)*, 9048125871) Springer.

Malainey, Mary E. A Consumer's Guide to Archaeological Science. 2010. (Manuals in Archaeological Method, Theory & Technique Ser.). (ENG., Illus.). xx, 600p. 169.00 *(978-1-4419-5703-0(0)*, 1441957030) Springer.

Malainey, Mary E. A Consumer's Guide to Archaeological Science: Analytical Techniques. 2012. (Manuals in Archaeological Method, Theory & Technique Ser.). (ENG., Illus.). 624p. pap. 59.95 ***(978-1-4614-3301-9(0)*,** 1461433010) Springer.

Marsden, Jerrold E. & Hoffman, Michael J. Elementary Classical Analysis. 3rd ed. 2014. (ENG., Illus.). 600p. (C). 128.95 *(978-0-7167-2886-3(9))* Worth Pubs., Inc.

Martinón-Torres, Marcos & Rehren, Thilo, eds. Archaeology, History & Science: Integrating Approaches to Ancient Materials. 2008. (Univ Col London Inst Arch Pub Ser.). (ENG., Illus.). 218p. 94.00 *(978-1-59874-340-1(6))* Left Coast Pr., Inc.

Mekuria Getachew, Yared & Abdel Maaboud Ismail Mohammed, Prof. Chemometrics Assisted Spectrophotometric Method. 2011. 80p. pap. ***(978-3-8443-1874-6(7))*** Lambert Academic Publishing.

Meyers, Robert A. Encyclopedia of Analytical Chemistry, 18 vols., Set. 2011. (ENG.). 16504p. 13500.00 *(978-1-119-99120-5(X)*, Wiley) Wiley, John & Sons, Inc.

Meyers, Robert A., ed. Encyclopedia of Analytical Chemistry: Applications, Theory & Instrumentation, 3 vols. 2011. (ENG., Illus.). 2188p. 890.00 *(978-0-470-97333-2(1)*, Wiley) Wiley, John & Sons, Inc.

Mieusset, Jean-Luc & Brinker, Udo H., eds. Molecular Encapsulation: Organic Reactions in Constrained Systems. 2010. (ENG., Illus.). 520p. 190.00 *(978-0-470-99807-6(5)*, Wiley) Wiley, John & Sons, Inc.

Miller, James & Miller, Jane C. Statistics & Chemometrics for Analytical Chemistry. 6th ed. 2010. (ENG., Illus.). 296p. pap. 97.50 *(978-0-273-73042-2(8)*, Prentice Hall) Pearson Education, Ltd. GBR. Dist: Trans-Atlantic Pubns., Inc.

Mittal, K. L., ed. Silanes & Other Coupling Agents, Vol. 4. 2007. (ENG.). 420p. 286.00 *(978-90-6764-452-5(8)*, CRC Press) Taylor & Francis Group GBR. Dist: Taylor & Francis Group.

Nedelkov, Dobrin & Nelson, Randall W., eds. New & Emerging Proteomic Techniques. 2010. (Methods in Molecular Biology Ser.). (Illus.). 248p. pap. 139.00 *(978-1-61737-615-3(9)*, 1617376159) Humana Pr.

Odegaard, Nancy, et al. Material Characterization Tests for Objects of Art. 2nd ed. 2007. (ENG., Illus.). 230p. 85.00 *(978-1-904982-09-8(3))* Archetype Pubns. GBR. Dist: National Bk. Network.

Oladepo, Sulayman. Characterization of Surface-Bound Molecular Architectures - Properties & Applications As Components of Nanodevices in a High Technology Industry. 2008. 160p. pap. *(978-3-639-06352-3(X))* VDM Verlag Dr. Mueller e.K.

Otto, Matthias. Chemometrics: Statistics & Computer Application in Analytical Chemistry. 2nd ed. 2007. (ENG., Illus.). 343p. pap. 110.00 *(978-3-527-31418-8(0)*, Wiley-VCH) Wiley, John & Sons, Inc.

Pajot, Bernard & Clerjaud, Bernard. Semiconducting & Insulating Crystals: Optical Absorption of Impurities & Defects. 2010. (Springer Series in Solid-State Sciences Ser.). (ENG., Illus.). xix, 474p. 229.00 *(978-3-540-95955-7(6)*, 3540959556) Springer.

Paquette, Leo A., et al. Handbook of Reagents for Organic Synthesis Set: Chiral Reagents for Asymmetric Synthesis, 4 vols. 2007. (ENG.). 2184p. 585.00 *(978-0-470-06652-2(0)*, Wiley) Wiley, John & Sons, Inc.

Park, Geriann P. & Crull, Anna W. Supercritical Fluids: Their Time Has Come. (Business Opportunity Report Ser.: Vol. 183). (Illus.). xvii, 179p. *(978-1-56965-030-1(6))* BCC Research.

Pavan, Manuela & Todeschini, Roberto. Scientific Data Ranking Methods: Theory & Applications. 2008. (Data Handling in Science & Technology Ser.: 27). (ENG., Illus.). 224p. 190.00 *(978-0-444-53020-2(7)*, Elsevier Science) Elsevier Science & Technology Bks.

Pawliszyn, Janusz, ed. Comprehensive Sampling & Sample Preparation: Analytical Techniques for Scientists. 2012. (ENG., Illus.). 3200p. 1595.00 ***(978-0-12-381373-2(5)*,** Academic Pr.) Elsevier Science & Technology Bks.

Pollard, Mark, et al. Analytical Chemistry in Archaeology. 2007. (Cambridge Manuals in Archaeology Ser.). (ENG., Illus.). 418p. (C). 124.00 *(978-0-521-65209-4(X))*; per. 57.00 *(978-0-521-65572-9(2))* Cambridge Univ. Pr.

Rankenburg, Ivan. Application of the Difference Map Algorithm to Protein Structure Prediction. 2008. 204p. per. *(978-3-8364-7106-0(X))* VDM Verlag Dr. Mueller e.K.

Roesky, H. W. & Atwood, David A. Group 13 Chemistry II: Biological Aspects of Aluminum. 2010. (Structure & Bonding Ser.). (Illus.). x, 200p. pap. 239.00 *(978-3-642-07854-5(0)*, 3642078540) Springer.

Ropero-Miller, Jeri D., et al. Handbook of Workplace Drug Testing. 2nd ed. 2008. *(978-1-59425-090-3(1))* American Assn. for Clinical Chemistry, Inc.

Rouessac, Francis & Rouessac, Annick. Chemical Analysis: Modern Instrumentation Methods & Techniques. Rouessac, Francis & Rouessac, Annick, trs. from FRE. Brooks, Steve, tr. from FRE. 2nd rev. ed. 2007. (ENG., Illus.). 600p. 210.00 *(978-0-470-85902-5(4))*; per. 70.00 *(978-0-470-85903-2(2))* Wiley, John & Sons, Inc. (Wiley).

Routledge, Chapman, Hall Inc. Staff. Applications of Super Critical Fluids in Industrial Analysis. (Illus.). 240p. *(978-0-7514-0057-1(2))* Blackie Academic & Professional.

Royal Society of Chemistry Staff. Challenges in Green Analytical Chemistry. de la Guardia, Miguel & Garrigues, Salvador, eds. 2011. (RSC Green Chemistry Ser.). (ENG., Illus.). 330p. (C). 195.00 ***(978-1-84973-132-4(2))*** Royal Society of Chemistry, The GBR. Dist: Ingram Pub. Services.

—Combining & Reporting Analytical Results. Belli, Maria et al, eds. 2006. (Special Publication). (ENG., Illus.). 394p. 160.00 ***(978-0-85404-848-9(0))*** Royal Society of Chemistry, The GBR. Dist: Ingram Pub. Services.

—Nanoporous Gold: From an Ancient Technology to a High-Tech Material. Biener, Jürgen et al, eds. 2012. (ENG., Illus.). 264p. 216.00 ***(978-1-84973-374-8(0))*** Royal Society of Chemistry, The GBR. Dist: Ingram Pub. Services.

Rudroff, Florian. Enzymatic Baeyer-Villiger Oxidation for Natural Product Synthesis. 2008. 200p. pap. *(978-3-639-02093-9(6))* VDM Verlag Dr. Mueller e.K.

Rurack, Knut & Martinez-Manez, Ramon, eds. Supramolecular Chemistry of Organic-Inorganic Hybrid Materials. 2010. (ENG., Illus.). 782p. 158.00 *(978-0-470-37621-8(X)*, Wiley) Wiley, John & Sons, Inc.

Senapati, M. Advanced Engineering Chemistry. 2nd ed. 2008. (Illus.). 531p. 95.95 *(978-0-9778582-9-3(4))* Jones & Bartlett Learning, LLC.

Sesták, Jaroslav, et al, eds. Glassy & Amorphous Materials: Thermal analysis, structure & Properties. 2010. (Hot Topics in Thermal Analysis & Calorimetry Ser.). (ENG., Illus.). xvii, 380p. 189.00 *(978-90-481-2881-5(1)*, 9048128811) Springer.

Sigel, Astrid, et al, eds. Interplay between Metal Ions & Nucleic Acids. 2012. (Metal Ions in Life Sciences Ser.). (ENG., Illus.). xxxiii, 353p. 209.00 ***(978-94-007-2171-5(4)*,** 9400721714) Springer.

Sivasankar, B. Instrumental Methods of Analysis. 2012. (ENG., Illus.). 600p. 29.99 ***(978-0-19-807391-8(7))*** Oxford Univ. Pr., Inc.

Sliwa, Wanda & Kozlowski, Cezary. Calixarenes & Resorcinarenes: Synthesis, Properties & Applications. 2009. (ENG., Illus.). 324p. 205.00 *(978-3-527-32263-3(9)*, Wiley-VCH) Wiley, John & Sons, Inc.

Smith, Mike. OCR A2 Chemistry: Rings, Polymers & Analysis. 2009. 96p. pap., stu. ed. 22.50 *(978-0-340-95758-5(1))* Hodder Education GBR. Dist: Trans-Atlantic Pubns., Inc.

Steed, Jonathan W., et al. Core Concepts in Supramolecular Chemistry & Nanochemistry. 2007. (ENG., Illus.). 320p. 169.00 *(978-0-470-85866-0(4)*, Wiley) Wiley, John & Sons, Inc.

Technology Research Editors, ed. Chemical Analysis of Ceramic Materials, 2007 Ed. 2007. pap. 118.50 *(978-1-60030-302-9(1)*, Search-In-Print) CSA Journal Division.

Telepchak, Michael J. Forensic & Clinical Applications of Solid Phase Extraction. 2010. (Forensic Science & Medicine Ser.). 384p. pap. 149.00 *(978-1-61737-114-1(9)*, 1617371149) Humana Pr.

Thiellement, Hervé, ed. Plant Proteomics: Methods & Protocols. 2010. (Methods in Molecular Biology Ser.). (Illus.). 416p. pap. 199.00 *(978-1-61737-686-3(8)*, 1617376868) Humana Pr.

Thijssen, Pierre. State Estimation in Chemometrics: The Kalman Filter & Beyond. 2008. (ENG.). 132p. pap. 85.00 *(978-1-904275-33-6(8))* Woodhead Publishing Ltd. GBR. Dist: Ingram Pub. Services.

Trimm, Harold H., ed. Analytical Chemistry: Methods & Applications. 2011. (Research Progress in Chemistry Ser.). (ENG.). 380p. 99.95 *(978-1-926692-58-6(6))* Apple Academic Pr., Inc. CAN. Dist: Taylor & Francis Group.

Švarc-Gajic, Jaroslava. Samples & Sample Preparation in Analytical Chemistry. 2012. (Chemistry Research & Applications Chemical Engineering Methods & Technology Ser.). 285p. 140.00 ***(978-1-62100-269-7(1))*** Nova Science Pubs., Inc.

Venn, Richard F., ed. Principles & Practice of Bioanalysis. 2nd rev. ed. 2008. (ENG., Illus.). 344p. 99.95 *(978-0-8493-3857-1(3)*, CRC Press) Taylor & Francis Group GBR. Dist: Taylor & Francis Group.

Vetter, Thomas W. & Guthrie, William F. Quantification of Measurement Uncertainty in Analytical Chemistry: Practical Tools & Applications. 2009. (ENG., Illus.). 300p. 139.95 *(978-1-4200-9505-0(6))* CRC Pr. LLC.

Wang, Liya. Analysis of Nmr Chemical Shifts in Peptide & Protein Structure Determination. 2008. 236p. per. *(978-3-8364-5773-6(4))* VDM Verlag Dr. Mueller e.K.

Wankat, Phillip C. Separation Process Engineering. 2nd rev. ed. 2006. (ENG., Illus.). 704p. 144.00 *(978-0-13-084789-8(5))* Prentice Hall PTR.

Wenclawiak, Bernd W., et al, eds. Quality Assurance in Analytical Chemistry: Training & Teaching. 2nd ed. 2010. (ENG., Illus.). xviii, 331p. 99.00 *(978-3-642-13608-5(7)*, 3642136087) Springer.

WFohler, Friedrich. The Analytical Chemist's Assistant: A Manual of Chemical Analysis, Both Qualitative & Quantitative of Natural & Artificial inorganic Compounds, To. 2006. 340p. per. 23.99 *(978-1-4255-3453-0(8))* MPublishing.

Wuerz, Stephen W. Chemistry for EPA Compliance: Reading & Writing EPA Reports. 2010. 350p. 89.95 *(978-0-470-38842-6(0)*, Wiley-Interscience) Wiley, John & Sons, Inc.

Xie, Yan. Chemical Signal Analysis with Fourier Microfluidics. 2009. 176p. pap. *(978-3-639-16082-6(7))* VDM Verlag Dr. Mueller e.K.

CHEMISTRY, ANALYTIC—LABORATORY MANUALS

Abrams, Binyomin. Analytical Chemistry Lab Manual. rev. ed. 2011. (ENG.). 202p. spiral bd. 60.30 *(978-0-7575-8433-6(0))* Kendall Hunt Publishing Co.

—Quantitative Analytical Chemistry Laboratory. rev. ed. 2010. (ENG.). 110p. spiral bd. 38.00 *(978-0-7575-7482-5(3))* Kendall Hunt Publishing Co.

Abrams, Jerry & Abrams, Binyomin. General & Quantitative Analytical Chemistry Laboratory I. rev. ed. 2009. (ENG.). 108p. spiral bd. 67.71 *(978-0-7575-7026-1(7))* Kendall Hunt Publishing Co.

McMahon, Robert J., ed. Avidin-Biotin Interactions: Methods & Applications. 2010. (Methods in Molecular Biology Ser.). (Illus.). xiv, 232p. pap. 119.00 *(978-1-61737-657-3(4)*, 1617376574) Humana Pr.

CHEMISTRY, ANALYTIC—PROBLEMS, EXERCISES, ETC.

Basic Chemistry Concepts & Exercises. 2011. 59.95 ***(978-1-4398-1338-6(8)*,** CRC Press) Taylor & Francis Group GBR. Dist: Taylor & Francis Group.

Harris, Daniel C. Exploring Chemical Analysis. (ENG.). (C). 4th ed. 2008. 200p. pap. 60.95 *(978-1-4292-1004-1(4))* 5th ed. 2012. 640p. pap. 137.95 ***(978-1-4292-7503-3(0))*** Freeman, W. H. & Co.

CHEMISTRY, ANALYTIC—QUALITATIVE

see also Spectrum Analysis

Eliot, Charles William. A Compendious Manual of Qualitative Chemical Analysis by Charles W Eliot-[and] Frank H Storer. 2006. 208p. per. 20.99 *(978-1-4255-1724-3(2))* MPublishing.

Masterton, William L. & Hurley, Cecile N. Chemistry: Principles & Reactions: Study Guide & Workbook. 7th ed. 2011. (ENG.). 432p. (C). spiral bd. 89.95 *(978-1-111-57059-0(0))* Brooks/Cole.

Oncel, Cinar. Chemical Synthesis of Multi Cation Oxide Powders. 2010. 180p. pap. *(978-3-8383-1848-6(X))* Lambert Academic Publishing.

Prichard, Elizabeth & Barwick, Victoria. Quality Assurance in Analytical Chemistry. 2007. (Analytical Techniques in the Sciences (AnTs) * Ser.: 23). (ENG., Illus.). 316p. 179.00 *(978-0-470-01203-1(X))*; per. 79.00 *(978-0-470-01204-8(8))* Wiley, John & Sons, Inc. (Wiley-Interscience).

Sorum, C. H. Introduction to Semimicro Qualitative Analysis. 2007. (ENG.). 212p. per. *(978-1-4067-1917-8(X))* Read Bks.

Wild, F. Characterization of Organic Compounds. 2011. 314p. 50.95 ***(978-1-258-08486-8(4))*** Literary Licensing, LLC.

CHEMISTRY, ANALYTIC—QUANTITATIVE

see also Distillation, Fractional; Electrochemical Analysis; Volumetric Analysis

Abrams, Jerry & Abrams, Binyomin. Intensive General & Quantitative Analytical Chemistry Laboratory I. rev. ed. 2009. (ENG.). 106p. spiral bd. 67.71 *(978-0-7575-7027-8(5))* Kendall Hunt Publishing Co.

Al Kobaisi, Mohammad. Molecularly Imprinted Polymers for Qcm-Based Sensors. 2010. 276p. pap. *(978-3-639-22583-9(X))* VDM Verlag Dr. Mueller e.K.

Baran, Mette. The Impact of Looping in Middle School. 2011. 260p. pap. ***(978-3-8433-9075-0(4))*** Lambert Academic Publishing.

Chen, Tao. Measurement & Assessment of Survey Quality. 2011. 208p. pap. ***(978-3-8443-8461-1(8))*** Lambert Academic Publishing.

Colombo, Simone P. & Rizzo, Christian L. Numerical Simulation Research Progress. 2008. 89.00 *(978-1-60456-783-0(X))* Nova Science Pubs., Inc.

Cram101 Textbook Reviews & Cram101 Textbook Reviews. Outlines & Highlights for Trace Quantitative Analysis by Mass Spectrometry by Cecilia Basic, Isbn: 9780470057711 0470057718. 2011. 140p. pap. 28.95 ***(978-1-61812-057-1(3))*** Cram101 Inc.

De Bièvre, Paul & Günzler, Helmut. Measurement Uncertainty in Chemical Analysis. 2010. xii, 283p. pap. 179.00 *(978-3-642-07884-2(2)*, 3642078842) Springer.

De Bièvre, Paul & Günzler, Helmut, eds. Traceability in Chemical Measurement. 2010. xi, 297p. pap. 249.00 *(978-3-642-07883-5(4)*, 3642078834) Springer.

Draux, Roland & BIJLEVELD, Henny-Annie. Functionalistische Benadering Van de Eenheid Zin. 2011. 92p. pap. ***(978-3-8433-8608-1(0))*** Lambert Academic Publishing.

Duncan, Mark W., et al. The Principles of Quantitative Mass Spectrometry. 2006. (Illus.). ix, 141p. pap. *(978-0-9786058-0-3(2))* Rockpool Productions LLC.

Hage, David S. & Carr, James R. Analytical chemistry pie no us Sale. 2011. (Illus.). 720p. pap. *(978-0-321-70680-5(3))* Prentice Hall PTR.

—Student Solutions Manual for Analytical Chemistry & Quantitative Analysis. 2010. (ENG.). 456p. (C). pap. 73.33 *(978-0-321-70551-8(3)*, Prentice Hall) Prentice Hall PTR.

Hage, David S. & McLaughlin, Charles J. In Class Worksheets & Additional Beyond the Book Assignments for Analytical Chemistry & Quantitative Analysis. 2010. (ENG.). 30p. (C). pap. 25.60 *(978-0-321-75082-2(9)*, Prentice Hall) Prentice Hall PTR.

Harris, Daniel C. Quantitative Chemical Analysis. 8th ed. 2010. (ENG.). 750p. (C). 189.95 *(978-1-4292-1815-3(0))* Freeman, W. H. & Co.

Harris, Daniel C. Quantitative Chemical Analysis Solution Manual. 8th rev. ed. 2010. (ENG.). 335p. (C). pap. 53.95 ***(978-1-4292-3123-7(8))*** Freeman, W. H. & Co.

Jella, Noordin. Mathematical Programming. 2011. 312p. pap. ***(978-3-8443-8432-1(4))*** Lambert Academic Publishing.

Kaastra, Jelle, ed. Clusters of Galaxies: Beyond the Thermal View. 2008. (ENG., Illus.). vi, 418p. 179.00 *(978-0-387-78874-6(3)*, 0387788743) Springer.

Kibreab, Ermias. Spss in Social Science Research. 2011. 128p. pap. ***(978-3-8443-0187-8(9))*** Lambert Academic Publishing.

Lapkin, Alexei & Constable, David, eds. Green Chemistry Metrics: Measuring & Monitoring Sustainable Processes. 2008. (ENG., Illus.). 344p. 140.00 *(978-1-4051-5968-5(5)*, Wiley-Blackwell) Wiley, John & Sons, Inc.

Li, Na, et al. Quantitative Chemical Analysis. 2009. (Illus.). *(978-7-301-15659-9(6))* Beijing University Pr.

Lindsey, Richard R. & Schachter, Barry, eds. How I Became a Quant: Insights from 25 of Wall Street's Elite. 2007. (ENG., Illus.). 386p. 29.95 *(978-0-470-05062-0(4)*, Wiley) Wiley, John & Sons, Inc.

Milman, Boris L. Chemical Identification & its Quality Assurance. 2011. (Illus.). xviii, 281p. 129.00 *(978-3-642-15360-0(7)*, 3642153607) Springer.

Prescott, A. B. (Albert Benjamin). Outlines of Proximate Organic Analysis. 2006. 248p. per. 20.99 *(978-1-4255-2129-5(0))* MPublishing.

Storer, Francis Humphreys. A Cyclopaedia of Quantitative Chemical Analysis by Frank H Storer. 2006. 244p. per. 20.99 *(978-1-4255-2140-0(1))* MPublishing.

Thorpe, T. E. Quantitative Chemical Analysis by T E Thorpe. 2006. 400p. per. 26.99 *(978-1-4255-4291-7(3))* MPublishing.

Wild. Estimation Organic Compounds. 2009. (ENG.). 248p. pap. 53.00 *(978-0-521-11275-8(3))* Cambridge Univ. Pr.

Yang, Yirong. Quantitative Analysis & Improvement of Retinal Image Quality. 2008. 76p. pap. *(978-3-639-05067-7(3))* VDM Verlag Dr. Mueller e.K.

CHEMISTRY, BIOLOGICAL

see Biochemistry

CHEMISTRY, BOTANICAL

see Botanical Chemistry

CHEMISTRY, CLINICAL

see Clinical Chemistry

CHEMISTRY, DIAGNOSTIC

see Clinical Chemistry

CHEMISTRY, DENTAL

see Dental Chemistry

CHEMISTRY, ENVIRONMENTAL

see Environmental Chemistry

CHEMISTRY, FORENSIC

see also Medical Jurisprudence; Poisons

Almirall, Jose R. & Winefordner, James D. Forensic Chemistry. Almirall, Jose R., ed. 2013. (Chemical Analysis: A Series of Monographs on Analytical Chemistry & Its Applications Ser.). (ENG.). 320p. 84.95 *(978-0-471-67533-4(4)*, Wiley-Interscience) Wiley, John & Sons, Inc.

Aspatore, Inc Staff, contrib. by. Understanding DUI Scientific Evidence: Leading Defense Attorneys on Understanding Chemical & Field Sobriety Testing Procedures, Analyzing the Validity of Results, & Developing Trial Strategies. 2nd ed. 2009. (Illus.). 557p. *(978-0-314-90467-6(0))* Aspatore Bks.

Bayne, Shirley & Carlin, Michelle. Forensic Applications of High Performance Liquid Chromatography. 2010. (Analytical Concepts in Forensic Chemistry Ser.). (ENG., Illus.). 272p. (C). pap. 62.95 *(978-1-4200-9191-5(3)*, CRC Press) Taylor & Francis Group GBR. Dist: Taylor & Francis Group.

Bell, Suzanne. Forensic Chemistry. 2nd rev. ed. 2012. (ENG., Illus.). 648p. (C). 169.93 ***(978-0-321-76575-8(3)*,** Prentice Hall) Prentice Hall PTR.

—Solutions Manual for Forensic Chemistry. 2nd ed. 2012. (ENG.). 144p. (C). pap. 68.40 ***(978-0-321-76607-6(5)*,** Prentice Hall) Prentice Hall PTR.

Cliff, John B. & Kreuzer-Martin, Helen, eds. Chemical & Physical Signatures for Microbial Forensics. 2009. (Infectious Disease Ser.). (ENG.). 350p. 139.00 *(978-1-60327-217-9(8))* Humana Pr.

Cobb, Cathy. Crime Scene Chemistry for the Armchair Sleuth. 2007. (ENG., Illus.). 1p. 27.98 *(978-1-59102-505-4(2))* Prometheus Bks., Pubs.

Collins, David. Forensic Chemistry Module. 2006. 32p. (C). pap. 30.95 *(978-0-7593-9085-0(1))* CENGAGE Learning Custom Publishing.

Cram101 Textbook Reviews. Outlines & Highlights for Investigating Chemistry: A Forensic Science Approach by Matthew Johll, ISBN. 2010. 182p. pap. 36.95 *(978-1-61698-577-6(1))* Cram101 Inc.

—Outlines & Highlights for Investigating Chemistry: A Forensic Science Perspective by Matthew Johll, ISBN. 2010. 154p. pap. 35.95 *(978-1-61698-579-0(8))* Cram101 Inc.

Froede, Richard C. & Pitluck, Haskell M. The Scientific Expert in Court: Principles & Guidelines. 2nd ed. 2009. *(978-1-59425-094-1(4))*, American Assn. for Clinical Chemistry, Inc.

Gesser, Hyman Davidson, et al, eds. Forensic Chemistry & the Expert Witness. 2010. (Laws & Legislation Ser.). 89.00 *(978-1-60876-807-3(4))* Nova Science Pubs., Inc.

Goulka, Jeremiah, et al. Toward a Comparison of DNA Profiling & Databases in the United States & England. 2011. 35p. 16.00 *(978-0-8330-5121-9(0))* RAND Corp., The.

Jenkins, Amanda J., ed. Drug Testing in Alternate Biological Specimens. 2010. (Forensic Science & Medicine Ser.). (Illus.). xxi, 186p. pap. 149.00 *(978-1-61737-732-7(5)*, 1617377325) Humana Pr.

Johll & Johll, Matthew E. Investigating Chemistry: A Forensic Science Perspective. 2nd ed. 3910. (Illus.). 485p. *(978-1-4292-2241-9(7))* Freeman, W. H. & Co.

Johll, Matthew. Investigating Chemistry. 2nd ed. 2009. (ENG.). 495p. (C). 77.95 *(978-1-4292-3951-6(4))* Freeman, W. H. & Co.

—Investigating Chemistry: A Forensic Science Perspective. 2nd ed. 2008. (ENG., Illus.). 704p. (C). 134.95 *(978-1-4292-0989-2(5))* Freeman, W. H. & Co.

—Investigating Chemistry: Introductory Chemistry from a Forensic Science Perspective. 3rd ed. 2012. (ENG.). 512p. (C). 134.95 ***(978-1-4292-5522-6(6))*** Freeman, W. H. & Co.

—Investigating Chemistry (High School) 3rd ed. 2012. (ENG.). 490p. 154.95 ***(978-1-4641-0277-6(5))*** Freeman, W. H. & Co.

Johll, Matthew. Lab Manual for Investigating Chemistry. 2nd ed. 2008. (ENG.). 220p. (C). pap. 76.95 *(978-1-4292-2243-3(3))* Freeman, W. H. & Co.

Karch, Steven B., ed. Workplace Drug Testing. 2007. (ENG., Illus.). 208p. 89.95 *(978-1-4200-5448-4(1)*, CRC Press) Taylor & Francis Group GBR. Dist: Taylor & Francis Group.

Khan, Javed, et al. Basic Principles of Forensic Chemistry. 2011. (ENG., Illus.). xxii, 353p. 99.00 *(978-1-934115-06-0(1)*, 193411506*) Springer.

King, Leslie A. Forensic Chemistry of Substance Misuse: A Guide to Drug Control Edition. 2009. (ENG., Illus.). 276p. (C). 80.00 *(978-0-85404-178-7(8))* Royal Society of Chemistry, The GBR. Dist: Ingram Pub. Services.

Kintz, Pascal. Analytical & Practical Aspects of Drug Testing in Hair. 2006. (Forensic Science Ser.). (ENG., Illus.). 382p. 157.95 *(978-0-8493-6450-1(7)*, CRC Press) Taylor & Francis Group GBR. Dist: Taylor & Francis Group.

Koblinsky, Lawrence F. & Levine, Louis, eds. Forensic Chemistry Handbook. 2011. (ENG., Illus.). 560p. 125.00 *(978-0-471-73954-3(5)*, Wiley) Wiley, John & Sons, Inc.

Ludlow, Fitz Hugh. The Hasheesh Eater: Being Passages from the Life of a Pythagorean. Rachman, Stephen, ed. 2006. (Subterranean Lives Ser.). (ENG.). 360p. 68.00 *(978-0-8135-3868-6(8))* Rutgers Univ. Pr.

McCord, Bruce R. & Almirall, Jose R. Forensic Chemistry Laboratory Manual. 2007. (Chemical Analysis: A Series of Monographs on Analytical Chemistry & Its Applications Ser.). 150p. pap. 39.95 *(978-0-471-78244-5(0)*, Wiley-Interscience) Wiley, John & Sons, Inc.

McCubbins, Sara & Codron, Angela. Forensics in Chemistry: The Case of Kirsten K. 2012. ***(978-1-936137-36-7(4))***; E-Book ***(978-1-936959-83-9(6))*** National Science Teachers Assn.

McLaughlin, Eugene D. & Breaux, Levan A. Chemical Mineralogy, Smelting & Metallization. 2009. 370p. 98.00 *(978-1-60692-853-0(3))* Nova Science Pubs., Inc.

Meier-Augenstein, Wolfram. Stable Isotope Forensics: An Introduction to the Forensic Application of Stable Isotope Analysis. 2010. (Developments in Forensic Science Ser.). (ENG., Illus.). 296p. 135.00 *(978-0-470-51705-5(0)*, Wiley) Wiley, John & Sons, Inc.

Meloan, Clifton E., et al. Lab Manual for Criminalistics: An Introduction to Forensic Science. 10th ed. 2010. (ENG.). 352p. (C). pap. 83.60 *(978-0-13-509944-5(7)*, Prentice Hall) Prentice Hall PTR.

Newton, David. Forensic Chemistry. 2008. (New Chemistry Ser.). (Illus.). 208p. (gr. 6-12). pap. 12.95 *(978-0-8160-7800-4(9)*, Checkmark Bks.) Facts On File, Inc.

Petersen, John R. & Mohammad, Amin A., eds. Clinical & Forensic Applications of Capillary Electrophoresis. 2010. (Pathology & Laboratory Medicine Ser.). (Illus.). 456p. pap. 169.00 *(978-1-61737-113-4(0)*, 1617371130) Humana Pr.

Powell, Jason. Investigating Chemistry. 2nd ed. 2008. (ENG.). 75p. (C). pap. 49.95 *(978-1-4292-2242-6(5))* Freeman, W. H. & Co.

Rao, Kalipatnapu N. Forensic Toxicology: Medico-legal Case Studies. 2012. (ENG., Illus.). 289p. 99.95 *(978-1-4398-6681-8(3)*, CRC Press) Taylor & Francis Group GBR. Dist: Taylor & Francis Group.

Rapley, Ralph & Whitehouse, David, eds. Molecular Forensics. 2007. (ENG., Illus.). 258p. 189.95 *(978-0-470-02495-9(X)*, Wiley) Wiley, John & Sons, Inc.

Ropero-Miller, Jeri D., et al. Handbook of Workplace Drug Testing. 2nd ed. 2008. *(978-1-59425-090-3(1))* American Assn. for Clinical Chemistry, Inc.

Saferstein, Richard. Criminalistics: An Introduction to Forensic Science. 10th ed. 2010. (ENG., Illus.). 576p. (C). 153.20 *(978-0-13-504520-6(7)*, Prentice Hall) Prentice Hall PTR.

Telepchak, Michael J. Forensic & Clinical Applications of Solid Phase Extraction. 2010. (Forensic Science & Medicine Ser.). 384p. pap. 149.00 *(978-1-61737-114-1(9)*, 1617371149) Humana Pr.

Telepchak, Michael J., et al. Forensic & Clinical Applications of Solid Phase Extraction. 2nd ed. 2010. (Forensic Science & Medicine Ser.). (ENG.). 500p. 149.00 *(978-1-60327-358-9(1)*, 1603273581) Humana Pr.

Tibbett, Mark & Carter, David O., eds. Soil Analysis in Forensic Taphonomy: Chemical & Biological Effects of Buried Human Remains. 2008. (ENG., Illus.). 352p. 109.95 *(978-1-4200-6991-4(8)*, CRC Press) Taylor & Francis Group GBR. Dist: Taylor & Francis Group.

Weissmann, Elke. The Forensic Sciences of CsI. 2010. 224p. pap. *(978-3-639-26709-9(5))* VDM Verlag Dr. Mueller e.K.

Whitehouse, David, ed. Molecular Forensics. 2007. (ENG., Illus.). 258p. per. 89.95 *(978-0-470-02496-6(8)*, Wiley) Wiley, John & Sons, Inc.

CHEMISTRY, INDUSTRIAL

see Chemical Engineering; Chemistry, Technical

CHEMISTRY, INORGANIC

see also Electric Furnaces; Inorganic Compounds; Metals; Platinum Group also names and classes of inorganic compounds

Acar, Selçuk. Sodium Amide - Sodium Tetrahydridoborate System. 2010. 120p. pap. *(978-3-8383-6496-4(1))* Lambert Academic Publishing.

Alberto, Roger & Metzler-Nolte, Nils, eds. Medicinal Inorganic Chemistry: Concepts, Applications & Perspectives. 2010. 370p. 215.00 *(978-3-527-32266-4(3)*, Wiley-VCH) Wiley, John & Sons Inc.

Amouri, Hanie, et al. Chirality in Transition Metal Chemistry: Molecules, Supramolecular Assemblies & Materials. (Inorganic Chemistry: a Textbook Ser.). (ENG., Illus.). 260p. 2009. pap. 80.00 *(978-0-470-06054-4(9))* 2008. 215.00 *(978-0-470-06053-7(0))* Wiley, John & Sons, Inc. (Wiley).

Bakac, A. Physical Inorganic Chemistry: Principles, Methods, & Models, 2 vols. 2010. (ENG., Illus.). 518p. 160.00 *(978-0-470-22419-9(3)*, Wiley) Wiley, John & Sons, Inc.

—Physical Inorganic Chemistry: Reactions, Processes, & Applications, 2 vols. 2010. (ENG., Illus.). 624p. 160.00 *(978-0-470-22420-5(7)*, Wiley) Wiley, John & Sons, Inc.

Bakac, Andreja, ed. Physical Inorganic Chemistry, 2 vols., Set. 2010. (ENG., Illus.). 1000p. 260.00 *(978-0-470-58022-6(4)*, Wiley) Wiley, John & Sons, Inc.

BarCharts, Inc. Inorganic Chemistry. 2010. (ENG.). 6p. 5.95 *(978-1-4232-1431-1(5))* Barcharts, Inc.

Barker, George Frederick. A Text Book of Elementary Chemistry, Theoretical & Inorganic by George F Barker. 2006. 356p. per. 26.99 *(978-1-4255-3638-1(7))* MPublishing.

Bartecki, Adam, et al. The Color of Metal Compounds. 2nd rev. ed. 2012. (ENG., Illus.). 392p. 149.95 *(978-1-4398-3900-3(X)*, CRC Press) Taylor & Francis Group GBR. Dist: Taylor & Francis Group.

Becker, Johanna Sabine & Becker, Sabine. Inorganic Mass Spectrometry: Principles & Applications. 2008. (ENG., Illus.). 514p. 230.00 *(978-0-470-01200-0(5)*, Wiley-Interscience) Wiley, John & Sons, Inc

Bocarsly, Andrew & Mingos, David Michael P., eds. Fuel Cells & Hydrogen Storage. 2011. (Structure & Bonding Ser.). (ENG., Illus.). xi, 205p. 259.00 ***(978-3-642-21779-1(6)***, 3642217796) Springer.

Bose, Arun C., ed. Inorganic Membranes for Energy & Environmental Applications. 2010. (ENG., Illus.). xiv, 322p. pap. 79.95 *(978-1-4419-2237-3(7)*, 1441922377) Springer.

Bouyou, Pierre-Aymeric, et al. Fate of Silver in an Aquatic System Inhabited by Hediste Diversicolor: Comparative Study Between Ionic Silver & Silver Nanoparticles. 2011. 76p. pap. ***(978-3-639-33804-1(9))*** VDM Verlag Dr. Mueller e.K.

Chio, Chi Hong. Raman Spectroscopy - a Study of Iron Sulfate Minerals. 2009. 136p. pap. *(978-3-639-12449-1(9))* VDM Verlag Dr. Mueller e.K.

Cotton. Basic Inorganic Chemistry Solutions. 3rd ed. (Illus.). 1080p. *(978-0-471-37197-7(1))* Wiley, John & Sons, Inc.

Cram101 Textbook Reviews. Outlines & Highlights for Descriptive Inorganic Chemistry by Geoff Rayner-Canham, Tina Overton, Isbn: 9780716789635. 2010. 244p. pap. 31.95 *(978-1-61698-546-2(1))* Cram101 Inc.

—Outlines & Highlights for Inorganic Chemistry by Catherine Housecroft, Isbn: 9780131755536 0131755536. 2011. 694p. pap. 42.95 ***(978-1-61812-266-7(5))*** Cram101 Inc.

—Outlines & Highlights for Inorganic Chemistry by Duward Shriver. 2011. 386p. pap. 34.95 ***(978-1-61812-355-8(6))*** Cram101 Inc.

Cram101 Textbook Reviews & Cram101 Textbook Reviews. Outlines & Highlights for Inorganic Chemistry by James House, Isbn: 9780123567864. 2011. 446p. pap. 36.95 ***(978-1-61812-041-0(7))*** Cram101 Inc.

Cram101 Textbook Reviews Staff. Outlines & Highlights for Descriptive Inorganic Chemistry by Geoff Rayner-Canham, Tina Overton, Isbn: 9780716789635. 2009. 216p. pap. 30.95 *(978-1-4288-7444-2(5))* Cram101 Inc.

—Outlines & Highlights for Inorganic Chemistry by Gary L Miessler, Isbn: 9780130354716. 2009. 206p. pap. 30.95 *(978-1-4288-9732-8(1))* Cram101 Inc.

—Outlines & Highlights for Inorganic Chemistry by Miessler Isbn: 0131201980. 2007. 280p. pap. 15.95 *(978-1-4288-3074-5(X))* Cram101 Inc.

Daams, J., et al, contrib. by. Crystal Structures of Inorganic Compounds. 2007. (Landolt-Börnstein: Numerical Data & Functional Relationships in Science & Technology Ser.). (Illus.). xiv, 510p. 8489.00 *(978-3-540-25851-3(5))* Springer.

Dalton, John. A New System of Chemical Philosophy Set, 3 vols. reprint ed. lib. bdg. 375.00 *(978-0-7222-3059-6(1))* Library Reprints, Inc.

Darling, Stephen D. Molecular Visions: the Flexible Molecular Model Kit. 2006. (ENG.). (C). 36.20 *(978-0-13-233470-9(4)*, Prentice Hall) Prentice Hall PTR.

Denmark, Scott E. Organic Reactions Vol. 77, Vol. 77a. 2012. (Organic Reactions Ser.: 86). (ENG.). 640p. 149.95 ***(978-1-118-16380-1(X)***, Wiley) Wiley, John & Sons, Inc.

Denniston, Katherine, et al. Loose Leaf General, Organic & Biochemistry. 7th ed. 2010. (ENG.). (C). ring bd. 147.33 *(978-0-07-740174-0(3)*, 0077401743, McGraw-Hill Science, Engineering & Mathematics) McGraw-Hill Higher Education.

Ebsworth, E. A. V., et al, eds. New Pathways in Inorganic Chemistry. 2011. (ENG.). 424p. pap. 50.00 *(978-0-521-27913-0(5))* Cambridge Univ. Pr.

Eliot, Charles William. A Manual of Inorganic Chemistry, Arranged to Facilitate the Experimental Demonstration of the Facts & Principles of the Science by Charles W Eliot. 2006. 684p. per. 36.99 *(978-1-4255-6844-3(0))* MPublishing.

Fackler, John P., Jr. & Falvello, Larry, eds. Techniques in Inorganic Chemistry. 2010. (ENG., Illus.). 219p. 119.95 *(978-1-4398-1514-4(3)*, CRC Press) Taylor & Francis Group GBR. Dist: Taylor & Francis Group.

Fukuda, Yutaka, ed. Inorganic Chromotropism: Basic Concepts & Applications of Colored Materials. (ENG., Illus.). xv, 378p. 2010. pap. 265.00 *(978-3-642-09141-4(5)*, 3642091415) 2007. 265.00 *(978-3-540-72311-0(0)*, 3540723110) Springer.

Glass, Richard S. Sulfur's Role in the Modern World. 2011. 350p. 179.00 *(978-90-481-3837-1(X)*, 904813837X) Springer.

Gütlich, Philipp & Goodwin, Harold A. Spin Crossover in Transition Metal Compounds III. 2010. (Topics in Current Chemistry Ser.). (Illus.). xiv, 268p. pap. 299.00 *(978-3-642-07327-4(1)*, 3642073271) Springer.

Gütlich, Philipp & Goodwin, Harold A., eds. Spin Crossover in Transition Metal Compounds I. 2010. (Topics in Current Chemistry Ser.). (Illus.). xiii, 341p. pap. 379.00 *(978-3-642-07326-7(3)*, 3642073263) Springer.

—Spin Crossover in Transition Metal Compounds II. 2010. (Topics in Current Chemistry Ser.). xiv, 294p. pap. 379.00 *(978-3-642-07328-1(X)*, 364207328X) Springer.

Gutmann, V., ed. Inorganic Solution Chemistry. *(978-965-294-064-3(X))* Freund Publishing Hse., Ltd.

Hirota, E., et al. Inorganic Molecules: (Supplement to II/7, II/15, II/21, II/23, II/25) 2006. (Landolt-Börnstein: Numerical Data & Functional Relationships in Science & Technology Ser.). viii, 169p. 2589.00 *(978-3-540-37250-9(4)*, 3540372504) Springer.

Holliday, Richard & Cortis, Christopher. Gold: Science & Applications. 2009. (ENG., Illus.). 444p. 247.95 *(978-1-4200-6523-7(8)*, CRC Press) Taylor & Francis Group GBR. Dist: Taylor & Francis Group.

House, James E. Inorganic Chemistry. 2008. (ENG., Illus.). 864p. (C). pap. 99.95 *(978-0-12-356786-4(6)*, Academic Pr.) Elsevier Science & Technology Bks.

House, James E. & House, Kathleen A. Descriptive Inorganic Chemistry. 2nd ed. 2010. (ENG., Illus.). 592p. (C). pap. 94.95 *(978-0-12-088755-2(X)*, Academic Pr.) Elsevier Science & Technology Bks.

Housecroft, Catherine E. Inorganic Chemistry. 3rd ed. 2007. (ENG.). 368p. (C). pap. 46.10 *(978-0-13-204849-1(3)*, Prentice Hall) Prentice Hall PTR.

Housecroft, Catherine E. & Sharpe, Alan G. Inorganic Chemistry. 3rd rev. ed. 2007. (ENG., Illus.). 1136p. (C). per. 224.53 *(978-0-13-175553-6(6)*, Prentice Hall) Prentice Hall PTR.

Huheey, James E., et al. Anorganische Chemie: Prinzipien von Struktur und Reaktivität. Steudel, Ralf, ed. 4th ed. 2012. (De Gruyter Studium Ser.).Tr. of Inorganic Chemistry. (GER & ENG., Illus.). 1310p. (C). (gr. 13-16). pap. 112.00 ***(978-3-11-024907-1(3))*** De Gruyter, Walter Inc.

Husain, Ahmad. Physico-Chemical Studies of Metal Complexes with N & S Donor Ligands. 2011. 168p. pap. ***(978-3-8443-1221-8(8))*** Lambert Academic Publishing.

Inorganic Reactions & Methods: Formation of Bonds to Transition & Inner-Transition Metals, 18 vols., Set. Incl. Inorganic Reactions & Methods Pt. 1, Vol. 3: The Formation of Bonds to Halogens. Zuckerman, J. J., ed. 710p. 1989. pap. 250.00 *(978-0-89573-253-8(X))*; Inorganic Reactions & Methods Pt. 1, Vol. 07: The Formation of Bonds to N, P, As, Sb, Bi. Zuckerman, J. J., ed. 385p. 1988. pap. 250.00 *(978-0-89573-257-6(2))*; Inorganic Reactions & Methods Pt. 1, Vol. 9: The Formation of Bonds to C, Si, Ge, Sn, Pb. Hagen, Arnulf P. & Zuckerman, J. J., eds. 604p. 1991. pap. 250.00 *(978-0-89573-259-0(9))*; Inorganic Reactions & Methods Pt. 4, Vol. 12B: The Formation of Bonds to C, Si, Ge, Sn, Pb. Zuckerman, J. J. & Hagen, Arnulf P., eds. 631p. 1990. pap. 250.00 *(978-0-89573-278-1(5))*; Inorganic Reactions & Methods Vol. 1, Pt. 1: The Formation of Bonds to Hydrogen. Zuckerman, J. J., ed. 326p. 1986. pap. 250.00 *(978-0-89573-251-4(3))*; Inorganic Reactions & Methods Vol. 2, Pt. 2: The Formation of Bonds to Hydrogen. Zuckerman, J. J., ed. 476p. 1987. pap. 250.00 *(978-0-89573-252-1(1))*; Inorganic Reactions & Methods Vol. 4, Pt. 2: The Formation of Bonds to Halogens. Zuckerman, J. J. Hagen, Arnulf P., ed. 491p. 1991. pap. 250.00 *(978-0-89573-254-5(8))*; Inorganic Reactions & Methods Vol. 10, Pt. 2: The Formation of Bonds to C, Si, Ge, Sn, Pb. Zuckerman, J. J., ed. 506p. 1989. pap. 250.00 *(978-0-89573-260-6(2))*; Inorganic Reactions & Methods Vol. 13: The Formation of Bonds to B, Al, Ga, In, Tl & to Elements of Groups One & Two. Hagen, Arnulf P. & Zuckerman, J. J., eds. (Illus.). 571p. 1991. pap. 220.00 *(978-0-89573-263-7(7))*; Inorganic Reactions & Methods Vol. 15: Electron-Transfer & Electrochemical Reactions, Photochemical & Other Energized Reactions. Zuckerman, J. J., ed. 423p. 1986. pap. 250.00 *(978-0-89573-265-1(3))*; Inorganic Reactions & Methods Vol. 16: Reactions Catalyzed by Inorganic Compounds. Hagen, Arnulf P. & Zuckerman, J. J., eds. 655p. 1993. pap. 220.00 *(978-0-89573-266-8(1))*; Inorganic Reactions & Methods Vol. 06, Pts. 2: The Formation of Bonds to O, S, Se, Te, Po. Hagen, Arnulf P. & Zuckerman, J. J., eds. 1993. lib. bdg. 250.00 *(978-0-89573-256-9(4))*; Inorganic Reactions & Methods Vols. 08, Pts. 2: The Formation of Bonds to N, P, As, Sb, Bi. Hagen, Arnulf P. & Zuckerman, J. J., eds. (Illus.). 483p. 1994. pap. 250.00 *(978-0-89573-258-3(0))*; Oligomerization & Polymerization Formation of Intercalation Compounds. Zuckerman, J. J. & Hagen, Arnulf P., eds. 431p. 1990. pap. 250.00 *(978-0-89573-267-5(X))*; Vol. 05. Inorganic Reactions & Methods: The Formation of Bonds to O, S, Se, Te, Po (Pt. 1) Zuckerman, J. J. & Hagen, Arnulf P., eds. 567p. 1991. pap. 250.00 *(978-0-89573-255-2(6))*; Vol. 11. Formation of Bonds to C, Si, Ge, Sn, Pb. Zuckerman, J. J., ed. 594p. 1988. pap. 250.00 *(978-0-89573-261-3(0))*; Vol. 12A. Inorganic Reactions & Methods: The Formation of Bonds to C, Si, Ge, Sn, Pb. Hagen, Arnulf P. & Zuckerman, J. J., eds. 453p. 1990. pap. 250.00 *(978-0-89573-262-0(9))*; Vol. 14. Inorganic Reactions & Methods: The Formation of Bonds to Transition Metals, Oxidative Additions & Reductive Eliminations, Insertion Reactions & Their Reverse. Hagen, Arnulf P. & Zuckerman, J. J., eds. 1993. 250.00 *(978-0-89573-264-4(5))*; Vol. 18. Inorganic Reactions & Methods: The Formation of Ceramics. Hagen, Arnulf P. & Zuckerman, J. J., eds. 1993. 220.00 *(978-0-89573-268-2(8))*; 4200.00 *(978-0-89573-250-7(5)*, Wiley-VCH) Wiley, John & Sons, Inc.

Janiak, Christoph, et al. Riedel Moderne Anorganische Chemie. Meyer, Hans-Jürgen, ed. 4th ed. 2012. (De Gruyter Studium Ser.). (GER., Illus.). XI, 916p. (C). (gr. 13-16). pap. 98.00 ***(978-3-11-024900-2(6))*** De Gruyter, Walter Inc.

Kalia, Shashi & Lumba, Kamakshi. Dithiocarbazates & Their Transition Metal Complexes. 2010. 96p. pap. *(978-3-8383-1972-8(9))* Lambert Academic Publishing.

Kaplan. KTPA MCAT Organic Chemistry. 2010. (ENG.). 464p. pap. 45.00 *(978-1-60714-825-8(0))* Kaplan Publishing.

Karlin. Progress in Inorganic Chemistry Bundle. 2008. (Progress in Inorganic Chemistry Ser.). 3932p. 912.00 *(978-0-470-38790-0(4)*, Wiley-Interscience) Wiley, John & Sons, Inc.

Karlin, Kenneth D. Progress in Inorganic Chemistry. (Progress in Inorganic Chemistry Ser.: 55). (ENG., Illus.). Volume 55. 2007. 776p. 233.00 *(978-0-471-68242-4(X))*Volume 56. 2009. 586p. 227.00 *(978-0-470-39547-9(8))* Wiley, John & Sons, Inc. (Wiley-Interscience).

Karlin, Kenneth D., ed. Progress in Inorganic Chemistry, Volume 57. 2011. (Progress in Inorganic Chemistry Ser.: 113). (ENG.). 624p. 149.95 ***(978-1-118-01063-1(9)***, Wiley) Wiley, John & Sons, Inc.

Kaushal, Raj & Sarvjeet Singh. Ed Ligand Zirconium Complexes. 2011. 172p. pap. ***(978-3-8443-0494-7(0))*** Lambert Academic Publishing.

Khalili, Fawwaz & K. Mohammad, Ahmad. Adsorption of Actinides. 2011. 112p. pap. ***(978-3-8443-1058-0(4))*** Lambert Academic Publishing.

Kolev, Tsonko. Quantum Chemical, Spectroscopic & Structural Study of Hydrochlorides, Hydrogens Squarates & Ester Amides of Squaric Acid of Amina. 2008. (Illus.). viii, 95p. pap. 39.00 *(978-1-60456-431-0(8))* Nova Science Pubs., Inc.

Kornshead, W. B. Inorganic Chemistry: For Use in Science Classes & Higher & Middle Schools. by Dr. W. B. Kernshead ... 2006. 192p. per. 18.99 *(978-1-4255-1557-7(6))* MPublishing.

Krivovichev, Sergey, et al, eds. Structural Chemistry of Inorganic Actinide Compounds. 2006. (ENG.). 504p. 260.00 *(978-0-444-52111-8(9))*, Elsevier Science) Elsevier Science & Technology Bks.

Lalena, John N. & Cleary, David A. Principles of Inorganic Materials Design. 2nd ed. 2010. (ENG., Illus.). 585p. 163.00 *(978-0-470-40403-4(5)*, Wiley) Wiley, John & Sons, Inc.

Langová, 'árka. Acid-Base Properties of Oxide Systems in Melts & Aqueous Solutions. 2011. 96p. pap. ***(978-3-8443-1474-8(1))*** Lambert Academic Publishing.

Li, Wai-Kee, et al. Advanced Structural Inorganic Chemistry. 2008. (International Union of Crystallography Texts on Crystallography Ser.). (ENG., Illus.). 848p. 165.00 *(978-0-19-921694-9(0))*; 688p. pap. 85.00 *(978-0-19-921695-6(9))* Oxford Univ. Pr., Inc.

Louie, Steven G. & Cohen, Marvin L. Conceptual Foundations of Materials: A Standard Model for Ground-And Excited-State Properties. 2006. (Contemporary Concepts of Condensed Matter Science Ser.: 2). (ENG., Illus.). 244p. 195.00 *(978-0-444-50976-5(3)*, Elsevier Science) Elsevier Science & Technology Bks.

Lucke-Wold, Brandon. Embarking on New Paths in the World of Metallacarboranes. 2011. 80p. pap. ***(978-3-8454-1210-8(0))*** Lambert Academic Publishing.

Mallayan, Palaniandavar & M. Ruthenium Complexes of Thioether Ligands. 2010. 180p. pap. *(978-3-639-23888-4(5))* VDM Verlag Dr. Mueller e.K.

Matsumoto, Kiyoshi & Hayashi, Naoto. Heterocyclic Supramolecules II. 2009. (Topics in Heterocyclic Chemistry Ser.). (ENG.). ix, 157p. 219.00 *(978-3-642-02040-7(2)*, 3642020402) Springer.

Mellor, Joseph W. A Comprehensive Treatise on Inorganic & Theoretical Chemistry. reprint ed. lib. bdg. 2000.00 *(978-0-7222-3060-2(5))* Library Reprints, Inc.

Meyer, Gerd, et al, eds. Inorganic Chemistry in Focus III. 2006. (ENG., Illus.). 375p. pap. 175.00 *(978-3-527-31510-9(1)*, Wiley-VCH) Wiley, John & Sons, Inc.

Miessler, Gary & Tarr, Donald A. Solution Manual for Inorganic Chemistry. 4th ed. 2010. (ENG.). 176p. (C). pap. 44.27 (978-0-13-612867-0(X), Prentice Hall) Prentice Hall PTR.

Miessler, Gary L. & Tarr, Donald A. Inorganic Chemistry. 4th ed. 2011. (Illus.). 720p. pap. (978-0-13-615383-2(6)) Prentice Hall PTR.

—Inorganic Chemistry. 4th ed. 2010. (ENG., Illus.). 720p. (C). pap. 184.13 (978-0-13-612866-3(1), Prentice Hall) Prentice Hall PTR.

Mingos, David Michael P. Magnetic Functions Beyond the Spin-Hamiltonian. 2010. (Structure & Bonding Ser.). (Illus.). x, 276p. pap. 389.00 (978-3-642-06543-9(0), 3642065430) Springer.

Molloy, Kieran C. Group Theory for Chemists: Fundamental Theory & Applications. 2nd ed. 2011. (Woodhead Publishing in Materials Ser.). (ENG., Illus.). 232p. pap. 60.00 (978-0-85709-240-3(5)) Woodhead Publishing Ltd. GBR. Dist: Ingram Pub. Services.

Morrison, Desiree A., ed. Handbook of Inorganic Chemistry Research. 2010. (Chemistry Research & Applications Ser.). (Illus.). xiii, 446p. 195.00 (978-1-61668-010-7(5)) Nova Science Pubs., Inc.

Müller, Ulrich. Inorganic Structural Chemistry. 2nd rev. ed. 2006. (Inorganic Chemistry: a Textbook Ser.: 22). (ENG., Illus.). 280p. 180.00 (978-0-470-01864-4(X)); per. 65.00 (978-0-470-01865-1(8)) Wiley, John & Sons, Inc. (Wiley).

Muramatsu, Atsushi & Miyashita, Tokuji, eds. Nano-hybridization of Organic-Inorganic Materials. 2009. (Advances in Materials Research Ser.). (ENG., Illus.). xvii, 288p. 199.00 (978-3-540-92232-2(6), 3540922326) Springer.

Nakamoto, Kazuo. Infrared & Raman Spectra of Inorganic & Coordination Compounds Pt. A: Theory & Applications in Inorganic Chemistry, 2 vols. 6th ed. 2009. (ENG., Illus.). 432p. 134.00 (978-0-471-74339-2(9), Wiley-Interscience) Wiley, John & Sons, Inc.

Nielsen, Lauge Fuglsang. Composite Materials: Properties as Influenced by Phase Geometry. 2010. (Illus.). xv, 259p. pap. 135.00 (978-3-642-06367-1(5), 3642063675) Springer.

Paquette, Leo A., et al. Handbook of Reagents for Organic Synthesis Set: Chiral Reagents for Asymmetric Synthesis, 4 vols. 2007. (ENG.). 2184p. 585.00 (978-0-470-06652-2(0), Wiley) Wiley, John & Sons, Inc.

Pellissier, Hélène, ed. Recent Developments in Asymmetric Organocatalysis. 2010. (RSC Catalysis Ser.). (Illus.). 260p. (C). 195.00 **(978-1-84973-054-9(7))** Royal Society of Chemistry, The GBR. Dist: Ingram Pub. Services.

Pulford, Ian & Flowers, Hugh. Environmental Chemistry at a Glance. 2006. (Chemistry at a Glance Ser.). (ENG., Illus.). 144p. per. 41.99 (978-1-4051-3532-0(8), Wiley-Blackwell) Wiley, John & Sons, Inc.

Rayner-Canham, Geoff & Overton, Tina. Descriptive Inorganic Chemistry. 5th ed. 2009. (ENG., Illus.). 650p. (C). 134.95 (978-1-4292-1814-6(2)) Freeman, W. H. & Co.

Reimann, E. & Roy, S. Fortschritte der Chemie Organischer Naturstoffe/Progress in the Chemistry of Organic Natural Products Volume 88. Herz, W. & Falk, H., eds. 2007. (Fortschritte der Chemie organischer Naturstoffe / Progress in the Chemistry of Organic Natural Products Ser.). (Illus.). 212p. 239.00 (978-3-211-20688-1(4), 3211206884) Springer.

Rich, Ronald. Inorganic Reactions in Water. 2010. (ENG., Illus.). xxii, 521p. pap. 279.00 (978-3-642-09324-1(8), 3642093248) Springer.

Rich, Ronald L. Inorganic Reactions in Water. 2008. (ENG., Illus.). xxii, 521p. 279.00 (978-3-540-73961-6(0), 3540739610) Springer.

Riedel, Erwin. Allgemeine und Anorganische Chemie. 9th ed. 2008. (De Gruyter Lehrbuch Ser.).Tr. of General & Inorganic Chemistry. (GER., Illus.). X, 432p. (C). pap. (978-3-11-020277-9(8)) de Gruyter, Walter GmbH & Co. KG.

Riedel, Erwin & Janiak, Christoph. Anorganische Chemie. 7th ed. 2007.Tr. of Inorganic Chemistry. (Illus.). 961p. 98.00 (978-3-11-018903-2(8)) De Gruyter, Walter Inc.

—Anorganische Chemie: Mit DVD. 8th ed. 2011. (De Gruyter Studium Ser.).Tr. of Inorganic Chemistry. (GER., Illus.). 978p. (C). 105.00 (978-3-11-022566-2(2)) De Gruyter, Walter Inc.

Riedel, Erwin & Meyer, Hans-Jargen. Allgemeine und Anorganische Chemie. 10th ed. 2010. (De Gruyter Studium Ser.).Tr. of General & Inorganic Chemistry. (GER., Illus.). X, 452p. (C). pap. 56.00 (978-3-11-022781-9(9)) De Gruyter, Walter Inc.

Rodgers, Glen E. Descriptive in Organic, Coordination, & Solid State Chemistry. 3rd ed. 2011. (ENG.). 656p. (C). 235.95 (978-0-8400-6846-0(8)) Brooks/Cole.

Roesky, H. W. & Atwood, D. A. Group 13 Chemistry I: Fundamental New Developments. 2010. (Structure & Bonding Ser.). x, 171p. pap. 199.00 (978-3-642-07816-3(8), 3642078168) Springer.

—Group 13 Chemistry III: Industrial Applications. 2010. (Structure & Bonding Ser.). (Illus.). x, 207p. pap. 259.00 (978-3-642-07905-4(9), 3642079059) Springer.

Scott, Robert A., ed. Applications of Physical Methods to Inorganic & Bioinorganic Chemistry. 2007. (EIC Bks.: 2). (ENG., Illus.). 594p. 255.00 (978-0-470-03217-6(0), Wiley-Interscience) Wiley, John & Sons, Inc.

Scott, Robert A. & Lukehart, Charles M., eds. Nanomaterials: Inorganic & Bioinorganic Perspectives. 2009. (EIC Bks.). (ENG., Illus.). 856p. 390.00 (978-0-470-51644-7(5), Wiley) Wiley, John & Sons, Inc.

Scrivener, Karen & Young, Francis. Introduction to the Chemistry of Inorganic Cements. 2010. 320p. pap. 59.95 (978-0-415-54801-4(2), Taylor & Francis) Taylor & Francis Group GBR. Dist: Taylor & Francis Group.

Shriver, Duward & Atkins, Peter. Inorganic Chemistry. 5th ed. 2009. (ENG.). 830p. (C). 155.95 (978-1-4292-1820-7(7)) Freeman, W. H. & Co.

Shriver, Duward, et al. Inorganic Chemistry. 4th ed. 2006. (ENG.). 300p. (C). pap. 44.95 (978-0-7167-7053-4(9)) Freeman, W. H. & Co.

Sigel, Astrid, et al, eds. Interplay between Metal Ions & Nucleic Acids. 2012. (Metal Ions in Life Sciences Ser.). (ENG., Illus.). xxxiii, 353p. 209.00 **(978-94-007-2171-5(4)**, 9400721714) Springer.

Smith, Janice Gorzynski. Student Study Guide/Solutions Manual for Principles of General, Organic & Biochemistry. 2011. (ENG.). 384p. (C). pap. 61.67 (978-0-07-738562-0(4), 0077385624, McGraw-Hill Science, Engineering & Mathematics) McGraw-Hill Higher Education.

Solomon, Edward I., et al, eds. Computational Inorganic & Bioinorganic Chemistry. 2009. (EIC Bks.). (ENG., Illus.). 614p. 230.00 (978-0-470-69997-3(3), Wiley) Wiley, John & Sons, Inc.

Tan, Jeanne & Chan, Kim Seng. Understanding Advanced Physical Inorganic Chemistry: The Learner's Approach. 2010. 488p. pap. 28.00 (978-981-4317-26-9(8)) World Scientific Publishing Co., Inc.

Trimm, Harold H., ed. Inorganic Chemistry: Reactions, Structure & Mechanisms. 2011. (Research Progress in Chemistry Ser.). (ENG.). 332p. 99.95 (978-1-926692-59-3(4)) Apple Academic Pr., Inc. CAN. Dist: Taylor & Francis Group.

Turova, Nataliya. Inorganic Chemistry in Tables. 2011. (ENG., Illus.). iv, 157p. pap. 49.95 (978-3-642-20486-9(4), 3642204864) Springer.

Valentine, Joan Selverstone. Biological Inorganic Chemistry: Structure & Reactivity. 2006. (Illus.). 739p. 98.25 (978-1-891389-43-6(2)) Univ. Science Bks.

van Eldik, Rudi, ed. Advances in Inorganic Chemistry. 2008. (Advances in Inorganic Chemistry Ser.). (ENG.). 296p. 258.00 (978-0-12-373977-3(2), Academic Pr.) Elsevier Science & Technology Bks.

van Eldik, Rudi, et al, eds. Advances in Inorganic Chemistry: Theoretical & Computational Inorganic Chemistry. 2010. (ENG.). 536p. 258.00 (978-0-12-380874-5(X), Academic Pr.) Elsevier Science & Technology Bks.

van Eldik, Rudi & Bowman-James, Kristin, eds. Advances in Inorganic Chemistry: Template Effects & Molecular Organization. 2006. (Advances in Inorganic Chemistry Ser.). (ENG.). 332p. 258.00 (978-0-12-023659-6(1), Academic Pr.) Elsevier Science & Technology Bks.

van Eldik, Rudi & Hubbard, Colin D., eds. Advances in Inorganic Chemistry: Theoretical & Computational Inorganic Chemistry. 2009. (Advances in Inorganic Chemistry Ser.). (ENG.). 668p. 258.00 (978-0-12-375033-4(4), Academic Pr.) Elsevier Science & Technology Bks.

Villars, Pierre & Cenzual, Karin, eds. Inorganic. 2009. (Landolt-Börnstein: Numerical Data & Functional Relationships in Science & Technology Ser.). (Illus.). xiv, 511p. 6739.00 (978-3-540-69948-4(1)) Springer.

Vollath, Dieter & Wedemeyer, Horst. Uranium Dioxide, UO2, Preparation & Crystallographic Properties. 8th ed. 2007. (Gmelin Handbook of Inorganic & Organometallic Chemistry - 8th edition / U. Uran. Uranium (System-Nr. 55) Ser.). 156p. 425.00 (978-3-540-93509-4(6)) Springer.

Wells, Alexander Frank. Structural Inorganic Chemistry. 2012. (ENG., Illus.). 1416p. pap. 99.99 **(978-0-19-965763-6(7))** Oxford Univ. Pr., Inc.

Whangbo, Myung-Hwan, et al. Electronic Instabilities & Orbital Interactions in Low-Dimensional Conducting Materials. 2011. 59.95 **(978-0-471-09928-4(7)**, Wiley) Wiley, John & Sons, Inc.

Winpenny, Richard. Single Molecule Magnets & Related Phenomena. 2006. (Structure & Bonding Ser.: Vol. 122). (Illus.). xiv, 262p. 309.00 (978-3-540-33239-8(1), 3540332391) Springer.

Woollins, J. Derek, ed. Inorganic Experiments. 3rd ed. 2010. (ENG., Illus.). 482p. 80.00 (978-3-527-32472-9(0), Wiley-VCH) Wiley, John & Sons, Inc.

Wu, Xin-Tao. Controlled Assembly & Modification of Inorganic Systems. 2009. (Structure & Bonding Ser.). (ENG., Illus.). xv, 208p. 299.00 (978-3-642-01561-8(1), 3642015611) Springer.

Yen, William M., et al, eds. Fundamentals of Phosphors. 2006. (ENG., Illus.). 352p. 102.95 (978-1-4200-4367-9(6), CRC Press) Taylor & Francis Group GBR. Dist: Taylor & Francis Group.

—Measurements of Phosphor Properties. 2006. (ENG., Illus.). 160p. 95.95 (978-1-4200-4365-5(X), CRC Press) Taylor & Francis Group GBR. Dist: Taylor & Francis Group.

Zanello, Piero, et al. Inorganic Electrochemistry: Theory, Practice & Application. 2nd ed. 2011. (ENG., Illus.). 700p. (C). 160.00 **(978-1-84973-071-6(7))** Royal Society of Chemistry, The GBR. Dist: Ingram Pub. Services.

Zlatic, Veljko & Hewson, Alex C., eds. Properties & Applications of Thermoelectric Materials: The Search for New Materials for Thermoelectric Devices. 2009. (NATO Science for Peace & Security Series B: Physics & Biophysics Ser.). (Illus.). xv, 340p. 309.00 (978-90-481-2890-7(0)); (ENG., pap. 159.00 (978-90-481-2891-4(9)) Springer.

CHEMISTRY, INORGANIC—LABORATORY MANUALS

Cerny, Kenneth F. & Schwartz, Marietta H. Laboratory Manual for Organic Chemistry. 2nd rev. ed. 2009. (ENG.). 216p. spiral bd. 38.54 (978-0-7575-4473-6(8)) Kendall Hunt Publishing Co.

Zubricky, James. An Introduction to Organic Instrumental Analysis. 2nd rev. ed. 2010. (ENG.). 84p. spiral bd. 38.05 (978-0-7575-7510-5(2)) Kendall Hunt Publishing Co.

CHEMISTRY, INORGANIC—SYNTHESIS

see Inorganic Compounds—Synthesis

CHEMISTRY, LEGAL

see Chemistry, Forensic

CHEMISTRY, MEDICAL

see Clinical Chemistry

CHEMISTRY, MEDICAL AND PHARMACEUTICAL

see Pharmaceutical Chemistry

CHEMISTRY, MICROBIOLOGICAL

see Microbiological Chemistry

CHEMISTRY, MINERALOGICAL

see Mineralogical Chemistry

CHEMISTRY, NUCLEAR

see Nuclear Chemistry

CHEMISTRY, ORGANIC

see also Bioinorganic Chemistry; Bioorganic Chemistry; Carbon Compounds; Condensation Products (Chemistry); Organic Compounds; Physical Organic Chemistry; Radicals (Chemistry); Stereochemistry; Surface Active Agents

also names of classes of organic compounds, e.g. Alkaloids; Carbohydrates; Proteins; also names of individual organic substances, e.g. Benzene

Abrahamson, Julie K. Guided Inquiry Explorations into Organic & Biochemistry. 2009. 144p. pap. 37.95 (978-1-935551-58-4(2)) Univ. Readers.

Agranovich, Vladimir. Excitations in Organic Solids. 2009. (International Series of Monographs on Physics Ser.). (ENG., Illus.). 512p. 145.00 (978-0-19-923441-7(8)) Oxford Univ. Pr., Inc.

Akiba, Kin-ya. Organo Main Group Chemistry. 2011. (ENG., Illus.). 288p. pap. 79.95 (978-0-470-45033-8(9), Wiley) Wiley, John & Sons, Inc.

Al-Faiyz, Yasair. Hydroxamic Acid Chemistry. 2009. 216p. pap. (978-3-639-20719-4(X)) VDM Verlag Dr. Mueller e.K.

Alam, Mahmood, ed. Arkivoc 2007 Commemorative for Prof Atta-Ur-Rahman. 2007. 388p. per. 20.00 (978-1-59730-092-6(6)) Arkat USA, Inc.

Allen, D. W. Organophosphorus Chemistry, Vol. 36. 2007. (Specialist Periodical Reports). (ENG.). 358p. 448.00 (978-0-85404-354-5(3)) Royal Society of Chemistry, The GBR. Dist: Ingram Pub. Services.

Allen, D. W., et al. Organophosphorus Chemistry, Vol. 35. 2006. (Specialist Periodical Reports). (ENG.). 582p. 448.00 (978-0-85404-349-1(7)) Royal Society of Chemistry, The GBR. Dist: Ingram Pub. Services.

Alvarez-Builla, Julio, et al, eds. Modern Heterocyclic Chemistry, 4 vols., Set. 2011. (ENG., Illus.). 2530p. 810.00 **(978-3-527-33201-4(4)**, Wiley-VCH) Wiley, John & Sons, Inc.

Amir, Faheem. Structure Elucidation of Pentacyclic Triterpenes. 2011. 76p. pap. **(978-3-8443-8900-5(8))** Lambert Academic Publishing.

Andraos, John. The Algebra of Organic Synthesis: Green Metrics, Design Strategy, Route Selection, & Optimization. 2011. (ENG., Illus.). 1221p. 189.95 (978-1-4200-9328-5(2), CRC Press) Taylor & Francis Group GBR. Dist: Taylor & Francis Group.

Anstein, Stefanie & Kremer, Gerhard. Analysing Names of Organic Chemical Compounds. 2008. 112p. per. (978-3-8364-6985-2(5)) VDM Verlag Dr. Mueller e.K.

Ardrey, Robert, et al. Techniques of Modern Organic Mass Spectrometry. 2010. (Analytical Techniques in the Sciences (AnTs) #8727; Ser.). (ENG.). 384p. pap. (978-0-470-86995-6(X), Wiley-Blackwell) Wiley, John & Sons, Ltd.

Arnold, Melvin T. Essentials of General Organic & Biochemistry. tchr. ed. (978-0-03-005649-9(7)) Saunders College Publishing.

—Essentials of General Organic Biochemistry. 100p. pap. (978-0-03-005687-1(X)) Saunders College Publishing.

Arseniyadis, Stellios & Cossy, Janine, eds. Modern Tools for the Synthesis of Complex Bioactive Molecules. 2012. (ENG.). 612p. 149.95 (978-0-470-61618-5(0), Wiley) Wiley, John & Sons, Inc.

Bachrach, Steven M. Computational Organic Chemistry. 2007. (ENG., Illus.). 496p. 156.00 (978-0-471-71342-5(2), Wiley-Interscience) Wiley, John & Sons, Inc.

Bansal, Raj K. Phosphorous Heterocycles I. 2009. (Topics in Heterocyclic Chemistry Ser.). (ENG., Illus.). ix, 314p. 389.00 (978-3-642-00337-0(0), 3642003370) Springer.

Bateman, Graham, ed. Organic Chemistry & Biochemistry. 2011. (Facts at Your Fingertips: Introducing Chemistry Ser.). 64p. (YA). (gr. 7-12). lib. bdg. 35.65 (978-1-936333-14-1(7)) Brown Bear Bks.

Beale, John M. & Block, John, eds. Organic Medicinal & Pharmaceutical Chemistry. 12th rev. ed. 2010. (ENG., Illus.). 1008p. 98.99 (978-0-7817-7929-6(4)) Lippincott Williams & Wilkins.

Begtrup, Mikael, ed. Arkivoc 2001 Commemorative for Prof Kalevi Pihlaja. 2006. 124p. per. 20.00 (978-1-59730-051-3(9)) Arkat USA, Inc.

—Arkivoc 2001 Commemorative for Prof Kjell Undheim. 2006. 108p. per. 20.00 (978-1-59730-058-2(6)) Arkat USA, Inc.

—Arkivoc 2001 Commemorative for Prof Miha Tisler. 2006. 168p. per. 20.00 (978-1-59730-053-7(5)) Arkat USA, Inc.

—Arkivoc 2006 Commemorative for Dr Edmunds Lukevics. 2007. 172p. per. 20.00 (978-1-59730-079-7(9)) Arkat USA, Inc.

—Arkivoc 2007 Commemorative for Prof Waldemar Adam. 2007. 416p. per. 20.00 (978-1-59730-093-3(4)) Arkat USA, Inc.

Begtrup, Mikael, et al, eds. Arkivoc 2000 General Papers. 2007. (ENG.). 132p. per. 20.00 (978-1-59730-048-3(9)); 100p. per. 20.00 (978-1-59730-043-8(8)); (ENG.). 112p. per. 20.00 (978-1-59730-044-5(6)); (ENG.). 188p. per. 20.00 (978-1-59730-046-9(2)) Arkat USA, Inc.

—Arkivoc 2007 General Papers. 2008. 348p. per. 20.00 (978-1-59730-099-5(3)) Arkat USA, Inc.

Begtrup, Mikael & Ramsden, Christopher, eds. Arkivoc 2006 General Papers. 2007. 228p. per. 20.00 (978-1-59730-103-9(5)) Arkat USA, Inc.

Beilstein's Handbook Supplementary Ser. 27. (Beilstein's Handbuch der Organischen Chemie Ser.). (C). 1960.00 (978-3-89536-067-1(8)); 4th ed. 1960.00 (978-3-89536-066-4(X)) Beilstein Informationssysteme GmbH DEU. Dist: Springer.

Bell, Les. What's Cooking in Chemistry? How Leading Chemists Succeed in the Kitchen. Güntner, Carlos E. et al, eds. 2nd ed. 2009. (Erlebnis Wissenschaft Ser.: 5). (ENG.). 243p. pap. 20.95 (978-3-527-32621-1(9), Wiley-VCH) Wiley, John & Sons, Inc.

Bello, Isaac, et al. An Antioxidant from Nature. 2010. 76p. pap. (978-3-8383-7794-0(X)) Lambert Academic Publishing.

Bettelheim, Frederick. Introduction to General, Organic & Biochemistry, Hybrid. 10th ed. 2012. (Cengage Learningrsquo;s New Hybrid Editions! Ser.). (ENG.). 768p. (C). pap. 165.95 **(978-1-133-10982-2(9))** Brooks/Cole.

Bhakuni, Dewan S. & Rawat, D. S. Bioactive Marine Natural Products. 2010. xv, 400p. pap. 219.00 (978-90-481-6875-0(9), 9048168759) Springer.

Bloch, Daniel. Organic Chemistry Demystified 2/E. 2nd ed. 2012. (Demystified Ser.). (ENG., Illus.). 640p. pap. 20.00 **(978-0-07-176797-2(5)**, 0071767975) McGraw-Hill Professional Publishing.

Bozec, Hubert Le & Guerchais, Véronique. Molecular Organometallic Materials for Optics. 2009. (Topics in Organometallic Chemistry Ser.). (ENG., Illus.). x, 230p. 299.00 (978-3-642-01865-7(3), 3642018653) Springer.

Brown, Kate. General, Organic & Biochemistry. 2nd ed. Date not set. (Chemistry Ser.). tchr. ed. 1.00 (978-0-87150-774-7(9)); stu. ed. 14.25 net. (978-0-87150-772-3(2)); (Illus.). 809p. 44.25 net. (978-0-87150-762-4(5)) Brooks/Cole. (Brooks/Cole).

—Introduction to Organic & Biochemistry. 3rd ed. Date not set. (Chemistry Ser.). stu. ed. 12.50 net. (978-0-87150-739-6(0), Brooks/Cole) Brooks/Cole.

—A New Introduction to Organic Chemistry. Date not set. (Illus.). 378p. pap. 31.50 (978-0-582-35128-8(6)) Addison-Wesley Longman, Ltd. GBR. Dist: Trans-Atlantic Pubns., Inc.

Brown, Kate & Clapp. General, Organic & Biochemistry. 2nd ed. Date not set. (Chemistry Ser.). lab manual ed. 21.25 net. (978-0-87150-773-0(0), Brooks/Cole) Brooks/Cole.

Brown, William & Foote, Christopher S. Organic Chemistry. 5th ed. 2010. (ENG.). 800p. (C). pap. 151.95 (978-0-538-49765-7(3)) Brooks/Cole.

Brown, William, et al. Organic Chemistry. 6th ed. 2011. (Cengage Learningrsquo;s New Hybrid Editions! Ser.). (ENG.). (C). 1056p. pap. 154.95 (978-1-111-98776-3(9)); 1296p. 275.95 (978-0-8400-5498-2(X)) Brooks/Cole.

Brown, William H. & Poon, Thomas. Introduction to Organic Chemistry. 4th ed. 2010. (ENG.). (C). 896p. 205.95 (978-0-470-12923-4(9)); 720p. pap. 82.95 (978-0-470-55494-4(0)) Wiley, John & Sons, Inc. (Wiley).

—Introduction to Organic Chemistry, 4th Edition Binder Ready Version. 2010. (ENG.). 912p. (C). ring bd. 129.95 (978-0-470-60153-2(1), Wiley) Wiley, John & Sons, Inc.

Brown, William H., et al. Organic Chemistry, Enhanced Edition. 5th ed. 2010. (Available Titles OWL Ser.). (ENG.). 1248p. (C). 244.95 (978-0-538-49675-9(4)) Brooks/Cole.

Bruice, Paula Y. Organic Chemistry Study Guide & Solutions Manual, Books a la Carte Edition. 6th ed. 2011. (ENG.). 888p. (C). ring bd. 72.53 (978-0-321-77437-8(X), Prentice Hall) Prentice Hall PTR.

Bruice, Paula Yurkanis. Essential Organic Chemistry. 2nd ed. (ENG.). 624p. (C). 2010. ring bd. 107.47 (978-0-321-69389-1(2)) 2009. 179.07 (978-0-321-59695-6(1)) Prentice Hall PTR. (Prentice Hall).

—Essential Organic Chemistry: International Edition. 2nd ed. 2010. (Illus.). 624p. pap. (978-0-321-64416-9(6)) Prentice Hall PTR.

—Organic Chemistry. 5th ed. 2007. (978-0-13-242631-2(5)) Pearson Education Canada.

—Organic Chemistry. 5th ed. 2006. (ENG.). (C). 223.80 (978-0-13-241513-2(5), Prentice Hall) 5th rev. ed. 2007. (Illus.). 1440p. pap. (978-0-13-199631-1(2)) 6th ed. 2010. (ENG.). 1440p. (C). ring bd. 140.47 (978-0-321-72701-5(0), Prentice Hall) 6th ed. 2010. (ENG.). 1440p. (C). 234.07 (978-0-321-66313-9(6), Prentice Hall) 6th ed. 2010. (ENG.). (C). 44.07 (978-0-321-70693-5(5), Prentice Hall) Prentice Hall PTR.

—Study Guide & Solutions Manual for Essential Organic Chemistry. 2nd ed. 2009. (ENG.). 312p. (C). pap. 74.33 (978-0-321-59258-3(1), Prentice Hall) Prentice Hall PTR.

—Study Guide & Solutions Manual for Organic Chemistry. 6th ed. 2010. (ENG.). 856p. (C). pap. 120.80 (978-0-321-67682-5(3), Prentice Hall) Prentice Hall PTR.

Buddrus, Joachim & Schmidt, Bernd. Grundlagen der Organischen Chemie. 4th ed. 2011. (De Gruyter Studium Ser.). (C). 70.00 **(978-3-11-024894-4(8))**; (Illus.). xxv, 946p. E-Book 700.00 **(978-3-11-024640-7(6))** De Gruyter, Walter Inc.

Buenzli-Tripp Ursula Staff. Systematic Chemical Nomenclature of Organic Organometallic & Co. 2007. 636p. 194.95 (978-1-4200-4615-1(2)) CRC Pr. LLC.

Burns, Jason H. Commodity Futures Trading Commision: Modern Tendencies in Organic & Bioorganic Chemistry: Today & Tomorrow. 2008. (Illus.). pap. 39.00 (978-1-60456-296-5(X)) Nova Science Pubs., Inc.

Carey, Francis. Organic Chemistry. 8th ed. 2010. (ENG.). (C). 256.33 (978-0-07-740572-4(2), 0077405722, McGraw-Hill Science, Engineering & Mathematics) McGraw-Hill Higher Education.

—Package: Organic Chemistry with Solutions Manual & Connect Plus Access Card. 8th ed. 2010. (ENG.). (C). pap. 318.00 (978-0-07-749782-8(1), 0077497821, McGraw-Hill Science, Engineering & Mathematics) McGraw-Hill Higher Education.

Carey, Francis & Giuliano, Robert. Loose Leaf Organic Chemistry. 8th ed. 2010. (ENG.). (C). 173.33 *(978-0-07-740176-4(X)*, 007740176X, McGraw-Hill Science, Engineering & Mathematics) McGraw-Hill Higher Education.
Carey, Francis A. Organic Chemistry. 7th rev. ed. 2007. (ENG., Illus.). 1312p. (C). 213.75 *(978-0-07-331184-5(7)*, 0073311847, McGraw-Hill Science, Engineering & Mathematics) McGraw-Hill Higher Education.
—Spartan model CD-ROM. 7th ed. 2007. (ENG.). (C). cd-rom 35.00 *(978-0-07-304795-9(3)*, 0073047953, McGraw-Hill Science, Engineering & Mathematics) McGraw-Hill Higher Education.
Carey, Francis A. & Giuliano, Robert M. Organic Chemistry. 8th ed. 2010. *(978-0-07-340261-1(3))* McGraw-Hill Cos., The.
—Organic Chemistry. 8th ed. 2010. (ENG., Illus.). 1280p. (C). 247.33 *(978-0-07-735477-0(X)*, 007735477X, McGraw-Hill Science, Engineering & Mathematics) McGraw-Hill Higher Education.
Carey, Francis A. & Sundberg, Richard J. Advanced Organic Chemistry: Part A: Structure & Mechanisms. 5th rev. ed. 2007. (Advanced Organic Chemistry / Part A: Structure & Mechanisms Ser.). (Illus.). xxi, 1199p. pap. 59.95 *(978-0-387-68346-1(1))* Springer.
—Advanced Organic Chemistry: Part B: Reactions & Synthesis. 5th rev. ed. 2007. (Advanced Organic Chemistry / Part B: Reactions & Synthesis Ser.). (Illus.). 1321p. 119.00 *(978-0-387-68350-8(X))*; per. 59.95 *(978-0-387-68354-6(2))* Springer.
—Advanced Organic Chemistry Part A: Structure & Mechanisms. 5th rev. ed. 2007. (Advanced Organic Chemistry / Part A: Structure & Mechanisms Ser.). (Illus.). 1199p. 119.00 *(978-0-387-44897-8(7))* Springer.
Carroll, Felix A. Perspectives on Structure & Mechanism in Organic Chemistry. tchr. ed. *(978-0-534-24949-6(3))* Brooks/Cole.
Chagal, Leonid. Diamines in Catalysis & in Biological Systems. 2010. 112p. pap. *(978-3-8383-0652-0(X))* Lambert Academic Publishing.
Chan, Kim Seng & Tan, Jeanne. Understanding Advanced Organic & Analytical Chemistry: The Learner's Approach. 2011. 556p. pap. 34.00 ***(978-981-4374-98-9(9))*** World Scientific Publishing Co., Inc.
Chaudhary, Anu. Name Reactions in Organic Chemistry. 2011. 72p. pap. ***(978-3-8443-1177-8(7))*** Lambert Academic Publishing.
Chikkali, Samir. Catechol Phosphines: Metal Assisted Self-assembly & Application. 2008. 200p. pap. *(978-3-639-07138-2(7))* VDM Verlag Dr. Mueller e.K.
Cirrincione, Girolamo, ed. Arkivoc 2006 Special Issue Ichc-20. 2007. 536p. per. 20.00 *(978-1-59730-081-0(0))* Arkat USA, Inc.
—Arkivoc 2006 Special Issue Plenary & Invited Lectures of Joint Italian-Swiss Medicinal Chemistry Meeting. 2007. 156p. per. 20.00 *(978-1-59730-082-7(9))* Arkat USA, Inc.
—Arkivoc 2007 Commemorative for Prof Alain Krief. 2008. 432p. per. 20.00 *(978-1-59730-095-7(0))* Arkat USA, Inc.
Clayden, Jonathan, et al. Organic Chemistry. 2nd ed. 2012. (ENG., Illus.). 1,250p. 134.00 ***(978-0-19-927029-3(5))*** Oxford Univ. Pr., Inc.
Consumer Dummies Staff, et al. Organic Chemistry II for Dummies. 2010. (ENG., Illus.). 384p. pap. 19.99 *(978-0-470-17815-7(9)*, For Dummies) Wiley, John & Sons, Inc.
Cooper, Caroline. Organic Chemist's Desk Reference. 2nd rev. ed. 2010. (ENG., Illus.). 280p. 79.95 *(978-1-4398-1164-1(4)*, CRC Press) Taylor & Francis Group GBR. Dist: Taylor & Francis Group.
Cordes, Eugene H. The Tao of Chemistry & Life: A Scientific Journey. 2009. (ENG., Illus.). 432p. 59.95 *(978-0-19-536963-2(7))* Oxford Univ. Pr., Inc.
Crabtree, Robert & Mingos, Mike. Comprehensive Organometallic Chemistry III Set: From Fundamentals to Applications, 13 vols. 2006. (ENG., Illus.). 9000p. 8670.00 *(978-0-08-044590-8(X)*, Elsevier Science) Elsevier Science & Technology Bks.
Crabtree, Robert H. Advanced Organic Chemistry for University of Maryland Eastern Shore. 10th ed. 2011. 652p. pap. 83.95 ***(978-0-470-95579-6(1)***, Wiley) Wiley, John & Sons, Inc.
Cram101 Textbook Reviews. Outlines & Highlights for General Organic & Biochemistry: Connecting Chemistry to Your Life by Ira Blei, George Odian, ISBN. 2010. 240p. pap. 31.95 *(978-1-61698-607-0(7))* Cram101 Inc.
—Outlines & Highlights for General, Organic, & Biological Chemistry: Structures of Life by Timberlake, Karen. 2010. 680p. pap. 41.95 *(978-1-4288-5324-9(3))* Cram101 Inc.
—Outlines & Highlights for General, Organic & Biological Chemistry by Janice Gorzynski Smith, Isbn: 9780077274290. 2010. 302p. pap. 32.95 *(978-1-61698-554-7(2))* Cram101 Inc.
Cram101 Textbook Reviews Staff. Outlines & Highlights for Foundations of General, Organic, & Biochemistry by Denniston, Isbn: 0073511064. 2007. 128p. per. 11.95 *(978-1-4288-5732-2(X))* Cram101 Inc.
—Outlines & Highlights for Organic Chemistry by Bruice, Isbn: 0131407481. 2007. 532p. pap. 21.95 *(978-1-4288-3026-4(X))* Cram101 Inc.
—Outlines & Highlights for Organic Chemistry by Mcmurry, Isbn: 0534389996. 2007. 500p. pap. 20.95 *(978-1-4288-3046-2(4))* Cram101 Inc.
Crawford, Nathan. Laying Foundations in General & Organic Chemistry. rev. ed. 2009. (ENG.). 62p. spiral bd. 22.00 *(978-0-7575-6531-1(X))* Kendall Hunt Publishing Co.
Crego-Calama, Mercedes & Reinhoudt, David N. Supramolecular Chirality. 2010. (Topics in Current Chemistry Ser.). (Illus.). xii, 312p. pap. 379.00 *(978-3-642-06878-2(2)*, 3642068782) Springer.
Crews, Phillip, et al. Organic Structure Analysis, 1 vol. 2nd ed. 2009. (ENG., Illus.). 656p. (C). 164.95 *(978-0-19-533604-7(6))* Oxford Univ. Pr., Inc.
Dalton, David R. Foundations of Organic Chemistry: Unity & Diversity of Structures, Pathways, & Reactions. 2011. (ENG., Illus.). 1440p. 149.95 *(978-0-470-47908-7(6)*, Wiley) Wiley, John & Sons, Inc.
Darling, Stephen D. Molecular Visions: the Flexible Molecular Model Kit. 2006. (ENG.). (C). 36.20 *(978-0-13-233470-9(4)*, Prentice Hall) Prentice Hall PTR.
Darling, Steve. Organic Molecular Model Kit. 2006. (ENG.). (C). 28.47 *(978-0-13-233471-6(2)*, Prentice Hall) Prentice Hall PTR.
De Stanto, et al. Chemistry of Heterocyclic Compounds: Seven-Membered Rings with Two Heteroatoms. 2008. 99.95 *(978-0-471-80774-2(5)*, Wiley) Wiley, John & Sons, Inc.
Denmark, Scott E. Organic Reactions. (Organic Reactions Ser.: 76). (ENG.). Volume 73. 2009. 624p. 166.00 *(978-0-470-43690-5(5)*, Wiley-Interscience)Volume 78. 2012. 592p. 149.95 ***(978-1-118-35636-4(5)***, Wiley) Wiley, John & Sons, Inc.
Denmark, Scott E., ed. Organic Reactions. (Organic Reactions Ser.: 78). (ENG.). Volume 72. 2008. 704p. 166.00 *(978-0-470-42374-5(5)*, Wiley-Interscience)Volume 74. 2009. 705p. 156.00 *(978-0-470-53048-1(0)*, Wiley)Volume 75. 2011. 880p. 175.00 *(978-0-470-88907-7(1)*, Wiley)Volume 76. 2011. 584p. 149.95 *(978-0-470-63843-9(5)*, Wiley) Wiley, John & Sons, Inc.
Denmark, Scott E. & Overman, Larry E., eds. Organic Reactions, Vol. 71. 2008. (Organic Reactions Ser.: 75). (ENG., Illus.). 772p. 178.00 *(978-0-470-09899-8(6)*, Wiley-Interscience) Wiley, John & Sons, Inc.
Denniston, K. J. & Topping, Joseph J. Foundations of General, Organic, & Biochemistry. 2007. 167.19 *(978-0-07-351106-1(4))* McGraw-Hill Higher Education.
—General, Organic, & Biochemistry. 7th ed. 2010. *(978-0-07-340262-8(1))* McGraw-Hill Cos., The.
Denniston, K. J., et al. General, Organic, & Biochemistry. 6th ed. 2007. *(978-0-07-351110-8(2))* McGraw-Hill Cos., The.
Denniston, Katherine. General, Organic, & Biochemistry. 7th ed. 2010. (ENG.). (C). 219.33 *(978-0-07-740574-8(9)*, 007405749, McGraw-Hill Science, Engineering & Mathematics) McGraw-Hill Higher Education.
Denniston, Katherine, et al. Chemistry (from General, Organic, & Biochemistry) 7th ed. 2010. (ENG.). 416p. (C). pap. 96.67 *(978-0-07-739764-7(9)*, 0077397649, McGraw-Hill Science, Engineering & Mathematics) McGraw-Hill Higher Education.
—A Laboratory Manual for General, Organic & Biochemistry. 7th ed. 2010. (ENG., Illus.). 448p. (C). spiral bd., lab manual ed. 98.00 *(978-0-07-729672-8(9)*, 0077296729, McGraw-Hill Science, Engineering & Mathematics) McGraw-Hill Higher Education.
—Organic & Biochemistry (from General, Organic, & Biochemistry) 7th ed. 2010. (ENG.). (C). pap. 122.33 *(978-0-07-739763-0(0)*, 0077397630, McGraw-Hill Science, Engineering & Mathematics) McGraw-Hill Higher Education.
—Student Study Guide/Solutions Manual General, Organic & Biochemistry. 7th ed. 2010. (ENG.). 576p. (C). pap. 68.67 *(978-0-07-729673-5(7)*, 0077296737, McGraw-Hill Science, Engineering & Mathematics) McGraw-Hill Higher Education.
Denniston, Katherine J. & Topping, Joseph J. Foundations of General, Organic, & Biochemistry. 2007. (ENG., Illus.). 688p. (C). 184.00 *(978-0-07-331153-8(9)*, 0073311839, McGraw-Hill Science, Engineering & Mathematics) McGraw-Hill Higher Education.
Denniston, Katherine J., et al. General, Organic & Biochemistry. (ENG.). 928p. (C). 6th ed. 2007. Illus.). 175.94 *(978-0-07-722141-6(9)*, 0077221419) 7th ed. 2010. 210.33 *(978-0-07-735480-0(X)*, 007735480X) McGraw-Hill Higher Education. (McGraw-Hill Science, Engineering & Mathematics).
Dicks, Andrew, ed. Green Organic Chemistry in Lecture & Labartory. 2011. (Sustainability Ser.). (ENG., Illus.). 299p. 149.95 *(978-1-4398-4076-4(8)*, CRC Press) Taylor & Francis Group GBR. Dist: Taylor & Francis Group.
Díez-González, Silvia & Royal Society of Chemistry Staff. N-Heterocyclic Carbenes: From Laboratory Curiosities to Efficient Synthetic Tools. 2010. (RSC Catalysis Ser.). (ENG., Illus.). 468p. (C). 195.00 ***(978-1-84973-042-6(3))*** Royal Society of Chemistry, The GBR. Dist: Ingram Pub. Services.
Dingle, Adrian. Organic Chemistry: Reactions & Applications. 2012. (ENG., Illus.). 250p. pap. 35.00 *(978-1-84331-390-8(1))* Anthem Pr. GBR. Dist: Books International, Inc.
Eguchi, Shoji. Bioactive Heterocyles I. 2010. (Topics in Heterocyclic Chemistry Ser.). xiv, 220p. pap. 239.00 *(978-3-642-06998-7(3)*, 3642069983) Springer.
Erickson, John G. Chemistry of Heterocyclic Compounds: The 1,2,3- & 1,2,4-Triazines, Tetrazines & Pentazines. 2007. (Chemistry of Heterocyclic Compounds: A Series of Monographs). (ENG., Illus.). 274p. 499.00 *(978-0-470-18273-4(3)*, Wiley) Wiley, John & Sons, Inc.
Eycken, Erik van der & Kappe, C. Oliver. Microwave-Assisted Synthesis of Heterocycles. 2010. (Topics in Heterocyclic Chemistry Ser.). xiv, 309p. pap. 269.00 *(978-3-642-06815-7(4)*, 3642068154) Springer.
Faber, Kurt. Biotransformations in Organic Chemistry: A Textbook. 6th ed. 2011. (ENG., Illus.). xi, 423p. pap. 79.95 *(978-3-642-17392-9(6)*, 3642173926) Springer.
Fermini, Bernard. Ion Channels. 2008. (Topics in Medicinal Chemistry Ser.). 239.00 *(978-3-540-79728-9(9)*, 3540797289) Springer.
Fermini, Bernard & Priest, Birgit. Ion Channels. 2010. (Topics in Medicinal Chemistry Ser.). (Illus.). xiv, 171p. pap. 239.00 *(978-3-642-09855-0(X)*, 364209855X) Springer.
Fessenden. Organic Chemistry. 2nd ed. Date not set. (Chemistry Ser.). tchr. ed. 1.00 *(978-0-87150-369-5(7)*, Brooks/Cole) Brooks/Cole.
—Organic Chemistry. 5th ed. stu. ed. 106.20 net. *(978-0-534-31844-4(4))* CENGAGE Learning.
Finch, A. F., ed. Theilheimer's Synthetic Methods of Organic Chemistry. (Theilheimer's Synthetic Methods of Organic Chemistry Ser.). 430p. *(978-3-8055-8217-9(X))*; Vol. 61. (Illus.). *(978-3-8055-7451-8(7))*; Vol. 62. (Illus.). *(978-3-8055-7452-5(5))*; Vol. 63. *(978-3-8055-7601-7(3))*; Vol. 64. *(978-3-8055-7679-6(X))*; Vol. 65. *(978-3-8055-7821-9(0))*; Vol. 66. *(978-3-8055-7854-7(7))*; Vol. 67. *(978-3-8055-7988-9(8))* Karger, S. AG.
—Theilheimer's Synthetic Methods of Organic Chemistry, Vol. 68. rev. ed. (Theilheimer Ser.). 398p. *(978-3-8055-7989-6(6))* Karger, S. AG.
—Theilheimer's Synthetic Methods of Organic Chemistry, Vol. 69. 2006th ed. (Theilheimer's Synthetic Methods of Organic Chemistry Ser.). (Illus.). *(978-3-8055-8147-9(5))* Karger, S. AG.
Fleming, Steve A. & Jones, Maitland, Jr. Organic Chemistry. 4th ed. 2009. (ENG.). 1220p. (C). 150.00 net. incl. cd-rom *(978-0-393-93149-5(8)*, 93149) Norton, W. W. & Co., Inc.
Fortschritte der Chemie organischer Naturstoffe / Progress in the Chemistry of Organic Natural Products 88. 2010. (Fortschritte der Chemie Organischer Naturstoffe Progress in the Chemistry of Organic Natural Products Ser.). (Illus.). ix, 212p. pap. 239.00 *(978-3-211-99872-4(1)*, 3211998721) Springer.
Fox, Marye Anne & Whitesell, James. Organic Chemistry: Test Bank. 2nd ed. Date not set. (Chemistry Ser.). pap. 10.00 *(978-0-7637-0492-6(X))* Jones & Bartlett Learning, LLC.
Frost, Laura D. & Deal, S. Todd. General, Organic, & Biological Chemistry. 2011. (ENG.). (C). ring bd. 110.20 ***(978-0-321-79590-8(3)***, Prentice Hall) Prentice Hall PTR.
Fuchs, Philip L., ed. Reagents for Silicon-Mediated Organic Synthesis. 2011. (Hdbk of Reagents for Organic Synthesis Ser.). (ENG., Illus.). 854p. 155.00 ***(978-0-470-71023-4(3)***, Wiley) Wiley, John & Sons, Inc.
Fujita, Shinsaku. Organic Chemistry of Photography. 2010. (ENG., Illus.). xix, 587p. pap. 289.00 *(978-3-642-05902-5(3)*, 3642059023) Springer.
Fuller, T., ed. Organic Photovoltaics. 2007. (ECS Transactions Ser.). 11p. pap. 27.00 *(978-1-60423-375-9(3))* Curran Assocs., Inc.
Garoutte, Michael P. General, Organic, & Biological Chemistry: A Guided Inquiry. 11th ed. 2006. (ENG., Illus.). 216p. (C). pap. 66.95 *(978-0-471-76359-8(4)*, Wiley) Wiley, John & Sons, Inc.
Ghafoori, Emad & Flynn, Peter. The Economics of Energy from Animal Manure. 2008. 164p. pap. *(978-3-8364-9545-5(7))* VDM Verlag Dr. Mueller e.K.
Gilbert, John C. & Martin, Stephen F. Experimental Organic Chemistry: A Miniscale & Microscale Approach. 5th ed. 2010. (Available Titles CourseMate Ser.). (ENG.). 960p. (C). 243.95 *(978-1-4390-4914-3(9))* Brooks/Cole.
Gilchrist, Tom, ed. Arkivoc 2001 Commemorative for Prof Donald Cameron. 2006. 180p. per. 20.00 *(978-1-59730-055-1(1))* Arkat USA, Inc.
Gillingham, Dennis. A Synthesis of Baconipyrone Through New Catalytic Asymmetric Methods. 2008. 148p. pap. *(978-3-8364-9216-4(4))* VDM Verlag Dr. Mueller e.K.
Gilkson, M. V. & Mastalerz, M., eds. Organic Matter & Mineralisation: Thermal Alteration, Hydrocarbon Generation & Role in Metallogenesis: Thermal Alteration, Hydrocarbon Generation & Role in Metallogenesis. 2010. 454p. pap. 204.00 *(978-90-481-4019-0(6)*, 9048140196) Springer.
Glycoscience - Chemistry & Chemical Biology I-III. 2008. 1689.00 *(978-3-540-36157-2(X)*, 354036157X); 1349.00 *(978-3-540-30429-6(0))* Springer.
Gray, Gary R. Flash Cards for Organic Chemistry I. rev. ed. 2010. (ENG.). 44p. ring bd. 20.08 *(978-0-7575-4301-2(4))* Kendall Hunt Publishing Co.
Gribble, Gordon W. & Joule, John A., eds. Progress in Heterocyclic Chemistry. 2011. (Progress in Heterocyclic Chemistry Ser.: 23). (ENG.). 550p. 185.00 ***(978-0-08-096805-6(8))*** Elsevier Science & Technology Bks.
Gribble, Gordon W. & Joule, John A., eds. Progress in Heterocyclic Chemistry, Vol. 22. 2010. (Progress in Heterocyclic Chemistry Ser.: 22). (ENG.). 592p. 185.00 *(978-0-08-096685-4(3))* Elsevier Science & Technology Bks.
Guch, Ian & Wayman, Kjirsten. Organic Chemistry - The Complete Idiot's Guide. 2008. (Complete Idiot's Guide Ser.). (ENG., Illus.). 384p. (gr. 12-18). 18.95 *(978-1-59257-753-8(9)*, Alpha Bks.) Penguin Group (USA) Inc.
Guinn, Denise & Brewer, Rebecca. Essentials of General, Organic & Biochemistry. 2009. (ENG.). 640p. (C). 124.95 *(978-0-7167-6121-1(1))* Freeman, W. H. & Co.
Gupta, Radha R., et al. Heterocyclic Chemistry II: Five-Membered Heterocycles. 2010. (ENG., Illus.). xi, 638p. pap. 149.00 *(978-3-642-08460-7(5)*, 3642084605) Springer.
H. Mohamed, Zeinhom, et al. Photodegradation of Some Dye Pollutants. 2011. 204p. pap. ***(978-3-8443-0401-5(0))*** Lambert Academic Publishing.
Harmata, Michael, ed. Silver in Organic Chemistry. 2010. (ENG., Illus.). 402p. 116.00 *(978-0-470-46611-7(1)*, Wiley) Wiley, John & Sons, Inc.
Harmsen, J. & Powell, Joseph B., eds. Sustainable Development in the Process Industries: Cases & Impact. 2010. (ENG., Illus.). 270p. 94.95 *(978-0-470-18779-1(4))* American Institute of Chemical Engineers.
Hart, Harold, et al. Organic Chemistry: A Short Course. 13th ed. 2011. (Textbooks Available with Cengage YouBook Ser.). (ENG.). 608p. (C). 211.95 *(978-1-111-42556-2(6))* Brooks/Cole.
Hein, Morris, et al. Introduction to General, Organic, & Biochemistry. 10th ed. 2011. (ENG., Illus.). 1120p. (C). 212.95 *(978-0-470-59880-1(8)*, Wiley) Wiley, John & Sons, Inc.
Heinonen, Pertti. Water Quality Measurements, 6 vols., Set. 2008. (ENG.). 1988p. 1300.00 *(978-0-470-77959-0(4)*, Wiley) Wiley, John & Sons, Inc.
Hill, Lisa. The Properties of Elements & Compounds, 1 vol. 2008. (Sci-Hi: Physical Science Ser.). (ENG.). 48p. (gr. 4-4). pap. 8.99 *(978-1-4109-3260-0(5)*, Sci-Hi) Heinemann-Raintree.
Hill, Richard & Barbaro, John. Experiments in Organic Chemistry. 2nd ed. (Illus.). 300p. (C). pap. 29.95 *(978-0-89892-218-9(6))* Contemporary Publishing Co. of Raleigh, Inc.
Ho, Tse-Lok. Fiesers' Reagents for Organic Synthesis. (Fiesers' Reagents for Organic Synthesis Ser.: 39). (ENG., Illus.). Volume 24. 2nd ed. 2008. 524p. 184.00 *(978-0-470-22554-7(8))*Volume 25. 2009. 571p. 166.00 *(978-0-470-43375-1(2))*Volumes 1-25, and Collective Index for Volumes 1-2. 2nd ed. 2010. 3000p. 3310.00 *(978-0-470-52111-3(2))* Wiley, John & Sons, Inc. (Wiley).
—Fiesers' Reagents for Organic Synthesis, Fiesers' Reagents for Organic Synthesis, Volume 23. 2006. (Fiesers' Reagents for Organic Synthesis Ser.: 23). (ENG.). 533p. 184.00 *(978-0-471-68243-1(8)*, Wiley-Interscience) Wiley, John & Sons, Inc.
Houk, K. N. & Vogel. Advanced Organic Chemistry. 2008. 1088p. 110.00 *(978-0-8153-4167-3(9)*, Garland Science) Taylor & Francis Group.
Ikan, Raphael, ed. Natural & Laboratory Simulated Thermal Geochemical Processes. 2010. 408p. pap. 189.00 *(978-90-481-6306-9(4)*, 9048163064) Springer.
Ikediobi, Christopher & Onyeozili, Edith. General Experimental Organic Chemistry. rev. ed. 2011. (ENG.). 224p. pap. 65.60 *(978-0-7575-8127-4(7))* Kendall Hunt Publishing Co.
Ila, Hiriyakkanavar, ed. Arkivoc 2007 Commemorative for Prof Jan Epsztajn. 2007. 240p. per. 20.00 *(978-1-59730-091-9(8))* Arkat USA, Inc.
Ila, Hiriyakkanavar & Schantl, Joachim, eds. Arkivoc 2006 General Papers. 2007. 244p. per. 20.00 *(978-1-59730-096-4(9))* Arkat USA, Inc.
Iskra, Jernej, ed. Halogenated Heterocycles: Synthesis, Application & Environment. 2012. (Topics in Heterocyclic Chemistry Ser.). (ENG., Illus.). ix, 316p. 309.00 ***(978-3-642-25102-3(1)***, 3642251021) Springer.
Jamshed, Hashim. C-C Coupling Reactions for the Synthesis of Carbostyrils Derivatives. 2010. 96p. pap. *(978-3-639-24934-7(8))* VDM Verlag Dr. Mueller e.K.
Jones, M. Organic Chemistry/Darling Mode. Date not set. (C). pap. *(978-0-393-10210-9(6))* Norton, W. W. & Co., Inc.
Joule, John A. & Mills, Keith. Heterocyclic Chemistry. 5th ed. 2010. (ENG., Illus.). 718p. 195.00 *(978-1-4051-9365-8(4)*, Wiley-Blackwell) Wiley, John & Sons, Inc.
Kajzar, F., et al, eds. Photoactive Organic Materials: Science & Applications: Science & Applications. 2010. (NATO Science Partnership Sub-Series: 3: Ser.). 588p. pap. 499.00 *(978-90-481-4681-9(X)*, 904814681X) Springer.
Kaplan Higher Education Staff. Kaplan MCAT Organic Chemistry Review. 2010. (ENG.). 448p. pap. 45.00 *(978-1-60714-641-4(X))* Kaplan Publishing.
Karty, Joel. Get Ready for Organic Chemistry. 2nd rev. ed. 2011. (ENG.). 288p. (C). pap. 49.20 ***(978-0-321-77412-5(4)***, Prentice Hall) Prentice Hall PTR.
Katritzky, Alan R., et al. A Review of the Literature, 1995-2007 Vols. 1-15, Set, 15 vols. 2008. (Advances in Heterocyclic Chemistry Ser.). (ENG., Illus.). 12500p. 10300.00 *(978-0-08-044991-3(3)*, Elsevier Science) Elsevier Science & Technology Bks.
Kazmierski, Wieslaw M., ed. Peptidomimetics Protocols. 2010. (Methods in Molecular Medicine Ser.). 576p. pap. 149.00 *(978-1-61737-059-5(2)*, 1617370592) Humana Pr.
Keese, Reinhart, et al. Practical Organic Synthesis: A Student's Guide. 2006. (ENG., Illus.). 208p. stu. ed. 130.00 *(978-0-470-02965-7(X))*; stu. ed., per. 60.00 *(978-0-470-02966-4(8))* Wiley, John & Sons, Inc. (Wiley).
Kiihne, S. R. & de Groot, H. J. M., eds. Perspectives on Solid State NMR in Biology. 2010. (Focus on Structural Biology Ser.). (Illus.). 248p. pap. 159.00 *(978-90-481-5744-0(7)*, 9048157447) Springer.
Kinghorn, A. Douglas, et al, eds. Fortschritte der Chemie organischer Naturstoffe / Progress in the Chemistry of Organic Natural Products / Volume 92. 2010. (Fortschritte der Chemie organischer Naturstoffe / Progress in the Chemistry of Organic Natural Products Ser.). (Illus.). xi, 175p. 299.00 *(978-3-211-99660-7(5)*, 3211996605) Springer.
Kjellin, Mikael & Johansson, Ingegärd, eds. Surfactants from Renewable Resources. 2010. (Wiley Series in Renewable Resource Ser.). (ENG., Illus.). 336p. 155.00 *(978-0-470-76041-3(9)*, Wiley) Wiley, John & Sons, Inc.
Klauk, Hagen, ed. Organic Electronics: Materials, Manufacturing, & Applications. 2006. (ENG., Illus.). 446p. 215.00 *(978-3-527-31264-1(1)*, Wiley-VCH) Wiley, John & Sons, Inc.
Klein, David R. Organic Chemistry. 2011. (ENG., Illus.). 1360p. (C). 241.95 *(978-0-471-75614-9(8)*, Wiley) Wiley, John & Sons, Inc.
—Organic Chemistry. 2011. 1392p. (C). ring bd. 143.95 *(978-0-470-91780-0(6)*, Wiley) Wiley, John & Sons, Inc.
—Organic Chemistry: As a Second Language. 3rd ed. 2011. (ENG.). 356p. (C). pap. 46.95 ***(978-1-118-14434-3(1)***, Wiley) Wiley, John & Sons, Inc.
—Organic Chemistry: As a Second Language - First Semester Topics. 3rd ed. 2011. (ENG.). 400p. (C). pap. 35.95 *(978-1-118-01040-2(X)*, Wiley) Wiley, John & Sons, Inc.
—Organic Chemistry As a Second Language, Vols. 1 & 2. 2008. (Wiley Plus Products Ser.). pap. 32.95 *(978-0-470-14341-4(X)*, Wiley) Wiley, John & Sons, Inc.
—Organic Chemistry for University of Texas Brownsville. 2011. 1210p. (C). pap. 128.95 ***(978-1-118-11481-0(7)***, Wiley) Wiley, John & Sons, Inc.
—Student Study Guide & Solutions Manual T/a Organic Chemistry, 1E Preliminary Edition Volume 2 Binder Ready Version. 2011. (C). ring bd. 19.95 *(978-0-470-73426-1(4)*, Wiley) Wiley, John & Sons, Inc.

C

Klein, David R. WP Course Organic Chemistry. 2011. (C). 82.95 ***(978-0-470-91429-8(7)***, Wiley) Wiley, John & Sons, Inc.

Knipe, A. C., ed. Organic Reaction Mechanisms, 1999-2003, 5 vols., Set. 2008. (ENG.). 3400p. 2950.00 *(978-0-470-77955-2(1)*, Wiley) Wiley, John & Sons, Inc.

—Organic Reaction Mechanisms 2004. 2008. (Organic Reaction Mechanisms Ser.: 118). (ENG.). 712p. 710.00 *(978-0-470-01847-7(X)*, Wiley) Wiley, John & Sons, Inc.

—Organic Reaction Mechanisms 2008. 2011. (Organic Reaction Mechanisms Ser.). (ENG.). 548p. 500.00 *(978-0-470-74981-4(4)*, Wiley) Wiley, John & Sons, Inc.

Knipe, A. C. & Knipe, Chris, eds. Organic Reaction Mechanisms 2003. 2007. (Organic Reaction Mechanisms Ser.: 120). (ENG.). 644p. 710.00 *(978-0-470-01490-5(3)*, Wiley) Wiley, John & Sons, Inc.

Knipe, Chris & Knipe, A. C., eds. Organic Reaction Mechanisms 2009. 2012. (Organic Reaction Mechanisms Ser.). (ENG.). 786p. 545.00 ***(978-0-470-68594-5(8)***, Wiley) Wiley, John & Sons, Inc.

Kobayashi, Nagao & Muranaka, Atsuya. Circular Dichroism & Magnetic Circular Dichroism Spectroscopy for Organic Chemists. 2011. (ENG., Illus.). 216p. 160.00 ***(978-1-84755-869-5(0))*** Royal Society of Chemistry, The GBR. Dist: Ingram Pub. Services.

Kolev, Tsonko. Quantum Chemical, Spectroscopic & Structural Study of Hydrochlorides, Hydrogens Squarates & Ester Amides of Squaric Acid of Amina. 2008. (Illus.). viii, 95p. pap. 39.00 *(978-1-60456-431-0(8))* Nova Science Pubs., Inc.

Kouadio, Kay I. Organic Chemistry I: Lecture Templates. 2nd rev. ed. 2011. (ENG.). 392p. pap. 49.99 ***(978-0-7575-9111-2(6))*** Kendall Hunt Publishing Co.

—Organic Chemistry Ii: Lecture Templates. 2nd rev. ed. 2011. (ENG.). 530p. pap. 49.99 ***(978-0-7575-9112-9(4))*** Kendall Hunt Publishing Co.

Krapcho, Paul, ed. Arkivoc 2001 Commemorative for Prof Alfred Hassner. 2006. 84p. per. 20.00 *(978-1-59730-052-0(7))* Arkat USA, Inc.

—Arkivoc 2001 Commemorative for Prof O S Tee. 2007. 252p. per. 20.00 *(978-1-59730-060-5(8))* Arkat USA, Inc.

Krapcho, Paul, et al, eds. Arkivoc 2001 General Papers. 2007. 280p. per. 20.00 *(978-1-59730-049-0(7))* Arkat USA, Inc.

Kräutler, Bernhard & Sahu, N. P. Fortschritte der Chemie organischer Naturstoffe / Progress in the Chemistry of Organic Natural Products. 2010. (Fortschritte der Chemie Organischer Naturstoffe Progress in the Chemistry of Organic Natural Products Ser.). (Illus.). vii, 163p. pap. 219.00 *(978-3-211-99907-3(8)*, 3211999078) Springer.

Larhed, Mats & Olofsson, Kristofer. Microwave Methods in Organic Synthesis. 2010. (Topics in Current Chemistry Ser.). (Illus.). xii, 289p. pap. 419.00 *(978-3-642-07182-9(1)*, 3642071821) Springer.

Larson, Gerald L. & Fry, James L. Ionic & Organometallic-Catalyzed Organosilane Reductions. 2009. (Organic Reactions Ser.: 81). (ENG., Illus.). 756p. pap., instr.'s hndbk. ed. 111.00 *(978-0-470-54787-8(1)*, Wiley) Wiley, John & Sons, Inc.

Lednicer, Daniel. The Organic Chemistry of Drug Synthesis, Volume 7. 2007. (Organic Chemistry Series of Drug Synthesis Ser.: 8). (ENG.). 272p. 156.00 *(978-0-470-10750-8(2)*, Wiley-Interscience) Wiley, John & Sons, Inc.

Lee, Moses. Heterocyclic Antitumor Antibiotics. 2010. (Topics in Heterocyclic Chemistry Ser.). xiv, 252p. pap. 199.00 *(978-3-642-06814-0(6)*, 3642068146) Springer.

Lehman, John W. Operational Organic Chemistry: A Problem-Solving Approach to the Laboratory Course. 4th ed. 2008. (ENG., Illus.). 912p. (C). 160.20 *(978-0-13-600092-1(4)*, Prentice Hall) Prentice Hall PTR.

Levy, Daniel E. Arrow-Pushing in Organic Chemistry: An Easy Approach to Understanding Reaction Mechanisms. 2008. (ENG., Illus.). 320p. pap. 42.50 *(978-0-470-17110-3(3)*, Wiley-Interscience) Wiley, John & Sons, Inc.

Li, Chao-Jun & Chan, Tak-Hang. Comprehensive Organic Reactions in Aqueous Media. 2nd rev. ed. 2007. (ENG., Illus.). 417p. 166.00 *(978-0-471-76129-7(X)*, Wiley-Interscience) Wiley, John & Sons, Inc.

Li, Jie Jack. Name Reactions: A Collection of Detailed Mechanisms & Synthetic Applications. 4th ed. 2009. (ENG., Illus.). xxii, 621p. 99.00 *(978-3-642-01052-1(0)*, 3642010520) Springer.

—Name Reactions: A Collection of Detailed Reaction Mechanisms. 3rd rev. ed. 2006. (Illus.). 652p. 99.00 *(978-3-540-30030-4(9)*, 3540300309) Springer.

—Name Reactions in Heterocyclic Chemistry, Vol. 2. 2011. (Comprehensive Name Reactions Ser.: 6). (ENG., Illus.). 704p. 149.95 *(978-0-470-08508-0(8)*, Wiley) Wiley, John & Sons, Inc.

Li, Jie Jack & Corey, E. J. Name Reactions Series. 2010. (Comprehensive Name Reactions Ser.). (ENG.). 3718p. 720.00 *(978-0-470-94032-7(8)*, Wiley) Wiley, John & Sons, Inc.

Lindhorst, Thisbe K. Essentials of Carbohydrate Chemistry & Biochemistry. 3rd ed. 2007. (ENG., Illus.). 332p. pap. 90.00 *(978-3-527-31528-4(4)*, Wiley-VCH) Wiley, John & Sons, Inc.

Loudon, Marc. Organic Chemistry. 5th ed. 2009. (ENG., Illus.). 1469p. (C). 125.00 *(978-0-9815194-3-2(1)*, Roberts & Co. Pubs.) Roberts & Co.

—Study Guide & Solutions Manual to Accompany Organic Chemistry. 5th ed. 2009. (ENG., Illus.). 759p. (C). (gr. 14-15). pap. 62.50 *(978-0-9815194-4-9(X))* Roberts & Co.

Mahrwald, Rainer, ed. Enantioselective Organocatalyzed Reactions II: Asymmetric C-C Bond Formation Processes, 2 vols. 2011. (ENG., Illus.). xiii, 386p. 189.00 *(978-90-481-3866-1(3)*, 9048138663) Springer.

Mannam, Sreedevi & Sekar, Govindasamy. Alcohol Oxidation. 2010. 196p. pap. *(978-3-639-25834-9(7))* VDM Verlag Dr. Mueller e.K.

Marchand, Alan, ed. Arkivoc 2001 Commemorative for Prof B S Thyagarajan. 2006. 100p. per. 20.00 *(978-1-59730-059-9(4))* Arkat USA, Inc.

—Arkivoc 2005 Commemorative Organic Chemistry in Ukraine. 2006. 112p. per. 20.00 *(978-1-59730-036-0(5))* Arkat USA, Inc.

—Arkivoc 2007 Commemorative for Prof Ernst Anders. 2007. 204p. per. 20.00 *(978-1-59730-088-9(8))* Arkat USA, Inc.

Marchand, Alan, et al, eds. Arkivoc 2006 General Papers. 2008. 296p. per. 20.00 *(978-1-59730-101-5(9))* Arkat USA, Inc.

Marchand, Alan & Ramsden, Christopher, eds. Arkivoc 2005 General Papers. 2006. 228p. per. 20.00 *(978-1-59730-074-2(8))* Arkat USA, Inc.

—Arkivoc 2006 General Papers. 2007. 196p. per. 20.00 *(978-1-59730-102-2(7))* Arkat USA, Inc.

Marchand, Alan & Zhdankin, Viktor, eds. Arkivoc 2006 General Papers. 2007. 224p. per. 20.00 *(978-1-59730-104-6(3))* Arkat USA, Inc.

Martin, Robert. Aromatic Hydroxyketones: Preparation & Physical Properties, Vol. 1. 3rd ed. 2011. (ENG., Illus.). 2800p. 1600.00 *(978-1-4020-9786-7(7)*, 1402097867) Springer.

Maskat, Norhayati & Sin, Tan. The Influence of Piagetian Reasoning Ability in Organic Chemistry. 2010. 68p. pap. *(978-3-639-24374-1(9))* VDM Verlag Dr. Mueller e.K.

Maskill, Howard, ed. The Investigation of Organic Reactions & Their Mechanisms. 2007. (ENG., Illus.). 392p. 225.00 *(978-1-4051-3142-1(X)*, Wiley-Blackwell) Wiley, John & Sons, Inc.

Materials Research Society ( ) Staff, compiled by. Organic Electronics: Materials, Devices, & Applications. 2007. (Materials Research Society Symposium Proceedings Ser.). 402p. pap. 115.00 *(978-1-60423-417-6(2))* Curran Assocs., Inc.

Matsumoto, Kiyoshi & Hayashi, Naoto. Heterocyclic Supramolecules II. 2009. (Topics in Heterocyclic Chemistry Ser.). (ENG.). ix, 157p. 219.00 *(978-3-642-02040-7(2)*, 3642020402) Springer.

Mcdougal, Owen & Steiner, Rick. General, Organic & Biological Chemistry. 2006. pap., stu. ed. 43.95 *(978-0-471-69942-2(X))* Wiley, John & Sons, Inc.

Mcmurry. Intl Stdt Edition-Organic Chemistry. 7th rev. ed. 2008. (Illus.). 1376p. pap. 246.95 *(978-0-495-11628-8(9))* Brooks/Cole.

—Pac W/Thomsonnow-Organic Chemistry. 7th ed. 2008. (Illus.). xxiv, 1224p. *(978-0-495-31868-2(X))* Brooks/Cole.

McMurry, John. Organic Chemistry. 4th ed. 88.31 net. *(978-0-534-33276-1(5))*; 81.00 net. *(978-0-534-33255-6(2))* Brooks/Cole.

—Organic Chemistry: A Biological Approach. 2007. (Illus.). xxvi, 1015p. *(978-0-495-01526-0(1))* Brooks/Cole.

McMurry, John & McMurry. Organic Chemistry: With Biological Applications, International Edition. 2011. 1152p. pap. 249.95 *(978-0-495-39147-0(6))* Brooks/Cole.

McMurry, John, et al. Study Guide & Selected Solutions Manual for Fundamentals of General, Organic, & Biological Chemistry. 6th ed. 2009. (ENG.). 432p. (C). pap. 69.87 *(978-0-321-61239-7(6)*, Prentice Hall) Prentice Hall PTR.

McMurry, John E. Fundamentals of Organic Chemistry. 7th ed. 2010. (Available Titles OWL Ser.). (ENG.). (C). 672p. 226.95 *(978-1-4390-4971-6(8))*; 464p. pap., stu. ed. 100.95 *(978-1-4390-4972-3(6))* Brooks/Cole.

—Organic Chemistry. (Cengage Learningrsquo;s New Hybrid Editions! Ser.). (ENG., (C). 8th ed. 2011. Illus.). 1104p. pap. 154.95 *(978-1-111-58157-2(6))* 8th ed. 2011. 1376p. 276.95 *(978-0-8400-5444-9(0))* Vol. 2. 7th ed. 2009. 768p. 137.95 *(978-1-4390-4931-0(9))* Brooks/Cole.

—Organic Chemistry, Vol. 1. 7th ed. 2009. (ENG.). 656p. (C). 146.95 *(978-0-538-73395-3(0))* Cengage South-Western.

—Organic Chemistry: A Biological Approach. 2nd ed. 2010. (Available Titles OWL Ser.). (ENG.). 1152p. (C). 280.95 *(978-0-495-39144-9(1))* Brooks/Cole.

—Organic Chemistry Study Guide & Student Solutions Manual. 8th ed. 2011. (ENG.). 928p. (C). pap. 157.95 *(978-0-8400-5445-6(9))* Brooks/Cole.

Medvedevskikh, Y. G. Organic & Physical Chemistry Using Chemical Kinetics: Prospects & Developments. 2007. 145.00 *(978-1-60021-763-0(X))* Nova Science Pubs., Inc.

Mehmetli, Ebru & Koumanova, Bogdana. The Fate of Persistent Organic Pollutants in the Environment: [proceedings of the NATO Advanced Research Workshop on the Fate of Persistent Organic Pollutants in the Environment, Istanbul, Turkey, 25-27 April 2007]. Mehmetli, Ebru & Koumanova, Bogdana, eds. 2007. (NATO Science for Peace & Security Series C: Environmental Security Ser.). (Illus.). 492p. 249.00 *(978-1-4020-6640-5(6)*, 1402066406) Springer.

Mehmetli, Ebru & Koumanova, Bogdana, eds. The Fate of Persistent Organic Pollutants in the Environment. 2007. (NATO Science for Peace & Security Series C: Environmental Security Ser.). (ENG., Illus.). 492p. per. 129.00 *(978-1-4020-6641-2(4))* Springer.

Mehta, Surinder & Kaur, Khushwinder. Influence of Additives on Microstructure of Reverse Micelles. 2011. 196p. pap. ***(978-3-8433-9162-7(9))*** Lambert Academic Publishing.

Mizuno, Noritaka. Modern Heterogeneous Oxidation Catalysis: Design, Reactions & Characterization. 2009. (ENG., Illus.). 356p. 249.00 *(978-3-527-31859-9(3)*, Wiley-VCH) Wiley, John & Sons, Inc.

Mohrig, Jerry R., et al. Techniques in Organic Chemistry. 3rd ed. 2010. (ENG.). 312p. (C). pap. 59.95 *(978-1-4292-1956-3(4))* Freeman, W. H. & Co.

Molander, Gary. Catalyst Components for Coupling Reactions. 2008. (Hdbk of Reagents for Organic Synthesis Ser.). (ENG., Illus.). 690p. 220.00 *(978-0-470-51811-3(1)*, Wiley) Wiley, John & Sons, Inc.

Moore, John & Langley, Richard H. McGraw-Hill's 500 MCAT Organic Chemistry Questions to Know by Test Day. 2012. (ENG., Illus.). 256p. (C). pap. 25.00 ***(978-0-07-178275-3(3)***, 0071782753) McGraw-Hill Cos., The.

Muramatsu, Atsushi & Miyashita, Tokuji, eds. Nano-hybridization of Organic-Inorganic Materials. 2009. (Advances in Materials Research Ser.). (ENG., Illus.). xvii, 288p. 199.00 *(978-3-540-92232-2(6)*, 3540922326) Springer.

Muthyala, Ramaiah, ed. Arkivoc 2005 Commemorative for Prof Rosa Lederkremer. 2006. 408p. per. 20.00 *(978-1-59730-040-7(3))* Arkat USA, Inc.

Nubbemeyer, Udo & Hiersemann, Martin, eds. The Claisen Rearrangement: Methods & Applications. 2007. (ENG., Illus.). 591p. 265.00 *(978-3-527-30825-5(3)*, Wiley-VCH) Wiley, John & Sons, Inc.

Nyokong, Tebello & Ahsen, Vefa, eds. Photosensitizers in Medicine, Environment, & Security. 2012. (ENG., Illus.). xvi, 662p. 259.00 *(978-90-481-3870-8(1)*, 9048138701) Springer.

Olah, George A. & Klumpp, Douglas A. Superelectrophiles & Their Chemistry. 2007. (ENG., Illus.). 301p. 166.00 *(978-0-470-04961-7(8)*, Wiley-Interscience) Wiley, John & Sons, Inc.

O'Lenick, Anthony J. & O'Lenick, Thomas. Organic Chemistry for the Cosmetic Chemist. 2008. 318p. 179.00 *(978-1-932633-32-0(4))* Allured Business Media.

Ollevier, Thierry, ed. Bismuth-Mediated Organic Reactions. 2012. (Topics in Current Chemistry Ser.). (ENG., Illus.). xiv, 277p. 309.00 ***(978-3-642-27238-7(X)***, 364227238X) Springer.

Overman, Larry E. Organic Reactions. 2006. 576p. 125.00 *(978-0-470-04153-6(6)*, Wiley) Wiley, John & Sons, Inc.

—Organic Reactions, Vol. 69. Denmark, Scott E., ed. 2007. (Organic Reactions Ser.: 71). (ENG.). 704p. 178.00 *(978-0-470-22397-0(9)*, Wiley-Interscience) Wiley, John & Sons, Inc.

—Organic Reactions, Volumes 1 - 74. 2010. (Organic Reactions Ser.: 83). (ENG.). 8200.00 *(978-0-470-63218-5(6)*, Wiley) Wiley, John & Sons, Inc.

Overman, Larry E., ed. Organic Reactions, Volumes 1 - 73. 2009. (Organic Reactions Ser.: 79). (ENG.). 8050.00 *(978-0-470-52304-9(2)*, Wiley) Wiley, John & Sons, Inc.

Overman, Larry E., et al, eds. Organic Reactions, Vol. 70. 2008. (Organic Reactions Ser.: 72). (ENG., Illus.). 656p. 178.00 *(978-0-470-25453-0(X)*, Wiley-Interscience) Wiley, John & Sons, Inc.

Pandithavidana, Dinesh. Photoswitchable Nine-Membered Cyclic Enediynes & Enyne-Allenes. 2011. 148p. pap. ***(978-3-8443-2287-3(6))*** Lambert Academic Publishing.

Pascoe. Organic Chemistry 1 And 2: A Student Workbook. rev. ed. 2011. (ENG.). 330p. spiral bd. 59.99 ***(978-0-7575-9371-0(2))*** Kendall Hunt Publishing Co.

Pignataro, Bruno, ed. Tomorrow's Chemistry Today: Concepts in Nanoscience, Organic Materials & Environmental Chemistry. (Illus.). 2008. 493p. 145.00 *(978-3-527-31918-3(2))* 2nd ed. 2009. (ENG., 464p. 153.00 *(978-3-527-32623-5(5)*, Wiley-VCH) Wiley, John & Sons, Inc.

Pirrung, Michael C. The Synthetic Organic Chemist's Companion. 2007. (ENG., Illus.). 208p. pap. 65.95 *(978-0-470-10707-2(3)*, Wiley-Interscience) Wiley, John & Sons, Inc.

Pozharskii, Alexander F., et al. Heterocycles in Life & Society: An Introduction to Heterocyclic Chemistry, Biochemistry & Applications. 2nd ed. 2011. (ENG., Illus.). 396p. pap. 59.96 *(978-0-470-71410-2(7))*; 150.00 *(978-0-470-71411-9(5))* Wiley, John & Sons, Inc. (Wiley).

Qiu, Zaozao. Late Transition Metal-Carboryne Complexes: Synthesis, Structure, Bonding, & Reaction with Alkenes & Alkynes. 2012. (Springer Theses Ser.). (ENG., Illus.). xviii, 133p. 129.00 ***(978-3-642-24360-8(6)***, 3642243606) Springer.

Quin, Louis D. & Tyrell, John. Fundamentals of Heterocyclic Chemistry: Importance in Nature & in the Synthesis of Pharmaceuticals. 2010. (ENG., Illus.). 327p. 83.95 *(978-0-470-56669-5(8)*, Wiley) Wiley, John & Sons, Inc.

Ragazzon, Patricia. Interactions of Flavones & Related Compounds with Nucleic Acids. 2009. 260p. pap. *(978-3-639-15767-3(2))* VDM Verlag Dr. Mueller e.K.

Ramsden, Christopher, ed. Arkivoc 2000 Commemorative for Prof Gurnos Jones. 2007. 284p. per. 20.00 *(978-1-59730-045-2(4))* Arkat USA, Inc.

—Arkivoc 2006 Commemorative for Prof Jim Coxon. 2007. 256p. per. 20.00 *(978-1-59730-077-3(2))* Arkat USA, Inc.

—Arkivoc 2007 Special Issue for the Rsc Heterocyclic Group. 2006. 196p. per. 20.00 *(978-1-59730-085-8(3))* Arkat USA, Inc.

Rappaport, Zvi. The Chemistry of Functional Chemistry Groups, 10 vols., Sets. 1-2. 2008. (ENG.). 13282p. 11500.00 *(978-0-470-77954-5(3)*, Wiley) Wiley, John & Sons, Inc.

—The Chemistry of Functional Groups. 2008. (ENG.). 6010p. 6800.00 *(978-0-470-77953-8(5)*, Wiley) Wiley, John & Sons, Inc.

Raymond, Kenneth W. General Organic & Biological Chemistry. 3rd ed. (ENG., Illus.). (C). 2010. 624p. 188.95 *(978-0-470-50476-5(5))* 2009. 349p. pap., pupil's gde. ed. 61.95 *(978-0-470-55495-1(9))* Wiley, John & Sons, Inc. (Wiley).

—General, Organic, & Biological Chemistry: An Integrated Approach, Binder Ready Book. 2nd ed. 2007. (ENG.). 656p. (C). ring bd. 113.95 *(978-0-470-27985-4(0)*, Wiley) Wiley, John & Sons, Inc.

—General Organic & Biological Chemistry: An Integrated Approach with Wiley Plus Set. rev. ed. 2006. 82.00 net. *(978-0-470-10394-4(9))* Wiley, John & Sons, Inc.

—General, Organic, & Biological Chemistry: Anintegrated Approach. 2nd ed. 2008. (ENG., Illus.). 640p. (C). stu. ed., per. 61.95 *(978-0-470-22844-9(X)*, Wiley) Wiley, John & Sons, Inc.

Rees, Charles, ed. Arkivoc 2000 Commemorative for Prof Otto Meth-Cohn. 2007. 216p. per. 20.00 *(978-1-59730-047-6(0))* Arkat USA, Inc.

Rehman, Wajid, et al. The Biologically Potent Mannich Bases. 2010. 68p. pap. *(978-3-639-24476-2(1))* VDM Verlag Dr. Mueller e.K.

Rich, James & Lowary, Todd. Carbohydrate Chemistry: Principles & Approaches from Organic Chemistry. 2007. (Illus.). 376p. 79.99 *(978-0-8138-2777-3(9)*, Wiley-Blackwell) Wiley, John & Sons, Inc.

Rocke, Alan J. Image & Reality: Kekulé, Kopp, & the Scientific Imagination. 2010. (Synthesis Ser.). (ENG., Illus.). 416p. 45.00 *(978-0-226-72332-7(1))* Univ. of Chicago Pr.

Rokita, Steven. Carbon-Centered Free Radicals & Radical Cations: Structure, Reactivity, & Dynamics. Forbes, Malcolm D., ed. 2010. (Wiley Series of Reactive Intermediates in Chemistry & Biology Ser.: 2). (ENG., Illus.). 370p. 139.00 *(978-0-470-39009-2(3)*, Wiley) Wiley, John & Sons, Inc.

Roy, Biswajit Gopal & Bikas Mandal, Sukhendu. Enantiopure Nucleosides from Carbohydrates. 2011. 168p. pap. ***(978-3-8443-9248-7(3))*** Lambert Academic Publishing.

Royal Society of Chemistry Staff. Organophosphorus Chemistry, Vol. 37. Tebby, J. C., ed. 2008. (Specialist Periodical Reports). (ENG.). 324p. 448.00 *(978-0-85404-359-0(4))* Royal Society of Chemistry, The GBR. Dist: Ingram Pub. Services.

—Organophosphorus Chemistry, Vol. 38. Allen, D. W. & Tebby, J. C., eds. 2009. (Specialist Periodical Reports). (ENG.). 385p. 480.00 *(978-1-84755-920-3(4))* Royal Society of Chemistry, The GBR. Dist: Ingram Pub. Services.

—Organophosphorus Chemistry, Vol. 39. Allen, D. W. et al, eds. 2010. (Specialist Periodical Reports). (ENG.). 408p. 480.00 ***(978-1-84755-058-3(4))*** Royal Society of Chemistry, The GBR. Dist: Ingram Pub. Services.

Sahai, Mahendra, et al. Fortschritte der Chemie organischer Naturstoffe / Progress in the Chemistry of Organic Natural Products, Vol. 93. Kinghorn, A. Douglas et al, eds. 2010. (Fortschritte der Chemie organischer Naturstoffe Progress in the Chemistry of Organic Natural Products Ser.). (Illus.). xv, 264p. 359.00 *(978-3-7091-0139-1(5)*, 3709101395) Springer.

Santos, Leonardo S., ed. Reactive Intermediates: MS Investigations in Solution. 2010. (ENG., Illus.). 341p. 170.00 *(978-3-527-32351-7(1)*, Wiley-VCH) Wiley, John & Sons, Inc.

Schantl, Joachim, ed. Arkivoc 2001 Commemorative for Prof Academician M G Voronkov. 2006. 200p. per. 20.00 *(978-1-59730-057-5(8))* Arkat USA, Inc.

—Arkivoc 2001 Commemorative for Prof Fritz Sauter. 2007. 184p. per. 20.00 *(978-1-59730-050-6(0))* Arkat USA, Inc.

—Arkivoc 2006 Commemorative for Prof Armand Lattes. 2007. 256p. per. 20.00 *(978-1-59730-078-0(0))* Arkat USA, Inc.

Schrader, Bernhard. Kurzes Lehrbuch der Organischen Chemie. 2nd ed. (De Gruyter Lehrbuch Ser.).Tr. of Compact Textbook of Organic Chemistry. (GER.). XII, 368p. (C). 210.00 ***(978-3-11-178762-6(1))*** De Gruyter, Walter Inc.

Schrader, Bernhard & Rademacher, Paul. Kurzes Lehrbuch der Organischen Chemie. 3rd ed. 2009.Tr. of Compact Textbook of Organic Chemistry. (GER., Illus.). XVII, 386p. (C). pap. 52.00 *(978-3-11-020360-8(X))* De Gruyter, Walter Inc.

Scriven, Eric, ed. Arkivoc 2001 Commemorative for Prof R a Abramovitch. 2006. 148p. per. 20.00 *(978-1-59730-054-4(3))* Arkat USA, Inc.

Semple, Edward, ed. Arkivoc 2007 Commemorative for Prof Madeleine Joullit. 2007. 176p. per. 20.00 *(978-1-59730-097-1(7))* Arkat USA, Inc.

Sharma, Deepa. Advanced Organic Chemistry. 2009. (Illus.). 450p. *(978-1-906574-18-5(9))* New Age Science, Ltd.

Singh, A. K. Alkyl Aryl Sulfonates. 2010. 348p. pap. *(978-3-8383-6836-8(3))* Lambert Academic Publishing.

Sloop, Joseph C. Succeeding in Organic Chemistry: A Systematic Problem-Solving Approach to Mastering Structure, Function & Mechanism. 2010. 144p. pap. 32.95 *(978-1-4520-1737-2(9))* AuthorHouse.

Smith, Dennis A., ed. Metabolism, Pharmacokinetics & Toxicity of Functional Groups: Impact of Chemical Building Blocks on ADMET. 2010. (RSC Drug Discovery Ser.). (ENG., Illus.). 544p. 232.00 ***(978-1-84973-016-7(4))*** Royal Society of Chemistry, The GBR. Dist: Ingram Pub. Services.

Smith, Janice. General Organic & Biological Chemistry. 2009. (ENG.). (C). ring bd., ring bd. 147.33 *(978-0-07-736666-7(2)*, 0077366662, McGraw-Hill Science, Engineering & Mathematics) McGraw-Hill Higher Education.

—Loose Leaf Organic Chemistry. 3rd ed. 2010. (ENG.). (C). ring bd. 173.33 *(978-0-07-740175-7(1)*, 0077401751, McGraw-Hill Science, Engineering & Mathematics) McGraw-Hill Higher Education.

—Organic Chemistry. 3rd ed. 2010. (ENG.). (C). pap. 251.00 *(978-0-07-750023-8(7)*, 0077500237); 256.33 *(978-0-07-740571-7(4)*, 0077405714) McGraw-Hill Higher Education. (McGraw-Hill Science, Engineering & Mathematics).

Smith, Janice G. Organic Chemistry. 2nd ed. 2007. *(978-0-07-304986-1(7))* 3rd ed. 2010. *(978-0-07-337562-5(4))* McGraw-Hill Cos., The.

Smith, Janice Gorzynski. Loose Leaf Version for Principles of General, Organic, & Biochemistry. 2011. (ENG.). (C). ring bd. 130.00 *(978-0-07-743138-9(3)*, 0077431383, McGraw-Hill Science, Engineering & Mathematics) McGraw-Hill Higher Education.

—Organic Chemistry. (ENG., Illus.). (C). 2nd ed. 2007. 1280p. 213.75 *(978-0-07-332749-5(2)*, 0073327492) 3rd ed. 2010. 1312p. 247.33 *(978-0-07-735472-5(9)*, 0077354729) McGraw-Hill Higher Education. (McGraw-Hill Science, Engineering & Mathematics).

—Package: Principles of General, Organic & Biochemistry. 2011. (ENG.). (C). 194.66 *(978-0-07-746845-3(7)*, 0077468457, McGraw-Hill Science, Engineering & Mathematics) McGraw-Hill Higher Education.

—Principles of General, Organic, & Biological Chemistry. 2011. (ENG., Illus.). 736p. (C). 185.67 (978-0-07-351115-3(3), 0073511153, McGraw-Hill Science, Engineering & Mathematics) McGraw-Hill Higher Education.

Smith, Janice Gorzynski & Berk, Erin Smith. Organic Chemistry Student Study Guide/Solutions Manual. 2nd ed. 2007. (ENG., Illus.). 736p. (C). per. 133.33 (978-0-07-304987-8(5), 0073049875, McGraw-Hill Science, Engineering & Mathematics) McGraw-Hill Higher Education.

—Student Study Guide/Solutions Manual to accompany General, Organic & Biological Chemistry. 2009. (ENG.). 528p. (C). pap. 68.67 (978-0-07-302658-9(1), 0073026581, McGraw-Hill Science, Engineering & Mathematics) McGraw-Hill Higher Education.

Smith, Michael. Organic Chemistry. 2nd ed. 2006. (Collins College Outlines Ser.). (ENG., Illus.). 624p. pap. 15.95 (978-0-06-088154-2(2)) HarperCollins Pubs.

—Organic Chemistry: An Acid-Base Approach. 2010. (ENG., Illus.). 1592p. (C). 139.95 (978-1-4200-7920-3(4), CRC Press) Taylor & Francis Group GBR. Dist: Taylor & Francis Group.

Smith, Michael B. & March, Jerry. March's Advanced Organic Chemistry: Reactions, Mechanisms, & Structure. 6th rev. ed. 2007. (ENG., Illus.). 2384p. 120.00 (978-0-471-72091-1(7), Wiley-Interscience) Wiley, John & Sons, Inc.

Smith, Ross. Extracting Reality from Organic Theory. 2011. 60p. pap. (978-3-8443-0570-8(X)) Lambert Academic Publishing.

So, Franky, ed. Organic Electronics: Materials, Processing, Devices & Applications. 2009. (ENG., Illus.). 581p. 154.95 (978-1-4200-7290-7(0), CRC Press) Taylor & Francis Group GBR. Dist: Taylor & Francis Group.

Solomon, Anand & S. Rajan, S. Studies on Antifeedants from Meliaceae Family. 2011. 296p. pap. (978-3-8443-1258-4(7)) Lambert Academic Publishing.

Solomons. Organic Chemistry 10E Binder Ready Version with Binder Student Study Guide/Solutions Manual Molecular Model Kit & WileyPLUS Set. 2011. pap. (978-0-470-93606-1(1)) Wiley, John & Sons, Inc.

—Organic Chemistry 10E Volume 1 for Northern Arizona University with WileyPLUS Set. 2011. pap. (978-0-470-93591-0(X)) Wiley, John & Sons, Inc.

—Organic Chemistry 10E with Study Guide/Solutions Manual Organic Chem as a 2nd Language I 2E Lab Survival Manual 8E & WileyPLUS Set. 2011. (978-0-470-93614-6(2)) Wiley, John & Sons, Inc.

Solomons, T. W. Graham. Wiley Plus/Blackboard Stand-Alone to Accompany Organic Chemistry. 9th ed. 2007. pap. 0.01 (978-0-470-09953-7(4), Wiley) Wiley, John & Sons, Inc.

Solomons, T. W. Graham & Fryhle, Craig B. Organic Chemistry. 8th ed. 2006. pap. 83.95 (978-0-470-07961-4(4)) 9th rev. ed. 2007. (ENG., Illus.). 1280p. (C). 231.95 (978-0-471-68496-1(1), Wiley) 10th ed. 2010. (ENG.). 744p. (C). pap., pupil's gde. ed. 125.95 (978-0-470-47839-4(X), Wiley) 10th ed. 2009. (ENG.). 1272p. (C). 231.95 (978-0-470-40141-5(9), Wiley) Wiley, John & Sons, Inc.

—Organic Chemistry, Binder Ready Version. 9th ed. 2007. (ENG.). 1280p. (C). ring bd. 143.95 (978-0-471-75237-0(1), Wiley) Wiley, John & Sons, Inc.

—WP Course Organic Chemistry. 10th ed. 2010. (C). 77.95 (978-0-470-57859-9(9), Wiley) Wiley, John & Sons, Inc.

Song, Choong Eui, ed. Cinchona Alkaloids in Synthesis & Catalysis: Ligands, Immobilization & Organocatalysis. 2009. (ENG., Illus.). 546p. 205.00 (978-3-527-32416-3(X), Wiley-VCH) Wiley, John & Sons, Inc.

Spessard, Gary. Advanced Organic Chemistry. 2007. (Illus.). 800p. pap. (978-0-632-04334-7(2), Wiley-Blackwell) Wiley, John & Sons, Ltd.

Stephens, Philip John, et al. Vcd Spectroscopy for Organic Chemists. 2012. (ENG., Illus.). 310p. 149.95 (978-1-4398-2171-8(2), CRC Press) Taylor & Francis Group GBR. Dist: Taylor & Francis Group.

Stevens, Christian, ed. Arkivoc 2006 General Papers. 2007. 148p. per. 20.00 (978-1-59730-075-9(6)) Arkat USA, Inc.

—Arkivoc 2007 Commemorative for Prof Joan Bosch. 2008. 480p. per. 20.00 (978-1-59730-089-6(6)) Arkat USA, Inc.

Stevens, Christian & Turnbull, Kenneth, eds. Arkivoc 2005 General Papers. 2007. 252p. per. 20.00 (978-1-59730-076-6(4)) Arkat USA, Inc.

Stoker, H. Stephen. General, Organic & Biological Chemistry. 4th ed. 2006. (ENG.). 432p. (C). pap., lab manual ed. 110.95 (978-0-618-60608-5(4), 354232) Brooks/Cole.

Straumanis, Andrei. Organic Chemistry: Guided Inquiry for Recitation, Volume 2. 2011. (ENG.). 224p. (C). pap. 23.95 (978-1-111-57398-0(0)) Brooks/Cole.

—Organic Chemistry Vol. 1: Guided Inquiry for Recitation. 2011. (ENG.). 224p. (C). pap. 23.95 (978-1-111-57399-7(9)) Brooks/Cole.

—Straumanis' Organic Chemistry: A Guided Inquiry for Recitation. 2011. (ENG.). 160p. (C). pap. 29.95 (978-1-111-57817-6(6)) Brooks/Cole.

Stumbraite, Jolanta, et al. 1-Phenyl-1,2,3,4-Tetrahydroquinoline Based Electroactive Materials. 2010. 168p. pap. (978-3-8383-4498-0(7)) Lambert Academic Publishing.

Subba Rao, G. G. S. R., ed. Arkivoc 2001 Commemorative for Prof T Govindachari. 2006. 192p. per. 20.00 (978-1-59730-056-8(X)) Arkat USA, Inc.

Suggs, J. William & Zimmt, Matthew. Organic Chemistry. 2009. (C). pap. 70.95 (978-0-471-69260-7(3), Wiley) Wiley, John & Sons, Inc.

Swain, Frederick M. Non-Marine Organic Geochemistry. 2010. (Cambridge Earth Science Ser.). (ENG., Illus.). 460p. pap. 28.99 (978-0-521-15510-6(X)) Cambridge Univ. Pr.

Thonggom, Rattapom, et al, eds. Emerging Topics in Organic Chemistry. 2008. (Illus.). vii, 259p. 120.00 (978-1-60456-633-8(7)) Nova Science Pubs., Inc.

Tiekink, Edward R. T., et al, eds. Organic Crystal Engineering: Frontiers in Crystal Engineering. 2010. (ENG., Illus.). 336p. 260.00 (978-0-470-31990-1(9), Wiley) Wiley, John & Sons, Inc.

Timberlake, Karen C. Chemistry: An Introduction to General, Organic, & Biological Chemistry with MasteringChemistry(r). 11th rev. ed. 2011. (ENG.). 744p. (C). 194.07 (978-0-321-74104-2(8), Prentice Hall) Prentice Hall PTR.

Toda, Fumio, ed. Organic Solid-State Reactions. 2010. 288p. pap. 184.00 (978-90-481-5923-9(7), 9048159237) Springer.

Todres, Zory Vlad. Chalcogenadiazoles: Chemistry & Applications. 2011. (ENG., Illus.). 310p. 199.95 (978-1-4200-6607-4(2), CRC Press) Taylor & Francis Group GBR. Dist: Taylor & Francis Group.

Tozer-Hotchkiss, G., ed. Theilheimer's Synthetic Methods of Organic Chemistry. (Theilheimer's Synthetic Methods of Organic Chemistry Ser.). 2011. (ENG.). 492p. (978-3-8055-9864-4(5)) 2007. (Illus.). 412p. (978-3-8055-8404-3(0)) Karger, S. AG.

Tozer-Hotchkiss, G., ed. & contrib. by. Theilheimer's Synthetic Methods of Organic Chemistry. (Theilheimer's Synthetic Methods of Organic Chemistry Ser.). 2011. 460p. (978-3-8055-9678-7(2)) 2010. 474p. (978-3-8055-9390-8(2)) 2009. (ENG.). 458p. (978-3-8055-9235-2(3)) 2009. 428p. (978-3-8055-9069-3(5)) 2008. 456p. (978-3-8055-8639-9(6))Vol 76. 2010. 458p. (978-3-8055-9572-8(7)) Karger, S. AG.

Traynham, James G. Organic Nomenclature: A Programmed Introduction. 6th rev. ed. 2008. (ENG., Illus.). 160p. (C). pap. 59.73 (978-0-13-017868-8(3), Prentice Hall) Prentice Hall PTR.

Trimm, Harold H., ed. Organic Chemistry: Structure & Mechanisms. 2011. (Research Progress in Chemistry Ser.). (ENG.). 384p. 99.95 (978-1-926692-60-9(8)) Apple Academic Pr., Inc. CAN. Dist: Taylor & Francis Group.

Turnbull, Kenneth, ed. Arkivoc 2006 General Papers. 2007. 244p. per. 20.00 (978-1-59730-084-1(5)) Arkat USA, Inc.

Turnbull, Kenneth, et al, eds. Arkivoc 2007 General Papers. 2008. 304p. per. 20.00 (978-1-59730-098-8(5)); 340p. per. 20.00 (978-1-59730-106-0(X)) Arkat USA, Inc.

Turnbull, Kenneth & Waring, Anthony, eds. Arkivoc 2007 General Papers. 2007. 260p. per. 20.00 (978-1-59730-086-5(1)) Arkat USA, Inc.

Turro, Nicholas J., et al. Modern Molecular Photochemistry of Organic Molecules. 2010. (Illus.). 1120p. (C). 134.50 (978-1-891389-25-2(4)) Univ. Science Bks.

Verschueren, Karel. Verschueren Network. 5th ed. 2009. (ENG.). 4p. 1570.00 (978-0-470-48472-2(1), Wiley) Wiley, John & Sons, Inc.

Vollath, Dieter & Wedemeyer, Horst. Uranium Dioxide, UO2, Preparation & Crystallographic Properties. 8th ed. 2007. (Gmelin Handbook of Inorganic & Organometallic Chemistry - 8th edition / U. Uran. Uranium (System-Nr. 55) Ser.). 156p. 425.00 (978-3-540-93509-4(6)) Springer.

Vollhardt, K. Peter C. & Schore, Neil E. Organic Chemistry. 6th ed. 2010. (ENG.). 1203p. (C). 190.95 (978-1-4292-0494-1(X)) Freeman, W. H. & Co.

Vollhardt, Peter & Schore, Neil. Organic Chemistry: Structure & Function. 6th ed. 2010. 250.00 (978-1-4292-7731-0(9)); ring bd. 138.95 (978-1-4292-7732-7(7)) Freeman, W. H. & Co.

Wade, L. G., Jr. Organic Chemistry. 8th ed. (ENG.). (C). 2012. 1328p. ring bd. 150.47 (978-0-321-77387-6(X)) 2011. 1320p. 244.07 (978-0-321-76814-8(0)) Prentice Hall PTR. (Prentice Hall).

Wade, L. G., Jr. & Simek, Jan. Organic Chemistry. 7th ed. 2011. (ENG.). 712p. (C). ring bd., pupil's gde. ed. 84.73 (978-0-321-77417-0(5), Prentice Hall) Prentice Hall PTR.

Wade, Leroy G., Jr. Organic Chemistry. 7th ed. 2009. (ENG.). 1320p. (C). 234.07 (978-0-321-59231-6(X), Prentice Hall) Prentice Hall PTR.

Wade, Leroy G. Organic Chemistry. 8th rev. ed. 2011. (ENG.). 1320p. (C). 234.07 (978-0-321-76841-4(8), Prentice Hall) Prentice Hall PTR.

Wade, LeRoy G. Organic Chemistry, Books a la Carte Edition. 8th ed. 2012. (ENG.). 1320p. (C). ring bd. 140.47 (978-0-321-77769-0(7), Prentice Hall) Prentice Hall PTR.

Wade, LeRoy G. & Simek, Jan. Student Solutions Manual for Organic Chemistry. 7th ed. 2009. (ENG.). 712p. (C). pap. 121.00 (978-0-321-59871-4(7), Prentice Hall) Prentice Hall PTR.

Wang, Ying. Equilibrium Hydrogen Isotope Fractionation in Organic Molecules. 2010. 192p. pap. (978-3-639-04701-1(X)) VDM Verlag Dr. Mueller e.K.

Wang, Zerong. Comprehensive Organic Name Reactions & Reagents, 3 vols. 2009. (ENG., Illus.). 1368p. 198.33 (978-0-470-53346-8(3)); Vol. 1. 1304p. 198.34 (978-0-470-28662-3(8)); Vol. 2. 987p. 198.33 (978-0-470-28563-0(6)) Wiley, John & Sons, Inc. (Wiley-Interscience).

Waring, Anthony, ed. Arkivoc 2006 Commemorative for Prof Giuseppe Bartoli. 2007. 216p. per. 20.00 (978-1-59730-080-3(2)) Arkat USA, Inc.

—Arkivoc 2007 Commemorative for Prof Lutz Tietze. 2007. 328p. per. 20.00 (978-1-59730-090-2(X)) Arkat USA, Inc.

Waring, Anthony, et al, eds. Arkivoc 2006 General Papers. 2008. 196p. per. 20.00 (978-1-59730-100-8(0)) Arkat USA, Inc.

Waser, Mario. Asymmetric Organocatalysis in Natural Product Syntheses. 2012. (Progress in the Chemistry of Organic Natural Products Ser.: 96). (ENG., Illus.). vi, 200p. 259.00 (978-3-7091-1162-8(5), 3709111625) Springer.

Watts, W. E., et al, eds. Organic Reaction Mechanisms 2005. 2009. (Organic Reaction Mechanisms Ser.: 119). (ENG.). 594p. 710.00 (978-0-470-03403-3(3), Wiley) Wiley, John & Sons, Inc.

(WCS)Organic Chemistry 9e Binder Ready Version with Binder, Wiley Plus & iClick Set. 2007. (Wiley Plus Products Ser.). pap. 96.00 net. (978-0-470-89645-7(0)) Wiley, John & Sons, Inc.

Wepplo, Peter. A Guide to Organic Chemistry Mechanisms: A Guide to Organic Chemistry Mechanisms. 2008. (ENG.). (C). pap., pupil's gde. ed. 49.95 (978-0-9779313-0-9(7)) CurvedArrowPress.

WFohler, Friedrich. Wfohler's Outlines of Organic Chemistry. 2006. 568p. per. 32.99 (978-1-4255-6201-4(9)) MPublishing.

Whitmore, Frank C. Organic Chemistry, Volume Two: Part III: Aromatic Compounds Part IV: Heterocyclic Compounds Part V: Organophosphorus & Organometallic Compounds. 2011. (Dover Books on Chemistry Ser.). (ENG.). 416p. pap. 24.95 (978-0-486-60701-6(1)) Dover Pubns., Inc.

Whitmore, Frank C. & Chemistry Associates Staff. Organic Chemistry, Volume One: Part I: Aliphatic Compounds Part II: Alicyclic Compounds. 2011. (Dover Books on Chemistry Ser.). (ENG.). 608p. pap. 24.95 (978-0-486-60700-9(3)) Dover Pubns., Inc.

Wild. Estimation Organic Compounds. 2009. (ENG.). 248p. pap. 53.00 (978-0-521-11275-8(3)) Cambridge Univ. Pr.

Wild, F. Characterization of Organic Compounds. 2011. 314p. 50.95 (978-1-258-08486-8(4)) Literary Licensing, LLC.

Williams, Dudley H. & Fleming, Ian. Spectroscopic Methods in Organic Chemistry. 6th ed. 2007. 304p. pap. 89.98 (978-0-07-711812-9(X)) McGraw-Hill Education.

Winter, Arthur. Organic Chemistry I Workbook for Dummies. 2008. (ENG., Illus.). 360p. pap., wbk. ed. 19.99 (978-0-470-25151-5(4), For Dummies) Wiley, John & Sons, Inc.

Wittmann, Christine. Immobilisation of DNA on Chips II. 2010. (Topics in Current Chemistry Ser.). xvi, 199p. pap. 179.00 (978-3-642-06666-5(6), 3642066666) Springer.

Xu, Libin. Designing Models to Elucidate Radical Reaction Mechanisms. 2008. 188p. pap. (978-3-639-05150-6(5)) VDM Verlag Dr. Mueller e.K.

Yalkowsky, Samuel H. & Jain, Parijat. Aqueous Solubility Data. 2nd ed. 2010. (ENG., Illus.). 1620p. instr.'s hndbk. ed. 420.00 (978-1-4398-0245-8(9), CRC Press) Taylor & Francis Group GBR. Dist: Taylor & Francis Group.

Yaws, Carl L. Thermophysical Properties of Chemicals & Hydrocarbons. 2008. (ENG., Illus.). 800p. 305.00 (978-0-8155-1596-8(0)) William Andrew, Inc.

Yoder, Claude H., et al. The Bridge to Organic Chemistry: Concepts & Nomenclature. 2010. (ENG., Illus.). 112p. pap. 19.95 (978-0-470-52676-7(9), Wiley) Wiley, John & Sons, Inc.

Yoshida, Jun-Ichi. Flash Chemistry: Fast Organic Synthesis in Microsystems. 2008. (ENG., Illus.). 244p. 179.00 (978-0-470-03586-3(2), Wiley) Wiley, John & Sons, Inc.

Yu, Jin-Quan & Shi, Zhangjie, eds. C-H Activation. 2010. (Topics in Current Chemistry Ser.). (ENG., Illus.). xii, 380p. 359.00 (978-3-642-12355-9(4), 3642123554) Springer.

Zaikov, Gennadii Efremovich, ed. Modern Tendencies in Organic & Bioorganic Chemistry: Today & Tomorrow. 2008. (Illus.). viii, 423p. 185.00 (978-1-60456-295-8(1)) Nova Science Pubs., Inc.

Zhdankin, Viktor, ed. Arkivoc 2006 Special Issue Reviews & Accounts. 2007. 376p. per. 20.00 (978-1-59730-083-4(7)) Arkat USA, Inc.

—Arkivoc 2007 Commemorative for Prof Berhanu M Abegaz. 2008. 164p. per. 20.00 (978-1-59730-094-0(2)) Arkat USA, Inc.

CHEMISTRY, ORGANIC—EXPERIMENTS

Bhowmik-Behnia. Microscale Experiments in Organic Chemistry. rev. ed. 2011. (ENG.). 138p. spiral bd. 37.99 (978-0-7575-9688-9(6)) Kendall Hunt Publishing Co.

Cram101 Textbook Reviews Staff. Outlines & Highlights for Operational Organic Chemistry: A Problem-Solving Approach to the Laboratory Course by John W. Lehman, ISBN. 2009. 78p. pap. 27.95 (978-1-4288-8173-0(5)) Cram101 Inc.

Hall, James W. Experimental Chemistry: An Atoms First Approach. 2011. (ENG.). 624p. (C). pap., lab manual ed. 125.95 (978-0-8400-6585-8(X)) Brooks/Cole.

Williamson, Kenneth L. & Masters, Katherine M. Techniques Labs for Macroscale & Microscale Organic Experiments. 6th ed. 2011. (ENG.). 336p. (C). pap. 119.95 (978-1-111-43041-2(1)) Brooks/Cole.

CHEMISTRY, ORGANIC—HISTORY

Russell, Colin A. From Atoms to Molecules: Studies in the History of Chemistry from the 19th Century. 2010. (Variorum Collected Studies). (Illus.). 342p. 165.00 (978-0-7546-6855-8(X)) Ashgate Publishing Co.

CHEMISTRY, ORGANIC—LABORATORY MANUALS

Belostotskii. Conformational Concept for Synthetic... 2011. 107.00 (978-981-281-409-8(4)) World Scientific Publishing Co., Inc.

Bettelheim, Frederick A., et al. Lab Experiments for Organic & Biochemistry. 6th ed. 2007. (Illus.). xxiii, 554p. (978-0-495-10656-2(9)); (978-0-495-18998-5(7)) Brooks/Cole.

Brown, William H., et al. Organic Chemistry - Study Guide with Student Solutions Manual. 6th ed. 2011. (ENG.). 848p. (C). pap. 151.95 (978-1-111-42681-1(3)) Brooks/Cole.

Brunke, Kathleen & Carney, Jeffrey. Organic Chemistry 321 & 322 Lab Manual, 2nd Ed. , Fall 2011. 2011. (C). spiral bd. (978-1-60036-465-5(9)) Academx Publishing Services, Inc.

Caron, Stéphane, ed. Practical Synthetic Organic Chemistry: Reactions, Principles, & Techniques. 2011. (ENG., Illus.). 872p. pap. 99.95 (978-0-470-03733-1(4), Wiley) Wiley, John & Sons, Inc.

Cerny, Kenneth F. & Schwartz, Marietta H. Laboratory Manual for Organic Chemistry. 3rd rev. ed. 2010. (ENG.). 224p. spiral bd. 43.95 (978-0-7575-8286-8(9)) Kendall Hunt Publishing Co.

Cram101 Textbook Reviews. Outlines & Highlights for Introduction to Organic Laboratory Techniques: A Microscale Approach by Donald L. Pavia, Gary M. Lampman, George S. Kriz, Ra. 2010. 76p. pap. 27.95 (978-1-61698-563-9(1)) Cram101 Inc.

—Outlines & Highlights for Multiscale Operational Organic Chemistry: A Problem Solving Approach to the Laboratory, Vol. 2 by John W Lehman, ISBN. 2010. 188p. pap. 30.95 (978-1-61698-559-2(3)) Cram101 Inc.

Cram101 Textbook Reviews Staff. Outlines & Highlights for Introduction to Organic Laboratory Techniques: A Microscale Approach by Donald L. Pavia, Gary M. Lampman, George S. Kriz, Ra. 2009. 66p. pap. 27.95 (978-1-4288-8172-3(7)) Cram101 Inc.

—Outlines & Highlights for Multiscale Operational Organic Chemistry: A Problem Solving Approach to the Laboratory, Vol. 2 by John W Lehman, ISBN. 2009. 164p. pap. 29.95 (978-1-4288-8176-1(X)) Cram101 Inc.

—Outlines & Highlights for Organic Laboratory Techniques by Fessenden, Ralph J / Fessenden, Joan S , Isbn: 9780534379810. 2009. 56p. pap. 26.95 (978-1-4288-8183-9(2)) Cram101 Inc.

Fijolek, Hilary. Organic Chemistry I Laboratory Manual. rev. ed. 2010. (ENG.). 172p. spiral bd. 72.12 (978-0-7575-6896-1(3)) Kendall Hunt Publishing Co.

Hein, Morris, et al. Introduction to General Organic & Biochemistry. 10th ed. 2011. (ENG.). 512p. (C). pap., lab manual ed. 142.95 (978-0-470-59881-8(6), Wiley) Wiley, John & Sons, Inc.

Johnson, Paul G. & Patil, Sujata. Microscale & Miniscale Laboratory Investigations in Organic Chemistry. 2nd rev. ed. 2010. (ENG.). 334p. spiral bd. 89.60 (978-0-7575-5211-3(0)) Kendall Hunt Publishing Co.

Kim, Jaegwon, et al. Experiments in Organic Chemistry I Laboratory (CHEM 201), Fifth Ed. 2006. (C). spiral bd. (978-1-932768-84-8(X)) Academx Publishing Services, Inc.

Landesberg, Joseph M. eneral, Organic, & Biochemistry - Laboratory Experiments. 2011. (ENG.). 256p. (C). pap. 69.95 (978-1-111-42661-3(9)) Brooks/Cole.

Landrie, Chad. Organic Chemistry Laboratory I, No. 233. rev. ed. 2009. (ENG.). 132p. spiral bd., lab manual ed. 32.05 (978-0-7575-6240-2(X)) Kendall Hunt Publishing Co.

Lehman, John W. Laboratory Techniques for Organic Chemistry: Standard Scale & Microscale. 2nd ed. 2008. (ENG. Illus.). 488p. (C). per. 83.07 (978-0-13-159381-7(1), Prentice Hall) Prentice Hall PTR.

—Microscale Operational Organic Chemistry Vol 3: A Problem Solving Approach to the Laboratory. 2nd ed. 2008. 816p. (C). 98.67 (978-0-13-158716-8(1), Prentice Hall) Prentice Hall PTR.

—Multiscale Operational Organic Chemistry Vol. 2: A Problem Solving Approach to the Laboratory. 2nd ed. 2008. (ENG., Illus.). 984p. (C). 154.33 (978-0-13-241375-6(2), Prentice Hall) Prentice Hall PTR.

Macaulay, David B., et al. General, Organic & Biological Chemistry: An Integrated Approach. 2nd ed. 2009. (ENG.). 344p. (C). pap., lab manual ed. 88.95 (978-0-470-56171-3(8), Wiley) Wiley, John & Sons, Inc.

Mariappan, Manoharan. Organic Chemistry Laboratory Manual. rev. ed. 2009. (ENG.). 82p. spiral bd. 33.80 (978-0-7575-6841-1(6)) Kendall Hunt Publishing Co.

Mayo, Dana W., et al. Microscale Organic Laboratory: With Multistep & Multiscale Syntheses. 5th ed. 2010. (ENG., Illus.). 704p. (C). 200.95 (978-0-471-21502-8(3), Wiley) Wiley, John & Sons, Inc.

Pavia, Donald L., et al. A Small Scale Approach to Organic Laboratory Techniques. 3rd ed. 2010. (Available Titles CourseMate Ser.). (ENG.). 1024p. (C). 246.95 (978-1-4390-4932-7(7)) Brooks/Cole.

Pedersen, Steven F. & Myers, Arlyn M. Understanding the Principles of Organic Chemistry: A Laboratory Course, Reprint. 2010. (Available Titles CengageNOW Ser.). (ENG.). 432p. (C). 154.95 (978-1-111-42816-7(6)) Brooks/Cole.

Prescott, A. B. (Albert Benjamin). Outlines of Proximate Organic Analysis. 2006. 248p. per. 20.99 (978-1-4255-2129-5(0)) MPublishing.

Rosenberg, Robert C. Experimental Organic Chemistry: 2006-2007 Howard Univ. Edition. 2006. (C). per. (978-1-60035-038-1(6)) Academx Publishing Services, Inc.

Tietze, Lutz F., et al. Reactions & Syntheses: In the Organic Chemistry Laboratory. 3rd ed. 2007. (ENG., Illus.). 598p. pap. 115.00 (978-3-527-31223-8(4), Wiley-VCH) Wiley, John & Sons, Inc.

Timberlake, Karen C. Lab Manual for General, Organic, & Biological Chemistry. 2nd ed. 2010. (ENG.). 624p. (C). pap. 97.40 (978-0-321-69529-1(1), Prentice Hall) Prentice Hall PTR.

Uncw - Chemistry Dept Staff. Organic Chemistry: Chemistry 211-212 Laboratory Manual. 2nd rev. ed. 2010. (ENG.). 276p. spiral bd. 54.31 (978-0-7575-8241-7(9)) Kendall Hunt Publishing Co.

Vinod, T. K. & Craine, Leslie E. Organic Chemistry: A Short Course -Laboratory Manual. 13th ed. 2011. (ENG.). 512p. (C). pap. 118.95 (978-1-111-42584-5(1)) Brooks/Cole.

Williamson, Kenneth L. & Masters, Katherine M. Macroscale & Microscale Organic Experiments. 6th ed. 2010. (Available Titles CourseMate Ser.). (ENG.). 816p. (C). 230.95 (978-0-538-73333-5(0)) Brooks/Cole.

—Techniques Labs for Macroscale & Microscale Organic Experiments. 6th ed. 2011. (ENG.). 336p. (C). pap. 119.95 (978-1-111-43041-2(1)) Brooks/Cole.

Zubrick, James W. The Organic Chem: A Student's Guide to Techniques. 8th ed. 2010. (ENG., Illus.). 376p. (C). pap., stu. ed., lab manual ed. 74.95 (978-0-470-49437-0(9), Wiley) Wiley, John & Sons, Inc.

Zubrick, James W. & Peterson Kathleen A. Elementary Organic Laboratory II; Chem 21224: The Organic Chem Lab Survival Manual. 2007. (ENG., Illus.). 114p. (C). pap. 56.95 (978-0-470-13036-0(9), Wiley) Wiley, John & Sons, Inc.

CHEMISTRY, ORGANIC—OUTLINES, SYLLABI, ETC.

Blei & Odian & Cram101 Textbook Reviews Staff. General, Organic, & Biochemistry. 2007. 284p. per. 15.95 (978-1-4288-2932-9(6)) Cram101 Inc.

Brown & Foote & Cram101 Textbook Reviews Staff. Organic Chemistry. 2007. 464p. per. 19.95 (978-1-4288-2938-1(5)) Cram101 Inc.

Cassidy, Patrick E. & David, Wendi M. Summary of Key Concepts, Organic Chemistry: Semesters One & Two. rev. ed. 2008. (ENG.). 130p. ring bd. 54.59 *(978-0-7575-5207-6(2))* Kendall Hunt Publishing Co.

Cram101 Textbook Reviews. Outlines & Highlights for Chemistry for Today: General, Organic, & Biochemistry by Spencer L. Seager, Michael R. Slabaugh, ISBN. 2010. 148p. pap. 29.95 *(978-1-61698-580-6(1))* Cram101 Inc.

—Outlines & Highlights for Essentials of General, Organic, & Biological Chemistry by H Stephen Stoker, Sharon K Stoffels, Isbn: 9780618192823. 2010. 154p. pap. 29.95 *(978-1-61698-613-1(1))* Cram101 Inc.

—Outlines & Highlights for Fundamentals of Organic Chemistry by John E Mcmurry, Eric E Simanek, Isbn: 9780495012030. 2010. 212p. pap. 30.95 *(978-1-61698-566-0(6))* Cram101 Inc.

—Outlines & Highlights for Fundamentals of Organic Chemistry by John E Mcmurry, Isbn: 9781439049716 1439049718. 2011. 280p. pap. 32.95 ***(978-1-61490-199-0(6))*** Cram101 Inc.

—Outlines & Highlights for General, Organic, & Biological Chemistry by H Stephen Stoker, Isbn: 9780547152813 0547152817. 2011. 560p. pap. 38.95 ***(978-1-61490-182-2(1))*** Cram101 Inc.

—Outlines & Highlights for General Organic & Biological Chemistry by Kenneth W Raymond, Isbn: 9780470504765 0470504765. 2011. 366p. pap. 34.95 ***(978-1-61490-185-3(6))*** Cram101 Inc.

—Outlines & Highlights for General, Organic, & Biological Chemistry by Laura D Frost, Isbn: 9780805381788 0805381783. 2011. 272p. pap. 32.95 ***(978-1-61490-181-5(3))*** Cram101 Inc.

—Outlines & Highlights for Industrial Organic Chemistry by Hans-J?Rgen Arpe. 2011. 170p. pap. 29.95 ***(978-1-61905-437-0(X))*** Cram101 Inc.

—Outlines & Highlights for Introduction to General, Organic & Biochemistry in the Laboratory by Leo R Best, Morris Hein, Scott Pattison, Susan Aren. 2010. 202p. pap. 30.95 *(978-1-61698-610-0(7))* Cram101 Inc.

—Outlines & Highlights for Introduction to Organic Chemistry by Brown, William H / Poon, Thomas, Isbn: 9780471444510. 2010. 228p. pap. 31.95 *(978-1-61698-561-5(5))* Cram101 Inc.

—Outlines & Highlights for Introduction to Organic Laboratory Techniques: A Microscale Approach by Donald L. Pavia, Gary M. Lampman, George S. Kriz, Ra. 2010. 76p. pap. 27.95 *(978-1-61698-563-9(1))* Cram101 Inc.

—Outlines & Highlights for Multiscale Operational Organic Chemistry: A Problem Solving Approach to the Laboratory, Vol. 2 by John W Lehman, ISBN. 2010. 188p. pap. 30.95 *(978-1-61698-559-2(3))* Cram101 Inc.

—Outlines & Highlights for Operational Organic Chemistry: A Problem-Solving Approach to the Laboratory Course by John W. Lehman, ISBN. 2010. 90p. pap. 27.95 *(978-1-61698-562-2(3))* Cram101 Inc.

—Outlines & Highlights for Organic & Biochemistry for Today by Spencer L Seager, Michael R Slabaugh, Isbn. 2010. 82p. pap. 27.95 *(978-1-61698-612-4(3))* Cram101 Inc.

—Outlines & Highlights for Organic & Biological Chemistry by H Stephen Stoker. 2011. 442p. pap. 36.95 ***(978-1-61905-782-1(4))*** Cram101 Inc.

—Outlines & Highlights for Organic Chemistry by K Peter C Vollhardt, Neil E Schore, Peter C , Isbn: 9780716799498. 2010. 426p. pap. 35.95 *(978-1-61698-565-3(8))* Cram101 Inc.

—Outlines & Highlights for Organic Chemistry by Leroy Wade, Isbn: 9780131478718. 2010. 382p. pap. 34.95 *(978-1-61698-564-6(X))* Cram101 Inc.

—Outlines & Highlights for Organic Chemistry by Paula y Bruice. 2011. 508p. pap. 37.95 ***(978-1-61905-783-8(2))*** Cram101 Inc.

—Outlines & Highlights for Organic Chemistry by Paula Yurkanis Bruice, Isbn: 9780131963160 9780132415132 9780131996311 0132415135 9780132248266. 2011. 304p. pap. 32.95 ***(978-1-4288-8175-4(1))*** Cram101 Inc.

—Outlines & Highlights for Organic Chemistry by T W Graham Solomons, Craig B Fryhle, Isbn: 9780471684961. 2010. 404p. pap. 35.95 *(978-1-61698-569-1(0))* Cram101 Inc.

—Outlines & Highlights for Organic Chemistry by William H Brown, Christopher S Foote, Brent L Iverson, Isbn: 97805344677. 2010. 166p. pap. 41.95 *(978-1-61698-567-7(4))* Cram101 Inc.

—Outlines & Highlights for Organic Chemistry by William H Brown, Isbn: 9780495388579. 2010. 100p. pap. 27.95 *(978-1-61698-568-4(2))* Cram101 Inc.

Cram101 Textbook Reviews & Cram101 Textbook Reviews. Outlines & Highlights for Advanced Organic Chemistry, Part: Structure & Mechanisms by Francis A. Carey, ISBN. 2011. 228p. pap. 31.95 ***(978-1-61490-462-5(6))*** Cram101 Inc.

—Outlines & Highlights for Advanced Organic Chemistry, Part B by Francis a Carey, Isbn: 9780387683546 0387683542. 2011. 224p. pap. 30.95 ***(978-1-61490-460-1(X))*** Cram101 Inc.

—Outlines & Highlights for Chemistry for Today: General, Organic, & Biochemistry by Spencer L. Seager, Michael R. Slabaugh, ISBN. 2011. 436p. pap. 36.95 ***(978-1-61461-759-4(7))*** Cram101 Inc.

—Outlines & Highlights for Introduction to Organic & Biochemistry by Frederick a Bettelheim, Isbn: 9780495391166 0495391166. 2011. 278p. pap. 32.95 ***(978-1-61490-783-1(8))*** Cram101 Inc.

—Outlines & Highlights for Marchs Advanced Organic Chemistry: Reactions, Mechanisms, & Structure by Michael B. Smith, ISBN. 2011. 430p. pap. 36.95 ***(978-1-61490-789-3(7))*** Cram101 Inc.

—Outlines & Highlights for Organic Chemistry: A Biological Approach by John E. Mcmurry, ISBN. 2011. 172p. pap. 29.95 ***(978-1-61461-775-4(9))*** Cram101 Inc.

—Outlines & Highlights for Organic Chemistry by Jones, Isbn: 9780393114058. 2011. 480p. pap. 37.95 ***(978-1-61461-752-5(X))*** Cram101 Inc.

—Outlines Joseph J Topping; Robert L Caret, Isbn: 9780077354800 9780073. 2011. 268p. pap. 31.95 ***(978-1-61461-760-0(0))*** Cram101 Inc.

—Outlines Maitland Jones Jr , Isbn: 9780393931495. 2011. 460p. pap. 36.95 ***(978-1-61461-753-2(8))*** Cram101 Inc.

—Outlines Thomas Poon, Isbn: 9780470129234. 2011. 216p. pap. 30.95 ***(978-1-61461-751-8(1))*** Cram101 Inc.

Cram101 Textbook Reviews Staff. Outlines & Highlights for Essential Organic Chemistry by Paula y Bruice, Isbn: 9780321596956. 2009. 178p. pap. 29.95 *(978-1-4288-9071-8(8))* Cram101 Inc.

—Outlines & Highlights for General, Organic, & Biochemistry by Katherine J Denniston, Isbn: 9780077221416. 2009. 412p. pap. 35.95 *(978-1-4288-8682-7(6))* Cram101 Inc.

—Outlines & Highlights for General, Organic, & Biological Chemistry: An Integrated Approach by Kenneth W. Raymond, ISBN. 2009. 136p. pap. 28.95 *(978-1-4288-8297-3(9))* Cram101 Inc.

—Outlines & Highlights for General, Organic, & Biological Chemistry by H Stephen Stoker, Isbn: 9780618606061. 2009. 386p. pap. 34.95 *(978-1-4288-9657-4(0))* Cram101 Inc.

—Outlines & Highlights for Introduction to Organic Laboratory Techniques: A Microscale Approach by Donald L. Pavia, Gary M. Lampman, George S. Kriz, Ra. 2009. 66p. pap. 27.95 *(978-1-4288-8172-3(7))* Cram101 Inc.

—Outlines & Highlights for Multiscale Operational Organic Chemistry: A Problem Solving Approach to the Laboratory, Vol. 2 by John W Lehman, ISBN. 2009. 164p. pap. 29.95 *(978-1-4288-8176-1(X))* Cram101 Inc.

—Outlines & Highlights for Organic & Biochemistry, Chapters 10-23 from General, Organic, & Biochemistry by Katherine J Denniston, Isbn: 9780077240. 2009. 176p. pap. 29.95 *(978-1-4288-9054-1(8))* Cram101 Inc.

—Outlines & Highlights for Organic Chemistry by Carey, Isbn: 0073047872. 2007. 416p. per. 18.95 *(978-1-4288-5712-4(5))* Cram101 Inc.

—Outlines & Highlights for Organic Chemistry by Francis a Carey, Isbn: 9780073047874. 2009. 576p. pap. 39.95 *(978-1-4288-8482-3(3))* Cram101 Inc.

—Outlines & Highlights for Organic Chemistry by Janice Gorzynski Smith, Isbn: 9780073327495. 2009. 474p. pap. 36.95 *(978-1-4288-9086-2(6))* Cram101 Inc.

—Outlines & Highlights for Organic Chemistry by Joseph M Hornback, Isbn: 9780534389512. 2009. 382p. pap. 34.95 *(978-1-4288-8526-4(9))* Cram101 Inc.

—Outlines & Highlights for Organic Chemistry by K Peter C Vollhardt, Neil E Schore, Peter C , Isbn: 9780716799498. 2009. 370p. pap. 34.95 *(978-1-4288-8170-9(0))* Cram101 Inc.

—Outlines & Highlights for Organic Chemistry by L G G Wade, Leroy Wade, Isbn: 9780131478718. 2009. 332p. pap. 33.95 *(978-1-4288-8171-6(9))* Cram101 Inc.

—Outlines & Highlights for Organic Chemistry by Leroy G Wade, Isbn: 9780131699571. 2009. 238p. pap. 31.95 *(978-1-4288-8474-8(2))* Cram101 Inc.

—Outlines & Highlights for Organic Chemistry by Mcmurry, Isbn: 0495112585. 2009. 316p. pap. 33.95 *(978-1-4288-6739-0(2))* Cram101 Inc.

—Outlines & Highlights for Organic Chemistry by T W Graham Solomons, Craig B Fryhle, Isbn: 9780471684961. 2009. 338p. pap. 33.95 *(978-1-4288-8166-2(2))* Cram101 Inc.

—Outlines & Highlights for Organic Chemistry, Enhanced Edition, Volume 1 by John E Mcmurry, Isbn: 9780538733953. 2009. 272p. pap. 32.95 *(978-1-4288-8824-1(1))* Cram101 Inc.

—Outlines & Highlights for Organic Laboratory Techniques by Fessenden, Ralph J / Fessenden, Joan S , Isbn: 9780534379810. 2009. 56p. pap. 26.95 *(978-1-4288-8183-9(2))* Cram101 Inc.

—Outlines & Highlights for Techniques in Organic Chemistry: Miniscale, Standard-Taper Microscale, Williamson Microscale by Jerry R. Mohrig, ISBN. 2009. 68p. pap. 27.95 *(978-1-4288-8862-3(4))* Cram101 Inc.

Hathaway, Bruce A. E-Z Organic Chemistry. 2nd ed. 2011. (Barron's E-Z Ser.). 448p. pap. 16.99 *(978-0-7641-4467-7(7))* Barron's Educational Series, Inc.

Loudon & Cram101 Textbook Reviews Staff. Organic Chemistry. 2007. 340p. per. 16.95 *(978-1-4288-3056-1(1))* Cram101 Inc.

Meislich, Herbert, et al. Organic Chemistry. 4th ed. 2009. (Schaum's Outline Ser.). (ENG., Illus.). 512p. (C). pap. 18.95 *(978-0-07-162512-8(7),* 0071625127) McGraw-Hill Cos., The.

—Organic Chemistry: The Fast Way to Top Grades. 2nd ed. 2010. (Schaum's Easy Outlines Ser.). (ENG., Illus.). 144p. (C). pap. 11.00 *(978-0-07-174590-1(4),* 0071745904) McGraw-Hill Cos., The.

CHEMISTRY, ORGANIC—PROBLEMS, EXERCISES, ETC.

Carey, Francis, et al. Solutions Manual Organic Chemistry. 8th ed. 2010. (ENG., Illus.). 864p. (C). pap. 133.33 *(978-0-07-329397-4(0),* 0073293970, McGraw-Hill Science, Engineering & Mathematics) McGraw-Hill Higher Education.

Cram101 Textbook Reviews & Cram101 Textbook Reviews. Outlines Maitland Jones Jr , Isbn: 9780393931495. 2011. 460p. pap. 36.95 ***(978-1-61461-753-2(8))*** Cram101 Inc.

Hart, Harold, et al. Organic Chemistry: A Short Course - Study Guide & Solutions Manual. 13th ed. 2011. (ENG.). 432p. (C). pap. 102.95 *(978-1-111-42585-2(X))* Brooks/Cole.

Hathaway, Bruce A. E-Z Organic Chemistry. 2nd ed. 2011. (Barron's E-Z Ser.). 448p. pap. 16.99 *(978-0-7641-4467-7(7))* Barron's Educational Series, Inc.

Jain, Ahamindra. Organic Chemistry Workbook: Additional Problems. 5th ed. 2007. (ENG.). 144p. (C). pap. 46.95 *(978-1-4292-0247-3(5))* Freeman, W. H. & Co.

Jenkins, Jerry. Workbook for Organic Chemistry. 6th rev. ed. 2009. (ENG.). 512p. (C). pap. 48.95 *(978-1-4292-4758-0(4))* Freeman, W. H. & Co.

Jones, Maitland, et al. Organic Chemistry. 4th ed. 2010. (ENG.). 844p. (C). pap., pupil's gde. ed. 80.00 net. *(978-0-393-93500-4(0),* 93500) Norton, W. W. & Co., Inc.

Klein. Student Study Guide & Solutions Manual T/a Organic Chemistry , 1E Binder Ready Version. 2010. (ENG.). 720p. (C). ring bd. 73.95 *(978-0-470-92661-1(9),* Wiley) Wiley, John & Sons, Inc.

Klein, David R. Organic Chemistry. 2011. (ENG.). 720p. (C). pap., pupil's gde. ed. 118.95 *(978-0-471-75739-9(X),* Wiley) Wiley, John & Sons, Inc.

—Organic Chemistry I: Translating the Basic Concepts. 2nd rev. ed. 2007. (ENG., Illus.). 384p. (C). per. 42.95 *(978-0-470-12929-6(8),* Wiley) Wiley, John & Sons, Inc.

Meislich, Herbert, et al. Organic Chemistry. 4th ed. 2009. (Schaum's Outline Ser.). (ENG., Illus.). 512p. (C). pap. 18.95 *(978-0-07-162512-8(7),* 0071625127) McGraw-Hill Cos., The.

—Organic Chemistry: The Fast Way to Top Grades. 2nd ed. 2010. (Schaum's Easy Outlines Ser.). (ENG., Illus.). 144p. (C). pap. 11.00 *(978-0-07-174590-1(4),* 0071745904) McGraw-Hill Cos., The.

Newman, Donald & Boxer, Robert J. Organic Chemistry Exam File. 2nd ed. 2007. (ENG.). 414p. pap. 17.95 *(978-1-4195-1808-9(9))* Kaplan Publishing.

Odian, George & Blei, Ira. General, Organic, & Biochemistry for Nursing & Allied Health. 2nd ed. 2009. (Schaum's Outline Ser.). (ENG., Illus.). 528p. (C). pap. 20.00 *(978-0-07-161165-7(7),* 0071611657) McGraw-Hill Cos., The.

Organic Chemistry. 2011. (C). 139.95 ***(978-1-4200-7921-0(2),*** CRC Press) Taylor & Francis Group GBR. Dist: Taylor & Francis Group.

Pascoe, Keith. Organic Chemistry 1 And 2: A Student Workbook. rev. ed. 2010. (ENG.). 330p. spiral bd. 56.06 *(978-0-7575-8271-4(0))* Kendall Hunt Publishing Co.

Reingold & Reingold, David. (Juniata PA) Organic Chemistry or the HAPPY CARBON, an Introductory Text Emphasizing Biological Connections. 2nd ed. 2011. (ENG.). 833p. (C). 165.00 ***(978-0-07-804324-6(7),*** 0078043247) McGraw-Hill Cos., The.

Smith, Janice & Berk, Erin Smith. Study Guide/Solutions Manual for Organic Chemistry. 3rd ed. 2010. (ENG.). 736p. (C). pap. 133.33 *(978-0-07-729665-0(6),* 0077296656, McGraw-Hill Science, Engineering & Mathematics) McGraw-Hill Higher Education.

Straumanis, Andrei. Organic Chemistry. 2nd ed. 2008. (ENG., Illus.). 528p. (C). pap. 92.95 *(978-0-618-97412-2(1))* Brooks/Cole.

Taber, Douglass F. Organic Spectroscopic Structure Determination: A Problem-Based Learning Approach. 2007. (ENG., Illus.). 272p. per. 34.95 *(978-0-19-531470-0(0))* Oxford Univ. Pr., Inc.

CHEMISTRY, ORGANIC—SYNTHESIS

see Organic Compounds—Synthesis

CHEMISTRY, ORGANOMETALLIC

see Organometallic Chemistry

CHEMISTRY, PHARMACEUTICAL

see Pharmaceutical Chemistry

CHEMISTRY, PHOTOGRAPHIC

see Photographic Chemistry

CHEMISTRY, PHYSICAL AND THEORETICAL

see also Absorption; Allotropy; Atmospheric Chemistry; Atomic Mass; Atomic Theory; Atomic Weights; Atoms; Catalysis; Chemical Affinity; Chemical Bonds; Chemical Equilibrium; Chemical Reaction, Conditions and Laws of; Chemical Structure; Colloids; Coordination Compounds; Crystallization; Dipole Moments; Electrochemistry; Electrolysis; Electrolytes; Flocculation; Fusion; Hydrogen Bonding; Instrumental Analysis; Isomerism; Melting Points; Molecular Theory; Molecular Weights; Nuclear Chemistry; Nucleation; Periodic Law; Phase Rule and Equilibrium; Photochemistry; Physical Organic Chemistry; Quantum Chemistry; Radiation Chemistry; Radiochemistry; Relaxation Phenomena; Solid State Chemistry; Solubility; Solution (Chemistry); Sonochemistry; Stoichiometry; Surface Chemistry; Thermochemistry; Thermodynamics; Valence (Theoretical Chemistry)

Abdel-Azeim, Safwat. Protein Ligand Binding Interactions. 2010. 200p. pap. *(978-3-639-27790-6(2))* VDM Verlag Dr. Mueller e.K.

Adam, Gerold, et al. Physikalische Chemie und Biophysik. 4th ed. (Springer-Lehrbuch Ser.). (Illus.). XIII, 617p. pap. 54.95 *(978-3-540-00066-2(6),* 3540000666) Springer.

—Physikalische Chemie und Biophysik. 5th ed. 2011. 644p. pap. ***(978-3-642-00423-0(7))*** Springer Singapore Pte. Ltd.

Adil, Hadeel, et al. New Stabilizers for Pvc Based on Benzothiazole Complexes. 2011. 76p. pap. ***(978-3-8443-2358-0(9))*** Lambert Academic Publishing.

Ahmad, Afaq. Interferences in the Photo Detachment of Negative Ion Systems. 2010. 128p. pap. *(978-3-639-25580-5(1))* VDM Verlag Dr. Mueller e.K.

Allen, James & Allen, James P. Biophysical Chemistry. 2008. (ENG., Illus.). 512p. 129.95 *(978-1-4051-2436-2(9),* Wiley-Blackwell) Wiley, John & Sons, Inc.

Arnold, Samuel V., ed. Chemical Physics Research Trends. 2007. (Horizons in World Physics Ser.). 352p. 129.00 *(978-1-60021-554-4(8))* Nova Science Pubs., Inc.

Arora, Pinklesh & R.P. Singh. Interaction of Metal-Ions & Surfactants with Proteins. 2010. 260p. pap. *(978-3-8383-8038-4(X))* Lambert Academic Publishing.

Atkins, et al. Physical Chemistry Vol 2: Quantum Chemistry, 2 vols. 9th ed. 2010. (ENG., Illus.). 435p. (C). pap. 89.95 *(978-1-4292-3126-8(2))* Freeman, W. H. & Co.

—Physical Chemistry Volume 1: Thermodynamics & Kinetics, 2 vols. 9th ed. 2010. (ENG., Illus.). 435p. (C). pap. 89.95 *(978-1-4292-3127-5(0))* Freeman, W. H. & Co.

Atkins, Peter. Physical Chemistry. (C). tchr. ed. 18.00 *(978-0-7167-2562-6(2))* Freeman, W. H. & Co.

Atkins, Peter & de Paula, Julio. Elements of Physical Chemistry. 5th ed. 2009. (ENG., Illus.). 630p. (C). pap. 128.95 *(978-1-4292-1813-9(4))* Freeman, W. H. & Co.

Atkins, Peter & De Paula, Julio. Physical Chemistry Vol. 1: Thermodynamics & Kinetics. 2006. 512p. (C). 60.00 net. *(978-0-7167-8567-5(6))* Freeman, W. H. & Co.

—Physical Chemistry Vol. 2: Quantum Chemistry & Spectroscopy. 2006. 512p. (C). 60.00 net. *(978-0-7167-8569-9(2))* Freeman, W. H. & Co.

Atkins, Peter & dePaula, Julio. Physical Chemistry Soluitons Manual. 5th ed. 2008. 370p. (C). pap. 47.95 *(978-1-4292-2400-0(2))* Freeman, W. H. & Co.

—Physical Chemistry. 9th ed. 2009. (ENG., Illus.). 1060p. (C). 155.95 *(978-1-4292-1812-2(6))* Freeman, W. H. & Co.

—Physical Chemistry for the Life Sciences Solutions Manual. 2nd ed. 2011. (ENG.). 225p. (C). pap. 49.95 *(978-1-4292-3125-1(4))* Freeman, W. H. & Co.

Atkins, Peter, et al. Physical Chemistry. 8th ed. 2006. (ENG.). 300p. (C). pap. 57.95 *(978-0-7167-6206-5(4))* Freeman, W. H. & Co.

Aydin, Metin. Photofragmentation Spectroscopy. 2009. 292p. pap. *(978-3-639-15289-0(1))* VDM Verlag Dr. Mueller e.K.

Balaz, Peter. Mechanochemistry in Nanoscience & Minerals Engineering. 2008. (ENG., Illus.). xiv, 414p. 159.00 *(978-3-540-74854-0(7),* 3540748547) Springer.

Barkan, Diana Kormos. Walther Nernst & the Transition to Modern Physical Science. 2011. (ENG., Illus.). 302p. pap. 36.99 *(978-0-521-17629-3(8))* Cambridge Univ. Pr.

Battaglia, F. & George, T. F. Fundamentals in Chemical Physics. 2010. 326p. pap. 259.00 *(978-90-481-5082-3(5),* 9048150825) Springer.

Behrens, J. P. & Behr, Amo. Supramolecular Chemistry, 7 vols., Set. 2008. (ENG.). 2504p. 2900.00 *(978-0-470-77949-1(7),* Wiley) Wiley, John & Sons, Inc.

Belostotskii. Conformational Concept for Synthetic... 2011. 107.00 *(978-981-281-409-8(4))* World Scientific Publishing Co., Inc.

Bergethon, Peter R. The Physical Basis of Biochemistry: The Foundations of Molecular Biophysics. 2nd ed. 2010. (ENG., Illus.). xxx, 950p. 89.95 *(978-1-4419-6323-9(5),* 1441963235) Springer.

Bergethon, Peter R. & Hallock, Kevin. The Physical Basis of Biochemistry: Solutions Manual to the Second Edition. 2010. (ENG., Illus.). x, 146p. pap. 39.95 *(978-1-4419-7363-4(X),* 144197363X) Springer.

Binder, Wolfgang. Hydrogen Bonded Polymers. 2007. (Advances in Polymer Science Ser.: Vol. 207). (Illus.). xii, 206p. 279.00 *(978-3-540-68587-6(1))* Springer.

Birdi, K. S. Introduction to Electrical Interfacial Phenomena. 2010. (ENG., Illus.). 180p. 119.95 *(978-1-4200-5369-2(8),* CRC Press) Taylor & Francis Group GBR. Dist: Taylor & Francis Group.

Blaser, Hans Ulrich & Federsel, Hans-Jürgen, eds. Asymmetric Catalysis on Industrial Scale: Challenges, Approaches & Solutions. 2nd ed. 2010. (ENG., Illus.). 580p. 360.00 *(978-3-527-32489-7(5),* Wiley-VCH) Wiley, John & Sons, Inc.

Boeyens, Jan C. A. Chemical Cosmology. 2010. (ENG.). xvii, 419p. 189.00 *(978-90-481-3827-2(2),* 9048138272) Springer.

—Chemistry from First Principles. 2010. (Illus.). xviii, 322p. pap. 109.00 *(978-90-481-7907-7(6),* 9048179076) Springer.

Boeyens, Jan C. A. & Boeyens, J. C. A. Chemistry from First Principles. 2008. (Illus.). xvii, 321p. 109.00 *(978-1-4020-8545-1(1))* Springer.

Bowman-James, Kristin, et al, eds. Anion Coordination Chemistry. 2012. (ENG., Illus.). 574p. 215.00 ***(978-3-527-32370-8(8),*** Wiley-VCH) Wiley, John & Sons, Inc.

Broglia, R. A., et al. Solid State Physics of Finite Systems: Metal Clusters, Fullerenes, Atomic Wires. 2010. (Advanced Texts in Physics Ser.). (Illus.). xi, 234p. 139.00 *(978-3-642-05911-7(2),* 3642059112) Springer.

Brown, Kate. Physical Chemistry. 3rd ed. Date not set. (Illus.). 496p. pap. 31.50 *(978-0-582-35365-7(3))* Addison-Wesley Longman, Ltd. GBR. Dist: Trans-Atlantic Pubns., Inc.

Buxbaum, Engelbert. Biophysical Chemistry of Proteins: An Introduction to Laboratory Methods. 2010. (ENG., Illus.). xvi, 510p. 209.00 *(978-1-4419-7250-7(1),* 1441972501) Springer.

Carre, Antoine. Development of Empirical Potentials for Amorphous Silic. 2008. 180p. pap. *(978-3-8364-9129-7(X))* VDM Verlag Dr. Mueller e.K.

Chakraborty, Aniruddha. Nano Devices, 2d Electron Solvation & Curve Crossing Problems. 2010. 152p. pap. *(978-3-8383-9210-3(8))* Lambert Academic Publishing.

Ciolacu, Diana & Popa, Valentin I., eds. Celluose Allomorphs: Structure, Accessibility & Reactivity. 2010. (Polymer Science & Technology Ser.). (Illus.). x, 69p. pap. 43.00 *(978-1-61668-323-8(6))* Nova Science Pubs., Inc.

Cooke, Josiah Parsons. The New Chemistry. 2009. 212p. pap. *(978-0-217-12335-8(X))* Books LLC.

—The New Chemistry. 2006. 340p. per. 23.99 (978-1-4255-3436-3(8)) MPublishing.
Cragg, Peter J. Supramolecular Chemistry: From Biological Inspiration to Biomedical Applications. 2010. (ENG., Illus.). xv, 260p. 129.00 (978-90-481-2581-4(2), 9048125812) Springer.
Cram101 Textbook Reviews. Outlines & Highlights for Chemistry: Molecular Approach by Tro, Nivaldo Jose, ISBN. 2010. 424p. pap. 35.95 (978-1-61698-591-2(7)) Cram101 Inc.
—Outlines & Highlights for Elements of Physical Chemistry by Peter Atkins, Julio de Paula, Isbn: 9780716773290. 2010. 172p. pap. 29.95 (978-1-61698-463-2(5)) Cram101 Inc.
—Outlines & Highlights for Elements of Physical Chemistry by Peter Atkins, Julio de Paula, Isbn: 9781429218139. 2010. 122p. pap. 35.95 (978-1-61698-547-9(X)) Cram101 Inc.
—Outlines & Highlights for Physical Chemistry: For the Biosciences by Raymond Chang, ISBN. 2010. 120p. pap. 28.95 (978-1-61698-552-3(6)) Cram101 Inc.
—Outlines & Highlights for Physical Chemistry: For the Chemical & Biological Sciences by Raymond Chang, ISBN. 2010. 90p. pap. 27.95 (978-1-61698-544-8(5)) Cram101 Inc.
—Outlines & Highlights for Physical Chemistry by Ira N Levine, Isbn: 9780072538625. 2010. 246p. pap. 31.95 (978-1-61698-549-3(6)) Cram101 Inc.
—Outlines & Highlights for Physical Chemistry by Robert G Mortimer. 2011. 492p. pap. 37.95 (978-1-61905-731-9(X)) Cram101 Inc.
—Outlines & Highlights for Physical Chemistry by Thomas Engel, Philip Reid, Isbn: 9780805338423. 2010. 66p. pap. 27.95 (978-1-61698-553-0(4)) Cram101 Inc.
—Outlines & Highlights for Physical Chemistry for the Life Sciences by Peter Atkins, Julio de Paula, Isbn: 9780716786283. 2010. 136p. pap. 28.95 (978-1-61698-551-6(8)) Cram101 Inc.
—Outlines & Highlights for Physical Chemistry, Volume 1 by Peter Atkins, Isbn: 9780716774341 9780716785675 0716785676 0716774348. 2011. 100p. pap. 27.95 (978-1-61812-225-4(8)) Cram101 Inc.
—Outlines & Highlights for the Physical Chemistry of Materials: Energy & Environmental Applications by Rolando M. A. Roque-Malherbe, ISBN. 2011. 78p. pap. 27.95 (978-1-4288-0405-0(6)) Cram101 Inc.
Cram101 Textbook Reviews & Cram101 Textbook Reviews. Outlines & Highlights for Physical Chemistry by Thomas Engel, Isbn: 9780321615053 0321615050. 2011. 136p. pap. 28.95 (978-1-61490-707-7(2)) Cram101 Inc.
Cram101 Textbook Reviews Staff. Outlines & Highlights for Chemistry: Molecular Approach by Tro, Nivaldo Jose, ISBN. 2009. 366p. pap. 34.95 (978-1-4288-7430-5(5)) Cram101 Inc.
—Outlines & Highlights for Elements of Physical Chemistry by Peter Atkins, Julio de Paula, Isbn: 9780716773290. 2009. 152p. pap. 29.95 (978-1-4288-8310-9(X)) Cram101 Inc.
—Outlines & Highlights for Physical Chemistry: A Molecular Approach by Mcquarrie ISBN. 2007. 260p. pap. 14.95 (978-1-4288-3076-9(6)) Cram101 Inc.
—Outlines & Highlights for Physical Chemistry: For the Chemical & Biological Sciences by Raymond Chang, ISBN. 2009. 80p. pap. 27.95 (978-1-4288-8185-3(9)) Cram101 Inc.
—Outlines & Highlights for Physical Chemistry by Peter Atkins, Isbn: 9780716787594. 2009. 218p. pap. 30.95 (978-1-4285-9568-3(X)) Cram101 Inc.
—Outlines & Highlights for Physical Chemistry by Thomas Engel, Philip Reid, Isbn: 9780805338423. 2009. 58p. pap. 26.95 (978-1-4288-8177-8(8)) Cram101 Inc.
—Outlines & Highlights for Physical Chemistry by Tinoco, Isbn: 013095943x. 2007. 264p. pap. 14.95 (978-1-4288-3022-6(7)) Cram101 Inc.
—Outlines & Highlights for Physical Chemistry for the Life Sciences by Peter Atkins, Julio de Paula, Isbn: 9780716786283. 2009. 122p. pap. 28.95 (978-1-4288-8179-2(4)) Cram101 Inc.
Crego-Calama, Mercedes & Reinhoudt, David N. Supramolecular Chirality. 2010. (Topics in Current Chemistry Ser.). (Illus.). xii, 312p. pap. 379.00 (978-3-642-06876-2(2), 3642068782) Springer.
Davis, William M. & Dykstra, Clifford E. Physical Chemistry. 2nd ed. 2011. (Illus.). (ENG.). 519p. 99.95 (978-1-4398-1077-4(X)); 700p. 99.95 (978-1-4398-1079-8(6)) Taylor & Francis Group GBR. (CRC Press). Dist: Taylor & Francis Group.
Day. Molecules into Materials. 199.00 (978-981-270-038-4(2)) World Scientific Publishing Co., Inc.
De Riepen, Magdalena R. La Quimica Hacia la Conquista del Sol. (Ciencia para Todos Ser.). (SPA.). pap. 6.99 (978-968-16-2397-5(5)) Fondo de Cultura Economica USA.
Dhar, Anirban. Fabrication of Rare Earth Doped Optical Fibre Using Mcvd Process. 2010. 156p. pap. (978-3-8383-4093-7(0)) Lambert Academic Publishing.
Dickinson Eric Staff. Surfactants & Proteins in Food Technology & Processing. 2009. 400p. 139.95 (978-1-57444-530-5(8)) CRC Pr. LLC.
Dodziuk, Helena. Introduction to Supramolecular Chemistry. 2010. (Illus.). 368p. pap. 229.00 (978-90-481-5913-0(X), 904815913X) Springer.
Donnio, B., et al, contrib. by. Supramolecular Polymers/Polymeric Betains/Oligomers. 2010. (Advances in Polymer Science Ser.). x, 301p. pap. 329.00 (978-3-642-06872-0(3), 3642068723) Springer.
Dyer, Chris K., et al, eds. Encyclopedia of Electrochemical Power Sources, 5 vols., Set. 2009. (ENG.). 4538p. 2365.00 (978-0-444-52093-7(7), Elsevier Science) Elsevier Science & Technology Bks.
Ebel, Adolf, et al, eds. Tropospheric Modelling & Emission Estimation: Chemical Transport & Emission Modelling on Regional, Global & Urban Scales Chemistry Chemistry. 2010. (Transport & Chemical Transformation of Pollutants in the Troposphere Ser.). (ENG., Illus.). xxiv, 440p. pap. 239.00 (978-3-642-08319-8(6), 3642083196) Springer.
Ellison, Mark D. & Schoolcraft, Tracy A., eds. Advances in Teaching Physical Chemistry. 2007. (American Chemical Society Publication). (ENG.). 364p. 150.00 (978-0-8412-3998-2(3)) American Chemical Society.
Engel, Thomas & Reid, Philip. Physical Chemistry. (ENG., (C). 2nd ed. 2009. Illus.). 1088p. 176.00 (978-0-321-61505-3(0)) 3rd rev. ed. 2012. 1104p. 186.00 (978-0-321-76620-5(2)) 3rd ed. 2012. (Illus.). 1128p. 176.00 (978-0-321-81200-1(X)) Prentice Hall PTR. (Prentice Hall).
—Physical Chemistry, Books a la Carte Edition. 3rd ed. 2012. (ENG.). 1128p. (C). ring bd. 105.60 (978-0-321-81534-7(3), Prentice Hall) Prentice Hall PTR.
—Physical Chemistry, Books a la Carte Plus MasteringChemistry(r). 3rd ed. 2012. (ENG.). (C). ring bd. 115.60 (978-0-321-81517-0(3), Prentice Hall) Prentice Hall PTR.
Engel, Thomas & Reid, Philip. Student Solutions Manual for Physical Chemistry. 2nd ed. 2009. (ENG.). 288p. (C). pap. 47.93 (978-0-321-61626-5(X), Prentice Hall) Prentice Hall PTR.
Engel, Tom & Reid, Phil. Student Solution Manual for Physical Chemistry. 3rd ed. 2012. (ENG.). 200p. (C). pap. 47.93 (978-0-321-76668-7(7), Prentice Hall) Prentice Hall PTR.
Evanseck, Jeffrey D., et al. Computational Chemistry. 2009. 736p. 90.00 (978-0-8153-4144-4(X), Garland Science) Taylor & Francis Group.
Fabbrizzi, L. & Poggi, Antonio, eds. Transition Metals in Supramolecular Chemistry. 2010. (NATO Science Series C: (closed) Ser.). 464p. pap. 449.00 (978-90-481-4483-9(3), 9048144833) Springer.
Fages, Frederic. Low Molecular Mass Gelators: Design, Self-Assembly, Function. 2010. (Topics in Current Chemistry Ser.). (Illus.). xii, 283p. pap. 389.00 (978-3-642-06459-3(0), 3642064590) Springer.
Fawwaz, Osama. Theoretical Calculation of the Electronic States of the Molecule Narb. 2010. 148p. pap. (978-3-8383-7604-2(8)) Lambert Academic Publishing.
Field, Martin J. A Practical Introduction to the Simulation of Molecular Systems. 2nd rev. ed. 2007. (ENG., Illus.). 344p. 148.99 (978-0-521-85252-4(8)) Cambridge Univ. Pr.
Fink, Johannes Karl. Physical Chemistry in Depth. 2009. (ENG., Illus.). xviii, 588p. 99.00 (978-3-642-01013-2(X), 364201013X) Springer.
Florence, A. T. & Attwood, D. Physicochemical Principles of Pharmacy. 5th ed. 2011. (Illus.). 528p. pap. 65.00 (978-0-85369-984-2(4)) Pharmaceutical Pr. GBR. Dist: Smith Fulfillment Services.
Frazer, Andrew. Chemistry Fundamentals 1A Workbook. rev. ed. 2011. (ENG.). 138p. spiral bd. 28.50 (978-0-7575-7431-3(9)) Kendall Hunt Publishing Co.
Gale, Philip A. & Dehaen, Wim, eds. Anion Recognition in Supramolecular Chemistry. 2010. (Topics in Heterocyclic Chemistry Ser.). (Illus.). x, 365p. 409.00 (978-3-642-15443-0(3), 3642154433) Springer.
Garland, Carl W., et al. Experiments in Physical Chemistry. 8th ed. 2008. (ENG., Illus.). 752p. (C). 110.33 (978-0-07-282842-9(0), 0072828420, McGraw-Hill Science, Engineering & Mathematics) McGraw-Hill Higher Education.
Gheorghita, Ligia. Passivation Kinetics at Semiconductor Interfaces. 2011. 168p. pap. (978-3-8443-8223-5(2)) Lambert Academic Publishing.
Gitterman, Moshe. Chemistry Versus Physics: Chemical Reactions near Critical Points. 2009. 148p. 65.00 (978-981-4291-20-0(X)) World Scientific Publishing Co., Inc.
Gnanou, Yves & Fontanille, Michel. Organic & Physical Chemistry of Polymers. 2008. (ENG., Illus.). 632p. 128.00 (978-0-471-72543-5(9), Wiley-Interscience) Wiley, John & Sons, Inc.
Goodson, David Z. Mathematical Methods for Physical & Analytical Chemistry. 2011. (ENG., Illus.). 408p. 99.95 (978-0-470-47354-2(1), Wiley) Wiley, John & Sons, Inc.
Hammes, Gordon G. Physical Chemistry for the Biological Sciences. 2007. (Methods of Biochemical Analysis Ser.: 138). (ENG., Illus.). 388p. 122.00 (978-0-470-12202-0(1), Wiley-Interscience) Wiley, John & Sons, Inc.
Hampel, Frank. Theoretical Molecular Structure. 2009. (Landolt-Börnstein: Numerical Data & Functional Relationships in Science & Technology - New Series / Molecules & Radicals Ser.). 240p. 6199.00 (978-3-540-60329-0(8)) Springer.
Hansen, Peter W. Chemical Physics Research Developments. 2011. (978-1-61122-068-1(8)) Nova Science Pubs., Inc.
Harrison, Roy M. IUPAC Series on Analytical & Physical Chemistry of Environmental Systems, 6 vols., Set. 2008. (ENG.). 3524p. 2500.00 (978-0-470-77958-3(6), Wiley) Wiley, John & Sons, Inc.
He, Qiang, et al. Molecular Assembly of Biomimetic Systems. 2011. (ENG., Illus.). 202p. pap. 210.00 (978-3-527-32542-9(5), Wiley-VCH) Wiley, John & Sons, Inc.
Higson, Séamus & Davis, Frank. Macrocycles: Construction, Chemistry & Nanotechnology Applications. 2011. (ENG., Illus.). 608p. 180.00 (978-0-470-71462-1(X)); pap. 70.00 (978-0-470-71463-8(8)) Wiley, John & Sons, Inc. (Wiley).
Hossain, Akm Motahar. An Analysis of the Physico-Chemical Characteristics of Hils. 2010. 148p. pap. (978-3-639-26803-4(2)) VDM Verlag Dr. Mueller e.K.
Hsin, Tse-Ming. Detecting Molecular Properties by Various Laser-Based Techniques. 2010. 124p. pap. (978-3-8383-7241-9(7)) Lambert Academic Publishing.
Hsu, Jyh-Ping & Spasic, Aleksandar M. Interfacial Electroviscoelasticity & Electrophoresis. 2010. (ENG., Illus.). 194p. 139.95 (978-1-4398-0352-3(8), CRC Press) Taylor & Francis Group GBR. Dist: Taylor & Francis Group.
Ibhadon, A. O. Physical Chemistry Examinations. 2009. pap. 42.00 (978-1-60692-345-0(5)) Nova Science Pubs., Inc.
Iglesias, Rodrigo Alejandro & Dassie, Sergio Alberto, eds. Ion Transfer at Liquid/Liquid Interfaces. 2010. (Chemistry Research & Applications Ser.). 118p. pap. 43.00 (978-1-61668-684-0(7), Nova Novinka) Nova Science Pubs., Inc.
Inamuddin, M. & Mohammad, Ali, eds. Green Solvents I: Properties & Applications in Chemistry. 2012. (ENG., Illus.). xviii, 427p. 189.00 (978-94-007-1711-4(3), 9400717113) Springer.
Islam, Nazmul. A Sar Rationale of the Toxicity of Pcbs. 2010. 96p. pap. (978-3-8383-7670-7(6)) Lambert Academic Publishing.
—Semi-Empirical & Dft Studies of the Periodic Parameters. 2010. 204p. pap. (978-3-8383-8551-8(9)) Lambert Academic Publishing.
Israelachvili, Jacob N. Intermolecular & Surface Forces. 3rd rev. ed. 2011. (ENG.). 704p. 109.95 (978-0-12-391927-4(4), Academic Pr.) Elsevier Science & Technology Bks.
Kalsi, P. S. & Kalsi, J. P. Bioorganic, Bioinorganic & Supramolecular Chemistry. 2nd ed. 2011. (Illus.). 414p. pap. (978-1-906574-79-6(0)) New Age Science, Ltd.
Kntt, Agnes. Studies of Acid-Base Equilibria in Non-Aqueous Medi. 2008. 172p. pap. (978-3-639-10863-7(9)) VDM Verlag Dr. Mueller e.K.
Komatsuzaki, Tamiki, et al. Advances in Chemical Physics, Advancing Theory for Kinetics & Dynamics of Complex, Many-Dimensional Systems: Clusters & Proteins, Volume 145. 2011. (Advances in Chemical Physics Ser.: 312). (ENG., Illus.). 272p. 195.00 (978-0-470-64371-6(4), Wiley) Wiley, John & Sons, Inc.
Komatsuzaki, Tamiki, et al, eds. Single Molecule Biophysics Vol. 146: Experiments & Theories. 2011. (Advances in Chemical Physics Ser.: 314). (ENG., Illus.). 512p. 195.00 (978-1-118-05780-3(5), Wiley) Wiley, John & Sons, Inc.
Kuhn. Organised Monolayers. 280p. 140.00 (978-0-471-49018-0(0)) Wiley, John & Sons, Inc.
Kunes, Josef. Dimensionless Physical Quantities in Science & Engineering. 2012. (ENG.). 454p. 150.00 (978-0-12-416013-2(1)) Elsevier Science & Technology Bks.
Kushawaha, Rajesh Kumar & Bapat, Bhas. Fragmentation Dynamics of Molecular Ions. 2011. 116p. pap. (978-3-8443-0255-4(7)) Lambert Academic Publishing.
Laguna, Antonio, ed. Modern Supramolecular Gold Chemistry: Gold-Metal Interactions & Applications. 2008. (ENG., Illus.). 525p. 245.00 (978-3-527-32029-5(6), Wiley-VCH) Wiley, John & Sons, Inc.
Lapherty, James N. New Trends in Chemical Physics Research. 2011. (Chemistry Research & Applications Physics Research & Technology Ser.). 367p. 129.00 (978-1-61668-535-5(2)) Nova Science Pubs., Inc.
Leone, Stephen R., ed. Annual Review of Physical Chemistry, Vol. 58. 2007. 758p. pap. 197.00 (978-0-8243-1058-5(6)) Annual Reviews, Inc.
Leone, Stephen R., ed. Annual Review of Physical Chemistry 2011. 2011. 681p. pap. 86.00 (978-0-8243-1062-2(4)) Annual Reviews, Inc.
Leszczynski, Jerzy & Shukla, Manoj K., eds. Practical Aspects of Computational Chemistry I: An Overview of the Last Two Decades & Current Trends, 2 vols. 2012. (ENG., Illus.). xv, 680p. 229.00 (978-94-007-0918-8(8), 9400709188) Springer.
Levine, Ira N. Physical Chemistry. 6th ed. 2008. (ENG., Illus.). 1008p. (C). 226.67 (978-0-07-253862-5(7), 0072538627, McGraw-Hill Science, Engineering & Mathematics) McGraw-Hill Higher Education.
Lewars, Errol G. Computational Chemistry: Introduction to the Theory & Applications of Molecular & Quantum Mechanics. 2nd ed. 2011. (ENG., Illus.). xvi, 664p. pap. 99.00 (978-90-481-3861-6(2), 9048138612) Springer.
Li. Name Reactions for Homologation, 2 vols., Pt. 1. Li, Jie Jack, ed. 2009. (Comprehensive Name Reactions Ser.: 5). (ENG., Illus.). 719p. 166.00 (978-0-470-08507-3(X), Wiley) Wiley, John & Sons, Inc.
Li, Jie Jack, ed. Name Reactions for Homologation, 2 vols., Pt. 2. 2009. (Comprehensive Name Reactions Ser.: 8). (ENG., Illus.). 859p. 166.00 (978-0-470-46498-4(4), Wiley) Wiley, John & Sons, Inc.
Li, Jie Jack & Li. Name Reactions for Homologation, 2 pts., Set. Li, Jie Jack, ed. 2009. (Comprehensive Name Reactions Ser.: 9). (ENG., Illus.). 1520p. 249.00 (978-0-470-46721-3(5), Wiley) Wiley, John & Sons, Inc.
Linder, Bruno. Elementary Physical Chemistry. 2010. 160p. 42.00 (978-981-4299-66-4(9)) World Scientific Publishing Co., Inc.
Luisi, Pier Luigi & Chiarabelli, Cristiano, eds. Chemical Synthetic Biology. 2011. (ENG., Illus.). 384p. 155.00 (978-0-470-71397-6(6), Wiley) Wiley, John & Sons, Inc.
Madelung, Otfried. Numerical Data & Functional Relationships in Science & Technology: Group 4 - Physical Chemistry, Vol. 12. 2006. (Landolt-Börnstein: Numerical Data & Functional Relationships in Science & Technology Ser.). (Illus.). ix, 564p. 5931.00 (978-3-540-60347-4(6), 3540603476) Springer.
Makai, Mihály. Group Theory Applied to Boundary Value Problems with Applications to Reactor Physics. Mercê, Ana Lucia Ramalho et al, eds. 2010. (Chemistry Research & Applications Ser.). 195.00 (978-1-61728-785-5(7)) Nova Science Pubs., Inc.
Marciniec, Bogdan. Hydrosilation: A Comprehensive Review on Recent Advances. 2008. (Advances in Silicon Science Ser.). (ENG., Illus.). xxiv, 408p. 429.00 (978-1-4020-8171-2(5)) Springer.
Mark, James E. Physical Properties of Polymers Handbook. 2nd rev. ed. 2006. (Illus.). 1076p. 395.00 (978-0-387-31235-4(8), 0387312358) Springer.
Maruani, J., et al, eds. Advanced Topics in Theoretical Chemical Physics. 2010. (Progress in Theoretical Chemistry & Physics Ser.). 528p. pap. 239.00 (978-90-481-6401-1(X), 904816401X) Springer.
Matsumoto, Kiyoshi. Heterocyclic Supramolecules I. 2010. (Topics in Heterocyclic Chemistry Ser.). (Illus.). xiv, 201p. pap. 269.00 (978-3-642-08787-5(6), 3642087876) Springer.
Mazziotti, David A., ed. Reduced-Density-Matrix Mechanics: With Application to Many-Electron Atoms & Molecules. 2007. (Advances in Chemical Physics Ser.: 165). (ENG., Illus.). 574p. 233.00 (978-0-471-79056-3(7), Wiley-Interscience) Wiley, John & Sons, Inc.
Möller, Detlev. Chemistry of the Climate System. 2011. (ENG., Illus.). XVII, 722p. 335.00 (978-3-11-174040-9(4)) De Gruyter, Walter Inc.
McMillan, Paul F. & Meersman, Filip. High Pressure Chemistry. 2011. (ENG.). 300p. 139.00 (978-90-481-3868-5(X), 904813868X) Springer.
McQuarrie, Donald A. Mathematics for Physical Chemistry: Opening Doors. 2008. (Illus.). 345p. pap. 48.00 (978-1-891389-56-6(4)) Univ. Science Bks.
Medvedevskikh, Y. G. Organic & Physical Chemistry Using Chemical Kinetics: Prospects & Developments. 2007. 145.00 (978-1-60021-763-0(X)) Nova Science Pubs., Inc.
Mellor, Joseph W. A Comprehensive Treatise on Inorganic & Theoretical Chemistry. reprint ed. lib. bdg. 2000.00 (978-0-7222-3060-2(5)) Library Reprints, Inc.
—Higher Mathematics for Students of Chemistry & Physics. 2007. 664p. per. 26.95 (978-1-60206-569-7(1)) Cosimo, Inc.
Mennucci, Benedetta & Cammi, Roberto, eds. Continuum Solvation Models in Chemical Physics: From Theory to Applications. 2008. (ENG., Illus.). 636p. 310.00 (978-0-470-02938-1(2), Wiley) Wiley, John & Sons, Inc.
Metzger, Robert M., ed. Unimolecular & Supramolecular Electronics I: Chemistry & Physics Meet at Metal-Molecule Interfaces, 2 vols. 2012. (Topics in Current Chemistry Ser.). (ENG., Illus.). xi, 307p. 349.00 (978-3-642-27283-7(5), 3642272835) Springer.
Mewes, D. Multiphase Gas-liquid Flows: Experimental Methods, Modelling, Technical Applications. 2009. (ENG.). 300p. 170.00 (978-3-527-31197-2(1), Wiley-VCH) Wiley, John & Sons, Inc.
Micha, David. Kinetics in Condensed Matter & at Interfaces. 2010. (ENG.). 400p. 130.00 (978-0-470-38371-1(2), Wiley-Interscience) Wiley, John & Sons, Inc.
Mihai Barboiu, Mihai & Peinemann, Klaus-Viktor, eds. Handbook of Molecular Self-Assembly: Principles, Fabrication & Devices. 2011. 400p. 199.00 (978-981-4303-63-7(1)) Pan Stanford Publishing SGP. Dist: Independent Pubs. Group.
Mills, Ian, et al, eds. Quantities, Units & Symbols in Physical Chemistry. 3rd rev. ed. 2007. (ENG., Illus.). 248p. (C). 64.00 (978-0-85404-433-7(7)) Royal Society of Chemistry, The GBR. Dist: Ingram Pub. Services.
Molloy, Kieran C. Group Theory for Chemists: Fundamental Theory & Applications. 2nd ed. 2011. (Woodhead Publishing in Materials Ser.). (ENG., Illus.). 232p. pap. 60.00 (978-0-85709-240-3(5)) Woodhead Publishing Ltd. GBR. Dist: Ingram Pub. Services.
Monti, Oliver L. A. & Prezhdo, Oleg V. Physical Chemistry of Interfaces & Nanomaterials VIII: 2-4 August 2009, San Diego, California, United States. 2009. (Proceedings of SPIE Ser.). (Illus.). 126p. pap. 70.00 (978-0-8194-7686-9(2)) SPIE.
Moore, Walter John. Physikalische Chemie. Hummel, Dieter O., ed. (GER.). XVI, 1134p. 644.00 (978-3-11-216585-0(3)); 431.00 (978-3-11-003501-8(4)) De Gruyter, Walter Inc.
Nakamura, Takayoshi, et al. Chemistry of Nanomolecular Systems: Towards the Realization of Molecular Devices. 2010. (Springer Series in Chemical Physics Ser.). (Illus.). xviii, 198p. pap. 119.00 (978-3-642-07910-8(5), 3642079105) Springer.
Narayanan, Ajeetha. Role of Oxygen on Phase Behavior of Liquid Crystals. 2010. 120p. pap. (978-3-639-23063-3(3)) VDM Verlag Dr. Mueller e.K.
Niyazi, Farukh Fatehovich, et al. Stabilization & Modification of Cellulose Diacetate. 2008. pap. 35.00 (978-1-60692-002-2(2)) Nova Science Pubs., Inc.
Novak, C., ed. Physicochemical Characterization of Pharmaceuticals: Applications of Thermal Analysis & Other Techniques for Pharmaceuticals & Other Substances. 2008. 900p. 649.00 (978-1-4020-3164-9(5), 1402031645) Springer.
O'Donnell, T. J. Design & Use of Relational Databases in Chemistry. 2008. (ENG., Illus.). 224p. 139.95 (978-1-4200-6442-1(8), CRC Press) Taylor & Francis Group GBR. Dist: Taylor & Francis Group.
Ohshima, Hiroyuki. Biophysical Chemistry of Biointerfaces. 2010. (ENG., Illus.). 547p. 142.00 (978-0-470-16935-3(4), Wiley) Wiley, John & Sons, Inc.
Papadopoulos, Manthos G., et a, eds. Non-Linear Optical Properties of Matter: From molecules to condensed Phases. 2010. (Challenges & Advances in Computational Chemistry & Physics Ser.). xvii, 676p. pap. 439.00 (978-90-481-7211-5(X), 904817211X) Springer.
Patterson, Gary. Physical Chemistry of Macromolecules. 2nd ed. 2007. (ENG., Illus.). 152p. (C). 87.95 (978-0-8247-9467-5(2), CRC Press) Taylor & Francis Group GBR. Dist: Taylor & Francis Group.
Peiris, Suhithi M., et al. Static Compression of Energetic Materials. 2008. (Shock Wave & High Pressure Phenomena Ser.). (Illus.). 350p. 199.00 (978-3-540-68146-5(9)) Springer.
Piazza, Roberto. Soft Matter: The stuff that dreams are made Of. 2011. Orig. Title: La materia dei Sogni. (ENG., Illus.). xiv, 279p. pap. 24.95 (978-94-007-0584-5(0), 9400705840) Springer.

Pifat-Mrzljak, Greta, ed. Supramolecular Structure & Function 9. 2010. viii, 320p. pap. 139.00 *(978-90-481-7649-6(2)*, 9048176492) Springer.

Plattes, Mario. The Effect of Ultrasound on Electrochemical Processes. 2009. 264p. pap. *(978-3-639-14143-6(1))* VDM Verlag Dr. Mueller e.K.

Poitrowiak, Piotr. Physical Chemistry of Interfaces & Nanomaterials VI: 26-28 August, 2007, San Diego, California, USA. Rumbles, G., tr. 2007. (Proceedings of SPIE Ser.). (Illus.). 84p. pap. 70.00 *(978-0-8194-6791-1(X))* SPIE.

Prigogine, Ilya, et al. Advances in Chemical Physics, Volume 137. 2008. (Advances in Chemical Physics Ser.: 133). (ENG.). 253p. 233.00 *(978-0-471-43573-0(2)*, Wiley-Interscience) Wiley, John & Sons, Inc.

Putz, Mihai V., ed. Carbon Bonding & Structures: Advances in Physics & Chemistry. 2011. (Carbon Materials: Chemistry & Physics Ser.). (ENG., Illus.). xii, 445p. 189.00 ***(978-94-007-1732-9(6)***, 9400717326) Springer.

Ramachandran, K. I., et al. Computational Chemistry & Molecular Modeling: Principles & Applications. (ENG., Illus.). xxi, 397p. 2010. pap. 99.00 *(978-3-642-09598-6(4)*, 3642095984) 2008. 99.00 *(978-3-540-77302-3(9)*, 3540773029) Springer.

Rastogi, R. P. Introduction to Non-Equilibrium Physical Chemistry: Towards Complexity & Non-Linear Science. 2007. (ENG., Illus.). 356p. 175.00 *(978-0-444-52188-0(7)*, Elsevier Science) Elsevier Science & Technology Bks.

Rice & Rice, Stuart A. Advances in Chemical Physics, Volume 135, Prigogine Special Volume. 2007. (Advances in Chemical Physics Ser.: 133). (ENG., Illus.). 332p. 233.00 *(978-0-471-68233-2(0)*, Wiley-Interscience) Wiley, John & Sons, Inc.

Rice, Francis Owen & Teller, Edward. The Structure of Matter. 2011. 374p. 53.95 ***(978-1-258-05545-5(7))*** Literary Licensing, LLC.

Rice, Stuart A. Advances in Chemical Physics. (Advances in Chemical Physics Ser.). (ENG.). 2013. 195.00 *(978-0-470-93235-3(X)*, Wiley) Vol. 136. 2007. (Illus.). 318p. 233.00 *(978-0-471-68232-5(2)*, Wiley-Interscience) Vol. 144. 2010. 254p. 216.00 *(978-0-470-54786-1(3)*, Wiley)Volume 138. 2008. 464p. 216.00 *(978-0-471-68234-9(9)*, Wiley-Interscience) Wiley, John & Sons, Inc.

Rice, Stuart A., contrib. by. Advances in Chemical Physics, Vol. 139. 2008. (Advances in Chemical Physics Ser.: 305). (ENG.). 634p. 216.00 *(978-0-470-25389-2(4)*, Wiley-Interscience) Wiley, John & Sons, Inc.

Rice, Stuart A., ed. Advances in Chemical Physics. (Advances in Chemical Physics Ser.: 300). (ENG.). Vol. 140. 2008. 290p. 205.00 *(978-0-470-22688-9(9)*, Wiley-Interscience) Vol. 141. 2009. 563p. 205.00 *(978-0-470-41713-3(7)*, Wiley-Interscience) Vol. 150. 2012. 372p. 195.00 ***(978-1-118-16784-7(8)***, Wiley)Volume 149. 2012. 306p. 195.00 ***(978-1-118-16793-9(7))*** Wiley) Wiley, John & Sons, Inc.

—Advances in Chemical Physics Bundle. 2008. (Advances in Chemical Physics Ser.: 306). (ENG.). 7670p. 2990.00 *(978-0-470-38791-7(2)*, Wiley-Interscience) Wiley, John & Sons, Inc.

Rice, Stuart A. & Dinner, Aaron R., eds. Advances in Chemical Physics. (Advances in Chemical Physics Ser.: 316). (ENG.). Vol. 147. 2011. 432p. 195.00 ***(978-1-118-12234-1(8))*** Vol. 148. 2012. 392p. 195.00 ***(978-1-118-12235-8(6))*** Wiley, John & Sons, Inc. (Wiley).

Rice, Stuart A. & Rice. Advances in Chemical Physics, Vol. 143. Rice, Stuart A., ed. 2009. (Advances in Chemical Physics Ser.: 310). (ENG.). 171p. 216.00 *(978-0-470-50025-5(5)*, Wiley) Wiley, John & Sons, Inc.

Rice, Stuart A., et al. Advances in Chemical Physics, Volume 142. 2009. (Advances in Chemical Physics Ser.: 309). (ENG.). 298p. 216.00 *(978-0-470-46499-1(2)*, Wiley) Wiley, John & Sons, Inc.

Rodgers, Glen E. Descriptive in Organic, Coordination, & Solid State Chemistry. 3rd ed. 2011. (ENG.). 656p. (C). 235.95 ***(978-0-8400-6846-0(8))*** Brooks/Cole.

Rogers, Donald W. Concise Physical Chemistry. 2011. (ENG., Illus.). 404p. pap. 79.95 *(978-0-470-52264-6(X)*, Wiley) Wiley, John & Sons, Inc.

Romo, Alfonso. Quimica, Universo, Tierra y Vida. (Ciencia para Todos Ser.). (SPA.). pap. 6.99 *(978-968-16-2705-8(9))* Fondo de Cultura Economica USA.

Roque-Malherbe, Rolando M. A. Physical Chemistry of Materials: Energy & Environmental Applications. 2009. (ENG., Illus.). 522p. 154.95 *(978-1-4200-8272-2(8)*, CRC Press) Taylor & Francis Group GBR. Dist: Taylor & Francis Group.

Roussel, Marc R. A Life Scientist's Guide to Physical Chemistry. 2012. (ENG., Illus.). 456p. (C). 140.00 ***(978-1-107-00678-2(3))***; pap. 60.00 ***(978-0-521-18696-4(X))*** Cambridge Univ. Pr.

Royal Society of Chemistry Staff. Modelling Molecular Structure & Reactivity in Biological Systems. Naidoo, Kevin J. et al, eds. 2006. (Special Publication: No. 304). (ENG., Illus.). 304p. 176.00 *(978-0-85404-668-3(2)*, 0854046682) Royal Society of Chemistry, The GBR. Dist: Ingram Pub. Services.

Rumbles, G. & Monti, Oliver L. A. Physical Chemistry of Interfaces & Nanomaterials VII: 11-12 August 2008, San Diego, California, USA. 2008. (Proceedings of SPIE Ser.). (Illus.). 100p. pap. 70.00 *(978-0-8194-7254-0(9))* SPIE.

Rurack, Knut & Martinez-Manez, Ramon, eds. Supramolecular Chemistry of Organic-Inorganic Hybrid Materials. 2010. (ENG., Illus.). 782p. 158.00 *(978-0-470-37621-8(X)*, Wiley) Wiley, John & Sons, Inc.

Samorì, Paolo & Cacialli, Franco, eds. Functional Supramolecular Architectures: For Organic Electronics & Nanotechnology, 2 vols. 2011. (ENG., Illus.). 1030p. 405.00 *(978-3-527-32611-2(1)*, Wiley-VCH) Wiley, John & Sons, Inc.

Schäfer, Rolf & Schmidt, Peter C., eds. Methods in Physical Chemistry, 2 vols. 2012. (ENG.). 898p. 335.00 ***(978-3-527-32745-4(2)***, Wiley-VCH) Wiley, John & Sons, Inc.

Schalley, Christoph A., et al. Templates in Chemistry II. 2010. (Topics in Current Chemistry Ser.). (Illus.). xii, 371p. pap. 449.00 *(978-3-642-06201-8(6)*, 3642062016) Springer.

Schalley, Christoph A., ed. Analytical Methods in Supramolecular Chemistry. (ENG., Illus.). 2007. 502p. 249.00 *(978-3-527-31505-5(5))* 22nd ed. 2012. 844p. 310.00 ***(978-3-527-32982-3(X))*** Wiley, John & Sons, Inc. (Wiley-VCH).

Schlüter, A. Dieter. Functional Molecular Nanostructures. 2010. (Topics in Current Chemistry Ser.). (Illus.). x, 327p. pap. 409.00 *(978-3-642-06015-1(3)*, 3642060153) Springer.

Schneider, Hans-Jorg, ed. Applications of Supramolecular Chemistry for 21st Century Technology. 2012. (ENG., Illus.). 453p. 99.95 ***(978-1-4398-4014-6(8)***, CRC Press) Taylor & Francis Group GBR. Dist: Taylor & Francis Group.

Seeboth, Arno & Lotzch, Detlef. Thermochromic Phenomena in Polymers. 2008. (Smithers Rapra Updates Ser.). (Illus.). 108p. *(978-1-84735-112-8(3))* iSmithers Rapra Publishing.

Shapiro, Alan E. Fits, Passions & Paroxysms: Physics, Method & Chemistry & Newton's Theories of Colored Bodies & Fits of Easy Reflection. 2009. (ENG.). 420p. pap. 29.99 *(978-0-521-11755-5(0))* Cambridge Univ. Pr.

Shillady, Donald. Essentials of Physical Chemistry. 2011. (ENG., Illus.). 510p. 79.95 *(978-1-4398-4097-9(0)*, CRC Press) Taylor & Francis Group GBR. Dist: Taylor & Francis Group.

Silva, Carlos. Physical Chemistry of Interfaces & Nanomaterials X. 2011. (Proceedings of SPIE Ser.). 118p. pap. 90.00 ***(978-0-8194-8708-7(2))*** SPIE.

Sinko, Patrick J. Martin's Physical Pharmacy & Pharmaceutical Sciences. 6th rev. ed. 2010. (ENG., Illus.). 672p. 88.99 *(978-0-7817-9766-5(7))* Lippincott Williams & Wilkins.

Smyth Wallace, James. Chemical Analysis of Firearms, Ammunition, & Gunshot Residue. 2008. (International Forensic Science & Investigation Ser.). (ENG., Illus.). 320p. 109.95 *(978-1-4200-6966-2(7)*, CRC Press) Taylor & Francis Group GBR. Dist: Taylor & Francis Group.

Span, Roland. Multiparameter Equations of State: An Accurate Source of Thermodynamic Property Data. 2010. (ENG., Illus.). xviii, 367p. pap. 159.00 *(978-3-642-08671-7(3)*, 3642086713) Springer.

Spitler, Mark & Willig, Frank. Physical Chemistry of Interfaces & Nanomaterials V: 15-17 August, 2006, San Diego, California, USA. 2006. (Proceedings of SPIE Ser.). (Illus.). 192p. pap. 80.00 *(978-0-8194-6404-0(X))* SPIE.

Starikov, Evgeni, et al, eds. Modern Methods for Theoretical Physical Chemistry of Biopolymers. 2006. (ENG., Illus.). 604p. 300.00 *(978-0-444-52220-7(4)*, Elsevier Science) Elsevier Science & Technology Bks.

Steed, Jonathan W. & Gale, Philip A. Supramolecular Chemistry Set: From Molecules to Nanomaterials, 8 vols. 2012. (ENG.). 4014p. 1995.00 ***(978-0-470-74640-0(8)***, Wiley) Wiley, John & Sons, Inc.

Steed, Jonathan W., et al. Core Concepts in Supramolecular Chemistry & Nanochemistry. 2007. (ENG., Illus.). 320p. 169.00 *(978-0-470-85866-0(4))*; per. 55.00 *(978-0-470-85867-7(2))* Wiley, John & Sons, Inc. (Wiley).

Tanford, Charles. Physical Chemistry of Macromolecules. 2007. (ENG.). reprint ed. per. 79.00 *(978-1-930217-19-5(6))* Edwards, R. T. Inc.

Teplyakov, Andrew & Dybowski, Cecil. Physical Chemistry. 2009. (ENG.). (C). pap., instr.'s hndbk. ed. 33.80 *(978-0-558-30403-4(6))* Pearson Learning Solutions.

Tilden, William A. Introduction to the Study of Chemical Philosophy; the Principles of Theoretical & Systematic Chemistry by William a Tilden. 2006. 300p. per. 23.99 *(978-1-4255-2824-9(4))* MPublishing.

Trimm, Harold H., ed. Physical Chemistry: Chemical Kinetics & Reaction Mechanisms. 2011. (Research Progress in Chemistry Ser.). (ENG.). 358p. 99.95 *(978-1-926692-61-6(6))* Apple Academic Pr., Inc. CAN. Dist: Taylor & Francis Group.

Tro, Nivaldo J. Books a la Carte for Principles of Chemistry: A Molecular Approach. (ENG.). (C). 2010. 888p. ring bd. 103.80 *(978-0-321-73234-7(0))* 2nd ed. 2012. 936p. ring bd. 103.80 ***(978-0-321-75177-5(9))*** Prentice Hall PTR. (Prentice Hall).

—Chemistry: A Molecular Approach. 2nd ed. 2010. (ENG.). (C). 1232p. 232.00 *(978-0-321-70615-7(3))*; 1224p. E-Book 126.67 *(978-0-321-67631-3(9))* Prentice Hall PTR. (Prentice Hall).

Tro, Nivaldo J., et al. Selected Solution Manual for Principles of Chemistry: A Molecular Approach. 2nd ed. 2012. (ENG.). 408p. (C). pap. 73.53 ***(978-0-321-75183-6(3)***, Prentice Hall) Prentice Hall PTR.

Tro, Nivaldo Jose. Principles of Chemistry: A Molecular Approach. 2009. (ENG., Illus.). 888p. (C). 173.00 *(978-0-321-56004-9(3)*, Prentice Hall) Prentice Hall PTR.

Tro, Nivaldo Jose, et al. Solutions Manual for Principles of Chemistry: A Molecular Approach. 2009. (ENG.). 702p. (C). pap. 76.60 *(978-0-321-58639-1(5)*, Prentice Hall) Prentice Hall PTR.

V, Ganesh. Ab Initio Treatment of Large Molecular Systems: Algorithm Development, Parallelization & Applications. 2010. 164p. pap. *(978-3-8383-5185-8(1))* Lambert Academic Publishing.

Van Kampen, N. G. Stochastic Processes in Physics & Chemistry. 3rd ed. 2007. (North-Holland Personal Library). (ENG., Illus.). 464p. per. 107.00 *(978-0-444-52965-7(9)*, North Holland) Elsevier Science & Technology Bks.

Varfolomeev, Sergei Dmitrievich. Biochemical Physics Frontal Research. 2006. 133p. 225.00 *(978-1-60021-425-7(8))* Nova Science Pubs., Inc.

—New Aspects of Biochemical Physics: Pure & Applied Science. 2006. 143p. (C). 169.00 *(978-1-60021-419-6(3))* Nova Science Pubs., Inc.

—Trends in Biochemical Physics Research. 2007. 89.00 *(978-1-60021-426-4(6))* Nova Science Pubs., Inc.

Vemulapalli, Gopala Krishna. Invitation to Physical Chemistry. 2010. (Illus.). 240p. 54.00 *(978-1-84816-301-0(0))* Imperial College Pr. GBR. Dist: World Scientific Publishing Co., Inc.

Vieil, Eric. Understanding Physics & Chemistry Using Formal Graphs. 2012. (ENG., Illus.). 815p. 159.95 *(978-1-4200-8612-6(X)*, CRC Press) Taylor & Francis Group GBR. Dist: Taylor & Francis Group.

Vincent, John J., et al. Chemistry: A Molecular Approach. 2008. (ENG.). 368p. (C). spiral bd., lab manual ed. 95.80 *(978-0-13-600696-1(5)*, Prentice Hall) Prentice Hall PTR.

Waldeck, David H., et al. Principles of Physical Chemistry. 2nd ed. 2009. (ENG., Illus.). 1084p. 143.95 *(978-0-470-08964-4(4)*, Wiley-Interscience) Wiley, John & Sons, Inc.

—Principles of Physical Chemistry. 2nd ed. 2010. (ENG., Illus.). 804p. pap. 31.95 *(978-0-470-56197-3(1)*, Wiley) Wiley, John & Sons, Inc.

Wang, Yan Alexander, et al, eds. Advanced Reviews in Theoretical Chemical Physics. 2009. (Progress in Theoretical Chemistry & Physics Ser.). 600p. 399.00 *(978-90-481-2601-9(0))* Springer.

Whelan, Colm T. & Mason, Nigel J., eds. Electron Scattering: From Atoms, Molecules, Nuclei & Bulk Matter. 2010. (Physics of Atoms & Molecules Ser.). vii, 340p. pap. 179.00 *(978-1-4419-3469-7(3)*, 1441934693) Springer.

Wirth, Thomas, ed. Hypervalent Iodine Chemistry: Modern Developments in Organic Synthesis. 2010. (Topics in Current Chemistry Ser.). (Illus.). x, 264p. pap. 359.00 *(978-3-642-07906-1(7)*, 3642079067) Springer.

Würthner, Frank. Supramolecular Dye Chemistry. 2010. (Topics in Current Chemistry Ser.). xii, 324p. pap. 409.00 *(978-3-642-06613-9(5)*, 3642066135) Springer.

Yates, John T., et al. Molecular Physical Chemistry for Engineers. 2007. (Illus.). 482p. 92.00 *(978-1-891389-27-6(0))* Univ. Science Bks.

Yersin, Hartmut. Transition Metal & Rare Earth Compounds: Excited States, Transitions, Interactions II. 2010. (Topics in Current Chemistry Ser.). (Illus.). x, 190p. pap. 239.00 *(978-3-642-08757-8(4)*, 3642087574) Springer.

Yersin, Hartmut, ed. Transition Metal & Rare Earth Compounds: Excited States, Transitions, Interactions I. 2012. (Topics in Current Chemistry Ser.). (ENG., Illus.). x, 186p. pap. 229.00 *(978-3-642-08758-5(2)*, 3642087582) Springer.

Yoder, Claude H., et al. The Bridge to Organic Chemistry: Concepts & Nomenclature. 2010. (ENG., Illus.). 112p. pap. 19.95 *(978-0-470-52676-7(9)*, Wiley) Wiley, John & Sons, Inc.

Zaikov, Gennadii Efremovich, ed. Progress in Chemical & Biochemical Physics, Kinetics & Thermodynamics. 2008. (C). 185.00 *(978-1-60456-079-4(7))* Nova Science Pubs., Inc.

Zaikov, Gennadii Efremovich & Kablov, V. K. Handbook of Condensed Phase Chemistry. 2009. (Illus.). x, 341p. 195.00 *(978-1-60741-734-7(0))* Nova Science Pubs., Inc.

Zaikov, Gennadii Efremovich & Kirshenbaum, Gerald S. Chemical Physics & Physical Chemistry: Step into the Future. 2007. (C). 225.00 *(978-1-60021-727-2(3))* Nova Science Pubs., Inc.

Zhou, Gongdu & Duan, Lianyun. Jie Gou Hua Xue Ji Chu. 4th ed. 2008. (CHI., Illus.). 362p. *(978-7-301-05773-5(3))* Beijing University Pr.

CHEMISTRY, PHYSICAL AND THEORETICAL—LABORATORY MANUALS

Cram101 Textbook Reviews. Outlines & Highlights for Experiments in Physical Chemistry by Carl W Garland, David P Shoemaker, Joseph W Nibler, Isbn: 9780072828429. 2010. 72p. pap. 27.95 *(978-1-61698-550-9(X))* Cram101 Inc.

Cram101 Textbook Reviews Staff. Outlines & Highlights for Experiments in Physical Chemistry by Carl W Garland, David P Shoemaker, Joseph W Nibler, Isbn: 9780072828429. 2009. 64p. pap. 27.95 *(978-1-4288-8180-8(8))* Cram101 Inc.

—Outlines & Highlights for Experiments in Physical Chemistry by Garland Isbn: 007231821x. 2008. 84p. pap. 10.95 *(978-1-4288-5914-2(4))* Cram101 Inc.

Palmer, W. G. Experimental Physical Chemistry. 2009. (ENG.). 336p. pap. 46.00 *(978-0-521-10495-1(5))* Cambridge Univ. Pr.

Wilson, Robb J. Hooked on Pchem Lab: Physical Chemistry Laboratory Manual. 2010. (ENG.). 258p. spiral bd. 67.89 *(978-0-7575-7447-4(5))* Kendall Hunt Publishing Co.

CHEMISTRY, PHYSICAL AND THEORETICAL—PROBLEMS, EXERCISES, ETC.

Atkins, et al. Student Solutions Manual for Physical Chemistry. 9th ed. 2010. (ENG.). 550p. (C). pap. 50.95 *(978-1-4292-3128-2(9))* Freeman, W. H. & Co.

Ilich, Predrag-Peter. Selected Problems in Physical Chemistry. 2009. 161p. pap. 39.95 *(978-3-642-04326-0(7)*, 3642043267) Springer.

Levine, Ira N. Physical Chemistry. 6th ed. 2008. (ENG.). 416p. (C). pap. 88.00 *(978-0-07-253863-2(5)*, 0072538635, McGraw-Hill Science, Engineering & Mathematics) McGraw-Hill Higher Education.

CHEMISTRY, PHYSICAL ORGANIC

see Physical Organic Chemistry

CHEMISTRY, PHYSIOLOGICAL

see Biochemistry

CHEMISTRY, QUANTUM

see Quantum Chemistry

CHEMISTRY, SOIL

see Soil Chemistry

CHEMISTRY, SOLID STATE

see Solid State Chemistry

CHEMISTRY, SURFACE

see Surface Chemistry

CHEMISTRY, SYNTHETIC INORGANIC

see Inorganic Compounds—Synthesis

CHEMISTRY, SYNTHETIC ORGANIC

see Organic Compounds—Synthesis

CHEMISTRY, TECHNICAL

see also Animal Products; Biochemical Engineering; Bleaching; Canning and Preserving; Ceramics; Chemical Engineering; Chemical Reactors; Chemurgy; Cleaning Compounds; Corrosion and Anti-Corrosives; Electrochemistry; Explosives; Extraction (Chemistry); Food—Analysis; High Pressure (Technology); Metallurgical Analysis; Photochemistry; Refrigerants; Separation (Technology); Synthetic Products; Tanning; Textile Chemistry; Wood—Chemistry; Workshop Recipes

also particular industries and products, e.g. Clay Industries; Dyes and Dyeing; Petroleum Products

Bakeev, Katherine A., ed. Process Analytical Technology: Spectroscopic Tools & Implementation Strategies for the Chemical & Pharmaceutical Industries. 2nd ed. 2010. (ENG., Illus.). 576p. 200.00 *(978-0-470-72207-7(X)*, Wiley) Wiley, John & Sons, Inc.

Centi, Gabriele, et al, eds. Sustainable Industrial Chemistry. 2009. (ENG., Illus.). 621p. 205.00 *(978-3-527-31552-9(7)*, Wiley-VCH) Wiley, John & Sons, Inc.

Chemical Process Monitoring Devices. 2007. per. 4250.00 *(978-1-59623-279-2(X))* BCC Research.

Council of Industrial Boiler Owners (CIBO) Staff, compiled by. 5th Industrial Emissions Control Technology Conference 2007. 2007. 997p. pap. 118.00 *(978-1-60423-382-7(6))* Curran Assocs., Inc.

Cram101 Textbook Reviews. Outlines & Highlights for Industrial Organic Chemistry by Hans-J?rgen Arpe. 2011. 170p. pap. 29.95 ***(978-1-61905-437-0(X))*** Cram101 Inc.

Deyev, German F. & Deyev, Dmitriy G. Physical Chemistry of Fusion Welding. 2010. 762p. 275.00 *(978-0-9820870-4-6(7))* IGI Pr.

Douroumis, Dionysios, ed. Hot-Melt Extrusion: Pharmaceutical Applications. 2012. (ENG.). 384p. 180.00 ***(978-0-470-71118-7(3)***, Wiley) Wiley, John & Sons, Inc.

Drieben-Holsche, B, et al. Grundriss der Chemischen Technik. 2012. (ENG.). 800p. 105.00 ***(978-3-527-30446-2(0)***, Wiley-VCH) Wiley, John & Sons, Inc.

Garrett, Peter R. Defoaming: Theory & Industrial Applications. 2nd rev. ed. 2010. (Surfactant Science Ser.). (ENG., Illus.). 480p. 199.95 *(978-1-4200-6041-6(4))* CRC Pr. LLC.

Gordon, B. Le Roy & Gordon, B. L. Chemical Arts & Technologies of Indigenous Americans. 2009. (Bar S Ser.). (Illus.). 167p. (C). bds. 90.00 *(978-1-4073-0390-1(2))* British Archaeological Reports Ltd. GBR. Dist: Brown, David Bk. Co., The.

Hagiopol, Cornel & Johnston, James W. Chemistry of Modern Papermaking. 2011. (ENG., Illus.). 431p. 179.95 *(978-1-4398-5644-4(3)*, CRC Press) Taylor & Francis Group GBR. Dist: Taylor & Francis Group.

Heaton, C.A. An Introduction to Industrial Chemistry. 2nd ed. 2008. 448p. pap. 69.95 *(978-0-216-92919-7(9))* Springer.

Hecht, Stefan & Huc, Ivan, eds. Foldamers: Structure, Properties, & Applications. 2007. (ENG., Illus.). 456p. 265.00 *(978-3-527-31563-5(2)*, Wiley-VCH) Wiley, John & Sons, Inc.

Imamoglu, Yavuz & Valerian, Dragutan. Metathesis Chemistry: From Nanostructure Design to Synthesis of Advanced Materials: Proceedings of the NATO Advanced Study Institute on New Frontiers in Technologies for Synthesis of Advanced Materials, Antalya, Turkey, 4-16 September 2006. 2007. (NATO Science Series II). (Illus.). 532p. 319.00 *(978-1-4020-6089-2(0))* Springer.

Islam, Rafiq. Natural & Processed Substances: Production, Uses & Effects. 2012. (Food Science & Technology Ser.). 149p. 95.00 *(978-1-61324-146-2(1))* Nova Science Pubs., Inc.

Jayakumar, R., et al, eds. Chitosan for Biomaterials I, 2 vols. 2011. (Advances in Polymer Science Ser.). (ENG., Illus.). xi, 236p. 259.00 ***(978-3-642-23113-1(6)***, 3642231136) Springer.

Jayakumar, Rangasamy, et al, eds. Chitosan for Biomaterials II, 2 vols. 2011. (Advances in Polymer Science Ser.). (ENG., Illus.). xi, 212p. 259.00 ***(978-3-642-24060-7(7)***, 3642240607) Springer.

Johnston, Jas. F. W. (James Finlay Weir). The Chemistry of Common Life by James F Johnston Illustrated with Numerous Wood Engravings + Eighth Edition. 2006. (Illus.). 316p. per. 23.99 *(978-1-4255-3077-8(X))*; (ENG., 388p. per. 26.99 *(978-1-4255-4131-6(3))* MPublishing.

—The Chemistry of Common Life by James F Johnston Illustratedwith Numerous Wood Engravings + 2006. (Illus.). 316p. per. 23.99 *(978-1-4255-3076-1(1))*; (ENG., 388p. per. 26.99 *(978-1-4255-4130-9(5))* MPublishing.

Kent, James A., ed. Handbook of Industrial Chemistry. 10th ed. 2006. 1374p. 809.00 *(978-0-387-34292-4(3)*, 0387342923) Springer.

Kirchner, Barbara & Vrabec, Jadran, eds. Multiscale Molecular Methods in Applied Chemistry. 2012. (Topics in Current Chemistry Ser.). (ENG., Illus.). xii, 326p. 349.00 ***(978-3-642-24967-9(1)***, 3642249671) Springer.

Kirk-Othmer. Kirk-Othmer Encyclopedia of Chemical Technology, 27 vols. Wiley-Interscience Publication Staff, ed. 5th rev. ed. 2006. (Kirk 5e Print Continuation Ser.: 5). (ENG., Illus.). Vol. 23. 912p. 426.00 *(978-0-471-48499-8(7))*Volume 24. 896p. 426.00 *(978-0-471-48498-1(9))* Wiley, John & Sons, Inc. (Wiley-Interscience).

Kirk-Othmer & Kirk-Othmer. Kirk-Othmer Encyclopedia of Chemical Technology, 27 vols. Wiley-Interscience Publication Staff, ed. 5th rev. ed. (Kirk 5e Print Continuation Ser.: 7). (ENG., Illus.). Volume 21. 2006. 896p. 426.00

(978-0-471-48502-5(0))Volume 25. 2007. 944p. 426.00 (978-0-471-48497-4(0))Volume 26. 2007. 1076p. 425.00 (978-0-471-48495-0(4)) Wiley, John & Sons, Inc. (Wiley-Interscience).

Kirk-Othmer, R. E. Encyclopedia of Chemical Technology. 5th ed. 2007. (Kirk 5e Print Continuation Ser.). 850p. 295.00 (978-0-470-08141-9(4), Wiley-Interscience) Wiley, John & Sons, Inc.

Kirk-Othmer, R. E. & Kirk-Othmer. Kirk-Othmer Encyclopedia of Chemical Technology, 27 vols., Volume 22. Wiley-Interscience Publication Staff, ed. 5th rev. ed. 2006. (Kirk 5e Print Continuation Ser.: 6). (ENG., Illus.). 900p. 426.00 (978-0-471-48501-8(2), Wiley-Interscience) Wiley, John & Sons, Inc.

Klerk, Arno de. Fischer-Tropsch Refining. 2011. (ENG., Illus.). 642p. 195.00 (978-3-527-32605-1(7), Wiley-VCH) Wiley, John & Sons, Inc.

Kulprathipanja, Santi, ed. Zeolites in Industrial Separation & Catalysis. 2010. (ENG., Illus.). 618p. 235.00 (978-3-527-32505-4(0), Wiley-VCH) Wiley, John & Sons, Inc.

Lalena, John N. & Cleary, David A. Principles of Inorganic Materials Design. 2nd ed. 2010. (ENG., Illus.). 585p. 163.00 (978-0-470-40403-4(5), Wiley) Wiley, John & Sons, Inc.

Laudon, Matthew & Romanowicz, Bart, eds. Cleantech Technical Proceedings. 2007. (Illus.). 346p. per. 139.95 (978-1-4200-6382-0(0)) CRC Pr. LLC.

Levey, Martin. Mediaeval Arabic Bookmaking & Its Relation to Early Chemistry & Pharmacology. 2011. 80p. 37.95 **(978-1-258-03182-4(5))** Literary Licensing, LLC.

Li, Jing. Thickness Variation Reduction for Vartm Process. 2009. 144p. pap. (978-3-639-12871-0(0)) VDM Verlag Dr. Mueller e.K.

Li, Zongjin & Liang, Wenquan. Advanced Concrete Technology. 2011. (ENG., Illus.). 528p. 145.00 (978-0-470-43743-8(X), Wiley) Wiley, John & Sons, Inc.

Mahler, Hanns-Christian. Analysis of Aggregates & Particles in Protein Pharmaceuticals. Jiskoot, Wim & Mahler, Hanns-Christian, eds. 2012. (ENG., Illus.). 472p. 125.00 **(978-0-470-49718-0(1)**, Wiley) Wiley, John & Sons, Inc.

McConville, Francis X. The Pilot Plant Real Book: A Unique Handbook for the Chemical Process Industry. 2nd num. ed. 2007. (Illus.). 320p. 114.95 (978-0-9721769-2-7(6)) FXM Engineering & Design.

Mohos, Ferenc Á. Confectionery & Chocolate Engineering: Principles & Applications. 2010. (ENG., Illus.). 712p. 269.95 (978-1-4051-9470-9(7), Wiley-Blackwell) Wiley, John & Sons, Inc.

Mujumdar, Arun S. Handbook of Industrial Drying. 3rd rev. ed. 2006. (ENG., Illus.). 1312p. 289.95 (978-1-57444-668-5(1), CRC Press) Taylor & Francis Group GBR. Dist: Taylor & Francis Group.

O'brien Robert J Staff. Synthesis Gas Chemistry Production & Utilization. 2009. 500p. 169.95 (978-1-57444-533-6(2), DK3400) Taylor & Francis Group.

Okoroanyanwu, Uzodinma. Chemistry & Lithography. (Illus.). 2011. (ENG.). xxix, 861p. 121.00 (978-1-118-03002-8(8)) 2010. 892p. 115.00 (978-0-8194-7562-6(9)) SPIE.

Pahari, A. & Chauhan, B. Engineering Chemistry. 2007. (Illus.). 600p. 98.95 (978-0-9778582-8-6(6)) Jones & Bartlett Learning, LLC.

Perozziello, Gerardo. Microfluidic System Interfacing. 2011. 96p. pap. **(978-3-8443-2770-0(3))** Lambert Academic Publishing.

Phlegm, H. K. The Role of the Chemist in Automotive Design. 2009. (ENG., Illus.). 216p. 144.95 (978-1-4200-7188-7(2), CRC Press) Taylor & Francis Group GBR. Dist: Taylor & Francis Group.

Pistikopoulos, E. N., et al, eds. 21st European Symposium on Computer Aided Process Engineering, 2 vols. 2011. (Computer Aided Chemical Engineering Ser.). (Illus.). 1136p. 570.00 (978-0-444-53711-9(2)) Elsevier Science & Technology Bks.

Plumlee Karl Staff. Solid-Acid Catalyzed Alkylation & Isomerization. 2009. 169.95 (978-1-57444-523-7(5)) CRC Pr. LLC.

Predel, Bruno, et al. Phase Diagrams & Heterogeneous Equilibria: A Practical Introduction. 2010. (Engineering Materials & Processes Ser.). (Illus.). xv, 349p. pap. 149.00 (978-3-642-05727-4(6), 3642057276) Springer.

Rähse, Wilfried. Produktdesign in der chemischen Industrie: Schnelle Umsetzung kundenspezifischer Lösungen. 2006. (VDI-Buch / Chemische Technik / Verfahrenstechnik Ser.). (Illus.). XII, 348p. 139.00 (978-3-540-25162-0(6), 3540251626) Springer.

Royal Society of Chemistry Staff. Advanced Oil Crop Biorefineries. Kazmi, Abbas, ed. 2011. (RSC Green Chemistry Ser.). (ENG., Illus.). 336p. (C). 195.00 (978-1-84973-135-5(7)) Royal Society of Chemistry, The GBR. Dist: Ingram Pub. Services.

Senapati, M. Advanced Engineering Chemistry. 2nd ed. 2008. (Illus.). 531p. 95.95 (978-0-9778582-9-3(4)) Jones & Bartlett Learning, LLC.

Siepmann, Juergen, et al, eds. Fundamentals & Applications of Controlled Release Drug Delivery. 2011. (Advances in Delivery Science & Technology Ser.). (ENG., Illus.). xiii, 592p. 239.00 **(978-1-4614-0880-2(6)**, 1461408806) Springer.

Society of Petroleum Engineers (SPE) Staff, compiled by. SPE International Symposium on Oilfield Chemistry 2007. 2007. 661p. pap. 131.00 (978-1-60423-753-5(8)) Curran Assocs., Inc.

Strom, E. Thomas & Rasmussen, Seth C., eds. 100+ Years of Plastics: Leo Baekeland & Beyond. 2012. (ACS Symposium Ser.: 1080). (ENG.). 208p. 150.00 **(978-0-8412-2677-7(6))** American Chemical Society.

Tao, Junhua, et al. Biocatalysis for the Pharmaceutical Industry: Discovery, Development & Manufacturing. 2008. (ENG., Illus.). 250p. 140.00 (978-0-470-82314-9(3), Wiley) Wiley, John & Sons, Inc.

Valerian, Dragutan. Metathesis Chemistry: From Nanostructure Design to Synthesis of Advanced Materials: Proceedings of the NATO Advanced Study Institute on New Frontiers in Technologies for Synthesis of Advanced Materials, Antalya, Turkey, 4-16 September 2006. Imamoglu, Yavuz & Dragutan, Valerian, eds. 2007. (NATO Science Series II). (Illus.). 532p. per. 139.00 (978-1-4020-6090-8(4)) Springer.

Vasiliu-Oprea, Cleopatra & Dan, Florin. Macromolecular Mechanochemistry. 2007. (ENG.). 456p. 180.00 (978-1-904602-54-5(1)) Cambridge International Science Publishing, Ltd. GBR. Dist: Ingram Pub. Services.

Wiley-Interscience Publication Staff, creator. Kirk-Othmer Chemical Technology & the Environment, 2 vols., Vol. 1. 2007. (ENG., Illus.). 2573p. 690.00 (978-0-470-10540-5(2), Wiley-Interscience) Wiley, John & Sons, Inc.

Wiley-VCH Staff, ed. Ullmann's Encyclopedia of Industrial Chemistry. 740th ed. 2012. (ENG.). 29456p. 8745.00 (978-3-527-32943-4(9), Wiley-VCH) Wiley, John & Sons, Inc.

Xie, Yan. Chemical Signal Analysis with Fourier Microfluidics. 2009. 176p. pap. (978-3-639-16082-6(7)) VDM Verlag Dr. Mueller e.K.

Zaikowski, Lori, et al, eds. Chemical Evolution II: From the Origins of Life to Modern Society, 1 vol. 2010. (ACS Symposium Ser.). (ENG., Illus.). 376p. 150.00 (978-0-8412-6980-4(7)) American Chemical Society.

Zibaseresht, Ramin. Approaches to Photo Activated Cytotoxins. 2011. 328p. pap. **(978-3-8443-8236-5(4))** Lambert Academic Publishing.

CHEMISTRY, TECHNICAL—DICTIONARIES

Ash, Michael & Ash, Irene. Industrial Chemical Thesaurus. 2nd ed. 2006. (ENG.). Volume 1. 844p. 326.00 (978-0-470-14429-9(7))Volume 2. 464p. 326.00 (978-0-470-14430-5(0)) Wiley, John & Sons, Inc. (Wiley).

Gross, Helmut. English-German Dictionary of Chemistry & Chemical Technology. (ENG & GER.). (978-0-7859-9341-4(X)) French & European Pubns., Inc.

Kirk-Othmer. Kirk-Othmer Concise Encyclopedia of Chemical Technology, 2 vols. 52nd rev. ed. 2007. (ENG., Illus.). 2762p. 570.00 (978-0-470-04748-4(8), Wiley-Interscience) Wiley, John & Sons, Inc.

Kirk-Othmer & Kirk-Othmer. Chemical Technology, Vols. 1-26. Seidel, Arza, ed. 5th rev. ed. 2007. (Kirk 5e Print Continuation Ser.: 2). (ENG.). 1084p. 425.00 (978-0-471-48496-7(2), Wiley-Interscience) Wiley, John & Sons, Inc.

Kirk-Othmer, R. E. Encyclopedia of Chemical Technology, Vol. 23. 5th ed. 2007. (Kirk 5e Print Continuation Ser.). 850p. 295.00 (978-0-470-08143-3(0), Wiley-Interscience) Wiley, John & Sons, Inc.

Wiley. Kirk-Othmer Food & Feed Technology, 2 vols. 2007. (ENG., Illus.). 1760p. 560.00 (978-0-470-17448-7(X), Wiley-Interscience) Wiley, John & Sons, Inc.

Wiley and Sons, Inc. Staff. Kirk-Othmer Separation Technology, 2 vols., Set. 2nd ed. 2008. (ENG.). 2544p. 730.00 (978-0-470-12741-4(4), Wiley-Interscience) Wiley, John & Sons, Inc.

Wiley-VCH, ed. Ullmann's Encyclopedia of Industrial Chemistry: Electronic Release 2007. 2007. 1100p. 1470.00 (978-3-527-31602-1(7)) Wiley, John & Sons, Inc.

CHEMISTRY, TECHNICAL—FORMULAE, RECEIPTS, PRESCRIPTIONS

Chandrasekaran, Chellappa. Essential Rubber Formulary: Formulas for Practitioners. 2007. (Plastics Design Library). (ENG.). 202p. 136.00 (978-0-8155-1539-5(1)) William Andrew, Inc.

Pensé-Lhéritier, Anne-Marie. Formulation. 2011. (ENG., Illus.). 352p. 145.00 (978-1-84821-259-6(3), Wiley-ISTE) Wiley, John & Sons, Inc.

Salmi, Tapio O., et al. Chemical Reaction Engineering & Reactor Technology. 2010. (Chemical Industries Ser.). (ENG., Illus.). 644p. (C). 119.95 (978-1-4200-9268-4(5), CRC Press) Taylor & Francis Group GBR. Dist: Taylor & Francis Group.

CHEMISTRY, TECHNICAL—HISTORY

Reinhardt, Carsten & Travis, Anthony S. Heinrich Caro & the Creation of Modern Chemical Industry. 2010. (Chemists & Chemistry Ser.). 480p. pap. 289.00 (978-90-481-5575-0(4), 9048155754) Springer.

CHEMISTRY, TECHNICAL—RESEARCH

Panel on Chemical Science and Technology & National Research Council. n Assessment of the National Institute of Standards & Technology Chemical Science & Technology Laboratory: Fiscal Year 2007. 2007. (ENG.). 38p. pap. 15.00 (978-0-309-11175-1(7)) National Academies Pr.

—An Assessment of the National Institute of Standards & Technology Chemical Science & Technology Laboratory: Fiscal Year 2009. 2009. (ENG.). 50p. pap. 21.00 (978-0-309-14509-1(0)) National Academies Pr.

CHEMISTRY, TEXTILE

see Textile Chemistry

CHEMISTRY, THEORETICAL

see Chemistry, Physical and Theoretical

CHEMISTRY, TOXICOLOGICAL

see Toxicological Chemistry

CHEMISTRY AS A PROFESSION

see Chemistry—Vocational Guidance

CHEMISTRY IN WARFARE

see Chemical Warfare

CHEMISTRY OF FOOD

see Food—Analysis; Food—Composition

CHEMISTS

see also Chemical Engineers; Pharmacists

Ahlberg. Nobel Lectures in Chemistry 2001-2005. 2008. 106.00 (978-981-279-444-4(1)) World Scientific Publishing Co., Inc.

Ahlberg, Per, ed. Chemistry 2001-2005. 2008. (Nobel Lectures in Chemistry Ser.). (Illus.). 481p. pap. 65.00 (978-981-279-445-1(X)) World Scientific Publishing Co., Inc.

Apotheker, Jan & Sarkadi, Livia Simon, eds. European Women in Chemistry. 2011. (ENG., Illus.). 256p. pap. 34.95 (978-3-527-32956-4(0), Wiley-VCH) Wiley, John & Sons, Inc.

Bader, Alfred. Chemistry & Art: Further Adventures of a Chemist Collector. 2009. (ENG., Illus.). 312p. 29.95 (978-0-297-85512-5(3)) Orion Publishing Group, Ltd. GBR. Dist: Independent Pubs. Group.

Balbes, Lisa M. Nontraditional Careers for Chemists: New Formulas in Chemistry. 2006. (ENG., Illus.). 320p. per. 27.95 (978-0-19-518367-2(3)) Oxford Univ. Pr., Inc.

Barkan, Diana Kormos. Walther Nernst & the Transition to Modern Physical Science. 2011. (ENG., Illus.). 302p. pap. 36.99 (978-0-521-17629-3(3)) Cambridge Univ. Pr.

Bartel, Hans-Georg & Huebener, Rudolf P. Walther Nernst: Pioneer of Physics & of Chemistry. 2007. (Illus.). 394p. 96.00 (978-981-256-560-0(4)) World Scientific Publishing Co., Inc.

Bell, Les. What's Cooking in Chemistry? How Leading Chemists Succeed in the Kitchen. Güntner, Carlos E. et al, eds. 2nd ed. 2009. (Erlebnis Wissenschaft Ser.: 5). (ENG.). 243p. pap. 20.95 (978-3-527-32621-1(9), Wiley-VCH) Wiley, John & Sons, Inc.

Bogert, Marston Taylor. Biographical Memoir of Charles Frederick Chandler, 1836-1925: National Academy of Sciences, Biographical Memoirs, V14, Fifth Memoir. 2011. 60p. 36.95 **(978-1-258-07758-7(2))** Literary Licensing, LLC.

Charles, Daniel. Master Mind: The Rise & Fall of Fritz Haber, the Nobel Laureate Who Launched the Age of Chemical Warfare. 2009. (ENG.). 313p. 25.00 (978-1-4379-6670-1(5)) DIANE Publishing Co.

Coffey, Patrick. Cathedrals of Science: The Personalities & Rivalries That Made Modern Chemistry. 2008. (ENG., Illus.). 416p. 29.95 (978-0-19-532134-0(0)) Oxford Univ. Pr., Inc.

Conrads, Hinderk, et al. Carl Neuberg — Biochemie, Politik und Geschichte: Lebenswege und Werk Eines Fast Verdrängten Forschers. 2006. (Geschichte und Philosophie der Medizin. History & Philosophy of Medicine Ser.). (GER., Illus.). 221p. (C). 68.00 (978-3-515-08894-7(6)) Steiner, Franz Verlag Wiesbaden GmbH DEU. Dist: Brown, David Bk. Co., The.

Cowan, George A. Manhattan Project to the Santa Fe Institute: The Memoirs of George A. Cowan. 2010. (ENG., Illus.). 184p. 27.95 (978-0-8263-4870-8(X)) Univ. of New Mexico Pr.

Curie, Marie, et al. Lettres: Marie Curie et Ses Filles. 2011. (FRE.). 416p. (978-2-7564-0457-8(8)) Pygmalion, Editions.

Dhar, Durga Nath & Dhar, Preeti. Noble Prize Winners in Chemistry, 1901-2009. 2011. 364p. pap. **(978-3-8443-0446-6(0))** Lambert Academic Publishing.

Emling, Shelley. Marie Curie & Her Daughters: The Private Lives of Science's First Family. 2012. (ENG., Illus.). 256p. 26.00 **(978-0-230-11571-2(3))** Palgrave Macmillan.

Fraser-Reid, Bert. From Sugar to Splenda: A Personal & Scientific Journey of a Carbohydrate Chemist & Expert Witness. 2012. (ENG., Illus.). xx, 216p. 129.00 **(978-3-642-22780-6(5)**, 3642227805) Springer.

French, Sidney J. Torch & Crucible: Life & Death of Antoine Lavoisier. 2011. 296p. 48.95 **(978-1-258-05888-3(X))** Literary Licensing, LLC.

Ghosh, Abhik, ed. Letters to a Young Chemist. 2011. (ENG., Illus.). 320p. pap. 39.95 (978-0-470-39043-6(3), Wiley-Interscience) Wiley, John & Sons, Inc.

Goh, (wong) Lai Yoong. Follow the Chemistry: Lure, Lore & Life - an Autobiography of Goh Lai Yoong. 2010. 176p. 34.00 (978-981-4304-00-9(X)) World Scientific Publishing Co., Inc.

Hager, Thomas. The Alchemy of Air: A Jewish Genius, a Doomed Tycoon, & the Scientific Discovery That Fed the World but Fueled the Rise of Hitler. (ENG.). 336p. 2009. pap. 15.00 (978-0-307-35179-1(3), Three Rivers Pr.) 2008. 24.95 (978-0-307-35178-4(5), Harmony) Crown Publishing Group.

Harrow, Benjamin. Eminent Chemists of Our Time. 2010. 310p. pap. 29.75 (978-1-143-00355-4(1)) 2009. 312p. 25.99 (978-1-103-93851-3(7)) 2009. 312p. pap. 19.99 (978-1-103-93843-8(6)) BiblioBazaar.

—Eminent Chemists of Our Time. 2009. 180p. pap. 19.99 (978-0-217-71240-8(1)) General Bks. LLC.

Hoffmann, Klaus. Schuld und Verantwortung. 2007. (GER.). 312p. 54.95 (978-3-540-56766-0(6)) Springer.

Hornblum, Allen M. The Invisible Harry Gold: The Man Who Gave the Soviets the Atom Bomb. (Illus.). 464p. 2011. (ENG.). pap. 20.00 (978-0-300-17757-2(7)) 2010. 32.50 (978-0-300-15676-8(6)) Yale Univ. Pr.

Jay, Mike. The Atmosphere of Heaven: The Unnatural Experiments of Dr. Beddoes & His Sons of Genius. 2009. (ENG., Illus.). 296p. 30.00 (978-0-300-12439-2(2)) Yale Univ. Pr.

—The Atmosphere of Heaven: The Unnatural Experiments of Dr Beddoes & His Sons of Genius. 2010. (ENG., Illus.). 304p. pap. 20.00 (978-0-300-16891-4(8)) Yale Univ. Pr.

Johnson, Steven. The Invention of Air: A Story of Science, Faith, Revolution, & the Birth of America. (ENG.). (gr. 12-18). 2009. 304p. 16.00 (978-1-59448-401-8(5), Riverhead Trade (Paperbacks)) 2008. 272p. 25.95 (978-1-59448-852-8(5), Riverhead Bks. (Hardcover)) Penguin Group (USA) Inc.

Lachman, Arthur. Borderland of the Unknown: The Life Story of Gilbert Newton Lewis, One of the World's Great Scientists. 2011. 194p. 42.95 **(978-1-258-06890-5(7))** Literary Licensing, LLC.

Michaels, Darren & Heinen, Peter. The Science of Stripping. 2009. 100p. pap. 20.95 (978-1-4327-3681-1(7)) Outskirts Pr., Inc.

Mirzayanov, Vil S. State Secrets: An Insider's Chronicle of the Russian Chemical Weapons Program. 2008. 624p. 43.95 (978-1-4327-1923-4(8)); pap. 29.95 (978-1-4327-2566-2(1)) Outskirts Pr., Inc.

Moran, Bruce T. Andreas Libavius & the Transformation of Alchemy: Separating Chemical Cultures with Polemical Fire. 2007. (Illus.). 351p. 49.95 (978-0-88135-395-2(7)) Watson Publishing International, LLC.

Numerof, Paul. In August 1945: A Memoir. 2006. (Illus.). 118p. (978-0-941232-35-7(2)) Los Alamos Historical Society.

Ogilvie, Marilyn Bailey. Marie Curie: A Biography. 2010. (ENG., Illus.). 180p. pap. 17.00 (978-1-61614-216-2(2)) Prometheus Bks., Pubs.

Osborne, Thomas B. Biographical Memoir of Samuel William Johnson, 1830-1909: National Academy of Sciences, Biographical Memoirs, V7, No. 8, July 1911. 2011. 24p. 35.95 **(978-1-258-07183-7(5))** Literary Licensing, LLC.

Priestley, Joseph & Cooper, Thomas. Memoirs of Dr. Joseph Priestley. 2010. (Cambridge Library Collection - Physical Sciences Ser.). (ENG.). 504p. pap. 35.99 (978-1-108-01419-9(4)); 452p. pap. 32.99 (978-1-108-01420-5(8)) Cambridge Univ. Pr.

Principe, Lawrence M. The Secrets of Alchemy. 2012. (Synthesis Ser.). (Illus.). 288p. 25.00 **(978-0-226-68295-2(1))** Univ. of Chicago Pr.

Quadbeck-Seeger, Hans-Jürgen. The Periodic Table Through History: Who Charted the Elements? 2007. (ENG.). 2p. 30.00 (978-3-527-32083-7(0), Wiley-VCH) Wiley, John & Sons, Inc.

Rao, C. N. R. Climbing the Limitless Ladder: A Life in Chemistry. 2010. 232p. 54.00 (978-981-4307-85-7(8)); pap. 29.00 (978-981-4307-86-4(6)) World Scientific Publishing Co., Inc.

Rayner-Canham, Marelene F. & Rayner-Canham, Geoffrey. Chemistry Was Their Life: Pioneering British Women Chemists, 1880-1949. 2008. (Illus.). xvii, 542p. 96.00 (978-1-86094-986-9(X)) World Scientific Publishing Co., Inc.

Redniss, Lauren. Radioactive: Marie & Pierre Curie - A Tale of Love & Fallout. 2010. (ENG.). 208p. 29.99 (978-0-06-135132-7(6)) HarperCollins Pubs.

Reed, Germaine M. Crusading for Chemistry: The Professional Career of Charles Holmes Herty. 2010. (ENG.). 498p. pap. 26.95 (978-0-8203-3552-0(5)) Univ. of Georgia Pr.

Reinhardt, Carsten & Travis, Anthony S. Heinrich Caro & the Creation of Modern Chemical Industry. 2010. (Chemists & Chemistry Ser.). 480p. pap. 289.00 (978-90-481-5575-0(4), 9048155754) Springer.

Rogers, David N. Nobel Laureate Contributions to 20th Century Chemistry. 2006. (ENG., Illus.). 668p. 160.00 (978-0-85404-356-9(X), 085404356X) Royal Society of Chemistry, The GBR. Dist: Ingram Pub. Services.

Rowlinson, John. Sir James Dewar 1842-1923: A Ruthless Chemist. 2012. (Science, Technology & Culture, 17001945 Ser.). (Illus.). 250p. 124.95 **(978-1-4094-0613-6(X))** Ashgate Publishing Co.

Smith, Edgar F. James Woodhouse A Pioneer in Chemistry 1. 2006. pap. 30.95 (978-1-4286-5722-9(3)) Kessinger Publishing, LLC.

Strauss, Anselm L., et al. The Professional Scientist a Study of American Chemists. 2011. (ENG.). 296p. pap. 34.95 (978-1-4128-1858-2(3)) Aldine Transaction.

Thorpe, Thomas E. Essays in Historical Chemistry. 2007. 392p. 48.95 (978-0-548-55266-7(5)); (ENG.). per. 33.95 (978-0-548-47727-4(2)) Kessinger Publishing, LLC.

Tietz, Norbert W. My Life: From Refugee to Teacher & Scientist, Living the American Dream. 2010. (978-1-59425-108-5(8), AACC Pr.) American Assn. for Clinical Chemistry, Inc.

Tilden, William Augustus. Famous Chemists; the Men & Their Work. 2011. 380p. pap. 31.95 **(978-1-4460-7167-0(7))** Aslan Pr.

Todd, Alexander. A Time to Remember: The Autobiography of a Chemist. 2009. (ENG.). 268p. pap. 27.99 (978-0-521-12673-1(8)) Cambridge Univ. Pr.

Wagner-Kyora, Georg. Vom 'nationalen' zum 'sozialistischen' Selbst: Zur Erfahrungsgeschichte deutscher Chemiker und Ingenieure im 20. Jahrhundert. 2009. (Beitrage zur Unternehmensgeschichte (BZUG) Ser.). (GER., Illus.). 795p. (C). pap. 127.00 (978-3-515-09262-3(5)) Steiner, Franz Verlag Wiesbaden GmbH DEU. Dist: Brown, David Bk. Co., The.

Woodward, Walter William. Prospero's America: John Winthrop, Jr., Alchemy, & the Creation of New England Culture, 1606-1676. 2010. (Published for the Omohundro Institute of Early American History & Culture, Williamsburg Virginia Ser.). (ENG., Illus.). 336p. 45.00 (978-0-8078-3301-8(0)) Univ. of North Carolina Pr.

Wunderlich, Bernhard. A Science Career Against all Odds: A Life of Survival, Study, Teaching & Travel in the 20th Century. 2010. (ENG., Illus.). xxx, 519p. 99.00 (978-3-642-11195-2(5), 3642111955) Springer.

CHEMOKINES

Here are entered works on cytokines that have chemotactic and inflammatory activities.

Bruserud, Oystein, ed. The Chemokine System in Experimental & Clinical Hematology. 2010. (Current Topics in Microbiology & Immunology Ser.). (Illus.). xii, 210p. 219.00 (978-3-642-12638-3(3), 3642126383) Springer.

Dâ€(tm)Ambrosio, Daniele & Sinigaglia, Francesco, eds. Cell Migration in Inflammation & Immunity: Methods & Protocols. 2010. (Methods in Molecular Biology Ser.). (Illus.). 288p. pap. 129.00 (978-1-61737-357-2(5), 1617373575) Humana Pr.

Fulton, Amy M. Chemokine Receptors in Cancer. 2009. (Cancer Drug Discovery & Development Ser.). (ENG., Illus.). 208p. 189.00 (978-1-60327-266-7(5)) Humana Pr.

Grinwald, Leah R. Chemokine Research Trends. 2007. 208p. 129.00 (978-1-60021-588-9(2)) Nova Science Pubs., Inc.

Handel, Tracy & Hamel, Damon. Chemokines, Part A, 2 vols. 2009. (ENG., Illus.). 400p. 187.00 (978-0-12-374908-6(5), Academic Pr.) Elsevier Science & Technology Bks.

—Chemokines, Part B, 2 vols. 2009. (ENG., Illus.). 350p. 187.00 (978-0-12-374907-9(7), Academic Pr.) Elsevier Science & Technology Bks.

Harrison, Jeffrey K. & Lukacs, Nicholas W. The Chemokine Receptors. 2007. (Receptors Ser.). (Illus.). 403p. 229.00 (978-1-58829-773-0(X)) Humana Pr.

Harrison, Jeffrey K. & Lukacs, Nicholas W., eds. The Chemokine Receptors. 2010. (Receptors Ser.). (Illus.). xiii, 403p. pap. 229.00 (978-1-61737-768-6(6), 1617377686) Humana Pr.

Jaramillo, Maritza. Malaria Immunopathology. 2009. 172p. pap. (978-3-639-13633-3(0)) VDM Verlag Dr. Mueller e.K.

Kotb, Malak & Calandra, Thierry, eds. Cytokines & Chemokines in Infectious Diseases Handbook. 2011. (Infectious Disease Ser.). (ENG., Illus.). 456p. pap. 169.00 (978-1-61737-247-6(1), 1617372471) Humana Pr.

Lane, Thomas E. Chemokines & Viral Infection. 2010. (Current Topics in Microbiology & Immunology Ser.). (Illus.). xii, 160p. pap. 159.00 (978-3-642-06717-4(4), 3642067174) Springer.

Letts, L. G., et al, eds. Chemokine Biology: Basic Research & Clinical Application: Basic Research & Clinical Application. 2007. (Progress in Inflammation Research Ser.). 259.00 (978-3-7643-7307-8(5), 3764373075) Birkhauser Boston.

Leurs, Rob, et al, eds. Chemokine Receptors as Drug Targets. 2010. (Methods & Principles in Medicinal Chemistry Ser.: 117). (ENG., Illus.). 408p. 195.00 (978-3-527-32118-6(7), Wiley-VCH) Wiley, John & Sons, Inc.

Linkes, W. P. Progress in Chemokine Research. 2007. 217p. 129.00 (978-1-60021-641-1(2)) Nova Science Pubs., Inc.

Mahalingam, Suresh, ed. Chemokines in Viral Infections. 2010. (Medical Intelligence Unit Ser.). 132p. pap. 159.00 (978-1-4419-3436-9(7), 1441934367) Springer.

Meucci, Olimpia, ed. Chemokine Receptors & Neuroaids: Beyond Co-Receptor Function & Links to Other Neuropathologies. 2010. (ENG., Illus.). xvi, 412p. 209.00 (978-1-4419-0792-9(0), 1441907920) Springer.

Neote, Kuldeep & Moser, Bernhard, eds. Chemokine Biology: Basic Research & Clinical Application: Vol. 2: Pathophysiology of Chemokines. 2007. (Progress in Inflammation Research Ser.). (Illus.). 168p. 229.00 (978-3-7643-7195-1(1), 3764371951) Birkhauser Boston.

Proudfoot, Amanda E. I., et al, eds. Chemokine Protocols. 2010. (Methods in Molecular Biology Ser.). (Illus.). 332p. pap. 139.00 (978-1-61737-151-6(3), 1617371513) Humana Pr.

Standiford, Theodore J. & Roman, Jesse, eds. Ars in Lung Biology & Disease. 2007. 100p. per. 16.00 (978-977-454-003-5(4)) Hindawi Publishing Corp.

Walker, Keith J., ed. Chemokines: Types, Functions, & Structural Characteristics. 2010. (Cell Biology Research Progress Ser.). 129.00 (978-1-61728-861-6(6), Nova Biomedical Bks.) Nova Science Pubs., Inc.

CHEMORECEPTORS

Collin, M. & Schuch, R., eds. Bacterial Sensing & Signaling. 2009. (Contributions to Microbiology Ser.). (ENG., Illus.). 230p. (978-3-8055-9132-4(2)) Karger, S. AG.

Gonzalez, Constancio, et al, eds. Arterial Chemoreceptors. 2009. (Advances in Experimental Medicine & Biology Ser.). (Illus.). xxvi, 462p. 219.00 (978-90-481-2258-5(9)) Springer.

Hurst, Jane L., et al, eds. Chemical Signals in Vertebrates 11. 2007. (Chemical Signals in Vertebrates Ser.). (ENG., Illus.). xxviii, 432p. 169.00 (978-0-387-73944-1(0), 0387739440) Springer.

Mason, R. T., et al, eds. Chemical Signals in Vertebrates 12. 2010. (ENG., Illus.). xii, 430p. pap. 289.00 (978-1-4419-3776-6(5), 1441937765) Springer.

Meyerhof, Wolfgang, et al, eds. Sensory & Metabolic Control of Energy Balance. 2010. (Results & Problems in Cell Differentiation Ser.). (Illus.). viii, 205p. 219.00 (978-3-642-14425-7(X), 364214425X) Springer.

Meyerhof, Wolfgang & Korsching, Sigrun. Chemosensory Systems in Mammals, Fishes, & Insects. 2009. (Results & Problems in Cell Differentiation Ser.). (ENG., Illus.). xvii, 261p. 169.00 (978-3-540-69918-7(X), 354069918X) Springer.

Meyerhof, Wolfgang & Korsching, Sigrun, eds. Chemosensory Systems in Mammals, Fishes, & Insects. 2010. (Results & Problems in Cell Differentiation Ser.). (ENG., Illus.). xvii, 261p. pap. 169.00 (978-3-642-08939-8(9), 3642089399) Springer.

Mirsky, Vladimir M. & Yatsimirsky, Anatoly, eds. Artificial Receptors for Chemical Sensors. 2011. (ENG., Illus.). 486p. 190.00 (978-3-527-32357-9(0), Wiley-VCH) Wiley, John & Sons, Inc.

Sooryadas, Daya I. Biomimetic Sensor for Invivo Applications. 2008. 92p. pap. (978-3-639-06946-4(3)) VDM Verlag Dr. Mueller e.K.

Zaccone, Giacomo. Airway Chemoreceptors in the Vertebrates: Structure, Evolution & Function. 2009. (ENG., Illus.). 464p. 139.95 (978-1-57808-614-6(0)) BIOS Scientific Publishers Ltd. GBR. Dist: Taylor & Francis Group.

CHEMOSURGERY

see also Cancer—Chemotherapy

Brody, Harold J. Chemical Peeling & Resurfacing. 3rd ed. 2008. (Illus.). xv, 240p. (978-1-60602-150-7(8)) Mosby.

Goldberg, David J. Facial Resurfacing. 2010. (ENG., Illus.). 168p. 165.95 (978-1-4051-9080-0(9), Wiley-Blackwell) Wiley, John & Sons, Inc.

Grimes, Pearl E. & Padova, Maria Pia de, eds. Color Atlas of Chemical Peels. 2010. (Illus.). xiv, 216p. pap. 219.00 (978-3-642-05959-9(7), 3642059597) Springer.

Gross, Kenneth G. & Steinman, Howard K. Mohs Surgery & Histopathology: Beyond the Fundamentals. Gross, Kenneth G. et al, eds. Gross, Ken et al, eds. 2009. (ENG., Illus.). 196p. 156.00 (978-0-521-88804-2(2)) Cambridge Univ. Pr.

Khunger, Niti. Step by Step Chemical Peels. 2010. (ENG., Illus.). 339p. 44.00 (978-0-07-166725-8(3), 0071667253) McGraw-Hill Professional Publishing.

Lee, Steven. Introduction to MOHS Cryotomy. 2006. 29.95 (978-1-59540-864-8(9), 1st World Publishing) 1st World Publishing, Inc.

Nouri, Keyvan, ed. Mohs Micrographic Surgery. 2012. (ENG., Illus.). xxi, 563p. 219.00 (978-1-4471-2151-0(1), 1447121511) Springer.

Rubin, Mark G. & Tung, Rebecca. Procedures in Cosmetic Dermatology Series: Chemical Peels. 2nd ed. 2010. (Procedures in Cosmetic Dermatology Ser.). (ENG., Illus.). 208p. 164.00 (978-1-4377-1924-6(4), Saunders) Elsevier - Health Sciences Div.

Tosti, Antonella, et al, eds. Color Atlas of Chemical Peels. 2nd ed. 2012. (ENG., Illus.). x, 211p. 189.00 (978-3-642-20269-8(1), 3642202691) Springer.

Vidimos, Allison T., et al. Mohs Surgery, an Issue of Dermatologic Clinics. 2011. (Clinics: Dermatology Ser.: 29-2). (ENG., Illus.). 248p. 110.00 (978-1-4557-0437-8(7), Saunders) Elsevier - Health Sciences Div.

CHEMOTACTIC CYTOKINES

see Chemokines

CHEMOTHERAPY

see also Diuretics and Diuresis; Drugs; Pharmacology; Photochemotherapy; Psychopharmacology

also subdivision Chemotherapy under diseases, e.g. Cancer— Chemotherapy

Abrams, Anne Collins, et al. Clinical Drug Therapy: Rationales for Nursing Practice. 9th rev. ed. 2008. (ENG., Illus.). 1068p. pap. 96.99 (978-0-7817-7769-8(0)); 240p. pap., pupil's gde. ed. 30.95 (978-0-7817-8248-7(1)) Lippincott Williams & Wilkins.

Adams, H. Richard. Veterinary Pharmacology & Therapeutics. Papich, Mark G. & Riviere, Jim E., eds. 9th ed. 2009. (ENG., Illus.). 1500p. 219.99 (978-0-8138-2061-3(8), Wiley-Blackwell) Wiley, John & Sons, Inc.

Adams, Michael & Holland, Leland Norman. Core Concepts in Pharmacology. 3rd ed. 2010. (ENG.). 768p. (C). pap. 66.00 (978-0-13-507759-7(1), Prentice Hall) Prentice Hall PTR.

Al-Nimer, Marwan S. M., ed. Pharmacological Intervention in Management of Neck Pain Disorders: A Review. 2010. (Pain & its Origins, Diagnosis & Treatments Ser.). pap. 49.00 (978-1-61728-221-8(9), Nova Biomedical Bks.) Nova Science Pubs., Inc.

Alemdaroglu, N. Ceren. Impact of Folate Absorption & Transport for Nutrition & Drug Targeting. 2008. 228p. pap. (978-3-639-01068-8(X)) VDM Verlag Dr. Mueller e.K.

Alldredge. Applied Therapeutics Cb. 10th rev. ed. 2012. (ENG.). 2960p. 193.95 (978-1-60913-713-7(2)) Lippincott Williams & Wilkins.

American College of Clinical Pharmacy Staff, contrib. by. Updates in Therapeutics: The Pharmacotherapy Preparatory Course, 2007. 2007. 756p. pap. 184.95 (978-1-932658-23-1(8)) American College of Clinical Pharmacy.

American Society of Health-System Pharmacists, creator. Consumer Drug Reference 2007. 2006. (Consumer Drug Reference Ser.). (ENG., Illus.). 1845p. 44.95 (978-1-933524-03-0(0)) Consumer Reports Bks.

American Society of Pain Educators Staff. Diabetic Peripheral Neuropathic Pain Guidelines Pocketcard: American Society of Pain Educators 2010. 2010. 10p. pap. 9.95 (978-0-9845053-8-8(5)) International Guidelines Ctr., Inc.

Arcangelo, Virginia Poole & Peterson, Andrew M. Pharmacotherapeutics for Advanced Practice. 3rd rev. ed. 2011. (ENG.). 1000p. pap. 114.95 (978-1-4511-1197-2(5)) Lippincott Williams & Wilkins.

Aronson, Jeffrey K., ed. Side Effects of Drugs Annual 30: A worldwide yearly survey of new data & trends in adverse drug Reactions. 2008. (ENG.). 672p. 353.00 (978-0-444-52767-7(2), Elsevier Science) Elsevier Science & Technology Bks.

Aschenbrenner, Diane S. & Venable, Samantha J. Drug Therapy in Nursing. 4th rev. ed. 2011. (ENG., Illus.). 384p. pap., pupil's gde. ed. 29.95 (978-1-60831-152-1(X)); 1152p. 96.95 (978-1-60831-151-4(1)) Lippincott Williams & Wilkins.

Aschenbrenner, Diane S. & Venable, Samantha J. Drug Therapy in Nursing: Diagnosis & Management of Sleep Problems in Children & Adolescents. 3rd ed. 2008. pap. 157.95 (978-1-60547-047-4(3)) Lippincott Williams & Wilkins.

Ash, Deborah Swartwood. ASHP's Management Pearls. 2008. 99.00 (978-1-58528-219-7(7)) American Society of Health-System Pharmacists(r).

Aubry, Jean-Michel, et al. Pharmacotherapy of Bipolar Disorders. 2007. (ENG.). 296p. 110.95 (978-0-470-05823-7(4), Wiley) Wiley, John & Sons, Inc.

Avidan, Alon Y., ed. The Interface of Sleep Medicine & Movement Disorders. 2011. (Contemporary Clinical Neuroscience Ser.). (ENG.). 500p. 159.00 (978-1-60327-189-9(9), 1603271899) Humana Pr.

Bailey, Clifford J., et al, eds. Metformin - The Gold Standard: A Scientific Handbook. 2008. (ENG., Illus.). 272p. 106.00 (978-0-470-72541-2(9), Wiley) Wiley, John & Sons, Inc.

Banning, Maggi. Medication Management in Care of Older People. 2007. (ENG., Illus.). 200p. pap. 66.99 (978-1-4051-5174-0(9), Wiley-Blackwell) Wiley, John & Sons, Inc.

Bartlett, John G., et al. 2012 Medical Management of HIV Infection. 16th ed. 2012. (ENG.). 603p. pap. 24.99 (978-0-9837111-0-0(0)) Knowledge Source Solutions, LLC.

Bindslev, Niels. Drug-Acceptor Interactions: Modeling theoretical tools to test & evaluate experimental equilibrium Effects. 2008. (Illus.). 428p. pap. (978-91-977071-0-7(4)) Co-Action Publishing.

Blanchard & Loeb, contrib. by. 2008 Nurse's Drug Handbook. 2007. (ENG.). 1184p. (C). pap. 39.95 (978-1-930138-44-5(X)) Delmar Cengage Learning.

Bledsoe, Bryan E. & Clayden, Dwayne E. Prehospital Emergency Pharmacology. 7th rev. ed. 2011. (ENG., Illus.). 560p. (C). 80.00 (978-0-13-513822-9(1), Prentice Hall) Prentice Hall PTR.

Blenkinsopp, Alison, et al. Symptoms in the Pharmacy: A Guide to the Management of Common Illness. 6th ed. 2008. (ENG., Illus.). 360p. pap., instr.'s gde. ed. 62.95 (978-1-4051-8079-5(X), Wiley-Blackwell) Wiley, John & Sons, Inc.

Boothe, Dawn Merton. Boothe's Small Animal Formulary. 6th ed. 2009. (ENG.). 248p. spiral bd. 47.95 (978-1-58326-097-5(8), AAHA Pr.) American Animal Hospital Assn. Pr.

Bradley, John S. & Nelson, John D. 2010-2011 Nelson's Pocket Book of Pediatric Antimicrobial Therapy. 18th ed. 2010. (Nelson's Pocket Book of Pediatric Antimicrobial Therapy Ser.). (ENG., Illus.). 168p. pap. 34.95 (978-1-58110-373-1(5)) American Academy of Pediatrics.

Brenner, George M., et al. Pharmacology: With STUDENT CONSULT Online Access. 3rd ed. 2009. (ENG., Illus.). 552p. (C). pap. 59.95 (978-1-4160-6627-9(6), Saunders) Elsevier - Health Sciences Div.

Britten, Nicky. Medicines & Society: Patients, Professionals & the Dominance of Pharmaceuticals. 2008. (ENG., Illus.). 224p. 95.00 (978-0-230-20510-9(0)); 256p. pap. 39.00 (978-1-4039-3541-0(6)) Palgrave Macmillan.

Brophy, Kathleen Marion & Webber, Karen. Clinical Drug Therapy for Canadian Practice. 2007. (Illus.). 1152p. pap. 74.95 (978-0-7817-6590-9(0)) Lippincott Williams & Wilkins.

Brophy, Kathleen Marion, et al. Clinical Drug Therapy: Second Canadian Edition. 2nd rev. ed. 2010. 1120p. pap. 74.95 (978-1-60547-517-2(3)) Lippincott Williams & Wilkins.

Brownstein, David. Drugs That Don't Work & Natural Therapies That Do. 2007. per. 15.00 (978-0-9660882-6-7(3)) Medical Alternative Pr.

Canaday, Bruce Robert. ASHP's Clinical Pearls. 2008. (Illus.). ix, 129p. 99.00 (978-1-58528-218-0(9)) American Society of Health-System Pharmacists(r).

Carpenter, James W. Exotic Animal Formulary. 4th ed. 2012. (ENG., Illus.). 744p. 59.95 (978-1-4377-2264-2(4), Saunders) Elsevier - Health Sciences Div.

Cashen, Amanda, et al. Hematology & Oncology Subspecialty Consult. 3rd rev. ed. 2012. (ENG., Illus.). 488p. pap. 49.95 (978-1-4511-1424-9(9)) Lippincott Williams & Wilkins.

Chabner, Bruce, et al. Harrison's Manual of Oncology. 2007. (ENG., Illus.). 644p. per. 92.00 (978-0-07-141189-9(5), 0071411895) McGraw-Hill Professional Publishing.

Chan, Paul. Outpatient & Primary Care Medicine, 2008 Edition. 2008th ed. 2007. pap. (978-1-934323-06-9(3)) Current Clinical Strategies Publishing.

—Outpatient & Primary Care Medicine CD-ROM, 2008 Edition. 2007. cd-rom (978-1-934323-07-6(1)) Current Clinical Strategies Publishing.

Chee, Frederick & Fernando, Tyrone. Closed-Loop Control of Blood Glucose. 2007. (Lecture Notes in Control & Information Sciences Ser.). (Illus.). 157p. pap. 129.00 (978-3-540-74030-8(9)) Springer.

Chisholm-Burns, Marie A., et al. Pharmacotherapy Principles & Practice. 2nd ed. 2010. (ENG., Illus.). 1904p. 162.00 (978-0-07-162180-9(6), 0071621806) McGraw-Hill Medical Publishing Div.

Chu, Edward. Pocket Guide to Chemotherapy Protocols. 3rd rev. ed. 2006. 179p. (C). spiral bd. 32.95 (978-0-7637-4310-9(0)) 4th rev. ed. 2008. 177p. spiral bd. 42.95 (978-0-7637-5372-6(6)) 5th rev. ed. 2009. 196p. spiral bd. 22.95 (978-0-7637-7911-5(3)) Jones & Bartlett Learning, LLC.

Ciccone, Charles D. & Ciccone, Charles. Pharmacology in Rehabilitation. 4th rev. ed. 2007. (Illus.). 679p. (C). pap. 76.95 (978-0-8036-1377-5(6)) Davis, F. A. Co.

Cohen, Suzy. La Farmacia: Tu Guía Personal de Salud - Consejos Asombrosos de la Farmacéutica Más Respetada de Estados Unidos. 2008. (SPA.). 432p. pap. 14.95 (978-0-06-155507-7(X), Rayo) HarperCollins Pubs.

Consumer Reports Staff & American Society of Health-System Pharmacists Staff. Consumer Drug Reference 2008. 2008. (Consumer Drug Reference Ser.). (ENG., Illus.). 1823p. 44.95 (978-1-933524-11-5(1)) Consumer Reports Bks.

Cooper, Steven J. & Kirkham, Tim, eds. Appetite & Body Weight: Integrative Systems & the Development of Anti-Obesity Drugs. 2006. (ENG., Illus.). 384p. 131.00 (978-0-12-370633-1(5), Academic Pr.) Elsevier Science & Technology Bks.

Cram101 Textbook Reviews. Outlines & Highlights for Core Concepts in Pharmacology by Norman Holland. 2011. 538p. pap. 38.95 (978-1-61906-043-2(4)) Cram101 Inc.

—Outlines & Highlights for Introduction to Clinical Pharmacology by Edmunds, Marilyn Winterton. 2011. 220p. pap. 30.95 (978-1-61906-008-1(6)) Cram101 Inc.

—Outlines & Highlights for Pharmacological Aspects of Nursing Care by Bonita E Broyles, Isbn: 9781401888862 1401888860. 2011. 602p. pap. 39.95 (978-1-61490-741-1(2)) Cram101 Inc.

—Outlines & Highlights for Pharmacology: A Nursing Process Approach by Joyce Lefever Kee. 2011. 472p. pap. 36.95 (978-1-61906-095-1(7)) Cram101 Inc.

—Outlines & Highlights for Pharmacology: A Nursing Process Approach by Kee, Hayes, Mccuistion. 2011. 668p. pap. 41.95 (978-1-61906-194-1(5)) Cram101 Inc.

—Outlines & Highlights for Pharmacology & the Nursing Process by Lilley, Harrington, Snyder. 2011. 314p. pap. 33.95 (978-1-61906-198-9(8)) Cram101 Inc.

—Outlines & Highlights for Principles of Pharmacology: The Pathophysiologic Basis of Drug Therapy by Golan, et Al... 2011. 368p. pap. 34.95 (978-1-4672-7257-5(4)) Cram101 Inc.

Cram101 Textbook Reviews & Cram101 Textbook Reviews. Outlines & Highlights for Clinical Drug Therapy: Rationales for Nursing Practice by Anne Collins Abrams. 2011. 484p. pap. 37.95 (978-1-61830-870-2(X)) Cram101 Inc.

—Outlines & Highlights for Current Pediatric Therapy by Fredric Burg, Isbn: 9780721605494. 2011. 104p. pap. 28.95 (978-1-61461-227-8(7)) Cram101 Inc.

—Outlines & Highlights for Drug Interactions Analysis & Management 2008 by Philip D Hansten. 2011. 228p. pap. 31.95 (978-1-61830-617-3(0)) Cram101 Inc.

—Outlines & Highlights for Drug Interactions Analysis & Management 2010 by Philip D Hansten. 2011. 254p. pap. 31.95 (978-1-61830-854-2(8)) Cram101 Inc.

—Outlines & Highlights for Essentials of Pharmacoeconomics by Karen L Rascati. 2011. 58p. pap. 26.95 (978-1-61830-848-1(3)) Cram101 Inc.

—Outlines & Highlights for Introduction to Clinical Pharmacology by Marilyn Winterton Edmunds. 2011. 176p. pap. 29.95 (978-1-61830-828-3(9)) Cram101 Inc.

—Outlines & Highlights for Oral Pharmacology for the Dental Hygienist by Mea a Weinberg. 2011. 306p. pap. 32.95 (978-1-61830-805-4(X)) Cram101 Inc.

—Outlines & Highlights for Pharmacology by George M Brenner PhD. 2011. 518p. pap. 37.95 (978-1-61830-643-2(X)) Cram101 Inc.

—Outlines & Highlights for Pharmacology for Nurses: A Pathophysiologic Approach by Michael Adams. 2011. 494p. pap. 37.95 (978-1-61830-646-3(4)) Cram101 Inc.

—Outlines & Highlights for Pharmacology for Nursing Care - Text & E-Book by Richard a Lehne. 2011. 604p. pap. 40.95 (978-1-61830-642-5(1)) Cram101 Inc.

—Outlines & Highlights for Pharmacology for the Health Care Professions by Christine Thorp. 2011. 354p. pap. 34.95 (978-1-61830-776-7(2)) Cram101 Inc.

—Outlines & Highlights for Pharmacotherapy: A Pathophysiologic Approach by Joseph T. Dipiro, ISBN. 2011. 682p. pap. 41.95 (978-1-61490-739-8(0)) Cram101 Inc.

—Outlines & Highlights for Pharmacotherapy Principles & Practice by Marie a Chisholm-Burns. 2011. 472p. pap. 36.95 (978-1-61830-942-6(0)) Cram101 Inc.

—Outlines & Highlights for Practical Pharmacology for the Pharmacy Technician by Joy Bellis Sakai. 2011. 354p. pap. 34.95 (978-1-61830-772-9(X)) Cram101 Inc.

—Outlines & Highlights for Roach's Introductory Clinical Pharmacology by Susan M Ford. 2011. 398p. pap. 35.95 (978-1-61830-753-8(3)) Cram101 Inc.

Cram101 Textbook Reviews Staff. Outlines & Highlights for Clinical Drug Therapy: Rationales for Nursing Practice by Anne Collins Abrams, ISBN. 2009. 146p. pap. 29.95 (978-1-4288-9197-5(8)) Cram101 Inc.

—Outlines & Highlights for Drug Therapy in Nursing by Diane S Aschenbrenner, Isbn: 9780781765879. 2009. 120p. pap. 28.95 (978-1-4288-9723-6(2)) Cram101 Inc.

Cuello, A. Claudio, ed. Pharmacological Mechanisms in Alzheimer's Therapeutics. 2007. (ENG., Illus.). xx, 324p. 159.00 (978-0-387-71521-6(5), 0387715215) Springer.

Cunha, Burke A. Antibiotic Essentials. 10th ed. 2011. 778p. pap. 24.95 (978-1-4496-2431-6(6)) Jones & Bartlett Learning, LLC.

—Antibiotics Essentials 2010. 9th rev. ed. 2010. 732p. pap. 28.95 (978-0-7637-9214-5(4)) Jones & Bartlett Learning, LLC.

Dale, Maureen M. & Haylett, Dennis G. Rang & Dale's Pharmacology Flash Cards. 2010. (ENG.). 656p. (C). 38.95 (978-1-4160-6150-2(9), Churchill Livingstone) Elsevier - Health Sciences Div.

Dasgupta, Amitava, ed. Handbook of Drug Monitoring Methods: Therapeutics & Drugs of Abuse. 2007. (ENG., Illus.). x, 446p. 129.00 (978-1-58829-780-8(2), 1588297802) Humana Pr.

Dasgupta, Amitava & Langman, Loralie J., eds. Pharmacogenomics in Clinical Therapeutics. 2nd ed. 2012. (ENG., Illus.). 256p. 124.95 (978-0-470-65734-8(0), Wiley-Blackwell) Wiley, John & Sons, Inc.

de Clercq, H., et al, eds. Concept & Practice of Therapeutic Teams: Proceedings of the 11th European Symposium on Clinical Pharmacy, Brussels 1982. 2011. (ENG.). 266p. pap. 35.99 (978-0-521-27917-8(8)) Cambridge Univ. Pr.

De Ponte, Francesco Saverio, ed. Bisphosphonates & Osteonecrosis of the Jaw: A Multidisciplinary Approach. 2011. (ENG., Illus.). xiii, 181p. 139.00 (978-88-470-2082-5(4), 8847020824) Springer.

Dean, Reginald L., et al. Opiate Receptors & Antagonists. 2009. (Contemporary Neuroscience Ser.). (Illus.). 525p. 179.00 (978-1-58829-881-2(7)) Humana Pr.

Del Rosso, James Q. Antibiotic Use in Dermatology, an Issue of Dermatologic Clinics. 2008. (Clinics: Dermatology Ser.: 27-1). (ENG., Illus.). 240p. 99.00 (978-1-4377-0468-6(9), Saunders) Elsevier - Health Sciences Div.

Delmar. 2008 PDR Nurse's Drug Handbook. Thomson Healthcare Staff, ed. 2007. 1800p. pap. 39.95 (978-1-56363-665-3(4)) PDR Network, LLC.

DeYoung, Eric M. How to Live a Happy, Healthy, Wealthy & Safe Life! The Missing Links in Conventional Medicine. 2011. 116p. pap. 14.95 (978-1-4269-5309-5(7)) Trafford Publishing.

Di Carlo, Isidoro & Biffi, Roberto, eds. Totally Implantable Venous Access Devices. 2011. (ENG., Illus.). 300p. 189.00 (978-88-470-2372-7(6), 8847023726) Springer.

DiPiro, Joseph, et al. Pharmacotherapy: A Pathophysiologic Approach. 8th ed. 2011. (ENG., Illus.). 2700p. (C). 203.00 *(978-0-07-170354-3(3)*, 0071703543) McGraw-Hill Medical Publishing Div.

Donald, P.R. & van Helden, P. D., eds. Antituberculosis Chemotherapy. 2011. (Progress in Respiratory Research Ser.). (ENG., Illus.). 252p. ***(978-3-8055-9627-5(8))*** Karger, S. AG.

Downie, George, et al. Pharmacology & Medicines Management for Nurses. 4th ed. 2008. (ENG., Illus.). 576p. pap. 55.95 *(978-0-443-10331-5(3)*, Churchill Livingstone) Elsevier - Health Sciences Div.

Drugs Treatments for Leading Endocrine & Metabolic Disease. 2007. per. 4250.00 *(978-1-59623-269-3(2))* BCC Research.

Duncan, Jill & Corcoran, Jason. Pediatric High-Alert Medications: Evidence-Based Safe Practices for Nursing Professionals. 2007. 168p. per. 129.00 *(978-1-60146-027-1(9))* Opus Communications.

Dyck, Erika. Psychedelic Psychiatry: LSD from Clinic to Campus. 2008. (ENG., Illus.). 216p. (gr. 17). 37.00 *(978-0-8018-8994-3(4))* Johns Hopkins Univ. Pr.

Edmunds, Marilyn Winterton. Introduction to Clinical Pharmacology. 7th ed. 2012. (ENG., Illus.). 512p. (C). pap. 63.95 ***(978-0-323-07398-1(0)***, Mosby) Elsevier - Health Sciences Div.

—Introduction to Clinical Pharmacology - Text & Study Guide Package. 7th ed. 2012. (ENG.). (C). pap. 84.51 ***(978-0-323-09667-6(0)***, Mosby) Elsevier - Health Sciences Div.

—Study Guide for Introduction to Clinical Pharmacology. 7th ed. 2012. (ENG.). 176p. (C). pap. 29.95 ***(978-0-323-07696-8(3)***, Mosby) Elsevier - Health Sciences Div.

Edmunds, Marilyn Winterton & Mayhew, Maren Stewart. Pharmacology for the Primary Care Provider. 3rd ed. 2008. (ENG., Illus.). 864p. (C). pap. 112.00 *(978-0-323-05131-6(6)*, Mosby) Elsevier - Health Sciences Div.

Ellermann, Jackie. The Mustard Seed. 2011. 192p. pap. 16.95 ***(978-1-4670-3630-6(7))*** AuthorHouse.

Elsevier. The Elsevier Pocket Guide to Oncology Drugs & Regimens. 2006. (ENG.). pap., instr.'s gde. ed. 29.95 *(978-1-4160-3422-3(6)*, Elsevier) Elsevier - Health Sciences Div.

Ewert, Ralf. Iloprost in Intensive Care Medicine. 2006. (UNI-MED Science Ser.). (Illus.). 112p. *(978-3-89599-943-7(1))* UNI-MED Verlag AG.

Extending the Cure: Policy Responses to the Growing Threat of Antibiotic Resistance. 2007. (ENG., Illus.). 192p. pap. 29.95 *(978-1-933115-57-3(2))* Routledge.

Facts and Comparisons Staff. Facts & Comparisons eAnswers 2012. 2011. (ENG.). cd-rom 270.00 ***(978-1-57439-333-0(2))*** Lippincott Williams & Wilkins.

Finch, Roger G., et al. Antibiotic & Chemotherapy: Expert Consult. 9th ed. 2010. (ENG., Illus.). 916p. 218.00 *(978-0-7020-4064-1(9)*, Saunders) Elsevier - Health Sciences Div.

Flanigan, Devin A., ed. Malaria Research Trends. 2007. (C). 129.00 *(978-1-60021-589-6(0))* Nova Science Pubs., Inc.

Ford, Susan M. & Roach, Sally S. Introductory Clinical Pharmacology, 2 vols. 9th rev. ed. 2009. (ENG., Illus.). 784p. pap. 73.99 *(978-1-60547-633-9(1))* Lippincott Williams & Wilkins.

Forum on Drug Discovery, Development and Translation Staff. Understanding the Benefits & Risks of Pharmaceuticals: Workshop Summary. 2007. (ENG.). 98p. pap. 21.00 *(978-0-309-10738-9(5))* National Academies Pr.

Frackiewicz, Edyta J., et al. Ethnicity in Drug Development & Therapeutics. 2011. (ENG.). 152p. pap. 36.99 *(978-0-521-29252-8(2))* Cambridge Univ. Pr.

Fulcher, Eugenia M., et al. Pharmacology: Principles & Applications - Text & Workbook Package: A Worktext for Allied Health Professionals. 2nd ed. 2008. (ENG.). (C). 98.91 *(978-1-4160-5576-1(2)*, Saunders) Elsevier - Health Sciences Div.

Gaebelein, Claude J. & Gleason, Brenda L. Contemporary Drug Information: An Evidence-Based Approach. 2007. (Illus.). 370p. per. 62.99 *(978-0-7817-8280-7(5))* Lippincott Williams & Wilkins.

Gaya, Andrew. Combination Studies with the Vascular Disrupting Agent Ca4p. 2011. 256p. pap. ***(978-3-8383-4353-2(0))*** Lambert Academic Publishing.

Gibaldi. Handbook of Evidence-Based Drug Therapy. 2007. 544p. pap. 179.00 *(978-0-471-45715-2(9)*, Wiley-Liss) Wiley, John & Sons, Inc.

Giguere, Steeve, et al, eds. Antimicrobial Therapy in Veterinary Medicine. 4th rev. ed. 2007. (ENG., Illus.). 626p. 157.99 *(978-0-8138-0656-3(9)*, Wiley-Blackwell) Wiley, John & Sons, Inc.

Gilbert, David N., et al, eds. The Sanford Guide to Antimicrobial Therapy. (Guide to Antimicrobial Therapy (Sanford) Ser.). 38th ed. 2008. 216p. pap. 13.45 *(978-1-930808-45-4(3))* 38th ed. 2008. (Illus.). 216p. pap. 39.95 *(978-1-930808-47-8(X))* 39th ed. 2009. (Illus.). 212p. pap. 39.95 *(978-1-930808-54-6(2))* Antimicrobial Therapy, Inc.

—The Sanford Guide to Antimicrobial Therapy 2008. 38th ed. 2008. (Guide to Antimicrobial Therapy (Sanford) Ser.). (Illus.). 216p. spiral bd. 29.95 *(978-1-930808-46-1(1))* Antimicrobial Therapy, Inc.

Gilbert, David N., et al. The Sanford Guide to Antimicrobial Therapy. 37th ed. 2007. (Guide to Antimicrobial Therapy (Sanford) Ser.). 202p. per. 12.95 *(978-1-930808-38-6(0))* Antimicrobial Therapy, Inc.

Golan. Principles of Pharmacology. 3rd rev. ed. 2011. (ENG.). 976p. pap. 82.99 *(978-1-60831-270-2(4))* Lippincott Williams & Wilkins.

Goldman, Mitchel P., et al. Sclerotherapy: Treatment of Varicose & Telangiectatic Leg Veins. 5th ed. 2011. (ENG., Illus.). 416p. 269.00 *(978-0-323-07367-7(0)*, Saunders) Elsevier - Health Sciences Div.

González-Moreno, S. Advances in Peritoneal Surface Oncology. 2010. (Recent Results in Cancer Research Ser.). (Illus.). xiii, 176p. pap. 139.00 *(978-3-642-06802-7(2)*, 3642068022) Springer.

Goode, Jean-Venable "Kelly" R., et al. Community Pharmacy Practice Case Studies. 2009. (ENG.). 316p. (C). pap. 48.95 *(978-1-58212-105-5(2))* American Pharmacists Assn.

Greene, Jeremy A. Prescribing by Numbers: Drugs & the Definition of Disease. 2008. (ENG., Illus.). 336p. (gr. 17). pap. 26.00 *(978-0-8018-9100-7(0))* Johns Hopkins Univ. Pr.

Greenwald, Mark. Human Experimental Therapeutic Models in Opioid Dependence. 2008. (Illus.). 82p. pap. 29.00 *(978-1-60456-807-3(0))* Nova Science Pubs., Inc.

Gullino, M. L., et al, eds. Recent Developments in Disease Management. 2009. (Plant Pathology in the 21st Century Ser.). (ENG., Illus.). xv, 377p. 199.00 *(978-1-4020-8803-2(5)*, 1402088035) Springer.

Gutierrez, Kathleen Jo. Pharmacotherapeutics: Clinical Reasoning in Primary Care. 2nd rev. ed. 2007. (ENG., Illus.). 1280p. (C). 120.00 *(978-1-4160-3287-8(8)*, Saunders) Elsevier - Health Sciences Div.

Hacker, Miles, et al. Pharmacology: Principles & Practice. 2009. (ENG., Illus.). 608p. (C). 92.95 *(978-0-12-369521-5(X)*, Academic Pr.) Elsevier Science & Technology Bks.

Hagberg, Carin A. Benumof's Airway Management. 2nd rev. ed. 2007. (ENG., Illus.). 1344p. 218.00 *(978-0-323-02233-0(2)*, Mosby) Elsevier - Health Sciences Div.

Hansen, Laura, et al, eds. Women's Health Across the Lifespan: A Pharmacotherapeutic Approach. 2010. (Illus.). 650p. 88.00 *(978-1-58528-194-7(8))* American Society of Health-System Pharmacists.

Hill, Pamela. Botox, Dysport, Dermal Fillers & Sclerotherapy. 2nd ed. 2010. (ENG.). 304p. (C). pap. 56.95 *(978-1-4354-3864-4(7)*, Milady Publishing Co.) Delmar Cengage Learning.

Hitner, Henry & Nagle, Barbara T. Pharmacology. 6th ed. 2011. (ENG., Illus.). 896p. (C). pap. 81.33 *(978-0-07-352086-5(1)*, 0073520861) McGraw-Hill Higher Education.

Holland, Norm & Adams, Michael P. MyNursingKit for Core Concepts in Pharmacology. 2010. (ENG.). (C). 34.80 *(978-0-13-215605-9(9)*, Prentice Hall) Prentice Hall PTR.

Holland, Norman, et al. Core Concepts in Pharmacology. 3rd ed. 2010. (ENG.). 240p. (C). pap., pupil's gde. ed. 28.20 *(978-0-13-612109-1(8)*, Prentice Hall) Prentice Hall PTR.

Hosseinzadeh, Leila, et al. Curcumin & Doxorubicin. 2011. 148p. pap. ***(978-3-8443-9921-9(6))*** Lambert Academic Publishing.

Hsu, Walter. Handbook of Veterinary Pharmacology. Reece, William O. et al, eds. 2008. (ENG., Illus.). 568p. pap. 88.99 *(978-0-8138-2837-4(6)*, Wiley-Blackwell) Wiley, John & Sons, Inc.

International Guidelines Center Staff. Hypoglycemic Disorders in Adults GUIDELINES Pocketcard 2010: The Endocrine Society (TES) 2010 (Illus.). 12p. 9.95 *(978-0-9846167-8-7(0))* International Guidelines Ctr., Inc.

Jackson, Stephen, et al, eds. Prescribing for Elderly Patients. 2009. (ENG., Illus.). 552p. 134.00 *(978-0-470-02428-7(3)*, Wiley) Wiley, John & Sons, Inc.

John Wiley and Sons Ltd. Staff. Wiley Handbook of Current & Emerging Drug Therapies, 4 vols., Vols. 1-4. 2006. (ENG., Illus.). 2664p. 1500.00 *(978-0-470-04098-0(X)*, Wiley-Interscience) Wiley, John & Sons, Inc.

Johns Hopkins Hospital, et al. Harriet Lane Handbook & Harriet Lane Handbook of Pediatric Antimicrobial Therapy Package. 2nd ed. 2011. (Mobile Medicine Ser.). (ENG.). pap. 79.95 ***(978-0-323-08723-0(X)***, Mosby) Elsevier - Health Sciences Div.

Johnston, Michael V. & Gross, Robert A. Principles of Drug Therapy in Neurology. 2nd ed. 2008. (Contemporary Neurology Ser.: Vol. 72). (ENG., Illus.) 512p. 99.00 *(978-0-19-514683-7(2))* Oxford Univ. Pr., Inc.

Jones & Bartlett Learning Staff. 2012 Nurse's Drug Handbook. 11th ed. 2011. 1276p. pap. 44.95 *(978-1-4496-3864-1(3))* Jones & Bartlett Learning, LLC.

Jones and Bartlett Publishers. Combination Drugs. 2nd rev. ed. 2009. (ENG.). 857p. pap., instr.'s hndbk. ed. 55.95 *(978-0-7637-6549-1(X))* Jones & Bartlett Learning, LLC.

—Nurse's Drug 2009. 2008. (ENG.). 1228p. pap., instr.'s hndbk. ed. 37.95 *(978-0-7637-6547-7(3))* Jones & Bartlett Learning, LLC.

Jordan, Sue. The Prescription Drug Guide for Nurses. 2008. (ENG., Illus.). 192p. (C). pap. 34.00 *(978-0-335-22547-7(0)*, 0335225470) McGraw-Hill Education GBR. Dist: McGraw-Hill Cos., The.

—Prescription Drug Guide for Nurses. 2008. (ENG.). 192p. (C). 116.95 *(978-0-335-22546-0(2)*, 0335225462, Open University Pr.) McGraw-Hill Education GBR. Dist: McGraw-Hill Cos., The.

Karch. Lippincott's Nursing Drug Guide 2011. 2010. (Illus.). 1536p. pap. 39.95 *(978-1-60913-234-7(3))* Lippincott Williams & Wilkins.

Katz, Michael, et al. Pharmacotherapy Principles & Practice Study Guide: A Case-Based Care Plan Approach. 2010. (ENG., Illus.). 480p. (C). pap. 58.00 *(978-0-07-170119-8(2)*, 0071701192) McGraw-Hill Medical Publishing Div.

Kaye, Alan. Perioperative Pharmacotherapy, an Issue of Anesthesiology Clinics. 2010. (Clinics: Surgery Ser.: 28-4). (ENG.). 105.00 *(978-1-4557-0585-6(3)*, Saunders) Elsevier - Health Sciences Div.

Kaye, Donald & Kaye, Keith S. Antibacterial Therapy & Newer Agents, an Issue of Infectious Disease Clinics. 2009. (Clinics: Internal Medicine Ser.: 23-4). (ENG., Illus.). xiv, 758p. 99.00 *(978-1-4377-1232-2(0)*, Saunders) Elsevier - Health Sciences Div.

Keogh, James. Schaum's Outline of Pharmacology. 2010. (Schaum's Outline Ser.). (ENG., Illus.). 384p. (C). pap. 21.95 *(978-0-07-162362-9(0)*, 0071623620) McGraw-Hill Cos., The.

Kerecsen, Laszlo & Pazdernik, Thomas L. Pharmacology. 3rd ed. 2010. (Rapid Review Ser.). (ENG., Illus.). 360p. (C). pap. 39.95 *(978-0-323-06812-3(X)*, Mosby) Elsevier - Health Sciences Div.

Kimmel, Stephen E. & Strom, Brian L., eds. Textbook of Pharmacoepidemiology. 2007. (ENG., Illus.). 518p. 179.00 *(978-0-470-02924-4(2)*, Wiley) Wiley, John & Sons, Inc.

Kleinberg, Michael E., ed. Managing Infections in Patients with Hematological Malignancies. 2009. (Contemporary Hematology Ser.). 300p. 219.00 *(978-1-58829-986-4(4))* Humana Pr.

Klenke, Elisabeth. Inhibition of Angiogenesis by Potential Chemopreventive Agents. 2008. 132p. pap. *(978-3-639-03630-5(1))* VDM Verlag Dr. Mueller e.K.

Koda-Kimble, Mary Anne, et al, eds. Handbook of Applied Therapeutics. 8th rev. ed. 2006. (Spiral Manual Ser.). (ENG., Illus.). 1104p. pap. 63.99 *(978-0-7817-9026-0(3))* Lippincott Williams & Wilkins.

Koning, Lee O., ed. Progress in Malaria Research. 2007. 129.00 *(978-1-60021-590-2(4))* Nova Science Pubs., Inc.

Krause, Walter. Drugs Compromising Male Sexual Health. 2008. (Illus.). 701p. 89.95 incl. cd-rom *(978-3-540-69859-3(0))* Springer.

Kräusslich, Hans-Georg & Bartenschlager, Ralf. Antiviral Strategies. 2008. (Handbook of Experimental Pharmacology Ser.: Vol. 1). (Illus.). 360p. 419.00 *(978-3-540-79085-3(3))* Springer.

Krausz, M., et al, contrib. by. Pharmakotherapie der Sucht. (GER., Illus.). *(978-3-8055-7482-2(7))* Karger, S. AG.

Lacy, Charles F., et al, eds. Drug Information Handbook: A Comprehensive Resource for All Clinicians & Healthcare Professionals. 18th ed. 2009. (Drug Information Handbook Ser.). 1875p. pap. 61.95 *(978-1-59195-254-1(9))* Lexi-Comp, Inc.

—Drug Information Handbook with International Trade Names Index. (Drug Information Handbook (International Ed) Ser.). 18th ed. 2009. 2215p. pap. 67.95 *(978-1-59195-255-8(7))* 19th ed. 2010. (Illus.). 2161p. pap. 69.95 *(978-1-59195-279-4(4))* 20th ed. 2011. (ENG.). 2263p. pap. 71.95 ***(978-1-59195-292-3(1))*** Lexi-Comp, Inc.

Lacy, Charles F., et al. Drug Information Handbook: A Comprehensive Resource for All Clinicians & Healthcare Professionals. 15th ed. 2007. (Drug Information Handbook Ser.). 2148p. per. 56.95 *(978-1-59195-203-9(4))* Lexi-Comp, Inc.

—Drug Information Handbook with International Trade Names Index. 15th ed. 2007. (Lexi-Comp's Drug Reference Handbooks Ser.). 2445p. per. 63.95 *(978-1-59195-204-6(2))* Lexi-Comp, Inc.

Lamonte, Jean R. Aromatase Inhibitors: Types, Mode of Action & Indications. 2009. (Cancer Etiology, Diagnosis & Treatments Ser.). 89.00 *(978-1-60741-711-8(1)*, Nova Biomedical Bks.) Nova Science Pubs., Inc.

Lednicer, Daniel. New Drug Discovery & Development. 2006. (ENG., Illus.). 190p. 127.00 *(978-0-470-00750-1(8)*, Wiley-Interscience) Wiley, John & Sons, Inc.

Lenz, Thomas L. Lifestyle Modifications in Pharmacotherapy. 2007. (ENG., Illus.). 416p. per. 55.99 *(978-0-7817-7651-6(1))* Lippincott Williams & Wilkins.

Levin, Bonnie & Schlesselman, Michael D. ASHP's Informatics Pearls. 2009. 99.00 *(978-1-58528-201-2(4))* American Society of Health-System Pharmacists(r).

Lincoff, A. Michael, ed. Platelet Glycoprotein IIb/IIIa Inhibitors in Cardiovascular Disease. 2nd ed. 2010. (Contemporary Cardiology Ser.). (Illus.). 440p. pap. 179.00 *(978-1-61737-408-1(3)*, 1617374083) Humana Pr.

Linda J. Dodds Staff. Drugs in Use, 4th Edition. 4th rev. ed. 2009. xxii, 666p. pap. 59.99 *(978-0-85369-791-6(4))* Pharmaceutical Pr. GBR. Dist: Smith Fulfillment Services.

Linn, William D., et al. Pharmacotherapy in Primary Care. 2008. (ENG., Illus.). 544p. pap. 72.00 *(978-0-07-145612-8(0)*, 0071456120) McGraw-Hill Medical Publishing Div.

Lippincott. MediQuik Drug Cards. 18th rev. ed. 2011. (ENG.). 912p. 43.99 ***(978-1-60913-623-9(3))*** Lippincott Williams & Wilkins.

Long, Paul F. & Costello, Ian, eds. Paediatric Drug Handling. 2007. (ULLA Postgraduate Pharmacy Ser.). (Illus.). 130p. 45.00 *(978-0-85369-686-5(1))* Pharmaceutical Pr. GBR. Dist: Smith Fulfillment Services.

Lüllmann, Heinz, et al. Pocket Atlas of Pharmacology. 4th ed. 2010. (ENG.). 408p. pap. 49.99 *(978-3-13-781704-8(8))* Thieme Medical Pubs., Inc.

LWW. Lippin Drugs Know Nclex-Rn. 4th rev. ed. 2012. (ENG.). 416p. pap. 24.95 ***(978-1-4511-7198-3(6))*** Lippincott Williams & Wilkins.

—Nursing Pharmacology Made Inc Easy Pb. 3rd rev. ed. 2012. (Incredibly Easy! Ser.). (ENG., Illus.). 736p. pap. 48.95 ***(978-1-4511-4624-0(8))*** Lippincott Williams & Wilkins.

LWW, ed. Craven, Fundamentals of Nursing, Abrams, Clinical Drug Therapy & Craig, Clinical Caculations Made Easy. 2009. pap. 188.95 *(978-1-60913-500-3(8))* Lippincott Williams & Wilkins.

Lyden, Patrick D., ed. Thrombolytic Therapy for Acute Stroke. 2nd ed. 2010. (Current Clinical Neurology Ser.). (Illus.). 392p. pap. 139.00 *(978-1-61737-540-8(3)*, 1617375403) Humana Pr.

Madhan, Ramesh, et al. Pharmacist's Intervention on Drug Therapy: Impact on Healthcare Cost. 2010. 80p. pap. *(978-3-8383-8040-7(1))* Lambert Academic Publishing.

Maida, Marybeth & Kiederer, Debbie. Beauty Pearls for Chemo Girls. 2009. (ENG.). 288p. pap. 14.95 *(978-0-8065-3118-2(5)*, Citadel Pr.) Kensington Publishing Corp.

Marx, Robert E. Oral & Intravenous Bisphosphonate-Induced Osteonecrosis of the Jaws: History, Etiology, Prevention, & Treatment. 2007. (Illus.). 150p. per. *(978-0-86715-462-7(4))* Quintessence Publishing Co., Inc.

Masor, Nathan. The New Psychiatry. 2011. 162p. 41.95 ***(978-1-258-07596-5(2))*** Literary Licensing, LLC.

Mayes, Rick, et al. Medicating Children: ADHD & Pediatric Mental Health. 2009. (Illus.). 360p. 44.00 *(978-0-674-03153-0(6))* Harvard Univ. Pr.

McCleane, Gary J. Pain Management: Expanding the Pharmacological Options. 2008. (ENG., Illus.). 200p. pap. 115.95 *(978-1-4051-7823-5(X)*, Wiley-Blackwell) Wiley, John & Sons, Inc.

Medical Letter Staff, intro. Handbook of Antimicrobial Therapy. 2008. 476p. pap. 35.00 net. *(978-0-9719093-8-0(5))* Medical Letter, Inc., The.

Midlöv, Patrik, et al. Drug-related problems in the Elderly. 2009. (ENG., Illus.). xii, 136p. 189.00 *(978-90-481-2445-9(X)*, 904812445X) Springer.

Miller, Monica L., et al. Acute Care Medicine: A Pharmacist's Guide. 2012. (ENG., Illus.). 256p. (C). pap. 50.00 ***(978-0-07-174580-2(7)***, 0071745807) McGraw-Hill Medical Publishing Div.

Mogensen, Carl Erik, ed. Pharmacotherapy of Diabetes: New Developments: Improving Life & Prognosis for Diabetic Patients. 2007. (ENG., Illus.). x, 289p. 139.00 *(978-0-387-69736-9(5)*, 0387697365) Springer.

Mosby. Mosby's Drug Reference for Health Professions. 3rd ed. 2011. (ENG.). 1744p. pap. 48.95 *(978-0-323-07736-1(6)*, Mosby) Elsevier - Health Sciences Div.

North American Companion Animal Formulary, 7th Edition Revised. 2007. spiral bd. 50.00 *(978-1-889750-91-0(3))* North American Compendiums, Inc.

North-Lewis, Penny, ed. Drugs & the Liver: A Guide to Drug Handling in Liver Dysfunction. 2008. (Illus.). 344p. pap. 57.50 *(978-0-85369-710-7(8))* Pharmaceutical Pr. GBR. Dist: Smith Fulfillment Services.

Olfman, Sharna. Bipolar Children: Cutting-Edge Controversy, Insights, & Research, 1 vol. 2007. (Childhood in America Ser.). (Illus.). 176p. 39.95 *(978-0-275-99730-4(8)*, C9730, Praeger Pubs.) Greenwood Publishing Group, Inc.

Onwuamah, Chika Kingsley, et al. Mouse Cellular Immune Response to Plasmodium Berghei Nk65 Infection. 2010. 92p. pap. *(978-3-8383-7841-1(5))* Lambert Academic Publishing.

O'reilly Eileen M Staff. Chemotherapy for Gastrointestinal Neoplasms. 2010 (Illus.). 179.95 *(978-0-8493-8499-8(0)*, Informa Healthcare) Taylor & Francis Group GBR. Dist: Taylor & Francis Group.

Pandi-Perumal, S. R., et al, eds. Sleep Disorders: Diagnosis & Therapeutics. 2008. (ENG., Illus.). 770p. 399.95 *(978-0-415-43818-6(7)*, Informa Healthcare) Taylor & Francis Group GBR. Dist: Taylor & Francis Group.

Panus, Peter, et al. Pharmacology for the Physical Therapist. 2008. (ENG., Illus.). 608p. (C). 74.00 *(978-0-07-146043-9(8)*, 0071460438) McGraw-Hill Medical Publishing Div.

Papadopoulos, John. Pocket Guide to Critical Care Pharmacotherapy. 2007. (Illus.). 207p. *(978-1-934115-45-9(2))* American Academy of Pediatrics.

Patient Compliance with Medications: Issues & Opportunities. 2007. (ENG., Illus.). 232p. 60.00 *(978-0-7890-2609-5(0))*; per. 34.00 *(978-0-7890-2610-1(4))* Taylor & Francis Group. (Informa Healthcare).

PDR Staff. PDR Concise Drug Guide for Advanced Practice Clinicians 2009. Reuters, Thomson, ed. 2008. (ENG.). 1400p. pap. 44.95 *(978-1-56363-718-6(9))* PDR Network, LLC.

Phelps, Stephanie J., et al. Pediatric Injectable Drugs: The Teddy Bear Book. 9th ed. (Illus.). 702p. E-Book 299.00 *(978-1-58528-243-2(X))* American Society of Health-System Pharmacists.

Pinedo, H. M. & Smorenburg, C H, eds. Drugs Affecting Growth of Tumours 2006. (Milestones in Drug Therapy Ser.). (Illus.). 237p. 199.00 *(978-3-7643-2196-3(2)*, 3764321962) Birkhauser Verlag AG CHE. Dist: Springer.

Plumb, Donald C. Plumb's Veterinary Drug Handbook. 7th ed. 2011. (ENG.) 1208p. pap. 79.99 ***(978-0-470-95964-0(9)***, Wiley-Blackwell) Wiley, John & Sons, Inc.

—Veterinary Drug Handbook. 7th ed. 2011. (ENG.). 1584p. pap. 79.99 ***(978-0-470-95965-7(7)***, Wiley) Wiley, John & Sons, Inc.

Pojskic, Nedzad & D. MacKeigan, Linda. Physician Collaboration with Pharmacists on Drug Therapy Management. 2010. 112p. pap. *(978-3-8383-0265-2(6))* Lambert Academic Publishing.

Porché, Robert A. High-Alert Medications: Strategies for Improving Safety. 2008. (Illus.). x, 124p. *(978-1-59940-209-3(2))* Joint Commission Resources.

Prescher-Hughes, Debra S. Nurse's Chemotherapy Quick Pocket Reference. 2008. (ENG.). 208p. pap. 41.95 *(978-0-7637-5824-0(8))* Jones & Bartlett Learning, LLC.

Prescription Psychotropic Drug Use among Children in Foster Care: Hearing Before the Subcommittee on Income Security & Family Support of the Committee on Ways & Means, U.S. House of Representatives, One Hundred Tenth Congress, Second Session, May 8, 2008. 2009. (Illus.). iii, 89p. *(978-0-16-082699-3(3)*, 552-070-38716-1) United States Government Printing Office.

Raofi, Saeid & Schappert, Susan M. Medication Therapy in Ambulatory Medical Care: United States, 2003-04. 2006. (DHHS Publication Ser.: Nos. 2007-1734). (Illus.). 40p. *(978-0-8406-0610-5(9)*, Centers for Disease Control & Prevention) United States Government Printing Office.

Reeves. Entry Inhibitors in HIV Therapy. 2007. (Milestones in Drug Therapy Ser.). (Illus.). ix, 200p. 199.00 ***(978-3-7643-7782-3(8)***, 3764377828) Birkhauser Verlag AG CHE. Dist: Springer.

Reuters, Thomson & Alexander, Ivy. 2010 PDR Nurse's Drug Handbook. 2009. 2000p. pap. 41.95 *(978-1-56363-746-9(4)*, Physician's Desk Reference (PDR)) PDR Network, LLC

Richards, Duncan, et al. Oxford Handbook of Practical Drug Therapy. 2nd ed. 2012. (Oxford Handbooks Ser.). (Illus.). 800p. pap. 52.95 *(978-0-19-956285-5(7))* Oxford Univ. Pr., Inc.

Rickles, Nathaniel M., et al. Social & Behavioral Aspects of Pharmaceutical Care. 2nd rev. ed. 2009. 484p. pap. 91.95 *(978-0-7637-6408-1(6))* Jones & Bartlett Learning, LLC.

Sakai, Joy, et al. Practical Pharmacology for the Pharmacy Technician. 2008. (LWW Pharmacy Technician Education Ser.). (ENG., Illus.). 688p. pap. 68.99 *(978-0-7817-7348-5(2))* Lippincott Williams & Wilkins.

Saltz, Leonard B. Colorectal Cancer: Evidence-Based Chemotherapy Strategies. 2006. (Current Clinical Oncology Ser.). (Illus.). 292p. 115.00 *(978-1-58829-751-8(9))*, 1588297519) Humana Pr.

Saltz, Leonard B., ed. Colorectal Cancer: Evidence-based Chemotherapy Strategies. 2010. (Current Clinical Oncology Ser.). (Illus.). 304p. pap. 115.00 *(978-1-61737-756-3(2)*, 1617377562) Humana Pr.

Sax, Paul E., et al. HIV Essentials 2010. 3rd rev. ed. 2009. 252p. pap. 24.95 *(978-0-7637-7709-8(9))* Jones & Bartlett Learning, LLC.

—HIV Essentials 2011. 4th ed. 2010. 258p. pap. 24.95 *(978-1-4496-1339-6(X))* Jones & Bartlett Learning, LLC.

Schwee, Martin. Die zulassungsüberschreitende Verordnung von Fertigarzneimitteln (off-Label-Use) Eine Untersuchung vorwiegend im Bereich des Rechts der Gesetzlichen Krankenversicherung unter besonderer Berücksichtigung der sozialgerichtlichen Rechtsprechung. 2008. (Recht & Medizin Ser.). 186p. pap. 56.95 *(978-3-631-57175-0(5))* Lang, Peter GmbH, Europaischer Verlag der Wissenschaften DEU. Dist: Lang, Peter.

Schwinghammer, Terry, et al. Casebook of Pharmacotherapy & Pharmacotherapy: A Pathophysiologic Approach 8th ed. 2011. (ENG.). pap. 240.00 *(978-0-07-175392-0(3)*, 0071753923) McGraw-Hill Professional Publishing.

Schwinghammer, Terry L. & Koehler, Julia M. Pharmacotherapy: A Patient-Focused Approach. 8th ed. 2011. (ENG., Illus.). 450p. pap. 58.00 *(978-0-07-174626-7(9)*, 0071746269) McGraw-Hill Medical Publishing Div.

Scott, David L., et al. Inflammatory Arthritis in Clinical Practice. 2007. (Illus.). 116p. pap. 69.95 *(978-1-84628-932-3(7))* Springer.

Sechi, GianPietro, ed. Drug Related Encephalopathies. 2008. 89.00 *(978-1-60456-745-8(7))* Nova Science Pubs., Inc.

Selzer, P. M. Antiparasitic & Antibacterial Drug Discovery: From Molecular Targets to Drug Candidates. Selzer, Paul M., ed. 2009. (Drug Discovery in Infectious Diseases Ser.). (ENG., Illus.). 509p. 239.95 *(978-3-527-32327-2(9)*, Wiley-VCH) Wiley, John & Sons, Inc.

Semla, Todd P., et al, eds. Geriatric Dosage Handbook: Including Clinical Recommendations & Monitoring Guidelines. 15th ed. 2009. (Geriatric Dosage Handbook Ser.). (ENG., Illus.). 2063p. pap. 53.95 *(978-1-59195-274-9(3))* Lexi-Comp, Inc.

Semla, Todd P., et al. Geriatric Dosage Handbook: Including Clinical Recommendations & Monitoring Guidelines. 13th ed. 2007. (Lexi-Comp's Drug Reference Handbooks Ser.). (Illus.). 1886p. per. 48.95 *(978-1-59195-226-8(3))* Lexi-Comp, Inc.

Shannon, Margaret, et al. Prentice Hall Health Professional's Drug Guide. 2007. 1763p. per. 39.95 *(978-0-13-513408-5(0))* Prentice Hall PTR.

Shea, Shawn Christopher. Improving Medication Adherence: How to Talk with Patients about Their Medications. 2006. 184p. per. 46.99 *(978-0-7817-9622-4(9))* Lippincott Williams & Wilkins.

Si-Shen Feng Staff. Chemotherapeutic Engineering. 2010. (ENG., Illus.). 500p. 139.95 *(978-0-8493-9084-5(2))* CRC Pr. LLC.

Silberman, Howard & Silberman, Allan W., eds. Principles & Practice of Surgical Oncology: A Multidisciplinary Approach to Difficult Problems. 2009. (ENG.). 1200p. 248.99 *(978-0-7817-6546-6(3))* Lippincott Williams & Wilkins.

Silverman, Daniel H. & Davidson, Idelle. Your Brain after Chemo: A Practical Guide to Lifting the Fog & Getting Back Your Focus. 2009. (ENG.). 304p. 25.00 *(978-0-7382-1259-3(8))* Da Capo Pr., Inc.

Sisson, Evan, rev. AADE Quick Guide to Medications. 2008. vii, 40p. pap. *(978-1-881876-25-0(X))* American Assn. of Diabetes Educators.

Skidmore-Roth, Linda, et al. Mosby's Drug Guide for Nurses, with 2012 Update; Pagana: Mosby's Diagnostic & Laboratory Test Reference, 10e; & Mosby's Dictionary of Medicine, Nursing & Health Professions, 8e Package. 9th ed. 2011. (ENG.). pap. 99.95 *(978-0-323-09726-0(X)*, Mosby) Elsevier - Health Sciences Div.

Soriano, Nathaniel. Glioblastoma Treatment with 2, 5-Dimethyl-Celecoxib (Dmc) in Vitro. 2008. 48p. pap. *(978-3-639-02829-4(5))* VDM Verlag Dr. Mueller e.K.

Southern California Evidence-Based Practice Center/RAND Staff, contrib. by. Antiretoviral (ARV) Drug Resistance in the Developing World. 2007. (AHRQ Publication Ser.: No. 156). viii, 74p. *(978-1-58763-267-9(5))* Agency for Healthcare Research & Quality.

Spencer, Peter & Holt, Walter. Anticancer Drugs: Design, Delivery & Pharmacology. 2009. 129.00 *(978-1-60741-004-1(4))* Nova Science Pubs., Inc.

Springhouse Publishing Company Staff, ed. I. V. Therapy. 4th rev. ed. 2009. (Incredibly Easy! Ser.). (ENG., Illus.). 384p. pap. 46.95 *(978-1-60547-198-3(4))* Lippincott Williams & Wilkins.

—Psychiatric Disorders. 2009. (ENG.). 384p. pap. 41.99 *(978-1-60547-051-1(1))* Lippincott Williams & Wilkins.

Stahl, Stephen & Stahl, Stephen M. Mood Stabilizers. 2009. (Stahl's Illustrated Ser.). (ENG., Illus.). 176p. pap. 41.99 *(978-0-521-75849-9(1))* Cambridge Univ. Pr.

Staines, Henry M. & Krishna, Sanjeev, eds. Treatment & Prevention of Malaria: Antimalarial Drug Chemistry, Action & Use. 2012. (Milestones in Drug Therapy Ser.). (ENG., Illus.). x, 315p. 189.00 ***(978-3-0346-0479-6(3)***, 3034604793) Birkhauser Verlag AG CHE. Dist: Springer.

Strom, Brian L. & Kimmel, Stephen E., eds. Textbook of Pharmacoepidemiology. 2007. (ENG., Illus.). 518p. per. 90.00 *(978-0-470-02925-1(0)*, Wiley) Wiley, John & Sons, Inc.

Swearingen, Brooke & Biller, Beverly M. K., eds. Diagnosis & Management of Pituitary Disorders. 2008. (Contemporary Endocrinology Ser.). (Illus.). 518p. 189.00 *(978-1-58829-922-2(8)*, 1588299228) Springer.

Taraschenko, Olga. 18-Methoxycoronaridine & the Habenulo-Interpeduncular Pathway. 2009. 192p. pap. *(978-3-639-13774-3(4))* VDM Verlag Dr. Mueller e.K.

Thomson Micromedex, creator. Drug Information for the Health Care Professional. 27th rev. ed. 2007. (USP DI: V. 1 Drug Information for the Health Care Professional Ser.). (Illus.). 3218p. 174.00 *(978-1-56363-574-8(7))* PDR Network, LLC.

Thorp, Christine M. Pharmacology for the Health Care Professions. 2008. (ENG., Illus.). 376p. 146.95 *(978-0-470-51018-6(8)*, Wiley) Wiley, John & Sons, Inc.

—Pharmacology for the Health Care Professions. 2008. (ENG., Illus.). 376p. pap. 69.95 *(978-0-470-51017-9(X)*, Wiley) Wiley, John & Sons, Inc.

UNAIDS. Guidelines for the Treatment of Malaria. 2nd rev. ed. 2010. (Nonseral Publication). (ENG.). 194p. pap. 24.00 *(978-92-4-154792-5(8))* World Health Organization.

Urban, Carol & Adams, Michael. Pharmacology: Connections to Nursing Practice. 2nd rev. ed. 2012. (ENG.). 1560p. (C). 104.00 ***(978-0-13-281442-3(0)***, Prentice Hall) Prentice Hall PTR.

van Mil, Jose. Healthy Eating with Chemotherapy. 2009. (ENG.). 160p. pap. 16.95 *(978-1-904920-88-5(8))* Kyle Bks. GBR. Dist: National Bk. Network.

Veale, David & Neziroglu, Fugen. Body Dysmorphic Disorder: A Treatment Manual. 2010. (ENG., Illus.). 488p. pap. 72.95 *(978-0-470-85121-0(X)*, Wiley) Wiley, John & Sons, Inc.

Waldman, Scott A. & Terzic, Andre. Pharmacology & Therapeutics. 2008. (ENG., Illus.). 1054p. 218.00 *(978-1-4160-6098-7(7)*, Saunders) Elsevier - Health Sciences Div.

—Pharmacology & Therapeutics: Principles to Practice. 2008. (ENG., Illus.). 1536p. 164.00 *(978-1-4160-3291-5(6)*, Saunders) Elsevier - Health Sciences Div.

Walker, Ida. Recreational Ritalin: The Not-So-Smart Drug. 2012. ***(978-1-4222-2439-7(2))***; ***(978-1-4222-2458-8(9))*** Mason Crest Pubs.

Walker, Roger & Whittlesea, Cate. Clinical Pharmacy & Therapeutics. 4th ed. 2007. *(978-0-443-10286-8(4)*, Churchill Livingstone) Elsevier - Health Sciences Div.

Walker, Roger & Whittlesea, Cate, eds. Clinical Pharmacy & Therapeutics. 5th ed. 2011. (ENG., Illus.). 998p. (C). pap. 81.95 ***(978-0-7020-4293-5(5)***, Churchill Livingstone) Elsevier - Health Sciences Div.

Wang, Paul & Al-Ahmad, Amin. Advances in ICD Therapy: Cardiac Electrophysiology Clinics. 2011. (Clinics: Internal Medicine Ser.: 3-3). (ENG.). 75.00 *(978-1-4557-0424-8(5)*, Saunders) Elsevier - Health Sciences Div.

Waring, Michael, ed. Sequence-Specific DNA Binding Agents. 2006. (RSC Biomolecular Sciences Ser.). (ENG., Illus.). 270p. 149.00 *(978-0-85404-370-5(5)*, 0854043705) Royal Society of Chemistry, The GBR. Dist: Ingram Pub. Services.

Waun MA LPC BCPCC, Deborah. Survivor's Guide to Chemo, 1 vol. 2009. 96p. pap. 16.95 *(978-1-60813-089-4(4))* PublishAmerica, Inc.

Wecker, Lynn, et al. Brody's Human Pharmacology: With STUDENT CONSULT Online Access. 5th ed. 2009. (ENG., Illus.). 719p. (C). pap. 79.95 *(978-0-323-05374-7(2)*, Mosby) Elsevier - Health Sciences Div.

Weinberg, Mea A., et al. Oral Pharmacology for the Dental Hygienist. 2nd rev. ed. 2012. (ENG.). 360p. (C). pap. 77.47 ***(978-0-13-255992-8(7)***, Prentice Hall) Prentice Hall PTR.

Weissman, Sidney, et al. Integrating Psychological & Biological Therapies. 2008. (Psychotherapy in Clinical Practice Ser.). (ENG., Illus.). 176p. pap. 49.99 *(978-0-7817-5102-5(0))* Lippincott Williams & Wilkins.

Wells, Barbara, et al. Pharmacotherapy Handbook, Eighth Edition. 8th ed. 2011. (ENG., Illus.). 1164p. pap. 55.00 ***(978-0-07-174834-6(2)***, 0071748342) McGraw-Hill Medical Publishing Div.

Whipple, Jody. Tell Me What to Eat During Chemotherapy. 2008. (Tell Me What to Eat Ser.). 192p. pap. 12.99 *(978-1-60163-045-2(X))* Career Pr., Inc.

Wilding, John P. H., ed. Pharmacotherapy of Obesity. 2007. (Milestones in Drug Therapy Ser.). (Illus.). x, 120p. 179.00 *(978-3-7643-7138-8(2))* Birkhauser Verlag AG CHE. Dist: Springer.

Wiley. Wiley Handbook of Current & Emerging Drug Therapies, Volume 1, 8 vols. 2007. (Illus.). *(978-0-470-10250-3(0)*, Wiley-Interscience) Wiley, John & Sons, Inc.

—Wiley Handbook of Current & Emerging Drug Therapies, Volume 2, 8 vols. 2007. (Illus.). *(978-0-470-10251-0(9)*, Wiley-Interscience) Wiley, John & Sons, Inc.

—Wiley Handbook of Current & Emerging Drug Therapies, Volume 3, 8 vols. 2007. (Illus.). *(978-0-470-10252-7(7)*, Wiley-Interscience) Wiley, John & Sons, Inc.

—Wiley Handbook of Current & Emerging Drug Therapies, Volume 4, 8 vols. 2007. (Illus.). *(978-0-470-10253-4(5)*, Wiley-Interscience) Wiley, John & Sons, Inc.

—Wiley Handbook of Current & Emerging Drug Therapies, Volume 5. 2007. *(978-0-470-10254-1(3)*, Wiley-Interscience) Wiley, John & Sons, Inc.

—Wiley Handbook of Current & Emerging Drug Therapies, Volume 6. 2007. *(978-0-470-10255-8(1)*, Wiley-Interscience) Wiley, John & Sons, Inc.

—Wiley Handbook of Current & Emerging Drug Therapies, Volume 7. 2007. *(978-0-470-10256-5(X)*, Wiley-Interscience) Wiley, John & Sons, Inc.

—Wiley Handbook of Current & Emerging Drug Therapies, Volume 8. 2007. *(978-0-470-10257-2(8)*, Wiley-Interscience) Wiley, John & Sons, Inc.

Wiley and Sons, Inc. Staff. Current & Emerging Drug Therapies, 4 vols., Vols. 5-8. 2007. (ENG., Illus.). 3120p. instr.'s hndbk. ed. 1500.00 *(978-0-470-04099-7(8)*, Wiley-Interscience) Wiley, John & Sons, Inc.

Wilkes, Gail & Barton-Burke, Margaret. 2010 Oncology Nursing Drug Handbook. 14th rev. ed. 2009. 1360p. pap. 102.95 *(978-0-7637-8124-8(X))* Jones & Bartlett Learning, LLC.

Wilkes, Gail M. & Barton-Burke, Margaret. 2008 Oncology Nursing Drug Handbook. 2007. 1220p. pap. 88.95 *(978-0-7637-5563-8(X))* Jones & Bartlett Learning, LLC.

Wilkes, Gail M., et al. 2009 Oncology Nursing Drug Handbook. 13th ed. 2008. 1298p. pap. 104.95 *(978-0-7637-6585-9(6))* Jones & Bartlett Learning, LLC.

Williamson, Steve & Polwart, Calum. The Oral Anticancer Medicine Handbook. 2009. 193p. pap. 21.50 *(978-1-4092-4044-0(4))* Lulu Enterprises Inc.

Wilson, Billie Ann, et al. Pearson Nurse's Drug Guide 2011. 2010. (ENG.). 1792p. (C). 41.95 *(978-0-13-214926-6(5)*, Prentice Hall) Prentice Hall PTR.

—Pearson Nurse's Drug Guide 2011. 2010. (ENG.). 1792p. (C). 43.80 *(978-0-13-214970-9(2)*, Prentice Hall) Prentice Hall PTR.

Wilson, Billie Ann, et al. Pearson Nurse's Drug Guide 2013. 2nd rev. ed. 2012. (ENG.). 1792p. (C). 42.95 ***(978-0-13-296489-0(9))***; 42.95 ***(978-0-13-297485-1(1))*** Prentice Hall PTR. (Prentice Hall).

Wilson, Eric G. Against Happiness: In Praise of Melancholy. 2009. (ENG., Illus.). 176p. pap. 12.00 *(978-0-374-53166-9(8))* Farrar, Straus & Giroux.

Wilson, James W. & Estes, Lynn, eds. Mayo Clinic Antimicrobial Therapy Quick Reference Guide. 2008. 352p. pap. 29.95 *(978-1-4200-6713-2(3)*, Informa Healthcare) Taylor & Francis Group GBR. Dist: Taylor & Francis Group.

Wolverton, Stephen E. Comprehensive Dermatologic Drug Therapy. 2nd rev. ed. 2007. (ENG., Illus.). 1104p. pap. 152.00 *(978-1-4160-3328-8(9)*, Saunders) Elsevier - Health Sciences Div.

Woo, Teri M. & Wynne, Anita L. Pharmacotherapeutics for Nurse Practitioner Prescribers. 3rd rev. ed. 2011. (Illus.). 1376p. 135.00 *(978-0-8036-2235-7(X))* Davis, F. A. Co.

Woodrow, Ruth. Essentials of Pharmacology for Health Occupations. 4th ed. 2007. pap. 16.95 *(978-1-4288-1900-9(2))* Cram101 Inc.

Woodrow, Ruth, et al. Essentials of Pharmacology for Health Occupations. 6th ed. 2010. (New Releases for Health Science Ser.). (ENG., Illus.). 624p. (C). pap. 97.95 *(978-1-4354-8033-9(3))* Delmar Cengage Learning.

—Study Guide for Woodrow/Colbert/Smith's Essentials of Pharmacology for Health Occupations. 6th ed. 2010. (ENG.). 176p. (C). pap. 43.95 *(978-1-4354-8037-7(6))* Delmar Cengage Learning.

World Health Organization. Guidelines for the Programmatic Management of Drug-resistant Tuberculosis: Emergency Update 2008. 2009. (Nonserial Publication Ser.). (ENG.). 268p. pap. 30.00 *(978-92-4-154758-1(8))* World Health Organization.

—Malaria Rapid Diagnostic Test Performance 2008: Results of WHO Product Testing of RDTs. 2009. (DOCUMENTS for SALE Ser.). (ENG.). 104p. pap. 30.00 *(978-92-4-159807-1(7))* World Health Organization.

—WHO Guidelines on Pharmacological Treatment of Persisting Pain in Children with Medical Illnesses. 2012. 250p. pap. 30.00 *(978-92-4-154812-0(6))* World Health Organization.

Yaffe, Sumner J. & Aranda, Jacob V., eds. Neonatal & Pediatric Pharmacology: Therapeutic Principles in Practice. 4th rev. ed. 2010. (ENG., Illus.). 1072p. 256.99 *(978-0-7817-9538-8(9))* Lippincott Williams & Wilkins.

Yue, Eddy W., et al. Inhibitors of Cyclin-Dependent Kinases as Anti-Tumor Agents. 2006. (Enzyme Inhibitors Ser.: Vol. 3). (ENG., Illus.). 448p. 189.95 *(978-0-8493-3774-1(7)*, CRC Press) Taylor & Francis Group GBR. Dist: Taylor & Francis Group.

Zee, Anke-Hilse Maitland-van der & Daly, Ann K., eds. Pharmacogenetics & Individualized Therapy. 2012. (ENG.). 510p. 115.00 ***(978-0-470-43354-6(X)***, Wiley) Wiley, John & Sons, Inc.

Zook, Virginia. Ramblings of a Single-Breasted Mattress Thrasher: Or: A Funny Thing Happened to Me on the Way to Chemo. 2008. 84p. pap. 16.95 *(978-1-60703-195-6(7))* PublishAmerica, Inc.

CHEMOTHERAPY—COMPLICATIONS

see Drugs—Side Effects

CHEMURGY

see also Synthetic Products

Haynes, Williams. Southern Horizons. 2010. 338p. pap. 31.75 *(978-1-171-84611-6(8))* BiblioBazaar.

—Southern Horizons. 2010. 138p. pap. 22.63 *(978-1-153-55313-1(9))* General Bks. LLC.

CHENEY, RICHARD B., 1941-

Barnett, Thomas P. M. Great Powers: America & the World after Bush. 2010. (ENG.). 496p. (gr. 12-18). 16.00 *(978-0-425-23225-5(5)*, Berkley Trade) Penguin Group (USA) Inc.

Buick, Robert Clayton. Evil Dynasty. 2011. 144p. pap. 19.99 ***(978-1-4500-0478-7(4))*** Xlibris Corp.

Cheney, Dick. In My Time: A Personal & Political Memoir. (ENG., Illus.). 576p. 2012. pap. 16.00 ***(978-1-4391-7622-1(1))*** 2011. 35.00 *(978-1-4391-7619-1(1))* Threshold Editions. (Threshold Editions).

Cheney, Lynne. Blue Skies, No Fences: A Memoir of Childhood & Family. 2009. (ENG., Illus.). 320p. pap. 15.00 *(978-1-4165-3289-7(7)*, Threshold Editions) Threshold Editions.

Cheney, Mary. Now It's My Turn: A Daughter's Chronicle of Political Life. 2008. (ENG.). 256p. pap. 17.95 *(978-1-4165-2290-4(5)*, Threshold Editions) Threshold Editions.

Christie, Ron. Black in the White House: Life Inside George W. Bush's West Wing, 0 vols. 2009. 328p. pap. 14.99 *(978-1-59555-285-3(5))* Nelson, Thomas Inc.

Gellman, Barton. Angler: The Cheney Vice Presidency. 2009. (ENG.). 512p. (gr. 12-18). 18.00 *(978-0-14-311616-5(9)*, Penguin (Non-Classics)) Penguin Group (USA) Inc.

Hayes, Stephen F. Cheney: The Untold Story of America's Most Powerful & Controversial Vice President. 2007. (ENG.). 592p. 27.99 *(978-0-06-072346-0(7))* HarperCollins Pubs.

Montgomery, Bruce P. The Bush-Cheney Administration's Assault on Open Government, 1 vol. 2008. 232p. 49.95 *(978-0-275-99904-9(1)*, C9904, Praeger Pubs.) Greenwood Publishing Group, Inc.

—Richard B. Cheney & the Rise of the Imperial Vice Presidency, 1 vol. 2009. 248p. 49.95 *(978-0-313-35620-9(3)*, C35620, Praeger Pubs.) Greenwood Publishing Group, Inc.

Phillips, Peter & Loo, Dennis, eds. Impeach the President: The Case Against Bush & Cheney. 2006. (ENG., Illus.). 352p. per. 17.95 *(978-1-58322-743-5(1))* Seven Stories Pr.

Sammon, Bill. The Evangelical President: George Bush's Struggle to Spread a Moral Democracy Throughout the World. 2007. (ENG.). 232p. 27.95 *(978-1-59698-518-6(6))* Regnery Publishing, Inc., An Eagle Publishing Co.

Sands, Philippe. Torture Team: Rumsfeld's Memo & the Betrayal of American Values. (ENG., 2009. Illus.). 288p. pap. 16.95 *(978-0-230-61443-7(4))* 2008. 272p. 26.95 *(978-0-230-60390-5(4))* Palgrave Macmillan.

Thoreau, Jackson. Born to Cheat: How Bush, Cheney, Rove & Co. Broke the Rules - from the Sandlot to the White House. 2007. 256p. per. 19.95 net. *(978-1-881365-53-2(0))* Shay Publications/Random Publishers.

Vidal, Gore. Dreaming War: Blood for Oil & the Cheney-Bush Junta. 2007. (Nation Bks.). (ENG.). 197p. pap. 11.95 *(978-1-56025-502-4(1))* Basic Bks.

Warshaw, Shirley Anne. The Co-Presidency of Bush & Cheney. 2009. (ENG.). 320p. 29.95 *(978-0-8047-5818-5(2))* Stanford Univ. Pr.

CHENNAULT, CLAIRE LEE, 1890-1958

Ford, Daniel. Flying Tigers: Claire Chennault & His American Volunteers, 1941-1942. 2007. (ENG., Illus.). 400p. pap. 15.99 *(978-0-06-124655-5(7)*, HarperPerennial) HarperCollins Pubs.

Samson, Jack. The Flying Tiger: The True Story of General Claire Chennault & the U. S. 14th Air Force in China. movie tie-in ed. 2011. (ENG., Illus.). 488p. pap. 18.95 *(978-0-7627-7283-4(2)*, Lyons Pr.) Globe Pequot Pr., The.

CHER, 1946-

Howard, Josiah. Cher: Strong Enough. 2012. (ENG.). 240p. pap. 19.95 ***(978-0-85965-484-5(2))*** Plexus Publishing, Ltd. GBR. Dist: Perseus-PGW.

CHERAW INDIANS

see Indians of North America—East (U.S.)

CHERNOBYL NUCLEAR ACCIDENT, CHORNOBYL, UKRAINE, 1986

Bertell, Rosalie & Tchertkoff, Wladimir, told to. Chernobyl: The Hidden Legacy. 2007. (Illus.). 240p. pap. 45.00 *(978-1-904563-58-7(9))* Trolley GBR. Dist: Prestel Publishing.

Burlakova, E. 20 Years after the Chernobyl Accident: Past, Present & Future. 2006. 89.00 *(978-1-60021-249-9(2))* Nova Science Pubs., Inc.

Burlakova, Elena B. & Naydich, Valeria I., eds. Lessons of Chernobyl: 25 Years Later. 2011. ***(978-1-61324-516-3(5))*** Nova Science Pubs., Inc.

Cheney, Glenn Alan. Journey to Chernobyl: Encounters in a Radioactive Zone. 2006. (Illus.). 222p. per. 16.95 *(978-0-89733-552-2(X))* Academy Chicago Pubs., Ltd.

Krementschouk, Andrej, photos by. Andrej Krementschouk - CHERNOBYL ZONE (I) 2011. (ENG., Illus.). 120p. 80.00 ***(978-3-86828-200-9(9))*** Kehrer Verlag Heidelberg, Klaus Kehrer DEU. Dist: Consortium Bk. Sales & Distribution.

The Legacy of Chornobyl: Health & Safety 20 Years Later: Hearing Before the Commission on Security & Cooperation in Europe, One Hundred Ninth Congress, Second Session, April 25, 2006. 2007. iii, 43p. *(978-0-16-079910-5(4)*, 552-070-36747-1) United States Government Printing Office.

Onishi, Yasuo, et al, eds. Chernobyl - What Have We Learned? The Successes & Failures to Mitigate Water Contamination over 20 Years. 2006. (Environmental Pollution Ser.: Vol. 12). (Illus.). x, 289p. 179.00 *(978-1-4020-5348-1(7)*, 1402053487) Springer.

Schirmböck, Thomas. Andrej Krementschouk - Chernobyl Zone (II) 2012. (ENG., Illus.). 88p. pap. 40.00 ***(978-3-86828-210-8(6))*** Kehrer Verlag Heidelberg, Klaus Kehrer DEU. Dist: Consortium Bk. Sales & Distribution.

Shibata, Yoshisada, et al, eds. Radiation Risk Perspectives: Proceedings of the Second Nagasaki Symposium of International Consortium for Medical Care of Hibakusha & Radiation Life Science, Nagasaki, Japan, 26-27 July 2006. 2007. (International Congress Ser.: 1299). (ENG.). 328p. 195.00 *(978-0-444-52888-9(1)*, Elsevier) Elsevier - Health Sciences Div.

Smith, John. Chernobyl (Routledge Revivals) The Long Shadow. 2011. (Routledge Revivals Ser.). (ENG.). 224p. 120.00 *(978-0-415-67597-0(9))* Routledge.

University of Alberta Staff, et al, contrib. by. Commemoration of the Chernobyl Disaster: The Human Experience Twenty Years Later: Conference Proceedings. 2007. (Illus.). 82p. *(978-1-933549-19-4(X))* Woodrow Wilson Interantional Ctr. fo Scholars.

Yaroshinska, Alla, et al. Chernobyl: Crime without Punishment. 2011. 409p. 39.95 ***(978-1-4128-4296-9(4))*** Transaction Pubs.

CHEROKEE INDIAN REMOVAL, 1838
see Trail of Tears, 1838

CHEROKEE INDIANS
see Five Civilized Tribes; Indians of North America—Southern States

CHEROKEE LANGUAGE

Cushman, Ellen. The Cherokee Syllabary: Writing the People's Perseverance. 2011. (ENG., Illus.). 256p. 34.95 *(978-0-8061-4220-3(0))* Univ. of Oklahoma Pr.

Icon Group International, Inc. Staff, compiled by. Webster's Cherokee - English Thesaurus Dictionary. 2008. 56p. ring bd. 28.95 incl. audio compact disk *(978-0-497-83466-1(9))* Icon Group International, Inc.

Joyner, Michael. Cherokee Lessons - Introductory Edition. 2010. 104p. pap. 9.95 *(978-0-557-68640-7(7))* Lulu Enterprises Inc.

Mooney, James. The Sacred Formulas of the Cherokees. 2007. 112p. (ENG.). 24.95 *(978-1-934451-96-0(7))*; per. 14.99 *(978-1-934451-95-3(9))* Wilder Pubns., Ltd.

CHEROKEE REMOVAL, 1838
see Trail of Tears, 1838

CHERUBIM
see Angels

CHESAPEAKE AND DELAWARE CANAL

Barry, David A. A History of the Chesapeake & Delaware Canal. 2010. (Landmarks Ser.). 128p. pap. 19.99 *(978-1-59629-864-4(2))* History Pr., The.

CHESAPEAKE AND OHIO CANAL (MD. AND WASHINGTON, D.C.)

Camagna, Dorothy. C & O Canal. 2007. pap. 24.95 *(978-1-58979-214-2(9))* Taylor Trade Publishing.

Sabatke, Mark D. Discovering the C&O Canal: And Adjacent Potomac River. 2007. (ENG., Illus.). 176p. per. 19.95 *(978-0-88400-331-1(0))* Schreiber Publishing, Inc.

CHESAPEAKE BAY (MD. AND VA.)

Buckley, Michael. Voices of the Chesapeake Bay. 2008. (Illus.). 464p. pap. 19.95 *(978-0-9787278-5-7(1))*; 463p. *(978-0-9787278-8-8(6))* Geared Up LLC.

Chambers, Erve. Heritage Matters: Heritage, Culture, History, & Chesapeake Bay. 2006. *(978-0-943676-66-1(5))* Univ. of Maryland, Sea Grant Program.

Chewning, Alpheus J. Virginia Beach Shipwrecks. 2008. pap. 19.99 *(978-1-59629-474-5(4))* History Pr., The.

Dickon, Chris. Chesapeake Bay Steamers. 2006. (Images of America Ser.). (ENG., Illus.). 128p. per. 21.99 *(978-0-7385-4373-4(X))* Arcadia Publishing.

Ernst, Howard R. Fight for the Bay: Why a Dark Green Environmental Awakening Is Needed to Save the Chesapeake Bay. 2009. (ENG., Illus.). 164p. 44.00 *(978-0-7425-6323-0(5))*; pap. 19.95 *(978-0-7425-6324-7(3))* Rowman & Littlefield Publishers, Inc.

Eshelman, Ralph E., et al. A Travel Guide to the War of 1812 in the Chesapeake: Eighteen Tours in Maryland, Virginia, & the District of Columbia. 2011. (Johns Hopkins Books on the War Of 1812 Ser.). (ENG., Illus.). 296p. (gr. 17). 65.00 *(978-0-8018-9836-5(6))*; pap. 24.95 *(978-0-8018-9837-2(4))* Johns Hopkins Univ. Pr.

—The War of 1812 in the Chesapeake: A Reference Guide to Historic Sites in Maryland, Virginia, & the District of Columbia. 2010. (Johns Hopkins Books on the War Of 1812 Ser.). (ENG., Illus.). 424p. (gr. 17). 67.00 *(978-0-8018-9235-6(X))* Johns Hopkins Univ. Pr.

Gellis, Allen C. Sources, Transport, & Storage of Sediment at Selected Sites in the Chesapeake Bay Watershed. 2009. (Illus.). ix, 95p. *(978-1-4113-2360-5(2))* United States Geological Survey.

Germanotta, Anthony F., Jr. Insiders' Guide to Hampton Roads: Virginia Beach, Norfolk & Newport News. 2011. (Insiders' Guide Ser.). (ENG., Illus.). 288p. pap. 18.95 *(978-0-7627-6017-6(6)*, Insiders' Guide) Globe Pequot Pr., The.

Harper, Raymond L. Chesapeake, Virginia: A History. 2007. pap. 19.99 *(978-1-59629-351-9(9))* History Pr., The.

Horton, Tom. An Island Out of Time: A Memoir of Smith Island in the Chesapeake. 2008. (ENG.). 336p. pap. 15.95 *(978-0-393-33146-2(6)*, 33146) Norton, W. W. & Co., Inc.

Katalkina, Anna. Flying above Chesapeake Bay. 2008. (Illus.). 144p. 29.95 *(978-1-885435-93-4(2))* Twin Lights Pubs., Inc.

Kolarek, Frances. Vanishing Islands: A Story of History's Invisible People on Islands in the Chesapeake Bay-How They Lived & Worked & Played. 2008. 190p. pap. 22.00 *(978-0-7884-4901-7(X))* Heritage Bks.

Matuszeski, William. Inquiry in a Culture of Consensus: Science & Management for the Chesapeake Bay. 2008. *(978-0-943676-68-5(1))* Univ. of Maryland, Sea Grant Program.

Miller, Joanne. Chesapeake Bay. 2nd ed. 2008. (Moon Handbooks Ser.). (ENG., Illus.). 304p. per. 18.95 *(978-1-56691-928-9(2))* Westview Pr.

Mills, Eric. Chesapeake Bay in the Civil War. 2007. (Illus.). 315p. per. 29.95 *(978-0-87033-591-4(X)*, Cornell Maritime Pr./Tidewater Pubs.) Schiffer Publishing, Ltd.

Powers, Robert C. The Unknown Horizon: A Story of the Chesapeake Native Americans. 2008. 288p. pap. 19.95 *(978-0-9769773-8-4(9))* Powerful Pub. LLC.

Protecting & Restoring America's Great Waters: Hearing Before the Subcommittee on Water Resources & Environment of the Committee on Transportation & Infrastructure, House of Representatives, One Hundred Tenth Congress, Second Session, July 30, 2008. 2008. (Illus.). xvi, 159p. *(978-0-16-083843-9(6)*, 552-070-39540-7) United States Government Printing Office.

Rountree, Helen C., et al. John Smith's Chesapeake Voyages, 1607-1609. 2008. (ENG.). 402p. pap. 19.95 *(978-0-8139-2728-2(5))* Univ. Pr. of Virginia.

Shomette, Donald G. Pirates on the Chesapeake: Being a True History of Pirates, Picaroons, & Raiders on Chesapeake Bay, 1610-1807. 2008. (Illus.). 344p. pap. 22.95 *(978-0-87033-607-2(X)*, Cornell Maritime Pr./Tidewater Pubs.) Schiffer Publishing, Ltd.

—Shipwrecks on the Chesapeake: Maritime Disasters on Chesapeake Bay & Its Tributaries, 1608- 1978. 2007. (Illus.). 324p. per. 19.95 *(978-0-87033-597-6(9)*, Cornell Maritime Pr./Tidewater Pubs.) Schiffer Publishing, Ltd.

Sullivan, C. John. Chesapeake Bay Retrievers, Decoys & Long Guns: Tales of Carroll's Island Ducking Club. 2008. (Illus.). 159p. pap. 21.99 *(978-1-59629-462-2(0))* History Pr., The.

Tigner, James, Jr. Yesterday on the Chesapeake Bay. 2007. (Illus.). 160p. 39.95 *(978-0-7643-2597-7(3))* Schiffer Publishing, Ltd.

Tigner, Jr. & Tigner, James. Steamboat Days on the Chesapeake: Betterton & Tolchester Beach, Maryland. 2009. (Illus.). 128p. bds. 29.99 *(978-0-7643-3109-1(4))* Schiffer Publishing, Ltd.

Walsh, Lorena S. Motives of Honor, Pleasure, & Profit: Plantation Management in the Colonial Chesapeake, 1607-1763. 2010. (Published for the Omohundro Institute of Early American History & Culture, Williamsburg, Virginia Ser.). (ENG., Illus.). 736p. 70.00 *(978-0-8078-3234-9(0))* Univ. of North Carolina Pr.

Wennersten, John. The Oyster Wars of Chesapeake Bay. 2007. 164p. pap. 19.95 *(978-0-615-18250-6(X))* Wennersten, John R.

Whitman, T. Stephen. Challenging Slavery in the Chesapeake: Black & White Resistance to Human Bondage, 1775-1865. 2006. (ENG., Illus.). 320p. (gr. 17). per. 20.00 *(978-0-938420-96-5(8))* Maryland Historical Society.

Williams, John Page. Chesapeake: Exploring the Water Trail of Captain John Smith. (Illus.). 2007. (ENG.). 192p. per. 12.95 *(978-1-4262-0069-4(2)*, National Geographic) 2006. 191p. *(978-0-7922-5557-4(7))* 2006. 191p. *(978-0-7922-5556-7(9))* National Geographic Society.

Williams, Marlyse. Land Application of Wastewater in the Chesapeake Bay Watershed. 2008. 212p. pap. *(978-3-639-08017-9(3))* VDM Verlag Dr. Mueller e.K.

Wright, Emmett L. Decision Making: The Chesapeake. 2nd ed. (Interdisciplinary Environmental Education Curriculum Unit Ser.). 14.95 *(978-0-943675-25-8(8))* Univ. of Maryland, Sea Grant Program.

CHESAPEAKE BAY RETRIEVERS

Hammond, Charmaine. On Toby's Terms. 2010. (ENG.). 264p. pap. 14.95 *(978-0-9843081-4-9(8))* Youngs, Bettie Bks.

Linzy, Jan, et al. Chesapeake Bay Retriever Champions, 2006-2010. 2011. (Illus.). 138p. spiral bd. 46.95 *(978-1-55893-328-6(X))* Camino E.E. & Bk. Co.

Sullivan, C. John. Chesapeake Bay Retrievers, Decoys & Long Guns: Tales of Carroll's Island Ducking Club. 2008. (Illus.). 159p. pap. 21.99 *(978-1-59629-462-2(0))* History Pr., The.

CHESHIRE (ENGLAND)

AA Publishing Staff. Lancashire & Cheshire. 2nd ed. 2008. (50 Walks Ser.). (ENG., Illus.). 144p. pap. 19.95 *(978-0-7495-6056-0(8))* Automobile Assn. GBR. Dist: Independent Pubs. Group.

Darlington, Thomas. The Folk-Speech of South Cheshire. 2010. 488p. pap. 38.75 *(978-1-141-95551-0(2))* BiblioBazaar.

—The Folk-Speech of South Cheshire. 2010. 260p. pap. 34.05 *(978-1-152-46278-6(4))* General Bks. LLC.

—The Folk-Speech of South Cheshire. 2007. (ENG.). 460p. 52.95 *(978-0-548-22758-9(5))*; per. 37.95 *(978-1-4325-5002-8(0))* Kessinger Publishing, LLC.

Hartwell, Clare, et al. Cheshire. 2011. (Pevsner Architectural Guides). (ENG., Illus.). 800p. 85.00 *(978-0-300-17043-6(2))* Yale Univ. Pr.

Pevsner, Nikolaus. Cheshire. (Buildings of England Ser.). (Illus.). 448p. 45.00 *(978-0-14-071042-7(6))* Penguin Group (USA) Inc.

CHESHIRE (ENGLAND)—DESCRIPTION AND TRAVEL

Gerrard, David. The Hidden Places of Lancashire & Cheshire. 6th rev. ed. 2009. (Illus.). 200p. pap. 14.95 *(978-1-904434-83-2(5))* Travel Publishing, Ltd. GBR. Dist: Casemate Pubs. & Bk. Distributors, LLC.

Mike, Gerrard. Lancashire & Cheshire Hidden Places/7. 7th rev. ed. 2011. (Illus.). 252p. pap. 14.95 *(978-1-907462-01-6(5))* Travel Publishing, Ltd. GBR. Dist: Casemate Pubs. & Bk. Distributors, LLC.

Mowl, Timothy & Mako, Marion. The Historic Gardens of England: Cheshire. 2008. (ENG.). 192p. pap. 41.95 *(978-0-7524-4575-5(8))* History Pr. Ltd., The GBR. Dist: Independent Pubs. Group.

CHESHIRE (ENGLAND)—HISTORY

Browning, Beryl. Puritans & Nonconformist Ministers. 2008. 153p. pap. 24.50 *(978-1-4092-1955-2(0))* Lulu Enterprises Inc.

Wilkes, Sue. Regency Cheshire. 2010. (ENG., Illus.). 288p. 32.95 *(978-0-7090-8530-0(3))* Hale, Robert Ltd. GBR. Dist: Independent Pubs. Group.

CHESNUT, MARY BOYKIN MILLER, 1823-1886

Chesnut, Mary, et al. Mary Chesnut's Illustrated Diary, 2 vols., Set.Vol. 1. 2011. (ENG., Illus.). 848p. 75.00 *(978-1-58980-853-9(3))* Pelican Publishing Co., Inc.

Chesnut, Mary Boykin. Mary Chesnut's Diary. 2011. (ENG.). 384p. (gr. 12). 15.00 *(978-0-14-310606-7(6)*, Penguin Classics) Penguin Group (USA) Inc.

Chesnut, Mary Boykin Miller. A Diary from Dixie. 2010. 482p. pap. 37.75 *(978-1-143-11749-7(2))* BiblioBazaar.

—A Diary from Dixie. 2009. 302p. pap. *(978-1-150-64327-9(7))* Books LLC.

Chesnut, Mary Boykin Miller & Martin, Isabella D. A Diary from Dixie. 2010. 488p. pap. 38.75 *(978-1-145-75848-3(7))* BiblioBazaar.

Stern, Julia A. Mary Chesnut's Civil War Epic. 2010. (ENG., Illus.). 352p. 45.00 *(978-0-226-77328-5(0)*, Univ. of Chicago Pr.

CHESNUTT, CHARLES WADDELL, 1858-1932

Chesnutt, Charles W. The Conjure Stories. Stepto, Robert B. & Greeson, Jennifer Rae, eds. 2011. (Norton Critical Editions Ser.). (ENG., Illus.). 384p. (C). pap. 12.00 net. *(978-0-393-92780-1(6)*, 92780) Norton, W. W. & Co., Inc.

Chesnutt, Helen M. Charles Waddell Chesnutt: Pioneer of the Color Line. 2011. (ENG.). 334p. pap. 40.00 *(978-0-8078-9636-5(5))* Univ. of North Carolina Pr.

Izzo, David Garrett & Orban, Maria. Charles Chesnutt Reappraised: Essays on the First Major African American Fiction Writer. 2009. (ENG.). 246p. pap. 39.95 *(978-0-7864-4111-2(9))* McFarland & Co., Inc. Pubs.

Simmons, Ryan. Chesnutt & Realism: A Study of the Novels. 2nd ed. 2006. (Studies in American Literary Realism & Naturalism). (Illus.). 208p. 39.95 *(978-0-8173-1520-7(9))* Univ. of Alabama Pr.

Wilson, Matthew. Whiteness in the Novels of Charles W. Chesnutt. 2009. (ENG.). 256p. pap. 25.00 *(978-1-60473-248-1(2))* Univ. Pr. of Mississippi.

CHESS
see also Chessmen; Chinese Chess

Aagaard, Jacob. The Attacking Manual 2: Technique & Praxis. (Illus.). 320p. pap. 34.95 *(978-91-976004-1-5(5))* Quality Chess Europe SWE. Dist: SCB Distributors.

Adams, Weaver W. White to Play & Win. 2007. 170p. per. 14.95 *(978-0-923891-83-1(8))* Ishi Pr. International.

Ajedrez Super Facil.Tr. of Super Simple Chess. (SPA.). 8.98 *(978-968-403-437-2(7))* Selector, S.A. de C.V. MEX. Dist: AIMS International Bks., Inc.

Alberston, Bruce & Wilson, Fred. 212 Surprising Checkmates. 2011. (ENG.). 156p. pap. 9.95 *(978-1-936490-23-3(4))* Russell Enterprises, Inc.

Albertson, Bruce. 51 Chess Openings for Beginners. 2007. (ENG., Illus.). 176p. pap. 12.95 *(978-1-58042-212-3(8))* Cardoza Publishing.

Alburt, Lev & Lawrence, Al. Chess for the Gifted & Busy: A Short but Comprehensive Course from Beginner to Expert. 2011. (Comprehensive Chess Course Ser.). (ENG., Illus.). 304p. pap. 19.95 *(978-1-889323-24-4(1)*, 889324, Chess Information & Research Ctr.) Alburt, Lev.

Alburt, Lev & Pelts, Roman. Comprehensive Chess Course - Learn Chess in 12 Lessons. 5th ed. 2011. (Comprehensive Chess Course Ser.). (ENG., Illus.). 144p. pap. 16.95 *(978-1-889323-23-7(3)*, 889323, Chess Information & Research Ctr.) Alburt, Lev.

Alburt, Lev, et al. Pirc Alert! A Complete Defense Against 1. E4. 2nd rev. ed. 2009. (ENG., Illus.). 448p. pap. 34.95 *(978-1-889323-19-0(5)*, 889319, Chess Information & Research Ctr.) Alburt, Lev.

Alekhine, Alexander. New York 1927. 2011. (ENG.). 168p. pap. 19.95 *(978-1-888690-83-5(6))* Russell Enterprises, Inc.

Aplin, Nick & Karolyi, Tibor. Kasparov's Fighting Chess 1993-1998. 2006. (Batsford Chess Bks.). (ENG., Illus.). 304p. per. 22.95 *(978-0-7134-8994-1(4)*, Batsford, B. T. Ltd.) Anova Bks. GBR. Dist: Sterling Publishing Co., Inc.

Aramil, William. The Complete Idiot's Guide to Chess Openings. 2008. (Complete Idiot's Guide Ser.). (ENG.) 208p. (gr. 12-18). 12.95 *(978-1-59257-776-7(8)* Alpha Bks.) Penguin Group (USA) Inc.

Arrobal. Exitos y Fracasos en el Tablero (Success & Failures in the Chess Board) (SPA.). 198p. *(978-84-8019-339-9(5))* Paidotribo, Editorial S.L.

Ashley, Maurice. The Most Valuable Skills in Chess. 2009. (ENG., Illus.). 160p. pap. 17.95 *(978-1-904600-87-9(5))* Gambit Pubns., Ltd. GBR. Dist: Perseus Distribution.

Atherton, Michael. Cognitive Transfer in Chess Playing. 2009. 60p. pap. *(978-3-639-18796-0(2))* VDM Verlag Dr. Mueller e.K.

Avni, Amatzia. The Amazing Chess Adventures of Baron Munchausen. 2011. (ENG., Illus.). 200p. 21.95 *(978-1-936277-32-2(8))* Mongoose Pr.

Baofu, Peter. The Future of Post-Human Chess: A Preface to a New Theory of Tactics AndStrategy. 2011. 464p. 80.00 *(978-1-907343-18-6(0))* Cambridge International Science Publishing, Ltd. GBR. Dist: Ingram Pub. Services.

Bauer, Christian. Play the Scandinavian. 2010. (ENG.). 344p. pap. 29.95 *(978-1-906552-55-8(X))* Quality Chess Europe SWE. Dist: SCB Distributors.

Beim, Valeri. Back to Basics: Strategy. 2011. (Back to Basics Chess Ser.). (ENG.). 192p. pap. 22.95 *(978-1-888690-49-1(6))* Russell Enterprises, Inc.

Bird, David & Saunders, John. The Complete Step-by-Step Guide to Chess & Bridge: How to play, winning strategies, rules & History. 2010. (ENG., Illus.). 512p. 35.00 *(978-0-7548-2062-8(9))* Anness Publishing GBR. Dist: National Bk. Network.

Bogdanov, Valentin. The Grünfeld. 2009. (Chess Explained Ser.). (ENG., Illus.). 127p. pap. 24.95 *(978-1-906454-06-7(X))* Gambit Pubns., Ltd. GBR. Dist: Perseus Distribution.

—Play the Alekhine. 2010. (ENG., Illus.). 112p. pap. 19.95 *(978-1-906454-15-9(9))* Gambit Pubns., Ltd. GBR. Dist: Perseus Distribution.

Bojkov, Dejan & Georgiev, Vladimir. A Course in Chess Tactics. 2010. (ENG., Illus.). 160p. pap. 22.95 *(978-1-906454-14-2(0))* Gambit Pubns., Ltd. GBR. Dist: Perseus Distribution.

Bologan, Victor. Chebanenko Slav Accord Bologan. 2008. (ENG., Illus.). 240p. pap. 29.95 *(978-90-5691-246-8(1)*, New In Chess,Csi) Continental Sales, Inc.

Borders, Mark. The Self-Improvement of Chess. 2007. 216p. pap. 19.95 *(978-1-4303-2764-6(2))* Lulu Enterprises Inc.

Boris, Gulko & Joel. Lessons with A Grandmaster. 2011. (ENG.). 298p. pap. 27.95 *(978-1-85744-668-5(2))* Everyman Chess GBR. Dist: Globe Pequot Pr., The.

Bosch, Jeroen. The Chess Combat Simulator: Test & Improve Your Chess with 50 Instructive Grandmaster Games. 2006. (ENG., Illus.). 272p. per. 24.95 *(978-90-5691-186-7(4)*, New In Chess,Csi) Continental Sales, Inc.

Bronstein, David & Fürstenberg, Tom. The Sorcerer's Apprentice. 2009. (ENG.). 384p. pap. 34.95 *(978-90-5691-272-7(0)*, New In Chess,Csi) Continental Sales, Inc.

Brunthaler, Heinz. Chess for Kids & Parents: From the Start till the First Tournament. 2006. (Illus.). 205p. per. 11.95 *(978-91-976004-5-3(8))* Quality Chess Europe SWE. Dist: SCB Distributors.

Burgess, Graham & Nunn, John, eds. The Mammoth Book of Chess. 2010. (ENG.). 560p. pap. 13.95 *(978-0-7624-3726-9(X))* Running Pr. Bk. Pubs.

Byfield, Brian. Learn Chess in 10 Minutes. 2011. (ENG., Illus.). 64p. 9.95 *(978-1-84994-015-3(0)*, Batsford, B. T. Ltd.) Anova Bks. GBR. Dist: Sterling Publishing Co., Inc.

Byfield, Brian & Orpin, Alan. Learn Chess Quick: How to Play the World's Greatest Board Game, & Win. 2010. (ENG., Illus.). 144p. (gr. 8). pap. 14.95 *(978-1-906388-66-9(0)*, Batsford, B. T. Ltd.) Anova Bks. GBR. Dist: Sterling Publishing Co., Inc.

Capablanca, Jose R. Chess Fundamentals. 256p. 2010. pap. 22.36 *(978-1-163-15857-9(7))* 2008. 42.95 *(978-1-4366-9127-7(3))* 2007. (ENG.). per. 27.95 *(978-1-4325-6864-1(7))* Kessinger Publishing, LLC.

Caxton, William. Game & Playe of the Chesse: A Verbatim Reprint of the First Edition 1474. 2007. (ENG.). 180p. pap. 19.99 *(978-1-4264-4276-6(9))*; 198p. pap. 21.99 *(978-1-4264-4340-4(4))* BiblioBazaar.

Charushin, Victor. The Steeplechase Vol. 5: The Tactitian's Handbook. (Illus.). 128p. pap. 15.95 *(978-1-886846-15-9(4))* Pickard & Son Publishing.

Cheng, Ray. Practical Chess Exercises: 600 Lessons from Tactics to Strategy. 2007. 216p. per. 17.95 *(978-1-58736-801-1(3))* Wheatmark.

Chess & Education: Selected Essays from the Koltanowski Conference. 2006. pap. 25.00 *(978-0-9786742-0-5(0))* Univ. of Texas at Dallas Chess Program, The.

Cluley, William. The Philosophy of Chess. 2007. (ENG.). 114p. 34.95 *(978-0-548-15286-7(1))*; pap. 19.95 *(978-1-4304-4663-7(3))* Kessinger Publishing, LLC.

Collins, Sam. Gambit Busters: Take It, Keep It, & Win! 2011. (ENG.). 208p. pap. 26.95 *(978-1-85744-642-5(9))* Everyman Chess GBR. Dist: Globe Pequot Pr., The.

Craig, Pritchett. Chess Secrets? Giants of Innovation. 2011. (ENG.). 288p. pap. 27.95 *(978-1-85744-671-5(2))* Everyman Chess GBR. Dist: Globe Pequot Pr., The.

Crouch, Colin. The Great Attackers: Learn from Kasparov, Tal & Stein. 2009. (ENG., Illus.). 272p. pap. 26.95 *(978-1-85744-579-4(1))* Everyman Chess GBR. Dist: Globe Pequot Pr., The.

—How to Defend in Chess: Learn from the World Champions. 2007. (ENG., Illus.). 224p. per. 24.95 *(978-1-904600-83-1(2))* Gambit Pubns., Ltd. GBR. Dist: Perseus Distribution.

—Modern Chess - Move by Move: A Step-by-Step Guide to Brilliant Chess. 2009. (ENG., Illus.). 414p. pap. 29.95 *(978-1-85744-599-2(6))* Everyman Chess GBR. Dist: Globe Pequot Pr., The.

Davies, Nigel. The Rules of Winning Chess. 2009. (ENG., Illus.). 192p. pap. 26.95 *(978-1-85744-596-1(1))* Everyman Chess GBR. Dist: Globe Pequot Pr., The.

de Groot, Adriaan D. Thought & Choice in Chess. 2008. (Amsterdam Academic Archive Ser.). (ENG.). 484p. pap. *(978-90-5356-998-6(7))* Amsterdam Univ. Pr.

Dean, George & Brady, Maxine. Chess Masterpieces: One Thousand Years of Extraordinary Chess Sets. 2010. (ENG., Illus.). 272p. 65.00 *(978-0-8109-4923-2(7))* Abrams.

del Rosario, Frisco. Capablanca: A Primer of Checkmate. 2010. (ENG., Illus.). 176p. pap. 19.95 *(978-1-936277-02-5(6))* Mongoose Pr.

Denker, Arnold & Parr, Larry. The Bobby Fischer I Knew & Other Stories. 2008. (ENG., Illus.). 366p. (Orig.). pap. 25.95 *(978-0-923891-43-5(9))* Ishi Pr. International.

Desjarlais, Robert R. Counterplay: An Anthropologist at the Chessboard. (ENG., Illus.). 2012. 266p. pap. 19.95 *(978-0-520-27260-6(9))* 2011. 276p. 50.00 *(978-0-520-26739-8(7))* Univ. of California Pr.

Dvoretsky, Mark. Dvoretsky's Analytical Manual: Practical Training for the Ambitious Chessplayer. 2008. (ENG.). 400p. pap. 34.95 *(978-1-888690-47-7(X))* Russell Enterprises, Inc.

—Tragicomedy in the Endgame: Instructive Mistakes of the Masters. 2011. (ENG.). 288p. pap. 29.95 *(978-1-936490-04-2(8))* Russell Enterprises, Inc.

Dvoretsky, Mark & Yusupov, Artur. Secrets of Creative Thinking: School of Future Champions 5. 2009. (Progress in Chess Ser.). (ENG.). 206p. pap. 39.95 *(978-3-283-00519-1(2))* Edition Olms DEU. Dist: Independent Pubs. Group.

—Secrets of Endgame Technique. 2007. (Dvoretsky School of Future Chess Champions Ser.). (ENG.). 200p. pap. 39.95 *(978-3-283-00517-7(6))* Edition Olms DEU. Dist: Independent Pubs. Group.

—Secrets of Opening Preparation Vol. 2: School of Future Champions 2. Neat, Ken, ed. 2007. (Dvoretsky School of Future Chess Champions Ser.). (ENG., Illus.). 220p. per. 39.95 *(978-3-283-00516-0(8))* Edition Olms DEU. Dist: Independent Pubs. Group.

—Secrets of Positional Play. 2009. (Progress in Chess Ser.). (ENG.). 240p. pap. 39.95 *(978-3-283-00518-4(4))* Edition Olms DEU. Dist: Independent Pubs. Group.

Eade, James. Chess. 3rd ed. 2011. (ENG.). 384p. pap. 22.99 *(978-1-118-01695-4(5)*, For Dummies) Wiley, John & Sons, Inc.

C

Edwards, Jon. Sacking the Citadel: The History, Theory & Practice of the Classic Bishop Sacrifice. 2011. (ENG.). 400p. pap. 24.95 *(978-1-888690-74-3(7))* Russell Enterprises, Inc.

—Teach Yourself Visually Chess. 2006. (ENG., Illus.). 304p. per. 24.99 *(978-0-470-04983-9(9),* Visual) Wiley, John & Sons, Inc.

Eingorn, Viacheslav & Bogdanov, Valentin. French. Giddins, Steve, tr. 2008. (Chess Explained Ser.). (ENG., Illus.). 124p. pap. 23.95 *(978-1-904600-95-4(6))* Gambit Pubns., Ltd. GBR. Dist: Perseus Distribution.

Emms, John. The Survival Guide to Competitive Chess: Improve Your Results Now! 2007. (ENG., Illus.). 192p. per. 24.95 *(978-1-85744-412-4(4))* Everyman Chess GBR. Dist: Globe Pequot Pr., The.

Emms, John, et al. Dangerous Weapons: Anti-Sicilians. 2009. (ENG., Illus.). 192p. pap. 24.95 *(978-1-85744-585-5(6))* Everyman Chess GBR. Dist: Globe Pequot Pr., The.

Euwe, Max. Judgment & Planning in Chess. 2011. (Illus.). 200p. pap. 19.95 ***(978-4-87187-471-7(0))*** Ishi Pr. International.

Euwe, Max, et al. The Logical Approach to Chess. 2011. (Illus.). 228p. pap. 25.95 ***(978-4-87187-472-4(9))*** Ishi Pr. International.

Evans, Larry. New Ideas in Chess. 2011. (ENG.). 200p. pap. 14.95 *(978-1-58042-274-1(8))* Cardoza Publishing.

—This Crazy World of Chess. 2009. (ENG.). 320p. pap. 12.95 *(978-1-58042-237-6(3))* Cardoza Publishing.

—10 Most Common Chess Mistakes. 2011. (ENG.). 256p. pap. 14.95 *(978-1-58042-269-5(6))* Cardoza Publishing.

Fabrego, Lluis Comas. True Lies in Chess. Carballo, Manuel Perez, tr. 2007. (Illus.). 160p. per. 29.99 *(978-91-976005-7-6(1))* Quality Chess Europe SWE. Dist: SCB Distributors.

Fadul, Jose A. Lessons in Chess, Lessons in Life. 2008. 139p. pap. 54.95 *(978-0-557-02158-1(8))* Lulu Enterprises Inc.

—More Lessons in Chess & in Life. 2009. 161p. pap. 52.50 *(978-0-557-04967-7(9))* Lulu Enterprises Inc.

Fadul, Jose A. & Canlas, Reynaldo Nuelito Q. Chess Therapy. 2009. 112p. pap. 39.95 *(978-0-557-07630-7(7))* Lulu Enterprises Inc.

—Chess Therapy (2nd Edition) 2010. 110p. 32.50 *(978-0-557-28578-5(X))* Lulu Enterprises Inc.

Fadul, Jose A. & Canlas, Reynaldo Q. Chess Therapy. 2009. 114p. 32.50 *(978-0-557-14875-2(8))*; (ENG.). 92p. pap. 16.68 *(978-0-557-08693-1(0))* Lulu Enterprises Inc.

Fine, Reuben. Chess the Easy Way. 2009. (ENG., Illus.). 200p. pap. 25.95 *(978-0-923891-50-3(1))* Ishi Pr. International.

—The Psychology of the Chess Player. 2009. (ENG., Illus.). 102p. pap. 16.95 *(978-4-87187-815-9(5))* Ishi Pr. International.

Fischer, Bobby, et al. Bobby Fischer Teaches Chess. 2010. (Illus.). 356p. pap. *(978-0-923891-60-2(9))* Ishi Pr. International.

Flear, Glenn. Tactimania. 2011. (ENG., Illus.). 248p. pap. 27.95 ***(978-1-906552-98-5(3))*** Quality Chess Europe SWE. Dist: SCB Distributors.

Franco, Zenon. Counter-Attack! 2009. (ENG., Illus.). 224p. pap. 14.95 *(978-1-906454-09-8(4))* Gambit Pubns., Ltd. GBR. Dist: Perseus Distribution.

Francuski, Branislav. Back to Basics: Fundamentals. 2008. (ChessCafe Back to Basics Chess Ser.). (ENG.). 192p. pap. 22.95 *(978-1-888690-42-2(9))* Russell Enterprises, Inc.

Fredericks, Mariah. Neurotic Girl's Guide, No. 2. Date not set. *(978-0-312-32355-4(7))* St. Martin's Pr.

French, Peter. The Little Book of Chess Tips. 2007. (Little Book Ser.). (ENG.). 112p. pap. 4.95 *(978-1-904573-68-5(1))* Absolute Pr. GBR. Dist: Independent Pubs. Group.

Ftacnik, Lubomir. Grandmaster Repertoire 6: The Sicilian Defence. 2010. (Illus.). 320p. 34.95 *(978-1-906552-08-4(8))* Quality Chess UK LLP GBR. Dist: SCB Distributors.

Gaprindashvili, Paata. Critical Moments in Chess. 2010. (ENG., Illus.). 272p. pap. 22.95 *(978-1-906388-65-2(2),* Batsford, B. T. Ltd.) Anova Bks. GBR. Dist: Sterling Publishing Co., Inc.

Georgiev, Kiril & Kolev, Atanas. The Sharpest Sicilian. 2007. pap. *(978-954-8782-56-2(1))* Chess Stars.

Gershon, Alik & Nor, Igor. San Luis 2005. 2007. (ENG., Illus.). 442p. pap. 29.95 *(978-91-976005-2-1(0))* Quality Chess Europe SWE. Dist: SCB Distributors.

Geuzendam, Dirk Jan ten & Timman, Jan, eds. New in Chess Magazine 2011/2. 2011. 106p. pap. 12.75 ***(978-90-5691-348-9(4),*** New In Chess,Csi) Continental Sales, Inc.

—New in Chess Magazine 2011/3. 2011. (ENG.). 106p. pap. 12.75 ***(978-90-5691-349-6(2),*** New In Chess,Csi) Continental Sales, Inc.

—New In Chess, the magazine 2011 #5. 5th ed. 2011. (ENG.). 106p. pap. 12.75 ***(978-90-5691-351-9(4),*** New In Chess,Csi) Continental Sales, Inc.

—New In Chess, the magazine 2011 #6. 6th ed. 2011. (ENG.). 106p. pap. 12.75 ***(978-90-5691-352-6(2),*** New In Chess,Csi) Continental Sales, Inc.

Geuzendam, Ten. New in Chess, Magazine. Timman, ed. 2007. (ENG.). 96p. pap. 11.50 *(978-90-5691-209-3(7))*; pap. 11.50 *(978-90-5691-208-6(9))*; pap. 11.50 *(978-90-5691-199-7(6))*; pap. 11.50 *(978-90-5691-198-0(8))*; pap. 11.50 *(978-90-5691-197-3(X))* Continental Sales, Inc. (New In Chess,Csi).

Giddins, Steve. 101 Chess Questions Answered. 2008. (ENG., Illus.). 127p. pap. 14.95 *(978-1-906454-00-5(0))* Gambit Pubns., Ltd. GBR. Dist: Perseus Distribution.

Giddins, Steve & Bosch, Jeroen. Chess Instructor 2009. 2008. (ENG.). 230p. pap. 26.95 *(978-90-5691-247-5(X),* New In Chess,Csi) Continental Sales, Inc.

Girona, Pablo Castro & Castro Girona, Pablo. Iniciacion al Ajedrez para Ninos.Tr. of Introduction to Chess for Children. (SPA.). 288p. 12.95 *(978-84-8019-317-7(4))* Paidotribo, Editorial S.L. ESP. Dist: Libros Sin Fronteras.

Goldowsky, Howard. Engaging Pieces: Interviews & Prose for the Chess Fan. 2007. 240p. per. 20.95 *(978-0-9790488-2-1(6))* Daowood & Brighton.

Gormally, Daniel. Calculate Like a Grandmaster: Learn from the World-Class Attacking Players. 2010. (ENG., Illus.). 288p. pap. 19.95 *(978-1-906388-69-0(5),* Batsford, B. T. Ltd.) Anova Bks. GBR. Dist: Sterling Publishing Co., Inc.

Gormally, Danny. Play Chess Like the Pros. 2010. (ENG., Illus.). 288p. pap. 26.95 *(978-1-85744-627-2(5))* Everyman Chess GBR. Dist: Globe Pequot Pr., The.

Gray, Daniel & Lawrence, Al. Knack Chess for Everyone: A Step-by-Step Guide to Rules, Moves & Winning Strategies. 2010. (Knack: Make It Easy Ser.). (ENG., Illus.). 256p. pap. 19.95 *(978-1-59921-510-5(1),* Knack) Globe Pequot Pr., The.

Grivas, Efstratios. Modern Chess Planning: A Practical Training Course in Logical Chess. 2007. (ENG., Illus.). 143p. per. 14.95 *(978-1-904600-68-8(9))* Gambit Pubns., Ltd. GBR. Dist: Perseus Distribution.

Grooten, Herman. Chess Strategy for Club Players: The Road to Positional Advantage. 2009. (ENG.). 400p. pap. 29.95 *(978-90-5691-268-0(2),* New In Chess,Csi) Continental Sales, Inc.

Gulko, Boris, et al. The KGB Plays Chess: The Soviet Secret Police & the Fight for the World Chess Crown. 2010. (ENG.). 192p. pap. 19.95 *(978-1-888690-75-0(5))* Russell Enterprises, Inc.

Hale, Benjamin, ed. Philosophy Looks at Chess. 2008. (ENG.). 288p. pap. 28.00 *(978-0-8126-9633-2(6))* Open Court Publishing Co.

Hanauer, Milton L. Chess Made Simple. 2009. (ENG., Illus.). 192p. pap. 24.95 *(978-0-923891-26-8(9))* Ishi Pr. International.

Hansen, Lars Bo. Improve Your Chess - By Learning from the Champions. 2009. (ENG., Illus.). 192p. pap. 24.95 *(978-1-906454-12-8(4))* Gambit Pubns., Ltd. GBR. Dist: Perseus Distribution.

Harkness, Kenneth. Blue Book & Encyclopedia of Chess. 2008. (Illus.). 350p. per. 24.95 net. *(978-0-923891-92-3(7))* Ishi Pr. International.

Harkness, Kenneth & Chernev, Irving. An Invitation to Chess. 2008. (Illus.). 200p. per. 17.95 *(978-0-923891-93-0(5))* Ishi Pr. International.

Hartson, William. Improve Your Chess. 2011. (Teach Yourself Ser.). (ENG., Illus.). 166p. pap. 15.95 *(978-1-4441-0308-3(3),* Hodder & Stoughton) Hodder General Publishing Div. GBR. Dist: Independent Pubs. Group.

—Teach Yourself Better Chess. 3rd rev. ed. 2007. (Teach Yourself: Games/Hobbies/Sports Ser.). (ENG., Illus.). 176p. per. 10.95 *(978-0-07-154872-4(6),* 0071548726) McGraw-Hill Cos., The.

Hartston, William. Win at Chess. 2011. (Teach Yourself: Reference Ser.). (ENG.). 240p. pap. 15.00 *(978-0-07-175476-7(8),* 0071754768) McGraw-Hill Cos., The.

Healy, John. Coffee House Chess Tactics. 2010. (ENG.). 128p. pap. 17.95 *(978-90-5691-328-1(X),* New In Chess,Csi) Continental Sales, Inc.

Hearst, Eliot & Knott, John. Blindfold Chess: History, Psychology, Techniques, Champions, World Records, & Important Games. 2008. (ENG., Illus.). 445p. 65.00 *(978-0-7864-3444-2(9))* McFarland & Co., Inc. Pubs.

Heisman, Dan. Back to Basics: Tactics. 2010. (ChessCafe Back to Basics Chess Ser.). (Illus.). 192p. pap. 21.95 *(978-1-888690-33-0(X))* Russell Enterprises, Inc.

—The Improving Annotator: From Beginner to Master. rev. exp. ed. 2011. 192p. pap. 19.95 *(978-1-936277-04-9(2))* Mongoose Pr.

Heisman, Dan & Müller, Karsten. Test & Improve Your Defensive Skill!, Bk. 3. 2007. (ChessCafe Back to Basics Chess Ser.). (ENG.). 192p. pap. 22.95 *(978-1-888690-34-7(8))* Russell Enterprises, Inc.

Herron, John. Total Chess: Learn, Teach & Play the Easy 1-2-3 Way. 2011. (ENG., Illus.). 389p. (J). per. 19.95 *(978-0-9798366-2-6(X))* HairBall Publishing.

Hertan, Charles. Forcing Chess Moves: The Key to Better Calculation. 2008. (ENG., Illus.). 320p. pap. 28.95 *(978-90-5691-243-7(7),* New In Chess,Csi) Continental Sales, Inc.

Horowitz, I. A. Solitaire Chess. 2009. (ENG., Illus.). 164p. pap. 19.95 *(978-4-87187-823-4(6))* Ishi Pr. International.

Horowitz, I. A. & Reinfeld, Fred. First Book of Chess. 2009. 134p. 35.95 *(978-1-104-84024-2(3))* 2007. (ENG.). 132p. per. 20.95 *(978-0-548-45035-2(8))* Kessinger Publishing, LLC.

Hortilosa, Andres D. Improve Your Chess at Any Age. 2010. (ENG., Illus.). 192p. pap. 26.95 *(978-1-85744-618-0(6))* Everyman Chess GBR. Dist: Globe Pequot Pr., The.

Hudson, Orrin C. One Move at a Time: How to Play & Win at Chess & Life! 2007. (Illus.). 226p. per. 14.95 *(978-1-933174-95-2(1))* 10 Finger Pr.

Ives, Rob & Black, Kell. Paper Chess: Create Your Own Chess Set with a Detachable Board & 2 Full Sets of Punch-Out Pieces. 2009. (ENG.). 80p. pap. 19.95 *(978-0-7624-3744-3(8))* Running Pr. Bk. Pubs.

Jacobus & Adams, Jenny. The Game & Playe of the Chesse. 2008. *(978-1-58044-130-8(0))* Medieval Institute Pubns.

Jacobus de Cessolis. The Book of Chess. 2008.Tr. of Liber de moribus hominum et officiis Nobilium. (ENG., Illus.). 148p. pap. 20.00 *(978-1-59910-010-4(X))* Italica Pr.

Karpov, Anatoly. How to Play the English Opening. 2007. (Batsford Chess Bks.). (ENG., Illus.). 144p. per. 21.95 *(978-0-7134-9065-7(9),* Batsford, B. T. Ltd.) Anova Bks. GBR. Dist: Sterling Publishing Co., Inc.

Karpov, Anatoly & Mazukevich, Anatoly. Find the Right Plan with Anatoly Karpov. 2010. (ENG., Illus.). 256p. pap. 22.95 *(978-1-906388-68-3(7),* Batsford, B. T. Ltd.) Anova Bks. GBR. Dist: Sterling Publishing Co., Inc.

Karpov, Anatoly, et al. Chess & the Art of Negotiation: Ancient Rules for Modern Combat, 1 vol. 2006. 128p. 34.95 *(978-0-275-99065-7(6),* C9065, Praeger Pubs.) Greenwood Publishing Group, Inc.

Kasparov, Garry. Checkmate Tactics. 2010. (Illus.). 96p. pap. 16.95 *(978-1-85744-626-5(7))* Everyman Chess GBR. Dist: Globe Pequot Pr., The.

—Garry Kasparov on Modern Chess Pt. 2: Kasparov vs Karpov 1975-1985, 4 vols. 2008. (ENG., Illus.). 350p. 45.00 *(978-1-85744-433-9(7))* Everyman Chess GBR. Dist: Globe Pequot Pr., The.

—How Life Imitates Chess: Making the Right Moves, from the Board to the Boardroom. 2008. (ENG., Illus.). 240p. pap. 16.00 *(978-1-59691-388-2(6))* Bloomsbury Publishing.

—Revolution in the 70's, Part One: Garry Kasparov on Modern Chess, 4 vols. 2007. (Everyman Chess Ser.). (ENG., Illus.). 416p. 45.00 *(978-1-85744-422-3(1))* Everyman Chess GBR. Dist: Globe Pequot Pr., The.

Katz, Rosalyn. Start Playing Chess Today! 2011. (ENG.). 96p. pap. 8.95 *(978-1-58042-286-4(1))* Cardoza Publishing.

Katz, Rosalyn B. & Katz, David Lawrence. Play Better Chess Today! 2011. (ENG.). 96p. pap. 8.95 *(978-1-58042-287-1(X))* Cardoza Publishing.

Keene, Ray & Simpole, Julian. Petrosian vs the Elite: 71 Victories by the Master of Manoeuvre 1946-1983. 2007. (Illus.). 299p. per. 21.95 *(978-0-7134-9049-7(7),* Batsford, B. T. Ltd.) Anova Bks. GBR. Dist: Sterling Publishing Co., Inc.

Keene, Raymond D. Chessman Quarterly - 1968. 2007. pap. *(978-1-84382-155-7(9))* Hardinge Simpole Publishing.

—Chessman Quarterly - 1969. 2007. pap. *(978-1-84382-156-4(7))* Hardinge Simpole Publishing.

—Grandmaster Tactics. 2008. (Illus.). 388p. per. *(978-1-84382-188-5(5))* Hardinge Simpole Publishing.

Khenkin, Victor. 1000 Checkmate Combinations. 2011. (ENG.). 352p. pap. 21.95 *(978-1-906388-70-6(9),* Batsford, B. T. Ltd.) Anova Bks. GBR. Dist: Sterling Publishing Co., Inc.

Khmelnitsky, Igor. Chess Exam & Training Guide: Rate Yourself & Learn How to Improve! 2007. (Chess Exams Ser.). (ENG.). 208p. per. 19.95 *(978-0-9754761-1-6(4))* IamCoach.com Publishing.

Kitsis, Aleksandr. Chess, Step by Step: From Beginner to Champion. 2009. 148p. pap. 21.98 *(978-0-557-13168-6(5))* Lulu Enterprises Inc.

Koltanowski, George & Finkelstein, Milton. Chess Enterprises Strategies. (Illus.). 182p. pap. 8.95 *(978-0-945470-78-6(9))* Chess Enterprises.

Konikowski, Jerzy & Soszynski, Marek. The Fearsome Four Pawns Attack. 2006. (Illus.). 283p. per. 24.95 *(978-1-888690-27-9(5))* Russell Enterprises, Inc.

Kotronias, Vassilios. The Grandmaster Battle Manual. 2011. (ENG., Illus.). 352p. pap. 34.95 *(978-1-906552-52-7(5))* Quality Chess Europe SWE. Dist: SCB Distributors.

Lamprecht, Frank & Muller, Karsten. Secrets of Pawn Endings. Becker, Marc, tr. 2008. (ENG., Illus.). 287p. per. 29.95 *(978-1-904600-88-6(3))* Gambit Pubns., Ltd. GBR. Dist: Perseus Distribution.

Lane, Gary. The Greatest Ever Chess Tricks & Traps. 2008. (ENG.). 192p. pap. 24.95 *(978-1-85744-577-0(5))* Everyman Chess GBR. Dist: Globe Pequot Pr., The.

—Guia para el Jugador de Ataque (Guide for the Attack Player) (SPA.). 156p. *(978-84-8019-382-5(4))* Paidotribo, Editorial S.L.

—Improve Your Chess in 7 Days. 2007. (ENG., Illus.). 160p. per. 17.95 *(978-0-7134-9050-3(0),* Batsford, B. T. Ltd.) Anova Bks. GBR. Dist: Sterling Publishing Co., Inc.

—Sharpen Your Chess Tactics in 7 Days. 2009. (ENG., Illus.). 224p. pap. 17.95 *(978-1-906388-28-7(8),* Batsford, B. T. Ltd.) Anova Bks. GBR. Dist: Sterling Publishing Co., Inc.

Lasker. Common Sense in Chess. pap. 3.95 *(978-0-679-14006-1(9))* Fodor's Travel Pubns.

Lasker, Edward. Chess Strategy. 2010. 244p. pap. 8.99 *(978-1-4209-3451-9(1))* Digireads.com.

—Chess Strategy. 2010. (Illus.). 200p. pap. 28.39 *(978-1-153-59524-7(9))* General Bks. LLC.

Lasker, Emanuel. Common Sense in Chess. 2010. (ENG.). 144p. pap. 21.75 *(978-1-171-65196-3(1))* BiblioBazaar.

—Common Sense in Chess. Alberston, Bruce, ed. 2008. (Illus.). 127p. per. 19.95 *(978-1-888690-40-8(2))* Russell Enterprises, Inc.

—Lasker's Manual of Chess. 2009. (ENG.). 350p. pap. 29.95 *(978-1-888690-50-7(X))* Russell Enterprises, Inc.

—St. Petersburg 1909: The Famous Tournament Book by the Second World Chess Champion. 2008. 192p. pap. 19.95 *(978-1-888690-46-0(1))* Russell Enterprises, Inc.

Levens, David. Basic Chess. 2007. (ENG., Illus.). 144p. per. 9.95 *(978-0-600-60804-2(2),* Hamlyn) Octopus Publishing Group GBR. Dist: Hachette Bk. Group.

Levitt, Jonathan & Friedgood, David. Secrets of Spectacular Chess. 2nd ed. 2008. (ENG., Illus.). 192p. pap. 24.95 *(978-1-85744-551-0(1))* Everyman Chess GBR. Dist: Globe Pequot Pr., The.

Lipnitsky, Isaac. Questions of Modern Chess Theory: A Soviet Classic. 2008. (ENG.). 250p. pap. 29.95 *(978-1-906552-03-9(7))* Quality Chess Europe SWE. Dist: SCB Distributors.

Loheac-Ammoun, Frank & Lohéac-Ammoun, Frank. Compruebe Su Nivel de Ajedrez (Prove Your Chess Level) (SPA.). 312p. *(978-84-8019-241-5(0))* Paidotribo, Editorial S.L.

Long, Sara. Chess Crymz & Other Business. Date not set. *(978-0-938650-90-4(4))* Thinkers' Pr., Inc.

Magner, James. Chess Juggler: Balancing Career, Family & Chess in the Modern World. 2011. (ENG.). 176p. pap. 19.95 ***(978-1-936490-12-7(9))*** Russell Enterprises, Inc.

Marin, Mihail. Beating the Open Games. 2nd ed. 2007. (Illus.). 288p. per. 34.95 *(978-91-976004-3-9(1))* Quality Chess Europe SWE. Dist: SCB Distributors.

Marin, Mihail & Garrett, Yuri. Reggio Emilia 2007/2008. 2009. 208p. pap. 29.95 *(978-1-906552-32-9(0))* Quality Chess Europe SWE. Dist: SCB Distributors.

McDonald, Neil. Chess Success: Planning after the Opening. 2008. (Batsford Chess Bks.). (ENG., Illus.). 256p. per. 21.95 *(978-0-7134-9071-8(3),* Batsford, B. T. Ltd.) Anova Bks. GBR. Dist: Sterling Publishing Co., Inc.

Mednis, Edmar. Como Convertirse en un Autentico Jugador de Auedrez (How to Become a True Chess Player) (SPA.). 138p. *(978-84-8019-384-9(0))* Paidotribo, Editorial S.L.

Mitchell, David A. David a Mitchell's Checkers. 2011. 188p. pap. 11.95 ***(978-1-61646-088-4(1))*** Coachwhip Pubns.

Moise, Frantzley. Chess 4 Life: Life 4 Chess. 2011. 44p. 21.00 *(978-1-4520-9665-0(1))* AuthorHouse.

More, Ramon Crusi & Crusi More, Ramón. Ataques Contra Enroque (Attacks Against Castling) (SPA.). 164p. *(978-84-8019-245-3(3))* Paidotribo, Editorial S.L.

Moskalenko, Viktor. The Fabulous Budapest Gambit: Much More Than Just a Sharp Surprise Weapon. 2008. (ENG., Illus.). 244p. per. 24.95 *(978-90-5691-224-6(0),* New In Chess,Csi) Continental Sales, Inc.

—Flexible French. 2008. (ENG., Illus.). 230p. pap. 24.95 *(978-90-5691-245-1(3),* New In Chess,Csi) Continental Sales, Inc.

—Revolutionize Your Chess: A Brand New System to Become a Better Player. 2010. (ENG.). 352p. pap. 29.95 *(978-90-5691-295-6(X),* New In Chess,Csi) Continental Sales, Inc.

Narula, Gautam Rajhar. The Novice Chess Players Manual: A Step-by-Step Guide & Workbook for the Budding Chess Player. 2nd ltd. ed. 2006. per. 14.95 *(978-0-9776659-0-7(9))* Kavita Media LLC.

Neiman, Emmanuel & Afek, Yochanan. Invisible Chess Moves: Discover Your Blind Spots & Stop. 2011. (ENG.). 224p. pap. 23.95 *(978-90-5691-368-7(9),* New In Chess,Csi) Continental Sales, Inc.

Neishstadt, Jakov. Improve Your Chess Tactics: 700 Practical Lessons & Exercises. 2011. (ENG.). 384p. pap. 19.95 *(978-90-5691-334-2(4),* New In Chess,Csi) Continental Sales, Inc.

New In Chess. New in Chess Magazine 2011/4. 2011. (ENG.). 100p. pap. 12.75 ***(978-90-5691-350-2(6),*** New In Chess,Csi) Continental Sales, Inc.

—New in Chess V20065. 2006. (ENG.). 96p. pap. 9.95 *(978-90-5691-179-9(1),* New In Chess,Csi) Continental Sales, Inc.

—New in Chess V20066. 2006. (ENG.). 96p. pap. 11.50 *(978-90-5691-183-6(X),* New In Chess,Csi) Continental Sales, Inc.

—New in Chess V20067. 2006. (ENG.). 96p. pap. 11.50 *(978-90-5691-181-2(3),* New In Chess,Csi) Continental Sales, Inc.

—New in Chess V20068. 2006. (ENG.). 96p. pap. 11.50 *(978-90-5691-182-9(1),* New In Chess,Csi) Continental Sales, Inc.

—New in Chess Yearbook 98: The Chess Player's Guide to Opening News. 2011. (ENG.). 250p. 38.95 ***(978-90-5691-338-0(7))***; pap. 29.95 ***(978-90-5691-337-3(9))*** Continental Sales, Inc. (New In Chess,Csi).

—New in Chess Yearbook 99: The Chess Player's Guide to Opening News. 2011. 250p. (ENG.). 38.95 ***(978-90-5691-357-1(3))***; pap. 29.95 ***(978-90-5691-356-4(5))*** Continental Sales, Inc. (New In Chess,Csi).

New In Chess, ed. New in Chess Magazine 2011 / 1. 2011. 105p. pap. 12.75 *(978-90-5691-347-2(6),* New In Chess,Csi) Continental Sales, Inc.

Nimzowitsch, Aaron. My System: A Chess Manual on Totally New Principles. 2007. (Chess Classics Ser.). (Illus.). 316p. per. 29.95 *(978-91-976005-3-8(9))* Quality Chess Europe SWE. Dist: SCB Distributors.

Nimzowitsch, Aron. Blockade Die Blockade. 2006. (Illus.). 155p. pap. *(978-1-84382-182-3(6))* Hardinge Simpole Publishing.

Nunn, John. Secrets of Practical Chess. 2nd enl. rev. ed. 2007. (ENG., Illus.). 254p. per. 24.95 *(978-1-904600-70-1(0))* Gambit Pubns., Ltd. GBR. Dist: Perseus Distribution.

—Winning Quickly at Chess. 2008. (Grandmaster Secrets Ser.). (ENG., Illus.). 255p. per. 14.95 *(978-1-904600-89-3(1))* Gambit Pubns., Ltd. GBR. Dist: Perseus Distribution.

Panamericana Staff. Ajedrez (Chess) (SPA.). 5.95 *(978-958-30-0042-3(6))* Panamericana Editorial COL. Dist: AIMS International Bks., Inc.

Pandolfini, Bruce. Chess Movies 1: Quick Tricks. 2010. (Pandolfini Chess Library). (ENG.). 192p. pap. 19.95 *(978-1-888690-72-9(0))* Russell Enterprises, Inc.

—Chess Movies 2: The Means & Ends. 2011. (Pandolfini Chess Library). (ENG.). 192p. pap. 19.95 *(978-1-888690-73-6(9))* Russell Enterprises, Inc.

—Let's Play Chess: A Step by Step Guide for New Players. 2nd rev. ed. 2008. (Pandolfini Chess Library). (ENG.). 224p. pap. 19.95 *(978-1-888690-52-1(6))* Russell Enterprises, Inc.

Pfleger, Helmut. Taktik und Witz Im Schach. (Praxis Schach Ser.: Bd. 8). (GER.). 182p. *(978-3-283-00252-7(5))* Olms, Georg Verlag AG.

Pinski, Jan. King's Gambit. 2007. (Illus.). 256p. pap. 29.95 *(978-91-976004-9-1(0))* Quality Chess Europe SWE. Dist: SCB Distributors.

Polugaevsky, Lev. Grandmaster Preparation. 2011.Tr. of Rozhdeniye Varianta. (Illus.). 258p. pap. 25.95 ***(978-4-87187-451-9(6))*** Ishi Pr. International.

Ponterotto, Joseph G. A Psychobiography of Bobby Fischer: Understanding the Genius, Mystery, & Psychological Decline of a World Chess Champion. 2012. ***(978-0-398-08742-5(3))***; pap. *(978-0-398-08740-1(7))* Thomas, Charles C. Pub., Ltd.

Pritchett, Craig. Chess for Rookies: Learn to Play, Win & Enjoy! 2009. (ENG., Illus.). 352p. pap. 21.95 *(978-1-85744-535-0(X))* Everyman Chess GBR. Dist: Globe Pequot Pr., The.

Prithard, D. B. Encyclopedia of Chess Variants. (Illus.). 372p. *(978-0-9524142-0-9(1))* Games & Puzzles Pubns.

Purdy & Steiner. The Chess World Editors. Date not set. pap. *(978-0-938650-82-9(3))* Thinkers' Pr., Inc.

Raetsky, Alexander & Chetverik, Maxim. No Passion for Chess Fashion: Fierce Openings for Your New Repertoire. 2011. (ENG.). 234p. pap. 24.95 ***(978-1-936277-26-1(3))*** Mongoose Pr.

Rasskin-Gutman, Diego & Klosky, Deborah. Chess Metaphors: Artificial Intelligence & the Human Mind. 2012. (ENG., Illus.). 232p. (gr. 17). pap. 12.95 ***(978-0-262-51749-2(3))*** MIT Pr.

Rasskin-Gutman, Diego & Rasskin-Gutman, D. Chess Metaphors: Artificial Intelligence & the Human Mind. Klosky, Deborah, tr. from SPA. 2009. (ENG., Illus.). 232p. (gr. 17). 24.95 *(978-0-262-18267-6(X))* MIT Pr.

Réti, Richard. Masters of the Chessboard. 2011. (ENG.). 216p. pap. 19.95 ***(978-1-936490-21-9(8))*** Russell Enterprises, Inc.

Reti, Richard. Modern Ideas in Chess. 2009. (ENG., Illus.). 242p. pap. 24.95 *(978-4-87187-824-1(4))* Ishi Pr. International.

Rice, Bob. Three Moves Ahead: What Chess Can Teach You about Business. 2008. (ENG., Illus.). 224p. 24.95 *(978-0-470-17821-8(3),* Jossey-Bass) Wiley, John & Sons, Inc.

Richey, Robert J. Key Chess Puzzles: Sacrificial Chess. 2011. 160p. pap. 11.70 *(978-1-4520-8753-5(9))* AuthorHouse.

Romero, Alfonso & Gonzalez De La Nava, Amador. The Ultimate Chess Strategy Book, Vol. 1. 2008. (ENG., Illus.). 207p. pap. 14.95 *(978-1-904600-84-8(0))* Gambit Pubns., Ltd. GBR. Dist: Perseus Distribution.

Root, Alexey W. The Living Chess Game: Fine Arts Activities for Kids 9-14, 1 vol. (Illus.). 102p. pap. 30.00 *(978-1-59884-380-4(X),* A2704P); 2010. E-Book *(978-1-59884-381-1(8))* Libraries Unlimited, Inc.

—People, Places, Checkmates: Teaching Social Studies with Chess, 1 vol. 2010. 146p. pap. 25.00 *(978-1-59158-850-4(2),* TIP8850) Libraries Unlimited, Inc.

—Read, Write, Checkmate: Enrich Literacy with Chess Activities, 1 vol. 2009. (Illus.). 128p. pap. 25.00 *(978-1-59158-754-5(9),* TIP8754, Teacher Ideas Pr.) Libraries Unlimited, Inc.

—Science, Math, Checkmate: 32 Chess Activities for Inquiry & Problem Solving, 1 vol. 2008. (Illus.). 144p. per. 25.00 *(978-1-59158-571-8(6),* TIP8571, Teacher Ideas Pr.) Libraries Unlimited, Inc.

Saunders, John. Advanced Chess: Rules, Skills, Tactics & Strategic Play. 2009. (ENG., Illus.). 128p. pap. 17.99 *(978-1-84476-659-8(4,)* Anness Publishing GBR. Dist: National Bk. Network.

Sawyer, Tim. The Alekhine Defense Playbook. (Illus.). 160p. pap. 21.95 *(978-1-886846-16-6(2))* Pickard & Son Publishing.

Schandorff, Lars. Grandmaster Repertoire 7: The Caro-Kann. 2010. (Grandmaster Repertoire Ser.). (ENG.). 240p. pap. 29.95 *(978-1-906552-56-5(8))* Quality Chess Europe SWE. Dist: SCB Distributors.

Schiller, Eric. Chess: Every Thing You Need to Know to Win at Chess. 2006. (Big Book Of... Ser.). (ENG., Illus.). 320p. pap. 17.95 *(978-1-58042-133-1(4))* Cardoza Publishing.

—Learn from Bobby Fischer's Greatest Games. 2009. (ENG.). 224p. pap. 14.95 *(978-1-58042-235-2(7))* Cardoza Publishing.

—7 Steps to Better Chess. 2010. (ENG.). 192p. pap. 14.95 *(978-1-58042-240-6(3))* Cardoza Publishing.

Seck, Chris. How to Beat a Grandmaster: Secrets Every Amateur Should Know about Playing the Pros. 2009. 112p. pap. 14.99 *(978-1-4389-5164-5(7))* AuthorHouse.

Seirawan, Yasser. Chess Duels: My Games with the World Champions. 2010. (ENG., Illus.). 432p. 35.00 *(978-1-85744-587-9(2))* Everyman Chess GBR. Dist: Globe Pequot Pr., The.

Shaw, John. Grandmaster versus Amateur. Aagaard, Jacob, ed. 2011. (ENG.). 288p. pap. 29.95 *(978-1-906552-84-8(3))* Quality Chess Europe SWE. Dist: SCB Distributors.

Shipov, Sergey. The Complete Hedgehog. 2011. pap. 29.95 *(978-1-936277-22-3(0))* Mongoose Pr.

Silman, Jeremy. How to Reassess Your Chess, 4th Edition. 4th ed. 2010. (ENG., Illus.). 672p. pap. 29.95 *(978-1-890085-13-1(8))* Silman-James Pr.

Smith, Dale. The Tao of the Chessboard. 2008. 140p. pap. 14.95 *(978-1-59858-673-2(4))* Dog Ear Publishing, LLC.

Snyder, Robert M. More Unbeatable Chess Lessons: Instruction for the Advanced Player. 2007. 264p. per. 19.95 *(978-0-595-45346-7(5))* iUniverse, Inc.

—Unbeatable Chess Lessons. 2007. 232p. per. 18.95 *(978-0-595-45344-3(9))* iUniverse, Inc.

—Winning Chess Tournaments: Methods & Materials Training Guide. 2007. 228p. per. 18.95 *(978-0-595-45347-4(3))* iUniverse, Inc.

Soltis, Andrew. Studying Chess Made Easy. 2010. (ENG., Illus.). 256p. pap. 22.95 *(978-1-906388-67-6(9),* Batsford, B. T. Ltd.) Anova Bks. GBR. Dist: Sterling Publishing Co., Inc.

—Transpo Tricks in Chess: Finesse Your Chess Moves & Win. 2007. (Batsford Chess Bks.). (ENG., Illus.). 224p. per. 21.95 *(978-0-7134-9051-0(9),* Batsford, B. T. Ltd.) Anova Bks. GBR. Dist: Sterling Publishing Co., Inc.

—What It Takes to Become a Chess Master. 2012. (ENG., Illus.). 208p. pap. 19.95 ***(978-1-84994-026-9(6),*** Batsford, B. T. Ltd.) Anova Bks. GBR. Dist: Sterling Publishing Co., Inc.

Soltis, Andrew. 300 Wisest Things Said about Chess: With 300 Annotated Positions. 2008. (ENG., Illus.). 304p. pap. 21.95 *(978-1-906388-00-3(8),* Batsford, B. T. Ltd.) Anova Bks. GBR. Dist: Sterling Publishing Co., Inc.

Sosonko, Genna. Russian Silhouettes. 2009. (ENG.). 240p. pap. 24.95 *(978-90-5691-293-2(3),* New In Chess,Csi) Continental Sales, Inc.

Sosonko, Genna, ed. New in Chess Yearbook: The Chess Player's Guide to Opening News. (ENG.). 2011. 250p. 38.95 *(978-90-5691-336-6(0))* 2006. (Illus.). 248p. pap. 26.95 *(978-90-5691-173-7(2))* Vol. 96. 2010. 250p. 38.95 *(978-90-5691-304-5(2))* Vol. 96. 2010. 250p. pap. 29.95 *(978-90-5691-303-8(4))* Continental Sales, Inc. (New In Chess,Csi).

—New in Chess Yearbook 95: The Chess Player's Guide to Opening News. 2010. (ENG.). 250p. 38.95 *(978-90-5691-302-1(6));* pap. 29.95 *(978-90-5691-301-4(8))* Continental Sales, Inc. (New In Chess,Csi).

Sosonko Genna & Boel Peter, eds. Yearbook V80. 2006. (ENG.). 248p. pap. 28.95 *(978-90-5691-175-1(9),* New In Chess,Csi) Continental Sales, Inc.

Speelman, Jon. Preparacion de Finales (Prepare the End Plays - Chess) (SPA.). 188p. *(978-84-8019-242-2(9))* Paidotribo, Editorial S.L.

Speelman, Jon, et al. BCE: Batsford Chess Endings. (Illus.). 448p. pap. *(978-0-7134-4420-9(7),* Batsford, B. T. Ltd.) Anova Bks.

Stark, Kevin. Checkmate for Children. 2010. (ENG.). 144p. pap. 14.95 *(978-90-5691-309-0(3),* New In Chess,Csi) Continental Sales, Inc.

Suba, Mihai. Dynamic Chess Strategy. 2010. (ENG.). 208p. pap. 19.95 *(978-90-5691-325-0(5),* New In Chess,Csi) Continental Sales, Inc.

—Positional Chess Sacrifices. 2011. (ENG.). 352p. pap. 34.95 *(978-1-906552-86-2(X))* Quality Chess Europe SWE. Dist: SCB Distributors.

Succar, Mohammad. The History of Chess. 2011. 588p. pap. 46.95 ***(978-1-4620-5021-5(2))*** iUniverse, Inc.

Sukhin, Igor. Chess Camp: Volume 1: Move, Attack, & Capture. 2010. (ENG.). 116p. 11.95 *(978-1-936277-07-0(7))* Mongoose Pr.

—Chess Camp Vol. 2: Simple Checkmates. 2010. (ENG.). 116p. 11.95 *(978-1-936277-08-7(5))* Mongoose Pr.

—Chess Camp Vol. 3: Checkmates with Many Pieces. 2010. (ENG.). 116p. 11.95 *(978-1-936277-09-4(3))* Mongoose Pr.

Sundberg, Stephanie, MAT. Why We Should Teach Children Chess in Schools. 2009. 52p. pap. 14.98 *(978-0-557-06981-1(5))* Lulu Enterprises Inc.

Taylor, Julian. The Major Transition. 2010. (Illus.). 102p. pap. *(978-1-907652-07-3(8))* Grosvenor Hse. Publishing Ltd.

Taylor, Timothy. Pawn Sacrifice! Winning at chess the adventurous Way! 2008. (ENG.). 192p. pap. 24.95 *(978-1-85744-565-7(1))* Everyman Chess GBR. Dist: Globe Pequot Pr., The.

—True Combat Chess: Winning Battles over the Board. 2009. (ENG., Illus.). 192p. pap. 24.95 *(978-1-85744-584-8(8))* Everyman Chess GBR. Dist: Globe Pequot Pr., The.

Timman, Jan. On the Attack: The Art of Attacking Chess According to the Modern Masters. Verhagen, Piet, tr. 2006. (ENG., Illus.). 240p. pap. 27.95 *(978-90-5691-187-4(2),* New In Chess,Csi) Continental Sales, Inc.

Timman, Jan & Geuzendam, Dirk Jan ten, eds. New in Chess, the Magazine. 104p. 2011. pap. 12.75 *(978-90-5691-323-6(9))* 2011. pap. 12.75 *(978-90-5691-322-9(0))* 2010. (ENG.). pap. 12.75 *(978-90-5691-321-2(2))* 2010. (ENG.). pap. 12.50 *(978-90-5691-320-5(4))* Continental Sales, Inc. (New In Chess,Csi).

Tolbert, Herman Sr. Corridors: (the geometry, physics & mathematics of chess) Vol 1. 2011. 78p. pap. 15.99 ***(978-1-4653-6173-8(1))*** Xlibris Corp.

Tortoza, Carlos. Check Mate & Words Game: Postal Chess: Chess, Friendship & Philosophy! 2006. (ENG.). 200p. per. 18.95 *(978-1-59800-288-1(0))* Outskirts Pr., Inc.

Tykodi, Ralph, compiled by. C. J. S. Purdy's Fine Art of Chess Annotations & Other Thoughts, 5. Date not set. pap. *(978-0-938650-86-7(6))* Thinkers' Pr., Inc.

Uhlmann, Wolfgang & Schmidt, Gerhard. Open Files. 2010. (Progress in Chess Ser.). (ENG.). 164p. 35.00 *(978-3-283-01006-5(4))* Edition Olms DEU. Dist: Independent Pubs. Group.

Varas, Nancy. Chess for Fun: Chess game Module -7d. 2006. (Illus.). 12p. 5.00 *(978-0-9726946-9-8(2))* Varas, Reny.

Vigorito, David. The Main-Line Slav. 2009. (Chess Explained Ser.). (ENG., Illus.). 111p. pap. 24.95 *(978-1-906454-05-0(1))* Gambit Pubns., Ltd. GBR. Dist: Perseus Distribution.

Villa, Jesus De La. Dismantling the Sicilian: A Complete Repertoire for White. 2009. (ENG., Illus.). 336p. pap. 26.95 *(978-90-5691-294-9(1),* New In Chess,Csi) Continental Sales, Inc.

Volokitin, Andrei & Grabinsky, Vladimir. Perfect Your Chess. Giddins, Steve, tr. 2007. (ENG., Illus.). 159p. per. 28.95 *(978-1-904600-82-4(4))* Gambit Pubns., Ltd. GBR. Dist: Perseus Distribution.

Wainwright, Michael. Faulkner's Gambit: Chess & Literature. 2011. (ENG., Illus.). 230p. 85.00 ***(978-0-230-33860-9(7))*** Palgrave Macmillan.

Ward, Barbara. Starting Out? Chess Tactics & Check. 2007. (ENG.). cd-rom 23.95 *(978-1-85744-606-7(2))* Everyman Chess GBR. Dist: Globe Pequot Pr., The.

Watkins, John. Across the Board - the Mathematics of Chessboard Problems. 2012. (Princeton Puzzlers Ser.). (ENG., Illus.). 272p. pap. 18.95 ***(978-0-691-15498-5(8))*** Princeton Univ. Pr.

Watkins, John J. Across the Board: The Mathematics of Chessboard Problems. 2007. (Princeton Puzzlers Ser.). (ENG., Illus.). 272p. (C). per. 25.95 *(978-0-691-13062-0(0))* Princeton Univ. Pr.

Weinreb, Michael. Game of Kings: A Year among the Oddballs & Geniuses Who Make up America's Top High School Chess Team. 2007. (ENG.). 304p. (gr. 12-18). 15.00 *(978-1-59240-338-7(7),* Gotham) Penguin Group (USA) Inc.

Wells, Adam. Football & Chess. 2007. (Illus.). 176p. per. *(978-1-84382-186-1(9))* Hardinge Simpole Publishing.

Williams, Simon. How to Crush Your Chess Opponents. 2008. (ENG.). 109p. pap. 14.95 *(978-1-904600-99-2(9))* Gambit Pubns., Ltd. GBR. Dist: Perseus Distribution.

Wilson, Fred & Alberston, Bruce. 200 Capture Mates: One & Two Move Checkmates. 2007. (ENG., Illus.). 144p. pap. 12.95 *(978-1-58042-215-4(2))* Cardoza Publishing.

—606 Puzzles for Chess Nuts. 2008. (Mensa Ser.). (ENG., Illus.). 368p. pap. 9.95 *(978-1-4027-6022-8(1),* Sterling Publishing Co., Inc.

Wiseman, Paul. Wiseman's Chess Primer. 2011. 202p. pap. ***(978-1-907611-92-6(4))*** Paragon Publishing, Rothersthorpe.

Yakovlev, Nikolay. Chess Blueprints: Planning in the Middlegame. 2010. (ENG., Illus.). 272p. pap. 24.95 *(978-1-936277-01-8(8))* Mongoose Pr.

Yusupov, Artur. Boost Your Chess 1: The Fundamentals. 2010. (Illus.). 288p. pap. 29.95 *(978-1-906552-43-4(1))* Quality Chess Europe SWE. Dist: SCB Distributors.

—Boost Your Chess 2 with Artur Yusupov. 2010. (Beyond the Basics Ser.). (ENG., Illus.). 288p. pap. 29.95 *(978-1-906552-43-5(6))* Quality Chess Europe SWE. Dist: SCB Distributors.

—Build up your Chess with Artur Yusupov: The Fundamentals Volume I. 2008. (ENG., Illus.). 276p. pap. 29.95 *(978-1-906552-01-5(0))* Quality Chess Europe SWE. Dist: SCB Distributors.

—Build up your Chess with Artur Yusupov 2: Beyond the Basics. 2009. (Illus.). 276p. pap. 29.95 *(978-1-906552-10-7(X))* Quality Chess Europe SWE. Dist: SCB Distributors.

—Chess Evolution 1 with Artur Yusupov. 2011. (Chess Evolution Ser.). (ENG.). 288p. pap. 29.95 *(978-1-906552-45-9(2))* Quality Chess Europe SWE. Dist: SCB Distributors.

Zadorozny, Michael. Chess for everyone series: learning to checkmate, book One: Basics. 2006. (J). per. 24.95 *(978-0-9789584-0-4(3))* Chess On My Mind Productions, Inc.

Ziegler, Ari. Mating the Castled King. 2007. (Illus.). 208p. pap. 24.95 *(978-91-975244-3-8(3))* Quality Chess Europe SWE. Dist: SCB Distributors.

CHESS—BIBLIOGRAPHY

Di Felice, Gino. Chess Periodicals: An Annotated International Bibliography, 1836-2008. 2010. (ENG., Illus.). 357p. pap. 49.95 *(978-0-7864-4643-8(9))* McFarland & Co., Inc. Pubs.

Linde, Antonius van der. Geschichte und Litteratur des Schachspiels, 2 vols. 2007. (GER., Illus.). 1130p. 145.00 *(978-1-57898-459-6(9))* Martino Publishing.

Van der Linde, Antonius. Geschichte und Litteratur des Schachspiels, 2 vols. in 1. (Tschaturanga Ser.: Vol. 20). (GER., Illus.). 1093p. reprint ed. *(978-3-283-00079-0(4))* Olms, Georg Verlag AG.

CHESS—BIOGRAPHY

see also names of chess players, e.g. Fischer, Bobby, 1943-

Beim, Valeri. Paul Morphy: A Modern Perspective. 2006. (Illus.). 164p. per. 17.95 *(978-1-888690-26-2(7))* Russell Enterprises, Inc.

Benjamin, Joel. American Grandmaster: Four Decades of Chess Adventures. 2008. (Everyman Chess Ser.). (ENG., Illus.). 272p. per. 24.95 *(978-1-85744-552-7(X))* Everyman Chess GBR. Dist: Globe Pequot Pr., The.

Bernstein, Sidney. Combat My 50 Years at the Chessboard. 2009. 118p. pap. 25.95 net. *(978-0-923891-30-5(7))* Ishi Pr. International.

Bisguier, Arthur & Berry, Newton. Art of Bisguier: Selected Games 1961-2003. 2008. (ENG.). 272p. pap. 29.95 *(978-1-888690-36-1(4))* Russell Enterprises, Inc.

Bisguier, Arthur & Maddox, Don. Bisguier! The Career of IGM Arthur Bisguier. (ChessBase University American Grandmaster Ser.). (Illus.). 64p. (Orig.). pap. 10.95 *(978-1-883358-03-7(5))* R&D Publishing.

Brady, Frank. Endgame: Bobby Fischer's Remarkable Rise & Fall - From America's Brightest Prodigy to the Edge of Madness. 2011. (ENG., Illus.). 416p. 25.99 *(978-0-307-46390-6(7),* Crown) Crown Publishing Group.

Centre-Stage & Behind the Scenes: A Personal Memoir. 2011. (ENG.). 272p. pap. 32.95 *(978-90-5691-364-9(6),* New In Chess,Csi) Continental Sales, Inc.

Donaldson, John & Minev, Nikolay. The Life & Games of Akiva Rubinstein: Volume 1: Uncrowned King. 2nd rev. ed. 2007. (Illus.). 402p. per. 29.95 *(978-1-888690-29-3(1))* Russell Enterprises, Inc.

Elo, Arpad E. The Rating of Chess Players, Past & Present. 2008. (Illus.). 206p. pap. 25.95 net. *(978-0-923891-27-5(7))* Ishi Pr. International.

Fishbein, Alex. Fishbein! The Chess Career of Alex Fishbein. (ChessBase University American Grandmaster Ser.). 64p. (Orig.). pap. 10.95 *(978-1-883358-14-3(0))* R&D Publishing.

Ftacnik, Lubomir, et al. Champions of the New Millennium. 2008. (ENG., Illus.). 400p. pap. 39.95 *(978-1-906552-02-2(9))* Quality Chess Europe SWE. Dist: SCB Distributors.

Henley, Ron. Henley! The Chess Career of Ron Henley. (ChessBase University American Grandmaster Ser.). (Illus.). 64p. (Orig.). pap. 10.95 *(978-1-883358-13-6(2))* R&D Publishing.

Hilbert, John S. & Lahde, Peter P. Albert Beauregard Hodges: The Man Chess Made. 2008. (ENG., Illus.). 550p. 55.00 *(978-0-7864-3220-2(9))* McFarland & Co., Inc. Pubs.

Hook, Bill. Hooked on Chess: A Memoir. 2007. (ENG., Illus.). 180p. pap. 22.95 *(978-90-5691-220-8(8),* New In Chess,Csi) Continental Sales, Inc.

Kalkamjozov, Zhivko. The Genius & the Misery of Chess. 2008. (ENG.). 224p. pap. 19.95 *(978-0-9791482-3-1(5))* Mongoose Pr.

Kasparov, Garry. Garry Kasparov on Garry Kasparov, Part 1: 1973-1985. 2011. (ENG.). 520p. 45.00 *(978-1-85744-672-2(0))* Everyman Chess GBR. Dist: Globe Pequot Pr., The.

Lahde, Peter P. Isaac Kashdan, American Chess Grandmaster: A Career Summary with 757 Games. 2009. (ENG., Illus.). 360p. 55.00 *(978-0-7864-3296-7(9))* McFarland & Co., Inc. Pubs.

Lawson, David. Paul Morphy: The Pride & Sorrow of Chess. Aiello, Thomas, ed. 2010. pap. 20.00 *(978-1-887366-97-7(0))* Univ. of Louisiana at Lafayette Pr.

Mueller, Karsten. Bobby Fischer: The Career & Complete Games of the American World Chess Champion. 2009. 476p. pap. 39.95 *(978-1-888690-59-0(3));* (ENG., Illus.). 408p. 79.95 *(978-1-888690-68-2(2))* Russell Enterprises, Inc.

Purdy. World Champions at Work. Date not set. pap. 25.00 *(978-0-938650-81-2(5))* Thinkers' Pr., Inc.

Reti, Richard. Masters of the Chessboard. 2008. (ENG.). 432p. pap. 25.95 *(978-0-923891-48-0(X))* Ishi Pr. International.

Soltis, Andrew. Confessions of a Grandmaster. Date not set. (Orig.). pap. 25.00 *(978-0-938650-69-0(6))* Thinkers' Pr., Inc.

Sosonko, Genna. New in Chess Yearbook 89: The Chess Player's Guide to Opening News. 2009. (ENG.). 250p. 38.95 *(978-90-5691-251-2(8),* New In Chess,Csi) Continental Sales, Inc.

Sosonko, Genna, ed. New in Chess Yearbook V89. 2009. (ENG.). 250p. pap. 29.95 *(978-90-5691-250-5(X),* New In Chess,Csi) Continental Sales, Inc.

Steinitz, William. The Steinitz Papers: Letters & Documents of the First World Chess Champion. Landsberger, Kurt & Soltis, eds. alt. ed. 2010. (ENG., Illus.). 360p. pap. 45.00 *(978-0-7864-4704-6(4))* McFarland & Co., Inc. Pubs.

Urcan, Olimpiu G. Adolf Albin in America: A European Chess Master's Sojourn, 1893-1895. 2008. (ENG., Illus.). 286p. 49.95 *(978-0-7864-3010-9(9))* McFarland & Co., Inc. Pubs.

—Julius Finn: A Chess Master's Life in America, 1871-1931. 2010. (ENG., Illus.). 286p. 49.95 *(978-0-7864-4233-6(2))* McFarland & Co., Inc. Pubs.

Urcan, Olimpiu G. & Braunwarth, Peter Michael. Arthur Kaufmann: A Chess Biography, 1872-1938. 2012. (ENG., Illus.). 274p. pap. 45.00 *(978-0-7864-6145-5(4))* McFarland & Co., Inc. Pubs.

Urcan, Olimpiu G. & Hilbert, John S. William H. K. Pollock: A Chess Biography 2012. (ENG.). [288]p. 49.95 ***(978-0-7864-5868-4(2))*** McFarland & Co., Inc. Pubs.

van Winsen, Joost. James Mason in America: The Early Chess Career, 1867-1878. 2010. (ENG., Illus.). 384p. 49.95 *(978-0-7864-4892-0(X))* McFarland & Co., Inc. Pubs.

Verwer, Renzo. Bobby Fischer for Beginners: Most Famous Chess Player Explained. 2010. (ENG.). 128p. pap. 16.95 *(978-90-5691-315-1(8),* New In Chess,Csi) Continental Sales, Inc.

Wade, Robert G. Soviet Chess. 2011. (Illus.). 288p. pap. 25.95 ***(978-4-87187-457-1(5))*** Ishi Pr. International.

Waitzkin, Josh. The Art of Learning: A Journey in the Pursuit of Excellence. 2008. (ENG.). 288p. pap. 15.00 *(978-0-7432-7746-4(5),* Free Pr.) Free Pr.

Winter, Edward. Capablanca: A Compendium of Games, Notes, Articles, Correspondence, Illustrations & Other Rare Archival Materials on the Cuban Chess Genius Jose Raul Capablanca, 1888-1942. alt. ed. 2011. (ENG., Illus.). 359p. pap. 35.00 *(978-0-7864-6634-4(0))* McFarland & Co., Inc. Pubs.

CHESS—COLLECTIONS OF GAMES

see also Chess—Tournaments

also collections of games of one payer under individual's name, e.g. Karpov, Anatoly, 1951-

Alburt, Lev. Chess Training: 300 Most Important Positions. 3rd ed. 2010. (Comprehensive Chess Course Ser.). (ENG., Illus.). 188p. pap. 17.95 *(978-1-889323-22-0(5),* 889322, Chess Information & Research Ctr.) Alburt, Lev.

Alburt, Lev & Lawrence, Al. Chess Training Bk. 2: How to Spot Tactics & How Far Ahead to Calculate. 2008. (ENG., Illus.). 192p. pap. 18.95 *(978-1-889323-17-6(9),* Chess Information & Research Ctr.) Alburt, Lev.

Alburt, Lev & Palatnik, Sam. Chess Strategy for the Tournament Player. 3rd ed. 2010. (Comprehensive Chess Course Ser.). (ENG., Illus.). 352p. pap. 24.95 *(978-1-889323-21-3(7),* 889321, Chess Information & Research Ctr.) Alburt, Lev.

Alburt, Lev, et al. Chess Openings for Black, Explained: A Complete Repertoire. 2nd ed. 2009. (ENG.). 224p. pap. 29.95 *(978-1-889323-18-3(7),* 889318, Chess Information & Research Ctr.) Alburt, Lev.

Alekhine, Alexander. New York 1924. 2009. (Illus.). 352p. pap. 29.95 *(978-1-888690-48-4(8))* Russell Enterprises, Inc.

Bernstein, Sidney. Combat My 50 Years at the Chessboard. 2009. 118p. pap. 25.95 net. *(978-0-923891-30-5(7))* Ishi Pr. International.

Bird, H. E. Chess Masterpieces Comprising A Collecti. 2006. pap. 21.95 *(978-1-4286-4135-8(1))* Kessinger Publishing, LLC.

Bologan, Victor. Victor Bologan: Selected Games 1985-2004. 2007. (Illus.). 236p. per. 29.95 *(978-1-888690-37-8(2))* Russell Enterprises, Inc.

Brady, Frank. Endgame: Bobby Fischer's Remarkable Rise & Fall - From America's Brightest Prodigy to the Edge of Madness. 2011. (ENG., Illus.). 416p. 25.99 *(978-0-307-46390-6(7),* Crown) Crown Publishing Group.

—Endgame: Bobby Fischer's Remarkable Rise & Fall - from America's Brightest Prodigy to the Edge of Madness. 2012. (ENG.). 432p. pap. 16.00 *(978-0-307-46391-3(5))* Broadway Bks.

Burger, Robert E. The Chess of Bobby Fischer. 2011. (Illus.). 348p. pap. 25.95 ***(978-4-87187-455-7(9))*** Ishi Pr. International.

Burgess, Graham. New Ideas in the Alekhine Defence. (Illus.). 128p. pap. *(978-0-7134-7833-4(0),* Batsford, B. T. Ltd.) Anova Bks.

C

Burgess, Graham, et al. The Mammoth Book of the World's Greatest Chess Games. 2010. (ENG.). 704p. pap. 13.95 *(978-0-7624-3995-9(5))* Running Pr. Bk. Pubs.

Colin, Crouch. Analyse Your Chess. 2011. (ENG.). 240p. pap. 26.95 *(978-1-85744-670-8(4))* Everyman Chess GBR. Dist: Globe Pequot Pr., The.

Dreev, Alexey. My One Hundred best Games. 2007. 300p. pap. *(978-954-8782-55-5(3))* Chess Stars.

Euwe, Max. Bobby Fischer - the Greatest? 2011. (Illus.). 218p. pap. 25.95 ***(978-4-87187-470-0(2))*** Ishi Pr. International.

Evans, Larry. Vienna 1922. 2011. (ENG.). 144p. pap. 19.95 *(978-1-936490-02-8(1))* Russell Enterprises, Inc.

The Final Theory of Chess. 2008. pap. *(978-0-9815677-0-9(3))* Phillidor Pr.

Fischer, Bobby. Bobby Fischer's Games of Chess. 2008. (Illus.). pap. 25.95 *(978-0-923891-46-6(3))* Ishi Pr. International.

—My 60 Memorable Games. 2009. (ENG.). 384p. pap. 22.95 *(978-1-906388-30-0(X))*, Batsford, B. T. Ltd.) Anova Bks. GBR. Dist: Sterling Publishing Co., Inc.

—My 60 Memorable Games. 2009. (Illus.). 384p. pap. 29.95 *(978-0-923891-58-9(7))* Ishi Pr. International.

Franco, Zenon. The Art of Attacking Chess. Adams, Phil, tr. from SPA. 2008. (ENG., Illus.). 254p. pap. 14.95 *(978-1-904600-97-8(2))* Gambit Pubns., Ltd. GBR. Dist: Perseus Distribution.

Greet, Andrew. Play the Queen's Indian. 2009. (ENG., Illus.). 256p. pap. 24.95 *(978-1-85744-580-0(5))* Everyman Chess GBR. Dist: Globe Pequot Pr., The.

Guezendam, Dirk Jan Ten & Timman, Jan, eds. New in Chess Magazine 2010, Vol. 4. 2010. (ENG.). 106p. pap. 12.50 *(978-90-5691-319-9(0))*, New In Chess,Csi) Continental Sales, Inc.

—New in Chess, the magazine. 2010. (ENG.). 106p. Vol. 1. pap. 12.50 *(978-90-5691-316-8(6))* Vol. 2. pap. 12.50 *(978-90-5691-317-5(4))* Vol. 3. pap. 12.50 *(978-90-5691-318-2(2))* Continental Sales, Inc. (New In Chess,Csi).

Hansen, Lars Bo. How Chess Games Are Won & Lost. 2008. (ENG., Illus.). 254p. pap. 29.95 *(978-1-906454-01-2(9))* Gambit Pubns., Ltd. GBR. Dist: Perseus Distribution.

Harding, Tim. Correspondence Chess in Britain & Ireland, 1824-1987. 2010. (ENG., Illus.). 439p. pap. 49.95 *(978-0-7864-4553-0(X))* McFarland & Co., Inc. Pubs.

Hilton, Jonathan & Ippolito, Dean. Wojo's Weapons: Winning with White, Volume 1. 2010. (ENG.). 408p. pap. 29.95 *(978-0-9791482-0-0(0))* Mongoose Pr.

Houska, Jovanka. Starting Out: The Scandinavian. 2009. (ENG., Illus.). 320p. pap. 25.95 *(978-1-85744-582-4(1))* Everyman Chess GBR. Dist: Globe Pequot Pr., The.

Huegel, Tony & Alburt, Lev. Colorado Byways: 80 Roads Adventure West of Denver. 2012. (ENG.). 224p. pap. 17.95 ***(978-1-889323-25-1(X)***, 889325, Chess Information & Research Ctr.) Alburt, Lev.

Karolyi, Tibor. Karpov's Strategic Wins 1: the Making of A Champion: 1961-1985, 2 vols. 2011. (ENG., Illus.). 360p. pap. 29.95 *(978-1-906552-41-1(X))* Quality Chess Europe SWE. Dist: SCB Distributors.

—Karpov's Strategic Wins 2: the Prime Years: 1986-2009, 2 vols. 2011. (ENG., Illus.). 360p. pap. 29.95 *(978-1-906552-42-8(8))* Quality Chess Europe SWE. Dist: SCB Distributors.

Karpov, Anatoly. My Best Games. Neat, Ken, tr. 2008. (Progress in Chess Ser.). (ENG., Illus.). 295p. pap. 39.95 *(978-3-283-01002-7(1))* Edition Olms DEU. Dist: Independent Pubs. Group.

Karpov, Anatoly & Henley, Ron. Elista Diaries: Karpov-Kamsky, Karpov-Anand, Anand Mexico City 2007 World Chess Championship Matches. 2007. (Illus.). 414p. per. *(978-0-923891-97-8(8))* Ishi Pr. International.

Kasparov, Garry. Garry Kasparov on Modern Chess, Part 4: Kasparov v Karpov 1988-2009, 4 vols. 2010. (ENG., Illus.). 432p. 45.00 *(978-1-85744-652-4(6))* Everyman Chess GBR. Dist: Globe Pequot Pr., The.

—Kasparov vs Karpov 1986-1987, 4 vols. 2009. (ENG., Illus.). 436p. 45.00 *(978-1-85744-625-8(9))* Everyman Chess GBR. Dist: Globe Pequot Pr., The.

Kaufeld, Jurgen. Grandmaster Chess Strategy: What Amateurs Can Learn from Ulf Andersson's Positional Masterpieces. 2011. (ENG.). 224p. pap. 24.95 *(978-90-5691-346-5(8))*, New In Chess,Csi) Continental Sales, Inc.

King, Daniel. Kasparov V Deeper Blue. (Illus.). 96p. pap. *(978-0-7134-8322-2(9))*, Batsford, B. T. Ltd.) Anova Bks.

Korchnoi, Victor. My Best Games. 2011. (ENG.). 416p. pap. 29.95 *(978-3-283-01019-5(6))* Edition Olms DEU. Dist: Independent Pubs. Group.

Langrock, Hannes. The Modern Morra Gambit: A Dynamic Weapon against the Sicilian. 2nd rev. ed. 2011. (ENG.). 320p. pap. 29.95 ***(978-1-936490-30-1(7))*** Russell Enterprises, Inc.

Levy, David N. L. Sacrifices in the Sicilian. 2009. (ENG., Illus.). 176p. pap. 24.95 *(978-4-87187-811-1(2))* Ishi Pr. International.

Marin, Mihail. A Spanish Repertoire for Black. 2007. (Illus.). 231p. per. 29.95 *(978-91-976005-0-7(4))* Quality Chess Europe SWE. Dist: SCB Distributors.

Maroczy, Geza & Capablanca, Jose Raul. London 1922/the 1921 World Chess Championship Match. 2010. (Illus.). 128p. pap. *(978-1-888690-61-3(5))* Russell Enterprises, Inc.

McDonald, Neil. The Art of Planning in Chess: Move by Move. 2006. (Batsford Chess Bks.). (ENG., Illus.). 256p. per. 21.95 *(978-0-7134-9025-1(X))*, Batsford, B. T. Ltd.) Anova Bks. GBR. Dist: Sterling Publishing Co., Inc.

Minev, Nikolay. David Bronstein: Fifty Great Short Games. 2008. 97p. pap. 19.49 *(978-0-9661889-2-9(6))* Chess Library, The.

—Tony Miles: Fifty Great Short Games. 2008. 90p. per. 19.25 *(978-0-9661889-3-6(4))* Chess Library, The.

Mueller, Karsten. Bobby Fischer: The Career & Complete Games of the American World Chess Champion. 2009. 476p. pap. 39.95 *(978-1-888690-59-0(3))*; (ENG., Illus.). 408p. 79.95 *(978-1-888690-68-2(2))* Russell Enterprises, Inc.

NIC Editorial Team. New in Chess:Magazine 2007-06. 2007. (ENG.). 106p. pap. 11.50 *(978-90-5691-215-4(1))*, New In Chess,Csi) Continental Sales, Inc.

—New in Chess:Magazine 2007-07. 2007. (ENG.). 96p. pap. 11.50 *(978-90-5691-216-1(X))*, New In Chess,Csi) Continental Sales, Inc.

—New in Chess:Magazine 2007-08. 2008. (ENG.). 96p. pap. 11.50 *(978-90-5691-217-8(8))*, New In Chess,Csi) Continental Sales, Inc.

Nimzowitsch, Aron. Chess Praxis: The Praxis of My System. 2007. (Chess Classics Ser.). 215p. per. 21.95 *(978-91-85779-00-0(8))* Quality Chess Europe SWE. Dist: SCB Distributors.

Paige, Roger Leslie. Hampshire Chess Games, 1950 to 1970. 2008. (Illus.). 523p. pap. *(978-1-897312-79-7(2))* Adlibbed, Ltd.

Palliser, Richard, et al. Dangerous Weapons: The Dutch. 2009. (ENG., Illus.). 192p. pap. 26.95 *(978-1-85744-624-1(0))* Everyman Chess GBR. Dist: Globe Pequot Pr., The.

Popov, Vladimir. Chess Lessons. 2011. (ENG.). 192p. pap. 25.95 *(978-1-906552-82-4(7))* Quality Chess Europe SWE. Dist: SCB Distributors.

Reinfeld, Fred. Great Short Games of the Chess Masters. 2011. 222p. 44.95 ***(978-1-258-08017-4(6))*** Literary Licensing, LLC.

Shipov, Sergey. The Complete Hedgehog, Volume 1. 2009. (ENG., Illus.). 532p. pap. 29.95 *(978-0-9791482-1-7(9))* Mongoose Pr.

Skjoldager, Per & Nielsen, Jo Erik. Aron Nimzowitsch: On the Road to Chess Mastery, 1886-1924. 2012. (ENG.). 49.95 ***(978-0-7864-6539-2(5))*** McFarland & Co., Inc. Pubs.

Sosonko, Genna. New in Chess Yearbook 85: The Chess Player's Guide to Opening News. 2008. (ENG.). 248p. pap. 28.95 *(978-90-5691-234-5(8))*, New In Chess,Csi) Continental Sales, Inc.

Sosonko, Genna. New in Chess Yearbook 85: The Chess Player's Guide to Opening News. 2008. (ENG.). 248p. 36.95 *(978-90-5691-235-2(6))*, New In Chess,Csi) Continental Sales, Inc.

—New in Chess Yearbook 89: The Chess Player's Guide to Opening News. 2009. (ENG.). 250p. 38.95 *(978-90-5691-251-2(8))*, New In Chess,Csi) Continental Sales, Inc.

—New in Chess Yearbook 94. 2010. (ENG.). 250p. 38.95 *(978-90-5691-312-0(3))*; pap. 29.95 *(978-90-5691-311-3(5))* Continental Sales, Inc. (New In Chess,Csi).

Sosonko, Genna, ed. New In Chess Yearbook 92: The Chess Player's Guide to Opening News. 2009. (Yearbook Ser.). (ENG.). 250p. 38.95 *(978-90-5691-287-1(9))*; pap. 29.95 *(978-90-5691-288-8(7))* Continental Sales, Inc. (New In Chess,Csi).

—New In Chess Yearbook 93: The Chess Player's Guide to Opening News. 2010. (Yearbook Ser.). (ENG.). 250p. 38.95 *(978-90-5691-290-1(9))*; pap. 29.95 *(978-90-5691-289-5(5))* Continental Sales, Inc. (New In Chess,Csi).

—New in Chess Yearbook V86. 2008. (ENG.). 250p. 36.95 *(978-90-5691-237-6(2))*; pap. 28.95 *(978-90-5691-236-9(4))* Continental Sales, Inc. (New In Chess,Csi).

—New in Chess Yearbook V87. 2008. (ENG.). 250p. 36.95 *(978-90-5691-239-0(9))*; pap. 28.95 *(978-90-5691-238-3(0))* Continental Sales, Inc. (New In Chess,Csi).

—New in Chess Yearbook V88. 2008. (ENG.). 250p. 38.95 *(978-90-5691-249-9(6))*; pap. 29.95 *(978-90-5691-248-2(8))* Continental Sales, Inc. (New In Chess,Csi).

—New in Chess Yearbook V89. 2009. (ENG.). 250p. pap. 29.95 *(978-90-5691-250-5(X))*, New In Chess,Csi) Continental Sales, Inc.

—Yearbook 82: The Chess Player's Guide to Opening News. 2007. (ENG.). 248p. 36.95 *(978-90-5691-192-8(9))*; pap. 28.95 *(978-90-5691-191-1(0))* Continental Sales, Inc. (New In Chess,Csi).

—Yearbook 83: The Chess Player's Guide to Opening News. 2007. (ENG.). 248p. 36.95 *(978-90-5691-207-9(0))*; pap. 28.95 *(978-90-5691-206-2(2))* Continental Sales, Inc. (New In Chess,Csi).

Steinitz, William. Sixth American Chess Congress, New York 1889. 2009. (ENG., Illus.). 656p. pap. 29.95 *(978-4-87187-847-0(3))* Ishi Pr. International.

Stohl, Igor. Instructive Modern Chess Masterpieces. enl. ed. 2009. (ENG.). 448p. pap. 34.95 *(978-1-906454-08-1(6))* Gambit Pubns., Ltd. GBR. Dist: Perseus Distribution.

Suetin, Alexey. Soviet Chess Strategy. 2nd ed. 2010. (Chess Classics Ser.). (ENG., Illus.). 240p. pap. 29.95 *(978-1-906552-20-6(7))* Quality Chess UK LLP GBR. Dist: SCB Distributors.

Verwer, Renzo. Bobby Fischer for Beginners: Most Famous Chess Player Explained. 2010. (ENG.). 128p. pap. 16.95 *(978-90-5691-315-1(8))*, New In Chess,Csi) Continental Sales, Inc.

Vigorito, David. Play the Semi-Slav. 2008. (Illus.). 277p. pap. 25.95 *(978-91-85779-01-7(6))* Quality Chess Europe SWE. Dist: SCB Distributors.

Wade, Robert G. Soviet Chess. 2011. (Illus.). 288p. pap. 25.95 ***(978-4-87187-457-1(5))*** Ishi Pr. International.

Wade, Robert G. & O'Connell, Kevin J. The Complete Games of Bobby Fischer. 2009. (ENG., Illus.). 486p. pap. 29.95 *(978-0-923891-37-4(4)*, GS24) Ishi Pr. International.

CHESS—COMBINATIONS

see Chess—Middle Games

CHESS—COMPUTER PROGRAMS

see Computer Chess

CHESS—DATA PROCESSING

see Computer Chess

CHESS—DICTIONARIES

Horton, Byrne J. Dictionary of Modern Chess. *(978-0-8022-0746-3(4))* Philosophical Library, Inc.

CHESS—END GAMES

Benko, Pal. Pal Benko's Endgame Laboratory. 2007. 300p. per. 24.95 *(978-0-923891-88-6(9))* Ishi Pr. International.

Delavilla, Jesus. 100 Endgames You Must Know. 2008. (ENG., Illus.). 220p. pap. 24.95 *(978-90-5691-244-4(5))*, New In Chess,Csi) Continental Sales, Inc.

Dvoretsky, Mark. Dvoretsky's Endgame Manual. 3rd rev. ed. 2011. (ENG.). 404p. pap. 34.95 *(978-1-936490-13-4(7))* Russell Enterprises, Inc.

Flear, Glenn. Practical Endgame Play - Beyond the Basics: The Definitive Guide to the Endgames That Really Matter. 2007. (Everyman Chess Ser.). (ENG., Illus.). 544p. per. 40.00 *(978-1-85744-555-8(4))* Everyman Chess GBR. Dist: Globe Pequot Pr., The.

Giddins, Steve. 101 Chess Endgame Tips. 2007. (ENG., Illus.). 111p. per. 19.95 *(978-1-904600-66-4(2))* Gambit Pubns., Ltd. GBR. Dist: Perseus Distribution.

Grivas, Efstratios. Practical Endgame Play - Mastering the Basics: The Essential Guide to Endgame Fundamentals. 2008. (Everyman Chess Ser.). (ENG., Illus.). 320p. pap. 25.95 *(978-1-85744-556-5(2))* Everyman Chess GBR. Dist: Globe Pequot Pr., The.

Hansen, Carsten. Back to Basics: Endings. 2008. (ChessCafe Back to Basics Chess Ser.). (ENG.). 192p. pap. 22.95 *(978-1-888690-45-3(3))* Russell Enterprises, Inc.

Karolyi, Tibor & Aplin, Nick. Endgame Virtuoso Anatoly Karpov: The Exceptional Endgame Skills of the 12th World Champion. 2007. (ENG., Illus.). 360p. pap. 28.95 *(978-90-5691-202-4(X))*, New In Chess,Csi) Continental Sales, Inc.

Kasparyan, Ghenrikh M. Domination in 2,545 Endgame Studies. 2007. 546p. per. 24.95 net. *(978-0-923891-87-9(0))* Ishi Pr. International.

Nunn, John. Nunn's Chess Endings, 2 vols., Vol. 2. 2010. (ENG., Illus.). 336p. pap. 29.95 *(978-1-906454-23-4(X))* Gambit Pubns., Ltd. GBR. Dist: Perseus Distribution.

—Nunn's Chess Endings Volume 1, 2 vols. 2010. (ENG., Illus.). 320p. pap. 29.95 *(978-1-906454-21-0(3))* Gambit Pubns., Ltd. GBR. Dist: Perseus Distribution.

—Secrets of Minor-Piece Endings. (Illus.). 288p. pap. *(978-0-7134-7727-6(X))*, Batsford, B. T. Ltd.) Anova Bks.

—Understanding Chess Endgames. 2009. (ENG., Illus.). 224p. pap. 24.95 *(978-1-906454-11-1(6))* Gambit Pubns., Ltd. GBR. Dist: Perseus Distribution.

—1001 Deadly Checkmates. 2011. (ENG.). 304p. pap. 24.95 *(978-1-906454-25-8(6))* Gambit Pubns., Ltd. GBR. Dist: Perseus Distribution.

Pajeken, Wolfgang & Muller, Karsten. How to Play Chess Endgames. Adams, Phil, tr. 2008. (ENG., Illus.). 351p. per. 34.95 *(978-1-904600-86-2(7))* Gambit Pubns., Ltd. GBR. Dist: Perseus Distribution.

Pandolfini, Bruce. Endgame Workshop: Principles for the Practical Player. 2008. (Pandolfini Chess Library). (ENG.). 224p. pap. 19.95 *(978-1-888690-53-8(4))* Russell Enterprises, Inc.

—Pandolfini's Chess Challenges: 111 Winning Endgames. I.t. ed. 2007. (Chess Ser.). (ENG., Illus.). 256p. pap. 9.95 *(978-0-375-72206-6(8))*, Random Hse. Puzzles & Games) Random Hse. Information Group.

Sharnkovich, Leonid & Schiller, Eric. Saving Lost Positions: A Chess Works Publication. 2011. (Illus.). 140p. pap. 14.95 ***(978-4-87187-441-0(9))*** Ishi Pr. International.

Timman, Jan. The Art of the Endgame: My Journeys in the Turbulent World of Endgame Studies. 2012. (ENG.). 240p. pap. 27.95 ***(978-90-5691-369-4(7)***, New In Chess,Csi) Continental Sales, Inc.

Troitzki, A. A. Collection of Chess Studies, with a Supplement on the Theory of End-Game of Two Knights Against Pawns. 270p. reprint ed. lib. bdg. 31.20 *(978-3-283-00114-8(6))* Edition Olms DEU. Dist: Lubrecht & Cramer, Ltd.

Troitzky, Alexey Alexeyevich. Collection of Chess Studies by Troitzky: With a Supplement on the Theory of the End-game of Two Knights Against Pawns. 2006. Orig. Title: Collection of Chess Studies. 270p. reprint ed. per. 19.95 net. *(978-0-923891-10-7(2))* Ishi Pr. International.

Whitaker, Norman T. & Hartleb, Glenn E. 365 Selected Chess Endgames, One for Each Day of the Year. 2007.Tr. of 365 Ausgewahlte Endspiele, Eines Fur jeden Tag Im Jahr. 380p. per. 19.95 *(978-0-923891-84-8(6))* Ishi Pr. International.

CHESS—HISTORY

Adams, Jenny. Power Play: The Literature & Politics of Chess in the Late Middle Ages. 2006. (Middle Ages Ser.). (Illus.). 264p. (C). 59.95 *(978-0-8122-3944-7(X))* Univ. of Pennsylvania Pr.

Bird, Henry Edward. Chess History & Reminiscences. (ENG.). 2007. 194p. pap. 19.99 *(978-1-4264-1898-3(1))* 2008. 405p. pap. 34.75 *(978-1-4264-2009-2(9))* BiblioBazaar.

Darlow, Mike. Woodturning Chessmen. 2008. (Darlow's Woodturning Ser.). (ENG., Illus.). 168p. pap. 24.95 *(978-1-56523-373-7(5))* Fox Chapel Publishing Co., Inc.

Fadul, Jose A. Lessons in Chess, Lessons in Life. 2008. 139p. 24.50 *(978-0-557-01191-9(4))* Lulu Enterprises Inc.

Hesse, Christian. The Joys of Chess: Heroes, Battles & Brilliancies. 2011. (ENG.). 416p. pap. 34.95 *(978-90-5691-355-7(7)*, New in Chess) Continental Sales, Inc.

Hillyer, Martin ère. Thomas Frere & the Brotherhood of Chess: A History of 19th Century Chess in New York City. 2006. (ENG., Illus.). 223p. 45.00 *(978-0-7864-2327-9(7))* McFarland & Co., Inc. Pubs.

Levitt, Gerald M. The Turk, Chess Automaton. alt. ed. 2006. (ENG., Illus.). 268p. per. 45.00 *(978-0-7864-2903-5(8))* McFarland & Co., Inc. Pubs.

Linde, Antonius van der. Geschichte und Litteratur des Schachspiels, 2 vols. 2007. (GER., Illus.). 1130p. 145.00 *(978-1-57898-459-6(9))* Martino Publishing.

Nugent, Brian. The Irish Invented Chess! 2010. 105p. pap. 16.12 *(978-0-9556812-6-4(X))* Nugent, Brian IRL. Dist: Lulu Enterprises Inc.

Richey, Robert J. Blitz Chess Puzzles: The Art of Sacrifice. 2010. 96p. pap. 10.49 *(978-1-4520-4797-3(9))* AuthorHouse.

Shenk, David. The Immortal Game: A History of Chess or How 32 Carved Pieces on a Board Illuminated Our Understanding of War, Art, Science, & the Human Brain. 2007. (ENG., Illus.). 352p. pap. 16.00 *(978-1-4000-3408-6(6)*, Anchor) Knopf Doubleday Publishing Group.

Soltis, Andrew. Confessions of a Grandmaster. Date not set. (Orig.). pap. 25.00 *(978-0-938650-69-0(6))* Thinkers' Pr., Inc.

Soltis, Andy & McCormick, Gene H. The United States Chess Championship, 1845-1996. 2nd rev. alt. ed. 2006. (ENG., Illus.). 247p. per. 39.95 *(978-0-7864-2856-4(2))* McFarland & Co., Inc. Pubs.

CHESS—MIDDLE GAMES

Giddins, Steve. 50 Ways to Win at Chess. 2007. (ENG., Illus.). 173p. per. 14.95 *(978-1-904600-85-5(9))* Gambit Pubns., Ltd. GBR. Dist: Perseus Distribution.

Heisman, Dan. Elements of Positional Evaluation: How the Pieces Get Their Power. 4th ed. 2010. (Illus.). 216p. pap. 19.95 *(978-1-888690-58-3(5))* Russell Enterprises, Inc.

Lane, Gary. Prepare to Attack. 2011. (ENG.). 192p. pap. 26.95 *(978-1-85744-650-0(X))* Everyman Chess GBR. Dist: Globe Pequot Pr., The.

Naroditsky, Daniel. Mastering Positional Chess. 2010. (ENG.). 240p. pap. 23.95 *(978-90-5691-310-6(7)*, New In Chess,Csi) Continental Sales, Inc.

Nunn, John. Understanding Chess Middlegames. 2012. (ENG.). 232p. pap. 24.95 *(978-1-906454-27-2(2))* Gambit Pubns., Ltd. GBR. Dist: Perseus Distribution.

—1001 Deadly Checkmates. 2011. (ENG.). 304p. pap. 24.95 *(978-1-906454-25-8(6))* Gambit Pubns., Ltd. GBR. Dist: Perseus Distribution.

Sokolov, Ivan. Winning Chess Middlegames: An Essential Guide to Pawn Structures. 2009. (ENG.). 260p. pap. 29.95 *(978-90-5691-264-2(X)*, New In Chess,Csi) Continental Sales, Inc.

Sukhin, Igor. Chess Gems: 1,000 Combinations You Should Know. 2007. (ENG.). 336p. per. 24.95 *(978-0-9791482-5-5(1))* Mongoose Pr.

Vukovic, Vladimir. The Chess Sacrifice: Technique Art & Risk in Sacrificial Chess. 2009. (ENG., Illus.). 236p. pap. 24.95 *(978-4-87187-820-3(1))* Ishi Pr. International.

CHESS—OPENINGS

Aagaard, Jacob & Ntirlis, Nikolaos. Grandmaster Repertoire 10: The Tarrasch Defence. 2011. (Grandmaster Repertoire Ser.). (ENG.). 400p. pap. 34.95 ***(978-1-906552-91-6(6))*** Quality Chess Europe SWE. Dist: SCB Distributors.

Aagaard, Jacob & Shaw, John, eds. Experts vs. the Sicilian. 2nd ed. 2006. (Illus.). 228p. per. 27.50 *(978-91-975244-6-9(8))* Quality Chess Europe SWE. Dist: SCB Distributors.

Albertson, Bruce. Chess Opening Trap of the Day. 2007. (ENG.). 224p. pap. 14.95 *(978-1-58042-217-8(9))* Cardoza Publishing.

Alburt, Lev, et al. Chess Openings for Black, Explained: A Complete Repertoire. 2nd ed. 2009. (ENG.). 224p. pap. 29.95 *(978-1-889323-18-3(7)*, 889318, Chess Information & Research Ctr.) Alburt, Lev.

—Chess Openings for White, Explained: Winning with 1. E4. 2006. (ENG., Illus.). 448p. per. 29.95 *(978-1-889323-11-4(X))* Alburt, Lev.

—Chess Openings for White, Explained: Winning with 1.E4. 2nd ed. 2010. (Comprehensive Chess Course Ser.). (ENG., Illus.). 548p. pap. 29.95 *(978-1-889323-20-6(9)*, 889320, Chess Information & Research Ctr.) Alburt, Lev.

Alterman, Boris. The Alterman Gambit Guide: Black Gambits. 2011. (Alterman Gambit Guide Ser.). (ENG.). 400p. pap. 25.99 *(978-1-906552-54-1(1))* Quality Chess Europe SWE. Dist: SCB Distributors.

—The Alterman Gambit Guide: White Gambits. 2010. (Illus.). 440p. pap. 25.95 *(978-1-906552-53-4(3))* Quality Chess Europe SWE. Dist: SCB Distributors.

Aramil, William. The Complete Idiot's Guide to Chess Openings. 2008. (Complete Idiot's Guide Ser.). (ENG.). 208p. (gr. 12-18). 12.95 *(978-1-59257-776-7(8)*, Alpha Bks.) Penguin Group (USA) Inc.

Avrukh, Boris. Grandmaster Repertoire 1: 1. d4 Volume One, 2 vols. 2009. (Illus.). 288p. pap. 29.95 *(978-1-906552-05-3(3))* Quality Chess Europe SWE. Dist: SCB Distributors.

—Grandmaster Repertoire 2: 1. d4 Volume Two, 2 vols. 2009. (Illus.). 320p. pap. 34.95 *(978-1-906552-33-6(9))* Quality Chess Europe SWE. Dist: SCB Distributors.

—Grandmaster Repertoire 8: The Grünfeld Defence. 2011. (Grandmaster Repertoire Ser.). (ENG., Illus.). 352p. pap. 29.95 *(978-1-906552-75-6(4))* Quality Chess Europe SWE. Dist: SCB Distributors.

Avrukh, Boris. Grandmaster Repertoire 9: The Granfeld Defence Vol. 2. 2011. (Grandmaster Repertoire Ser.). (ENG., Illus.). 264p. pap. 29.95 ***(978-1-907982-00-2(0))*** Quality Chess Europe SWE. Dist: SCB Distributors.

Barsky, Vladimir. The Ragozin Complex: A Guide for White & Black. 2011. (ENG.). 272p. pap. 27.95 ***(978-90-5691-370-0(0)***, New In Chess,Csi) Continental Sales, Inc.

Bauer, Christian. The Philidor Files: Detailed Coverage of a Dynamic Opening. 2007. (Everyman Chess Ser.). (ENG., Illus.). 304p. per. 24.95 *(978-1-85744-436-0(1))* Everyman Chess GBR. Dist: Globe Pequot Pr., The.

Bern, Ivar, et al. Win with the Stonewall Dutch. 2009. (ENG.). 208p. pap. 29.95 *(978-1-906454-07-4(8))* Gambit Pubns., Ltd. GBR. Dist: Perseus Distribution.

Bologan, Victor. The Rossolimo Sicilian: A Powerful Anti-Sicilian that Avoids Tons of Theory. 2011. (ENG.). 256p. pap. 24.95 *(978-90-5691-345-8(X)*, New in Chess) Continental Sales, Inc.

Bosch, Jeroen. Secrets of Opening Surprises. 2009. (ENG., Illus.). 144p. Vol. 10. pap. 21.95 *(978-90-5691-260-4(7))* Vol. 11. pap. 21.95 *(978-90-5691-273-4(9))* Continental Sales, Inc. (New In Chess,Csi).

Bosch, Jeroen, ed. Secrets of Opening Surprises V09. 2008. (ENG., Illus.). 144p. pap. 21.95 *(978-90-5691-241-3(0)*, New In Chess,Csi) Continental Sales, Inc.

—Secrets of Opening Surprises, Vol. 13. 2011. (ENG.). 144p. pap. 21.95 *(978-90-5691-341-0(7)*, New In Chess,Csi) Continental Sales, Inc.

—Secrets of Opening Surprises, Volume 7. 2007. (Secrets of Opening Surprises Ser.). (ENG., Illus.). 144p. per. 21.95 *(978-90-5691-204-8(6)*, New In Chess,Csi) Continental Sales, Inc.

—SOS - Secrets of Opening Surprises Vol. 11: No Time to Study Chess Opening Theory? 12th ed. 2010. (Secrets of Opening Surprises Ser.). (ENG., Illus.). 144p. pap. 21.95 *(978-90-5691-298-7(4)*, New In Chess,Csi) Continental Sales, Inc.

—SOS: Secrets of Opening Surprises, Volume 8, 8. 2008. (SOS: Secrets of Opening Surprises Ser.). (ENG., Illus.). 144p. pap. 21.95 *(978-90-5691-222-2(4)*, New In Chess,Csi) Continental Sales, Inc.

Bronznik, Valeri. 1.d4 - Beat the Guerrillas: A Powerful Repertoire Against Annoying Black Sidelines. 2011. (ENG.). 224p. pap. 24.95 ***(978-90-5691-373-1(5)***, New In Chess,Csi) Continental Sales, Inc.

Brunello, Sabino. Attacking the Spanish: Marshall, Schliemann & Gajewski. 2009. (Illus.). 176p. pap. 29.95 *(978-1-906552-17-6(7))* Quality Chess Europe SWE. Dist: SCB Distributors.

Burgess, Graham. New Ideas in the Alekhine Defence. (Illus.). 128p. pap. *(978-0-7134-7833-4(0)*, Batsford, B. T. Ltd.) Anova Bks.

Cherniaev, Alexander & Prokuronov, Eduard. The New Old Indian. 2011. (ENG.). 160p. pap. 26.95 ***(978-1-85744-667-8(4))*** Everyman Chess GBR. Dist: Globe Pequot Pr., The.

Cherniaev, Alexander & Prokuronov, Eduard. The Samisch King's Indian Uncovered. 2008. (Everyman Chess Ser.). (ENG., Illus.). 192p. per. 24.95 *(978-1-85744-540-4(6))* Everyman Chess GBR. Dist: Globe Pequot Pr., The.

Chetverik, Maxim & Raetsky, Alex. Queen's Gambit Accepted. 2006. (Starting Out - Everyman Chess Ser.). (ENG., Illus.). 176p. per. 23.95 *(978-1-85744-415-5(9))* Everyman Chess GBR. Dist: Globe Pequot Pr., The.

Colin, Crouch. Analyse Your Chess. 2011. (ENG.). 240p. pap. 26.95 *(978-1-85744-670-8(4))* Everyman Chess GBR. Dist: Globe Pequot Pr., The.

Collins, Sam. Chess Explained: The c3 Sicilian: A New Approach to Understanding the Chess Openings. 2007. (ENG., Illus.). 111p. per. 19.95 *(978-1-904600-71-8(9))* Gambit Pubns., Ltd. GBR. Dist: Perseus Distribution.

—French Advance CD. 2007. (ENG.). cd-rom 23.95 *(978-1-85744-604-3(6))* Everyman Chess GBR. Dist: Globe Pequot Pr., The.

Cox, John. Declining the Queen's Gambit. 2011. (ENG.). 208p. pap. 26.95 *(978-1-85744-640-1(2))* Everyman Chess GBR. Dist: Globe Pequot Pr., The.

—Sicilian Sveshnikov. 2007. (Starting Out Ser.). (ENG., Illus.). 192p. per. 24.95 *(978-1-85744-431-5(0))* Everyman Chess GBR. Dist: Globe Pequot Pr., The.

—Starting Out: 1 D4! A Reliable Repertoire for the Improving Player. 2006. (Starting Out - Everyman Chess Ser.). (ENG., Illus.). 240p. per. 24.95 *(978-1-85744-417-9(5))* Everyman Chess GBR. Dist: Globe Pequot Pr., The.

Cyrus, Lakdawala. A Ferocious Opening Repertoire. 2011. (ENG.). 304p. pap. 27.95 *(978-1-85744-661-6(5))* Everyman Chess GBR. Dist: Globe Pequot Pr., The.

Cyrus, Lakdawala. 1 D6? Move by Move. 2012. (ENG.). 400p. pap. 29.95 ***(978-1-85744-683-8(6))*** Everyman Chess GBR. Dist: Globe Pequot Pr., The.

David, Vigorito. Attacking Chess? The King's Indian. 2011. (ENG.). 368p. pap. 27.95 ***(978-1-85744-664-7(X))*** Everyman Chess GBR. Dist: Globe Pequot Pr., The.

Davies, Nigel. Gambiteer I: A Hard-Hitting Chess Opening Repertoire for White. 2007. (Everyman Chess Ser.). (ENG., Illus.). 192p. per. 24.95 *(978-1-85744-516-9(3))* Everyman Chess GBR. Dist: Globe Pequot Pr., The.

—Gambiteer II: A Hard-Hitting Chess Opening Repertoire for Black. 2007. (ENG., Illus.). 192p. per. 24.95 *(978-1-85744-536-7(8))* Everyman Chess GBR. Dist: Globe Pequot Pr., The.

—Play 1e4 1e5 Cd. 2007. (ENG.). cd-rom 23.95 *(978-1-85744-607-4(0))* Everyman Chess GBR. Dist: Globe Pequot Pr., The.

—Play the Catalan. 2009. (ENG., Illus.). 192p. pap. 24.95 *(978-1-85744-591-6(0))* Everyman Chess GBR. Dist: Globe Pequot Pr., The.

—Starting Out: The Modern. 2008. (ENG.). 192p. pap. 24.95 *(978-1-85744-566-4(X))* Everyman Chess GBR. Dist: Globe Pequot Pr., The.

De Firmian, Nick. Modern Chess Openings. 15th l.t. ed. 2008. (Chess Ser.). (ENG., Illus.). 768p. pap. 29.95 *(978-0-8129-3682-7(5)*, Random Hse. Puzzles & Games) Random Hse. Information Group.

Dembo, Yelena. Fighting the Anti-King's Indians. 2008. (ENG., Illus.). 192p. pap. 24.95 *(978-1-85744-575-6(9))* Everyman Chess GBR. Dist: Globe Pequot Pr., The.

—Play the Grunfeld: Detailed Coverage of This Kasparov Favourite. 2007. (ENG., Illus.). 192p. per. 24.95 *(978-1-85744-521-3(X))* Everyman Chess GBR. Dist: Globe Pequot Pr., The.

Djuric, Stefan. Chess Opening Essentials Volume 4. 2010. (ENG.). 320p. pap. 28.95 *(978-90-5691-308-3(5)*, New In Chess,Csi) Continental Sales, Inc.

Djuric, Stefan, et al. Chess Opening Essentials: 1.d4-d5 / 1.d4-various / Queen's Gambits, Vol. 2. 2009. (Chess Opening Essentials Ser.). (ENG.). 288p. pap. 32.95 *(978-90-5691-269-7(0)*, New In Chess,Csi) Continental Sales, Inc.

—Chess Opening Essentials: Indian Defences, Vol. 3. 2009. (ENG.). 336p. pap. 32.95 *(978-90-5691-270-3(4)*, New In Chess,Csi) Continental Sales, Inc.

—Chess Opening Essentials: The Complete 1. e4. 2007. (Chess Opening Essentials Ser.). (ENG., Illus.). 358p. per. 29.95 *(978-90-5691-203-1(8)*, New in Chess) Continental Sales, Inc.

Donaldson, John & Hansen, Carsten. A Strategic Opening Repertoire. 2nd ed. 2008. (Illus.). 272p. per. 29.95 *(978-1-888690-41-5(0))* Russell Enterprises, Inc.

Eade, James. Chess Openings for Dummies. 2010. (ENG., Illus.). 384p. pap. 21.99 *(978-0-470-60364-2(X)*, For Dummies) Wiley, John & Sons, Inc.

Edwards, Jon & Henley, Ron. The Winawer! A Mainline French Variation. (ChessBase University Power Play! Ser.). (Illus.). 64p. (Orig.). pap. 10.95 *(978-1-883358-10-5(8))* R&D Publishing.

Eingorn, Viacheslav. Creative Chess Opening Preparation: How to Seize the Initiative & Pose Novel Problems for the Opponent. Sugden, John, tr. 2006. (ENG.). 158p. per. 14.95 *(978-1-904600-58-9(1))* Gambit Pubns., Ltd. GBR. Dist: Perseus Distribution.

Emms, John. Beating 1e4 E5: A Repertoire for White in the Open Games. 2010. (ENG., Illus.). 224p. pap. 26.95 *(978-1-85744-617-3(8))* Everyman Chess GBR. Dist: Globe Pequot Pr., The.

—Discovering Chess Openings: Building a Repertoire from Basic Principles. 2006. (ENG.). 192p. pap. 24.95 *(978-1-85744-419-3(1))* Everyman Chess GBR. Dist: Globe Pequot Pr., The.

—Starting Out? Scotch CD. 2007. (ENG.). cd-rom 23.95 *(978-1-85744-600-5(3))* Everyman Chess GBR. Dist: Globe Pequot Pr., The.

—Starting Out: the c3 Sicilian: Dazzle your Opponents! 2008. (ENG.). 192p. pap. 24.95 *(978-1-85744-570-1(8))* Everyman Chess GBR. Dist: Globe Pequot Pr., The.

Emms, John & Palliser, Richard. The Sicilian: Dazzle Your Opponents. 2006. (Dangerous Weapons Ser.). (ENG.). 304p. per. 24.95 *(978-1-85744-423-0(X))* Everyman Chess GBR. Dist: Globe Pequot Pr., The.

Emms, John, et al. Dangerous Weapons: 1 E4 E5: Dazzle Your Opponents in the Open Games! 2008. (Dangerous Weapons Ser.). (ENG., Illus.). 336p. pap. 25.95 *(978-1-85744-542-8(2))* Everyman Chess GBR. Dist: Globe Pequot Pr., The.

—The Nimzo-Indian. 2006. (Dangerous Weapons Ser.). (ENG., Illus.). 272p. per. 27.95 *(978-1-85744-424-7(8))* Everyman Chess GBR. Dist: Globe Pequot Pr., The.

Emms, Johns. The Sicilian. 2nd ed. 2009. (Starting Out - Everyman Chess Ser.). (ENG., Illus.). 304p. pap. 25.95 *(978-1-85744-588-6(0))* Everyman Chess GBR. Dist: Globe Pequot Pr., The.

Ernst, Sipke & Van Der Stricht, Geert. Tactics in the Chess Opening 5: Indian Defences: Catalan & Benoni. 2007. (Tactics in the Chess Opening Ser.). (ENG., Illus.). 240p. pap. 21.95 *(978-90-5691-201-7(1)*, New In Chess,Csi) Continental Sales, Inc.

—Tactics in the Chess Opening 6: Gambits & Flank Openings. 2007. (Tactics in the Chess Opening Ser.). (ENG., Illus.). 240p. per. 21.95 *(978-90-5691-221-5(6)*, New In Chess,Csi) Continental Sales, Inc.

Facaros, Dana & Pauls, Michael. Provence. 5th ed. 2009. (Illus.). 344p. pap. *(978-1-86011-409-0(1))* Cadogan Guides GBR. Dist: Globe Pequot Pr., The.

—Provence. 5th ed. 2009. (ENG., Illus.). 328p. pap. 21.95 *(978-1-56656-760-2(2))* Interlink Publishing Group, Inc.

Franco, Zenon. The English Opening. 2006. (Chess Explained Ser.). (ENG., Illus.). 111p. per. 19.95 *(978-1-904600-59-6(X))* Gambit Pubns., Ltd. GBR. Dist: Perseus Distribution.

—The Modern Benoni. Carballo, Manuel Perez, tr. from SPA. 2007. (Chess Explained Ser.). (ENG., Illus.). 112p. per. 23.95 *(978-1-904600-77-0(8))* Gambit Pubns., Ltd. GBR. Dist: Perseus Distribution.

Gallagher, Joe. Starting Out? Kings Indian CD. 2007. (ENG.). cd-rom 23.95 *(978-1-85744-609-8(7))* Everyman Chess GBR. Dist: Globe Pequot Pr., The.

Gawain, Jones. How to Beat the Sicilian Defence. 2011. (ENG.). 352p. pap. 29.95 *(978-1-85744-663-0(1))* Everyman Chess GBR. Dist: Globe Pequot Pr., The.

Greet, Andrew. Play the Queen's Indian. 2009. (ENG., Illus.). 256p. pap. 24.95 *(978-1-85744-580-0(5))* Everyman Chess GBR. Dist: Globe Pequot Pr., The.

—Play the Ruy Lopez: A Complete Repertoire in a Famous Opening. 2007. (ENG., Illus.). 376p. per. 28.95 *(978-1-85744-427-8(2))* Everyman Chess GBR. Dist: Globe Pequot Pr., The.

—Starting Out: the Accelerated Dragon: Fundamental Coverage of a Dynamic Sicilian. 2008. (ENG., Illus.). 320p. pap. 25.95 *(978-1-85744-530-5(9))* Everyman Chess GBR. Dist: Globe Pequot Pr., The.

Hansen, Carsten. Back to Basics: Openings. 2008. (ChessCafe Back to Basics Chess Ser.). (ENG.). 192p. pap. 22.95 *(978-1-888690-44-6(5))* Russell Enterprises, Inc.

Harvey, Bill. The Gambit Files: Tactical Themes to Sharpen Your Play. 2011. 156p. pap. 15.95 *(978-1-936277-11-7(5))* Mongoose Pr.

Hellsten, Johan. Play the Sicilian Kan: A Dynamic & Flexible Repertoire for Black. 2008. (ENG.). 192p. pap. 27.95 *(978-1-85744-581-7(3))* Everyman Chess GBR. Dist: Globe Pequot Pr., The.

Hilton, Jonathan & Ippolito, Dean. Wojo's Weapons: Winning with White. 2011. pap. 29.95 *(978-1-936277-23-0(9))* Mongoose Pr.

—Wojo's Weapons: Winning with White, Volume 1. 2010. (ENG.). 408p. pap. 29.95 *(978-0-9791482-0-0(0))* Mongoose Pr.

Hodges, Paul H. The Caro-Kann! (ChessBase University Power Play! Ser.). (Illus.). 64p. (Orig.). pap. 10.95 *(978-1-883358-09-9(4))* R&D Publishing.

Horowitz, I. A. How to Win in the Chess Openings. 2009. (ENG., Illus.). 204p. pap. 18.95 *(978-0-923891-28-2(5)*, GS19) Ishi Pr. International.

Houska, Jovanka. Play the Caro-Kann: A Complete Chess Opening Repertoire Against 1e4. 2007. (Everyman Chess Ser.). (ENG., Illus.). 192p. per. 24.95 *(978-1-85744-434-6(5))* Everyman Chess GBR. Dist: Globe Pequot Pr., The.

—Starting Out: The Scandinavian. 2009. (ENG., Illus.). 320p. pap. 25.95 *(978-1-85744-582-4(1))* Everyman Chess GBR. Dist: Globe Pequot Pr., The.

John, Emms. The Nimzo-Indian? Move by Move. 2011. (ENG.). 368p. pap. 29.95 ***(978-1-85744-666-1(6))*** Everyman Chess GBR. Dist: Globe Pequot Pr., The.

Johnsen, Sverre & Johannessen, Leif Erlend. The Ruy Lopez: A Guide for Black: A Reliable Defence with More Than a Spark of Aggression. 2007. (ENG., Illus.). 207p. per. 14.95 *(978-1-904600-67-1(0))* Gambit Pubns., Ltd. GBR. Dist: Perseus Distribution.

Jones, Gawain. Starting Out: Sicilian Grand Prix Attack. 2008. (ENG.). 176p. pap. 24.95 *(978-1-85744-547-3(3))* Everyman Chess GBR. Dist: Globe Pequot Pr., The.

Karpov, Anatoly & Podgaets, Mikhail. Caro-Kann Defence: Advance Variation & Gambit System. Adams, Jimmy, tr. 2006. (Batsford Chess Bks.). (ENG., Illus.). 244p. per. *(978-0-7134-9010-7(1)*, Batsford, B. T. Ltd.) Anova Bks. GBR. Dist: Sterling Publishing Co., Inc.

—Caro-Kann Defence: Panov Attack. Adams, Jimmy, tr. 2006. (Batsford Chess Bks.). (ENG., Illus.). 244p. per. 22.95 *(978-0-7134-9011-4(X)*, Batsford, B. T. Ltd.) Anova Bks. GBR. Dist: Sterling Publishing Co., Inc.

Keene, Raymond & Levy, David. How to Play the Opening in Chess. 2nd ed. (Illus.). 160p. reprint ed. pap. *(978-0-7134-7115-1(8)*, Batsford, B. T. Ltd.) Anova Bks.

Khalifman, Alexander. Opening for White According to Anand Vol. 8: Sicilian Defence. 2006. (YA). pap. *(978-954-8782-53-1(7))* Chess Stars.

—Opening for White According to Kramnik 1. NF3, Vol. 1b. 2nd rev. ed. 2006. pap. *(978-954-8782-50-0(2))* Chess Stars.

Konikowski, Jerzy & Soszynski, Marek. 1. B4: Theory & Practice of the Sokolsky Opening. 2009. (ENG., Illus.). 276p. pap. 29.95 *(978-1-888690-65-1(8))* Russell Enterprises, Inc.

Lakdawala, Cyrus. Play the London System. 2010. (ENG.). 256p. pap. 26.95 *(978-1-85744-639-5(9))* Everyman Chess GBR. Dist: Globe Pequot Pr., The.

Lakdawala, Cyrus. The Slav: Move by Move. 2011. (ENG.). 416p. pap. 29.95 ***(978-1-85744-678-4(X))*** Everyman Chess GBR. Dist: Globe Pequot Pr., The.

Langrock, Hannes. The Modern Morra Gambit: A Dynamic Weapon against the Sicilian. 2nd rev. ed. 2011. (ENG.). 320p. pap. 29.95 ***(978-1-936490-30-1(7))*** Russell Enterprises, Inc.

Lapshun, Yury & Conticello, Nick. Play 1b4! Shock Your Opponents with the Sokolsky. 2008. (Everyman Chess Ser.). (ENG., Illus.). 192p. pap. 24.95 *(978-1-85744-560-2(0))* Everyman Chess GBR. Dist: Globe Pequot Pr., The.

Larsen, Bent & Zeuthen, Steffen. Zoom 001 Zero Hour for Operative Chess Opening Models. 2011. (Illus.). 364p. pap. 25.95 ***(978-4-87187-450-2(6))*** Ishi Pr. International.

Levy, David N. L. Sacrifices in the Sicilian. 2009. (ENG., Illus.). 176p. pap. 24.95 *(978-4-87187-811-1(2))* Ishi Pr. International.

Marin, Mihail. Grandmaster Repertoire 3: The English Opening. 2009. (Illus.). 320p. pap. 29.95 *(978-1-906552-04-6(5))* Quality Chess UK LLP GBR. Dist: SCB Distributors.

—Grandmaster Repertoire 4: The English Opening, Vol. 2. 2010. (Grandmaster Repertoire Ser.). (ENG., Illus.). 400p. pap. 34.95 *(978-1-906552-38-1(X))* Quality Chess UK LLP GBR. Dist: SCB Distributors.

—Grandmaster Repertoire 5: The English Opening 1. c4 c5 - Volume Three. 2010. (Grandmaster Repertoire Ser.). (ENG., Illus.). 320p. pap. 34.95 *(978-1-906552-59-6(2))* Quality Chess Europe SWE. Dist: SCB Distributors.

—A Spanish Repertoire for Black. 2007. (Illus.). 231p. per. 29.95 *(978-91-976005-0-7(4))* Quality Chess Europe SWE. Dist: SCB Distributors.

Markos, Jan. Beat the KID: Three lines against the King's Indian. 2009. (Illus.). 320p. pap. 29.95 *(978-1-906552-15-2(0))* Quality Chess Europe SWE. Dist: SCB Distributors.

Martin, Andrew. Starting Out? Sicilian Dragon CD. 2007. (ENG.). cd-rom 23.95 *(978-1-85744-602-9(X))* Everyman Chess GBR. Dist: Globe Pequot Pr., The.

McDonald, Neil. How to Play Against 1 E4. 2009. (ENG., Illus.). 192p. pap. 24.95 *(978-1-85744-586-2(4))* Everyman Chess GBR. Dist: Globe Pequot Pr., The.

—Play the Dutch. 2010. (ENG.). 176p. pap. 26.95 *(978-1-85744-641-8(0))* Everyman Chess GBR. Dist: Globe Pequot Pr., The.

—Starting Out: 1e4. 2006. (Starting Out - Everyman Chess Ser.). (ENG., Illus.). 192p. per. 24.95 *(978-1-85744-416-2(7))* Everyman Chess GBR. Dist: Globe Pequot Pr., The.

—Starting Out? 1e4 CD. 2007. (ENG.). cd-rom 23.95 *(978-1-85744-610-4(0))* Everyman Chess GBR. Dist: Globe Pequot Pr., The.

—Starting Out: The Reti. 2010. (ENG.). 208p. pap. 26.95 *(978-1-85744-622-7(4))* Everyman Chess GBR. Dist: Globe Pequot Pr., The.

—Starting Out: Queen's Gambit Declined. 2006. (Starting Out - Everyman Chess Ser.). (ENG., Illus.). 192p. per. 23.95 *(978-1-85744-426-1(4))* Everyman Chess GBR. Dist: Globe Pequot Pr., The.

Moskalenko, Viktor. The Wonderful Winawer: Strategic Ideas & Surprise Weapons for Dynamic Chess Players. 2010. (ENG.). 240p. pap. 23.95 *(978-90-5691-327-4(1)*, New In Chess,Csi) Continental Sales, Inc.

Muller, Karsten & Knaack, Rainer. 222 Opening Traps: After 1. D4. 2008. (Progress in Chess Ser.). (ENG.). 200p. pap. 29.95 *(978-3-283-01005-8(6))* Edition Olms DEU. Dist: Independent Pubs. Group.

—222 Opening Traps: After 1.E4. 2007. (Progress in Chess Ser.). (ENG.). 200p. pap. 29.95 *(978-3-283-01004-1(8))* Edition Olms DEU. Dist: Independent Pubs. Group.

Nakamura, Hikaru, et al. Secrets of Opening Surprises: Volume 5. Bosch, Jeroen, ed. 2006. (SOS: Secrets of Opening Surprises Ser.). (ENG., Illus.). 144p. pap. 21.95 *(978-90-5691-170-6(8)*, New In Chess,Csi) Continental Sales, Inc.

Neil, Mcdonald. The Ruy Lopez? Move by Move. 2011. (ENG.). 320p. pap. 27.95 ***(978-1-85744-669-2(0))*** Everyman Chess GBR. Dist: Globe Pequot Pr., The.

Nijboer, Friso & Van Der Stricht, Geert. Tactics in the Chess Opening 4: Queen's Gambits (Trompowsky & Torre) 2006. (Tactics in the Chess Opening Ser.). (ENG., Illus.). 240p. per. 21.95 *(978-90-5691-172-0(4)*, New In Chess,Csi) Continental Sales, Inc.

Obodchuk, Andrey. The Four Knights Game: New Adventures in an Old Chess Opening. 2011. (ENG.). 240p. pap. 23.95 ***(978-90-5691-372-4(7)***, New In Chess,Csi) Continental Sales, Inc.

Odessky, Ilya & Odesskii, I. Play 1.b3! The Nimzo-Larsen Attack: A Friend for Life. 2008. (ENG., Illus.). 230p. pap. 26.95 *(978-90-5691-256-7(9)*, New In Chess,Csi) Continental Sales, Inc.

Palliser, Richard. Starting Out: The Colle. 2007. (ENG., Illus.). 192p. pap. 24.95 *(978-1-85744-527-5(9))* Everyman Chess GBR. Dist: Globe Pequot Pr., The.

Palliser, Richard. Beating Unusual Chess Openings: Dealing with the English, Reti, King's Indian Attack & Other Annoying Systems. 2007. (Everyman Chess Ser.). (ENG., Illus.). 224p. per. 24.95 *(978-1-85744-429-2(9))* Everyman Chess GBR. Dist: Globe Pequot Pr., The.

—D-Pawn Attacks: The Colle-Zukertort, Barry & 150 Attacks. 2008. (ENG.). 272p. pap. 27.95 *(978-1-85744-578-7(3))* Everyman Chess GBR. Dist: Globe Pequot Pr., The.

—Fighting the Anti-Sicilians: Combating 2 C3, the Closed, the Morra Gambit & Other Tricky Ideas. 2007. (Everyman Chess Ser.). (ENG., Illus.). 256p. per. 26.95 *(978-1-85744-520-6(1))* Everyman Chess GBR. Dist: Globe Pequot Pr., The.

—Starting Out? Closed Sicilian CD. 2007. (ENG.). cd-rom 23.95 *(978-1-85744-603-6(8))* Everyman Chess GBR. Dist: Globe Pequot Pr., The.

—Starting Out? Sicilian Najdorf CD. 2007. (ENG.). cd-rom 23.95 *(978-1-85744-601-2(1))* Everyman Chess GBR. Dist: Globe Pequot Pr., The.

—Starting Out: the Trompowsky Attack. 2009. (ENG.). 272p. pap. 24.95 *(978-1-85744-562-6(7))* Everyman Chess GBR. Dist: Globe Pequot Pr., The.

Palliser, Richard & Vigus, James. The Pirc & Modern. 2009. (ENG.). 192p. pap. 24.95 *(978-1-85744-594-7(5))* Everyman Chess GBR. Dist: Globe Pequot Pr., The.

Palliser, Richard, et al. Dangerous Weapons: The Dutch. 2009. (ENG., Illus.). 192p. pap. 26.95 *(978-1-85744-624-1(0))* Everyman Chess GBR. Dist: Globe Pequot Pr., The.

—Dangerous Weapons: the Benoni & Benko: Dazzle your Opponents! 2008. (ENG.). 192p. pap. 25.95 *(978-1-85744-571-8(6))* Everyman Chess GBR. Dist: Globe Pequot Pr., The.

—The King's Indian: Dazzle Your Opponents! 2009. (ENG.). 272p. pap. 24.95 *(978-1-85744-593-0(7))* Everyman Chess GBR. Dist: Globe Pequot Pr., The.

—The Queens Gambit: Dazzle Your Opponents! 2008. (Dangerous Weapons Ser.). (ENG.). 240p. pap. 24.95 *(978-1-85744-546-6(5))* Everyman Chess GBR. Dist: Globe Pequot Pr., The.

Pallister, Kosten, et al. Flank Openings: Dazzle Your Opponents! 2008. (ENG., Illus.). 256p. pap. 24.95 *(978-1-85744-583-1(X))* Everyman Chess GBR. Dist: Globe Pequot Pr., The.

Panczyk, Krzysztof & Ilczuk, Jacek. The Classical King's Indian Uncovered. 2009. (ENG.). 384p. pap. 25.95 *(978-1-85744-517-6(1))* Everyman Chess GBR. Dist: Globe Pequot Pr., The.

Pavlovic, Milos. The Cutting Edge 1 - the Open Sicilian 1. 2010. (Cutting Edge Ser.). (ENG., Illus.). 224p. pap. 27.95 *(978-1-906552-57-2(6))* Quality Chess Europe SWE. Dist: SCB Distributors.

—The Cutting Edge 2: Sicilian Najdorf 6.Be3. 2011. (Cutting Edge Ser.). (ENG.). 384p. pap. 29.95 *(978-1-906552-77-0(0))* Quality Chess Europe SWE. Dist: SCB Distributors.

—Fighting the Ruy Lopez. 2009. (ENG.). 192p. pap. 25.95 *(978-1-85744-590-9(2))* Everyman Chess GBR. Dist: Globe Pequot Pr., The.

Pritchett, Craig. Play the English: An Active Opening Repertoire for White. 2008. (Everyman Chess Ser.). (ENG., Illus.). 192p. per. 24.95 *(978-1-85744-545-9(7))* Everyman Chess GBR. Dist: Globe Pequot Pr., The.

—Sicilian Scheveningen. 2006. (Starting Out - Everyman Chess Ser.). (ENG., Illus.). 192p. per. 23.95 *(978-1-85744-413-1(2))* Everyman Chess GBR. Dist: Globe Pequot Pr., The.

Raetsky, Alexander & Chetverik, Maxim. Starting Out: Classical Sicilian. 2007. (ENG., Illus.). 192p. per. 24.95 *(978-1-85744-537-4(6))* Everyman Chess GBR. Dist: Globe Pequot Pr., The.

Rizzitano, James. Chess Explained: the Queen's Gambit Declined. 2007. (Chess Explained Ser.). (ENG., Illus.). 128p. per. 23.95 *(978-1-904600-80-0(8))* Gambit Pubns., Ltd. GBR. Dist: Perseus Distribution.

—Chess Explained: the Taimanov Sicilian. 2006. (Chess Explained Ser.). (ENG., Illus.). 111p. per. 19.95 *(978-1-904600-62-6(X))* Gambit Pubns., Ltd. GBR. Dist: Perseus Distribution.

—Play the Najdorf Sicilian. 2010. (ENG., Illus.). 128p. pap. 22.95 *(978-1-906454-16-6(7))* Gambit Pubns., Ltd. GBR. Dist: Perseus Distribution.

Rogers, Ian, et al, contrib. by. Secrets of Opening Surprises: Volume 6. 2007. (SOS: Secrets of Opening Surprises Ser.). (ENG., Illus.). 144p. pap. 21.95 *(978-90-5691-193-5(7)*, New in Chess,Csi) Continental Sales, Inc.

Schandorff, Lars. Playing the Queen's Gambit: A Grandmaster Guide. 2009. 256p. pap. 27.95 *(978-1-906552-18-3(5))* Quality Chess Europe SWE. Dist: SCB Distributors.

C

Scheerer, Chris. Greatest Ever Chess Opening Ideas! 2008. (ENG.). 192p. pap. 25.95 *(978-1-85744-561-9(9))* Everyman Chess GBR. Dist: Globe Pequot Pr., The.

Scherbakov, Ruslan. The Triangle System: Challenging White in the Semi-Slav. 2012. (ENG.). 448p. pap. 29.95 *(978-1-85744-644-9(5))* Everyman Chess GBR. Dist: Globe Pequot Pr., The.

Schiller, Eric. Secrets of the Sicilian Dragon Revised. 2011. (ENG.). 192p. pap. 14.95 *(978-1-58042-279-6(9))* Cardoza Publishing.

—World Champion Openings. 2009. (ENG.). 400p. pap. 19.95 *(978-1-58042-253-6(5))* Cardoza Publishing.

Schiller, Eric & Shamkovich, Leonid. Spanish Gambits updated in 2011: Chess Works Publication. 2011. (Illus.). 128p. pap. 15.95 ***(978-4-87187-440-3(0))*** Ishi Pr. International.

Shaw, John. Experts on the Anti-Sicilian. Aagaard, Jacob, ed. 2011. (ENG.). 288p. pap. 29.95 *(978-1-906552-80-0(0))* Quality Chess Europe SWE. Dist: SCB Distributors.

—The King's Gambit. 2011. (ENG.). 224p. pap. 29.95 *(978-1-906552-71-8(1))* Quality Chess Europe SWE. Dist: SCB Distributors.

Shipov, Sergey. The Complete Hedgehog, Volume 1. 2009. (ENG., Illus.). 532p. pap. 29.95 *(978-0-9791482-1-7(9))* Mongoose Pr.

Snyder, Robert M. Winning Chess Traps: Opening Tactics for the Advanced Beginner & Intermediate Player. 2007. 232p. per. 18.95 *(978-0-595-45345-0(7))* iUniverse, Inc.

Sokolov, Ivan. The Ruy Lopez Revisited: Offbeat Weapons & Unexplored Resources. 2010. (ENG., Illus.). 240p. pap. 27.95 *(978-90-5691-297-0(6)*, New In Chess,Csi) Continental Sales, Inc.

Sosonko, Genna. New in Chess Yearbook 84: The Chess Player's Guide to Opening News. 2007. (ENG.). 246p. pap. 28.95 *(978-90-5691-212-3(7)*, New In Chess,Csi) Continental Sales, Inc.

—New in Chess Yearbook 85: The Chess Player's Guide to Opening News. 2008. (ENG.). 248p. pap. 28.95 *(978-90-5691-234-5(8)*, New In Chess,Csi) Continental Sales, Inc.

Sosonko, Genna. New in Chess Yearbook 81: The Chess Player's Guide to Opening News. 2007. (ENG.). 248p. 36.95 *(978-90-5691-190-4(2)*, New In Chess,Csi) Continental Sales, Inc.

—New in Chess Yearbook 84: The Chess Player's Guide to Opening News. 2007. (ENG.). 246p. 36.95 *(978-90-5691-213-0(5)*, New In Chess,Csi) Continental Sales, Inc.

—New in Chess Yearbook 85: The Chess Player's Guide to Opening News. 2008. (ENG.). 248p. 36.95 *(978-90-5691-235-2(6)*, New In Chess,Csi) Continental Sales, Inc.

—New in Chess Yearbook 94. 2010. (ENG.). 250p. 38.95 *(978-90-5691-312-0(3))*; pap. 29.95 *(978-90-5691-311-3(5))* Continental Sales, Inc. (New In Chess,Csi).

Sosonko, Genna, ed. The Chess Player's Guide to Opening News 100. (ENG.). 2011. 280p. 38.95 ***(978-90-5691-359-5(X))*** 2011. 280p. pap. 29.95 ***(978-90-5691-358-8(1))***Volume 101. 2012. 250p. 39.95 ***(978-90-5691-361-8(1))*** Continental Sales, Inc. (New In Chess,Csi).

—New in Chess Yearbook: The Chess Player's Guide to Opening News. 2011. 250p. pap. 29.95 *(978-90-5691-335-9(2)*, New In Chess,Csi) Continental Sales, Inc.

—New in Chess Yearbook 101: The\Chess Player's Guide to Opening News, Volume 101. 2012. (ENG.). 250p. pap. 33.95 ***(978-90-5691-360-1(3)***, New In Chess,Csi) Continental Sales, Inc.

—New In Chess Yearbook 90: The Chess Player's Guide to Opening News. 2009. (ENG.). 250p. 38.95 *(978-90-5691-253-6(4))*; pap. 29.95 *(978-90-5691-252-9(6))* Continental Sales, Inc. (New In Chess,Csi).

—New In Chess Yearbook 91: The Chess Player's Guide to Opening News. 2009. (ENG.). 250p. 38.95 *(978-90-5691-266-6(6))*; pap. 29.95 *(978-90-5691-265-9(8))* Continental Sales, Inc. (New In Chess,Csi).

—New In Chess Yearbook 92: The Chess Player's Guide to Opening News. 2009. (Yearbook Ser.). (ENG.). 250p. 38.95 *(978-90-5691-287-1(9))*; pap. 29.95 *(978-90-5691-288-8(7))* Continental Sales, Inc. (New In Chess,Csi).

—New In Chess Yearbook 93: The Chess Player's Guide to Opening News. 2010. (Yearbook Ser.). (ENG.). 250p. 38.95 *(978-90-5691-290-1(9))*; pap. 29.95 *(978-90-5691-289-5(5))* Continental Sales, Inc. (New In Chess,Csi).

—New in Chess Yearbook V86. 2008. (ENG.). 250p. 36.95 *(978-90-5691-237-6(2))*; pap. 28.95 *(978-90-5691-236-9(4))* Continental Sales, Inc. (New In Chess,Csi).

—New in Chess Yearbook V87. 2008. (ENG.). 250p. 36.95 *(978-90-5691-239-0(9))*; pap. 28.95 *(978-90-5691-238-3(0))* Continental Sales, Inc. (New In Chess,Csi).

—New in Chess Yearbook V88. 2008. (ENG.). 250p. 38.95 *(978-90-5691-249-9(6))*; pap. 29.95 *(978-90-5691-248-2(8))* Continental Sales, Inc. (New In Chess,Csi).

—Yearbook 82: The Chess Player's Guide to Opening News. 2007. (ENG.). 248p. 36.95 *(978-90-5691-192-8(9))*; pap. 28.95 *(978-90-5691-191-1(0))* Continental Sales, Inc. (New In Chess,Csi).

—Yearbook 83: The Chess Player's Guide to Opening News. 2007. (ENG.). 248p. 36.95 *(978-90-5691-207-9(0))*; pap. 28.95 *(978-90-5691-206-2(2))* Continental Sales, Inc. (New In Chess,Csi).

Storey, Charlie. The Sniper: Play 1... G6, ... Bg7 & ... C5! 2011. (ENG.). 176p. pap. 26.95 *(978-1-85744-643-2(7))* Everyman Chess GBR. Dist: Globe Pequot Pr., The.

Summerscale, Johnsen, et al. Killer Chess Opening Repertoire. enl. ed. 2010. (ENG.). 192p. pap. 19.95 *(978-1-906454-18-0(3))* Gambit Pubns., Ltd. GBR. Dist: Perseus Distribution.

Sveshnikov, Evgeny. The Complete c3 Sicilian. 2010. (ENG.). 575p. pap. 34.95 *(978-90-5691-329-8(8)*, New In Chess,Csi) Continental Sales, Inc.

—French Defence Advance Variation Vol. 1: Basic Course. 2008. (Progress in Chess Ser.). (ENG., Illus.). 176p. per. 29.95 *(978-3-283-00523-8(0))* Edition Olms DEU. Dist: Independent Pubs. Group.

—French Defence Advance Variation Vol. 2: White Repertoire for Tournament Players. 2008. (Progress in Chess Ser.). (ENG., Illus.). 152p. pap. 29.95 *(978-3-283-00524-5(9))* Edition Olms DEU. Dist: Independent Pubs. Group.

Taylor, Timothy. Beating the King's Indian & Grunfeld. 2006. (Everyman Chess Ser.). (ENG., Illus.). 224p. per. 23.95 *(978-1-85744-428-5(0))* Everyman Chess GBR. Dist: Globe Pequot Pr., The.

—The Budapest Gambit. 2009. (ENG.). 240p. pap. 24.95 *(978-1-85744-592-3(9))* Everyman Chess GBR. Dist: Globe Pequot Pr., The.

—Slay the Spanish! 2011. (ENG., Illus.). 288p. pap. 27.95 *(978-1-85744-637-1(2))* Everyman Chess GBR. Dist: Globe Pequot Pr., The.

Tzermiadianos, Andreas. How to Beat the French Defence: The Essential Guide to the Tarrasch. 2008. (ENG.). 192p. pap. 25.95 *(978-1-85744-567-1(8))* Everyman Chess GBR. Dist: Globe Pequot Pr., The.

van der Sterren, Paul. FCO - Fundamental Chess Openings. 2009. (ENG.). 448p. pap. 29.95 *(978-1-906454-13-5(2))* Gambit Pubns., Ltd. GBR. Dist: Perseus Distribution.

Vanrekom, Jerry & Janssen, Leo. Black Lion: The Chess Predator's Choice Against Both 1.e4 & 1.d4. 2009. (ENG.). 280p. pap. 27.95 *(978-90-5691-257-4(7)*, New In Chess,Csi) Continental Sales, Inc.

Vera, Reinaldo. The Meran Semi-Slav. Adams, Phil, tr. 2007. (Chess Explained Ser.). (ENG., Illus.). 112p. per. 23.95 *(978-1-904600-81-7(6))* Gambit Pubns., Ltd. GBR. Dist: Perseus Distribution.

—Nimzo-Indian. Adams, Phil, tr. 2008. (Chess Explained Ser.). (ENG., Illus.). 111p. pap. 23.95 *(978-1-904600-72-5(7))* Gambit Pubns., Ltd. GBR. Dist: Perseus Distribution.

Vigorito, David. Challenging the Nimzo-Indian. 2007. (Illus.). 325p. per. 29.95 *(978-91-976005-5-2(5))* Quality Chess Europe SWE. Dist: SCB Distributors.

—Play the Semi-Slav. 2008. (Illus.). 277p. pap. 25.95 *(978-91-85779-01-7(6))* Quality Chess Europe SWE. Dist: SCB Distributors.

—Understanding the Marshall Attack. 2010. (ENG.). 176p. pap. 23.95 *(978-1-906454-17-3(5))* Gambit Pubns., Ltd. GBR. Dist: Perseus Distribution.

Vigus, James. The Pirc in Black & White: Detailed Coverage of an Enterprising Chess Opening. 2007. (Everyman Chess Ser.). (ENG., Illus.). 384p. per. 25.95 *(978-1-85744-432-2(9))* Everyman Chess GBR. Dist: Globe Pequot Pr., The.

—Play the Slav. 2008. (ENG., Illus.). 192p. pap. 26.95 *(978-1-85744-557-2(0))* Everyman Chess GBR. Dist: Globe Pequot Pr., The.

Wahls, Matthias. The Modern Scandinavian: Themes, Structures & Plans in an Increasingly Popular Chess Opening. 2011. 384p. pap. 29.95 *(978-90-5691-344-1(1)*, New In Chess,Csi) Continental Sales, Inc.

Ward, Barbara. Chess Tactics & Checkmates. 2006. (Starting Out - Everyman Chess Ser.). (ENG.). 176p. per. 23.95 *(978-1-85744-418-6(3))* Everyman Chess GBR. Dist: Globe Pequot Pr., The.

—Play the Queens Gambit CD. 2007. (ENG.). cd-rom 23.95 *(978-1-85744-608-1(9))* Everyman Chess GBR. Dist: Globe Pequot Pr., The.

Watson, John. The French. 2007. (Dangerous Weapons Ser.). (ENG., Illus.). 192p. per. 25.95 *(978-1-85744-435-3(3))* Everyman Chess GBR. Dist: Globe Pequot Pr., The.

—Mastering the Chess Openings. (ENG., Illus.). Vol. 3. 2008. 351p. pap. 29.95 *(978-1-904600-98-5(0))* Vol. 4. 2010. 336p. pap. 29.95 *(978-1-906454-19-7(1))* Gambit Pubns., Ltd. GBR. Dist: Perseus Distribution.

—Mastering the Chess Openings: Unlocking the Mysteries of the Modern Chess Openings. 2006. (ENG., Illus.). 334p. per. 29.95 *(978-1-904600-60-2(3))* Gambit Pubns., Ltd. GBR. Dist: Perseus Distribution.

—Mastering the Chess Openings Vol. 2: Unlocking the Mysteries of the Modern Chess Openings. 2007. (ENG., Illus.). 318p. per. 29.95 *(978-1-904600-69-5(7))* Gambit Pubns., Ltd. GBR. Dist: Perseus Distribution.

Wells, Peter. Grandmaster Secrets: the Caro-Kann. 2007. (ENG.). 175p. per. 29.95 *(978-1-904600-61-9(1))* Gambit Pubns., Ltd. GBR. Dist: Perseus Distribution.

Williams, Simon. Attacking Chess - The French: A Dynamic Repertoire for Black. 2011. (ENG.). 320p. pap. 27.95 *(978-1-85744-646-3(1))* Everyman Chess GBR. Dist: Globe Pequot Pr., The.

—The New Sicilian Dragon. 2009. (ENG.). 224p. pap. 24.95 *(978-1-85744-615-9(1))* Everyman Chess GBR. Dist: Globe Pequot Pr., The.

Wisnewski, Christoph. Play 1... Nc6! A Complete Chess Opening Repertoire for Black. 2007. (Everyman Chess Ser.). (ENG., Illus.). 192p. per. 24.95 *(978-1-85744-522-0(8))* Everyman Chess GBR. Dist: Globe Pequot Pr., The.

Yakovich, Yuri. Sicilian Attacks: Powerful Charges & Typical Tactics. 2011. (ENG.). 208p. pap. 21.95 *(978-90-5691-332-8(8)*, New In Chess,Csi) Continental Sales, Inc.

Yapshun, Yury & Conticello, Nick. Seven Ways to Smash the Sicilian. 2009. (ENG., Illus.). 192p. pap. 24.95 *(978-1-85744-595-4(3))* Everyman Chess GBR. Dist: Globe Pequot Pr., The.

CHESS—PICTORIAL WORKS

Benson, Harry. Bobby Fischer. 2011. (ENG., Illus.). 144p. 39.95 *(978-1-57687-581-0(4))* powerHouse Cultural Entertainment, Inc.

Orozco, Gabriel, illus. The Samurai Tree Invariants, 1 vol. 2007. (ENG.). 676p. pap. 100.00 *(978-3-86560-166-7(9))* Verlag der Buchhandlung Walther Konig DEU. Dist: D.A.P./Distributed Art Pubs.

CHESS—PROBLEMS

see Chess Problems

CHESS—TOURNAMENTS

Alekhine, Alexander. New York 1924. 2009. (Illus.). 352p. pap. 29.95 *(978-1-888690-48-4(8))* Russell Enterprises, Inc.

—Nottingham 1936. 2009. (ENG., Illus.). 200p. pap. 24.95 *(978-1-888690-63-7(1))* Russell Enterprises, Inc.

Botvinnik, Mikhail. Botvinnik - Petrosian: 1963 World Chess Championship Match. 2010. (ENG.). 144p. pap. 22.95 *(978-90-5691-314-4(X)*, New In Chess,Csi) Continental Sales, Inc.

Christiansen, Larry, et al. On Top of the Chess World: The 1995 World Chess Championships. Date not set. (Competitive Chess Ser.). (Illus.). 100p. (Orig.). pap. 14.95 *(978-1-886040-20-5(6))* Hypermodern Pr.

Di Felice, Gino. Chess Results, 1921-1930: A Comprehensive Record with 940 Tournament Crosstables & 210 Match Scores. 2006. (ENG., Illus.). 354p. per. 49.95 *(978-0-7864-2642-3(X))* McFarland & Co., Inc. Pubs.

—Chess Results, 1931-1935: A Comprehensive Record with 1,065 Tournament Crosstables & 190 Match Scores. 2006. (ENG., Illus.). 424p. per. 49.95 *(978-0-7864-2723-9(X))* McFarland & Co., Inc. Pubs.

—Chess Results, 1936-1940: A Comprehensive Record with 990 Tournament Crosstables & 125 Match Scores. 2007. (ENG., Illus.). 392p. per. 49.95 *(978-0-7864-2748-2(5))* McFarland & Co., Inc. Pubs.

—Chess Results, 1941-1946: A Comprehensive Record with 810 Tournament Crosstables & 80 Match Scores, with Sources. 2008. (ENG., Illus.). 376p. pap. 49.95 *(978-0-7864-3819-8(3))* McFarland & Co., Inc. Pubs.

—Chess Results, 1947-1950: A Comprehensive Record with 980 Tournament Crosstables & 155 Match Scores with Sources. 2008. (ENG., Illus.). 496p. pap. 49.95 *(978-0-7864-3820-4(7))* McFarland & Co., Inc. Pubs.

—Chess Results, 1951-1955: A Comprehensive Record with 1,620 Tournament Crosstables & 144 Match Scores, with Sources. 2010. (ENG., Illus.). 606p. pap. 49.95 *(978-0-7864-4801-2(6))* McFarland & Co., Inc. Pubs.

—Chess Results, 1956-1960: A Comprehensive Record with 1,385 Tournament Crosstables & 142 Match Scores, with Sources. 2010. (ENG., Illus.). 582p. pap. 49.95 *(978-0-7864-4803-6(2))* McFarland & Co., Inc. Pubs.

Euwe, Max & Timman, Jan. Fischer World Champion: The Acclaimed Classic about the 1972 Fischer-Spassky Match. 3rd ed. 2009. (ENG.). 195p. pap. 24.95 *(978-90-5691-263-5(1)*, New In Chess,Csi) Continental Sales, Inc.

Evans, Larry. Vienna 1922. 2011. (ENG.). 144p. pap. 19.95 *(978-1-936490-02-8(1))* Russell Enterprises, Inc.

Forster, Richard. The Zurich Chess Club, 1809-2009. 2011. (ENG., Illus.). 448p. 55.00 *(978-0-7864-6064-9(4))* McFarland & Co., Inc. Pubs.

Golombek, Harry. Reykjavik 1972. 2007. (Illus.). 205p. pap. *(978-1-84382-187-8(7))* Hardinge Simpole Publishing.

Groningen International Chess Tournament 1946. 2007. (Illus.). 164p. pap. *(978-1-84382-184-7(2))* Hardinge Simpole Publishing.

Johnson, Daniel. White King & Red Queen: How the Cold War Was Fought on the Chessboard. 2008. (ENG., Illus.). 384p. 26.00 *(978-0-547-13337-9(5))* Houghton Mifflin Harcourt Trade & Reference Pubs.

Kaikamjozov, Zhivko. The Genius & the Misery of Chess. 2008. (ENG.). 224p. pap. 19.95 *(978-0-9791482-3-1(5))* Mongoose Pr.

Karolyi, Tibor & Aplin, Nick. Kasparov: How His Predecessors Misled Him about Chess. 2009. (ENG., Illus.). 272p. pap. 22.95 *(978-1-906388-26-3(1)*, Batsford, B. T. Ltd.) Anova Bks. GBR. Dist: Sterling Publishing Co., Inc.

Karpov, Anatoly & Henley, Ron. Elista Diaries: Karpov-Kamsky, Karpov-Anand, Anand Mexico City 2007 World Chess Championship Matches. 2007. (Illus.). 414p. per. *(978-0-923891-97-8(8))* Ishi Pr. International.

Knobloch, Darrel. How to Start & Run A Scholastic Chess Program: How to Organize & Run a Successful Chess Program for a School, Library, Aftercare or Recreation Center. 2010. 127p. pap. 17.95 *(978-1-4327-6476-0(4))* Outskirts Pr., Inc.

Lawson, Dominic. Inner Game. 2008. 264p. pap. *(978-1-84382-137-3(0))* Hardinge Simpole Publishing.

Maroczy, Geza & Capablanca, Jose Raul. London 1922/the 1921 World Chess Championship Match. 2010. (Illus.). 128p. pap. *(978-1-888690-61-3(5))* Russell Enterprises, Inc.

Paige, Roger Leslie. Hampshire Chess Games, 1950 to 1970. 2008. (Illus.). 523p. pap. *(978-1-897312-79-7(2))* Adlibbed, Ltd.

Sloan, Sam. Showdown in Siberia: The 2010 World Chess Olympiad in Khanty-Mansiysk, Russia. 2010. (ENG., Illus.). 300p. per. 29.95 *(978-0-923891-89-3(7))* Ishi Pr. International.

Soltis, Andy. The United States Chess Championship, 1845-2011, 3d Ed. 3rd rev. ed. 2011. (ENG.). 286p. pap. 45.00 ***(978-0-7864-6528-6(X))*** McFarland & Co., Inc. Pubs.

Soltis, Andy & McCormick, Gene H. The United States Chess Championship, 1845-1996. 2nd rev. alt. ed. 2006. (ENG., Illus.). 247p. per. 39.95 *(978-0-7864-2856-4(2))* McFarland & Co., Inc. Pubs.

Topalov, Veselin & Ginchev, Zhivko. Topalov-Kramnik 2006 World Chess Championship: On the Edge in Elista. 2007. (Illus.). 220p. per. 29.95 *(978-1-888690-39-2(9))* Russell Enterprises, Inc.

CHESS—VARIANTS

see Chess Variations

CHESS GAMES

see Chess—Collections of Games

CHESS OPENINGS

see Chess—Openings

CHESS PROBLEMS

Alberston, Bruce. Chess Mazes 2. 2008. (ENG.). 144p. pap. 17.95 *(978-1-888690-35-4(6))* Russell Enterprises, Inc.

Anderson, Ian. Chess Visualization Course. 2007. (Illus.). pap. *(978-0-9795940-2-1(2))* Gelvert Publishing LLC.

Brecher, Erwin & Barden, Leonard. One Move & You're Dead! 2010. (ENG., Illus.). 192p. pap. 14.95 *(978-1-84732-347-7(2))* Carlton Bks., Ltd. GBR. Dist: Independent Pubs. Group.

Burgess, Graham. The Gambit Book of Instructive Chess Puzzles. 2011. (ENG.). 160p. pap. 16.95 *(978-1-906454-28-9(0))* Gambit Pubns., Ltd. GBR. Dist: Perseus Distribution.

Colin, Crouch. Analyse Your Chess. 2011. (ENG.). 240p. pap. 26.95 *(978-1-85744-670-8(4))* Everyman Chess GBR. Dist: Globe Pequot Pr., The.

Franco, Zenon. The Giant Chess Puzzle Book. 2010. (ENG., Illus.). 288p. pap. 26.95 *(978-1-906454-20-3(5))* Gambit Pubns., Ltd. GBR. Dist: Perseus Distribution.

Giddins, Steve. 50 Ways to Win at Chess. 2007. (ENG., Illus.). 173p. per. 14.95 *(978-1-904600-85-5(9))* Gambit Pubns., Ltd. GBR. Dist: Perseus Distribution.

Gosling, Brian. John Brown: the Forgotten Chess Composer? 50 chess problems by John Brown. 2011. (ENG.). 220p. pap. ***(978-1-84876-729-4(3))*** Troubadour Publishing Ltd.

Kaufeld, Jurgen. Grandmaster Chess Strategy: What Amateurs Can Learn from Ulf Andersson's Positional Masterpieces. 2011. (ENG.). 224p. pap. 24.95 *(978-90-5691-346-5(8)*, New In Chess,Csi) Continental Sales, Inc.

Khmelnitsky, Igor. Chess Exam & Training Guide: Rate Yourself & Learn How to Improve! 2007. (Chess Exams Ser.). (ENG.). 208p. per. 19.95 *(978-0-9754761-1-6(4))* IamCoach.com Publishing.

Müller, Karsten. The ChessCafe Puzzle Book 2: Test & Improve Your Positional Intuition. 2008. (ChessCafe Puzzle Book Ser.). (ENG.). 250p. pap. 24.95 *(978-1-888690-43-9(7))* Russell Enterprises, Inc.

Nunn, John. John Nunn's Chess Puzzle Book. enl. ed. 2009. (ENG.). 335p. pap. 24.95 *(978-1-906454-03-6(5))* Gambit Pubns., Ltd. GBR. Dist: Perseus Distribution.

Palliser, Richard. The Complete Chess Workout: Train Your Brain with 1500 Puzzles! 2007. (Everyman Chess Ser.). (ENG.). 360p. pap. 29.95 *(978-1-85744-532-9(5))* Everyman Chess GBR. Dist: Globe Pequot Pr., The.

Shahade, Jennifer, ed. Play Like a Girl! Tactics By 9Queens. 2011. 100p. 14.95 *(978-1-936277-03-2(4))* Mongoose Pr.

Smullyan, Raymond M. The Chess Mysteries of Sherlock Holmes: Fifty Tantalizing Problems of Chess Detection. 2012. (Dover Recreational Math Ser.). (ENG.). 192p. pap. 12.95 ***(978-0-486-48201-9(4))*** Dover Pubns., Inc.

Yakovlev, Nikolay. Chess Blueprints: Planning in the Middlegame. 2010. (ENG., Illus.). 272p. pap. 24.95 *(978-1-936277-01-8(8))* Mongoose Pr.

CHESS VARIATIONS

see also Chinese Chess; Shogi

Chess Variants: Chess Variant, Shogi, Xiangqi, Chess960, Baroque Chess, Shatranj, Three-Dimensional Chess, Avalanche Chess, Bughouse Chess. 2010. 488p. pap. 14.14 *(978-1-157-08625-3(X))* General Bks. LLC.

Llc, Books. Chess Variants: Capablanca Chess Variants, Fairy Chess, Fairy Chess Pieces, Shogi, Xiangqi, Chess960, Baroque Chess, Shatranj. 2010. 494p. pap. 55.69 *(978-1-156-07308-7(1))* General Bks. LLC.

Yusupov, Artur. Boost Your Chess 3 with Artur Yusupov. 2011. (Boost your Chess Ser.). (ENG.). 288p. pap. 29.95 *(978-1-906552-44-2(4))* Quality Chess Europe SWE. Dist: SCB Distributors.

CHESSMAN, CARYL, 1921-1960

Chessman, Caryl. Cell 2455, Death Row: A Condemned Man's Own Story. 2006. (ENG., Illus.). 336p. per. 15.95 *(978-0-7867-1815-3(3))* Da Capo Pr., Inc.

CHESSMEN

Caldwell, David, et al. The Lewis Chessmen Unmasked. 2011. (ENG., Illus.). 80p. 15.95 *(978-1-905267-46-0(0))* NMS Enterprises Ltd. - Publishing GBR. Dist: National Bk. Network.

Darlow, Mike. Woodturning Chessmen. 2008. (Darlow's Woodturning Ser.). (ENG., Illus.). 168p. pap. 24.95 *(978-1-56523-373-7(5))* Fox Chapel Publishing Co., Inc.

Kape, Jim. Wooden Chess Sets: 15 One-of-a-Kind Projects for the Scroll Saw. 2010. (Illus.). 136p. pap. 19.95 *(978-1-56523-457-4(X))* Fox Chapel Publishing Co., Inc.

Liddell, Donald M. Chessmen. 2008. (Illus.). 180p. pap. 29.95 *(978-0-923891-42-8(0))* Ishi Pr. International.

CHEST

see also Aorta; Heart; Lungs; Mediastinum; Pericardium; Respiratory Organs

Baert, A. L., frwd. Pediatric Chest Imaging: Chest Imaging in Infants & Children. 2nd rev. ed. 2007. (Medical Radiology / Diagnostic Imaging Ser.). (Illus.). 510p. 319.00 *(978-3-540-32675-5(8))*, 3540326758) Springer.

Deslauriers, Jean. Thoracic Anatomy, Part II, an Issue of Thoracic Surgery Clinics, 2 vols. 2011. (Clinics: Surgery Ser.: 21-2). (ENG., Illus.). 200p. 105.00 *(978-1-4377-2269-7(5)*, Saunders) Elsevier - Health Sciences Div.

Federle, Michael P., et al. Chest, Abdomen, Pelvis. 2006. (Diagnostic & Surgical Imaging Anatomy Ser.). (ENG., Illus.). 1250p. 249.00 *(978-1-931884-33-4(1))* Lippincott Williams & Wilkins.

Gotway, Michael. Netter's Correlative Imaging: Cardiothoracic Anatomy: With Online Access. 2012. (Netter Clinical Science Ser.). (ENG., Illus.). 448p. 199.00 ***(978-1-4377-0440-2(9)***, Saunders) Elsevier - Health Sciences Div.

Human Kinetics. Core Assessment & Training. 2010. (ENG., Illus.). 160p. 44.00 *(978-0-7360-7384-4(1))* Human Kinetics Pubs.

Lucaya, Javier & Strife, Janet L., eds. Pediatric Chest Imaging: Chest Imaging in Infants & Children. 2nd ed. 2011. (Medical Radiology / Diagnostic Imaging Ser.). (ENG., Illus.). x, 450p. pap. 319.00 *(978-3-642-06917-8(7),* 3642069177) Springer.

Martin, Justin McCory. Heart. 2010. 16p. ***(978-0-545-24799-3(3))*** Scholastic, Inc.

Mathis, Gebhard. Chest Sonography. Mathis, Gebhard, ed. 3rd ed. 2011. (ENG., Illus.). vii, 249p. 139.00 ***(978-3-642-21246-8(8),*** 3642212468) Springer.

Rémy-Jardin, Martine & Remy, Jacques. Integrated Cardiothoracic Imaging with MDCT. 2010. (Medical Radiology / Diagnostic Imaging Ser.). (Illus.). xii, 444p. pap. 139.00 *(978-3-642-09146-9(6),* 3642091466) Springer.

CHEST—DISEASES

see also Chest—Radiography; Tuberculosis

Clarke, Christopher & Dux, Anthony. Chest X-Rays for Medical Students. 2011. (ENG., Illus.). 140p. pap. 29.95 *(978-0-470-65619-8(0),* Wiley-Blackwell) Wiley, John & Sons, Inc.

Cram101 Textbook Reviews. Outlines & Highlights for Chest Pain: Advanced Assessment & Management Skills by John Albarran, ISBN. 2011. 428p. pap. 35.95 ***(978-1-61461-446-3(6))*** Cram101 Inc.

Donoghue, V., ed. Radiological Imaging of the Neonatal Chest. 2nd rev. ed. 2007. (Medical Radiology / Diagnostic Imaging Ser.). (Illus.). 362p. 209.00 *(978-3-540-33748-5(2))* Springer.

Donoghue, Veronica B., ed. Radiological Imaging of the Neonatal Chest. 2nd ed. 2012. (Medical Radiology / Diagnostic Imaging Ser.). (ENG., Illus.). x, 366p. pap. 209.00 *(978-3-642-07030-3(2),* 3642070302) Springer.

Folio, Les R. Chest Imaging: An Algorithmic Approach to Learning. 2011. (ENG., Illus.). xvii, 147p. pap. 49.95 ***(978-1-4614-1316-5(8),*** 1461413168) Springer.

Gibbons, Peter & Tehan, Philip. Manipulation of the Spine, Thorax, & Pelvis: An Osteopathic Perspective. 3rd ed. 2009. (ENG., Illus.). 304p. pap. 112.00 *(978-0-7020-3130-4(5),* Churchill Livingstone) Elsevier - Health Sciences Div.

Hecht, Alan & Finer, Kim R. Tuberculosis. 2nd rev. ed. 2011. (Deadly Diseases & Epidemics Ser.). 128p. (C). (gr. 9). 34.95 *(978-1-61753-017-3(4),* Chelsea Hse.) Facts On File, Inc.

Homasson, Jean-Paul & Bell, Nicolas. Cryotherapy in Chest Medicine. (Illus.). 110p. (C). 93.00 *(978-2-287-00379-0(7))* Springer France FRA. Dist: Springer.

Kinnear, William & Kumaran, Maruti. Ultrasound of the Chest: A Guide for Clinicians. 2010. (ENG.). 68p. pap. 24.95 *(978-1-904761-42-6(9))* Nottingham Univ. Pr. GBR. Dist: Independent Pubs. Group.

Mehta, Atul C. Interventional Pulmonology, an Issue of Clinics in Chest Medicine. 2010. (Clinics: Internal Medicine Ser.: 31-1). (ENG., Illus.). xii, 177p. 105.00 *(978-1-4377-1202-5(9),* Saunders) Elsevier - Health Sciences Div.

Miller, M.D., Albert. Chest Pain: When & When Not to Worry, 1 vol. 2009. (ENG., Illus.). 152p. pap. 14.95 *(978-1-935235-03-3(6))* Selfhelp Success Bks., L.L.C.

Muller, Nestor L. & Silva, C. Isabela S. The Teaching Files: Chest: Expert Consult - Online & Print. 2009. (Teaching Files in Radiology Ser.). (ENG., Illus.). 448p. (C). 142.00 *(978-1-4160-6110-6(X),* Saunders) Elsevier - Health Sciences Div.

Niederman, Michael. Respiratory Tract Infections - Advances in Diagnosis, Management, & Prevention: Clinics in Chest Medicine. 2011. (Clinics: Internal Medicine Ser.: 32-3). (ENG., Illus.). xiv, 417p. 110.00 *(978-1-4557-1023-2(7),* Saunders) Elsevier - Health Sciences Div.

Peacock, William Franklin & Cannon, Christopher P. Short Stay Management of Chest Pain. Peacock, William Franklin & Cannon, Christopher P., eds. 2009. (Contemporary Cardiology Ser.). (ENG., Illus.). 272p. 219.00 *(978-1-60327-947-5(4),* 1603279474) Humana Pr.

Rosado-de-Christenson, Melissa L. & Abbott, Gerald F. Chest. 2nd rev. ed. 2012. (ENG., Illus.). 980p. 339.00 ***(978-1-931884-75-4(7))*** Lippincott Williams & Wilkins.

Weber, Sophie M., ed. Chest Pain: Causes, Diagnosis, & Treatment. 2010. (Cardiology Research & Clinical Developments Ser.). (Illus.). x, 149p. 59.00 *(978-1-61728-112-9(3),* Nova Biomedical Bks.) Nova Science Pubs., Inc.

CHEST—DISEASES—DIAGNOSIS

see also Auscultation

Carr, Robert B., et al. Chest. 2010. (EXPERTddx™ Ser.). (ENG.). 500p. 299.00 *(978-1-931884-12-9(9))* Lippincott Williams & Wilkins.

Collins, Jannette & Stern, Eric J. Chest Radiology: The Essentials. 2nd rev. ed. 2007. (ENG., Illus.). 352p. 100.00 *(978-0-7817-6314-1(2))* Lippincott Williams & Wilkins.

Corne, Jonathan, et al. 100 Chest X-Ray Problems. 2007. (ENG., Illus.). 212p. pap. 34.95 *(978-0-443-07012-9(1),* Churchill Livingstone) Elsevier - Health Sciences Div.

Crundwell, Neil & Joarder, Rita, eds. Chest X-Ray in Clinical Practice. 2009. (ENG., Illus.). 128p. pap. 49.95 *(978-1-84882-098-2(4),* 1848820984) Springer.

Eslick, Guy D. Epidemiology of Non-Cardiac Chest Pain. 2008. 212p. pap. *(978-3-639-05442-2(3))* VDM Verlag Dr. Mueller e.K.

Eslick, Guy D. & Yelland, Michael. Chest Pain: Medical Clinics of North America. 2010. (Clinics: Internal Medicine Ser.: 94-2). (ENG., Illus.). xiv, 202p. 79.00 *(978-1-4377-1835-5(3),* Saunders) Elsevier - Health Sciences Div.

Fass, Ronnie & Eslick, Guy, eds. Noncardiac Chest Pain: A Growing Medical Problem. 2007. (Illus.). 188p. 99.95 *(978-1-59756-176-1(2))* Plural Publishing, Inc.

Ferguson, Mark K. Imaging of Thoracic Diseases, an Issue of Thoracic Surgery Clinics. 2010. (Clinics: Surgery Ser.: 20-1). (ENG.). 105.00 *(978-1-4377-2268-0(7),* Saunders) Elsevier - Health Sciences Div.

Hartman, Thomas, ed. Pearls & Pitfalls in Thoracic Imaging: Variants & Other Difficult Diagnoses. 2011. (ENG., Illus.). 234p. 99.00 ***(978-0-521-11907-8(3))*** Cambridge Univ. Pr.

Hodler, Jarg, et al, eds. Diseases of the Heart, Chest & Breast 2011-2014: Diagnostic Imaging & Interventional Techniques. 2011. (Illus.). 280p. pap. 109.00 *(978-88-470-1937-9(0),* 8847019370) Springer.

Hofer, Matthias. The Chest X-Ray: A Systematic Teaching Atlas. Abanador, N. et al, eds. 2006. (ENG.). 224p. pap. 54.99 *(978-1-58890-554-3(3))* Thieme Medical Pubs., Inc.

Kartikeyan, D. & Chegu, Deepa. Chest X-Ray Made Easy. 2007. (Made Easy Ser.). (Illus.). 180p. pap. 29.95 *(978-1-905740-59-8(X))* Anshan GBR. Dist: Publishers Storage & Shipping.

Lewis, Michael I. & McKenna, Robert J. Medical Management of the Thoracic Surgery Patient: Expert Consult - Online & Print. 2009. (ENG., Illus.). 560p. 170.00 *(978-1-4160-3993-8(7),* Saunders) Elsevier - Health Sciences Div.

Lynch, David A., et al. Imaging of Diseases of the Chest. 5th ed. 2009. (ENG., Illus.). 1208p. 345.00 *(978-0-7234-3496-2(4),* Mosby) Elsevier - Health Sciences Div.

Matsushima, Toshiharu. Diseases of the Chest: Imaging Diagnosis Based on Pattern Classification. 2006. (ENG., Illus.). 183p. 119.99 *(978-1-58890-562-8(4))* Thieme Medical Pubs., Inc.

Moran, Cesar A. & Suster, Saul. Diagnostic Pathology: Thoracic. 2011. (ENG., Illus.). 800p. 299.00 *(978-1-931884-49-5(8))* Lippincott Williams & Wilkins.

Moskowitz, Harold. I. C. U. Chest Radiology: Principles & Case Studies. 2010. (ENG., Illus.). 183p. 99.95 *(978-0-470-45034-5(7),* Wiley-Blackwell) Wiley, John & Sons, Inc.

Muller, Nestor L. & Silva, C. Isabela S. Imaging of the Chest, 2 vols., Set. 2008. (Expert Radiology Ser.). (ENG., Illus.). 1608p. 329.00 *(978-1-4160-4048-4(X),* Saunders) Elsevier - Health Sciences Div.

Parker, Mark S. & Abbott, Gerald F. Chest Imaging Case Atlas. De Christenson, Melissa, ed. 2012. (ENG., Illus.). 1104p. 159.99 ***(978-1-60406-590-9(7))*** Thieme Medical Pubs., Inc.

Sarosi, George A. & Knox, Kenneth S. Fungal Disease, an Issue of Clinics in Chest Medicine. 2009. (Clinics: Internal Medicine Ser.: 30-2). (ENG., Illus.). 240p. 99.00 *(978-1-4377-0461-7(1),* Saunders) Elsevier - Health Sciences Div.

Tagney, Jenny & Albarran, John W., eds. Chest Pain: Advanced Assessment & Management Skills. 2007. (ENG., Illus.). 280p. pap. 66.99 *(978-1-4051-4422-3(X),* Wiley-Blackwell) Wiley, John & Sons, Inc.

White, Charles S. & Boiselle, Phillip M., eds. New Techniques in Cardiothoracic Imaging. 2007. (ENG., Illus.). 234p. 250.00 *(978-0-8493-9019-7(2),* Informa Healthcare) Taylor & Francis Group GBR. Dist: Taylor & Francis Group.

CHEST—RADIOGRAPHY

Berry. Mini Atlas of Diagnostic Radiology: Emergency & Chest Radiology. 2009. (Anshan Gold Standard Mini Atlas Ser.). (ENG., Illus.). 350p. pap. 34.95 incl. cd-rom *(978-1-905740-15-4(8))* Anshan GBR. Dist: Publishers Storage & Shipping.

Bhalla, Sanjeev. Thoracic Multidetector CT Comes of Age: Radiologic Clinics of North America. 2010. (Clinics: Radiology Ser.: 48-1). (ENG.). 105.00 *(978-1-4377-1514-9(1),* Saunders) Elsevier - Health Sciences Div.

Bhalla, Sanjeev, et al. Chest Imaging Cases, 1 vol. 2012. (Cases in Radiology Ser.). (ENG., Illus.). 336p. pap. 59.99 ***(978-0-19-539453-5(4))*** Oxford Univ. Pr., Inc.

Boiselle, Phillip M., et al. Thoracic Imaging. 2nd ed. 2010. (Case Review Ser.). (ENG., Illus.). 356p. pap. 54.95 *(978-0-323-02999-5(X),* Mosby) Elsevier - Health Sciences Div.

Bolliger, C. T., et al, eds. Clinical Chest Ultrasound: From the ICU to the Bronchoscopy Suite. 2008. (Progress in Respiratory Research Ser.). (Illus.). 250p. *(978-3-8055-8642-9(6))* Karger, S. AG.

Briggs, Greg. Chest X-Rays. 2nd ed. 2008. (ENG., Illus.). 232p. pap. 46.00 *(978-0-07-013877-3(X),* 007013877X) McGraw-Hill Australia AUS. Dist: McGraw-Hill Cos., The.

Clarke, Christopher & Dux, Anthony. Chest X-Rays for Medical Students. 2011. (ENG., Illus.). 140p. pap. 29.95 *(978-0-470-65619-8(0),* Wiley-Blackwell) Wiley, John & Sons, Inc.

Coche, Emmanuel E., et al. Comparative Interpretation of CT & Standard Radiography of the Chest. 2010. (Medical Radiology / Diagnostic Imaging Ser.). (ENG., Illus.). 300p. 319.00 *(978-3-540-79941-2(9),* 3540799419) Springer.

Collins, Jannette & Stern, Eric J. Chest Radiology: The Essentials. 2nd rev. ed. 2007. (ENG., Illus.). 352p. 100.00 *(978-0-7817-6314-1(2))* Lippincott Williams & Wilkins.

Corne, Jonathan & Pointon, Kate. Chest X-Ray Made Easy. 3rd ed. 2009. (Made Easy Ser.). (ENG., Illus.). 184p. (C). pap. 39.95 *(978-0-443-06922-2(0),* Churchill Livingstone) Elsevier - Health Sciences Div.

Crundwell, Neil & Joarder, Rita, eds. Chest X-Ray in Clinical Practice. 2009 (ENG., Illus.). 128p. pap. 49.95 *(978-1-84882-098-2(4),* 1848820984) Springer.

de Lacey, Gerald, et al. The Chest X-Ray: A Survival Guide. 2008. (ENG., Illus.). 352p. pap., instr.'s gde. ed. 62.95 *(978-0-7020-3046-8(5),* Saunders) Elsevier - Health Sciences Div.

Folio, Les R. Chest Imaging: An Algorithmic Approach to Learning. 2011. (ENG., Illus.). xvii, 147p. pap. 49.95 ***(978-1-4614-1316-5(8),*** 1461413168) Springer.

Goodman, Lawrence R. Principles of Chest Roentgenology: A Programmed Text. 3rd rev. ed. 2006. (ENG., Illus.). 272p. pap. 76.95 *(978-1-4160-2923-6(0),* Saunders) Elsevier - Health Sciences Div.

Gurney, Jud W., et al. HRCT of the Lung: Anatomic Basis, Imaging Features, Differential Diagnosis. 2009. (ENG., Illus.). 600p. 229.00 *(978-1-931884-16-7(1))* Lippincott Williams & Wilkins.

Hartman, Thomas, ed. Pearls & Pitfalls in Thoracic Imaging: Variants & Other Difficult Diagnoses. 2011. (ENG., Illus.). 234p. 99.00 ***(978-0-521-11907-8(3))*** Cambridge Univ. Pr.

Hofer, Matthias. The Chest X-Ray: A Systematic Teaching Atlas. Abanador, N. et al, eds. 2006. (ENG.). 224p. pap. 54.99 *(978-1-58890-554-3(3))* Thieme Medical Pubs., Inc.

Jeremic, Branislav, ed. Advances in Radiation Oncology in Lung Cancer. 2nd ed. 2011. (Medical Radiology / Radiation Oncology Ser.). (ENG., Illus.). xviii, 843p. 359.00 ***(978-3-642-19924-0(0),*** 3642199240) Springer.

Joarder, Rita & Crundwell, Neil. Case Studies in Chest Imaging. 2011. (ENG., Illus.). xii, 304p. 139.00 ***(978-0-85729-837-9(2),*** 0857298372) Springer.

Kartikeyan, D. & Chegu, Deepa. Chest X-Ray Made Easy. 2007. (Made Easy Ser.). (Illus.). 180p. pap. 29.95 *(978-1-905740-59-8(X))* Anshan GBR. Dist: Publishers Storage & Shipping.

Kinnear, William & Kumaran, Maruti. Ultrasound of the Chest: A Guide for Clinicians. 2010. (ENG.). 68p. pap. 24.95 *(978-1-904761-42-6(9))* Nottingham Univ. Pr. GBR. Dist: Independent Pubs. Group.

Kirchner, Johannes. Chest Radiology - A Resident's Manual. 2011. (ENG., Illus.). 300p. pap. 109.99 *(978-3-13-153871-0(6))* Thieme Medical Pubs., Inc.

Lange, Sebastian & Walsh, Geraldine. Radiology of Chest Diseases. 3rd ed. 2006. 139.95 *(978-3-13-740703-4(6));* (ENG., Illus.). 389p. 149.99 *(978-1-58890-447-8(4))* Thieme Medical Pubs., Inc.

Lee, Kyung Soo, et al. Muller's Diseases of the Lung: Radiologic & Pathologic Correlations. 2nd rev. ed. 2011. (ENG., Illus.). 520p. 179.95 ***(978-1-4511-1116-3(9))*** Lippincott Williams & Wilkins.

Mathis, Gebhard, ed. Chest Sonography. 2nd ed. 2010. (Illus.). xiv, 242p. pap. 159.00 *(978-3-642-09143-0(0),* 3642091490) Springer.

Matsushima, Toshiharu. Diseases of the Chest: Imaging Diagnosis Based on Pattern Classification. 2006. (ENG., Illus.). 183p. 119.99 *(978-1-58890-562-8(4))* Thieme Medical Pubs., Inc.

McLoud, Theresa C. Thoracic Radiology: The Requisites. 2nd ed. 2010. (Requisites in Radiology Ser.). (ENG., Illus.). 442p. 110.00 *(978-0-323-02790-8(3),* Mosby) Elsevier - Health Sciences Div.

Misra, Rakesh, et al. A-Z of Chest Radiology. 2007. (ENG., Illus.). 224p. pap. 68.99 *(978-0-521-69148-2(6))* Cambridge Univ. Pr.

Moskowitz, Harold. I. C. U. Chest Radiology: Principles & Case Studies. 2010. (ENG., Illus.). 183p. 99.95 *(978-0-470-45034-5(7),* Wiley-Blackwell) Wiley, John & Sons, Inc.

Muller, Nestor L. & Silva, C. Isabela. Imaging of Pulmonary Infections. Lee, Kyung Soo & Franquet, Tomás, eds. 2006. (Illus.). 192p. 168.99 *(978-0-7817-7232-7(X))* Lippincott Williams & Wilkins.

Muller, Nestor L. & Silva, C. Isabela S. The Teaching Files: Chest: Expert Consult - Online & Print. 2009. (Teaching Files in Radiology Ser.). (ENG., Illus.). 448p. (C). 142.00 *(978-1-4160-6110-6(X),* Saunders) Elsevier - Health Sciences Div.

Reed, James C. Chest Radiology: Plain Film Patterns & Differential Diagnoses. 6th ed. 2010. (ENG., Illus.). 480p. 130.00 *(978-1-4377-2345-8(4),* Mosby) Elsevier - Health Sciences Div.

Rosado-de-Christenson, Melissa L. & Abbott, Gerald F. Chest. 2nd rev. ed. 2012. (ENG., Illus.). 980p. 339.00 ***(978-1-931884-75-4(7))*** Lippincott Williams & Wilkins.

Schild, Steven E. Thoracic Malignancies. 2010. 289.00 *(978-1-933864-89-1(3))* Demos Medical Publishing, LLC.

Srichai, Monvadi B. Computed Tomography & Magnetic Resonance of the Thorax. Naidich, David P. et al, eds. 4th rev. ed. 2007. (ENG., Illus.). 900p. 178.99 *(978-0-7817-5765-2(7))* Lippincott Williams & Wilkins.

Stern, Eric J., et al. High-Resolution CT of the Chest: Comprehensive Atlas. 3rd rev. ed. 2009. (ENG., Illus.). 368p. 178.99 *(978-0-7817-9190-8(1))* Lippincott Williams & Wilkins.

Vidyasagar, B. Principles & Interpretation of Chest X-Rays. 2007. (Illus.). 157p. pap. 29.99 incl. cd-rom *(978-1-905740-07-9(7))* Anshan GBR. Dist: Publishers Storage & Shipping.

Webb, W. Richard & Higgins, Charles B. Thoracic Imaging: Pulmonary & Cardiovascular Radiology. 2nd rev. ed. 2010. (ENG.). 928p. 239.00 *(978-1-60547-976-7(4))* Lippincott Williams & Wilkins.

CHEST—SURGERY

Bhalla, Sanjeev. Thoracic Multidetector CT Comes of Age: Radiologic Clinics of North America. 2010. (Clinics: Radiology Ser.: 48-1). (ENG.). 105.00 *(978-1-4377-1514-9(1),* Saunders) Elsevier - Health Sciences Div.

Brunelli, Alessandro. Air Leak after Pulmonary Resection, an Issue of Thoracic Surgery Clinics. 2010. (Clinics: Surgery Ser.: 20-3). (ENG., Illus.). ix, 346p. 105.00 *(978-1-4377-1881-2(7),* Saunders) Elsevier - Health Sciences Div.

Choong, Cliff K. C. Update on Surgical & Endoscopic Management of Emphysema: Thoracic Surgery Clinics. rev. ed. 2009. (Clinics: Surgery Ser.: 19-2). (ENG.). 240p. 99.00 *(978-1-4377-0552-2(9),* Saunders) Elsevier - Health Sciences Div.

Cram101 Textbook Reviews. Outlines & Highlights for a Practical Approach to Cardiac Anesthesia by Frederick a Hensley. 2011. 624p. pap. 40.95 ***(978-1-61905-705-0(0))*** Cram101 Inc.

Danto, Arthur C. & Moeller, Hans-Georg. Cardiothoracic Surgery in China: Past, Present & Future. Wang, Song, ed. 2007. (ENG., Illus.). 550p. (gr. 17). 70.00 *(978-962-996-321-7(3))* Chinese Univ. of Hong Kong, The HKG. Dist: Columbia Univ. Pr.

Darling, Gail. Surgical Conditions of the Diaphragm, an Issue of Thoracic Surgery Clinics. 2009. (Clinics: Surgery Ser.: 19-4). (ENG., Illus.). x, 420p. 99.00 *(978-1-4377-1392-3(0),* Saunders) Elsevier - Health Sciences Div.

DeMeester, Steven R. Tracheobronchial, Pulmonary & Mediastinal Problems in General Thoracic Surgery: Surgical Clinics of North America. 2010. (Clinics: Surgery Ser.: 90-5). (ENG., Illus.). xii, 920p. 99.00 *(978-1-4377-2615-2(1),* Saunders) Elsevier - Health Sciences Div.

Dienemann, Hendrik C., et al, eds. Chest Surgery. 2012. (Springer Surgery Atlas Ser.). (ENG., Illus.). 400p. 139.00 *(978-3-642-12043-5(1),* 3642120431) Springer.

Ferguson, Mark K. Imaging of Thoracic Diseases, an Issue of Thoracic Surgery Clinics. 2010. (Clinics: Surgery Ser.: 20-1). (ENG.). 105.00 *(978-1-4377-2268-0(7),* Saunders) Elsevier - Health Sciences Div.

—Thoracic Surgery Atlas. 2007. (ENG., Illus.). 325p. 235.00 *(978-0-7216-0325-4(4),* Saunders) Elsevier - Health Sciences Div.

Ferguson, Mark K., ed. Difficult Decisions in Thoracic Surgery: An Evidence-Based Approach. (Illus.). 2006. 525p. 169.00 *(978-1-84628-384-0(1),* 1846283841) 2nd ed. 2011. (ENG., xxii, 504p. 139.00 *(978-1-84996-364-0(9),* 1849963649) Springer.

Franco, Kenneth L. & Thourani, Vinod H. Cardiothoracic Surgery Review. 2011. (ENG., Illus.). 1770p. 279.00 *(978-1-60913-235-4(1))* Lippincott Williams & Wilkins.

Galanski, Michael. Thoracic Imaging. 2010. (ENG., Illus.). 368p. pap. 59.99 *(978-3-13-145131-6(9))* Thieme Medical Pubs., Inc.

Gillham, Michael, et al. Cardiothoracic Critical Care. 2007. (ENG., Illus.). 672p. 99.95 *(978-0-7506-7572-7(1),* Butterworth-Heinemann) Elsevier - Health Sciences Div.

Gossot, Daniel, et al. Surgical Thoracoscopy. (Illus.). (C). 90.00 *(978-2-287-00363-9(0))* Springer France FRA. Dist: Springer.

Grondin, Sean C. & Pearson, F. Griffith. From Residency to Retirement: Building a Successful Career in Thoracic Surgery - Thoracic Surgery Clinics. 2011. (Clinics: Surgery Ser.: 21-3). (ENG., Illus.). 144p. 110.00 ***(978-1-4557-1190-1(X),*** Saunders) Elsevier - Health Sciences Div.

Hartigan, Philip M., ed. Practical Handbook of Thoracic Anesthesia. 2012. (ENG., Illus.). xviii, 628p. pap. 69.95 *(978-0-387-88492-9(0),* 0387884920) Springer.

Jobe, Blair A. Advances in the Management of Benign Esophageal Diseases, an Issue of Thoracic Surgery Clinics. 2011. (Clinics: Surgery Ser.: 21-4). (ENG., Illus.). xi, 450p. 110.00 ***(978-1-4557-1139-8(4),*** Saunders) Elsevier - Health Sciences Div.

Kaiser, Larry R., et al, eds. Mastery of Cardiothoracic Surgery. 2nd rev. ed. 2006. (ENG., Illus.). 1088p. 265.99 *(978-0-7817-5209-1(4))* Lippincott Williams & Wilkins.

Kaplan, Joel A. Essentials of Cardiac Anesthesia: A Volume in Essentials of Anesthesia & Critical Care. 2008. (ENG., Illus.). 768p. pap. 76.95 *(978-1-4160-3786-6(1),* Saunders) Elsevier - Health Sciences Div.

Katlic, Mark R., ed. Cardiothoracic Surgery in the Elderly. 2011. (ENG., Illus.). xxv, 654p. 239.00 *(978-1-4419-0891-9(9),* 1441908919) Springer.

Klein, Andrew, et al, eds. Core Topics in Cardiothoracic Critical Care. 2008. (ENG., Illus.). 564p. 95.00 *(978-0-521-87283-6(9))* Cambridge Univ. Pr.

KRASNA. Atlas Thoracosco Surg 2e. 2nd ed. 2009. 139.95 *(978-0-8247-4788-6(7),* Informa Healthcare) Taylor & Francis Group GBR. Dist: Taylor & Francis Group.

Lee, Edward Y. Advances in Pediatric Thoracic Imaging, an Issue of Radiologic Clinics of North America. 2011. (Clinics: Radiology Ser.: 49-5). (ENG., Illus.). x, 806p. 110.00 *(978-1-4557-1151-2(9),* Saunders) Elsevier - Health Sciences Div.

Lewis, Michael I. & McKenna, Robert J. Medical Management of the Thoracic Surgery Patient: Expert Consult - Online & Print. 2009. (ENG., Illus.). 560p. 170.00 *(978-1-4160-3993-8(7),* Saunders) Elsevier - Health Sciences Div.

Little, Alex G. & Merrill, Walter H., eds. Complications in Cardiothoracic Surgery: Avoidance & Treatment. 2nd ed. 2009. (ENG., Illus.). 496p. 165.95 *(978-1-4051-8103-7(6),* Wiley-Blackwell) Wiley, John & Sons, Inc.

Marshall, M. Blair. Current Management Guidelines in Thoracic Surgery, an Issue of Thoracic Surgery Clinics. 2011. (Clinics: Surgery Ser.: 22-1). (ENG.). 115.00 ***(978-1-4557-3943-1(X),*** Saunders) Elsevier - Health Sciences Div.

Martin, Donald E., et al, eds. A Practical Approach to Cardiac Anesthesia. 4th rev. ed. 2007. (Practical Approach Ser.). (ENG., Illus.). 816p. per. 92.95 *(978-0-7817-9533-3(8))* Lippincott Williams & Wilkins.

McKenna, Robert J., Jr., et al. Atlas of Minimally Invasive Thoracic Surgery. 2010. (ENG., Illus.). 336p. 218.00 *(978-1-4160-6263-9(7),* Saunders) Elsevier - Health Sciences Div.

Morris, Charles R. The Surgeons: Life & Death in a Top Heart Center. (ENG.). 336p. 2008. pap. 15.95 *(978-0-393-33400-5(7),* 33400) 2007. (Illus.). 24.95 *(978-0-393-06562-6(6),* 6562) Norton, W. W. & Co., Inc.

Parikh, Dakshesh, et al, eds. Pediatric Thoracic Surgery. 2009. (ENG., Illus.). xvi, 614p. 299.00 *(978-1-84800-902-8(X))* Springer.

Reves, J. G., et al. Atlas of Cardiothoracic Anesthesia. 2nd ed. 2009. (Illus.). 230p. 319.00 *(978-1-57340-278-1(8))* Current Medicine Group LLC.

Rocco, Gaetano. Chest Wall Surgery, an Issue of Thoracic Surgery Clinics. 2010. (Clinics: Surgery Ser.: 20-4). (ENG., Illus.). xi, 454p. 105.00 *(978-1-4377-2724-1(7),* Saunders) Elsevier - Health Sciences Div.

C

Sabiston, David C., et al. Surgery of the Chest, 2 vols., Set. 8th ed. 2009. (ENG., Illus.). 2520p. (C). 365.00 *(978-1-4160-5225-8(9)*, Saunders) Elsevier - Health Sciences Div.

Schwarz, Tobias & Johnson, Victoria, eds. BSAVA Manual of Canine & Feline Thoracic Imaging. 2008. (BSAVA British Small Animal Veterinary Association Ser.). (ENG., Illus.). 408p. pap. 146.99 *(978-0-905214-97-9(8))* British Small Animal Veterinary Assn. (BSAVA) GBR. Dist: Wiley, John & Sons, Inc.

Shields, Thomas W., et al, eds. General Thoracic Surgery, 2 vols. 7th rev. ed. 2009. (ENG., Illus.). 2672p. 414.99 *(978-0-7817-7982-1(0))* Lippincott Williams & Wilkins.

Slinger, Peter. Principles & Practice of Anesthesia for Thoracic Surgery. 2011. (ENG., Illus.). xix, 732p. 179.00 *(978-1-4419-0183-5(3)*, 1441901833) Springer.

Sugarbaker, David J., et al. Adult Chest Surgery. 2009. (ENG., Illus.). 1264p. 338.00 *(978-0-07-143414-0(3)*, 0071434143) McGraw-Hill Professional Publishing.

Urschel, Harold C., Jr. Thoracic Oncology. (Handbooks Ser.). (Illus.). 45.00 *(978-1-57059-674-2(3))* Landes Bioscience.

Verhoye, Jean-Philippe, et al, eds. Thoracic Aortic Diseases. 2006. (Illus.). 387p. 359.00 *(978-3-540-25734-9(9)*, 3540257349) Springer.

Wasnick, John, et al. Cardiac Anesthesia & Transesophageal Echocardiography. 2011. (ENG., Illus.). 332p. pap. 78.00 *(978-0-07-171798-4(6)*, 0071717986) McGraw-Hill Professional Publishing.

Wasnick, John D. Cardiac Anesthesia & Transesophageal Echocardiography. 2011. (Illus.). xii, 319p. *(978-0-07-163458-8(4))*; pap. *(978-0-07-163457-1(6))* McGraw-Hill Professional Publishing.

Wilkinson, Jonathan, et al. Thoracic Anaesthesia. 2011. (ENG., Illus.). 786p. pap. 85.00 *(978-0-19-956309-8(8))* Oxford Univ. Pr., Inc.

Yang, Stephen C. & Ferguson, Mark K. Thoracic Surgery in the Elderly, an Issue of Thoracic Surgery Clinics. 2009. (Clinics: Surgery Ser.: 19-3). (ENG.). 99.00 *(978-1-4377-1391-6(2)*, Saunders) Elsevier - Health Sciences Div.

Yim, Anthony P. C., et al. Minimally Invasive Thoracic Surgery. 2008. (ENG.). 1206p. (gr. 17). pap. 290.00 *(978-962-996-367-5(1))* Chinese Univ. of Hong Kong, The HKG. Dist: Columbia Univ. Pr.

Yuh, David Daiho, et al. The Johns Hopkins Manual of Cardiothoracic Surgery. 2006. (ENG., Illus.). 1488p. 199.00 *(978-0-07-141652-8(8)*, 0071416528) McGraw-Hill Professional Publishing.

Zwischenberger, Joseph B. Atlas of Thoracic Surgical Techniques. 2010. (ENG., Illus.). 448p. 274.00 *(978-1-4160-4017-0(X)*, Saunders) Elsevier - Health Sciences Div.

CHESTER (DIOCESE)

Holland, Robert. A Glossary of Words Used in the County of Chester. 2009. 416p. pap. *(978-1-151-14845-2(8))* Books LLC.

—A Glossary of Words Used in the County of Chester. 2008. 528p. 55.95 *(978-1-4365-4670-6(2))* 2007. (ENG.). 532p. per. 40.95 *(978-0-548-71552-9(1))* Kessinger Publishing, LLC.

CHESTER CATHEDRAL

Scala Publishing. Chester Cathedral. 2010. (ENG., Illus.). 48p. pap. 10.00 *(978-1-85759-591-8(2))* Scala, Editions FRA. Dist: National Bk. Network.

CHESTER COUNTY (PA.)

Brody, Susannah Wilson. Remembering Chester County: Stories from Valley Forge to Coatesville. 2010. (American Chronicles Ser.). 128p. pap. 19.99 *(978-1-59629-953-5(3))* History Pr., The.

Chester Historical Preservation Committee. Chester. 2008. (Postcard History Ser.). (ENG.). 128p. pap. 21.99 *(978-0-7385-6348-0(X))* Arcadia Publishing.

Devereux, Antelo, Jr. Chester County Out & About. 2011. 45.00 *(978-0-7643-3625-6(8))* Schiffer Publishing, Ltd.

Martino, Vincent, Jr. Northern Chester County. 2006. (Postcard History Ser.). (ENG., Illus.). 128p. per. 19.99 *(978-0-7385-4571-4(6))* Arcadia Publishing.

McCullough, Kevin & Meyers, Larry. 2011 Chester County Data Book. McCullough, Kevin, ed. 2011. (Illus.). 162p. pap. 45.00 *(978-1-58036-715-8(1))* Pennsylvania State Data Ctr.

Mowday, Bruce Edward. Chester County Mushroom Farming. 2008. (IOA Ser.). (ENG., Illus.). 128p. pap. 19.99 *(978-0-7385-5658-1(0))* Arcadia Publishing.

CHESTER PLAYS

Lumiansky, Robert M. & Mills, David. The Chester Mystery Cycle: Essays & Documents. 2011. (ENG.). 352p. pap. 50.00 ***(978-0-8078-9715-7(9))*** Univ. of North Carolina Pr.

CHESTERFIELD, PHILIP DORMER STANHOPE, EARL OF, 1694-1773

Chesterfield, Earl of. Chesterfield's Letters to His Son 1746 - 1771. 2007. 656p. per. *(978-1-4068-4539-6(6))* Echo Library.

Chesterfield, Lord. Lord Chesterfield's Letters. Roberts, David, ed. 2008. (Oxford World's Classics Ser.). (ENG.). 480p. pap. 16.95 *(978-0-19-955484-3(6))* Oxford Univ. Pr., Inc.

Craig, William Henry. Life of Lord Chesterfield: an Account of the Ancestry, Personal. 2007. (ENG.). 380p. per. 33.95 *(978-1-4304-4421-3(5))* Kessinger Publishing, LLC.

Gulick, Sidney L., ed. Two Burlesques of Lord Chesterfield's Letters: The Graces, 1774, the Fine Gentleman's Etiquette 1776. 2011. 54p. 36.95 ***(978-1-258-06329-0(8))*** Literary Licensing, LLC.

Hill, George Birkbeck. Lord Chesterfield's Worldly Wisdom: Selections from His Letters & Characters. 2008. 288p. pap. *(978-1-4097-9351-9(6))* Read Bks.

Stanhope, Philip Dormer. The Letters of Philip Dormer Stanhope, Earl of Chesterfield V2. Mahon, Lord, ed. 2007. (ENG.). 490p. 53.95 *(978-0-548-15631-5(X))*; 492p. per. 38.95 *(978-1-4304-5094-8(0))* Kessinger Publishing, LLC.

CHESTERTON, G. K. (GILBERT KEITH), 1874-1936

Belmonte, Kevin. The Quotable Chesterton: The Wit & Wisdom of G. K. Chesterton. 2011. 336p. pap. 15.99 *(978-1-59555-205-1(7))* Nelson, Thomas Inc.

Chesteron, G. K. Orthodoxy. 2008. 288p. pap. *(978-1-4097-6940-8(2))* Read Bks.

Chesterson, Gilbert K. Heretics. 2009. 140p. 29.99 *(978-1-59547-535-0(4))* NuVision Pubns., LLC.

Chesterton & Chesterton, G. K. Orthodoxy. 2007. (B&N Library of Essential Reading Ser.). (ENG.). 176p. pap. 8.95 *(978-0-7607-8631-4(3))* Barnes & Noble, Inc.

Chesterton, Cecil & Perry, Michael W. G.K. Chesterton, a Criticism. 2007. (Illus.). 179p. *(978-1-58742-060-3(0))* Inkling Bks.

Chesterton, G. K. The Appetite of Tyranny, Including Letters to an Old Garibaldian. reprint ed. lib. bdg. 98.00 *(978-0-7426-3031-4(5))*; lib. bdg. 98.00 *(978-0-7426-3033-8(1))* Classic Bks.

—Collected Works of G. K. Chesterton - The Illustrated London News, Vol. 36. 2011. 612p. 39.95 *(978-0-89870-838-7(9))*; pap. 29.95 *(978-0-89870-839-4(7))* Ignatius Pr.

—Defiant Joy: The Remarkable Life & Impact of G. K. Chesterton. 2011. 336p. pap. 16.99 *(978-1-59555-201-3(4))* Nelson, Thomas Inc.

—Heretics. 2009. 152p. pap. 8.99 *(978-1-60450-616-7(4)*, Serenity Pubs.) Arc Manor.

—Heretics. 2008. 172p. 25.99 *(978-0-554-21477-1(6))* 2008. 172p. 22.99 *(978-0-554-30780-0(4))* 2006. (ENG.). 176p. pap. 19.99 *(978-1-4264-0088-9(8))* 2006. (ENG.). 170p. pap. 21.99 *(978-1-4264-0217-3(1))* BiblioBazaar.

—Heretics. 2007. (ENG.). 176p. per. 10.95 *(978-1-60206-845-2(3))* Cosimo, Inc.

—Heretics. 2006. (ENG.). pap. *(978-1-4065-1003-4(3))* Dodo Pr.

—Heretics. 2007. 216p. pap. 9.99 *(978-1-59986-898-1(9))* Filiquarian Publishing, LLC.

—Heretics. 2007. (Hendrickson Christian Classics Ser.). 179p. 10.95 *(978-1-59856-015-2(8))*; 7.97 *(978-1-59856-305-4(X))* Hendrickson Pubs. Marketing, LLC.

—Orthodoxy. 2008. 196p. 22.95 *(978-1-4218-9480-5(7))*; pap. 15.95 *(978-1-4218-9380-8(0))* 1st World Publishing, Inc. (1st World Library - Literary Society).

—Orthodoxy. 2008. 140p. pap. 8.99 *(978-1-60450-585-6(0)*, Serenity Pubs.) Arc Manor.

—Orthodoxy. 2008. 176p. 22.99 *(978-0-554-33475-2(5))* 2008. 176p. 25.99 *(978-0-554-24172-2(2))* 2007. (ENG.). 156p. pap. 19.99 *(978-1-4264-5897-2(5))* BiblioBazaar.

—Orthodoxy. 2011. 142p. pap. 12.99 ***(978-1-61203-253-5(2))*** Bottom of the Hill Publishing.

—Orthodoxy. 2007. 168p. per. 11.95 *(978-1-60206-757-8(0))* Cosimo, Inc.

—Orthodoxy. 2006. (ENG.). pap. *(978-1-4065-1002-7(5))* Dodo Pr.

—Orthodoxy. l.t. ed. 2006. pap. *(978-1-4068-2223-6(X))* Echo Library.

—Orthodoxy. 2008. 172p. pap. 11.95 *(978-1-60096-675-0(6))*; 168p. pap. 11.95 *(978-1-60096-527-2(X))* Editorium, The.

—Orthodoxy. 2007. 200p. pap. 9.99 *(978-1-59986-821-9(0))* Filiquarian Publishing, LLC.

—Orthodoxy, 1 vol. 2009. (Moody Classics Ser.). (ENG.). 240p. pap. 7.99 *(978-0-8024-5657-1(X))* Moody Pubs.

—Orthodoxy. 2007. (ENG.). 152p. pap. 10.45 *(978-1-60424-866-1(1)*, Book Jungle) Standard Pubns., Inc.

—Orthodoxy: The classic of Christian Apologetics. 2010. 172p. pap. 14.95 *(978-1-60444-082-9(1))* IndoEuropeanPublishing.com.

—The Universe According to G. K. Chesterton: A Dictionary of the Mad, Mundane & Metaphysical. Ahlquist, Dale, ed. 2011. (ENG.). 144p. pap. 7.95 *(978-0-486-48115-9(8))* Dover Pubns., Inc.

—Varied Types. 2010. 294p. pap. 28.75 *(978-1-143-45598-8(3))* 2010. 290p. pap. 28.75 *(978-1-141-68590-5(6))* 2009. 280p. 34.99 *(978-1-116-98542-9(X))* 2009. (ENG.). 278p. pap. 21.99 *(978-1-116-98544-3(6)*, BiblioLife) 2009. 280p. pap. 26.75 *(978-1-116-98543-6(8))* 2009. 280p. 30.99 *(978-1-113-38821-6(8))* 2009. 280p. pap. 26.75 *(978-1-113-38819-3(6))* BiblioBazaar.

—Varied Types. 2009. 62p. pap. *(978-1-4589-9188-1(1))* Books LLC.

—Varied Types. 2008. (ENG.). 116p. per. *(978-1-4065-9097-5(5))* Dodo Pr.

—Varied Types. 2006. (ENG.). pap. *(978-1-4068-0320-4(0))* Echo Library.

Clark, Stephen R. L. G. K. Chesterton: Thinking Backward, Looking Forward. 2006. 288p. 29.95 *(978-1-59947-104-4(3))* Templeton Pr.

Evans, Maurice. G. K. Chesterton. 2011. (ENG.). 168p. pap. 34.99 ***(978-1-107-65014-5(3))*** Cambridge Univ. Pr.

Hillier, Bevis. Wit & Wisdom of G K Chesterton. 2011. (ENG., Illus.). 312p. 24.95 *(978-1-4411-7958-6(5))* Continuum International Publishing Group, Ltd. GBR. Dist: National Bk. Network.

Hurley, Michael D. G. K. Chesterton. 2012. (Writers & Their Work Ser.). (ENG.). 128p. (C). 80.00 *(978-0-7463-1210-0(5))*; pap. 26.00 *(978-0-7463-1211-7(3))* Northcote Hse. Publishers, Ltd. GBR. Dist: Brown, David Bk. Co., The.

Ker, Ian. G. K. Chesterton: A Biography. (ENG., Illus.). 2012. 784p. pap. 35.00 ***(978-0-19-965576-2(6))*** 2011. 688p. 65.00 *(978-0-19-960128-8(3))* Oxford Univ. Pr., Inc.

Mackey, Aidan. G. K. Chesterton: A Prophet for the 21st Century. 2009. (ENG.). 37p. pap. 8.95 *(978-1-932528-53-4(9))* IHS Pr.

McCleary, Joseph. The Historical Imagination of G. K. Chesterton: Locality, Patriotism, & Nationalism. 2009. (Studies in Major Literary Authors Ser.). (ENG., Illus.). 172p. (C). 125.00 *(978-0-415-99175-9(7))* Routledge.

Milbank, Alison. Chesterton & Tolkien as Theologians. 2009. (ENG.). 202p. 39.95 *(978-0-567-39041-7(1)*, T&T Clark Int'l) Continuum International Publishing Group, Ltd. GBR. Dist: National Bk. Network.

Morris, Kevin L. & Chesterton, G. K. The Truest Fairy Tale: An Anthology of the Religious Writings of G. K. Chesterton. 2007. (ENG.). 244p. pap. 40.00 *(978-0-7188-3061-8(X))* Lutherworth Pr., The GBR. Dist: Brown, David Bk. Co., The.

Nichols, Aidan. G. K. Chesterton, Theologian. 2009. pap. 16.95 *(978-1-933184-50-0(7))* Sophia Institute Pr.

Oddie, William. Chesterton & the Romance of Orthodoxy: The Making of GKC, 1874-1908. 2010. (ENG.). 416p. pap. 29.95 *(978-0-19-958201-3(7))* Oxford Univ. Pr., Inc.

Perry, Michael W., ed. G. K. Chesterton, a Criticism. 2007. (Illus.). 179p. pap. 14.95 *(978-1-58742-059-7(7))* Inkling Bks.

Robbins, Harold. The Last of the Realists: A Distributist Biography of G. K. Chesterton. 2010. (Illus.). 160p. pap. 22.95 *(978-1-932528-01-5(6))* IHS Pr.

Schwartz, Adam. The Third Spring: G. K. Chesterton, Graham Greene, Christopher Dawson, & David Jones. 2012. (ENG.). 432p. pap. 34.95 ***(978-0-8132-1982-0(5))*** Catholic Univ. of America Pr.

Scott, William T. Chesterton & Other Essays. 2007. 272p. 42.95 *(978-0-548-01604-6(6))* Kessinger Publishing, LLC.

Seaber, Luke. G. K. Chesterton's Literary Influence on George Orwell: A Surprising Irony. 2011. (ENG., Illus.). 416p. 139.95 ***(978-0-7734-2580-4(2))*** Mellen, Edwin Pr., The.

Stapleton, Julia. Christianity, Patriotism, & Nationhood: The England of G. K. Chesterton. 2009. (ENG., Illus.). 250p. 83.99 *(978-0-7391-2613-4(X))*; pap. 34.99 *(978-0-7391-2614-1(8))* Lexington Bks.

Stapleton, Julia, ed. G K Chesterton at the Daily News, Part I: Literature, Liberalism & Revolution, 1901-1913, 4 vols. 2011. (Pickering Masters Ser.). (ENG.). 1696p. 625.00 *(978-1-84893-212-8(X))* Pickering & Chatto Pubs., Ltd. GBR. Dist: Ashgate Publishing Co.

Ward, Maisie. Gilbert Keith Chesterton. 2009. 384p. 31.99 *(978-0-559-11097-9(9))*; 392p. 29.99 *(978-0-559-11916-3(X))*; 384p. 29.99 *(978-0-559-11110-5(X))*; 392p. 31.99 *(978-0-559-11903-3(8))*; 384p. pap. 33.75 *(978-0-559-11101-3(0))*; 384p. pap. 20.99 *(978-0-559-11108-2(8))*; 392p. pap. 33.75 *(978-0-559-11908-8(9))*; 392p. pap. 32.75 *(978-0-559-11912-5(7))* BiblioBazaar.

Wood, Ralph C. Chesterton: The Nightmare Goodness of God. 2011. (Making of Christian Imagination Ser.). (ENG.). 358p. 34.95 *(978-1-60258-161-6(4))* Baylor Univ. Pr.

CHESTS

Gibson, Scott & Turner, Peter. Blanket Chests: Outstanding Designs from 30 of the World's Finest Furniture Makers. 2011. (ENG., Illus.). 176p. pap. 24.95 *(978-1-60085-299-2(8))* Taunton Pr., Inc.

Koizumi, Kazuko. Traditional Japanese Chests: A Definitive Guide, 1 vol. Frew, Gavin, tr. from JPN. 2010. (ENG., Illus.). 152p. 50.00 *(978-4-7700-3112-9(2))* Kodansha America, Inc.

Matsele, Virginia, et al. He Hellenike Kasela. 2010. (GRE & GER., Illus.). 296p. (C). 90.00 ***(978-960-6878-12-1(0))*** Kapon, Ekdoseis GRC. Dist: ISD.

Roe, Fred. Ancient Church Chests & Chairs. 2007. 144p. per. *(978-1-905217-80-9(3))* Mills, Jeremy Publishing.

CHETAHS

see Cheetah

CHEVELLE AUTOMOBILE

Chevelle SS 1964-1972: A Muscle Car Source Book. 2nd ed. 2007. (Illus.). 128p. per. 19.95 *(978-0-9729869-3-9(6))* JC Publishing.

Portman, Michael. Chevelles. 2011. (Wild Wheels Ser.). (Illus.). 32p. (gr. 3-6). pap. 10.50 *(978-1-4339-4744-5(7)*, Stevens, Gareth Learning Library) Stevens, Gareth Publishing LLLP.

CHEVROLET AUTOMOBILE

see also Camaro Automobile; Chevelle Automobile; Chevy II Automobile; Corvair Automobile; Corvette Automobile; Nova Automobile

Arculus, Paul. Durant's Right-Hand Man. 2011. 368p. ***(978-1-77067-782-1(8))***; pap. ***(978-1-77067-783-8(6))*** FriesenPress.

Atherton, Larry & Schreib, Larry. How to Rebuild the Small Block Chevrolet. 2nd rev. ed. 2009. 160p. pap. 24.95 *(978-1-934709-00-9(X)*, S-A Design) CarTech, Inc.

Baechtel, John. Small-Block Chevy Performance 1955-1996. 2006. (ENG., Illus.). 144p. pap. 19.95 *(978-1-932494-15-0(4)*, S-A Design) CarTech, Inc.

Banacki, Walter J. Camaro Z28 Is Back! 2009. 60p. pap. 15.49 *(978-1-4389-4364-0(4))* AuthorHouse.

Benty, Cam & Super Chevy Magazine Editors. Chevy LS Engine Buildups HP1567. 2011. (ENG.). 224p. (gr. 12). 21.95 *(978-1-55788-567-8(2)*, HP Trade) Penguin Group (USA) Inc.

Burt, William. Chevrolet Camaro, 1967-1972. 2006. (MuscleCarTech Ser.). (ENG., Illus.). 112p. pap. 22.95 *(978-1-58007-100-0(7)*, MuscleCarTech) Specialty Pr. Pubs. & Wholesalers, Inc.

Chilton Automotive Editorial Staff. GM Celebrity - Century, 1982-95. 448p. pap. 16.95 *(978-0-8019-8689-5(3))* Nichols Publishing Co.

Dufur, Tom. How to Build Killer Big-Block Chevy Engines. 2012. (Illus.). 144p. pap. 24.95 ***(978-1-934709-28-3(X))*** CarTech, Inc.

Edsall, Larry. Chevrolet Volt: Charging into the Future. 2010. (ENG., Illus.). 144p. 30.00 *(978-0-7603-3893-3(0)*, 0760338930, Motorbooks) MBI Publishing Co. LLC.

Freiburger, David & Hot Rod Magazine Staff. Hot Rod Horsepower Handbook: Big-Block Chevy. rev. ed. 2006. (Motorbooks Workshop). (ENG., Illus.). 160p. per. 24.95 *(978-0-7603-2783-8(1)*, 0760327831, Motorbooks) MBI Publishing Co. LLC.

Genat, Robert. Chevy SS: 50 Years of Super Sport. 2007. (ENG., Illus.). 348p. 50.00 *(978-0-7603-2979-5(6)*, 0760329796, Motorbooks) MBI Publishing Co. LLC.

Genat, Robert. Chevy SS: The Super Sport Story. 2012. (ENG., Illus.). 348p. pap. 32.99 ***(978-0-7603-4297-8(0)***, 0760342970, Motorbooks) MBI Publishing Co. LLC.

Gunnell, John. Standard Catalog of Chevy, 1912-2001: 90 Years of History, Photos, Technical Data & Pricing. 2011. (ENG.). 448p. pap. 24.99 ***(978-1-4402-3051-6(X))*** Krause Pubns.

Handzel, Will. How to Build High-Performance Chevy LS1/LS6 V-8s: Modifying & Tuning Gen3 Engines for GM Cars & Pickups. 2008. 160p. pap. 24.95 *(978-1-932494-88-4(X))* CarTech, Inc.

Hansen, Graham. High-Performance Chevy Small-Block Cylinder Heads. 2007. (Cartech Ser.). (ENG., Illus.). 144p. pap. 24.95 *(978-1-932494-31-0(6)*, S-A Design) CarTech, Inc.

Hart, Lou. Chevy-Powered Drag Racing. 2010. (Photo Gallery Ser.). (ENG., Illus.). 160p. pap. 32.95 *(978-1-58388-271-9(5)*, 1583882715) Iconografix, Inc.

Haynes, John. Chevrolet & GMC Full-Size Vans: 1996 Thru 2010. 2011. (Haynes Repair Manual Ser.). (ENG., Illus.). 288p. pap. 24.95 ***(978-1-56392-887-1(6)***, 1563928876) Haynes Manuals, Inc.

Haynes Manuals, Editors of. Chevrolet Silverado & GMC Sierra, 2007 Thru 2012. 2012. (Haynes Repair Manual Ser.). (ENG., Illus.). 384p. pap. 26.95 ***(978-1-56392-972-4(4)***, 1563929724) Haynes Manuals, Inc.

Haynes, Max. Chevrolet Colorado GMC Canyon 2004 Thru 2010. 2011. (ENG., Illus.). 300p. pap. 24.95 *(978-1-56392-898-7(1)*, 1563928981) Haynes Manuals, Inc.

—Chevrolet S-10 & GMC Sonoma Pick-Ups: Chevrolet S-10 & GMC Sonoma Pick-Ups (1994-2004) Chevrolet Blazer & GMC Jimmy (1995-2004) GMC Envoy (1998-2001) Oldsmobile Bravada & Isuzu Hombre (1906-2001) 2008. (Haynes Repair Manual Ser.). (ENG., Illus.). 287p. pap. 26.95 *(978-1-56392-728-7(4)*, 1563927284) Haynes Manuals, Inc.

Henderson, Shawn. Chevy LS Engine Conversion Handbook. 2011. (ENG.). 192p. 23.95 *(978-1-55788-566-1(4)*, HP Trade) Penguin Group (USA) Inc.

Huntimer, Tony. How to Rebuild the Big-Block Chevrolet. 2009. 144p. pap. 24.95 *(978-1-932494-53-2(7))* CarTech, Inc.

Kibler, Jeff & Haynes, John H. Chevrolet Silverado GMC Sierra: 1999 Thru 2006 2WD & 4WD. Freund, Ken, ed. 2008. (Haynes Repair Manual Ser.). (ENG., Illus.). 352p. per. 26.95 *(978-1-56392-681-5(4)*, 1563926814) Haynes Manuals, Inc.

Lafontaine, Pierre & Lewis, David. Chevy Small-Block V-8 Interchange Manual. 2nd ed. 2009. (Motorbooks Workshop Ser.). (ENG., Illus.). 176p. pap. 24.99 *(978-0-7603-3166-8(9)*, 0760331669, Motorbooks) MBI Publishing Co. LLC.

Mavrigian, Mike. How to Rebuild Big-Block Chevy Engines, 1991-2000 Gen V & Gen VI: Step-by-Step Disassembly, Reconditioning & Final Assembly. 2009. (ENG.). 208p. (gr. 12-18). 21.95 *(978-1-55788-550-0(8)*, HP Trade) Penguin Group (USA) Inc.

Mueller, Mike. El Camino by Chevrolet. 2008. (ENG., Illus.). 112p. pap. 24.95 *(978-1-58388-215-3(4)*, 1583882154) Iconografix, Inc.

Petralia, Mike. Small-Block Chevy Bolt-on Horsepower. 2006. (ENG.). 144p. pap. 24.95 *(978-1-932494-17-4(0)*, S-A Design) CarTech, Inc.

Publications International Staff. Chevy Classics. 2008. 128p. 10.98 *(978-1-4127-1524-9(5))* Publications International, Ltd.

Santucci, Leo. Chevrolet Inline Six-Cylinder Power Manual 2nd Edition. 2011. (ENG., Illus.). 224p. pap. 29.95 *(978-1-931128-27-8(8)*, 1931128278) California Bill's Automotive Handbooks.

Schweid, Richard. Che's Chevrolet, Fidel's Oldsmobile: On the Road in Cuba. 2008. (ENG., Illus.). 256p. per. 20.95 *(978-0-8078-5887-5(0))* Univ. of North Carolina Pr.

Staffel, Ed. Chevrolet Small Block Parts Interchange Manual. 2010. (Illus.). 144p. pap. 24.95 *(978-1-934709-23-8(9)*, S-A Design) CarTech, Inc.

Storer, Jay. Chilton General Motors Colorado Canyon: 2004-06 Repair Manual. 2007. (Chilton's Total Car Care Repair Manuals Ser.). (ENG., Illus.). 304p. pap. 29.95 *(978-1-56392-673-0(3))* Haynes,Chilton.

—General Motors: Chevrolet Colorado & GMC Canyon: 2004 Thru 2010. 2011. (ENG.). 336p. pap. 29.95 *(978-1-56392-900-7(7))* Haynes,Chilton.

Stubblefield, Mike. General Motors Impala & Monte Carlo. 2009. (ENG., Illus.). 352p. pap. 29.95 *(978-1-56392-709-6(8))* Haynes,Chilton.

Vizard, David. How to Build Max-Performance Chevy Big-Blocks on a Budget. 2011. (Illus.). 144p. *(978-1-934709-38-2(7))* CarTech, Inc.

—How to Build Max-Performance Chevy Small Blocks on a Budjet! 2009. 160p. pap. 24.95 *(978-1-932494-84-6(7))* CarTech, Inc.

CHEVY II AUTOMOBILE

Clarke, R. M., compiled by. Blazer & Jimmy, 1983-1994: Chevy Blazer. S-10. K-5. K-10. V. K-1500. GMC Jimmy. S-15. K-15. V. Yukon. 2008. (Limited Edition Extra Ser.). (ENG., Illus.). 136p. pap. 24.95 *(978-1-85520-754-7(0)*, 1855207540) Brooklands Bks. GBR. Dist: MBI Distribution Services/Quayside Distribution.

—Chevy Blazer & Jimmy, 1969-1982. ltd. ed. 2008. (ENG., Illus.). 136p. pap. 24.95 *(978-1-85520-753-0(2)*, 1855207532) Brooklands Bks. GBR. Dist: MBI Distribution Services/Quayside Distribution.

Marion, Doug. Chevy II Nova: Production Details, History & Performance for Every Model. 2008. (ENG., Illus.). 224p. pap. 24.99 *(978-0-89689-658-1(7))* Krause Pubns.

Mavrigian, Mike. Building the Chevy LS Engine: Rebuilding & Performance Modifications for Chevy Ls Engines, Featuring a Buildup of an Ls2. Includes Added Information on Ls3, Ls7, & Ls9. 2010. (ENG.). 208p. (gr. 12). 21.95 *(978-1-55788-559-3(1)*, HP Trade) Penguin Group (USA) Inc.

Publications International Staff. Chevrolet Trucks. Consumer Guide Editors, ed. 2010. 192p. 13.98 *(978-1-4127-1686-4(1))* Publications International, Ltd.

CHEWA DIALECT

see also Nyanja Language

Euro Talk. Talk Now! Chichewa. 2008. 29.99 *(978-1-84352-433-5(3))* TOPICS Entertainment.

Megerdoomian, Karine. Beyond Words & Phrases. 2009. 216p. pap. *(978-3-639-15763-5(X))* VDM Verlag Dr. Mueller e.K.

Mwanza, David Sani & Bwanali, Alick Kadango. Tiyankhule ChiChewa: Let's Speak ChiChewa: (A First-Year Textbook) 2011. (NYA & ENG.). pap. ***(978-1-59703-022-9(8))*** Global Academic Publishing.

CHEWING

see Mastication

CHEYENNE (WYO.)

Van Pelt, Lori. Capital Characters of Old Cheyenne. 2006. (Dreamers & Schemers Ser.). (Illus.). 287p. *(978-0-931271-74-8(6))* High Plains Pr.

Weidel, Nancy. Cheyenne: 1867-1917. 2009. (Images of America Ser.). (ENG., Illus.). 128p. pap. 21.99 *(978-0-7385-5893-6(1))* Arcadia Publishing.

CHEYENNE INDIANS

see Indians of North America—West (U.S.)

CHEYENNE LANGUAGE

Icon Group International, Inc. Staff, compiled by. Webster's Cheyenne - English Thesaurus Dictionary. 2008. 60p. ring bd. 28.95 incl. audio compact disk *(978-0-497-83467-8(7))* Icon Group International, Inc.

CHI (CHINESE PHILOSOPHY)

see Qi (Chinese Philosophy)

CHI KUNG

see Qi Gong

CHIANG, KAI-SHEK, 1887-1975

Fenby, Jonathan. Generalissimo: Chiang Kai-Shek & the China He Lost. 2006. (Illus.). 562p. reprint ed. 35.00 *(978-1-4223-5775-0(9))* DIANE Publishing Co.

Heiferman, Ronald Ian. The Cairo Conference of 1943: Roosevelt, Churchill, Chiang Kai-Shek & Madame Chiang. 2011. (ENG., Illus.). 207p. pap. 45.00 *(978-0-7864-4804-3(0))* McFarland & Co., Inc. Pubs.

Jingping, Wu. Select Telegrams Between Chiang Kai-Shek & T. V. Soong, 1940-1943. Kuo, Tai-chun, ed. 2008. (TV soong Ser.). (CHI & ENG., Illus.). 384p. pap. 15.00 *(978-7-309-05956-4(5))* Hoover Institution Pr.

Li, Baoming. "Guo Jia Hua" Ming Yi Xia de "Si Shu Hua" Jiang Jieshi Dui Guo Min Ge Ming Jun de Kong Zhi Yan Jiu. 2010. *(978-7-5097-1414-0(1))* China Social Science Documentation Publishing Hse.

Long, Jianyu. Mao Zedong, Jiang Jieshi de Ren Sheng Dao Lu. 2010. (CHI., Illus.). *(978-7-80257-117-4(0))* ET Pr.

Pakula, Hannah. The Last Empress: Madame Chiang Kai-shek & the Birth of Modern China. 2010. (ENG., Illus.). 816p. pap. 20.00 *(978-1-4391-4894-5(5))* Simon & Schuster.

Taylor, Jay. The Generalissimo: Chiang Kai-Shek & the Struggle for Modern China. 2011. (ENG., Illus.). 752p. pap. 19.95 *(978-0-674-06049-4(0)*, Belknap Pr.) Harvard Univ. Pr.

CHIANG, MAY-LING SOONG, 1897-2003

Chiang, Ching-Kuo, et al. Jiang Jingguo Shu Xin Ji: Yu Song Meiling Wang Lai Han Dian = Chiang Ching-Kuo's Telegram Correspondence with Madame Chiang Kai-Shek, 2 vols. 2009. (CHI., Illus.). *(978-986-01-9590-3(0))* Academia Sinica.

DeLong, Thomas A. Madame Chiang Kai-Shek & Miss Emma Mills: China's First Lady & Her American Friend. 2007. (ENG., Illus.). 264p. per. 39.95 *(978-0-7864-2980-6(1))* McFarland & Co., Inc. Pubs.

Heiferman, Ronald Ian. The Cairo Conference of 1943: Roosevelt, Churchill, Chiang Kai-Shek & Madame Chiang. 2011. (ENG., Illus.). 207p. pap. 45.00 *(978-0-7864-4804-3(0))* McFarland & Co., Inc. Pubs.

Pakula, Hannah. The Last Empress: Madame Chiang Kai-shek & the Birth of Modern China. 2010. (ENG., Illus.). 816p. pap. 20.00 *(978-1-4391-4894-5(5))* Simon & Schuster.

Tyson Li, Laura, et al. Madame Chiang Kai-Shek: China's Eternal First Lady. 2007. (ENG., Illus.). 576p. per. 17.00 *(978-0-8021-4322-8(9)*, Grove Pr.) Grove/Atlantic, Inc.

Yang, Shubiao & Yang, Jing. Song Meiling Zhuan. 2010. (CHI.). 256p. *(978-7-308-06772-0(6))* Zhejiang Univ. Electronic & Audio-Video Pr.

CHIAPAS (MEXICO)

Bardacke, Frank, tr. & afterword by. Shadows of Tender Fury: The Letters & Communiques of Subcomandante Marcos & the Zapatista Army of National Liberation. (Illus.). 272p. 38.00 *(978-0-85345-917-0(7))* Monthly Review Pr.

Barmeyer, Niels. Developing Zapatista Autonomy: Conflict & NGO Involvement in Rebel Chiapas. 2009. (ENG., Illus.). 308p. (C). pap. 29.95 *(978-0-8263-4584-4(0))* Univ. of New Mexico Pr.

Chiapas, Revista. Chiapas 14. (SPA.). 176p. *(978-968-411-604-7(7))* Ediciones Era.

di Piramo, Daniela. Political Leadership in Zapatista Mexico: Marcos, Celebrity, & Charismatic Authority. 2010. (Illus.). 150p. 68.00 *(978-1-935049-21-0(6))* FirstForumPress.

Faleschini, Jake. The Causes of the Zapatista Rebellion in Chiapas: Bringing the Peasant Back In. 2008. 132p. pap. *(978-3-639-02871-3(6))* VDM Verlag Dr. Mueller e.K.

Hernandez Castillo, R. Aida, et al, eds. Dissident Women: Gender & Cultural Politics in Chiapas. 2006. (Louann Atkins Temple Women & Culture Ser.: Bk. 14). (ENG., Illus.). 318p. mass mkt. 22.95 *(978-0-292-71440-3(8))* Univ. of Texas Pr.

Núñez Rodríguez, Carlos Juan. La Marcha de la Dignidad Indígena Como Búsqueda de la Autonomía. 2009. (SPA.). 239p. 16.00 *(978-970-722-773-6(7))* Plaza y Valdes, S.A. de C.V. MEX. Dist: Sony Electronics.

Rabasa, José. Without History: Subaltern Studies, the Zapatista Insurgency, & the Specter of History. 2010. (Pitt Illuminations Ser.). (ENG., Illus.). 416p. (C). pap. 28.50 *(978-0-8229-6065-2(6))* Univ. of Pittsburgh Pr.

Ross, John. Zapatistas! Making Another World Possible - Chronicles of Resistance 2000-2006. 2006. (ENG.). 354p. per. 15.95 *(978-1-56025-874-2(8)*, Nation Bks.) Basic Bks.

Stephens, John Lloyd. Incidents of Travel in Central America, Chiapas, & Yucatan. 2010. (Cambridge Library Collection - Archaeology Ser.). (ENG.). 550p. pap. 39.99 *(978-1-108-01729-9(0))*; (Illus.). 472p. pap. 34.99 *(978-1-108-01728-2(2))* Cambridge Univ. Pr.

Visquerra Tischler, Serbio. Tiempo Y Emancipación. Mijail Bajtín Y Walter Benjamin En La Selva Lacandona., Vol. 3. 2008. (SPA.). 80p. pap. *(978-99922-61-73-0(0))* F & G Editores.

Washbrook, Sarah. Producing Modernity in Mexico: Labour, Race, & the State in Chiapas, 1876-1914. 2012. (ENG., Illus.). 400p. 150.00 ***(978-0-19-726497-3(2))*** Oxford Univ. Pr., Inc.

Washbrook, Sarah, ed. Rural Chiapas Ten Years after the Zapatista Uprising. 2007. (Illus.). 304p. 160.00 *(978-0-415-39490-1(2))* Routledge.

CHICAGO (ILL.)

see also Chicago Metropolitan Area (Ill.)

Hiles, Gary. A Simple Guide to Getting an Athletic Scholarship. 2011. 180p. pap. 24.99 ***(978-1-60844-754-1(5))*** Dog Ear Publishing, LLC.

The Port of Chicago, Illinois. (Port Ser.: Vol. 46). per. 8.50 *(978-0-16-001765-0(3))* United States Government Printing Office.

CHICAGO (ILL.)—ART INSTITUTE

see Art Institute of Chicago

CHICAGO (ILL.)—BIOGRAPHY

Abitong, Bill. It's Like Life's Mirror-If You Can See Things Clearly You Can Change Anything! 2010. 96p. pap. 21.30 *(978-0-557-31288-7(4))* Lulu Enterprises Inc.

Archer, Jacque Day & Santoro, Jamie Wirsbinski. Rogers Park. 2007. (Images of America Ser.). (ENG., Illus.). 128p. per. 21.99 *(978-0-7385-4139-6(7))* Arcadia Publishing.

Arredondo, Ramón & Arredondo, Trisha. Maria's Journey. 2010. pap. *(978-0-87195-286-8(6))* Indiana Historical Society.

Baatz, Simon. For the Thrill of It: Leopold, Loeb, & the Murder That Shocked Jazz Age Chicago. 2008. (ENG., Illus.). 560p. 27.95 *(978-0-06-078100-2(9))* HarperCollins Pubs.

Balken, Debra Bricker, text. John Storrs: Abstract Forms of The 1930s. 2008. (Illus.). 24p. *(978-0-9777686-8-4(6))* Carberry, Valerie Gallery, Inc.

Ballowe, James. A Man of Salt & Trees: The Life of Joy Morton. 2009. (Illus.). 318p. 28.95 *(978-0-87580-398-2(9))* Northern Illinois Univ. Pr.

Baugher, Shirley. Hidden History of Old Town. 2011. (Illus.). 130p. pap. 17.99 ***(978-1-60949-207-6(2))*** History Pr., The.

Bear, Marjorie Warvelle. A Mile Square of Chicago. 2007. (Illus.). 549p. pap. 48.00 *(978-0-9633995-4-0(3))* TIPRAC.

Bell, Debbie. Leave Us Alone & Let Us Shine. 2010. 68p. pap. 10.57 *(978-1-4269-3968-6(X))* Trafford Publishing.

Bezkorovainy, Anatoly. All Was Not Lost: Journey of a Russian Immigrant from Riga to Chicagoland. 2008. 692p. 36.49 *(978-1-4343-6457-9(7))*; pap. 30.00 *(978-1-4343-6458-6(5))* AuthorHouse.

Bilek, Art. The First Vice Lord: Big Jim Colosimo & the Ladies of the Levee. 2008. (ENG., Illus.). 319p. 24.95 *(978-1-58182-639-5(7))* Turner Publishing Co.

Black, Timuel D., Jr. Bridges of Memory: Chicago's Second Generation of Black Migration. 2008. (ENG., Illus.). 392p. per. 22.95 *(978-0-8101-5194-9(4))* Northwestern Univ. Pr.

Bond, Alma Halbert. Michelle Obama, a Biography. 2012. (Illus.). xvi, 167p. E-Book ***(978-0-313-38105-8(4)***, Greenwood Pr.) Greenwood Publishing Group, Inc.

Bottoni, Maurizio. The Cost of Unethical Behavior: A pending issue at the Argonne National Laboratory. 2010. 204p. pap. 14.49 *(978-1-4389-6709-7(8))* AuthorHouse.

Brabec, Barbara. The Drummer Drives! 2010. pap. *(978-1-4507-0915-6(X))* Independent Pub.

Brown, Allen, et al. Our Legacies: Writings from Chicago's Older Gay Men. 2011. 236p. pap. 18.95 *(978-1-4502-9168-2(6))* iUniverse, Inc.

Brown, Didi. A Spoon of God. 2008. 328p. (ENG.). 27.99 *(978-1-60477-365-1(0))*; per. 17.99 *(978-1-60477-364-4(2))* Xulon Pr., Inc.

Brown, Jeffrey A. Funny Misshapen Body: A Memoir. 2009. (ENG.). 320p. pap. 16.00 *(978-1-4165-4947-5(1)*, Touchstone) Touchstone.

Brown, Jr & Brown, Joan L. Jr Part II: You Can't Live Forever. 2009. 708p. pap. 25.99 *(978-1-4490-2664-6(8))* AuthorHouse.

Budge, Harry W. The Cloudbase Chronicles - Life at the Top: Living & Working at Chicago's John Hancock Center - an Engineer's Tale. 2009. 194p. pap. 14.95 *(978-1-4327-4733-6(9))* Outskirts Pr., Inc.

Buettner, Brad & Buettner, Mary. Growing up & Finding Her. 2011. 376p. 31.95 *(978-1-4502-9102-6(3))*; pap. 21.95 *(978-1-4502-9104-0(X))* iUniverse, Inc.

Bus, Anthony. A Mother's Plea: Lifting the Veil in Sanctuary. 2008. (ENG., Illus.). 317p. per. 16.95 *(978-1-59614-184-1(0))* Marian Pr.

Cain, Michael J. The Tangled Web: The Life & Death of Richard Cain - Chicago Cop & Mafia Hitman. 2009. (ENG.). 240p. pap. 14.95 *(978-1-60239-341-7(9)*, 239341) Skyhorse Publishing Co., Inc.

Calabrese, Frank, Jr., et al. Operation Family Secrets: How a Mobster's Son & the FBI Brought down Chicago's Murderous Crime Family. lt. ed. 2011. 525p. 30.99 ***(978-1-4104-3830-0(9))*** Thorndike Pr.

Chambers, Catherine Bourke. Just a Boy from Home: With songs, stories & Recipes. 2008. 336p. 28.49 *(978-1-4343-6790-7(8))*; pap. 17.99 *(978-1-4343-6789-1(4))* AuthorHouse.

Chambers, Charles D. Life's Journey of an Immigrant. 2010. 108p. 21.49 *(978-1-4490-9888-9(6))*; (ENG.). pap. 10.99 *(978-1-4490-9889-6(4))* AuthorHouse.

Chasnoff, Joel. The 188th Crybaby Brigade: A Skinny Jewish Kid from Chicago Fights Hezbollah - A Memoir. 2010. (ENG., Illus.). 288p. 25.00 *(978-1-4165-4932-1(3)*, Free Pr.) Free Pr.

Chicago Tribune Staff. Bears Roar: Meet the Men Who Put the Swagger Back in Chicago Football. 2007. (ENG., Illus.). 128p. per. 12.95 *(978-1-60078-001-1(6))* Triumph Bks.

Chojnacki, Paul E. Lick Stick Count or Pour: Pharmacy Before the Pharm D. 2011. 80p. pap. 15.95 ***(978-1-4327-7616-9(9))*** Outskirts Pr., Inc.

Cicero, Frank. Relative Strangers: Italian Protestants in the Catholic World. 2011. (ENG.). 250p. 32.50 *(978-0-89733-615-4(1))* Academy Chicago Pubs., Ltd.

Ciezadlo, Janina & Rosemont, Penelope, eds. Armitage Avenue Transcendentalists: Chicago Stories by Nelson Algren, Studs Terkel, 2010. (Illus.). 160p. pap. 15.00 *(978-0-88286-290-3(1))* Kerr, Charles H. Publishing Co.

Cohen, Rich. Machers & Rockers: Chess Records & the Business of Rock & Roll. 2006. (Illus.). 220p. reprint ed. 23.00 *(978-1-4223-5588-6(8))* DIANE Publishing Co.

Cunningham, James. Howling like Wolves from Longwood Drive: Chicago Teenagers in the Great Depression. 2010. 124p. pap. 13.00 *(978-1-4269-2721-8(5))* Trafford Publishing.

Dawson, Garth Clark. Here's Fifty: The First hundred Years are the Hardest. Edmund T. Mazur. 2008. 280p. pap. 20.95 *(978-0-595-52744-1(2))* iUniverse, Inc.

Derrick, Gregory J. Revolution's Revelation. 2010. 258p. pap. 19.99 *(978-1-4415-9936-0(3))* Xlibris Corp.

Dickerson, Dennis C. African American Preachers & Politics: The Careys of Chicago. (Margaret Walker Alexander Series in African American Studies). (ENG., Illus.). 2011. 304p. pap. 30.00 ***(978-1-61703-193-9(3))*** 2010. 236p. 65.00 *(978-1-60473-427-0(2))* Univ. Pr. of Mississippi.

Drummond, John. It Ain't Pretty but It's Real. 2008. 272p. per. 20.00 *(978-1-58374-175-7(5))* Chicago Spectrum Pr.

Eddy former Lt, George. Fly Boy Navy Wings & Willing Women W. 2006. pap. 8.95 *(978-1-59800-734-3(3))* Outskirts Pr., Inc.

El, Molino. Stimulus Distiller: A Blue Flame (Test) 2010. 56p. pap. 19.95 *(978-1-4520-5518-3(1))* AuthorHouse.

Ellis, Johnny L. & Rose, Abraham. Johnny & His Rose: A True Story of Eternal Love. 2007. (ENG., Illus.) 93p. per. 15.00 *(978-0-9789461-2-8(X))* His Rose, Inc.

Fallows, Alice Katharine. Everybody's Bishop: Being the Life & Times of Samuel Fallows. 2011. 526p. 60.95 ***(978-1-258-02643-1(0))*** Literary Licensing, LLC.

Fringero, Valarie Kent. Change to Shame. 2011. 74p. pap. 15.99 ***(978-1-4568-0989-8(X))*** Xlibris Corp.

Gateley, Edwina. In God's Womb. 2009. (Illus.). 192p. pap. 20.00 *(978-1-57075-847-8(6))* Orbis Bks.

Golin, Milton. Delivery: From Ferrying Warplanes Across Oceans to Bringing Heroic News from a Megaflood. 2010. 116p. (ENG.). 22.95 *(978-1-4502-2649-3(3))*; pap. 12.95 *(978-1-4502-1989-1(6))* iUniverse, Inc.

Gracey, Douglas R. Intern in the Promised Land: Cook County Hospital. 128p. 2009. 23.95 *(978-1-4401-1251-5(7))* 2008. pap. 13.95 *(978-1-4401-1249-2(5))* iUniverse, Inc.

Haas, Jeffrey. The Assassination of Fred Hampton: How the FBI & the Chicago Police Murdered a Black Panther. 2011. (ENG.). 384p. pap. 16.95 *(978-1-56976-709-2(2)*, Hill, Lawrence Bks.) Chicago Review Pr., Inc.

Harpster, Jack. The Railroad Tycoon Who Built Chicago: A Biography of William B. Ogden. 2009. (ENG.). 328p. 29.95 *(978-0-8093-2917-5(4))* Southern Illinois Univ. Pr.

Hawkins, Florence Nnyala. Sot. 2008. 76p. pap. 10.49 *(978-1-4389-1916-4(6))* AuthorHouse.

Hicks, Hadley. So You Wanna Be a Legend. So Did I. The Reflections of a Teacher-Coach - A Search for Significance. 2010. 372p. pap. 24.95 *(978-1-4497-0231-1(7)*, WestBow Pr.) Author Solutions, Inc.

Hines, Thomas S. Burnham of Chicago: Architect & Planner. 2nd ed. 2008. (ENG., Illus.). 474p. pap. 22.50 *(978-0-226-34172-9(0))* Univ. of Chicago Pr.

Holliday, Norma Jean. The Larry Holliday Story. 2008. 320p. per. 16.95 *(978-1-4327-1798-8(7))* Outskirts Pr., Inc.

Hopkins, Jerry. In the Name of the Boss Upstairs: The Father Ray Brennan Story. 2006.Tr. of Au nom du Patron d'en Haut, Histoire du Pere Ray Brennan. (FRE., Illus.). 337p. pap. 15.00 *(978-0-9759284-4-8(9))* Vincent, Thomas J. Foundation Inc.

Humble, Ronald D. Frank Nitti: The True Story of Chicago's Notorious Enforcer. 2008. (ENG., Illus.). 320p. 23.95 *(978-1-56980-342-4(0))* Barricade Bks., Inc.

Ind, Peter. Lennie Tristano & His Legacy. 2008. (Popular Music History Ser.). (ENG.). 192p. (C). pap. 19.95 *(978-1-84553-281-9(3))* Equinox Publishing Ltd. GBR. Dist: ISD.

Jankovsky, Jason Alan & Trader X. The Art of the Trade: What I Learned (and Lost) Trading the Chicago Futures Markets. 2008. (ENG.). 208p. 29.95 *(978-0-470-13899-1(8)*, Wiley) Wiley, John & Sons, Inc.

Janssen, Marian. Not at All What One Is Used To: The Life & Times of Isabella Gardner. 2010. (ENG., Illus.). 392p. 34.95 *(978-0-8262-1898-8(9))* Univ. of Missouri Pr.

Johnson, Moriah. The Book of Restoration & Hope. 2011. 56p. pap. 8.95 ***(978-1-4620-3377-5(6))*** iUniverse, Inc.

Kakaletris, George. Within the Warrior: There Lived A Broken Child. 2007. 536p. per. 31.46 *(978-1-4120-9383-5(X))* Trafford Publishing.

Kalmbach, Sally Sexton. The Jewel of the Gold Coast: Mrs. Potter Palmer's Chicago. 2009. (Illus.). 96p. pap. 17.95 *(978-0-9818126-6-3(X))* Ampersand, Inc.

KAUTH, Agnes Koudelka. Life Is full of Smiles. 2008. 172p. pap. 19.96 *(978-1-4357-4256-7(7))* Lulu Enterprises Inc.

Kersten, Jason. The Art of Making Money: The Story of a Master Counterfeiter. 2010. (ENG.). 304p. (gr. 12). 16.00 *(978-1-59240-557-2(6)*, Gotham) Penguin Group (USA) Inc.

Kiel, Donna. He Was There Even When I Was Unaware & So Was Ms. 2009. 108p. 19.99 *(978-1-60791-422-8(0))*; pap. 11.99 *(978-1-60791-421-1(2))* Xulon Pr., Inc.

Klatt, Wayne. King of the Gold Coast: Cap'n Streeter, the Millionaires & the Story of Lake Shore Drive. 2011. 160p. pap. 19.99 ***(978-1-60949-320-2(6))*** History Pr., The.

Kohl, Beth. Embryo Culture: Making Babies in the Twenty-First Century. 2010. (ENG.). 288p. 24.00 *(978-1-4379-7129-3(6))* DIANE Publishing Co.

Krieman, Jade Dean. An Endless Journey. 2011. 184p. 29.99 ***(978-1-4568-7014-0(9))***; pap. 19.99 ***(978-1-4568-7013-3(0))*** Xlibris Corp.

Kuecher, Gerald J. Fruitcake Hill: A History & Memoir of Life on the Hill in a Family Of 15. 2008. (Illus.). 92p. pap. *(978-0-9809995-0-1(2)*, CCB Publishing) CCB Publishing.

Kulkarni, Mauktik. A Ghost of Che: A Motorcycle Ride Through Space, Time, Life & Love. 2009. 156p. pap. 14.95 *(978-1-4401-6109-4(7))* iUniverse, Inc.

Lane, Ernest P. Biographical Memoir of Ernest Julius Wilczynski, 1876-1932: National Academy of Sciences, Biographical Memoirs V16, Sixth Memoir. 2011. 38p. 35.95 ***(978-1-258-07166-0(5))*** Literary Licensing, LLC.

Latourette, K. s. & Laufer, Berthold. Biographical Memoir of Berthold Laufer, 1874-1934: National Academy of Sciences Biographical Memoirs, V18, Third Memoir. 2011. 34p. 35.95 ***(978-1-258-06839-4(7))*** Literary Licensing, LLC.

Layner, John Steven & Layner, June Evelyn. Yesterday. 2007. 112p. (ENG.). 18.95 *(978-1-4327-0421-6(4))*; per. 9.95 *(978-1-4327-0412-4(5))* Outskirts Pr., Inc.

Ledermann, Robert P. State Street: One Brick at a Time. 2011. (Illus.). 160p. pap. 22.99 ***(978-1-60949-294-6(3))*** History Pr., The.

Lemons, Lawrence Todd. Reinforcements, 1 vol. 2009. 83p. pap. 16.95 *(978-1-60610-262-6(1))* PublishAmerica, Inc.

Len Small: Gov. Len Small in the 1920s, When Al Capone Owned the Top Officials in Illinois: Governors & Gangsters. 2009. (Illus.). 297p. *(978-0-9824080-0-1(5))* Side Show Bks.

Letto, Heather. Plan V: Plan A Didn't Work - Plan B Sucked - Plan C Was Worse Than Plan A, 1 vol. 2010. 230p. pap. 24.95 *(978-1-4489-4084-4(2))* PublishAmerica, Inc.

Levoy, Hughie Boy. Chicago Kid: From Whence I Came. 2011. 282p. pap. 19.99 ***(978-1-4653-4086-3(6))***; 29.99 ***(978-1-4628-5341-0(2))*** Xlibris Corp.

Lindberg, Richard C. Heartland Serial Killers: Belle Gunness, Johann Hoch, & Murder for Profit in Gaslight Era Chicago. 2011. (ENG., Illus.). 272p. 28.95 *(978-0-87580-436-1(5))* Northern Illinois Univ. Pr.

Longo, Sam. Bellmen Don't Get Golden Parachutes. 2010. 200p. 25.99 *(978-1-4490-1273-1(6))*; pap. 15.95 *(978-1-4490-1272-4(8))* AuthorHouse.

Lyles, Darrin. Operations Power up in Christ: Overcoming the Worst of Times. 2008. 100p. pap. 12.95 *(978-0-9802398-2-9(6))* Williams, Benjamin Publishing.

Lyon, Andrea. Angel of Death Row: My Life as a Death Penalty Defense Lawyer. 2010. (ENG., Illus.). 288p. 24.95 *(978-1-60714-434-2(4))* Kaplan Publishing.

Macaluso, Lou. Clown Town. 2008. 244p. 32.00 *(978-1-59858-637-4(8))*; pap. 14.00 *(978-1-59858-670-1(X))* Dog Ear Publishing, LLC.

Magrady, Charles A. Charlie's Way: Teacher & Pilot - The Rest of the Story. 2008. 158p. pap. 24.95 *(978-1-60703-770-5(X))* PublishAmerica, Inc.

Mangino, Gary. College Educated: A Story of My Life in Hockey. 2007. (ENG.). 140p. per. 24.95 *(978-1-4241-5925-3(3))* PublishAmerica, Inc.

Markelis, Daiva. White Field, Black Sheep: A Lithuanian-American Life. 2010. (ENG., Illus.). 216p. 22.50 *(978-0-226-50530-5(8))* Univ. of Chicago Pr.

McBride, Peter. As an Architect. 2011. 206p. pap. 24.95 ***(978-1-4560-7951-2(4))*** PublishAmerica, Inc.

C

McClelland, Edward. Young Mr. Obama: Chicago & the Making of a Black President. 2010. (ENG., Illus.). 288p. 24.00 *(978-1-60819-060-7(9))* Bloomsbury Publishing.

Miller, Alexander. The Heart of a City. 2007. 304p. per. 21.95 *(978-0-595-41899-2(6))* iUniverse, Inc.

Miller, Tom. No Regrets. 2011. 82p. 24.99 ***(978-1-4628-9865-7(3))***; pap. 15.99 ***(978-1-4628-9864-0(5))*** Xlibris Corp.

Moore, Kenneth Nathan. Saving the African American Community from Violence: Growing up tough in Chicago. 2011. 180p. pap. 19.99 ***(978-1-4568-1226-3(2))*** Xlibris Corp.

Muir, Ruth C. Three Surnames & a Jr. 2010. 168p. pap. 13.96 *(978-1-4269-3938-9(8))* Trafford Publishing.

Myers, P. L. Gate to Gate. 2010. 200p. pap. 14.99 *(978-0-557-26147-5(3))* Lulu Enterprises Inc.

O'Neill, Francis. Chief O'Neill's Sketchy Recollections of an Eventful Life in Chicago. Skerrett, Ellen & Lesch, Mary, eds. 2008. (ENG., Illus.). 336p. 28.95 *(978-0-8101-2465-3(3))* Northwestern Univ. Pr.

Pae, James. Letters to Gabriel: My Enduring Memories as an Immigrant in America. 2010. 124p. 23.95 *(978-1-4502-1414-8(2))*; pap. 13.95 *(978-1-4502-1413-1(4))* iUniverse, Inc.

Palazzolo, Tom. At Maxwell Street: Chicago's Historic Marketplace Recalled in Words an Photographs. 2008. (Illus.). 90p. 40.00 *(978-0-9789676-1-1(5))* Wicker Pk. Pr., Ltd.

Parks, Chester. The Old Neighborhood... & Beyond. 2006. pap. 16.97 *(978-0-9727840-7-8(1))* Mystic Pubs.

Peterson, Paul O. Pop's Story. 2011. 376p. 30.74 ***(978-1-4269-6612-5(1))***; pap. 20.74 ***(978-1-4269-6611-8(3))*** Trafford Publishing.

Pick, Grant. The People Are the News: Grant Pick's Chicago Stories. Pick, John, ed. 2009. (ENG.). 296p. pap. 18.95 *(978-0-8101-2580-3(3))* Northwestern Univ. Pr.

Piper, Jason. Back to Suburbia. 2011. 144p. pap. 14.95 *(978-1-4502-6467-9(0))* iUniverse, Inc.

Price, Tom. Last Hand: A Suburban Memoir of Cards & the Cold War Era. 2009. 264p. pap. 26.95 *(978-1-4401-3619-1(X))* iUniverse, Inc.

Priest, Lord. From Foot Soldier to Elite. 2011. 80p. pap. 14.99 ***(978-1-4634-1074-2(3))*** AuthorHouse.

Ramirez, Leonard G., et al. Chicanas of 18th Street: Narratives of a Movements from Latino Chicago. 2011. (Latinos in Chicago & Midwest Ser.). (ENG., Illus.). 272p. 80.00 *(978-0-252-03618-7(2))*; pap. 27.00 *(978-0-252-07812-5(8))* Univ. of Illinois Pr.

Ratliff, Stanley. A Dream, A Goal, Never a Reality. 2008. 120p. pap. 12.99 *(978-1-4343-6622-1(7))* AuthorHouse.

Reimers, Lois. Hattie: She Was Wired Differently. 2011. 207p. pap. 14.95 ***(978-1-4327-7405-9(0))*** Outskirts Pr., Inc.

Rica, Frede'. A Burden Has Been Lifted. 2008. 60p. pap. 16.95 *(978-1-60563-832-4(3))* PublishAmerica, Inc.

Richards, Bob. Secrets from the Tower: An O'Hare Air Traffic Controller's Personal Stories of Life & Aviation. 2007. 376p. per. 25.00 *(978-0-9787113-9-9(4),* Ithaca Pr.) Authors & Artists Publishers of New York, Inc.

Riley, Jim. Oh Really, Riley? The Story of Riley's Trick Shop & the Family behind It. 2010. 192p. 26.95 *(978-1-4502-6549-2(9))*; pap. 16.95 *(978-1-4502-6547-8(2))* iUniverse, Inc.

Sanchez, Reymundo. My Bloody Life. 2011. 15.44 *(978-0-7848-3416-9(4),* Everbind) Marco Bk. Co.

Sanchez, Reymundo & Rodriguez, Sonia. Lady Q: The Rise & Fall of a Latin Queen. 2010. (ENG.). 288p. pap. 16.95 *(978-1-56976-285-1(6))* Chicago Review Pr., Inc.

Sawyers, June Skinner. Chicago Portraits. 2nd ed. 2012. (ENG.). 376p. pap. 34.95 *(978-0-8101-2649-7(4))* Northwestern Univ. Pr.

Scott, Mike. Great American Youth: A True Saga. 2011. 256p. pap. 16.00 *(978-1-4567-6043-4(2))* AuthorHouse.

Selander, Joyce. Joyce, Queen of the Mountain: Female Courage & Hand-to-Hand Combat in the World's Largest Money Pit. 2011. 180p. 26.95 ***(978-1-4620-4207-4(4))***; pap. 16.95 ***(978-1-4620-4205-0(8))*** iUniverse, Inc.

Serritella, Anthony. Book Joint for Sale: Memoirs of a Bookie. 2011. 238p. pap. 14.95 ***(978-1-4567-4335-2(X))***; pap. 24.95 ***(978-1-4567-4334-5(1))*** AuthorHouse.

Shorter Jr., Theodore (Ted). Lovingly & Orderly: A Son's Lament. 2010. 448p. pap. *(978-1-4251-4207-0(9))* Trafford Publishing (UK) Ltd.

Simonis, George. The House on Orchard Street. 2007. 242p. (YA). pap. 22.96 *(978-1-4303-2995-4(5))* Lulu Enterprises Inc.

—Last Train Home. 2009. 220p. pap. 21.95 *(978-0-557-09668-8(5))* Lulu Enterprises Inc.

Soucek, Gayle. Marshall Fields: The Store that Helped Build Chicago. 2010. (Landmarks Ser.). (ENG., Illus.). 160p. pap. 19.99 *(978-1-59629-854-5(5))* History Pr., The.

Spoula, Michael J. Glimpses of God. 2011. 416p. pap. 29.95 ***(978-1-4626-2598-7(3))*** PublishAmerica, Inc.

Steinberg, Ellen FitzSimmons & Hanson, Eleanor Hudera. Learning to Cook In 1898: A Chicago Culinary Memoir. 2007. (Great Lakes Bks.). 218p. per. 19.95 *(978-0-8143-3364-8(8))* Wayne State Univ. Pr.

Steinberg, Neil. Drunkard: A Hard-Drinking Life. 2009. (ENG.). 288p. (gr. 12-18). 15.00 *(978-0-452-29543-8(2),* Plume) Penguin Group (USA) Inc.

Stout, M. F. One Weekend. 2009. 328p. 28.49 *(978-1-4343-9395-1(X))*; pap. 17.99 *(978-1-4343-9394-4(1))* AuthorHouse.

Streiker, Lowell. Of Boys & Guns. 2007. 260p. pap. 19.95 *(978-1-4303-0560-6(6))* Lulu Enterprises Inc.

Sullivan, Karla. Imagine That. 2007. 76p. per. 16.95 *(978-1-4241-1154-1(4))* PublishAmerica, Inc.

Tesich, Nadja. To Die in Chicago. 2010. 204p. pap. 17.95 *(978-1-4502-3389-7(9))* iUniverse, Inc.

Thomopoulos, Nick T. 100 Years: From Greece to Chicago & Back. 2011. 206p. 29.99 ***(978-1-4568-0144-1(9))***; pap. 19.99 ***(978-1-4568-0143-4(0))*** Xlibris Corp.

Thomsen, Richard. Is God on Our Side? My Side? Your Side? Their Side? 2010. 253p. 29.95 *(978-1-4327-6053-3(X))*; (Illus.). pap. 15.95 *(978-1-4327-6038-0(6))* Outskirts Pr., Inc.

Tipre, Vincent. Six Summers - a Memoir. 2007. 256p. per. 12.95 *(978-1-59858-412-7(X))* Dog Ear Publishing, LLC.

Tipre, Vincent. The Tennis Baseball League. 2011. 148p. pap. 12.95 ***(978-1-4575-0346-7(8))*** Dog Ear Publishing, LLC.

Trinidad, David & Powell, D. A. By Myself, an Autobiography. 2009. (ENG.). 52p. pap. 9.00 *(978-1-933527-29-1(3))* Turtle Point Pr.

Tukiendorf, Bogdan. The Long, Hard Road: From Nazi-Occupied Poland to Freedom in America. 2010. pap. 13.99 *(978-1-61566-152-7(2))* Tate Publishing & Enterprises, LLC.

Turck, W. C. Everything for Love: A memoir of love & War. 2009. 292p. pap. 21.95 *(978-1-4401-3292-6(5))* iUniverse, Inc.

Unger, Rudolph M. The Community of Fuller Park: Those Were the Days My Friends. (Illus.). 352p. reprint ed. pap. 26.00 *(978-0-9710761-1-2(1))* Unger, Rudolph M.

Virtue, John. The Model American Abroad. 2007. 280p. pap. 19.99 *(978-1-59092-405-1(3))* Orchard House Pr.

Wade, Dwyane. A Father First: How My Life Became Bigger Than Basketball. 2012. (ENG.). 320p. 26.99 ***(978-0-06-213615-2(1)***, Morrow, William & Co.) HarperCollins Pubs.

Walker, Sabrina L. Actions Speak Louder Than Words: Is an Informative Documentation of the Personal Roles Individuals Play while in Sexual Relationships. These Roles Are Clearly Stated but Often Construed Due to What Is Seen Compared to What Is Felt. 2008. 89p. pap. 16.95 *(978-1-60563-221-6(X))* PublishAmerica, Inc.

Watanuki, Kumiko. Spotkanie Wschodu Z Zachodem. 2010. 102p. pap. 15.99 *(978-1-4500-4254-3(6))* Xlibris Corp.

Watson, Douglas Duane. Pretzels & Ginger Ale. 2011. 140p. pap. 24.95 ***(978-1-4560-3720-8(X))*** PublishAmerica, Inc.

Wilborn, Carlton. Front & Center: How I Learned to Live There. 2007. 24.95 *(978-0-9790052-0-6(5))* Treelife Publishing.

Willis, R. Elliot. Finding Grace on a Less Traveled Road: A Cancer Doctor Reflects on Living & Dying. 2008. 212p. 27.95 *(978-1-4401-1128-0(6))*; pap. 17.95 *(978-1-4401-1126-6(X))* iUniverse, Inc.

Wysocki, Bernard. Learn to Live, Love, Laugh. 2011. 60p. pap. 9.95 ***(978-1-4620-6266-9(0))*** iUniverse, Inc.

Zipperstein, Steven J. Rosenfeld's Lives: Fame, Oblivion, & the Furies of Writing. 2011. (ENG., Illus.). 288p. pap. 20.00 *(978-0-300-17153-2(6))* Yale Univ. Pr.

CHICAGO (ILL.)—BOARD OF TRADE

see Chicago Board of Trade

CHICAGO (ILL.)—BUILDINGS, STRUCTURES, ETC.

Bosch, Jennifer Marjorie & Pridmore, Jay, texts. A View from the River: The Chicago Architecture Foundation River Cruise. 2008. 96p. pap. 15.95 *(978-0-7649-4532-8(7))* Pomegranate Communications, Inc.

Cannon, Patrick F. Prairie Metropolis: Chicago & the Birth of a New American Home. 2008. (Illus.). 160p. 39.95 *(978-0-7649-4595-3(5))* Pomegranate Communications, Inc.

Cannon, Patrick F. & Sullivan, Louis H. Louis Sullivan: Creating a New American Architecture. 2011. (Illus.). 192p. 39.95 *(978-0-7649-5771-0(6))* Pomegranate Communications, Inc.

Chappell, Sally A. Kitt. Chicago's Urban Nature: A Guide to the City's Architecture + Landscape. 2007. (ENG., Illus.). 300p. 47.50 *(978-0-226-10139-2(8))*; pap. 20.00 *(978-0-226-10140-8(1))* Univ. of Chicago Pr.

Charles W. Moore Center for the Study of Place Staff. Placenotes — Chicago Art & Architecture. 2008. (ENG.). 1p. 19.95 *(978-0-9766493-8-0(1))* Moore Ctr. Pr.

Cuno, James B., et al. The Modern Wing: Renzo Piano & the Art Institute of Chicago. 2009. (Illus.). 167p. pap. *(978-0-86559-231-5(4))* Art Institute of Chicago.

Day, Jacque E. & Santoro, Jamie Wirsbinski. West Ridge. 2008. (Images of America Ser.). (Illus.). 128p. pap. 19.99 *(978-0-7385-6150-9(9))* Arcadia Publishing.

Daza, Ricardo, ed. Looking for Mies. 2008. 200p. pap. *(978-84-96954-37-3(4))* Actar Birkhauser Distribution.

Feldman, Roberta M. & Wheaton, Jim, eds. The Chicago Greystone in Historic North Lawndale. 2007. (Illus.). 120p. per. 14.95 *(978-0-9789650-0-6(0))* City Design Ctr.

Furse, Ray. City in Time: Chicago. 2007. (City in Time Ser.). (ENG., Illus.). 144p. 14.95 *(978-1-4027-3299-7(6))* Sterling Publishing Co., Inc.

Garfinkle, Charlene G., et al. Women Building History: Public Art at the 1893 Columbian Exposition. 2011. (ENG., Illus.). 279p. 49.95 *(978-0-520-24111-4(8))* Univ. of California Pr.

Gyure, Dale Allen. The Chicago Schoolhouse: High School Architecture & Educational Reform, 1856-2006. 2011. (Center for American Places - Center Books on American Places Ser.). (ENG., Illus.). 240p. 40.00 *(978-1-935195-19-1(0))* Ctr. for American Places, Inc.

Keegan, Edward & Chicago Architecture Foundation Staff. Chicago Architecture: 1885 to Today. 2008. (Universe Architecture Ser.). (ENG., Illus.). 224p. pap. 29.95 *(978-0-7893-1533-5(5))* Universe Publishing.

Lowe, David Garrard. Lost Chicago. 2010. (ENG., Illus.). 272p. pap. 35.00 *(978-0-226-49432-6(2))* Univ. of Chicago Pr.

Marjanovic, Igor, et al. Marina City: Bertrand Goldberg's Urban Vision. 2010. (ENG., Illus.). 176p. pap. 35.00 *(978-1-56898-863-4(X))* Princeton Architectural Pr.

McNulty, Elizabeth. Chicago. 2007. (Then & Now Thunder Bay Ser.). (ENG., Illus.). 144p. pap. 12.95 *(978-1-59223-732-6(0),* Thunder Bay Pr.) Advantage Pubs. Group.

Merwood-Salisbury, Joanna. Chicago 1890: The Skyscraper & the Modern City. 2009. (Chicago Architecture & Urbanism Ser.). (ENG., Illus.). 208p. 45.00 *(978-0-226-52078-0(1))* Univ. of Chicago Pr.

Noelle, Christina. Urban Loft: How Chicago Redefined the Architecture. 2008. (Illus.). 168p. 49.95 *(978-0-9672215-5-7(2))* Bridge Hse. Publishing, Inc.

O'Gorman, Thomas J. Chicago from the Air Then & Now. 2010. (ENG.). 144p. 19.95 *(978-1-60710-009-6(6),* Thunder Bay Pr.) Advantage Pubs. Group.

Roche, R. Samuel. Plans of Chicago. 2010. (Illus.). 160p. 45.00 *(978-0-615-28220-6(2))* Architects Research Foundation.

Schrenk, Lisa D. Building a Century of Progress: The Architecture of Chicago's 1933-34 World's Fair. 2007. (Illus.). 368p. 39.95 *(978-0-8166-4836-8(0))* Univ. of Minnesota Pr.

Siry, Joseph M. Carson Pirie Scott: Louis Sullivan & the Chicago Department Store. 2012. (Chicago Architecture & Urbanism Ser.). (ENG., Illus.). 304p. pap. 50.00 *(978-0-226-76137-4(1))* Univ. of Chicago Pr.

Skyline: Chicago: The Series. 6.95 *(978-1-880005-10-1(7))* Perspectives International, Inc.

Slavick, Ann. Hour Chicago: Twenty-Five Self-Guided 60-Minute Tours of Chicago's Great Architecture & Art. 2008. (ENG., Illus.). 272p. pap. 16.95 *(978-1-56663-743-5(0))* Dee, Ivan R. Pub.

Vernon, Christopher. Graceland Cemetery: A Design History. 2011. (Illus.). 208p. 39.95 ***(978-1-55849-926-3(1))*** Univ. of Massachusetts Pr.

Waldheim, Charles & Ray, Katerina Ruedi, eds. Chicago Architecture: Histories, Revisions, Alternatives. 2007. (Chicago Architecture & Urbanism Ser.). (Illus.). 442p. per. 25.00 *(978-0-226-87039-7(1))* Univ. of Chicago Pr.

Walker, Matthew. Chicago Book. 2008. *(978-0-9704875-3-7(3))* Walker, Matthew D. Publishing.

Wallpaper Editors, ed. Wallpaper City Guide Chicago 2012. 2012. (ENG., Illus.). 128p. pap. 9.95 ***(978-0-7148-6299-6(1))*** Phaidon Pr., Inc.

Whitman Publishing Staff, ed. Chicago A Past to Present Photo Tour. 2010. (Illus.). 120p. 12.95 *(978-0-7948-3063-2(3))* Whitman Publishing LLC.

CHICAGO (ILL.)—DESCRIPTION AND TRAVEL

Adams, Rosemary K. Remembering Christmas in Chicago. 2010. (Remembering Ser.). (ENG., Illus.). 134p. pap. 16.95 *(978-1-59652-696-9(3))* Turner Publishing Co.

Algren, Nelson. Chicago: City on the Make. 60th anniv. ed. 2011. 152p. pap. 17.00 *(978-0-226-01386-2(3))* Univ. of Chicago Pr.

Appelbaum, Stanley. Spectacle in the White City: The Chicago 1893 World's Fair. 2009. (Calla Editions Ser.). (ENG., Illus.). 176p. 50.00 *(978-1-60660-006-1(0))* Dover Pubns., Inc.

Attini, Antonio, photos by. Chicago from the Air. (Illus.). 160p. *(978-88-8095-754-6(6))* White Star Publishers, Inc.

Bachrach, Julia S. The City in a Garden: A Photographic History of Chicago's Parks Second Edition. 2nd ed. 2012. (Center for American Places - Center Books on American Places Ser.). (Illus.). 224p. pap. 37.50 *(978-1-935195-22-1(0))* Ctr. for American Places, Inc.

Bakija, compiled by. Chicago in Focus: Portrait of a City Through the Eyes of Its People, 1 vols., vol. 1. 2010. 64p. pap. 19.95 *(978-0-615-36236-6(2))* Dream Town.

Becker, Edwin F. True Haunting. 2011. 184p. pap. 14.49 ***(978-1-4634-0862-6(5))***; 24.99 ***(978-1-4634-0861-9(7))*** AuthorHouse.

Bielski, Ursula. Chicago Haunts. 2009. 296p. pap. 15.95 *(978-1-933272-13-9(9))* Thunder Bay Pr.

—Chicago Haunts 3. 2009. 224p. pap. 15.95 *(978-1-933272-15-3(5))* Thunder Bay Pr.

—More Chicago Haunts. 2008. 312p. pap. 15.95 *(978-1-933272-14-6(7))* Thunder Bay Pr.

Blessing, Anna H. Rather Chicago: A Compendium of Desirable Independent Eating - Shopping Establishments. 2011. (Rather Ser.). (ENG.). 192p. pap. 15.95 *(978-0-9833145-3-0(5))* Cabazon Bks.

Breitberg, Pamela. The Prairie - a Photographic Introduction to the Midwest Prairie. 2011. 142p. pap. 56.50 ***(978-1-4583-3893-8(2))*** Lulu Enterprises Inc.

Britt, Raymond. Chicago Marathon. 2009. 128p. pap. 21.99 *(978-0-7385-7718-0(9))* Arcadia Publishing.

Bronsky, Eric & Samors, Neal. Downtown Chicago in Transition. 2007. (Illus.). 256p. 39.50 *(978-0-9797892-0-5(6),* Chicago's Bks. Pr.) Chicago's Neighborhoods, Inc.

Brooks, Rachel. Chicago Ghosts. 2008. (Illus.). 160p. pap. 14.95 *(978-0-7643-2742-1(9))* Schiffer Publishing, Ltd.

Browne, Gay & Green Media Group LLC Staff. Chicago: Eat, Shop, Live Green - The Definitive Guide to More Than 1,300 Eco-Friendly Businesses & Resources. 2010. (Greenopia Ser.). (ENG.). 340p. pap. 17.95 *(978-0-9785064-5-2(6))* Green Media Group, LLC, The.

cahan, richard & williams, michael. The Lost Panoramas: When Chicago Changed its River & the Land Beyond. 2011. (ENG., Illus.). 160p. 45.00 ***(978-0-9785450-7-9(9))*** CityFiles Pr.

Chamberlin, Everett. Chicago & Its Suburbs. 2010. 538p. pap. 40.75 *(978-1-142-31955-7(5))* BiblioBazaar.

—Chicago & Its Suburbs. 508p. 2010. 44.76 *(978-1-169-80192-9(7))* 2010. pap. 32.76 *(978-1-163-30422-8(0))* 2010. 55.95 *(978-1-161-65524-7(7))* 2007. (ENG.). per. 40.95 *(978-1-4326-5794-9(1))* Kessinger Publishing, LLC.

Chicago Impressions. 2007. (Illus.). 80p. per. 12.95 *(978-1-56037-474-9(8))* Farcountry Pr.

Childers, Scott. Chicago's WLS Radio. 2008. (Images of America Ser.). (ENG., Illus.). 128p. pap. 21.99 *(978-0-7385-6194-3(0))* Arcadia Publishing.

Cohen, Ronald D. & Riesman, Bob, eds. Chicago Folk: Images of the Sixties Music Scene. 2009. (ENG., Illus.). 180p. pap. 22.95 *(978-1-55022-873-1(0))* ECW Pr. CAN. Dist: Independent Pubs. Group.

Cotter, Amelia. This House: The True Story of a Girl & a Ghost. Jacksier, Michelle, ed. 2nd ed. 2011. 108p. (YA). pap. 9.95 ***(978-0-9790401-8-4(3))*** Black Oak Media, Inc.

Cronon. Nature S Metropolis. 2006. 107p. pap. 9.95 *(978-1-4288-0998-7(8))* Cram101 Inc.

Cruz, Wilfredo. Chicago Latinos at Work. 2010. (Images of America Ser.). (ENG., Illus.). 128p. pap. 21.99 *(978-0-7385-7793-7(6))* Arcadia Publishing.

Darien Historical Society. Darien. 2012. (Images of America Ser.). (ENG., Illus.). 128p. pap. 21.99 ***(978-0-7385-9186-5(6))*** Arcadia Publishing.

Davros, Michael George. Greeks in Chicago. 2009. (Images of America Ser.). (ENG., Illus.). 128p. pap. 21.99 *(978-0-7385-6171-4(1))* Arcadia Publishing.

Day, Jacque E. & Santoro, Jamie Wirsbinski. West Ridge. 2008. (Images of America Ser.). (Illus.). 128p. pap. 19.99 *(978-0-7385-6150-9(9))* Arcadia Publishing.

Dorfman, Ron, ed. Harold! Photographs from the Harold Washington Years. 2007. (ENG., Illus.). 224p. per. 19.95 *(978-0-8101-2446-2(7))* Northwestern Univ. Pr.

Dougherty, Monica & Sammons, Mary Beth. The Irish American Heritage Center. 2011. (Images of America Ser.). (Illus.). 128p. pap. 21.99 *(978-0-7385-8288-7(3))* Arcadia Publishing.

Duffey, Bernard I. The Chicago Renaissance in American Letters: A Critical History. 2011. 294p. 48.95 ***(978-1-258-04728-3(4))*** Literary Licensing, LLC.

Dybek, Stuart, frwd. Barrio: Photographs from Chicago's Pilsen & Little Village. 2006. (Chicago Visions & Revisions Ser.). (Illus.). 128p. 35.00 *(978-0-226-13505-2(5))* Univ. of Chicago Pr.

Farrar, Ellen S. The Magnificent Mile Lights Festival. 2008. (Images of America Ser.). (ENG., Illus.). 128p. pap. 21.99 *(978-0-7385-6184-4(3))* Arcadia Publishing.

Ford, Anne. Peaceful Places - Chicago: 119 Tranquil Sites in the Windy City & Beyond. 2011. (Peaceful Places Ser.). (ENG., Illus.). 240p. pap. 14.95 *(978-0-89732-534-9(6))* Menasha Ridge Pr., Inc.

Franciscan Fathers. A Picture Story: St. Peter's New Church & Friary, Madison at Clark Street, Chicago, Illinois. 2011. 20p. pap. 35.95 ***(978-1-258-00936-6(6))*** Literary Licensing, LLC.

Freeman, Nick. Food, Lodging, Liquor: Signs You're in Chicago. 2008. pap. 22.95 *(978-1-893121-69-0(0))* Everything Goes Media, LLC.

Furse, Ray. City in Time: Chicago. 2007. (City in Time Ser.). (ENG., Illus.). 144p. 14.95 *(978-1-4027-3299-7(6))* Sterling Publishing Co., Inc.

Globe Pequot Press Staff. Chicago: 57 Things Every Self-Respecting Chicagoan Must Know about the Windy City. 2009. 224p. pap. 12.95 *(978-0-7627-5523-3(7))* Globe Pequot Pr., The.

Grandin, Madame Léon, et al. A Parisienne in Chicago: Impressions of the World's Columbian Exposition. 2010. (ENG., Illus.). 264p. 50.00 *(978-0-252-03515-5(3))* Univ. of Illinois Pr.

Green, Larry W. Water Tanks of Chicago: A Vanishing Urban Legcy. 2007. (Illus.). 50p. per. 19.95 *(978-0-9789676-0-4(7))* Wicker Pk. Pr., Ltd.

Hanson, Karen. Today's Chicago Blues. 2007. (Illus.). 238p. per. 15.95 *(978-1-893121-19-5(4))* Everything Goes Media, LLC.

Houlihan Kennedy, Bridget. Chicago's South Side Irish Parade. 2010. (Images of America Ser.). (ENG., Illus.). 128p. pap. 21.99 *(978-0-7385-7722-7(7))* Arcadia Publishing.

Hudson, John C. Chicago: A Geography of the City & Its Region. 2006. (Center for American Places-Center Books on American Places Ser.: Vol. 10). (Illus.). 356p. 45.00 *(978-0-226-35806-2(2))* Univ. of Chicago Pr.

Johnson, Raymond. Chicago's Haunt Detective. 2011. (Illus.). 160p. *(978-0-7643-3718-5(1),* Schiffer Publishing Ltd) Schiffer Publishing, Ltd.

Jones, Wilbert, et al. Chicago's Gold Coast. 2012. (Images of America Ser.). (ENG., Illus.). 128p. pap. 21.99 ***(978-0-7385-9177-3(7))*** Arcadia Publishing.

Kelly, John. Chicago Stations & Trains Photo Archive. 2008. (Photo Archive Ser.). (ENG., Illus.). 128p. pap. 29.95 *(978-1-58388-216-0(2),* 1583882162) Iconografix, Inc.

Klatt, Mary Beth. Chicago's Fashion History: 1865-1945. 2010. (Images of America Ser.). (Illus.). 128p. pap. 21.99 *(978-0-7385-8432-4(0))* Arcadia Publishing.

Klekowski, James J. 1990 So Long Old Comiskey Park. 2006. 25.00 *(978-0-9714950-2-9(5),* 10000) Ellis Avenue Studios.

Kogan, Rick. Sidewalks: Portraits of Chicago. (ENG., Illus.). 2008. 248p. pap. 21.95 *(978-0-8101-5193-2(6))* 2006. 256p. 32.00 *(978-0-8101-2349-6(5))* Northwestern Univ. Pr.

—Sidewalks: Volume 2: Reflections on Chicago. 2009. (Illus.). 256p. 40.00 *(978-0-9841265-0-7(3))* Sidewalks Bk. Co.

Kronish, Elisa & Glusac, Elaine. Top 10 Chicago. 2012. (Eyewitness top 10 travel Guide Ser.). (ENG.). 128p. 14.00 *(978-0-7566-8454-9(4))* Dorling Kindersley Publishing, Inc.

Littman, Margaret. Little Black Book of Chicago: The Indispensible Guide to the Windy City. 2008. (Little Black Book Ser.). 215p. spiral bd. 12.95 *(978-1-59359-812-9(2))* Peter Pauper Pr. Inc.

Locken, E. Travel Journal Chicago. 2010. 192p. pap. 19.99 *(978-0-557-41572-4(1))* Lulu Enterprises Inc.

Lynch, Christopher. When Hollywood Landed at Chicago's Midway Airport: The Photos & Stories of Mike Rotunno. 2012. 160p. pap. 19.99 ***(978-1-60949-592-3(6))*** History Pr., The.

Magallon, Frank S. Chicago's Little Village: Lawndale-Crawford. 2010. (Images of America Ser.). (ENG., Illus.). 128p. pap. 21.99 *(978-0-7385-7737-1(5))* Arcadia Publishing.

McCue, Craig S. & West Des Moines Historical Society. West des Moines & Valley Junction. 2009. (Images of America Ser.). (ENG., Illus.). 128p. pap. 21.99 *(978-0-7385-6188-2(6))* Arcadia Publishing.

Milan, Jon. Old Chicago Road: US-12 from Detroit to Chicago. 2011. (Images of America Ser.). (ENG., Illus.). 128p. pap. 21.99 ***(978-0-7385-7810-1(X))*** Arcadia Publishing.

Moore Hill, Candace. Bahá'í Temple. 2010. (Images of America Ser.). (ENG., Illus.). 128p. pap. 21.99 *(978-0-7385-8421-8(5))* Arcadia Publishing.

Museum of Broadcast Communications Staff. Chicago Television. Berger, Daniel & Jajkowski, Steve, eds. 2010. (ENG., Illus.). 144p. pap. 26.99 *(978-0-7385-7713-5(8))* Arcadia Publishing.

Nathan, Jo Ann, et al. Inspired by Nature: The Garfield Park Conservatory & Chicago's West Side. 2007. (Illus.). 160p. pap. 25.00 *(978-0-9794125-0-9(1))* Garfield Park Conservatory Alliance.

Ogorek, Cynthia L. The Lincoln Highway Around Chicago. 2008. (Images of America Ser.). (ENG., Illus.). 128p. pap. 19.99 *(978-0-7385-5197-5(X))* Arcadia Publishing.

O'Gorman, Thomas J. Chicago from the Air Then & Now. 2010. (ENG.). 144p. 19.95 *(978-1-60710-009-6(6),* Thunder Bay Pr.) Advantage Pubs. Group.

Packer, Robert A. Chicago's Forgotten Synagogues. 2007. (Images of America Ser.). (ENG., Illus.). 128p. per. 19.99 *(978-0-7385-5152-4(X))* Arcadia Publishing.

Pero, Peter Nicholas. Chicago Italians at Work. 2009. (Images of America Ser.). (ENG., Illus.). 128p. pap. 21.99 *(978-0-7385-6187-5(8))* Arcadia Publishing.

Peterson, Paul Michael. Chicago Stadium. 2011. (Images of Sports Ser.). (ENG., Illus.). 128p. pap. 21.99 ***(978-0-7385-8307-5(3))*** Arcadia Publishing.

Peterson, Paul Michael. Chicago's Soldier Field. 2007. (Images of Sports Ser.). (ENG., Illus.). 128p. per. 19.99 *(978-0-7385-5150-0(3),* Arcadia Publishing.

Rand McNally, creator. Rand Mcnally Chicago & Cook County Street Guide. 57th ed. 2008. (Rand Mcnally Chicago/Cook County Street Guide Ser.). (Illus.). pap. 19.95 *(978-0-528-87429-1(2))* Rand McNally.

Rinker, Kimberly A. Chicago's Horse Racing Venues. 2009. (Images of America Ser.). (ENG., Illus.). 128p. pap. 21.99 *(978-0-7385-6060-9(4))* Arcadia Publishing.

Schiecke, Konrad. Downtown Chicago's Historic Movie Theatres. 2011. (ENG., Illus.). 201p. pap. 49.95 ***(978-0-7864-6590-3(5))*** McFarland & Co., Inc. Pubs.

Scott, Markus. Voices from the Chicago Grave: They're Calling. Will You Answer? 2008. 328p. pap. 16.95 *(978-1-933272-19-1(8))* Thunder Bay Pr.

Shay, Art. Chicago's Nelson Algren. 2007. (ENG., Illus.). 208p. per. 19.95 *(978-1-58322-764-0(4))* Seven Stories Pr.

St. Mary's Catholic Church, compiled by. Old St. Mary's Catholic Church 175th Anniversary: 1833-2008 A Future for the Church Brighter than any Past. 2008. (Illus.). 96p. lib. bdg. 40.00 *(978-1-934729-12-0(4))* M.T. Publishing Co., Inc.

Sternstein, Malynne. Czechs of Chicagoland. 2008. (Images of America Ser.). (ENG., Illus.). 128p. pap. 21.99 *(978-0-7385-5178-4(3))* Arcadia Publishing.

Streetwise Maps Inc., des. & rev. Artwise Chicago Museum Map - Laminated Museum Map of Chicago, Illinois - Streetwise Maps. 2004th ed. 2007. (Artwise Ser.). (ENG., Illus.). 7.95 *(978-0-935039-50-4(3),* Artwise) Streetwise Maps, Inc.

Taylor, Troy, et al. Weird Chicago. 2008. 368p. pap. 20.00 *(978-1-892523-59-4(0))* Whitechapel Productions Pr.

Thompson, Lowell. African Americans in Chicago. 2012. (Images of America Ser.). (ENG., Illus.). 128p. pap. 21.99 ***(978-0-7385-8853-7(9))*** Arcadia Publishing.

Thunder Bay Press Staff, ed. Greetings from Chicago. 2011. (ENG., Illus.). 36p. 19.95 *(978-1-60710-220-5(X),* Thunder Bay Pr.) Advantage Pubs. Group.

Tyre, William H. Chicago's Historic Prairie Avenue. 2008. (Images of America (Arcadia Publishing) Ser.). (ENG., Illus.). 128p. pap. 21.99 *(978-0-7385-5212-5(7));* 15p. pap. 7.99 *(978-0-7385-2527-3(8))* Arcadia Publishing.

Vitti, Jim. Chicago Cubs: Baseball on Catalina Island. 2010. (Images of Baseball Ser.). (ENG., Illus.). 128p. pap. 21.99 *(978-0-7385-7795-1(2))* Arcadia Publishing.

Walker, Matthew. Chicago Book. 2008. *(978-0-9704875-3-7(3))* Walker, Matthew D. Publishing.

Whitman Publishing Staff, ed. Chicago A Past to Present Photo Tour. 2010. (Illus.). 120p. 12.95 *(978-0-7948-3063-2(3))* Whitman Publishing LLC.

Williams, Michael, et al. Chicago: City on the Move. 2007. (Illus.). 256p. 39.95 *(978-0-9785450-3-1(6))* CityFiles Pr.

The Windies' City: Chicago's Historical Hidden Treasures. 2006. pap. 12.95 *(978-0-9710487-3-7(8),* 0971048738) Highlights of Chicago Pr.

Witter, David Anthony. Oldest Chicago. 2011. 257p. pap. 16.95 *(978-1-893121-44-7(5))* Everything Goes Media, LLC.

Wolf, Michael, photos by. The Transparent City. 2008. (ENG., Illus.). 112p. 60.00 *(978-1-59711-076-1(0))* Aperture Foundation, Inc.

Worek, Jordan. Chicago. Liebman, Dan, ed. 2009. (America the BeautifulAmerica the BeautifulAmerica the Beautiful Ser.). (ENG., Illus.). 96p. 18.95 *(978-1-55407-543-0(2))* Firefly Bks., Ltd.

CHICAGO (ILL.)—DIRECTORIES

Bergquist, Kathie, et al. Not for Tourists Guide to Chicago. 2007. (Not for Tourists Guide to Chicago Ser.). (Illus.). 363p. 18.95 *(978-0-9793945-4-6(6))* Not for Tourists, Inc.

Kaufman, Carrie L., ed. The Book: An Actor's Guide to Chicago, 7th Edition. 2007. im. lthr. 15.00 *(978-1-892296-05-4(5))* PerformInk Bks., Ltd.

Macoy, Robert. The Masonic Manual, a Pocket Companion for the Initiated;Containing the Rituals of Freemasonry, Embraced in the Degrees of the Lodge, Chapter & Enca. 2006. 324p. per. 23.99 *(978-1-4255-3145-4(8))* MPublishing.

Not for Tourists Staff. Chicago 2009. 7th rev. ed. 2008. (Illus.). 448p. 19.95 *(978-0-9814887-4-5(9))* Not for Tourists, Inc.

Not For Tourists Staff. Not for Tourists Guide to Chicago: 2012. 2011. (ENG., Illus.). 432p. pap. 19.95 ***(978-1-61608-527-8(4),*** 608527, Not For Tourist) Skyhorse Publishing Co., Inc.

CHICAGO (ILL.)—ECONOMIC CONDITIONS

Duis, Perry R. Challenging Chicago: Coping with Everyday Life, 1837-1920. 2006. (Illus.). 448p. per. 22.95 *(978-0-252-07415-8(7))* Univ. of Illinois Pr.

Goddard, Leslie. Remembering Marshall Field's. 2011. (Images of America Ser.). (Illus.). 128p. pap. 21.99 *(978-0-7385-8368-6(5))* Arcadia Publishing.

Holton, Lisa. For Members Only: A History & Guide to Chicago's Oldest Private Clubs. 2008. (Illus.). 317p. pap. 18.95 *(978-1-893121-28-7(3))* Everything Goes Media, LLC.

Hyra, Derek S. The New Urban Renewal: The Economic Transformation of Harlem & Bronzeville. 2008. (Illus.). 224p. 22.50 *(978-0-226-36604-3(9))* Univ. of Chicago Pr.

Icon Group International, Inc. Staff, compiled by. The 2006 Economic & Product Market Databook for Chicago , United States. 2006. 618p. ring bd. 95.00 *(978-0-497-80356-8(9))* Icon Group International, Inc.

Ledermann, Robert P. State Street: One Brick at a Time. 2011. (Illus.). 160p. pap. 22.99 ***(978-1-60949-294-6(3))*** History Pr., The.

Lewis, Robert D. Chicago Made - Factory Networks in the Industrial Metropolis. 2008. (Historical Studies of Urban America Ser.). (ENG., Illus.). 364p. 40.00 *(978-0-226-47701-5(0))* Univ. of Chicago Pr.

Peerbolte, Gregory T. Randhurst: Suburban Chicago's Grandest Shopping Center. 2011. *(978-1-60949-147-5(5))* History Pr., The.

Soucek, Gayle. Marshall Fields: The Store that Helped Build Chicago. 2010. (Landmarks Ser.). (ENG., Illus.). 160p. pap. 19.99 *(978-1-59629-854-5(5))* History Pr., The.

Zeiger, Sheldon. Stick It to Your Ticket: The Unofficial Guide to Beating Your Parking Ticket in Chicago. 2009. 79p. pap. 12.95 *(978-0-9822346-0-0(0))* Zeiger.

CHICAGO (ILL.)—FIRE, 1871

see Great Fire, Chicago, Ill., 1871

CHICAGO (ILL.)—GUIDEBOOKS

AA Publishing Staff & Grinnell, Max. Chicago. 2009. (Great Walks Ser.). (ENG., Illus.). 176p. pap. 15.99 *(978-0-470-45375-9(3),* Frommers) Wiley, John & Sons, Inc.

Ashley, Julie. Newcomer's Handbook for Moving to & Living in Chicago: Including Evanston, Oak Park, Schaumburg, Wheaton, & Naperville. 5th rev. ed. 2008. 416p. pap. 24.95 *(978-0-912301-87-7(2))* First Bks.

Atkinson, Kim & Roufos, Anna, eds. Forbes City Guide Chicago 2010. 2010. (City Guide Ser.). (ENG., Illus.). 192p. pap. 13.95 *(978-1-936010-05-9(4))* Five Star Travel Corp., The.

August, Krista. Giants in the Park: A Guide to Portrait Statues in Chicago's Lincoln Park. 2011. (ENG., Illus.). 120p. pap. 20.00 *(978-0-615-42737-9(5))* Lincoln Park Pr.

Avalon Travel Publishing Staff. Chicago. Young, Sabrina, ed. 3rd ed. 2008. (Moon Metro Ser.). (ENG., Illus.). 136p. pap. 16.95 *(978-1-56691-975-3(4))* Westview Pr.

Bergquist, Kathie, et al. Not for Tourists Guide to Chicago. 2007. (Not for Tourists Guide to Chicago Ser.). (Illus.). 363p. 18.95 *(978-0-9793945-4-6(6))* Not for Tourists, Inc.

Blackwell, Elizabeth Canning. Frommer's Chicago. 17th ed. 2012. (Frommer's Color Complete Ser.). (ENG., Illus.). 384p. pap. 19.99 ***(978-1-118-01720-3(X),*** Frommers) Wiley, John & Sons, Inc.

Blessing, Anna H. Eat. shop Chicago: The Indispensable Guide to Inspired, Locally Owned Eating & Shopping Establishments. 3rd ed. 2009. (ENG.). 192p. pap. 14.95 *(978-0-9823254-3-8(6))* Cabazon Bks.

Bond, Barbara I. Moon Take a Hike Chicago: Hikes within Two Hours of the City. 2011. (Moon Outdoors Ser.). (ENG., Illus.). 320p. pap. 17.99 *(978-1-59880-761-5(7))* Avalon Travel Publishing.

Bosch, Jennifer Marjorie & Pridmore, Jay, texts. A View from the River: The Chicago Architecture Foundation River Cruise. 2008. 96p. pap. 15.95 *(978-0-7649-4532-8(7))* Pomegranate Communications, Inc.

Browne, Gay. Greenopia: Chicago. 2009. 272p. pap. 17.95 *(978-1-58479-782-1(7))* Stewart, Tabori & Chang.

Cavalieri, Nate & Lonely Planet Staff. Chicago. 2009. (Best Of Ser.). (ENG., Illus.). 176p. pap. 14.99 *(978-1-74179-292-8(4))* Lonely Planet Pubns.

Chappell, Sally A. Kitt. Chicago's Urban Nature: A Guide to the City's Architecture + Landscape. 2007. (ENG., Illus.). 300p. 47.50 *(978-0-226-10139-2(8));* pap. 20.00 *(978-0-226-10140-8(1))* Univ. of Chicago Pr.

Charles W. Moore Center for the Study of Place Staff. Placenotes — Chicago Art & Architecture. 2008. (ENG.). 1p. 19.95 *(978-0-9766493-8-0(1))* Moore Ctr. Pr.

Chicago. 2009. (SMART GUIDE Ser.). (Illus.). 144p. 11.95 *(978-981-258-978-1(3))* Insight Guides.

Chicago. (Rand Mcnally Wall Maps Ser.). 229.00 *(978-0-528-86122-2(0))* Rand McNally.

Chicago. 2012. (Select Ser.). (Illus.). 192p. pap. 15.00 ***(978-1-78005-280-9(4))*** APA Publications Services SGP. Dist: Ingram Pub. Services.

Cohn, Scotti. Chicago Curiosities: Quirky Characters, Roadside Oddities & Other Offbeat Stuff. 2011. (Curiosities Ser.). (ENG., Illus.). 192p. pap. 15.95 *(978-0-7627-5984-2(4))* Globe Pequot Pr., The.

DK Publishing. DK Eyewitness Travel Guide: Chicago: Chicago. 2012. (Eyewitness travel Guide Ser.). (ENG.). 216p. pap. 20.00 ***(978-0-7566-8575-1(3))*** Dorling Kindersley Publishing, Inc.

Dorling Kindersley Publishing Staff. Chicago. 2010. (Eyewitness Travel Guides). (ENG.). 216p. pap. 20.00 *(978-0-7566-6181-6(1))* Dorling Kindersley Publishing, Inc.

Drake, Elisa. Day Trips from Chicago: Getaway Ideas for the Local Traveler. 2011. (Day Trips Ser.). (ENG., Illus.). 232p. pap. 14.95 *(978-0-7627-6459-4(7))* Globe Pequot Pr., The.

Elkins, Elizabeth A. Jean Lafitte International: Chicago. Elkins, Elizabeth A., ed. Date not set. (Jean Lafitte International Ser.). 212p. (Orig.). pap. 20.00 *(978-0-9701864-9-2(5))* E E Productions.

Entertainment Publications, Inc. Staff, compiled by. Chicago South 2009 Entertainment Book. 2008. pap. 25.00 *(978-1-59878-620-0(2))* Entertainment Pubns., Inc.

—Chicago West 2009 Entertainment Book. 2008. pap. 25.00 *(978-1-59878-609-5(1))* Entertainment Pubns., Inc.

Fodor's Travel Publications, Inc. Staff. Fodor's Chicago 2012. 2011. (Full-Color Gold Guides). (ENG., Illus.). 368p. pap. 18.99 *(978-0-679-00958-0(2),* Fodor's) Fodor's Travel Pubns.

—Fodor's Chicago's 25 Best, 7th Edition. 2011. (25 Best Ser.). (ENG & ABK.). 128p. pap. 11.99 *(978-1-4000-0541-3(8),* Fodor's) Fodor's Travel Pubns.

Forbes Travel Guide. Forbes City Guide 2011 Chicago. 2010. (Forbes Travel Guide City Guide Ser.). (ENG.). 192p. pap. 13.95 *(978-1-936010-98-1(4))* Five Star Travel Corp., The.

Hargraves, Orin. Cultureshock Chicago, 1 vol. 2011. (ENG.). 240p. pap. 15.95 *(978-0-7614-6055-8(1))* Marshall Cavendish Corp.

Henry de Tessan, Christina. Chicago: 50 Adventures on Foot. 2007. (City Walks Ser.: CITY). (ENG., Illus.). 14.95 *(978-0-8118-5558-7(9))* Chronicle Bks. LLC.

Insight Guides Staff & Hardy, Pam. Chicago. 2006. (Pocket Guides). (Illus.). 97p. 13.95 *(978-0-88729-289-7(5))* Insight Guides.

Iversen, Jean. Chicago: Your Guide to Bring-Your-Own-Bottle Restaurants & Wine & Spirits Stores in Chicago. 3rd ed. 2009. (BYOB Guides). (ENG.). 208p. pap. 13.95 *(978-0-9764131-3-4(2))* BYOB Chicago Inc.

Keating, Ann Durkin, ed. Chicago Neighborhoods & Suburbs: A Historical Guide. 2008. (ENG., Illus.). 344p. pap., instr.'s gde. ed. 25.00 *(978-0-226-42883-3(4))* Univ. of Chicago Pr.

Kyi, Tanya Lloyd & Kyi, Tanya Lloyd. Chicago. rev. ed. 2010. (ENG., Illus.). 96p. pap. 12.95 *(978-1-55285-599-7(6))* Whitecap Bks., Ltd. CAN. Dist: Midpoint Trade Bks., Inc.

Langer, Jeff. Chi-Town. 2009. 164p. pap. 19.99 *(978-1-4415-2362-4(6))* Xlibris Corp.

Littman, Margaret. The Dog Lover's Companion to Chicago: The Inside Scoop on Where to Take Your Dog. 2nd ed. 2006. (Dog Lover's Companion Guides). (ENG., Illus.). 260p. per. 17.95 *(978-1-56691-870-1(7))* Avalon Travel Publishing.

Littman, Margaret, et al. Must Sees Chicago Michelin. 2nd ed. 2009. (Must Sees Ser.). (ENG., Illus.). 160p. pap. 11.99 *(978-1-906261-63-4(6))* Michelin Travel & Lifestyle.

Lonely Planet Staff & Zimmerman, Karla. Lonely Planet Chicago, 30 vols. 6th rev. ed. 2011. (City Guide Ser.). (ENG., Illus.). 280p. pap. 18.99 *(978-1-74179-412-0(9))* Lonely Planet Pubns.

McLaughlin, John. 48 Hours Chicago: Timed Tours for Short Stays. 2009. (ENG., Illus.). 32p. 7.95 *(978-0-7627-4925-6(3))* Globe Pequot Pr., The.

Meek Schuldt, Lori. Chicago: Where to Go & What to Do with the Kids. 2009. (Are We Almost There? Ser.). (ENG., Illus.). 64p. 7.95 *(978-0-7627-5284-3(X))* Globe Pequot Pr., The.

Menasha Ridge Press Staff, et al. The Unofficial Guide to Chicago. 8th ed. 2009. (Unofficial Guides: 222). (ENG., Illus.). 384p. pap. 17.99 *(978-0-470-37999-8(5),* Wiley) Wiley, John & Sons, Inc.

Michelin Travel & Lifestyle. MICHELIN Guide Chicago 2012. 2nd ed. 2011. (ENG.). 352p. pap. 18.99 *(978-2-06-716530-4(5))* Michelin Travel & Lifestyle.

—Michelin Must Sees Chicago. 3rd ed. 2012. (ENG.). 160p. pap. 11.99 *(978-1-907099-39-7(5))* Michelin Travel & Lifestyle.

Mobil US City Gd. Chicago 2009. 2009. (CITY GUIDE-DOMESTIC Ser.). 192p. 16.95 *(978-0-8416-0733-0(8))* Langenscheidt Publishing Group.

Morgan, Adam. Best Hikes near Chicago. 2011. (Best Hikes near Ser.). (ENG., Illus.). 208p. pap. 18.95 *(978-0-7627-6120-3(2),* Falcon Guides) Globe Pequot Pr., The.

Not For Tourists. Not for Tourists Guide to Chicago, 9th Edition. 9th ed. 2010. (Not for Tourists Ser.). (ENG., Illus.). 440p. pap. 21.99 *(978-0-9795339-6-9(1))* Not For Tourists, Inc.

Not for Tourists Staff. Chicago 2009. 7th rev. ed. 2008. (Illus.). 448p. 19.95 *(978-0-9814887-4-5(9))* Not for Tourists, Inc.

Not For Tourists Staff. Chicago 2010. 2009. (Not for Tourists Guidebooks Ser.). (ENG., Illus.). 440p. pap. 19.99 *(978-0-9815591-3-1(1))* Not For Tourists, Inc.

Not For Tourists Staff. Not for Tourists Guide to Chicago: 2012. 2011. (ENG., Illus.). 432p. pap. 19.95 ***(978-1-61608-527-8(4),*** 608527, Not For Tourist) Skyhorse Publishing Co., Inc.

Not for Tourists Staff, creator. Not for Tourists Guide to Chicago. 4th ed. 2006. (Not for Tourists Guide to Chicago Ser.). (Illus.). 363p. 16.95 *(978-0-9778031-3-2(9),* Not For Tourists) Not for Tourists, Inc.

Oehlsen, Nadia. Chicago: Secrets of Living the Good Life — For Free! 2nd ed. 2009. (Cheap Bastard Ser.). (ENG., Illus.). 320p. pap. 14.95 *(978-0-7627-5023-8(5))* Globe Pequot Pr., The.

Olvera, Jennifer. Food Lovers' Guide to Chicago: Best Local Specialties, Markets, Recipes, Restaurants, & Events. 2011. (Food Lovers' Ser.). (ENG., Illus.). 480p. pap. 15.95 *(978-0-7627-7015-1(5))* Globe Pequot Pr., The.

Pistolesi, Andrea. Chicago. (Illus.). 64p. pap. *(978-88-7009-887-7(7))* Casa Editrice Bonechi.

PopOut Products. Chicago Inside Out. 2010. 64p. 10.95 *(978-1-84587-801-6(9))* Globe Pequot Pr., The.

Rand McNally, creator. Rand Mcnally Chicago 7-County Street Guide: Cook, Dupage, Kane, Kendall, Lake, Mchenry, Will. 2007. (Rand Mcnally Chicago 7 Counties Street Guide: Cook, Dupage, Kane, Ser.). (Illus.). 34.95 *(978-0-528-86089-8(5))* Rand McNally.

Rough Guides. The Rough Guide to Chicago. 4th ed. 2012. (Rough Guide To... Ser.). (ENG., Illus.). 288p. 19.99 *(978-1-4053-8983-9(4))* Rough Guides, Ltd. GBR. Dist: Dorling Kindersley Publishing, Inc.

Rough Guides Staff. Chicago. 3rd ed. 2009. (Rough Guide Travel Guides). (ENG., Illus.). 320p. (gr. 12). pap. 19.99 *(978-1-84836-070-9(3))* Rough Guides, Ltd. GBR. Dist: Dorling Kindersley Publishing, Inc.

Solzman, David M. The Chicago River: An Illustrated History & Guide to the River & Its Waterways. 2nd ed. 2006. (ENG., Illus.). 302p. per. 20.00 *(978-0-226-76801-4(5))* Univ. of Chicago Pr.

Stengele, Anbritt. Sports Traveler Chicago. 2009. 219p. pap. 15.95 *(978-1-893121-22-5(4))* Everything Goes Media, LLC.

Stockwell, David. Chicago. Baldini, Anna, ed. (Illus.). 96p. *(978-88-8029-628-7(0))* Casa Editrice Bonechi.

Streetwise Maps Inc., des. & rev. Artwise Chicago Museum Map - Laminated Museum Map of Chicago, Illinois - Streetwise Maps. 2004th ed. 2007. (Artwise Ser.). (ENG., Illus.). 7.95 *(978-0-935039-50-4(3),* Artwise) Streetwise Maps, Inc.

Stroeve, Wilbert & Akerman, James R., photos by. Chicago to Lake Geneva, Then & Now: Retracing the Route of H. Sargent Michaels' 1905 Photographic Guide for Motorists. 2008. (Illus.). 160p. pap. 17.95 *(978-0-911028-82-9(X))* Newberry Library.

Tiebert, Laura. Frommer's Chicago Day by Day. 3rd ed. 2012. (Frommer's Day by Day - Pocket Ser.: 239). (ENG.). 192p. pap. 13.99 ***(978-1-118-16716-8(3),*** Frommers) Wiley, John & Sons, Inc.

Tiebert, Laura. Frommer's Chicago Free & Dirt Cheap. 2010. (Frommer's Free & Dirt Cheap Ser.: 87). (ENG., Illus.). 320p. pap. 16.99 *(978-0-470-73650-0(X),* Wiley) Wiley, John & Sons, Inc.

Tiebert, Laura & Tiebert. Chicago with Kids. 4th ed. 2009. (Frommer's with Kids Ser.: 46). (ENG., Illus.). 320p. pap. 17.99 *(978-0-470-39324-6(6),* Frommers) Wiley, John & Sons, Inc.

—Frommer's Chicago Day by Day. 2nd ed. 2009. (Frommer's Day by Day - Pocket Ser.: 47). (ENG., Illus.). 192p. pap. 12.99 *(978-0-470-42208-3(4),* Frommers) Wiley, John & Sons, Inc.

Time Out Guides Staff. Time Out Chicago. 5th ed. 2009. (Time Out Guides). (ENG., Illus.). 330p. 19.95 *(978-1-84670-138-2(4))* Time Out Guides Ltd. GBR. Dist: Perseus-PGW.

Van Dam Chicago Atlas. Date not set. pap. *(978-0-312-18769-9(6),* St. Martin's Griffin) St. Martin's Pr.

Ver Berkmoes, Ryan. Walking Chicago: 31 Tours of the Windy City's Classic Bars, Scandalous Sites, Historic Architecture, Dynamic Neighborhoods, & Famous Lakeshore. 2008. (Walking Ser.). (ENG.). 264p. pap. 19.95 *(978-0-89997-416-3(3))* Wilderness Pr.

Villaire, Ted. Best Bike Rides Chicago: The Greatest Recreational Rides in the Metro Area. 2011. (Best Bike Rides Ser.). (ENG., Illus.). 272p. pap. 18.95 *(978-0-7627-4689-7(0),* Falcon Guides) Globe Pequot Pr., The.

—Chicago: Including the Collar Counties & Northwest Indiana. 2010. (Easy Hikes Close to Home Ser.). (ENG., Illus.). 96p. pap. 8.95 *(978-0-89732-889-0(2))* Menasha Ridge Pr., Inc.

—60 Hikes Within 60 Miles: Chicago: Including Aurora, Northwest Indiana, & Waukegan. 2nd ed. 2008. (60 Hikes within 60 Miles Ser.). (ENG., Illus.). 248p. pap. 16.95 *(978-0-89732-663-6(6))* Menasha Ridge Pr., Inc.

Wallpaper Editors, ed. Wallpaper City Guide Chicago 2012. 2012. (ENG., Illus.). 128p. pap. 9.95 ***(978-0-7148-6299-6(1))*** Phaidon Pr., Inc.

Wallpaper Magazine Editors. Wallpaper City Guide: Chicago. Moloney, Rachael, ed. 2007. (ENG., Illus.). 128p. pap. 8.95 *(978-0-7148-4738-2(0))* Phaidon Pr., Inc.

Where Magazine Staff. WHERE Chicago / Shop: Great Shopping Wherever You Are. 2008. (ENG., Illus.). 96p. 9.95 *(978-0-7627-4627-9(0))* Globe Pequot Pr., The.

C

Worrell, Jennifer, ed. Hungry? Chicago: The Lowdown on Where the Real People Eat! 2009. 224p. pap. 14.95 *(978-1-893329-51-5(8)*, Glove Box Guides) Hungry City Guides.

Zagat Survey Staff. Chicago Dating (And Dumping) Guide. 2009. (ENG.). 80p. pap. 6.95 *(978-1-60478-197-7(1))* Zagat Survey.

—Chicago Game Day 2009-10, Pack. 2009. NAp. pap. 19.95 *(978-1-60478-227-1(7))* Zagat Survey.

—Chicago Restaurants 2003/2004. rev. ed. (ENG.). 240p. pap. 12.95 *(978-1-57006-521-7(7))* Zagat Survey.

—2008/09 Chicago ZAGAT. com & Book Pack. 2008. (ENG.). 34.90 *(978-1-57006-987-1(5))* Zagat Survey.

—2008/09 Chicago ZAGAT to Go Pack. 2008. (ENG.). 34.90 *(978-1-57006-988-8(3))* Zagat Survey.

—2011/12 Chicago Restaurants. 2011. (ZAGAT Restaurant Guides). (ENG.). 272p. pap. 14.95 *(978-1-60478-351-3(6))* Zagat Survey.

Zagat Survey Staff, creator. Chicago Restaurants. 2007. (Zagat to Go Packs Ser.). (ENG.). 34.90 *(978-1-57006-923-9(9))* Zagat Survey.

—Zagat Chicago Restaurants. rev. ed. 2007. (ENG., Illus.). 268p. per. 13.95 *(978-1-57006-878-2(X))* Zagat Survey.

—Zagat. com Chicago Restaurants. 2007. (ENG.). 29.95 *(978-1-57006-934-5(4))* Zagat Survey.

Zagat Survey Staff, ed. BOXED/Chicago Rest. /Zagat to Go 2009/10. 2008. *(978-1-60478-204-2(8))* Zagat Survey.

—Chicago 2009/10. 2008. (ENG.). pap. *(978-1-60478-203-5(X))* Zagat Survey.

—Chicago Dining Deals. 2009. (ENG.). 80p. pap. 5.95 *(978-1-60478-133-5(5))* Zagat Survey.

—Chicago Restaurants- 2009/10. 2008. (ENG.). 256p. pap. 14.95 *(978-1-60478-162-5(9))* Zagat Survey.

Zimmerman, Karla & Zimmerman. Chicago: Day Trips, Weekend Getaways, Easy Planning, Quick Access, Best Places to Visit. 2009. (Great Escapes Ser.). (ENG., Illus.). 172p. pap. 16.95 *(978-0-88150-844-4(6)*, 150844) Countryman Pr.

CHICAGO (ILL.)—HAYMARKET SQUARE RIOT, 1886

see Haymarket Square Riot, Chicago, Ill., 1886

CHICAGO (ILL.)—HISTORY

Abbott, Karen. Sin in the Second City: Madams, Ministers, Playboys, & the Battle for America's Soul. 2008. (ENG., Illus.). 400p. pap. 15.00 *(978-0-8129-7599-4(5)*, Random Hse. Trade Paperbacks) Random House Publishing Group.

Alaspa, Brian W. Chicago Crime Stories: Rich Gone Wrong. 2008. (Illus.). 128p. pap. 14.99 *(978-0-7643-3114-5(0))* Schiffer Publishing, Ltd.

Alaspa, Bryan W. Chicago Disasters. 2010. (Illus.). 128p. pap. 14.99 *(978-0-7643-3395-8(X))* Schiffer Publishing, Ltd.

Algren, Nelson. Chicago: City on the Make. 60th anniv. ed. 2011. 152p. pap. 17.00 *(978-0-226-01386-2(3))* Univ. of Chicago Pr.

Andreas, A. T. History of Chicago, 3 vols., Set. (Illus.). reprint ed. lib. bdg. 375.00 *(978-0-7222-0058-2(7))* Library Reprints, Inc.

Ansell, David. County: Life, Death & Politics at Chicago's Public Hospital. 2011. (ENG., Illus.). 256p. 29.95 *(978-0-89733-620-8(6))* Academy Chicago Pubs., Ltd.

Appelbaum, Stanley. Spectacle in the White City: The Chicago 1893 World's Fair. 2009. (Calla Editions Ser.). (ENG., Illus.). 176p. 50.00 *(978-1-60660-006-1(0))* Dover Pubns., Inc.

Archer, Jacque Day & Santoro, Jamie Wirsbinski. Rogers Park. 2007. (Images of America Ser.). (ENG., Illus.). 128p. per. 21.99 *(978-0-7385-4139-6(7))* Arcadia Publishing.

Austin, Andy. Rule 53: Capturing Hippies, Spies, Politicians, & Murderers in an American Courtroom. 2008. 416p. pap. 19.95 *(978-1-893121-53-9(4))* Everything Goes Media, LLC.

Bachrach, Julia S. The City in a Garden: A Photographic History of Chicago's Parks Second Edition. 2nd ed. 2012. (Center for American Places - Center Books on American Places Ser.). (Illus.). 224p. pap. 37.50 *(978-1-935195-22-1(0))* Ctr. for American Places, Inc.

Baim, Tracy, ed. Out & Proud in Chicago: An Overview of the City's Gay Community. 2008. (ENG., Illus.). 224p. 30.00 *(978-1-57284-100-0(1))* Surrey Bks.

Bakija, compiled by. Chicago in Focus: Portrait of a City Through the Eyes of Its People, 1 vols., vol. 1. 2010. 64p. pap. 19.95 *(978-0-615-36236-6(2))* Dream Town.

Baldwin, Davarian L. Chicago's New Negroes: Modernity, the Great Migration, & Black Urban Life. 2007. (ENG., Illus.). 384p. 69.95 *(978-0-8078-3099-4(2))*; per. 27.95 *(978-0-8078-5799-1(8))* Univ. of North Carolina Pr.

Ballowe, James. A Man of Salt & Trees: The Life of Joy Morton. 2009. (Illus.). 318p. 28.95 *(978-0-87580-398-2(9))* Northern Illinois Univ. Pr.

Baugher, Shirley. Hidden History of Old Town. 2011. (Illus.). 130p. pap. 17.99 ***(978-1-60949-207-6(2))*** History Pr., The.

Bielski, Ursula. Chicago Haunts 3. 2009. 224p. pap. 15.95 *(978-1-933272-15-3(5))* Thunder Bay Pr.

Borzo, Greg. The Chicago L. 2007. (ENG., Illus.). 168p. per. 26.99 *(978-0-7385-5100-5(7))* Arcadia Publishing.

Brandt, Nat. Chicago Death Trap: The Iroquois Theatre Fire Of 1903. 2006. (ENG., Illus.). 240p. per. 17.95 *(978-0-8093-2721-8(X))* Southern Illinois Univ. Pr.

Branigan, Michael. A History of Chicago's O'Hare Airport. 2011. 160p. pap. 19.99 ***(978-1-60949-434-6(2))*** History Pr., The.

Brinkmann, Tobias. Sundays at Sinai: A Jewish Congregation in Chicago. 2012. (Historical Studies of Urban America Ser.). (ENG., Illus.). 384p. 45.00 ***(978-0-226-07454-2(4))*** Univ. of Chicago Pr.

Britt, Raymond. Chicago Marathon. 2009. 128p. pap. 21.99 *(978-0-7385-7718-0(9))* Arcadia Publishing.

Brown, Damon & Anderson, Pamela. Playboy's Greatest Covers. 2012. (ENG.). 320p. 35.00 *(978-1-4027-8014-1(1))* Sterling Publishing Co., Inc.

cahan, richard & williams, michael. The Lost Panoramas: When Chicago Changed its River & the Land Beyond. 2011. (ENG., Illus.). 160p. 45.00 ***(978-0-9785450-7-9(9))*** CityFiles Pr.

Catrambone, Kathy & Shubart, Ellen. Taylor Street: Chicago's Little Italy. 2007. (Images of America Ser.). (Illus.). 127p. per. 19.99 *(978-0-7385-5107-4(4))* Arcadia Publishing.

Chamberlin, Everett. Chicago & Its Suburbs. 2010. 538p. pap. 40.75 *(978-1-142-31955-7(5))* BiblioBazaar.

—Chicago & Its Suburbs. 508p. 2010. 44.76 *(978-1-169-80192-9(7))* 2010. pap. 32.76 *(978-1-163-30422-8(0))* 2010. 55.95 *(978-1-161-65524-7(7))* 2007. (ENG.). per. 40.95 *(978-1-4326-5794-9(1))* Kessinger Publishing, LLC.

Chicago Magazine the West As It Is. 2006. 460p. per. 29.99 *(978-1-4255-5066-0(5))* MPublishing.

Childers, Scott. Chicago's WLS Radio. 2008. (Images of America Ser.). (ENG., Illus.). 128p. pap. 21.99 *(978-0-7385-6194-3(0))* Arcadia Publishing.

Clark, David G. Route 66 in Chicago. 2007. (Images of America Ser.). (ENG., Illus.). 128p. per. 21.99 *(978-0-7385-5138-8(4))* Arcadia Publishing.

Cohn, Scotti. It Happened in Chicago. 2009. (It Happened in Ser.). (ENG., Illus.). 176p. pap. 14.95 *(978-0-7627-5056-6(1))* Globe Pequot Pr., The.

Colbert, Elias. Chicago & the Great Conflagration. 2009. (City Ser.). (ENG.). 556p. pap. 32.95 *(978-1-4290-2214-9(0))* Applewood Bks.

—Chicago & the Great Conflagration. 2009. 374p. pap. *(978-0-217-19273-6(4))* Books LLC.

Conzen, Michael P. & Dillon, Diane, eds. Mapping Manifest Destiny: Chicago & the American West. 2008. (Illus.). 120p. pap. 27.95 *(978-0-911028-81-2(1))* Newberry Library.

Curtis, Edward E., IV. Black Muslim Religion in the Nation of Islam, 1960-1975. 2006. (ENG., Illus.). 256p. per. 22.00 *(978-0-8078-5771-7(8))* Univ. of North Carolina Pr.

Dale, Elizabeth. The Chicago Trunk Murder: Law & Justice at the Turn of the Century. 2011. (ENG., Illus.). 167p. 32.00 *(978-0-87580-440-8(3))* Northern Illinois Univ. Pr.

Danahey, Mike & Hantschel, Allison. Chicago's Historic Irish Pubs. 2011. (Images of America Ser.). (Illus.). 128p. pap. 21.99 *(978-0-7385-8391-4(X))* Arcadia Publishing.

Darien Historical Society. Darien. 2012. (Images of America Ser.). (ENG., Illus.). 128p. pap. 21.99 ***(978-0-7385-9186-5(6))*** Arcadia Publishing.

Davis, Calvin. Inner City Hoops: A History of Chicago Basketball. 2007. 132p. pap. 9.95 *(978-1-4327-0038-6(3))* Outskirts Pr., Inc.

Davros, Michael George. Greeks in Chicago. 2009. (Images of America Ser.). (ENG., Illus.). 128p. pap. 21.99 *(978-0-7385-6171-4(1))* Arcadia Publishing.

Day, Jacque E. & Santoro, Jamie Wirsbinski. West Ridge. 2008. (Images of America Ser.). (Illus.). 128p. pap. 19.99 *(978-0-7385-6150-9(9))* Arcadia Publishing.

Dennis, Michael. The Memorial Day Massacre: Chicago, Labor, & the Movement for Industrial Democracy. 2010. (ENG.). 288p. 89.00 *(978-0-230-61821-3(9))* Palgrave Macmillan.

Deuchler, Douglas. Cicero Revisited. 2006. (Images of America Ser.). (ENG., Illus.). 128p. per. 21.99 *(978-0-7385-4107-5(9))* Arcadia Publishing.

Dougherty, Monica & Sammons, Mary Beth. The Irish American Heritage Center. 2011. (Images of America Ser.). (Illus.). 128p. pap. 21.99 *(978-0-7385-8288-7(3))* Arcadia Publishing.

Farrar, Ellen S. The Magnificent Mile Lights Festival. 2008. (Images of America Ser.). (ENG., Illus.). 128p. pap. 21.99 *(978-0-7385-6184-4(3))* Arcadia Publishing.

Fernandez, Lilia. Brown in the Windy City: Mexicans & Puerto Ricans in Postwar Chicago. 2012. (Historical Studies of Urban America Ser.). (Illus.). 384p. 45.00 ***(978-0-226-24425-9(3))*** Univ. of Chicago Pr.

Ferraro, Thomas E. Niles: The Early Years. 2012. (Images of America Ser.). (ENG., Illus.). 128p. pap. 21.99 ***(978-0-7385-8306-8(5))*** Arcadia Publishing.

Fitzpatrick, Tony. The Wonder Vol. 3: Portraits of a Remembered City: City of Monsters, City of Ghosts. 2008. (Illus.). 128p. 30.00 *(978-0-86719-696-2(3))* Last Gasp of San Francisco.

Flood, Dawn Rae. Rape in Chicago: Race, Myth, & the Courts. 2012. (Women in American History Ser.). (ENG., Illus.). 272p. 55.00 ***(978-0-252-03689-7(1))*** Univ. of Illinois Pr.

Foster, Thomas Dove. A Letter from the Fire: Being an Account of the Great Chicago Fire Written In 1871. 2011. 46p. 35.95 ***(978-1-258-01064-5(X))*** Literary Licensing, LLC.

Freeman, Nick. Food, Lodging, Liquor: Signs You're in Chicago. 2008. pap. 22.95 *(978-1-893121-69-0(0))* Everything Goes Media, LLC.

Frese, Rita L., et al, eds. From Lumber Hookers to the Hooligan Fleet: A Treasury of Chicago Maritime History. 2008. (Illus.). 379p. pap. 19.95 *(978-1-893121-30-0(5))* Everything Goes Media, LLC.

Furse, Ray. City in Time: Chicago. 2007. (City in Time Ser.). (ENG., Illus.). 144p. 14.95 *(978-1-4027-3299-7(6))* Sterling Publishing Co., Inc.

Ganz, Cheryl R. The 1933 Chicago World's Fair: A Century of Progress. 2012. (ENG., Illus.). 272p. pap. 21.95 ***(978-0-252-07852-1(7))*** Univ. of Illinois Pr.

Genzen, Jonathan. The Chicago River: A History in Pictures. 2007. (Illus.). 96p. 19.95 *(978-1-56579-553-2(9))* Westcliffe Pubs.

Gibson, Dawn-Marie. A History of the Nation of Islam: Race, Islam, & the Quest for Freedom, 1 vol. 2012. 239p. 48.00 ***(978-0-313-39807-0(0)***, A3607C) Greenwood Publishing Group, Inc.

Goddard, Leslie. Remembering Marshall Field's. 2011. (Images of America Ser.). (Illus.). 128p. pap. 21.99 *(978-0-7385-8368-6(5))* Arcadia Publishing.

Goodspeed, Edgar Johnson. History of the Great Fires in Chicago & the West a Proud Career Arrested by Sudden & Awful Calamity, Towns & Counties Laid Waste by the Deva. 2006. 684p. per. 36.99 *(978-1-4255-6816-0(5))* MPublishing.

Guy, Roger. From Diversity to Unity: Southern & Appalachian Migrants in Uptown Chicago, 1950-1970. 2007. (ENG.). 140p. 57.99 *(978-0-7391-1833-7(1))* Lexington Bks.

Harpster, Jack. The Railroad Tycoon Who Built Chicago: A Biography of William B. Ogden. 2009. (ENG.). 328p. 29.95 *(978-0-8093-2917-5(4))* Southern Illinois Univ. Pr.

Harris, Neil. The Chicagoan: A Lost Magazine of the Jazz Age. 2008. (ENG., Illus.). 400p. 65.00 *(978-0-226-31761-8(7))* Univ. of Chicago Pr.

Hatch, HATCH, Anthony P. Tinder Box: The Iroquois Theater Disaster 1903. 2010. (ENG.). pap. 17.95 *(978-0-89733-609-3(7))* Academy Chicago Pubs., Ltd.

Hawcock, David & League Baseball Organisation Staff. Wrigley Field. 2010. (ENG., Illus.). 16p. 25.00 *(978-0-7893-2016-2(9))* Universe Publishing.

Helmer, William J., ed. Al Capone & His American Boys: Memoirs of a Mobster's Wife. 2011. (ENG., Illus.). 400p. 29.95 *(978-0-253-35606-2(7)*, 0253356067) Indiana Univ. Pr.

Holderfield, William J. Schaumburg's Woodfield Mall. 2007. (Images of America Ser.). (ENG., Illus.). 128p. per. 19.99 *(978-0-7385-5102-9(3))* Arcadia Publishing.

Houlihan Kennedy, Bridget. Chicago's South Side Irish Parade. 2010. (Images of America Ser.). (ENG., Illus.). 128p. pap. 21.99 *(978-0-7385-7722-7(7))* Arcadia Publishing.

Inter Ocean Publishing Co. Chicago's First Half Century, 1833-1883. 2010. (Historiography Ser.). 212p. pap. 15.95 *(978-1-4290-2294-1(9))* Applewood Bks.

Jacob, Mark, et al. Chicago under Glass: Early Photographs from the Chicago Daily News. 2007. (Illus.). 272p. 45.00 *(978-0-226-08930-0(4))* Univ. of Chicago Pr.

Janda, Steven Andrew. The Emerald Home Run. 2011. 320p. pap. 29.95 ***(978-1-60911-498-5(1)***, Strategic Bk. Publishing) AEG Literary Publishing Services, Inc.

Jones, Wilbert, et al. Chicago's Gold Coast. 2012. (Images of America Ser.). (ENG., Illus.). 128p. pap. 21.99 ***(978-0-7385-9177-3(7))*** Arcadia Publishing.

Kalmbach, Sally Sexton. The Jewel of the Gold Coast: Mrs. Potter Palmer's Chicago. 2009. (Illus.). 96p. pap. 17.95 *(978-0-9818126-6-3(X))* Ampersand, Inc.

Keating, Ann Durkin. Rising up from Indian Country: The Battle of Fort Dearborn & the Birth of Chicago. 2012. (Illus.). 328p. 30.00 ***(978-0-226-42896-3(6))*** Univ. of Chicago Pr.

Keating, Ann Durkin, ed. Chicago Neighborhoods & Suburbs: A Historical Guide. 2008. (ENG., Illus.). 344p. pap., instr.'s gde. ed. 25.00 *(978-0-226-42883-3(4))* Univ. of Chicago Pr.

Keller Bourland, Kate & Grimes, Bill. Effingham County. 2009. (Images of America Ser.). (ENG., Illus.). 128p. pap. 21.99 *(978-0-7385-6064-9(2))* Arcadia Publishing.

Kent, Cheryl. Millennium Park Chicago. 2011. (ENG., Illus.). 152p. pap. 19.95 *(978-0-8101-2682-4(6))* Northwestern Univ. Pr.

Klatt, Mary Beth. Chicago's Fashion History: 1865-1945. 2010. (Images of America Ser.). (Illus.). 128p. pap. 21.99 *(978-0-7385-8432-4(0))* Arcadia Publishing.

Klatt, Wayne. King of the Gold Coast: Cap'n Streeter, the Millionaires & the Story of Lake Shore Drive. 2011. 160p. pap. 19.99 ***(978-1-60949-320-2(6))*** History Pr., The.

Kogan, Rick. A Chicago Tavern: A Goat, a Curse, & the American Dream. 2006. (Illus.). 115p. per. 10.00 *(978-1-893121-49-2(6))* Everything Goes Media, LLC.

—Sidewalks: Portraits of Chicago. 2006. (ENG., Illus.). 256p. 32.00 *(978-0-8101-2349-6(5))* Northwestern Univ. Pr.

Korst, Kevin. Oak Lawn. 2012. (Images of America Ser.). (ENG., Illus.). 128p. pap. 21.99 ***(978-0-7385-9360-9(5))*** Arcadia Publishing.

Krist, Gary. City of Scoundrels: The 12 Days of Disaster That Gave Birth to Modern Chicago. 2012. (ENG.). 368p. 26.00 *(978-0-307-45429-4(0))* Crown Publishing Group.

Kritzberg, Barry. Morgan Park Academy Vol. 1: A History. 2007. 340p. 33.95 *(978-0-595-89622-6(7))*; per. 23.95 *(978-0-595-44055-9(X))* iUniverse, Inc.

Kyi, Tanya Lloyd. Chicago. 2010. (ENG., Illus.). 96p. 19.95 *(978-1-55285-026-8(9))* Whitecap Bks., Ltd. CAN. Dist: Midpoint Trade Bks., Inc.

Lambert, Emily. The Futures: The Rise of the Speculator & the Origins of the World's Biggest Markets. 2012. (ENG.). 248p. (gr. 9). pap. 15.99 ***(978-0-465-02841-2(1))*** Basic Bks.

Ledermann, Robert P. State Street: One Brick at a Time. 2011. (Illus.). 160p. pap. 22.99 ***(978-1-60949-294-6(3))*** History Pr., The.

Lesy, Michael. Murder City: The Bloody History of Chicago in the Twenties. 2007. (ENG., Illus.). 224p. 25.95 *(978-0-393-06030-0(6)*, 6030) Norton, W. W. & Co., Inc.

Ling, Huping. Chinese Chicago: Race, Transnational Migration, & Community Since 1870. 2012. (Asian America Ser.). (ENG., Illus.). 336p. 80.00 ***(978-0-8047-7558-8(3))***; pap. 24.95 ***(978-0-8047-7559-5(1))*** Stanford Univ. Pr.

Lowe, David Garrard. Lost Chicago. 2010. (ENG., Illus.). 272p. pap. 35.00 *(978-0-226-49432-6(2))* Univ. of Chicago Pr.

Magallon, Frank S. Chicago's Little Village: Lawndale-Crawford. 2010. (Images of America Ser.). (ENG., Illus.). 128p. pap. 21.99 *(978-0-7385-7737-1(5))* Arcadia Publishing.

Maloof, John. Portage Park. 2008. (Images of America Ser.). (ENG., Illus.). 128p. pap. 21.99 *(978-0-7385-5229-3(1))* Arcadia Publishing.

Manley, Theodoric, Jr. The Way They Saw It: The Changing Face of Bronzeville. 2008. 200p. pap. 23.00 *(978-0-8059-7507-9(1))* Dorrance Publishing Co., Inc.

McCue, Craig S. & West Des Moines Historical Society. West des Moines & Valley Junction. 2009. (Images of America Ser.). (ENG., Illus.). 128p. pap. 21.99 *(978-0-7385-6188-2(6))* Arcadia Publishing.

McNulty, Elizabeth. Chicago. 2007. (Then & Now Thunder Bay Ser.). (ENG., Illus.). 144p. pap. 12.95 *(978-1-59223-732-6(0)*, Thunder Bay Pr.) Advantage Pubs. Group.

Messer-Kruse, Timothy. The Trial of the Haymarket Anarchists: Terrorism & Justice in the Gilded Age. 2011. (ENG., Illus.). 244p. 90.00 *(978-0-230-11660-3(4))*; pap. 30.00 *(978-0-230-12077-8(6))* Palgrave Macmillan.

Milan, Jon. Old Chicago Road: US-12 from Detroit to Chicago. 2011. (Images of America Ser.). (ENG., Illus.). 128p. pap. 21.99 ***(978-0-7385-7810-1(X))*** Arcadia Publishing.

Moore Hill, Candace. Bahá'í Temple. 2010. (Images of America Ser.). (ENG., Illus.). 128p. pap. 21.99 *(978-0-7385-8421-8(5))* Arcadia Publishing.

Murphy, John. Secrets of the Snake Charmer: Snakes in the 21st Century. 2010. 420p. pap. 36.95 *(978-1-4502-2126-9(2))* iUniverse, Inc.

Neu, Denese. Chicago Beer: A High-Gravity History of Windy City Brewing. 2011. 128p. pap. 19.99 ***(978-1-60949-125-3(4))*** History Pr., The.

Ogorek, Cynthia L. The Lincoln Highway Around Chicago. 2008. (Images of America Ser.). (ENG., Illus.). 128p. pap. 19.99 *(978-0-7385-5197-5(X))* Arcadia Publishing.

O'Gorman, Thomas J. Chicago from the Air Then & Now. 2010. (ENG.). 144p. 19.95 *(978-1-60710-009-6(6)*, Thunder Bay Pr.) Advantage Pubs. Group.

Oswalt, Rusty & Longnecker, Eric. 'Chi-Town Slaughter' Uncensored. 2007. 132p. per. 19.95 *(978-1-4327-0055-3(3))* Outskirts Pr., Inc.

Packer, Robert A. Chicago's Forgotten Synagogues. 2007. (Images of America Ser.). (ENG., Illus.). 128p. per. 19.99 *(978-0-7385-5152-4(X))* Arcadia Publishing.

Pacyga, Dominic A. Chicago: A Biography. (ENG., Illus.). 472p. 2011. pap. 22.50 *(978-0-226-64428-8(6))* 2009. 35.00 *(978-0-226-64431-8(6))* Univ. of Chicago Pr.

Palazzolo, Tom. At Maxwell Street: Chicago's Historic Marketplace Recalled in Words an Photographs. 2008. (Illus.). 90p. 40.00 *(978-0-9789676-1-1(5))* Wicker Pk. Pr., Ltd.

Parsons, Albert & Spies, August. The Haymarket Trial: Selected Testimony from the Trial of the Chicago Anarchists. Flank, Lenny, ed. 2011. 404p. pap. 16.99 ***(978-1-61001-006-1(X))*** Red & Black Pubs.

Pero, Peter N. Chicago's Pilsen Neighborhood. 2011. (Images of America Ser.). (Illus.). 128p. pap. 21.99 *(978-0-7385-8334-1(0))* Arcadia Publishing.

Pero, Peter Nicholas. Chicago Italians at Work. 2009. (Images of America Ser.). (ENG., Illus.). 128p. pap. 21.99 *(978-0-7385-6187-5(8))* Arcadia Publishing.

Peterson, Paul Michael. Chicago Stadium. 2011. (Images of Sports Ser.). (ENG., Illus.). 128p. pap. 21.99 ***(978-0-7385-8307-5(3))*** Arcadia Publishing.

Peterson, Paul Michael. Chicago's Soldier Field. 2007. (Images of Sports Ser.). (ENG., Illus.). 128p. per. 19.99 *(978-0-7385-5150-0(3))* Arcadia Publishing.

Pierce, Bessie Louise. A History of Chicago Vol. 3: The Rise of a Modern City, 1871-1893. 2007. (Illus.). 640p. per. 42.50 *(978-0-226-66842-0(8))* Univ. of Chicago Pr.

—A History of Chicago, Volume I: The Beginning of a City 1673-1848, 3 vols. 2007. (ENG., Illus.). 520p. per. 37.50 *(978-0-226-66839-0(8))* Univ. of Chicago Pr.

—A History of Chicago, Volume II: From Town to City 1848-1871, 3 vols. 2007. (ENG., Illus.). 614p. per. 42.50 *(978-0-226-66840-6(1))* Univ. of Chicago Pr.

Rangaswamy, Padma. Namastt Americ. 2007. 388p. per. 25.95 *(978-0-271-02775-3(4))* Pennsylvania State Univ. Pr.

Reed, Christopher Robert. The Rise of Chicago's Black Metropolis, 1920-1929. 2011. (New Black Studies Ser.). (ENG., Illus.). 288p. 55.00 *(978-0-252-03623-1(9))* Univ. of Illinois Pr.

Rinker, Kimberly A. Chicago's Horse Racing Venues. 2009. (Images of America Ser.). (ENG., Illus.). 128p. pap. 21.99 *(978-0-7385-6080-9(4))* Arcadia Publishing.

Robinson, Guy. Do You Know Chicago? A Challenging Little Quiz about the Amazing People, Great Places, & Illustrious History of the Second City. 2008. (ENG.). 48p. pap. 5.95 *(978-1-4022-1298-7(4))* Sourcebooks, Inc.

Rosemont, Franklin & Roediger, David, eds. Haymarket Scrapbook: 25th Anniversary Edition. 25th ed. 2012. (ENG., Illus.). 272p. pap. 23.00 ***(978-1-84935-080-8(9))*** AK Pr. GBR. Dist: Consortium Bk. Sales & Distribution.

Roth, Walter. Avengers & Defenders. 2008. (ENG.). 240p. pap. 16.95 *(978-0-89733-573-7(2))* Academy Chicago Pubs., Ltd.

Schirado, Roberta H. J. & Rockford Historical Society. Rockford. 2009. (Images of America Ser.). (ENG., Illus.). 128p. pap. 21.99 *(978-0-7385-6073-1(1))* Arcadia Publishing.

Schneidhorst, Amy C. Building a Just & Secure World: Popular Front Women's Struggle for Peace & Justice in Chicago During the 1960s. 2011. (ENG., Illus.). 272p. 120.00 *(978-1-4411-0972-9(2))* Continuum International Publishing Group, Ltd. GBR. Dist: National Bk. Network.

Smith, Carl. The Plan of Chicago: Daniel Burnham & the Remaking of the American City. (Chicago Visions & Revisions Ser.). (ENG., Illus.). 2007. 202p. per. 12.00 *(978-0-226-76472-6(9))* 2006. 184p. 22.00 *(978-0-226-76471-9(0))* Univ. of Chicago Pr.

Soucek, Gayle. Chicago Calamities: Disaster in the Windy City. 2010. (Disaster Ser.). (ENG., Illus.). 112p. pap. 19.99 *(978-1-60949-034-8(7))* History Pr., The.

Souter, Gerry & Souter, Janet. The Chicago Air & Water Show: A History of Wings above the Waves. 2010. (ENG., Illus.). 168p. pap. 19.99 *(978-1-59629-837-8(5))* History Pr., The.

Sternstein, Malynne. Czechs of Chicagoland. 2008. (Images of America Ser.). (ENG., Illus.). 128p. pap. 21.99 *(978-0-7385-5178-4(3))* Arcadia Publishing.

Storch, Randi. Red Chicago: American Communism at Its Grassroots, 1928-35. 2007. (Working Class in American History Ser.). (Illus.). 320p. (C). 35.00 *(978-0-252-03206-6(3))* Univ. of Illinois Pr.

Swist, Jeannette. Back of the Yards. 2007. (Images of America Ser.). (ENG., Illus.). 128p. per. 21.99 *(978-0-7385-5054-1(X))* Arcadia Publishing.

Taylor, Troy. Resurrection Mary. 2007. 188p. per. 16.95 *(978-1-892523-50-1(7))* Whitechapel Productions Pr.

Taylor, Troy, et al. Weird Chicago. 2008. 368p. pap. 20.00 *(978-1-892523-59-4(0))* Whitechapel Productions Pr.

Thompson, Lowell. African Americans in Chicago. 2012. (Images of America Ser.). (ENG., Illus.). 128p. pap. 21.99 ***(978-0-7385-8853-7(9))*** Arcadia Publishing.

Tyre, William H. Chicago's Historic Prairie Avenue. 2008. (Images of America (Arcadia Publishing) Ser.). (ENG., Illus.). 128p. pap. 21.99 *(978-0-7385-5212-5(7))*; 15p. pap. 7.99 *(978-0-7385-2527-3(8))* Arcadia Publishing.

Unger, Rudolph M. The Community of Fuller Park: Those Were the Days My Friends. (Illus.). 352p. reprint ed. pap. 26.00 *(978-0-9710761-1-2(1))* Unger, Rudolph M.

Vickers, Raymond. Panic in the Loop: Chicago's Banking Crisis of 1932. 2011. (ENG.). 348p. 80.00 ***(978-0-7391-6640-6(9))*** Lexington Bks.

Vickers, Raymond B. Panic in the Loop: Chicago's Banking Crisis of 1932. 2011. ***(978-0-7391-6642-0(5))*** Lexington Bks.

Vitti, Jim. Chicago Cubs: Baseball on Catalina Island. 2010. (Images of Baseball Ser.). (ENG., Illus.). 128p. pap. 21.99 *(978-0-7385-7795-1(2))* Arcadia Publishing.

Walker, Matthew. Chicago Book. 2008. *(978-0-9704875-3-7(3))* Walker, Matthew D. Publishing.

Whitman Publishing Staff, ed. Chicago A Past to Present Photo Tour. 2010. (Illus.). 120p. 12.95 *(978-0-7948-3063-2(3))* Whitman Publishing LLC.

The Windies' City: Chicago's Historical Hidden Treasures. 2006. pap. 12.95 *(978-0-9710487-3-7(8),* 0971048738) Highlights of Chicago Pr.

Witter, David Anthony. Oldest Chicago. 2011. 257p. pap. 16.95 *(978-1-893121-44-7(5))* Everything Goes Media, LLC.

Wright, John S. Chicago: Past, Present, Future. Relations to the Great interior, & to the Continent. by John S. Wright. 2006. 500p. per. 29.99 *(978-1-4255-5521-4(7))* MPublishing.

CHICAGO (ILL.)—HISTORY—ANECDOTES

Kuenster, John. Remembrances of the Angels: A 50th Anniversary Retrospective on the Fire No One Can Forget. 2008. (ENG.). 192p. 22.50 *(978-1-56663-800-5(3))* Dee, Ivan R. Pub.

CHICAGO (ILL.)—IN LITERATURE

Bloom, Harold. The House on Mango Street. 2nd rev. ed. 2010. (Bloom's Guides). 122p. (C). (gr. 9-18). 30.00 *(978-1-60413-812-2(2),* Chelsea Hse.) Facts On File, Inc.

—The Jungle - Upton Sinclair. 2nd rev. ed. 2010. (Bloom's Modern Critical Interpretations Ser.). 192p. (C). (gr. 9). 45.00 *(978-1-60413-887-0(4),* Chelsea Hse.) Facts On File, Inc.

Duffey, Bernard I. The Chicago Renaissance in American Letters: A Critical History. 2011. 294p. 48.95 ***(978-1-258-04728-3(4))*** Literary Licensing, LLC.

Fanning, Charles. Finley Peter Dunne & Mr Dooley: The Chicago Years. 2008. 312p. pap. 30.00 *(978-1-59740-420-4(9))* ACLS Humanities E-Book.

Kaser, James. The Chicago of Fiction: A Resource Guide. 2011. (ENG.). 672p. 100.00 *(978-0-8108-7724-5(4))* Scarecrow Pr., Inc.

CHICAGO (ILL.)—JUVENILE LITERATURE

Olson, Kay Melchisedech. The Great Chicago Fire Of 1871. 2006. (Graphic Library: Disasters in History Ser.). (ENG., Illus.). 32p. (gr. 3-4). per. 7.95 *(978-0-7368-6875-4(5),* Graphic Library) Capstone Pr., Inc.

CHICAGO (ILL.)—MAPS

American Map Corp, creator. Chicagoland Seven County, Illinos Large Type Street Atlas. 2007. (American Map Ser.). 39.95 *(978-0-8416-2716-1(9))* American Map Corp.

American Map Corporation. Seven County, il Atlas. 2007. pap. 21.95 *(978-84-16627-17-2(7))* American Map Corp.

American Map Corporation, creator. City of Chicago/Suburban Cook County Street Atlas: Includes the Chicagoland Grid Coordinate System. 2006. (Illus.). 124p. 19.95 *(978-0-8416-2666-9(9))* American Map Corp.

Bergquist, Kathie, et al. Not for Tourists Guide to Chicago. 2007. (Not for Tourists Guide to Chicago Ser.). (Illus.). 363p. 18.95 *(978-0-9793945-4-6(6))* Not for Tourists, Inc.

Fodor's Travel Publications, Inc. Staff. Chicago. 4th ed. 2009. (Flashmaps Ser.). (ENG.). 128p. 10.95 *(978-1-4000-1630-3(4),* Fodor's) Fodor's Travel Pubns.

Knopf Guides. Knopf MapGuide: Chicago. 2009. (ENG.). 48p. pap. 10.95 *(978-0-307-27084-9(X),* Knopf) Knopf Doubleday Publishing Group.

MapEasy Inc Staff. Chicago Mini Map. 2009. 6.95 *(978-1-878979-39-1(6))* Mapeasy, Inc.

Not for Tourists Staff. Chicago 2009. 7th rev. ed. 2008. (Illus.). 448p. 19.95 *(978-0-9814887-4-5(9))* Not for Tourists, Inc.

Not For Tourists Staff. Not for Tourists Guide to Chicago: 2012. 2011. (ENG., Illus.). 432p. pap. 19.95 ***(978-1-61608-527-8(4),*** 603527, Not For Tourist) Skyhorse Publishing Co., Inc.

Rand McNally, creator. Rand Mcnally Chicago 7-County Street Guide: Cook, Dupage, Kane, Kendall, Lake, Mchenry, Will. 2007. (Rand Mcnally Chicago 7 Counties Street Guide: Cook, Dupage, Kane, Ser.) (Illus.). 34.95 *(978-0-528-86089-8(5))* Rand McNally.

—Rand Mcnally Chicago & Cook County Street Guide. 2007. (Rand Mcnally Chicago/Cook County Street Guide Ser.). (Illus.). pap. 19.95 *(978-0-528-86087-4(9))* Rand McNally.

CHICAGO (ILL.)—POLICE

see Police—Illinois—Chicago

CHICAGO (ILL.)—POLITICS AND GOVERNMENT

Dickerson, Dennis C. African American Preachers & Politics: The Careys of Chicago. 2010. (Margaret Walker Alexander Series in African American Studies). (ENG., Illus.). 236p. 65.00 *(978-1-60473-427-0(2))* Univ. Pr. of Mississippi.

Dorfman, Ron, ed. Harold! Photographs from the Harold Washington Years. 2007. (ENG., Illus.). 224p. per. 19.95 *(978-0-8101-2446-2(7))* Northwestern Univ. Pr.

Hajnal, Zoltan L. Changing White Attitudes Toward Black Political Leadership. 2006. (ENG.). 230p. 71.99 *(978-0-521-85747-5(3))*; (Illus.). per. 26.99 *(978-0-521-67415-7(8))* Cambridge Univ. Pr.

Janowitz, Rebecca. Culture of Opportunity: Obama's Chicago - The People, Politics, & Ideas of Hyde Park. 2010. (ENG.). 256p. pap. 26.95 *(978-1-56663-833-3(X))* Dee, Ivan R. Pub.

Merriner, James L. Grafters & Goo Goos: Corruption & Reform in Chicago. 2008. (ENG., Illus.). 344p. pap. 19.95 *(978-0-8093-2874-1(7))* Southern Illinois Univ. Pr.

Stead, William T. If Christ Came to Chicago! A Plea for the Union of All Who Love in the Service of All Who Suffer. 472p. reprint ed. 98.00 *(978-0-7222-1842-6(7))* Library Reprints, Inc.

Stricherz, Mark. Why the Democrats Are Blue: How Secular Liberals Hijacked the People's Party. 2007. (ENG.). 350p. 29.95 *(978-1-59403-205-9(X))* Encounter Bks.

CHICAGO (ILL.)—POPULATION

Baldwin, Davarian L. Chicago's New Negroes: Modernity, the Great Migration, & Black Urban Life. 2007. (ENG., Illus.). 384p. per. 27.95 *(978-0-8078-5799-1(8))* Univ. of North Carolina Pr.

CHICAGO (ILL.)—RIOTS

see Haymarket Square Riot, Chicago, Ill., 1886; Riots—Illinois—Chicago

CHICAGO (ILL.)—SOCIAL CONDITIONS

Agic, Senad. Imigracija I Asimilacija: Iskustvo Bosanskih Muslimana U Chicagu. 2010. (Illus.). 197p. *(978-9958-622-53-3(X))* Connectum.

Allen, Joe. People Wasn't Made to Burn: A True Story of Housing, Race, & Murder in Chicago. 2011. (ENG., Illus.). 328p. ***(978-1-60846-126-4(2))*** Pluto Pr.

Anderson, Nels. The Hobo: The Sociology of the Homeless Man. Park, Robert E., ed. 2011. 338p. 50.95 ***(978-1-258-04807-5(8))*** Literary Licensing, LLC.

Arredondo, Gabriela F. Mexican Chicago: Race, Identity, & Nation, 1916-39. 2008. (Statue of Liberty Ellis Island Ser.). (Illus.). 272p. 62.00 *(978-0-252-03269-1(1))*; pap. 26.00 *(978-0-252-07497-4(1))* Univ. of Illinois Pr.

Bachin, Robin F. Building the South Side: Urban Space & Civic Culture in Chicago, 1890-1919. 2008. (Historical Studies of Urban America Ser.). (ENG., Illus.). 448p. pap. 25.00 *(978-0-226-03394-5(5))* Univ. of Chicago Pr.

Baldwin, Davarian L. Chicago's New Negroes: Modernity, the Great Migration, & Black Urban Life. 2007. (ENG., Illus.). 384p. 69.95 *(978-0-8078-3099-4(2))*; per. 27.95 *(978-0-8078-5799-1(8))* Univ. of North Carolina Pr.

Bennett, Larry. The Third City: Chicago & American Urbanism. 2010. (Chicago Visions & Revisions Ser.). (ENG., Illus.). 256p. 22.50 *(978-0-226-04293-0(6))* Univ. of Chicago Pr.

Bennett, Larry, et al, eds. The New Chicago: A Social & Cultural Analysis. 2006. (Illus.). 384p. 90.50 *(978-1-59213-087-0(9))* Temple Univ. Pr.

—The New Chicago: A Social & Cultural Analysis. 2006. (Illus.). 384p. per. 44.95 *(978-1-59213-088-7(7))* Temple Univ. Pr.

Black, Timuel D., Jr. Bridges of Memory: Chicago's Second Generation of Black Migration. 2008. (ENG., Illus.). 392p. per. 22.95 *(978-0-8101-5194-9(4))* Northwestern Univ. Pr.

Ciezadlo, Janina & Rosemont, Penelope, eds. Armitage Avenue Transcendentalists: Chicago Stories by Nelson Algren, Studs Terkel, 2010. (Illus.). 160p. pap. 15.00 *(978-0-88286-290-3(1))* Kerr, Charles H. Publishing Co.

Cressey, Paul Goalby. The Taxi-Dance Hall: A Sociological Study in Commercialized Recreation & City Life. 2008. (University of Chicago Sociological Ser.). (Illus.). 334p. pap. 30.00 *(978-0-226-12051-5(1))* Univ. of Chicago Pr.

Cruz, Wilfredo. Chicago Latinos at Work. 2010. (Images of America Ser.). (ENG., Illus.). 128p. pap. 21.99 *(978-0-7385-7793-7(6))* Arcadia Publishing.

—City of Dreams: Latino Immigration to Chicago. 2007. (ENG., Illus.). 240p. per. 38.99 *(978-0-7618-3820-3(1))* Univ. Pr. of America, Inc.

Cunningham, James. Howling like Wolves from Longwood Drive: Chicago Teenagers in the Great Depression. 2010. 124p. pap. 13.00 *(978-1-4269-2721-8(5))* Trafford Publishing.

Cutler, Irving. The Jews of Chicago: From Shtetl to Suburb. 2008. (Ethnic History of Chicago Ser.). (ENG.). 336p. pap. 24.95 *(978-0-252-07644-2(3))* Univ. of Illinois Pr.

De la Croix, St Sukie. Chicago Whispers: A History of LGBT Chicago Before Stonewall. 2012. E-Book ***(978-0-299-28693-4(2))***; (ENG.). 312p. pap. 29.95 ***(978-0-299-28694-1(0))*** Univ. of Wisconsin Pr.

Donovan, Frances R. The Woman Who Waits. 2009. 118p. pap. 14.14 *(978-1-151-04806-6(2))* General Bks. LLC.

Duis, Perry R. Challenging Chicago: Coping with Everyday Life, 1837-1920. 2006. (Illus.). 448p. per. 22.95 *(978-0-252-07415-8(7))* Univ. of Illinois Pr.

Green, Adam & Green, A. Selling the Race: Culture, Community, & Black Chicago, 1940-1955. 2009. (Historical Studies of Urban America Ser.). (ENG., Illus.). 328p. pap. 20.00 *(978-0-226-30640-7(2))* Univ. of Chicago Pr.

Green, James. Death in the Haymarket: A Story of Chicago, the First Labor Movement, & the Bombing That Divided Gilded Age America. 2007. (ENG., Illus.). 400p. pap. 16.95 *(978-1-4000-3322-5(5),* Anchor) Knopf Doubleday Publishing Group.

Hickman, Tommie N. From Violence to the Violin: Disturbing Information about Violence & Crime in Chicago, 1 vol. 2010. 63p. pap. 16.95 *(978-1-4489-5390-5(1))* PublishAmerica, Inc.

Hong, Soo. A Cord of Three Strands: A New Approach to Parent Engagement in Schools. 2011. (Illus.). 240p. 49.95 *(978-1-934742-82-2(1))*; pap. 29.95 *(978-1-934742-54-9(6))* Harvard Education Publishing Group (HEPG).

Janowitz, Rebecca. Culture of Opportunity: Obama's Chicago - The People, Politics, & Ideas of Hyde Park. 2010. (ENG.). 256p. pap. 26.95 *(978-1-56663-833-3(X))* Dee, Ivan R. Pub.

Jentz, John B. & Schneirov, Richard. Chicago in the Age of Capital: Class, Politics, & Democracy During the Civil War & Reconstruction. 2012. (Working Class in American History Ser.). (ENG., Illus.). 320p. 55.00 ***(978-0-252-03683-5(2))*** Univ. of Illinois Pr.

Joiner, Thekla Ellen. Sin in the City: Chicago & Revivalism, 1880-1920. 2007. (ENG., Illus.). 288p. (C). 44.95 *(978-0-8262-1743-1(5))* Univ. of Missouri Pr.

Kenosha (Wis.) Ordinances, etc. Staff. The Revised Charter & Ordinances of the City of Kenosha, with the by-Laws of the Council. 2006. 176p. per. 18.99 *(978-1-4255-1352-8(2))* MPublishing.

Lan, Shanshan. Diaspora & Class Consciousness: Chinese Immigrant Workers in Multiracial Chicago. 2011. (Studies in Asian Americans Ser.). (ENG., Illus.). 218p. (C). 125.00 *(978-0-415-89036-6(5))* Routledge.

Lesy, Michael. Murder City: The Bloody History of Chicago in the Twenties. 2008. (ENG., Illus.). 352p. per. 15.95 *(978-0-393-33059-5(1),* 33059) Norton, W. W. & Co., Inc.

Manley, Theodoric, Jr. The Way They Saw It: The Changing Face of Bronzeville. 2008. 200p. pap. 23.00 *(978-0-8059-7507-9(1))* Dorrance Publishing Co., Inc.

Ortega, Pe. A Spatial Decision Support System Approach for Interagency Partnership. 2010. 216p. pap. *(978-3-639-25854-7(1))* VDM Verlag Dr. Mueller e.K.

Pallares, Amalia & Flores-Gonzalez, Nilda. Marcha: Latino Chicago & the Immigrant Rights Movement. 2010. (Latinos in Chicago & Midwest Ser.). (ENG., Illus.). 320p. 85.00 *(978-0-252-03529-6(1))*; pap. 30.00 *(978-0-252-07716-6(4))* Univ. of Illinois Pr.

Park, Jung-Sun. Chicago Korean-Americans: Identity & Politics in a Transnational Community. 2007. (Asian Americans Ser.). (ENG.). 208p. 125.00 *(978-0-415-94881-4(9))* Routledge.

Pick, Grant. The People Are the News: Grant Pick's Chicago Stories. Pick, John, ed. 2009. (ENG.). 296p. pap. 18.95 *(978-0-8101-2580-3(3))* Northwestern Univ. Pr.

Preib, Martin. The Wagon & Other Stories from the City. (Chicago Visions & Revisions Ser.). 176p. 2011. pap. 14.00 *(978-0-226-67982-2(9))* 2010. 20.00 *(978-0-226-67980-8(2))* Univ. of Chicago Pr.

Ramirez, Leonard G., et al. Chicanas of 18th Street: Narratives of a Movements from Latino Chicago. 2011. (Latinos in Chicago & Midwest Ser.). (ENG., Illus.). 272p. 80.00 *(978-0-252-03613-7(2))*; pap. 27.00 *(978-0-252-07812-5(8))* Univ. of Illinois Pr.

Rangaswamy, Padma. Namastt Americ. 2007. 388p. per. 25.95 *(978-0-271-02775-3(4))* Pennsylvania State Univ. Pr.

Residents of Hull-House. Hull-House Maps & Papers: A Presentation of Nationalities & Wages in a Congested District of Chicago, Together with Comments & Essays on Problems Growing Out of the Social Conditions. 2007. (Illus.). 200p. 50.00 *(978-0-252-03134-2(2))* Univ. of Illinois Pr.

Roth, Walter. Avengers & Defenders. 2008. (ENG.). 240p. pap. 16.95 *(978-0-89733-573-7(2))* Academy Chicago Pubs., Ltd.

Royko, Mike. Early Royko: Up Against It in Chicago. 2010. (ENG.). 232p. pap. 16.00 *(978-0-226-73077-6(8))* Univ. of Chicago Pr.

Rua, Merida M. A Grounded Identidad: Making New Lives in Chicago's Puerto Rican Neighborhoods. 2012. (ENG., Illus.). 224p. 49.95 ***(978-0-19-976026-8(8))*** Oxford Univ. Pr., Inc.

Sanchez, Reymundo. My Bloody Life. 2011. 15.44 *(978-0-7848-3416-9(4),* Everbind) Marco Bk. Co.

Scott, Mike. Great American Youth: A True Saga. 2011. 256p. pap. 16.00 *(978-1-4567-6043-4(2))* AuthorHouse.

Skok, Deborah A. More Than Neighbors: Catholic Settlements & Day Nurseries in Chicago, 1893-1930. 2007. (Illus.). 251p. 38.00 *(978-0-87580-374-6(1))* Northern Illinois Univ. Pr.

Smith, Carl. Urban Disorder & the Shape of Belief: The Great Chicago Fire, the Haymarket Bomb, & the Model Town of Pullman. 2nd ed. 2007. (Illus.). 407p. per. 27.50 *(978-0-226-76424-5(9))* Univ. of Chicago Pr.

Sorokina, Tatiana. The Legal Alien's Guide: Building a Career & Life in Chicago, Illinois. 2007. 120p. (ENG.). 24.95 *(978-0-595-68855-5(1))*; per. 14.95 *(978-0-595-44622-3(1))* iUniverse, Inc.

Street, Paul L. Racial Oppression in the Global Metropolis: A Living Black Chicago History. 2007. (ENG.). 328p. 85.00 *(978-0-7425-4081-1(2))*; per. 32.95 *(978-0-7425-4082-8(0))* Rowman & Littlefield Publishers, Inc.

Taylor, Troy. Murder & Mayhem in Chicago's Vice Districts. 2009. (Murder & Mayhem Ser.). 112p. pap. 19.99 *(978-1-59629-692-3(5))* History Pr., The.

Tracy, Steven C. Writers of the Black Chicago Renaissance. 2011. (ENG.). 536p. 50.00 ***(978-0-252-03639-2(5))*** Univ. of Illinois Pr.

Venkatesh, Sudhir Alladi & Venkatesh, Sudhir. Gang Leader for a Day: A Rogue Sociologist Takes to the Streets. 2008. (ENG.). 320p. (gr. 12-18). 16.00 *(978-0-14-311493-2(X),* Penguin (Non-Classics)); 25.95 *(978-1-59420-150-9(1),* Penguin Pr. HC, The) Penguin Group (USA) Inc.

Walley, Christine J. Exit Zero: Family & Class in Postindustrial Chicago. 2012. 240p. pap. 27.50 ***(978-0-226-87180-6(0))***; (Illus.). 85.00 ***(978-0-226-87179-0(7))*** Univ. of Chicago Pr.

Westhoff, Laura M. A Fatal Drifting Apart: Democratic Social Knowledge & Chicago Reform. 2007. (URBAN LIFE & URBAN LANDSCAPE Ser.). (ENG.). 309p. 47.95 *(978-0-8142-1058-1(9))*; cd-rom 9.95 *(978-0-8142-9137-5(6))* Ohio State Univ. Pr.

Wilson, Samuel Paynter. The Story of Lena Murphy the White Slave: And Other Startling Revelations. fac. lt. ed. 2010. 48p. pap. 6.95 *(978-1-61033-442-6(6),* TGS Publishing) TGS.

Wilson, William Julius & Taub, Richard P. There Goes the Neighborhood: Racial, Ethnic, & Class Tensions in Four Chicago Neighborhoods & Their Meaning for America. 2007. (Vintage Ser.). (ENG., Illus.). 240p. pap. 14.95 *(978-0-679-72418-6(4),* Vintage) Knopf Doubleday Publishing Group.

Zimmerman, Marc. Defending Their Own in the Cold: The Cultural Turns of U. S. Puerto Ricans. 2011. (Latinos in Chicago & Midwest Ser.). (ENG., Illus.). 232p. 55.00 ***(978-0-252-03646-0(8))*** Univ. of Illinois Pr.

CHICAGO (ILL.)—SOCIAL LIFE AND CUSTOMS

Adams, Rosemary. Historic Photos of Christmas in Chicago. 2008. (Historic Photos Ser.). (ENG.). 205p. 39.95 *(978-1-59652-511-5(8))* Turner Publishing Co.

Adams, Rosemary K. Remembering Christmas in Chicago. 2010. (Remembering Ser.). (ENG., Illus.). 134p. pap. 16.95 *(978-1-59652-696-9(3))* Turner Publishing Co.

Addams, Jane. A New Conscience & an Ancient Evil. 2009. 236p. 23.99 *(978-1-103-95606-7(X))* 2009. 236p. pap. 17.99 *(978-1-103-95598-5(5))* 2008. 124p. 24.99 *(978-0-554-26130-0(8))* 2008. 124p. 21.99 *(978-0-554-35433-0(0))* 2007. (ENG.). 112p. pap. 18.99 *(978-1-4346-0494-1(2))* 2007. 122p. pap. 19.99 *(978-1-4346-0527-6(2))* BiblioBazaar.

—A New Conscience & an Ancient Evil. 2009. 80p. pap. *(978-0-217-42760-9(X))*; 86p. pap. *(978-0-217-15328-7(3))*. 80p. pap. *(978-1-4432-6779-3(1))*; 82p. pap. *(978-1-4432-6781-6(3))* Books LLC.

—A New Conscience & an Ancient Evil. 2007. (ENG.). 230p. 41.95 *(978-0-548-01157-7(5))* Kessinger Publishing, LLC.

Arredondo, Ramón & Arredondo, Trisha. Maria's Journey. 2010. pap. *(978-0-87195-286-8(6))* Indiana Historical Society.

Baugher, Shirley. Hidden History of Old Town. 2011. (Illus.). 130p. pap. 17.99 ***(978-1-60949-207-6(2))*** History Pr., The.

Bear, Marjorie Warvelle. A Mile Square of Chicago. 2007. (Illus.). 549p. pap. 48.00 *(978-0-9633995-4-0(3))* TIPRAC.

Bruno, Robert Anthony. Justified by Work: Identity & the Meaning of Faith in Chicago's Working-Class Churc. 2008. (ENG.). cd-rom 14.95 *(978-0-8142-9175-7(9))* Ohio State Univ. Pr.

—Justified by Work: Identity & the Meaning of Faith in Chicago's Working-Class Churches. 2008. (ENG.). 304p. 104.95 *(978-0-8142-1095-6(3))*; pap. 39.95 *(978-0-8142-5134-8(X))* Ohio State Univ. Pr.

Ciezadlo, Janina & Rosemont, Penelope, eds. Armitage Avenue Transcendentalists: Chicago Stories by Nelson Algren, Studs Terkel, 2010. (Illus.). 160p. pap. 15.00 *(978-0-88286-290-3(1))* Kerr, Charles H. Publishing Co.

Coppock, Chet. Fat Guys Shouldn't Be Dancin' at Halftime: An Irreverent Romp Through Chicago Sports. 2009. (ENG.). 304p. pap. 14.95 *(978-1-60078-269-5(8))* Triumph Bks.

Cordwell, Colin, et al. Tales from the Red Lion. Weagly, John & Dubnick, Andrea, eds. 2007. per. 13.00 *(978-0-9773856-2-3(8))* Twilight Tales, Inc.

Dougherty, Monica & Sammons, Mary Beth. The Irish American Heritage Center. 2011. (Images of America Ser.). (Illus.). 128p. pap. 21.99 *(978-0-7385-8288-7(3))* Arcadia Publishing.

Duis, Perry R. Challenging Chicago: Coping with Everyday Life, 1837-1920. 2006. (Illus.). 443p. per. 22.95 *(978-0-252-07415-8(7))* Univ. of Illinois Pr.

Feiling, Thomas. Cocaine Nation: How the White Trade Took over the World. 2010. (ENG., Illus.). 356p. 27.95 *(978-1-60598-101-7(X),* 605101) Pegasus Bks.

C

Hargraves, Orin. Chicago. 2007. (Culture Shock! A Survival Guide to Customs & Etiquette Ser.). (Illus.). 270p. per. 15.95 *(978-0-7614-5400-7(4))* Marshall Cavendish Corp.

—Cultureshock Chicago, 1 vol. 2011. (ENG.). 240p. pap. 15.95 *(978-0-7614-6055-8(1))* Marshall Cavendish Corp.

Heap, Chad. Slumming: Sexual & Racial Encounters in American Nightlife, 1885-1940. 2010. (Historical Studies of Urban America Ser.). (Illus.). 432p. pap. 25.00 *(978-0-226-32244-5(0))* Univ. of Chicago Pr.

Heap, Chad & Heap, Chad C. Slumming: Sexual & Racial Encounters in American Nightlife, 1885-1940. 2009. (Historical Studies of Urban America Ser.). (ENG., Illus.). 432p. 35.00 *(978-0-226-32243-8(2))* Univ. of Chicago Pr.

Houlihan Kennedy, Bridget. Chicago's South Side Irish Parade. 2010. (Images of America Ser.). (ENG., Illus.). 128p. pap. 21.99 *(978-0-7385-7722-7(7))* Arcadia Publishing.

Jacob, Mark, et al. Chicago under Glass: Early Photographs from the Chicago Daily News. 2007. (Illus.). 272p. 45.00 *(978-0-226-08930-0(4))* Univ. of Chicago Pr.

Kogan, Rick. Sidewalks: Portraits of Chicago. (ENG., Illus.). 2008. 248p. pap. 21.95 *(978-0-8101-5193-2(6))* 2006. 256p. 32.00 *(978-0-8101-2349-6(5))* Northwestern Univ. Pr.

—Sidewalks: Volume 2: Reflections on Chicago. 2009. (Illus.). 256p. 40.00 *(978-0-9841265-0-7(3))* Sidewalks Bk. Co.

Ledermann, Robert P. State Street: One Brick at a Time. 2011. (Illus.). 160p. pap. 22.99 ***(978-1-60949-294-6(3))*** History Pr., The.

Lynch, Christopher. When Hollywood Landed at Chicago's Midway Airport: The Photos & Stories of Mike Rotunno. 2012. 160p. pap. 19.99 ***(978-1-60949-592-3(6))*** History Pr., The.

Magallon, Frank S. Chicago's Little Village: Lawndale-Crawford. 2010. (Images of America Ser.). (ENG., Illus.). 128p. pap. 21.99 *(978-0-7385-7737-1(5))* Arcadia Publishing.

Peerbolte, Gregory T. Randhurst: Suburban Chicago's Grandest Shopping Center. 2011. *(978-1-60949-147-5(5))* History Pr., The.

Pick, Grant. The People Are the News: Grant Pick's Chicago Stories. Pick, John, ed. 2008. (ENG., Illus.). 296p. 26.95 *(978-0-8101-2445-5(9))* Northwestern Univ. Pr.

Royko, Mike. Early Royko: Up Against It in Chicago. 2010. (ENG.). 232p. pap. 16.00 *(978-0-226-73077-6(8))* Univ. of Chicago Pr.

Ruane, John Bernard. Parish the Thought: An Inspirational Memoir of Growing up Catholic in the 1960s. 2008. (ENG., Illus.). 288p. pap. 16.00 *(978-1-4165-8949-5(X))* Gallery Pr., The IRL. Dist: Simon & Schuster, Inc.

Samarov, Dmitry. Hack: Stories from a Chicago Cab. 2011. (ENG., Illus.). 124p. 20.00 *(978-0-226-73473-6(0))* Univ. of Chicago Pr.

Shay, Art. Chicago's Nelson Algren. 2007. (ENG., Illus.). 208p. per. 19.95 *(978-1-58322-764-0(4))* Seven Stories Pr.

Souter, Gerry & Souter, Janet. The Chicago Air & Water Show: A History of Wings above the Waves. 2010. (ENG., Illus.). 168p. pap. 19.99 *(978-1-59629-837-8(5))* History Pr., The.

Stead, William T. If Christ Came to Chicago! A Plea for the Union of All Who Love in the Service of All Who Suffer. 472p. reprint ed. 98.00 *(978-0-7222-1842-6(7))* Library Reprints, Inc.

Steinberg, Ellen FitzSimmons & Hanson, Eleanor Hudera. Learning to Cook In 1898: A Chicago Culinary Memoir. 2007. (Great Lakes Bks.). 218p. per. 19.95 *(978-0-8143-3364-8(8))* Wayne State Univ. Pr.

Thompson, Lowell. African Americans in Chicago. 2012. (Images of America Ser.). (ENG., Illus.). 128p. pap. 21.99 ***(978-0-7385-8853-7(9))*** Arcadia Publishing.

=Williams, Carla, ed. Articles of Faith: African-American Community Churches in Chicago. 2009. (Center for American Places - Center Books on American Places Ser.). (ENG., Illus.). 96p. 50.00 *(978-1-930066-97-7(X))* Ctr. for American Places, Inc.

Zurawski, Joseph W. Polish Chicago: Our History - Our Recipes. 2007. (ENG.). 240p. 37.50 *(978-0-9774512-2-7(4))* Bradley, G. Publishing, Inc.

CHICAGO (ILL.)—WORLD'S COLUMBIAN EXPOSITION, 1893

see World's Columbian Exposition (1893: Chicago, Ill.)

CHICAGO, BURLINGTON AND QUINCY RAILROAD COMPANY

Burg, Thomas E., ed. Burlington Route Steam: Locomotive Photos from the Roy Campbell Collection. 2008. (Illus.). 148p. pap. 29.95 *(978-0-9795752-8-2(2))* Merrill Publishing Assocs.

Overton, R. C. The First Ninety Years: An Historical Sketch of the Burlington Railroad, 1850-1940. (Illus.). 40p. reprint ed. lib. bdg. 88.00 *(978-0-7222-0618-8(6))* Library Reprints, Inc.

Perkins, Charles Elliott & Perkins, Edith Forbes. Family Letters & Reminiscences, 1865-1907, V1-2: Charles Elliott Perkins & Edith Forbes Perkins. Cunningham, Edith Perkins, ed. 2011. 746p. 71.95 ***(978-1-258-07929-1(1))*** Literary Licensing, LLC.

CHICAGO, MILWAUKEE, ST. PAUL, AND PACIFIC RAILROAD COMPANY

Burg, Thomas E., ed. Milwaukee Road Steam in the West: Locomotive Photos from the Roy Campbell Collection. 2008. (Illus.). 129p. pap. 29.95 *(978-0-9795752-3-5(0))* Merrill Publishing Assocs.

Burg, Thomas E. & Storozuk, Bob. Route of the North Woods Hiawatha: The Milwaukee Road's Wisconsin Valley Line. 2010. (Illus.). 113p. ***(978-0-9795752-9-7(X))*** Merrill Publishing Assocs.

Lorenzsonn, Axel. Steam & Cinders: The Advent of Railroads in Wisconsin. 2009. (ENG., Illus.). 352p. 29.95 *(978-0-87020-385-5(1))* Wisconsin Historical Society.

Scribbins, Jim. The Hiawatha Story. 2007. (Fesler-Lampert Minnesota Heritage Ser.). (Illus.). 272p. pap. 29.95 *(978-0-8166-5003-3(9))* Univ. of Minnesota Pr.

—Milwaukee Road Remembered. 2008. (Illus.). 168p. (Orig.). pap. 29.95 *(978-0-8166-5625-7(6))* Univ. of Minnesota Pr.

CHICAGO, UNIVERSITY OF

see University of Chicago

CHICAGO BEARS (FOOTBALL TEAM)

Chicago Tribune Sports and Photo Staff, creator. Super Bears: The Remarkable Story of the 2006 Chicago Bears. 2007. (ENG., Illus.). 128p. per. 14.95 *(978-1-60078-032-5(6))* Triumph Bks.

Chicago Tribune Staff. Bears Roar: Meet the Men Who Put the Swagger Back in Chicago Football. 2007. (ENG., Illus.). 128p. per. 12.95 *(978-1-60078-001-1(6))* Triumph Bks.

Claerbaut, David. Bears Essential: Everything You Need to Know to Be a Real Fan! 2006. (Essential: Everything You Need to Know to Be a Real Fan Ser.). (ENG., Illus.). 180p. 19.95 *(978-1-57243-843-9(6))* Triumph Bks.

Crist, John. 100 Things Bears Fans Should Know & Do Before They Die. 2013. (100 Things... Fans Should Know Ser.). (ENG.). 256p. pap. 14.95 ***(978-1-60078-412-5(7))*** Triumph Bks.

Davis, Jeff. Papa Bear: The Life & Legacy of George Halas. 2006. (ENG.). 544p. pap. 16.95 *(978-0-07-147741-3(1), 007147741I)* McGraw-Hill Cos., The.

Delsohn, Steve. Da Bears! How the 1985 Monsters of the Midway Became the Greatest Team in NFL History. (Illus.). 2011. (ENG.). 280p. pap. 14.00 *(978-0-307-46468-2(7)*, Three Rivers Pr.) 2010. 272p. 24.99 *(978-0-307-46467-5(9)*, Crown) Crown Publishing Group.

Ditka, Mike & Telander, Rick. The '85 Bears: We Were the Greatest. 2010. (ENG.). 256p. 26.95 *(978-1-60078-508-5(5))* Triumph Bks.

Freedman, Lew. Game of My Life: Chicago Bears: Memorable Stories of Bears Football. 2006. (Illus.). 225p. 24.95 *(978-1-59670-100-7(5))* Sports Publishing, LLC.

—Game of My Life Chicago Bears: Memorable Stories of Bears Football. 2nd ed. 2008. (Illus.). 256p. pap. 16.95 *(978-1-59670-339-1(3))* Sports Publishing, LLC.

—The 50 Greatest Plays in Chicago Bears Football History. 2008. (50 Greatest Plays Ser.). (ENG.). 224p. 24.95 *(978-1-60078-122-3(5))* Triumph Bks.

Jiggetts, Dan & Mitchell, Fred. "Then Ditka Said to Payton..." The Best Chicago Bears Stories Ever Told. 2008. (Best Sports Stories Ever Told Ser.). (ENG.). 192p. 22.95 *(978-1-57243-985-6(8))* Triumph Bks.

John Mullin. Tales from the Chicago Bears Sidelines. 2007. (Tales Ser.). (Illus.). 192p. pap. 15.95 *(978-1-59670-246-2(X))* Sports Publishing, LLC.

Johnson, Steve. Chicago Bears Trivia Teasers. 2006. (Illus.). 147p. per. 16.95 *(978-1-931599-76-4(9)*, Trails Bks.) Big Earth Publishing.

Klein, Fred & Anderson, Mark. For the Love of the Bears. 2010. 48p. *(978-1-60078-262-6(0))* Triumph Bks.

McCaskey, Patrick & Sandrolini, Mike. Bear with Me: A Family History of George Halas & the Chicago Bears. 2009. (ENG.). 240p. 24.95 *(978-1-60078-128-5(4))* Triumph Bks.

McMichael, Steve, et al. Amazing Tales from the Chicago Bears Sideline: A Collection of the Greatest Bears Stories Ever Told. 2011. (Tales from the Team Ser.). (ENG., Illus.). 384p. 24.95 *(978-1-61321-026-0(4)*, 613026) Skyhorse Publishing Co., Inc.

Mullin, John. The Best Chicago Sports Arguments: The 100 Most Controversial, Debatable Questions for Die-Hard Chicago Fans. 2006. (Best Sports Arguments Ser.). (ENG., Illus.). 272p. per. 14.95 *(978-1-4022-0821-8(9))* Sourcebooks, Inc.

Sayers, Gale & Mitchell, Fred. Sayers: My Life & Times. 2007. (ENG.). 240p. 24.95 *(978-1-57243-995-5(5))* Triumph Bks.

Super Bowl Indianapolis Colts. 2010. pap. 19.95 *(978-0-615-35073-8(9))* Sport-Publishing llc.

CHICAGO BLACKHAWKS (HOCKEY TEAM)

Bamford, Tab. 100 Things Blackhawks Fans Should Know & Do Before They Die. 2011. (100 Things... Fans Should Know Ser.). (ENG.). 256p. pap. 14.95 *(978-1-60078-652-5(9))* Triumph Bks.

Chicago Tribune Staff. Hawkeytown: Chicago Balckhawks' Run for the 2010 Stanley Cup. 2010. (ENG.). 128p. pap. 14.95 *(978-1-60078-528-3(X))* Triumph Bks.

—Hawkeytown: Chicago Blackhawks' Run for the 2010 Stanley Cup. 2010. E-Book 14.95 *(978-1-61749-110-8(1))* Triumph Bks.

Mikita, Stan & Verdi, Bob. Forever a Blackhawk. 2011. (ENG.). 208p. 26.95 ***(978-1-60078-614-3(6))*** Triumph Bks.

CHICAGO BOARD OF TRADE

Harcourt, Bernard E. The Illusion of Free Markets: Punishment & the Myth of Natural Order. 2011. (Illus.). 336p. 29.95 *(978-0-674-05726-5(0))* Harvard Univ. Pr.

CHICAGO BULLS (BASKETBALL TEAM)

Chicago Tribune Staff. TBD Chicago Bulls NBA Champions. 2011. 128p. pap. 14.95 ***(978-1-60078-684-6(7))*** Triumph Bks.

Frisch, Aaron. Chicago Bulls. 2008. (NBA Champions Ser.). (Illus.). 24p. (J). (gr. 1-4). lib. bdg. 24.25 *(978-1-58341-505-4(X))* Creative Co., The.

Sandrolini, Mike & McDill, Kent. 100 Things Bulls Fans Should Know & Do Before They Die. 2012. (100 Things... Fans Should Know Ser.). (ENG.). 256p. pap. 14.95 *(978-1-60078-650-1(2))* Triumph Bks.

CHICAGO CUBS (BASEBALL TEAM)

Ahrens, Art. Chicago Cubs: Tinker to Evers to Chance. 2007. (Images of Baseball Ser.). (ENG., Illus.). 128p. per. 19.99 *(978-0-7385-5130-2(9))* Arcadia Publishing.

Bissinger, Buzz. 3 Nights in August: Strategy, Heartbreak, & Joy Inside the Mind of a Manager. 2008. (Playaway Adult Fiction Ser.). 54.99 *(978-1-60640-938-1(7))* Findaway World, LLC.

Bogen, Gil. The Billy Goat Curse: Losing & Superstition in Cubs Baseball since World War II. 2008. (ENG., Illus.). 228p. pap. 29.95 *(978-0-7864-3354-4(X))* McFarland & Co., Inc. Pubs.

Castle, George. Entangled in Ivy. 2007. (Illus.). 273p. per. 16.95 *(978-1-59670-189-2(7))* Sports Publishing, LLC.

Chicago Cubs Staff. Ron Santo: Always a Cub. 2011. 29.95 ***(978-1-60078-635-8(9))*** Triumph Bks.

Chicago Cubs Staff & Triumph Books Staff. Chicago Cubs Cookbook: All-Star Recipes from Your Favorite Players. 2010. (ENG.). 144p. 16.95 *(978-1-60078-527-6(1))* Triumph Bks.

Deporter, Hoodoo. 2008. (Illus.). 176p. 24.99 *(978-0-9820512-0-7(4))* Rare Air, Ltd.

Edward, James. Cubs Win, Cubs Win, A Tale. 2007. 180p. per. 10.95 *(978-1-4327-1292-1(6))* Outskirts Pr., Inc.

Fast, Darcy. The Missing Cub. 2007. (ENG.). 240p. 24.99 *(978-1-60477-514-3(9))* Xulon Pr., Inc.

Fast, Darcy & Kravetz, Jonathan. The Missing Cub. 2007. 240p. per. 14.99 *(978-1-60477-277-7(8))* Xulon Pr., Inc.

Feldmann, Doug. Miracle Collapse: The 1969 Chicago Cubs. 2009. (ENG., Illus.). 304p. pap. 17.95 *(978-0-8032-2637-1(3)*, Bison Bks.) Univ. of Nebraska Pr.

Freedman, Lew. Chicago Cubs: Memorable Stories of Cubs Baseball. 2007. (Game of My Life Ser.). (Illus.). 244p. 24.95 *(978-1-59670-173-1(0))* Sports Publishing, LLC.

Fromm, Chris. Greatest Moments in Cubs History. 2010. 110p. pap. 12.99 *(978-0-557-68132-7(4))* Lulu Enterprises Inc.

Gordon, Dan, ed. Your Brain on Cubs: Inside the Heads of Players & Fans. 2008. (Illus.). 150p. 19.95 *(978-1-932594-28-7(0))* Dana Pr., The.

Greenfield, Jimmy. 100 Things Cubs Fans Should Know & Do Before They Die. 2012. (100 Things... Fans Should Know Ser.). (ENG.). 256p. pap. 14.95 ***(978-1-60078-662-4(6))*** Triumph Bks.

Hanley, John & DeLuca, Chris. Classic Cubs: A Tribute to the Men & Magic of Wrigley Field. 2008. (ENG., Illus.). 186p. 24.95 *(978-1-58182-637-1(0))* Turner Publishing Co.

Jacover, Jerry. Merkle's Curse: Why the Chicago Cubs Have Not Won a World Series Since 1908. 2008. 386p. pap. 19.99 *(978-1-60462-935-4(5))* Tate Publishing & Enterprises, LLC.

Jenkins, Fergie & Freedman, Lew. Fergie: My Life from the Cubs to Cooperstown. 2009. (ENG.). 224p. 24.95 *(978-1-60078-171-1(3))* Triumph Bks.

Johnson, Steve. Chicago Cubs Yesterday & Today. 2008. (ENG., Illus.). 144p. 26.95 *(978-0-7603-3246-7(0)*, 0760332460, MVP Bks.) MBI Publishing Co. LLC.

Lechner, Tammy. The Chicago Cubs: Our Team, Our Dream: A Cubs Fan's Journey into Baseball's Greatest Romance. 2007. (ENG., Illus.). 206p. 27.95 *(978-1-60078-070-7(9))* Triumph Bks.

Logan, Bob & Cava, Pete. Amazing Tales from the Chicago Cubs Dugout: A Collection of the Greatest Cubs Stories Ever Told. 2012. (Tales from the Team Ser.). (ENG., Illus.). 462p. 24.95 ***(978-1-61321-022-2(1)**, 613022)* Skyhorse Publishing Co., Inc.

Matthews, George R. When the Cubs Won It All: The 1908 Championship Season. 2009. (ENG., Illus.). 234p. pap. 29.95 *(978-0-7864-3495-4(3))* McFarland & Co., Inc. Pubs.

McArdle, Jim. Living the Dream: An Inside Account of the 2008 Cubs Season. 2009. (ENG.). 272p. 19.95 *(978-1-60078-158-2(6))* Triumph Bks.

McGrath, Dan & Vanderberg, Bob. 162 - 0: A Cubs Perfect Season. 2011. (162-0: Imagine... Ser.). (ENG.). 288p. pap. 16.95 *(978-1-60078-362-3(7))* Triumph Bks.

Nemec, David & Flatow, Scott. The Ultimate Chicago Cubs Baseball Challenge. 2007. (ENG.). 192p. per. 10.95 *(978-1-58979-327-9(7))* Taylor Trade Publishing.

New York Times Staff, as told by. The New York Times - Greatest Moments in Cubs History. 2007. *(978-1-934653-05-0(5))* RetroGraphics Publishing Inc.

Quigley, Brendan E. Chicago Cubs Crossword Puzzle Book. 2009. (ENG.). 64p. pap. 7.95 *(978-1-60433-034-2(1))* Cider Mill Pr. Bk. Pubs., LLC.

Roberts, Randy & Cunningham, Carson. Before the Curse: The Chicago Cubs' Glory Years, 1870-1945. 2011. (ENG., Illus.). 296p. pap. 21.95 ***(978-0-252-07816-3(0))*** Univ. of Illinois Pr.

Robinson, Guy. Do You Know the Chicago Cubs? Test Your Expertise with These Fastball Questions (and a Few Curves) about Your Favorite Team's Hurlers, Sluggers, Stats & Most Memorable Moments. 2008. (ENG.). 48p. pap. 5.95 *(978-1-4022-1421-9(9))* Sourcebooks, Inc.

Rogers, Phil. Ernie Banks: Mr. Cub & the Summer Of '69. 2011. (ENG.). 272p. 24.95 *(978-1-60078-519-1(0))* Triumph Bks.

Shea, Stuart, ed. Wrigley Season Ticket 2007: An Annual Guide to Chicago Cubs Baseball. annuals 2007. (Illus.). 112p. per. 14.95 *(978-0-9777436-7-4(5))* Maple Street Press LLC.

Silverman, Matthew, et al. Cubs by the Numbers: A Complete Team History of the Cubbies by Uniform Number. 2009. (ENG., Illus.). 320p. pap. 14.95 *(978-1-60239-372-1(9)*, 239372) Skyhorse Publishing Co., Inc.

Snyder, John. 365 Oddball Days in Chicago Cubs History. 2010. (ENG.). 384p. pap. 14.95 *(978-1-57860-343-5(9))* Clerisy Pr.

Stout, Glenn. The Cubs: The Complete Story of Chicago Cubs Baseball. 2007. (ENG., Illus.). 480p. 40.00 *(978-0-618-59500-6(7))* Houghton Mifflin Harcourt Publishing Co.

Swyers, Holly. Wrigley Regulars: Finding Community in the Bleachers. 2010. (ENG.). 200p. pap. 25.00 *(978-0-252-07740-1(7))*; 65.00 *(978-0-252-03550-0(X))* Univ. of Illinois Pr.

Vitti, Jim. Chicago Cubs: Baseball on Catalina Island. 2010. (Images of Baseball Ser.). (ENG., Illus.). 128p. pap. 21.99 *(978-0-7385-7795-1(2))* Arcadia Publishing.

Vorwald, Bob. Cubs Forever: Memories from the Men Who Lived Them. 2008. (ENG., Illus.). 192p. 29.95 *(978-1-60078-044-8(X))* Triumph Bks.

—What It Means to Be a Cub: The North Side's Greatest Players Talk about Cubs Baseball. 2010. (What It Means to Be Ser.). (ENG.). 320p. 24.95 *(978-1-60078-277-0(9))* Triumph Bks.

Weisberger, Bernard A. When Chicago Ruled Baseball: The Cubs-White Sox World Series of 1906. 2007. (ENG., Illus.). 240p. per. 14.95 *(978-0-06-059237-0(0)*, William Morrow Paperbacks) HarperCollins Pubs.

Williams, Billy & Mitchell, Fred. Billy Williams: My Sweet-Swinging Lifetime with the Cubs. 2008. (ENG., Illus.). 256p. 24.95 *(978-1-60078-050-9(4))* Triumph Bks.

Wolfe, R. Ron Santo: A Perfect 10. 2011. 264p. 24.95 ***(978-0-9846278-2-0(0))*** Lone Wolfe Pr.

Wood, Gerald C. & Hazucha, Andrew, eds. Northsiders: Essays on the History & Culture of the Chicago Cubs. 2008. (ENG., Illus.). 229p. pap. 39.95 *(978-0-7864-3623-1(9))* McFarland & Co., Inc. Pubs.

CHICAGO IN LITERATURE

see Chicago (Ill.)—In Literature

CHICAGO-LAMBETH QUADRILATERAL

see Lambeth Quadrilateral

CHICAGO METROPOLITAN AREA (ILL.)

Kozlowski, Phyllis J. The Chicago River Architecture Tour. 2008. 113p. pap. 12.00 *(978-1-893121-33-1(X))* Everything Goes Media, LLC.

Schwieterman, Joseph P. & Mammoser, Alan P. Beyond Burnham: An Illustrated History of Planning for the Chicago Region. Shuler, John A., ed. & afterword by by. 2009. (ENG., Illus.). 232p. pap. 19.95 *(978-0-9823156-1-3(9))* Lake Forest College Pr.

CHICAGO SCHOOL OF ECONOMICS

Blanchard, Kathryn D. The Protestant Ethic or the Spirit of Capitalism: Christians, Freedom, & Free Markets. 2010. 262p. pap. 29.00 *(978-1-60608-659-9(6)*, Cascade Bks.) Wipf & Stock Pubs.

Emmett. The Elgar Companion to the Chicago Law School of Economics. 2010. (Elgar Original Reference Ser.). 360p. 206.00 *(978-1-84064-874-4(0))* Elgar, Edward Publishing, Inc.

Emmett, Ross B. The Elgar Companion to the Chicago School of Economics. 2012. (Elgar Original Reference Ser.). 360p. pap. 55.00 ***(978-1-84980-867-5(8))*** Elgar, Edward Publishing, Inc.

Emmett, Ross B. Frank Knight & the Chicago School in American Economics. Gammon, Sean, ed. 2009. (Routledge Studies in the History of Economics Ser.). (Illus.). X, 166p. 135.00 *(978-0-415-77500-7(0))* Routledge.

Hammond, J. Daniel & Hammond, Claire H., eds. Making Chicago Price Theory: Friedman-Stigler Correspondence 1945-1958. 2006. (Routledge Studies in History of Economics Ser.). (ENG., Illus.). 165p. (C). 150.00 *(978-0-415-70078-8(7)*, RU0787X) Routledge.

Harcourt, Bernard E. The Illusion of Free Markets: Punishment & the Myth of Natural Order. 2011. (Illus.). 336p. 29.95 *(978-0-674-05726-5(0))* Harvard Univ. Pr.

Horn, Rob van, et al, eds. Building Chicago Economics: New Perspectives on the History of America's Most Powerful Economics Program. 2011. (Historical Perspectives on Modern Economics Ser.). (ENG., Illus.). 440p. 110.00 *(978-1-107-01341-4(0))* Cambridge Univ. Pr.

Kenway, Peter. From Keynesianism to Monetarism: The evolution of UK macroeconometric Models. 2011. (Routledge Revivals Ser.). (ENG.). 228p. 115.00 *(978-0-415-61234-0(9))* Routledge.

Kindleberger. Keynesianism vs. Monetarism. 2007. 272p. 39.95 *(978-0-415-43671-7(0))* Routledge.

McKee, Bob. New Monetarism New Edition. 2008. 123p. pap. 20.95 *(978-1-4357-4570-4(1))* Lulu Enterprises Inc.

Mosini, Valeria. Reassessing the Paradigm of Economics. 2011. (Routledge INEM Advances in Economic Methodology Ser.). (ENG., Illus.). 176p. (C). 115.00 *(978-0-415-57511-9(7))* Routledge.

Nell, Edward, ed. Free Market Conservatism: A Critique of Theory & Practice. 2009. (Routledge Revivals Ser.). 264p. 110.00 *(978-0-415-56715-2(7))* Routledge.

—Free Market Conservatism (Routledge Revivals) 2009. 264p. pap. 39.95 *(978-0-415-57047-3(6))* Routledge.

Taylor, C. T. A Macroeconomic Regime for the 21st Century: Towards a New Economic Order. 2011. (ENG., Illus.). 272p. (C). 176.00 *(978-0-415-59897-2(4))*; pap. 47.95 *(978-0-415-59898-9(2))* Routledge.

Van Overtveldt, Johan. The Chicago School: How the University of Chicago Assembled the Thinkers Who Revolutionized Economics & Business. (ENG.). 432p. 2009. 25.00 *(978-1-932841-19-0(9))* 2007. 35.00 *(978-1-932841-14-5(8))* Agate Publishing, Inc.

CHICAGO SCHOOL OF SOCIOLOGY

Salerno, Roger A. Sociology Noir: Studies at the University of Chicago in Loneliness, Marginality & Deviance, 1915-1935. 2007. (ENG., Illus.). 196p. per. 39.95 *(978-0-7864-2990-5(9))* McFarland & Co., Inc. Pubs.

Wilcox, Clifford. Robert Redfield & the Development of American Anthropology. 2006. (ENG., Illus.). 246p. per. 29.50 *(978-0-7391-1777-4(7))* Lexington Bks.

CHICAGO SCHOOL OF THEOLOGY

Peden, Creighton. Life & Thought of Bernard Eugene Meland, American Constructive Theologian, 1899-1993. 2010. 199p. *(978-1-4438-2406-4(2))* Cambridge Scholars Pub.

CHICAGO SOCIOLOGISTS

see Chicago School of Sociology

CHICAGO STRIKE, 1894

see Pullman Strike, 1894

CHICAGO TRIBUNE

Muti, Riccardo. Riccardo Muti: An Autobiography - First the Music, Then the Words. 2011. (ENG., Illus.). 244p. 29.95 *(978-0-8478-3724-3(6))* Rizzoli International Pubns., Inc.

Unger, Rudolph M. The Chicago Tribune News Staff, 1920s-1960s. 120p. reprint ed. pap. 12.00 *(978-0-9710761-0-5(3))* Unger, Rudolph M.

CHICAGO WHITE SOX (BASEBALL TEAM)

Anderson, Wayne. The Chicago Black Sox Trial: A Primary Source Account. 2009. (Great Trials of the Twentieth Century Ser.). 64p. (gr. 5-8). 58.50 *(978-1-61513-213-3(9))* Rosen Publishing Group, Inc., The.

Asinof, Eliot. Eight Men Out. 29.95 *(978-0-8488-1567-7(X))* Amereon LTD.

Brown, Warren. The Chicago White Sox. 2007. (Writing Sports Ser.). (Illus.). 258p. per. 18.00 *(978-0-87338-895-5(X))* Kent State Univ. Pr.

Carney, Gene. Burying the Black Sox: How Baseball's Cover-up of the 1919 World Series Fix Almost Succeeded. 2007. (Illus.). 383p. per. 17.95 *(978-1-59797-108-9(1))* Potomac Bks., Inc.

Felber, Bill. Under Pallor, under Shadow: The 1920 American League Pennant Race That Rattled & Rebuilt Baseball. 2011. (ENG.). 304p. 26.95 *(978-0-8032-3471-0(6))* Univ. of Nebraska Pr.

Fleitz, David L. Shoeless: The Life & Times of Joe Jackson. l.t. alt. ed. 2007. (ENG., Illus.). 455p. per. 39.95 *(978-0-7864-3312-4(4))* McFarland & Co., Inc. Pubs.

Freedman, Lew. Early Wynn, the Go-Go White Sox & the 1959 World Series. 2009. (ENG., Illus.). 223p. pap. 29.95 *(978-0-7864-4442-7(8))* McFarland & Co., Inc. Pubs.

—Game of My Life: White Sox: Memorable Stories of Chicago White Sox Baseball. 2008. (Game of My Life Ser.). (Illus.). 221p. 24.95 *(978-1-59670-291-2(5))* Sports Publishing, LLC.

—White Sox Essential: Everything You Need to Know to Be a Real Fan! 2007. (Essential (Triumph) Ser.). (ENG., Illus.). 208p. 19.95 *(978-1-57243-932-0(7))* Triumph Bks.

Freedman, Lew & Pierce, Billy. "Then Ozzie Said to Harold..." The Best Chicago White Sox Stories Ever Told. 2008. (Best Sports Stories Ever Told Ser.). (ENG., Illus.). 239p. 22.95 *(978-1-60078-063-9(6))* Triumph Bks.

Frommer, Harvey. Shoeless Joe & Ragtime Baseball. 2008. (ENG., Illus.). 264p. pap. 16.95 *(978-0-8032-1862-8(1))*, Bison Bks.) Univ. of Nebraska Pr.

Gonzales, Mark. The Good, the Bad, & the Ugly: Chicago White Sox - Heart Pounding, Jaw Dropping, & Gut-Wrenching Moments from Chicago White Sox Hist. 2009. (Good, the Bad, & the Ugly Ser.). (ENG.). 224p. pap. 14.95 *(978-1-60078-203-9(5))* Triumph Bks.

Lindberg, Richard C. Total White Sox: The Definitive Encyclopedia of the Chicago White Sox. 3rd ed. 2011. (ENG.). 768p. 29.95 *(978-1-60078-404-0(6))* Triumph Bks.

Lynch, Michael T. It Ain't So: A Might-Have-Been History of the White Sox in 1919 & Beyond. 2009. (ENG., Illus.). 365p. pap. 39.95 *(978-0-7864-4189-1(5))* McFarland & Co., Inc. Pubs.

MacRae, Sloan. The Chicago White Sox. 2012. (Illus.). 24p. (J). 49.50 *(978-1-4488-5156-0(4))*; pap. 8.25 *(978-1-4488-5155-3(6))*; lib. bdg. 21.25 *(978-1-4488-5011-2(8))* Rosen Publishing Group, Inc., The.

Margalus, Jim. White Sox Outsider 2010. 2010. 246p. pap. 19.95 *(978-0-557-33749-1(6))* Lulu Enterprises Inc.

Margalus, Jim. White Sox Outsider 2011. 2011. 236p. pap. 19.95 ***(978-1-257-02434-6(5))*** Lulu Enterprises Inc.

Roeper, Richard. Sox & the City: A Fan's Love Affair with the White Sox from the Heartbreak of '67 to the Wizards of Oz. (ENG., Illus.). 240p. 2007. per. 14.95 *(978-1-55652-679-4(2))* 2006. 19.95 *(978-1-55652-650-3(4))* Chicago Review Pr., Inc.

Smiles, Jack. Big Ed Walsh: The Life & Times of a Spitballing Hall of Famer. 2007. (ENG., Illus.). 238p. per. 29.95 *(978-0-7864-3278-3(C))* McFarland & Co., Inc. Pubs.

Sports Publishing LLC Staff. 2006 World Series Champions. 2006. (World Series Champions Ser.). (Illus.). 128p. 19.95 *(978-1-59670-114-4(5))*; pap. 14.95 *(978-1-59670-112-0(9))* Sports Publishing, LLC.

Stinson, Mitchell Conrad. Edd Roush: A Biography of the Cincinnati Reds Star. 2010. (ENG., Illus.). 256p. pap. 29.95 *(978-0-7864-4407-6(X))* McFarland & Co., Inc. Pubs.

Vorwald, Bob. What It Means to Be a White Sox: The South Side's Greatest Players Talk about White Sox Baseball. 2010. (What It Means to Be Ser.). (ENG.). 336p. 24.95 *(978-1-60078-278-7(7))* Triumph Bks.

Weisberger, Bernard A. When Chicago Ruled Baseball: The Cubs-White Sox World Series of 1906. 2007. (ENG., Illus.). 240p. per. 14.95 *(978-0-06-059237-0(0)*, William Morrow Paperbacks) HarperCollins Pubs.

Zminda, Don, et al, eds. Go-Go to Glory: The 1959 Chicago White Sox. 2009. (Illus.). 247p. pap. 19.95 *(978-0-87946-386-1(4))* ACTA Pubns.

CHICAGO WORLD'S FAIR (1893: CHICAGO, ILL.)

see World's Columbian Exposition (1893: Chicago, Ill.)

CHICANAS

see Mexican American Women

CHICANERY

see Deception

CHICANOS

see Mexican Americans

CHICHEN ITZA SITE (MEXICO)

Chichen Itza Ciudad Sagrada. (SPA.). 13.95 *(978-84-345-2783-7(2))* SM Ediciones ESP. Dist: AIMS International Bks., Inc.

Kowalski, Jeff Karl, et al. Twin Tollans: Chichén Itzá, Tula, & the Epiclassic to Early Postclassic Mesoamerican World. Kristan-Graham, Cynthia, ed. 2nd rev. ed. 2011. (Dumbarton Oaks Pre-Columbian Symposia & Colloquia Ser.). (ENG., Illus.). 432p. pap. 50.00 *(978-0-88402-372-2(9))* Dumbarton Oaks.

Morris, Earl H., et al. The Temple of the Warriors at Chichen Itza, Yucatan, 2 vols., Set. (Carnegie Institution of Washington Publications: No. 406). reprint ed. 104.50 *(978-0-404-16280-1(0))* AMS Pr., Inc.

Ruppert, Karl. Chichen Itza: Architectural Notes & Plans. (Carnegie Institution of Washington Publications: No. 595). reprint ed. 42.50 *(978-0-404-16279-5(7))* AMS Pr., Inc.

Svadihatra, Julia. The Priest: Ancient Priest of Chichen Itza Reincarnated. 2009. 188p. pap. 16.95 *(978-1-4401-4117-1(7))* iUniverse, Inc.

—The Re-Birth of an Atlantean Queen. 2009. 444p. pap. 27.95 *(978-1-4401-4115-7(0))* iUniverse, Inc.

—Who Is Chak Mol? 2009. 64p. pap. 9.95 *(978-1-4401-4112-6(6))* iUniverse, Inc.

CHICHESTER, FRANCIS CHARLES, SIR, 1901-1972

Chichester, Francis. The Lonely Sea & the Sky. 2012. (ENG., Illus.). 432p. pap. 15.95 ***(978-1-84953-201-3(X))*** Summerdale Pubs. GBR. Dist: Independent Pubs. Group.

Gelder, Paul & Fisher, Bob. A Legend Sails Again. 2008. (ENG., Illus.). 256p. 44.95 *(978-0-470-72443-9(9)*, Wiley) Wiley, John & Sons, Inc.

CHICKAMAUGA, BATTLE OF, GA., 1863

Addison, Stephen O. Seen the Glory: The Story of the Oldest Person of Our Country 1820-1943. 2006. (Illus.). 80p. per. 9.95 *(978-1-59091-057-3(5))* Eastern National.

Baumgartner, Richard. Blue Lightning: Wilder's Mounted Infantry Brigade in the Battle of Chickamauga. 2nd exp. ed. 2007. (Illus.). 392p. 32.95 *(978-1-885033-35-2(4))* Blue Acorn Pr.

Boynton, Henry V. The Battles of Chickamauga & Chattanooga & the Organizations Engaged. 2010. (ENG.). 34.95 *(978-1-57233-694-0(3))*, Univ. of Tennessee Pr.

Gracie, Archibald. The Truth about Chickamauga. 2007. (ENG.). 492p. per. 38.95 *(978-1-4325-3126-3(3))* Kessinger Publishing, LLC.

Hoobler, James A. Historic Photos of Chickamauga Chattanooga. 2007. (Historic Photos Ser.). (ENG., Illus.). 205p. 39.95 *(978-1-59652-412-5(X))* Turner Publishing Co.

Military Historical Society of Massachusetts Staff. The Campaigns in Kentucky & Tennessee Including the Battle of Chickamauga 1862-1864. 557p. reprint ed. 98.00 *(978-0-7222-8340-0(7))* Library Reprints, Inc.

Powell, David. Failure in the Saddle: Nathan Bedford Forrest, Joe Wheeler, & the Confederate Cavalry in the Chickamauga Campaign. 2010. (Illus.). 408p. 34.95 *(978-1-932714-87-6(1))* Savas Beatie.

—The Maps of Chickamauga: An Atlas of the Chickamauga Campaign, Including the Tullahoma Operations, June 22 - September 23, 1863. 2009. (Illus.). 320p. 39.95 *(978-1-932714-72-2(3))* Savas Beatie.

Smith, Timothy B. A Chickamauga Memorial: The Establishment of America's First Civil War National Military Park. 2009. (ENG.). 43.00 *(978-1-57233-679-7(X))* Univ. of Tennessee Pr.

Tucker, Glenn. Chickamauga: Bloody Battle in the West. 2011. 450p. 56.95 ***(978-1-258-06949-0(0))*** Literary Licensing, LLC.

Turchin, John Basil. Chickamauga: Noted Battles for the Union During the Civil War in the United States of America 1861-1865. 295p. reprint ed. 98.00 *(978-0-7222-8050-8(5))* Library Reprints, Inc.

Wakefield, John F. Battle of Chickamauga. 2008. (Illus.). 67p. pap. *(978-0-943465-40-1(0))* Honors Pr.

Woodworth, Steven E., ed. The Chickamauga Campaign. 2010. (Civil War Campaigns in the Heartland Ser.). (ENG., Illus.). 216p. 24.95 *(978-0-8093-2980-9(8))* Southern Illinois Univ. Pr.

CHICKASAW INDIANS

see Five Civilized Tribes; Indians of North America—Southern States

CHICKEN POX

see Chickenpox

CHICKENPOX

Doerr, Hans Wilhelm & Gross, G. Herpes Zoster. (Monographs in Virology: Vol. 26). (Illus.). ix, 193p. *(978-3-8055-7982-7(9))* Karger, S. AG.

Goldman, Gary S., ed. The Chickenpox Vaccine: A New Epidemic of Disease & Corruption. 2006. (ENG., Illus.). 300p. 25.00 net. *(978-0-9788383-2-4(7))* Medical Veritas International Inc.

Orrin, Mark. The Chickenpox Vaccine: A new epidemic of disease & Corruption. Goldman, Gary, ed. 2006. 300p. per. 14.95 *(978-0-9788383-1-7(9))* Virtualbookworm.com Publishing, Inc.

Powell, Jillian. Chickenpox. 2008. (Feeling Sick? Ser.). (Illus.). 23p. (J). (gr. 1-4). lib. bdg. 27.10 *(978-1-84234-469-9(2))* Cherrytree Pubns., Inc.

CHICKENS

see Poultry

CHICOPEE (MASS.)

Jendrysik, Stephen R. Chicopee in The 1940s. 2007. (Images of America Ser.). (ENG., Illus.). 128p. per. 19.99 *(978-0-7385-5514-0(2))* Arcadia Publishing.

CHIEF EXECUTIVE OFFICERS

Alanne, Artsi. Paid to Perform. 2010. 72p. pap. *(978-3-8383-8896-0(8))* Lambert Academic Publishing.

Amernic, Joel & Craig, Russell. CEO-Speak: The Language of Corporate Leadership. 2007. (ENG.). 256p. (C). per. *(978-0-7735-3320-2(6))* McGill-Queen's Univ. Pr.

Arcand, Jean-Philippe. Entering the Ipo Process - Impacts of Replacing the Firm Founder & Ceo. 2008. 120p. per. *(978-3-8364-3676-2(0))* VDM Verlag Dr. Mueller e.K.

Aspatore Books Staff, compiled by. Achieving Success as a CEO: Leading CEOs on Formulating a Leadership Plan, Identifying Success, & Working with the Management Team (Inside the Minds) 2008. 160p. pap. 65.00 *(978-0-314-98713-6(4))* Aspatore Bks.

—The First Year as the CEO of a Company: Leading CEOs on Understanding the Company Culture, Working with the Management Team, & Developing a Vision for the Company (Inside the Minds) 2008. pap. *(978-0-314-19563-0(7))* Aspatore Bks.

Axelrod, Alan. Gandhi, CEO: 14 Principles to Guide & Inspire Modern Leaders. 2010. (CEO Ser.). (ENG.). 224p. 22.95 *(978-1-4027-5806-5(5))* Sterling Publishing Co., Inc.

—Julius Caesar, CEO: 6 Principles to Guide &Inspire Modern Leaders. 2012. (CEO Ser.). (ENG.). 248p. 22.95 ***(978-1-4027-8484-2(8))*** Sterling Publishing Co., Inc.

—Napoleon, CEO: 6 Principles to Guide & Inspire Modern Leaders. 2011. (CEO Ser.). (ENG.). 288p. 22.95 *(978-1-4027-7906-0(2))* Sterling Publishing Co., Inc.

Axelrod, Alan. Theodore Roosevelt, CEO: 7 Principles to Guide & Inspire Modern Leaders. 2012. (CEO Ser.). (ENG.). 272p. 22.95 ***(978-1-4027-8483-5(X))*** Sterling Publishing Co., Inc.

Axelrod, Nancy R. Chief Executive Succession Planning: Essential Guidance for Boards & CEOs. 2nd ed. 2009. *(978-1-58686-114-8(X))* National Ctr. for Nonprofit Boards.

Bates, Suzanne. Discover Your CEO Brand: Secrets to Embracing & Maximizing Your Unique Value As a Leader. 2011. (ENG., Illus.). 256p. 25.00 ***(978-0-07-176286-1(8))***, 0071762868) McGraw-Hill Cos., The.

Bathula, Hanoku & Singh Gaur, Sanjaya. Board Characteristics & Firm Performance. 2011. 144p. pap. ***(978-3-8433-6307-5(2))*** Lambert Academic Publishing.

Beckwith, A. Lashamda. When You're Happy with You. 2011. 282p. 26.99 ***(978-1-61379-066-3(X))***; pap. 16.99 ***(978-1-61215-597-5(9))*** Xulon Pr., Inc.

Benton, D. A. CEO Material: How to Be a Leader in Any Organization. 2009. (ENG.). 256p. 24.95 *(978-0-07-160545-8(2)*, 0071605452) McGraw-Hill Cos., The.

Bez, Ulrich. Mr. Aston Martin. 2012. (ENG & GER., Illus.). 408p. 110.00 ***(978-3-8327-9542-9(1))*** teNeues Publishing Co.

Bhandarker, Asha & Singh, Pritam. In Search of Change Maestros. 2011. (Response Bks.). (Illus.). 532p. (C). 50.00 *(978-81-321-0586-2(9)*, B05862C) SAGE Pubns., Inc.

Binder, Gordon & Bashe, Philip. Science Lessons: What the Business of Biotech Taught Me about Management. 2008. (ENG., Illus.). 292p. 29.95 *(978-1-59139-861-5(4))* Harvard Business Review Pr.

Black, John R. & Miller, David. The Toyota Way to Healthcare Excellence: Increase Efficiency & Improve Quality with Lean. 2008. 77.00 *(978-1-56793-293-5(2))* Health Administration Pr.

Bragg, Steven M. The Essential Controller: An Introduction to What Every Financial Manager Must Know. 2nd ed. 2012. (Wiley Corporate F&a Ser.: 582). (ENG.). 277p. pap. 60.00 ***(978-1-118-16997-1(2)***, Wiley) Wiley, John & Sons, Inc.

Bragg, Steven M. The New CEO Corporate Leadership Manual: Strategic & Analytical Tools for Growth. 2011. (ENG., Illus.). 344p. 125.00 *(978-0-470-91287-4(1)*, Wiley) Wiley, John & Sons, Inc.

Braksick, Leslie W. & Hillgren, James S. Preparing CEOs for Success. Schroyer, Fred, ed. 2010. 216p. pap. 19.95 *(978-0-692-00790-7(3))* H.J. Heinz Co.

Branson, Douglas M. The Last Male Bastion: Gender & the CEO Suite in America's Public Companies. 2009. (ENG., Illus.). 288p. 110.00 *(978-0-415-87295-9(2))*; 270p. pap. 39.95 *(978-0-415-87296-6(0))* Routledge.

Browne, John. Beyond Business. 2010. (ENG., Illus.). 336p. 35.00 *(978-0-297-85915-4(3))* Orion Publishing Group, Ltd. GBR. Dist: Independent Pubs. Group.

—Beyond Business: An Inspirational Memoir from a Remarkable Leader. 2011. (ENG., Illus.) 344p. 16.95 *(978-0-7538-2835-9(9))* Orion Publishing Group, Ltd. GBR. Dist: Independent Pubs. Group.

Bryant, Adam. Corner Office: Indispensable & Unexpected Lessons from CEOs on How to Lead & Succeed. 2011. (ENG.). 272p. 25.00 *(978-0-8050-9306-3(0)*, Times Bks.) Holt, Henry & Co.

Buchholz, Todd G. Lasting Lessons from the Corner Office: Essential Wisdom from the Twentieth Century's Greatest Entrepreneurs. 2009. (ENG.). 320p. pap. 16.99 *(978-0-06-119763-5(7)*, Harper Paperbacks) HarperCollins Pubs.

—New Ideas from Dead CEOs: Lasting Lessons from the Corner Office. 2007. 320p. 26.95 *(978-0-06-119762-8(9)*, Collins) HarperCollins Pubs.

Carlson, Mim & Donohoe, Margaret. The Executive Director's Guide to Thriving as a Nonprofit Leader. 2nd ed. 2010. (Jossey-Bass Nonprofit Guidebook Ser.: 7). (ENG., Illus.). 352p. pap. 38.00 *(978-0-470-40749-3(2)*, Jossey-Bass) Wiley, John & Sons, Inc.

Carpenter, Jennifer & Yermack, D., eds. Executive Compensation & Shareholder Value: Theory & Evidence. 2010. (New York University Salomon Center Series on Financial Markets & Institutions Ser.). 176p. pap. 139.00 *(978-1-4419-5041-3(9)*, 1441950419) Springer.

Carver, Miriam, et al. Evaluating CEO & Board Performance, Volume 5. 2nd rev. ed. 2009. (J-B Carver Board Governance Ser.: 28). (ENG., Illus.). 40p. pap. 16.00 *(978-0-470-39256-0(8)*, Jossey-Bass) Wiley, John & Sons, Inc.

Casey, Tom, et al. Talent Readiness: The Future Is Now. 2010. (ENG.). 119p. pap. 14.99 *(978-1-59932-221-6(8))* Advantage Media Group.

Chan, Ronald. Behind the Berkshire Hathaway Curtain: Lessons from Warren Buffett's Top Business Leaders. 2010. (ENG., Illus.). 178p. 24.95 *(978-0-470-56062-4(2)*, Wiley) Wiley, John & Sons, Inc.

Changzheng, Zhang, ed. Manipulation Effect of Managerial Discretion on Managerial Compensation: Evidence from Listed Firms in China. 2010. (Management Science - Theory & Applications Ser.). (Illus.). x, 213p. 89.00 *(978-1-60876-460-0(5))* Nova Science Pubs., Inc.

Cheng, Victor. Extreme Revenue Growth: Startup Secrets to Growing Your Sales from $1 Million to $25 Million in Any Industry. 2010. 202p. pap. 16.95 *(978-0-9841835-1-7(5))* Innovation Pr.

Clutterbuck, David. The Talent Wave: Why Succession Planning Fails & What to Do about It. 2012. (ENG.). 256p. pap. 39.95 ***(978-0-7494-5697-9(3))*** Kogan Page, Ltd. GBR. Dist: Ingram Pub. Services.

Conference Board Staff, contrib. by. CEO Challenge 2008: Top 10 Challenges - Financial Crisis Edition. 2008. (Illus.). 10p. pap. *(978-0-8237-0943-4(4))* Conference Board, Inc., The.

Conger. Boardroom Realities: Building Leaders Across Your Board. Conger, Jay A., ed. 2009. (ENG., Illus.). 544p. 55.00 *(978-0-470-39178-5(2)*, Jossey-Bass) Wiley, John & Sons, Inc.

Cross, Stuart. The Ceo's Strategy Handbook. 2011. 212p. pap. 29.95 ***(978-1-906403-66-9(X))*** Global Professional Publishing GBR. Dist: Stylus Publishing, LLC.

D'Arienzo, Bill. By George! Lessons in Leadership from George Washington, CEO. 2010. pap. 10.99 *(978-1-61663-017-1(5))* Tate Publishing & Enterprises, LLC.

De la Vega, Ralph & Brown, Paul B. Obstacles Welcome: How to Turn Adversity into Advantage in Business & in Life, 0 vols. 2010. (Christian Encounters Ser.). (Illus.). 192p. pap. 12.00 *(978-1-59555-109-2(3))* Nelson, Thomas Inc.

Dutta, Soumitra, et al, eds. Innovating at the Top: How Global CEOs Drive Innovation for Growth & Profit. 2008. (ENG.). 256p. 53.00 *(978-0-230-57573-8(0))* Palgrave Macmillan.

Dym, Barry, et al. Managing Leadership Transition for Nonprofits: Passing the Torch to Sustain Organizational Excellence. 2011. (ENG.). 368p. 49.99 *(978-0-13-704765-9(7))* FT Press.

Ericson, Richard N. The New Standards: Methods for Linking Business Performance & Executive Incentive Pay. 2nd ed. 2010. (ENG., Illus.). 336p. 78.95 *(978-0-470-55989-5(6)*, Wiley) Wiley, John & Sons, Inc.

Fifer, Bob & Quick, Gordon. The Enlightened CEO: How to Succeed at the Toughest Job in Business. 2007. iii, 327p. *(978-1-934380-10-9(5))* Franklin Hall Publishing.

Flynn, Outi. Meeting, & Exceeding Expectations: A Guide to Better Nonprofit Board Meetings. 2nd ed. 2009. *(978-1-58686-115-5(8))* National Ctr. for Nonprofit Boards.

Frisch, Bob. Who's in the Room? How Great Leaders Structure & Manage the Teams Around Them. 2012. (ENG.). 208p. 29.95 ***(978-1-118-06787-1(8)***, Jossey-Bass) Wiley, John & Sons, Inc.

Gardner, Karen, ed. Better CEO-Board Relations: Practical Advice for a Successful Partnership. 2007. 147p. per. *(978-1-55648-341-7(4)*, 196901, AHA Pr.) Health Forum.

—The Excellent Board II: New, Practical Solutions for Health Care Trustees & Ceos. 2nd ed. 2007. (Illus.). 434p. per. 95.00 *(978-1-55648-350-9(3)*, AHA Pr.) Health Forum.

Giarratana, Neil. CEO Priorities: Everything You Need to Know to Lead & Succeed. 2010. E-Book 15.99 *(978-1-60163-723-9(3))* Career Pr., Inc.

—CEO Priorities: Master the Art of Surviving at the Top. 2010. (ENG.). 1p. pap. 15.99 *(978-1-60163-126-8(X))* Career Pr., Inc.

Gillespie, John & Zweig, David. Money for Nothing: How CEOs & Boards Are Bankrupting America. 2011. (ENG.). 336p. pap. 15.00 *(978-1-4165-9770-4(0)*, Free Pr.) Free Pr.

—Money for Nothing: How CEOs & Boards Enrich Themselves While Bankrupting America. 2010. (ENG. Illus.). 320p. 27.00 *(978-1-4165-5993-1(0)*, Free Pr.) Free Pr.

Goldsmith, Marshall. Succession: Are You Ready? 2009. (Memo to the CEO: Ser.). (ENG., Illus.). 130p. 18.00 *(978-1-4221-1823-8(1))* Harvard Business Review Pr.

Gottschalk, Petter. Cio & Corporate Strategic Management: Changing Role of CIO to CEO. 2006. (Illus.). 296p. 94.95 *(978-1-59904-423-1(4))* IGI Global.

C

Griffiths, Tony. Corporate Catalyst: A Chronicle of the (Mis)Management of Canadian Business from a Veteran Insider. 2012. (ENG.). 320p. 36.95 ***(978-1-118-15286-7(7)***, Wiley) Wiley, John & Sons, Inc.

Hack, Richard. The Rise & Fall of Michael Eisner. 2006. 288p. 27.95 *(978-1-59777-535-9(5))* Phoenix Bks., Inc.

Hari, P. K. Excel for the CEO. 2006. (Excel for Professionals Ser.). (ENG., Illus.). 349p. pap. 24.95 *(978-1-932802-17-7(7))* Tickling Keys, Inc.

Hay Group Staff. China's CEO Challeng: An Inside Story of Leadership at the Crossroads. 2008. 256p. pap. 19.95 *(978-0-470-82269-2(4))* Wiley, John & Sons, Inc.

Hindery, Leo. It Takes a CEO: It's Time to Lead with Integrity. 2010. (ENG.). 208p. pap. 14.99 *(978-0-7432-6986-5(1)*, Free Pr.) Free Pr.

Hoflich, Peter & Asian Banker Staff. Asia's Banking CEOs: The Future of Finance in the Asia. 2008. (ENG., Illus.). 250p. 42.00 *(978-0-470-82359-0(3)*, Wiley) Wiley, John & Sons, Inc.

Isaacson, Walter. Steve Jobs. 2011. (Vintage Espanol Ser.). (SPA., Illus.). 752p. pap. 17.95 ***(978-0-307-95028-4(X)***, Vintage) Knopf Doubleday Publishing Group.

—Steve Jobs. 2011. (SPA.). pap. ***(978-1-4516-4854-6(5))***; (ENG., Illus.). 656p. 35.00 ***(978-1-4516-4853-9(7))*** Simon & Schuster.

—Steve Jobs. l.t. ed. 2011. (ENG.). 630p. 35.99 ***(978-1-4104-4522-3(4))*** Thorndike Pr.

Isdell, Neville & Beasley, David. Inside Coca Cola. 2011. (Illus.). 288p. pap. 16.00 ***(978-1-250-00498-7(5))*** St. Martin's Pr.

Jensen, Michael C., et al. CEO Pay & What to Do about It: Restoring Integrity to Both Executive Compensation & Capital-Market Relations. 2013. (ENG., Illus.). 256p. 35.00 *(978-1-4221-0117-9(7))* Harvard Business Review Pr.

Kase, Kimio & Jacopin, Tanguy. CEOs As Leaders & Strategy Designers: Explaining the Success of Spanish Banks. 2008. (Palgrave Macmillan Studies in Banking & Financial Institutions Ser.). (ENG., Illus.). 288p. 100.00 *(978-0-230-54295-2(6))* Palgrave Macmillan.

Kay, Ira & Van Putten, Steve. Myths & Realities of Executive Pay. 2007. (ENG., Illus.). 278p. 29.00 *(978-0-521-87195-2(6))* Cambridge Univ. Pr.

Kelly, Kevin. Top Jobs: How They Are Different & What You Need to Succeed. 2009. (ENG.). 208p. 22.99 *(978-0-13-712781-8(2))* FT Press.

Kenemore, Scott. Z. E. O. How to Get A(Head) in Business. 2009. (Zen of Zombie Ser.). (ENG., Illus.). 272p. pap. 12.95 *(978-1-60239-648-7(5)*, 239648) Skyhorse Publishing Co., Inc.

Khoury, Sam. Business Is Hard-Failure Is Optional: Ceos' Choices & Challenges. 2009. 112p. 16.95 *(978-0-9802377-1-9(8))* For-CEOs-Only.

Kissman, Katha. Trouble at the Top: The Nonprofit Board's Guide to Managing an Imperfect Chief Executive. 2009. *(978-1-58686-112-4(3))* National Ctr. for Nonprofit Boards.

Klepper, William M. The CEO's Boss: Tough Love in the Board Room. 2010. (Columbia Business School Publishing Ser.). E-Book 23.99 *(978-0-231-52063-8(8))* Columbia Univ. Pr.

—The CEO's Boss: Tough Love in the Boardroom. 2010. (Columbia Business School Publishing Ser.). (ENG., Illus.). 192p. (gr. 17). 29.95 *(978-0-231-14988-4(3))* Columbia Univ. Pr.

Kuta, Mark, Jr. Think Like A CEO: Sell to Any Company in Any Industry... BETTER & FASTER than a Harvard MBA. 2007. (Illus.). 304p. 39.95 *(978-0-9713031-2-6(6))* Flow Publishing.

Lagakis, Vasiliki. Female Chief Executive Officers. 2009. 204p. pap. *(978-3-639-12196-4(1))* VDM Verlag Dr. Mueller e.K.

Leach, Steve. Managing in a Political World: The Life Cycle of Local Authority Chief Executives. 2010. (ENG., Illus.). 176p. 100.00 *(978-0-230-24562-4(5))* Palgrave Macmillan.

Lencioni, Patrick M. The Five Temptations of a CEO: A Leadership Fabel. 10th anniv. ed. 2008. (J-B Lencioni Ser.: 32). (ENG., Illus.). 160p. 24.95 *(978-0-470-26758-5(5)*, Jossey-Bass) Wiley, John & Sons, Inc.

Liew, Mun Leong. Building People Vol. 2: Sunday Emails from a CEO. 2010. (ENG., Illus.). 200p. pap. 17.95 *(978-0-470-82786-4(6)*, Wiley) Wiley, John & Sons, Inc.

Liew, Mun Leong. Building People: Sunday Emails from a Ceo, Volume 2 (Bilingual) 2011. (ENG & CHI.). 512p. pap. 22.95 ***(978-0-470-82790-1(4)***, Wiley) Wiley, John & Sons, Inc.

Long, Weldon. The Upside of Fear. 2009. 199p. 19.95 ***(978-1-60832-000-4(6)***, Greenleaf Book Group Pr.) Greenleaf Book Group.

Lowe, Janet. Jack Welch Speaks: Wit & Wisdom from the World's Greatest Business Leader. 2nd rev. ed. 2007. (ENG.). 304p. 19.95 *(978-0-470-15261-4(3)*, Wiley) Wiley, John & Sons, Inc.

Marshall, Paula. Sometimes Being a CEO Looks Pretty Tough... 2009. (Illus.). 103p. pap. 11.99 *(978-0-88144-352-3(2))* Yorkshire Publishing Group.

Marwood, Maurice E. Professional Nomad. 2009. 274p. pap. 25.00 *(978-1-4251-8035-5(3))* Trafford Publishing.

Mattson, David & Parinello, Anthony. Five Minutes with Vito: Making the Most of Your Selling Time with the Very Important Top Officer. 2008. 224p. pap. 14.95 *(978-0-9786078-3-8(X))* Pegasus Media World.

Mcafee, Michael. Ceos As Volunteer Leaders. 2008. 196p. pap. *(978-3-639-07487-1(4))* VDM Verlag Dr. Mueller e.K.

McCann, Peter. Turnarounds: Brains, Guts & Stamina. 2009. 184p. pap. 22.00 *(978-1-4251-9099-6(5))* Trafford Publishing.

McFarland, Linda, et al. Sitting on a File Cabinet, Naked, with a Gun: True Stories of Silicon Valley CEO Assistants. 2009. 140p. 21.49 *(978-1-4490-3158-9(7))*; pap. 14.99 *(978-1-4490-3159-6(5))* AuthorHouse.

McGinn, Peter. Partnership of Equals: Practical Strategies for Healthcare CEO's & their Boards. 2009. (ENG.). 73p. 77.00 *(978-1-56793-311-6(4))* Health Administration Pr.

McLaughlin, Thomas A. & Backlund, Addie Nelson. Moving Beyond Founder's Syndrome to Nonprofit Success. 2008. *(978-1-58686-096-7(8))* National Ctr. for Nonprofit Boards.

Meyer, Irma. The Significance of the Ceo's Internal Communication Programme. 2009. 192p. pap. *(978-3-639-16638-5(8))* VDM Verlag Dr. Mueller e.K.

Miller, Norman. Beyond the Norm, 0 vols. 2009. 224p. pap. 12.99 *(978-1-59555-331-7(2))* Nelson, Thomas Inc.

Monks, Robert A. G. Corpocracy: How CEOs & the Business Roundtable Hijacked the World's Greatest Wealth Machine - And How to Get It Back. 2007. (ENG.). 272p. 29.95 *(978-0-470-14509-8(9)*, Wiley) Wiley, John & Sons, Inc.

Murray, Alan. Revolt in the Boardroom: The New Rules of Power in Corporate America. 2008. (ENG.). 272p. pap. 14.95 *(978-0-06-088248-8(4)*, Collins) HarperCollins Pubs.

Murray, Kevin. The Language of Leaders: How Top Ceos Communicate to Inspire, Influence & Achieve Results. 2012. (ENG., Illus.). 240p. 34.95 *(978-0-7494-6396-0(1))* Kogan Page, Ltd. GBR. Dist: Ingram Pub. Services.

Myatt, Mike. Leadership Matters the Ceo Survival Manual: What it takes to reach the c-suite & stay There. 2007. 212p. 29.95 *(978-1-4327-1773-5(1))* Outskirts Pr., Inc.

Nolop, Bruce. The Essential CFO: A Corporate Finance Playbook. 2012. (Wiley Corporate F&a Ser.: 585). (ENG.). 349p. pap. 60.00 ***(978-1-118-17304-6(X)***, Wiley) Wiley, John & Sons, Inc.

Northup, Tom. Five Hidden Mistakes CEOs Make: How to Unlock the Secrets that Drive Growth & Profitability. 2008. 132p. pap. 19.99 *(978-0-9752671-5-8(9))* Solutions Pr.

Oliver, Jamie & Goodwin, Tony. How They Blew It: The CEO's & Entrepreneurs Behind Some of the World's Most Catastrophic Business Failures. 2010. (ENG.). 224p. pap. 19.95 *(978-0-7494-6065-5(2))* Kogan Page, Ltd. GBR. Dist: Ingram Pub. Services.

Parinello, Anthony. Secrets of VITO: Think & Sell Like a CEO. 2006. (ENG.). 288p. per. 17.95 *(978-1-59918-033-5(2)*, 1599180332) Entrepreneur Pr. dba Entrepreneur Media, Inc.

Phillips, Jack J. & Phillips, Jack. Measuring for Success. 2009. (ENG., Illus.). 296p. pap. 38.95 *(978-1-56286-588-7(9))* American Society for Training & Development.

Porrini, Patrizia, et al. Above the Board: How Ethical CEOs Create Honest Corporations. 2008. (ENG.). 240p. 27.95 *(978-0-07-149631-5(9)*, 0071496319) McGraw-Hill Cos., The.

Preston, Donald. I Love You One Thousand Houses: A Memoir. 2009. 204p. pap. 17.95 *(978-1-4401-4384-7(6))* iUniverse, Inc.

Prybil, Lawrence. Governance in High-Performing Community Health Systems: A Report on Trustee & CEO Views. 2009. 58p. pap. 10.00 *(978-0-9815532-1-4(4))* Thornton, Grant LLP.

Redmond, Andrea & Crisafulli, Patricia B. Comebacks: Powerful Lessons from Leaders Who Endured Setbacks & Recaptured Success on Their Terms. 2010. (ENG.). 256p. 27.95 *(978-0-470-58375-3(4)*, Jossey-Bass) Wiley, John & Sons, Inc.

ReedLogic, ed. Management Strategies for CEOs of VC Backed Companies. 2007. cd-rom 999.95 *(978-1-59701-202-7(5))* Aspatore Bks.

Renteria, Robert J. Desde el Barrio Al Exito. 2009. (ENG.). 112p. pap. 14.95 *(978-0-9822206-5-8(0))* Writer of the Round Table Pr.

Ribas, Vinny. Ceo Secrets. 2007. 216p. per. 17.95 *(978-1-933912-27-1(8))* Westview Publishing Co., Inc.

Rosen, Scott D. Wisdom at the Top: Lessons on Leadership & Life from 35 CEOs. 2010. 188p. 29.95 *(978-1-4520-3512-3(1))*; pap. 19.95 *(978-1-4520-3513-0(X))* AuthorHouse.

Sayles, Leonard R. & Smith, Cynthia J. The Rise of the Rogue Executive: How Good Companies Go Bad & How to Stop the Destruction. 2011. (ENG.). 288p. pap. 32.99 ***(978-0-13-290616-6(3))*** FT Press.

Spencer, Signe, et al. The Indian CEO: A Portrait of Excellence. 2007. (Response Bks.). (Illus.). 264p. (C). per. 34.00 *(978-0-7619-3362-5(X)*, B3362XP) SAGE Pubns., Inc.

Tappin, Steve & Cave, Andrew. The New Secrets of CEOs: 200 Global Chief Executives on Leading. 2010. (ENG.). 230p. pap. 19.95 *(978-1-85788-543-9(0))* Ebsco Publishing.

Tebbe, Don. Chief Executive Transitions: How to Hire & Support a Nonprofit CEO. 2008. viii, 113p. pap. *(978-1-58686-086-8(0))* National Ctr. for Nonprofit Boards.

Thomas, Mark, et al. The Complete CEO: The Executive's Guide to Consistent Peak Performance. 2006. (ENG., Illus.). 260p. per. 29.95 *(978-1-84112-728-6(0)*, Capstone) Wiley, John & Sons, Inc.

Urseth, William. Death Spiral: The Collapse of Cinar, Norshield & Mount Real. 2009. (ENG., Illus.). 288p. 27.95 *(978-1-55022-844-1(7))* ECW Pr. CAN. Dist: Independent Pubs. Group.

Vogel, Brian H. & Quatt, Charles W. Nonprofit Executive Compensation: Planning, Performance, & Pay. 2nd ed. 2009. *(978-1-58686-117-9(4))* National Ctr. for Nonprofit Boards.

Waller, Graham, et al. The CIO Edge: Seven Leadership Skills You Need to Drive Results. 2010. (ENG., Illus.). 240p. 29.95 *(978-1-4221-6637-6(6))* Harvard Business Review Pr.

Weil, Steven E. Ask Papa Jack: Wisdom from the World's Oldest CEO. 2009. (ENG.). 15.95 *(978-1-55566-428-2(8))* Johnson Bks.

Wells, George D. & Padberg, Nancy Shonka. The American Dream in A Kilt: CEO Shares Secrets on Leadership, Life & Laughter. 2006. 21.95 *(978-1-59594-076-6(6)*, Wingspan Pr.) WingSpan Publishing.

Williams, Sherill K. & McGinnis, Kathleen A. Getting the Best from Your Board: An Executive's Guide to a Successful Partnership. 2006. x, 63p. pap. *(978-1-58686-091-2(7))* National Ctr. for Nonprofit Boards.

Williams, Sherill K., et al. Building the Governance Partnership: The Chief Executive's Guide to Getting the Best from the Board. 2011. *(978-1-58686-124-7(7))* National Ctr. for Nonprofit Boards.

Wolfred, Timothy. Managing Executive Transitions: A Guide for Nonprofits. 2009. (ENG.). 165p. pap. 29.95 *(978-0-940069-57-2(1)*, Fieldstone Alliance) Turner Publishing Co.

WorldatWork, ed. & illus. Executive Compensation: A Collection of Articles from WorldatWork. 2010. (ENG.). 288p. pap. 39.95 *(978-1-57963-317-2(X))* WorldatWork.

Yaverbaum, Eric. Leadership Secrets of the World's Most Successful CEDs. 2006. 275p. reprint ed. 22.00 *(978-1-4223-5313-4(3))* DIANE Publishing Co.

Zimmerman, Karen. The Psychic Next Door: Ordinary People with Extraordinary Powers. 2011. 138p. pap. 8.95 ***(978-1-60076-316-8(2))*** StoneGarden.net Publishing.

Zweigenhaft, Richard & Domhoff, G. William. The New CEOs: Women, African American, Latino, & Asian American Leaders of Fortune 500 Companies. 2011. (ENG., Illus.). 216p. 37.95 *(978-1-4422-0765-3(5))* Rowman & Littlefield Publishers, Inc.

CHIEF JUSTICES

see Judges

CHIEFDOMS

Boada Rivas, Ana María. The Evolution of Social Hierarchy in a Muisca Chiefdom of the Northern Andes of Colombia /la Evolucion de Jerarquia Social en un Cacicazgo Muisca de Los Andes Septentrionales de Colombia. 2007. (University of Pittsburgh Memoirs in Latin American Archaeology Ser.). (SPA & ENG., Illus.). 272p. pap. 38.00 *(978-1-877812-83-5(6))* Univ. of Pittsburgh Ctr. for Comparative Archaeology.

Buur, Lars & Kyed, Helene Maria. State Recognition & Democratization in Sub-Saharan Africa: A New Dawn for Traditional Authorities? 2007. (Governance, Security & Development Ser.). (ENG.). 256p. 95.00 *(978-0-230-60033-1(6))* Palgrave Macmillan.

Carton, Benedict, et al, eds. Zulu Identities: Being Zulu, Past & Present. 2009. (Columbia/Hurst Ser.). (ENG.). 688p. (gr. 17). pap. 34.50 *(978-0-231-70059-7(8))* Columbia Univ. Pr.

Chiloane, Lesley. Compromised Democracy. 2010. 186p. pap. 19.99 *(978-1-4535-3991-0(3))* Xlibris Corp.

Christie, Jessica Joyce & Sarro, Patricia Joan, eds. Palaces & Power in the Americas: From Peru to the Northwest Coast. 2010. (ENG., Illus.). 432p. pap. 35.00 *(978-0-292-72599-7(X))* Univ. of Texas Pr.

Cuellar, Andrea M. The Quijos Chiefdoms: Social Change & Agriculture in the Eastern Andes of Ecuador = Los Cacicazgos Quijos: Cambio Social y Agricultura en los Andes Orientales del Ecuador. 2009. (ENG & SPA., Illus.). 206p. pap. *(978-1-877812-87-3(0))* Univ. of Pittsburgh Ctr. for Comparative Archaeology.

Drennan, Robert D., ed. Prehispanic Chiefdoms in the Valle de la Pata, Volume 5: Regional Settlement Patterns = Cacicazgos prehispanicos del Valle de la Plata, Tomo 5: Patrones de asentamiento Regionales, Vol. 5. 2006. (University of Pittsburgh Memoirs in Latin American Archaeology Ser.: No. 16). (SPA & ENG., Illus.). 236p. pap. 36.00 *(978-1-877812-82-8(X))* Univ. of Pittsburgh Ctr. for Comparative Archaeology.

Fokwang, Jude. Mediating Legitimacy: Chieftaincy & Democratisation in Two African Chiefdoms. 2009. 140p. pap. *(978-9956-558-64-3(8))* Langaa Research & Publishing Common Initiative Group CMR. Dist: Michigan State Univ. Pr.

Gibson, D. Blair. From Chiefdom to State in Early Ireland. 2012. (ENG., Illus.). 107p. 99.00 ***(978-1-107-01563-0(4))*** Cambridge Univ. Pr.

Gulbrandsen, Ørnulf. The State & the Social: State Formation in Botswana & Its Precolonial & Colonial Genealogies. 2012. (ENG.). 362p. 120.00 ***(978-0-85745-297-9(5))*** Berghahn Bks., Inc.

Haller, Mikael John. Asiento Viejo & the Development of the Rio Parita Chiefdom, Panama = el Asiento Viejo y el Desarrollo del Cacicazgo del Rio Parita, Panama. 2008. (ENG & SPA., Illus.). 228p. pap. 39.00 *(978-1-877812-86-6(2))* Univ. of Pittsburgh Ctr. for Comparative Archaeology.

Helms, Mary W. Access to Origins: Affines, Ancestors, & Aristocrats. 2010. (ENG., Illus.). 272p. pap. 25.00 *(978-0-292-72374-0(1))* Univ. of Texas Pr.

Jackson, Paula, et al. South African Governance in Review: Anti-Corruption, Local Government, Traditional Leadership. 2010. (ENG.). 64p. pap. 15.95 *(978-0-7969-2278-6(0))* Human Sciences Research Council ZAF. Dist: Independent Pubs. Group.

Kirch, Patrick Vinton. How Chiefs Became Kings: Divine Kingship & the Rise of Archaic States in Ancient Hawai'i. 2010. (ENG., Illus.). 288p. 39.95 *(978-0-520-26725-1(7))* Univ. of California Pr.

Knight, Vernon James, Jr. & Steponaitis, Vincas P., eds. Archaeology of the Moundville Chiefdom. 2nd rev. ed. 2007. (Illus.). 226p. per. 29.95 *(978-0-8173-5421-3(2))* Univ. of Alabama Pr.

Merry, Sally Engle & Brenneis, Donald Lawrence. Law & Empire in the Pacific: Fiji & Hawaii. (Advanced Seminar Ser.). 314p. pap. 19.95 *(978-1-930618-25-1(5))* School for Advanced Research Pr./SAR Pr.

Pauketat, Timothy R. Chiefdoms & Other Archaeological Delusions. Pauketat, Timothy R., ed. 2007. (Issues in Eastern Woodlands Archaeology Ser.). (ENG., Illus.). 270p. 75.00 *(978-0-7591-0828-8(5))*; pap. 29.95 *(978-0-7591-0829-5(3))* AltaMira Pr.

Petersen, Glenn. Traditional Micronesian Societies: Adaptation, Integration, & Political Organization. 2009. (Illus.). 328p. 42.00 *(978-0-8248-3248-3(5))* Univ. of Hawaii Pr.

Sharma, Keshav. Reinventing African Chieftaincy in the Age of AIDS, Gender, Governance, & Development. Ray, Donald Iain & Quinlan, Tim, eds. 2011. (Illus.). 594p. pap. 44.95 *(978-1-55238-498-5(5))* Univ. of Calgary Pr. CAN. Dist: Michigan State Univ. Pr.

Ubink, Janine. Traditional Authorities in Africa: Resurgence in an Era of Democratisation. 2008. (Law, Governance, & Development Ser.). 39p. pap. *(978-90-8728-052-9(1)*, Leiden Univ. Pr.) Amsterdam Univ. Pr.

Vaughan, Olufemi. Nigerian Chiefs: Traditional Power in Modern Politics, 1890s-1990s. 2006. (Rochester Studies in African History & the Diaspora Ser.: Volume 7). (Illus.). 310p. per. 34.95 *(978-1-58046-249-5(9))* Univ. of Rochester Pr.

Williams, J. Michael & Herbst, Jeffrey. Chieftaincy, the State, & Democracy: Political Legitimacy in Post-Apartheid South Africa. 2009. (ENG.). 300p. 65.00 *(978-0-253-35418-1(8)*, 0253354188); (Illus.). pap. 24.95 *(978-0-253-22155-1(2)*, 0253221552) Indiana Univ. Pr.

Wright, Henry Tutwiler. Early State Formation in Central Madagascar: An Archaeological Survey of Western Avaradrano. 2007. (Illus.). 311p. 38.00 *(978-0-915703-63-0(7))* Univ. of Michigan, Museum of Anthropology, Pubns. Dept.

Zaken, Mordechai. Jewish Subjects & Their Tribal Chieftans in Kurdistan: A Study in Survival. 2007. (Jewish Identities in a Changing World Ser.). (Illus.). 375p. *(978-90-04-16190-0(2))* BRILL.

CHIEFS OF POLICE

see Police Chiefs

CHIHUAHUA (MEXICO)

Arrieta, Yolanda Herrera & Peterson, Paul M. Muhlenbergia (Poaceae) de Chihuahua, Mexico. 2006. (SIDA, Botanical Miscellany Ser.: 29). (SPA.). pap. *(978-1-889878-16-4(2))* Botanical Research Institute of Texas.

Evans, George. Mexican Gold Trail: The Journey of a Forty-Niner. Dumke, Glenn S., ed. 2006. (Huntington Library Classics Ser.). (Illus.). 340p. per. 24.95 *(978-0-87328-222-2(1))* Huntington Library Pr.

Remington, Frederic. Pony Tracks. 2009. 286p. 24.99 *(978-1-110-80967-7(0))*; pap. 18.99 *(978-1-110-80965-3(4))* BiblioBazaar.

—Pony Tracks. 2009. 106p. pap. 14.14 *(978-0-217-86696-5(4))* General Bks. LLC.

—Pony Tracks. 2007. (ENG.). 298p. 43.95 *(978-0-548-26938-1(6))*; 300p. per. 28.95 *(978-1-4326-7388-8(2))* Kessinger Publishing, LLC.

Turpin, Solveig A. & Eling, Herbert H., Jr., eds. Dust, Smoke, & Tracks: Two Accounts of Nineteenth Century Mexican Military Expeditions to Northern Coahuila & Chihuahua. Eling, Noemi Galvan, tr. from SPA. 2009. (Illus.). 194p. pap. 20.00 *(978-0-9707709-7-4(9))* Sul Ross State Univ., Ctr. for Big Bend Studies.

VanPool, Christine S. & VanPool, Todd L. Signs of the Casas Grandes Shamans. 2007. (ENG., Illus.). 192p. 35.00 *(978-0-87480-874-2(X))* Univ. of Utah Pr.

Villaseñor, Victor. Lion Eyes. 2011. (ENG., Illus.). 456p. 27.95 *(978-1-4019-3200-8(2))* Hay Hse., Inc.

CHIHUAHUA (DOG BREED)

Bollinger, Linda C. Chihuahua, 1 vol. 2011. (ENG.). 144p. 15.95 *(978-0-7938-3716-8(2))* TFH Pubns., Inc.

Chipperton, Sue & Dyball, Rennie. A Famous Dog's Life: The Story of Gidget, America's Most Beloved Chihuahua. 2011. (ENG.). 288p. (gr. 12). 15.00 *(978-0-451-23309-7(3)*, N A L Trade) Penguin Group (USA) Inc.

Coile, D. Caroline. The Chihuahua Handbook. 2nd ed. 2010. (Barron's Pet Handbooks Ser.). (ENG., Illus.). 176p. pap. 12.99 *(978-0-7641-4330-4(1))* Barron's Educational Series, Inc.

Dog Fancy Magazine, compiled by. Chihuahua. 2010. (Smart Owner's Guide Ser.). (ENG.). 176p. (gr. 6). 17.95 *(978-1-59378-764-6(2))* Kennel Club Bks.

Dog Fancy Staff, compiled by. Chihuahua. 2010. (Smart Owner's Guide Ser.). (ENG.). 176p. (gr. 6). pap. 15.95 *(978-1-59378-748-6(0))* Kennel Club Bks.

Fernandez, Amy. Chihuahuas. 2009. *(978-0-7641-6968-7(8))*; (ENG., Illus.). 192p. 18.99 *(978-0-7641-9656-0(1))* Barron's Educational Series, Inc.

Gewirtz, Elaine Waldorf. The Chihuahua. 2011. *(978-1-932904-81-9(6))*; 34.95 *(978-1-932904-75-8(1))* Eldorado Ink.

—Chihuahua: Your Happy Healthy Pet. 2nd rev. ed. 2006. (Happy Healthy Pet Ser.: 73). (ENG., Illus.). 144p. 12.99 *(978-0-470-03794-2(6)*, Howell Bk. Hse.) Wiley, John & Sons, Inc.

Landau, Elaine. Chihuahuas Are the Best! 2010. (Best Dogs Ever Ser.). 32p. (J). (gr. 2-4). lib. bdg. 25.26 *(978-1-58013-567-2(6)*, Lerner Pubns.) Lerner Publishing Group.

Leibstein, Mira. Training Your Chihuahua. 2011. (Training Your Dog Ser.). (ENG.). 160p. pap. 12.99 *(978-0-7641-4686-2(6))* Barron's Educational Series, Inc.

Linzy, Jan, et al. Chihuahua Champions, 2005-2007. 2008. (Illus.). 189p. spiral bd. 46.95 *(978-1-55893-239-5(9))* Camino E.E. & Bk. Co.

Miller, Richard. Chihuahuas. 2006. (Animal Planet Pet Care Library). (Illus.). 111p. 11.95 *(978-0-7938-3754-0(5))* TFH Pubns., Inc.

Murray, Jenni. My Boy Butch: The Heart-Warming True Story of a Little Dog Who Made Life Worth Living Again. 2012. (ENG., Illus.). 240p. 12.95 ***(978-0-00-743780-1(3))*** HarperCollins Pubs. Ltd. GBR. Dist: Independent Pubs. Group.

Payne, Susan. The Chihuahua. 2009. (Kennel Club Classics: Ser.). (ENG., Illus.). 200p. 39.95 *(978-1-59378-681-6(6))*; pap. 22.95 *(978-1-59378-691-5(3))* Kennel Club Bks.

Rehm, Diane. Life with Maxie, 1 vol. 2010. (ENG., Illus.). 64p. 12.99 *(978-1-4236-1627-6(8))* Gibbs Smith, Publisher.

Sovey, Melissa. ChiWOWhua! Undersized, Underfoot & over the Top. 2008. (ENG., Illus.). 96p. 14.95 *(978-1-59543-819-5(X))* Willow Creek Pr., Inc.

White, Debra J. Chihuahua, 1 vol. 2010. (DogLife Ser.). (ENG., Illus.). 224p. (J). 19.95 *(978-0-7938-3605-5(0))* TFH Pubns., Inc.

CHIHUAHUA DOGS

see Chihuahua (Dog Breed)

CHIHUAHUA EXPEDITION, 1846-1847

see Doniphan's Expedition, 1846-1847

CHILD, FRANCIS JAMES, 1825-1896

Brown, Mary Ellen. Child's Unfinished Masterpiece: The English & Scottish Popular Ballads. 2011. (ENG., Illus.). 296p. 45.00 *(978-0-252-03594-4(1))* Univ. of Illinois Pr.

CHILD, JULIA, 1912-2004

Barr, Nancy Verde. Backstage with Julia: My Years with Julia Child. 2008. (ENG., Illus.). 285p. pap. 14.95 *(978-0-470-27637-2(1)*, Wiley) Wiley, John & Sons, Inc.

Child, Julia & Prud'homme, Alex. My Life in France. 2007. (ENG., Illus.). 368p. pap. 16.00 *(978-0-307-27769-5(0)*, Anchor) Knopf Doubleday Publishing Group.

—My Life in France. movie tie-in ed. 2009. (ENG.). 432p. mass mkt. 7.99 *(978-0-307-47501-5(8))* Knopf, Alfred A. Inc.

Conant, Jennet. A Covert Affair: When Julia Child & Paul Child in the OSS They Had No Way of Knowing That Their Adventures with the Spy Service Would Lead Them into a World of Intrigue and, Because of one Idealistic but Reckless Colleague, a Terrifying FBI Investigation. 2011. (ENG., Illus.). 416p. pap. 16.00 ***(978-1-4391-6353-5(7))*** Simon & Schuster.

Fitch, Noel Riley. Appetite for Life: The Biography of Julia Child. 2012. (ENG., Illus.). 608p. pap. 18.95 ***(978-0-307-94838-0(2)***, Anchor) Knopf Doubleday Publishing Group.

Polan, Dana. Julia Child's the French Chef. 2011. (Spin Offs Ser.). (ENG., Illus.). 312p. 84.95 *(978-0-8223-4859-7(4))*; pap. 23.95 *(978-0-8223-4872-6(1))* Duke Univ. Pr.

Powell, Julie. Julie & Julia. movie tie-in ed. 2009. (ENG.). 352p. pap. 14.99 *(978-0-316-04427-1(X))* Little Brown & Co.

—Julie & Julia: My Year of Cooking Dangerously. (ENG.). 2006. 336p. per. 14.99 *(978-0-316-01326-0(9)*, Back Bay Bks.) 2009. 400p. mass mkt. 7.99 *(978-0-316-04251-2(X))* Little Brown & Co.

Reardon, Joan. As Always, Julia: The Letters of Julia Child & Avis Devoto. 2012. (ENG., Illus.). 432p. pap. 15.95 ***(978-0-547-57748-7(5)***, Mariner Bks.) Houghton Mifflin Harcourt Trade & Reference Pubs.

Reardon, Joan, ed. As Always, Julia: The Letters of Julia Child & Avis Devoto. 2010. (ENG., Illus.). 432p. 26.00 *(978-0-547-41771-4(3))* Houghton Mifflin Harcourt Trade & Reference Pubs.

Shapiro, Laura. Julia Child: A Life. 2010. audio compact disk 29.95 *(978-1-59316-494-2(7))* Listen & Live Audio, Inc.

—Julia Child: A Life. 2009. (ENG.). 208p. (gr. 12-18). pap. 14.00 *(978-0-14-311644-8(4)*, Penguin (Non-Classics)) Penguin Group (USA) Inc.

Spitz, Bob. Dearie: The Remarkable Life of Julia Child. l.t. ed. 2012. (ENG.). 794p. pap. 29.00 ***(978-0-307-99083-9(4))*** Random Hse. Large Print.

CHILD, MRS. (LYDIA MARIA), 1802-1880

Beach, Seth Curtis. Daughters of the Puritans: A Group of Brief Biographies. 286p. reprint ed. 98.00 *(978-0-7222-8381-3(4))* Library Reprints, Inc.

Child, Lydia Maria. Letters of Lydia Maria Child, with a Biographical Introduction by John G Whittier & an Appendix by Wendell Phillips. 2006. 328p. per. 23.99 *(978-1-4255-3287-1(X))* MPublishing.

Gould, Philip. Covenant & Republic: Historical Romance & the Politics of Puritanism. 2009. (Cambridge Studies in American Literature & Culture Ser.). (ENG.). 292p. pap. 42.00 *(978-0-521-55532-6(9))* Cambridge Univ. Pr.

CHILD, INNER

see Inner Child

CHILD ABUSE

see also Abused Children; Battered Child Syndrome; Child Pornography; Child Sexual Abuse; Children—Crimes Against; Interviewing in Child Abuse; Munchausen Syndrome by Proxy; Psychological Child Abuse; Shaken Baby Syndrome

Abuse: A Quick Reference Guide, 2 vols. Incl. Early Recognition of Child Abuse & Neglect: A Quick Reference Guide. Otterman, Gabriel J. & Elliot, Diana M., eds. (Illus.). 34p. 1996. spiral bd. 9.95 *(978-1-887272-06-3(2))*; Early Recognition of Domestic Violence: A Quick Reference Guide. Robertson, Jennifer L. & Chambliss, Linda R., eds. (Illus.). 40p. 1997. pap. 9.95 *(978-1-887272-09-4(7))*; Early Recognition of Elder Abuse. Weinberg, Andrew D. & Wei, Jeanne Y., eds. 36p. 1995. spiral bd. 9.95 *(978-1-887272-05-6(4))*; *(978-1-887272-07-0(0))* American Medical Publishing Co., Inc.

Achong, Lanakila Michael. Haole Boy: The Adoption of Diversity. 2008. 248p. 29.95 *(978-1-4401-0832-7(3))*; pap. 19.95 *(978-1-4401-0830-3(7))* iUniverse, Inc.

Adams, Marge Zwack. Vowed to Protect. 2006. 264p. per. 16.95 *(978-1-933912-02-8(2))* Westview Publishing Co., Inc.

Alexander, Randell. Child Fatality Review Guide/Atlas Set: An Interdisciplinary Guide & Photographic Reference. 2007. (ENG., Illus.). 832p. 175.00 *(978-1-878060-58-7(9))* STM Learning, Inc.

Alexander, Randell & Case, Mary E. Child Fatality Review Quick-Reference: For Health Care, Social Service, & Law Enforcement Professionals. 2011. (ENG., Illus.). 400p. spiral bd. 55.00 *(978-1-878060-59-4(7))* STM Learning, Inc.

Anderson, Kim M. Enhancing Resilience in Survivors of Family Violence. 2009. 264p. *(978-0-8261-1139-5(4))* Springer.

ANEP, et al. Mapa de ruta en el ámbito escolar para las situaciones de maltrato y abuso sexual que viven niños, niñas y Adolescentes. 2007.Tr. of Roadmap in school environment for situations of child abuse & sexual abuse suffered by children & Adolescents. (SPA.). 60p. per. *(978-92-806-4176-9(X))* United Nations Children's Fund, The (UNICEF).

Armstrong, Valerie Diane. Family Tides. 2008. 68p. pap. 10.49 *(978-1-4343-7238-3(3))* AuthorHouse.

Aronin, Romulo. Your Child's Substance Abuse. rev. ed. 2010. 128p. pap. 22.95 *(978-0-7637-7981-8(4))* Jones & Bartlett Learning, LLC.

Ault, Caroline, et al. For the Love of My Children: The True Story of One Woman's Struggle to Escape a Brutal British Cult. 2010. (ENC.). 288p. 12.95 *(978-0-00-734092-7(3))* HarperCollins Pubs. Ltd. GBR. Dist: Independent Pubs. Group.

Baker, Amy J. L. Adult Children of Parental Alienation: The Ties That Bind Children to Emotionally Abusive Parents. 2006. *(978-0-7658-0351-1(8))* Transaction Pubs.

Baker, Delma. Why Didn't I Listen to My Parents, but You Don't Have to Commit Suicide I Didn't. 2011. 82p. pap. 19.95 ***(978-1-4560-0221-3(X))*** PublishAmerica, Inc.

BarCharts, Inc. Child Abuse/Mandated Reporter Reference Guide. 2009. 4p. 1.57 *(978-1-4232-0149-6(3))* Barcharts, Inc.

Barker, Carole. Crush: VERB 1) to press or squeeze with a force that deforms or Destroys. 2008. 172p. pap. 15.95 *(978-0-595-52225-5(4))* iUniverse, Inc.

Beahn, Danielle. The Dynamics of Child Abuse & Neglect. 2009. 128p. pap. *(978-3-639-20965-5(6))* VDM Verlag Dr. Mueller e.K.

Belvin, Charles. Eve Still Hasn't Learned. 2006. 68p. per. 13.95 *(978-0-9773973-6-5(X))* Cole Publishing.

Black, Latoya. The Tears Behind My Smile. 2011. 120p. 23.99 ***(978-1-4634-0774-2(2))***; pap. 16.99 ***(978-1-4634-0775-9(0))*** AuthorHouse.

Book, Lauren. It's OK to Tell: A Story of Hope & Recovery. 2011. (ENG.). 224p. 19.95 *(978-1-935212-43-0(5))* Easton Studio Pr., LLC.

Bottoms, Bette & Quas, Jodi A., eds. Emerging Directions in Child Maltreatment Research: Perspectives on Theory, Research, Practice, & Policy, Volume 62, Number 4, 2006. 2006. (Journal of Social Issues Ser.: 2). (ENG., Illus.). 228p. pap. 47.95 *(978-1-4051-6723-9(8)*, Wiley-Blackwell) Wiley, John & Sons, Inc.

Bowman, Billye Graham. Abuse Buster: the Second Step: A Spiritual Solution for Healing the Adult Symptoms of Childhood Abuse. 2006. 200p. per. 13.95 *(978-1-59886-429-8(7))* Tate Publishing & Enterprises, LLC.

Bratcher, Sarah. Freed to Tell. 2009. 216p. pap. 15.99 *(978-1-60791-366-5(6))* Xulon Pr., Inc.

Brenner, Norm. Wanker. 2011. 136p. 29.99 ***(978-1-4628-8807-8(0))*** Xlibris Corp.

Bridges, Sanaria B. Through the Eyes of the Innocent: A Diary of Child Abuse. 2010. 80p. pap. 10.95 ***(978-1-4502-3948-6(X))*** iUniverse, Inc.

Brouwer, Thomas P. Parents with Substance Use Disorders & Child Protection Issues. 2011. (Children's Issues, Laws & Programs Ser.). viii, 280p. 195.00 *(978-1-60692-400-6(1))* Nova Science Pubs., Inc.

Brown, Brenda Fewtrell. Lollipops, Bubblegum, Death & Lies: A Young Life Scarred by a Culture of Silence. 2011. (Illus.). 396p. pap. 21.14 *(978-1-4520-5316-5(2))* AuthorHouse.

Brown, Catherine. Laughter Calls Me: A Young Woman's Search for Truth Leads to a Courageous Battle to Save Her Children. 2nd ed. 2007. (ENG., Illus.). 160p. pap. 12.95 *(978-0-9721512-6-9(5))* Lighthouse Trails Publishing Co.

Bryant, Nick. The Franklin Scandal: A Story of Powerbrokers, Child Abuse & Betrayal. (Illus.). 2012. 656p. pap. 19.95 *(978-1-936296-07-1(1))* 2009. (ENG., 672p. 24.95 *(978-0-9777953-5-2(7))* Trine Day.

Burch, Cynthia. You'll See Jesus on My Face. 2011. 144p. pap. 12.95 ***(978-1-60920-014-5(4))*** Ajoyin Publishing, Inc.

Burns, Kate. Child Abuse. 2007. (History of Issues Ser.). (ENG.). 242p. (gr. 10-12). lib. bdg. 39.70 *(978-0-7377-2861-3(2)*, Greenhaven Pr., Inc.) Cengage Gale.

Burns, Lynch. Children's Rights & Child Protection: Critical Times, Critical Issues In Ireland. Burns, Kenneth & Lynch, Deborah, eds. 2012. (ENG., Illus.). 256p. 100.00 ***(978-0-7190-8627-4(2))*** Manchester Univ. Pr. GBR. Dist: Macmillan.

Butler-Derge, Shirley R. Child Abuse & Neglect Prevention Strategies: Milwaukee County, 1 vol. 2010. 196p. pap. 24.95 *(978-1-4489-5996-9(9))* PublishAmerica, Inc.

Caddick, Veronica. Looking Through the Mirror: An Inner Journey to Freedom from Childhood Abuse. 2nd ed. 2009. 135p. pap. *(978-1-906628-05-5(X))* Checkpoint Pr.

Cahn, Dudley D. Family Violence: Communication Processes. 2009. (SUNY series in Communication Studies). 240p. 70.00 *(978-0-7914-9375-5(X))* State Univ. of New York Pr.

Cahn, Dudley D., Jr., ed. Family Violence: Communication Processes. 2010. (SUNY series in Communication Studies). 240p. pap. 24.95 *(978-0-7914-9376-2(8)*, Suny Pr.) State Univ. of New York Pr.

Cain, E. B. One Day, One Life: The Ghost of Child Abuse, 1 vol. 2010. 210p. pap. 24.95 *(978-1-60672-064-6(3))* PublishAmerica, Inc.

Carroll, Julia. Healed by Light. 2008. 244p. per. 38.98 *(978-1-60461-822-8(1))* Reiki Touch Institute of Holistic Medicine Publishing.

Case, Paula. Compensating Child Abuse in England & Wales. 2007. (ENG.). 336p. 105.00 *(978-0-521-86402-2(X))* Cambridge Univ. Pr.

Caspi, Jonathan. Sibling Aggression: Assessment & Treatment. 2011. 250p. pap. ***(978-0-8261-2415-9(1))***; E-Book ***(978-0-8261-2416-6(X))*** Springer.

Cedeno, Elna V. Stop the Silence: Can You Hear Us? 2006. 15.95 *(978-0-9773476-0-5(5))* Cedeno, Elna V.

Chadwick, David L., et al. Child Maltreatment 4E; Set with CD-ROM: A Clinical Guide & Reference & A Comprehensive Photographic Reference Identifying Potential Child Abuse, 2 vols. 4th ed. 2012. (Illus.). 375.00 incl. cd-rom *(978-1-878060-94-5(5))* STM Learning, Inc.

Challenges Facing the Child Welfare System: Hearing Before the Subcommittee on Income Security & Family Support of the Committee on Ways & Means, U.S. House of Representatives, One Hundred Tenth Congress, First Session, May 15, 2007. 2008. (Illus.). iii, 136p. *(978-0-16-081803-5(6)*, 552-070-38009-4) United States Government Printing Office.

Chan, Edward Ko Ling, ed. Child Protection in Chinese Societies: Challenges & Policies. 2012. ***(978-1-61942-879-9(2))*** Nova Science Pubs., Inc.

Chapman, Vernon & Burton, Allan, eds. Child Fatalities Due to Maltreatment: The Role of Quality Data. 2012. 230p. pap. ***(978-1-61942-342-8(1))*** Nova Science Pubs., Inc.

Chibaya Mbuya, John. Women & Child Abuse. 2010. 240p. pap. *(978-3-8383-7083-5(X))* Lambert Academic Publishing.

Child Abuse. pap. *(978-0-660-16744-2(1))* Canadian Government Publishing.

Child Abuse & Domestic Violence. 2011. pap. 58.00 *(978-1-4144-4856-5(2))* Cengage Gale.

A Child & a Monster, 1 vol. 2010. 60p. pap. 19.95 *(978-1-4489-4363-0(9))* PublishAmerica, Inc.

Clements, Paul T. & Burgess, Ann W. Nursing Approach to the Evaluation of Child Maltreatment 2E. 2nd ed. 2012. (ENG., Illus.). pap. 75.00 *(978-1-878060-17-4(1))* STM Learning, Inc.

Cobley, Cathy & Sanders, Tom, eds. Non-Accidental Head Injury in Young Children: Medical, Legal & Social Responses. 2006. (ENG., Illus.). 192p. per. *(978-1-84310-360-8(5))* Kingsley, Jessica Ltd.

Cole-Kelly, Candace. Beyond the Mask. 2006. 200p. per. 16.95 *(978-0-9773973-7-2(8))* Cole Publishing.

Cost, Bettyjo. Redeemed by Love: Reflections on Survival. 2008. 148p. pap. 14.95 *(978-0-595-52585-0(7))* iUniverse, Inc.

Council of Europe Staff. Eradicating violence against Children: Council of Europe Actions. 2008. (Building a Europe for & with Children Monograph Ser.). 135p. pap. 38.00 *(978-92-871-6432-2(0))* Council of Europe FRA. Dist: Manhattan Publishing Co.

Cram101 Textbook Reviews. Outlines & Highlights for Child Abuse: Towards a Knowledge Base by Corby. 2010. 130p. pap. 28.95 *(978-1-61698-934-7(3))* Cram101 Inc.

Cram101 Textbook Reviews & Cram101 Textbook Reviews. Outlines & Highlights for Child Maltreatment: An Introduction by Cindy Miller-Perrin, ISBN 2011. 176p. pap. 29.95 ***(978-1-61461-014-4(2))*** Cram101 Inc.

—Outlines & Highlights for Childhood Denied by Kathleen Reardon, Isbn: 9781412939768. 2011. 178p. pap. 29.95 ***(978-1-61461-083-0(5))*** Cram101 Inc.

—Outlines & Highlights for Tell Me What Happened: Structured Investigative Interviews of Child Victims & Witnesses by Michael E. Lamb (University Of. 2011. 220p. pap. 30.95 ***(978-1-4288-4717-0(0))*** Cram101 Inc.

—Outlines & Highlights for Understanding Child Abuse & Neglect by Cynthia Crosson-Tower, Isbn: 9780205769155 0205769152. 2011. 170p. pap. 29.95 ***(978-1-4288-9068-8(8))*** Cram101 Inc.

Crosson-Tower & Cram101 Textbook Reviews Staff. Understanding Child Abuse & Neglect. 2007. 136p. per. 11.95 *(978-1-4288-1984-9(3))* Cram101 Inc.

Crosson-Tower, Cynthia. A Clergy Guide to Child Abuse & Neglect. 2006. 256p. per. *(978-0-8298-1595-5(3))* Pilgrim Pr., The/United Church Pr.

—Understanding Child Abuse & Neglect. 8th ed. 2009. (ENG.). 448p. (C). pap. 101.80 *(978-0-205-76915-5(2)*, Prentice Hall) Prentice Hall PTR.

Crouse, Janice. Children at Risk: The Precarious State of Children's Well-Being in America. 2009. (ENG.). 224p. 34.95 *(978-1-4128-1076-0(0))* Transaction Pubs.

Curry, Lynne. The Deshaney Case: Child Abuse, Family Rights, & the Dilemma of State Intervention. 2007. (Landmark Law Cases & American Society Ser.). 164p. *(978-0-7006-1496-7(6))*; per. *(978-0-7006-1497-4(4))* Univ. Pr. of Kansas.

Cutler, Erin and Derek. Not Backing Down, 1 vol. 2010. 80p. pap. 19.95 *(978-1-4489-5376-9(6))* PublishAmerica, Inc.

Daro, Deborah, ed. World Perspectives on Child Abuse. 7th ed. 2006. (Illus.). vi, 203p. per. 45.00 *(978-0-9787530-0-9(3))* ISPCAN.

Davidson, Julia & Hamerton, Christopher. International Perspectives on Child Victimisation. 2012. (ENG.). 208p. 125.00 *(978-0-415-57957-5(0))* Routledge.

Davies, Liz. Protecting Children: A resource Book. 2nd ed. 2010. (ENG., Illus.). 136p. pap. *(978-1-905179-07-7(3)*, Lonely Scribe) Armadillo Design Ltd.

Degun-Mather, Marcia. Hypnosis, Dissociation & Survivors of Child Abuse: Understanding & Treatment. 2006. (ENG., Illus.). 256p. 155.00 *(978-0-470-03254-1(5)*, Wiley) Wiley, John & Sons, Inc.

Dell, Pickle. Through a Mother's Pain, the Child Cries. 2011. 92p. pap. 13.99 *(978-1-4520-7459-7(3))* AuthorHouse.

DeMeo, James. Saharasia: The 4000 BCE Origins of Child Abuse, Sex-Repression, Warfare & Social Violence, in the Deserts of the Old World. rev. exp. ed. 2011. (ENG., Illus.). 480p. pap. 39.00 ***(978-0-9802316-4-9(7))*** Natural Energy Works.

Devon, Raymond T., ed. Working with the Courts in Child Protection. 2010. (Children's Issues, Laws & Programs Ser.). (Illus.). 185p. 69.00 *(978-1-61668-303-0(1))* Nova Science Pubs., Inc.

Dietrich, Anne. When the Hurting Continues. 2008. 120p. pap. *(978-3-639-02345-9(5))* VDM Verlag Dr. Mueller e.K.

Doak, Melissa J. Child Abuse & Domestic Violence. 2009. (Information Plus Reference Ser.). (ENG.). 168p. pap. 58.00 *(978-1-4144-3371-4(9))* Cengage Gale.

Dodge, Kenneth A. Preventing Child Maltreatment: Community Approaches. Dodge, Kenneth A. & Coleman, Doriane Lambelet, eds. 2009. (Duke Series in Child Develpment & Public Policy Ser.). (ENG., Illus.). 203p. 45.00 *(978-1-59385-973-2(2))* Guilford Pubns., Inc.

Dolly. The Blood of Ten Souls. 2009. 192p. 24.99 *(978-1-4389-3792-2(X))*; pap. 14.70 *(978-1-4389-3791-5(1))* AuthorHouse.

Douglas, Ed. No Peace Within: Tidbits of Gold in God's Holy Words. 2009. 112p. pap. 16.49 *(978-1-4490-1697-5(9))* AuthorHouse.

Doyle, Celia. Working with Abused Children: Focus on Child. 4th rev. ed. 2012. (Practical Social Work Ser.). (ENG., Illus.). 304p. (C). pap. 31.00 ***(978-0-230-29794-4(3))*** Palgrave Macmillan.

Doyle, Hilarie Rose. Anatomy of Abuse & the Forgiveness Factor, 1 vol. 2009. 82p. pap. 16.95 *(978-1-4241-8910-6(1))* PublishAmerica, Inc.

Dubowitz, Howard & Merrick, Joav. International Aspects of Child Abuse & Neglect. 2011. (Series: Health & Human Development Ser.). xxii, 286p. pap. 69.00 *(978-1-61122-049-0(1))* Nova Science Pubs., Inc.

Dubowitz, Howard & Merrick, Joav, eds. International Aspects of Child Abuse & Neglect. 2010. (Health & Human Development (Joav Merrick - Series Editor - National Institute of Child Health & Human Development, Ministry of Social Affairs, Jerusalem Ser.). (Illus.). xxii, 286p. 125.00 *(978-1-60876-703-8(5))* Nova Science Pubs., Inc.

Ebbe, Obi N. I. & Das, Dilip K., eds. Criminal Abuse of Women & Children: An International Perspective. 2009. (ENG., Illus.). 396p. 124.95 *(978-1-4200-8803-8(3)*, CRC Press) Taylor & Francis Group GBR. Dist: Taylor & Francis Group.

Einhorn, Lois. Forgiveness & Child Abuse: Would YOU Forgive? 2010. (Illus.). 214p. 22.95 *(978-1-931741-69-9(7))* Reed, Robert D. Pubs.

Ewart, Heyward Bruce. Am I Bad ? Recovering from Abuse. 2007. (ENG.). 200p. per. *(978-1-932690-33-0(6))* Loving Healing Pr., Inc.

Feerick, Margaret M. & Flanzer, Sally, eds. Child Abuse & Neglect: Definitions, Classifications, & a Framework for Research. 2006. (Illus.). 404p. *(978-1-55766-759-5(4)*, 7594) Brookes, Paul H. Publishing Co.

Fiket, Craig S. & Grotti, Amy W. The Child Abuse Prevention & Treatment Act with a Summary of State Laws. 2012. (Children's Issues, Laws & Programs Ser.). 245p. 95.00 ***(978-1-62100-051-8(6))*** Nova Science Pubs., Inc.

Finkelhor, David. Childhood Victimization: Violence, Crime & Abuse in the Lives of Young People. 2008. (Interpersonal Violence Ser.). (ENG., Illus.). 256p. 39.99 *(978-0-19-534285-7(2))* Oxford Univ. Pr., Inc.

Finn, Mickey. In My Own Words (Still Running) 2011. 228p. pap. 17.09 ***(978-1-4567-7999-3(0))*** AuthorHouse.

Fitzgibbon, Wendy. Probation & Social Work on Trial: Violent Offenders & Child Abusers. 2011. (ENG., Illus.). 208p. 85.00 ***(978-0-230-27537-9(0))*** Palgrave Macmillan.

Flannery, Tony, ed. Responding to the Ryan Report. 2010. (ENG.). 233p. pap. 27.95 *(978-1-85607-673-9(3))* Columba Pr. IRL. Dist: Dufour Editions, Inc.

Fontes, Lisa Aronson. Child Abuse & Culture: Working with Diverse Families. 2008. (ENG., Illus.). 239p. pap. 27.00 *(978-1-59385-643-4(1))* Guilford Pubns., Inc.

Foote, G. W. The Child Convict. 2009. 144p. 22.75 *(978-1-60860-092-2(0)*, Strategic Bk. Publishing) AEG Literary Publishing Services, Inc.

The Forgotten Children: Hungry. Hopeless. Running for their Lives. 2006. per. 14.95 *(978-0-9788041-0-7(4))* World Help Inc.

Forum on Global Violence Prevention & Institute of Medicine. Preventing Violence Against Women & Children: Workshop Summary. 2011. (ENG.). 236p. pap. 54.00 ***(978-0-309-21151-2(4))*** National Academies Pr.

Franklin, Stuart. A Holocaust of Innocence: An Innocence of Childhood Lost. 2008. 144p. pap. 14.95 *(978-1-4327-3139-7(4))* Outskirts Pr., Inc.

Frasier, Lori, et al. Abusive Head Trauma in Infants & Children; A Clinical Guide/Color Atlas: A Medical, Legal, & Forensic Reference. 2006. (Illus.). 630p. 175.00 *(978-1-878060-58-6(6))* STM Learning, Inc.

Fromm Reed, Suzette. Processes That Mediate the Effect of Community Factors on Child Maltreatment. 2008. 100p. per. *(978-3-8364-5947-1(7))* VDM Verlag Dr. Mueller e.K.

Frost, Sasha. The Letting Go. 2011. 144p. 23.14 ***(978-1-4269-6310-0(6))*** Trafford Publishing.

Giardino, Angelo P. Helping Children Affected by Abuse: A Parent's & Teacher's Handbook for Increasing Awareness. 2007. (ENG., Illus.). 218p. 26.00 *(978-1-878060-98-3(8))* STM Learning, Inc.

Giardino, Angelo P., et al. Physical Abuse & Neglect: A Training Curriculum. 2008. (ENG., Illus.). 259p. spiral bd. 200.00 *(978-1-878060-79-2(1))* STM Learning, Inc.

Giardino, Eileen R. & Giardino, Angelo P. Nursing Approach to Child Maltreatment Curriculum: A Training Curriculum. 2012. (ENG., Illus.). spiral bd. 200.00 *(978-1-878060-72-3(4))* STM Learning, Inc.

Gil, Eliana. Helping Abused & Traumatized Children: Integrating Directive & Nondirective Approaches. 2006. (ENG., Illus.). 254p. 50.00 *(978-1-59385-334-1(3))* Guilford Pubns., Inc.

Gil, Eliana, ed. Working with Children to Heal Interpersonal Trauma: The Power of Play. 2010. (ENG., Illus.). 336p. 40.00 (978-1-60623-892-9(2)) Guilford Pubns., Inc.

Gilbert, Neil, et al, eds. Child Protection Systems: International Trends & Orientations, 1 vol. 2011. (International Policy Exchange Ser.). (ENG., Illus.). 288p. 55.00 (978-0-19-979335-8(2)) Oxford Univ. Pr., Inc.

Goel, Suresh. Psychosocial Aspects of Domestic Violence. 2009. 301p. 47.50 (978-81-7533-217-1(4)) M. D. Pubns. Pvt, Ltd. IND. Dist: Coronet Bks.

Gorky, Maksim & Hettlinger, Graham. Childhood. 2010. (978-1-56663-906-4(9)) Dee, Ivan R. Pub.

Grace, Sharon. When the Trust Is Broken: Just When You Think Your Children are Safe, Think Again. 2010. (ENG.). 112p. pap. 14.95 (978-1-60037-732-7(7)) Morgan James Publishing.

Gray, Elizabeth. I Relived My Nightmare from Hell: Overcoming Abuse & Agoraphobia. 2009. 100p. pap. 13.95 (978-1-4389-5367-0(4)) AuthorHouse.

Green, Nicole M. Veil of Secrecy: My Life Story. 2011. 188p. pap. 15.00 **(978-1-4634-1881-6(7))** AuthorHouse.

Gresell, Charity Shae. The Dark Path of Innocents. 2011. 106p. pap. 19.95 **(978-1-4560-0325-8(9))** PublishAmerica, Inc.

Grover, Linda. The Story Never Told, 1 vol. 2010. 184p. pap. 24.95 (978-1-4512-0953-2(3)) PublishAmerica, Inc.

Gumbel, Elisabeth Ann, et al. APIL Guide to Abuse Compensation Claims. 2nd rev. ed. 2011. (ENG.). 400p. pap. (978-1-84661-255-8(1)) Jordan Publishing, Ltd.

Hamilton, Marci. Justice Denied: What America Must Do to Protect Its Children. 2008. (ENG.). 168p. 26.00 (978-0-521-88621-5(X)) Cambridge Univ. Pr.

Hamilton, Marci A. Justice Denied: What America Must Do to Protect its Children. 2012. (ENG.). 176p. pap. 18.99 **(978-1-107-67312-0(7))** Cambridge Univ. Pr.

Hannah, Mo Therese & Goldstein, Barry. Domestic Violence, Abuse, & Child Custody: Legal Strategies & Policy Issues. 2010. (978-1-887554-76-3(9)) Civic Research Institute, Inc.

Harder, Jeannette. Let the Children Come: Preparing Faith Communities to End Child Abuse & Neglect. 2010. 213p. pap. 12.99 (978-0-8361-9518-7(3)) Herald Pr.

Harne, Lynne. Violent Fathering & the Risks to Children: The Need for Change. 2011. (Illus.). 216p. 85.00 (978-1-84742-917-9(3)) Policy Pr. GBR. Dist: Chicago Distribution Ctr.

Harris, Leslie J. & Teitelbaum, Lee E. Children, Parents, & the Law: Public & Private Authority in the Home, Schools, & Juvenile Courts. 2nd ed. 2007. 144.00 (978-0-7355-6363-6(2)); xxxi, 769p. (978-0-7355-6365-0(9)) Wolters Kluwer Law & Business. (Aspen Pubs.).

Hatchell, Rodney Ray. Everything but Love, 1 vol. 2010. 140p. pap. 24.95 (978-1-4489-4366-1(3)) PublishAmerica, Inc.

Haywood, Della W. Years of a Lotus: Memoir of a Lust Baby. 2010. pap. 15.95 (978-0-7414-5868-1(3)) Infinity Publishing.

Heim, Richard. 'Crucifixion' of the Child. 2009. 156p. 22.49 (978-1-4490-3212-8(5)); pap. 13.49 (978-1-4490-3213-5(3)) AuthorHouse.

Heimlich, Janet. Breaking Their Will: Shedding Light on Religious Child Maltreatment. 2011. (ENG.). 360p. pap. 20.00 (978-1-61614-405-0(X)) Prometheus Bks., Pubs.

Helander, Einar. Children & Violence: The World of the Defenceless. 2008. (ENG., Illus.). 288p. 105.00 (978-0-230-57394-9(0)) Palgrave Macmillan.

Hendrix, Ervin. One Voice: Speak Out, America-Raise Your Voice-It Matters! 2009. 200p. pap. 19.95 (978-1-4269-0031-0(7)) Trafford Publishing.

Hicks, Tim. Walking with My Savior. 2008. 172p. pap. 14.96 (978-1-4357-6051-6(4)) Lulu Enterprises Inc.

Higgins, Jeff V. & Brady, Christopher M. Child Sex Trafficking in the United States. 2012. pap. **(978-1-62100-266-6(7))** Nova Science Pubs., Inc.

Hobart, Christine & Frankel, Jill. Good Practice in Safeguarding Children 3rd Edition. Walker, Miranda, ed. 3rd rev. ed. 2009. (ENG., Illus.). 224p. pap. 57.50 **(978-1-4085-0491-8(X))** Nelson Thornes Ltd. GBR. Dist: Trans-Atlantic Pubns., Inc.

Horwath, Jan. Child Neglect: Planning & Intervention. 2013. (ENG.). 208p. (C). pap. 32.95 (978-0-230-20666-3(2)) Palgrave Macmillan.

Howe, Mark L., et al, eds. Stress, Trauma, & Children's Memory Development: Neurobiological, Cognitive, Clinical, & Legal Perspectives. 2008. (ENG., Illus.). 352p. 55.00 (978-0-19-530845-7(X)) Oxford Univ. Pr., Inc.

Howitt, Rene. Whose Best Interest? A Fight to Save Two American Kids. 2007. 255p. per. 14.99 (978-1-59886-822-7(5)) Tate Publishing & Enterprises, LLC.

Hoyano, Laura & Keenan, Caroline. Child Abuse: Law & Policy Across Boundaries. 2010. 1,080p. pap. 99.00 (978-0-19-957156-7(2)) Oxford Univ. Pr., Inc.

Hugs to Heartbreak: A Parent's Journey Through Parental Alienation. 2007. per. 17.95 (978-0-9796960-0-8(3)) Family's Heartbreak, LLC, A.

Jackson, Mollee. I Am Hope, 1 vol. 2010. 274p. pap. 27.95 (978-1-4489-7015-5(6)) PublishAmerica, Inc.

Kagan, Richard. Real Life Heroes: Practitioner's Manual. 2007. (ENG., Illus.). 220p. per. 44.95 (978-0-7890-2952-2(9)) Routledge.

Kampmark, Binoy. Sacred Child: The Politics of Child Abuse & Abusers in the Twenty-First Century. 2011. ix, 114p. **(978-1-61324-155-4(0))** Nova Science Pubs., Inc.

Kay, Janet. Protecting Children. pap. (978-0-8264-5802-5(5)) Continuum International Publishing Group, Ltd.

Kelly, Judith. Rock Me Gently: A True Story of a Convent Childhood. 2006. (ENG., Illus.). 288p. per. 15.95 (978-0-7475-8714-9(0)) Bloomsbury Publishing Plc GBR. Dist: Independent Pubs. Group.

Key, Craig. The Deadly Game of Tug of War: The Kelsey Smith-Briggs Story. 2008. (ENG.). 168p. pap. 16.95 (978-1-60037-311-4(9)) Morgan James Publishing.

Kiesbye, Stefan. Child Abuse & Neglect. 2007. (Social Issues Firsthand Ser.). (Illus.). 112p. (YA). (gr. 10-12). lib. bdg. 31.80 (978-0-7377-4272-5(0), LML02109-244145, Greenhaven Pr., Inc.) Cengage Gale.

Kyle, John Edward. Going Against the Grain. 2011. 292p. 29.99 **(978-1-4568-8503-8(0))**; pap. 19.99 **(978-1-4568-8502-1(2))** Xlibris Corp.

Lamb, Michael E., et al. Tell Me What Happened: Structured Investigative Interviews of Child Victims & Witnesses. 2008. (Wiley Series in Psychology of Crime, Policing & Law Ser.). (ENG.). 386p. pap. 71.95 (978-0-470-51866-3(9)); 172.95 (978-0-470-51865-6(0)) Wiley, John & Sons, Inc. (Wiley).

Lavoie, Henri. Not Me Not Ever the Road Map of an Oppo. 2007. pap. 12.95 (978-1-59800-996-5(6)) Outskirts Pr., Inc.

Lawrence, Abigail. Invisible Tears: The Abuse the Rebellion the Survival despite all Odds. 2010. 228p. pap. 14.49 (978-1-4490-7002-1(7)) AuthorHouse.

Levesque, Roger J. R. Child Maltreatment & the Law: Returning to First Principles. (ENG.). x, 217p. 2010. pap. 54.95 (978-1-4419-2731-6(X), 144192731X) 2008. 54.95 (978-0-387-79917-9(6), 0387799176) Springer.

Lisa, Mona. Forgotten Child: Series 1. 2011. 70p. pap. 19.95 **(978-1-4626-0398-5(X))** PublishAmerica, Inc.

Machel, Graca. The Impact of War on Children: A Review of Progress since the 1996 United Nations Report on the Impact of Armed Conflict on Children. (ENG., Illus.). 176p. (978-0-7748-0867-5(5)) Univ. of British Columbia Pr.

MacKenzie, Miranda. Pilgrimage Toward the Light: One Woman's Journey Away from the Darkness of Complex Childhood Abuse. 2011. 296p. pap. 17.95 **(978-1-60976-939-0(2)**, Strategic Bk. Publishing) AEG Literary Publishing Services, Inc.

Mahendra, B. A Family Psychiatric Practice. 2010. (ENG.). 306p. pap. (978-1-84661-224-4(1)) Jordan Publishing, Ltd.

MAKHENE, E. D. W. A. R. D. R. W. What's that, Mummy? 2008. 92p. pap. 16.95 (978-1-4357-0856-3(3)) Lulu Enterprises Inc.

Maley, April J. I Will Not Be Silent. 2010. 176p. pap. 13.95 (978-1-60844-433-5(3)) Dog Ear Publishing, LLC.

Marsh, Samantha. Sometimes, Society Fails. 2006. 76p. pap. 16.95 (978-1-4241-4620-8(8)) PublishAmerica, Inc.

Martin, Lena C. Desperate for Love: Overcoming with Prayer. 2007. 436p. per. 18.95 (978-1-4327-0209-0(2)) Outskirts Pr., Inc.

Martin, Rose. Shannon - Betrayed from Birth. 2009. (ENG., Illus.). 278p. pap. 13.95 (978-1-84454-862-0(7)) Blake, John Publishing, Ltd. GBR. Dist: Independent Pubs. Group.

Matthews, Sherry. We Were Not Orphans: Stories from the Waco State Home. 2011. (ENG., Illus.). 234p. 29.95 (978-0-292-72559-1(0)) Univ. of Texas Pr.

Mayhew, Lisa. Child Death Investigations: Interdisciplinary Techniques from Cradle to Court. 2007. 20.00 (978-1-59460-209-2(3)) Carolina Academic Pr.

McCord, Joan. Crime & Family: Selected Essays of Joan Mccord. 2007. (Illus.). 320p. per. 29.95 (978-1-59213-558-5(7)) Temple Univ. Pr.

McCoy, Monica L. Child Abuse & Neglect. 2009. (ENG., Illus.). 312p. (C). 69.95 (978-0-8058-6244-7(7), Psychology Press) Taylor & Francis Group GBR. Dist: Taylor & Francis Group.

McKnight, Patricia A. My Justice. 2011. 276p. pap. 16.25 (978-1-4520-7169-5(1)) AuthorHouse.

McPherson, Sandra B. & Afsarifard, Farshid. Equivocal Child Abuse. 2011. (ENG., Illus.). 304p. 99.95 (978-1-4398-4776-3(2), Taylor & Francis) Taylor & Francis Group GBR. Dist: Taylor & Francis Group.

McShane, John. It Must Never Happen Again: The Lessons Learned from the Short Life & Terrible Death of Baby P. 2009. (ENG., Illus.). 288p. pap. 14.95 (978-1-84454-789-0(2)) Blake, John Publishing, Ltd. GBR. Dist: Independent Pubs. Group.

Meadow, Roy, et al. ABC of Child Protection. 4th rev. ed. 2007. (ABC Ser.: 112). (ENG., Illus.). 120p. pap. 59.95 (978-0-7279-1817-8(6)) Wiley, John & Sons, Inc.

Medina, Sarah. Abuse & Neglect. 2008. (Emotional Health Issues Ser.). (Illus.). 48p. (YA). (gr. 7-12). lib. bdg. 31.00 (978-0-8368-9198-0(8)) Stevens, Gareth Publishing LLLP.

Melton, Joy Thornburg. Safe Sanctuaries: Reducing the Risk of Abuse in the Church for Children & Youth. 2008. 144p. pap. 25.00 (978-0-88177-543-3(6)) Upper Room Bks.

Merrick. Social Work & Child Abuse: Still Walking the Tightrope? 2nd rev. ed. 2006. 256p. 49.95 (978-0-415-35415-8(3)) Routledge.

Merrick, Dave. Social Work & Child Abuse: Still Walking the Tightrope? 2nd rev. ed. 2006. 239p. 160.00 (978-0-415-35414-1(5)) Routledge.

Miller, Alice. Breaking down the Wall of Silence: The Liberating Experience of Facing Painful Truth. 2008. (ENG.). 186p. pap. 16.99 (978-0-465-01504-7(2)) Basic Bks.

Miller-Perrin, Cindy L. Child Maltreatment: An Introduction. Perrin, Robin D., ed. 2nd rev. ed. 2006. (Illus.). 496p. (C). pap. 67.00 (978-1-4129-2668-3(8), B26688P) SAGE Pubns., Inc.

Miller-Perrin, Cindy L. & Perrin, Robin D. (Dale). Child Maltreatment: An Introduction. 3rd ed. 2012. 472p. (C). pap. 67.00 **(978-1-4522-0579-3(5)**, B05793P) SAGE Pubns., Inc.

Morinsliva. Through My Eyes. 2011. 100p. pap. 15.00 **(978-1-60911-633-0(X)**, Eloquent Bks.) AEG Literary Publishing Services, Inc.

Munro, Eileen. Child Protection. 2007. (SAGE Course Companions Ser.). (Illus.). 200p. (C). per. 34.00 (978-1-4129-1179-5(6), B11788P) SAGE Pubns., Ltd. GBR. Dist: SAGE Pubns., Inc.

Myers, John E. B. & American Professional Society on the Abuse of Children Staff. The APSAC Handbook on Child Maltreatment. Greenbaum, Jordan, ed. 3rd ed. 2010. 464p. (C). pap. 86.00 (978-1-4129-6681-8(7), B66818P) SAGE Pubns., Inc.

Narisetti, Innaiah. Forced into Faith: How Religion Abuses Children's Rights. 2008. (ENG.). 100p. pap. 9.98 (978-1-59102-606-8(7)) Prometheus Bks., Pubs.

Nat. Distr. Attorneys Assoc., et al. Investigation & Prosecution of Child Abuse, Neglect, & Exploitation. 2012. (ENG., Illus.). 700p. 145.00 (978-1-878060-44-0(9)) STM Learning, Inc.

Norris-Bernal, J. E. Forgiving Others & Trusting God ... A Handbook for Survivors of Child Abuse Experience Healing for Deep Wounds that Hinder Your Relationship with the Father. 2011. 382p. pap. 23.99 (978-1-61215-614-9(2)) Xulon Pr., Inc.

O'Brien, M. J. Beaten down by the System, but Not Beaten. 2011. 388p. pap. 29.95 **(978-1-4560-6549-2(1))** PublishAmerica, Inc.

Office of Management and Budget (U.S.), compiled by. Cases of Child Neglect & Abuse at Private Residential Treatment Facilities: Hearing Before the Committee on Education & Labor, U. S. House of Representatives, One Hundred Tenth Congress, First Session, Hearing Held in Washington, DC, October 10, 2007. 2008. (ENG., Illus.). iii, 138p. pap. 102.00 (978-0-16-080875-3(8), 552-070-37425-6, Office of Management & Budget) United States Government Printing Office.

O'Keeffe, Toni. Those Who Trespass Against Us. 2007. 252p. 29.95 (978-1-4251-6734-9(9)) Trafford Publishing.

Olive, M. Foster. Child Abuse & Stress Disorders. 2007. (Psychological Disorders Ser.). (Illus.). 120p. (YA). (gr. 7-12). lib. bdg. 37.50 (978-0-7910-9006-0(X)) Facts On File, Inc.

Olson, Diane & Friedrich, Laura Dean. Weaving A Just Future for Children. 2008. 160p. pap. 15.00 (978-0-88177-547-1(9)) Upper Room Bks.

O'Neill, Terence. Someone to Love Us: The Shocking True Story of Two Brothers Fostered into Brutality & Neglect. 2010. (ENG.). 320p. 12.95 (978-0-00-735018-6(X)) HarperCollins Pubs. Ltd. GBR. Dist: Independent Pubs. Group.

Orozco, Michael. Investigating the Death of Innocents. 2010. (Illus.). 224p. pap. 15.00 (978-1-935437-22-2(4)) Imago Pr.

Osborne, Sheree. Broken Wings: A Story of Breathtaking Joy, Hope, & Love. 2006. (ENG.). 232p. per. 12.99 (978-1-86024-557-2(9)) Authentic Media.

Owens, Derek. Memory's Wake. 2011. **(978-1-933132-86-0(8))** Spuyten Duyvil.

Pal, D. D. Gach. Child Neglect & Crimes in Southern Sudan. 2011. 120p. pap. **(978-3-8443-8177-1(5))** Lambert Academic Publishing.

Palusci, Vincent J. & Fischer, Howard. Child Abuse & Neglect: A Diagnostic Guide for Physicians, Surgeons, Pathologists, Dentists, Nurses & Social Workers. 2010. (ENG., Illus.). 272p. 120.00 (978-1-84076-123-8(7)) Manson Publishing, Ltd. GBR. Dist: Thieme Medical Pubs., Inc.

Parens, Erik, ed. Surgically Shaping Children: Technology, Ethics, & the Pursuit of Normality. 2008. (ENG., Illus.). 304p. (gr. 17). pap. 25.00 (978-0-8018-9090-1(X)) Johns Hopkins Univ. Pr.

Patton, Stacey. That Mean Old Yesterday: A Memoir. 2008. (ENG.). 336p. pap. 20.99 (978-0-7432-9311-2(8), Washington Square Pr.) Washington Square Pr.

Payne, Brian K. & Gainey, Randy R. Family Violence & Criminal Justice: A Life-Course Approach. 3rd ed. 2009. (ENG.). 460p. (C). pap. 47.95 (978-1-4224-6138-9(6)) Anderson Publishing Co.

Pearce, John W. & Pezzot-Pearce, Terry Dianne. Psychotherapy of Abused & Neglected Children. 2nd rev. ed. 2006. (ENG., Illus.). 411p. 50.00 (978-1-59385-213-9(4)) Guilford Pubns., Inc.

Pennington, Lucinda. They Meant it for Evil. 2011. pap. 11.99 **(978-1-61346-093-1(7))** Tate Publishing & Enterprises, LLC.

Powlison, David. Recovering from Child Abuse: Healing & Hope for Victims. 2008. (ENG.). 24p. 3.99 (978-1-934885-47-5(9)) New Growth Pr.

Presley, Jennifer Aron. The Jennifer Presley Project. 2011. (ENG.). 164p. pap. 13.95 **(978-1-4327-7343-4(7))** Outskirts Pr., Inc.

Proykov, Todor. Opening the Pandora's Box: The Child Abuse Discourse. 2010. 132p. pap. (978-3-8383-5003-5(0)) Lambert Academic Publishing.

Pughe, Billy & Philpot, Terry. Living Alongside a Child's Recovery: Therapeutic Parenting with Traumatized Children. 2007. (ENG.). 144p. per. (978-1-84310-328-8(1)) Kingsley, Jessica Ltd.

Raja, Imran. Frozen Wounds: Child abuse casts a shadow the length of a Lifetime. 2009. 224p. pap. 14.49 (978-1-4389-4166-0(8)) AuthorHouse.

Richards, Nancy. Heal & Forgive II: The Journey from Abuse & Estrangement to Reconciliation. 2008. 172p. pap. 16.00 (978-1-57733-220-6(2)) Blue Dolphin Publishing, Inc.

Richardson, Kim Michele. The Unbreakable Child. 2nd rev. ed. 2010. (ENG., Illus.). 218p. pap. 15.95 (978-1-933016-91-7(4)) Behler Pubns., LLC.

Richardson, Tom I. & Williams, Marsha V. Child Abuse & Violence. 2008. (C). 90.00 (978-1-60456-128-9(9)) Nova Science Pubs., Inc.

Roman, Noama Malva. Guilty at Birth: A True Story. 2009. 152p. pap. 14.95 (978-1-4401-3462-3(6)) iUniverse, Inc.

Ronquillo, Victor. Los NiNtilde;Os de Nadie. 2007. (SPA.). 200p. pap. 18.95 (978-970-710-262-0(4)) B. Mexico, Ediciones, S.A. de C.V. MEX. Dist: Ediciones Urano S. A.

Rothgeb, Carol & Cupp, Scott. No One Can Hurt Him Anymore. 2010. (ENG.). 320p. 6.99 (978-0-7860-2755-2(X), Pinnacle Bks.) Kensington Publishing Corp.

Russell, Joel Lee. Escaping Death's Sting: A Combat Marine Life's Story. 2010. 320p. 28.50 (978-1-60911-019-2(6), Eloquent Bks.) AEG Literary Publishing Services, Inc.

Sabatino, Catherine Ann. Voices in the Midst: Catherine Ann Sabatino. 2010. 336p. 28.49 (978-1-4490-9527-7(5)); pap. 17.99 (978-1-4490-9528-4(3)) AuthorHouse.

Sabbagh, Karl. Remembering our Childhood: How Memory Betrays Us. 2011. (ENG., Illus.). 240p. pap. 19.95 (978-0-19-921841-7(2)) Oxford Univ. Pr., Inc.

Saunders, Bernadette J. & Goddard, Chris. Physical Punishment in Childhood: The Rights of the Child. 2010. (ENG., Illus.). 284p. 110.95 (978-0-470-68256-2(6), Wiley) Wiley, John & Sons, Inc.

Saunders, Bernadette J. & Goddard, Christopher Rex. Physical Punishment in Childhood: The Rights of the Child. 2010. (ENG., Illus.). 284p. pap. 54.95 (978-0-470-72706-5(3), Wiley) Wiley, John & Sons, Inc.

Savage, William. Through the Eyes of an Angry Child: The Untold Story. 2011. 134p. 29.99 **(978-1-4535-4511-9(5))**; pap. 19.99 **(978-1-4535-4510-2(7))** Xlibris Corp.

Sax, Robin. Predators & Child Molesters: What Every Parent Needs to Know to Keep Kids Safe. 2009. (ENG.). 224p. pap. 17.98 (978-1-59102-712-6(8)) Prometheus Bks., Pubs.

Schrock, Orva. Worthless Boy: A Memoir. 2011. (ENG.). 98p. 14.95 **(978-1-4327-8042-5(5))** Outskirts Pr., Inc.

Schwartz Lita Linzer & Isser Natalie K. Child Homicide: Parents Who Kill. 2nd ed. 2006. (ENG., Illus.). 297p. 99.95 (978-0-8493-9366-2(3), CRC Press) Taylor & Francis Group GBR. Dist: Taylor & Francis Group.

Settles, Linda. The Girl among Thorns: Why Did She Stay So Long. 2010. (ENG.). 290p. pap. 12.99 (978-0-9790238-6-6(6)) Edict House Publishing Group, LLC.

Sheehan, Rosemary, et al, eds. Vulnerable Children & the Law: International Evidence for Improving Child Welfare, Child Protection & Children's Rights. 2012. (ENG., Illus.). 304p. pap. **(978-1-84905-868-1(7))** Kingsley, Jessica Ltd.

Sheppard, Dawn. The Hidden Legacy of the Millers. 2010. 191p. pap. 16.99 (978-0-557-35585-3(0)) Lulu Enterprises Inc.

Silberg, Joy L. The Child Survivor: Healing Developmental Trauma & Dissociation. 2012. (ENG.). 272p. 95.00 (978-0-415-88994-0(4)); pap. 34.95 (978-0-415-88995-7(2)) Routledge.

Simari. Maltrato y Abuso Sexual de Ninos. (Serie Actualidades - Actualities Ser.).Tr. of Mistreatment & Sexual Abuse of Children. (SPA.). 2.29 (978-1-56063-661-8(0), 496252) Editorial Unilit.

Sirotnak, Andrew. Child Abuse & Neglect - Advancements & Challenges in the 21st Century: Pediatric Clinics of North America. 2009. (Clinics: Internal Medicine Ser.: 56-2). (ENG., Illus.). 240p. 78.00 (978-1-4377-0519-5(7), Saunders) Elsevier - Health Sciences Div.

Spiteri, Ylenia & Galea, Elizabeth M. Psychology of Neglect. 2012. (Psychology Research Progress Psychology of Emotions, Motivations & Actions Ser.). 212p. 95.00 **(978-1-62100-180-5(6))** Nova Science Pubs., Inc.

Stone, Martha & Stone, Jonathan. Fight Like a Tiger Would for Her Cubs. 2010. 35p. pap. 8.50 (978-1-4461-5881-4(0)) Lulu Enterprises Inc.

Taiwo, Ola Lydia. What a Life! 2009. 72p. pap. 9.95 (978-1-60693-982-6(3), Strategic Bk. Publishing) AEG Literary Publishing Services, Inc.

Tenaglia-Webster, Maria. Slavery. 2009. (GLOBAL VIEWPOINTS Ser.). (ENG.). 224p. pap. 26.50 (978-0-7377-4473-6(1)); (Illus.). pap. 38.45 (978-0-7377-4472-9(3)) Cengage Gale. (Greenhaven Pr., Inc.).

Tocholke, Bernie. Torn Asunder. 2008. 152p. 22.49 (978-1-4389-2329-1(5)); pap. 11.99 (978-1-4389-2330-7(9)) AuthorHouse.

Touher, Patrick. Fear of the Collar: The True Story of the Boy They Couldn't Break. 2007. (ENG., Illus.). 272p. pap. 12.95 (978-0-09-191766-1(2)) Ebury Publishing GBR. Dist: Independent Pubs. Group.

Tracy, Steven R. Mending the Soul: Understanding & Healing Abuse. 2008. (ENG., Illus.). 272p. pap. 16.99 (978-0-310-28529-8(1)) Zondervan.

Trappler, Brian. Identifying & Recovering from Psychological Trauma: A Psychiatrist's Guide for Victims of Childhood Abuse, Spousal Battery, & Political Terrorism. 2009. (ENG.). 208p. pap. 22.95 (978-1-884092-76-3(4), Gordian Knot Bks.) Altschuler, Richard & Assocs., Inc.

Tree of Knowledge Press: We Educate Children One Child at a Time. Lost, Bad, & Evil (3 Stages of Child Abuse) Why Are My Family Members Dysfunctional, Disturbed, or Insane? 2011. 125p. pap. 21.99 (978-1-885872-39-5(9)) Tree of Knowledge Pr.

Trent, Michael E. & Buess, Terese M. Investigation & Prosecution of Child Sexual Abuse. 2007. 304p. pap. 40.00 (978-0-9796993-6-8(3)) Texas District & County Attorneys Assn.

Trigs, Janet & Trigs, Anton. Annabelle's Early Years: Trauma & Despair. 2011. 156p. pap. 15.66 **(978-1-4567-7938-2(9))** AuthorHouse.

Turnell, Andrew & Essex, Susanne. Working with Denied Child Abuse: The Resolutions Approach. 2006. (Illus.). 224p. 130.00 (978-0-335-21656-7(0), 9780335216567, Open University Pr.); (ENG., pap. 49.00 (978-0-335-21657-4(9), 0335216579) McGraw-Hill Education GBR. Dist: McGraw-Hill Cos., The.

Ventrell, Marvin R. Trial Advocacy for the Child Welfare Lawyer: Telling the Story of the Family. 2011. (978-1-60156-149-7(0)) National Institute for Trial Advocacy.

Vieth, Victor I., et al. Investigation of Child Maltreatment Quick Reference: For Healthcare, Social Service, & Law Enforcement Professionals. 2012. (ENG., Illus.). 350p. spiral bd. 52.00 (978-1-878060-45-7(7)) STM Learning, Inc.

Vincent-Lum, Sharon. Children Experiencing Domestic Abuse. Stafford, Anne, ed. 2010. 110p. pap. 26.95 (978-1-903765-97-5(8)) Dunedin Academic Pr. GBR. Dist: International Specialized Bk. Services.

Vincent, Sharon. Learning from Child Deaths & Serious Abuse. 2010. 133p. pap. 26.95 *(978-1-903765-96-8(X))* Dunedin Academic Pr. GBR. Dist: International Specialized Bk. Services.

Watson, Douglas Duane. Pretzels & Ginger Ale. 2011. 140p. pap. 24.95 ***(978-1-4560-3720-8(X))*** PublishAmerica, Inc.

Wekerle, Christine, et al. Childhood Maltreatment. 2006. (Advances in Psychotherapy — Evidence-Based Practice Ser.: Vol. 4). (Illus.). 100p. pap. 29.80 *(978-0-88937-314-3(0))* Hogrefe Publishing.

Western Schools. The Body Never Lies. 2007. wbk. ed. 69.95 *(978-1-57801-206-0(6))* Western Schls.

Whitman, Jennifer. Of Hushed Silence: A Story of Child Abuse. 2011. 108p. 22.99 ***(978-1-4634-3747-3(1))***; pap. 15.99 ***(978-1-4634-3749-7(8))*** AuthorHouse.

Wood, Darla. The Little Girl in the Corner, 1 vol. 2010. 48p. pap. 16.95 *(978-1-4489-5310-3(3))* PublishAmerica, Inc.

World Vision International. Protecting Children: Improving the ICC to respond to Children & Armed Conflict. 2010. 36p. *(978-0-9822649-5-9(X))* World Vision International.

CHILD ABUSE—PREVENTION

Ammerman, Robert T. & Hersen, Michel, eds. Children at Risk. 2010. (ENG.). 332p. pap. 89.95 *(978-1-4419-3214-3(3),* 1441932143) Springer.

Bailey, Judith A. & Cottom, Robert I. Programs & Interventions for Maltreated Children & Families at Risk. Rubin, Allen, ed. 2011. (Clinician's Guide to Evidence-Based Practice Ser.: 5). (ENG.). 354p. pap. 55.00 *(978-0-470-89063-9(0),* Wiley) Wiley, John & Sons, Inc.

Barker, Judy & Hodes, Deborah. The Child in Mind. 3rd rev. ed. 2007. (Illus.). 128p. 31.95 *(978-0-415-42602-2(2))* Routledge.

—The Child in Mind: A Child Protection Handbook. 4th rev. ed. 2012. (ENG.). 136p. 115.00 *(978-0-415-60995-1(X))*; pap. 31.95 *(978-0-415-60996-8(8))* Routledge.

Brown, Sue. Spirit Unbroken: A Journey of Hope, Survival, & Beating the Odds. 2008. 200p. pap. 24.95 *(978-1-60563-408-1(5))* PublishAmerica, Inc.

Chadwick, David L. The Child Abuse Doctors. 2010. (Illus.). 192p. lib. bdg. 35.00 *(978-1-878060-69-3(4))* STM Learning, Inc.

Cram101 Textbook Reviews & Cram101 Textbook Reviews. Outlines & Highlights for Apsac Handbook on Child Maltreatment by Jordan Greenbaum, Isbn: 9781412966818. 2011. 180p. pap. 29.95 ***(978-1-61461-141-7(6))*** Cram101 Inc.

—Outlines & Highlights for Effective Child Protection by Eileen Munro, Isbn: 9781412946940. 2011. 86p. pap. 27.95 ***(978-1-61461-076-2(2))*** Cram101 Inc.

Daniel, Brigid, et al. Recognizing & Helping the Neglected Child: Evidence-Based Practice for Assessment & Intervention. 2011. (ENG., Illus.). 176p. pap. ***(978-1-84905-093-7(7))*** Kingsley, Jessica Ltd.

Daro, Deborah. Confronting Child Abuse. 2007. (ENG.). 368p. pap. 23.95 *(978-1-4165-7334-0(8),* Free Pr.) Free Pr.

Daro, Deborah, ed. World Perspectives on Child Abuse: Eighth Edition (2008) 8th ed. 2008. (Illus.). vi, 242p. pap. 35.00 *(978-0-9787530-1-6(1))* ISPCAN.

Davidson, Julia & Gottschalk, Petter, eds. Internet Child Abuse: Current Research & Policy. 2010. (Illus.). 216p. 125.00 *(978-0-415-55980-5(4),* Routledge Cavendish) Taylor & Francis Group GBR. Dist: Taylor & Francis Group.

Dawes, Mark & Jones, Deborah. Understanding Unreasonable Force. 2007. 180p. per. *(978-1-84667-030-5(6))* Derwent Pr., The.

Dedel, Kelly. Child Abuse & Neglect in the Home. 2010. 72p. pap. *(978-1-935676-00-3(8))* U.S. Dept. of Justice-COPS.

Duncan, Karen A. Female Sexual Predators: Understanding Them to Protect Our Children & Youths, 1 vol. 2010. (Forensic Psychology Ser.). 241p. 44.95 *(978-0-313-36629-1(2),* C36629, Praeger Pubs.) Greenwood Publishing Group, Inc.

Erooga, Marcus. Creating Safer Organisations: Practical Steps to Prevent the Abuse of Children by Those Working with Them. 2012. (Wiley Child Protection & Policy Ser.). (ENG.). 210p. 119.95 ***(978-1-119-97269-3(8))***; pap. 49.95 ***(978-1-119-97268-6(X))*** Wiley, John & Sons, Inc. (Wiley).

Galano, Joseph, ed. The Healthy Families America Initiative: Integrating Research, Theory & Practice. 2007. (ENG., Illus.). 256p. pap. 45.95 *(978-0-7890-3681-0(9))* Routledge.

Giardino, Angelo P., et al. Child Safety: A Pediatric Guide for Parents, Teachers, Nurses, & Caregivers. 2007. (ENG., Illus.). 341p. 33.00 *(978-1-878060-67-9(8))* STM Learning, Inc.

Gray, Jenny, ed. World Perspectives on Child Abuse: Ninth Edition (2010) 2010. lib. bdg. 45.00 *(978-0-9787530-2-3(X))* ISPCAN.

Hirschy, Sharon & Wilkinson, Elaine. Protecting Our Children: Understanding & Preventing Abuse & Neglect in Early Childhood. 2009. (ENG., Illus.). 288p. (C). pap. 46.95 *(978-1-4283-6124-9(3))* Delmar Cengage Learning.

Hobart, Christine & Frankel, Jill. Good Practice in Safeguarding Children 3rd Edition. Walker, Miranda, ed. 3rd rev. ed. 2009. (ENG., Illus.). 224p. pap. 57.50 ***(978-1-4085-0491-8(X))*** Nelson Thornes Ltd. GBR. Dist: Trans-Atlantic Pubns., Inc.

Housden, Leslie. Prevention of Cruelty to Children. *(978-0-8022-0748-7(0))* Philosophical Library, Inc.

Hunter, Sue, et al. I'M a Great Little Kid, 1 vol. 2009. (ENG.). 272p. (J). spiral bd. 24.95 *(978-1-896764-69-6(X))* Second Story Pr. CAN. Dist: Orca Bk. Pubs. USA.

Kay, Janet. Protecting Children. pap. *(978-0-8264-5802-5(5))* Continuum International Publishing Group, Ltd.

Kirton, Beatrice E. Understanding Child Abuse & Neglect in Contemporary Caribbean Society: A Recipe for Change. 2011. 272p. pap. 19.95 ***(978-1-4670-3832-4(6))*** AuthorHouse.

Langwith, Jacqueline, ed. Child Abuse. 2011. (Introducing Issues with Opposing Viewpoints Ser.). (Illus.). 144p. (YA). (gr. 9-12). 35.75 *(978-0-7377-5672-2(1))* Cengage Gale.

Lutzker, John R., ed. Handbook of Child Abuse Research & Treatment. 2012. (Issues in Clinical Child Psychology Ser.). (ENG.). 596p. pap. 199.00 *(978-1-4419-3278-5(X),* 144193278X) Springer.

Mcfall, Michael. Licensing Parents: Family, State, & Child Maltreatment. 2010. (ENG.). 248p. pap. 32.95 *(978-0-7391-2914-2(7))* Lexington Bks.

McFall, Michael T. Licensing Parents: Family, State, & Child Maltreatment. 2009. (ENG.). 248p. 78.99 *(978-0-7391-2913-5(9))* Lexington Bks.

Myers, John E. B., ed. Child Maltreatment: A Collection of Readings. 2011. (Illus.). 384p. (C). pap. 36.00 *(978-1-4129-9506-1(X),* B95061P) SAGE Pubns., Inc.

Powell, Catherine. Safeguarding Children & Young People: A Practice Companion for Nurses & Midwives. 2011. (ENG.). 176p. (C). pap. 39.00 ***(978-0-335-23614-5(6)***, 0335236146) McGraw-Hill Education GBR. Dist: McGraw-Hill Cos., The.

Preventing Child Abuse & Improving Responses to Families in Crisis: Hearing Before the Subcommittee on Healthy Families & Communities, Committee on Education & Labor, U.S. House of Representatives, One Hundred Eleventh Congress, First Session, Hearing Held in Washington, DC, November 5, 2009. 2010. (Illus.). iii, 123p. *(978-0-16-086315-8(5),* 552-070-41402-9) United States Government Printing Office.

Protecting Children, Strengthening Families: Reauthorizing CAPTA: Hearing Before the Subcommittee on Children & Families of the Committee on Health, Education, Labor, & Pensions, United States Senate, One Hundred Tenth Congress, Second Session, on Examining Reauthorization of the Child Abuse Prevention & Treatment ACT (CAPTA) (Public Law 93-247), Focusing on Protecting Children & Strengthening Families, June 26, 2008. 2009. iii, 83p. *(978-0-16-084909-1(8),* 552-070-40305-1) United States Government Printing Office.

Schlaack, Holly. Invisible Kids: Marcus Fiesel's Legacy: One Short Life, One Terrible Death & 12 Things YOU Can Do to Improve the Lives of Foster Children. 2009. 201p. pap. 18.95 *(978-0-615-22976-8(X))* Advocacy Publishing.

Seth, Joshua B. Offenders & Abuse: An Awareness Guide to Shielding the Community. 2009. (ENG.). 511p. pap. 34.95 *(978-1-60813-129-7(7))* PublishAmerica, Inc.

Shannon, Joyce, ed. Child Abuse Sourcebook. 2nd rev. ed. 2009. (Health Reference Ser.). 632p. lib. bdg. 93.00 *(978-0-7808-1037-2(6))* Omnigraphics, Inc.

Shelton, William. It's Okay, You're with My Father: (A Child Abuse Investigator's Call to the Church) 2011. 104p. pap. 10.00 ***(978-1-4497-2078-0(1)***, WestBow Pr.) Author Solutions, Inc.

Sinason, Valerie, et al. Psychoanalytic Psychotherapies in the Treatment & Care of Individuals who have Experienced Sexual Abuse, Violence & Neglect in Childhood: Victims of Violence & Abuse Prevention Program Guideline. 2008. 120p. pap. 41.00 *(978-1-85575-639-7(0))* Karnac Bks. GBR. Dist: Stylus Publishing, LLC.

The Spanking Writers. 2008. 40.95 *(978-0-9558483-0-8(X))* Abelard Bks. GBR. Dist: Lulu Enterprises Inc.

Sterne. Domestic Violence & Children: A Handbook for Schools & Early Years Settings. 2009. (ENG., Illus.). 160p. (C). 37.95 *(978-0-415-46551-9(6))* Routledge.

Sterne, Abigail & Poole, Liz. Domestic Violence & Children: A Handbook for Schools & Early Years Settings. 2009. (ENG., Illus.). 160p. (C). 130.00 *(978-0-415-55632-3(5))* Routledge.

Vissing, Yvonne Marie & Vissing, Yvonne. How to Keep Your Children Safe: A Guide for Parents. 2007. (ENG., Illus.). 216p. pap. 12.95 *(978-1-58465-529-9(1))* Univ. Pr. of New England.

Whitaker, Daniel J. & Lutzker, John R., eds. Preventing Partner Violence: Research & Evidence-Based Intervention Strategies. 2009. 320p. 59.95 *(978-1-4338-0434-2(4))* American Psychological Assn.

Whitney, Ben. Social Inclusion in Schools: Improving Outcomes, Raising Standards. 2007. (David Fulton Bks.). (Illus.). 112p. per. 37.50 *(978-1-84312-474-0(2))* Routledge.

Zero to Three (Organization) Staff, contrib. by. Preventing Child Abuse & Neglect: Parent-Provider Partnerships in Child Care. 2006. *(978-0-943657-98-1(9))* Zero To Three Pr.

CHILD ABUSE—REPORTING

Abuse: A Quick Reference Guide, 2 vols. Incl. Early Recognition of Child Abuse & Neglect: A Quick Reference Guide. Otterman, Gabriel J. & Elliot, Diana M., eds. (Illus.). 34p. 1996. spiral bd. 9.95 *(978-1-887272-06-3(2))*; Early Recognition of Domestic Violence: A Quick Reference Guide. Robertson, Jennifer L. & Chambliss, Linda R., eds. (Illus.). 40p. 1997. pap. 9.95 *(978-1-887272-09-4(7))*; Early Recognition of Elder Abuse. Weinberg, Andrew D. & Wei, Jeanne Y., eds. 36p. 1995. spiral bd. 9.95 *(978-1-887272-05-6(4))*; *(978-1-887272-07-0(0))* American Medical Publishing Co., Inc.

Chadwick, David L., et al. Child Maltreatment 4E; Set with CD-ROM: A Clinical Guide & Reference & A Comprehensive Photographic Reference Identifying Potential Child Abuse, 2 vols. 4th ed. 2012. (Illus.). 375.00 incl. cd-rom *(978-1-878060-94-5(5))* STM Learning, Inc.

Giardino, Angelo P. & Alexander, Randell. Child Abuse Quick Reference 2E: For Healthcare, Social Service, & Law Enforcement Professionals. 2nd rev. ed. 2006. (ENG., Illus.). 448p. spiral bd. 52.00 *(978-1-878060-60-0(0))* STM Learning, Inc.

Lau, Kenneth J., et al. Mandated Reporting of Child Abuse & Neglect: A Practical Guide for Social Workers. 2008. 224p. 45.00 *(978-0-8261-1098-5(3))* Springer Publishing Co., Inc.

Reardon, Kathleen Kelley & Noblet, Christopher T. Childhood Denied: Ending the Nightmare of Child Abuse & Neglect. 2008. 256p. (C). 82.00 *(978-1-4129-3976-8(3),* B39763C); (Illus.). pap. 35.00 *(978-1-4129-3977-5(1),* B39763P) SAGE Pubns., Inc.

CHILD ABUSE SURVIVORS

see Adult Child Abuse Victims

CHILD ABUSE VICTIMS

see Abused Children

CHILD ABUSE VICTIMS, ADULT

see Adult Child Abuse Victims

CHILD ACTORS

Cameron, Barbara. A Full House of Growing Pains: A Hollywood Mother's Journey. 2006. (Illus.). 245p. 19.99 *(978-0-88270-189-9(4))* Bridge-Logos Foundation.

Coghlan, Frank. They Still Call Me Junior: Autobiography of a Child Star; with a Filmography. alt. ed. 2011. (ENG., Illus.). 383p. pap. 29.95 *(978-0-7864-6381-7(3))* McFarland & Co., Inc. Pubs.

Cole, Julie Dawn & Esslinger, Michael. I Want It Now! a Memoir of Life on the Set of Willy Wonka & the Chocolate Factory. 2011. 252p. pap. 21.95 ***(978-1-59393-074-5(7))*** BearManor Media.

Diamond, Dustin. Behind the Bell. 2009. (ENG., Illus.). 311p. 25.00 *(978-0-9812396-9-9(2))* Transit Publishing (Transit Editeur Inc.) CAN. Dist: Midpoint Trade Bks., Inc.

Hawes, Jo. Children in Theatre: From the Audition to Working in Professional Theatre: A Guide for Children & Their Parents. 2012. (ENG.). 180p. pap. 30.95 ***(978-1-84943-127-9(2))*** Oberon Bks., Ltd. GBR. Dist: Consortium Bk. Sales & Distribution.

Kaye, Darwood. Finding Waldo: From Little Rascal to Adventist Pastor. 2009. 15.99 *(978-0-8163-2376-0(3))* Pacific Pr. Publishing Assn.

Knowlden, Marilyn. Little Girl in Big Pictures. 2011. 456p. pap. 24.95 ***(978-1-59393-638-9(9))*** BearManor Media.

Lamb, Edel. Performing Childhood in the Early Modern Theatre: The Children's Playing Companies (1599-1613) 2008. (Early Modern Literature in History Ser.). (ENG., Illus.). 224p. 89.00 *(978-0-230-20261-0(6))* Palgrave Macmillan.

Lury, Karen. The Child in Film: Tears, Fears, & Fairy Tales. 2010. (Rutgers Series in Childhood Studies). (ENG.). 220p. (C). 72.00 *(978-0-8135-4895-1(0))*; pap. 24.95 *(978-0-8135-4896-8(9))* Rutgers Univ. Pr.

O'Connor, Jane Catherine. The Cultural Significance of the Child Star. (Routledge Advances in Sociology Ser.). (ENG., Illus.). 190p. 2012. pap. 42.95 ***(978-0-415-54267-8(7))*** 2007. 125.00 *(978-0-415-96157-8(2))* Routledge.

Ott, Meredith. Child Actor Ethics. 2010. 72p. pap. *(978-3-8383-8707-9(4))* Lambert Academic Publishing.

People Magazine Editors. Child Stars Then & Now: Catching up with More Than 100 Showbiz Kids. Where Are They Today? Durkee, Cutler, ed. 2008. (ENG., Illus.). 144p. (YA). (gr. 7-17). 29.95 *(978-1-60320-014-1(2),* People Bks.) Time Home Entertainment, Inc.

Sweetin, Jodie. Unsweetined: A Memoir. (ENG., Illus.). 256p. 2010. pap. 15.00 *(978-1-4391-5269-0(1))* 2009. 25.99 *(978-1-4391-5268-3(3))* Gallery Pr., The IRL. Dist: Simon & Schuster, Inc.

Thomas, Jr. & Menefee, David. Otay! - the Billy Buckwheat Thomas Story. 2010. 100p. pap. 14.95 *(978-1-59393-519-1(6))* BearManor Media.

Thomas, Jr. & Menefee, David W. Otay! - the Billy Buckwheat Thomas Story. 2010. 160p. 24.95 *(978-1-59393-207-7(3))* BearManor Media.

CHILD-ADULT RELATIONSHIPS

see Children and Adults

CHILD ADVOCACY (LAW)

see Legal Assistance to Children

CHILD ANALYSIS

Bond, Alma Halbert. Margaret Mahler: A Biography of the Psychoanalyst. 2008. (ENG., Illus.). 251p. pap. 45.00 *(978-0-7864-3355-1(8))* McFarland & Co., Inc. Pubs.

Frank, Elizabe, Claudia;Spillius. Melanie Klein in Berlin: Her First Psychoanalyses of Children. 2009. (New Library of Psychoanalysis Ser.). (ENG., Illus.). 504p. (C). 125.00 *(978-0-415-48497-8(9))*; pap. 42.50 *(978-0-415-48498-5(7))* Routledge.

Freud, Anna. Psychoanalysis for Teachers & Parents. 2007. (ENG.). 124p. pe. *(978-1-4067-4736-2(X))* Read Bks.

Gunter, Michael. Technique in Child & Adolescent Analysis. 2010. (Illus.). 156p. pap. 37.95 *(978-1-85575-715-8(X))* Karnac Bks. GBR. Dist: Stylus Publishing, LLC.

Gunter, Michael & Franieck, M. Leticia. On Latency: Individual Development, Narcissistic Impulse, Reminiscence & Cultural Ideal. 2010. 140p. pap. 28.95 *(978-1-85575-740-0(0))* Karnac Bks. GBR. Dist: Stylus Publishing, LLC.

Hall. Theory Practice Child Psychoanalysis: An Introduction to the Work of Francoise Dolto. 2009. 320p. pap. 39.95 *(978-1-85575-574-1(2))* Karnac Bks. GBR. Dist: Stylus Publishing, LLC.

Horne, Ann. Through Assessment to Consultation. 2009. (ENG.). 208p. (C). 100.00 *(978-0-415-46289-1(4))* Routledge.

Horne, Ann & Lanyado, Monica, eds. Through Assessment to Consultation: Independent Psychoanalytic Approaches with Children & Adolescents. 2009. (ENG.). 208p. (C). pap. 34.95 *(978-0-415-46290-7(8))* Routledge.

Institute of Psycho-Analysis Staff, contrib. by. Psychoanalytic Study of the Child. viii, 544p. *(978-0-7012-0401-3(X),* Hogarth Pr.) Random Hse.

King, Robert A. The Psychoanalytic Study of the Child, Vol. 63. Abrams, Samuel et al, eds. 2009. (Psychoanalytic Study of the Child Ser.). (ENG., Illus.). 336p. 65.00 *(978-0-300-14099-6(1))* Yale Univ. Pr.

King, Robert A., et al, eds. The Psychoanalytic Study of the Child. (Psychoanalytic Study of the Child Ser.). (ENG.). Vol. 62. 2008. 384p. 65.00 *(978-0-300-12540-5(2))* Vol. 64. 2010. (Illus.). 368p. 75.00 *(978-0-300-15329-3(5))* Vol. 65. 2012. (Illus.). 384p. 65.00 ***(978-0-300-16544-9(7))*** Yale Univ. Pr.

Lanyado, Monica. The Handbook of Child & Adolescent Psychotherapy: Psychoanalytic Approaches. 2nd ed. 2009. (ENG., Illus.). 480p. (C). instr.'s hndbk. ed. 105.00 *(978-0-415-46368-3(8))* Routledge.

—The Handbook of Child & Adolescent Psychotherapy: Psychoanalytic Approaches. Lanyado, Monica & Horne, Ann, eds. 2nd rev. ed. 2009. (ENG., Illus.). 480p. (C). 39.95 *(978-0-415-46369-0(6))* Routledge.

Midgley, Nick. Child Psychotherapy & Research: New Approaches, Emerging Findings. Grainger, Eve et al, eds. 2009. (ENG., Illus.). 248p. (C). 110.00 *(978-0-415-42202-4(7))* Routledge.

—Child Psychotherapy & Research: New Approaches, Emerging Findings. Nesic-Vuckovic, Tanja et al, eds. 2009. (ENG., Illus.). 248p. (C). pap. 40.00 *(978-0-415-42203-1(5))* Routledge.

Miller, Jill & Elliot-Neely, Carla, eds. Work of Hansi Kennedy. 2008. (Illus.). 336p. pap. 58.50 *(978-1-85575-523-9(8))* Karnac Bks. GBR. Dist: Stylus Publishing, LLC.

Rey-Flaud, Henri. Les Enfants de L'indicible Peur: Nouveau Regard Sur L'autisme. 2010. (FRE., Illus.). 519p. *(978-2-7007-0402-0(9))* Montaigne, Editions.

Roth, Silke. Encounters with Melanie Klein: Selected Papers of Elizabeth Spillius 2007. (New Library of Psychoanalysis Ser.). (ENG., Illus.). 264p. (C). 125.00 *(978-0-415-41998-7(0))* Routledge.

Spillius, Elizabeth Bott. Encounters with Melanie Klein. Roth, Priscilla & Rusbridger, Richard, eds. 2007. (New Library of Psychoanalysis Ser.). (ENG., Illus.). 264p. (C). per. 42.50 *(978-0-415-41999-4(9))* Routledge.

Tuber, Steven. Attachment, Play, & Authenticity: A Winnicott Primer. 2008. (ENG.). 224p. 78.99 *(978-0-7657-0541-9(9))*; per. 41.99 *(978-0-7657-0542-6(7))* Rowman & Littlefield Publishers, Inc. (Aronson, Jason).

Winnicott. Psycho-Analytic Explorations. 2010. 614p. pap. 57.95 *(978-1-85575-853-7(9))* Karnac Bks. GBR. Dist: Stylus Publishing, LLC.

Youell, Biddy. The Learning Relationship: Psychoanalytic Thinking in Education. 2006. (Tavistock Clinic Ser.). 192p. per. 36.00 *(978-1-85575-227-6(1))* Karnac Bks. GBR. Dist: Stylus Publishing, LLC.

CHILD AND ADULT

see Children and Adults

CHILD AND MOTHER

see Mother and Child

CHILD AND PARENT

see Parent and Child

CHILD ARTISTS

Beck, Walter. Self-Development in Drawing As Interpreted by the Genius of Romano. 2006. (ENG.). 304p. per. 28.95 *(978-1-4286-6040-3(2))* Kessinger Publishing, LLC.

Gerhardt, Melissa K. So You Think Your Kid Can Dance?, 1 vol. 2009. 73p. pap. 16.95 *(978-1-60836-718-4(5))* PublishAmerica, Inc.

Milbrath, Constance & Trautner, Hanns M., eds. Children's Understanding & Production of Pictures, Drawings, & Art: Theoretical & Empirical Approaches. 2007. (Illus.). 352p. pap. 44.00 *(978-0-88937-350-1(7))* Hogrefe Publishing.

Miller, Eileen. The Girl Who Spoke with Pictures: Autism Through Art. 2008. (ENG., Illus.). 208p. *(978-1-84310-889-4(5))* Kingsley, Jessica Ltd.

Mitlin, Mariell & Anderson, Carole. Mariell Mitlin. Paintings & Graphics. 2007. 100p. per. *(978-0-9787293-2-5(3))* Mitlin & Assocs.

Raczka, Bob. Before They Were Famous: How Seven Artists Got Their Start. 2011. (Bob Raczka's Art Adventures Ser.). pap. 9.95 ***(978-0-7613-7300-1(4)***, Millbrook Pr.) Lerner Publishing Group.

Selfe, Lorna. Nadia Revisited. 2011. (ENG., Illus.). 272p. (C). 54.95 *(978-1-84872-038-1(6),* Psychology Press) Taylor & Francis Group GBR. Dist: Taylor & Francis Group.

Szekely. Art Teaching. 2011. (ENG., Illus.). 456p. pap. 89.95 *(978-0-415-99058-5(0))* Routledge.

Weissberger, Jose A., ed. They Still Draw Pictures: A Collection of Sixty Drawings Made by Spanish Children During the War. 2011. 78p. 37.95 ***(978-1-258-05636-0(4))*** Literary Licensing, LLC.

CHILD AUTHORS

Here are entered works on child authors and-or discussions of their works. Collections of works published for children are entered under Children's Literature. Works on the reading interests of children, and-or lists of books read by or recommended for children, are entered under Children—Books and Reading. Collections of literary works or individual literary works written by children under 15 years of age are entered under Children's Writings.

Fuentes. Diary of a Dirty Boy. Date not set. 14.50 *(978-1-888425-14-7(8))* Ophelia Editions.

Shore, Emily. Journal of Emily Shore. 2009. 230p. pap. 20.59 *(978-1-150-35352-9(X))* General Bks. LLC.

C

—Journal of Emily Shore. 373p. reprint ed. 98.00 (978-0-7222-1747-4(1)) Library Reprints, Inc.

Tunks, Karyn Wellhousen & Giles, Rebecca McMahon. Write Now! Publishing with Young Authors, PreK-Grade 2. 2007. (Illus.). 112p. pap. 20.00 (978-0-325-00911-7(2), E00911) Heinemann.

Wadelton, Tommy. My Father Is a Quiet Man. 2007. (ENG.). 178p. 37.95 (978-0-548-06433-7(4)) Kessinger Publishing, LLC.

CHILD BEHAVIOR

see Child Psychology; Child Rearing; Etiquette for Children and Teenagers

CHILD BEHAVIOR DISORDERS

see Behavior Disorders in Children

CHILD BIRTH

see Childbirth

CHILD CARE

see also Child Rearing; Children—Institutional Care

Alcott, William A. The Young Mother: Management of Children in Regard to Health. 2007. (ENG.). 202p. pap. 20.99 (978-1-4346-2153-5(7)); 226p. pap. 22.99 (978-1-4346-2213-6(4)) BiblioBazaar.

Alcott, William A. The Young Mother: Management of Children in Regard to Health. 2007. (ENG.). 210p. pap. 20.99 (978-1-4264-0877-9(3)) 2006. 194p. pap. 21.99 (978-1-4264-0858-8(7)) BiblioBazaar.

American Academy of Pediatrics. Patient Education for Children, Teens, & Parents: Patient Education Compendium. 4th ed. 2011. (ENG.). 464p. pap. 119.95 **(978-1-58110-566-7(5))** American Academy of Pediatrics.

American Academy Of Pediatrics, et al. Caring for Your Baby & Young Child: Birth to Age 5. 5th ed. 2009. (ENG., Illus.). 928p. pap. 22.00 (978-0-553-38630-1(1)) Random House Publishing Group.

American Academy of Pediatrics (AAP) Staff. Paediatric First Aid for Carers & Teachers. rev. ed. 2009. 336p. pap. 16.95 (978-0-7637-8263-4(7)) Jones & Bartlett Learning, LLC.

American Academy of Pediatrics Staff. El Cuidado de su Hijo Pequeno: Desde Que Nace Hasta Los Cincos Anos. 2nd ed. 2006. (SPA & ENG., Illus.). 896p. pap. 21.00 (978-0-553-38423-9(6), Bantam) Random House Publishing Group.

American Academy of Pediatrics Staff, contrib. by. Patient Education for Children, Teens, & Parents. 3rd ed. 2007. (Illus.). xii, 436p. (978-1-58110-231-4(3)) American Academy of Pediatrics.

Aronson & Cram101 Textbook Reviews Staff. Healthy Young Children. 2007. 60p. per. 9.95 (978-1-4288-2052-4(3)) Cram101 Inc.

Auerbach, Stevanne. Child Care - A Comprehensive Guide Vol. 2: Model Programs & Their Components, 4 vols. 2011. 320p. pap. 21.95 (978-1-4502-3195-4(0)) iUniverse, Inc.

—Child Care: A Comprehensive Guide: Creative Homes & Centers: Foreword by Edward Zigler, PhD. 2011. 300p. pap. 21.95 (978-1-4502-3199-2(3)) iUniverse, Inc.

—Child Care: A Comprehensive Guide: Rationale for Child Care Services Programs vs Politics. 2011. 252p. pap. 21.95 (978-1-4502-3194-7(2)) iUniverse, Inc.

Auerbach, Stevanne. Confronting the Child Care Crisis. 2011. 144p. pap. 21.95 **(978-1-4502-3518-1(2))** iUniverse, Inc.

Australian Women's Weekly Staff. Baby Health. (Australian Women's Weekly Parenting Guides). (Illus.). 64p. pap. 5.95 (978-1-86396-225-4(5)) ACP Publishing Pty, Ltd. AUS. Dist: Graphic Arts Ctr. Publishing Co.

Azar. When the Tooth Fairy Is Not Enough. 2008. 24p. pap. 18.99 (978-1-4389-2748-0(7)) AuthorHouse.

Baillargeon, Denyse & Wilson, W. Donald. Babies for the Nation: The Medicalization of Motherhood in Quebec, 1910-1970. 2009. (Studies in Childhood & Family in Canada Ser.). (ENG.). 342p. pap. 42.95 (978-1-55458-058-3(7)) Wilfrid Laurier Univ. Pr. CAN. Dist: Univ. of Toronto Pr.

Baker, Heather, et al. Come Cook with Me. 2010. (978-1-60617-146-2(1)) Teaching Strategies, Inc.

Beare, Sr. Parenting: A View from the Therapist's Chair. 2009. 163p. 28.97 (978-0-557-17169-9(5)); pap. 18.97 (978-0-557-17194-1(6)) Lulu Enterprises Inc.

Belenky Ph. D., Robert. Tales of Priut Almus. 2009. 320p. 32.95 (978-1-4401-3153-0(8)); pap. 22.95 (978-1-4401-3151-6(1)) iUniverse, Inc.

Bergen, Doris, et al. Educating & Caring for Very Young Children: The Infant/Toddler Curriculum. 2nd rev. ed. 2008. (Early Childhood Education Ser.). (ENG., Illus.). 224p. pap. 26.95 (978-0-8077-4920-3(6)) Teachers College Pr., Teachers College, Columbia Univ.

Berke, Kai-Lee, et al. A Trainer's Guide to the Creative Curriculum for Infants, Toddlers & Twos. 2007. (978-1-933021-37-9(3)) Teaching Strategies, Inc.

Berry, Judy O. Lifespan Perspectives on the Family & Disability. 2nd ed. 2008. pap. 73.00 (978-1-4164-0379-1(5)) PRO-ED, Inc.

Bigmore, Jenny & Davey, Jill. Child Care Social Work. 2009. (Illus.). 105p. pap. (978-1-84445-180-7(1)) Learning Matters Ltd.

Blackard, Sandra R. SAY WHAT YOU SEE for Parents & Teachers. 4th ed. 2008. (ENG., Illus.). 56p. 7.95 (978-0-9800015-0-1(1)) Language of Listening.

Blaine, Tasha. Just Like Family: Inside the Lives of Nannies, the Parents They Work for, & the Children They Love. (ENG.). 336p. 2010. pap. 14.95 (978-0-547-33583-4(0), Mariner Bks.) 2009. 25.00 (978-0-15-101051-6(X)) Houghton Mifflin Harcourt Trade & Reference Pubs.

Bloch, Marianne N. Governing Young Children, Families, & Their Care: A Critical Policy Analysis of Early Education & Child Care. 2013. (Critical Cultural Studies of Childhood Ser.). (ENG., Illus.). 256p. 85.00 (978-0-230-62177-0(5)) Palgrave Macmillan.

Bounds, Bill. Forty Weeks of Keeping Your Head Down: A Chronicle of One Man's Journey from Guy to Father. 2010. 200p. pap. 16.95 (978-1-4502-0391-3(4)) iUniverse, Inc.

Bouyer, Rene-Jean. Les Mémoires D'un Bébé: Un Siècle D'éducation de L'enfant de Pasteur à Dolto. 2010. (FRE., Illus.). 221p. (978-2-35013-232-7(3)) Gawsewitch, Jean-Claude.

Bowen Shea, Sarah & Schlosberg, Suzanne. The Essential Breastfeeding Log: A Feedings Tracker & Baby-Care Organizer for Nursing Moms. 2009. (ENG.). 240p. pap. 15.00 (978-0-345-50649-8(9), Ballantine Bks.) Random House Publishing Group.

Bowlby, Sophia. Interdependency & Care over the Lifecourse. 2009. (Relationships & Resources Ser.). (Illus.). 224p. 110.00 (978-0-415-43466-9(1)) Routledge.

Bowlby, Sophia, et al. Interdependency & Care over the Lifecourse. 2010. (Relationships & Resources Ser.). (ENG., Illus.). 200p. (C). 40.95 (978-0-415-43467-6(X)) Routledge.

Brown-Quinn, Christine. Step Aside Superwoman! Career & Family Is for Any Woman. 2010. 168p. pap. (978-1-907498-38-1(9), Book Shaker) Lean Marketing Pr.

Brown, Tamara. Raising Brooklyn: Nannies, Childcare, & Caribbeans Creating Community. 2011. (ENG.). 240p. 75.00 (978-0-8147-9142-4(5)); pap. 22.00 (978-0-8147-9143-1(3)) New York Univ. Pr.

Bruce, Tina, ed. Early Childhood: A Guide for Students. (Illus.). (C). 2006. 344p. 116.00 (978-1-4129-2075-9(2), B20752C) 2006. 344p. per. 47.95 (978-1-4129-2076-6(0), B20752P) 2nd ed. 2010. 440p. 112.00 (978-1-84860-223-6(5), B02236C) 2nd ed. 2010. 440p. pap. 46.00 (978-1-84860-224-3(3), B02236P) SAGE Pubns., Ltd. GBR. Dist: SAGE Pubns., Inc.

Calder, Martin C., ed. Contemporary Risk Assessment in Safeguarding Children. 2008. (Illus.). 290p. pap. 65.00 (978-1-905541-20-1(1)) Russell Hse. Publishing Ltd. GBR. Dist: International Specialized Bk. Services.

Cameron, Claire & Moss, Peter, eds. Social Pedagogy & Working with Children & Young People: Where Care & Education Meet. 2011. (ENG., Illus.). 224p. pap. (978-1-84905-119-4(4)) Kingsley, Jessica Ltd.

Cameron, Hector Charles. The Nervous Child. 2008. 152p. 24.99 (978-0-554-27768-4(9)) 2008. 152p. 21.99 (978-0-554-37071-2(9)) 2007. (ENG.). 134p. pap. 18.99 (978-1-4346-3956-1(8)) 2007. (ENG.). 148p. pap. 19.99 (978-1-4346-3957-8(6)) BiblioBazaar.

—The Nervous Child. 2008. 136p. pap. (978-1-4099-1270-5(1)) Dodo Pr.

—The Nervous Child. 2007. 100p. per. (978-1-4068-4169-5(2)) Echo Library.

Cannella, Gaile Sloan & Soto, Lourdes Diaz. Childhoods: A Handbook. 2010. (Rethinking Childhood Ser.). 416p. (C). 155.95 (978-1-4331-0451-0(2)); pap. 49.95 (978-1-4331-0450-3(4)) Lang, Peter Publishing, Inc.

Capps, Ronald R. A Parent's Guide to Locating Responsible Child Care. 2007. pap. (978-0-9801657-0-8(9)) Masters Level Publishing, LLC.

Chalmers, Almarie. The Ball Is in Your Court: Embracing Your Child's Dreams. 2010. (ENG.). 100p. pap. 13.99 (978-1-59932-213-1(7)) Advantage Media Group.

Child Care Skills. 2008. (C). pap., stu. ed., wbk. ed. 10.95 (978-1-4018-8231-0(5)) Delmar Cengage Learning.

Child Care Skills Student Motivation Kit. 2008. (C). 132.00 (978-1-4018-8230-3(7)) Delmar Cengage Learning.

Clark County Fire District 11 Staff. Child Life: A Safety Course Designed for Child Care. 39p. pap. 8.00 (978-0-9637692-0-6(0)) Clark County Fire District Number 11.

Clifford-Poston, Andrea. A Playworkers Guide to Understanding Children's Behaviour: Working with the 8-12 Age Group. 2008. 240p. pap. 38.95 (978-1-85575-494-2(0)) Karnac Bks. GBR. Dist: Stylus Publishing, LLC.

Collinge, Justin. Understanding Edward. 2010. 156p. pap. 20.95 (978-1-4466-4509-3(6)) Lulu Enterprises Inc.

Comfort, Randy Lee. Searching to Be Found: Understanding & Helping Adopted & Looked after Children with Attention Difficulties. 2008. 206p. pap. 38.95 (978-1-85575-464-5(9)) Karnac Bks. GBR. Dist: Stylus Publishing, LLC.

Committee on Early Childhood Care and Education Workforce: A Workshop, et al. The Early Childhood Care & Education Workforce: Challenges & Opportunities: A Workshop Report. 2012. (ENG.). 224p. pap. 47.00 **(978-0-309-21934-1(5))** National Academies Pr.

Committee on the Future of Emergency Care in the United States Health System. Emergency Care for Children: Growing Pains. 2007. (ENG., Illus.). 360p. 43.95 (978-0-309-10171-4(9)) National Academies Pr.

Cram101 Textbook Reviews. Outlines & Highlights for Caring for School-Age Children by Phyllis M Click, Jennifer Parker, Isbn: 9781428318199 1428318194. 2011. 132p. pap. 28.95 **(978-1-61812-259-9(2))** Cram101 Inc.

—Outlines & Highlights for Health, Safety, & Nutrition for the Young Child by Lynn R Marotz, Isbn: 9781428320703. 2010. 82p. pap. 27.95 (978-1-61698-190-7(3)) Cram101 Inc.

—Outlines & Highlights for Infants, Toddlers, & Caregivers: A Curriculum of Respectful, Responsive Care & Education by Janet Gonzalez-Mena, ISBN. 2010. 78p. pap. 27.95 (978-1-61698-097-9(4)) Cram101 Inc.

Cram101 Textbook Reviews. Outlines & Highlights for Maternal & Child Nursing Care by J Ball & R Bindler. 2011. 686p. pap. 42.95 **(978-1-61905-548-3(1))** Cram101 Inc.

Cram101 Textbook Reviews & Cram101 Textbook Reviews. Outlines & Highlights for Early Childhood: A Guide for Students by Tina Bruce, ISBN. 2011. 62p. pap. 27.95 **(978-1-61461-069-4(X))**; pap. 27.95 **(978-1-61461-115-8(7))** Cram101 Inc.

—Outlines & Highlights for Early Childhood Education & Care: Policy & Practice by Margaret Clark, ISBN. 2011. 56p. pap. 26.95 **(978-1-61461-117-2(3))** Cram101 Inc.

—Outlines & Highlights for Infants & Toddlers, Curriculum & Teaching by Linda D Watson, Isbn: 9781418016623. 2011. 174p. pap. 29.95 **(978-1-61744-865-2(6))** Cram101 Inc.

—Outlines & Highlights for Introduction to Early Childhood: A Multidisciplinary Approach by Tim Waller, ISBN. 2011. 92p. pap. 27.95 **(978-1-61461-103-5(3))** Cram101 Inc.

El Currículo Creativo para Educación Preescolar. 5th ed. 2010. (SPA.). (978-1-60617-395-4(2)); 535p. **(978-1-60617-396-1(0))** Teaching Strategies, Inc.

Curtis, Audrey & O'Hagan, Maureen. Care & Education in Early Childhood: A Student's Guide to Theory & Practice. 2nd rev. ed. 2008. (Illus.). VI, 202p. pap. 41.95 (978-0-415-45757-6(2)) Routledge.

Dalli, Carmen & Urban, Mathias, eds. Professionalism in Early Childhood Education & Care. 2012. (ENG.). 164p. (C). pap. 45.95 **(978-0-415-50892-6(4))** Routledge.

Dalli, Carmen & Urban, Mathias, eds. Professionalism in Early Childhood Education & Care: International Perspectives. 2010. (ENG., Illus.). 176p. (C). 125.00 (978-0-415-57405-1(6)) Routledge.

Daubert, Thomas. Your House Their House: The Best & Worst of Residential Child Care. 2011. 156p. pap. 11.70 **(978-1-4634-3487-8(1))** AuthorHouse.

Davies, Kim. Baby & Childcare the Pure & Natural Way: Raising Your Baby & Child the Way Nature Intended, from Birth Right Through to the Age Of 5. 2007. (ENG., Illus.). 256p. 29.99 (978-0-7548-1672-0(9)) Anness Publishing GBR. Dist: National Bk. Network.

—Natural Baby Care: Raising Your Child the Way Nature Intended. 2008. (ENG., Illus.). 160p. pap. 18.99 (978-1-84476-365-8(X)) Anness Publishing GBR. Dist: National Bk. Network.

Davis, Mary Ellen. The Grandparenting Journey: Leading the Way. 2010. 64p. pap. 23.49 (978-1-4490-7156-1(2)) AuthorHouse.

Dawes, Mark & Jones, Deborah. Understanding Unreasonable Force. 2007. 180p. per. (978-1-84667-030-5(6)) Derwent Pr., The.

Djedje, Derahonon/Adrienne, creator. Caregiver Timesheet Pad. 2007. (ENG., Illus.). 200p. spiral bd. 13.89 (978-0-9749007-0-4(2)) Business Mind, Inc.

Dodge, Diane Trister. The Creative Curriculum for Preschool: Volume 1: The Foundation. 5th ed. 2010. (978-1-60617-372-5(3)); (978-1-60617-371-8(5)); (978-1-60617-370-1(7)); (978-1-60617-369-5(3)); (978-1-60617-373-2(1)) Teaching Strategies, Inc.

Dodge, Diane Trister, et al. The Creative Curriculum for Infants, Toddlers & Twos. 2nd ed. 2010. (978-1-60617-415-9(0)) 2010. (978-1-60617-417-3(7)) 2010. (978-1-60617-416-6(9)) 2006. (Illus.). xviii, 447p. pap. (978-1-879537-99-6(0)) Teaching Strategies, Inc.

Dodge, Diane Trister, et al. El Currículo Creativo para Niños de 0 a 3 Años. 2nd ed. (SPA & ENG.). 2011. **(978-1-60617-426-5(6))** 2008. (978-1-933021-40-9(3)) Teaching Strategies, Inc.

Eagle, Rita. Help Him Make You Smile: The Development of Intersubjectivity in the Atypical Child. 2007. (Psychological Issues Ser.). (ENG.). 336p. 93.50 (978-0-7657-0496-2(X)); pap. 41.99 (978-0-7657-0497-9(8)) Rowman & Littlefield Publishers, Inc. (Aronson, Jason).

Emlen, Arthur. Solving the Childcare & Flexibility Puzzle: How Working Parents Make the Best Feasible Choices & What That Means for Public Policy. 2010. 122p. pap. 25.95 (978-1-59942-868-0(7)) Universal Pubs.

Exley, Helen. Little Baby, Little Treasure. 2009. (ENG., Illus.). 240p. 7.50 (978-1-84634-317-9(8)) Exley, Helen Giftbooks GBR. Dist: National Bk. Network.

Eyal, Gil. The Autism Matrix: The Social Origins of the Autism Epidemic. 2010. (ENG., Illus.). 240p. 69.95 (978-0-7456-4399-1(X)); pap. 24.95 (978-0-7456-4400-4(7)) Polity Pr. GBR. Dist: Wiley, John & Sons, Inc.

Faull, Jan & McLean Oliver, Jennifer. Amazing Minds: The Science of Nurturing Your Child's Developing Mind with Games, Activites & More. 2010. (ENG.). 368p. (gr. 12). 15.00 (978-0-425-23224-8(7), Berkley Trade) Penguin Group (USA) Inc.

Felix, Nancy. Oh My, Au Pair! A Complete Guide to Hiring & Hosting an Au Pair. 2009. 188p. pap. 15.95 (978-1-60844-250-8(0)) Dog Ear Publishing, LLC.

Fields, Denise & Brown, Ari. Toddler 411: Clear Answers & Smart Advice for Your Toddler. 3rd rev. ed. 2010. (ENG.). 576p. pap. 14.95 (978-1-889392-38-7(3)) Windsor Peak Pr.

Fields, Denise & Fields, Alan. Baby Bargains: Secrets to Saving 20% to 50% on baby furniture, gear, clothes, toys, maternity wear & much, much More! 9th rev. ed. 2011. (ENG.). 608p. pap. 17.95 (978-1-889392-40-0(5)) Windsor Peak Pr.

Fitter, Jay Scott. Respect Your Children: A Practical Guide to Effective Parenting. 2010. 144p. 24.95 (978-1-4502-2068-2(1)); pap. 14.95 (978-1-4502-2066-8(5)) iUniverse, Inc.

Folks, Homer. The Care of Destitute, Neglected, & Delinquent Children. 2010. 276p. pap. 27.75 (978-1-141-50910-2(5)) 2010. 164p. pap. 21.75 (978-1-141-46753-2(4)) 2010. 274p. pap. 27.75 (978-1-141-63425-5(2)) 2010. 150p. pap. 21.75 (978-1-143-07198-0(0)) 2009. 264p. 30.99 (978-1-110-42075-9(7)) 2009. 264p. pap. 26.75 (978-1-110-42074-2(9)) 2009. (ENG.). 262p. pap. 23.99 (978-1-110-42073-5(0), BiblioLife) 2009. (ENG.). 262p. pap. 21.99 (978-1-110-42072-8(2), BiblioLife) 2009. 264p. 24.99 (978-1-103-42551-8(X)) 2009. 264p. pap. 18.99 (978-1-103-42549-5(8)) 2008. 148p. 21.99 (978-0-559-24727-9(3)) 2008. 148p. pap. 20.75 (978-0-559-24725-5(7)) BiblioBazaar.

—The Care of Destitute, Neglected, & Delinquent Children. 2009. 102p. pap. 14.14 (978-0-217-57467-9(X)) General Bks. LLC.

—The Care of Destitute, Neglected, & Delinquent Children. 2006. 144p. pap. 16.99 (978-1-4255-7214-3(6)) MPublishing.

Fontana, Gina. The Abc's of Child Care Management. rev. ed. 2007. (ENG.). 132p. spiral bd. 62.00 (978-0-7575-4523-8(8)) Kendall Hunt Publishing Co.

Ford, Gina. The Contented Baby with Toddler Book. 2010. (ENG., Illus.). 338p. pap. 17.95 (978-0-09-192958-9(X)) Random Hse. GBR. Dist: Independent Pubs. Group.

Foster, Lisa K. Child Care Funding Sources for California School Districts. 2008. iii, 56p. (978-1-58703-244-8(9)) California Research Bureau.

Foster, Maggie. Rainbows & Teardrops: Inside the Heart & Mind of a Child. 2011. (Illus.). 88p. pap. 12.52 (978-1-4520-6971-5(9)) AuthorHouse.

Fousekis, Natalie Marie. Demanding Child Care: Women's Activism & the Politics of Welfare, 1940-71. 2011. (Women in American History Ser.). (ENG., Illus.). 264p. 50.00 (978-0-252-03625-5(5)) Univ. of Illinois Pr.

Frankel, Jill & Hobart, Christine. Good Practice in Childminding: A Handbook for the Diploma in Home-Based Childcare. Walker, Miranda, ed. 4th rev. ed. 2009. (ENG., Illus.). 336p. pap. 57.50 **(978-1-4085-0493-2(6))** Nelson Thornes Ltd. GBR. Dist: Trans-Atlantic Pubns., Inc.

Franz, S. Cornelia. Common Sense Pediatrics: Combining Alternative & Traditional Medicine in Everyday Practice. 2008. 224p. pap. 19.99 (978-1-4343-6910-9(2)) AuthorHouse.

Garcia, Marito, et al. Africa's Future, Africa's Challenge: Early Childhood Care & Development in Sub Saharan Africa. 2007. (Directions in Development Ser.). 40.00 (978-0-8213-7054-4(5)) World Bank Pubns.

Gardner, Helen. The Concept of Family. 2010. 308p. pap. (978-3-639-22095-7(1)) VDM Verlag Dr. Mueller e.K.

Gaston, Lynn & Gaston, Randy. Three Times the Love: Finding Answers & Hope for Our Triplets with Autism. 2010. (ENG.). 240p. (gr. 12-18). 15.00 (978-1-58333-379-2(7), Avery) Penguin Group (USA) Inc.

Gates, Susan M., et al. Examining Child Care Need among Military Families. 2006. (Illus.). 114p. per. 20.00 (978-0-8330-3902-6(4)) RAND Corp., The.

Goforth, Debbie. Scars of Love: Tears of Hope. 2007. 199p. per. 16.95 (978-0-9796458-0-8(8)) At Risk Educational Services.

Gonzalez-Mena & Cram101 Textbook Reviews Staff. Diversity in Early Care & Education: Honoring Differences. 2007. 60p. per. 9.95 (978-1-4288-2090-6(6)); per. 9.95 (978-1-4288-2088-3(4)) Cram101 Inc.

Gonzalez-Mena, et al. Infants, Toddlers, & Caregivers: A Curriculum of Respectful, Responsive, Relationship-Based Care & Education. 9th ed. 2011. (ENG., Illus.). 416p. (C). pap. 102.33 (978-0-07-802435-1(8), 0078024358) McGraw-Hill Cos., The.

Gonzalez-Mena, Janet. The Caregiver's Companion. 8th ed. 2008. (ENG.). 160p. (C). pap. 40.33 (978-0-07-722691-6(7), 0077226917) McGraw-Hill Cos., The.

Gonzalez-Mena, Janet & Eyer, Dianne Widmeyer. The Caregiver's Companion. 9th ed. 2011. (ENG.). 192p. (C). pap. 40.33 **(978-0-07-749035-5(5)**, 0077490355) McGraw-Hill Cos., The.

Gonzalez-Mena, Janet, et al. Making Links: A Collaborative Approach to Planning & Practice in Early Childhood Programs. 2007. (ENG.). 192p. 36.95 (978-0-8077-4843-5(9)) Teachers College Pr., Teachers College, Columbia Univ.

Greco, Dana M. Please Don't Buy Me Ice Cream: A child's rules for priceless Parenting. 2008. 76p. pap. 12.95 (978-1-4327-2771-0(0)) Outskirts Pr., Inc.

Griffin, M. A. Ed. The Day I Took off My Cape: An NBA Wife's Journey to Finding Family Balance. 2010. 116p. 23.95 (978-1-4389-4741-9(0)) AuthorHouse.

Groark, Christina J., et al, eds. Evidence-Based Practices & Programs for Early Childhood Care & Education. 2006. (Illus.). 216p. 82.95 (978-1-4129-2614-0(9), B26149C); pap. 36.95 (978-1-4129-2615-7(7), B26149P) Corwin Pr.

Hagelin, Rebecca. 30 Ways in 30 Days to Take Back Your Family. 2009. (ENG.). 310p. 24.95 (978-1-59698-568-1(2)) Regnery Publishing, Inc., An Eagle Publishing Co.

Hagemann, Karen, et al, eds. Children, Families, & States: Time Policies of Childcare, Preschool & Primary Education in Europe. 2011. (CEH Ser.). (Illus.). 456p. 95.00 (978-0-85745-096-8(4)) Berghahn Bks., Inc.

Hale, Liisa & Copenhagen Bainer, Claire. Second Home: A Day in the Life of a Model Early Childhood Program. 2007. (ENG., Illus.). 280p. (J). 49.95 (978-1-929610-92-1(0)) Redleaf Pr.

Hale, Rachael. My Life As a Baby: A Five Year Record. 2009. (ENG.). 80p. 14.99 (978-0-7407-7674-8(6)) Andrews McMeel Publishing.

Hall, G. Stanley. Youth: Its Education, Regimen, & Hygiene. 2007. (ENG.). 312p. per. (978-1-4065-1591-6(4)) Dodo Pr.

Hamlyn. 50 Ways to Tame a Toddler: How to Charm & Disarm Your Diminutive Adversary... the British Way. 2009. (ENG.). pap. 6.99 (978-0-600-62038-9(7), Hamlyn) Octopus Publishing Group GBR. Dist: Hachette Bk. Group.

Hancock, Ange-Marie. Solidarity Politics for Millennials: A Guide to Ending the Oppression Olympics. 2011. (Politics of Intersectionality Ser.). (ENG., Illus.). 208p. 85.00 (978-0-230-10800-4(8)) Palgrave Macmillan.

Harris, Nonie. Comparing Child Care Subsidy Policies in California & Australi. 2010. 224p. pap. (978-3-8383-2009-0(3)) Lambert Academic Publishing.

Harter, Susan. The Construction of the Self: Developmental & Sociocultural Foundations. 2nd rev. ed. 2012. (ENG., Illus.). 440p. 55.00 **(978-1-4625-0297-4(0))** Guilford Pubns., Inc.

Hein, Catherine & Cassirer, Naomi. Workplace Solutions for Childcare. 2010. (ENG., Illus.). 400p. pap. 40.00 (978-92-2-122035-0(4)) International Labour Office.

Hendrick, Gladys W. My First Three Hundred Babies. rev. ed. (Illus.). (Orig.). pap. 13.95 (978-0-9600400-0-1(5)) Hurst Publishing.

Hewitt, Deborah. So This Is Normal Too? 2nd ed. 2011. (ENG.). 280p. pap. 29.95 (978-1-60554-072-6(2)) Redleaf Pr.

Hobart, Christine & Frankel, Jill. Good Practice in Childminding: A Handbook for the Diploma in Home-Based Childcare. Walker, Miranda, ed. 4th ed. 2006. (ENG., Illus.). 272p. pap. 52.50 (978-0-7487-9764-6(5)) Nelson Thornes Ltd. GBR. Dist: Trans-Atlantic Pubns., Inc.

Hockenberry, Marilyn J. & Wilson, David. Virtual Clinical Excursions 3. 0 for Wong's Nursing Care of Infants & Children. 9th ed. 2010. (ENG.). 192p. (C). 64.95 (978-0-323-07972-3(5), Mosby) Elsevier - Health Sciences Div.

—Wong's Nursing Care of Infants & Children - Text & Study Guide Package. 9th ed. 2010. (ENG.). (C). 124.16 (978-0-323-09695-9(6), Mosby) Elsevier - Health Sciences Div.

—Wong's Nursing Care of Infants & Children - Text & Virtual Clinical Excursions 3. 0 Package. 9th ed. 2010. (ENG.). (C). 143.00 (978-0-323-07973-0(3), Mosby) Elsevier - Health Sciences Div.

Hockenberry, Marilyn J., et al. Wong's Nursing Care of Infants & Children - Text & Mosby's Care of Infants & Children Nursing Video Skills Package. 9th ed. 2011. (ENG.). (C). 134.00 (978-0-323-09729-1(4), Mosby) Elsevier - Health Sciences Div.

Hogan, Mary Ann. Pearson Reviews & Rationales: Maternal-Newborn Nursing. 3rd rev. ed. 2012. (ENG., Illus.). 336p. (C). pap. 39.95 (978-0-13-295686-4(1), Prentice Hall) Prentice Hall PTR.

Homan, Sidney R. A Fish in the Moonlight: Growing up in the Bone Marrow Unit. 2008. 226p. 24.95 (978-1-55753-486-6(1)) Purdue Univ. Pr.

Horwath, Jan. Child Neglect: Planning & Intervention. 2013. (ENG.). 208p. (C). pap. 32.95 (978-0-230-20666-3(2)) Palgrave Macmillan.

Howard, Justine & McInnes, Karen. Companion to Professional Play Practice. 2012. (ENG.). 192p. (C). 125.00 (978-0-415-67808-7(0)); pap. 80.00 (978-0-415-67813-1(7)) Routledge.

Howe, Winfred Lewis. A Treatise on the Care of the Expectant Mother During Pregnancy And Childbirth, & the Care of the Child from Birth until Puberty. 2007. pap. 16.95 (978-1-4304-5138-9(6)) Kessinger Publishing, LLC.

Hughes, Daniel A. Attachment-Focused Parenting: Effective Strategies to Care for Children. 2009. (ENG.). 272p. 29.95 (978-0-393-70555-3(2), 70555) Norton, W. W. & Co., Inc.

Hwa-Froelich, Deborah A. Supporting Development in Internationally Adopted Children. 2011. (ENG.). 256p. pap. 39.95 (978-1-59857-191-2(5)) Brookes, Paul H. Publishing Co.

Improving Early Childhood Development Policies & Practices: Hearing Before the Subcommittee on Early Childhood, Elementary & Secondary Education, Committee on Education & Labor, U.S. House of Representatives, One Hundred Eleventh Congress, First Session, Hearing Held in Washington, DC, March 19, 2009. 2009. (Illus.). iii, 66p. (978-0-16-083539-1(9), 552-070-39262-9) United States Government Printing Office.

Iwaniec, Dorota, ed. The Child's Journey Through Care: Placement Stability, Care Planning, & Achieving Permanency. 2006. (ENG., Illus.). 304p. 164.95 (978-0-470-01137-9(8)); per. 65.00 (978-0-470-01138-6(6)) Wiley, John & Sons, Inc. (Wiley).

Johnson, Rucker C., et al. Mothers' Work & Children's Lives: Low-Income Families after Welfare Reform. 2009. (ENG.). 160p. 40.00 (978-0-88099-358-6(8)); pap. 18.00 (978-0-88099-356-2(1)) Upjohn, W.E. Institute for Employment Research.

Jonas, Nico. The Adenoid in Children. 2010. 64p. pap. (978-3-8383-2125-7(1)) Lambert Academic Publishing.

Juul, Jesper. Your Competent Child: Toward A New Paradigm in Parenting & Education. 2011. 236p. 33.95 (978-1-4525-3892-1(1)); pap. 17.95 (978-1-4525-3890-7(5)) Balboa Pr.

Kagan, Sharon Lynn, et al. Early Care & Education Teaching Workforce at Fulcrum: An Agenda for Reform. 2007. (Early Childhood Education Ser.). (ENG., Illus.). 192p. pap. 32.95 (978-0-8077-4827-5(7)) Teachers College Pr., Teachers College, Columbia Univ.

Kantola, Johanna. Feminists Theorize the State. annot. ed. 2006. (ENG.). 256p. 95.00 (978-0-230-00025-4(8)) Palgrave Macmillan.

Karnopp, Jennifer. Focus on Babies: How-Tos & What-To-Dos When Caring for Infants. 2012. (Focus on Providing Child Care Ser.). (ENG.). 136p. pap. 19.95 (978-0-87659-379-0(1)) Gryphon Hse., Inc.

Kaur, Gurupdesh, et al. Alternate Child Care Strategies & Development of Pre-School Children. 2011. 108p. pap. (978-3-8443-9938-7(0)) Lambert Academic Publishing.

Kay, S. & Kay, Janet. Good Practice in the Early Years. 3rd ed. 2012. (ENG., Illus.). 336p. pap. 34.95 (978-0-8264-9004-9(2)) Continuum International Publishing Group, Ltd. GBR. Dist: National Bk. Network.

Kellett, Mary. Children's Perspectives on Integrated Services: Every Child Matters in Policy & Practice. 2011. (Interagency Working in Health & Social Care Ser.). (ENG., Illus.). 256p. (C). pap. 32.95 (978-0-230-23039-2(3)) Palgrave Macmillan.

Kemp, Paul. The Daddy Diaries. 2008. 272p. pap. 14.00 (978-1-60693-233-9(0), Eloquent Bks.) AEG Literary Publishing Services, Inc

Kirton, Derek. Child Social Work Policy & Practice. 2008. (Illus.). 240p. (C). 109.00 (978-1-4129-2054-4(X), B2054XC); pap. 49.00 (978-1-4129-2055-1(8), B2054XP) SAGE Pubns., Ltd. GBR. Dist: SAGE Pubns., Inc.

Kompare, Tara. The Colic Chronicles: A Mother's Survival Guide to Calming Your Baby While Keeping Your Cool. 2008. (ENG.). 192p. pap. 14.95 (978-0-7382-1169-5(9)) Da Capo Pr., Inc.

Kuttner, Leora. A Child in Pain: How to Help, What to Do. 2008. (Illus.). 271p. pap. (978-1-84590-119-6(3)) Crown House Publishing, Whaley Bridge.

Lab-Volt Staff. Child Development & Child Care: TD Facs ESeries. 2010. 19p. 3.00 (978-1-60533-116-4(3)); 81p. 9.00 (978-1-60533-117-1(1)); 48p. ring bd. 6.00 (978-1-60533-075-4(2)) Lab-Volt Systems, Inc.

Lally, J. Ronald, et al, eds. Concepts for Care: 20 Essays on Infant/Toddler Development & Learning. 2006. (ENG., Illus.). 144p. pap. 21.95 (978-0-914409-39-7(5)) WestEd.

LaRowe, Michelle, et al. Beyond Parenting Basics: The International Nanny Association's Official Guide to In-Home Child Care. 2nd ed. 2010. 152p. (978-0-615-31241-5(1)) International Nanny Assn.

Leach, Penelope. Child Care Today: Getting It Right for Everyone. 2010. (Vintage Ser.). (ENG.). 368p. pap. 16.95 (978-1-4000-7721-2(4), Vintage) Knopf Doubleday Publishing Group.

Lee, Allison. Working Mum's Guide to Childcar: How to Choose & Manage the Right Childcare for Your Child. 2nd ed. 2010. (Illus.). 179p. pap. 26.00 (978-1-84528-378-0(3)) How To Books GBR. Dist: Parkwest Pubns., Inc.

Levene, Alysa. Childcare, Health & Mortality at the London Foundling Hospital, 1741-1800. 2007. (ENG., Illus.). 224p. 79.00 (978-0-7190-7354-0(5)) Manchester Univ. Pr. GBR. Dist: Macmillan.

Levine, Valerie & Levine, Valerie J. Break the Co-Sleeping Habit: How to Set Bedtime Boundaries - And Raise a Secure, Happy, Well-Adjusted Child. 2009. (ENG.). 240p. pap. 14.95 (978-1-59869-901-2(6)) Adams Media Corp.

Lie, Mabel. Towards Equal Voices. 2010. 404p. pap. (978-3-8383-4470-6(7)) Lambert Academic Publishing.

Line, Mommies. CHILD CARE for Mommies. 2008. 96p. pap. 12.95 (978-0-557-02106-2(5)) Lulu Enterprises Inc.

Mace, Ruth & Bentley, Gillian, eds. Substitute Parents: Biological & Social Perspective on Alloparenting Across Human Societies. 2009. (Illus.). 372p. 95.00 (978-1-84545-106-6(6)) Berghahn Bks., Inc.

Marks, Melissa & Marsh, Diane. How to Talk to Families about Child & Adolescent Mental Illness. 2009. (ENG.). 256p. pap. 21.95 (978-0-393-70570-6(6), 70570) Norton, W. W. & Co., Inc.

Maroni, Lesley. Understanding 4-5-Year-Olds. 2007. (Understanding Your Child (Jessica Kingsley Publishers) Ser.). (ENG.). 8p. per. (978-1-84310-534-3(9)) Kingsley, Jessica Ltd.

Marotz, Lynn R. Cengage Advantage Books: Health, Safety, & Nutrition for the Young Child. 8th ed. 2011. (ENG.). 576p. (C). ring bd. 121.95 (978-1-111-35580-7(0)) Wadsworth.

—Health, Safety, & Nutrition for the Young Child. 8th ed. 2011. (Whatsquo;s New in Early Childhood Ser.). (ENG.). 576p. (C). pap. 165.95 (978-1-111-29837-1(8)) Wadsworth.

Marty, Martin E. The Mystery of the Child. 2007. (Religion, Marriage, & Family Ser.). 257p. 24.00 (978-0-8028-1766-2(1)) Eerdmans, William B. Publishing Co.

May, Helen. Politics in the Playground: The World of Early Childhood in New Zealand. rev. ed. 2009. 366p. pap. 49.95 (978-1-877372-68-1(4)) Otago University Pr. NZL. Dist: International Specialized Bk. Services.

McCracken, Jean Byler. Peace with Child Care: Secrets to Finding Day Care You Can Trust from a Veteran Child Care Provider. 2007. 261p. (978-0-9790349-0-9(6)) Faithwell Pr.

Meggitt, Carolyn, et al. Cache Level 3 Child Care & Education. 2nd ed. 2012. (Illus.). 624p. pap. 49.95 (978-1-4441-7099-3(6)) Hodder Arnold Pubs.

Minett, Pamela. Child Care & Development. 6th ed. 2010. (ENG., Illus.). 344p. 35.00 (978-1-4441-1713-4(0)) Hodder Arnold Pubs.

Mupanduki, Stellah. God's Little Flock Healed: They will rise on wings like Eagles. 2010. 220p. 30.00 (978-1-4520-1985-7(1)) AuthorHouse.

Nora, Anya. How to Reduce the Stress of Being a Mum & Enjoy Time with Your Newborn Baby. 2010. 68p. pap. 14.95 (978-1-4452-6359-5(9)) Lulu Enterprises Inc.

Nutbrown, Cathy. Key Concepts in Early Childhood Education & Care. 2nd ed. 2011. (SAGE Key Concepts Ser.). (Illus.). 192p. (C). 104.00 (978-1-84920-400-2(4), B04002C); pap. 39.00 (978-1-84920-401-9(2), B04002P) SAGE Pubns., Ltd. GBR. Dist: SAGE Pubns., Inc.

Nutbrown, Cathy & Page, Jools. Working with Babies & Children: From Birth to Three. 2008. (Illus.). 224p. (C). 98.00 (978-1-4129-4673-5(5), B46735C); pap. 49.00 (978-1-4129-4674-2(3), B46735P) SAGE Pubns., Ltd. GBR. Dist: SAGE Pubns., Inc.

Ochiai Molony Staff. Asia's New Mothers. 2007. (Illus.). 240p. (C). (978-1-905246-37-3(4)) BRILL.

Oesterreich, Lesia. Heart Land Family Child Care Hand Book: Information, Ideas, & Resorces for the Home Care Provider. 2007. 426p. pap. 10.00 (978-0-9700528-6-5(3)) Iowa State Univ. Extension.

Okwany, Auma, et al. The Role of Local Knowledge & Culture in Child Care in Africa: A Sociological Study of Several Ethnic Groups in Kenya & Uganda. 2011. 168p. (978-0-7734-1583-6(1)) Mellen, Edwin Pr., The.

Ollhoff, Laurie & Ollhoff, Jim. Giving Children Their Childhood Back: Relearning the Purpose of Out-Of-School Time. 2006. (978-0-9786018-0-5(7)) Sparrow Media Group, Inc.

Oppenheimer, Louis & Barrett, Martyn, eds. National Identity & Ingroup-Outgroup Attitudes in Children: The Role of Socio-Historical Settings. 2011. (Special Issues of the European Journal of Developmental Psychology Ser.). (ENG.). 132p. pap. 39.95 (978-1-84872-742-7(9), Psychology Press) Taylor & Francis Group GBR. Dist: Taylor & Francis Group.

Palmer, Linda Folden. The Baby Bond. 2009. (ENG.). 432p. pap. 16.99 (978-1-4022-2657-1(8)) Sourcebooks, Inc.

Perrone, Marta. Help!! How to Find, Hire, Train & Maintain Your Household Help. 2006. (Illus.). 256p. per. 24.95 (978-1-930754-84-3(1)) Durban House Pr., Inc.

Peter Kabanya, Mwaniki. Child Care Practices & Malaria Severity in Children under Five Years. 2011. 140p. pap. (978-3-8443-2538-6(7)) Lambert Academic Publishing.

Petty, Karen. Deployment: Strategies for Working with Kids in Military Families. 2009. (ENG., Illus.). 180p. pap. 24.95 (978-1-933653-74-7(4)) Redleaf Pr.

Pfau-Effinger, Birgit & Rostgaard, Tine, eds. Care between Work & Welfare in European Societies. 2011. (ENG., Illus.). 256p. 85.00 (978-0-230-29129-4(5)) Palgrave Macmillan.

Polakow, Valerie. Who Cares for Our Children? The Child Care Crisis in the Other America. 2007. (ENG., Illus.). 240p. 46.00 (978-0-8077-4775-9(0)); pap. 21.95 (978-0-8077-4774-2(2)) Teachers College Pr., Teachers College, Columbia Univ.

A Practical Guide to Estate Planning for a Family with a Special Needs Child. 2009. pap. (978-0-8318-9992-9(1)) American Law Institute.

Pratney, Winkie. Devil Take the Youngest. 2009. 273p. pap. 18.97 (978-0-557-21791-5(1)) Lulu Enterprises Inc.

Pringle-Reid, Vertie. Smile Bandages: Loving the Unlovable. 2009. 176p. 22.95 (978-1-4389-3740-3(7)); pap. 15.95 (978-1-4389-3739-7(3)) AuthorHouse.

Puryear, Lucy J. & Puryear, Lucy. Understanding Your Moods When You're Expecting: Emotions, Mental Health, & Happiness - Before, During, & after Pregnancy. 2008. (ENG.). 256p. pap. 14.95 (978-0-547-05362-2(2)) Houghton Mifflin Harcourt Trade & Reference Pubs.

Qvortrup, Jens & Kjorholt, Anne-Trine, eds. The Modern Child & the Flexible Labour Market: Early Childhood Education & Care. 2011. (Studies in Childhood & Youth Ser.). (ENG., Illus.). 272p. (C). 85.00 (978-0-230-57932-3(9)) Palgrave Macmillan.

Raikes, Helen H., et al. Extending the Dance in Infant & Toddler Caregiving: Enhancing Attachment & Relationships. 2009. (Illus.). 224p. pap. 29.95 (978-1-55766-859-2(0)) Brookes, Paul H. Publishing Co.

Razavi, Shahra, ed. Seen, Heard & Counted: Rethinking Care in a Development Context. 2012. (Development & Change Special Issues Ser.: 4). (ENG.). 276p. pap. 34.95 (978-1-4443-6153-7(8), Wiley-Blackwell) Wiley, John & Sons Inc.

Redleaf, Rhoda. Hey Kids! Out the Door, Let's Explore! 2009. (ENG.). 304p. pap. 24.95 (978-1-933653-91-4(4)) Redleaf Pr.

Reisser, Paul C. Baby & Child Care: From Pre-Birth Through the Teen Years. rev. ed. 2007. (ENG., Illus.). 928p. 29.97 (978-1-4143-1305-4(5)) Tyndale Hse. Pubs.

Reno, Hilde. Handbook for Early Childhood Administrators: Directing with a Mission. 2007. (ENG., Illus.). 304p. per. 56.99 (978-0-205-46980-2(9)) Allyn & Bacon, Inc.

Riegel, Courtney. Through a Mother's Eyes: A Spiral down the Autism Spectrum. 2006. 94p. per. 9.99 (978-1-59886-590-5(0)) Tate Publishing & Enterprises, LLC.

Riley, Douglas A. What Your Explosive Child Is Trying to Tell You: Discovering the Pathway from Symptoms to Solutions. 2008. (ENG.). 272p. pap. 14.95 (978-0-618-70081-3(1)) Houghton Mifflin Harcourt Trade & Reference Pubs.

Roehr, Merle. There Came a Child: Insights into Christian Childcare. 2010. 108p. 21.49 (978-1-4490-7962-8(8)); pap. 10.99 (978-1-4490-7961-1(X)) AuthorHouse.

Ruffin-Rusher, Janette. Tyler's Pain. 2010. 108p. 22.95 (978-1-4502-6135-4(1)); pap. 12.95 (978-1-4502-6137-1(X)) iUniverse, Inc.

Ruffman, Jill V. & Sladek, Marjorie B. Now, What Do We Do? How to Manage Your Child's Critical Medical Needs: A Guided Journal for Parents & Child Advocates, 1. 2006. (Illus.). 179p. spiral bd. 19.95 (978-0-9766323-0-6(6)) Ruffman, Sladek Publishing Co.

Sayer, Tony. Critical Practice in Working with Children. 2008. (ENG., Illus.). 224p. pap. 39.00 (978-0-230-54319-5(7)) Palgrave Macmillan.

Scheiwe, Kirsten & Willekens, Harry, eds. Childcare & Preschool Development in Europe: Institutional Perspectives. 2009. (ENG., Illus.). 288p. 100.00 (978-0-230-53744-6(8)) Palgrave Macmillan.

Schweizer, Sally. Well, I Wonder: Childhood in the Modern World: A Handbook for Parents, Carers & Teachers. 2007. (Bringing Spirit to Life Ser.). (Illus.). 224p. per. (978-1-85584-124-6(X)) Steiner, Rudolf Pr.

Segal, Marilyn, et al. All about Child Care & Early Education: A Comprehensive Resource for Child Care Professionals. 2nd rev. ed. 2011. (ENG.). 384p. (C). pap. 47.40 (978-0-13-265545-3(4)) Allyn & Bacon, Inc.

Segal, Marilyn, et al. All about Child Care & Early Education: A Trainee's Manual for Child Care Professionals. 2nd ed. 2011. (ENG.). 288p. (C). pap. 25.00 (978-0-13-269865-8(X), Prentice Hall) Prentice Hall PTR.

Senator, Susan. The Autism Mom's Survival Guide (For Dads, Too!) Creating a Balanced & Happy Life While Raising a Child with Autism. 2010. (ENG.). 208p. pap. 16.95 (978-1-59030-753-3(4), Trumpeter) Shambhala Pubns., Inc.

Shapiro, Lawrence E., et al. The Baby Emergency Handbook: Lifesaving Information Every Parent Needs to Know. 2008. (ENG., Illus.). 192p. pap. 14.95 (978-1-57224-566-2(2)) New Harbinger Pubns.

Shaughnessy, Michael F. & Kleyn, Kinsey. Handbook of Early Childhood Education. 2012. (Education in a Competitive & Globalizing World Ser.). 238p. 140.00 (978-1-61324-154-7(2)) Nova Science Pubs., Inc.

Sheppard, Heidi. Childrens Care, Learning & Development. 2006. (ENG.). cd-rom 273.00 (978-0-7487-8399-1(7)) Nelson Thornes Ltd. GBR. Dist: International Specialized Bk. Services.

Singer, Jen. Stop Second-Guessing Yourself — The Preschool Years: The Field-Tested Guide to Confident Parenting. 2009. (Momma Said Ser.). (ENG.). 264p. pap. 14.95 (978-0-7573-1417-9(1)) Health Communications, Inc.

Singh, Mahesh Nath. Child Care & Utilization of Reproductive Health Services in Maharashtra. 2011. 80p. pap. (978-3-639-34073-0(6)) VDM Verlag Dr. Mueller e.K.

Sipilä, Jorma, et al. Cash for Childcare: The Consequences for Caring Mothers. 2011. (Illus.). 176p. 110.00 (978-1-84980-423-3(0)) Elgar, Edward Publishing, Inc.

Smith Koslowski, Alison. Who Cares? 2008. (Illus.). 332p. pap. (978-3-639-07101-6(8)) VDM Verlag Dr. Mueller e.K.

Smyth, Tracy & Dewar, Tammy. Raising the Village: How Individuals & Communities Can Work Together to Give Our Children a Stronger Start in Life. 2009. (978-1-926645-10-0(3)) BPS Bks.

Sorte, Joanne, et al. Nutrition, Health, & Safety for Young Children: Promoting Wellness. 2010. (ENG.). 696p. (C). pap. 109.20 (978-0-13-234941-3(8), Prentice Hall) Prentice Hall PTR.

—Nutrition, Health, & Safety for Young Children: Promoting Wellness (with MyEducationLab) 2010. (ENG.). 544p. (C). pap. 115.87 (978-0-13-138120-9(2), Prentice Hall) Prentice Hall PTR.

Southwood, Sue. Fast Facts for Child Care Early Years. 2007. (978-1-86201-348-3(9)) National Institute of Adult Continuing Education.

Spock, M.D., Benjamin & Needlman, Robert. Dr. Spock's Baby & Child Care: 9th Edition. 9th ed. 2011. (ENG., Illus.). 1168p. mass mkt. 8.99 (978-1-4391-8929-0(3)) Pocket Books.

Spock, Benjamin M. & Needlman, Robert. Dr. Spock's Baby & Child Care: 9th Edition. 9th ed. 2012. (ENG., Illus.). 1152p. pap. 19.99 (978-1-4391-8928-3(5)) Gallery Pr., The IRL. Dist: Simon & Schuster, Inc.

Stafford, Wess & Merrill, Dean. Just a Minute: In the Heart of a Child, One Moment... Can Last Forever. 2012. (ENG.). 224p. 19.99 (978-0-8024-0472-5(3)) Moody Pubs.

Sullivan, Lori. Overcoming Autism: A Parent's Guide. 2009. 148p. 28.95 (978-1-4490-2993-7(0)); pap. 19.95 (978-1-4490-2992-0(2)) AuthorHouse.

Swanson, David. Help — My Kid Is Driving Me Crazy: The 17 Ways Kids Manipulate Their Parents, & What You Can Do about It. 2009. (ENG.). 240p. (gr. 12-18). 14.95 (978-0-399-53526-0(8), Perigee Trade) Penguin Group (USA) Inc.

Swim, Terri & Watson, Linda D. Infants & Toddlers: Curriculum & Teaching. 6th rev. ed. 2007. (ENG., Illus.). 496p. (C). per. 146.95 (978-1-4180-1662-3(4)) Delmar Cengage Learning.

—Infants & Toddlers: Curriculum & Teaching. 7th ed. 2010. (Available Titles CourseMate Ser.). (ENG.). 528p. (C). pap. 163.95 (978-0-495-80786-5(9)) Wadsworth.

Taylor, Kay. Free Mother to Good Home: A Handbook & Survival Guide for Good Parents, Stepparents & Grandparents. 2011. 232p. 33.95 (978-1-4525-4004-7(7)); pap. 16.99 (978-1-4525-4003-0(9)) Balboa Pr.

Thomas, Margaret, et al. Love & Limits in & Out of Child Care: What Your Child Care Provider & Your Pediatrician Want You to Know. 2008. (ENG., Illus.). 224p. 40.00 (978-0-8018-8797-0(6)); pap. 16.95 (978-0-8018-8798-7(4)) Johns Hopkins Univ. Pr.

Timpson, Annis May. Driven Apart: Women's Employment Equality & Child Care in Canadian Public Policy. (ENG.). 352p. pap. (978-0-7748-0821-7(7)) Univ. of British Columbia Pr.

Ulker, Riza. Human Gaze & Autism. 2010. 88p. pap. (978-3-639-26339-8(1)) VDM Verlag Dr. Mueller e.K.

United Nations Children's Fund. The Child Care Transition: A League Table of Early Childhood Education & Care in Economically Advanced Countries. 2009. 36p. pap. 15.00 (978-88-89129-70-8(0)) United Nations Children's Fund, The (UNICEF).

Vickers, Margaret H. Working & Caring for a Child with Chronic Illness: Disconnected & Doing It All. 2006. (ENG.). 256p. 100.00 (978-1-4039-9767-8(5)) Palgrave Macmillan.

Vissing, Yvonne Marie & Vissing, Yvonne. How to Keep Your Children Safe: A Guide for Parents. 2007. (ENG., Illus.). 216p. pap. 12.95 (978-1-58465-529-9(1)) Univ. Pr. of New England.

Wahlgren, Anna. For the Love of Children: Childcare & Child Rearing 0-16 Years. 2009. 726p. 39.95 (978-91-977736-2-1(X)) Wahlgren, Anna AB SWE. Dist: AtlasBooks Distribution.

Waldfogel, Jane. What Children Need. 2010. (Family & Public Policy Ser.). (Illus.). 288p. pap. 19.95 (978-0-674-04640-5(4)) Harvard Univ. Pr.

Waller, Tim, ed. An Introduction to Early Childhood: A Multidisciplinary Approach. 2nd ed. 2009. (Illus.). 264p. (C). 112.00 (978-1-84787-517-4(3), B75174C); pap. 45.00 (978-1-84787-518-1(1), B75174P) SAGE Pubns., Ltd. GBR. Dist: SAGE Pubns., Inc.

Waller, Tim & Clark, Margaret Macdonald. Early Childhood Education & Care Policy & Practice. Waller, Tim & Clark, Margaret M., eds. 2007. (Illus.). 208p. (C). 130.00 (978-1-4129-3571-5(7), B35717C); per. 47.00 (978-1-4129-3572-2(5), B35717P) SAGE Pubns., Ltd. GBR. Dist: SAGE Pubns., Inc.

Washington, Carletta D. A Mother's Reflection. 2010. 142p. pap. 12.95 (978-0-9819913-4-4(3)) Prioritybooks Pubns.

Weissbluth, Marc. Healthy Sleep Habits, Happy Twins: A Step-by-Step Program for Sleep-Training Your Multiples. 2009. (ENG., Illus.). 192p. pap. 14.00 (978-0-345-49779-6(1), Ballantine Bks.) Random House Publishing Group.

C

What Role Does & What Role Should the Media Play in Choosing Our Candidates for National Office? 2nd rev. ed. 2008. pap. *(978-0-915915-51-4(0),* Harry Singer Foundation) Wellington Pubns.
Wright, Hazel. Women Studying Childcare: Integrating Lives Through Adult Education. 2011. (Illus.). 188p. pap. 34.95 *(978-1-85856-485-2(9))* Trentham Bks. Ltd. GBR. Dist: Stylus Publishing, LLC.
Yang, Juhua. Beyond Birth Control. 2008. 392p. per. *(978-3-8364-3925-1(5))* VDM Verlag Dr. Mueller e.K.
Yoshida, Yuko. Raising Children with Asperger's Syndrome & High-Functioning Autism: Championing the Individual. Sanders, Esther & Hirano, Cathy, trs. from JPN. 2012. (ENG., Illus.). 256p. pap. ***(978-1-84905-317-4(0))*** Kingsley, Jessica Ltd.
Zero to Three (Organization) Staff, contrib. by. Preventing Child Abuse & Neglect: Parent-Provider Partnerships in Child Care. 2006. *(978-0-943657-98-1(9))* Zero To Three Pr.
Zigler, Edward F., et al. The Tragedy of Child Care in America. 2009. (ENG.). 240p. 40.00 *(978-0-300-12233-6(0))* Yale Univ. Pr.
Zimmerman, Karen. Helping Your Child Grow & Develop. 2nd ed. 2009. (ENG., Illus.). 240p. 30.00 *(978-1-60525-128-8(3))* Goodheart-Willcox Pub.

CHILD CARE CENTERS
see Day Care Centers

CHILD CARE SERVICES
see also Babysitting; Day Care Centers; Family Day Care; Foster Home Care
Alison Haynes Staff. Childcare Arrangements: Employment & Tax Consequences. 2010. 320p. 89.95 *(978-1-904905-29-5(3))* Spiramus Pr. GBR. Dist: International Specialized Bk. Services.
Allison, Alexandra. Outstanding Child Care with a Professional Nanny. 38p. (Orig.). pap. 29.99 *(978-1-878235-24-4(9))* Taylor Publishing.
Amery, Justin, ed. Children's Palliative Care in Africa. 2009. (ENG., Illus.). 336p. pap. 59.95 *(978-0-19-956796-6(4))* Oxford Univ. Pr., Inc.
Anning, Angela, et al. Developing Multi-Professional Teamwork for Integrated Children's Services: Research, Policy & Practice. 2006. (Illus.). 156p. (C). pap. 57.00 *(978-0-335-21978-0(0),* 0335219780, Open University Pr.) McGraw-Hill Education GBR. Dist: McGraw-Hill Cos., The.
—Developing Multiprofessional Teamwork for Integrated Children's Services. 2006. (ENG., Illus.). 156p. (C). 162.00 *(978-0-335-21979-7(9),* 0335219799, Open University Pr.) McGraw-Hill Education GBR. Dist: McGraw-Hill Cos., The.
Ashcraft, Michael & Ashcraft, Chelsea. Leading to Learn: Organizational Leadership for the Child Care & Youth Development Director. 2011. pap. 16.00 *(978-0-9829526-1-0(9))* Sparrow Media Group, Inc.
Auerbach, Stevanne. Child Care - A Comprehensive Guide Vol. 4: Special Needs & Services - Foreword by Jeanette Watson, 4 vols. 2011. 256p. pap. 21.95 ***(978-1-4502-3224-1(8))*** iUniverse, Inc.
—Child Care: A Comprehensive Guide: Creative Homes & Centers: Foreword by Edward Zigler, PhD. 2011. 300p. pap. 21.95 *(978-1-4502-3199-2(3))* iUniverse, Inc.
—Child Care: A Comprehensive Guide: Rationale for Child Care Services Programs vs Politics. 2011. 252p. pap. 21.95 *(978-1-4502-3194-7(2))* iUniverse, Inc.
Boucher, Michelle. Bon Voyage: Leaving the Kids Home, the Complete Guide to Overnight Childcare. Date not set. (Illus.). 110p. (Orig.). pap. 10.00 *(978-0-9658110-1-9(8))* Hands of the Sun Publishing.
Bray, Ilona. Nannies & au Pairs: Hiring In-Home Child Care. 2010. (ENG., Illus.). 242p. pap. 19.99 *(978-1-4133-1190-7(3))* NOLO.
Bumgarner, Marlene. Working with School-Age Children. 2010. (ENG.). 352p. (C). pap. 76.00 *(978-0-13-208085-9(0),* Prentice Hall) Prentice Hall PTR.
Cameron, Claire & Moss, Peter, eds. Social Pedagogy & Working with Children & Young People: Where Care & Education Meet. 2011. (ENG., Illus.). 224p. pap. *(978-1-84905-119-4(4))* Kingsley, Jessica Ltd.
Catano, Francis N. Childcare Worker Assumptions about Caring. 2008. 160p. pap. *(978-3-639-03414-1(7))* VDM Verlag Dr. Mueller e.K.
Chandler, Karen. Administering for Quality: Canadian Early Childhood Development Programs, Third Edition. 3rd ed. 2008. (ENG.). 295p. (C). pap. *(978-0-13-205175-0(3))* Pearson Education Canada.
Cochran, Moncrieff. Finding Our Way: The Future of American Early Care & Education. 2007. *(978-1-934019-13-9(5))* Zero To Three Pr.
Dahlberg, Gunilla, et al. Beyond Quality in Early Childhood Education & Care: Languages of Evaluation. 2nd rev. ed. 2007. (ENG.). 232p. (C). 180.00 *(978-0-415-41848-5(8));* per. 43.95 *(978-0-415-41849-2(6))* Routledge.
Donoghue, Elaine A. & Kraft, Colleen A. Managing Chronic Health Needs in Child Care & Schools: A Quick Reference Guide. 2009. (ENG.). 214p. pap. 47.00 *(978-1-58110-299-4(2))* American Academy of Pediatrics.
Entrepreneur Press Staff & Lynn, Jacquelyn. Start Your Own Child-Care Service. 3rd ed. 2010. (ENG.). 240p. pap. 19.95 *(978-1-59918-403-6(6),* 1599184036) Entrepreneur Pr. dba Entrepreneur Media, Inc.
Epulani, Francis. Greatest Caring Secrets Revealed: As Promised. 2010. 180p. pap. 14.49 *(978-1-4490-6468-6(X))* AuthorHouse.
Friendly, Martha & Prentice, Susan. Childcare. 2009. (About Canada Ser.). (ENG.). 150p. pap. 17.95 *(978-1-55266-291-5(8))* Fernwood Publishing Co., Ltd. CAN. Dist: Independent Pubs. Group.
Gasper, Michael. Multi-agency Working in the Early Years: Challenges & Opportunities. 2010. (Illus.). 176p. (C). 112.00 *(978-1-84787-527-3(0),* B75273C); pap. 39.00 *(978-1-84787-528-0(9),* B75273P) SAGE Pubns., Ltd. GBR. Dist: SAGE Pubns., Inc.
Gonzalez-Mena, Janet, et al. Making Links: A Collaborative Approach to Planning & Practice in Early Childhood Programs. 2007. (ENG.). 192p. 36.95 *(978-0-8077-4843-5(9))* Teachers College Pr., Teachers College, Columbia Univ.
Green, Chamayne N. The Inside Scoop: Tips from a Family Child Care Professional. 2009. (ENG.). 104p. pap. 17.95 *(978-1-60554-004-7(8))* Redleaf Pr.
Herr, Ed.D., Judy, Judy. Working with Young Children. 7th ed. 2011. 184p. pap. 18.00 ***(978-1-60525-437-1(1));*** 310p. (gr. 9-14). pap. 22.64 ***(978-1-60525-438-8(X));*** (ENG., Illus.). 912p. (gr. 9-14). 78.00 ***(978-1-60525-436-4(3))*** Goodheart-Willcox Pub.
Hong, Sung-A. Ch'wiop Pumo Ui Chanyo Yangyuk Chiwon Sobisu Hyoyurhwa Pangan. 2010. (KOR., Illus.). xxi, 272p. *(978-89-8491-346-2(4))* Korean Women's Development Institute.
Investing in Early Education: Paths to Improving Children's Success: Hearing Before the Committee on Education & Labor, U.S. House of Representatives, One Hundred Tenth Congress, Second Session, Hearing Held in Washington, DC, January 23, 2008. 2008. (Illus.). iii, 81p. *(978-0-16-081550-8(9),* 552-070-37893-6) United States Government Printing Office.
Ito, Shuhei. Hoiku Seido Kaikaku to Jido Fukushiho No Yukue. 2010. (JPN., Illus.). 207p. *(978-4-7803-0336-0(2))* Kamogawa Shuppan.
Johnson, Jeff A. Keeping Your Smile: Caring for Children with Joy, Love, & Intention. 2010. (ENG.). 184p. pap. 17.95 *(978-1-933653-85-3(X))* Redleaf Pr.
Jones, Nick & Sundet. Developing an Empirically Based Practice Initiative: A Case Stud. 2007. (ENG., Illus.). 210p. 150.00 *(978-0-7890-3345-1(3))* Routledge.
Kagan, Sharon Lynn & Kauerz, Kristie. Early Childhood Systems: Transforming Early Learning. 2012. (ENG.). 336p. 68.00 ***(978-0-8077-5297-5(5))*** Teachers College Pr., Teachers College, Columbia Univ.
Kagan, Sharon Lynn & Kauerz, Kristie, eds. Early Childhood Systems: Transforming Early Learning. 2012. (ENG.). 336p. pap. 31.95 ***(978-0-8077-5296-8(7))*** Teachers College Pr., Teachers College, Columbia Univ.
Karnopp, Jennifer. Focus on Babies: How-Tos & What-To-Dos When Caring for Infants. 2012. (Focus on Providing Child Care Ser.). (ENG.). 136p. pap. 19.95 ***(978-0-87659-379-0(1))*** Gryphon Hse., Inc.
Kellett, Mary. Children's Perspectives on Integrated Services: Every Child Matters in Policy & Practice. 2011. (Interagency Working in Health & Social Care Ser.). (ENG., Illus.). 256p. (C). pap. 32.95 *(978-0-230-23039-2(3))* Palgrave Macmillan.
Khan, Masreka & Dey, Soma. Illusions of Motherhood: Assertions & realities of care Work. 2011. 80p. pap. ***(978-3-8443-9251-7(3))*** Lambert Academic Publishing.
Lancaster, Y. Penny & Kirby, Perpetua. Listening to Young Children. 2nd ed. 2010. (ENG., Illus.). 254p. 345.95 *(978-0-335-24127-9(1),* 0335241271) McGraw-Hill Education GBR. Dist: McGraw-Hill Cos., The.
Langford, Tom. Alberta's Day Care Controversy: From 1908 to 2009 & Beyond. 2011. (ENG.). 330p. pap. 41.95 *(978-1-926836-02-7(2))* UBC Pr. CAN. Dist: Univ. of Washington Pr.
Lee, Allison. The Parent's Guide to Childcare: How to Choose & Manage the Right Care for Your Child. 2008. 166p. pap. *(978-1-84528-220-2(5))* How To Books.
—Starting Your Own Childminding Business: How to Set up High Quality Childcare in Your Own Home. 2006. (Illus.). 180p. per. 26.00 *(978-1-84528-097-0(0))* How To Books GBR. Dist: Parkwest Pubns., Inc.
—Working Mum's Guide to Childcar: How to Choose & Manage the Right Childcare for Your Child. 2nd ed. 2010. (Illus.). 179p. pap. 26.00 *(978-1-84528-378-0(3))* How To Books GBR. Dist: Parkwest Pubns., Inc.
Leira, Arnlaug. Welfare States & Working Mothers: The Scandinavian Experience. 2009. (ENG.). 216p. pap. 32.99 *(978-0-521-12509-3(X))* Cambridge Univ. Pr.
Lindamood, Judy B. & Lindamood, Robert L. Considering the Care of Children: A Guide to Cross-National Perspectives (2nd Edition) 2nd rev. ed. 2008. (ENG., Illus.). 260p. (C). spiral bd. *(978-0-9741587-1-6(2),* 092007) Familiae, Inc.
Lindon, Jennie. Equality & Inclusion in Early Years: Linking Theory & Practice. 2nd ed. 2012. (ENG., Illus.). 224p. pap. 45.00 ***(978-1-4441-4550-2(9))*** Hodder Arnold Pubs.
Lloyd, Eva & Penn, Helen, eds. Childcare Markets: Can They Deliver an Equitable Service? 2012. 264p. 110.00 ***(978-1-84742-933-9(5))*** Policy Pr. GBR. Dist: Chicago Distribution Ctr.
Martin, Lucy. The Childcare Bible: The Ultimate Guide to All Forms of Childcare. 2009. (ENG.). 352p. 27.95 *(978-0-09-192426-3(X))* Random Hse. GBR. Dist: Independent Pubs. Group.
McCracken, Jean Byler. Peace with Child Care: Secrets to Finding Day Care You Can Trust from a Veteran Child Care Provider. 2007. 261p. *(978-0-9790349-0-9(6))* Faithwell Pr.
Melhuish, Edward C. Early Childhood Care & Education: International Perspectives. Petrogiannis, Konstantinos, ed. 2006. 182p. 170.00 *(978-0-415-38368-4(4))* Routledge.
Melhuish, Edward C. & Petrogiannis, Konstantinos, eds. Early Childhood Care & Education: International Perspectives. 2006. 182p. per. 52.95 *(978-0-415-38369-1(2))* Routledge.
Millam, Rosalind. Anti-Discriminatory Practice: A Guide for Those Working with Children & Young People. 3rd rev. ed. 2011. (ENG., Illus.). 384p. 44.95 *(978-1-4411-7741-4(8))* Continuum International Publishing Group, Ltd. GBR. Dist: National Bk. Network.
Murray, Kris. The Ultimate Child Care Marketing Guide: Tactics, Tools, & Strategies for Success. 2012. (ENG.). 200p. pap. 29.95 ***(978-1-60554-083-2(8))*** Redleaf Pr.
Musial, Tina. How to Open & Operate a Financially Successful Child Care Service. 2007. (ENG., Illus.). 288p. pap. 39.95 *(978-1-60138-115-6(8))* Atlantic Publishing Co.
Neuman, Michelle, et al, eds. Professionals in early childhood education & care systems: European profiles & perspectives. 2010. 525p. pap. 75.95 *(978-3-86649-249-3(9))* Budrich-Esser, Barbara DEU. Dist: International Specialized Bk. Services.
Pearl, David. Care Standards Legislation Handbook. 7th rev. ed. 2009. (ENG.). 808p. pap. *(978-1-84661-165-0(2))* Jordan Publishing, Ltd.
Powell, Douglas R. Who's Watching the Babies? Improving Family, Friend, & Neighbor Care. 2008. *(978-1-934019-21-4(6))* Zero To Three Pr.
Read, Veronica. Developing Attachment in Early Years Settings: Nurturing Secure Relationships from Birth to Five Years. 2009. (ENG., Illus.). 144p. 33.95 *(978-0-415-49164-8(9));* XII, 132p. 105.00 *(978-0-415-49163-1(0))* Fulton, David Pubs. GBR. Dist: Taylor & Francis Group.
Robinson, Maria. Child Development 0-8: A Journey Through the Early Years. 2007. (ENG., Illus.). 256p. (C). pap. 45.00 *(978-0-335-22097-7(5),* 0335220975) McGraw-Hill Education GBR. Dist: McGraw-Hill Cos., The.
—Child Development from Birth to Eight: A Journey Through the Early Years. 2008. (Illus.). 241p. 156.95 *(978-0-335-22098-4(3),* 9780335220984, Open University Pr.) McGraw-Hill Education GBR. Dist: McGraw-Hill Cos., The.
Sheppard, Lori. Daycare Seen Through a Teacher's Eyes: A Guide for Teachers & Parents, 1 vol. 2010. 68p. pap. 19.95 *(978-1-4489-4264-0(0))* PublishAmerica, Inc.
Sultana, A. Shahin. Quality in Early Childhood Care & Education: A Study of Chennai Corporation Nursery Schools. 2009. (Illus.). xvi, 180p. *(978-81-7831-191-3(7),* Library of Congress — New Delhi Overseas Office) Manak Pubns. Pvt., Ltd.
Taffy Gallagher. Program Full: Your Guide to Successful Childcare Marketing. 2010. 148p. pap. 14.95 *(978-1-4401-9680-5(X))* iUniverse, Inc.
—100 Ideas to Market Your Childcare Business. 2009. 152p. pap. 14.95 *(978-1-4401-8006-4(7))* iUniverse, Inc.
Talan, Teri N. & Bloom, Paula Jorde. Escala de Evaluacion de la Administracion de Negocios. 2010. 56p. pap. 20.95 *(978-0-8077-5166-4(9))* Teachers College Pr., Teachers College, Columbia Univ.
Tran, Henry. Stability in Nonmaternal Child Care Arrangements. 2009. 148p. pap. *(978-3-639-09566-1(9))* VDM Verlag Dr. Mueller e.K.
Vered, Karen Orr. Children & Media Outside the Home: Playing & Learning in after-School Care. 2008. (ENG., Illus.). 256p. 89.00 *(978-0-230-53729-3(4))* Palgrave Macmillan.
Wood, Karren/Ikeda & Youcha, Victoria. The ABCs of the ADA: Your Early Childhood Program's Guide to the Americans with Disabilities Act. 2nd ed. 2008. (Illus.). 256p. 29.95 *(978-1-55766-933-9(3))* Brookes, Paul H. Publishing Co.
Zaslow, Martha, et al, eds. Quality Measurement in Early Childhood Settings. 2011. (Illus.). 456p. pap. 44.95 *(978-1-59857-161-5(3))* Brookes, Paul H. Publishing Co.
Zellman, Gail. Assessing the Validity of the Qualistar Early Learning Quality Rating & Improvement System As a Tool for Improving Child-Care Quality. 2008. 128p. pap. 32.50 *(978-0-8330-4495-2(8))* RAND Corp., The.
Zellman, Gail L. & Perlman, Michael. Child-Care Quality Rating & Improvement Systems in Five Pioneer States: Implementation Issues & Lessons Learned. 2008. 90p. pap. 25.00 *(978-0-8330-4551-5(2),* mg-795) RAND Corp., The.
Zigler, Edward F. Child Care Choices. 2007. (ENG.). 272p. pap. 19.95 *(978-1-4165-7333-3(X),* Free Pr.) Free Pr.

CHILD CARE WORKERS
see also Babysitters; Governesses; Wet Nurses
Boone, Beverly. Basic Training for Residential Childcare Workers: A Practical Guide for Improving Service to Children. 2011. 224p. pap. 36.95 ***(978-0-398-08708-1(3))*** Thomas, Charles C. Pub., Ltd.
Bray, Ilona. Nannies & au Pairs: Hiring In-Home Child Care. 2010. (ENG., Illus.). 242p. pap. 19.99 *(978-1-4133-1190-7(3))* NOLO.
Bumgarner, Marlene. Working with School-Age Children. 2010. (ENG.). 352p. (C). pap. 76.00 *(978-0-13-208085-9(0),* Prentice Hall) Prentice Hall PTR.
Catano, Francis N. Childcare Worker Assumptions about Caring. 2008. 160p. pap. *(978-3-639-03414-1(7))* VDM Verlag Dr. Mueller e.K.
Clanchy, Kate. Antigona & Me. 2009. (ENG.). 288p. pap. 17.95 *(978-0-330-44933-5(8),* Macmillan) Pan Macmillan GBR. Dist: Trans-Atlantic Pubns., Inc.
Daniel, Brigid, et al. Child Development for Child Care & Protection Workers. 2nd ed. 2010. (ENG., Illus.). 336p. pap. *(978-1-84905-068-5(6))* Kingsley, Jessica Ltd.
Eberts, Marjorie & Gisler, Margaret. Careers in Child Care. 3rd ed. 2007. (ENG.). 192p. per. 16.95 *(978-0-07-148211-0(3),* 0071482113) McGraw-Hill Cos., The.
—Careers in Child Care. 3rd ed. 2007. (Careers In Ser.). (ENG., Illus.). 232p. 29.35 *(978-1-4178-1021-5(1),* Turtleback) Turtleback Bks.
Elliot, Enid. We're Not Robots: The Voices of Daycare Providers. 2006. (SUNY Series, Early Childhood Education). 199p. per. 29.95 *(978-0-7914-6942-2(5))* State Univ. of New York Pr.
Elliot, Enid & Gonzalez Mena, Janet. We're Not Robots: The Voices of Daycare Providers. 2006. (SUNY Series, Early Childhood Education). 176p. (C). 65.50 *(978-0-7914-6941-5(7))* State Univ. of New York Pr.
Gonzalez-Mena, Janet & Eyer, Dianne Widmeyer. Infants, Toddlers, & Caregivers: A Curriculum of Respectful, Responsive Care & Education. 8th ed. 2008. (ENG., Illus.). 400p. (C). pap. 102.33 *(978-0-07-337854-1(2),* 0073378542) McGraw-Hill Cos., The.
Gonzalez-Mena, Janet, et al. Making Links: A Collaborative Approach to Planning & Practice in Early Childhood Programs. 2007. (ENG.). 192p. 36.95 *(978-0-8077-4843-5(9))* Teachers College Pr., Teachers College, Columbia Univ.
Green, Chamayne N. The Inside Scoop: Tips from a Family Child Care Professional. 2009. (ENG.). 104p. pap. 17.95 *(978-1-60554-004-7(8))* Redleaf Pr.
Harms, Thelma & Cryer, Debby. Video Guide & Training Workbook for the FCCERS-R. 2007. (ENG.). 40p. pap. 4.00 *(978-0-8077-4826-8(9))* Teachers College Pr., Teachers College, Columbia Univ.
Harms, Thelma, et al. Escala de Calificacion Del Ambiente de Cuidado Infantil en Familia. 2010. (SPA.). 88p. pap. 19.95 *(978-0-8077-4879-4(X))* Teachers College Pr., Teachers College, Columbia Univ.
—Family Child Care Environment Rating Scale. 2007. (ENG., Illus.). 88p. pap. 20.95 *(978-0-8077-4725-4(4))* Teachers College Pr., Teachers College, Columbia Univ.
Herr, Ed.D., Judy, Judy. Mastering CDA Competencies Using Working with Young Children. 7th ed. 2011. (ENG.). 272p. (gr. 9-14). pap. 36.00 ***(978-1-60525-445-6(2))*** Goodheart-Willcox Pub.
—Working with Young Children. 7th ed. 2011. 184p. pap. 18.00 ***(978-1-60525-437-1(1));*** 310p. (gr. 9-14). pap. 22.64 ***(978-1-60525-438-8(X));*** (ENG., Illus.). 912p. (gr. 9-14). 78.00 ***(978-1-60525-436-4(3))*** Goodheart-Willcox Pub.
Johnson, Jeff A. Finding Your Smile Again: A Child Care Professional's Guide to Reducing Stress & Avoiding Burnout. 2007. (ENG., Illus.). 160p. (J). per. 14.95 *(978-1-929610-93-8(9))* Redleaf Pr.
—Keeping Your Smile: Caring for Children with Joy, Love, & Intention. 2010. (ENG.). 184p. pap. 17.95 *(978-1-933653-85-3(X))* Redleaf Pr.
Karoly, Lynn A. A Golden Opportunity: Advancing California's Early Care & Education Workforce Professional Development System, 1 vol. 2012. (ENG., Illus.). 172p. (C). pap. 25.00 ***(978-0-8330-6011-2(2))*** RAND Corp., The.
Keith-Lucas, Alan. Group Child Care as a Family Service. 2011. (ENG.). 283p. pap. 40.00 *(978-0-8078-9696-9(9))* Univ. of North Carolina Pr.
Kovach, Beverly & Da Ros-Voseles, Denise. Being with Babies: Understanding & Responding to the Infants in Your Care. 2008. (ENG., Illus.). 192p. pap. 24.95 *(978-0-87659-062-1(8))* Gryphon Hse., Inc.
Lally, et al. Infant/Toddler Caregiving. 2nd ed. 2009. (Illus.). x, 85p. *(978-0-8011-1701-5(1))* California Dept. of Education.
LaRowe, Michelle, et al. Beyond Parenting Basics: The International Nanny Association's Official Guide to In-Home Child Care. 2nd ed. 2010. 152p. ***(978-0-615-31241-5(1))*** International Nanny Assn.
Lee, Allison. How to Be an Outstanding Childminder. 2009. (ENG., Illus.). 152p. 24.95 *(978-1-84706-496-7(5))* Continuum International Publishing Group, Ltd. GBR. Dist: National Bk. Network.
Lee, Allison & Lee. The Inside Guide to Being a Childminder. 2008. (ENG.). 152p. 24.95 *(978-0-8264-9895-3(7))* Continuum International Publishing Group, Ltd. GBR. Dist: National Bk. Network.
Lee, Allison, et al. Childminder's Guide to Child Development. 2009. (ENG., Illus.). 128p. 29.95 *(978-1-84706-085-3(4))* Continuum International Publishing Group, Ltd. GBR. Dist: National Bk. Network.
Lindamood, Judy B. & Lindamood, Robert L. Considering the Care of Children: A Guide to Cross-National Perspectives (2nd Edition) 2nd rev. ed. 2008. (ENG., Illus.). 260p. (C). spiral bd. *(978-0-9741587-1-6(2),* 092007) Familiae, Inc.
Maddalone, Guy. How to Hire a Nanny. 2006. (Illus.). 285p. per. 19.95 *(978-1-57248-565-5(5),* 1261106, Sphinx Publishing) Sourcebooks, Inc.
Miller, Daniel & Burikova, Zuzana. Au Pair. 2010. (ENG., Illus.). 240p. 69.95 *(978-0-7456-5011-1(2));* pap. 22.95 *(978-0-7456-5012-8(0))* Polity Pr. GBR. Dist: Wiley, John & Sons, Inc.
Mukherjee, Diganta. Child Labour & Child Work. 2010. 436p. pap. *(978-3-8383-3128-7(1))* Lambert Academic Publishing.
Neuman, Michelle, et al, eds. Professionals in early childhood education & care systems: European profiles & perspectives. 2010. 525p. pap. 75.95 *(978-3-86649-249-3(9))* Budrich-Esser, Barbara DEU. Dist: International Specialized Bk. Services.
Perrone, Marta. Help!! How to Find, Hire, Train & Maintain Your Household Help. 2006. (Illus.). 256p. per. 24.95 *(978-1-930754-84-3(1))* Durban House Pr., Inc.
Pierce, Debra. The CDA Prep Guide: The Complete Review Manual for the Child Development Associate Credential. 2nd ed. 2011. (ENG.). 212p. pap. 19.95 ***(978-1-60554-105-1(2))*** Redleaf Pr.
Wright, Hazel. Women Studying Childcare: Integrating Lives Through Adult Education. 2011. (Illus.). 188p. pap. 34.95 *(978-1-85856-485-2(9))* Trentham Bks. Ltd. GBR. Dist: Stylus Publishing, LLC.

CHILD CUSTODY
see Custody of Children

CHILD DEATH
see Children—Death

CHILD DEVELOPMENT
Here are entered works on the physical, psychological and social growth of normal children. Works on the psychological growth and characteristics of children are entered under Child Psychology.
see also Child Psychology; Children—Growth; Motor Ability in Children; Play Groups

Aaron, Jane E. & Riley, Kathryn. Developmental Exercises for the Little. 7th ed. 2009. (ENG.). 110p. (C). pap. 19.20 *(978-0-205-70197-1(3))* Longman Publishing Group.

Adamkin, David H. Nutritional Strategies for the Very Low Birthweight Infant. 2009. (ENG., Illus.). 208p. pap. 44.99 *(978-0-521-73246-8(6)*, Cambridge Univ. Pr.

Adams, Harry. Justice for Children: Autonomy Development & the State. 2009. 264p. pap. 29.95 *(978-0-7914-7332-0(5))* 2008. 254p. 70.00 *(978-0-7914-7331-3(7))* State Univ. of New York Pr.

Adams Ph. D., Jerry. Discipline Without Anger: A Parent's Guide to Teaching Children Responsible Behavior. 2008. 260p. pap. 14.49 *(978-1-4343-7537-7(4))* AuthorHouse.

Adler, Alfred & Wolfe, W. Beran. The Pattern of Life. 2011. 280p. pap. 13.95 ***(978-1-61427-108-2(2))*** Martino Publishing.

Agis, Derya. Training of the Bahá'í Child Educators. 2011. 84p. pap. ***(978-3-8443-1882-1(8))*** Lambert Academic Publishing.

Aina, Tade Akin, et al, eds. Beyond Benign Neglect: Early Childhood Care, Development & Nutrition in Metropolitan Lagos, Nigeria. 2008. 220p. pap. *(978-978-023-205-4(2))* Malthouse Press Ltd, Nigeria NGA. Dist: Michigan State Univ. Pr.

Aitken, Stuart. Global Childhoods: Globalization, Development & Young People. 2007. pap. 40.00 *(978-0-415-49488-5(5))* Routledge.

Aitken, Stuart, ed. Global Childhoods: Globalization, Development & Young People. 2008. (ENG., Illus.). 200p. 140.00 *(978-0-415-41145-5(9))* Routledge.

Akanda, Md. Zahir Uddin & Akanda, Zahir Uddin. Father's Role in Enhancing Children's Development. 2011. 60p. pap. ***(978-3-8454-1886-5(9))*** Lambert Academic Publishing.

Akhtar, Monisha C. Play & Playfulness: Developmental, Cultural, & Clinical Aspects. 2010. *(978-0-7657-0762-8(4)*, Aronson, Jason) Rowman & Littlefield Publishers, Inc.

Akhtar, Salman. The Mother & Her Child: Clinical Aspects of Attachment, Separation, & Loss. 2011. E-Book ***(978-0-7657-0834-2(5)***, Aronson, Jason) Rowman & Littlefield Publishers, Inc.

Aleksandrowicz, Dov R. & Aleksandrowicz, Malca. The Injured Self: The Psychopathology & Psychotherapy of Developmental Deviations. 2011. 270p. pap. 34.95 *(978-1-85575-842-1(3))* Karnac Bks. GBR. Dist: Stylus Publishing, LLC.

Ali, Munir Muztaba. How Folk & Fairy Tales Aid Children's Growth & Maturity: An Analysis of Their Need Fulfillment Imagery. 2009. (Illus.). 192p. 99.95 *(978-0-7734-4706-6(7))* Mellen, Edwin Pr., The.

Allen, K Eileen & Marotz, Lynn R. Developmental Profiles: Pre-Birth Through Twelve. 5th rev. ed. 2006. (ENG., Illus.). 320p. (C). pap. 93.95 *(978-1-4180-2907-4(6))* Delmar Cengage Learning.

American Academy Of Pediatrics, et al. Caring for Your Baby & Young Child: Birth to Age 5. 5th ed. 2009. (ENG., Illus.). 928p. pap. 22.00 *(978-0-553-38630-1(1))* Random House Publishing Group.

American Academy of Pediatrics Staff. The Wonder Years: Helping Your Baby & Young Child Successfully Negotiate the Major Developmental Milestones. Altmann, Tanya Remer, ed. 2007. (ENG., Illus.). 224p. pap. 15.00 *(978-0-553-38397-3(3)*, Bantam) Random House Publishing Group.

Anandalakshmy, S., et al. Researching Families & Children Culturally Appropriate Methods. Anandalakshmy, S. et al, eds. 2008. (Illus.). 252p. (C). pap. 29.95 *(978-81-7829-872-6(4)*, B98726P) SAGE Pubns., Inc.

Andrews, Jac & Istvanffy, Peter, eds. Exceptional Life Journeys: Stories of Childhood Disorder. 2011. (ENG.). 306p. 64.95 *(978-0-12-385216-8(1))* Elsevier Science & Technology Bks.

Ann Roberts, Avril Harpie. From Birth to Three - Series 4 Pack. 2006. (From Birth to Three Ser.). 59.95 *(978-1-84312-458-0(0))* Fulton, David Pubs. GBR. Dist: Taylor & Francis Group.

Ansell, Nicola. Children, Youth & Development. 2nd rev. ed. 2013. (Routledge Perspectives on Development Ser.). (ENG., Illus.). 336p. (C). 128.00 *(978-0-415-61719-2(7))*; pap. 44.95 *(978-0-415-61720-8(0))* Routledge.

Apel, Kenn. Be-Yond Ba-By Talk: From Speaking to Spelling - A Guide to Language & Literacy Development for Parents & Caregivers. 2012. (ENG.). 304p. pap. 15.00 ***(978-0-307-95228-8(2)***, Three Rivers Pr.) Crown Publishing Group.

Arce, EdD, Eve-Marie, Eve-Marie. Twins & Supertwins: A Handbook for Early Childhood Professionals. 2010. (ENG.). 200p. pap. 29.95 ***(978-1-60554-030-6(7))*** Redleaf Pr.

Armstrong, Thomas. The Best Schools: How Human Development Research Should Inform Educational Practice. 2006. (Illus.). 182p. per. 23.95 *(978-1-4166-0457-0(X))*, Assn. for Supervision & Curriculum Development.

Arnold, Cheryl & Fisch, Ralph. The Impact of Complex Trauma on Development. 2011. (ENG.). 288p. 75.00 ***(978-0-7657-0882-3(5)***, Aronson, Jason) Rowman & Littlefield Publishers, Inc.

Ashy, Majed. Childhood Experiences, Social Interactions, & Physical Health. 2008. 120p. pap. *(978-3-639-06232-8(9))* VDM Verlag Dr. Mueller e.K.

Avan, Bilal Iqbal, ed. Early Childhood Development: From Understanding to Initiatives. 2008. (ENG., Illus.). 256p. pap. 39.95 *(978-0-19-547389-6(2))* Oxford Univ. Pr., Inc.

Aves, Corinne. Understanding 6-7-Year-Olds. 2006. (Understanding Your Child Ser.). (ENG.). 8p. per. *(978-1-84310-467-4(9))* Kingsley, Jessica Ltd.

Axness, Marcy. Parenting for Peace: Raising the Next Generation of Peacemakers. 2012. (ENG.). 320p. pap. 18.95 *(978-1-59181-176-3(7))* Sentient Pubns.

Azzopardi, Charlie. Telling your child about Separation. 2008. (ENG & MLT.). 79p. (C). pap. 10.00 *(978-99932-7-240-3(X))* Midsea Bks. Ltd. MLT. Dist: Brown, David Bk. Co., The.

—Will They Still Love Me? 2008. (ENG & MLT.). 16p. (C). pap. 9.00 *(978-99932-7-242-7(6))* Midsea Bks. Ltd. MLT. Dist: Brown, David Bk. Co., The.

Baartz, Ama. I Am Inspiration! Emotional Intelligence, Key to Success. 2011. 168p. pap. 61.95 ***(978-1-4525-3716-0(X))*** Get Published.

Babocsai, Lysett. When Vacuum Cleaners Bark & Dogs Buzz. 2008. 84p. pap. *(978-3-639-03044-0(3))* VDM Verlag Dr. Mueller e.K.

Bagnato, Stephen J., et al. LINKing Authentic Assessment & Early Childhood Intervention: Best Measures for Best Practices, Second Edition. 2nd ed. 2010. (Illus.). 400p. pap. 49.95 *(978-1-59857-047-2(1)*, Brookes, Paul H. Publishing Co.

Bahr, Diane. Nobody Ever Told Me (or my Mother) That! Everything from Bottles & Breathing to Healthy Speech Development. 2010. (ENG., Illus.). 390p. (gr. -1 — 1). pap. 24.95 *(978-1-935567-20-2(9))* Sensory Resources.

Bailey, Sue. The Young Mind: An Essential Guide to Mental Health for Young Adults, Parents & Teachers. Shooter, Mike, ed. 2012. (ENG.). 400p. pap. 14.95 *(978-0-553-82418-6(X))* Transworld Publishers Ltd. GBR. Dist: Independent Pubs. Group.

Baker, Jed. No More Meltdowns: Positive Strategies for Dealing with & Preventing Out-of-Control Behavior. 2008. (ENG.). 150p. pap. 14.95 *(978-1-932565-62-1(0))* Future Horizons, Inc.

Ball, Jessica & Pence, Alan. Supporting Indigenous Children's Development: Community-University Partnerships. 2006. (ENG., Illus.). 160p. pap. *(978-0-7748-1231-3(1))* Univ. of British Columbia Pr.

Bancroft Symanski, Barbara. Successful Children: One Teacher's Viewpoint: Step by Step. 2010. (Illus.). 96p. pap. 17.95 *(978-1-936198-07-8(X))* Hillcrest Publishing Group, Inc.

Barbarin, Oscar A. & Wasik, Barbara Hanna. Handbook of Child Development & Early Education: Research to Practice. Barbarin, Oscar A. & Wasik, Barbara Hanna, eds. 2009. (ENG., Illus.). 624p. (gr. -1-3). 95.00 *(978-1-60623-302-3(5))* Guilford Pubns., Inc.

Barbour, Chandler, et al. Families, Schools, & Communities: Building Partnerships for Educating Children. (ENG., (C). 4th ed. 2007. Illus.). 432p. per. 96.67 *(978-0-13-239282-2(8))* 5th ed. 2010. 416p. pap. 99.40 *(978-0-13-703546-5(2))* Prentice Hall PTR. (Prentice Hall).

Barker, Richard, ed. Making Sense of Every Child Matters: Multi-Professional Practice Guidance. 2008. (Illus.). 224p. pap. 35.95 *(978-1-84742-011-4(7))* Policy Pr. GBR. Dist: Chicago Distribution Ctr.

Barnes, Jacqueline. Down Our Way: The Relevance of Neighbourhoods for Parenting & Child Development. 2007. (ENG., Illus.). 306p. 184.00 *(978-0-470-03072-1(0)*, Wiley) Wiley, John & Sons, Inc.

Bauer, Patricia J., et al, eds. Advances in Child Development & Behavior. 2009. (Advances in Child Development & Behavior Ser.: 37). (ENG.). 400p. 107.00 *(978-0-12-374470-8(9)*, Academic Pr.) Elsevier Science & Technology Bks.

Bayer, Tedi. My Child Speaks Ten Languages. 2009. 279p. pap. 20.00 *(978-0-9801270-6-5(8))* Seven Locks Pr.

Beaty, Janice J. Observing Development of the Young Child. 7th ed. 2008. (ENG., Illus.). 480p. (C). pap. 73.20 *(978-0-13-502589-5(3)*, Prentice Hall) Prentice Hall PTR.

—Preschool Appropriate Practices. 3rd ed. 2008. (ENG., Illus.). 400p. (C). pap. 84.95 *(978-1-4283-0448-2(7))* Delmar Cengage Learning.

—Skills for Preschool Teachers. 9th rev. ed. 2011. (ENG.). 416p. (C). pap. 66.40 *(978-0-13-038840-7(8)*, Prentice Hall) Prentice Hall PTR.

Becker, Nettie & Becker, Paul. Developing Quality Care for Young Children: How to Turn Early Care Settings into Magical Places. 2008. (Illus.). 200p. 70.95 *(978-1-4129-6565-1(9)*, B65651C); pap. 29.95 *(978-1-4129-6566-8(7)*, B65651P) Corwin Pr.

Beckley, Pat & Marland, Harriet. Problem Solving, Reasoning & Numeracy. 2011. (Supporting Development in the Early Years Foundation Stage Ser.). (ENG., Illus.). 144p. 100.00 *(978-1-4411-8959-2(9))* Continuum International Publishing Group, Ltd. GBR. Dist: National Bk. Network.

Beckley, Pat, et al. Implementing the Early Years Foundation Stage. 2009. (ENG., Illus.). 280p. (C). 127.00 *(978-0-335-23616-9(2)*, 0335236162) McGraw-Hill Education GBR. Dist: McGraw-Hill Cos., The.

—Problem Solving, Reasoning & Numeracy. 2011. (Supporting Development in the Early Years Foundation Stage Ser.). (ENG., Illus.). 144p. pap. 29.95 *(978-1-4411-6474-2(X))* Continuum International Publishing Group, Ltd. GBR. Dist: National Bk. Network.

Bee, Helen & Boyd, Denise. The Developing Child. 11th ed. 2006. (Illus.). pap. 73.33 *(978-0-205-50247-9(4))* Allyn & Bacon, Inc.

Bee, Helen L. & Boyd, Denise. The Developing Child, Books a la Carte Edition. 13th ed. 2011. (ENG.). 576p. (C). ring bd. 108.67 ***(978-0-205-25635-8(X)***, Prentice Hall) Prentice Hall PTR.

Bee, Helen L. & Boyd, Denise A. The Developing Child. 13th rev. ed. 2011. (ENG.) 592p. (C). 166.67 ***(978-0-205-25602-0(3)***, Prentice Hall) Prentice Hall PTR.

Beese, Renee. You Are It: A Children's Book for Expanding Adults. 2011. 32p. pap. 16.00 ***(978-1-4634-1616-4(4))*** AuthorHouse.

Behera, Deepak Kumar. Childhoods in South Asia. 2007. xi, 356p. *(978-81-317-0415-8(7))* Addison-Wesley Longman, Inc.

Belenky Ph D., Robert. Tales of Priut Almus. 2009. 320p. 32.95 *(978-1-4401-3153-0(8))*; pap. 22.95 *(978-1-4401-3151-6(1))* iUniverse, Inc.

Belsky, Janet. Exploring Human Development. 2007. (ENG.). (C). stu. ed. 18.95 incl. cd-rom *(978-0-7167-7264-4(7))* Freeman, W. H. & Co.

Ben-Arieh, Asher & Froenes, Ivar, eds. Handbook of Child Well-Being: Theory, Indicators, Measures & Policies. 2011. (Illus.). 1200p. 1349.00 *(978-90-481-9062-1(2)*, 9048190622) Springer.

Benson, Janette B. Advances in Child Development & Behavior. 2011. (Advances in Child Development & Behavior Ser.: 40). (ENG., Illus.). 480p. 107.00 ***(978-0-12-386491-8(7)***, Academic Pr.) Elsevier Science & Technology Bks.

Benson, Janette B., contrib. by. Advances in Child Development & Behavior. 2012. (Advances in Child Development & Behavior Ser.: 42). (ENG.). 398p. 107.00 ***(978-0-12-394388-0(4)***, Academic Pr.) Elsevier Science & Technology Bks.

Benson, Peter L. Parent, Teacher, Mentor, Friend: How Every Adult Can Change Kids' Lives. 2010. (ENG., Illus.). 256p. pap. 7.95 *(978-1-57482-283-0(7))* Search Institute.

Bentham, Susan. A Teaching Assistant's Guide to Child Development & Psychology. 2nd rev. ed. 2011. (ENG., Illus.). 232p. 125.00 *(978-0-415-56922-4(2))*; pap. 35.95 *(978-0-415-56923-1(0))* Routledge.

Beresin, Anna R. Recess Battles: Playing, Fighting, & Storytelling. (ENG.). 144p. 2011. pap. 30.00 ***(978-1-61703-204-2(2))*** 2010. (Illus.). 50.00 *(978-1-60473-739-4(5))* Univ. Pr. of Mississippi.

Bergen, Doris, et al. Educating & Caring for Very Young Children: The Infant/Toddler Curriculum. 2nd rev. ed. 2008. (Early Childhood Education Ser.). (ENG., Illus.). 224p. pap. 26.95 *(978-0-8077-4920-3(6))* Teachers College Pr., Teachers College, Columbia Univ.

Berger. The Developing Person Through the Life Span. 7th rev. ed. 2007. (ENG., Illus.). 667p. (C). pap. 143.95 *(978-0-7167-6080-1(0))* Worth Pubs., Inc.

Berger & Berger, Kathleen Stassen. The Developing Person Through the Life Span. 8th rev. ed. 2011. (ENG.). 667p. (C). 155.95 *(978-1-4292-3203-6(X))* Worth Pubs., Inc.

Berger, Kathleen Stassen. The Developing Person. 5th ed. 2007. 160p. per. 11.95 *(978-1-4288-1940-5(1))* Cram101 Inc.

—The Developing Person Through Childhood & Adolescence. 8th ed. 2008. (ENG.). 608p. (C). 149.95 *(978-1-4292-1647-0(6))*; (Illus.). pap. 137.95 *(978-1-4292-2080-4(5))* Worth Pubs., Inc.

—Developing Person Through Childhood & Adolescence. (ENG.). (C). 8th ed. 2009. 608p. 87.95 *(978-1-4292-4437-4(2))* 9th ed. 2011. 672p. 149.95 ***(978-1-4292-4351-3(1))*** Worth Pubs., Inc.

—The Developing Person Through the Life Span. 7th rev. ed. 2007. (ENG., Illus.). 406p. (C). pap., pupil's gde. ed. 30.95 *(978-0-7167-6092-4(4))* Worth Pubs., Inc.

Berger, Kathleen Stassen & Straub, Richard O. The Developing Person Through Childhood & Adolescence. 8th ed. 2008. (ENG.). 404p. (C). pap., stu. ed. 30.95 *(978-1-4292-1782-8(0))* Worth Pubs., Inc.

Bergese, Rebecca. Understanding 10-11-year-Olds. 2008. (ENG.). 80p. pap. *(978-1-84310-674-6(4))* Kingsley, Jessica Ltd.

Bergin, David & Bergin, Christi. Child Development in Your Classroom. 2011. (Whatâ€(tm)s New in Education Ser.). (ENG.). 704p. (C). pap. 135.95 *(978-1-111-18634-0(0))* Wadsworth.

Berk & Cram101 Textbook Reviews Staff. Child Development. 2007. 156p. per. 12.95 *(978-1-4288-1964-1(9))* Cram101 Inc.

Berk, Laura E. Child Development. 8th ed. 2008. (ENG.). 800p. (C). 167.67 *(978-0-205-61559-9(7))* Allyn & Bacon, Inc.

—Child Development. 9th ed. 2012. ***(978-0-205-14977-3(4))***; (ENG.). 816p. (C). 167.67 ***(978-0-205-14976-6(6))*** Pearson Education.

—Child Development. 8th ed. 2009. (ENG.). 800p. (C). 96.20 *(978-0-205-66266-1(8)*, Prentice Hall) Prentice Hall PTR.

—Child Development, Books a la Carte Edition. 9th ed. 2012. (ENG.). 816p. (C). ring bd 109.33 ***(978-0-205-85435-6(4)***, Prentice Hall) Prentice Hall PTR.

—Infants & Children: Prenatal Through Middle Childhood. 4th ed. 2006. pap. 11.95 *(978-1-4288-1304-5(7))* Cram101 Inc.

—Infants & Children: Prenatal Through Middle Childhood. 7th ed. 2010. (ENG.). 672p. (C). pap. 135.00 *(978-0-205-83191-3(5)*, Prentice Hall) Prentice Hall PTR.

—Infants, Children & Adolescents. 4th ed. 2006. pap. 12.95 *(978-1-4288-1305-2(5))* Cram101 Inc.

—Infants, Children, & Adolescents. 7th rev. ed. 2010. (ENG.). 816p. (C). 167.60 *(978-0-205-71816-0(7)*, Prentice Hall) Prentice Hall PTR.

—Study Guide for Infants, Children & Adolescents. 7th rev. ed. 2011. (ENG.). 448p. (C). pap. 37.40 *(978-0-205-01051-6(2)*, Prentice Hall) Prentice Hall PTR.

—A Window on Child Development DVD Guide for Child Development. 8th ed. 2008. 128p. (C). pap. 5.00 *(978-0-205-62680-9(7)*, Allyn & Bacon) Pearson Education Canada CAN. Dist: Pearson Education.

Berke, Jennifer E. & Martin, Sue. See How They Grow: Infants & Toddlers. 2006. (ENG., Illus.). 400p. (C). pap. 70.95 *(978-1-4180-1922-8(4))* Delmar Cengage Learning.

Berke, Kai-Lee, et al. A Trainer's Guide to the Creative Curriculum for Infants, Toddlers & Twos. 2007. *(978-1-933021-37-9(3))* Teaching Strategies, Inc.

Bernier, Raphael & Gerdts, Jennifer. Autism Spectrum Disorders: A Reference Handbook, 1 vol. 2010. (Contemporary World Issues Ser.). (Illus.). 324p. 55.00 *(978-1-59884-334-7(6)*, A2264C) ABC-CLIO, LLC.

Bess, Cindy Rzasa. The View from the Little Chair in the Corner: Improving Teacher Practice & Early Childhood Learning. 2010. (ENG.). 168p. 68.00 *(978-0-8077-5040-7(9))*; pap. 23.95 *(978-0-8077-5039-1(5))* Teachers College Pr., Teachers College, Columbia Univ.

Biggeri, Mario, et al, eds. Children & the Capability Approach. 2011. (Studies in Childhood & Youth Ser.). (ENG., Illus.). 392p. 90.00 *(978-0-230-28481-4(7))* Palgrave Macmillan.

Biglan, Anthony, et al, eds. Preventing Youth Problems. 2010. (Issues in Children's & Families' Lives Ser.). 196p. pap. 84.95 *(978-1-4419-3398-0(0)*, 1441933980) Springer.

Bigner, Jerry J. Parent-Child Relations: An Introduction to Parenting. 8th ed. 2008. (ENG.). 408p. (C). pap. 105.00 *(978-0-13-500219-3(2)*, Prentice Hall) Prentice Hall PTR.

Billman & Sherman & Cram101 Textbook Reviews Staff. Observation & Participation in Early Childhood Settings. 2007. 68p. per. 10.95 *(978-1-4288-1968-9(1))* Cram101 Inc.

Bindler, Ruth McGillis W., et al. Clinical Handbook for Child Health Nursing: Partnering with Children & Families. 2nd ed. 2009. (ENG., Illus.). 744p. (C). pap. 48.95 *(978-0-13-500506-4(X)*, Prentice Hall) Prentice Hall PTR.

Bishop-Josef, Sandra J., et al, eds. Child Development & Social Policy: Knowledge for Action. 2006. (Decade of Behavior Ser.). (Illus.). 311p. 39.95 *(978-1-59147-425-8(6))* American Psychological Assn.

Bishop, Ronald. When Play Was Play: Why Pick-Up Games Matter. 2009. (Excelsior Editions Ser.). 208p. 65.00 *(978-1-4384-2603-7(8))*; pap. 24.94 *(978-1-4384-2604-4(6))* State Univ. of New York Pr.

Bjorklund, David F. Why Youth Is Not Wasted on the Young: Immaturity in Human Development. 2007. (ENG., Illus.). 288p. 110.95 *(978-1-4051-4951-8(5))*; pap. 35.95 *(978-1-4051-4952-5(3))* Wiley, John & Sons, Inc. (Wiley-Blackwell).

Bjorklund, David F. (David F. Bjorklund) & Hernández Blasi, Carlos. Child & Adolescent Development. 2011. (ENG.). 288p. (C). pap., pupil's gde. ed. 39.95 *(978-0-495-89706-4(X))* Wadsworth.

—Child & Adolescent Development: An Evolutionary Perspective. 2011. (ENG.). 800p. (C). 144.95 *(978-0-495-09563-7(X))* Wadsworth.

—Child & Adolescent Development: An Integrated Approach. 2011. (ENG., Illus.). 800p. (C). ring bd. 97.95 *(978-0-495-89740-8(X))* Wadsworth.

Blake, Sally, et al. Child Development & the Use of Technology: Perspectives, Applications & Experiences. 2011. ***(978-1-61350-319-5(9))***; ***(978-1-61350-317-1(2))***; E-Book ***(978-1-61350-318-8(0))*** IGI Global.

Blake, Simon, et al. Promoting Emotional & Social Development in Schools: A Practical Guide. 2007. (Illus.). 144p. 65.00 *(978-1-4129-0730-9(6)*, B07306C); per. 30.00 *(978-1-4129-0731-6(4)*, B07306P) SAGE Pubns., Ltd. GBR. Dist: SAGE Pubns., Inc.

Blundell, David. Education & Constructions of Childhood. 2012. (Contemporary Issues in Education Studies). (ENG.). 224p. 130.00 *(978-1-4411-7884-8(8))* Continuum International Publishing Group, Ltd. GBR. Dist: National Bk. Network.

Blundell, David S. Education & Constructions of Childhood. 2012. (Contemporary Issues in Education Studies). (ENG.). 224p. 39.95 *(978-1-84706-025-9(0))* Continuum International Publishing Group, Ltd. GBR. Dist: National Bk. Network.

Bock, John & Gaskins, Suzanne. The Anthropology of Learning in Childhood. Lancy, David F., ed. 2010. (ENG., Illus.). 410p. 90.00 *(978-0-7591-1322-0(X))* AltaMira Pr.

Bohlin, Lisa, et al. EdPsych: Modules. 2008. (ENG., Illus.). 688p. (C). pap. 157.67 *(978-0-07-337850-3(X)*, 007337850X) McGraw-Hill Cos., The.

Booth. Disparities in School Readiness. 2007. (ENG.). 320p. 105.95 *(978-0-8058-6435-9(0)*, Psychology Press) Taylor & Francis Group GBR. Dist: Taylor & Francis Group.

Booth, Alan & Crouter, Ann C., eds. Disparities in School Readiness: How Families Contribute to Transitions into School. 2007. (ENG., Illus.). 320p. per. 44.95 *(978-0-8058-5981-2(0)*, Psychology Press) Taylor & Francis Group GBR. Dist: Taylor & Francis Group.

Borgnon, Liselotte & Olsson, Liselott Mariett. Movement & Experimentation in Young Children's Learning: Deleuze & Guattari in Early Childhood Education. 2009. (Contesting Early Childhood Ser.). (ENG., Illus.). 234p. 140.00 *(978-0-415-46866-4(3))* Routledge.

Borkowski, John G. & Weaver, Chelsea M., eds. Prevention: The Science & Art of Promoting Health Child & Adolescent Development. 2006. 298p. per. 39.95 *(978-1-55766-868-4(X)*, 868X) Brookes, Paul H. Publishing Co.

Borovska, Pavlina. English with Pre-Schoolers. 2010. 56p. pap. *(978-3-8383-7195-5(X))* Lambert Academic Publishing.

Bouchard, Caroline & Fréchette, Nathalie. Le Développement Global de L'enfant de 6 à 12 Ans en Contextes éducatifs. 2011. (FRE., Illus.). xxiii, 554p. *(978-2-7605-2444-6(2))* Presses de l'Universite du Quebec.

Bowers, Edmond P., et al, eds. Thriving in Childhood & Adolescence - The Role of Self Regulation Processes. 2011. (J-B CAD Single Issue Child & Adolescent Development Ser.: 104). (ENG.). 112p. pap. 29.00 *(978-1-118-09410-5(7)*, Jossey-Bass) Wiley, John & Sons, Inc.

Bowers, Jill & Decker, Celia Anita. Child Development:Early Stages Through Age 12 ExamView Assessment Suite. 2010. cd-rom 200.00 *(978-1-60525-298-8(0))* Goodheart-Willcox Pub.

Bowman, Viviana, ed. Scholarly Resources for Children & Childhood Studies: A Research Guide & Annotated Bibliography. 2007. (ENG., Illus.). 298p. per. 60.00 *(978-0-8108-5874-9(6))* Scarecrow Pr., Inc.

Boyd, Denise & Bee, Helen L. The Growing Child. 2009. (ENG., Illus.). 656p. (C). pap. 154.40 *(978-0-205-54596-4(3))* Allyn & Bacon, Inc.

Bracken, Bruce A. & Nagle, Richard J., eds. Psychoeducational Assessment of Preschool Children. 4th rev. ed. 2006. (ENG., Illus.). 504p. 100.00 *(978-0-8058-5263-9(8))* Routledge.

C

Bradford, Helen. Appropriate Environments for Children Under 3. 2011. (Supporting Children Ser.). (ENG., Illus.). 104p. 105.00 *(978-0-415-61262-3(4))*; pap. 28.95 *(978-0-415-61263-0(2))* Routledge.

—Communication, Language & Literacy in the Early Years Foundation Stage. 2009. (Practical Guidance in the EYFS Ser.). (ENG.). 144p. 120.00 *(978-0-415-47835-9(9))* Fulton, David Pubs. GBR. Dist: Taylor & Francis Group.

—Communication, Language & Literacy in the Early Years Foundation Stage: Supporting the Framework Through the Use of Story, 7 vols. 2009. (Practical Guidance in the EYFS Ser.). (Illus.). 96p. pap. 31.95 *(978-0-415-47427-6(2))* Fulton, David Pubs. GBR. Dist: Taylor & Francis Group.

—Planning & Observation with Children Under 3. 2012. (Supporting Children Ser.). (ENG., Illus.). 112p. 115.00 *(978-0-415-61267-8(5))*; pap. 28.95 *(978-0-415-61268-5(3))* Routledge.

—The Well Being of Children Under 3. 2012. (Supporting Children from Birth to Three Ser.). (ENG., Illus.). 120p. 105.00 *(978-0-415-61270-8(5))*; pap. 28.95 *(978-0-415-61272-2(1))* Routledge.

Bradley, Elizabeth & Emanuel, Louise. "What Can the Matter Be?" Therapeutic Interventions with Parents, Infants, & Young Children: The Work of the Tavistock Clinic under Fives Service. Bradley, Elizabeth & Emanuel, Louise, eds. 2008. (Tavistock Clinic Ser.). 320p. pap. 38.95 *(978-1-85575-340-2(5))* Karnac Bks. GBR. Dist: Stylus Publishing, LLC.

Bradley, Reb. Born Liberal, Raised Right: How to Rescue America from Moral Decline - One Family at a Time. 2008. 192p. 25.95 *(978-1-935071-00-6(9))* WND Bks, Inc.

Bray, Rachel, et al. Growing up in the New South Africa: Childhood & Adolescence in Post-Apartheid Cape Town. 2010. (ENG.). 448p. pap. 34.95 *(978-0-7969-2313-4(2))* Human Sciences Research Council ZAF. Dist: Independent Pubs. Group.

Brazelton, T. Berry & Sparrow, Joshua D. Touchpoints-Birth to Three: Your Child's Emotional & Behavioral Development. 2nd rev. ed. 2006. (ENG., Illus.). 528p. per. 17.95 *(978-0-7382-1049-0(8))* Da Capo Pr., Inc.

Bredekamp & Bredekamp, Sue. Effective Practices in Early Childhood Education: Building a Foundation, Student Value Edition. 2011. (ENG.). 512p. (C). ring bd. 90.60 ***(978-0-13-277942-5(0)***, Prentice Hall) Prentice Hall PTR.

Bredekamp, Sue. Effective Practices in Early Childhood Education: Building a Foundation (with MyEducationLab) 2010. (ENG.). 576p. (C). 141.33 *(978-0-13-801999-0(1)*, Prentice Hall) Prentice Hall PTR.

Bredekamp, Virginia Susan & Bredekamp, Sue. Effective Practices in Early Childhood Education: Building a Foundation. 2010. (ENG.). 576p. (C). 139.40 *(978-0-205-51532-5(0)*, Prentice Hall) Prentice Hall PTR.

Brielmaier, Kate, ed. Activities on the Go: One-on-One Fun for Kids & Adults. 2009. (ENG., Illus.). 104p. pap. 9.95 *(978-1-57482-271-7(3))* Search Institute.

Briers, Stephen. How Your Child Thinks: Give Your Child the Superpowers to Be a Happy, Healthy Person. 2009. (ENG., Illus.). 272p. pap. 18.99 *(978-0-13-815674-9(3))* FT Press.

Brisbane & Glencoe McGraw-Hill Staff. The Developing Child Student Edition. 2nd ed. 2008. (ENG.). (C). 63.72 *(978-0-07-888360-6(1)*, 0078883601) McGraw-Hill Higher Education.

Broadhead, Pat & Woolley, Richard. Personal, Social & Emotional Development. 2011. (Supporting Development in the Early Years Foundation Stage Ser.). (ENG., Illus.). 160p. 100.00 *(978-1-4411-3371-7(2))* Continuum International Publishing Group, Ltd. GBR. Dist: National Bk. Network.

Broadhead, Pat, et al. Personal, Social & Emotional Development. 2011. (Supporting Development in the Early Years Foundation Stage Ser.). (ENG., Illus.). 160p. pap. 29.95 *(978-1-84706-567-4(8))* Continuum International Publishing Group, Ltd. GBR. Dist: National Bk. Network.

Brock, Avril & Rankin, Carolynn. Professionalism in the Interdisciplinary Early Years Team. Brock, Avril & Rankin, Carolynn, eds. 2011. (ENG., Illus.). 224p. pap. 34.95 *(978-1-4411-1408-2(4))* Continuum International Publishing Group, Ltd. GBR. Dist: National Bk. Network.

—Professionalism in the Interdisciplinary Early Years Team: Supporting Young Children & Their Families. Brock, Avril & Rankin, Carolynn, eds. 2011. (ENG., Illus.). 224p. 120.00 *(978-1-4411-3706-7(8))* Continuum International Publishing Group, Ltd. GBR. Dist: National Bk. Network.

Bronson, Po & Merryman, Ashley. NurtureShock: New Thinking about Children. (ENG.). 352p. 2011. pap. 14.99 *(978-0-446-50413-3(0))* 2009. 24.99 *(978-0-446-50412-6(2))* Grand Central Publishing. (Twelve).

Brott, Armin A. Fathering Your School-Age Child: A Dad's Guide to the Wonder Years - 3 To 9. 2007. (ENG., Illus.). 255p. per. 12.95 *(978-0-7892-0924-5(1))* Abbeville Pr., Inc.

Brown, Fraser & Patte, Michael. Rethinking Children's Play. 2013. (New Childhoods Ser.). (ENG.). 172p. 120.00 *(978-1-4411-7366-9(8))*; pap. 34.95 *(978-1-4411-9469-5(X))* Continuum International Publishing Group, Ltd. GBR. Dist: National Bk. Network.

Brown, Fraser & Taylor, Chris. Foundations of Playwork. 2008. (ENG., Illus.). 344p. (C). pap. 40.00 *(978-0-335-22291-9(9)*, 0335222919); 117.00 *(978-0-335-22292-6(7)*, 0335222927) McGraw-Hill Education GBR. Dist: McGraw-Hill Cos., The.

The BROWN UNIVERSITY CHILD & ADOLESCENT BEHAVIOR Letter, 27/5. 2011. 16.58 *(978-1-118-02027-2(8)*, Wiley) Wiley, John & Sons, Inc.

The BROWN UNIVERSITY CHILD & ADOLESCENT BEHAVIOR Letter, 27/6. 2011. 16.58 *(978-1-118-02028-9(6)*, Wiley) Wiley, John & Sons, Inc.

The BROWN UNIVERSITY CHILD & ADOLESCENT PSYCHOPHARMACOLOGY UPDATE 13/05. 2011. 16.58 *(978-1-118-02015-9(4)*, Wiley) Wiley, John & Sons, Inc.

The BROWN UNIVERSITY CHILD & ADOLESCENT PSYCHOPHARMACOLOGY UPDATE 13/06. 2011. 16.58 *(978-1-118-02016-6(2)*, Wiley) Wiley, John & Sons, Inc.

Browne, Kate & Gordon, Ann. To Teach Well: An Early Childhood Practicum Guide. 2008. (ENG.). 264p. (C). pap. 42.80 *(978-0-13-199502-4(2)*, Prentice Hall) Prentice Hall PTR.

Browne-Miller, Angela. Raising Thinking Children & Teens: Guiding Mental & Moral Development, 1 vol. 2009. (Illus.). 204p. 39.95 *(978-0-313-35876-0(1)*, C35876, Praeger Pubs.) Greenwood Publishing Group, Inc.

Bruce, Tina. Learning Through Play: For Babies, Toddlers & Young Children. 2nd rev. ed. 2011. (ENG., Illus.). 144p. pap. 35.00 *(978-1-4441-3716-3(6))* Hodder Arnold Pubs.

Bukatko & Daehler & Cram101 Textbook Reviews Staff. Child Development. 2007. 216p. per. 13.95 *(978-1-4288-1974-0(6))* Cram101 Inc.

Bukatko, Danuta. Child & Adolescent Development: A Chronological Approach. 2007. (ENG., Illus.). 720p. (C). 195.95 *(978-0-618-34920-3(0)*, 308200) Wadsworth.

—Child Development: A Thematic Approach. 6th ed. 2011. (ENG.). 288p. (C). pap., pupil's gde. ed. 60.95 *(978-0-618-61864-4(3))* Wadsworth.

Bukatko, Danuta & Daehler, Marvin. Cengage Advantage Books: Child Development: A Thematic Approach. 6th ed. 2011. (ENG.). 752p. (C). ring bd. 146.95 *(978-1-111-34534-1(1))* Wadsworth.

Bukatko, Danuta & Daehler, Marvin W. Child Development: A Thematic Approach. 6th ed. 2011. (ENG.). 752p. (C). 209.95 *(978-0-618-60865-2(6))* Wadsworth.

Bumgarner, Marlene. Working with School-Age Children. 2010. (ENG.). 352p. (C). pap. 76.00 *(978-0-13-208085-9(0)*, Prentice Hall) Prentice Hall PTR.

Burkett, Jillian. What Children Really Want from Their Parents. 2011. 214p. pap. 25.00 ***(978-1-257-10569-4(8))*** Lulu Enterprises Inc.

Burns, Jim. Uncommon Object Lessons & Discussion Starters. 2010. (Uncommon Ser.). (ENG.). 224p. (YA). (gr. 6-12). 34.99 *(978-0-8307-5098-6(3))* Gospel Light Pubns.

Burt, Sandra & Perlis, Linda. Raising a Successful Child: Discover & Nurture Your Child's Talents. 2006. (ENG., Illus.). 272p. per. 14.95 *(978-1-56975-564-8(7))* Ulysses Pr.

Buss, Emily & Maclean, Mavis. The Law & Child Development. 2010. (Library of Essays in Child Welfare & Development Ser.). (Illus.). 516p. 275.00 *(978-0-7546-2811-8(6))* Ashgate Publishing Co.

Butch. Playin' to Win: A Surgeon, Scientist & Parent Examines the Upside of Video Games. (ENG.). 2009. pap. 16.95 *(978-1-60037-361-9(5))* 2008. 26.95 *(978-1-60037-362-6(3))* Morgan James Publishing.

Butler, Carly W. Talk & Social Interaction in the Playground. 2008. (Directions in Ethnomethodology & Conversation Analysis Ser.). 230p. 114.95 *(978-0-7546-7416-0(9))* Ashgate Publishing Co.

Buysse, Virginia & Wesley, Patricia, eds. Evidence-Based Practice in the Early Childhood Field. 2006. (Illus.). 258p. per. 34.95 *(978-0-943657-95-0(4))* Zero To Three Pr.

CAD. Beyond the Family: Contexts of Immigrant Children's Development - New Directions for Child & Adolescent Development. Way, Niobe & Yoshikawa, Hirokazu, eds. 2008. (J-B CAD Single Issue Child & Adolescent Development Ser.: 91). (ENG.). 112p. pap. 29.00 *(978-0-470-41730-0(7)*, Jossey-Bass) Wiley, John & Sons, Inc.

—Children's Moral Emotions & Moral Cognition: Developmental & Educational Perspectives. Latzko, Brigitte & Malti, Tina, eds. 2010. (J-B CAD Single Issue Child & Adolescent Development Ser.: 100). (ENG., Illus.). 112p. pap. 29.00 *(978-0-470-90388-9(0)*, Jossey-Bass) Wiley, John & Sons, Inc.

CAD & Diamond, Lisa M. Rethinking Positive Adolescent Female Sexual Development. 2006. (J-B CAD Single Issue Child & Adolescent Development Ser.: 82). (ENG., Illus.). 104p. per. 29.00 *(978-0-7879-8735-0(2)*, Jossey-Bass) Wiley, John & Sons, Inc.

CAD (Child and Adolescent Development) Staff & Diamond, Lisa M. The Modernization of Youth Transitions in Europe, No. 113. Bois-Reymond, Manuela du & Chisholm, Lynne, eds. 2006. (J-B CAD Single Issue Child & Adolescent Development Ser.: 83). (ENG.). 104p. pap. 29.00 *(978-0-7879-8889-0(8)*, Jossey-Bass) Wiley, John & Sons, Inc.

Cahill, Donald & Cahill, Maureen. The Goal Mine with Goal Digger CD. 2007. 328p. per. 29.95 *(978-0-941457-49-1(4))* IEP Publishing.

Calarco, Donald Charles. Tell Me the Truth Is Santa for Real? A 5yr Old's Own Story! 2009. 55p. pap. 11.95 *(978-1-4327-2325-5(1))* Outskirts Pr., Inc.

Calkins, Susan D. & Bell, Martha Ann. Child Development at the Intersection of Emotion & Cognition. 2009. (Illus.). 264p. 69.95 *(978-1-4338-0686-5(X))*; x, 261p. E-Book *(978-1-4338-0687-2(8))* American Psychological Assn.

Calvert, Sandra L. & Wilson, Barbara J., eds. The Handbook of Children, Media & Development. (Handbooks in Communication & Media Ser.: 10). (ENG., Illus.). 640p. 2011. pap. 49.95 *(978-1-4443-3694-8(0))* 2008. 219.95 *(978-1-4051-4417-9(3))* Wiley, John & Sons, Inc. (Wiley-Blackwell).

Campbell, Susan B. Behavior Problems in Preschool Children: Clinical & Developmental Issues. 2nd rev. ed. 2006. (ENG.). 334p. pap. 30.00 *(978-1-59385-377-8(7))* Guilford Pubns., Inc.

Cannella, Gaile Sloan & Soto, Lourdes Diaz. Childhoods: A Handbook. 2010. (Rethinking Childhood Ser.). 416p. (C). 155.95 *(978-1-4331-0451-0(2))*; pap. 49.95 *(978-1-4331-0450-3(4))* Lang, Peter Publishing, Inc.

Carey, William B., et al. Developmental-Behavioral Pediatrics: Expert Consult - Online & Print. 4th ed. 2009. (ENG., Illus.). 1060p. 194.00 *(978-1-4160-3370-7(X)*, Saunders) Elsevier - Health Sciences Div.

Carini, Patricia F. & Himley, Margaret. Jenny's Story: Taking the Long View of the Child - Prospect's Philosophy in Action. 2010. (ENG.). 216p. 62.00 *(978-0-8077-5052-0(2))*; pap. 29.95 *(978-0-8077-5051-3(4))* Teachers College Pr., Teachers College, Columbia Univ.

Carta, Judith, et al. Using IGDIs: Monitoring Progress & Improving Intervention for Infants & Young Children. 2010. (Illus.). 264p. pap. 34.95 *(978-1-59857-065-6(X))* Brookes, Paul H. Publishing Co.

Carter, Carrie. Think Your Way to Riches Kid's Style. 2007. (ENG.). per. 17.95 *(978-1-60037-337-4(2))* Morgan James Publishing.

Carter, Christine. Raising Happiness: 10 Simple Steps for More Joyful Kids & Happier Parents. 2010. (ENG., Illus.). 256p. 24.00 *(978-0-345-51561-2(7)*, Ballantine Bks.) Random House Publishing Group.

Carter, William Lee. Putting Humpty Dumpty Back Together: Parenting a Distressed Child. 2009. 176p. pap. 15.00 *(978-0-9841080-0-8(9))* Restoration Pubns.

Caruso, Joseph J. & Fawcett, M. Temple. Supervision in Early Childhood Education: A Developmental Perspective. 3rd ed. 2006. (Early Childhood Education Ser.). (ENG., Illus.). 288p. pap. 25.95 *(978-0-8077-4731-5(9))* Teachers College Pr., Teachers College, Columbia Univ.

Castle, Kathryn. Early Childhood Teacher Research. 2011. (ENG., Illus.). 208p. 130.00 *(978-0-415-87758-9(X))*; pap. 28.95 *(978-0-415-87759-6(8))* Routledge.

Castro, Dina C., et al. New Voices ~ Nuevas Voces: A Handbook on Cultural & Linguistic Diversity in Early Childhood. 2010. (Illus.). 184p. pap. 34.95 *(978-1-59857-046-5(3))* Brookes, Paul H. Publishing Co.

Catty, Nancy. Theory & Practice of Education. 2006. 260p. per. *(978-1-4067-2080-8(1)*, Hesperides Pr.) Read Bks.

Cave, Peter. Primary School in Japan: Self, Individuality & Learning in Elementary Education. 2009. 248p. pap. 39.95 *(978-0-415-54536-5(6))* 2007. (ENG., Illus.). 264p. (C). 160.00 *(978-0-415-44679-2(1))* Routledge.

Cbl. The Brown University Child & Adolescent Behavior Letter. 2011. (ENG.). 16.58 *(978-1-118-02033-3(2))*; 16.58 *(978-1-118-02032-6(4)*, Wiley); 16.58 *(978-1-118-02030-2(8)*, Wiley) Wiley, John & Sons, Inc.

—The Brown University Child & Adolescent Behavior Letter, 27/11. 2011. 16.58 ***(978-1-118-02034-0(0)***, Wiley) Wiley, John & Sons, Inc.

Cbl. The BROWN UNIVERSITY CHILD & ADOLESCENT BEHAVIOR Letter, 27/7. 2011. 16.58 *(978-1-118-02029-6(4)*, Wiley) Wiley, John & Sons, Inc.

Chabon, Shelly S. & Cohn, Ellen R. The Communication Disorders Casebook: Learning by Example. 2010. (ENG.). 576p. (C). pap. 88.40 *(978-0-205-61012-9(9))* Allyn & Bacon, Inc.

Chaplain, Mark A.J. & Takahashi, K., eds. Beyond the Dyad: Conceptualization of Social Networks, Vol. 48. (Illus.). 114p. *(978-3-8055-7897-4(0))* Karger, S. AG.

Charlesworth & Cram101 Textbook Reviews Staff. Understanding Child Development. 2007. 212p. per. 13.95 *(978-1-4288-1970-2(3))* Cram101 Inc.

Charlesworth, Rosalind. Child Development PET. 7th ed. 2007. (ENG.). 208p. (C). pap. 24.95 *(978-1-4180-3816-8(4))* Delmar Cengage Learning.

—Understanding Child Development. 8th ed. 2010. (Whatrsquo;s New in Early Childhood Ser.). (ENG.). 768p. (Orig.). (C). pap. 165.95 *(978-0-495-80930-2(6))* Delmar Cengage Learning.

Chen, Xinyin & Rubin, Kenneth H., eds. Socioemotional Development in Cultural Context. 2011. (Social, Emotional, & Personality Development in Context Ser.). (ENG.). 342p. 60.00 *(978-1-60918-186-4(7))* Guilford Pubns., Inc.

Chesaina, Ciarunji. The Significance of Oral Literature in Children's Development. 2010. 48p. pap. *(978-3-8383-0121-1(8))* Lambert Academic Publishing.

Chesebrough, Elda, et al, eds. A Blueprint for the Promotion of Pro-Social Behavior in Early Childhood. 2010. (Issues in Children's & Families' Lives Ser.). 320p. pap. 119.00 *(978-1-4419-3430-7(8)*, 1441934308) Springer.

Child and Adolescent Development Staff (CAD). The Intersections of Personal & Social Identities: New Directions for Child & Adolescent Development. Radmacher, Kimberly Ann et al, eds. 2008. (J-B CAD Single Issue Child & Adolescent Development Ser.: 90). (ENG.). 112p. pap. 29.00 *(978-0-470-37283-8(4)*, Jossey-Bass) Wiley, John & Sons, Inc.

—Social Interaction & the Development of Executive Function, No. 123. Carpendale, Jeremy I. M. & Lewis, Charlie, eds. 2009. (J-B CAD Single Issue Child & Adolescent Development Ser.: 93). (ENG., Illus.). 112p. pap. 29.00 *(978-0-470-48901-7(4)*, Jossey-Bass) Wiley, John & Sons, Inc.

Childhood Emotional Abuse: Mediating & Noderating Processes Af. 2008. (ENG., Illus.). 176p. 110.00 *(978-0-7890-3711-4(4))* Routledge.

Chisholm, James. Navajo Infancy: An Ethological Study of Child Development. 2009. (ENG., Illus.). 285p. pap. 29.95 *(978-0-202-36251-9(5))* Aldine Transaction.

Chouinard, Michelle M. Children's Questions. 2007. (Monographs of the Society for Research in Child Development Ser.). (ENG.). 132p. pap. 47.95 *(978-1-4051-7633-0(4)*, Wiley-Blackwell) Wiley, John & Sons, Inc.

Chute, Douglas L., et al, eds. Pediatric Neuropsychology: The Stein Family Fellow & Drexel University Symposium. 2011. (Special Issues of the Clinical Neuropsychologist Ser.). (ENG.). 200p. pap. 76.99 ***(978-1-84872-752-6(6)***, Psychology Press) Taylor & Francis Group GBR. Dist: Taylor & Francis Group.

Cioni, Giovanni & Mercuri, Eugenio. Neurological Assessment in the First Two Years of Life: Instruments for the Follow-Up of High-Risk Newborns. 2008. (Clinics in Developmental Medicine Ser.). (ENG., Illus.). 256p. 158.00 *(978-1-898683-54-4(9))* Mac Keith Pr. GBR. Dist: Wiley, John & Sons, Inc.

Clark, Cindy, ed. Transactions at Play. 2009. (Play & Cultural Studies). (ENG., Illus.). 200p. pap. 31.50 *(978-0-7618-4485-3(6))* Univ. Pr. of America, Inc.

Clark, Cindy Dell. In A Younger Voice: Doing Child-Centered Qualitative Research. 2010. (Child Development in Cultural Context Ser.). (ENG., Illus.). 272p. 39.95 *(978-0-19-537659-3(5))* Oxford Univ. Pr., Inc.

Clark, Margaret M. & Tucker, Stanley. Early Childhoods in a Changing World. 2010. 186p. pap. 34.95 *(978-1-85856-473-9(5))* Trentham Bks. Ltd. GBR. Dist: Stylus Publishing, LLC.

Clark, Megan. Today's Toddler: Things We Worry about (but Probably Shouldn't) 2009. pap. 9.99 *(978-1-60799-451-0(8))* Tate Publishing & Enterprises, LLC.

Clarkson, Patricia K. A Developmental Approach to Educating Young Children. Daniels, Denise H., ed. 2010. (Classroom Insights from Educational Psychology Ser.). (Illus.). 208p. pap. 27.95 *(978-1-4129-8114-9(X)*, B81149P) Corwin Pr.

Clements, Dougla, et al. Learning & Teaching Early Math: The Learning Trajectories Approach. 2009. (Studies in Mathematical Thinking & Learning Ser.). (ENG., Illus.). 344p. 165.00 *(978-0-415-99591-7(4))*; pap. 53.95 *(978-0-415-99592-4(2))* Routledge.

Clements, Douglas H. & Sarama, Julie A. Early Childhood Mathematics Education Research: Learning Trajectories for Young Children. 2009. (Studies in Mathematical Thinking & Learning Ser.). (ENG., Illus.). 410p. 160.00 *(978-0-8058-6308-6(7))* Routledge.

Click, Phyllis M. & Parker, Jennifer. Caring for School-Age Children. 6th ed. 2011. (PSY 681 Ethical, Historical, Legal, & Professional Issues in School Psychology Ser.). (ENG.). 416p. (C). pap. 123.95 *(978-1-111-29813-5(0))* Wadsworth.

Clinton, Hillary Rodham & Clinton, Hillary Rodham. It Takes a Village: And Other Lessons Children Teach Us. 2006. (ENG., Illus.). 352p. 25.00 *(978-1-4165-4064-9(4))* Simon & Schuster.

Coch, Donna, et al, eds. Human Behavior, Learning, & the Developing Brain: Typical Development. 2010. (ENG.). 412p. pap. 35.00 *(978-1-60623-968-1(6))* Guilford Pubns., Inc.

Cohen, Dorothy H., et al. Observing & Recording the Behavior of Young Children. 5th rev. ed. 2008. (ENG.). 264p. pap. 22.95 *(978-0-8077-4882-4(X))* Teachers College Pr., Teachers College, Columbia Univ.

Cohen, Libby G. & Spenciner, Loraine J. Assessment of Children & Youth with Special Needs. 4th ed. 2010. (ENG.). 432p. (C). pap. 129.80 *(978-0-13-705453-4(X)*, Prentice Hall) Prentice Hall PTR.

Cole & Cole & Cram101 Textbook Reviews Staff. The Development of Children. 2007. 180p. per. 12.95 *(978-1-4288-1962-7(2))* Cram101 Inc.

Cole, Cole. The Development of Children. 2006. pap. 12.95 *(978-1-4288-1334-2(9))* Cram101 Inc.

Cole, Elizabeth B. & Flexer, Carol A. Children with Hearing Loss: Developing Listening & Talking Birth to Six. 2007. pap. 65.00 *(978-1-59756-158-7(4))* Plural Publishing, Inc.

College of DuPage Press. The Thinking Nurse... a board Game: Caring for the Infant. 2007. 49.95 net. *(978-1-932514-06-3(6))* College of DuPage Pr.

Compton, Ashley & Taylor, Kathleen. Creative Development. 2011. (Supporting Development in the Early Years Foundation Stage Ser.). (ENG., Illus.). 160p. 100.00 *(978-1-4411-6330-1(1))*; pap. 37.95 *(978-1-4411-7222-8(X))* Continuum International Publishing Group, Ltd. GBR. Dist: National Bk. Network.

Connerr, Helyn. Learning Without Tears: Discover How the Mercury Model Can - Identify a Child's Unique Learning Style - Unlock a Child's True Potential - Turn Tension into Talking. 2008. (ENG., Illus.). 224p. per. 14.95 *(978-1-905857-53-1(5)*, Watkins Publishing) Duncan Baird Pubs. GBR. Dist: Sterling Publishing Co., Inc.

Consumer Dummies Staff, et al. Child Psychology & Development for Dummies. 2011. (ENG., Illus.). 384p. pap. 19.99 *(978-0-470-91885-2(3)*, For Dummies) Wiley, John & Sons, Inc.

Cook, Greg & Cook, Joan Littlefield. Child Development: Principles & Perspectives. 2nd ed. 2008. (ENG., Illus.). 624p. (C). per. 167.67 *(978-0-205-49406-4(4))* Allyn & Bacon, Inc.

—Practice Tests for the World of Children for World of Children. 2nd ed. 2010. (ENG.). 432p. (C). pap., pupil's gde. ed. 28.20 *(978-0-205-77861-4(5))* Allyn & Bacon, Inc.

Cook, Joan Littlefield & Cook, Greg. Child Development: Principles & Perspectives. 2nd ed. 2010. (ENG.). (C). ring bd. 116.00 *(978-0-205-02185-7(9)*, Prentice Hall) Prentice Hall PTR.

—Child Development: Principles & Perspectives, Books a la Carte Plus MyDevelopmentLab Pegasus. 2nd ed. 2010. (ENG.). (C). ring bd. 116.00 *(978-0-205-74789-4(2)*, Prentice Hall) Prentice Hall PTR.

—The World of Children. 2nd ed. 2009. (ENG.). 656p. (C). 154.40 *(978-0-205-68592-9(7)*, Prentice Hall) Prentice Hall PTR.

—World of Children. 2nd ed. 2010. (ENG.). (C). 46.67 *(978-0-205-72908-1(8))*; 656p. 109.33 *(978-0-205-80589-1(2))* Prentice Hall PTR. (Prentice Hall).

Cooper, Carol. Your Clever Baby: How to Make the Most of Your Child's Potential. 2007. (Illus.). 144p. pap. *(978-1-84597-369-8(0))* Ryland Peters & Small.

Cooper, Linda & Doherty, Jonathan. Physical Development. 2011. (Supporting Development in the Early Years Foundation Stage Ser.). (ENG., Illus.). 144p. 90.00 *(978-1-4411-2400-5(4))* Continuum International Publishing Group, Ltd. GBR. Dist: National Bk. Network.

Cooper, Linda & Woolley, Richard. Knowledge & Understanding of the World. 2011. (Supporting Development in the Early Years Foundation Stage Ser.). (ENG., Illus.). 160p. 100.00 *(978-1-4411-5432-3(9))*; pap. 29.95 *(978-1-4411-3762-3(9))* Continuum International Publishing Group, Ltd. GBR. Dist: National Bk. Network.

Coping and Development Staff. Coping & the Development of Regulation No. 124: New Directions for Child & Adolescent Development. Skinner, Ellen A. & Zimmer-Gembeck, Melanie J., eds. 2009. (J-B CAD Single Issue Child &

Adolescent Development Ser.: 94). (ENG., Illus.). 108p. pap. 29.00 (978-0-470-53137-2(1), Jossey-Bass) Wiley, John & Sons, Inc.

Copley, Juanita V., et al. Mathematics: The Creative Curriculum Approach. 2007. (978-1-879537-88-0(5)) Teaching Strategies, Inc.

Copple, Carol & Bredekamp, Sue, eds. Developmentally Appropriate Practice in Early Childhood Programs Serving Children from Birth through Age 8. 3rd ed. 2009. 350p. pap. 35.00 (978-1-928896-64-7(2)) National Assn. for the Education of Young Children.

Copple, Carol, et al. Basics of Developmentally Appropriate Practice: An Introduction for Teachers of Infants & Toddlers. 2011. (Illus.). 116p. pap. 20.00 (978-1-928896-73-9(1)) National Assn. for the Education of Young Children.

Cousins, Lynn. Shaping Children's Behaviour in the Early Years. 2010. (ENG., Illus.). 235p. pap. 45.00 (978-1-4082-2502-8(6)) Longman Publishing Group.

Covington, Frederick B. Things I Know. 2010. 23p. (J). pap. 15.95 (978-1-4327-5352-8(5)) Outskirts Pr., Inc.

Cowie, Helen. From Birth to Sixteen Years: Children's Physical, Social, Emotional & Cognitive Development. 2012. (ENG., Illus.). 224p. 115.00 (978-0-415-60265-5(3)); pap. 23.95 (978-0-415-60266-2(1)) Routledge.

Cowie, Helen & Blades, Mark. Understanding Children's Development. Smith, Peter, ed. 5th ed. 2011. (Basic Psychology Ser.: 3). (ENG., Illus.). 830p. pap. 69.95 (978-1-4051-7601-9(6), Wiley-Blackwell) Wiley, John & Sons, Inc.

Cowles, Jacqueline Messineo. The Therapist's Cookbook, 1 vol. 2010. 74p. pap. 19.95 (978-1-4489-3881-0(3)) PublishAmerica, Inc.

Cox, Adam J. No Mind Left Behind: Understanding & Fostering Executive Control — the Eight Essential Brain SkillsEvery Child Needs to Thrive. 2008. (ENG.). 288p. (gr. 12-18). 15.95 (978-0-399-53455-3(5), Perigee Trade) Penguin Group (USA) Inc.

Cpu. The Brown University Child & Adolescent Psychopharmacology. 2011. 16.58 (978-1-118-02020-3(0)); 16.58 (978-1-118-02019-7(7)); 16.58 (978-1-118-02018-0(9)); 16.58 (978-1-118-02017-3(0)) Wiley, John & Sons, Inc. (Wiley).

Cram101 Textbook Reviews. Outlines & Highlights for Art & Creative Development for Young Children by J Englebright Fox. 2011. 144p. pap. 28.95 (978-1-61905-222-2(9)) Cram101 Inc.

—Outlines & Highlights for Cengage Advantage Books: Child & Adolescent Development by David Bjorklund, ISBN. 2011. 122p. pap. 28.95 (978-1-4288-4279-3(9)) Cram101 Inc.

—Outlines & Highlights for Child & Adolescent Development: An Advanced Course by William Damon, ISBN. 2010. 174p. pap. 29.95 (978-1-61654-494-2(5)) Cram101 Inc.

—Outlines & Highlights for Child & Adolescent Development by Anita E Woolfolk. 2011. 246p. pap. 31.95 (978-1-61905-181-2(8)) Cram101 Inc.

—Outlines & Highlights for Child & Adolescent Development in Your Classroom by Christi Bergin. 2011. 154p. pap. 29.95 (978-1-61905-182-9(6)) Cram101 Inc.

—Outlines & Highlights for Child Development by John W Santrock, Isbn: 9780073370637. 2010. 86p. pap. 27.95 (978-1-61698-728-2(6)) Cram101 Inc.

—Outlines & Highlights for Childhood: Voyages in Development by Spencer A. Rathus. 2011. 180p. pap. 29.95 (978-1-61698-053-5(2)) Cram101 Inc.

—Outlines & Highlights for Children, Play, & Development by Fergus P Hughes. 2011. 192p. pap. 30.95 (978-1-61654-978-7(5)) Cram101 Inc.

—Outlines & Highlights for Development of Children by Cynthia Lightfoot, Isbn: 9781429202251. 2010. 218p. pap. 30.95 (978-1-61654-990-9(4)) Cram101 Inc.

—Outlines & Highlights for Disorders of Childhood: Development & Psychopathology by Robin Hornik Parritz. 2011. 120p. pap. 28.95 (978-1-61905-159-1(1)) Cram101 Inc.

—Outlines & Highlights for How Children Develop & Video Tool Kit for Human Development by Robert S Siegler. 2011. 276p. pap. 32.95 (978-1-4672-6670-3(1)) Cram101 Inc.

—Outlines & Highlights for Infancy & Childhood by Charlotte Patterson, Isbn: 9780073355894. 2010. 68p. pap. 27.95 (978-1-61698-724-4(3)) Cram101 Inc.

—Outlines & Highlights for Infant & Toddler Development & Responsive Program Planning: A Relationship-Based Approach by Donna S. Wittmer, Sandy Pet. 2010. 62p. pap. 27.95 (978-1-61698-663-6(8)) Cram101 Inc.

—Outlines & Highlights for Infants & Toddlers: Development & Curriculum Planning by Penny Deiner, ISBN. 2010. 66p. pap. 27.95 (978-1-61698-667-4(0)) Cram101 Inc.

—Outlines & Highlights for Infants, Toddlers, & Caregivers: A Curriculum of Respectful, Responsive Care & Education by Janet Gonzalez-Mena, ISBN. 2010. 78p. pap. 27.95 (978-1-61698-097-9(4)) Cram101 Inc.

—Outlines & Highlights for Life Span: Human Development for Helping Professionals by Broderick & Blewitt. 2010. 194p. pap. 30.95 (978-1-61698-999-6(8)) Cram101 Inc.

Cram101 Textbook Reviews & Cram101 Textbook Reviews. Outlines & Highlights for Advances in Child Development & Behavior. 9780120097340. 2011. 82p. pap. 27.95 (978-1-61461-140-0(8)) Cram101 Inc.

—Outlines & Highlights for an Introduction to Early Childhood Studies by Nigel Thomas, Isbn: 9781847871671. 2011. 176p. pap. 29.95 (978-1-61461-127-1(0)) Cram101 Inc.

—Outlines & Highlights for Beginnings & Beyond: Foundations in Early Childhood Education by Ann Gordon, ISBN. 2011. 62p. pap. 27.95 (978-1-61461-133-2(5)) Cram101 Inc.

—Outlines & Highlights for Behavioral, Social, & Emotional Assessment of Children & Adolescents by Kenneth Merrell, Isbn: 9780805853704. 2011. 72p. pap. 27.95 (978-1-61698-263-8(2)) Cram101 Inc.

—Outlines & Highlights for Cengage Advantage Books: Child Development. 2011. 140p. pap. 28.95 (978-1-61461-019-9(3)) Cram101 Inc.

—Outlines & Highlights for Child & Adolescent Development: An Integrated Approach by David Bjorklund, ISBN. 2011. 206p. pap. 30.95 (978-1-61461-123-3(8)) Cram101 Inc.

—Outlines & Highlights for Child Development: An Active Learning Approach by Laura E. Levine, ISBN. 2011. 228p. pap. 31.95 (978-1-4288-3703-4(5)) Cram101 Inc.

—Outlines & Highlights for Child Neuropsychology: Concepts, Theory & Practice by Jonathan Reed, ISBN. 2011. 326p. pap. 33.95 (978-1-4288-1926-9(6)) Cram101 Inc.

—Outlines & Highlights for Children & Their Development by Robert V Kail, Isbn: 9780205654154. 2011. 144p. pap. 28.95 (978-1-61744-977-2(6)) Cram101 Inc.

—Outlines & Highlights for Developing Child, the by Helen Bee, Isbn: 9780205744473. 2011. 108p. pap. 28.95 (978-1-61461-068-7(1)) Cram101 Inc.

—Outlines & Highlights for Development of Geocentric Spatial Language & Cognition: An Eco-cultural Perspective by Pierre Dasen, ISBN. 2011. 66p. pap. 27.95 (978-1-61461-954-3(9)) Cram101 Inc.

—Outlines & Highlights for Early Childhood: A Guide for Students by Tina Bruce, ISBN. 2011. 62p. pap. 27.95 (978-1-61461-115-8(7)); pap. 27.95 (978-1-61461-069-4(X)) Cram101 Inc.

—Outlines & Highlights for Early Childhood Curriculum: Developmental Bases for Learning & Teaching by Sue Wortham, ISBN. 2011. 340p. pap. 33.95 (978-1-4288-6143-5(2)) Cram101 Inc.

—Outlines & Highlights for Early Childhood Development by Jeffrey Trawick-Smith, Isbn: 9780131198050. 2011. 214p. pap. 30.95 (978-1-61744-985-7(7)) Cram101 Inc.

—Outlines & Highlights for Effective Practices in Early Childhood Education: Building a Foundation by Virginia Susan Bredekamp, ISBN. 2011. 322p. pap. 33.95 (978-1-61461-090-8(8)) Cram101 Inc.

—Outlines & Highlights for Guiding Childrens Social Development & Learning by Marjorie Kostelnik, Isbn: 9781111301255. 2011. 220p. pap. 30.95 (978-1-4288-4280-9(2)) Cram101 Inc.

—Outlines & Highlights for Hdev by Spencer a Rathus. 2011. 116p. pap. 28.95 (978-1-61830-318-9(X)) Cram101 Inc.

—Outlines & Highlights for Hdev by Spencer a Rathus, Isbn: 9780495601524. 2011. 136p. pap. 28.95 (978-1-61744-872-0(9)) Cram101 Inc.

—Outlines & Highlights for Infants & Toddlers, Curriculum & Teaching by Linda D Watson, Isbn: 9781418016623. 2011. 174p. pap. 29.95 (978-1-61744-865-2(6)) Cram101 Inc.

—Outlines & Highlights for Introducing Child Psychology by H Rudolph Schaffer. 2011. 136p. pap. 30.95 (978-1-61830-300-4(7)) Cram101 Inc.

—Outlines & Highlights for Introduction to Early Childhood Education: Preschool Through Primary Grades by Jo Brewer, ISBN. 2011. 274p. pap. 32.95 (978-1-61461-061-8(4)) Cram101 Inc.

—Outlines & Highlights for Language Development in Early Childhood by Beverly W Otto, Isbn: 9780135019696 0135019699. 2011. 348p. pap. 33.95 (978-1-61490-836-4(2)) Cram101 Inc.

—Outlines & Highlights for Meaningful Assessments of the Young Child by Margaret B Puckett, Isbn: 9780132237598. 2011. 94p. pap. 27.95 (978-1-61744-712-9(9)) Cram101 Inc.

—Outlines & Highlights for Observing Development of the Young Child by Janice J Beaty, Isbn: 9780131700130. 2011. 158p. pap. 29.95 (978-1-4288-5083-5(X)) Cram101 Inc.

—Outlines & Highlights for Observing Development of the Young Child by Janice J Beaty, Isbn: 9780135025895. 2011. 80p. pap. 27.95 (978-1-61744-920-8(2)) Cram101 Inc.

—Outlines & Highlights for Positive Child Guidance by Darla Ferris Miller, Isbn: 9781435418592. 2011. 218p. pap. 30.95 (978-1-61744-290-2(9)) Cram101 Inc.

—Outlines & Highlights for Preschool Appropriate Practices by Janice J Beaty, Isbn: 9781428304482. 2011. 132p. pap. 28.95 (978-1-61744-304-6(2)) Cram101 Inc.

—Outlines & Highlights for Skills for Preschool Teachers by Janice J Beaty, Isbn: 9780131583788. 2011. 152p. pap. 29.95 (978-1-61744-247-6(X)) Cram101 Inc.

—Outlines & Highlights for the Cambridge Encyclopedia of Child Development by with Ronald G Barr Edited by Brian Hopkins, Isbn: 9780521651172. 2011. 216p. pap. 30.95 (978-1-4288-6489-4(X)) Cram101 Inc.

—Outlines & Highlights for Understanding Child Development by Rosalind Charlesworth, Isbn: 9780495809302. 2011. 370p. pap. 34.95 (978-1-61461-106-6(8)) Cram101 Inc.

—Outlines & Highlights for Young Children with Special Needs by Stephen R Hooper, Isbn: 9780131590144. 2011. 88p. pap. 27.95 (978-1-61698-392-5(2)) Cram101 Inc.

Cram101 Textbook Reviews Staff. Outlines & Highlights for Child & Adolescent Development Childhood & Adolescence. 2008. 160p. pap. 12.95 (978-1-4288-5815-2(6)) Cram101 Inc.

—Outlines & Highlights for Child Development: Principles & Perspectives by Joan Littlefield Cook, ISBN. 2009. 64p. pap. 27.95 (978-1-4288-8762-6(8)) Cram101 Inc.

—Outlines & Highlights for Child Development & Education by Mcdevitt, Isbn: 0131188178. 2008. 220p. pap. 13.95 (978-1-4288-6011-7(8)) Cram101 Inc.

—Outlines & Highlights for Child Development by Berk, Isbn: 0205449131. 2008. 352p. pap. 16.95 (978-1-4288-5959-3(4)) Cram101 Inc.

—Outlines & Highlights for Child Development by Feldman, Isbn: 0131732471. 2008. 176p. pap. 12.95 (978-1-4288-5964-7(0)) Cram101 Inc.

—Outlines & Highlights for Child Development by John W Santrock, Isbn: 9780073370637. 2009. 72p. pap. 27.95 (978-1-4288-8012-2(7)) Cram101 Inc.

—Outlines & Highlights for Child Development by Laura E Berk, Isbn: 9780205615599. 2009. 126p. pap. 28.95 (978-1-4288-8559-2(5)) Cram101 Inc.

—Outlines & Highlights for Child Development by Patterson, Isbn: 9780072347951. 2008. 188p. pap. 12.95 (978-1-4288-5960-9(8)) Cram101 Inc.

—Outlines & Highlights for Child Development by Robert S Feldman, Isbn: 9780205655021. 2009. 66p. pap. 27.95 (978-1-4288-8759-6(8)) Cram101 Inc.

—Outlines & Highlights for Childhood. 2008. 136p. pap. 11.95 (978-1-4288-5816-9(4)) Cram101 Inc.

—Outlines & Highlights for Children & Their Development by Kail, Isbn: 013194911x. 2008. 192p. pap. 13.95 (978-1-4288-5957-9(8)) Cram101 Inc.

—Outlines & Highlights for Children by Santrock, Isbn: 9780073382609. 2008. 180p. pap. 12.95 (978-1-4288-5953-1(5)) Cram101 Inc.

—Outlines & Highlights for Child's World: Infancy through Adolescence by Papalia, ISBN. 2008. 316p. per. 15.95 (978-1-4288-5781-0(8)) Cram101 Inc.

—Outlines & Highlights for Developing Child, the by Helen Bee, Isbn: 9780205685936. 2009. 60p. pap. 27.95 (978-1-4288-8557-8(9)) Cram101 Inc.

—Outlines & Highlights for Infants & Children: Prenatal Through Middle Childhood by Berk, ISBN. 2008. 332p. pap. 16.95 (978-1-4288-6040-7(1)) Cram101 Inc.

—Outlines & Highlights for Infants & Toddlers: Development & Curriculum Planning by Penny Deiner, ISBN. 2009. 64p. pap. 27.95 (978-1-4288-8077-1(1)) Cram101 Inc.

—Outlines & Highlights for Infants, Children, & Adolescents by Berk, Isbn: 0205511384. 2008. 396p. pap. 17.95 (978-1-4288-5976-0(4)) Cram101 Inc.

—Outlines & Highlights for Middle Childhood to Middle Adolescence: Development from Ages 8 to 18 by Blume, ISBN. 2008. 152p. pap. 12.95 (978-1-4288-5975-3(6)) Cram101 Inc.

—Outlines & Highlights for the Developing Child by Bee, Isbn: 0205474535. 2008. 224p. pap. 13.95 (978-1-4288-6021-6(5)) Cram101 Inc.

—Outlines & Highlights for the Growing Child by Denise Boyd, Helen Bee, Isbn: 9780205545964. 2009. 64p. pap. 27.95 (978-1-4288-8776-3(8)) Cram101 Inc.

—Outlines & Highlights for the World of Children by Cook, Isbn: 0205447430. 2008. 224p. pap. 13.95 (978-1-4288-6281-4(1)) Cram101 Inc.

—Outlines & Highlights for Theories of Development Comparing Theories of Child Development by Thomas, Isbn: 0534607179. 2008. 180p. pap. 12.95 (978-1-4288-6018-6(5)) Cram101 Inc.

Crawford, Catherine. The Highly Intuitive Child: A Guide to Understanding & Parenting Unusually Sensitive & Empathic Children. 2009. (ENG.). 264p. pap. 15.95 (978-0-89793-509-8(8)) Hunter Hse., Inc.

Crosnoe, Robert. Mexican Roots, American Schools: Helping Mexican Immigrant Children Succeed. 2006. (ENG., Illus.). 184p. 55.00 (978-0-8047-5522-1(1)); per. 21.95 (978-0-8047-5523-8(X)) Stanford Univ. Pr.

Cross, Aerial. Come & Play: Sensory Integration Strategies for Children with Play Challenges. 2010. (ENG.). 200p. pap. 29.95 (978-1-60554-022-1(6)) Redleaf Pr.

Croudo, Sonny. A Success Story of a Single Parent: The Best Father - the Coolest Dad. 2009. 112p. pap. 19.99 (978-1-4415-7992-8(3)) Xlibris Corp.

Cummings, E. Mark & Davies, Patrick T. Marital Conflict & Children: An Emotional Security Perspective. (Guilford Series on Social & Emotional Development Ser.). (ENG.). 320p. 2011. pap. 30.00 (978-1-4625-0329-2(2)) 2010. (Illus.). 50.00 (978-1-60623-519-5(2)) Guilford Pubns., Inc.

Cunningham, Rebekah. Mismatch Negativity in Typically Developing Children. 2010. 64p. pap. (978-3-8383-3734-0(4)) Lambert Academic Publishing.

El Currículo Creativo para Educación Preescolar. 5th ed. 2010. (SPA.). (978-1-60617-395-4(2)) Teaching Strategies, Inc.

Daly, Mary, ed. Parenting in contemporary Europe: A positive Approach. 2007. 175p. pap. 29.00 (978-92-871-6135-2(6)) Council of Europe FRA. Dist: Manhattan Publishing Co.

Daniel, Becky. Play, Baby, Play: Daily Affirmations for Toddlers. (Illus.). 388p. pap. 10.00 (978-1-885412-01-0(0)) Daniel, Rebecca A.

Daniel, Brigid, et al. Child Development for Child Care & Protection Workers. 2nd ed. 2010. (ENG., Illus.). 336p. pap. (978-1-84905-068-5(6)) Kingsley, Jessica Ltd.

Davies, Douglas D. Child Development: A Practitioner's Guide. 3rd rev. ed. 2010. (Social Work Practice with Children & Families Ser.). (ENG.). 494p. 65.00 (978-1-60623-909-4(0)) Guilford Pubns., Inc.

Davies, Kim. Caring for Your Toddler: Raising Your Child the Way Nature Intended. 2008. (ENG., Illus.). 96p. pap. 14.99 (978-1-84476-482-2(6)) Anness Publishing GBR. Dist: National Bk. Network.

Davis, Susan Elisabeth, et al. Play & Learn: 1001 Fun Activities for Your Baby & Child. 2008. (Gymboree Play & Music Ser.). (ENG., Illus.). 240p. pap. 24.95 (978-1-55470-033-2(7)) Key Porter Bks. CAN. Dist: Perseus-PGW.

Davydov, Vasilii Vasilevich. Problems of Developmental Instruction: A Theoretical & Experimental Psychological Study. Davydov, V. V., ed. 2008. 246p. 98.00 (978-1-60456-552-2(7)) Nova Science Pubs., Inc.

Dawson, Peg & Guare, Richard. Coaching Students with Executive Skills Deficits. 2012. (Guilford Practical Intervention in the Schools Ser.). (ENG., Illus.). 240p. (gr. k-12). pap. 35.00 (978-1-4625-0375-9(6)) Guilford Pubns., Inc.

Dawson, Peg & Guare, Richard. Smart but Scattered: The Revolutionary Executive Skills Approach to Helping Kids Reach Their Potential. 2009. (ENG., Illus.). 314p. pap. 17.95 (978-1-59385-445-4(5)) Guilford Pubns., Inc.

De Ste Croix, Mark & Korff, Thomas, eds. Paediatric Biomechanics & Motor Control. 2011. (Routledge Research in Sport & Exercise Science Ser.). (ENG., Illus.). 336p. (C). 145.00 (978-0-415-58018-2(8)) Routledge.

Deacon, Caroline. Teach Yourself Your Baby's Development. 2008. (Teach Yourself Ser.). (ENG.). 192p. pap. 16.00 (978-0-07-154501-3(8), 0071545018) McGraw-Hill Cos., The.

—Your Toddler's Development. 2008. (Teach Yourself: Parenting Ser.). (ENG.). 192p. pap. 12.95 (978-0-07-158314-5(9), 0071583149) McGraw-Hill Cos., The.

Deans, Jan, et al. Developing Everyday Coping Skills in the Early Years: Proactive Strategies for Supporting Social & Emotional Development. 2012. (Illus.). 128p. E-Book (978-1-4411-8799-4(5)); E-Book (978-1-4411-6010-2(8)) Continuum International Publishing Group, Ltd.

Decker, Celia Anita. Child Development: Early Stages Through Age 12. 7th ed. 2010. (ENG.). (gr. 9-12). 720p. 74.64 (978-1-60525-293-3(X)); 184p. pap., wbk. ed. 16.64 (978-1-60525-295-7(6)) Goodheart-Willcox Pub.

—Child Development: Early Stages Through Age 12 PowerPoint-Individual License. 2010. cd-rom 140.00 (978-1-60525-299-5(9)) Goodheart-Willcox Pub.

—Child Development: Early Stages Through Age 12 Teacher's Edition. 2010. 96.00 (978-1-60525-294-0(8)) Goodheart-Willcox Pub.

—Child Development: Early Stages Through Age 12 (Teacher's Power Point Presentations, Site License. 7th ed. 2010. cd-rom 420.00 (978-1-60525-300-8(6)) Goodheart-Willcox Pub.

—Child Development: Early Stages Through Age 12 Teacher's Resource CD. 2010. cd-rom 240.00 (978-1-60525-297-1(2)) Goodheart-Willcox Pub.

—Child Development: Early Stages Through Age 12 Teacher's Resource Guide. 2010. pap. 98.00 (978-1-60525-296-4(4)) Goodheart-Willcox Pub.

DeFleur, Margaret H. & DeFleur, Melvin L. Mass Communication Theories: Explaining Origins, Processes, & Effects. 4th ed. 2009. (ENG.). 400p. (C). pap. 67.60 (978-0-205-33172-7(6)) Allyn & Bacon, Inc.

Dehart & Sroufe & Cooper & Cram101 Textbook Reviews Staff. Child Development: Its Nature & Course. 2007. 188p. per. 12.95 (978-1-4288-2042-5(6)) Cram101 Inc.

Deiner, Penny Low. Infants & Toddlers: Development & Curriculum Planning. 2nd rev. ed. 2008. (ENG., Illus.). 784p. (C). pap. 133.95 (978-1-4283-1824-3(0)) Delmar Cengage Learning.

Delaney, Tara. Sensory Processing Disorder: Practical Answers to the Top 275 Questions Parents Ask. 2008. (ENG., Illus.). 240p. pap. 14.95 (978-1-4022-1123-2(6)) Sourcebooks, Inc.

DeLany, Janet V. & Pendzick, Margaret J. Working with Children & Adolescents: A Guide for the Occupational Therapy Assistant. 2007. (ENG., Illus.). 544p. (C). per. 60.00 (978-0-13-171917-0(3), Prentice Hall) Prentice Hall PTR.

Denzin, Norman. Childhood Socialization. 2nd rev. ed. 2009. (ENG.). 250p. pap. 29.95 (978-1-4128-1059-3(0)) Transaction Pubs.

Development of Young Childrenstudent Motivation K. 2008. (C). 132.00 (978-1-4018-8227-3(7)) Delmar Cengage Learning.

Development of Young Childrenstudent Workbook. 2008. (C). pap. 10.95 (978-1-4018-8228-0(5)) Delmar Cengage Learning.

Dewey, John. The School & Society & the Child & the Curriculum. 2008. (Illus.). 128p. pap. (978-1-60796-056-0(7)) Editorial Benei Noaj.

Dex, Shirley, et al, eds. Children of the 21st Century: The first five Years. 2010. (Illus.). 320p. 85.00 (978-1-84742-476-1(7)) Policy Pr. GBR. Dist: Chicago Distribution Ctr.

—Children of the 21st Century: The First Five Years. 2010. (Illus.). 320p. pap. 39.95 (978-1-84742-475-4(9)) Policy Pr. GBR. Dist: Chicago Distribution Ctr.

Dicker, Sheryl. Reversing the Odds: Improving Outcomes for Babies in the Child Welfare System. 2009. 216p. pap. 29.95 (978-1-55766-961-2(9)) Brookes, Paul H. Publishing Co.

Diller, Lawrence H. The Last Normal Child: Essays on the Intersection of Kids, Culture, & Psychiatric Drugs, 1 vol. annot. ed. 2006. (Childhood in America Ser.). 160p. 39.95 (978-0-275-99096-1(6), C9096, Praeger Pubs.) Greenwood Publishing Group, Inc.

Diniz, Felipe. Estimating a Technology of Cognitive Skill Formation in Brazil. 2009. 72p. pap. (978-3-639-14574-8(7)) VDM Verlag Dr. Mueller e.K.

Doctor McGougain. I Am Free. 2011. 24p. pap. 12.99 (978-1-4634-0217-4(1)) AuthorHouse.

Dodge, Diane Trister, et al. The Creative Curriculum for Family Child Care. 2nd ed. 2009. (978-1-60617-074-8(0)); (978-1-60617-075-5(9)) Teaching Strategies, Inc.

—The Creative Curriculum for Infants, Toddlers & Twos. 2nd ed. 2010. (978-1-60617-416-6(9)) 2010. (978-1-60617-415-9(0)) 2010. (978-1-60617-417-3(7)) 2006. (Illus.). xviii, 447p. pap. (978-1-879537-99-6(0)) Teaching Strategies, Inc.

Dodge, Diane Trister, et al. El Currículo Creativo para Niños de 0 a 3 Años. 2nd ed. (SPA & ENG.). 2011. (978-1-60617-426-5(6)) 2008. (978-1-933021-40-9(3)) Teaching Strategies, Inc.

C

Doherty, Jonathan & Hughes, Malcolm. Child Development: Theory & Practice. 2009. (Illus.). 608p. pap. 82.50 (978-1-4058-2127-8(2)) Addison-Wesley Longman, Inc.

Dolya, Galina. Vygotsky in Action in the Early Years: The 'Key to Learning' Curriculum. 2009. (ENG., Illus.). 176p. pap. 49.95 (978-0-415-55229-5(X)) Routledge.

Doman, Glenn & Doman, Douglas. Fit Baby, Smart Baby, Your Baby! 2012. (ENG., Illus.). 288p. pap. (978-0-7570-0376-9(1)) Square One Pubs.

Dombro, Amy Laura, et al. Powerful Interactions: How to Connect with Children to Extend Their Learning. 2011. (Illus.). 150p. spiral bd. 30.00 (978-1-928896-72-2(3)) National Assn. for the Education of Young Children.

Domellöf, Erik. Development of Functional Asymmetries in Young Infants - a Sensory-Motor Approach. 2008. 60p. pap. (978-3-639-04422-5(3)) VDM Verlag Dr. Mueller e.K.

Dorling Kindersley Publishing Staff. Baby Development Everything You Need to Know. 2012. (ENG.). 192p. 14.95 (978-0-7566-9190-5(7)) Dorling Kindersley Publishing, Inc.

Douglas, Jo, et al. A Community Health Approach to the Assessment of Infants & Their Parents: The Care Programme. 2006. (ENG., Illus.). 234p. 150.00 (978-0-470-09251-4(3), Wiley) Wiley, John & Sons, Inc.

Dowling, Marion. Young Children's Personal, Social & Emotional Development. 3rd ed. 2009. (Illus.). 240p. (C). 112.00 (978-1-84860-105-5(0), B01055C); pap. 45.00 (978-1-84860-106-2(9), B01055P) SAGE Pubns., Ltd. GBR. Dist: SAGE Pubns., Inc.

Drake, Jane. Planning for Children's Play & Learning: Meeting children's needs in the later stages of EYFS. 3rd rev. ed. 2009. (ENG., Illus.). 256p. 130.00 (978-0-415-48593-7(2)); pap. 37.95 (978-0-415-48597-5(5)) Routledge.

Driscoll & Nagel & Cram101 Textbook Reviews Staff. Early Childhood Education: Birth - 8. 2007. 92p. per. 10.95 (978-1-4286-1994-8(0)) Cram101 Inc.

Driscoll, Amy & Nagel, Nancy G. Early Childhood Education: Birth - 8: the World of Children, Families, & Educators. 4th ed. 2007. (ENG., Illus.). 496p. (C). 139.80 (978-0-205-53604-7(2)) Allyn & Bacon, Inc.

Drysdale, Maureen & Rye, B. J. Clashing Views in Adolescence. 2nd ed. 2008. (Taking Sides Ser.). (ENG.). 480p. (C). pap. 48.00 (978-0-07-351536-6(1), 0073515361, McGraw-Hill/Dushkin) McGraw-Hill Higher Education.

Duke Medical Center Child Development Staff. The Duke Guide to Baby's 1st Year. (978-0-449-90317-9(6), Fawcett) Random House Publishing Group.

Duncan, Tami & Rosner, Bryan. The Lyme-Autism Connection: Unveiling the Shocking Link Between Lyme Disease & Childhood Developmental Disorders. 2008. 288p. pap. 25.95 (978-0-9763797-5-1(9)) BioMed Publishing Group.

Dunckel, Lindsay. Goodness-of-Fit in Infancy. 2009. 132p. pap. (978-3-639-16922-5(0)) VDM Verlag Dr. Mueller e.K.

Dupree, Tj. Memorable Parenting Moments: Conversations with Family. 2007. 108p. per. 94.95 (978-1-4241-9159-8(9)) PublishAmerica, Inc.

Dupuis, Mélodie. Kind: Kids Independent, Not Dependent. 2010. 130p. pap. 10.95 (978-1-60911-887-7(1), Eloquent Bks.) AEG Literary Publishing Services, Inc.

Dutwin, David. Unplug Your Kids: A Parent's Guide to Raising Happy, Active, & Well-Adjusted Children in the Digital Age. 2009. (ENG., Illus.). 256p. pap. 14.95 (978-1-59869-804-6(4)) Adams Media Corp.

Ebbeck, Marjory & Waniganayake, Manjula, eds. Play in Early Childhood Education: Learning in Diverse Contexts. 2010. (ENG., Illus.). 75.00 (978-0-19-556904-9(0)) Oxford Univ. Pr., Inc.

Eccles/Meece. Handbook of Research on Schools, Schooling & Human Development. 2008. (Illus.). 704p. pap. 119.95 (978-0-8058-5949-2(7)) Erlbaum, Lawrence Assocs., Inc.

—Handbook of Research on Schools, Schooling & Human Development. 2010. (ENG., Illus.). 536p. 305.00 (978-0-8058-5948-5(9)) Routledge.

Eden, Alvin. Positive Parenting: Raising Healthy Children from Birth to Three Years. 2007. (ENG., Illus.). 288p. pap. 15.95 (978-1-57826-252-6(6), Hatherleigh Pr.) Hatherleigh Co., Ltd., The.

Edmiston, Brian. Forming Ethical Identities in Early Childhood Play. 2007. (Contesting Early Childhood Ser.). (Illus.). 224p. pap. 42.50 (978-0-415-43548-2(X)); 170.00 (978-0-415-43547-5(1)) Routledge.

Edwards, Glenna S. & Henriques, Karen. Mr. Emotions & Friends: Coping & Social Skills Activities for Students in Grades Pre-K through Third Grade. 2009. (Illus.). 78p. pap. 39.95 (978-1-4327-3509-8(8)) Outskirts Pr., Inc.

Egan, Amy, et al. Is It a Big Problem or a Little Problem? When to Worry, When Not to Worry, & What to Do. 2007. (ENG., Illus.). 352p. pap. 15.95 (978-0-312-35412-1(6), St. Martin's Griffin) St. Martin's Pr.

Egan, Kieran. Primary Understanding: Education in Early Childhood. 2012. (Routledge Library Editions: Education Ser.). (ENG.). 308p. 130.00 (978-0-415-67243-6(0)) Routledge.

Eisenberg, Zena. From Now to Then. 2010. 116p. pap. (978-3-8383-7605-9(6)) Lambert Academic Publishing.

Ek, Ulla. Children with Visual Disorders - Cognitive Development, Developmental Disorders & Consequences for Treatment & Counselling. 2008. 72p. pap. (978-3-639-05867-3(4)) VDM Verlag Dr. Mueller e.K.

Eke, Richard. Whose Childhood Is It? The Roles of Children, Adults & Policy Makers. Lee, Mandy & Butcher, Helen, eds. 2009. (ENG., Illus.). 224p. 130.00 (978-1-4411-7357-7(9)) Continuum International Publishing Group, Ltd. GBR. Dist: National Bk. Network.

Eke, Richard & Lee, Mandy, eds. Whose Childhood Is It? The Roles of Children, Adults & Policy Makers. 2009. (ENG., Illus.). 224p. 39.95 (978-0-8264-9981-3(3)) Continuum International Publishing Group, Ltd. GBR. Dist: National Bk. Network.

El-Sheikh, Mona, et al. Marital Conflict & Children's Externalizing Behavior: Interactions Between Parasympathetic & Sympathetic Nervous System Activity. 2009. (Monographs of the Society for Research in Child Development Ser.). (ENG., Illus.). 200p. pap. 39.95 (978-1-4051-9942-1(3), Wiley-Blackwell) Wiley, John & Sons, Inc.

Ellis, Mesha L., et al. The SAGE Handbook of Child Development, Multiculturalism, & Media. 2008. (Illus.). 528p. 150.00 (978-1-4129-4915-6(7), B49157C) SAGE Pubns., Inc.

Else, Perry & Else. Value of Play. 2009. (ENG., Illus.). 184p. 39.95 (978-0-8264-9565-5(6)) Continuum International Publishing Group, Ltd. GBR. Dist: National Bk. Network.

—The Value of Play. 2009. (ENG., Illus.). 184p. 130.00 (978-0-8264-4809-5(7)) Continuum International Publishing Group, Ltd. GBR. Dist: National Bk. Network.

Endtinger, Stuckmann, S. Traumwelt von Kindern und Jugendlichen: Entwicklung - Verstandnis - Therapeutischer Umgang. Riecher-Rössler, Anita & Steiner, M., eds. (Bibliotheca Psychiatrica Ser.). (GER., Illus.). (978-3-8055-8067-0(3)) Karger, S. AG.

Engel, Susan. Red Flags or Red Herrings? Predicting Who Your Child Will Become. 2011. (ENG.). 288p. 24.00 (978-1-4391-5011-5(7), Beyond Words/Atria Bks.) Atria Bks.

Enzer & Goin. 1st Chance-Social Emotions. pap. 15.95 (978-0-8027-7263-3(3)) Walker & Co.

Erk, Robert R. Counseling Treatment for Children & Adolescents with DSM-IV-TR Disorders. 2nd ed. 2007. (ENG., Illus.). 480p. (C). pap. 129.80 (978-0-13-230262-3(4), Prentice Hall) Prentice Hall PTR.

Esolen, Anthony. Ten ways to destroy the imagination of your Child. 2010. (ENG.). 320p. 26.95 (978-1-935191-88-9(8)) ISI Bks.

Essa, Eva L. & Burnham, Melissa M., eds. Informing Our Practice: Useful Research on Young Children's Development. 2009. 258p. pap. 26.00 (978-1-928896-65-4(0)) National Assn. for the Education of Young Children.

Esteban, Esther Joos. The Work of Children: Helping Children Understand the Meaning, Purpose, & Value of Work. 2009. 103p. pap. 9.95 (978-1-59417-082-9(7)) Scepter Pubs., Inc.

Evans, Gary W. & Wachs, Theodore D. Chaos & Its Influence on Children's Development: An Ecological Perspective. 2009. (Illus.). 275p. 59.95 (978-1-4338-0565-3(0)) American Psychological Assn.

Evans, Subhadra & Keenan, Thomas. An Introduction to Child Development. 2nd ed. 2009. (SAGE Foundations of Psychology Ser.). (Illus.). 424p. (C). 112.00 (978-1-4129-1114-6(1), B11141C); pap. 58.00 (978-1-4129-1115-3(X), B11141P) SAGE Pubns., Ltd. GBR. Dist: SAGE Pubns., Inc.

Faegre, Marion E. & Anderson, John E. Child Care & Training. 2009. (ENG.). 334p. pap. 60.00 (978-0-8166-0157-8(7)) Univ. of Minnesota Pr.

Fairview Health Services Staff, contrib. by. The New Family: Your Child's Early Months. 2nd ed. 2010. (978-1-57749-240-5(4)) Taylor Trade Publishing.

Falk, Beverly. Defending Childhood: Keeping the Promise of Early Education. 2012. (Early Childhood Education Ser.). (ENG., Illus.). 288p. pap. 29.95 (978-0-8077-5310-1(6)) Teachers College Pr., Teachers College, Columbia Univ.

Falk, Beverly, ed. Defending Childhood: Keeping the Promise of Early Education. 2012. (Early Childhood Education Ser.). (ENG., Illus.). 288p. 68.00 (978-0-8077-5311-8(4)) Teachers College Pr., Teachers College, Columbia Univ.

Farkas, L. C. S. W., et al. Resilient Children. 2011. 150p. pap. 18.95 (978-1-60594-695-5(8), Llumina Pr.) Aeon Publishing Inc.

Farley, Thelma A. Parenting Developmentally: Living the Passion, Power & Perks. 2009. 248p. pap. 15.95 (978-1-4327-4438-0(0)) Outskirts Pr., Inc.

Farooqi, Aijaz. School-Age Outcomes of Children Born at the Limit of Viability - Functional Limitations, Growth, Mental Health, Social Compentencies, Executive Functi. 2008. 104p. pap. (978-3-639-05575-7(6)) VDM Verlag Dr. Mueller e.K.

Faull, Jan & McLean Oliver, Jennifer. Amazing Minds: The Science of Nurturing Your Child's Developing Mind with Games, Activites & More. 2010. (ENG.). 368p. (gr. 12). 15.00 (978-0-425-23224-8(7), Berkley Trade) Penguin Group (USA) Inc.

Feeney, Stephanie, et al. Who Am I in the Lives of Children? An Introduction to Early Childhood Education. 8th ed. 2008. (ENG.). (C). 528p. 146.07 (978-0-13-610111-6(9)); (Illus.). 512p. 139.40 (978-0-13-715193-6(4)) Prentice Hall PTR. (Prentice Hall).

—Who Am I in the Lives of Children? An Introducton to Early Childhood Education. 9th rev. ed. 2012. (ENG.). 592p. (C). pap. 139.40 (978-0-13-265704-4(X), Prentice Hall) Prentice Hall PTR.

—Who Am I in the Lives of Children? an Introducton to Early Childhood Education, Student Value Edition. 9th ed. 2012. (ENG.). 512p. (C). ring bd. 90.67 (978-0-13-288829-5(7), Prentice Hall) Prentice Hall PTR.

Feldman & Cram101 Textbook Reviews Staff. Child Development. 2007. 180p. per. 12.95 (978-1-4288-1998-6(3)) Cram101 Inc.

Feldman, Robert S. Child Development. (ENG.). 552p. (C). 5th ed. 2008. 167.60 (978-0-205-65502-1(5)) 6th ed. 2011. (Illus.). 166.67 (978-0-205-25354-8(7)) Prentice Hall PTR. (Prentice Hall).

Ferguson, Christine Jeandheur & Dettore, Ernest. To Play or Not to Play: Is It Really a Question? 2007. (Illus.). 101p. pap. (978-0-87173-170-8(3)) Assn. for Childhood Education International.

Fernyhough, Charles. A Thousand Days of Wonder: A Scientist's Chronicle of His Daughter's Developing Mind. 2010. (ENG.). 272p. (gr. 12). 16.00 (978-1-58333-397-6(5), Avery) Penguin Group (USA) Inc.

Fidler, Deborah J. Early Development in Neurogenetic Disorders. 2011. (ENG.). 334p. 198.00 (978-0-12-374478-4(4), Academic Pr.) Elsevier Science & Technology Bks.

Fiedler, Anselm & Kuester, Isidor, eds. Child Development & Child Poverty. 2010. (Children's Issues, Laws & Programs Ser.). (Illus.). xii, 304p. 129.00 (978-1-60741-816-0(9)) Nova Science Pubs., Inc.

Fields, Marjorie V., et al. Let's Begin Reading Right: A Developmental Approach to Emergent Literacy. 6th ed. 2007. (ENG., Illus.). 448p. (C). per. 83.80 (978-0-13-159502-6(4), Prentice Hall) Prentice Hall PTR.

Fitzgerald, Hiram E., et al, eds. International Perspectives on Children & Mental Health Vol. 1: Development & Context, 2 vols. 2011. (Child Psychology & Mental Health Ser.). (Illus.). 500p. 124.95 (978-0-313-38298-7(0), A2697C, Praeger Pubs.) Greenwood Publishing Group, Inc.

Fitzsimmons, Michele L. & Bromley, M. Theresa. Kids on Track Checklists. 2010. 108p. 23.00 (978-1-4520-9212-6(5)); pap. 15.00 (978-1-4520-9211-9(7)) AuthorHouse.

Flanders, Judith. The Discovery of Neverland: The Transformation of Childhood 1500-1900. 2006. 352p. pap. 13.95 (978-0-06-059461-9(6)) HarperCollins Pubs.

Fleer, Marilyn. Early Learning & Development: Cultural-historical concepts in Play, 1 vol. 2010. (ENG., Illus.). 266p. (C). pap. 64.99 (978-0-521-12265-8(1)) Cambridge Univ. Pr.

Fleer, Marilyn, et al. Childhood Studies & the Impact of Globalization: Policies & Practices at Global & Local Levels. Hedegaard, Mariane & Tudge, Jonathan, eds. 2008. (World Yearbook of Education Ser.). (Illus.). 352p. 150.00 (978-0-415-99411-8(X)) Routledge.

Fletcher, Janice M. Grooming for Greatness: Preparing Children for Academic Excellence. 2009. 100p. pap. 10.49 (978-1-4389-0618-8(8)) AuthorHouse.

Flick, Grad L. Understanding & Managing Emotional & Behavior Disorders in the Classroom. 2010. (ENG.). 528p. (C). pap. 77.40 (978-0-13-041713-8(0), Prentice Hall) Prentice Hall PTR.

Flom, Ross, et al, eds. Gaze-Following: Its Development & Significance. 2006. (ENG., Illus.). 344p. 89.95 (978-0-8058-4750-5(2), Psychology Press) Taylor & Francis Group GBR. Dist: Taylor & Francis Group.

Fogel, Alan. Infancy: Infant, Family, & Society. 5th ed. 2008. (ENG., Illus.). 720p. pap. 53.00 net. (978-1-59738-016-4(4)) Sloan Publishing.

—Infant Development: A Topical Approach. 2010. (Illus.). 600p. (C). pap. 50.00 net. (978-1-59738-025-6(3)) Sloan Publishing.

Fontana, Gina. Child Growth & Development. rev. ed. 2007. (ENG.). 86p. spiral bd. 60.00 (978-0-7575-4686-0(2)) Kendall Hunt Publishing Co.

Fosarelli, Patricia D. ASAP: Ages, Stages, & Phases: From Infancy to Adolescense. 2006. 136p. per. 5.95 (978-0-7648-1501-0(6)) Liguori Pubns.

Fox, Jenifer. Your Child's Strengths: A Guide for Parents & Teachers. 2009. (ENG.). 368p. (gr. 12-18). 16.00 (978-0-14-311517-5(0), Penguin (Non-Classics)) Penguin Group (USA) Inc.

Fox, Louisa Lane. Love to the Little Ones: The Trials & Triumphs of Parents Through the Ages in Letters, Diaries, Memoirs & Essays. 2009. (ENG., Illus.). 304p. 24.95 (978-0-7112-2940-2(6)) Lincoln, Frances Ltd. GBR. Dist: Perseus-PGW.

Freiberg, Karen L. Annual Editions: Human Development 07/08. 35th rev. ed. 2006. (Annual Editions Ser.). 224p. (C). pap. 27.81 (978-0-07-351615-8(5), 9780073516158, McGraw-Hill/Dushkin) McGraw-Hill Higher Education.

Friedman, Joan A. Emotionally Healthy Twins: A New Philosophy for Parenting Two Unique Children. 2008. (ENG.). 256p. per. 15.95 (978-0-7382-1087-2(0)) Da Capo Pr., Inc.

Fromberg, Doris Pronin, ed. Play from Birth to Twelve: Contexts, Perspectives, & Meanings. 2nd rev. ed. 2006. (Illus.). 455p. 150.00 (978-0-415-95111-1(9)); (ENG., 480p. per. 47.95 (978-0-415-95112-8(7)) Routledge.

Frost, Joe L. A History of Children's Play & Play Environments: Toward a Contemporary Child-Saving Movement. 2009. (ENG., Illus.). 320p. 49.95 (978-0-415-80620-6(8)); 155.00 (978-0-415-80619-0(4)) Routledge.

Frost, Joe L., et al. Play & Child Development. 4th rev. ed. 2011. (ENG., Illus.). 512p. (C). pap. 91.20 (978-0-13-259683-1(0), Prentice Hall) Prentice Hall PTR.

Frydenberg, Erica, et al. Developing Everyday Coping Skills in the Early Years: Proactive Strategies for Supporting Social & Emotional Development. 2012. (ENG., Illus.). 172p. pap. 34.95 (978-1-4411-6104-8(X)) Continuum International Publishing Group, Ltd. GBR. Dist: National Bk. Network.

Fuller, Andrew. Bright Kid Challenge: Ending Conflict & Unlocking the Potential of Smart, Challenging Children. 2008. (ENG.). 224p. pap. 14.95 (978-1-4022-1212-3(7)) Sourcebooks, Inc.

Galinsky, Ellen. Mind in the Making: The Seven Essential Life Skills Every Child Needs. 2010. (ENG., Illus.). 256p. pap. 16.99 (978-0-06-173232-4(X), William Morrow Paperbacks) HarperCollins Pubs.

Gallagher, Mary & Karjala, Lynn. Taming Trauma Beasties. 2007. 72p. pap. 16.95 (978-0-9788571-4-1(3)) Thomas Max Publishing.

Gammage, Phillip. Children & Schooling. 2012. (Routledge Library Editions: Education Ser.). (ENG.). 224p. 115.00 (978-0-415-66431-8(4)) Routledge.

García Coll, Cynthia T. & Marks, Amy Kerivan. The Immigrant Paradox in Children & Adolescents: Is Becoming American a Developmental Risk? 2011. 69.95 (978-1-4338-1053-4(0)) American Psychological Assn.

García Coll, Cynthia T. & Marks, Amy Kerivan. Immigrant Stories: Ethnicity & Academics in Middle Childhood. 2009. (Child Development in Cultural Context Ser.). (Illus.). 304p. 39.95 (978-0-19-517459-5(3)) Oxford Univ. Pr., Inc.

Garcia, Marito, et al. Africa's Future, Africa's Challenge: Early Childhood Care & Development in Sub Saharan Africa. 2007. (Directions in Development Ser.). 40.00 (978-0-8213-7054-4(5)) World Bank Pubns.

Gardener, Judith K. & Gardener, Howard, eds. Classics in Child Development, 32 vols. 924.00 (978-0-405-06450-0(0), 409) Ayer Co. Pubs., Inc.

Garralda, Elena & Raynaud, Jean Philippe, eds. Brain, Mind, & Developmental Psychopathology in Childhood. 2012. (ENG.). 336p. (gr. 17). 85.00 (978-0-7657-0864-9(7)); pap. 36.99 (978-0-7657-0865-6(5)) Rowman & Littlefield Publishers, Inc. (Aronson, Jason).

Garralda, M. Elena & Raynaud, Jean Philippe. Brain, Mind, & Developmental Psychopathology in Childhood. 2012. (978-0-7657-0866-3(3), Aronson, Jason) Rowman & Littlefield Publishers, Inc.

Gaskins, Suzanne, ed. Play & Development: Evolutionary, Sociocultural, & Functional Perspectives. 2007. (Jean Piaget Symposium Ser.). (ENG., Illus.). 328p. 95.00 (978-0-8058-5261-5(1), Psychology Press) Taylor & Francis Group GBR. Dist: Taylor & Francis Group.

Gauvain, Mary & Cole, Michael. Readings on the Development of Children. 5th ed. 2008. (ENG., Illus.). 384p. (C). pap. 47.95 (978-1-4292-1649-4(2)) Worth Pubs., Inc.

Gazelle, Heidi & Rubin, Kenneth H., eds. Social Anxiety in Childhood: Bridging Developmental & Clinical Perspectives. 2010. (J-B CAD Single Issue Child & Adolescent Development Ser.: 98). (ENG.). 120p. pap. 29.00 (978-0-470-61805-9(1), Jossey-Bass) Wiley, John & Sons, Inc.

Gestwicki, Carol. Developmentally Appropriate Practice. 4th ed. 2010. (ENG.). 480p. (C). pap. 141.95 (978-1-111-18554-1(9)) Wadsworth.

Giampaolo, Sasso & Sasso, Giampaolo. The Development of Consciousness: An Integrative Model of Child Development, Neuroscience & Psychoanalysis. 2008. (EFPP Series (European Federation for Psychoanalytic Psychotherapy) Ser.). (Illus.). 300p. (C). pap. 42.75 (978-1-85575-482-9(7)) Karnac Bks. GBR. Dist: Stylus Publishing, LLC.

Gibbons, A. The Matrix Ate My Baby. 2007. 200p. per. (978-90-8790-234-6(4)) Sense Pubs.

Gibbons, Andrew. The Matrix Ate My Baby. 2008. 200p. (978-90-8790-235-3(2)) Sense Pubs.

Gill, Owen & Jack, Gordon. The Child & Family in Context: Developing Ecological Pratice in Disadvantaged Communities. 2007. (Illus.). 176p. pap. 37.95 (978-1-905541-15-7(5)) Russell Hse. Publishing Ltd. GBR. Dist: International Specialized Bk. Services.

Gillen, Julia. A International Perspectives on Early Childhood Research: A Day in the Life. Cameron, Catherine Ann, ed. 2010. (ENG., Illus.). 208p. 84.00 (978-0-230-23249-5(3)) Palgrave Macmillan.

Gimre, Amy. If I Could. 2009. 20p. pap. 12.99 (978-1-4389-7018-9(8)) AuthorHouse.

Gladney, Lawana S. If I Have to Tell You One More Time. (978-0-9630403-1-2(6)) Brown Bks. Publishing Group.

Glass, Cathy. Happy Kids: The Secrets to Raising Well-Behaved, Contented Children. 2010. (ENG.). 288p. (J). 12.95 (978-0-00-733925-9(9)) HarperCollins Pubs. Ltd. GBR. Dist: Independent Pubs. Group.

Gleason, Mary Margaret & Schechter, Daniel S. Infant & Early Childhood Mental Health, an Issue of Child & Adolescent Psychiatric Clinics of North America. 2009. (Clinics: Internal Medicine Ser.: 18-3). (ENG.). 240p. 99.00 (978-1-4377-1199-8(5), Saunders) Elsevier - Health Sciences Div.

Glenyn, Bernice C., et al, eds. Celiac Disease: Etiology, Diagnosis, & Treatment. 2008. (Illus.). xi, 261p. 129.00 (978-1-60692-634-5(9)) Nova Science Pubs., Inc.

Goba, Fairhope Dumile. Trends in Relation to the Involvement of Family in Children in Care. 2011. 216p. pap. (978-3-8443-9823-6(6)) Lambert Academic Publishing.

Goebel, Wolfgang & Glockler, Michaela. A Guide to Child Health. Creeger, Catherine, tr. from GER. 3rd rev. ed. 2007. (Illus.). 477p. pap. (978-0-86315-606-9(1)) Floris Bks.

Goelman, Hillel, et al, eds. New Approaches to Early Child Development: Rules, Rituals, & Realities. 2011. (Critical Cultural Studies of Childhood Ser.). (ENG.). 274p. 85.00 (978-0-230-10543-0(2)) Palgrave Macmillan.

Goke, Jayesimi. Critical Issues in Kindergarten & Primary Education. 2011. 140p. pap. (978-3-8454-1075-3(2)) Lambert Academic Publishing.

Goldstein, Sam & Naglieri, Jack A., eds. Encyclopedia of Child Behavior & Development, 3 vols. 2010. (ENG.). liv, 1591p. 949.00 (978-0-387-77579-1(X), 038777579X) Springer.

Gomez, Juan Carlos & Gomez, Juan-Carlos. Apes, Monkeys, Children, & the Growth of Mind. 2006. (Developing Child Ser.). (Illus.). 352p. per. 25.00 (978-0-674-02239-3(4)) Harvard Univ. Pr.

Goncu, Artin & Gaskins, Suzanne, eds. Play & Development: Evolutionary, Sociocultural, & Functional Perspectives. 2007. (Jean Piaget Symposia Ser.). (ENG.). 328p. per. 44.95 (978-0-8058-6314-7(1), Psychology Press) Taylor & Francis Group GBR. Dist: Taylor & Francis Group.

Goneng, Awang. Growing up in Trengganu. 2007. (ENG., Illus.). 336p. pap. 15.95 (978-981-05-8692-8(2)) Monsoon Bks. Pte. Ltd.

Gonzalez-Mena, et al. Infants, Toddlers, & Caregivers: A Curriculum of Respectful, Responsive, Relationship-Based Care & Education. 9th ed. 2011. (ENG., Illus.). 416p. (C). pap. 102.33 (978-0-07-802435-1(8), 0078024358) McGraw-Hill Cos., The.

Gonzalez-Mena, Janet. The Caregiver's Companion. 8th ed. 2008. (ENG.). 160p. (C). pap. 40.33 (978-0-07-722691-6(7), 0077226917) McGraw-Hill Cos., The.

Gonzalez-Mena, Janet & Eyer, Dianne Widmeyer. The Caregiver's Companion. 9th ed. 2011. (ENG.). 192p. (C). pap. 40.33 ***(978-0-07-749035-5(5)***, 0077490355) McGraw-Hill Cos., The.

Gonzalez-Mena, Janet & Eyer, Dianne Widmeyer. Infants, Toddlers, & Caregivers: A Curriculum of Respectful, Responsive Care & Education. 8th ed. 2008. (ENG., Illus.). 400p. (C). pap. 102.33 *(978-0-07-337854-1(2)*, 0073378542) McGraw-Hill Cos., The.

Goode, Caron B. Raising Intuitive Children. 2009. (ENG.). 1p. pap. 15.99 *(978-1-60163-051-3(4)*, New Page Bks.) Career Pr., Inc.

Goodenough, Elizabeth. Where Do the Children Play? A Study Guide to the Film. 2nd ed. 2010. (Illus.). 256p. pap. 27.50 ***(978-0-9823751-1-2(5))*** Alliance for Childhood.

Goodenough, Florence L. Experimental Child Study. 2007. (ENG.). 572p. per. *(978-1-4067-0443-3(1))* Read Bks.

Goodyer. Families & Child Development. Date not set. (Illus.). viii, 183p. pap. 48.00 *(978-0-582-22478-0(0))* Addison-Wesley Longman, Ltd. GBR. Dist: Trans-Atlantic Pubns., Inc.

Görlitz, Dietmar, et al, eds. Children, Cities, & Psychological Theories: Developing Relationships. (International Studies on Childhood & Adolescence Ser.). (ENG., Illus.). XI, 688p. 285.00 ***(978-3-11-175249-5(6))*** De Gruyter, Walter Inc.

Granott, Nira & Parziale, Jim, eds. Microdevelopment: Transition Processes in Development & Learning. 2009. (Cambridge Studies in Cognitive & Perceptual Development Ser.). (ENG., Illus.). 368p. pap. 48.00 *(978-0-521-10328-2(2))* Cambridge Univ. Pr.

Gray, Bryce T. Elephant in the Room. 2011. 24p. pap. 13.77 ***(978-1-4269-6979-9(1))*** Trafford Publishing.

Grayer, Dianna. I AM a Lot of Things. 2011. (ENG.). 40p. pap. 13.99 ***(978-1-4662-2466-7(5))*** CreateSpace.

Greenspan, Stanley I. & Greenspan, Nancy Thorndike. The Learning Tree: Overcoming Learning Disabilities from the Ground Up. 2010. (Merloyd Lawrence Book Ser.). (ENG., Illus.). 296p. 26.00 *(978-0-7382-1233-3(4))* Da Capo Pr., Inc.

Griffin, Richard. Child Development. 2007. (Very Short Introductions Ser.). (Illus.). 144p. 9.95 *(978-0-19-280308-5(5))* Oxford Univ. Pr., Inc.

Griffiths, Alex, et al. 101 Essential Lists on Managing Behaviour in the Primary School. 2006. (101 Essential Lists Ser.). (ENG.). 128p. 35.95 *(978-0-8264-8988-3(5))* Continuum International Publishing Group, Ltd. GBR. Dist: National Bk. Network.

—101 Essential Lists on Managing Behaviour in the Secondary School. 2006. (101 Essential Lists Ser.). (ENG.). 128p. 35.95 *(978-0-8264-8864-0(1))* Continuum International Publishing Group, Ltd. GBR. Dist: National Bk. Network.

Groark, Christina J., et al, eds. Early Childhood Intervention: Shaping the Future for Children with Special Needs & Their Families, 3 vols. 2011. (Illus.). 876p. 154.95 *(978-0-313-37793-8(6)*, C37793) Greenwood Publishing Group, Inc.

Grolnick, Wendy S. & Seal, Kathy. Pressured Parents, Stressed-Out Kids: Dealing with Competition While Raising a Successful Child. 2008. (ENG., Illus.). 235p. per. 18.98 *(978-1-59102-566-5(4))* Prometheus Bks., Pubs.

Gross, Dana. Infancy: Development from Birth to Age 3. 2nd rev. ed. 2010. (ENG.). 512p. (C). 131.60 *(978-0-205-73419-1(7)*, Prentice Hall) Prentice Hall PTR.

Gruenberg, Sidonie Matzner. Your Child: Today & Tomorrow. 2008. 172p. 22.99 *(978-0-554-32445-6(8))* 2008. 172p. 25.99 *(978-0-554-23142-6(5))* 2007. (ENG.). 154p. pap. 19.99 *(978-1-4264-3793-9(5))* 2007. (ENG.). 304p. pap. 24.99 *(978-1-4264-3863-9(X))* BiblioBazaar.

—Your Child: Today & Tomorrow. 2008. 144p. pap. *(978-1-4099-4723-3(8))* Dodo Pr.

—Your Child: Today & Tomorrow. 2007. 112p. per. *(978-1-4068-6264-5(9))* Echo Library.

Grych, John H. & Fincham, Frank D., eds. Interparental Conflict & Child Development: Theory, Research & Applications. 2011. (ENG., Illus.). 492p. pap. 45.00 *(978-0-521-65829-4(2))* Cambridge Univ. Pr.

Guernsey, Lisa. Into the Minds of Babes: How Screen Time Affects Children from Birth to Age Five. 2007. (ENG.). 304p. (gr. 9). 25.00 *(978-0-465-02798-9(9))* Basic Bks.

Guernsey, Lisa. Screen Time: How Electronic Media — From Baby Videos to Educational Software — Affects Your Young Child. 2012. (ENG.). 336p. (gr. 9). pap. 15.99 ***(978-0-465-02980-8(9))*** Basic Bks.

Guldberg, Helene. Reclaiming Childhood: Freedom & Play in an Age of Fear. 2009. 206p. 150.00 *(978-0-415-47722-2(0))*; (ENG.). 216p. pap. 31.95 *(978-0-415-47723-9(9))* Routledge.

Gullotta, Thomas P. & Blau, Gary. Handbook of Childhood Behavioral Issues: Evidence-Based Approaches to Prevention & Treatment. 2007. (ENG., Illus.). 432p. 125.00 *(978-0-415-95461-7(4))* Routledge.

Gullotta, Thomas P. & Blau, Gary, eds. Family Influences on Childhood Behavior & Development: Evidence-Based Prevention & Treatment Approaches. 2008. (ENG., Illus.). 360p. 52.95 *(978-0-415-96532-3(2))* Routledge.

Gunter, Michael & Franieck, M. Leticia. On Latency: Individual Development, Narcissistic Impulse, Reminiscence & Cultural Ideal. 2010. 140p. pap. 28.95 *(978-1-85575-740-0(0))* Karnac Bks. GBR. Dist: Stylus Publishing, LLC.

Gurian Institute Staff, et al. It's a Baby Boy! The Unique Wonders & Special Nature of Your Son from Pregnancy to Two Years. 2009. (ENG., Illus.). 160p. pap. 15.95 *(978-0-470-24338-1(4)*, Jossey-Bass) Wiley, John & Sons, Inc.

—It's a Baby Girl! The Unique Wonder & Special Nature of Your Daughter from Pregnancy to Two Years. 2009. (ENG.). 160p. pap. 15.95 *(978-0-470-24339-8(2)*, Jossey-Bass) Wiley, John & Sons, Inc.

Gurian, Michael. Nurture the Nature: Understanding & Supporting Your Child's Unique Core Personality. 2007. (ENG.). 368p. 24.95 *(978-0-7879-8633-9(X)*, Jossey-Bass) Wiley, John & Sons, Inc.

Gurian, Michael & Gurian. Nurture the Nature: Understanding & Supporting Your Child's Unique Core Personality. 2009. (ENG.). 368p. pap. 16.95 *(978-0-470-32252-9(7)*, Jossey-Bass) Wiley, John & Sons, Inc.

Gutstein, Steven, ed. The Relationship Development Intervention Program & Education. 2007. 259p. per. 22.50 *(978-0-9777186-1-0(1))* Connections Center.

Haaften, A. W. van, et al, eds. Philosophy of Development: Reconstructing the Foundations of Human Development & Education. 2010. (Philosophy & Education Ser.). 302p. pap. 269.00 *(978-90-481-4770-3(0)*, 9048147700) Springer.

Haith, Marshall M. & Benson, Janette B., eds. Encyclopedia of Infant & Early Childhood Development, 3 vols., Set. 2008. (ENG., Illus.). 2200p. 1230.00 *(978-0-12-370460-3(X)*, Academic Pr.) Elsevier Science & Technology Bks.

Hall, G. Stanley. Aspects of Child Life & Education. 2009. (ENG.). 337p. 36.99 *(978-1-117-69907-3(2))*; 337p. pap. 30.75 *(978-1-117-69908-0(0))*; 345p. 36.99 *(978-1-117-09348-2(4))*; 345p. pap. 23.99 *(978-1-117-09350-5(6)*, BiblioLife); 345p. pap. 31.75 *(978-1-117-09349-9(2))* BiblioBazaar.

Hall, Nadia, et al. Your Guide to Nurturing Parent-Child Relationships: Positive Parenting Activities for Home Visitors. 2007. (Illus.). 273p. spiral bd. 49.95 *(978-1-55766-907-0(4))* Brookes, Paul H. Publishing Co.

Hall, Sharon & Hall, Sharon K. Raising Kids in the 21st Century: The Science of Psychological Health for Children. 2008. (ENG., Illus.). 192p. pap. 29.95 *(978-1-4051-5806-0(9)*, Wiley-Blackwell) Wiley, John & Sons, Inc.

Hallam, Rena A. & Rous, Beth S. Tools for Transition in Early Childhood: A Step-by-Step Guide for Agencies, Teachers, & Families. 2006. (Illus.). 204p. pap. 32.95 *(978-1-55766-735-9(7))* Brookes, Paul H. Publishing Co.

Hallissy, Jennifer. The Write Start: A Guide to Nurturing Writing at Every Stage, from Scribbling to Forming Letters & Writing Stories. 2010. (ENG., Illus.). 160p. pap. 17.95 *(978-1-59030-837-0(9)*, Trumpeter) Shambhala Pubns., Inc.

Hamlett, Tiffany, et al. Content Analysis of Aggression in Television Programs for Preschoolers. 2010. 76p. pap. *(978-3-639-18648-2(6))* VDM Verlag Dr. Mueller e.K.

Hammond, Ruth Anne. Respecting Babies: A New Look at Magda Gerber's RIE Approach. 2009. *(978-1-934019-35-1(6))* Zero To Three Pr.

Handscomb, Graham & Cockburn, Anne, eds. Teaching Children 3-11: A Student's Guide. 3rd ed. 2011. (Illus.). 368p. (C). 115.00 ***(978-0-85702-486-2(8)***, B24862C); pap. 44.00 ***(978-0-85702-487-9(6)***, B24862P) SAGE Pubns., Ltd. GBR. Dist: SAGE Pubns., Inc.

Hanks, Scott. Take Heed to Thyself. 2007. spiral bd. 7.00 *(978-0-9799518-5-5(2))* Hanks, Scott.

Hanser, Christina. The Law of Attraction for Children. 2010. 32p. pap. 12.99 *(978-1-4520-0996-4(1))* AuthorHouse.

Harris. The Tavistock Model: Papers on Child Development & Psychoanalytic Training. 2011. (Harris Meltzer Trust Ser.). 440p. pap. 41.95 ***(978-1-78049-009-0(7))*** Karnac Bks. GBR. Dist: Stylus Publishing, LLC.

—Thinking about Infants Young Children. 2011. (Harris Meltzer Trust Ser.). (Illus.). 130p. 32.95 ***(978-1-78049-010-6(0))*** Karnac Bks. GBR. Dist: Stylus Publishing, LLC.

Harris, Judith Rich. The Nurture Assumption: Why Children Turn Out the Way They Do. 2nd rev. ed. 2009. (ENG., Illus.). 480p. pap. 16.95 *(978-1-4391-0165-0(5)*, Free Pr.) Free Pr.

Harris, Yvette R. & Graham, James A. The African American Child: Development & Challenges. 2007. (C). 50.00 *(978-0-8261-2756-3(8))* Springer Publishing Co., Inc.

Harrison, Elizabeth. A Study of Child Nature from the Kindergarten Standpoint. 2009. 80p. pap. 14.14 *(978-1-151-62346-1(6))* General Bks. LLC.

Hart, Craig, ed. Parenting & Child Guidance Readings. 2006. (C). pap. 29.75 *(978-0-8425-2648-7(X)*, Academic Publishing) Brigham Young Univ.

Hartley-Brewer, Elizabeth. Making Friends: A Guide to Understanding & Nurturing Your Child's Friendships. 2009. (ENG.). 224p. pap. 13.00 *(978-0-7382-1323-1(3))* Da Capo Pr., Inc.

Hatch, J. Amos. Cognitive-Behavioral Therapy for Depression: A Practical Guide to Management & Treatment. 2007. (Changing Images of Early Childhood Ser.). 240p. pap. 27.95 *(978-0-415-95340-5(5))* Routledge.

—Early Childhood Qualitative Research. 2006. (Changing Images of Early Childhood Ser.). 251p. per. 38.95 *(978-0-415-95341-2(3))* Routledge.

Hatch, J. Amos, ed. Early Childhood Qualitative Research. 2006. (Changing Images of Early Childhood Ser.). 251p. 150.00 *(978-0-415-95472-3(X))* Routledge.

Health & Welfare of Art Children. 2nd ed. 2006. (Reproductive Medicine & Assisted Reproductive Techniques Ser.). (Illus.). 206p. 110.00 *(978-0-415-37930-4(X))* Taylor & Francis Group.

Heaphy, Cheryl. What's That? 2009. 32p. pap. 12.95 *(978-1-4327-2135-0(6))* Outskirts Pr., Inc.

Heath, John F. When Bright Kids Can't Learn: How New Brain Research Can Help Your Child. 2007. (Illus.). 98p. pap. 15.95 *(978-0-9785423-0-6(4))* IQ Express.

Hedegaard, Mariane. Children, Childhood, & Everyday Life: Children's Perspective. 2012. ***(978-1-61735-735-0(9))***; pap. ***(978-1-61735-734-3(0))*** Information Age Publishing, Inc.

Hedegaard, Mariane, et al, eds. Motives in Children's Development: Cultural-Historical Approaches. 2011. (ENG., Illus.). 238p. 90.00 ***(978-0-521-76742-2(3))*** Cambridge Univ. Pr.

Hedegaard, Marianne & Fleer, Marilyn. Studying Children. 2008. (ENG., Illus.). 232p. (C). 127.00 *(978-0-335-23479-0(8)*, 0335234798) McGraw-Hill Education GBR. Dist: McGraw-Hill Cos., The.

—Studying Children: A Cultural-Historical Approach. 2008. (ENG., Illus.). 232p. (C). pap. 45.00 *(978-0-335-23478-3(X)*, 033523478X) McGraw-Hill Education GBR. Dist: McGraw-Hill Cos., The.

Hegarty, Lorna. A Wealth of Parenting. 2008. 176p. per. *(978-0-9783204-4-7(1))* Aaspirations.

Heidemann, Sandra & Hewitt, Deborah. Play: The Pathway from Theory to Practice. 2nd ed. 2009. (ENG., Illus.). 160p. pap. 29.95 *(978-1-933653-73-0(6))* Redleaf Pr.

Heim, Susan & Engel-Smothers, Holly. Boosting Your Baby's Brain Power. 2008. (SPA.). 150p. pap. 15.95 *(978-0-910707-90-9(1))* Great Potential Pr., Inc.

HEITMEYER, J. I. M. & BRIM, Mark. Say no before jail says yes - school Version. 2010. 423p. pap. 29.97 *(978-0-557-24049-4(2))* Lulu Enterprises Inc.

Helman, Lori, et al. Words Their Way: Letter-Name Alphabetic Sorts for Spanish-Speaking English Learners. 5th ed. 2008. (Words Their Way Ser.). (SPA & ENG., Illus.). 160p. (C). pap. 24.99 *(978-0-13-242103-4(8)*, Prentice Hall) Prentice Hall PTR.

Helping Your Child Cope with Divorce. 12.00 *(978-0-687-08877-5(1))* Abingdon Pr.

Helping Your Child Cope with Grief. 12.00 *(978-0-687-08904-8(2))* Abingdon Pr.

Hendrick, Joanne & Weissman, Patricia. Total Learning: Developmental Curriculum for the Young Child. (C). 7th rev. ed. 2006. (Illus.). 432p. per. 109.33 *(978-0-13-222566-3(2))* 8th ed. 2010. 408p. pap. 114.67 *(978-0-13-703411-6(3))* Prentice Hall PTR. (Prentice Hall).

—Total Learning: Developmental Curriculum for the Young Child (with MyEducationLab) 8th ed. 2010. (ENG.). 408p. (C). pap. 118.67 *(978-0-13-138117-9(2)*, Prentice Hall) Prentice Hall PTR.

Henry, C. Jeya K. & Ulijaszek, Stanley J., eds. Long-term Consequences of Early Environment: Growth, Development & the Lifespan Developmental Perspective. 2009. (Society for the Study of Human Biology Symposium Ser.). (ENG., Illus.). 268p. pap. 40.00 *(978-0-521-11821-7(2))* Cambridge Univ. Pr.

Herman, Conner & Ryan, Kira. The Dream Sleeper: A Three-Part Plan for Getting Your Baby to Love Sleep. 2012. (ENG., Illus.). 288p. pap. 17.95 ***(978-1-118-01842-2(7)***, Jossey-Bass) Wiley, John & Sons, Inc.

Herr & Swim & Cram101 Textbook Reviews Staff. Creative Resources for Infants & Toddlers. 2007. 60p. per. 9.95 *(978-1-4288-2002-9(7))* Cram101 Inc.

Herr, Judy. Working with Young Children. 6th ed. 2007. (ENG.). 733p. (gr. 9-12). 73.28 *(978-1-59070-813-2(X))* Goodheart-Willcox Pub.

Hewitt, Deborah. So This Is Normal Too? 2nd ed. 2011. (ENG.). 280p. pap. 29.95 ***(978-1-60554-072-6(2))*** Redleaf Pr.

Heyen, Gina. Learning with Matthew: A Caregiver's Guide to Problem Solving School Issues with Their Child. 2007. 52p. per. 7.99 *(978-1-59886-695-7(8))* Tate Publishing & Enterprises, LLC.

Heyman, Richard. Tough Conversations with Your Kids: From Sex to Family Values Tackle Any Topic with Sensitivity & Smarts. 2009. (ENG.). 224p. pap. 9.95 *(978-1-59869-878-7(8))* Adams Media Corp.

Hinitz, Blythe F., ed. Contemporary Perspectives on Early Childhood Education History. 2012. (ENG.). 240p. 145.00 *(978-0-415-89278-0(3))*; pap. 36.95 *(978-0-415-89279-7(1))* Routledge.

Hinshelwood, Lisa. Empowering Parents: Real-Life Strategies for Raising Children. 2010. 164p. pap. 12.00 *(978-0-557-36249-3(0))* Lulu Enterprises Inc.

Hobart, Christine & Frankel, Jill. A Practical Guide to Child Observation & Assessment. Walker, Miranda, ed. 4th rev. ed. 2009. (Illus.). 200p. pap. 22.50 *(978-1-4085-0488-8(X))* Nelson Thornes Ltd. GBR. Dist: International Specialized Bk. Services.

Hobson, Peter N., et al, eds. Foundations for Self-Awareness: An Exploration Through Autism. 2006. (Monographs of the Society for Research in Child Development Ser.). (ENG., Illus.). 200p. pap. 38.95 *(978-1-4051-6722-2(X)*, Wiley-Blackwell) Wiley, John & Sons, Inc.

Holewa, Lisa & Rice, Joan. What Kindergarten Teachers Know: Practical & Playful Ways for Parents to Help Children Listen, Learn, & Cooperate at Home. 2008. (ENG., Illus.). 224p. (gr. 12-18). 13.95 *(978-0-399-53424-9(5)*, Perigee Trade) Penguin Group (USA) Inc.

Hollander, Dana. Exemplarity & Chosenness: Rosenzweig & Derrida on the Nation of Philosophy. 2008. (Cultural Memory in the Present Ser.). (ENG., Illus.). 296p. 60.00 *(978-0-8047-5521-4(3))* Stanford Univ. Pr.

Holliday, H. Reconnecting, Redirecting, & Redefining 21st Century Males. 2011. (ENG., Illus.). 168p. 50.00 *(978-1-61048-475-6(4))*; pap. 24.95 *(978-1-61048-476-3(2))* Rowman & Littlefield Education.

Holliday, H. E. Reconnecting, Redirecting, & Redefining 21st Century Males. 2011. ***(978-1-61048-477-0(0))*** Rowman & Littlefield Education.

Holt, K. S. Movement & Child Development. (C). *(978-0-901260-45-1(2))* Mac Keith Pr. GBR. Dist: Cambridge Univ. Pr.

Holton, Gerald & Sonnert, Gerhard. What Happened to the Children Who Fled Nazi Persecution. 2006. (ENG., Illus.). 280p. 89.00 *(978-1-4039-7625-3(2))* Palgrave Macmillan.

Hooper, Jeni. What Children Need to Be Happy, Confident & Successful: Step by Step Positive Psychology to Help Children Flourish. 2012. (ENG., Illus.). 160p. pap. ***(978-1-84905-239-9(5))*** Kingsley, Jessica Ltd.

Hooper, Stephen & Umansky, Warren. Young Children with Special Needs. 5th ed. 2008. (ENG., Illus.). 544p. (C). pap. 116.00 *(978-0-13-159014-4(6)*, Prentice Hall) Prentice Hall PTR.

Hornbeak, Denise C. The SuperConfitelligent Child: Loving to Learn through Movement & Play. 2008. 178p. pap. 19.95 *(978-0-9800134-0-5(2))* PEAK Producers.

Horne, Arthur, et al. A Parent's Guide to Understanding & Responding to Bullying: The Bully Buster's Approach. 2008. 164p. pap. 22.95 *(978-0-87822-596-5(X))* Research Pr.

Hörschelmann, Kathrin. Children, Youth & the City. 2011. (Routledge Critical Introductions to Urbanism & the City Ser.). (ENG., Illus.). 256p. (C). pap. 42.95 *(978-0-415-37692-1(0))* Routledge.

Howard, Justine & McInnes, Karen. Companion to Professional Play Practice. 2012. (ENG.). 192p. (C). 125.00 *(978-0-415-67808-7(0))*; pap. 80.00 *(978-0-415-67813-1(7))* Routledge.

Howard, Vikki F., et al. Very Young Children with Special Needs: A Foundation for Educators, Families, & Service Providers. 4th ed. 2009. (ENG.). 544p. (C). pap. 116.00 *(978-0-13-208088-0(5)*, Prentice Hall) Prentice Hall PTR.

Howe, Christine. Peer Groups & Children's Development. 2010. (Understanding Children's Worlds Ser.: 13). (ENG., Illus.). 248p. 104.95 *(978-1-4051-7945-4(7))*; pap. 44.95 *(978-1-4051-7944-7(9))* Wiley, John & Sons, Inc. (Wiley-Blackwell).

Howes, Carollee. Culture & Child Development in Early Childhood Programs: Practices for Quality Education & Care. 2010. (ENG., Illus.). 216p. pap. 31.95 *(978-0-8077-5020-9(4))* Teachers College Pr., Teachers College, Columbia Univ.

Howlin, Patricia. Behavioural Approaches to Problems in Childhood. 2007. (Clinics in Developmental Medicine Ser.: Vol. 146). (ENG., Illus.). 172p. 77.95 *(978-1-898683-12-4(3))* Mac Keith Pr. GBR. Dist: Wiley, John & Sons, Inc.

H.R. 2343: The Education Begins at Home ACT: Hearing Before the Committee on Education & Labor, U.S. House of Representatives, One Hundred Tenth Congress, Second Session, Hearing Held in Washington, DC, June 11, 2008. 2008. iii, 85p. *(978-0-16-081553-9(3)*, 552-070-37896-1) United States Government Printing Office.

Hudziak, James J. Developmental Psychopathology & Wellness: Genetic & Environmental Influences. 2008. (Illus.). 320p. pap. 74.00 *(978-1-58562-279-5(6))* American Psychiatric Publishing, Inc.

Hughes & Cram101 Textbook Reviews Staff. Children, Play, & Development. 2007. 60p. per. 9.95 *(978-1-4288-2034-0(5))* Cram101 Inc.

Hughes, Bob. Evolutionary Playwork. 2nd rev. ed. 2011. (ENG., Illus.). 424p. (C). 150.00 *(978-0-415-55084-0(X))*; pap. 49.95 *(978-0-415-55085-7(8))* Routledge.

Hughes, Fergus P. Children, Play, & Development. 4th ed. 2009. (Illus.). 384p. (C). pap. 61.00 *(978-1-4129-6769-3(4)*, B67693P) SAGE Pubns., Inc.

Hughes, William. Social Understanding & Social Lives. 2011. (Essays in Developmental Psychology Ser.). (ENG., Illus.). 256p. 49.95 *(978-1-84169-735-2(4)*, Psychology Press) Taylor & Francis Group GBR. Dist: Taylor & Francis Group.

Hummel, Katherine & Darragh Lantry, Noreen. Building Baby's Brain Power: Hundreds of One-Minute Brain Stimulating Activities for Baby's First Years. 2007. (Illus.). 229p. per. 14.95 *(978-0-9671289-1-7(9))* B E T A Ctr., Inc.

—Fortaleciendo la Facultad Cerebral del Bebe: Hundreds of One-Minute Brain Stimulating Activities for Baby's First Years. 2007. (Illus.). 230p. per. 14.95 *(978-0-9671289-3-1(5))* B E T A Ctr., Inc.

Huston, Aletha C. & Ripke, Marika N., eds. Development Contexts in Middle Childhood: Bridges to Adolescence & Adulthood. 2010. (Cambridge Studies in Social & Emotional Development Ser.). (ENG.). 478p. pap. 34.99 *(978-0-521-17554-8(2))* Cambridge Univ. Pr.

Hwa-Froelich, Deborah A. Supporting Development in Internationally Adopted Children. 2011. (ENG.). 256p. pap. 39.95 ***(978-1-59857-191-2(5))*** Brookes, Paul H. Publishing Co.

Hyndman, Robert. Connecting School Culture to Boys' Learning. 2008. 116p. pap. *(978-3-639-03358-8(2))* VDM Verlag Dr. Mueller e.K.

Investing in Early Education: Paths to Improving Children's Success: Hearing Before the Committee on Education & Labor, U.S. House of Representatives, One Hundred Tenth Congress, Second Session, Hearing Held in Washington, DC, January 23, 2008. 2008. (Illus.). iii, 81p. *(978-0-16-081550-8(9)*, 552-070-37893-6) United States Government Printing Office.

IRIS Media Staff, creator. Carescapes - Promoting Children's Social Competence: A Guide for Family Child Care Providers, 1 disc. 2007. DVD 40.00 *(978-1-932969-18-4(7))* IRIS Media, Inc.

Irlen, Helen & Trivieri, Larry. The Irlen Revolution: A Guide to Overcoming Learning Disabilities. 2008. (ENG.). 240p. pap. 17.95 *(978-0-7570-0236-6(6))* Square One Pubs.

Isaacs, Larry & Payne, V. Gregory. Human Motor Development: A Lifespan Approach. 8th ed. 2011. (ENG., Illus.). 608p. (C). 147.00 *(978-0-07-802249-4(5)*, 0078022495) McGraw-Hill Cos., The.

Izumi-Taylor, Satomi & Blake, Sally, eds. Technology for Early Childhood Education & Socialization: Developmental Applications & Methodologies. 2009. 294p. 180.00 *(978-1-60566-784-3(6))* IGI Global.

Jaffe, Peter G., et al. Growing up with Domestic Violence. 2011. (Illus.). 78p. pap. 29.80 *(978-0-88937-336-5(1))* Hogrefe Publishing.

Jalongo, Mary Renck, ed. Enduring Bonds: The Significance of Interpersonal Relationships in Young Children's Lives. 2007. (Educating the Young Child Ser.). (Illus.). 224p. 149.00 *(978-0-387-74524-4(6))* Springer.

C

—Enduring Bonds: The Significance of Interpersonal Relationships in Young Children's Lives. 2007. (Educating the Young Child Ser.). 224p. per. 59.95 (978-0-387-75937-1(9)) Springer.

James, Allison & Christensen, Pia Monrad. Research with Children: Perspectives & Practices. Christensen, Pia & James, Allison, eds. 2nd rev. ed. 2008. (Illus.). (ENG.). 312p. (C). 45.95 (978-0-415-41684-9(1)); XVI, 296p. 150.00 (978-0-415-41683-2(3)) Routledge.

Jana, Laura A. & Shu, Jennifer. Heading Home with Your Newborn: From Birth to Reality. 2nd ed. 2010. (ENG.). 375p. pap. 15.95 (978-1-58110-444-8(8)) American Academy of Pediatrics.

Jensen, Lene Arnett & Mortimer, Jeylan T., eds. Social Class & Transitions to Adulthood: New Directions for Child & Adolescent Development. 2008. (J-B CAD Single Issue Child & Adolescent Development Ser.: 89). (ENG.). 112p. pap. 29.00 (978-0-470-29362-1(4), Jossey-Bass) Wiley, John & Sons, Inc.

Johansen Psy.D., Thor M. Disruptive Kids: A Guide for Parents. 2008. 192p. pap. 18.95 (978-1-4343-6293-3(0)) AuthorHouse.

John, Jaiya. Reflection Pond. 2007. (ENG.). 228p. per. 17.00 (978-0-9713308-2-5(4)) Soul Water Rising.

Johnson, Eileen. The Children's Bill of Emotional Rights: A Guide to the Needs of Children. 2011. (ENG., Illus.). 272p. (gr. 17). 60.00 **(978-0-7657-0850-2(7)**, Aronson, Jason) Rowman & Littlefield Publishers, Inc.

Johnston, Jane, et al. Physical Development. Nahmad-Williams, Lindy, ed. 2011. (Supporting Development in the Early Years Foundation Stage Ser.). (ENG., Illus.). 144p. 27.95 (978-1-4411-9244-8(1)) Continuum International Publishing Group, Ltd. GBR. Dist: National Bk. Network.

Jones-Smith, Elsie. Nurturing Nonviolent Children: A Guide for Parents, Educators, & Counselors, 1 vol. 2008. (Contributions in Psychology Ser.). (Illus.). 336p. 39.95 (978-0-275-98403-8(6), C8403, Praeger Pubs.) Greenwood Publishing Group, Inc.

Juniper, Aaron. Paternal Matters. 2009. 128p. pap. (978-3-639-16072-7(X)) VDM Verlag Dr. Mueller e.K.

Junn, Ellen & Boyatzis, Chris. Annual Editions: Child Growth & Development 12/13. 19th ed. 2011. (Annual Editions Ser.). (ENG., Illus.). 224p. (C). pap. 44.00 (978-0-07-805107-4(X), 007805107X, McGraw-Hill/Dushkin) McGraw-Hill Higher Education.

—Child Growth & Development 11/12. annuals 18th ed. 2010. (Annual Editions Ser.). (ENG., Illus.). 224p. (C). pap. 44.00 (978-0-07-805075-6(8), 0078050758, McGraw-Hill/Dushkin) McGraw-Hill Higher Education.

Junn, Ellen, et al. Child Growth & Development 10/11. 17th ed. 2009. (Annual Editions Ser.). (ENG., Illus.). 176p. (C). pap. 44.00 (978-0-07-812784-7(X), 007812784X, McGraw-Hill/Dushkin) McGraw-Hill Higher Education.

Kagan, Jerome, et al. Preservation of Two Infant Temperaments into Adolescence. 2007. (Monographs of the Society for Research in Child Development Ser.). (ENG., Illus.). 132p. pap. 42.95 (978-1-4051-8011-5(0), Wiley-Blackwell) Wiley, John & Sons, Inc.

Kagan, Sharon Lynn & Tarrant, Kate, eds. Transitions for Young Children: Creating Connections Across Early Childhood Systems. 2010. (Illus.). 360p. pap. 39.95 (978-1-59857-083-0(8)) Brookes, Paul H. Publishing Co.

Kail. Children & Their Development. 6th rev. ed. 2011. (ENG.). 592p. (C). 109.33 (978-0-205-03603-5(1), Prentice Hall) Prentice Hall PTR.

Kail & Cavanaugh. Human Development. 2nd ed. 60.80 net. (978-0-534-32952-5(7)) Wadsworth.

Kail & Cram101 Textbook Reviews Staff. Children. 2007. 156p. per. 12.95 (978-1-4288-2038-8(8)) Cram101 Inc.

—Children & Their Development. 2007. 152p. per. 12.95 (978-1-4288-2028-9(0)) Cram101 Inc.

Kail & Kail, Robert V. Children & Their Development. 6th rev. ed. 2011. (ENG., Illus.). 592p. (C). 167.60 **(978-0-205-03494-9(2)**, Prentice Hall) Prentice Hall PTR.

Kail, Robert. Children & Their Development. rev. ed. 2011. (ENG.). (C). 46.67 (978-0-205-03602-8(3), Prentice Hall) Prentice Hall PTR.

Kail, Robert V., Jr. Children & Their Development. 6th ed. 2011. (ENG.). (C). ring bd. 116.00 (978-0-205-21603-1(X), Prentice Hall) Prentice Hall PTR.

Kail, Robert V. Children & Their Development, Books a la Carte Edition. 6th ed. 2011. (ENG., Illus.). 576p. (C). ring bd. 109.20 **(978-0-205-19333-2(1)**, Prentice Hall) Prentice Hall PTR.

Kail, Robert V., ed. Advances in Child Development & Behavior. (Advances in Child Development & Behavior Ser.: 36). (ENG., 2008. Illus.). 520p. 107.00 (978-0-12-374317-6(6)) 2007. 426p. 107.00 (978-0-12-009735-7(4)) 2006. (Illus.). 418p. 107.00 (978-0-12-009734-0(6)) Elsevier Science & Technology Bks. (Academic Pr.).

Kalish, Chuck W. & Sabbagh, Mark A., eds. Conventionality in Cognitive Development - How Children Acquire Shared Representation in Language, Thought, & Action: New Directions for Child & Adolescent Development. 2007. (J-B CAD Single Issue Child & Adolescent Development Ser.: 85). (ENG., Illus.). 112p. per. 29.00 (978-0-7879-9697-0(1), Jossey-Bass) Wiley, John & Sons, Inc.

Kaplan, Paul S. A Child's Odyssey: Child & Adolescent Development, Including InfoTrac College Edition. (978-0-534-74502-8(4)) Wadsworth.

Karniol, Rachel. Social Development As Preference Management: How Infants, Children, & Parents Get What They Want from One Another. 2010. (ENG., Illus.). 376p. (C). 99.00 (978-0-521-11950-4(2)); pap. 39.99 (978-0-521-13530-6(3)) Cambridge Univ. Pr.

Karp, Harvey. Happiest Toddler on the Block: How to Eliminate Tantrums & Raise a Patient, Respectful & Cooperative One-to Four-Year-Old. rev. ed. 2008. (ENG., Illus.). 336p. 24.00 (978-0-553-80521-5(5), Bantam) Random House Publishing Group.

—The Happiest Toddler on the Block: How to Eliminate Tantrums & Raise a Patient, Respectful, & Cooperative One-To Four-Year-Old. rev. ed. 2008. (ENG., Illus.). 336p. pap. 15.00 (978-0-553-38442-0(2), Bantam) Random House Publishing Group.

Karpov, Yuriy V. The Neo-Vygotskian Approach to Child Development. 2006. (ENG., Illus.). 300p. (C). per. 35.99 (978-0-521-69613-5(5)) Cambridge Univ. Pr.

Kassem, Derek. Childhood & Youth Studies: Critical Issues. Murphy, Lisa & Taylor, Elizabeth, eds. 2009. (ENG., Illus.). 240p. (C). pap. 39.95 (978-0-415-46889-3(2)) Routledge.

—Key Issues in Childhood & Youth Studies. Murphy, Lisa & Taylor, Elizabeth, eds. 2009. (ENG., Illus.). 240p. (C). 125.00 (978-0-415-46888-6(4)) Routledge.

Kaur, Gurupdesh, et al. Alternate Child Care Strategies & Development of Pre-School Children. 2011. 108p. pap. **(978-3-8443-9938-7(0))** Lambert Academic Publishing.

Kay, Janet & Kay. Behavioural, Emotional & Social Difficulties: A Guide for the Early Years. 2007. (Sen in the Early Years Ser.). (ENG.). 160p. 21.95 (978-0-8264-8469-7(7)) Continuum International Publishing Group, Ltd. GBR. Dist: National Bk. Network.

Kedar, Yarden. The Role of Functional Categories in First Language Acquisition. 2009. 144p. pap. (978-3-8364-6387-4(3)) VDM Verlag Dr. Mueller e.K.

Kellam, Theresa. The Parent Survival Guide: From Chaos to Harmony in Ten Weeks or Less. 2008. (ENG., Illus.). 264p. 19.95 (978-0-415-98934-3(5)) Routledge.

Kellet, Mary. Rethinking Children & Research: Attitudes in Contemporary Society. 2010. (New Childhoods Ser.). (ENG., Illus.). 176p. 120.00 (978-1-4411-2913-0(8)) Continuum International Publishing Group, Ltd. GBR. Dist: National Bk. Network.

Kellett, Mary. Rethinking Children & Research: Attitudes in Contemporary Society. 2010. (New Childhoods Ser.). (ENG., Illus.). 176p. 34.95 (978-1-84706-323-6(3)) Continuum International Publishing Group, Ltd. GBR. Dist: National Bk. Network.

Kernberg, Paulina F. Beyond the Reflection: The Role of the Mirror Paradigm in Clinical Practice. 2007. (ENG., Illus.). 232p. pap. 26.00 (978-1-59051-071-1(2)) Other Pr., LLC.

Khonsari, Terri A. Raising a Superstar: Simple Strategies to Bring Out the Brilliance in Every Child. 2007. (ENG., Illus.). 137p. per. 14.99 (978-1-59932-046-5(0), Advantage) Advantage Media Group.

—Raising a Superstar: Simple Strategies to Bring Out the Brilliance in Every Child. 2008. (ENG.). pap. 14.99 (978-1-60037-356-5(9)) Morgan James Publishing.

Kilvington, Jacky & Wood, Ali. Reflective Playwork: For All Who Work with Children. 2010. (ENG., Illus.). 184p. 34.95 (978-0-8264-9764-2(0)) Continuum International Publishing Group, Ltd. GBR. Dist: National Bk. Network.

Kilvington, Jacky & Wood, Ali. Reflective Playwork: For All Who Work with Children. 2010. (ENG., Illus.). 184p. 120.00 (978-1-4411-6768-2(4)) Continuum International Publishing Group, Ltd. GBR. Dist: National Bk. Network.

King, Robert A., et al, eds. The Psychoanalytic Study of the Child, Vol. 64. 2010. (Psychoanalytic Study of the Child Ser.). (ENG., Illus.). 368p. 75.00 (978-0-300-15329-3(5)) Yale Univ. Pr.

Kivanc, D. Y. May I Call You Mommy. 2010. 36p. pap. 15.49 (978-1-4520-1125-7(7)) AuthorHouse.

Klass, Carol S. The Home Visitor's Guidebook. 3rd ed. 2008. 544p. per. 49.95 (978-1-55766-903-2(1)) Brookes, Paul H. Publishing Co.

Kleine, Karynne L. M. Treasure Chest II: Problem-Solving Activities, Brain Stretchers, & Active Games. 2009. (978-1-56090-231-7(0)) National Middle Schl. Assn.

Kline, Kathleen Kovner, ed. Authoritative Communities: The Scientific Case for Nurturing the Whole Child. 2007. (Search Institute Series on Developmentally Attentive Community & Society Ser.). (Illus.). 386p. 79.95 (978-0-387-72720-2(5), 0387727205) Springer.

Kloo, Daniela. Theory of Mind & Executive Functions. 2008. 200p. pap. (978-3-639-01139-5(2)) VDM Verlag Dr. Mueller e.K.

Konner, Melvin. The Evolution of Childhood: Relationships, Emotion, Mind. 2011. (ENG., Illus.). 960p. pap. 22.50 (978-0-674-06201-6(9), Belknap Pr.) Harvard Univ. Pr.

Kontopodis, Michalis, et al, eds. Children, Development & Education: Cultural, Historical, Anthropological Perspectives. 2011. (International perspectives on early childhood education & Development Ser.). (ENG., Illus.). vii, 264p. 139.00 (978-94-007-0242-4(6), 9400702426) Springer.

Koplow, Lesley. Bears Bears Everywhere! Supporting Children's Emotional Health in the Classroom. 3rd ed. 2008. (ENG., Illus.). 128p. pap. 20.95 (978-0-8077-4903-6(6)) Teachers College Pr., Teachers College, Columbia Univ.

Koralek, Derry & Gillespie, Linda, eds. Spotlight on Infants & Toddlers. 2011. (Illus.). 80p. pap. 14.00 **(978-1-928896-76-0(6))** National Assn. for the Education of Young Children.

Kostelnik, Marjorie J., et al. Guiding Children's Social Development & Learning. 7th ed. 2011. (Whatsquo;s New in Early Childhood Ser.). (ENG.). 560p. (C). pap. 137.95 (978-1-111-30125-5(5)) Wadsworth.

Kostelnik, Marjorie J., et al. Developmentally Appropriate Curricula: Best Practices in Early Childhood Education. 5th ed. 2010. (ENG.). 576p. (C). pap. 120.00 (978-0-13-138144-5(X), Prentice Hall) Prentice Hall PTR.

—Developmentally Appropriate Curriculum: Best Practices in Early Childhood Education. 5th ed. 2010. (ENG., Illus.). 552p. (C). pap. 113.33 (978-0-13-703553-3(5), Prentice Hall) Prentice Hall PTR.

Kovner Kline, Kathleen, ed. Authoritative Communities: The Scientific Case for Nurturing the Whole Child. 2010. (Search Institute Series on Developmentally Attentive Community & Society Ser.). xxvi, 390p. pap. 79.95 (978-1-4419-2491-9(4), 1441924914) Springer.

Kramer, Laurie & Conger, Katherine J., eds. Siblings As Agents of Socialization: New Directions for Child & Adolescent Development, No. 126. 2009. (J-B CAD Single Issue Child & Adolescent Development Ser.: 97). (ENG.). 120p. pap. 29.00 (978-0-470-61459-4(5), Jossey-Bass) Wiley, John & Sons, Inc.

Kramer, Paula & Kramer, Paula. Frames of Reference for Pediatric Occupational Therapy. Hinojosa, Jim, ed. 3rd rev. ed. 2009. (ENG., Illus.). 602p. 84.99 (978-0-7817-6826-9(8)) Lippincott Williams & Wilkins.

Kuriansky, Judy & Hand, Edie. 31 Things to Raise a Child's Self-Esteem. 2010. (Good Things to Know Ser.). (ENG.). 174p. pap. 9.99 (978-1-59652-582-5(7)) Turner Publishing Co.

Kurtz, Lisa A. & Kurtz, Lisa. Understanding Motor Skills in Children. 2007. (ENG., Illus.). 16p. pap. (978-1-84310-865-8(8)) Kingsley, Jessica Ltd.

Kytts, Marketta. Children in Outdoor Contexts: Affordances & Independent Mobility in the Assessment of Environmental Child Friendliness. 2008. 208p. pap. (978-3-639-08841-0(7)) VDM Verlag Dr. Mueller e.K.

La Barre, Frances & Frank, Ruella. The First Year of the Rest of Your Life: Movement, Development, & Psychotherapeutic Change. 2010. (ENG., Illus.). 200p. (C). 120.00 (978-0-415-87639-1(7)); pap. 36.95 (978-0-415-87640-7(0)) Routledge.

Lab-Volt Staff. Child Development & Child Care: TD Facs ESeries. 2010. 81p. 9.00 (978-1-60533-117-1(1)); 19p. 3.00 (978-1-60533-116-4(3)); 48p. ring bd. 6.00 (978-1-60533-075-4(2)) Lab-Volt Systems, Inc.

Ladd, Gary W. Appraising the Human Developmental Sciences: Essays in Honor of Merrill-Palmer Quarterly. 2007. (Illus.). 404p. per. 34.95 (978-0-8143-3342-6(7)) Wayne State Univ. Pr.

Laffey, John. Nurture a Brighter Child. 2008. 124p. pap. 20.95 (978-1-4092-2235-4(7)) Lulu Enterprises Inc.

LaFreniere, Peter J. Emotional Development: A Biosocial Perspective, with InfoTrac College Edition. (978-0-534-74504-2(0)) Wadsworth.

Laird, Wendy. Rambling Squirrel. 2010. (Illus.). 26p. (J). pap. 16.95 (978-1-4327-3876-1(3)) Outskirts Pr., Inc.

Lake-Smith. Child Family & Community. 2011. (ENG.). 154p. pap. 59.95 **(978-0-7575-9552-3(9))** Kendall Hunt Publishing Co.

Lally, J. Ronald, et al, eds. Concepts for Care: 20 Essays on Infant/Toddler Development & Learning. 2006. (ENG., Illus.). 144p. pap. 21.95 (978-0-914409-39-7(5)) WestEd.

Lamoreaux, Antoinette Abe. Unfolding Life. 2006. pap. (978-1-4068-1421-7(0)) Echo Library.

Lancaster, Karen. AS Level Health & Social Care (for Edexcel) Revision Guide for Unit 1: Human Growth & Development. 2007. 152p. pap. 23.50 (978-1-84753-369-2(8)) Lulu Enterprises Inc.

Lancaster, Lesley. The Multimodality of Mark-making in Early Childhood. 2012. (Routledge Studies in Multimodality Ser.). (ENG.). 192p. (C). 125.00 (978-0-415-87231-7(6)) Routledge.

Lancy, David F. The Anthropology of Childhood: Cherubs, Chattel, Changelings. 2008. (ENG., Illus.). 480p. 109.00 (978-0-521-88773-1(9)); 488p. pap. 40.00 (978-0-521-71603-1(9)) Cambridge Univ. Pr.

Landy, Sarah. Pathways to Competence: Encouraging Healthy Social & Emotional Development in Young Children. 2nd ed. 2009. 672p. pap. 59.95 (978-1-55766-891-2(4)) Brookes, Paul H. Publishing Co.

Lange-Küttner, Christiane & Vinter, Annie. Drawing & the Non-Verbal Mind: A Life-Span Perspective. Lange-Küttner, Christiane & Vinter, Annie, eds. 2008. (ENG., Illus.). 360p. 110.00 (978-0-521-87205-8(7)) Cambridge Univ. Pr.

Langston, Ann & Abbott, Lesley. Playing to Learn: Developing High Quality Experiences for Babies & Toddlers. 2007. (Illus.). 56p. (C). pap. 201.00 (978-0-335-22238-4(2), 0335222382, Open University Pr.) McGraw-Hill Education GBR. Dist: McGraw-Hill Cos., The.

Laverick, DeAnna M. & Renck Jalongo, Mary, eds. Transitions to Early Care & Education: International Perspectives for Making Schools Ready for Young Children. 2011. (Educating the Young Child Ser.). (ENG.). xv, 204p. 139.00 (978-94-007-0572-2(7), 9400705727) Springer.

Lawlis, Frank. The IQ Answer: Maximizing Your Child's Potential. 2007. (ENG.). 272p. (gr. 12-18). 15.00 (978-0-452-28868-3(1), Plume) Penguin Group (USA) Inc.

Lebeer, Jo, ed. With A Different Glance [Includes Dvd]: Dynamic Assesment of Functioning of Children at Development & Inclusive Learning. 2011. 288p. pap. 87.50 **(978-90-441-2802-4(7))** Garant Uitgevers N.V. BEL. Dist: Coronet Bks.

Lee, Allison. Childminder's Guide to Play & Activities. 2007. (ENG., Illus.). 176p. 29.95 (978-0-8264-9464-1(1)) Continuum International Publishing Group, Ltd. GBR. Dist: National Bk. Network.

Lee, Allison, et al. Childminder's Guide to Child Development. 2009. (ENG., Illus.). 128p. 29.95 (978-1-84706-085-3(4)) Continuum International Publishing Group, Ltd. GBR. Dist: National Bk. Network.

Lee, Ilchi. Power Brain Kids: 12 Easy Lessons to Ignite Your Child's Potential. 2010. 118p. pap. 16.95 (978-1-935127-35-2(7)) BEST Life Media.

—Power Brain Kids: 12 Easy Lessons to Ignite Your Child's Potential. 2007. (Illus.). 118p. per. 18.95 (978-1-932843-19-4(1)) Healing Society, Inc.

Lee, Kyunghwa & Vagle, Mark D., eds. Developmentalism in Early Childhood & Middle Grades Education: Critical Conversations on Readiness & Responsiveness. 2010. (Critical Cultural Studies of Childhood Ser.). (ENG.). 274p. 89.00 (978-0-230-61980-7(0)) Palgrave Macmillan.

Leiderman, Roni Cohen & Masi, Wendy. Let's Play & Learn Together: Fill Your Baby's Day with Creative Activities That Are Super Fun & Enhance Development. 2012. (ENG., Illus.). 176p. pap. 18.99 (978-1-59233-495-7(4), 1592334954) Quayside.

Lentze, M. J., ed. Growth in Children - A Global Perspective. 2008. (Illus.). 48p. pap. (978-3-8055-8493-7(8)) Karger, S. AG.

Lester, Barry M., et al, eds. Resilience in Children, Vol. 1094. 2007. (Annals of the New York Academy of Sciences Ser.: 4). (ENG., Illus.). 400p. pap. 139.95 (978-1-57331-643-9(1), Wiley-Blackwell) Wiley, John & Sons, Inc.

Lester, Barry M. & Sparrow, Joshua D., eds. Nurturing Children & Families: Building on the Legacy of T. Berry Brazelton. 2010. (ENG., Illus.). 416p. 49.95 (978-1-4051-9600-0(9), Wiley-Blackwell) Wiley, John & Sons, Inc.

Levenstein, Phyllis & Levenstein, Susan. Messages from Home: The Parent-Child Home Program for Overcoming Educational Disadvantage. 2nd ed. 2008. (ENG., Illus.). 288p. (C). 83.50 (978-1-59213-676-6(1)); pap. 30.95 (978-1-59213-677-3(X)) Temple Univ. Pr.

Levine, Laura E. & Munsch, Joyce. Child Development: An Active Learning Approach. 2010. 704p. (C). ring bd. 62.00 (978-1-4129-8918-3(3), B68508M); (Illus.). pap. 83.00 (978-1-4129-6850-8(X), B68508P) SAGE Pubns., Inc.

Lewin-Benham, Ann. Infants & Toddlers at Work: Using Reggio-Inspired Materials to Support Brain Development. 2010. (Early Childhood Education Ser.). (ENG.). 192p. pap. 27.95 (978-0-8077-5107-7(3)); 62.00 (978-0-8077-5108-4(1)) Teachers College Pr., Teachers College, Columbia Univ.

—Powerful Children: Understanding How to Teach & Learn Using the Reggio Approach. 2008. (Early Childhood Education Ser.). (ENG., Illus.). 216p. pap. 27.95 (978-0-8077-4883-1(8)); 60.00 (978-0-8077-4884-8(6)) Teachers College Pr., Teachers College, Columbia Univ.

Lewin, Vivienne & Sharp, Belinda, eds. Siblings in Development: A Psychoanalytic View. 2009. 192p. pap. 41.00 (978-1-85575-684-7(6)) Karnac Bks. GBR. Dist: Stylus Publishing, LLC.

Lewis, Betsy. All Seventh Graders Smell! 2008. 60p. pap. 7.00 (978-1-4357-1306-2(0)) Lulu Enterprises Inc.

Lievegoed, Bernard C. J. Phases of Childhood: Growing in Body, Soul & Spirit. Langham, Tony & Peters, Plym, trs. from DUT. 3rd rev. ed. (Illus.). 208p. pap. 19.95 (978-0-86315-481-2(6)) Floris Bks. GBR. Dist: SteinerBooks, Inc.

Lightfoot, Cynthia. Development of Children (Loose Leaf) 7th ed. 2012. (ENG.). 667p. (C). 87.95 **(978-1-4292-9749-3(2))** Worth Pubs., Inc.

Lightfoot, Cynthia, et al. The Development of Children. (ENG., 667p. (C). 6th rev. ed. 2008. Illus.). 146.95 (978-1-4292-0225-1(4)) 7th ed. 2012. 152.95 **(978-1-4292-4328-5(7))** Worth Pubs., Inc.

—The Development of Children Study Guide. 6th ed. 2009. (ENG., Illus.). 404p. (C). pap., stu. ed. 29.95 (978-1-4292-1783-5(9)) Worth Pubs., Inc.

Lillas, Connie & Turnbull, Janiece. Infant/Child Mental Health, Early Intervention, & Relationship-Based Therapies: A Neurorelational Framework for Interdisciplinary Practice. 2009. (Norton Series on Interpersonal Neurobiology Ser.). (ENG., Illus.). 420p. 52.00 (978-0-393-70425-9(4), 70425) Norton, W. W. & Co., Inc.

Linder, Toni W. Administration Guide for. 2008. (Illus.). 384p. spiral bd. 54.95 (978-1-55766-873-8(6)) Brookes, Paul H. Publishing Co.

—Transdisciplinary Play-Based Assessment: A Functional Approach to Working with Young Children. 2nd ed. 2008. 384p. spiral bd. 54.95 (978-1-55766-871-4(X)) Brookes, Paul H. Publishing Co.

—Transdisciplinary Play-Based Intervention: Guidelines for Developing a Meaningful Curriculum for Young Children. 2nd ed. 2008. 608p. spiral bd. 59.95 (978-1-55766-872-1(8)) Brookes, Paul H. Publishing Co.

Lindon, Jennie. Understanding Child Development: Linking Theory & Practice. (ENG., 2nd ed. 2010. Illus.). 296p. pap. 39.95 (978-1-4441-0284-0(2)) 3rd rev. ed. 2012. 288p. pap. 42.95 **(978-1-4441-6718-4(9))** Hodder Arnold Pubs.

—Understanding Children & Young People: Development from 5-18 Years. 2007. (ENG., Illus.). 272p. pap. 45.00 (978-0-340-93910-9(9)) Hodder Education GBR. Dist: Oxford Univ. Pr., Inc.

Lindon, Jennie. Understanding Children's Behaviour 0-11 Years: Play, Development & Learning. 2012. (ENG., Illus.). 224p. pap. 45.00 **(978-1-4441-7097-9(X))** Hodder Arnold Pubs.

Livingstone, Tessa. Child of Our Time: Early Learning. 2008. (ENG., Illus.). 224p. pap. 29.95 (978-0-593-05927-2(1)) Transworld Publishers Ltd. GBR. Dist: Independent Pubs. Group.

Loehr, Jamie & Meyers, Jen. Baby's First Year. 2007. (ENG.). 352p. mass mkt. 6.99 (978-1-4022-0935-2(5)) Sourcebooks, Inc.

Long, Fiachra. Educating the Postmodern Child: The Struggle for Learning in a World of Virtual Realities. 2013. (ENG.). 208p. 130.00 (978-1-4411-0387-1(2)) Continuum International Publishing Group, Ltd. GBR. Dist: National Bk. Network.

Losardo, Angela & Syverson, Angela Notari. Alternative Approaches to Assessing Young Children, Second Edition. 2nd ed. 2011. (Illus.). 272p. pap. 39.95 (978-1-59857-087-8(0)) Brookes, Paul H. Publishing Co.

Loughlin, Gerald M. & Marcus, Carole, eds. Sleep in Children Set: Developmental Changes in Sleep Patterns, 2 vols. 2nd rev. ed. 2008. (ENG., Illus.). 1080p. 370.00 (978-1-4200-8001-8(6), Informa Healthcare) Taylor & Francis Group GBR. Dist: Taylor & Francis Group.

Lowe, Edward, ed. Making It Work: Low-Wage Employment, Family Life, & Child Development. 2006. (Illus.). 427p. (978-0-87154-972-3(7)) Russell Sage Foundation.

Lowe, Edward, et al, eds. Making It Work: Low-Wage Employment, Family Life, & Child Development. 2009. (Illus.). 427p. pap. 19.95 *(978-0-87154-973-0(5))* Russell Sage Foundation.

Lowe, Fergus & Lowe, Brigid. Brain Training for Babies: A Teach Yourself Guide. 2011. (Teach Yourself: General Reference Ser.). (ENG.). 224p. pap. 15.00 *(978-0-07-176980-8(3),* 0071769803) McGraw-Hill Cos., The.

Lubawy, Joy. Visions of Creativity in Early Childhood: Connecting Theory, Practice, & Reflection. 2010. (ENG.). 264p. pap. 59.95 *(978-1-60554-038-2(2))* Redleaf Pr.

Luby, Joan L., ed. Handbook of Preschool Mental Health: Development, Disorders, & Treatment. (ENG., Illus.). 430p. 2009. pap. 35.00 *(978-1-60623-350-4(5))* 2006. 60.00 *(978-1-59385-313-6(0))* Guilford Pubns., Inc.

Lucas, A., et al, eds. Importance of Growth for Health & Development: 65th Nestlé Nutrition Institute Workshop, Pediatric Program, Kuala Lumpur, March 2009. 2010. (Nestlé Nutrition Institute Workshop Series: Clinical & Performance Program Ser.). (ENG., Illus.). 252p. *(978-3-8055-9304-5(X))* Karger, S. AG.

Luke, Barbara & Eberlein, Tamara. When You're Expecting Twins, Triplets, or Quads: Proven Guidelines for a Healthy Multiple Pregnancy. 3rd ed. 2010. (ENG., Illus.). 432p. pap. 19.99 *(978-0-06-180307-9(3),* William Morrow Paperbacks) HarperCollins Pubs.

Lupyan, Gary & Rakison, David H. Developing Object Concepts in Infancy: An Associative Learning Perspective. 2008. (Monographs of the Society for Research in Child Development Ser.). (ENG., Illus.). 160p. pap. 49.95 *(978-1-4051-8766-4(2),* Wiley-Blackwell) Wiley, John & Sons, Inc.

Luvmour, Josette. Adult Development: Emergent Wisdom in the Family Context. 2010. 160p. pap. *(978-3-8383-5501-6(6))* Lambert Academic Publishing.

Lyons (Nubian Sphinx), Stanley J. School Boy: (the Hated, the Accused, & the Terrorized) 2011. 62p. pap. 19.95 ***(978-1-4626-4169-7(5))*** PublishAmerica, Inc.

MacGregor, Janet. Introduction to the Anatomy & Physiology of Children: A Guide for Students of Nursing, Child Care & Health. 2nd rev. ed. 2008. (Illus.). XIV, 258p. 43.95 *(978-0-415-44624-2(4));* 150.00 *(978-0-415-44623-5(6))* Routledge.

MacIntyre, Christine. Understanding the Developing Child: A student & practitioner guide to the vital years from birth to Three. 2011. (ENG., Illus.). 128p. (C). pap. 30.95 *(978-0-415-66978-8(2));* 104.00 *(978-0-415-66977-1(4))* Routledge.

MacIntyre, Christine. Understanidng Children's Development in the Early Years. 2007. (Nursery World/Routledge Essential Guides for Early Years Practitioners Ser.). (Illus.). 129p. 145.00 *(978-0-415-41287-2(0))* Routledge.

—Understanidng Children's Development in the Early Years: Questions Practitioners Frequently Ask. 2007. (Nursery World/Routledge Essential Guides for Early Years Practitioners Ser.). (Illus.). 129p. per. 32.50 *(978-0-415-41288-9(9))* Routledge.

MacKenzie, Gaye. Sandpit Dilemmas - Challenges of Researching Young Children. 2008. 140p. pap. *(978-3-639-01772-4(2))* VDM Verlag Dr. Mueller e.K.

Maestas, Nicole & Gaillot, Sarah J. An Outcome Evaluation of the Success for Kids Program. 2011. 70p. pap. 17.00 *(978-0-8330-5124-0(5),* TR-575-1) RAND Corp., The.

Magumise, Johnson & Chikwiri, Elizabeth. Community Involvement in the Early Childhood Development Programme. 2011. 108p. pap. ***(978-3-8443-1437-3(7))*** Lambert Academic Publishing.

Maholmes, Valerie. The Oxford Handbook of Poverty & Child Development, 1 vol. King, Rosalind B., ed. 2012. (Oxford Library of Psychology Ser.). (ENG.). 768p. 150.00 ***(978-0-19-976910-0(9))*** Oxford Univ. Pr., Inc.

Malenfant, Nicole. Routines & Transitions: A Guide for Early Childhood Professionals. 2006. (ENG.). 300p. pap. 34.95 *(978-1-933653-04-4(3))* Redleaf Pr.

Martin, Art. Reparenting Yourself. 2009. 164p. pap. 19.97 *(978-1-891962-12-7(4))* Personal Transformation Pr.

Martin, Carol Lynn & Fabes, Richard. Discovering Child Development. 2nd ed. 2008. (ENG.). 688p. (C). pap. 183.95 *(978-0-547-00361-0(7),* 1029093) CENGAGE Learning.

Mashumba, K. Every Child Needs Nothing but Love. 2007. 48p. per. 16.95 *(978-1-4241-8977-9(2))* PublishAmerica, Inc.

Masten, Ann S. Multilevel Dynamics in Developmental Psychopathology: Pathways to the Future. 2007. (Minnesota Symposia on Child Psychology Ser.). (ENG., Illus.). 368p. 94.95 *(978-0-8058-6162-4(9),* Psychology Press) Taylor & Francis Group GBR. Dist: Taylor & Francis Group.

Mauro, Terri. 50 Ways to Support Your Child's Special Education: From IEPs to Assorted Therapies, an Empowering Guide to Taking Action, Every Day. 2009. (ENG.). 224p. pap. 12.95 *(978-1-60550-112-3(3))* Adams Media Corp.

May, Pamela. Child Development in Practice: Responsive Teaching & Learning from Birth to Five. 2010. (ENG., Illus.). 184p. (C). pap. 30.95 *(978-0-415-49755-8(8))* Fulton, David Pubs. GBR. Dist: Taylor & Francis Group.

—Child Development in Practice: Responsive Teaching & Learning from Birth to Five. 2010. (ENG., Illus.). 184p. (C). 96.00 *(978-0-415-49753-4(1))* Routledge.

—Creative Development in the Early Years Foundation Stage, 7 vols. 2009. (Practical Guidance in the EYFS Ser.). (ENG., Illus.). 144p. pap. 31.95 *(978-0-415-47653-9(4))* Fulton, David Pubs. GBR. Dist: Taylor & Francis Group.

Mayes, Linda & Lewis, Michael, eds. The Environment of Human Development: A Handbook of Theory & Measurement. 2012. (Cambridge Handbooks in Psychology Ser.). (ENG., Illus.). 704p. 140.00 ***(978-0-521-86882-2(3))*** Cambridge Univ. Pr.

Mayesky, Mary. Cengage Advantage Books: Creative Activities for Young Children. 10th ed. 2011. (ENG.). 704p. (C). ring bd. 113.95 *(978-1-111-35582-1(7))* Wadsworth.

—Creative Activities for Young Children. 10th ed. 2011. (Whatrsquo;s New in Early Childhood Ser.). (ENG.). 688p. (C). pap. 163.95 *(978-1-111-29809-8(2))* Wadsworth.

Maynard, Trisha & Thomas, Nigel, eds. An Introduction to Early Childhood Studies. 2nd ed. 2009. (Illus.). 320p. (C). 112.00 *(978-1-84787-167-1(4),* B71671C); pap. 51.00 *(978-1-84787-168-8(2),* B71671P) SAGE Pubns., Ltd. GBR. Dist: SAGE Pubns., Inc.

McAfee, Oralie & Leong, Deborah J. Assessing & Guiding Young Children's Development & Learning. 5th ed. 2010. (ENG.). 288p. (C). pap. 84.20 *(978-0-13-704127-5(6),* Prentice Hall) Prentice Hall PTR.

McCardle, Peggy D. How Animals Affect Us: Examining the Influence of Human-Animal Interaction on Child Development & Human Health. 2010. (Illus.). xvi, 226p. E-Book *(978-1-4338-0866-1(8))* American Psychological Assn.

McCardle, Peggy D., et al, eds. How Animals Affect Us: Examining the Influence of Human-Animal Interaction on Child Development & Human Health. 2010. (Illus.). 240p. 59.95 *(978-1-4338-0865-4(X))* American Psychological Assn.

McCarroll, Elizabeth M. The Quality of Mother-Child Interaction in Early Adolescence. 2008. 140p. pap. *(978-3-639-06333-2(3))* VDM Verlag Dr. Mueller e.K.

McCartney, Kathleen & Phillips, Deborah, eds. Blackwell Handbook of Early Childhood Development. 2008. (Blackwell Handbooks of Developmental Psychology Ser.). (ENG., Illus.). 680p. pap. 59.95 *(978-1-4051-7661-3(X),* Wiley-Blackwell) Wiley, John & Sons, Inc.

McClelland, Kylie. Extreme Parenting: Raising children who have Disabilities. 2011. 300p. 29.99 ***(978-1-4568-3761-7(3));*** pap. 19.99 ***(978-1-4568-3760-0(5))*** Xlibris Corp.

McClure, Robin. Toddler's Busy Book: Over 500 Creative Games, Activities, Crafts, & Recipes for Your Very Busy Toddler. 2007. (ENG.). 352p. mass mkt. 6.99 *(978-1-4022-0936-9(3))* Sourcebooks, Inc.

—Toddler's Busy Book: Over 500 Creative Games, Activities, Crafts & Recipes for Your Very Busy Toddler. 2007. (Playskool Ser.). (ENG., Illus.). 304p. pap. 19.99 *(978-1-4022-0933-8(9))* Sourcebooks, Inc.

McClure, Robin & Iannelli, Vincent. Baby's First Year: Your Child's First Twelve Months. 2009. (Knack: Make It Easy Ser.). (ENG., Illus.). 256p. pap. 19.95 *(978-1-59921-503-7(9),* Knack) Globe Pequot Pr., The.

McClure, Robin, et al. Raising Your Toddler: A Complete Illustrated Guide from First Steps to Preschool. 2010. (Knack: Make It Easy Ser.). (ENG., Illus.). 256p. pap. 19.95 *(978-1-59921-620-1(5),* Knack) Globe Pequot Pr., The.

McDevitt, Teresa, et al. Child Development & Education. 4th ed. 2008. (MyEducationLab Ser.). (ENG.). 720p. (C). pap. 135.00 *(978-0-13-713383-3(9),* Prentice Hall) Prentice Hall PTR.

McDevitt, Teresa M. & Ormrod, Jeanne E. Child Development & Education (with MyEducationLab) 4th ed. 2008. (ENG.). 720p. (C). pap. 141.67 *(978-0-13-610129-1(1),* Prentice Hall) Prentice Hall PTR.

McDevitt, Teresa M. & Ormrod, Jeanne Ellis. Child Development & Education. 5th rev. ed. 2012. (ENG.). 768p. (C). pap. 140.00 ***(978-0-13-248620-0(2))*** Allyn & Bacon, Inc.

—Child Development & Education, Student Value Edition. 5th ed. 2012. (ENG.). 672p. (C). ring bd. 91.00 ***(978-0-13-289301-5(0),*** Prentice Hall) Prentice Hall PTR.

McEvoy, Victoria Rogers. The 24/7 Baby Doctor: A Harvard Pediatrician Answers All Your Questions from Birth to One Year. 2010. (ENG.). 296p. pap. 16.95 *(978-0-7627-5335-2(8),* Lyons Pr.) Globe Pequot Pr., The.

McGraw-Hill-Glencoe Staff, creator. The Developing Child Student Activity Workbook. 2009. (Illus.). 179p. pap. 18.50 *(978-0-07-888433-7(0))* McGraw-Hill Cos., The.

The Meaning of Life: A Child's Book of Existential Psychology. 2007. *(978-0-9794108-0-2(0))* Trans Limbic Pr.

Medina, John. Brain Rules for Baby: How to Raise a Smart & Happy Child from Zero to Five. 2011. (ENG.). 294p. pap. 15.00 *(978-0-9832633-0-2(2))* Pear Pr.

Meece, Judith L., et al. Child & Adolescent Development for Educators. 3rd rev. ed. 2007. (ENG., Illus.). 640p. (C). per. 107.67 *(978-0-07-352576-1(6),* 0073525766) McGraw-Hill Cos., The.

Meggitt, Carolyn. Understand Child Development: Teach Yourself. 2012. (Teach Yourself Ser.). (ENG.). 208p. pap. 19.95 ***(978-1-4441-3799-6(9),*** Hodder & Stoughton) Hodder General Publishing Div. GBR. Dist: Independent Pubs. Group.

Meggitt, Carolyn, et al. Cache Level 3 Child Care & Education. 2nd ed. 2012. (Illus.). 624p. pap. 49.95 ***(978-1-4441-7099-3(6))*** Hodder Arnold Pubs.

Meier, Deborah, et al. Playing for Keeps: Life & Learning on a Public School Playground. 2010. (ENG., Illus.). 144p. pap. 19.95 *(978-0-8077-5095-7(6))* Teachers College Pr., Teachers College, Columbia Univ.

Menezes, Edirle. Children S Play & the Socio-Cultural Nature of Subjectivity. 2008. 156p. pap. *(978-3-639-08771-0(2))* VDM Verlag Dr. Mueller e.K.

Mercer, Jean A. & Mercer, Jean. Child Development: Myths & Misunderstandings. 2009. 296p. (C). pap. 32.00 *(978-1-4129-5646-8(3),* B56463P) SAGE Pubns., Inc.

Mercogliano, Chris. In Defense of Childhood: Protecting Kids' Inner Wildness. 2008. (ENG.). 224p. pap. 16.00 *(978-0-8070-3287-9(5))* Beacon Pr.

Merrell, Kenneth W. Behavioral, Social, & Emotional Assessment of Children & Adolescents. 3rd rev. ed. 2007. (ENG., Illus.). 560p. 110.00 *(978-0-8058-5370-4(7))* Routledge.

—Strong Kids: A Social & Emotional Learning Curriculum. 2007. (Strong Kids Curricula Ser.). (Illus.). 174p. pap. 36.95 incl. cd-rom *(978-1-55766-931-5(7));* 176p. pap. 36.95 incl. cd-rom *(978-1-55766-930-8(9))* Brookes, Paul H. Publishing Co.

—Strong Teens: A Social & Emotional Learning Curriculum. 2007. (Strong Kids Curricula Ser.). (Illus.). 176p. pap. 36.95 incl. cd-rom *(978-1-55766-932-2(5))* Brookes, Paul H. Publishing Co.

Merrell, Kenneth W., et al. Strong Start: A Social & Emotional Learning Curriculum. 2007. (Strong Kids Curricula Ser.). (Illus.). 132p. pap. 36.95 incl. cd-rom *(978-1-55766-929-2(5))* Brookes, Paul H. Publishing Co.

Merrick, Joav. Child Health & Human Development Yearbook 2009. 2011. (Health & Human Development (Joav Merrick - Ser. Editor - National Institute of Child Health & Human Development, Ministry of Social Affairs, Jerusalem) Ser.). 295.00 *(978-1-61668-912-4(9))* Nova Science Pubs., Inc.

Merrick, Joav, ed. Child & Adolescent Health Yearbook 2008. 2009. 145.00 *(978-1-60692-866-0(X))* Nova Science Pubs., Inc.

—Child Health & Human Development Yearbook 2008. 2009. 145.00 *(978-1-60692-979-7(8))* Nova Science Pubs., Inc.

Merz, Eva-Maria. Caring for Your Loved Ones? 2010. 176p. pap. *(978-3-8383-4941-1(5))* Lambert Academic Publishing.

Miller, Arnold. The Miller Method: Developing the Capacities of Children on the Autism Spectrum. 2007. (ENG., Illus.). 32p. *(978-1-84310-722-4(8))* Kingsley, Jessica Ltd.

Miller, Sue, et al. Studying Childhood & Early Childhood: A Guide for Students. 2nd ed. 2010. (SAGE Study Skills Ser.). (Illus.). 160p. (C). 112.00 *(978-1-84920-134-6(X),* B01346C); pap. 43.00 *(978-1-84920-135-3(8),* B01346P) SAGE Pubns., Ltd. GBR. Dist: SAGE Pubns., Inc.

Miller, Toby & Miller, Darla Ferris. Guidance & Behavior Management PET. 5th ed. 2006. (ENG.). 128p. (C). pap. 23.95 *(978-1-4180-3098-6(8))* Wadsworth.

Minett, Pamela. Child Care & Development. 6th ed. 2010. (ENG., Illus.). 344p. 35.00 *(978-1-4441-1713-4(0))* Hodder Arnold Pubs.

Miranda, Pat & Lacono, Teresa. Autism & Augmentative & Alternative Communication (AAC) 2008. (Illus.). 504p. 54.95 *(978-1-55766-953-7(8))* Brookes, Paul H. Publishing Co.

Mix, Kelly S., et al, eds. The Spatial Foundations of Cognition & Language: Thinking Through Space. 2010. (Explorations in Language & Space Ser.). (ENG., Illus.). 288p. 120.00 *(978-0-19-955324-2(6))* Oxford Univ. Pr., Inc.

Modin, Bitte. Setting the Scene for Life - Longitudinal Studies of Early Social Disadvantage & Later Life Chances. 2008. 144p. pap. *(978-3-639-05166-7(1))* VDM Verlag Dr. Mueller e.K.

Montgomery, Douglas C. & Montgomery, Heather. An Introduction to Childhood: Anthropological Perspectives on Children's Lives. 2008. (ENG.). 296p. 99.95 *(978-1-4051-2591-8(8),* Wiley-Blackwell) Wiley, John & Sons, Inc.

Montgomery, Heather. An Introduction to Childhood: Anthropological Perspectives on Children's Lives. 2008. (ENG.). 296p. pap. 38.95 *(978-1-4051-2590-1(X),* Wiley-Blackwell) Wiley, John & Sons, Inc.

Montie, Jeanne, et al. The Role of Preschool Experience in Children's Development: Longitudinal Findings from 10 Countries. 2007. pap. *(978-1-57379-310-0(8))* High/Scope Pr.

Moore, Lynn. The Everything Parent's Guide to Children with Special Needs: A Reassuring, Informative Guide to Your Child's Well-Being & Happiness. 2009. (ENG.). 320p. pap. 14.95 *(978-1-60550-163-5(8))* Adams Media Corp.

Morehead-Coleman, Dorothy. Child Development in the 1997 Society Reading Development for the Beginner Phonics Particularly the Inner City. Date not set. 120p. pap. 30.00 *(978-0-9669926-0-1(1))* Coleman, Dorothy Morehead.

Morgan, Linda. Beyond Smart: Boosting Your Child's Social, Emotional, & Academic Potential. 2010. (ENG.). 148p. pap. 14.95 *(978-0-9823454-2-9(9))* ParentMap.

Morris, Desmond. Amazing Baby. 2008. (ENG., Illus.). 208p. 40.00 *(978-1-55407-419-8(3))* Firefly Bks., Ltd.

—Child: How Children Think, Learn & Grow in the Early Years. 2010. (ENG., Illus.). 192p. 29.99 *(978-0-600-61994-9(X),* Hamlyn) Octopus Publishing Group GBR. Dist: Hachette Bk. Group.

Mosiman, Mike & Mosiman, Renee. The Smarter Preschooler: Unlocking Your Child's Intellectual Potential. 2009. (ENG., Illus.). 224p. pap. 14.95 *(978-0-9816426-5-9(9))* Brighter Insights.

Mould, Claire & Fabian, Hilary, eds. Development & Learning for Very Young Children. 2009. (Illus.). 184p. (C). 112.00 *(978-1-84787-392-7(8),* B73927C); pap. 45.00 *(978-1-84787-393-4(6),* B73927P) SAGE Pubns., Ltd. GBR. Dist: SAGE Pubns., Inc.

Moyles, Janet & Papatheodorou, Theodora, eds. Learning Together in the Early Years: Exploring Relational Pedagogy. 2008. (Illus.). XVIII, 238p. 44.95 *(978-0-415-46933-3(3))* Routledge.

Myers, Gene. The Significance of Children & Animals: Social Development & Our Connection to Other Species. 2nd rev. ed. 2006. (New Directions in the Human-Animal Bond Ser.). (ENG.). 248p. per. 29.95 *(978-1-55753-429-3(2))* Purdue Univ. Pr.

Naigles, Letitia R., et al. Flexibility in Early Verb Use - Evidence from a Multiple-N Diary Study. 2009. (Monographs of the Society for Research in Child Development Ser.). (ENG., Illus.). 300p. pap. 47.95 *(978-1-4443-3357-2(7),* Wiley-Blackwell) Wiley, John & Sons, Inc.

Narramore, Bruce S. Por Que Se Portan Mal los Ninos? Why Children Misbehave? (SPA.). 176p. *(978-84-7228-647-4(9),* 220708) Clie, Editorial.

Naudeau, Sophie. Investing in Young Children: An Early Childhood Development Guide for Policy Dialogue & Project Preparation. 2010. (Directions in Development Ser.). (Illus.). (ENG.). 320p. pap. 30.00 *(978-0-8213-8526-5(7),* 9780821385265); xix, 294p. *(978-0-8213-8528-9(3))* World Bank Pubns.

Nauman, Ann K. & Kirylo, James D. Curriculum Development: Perspectives from Around the World. 2010. pap. *(978-0-87173-176-0(2))* Assn. for Childhood Education International.

Nayar, Monisha & Akhtar, Monisha C. Play & Playfulness: Developmental, Cultural, & Clinical Aspects. 2011. (ENG.). 252p. 65.00 *(978-0-7657-0760-4(8),* Aronson, Jason) Rowman & Littlefield Publishers, Inc.

Neaum, Sally. Child Development for Early Childhood Studies. 2010. (ENG., Illus.). 156p. pap. *(978-1-84445-474-7(6))* Learning Matters Ltd.

Neel, Ruby. The Gift of Giving. 2010. 32p. pap. 14.49 *(978-1-4490-7069-4(8))* AuthorHouse.

Negri, Romana. The Story of Infant Development: Observational Work with Martha Harris. Williams, Meg Harris, ed. 2007. (Harris Meltzer Trust Ser.). (Illus.). 260p. per. 45.00 *(978-1-85575-414-0(2))* Karnac Bks. GBR. Dist: Stylus Publishing, LLC.

Nelsen, Jane, et al. Positive Discipline - The First Three Years: From Infant to Toddler — Laying the Foundation for Raising a Capable, Confident Child. 2nd ed. 2007. (Positive Discipline Library). (ENG., Illus.). 304p. pap. 16.99 *(978-0-307-34159-4(3),* Three Rivers Pr.) Crown Publishing Group.

Nelson, Gerald E. The One-Minute Scolding: The Amazingly Effective Approach to Child Discipline. 2009. 160p. 29.99 *(978-1-4363-9555-7(0));* pap. 19.99 *(978-1-4363-9554-0(2))* Xlibris Corp.

Neufeld, Gordon. Regreso Al Vinculo Familiar. 2008. 356p. pap. 24.95 *(978-0-9777899-5-5(0))* Hara Pr., USA, LLC.

Neufeld, Gordon & Maté, Gabor. Hold on to Your Kids: Why Parents Need to Matter More Than Peers. 2006. (ENG.). 320p. pap. 16.00 *(978-0-375-76028-0(8),* Ballantine Bks.) Random House Publishing Group.

Neville, Helen F. Is This a Phase? Child Development & Parent Strategies, Birth to 6 Years. 2006. (ENG., Illus.). 220p. pap. 22.95 *(978-1-884734-63-2(4))* Parenting Pr., Inc.

Neville, Helen Fowler. Is This a Phase? Child Development & Parent Strategies, Birth to 6 Years. 2006. (ENG., Illus.). 220p. lib. bdg. 42.95 *(978-1-884734-64-9(2))* Parenting Pr., Inc.

Newman, Sarah. Small Steps Forward: Using Games & Activities to Help Your Pre-School Child with Special Needs. 2nd ed. 2008. (ENG., Illus.). 272p. pap. *(978-1-84310-693-7(0))* Kingsley, Jessica Ltd.

Newton, Ruth P. The Attachment Connection: Parenting a Secure & Confident Child Using the Science of Attachment Theory. 2008. (ENG., Illus.). 240p. pap. 16.95 *(978-1-57224-520-4(4))* New Harbinger Pubns.

Nicholson, Barbara & Parker, Lysa. Attached at the Heart: 8 Proven Parenting Principles for Raising Connected & Compassionate Children. 2009. 380p. pap. 23.95 *(978-1-935278-86-3(X),* iUniverse Star) iUniverse, Inc.

Niemann, Sandy, et al. Ayudar a Los Niños Sordos: Apoyo Familiar y Comunitario para Niños Que No Oyen Bien. 2008. (SPA.). pap. *(978-0-942364-47-7(3))* Hesperian Foundation, The.

Nilsen, Barbara Ann. Observation & Assessment. 4th ed. 2007. (ENG.). 228p. (C) pap. 24.95 *(978-1-4180-7279-7(6))* Wadsworth.

—Week by Week: Plans for Documenting Children's Development. 5th ed. 2010. (Whatrsquo;s New in Early Childhood Ser.). (ENG.). 432p. (C). pap. 126.95 *(978-0-495-81317-0(6))* Cengage South-Western.

—Week by Week: Plans for Documenting Children's Development, Reprint. 4th ed. 2009. (ENG.). 416p. (C). pap. 112.95 *(978-1-4390-4376-9(0))* Delmar Cengage Learning.

Nittrouer, Susan. Early Development of Children with Hearing Loss. 2009. (Illus.). 1000p. pap. 79.95 *(978-1-59756-323-9(4))* Plural Publishing, Inc.

Noel, Lynette T. The Night Nopat Was Left Out. 2011. 16p. 8.50 *(978-1-4567-2971-4(3))* AuthorHouse.

Nosarti, Chiara, et al, eds. Neurodevelopmental Outcomes of Preterm Birth: From Childhood to Adult Life. 2010. (ENG., Illus.). 288p. 99.00 *(978-0-521-87179-2(4))* Cambridge Univ. Pr.

Nurse, Angela D. Physical Development in the Early Years Foundation Stage. 2009. (Practical Guidance in the EYFS Ser.). (Illus.). 8p. 120.00 *(978-0-415-47906-6(1));* pap. 31.95 *(978-0-415-47905-9(3))* Taylor & Francis Group.

Nurse, Angela D., et al. Practical Guidance in the Early Years Foundation Stage Set, 7 vols. 2009. (Practical Guidance in the EYFS Ser.). (Illus.). 172.00 *(978-0-415-47862-5(6))* Taylor & Francis Group.

Observation Planning & Assessment in the Early Years. 2012. 115.00 ***(978-0-415-57688-8(1))*** Routledge.

O'Connor, Anne. Understanding Transitions in the Early Years. 2012. (ENG., Illus.). 144p. (C). 135.00 ***(978-0-415-59857-6(5));*** pap. 35.95 ***(978-0-415-59858-3(3))*** Routledge.

O'Donnell, Nina Sazer. Early Childhood Action Tips. 19p. pap. 9.00 *(978-1-888324-27-3(9))* Families & Work Institute.

Okwany, Auma, et al. The Role of Local Knowledge & Culture in Child Care in Africa: A Sociological Study of Several Ethnic Groups in Kenya & Uganda. 2011. 168p. ***(978-0-7734-1583-6(1))*** Mellen, Edwin Pr., The.

O'Loughlin, Michael. The Subject of Childhood. 2008. (Rethinking Childhood Ser.). 99.95 *(978-1-4331-0347-6(8));* pap. 32.95 *(978-1-4331-0120-5(3))* Lang, Peter Publishing, Inc.

Olson, Sheryl L. & Sameroff, Arnold J., eds. Biopsychosocial Regulatory Processes in the Development of Childhood Behavioral Problems. 2009. (ENG., Illus.). 352p. 99.00 *(978-0-521-84813-8(X))* Cambridge Univ. Pr.

C

Oneka, Angelo. How to Protect Your Child from Harm & Dangers. 2011. 86p. pap. 19.95 ***(978-1-4560-6582-9(3))*** PublishAmerica, Inc.

Oppenheimer, Sharifa. Heaven on Earth: A Handbook for Parents of Young Children. 2006. (Illus.). 235p. per. 25.00 *(978-0-88010-566-8(6))* SteinerBooks, Inc.

Otto, Beverly W. Language Development in Early Childhood Education. 3rd ed. 2009. (ENG.). 456p. (C). pap. 73.20 *(978-0-13-501969-6(9)*, Prentice Hall) Prentice Hall PTR.

Owusu-Bempah, Kwame. The Wellbeing of Children in Care: A New Approach for Improving Developmental Outcomes. 2010. (ENG.). 192p. (C). 125.00 *(978-0-415-47939-4(8))*; pap. 39.95 *(978-0-415-47940-0(1))* Routledge.

Paciorek, Karen Menke. Annual Editions: Early Childhood Education 12/13. 33rd ed. 2012. (Annual Editions Ser.). (ENG., Illus.). 240p. (C). pap. 44.00 ***(978-0-07-805126-5(6)***, 0078051266, McGraw-Hill/Dushkin) McGraw-Hill Higher Education.

Page, Tom & Thorsteinsson, Gisli. Playful Learning. 2011. 68p. pap. ***(978-3-8454-0665-7(8))*** Lambert Academic Publishing.

Palm Beach Community College & Children and Families Research Group Staff. Developmentally Appropriate Practices for School-Age Children (5-12 Years) rev. ed. 2009. (ENG.). 160p. pap. 18.30 *(978-0-7575-5480-3(6))* Kendall Hunt Publishing Co.

—Practicas Apropiades del Desarrollo para Lactantes & Ninos de 1 a 3 Anos de Edad. rev. ed. 2008. (ENG.). 124p. pap. 15.97 *(978-0-7575-5488-9(1))* Kendall Hunt Publishing Co.

Palm Beach Community College Staff & Department of Children and Families Staff. Practicas Apropiadad del Desarrollo para Ninos Jovenes (3-5 Anos) rev. ed. 2010. (ENG.). 132p. pap. 17.14 *(978-0-7575-5489-6(X))* Kendall Hunt Publishing Co.

Palm Beach Community Staff & Children and Families Research Group Staff. Developmentally Appropriate Practices for Infants & Toddlers. rev. ed. 2010. (ENG.). 126p. pap. 15.97 *(978-0-7575-5475-9(X))* Kendall Hunt Publishing Co.

—Developmentally Appropriate Practices for Young Children (3-5 Years) rev. ed. 2010. (ENG.). 132p. pap. 17.14 *(978-0-7575-5477-3(6))* Kendall Hunt Publishing Co.

Palmer, Sue. Toxic Childhood: How the Modern World Is Damaging Our Children & What We Can Do about It. 2007. (ENG.). 384p. pap. 12.95 *(978-0-7528-8091-4(8))* Orion Bks. Ltd. GBR. Dist: Sterling Publishing Co., Inc.

Pangrazi, Robert P. Dynamic Physical Education Curriculum Guide: Lesson Plans for Implementation. 16th ed. 2009. (ENG.). 352p. (C). pap. 57.07 *(978-0-321-56164-0(3))* Benjamin-Cummings Publishing Co.

Papalia, Diane E. & Feldman, Ruth Duskin. A Child's World: Infancy Through Adolescence. 12th ed. 2010. (ENG., Illus.). 608p. (C). 178.33 *(978-0-07-353204-2(5)*, 0073532045) McGraw-Hill Cos., The.

Papalia, Diane E., et al. A Child's World: Infancy Through Adolescence. 11th ed. 2007. (ENG., Illus.). 640p. (C). 177.00 *(978-0-07-353197-7(9)*, 0073531979) McGraw-Hill Cos., The.

Papalia, Olds & Cram101 Textbook Reviews Staff. A Child's World: Infancy Through Adolescence. 2007. 280p. per. 15.95 *(978-1-4288-2700-4(5))* Cram101 Inc.

Papatheodorou, Theodora, et al. Child Observation for Learning & Research. rev. ed. 2012. (ENG., Illus.). 200p. pap. 55.00 ***(978-1-4058-2467-5(0))*** Longman Publishing Group.

Papatheordorou, Theodora. Learning Together in the Early Years: Exploring Relational Pedagogy. Moyles, Janet, ed. 2008. (Illus.). XVIII, 238p. 170.00 *(978-0-415-46932-6(5))* Routledge.

Parizkova, Jana. Nutrition, Physical Activity, & Health in Early Life. 2nd rev. ed. 2009. (ENG., Illus.). 428p. 144.95 *(978-1-4200-8231-9(0)*, CRC Press) Taylor & Francis Group GBR. Dist: Taylor & Francis Group.

Parke, Ross D. & Clarke-Stewart, Alison. Social Development. 2010. (ENG., Illus.). 618p. (C). 197.95 *(978-0-470-59905-1(7)*, Wiley) Wiley, John & Sons, Inc.

Patel, Dilip R. & Greydanus, Donald E., eds. Adolescence & Sports. 2010. (Health & Human Development (Joav Merrick - Series Editor - National Institute of Child Health & Human Development, Ministry of Social Affairs, Jerusalem) Ser.). 157p. 89.00 *(978-1-60876-702-1(7))* Nova Science Pubs., Inc.

Patterson, Charlotte J. Infancy & Childhood. 2008. (ENG., Illus.). 592p. (C). pap. 138.33 *(978-0-07-335589-4(5)*, 0073355895) McGraw-Hill Cos., The.

Patterson, Gale. Fresh Eggs or Hard Boiled? How We Raise & Educate Our Children. 2012. ***(978-1-58982-848-3(8))*** American Bk. Publishing Group.

Paxton, Katherine & Estay, Irene A. Counseling People on the Autism Spectrum: A Practical Approach. 2007. (ENG., Illus.). 176p. per. *(978-1-84310-552-7(7))* Kingsley, Jessica Ltd.

Payne, Kim John & Ross, Lisa M. Simplicity Parenting: Using the Extraordinary Power of Less to Raise Calmer, Happier, & More Secure Kids. 2009. (ENG.). 256p. 25.00 *(978-0-345-50797-6(5)*, Ballantine Bks.) Random House Publishing Group.

Payne, V. Gregory & Isaacs, Larry D. Human Motor Development: A Lifespan Approach. 7th rev. ed. 2007. (ENG., Illus.). 552p. (C). 147.00 *(978-0-07-352362-0(3)*, 0073523623) McGraw-Hill Cos., The.

Pedersen, Amy B. The Miracle of Me: From conception to Birth. 2007. lib. bdg. 19.99 *(978-1-59872-879-8(2))* Instant Pub.

Pediatrists. The Baby Care Book: Absolutely Everything You Need to Know about Your Fabulous Baby. 2010. 99p. pap. 19.95 *(978-1-4327-5783-0(0))* Outskirts Pr., Inc.

Peele, Amy S. Aunt Mary's Guide to Raising Children the Old-Fashioned Way. 2009. 184p. pap. 15.95 *(978-0-557-08442-5(3))* Lulu Enterprises Inc.

Pendleton McClain. The Intentional Parenting Plan: Tipp. 2009. 172p. pap. 20.99 *(978-1-4389-9740-7(X))* AuthorHouse.

Penn, Helen. Understanding Early Childhood: Issues & Controversies. 2nd ed. 2008. (ENG., Illus.). 232p. (C). pap. 45.00 *(978-0-335-22550-7(0)*, 0335225500) McGraw-Hill Education GBR. Dist: McGraw-Hill Cos., The.

Percy, Bernard, et al. How to Grow a Child: A Child's Advice to Parents. 2009. 134p. pap. 15.95 *(978-1-888045-24-6(8))* Action Publishing, LLC.

Persaud, Raj. The Young Mind. Bailey, Sue & Shooter, Mike, eds. 2009. (ENG., Illus.). 420p. pap. 29.99 *(978-0-593-06138-1(1))* Transworld Publishers Ltd. GBR. Dist: Independent Pubs. Group.

Petty, Karen. Developmental Milestones of Young Children. 2009. (Redleaf Quick Guides). (ENG., Illus.). 50p. pap. 14.95 *(978-1-60554-005-4(6))* Redleaf Pr.

Phillips, Ronnie. Parent Involvement Is Non-Negotiable. 2009. 96p. pap. 13.95 *(978-1-4327-4328-4(7))* Outskirts Pr., Inc.

Piaget, Jean. The Language & Thought of the Child. 2007. (ENG., Illus.). 272p. per. *(978-1-4067-2832-3(2))* Read Bks.

Pica, Rae. Experiences in Music & Movement: Birth to Age Eight. 5th ed. 2012. (ENG., Illus.). 368p. (C). pap. 118.95 ***(978-1-111-83805-8(4))*** Wadsworth.

Pickhardt, Carl E. Stop the Screaming: How to Turn Angry Conflict with Your Child into Positive Communication. 2009. (ENG.). 240p. pap. 14.95 *(978-0-230-60645-6(8))* Palgrave Macmillan.

Pierce, Anne. Ships without a Shore: America's Undernurtured Children. 2009. (ENG., Illus.). 276p. pap. 29.95 *(978-1-4128-1090-6(6))* Transaction Pubs.

Pillow, Bradford H. Children's Discovery of the Active Mind: Phenomenological Awareness, Social Experience, & Knowledge about Cognition. 2011. (SpringerBriefs in Psychology / SpringerBriefs in Child Development Ser.). (ENG., Illus.). xi, 99p. pap. 49.95 ***(978-1-4614-2247-1(7)***, 1461422477) Springer.

Plummer, Deborah M. Focussing & Calming Games & Activities for Children. 2012. (ENG., Illus.). 176p. pap. ***(978-1-84905-143-9(7))*** Kingsley, Jessica Ltd.

Pollock, David. Third Culture Kids, Revised Edition: The Experience of Growing up among Worlds. 2009. (ENG., Illus.). 360p. pap. 19.95 *(978-1-85788-525-5(2))* Ebsco Publishing.

Poncin, Yann B., et al. Lewis's Child & Adolescent Psychiatry Review: 1400 Questions to Help You Pass the Boards. 4th rev. ed. 2009. (ENG.). 272p. pap. 68.99 *(978-0-7817-9507-4(9))* Lippincott Williams & Wilkins.

Pope, Liston. Newell Gilbert's Boyhood. Pope, Liston, ed. 2006. (Liston Pope's Works: Vol. 5). 615p. 44.95 *(978-0-9638900-8-5(5))* Mantis Pr.

Posner, Michael I. & Rothbart, Mary K. Educating the Human Brain. 2006. (Illus.). 263p. 39.95 *(978-1-59147-381-7(0))* American Psychological Assn.

Powell, Craig M. & Monteggia, Lisa M. The Autisms: Molecules to Model Systems. 2012. (ENG.). 416p. 145.00 ***(978-0-19-974431-2(9))*** Oxford Univ. Pr., Inc.

Prasad, Deepesh Chandra. Fundamentals of Child Psychology. 2008. (Illus.). 393p. 62.50 *(978-81-7533-145-7(3))* M. D. Pubns. Pvt, Ltd. IND. Dist: Coronet Bks.

Presseau, Emily & Stires, Susan. Encouraging Enthusiastic Readers. 2010. 68p. pap. *(978-3-8383-5483-5(4))* Lambert Academic Publishing.

Preyer, William. Mental Development in the Child. Brown, H. W., tr. from GER. (Brainedness, Handedness, & Mental Abilities Ser.). reprint ed. 42.50 *(978-0-404-60887-3(6))* AMS Pr., Inc.

Principe, Gabrielle F. Your Brain on Childhood: The Unexpected Side Effects of Classrooms, Ballparks, Family Rooms, & the Minivan. 2011. (ENG.). 275p. pap. 17.00 *(978-1-61614-425-8(4))* Prometheus Bks., Pubs.

Probert, Rebecca, et al. Responsible Parents & Parental Responsibility. Probert, Rebecca et al, eds. 2009. (ENG.). 354p. pap. 114.00 *(978-1-84113-880-0(0))* Hart Publishing Ltd. GBR. Dist: International Specialized Bk. Services.

Proykov, Todor. Opening the Pandora's Box: The Child Abuse Discourse. 2010. 132p. pap. *(978-3-8383-5003-5(0))* Lambert Academic Publishing.

Pryce, Tony. Circle Time Sessions for Relaxation & Imagination. rev. ed. 2007. (Lucky Duck Bks.). (Illus.). 96p. per. 27.00 *(978-1-4129-2018-6(3)*, B20175P) SAGE Pubns., Ltd. GBR. Dist: SAGE Pubns., Inc.

Puckett, Margaret B. & Black, Janet K. Understanding Preschooler Development. 2007. (ENG., Illus.). 120p. (J). per. 19.95 *(978-1-933653-03-7(5))* Redleaf Pr.

Puckett, Margaret B., et al. The Young Child: Development from Prebirth Through Age Eight. 5th ed. 2008. (ENG.). 600p. (C). pap. 105.00 *(978-0-13-514776-4(X)*, Prentice Hall) Prentice Hall PTR.

Pulley, Leland E. Topics to Discuss with Children & Adolescents Pulley, Leland E., ed. 2007. (Illus.). 470p. 29.50 *(978-0-9611282-5-8(9))* Leland Pulley Co.

Quinn, Karen. Testing for Kindergarten: Simple Strategies to Help Your Child Ace the Tests for: Public School Placement, Private School Admissions, Gifted Program Qualification. 2010. (ENG., Illus.). 272p. pap. 15.99 *(978-1-4165-9107-8(9)*, Touchstone) Touchstone.

Qvortrup, Jens, et al, eds. The Palgrave Handbook of Childhood Studies. (ENG., Illus.). 500p. 2011. pap. 60.00 *(978-0-230-53261-8(6))* 2009. 231.00 *(978-0-230-53260-1(8))* Palgrave Macmillan.

R&S Information LLC Staff. Healthy Baby, Happy Home; Create a Safe Green Home for Your Baby. 2009. 182p. pap. 17.95 *(978-1-935097-38-9(5))* Hillcrest Publishing Group, Inc.

Ramirez, Tami. Being a Baby, 1 vol. 2009. pap. 24.95 *(978-1-60813-960-6(3))* PublishAmerica, Inc.

Rao, Anthony & Seaton, Michelle. The Way of Boys: Promoting the Social & Emotional Development of Young Boys. 2010. (ENG.). 304p. pap. 14.99 *(978-0-06-170783-4(X)*, Harper Paperbacks) HarperCollins Pubs.

—The Way of Boys: Raising Healthy Boys in a Challenging & Complex World. 2009. 304p. 25.99 *(978-0-06-170782-7(1)*, Morrow, William & Co.) HarperCollins Pubs.

Rathus, Spencer A. Childhood: Voyages in Development. (ENG., (C). 3rd rev. ed. 2007. Illus.). 584p. per. 136.95 *(978-0-495-50461-0(0))* 4th ed. 2010. 560p. pap. 80.95 *(978-0-495-90437-3(6))* 4th ed. 2010. 560p. pap. 153.95 *(978-0-495-90433-5(3))* Wadsworth.

—Childhood & Adolescence: Voyages in Development. (ENG.). (C). 3rd ed. 2007. 712p. ring bd. 67.95 *(978-0-495-50458-0(0))* 3rd ed. 2007. (Illus.). 712p. per. 156.95 *(978-0-495-50390-3(8))* 4th ed. 2010. 672p. pap. 175.95 *(978-0-495-90408-3(2))* 4th ed. 2010. 672p. ring bd. 75.95 *(978-0-495-90436-6(8))* Wadsworth.

—HDEV. 2nd ed. 2011. (PSY 232 Developmental Psychology Ser.). (ENG.). 416p. pap. 69.95 *(978-1-111-51982-7(X))* Wadsworth.

—Observation Worksheets for Rathus' Childhood & Adolescence: Voyages in Development, 4th. 4th ed. 2010. (ENG.). 64p. (C). pap. 41.95 *(978-0-8400-3240-9(4))* Wadsworth.

Reisser, Paul C. Baby & Child Care: From Pre-Birth Through the Teen Years. rev. ed. 2007. (ENG., Illus.). 928p. 29.97 *(978-1-4143-1305-4(5))* Tyndale Hse. Pubs.

Reney, Evelyn. Tunnel of Vision. 2006. pap. 13.99 *(978-1-4259-6912-7(7))* AuthorHouse.

Reno, Hilde. Handbook for Early Childhood Administrators: Directing with a Mission. 2007. (ENG., Illus.). 304p. per. 56.99 *(978-0-205-46980-2(9))* Allyn & Bacon, Inc.

Researcher, C. Q. Childhood & Adolescence in Society: Selections from CQ Researcher. 2011. (Illus.). 336p. (C). pap. 36.00 *(978-1-4129-9434-7(9)*, B94347P) SAGE Pubns., Inc.

Reutzel, D. Ray & Cooter, Robert B. Strategies for Reading Assessment & Instruction: Helping Every Child Succeed. 4th ed. 2010. (ENG.). 480p. (C). pap. 106.00 *(978-0-13-704838-0(6))* Allyn & Bacon, Inc.

—Strategies for Reading Assessment & Instruction: Helping Every Child Succeed (with MyEducationLab) 4th ed. 2010. (ENG.). 480p. (C). pap. 112.67 *(978-0-13-138151-3(2)*, Prentice Hall) Prentice Hall PTR.

Reznick, Charlotte. The Power of Your Child's Imagination: How to Transform Stress & Anxiety into Joy & Success. 2009. (ENG.). 320p. (gr. 12-18). 14.95 *(978-0-399-53507-9(1)*, Perigee Trade) Penguin Group (USA) Inc.

Riley, Dave. Intellectual Development: Connecting Science & Practice in Early Childhood Settings. 2008. (Redleaf Professional Library). (ENG.). 160p. pap. 24.95 *(978-1-933653-63-1(9))* Redleaf Pr.

Riley, Dave, et al. Social & Emotional Development: Connecting Science & Practice in Early Childhood Settings. 2007. (ENG., Illus.). 144p. per. 24.95 *(978-1-933653-30-3(2))* Redleaf Pr.

Rispoli, Luciano. The Basic Experience & the Development of the Self: Development from the Point of View of Functional Psychotherapy. 2008. 460p. pap. *(978-3-03911-750-5(5))* Lang, Peter.

Rivers, Caryl & Barnett, Rosalind C. The Truth about Girls & Boys: Challenging Toxic Stereotypes about Our Children. 2011. (Illus.). 192p. E-Book ***(978-0-231-52530-5(3))***; (ENG., 240p. (gr. 17). 24.50 *(978-0-231-15162-7(4))* Columbia Univ. Pr.

Roberts-Holmes, Guy. Doing Your Early Research Project. 2nd ed. 2011. (Illus.). 232p. (C). 104.00 *(978-1-84920-519-1(1)*, B05191C); pap. 45.00 *(978-1-84920-520-7(5)*, B05191P) SAGE Pubns., Ltd. GBR. Dist: SAGE Pubns., Inc.

Robinson, Kerry. Innocence, Knowledge & the Construction of Childhood: The Contradictory Nature of Sexuality & Censorship in Children's Contemporary Lives. 2012. (ENG.). 160p. (C). 130.00 *(978-0-415-60967-8(4))*; pap. 39.95 *(978-0-415-60763-6(9))* Routledge.

Robinson, Lena. Cross-Cultural Child Development for Social Workers. 2007. (ENG.). 208p. pap. 34.00 *(978-0-333-72610-5(3))* Palgrave Macmillan.

Robinson, Maria. Child Development 0-8: A Journey Through the Early Years. 2007. (ENG., Illus.). 256p. (C). pap. 45.00 *(978-0-335-22097-7(5)*, 0335220975) McGraw-Hill Education GBR. Dist: McGraw-Hill Cos., The.

—Child Development from Birth to Eight: A Journey Through the Early Years. 2008. (Illus.). 241p. 156.95 *(978-0-335-22098-4(3)*, 9780335220984, Open University Pr.) McGraw-Hill Education GBR. Dist: McGraw-Hill Cos., The.

Rodrigues, Luis Paulo. Assessing Motor Affordances in the Home Environment. 2009. 60p. pap. *(978-3-639-18687-1(7))* VDM Verlag Dr. Mueller e.K.

Roehlkepartain, Jolene L. Parenting Preschoolers with a Purpose: Caring for Your Kids & Yourself. 2006. (ENG., Illus.). 232p. pap. 13.95 *(978-1-57482-239-7(X))* Search Institute.

Rogers, Sally J. & Dawson, Geraldine. Early Start Denver Model for Young Children with Autism: Promoting Language, Learning, & Engagement. 2009. (ENG., Illus.). 297p. 75.00 *(978-1-60623-632-1(6))*; pap. 50.00 *(978-1-60623-631-4(8))* Guilford Pubns., Inc.

Roggman, Lori A., et al. Developmental Parenting: A Guide for Early Childhood Practitioners. 2008. 224p. pap. 29.95 *(978-1-55766-976-6(7))* Brookes, Paul H. Publishing Co.

Roizen, Michael F. & Oz, Mehmet C. You - Raising Your Child: The Owner's Manual from First Breath to First Grade. 2010. (ENG., Illus.). 496p. 24.99 *(978-1-4391-0948-9(6)*, Free Pr.) Free Pr.

Roth, Ilona & Rezaie, Payam, eds. Researching the Autism Spectrum: Contemporary Perspectives. 2011. (Illus.). 418p. pap. 59.00 *(978-0-521-73686-2(2))* Cambridge Univ. Pr.

Rothbart, Mary K. Becoming Who We Are: Temperament & Personality in Development. 2011. (Guilford Series on Social & Emotional Development Ser.). (ENG., Illus.). 324p. 40.00 *(978-1-60918-069-0(0))* Guilford Pubns., Inc.

Rothbart, Mary Klevjord. Becoming Who We Are: Temperament & Personality in Development. 2011. (Illus.). xi, 324p. ***(978-1-60918-070-6(4))*** Guilford Pubns., Inc.

Rowe, Stuart H. Physical Nature of the Child & How to. 2006. pap. 26.95 *(978-1-4286-3534-0(3))* Kessinger Publishing, LLC.

Rowlands, Fiona. Preschool Children & Free Play. 2008. 144p. pap. *(978-3-639-04125-5(9))* VDM Verlag Dr. Mueller e.K.

Rudd, Betty. Help Your Child Develop Emotional Literacy: The Parents' Guide to Happy Children. 2009. (Help Your Child to Succeed Ser.). (ENG., Illus.). 128p. 24.95 *(978-1-85539-467-4(7)*, Network Continuum Education) Continuum International Publishing Group, Ltd. GBR. Dist: National Bk. Network.

Rush, Dathan R. & Shelden, M'Lisa L. The Early Childhood Coaching Handbook. 2011. (Illus.). 240p. pap. 34.95 *(978-1-59857-067-0(6))* Brookes, Paul H. Publishing Co.

Rutledge, Rebecca. Toddler Years. 2007. (ENG.). 352p. mass mkt. 6.99 *(978-1-4022-0958-1(4))* Sourcebooks, Inc.

S. H. Jacob. Your Baby's Mind: How to Make the Most of the Critical First Two Years. 2009. 332p. pap. 19.99 *(978-1-4343-6936-9(6))* AuthorHouse.

Sachs, Bernard. The Normal Child & How to Keep It Normal in Mind & Morals. 2011. 116p. 39.95 ***(978-1-258-05729-9(8))*** Literary Licensing, LLC.

Safford, Kimberley, et al, eds. Small-Scale Research in Primary Schools: A Reader for Learning & Professional Development. 2010. (ENG., Illus.). 240p. pap. 36.95 *(978-0-415-58560-6(0))* Routledge.

—Small-Scale Research in Primary Schools: A Reader for Learning & Professional Development. 2010. (ENG., Illus.). 240p. 140.00 *(978-0-415-58559-0(7)*, Routledge) Taylor & Francis Group GBR. Dist: Taylor & Francis Group.

Sam Goldstein. A Different Kind of Resilience: Collected Essays, 1999-2009. 2010. 300p. pap. 21.95 *(978-1-4502-0672-3(7))* iUniverse, Inc.

Sandas, Ilyne & Siegel, Christine. The Everything Parent's Guide to Children with Anxiety: Professional Advice to Help Your Child Feel Confident, Happy, & Secure. 2008. (ENG.). 304p. pap. 14.95 *(978-1-59869-686-8(6))* Adams Media Corp.

Sandberg, Elisabeth. Normal Cognitive Development in Childhood. Spritz, Becky L., ed. 2009. (ENG., Illus.). 267p. 36.95 *(978-0-415-99183-4(8))* Routledge.

Santrock. Child Development. 12th ed. 2009. pap. *(978-0-07-128081-5(2))* McGraw-Hill Cos., The.

Santrock. Children. 12th ed. 2012. (ENG., Illus.). 640p. (C). pap. 176.67 ***(978-0-07-803512-8(0)***, 0078035120) McGraw-Hill Cos., The.

Santrock & Cram101 Textbook Reviews Staff. Child Development. 2007. 252p. per. 14.95 *(978-1-4288-2132-3(5))* Cram101 Inc.

—Children. 2007. 276p. per. 15.95 *(978-1-4288-2134-7(1))* Cram101 Inc.

Santrock, John W. Child Development. 12th ed. 2008. (ENG., Illus.). 704p. (C). 169.33 *(978-0-07-337063-7(0)*, 0073370630) McGraw-Hill Cos., The.

—Child Development: An Introduction. 13th ed. 2010. (ENG., Illus.). 648p. (C). 173.33 *(978-0-07-353208-0(8)*, 0073532088) McGraw-Hill Cos., The.

—Children. (Illus.). 9th ed. 2007. pap. *(978-0-07-310730-1(1))* 11th ed. 2009. (ENG., 704p. (C). pap. 176.67 *(978-0-07-353200-4(2)*, 0073532002) McGraw-Hill Cos., The.

Saracho, Olivia N. & Spodek, Bernard. Contemporary Perspectives on Social Learning in Early Childhood Education. 2007. (Contemporary Perspectives in Early Childhood Education Ser.). (C). (ENG.). 340p. *(978-1-59311-743-6(4))*; xx, 317p. pap. *(978-1-59311-742-9(6))* Information Age Publishing, Inc.

Saracho, Olivia N. & Spodek, Bernard. Handbook of Research on the Education of Young Children. 3rd ed. 2012. pap. ***(978-0-415-88435-8(7))*** Routledge.

Saracho, Olivia N. & Spodek, Bernard, eds. Handbook of Research on the Education of Young Children. 3rd rev. ed. 2012. (ENG., Illus.). 552p. (C). 295.00 ***(978-0-415-88434-1(9))*** Routledge.

Sarama, Julie A. Early Childhood Mathematics Education Research: Learngin Trajectories for Young Children. 2009. (Studies in Mathematical Thinking & Learning Ser.). (Illus.). 410p. pap. 70.95 *(978-0-8058-6309-3(5))* Routledge.

Sassé, Margaret. Active Baby, Healthy Brain: 135 Fun Exercises & Activities to Maximize Your Child's Brain Development from Birth Through Age 5 1/2. 2010. (ENG., Illus.). 160p. pap. 15.95 *(978-1-61519-006-5(6)*, 1615190066) Experiment LLC, The.

Sawyer, Aenor, ed. Bone Densitometry in Growing Patients. 2010. (Current Clinical Practice Ser.). (Illus.). 350p. pap. 149.00 *(978-1-61737-685-6(X)*, 161737685X) Humana Pr.

Sawyer, Aenor J., et al, eds. Bone Densitometry in Growing Patients: Guidelines for Clinical Practice. 2006. (Current Clinical Practice Ser.). (Illus.). 226p. 149.00 *(978-1-58829-634-4(2)*, 1588296342) Humana Pr.

Scheiwe, Kirsten & Willekens, Harry, eds. Childcare & Preschool Development in Europe: Institutional Perspectives. 2009. (ENG., Illus.). 288p. 100.00 *(978-0-230-53744-6(8))* Palgrave Macmillan.

Schiefelbusch, Richard L. & Schroeder, Stephen R. Doing Science & Doing Good: A History of the Bureau of Child Research & the Schiefelbusch Institute for Life Span Studies at the University of Kansas. 2006. (Illus.). 568p. *(978-1-55766-912-4(0))* Brookes, Paul H. Publishing Co.

Schirrmacher, Robert & Fox, J. Englebright. Art & Creative Development for Young Children. 6th ed. 2008. (ENG., Illus.). 416p. (C). per. 128.95 *(978-1-4283-5920-8(6))* Delmar Cengage Learning.

—Art & Creative Development for Young Children. 7th ed. 2011. (Whatrsquo;s New in Early Childhood Ser.). (ENG.). 368p. (C). pap. 134.95 *(978-0-495-91312-2(X))* Wadsworth.

Schlemmer, Phil & Schlemmer, Dori. Teaching Kids to Be Confident, Effective Communicators: Differentiated Projects to Get All Students Writing, Speaking,

& Presenting. rev. ed. 2011. (ENG.). 240p. (gr. k-6). 35.99 (978-1-57542-371-5(5)) Free Spirit Publishing, Inc.

Schlessinger, Laura & Schlessinger, L. Bad Childhood — - Good Life: How to Blossom & Thrive in Spite of an Unhappy Childhood. 2007. (ENG.). 272p. pap. 13.95 (978-0-06-057787-2(8), HarperPerennial) HarperCollins Pubs.

Schmidt, Louis & Segalowitz, Sidney J., eds. Developmental Psychophysiology. 2007. (ENG., Illus.). 484p. 107.00 (978-0-521-82106-3(1)) Cambridge Univ. Pr.

Schmukler, Anita G., et al. Ethical Practice in Child & Adolescent Analysis & Psychotherapy: Protecting Safety in a Therapeutic Environment. 2011. (ENG.). 132p. (gr. 17). 55.00 (978-0-7657-0818-2(3), Aronson, Jason) Rowman & Littlefield Publishers, Inc.

Schore, Allan & Schore, Judith Rothman. Reader's Guide to Affect Regulation & Neurobiology. 2008. 272p. 39.95 (978-0-393-70480-8(7)) Norton, W. W. & Co., Inc.

Schulz, Marc S. Strengthening Couple Relationships for Optimal Child Development: Lessons from Research & Intervention. 2009. (Illus.). 244p. 59.95 (978-1-4338-0547-9(2)) American Psychological Assn.

Schweizer, Sally. Well, I Wonder: Childhood in the Modern World: A Handbook for Parents, Carers & Teachers. 2007. (Bringing Spirit to Life Ser.). (Illus.). 224p. per. (978-1-85584-124-6(X)) Steiner, Rudolf Pr.

Sclafani, Joseph D. The Educated Parent 2: Child Rearing in the 21st Century. 2012. xviii, 248p. E-Book (978-0-313-39777-6(5), Praeger Pubs.); 2nd ed. 248p. 48.00 (978-0-313-39776-9(7), A3593C) Greenwood Publishing Group, Inc.

Screen, Robert Martin & Lee-Wilkerson, Dorian. HIV, Substance Abuse, & Communication Disorders in Children. 2007. 110p. 175.00 (978-0-7890-2711-5(9)); per. 49.95 (978-0-7890-2712-2(7)) Routledge.

Segal, Marilyn, et al. All about Child Care & Early Education: A Comprehensive Resource for Child Care Professionals. 2nd rev. ed. 2011. (ENG.). 384p. (C). pap. 47.40 (978-0-13-265545-3(4)) Allyn & Bacon, Inc.

Segal, Marilyn, et al. All about Child Care & Early Education: A Trainee's Manual for Child Care Professionals. 2nd ed. 2011. (ENG.). 288p. (C). pap. 25.00 (978-0-13-269865-8(X), Prentice Hall) Prentice Hall PTR.

Selg, Peter. The Therapeutic Eye: How Rudolf Steiner Observed Children. 2008.Tr. of therapeutische Blick. 120p. pap. 15.00 (978-0-88010-594-1(1)) SteinerBooks, Inc.

Sharman, Carole, et al. Observing Children & Young People. 4th ed. 2007. (ENG., Illus.). 184p. 29.95 (978-0-8264-9273-9(8)) Continuum International Publishing Group, Ltd. GBR. Dist: National Bk. Network.

Shaughnessy, Michael F. & Kleyn, Kinsey. Handbook of Early Childhood Education. 2012. (Education in a Competitive & Globalizing World Ser.). 238p. 140.00 (978-1-61324-154-7(2)) Nova Science Pubs., Inc.

Shek, Daniel T.L., ed. Quality of Life of Chinese People in a Changing World. 2010. (Social Indicators Research Ser.). (Illus.). vi, 198p. 79.95 (978-94-007-0223-3(X), 940070223X) Springer.

Shek, Daniel T.L., et al, eds. Positive Youth Development: Evaluation & Future Directions in a Chinese Context. 2010. (Health & Human Development (Joav Merrick - Series Editor - National Institute of Child Health & Human Development, Ministry of Social Affairs, Jerusalem) Ser.). 135.00 (978-1-60876-830-1(9)) Nova Science Pubs., Inc.

Sheppard, Heidi. Childrens Care, Learning & Development. 2006. (ENG.). cd-rom 273.00 (978-0-7487-8399-1(7)) Nelson Thornes Ltd. GBR. Dist: International Specialized Bk. Services.

Sheppard, Philip. Music Makes Your Child Smarter. (ENG.) 347p. 2008. pap. 19.95 (978-0-8256-7360-3(7), OP52723) 2007. (Illus.). 22.95 (978-0-8256-7331-3(3), OP51689) Omnibus Pr.

Sheppy, Sue. Personal, Social & Emotional Development in the Early Years Foundation Stage, 7 vols. 2009. (Practical Guidance in the EYFS Ser.). (Illus.). 176p. pap. 31.95 (978-0-415-47180-0(X)) Fulton, David Pubs. GBR. Dist: Taylor & Francis Group.

Sheridan, Mary D., et al. From Birth to Five Years: Children's Developmental Progress. 3rd rev. ed. 2007. (ENG., Illus.). 112p. pap. 19.95 (978-0-415-42365-6(1)) Routledge.

—Play in Early Childhood. 3rd rev. ed. 2011. (ENG., Illus.). 104p. 115.00 (978-0-415-57789-2(6)); pap. 24.95 (978-0-415-57790-8(X)) Routledge.

Sherman, Richard & Harris, Scott. Divorcing with Kids: An Interactive Workbook for Parents & their Children. 2007. 60p. per. 9.95 (978-0-595-44037-5(1)) iUniverse, Inc.

Shinn, Millicent Washb. Biography of A Baby. 2006. pap. 27.95 (978-1-4286-4151-8(3)) Kessinger Publishing, LLC.

Shrimali, Shyam. Child Development. 2008. 476p. (C). 45.00 (978-81-316-0181-5(1)) Rawat Pubns. IND. Dist: International Specialized Bk. Services.

Siegel, Daniel J. & Bryson, Tina Payne. The Whole-Brain Child: 12 Revolutionary Strategies to Nurture Your Child's Developing Mind, Survive Everyday Parenting Struggles, & Help Your Family Thrive. 2011. (ENG.). 192p. 24.00 (978-0-553-80791-2(9), Delacorte Pr) Random House Publishing Group.

Siegel-Maier, Karyn. Happy Baby, Happy You: 500 Ways to Nurture the Bond with Your Baby. 2009. (ENG., Illus.). 296p. pap. 10.95 (978-1-60342-141-6(6), 1603421416) Storey Publishing, LLC.

Siegler, et al. How Children Develop (Looseleaf) 3rd ed. 2010. (ENG.). 600p. (C). 87.95 (978-1-4292-6352-8(0)) Worth Pubs., Inc.

Siegler, Robert S., et al. How Children Develop. 3rd ed. 2010. (ENG., Illus.). 600p. (C). 152.95 (978-1-4292-1790-3(1)) Worth Pubs., Inc.

Silberg, Joy L. The Child Survivor: Healing Developmental Trauma & Dissociation. 2012. (ENG.). 272p. 95.00 (978-0-415-88994-0(4)); pap. 34.95 (978-0-415-88995-7(2)) Routledge.

Silvers, Carolyn Long. Cherubs & Chimps: A Year in Pre-K. 2011. 36p. pap. 16.99 (978-1-4634-3017-7(5)) AuthorHouse.

Simon, Rita James & Roorda, Rhonda M. In Their Siblings' Voices: White Non-Adopted Siblings Talk about Their Experiences Being Raised with Black & Biracial Brothers & Sisters. 2009. (ENG.). 248p. (gr. 17). pap. 24.50 (978-0-231-14851-1(8)); (Illus.). 74.50 (978-0-231-14850-4(X)) Columbia Univ. Pr.

Sinclair, Leslie V. Autism Spectrum Disorder: A Supplemental Curriculum for Life's Lessons. 2008. (ENG.). 300p. pap. 34.95 (978-1-59624-085-8(7)) Cleveland Clinic Pr.

Singh, Manjari. Introducing & Reviewing Preterm Delivery & Low Birth Weight. 2011. 72p. pap. (978-3-8443-9002-5(2)) Lambert Academic Publishing.

Siraj-Blatchford, Iram. Early Childhood Matters: Evidence from the Effective Pre-school & Primary Education Project. Melhuish, Edward C. et al, eds. 2009. (Illus.). 176p. 140.00 (978-0-415-48242-4(9)) Routledge.

Siraj-Blatchford, Iram, et al, eds. Early Childhood Matters: Evidence from the Effective Pre-school & Primary Education Project. 2009. (Illus.). 176p. pap. 47.95 (978-0-415-48243-1(7)) Routledge.

Sklarew, Bruce & Sklarew, Myra, eds. The Journey of Child Development. 2010. (ENG.). 304p. (C). 39.95 (978-0-415-87664-3(8)) Routledge.

Slater, Alan & Bremner, Gavin, eds. An Introduction to Developmental Psychology. 2nd ed. 2011. (BPS Textbooks in Psychology Ser.: 7). (ENG., Illus.). 800p. pap. 71.95 (978-1-4051-8652-0(6), Wiley-Blackwell) Wiley, John & Sons, Inc.

Slater, Alan & Lewis, Michael, eds. Introduction to Infant Development. 2nd rev. ed. 2007. (Illus.). 405p. (Orig.). (C). per. 64.95 (978-0-19-928305-7(2)) Oxford Univ. Pr., Inc.

Smidt, Sandra. The Developing Child in the 21st Century: A Global Perspective on Child Development. 2006. (Illus.). 150p. 160.00 (978-0-415-38569-5(5)); per. 34.95 (978-0-415-38570-1(9)) Routledge.

—A Guide to Early Years Practice. 3rd rev. ed. 2007. (Illus.). 189p. per. 34.95 (978-0-415-41604-7(3)) Routledge.

—Introducing Vygotsky: A Guide for Practitioners & Students in Early Years Education. 2009. (ENG., Illus.). 192p. (C). stu. ed. 150.00 (978-0-415-48055-0(8)); pap. 33.95 (978-0-415-48057-4(4)) Routledge.

Smith, Maggie & Dukes, Chris. Building Better Behaviour in the Early Years. 2009. (Hands on Guides). (Illus.). 120p. 112.00 (978-1-84787-519-8(X), B75198C); pap. 45.00 (978-1-84787-520-4(3), B75198P) SAGE Pubns., Ltd. GBR. Dist: SAGE Pubns., Inc.

Smith, Peter, et al. Children & Play: Understanding Children's Worlds. 2009. (Understanding Children's Worlds Ser.: 5). (ENG., Illus.). 272p. pap. 39.95 (978-0-631-23522-4(1), Wiley-Blackwell) Wiley, John & Sons, Inc.

Smuts, Alice. Science in the Service of Children, 1893-1935. 2008. (ENG., Illus.). 398p. pap. 32.00 (978-0-300-14435-2(0)) Yale Univ. Pr.

Smyth, Tracy & Dewar, Tammy. Raising the Village: How Individuals & Communities Can Work Together to Give Our Children a Stronger Start in Life. 2009. (978-1-926545-10-0(3)) BPS Bks.

Snow, McGaha & Cram101 Textbook Reviews Staff. Infant Development. 2007. 156p. per. 12.95 (978-1-4288-2064-7(7)) Cram101 Inc.

Sobko, Kristina. Temperament & Computer Play Patterns in Preschool Age Children. 2008. 52p. pap. (978-3-639-01390-0(5)) VDM Verlag Dr. Mueller e.K.

Solomon, Elbert D. & Dear, Martha R. Unleash the Greatness in Your Youth: 6th Grade. 2007. (Illus.). 148p. (J). (gr. 5-7). per. 19.95 (978-1-891187-17-9(1)) I Care Products & Services.

Sommer, Dion. A Childhood Psychology: Developing in a Changing World. 2012. (ENG., Illus.). 304p. (C). pap. 40.00 (978-0-230-25224-0(9)) Palgrave Macmillan.

—A Childhood Psychology: Young Children in Changing Times. 2012. (ENG., Illus.). 304p. (C). 95.00 (978-0-230-36194-2(3)) Palgrave Macmillan.

Sommer, Dion, et al. Child Perspectives & Children's Perspectives in Theory & Practice. 2010. (International perspectives on early childhood education & Development Ser.). (Illus.). xvii, 233p. 159.00 (978-90-481-3315-4(7), 9048133157) Springer.

Sparling, Joseph. Creative Curriculum Learning Games: 24-36 Months. 2007. pap. 29.34 (978-1-933021-60-7(8)) Teaching Strategies, Inc.

Spencer, Celia. A Classroom of Individuals: 50 Short Stories along with Educational Quotes. 2010. 236p. 24.99 (978-1-4490-8421-9(4)) AuthorHouse.

Speranza, Hallie & Hazen-Swann, Nancy. Hdf 113L Child Development Laboratory Course Manual. rev. ed. 2008. (ENG.). 76p. spiral bd. 58.10 (978-0-7575-3929-9(7)) Kendall Hunt Publishing Co.

Spitz, Ellen Handler. The Brightening Glance: Imagination & Childhood. 2007. (ENG.). 272p. pap. 14.95 (978-0-385-72005-2(X), Anchor) Knopf Doubleday Publishing Group.

Spodek, Bernard & Saracho, Olivia N. Contemporary Perspectives on Socialization & Social Development in Early Childhood Education. 2007. (Contemporary Perspectives in Early Childhood Education Ser.). 344p. (C). per. (978-1-59311-633-0(0)) Information Age Publishing, Inc.

—Contemporary Perspectives on Socialization & Social Development in Early Childhood Education. 2007. (Contemporary Perspectives in Early Childhood Education Ser.). (ENG.). 344p. (C). (978-1-59311-634-7(9)) Information Age Publishing, Inc.

Sprenger, Marilee B., ed. The Developing Brain: Birth to Age Eight. 2008. (Illus.). 144p. 72.95 (978-1-4129-5534-8(3), B55343C); per. 31.95 (978-1-4129-5535-5(1), B55343P) Corwin Pr.

Squires & Bricker, creator. ASQ-3 Quick Start Guide: Ages & Stages Questionnaires. 3rd ed. 2009. 4p. pap. 24.95 (978-1-59857-005-2(6)) Brookes, Paul H. Publishing Co.

Squires, Jane. ASQ-3 User's Guide. 2009. (978-1-59857-004-5(8)) Brookes, Paul H. Publishing Co.

Squires, Jane & Bricker, Diane D. Ages & Stages Questionnaires in Spanish: A Parent-Completed Child Monitoring System. 3rd ed. 2009. (SPA.). 225.00 (978-1-59857-003-8(X)) Brookes, Paul H. Publishing Co.

Sroufe, L. Alan, et al. The Development of the Person: The Minnesota Study of Risk & Adaptation from Birth to Adulthood. 2009. (ENG.). 384p. pap. 40.00 (978-1-60623-249-1(5)) Guilford Pubns., Inc.

St. Petersburg Times Staff. The Effects of Early Social-Emotional & Relationship Experience on the Development of Young Orphanage Children. 2009. (Monographs of the Society for Research in Child Development Ser.: 2). (ENG., Illus.). 300p. pap. 39.95 (978-1-4051-9599-7(1), Wiley-Blackwell) Wiley, John & Sons, Inc.

Stamm, Jill & Spencer, Paula. Bright from the Start: The Simple, Science-Backed Way to Nurture Your Child's Developing Mind, from Birth to Age 3. 2007. (ENG., Illus.). 368p. (gr. 12-18). 26.00 (978-1-59240-285-4(2), Gotham) Penguin Group (USA) Inc.

Starkman, Neal, et al. Great Places to Learn: Creating Asset-Building Schools That Help Students Succeed. 2nd ed. 2006. (ENG., Illus.). 216p. pap. 34.95 (978-1-57482-245-8(4)) Search Institute.

Steed, Elizabeth A., et al. Preschool-Wide Evaluation Tool (PreSET) Manual, Research Edition: Assessing Universal Program-Wide Positive Behavior Support in Early Childhood. 2012. (ENG.). 128p. pap. 50.00 (978-1-59857-207-0(5)) Brookes, Paul H. Publishing Co.

Steele, Robin. The Effects of Encouragement. 2010. 100p. pap. (978-3-8383-9334-6(1)) Lambert Academic Publishing.

Steinberg, Laurence, et al. Development: Infancy Through Adolescence. 2010. (Available Titles CengageNOW Ser.). (ENG.). 576p. (C). 148.95 (978-0-618-72155-9(X)) Wadsworth.

—Development: Infancy Through Adolescence. 2010. (ENG.). 576p. (C). pap. 117.95 (978-0-8400-3307-9(9)) Wadsworth.

—Steinberg's Development: Infancy Through Adolescence. 2010. (ENG.). 272p. (C). pap., pupil's gde. ed. 58.95 (978-0-618-60990-1(3)) Wadsworth.

Steinberg, Laurence D. Child Development. 2011. (Illus.). xx, 465p. pap. 34.99 (978-0-324-82960-0(4)) Wadsworth.

Steinberg, Shirley R. & Kincheloe, Joe L., eds. Kinderculture: The Corporate Construction of Childhood. 3rd ed. 2011. (ENG.). 320p. (C). pap. 35.00 (978-0-8133-4489-8(1)) Westview Pr.

Steiner, Rudolf. Educating Children Today. 2008. 81p. pap. (978-1-85584-206-9(6)) Sophia Bks.

Stern, Katie Barko. Younique: Multiples Are One of a Kind. 2010. 20p. 10.99 (978-1-4389-1598-2(6)) AuthorHouse.

Sternberg, Robert J., et al. Explorations in Giftedness. 2010. (ENG.). 320p. (C). pap. 29.99 (978-0-521-74009-8(6)); (Illus.). 90.00 (978-0-521-51854-3(7)) Cambridge Univ. Pr.

Stiles, Joan, et al. Neural Plasticity & Cognitive Development: Insights from Children with Perinatal Brain Injury, 1 vol. 2012. (ENG.). 384p. 79.99 (978-0-19-538994-4(6)) Oxford Univ. Pr., Inc.

Strauss, Michaela. Understanding Children's Drawings: Tracing the Path of Incarnation. Wehrle, Pauline, tr. from GER. 2008. (Illus.). 96p. (978-1-85584-199-4(1)) Steiner, Rudolf Pr.

Summers, Susan J. & Chazan-Cohen, Rachel, eds. Understanding Early Childhood Mental Health: A Practical Guide for Professionals. 2011. 296p. pap. 39.95 (978-1-59857-075-5(7)) Brookes, Paul H. Publishing Co.

Swim, Terri & Watson, Linda D. Infants & Toddlers: Curriculum & Teaching. 6th rev. ed. 2007. (ENG., Illus.). 496p. (C). per. 146.95 (978-1-4180-1662-3(4)) Delmar Cengage Learning.

Switzer, Daniel L. Train up a Child: Successful Parenting for the Next Generation. 2007. 158p. per. 12.99 (978-1-880226-37-7(5)) Messianic Jewish Pubs.

Talbot, James C. The Road to Positive Discipline: A Parent's Guide. 2009. 165p. pap. 14.95 (978-0-578-01058-8(5)) TNT Publishing.

Tarlov, Alvin R. & Debbink, Michelle Precourt, eds. Investing in Early Childhood Development: Evidence to Support a Movement for Educational Change. 2008. (ENG., Illus.). 272p. 89.00 (978-1-4039-7993-3(6)) Palgrave Macmillan.

Tate, Marcia L. (LaVerne). Preparing Children for Success in School & Life: 20 Ways to Enhance Your Child's Brain Power. 2011. 208p. pap. 19.95 (978-1-4129-8844-5(6), B88445P) Corwin Pr.

Taylor, Julia V. & Trice-Black, Shannon. G. I. R. L. S. , Girls in Real Life Situations, Grades 6-12 (Book & CD) Group Counseling Activities for Enhancing Social & Emotional Development. 2007. (ENG.). 240p. spiral bd. 37.95 (978-0-87822-540-8(4)) Research Pr.

Teaford, Patricia & Wheat, Jan. HELP 3-6: Activities at Home. 2nd ed. 2010. (Illus.). xvi, 294p. (978-0-89718-208-9(1)) VORT Corp.

Teaford, Patricia, et al. HELP 3-6. 2nd ed. 2010. (978-0-89718-206-5(5)); (978-0-89718-239-3(1)) VORT Corp.

—HELP 3-6: Curriculum Guide. 2nd ed. 2010. xvi, 234p. (978-0-89718-207-2(3)) VORT Corp.

Tekin, Ali. Psychological Factors of Parent Involvement. 2009. 216p. pap. (978-3-639-10935-1(X)) VDM Verlag Dr. Mueller e.K.

TExES Exam Secrets Test Prep Staff, ed. TExES (202) AAFCS Human Development & Family Studies 8-12 Exam Flashcard Study System: TExES Test Practice Questions & Review for the Texas Examinations of Educator Standards. 2011. (C). 62.99 (978-1-61403-742-2(6)) Mometrix Media LLC.

—TExES (202) AAFCS Human Development & Family Studies 8-12 Exam Secrets Study Guide: TExES Test Review for the Texas Examinations of Educator Standards. 2011. (C). 62.99 (978-1-61403-741-5(8)) Mometrix Media LLC.

Thomas, Margaret, et al. Love & Limits in & Out of Child Care: What Your Child Care Provider & Your Pediatrician Want You to Know. 2008. (ENG., Illus.). 224p. 40.00 (978-0-8018-8797-0(6)); pap. 16.95 (978-0-8018-8798-7(4)) Johns Hopkins Univ. Pr.

Thomas, Murray R. & Iding, Marie K. Explaining Conversations: A Developmental Social Exchange Theory. 2011. (ENG.). 218p. (gr. 17). 65.00 (978-0-7657-0872-4(8), Aronson, Jason) Rowman & Littlefield Publishers, Inc.

Thomas, R. Murray & Iding, Marie K. Explaining Conversations: A Developmental Social Exchange Theory. 2012. (978-0-7657-0877-9(9), Aronson, Jason) Rowman & Littlefield Publishers, Inc.

Thompson, D. Carr. How to Grow Science & Math Kids. 2010. 58p. pap. 12.00 (978-0-557-28910-3(6)) Lulu Enterprises Inc.

Thompson, Michael & Barker, Teresa. It's a Boy! Your Son's Development from Birth to Age 18. 2009. (ENG., Illus.). 480p. pap. 17.00 (978-0-345-49396-5(6), Ballantine Bks.) Random House Publishing Group.

Thompson, Patrick A. Elevating School Readiness & Child Development with the Head Start Program (with DVD) 2011. (Education in a Competitive & Globalizing World Ser.). 295.00 (978-1-61209-141-9(5)) Nova Science Pubs., Inc.

Thompson, Richard H. The Handbook of Child Life: A Guide for Pediatric Psychosocial Care. 2009. 378p. 79.95 (978-0-398-07831-7(9)); pap. 55.95 (978-0-398-07832-4(7)) Thomas, Charles C. Pub., Ltd.

Thwaites, Alan. 100 Ideas for Teaching Problem Solving, Reasoning & Numeracy. 2008. (100 Ideas for the Early Years Ser.). (ENG., Illus.). 136p. 19.95 (978-0-8264-9905-9(8)) Continuum International Publishing Group, Ltd. GBR. Dist: National Bk. Network.

Toomela, Aaro, ed. Systemic Person-Oriented Study of Child Development in Early Primary School. 2010. 298p. 72.95 (978-3-631-58764-5(3)) Lang, Peter GmbH, Europaischer Verlag der Wissenschaften DEU. Dist: Lang, Peter.

Tough, Paul. How Children Succeed: Rethinking Character & Intelligence. 2012. (ENG.). 272p. 27.00 (978-0-547-56465-4(1)) Houghton Mifflin Harcourt Trade & Reference Pubs.

Travers Simon, Joan. Mind the Gap? 2010. 312p. pap. (978-3-8383-5924-3(0)) Lambert Academic Publishing.

Trawick-Smith, Jeffrey W. & Trawick-Smith, Jeffrey. Early Childhood Development: A Multicultural Perspective. 5th ed. 2008. (ENG., Illus.). 576p. (C). pap. 105.00 (978-0-13-501646-6(0), Prentice Hall) Prentice Hall PTR.

Tyano, Sam, et al. Parenthood & Mental Health: A Bridge Between Infant & Adult Psychiatry. 2010. (World Psychiatric Association Ser.). (ENG., Illus.). 484p. 104.95 (978-0-470-74722-3(6), Wiley) Wiley, John & Sons, Inc.

Ungar, Michael. Too Safe for Their Own Good: How Risk & Responsibility Help Teens Thrive. 2007. (ENG., Illus.). 240p. pap. 18.95 (978-0-7710-8708-0(X), McClelland & Stewart) McClelland & Stewart CAN. Dist: Random Hse., Inc.

United Nations Children's Fund. The Child Care Transition: A League Table of Early Childhood Education & Care in Economically Advanced Countries. 2009. 36p. pap. 15.00 (978-88-89129-70-8(0)) United Nations Children's Fund, The (UNICEF).

Valinejad, Carol. How to Have a Happy Toddler: Responding to Your Child's Emotional Needs From 0 - 4. 2006. (ENG., Illus.). 144p. pap. 14.95 (978-0-600-61601-6(0), Hamlyn) Octopus Publishing Group GBR. Dist: Hachette Bk. Group.

Valman, Bernard & Thomas, Roslyn. ABC of the First Year. 6th ed. 2009. (ABC Ser.: 42). (ENG., Illus.). 136p. pap. 55.95 (978-1-4051-8037-5(4)) Wiley, John & Sons, Inc.

Van Hemel, Susan B. Early Childhood Assessment: Why, What, & How. Snow, Catherine E., ed. 2008. (ENG., Illus.). 520p. 59.95 (978-0-309-12465-2(4)) National Academies Pr.

van Nijnatten, Carolus. Children's agency, children's Welfare: A dialogical approach to child development, policy & Practice. 2010. 168p. 99.00 (978-1-84742-489-1(9)) Policy Pr. GBR. Dist: Chicago Distribution Ctr.

VanderVen, Karen. Promoting Positive Development in Early Childhood: An Ecological Framework. 2008. (Search Institute Series on Developmentally Attentive Community & Society Ser.). 350p. 149.00 (978-0-387-79921-6(4)) Springer.

—Promoting Positive Development in Early Childhood: Building Blocks for a Successful Start. 2010. (Search Institute Series on Developmentally Attentive Community & Society Ser.). xvi, 168p. pap. 49.95 (978-1-4419-8136-3(5), 1441981365) Springer.

Vishnyakova, Natalie F. The Abcs of Creativity, Talent, & Spirituality: Practical Psychology of Children's Potential Self-development. 2011. 618p. 34.99 (978-1-4653-4095-5(5)); pap. 23.99 (978-1-4653-4094-8(7)) Xlibris Corp.

Vitale, Judi. Babystrology: The Astrological Guide to Your Little Star. 2012. (ENG.). 224p. 15.95 (978-1-4405-3888-9(3)) Adams Media Corp.

Waldfogel, Jane. What Children Need. 2010. (Family & Public Policy Ser.). (Illus.). 288p. pap. 19.95 (978-0-674-04640-5(4)) Harvard Univ. Pr.

Waldren, Jacqueline & Kaminski, Ignacy-Marek. Learning from the Children: Childhood, Culture & Identity in a Changing World. 2012. E-Book (978-0-85745-326-6(2)) Berghahn Bks., Inc.

C

Waldren, Jacqueline & Kaminski, Ignacy-Marek, eds. Learning from the Children: Childhood, Culture & Identity in a Changing World. 2012. (ENG.). 212p. 60.00 ***(978-0-85745-325-9(4))*** Berghahn Bks., Inc.

Walker, Kathy. Play Matters: Engaging Children in Learning. 2007. 96p. pap. 59.95 incl. audio compact disk *(978-0-86431-639-4(9))* ACER Pr. AUS. Dist: International Specialized Bk. Services.

Walker, Peter. Developmental Baby Massage: Therapeutic Touch Techniques for Making Your Baby Stronger, Healthier, & Happier. 2011. (ENG., Illus.). 96p. 19.99 *(978-1-59233-483-4(0)*, 1592334830) Quayside.

Walsh, David. Smart Parenting, Smarter Kids: The One Brain Book You Need to Help Your Child Grow Brighter, Healthier, & Happier. (ENG.). 304p. 2012. pap. 15.00 ***(978-1-4391-2119-1(2))*** 2011. lib. bdg. 25.00 *(978-1-4391-2117-7(6))* Free Pr. (Free Pr.).

Wang, Sam & Aamodt, Sandra. Welcome to Your Child's Brain: How the Mind Grows from Conception to College. 2011. (ENG., Illus.). 336p. 26.00 *(978-1-59691-649-4(4))* Bloomsbury Publishing.

Wardle & Cram101 Textbook Reviews Staff. Introduction to Early Childhood Education. 2007. 116p. per. 11.95 *(978-1-4288-2044-9(2))* Cram101 Inc.

Wardle, Francis. Approaches to Early Childhood & Elementary Education. 2009. (Education in a Competitive & Globalizing World Ser.). (Illus.). xv, 456p. 79.00 *(978-1-60741-643-2(3))* Nova Science Pubs., Inc.

Warner, Penny, contrib. by. Baby Play & Learn. (Illus.). ix, 181p. *(978-0-88166-328-0(X))* Meadowbrook Pr.

Washburne, Marion Foster. Study of Child Life. 2010. (Illus.). 218p. pap. 24.75 *(978-1-142-99626-0(3))* BiblioBazaar.

Watkinson, Jane. Let's Play! Promoting Active Playgrounds. 2009. (ENG., Illus.). 120p. (gr. k-6). 26.00 *(978-0-7360-7001-0(X))* Human Kinetics Pubs.

Watts, Ann. Every Nursery Needs A Garden. 2011. (ENG., Illus.). 144p. 104.00 *(978-0-415-59130-0(9))* Routledge.

Weigle, Luther Allen. The Pupil & the Teacher. 2007. (ENG.). 216p. 39.95 *(978-0-548-01815-6(4))* Kessinger Publishing, LLC.

Weinert, Franz E. & Schneider, Wolfgang, eds. Individual Development from 3 To 12: Findings from the Munich Longitudinal Study. 2011. (ENG., Illus.). 372p. pap. 39.99 *(978-0-521-17634-7(4))* Cambridge Univ. Pr.

Weiss, Lawrence G., et al, eds. Bayley-III Clinical Use & Interpretation. 2010. (Practical Resources for the Mental Health Professional Ser.). (ENG., Illus.). 256p. 61.95 *(978-0-12-374177-6(7)*, Academic Pr.) Elsevier Science & Technology Bks.

Wellman, Glo. Guiding Their Way - Day by Day. 2008. 252p. pap. 15.95 *(978-1-4327-3647-7(7))* Outskirts Pr., Inc.

Wesley, Patricia W. & Buysse, Virginia, eds. The Quest for Quality: Promising Innovations for Early Childhood Programs. 2010. (Illus.). 224p. pap. 39.95 *(978-1-59857-086-1(2))* Brookes, Paul H. Publishing Co.

WEST-E Exam Secrets Test Prep Staff, ed. WEST-E Early Childhood Special Education (071) Secrets Study Guide: WEST-E Test Review for the Washington Educator Skills Tests-Endorsements. 2011. (C). 62.99 *(978-1-61403-764-4(7))* Mometrix Media LLC.

Whitebread, David. Developmental Psychology & Early Childhood Education: A Guide for Students & Practitioners. 2011. (Illus.). 184p. (C). 100.00 ***(978-1-4129-4712-1(X)***, B47121C); pap. 38.00 ***(978-1-4129-4713-8(8)***, B47121P) SAGE Pubns., Ltd. GBR. Dist: SAGE Pubns., Inc.

Whitehead, Marian. Supporting Language & Literacy Development in the Early Years. 2nd ed. 2009. (ENG., Illus.). 200p. pap. 45.00 *(978-0-335-23427-1(5)*, 0335234275) McGraw-Hill Education GBR. Dist: McGraw-Hill Cos., The.

Willemsen, Jan. Children's Rights & Human Development. 2010. (Illus.). 964p. pap. 189.00 *(978-94-000-0032-2(4))* Intersentia Uitgevers N.V. BEL. Dist: International Specialized Bk. Services.

Wilson, Trevor. Development Following Premature Birth. 2009. 240p. pap. *(978-3-639-13294-6(7))* VDM Verlag Dr. Mueller e.K.

Wilson, Victoria. Teach Yourself Developing Your Child's Creativity. 2009. (Teach Yourself: Parenting Ser.). (ENG.). 192p. pap. 14.95 *(978-0-07-162583-8(6)*, 0071625836) McGraw-Hill Cos., The.

Winicott, D W. The Family & Individual Development. 2006. (Routledge Classics Ser.). (ENG.). 288p. per. 24.95 *(978-0-415-40277-4(8))* Routledge.

Wittmer, Donna S. & Petersen, Sandy. Infant & Toddler Development & Responsive Program Planning: A Relationship-Based Approach. 2nd ed. 2009. (ENG.). 432p. (C). pap. 85.60 *(978-0-13-715263-6(9)*, Prentice Hall) Prentice Hall PTR.

Wolchik, Sharlene & Sandler, Irwin N., eds. Handbook of Children's Coping: Linking Theory & Intervention. 2010. (Issues in Clinical Child Psychology Ser.). 566p. pap. 149.00 *(978-1-4419-3269-3(0)*, 1441932690) Springer.

Wolraich, Mark Lee, et al. Developmental-Behavioral Pediatrics: Evidence & Practice. 2007. (ENG., Illus.). 1008p. 148.00 *(978-0-323-04025-9(X)*, Mosby) Elsevier - Health Sciences Div.

Wood, Chip. Yardsticks: Children in the Classroom Ages 4-14. 3rd ed. 2007. (Illus.). 240p. (ENG.). 28.00 *(978-1-892989-21-5(2)*, 191); pap. 18.00 *(978-1-892989-19-2(0)*, 134) Northeast Foundation for Children, Inc.

Woodacre, Emily. The First Fifty Words. 2008. 64p. pap. *(978-3-639-01777-9(3))* VDM Verlag Dr. Mueller e.K.

Woodward, Sharon. Family Child Care Curriculum: Teaching through Quality Care. 2010. (ENG.). 304p. pap. 39.95 *(978-1-60554-012-2(9))* Redleaf Pr.

Woolfolk, et al. Child & Adolescent Development, Student Value Edition. 2011. (ENG.). 592p. (C). ring bd. 84.00 ***(978-0-13-277939-5(0))*** Allyn & Bacon, Inc.

Woolfolk, Anita & Perry, Nancy E. Child & Adolescent Development. rev. ed. 2011. (ENG., Illus.). 696p. (C). pap. 135.00 *(978-0-13-702311-0(1))* Allyn & Bacon, Inc.

Woolum, Kayren. The Effects of Music in the Early Childhood Classroom. 2009. 54p. pap. *(978-3-639-18258-3(8))* VDM Verlag Dr. Mueller e.K.

World Bank Group Staff, et al. The Promise of Early Childhood Development in Latin America & the Caribbean. 2009. (Latin American Development Forum Ser.). (ENG., Illus.). 220p. pap. 40.00 *(978-0-8213-7759-8(0)*, 9780821377598) World Bank Pubns.

World Health Organization. WHO Child Growth Standards: Growth Velocity Based on Weight Length & Head Circumference - Methods & Development. 2009. (Nonserial Publication Ser.). (ENG., Illus.). 261p. pap. 60.00 *(978-92-4-154763-5(4))* World Health Organization.

World Health Organization Staff, contrib. by. International Classification of Fnctioning, Disability & Halth - Children & Youth Version ICF-CY. 2007. (Nonserial Publication). (ENG.). 349p. pap. 60.00 *(978-92-4-154732-1(4))* World Health Organization.

World Health Organization Staff & World Health Organization, Nutrition for Health and Development Staff, contrib. by. Who Child Growth Standards: Head Circumference-for-Age, Arm Circumference-For Age, Triceps Skinfold-for-Age & Subscapular Skinfold-For Age. 2007. (Nonserial Publication). (ENG.). 234p. pap. 48.00 *(978-92-4-154718-5(9))* World Health Organization.

Wortham, Sue C. Early Childhood Curriculum: Developmental Bases for Learning & Teaching. 5th ed. 2009. (ENG., Illus.). 456p. (C). pap. 116.00 *(978-0-13-715233-9(7)*, Prentice Hall) Prentice Hall PTR.

—Early Childhood Curriculum: Developmental Bases for Learning & Teaching (with MyEducationLab) 5th ed. 2010. (ENG.). 456p. (C). pap. 122.67 *(978-0-13-254543-3(8)*, Prentice Hall) Prentice Hall PTR.

Yanowitz, Karen L. & Bukatko, Danuta. Child & Adolescent Development: A Chronological Approach. 2007. (ENG.). 256p. (C). per., pupil's gde. ed. 55.95 *(978-0-618-34922-7(7)*, 308202) Wadsworth.

You, Wen. Time Well Spent: How Watching Time can Reduce the Chances of Having Overweight Children. 2008. 152p. pap. *(978-3-8364-3926-8(3))* VDM Verlag Dr. Mueller e.K.

Youell & Youell, Biddy. Understanding 8-9-Year-Olds. 2008. (ENG., Illus.). 80p. pap. *(978-1-84310-673-9(6))* Kingsley, Jessica Ltd.

Young, Gerald. Development & Causality: Neo-Piagetian Perspectives. 2011. (ENG., Illus.). xxxviii, 849p. 179.00 *(978-1-4419-9421-9(1)*, 1441994211) Springer.

Young, Mary E. Early Child Development from Measurement to Action: A Priority for Growth & Equity. Young, Mary Eming & Richardson, Linda, eds. 2007. (Stand Alone Ser.). (ENG., Illus.). 324p. per. 35.00 *(978-0-8213-7086-5(3)*, 9780821370865) World Bank Pubns.

Youth Development Staff. Afterschool Around the Globe No. 116: Policy, Practices, & Youth Voice - New Directions for Youth Development. Capece, Jen Hilmer et al, eds. 2008. (J-B MHS Single Issue Mental Health Services Ser.: 90). (ENG.). 168p. pap. 29.00 *(978-0-470-28239-7(8)*, Jossey-Bass) Wiley, John & Sons, Inc.

Zairi, Alweena. Raising Children's Learning & Performance. 2010. 336p. pap. *(978-3-8383-8657-7(4))* Lambert Academic Publishing.

Zambo, Debby & Hansen, Cory Cooper. Child Development Through the Eyes of Children's Authors: Using Picture Books to Understand Theory. 2006. (Illus.). 78p. per. 10.00 *(978-0-13-199363-1(1))* Prentice Hall PTR.

Zembar, Mary Jo & Blume, Libby Balter. Middle Childhood Development: A Contextual Approach. 2008. (ENG., Illus.). 528p. (C). per. 117.40 *(978-0-13-171881-4(9)*, Prentice Hall) Prentice Hall PTR.

Zevalkink, Jolien, et al, eds. Mentalising in Child Therapy: Guidelines for Clinical Practitioners. 2008. (Illus.). 266p. pap. 52.95 *(978-1-85575-581-9(5))* Karnac Bks. GBR. Dist: Stylus Publishing, LLC.

Zigler, Edward F. Child Care Choices. 2007. (ENG.). 272p. pap. 19.95 *(978-1-4165-7333-3(X)*, Free Pr.) Free Pr.

Zurawski, Elizabeth. Ian's Guide: Information for Children with Special Medical Needs. 2008. 73p. pap. 16.95 *(978-1-60672-014-1(7))* PublishAmerica, Inc.

Zych, Marta. The Ability of Orphanages to Meet Child Development Needs. 2011. 100p. pap. ***(978-3-8433-8335-6(9))*** Lambert Academic Publishing.

CHILD DEVELOPMENT—FEDERAL AID

see Federal Aid to Child Development

CHILD DEVELOPMENT DEVIATIONS

see also Developmentally Disabled Children

Augustyn, Marilyn C., et al, eds. The Zuckerman Parker Handbook of Developmental & Behavioral Pediatrics for Primary Care. 3rd rev. ed. 2010. (ENG., Illus.). 560p. pap. 74.99 *(978-1-60831-914-5(8))* Lippincott Williams & Wilkins.

Batshaw, Mark L., et al, eds. Children with Disabilities, Sixth Edition. 6th ed. 2007. (ENG., Illus.). 792p. 79.95 *(978-1-55766-858-5(2))* Brookes, Paul H. Publishing Co.

Carey, William B., et al. Developmental-Behavioral Pediatrics: Expert Consult - Online & Print. 4th ed. 2009. (ENG., Illus.). 1060p. 194.00 *(978-1-4160-3370-7(X)*, Saunders) Elsevier - Health Sciences Div.

Cline, Foster W. & Greene, Lisa C. Parenting Children with Health Issues: Essential Tools, Tips, & Tactics for Raising Kids with Chronic Illness, Medical Conditions & Special Healthcare Needs. 2007. (Illus.). 384p. per. 24.95 *(978-1-930429-89-5(4))* Love & Logic Institute, Inc.

Coleman, Mary & Gillberg, Christopher. The Autisms, 1 vol. 4th ed. 2011. (ENG., Illus.). 432p. 115.00 ***(978-0-19-973212-8(4))*** Oxford Univ. Pr., Inc.

Cram101 Textbook Reviews & Cram101 Textbook Reviews. Outlines & Highlights for Understanding Physical, Health, & Mulitiple Disabilities by Kathryn Wolff Heller, Paul a Alberto, Paula E Forney, Isbn. 2011. 268p. pap. 31.95 ***(978-1-61490-535-6(5))*** Cram101 Inc.

Diamant, Rachel B. Positioning for Play: Interactive Activities to Enhance Movement & Sensory Exploration. 2nd ed. 2009. 67.00 *(978-1-4164-0431-6(7))* PRO-ED, Inc.

Lipina, Sebastián J. & Colombo, Jorge A. Poverty & Brain Development During Childhood: An Approach from Cognitive Psychology & Neuroscience. 2009. (Illus.). 184p. 49.95 *(978-1-4338-0445-8(X))* American Psychological Assn.

McCarthy, Jenny & Kartzinel, Jerry. Healing & Preventing Autism: A Complete Guide. 2010. (ENG., Illus.). 416p. (gr. 12-18). 16.00 *(978-0-452-29592-6(0)*, Plume) Penguin Group (USA) Inc.

Odom, Samuel L., et al, eds. Handbook of Developmental Disabilities. 2007. (ENG., Illus.). 654p. (gr. -1). 85.00 *(978-1-59385-485-0(4))* Guilford Pubns., Inc.

Reichow, Brian, et al, eds. Evidence-Based Practices & Treatments for Children with Autism. 2010. xviii, 408p. 179.00 *(978-1-4419-6973-6(X)*, 144196973X) Springer.

Ron, Mayra. Diary of a Crazy Woman: One Woman's Fight to Help Her Son with Autism Find a Place in the World. 2009. (Illus.). 163p. pap. 14.99 *(978-1-60696-430-9(5))* Tate Publishing & Enterprises, LLC.

Sears, Robert. The Autism Book: What Every Parent Needs to Know about Early Detection, Treatment, Recovery, & Prevention. 2010. (ENG.). 416p. pap. 14.99 *(978-0-316-04280-2(3))* Little Brown & Co.

Siri, Ken & Lyons, Tony. Cutting-Edge Therapies for Autism 2011-2012. 2011. (ENG., Illus.). 528p. pap. 17.95 *(978-1-61608-252-9(6)*, 608252) Skyhorse Publishing Co., Inc.

Squires & Bricker, creator. ASQ-3 Quick Start Guide: Ages & Stages Questionnaires. 3rd ed. 2009. 4p. pap. 24.95 *(978-1-59857-005-2(6))* Brookes, Paul H. Publishing Co.

Squires, Jane. ASQ-3 User's Guide. 2009. *(978-1-59857-004-5(8))* Brookes, Paul H. Publishing Co.

Squires, Jane & Bricker, Diane D. Ages & Stages Questionnaires in Spanish: A Parent-Completed Child Monitoring System. 3rd ed. 2009. (SPA.). 225.00 *(978-1-59857-003-8(X))* Brookes, Paul H. Publishing Co.

Williams, Keith E. & Foxx, Richard M. Eating Problems of Children with Autism Spectrum Disorders & Developmental Disabilities: Interventions for Professionals & Parents. 2008. xv, 204p. 55.00 *(978-1-4164-0248-0(9))* PRO-ED, Inc.

Woliver, Robbie. Alphabet Kids - From ADD to Zellweger Syndrome: A Guide to Developmental, Neurobiological & Psychological Disorders for Parents & Professionals. 2008. (ENG.). 384p. *(978-1-84310-880-1(1))* Kingsley, Jessica Ltd.

CHILD DISCIPLINE

see Discipline of Children

CHILD EGO STATE

see Inner Child

CHILD EMOTIONAL ABUSE

see Psychological Child Abuse

CHILD ENDOWMENT

see Family Allowances

CHILD HEALTH

see Child Welfare; Children—Health and Hygiene

CHILD HEALTH SERVICES

see also Immunization of Children

Ajala, Aderemi Suleiman. Rural Health Provisioning: Socio-cultural Factors Influencing Maternal & Child Health Care in Osun State, Nigeria. 2009. 106p. 28.95 *(978-3-631-59023-2(7))* Lang, Peter GmbH, Europaischer Verlag der Wissenschaften DEU. Dist: Lang, Peter.

Akinsola, Folasade. Low Vision in Children & Educational Services in Developing Country. 2010. 84p. pap. *(978-3-639-21559-5(1))* VDM Verlag Dr. Mueller e.K.

Allen, Kathryn G. Children's Health Insurance: States' SCHIP Enrollment & Spending Experiences & Considerations for Reauthorization. 2007. (Illus.). 44p. (C). pap. 20.00 *(978-1-4223-1560-6(6))* DIANE Publishing Co.

American Academy of Pediatrics Staff & American College of Emergency Physicians Staff, contrib. by. APLS: The Pediatric Emergency Medicine Resource. 5th ed. 2012. ***(978-1-4496-2445-3(6))*** Jones & Bartlett Publishers.

Arokiasamy, P. & Pradhan, J. Demand & Supply Aspects: Of Maternal & Child Health Care Services Utilization in India. 2011. 104p. pap. ***(978-3-639-32621-5(0))*** VDM Verlag Dr. Mueller e.K.

Austin, Michael J., ed. Evidence for Child Welfare Practice. 2009. (ENG., Illus.). 125.00 *(978-0-7890-3814-2(5))*; pap. 45.95 *(978-0-7890-3815-9(3))* Routledge.

Bailey, Judith A. & Cottom, Robert I. Programs & Interventions for Maltreated Children & Families at Risk. Rubin, Allen, ed. 2011. (Clinician's Guide to Evidence-Based Practice Ser.: 5). (ENG.). 354p. pap. 55.00 *(978-0-470-89063-9(0)*, Wiley) Wiley, John & Sons, Inc.

Barnhart. Foundations in Neonatal & Pediatric Respitory Care. rev. ed. 2011. pap. 72.95 *(978-0-7637-7827-9(3))* Jones & Bartlett Learning, LLC.

Benaroch, Roy. A Guide to Getting the Best Health Care for Your Child, 1 vol. 2007. (Praeger Series on Contemporary Health & Living Ser.). 192p. 44.95 *(978-0-275-99346-7(9)*, C9346, Praeger Pubs.) Greenwood Publishing Group, Inc.

Bennett, John C. Orthodontic Management of Uncrowded Class II Division One Malocclusion in Children. 2006. (ENG., Illus.). 153p. 133.00 *(978-0-323-05317-4(3)*, Mosby) Elsevier - Health Sciences Div.

Berkelhamer, Jay E. & Duarte, Charles. Emerging Government Issues with Medicaid & Children's Health: Leading Children's Health Experts on Improving Cost & Access to Health Care, Working with Advocacy Groups & Government Officials, & Campaigning for Health Care Reform (Inside the Minds) 2009. 124p. pap. *(978-0-314-19946-1(2))* Aspatore Bks.

Berman, Stephen. Getting It Right for Children: Stories of Pediatric Care & Advocacy. 2007. (ENG., Illus.). 256p. per. 30.00 *(978-1-58110-286-4(0))* American Academy of Pediatrics.

Bharj, Kuldip & Phillips, Mari. The Policy Context of Midwifery & Maternity Services. 2012. (ENG.). 192p. (C). pap. 39.95 *(978-0-415-67860-5(9))*; 130.00 *(978-0-415-67460-7(3))* Routledge.

Bick, Debra, et al. Postnatal Care. 2nd ed. 2008. (ENG., Illus.). 256p. pap. 56.95 *(978-0-443-10400-8(X)*, Churchill Livingstone) Elsevier - Health Sciences Div.

Bick, Debra, et al. Postnatal Care Text & Evolve eBooks Package. 2nd ed. 2011. (ENG., Illus.). 256p. (C). pap. 64.95 ***(978-0-7020-4117-4(3)***, Churchill Livingstone) Elsevier - Health Sciences Div.

Blair, Mitch, et al. Child Public Health. 2nd ed. 2010. (ENG., Illus.). 310p. (Orig.). pap. 59.95 *(978-0-19-954750-0(5))* Oxford Univ. Pr., Inc.

Block, Jennifer. Pushed: The Painful Truth about Childbirth & Modern Maternity Care. 2008. (ENG.). 344p. pap. 16.00 *(978-0-7382-1166-4(4))* Da Capo Pr., Inc.

Breastfeeding & Diseases. 2008. 144p. pap. 24.95 *(978-0-9815257-1-6(7))* Hale Publishing.

Briese, Volker, ed. Obesity & Pregnancy. 2010. (Pregnancy & Infants: Medical, Psychological & Social Issues Ser.). (Illus.). 192p. 49.00 *(978-1-60876-111-1(8))* Nova Science Pubs., Inc.

Brooks, Christie. Our Heartbreaking Choices. 2008. 420p. pap. 26.95 *(978-0-595-53047-2(8))* iUniverse, Inc.

Brown, J. Betrayal of Minds. 2007. (ENG.). 100p. per. *(978-1-84747-481-0(0))* Chipmunkapublishing.

Cartlidge, Patrick H. T., ed. Ethical, Legal & Social Aspects of Child Healthcare. 2007. (ENG., Illus.). 224p. pap. 69.95 *(978-0-08-044682-0(5)*, Elsevier) Elsevier - Health Sciences Div.

Chambers, Christine T. & Finley, G. Allen, eds. Pediatric Pain: A Clinical Casebook. 2008. (Contemporary Pain Medicine Ser.). (Illus.). 300p. 89.50 *(978-1-60327-050-2(7)*, 1603270507) Springer.

Chandra, Anita & Gresenz, Carole Roan. Health & Health Care among District of Columbia Youth. 2009. (Illus.). 216p. pap. 46.00 *(978-0-8330-4805-9(8)*, tr-751) RAND Corp., The.

Chapman, Rachel R. Family Secrets: Risking Reproduction in Central Mozambique. 2010. (ENG.). 280p. pap. 34.95 *(978-0-8265-1718-0(8))*; lib. bdg. 79.95 *(978-0-8265-1717-3(X))* Vanderbilt Univ. Pr.

Cheng, Shirley. Parental Rights in Children's Medical Care - Where Is Our Freedom to Say No? A Look at the Injustice of the American Medical System. 2008. 161p. pap. 14.97 *(978-0-615-14994-3(4))* Dance With Your Heart! Publishing.

Christensen, Randy. Ask Me Why I Hurt: The Kids Nobody Wants & the Doctor Who Heals Them. 2011. 288p. 24.99 *(978-0-307-71899-0(9))*; (ENG.). pap. 19.00 ***(978-0-307-71901-0(4))*** Broadway Bks.

Clements, Paul T. & Burgess, Ann W. Nursing Approach to the Evaluation of Child Maltreatment 2E. 2nd ed. 2012. (ENG., Illus.). pap. 75.00 *(978-1-878060-17-4(1))* STM Learning, Inc.

Comacchio, Cynthia R., et al. Healing the World's Children: Interdisciplinary Perspectives on Child Health in the Twentieth Century. 2008. (McGill-Queen's/Associated Medical Services Studies in the History of Medicine, H Ser.). (ENG., Illus.). 324p. *(978-0-7735-3399-8(0))* McGill-Queen's Univ. Pr.

Committee on Pediatric Health and Health Care Quality Measures, et al. Child & Adolescent Health & Health Care Quality: Measuring What Matters. 2011. (ENG.). 320p. pap. 50.00 ***(978-0-309-18623-0(4))*** National Academies Pr.

Committee on Strengthening Benefit-Cost Methodology for the Evaluation of Early Childhood Interventions, et al. Benefit-Cost Analysis for Early Childhood Interventions: Workshop Summary. 2009. (ENG.). 88p. pap. 21.00 *(978-0-309-14563-3(5))* National Academies Pr.

Covering Uninsured Children: The Impact of the August 17th CHIP Directive: Hearing Before the Subcommittee on Health Care of the Committee on Finance, United States Senate, One Hundred Tenth Congress, Second Session, April 9, 2008. 2008. (Illus.). iii, 146p. *(978-0-16-085855-0(0)*, 552-070-41067-8) United States Government Printing Office.

Cram101 Textbook Reviews & Cram101 Textbook Reviews. Outlines & Highlights for Preventing Childhood Obesity: Evidence Policy & Practice by Elizabeth Waters, ISBN. 2011. 196p. pap. 30.95 ***(978-1-61461-089-2(4))*** Cram101 Inc.

Cram101 Textbook Reviews Staff. Outlines & Highlights for Olds' Maternal-Newborn Nursing & Women's Health Across the Lifespan by Davidson Isbn. 2008. 200p. pap. 13.95 *(978-1-4288-5877-0(6))* Cram101 Inc.

Davies, Joanna H. & Hassell, Lynda L. Children in Intensive Care: A Survival Guide. 2nd rev. ed. 2007. (ENG., Illus.). 296p. vinyl bd. 39.95 *(978-0-443-10023-9(3)*, Churchill Livingstone) Elsevier - Health Sciences Div.

Davis-Floyd, Robbie. Birth Models That Work. Davis-Floyd, Robbie E. et al, eds. 2009. (ENG., Illus.). 320p. pap. 29.95 *(978-0-520-25891-4(6))* Univ. of California Pr.

Davis-Floyd, Robbie E., et al, eds. Birth Models That Work. 2009. (ENG., Illus.). 320p. 65.00 *(978-0-520-24863-2(5))* Univ. of California Pr.

Dempsey, Sharon. Extreme Parenting: Parenting Your Child with a Chronic Illness. 2008. (ENG.). 176p. pap. *(978-1-84310-619-7(1))* Kingsley, Jessica Ltd.

Department of Health & Human Services Fiscal Year 2008 Budget Request: Hearing Before the Committee on the Budget, House of Representatives, One Hundred Tenth Congress, First Session, Hearing Held in Washington, DC, February 13, 2007. 2007. iii, 52p. *(978-0-16-079912-9(0),* 552-070-36749-7) United States Government Printing Office.
Dorland Health, creator. The National Directory of Children, Youth & Families Services: The Professionals' Reference. 2008. (National Directory of Children, Youth & Families Services Ser.). 1036p. pap. 199.00 *(978-1-885461-26-1(7))* Contexo Media.
Douglas, Jo, et al. A Community Health Approach to the Assessment of Infants & Their Parents: The Care Programme. 2006. (ENG., Illus.). 234p. 150.00 *(978-0-470-09251-4(3),* Wiley) Wiley, John & Sons, Inc.
Dueger, Caroline & O'Callahan, Cliff. Working in International Child Health. 2nd ed. 2008. (ENG., Illus.). 275p. pap. 39.95 ***(978-1-58110-332-8(8))*** American Academy of Pediatrics.
Duncan, MD, FAAP, Paula. Bright Futures, Kit. Hagan, Jr., MD, FAAP, Joseph F & Shaw, RN, MPH, EdD, Judith S, eds. 3rd ed. 2007. (ENG.). 100p. cd-rom 325.00 ***(978-1-58110-225-3(9))*** American Academy of Pediatrics.
Duncan, Michael, ed. Reviews in Pediatric Exercise Science. 2012. (Pediatrics - Laboratory & Clinical Research/ Sports & Athletics Ser.). 274p. 165.00 ***(978-1-61470-978-7(5))*** Nova Science Pubs., Inc.
Ehiri, John, ed. Maternal & Child Health: Global Challenges, Programs, & Policies. 2009. (ENG., Illus.). xii, 688p. 99.00 *(978-0-387-89244-3(3),* 0387892443) Springer.
Ehrlich, Paul & Chiaramonte, Larry. Asthma Allergies Children: A Parent's Guide. 2010. 311p. pap. 18.95 *(978-0-9843832-0-7(4))* Third Avenue Bks.
Ejeta, Bekele Ababeye. Assessment of Factors Affecting Child Health Services Utilization. 2010. 108p. pap. *(978-3-639-26248-3(4))* VDM Verlag Dr. Mueller e.K.
Elliston, Sarah. Best Interests of the Child in Healthcare. 2006. (Biomedical Law & Ethics Library). 328p. 200.00 *(978-1-84472-043-9(8),* Routledge) Taylor & Francis Group GBR. Dist: Taylor & Francis Group.
—The Best Interests of the Child in Healthcare. 2007. (Biomedical Law & Ethics Library). 308p. per. 57.50 *(978-1-84472-042-2(X),* Routledge) Taylor & Francis Group GBR. Dist: Taylor & Francis Group.
Ewing, Mary T. State Children's Health Insurance Program (SCHIP) Ewing, Mary T., ed. 2008. 186p. 69.00 *(978-1-60456-333-7(8))* Nova Science Pubs., Inc.
Falola, Toyin & Heaton, Matthew M. Endangered Bodies: Women, Children, & Health in Africa. 2008. (Illus.). xii, 291p. *(978-1-59221-500-3(9));* 300p. pap. *(978-1-59221-501-0(7))* Africa World Pr.
Farooqi, Aijaz. School-Age Outcomes of Children Born at the Limit of Viability - Functional Limitations, Growth, Mental Health, Social Compentencies, Executive Functi. 2008. 104p. pap. *(978-3-639-05575-7(6))* VDM Verlag Dr. Mueller e.K.
Fergusson, Diana. Clinical Assessment & Monitoring in Children. 2008. (Essential Clinical Skills for Nurses Ser.). (ENG., Illus.). 352p. pap. 45.99 *(978-1-4051-3338-8(4),* Wiley-Blackwell) Wiley, John & Sons, Inc.
Finley, G. Allen, ed. Bringing Pain Relief to Children: Treatment Approaches. 2010. (ENG., Illus.). 256p. pap. 94.00 *(978-1-61737-682-5(5),* 1617376825) Humana Pr.
Fleming, Jennie & Boeck, Thilo, eds. Involving Children & Young People in Health & Social Care Research. 2012. (ENG.). 272p. (C). 145.00 *(978-0-415-66349-6(0))* Routledge.
Fordyce, Lauren & Maraesa, Aminata, eds. Risk, Reproduction, & Narratives of Experience. 2012. (ENG.). 256p. 69.95 ***(978-0-8265-1819-4(2));*** pap. 29.95 ***(978-0-8265-1820-0(6))*** Vanderbilt Univ. Pr.
The Future of CHIP: Improving the Health of America's Children: Hearing Before the Committee on Finance, United States Senate, One Hundred Tenth Congress, First Session, February 1, 2007. 2007. (Illus.). iv, 256p. *(978-0-16-080780-0(8),* 552-070-37398-5) United States Government Printing Office.
Giardino, Eileen R. & Giardino, Angelo P. Nursing Approach to Child Maltreatment Curriculum: A Training Curriculum. 2012. (ENG., Illus.). spiral bd. 200.00 *(978-1-878060-72-3(4))* STM Learning, Inc.
Golden, Janet & Weisz, George. Healing the World's Children: Interdisciplinary Perspectives on Child Health in the Twentieth Century. Comacchio, Cynthia, ed. 2008. (McGill-Queen's/Associated Medical Services Studies in the History of Medicine, H Ser.). (ENG., Illus.). 324p. pap. *(978-0-7735-3400-1(8))* McGill-Queen's Univ. Pr.
Gulati, S. C., ed. Population, Health & Human Resources in India's Development. 2011. (ENG., Illus.). 626p. 89.95 *(978-81-7188-785-9(6))* Academic Foundation IND. Dist: Independent Pubs. Group.
Gupta, Palak & Singh, Kalyani. Maternal Perception & Feeding Practices: Effect on Preschooler's Weight. 2011. 140p. pap. ***(978-3-8443-0376-6(6))*** Lambert Academic Publishing.
Hagan, Joseph F., Jr. Bright Futures: Guidelines for Health Supervision of Infants, Children, & Adolescents. Shaw, Judith & Duncan, Paula M., eds. 3rd ed. 2007. (ENG., Illus.). 83p. spiral bd. 14.95 *(978-1-58110-224-6(0))* American Academy of Pediatrics.
Hagan, Joseph F., Jr. & Duncan, Paula M. Bright Futures: Guidelines for Health Supervision of Infants, Children, & Adolescents. Shaw, Judith, ed. 3rd ed. 2007. (ENG., Illus.). 650p. pap. 64.95 *(978-1-58110-223-9(2))* American Academy of Pediatrics.
Hagger, Lynn. The Child as Vulnerable Patient: Protection & Empowerment. 2009. (Medical Law & Ethics Ser.). 268p. 124.95 *(978-0-7546-7252-4(2))* Ashgate Publishing Co.
Hall, David M. B. & Elliman, David. Health for All Children. 4th rev. ed. 2006. (ENG., Illus.). 424p. (Orig.). pap. 49.95 *(978-0-19-857084-4(8))* Oxford Univ. Pr., Inc.
Handler, Arden, et al, eds. Reducing Racial/Ethnic Disparities in Reproductive & Perinatal Outcomes: The Evidence for Population-Based Intervention. 2010. (ENG.). xx, 680p. 179.00 *(978-1-4419-1498-9(6),* 1441914986) Springer.
Harrison, Kelsey A. Sowing the Seeds of Safe Motherhood in Sub-Saharan Afric. 2010. (Illus.). 494p. *(978-1-906704-78-0(3))* Adonis & Abbey Publishers Ltd.
Health Care for Children in Foster Care: Hearing Before the Subcommittee on Income Security & Family Support of the Committee on Ways & Means, U.S. House of Representatives, One Hundred Tenth Congress, First Session, July 19, 2007. 2008. (Illus.). iii, 89p. *(978-0-16-082173-8(8),* 552-070-38308-5) United States Government Printing Office.
Heymann, Jody, et al, eds. Protecting Childhood in the AIDS Pandemic: Finding Solutions that Work. 1 vol. 2012. (ENG., Illus.). 336p. 55.00 ***(978-0-19-976512-6(X))*** Oxford Univ. Pr., Inc.
Hofmeyr, G. Justus, et al. Pregnancy & Childbirth. 2008. (Wiley Cochrane Series?? Ser.). (ENG.). 446p. pap. 72.00 *(978-0-470-51845-8(6),* Wiley) Wiley, John & Sons, Inc.
Houston, Michael & Sarvet, Barry D. Leadership & Management Core Competencies, an Issue of Child & Adolescent Psychiatric Clinics of North America. 2010. (Clinics: Internal Medicine Ser.: 19-1). (ENG., Illus.). xvii, 182p. 105.00 *(978-1-4377-1802-7(7),* Saunders) Elsevier - Health Sciences Div.
H.R. 5998, the Protecting Children's Health Coverage ACT of 2008: Hearing Before the Subcommittee on Health of the Committee on Energy & Commerce, House of Representatives, One Hundred Tenth Congress, Second Session, May 15, 2008. 2008. (Illus.). v, 129p. *(978-0-16-086866-5(1),* 552-070-41778-8) United States Government Printing Office.
Hussein, Julia, et al. Maternal & Perinatal Health in Developing Countries. 2012. (Illus.). 256p. 160.00 ***(978-1-84593-745-4(7))*** CABI GBR. Dist: Stylus Publishing, LLC.
Improving Children's Health: Strengthening Federal Child Nutrition Programs: Hearing Before the Committee on Education & Labor, U.S. House of Representatives, One Hundred Eleventh Congress, Second Session, Hearing Held in Washington, DC, March 2, 2010. 2010. (Illus.). iii, 57p. ***(978-0-16-087126-9(3),*** 552-070-41971-3) United States Government Printing Office.
Kamat, Deepak M. & Fischer, Philip R., eds. Textbook of Global Child Health. 2011. (ENG., Illus.). 856p. 59.95 ***(978-1-58110-523-0(1))*** American Academy of Pediatrics.
Kashyap, Aruna. No Tally of the Anguish: Accountability in Maternal Health Care in India. 2009. (Illus.). 150p. pap. ***(978-1-56432-547-1(4),*** Library of Congress — New Delhi Overseas Office) Human Rights Watch.
Kelsey, Janet & McEwing, Gillian. Clinical Skills in Child Health Practice. 2008. (ENG., Illus.). 448p. pap. 61.95 *(978-0-443-10340-7(2),* Churchill Livingstone) Elsevier - Health Sciences Div.
Kennedy, Margaret B., et al. Intrapartum Management Modules: A Perinatal Education Program. 4th rev. ed. 2008. (ENG., Illus.). 784p. pap. 62.99 *(978-0-7817-8168-8(X))* Lippincott Williams & Wilkins.
Kibel, Maurice, et al. Child Health for All. 4th ed. 2008. (ENG., Illus.). 576p. pap. 69.50 *(978-0-19-576495-6(1))* Oxford Univ. Pr., Inc.
Kilham, Henry, et al. Paediatrics Manual the Children's Hospital at Westmead Handbook. 2nd ed. 2009. (ENG.). 600p. pap. 49.95 *(978-0-07-027189-0(5),* 0070271895) McGraw-Hill Australia AUS. Dist: McGraw-Hill Cos., The.
Koplan, Jeffrey. Progress in Preventing Childhood Obesity: How Do We Measure Up? 2007. (ENG., Illus.). 494p. pap. 55.00 *(978-0-309-10208-7(1))* National Academies Pr.
Kotch, Jonathan B. Maternal & Child Health. 3rd ed. 2012. 552p. pap. 86.95 ***(978-1-4496-1159-0(1))*** Jones & Bartlett Learning, LLC.
Kronenfeld, Jennie J. Expansion of Publicly Funded Health Insurance in the United States: The Children's Health Insurance Program & Its Implications. 2006. (ENG., Illus.). 168p. 62.99 *(978-0-7391-0829-1(8))* Lexington Bks.
Ladewig, Patricia A., et al. Clinical Handbook for Contemporary Maternal-Newborn Nursing. 7th ed. 2009. (ENG., Illus.). 432p. (C). pap. 31.95 *(978-0-13-504725-5(0),* Prentice Hall) Prentice Hall PTR.
Larson, Jim & Lochman, John E. Helping Schoolchildren Cope with Anger, Second Edition: A Cognitive-Behavioral Intervention. 2nd ed. 2010. (ENG., Illus.). 222p. (gr. 3-6). pap. 30.00 *(978-1-60623-973-5(2))* Guilford Pubns., Inc.
Lederman, Regina & Weis, Karen. Psychosocial Adaptation to Pregnancy: Seven Dimensions of Maternal Role Development. 3rd ed. 2009. (ENG., Illus.). xv, 340p. 179.00 *(978-1-4419-0287-0(2),* 1441902872) Springer.
London, Marcia L., et al. Clinical Handbook for Olds' Maternal-Newborn Nursing. 9th ed. 2011. (ENG.). 432p. (C). pap. 26.00 *(978-0-13-211849-1(1),* Prentice Hall) Prentice Hall PTR.
Lyte, Geraldine & Hughes, Jane, eds. Developing Nursing Practice with Children & Young People. 2008. (ENG., Illus.). 256p. pap. 66.99 *(978-1-4051-5605-9(8),* Wiley-Blackwell) Wiley, John & Sons, Inc.
Maher, Dustin. Fit Moms for Life: How to Have Endless Energy to Out Play Your Kids. 2011. (ENG.). 204p. pap. 19.95 ***(978-1-61448-080-8(X))*** Morgan James Publishing.
Mars, Laura, ed. Complete Directory for Pediatric Disorders. 2011. 2500p. pap. 165.00 *(978-1-59237-742-8(4))* Grey Hse. Publishing.
McIntosh, Tania. A Social History of Maternity & Childbirth. 2012. (ENG., Illus.). 200p. (C). pap. 44.95 ***(978-0-415-56163-1(9))*** Routledge.
—A Social History of Maternity & Childbirth: Key Themes in Maternity Care. 2012. E-Book ***(978-0-203-12422-2(7))*** Routledge.
McNany, Dolores H., ed. Angels in Disguise: Stories from America's School Nurses. 2011. 164p. 25.95 ***(978-1-4620-0627-4(2));*** pap. 15.95 ***(978-1-4620-0626-7(4))*** iUniverse, Inc.
Mekonnen, Aemtsehay. Women Autonomy & Maternal. 2010. 72p. pap. *(978-3-639-23735-1(8))* VDM Verlag Dr. Mueller e.K.
Montanti, Elissa & Haupt, Jennifer. I'll Stand by You: One Woman's Mission to Heal the Children of the World. 2012. (ENG., Illus.). 288p. (gr. 12). 25.95 ***(978-0-525-95295-4(0),*** Dutton Adult) Penguin Group (USA) Inc.
Mosley, W. Henry & Chen, Lincoln C. Child Survival: Strategies for Research. 2008. (ENG., Illus.). 412p. pap. 50.00 *(978-0-521-07297-7(2))* Cambridge Univ. Pr.
Murkoff, Heidi, et al. Que Puedes Esperar Cuando Se Esta Esperando. 4th ed. 2010. (SPA & ENG., Illus.). 676p. pap. 15.95 *(978-0-7611-5738-0(7),* 0761157387) Workman Publishing Co., Inc.
Murray, Sharon Smith & McKinney, Emily Slone. Foundations of Maternal-Newborn & Women's Health Nursing. 5th ed. 2009. (ENG., Illus.). 1056p. (C). 91.95 *(978-1-4377-0259-0(7),* Saunders) Elsevier - Health Sciences Div.
—Foundations of Maternal-Newborn & Women's Health Nursing - Text & Virtual Clinical Excursions 3. 0 Package. 5th ed. 2009. (ENG.). (C). 126.95 *(978-1-4377-1538-5(9),* Saunders) Elsevier - Health Sciences Div.
National Directory of Children Youth & Families Services, creator. The National Directory of Children, Youth, & Families Services: The Professionals' Reference. 2007. (National Directory of Children, Youth & Families Services Ser.). 1438p. per. 179.00 *(978-1-885461-18-6(6))* National Directory CYF.
Nurse, Sharon. Maternal Neonatal Care. 2009. (Incredibly Easy! Ser.). (ENG., Illus.). 544p. pap. 42.95 *(978-1-901831-08-5(6))* Lippincott Williams & Wilkins.
Oberg, Cecilia. Children's Health in a Traditional Society. 2009. 87.00 *(978-1-60692-769-4(8))* Nova Science Pubs., Inc.
O'Luanaigh, Padraig & Carlson, Cindy. Midwifery & Public Health - Text & E-Book Package: Future Directions & New Opportunities. 2011. (ENG., Illus.). 286p. pap. 80.95 ***(978-0-7020-3569-2(6),*** Churchill Livingstone) Elsevier - Health Sciences Div.
Palfrey, Judith S. Child Health in America: Making a Difference Through Advocacy. 2006. (ENG., Illus.). 312p. (gr. 17). per. 32.00 *(978-0-8018-8453-5(5))* Johns Hopkins Univ. Pr.
—Child Health in America: Making a Difference Through Advocacy. 2006. (ENG., Illus.). 312p. (gr. 17). 67.00 *(978-0-8018-8452-8(7))* Johns Hopkins Univ. Pr.
Pan American Health Organization. Social Protection in Health Schemes for Mother Newborn & Child Populations: Lessons learned in Latin American Countries. 2009. (PAHO Occasional Publication Ser.). 177p. pap. 20.00 *(978-92-75-12841-1(3))* Pan American Health Organization (PAHO).
Pathak, Praveen Kumar. Wealth Inequalities & Use of Reproductive & Child Health Services. 2010. 164p. pap. *(978-3-639-25895-0(9))* VDM Verlag Dr. Mueller e.K.
Peate, Ian & Whiting, Lisa, eds. Caring for Children & Families. 2006. (Wiley Series in Nursing Ser.: 2). (ENG., Illus.). 316p. per. 66.99 *(978-0-470-01970-2(0),* Wiley) Wiley, John & Sons, Inc.
Perry, Deborah F., et al, eds. Social & Emotional Health in Early Childhood: Building Bridges Between Services & Systems. 2007. (Systems of Care for Children's Mental Health Ser.: 7). (Illus.). 404p. per. 39.95 *(978-1-55766-782-3(9))* Brookes, Paul H. Publishing Co.
Peters, Shawn Francis. When Prayer Fails: Faith Healing, Children, & the Law. 2007. (ENG.). 304p. 29.95 *(978-0-19-530635-4(X))* Oxford Univ. Pr., Inc.
Peterson, John. Children in Practice. 2012. (ENG.). 236p. pap. 35.00 ***(978-1-107-69523-8(6))*** Cambridge Univ. Pr.
Pinto, Sarah. Where There Is No Midwife: Birth & Loss in Rural India. 2011. (Fertility, Reproduction & Sexuality Ser.). (ENG.). 342p. pap. 37.95 ***(978-0-85745-153-8(7))*** Berghahn Bks., Inc.
Plant, Kathryn. Personal Development Matters: A Guide & Step-by-Step Educational Workbook for Helping Young People Aged Roughly 11-16 with Complex Needs to Get to Know Themselves Better. 2011. (Illus.). 224p. pap. 59.95 *(978-1-905541-69-0(4))* Russell Hse. Publishing Ltd. GBR. Dist: International Specialized Bk. Services.
Protections for Foster Children Enrolled in Clinical Trials: Hearing Before the Subcommittee on Human Resources of the Committee on Ways & Means, U.S. House of Representatives, One Hundred Ninth Congress, First Session, May 18, 2005. 2007. iii, 71p. *(978-0-16-079306-6(8),* 552-070-36384-0) United States Government Printing Office.
Pugh, Linda C., et al. Breastfeeding the Healthy Newborn. 2nd ed. 2007. *(978-0-86525-119-9(3))* March of Dimes Birth Defects Foundation.
Richardson, Greg, et al, eds. Child & Adolescent Mental Health Services: An Operational Handbook. 2nd ed. 2010. 336p. pap. *(978-1-904671-80-0(2))* Royal College of Psychiatrists.
The Rising Cost of Food & Its Impact on Federal Child Nutrition Programs: Hearing Before the Committee on Education & Labor, U.S. House of Representatives, One Hundred Tenth Congress, Second Session, Hearing Held in Washington, DC, July 9, 2008. 2008. (Illus.). iv, 95p. *(978-0-16-082198-1(3),* 552-070-38332-8) United States Government Printing Office.
Roberts, Helen. What Works in Reducing Inequalities in Child Health. 2nd rev. ed. 2012. 208p. pap. 32.95 ***(978-1-84742-996-4(3))*** Policy Pr. GBR. Dist: Chicago Distribution Ctr.
—What Works in Reducing Inequalities in Child Health? 2nd rev. ed. 2012. 208p. 89.95 ***(978-1-84742-997-1(1))*** Policy Pr. GBR. Dist: Chicago Distribution Ctr.
Roulstone. Prioritising Child Health. 2006. (Illus.). 136p. 49.95 *(978-0-415-37634-1(3))* Routledge.
Roulstone, Sue. Prioritising Child Health. 2006. (Illus.). 136p. 160.00 *(978-0-415-37633-4(5))* Routledge.
Roundtable on Health Disparities Staff, et al. Focusing on Children's Health: Community Approaches to Addressing Health Disparities - Workshop Summary. 2009. (ENG.). 132p. pap. 33.00 *(978-0-309-13785-0(3))* National Academies Pr.
Sahin, Nevin Hotun & Gungor, Ilkay. Birth Defects: Issues on Prevention & Promotion. 2010. (Health Care Issues, Costs & Access Ser.). viii, 131p. pap. 49.00 *(978-1-61668-967-4(6),* Nova Novinka) Nova Science Pubs., Inc.
Sharma, Sharad Kumar & Vong-ek, Panee. Levels of & Contextual Influences on Obstetric Morbidity in Thailand. 2010. 196p. pap. *(978-3-8383-3546-9(5))* Lambert Academic Publishing.
Singh, Lucky. Levels, Trends, & Determinants of Teenage Childbearing in Indi. 2010. 116p. pap. *(978-3-8383-8543-3(9))* Lambert Academic Publishing.
Sithong, Umakon. Reproductive Health Services among Minority Women. 2010. 76p. pap. *(978-3-8383-8015-5(0))* Lambert Academic Publishing.
Smith, David G. The Child Health Insurance Program: Past & Future. 2011. (ENG.). 121p. 34.95 *(978-1-4128-1869-8(9))* Transaction Pubs.
Sobo, Elisa J. & Kurtin, Paul S., eds. Optimizing Care for Young Children with Special Health Care Needs: Knowledge & Strategies for Navigating the System. 2007. (Illus.). 291p. per. 39.95 *(978-1-55766-854-7(X))* Brookes, Paul H. Publishing Co.
Springhouse Publishing Company Staff, ed. Straight A's in Maternal-Neonatal Nursing. 2nd rev. ed. 2007. (Straight A's Ser.). (ENG., Illus.). 448p. pap. 44.95 *(978-1-58255-693-2(8))* Lippincott Williams & Wilkins.
Standing Committee on Childhood Obesity Prevention Staff & Institute of Medicine. Legal Strategies in Childhood Obesity Prevention: Workshop Summary. 2011. (ENG., Illus.). 104p. pap. 33.00 ***(978-0-309-21019-5(4))*** National Academies Pr.
Stecklein, Hilary Pert. Recognizing Common Illnesses in Early Childhood Settings. 2009. (Redleaf Quick Guides). (ENG.). 50p. pap. 14.95 *(978-1-933653-67-9(1))* Redleaf Pr.
Stenton, Janice. Long Term Effects of Middle Ear Problems on Learning & Behaviour. 2010. 212p. pap. *(978-3-639-26924-6(1))* VDM Verlag Dr. Mueller e.K.
Taking to Scale Imci Implementation in Mongolia 2000-2008: Lessons Learnts. 2011. (WPRO Nonserial Publication Ser.). (ENG.). 57p. cd-rom 12.00 ***(978-92-9061-477-7(3))*** WHO Regional Office for the Western Pacific PHL. Dist: World Health Organization.
Tally, James E. One for the Kids: Creating Children's Healthcare of Atlanta. 2008. (Illus.). 141p. *(978-1-934144-31-2(2))* Indigo.
Teare, Jean, ed. Caring for Children with Complex Needs in the Community. 2008. (ENG., Illus.). 208p. pap. 62.99 *(978-1-4051-5177-1(3),* Wiley-Blackwell) Wiley, John & Sons, Inc.
Thompson, Richard H. The Handbook of Child Life: A Guide for Pediatric Psychosocial Care. 2009. 378p. 79.95 *(978-0-398-07831-7(9));* pap. 55.95 *(978-0-398-07832-4(7))* Thomas, Charles C. Pub., Ltd.
Tomlinson, Patrick & Philpot, Terry. A Child's Journey to Recovery: Assessment & Planning for Traumatized Children. 2007. (Delivering Recovery Ser.). (ENG., Illus.). 144p. per. *(978-1-84310-330-1(3))* Kingsley, Jessica Ltd.
Walker, Steven. Children & Adolescent Mental Health. 2011. (ENG., Illus.). 184p. pap. *(978-0-85725-057-5(4))* Learning Matters Ltd.
White. Global Case Studies in Maternal & Child Health. rev. ed. 2011. pap. 64.95 *(978-0-7637-8153-8(3))* Jones & Bartlett Learning, LLC.
World Bank Staff, contrib. by. The Human Resources for Health Situation in Ethiopia: Towards Attending Remaining Challenges. 2012. ***(978-0-8213-8958-4(0))*** World Bank Pubns.
World Health Organization: Commission on Information and Accountability for Women's and Children's Health. Keeping Promises, Measuring Results: Commission on Information & Accountability for Women's & Children's Health. 2012. (DOCUMENTS for SALE Ser.). (ENG.). 27p. 12.00 ***(978-92-4-156432-8(6))*** World Health Organization.
Yang, Weidong & Wen, Xiaoying. Child Health Care Support Programs for Deafness, Dental Services & down Syndrome. 2012. (Children's Issues, Laws & Programs Ser.). 161p. 125.00 ***(978-1-61470-970-1(X))*** Nova Science Pubs., Inc.
Zarbock, Sarah, ed. The Complete Directory for Pediatric Disorders. 4th ed. 2007. (Complete Directory for Pediatric Disorders Ser.). 1131p. per. 165.00 *(978-1-59237-150-1(7))* Grey Hse. Publishing.

CHILD LABOR

see also Age and Employment

Agaltsova, Marina. Elimination of Child Labor. 2010. 100p. pap. *(978-3-8383-8313-2(3))* Lambert Academic Publishing.
Agbu, Osita, ed. Children & Youth in the Labour Process in Africa. 2009. 232p. pap. *(978-2-86978-251-8(9))* Council for the Development of Social Science Research in Africa SEN. Dist: Michigan State Univ. Pr.
Akee, Randall K. Q., et al. Child Labor & the Transition Between School & Work. 2010. (Research in Labor Economics Ser.). 300p. 134.95 *(978-0-85724-000-2(5))* Emerald Group Publishing Ltd. GBR. Dist: Turpin Distribution Services Ltd.
Ali Meerza, Syed Imran. Role of Rural-Urban Migration in Increasing Rural Child Labor. 2010. 64p. pap. *(978-3-639-25809-7(6))* VDM Verlag Dr. Mueller e.K.

C

Ame, Robert. Children's Rights in Ghana: Reality or Rhetoric? 2011. (ENG., Illus.). 310p. 75.00 *(978-0-7391-4800-6(1))* Lexington Bks.

Amigó, María Florencia. Children Chasing Money. 2010. 244p. pap. *(978-3-639-26901-7(2))* VDM Verlag Dr. Mueller e.K.

Ansari, Mehnaz. A Study of Cognitive & Social Development in Working & School Children. 2011. 168p. pap. ***(978-3-8433-8842-9(3))*** Lambert Academic Publishing.

Awaleh, Mahad. Child Labor & Access to Education. 2008. 128p. pap. *(978-3-639-09403-9(4))* VDM Verlag Dr. Mueller e.K.

Bagchi, Subrata Sank. Child Labor & the Urban Third World: Toward a New Understanding of the Problem. 2010. (ENG.). 84p. pap. 16.99 *(978-0-7618-5298-8(0))* Univ. Pr. of America, Inc.

Beitz, Charles R. & Goodin, Robert E., eds. Global Basic Rights. 2009. (ENG.). 272p. 95.00 *(978-0-19-957026-3(4))* Oxford Univ. Pr., Inc.

Blum, Ann S. Domestic Economies: Family, Work, & Welfare in Mexico City, 1884-1943. 2010. (Engendering Latin America Ser.). (ENG., Illus.). 396p. pap. 30.00 *(978-0-8032-1359-3(X))* Univ. of Nebraska Pr.

Bourdillon, Michael F. C., et al. Rights & Wrongs of Children's Work. 2010. (Rutgers Series in Childhood Studies). (ENG., Illus.). 320p. (C). 75.00 *(978-0-8135-4888-3(8))* Rutgers Univ. Pr.

—Rights & Wrongs of Children's Work. 2010. (Rutgers Series in Childhood Studies). (ENG., Illus.). 320p. (C). pap. 26.95 *(978-0-8135-4889-0(6))* Rutgers Univ. Pr.

Browning, Wilt. Come Quittin' Time. 2007. 184p. per. 20.00 *(978-0-9790949-2-7(5))* Alabaster Bk. Pub.

Bwengye-Kahororo, Edward. Child Labour in Solid Waste Scavenging. 2011. 152p. pap. ***(978-3-8433-8783-5(4))*** Lambert Academic Publishing.

Celebi, Serife Pinar. An Investigation into Child Labour in Turkey. 2010. 96p. pap. *(978-3-639-25920-9(3))* VDM Verlag Dr. Mueller e.K.

Chapagai Chaulagai, Pratima. Child Labour in Domestic Affairs, Nepal. 2010. 64p. pap. *(978-3-639-26648-1(X))* VDM Verlag Dr. Mueller e.K.

Child Labor Enforcement: Are We Adequately Protecting Our Children?: Hearing Before the Subcommittee on Workforce Protections, Committee on Education & Labor, U.S. House of Representatives, One Hundred Tenth Congress, Second Session, Hearing Held in Washington, DC, September 23, 2008. 2008. iii, 34p. *(978-0-16-082280-3(7),* 552-070-38344-1) United States Government Printing Office.

Child Labour under Nigerian Laws. 2011. 440p. pap. ***(978-3-8443-1701-5(5))*** Lambert Academic Publishing.

Clopper, Edward N. Child Labor in City Streets. 2009. 292p. 30.99 *(978-1-113-65046-7(X))*; 292p. 34.99 *(978-1-113-65049-8(4))*; 292p. pap. 28.75 *(978-1-113-65045-0(1))*; 292p. pap. 27.75 *(978-1-113-65043-6(5))*; (ENG.). 291p. pap. 23.99 *(978-1-113-65041-2(9),* BiblioLife) BiblioBazaar.

Concern Worldwide. Dear President Obama... The Concern Worldwide 2009 Writing Competition. 2010. (ENG., Illus.). 256p. pap. 25.95 *(978-1-905785-65-0(8))* Liffey Pr., The IRL. Dist: Dufour Editions, Inc.

Craig, Gary, ed. Child slavery Now: A contemporary Reader. 2010. (Illus.). 360p. 85.00 *(978-1-84742-610-9(7))* Policy Pr. GBR. Dist: Chicago Distribution Ctr.

—Child Slavery Now: A Contemporary Reader. 2010. (Illus.). 360p. pap. 39.95 *(978-1-84742-609-3(3))* Policy Pr. GBR. Dist: Chicago Distribution Ctr.

Cram101 Textbook Reviews & Cram101 Textbook Reviews. Outlines & Highlights for Childhood & Child Labour in the British Industrial Revolution by Jane Humphries, Isbn: 9780521847568. 2011. 74p. pap. 27.95 ***(978-1-4288-6202-9(1))*** Cram101 Inc.

Crofts, Andrew. The Little Hero: One Boy's Fight for Freedom - Iqbal Masih's Story. 2006. (ENG.). 265p. per. 17.95 *(978-1-904132-84-4(7))* Vision Paperbacks GBR. Dist: Independent Pubs. Group.

Cullen, Holly. The Role of International Law in the Elimination of Child Labor. 2007. (Procedural Aspects of International Law Ser.). 303p. *(978-90-04-16285-3(2))* BRILL.

Day, David. The Bevin Boy: A History of the Use of Young Boys in British Mines During WWII. l.t. ed. 192p. 21.95 *(978-1-85695-162-3(6))* ISIS Large Print Bks. GBR. Dist: Transaction Pubs.

de Ruiter, Peter. A World for Children: Growing up Without Child Labour. 2009. 200p. pap. 35.00 *(978-94-6022-035-7(5))* Royal Tropical Institute Pr. (KIT (Koninklijk Instituut voor de Tropen) NLD. Dist: Stylus Publishing, LLC.

Derby, C. Nana. Contemporary Slavery. 2009. (ENG.). 166p. pap. 26.50 *(978-0-7618-4512-6(7))* Univ. Pr. of America, Inc.

Dikici Bilgin, Hasret. Working Street Children in Turkey & Romani. 2009. 148p. pap. *(978-3-639-13036-2(7))* VDM Verlag Dr. Mueller e.K.

Distributed Art Publishers Staff, contrib. by. Lewis Hine: From the Collections of George Eastman House, International Museum of Photography & Film Fondation Henri Cartier_Bresson, Paris September 7 - December 18, 2011 Fundación MAPFRE, Madrid February 6 - April 24, 2012 Nederlands Fotomuseum, Rotterdam September 15, 2012 - January 6, 2013. 2012. (ENG.). 264p. 65.00 ***(978-1-935202-76-9(6))*** D.A.P./Distributed Art Pubs.

Epstein, Irving, ed. The Greenwood Encyclopedia of Children's Issues Worldwide, 6 vols. 2007. (Illus.). 3048p. 599.95 *(978-0-313-33614-0(8),* GR3614, Greenwood Pr.) Greenwood Publishing Group, Inc.

Fassa, Anaclaudia Gastal, et al. Child Labour: A Public Health Perspective. 2010. (ENG., Illus.). 272p. 59.95 *(978-0-19-955858-2(2))* Oxford Univ. Pr., Inc.

Finkel, Michael. True Story: Murder, Memoir, Mea Culpa. 2006. (ENG.). 336p. pap. 14.95 *(978-0-06-058048-3(8),* HarperPerennial) HarperCollins Pubs.

Flannery, James L. The Glass House Boys of Pittsburgh: Law, Technology, & Child Labor. 2009. (ENG., Illus.). 240p. (C). 35.00 *(978-0-8229-4377-8(8))* Univ. of Pittsburgh Pr.

Fyfe, Alec & International Labour Office, International Labour Standards Dept Staff. The Worldwide Movement Agaist Child Labour: Progress & Future Directions. 2008. (ENG., Illus.). 94p. pap. 14.00 *(978-92-2-120017-8(5))* International Labour Office.

Gallop, Alan. Victoria's Children of the Dark: Life & Death Underground in Victorian England. 2010. (ENG., Illus.). 252p. pap. 18.95 *(978-0-7524-5698-0(9))* History Pr. Ltd., The GBR. Dist: Independent Pubs. Group.

Gonzales, Gizela M. Where the Children Are. 2011. (ENG.). 167p. pap. 50.00 *(978-971-94292-6-5(7))* Artpostasia Inc. PHL. Dist: National Bk. Network.

Gorshkov, Boris B. Russia's Factory Children: State, Society, & Law, 1800-1917. 2009. (Pitt Russian East European Ser.). (ENG., Illus.). 228p. (C). 60.00 *(978-0-8229-4383-9(2))*; pap. 25.95 *(978-0-8229-6048-5(6))* Univ. of Pittsburgh Pr.

Graham, Paul, ed. Inheriting Poverty? the Link Between Children's Wellbeing & Unemployment in South Afric. 2007. 144p. pap. *(978-1-920118-24-2(1))* IDASA Pubs. ZAF. Dist: Michigan State Univ. Pr.

Halder, Baby. A Life Less Ordinary: A Memoir. 2008. 192p. pap. 13.95 *(978-0-06-137398-5(2),* HarperPerennial) HarperCollins Pubs.

Haugen, David M., ed. Labor & Employment. 2012. (Teen Rights & Freedoms Ser.). (ENG., Illus.). 176p. (gr. 10-12). lib. bdg. 37.10 ***(978-0-7377-6402-4(3),*** Greenhaven Pr., Inc.) Cengage Gale.

Herath, Gamini & Sharma, Kishor, eds. Child Labour in South Asia. 2007. (Contemporary Employment Relations Ser.). (Illus.). 202p. 114.95 *(978-0-7546-7004-9(X))* Ashgate Publishing Co.

Herndon, Ruth Wallis & Murray, John E. Children Bound to Labor: The Pauper Apprentice System in Early America. 2009. (Illus.). 288p. 76.95 *(978-0-8014-4624-5(4))*; pap. 24.95 *(978-0-8014-7559-7(7))* Cornell Univ. Pr.

Hindman, Hugh D., ed. The World of Child Labor: An Historical & Regional Survey. 2009. (Illus.). 1032p. 199.00 *(978-0-7656-1707-1(2))* Sharpe, M.E. Inc.

Honeyman, Katrina. Child workers in England 1780-1820: Parish apprenticeship & the making of the early industrial labour Force. 2007. (Studies in Labour History Ser.). (Illus.). 354p. 134.95 *(978-0-7546-6272-3(1))* Ashgate Publishing Co.

Horner, Leonard. On the Employment of Children in Factories & Other Works in the United Kingdom & in Some Foreign Countries. 2009. 88p. pap. 14.14 *(978-1-151-42488-4(9))* General Bks. LLC.

Huberman, Jennifer. Ambivalent Encounters: Childhood, Tourism, & Social Change in Banaras, India. 2013. (Rutgers Series in Childhood Studies). (ENG.). 264p. 72.00 ***(978-0-8135-5407-5(1))***; pap. 28.95 ***(978-0-8135-5406-8(3))*** Rutgers Univ. Pr.

Humbert, Franziska. The Challenge of Child Labour in International Law. 2009. (Cambridge Studies in International & Comparative Law Ser.). (ENG.). 458p 113.00 *(978-0-521-76490-2(4))* Cambridge Univ. Pr. GBR. Dist: Cambridge Univ. Pr.

Humphries, Jane. Childhood & Child Labour in the British Industrial Revolution. (Cambridge Studies in Economic History - Second Ser.). (ENG., Illus.). 2011. 454p. pap. 34.99 ***(978-0-521-24896-9(5))*** 2010. 456p. 110.00 *(978-0-521-84756-8(7))* Cambridge Univ. Pr.

Hungerland, Beatrice, et al, eds. Working to Be Someone: Child Focused Research & Practice with Working Children. 2007. (ENG., Illus.). 272p. per. *(978-1-84310-523-7(3))* Kingsley, Jessica Ltd.

ILO. The End of Child Labour: Within Reach: Global Report under the Follow-up to the ILO Declaration on Fundamental Principles & Rights at Work. 2006. (ENG., Illus.). 127p. per. 29.95 *(978-92-2-116603-0(1))* International Labour Office.

Kaushal, Lata. Child Labour & Human Rights: A Social Dimension. 2009. 335p. 62.50 *(978-81-7533-219-5(0))* M. D. Pubns. Pvt, Ltd. IND. Dist: Coronet Bks.

Kayaalp, Dilek. Child Labor & Education. 2009. 104p. pap. *(978-3-639-13363-9(3))* VDM Verlag Dr. Mueller e.K.

Kenny, Mary. Hidden Heads of the Households: Child Labor in Urban Northeast Brazil. 2nd ed. 2008. (Teaching Culture: UTP Ethnographies for the Classroom Ser.). (ENG.). 160p. pap. *(978-1-4426-0084-3(5))* Univ. of Toronto Pr.

Khan, Ali. Representing Children: Power, Policy & the Discourse on Child Labour in the Football Manufacturing Industry of Sialkot. 2008. (ENG., Illus.). 240p. 45.00 *(978-0-19-547478-7(3))* Oxford Univ. Pr., Inc.

Khan, Rana Ejaz Ali. Child Labor in Pakistan. 2010. 368p. pap. *(978-3-639-24596-7(2))* VDM Verlag Dr. Mueller e.K.

Khanam, Rasheda. Child Labour & Schooling in Bangladesh. 2011. 204p. pap. ***(978-3-8443-1855-5(0))*** Lambert Academic Publishing.

Kielland, Anne. Child Labor Migration in Benin: Incentive, Constraint, or Agency? 2008. 120p. pap. *(978-3-639-06802-3(5))* VDM Verlag Dr. Mueller e.K.

Lee-Wright, Peter. Child Slaves. 2009. (Aid & Development Set Ser.). (ENG.). 302p. 110.00 *(978-1-84971-041-1(4))* Routledge.

Lieten, G. C. M., ed. Hazardous Child Labour in Latin America. 2010. (ENG., Illus.). xiv, 200p. 139.00 *(978-94-007-0176-2(4),* 9400701764) Springer.

López-Calva, Luis Felipe. Trabajo Infantil: Teoría y Lecciones de la América Latina. 2006. (Lecturas de el Trimestre Económico Ser.). (SPA., Illus.). 461p. pap. *(978-968-16-8120-3(7))* Fondo de Cultura Economica.

Malik, Muhammad Shahid. Child Labour. 2010. 124p. pap. *(978-3-8383-8499-3(7))* Lambert Academic Publishing.

Mapes, Kathleen. Sweet Tyranny: Migrant Labor, Industrial Agriculture, & Imperial Politics. 2009. (Working Class in American History Ser.). (ENG., Illus.). 336p. pap. 31.00 *(978-0-252-07667-1(2))* Univ. of Illinois Pr.

Mayers, Lynne. A Dangerous Place to Work! 2008. (Illus.). 108p. pap. 16.95 *(978-0-9556896-0-4(0))* Blaize Bailey Bks. GBR. Dist: Lulu Enterprises Inc.

McCarthy, James. Selim Aga: A Slave's Odyssey. 2007. (ENG., Illus.). 254p. 26.95 *(978-1-905222-17-9(3))* Luath Pr. Ltd. GBR. Dist: Ingram Pub. Services.

—Selim Aga: A Slave's Odyssey. 2007. 254p. (YA). 26.95 *(978-1-4115-2035-6(1))* Polyglot Pr., Inc.

Mccaw, Stewart. Galloping to Space. 2011. (Illus.). 104p. pap. 15.66 ***(978-1-4567-9363-0(2))*** AuthorHouse.

Mukherjee, Diganta. Child Labour & Child Work. 2010. 436p. pap. *(978-3-8383-3128-7(1))* Lambert Academic Publishing.

Mukherjee, Dipa. Child Workers in Indi. 2011. 100p. pap. ***(978-3-8443-0648-4(X))*** Lambert Academic Publishing.

Naqshbandi, M. Mudasir. Child Labor in Kashmir. 2011. 100p. pap. ***(978-3-8443-0637-8(4))*** Lambert Academic Publishing.

National Research Council. Approaches to Reducing the Use of Forced or Child Labor: Summary of a Workshop on Assessing Practice. 2009. (ENG.). 142p. pap. 34.75 *(978-0-309-14528-2(7))* National Academies Pr.

Nederveen Meerkerk, Elise van & Kristoffel, Lieten. Child Labour's Global Past, 1650-2000. 2011. (Illus.). 716p. *(978-3-0343-0517-4(6))* Lang, Peter.

Nogler, Luca & Pertile, Marco. Child Labour in a Globalized World: A Legal Analysis of ILO Action. Nesi, Giuseppe, ed. 2008. 492p. 144.95 *(978-0-7546-7222-7(0))* Ashgate Publishing Co.

Offit, Thomas A. Conquistadores de la Calle: Child Street Labor in Guatemala City. 2010. (ENG., Illus.). 240p. pap. 25.00 *(978-0-292-72150-0(1))* Univ. of Texas Pr.

Orazem, Peter F., et al. Child Labor & Education in Latin America: An Economic Perspective. 2009. (ENG., Illus.). 252p. 100.00 *(978-0-230-61459-8(0))* Palgrave Macmillan.

Parker, David L. & Parker, David. Before Their Time: The World of Child Labor. 2007. (ENG., Illus.). 160p. 35.00 *(978-1-59372-024-7(6),* 372024) Quantuck Lane Pr. & The Mill Road Collaborative, The.

Peow, See Hoon. Law & Child Labour in Malaysia: Case Study in a Chinese New Village. 2007. 168p. (C). pap. 28.50 *(978-967-978-937-9(3))* Pelanduk Pubns. Malaysia Sdn. Bhd MYS. Dist: Coronet Bks.

Przyborowska, Ewa. Child Labour & Demographic Transition in Thailand. 2011. 56p. pap. ***(978-3-8443-8407-9(3))*** Lambert Academic Publishing.

Rende, Sevint. Children's Work & Opportunities for Education. 2008. 144p. per. *(978-3-8364-3855-1(0))* VDM Verlag Dr. Mueller e.K.

Rifaey, Tonia. Child Labour in Old Cairo & the Roles Children Negotiate. 2010. 304p. pap. *(978-3-8383-2833-1(7))* Lambert Academic Publishing.

Rivera, Ian C. & Howard, Natasha M., eds. Child Labor in America. 2010. (Children's Issues, Laws & Programs Ser.). pap. 43.00 *(978-1-60876-769-4(8))* Nova Science Pubs., Inc.

Roche, Mary M. Doyle. Children, Consumerism, & the Common Good. 2009. (ENG.). 158p. 62.99 *(978-0-7391-2947-0(3))* Lexington Bks.

Rodríguez, Pablo & Mannarelli, María Emma. Historia de la Infancia en América Latina. 2007. (SPA., Illus.). 673p. pap. 33.00 *(978-958-710-218-5(5))* Universidad Externado de Colombia COL. Dist: Siglo del Hombre.

Rollings-Magnusson, Sandra. Heavy Burdens on Small Shoulders: The Labour of Pioneer Children on the Canadian Prairies. 2009. (ENG., Illus.). 192p. pap. 34.95 *(978-0-88864-509-8(0))* Univ. of Alberta Pr. CAN. Dist: Michigan State Univ. Pr.

Savio, Martina. Dynamics of Oppression & State Failure. 2010. 96p. pap. *(978-3-8383-8402-3(4))* Lambert Academic Publishing.

Schmidt, James D. Industrial Violence & the Legal Origins of Child Labor. 2010. (Cambridge Historical Studies in American Law & Society Ser.). (ENG., Illus.). 304p. 85.00 *(978-0-521-19865-3(8))*; pap. 27.99 *(978-0-521-15505-2(3))* Cambridge Univ. Pr.

Somçelik-Köksal, Aysegül. Working & Non-Working Children in Turkey. 2010. 80p. pap. *(978-3-8383-8003-2(7))* Lambert Academic Publishing.

Sosenski, Susana. Niños en Acción: El Trabajo Infantil en la Ciudad de México (1920-1934) 2010. (Estudios Históricos Ser.). (SPA., Illus.). 365p. pap. 48.99 *(978-607-462-053-5(9))* El Colegio de México, A.C., Biblioteca Miguel Cosio Villegas MEX. Dist: Fondo de Cultura Economica USA.

Spargo, John. The Bitter Cry of the Children. 2009. 148p. pap. 19.99 *(978-1-150-60309-9(7))* General Bks. LLC.

—The Bitter Cry of the Children. 2008. 428p. 51.95 *(978-1-4365-6792-3(0))* 2007. (ENG.). 432p. per. 36.95 *(978-0-548-77060-3(3))* Kessinger Publishing, LLC.

Sundue, Sharon Braslaw. Industrious in Their Stations: Young People at Work in Urban America, 1720-1810. 2009. (ENG.). 288p. (gr. 17). 45.00 *(978-0-8139-2713-8(7))* Univ. Pr. of Virginia.

Teele, Dawn L. If ratification does not affect compliance, why docountries bother? An investigation into child labor & the minimum age to work convention. 2008. 112p. pap. *(978-3-639-09369-8(0))* VDM Verlag Dr. Mueller e.K.

Tenaglia-Webster, Maria. Slavery. 2009. (GLOBAL VIEWPOINTS Ser.). (ENG.). 224p. pap. 26.50 *(978-0-7377-4473-6(1))*; (Illus.). pap. 38.45 *(978-0-7377-4472-9(3))* Cengage Gale. (Greenhaven Pr., Inc.).

Valencia, Lance K. & Hahn, Bryson J., eds. Employment & Labor Issues: Unemployment, Youth Employment & Child Labor. 2010. (Economic Issues, Problems & Perspectives Ser.). (Illus.). 243p. 129.00 *(978-1-60876-282-8(3))* Nova Science Pubs., Inc.

Van Vorst, Bessie. The Woman Who Toils: The Experiences of Two Ladies As Factory Girls. 163p. reprint ed. 88.00 *(978-0-7222-1868-6(0))* Library Reprints, Inc.

Vorst, Marie Van & John Van Vorst. The Woman Who Toils: Being the Experiences of Two Gentlewomen as Factor. 2007. 200p. pap. 19.99 *(978-1-4264-8471-1(2))*; 222p. pap. 22.99 *(978-1-4264-8529-9(8))* BiblioBazaar.

Walakira, Eddy. Interpretation of Child Labour in Ugand. 2010. 268p. pap. *(978-3-639-24634-6(9))* VDM Verlag Dr. Mueller e.K.

Wallace, Eileen. Children of the Labouring Poor: The Working Lives of Children in Nineteenth-Century Hertfordshire. 2010. (ENG., Illus.). 256p. pap. 33.95 *(978-1-905313-49-5(7))* Univ. of Hertfordshire Pr. GBR. Dist: Independent Pubs. Group.

Watkins, Christine. Child Labor & Sweatshops. 2010. (At Issue Ser.). (ENG.). 80-128p. pap. 22.50 *(978-0-7377-4875-8(3),* Greenhaven Pr., Inc.); (YA). (gr. 9-12). 31.80 *(978-0-7377-4874-1(5))* Cengage Gale.

Weiner, Myron, et al. Born Unfree - Child Labour, Education, & the State in India: An Omnibus - The Child & the State in India, Born to Work, & Child Rights in India (Extract) 2007. (ENG., Illus.). 740p. 65.00 *(978-0-19-567990-8(3))* Oxford Univ. Pr., Inc.

Wilkes, Sue. The Children History Forgot: Young Workers of the Industrial Age. 2011. (Illus.). 320p. 32.95 ***(978-0-7090-8972-8(4))*** Hale, Robert Ltd. GBR. Dist: Independent Pubs. Group.

Willis, Laurie, ed. Child Labor. 2011. (Issues that Concern You Ser.). (Illus.). 144p. 35.75 *(978-0-7377-5690-6(X),* Greenhaven Pr., Inc.) Cengage Gale.

Winrock International Staff, contrib. by. Child Labor Through Education: Drawn from Winrock Global CIRCLE Projects: Community-Based Innovations to Reduce Child Labor Through Education. 2008. *(978-1-57360-070-5(9))* Winrock International Institute for Agricultural Development.

CHILD MARRIAGE

Chester. Child-marriages, Divorces, & Ratifications. 256p. reprint ed. 98.00 *(978-0-7222-1816-7(8))* Library Reprints, Inc.

Crimes Associated with Polygamy: The Need for a Coordinated State & Federal Response: Hearing Before the Committee on the Judiciary, United States Senate, One Hundred Tenth Congress, Second Session, July 24, 2008. 2008. (Illus.). iii, 185p. *(978-0-16-081993-3(8),* 552-070-38165-1) United States Government Printing Office.

Magoke-Mhoja, Monica Elias. Child-Widows Silenced & Unheard. 2008. (Illus.). 288p. pap. 22.99 *(978-1-4343-7787-6(3))* AuthorHouse.

Minoui, Delphine & Ali, Nujood. I Am Nujood, Age 10 & Divorced. 2010. (ENG.). 192p. pap. 12.00 *(978-0-307-58967-5(6),* Three Rivers Pr.) Crown Publishing Group.

CHILD MARRIAGE—INDIA

Goswami, Sambodh. Female Infanticide & Child Marriage. 2007. (RAJ & ENG.). 424p. (C). 40.00 *(978-81-316-0112-9(9))* Rawat Pubns. IND. Dist: International Specialized Bk. Services.

Malabari, Behramji Merwanji. Infant Marriage & Enforced Widowhood in India: A Collection of Opinions, for & Against, Received by Mr. Behramji M. Malabari, from Representative Hindu Gentlemen & Official & Other Authorities. 109p. reprint ed. 88.00 *(978-0-7222-1815-0(X))* Library Reprints, Inc.

CHILD MENTAL HEALTH

see also Child Psychiatry; Child Psychopathology

Auger, Rick, ed. The School Counselor's Mental Health Sourcebook: Strategies to Help Students Succeed. 2010. (Illus.). 216p. pap. 36.95 *(978-1-4129-7273-4(6),* B72727P) Corwin Pr.

Bailey, Sue. The Young Mind: An Essential Guide to Mental Health for Young Adults, Parents & Teachers. Shooter, Mike, ed. 2012. (ENG.). 400p. pap. 14.95 *(978-0-553-82418-6(X))* Transworld Publishers Ltd. GBR. Dist: Independent Pubs. Group.

Bakewell, Lisa, ed. Mental Health Information for Teens. 3rd rev. ed. 2010. (Teen Health Ser.). 448p. (YA). lib. bdg. 69.00 *(978-0-7808-1087-7(2))* Omnigraphics, Inc.

Berthier, Dr Rolade Brizuela & Berthier, Rolade Brizuela. Intelligence, Giftedness: Pre-cradle to Post-grave. 2010. 240p. pap. 14.95 *(978-1-60976-296-4(7),* Eloquent Bks.) AEG Literary Publishing Services, Inc.

Brendtro, et al. Deep Brain Learning: Pathways to Potential with Challenging Youth. 2009. (Illus.). xvii, 169p. *(978-1-60725-789-9(0),* Debolsillo) Independent Pub.

Brown, J. Betrayal of Minds. 2007. (ENG.). 100p. per. *(978-1-84747-481-0(0))* Chipmunkapublishing.

Buckingham, David. The Material Child. 2011. (ENG.). 256p. 69.95 *(978-0-7456-4770-8(7))* Polity Pr. GBR. Dist: Wiley, John & Sons, Inc.

—The Material Child: Growing up in Consumer Culture. 2011. (ENG.). 256p. pap. 24.95 *(978-0-7456-4771-5(5))* Polity Pr. GBR. Dist: Wiley, John & Sons, Inc.

Bursztyn, Alberto. Childhood Psychological Disorders: Current Controversies. 2011. E-Book *(978-0-313-06406-7(7),* Praeger Pubs.) Greenwood Publishing Group, Inc.

Cabrera, Natasha, et al. Latina & Latino Children's Mental Health, 2 vols. 2011. (Child Psychology & Mental Health Ser.). (Illus.). 512p. 104.95 *(978-0-313-38296-3(4),* A2696C, Praeger Pubs.) Greenwood Publishing Group, Inc.

Cabrera, Natasha J., et al. Latina/O Children & Mental Health, 2 vols. 2011. (Illus.). E-Book *(978-0-313-38297-0(2))* ABC-CLIO, LLC.

Carter, William Lee. Putting Humpty Dumpty Back Together: Parenting a Distressed Child. 2009. 176p. pap. 15.00 *(978-0-9841080-0-8(9))* Restoration Pubns.

Clanton Harpine, Elaine. Group-Centered Prevention Programs for at-Risk Students. 2010. (ENG.). xx, 155p. 129.00 *(978-1-4419-7247-7(1),* 1441972471) Springer.

—Group Interventions in Schools: Promoting Mental Health for at-Risk Children & Youth. 2010. (ENG.). xv, 107p. pap. 44.95 *(978-1-4419-4587-7(3),* 1441945873) Springer.

Cram101 Textbook Reviews & Cram101 Textbook Reviews. Outlines & Highlights for Cultural Issues in Pediatric Mental Health, an Issue of Child & Adolescent Psychiatric Clinics of North America by Shashan. 2011. 86p. pap. 27.95 ***(978-1-61461-226-1(9))*** Cram101 Inc.

DeWine, Mike, ed. Mental Health in Children & Youth: Issues Throughout the Developmental Process: Congressional Hearing. 2006. 94p. (C). reprint ed. pap. 25.00 *(978-1-4223-0536-2(8))* DIANE Publishing Co.

Dishion, Thomas J. & Stormshak, Elizabeth A. Intervening in Children's Lives: An Ecological, Family-Centered Approach to Mental Health Care. 2006. (Illus.). 319p. 39.95 *(978-1-59147-428-9(0))* American Psychological Assn.

Doega, Zofia & John-Borys, Maria. Zdrowie Psychiczne Uczniów: Rózne Konteksty I Odniesienia. 2009. (POL., Illus.). 303p. *(978-83-226-1743-4(7))* Uniwersytet Slaski, Wydawnictwo.

Dosick, Wayne D., et al. Empowering Your Indigo Child: A Handbook for Parents of Children of Spirit. 2009. (ENG., Illus.). 1p. pap., instr.'s hndbk. ed. 15.95 *(978-1-57863-444-6(X),* Weiser Bks.) Red Wheel/Weiser.

Dyregrov, Atle. Grief in Children: A Handbook for Adults. 2nd ed. 2008. (ENG.). 144p. pap. *(978-1-84310-612-8(4))* Kingsley, Jessica Ltd.

Elkind, David. Hurried Child: Growing up Too Fast Too Soon. 25th anniv. ed. 2006. (ENG.). 288p. pap. 16.95 *(978-0-7382-1082-7(X))* Da Capo Pr., Inc.

Fitzgerald, Hiram E., et al, eds. International Perspectives on Children & Mental Health Vol. 1: Development & Context, 2 vols. 2011. (Child Psychology & Mental Health Ser.). (Illus.). 500p. 124.95 *(978-0-313-38298-7(0),* A2697C, Praeger Pubs.) Greenwood Publishing Group, Inc.

Foster, Susan. School Mental Health Services in the United States 2002-2003. 2006. (Illus.). 150p. (C). pap. 35.00 *(978-1-4223-0697-0(6))* DIANE Publishing Co.

Fritsch, Sandra L. Interface Between Pediatrics & Children's Mental Health: An Issue of Child & Adolescent Psychiatric Clinics of North America. 2010. (Clinics: Internal Medicine Ser.: 19-2). (ENG.). xvii, 184p. 105.00 *(978-1-4377-1946-8(5),* Saunders) Elsevier - Health Sciences Div.

Fritsch, Sandra L. & Trivedi, Harsh K. Interface Between Pediatrics & Children's Mental Health: Pediatric Clinics. 2011. (Clinics: Internal Medicine Ser.: 58-4). (ENG.). 88.00 ***(978-1-4557-1229-8(9),*** Saunders) Elsevier - Health Sciences Div.

Garralda, M. Elena. Increasing Awareness of Child & Adolescent Mental Health. 2010. (ENG., Illus.). 338p. 83.99 *(978-0-7657-0661-4(X),* Aronson, Jason) Rowman & Littlefield Publishers, Inc.

Garralda, M. Elena & Raynaud, Jean Philippe. Increasing Awareness of Child & Adolescent Mental Health. 2010. (Illus.). xvii, 319p. 34.95 *(978-0-7657-0663-8(6),* Aronson, Jason) Rowman & Littlefield Publishers, Inc.

Garralda, M. Elena & Raynaud, Jean-Philippe. Increasing Awareness of Child & Adolescent Mental Health. 2010. (ENG., Illus.). 338p. pap. 36.99 *(978-0-7657-0662-1(8),* Aronson, Jason) Rowman & Littlefield Publishers, Inc.

Goodheart, Kristin, et al, eds. Eating Disorders in Women & Children: Prevention, Stress Management, & Treatment. 2nd rev. ed. 2011. (ENG., Illus.). 456p. 129.95 *(978-1-4398-2481-8(9),* CRC Press) Taylor & Francis Group GBR. Dist: Taylor & Francis Group.

Goodman, Karen D. Music therapy groupwork with special needs Children: The Evolving Process. 2007. 318p. *(978-0-398-07739-6(8))* *(978-0-398-07740-2(1))* Thomas, Charles C. Pub., Ltd.

Harpine, Elaine Clanton. Group Interventions in Schools: Promoting Mental Health for At-Risk Children & Youth. 2008. (ENG.). xv, 107p. 44.95 *(978-0-387-77315-5(0),* 0387773150) Springer.

Herbert, Kenneth R. Childrens Mental Health: The History & Outcomes of a Mobile Crisis Service. 2008. 76p. pap. *(978-3-639-00909-5(6))* VDM Verlag Dr. Mueller e.K.

Hill, Nancy E., et al, eds. African American Children & Mental Health Vols. 1 & 2: Development & Context. 2011. (Child Psychology & Mental Health Ser.). (Illus.). 498p. 104.95 *(978-0-313-38302-1(2),* A2699C, Praeger Pubs.) Greenwood Publishing Group, Inc.

Hoagwood, Kimberly, et al, eds. Children's Mental Health Research: The Power of Partnerships, 1 vol. 2010. (ENG., Illus.). 224p. 34.95 *(978-0-19-530782-5(8))* Oxford Univ. Pr., Inc.

Hooper, Christine, et al. Child & Adolescent Mental Health Theory & Practice. 2nd rev. ed. 2012. (ENG., Illus.). 576p. pap. 45.00 ***(978-1-4441-4599-1(1))*** Hodder Arnold Pubs.

Hooper, Jeni. What Children Need to Be Happy, Confident & Successful: Step by Step Positive Psychology to Help Children Flourish. 2012. (ENG., Illus.). 160p. pap. ***(978-1-84905-239-9(5))*** Kingsley, Jessica Ltd.

Houston, Michael & Sarvet, Barry D. Leadership & Management Core Competencies, an Issue of Child & Adolescent Psychiatric Clinics of North America. 2010. (Clinics: Internal Medicine Ser.: 19-1). (ENG., Illus.). xvii, 182p. 105.00 *(978-1-4377-1802-7(7),* Saunders) Elsevier - Health Sciences Div.

Hughes, Tammy L. & Jimerson, Shane R. Identifying, Assessing, & Treating Conduct Disorder at School. 2007. (Developmental Psychopathology at School Ser.). X, 156p. 59.95 *(978-0-387-74393-6(6),* 0387743936) Springer.

Jensen, Peter S. & Hoagwood, Kimberly. Improving Children's Mental Health Through Parent Empowerment: A Guide to Assisting Families. 2008. (ENG., Illus.). 272p. (C). pap. 29.95 *(978-0-19-532090-9(5))* Oxford Univ. Pr., Inc.

Johnson, Eileen. The Children's Bill of Emotional Rights: A Guide to the Needs of Children. 2011. (ENG., Illus.). 272p. (gr. 17). 60.00 ***(978-0-7657-0850-2(7),*** Aronson, Jason) Rowman & Littlefield Publishers, Inc.

Kaila, H. L. Counsellor for School: A Child Mental Health Perspective. 2010. 357p. 57.50 *(978-81-7533-299-7(9))* M. D. Pubns. Pvt, Ltd. IND. Dist: Coronet Bks.

Larson, Jim & Lochman, John E. Helping Schoolchildren Cope with Anger, Second Edition: A Cognitive-Behavioral Intervention. 2nd ed. 2010. (ENG., Illus.). 222p. (gr. 3-6). pap. 30.00 *(978-1-60623-973-5(2))* Guilford Pubns., Inc.

Levine, Peter A. & Kline, Maggie. Trauma Through a Child's Eyes: Awakening the Ordinary Miracle of Healing; Infancy Through Adolescence. annot. ed. 2006. (ENG.). 536p. pap. 24.95 *(978-1-55643-630-7(0))* North Atlantic Bks.

Lyons, John S. & Weiner, Dana A. Behavioral Health Care: Assessment, Service Planning, & Total Clinical Outcomes Management. 2009. (Illus.). ***(978-1-887554-69-5(6))*** Civic Research Institute, Inc.

Mercogliano, Chris. In Defense of Childhood: Protecting Kids' Inner Wildness. 2008. (ENG.). 224p. pap. 16.00 *(978-0-8070-3287-9(5))* Beacon Pr.

Mohsin, Muhammad Naeem. Ecological Inventory Approach for Assessment & Training. 2011. 332p. pap. ***(978-3-8433-7427-9(9))*** Lambert Academic Publishing.

Olfman, Sharna & Robbins, Brent Dean. Drugging Our Children: How Profiteers Are Pushing Antipsychotics on Our Youngest, & What We Can Do to Stop It, 1 vol. 2012. (Childhood in America Ser.). 232p. 48.00 ***(978-0-313-39683-0(3),*** A3501C) Greenwood Publishing Group, Inc.

Persaud, Raj. The Young Mind. Bailey, Sue & Shooter, Mike, eds. 2009. (ENG., Illus.). 420p. pap. 29.99 *(978-0-593-06138-1(1))* Transworld Publishers Ltd. GBR. Dist: Independent Pubs. Group.

Probst, Barbara. When the Labels Don't Fit: A New Approach to Raising a Challenging Child. 2008. (ENG.). 288p. 13.95 *(978-0-307-39543-6(X),* Three Rivers Pr.) Crown Publishing Group.

Raines, James C. & Dibble, Nic T. Ethical Decision Making in School Mental Health. 2010. (SSWAA Workshop Ser.). (ENG., Illus.). 272p. pap. 24.95 *(978-0-19-973585-3(9))* Oxford Univ. Pr., Inc.

Sankar, D. Siva. Mental Health in Children, Vol. 5. *(978-0-915340-04-0(6))* PJD Pubns., Ltd.

Sarche, Michelle C. American Indian & Alaska Native Children & Mental Health: Development, Context, Prevention, & Treatment. 2011. E-Book ***(978-0-313-38305-2(7),*** Praeger Pubs.) Greenwood Publishing Group, Inc.

Schmidt Neven, Ruth. Core Principles of Assesement & Therapeutic Communication with Children: Towards the Promotion of Child & Family Wellbeing. 2010. (ENG., Illus.). 192p. (C). pap. 39.95 *(978-0-415-55243-1(5))* Routledge.

—Core Principles of Assesement & Therapeutic Communication with Children, Parents & Families: Towards the Promotion of Child & Family Wellbeing. 2010. (ENG., Illus.). 192p. (C). 100.00 *(978-0-415-55242-4(7))* Routledge.

Seifert, Kathryn. How Children Become Violent: Keeping Your Kids Out of Gangs, Terrorist Organizations, & Cults. 2006. (Illus.). 269p. per. 19.95 *(978-1-933531-48-6(1))* Acanthus Publishing.

Semrud-Clikeman, Margaret & Teeter Ellison, Phyllis Anne. Child Neuropsychology: Assessment & Interventions for Neurodevelopmental Disorders, 2nd Edition. 2nd ed. 2009. (ENG., Illus.). xix, 475p. 99.00 *(978-0-387-88962-7(0),* 0387889620) Springer.

Shaw, Richard J. & Demaso, David R. Clinical Manual of Pediatric Psychosomatic Medicine: Mental Health Consultation with Physically Ill Children & Adolescents. 2006. (Illus.). 411p. 72.00 *(978-1-58562-187-3(0),* 62187) American Psychiatric Publishing, Inc.

Shaw, Steven R. & McCabe, Paul C. Genetic & Acquired Disorders: Current Topics & Interventions for Educators. Shaw, Steven R. & McCabe, Paul C., eds. 2010. 192p. pap. 36.95 *(978-1-4129-6872-0(0),* B68713P) Corwin Pr.

—Psychiatric Disorders: Current Topics & Interventions for Educators. Shaw, Steven R. & McCabe, Paul C., eds. 2010. 184p. pap. 36.95 *(978-1-4129-6876-8(3),* B68751P) Corwin Pr.

Short, Rick Jay & Hess, Robyn S. Comprehensive Children's Mental Health Services in Schools & Communities. 2012. (School-Based Practice in Action Ser.). (ENG., Illus.). 187p. 95.95 *(978-0-415-80448-6(5));* pap. 34.95 *(978-0-415-80449-3(3))* Routledge.

Sink, Christopher A. Mental Health Interventions for School Counselors. 2010. (School Counseling Ser.). (ENG.). 208p. (C). pap. 47.95 *(978-0-618-75458-8(X))* Wadsworth.

Spicer, Paul, et al, eds. American Indian & Alaska Native Children & Mental Health: Development, Context, Prevention, & Treatment, 1 vol. 2011. (Child Psychology & Mental Health Ser.). (Illus.). 408p. 58.00 *(978-0-313-38304-5(9),* A2701C, Praeger Pubs.) Greenwood Publishing Group, Inc.

Stroul, Beth A. & Blau, Gary M. The System of Care Handbook: Transforming Mental Health Services for Children, Youth, & Families. 2008. (Systems of Care for Children's Mental Health Ser.). (Illus.). 760p. 74.95 *(978-1-55766-962-9(7))* Brookes, Paul H. Publishing Co.

Summers, Susan J. & Chazan-Cohen, Rachel, eds. Understanding Early Childhood Mental Health: A Practical Guide for Professionals. 2011. 296p. pap. 39.95 ***(978-1-59857-075-5(7))*** Brookes, Paul H. Publishing Co.

Vostanis, Panos, ed. Mental Health Interventions & Services for Vulnerable Children & Young People. 2007. (ENG., Illus.). 296p. pap. *(978-1-84310-489-6(X))* Kingsley, Jessica Ltd.

Walker, Steven. Children & Adolescent Mental Health. 2011. (ENG., Illus.). 184p. pap. *(978-0-85725-057-5(4))* Learning Matters Ltd.

Warner, Judith. We've Got Issues: Children & Parents in the Age of Medication. 2011. (ENG.). 336p. (gr. 12). 16.00 *(978-1-59448-497-1(X),* Riverhead Trade (Paperbacks)) Penguin Group (USA) Inc.

Williams, Jonathan J. & Hill, Peter D. A Handbook for the Assessment of Children's Behaviours. 2012. (ENG.). 622p. pap. 80.00 ***(978-1-119-97589-2(1),*** Wiley-Blackwell) Wiley, John & Sons, Inc.

Zeanah, Charles H., Jr., ed. Handbook of Infant Mental Health. 3rd ed. (ENG., 622p. 2009. Illus.). 75.00 *(978-1-60623-315-3(7))* 2012. pap. 45.00 ***(978-1-4625-0646-0(1))*** Guilford Pubns., Inc.

CHILD MOLESTING

see Child Sexual Abuse

CHILD MOLESTERS

Angela Banner; Robert Banner. The Perverse Plague. 2011. 462p. pap. 24.99 ***(978-1-61379-013-7(9))*** Xulon Pr., Inc.

Calder, Martin C., ed. Working with Children & Young People Who Sexually Abuse: Taking the Field Forward. 2007. (Illus.). 318p. pap. 65.00 *(978-1-905541-01-0(5))* Russell Hse. Publishing Ltd. GBR. Dist: International Specialized Bk. Services.

Davidson, Julia & Gottschalk, Petter, eds. Internet Child Abuse: Current Research & Policy. 2011. (ENG., Illus.). 216p. pap. 44.95 ***(978-0-415-69780-4(8),*** Routledge Cavendish) Taylor & Francis Group GBR. Dist: Taylor & Francis Group.

Ellison, Darlene. The Predator Next Door: Detect, Protect & Recover from Betrayal. 2009. (ENG.). 136p. pap. 14.95 *(978-0-9822864-0-1(6))* HTA Bks., LLC.

Faulkner, Joanne. The Importance of Being Innocent: Why We Worry about Children, 1 vol. 2010. 176p. pap. 32.99 *(978-0-521-14697-5(6))* Cambridge Univ. Pr.

Fowler, Jeff. A Practitioners' Tool for the Assessment of Adults Who Sexually Abuse Children. 2008. (ENG.). 160p. pap. *(978-1-84310-639-5(6))* Kingsley, Jessica Ltd.

Fragoso, Margaux. Tiger, Tiger: A Memoir. 2011. (ENG.). 336p. 26.00 *(978-0-374-27762-8(1))* Farrar, Straus & Giroux.

Frosh, Stephen & Emerson, Peter. Critical Narrative Analysis in Psychology: A Guide to Practice. rev. ed. 2009. (ENG.). 184p. pap. 37.00 *(978-0-230-59540-8(5))* Palgrave Macmillan.

Garris, Grant. Under the Red Velvet Cover: Conquering Victimhood & Breaking the Silence of Abuse, Corruption & Family Secrets - My Life Journey. 2010. 252p. pap. 16.95 *(978-1-4490-6910-0(X))* AuthorHouse.

Goode, Sarah Del. Understanding & Addressing Adult Sexual Attraction to Children. 2009. (ENG., Illus.). 228p. pap. 39.95 *(978-0-415-44626-6(0))* Routledge.

Goode, Sarah Del & Goode, Sarah D. Understanding & Addressing Adult Sexual Attraction to Children: A Study of Paedophiles in Contemporary Society. 2009. (ENG., Illus.). 240p. 140.00 *(978-0-415-44625-9(2))* Routledge.

Hall, Allan & Leidig, Michael. Girl in the Cellar: The Natascha Kampusch Story. 288p. 2010. mass mkt. 7.99 *(978-0-06-194529-8(3))* 2007. (Illus.). 24.95 *(978-0-06-134510-4(5))* HarperCollins Pubs.

Jasper, Margaret C. Missing & Exploited Children: How to Protect Your Child. 2006. (Legal Almanac Ser.). 232p. 47.00 *(978-0-19-532157-9(X))* Oxford Univ. Pr., Inc.

King, Gary C. Stolen in the Night: The True Story of a Family's Murder, a Kidnapping & the Child Who Survived. 2007. (ENG., Illus.). 256p. mass mkt. 7.99 *(978-0-312-94205-2(2),* St. Martin's Paperbacks) St. Martin's Pr.

Leon, Chrysanthi. Sex Fiends, Perverts, & Pedophiles: Understanding Sex Crime Policy in America. 2011. (ENG., Illus.). 263p. 70.00 *(978-0-8147-5258-6(6));* pap. 23.00 *(978-0-8147-5326-2(4))* New York Univ. Pr.

Leon, Chrysanthi S. Sex Fiends, Perverts, & Pedophiles: Understanding Sex Crime Policy in America. 2011. (Illus.). 272p. E-Book *(978-0-8147-5313-2(2))* New York Univ. Pr.

Marsh, Stefanie & Pancevski, Bojan. I'm No Monster: The Horrifying True Story of Josef Fritzl. 2011. (ENG.). 336p. (gr. 12). 9.99 *(978-0-425-24452-4(0),* Berkley) Penguin Group (USA) Inc.

McIntyre, Mike. Devil among Us: How Canada Failed to Stop a Pedophile. 2008. (ENG.). 320p. mass mkt. 11.95 *(978-1-894283-80-9(5))* Great Plains Pubns. CAN. Dist: Univ. of Toronto Pr.

Meyer, Anneke. The Child at Risk: Paedophiles, Media Responses & Public Opinion. 2007. (ENG., Illus.). 192p. 95.00 *(978-0-7190-7344-1(8))* Manchester Univ. Pr. GBR. Dist: Macmillan.

Philpot, Terry. Understanding Child Abuse: The Partners of Child Sex Offenders Tell Their Stories. 2009. X, 150p. pap. 43.95 *(978-0-415-45600-5(2))* 2008. 150p. 140.00 *(978-0-415-40949-0(7))* Routledge.

Reauthorization of the Adam Walsh ACT: Hearing Before the Subcommittee on Crime, Terrorism, & Homeland Security of the Committee on the Judiciary, House of Representatives, One Hundred Twelfth Congress, First Session, February 15, 2011. 2011. iii, 94p. ***(978-0-16-088615-7(5),*** 552-070-42784-8) United States Government Printing Office.

Sandoval, Terrell G. Adam Walsh Child Protection & Safety Act: Analysis & Law. 2010. (Children's Issues, Laws & Programs Ser.). 166p. 115.00 *(978-1-61668-808-0(4))* Nova Science Pubs., Inc.

Sauerwein, Kristina. Invisible Chains: Shawn Hornbeck & the Kidnapping Case That Shook the Nation. 2008. (ENG., Illus.). 336p. pap. 18.95 *(978-1-59921-344-6(3),* Lyons Pr.) Globe Pequot Pr., The.

Schinaia. On Paedophilia. 2010. 352p. pap. 41.95 *(978-1-85575-589-5(0))* Karnac Bks. GBR. Dist: Stylus Publishing, LLC.

Tirone Smith, Mary-Ann. Girls of Tender Age: A Memoir. 2007. (ENG., Illus.). 320p. pap. 19.99 *(978-0-7432-7978-9(6),* Free Pr.) Free Pr.

Turton, Jackie. Child Abuse Gender & Society. 2010. (ENG.). 160p. pap. 39.95 *(978-0-415-88294-1(X))* Routledge.

Wills, Laurie, ed. Sexual Predators. 2008. (Social Issues Firsthand Ser.). (ENG., Illus.). 127p. (J). (gr. 4-7). lib. bdg. 31.80 *(978-0-7377-4032-5(9),* Greenhaven Pr., Inc.) Cengage Gale.

Zilney, Laura, et al. Perverts & Predators. 2009. (Issues in Crime & Justice Ser.). (ENG.). 218p. pap. 27.50 *(978-0-7425-6623-1(4))* Rowman & Littlefield Publishers, Inc.

Zilney/Zilney. Perverts & Predators: The Making of Sexual Offending Laws. 2009. (Issues in Crime & Justice Ser.). (ENG.). 218p. 75.00 *(978-0-7425-6622-4(6))* Rowman & Littlefield Publishers, Inc.

CHILD MORTALITY

see Children—Mortality

CHILD MUSICIANS

Bancroft, Tony. Growing Your Musician: A Practical Guide for Band & Orchestra Parents. Bancroft, Tony, ed. 2nd ed. 2007. (ENG., Illus.). 162p. 55.00 *(978-1-57886-599-4(9));* pap. 21.95 *(978-1-57886-600-7(6))* Rowman & Littlefield Education.

Cooper, Barry. Child Composers & Their Works. 2009. (ENG.). 224p. 69.00 *(978-0-8108-6911-0(X))* Scarecrow Pr., Inc.

Revesz, G. The Psychology of a Musical Prodigy. 192p. 2008. 37.95 *(978-1-4366-7674-8(6))* 2007. (ENG.). per. 22.95 *(978-1-4325-8858-8(3))* Kessinger Publishing, LLC.

CHILD NEGLECT

see Child Abuse

CHILD PLACING

see Adoption; Foster Home Care

CHILD PORNOGRAPHY

Aspatore Books Staff, compiled by. Evidence Discovery in Internet Pornography Cases: Leading Lawyers on Obtaining, Examining, & Refuting Evidence During a Pornography Case (Inside the Minds) 2011. 152p. pap. 85.00 ***(978-0-314-27804-3(4))*** Aspatore Bks.

Aspatore Books Staff, compiled by. Strategies for Defending Internet Pornography Cases: Leading Lawyers on Analyzing Electronic Documents, Utilizing Expert Witnesses, & Explaining Technological Evidence. 2008. (Inside the Minds Ser.). 236p. pap. 90.00 *(978-0-314-19999-7(3))* Aspatore Bks.

Combating Child Pornography by Eliminating Pornographers' Access to the Financial Payment System: Hearing Before the Committee on Banking, Housing, & Urban Affairs, United States Senate, One Hundred Ninth Congress, Second Session, on Drawing Attention to the Problem of Child Pornography & to Highlight What Financial Service Companies Can Do to Eliminate It from the Financial Payment System, Tuesday, September 19, 2006. 2009. (Illus.). iii, 107p. *(978-0-16-084736-3(2),* 552-070-40213-6) United States Government Printing Office.

Combating the Sexual Exploitation of Children: Hearing Before the Commission on Security & Cooperation in Europe, One Hundred Ninth Congress, Second Session, September 27, 2006. 2007. iii, 98p. *(978-0-16-079402-5(1),* 552-070-36414-5) United States Government Printing Office.

Cooper, Sharon W., et al. Child Sexual Exploitation Quick Reference: For Healthcare, Social Service, & Law Enforcement Professionals. 2007. (ENG., Illus.). 384p. spiral bd. 52.00 *(978-1-878060-21-1(X))* STM Learning, Inc.

Data Retention As a Tool for Investigating Internet Child Pornography & Other Internet Crimes: Hearing Before the Subcommittee on Crime, Terrorism, & Homeland Security of the Committee on the Judiciary, House of Representatives, One Hundred Twelfth Congress, First Session, January 25, 2011. 2011. iii, 81p. ***(978-0-16-088295-1(8),*** 552-070-42600-1) United States Government Printing Office.

Davidson, Julia & Gottschalk, Petter, eds. Internet Child Abuse: Current Research & Policy. (Illus.). 216p. 2011. (ENG.). pap. 44.95 ***(978-0-415-69780-4(8))*** 2010. 125.00 *(978-0-415-55980-5(4))* Taylor & Francis Group GBR. (Routledge Cavendish). Dist: Taylor & Francis Group.

Dudley Gold, Susan. Child Pornography: John D. Ashcroft, Attorney General V. Free Speech Coalition. 2012. (J). 42.79 ***(978-1-60870-907-6(8))*** Marshall Cavendish Corp.

Fielding, Timmy. Untold Stories: How I Survived A Child Porn Ring. 2011. 232p. 28.95 ***(978-1-4620-4715-4(7));*** pap. 18.95 ***(978-1-4620-4714-7(9))*** iUniverse, Inc.

Gillespie, Alisdair A. Child Pornography. (ENG., Illus.). 392p. 2012. pap. 45.00 ***(978-0-415-66741-8(0))*** 2011. 135.00 *(978-0-415-49987-3(9))* Taylor & Francis Group GBR. (Routledge Cavendish). Dist: Taylor & Francis Group.

Gillespie, Alisdair A. & Gillespie, Alisdair. Child Exploitation & Communication Technologies. 2008. (Illus.). 160p. (C). pap. 39.95 *(978-1-905541-23-2(6))* Russell Hse. Publishing Ltd. GBR. Dist: International Specialized Bk. Services.

Hiber, Amanda. Child Pornography. 2009. (At Issue Ser.). (ENG., Illus.). 128p. (gr. 10-12). 31.80 *(978-0-7377-4288-6(7));* pap. 22.50 *(978-0-7377-4287-9(9))* Cengage Gale. (Greenhaven Pr., Inc.).

Howitt, Dennis & Sheldon, Kerry. Sex Offenders & the Internet. 2007. (ENG.). 312p. 155.00 *(978-0-470-02800-1(9));* per. 66.95 *(978-0-470-02801-8(7))* Wiley, John & Sons, Inc. (Wiley).

Milner, Claire & O'Donnell, Ian. Child Pornography: Crime, Computers & Society. 2011. (ENG., Illus.). 240p. (C). 84.95 *(978-1-84392-357-2(2))* Willan Publishing GBR. Dist: Taylor & Francis Group.

Nelson, David, ed. Online Pornography. 2012. (Opposing Viewpoints Ser.). (ENG., Illus.). 240p. (gr. 10-12). pap. 41.70 ***(978-0-7377-5906-8(2),*** Greenhaven Pr., Inc.); (YA). (gr. 9-12). lib. bdg. 28.90 ***(978-0-7377-5905-1(4))*** Cengage Gale.

O'Donnell, Ian & Milner, Claire. Child Pornography: Crime, Computers & Society. 2007. (Illus.). 259p. (C). pap. *(978-1-84392-356-5(4))* Willan Publishing.

Ost, Suzanne. Child Pornography & Sexual Grooming: Legal & Societal Responses. 2009. (Cambridge Studies in Law & Society Ser.). (ENG.). 288p. 95.00 *(978-0-521-88582-9(5))* Cambridge Univ. Pr.

Powell, Lynn. Framing Innocence: A Mother's Photographs, a Prosecutor's Zeal, & a Small Town's Response. (ENG., Illus.). 320p. 2011. pap. 17.95 *(978-1-59558-714-5(4))* 2010. 25.95 *(978-1-59558-551-6(6))* New Pr., The.

Priyadarsini, S. & Hartjen, Clayton A. The Global Victimization of Children: Problems & Solutions. 2011. (ENG., Illus.). xiii, 402p. 169.00 ***(978-1-4614-2178-8(0)***, 1461421780) Springer.

Protecting Children from Internet Pornographers ACT of 2011: Hearing Before the Subcommittee on Crime, Terrorism, & Homeland Security of the Committee on the Judiciary, House of Representatives, One Hundred Twelfth Congress, First Session, on H.R. 1981, July 12, 2011. 2011. iv, 88p. ***(978-0-16-089986-7(9)***, 552-070-43770-3) United States Government Printing Office.

Quayle, Ethel & Ribisl, Kurt M., eds. Internet Child Pornography. 2012. (ENG., Illus.). 296p. (C). 150.00 ***(978-0-415-68940-3(6))***; pap. 53.95 ***(978-0-415-68941-0(4))*** Routledge.

Sandoval, Terrell G. Adam Walsh Child Protection & Safety Act: Analysis & Law. 2010. (Children's Issues, Laws & Programs Ser.). 166p. 115.00 *(978-1-61668-808-0(4))* Nova Science Pubs., Inc.

Savirimuthu, Joseph. Online Child Safety: Law, Technology & Governance. 2012. (ENG., Illus.). 376p. 90.00 ***(978-0-230-24152-7(2))*** Palgrave Macmillan.

Sexual Exploitation of Children over the Internet: A Staff Report Prepared for the Use of the Committee on Energy & Commerce, U.S. House of Representatives, 109th Congress. 2007. v, 33p. *(978-0-16-078078-3(0)*, 552-070-35491-3) United States Government Printing Office.

Sher, Julian. Caught in the Web: Inside the Police Hunt to Rescue Children from Online Predators. 2008. (ENG.). 336p. pap. 15.95 *(978-0-7382-1171-8(0))* Da Capo Pr., Inc.

Smith, Sara M. Child Pornography & the Law in Canada: A New Agenda for the Information Age. 2011. (ENG.). 228p. (C). pap. 66.67 ***(978-0-558-75235-4(7))*** Pearson Learning Solutions.

United States Congress Senate Committee, creator. Challenges & Solutions for Protecting Our Children from Violence & Exploitation in the 21st Century. 2010. (ENG.). 154p. pap. 21.75 ***(978-1-240-54986-3(5)***, BiblioGov) BiblioBazaar.

CHILD PROSTITUTION

ABBE Research Division Staff. Children in Prostitution: Index & Medical Analysis of New Clinical/Research Information for All Nations. 2007. (Illus.). 160p. ring bd. 74.50 *(978-0-7883-4799-3(3)*, 07883-47993) ABBE Pubs. Assn. of Washington, D.C.

Alexzander, Rene. Branded Too Much Trouble: One Man's True Story, Every Child's Nightmare. 2011. 132p. 21.23 ***(978-1-4634-1626-3(1))***; pap. 14.99 ***(978-1-4634-1625-6(3))*** AuthorHouse.

Bryant, Nick. The Franklin Scandal: A Story of Powerbrokers, Child Abuse & Betrayal. 2012. (Illus.). 656p. pap. 19.95 *(978-1-936296-07-1(1))* Trine Day.

Clinton, Hillary Rodham, pref. Trafficking in Persons Report (10th Ed.) 2010. 372p. (C). pap. 45.00 *(978-1-4379-3716-9(0))* DIANE Publishing Co.

Combating the Sexual Exploitation of Children: Hearing Before the Commission on Security & Cooperation in Europe, One Hundred Ninth Congress, Second Session, September 27, 2006. 2007. iii, 98p. *(978-0-16-079402-5(1)*, 552-070-36414-5) United States Government Printing Office.

Cooper, Sharon W., et al. Child Sexual Exploitation Quick Reference: For Healthcare, Social Service, & Law Enforcement Professionals. 2007. (ENG., Illus.). 384p. spiral bd. 52.00 *(978-1-878060-21-1(X))* STM Learning, Inc.

Dank, Meredith L. The Commercial Sexual Exploitation of Children. 2011. 166p. 65.00 *(978-1-59332-409-4(X))* LFB Scholarly Publishing LLC.

Domestic Minor Sex Trafficking: Hearing Before the Subcommittee on Crime, Terrorism, & Homeland Security of the Committee on the Judiciary, House of Representatives, One Hundred Eleventh Congress, Second Session, September 15, 2010. 2011. (Illus.). iv, 407p. ***(978-0-16-087958-6(2)***, 552-070-42390-7) United States Government Printing Office.

Dorais, Michel & Corriveau, Patrice. Gangs & Girls: Understanding Juvenile Prostitution. 2009. (ENG., Illus.). 192p. (C). *(978-0-7735-3441-4(5))*; pap. *(978-0-7735-3442-1(3))* McGill-Queen's Univ. Pr.

Gillespie, Alisdair A. & Gillespie, Alisdair. Child Exploitation & Communication Technologies. 2008. (Illus.). 160p. (C). pap. 39.95 *(978-1-905541-23-2(6))* Russell Hse. Publishing Ltd. GBR. Dist: International Specialized Bk. Services.

Grant, David & Grant, Beth. Beyond the Soiled Curtain: Project Rescue's Fight for the Victims of the Sex-Slave Industry. 2007. (Illus.). 224p. pap. 14.95 *(978-1-880689-19-6(7))* Onward Bks., Inc.

In Our Own Backyard: Child Prostitution & Sex Trafficking in the United States: Hearing Before the Subcommittee on Human Rights & the Law of the Committee on the Judiciary, United States Senate, One Hundred Eleventh Congress, Second Session, February 24, 2010. 2010. iii, 87p. *(978-0-16-086764-4(9)*, 552-070-41685-4) United States Government Printing Office.

Landon, Maria. Daddy's Little Earner: A Heartbreaking True Story of a Brave Little Girl's Escape from Violence. 2008. (ENG.). 352p. pap. 12.95 *(978-0-00-726877-1(7))* HarperCollins Pubs. Ltd. GBR. Dist: Independent Pubs. Group.

Lloyd, Rachel. Girls Like Us: Fighting for a World Where Girls Are Not for Sale - A Memoir. (ENG.). 288p. 2012. pap. 15.99 ***(978-0-06-158206-6(9)***, HarperPerennial) 2011. (Illus.). 24.99 *(978-0-06-158205-9(0))* HarperCollins Pubs.

Malarek, Victor. The Johns: Sex for Sale & the Men Who Buy It. 2011. (ENG.). 328p. pap. 14.95 *(978-1-61145-012-5(8)*, 611012, Arcade Publishing) Skyhorse Publishing Co., Inc.

—The Natashas: The Horrific Inside Story of Slavery, Rape, & Murder in the Global Sex Trade. 2011. (ENG.). 320p. pap. 14.95 *(978-1-61145-326-3(7)*, 611326, Arcade Publishing) Skyhorse Publishing Co., Inc.

Mam, Somaly. The Road of Lost Innocence: The True Story of a Cambodian Heroine. 2009. (ENG.). 224p. pap. 15.00 *(978-0-385-52622-7(9))* Spiegel & Grau.

McCabe, Kimberly A. The Trafficking of Persons: National & International Responses. 2008. 176p. (C). pap. 32.95 *(978-0-8204-6327-8(2))* Lang, Peter Publishing, Inc.

Parrot, Andrea & Cummings, Nina. Sexual Enslavement of Girls & Women Worldwide, 1 vol. 2008. (Practical & Applied Psychology Ser.). (Illus.). 200p. 44.95 *(978-0-275-99291-0(8)*, C9291, Praeger Pubs.) Greenwood Publishing Group, Inc.

Priyadarsini, S. & Hartjen, Clayton A. The Global Victimization of Children: Problems & Solutions. 2011. (ENG., Illus.). xiii, 402p. 169.00 ***(978-1-4614-2178-8(0)***, 1461421780) Springer.

Robinson, Cynthia Cole. From the Classroom to the Corner: Female Dropouts' Reflections on Their School Years. 2006. 240p. (C). pap. 31.95 *(978-0-8204-8189-0(0))* Lang, Peter Publishing, Inc.

Rostagnol, Susana & Grabino, Valeria. Historias en el Silencio: Prostitución infantil y adolescente en Montevideo y área Metropolitana. 2007.Tr. of Stories of silence: child & adolescent prostitution in Montevideo & metropolitan Area. (SPA.). 120p. per. *(978-92-806-4236-0(7))* United Nations Children's Fund, The (UNICEF).

Roy, Norman Jean & Pearl, Mariane. Traffik. 2008. (ENG.). 224p. 50.00 *(978-1-57687-474-5(5))* powerHouse Cultural Entertainment, Inc.

Sanllorente, Jaume. Sonrisas de Bombay: El Viaje Que Cambió Mi Destino. 2007. (Plataforma Testimonio Ser.). (SPA., Illus.). 208p. pap. 26.95 ***(978-84-96981-01-0(0))*** Plataforma Editorial SL ESP. Dist: Independent Pubs. Group.

Sher, Julian. Somebody's Daughter: The Hidden Story of America's Prostituted Children & the Battle to Save Them. 2011. (ENG.). 352p. 24.95 *(978-1-56976-565-4(0))* Chicago Review Pr., Inc.

The Slave Across the Street: The true story of an American teen caught in human Trafficking. 2010. 160p. pap. 14.99 *(978-0-9823286-8-2(0))* Ampelon Publishing, LLC.

Stead, William T. The Maiden Tribute of Modern Babylon: The Report of the Secret Commission. Simpson, Antony E., ed. & anno. by. 2007. 207p. lib. bdg. 65.00 *(978-0-9791116-0-0(9))* True Bill Pr., The.

United Nations Children's Fund. South Asia in Action: Preventing & Responding to Child Trafficking - Child Rights-based Programme Practices. 2009. (Insight Innocenti Ser.). 42p. pap. 20.00 *(978-88-89129-77-7(8))* United Nations Children's Fund, The (UNICEF).

—Trafficking for Sexual Exploitation & other Exploitative Purposes. 2009. 24p. pap. 15.00 *(978-88-89129-21-0(2))* United Nations Children's Fund, The (UNICEF).

United Nations, Economic and Social Commission for Asia and the Pacific Staff. Pacific perspectives on the commercial sexual exploitation & sexual abuse of children & Youth. 2009. 132p. pap. 15.00 *(978-92-1-120552-7(2))* United Nations Pubns.

United Nations Staff, contrib. by. Toolkit for Implementing & Monitoring the East Asia & Pacific Regional Commitment & Action Plan Against Commercial Sexual Exploitation of Children. 2006. (ENG.). 184p. pap. 28.00 *(978-92-1-120470-4(4))* United Nations Pubns.

CHILD PSYCHIATRY

Here are entered works on the clinical and therapeutic aspects of mental disorders in children. Descriptive works on mental disorders of children are entered under Child Psychopathology. Works on mentally ill children themselves are entered under Mentally Ill Children.

see also Adolescent Psychiatry; Child Development Deviations; Child Mental Health; Child Psychology; Child Psychopathology; Child Psychotherapy; Cognition Disorders in Children; Infant Psychiatry; Mentally Ill Children; Problem Solving in Children; School Phobia

American Academy of Child and Adolescent Psychiatry (AACAP). Attention-Deficit / Hyperactivity Disorder GUIDELINES Pocketcard: American Academy of Child & Adolescent Psychiatry (2011) 2011. (ENG.). 6p. 9.95 ***(978-0-9846667-6-2(2))*** International Guidelines Ctr., Inc.

Arden, John B. & Linford, Lloyd. Brain-Based Therapy with Children & Adolescents: Evidence-Based Treatment for Everyday Practice. 2008. (ENG.). 324p. pap. 45.00 *(978-0-470-13891-5(2)*, Wiley) Wiley, John & Sons, Inc.

Banaschewski, Tobias & Rohde, L. A. Biological Child Psychiatry: Recent Trends & Developments. 2008. (Advances in Biological Psychiatry Ser.). (Illus.). 256p. *(978-3-8055-8482-1(2))* Karger, S. AG.

Bostic, Jeffrey Q. & Bagnell, Alexa L. Evidence-Based School Psychiatry - An Issue of Child & Adolescent Psychiatric Clinics of North America. 2012. (Clinics: Internal Medicine Ser.: 21-1). (ENG., Illus.). 960p. 115.00 ***(978-1-4557-3839-7(5)***, Saunders) Elsevier - Health Sciences Div.

Boston Process Study Group Staff. Change in Psychotherapy - A Unifying Paradigm. 2010. (ENG.). 368p. 35.00 *(978-0-393-70599-7(4)*, 70599) Norton, W. W. & Co., Inc.

Braaten, Ellen. How to Find Mental Health Care for Your Child. 2010. x, 265p. E-Book *(978-1-4338-0899-9(4))*; 280p. pap. 19.95 *(978-1-4338-0898-2(6))* American Psychological Assn.

Braaten, Ellen B. The Child Clinician's Report-Writing Handbook. 2007. (Clinician's Toolbox Ser.). (ENG.). 380p. (gr. -1-13). pap. 45.00 *(978-1-59385-395-2(5))* Guilford Pubns., Inc.

Brambring, Michael, et al, eds. Children at Risk: Assessment, Longitudinal Research & Intervention. (Prevention & Intervention in Childhood & Adolescence Ser.). (ENG.). XIV, 490p. 196.00 ***(978-3-11-179122-7(X))*** De Gruyter, Walter Inc.

Brohl, Kathryn. Working with Traumatized Children: A Handbook for Healing. 2007. pap. *(978-1-58760-097-5(8)*, CWLA Pr.) Child Welfare League of America, Inc.

Castell, Rolf. Hundert Jahre Kinder- und Jugendpsychiatrie. Castell, Rolf, ed. 2008. (GER.). 285p. (C). 60.00 *(978-3-89971-509-5(8))* Vandenhoeck & Ruprecht GmbH & Co. KG DEU. Dist: ISD.

Cepeda, Claudio. Clinical Manual for the Psychiatric Interview of Children & Adolescents. 2009. 59.00 *(978-1-58562-343-3(1))* American Psychiatric Publishing, Inc.

Cheng, Keith & Myers, Kathleen M., eds. Child & Adolescent Psychiatry: The Essentials. 2nd rev. ed. 2010. (ENG.). 560p. 94.99 *(978-1-60547-443-4(6))* Lippincott Williams & Wilkins.

Claveirole, Anne & Gaughan, Martin, eds. Understanding Children & Young People's Mental Health. 2010. (ENG., Illus.). 328p. pap. 47.99 *(978-0-470-72345-6(9)*, Wiley-Blackwell) Wiley, John & Sons, Inc.

Cobert. Tarascon Pediatric Psychiatrica. rev. ed. 2011. 298p. pap. 24.95 *(978-0-7637-7640-4(8)*, Tarascon) Jones & Bartlett Learning, LLC.

Cohen, Donald J. Life Is with Others: Selected Writings on Child Psychiatry. Martin, Andres & King, Robert A., eds. 2006. (ENG.). 304p. 37.00 *(978-0-300-11466-9(4))* Yale Univ. Pr.

Corcoran, Jacqueline. Mental Health Treatment for Children & Adolescents, 1 vol. 2010. (Evidence-Based Practice Ser.). (ENG., Illus.). 304p. 39.95 *(978-0-19-537571-8(8))* Oxford Univ. Pr., Inc.

Cram101 Textbook Reviews & Cram101 Textbook Reviews. Outlines & Highlights for Camps & Mental Health, an Issue of Child & Adolescent Psychiatric Clinics by Alicia Mcauliffe-Fogarty, Isbn: 97814160504. 2011. 70p. pap. 27.95 ***(978-1-61461-273-5(0))*** Cram101 Inc.

—Outlines & Highlights for Cultural Issues in Pediatric Mental Health, an Issue of Child & Adolescent Psychiatric Clinics of North America by Shashan. 2011. 86p. pap. 27.95 ***(978-1-61461-226-1(9))*** Cram101 Inc.

—Outlines & Highlights for Infant & Early Childhood Mental Health, an Issue of Child & Adolescent Psychiatric Clinics of North America by Mary Margaret. 2011. 98p. pap. 27.95 ***(978-1-61461-219-3(6))*** Cram101 Inc.

—Outlines & Highlights for Neuropsychiatric Genetic Syndromes, an Issue of Child & Adolescent Psychiatric Clinics by Doron Gothelf, Isbn: 97814160504. 2011. 86p. pap. 27.95 ***(978-1-61461-253-7(6))*** Cram101 Inc.

Cram101 Textbook Reviews Staff. Outlines & Highlights for Abnormal Child & Adolescent Psychology by Rita Wicks-Nelson, Allen C Israel, Isbn: 9780132359788. 2009. 140p. pap. 28.95 *(978-1-4288-7992-8(7))* Cram101 Inc.

Dulcan, Mina K., ed. Dulcan's Textbook of Child & Adolescent Psychiatry. 2009. (Illus.). 1104p. 249.00 *(978-1-58562-323-5(7))* American Psychiatric Publishing, Inc.

—Helping Parents, Youth, & Teachers Understand Medications for Behavioral & Emotional Problems: A Resource Book of Medication Information Handouts. 3rd ed. 2006. 733p. pap. 99.00 incl. cd-rom *(978-1-58562-253-5(2)*, 62253) American Psychiatric Publishing, Inc.

Dulcan, Mina K. & Lake, MaryBeth. Concise Guide to Child & Adolescent Psychiatry. 4th ed. 2011. (Illus.). 405p. pap. 53.00 ***(978-1-58562-416-4(0))*** American Psychiatric Publishing, Inc.

Elissa P. Benedek, M. d., et al. Principles & Practice of Child & Adolescent Forensic Mental Health. 2009. (ENG., Illus.). 531p. 135.00 *(978-1-58562-336-5(9))* American Psychiatric Publishing, Inc.

Enzer & Goin. 1st Chance-Social Emotions. pap. 15.95 *(978-0-8027-7263-3(3))* Walker & Co.

Ernst, Monique & Rumsey, Judith M., eds. Functional Neuroimaging in Child Psychiatry. 2010. (ENG., Illus.). 456p. pap. 52.00 *(978-0-521-12658-8(4))* Cambridge Univ. Pr.

Fitzgerald, Hiram E., et al, eds. International Perspectives on Children & Mental Health Vol. 1: Development & Context, 2 vols. 2011. (Child Psychology & Mental Health Ser.). (Illus.). 500p. 124.95 *(978-0-313-38298-7(0)*, A2697C, Praeger Pubs.) Greenwood Publishing Group, Inc.

Fritsch, Sandra L. & Trivedi, Harsh K. Interface Between Pediatrics & Children's Mental Health: Pediatric Clinics. 2011. (Clinics: Internal Medicine Ser.: 58-4). (ENG.). 88.00 ***(978-1-4557-1229-8(9)***, Saunders) Elsevier - Health Sciences Div.

Galanter, Cathryn A. & Jensen, Peter S. DSM-IV-TR Casebook & Treatment Guide for Child Mental Health. 2008. (Illus.). 752p. pap. 89.00 *(978-1-58562-310-5(5))* American Psychiatric Publishing, Inc.

Galatzer-Levy, Robert M., et al, eds. The Scientific Basis of Child Custody Decisions. 2nd ed. 2009. (ENG.). 499p. 90.00 *(978-0-470-03858-1(6)*, Wiley) Wiley, John & Sons, Inc.

Garralda, M. Elena. Culture & Conflict in Child & Adolescent Mental Health. 2008. (ENG., Illus.). 292p. per. 39.99 *(978-0-7657-0593-8(1)*, Aronson, Jason) Rowman & Littlefield Publishers, Inc.

—Increasing Awareness of Child & Adolescent Mental Health. 2010. (ENG., Illus.). 338p. 83.99 *(978-0-7657-0661-4(X)*, Aronson, Jason) Rowman & Littlefield Publishers, Inc.

Garralda, M. Elena & Raynaud, Jean Philippe. Culture & Conflict in Child & Adolescent Mental Health. 2008. (ENG., Illus.). 292p. 89.50 *(978-0-7657-0592-1(3)*, Aronson, Jason) Rowman & Littlefield Publishers, Inc.

—Increasing Awareness of Child & Adolescent Mental Health. 2010. (Illus.). xvii, 319p. 34.95 *(978-0-7657-0663-8(6)*, Aronson, Jason) Rowman & Littlefield Publishers, Inc.

Garralda, M. Elena & Raynaud, Jean-Philippe. Increasing Awareness of Child & Adolescent Mental Health. 2010. (ENG., Illus.). 338p. pap. 36.99 *(978-0-7657-0662-1(8)*, Aronson, Jason) Rowman & Littlefield Publishers, Inc.

Gillberg, Christopher, et al, eds. A Clinician's Handbook of Child & Adolescent Psychiatry. 2011. (ENG., Illus.). 764p. pap. 85.00 *(978-0-521-29484-3(3))* Cambridge Univ. Pr.

Goodman, R., et al. Kinderpsychiatrie kompakt. Rothenberger, A., tr. Orig. Title: R. Goodman, S. Scott, Child Psychiatry, Second Edition, ISBN 1405115246. XII, 465p. pap. 64.00 *(978-3-7985-1234-4(5)*, 3798512345); 2nd ed. 2006. XIV, 538p. pap. 69.95 *(978-3-7985-1612-0(X)*, 379851612X) Steinkopff, Dietrich DEU. Dist: Springer.

Green, Wayne Hugo. Child & Adolescent Clinical Psychopharmacology. 4th rev. ed. 2006. (ENG., Illus.). 400p. per. 87.50 *(978-0-7817-5950-2(1))* Lippincott Williams & Wilkins.

Greenberg, Rosalie. Bipolar Kids: Helping Your Child Find Calm in the Mood Storm. 2008. (ENG.). 316p. pap. 16.99 *(978-0-7382-1113-8(3))* Da Capo Pr., Inc.

Hendren. Child & Adolescent Psychiatry for the Specialty Board Review. 3rd rev. ed. 2007. (Continuing Education in Psychiatry & Psychology Ser.). (ENG.). 184p. 39.95 *(978-0-415-95598-0(X))* Routledge.

Houston, Michael & Sarvet, Barry D. Leadership & Management Core Competencies, an Issue of Child & Adolescent Psychiatric Clinics of North America. 2010. (Clinics: Internal Medicine Ser.: 19-1). (ENG., Illus.). xvii, 182p. 105.00 *(978-1-4377-1802-7(7)*, Saunders) Elsevier - Health Sciences Div.

Ivanenko, Anna, ed. Sleep & Psychiatric Disorders in Children & Adolescents. 2008. (ENG., Illus.). 432p. 200.00 *(978-1-4200-4807-0(4)*, Informa Healthcare) Taylor & Francis Group GBR. Dist: Taylor & Francis Group.

Joshi, Shashank & Pumariega, Andres. Cultural Issues in Pediatric Mental Health, an Issue of Child & Adolescent Psychiatric Clinics of North America. 2010. (Clinics: Internal Medicine Ser.: 19-4). (ENG., Illus.). xvii, 662p. 105.00 *(978-1-4377-2433-2(7)*, Saunders) Elsevier - Health Sciences Div.

Kendall, Philip C. & Comer, Jonathan. Childhood Disorders. 2nd rev. ed. 2010. (Clinical Psychology: A Modular Course Ser.). (ENG., Illus.). 304p. (C). 85.00 *(978-0-415-48641-5(6))*; pap. 29.95 *(978-0-415-48642-2(4))* Taylor & Francis Group GBR. (Psychology Press). Dist: Taylor & Francis Group.

King, Robert A., et al, eds. The Psychoanalytic Study of the Child, Vol. 61. 2007. (Psychoanalytic Study of the Child Ser.). (ENG., Illus.). 368p. 70.00 *(978-0-300-11996-1(8))* Yale Univ. Pr.

Klykylo, William M. & Kay, Jerald, eds. Clinical Child Psychiatry. 3rd ed. 2012. (ENG.). 564p. pap. 95.00 ***(978-1-119-99334-6(2)***, Wiley-Blackwell) Wiley, John & Sons, Inc.

Koletzko, B., et al. Paediatric Parenteral Nutrition: A Practical Reference Guide. 2008. (Illus.). 66p. pap. *(978-3-8055-8606-1(X))* Karger, S. AG.

Kothare, Sanjeev V. & Kotagal, Suresh. Sleep in Childhood Neurological Disorders. 2010. 324p. 85.00 *(978-1-933864-96-9(6))* Demos Medical Publishing, LLC.

Kruh, Ivan & Grisso, Thomas. Evaluation of Juveniles' Competence to Stand Trial. 2008. (Best Practices in Forensic Mental Health Assessment Ser.). (ENG., Illus.). 296p. (C). pap. 35.00 *(978-0-19-532307-8(6))* Oxford Univ. Pr., Inc.

Lillas, Connie & Turnbull, Janiece. Infant/Child Mental Health, Early Intervention, & Relationship-Based Therapies: A Neurorelational Framework for Interdisciplinary Practice. 2009. (Norton Series on Interpersonal Neurobiology Ser.). (ENG., Illus.). 420p. 52.00 *(978-0-393-70425-9(4)*, 70425) Norton, W. W. & Co., Inc.

Luby, Joan L., ed. Handbook of Preschool Mental Health: Development, Disorders, & Treatment. (ENG., Illus.). 430p. 2009. pap. 35.00 *(978-1-60623-350-4(5))* 2006. 60.00 *(978-1-59385-313-6(0))* Guilford Pubns., Inc.

Maximilian T. Badoy. Uncommon Sense. 2009. 108p. pap. 16.49 *(978-1-4389-0066-7(X))* AuthorHouse.

McCarroll, Elizabeth M. The Quality of Mother-Child Interaction in Early Adolescence. 2008. 140p. pap. *(978-3-639-06333-2(3))* VDM Verlag Dr. Mueller e.K.

McCarthy, Malia & Hendren, Robert L. Child & Adolescent Psychiatry for the General Psychiatrist, an Issue of Psychiatric Clinics. 2009. (Clinics: Internal Medicine Ser.: 32-1). (ENG., Illus.). 240p. 99.00 *(978-1-4377-0534-8(0)*, Saunders) Elsevier - Health Sciences Div.

McDougall, Tim, ed. Child & Adolescent Mental Health Nursing. 2006. (ENG., Illus.). 328p. pap. 66.99 *(978-1-4051-2801-8(1)*, Wiley-Blackwell) Wiley, John & Sons, Inc.

Midgley, Nick. Child Psychotherapy & Research: New Approaches, Emerging Findings. Grainger, Eve et al, eds. 2009. (ENG., Illus.). 248p. (C). 110.00 *(978-0-415-42202-4(7))* Routledge.

—Child Psychotherapy & Research: New Approaches, Emerging Findings. Nesic-Vuckovic, Tanja et al, eds. 2009. (ENG., Illus.). 248p. (C). pap. 40.00 *(978-0-415-42203-1(5))* Routledge.

Nass, Ruth D. & Frank, Yitzchak, eds. Cognitive & Behavioral Abnormalities of Pediatric Diseases, 1 vol. 2010. (ENG., Illus.). 752p. pap. *(978-0-19-534268-0(2))* Oxford Univ. Pr.

Oldfield, Amelia. Interactive Music Therapy in Child & Family Psychiatry. 2006. (ENG., Illus.). 192p. per. *(978-1-84310-444-5(X))* Kingsley, Jessica Ltd.

Olfman, Sharna. No Child Left Different. 2008. (ENG.). 260p. pap. 27.95 *(978-1-57886-774-5(6))* Rowman & Littlefield Education.

Poncin, Yann B., et al. Lewis's Child & Adolescent Psychiatry Review: 1400 Questions to Help You Pass the Boards. 4th rev. ed. 2009. (ENG.). 272p. pap. 68.99 *(978-0-7817-9507-4(9))* Lippincott Williams & Wilkins.

Randolph, Elizabeth M. The Childhood-onset Bipolar Disorder Test. 2006. 195.00 *(978-0-9718030-4-6(8))* RFR Pubns.

Robson, Kenneth S. The Children's Hour: A Life in Child Psychiatry. 2010. 160p. 24.00 *(978-0-615-39198-4(2))* Lyre Bks.

Rogers, James. Metamorphoses: Troubled Children over Four Decades. 2009. 147p. pap. 18.95 *(978-1-84624-354-7(8))* Book Guild, Ltd. GBR. Dist: Trans-Atlantic Pubns., Inc.

Root, Elizabeth E. Kids Caught in the Psychiatric Maelstrom: How Pathological Labels & Therapeutic Drugs Hurt Children & Families, 1 vol. 2009. 222p. 44.95 *(978-0-313-38122-5(4),* A2261C, Praeger Pubs.) Greenwood Publishing Group, Inc.

Rosoman, Clare. Therapy to Go: Gourmet Fast Food Handouts for Working with Child, Adolescent & Family Clients. 2008. (ENG., Illus.). 192p. pap. *(978-1-84310-643-2(4))* Kingsley, Jessica Ltd.

Rubin, Theodore I. Jordi - Lisa & David. 18.95 *(978-0-89190-588-2(X))* Amereon LTD.

Rutter, Michael. Rutter's Child & Adolescent Psychiatry. 5th ed. 2008. *(978-1-4051-4592-3(7),* Wiley-Blackwell) Wiley, John & Sons, Ltd.

Rutter, Michael, et al. Rutter's Child & Adolescent Psychiatry. 5th ed. (ENG.). 1248p. 2010. pap. 125.00 *(978-1-4051-4593-0(5))* 2008. (Illus.). 315.00 *(978-1-4051-4549-7(8))* Wiley, John & Sons, Inc. (Wiley-Blackwell).

Sadock, Benjamin James, et al. Kaplan & Sadock's Concise Textbook of Child & Adolescent Psychiatry. 10th ed. 2008. (ENG.). 264p. pap. 73.99 *(978-0-7817-9387-2(4))* Lippincott Williams & Wilkins.

Shen, Hong, et al. Study Guide to Child & Adolescent Psychiatry: A Companion to Dulcan's Textbook of Child & Adolescent Psychiatry. 2009. (Illus.). 350p. pap. 54.00 *(978-1-58562-353-2(9))* American Psychiatric Publishing, Inc.

Sicile-Kira, Chantal. 41 Things to Know about Autism. 2010. (Good Things to Know Ser.). (ENG.). 211p. pap. 9.99 *(978-1-59652-583-2(5))* Turner Publishing Co.

Skuse, David, et al. Child Psychology & Psychiatry: Frameworks for Practice. 2nd ed. 2011. (ENG., Illus.). 318p. pap. 65.95 *(978-0-470-97382-0(X),* Wiley) Wiley, John & Sons, Inc.

Steiner, Hans. Handbook of Developmental Psychiatry. 2011. 600p. 158.00 *(978-981-4324-81-6(7))* World Scientific Publishing Co., Inc.

—The Stanford University School of Medicine Handbook of Developmental Psychiatry for Children & Adolescents. 2009. 1120p. 175.00 *(978-0-7879-8435-9(3),* Jossey-Bass) Wiley, John & Sons, Inc.

Stubbe, Dorothy. Child & Adolescent Psychiatry. 2006. (Practical Guides in Psychiatry Ser.). (ENG.). 283p. per. 49.95 *(978-0-7817-7831-2(X))* Lippincott Williams & Wilkins.

Thomas, Prakash K. & Poncin, Yann. Psychopharmacology & Child Psychiatry Review: With 1200 Board-Style Questions, 1 vol. 2011. (ENG., Illus.). 240p. pap. 49.50 *(978-0-19-974468-8(8))* Oxford Univ. Pr., Inc.

Trivedi, Harsh K. & Kershner, Jeryl Dansky. Practical Child & Adolescent Psychiatry for Pediatrics & Primary Care. 2009. (Illus.). 230p. spiral bd. 49.00 *(978-0-88937-349-5(3))* Hogrefe Publishing.

Volkmar, Fred R., et al, eds. Lewis's Child & Adolescent Psychiatry: A Comprehensive Textbook. 4th rev. ed. 2007. (ENG., Illus.). 1088p. 245.99 *(978-0-7817-6214-4(6))* Lippincott Williams & Wilkins.

Volkmar, Fred R. & Martin, Andrés. Essentials of Lewis's Child & Adolescent Psychiatry. 2011. (ENG., Illus.). 432p. pap. 97.99 *(978-0-7817-7502-1(7))* Lippincott Williams & Wilkins.

Walker, Audrey M., et al, eds. Child & Adolescent Neurology for Psychiatrists. 2nd rev. ed. 2008. (ENG., Illus.). 480p. 106.99 *(978-0-7817-7191-7(9))* Lippincott Williams & Wilkins.

Warner, Judith. We've Got Issues: Children & Parents in the Age of Medication. 2011. (ENG.). 336p. (gr. 12). 16.00 *(978-1-59448-497-1(X),* Riverhead Trade (Paperbacks)) Penguin Group (USA) Inc.

Yiming. A Primer of Child Psychiatry. 2008. 133.00 *(978-981-277-991-5(4))* World Scientific Publishing Co., Inc.

Yiming, et al. A Primer of Child & Adolescent Psychiatry. 2008. xix, 486p. pap. 86.00 *(978-981-277-992-2(2))* World Scientific Publishing Co., Inc.

Zelan, Karen. Between Their World & Ours: Breakthroughs with Autistic Children. Date not set. mass mkt. *(978-0-312-98923-1(7),* St. Martin's Paperbacks) St. Martin's Pr.

Zelikovic, I. & Eisenstein, I., eds. Nephrology 2008. (Illus.). 122p. spiral bd. *(978-3-8055-8539-2(X))* Karger, S. AG.

CHILD PSYCHIATRY—CASE STUDIES

Holmes, Jo, et al. Creating Change for Complex Children & their Families: A Multi-Disciplinary Approach to Multi-Family Work. 2011. (ENG., Illus.). 256p. pap. *(978-1-84310-965-5(4))* Kingsley, Jessica Ltd.

Perry, Bruce & Szalavitz, Maia. The Boy Who Was Raised as a Dog: And Other Stories from a Child Psychiatrist's Notebook - What Traumatized Children Can Teach Us about Loss, Love & Healing. 2007. (ENG.). 288p. per. 15.95 *(978-0-465-05653-8(9))* Basic Bks.

CHILD PSYCHOANALYSIS

see Child Analysis

CHILD PSYCHOLOGICAL ABUSE

see Psychological Child Abuse

CHILD PSYCHOLOGY

Here are entered works on the psychological growth and characteristics of children. Works on the physical, psychological and social growth of normal children are entered under Child Development.

see also Anger in Children; Attachment Behavior; Child Development; Child Mental Health; Child Psychiatry; Child Rearing; Children and Adults; Cognition in Children; Creative Thinking in Children; Educational Psychology; Emotional Problems of Children; Emotions in Children; Grandparent and Child; Helping Behavior in Children; Infant Psychology; Interpersonal Communication in Children; Learning, Psychology of; Metacognition in Children; Moral Development; Passivity (Child Psychology); Prejudices in Children; Psychohistory; Race Awareness in Children; Sibling Rivalry; Stress in Children

Abbott, Jacob. Gentle Measures in the Management & Training of the Young. 2008. 292p. 25.99 *(978-0-554-33304-5(X))* 2008. 292p. 28.99 *(978-0-554-24001-5(7))* 2006. (ENG.). 256p. pap. 21.99 *(978-1-4264-0115-2(9))* 2006. (ENG.). 252p. pap. 23.99 *(978-1-4264-0244-9(9))* BiblioBazaar.

—Gentle Measures in the Management & Training of the Young: Or, the Principles on Which a Firm Parental Authority May Be Established & Maintained, Without Violence or Anger, & the Right Development of the Moral & Mental Capacities Be Promoted by Methods in Harmony with the Structure & the Characteristics of the Juvenile Mind. 2007. (ENG.). 258p. pap. 21.99 *(978-1-4264-5567-4(4));* 290p. pap. 23.99 *(978-1-4264-5615-2(8))* BiblioBazaar.

Abdullah, Nadia. Nadia Says; Get Creative, Parent! 2010. 129p. pap. 19.99 *(978-0-557-25819-2(7))* Lulu Enterprises Inc.

Activity Groups in Family-Centered Treatment: Psychiatric Occupational Therapy Approaches for Parents & Children. 2006. (ENG.). 188p. 73.95 *(978-0-7890-3509-7(X));* per. 34.95 *(978-0-7890-3510-3(3))* Routledge.

Adelson, Jill L. & Wilson, Hope E. Letting Go of Perfect: Overcoming Perfectionism in Kids & Teens. 2009. (ENG.). 200p. pap. 14.95 *(978-1-59363-362-2(9))* Prufrock Pr.

Al-Ghani, K.I. Learning about Friendship: Stories to Support Social Skills Training in Children with Asperger Syndrome & High Functioning Autism. 2010. (ENG., Illus.). 160p. pap. *(978-1-84905-145-3(3))* Kingsley, Jessica Ltd.

Aldridge-Askren, Carrie. Parent Attitude, Discipline, Aggression & Language in Young Children. 2010. 144p. pap. *(978-3-639-26896-6(2))* VDM Verlag Dr. Mueller e.K.

Alexander, Theron. Children & Adolescents: A Biocultural Approach to Psychological Development. 2007. (ENG., Illus.). 381p. pap. 29.95 *(978-0-202-30913-2(4))* Aldine Transaction.

Ali, Anees Janee, et al. Repatriate Children. 2011. 124p. pap. ***(978-3-8433-8395-0(2))*** Lambert Academic Publishing.

Altiero, Joann, ed. No More Stinking Thinking: A Workbook for Teaching Children Positive Thinking. 2007. (ENG., Illus.). 56p. per. *(978-1-84310-839-9(9))* Kingsley, Jessica Ltd.

Alvarez, Eduardo Manuel & Escobar, Arturo José, eds. Psychology of War. 2012. 230p. ***(978-1-61942-312-1(X))*** Nova Science Pubs., Inc.

Andrews, Jac & Istvanffy, Peter, eds. Exceptional Life Journeys: Stories of Childhood Disorder. 2011. (ENG.). 306p. 64.95 *(978-0-12-385216-8(1))* Elsevier Science & Technology Bks.

Anglada, Tracy & Hakala, Sheryl. Childhood Bipolar Disorder: Practical Answers to the Top 300 Questions Parents Ask. 2008. (ENG., Illus.). 320p. pap. 14.95 *(978-1-4022-1177-5(5))* Sourcebooks, Inc.

Appleton, Peter. Children's Anxiety: A Contextual Approach. 2008. (ENG., Illus.). 200p. (C). 120.00 *(978-0-415-41248-3(X))* Routledge.

Archer, Margaret. The Reflexive Imperative in Late Modernity. 2012. (ENG., Illus.). 352p. 95.00 ***(978-1-107-02095-5(6));*** pap. 36.99 ***(978-1-107-60527-5(X))*** Cambridge Univ. Pr.

Ardino, Vittoria, ed. Post-Traumatic Syndromes in Childhood & Adolescence: A Handbook of Research & Practice. 2011. (ENG., Illus.). 486p. instr.'s hndbk. ed. 144.95 *(978-0-470-99769-7(5),* Wiley) Wiley, John & Sons, Inc.

Aronica, Lou & Robinson, Ken. The Element: How Finding Your Passion Changes Everything. 2009. (ENG.). 288p. (gr. 12-18). 15.00 *(978-0-14-311673-8(8),* Penguin (Non-Classics)) Penguin Group (USA) Inc.

Ashy, Majed. Childhood Experiences, Social Interactions, & Physical Health. 2008. 120p. pap. *(978-3-639-06232-8(9))* VDM Verlag Dr. Mueller e.K.

Atkinson, C. Making Sense of Piaget. 2007. 240p. 180.00 *(978-0-415-40227-9(1))* Routledge.

Atwood, Robert W., et al. Adhd: Children Who Challenge. 2008. 288p. pap. 20.95 *(978-0-595-47665-7(1),* iUniverse, Inc.) iUniverse, Inc.

Aves, Corinne. Understanding 6-7-Year-Olds. 2006. (Understanding Your Child Ser.). (ENG.). 8p. per. *(978-1-84310-467-4(9))* Kingsley, Jessica Ltd.

Awoke, Tadesse. Psychological Problems of Physically Abused Children. 2011. 88p. pap. ***(978-3-639-32341-2(6))*** VDM Verlag Dr. Mueller e.K.

Babocsai, Lysett. When Vacuum Cleaners Bark & Dogs Buzz. 2008. 84p. pap. *(978-3-639-03044-0(3))* VDM Verlag Dr. Mueller e.K.

Bailey, Sue. The Young Mind: An Essential Guide to Mental Health for Young Adults, Parents & Teachers. Shooter, Mike, ed. 2012. (ENG.). 400p. pap. 14.95 *(978-0-553-82418-6(X))* Transworld Publishers Ltd. GBR. Dist: Independent Pubs. Group.

Bains, George Ann. A Child's Story: Going to School with Anxiety. 2009. 20p. 10.49 *(978-1-4389-8558-9(4))* AuthorHouse.

Barankin, Tatyana & Khanlou, Nazilla. Growing up Resilient: Ways to Build Resilience in Children & Youth. 2007. ***(978-0-88868-504-9(1))*** Centre for Addiction & Mental Health.

Barkley, Russell A. Barkley Functional Impairment Scale — Children & Adolescents (BFIS-CA) 2012. (ENG.). 166p. pap. 149.00 ***(978-1-4625-0395-7(0))*** Guilford Pubns., Inc.

Barrett, Justin L. Born Believers: The Science of Children's Religious Belief. 2012. (ENG.). 320p. 26.00 ***(978-1-4391-9654-0(0),*** Free Pr.) Free Pr.

Barricks, Jeri. I used to be Afraid. 2007. (Illus.). 36p. (J). 11.00 *(978-0-9743512-1-6(0))* Barricks, Jeri Ministry.

Bartram, Pamela. Understanding Your Young Child with Special Needs. 2007. (Understanding Your Child (Jessica Kingsley Publishers) Ser.). (ENG.). 88p. per. *(978-1-84310-533-6(0))* Kingsley, Jessica Ltd.

Bauer, Patricia J., ed. Varieties of Early Experience: Implications for the Development of Declarative Memory in Infancy. 2010. (Advances in Child Development & Behavior Ser.: 38). (ENG.). 234p. 107.00 *(978-0-12-374471-5(7),* Academic Pr.) Elsevier Science & Technology Bks.

Bauer, Patricia J., et al, eds. Advances in Child Development & Behavior. 2009. (Advances in Child Development & Behavior Ser.: 37). (ENG.). 400p. 107.00 *(978-0-12-374470-8(9),* Academic Pr.) Elsevier Science & Technology Bks.

Beard, R. M. An Outline of Piaget's Developmental Psychology. 2007. 160p. 180.00 *(978-0-415-40229-3(8))* Routledge.

Beaver, Rick. Educational Psychology Casework: A Practical Guide. 2nd ed. 2011. (ENG., Illus.). 256p. pap. *(978-1-84905-173-6(9))* Kingsley, Jessica Ltd.

Becerra. Death of a Parent in Childhood & Resilience in Adulthood. 2010. 148p. pap. *(978-3-639-25650-5(6))* VDM Verlag Dr. Mueller e.K.

Bee-Gates, Donna. I Want It Now: Navigating Childhood in a Materialistic World. 2007. (ENG.). 256p. pap. 14.95 *(978-0-230-60253-3(3))* Palgrave Macmillan.

Bee, Helen & Boyd, Denise. The Developing Child. 11th ed. 2006. (Illus.). pap. 73.33 *(978-0-205-50247-9(4))* Allyn & Bacon, Inc.

Bee, Helen L. & Boyd, Denise. The Developing Child, Books a la Carte Edition. 13th ed. 2011. (ENG.). 576p. (C). ring bd. 108.67 ***(978-0-205-25635-8(X),*** Prentice Hall) Prentice Hall PTR.

Bee, Helen L. & Boyd, Denise A. The Developing Child. 13th rev. ed. 2011. (ENG.). 592p. (C). 166.67 ***(978-0-205-25602-0(3),*** Prentice Hall) Prentice Hall PTR.

Bellous, Joyce E. Children, Spirituality, Loss & Recovery. Bellous, Joyce E., ed. 2009. 102p. 125.00 *(978-0-415-55136-6(6))* Routledge.

Ben-Arieh, Asher, et al. Measuring & Monitoring Children's Well-Being. 2010. (Social Indicators Research Ser.). 184p. pap. 139.00 *(978-90-481-5642-9(4),* 9048156424) Springer.

Benson, Janette B. Advances in Child Development & Behavior. 2011. (Advances in Child Development & Behavior Ser.: 40). (ENG., Illus.). 480p. 107.00 ***(978-0-12-386491-8(7),*** Academic Pr.) Elsevier Science & Technology Bks.

Benson, Janette B., contrib. by. Advances in Child Development & Behavior. 2012. (Advances in Child Development & Behavior Ser.: 42). (ENG.). 398p. 107.00 ***(978-0-12-394388-0(4),*** Academic Pr.) Elsevier Science & Technology Bks.

Benson, Peter L., et al. What Kids Need to Succeed: Proven, Practical Ways to Raise Good Kids (Revised & Updated 3rd Edition) 3rd ed. 2012. (ENG.). 256p. pap. 9.99 ***(978-1-57542-397-5(9))*** Free Spirit Publishing, Inc.

Bentham, Susan. A Teaching Assistant's Guide to Child Development & Psychology. 2nd rev. ed. 2011. (ENG., Illus.). 232p. 125.00 *(978-0-415-56922-4(2));* pap. 35.95 *(978-0-415-56923-1(0))* Routledge.

Bentzen, Warren R. Seeing Young Children: A Guide to Observing & Recording Behavior. 6th rev. ed. 2008. (ENG., Illus.). 528p. (C). per. 108.95 *(978-1-4180-7378-7(4))* Delmar Cengage Learning.

Berger, Kathleen Stassen. The Developing Person Through Childhood. 5th ed. 2008. (ENG.). 426p. (C). pap. 99.95 *(978-1-4292-1648-7(4))* Worth Pubs., Inc.

Bergese, Rebecca. Understanding 10-11-year-Olds. 2008. (ENG.). 80p. pap. *(978-1-84310-674-6(4))* Kingsley, Jessica Ltd.

Berry-Dee, Christopher & Morris, Steven. How to Make a Serial Killer: The Twisted Development of Innocent Children into the World's Most Sadistic Murderers. 2008. (ENG., Illus.). 276p. pap. 14.95 *(978-1-56975-654-6(6))* Ulysses Pr.

Bettelheim, Bruno & Sylvester, Emmy. Delinquency & Morality. 2011. 20p. pap. 35.95 ***(978-1-258-01448-3(3))*** Literary Licensing, LLC.

Beyond the Icarus Factor: Releasing the Free Spirit of Boys. 2008. (ENG.). 1p. per. 14.95 *(978-1-59477-228-3(2),* Park Street Pr.) Inner Traditions International, Ltd.

Bielski, Ursula. There's Something under the Bed: Children's Experiences with the Paranormal. 2010. (ENG.). 1p. pap. 14.99 *(978-1-60163-134-3(0),* New Page Bks.) Career Pr., Inc.

Biglan, Anthony, et al, eds. Preventing Youth Problems. 2010. (Issues in Children's & Families' Lives Ser.). 196p. pap. 84.95 *(978-1-4419-3398-0(0),* 1441933980) Springer.

Billington, Tom. Working with Children: Assessment, Representation & Intervention. 2006. (Illus.). 192p. (C). 124.00 *(978-1-4129-0869-6(8),* B08698C); per. 46.00 *(978-1-4129-0870-2(1),* B08698P) SAGE Pubns., Ltd. GBR. Dist: SAGE Pubns., Inc.

Bjorklund, David F. Children's Thinking. 5th ed. 2011. (ENG.). 688p. (C). pap. 155.95 *(978-1-111-34605-8(4))* Wadsworth.

Blair, Linda. The Happy Child: Everything You Need to Know to Raise Enthusiastic, Confident Children. 2011. (ENG.). 240p. pap. 13.95 *(978-0-7499-4071-3(9))* Piatkus Bks. GBR. Dist: Independent Pubs. Group.

Blake, Simon, et al. Promoting Emotional & Social Development in Schools: A Practical Guide. 2007. (Illus.). 144p. 65.00 *(978-1-4129-0730-9(6),* B07306C); per. 30.00 *(978-1-4129-0731-6(4),* B07306P) SAGE Pubns., Ltd. GBR. Dist: SAGE Pubns., Inc.

Bond, Helen, et al. Through Children's Eyes: President Obama & the Future Generation. 2012. (ENG.). 250p. pap. 27.99 ***(978-1-926780-06-1(X))*** Key Publishing Hse., Inc., The CAN. Dist: AtlasBooks Distribution.

Bonnah, Shelly. Profiles of Resistance. 2008. 56p. pap. *(978-3-639-06743-9(6))* VDM Verlag Dr. Mueller e.K.

Boothby, Neil, et al, eds. A World Turned Upside DOwn: Social Ecological Approaches to Children in War Zones. 2006. (Illus.). 288p. 69.95 *(978-1-56549-226-4(9));* pap. 27.95 *(978-1-56549-225-7(0))* Stylus Publishing, LLC.

Bouyer, Rene-Jean. Les Mémoires D'un Bébé: Un Siècle D'éducation de L'enfant de Pasteur à Dolto. 2010. (FRE., Illus.). 221p. *(978-2-35013-232-7(3))* Gawsewitch, Jean-Claude.

Bowen, Chris. Our Kids: Building Relationships in the Classroom. 2008. 148p. pap. 14.95 *(978-1-4327-2453-5(3))* Outskirts Pr., Inc.

Bowers, Ellen. The Everything Parent's Guide to the Strong-Willed Child: A positive approach to increase self-control, improve communication, & reduce Conflict. 2nd ed. 2012. (ENG.). 304p. pap. 15.95 ***(978-1-4405-3342-6(3))*** Adams Media Corp.

Bowers, Ellen & Pickhardt, Carl E. The Everything Parent's Guide to the Strong-Willed Child. 2nd ed. 2012. E-Book ***(978-1-4405-3848-3(4))*** Adams Media Corp.

Bowers, Jill & Decker, Celia Anita. Child Development:Early Stages Through Age 12 ExamView Assessment Suite. 2010. cd-rom 200.00 *(978-1-60525-298-8(0))* Goodheart-Willcox Pub.

Boxberger, Christine Cantrell. I Love You 'Cause You Love Me. 2006. 104p. pap. 10.95 *(978-0-7414-3214-8(5))* Infinity Publishing.

Brackett, Marc A. & Kremenitzer, Janet P. Creating Emotionally Literate Classrooms. 2011. per. 24.50 *(978-1-934032-18-3(2),* Dude Publishing) National Professional Resources, Inc.

Brafman. You & Your Five to Ten-Year-Olds. 2010. (Developmental Psychology Ser.). 120p. pap. 21.95 *(978-1-85575-703-5(6))* Karnac Bks. GBR. Dist: Stylus Publishing, LLC.

Brain, Christine. Psychology: Criminological & Child Psychology. 2009. (Illus.). 96p. pap., stu. ed. 22.50 *(978-0-340-94879-8(5))* Hodder Education GBR. Dist: Trans-Atlantic Pubns., Inc.

Brandell, Jerrold R. & Ringel, Shoshana. Attachment & Dynamic Practice: An Integrative Guide for Social Workers & Other Clinicians. 2007. (ENG.). 224p. (gr. 17). pap. 29.00 *(978-0-231-13391-3(X));* (Illus.). 90.00 *(978-0-231-13390-6(1))* Columbia Univ. Pr.

Brazelton, T. Berry & Sparrow, Joshua D. Touchpoints-Birth to Three: Your Child's Emotional & Behavioral Development. 2nd rev. ed. 2006. (ENG., Illus.). 528p. per. 17.95 *(978-0-7382-1049-0(8))* Da Capo Pr., Inc.

Brearley, M. & Hitchfield, E. A Teacher's Guide to Reading Piaget. 2007. 192p. 170.00 *(978-0-415-40234-7(4))* Routledge.

Breger, Louis. From Instinct to Identity: The Development of Personality. 2009. (ENG., Illus.). 389p. pap. 34.95 *(978-1-4128-0992-4(4))* Transaction Pubs.

Brendtro, et al. Deep Brain Learning: Pathways to Potential with Challenging Youth. 2009. (Illus.). xvii, 169p. *(978-1-60725-789-9(0),* Debolsillo) Independent Pub.

Briers, Stephen. How Your Child Thinks: Give Your Child the Superpowers to Be a Happy, Healthy Person. 2009. (ENG., Illus.). 272p. pap. 18.99 *(978-0-13-815674-9(3))* FT Press.

Broadhead, Pat & Woolley, Richard. Personal, Social & Emotional Development. 2011. (Supporting Development in the Early Years Foundation Stage Ser.). (ENG., Illus.). 160p. 100.00 *(978-1-4411-3371-7(2))* Continuum International Publishing Group, Ltd. GBR. Dist: National Bk. Network.

Broadhead, Pat, et al. Personal, Social & Emotional Development. 2011. (Supporting Development in the Early Years Foundation Stage Ser.). (ENG., Illus.). 160p. pap. 29.95 *(978-1-84706-567-4(8))* Continuum International Publishing Group, Ltd. GBR. Dist: National Bk. Network.

Brody, Sylvia. Beginning to Grow: Five Studies. 2009. 258p. pap. 27.50 *(978-0-615-30581-3(4))* International Psychoanalytic Bks.

Brom, Danny, et al. Treating Traumatized Children: Risk, Resilience, & Recovery. Pat-Horenczyk, Ruth & Ford, Julian D., eds. 2008. (ENG., Illus.). 304p. (C). 120.00 *(978-0-415-42636-7(7))* Routledge.

Bronson, Po & Merryman, Ashley. NurtureShock: New Thinking about Children. (ENG.). 352p. 2011. pap. 14.99 *(978-0-446-50413-3(0));* 2009. 24.99 *(978-0-446-50412-6(2))* Grand Central Publishing. (Twelve).

Brooks, Robert & Goldstein, Sam. Nurturing Resilience in Our Children. 2011. (ENG.). 288p. pap. 18.00 ***(978-0-07-138522-0(3),*** 0071385223) McGraw-Hill Cos., The.

Brown, G. & Desforges, C. Piaget's Theory. 2007. 208p. 180.00 *(978-0-415-40232-3(8))* Routledge.

Brown, Terry M. Rooms of the Mind: Quadrants for Success. 2010. 104p. pap. 12.95 *(978-1-4327-5512-6(9))* Outskirts Pr., Inc.

The BROWN UNIVERSITY CHILD & ADOLESCENT BEHAVIOR Letter, 27/5. 2011. 16.58 *(978-1-118-02027-2(8),* Wiley) Wiley, John & Sons, Inc.

The BROWN UNIVERSITY CHILD & ADOLESCENT BEHAVIOR Letter, 27/6. 2011. 16.58 *(978-1-118-02029-6(6),* Wiley) Wiley, John & Sons, Inc.

The BROWN UNIVERSITY CHILD & ADOLESCENT PSYCHOPHARMACOLOGY UPDATE 13/05. 2011. 16.58 (978-1-118-02015-9(4), Wiley) Wiley, John & Sons, Inc.

The BROWN UNIVERSITY CHILD & ADOLESCENT PSYCHOPHARMACOLOGY UPDATE 13/06. 2011. 16.58 (978-1-118-02016-6(2), Wiley) Wiley, John & Sons, Inc.

Brownell, Celia A. & Kopp, Claire B., eds. Socioemotional Development in the Toddler Years: Transitions & Transformations. 2010. (ENG.). 497p. pap. 40.00 (978-1-60623-946-9(5)) Guilford Pubns., Inc.

Brozovich, Richard. Say Goodbye to Being Shy: A Workbook to Help Kids Overcome Shyness. 2008. (Instant Help Ser.). (ENG.). 120p. (J). pap. 24.95 (978-1-57224-668-3(5)) Play2Grow.

Bruckisch, Rabea. Ressourcenorientierte Kunsttherapie mit Flüchtlingskindern: Ressourcenorientierte Arbeit mit Roma-Flüchtlingskindern im kunsttherapeutischen Setting einer Kunstwerkstatt. 2010. 100p. pap. (978-3-639-23605-7(X)) VDM Verlag Dr. Mueller e.K.

Bruehl, Mariah. Playful Learning: Develop Your Child's Sense of Joy & Wonder. 2011. (ENG., Illus.). 272p. pap. 22.95 (978-1-59030-819-6(0), Trumpeter) Shambhala Pubns., Inc.

Brunell, D. Edward. Car Conversations for Elementary School Kids. 2009. 56p. pap. 9.99 (978-0-557-14969-8(X)) Lulu Enterprises Inc.

Budd, Ken. The Voluntourist: A Six-Country Tale of Love, Loss, Fatherhood, Fate, & Singing Bon Jovi in Bethlehem. 2012. (ENG.). 464p. pap. 15.99 (978-0-06-194646-2(X), William Morrow Paperbacks) HarperCollins Pubs.

Budhal, Rishichand Sookai. Aggression. 2010. 164p. pap. (978-3-8383-6159-8(8)) Lambert Academic Publishing.

Buffolano, Sandra. Coping with Tourette Syndrome: A Workbook for Kids with Tic Disorders. 2008. (Instant Help Ser.). (ENG.). 136p. (J). pap. 16.95 (978-1-57224-632-4(4)) New Harbinger Pubns.

Bukowski, William M., et al, eds. Social & Emotional Development, 4 vols. 2009. (Critical Concepts in Psychology Ser.). (ENG., Illus.). 2560p. (C). 1675.00 (978-0-415-41202-5(1), Psychology Press) Taylor & Francis Group GBR. Dist: Taylor & Francis Group.

Bullock, Merry & Schneider, Wolfgang. Human Development from Early Childhood to Early Adulthood: Findings from a 20 Year Longitudinal Study. 2008. (ENG., Illus.). 296p. 135.00 (978-0-8058-6107-5(6), Psychology Press) Taylor & Francis Group GBR. Dist: Taylor & Francis Group.

Bullock, Merry, et al. Human Development from Early Childhood to Early Adulthood: Findings from a 20 Year Longitudinal Study. 2008. (ENG., Illus.). 296p. pap. 52.95 (978-0-8058-6108-2(4), Psychology Press) Taylor & Francis Group GBR. Dist: Taylor & Francis Group.

Burgan, Lori Collins. Moving with Kids: 25 Ways to Ease Your Family's Transition to a New Home. 2007. (ENG.). 144p. 19.95 (978-1-55832-342-1(2)); per. 9.95 (978-1-55832-343-8(0)) Harvard Common Pr.

Burkett, Jillian. What Children Really Want from Their Parents. 2011. 214p. pap. 25.00 (978-1-257-10569-4(8)) Lulu Enterprises Inc.

Burns, Donna, ed. When Kids Are Grieving: Addressing Grief & Loss in School. 2010. 128p. pap. 27.95 (978-1-4129-7490-5(9), B74905P) Corwin Pr.

Bursztyn, Alberto. Childhood Psychological Disorders: Current Controversies. 2011. E-Book (978-0-313-06406-7(7), Praeger Pubs.) Greenwood Publishing Group, Inc.

Butler, Kim. What happens to the Child. 2008. 97p. pap. 11.95 (978-1-4357-1911-8(5)) Lulu Enterprises Inc.

Butler, Richard J. & Green, David. The Child Within: Taking the Young Person's Perspective by Applying Personal Construct Psychology. 2nd ed. 2007. (ENG., Illus.). 246p. per. 52.95 (978-0-470-02998-5(6), Wiley) Wiley, John & Sons, Inc.

Butler, Richard W. & Green, David R. The Child Within: Taking the Young Person's Perspective by Applying Personal Construct Psychology. 2nd ed. 2007. (ENG.). 246p. 172.95 (978-0-470-02997-8(8), Wiley) Wiley, John & Sons, Inc.

Byrnes, James P. Cognitive Development & Learning in Instructional Contexts. 3rd ed. 2007. (ENG., Illus.). 464p. (C). per. 119.20 (978-0-205-50771-9(9)) Allyn & Bacon, Inc.

Cabrera, Natasha, et al. Latina & Latino Children's Mental Health, 2 vols. 2011. (Child Psychology & Mental Health Ser.). (Illus.). 512p. 104.95 (978-0-313-38296-3(4), A2696C, Praeger Pubs.) Greenwood Publishing Group, Inc.

Cabrera, Natasha J., et al. Latina/O Children & Mental Health, 2 vols. 2011. (Illus.). E-Book (978-0-313-38297-0(2)) ABC-CLIO, LLC.

CAD. Beyond the Family: Contexts of Immigrant Children's Development - New Directions for Child & Adolescent Development. Way, Niobe & Yoshikawa, Hirokazu, eds. 2008. (J-B CAD Single Issue Child & Adolescent Development Ser.: 91). (ENG.). 112p. pap. 29.00 (978-0-470-41730-0(7), Jossey-Bass) Wiley, John & Sons, Inc.

CAD Staff. Evidentiality No. 125: A Window into Language & Cognitive Development. Matsui, Tomoko & Fitneva, Stanka A., eds. 2009. (J-B CAD Single Issue Child & Adolescent Development Ser.: 95). (ENG.). 112p. pap. 29.00 (978-0-470-56965-8(4), Jossey-Bass) Wiley, John & Sons, Inc.

Campbell, Jack. Behavior Modification in the Classroom: Strategies for Teachers & Parents. 2009. 151p. pap. 17.95 (978-1-4327-2980-6(2)) Outskirts Pr., Inc.

Campbell, James E. Teachers & Mental Health: The Art of Accurate Speech & Other Ways to Help Students (Children) Not Become Psychiatric Patients. 2011. 112p. 24.99 (978-1-4634-1024-7(7)); pap. 19.99 (978-1-4634-1025-4(5)) AuthorHouse.

Campbell, Patricia. Songs in Their Heads: Music & Its Meaning in Children's Lives, Second Edition, 1 vol. 2nd ed. 2010. (ENG., Illus.). 336p. pap. 24.95 (978-0-19-538252-5(8)) Oxford Univ. Pr., Inc.

Campione, Joseph, et al, eds. Children's Learning in the Lab & in Schools. 2007. (Illus.). 264p. 95.00 (978-0-8058-5691-0(9)) Erlbaum, Lawrence Assocs., Inc.

Canfield, Jack L., et al. Chicken Soup for the Soul: Preteens Talk: Inspiration & Support for Preteens from Kids Just Like Them. 2008. (Chicken Soup for the Soul Ser.). (ENG.). 384p. pap. 14.95 (978-1-935096-00-9(1)) Chicken Soup for the Soul Publishing, LLC.

Cannella, Gaile Sloan & Soto, Lourdes Diaz. Childhoods: A Handbook. 2010. (Rethinking Childhood Ser.). 416p. (C). 155.95 (978-1-4331-0451-0(2)); pap. 49.95 (978-1-4331-0450-3(4)) Lang, Peter Publishing, Inc.

Caplan, Rochelle & Bursch, Brenda. How Many More Questions? Techniques for Clinical Interviews of Young Medically Ill Children. 2012. (ENG., Illus.). 304p. pap. 45.00 (978-0-19-984382-4(1)) Oxford Univ. Pr., Inc.

Carey, Tanith. Where Has My Little Girl Gone? How to Protect Your Daughter from Growing up Too Soon. 2011. (ENG.). 192p. pap. 14.95 (978-0-7459-5542-1(8)) Lion Hudson PLC GBR. Dist: Independent Pubs. Group.

Carey, William B., et al. Developmental-Behavioral Pediatrics: Expert Consult - Online & Print. 4th ed. 2009. (ENG., Illus.). 1060p. 194.00 (978-1-4160-3370-7(X), Saunders) Elsevier - Health Sciences Div.

Carroll, Annemaree, et al. Adolescent Reputations & Risk: Developmental Trajectories to Delinquency. 2009. (Advancing Responsible Adolescent Development Ser.). (ENG., Illus.). xviii, 208p. 109.00 (978-0-387-79987-2(7)) Springer.

Carroll, E. Thomas. Teddybears to Bombs. 2011. 120p. 21.23 (978-1-4490-6926-1(6)); pap. 10.68 (978-1-4490-6925-4(8)) AuthorHouse.

Carroll, Julia. Healed by Light. 2008. 244p. per. 38.98 (978-1-60461-822-8(1)) Reiki Touch Institute of Holistic Medicine Publishing.

Cash, Hilarie & McDaniel, Kim. Video Games & Your Kids: How Parents Stay in Control. 2008. (978-1-930461-05-5(4), Issues Pr.) Idyll Arbor, Inc.

Cashman, Orla & Twaite, James A. Toxic Wealth: How the Culture of Affluence Can Harm Us & Our Children, 1 vol. 2009. (Illus.). 216p. 34.95 (978-0-313-35991-0(1), C35991, Praeger Pubs.) Greenwood Publishing Group, Inc.

Cassidy, Jude & Shaver, Phillip R., eds. Handbook of Attachment: Theory, Research, & Clinical Applications. 2nd rev. ed. 2010. (ENG., Illus.). 1020p. 65.00 (978-1-60623-028-2(X)) Guilford Pubns., Inc.

—Handbook of Attachment, Second Edition: Theory, Research, & Clinical Applications. 2nd rev. ed. 2008. (ENG., Illus.). 1020p. 125.00 (978-1-59385-874-2(4)) Guilford Pubns., Inc.

Cave, Peter. Primary School in Japan: Self, Individuality & Learning in Elementary Education. 2009. 248p. pap. 39.95 (978-0-415-54536-5(6)) Routledge.

Cavett, Angela M. Structured Play-Based Interventions for Engaging Children & Adolescents in Therapy. 2010. pap. 29.95 (978-0-7414-6168-1(4)) Infinity Publishing.

Cbl. The Brown University Child & Adolescent Behavior Letter. 2011. (ENG.). 16.58 (978-1-118-02033-3(2)); 16.58 (978-1-118-02032-6(4), Wiley); 16.58 (978-1-118-02030-2(8), Wiley) Wiley, John & Sons, Inc.

—The Brown University Child & Adolescent Behavior Letter, 27/11. 2011. 16.58 (978-1-118-02034-0(0), Wiley) Wiley, John & Sons, Inc.

Cbl. The BROWN UNIVERSITY CHILD & ADOLESCENT BEHAVIOR Letter, 27/7. 2011. 16.58 (978-1-118-02029-6(4), Wiley) Wiley, John & Sons, Inc.

Cefai, Carmel. Promoting Resilience in the Classroom: A Guide to Developing Pupils' Emotional & Cognitive Skills. 2008. (Innovative Learning for All Ser.). (ENG., Illus.). 176p. pap. (978-1-84310-565-7(9)) Kingsley, Jessica Ltd.

Chadamoyo, Patrick & Dumbu, Emmanuel. The Effect of Socio-Economic Factors on Maternal & Infant Behaviours. 2011. 84p. pap. (978-3-8443-0267-7(0)) Lambert Academic Publishing.

Chamberlain, Alexander Francis. The Child: A Study in the Evolution of Man. 2007. (ENG.). 508p. 55.95 (978-0-548-01607-7(0)) Kessinger Publishing, LLC.

Chandler, Caroline, et al. Early Child Care: The New Perspectives. Dittmann, Laura, ed. 2008. (ENG.). 395p. pap. 34.95 (978-0-202-36218-2(3)) Aldine Transaction.

Chappell, Drew. Children under Construction: Critical Essays on Play as Curriculum. 2010. (Illus.). 328p. (C). pap. 35.95 (978-1-4331-0623-1(X)) Lang, Peter Publishing, Inc.

Chen, Rita. Early Childhood Identity: Construction, Culture, & the Self. 2009. (Rethinking Childhood Ser.). (Illus.). 216p. (C). 32.95 (978-1-4331-0161-8(0)) Lang, Peter Publishing, Inc.

Chen, Xinyin & Rubin, Kenneth H., eds. Socioemotional Development in Cultural Context. 2011. (Social, Emotional, & Personality Development in Context Ser.). (ENG.). 342p. 60.00 (978-1-60918-186-4(7)) Guilford Pubns., Inc.

Chenfeld, Mimi Brodsky. Celebrating Young Children & Their Teachers: The Mimi Brodsky Chenfeld Reader. 2007. (ENG., Illus.). 120p. (J). pap. 14.95 (978-1-933653-27-3(2)) Redleaf Pr.

Chesaina, Ciarunji. The Significance of Oral Literature in Children's Development. 2010. 48p. pap. (978-3-8383-0121-1(8)) Lambert Academic Publishing.

Chibashimba Christian, Amani. Child Soldiering Process. 2011. 56p. pap. (978-3-8443-3005-2(4)) Lambert Academic Publishing.

Child. Psychology & the Teacher - 8th Edition. 8th rev. ed. 2007. (ENG., Illus.). 628p. 160.00 (978-0-8264-8715-5(7)) Continuum International Publishing Group, Ltd. GBR. Dist: National Bk. Network.

Child and Adolescent Development Staff (CAD). Social Interaction & the Development of Executive Function, No. 123. Carpendale, Jeremy I. M. & Lewis, Charlie, eds. 2009. (J-B CAD Single Issue Child & Adolescent Development Ser.: 93). (ENG., Illus.). 112p. pap. 29.00 (978-0-470-48901-7(4), Jossey-Bass) Wiley, John & Sons, Inc.

Child, Dennis & Child. Psychology & the Teacher - 8th Edition. 8th ed. 2007. (ENG., Illus.). 628p. 55.00 (978-0-8264-8716-2(5)) Continuum International Publishing Group, Ltd. GBR. Dist: National Bk. Network.

Chouinard, Michelle M. Children's Questions. 2007. (Monographs of the Society for Research in Child Development Ser.). (ENG.). 132p. pap. 47.95 (978-1-4051-7633-0(4), Wiley-Blackwell) Wiley, John & Sons, Inc.

Church, Amelia. Preference Organisation & Peer Disputes: How Young Children Resolve Conflict. 2009. (Directions in Ethnomethodology & Conversation Analysis Ser.). 290p. 114.95 (978-0-7546-7441-2(X)) Ashgate Publishing Co.

Cicchetti, Dante & Gunnar, Megan R. Minnesota Symposia on Child Psychology Vol. 35: Meeting the Challenge of Translational Research in Child Psychology. 2009. (Minnesota Symposia on Child Psychology Ser.: 1). (ENG., Illus.). 329p. 140.00 (978-0-470-34513-9(6), Wiley) Wiley, John & Sons, Inc.

Cipani, Ennio. Decoding Challenging Classroom Behaviors: What Every Teacher & Paraeducator Should Know! 2011. (Illus.). 240p. pap. 34.95 (978-0-398-08674-9(5)) Thomas, Charles C. Pub., Ltd.

Claparede, Edouard. Experimental Pedagogy & the Psychology of the Child. Wozniak, Robert H., ed. 4th ed. (Classics in Psychology Ser.). (Illus.). 344p. (978-1-85506-696-0(3), Burns & Oates) Continuum International Publishing Group, Ltd.

Clark, Cindy, ed. Transactions at Play. 2009. (Play & Cultural Studies). (ENG., Illus.). 200p. pap. 31.50 (978-0-7618-4485-3(6)) Univ. Pr. of America, Inc.

Clifford-Poston, Andrea. A Playworkers Guide to Understanding Children's Behaviour: Working with the 8-12 Age Group. 2008. 240p. pap. 38.95 (978-1-85575-494-2(0)) Karnac Bks. GBR. Dist: Stylus Publishing, LLC.

—When Harry Hit Sally: Understanding Your Child's Behaviour. 2008. (ENG., Illus.). 276p. pap. 19.95 (978-1-84737-040-2(3)) Simon & Schuster, Ltd. GBR. Dist: Independent Pubs. Group.

Cohen, Cathi. Outnumbered. Not Outsmarted! A to Z Guide for Working with Children in Groups. 2008. (ENG.). 268p. pap. 14.95 (978-0-9714609-4-2(9)) Advantage Bks., LLC.

Cohen, David. How the Child's Mind Develops. 2nd ed. 2012. (ENG., Illus.). 224p. 62.50 (978-0-415-67765-3(3)); pap. 22.50 (978-0-415-67766-0(1)) Routledge.

Cohen, Judith A., et al, eds. Trauma-Focused CBT for Children & Adolescents: Treatment Applications. 2012. (ENG.). 308p. 40.00 (978-1-4625-0482-4(5)) Guilford Pubns., Inc.

Colace, Claudio. Freud's Observations on Children's Dreams & the Modern Dream Research. 2010. (Illus.). 260p. pap. 37.95 (978-1-85575-636-6(6)) Karnac Bks. GBR. Dist: Stylus Publishing, LLC.

Collinge, Justin. Understanding Edward. 2010. 156p. pap. 20.95 (978-1-4466-4509-3(6)) Lulu Enterprises Inc.

Collins, Margaret. Raising Self-Esteem in Primary Schools: A Whole School Training Programme. 2009. (Lucky Duck Bks.). (Illus.). 192p. 135.00 (978-1-84920-069-1(6), B00696C); pap. 56.00 (978-1-84860-775-0(X), B00696P) SAGE Pubns., Ltd. GBR. Dist: SAGE Pubns., Inc.

Colvin, Geoff, et al. Managing Noncompliance & Defiance in the Classroom: A Road Map for Teachers, Specialists, & Behavior Support Teams. 2009. 152p. 72.95 (978-1-4129-6088-5(6), B60885C) Corwin Pr.

Conde-Frazier, Elizabeth. Listen to the Children/Escuchemos a los Ninos: Conversations with Immigrant Families/Conversaciones con familias Inmigrantes. 2011. (ENG & SPA.). 160p. pap. 13.99 (978-0-8170-1661-6(9)) Judson Pr.

Connelly, Virginia. Just for Awhile. 2007. 104p. per. 11.95 (978-0-595-44809-8(7)) iUniverse, Inc.

Consumer Dummies Staff, et al. Child Psychology & Development for Dummies. 2011. (ENG., Illus.). 384p. pap. 19.99 (978-0-470-91885-2(3), For Dummies) Wiley, John & Sons, Inc.

Cook, Melissa H. & Hall, Karyn D. The Power of Validation: Arming Your Child Against Bullying, Peer Pressure, Addiction, Self-Harm, & Out-of-Control Emotions. 2011. (ENG.). 168p. pap. 16.95 (978-1-60882-033-7(5)) New Harbinger Pubns.

Cooper-Kahn, Joyce & Dietzel, Laurie C. Late, Lost & Unprepared: A Parents' Guide to Helping Children with Executive Functioning. 2008. 217p. pap. 19.95 (978-1-890627-84-3(4)) Woodbine Hse.

Cooper, Patricia M. The Classrooms All Young Children Need: Lessons in Teaching from Vivian Paley. 2009. (ENG.). 248p. 29.00 (978-0-226-11523-8(2)) Univ. of Chicago Pr.

Cousins, Lynn. Shaping Children's Behaviour in the Early Years. 2010. (ENG., Illus.). 235p. pap. 45.00 (978-1-4082-2502-8(6)) Longman Publishing Group.

Cox, Sue. Children as Decision Makers in Education: Sharing Experiences Across Cultures. Cox, Sue et al, eds. 2010. (ENG., Illus.). 192p. 140.00 (978-0-8264-2548-5(8)) Continuum International Publishing Group, Ltd. GBR. Dist: National Bk. Network.

Coyne, Phyllis, et al. Developing Leisure Time Skills for Persons with Autism: Structured Playtime Activities with Valuable Support Strategies for Adults. 2011. (ENG., Illus.). 228p. pap. 29.95 (978-1-935274-55-1(4)) Future Horizons, Inc.

Cozolino, Louis. The Social Neuroscience of Education: Optimizing Attachment & Learning in the Classroom. 2012. (ENG.). 304p. 37.50 (978-0-393-70609-3(5), 70609) Norton, W. W. & Co., Inc.

Cpu. The Brown University Child & Adolescent Psychopharmacology. 2011. 16.58 (978-1-118-02020-3(0)); 16.58 (978-1-118-02019-7(7)); 16.58 (978-1-118-02018-0(9)); 16.58 (978-1-118-02017-3(0)) Wiley, John & Sons, Inc. (Wiley).

Cram101 Textbook Reviews. Outlines & Highlights for Child Psychology: A Contemporary View Point by Ross D. Parke, Mary Gauvain, ISBN. 2010. 92p. pap. 27.95 (978-1-61698-726-8(X)) Cram101 Inc.

Cram101 Textbook Reviews. Outlines & Highlights for Seeing Young Children by Warren R Bentzen. 2011. 90p. pap. 27.95 (978-1-61654-115-6(6)) Cram101 Inc.

Cram101 Textbook Reviews & Cram101 Textbook Reviews. Outlines & Highlights for Abnormal Child & Adolescent Psychology by Jean E Dumas. 2011. 138p. pap. 28.95 (978-1-61830-364-6(3)) Cram101 Inc.

—Outlines & Highlights for Advances in Child Development & Behavior: 9780120097340. 2011. 82p. pap. 27.95 (978-1-61461-140-0(8)) Cram101 Inc.

—Outlines & Highlights for an Introduction to Early Childhood Studies by Nigel Thomas, Isbn: 9781847871671. 2011. 176p. pap. 29.95 (978-1-61461-127-1(0)) Cram101 Inc.

—Outlines & Highlights for Bridging: Assessement for Teaching & Learning in Early Childhood Classrooms by Jie-Qi Chen, ISBN. 2011. 68p. pap. 27.95 (978-1-4288-1885-9(5)) Cram101 Inc.

—Outlines & Highlights for Child Development: An Active Learning Approach by Laura E. Levine, ISBN. 2011. 228p. pap. 31.95 (978-1-4288-3703-4(5)) Cram101 Inc.

—Outlines & Highlights for Developing Child, the by Helen Bee, Isbn: 9780205744473. 2011. 108p. pap. 28.95 (978-1-61461-068-7(1)) Cram101 Inc.

—Outlines & Highlights for Differentiated Instructional Management: Work Smarter, Not Harder by Rita King, ISBN. 2011. 80p. pap. 27.95 (978-1-4288-6482-5(2)) Cram101 Inc.

—Outlines & Highlights for Handbook of Pediatric Psychology by Michael Roberts, Isbn: 9781606233283. 2011. 66p. pap. 27.95 (978-1-4288-6181-7(5)) Cram101 Inc.

—Outlines & Highlights for Introduction to Child Development by Subhadra Evans, Isbn: 9781412911146. 2011. 72p. pap. 27.95 (978-1-61461-097-7(5)) Cram101 Inc.

—Outlines & Highlights for Normal & Abnormal Fear & Anxiety in Children & Adolescents by Peter Muris, Isbn: 9780080450735 0080450733. 2011. 74p. pap. 27.95 (978-1-61654-043-2(5)) Cram101 Inc.

Cram101 Textbook Reviews Staff. Outlines & Highlights for Child Development by Feldman, Isbn: 0131732471. 2008. 176p. pap. 12.95 (978-1-4288-5964-7(0)) Cram101 Inc.

—Outlines & Highlights for Children & Their Development by Kail, Isbn: 013194911x. 2008. 192p. pap. 13.95 (978-1-4288-5957-9(8)) Cram101 Inc.

—Outlines & Highlights for the Developing Child by Bee, Isbn: 0205474535. 2008. 224p. pap. 13.95 (978-1-4288-6021-6(5)) Cram101 Inc.

—Outlines & Highlights for Theories of Development Comparing Theories of Child Development by Thomas, Isbn: 0534607179. 2008. 180p. pap. 12.95 (978-1-4288-6018-6(5)) Cram101 Inc.

Crenshaw, David A., ed. Child & Adolescent Psychotherapy: Wounded Spirits & Healing Paths. 2010. (ENG.). 178p. pap. 26.50 (978-0-7657-0599-0(0), Aronson, Jason) Rowman & Littlefield Publishers, Inc.

Crenshaw, David A. & Mordock, John B. Understanding & Treating the Aggression of Children: Fawns in Gorilla Suits. 2007. (ENG., Illus.). 312p. per. 36.99 (978-0-7657-0561-7(3), Aronson, Jason) Rowman & Littlefield Publishers, Inc.

Croft, Cindy. The Six Keys: Strategies for Promoting Children's Mental Health. 2007. (978-0-9786018-2-9(3)) Sparrow Media Group, Inc.

Cross, Richard. The Effect of Chronic Trauma in Children & Adolescents. 2011. pap. 34.95 (978-1-85575-499-7(1)) Karnac Bks. GBR. Dist: Stylus Publishing, LLC.

Cross, Tracy L. On the Social & Emotional Lives of Gifted Children. 4th rev. ed. 2010. (ENG.). 300p. pap. 24.95 (978-1-59363-498-8(6)) Prufrock Pr.

Crowley, Gerry. Winning Without Winning. 2nd rev. ed. 2010. 140p. pap. 14.99 (978-1-4520-4875-8(4)) AuthorHouse.

Crum, Thomas, et al. The New Conflict Cookbook: A Parent/Teacher Guide for Helping Young People Deal with Anger & Conflict. Date not set. 15.00 (978-1-877803-11-6(1)) Aiki Works, Inc.

Csóti, Márianna. Developing Children's Social, Emotional & Behavioural Skills. 2009. (ENG.). 152p. 35.95 (978-1-85539-471-1(5)) Continuum International Publishing Group, Ltd. GBR. Dist: National Bk. Network.

Cullen, K. Introducing Child Psych Prac Guid. 2011. (Introducing Ser.). (ENG., Illus.). 192p. pap. 9.95 (978-1-84831-258-6(X)) Totem Bks. GBR. Dist: Consortium Bk. Sales & Distribution.

Cunningham, Rebekah. Mismatch Negativity in Typically Developing Children. 2010. 64p. pap. (978-3-8383-3734-0(4)) Lambert Academic Publishing.

Curwin, Richard L., et al. Strategies for Successful Classroom Management: Helping Students Succeed Without Losing Your Dignity or Sanity. 2007. (Illus.). 176p. 66.95 (978-1-4129-3783-2(3), B37833C); per. 27.95 (978-1-4129-3784-9(1), B37833P) Corwin Pr.

Cusworth, Linda. The Impact of Parental Employment: Young People Well-Being & Educational Achievement. 2009. (Studies in Cash & Care Ser.). (Illus.). 260p. 114.95 (978-0-7546-7559-4(9)) Ashgate Publishing Co.

D. Smith. What Is a Trigger? 2009. 16p. pap. 8.49 (978-1-4389-6735-6(7)) AuthorHouse.

Daniel, Brigid, et al. Child Development for Child Care & Protection Workers. 2nd ed. 2010. (ENG., Illus.). 336p. pap. (978-1-84905-068-5(6)) Kingsley, Jessica Ltd.

Darden, Floyd. Drum Therapy. 2008. (ENG.). 180p. 25.95 (978-1-60594-105-9(0)); 184p. pap. 12.95 (978-1-60594-104-2(2)) Aeon Publishing Inc. (Lumina Pr.).
Daunic, Ann P., et al. Preventing Problem Behaviors: Schoolwide Programs & Classroom Practices. 2nd ed. 2010. (Illus.). 248p. pap. 38.95 (978-1-4129-7048-8(2), B70471P) Corwin Pr.
David, Jenny. Developmental Psychology of the Nursery Age Child. 2010. (Developmental Psychology Ser.). 100p. pap. 21.95 (978-1-85575-795-0(8)) Karnac Bks. GBR. Dist: Stylus Publishing, LLC.
Davydov, Vasilii Vasilevich. Problems of Developmental Instruction: A Theoretical & Experimental Psychological Study. Davydov, V. V., ed. 2008. 246p. 98.00 (978-1-60456-552-2(7)) Nova Science Pubs., Inc.
Dawson, Peg & Guare, Richard. Coaching Students with Executive Skills Deficits. 2012. (Guilford Practical Intervention in the Schools Ser.). (ENG., Illus.). 240p. (gr. k-12). pap. 35.00 **(978-1-4625-0375-9(5))** Guilford Pubns., Inc.
De Forrest, Terry. Child BehaviorImprove Your Child's Behavior: Simple Strategies That Really Work. rev. ed. 2009. (ENG.). 46p. pap. 14.49 (978-1-60250-072-3(X)) Kendall Hunt Publishing Co.
DeBellis, Valerie A. Navigating Through Discrete Mathematics in Prekindergarten Through Grade 5. 2009. (978-0-87353-608-0(8)) National Council of Teachers of Mathematics.
Decker, Celia Anita. Child Development: Early Stages Through Age 12. 7th ed. 2010. (ENG.). (gr. 9-12). 720p. 74.64 (978-1-60525-293-3(X)); 184p. pap., wbk. ed. 16.64 (978-1-60525-295-7(6)) Goodheart-Willcox Pub.
—Child Development: Early Stages Through Age 12 PowerPoint-Individual License. 2010. cd-rom 140.00 (978-1-60525-299-5(9)) Goodheart-Willcox Pub.
—Child Development: Early Stages Through Age 12 Teacher's Edition. 2010. 96.00 (978-1-60525-294-0(8)) Goodheart-Willcox Pub.
—Child Development: Early Stages Through Age 12 (Teacher's Power Point Presentations, Site License. 7th ed. 2010. cd-rom 420.00 (978-1-60525-300-8(6)) Goodheart-Willcox Pub.
—Child Development: Early Stages Through Age 12 Teacher's Resource CD. 2010. cd-rom 240.00 (978-1-60525-297-1(2)) Goodheart-Willcox Pub.
—Child Development: Early Stages Through Age 12 Teacher's Resource Guide. 2010. pap. 98.00 (978-1-60525-296-4(4)) Goodheart-Willcox Pub.
Dehn, Milton J. Long-Term Memory Problems in Children & Adolescents: Assessment, Intervention, & Effective Instruction. 2010. (ENG., Illus.). 408p. pap. 48.00 (978-0-470-43831-2(2), Wiley) Wiley, John & Sons, Inc.
Dennison, Trish. Sticks & Stones May Break My Bones but Words Can Hurt Forever: A Message from the Children in My Chair. 2010. 216p. 29.99 (978-1-4490-5560-8(5)); pap. 21.99 (978-1-4490-5559-2(1)) AuthorHouse.
DePalma, Renee & Atkinson, Elizabeth. Invisible Boundaries: Addressing Sexualities Equality in Children's Worlds. DePalma, Renee & Atkinson, Elizabeth, eds. 2008. (Illus.). 150p. pap. 32.95 (978-1-85856-430-2(1)) Trentham Bks. Ltd. GBR. Dist: Stylus Publishing, LLC.
DeRobertis, Eugene M. Humanizing Child Developmental Theory: A Holistic Approach. 2008. (Illus.). 264p. pap. 19.95 (978-0-595-44924-8(7)) iUniverse, Inc.
—Humanizing Child Developmental Theory: A Holistic Approach. 2008. (ENG., Illus.). 264p. 29.95 (978-0-595-69098-5(X)) iUniverse, Inc.
DeRosier, Melissa & Harrell, Amanda. S. S. grin-a: Group Interventions & Exercises for Enhancing Communication, Cooperation & Confidence with Adolescents. 2007. ring bd. (978-1-934409-08-4(1)) 3-C Institute for Social Development.
Desai, Murli. A Rights-Based Preventative Approach for Children's Psychosocial Well-being. 2010. (Children's Well-Being: Indicators & Research Ser.). 250p. 219.00 (978-90-481-9065-2(7), 9048190657) Springer.
Devanath, Sudipta. Parental Attitudes & Children's Sharing Behavior. 2010. 72p. pap. (978-3-639-26767-9(2)) VDM Verlag Dr. Mueller e.K.
Dicketmnller, Yvonne. Being Left Behind. 2008. 104p. pap. (978-3-8364-4620-4(0)) VDM Verlag Dr. Mueller e.K.
Diniz, Felipe. Estimating a Technology of Cognitive Skill Formation in Brazil. 2009. 72p. pap. (978-3-639-14574-8(7)) VDM Verlag Dr. Mueller e.K.
Dobson, James C. The New Strong-Willed Child. rev. ed. 2007. (ENG., Illus.). 288p. per. 14.99 (978-1-4143-1363-4(2)) Tyndale Hse. Pubs.
Doll, Beth. Transforming School Mental Health Services: Population-Based Approaches to Promoting the Competency & Wellness of Children. Doll, Beth & Cummings, Jack A., eds. 2007. (Illus.). 368p. 90.95 (978-1-4129-5328-3(6), B53286C) Corwin Pr.
—Transforming School Mental Health Services: Population-Based Approaches to Promoting the Competency & Wellness of Children. Cummings, Jack A., ed. 2007. (Joint Publication). (Illus.). 368p. per. 44.95 (978-1-4129-5329-0(4), B53286P) Corwin Pr.
Dombrowski, Stefan C. Maternal Fever During Pregnancy. 2009. 132p. pap. (978-3-639-12957-1(1)) VDM Verlag Dr. Mueller e.K.
Dombrowski, Stefan C. & Martin, Roy P. Prenatal Exposures: Psychological & Educational Consequences for Children. 2008. (ENG., Illus.). 461p. 69.95 (978-0-387-74397-4(9), 0387743979) Springer.
Dosani, Sabina. Banish the Bullies. 2008. (52 brilliant ideas Ser.). (Illus.). 256p. 14.99 (978-1-905940-29-5(7)) Infinite Ideas GBR. Dist: Sony Electronics.
Dowling, Marion. Young Children's Personal, Social & Emotional Development. 3rd ed. 2009. (Illus.). 240p. (C). 112.00 (978-1-84860-105-5(0), B01055C); pap. 45.00 (978-1-84860-106-2(9), B01055P) SAGE Pubns., Ltd. GBR. Dist: SAGE Pubns., Inc.
Dreikurs, Rudolf. Child Guidance & Education: Collected Papers. pap. 6.50 (978-0-918560-11-7(X)) Adler School of Professional Psychology.
Driussi, Lori. Cultivating Risk. 2008. 128p. pap. (978-3-639-03415-8(5)) VDM Verlag Dr. Mueller e.K.
D'Souza, Barnabe. From Ecstasy to Agony & Back: Journeying with Adolescents on the Street. 2011. (Illus.). 252p. (C) pap. 40.00 **(978-81-321-0703-3(9)**, B07033C) SAGE Pubns., Inc.
Edwards, Lindsey & Crocker, Susan. Psychological Processes in Deaf Children with Complex Needs: An Evidence-Based Practical Guide. 2007. (Illus.). 204p. pap. (978-1-84310-414-8(8)) Kingsley, Jessica Ltd.
Egan, Amy, et al. Is It a Big Problem or a Little Problem? When to Worry, When Not to Worry, & What to Do. 2007. (ENG., Illus.). 352p. pap. 15.95 (978-0-312-35412-1(6), St. Martin's Griffin) St. Martin's Pr.
Eicholz, Marti. A Child Is Speaking. 2009. 104p. pap. 24.99 (978-1-60693-940-6(8), Strategic Bk. Publishing) AEG Literary Publishing Services, Inc.
Eiderzen, Doug. The Metaphysics of the Model: Values within/toward the Attitude & Approach of Life. 2009. 92p. pap. 14.49 (978-1-4490-5480-9(3)) AuthorHouse.
Eileen Palmer And Katrina Wood. Early Childhood Inventory of Multiple Intelligences. 2008. 40p. pap. 21.99 (978-1-4363-6499-7(X)) Xlibris Corp.
Eisen, Andrew R. & Schaefer, Charles E. Separation Anxiety in Children & Adolescents: An Individualized Approach to Assessment & Treatment. 2007. (ENG.). 298p. pap. 30.00 (978-1-59385-482-9(X)) Guilford Pubns., Inc.
Ek, Ulla. Children with Visual Disorders - Cognitive Development, Developmental Disorders & Consequences for Treatment & Counselling. 2008. 72p. pap. (978-3-639-05867-3(4)) VDM Verlag Dr. Mueller e.K.
El-Sheikh, Mona, et al. Marital Conflict & Children's Externalizing Behavior: Interactions Between Parasympathetic & Sympathetic Nervous System Activity. 2009. (Monographs of the Society for Research in Child Development Ser.). (ENG., Illus.). 200p. pap. 39.95 (978-1-4051-9942-1(3), Wiley-Blackwell) Wiley, John & Sons, Inc.
Elkins, Don. Curry. 2011. 44p. pap. 16.95 **(978-1-4626-2681-6(5))** PublishAmerica, Inc.
Elliott, Delbert S., et al. Good Kids from Bad Neighborhoods: Successful Development in Social Context. 2006. (ENG., Illus.). 416p. (C). pap. 39.99 (978-0-521-68221-3(5)); 100.00 (978-0-521-86357-5(0)) Cambridge Univ. Pr.
Ellis, Mesha L., et al. The SAGE Handbook of Child Development, Multiculturalism, & Media. 2008. (Illus.). 528p. 150.00 (978-1-4129-4915-6(7), B49157C) SAGE Pubns., Inc.
Engel, Susan. Red Flags or Red Herrings? Predicting Who Your Child Will Become. 2011. (ENG.). 288p. 24.00 (978-1-4391-5011-5(7), Beyond Words/Atria Bks.) Atria Bks.
Enzer & Goin. 1st Chance-Social Emotions. pap. 15.95 (978-0-8027-7263-3(3)) Walker & Co.
Erhard-Weiss, Dana. Mothers' & Fathers' Judgments about Young Children's Autonomy. 2008. 92p. pap. (978-3-8364-3858-2(5)) VDM Verlag Dr. Mueller e.K.
Esolen, Anthony. Ten ways to destroy the imagination of your Child. 2010. (ENG.). 320p. 26.95 (978-1-935191-88-9(8)) ISI Bks.
Estrade, Patrick. You Are What You Remember: A Pathbreaking Guide to Understanding & Interpreting Your Childhood Memories. 2008. (ENG.). 272p. pap. 16.95 (978-1-60094-042-2(0), Da Capo Lifelong) Da Capo Pr., Inc.
Faegre, Marion E. & Anderson, John E. Child Care & Training. 2009. (ENG.). 334p. pap. 60.00 (978-0-8166-0157-8(7)) Univ. of Minnesota Pr.
Farkas, L. C. S. W., et al. Resilient Children. 2011. 150p. pap. 18.95 **(978-1-60594-695-5(8)**, Lumina Pr.) Aeon Publishing Inc.
Farnfield, Steve. A Practical Guide to Using Attachment Theory & Research with Children & Young People. 2008. 240p. pap. (978-1-84310-100-0(9)) Kingsley, Jessica Ltd.
Faulkner, Dorothy & Coates, Elizabeth, eds. Exploring Children's Creative Narratives. 2011. (ENG., Illus.). 288p. (C). 150.00 (978-0-415-56562-2(6)); pap. 46.95 (978-0-415-56563-9(4), Routledge.
Faupel, Adrian, et al. Anger Management. 2nd ed. 2010. (ENG., Illus.). 144p. instr.'s gde. ed. 36.95 (978-0-415-58071-7(4)) Routledge.
Fay, Jim & Fay, Charles. Love & Logic Powder Room Reader. 2009. pap. 11.95 (978-1-935326-05-2(8)) Love & Logic Institute, Inc.
Fedorov, Alexander. Children & Media Violence. 2010. 164p. pap. (978-3-8383-2580-4(X)) Lambert Academic Publishing.
Feldman, Robert S. Child Development. (ENG.). 552p. (C). 5th ed. 2008. 167.60 (978-0-205-65502-1(5)) 6th ed. 2011. (Illus.). 166.67 **(978-0-205-25354-8(7))** Prentice Hall PTR. (Prentice Hall).
Ferris, Lcsw-R. Balloons for Mary: A Children's Book about Grief & Coping with Death. 2009. 20p. pap. 14.95 (978-1-4490-1604-3(9)) AuthorHouse.
Fidler, Barbara Jo, et al. Children Who Resist Post-Separation Parental Contact: A Differential Approach for Legal & Mental Health Professionals, 1 vol. 2012. (American Psychology-Law Society Ser.). (ENG.). 328p. pap. 75.00 **(978-0-19-989549-6(X))** Oxford Univ. Pr., Inc.
Field, Andy P. & Hadwin, Julie A., eds. Information Processing Biases & Anxiety: A Developmental Perspective. 2010. (ENG., Illus.). 342p. 110.95 (978-0-470-99819-9(9), Wiley) Wiley, John & Sons, Inc.
Fife, Lynn H. Trouble at Home? Using the Dad Camp System with Children of Any Age. 2011. (ENG.). 133p. pap. 15.35 **(978-1-935359-94-4(0))** Book Pubs. Network.
Fink, Jeff & Halpern, Jon. More time to Teach: Responding to Student Behavior (facilitator's Guide) 2007. spiral bd 89.95 (978-0-9792204-4-9(0)) ChildSense.
—More time to Teach: Responding to Student Behavior (teacher's Guide) 2007. spiral bd. 19.95 (978-0-9792204-5-6(9)) ChildSense.
Flick, Grad L. Understanding & Managing Emotional & Behavior Disorders in the Classroom. 2010. (ENG.). 528p. (C). pap. 77.40 (978-0-13-041713-8(0), Prentice Hall) Prentice Hall PTR.
Frankel, Fred. Friends Forever: How Parents Can Help Their Kids Make & Keep Good Friends. 2010. (ENG.). 320p. pap. 14.95 (978-0-470-62450-0(7), Jossey-Bass) Wiley, John & Sons, Inc.
Freeman, Arthur, et al. Guide to Early Psychological Evaluation: Children & Adolescents. 2010. (ENG., Illus.). 160p. pap. 18.95 (978-0-393-70539-3(0), 70539) Norton, W. W. & Co., Inc.
Freud, Anna & Burlingham, Dorothy T. War & Children. Lehrman, Philip R., ed. 2011. 188p. 42.95 **(978-1-258-06196-8(1))** Literary Licensing, LLC.
Gagu Harris Eds, Amelia. Ants at Work: A Child's Introduction to Careers. 2011. 30p. 25.95 **(978-1-4327-7353-8(5))** Outskirts Pr., Inc.
Galatzer-Levy, Robert M., et al, eds. The Scientific Basis of Child Custody Decisions. 2nd ed. 2009. (ENG.). 499p. 90.00 (978-0-470-03858-1(6), Wiley) Wiley, John & Sons, Inc.
Gallagher, Mary & Karjala, Lynn. Taming Trauma Beasties. 2007. 72p. pap. 16.95 (978-0-9788571-4-1(3)) Thomas Max Publishing.
Gans, Joshua. Parentonomics: An Economist Dad Looks at Parenting. (ENG.). 256p. (gr. 17). 2010. pap. 12.95 (978-0-262-51497-2(4)) 2009. 22.95 (978-0-262-01278-2(2)) MIT Pr.
Garcia-Coll, C. The Impact of Immigration on Children's Development. 2011. (Contributions to Human Development Ser.). (ENG., Illus.). 154p. pap. **(978-3-8055-9798-2(3))** Karger, S AG.
Gardner, Yun. Affective Responses of Counselors to Child Sexual Abuse Disclosure. 2009. 120p. pap. (978-3-639-14343-0(4)) VDM Verlag Dr. Mueller e.K.
Gartrell, Dan. A Guidance Approach for the Encouraging Classroom. 5th ed. 2010. (ENG.). 608p. (C). pap. 118.95 (978-1-4283-6096-9(4)) Delmar Cengage Learning.
Gatto, Maureen. Children & Self-Efficacy. 2008. 88p. pap. (978-3-639-03021-1(4)) VDM Verlag Dr. Mueller e.K.
Gauvain, Mary & Cole, Michael. Readings on the Development of Children. 5th ed. 2008. (ENG., Illus.). 384p. (C) pap. 47.95 (978-1-4292-1649-4(2)) Worth Pubs., Inc.
Geber, B. A., ed. Piaget & Knowing. 2007. (Illus.). 272p. 180.00 (978-0-415-40230-9(1)) Routledge.
Gerard, Robert V. Icon Power for Kids: Quick-Fix Resolution of Problems for Kids Ages 8-10 Years. 2009. (J). pap. (978-1-880666-17-3(0)) Oughten Hse. Foundation, Inc.
Giardino, Angelo P. Helping Children Affected by Abuse: A Parent's & Teacher's Handbook for Increasing Awareness. 2007. (ENG., Illus.). 218p. 26.00 (978-1-878060-98-3(8)) STM Learning, Inc.
Gibson, Kathleen & Petersen, Anne, eds. Brain Maturation & Cognitive Development: Comparative & Cross-Cultural Perspectives. 2010. (ENG., Illus.). 390p. pap. 39.95 (978-0-202-36395-0(3)) Transaction Pubs.
Glenyn, Bernice C., et al, eds. Celiac Disease: Etiology, Diagnosis, & Treatment. 2008. (Illus.). xi, 261p. 129.00 (978-1-60692-634-5(9)) Nova Science Pubs., Inc.
Glicken, Morley D. Evidence-Based Practice with Emotionally Troubled Children & Adolescents. 2009. (Practical Resources for the Mental Health Professional Ser.). (ENG.). 664p. 72.95 (978-0-12-374523-1(3), Academic Pr.) Elsevier Science & Technology Bks.
Goba, Fairhope Dumile. Trends in Relation to the Involvement of Family in Children in Care. 2011. 216p. pap. **(978-3-8443-9823-6(6))** Lambert Academic Publishing.
Goldstein, Sam & Naglieri, Jack A., eds. Encyclopedia of Child Behavior & Development, 3 vols. 2010. (ENG.). liv, 1591p. 949.00 (978-0-387-77579-1(X), 038777579X) Springer.
Goodell, Nancy & Garrett, Ann. TLC for Frazzled Kids. 2010. 123p. pap. 14.95 (978-0-557-56041-7(1)) Lulu Enterprises Inc.
Goodenough, Florence L. Experimental Child Study. 2007. (ENG.). 572p. per. (978-1-4067-0443-3(1)) Read Bks.
Goodman, Greg S. & Goodman, Michael B. Educational Psychology Reader: The Art & Science of How People Learn. 2010. (Educational Psychology: Critical Pedagogical Perspectives Ser.). 744p. (C). pap. 69.95 (978-1-4331-0627-9(2)) Lang, Peter Publishing, Inc.
Goodman, Michael B. Educational Psychology Reader: The Art & Science of How People Learn. 2010. (Educational Psychology: Critical Pedagogical Perspectives Ser.). 744p. (C). 199.95 (978-1-4331-1072-6(5)) Lang, Peter Publishing, Inc.
Goodman, Robin F. & Fahnestock, Andrea Henderson. The Day Our World Changed: Children's Art Of 9/11. 2006. (Illus.). 128p. reprint ed. 20.00 (978-1-4223-5685-2(X)) DIANE Publishing Co.
Goodwin, Majorie Harness. The Hidden Life of Girls: Games of Stance, Status, & Exclusion. 2006. (Wiley-Blackwell Studies in Discourse & Culture Ser.). (ENG., Illus.). 344p. 108.95 (978-0-631-23424-1(1), Wiley-Blackwell) Wiley, John & Sons, Inc.
Gottlieb. Your Child Is Defiant: Why Is Nothing Working? 2011. 166p. pap. 19.98 **(978-1-257-10859-6(X))** Lulu Enterprises Inc.
Gray, Deborah D. Nurturing Adoptions: Creating Resilience after Neglect & Trauma. 2012. (ENG., Illus.). 514p. pap. **(978-1-84905-891-9(1))** Kingsley, Jessica Ltd.
Grayer, Dianna. I AM a Lot of Things. 2011. (ENG.). 40p. pap. 13.99 **(978-1-4662-2466-7(5))** CreateSpace.
Green, Christine. 100+ Fun Ideas for Playground Games. 2009. (Illus.). 110p. pap. (978-1-905780-40-2(0)) Brilliant Pubns.
Green, Michael & Piel, John A. Theories of Human Development: A Comparative Approach. 2nd ed. 2009. (ENG.). 464p. (C). pap. 91.40 (978-0-205-66568-6(3)) Allyn & Bacon, Inc.
Greene, Melissa L. Children's Social Competence: Theory & Intervention. 2010. (Children's Issues, Laws & Programs Ser.). pap. 43.00 (978-1-61668-861-5(0), Nova Novinka) Nova Science Pubs., Inc.
Greenspan, Stanley I. & Glovinsky, Cindy. Children & Babies with Mood Swings: New Insights for Parents & Professionals. 2007. (ENG.). 120p. pap. 24.95 (978-0-9767758-5-0(9)) Interdisciplinary Council on Developmental & Learning Disorders.
Greenspan, Stanley I. & Greenspan, Nancy Thorndike. The Learning Tree: Overcoming Learning Disabilities from the Ground Up. 2010. (Merloyd Lawrence Book Ser.). (ENG., Illus.). 296p. 26.00 (978-0-7382-1233-3(4)) Da Capo Pr., Inc.
Greydanus, Donald E. Clinical Pediatrics. 2010. 600p. instr.'s hndbk. ed. 129.00 (978-981-4280-49-5(6)) World Scientific Publishing Co., Inc.
Griffin, Linda. My Child Won't Listen: And Other Early Childhood Problems. 2009. 212p. pap. 14.49 (978-1-4389-1690-3(6)) AuthorHouse.
Griffin, Richard. Child Development. 2007. (Very Short Introductions Ser.). (Illus.). 144p. 9.95 (978-0-19-280308-5(5)) Oxford Univ. Pr., Inc.
Griffiths, Alex, et al. 101 Essential Lists on Managing Behaviour in the Primary School. 2006. (101 Essential Lists Ser.). (ENG.). 128p. 35.95 (978-0-8264-8988-3(5)) Continuum International Publishing Group, Ltd. GBR. Dist: National Bk. Network.
Griffiths, Fleur. Supporting Children's Creativity Through Music, Dance, Drama & Art: Creative Conversations in the Early Years. 2010. (ENG., Illus.). 140p. 120.00 (978-0-415-48965-2(2)); pap. 37.95 (978-0-415-48966-9(0)) Fulton, David Pubs. GBR. Dist: Taylor & Francis Group.
Grille, Robin. Parenting for a Peaceful World. 2009. (ENG.). 442p. pap. 29.95 (978-1-921004-14-8(2)) Longueville Media AUS. Dist: Consortium Bk. Sales & Distribution.
Guishard-Pine, Jeune, ed. Psychology, Race Equality & Working with Children. 2010. (Illus.). 228p. pap. 36.95 (978-1-85856-474-6(3)) Trentham Bks. Ltd. GBR. Dist: Stylus Publishing, LLC.
Gunter, Michael. Technique in Child & Adolescent Analysis. 2010. (Illus.). 156p. pap. 37.95 (978-1-85575-715-8(X)) Karnac Bks. GBR. Dist: Stylus Publishing, LLC.
Gunter, Michael & Franieck, M. Leticia. On Latency: Individual Development, Narcissistic Impulse, Reminiscence & Cultural Ideal. 2010. 140p. pap. 28.95 (978-1-85575-740-0(0)) Karnac Bks. GBR. Dist: Stylus Publishing, LLC.
Gurian, Michael. Nurture the Nature: Understanding & Supporting Your Child's Unique Core Personality. 2007. (ENG.). 368p. 24.95 (978-0-7879-8633-9(X), Jossey-Bass) Wiley, John & Sons, Inc.
Gurian, Michael & Gurian. Nurture the Nature: Understanding & Supporting Your Child's Unique Core Personality. 2009. (ENG.). 368p. pap. 16.95 (978-0-470-32252-9(7), Jossey-Bass) Wiley, John & Sons, Inc.
Habtamu, Mekonnen. Psychosocial Experience of Double Orphaned Children from Hiv/Aids: Children Can Not Live by Bread Alone: Psychosocial Experience of Double Orphans Before & after the Death of Their Parents from Hiv/Aids. 2011. 104p. pap. **(978-3-639-32793-9(4))** VDM Verlag Dr. Mueller e.K.
Haley, Arbegast. Social-Emotional Development in Early Childhood: From Birth Through Age Five. 2011. 180p. pap. **(978-3-639-33848-5(0))** VDM Verlag Dr. Mueller e.K.
Hall, Kathy, et al, eds. Interdisciplinary Perspectives on Learning to Read: Culture, Cognition & Pedagogy. 2010. (Routledge Psychology in Education Ser.). (ENG., Illus.). 272p. (C). 140.00 (978-0-415-56123-5(X)); pap. 47.95 (978-0-415-56124-2(8)) Routledge.
Hall, Sharon & Hall, Sharon K. Raising Kids in the 21st Century: The Science of Psychological Health for Children. 2008. (ENG., Illus.). 192p. pap. 29.95 (978-1-4051-5806-0(9), Wiley-Blackwell) Wiley, John & Sons, Inc.
Haner, Jean. The Wisdom of Your Child's Face: Discover Your Child's True Nature with Chinese Face Reading. 2010. (ENG., Illus.). 336p. pap. 15.95 (978-1-4019-2534-5(0)) Hay Hse., Inc.
Hannibal, Mary Ellen. Good Parenting Through Your Divorce: The Essential Guidebook to Helping Your Children Adjust & Thrive — Based on the Leading National Program. 2nd ed. 2006. (ENG.). 304p. per. 18.00 (978-1-56924-257-5(7)) Da Capo Pr., Inc.
Harps-Morrow, Verna. My Mommy Wears Army Boots. 2007. 36p. per. 17.95 (978-1-58961-465-9(8)) PageFree Publishing, Inc.
Harris. The Tavistock Model: Papers on Child Development & Psychoanalytic Training. 2011. (Harris Meltzer Trust Ser.). 440p. pap. 41.95 **(978-1-78049-009-0(7))** Karnac Bks. GBR. Dist: Stylus Publishing, LLC.
Harris, Rita, et al. Engaging with Complexity: Child & Adolescent Mental Health & Education. 2011. 256p. pap. 34.95 **(978-1-78049-003-8(8))** Karnac Bks. GBR. Dist: Stylus Publishing, LLC.
Harris, Sandra L. & Weiss, Mary Jane. Right from the Start: Behavioral Intervention for Young Children with Autism. 2nd ed. 2007. (Topics in Autism Ser.). (Illus.). 175p. per. 18.95 (978-1-890627-80-5(1)) Woodbine Hse.
Harrison, Elizabeth. A Study of Child Nature from the Kindergarten Standpoint. 2009. 80p. pap. 14.14 (978-1-151-62346-1(6)) General Bks. LLC.
Hart, Sura & Kindle-Hodson, Victoria. Respectful Parents, Respectful Kids: 7 Keys to Turn Family Conflict into Co-Operation. 2006. (ENG., Illus.). 208p. per. 17.95 (978-1-892005-22-9(0)) Puddledancer Pr.

C

Hartley-Brewer, Elizabeth. Making Friends: A Guide to Understanding & Nurturing Your Child's Friendships. 2009. (ENG.). 224p. pap. 13.00 *(978-0-7382-1323-1(3))* Da Capo Pr., Inc.

Hartley, Jennifer S. Psychology for Teaching Assistants: Second Edition. 2nd rev. ed. 2011. (Illus.). 230p. pap. 36.95 ***(978-1-85856-498-2(0))*** Trentham Bks. Ltd. GBR. Dist: Stylus Publishing, LLC.

Harvey, Pat & Penzo, Jeanine A. Parenting a Child Who Has Intense Emotions: Dialectical Behavior Therapy Skills to Help Your Child Regulate Emotional Outbursts & Aggressive Behaviors. 2009. (ENG.). 224p. pap. 18.95 *(978-1-57224-649-2(9))* New Harbinger Pubns.

Harwood, Debra. Exploring the Phenomenon of Teasing. 2008. 392p. pap. *(978-3-8364-8930-0(9))* VDM Verlag Dr. Mueller e.K.

Hatch, David. Violence & Teachers. 2009. 176p. pap. *(978-3-639-14952-4(1))* VDM Verlag Dr. Mueller e.K.

Healy, Maureen. Growing Happy Kids: How to Foster Inner Confidence, Success, & Happiness. 2012. (ENG.). 264p. pap. 14.95 ***(978-0-7573-1612-8(3))*** Health Communications, Inc.

Heard, Dorothy, et al. Attachment Therapy for Adolescents & Adults. 2009. (Illus.). 270p. pap. 36.95 *(978-1-85575-522-2(X))* Karnac Bks. GBR. Dist: Stylus Publishing, LLC.

Heide, Kathleen M. Kids Who Kill Their Parents. 2010. (Illus.). 336p. 35.00 *(978-0-19-517666-7(9))* Oxford Univ. Pr., Inc.

Hemsley, Steve & Morgans, Lucy. Boost Your Child?'s Confidence. 2008. (52 brilliant ideas Ser.). (Illus.). 256p. pap. 14.99 *(978-1-905940-47-9(5))* Infinite Ideas GBR. Dist: Sony Electronics.

Henig, Sherry. Sara Makes her Mother Proud & Learns Good Behavior: A Parent's Guide to Positive Proactive Parenting for the Oppositional Behavior of Preschoolers & Young Children. 2007. pap. 7.95 *(978-0-9777203-1-6(4))* Brenner Publishing, LLC.

Henry, Lucy. The Development of Working Memory in Children. 2011. (Discoveries & Explanations in Child Development Ser.). (Illus.). 384p. (C). 120.00 ***(978-1-84787-328-6(6)***, B73286C); pap. 45.00 ***(978-1-84787-329-3(4)***, B73286P) SAGE Pubns., Ltd. GBR. Dist: SAGE Pubns., Inc.

Henry, Sally. Bullying As a Social Pathology: A Peer Group Analysis. 2008. (Illus.). 276p. 109.95 *(978-0-7734-5196-4(X))* Mellen, Edwin Pr., The.

Herbert, Martin. Clinical Child & Adolescent Psychology: From Theory to Practice. 3rd ed. 2006. (Wiley Series in Clinical Psychology). (ENG.). 392p. 180.00 *(978-0-470-01256-7(0)*, Wiley) Wiley, John & Sons, Inc.

Heroman, Cate. Teaching Strategies GOLD: Objectives for Development & Learning: Birth Through Kindergarten. 2010. *(978-1-60617-312-1(X))* Teaching Strategies, Inc.

Hesketh, Diane. I Am Great! A Practical Toolkit for Developing Emotional Resilience in Children & Young People. 2012. (David Fulton / Nasen Ser.). (ENG.). 128p. pap. 44.95 ***(978-0-415-69583-1(X))*** Routledge.

Hetherington Et Al. & Cram101 Textbook Reviews Staff. Child Psychology: A Contemporary Viewpoint. 2007. 236p. per. 14.95 *(978-1-4288-2092-0(2))* Cram101 Inc.

Hinckley, Kevin. Parenting the Strong-Willed Child: Fortifying Our Youth & Healing Our Prodigals. 2008. *(978-1-59038-917-1(4))* Deseret Bk. Co.

Hinshelwood, Robert, et al. Introducing Melanie Klein. 2011. (Introducing Ser.). (ENG., Illus.). 176p. pap. 9.95 ***(978-1-84831-213-5(X))*** Totem Bks. GBR. Dist: Consortium Bk. Sales & Distribution.

Hirschfeld, Lawrence. Cornelia's Cradle. 2007. (ENG.). 320p. 26.00 *(978-0-300-11180-4(0))* Yale Univ. Pr.

Hirschland, Deborah. Collaborative Intervention in Early Childhood: Consulting with Parents & Teachers of 3- To 7-Year-Olds. 2008. (ENG., Illus.). 320p. 36.99 *(978-0-19-533120-2(6))* Oxford Univ. Pr., Inc.

Hodgins, Daniel J. Boys: Changing the Classroom, Not the Child. 2009. *(978-89-23-56894-4(5))* Wilderness Adventure Bks.

Hoge, Robert & Andrews, D. A., contrib. by. Evaluation for Risk of Violence in Juveniles. 2010. (Forensic mental health Assessment Ser.). (ENG.). 192p. pap. 35.00 *(978-0-19-537041-6(4))* Oxford Univ. Pr., Inc.

Holloway, G. E. T. Further Aspects of Piaget's Work. 2007. 176p. 180.00 *(978-0-415-40224-8(7))* Routledge.

Homrich, Barbara J. Autonomy Disturbance As a Psychological Characteristic in Anorexi. 2008. 164p. pap. *(978-3-639-02739-6(6))* VDM Verlag Dr. Mueller e.K.

Hooper, Jeni. What Children Need to Be Happy, Confident & Successful: Step by Step Positive Psychology to Help Children Flourish. 2012. (ENG., Illus.). 160p. pap. ***(978-1-84905-239-9(5))*** Kingsley, Jessica Ltd.

Hoover, John H. & Oliver, Ronald L. The Bullying Prevention Handbook: A Guide for Principals, Teachers, & Counselors. 2nd ed. 2008. (Illus.). 232p. pap. 29.95 incl. audio compact disk *(978-1-934009-11-6(3))* Solution Tree.

House, Richard & Loewenthal, Del. Childhood, Well-Being & A Therapeutic: Ethos. 2009. 250p. pap. 34.95 *(978-1-85575-633-5(1))* Karnac Bks. GBR. Dist: Stylus Publishing, LLC.

Howe, Mark L. The Nature of Early Memory: An Adaptive Theory of the Genesis & Development of Memory, 1 vol. 2011. (ENG.). 272p. 59.95 *(978-0-19-538141-2(6))* Oxford Univ. Pr., Inc.

Huberty, Thomas J. Anxiety & Depression in Children & Adolescents: Assessment, Intervention, & Prevention. 2012. (ENG., Illus.). xxv, 469p. 64.95 ***(978-1-4614-3108-4(5)***, 1461431085) Springer.

Hudley, Cynthia. You Did That on Purpose: Understanding & Changing Children's Aggression. 2008. (ENG.). 192p. 35.00 *(978-0-300-11085-2(5))* Yale Univ. Pr.

Huff, Mary Jo. Story Play: Building Language & Literacy One Story at a Time. 2011. (ENG.). 208p. pap. 16.95 *(978-0-87659-316-5(3))* Gryphon Hse., Inc.

Hughes, William. Social Understanding & Social Lives. 2011. (Essays in Developmental Psychology Ser.). (ENG., Illus.). 256p. 49.95 *(978-1-84169-735-2(4)*, Psychology Press) Taylor & Francis Group GBR. Dist: Taylor & Francis Group.

Hulac, David. Behavioral Interventions in Schools. 2010. (School-Based Practice in Action Ser.). (ENG., Illus.). 288p. pap. 34.95 *(978-0-415-87585-1(4))* Routledge.

Hulac, David, et al. Behavioral Interventions in Schools. 2010. (School-Based Practice in Action Ser.). (ENG., Illus.). 288p. 125.00 *(978-0-415-87584-4(6))* Routledge.

Hunter, Scott J. & Sparrow, Elizabeth P. Executive Function & Dysfunction. 2012. (ENG., Illus.). 296p. 99.00 ***(978-0-521-88976-6(6))*** Cambridge Univ. Pr.

Hurley, Kathy. Mommy, Why Do Bad Things Happen? 2009. 16p. pap. 8.49 *(978-1-4490-2630-1(3))* AuthorHouse.

Hyndman, Robert. Connecting School Culture to Boys' Learning. 2008. 116p. pap. *(978-3-639-03358-8(2))* VDM Verlag Dr. Mueller e.K.

James, Allison, et al, eds. Children, Food & Identity in Everyday Life. 2010. (Studies in Childhood & Youth Ser.). (ENG., Illus.). 208p. 89.00 *(978-0-230-57599-8(4))* Palgrave Macmillan.

James, Beverly. Handbook for Treatment of Attachment Problems in Children. 2008. (ENG.). 308p. pap. 20.95 *(978-1-4391-4300-1(5)*, Free Pr.) Free Pr.

Jana, Laura A. & Shu, Jennifer. Food Fights: Winning the Nutritional Challenges of Parenthood Armed with Insight, Humor, & a Bottle of Ketchup. 2012. (ENG.). 345p. pap. 14.95 ***(978-1-58110-585-8(1))*** American Academy of Pediatrics.

Jensen, Lene Arnett & Mortimer, Jeylan T., eds. Social Class & Transitions to Adulthood: New Directions for Child & Adolescent Development. 2008. (J-B CAD Single Issue Child & Adolescent Development Ser.: 89). (ENG.). 112p. pap. 29.00 *(978-0-470-29362-1(4)*, Jossey-Bass) Wiley, John & Sons, Inc.

Jervis, Kathe & Polland, Barbara K. Separation: Supporting Children in Their Preschool Transitions. 2007. 83p. pap. 7.00 *(978-1-928896-44-9(8))* National Assn. for the Education of Young Children.

Johansen Psy.D., Thor M. Disruptive Kids: A Guide for Parents. 2008. 192p. pap. 18.95 *(978-1-4343-6293-3(0))* AuthorHouse.

Johnson, Debresha. Mommie Don't Leave Me! 2010. 16p. 8.49 *(978-1-4520-0885-1(X))* AuthorHouse.

Johnson, Eileen. The Children's Bill of Emotional Rights: A Guide to the Needs of Children. 2011. (ENG., Illus.). 272p. (gr. 17). 60.00 ***(978-0-7657-0850-2(7)***, Aronson, Jason) Rowman & Littlefield Publishers, Inc.

Jones, Steven, et al. Why Kids Hate School. rev. ed. 2010. (ENG.). 266p. pap. 53.45 *(978-0-7575-4432-3(0))* Kendall Hunt Publishing Co.

Jongsma, Arthur E., Jr. The Child Psychotherapy: Treatment Planner. 2006. (PracticePlanners? Ser.). (ENG.). pap. 132.00 *(978-0-470-06714-7(4)*, Wiley) Wiley, John & Sons, Inc.

Joshi, Suman, et al. Courage, Heart & Wisdom: Essays on Autism. 2009. 365p. pap. 18.95 *(978-1-4327-1107-8(5))* Outskirts Pr., Inc.

Junefelt, Karen. Rethinking Egocentric Speech: Towards a New Hypothesis. 2007. 169.00 *(978-1-60021-724-1(9))* Nova Science Pubs., Inc.

Junn, Ellen & Boyatzis, Chris. Annual Editions: Child Growth & Development 12/13. 19th ed. 2011. (Annual Editions Ser.). (ENG., Illus.). 224p. (C). pap. 44.00 *(978-0-07-805107-4(X)*, 007805107X, McGraw-Hill/Dushkin) McGraw-Hill Higher Education.

—Child Growth & Development 11/12. annuals 18th ed. 2010. (Annual Editions Ser.). (ENG., Illus.). 224p. (C). pap. 44.00 *(978-0-07-805075-6(8)*, 0078050758, McGraw-Hill/Dushkin) McGraw-Hill Higher Education.

Junn, Ellen, et al. Child Growth & Development 10/11. 17th ed. 2009. (Annual Editions Ser.). (ENG., Illus.). 176p. (C). pap. 44.00 *(978-0-07-812784-7(X)*, 007812784X, McGraw-Hill/Dushkin) McGraw-Hill Higher Education.

Jupiter, Stephanie. The Power Codes: The Language & Habits of the Most Powerful People on the Planet. 2011. 88p. pap. 15.00 ***(978-1-4269-7574-5(0))*** Trafford Publishing.

Kaczmarek, Zofia. Do You Know How I Feel? 2008. 28p. pap. 8.49 *(978-1-4389-0518-1(1))* AuthorHouse.

Kader, Kashiefa. Children's Perceptions of 'screen' Violence. 2010. 116p. pap. *(978-3-8383-8055-1(X))* Lambert Academic Publishing.

Kail & Cram101 Textbook Reviews Staff. Children. 2007. 156p. per. 12.95 *(978-1-4288-2038-8(8))* Cram101 Inc.

—Children & Their Development. 2007. 152p. per. 12.95 *(978-1-4288-2028-9(0))* Cram101 Inc.

Kail, Robert V., ed. Advances in Child Development & Behavior. (Advances in Child Development & Behavior Ser.: 36). (ENG., 2008. Illus.). 520p. 107.00 *(978-0-12-374317-6(6))* 2007. 426p. 107.00 *(978-0-12-009735-7(4))* 2006. (Illus.). 418p. 107.00 *(978-0-12-009734-0(6))* Elsevier Science & Technology Bks. (Academic Pr.).

Kalikow, Kevin T. Your Child in the Balance: Solving the Psychiatric Medicine Dilemma. 2nd ed. 2012. (ENG.). 288p. pap. 21.95 *(978-0-393-70660-4(5)*, 70660) Norton, W. W. & Co., Inc.

Kampmann, Jennifer. The Well Being of Children: As Viewed through Their Conceptions of Death. 2008. 88p. pap. *(978-3-639-09416-9(6))* VDM Verlag Dr. Mueller e.K.

Kaplan, Paul S. A Child's Odyssey. 4th rev. ed. 2011. (ENG.). 688p. pap. 96.55 *(978-0-7575-4916-8(0))* Kendall Hunt Publishing Co.

Kaplan, Suzanne. Children in Genocide: Extreme Traumatization & Affect Regulation. 2008. (IPA: the International Psychoanalysis Library). (Illus.). 320p. (C). pap. 59.95 *(978-1-905888-15-3(5))* Karnac Bks. GBR. Dist: Stylus Publishing, LLC.

Kapornai, Krisztina. Early Neurodevelopmental Factors & Childhood Onset Depression. 2011. 64p. pap. ***(978-3-8433-9165-8(3))*** Lambert Academic Publishing.

Karpov, Yuriy V. The Neo-Vygotskian Approach to Child Development. 2006. (ENG., Illus.). 300p. (C). per. 35.99 *(978-0-521-69613-5(5))* Cambridge Univ. Pr.

Kay, Janet & Kay. Behavioural, Emotional & Social Difficulties: A Guide for the Early Years. 2007. (Sen in the Early Years Ser.). (ENG.). 160p. 21.95 *(978-0-8264-8469-7(7))* Continuum International Publishing Group, Ltd. GBR. Dist: National Bk. Network.

Kearney, Christopher. Getting Your Child to Say Yes to School: A Guide for Parents of Youth with School Refusal Behavior. 2007. (ENG., Illus.). 208p. per. 22.95 *(978-0-19-530630-9(9))* Oxford Univ. Pr., Inc.

Kearney, Christopher A. & Albano, Anne Marie. When Children Refuse School: A Cognitive-Behavioral Therapy Approach Parent Workbook. 2nd rev. ed. 2007. (Treatments That Work Ser.). (ENG., Illus.). 216p. per. 32.95 *(978-0-19-530829-7(8))* Oxford Univ. Pr., Inc.

—When Children Refuse School: A Cognitive-Behavioral Therapy Approach Therapist Guide. 2nd rev. ed. 2007. (Treatments That Work Ser.). (ENG., Illus.). 288p. (C). per. 42.95 *(978-0-19-530830-3(1))* Oxford Univ. Pr., Inc.

Keating, Daniel P., ed. Nature & Nurture in Early Child Development. 2010. (ENG., Illus.). 312p. 90.00 *(978-0-521-84040-8(6))* Cambridge Univ. Pr.

Kehily, Mary Jane. An Introduction to Childhood Studies. 2nd ed. 2008. (ENG.). 216p. (C). pap. 45.00 *(978-0-335-22870-6(4)*, 0335228704) McGraw-Hill Education GBR. Dist: McGraw-Hill Cos., The.

Kelman, Elaine & Whyte, Alison. Understanding Stammering or Stuttering: A Guide for Parents, Teachers & Other Professionals. 2012. (ENG.). 176p. pap. ***(978-1-84905-268-9(9))*** Kingsley, Jessica Ltd.

Kemp, Sally L. & Korkman, Marit. Essentials of NEPSY-II Assessment. 2010. (Essentials of Psychological Assessment Ser.: 69). (ENG., Illus.). 496p. pap. 38.95 *(978-0-470-43691-2(3)*, Wiley) Wiley, John & Sons, Inc.

Kendall, Anne & DeGangi, Georgia A. Effective Parenting for the Hard-to-Manage Child: A Skills-Based Book. 2007. (ENG., Illus.). 304p. per. 24.95 *(978-0-415-95546-1(7))* Routledge.

Kiel-Hinrichsen, Monika. Why Children Don't Listen: A Guide for Parents & Teachers. 2006. (Illus.). 185p. per. *(978-0-86315-574-1(X))* Floris Bks.

Killen, Melanie & Rutland, Adam. Children & Social Exclusion: Morality, Prejudice, & Group Identity. 2011. (Understanding Children's Worlds Ser.: 22). (ENG., Illus.). 248p. 104.95 *(978-1-4051-7651-4(2)*, Wiley-Blackwell) Wiley, John & Sons, Inc.

Killick, Steve. Emotional Literacy at the Heart of the School Ethos. rev. ed. 2006. (Lucky Duck Bks.). (Illus.). 208p. pap. 43.00 *(978-1-4129-1155-9(9)*, B11559P) SAGE Pubns., Ltd. GBR. Dist: SAGE Pubns., Inc.

Kim, Daniella. Infants' & Adults' Perception of Tone Chrom. 2009. 124p. pap. *(978-3-639-01831-8(1))* VDM Verlag Dr. Mueller e.K.

King, Robert A., et al, eds. The Psychoanalytic Study of the Child. (Psychoanalytic Study of the Child Ser.). (ENG., Illus.). 368p. Vol. 61. 2007. 70.00 *(978-0-300-11996-1(8))* Vol. 64. 2010. 75.00 *(978-0-300-15329-3(5))* Yale Univ. Pr.

Klein, Karin. Parent Connection, Grades Preschool-1. (Illus.). 80p. tchr. ed. 9.99 *(978-0-7847-0530-8(5)*, 03072) Standard Publishing.

Klingberg, Torkel. Grey Matter Garden: Memory & Brain Development in Children. 2012. (ENG.). 192p. 24.95 ***(978-0-19-991710-5(8))*** Oxford Univ. Pr., Inc.

Kloo, Daniela. Theory of Mind & Executive Functions. 2008. 200p. pap. *(978-3-639-01139-5(2))* VDM Verlag Dr. Mueller e.K.

Kohnstamm, Dolph. I am I - Sudden Flashes of Self-awareness in Childhood. 2007. 204p. per. *(978-1-84401-937-3(3))* Athena Pr.

Kohnstamm, Geldolph A. Jean Piaget: Number & Class in Children. 2011. (ENG.). 173p. pap. 29.95 ***(978-1-4128-4284-6(0))*** Aldine Transaction.

Koocher, Gerald & La Greca, Annette. The Parents' Guide to Psychological First Aid, 1 vol. 2010. (ENG., Illus.). 496p. pap. 27.95 *(978-0-19-538191-7(2))* Oxford Univ. Pr., Inc.

Kraus, Kurt L. Lenses: Applying Lifespan Development Theories in Counseling. 2008. (ENG.). 496p. (C). pap. 75.95 *(978-0-618-37030-6(7)*, 330920) CENGAGE Learning.

Krehbiel, James P. Troubled Childhood, Triumphant Life: Healing from the Battle Scars of Youth. 2010. (ENG.). 224p. pap. 14.95 *(978-0-88282-318-8(3))* New Horizon Pr. Pubs., Inc.

Kytts, Marketta. Children in Outdoor Contexts: Affordances & Independent Mobility in the Assessment of Environmental Child Friendliness. 2008. 208p. pap. *(978-3-639-08841-0(7))* VDM Verlag Dr. Mueller e.K.

Lab-Volt Staff. Finding Solutions: TD Facs ESeries. 2010. 81p. 9.00 *(978-1-60533-129-4(5))*; 44p. ring bd. 6.00 *(978-1-60533-130-0(9))* Lab-Volt Systems, Inc.

Labno, Jeannie. Commemorating the Polish Renaissance Child: Funeral Monuments & Their European Context. 2011. (Illus.). 472p. 134.95 *(978-0-7546-6825-1(8))* Ashgate Publishing Co.

Lack, Caleb W. Tornadoes, Children, & Posttraumatic Stress. 2008. 120p. pap. *(978-3-639-00387-1(X))* VDM Verlag Dr. Mueller e.K.

Ladd, Gary W. Appraising the Human Developmental Sciences: Essays in Honor of Merrill-Palmer Quarterly. 2007. (Illus.). 404p. per. 34.95 *(978-0-8143-3342-6(7))* Wayne State Univ. Pr.

Lamb, Winifred Wing Han & de Souza, Marian, eds. Children, Adolescents & Spirituality. 2008. (Interface: A Forum for Theology in the World Ser.). (ENG.). 168p. (C). pap. 10.00 *(978-1-920691-90-5(1))* ATF Pr. AUS. Dist: Brown, David Bk. Co., The.

Lamoreaux, Antoinette Abe. Unfolding Life. 2006. pap. *(978-1-4068-1421-7(0))* Echo Library.

Lampinen, James M. & Sexton-radek, Kathleen J., eds. Protecting Children from Violence: Evidence Based Interventions. 2010. (ENG., Illus.). 392p. 36.95 *(978-1-84872-841-7(7))*; 78.95 *(978-1-84872-840-0(9))* Taylor & Francis Group GBR. (Psychology Press). Dist: Taylor & Francis Group.

Landry, Deborah. Teachers'Perceptions of Student Behaviors During Testing. 2009. 172p. pap. *(978-3-639-13517-6(2))* VDM Verlag Dr. Mueller e.K.

Landry, Nicole E. R. The Mean Girl Motive: Negotiating Power & Femininity. 2008. (ENG.). 110p. pap. 17.95 *(978-1-55266-266-3(7))* Fernwood Publishing Co., Ltd. CAN. Dist: Independent Pubs. Group.

Landy, Sarah. Pathways to Competence: Encouraging Healthy Social & Emotional Development in Young Children. 2nd ed. 2009. 672p. pap. 59.95 *(978-1-55766-891-2(4))* Brookes, Paul H. Publishing Co.

Langelier, Pamela. Rebuilding Families: A Blueprint for Child Custody Team Evaluations. 2009. 116p. pap. 12.95 *(978-1-4401-2948-3(7))* iUniverse, Inc.

Larson, Christian. The Scientific Training of Children. 2007. 72p. per. 12.95 *(978-1-60206-195-8(5))* Cosimo, Inc.

Le Messurier, Mark & Nawana Parker, Madhavi. What's the Buzz? Games & Activities to Improve Social Skills. 2011. (ENG., Illus.). 256p. 47.95 *(978-0-415-58382-4(9))* Routledge.

Lee, Robert G. & Harris, Neil, eds. Relational Child, Relational Brain: Development & Therapy in Childhood & Adolescence. 2011. (ENG.). 382p. (C). pap. 39.95 ***(978-0-415-80776-0(X))*** Analytic Pr.

Lee, Steven W. & Eagle, John W. Ecobehavioral Consultation in Schools: Theory & Practice for School Psychologists, Special Educators, & School Counselors. 2010. (School-Based Practice in Action Ser.). (ENG.). 256p. 34.95 *(978-0-415-99343-2(1))*; 95.00 *(978-0-415-99342-5(3))* Routledge.

Lehman, Bob & Elaine. Raise Civilized Kids! Bring Back the Disciplines. 2010. pap. 14.99 *(978-1-60799-952-2(8))* Tate Publishing & Enterprises, LLC.

Leonard, Michael M. Youth, Gangs & God: Why Are Our Children Dying to Join Gangs? Leonard, Candice, ed. 2008. 68p. pap. 14.00 *(978-1-4251-6185-9(5))* Trafford Publishing.

Lester, Barry M. & Sparrow, Joshua D., eds. Nurturing Children & Families: Building on the Legacy of T. Berry Brazelton. 2010. (ENG., Illus.). 416p. 49.95 *(978-1-4051-9600-0(9)*, Wiley-Blackwell) Wiley, John & Sons, Inc.

Levine, Laura E. & Munsch, Joyce. Child Development: An Active Learning Approach. 2010. 704p. (C). ring bd. 62.00 *(978-1-4129-8918-3(3)*, B68508M); (Illus.). pap. 83.00 *(978-1-4129-6850-8(X)*, B68508P) SAGE Pubns., Inc.

Levine, Peter A. & Kline, Maggie. Trauma Through a Child's Eyes: Awakening the Ordinary Miracle of Healing; Infancy Through Adolescence. annot. ed. 2006. (ENG.). 536p. pap. 24.95 *(978-1-55643-630-7(0))* North Atlantic Bks.

Levy, Florence. Brain Circuits, Modularity, & Childhood Syndromes. 2011. 428p. pap. ***(978-3-8433-8568-8(8))*** Lambert Academic Publishing.

Lewis, James, III & Griffin, Dawn. Children Exposed to Violence: Current Issues, Interventions & Research. Zellner, Jennifer, ed. 2009. 266p. pap. 45.95 *(978-0-7890-3828-9(5))* Routledge.

—Children Exposed to Violence: Current Issues, Interventions & Research. Geffner, Bob & Zellner, Jennifer, eds. 2009. 266p. 130.00 *(978-0-7890-3827-2(7))* Routledge.

Lewis, Richard. Living by Wonder: Writings on the Imaginative Life of Childhood. 2006. (Illus.). 150p. per. 12.00 *(978-1-929299-05-8(2))* Touchstone Ctr. Pubns.

Lievegoed, Bernard C. J. Phases of Childhood: Growing in Body, Soul & Spirit. Langham, Tony & Peters, Plym, trs. from DUT. 3rd rev. ed. (Illus.). 208p. pap. 19.95 *(978-0-86315-481-2(6))* Floris Bks. GBR. Dist: SteinerBooks, Inc.

Lightfoot, Cynthia, et al. The Development of Children Study Guide. 6th ed. 2009. (ENG., Illus.). 404p. (C). pap., stu. ed. 29.95 *(978-1-4292-1783-5(9))* Worth Pubs., Inc.

Limón, Margarita & Mason, L., eds. Reconsidering Conceptual Change: Issues in Theory & Practice: Issues in Theory & Practice. 2010. 440p. pap. 269.00 *(978-90-481-5967-3(9)*, 9048159679) Springer.

Linder, Toni W. Administration Guide for. 2008. (Illus.). 384p. spiral bd. 54.95 *(978-1-55766-873-8(6))* Brookes, Paul H. Publishing Co.

Lindon, Jennie. Understanding Children's Behaviour 0-11 Years: Play, Development & Learning. 2012. (ENG., Illus.). 224p. pap. 45.00 ***(978-1-4441-7097-9(X))*** Hodder Arnold Pubs.

Lippitz, Wilfried & Martino, Daniel J. The Phenomenology of Childhood: The Nineteenth Annual Symposium of the Simon Silverman Phenomenology Center. 2006. *(978-0-9786572-5-3(X))* Duquesne Univ., Simon Silverman Phenomenology Ctr.

Lombardo, Gregory T. Understanding the Mind of Your Bipolar Child: The Complete Guide to the Development, Treatment, & Parenting of Children with Bipolar Disorder. 2008. (ENG., Illus.). 384p. pap. 14.99 *(978-0-312-35890-7(3)*, St. Martin's Griffin) St. Martin's Pr.

Long, Nicholas James, et al. The Angry Smile: The Psychology of Passive-Aggressive Behavior in Families, Schools, & Workplaces. 2nd ed. 2008. 26.00 *(978-1-4164-0423-1(6))* PRO-ED, Inc.

Lowenfeld, Margaret. Play in Childhood. 2008. (ENG., Illus.). 258p. pap. 42.50 *(978-1-84519-300-3(8))* Sussex Academic Pr. GBR. Dist: International Specialized Bk. Services.

Luby, Joan L., ed. Handbook of Preschool Mental Health: Development, Disorders, & Treatment. (ENG., Illus.). 430p. 2009. pap. 35.00 *(978-1-60623-350-4(5))* 2006. 60.00 *(978-1-59385-313-6(0))* Guilford Pubns., Inc.

Maciejewski, Charles. Adventure, Self-Efficacy, & Students of Color. 2008. 76p. pap. *(978-3-639-05000-4(2))* VDM Verlag Dr. Mueller e.K.

MacLaughlin, Sarah. What Not to Say: Tools for Talking with Young Children. 2010. (Illus.). 96p. 12.00 *(978-0-9654694-2-5(5))* Bay Island Bks.

Maffini, Helen & Bahman, Shahnaz. Developing Children's Emotional Intelligence. 2008. (ENG., Illus.). 144p. 34.95 *(978-0-8264-9974-5(0))* Continuum International Publishing Group, Ltd. GBR. Dist: National Bk. Network.

Mah, Ronald. The One-Minute Temper Tantrum Solution: Strategies for Responding to Children's Challenging Behaviors. 2008. 160p. 71.95 *(978-1-4129-5720-5(6),* B57206C); pap. 29.95 *(978-1-4129-5721-2(4),* B57206P) Corwin Pr.

Maholmes, Valerie & Lomonaco, Carmela Gina. Applied Research in Child & Adolescent Development. 2010. (ENG.). 340p. 94.95 *(978-1-84872-814-1(X));* pap., instr.'s gde. ed. 47.95 *(978-1-84872-815-8(8))* Taylor & Francis Group GBR. (Psychology Press). Dist: Taylor & Francis Group.

Main, Shiho. Childhood Re-Imagined: Images & Narratives of Development in Analytical Psychology. 2008. (ENG., Illus.). 216p. (C). 42.50 *(978-0-415-38496-4(6));* 110.00 *(978-0-415-38495-7(8))* Routledge.

Malik Aradhna & Malik, Aradhna. Media Screens: A Study of the Relationship Between Media Screen Exposure & Communicative Competence of 4 to 6-Year- Old Children. 2008. 128p. pap. *(978-3-639-03260-9(5))* VDM Verlag Dr. Mueller e.K.

Mallon, Brenda. Working with Bereaved Children & Young People. 2010. 168p. (C). 104.00 *(978-1-84920-370-8(9),* B03708C); pap. 41.00 *(978-1-84920-371-5(7),* B03708P) SAGE Pubns., Ltd. GBR. Dist: SAGE Pubns., Inc.

Manassis, Katharina. Keys to Parenting Your Anxious Child. 2nd rev. ed. 2008. (Barron's Parenting Keys Ser.). (ENG.). 192p. pap. 8.99 *(978-0-7641-3916-1(9))* Barron's Educational Series, Inc.

Manis, Frank & Radford, Mike. The Virtual Child. 2006. (C). pap. 16.00 *(978-0-13-175156-9(5),* Prentice Hall) Prentice Hall PTR.

Margalit, Malka. Lonely Children & Adolescents: Self-Perceptions, Social Exclusion, & Hope. (ENG., Illus.). xiv, 303p. 2011. pap. 44.95 ***(978-1-4614-2375-1(9),*** 1461423759) 2010. 169.00 *(978-1-4419-6283-6(2),* 1441962832) Springer.

Marion, Marian C. Guidance of Young Children. 8th ed. 2010. (ENG.). 416p. (C). pap. 82.80 *(978-0-13-703402-4(4),* Prentice Hall) Prentice Hall PTR.

—Guidance of Young Children (with MyEducationLab) 8th ed. 2010. (ENG.). 416p. (C). pap. 89.47 *(978-0-13-138119-3(3),* Prentice Hall) Prentice Hall PTR.

Maroni, Lesley. Understanding 4-5-Year-Olds. 2007. (Understanding Your Child (Jessica Kingsley Publishers) Ser.). (ENG.). 8p. per. *(978-1-84310-534-3(9))* Kingsley, Jessica Ltd.

Martin, Roy P. & Dombrowski, Stefan C. Prenatal Exposures: Psychological & Educational Consequences for Children. 2010. (ENG.). 461p. pap. 69.95 *(978-1-4419-4500-6(8),* 1441945008) Springer.

Mash, Eric J. & Barkley, Russell A., eds. Assessment of Childhood Disorders. 4th ed. 2009. (ENG.). 866p. pap. 50.00 *(978-1-60623-615-4(6))* Guilford Pubns., Inc.

Mash, Eric J. & Wolfe, David A. Abnormal Child Psychology. 4th ed. 2008. (Available Titles CengageNOW Ser.). (ENG.). 576p. (C). 214.95 *(978-0-495-50627-0(3))* Wadsworth.

Masten, Ann S. Multilevel Dynamics in Developmental Psychopathology: Pathways to the Future. 2007. (Minnesota Symposia on Child Psychology Ser.). (ENG., Illus.). 368p. 94.95 *(978-0-8058-6162-4(9),* Psychology Press) Taylor & Francis Group GBR. Dist: Taylor & Francis Group.

Matson, Johnny L., ed. Social Behavior & Skills in Children. 2009. (ENG.). x, 334p. 149.95 *(978-1-4419-0233-7(3),* 1441902333) Springer.

Mawson, W. B., ed. Collaborative Play in Early Childhood Education. 2010. (Children's Issues, Laws & Programs Ser.). 69.00 *(978-1-61728-946-0(9))* Nova Science Pubs., Inc.

Mayer, Elaine. Letters to Grand Children: Discovering Enchantment & Amazement. 2009. 240p. pap. 19.95 *(978-1-4269-1542-0(X))* Trafford Publishing.

Mayes, Linda & Lewis, Michael, eds. The Environment of Human Development: A Handbook of Theory & Measurement. 2012. (Cambridge Handbooks in Psychology Ser.). (ENG., Illus.). 704p. 140.00 ***(978-0-521-86882-2(3))*** Cambridge Univ. Pr.

Mayseless, Ofra & Scharf, Miri, eds. Attachment in Adolescence: Reflections & New Angles. 2007. (J-B CAD Single Issue Child & Adolescent Development Ser.: 87). (ENG., Illus.). 123p. per. 29.00 *(978-0-470-22560-8(2),* Jossey-Bass) Wiley, John & Sons, Inc.

McCready, Amy. If I Have to Tell You One More Time... The Revolutionary Program That Gets Your Kids to Listen Without Nagging, Reminding, or Yelling. (ENG., 320p. (gr. 12). 2012. Illus.). pap. 15.95 ***(978-0-399-16059-2(0))*** 2011. 24.95 *(978-1-58542-864-9(7))* Penguin Group (USA) Inc. (Tarcher).

McGuire, Patricia. Never Assume: Getting to Know Children Before Labeling Them. 2008. 112p. pap. 11.95 *(978-1-4327-1717-9(0),* Outskirts Pr., Inc.

McIlhaney, Joe S., Jr. & Bush, Freda McKissic. Hooked: New Science on How Casual Sex Is Affecting Our Children. 2008. (ENG.). 176p. 17.99 *(978-0-8024-5060-9(1))* Northfield Publishing.

McNeil, Frank. Learning with the Brain in Mind. 2008. (Illus.). 216p. tchr. ed. 128.00 *(978-1-4129-4525-7(9),* B45259C); pap. 38.95 *(978-1-4129-4526-4(7),* B45259P) SAGE Pubns., Ltd. GBR. Dist: SAGE Pubns., Inc.

The Meaning of Life: A Child's Book of Existential Psychology. 2007. *(978-0-9794108-0-2(0))* Trans Limbic Pr.

Menezes, Edirle. Chilcren S Play & the Socio-Cultural Nature of Subjectivity. 2008. 156p. pap. *(978-3-639-08771-0(2))* VDM Verlag Dr. Mueller e.K.

Mercogliano, Chris. In Defense of Childhood: Protecting Kids' Inner Wildness. 2008. (ENG.). 224p. pap. 16.00 *(978-0-8070-3287-9(5))* Beacon Pr.

Merleau-Ponty, Maurice. Child Psychology & Pedagogy: The Sorbonne Lectures, 1949-1952. Welsh, Talia, tr. from FRE. 2010. (Spep Ser.). (ENG.). 528p. 99.95 *(978-0-8101-2614-5(1));* pap. 34.95 *(978-0-8101-2616-9(8))* Northwestern Univ. Pr.

Merrell, Kenneth W. Home & Community Social Behavior Scales User's Guide. 2008. pap. *(978-1-55766-991-9(0))* Brookes, Paul H. Publishing Co.

Messay, Gebremariam Kotecho. The Psychological & Social Adjustment of Orphaned Children: The Case of Wolaita Soddo. 2011. 68p. pap. ***(978-3-639-32795-3(0))*** VDM Verlag Dr. Mueller e.K.

Messurier, Mark Le. Teaching Tough Kids: Simple & Proven Strategies for Student Success. 2009. (ENG., Illus.). 240p. pap. 42.95 *(978-0-415-46060-6(3))* Routledge.

Meyer, Manfred, ed. Children & the formal features of Television: Approaches & findings of experimental & formative Research. (Communication research & Broadcasting Ser.). (ENG.). 333p. ***(978-3-11-209618-5(5))*** Saur, K. G. Verlag GmbH & Co.

Midgley, Nick. Child Psychotherapy & Research: New Approaches, Emerging Findings. Grainger, Eve et al, eds. 2009. (ENG., Illus.). 248p. (C). 110.00 *(978-0-415-42202-4(7))* Routledge.

—Child Psychotherapy & Research: New Approaches, Emerging Findings. Nesic-Vuckovic, Tanja et al, eds. 2009. (ENG., Illus.). 248p. (C). pap. 40.00 *(978-0-415-42203-1(5))* Routledge.

Miller, Philip. The Really Good Fun Cartoon Book of NLP: A Simply & Graphic(al) Explanation of the Life Toolbox That Is NLP. 2008. (Illus.). 158p. pap. *(978-1-84590-115-8(0))* Crown Hse. Publishing.

Miller, Toby & Miller, Darla Ferris. Guidance & Behavior Management PET. 5th ed. 2006. (ENG.). 128p. (C). pap. 23.95 *(978-1-4180-3098-8(8))* Wadsworth.

Milner, Marion. Bothered by Alligators. 2012. (ENG., Illus.). 296p. 90.00 *(978-0-415-68455-2(2));* pap. 26.99 *(978-0-415-68456-9(0))* Routledge.

Mitchell. Fundamentals of Development. 2nd rev. ed. 2007. (ENG., Illus.). 248p. 39.95 *(978-1-84169-644-7(7),* Psychology Press) Taylor & Francis Group GBR. Dist: Taylor & Francis Group.

Mitchell, Claudia, et al, eds. Memory & Pedagogy. 2010. (Routledge Research in Education Ser.). (ENG., Illus.). 330p. (C). 125.00 *(978-0-415-88380-1(6))* Routledge.

Mitchell, Fenja. Psychology of Childhood Ed2. 2nd rev. ed. 2007. (ENG., Illus.). 248p. 90.00 *(978-0-86377-793-6(7),* Psychology Press) Taylor & Francis Group GBR. Dist: Taylor & Francis Group.

Modgil, S., et al, eds. Jean Piaget. 2007. 288p. 170.00 *(978-0-415-40226-2(3))* Routledge.

Moe, Gerald L. Heartfelt: ... Life Between the Lines. 2011. 124p. 21.95 *(978-1-4520-9963-7(4));* pap. 13.95 *(978-1-4520-9962-0(6))* AuthorHouse.

Moll, Albert. The Sexual Life of the Child. 2010. (ENG.). 360p. pap. 32.75 *(978-1-176-97803-4(9));* 366p. pap. 32.75 *(978-1-146-38516-9(1));* 362p. pap. 32.75 *(978-1-144-62015-6(5))* BiblioBazaar.

—The Sexual Life of the Child. 2009. 228p. pap. *(978-1-150-17453-7(6))* Books LLC.

—The Sexual Life of the Child. Paul, Eden, tr. 2009. 300p. pap. *(978-1-4099-4981-7(8))* Dodo Pr.

—The Sexual Life of the Child. 2010. (Illus.). 242p. pap. 32.38 *(978-1-153-81219-1(3))* General Bks. LLC.

—The Sexual Life of the Child. Paul, Eden, tr. fac. l.t. ed. 2010. (ENG.). 350p. pap. 23.95 *(978-1-61033-413-6(2),* TGS Publishing) TGS.

Mondy, Tim. Memoirs of Miracles. 2008. 232p. pap. 22.33 *(978-0-615-19877-4(5))* Mondy, Tim.

Montessori, Maria. The Absorbent Mind. 2008. 244p. pap. 11.99 *(978-1-60459-540-6(X))* Wilder Pubns., Ltd.

—Spontaneous Activity in Education. 2008. 272p. pap. 10.95 *(978-1-4385-0543-5(4));* (ENG.). pap. 11.45 *(978-1-4385-0967-9(7))* Standard Pubns., Inc. (Book Jungle).

Morales, Rosanna. Empowering Your Pupils Through Role-Play: Exploring Emotions & Building Resilience. 2007. (ENG., Illus.). 128p. pap. 37.50 *(978-0-415-44708-9(9))* Routledge.

Morgan, Angela. Constructing & Maintaining Disability. 2011. 240p. pap. ***(978-3-8443-3181-3(6))*** Lambert Academic Publishing.

Morgan, Jay. Fingerpainting in Psych Class: Artfully Applying Science to Better Work with Children & Teens. 2010. 352p. pap. 23.95 *(978-1-4401-6751-5(6))* iUniverse, Inc.

Morris, Desmond. Child: How Children Think, Learn & Grow in the Early Years. 2010. (ENG., Illus.). 192p. 29.99 *(978-0-600-61994-9(X),* Hamlyn) Octopus Publishing Group GBR. Dist: Hachette Bk. Group.

Mowder, Barbara, ed. Journal of Early Childhood VOL 3. 2007. (ENG.). 248p. pap. 40.00 *(978-0-944473-82-5(2))* Pace Univ. Pr.

Mowder, Barbara A., et al. Evidence-Based Practice in Infant & Early Childhood Psychology. Mowder, Barbara A. et al, eds. 2009. (ENG., Illus.). 792p. 163.00 *(978-0-470-39526-4(5),* Wiley) Wiley, John & Sons, Inc.

Mugubi, John. The Child Character in Adult Literature. 2010. 252p. pap. *(978-3-8383-8066-7(5))* Lambert Academic Publishing.

Mullen, Jodi Ann. Play Therapy Basic Training Workbook: A Guide to Learning & Living the Child-Centered Play Therapy Philosophy. Mentes, Emily, tr. 2007. (ENG & SPA., Illus.). 98p. pap. 23.95 *(978-0-9796287-0-2(9))* Integrative Counseling Services, PLLC.

Müller, Ulrich, et al, eds. The Cambridge Companion to Piaget. 2009. (Cambridge Companions to Philosophy Ser.). (ENG., Illus.). 440p. (C). 97.00 *(978-0-521-89858-4(7));* pap. 30.99 *(978-0-521-72719-8(7))* Cambridge Univ. Pr.

Murphy, Elizabeth & Meisgeier, Charles. MMTIC Manual: A Guide to the Development & Use of the Murphy-Meisgeier Type Indicator for Children. 2008. 107p. per. 25.00 *(978-0-935652-81-9(7))* Center for Applications of Psychological Type, Inc.

Murphy, Suzanne. A Place to Lay My Head. 2008. 260p. pap. *(978-3-639-08707-9(0))* VDM Verlag Dr. Mueller e.K.

Murray, Andrew. God's Best Secrets. 2011. 66p. pap. 5.95 ***(978-1-61427-155-0(0))*** Martino Publishing.

Myers, Gene. The Significance of Children & Animals: Social Development & Our Connection to Other Species. 2nd rev. ed. 2006. (New Directions in the Human-Animal Bond Ser.). (ENG.). 248p. per. 29.95 *(978-1-55753-429-3(2))* Purdue Univ. Pr.

Mysore padmaprasad, Shwetha & Mysore Padmaprasad, Shwetha. Working Memory & Complex Sentence Comprehension. 2011. 172p. pap. ***(978-3-8443-0742-9(7))*** Lambert Academic Publishing.

Neale, M. & Cardon, L. R. Methodology for Genetic Studies of Twins & Families. 2010. (NATO Science Series D: (closed) Ser.). 528p. pap. 559.00 *(978-90-481-4179-1(6),* 9048141796) Springer.

Neil, Dana. Welcome Baby Maizy! 2009. 52p. pap. 20.49 *(978-1-4389-2055-9(5))* AuthorHouse.

Nelsen, D. E. Childhood Dreams Really Do Come True. 2008. 276p. pap. 27.95 *(978-1-60610-919-9(7))* PublishAmerica, Inc.

Nelson, Katherine. Young Minds in Social Worlds: Experience, Meaning, & Memory. 2010. (Illus.). 330p. pap. 21.00 *(978-0-674-03486-0(4))* Harvard Univ. Pr.

Netmums Cookery Book Staff, et al. Toddling to Ten: Your Common Parenting Problems Solved - The Netmums Guide to the Challenges of Childhood. 2008. (ENG.). 416p. pap. 25.95 *(978-0-7553-1607-6(X))* Headline Bk. Publishing GBR. Dist: Independent Pubs. Group.

Netty. Full Stop to the Rescue, a Big Red Border Book. 2010. 38p. pap. 11.00 *(978-1-60911-109-0(5),* Strategic Bk. Publishing) AEG Literary Publishing Services, Inc.

Novak, Paul. Your Child's Brain. 2010. 84p. pap. 20.00 *(978-0-557-25396-8(9))* Lulu Enterprises Inc.

Nowinski, Joseph. The Divorced Child: Strengthening Your Family through the First Three Years of Separation. 2010. (ENG.). 240p. pap. 17.00 *(978-0-230-61772-8(7))* Palgrave Macmillan.

Nunes, T. & Bishop, D., eds. Learning Languages in Atypical Contexts Vol. 53, No. 5: Special Issue - Human Development 2010. 2011. (Illus.). 78p. pap. *(978-3-8055-9635-0(9))* Karger, S. AG.

Nunes, Terezinha & Bryant, Peter. Children's Reading & Spelling: Beyond the First Steps. 2009. (Understanding Children's Worlds Ser.). (ENG., Illus.). 320p. pap. 44.95 *(978-0-631-23403-6(9));* 116.95 *(978-0-631-23402-9(0))* Wiley, John & Sons, Inc. (Wiley-Blackwell).

Oakwater, Helen. Bubble Wrapped Children: How social networking Is transforming the face of 21st century Adoption. 2012. 202p. pap. ***(978-1-78092-097-9(0))*** MX Publishing, Ltd.

Olfman, Sharna. No Child Left Different. 2008. (ENG.). 260p. pap. 27.95 *(978-1-57886-774-5(6))* Rowman & Littlefield Education.

Olmsted, Sarah. Imagine Childhood: Exploring the World Through Nature, Imagination, & Play. 2012. (ENG., Illus.). 240p. pap. 19.95 ***(978-1-59030-970-4(7),*** Roost Books) Shambhala Pubns., Inc.

O'Loughlin, Michael. The Subject of Childhood. 2008. (Rethinking Childhood Ser.). 99.95 *(978-1-4331-0347-6(8));* pap. 32.95 *(978-1-4331-0120-5(3))* Lang, Peter Publishing, Inc.

Olson, Willard C. Problem Tendencies in Children: A Method for Their Measurement & Description. 2009. (ENG.). 110p. pap. 40.00 *(978-0-8166-6068-1(9))* Univ. of Minnesota Pr.

Oneka, Angelo. How to Protect Your Child from Harm & Dangers. 2011. 86p. pap. 19.95 ***(978-1-4560-6582-9(3))*** PublishAmerica, Inc.

Ong'era, Lynett. Managing Emotional & Behaviour Difficulties. 2011. 88p. pap. ***(978-3-639-33360-2(8))*** VDM Verlag Dr. Mueller e.K.

Onongha, Grace Igaba. Psycho-Social Factors in Stepparent-Stepchild Relationships in Nigeri. 2010. 528p. pap. *(978-3-639-26271-1(9))* VDM Verlag Dr. Mueller e.K.

Opare-Henaku, Annabella. What Is Worrying Children in Ghana? 2009. 68p. pap. *(978-3-639-19898-0(0))* VDM Verlag Dr. Mueller e.K.

Otten, Kaye & Tuttle, Jodie. How to Reach & Teach Children with Challenging Behavior: Practical, Ready-to-Use Interventions That Work. 2010. (J-B Ed: Reach & Teach Ser.: 7). (ENG., Illus.). 336p. pap. 29.95 *(978-0-470-50516-8(8),* Jossey-Bass) Wiley, John & Sons, Inc.

Otto, Hans-Uwe & Flösser, Gaby, eds. How to Organize Prevention: Political, Organizational, & Professional Challenges to Social Services. (Prevention & Intervention in Childhood & Adolescence Ser.). (ENG., Illus.). XVI, 424p. 252.00 ***(978-3-11-187943-7(7))*** De Gruyter, Walter Inc.

Owusu-Bempah, Kwame. Children & Separation: Socio-Genealogical Connectedness Perspective. 2007. (ENG., Illus.). 208p. 64.50 *(978-0-415-34212-4(0))* Routledge.

Packiam Alloway, Tracy. Improving Working Memory: Supporting Students' Learning. 2010. (Illus.). 136p. (C). 108.00 *(978-1-84920-747-8(X),* B07478C); pap. 41.00 *(978-1-84920-748-5(8),* B07478P) SAGE Pubns., Ltd. GBR. Dist: SAGE Pubns., Inc.

Painton, Mollie. Encouraging Your Child's Spiritual Intelligence. 2007. (ENG.). 192p. pap. 13.95 *(978-1-58270-149-3(0),* Beyond Words/Atria Bks.) Atria Bks.

Palka, Joe. Positive Penelope & Friends. 2010. 16p. 11.99 *(978-1-4520-1855-3(3))* AuthorHouse.

Palomares, Susanna. Anger Control & Conflict Management for Kids. 2011. 134p. pap. 25.95 ***(978-1-56499-078-5(8))*** Innerchoice Publishing.

Pantley, Elizabeth. The No-Cry Separation Anxiety Solution: Gentle Ways to Make Good-Bye Easy from Six Months to Six Years. 2010. (ENG., Illus.). 176p. pap. 16.95 *(978-0-07-159690-9(9),* 0071596909) McGraw-Hill Cos., The.

Papalia, Diane E., et al. A Child's World: Infancy Through Adolescence. 11th ed. 2007. (ENG., Illus.). 640p. (C). 177.00 *(978-0-07-353197-7(9),* 0073531979) McGraw-Hill Cos., The.

Parens, Henri. The Development of Aggression in Early Childhood. 2007. (ENG.). 436p. per. 57.99 *(978-0-7657-0510-5(9),* Aronson, Jason) Rowman & Littlefield Publishers, Inc.

—Handling Children's Aggression Constructively: Toward Taming Human Destructiveness. 2011. (ENG.). 300p. 65.00 *(978-0-7657-0687-4(3))* 2010. *(978-0-7657-0689-8(X))* Rowman & Littlefield Publishers, Inc. (Aronson, Jason).

Parens, Henri. Taming Aggression in Your Child: How to Avoid Raising Bullies, Delinquents, or Trouble-Makers. 2012. ***(978-0-7657-0898-4(1))*** 2011. (ENG.). 240p. (gr. 17). 70.00 ***(978-0-7657-0896-0(5))*** 2011. (ENG.). 240p. (gr. 17). pap. 29.99 ***(978-0-7657-0897-7(3))*** Rowman & Littlefield Publishers, Inc. (Aronson, Jason).

Parke, Ross & Gauvain, Mary. Child Psychology: A Contemporary View Point. 7th ed. 2008. (ENG., Illus.). 720p. (C). 173.33 *(978-0-07-338268-5(X),* 007338268X) McGraw-Hill Cos., The.

Parke, Ross D. & Clarke-Stewart, Alison. Social Development. 2010. (ENG., Illus.). 618p. (C). 197.95 *(978-0-470-59905-1(7),* Wiley) Wiley, John & Sons, Inc.

Parritz, Robin Hornik & Troy, Michael F. Disorders of Childhood: Development & Psychopathology. 2010. (ENG.). 488p. (C). 106.95 *(978-0-534-59274-5(0))* Wadsworth.

Partridge, Lee. Teaching Adolescent AD/HD Boys Through Self-Sufficient Reward Control: A Sociological Investigation. 2010. (Illus.). x, 257p. *(978-0-7734-3808-8(4))* Mellen, Edwin Pr., The.

Patel, Dilip R., et al. Behavioral Pediatrics. 3rd Edition. Greydanus, Donald E., ed. 2008. 89.00 *(978-1-60692-702-1(7))* Nova Science Pubs., Inc.

Payne, Ruby K. & Slocumb, Paul D. Boys in Poverty: A Framework for Understanding Dropout. 2010. 44.95 *(978-1-935249-86-3(X));* 160p. pap. 24.95 *(978-1-935542-22-3(2))* Solution Tree Pr.

Peacock, Gretchen Gimpel, et al, eds. Practical Handbook of School Psychology: Effective Practices for the 21st Century. 2009. (ENG., Illus.). 626p. (gr. k-12). 80.00 *(978-1-59385-697-7(0))* Guilford Pubns., Inc.

Pearman, Christopher B & Newhem, Ian Blake. Dream So Big: A Parent's Guide to Helping Your Child Believe & Achieve. 2010. (ENG.). 256p. 19.95 *(978-1-4405-0402-0(4))* Adams Media Corp.

Peile, Ed. The Normal Child. Bellman, Martin, ed. 11th ed. 2006. (ENG., Illus.). 224p. (C). pap. 69.95 *(978-0-443-05707-6(9),* Churchill Livingstone) Elsevier - Health Sciences Div.

Pellegrini, Anthony D. The Role of Play in Human Development, 1 vol. 2009. (ENG., Illus.). 288p. 49.95 *(978-0-19-536732-4(4))* Oxford Univ. Pr., Inc.

Pellegrini, Anthony D., ed. The Oxford Handbook of the Development of Play, 1 vol. 2010. (Oxford Library of Psychology Ser.). (ENG., Illus.). 416p. 135.00 *(978-0-19-539300-2(7))* Oxford Univ. Pr., Inc.

Percy, Bernard, et al. How to Grow a Child: A Child's Advice to Parents. 2009. 134p. pap. 15.95 *(978-1-888045-24-6(8))* Action Publishing, LLC.

Perez-Alvarez, Frederic & Timoneda-Gallart, Carme. Better Look at Intelligent Behavior: Cognition & Emotion. 2007. (C). 79.00 *(978-1-60021-742-5(7))* Nova Science Pubs., Inc.

Perez, Bernard. The First Three Years of Childhood. 2010. 334p. pap. 31.75 *(978-1-142-24881-9(X))* 2010. 360p. pap. 32.75 *(978-1-142-96708-6(5))* 2009. 328p. 36.99 *(978-1-115-54857-0(0))* 2009. 328p. 32.99 *(978-1-115-54868-7(9))* 2009. 328p. pap. 31.75 *(978-1-115-54869-4(7))* 2009. 328p. pap. 30.75 *(978-1-115-54870-0(0))* 2008. 328p. 28.99 *(978-0-559-74369-6(6))* 2008. 328p. pap. 30.75 *(978-0-559-74366-5(1))* BiblioBazaar.

—The First Three Years of Childhood. 2009. 204p. pap. 19.99 *(978-0-217-58601-6(5))* General Bks. LLC.

—The First Three Years of Childhood. Christie, Alice M., ed. 2008. 324p. 45.95 *(978-1-4366-4889-9(0));* pap. 30.95 *(978-0-548-89689-5(8))* Kessinger Publishing, LLC.

Perez, Bernard & Christie, Alice M. The First Three Years of Childhood. 2009. 328p. 36.99 *(978-1-117-66226-8(8),* BiblioLife); pap. 30.75 *(978-1-117-66227-5(6));* 36.99 *(978-1-115-75888-8(9));* 32.99 *(978-1-115-75889-5(6));* pap. 30.75 *(978-1-115-75891-8(8));* pap. 31.75 *(978-1-115-75890-1(X))* BiblioBazaar.

Peterkin, Allan. The Flyaway Blanket. 2011. (Illus.). 32p. (J). 14.95 ***(978-1-4338-1047-3(6),*** Magination Pr.) American Psychological Assn.

Petty, Karen. Developmental Milestones of Young Children. 2009. (Redleaf Quick Guides). (ENG., Illus.). 50p. pap. 14.95 *(978-1-60554-005-4(6))* Redleaf Pr.

Piaget, 14 vols. 2006. (Routledge Library Editions Ser.). (ENG.). 3584p. 2100.00 (978-0-415-40219-4(0)) Routledge.

Piaget, Jean. Behaviour & Evolution. 2007. 192p. 170.00 (978-0-415-40221-7(2)) Routledge.

—Child's Conception of Movement & Speed. 2007. (ENG.). 336p. 180.00 (978-0-415-40222-4(0)) Routledge.

—The Child's Conception of the World. 2nd ed. 2007. (ENG.). 432p. pap. 32.95 (978-0-7425-5951-6(3)) Rowman & Littlefield Publishers, Inc.

—The Child's Conception of Time. 2007. 304p. 180.00 (978-0-415-40223-1(9)) Routledge.

—The Mechanisms of Perception. 2007. 432p. 180.00 (978-0-415-40228-6(X)) Routledge.

—Success & Understanding. 2007. 256p. 180.00 (978-0-415-40233-0(6)) Routledge.

Pickhardt, Carl E. Why Good Kids Act Cruel: The Hidden Truth about the Pre-Teen Years. 2010. (ENG.). 320p. pap. 14.99 (978-1-4022-1944-3(X)) Sourcebooks, Inc.

Pickhardt, Carl E. & Iannelli, Vince. When Your Child Has a... Strong-Willed Personality. 2008. (ENG.). 224p. pap. 6.95 (978-1-59869-763-6(3)) Adams Media Corp.

Piette, Linda. Just Two More Bites! Helping Picky Eaters Say Yes to Food. 2006. (ENG., Illus.). 304p. per. 13.95 (978-1-4000-8109-7(2), Three Rivers Pr.) Crown Publishing Group.

Pirila, Silja & van der Meere, Jaap. The Meaning of Functional Motor Limitations in Childhood - a Monograph. 2008. 52p. pap. (978-3-639-09406-0(9)) VDM Verlag Dr. Mueller e.K.

Pitkeathley, Jill & Emerson, David. The Only Child: How to Survive Being One. 2011. (ENG.). 288p. pap. 16.95 (978-0-285-63148-9(9)) Souvenir Pr. Ltd. GBR. Dist: Independent Pubs. Group.

Plant, James S. Personality & the Cultural Pattern. 2007. (ENG.). 440p. per. (978-1-4067-4439-2(5)) Read Bks.

Plomin, Robert, et al. Nature & Nurture during Infancy & Early Childhood. 2006. (ENG., Illus.). 360p. (C). pap. 48.00 (978-0-521-03424-1(8)) Cambridge Univ. Pr.

Plummer, Deborah M. Focussing & Calming Games & Activities for Children. 2012. (ENG., Illus.). 176p. pap. **(978-1-84905-143-9(7))** Kingsley, Jessica Ltd.

Podolsky, Edward. The Jealous Child. 2011. 158p. 41.95 **(978-1-258-10032-2(0))** Literary Licensing, LLC.

Popkin, Michael H. Taming the Spirited Child: Strategies for Parenting Challenging Children Without Breaking Their Spirits. 2007. (ENG.). 288p. pap. 15.99 (978-0-7432-8689-3(8), Touchstone) Touchstone.

Porillo, Joseph. Sins of the Fathers: Suffer not the Children. 2009. 176p. 22.49 (978-1-4389-8981-5(4)); pap. 11.99 (978-1-4389-8980-8(6)) AuthorHouse.

Powers, Jean. The Brownie Elf. 2010. 24p. pap. 13.77 (978-1-4269-4308-9(3)) Trafford Publishing.

Prasad, Deepesh Chandra. Fundamentals of Child Psychology. 2008. (Illus.). 393p. 62.50 (978-81-7533-145-7(3)) M. D. Pubns. Pvt. Ltd. IND. Dist: Coronet Bks.

Preyer, William T. The Mind of the Child Pt. 2: The Development of the Intellect. 2007. (ENG.). 294p. pap. 21.99 (978-1-4346-3336-1(5)); 330p. pap. 24.99 (978-1-4346-3337-8(3)) BiblioBazaar.

Principe, Gabrielle F. Your Brain on Childhood: The Unexpected Side Effects of Classrooms, Ballparks, Family Rooms, & the Minivan. 2011. (ENG.). 275p. pap. 17.00 (978-1-61614-425-8(4)) Prometheus Bks., Pubs.

Principe, Gabrielle F., et al. Children's Memory: Psychology & the Law. 2013. (Understanding Children's Worlds Ser.). (ENG., Illus.). 224p. 89.95 (978-1-4051-1064-8(3)); pap. 39.95 (978-1-4051-1063-1(5)) Wiley, John & Sons, Inc. (Wiley-Blackwell).

Probst, Barbara. When the Labels Don't Fit: A New Approach to Raising a Challenging Child. 2008. (ENG.). 288p. pap. 13.95 (978-0-307-39543-6(X), Three Rivers Pr.) Crown Publishing Group.

Proctor, Curtis. Behavioral Indicators As Attachment Difficulties. 2008. 100p. pap. (978-3-639-07119-1(0)) VDM Verlag Dr. Mueller e.K.

Puckett, Margaret B., et al. The Young Child: Development from Prebirth Through Age Eight. 5th ed. 2008. (ENG.). 600p. (C). pap. 105.00 (978-0-13-514776-4(X), Prentice Hall) Prentice Hall PTR.

Quas, Jodi A., et al, eds. Emotion in Memory & Development: Biological, Cognitive, & Social Considerations. 2009. (Series in Affective Science Ser.). (ENG., Illus.). 448p. (C). 49.95 (978-0-19-532693-2(8)) Oxford Univ. Pr., Inc.

Quintana, Stephen M. & McKown, Clark. Handbook of Race, Racism, & the Developing Child. Quintana, Stephen M. & McKown, Clark, eds. 2007. (ENG., Illus.). 528p. 100.00 (978-0-470-04322-6(9), Wiley) Wiley, John & Sons, Inc.

Rahimi, Regina. Pervasive Vulnerabilities: Sexual Harassment in School. 2011. (C). pap. 139.95 **(978-1-4331-1280-5(9))**; pap. 34.95 **(978-1-4331-1279-9(5))** Lang, Peter Publishing, Inc.

Rahimi, Regina & Liston, Delores D. Pervasive Vulnerabilities: Sexual Harassment in School. 2012. E-Book **(978-1-4539-0258-5(9))** Lang, Peter Publishing, Inc.

Rao, Anthony & Seaton, Michelle. The Way of Boys: Promoting the Social & Emotional Development of Young Boys. 2010. (ENG.). 304p. pap. 14.99 (978-0-06-170783-4(X), Harper Paperbacks) HarperCollins Pubs.

Rapee, Ronald M., et al. Helping Your Anxious Child: A Step-by-Step Guide for Parents. 2nd rev. ed. 2008. (ENG., Illus.). 296p. pap. 17.95 (978-1-57224-575-4(1)) New Harbinger Pubns.

Rathus, Spencer A. Childhood & Adolescence: Voyages in Development. 4th ed. 2010. (ENG.). (C). 128p. pap. 42.95 (978-0-8400-3255-3(2)); 224p. pap., pupil's gde. ed. 72.95 (978-0-8400-3252-2(8)) Wadsworth.

Rauscher, Francis, ed. Neurosciences in Music Pedagogy. 2007. 79.00 (978-1-60021-834-7(2)) Nova Science Pubs., Inc.

Reddy, Linda A. Group Play Interventions for Children: Strategies for Teaching Prosocial Skills. 2011. pap. 49.95 **(978-1-4338-1055-8(7))** American Psychological Assn.

Reid. Teachers & Parents: The Anti Bully. 2009. 268p. pap. 24.95 (978-1-4389-5594-0(4)) AuthorHouse.

Reid, Vincent M., et al, eds. Social Cognition During Infancy: A Special Issue of the European Journal of Developmental Psychology. 2007. (Special Issues of the European Journal of Developmental Psychology Ser.). (ENG., Illus.). 128p. 74.50 (978-1-84169-832-8(6), Psychology Press) Taylor & Francis Group GBR. Dist: Taylor & Francis Group.

Reist, Michael. Raising Boys in a New Kind of World. 2012. (ENG., Illus.). 312p. pap. 24.99 (978-1-4597-0043-7(0)) Dundurn CAN. Dist: Ingram Pub. Services.

Remington, Robert & Zickefoose, Sherri. Runaway Devil: How Forbidden Love Drove a 12-Year-Old to Murder Her Family. 2010. (ENG., Illus.). 296p. pap. 17.95 (978-0-7710-7361-8(5), McClelland & Stewart) McClelland & Stewart CAN. Dist: Random Hse., Inc.

Requarth, Margo. After a Parent's Suicide: Helping Children Heal. 2006. 280p. per. 14.95 (978-0-9777468-0-4(1)) Healing Hearts Pr.

Rey, Joseph M., et al. Treating Child & Adolescent Depression. Birmaher, Boris, ed. 2009. (ENG., Illus.). 312p. 78.99 (978-0-7817-9569-2(9)) Lippincott Williams & Wilkins.

Reyes, Keith. Filicide As Child Sacrifice in the Judeo-Christian Worldview. 2009. 62p. pap. (978-3-639-16119-9(X)) VDM Verlag Dr. Mueller e.K.

Reynolds, Cecil R. & Fletcher-Janzen, Elaine, eds. Handbook of Clinical Child Neuropsychology. 3rd rev. ed. 2008. (ENG., Illus.). xiv, 814p. 183.00 (978-0-387-70708-2(5), 0387707085) Springer.

Reznick, Charlotte. The Power of Your Child's Imagination: How to Transform Stress & Anxiety into Joy & Success. 2009. (ENG.). 320p. (gr. 12-18). 14.95 (978-0-399-53507-9(1), Perigee Trade) Penguin Group (USA) Inc.

Richmond, R. G. Introduction to Piaget. 2007. 144p. 180.00 (978-0-415-40225-5(5)) Routledge.

Riffel, Laura A. Target the Behavior: Not the Student. 2010. 115p. pap. 25.00 (978-0-557-29357-5(X)) Lulu Enterprises Inc.

Riley, Dave, et al. Social & Emotional Development: Connecting Science & Practice in Early Childhood Settings. 2007. (ENG., Illus.). 144p. per. 24.95 (978-1-933653-30-3(2)) Redleaf Pr.

Roberts, Michael C. & Steele, Ric G., eds. Handbook of Pediatric Psychology. 4th rev. ed. 2009. (ENG.). 808p. 100.00 (978-1-60623-328-3(9)) Guilford Pubns., Inc.

Robinson, Ken. The Element: How Finding Your Passion Changes Everything. 2009. (ENG., Illus.). 288p. (gr. 12-18). 25.95 (978-0-670-02047-8(8), Viking Adult) Penguin Group (USA) Inc.

Robinson, Kerry. Innocence, Knowledge & the Construction of Childhood: The Contradictory Nature of Sexuality & Censorship in Children's Contemporary Lives. 2012. 160p. (C). 120.00 (978-0-415-60762-9(0)) Routledge.

Roeper, Annemarie. The I of the Beholder: A Guided Journey to the Essence of a Child. 2007. (Illus.). 127p. per. 18.95 (978-0-910707-78-7(2)) Great Potential Pr., Inc.

Rogers, Vanessa. Games & Activities for Exploring Feelings with Children: Giving Children the Confidence to Navigate Emotions & Friendships. 2011. (ENG., Illus.). 128p. pap. (978-1-84905-222-1(0)) Kingsley, Jessica Ltd.

Rosen, Larry D. Rewired: Understanding the iGeneration & the Way They Learn. 2010. (ENG., Illus.). 256p. pap. 17.00 (978-0-230-61478-9(7)) Palgrave Macmillan.

Ross, J. I Remember Me: Mnemonic Self-Reference Effects in Preschool Children. 2011. (Monographs of the Society for Research in Child Development (MONO) Ser.). (ENG.). 300p. pap. 39.95 **(978-1-118-25799-9(5)**, Wiley-Blackwell) Wiley, John & Sons, Inc.

Rotenberg, Ken J., ed. Disclosure Processes in Children & Adolescents. 2006. (Cambridge Studies in Social & Emotional Development Ser.). (ENG., Illus.). 248p. pap. 48.00 (978-0-521-02860-8(4)) Cambridge Univ. Pr.

Rotenberg, Ken J. & Hymel, Shelley, eds. Loneliness in Childhood & Adolescence. 2008. (ENG., Illus.). 416p. pap. 53.00 (978-0-521-08892-3(5)) Cambridge Univ. Pr.

Rothbart, Mary Klevjord. Becoming Who We Are: Temperament & Personality in Development. 2011. (Illus.). xi, 324p. **(978-1-60918-070-6(4))** Guilford Pubns., Inc.

Rowe, Salome G. Opened Vistas: Building Minds One Brain at the Time. 2010. 40p. pap. 24.99 (978-1-4520-8636-1(2)) AuthorHouse.

Rubin, Kenneth H., et al, eds. Handbook of Peer Interactions, Relationships, & Groups. 2011. (Social, Emotional, & Personality Development in Context Ser.). (ENG.). 654p. pap. 50.00 (978-1-60918-222-9(7)) Guilford Pubns., Inc.

Rubin, Kenneth H. & Coplan, Robert J., eds. The Development of Shyness & Social Withdrawal. 2010. (Social, Emotional, & Personality Development in Context Ser.). (ENG.). 336p. 55.00 (978-1-60623-522-5(2)) Guilford Pubns., Inc.

Rubin, Kenneth H., et al. Handbook of Peer Interactions, Relationships, & Groups. Rubin, Kenneth H. et al, eds. 2008. (Social, Emotional, & Personality Development in Context Ser.). (ENG., Illus.). 654p. 85.00 (978-1-59385-441-6(2)) Guilford Pubns., Inc.

Rubin, Lawrence C. Using Superheroes in Counseling & Play Therapy. 2007. (Illus.). 333p. 60.00 (978-0-8261-0269-0(7)) Springer Publishing Co., Inc.

Rubino, Joseph S. 31 Ways to Champion Children to Develop High Self-Esteem: An Empowerment Guidebook for Parents, Teachers, & Others. 2011. 173p. pap. 21.95 **(978-0-9728840-8-2(4))** Vision Works Publishing.

Ruset, Diana & Kalinowski, Michael. Is Mothers' Employment Status Correlated with Children's Behavioral Problems? 2008. 148p. pap. (978-3-639-00603-2(8)) VDM Verlag Dr. Mueller e.K.

Russell, Alex & Falconer, Tim. Drop the Worry Ball: How to Parent in the Age of Entitlement. 2012. (ENG.). 256p. pap. 17.95 **(978-1-118-12494-9(4)**, Wiley) Wiley, John & Sons, Inc.

Rutherford, Jesse Jayne & Nickerson, Kathleen. The Everything Parent's Guide to the Defiant Child: Reassuring advice to help your child manage explosive emotions & gain Self-control. 2010. (ENG.). 304p. pap. 14.95 (978-1-60550-369-1(X)) Adams Media Corp.

Rutherford, M. D. Child Development: Perspectives in Developmental Psychology. 2011. (ENG., Illus.). 514p. 124.95 (978-0-19-543298-5(3)) Oxford Univ. Pr., Inc.

Ryder, Verdene & Decker, Celia Anita. Parents & Their Children. 7th ed. 2009. (ENG.). 624p. 74.64 (978-1-59070-926-9(8)) Goodheart-Willcox Pub.

Rynsburger, Miska L. It's Time to Play Outside: 101 Ways for your Young Child to Enjoy Independent fun under the Sun. 2011. 132p. pap. 13.99 (978-1-4567-3204-2(8)) AuthorHouse.

Safer, Jeanne. Death Benefits: How Losing a Parent Can Change an Adult's Life — for the Better. 2010. (ENG.). 240p. pap. 15.95 (978-0-465-01857-4(2)) Basic Bks.

Salmon, Catherine & Schumann, Katrin. The Secret Power of Middle Children: How Middleborns Can Harness Their Unexpected & Remarkable Abilities. (ENG.). (gr. 12). 2012. 304p. pap. 16.00 **(978-0-452-29793-7(1)**, Plume) 2011. 288p. 25.95 (978-1-59463-080-4(1), Hudson Street Pr.) Penguin Group (USA) Inc.

Sammie & Tudie. Be a Thinker Not a Stinker: A story for kids & the big people they Love. 2009. 20p. pap. 10.99 (978-1-4389-9542-7(3)) AuthorHouse.

Santrock. Child Development. 12th ed. 2009. pap. (978-0-07-128081-5(2)) McGraw-Hill Cos., The.

Santrock, John W. Child Development. 12th ed. 2008. (ENG., Illus.). 704p. (C). 169.33 (978-0-07-337063-7(0), 0073370630) McGraw-Hill Cos., The.

—Children. (Illus.). 9th ed. 2007. pap. (978-0-07-310730-1(1)) 11th ed. 2009. (ENG., 704p. (C). pap. 176.67 (978-0-07-353200-4(2), 0073532002) McGraw-Hill Cos., The.

Sara Makes Her Mother Proud & Learns Good Behavior: The Complete Set. 2007. per. 13.95 (978-0-9777203-4-7(9)) Brenner Publishing, LLC.

Sassé, Margaret. Active Baby, Healthy Brain: 135 Fun Exercises & Activities to Maximize Your Child's Brain Development from Birth Through Age 5 1/2. 2010. (ENG., Illus.). 160p. pap. 15.95 (978-1-61519-006-5(6), 1615190066) Experiment LLC, The.

Saunders, Mel. A Depression Kid's Perspective. 2006. pap. 15.99 (978-1-60034-452-7(6)) Xulon Pr., Inc.

Saxon, Jill. How Children Develop. 3rd ed. 2010. (ENG.). 528p. (C). pap., stu. ed. 33.95 (978-1-4292-1791-0(X)) Worth Pubs., Inc.

Schab, Lisa M. & Schab, Lisa. The Divorce Workbook for Children: Help for Kids to Overcome Difficult Family Changes & Grow up Happy. 2008. (Instant Help Ser.). (ENG., Illus.). 152p. (J). (gr. 4-7). pap. 16.95 (978-1-57224-601-0(4)) Play2Grow.

Schafer, Alyson. Ain't Misbehavin' Tactics for Tantrums, Meltdowns, Bedtime Blues & Other Perfectly Normal Kid Behaviors. 2011. (ENG.). 288p. pap. 14.95 (978-0-470-67909-8(3), Wiley) Wiley, John & Sons, Inc.

Schiller, Pam. Start Smart! Building Brain Power in the Early Years. 2nd rev. ed. 2012. (ENG., Illus.). 160p. pap. 19.95 **(978-0-87659-393-6(7))** Gryphon Hse., Inc.

Schiltz, Karen L., et al. Beyond the Label: A Guide to Unlocking a Child's Educational Potential, 1 vol. 2011. (ENG., Illus.). 256p. pap. 24.95 (978-0-19-974705-4(9)) Oxford Univ. Pr., Inc.

Schmidt, Louis & Segalowitz, Sidney J., eds. Developmental Psychophysiology. 2007. (ENG., Illus.). 484p. 107.00 (978-0-521-82106-3(1)) Cambridge Univ. Pr.

Schutz, Paul A & Pekrun, Reinhard. Emotion in Education. 2007. (Educational Psychology Ser.). (ENG., Illus.). 368p. 90.95 (978-0-12-372545-5(3), Academic Pr.) Elsevier Science & Technology Bks.

Schwidder, Werner. Die Psychologismus-Kontroverse. 3rd ed. 2011. (Philosophie und psychologie im Dialog Ser.). (GER.). 142p. (C). pap. 27.00 **(978-3-525-45203-5(9))** Vandenhoeck & Ruprecht GmbH & Co. KG DEU. Dist: ISD.

Sclafani, Joseph D. The Educated Parent 2: Child Rearing in the 21st Century. 2012. xviii, 248p. E-Book **(978-0-313-39777-6(5)**, Praeger Pubs.); 2nd ed. 248p. 48.00 **(978-0-313-39776-9(7)**, A3593C) Greenwood Publishing Group, Inc.

Scott, Bruce. Free the Children. 2007. (ENG.). 288p. pap. 16.95 (978-1-55643-685-7(8)) North Atlantic Bks.

Scott, Phillip. A Voice for the Children, 1 vol. 2009. 57p. pap. 16.95 (978-1-61582-538-7(X)) PublishAmerica, Inc.

Seifert, Kathryn. How Children Become Violent - Parent Version. 2009. 51p. pap. 14.81 (978-0-557-06367-3(1)) Lulu Enterprises Inc.

Seltman, Muriel. Piaget's Logic. 2007. 384p. 170.00 (978-0-415-40231-6(X)) Routledge.

Semrud-Clikeman, Margaret & Ellison, Phyllis Anne Teeter. Child Neuropsychology: Assessment & Interventions for Neurodevelopmental Disorders. 2nd rev. ed. 2007. (Illus.). 330p. pap. 64.95 (978-0-387-47670-4(9)) Springer.

Senker, Cath. Getting along with Others. 2008. (Healthy Choices Ser.). (Illus.). 24p. (J). (gr. 4-7). lib. bdg. 21.25 (978-1-4042-4301-9(1), PowerKids Pr.) Rosen Publishing Group, Inc., The.

Shaffer, David R. & Kipp, Katherine. Developmental Psychology: Childhood & Adolescence. 8th ed. 2009. (Available Titles CengageNOW Ser.). (ENG.). 784p. (C). 195.95 (978-0-495-60171-5(3)); ring bd. 92.95 (978-0-495-59688-2(4)) Wadsworth.

Shapiro, Lawrence. Let's Be Friends: A Workbook to Help Kids Learn Social Skills & Make Great Friends. 2008. (Instant Help Ser.). (ENG.). 144p. (J). pap. 32.95 (978-1-57224-669-0(3)) Play2Grow.

Shapiro, Lawrence E. Learning to Listen, Learning to Care: A Workbook to Help Kids Learn Self-Control & Empathy. 2008. (Instant Help Ser.). (ENG., Illus.). 136p. (J). (gr. 4-7). per. 16.95 (978-1-57224-598-3(0)) Play2Grow.

Sharman, Carole, et al. Observing Children & Young People. 4th ed. 2007. (ENG., Illus.). 184p. 29.95 (978-0-8264-9273-9(8)) Continuum International Publishing Group, Ltd. GBR. Dist: National Bk. Network.

Shatkin, Jess P. Treating Child & Adolescent Mental Illness: A Practical, All-in-One Guide for Clinicians. 2009. (ENG., Illus.). 408p. 35.00 (978-0-393-70545-4(5), 70545) Norton, W. W. & Co., Inc.

Shemmings, David & Shemmings, Yvonne. Understanding Disorganized Attachment: Theory & Practice for Working with Children & Adults. 2011. (ENG., Illus.). 240p. pap. (978-1-84905-044-9(9)) Kingsley, Jessica Ltd.

Sheridan, Mary D., et al. From Birth to Five Years: Children's Developmental Progress. 3rd rev. ed. 2007. (ENG., Illus.). 112p. pap. 19.95 (978-0-415-42365-6(1)) Routledge.

Shipitsyna, Ludmila M. Psychology of Orphans. 2007. 244p. per. 18.95 (978-0-595-43018-5(X)) iUniverse, Inc.

Shrimali, Shyam. Child Development. 2008. 476p. (C). 45.00 (978-81-316-0181-5(1)) Rawat Pubns. IND. Dist: International Specialized Bk. Services.

Siegal, Michael. Marvelous Minds: The Discovery of What Children Know. 2008. (ENG., Illus.). 200p. 49.95 (978-0-19-920705-3(4)) Oxford Univ. Pr., Inc.

Sifers, Sarah K. Child Care Psychology. 2nd rev. ed. 2011. (ENG.). 134p. spiral bd. 60.36 **(978-0-7575-9674-2(6))** Kendall Hunt Publishing Co.

Sika, Nadine Mourad. Educational Reform in Egyptian Primary Schools since the 1990s: A Study of the Political Values & Behavior of Sixth Grade Students. 2010. (Illus.). iv, 311p. 119.95 (978-0-7734-3708-1(8)) Mellen, Edwin Pr., The.

Silbereisen, Rainer K. & Eye, Alexander von, eds. Growing up in Times of Social Change. (International Studies on Childhood & Adolescence Ser.). (ENG.). XVI, 344p. 210.00 **(978-3-11-182665-3(1))** De Gruyter, Walter Inc.

Silberg, Jackie. 125 Brain Games for Babies. 2nd rev. ed. 2012. (ENG., Illus.). 144p. pap. 16.95 **(978-0-87659-391-2(0))** Gryphon Hse., Inc.

Silfen, Roberta. 5 Minute Classroom Manager: Behavior in a Nutshell. 2011. 60p. 24.99 **(978-1-4653-6084-7(0))**; pap. 15.99 **(978-1-4653-6083-0(2))** Xlibris Corp.

Silvers, Carolyn Long. Cherubs & Chimps: A Year in Pre-K. 2011. 36p. pap. 16.99 **(978-1-4634-3017-7(5))** AuthorHouse.

Simms, Eva M. The Child in the World: Embodiment, Time, & Language in Early Childhood. 2008. (Landscapes of Childhood Ser.). (Illus.). 249p. pap. 29.95 (978-0-8143-3375-4(3)) Wayne State Univ. Pr.

Sisemore, Timothy. I Bet I Won't Fret: A Workbook to Help Children with Generalized Anxiety Disorder. 2008. (Instant Help Ser.). (ENG.). 152p. (J). pap. 32.95 (978-1-57224-658-4(8)) Play2Grow.

Sisemore, Timothy A. & Sisemore, Timothy. I Bet I Won't Fret: A Workbook to Help Children with Generalized Anxiety Disorder. 2008. (Instant Help Ser.). (ENG.). 152p. (J). (gr. 4-7). pap. 16.95 (978-1-57224-600-3(6)) Play2Grow.

Sisk, Dorothy, ed. Making Great Kids Greater: Easing the Burden of Being Gifted. 2008. (Illus.). 176p. 72.95 (978-1-4129-5871-4(7), B58714C); pap. 31.95 (978-1-4129-5872-1(5), B58714P) Corwin Pr.

Skuse, David, et al. Child Psychology & Psychiatry: Frameworks for Practice. 2nd ed. 2011. (ENG., Illus.). 318p. pap. 65.95 (978-0-470-97382-0(X), Wiley) Wiley, John & Sons, Inc.

Slater, Alan & Bremner, Gavin, eds. An Introduction to Developmental Psychology. 2nd ed. 2011. (BPS Textbooks in Psychology Ser.: 7). (ENG., Illus.). 800p. pap. 71.95 (978-1-4051-8652-0(6), Wiley-Blackwell) Wiley, John & Sons, Inc.

Sloss, Annunzio. Bags to Bridges: When Not Knowing Enough Is Too Much. 2009. 128p. pap. 14.95 (978-1-4327-3510-4(1)) Outskirts Pr., Inc.

Smiley, Kendra, et al. Journey of a Strong-Willed Child 2009. (ENG.). 144p. pap. 13.99 (978-0-8024-4353-3(2)) Moody Pubs.

Smith, Maggie & Dukes, Chris. Building Better Behaviour in the Early Years. 2009. (Hands on Guides). (Illus.). 120p. 112.00 (978-1-84787-519-8(X), B75198C); pap. 45.00 (978-1-84787-520-4(3), B75198P) SAGE Pubns., Ltd. GBR. Dist: SAGE Pubns., Inc.

Smith, Misty. Why the Abuse. 2008. 72p. pap. 12.69 (978-1-4389-2228-7(0)) AuthorHouse.

Smith, Peter K. & Connolly, Kevin J. The Ecology of Preschool Behaviour. 2010. (ENG.). 396p. pap. 32.99 (978-0-521-13387-6(4)) Cambridge Univ. Pr.

Smith, Peter K. & Hart, Craig H., eds. The Wiley-Blackwell Handbook of Childhood Social Development. 2nd ed. 2011. (Blackwell Handbooks of Developmental Psychology Ser.). (ENG., Illus.). 712p. 199.95 (978-1-4051-9679-6(3), Wiley-Blackwell) Wiley, John & Sons, Inc.

Sofroniou, Andreas. Psychology of Child Culture. 2009. 74p. pap. 20.95 (978-1-4092-7619-7(8)) Lulu Enterprises Inc.

Sokol, Bryan W., et al. Self & Social Regulation: Social Interaction & the Development of Social Understanding & Executive Functions, 1 vol. 2010. (ENG., Illus.). 472p. 65.00 (978-0-19-532769-4(1)) Oxford Univ. Pr., Inc.

Sommers, Peter Van. Drawing & Cognition: Descriptive & Experimental Studies of Graphic Production Processes. 2009. (ENG.). 300p. pap. 42.00 *(978-0-521-11063-1(7))* Cambridge Univ. Pr.

Soule, Amanda Blake. The Creative Family: How to Encourage Imagination & Nurture Family Connections. 2008. (ENG., Illus.). 224p. pap. 18.95 *(978-1-59030-471-6(3)*, Trumpeter) Shambhala Pubns., Inc.

Spitz, Ellen Handler. The Brightening Glance: Imagination & Childhood. 2007. (ENG.). 272p. pap. 14.95 *(978-0-385-72005-2(X)*, Anchor) Knopf Doubleday Publishing Group.

Sprick, Randy. Managing Noncompliance & Defiance in the Classroom: A Road Map for Teachers, Specialists, & Behavior Support Teams. 2009. 152p. pap. 29.95 *(978-1-4129-6089-2(4)*, B60885P) Corwin Pr.

Spurr, Pam. Your Child's Dreams. 2010. (ENG.). 160p. pap. 11.95 *(978-1-85906-288-3(1))* Connections Bk. Publishing, Ltd. GBR. Dist: Red Wheel/Weiser.

Squires, Jane. An Activity-Based Approach to Developing Young Children's Social & Emotional Competence. 2006. (Illus.). 276p. pap. 36.95 incl. cd-rom *(978-1-55766-737-3(3))* Brookes, Paul H. Publishing Co.

Srivastava, Smita. Toddlers' Use of Verb Constructions in Hindi: An Examination of Experimental & Everyday Contexts. 2009. 192p. pap. *(978-3-639-09167-0(1))* VDM Verlag Dr. Mueller e.K.

Sroufe, L. Alan, et al. The Development of the Person: The Minnesota Study of Risk & Adaptation from Birth to Adulthood. 2009. (ENG.). 384p. pap. 40.00 *(978-1-60623-249-1(5))* Guilford Pubns., Inc.

Stafford, Wess & Merrill, Dean. Just a Minute: In the Heart of a Child, One Moment... Can Last Forever. 2012. (ENG.). 224p. 19.99 ***(978-0-8024-0472-5(3))*** Moody Pubs.

Stamm, Jill. Bright from the Start: The Simple, Science-Backed Way to Nurture Your Child's Developing Mindfrom Birth to Age 3. 2008. (ENG.). 368p. (gr. 12-18). 17.00 *(978-1-59240-362-2(X)*, Gotham) Penguin Group (USA) Inc.

Stanescu, Dan Florin. Children of Parents with Acute Central Nervous System Injuries. 2010. 120p. pap. *(978-3-8383-0381-9(4))* Lambert Academic Publishing.

Stannard, Una. A Few Kind Words about Hate: The Dark Side of Family Life & the Bible. 1. 2007. 351p. 20.00 *(978-0-914142-03-4(8))* Germainbooks.

Stead, Gillian, ed. Oh, What You Said! A Journal for Recording Surprising Things Children Say. 2008. (ENG., Illus.). 120p. 14.95 *(978-1-55046-485-6(X))* Boston Mills Pr. CAN. Dist: Firefly Bks., Ltd.

Steemers, Jeanette. Creating Preschool Television: A Story of Commerce, Creativity & Curriculum. 2010. (ENG., Illus.). 256p. 95.00 *(978-0-230-57448-3(8))* Palgrave Macmillan.

Stein, Wendy, et al, contrib. by. No Putdowns: Creating a Healthy Learning Environment Through Encouragement, Understanding & Respect: Grades 6-8. 2006. (Illus.). 111p. per. 39.95 *(978-1-931636-65-0(5))* National Ctr. For Youth Issues.

Steinberg, Laurence, et al. Development: Infancy Through Adolescence. 2010. (Available Titles CengageNOW Ser.). (ENG.). 576p. (C). 148.95 *(978-0-618-72155-9(X))* Wadsworth.

Stern, Katie Barko. Younique: Multiples Are One of a Kind. 2010. 20p. 10.99 *(978-1-4389-1598-2(5))* AuthorHouse.

Stephenson, Kim & Roxborough, Tania. No, It's Not Ok: How to Stop the Cycle of Bullying. 2009. (ENG., Illus.). 228p. (gr. 12). 22.00 *(978-0-14-300667-1(3)*, Penguin Global) Penguin Group (USA) Inc.

Stevens, Willie G. An Analysis of Recidivism of Violent Behavior in an Elementary School. 2011. 240p. pap. 19.95 ***(978-1-4251-1801-3(1))*** Trafford Publishing.

Strober, Michael A. & Schneider, Meg F. Just a Little Too Thin: How to Pull Your Child Back from the Brink of an Eating Disorder. 2006. (ENG.). 256p. per. 16.95 *(978-0-7382-1079-7(X))* Da Capo Pr., Inc.

Sudbery, John. Human Growth & Development: An Introduction for Social Workers. 2009. (Student Social Work Ser.). (ENG., Illus.). 384p. (C). 140.00 *(978-0-415-43994-7(9))*; pap. 39.95 *(978-0-415-43995-4(7))* Routledge.

Sze, Susan & Cowden, Peter. What about my Child? 2009. 152p. pap. 47.95 *(978-1-4269-0594-0(7))* Trafford Publishing.

Szekely. Art Teaching. 2011. (ENG., Illus.). 456p. pap. 89.95 *(978-0-415-99058-5(0))* Routledge.

Taffe, Richard. Social Skills Training with Aggressive-Rejected Children. 2010. 180p. pap. *(978-3-8383-5108-7(8))* Lambert Academic Publishing.

Takikawa, Debby & Conley, Carrie. What Babies Want: Five Simple Steps to Calming & Communicating with Your Baby. 2011. (ENG.). 176p. pap. 14.95 *(978-0-9816368-2-5(9))* LifeTime Media, Inc.

Tanner, Amy E. The Child: His Thinking, Feeling, & Doing. enl. rev. ed. (Brainedness, Handedness, & Mental Abilities Ser.). reprint ed. 40.00 *(978-0-404-60894-1(9))* AMS Pr., Inc.

Tanner, R. E. S. Social Behaviour of Children: A Cross Cultural Assessment. 2007. 296p. *(978-81-8069-384-7(8))* Concept Publishing Co.

Targowska, Anna. Different Shades of Racism. 2008. 292p. pap. *(978-3-639-06330-1(9))* VDM Verlag Dr. Mueller e.K.

Tartas, Valérie. La construction du temps social par L'enfant: Préface de Jerome Bruner et Michel Bossard. 2008. (Exploration. Collection de la Société Suisse pour la Recherche en Education Ser.). 274p. pap. *(978-3-03911-761-1(0))* Lang, Peter.

Tessman, Lora Heims. Children of Parting Parents. 2nd ed. *(978-1-56821-055-1(8)*, Aronson, Jason) Rowman & Littlefield Publishers, Inc.

Thomas, Nancy, et al. Dandelion on My Pillow, Butcher Knife Beneath: The True Story of an Amazing Family That Lived with & Loved Kids Who Killed. 2010. (Illus.). 295p. pap. 19.95 *(978-0-9703525-2-1(2))* Families By Design.

Thompson, Denisse Rublee & Litwiller, Bonnie H. Navigating Through Problem Solving & Reasoning in Grade 6. 2009. (Illus.). viii, 120p. *(978-0-87353-607-3(X))* National Council of Teachers of Mathematics.

Thompson, Richard H. The Handbook of Child Life: A Guide for Pediatric Psychosocial Care. 2009. 378p. 79.95 *(978-0-398-07831-7(9))*; pap. 55.95 *(978-0-398-07832-4(7))* Thomas, Charles C. Pub., Ltd.

Thorndike, Edward Lee. Notes on Child Study. 2008. 152p. 36.95 *(978-1-4371-8793-9(5))*; pap. 21.95 *(978-1-4370-5692-1(X))* Kessinger Publishing, LLC.

Thwaites, Judith. 100 Ideas for Teaching Personal, Social & Emotional Development. 2008. (100 Ideas for the Early Years Ser.). (ENG., Illus.). 128p. 24.95 *(978-1-84706-382-3(9))* Continuum International Publishing Group, Ltd. GBR. Dist: National Bk. Network.

Tinglof, Christina Baglivi. Parenting School-Age Twins & Multiples. 2006. (ENG.). 256p. per. 17.95 *(978-0-07-146902-9(8)*, 0071469028) McGraw-Hill Cos., The.

Tough, Paul. How Children Succeed: Rethinking Character & Intelligence. 2012. (ENG.). 272p. 27.00 ***(978-0-547-56465-4(1))*** Houghton Mifflin Harcourt Trade & Reference Pubs.

Trahan, Arita & Eckroate, Norma. The Santa Story Revisited: How to Give Your Children a Santa They Will Never Outgrow. 2009. (Illus.). 176p. pap. 16.95 *(978-0-9825328-0-5(6))* Downstream Enterprises LLC.

Tree. Children & Discipline. 2011. 38p. pap. 16.95 ***(978-1-4626-4326-4(4))*** PublishAmerica, Inc.

Tronick, Ed. The Neurobehavioral & Social-Emotional Development of Infants & Children. 2007. (Norton Series on Interpersonal Neurobiology Ser.). (ENG., Illus.). 420p. 55.00 *(978-0-393-70517-1(X)*, 70517) Norton, W. W. & Co., Inc.

Trowell, Melody. Linguistic Stereotypes in Children's Animated Film: A Language Attitude Study. 2008. 60p. pap. *(978-3-639-11002-9(1))* VDM Verlag Dr. Mueller e.K.

Tuber, Steven. Attachment, Play, & Authenticity: A Winnicott Primer. 2008. (ENG.). 224p. 78.99 *(978-0-7657-0541-9(9))*; per. 41.99 *(978-0-7657-0542-6(7))* Rowman & Littlefield Publishers, Inc. (Aronson, Jason).

Tucci, J., et al. Children's sense of Safety: Children¿s experiences of childhood in contemporary Australia. 2008. 39p. spiral bd. *(978-0-9775355-3-8(3))* Australian Childhood Foundation.

Tudor, Keith, ed. The Adult is Parent to the Child: Transactional Analysis with Children & Young People. 2008. 300p. pap. 69.95 *(978-1-905541-17-1(1))* Russell Hse. Publishing Ltd. GBR. Dist: International Specialized Bk. Services.

Turecki, Stanley & Tonner, Leslie. El Nino Dificil de Criar.Tr. of Difficult Child. (SPA.). 14.00 *(978-958-04-4140-3(5))* Norma S.A. COL. Dist: Distribuidora Norma, Inc.

Turton, Jackie. Child Abuse, Gender & Society. 2007. (Routledge Research in Gender & Society Ser.). 152p. 143.00 *(978-0-415-36505-5(8))* Routledge.

Underwood, Marion K. & Rosen, Lisa H., eds. Social Development: Relationships in Infancy, Childhood, & Adolescence. 2011. (ENG., Illus.). 480p. 65.00 *(978-1-60918-233-5(2))* Guilford Pubns., Inc.

Ungar, Michael. Too Safe for Their Own Good: How Risk & Responsibility Help Teens Thrive. 2007. (ENG., Illus.). 240p. pap. 18.95 *(978-0-7710-8708-0(X)*, McClelland & Stewart) McClelland & Stewart CAN. Dist: Random Hse., Inc.

Unsworth, Anne. Eft for Children. 2009. (Illus.). 52p. pap. 20.49 *(978-1-4389-7094-3(3))* AuthorHouse.

Ushijima, Yoshitomo & Ando, Nobuo. Seishonen, 2 vols. 2010. (JPN., Illus.). *(978-4-87733-528-1(5))*; *(978-4-87733-529-8(3))* Kross Shuppan.

Valentina, Peshkova. The Phenomenon of a Genius: How to Wake up the Genius Inside a Child. 2007. (RUS.). 204p. per. 11.95 *(978-1-4327-1268-6(3))* Outskirts Pr., Inc.

Vasta, Ross, et al. Child Psychology: Development in a Changing Society. 5th ed. 2008. (ENG., Illus.). 784p. (C). 178.95 *(978-0-471-70649-6(3)*, Wiley) Wiley, John & Sons, Inc.

Verhulst, Frank C. & van der Ende, Jan. Assessment Scales in Child & Adolescent Psychiatry. 2006. (ENG., Illus.). 232p. 140.00 *(978-1-84184-534-0(5)*, DU5345) Taylor & Francis Group.

Vernon, Ann. Counseling Children & Adolescents. 4th ed. 2009. 528p. (C). 90.00 *(978-0-89108-340-5(5))* Love Publishing Co.

Vineyard, Catherine. Self-Concept in Children: The Relationship Between Self-Concept & Locus of Control, Sense of Inadequacy, & Self-Reliance. 2008. 64p. pap. *(978-3-639-01612-3(2))* VDM Verlag Dr. Mueller e.K.

Vishnyakova, Natalie F. The Abcs of Creativity, Talent, & Spirituality: Practical Psychology of Children's Potential Self-development. 2011. 618p. 34.99 ***(978-1-4653-4095-5(5))***; pap. 23.99 ***(978-1-4653-4094-8(7))*** Xlibris Corp.

Voss, Denise. Studying Stress in Pediatric Populations - Challenges & Opportunities. 2007. 112p. per. *(978-3-8364-2733-3(8))* VDM Verlag Dr. Mueller e.K.

Vygotskii, L. S., et al. Thought & Language. 2012. pap. ***(978-0-262-51771-3(X))*** MIT Pr.

Waddell, Charles Wilkin. An Introduction to Child Psychology. 2009. (Illus.). 260p. pap. *(978-0-217-17266-0(0))* Books LLC.

Waddle, Charles Wilkin. An Introduction to Child Psychology. 2010. 342p. pap. 31.75 *(978-1-178-35402-7(4))* BiblioBazaar.

Wagner, Barry M. Suicidal Behavior in Children & Adolescents. 2009. (Current Perspectives in Psychology Ser.). (ENG., Illus.). 326p. pap. 55.00 *(978-0-300-11250-4(5))* Yale Univ. Pr.

Waldren, Jacqueline & Kaminski, Ignacy-Marek. Learning from the Children: Childhood, Culture & Identity in a Changing World. 2012. E-Book ***(978-0-85745-326-6(2))*** Berghahn Bks., Inc.

Waldren, Jacqueline & Kaminski, Ignacy-Marek, eds. Learning from the Children: Childhood, Culture & Identity in a Changing World. 2012. (ENG.). 212p. 60.00 ***(978-0-85745-325-9(4))*** Berghahn Bks., Inc.

Walkerdine, Valerie. Children, Gender, Video Games: Towards a Relational Approach to Multimedia. 2009. (ENG.). 248p. pap. 33.00 *(978-0-230-58471-6(3))* Palgrave Macmillan.

Walsh, Brian R. Boys Should Be Boys: A Headmaster's Reflections. 2008. 216p. 29.95 *(978-0-9720307-6-2(X))* TMC Bks. L.L.C.

Watson, Casey. Crying for Help: The Shocking True Story of a Damaged Girl with a Dark Past. 2012. (ENG.). 304p. 12.95 ***(978-0-00-743658-3(0))*** HarperCollins Pubs. Ltd. GBR. Dist: Independent Pubs. Group.

Wattley, Linda D. Something about an Angel. 2007. 240p. per. 15.99 *(978-0-9798084-8-7(0))* Leading Lady Pubns.

Watts, A. F. Language & Mental Development of Child. 2006. 356p. per. *(978-1-4067-3333-4(4)*, Hesperides Pr.) Read Bks.

Webb, James T., et al. A Parent's Guide to Gifted Children. 2007. (Illus.). 390p. 32.95 *(978-0-910707-79-4(0))* Great Potential Pr., Inc.

Westman, Jack C. & Costello, Victoria. Child & Adolescent Psychology - Complete Idiot's Guide. 2011. (Complete Idiot's Guide Ser.). (ENG.). 400p. (gr. 12). 19.95 *(978-1-61564-063-8(0)*, Alpha Bks.) Penguin Group (USA) Inc.

White, Kate & Erskine, J. Terror Within & Without: Attachment & Disintegration - Clinical Work on the Edge. 2012. 330p. pap. 41.95 *(978-1-85575-637-3(4))* Karnac Bks. GBR. Dist: Stylus Publishing, LLC.

Wickersham, Joan & Hochman, Gail. The Suicide Index: Putting My Father's Death in Order. 2009. (ENG.). 336p. pap. 14.95 *(978-0-15-603380-0(1)*, Mariner Bks.) Houghton Mifflin Harcourt Trade & Reference Pubs.

Wilkinson, Simon. The Child's World of Illness: The Development of Health & Illness Behaviour. 2006. (ENG.). 300p. pap. 61.00 *(978-0-521-02904-9(X))* Cambridge Univ. Pr.

Williams, Dan. Above His Shoulders: A True Account of Sexual Abuse, Its Impact on Relationships, & the Emotional Survival & Healing. 2009. (Illus.). 242p. pap. 15.95 *(978-1-4327-3749-8(X))* Outskirts Pr., Inc.

Williamson, C. S. Throw Your Kid a Bone. 2007. 156p. pap. 14.95 *(978-1-4303-2519-2(4))* Lulu Enterprises Inc.

Wilson, Anthony. Creativity in Primary Education. Wilson, Anthony, ed. 2nd ed. 2009. (Illus.). 204p. pap. *(978-1-84445-198-2(4))* Learning Matters Ltd.

Wilson-Durham, Linda F. Peanut Butter, Jelly, & Love... 2010. pap. 7.99 *(978-1-61663-996-9(2))* Tate Publishing & Enterprises, LLC.

Wilson, Jim. The Performance of Practice: Enhancing the Repertoire of Therapy with Children & Families. 2007. (Systematic Thinking & Practice Ser.). 200p. per. 39.95 *(978-1-85575-526-0(2))* Karnac Bks. GBR. Dist: Stylus Publishing, LLC.

Winner, Michelle Garcia. A Politically Incorrect Look at Evidence-based Practices & Teaching Social Skills: A literature review & Discussion. 2008. pap. 20.00 *(978-0-9792922-5-5(5))* Think Social Publishing, Inc.

Wolfe, David A. Acting Out: Understanding & Reducing Aggressive Behaviour in Children & Youth. 2007. ***(978-0-88868-532-2(7))*** Centre for Addiction & Mental Health.

Wolraich, Mark Lee, et al. Developmental-Behavioral Pediatrics: Evidence & Practice. 2007. (ENG., Illus.). 1008p. 148.00 *(978-0-323-04025-9(X)*, Mosby) Elsevier - Health Sciences Div.

Wright, Jim, et al, contrib. by. No Putdowns: Grades 3-5: Creating a Healthy Learning Environment Through Encouragement, Understanding & Repsect, 3 bks. 2006. (Illus.). 294p. per. 39.95 *(978-1-931636-64-3(8))* National Ctr. For Youth Issues.

—No Putdowns: Grades K-2: Creating a Healthy Learning Environment Through Encouragement, Understanding & Repsect, 3 bks. 2006. (Illus.). 277p. per. 39.95 *(978-1-931636-63-6(X))* National Ctr. For Youth Issues.

Wright-Lee, Linda D. Oops!!! I'm a Parent. No One Told Me it Would be Hard Work: Learn Effective Parenting. Lee, David J., ed. pap. 23.95 *(978-0-9673754-6-5(0))* Wright On Time Publishing Co.

Wyatt, Randall C. & Seid, Erika L. Connecting with Our Kids: Making Parenting Count in the Lives of Children & Teens: Group Version. 2007. 59.00 *(978-1-60124-059-0(7))* Psychotherapy.net.

Youell & Youell, Biddy. Understanding 8-9-Year-Olds. 2008. (ENG., Illus.). 80p. pap. *(978-1-84310-673-9(6))* Kingsley, Jessica Ltd.

Young, Gerald. Development & Causality: Neo-Piagetian Perspectives. 2011. (ENG., Illus.). xxxviii, 849p. 179.00 *(978-1-4419-9421-9(1)*, 1441994211) Springer.

Your Child & Spirituality. 12.00 *(978-0-687-04912-7(1))* Abingdon Pr.

Zemi. The Source Within for Kids & Teens. 2009. 64p. pap. 13.45 *(978-1-4490-1589-3(1))* AuthorHouse.

Zevalkink, Jolien, et al, eds. Mentalising in Child Therapy: Guidelines for Clinical Practitioners. 2008. (Illus.). 266p. pap. 52.95 *(978-1-85575-581-9(5))* Karnac Bks. GBR. Dist: Stylus Publishing, LLC.

Zucker, Bonnie. Anxiety-Free Kids: An Interactive Guide for Parents & Children. 2008. (ENG.). 250p. pap. 16.95 *(978-1-59363-343-1(2))* Prufrock Pr.

CHILD PSYCHOLOGY—BIBLIOGRAPHY

Wilson, Louis N. Bibliography of Child Study. 2009. 80p. pap. *(978-0-217-44476-7(8))* Books LLC.

CHILD PSYCHOLOGY—JUVENILE LITERATURE

Baier, Jeanne M. The Twins Jeffrey & Jeanne. 2011. 28p. (gr. 2-4). pap. 19.95 ***(978-1-4269-7183-9(4))*** Trafford Publishing.

Frankel, Erin. Tough! 2012. (Weird! Ser.). (ENG.). 48p. (J). (gr. k-4). 15.99 ***(978-1-57542-400-2(2))*** Free Spirit Publishing, Inc.

—Weird! 2012. (Weird! Ser.). (ENG.). 48p. (J). (gr. k-4). 15.99 ***(978-1-57542-398-2(7))*** Free Spirit Publishing, Inc.

Triggle, David J. Understanding Drugs. 2011. (Understanding Drugs Ser.). (C). (gr. 9). 314.55 ***(978-0-7910-9959-9(8))***, Chelsea Hse.) Facts On File, Inc.

CHILD PSYCHOLOGY—METHODOLOGY

Colombo, Leone & Bianchi, Rachele. Preschool Children: Physical Activity, Behavioral Assessment & Developmental Challenges. 2010. (Children's Issues, Laws & Programs Ser.). (Illus.). 210p. 129.00 *(978-1-60876-026-8(X))* Nova Science Pubs., Inc.

Goodenough, Elizabeth. Where Do the Children Play? A Study Guide to the Film. 2nd ed. 2010. (Illus.). 256p. pap. 27.50 ***(978-0-9823751-1-2(5))*** Alliance for Childhood.

Hart, Angie & Blincow, Derek. Resilient Therapy: Working with Children & Families. 2007. (ENG., Illus.). 224p. (C). 95.00 *(978-0-415-40384-9(7))*; per. 37.50 *(978-0-415-40385-6(5))* Routledge.

Jensen, Arthur. Educational Differences (Rle Edu L) 2011. (Routledge Library Editions: Education Ser.). (ENG.). 472p. 150.00 ***(978-0-415-50624-3(7))*** Routledge.

Lane, Kathleen Lynne, et al. Systematic Screenings of Behavior to Support Instruction: From Preschool to High School. 2012. (ENG., Illus.). 260p. (gr. -1-12). 55.00 ***(978-1-4625-0342-1(X))***; pap. 35.00 ***(978-1-4625-0336-0(5))*** Guilford Pubns., Inc.

CHILD PSYCHOLOGY—OUTLINES, SYLLABI, ETC.

Cram101 Textbook Reviews. Outlines & Highlights for Child & Adolescent Development: An Advanced Course by William Damon, ISBN. 2010. 174p. pap. 29.95 *(978-1-61654-494-2(5))* Cram101 Inc.

—Outlines & Highlights for Childhood & Adolescence: Voyages in Development by Spencer A. Rathus, ISBN. 2011. 198p. pap. 30.95 ***(978-1-4288-7829-7(7))*** Cram101 Inc.

—Outlines & Highlights for Developing Person Through Childhood & Adolescence by Kathleen Stassen Berger. 2011. 146p. pap. 28.95 ***(978-1-4288-5994-4(2))*** Cram101 Inc.

Cram101 Textbook Reviews & Cram101 Textbook Reviews. Outlines & Highlights for Behavioral, Social, & Emotional Assessment of Children & Adolescents by Kenneth Merrell, Isbn: 9780805853704. 2011. 72p. pap. 27.95 ***(978-1-61698-263-8(2))*** Cram101 Inc.

—Outlines & Highlights for California School of Professional Psychology Handbook of Juvenile Forensic Psychology by Neil G Ribner. 2011. 72p. pap. 27.95 ***(978-1-61830-313-4(9))*** Cram101 Inc.

—Outlines & Highlights for Infant Perception & Cognition: Recent Advances, Emerging Theories, & Future Directions by Lisa Oakes, ISBN. 2011. 56p. pap. 26.95 ***(978-1-4288-6136-7(X))*** Cram101 Inc.

—Outlines & Highlights for Introducing Child Psychology by H Rudolph Schaffer. 2011. 196p. pap. 30.95 ***(978-1-61830-300-4(7))*** Cram101 Inc.

—Outlines & Highlights for Positive Child Guidance by Darla Ferris Miller, Isbn: 9781435418592. 2011. 218p. pap. 30.95 ***(978-1-61744-290-2(9))*** Cram101 Inc.

—Outlines & Highlights for the Handbook of Child & Adolescent Clinical Psychology: A Contextual Approach by Alan Carr. 2011. 94p. pap. 27.95 ***(978-1-61830-298-4(1))*** Cram101 Inc.

—Outlines & Highlights for Treatment of Childhood Disorders by Eric Mash, Isbn: 9781572309210. 2011. 528p. pap. 38.95 ***(978-1-61461-094-6(0))*** Cram101 Inc.

Cram101 Textbook Reviews Staff. Outlines & Highlights for Abnormal Child Psychology by Mash, Isbn. 2008. 144p. pap. 11.95 *(978-1-4288-5867-1(9))* Cram101 Inc.

—Outlines & Highlights for Children Ó S Thinking: Cognitive Development & Individual Differences by Bjorklund, ISBN. 2008. 160p. pap. 12.95 *(978-1-4288-5966-1(7))* Cram101 Inc.

—Outlines & Highlights for Children Ó S Thinking by Siegler, Isbn: 0131113844. 2008. 80p. pap. 10.95 *(978-1-4288-5952-4(7))* Cram101 Inc.

—Outlines & Highlights for Child's World: Infancy through Adolescence by Papalia, ISBN. 2008. 316p. per. 15.95 *(978-1-4288-5781-0(8))* Cram101 Inc.

—Outlines & Highlights for Developing Child, the by Helen Bee, Isbn: 9780205685936. 2009. 60p. pap. 27.95 *(978-1-4288-8557-8(9))* Cram101 Inc.

—Outlines & Highlights for Developmental Psychology: Childhood & Adolescence by Shaffer, ISBN. 2008. 152p. per. 12.95 *(978-1-4288-5789-6(3))* Cram101 Inc.

—Outlines & Highlights for Juvenile Delinquency: The Core by Siegel, ISBN. 2008. 116p. pap. 11.95 *(978-1-4288-6168-8(8))* Cram101 Inc.

—Outlines & Highlights for Juvenile Delinquency: Theory, Practice, & Law by Siegel ISBN. 2008. 144p. pap. 11.95 *(978-1-4288-6169-5(6))* Cram101 Inc.

—Outlines & Highlights for Juvenile Delinquency & Antisocial Behavior: A Developmental Perspective by Bartol, ISBN. 2008. 60p. pap. 9.95 *(978-1-4288-6150-3(5))* Cram101 Inc.

Dehart & Sroufe & Cooper & Cram101 Textbook Reviews Staff. Child Development: Its Nature & Course. 2007. 188p. per. 12.95 *(978-1-4288-2042-5(6))* Cram101 Inc.

Lane & Gresham & O'Shaughnessy & Cram101 Textbook Reviews Staff. Interventions for Children with or at Risk for Emotional & Behavioral Disorders. 2007. 104p. per. 10.95 *(978-1-4288-2018-0(3))* Cram101 Inc.

C

Papalia, Olds & Cram101 Textbook Reviews Staff. A Child's World: Infancy Through Adolescence. 2007. 280p. per. 15.95 (978-1-4288-2700-4(5)) Cram101 Inc.

CHILD PSYCHOPATHOLOGY

Here are entered descriptive works on mental disorders of children. Works on the clinical and therapeutic aspects of mental disorders are entered under Child Psychiatry. Works on mentally ill children themselves are entered under Mentally Ill Children.

see also Adolescent Psychopathology; Behavior Disorders in Children; Child Psychiatry; Cognition Disorders in Children; Emotional Problems of Children; Encopresis; Mentally Ill Children; Psychic Trauma in Children; Violence in Children

Achenbach, Thomas M. & Rescorla, Leslie A. Multicultural Understanding of Child & Adolescent Psychopathology: Implications for Mental Health Assessment. 2006. (ENG., Illus.). 322p. 45.00 (978-1-59385-348-8(3)) Guilford Pubns., Inc.

Aleksandrowicz, Dov R. & Aleksandrowicz, Malca. The/Injured Self: The Psychopathology & Psychotherapy of Developmental Deviations. 2011. 270p. pap. 34.95 (978-1-85575-842-1(3)) Karnac Bks. GBR. Dist: Stylus Publishing, LLC.

Austin, Vance L. & Sciarra, Daniel T. Children & Adolescents with Emotional & Behavioral Disorders. 2009. (ENG.). 504p. (C). pap. 123.60 (978-0-205-50176-2(1), Prentice Hall) Prentice Hall PTR.

Beauchaine, Theodore P. & Hinshaw, Stephen P., eds. Child & Adolescent Psychopathology. 2008. (ENG., Illus.). 720p. 110.00 (978-0-470-00744-0(3), Wiley) Wiley, John & Sons, Inc.

Becker-Weidman, Arthur, ed. Parenting for Attachment: Developing Connections & Healing Children. 2010. (ENG., Illus.). 306p. 73.50 (978-0-7657-0754-3(3), Aronson, Jason) Rowman & Littlefield Publishers, Inc.

Becker-Weidman, Arthur & Shell, Deborah. Parenting for Attachment: Developing Connections & Healing Children. 2010. (Illus.). (ENG.). 306p. pap. 31.50 (978-0-7657-0755-0(1)); xi, 293p. 29.95 (978-0-7657-0756-7(X)) Rowman & Littlefield Publishers, Inc. (Aronson, Jason).

Bilmes, Jenna & Welker, Tara. Common Psychological Disorders in Young Children: A Handbook for Early Childhood Professionals. 2006. (Redleaf Professional Library). (ENG.). 183p. per. 29.95 (978-1-929610-91-4(2)) Redleaf Pr.

Brown, Ronald T., et al. Childhood Mental Health Disorders: Evidence Base & Contextual Factors for Psychosocial, Psychopharmacological, & Combined Interventions. 2007. 207p. 49.95 (978-1-4338-0170-9(1)) American Psychological Assn.

Cavalli, Giulia. Theory of Mind & Emotion. 2010. 176p. pap. (978-3-639-21664-6(4)) VDM Verlag Dr. Mueller e.K.

Claveirole, Anne & Gaughan, Martin, eds. Understanding Children & Young People's Mental Health. 2010. (ENG., Illus.). 328p. pap. 47.99 (978-0-470-72345-6(9), Wiley-Blackwell) Wiley, John & Sons, Inc.

Copeland, Mary Ellen. Wellness Recovery Action Plan (WRAP) for Kids. 2007. (J). per. 0.00 (978-0-9631366-2-6(3)) Peach Pr.

Cram101 Textbook Reviews. Outlines & Highlights for Assessment of Childhood Disorders by Eric J Mash. 2011. 162p. pap. 29.95 (978-1-61905-143-0(5)) Cram101 Inc.

—Outlines & Highlights for Child & Adolescent Psychopathology by Stephen P Hinshaw, Isbn: 9780470007440. 2011. 150p. pap. 29.95 (978-1-61698-020-7(6)) Cram101 Inc.

—Outlines & Highlights for Disorders of Childhood: Development & Psychopathology by Robin Hornik Parritz. 2011. 120p. pap. 28.95 (978-1-61905-159-1(1)) Cram101 Inc.

Cram101 Textbook Reviews & Cram101 Textbook Reviews. Outlines & Highlights for Abnormal Child Psychology: A Developmental Perspective by Linda Wilmshurst. 2011. 206p. pap. 30.95 (978-1-61830-336-3(8)) Cram101 Inc.

—Outlines & Highlights for Introduction to Abnormal Child & Adolescent Psychology by Robert Weis, Isbn: 9781412926577 1412926572. 2011. 188p. pap. 30.95 (978-1-61654-234-4(9)) Cram101 Inc.

Cram101 Textbook Reviews Staff. Outlines & Highlights for Behavior Disorders of Childhood by Wicks-Nelson, Isbn: 0131539086. 2008. 96p. pap. 10.95 (978-1-4288-5937-1(3)) Cram101 Inc.

—Outlines & Highlights for Child Psychopathology by Haugaard, Isbn: 9780073405506. 2008. 160p. pap. 12.95 (978-1-4288-6013-1(4)) Cram101 Inc.

—Outlines & Highlights for Children & Adolescents with Emotional & Behavioral Disorders by VanCe L Austin, Isbn: 9780205501762. 2009. 118p. pap. 28.95 (978-1-4288-8818-0(7)) Cram101 Inc.

Dombrowski, Stefan C., et al. Assessing & Treating Low Incidence/High Severity Psychological Disorders of Childhood. 2011. (ENG.). xiv, 254p. 129.00 (978-1-4419-9969-6(8), 1441999698) Springer.

Dummett, Nicky, et al. Overcoming Teenage Low Mood & Depression: A Five Areas Approach. 2008. (ENG., Illus.). 328p. pap. 49.95 (978-0-340-94657-2(1)) Hodder Arnold Pubs.

Eagle, Rita. Help Him Make You Smile: The Development of Intersubjectivity in the Atypical Child. 2007. (Psychological Issues Ser.). (ENG.). 336p. 93.50 (978-0-7657-0496-2(X)); pap. 41.99 (978-0-7657-0497-9(8)) Rowman & Littlefield Publishers, Inc. (Aronson, Jason).

Eisen, Andrew R. & Engler, Linda B. Helping Your Socially Vulnerable Child: What to Do When Your Child Is Shy, Socially Anxious, Withdrawn, or Bullied. 2007. (ENG.). 216p. per. 15.95 (978-1-57224-458-0(5)) New Harbinger Pubns.

Elliott, Julian & Place, Maurice. Children in Difficulty: A Guide to Understanding & Helping. 3rd rev. ed. 2012. (ENG., Illus.). 296p. (C). 160.00 (978-0-415-67255-9(4)); pap. 44.95 (978-0-415-67263-4(5)) Routledge.

Fanti, Kostas Andrea. Development & Co-Development of Aggressive & Depressive Psychopathology - Infancy to Early Adolescence. 2008. 128p. pap. (978-3-639-00391-8(8)) VDM Verlag Dr. Mueller e.K.

Fattig, Michelle. Taming Tommy's Tantrums. 2007. 76p. pap. 10.99 (978-0-9795805-7-4(9)) Flower by the Water Publishing.

Freeman, Jennifer B. & Garcia, Abbe Marrs. Family-Based Treatment for Young Children with OCD. 2008. (ENG., Illus.). 112p. pap., wbk. ed. 24.95 (978-0-19-537364-6(2)) Oxford Univ. Pr., Inc.

Frick, Paul J., et al. Clinical Assessment of Child & Adolescent Personality & Behavior. 3rd ed. 2009. (ENG., Illus.). xi, 500p. 99.00 (978-0-387-89642-7(2), 0387896422) Springer.

Garralda, M. Elena & Flament, Martine. Working with Children & Adolescents: An Evidence-Based Approach to Risk & Resilience. annot. ed. 2006. (Book Series of the International Association for Child & Adolescent Psychiatry & Allied Professions). (ENG.). 224p. 63.99 (978-0-7657-0443-6(9), Aronson, Jason) Rowman & Littlefield Publishers, Inc.

Goldstein, Sam & Reynolds, Cecil R., eds. Handbook of Neurodevelopmental & Genetic Disorders in Children. 2nd rev. ed. 2010. (ENG., Illus.). 588p. 80.00 (978-1-60623-990-2(2)) Guilford Pubns., Inc.

Gowers, Simon G. Eating Disorders: Cognitive Behaviour Therapy with Children & Young People. 2009. (CBT with Children, Adolescents & Families Ser.). (ENG., Illus.). 200p. (C). 128.00 (978-0-415-44462-0(4)) Routledge.

Gullotta, Thomas P. & Blau, Gary. Handbook of Childhood Behavioral Issues: Evidence-Based Approaches to Prevention & Treatment. 2007. (ENG., Illus.). 432p. 125.00 (978-0-415-95461-7(4)) Routledge.

Gullotta, Thomas P. & Blau, Gary, eds. Family Influences on Childhood Behavior & Development: Evidence-Based Prevention & Treatment Approaches. 2008. (ENG., Illus.). 360p. 52.95 (978-0-415-96532-3(2)) Routledge.

Henry, Beth Friday. Mending Wounded Minds: Seeking Help for a Mentally Ill Child. 2006. (ENG.). 320p. pap. 14.95 (978-0-88282-242-6(X)) New Horizon Pr. Pubs., Inc.

Hobson, Peter. Autism & the Development of Mind. 2008. 104.00 (978-0-415-43335-8(5)) Routledge.

Hudziak, James J. Developmental Psychopathology & Wellness: Genetic & Environmental Influences. 2008. (Illus.). 320p. pap. 74.00 (978-1-58562-279-5(6)) American Psychiatric Publishing, Inc.

Ingram, Rick E. & Price, Joseph M., eds. Vulnerability to Psychopathology, Second Edition: Risk across the Lifespan. 2nd ed. (ENG.). 524p. 2010. pap. 40.00 (978-1-60918-148-2(4)) 2009. (Illus.). 65.00 (978-1-60623-347-4(5)) Guilford Pubns., Inc.

Kazdin, Alan E. Parent Management Training: Treatment for Oppositional, Aggressive, & Antisocial Behavior in Children & Adolescents. 2008. (ENG., Illus.). 424p. pap. 29.95 (978-0-19-538600-4(0)) Oxford Univ. Pr., Inc.

Kearney, Christopher A. Casebook in Child Behavior Disorders. 4th ed. 2009. (ENG.). 224p. (C). pap. 84.95 (978-0-495-60441-9(0)) Wadsworth.

Kendall, Philip C. & Comer, Jonathan. Childhood Disorders. 2nd rev. ed. 2010. (Clinical Psychology: A Modular Course Ser.). (ENG., Illus.). 304p. (C). 85.00 (978-0-415-48641-5(6)); pap. 29.95 (978-0-415-48642-2(4)) Taylor & Francis Group GBR. (Psychology Press). Dist: Taylor & Francis Group.

Kerig & Wenar & Cram101 Textbook Reviews Staff. Developmental Psychopathology. 2007. 316p. per. 16.95 (978-1-4288-2100-2(7)) Cram101 Inc.

Kutscher, Martin L. & Kutscher, Martin. Kids with A Syndrome Mix of Adhd, Ld, As. 2nd ed. 2007. (ENG., Illus.). 24p. pap. (978-1-84310-811-5(9)) Kingsley, Jessica Ltd.

Lucan, Dawn. My Back to School Memories. 2010. 12p. 14.95 (978-0-557-49659-4(4)) Lulu Enterprises Inc.

Mash, Eric J. & Barkley, Russell A., eds. Assessment of Childhood Disorders. 4th rev. ed. 2007. (ENG., Illus.). 866p. 90.00 (978-1-59385-493-5(5)) Guilford Pubns., Inc.

Matson, Johnny L., et al, eds. Assessing Childhood Psychopathology & Developmental Disabilities. 2010. x, 506p. pap. 89.95 (978-1-4419-8137-0(3), 1441981373) Springer.

—Treating Childhood Psychopathology & Developmental Disabilities. x, 457p. 2010. pap. 89.95 (978-1-4419-8141-7(1), 1441981411) 2008. (ENG.). 199.00 (978-0-387-09529-5(2), 0387095292) Springer.

Melillo, Robert & Leisman, Gerry. Neurobehavioral Disorders of Childhood: An Evolutionary Perspective. 2009. (ENG.). xii, 447p. pap. 59.95 (978-1-4419-1232-9(0), 1441912320) Springer.

The Mentally Subnormal Child. Date not set. (Technical Report Ser.). 46p. pap. 3.00 (978-92-4-120075-2(8)) World Health Organization.

Nurcombe, Barry, et al, eds. The Mental Health of Children & Adolescents: An Area of Global Neglect. 2007. (World Psychiatric Association Ser.). (ENG., Illus.). 256p. 110.95 (978-0-470-51245-6(8), Wiley) Wiley, John & Sons, Inc.

Olfman, Sharna. Bipolar Children: Cutting-Edge Controversy, Insights, & Research, 1 vol. 2007. (Childhood in America Ser.). (Illus.). 176p. 39.95 (978-0-275-99730-4(8), C9730, Praeger Pubs.) Greenwood Publishing Group, Inc.

Phares, Vicky. Understanding Abnormal Child Psychology. 2nd rev. ed. 2007. (ENG., Illus.). 566p. (C). 186.95 (978-0-471-72411-7(4), Wiley) Wiley, John & Sons, Inc.

Psychological Science, Association for, et al. Current Directions in Child Psychopathology. 2009. (Association for Psychological Science Readers Ser.). (ENG., Illus.). 208p. (C). pap. 45.40 (978-0-205-68013-9(5)) Allyn & Bacon, Inc.

Radke-Yarrow, Marian. Children of Depressed Mothers: From Early Childhood to Maturity. 2009. (ENG., Illus.). 236p. pap. 36.99 (978-0-521-10830-0(6)) Cambridge Univ. Pr.

Rutter, Michael, et al. Rutter's Child & Adolescent Psychiatry. 5th ed. 2010. (ENG.). 1248p. pap. 125.00 (978-1-4051-4593-0(5), Wiley-Blackwell) Wiley, John & Sons, Inc.

Rygaard, Niels P. Severe Attachment Disorder in Childhood: A Guide to Practical Therapy. 2010. (ENG., Illus.). xi, 213p. pap. 59.95 (978-3-211-99881-6(0), 3211998810) Springer.

Salekin, Randall T. & Lynam, Donald R., eds. Handbook of Child & Adolescent Psychopathy. 2010. (ENG., Illus.). 451p. 65.00 (978-1-60623-682-6(2)) Guilford Pubns., Inc.

Schofield, Michael. January First: A Child's Descent into Madness & Her Father's Struggle to Save Her. 2012. (ENG.). 288p. 25.00 (978-0-307-71908-9(1), Crown) Crown Publishing Group.

Shaw, Richard J. & DeMaso, David R., eds. Textbook of Pediatric Psychosomatic Medicine. 2010. (ENG., Illus.). 135.00 (978-1-58562-350-1(4)) American Psychiatric Publishing, Inc.

Silberg, Joy L. The Child Survivor: Healing Developmental Trauma & Dissociation. 2012. (ENG.). 272p. 95.00 (978-0-415-88994-0(4)); pap. 34.95 (978-0-415-88995-7(2)) Routledge.

Surace, Sandra. What's Wrong with My Child? Navigating through the maze of diagnostic Information. 2010. 316p. (ENG.). 32.99 (978-1-4520-1074-8(9)); pap. 24.99 (978-1-4520-1073-1(0)) AuthorHouse.

Talan, Kenneth H. Help Your Child or Teen Get Back on Track: What Parents & Professionals Can Do for Childhood Emotional & Behavioral Problems. (ENG., 2007. Illus.). 256p. pap. (978-1-84310-870-2(4)) 2nd ed. 2009. 288p. pap. (978-1-84310-914-3(X)) Kingsley, Jessica Ltd.

Wagemaker, A. Herbert. Psychiatric Medications & Our Children: A Parents Guide. (Illus.). 275p. (Orig.). pap. 17.95 (978-0-9654996-5-1(0)) Ponte Vedra Publishing.

Wilmshurst, Lind. Abnormal Child Psychology: A Developmental Perspective. 2008. (ENG., Illus.). 648p. 72.95 (978-0-415-95363-4(4)) Routledge.

Wilmshurst, Linda, ed. Child & Adolescent Psychopathology: A Casebook. 2nd ed. 2010. (Illus.). 384p. (C). pap. 42.00 (978-1-4129-8249-8(9), B82498P) SAGE Pubns., Inc.

World Health Organisation. Multiaxial Classification of Child & Adolescent Psychiatric Disorders: The ICD-10 Classification of Mental & Behavioural Disorders in Children & Adolescents. 2008. 312p. pap. 46.00 (978-0-521-06577-1(1)) Cambridge Univ. Pr.

CHILD PSYCHOTHERAPY

see also Child Analysis

Alvarez, Anne. Levels of Therapeutic Work & Levels of Pathology. 2012. (ENG., Illus.). 232p. (C). 128.00 (978-0-415-55486-2(1)); pap. 36.95 (978-0-415-55487-9(X)) Routledge.

Aumann, Kim & Hart, Angie. Helping Children with Complex Needs Bounce Back: Resilient Therapy for Parents & Professionals. 2009. (ENG., Illus.). 192p. pap. (978-1-84310-948-8(4)) Kingsley, Jessica Ltd.

Baggerly, Jennifer N., et al, eds. Child-Centered Play Therapy Research: The Evidence Base for Effective Practice. 2010. (ENG., Illus.). 528p. 65.00 (978-0-470-42201-4(7), Wiley) Wiley, John & Sons, Inc.

Barish, Kenneth M. Emotions in Child Psychotherapy: An Integrative Framework. 2009. (ENG.). 208p. 37.99 (978-0-19-536686-0(7)) Oxford Univ. Pr., Inc.

Becker-Weidman, Arthur. Developmental Dyadic Psychotherapy: Essential Practices & Methods. 2010. (978-0-7657-0795-6(0), Aronson, Jason) Rowman & Littlefield Publishers, Inc.

—Dyadic Developmental Psychotherapy: Essential Practices & Methods. 2010. (ENG.). 178p. 60.00 (978-0-7657-0793-2(4), Aronson, Jason) Rowman & Littlefield Publishers, Inc.

Becker-Weidman, Arthur, ed. Parenting for Attachment: Developing Connections & Healing Children. 2010. (ENG., Illus.). 306p. 73.50 (978-0-7657-0754-3(3), Aronson, Jason) Rowman & Littlefield Publishers, Inc.

Becker-Weidman, Arthur & Shell, Deborah. Parenting for Attachment: Developing Connections & Healing Children. 2010. (Illus.). (ENG.). 306p. pap. 31.50 (978-0-7657-0755-0(1)); xi, 293p. 29.95 (978-0-7657-0756-7(X)) Rowman & Littlefield Publishers, Inc. (Aronson, Jason).

Blake. Child & Adolescent Psychotherapy. 2011. 340p. pap. 46.95 (978-1-85575-898-8(9)) Karnac Bks. GBR. Dist: Stylus Publishing, LLC.

Blom, Rinda. The Handbook of Gestalt Play Therapy: Practical Guidelines for Child Therapists. 2006. (ENG., Illus.). 288p. per. (978-1-84310-459-9(8)) Kingsley, Jessica Ltd.

Bodiford McNeil, Cheryl & Hembree-Kigin, Toni. Parent-Child Interaction Therapy, 2nd Edition. 2nd ed. 2010. (Issues in Clinical Child Psychology Ser.). 445p. 189.00 (978-0-387-88638-1(9), 0387886389) Springer.

Boston Process Study Group Staff. Change in Psychotherapy - A Unifying Paradigm. 2010. (ENG.). 368p. 35.00 (978-0-393-70599-7(4), 70599) Norton, W. W. & Co., Inc.

Brems, Christiane. A Comprehensive Guide to Child Psychotherapy & Counseling. 3rd ed. 2008. (C). pap. 55.95 (978-1-57766-556-4(2)) Waveland Pr., Inc.

Briggs, Richard, et al, contrib. by. Relational Child Psychotherapy. 2010. 426p. pap. 37.00 (978-1-59051-422-1(X)) Other Pr., LLC.

Bromfield, Richard. Doing Child & Adolescent Psychotherapy: Adapting Psychodynamic Treatment to Contemporary Practice. 2nd ed. 2007. (ENG., Illus.). 320p. 78.00 (978-0-470-12181-8(5), Wiley) Wiley, John & Sons, Inc.

Browning, Robert & Stover, Donald. Behavior Modification in Child Treatment: An Experimental & Clinical Approach. 2009. (ENG., Illus.). 428p. pap. 45.95 (978-0-202-36293-9(0)) Aldine Transaction.

Burns, George W., ed. Healing with Stories: Your Casebook Collection for Using Therapeutic Metaphors. 2007. (ENG., Illus.). 304p. pap. 57.50 (978-0-471-78902-4(X), Wiley) Wiley, John & Sons, Inc.

Campher, Rosemary. Violent Child. 2008. (Forensic Psychotherapy Monograph Ser.). 286p. pap. 43.95 (978-1-85575-477-5(0)) Karnac Bks. GBR. Dist: Stylus Publishing, LLC.

Cattanach, Ann. Narrative Approaches in Play with Children. 2007. (ENG., Illus.). 224p. pap. (978-1-84310-588-6(8)) Kingsley, Jessica Ltd.

Christner, Ray W. & Stewart, Jessica, eds. Handbk Cbt Group Children & Adolescents: Specific Stteing & Popul. 2007. (ENG., Illus.). 552p. 65.95 (978-0-415-95254-5(9)) Routledge.

Cleve, Elisabeth. A Big & a Little One Is Gone: Crisis Therapy with a Two-Year-Old Boy. 2008. (Illus.). 216p. (C). pap. 39.95 (978-1-85575-541-3(6)) Karnac Bks. GBR. Dist: Stylus Publishing, LLC.

Cram101 Textbook Reviews & Cram101 Textbook Reviews. Outlines & Highlights for Counseling & Psychotherapy with Children & Adolescents: Theory & Practice for School & Clinical Settings by H. Thom. 2011. 112p. pap. 28.95 (978-1-61744-885-0(0)) Cram101 Inc.

Crenshaw, David A. Child & Adolescent Psychotherapy: Wounded Spirits & Healing Paths. 2008. (ENG., Illus.). 174p. 62.99 (978-0-7657-0598-3(2), Aronson, Jason) Rowman & Littlefield Publishers, Inc.

—Evocative Strategies in Child & Adolescent Psychotherapy. (ENG., Illus.). 312p. 2007. per. 39.99 (978-0-7657-0580-8(X)) 2006. 18.95 (978-0-7657-0414-6(5)) Rowman & Littlefield Publishers, Inc. (Aronson, Jason).

—Therapeutic Engagement of Children & Adolescents: Play, Symbol, Drawing, & Storytelling Strategies. 2008. (ENG., Illus.). 176p. 78.99 (978-0-7657-0570-9(2)); per. 39.99 (978-0-7657-0571-6(0)) Rowman & Littlefield Publishers, Inc. (Aronson, Jason).

DeGangi, Georgia. Kids' Club Letters: Narrative Tools for Stimulating Process & Dialogue in Therapy Groups for Children & Adolescents. 2009. (ENG., Illus.). 256p. 52.95 (978-0-415-99432-3(2)) Routledge.

Dodge, Kenneth A. & Rutter, Michael, eds. Gene-Environment Interactions in Developmental Psychopathology. 2011. (Duke Series in Child Develpment & Public Policy Ser.). (ENG.). 286p. 50.00 (978-1-60623-518-8(4)) Guilford Pubns., Inc.

Douglas. Containment & Reciprocity: Integrating Psychoanalytic Theory & Child Development Research for Work with Children. 2007. (ENG., Illus.). 184p. (C). 34.95 (978-0-415-39698-1(0)) Routledge.

Douglas, Hazel. Containment & Reciprocity: Integrating Concepts for Work with Children. 2007. (ENG., Illus.). 184p. (C). 95.00 (978-0-415-39697-4(2)) Routledge.

Drewes, Athena A., ed. Blending Play Therapy with Cognitive Behavioral Therapy: Evidence-Based & Other Effective Treatments & Techniques. 2009. (ENG., Illus.). 544p. 65.00 (978-0-470-17640-5(7), Wiley) Wiley, John & Sons, Inc.

Drewes, Athena A. & Mullen, Jodi Ann. Supervision Can Be Playful: Techniques for Child & Play Therapist Supervisors. 2008. (ENG., Illus.). 340p. 52.50 (978-0-7657-0533-4(8), Aronson, Jason) Rowman & Littlefield Publishers, Inc.

Durand, Mark V. & Hieneman, Meme. Helping Parents with Challenging Children: Positive Family Intervention. 2008. (Programs That Work Ser.). (ENG.). 144p. pap. 37.95 (978-0-19-533298-8(9)) Oxford Univ. Pr., Inc.

Durand, V. Mark & Hieneman, Meme. Helping Parents with Challenging Children Positive Family Intervention Parent Workbook. 2008. (Programs That Work Ser.). (ENG.). 144p. pap. 27.95 (978-0-19-533299-5(7)) Oxford Univ. Pr., Inc.

Eccleston, Juliet. Storytelling to Help Your Child. 2010. 92p. pap. (978-1-907172-87-8(4)) Pen Pr. Pubs., Ltd.

Elliott, Julian & Place, Maurice. Children in Difficulty: A Guide to Understanding & Helping. 3rd rev. ed. 2012. (ENG., Illus.). 296p. (C). 160.00 (978-0-415-67255-9(4)); pap. 44.95 (978-0-415-67263-4(5)) Routledge.

Ellis, Albert & Bernard, Michael E., eds. Rational Emotive Behavioral Approaches to Childhood Disorders: Theory, Practice & Research. 2010. (ENG.). xiv, 474p. pap. 69.95 (978-1-4419-3886-2(9), 1441938869) Springer.

Erk, Robert R. Counseling Treatment for Children & Adolescents with DSM-IV-TR Disorders. 2nd ed. 2007. (ENG., Illus.). 480p. (C). pap. 129.80 (978-0-13-230262-3(4), Prentice Hall) Prentice Hall PTR.

Field, Andy, et al, eds. Child Anxiety Theory & Treatment: A Special Issue of Cognition & Emotion. 2009. (Special Issues of Cognition & Emotion Ser.). (ENG., Illus.). 176p. 79.95 (978-1-84169-851-9(2), Psychology Press) Taylor & Francis Group GBR. Dist: Taylor & Francis Group.

French, Lyn & Klein, Reva, eds. Working with the Child Within. 2011. (ENG.). 256p. (C). 120.00 (978-0-415-59790-6(0)); pap. 36.99 (978-0-415-59791-3(9)) Routledge.

Friedman, Harriet & ROGERS-MITCHELL, R. I. E., eds. Supervision in Sandplay Therapy. 2007. (Supervision in the Arts Therapies Ser.). (ENG., Illus.). 248p. (C). 110.00 (978-0-415-41089-2(4)) Routledge.

Friedman, Harriet S. & Mitchell, Rie Rogers, eds. Supervision of Sandplay Therapy. 2007. (Supervision in the Arts Therapies Ser.). (ENG., Illus.). 248p. (C). per. 37.50 (978-0-415-41090-8(8)) Routledge.

Geldard, David & Geldard, Kathryn. Counselling Children: A Practical Introduction. 3rd ed. 2008. (Illus.). 328p. (C). 121.00 (978-1-4129-4833-3(9), B48333C) SAGE Pubns., Ltd. GBR. Dist: SAGE Pubns., Inc.

—Counselling Children: A Practical Introduction. 3rd ed. 2008. (Illus.). 328p. (C). per. 59.00 *(978-1-4129-4834-0(7)*, B48333P) SAGE Pubns., Ltd. GBR. Dist: SAGE Pubns., Inc.

Gil, Eliana. Helping Abused & Traumatized Children: Integrating Directive & Nondirective Approaches. 2011. (ENG., Illus.). 254p. pap. 26.00 *(978-1-60918-474-2(2))* Guilford Pubns., Inc.

Goldstein, Stanley. Shopping for A Shrink: Finding the Right Psychotherapist for You or Your Child /Sound Advice & Stories to Change Your Life. 2011. 358p. pap. 12.95 ***(978-0-9717705-5-3(7))*** Wyston Bks., Inc.

Gowers, Simon G. Eating Disorders: Cognitive Behaviour Therapy with Children & Young People. 2009. (CBT with Children, Adolescents & Families Ser.). (ENG., Illus.). 200p. (C). 128.00 *(978-0-415-44462-0(4))* Routledge.

Graziano, Anthony, ed. Behavior Therapy with Children, Vol. 2. 2008. (ENG., Illus.). 669p. pap. 59.95 *(978-0-202-36283-0(3))* Aldine Transaction.

Graziano, Anthony M. & Graziano, Anthony, eds. Behavior Therapy with Children, 2 vols. 2007. (ENG., Illus.). 470p. (gr. 11). pap. 34.95 *(978-0-202-30862-3(6))* Aldine Transaction.

Gunter, Michael. Winnicott's Squiggle Technique Practi. 2007. 223p. pap. 38.95 *(978-1-85575-419-5(3))* Karnac Bks. GBR. Dist: Stylus Publishing, LLC.

Haen, Craig, ed. Engaging Boys in Treatment. 2011. (Routledge Series on Counseling & Psychotherapy with Boys & Men Ser.). (ENG., Illus.). 346p. 125.00 *(978-0-415-87405-2(X))*; pap. 39.95 *(978-0-415-87406-9(8))* Routledge.

Hosin, Amer A., ed. Responses to Traumatized Children. 2007. (ENG., Illus.). 344p. 116.00 *(978-1-4039-9680-0(6))* Palgrave Macmillan.

Hughes, Tammy L. & Jimerson, Shane R. Identifying, Assessing, & Treating Conduct Disorder at School. 2007. (Developmental Psychopathology at School Ser.). X, 156p. 59.95 *(978-0-387-74393-6(6)*, 0387743936) Springer.

Jacobs, Linda & Wachs, Carol. Parent-Focused Child Therapy: Attachment, Identification, & Reflective Functions. 2006. (ENG.). 356p. 74.50 *(978-0-7657-0468-9(4))* Rowman & Littlefield Publishers, Inc.

Jaffe, Peter G., et al. Growing up with Domestic Violence. 2011. (Illus.). 78p. pap. 29.80 *(978-0-88937-336-5(1))* Hogrefe Publishing.

Jenkins, Peter & Daniels, Debbie. Therapy with Children: Children's Rights, Confidentiality & the Law. 2nd ed. 2010. (Ethics in Practice Ser.). (Illus.). 208p. (C). 108.00 *(978-1-84860-998-3(1)*, B09983C); pap. 44.00 *(978-1-84860-999-0(X)*, B09983P) SAGE Pubns., Ltd. GBR. Dist: SAGE Pubns., Inc.

Joiner, Lindsay. Creativity Unleashed: Therapeutic Activities & Character Education Ideas for Working with Children & Teens. 2011. (Illus.). 256p. pap. ***(978-1-84905-865-0(2))*** Kingsley, Jessica Ltd.

Jongsma, Arthur E., Jr. & Bruce, Timothy J. Evidence-Based Treatment Planning for Social Anxiety. 2010. (Evidence-Based Psychotherapy Treatment Planning Video Ser.: 14). (ENG.). mass mkt. 40.00 *(978-0-470-41507-8(X)*, Wiley) Wiley, John & Sons, Inc.

Jongsma, Arthur E. & Bruce, Timothy J. Treatment Planning for Disruptive Child & Adolescent Behavior. 2011. (Evidence-Based Psychotherapy Treatment Planning Video Ser.: 7). (ENG.). mass mkt. 40.00 *(978-0-470-41789-8(7))*;Set. mass mkt., wbk. ed. 55.25 *(978-1-118-02894-0(5))* Wiley, John & Sons, Inc. (Wiley).

Jongsma, Arthur E., Jr., et al. Child Psychotherapy Homework Planner. 2nd ed. (ENG.). 2007. (Practice Planners Ser.). cd-rom 100.00 *(978-0-471-73793-8(C))* 2006. (PracticePlanners Ser.: 210). (Illus.). 360p. pap. 55.00 *(978-0-471-78534-7(2))* Wiley, John & Sons, Inc. (Wiley).

—The Child Psychotherapy Progress Notes Planner. 3rd ed. 2007. (ENG.). (PracticePlanners? Ser.). cd-rom 125.00 *(978-0-471-78794-5(9))*; (PracticePlanners Ser.: 212). 408p. pap. 55.00 *(978-0-471-78536-1(9))* Wiley, John & Sons, Inc. (Wiley).

—The Child Psychotherapy Treatment Planner. 4th ed. 2006. (ENG.). (PracticePlanners? Ser.). cd-rom 175.00 *(978-0-471-78795-2(7))*; (PracticePlanners Ser. 211). 368p. pap. 55.00 *(978-0-471-78535-4(0))* Wiley, John & Sons, Inc. (Wiley).

Kaduson, Heidi Gerard & Schaefer, Charles E., eds. Short-Term Play Therapy for Children. 2nd rev. ed. 2006. (ENG., Illus.). 388p. 60.00 *(978-1-59385-330-3(0))* Guilford Pubns., Inc.

Kazdin, Alan E. Parent Management Training: Treatment for Oppositional, Aggressive, & Antisocial Behavior in Children & Adolescents. 2008. (ENG., Illus.). 424p. pap. 29.95 *(978-0-19-538600-4(0))* Oxford Univ. Pr., Inc.

Kelly-Zion, Sophronia & Schaefer, Charles E. Play Therapy for Very Young Children. 2008. (ENG., Illus.). 434p. 89.50 *(978-0-7657-0519-8(2)*, Aronson, Jason) Rowman & Littlefield Publishers, Inc.

Kelly-Zion, Sophronia, et al. Play Therapy for Very Young Children. 2008. (ENG.). 434p. pap. 52.50 *(978-0-7657-0520-4(6)*, Aronson, Jason) Rowman & Littlefield Publishers, Inc.

Kendall, Philip C., ed. Child & Adolescent Therapy, Fourth Edition: Cognitive-Behavioral Procedures. 4th rev. ed. 2011. (ENG., Illus.). 538p. 65.00 *(978-1-60623-561-4(3))* Guilford Pubns., Inc.

Kendall, Philip C. & Comer, Jonathan. Childhood Disorders. 2nd rev. ed. 2010. (Clinical Psychology: A Modular Course Ser.). (ENG., Illus.). 304p. (C). 85.00 *(978-0-415-48641-5(6))*; pap. 29.95 *(978-0-415-48642-2(4))* Taylor & Francis Group GBR. (Psychology Press). Dist: Taylor & Francis Group.

Kohen, Daniel P. & Olness, Karen. Hypnosis & Hypnotherapy with Children. 4th rev. ed. 2011. (ENG., Illus.). 558p. 59.95 *(978-0-415-87627-8(3))* Routledge.

Koplow, Lesley, ed. Unsmiling Faces: How Preschools Can Heal. 2nd rev. ed. 2007. (ENG.). 288p. pap. 27.95 *(978-0-8077-4803-9(X))*; (Illus.). 56.00 *(978-0-8077-4804-6(8))* Teachers College Pr., Teachers College, Columbia Univ.

Kourkoutas, Elias E., ed. Behavioral Disorders in Children: Ecosystemic Psychodynamic Interventions within the Family & School Context. 2011. (Children's Issues, Laws & Programs Ser.). 140.00 ***(978-1-61470-718-9(9))*** Nova Science Pubs., Inc.

Kratochwill, Thomas R. Handbook of Psychotherapy with Children & Adolescents, Second Edition. 2nd ed. 2009. pap. 89.95 *(978-0-8058-6226-3(9))* Erlbaum, Lawrence Assocs., Inc.

LeCroy, Craig Winston. Handbook of Evidence-Based Treatment Manuals for Children & Adolescents. 2nd ed. 2008. (ENG., Illus.). 560p. (C). 65.00 *(978-0-19-517741-1(X))* Oxford Univ. Pr., Inc.

Leigh, Lauraine, et al, eds. Dramatherapy with Children, Young People & Schools: Enabling creativity, sociability, communication & Learning. 2012. (ENG., Illus.). 304p. (C). 112.00 *(978-0-415-67076-0(4))*; pap. 36.99 *(978-0-415-67077-7(2))* Routledge.

Lowenstein, Liana. Assessment & Treatment Activities for Children, Adolescents, & Families: Practitioners Share Their Most Effective Techniques. 2008. 181p. *(978-0-9685199-4-3(6))* Champion Pr.

—Assessment & Treatment Activities for Children, Adolescents, & Families Vol. 2: Practitioners Share Their Most Effective Techniques. 2010. (Illus.). 157p. pap. 24.95 *(978-0-9685199-5-0(4))* Champion Pr. CAN. Dist: AtlasBooks Distribution.

—Assessment & treatment activities for children, adolescents, & families Volume Three: Practitioners share their most effective techniques. 2011. (Illus.). 208p. pap. ***(978-0-9685199-7-4(0))*** Champion Pr.

Lowenstein, Liana. Creative Interventions for Children of Divorce. 2006. (Illus.). 175p. *(978-0-9685199-3-6(8))* Champion Pr.

Lowenstein, Liana, ed. Creative Family Therapy Techniques: Play, Art, & Expressive Activities to Engage Children in Family Sessions. 2010. (Illus.). 352p. pap. *(978-0-9685199-6-7(2))* Champion Pr.

MacKenzie, Heather. Reaching & Teaching the Child with Autism Spectrum Disorder: Using Learning Preferences & Strengths. 2008. (ENG., Illus.). 240p. pap. *(978-1-84310-623-4(X))* Kingsley, Jessica Ltd.

Manassis, Katharina. Problem Solving in Child & Adolescent Psychotherapy: A Skills-Based, Collaborative Approach. 2012. (ENG.). 208p. 30.00 ***(978-1-4625-0370-4(5))*** Guilford Pubns., Inc.

Martyn, Dorothy W. Beyond Deserving: Children, Parents, & Responsibility Revisited. 2007. 170p. per. 14.00 *(978-0-8028-4422-4(7))* Eerdmans, William B. Publishing Co.

Mayer, Matthew J., et al, eds. Cognitive-Behavioral Interventions for Emotional & Behavioral Disorders: School-Based Practice. 2011. (ENG.). 420p. (gr. k-12). pap. 30.00 *(978-1-60918-481-0(5))* Guilford Pubns., Inc.

McCarthy, Dennis, ed. Speaking about the Unspeakable: Non-Verbal Methods & Experiences in Therapy with Children. 2008. (ENG., Illus.). 180p. pap. *(978-1-84310-879-5(8))* Kingsley, Jessica Ltd.

McKay, Dean & Storch, Eric A. Cognitive-Behavior Therapy for Children: Treating Complex & Refractory Cases. 2009. (Illus.). 608p. *(978-0-8261-1686-4(8))* Springer.

McNeil, Cheryl Bodiford & Hembree-Kigin, Toni L. Parent-Child Interaction Therapy. 2nd ed. 2011. (Issues in Clinical Child Psychology Ser.). (Illus.). xvii, 483p. pap. 49.95 *(978-1-4419-9575-9(7)*, 1441995757) Springer.

Mennuti, Rosemary B., et al, eds. Cognitive-Behavioral Interventions in Educational Settings: A Handbook for Practice. 2nd rev. ed. 2012. (ENG., Illus.). 782p. 62.95 ***(978-0-415-80740-1(9))*** Routledge.

Midgley, Nick. Child Psychotherapy & Research: New Approaches, Emerging Findings. Grainger, Eve et al, eds. 2009. (ENG., Illus.). 248p. (C). 110.00 *(978-0-415-42202-4(7))* Routledge.

—Child Psychotherapy & Research: New Approaches, Emerging Findings. Nesic-Vuckovic, Tanja et al, eds. 2009. (ENG., Illus.). 248p. (C). pap. 40.00 *(978-0-415-42203-1(5))* Routledge.

Midgley, Nick & Vrouva, Ioanna, eds. Keeping Children in Mind: Mentalization-based Interventions with Children, Young People & their Families. 2012. (ENG., Illus.). 240p. (C). pap. 36.95 *(978-0-415-60525-0(3))* Routledge.

—Keeping Children in Mind: Mentalization-Based Interventions with Children, Young People & Their Families. 2012. (ENG., Illus.). 240p. (C). 128.00 *(978-0-415-60523-6(7))* Routledge.

Morris, Richard J. & Kratochwill, Thomas R., eds. The Practice of Child Therapy. 4th rev. ed. 2007. (Illus.). 587p. 210.00 *(978-0-8058-5328-5(6))*; per. 98.95 *(978-0-8058-5329-2(4))* Erlbaum, Lawrence Assocs., Inc.

Munns, Evangeline. Applications of Family & Group Theraplay. 2009. (ENG.). 316p. 83.99 *(978-0-7657-0594-5(X)*, Aronson, Jason) Rowman & Littlefield Publishers, Inc.

Norton, Christine L. Innovative Interventions in Child & Adolescent Mental Health. 2010. (ENG., Illus.). 208p. 135.00 *(978-0-415-87984-2(1))*; pap. 35.95 *(978-0-415-87985-9(X))* Routledge.

Oaklander, Violet. Hidden Treasure: A Map to the Child's Inner Self. 2007. 256p. per. 39.95 *(978-1-85575-490-4(8))* Karnac Bks. GBR. Dist: Stylus Publishing, LLC.

Oppenheim, David & Goldsmith, Douglas F., eds. Attachment Theory in Clinical Work with Children: Bridging the Gap Between Research & Practice. (ENG.). 256p. 2011. pap. 27.00 *(978-1-60918-482-7(3))* 2007. (Illus.). 50.00 *(978-1-59385-448-5(X))* Guilford Pubns., Inc.

Painter, Kirstin. Evidence-Based Practice Model for Youth with Externalizing Disorders. 2010. 140p. pap. *(978-3-8383-0253-9(2))* Lambert Academic Publishing.

Papousek, Mechthild, et al. Disorders of Behavioral & Emotional Regulation in the First Years of Life: Early Risks & Intervention in the Developing Parent-Infant Relationships. 2007. *(978-1-934019-17-7(8))* Zero To Three Pr.

Pearce, John W. & Pezzot-Pearce, Terry Dianne. Psychotherapy of Abused & Neglected Children. 2nd rev. ed. 2006. (ENG., Illus.). 411p. 50.00 *(978-1-59385-213-9(4))* Guilford Pubns., Inc.

Pernicano, Pat. Family-Focused Trauma Intervention: Using Metaphor & Play with Victims of Abuse & Neglect. 2010. (ENG., Illus.). 212p. 52.50 *(978-0-7657-0772-7(1)*, Aronson, Jason) Rowman & Littlefield Publishers, Inc.

—Metaphorical Stories for Child Therapy: Of Magic & Miracles. 2010. (ENG.). 136p. 47.50 *(978-0-7657-0781-9(0)*, Aronson, Jason) Rowman & Littlefield Publishers, Inc.

Peters, Todd & Freeman, Jennifer. Cognitive Behavioral Therapy - An Issue of Child & Adolescent Psychiatric Clinics of North America. 2011. (Clinics: Internal Medicine Ser.: 20-2). (ENG., Illus.). xvi, 180p. 110.00 *(978-1-4557-0428-6(8)*, Saunders) Elsevier - Health Sciences Div.

Prout, H. Thompson & Brown, Douglas T., eds. Counseling & Psychotherapy with Children & Adolescents: Theory & Practice for School & Clinical Settings. 4th rev. ed. 2007. (ENG., Illus.). 480p. 152.00 *(978-0-471-77091-6(4)*, Wiley) Wiley, John & Sons, Inc.

Pughe, Billy & Philpot, Terry. Living Alongside a Child's Recovery: Therapeutic Parenting with Traumatized Children. 2007. (ENG.). 144p. per. *(978-1-84310-328-8(1))* Kingsley, Jessica Ltd.

Raicar, Alexandra Maeja. Child-Centred Attachment Therapy. 2009. (United Kingdom Council for Psychotherapy Ser.). (Illus.). 152p. pap. 36.95 *(978-1-85575-505-5(X))* Karnac Bks. GBR. Dist: Stylus Publishing, LLC.

Reaven, Judy, et al. Facing Your Fears Facilitator's Manual: Group Therapy for Managing Anxiety in Children with High-Functioning Autism Spectrum Disorders. 2011. (Illus.). xiii, 169p. 89.95 *(978-1-59857-178-3(8))* Brookes, Paul H. Publishing Co.

Recob, Amy. Bibliotherapy: When Kids Need Books. 2008. 224p. pap. 18.95 *(978-0-595-52530-0(X))* iUniverse, Inc.

Regan, Kathy. Opening Our Arms: Helping Troubled Kids Do Well. 2006. (ENG., Illus.). 224p. pap. 16.95 *(978-0-923521-94-3(1))* Bull Publishing Co.

Rispoli, Luciano. The Basic Experience & the Development of the Self: Development from the Point of View of Functional Psychotherapy. 2008. 460p. pap. *(978-3-03911-750-5(5))* Lang, Peter.

Roff, Hermione. Reflective Interpersonal Therapy for Children & Parents (RICAP) Mind That Child! A New Way of Helping Parents & Children with Extreme Conduct Disorder. 2008. (ENG., Illus.). 318p. 144.95 *(978-0-470-98648-6(4)*, Wiley) Wiley, John & Sons, Inc.

Rosenfeld, George W. Beyond Evidence-Based Psychotherapy: Fostering the Eight Sources of Change in Child & Adolescent Treatment. 2008. (Counseling & Psychotherapy Ser.). (ENG.). 284p. 42.50 *(978-0-415-99336-4(9))*; 125.00 *(978-0-415-99335-7(0))* Routledge.

Rubin, Lawrence C., ed. Popular Culture in Counseling, Pschotherapy, & Play-Based Interventions. 2008. (Illus.). 372p. 48.00 *(978-0-8261-0118-1(6))* Springer Publishing Co., Inc.

Rustin, Margaret. Work Discussion: Learning from Reflective Practice in Work with Children & Families. 2009. 330p. pap. 38.95 *(978-1-85575-644-1(7))* Karnac Bks. GBR. Dist: Stylus Publishing, LLC.

Saxe, Glenn N., et al. Collaborative Treatment of Traumatized Children & Teens: The Trauma Systems Therapy Approach. (ENG., Illus.). 338p. 2009. pap. 35.00 *(978-1-60623-349-8(1))* 2006. 60.00 *(978-1-59385-315-0(7))* Guilford Pubns., Inc.

Scalzo. Therapy with Children: An Existential Perspective. 2010. (United Kingdom Council for Psychotherapy Ser.). 180p. pap. 28.95 *(978-1-85575-730-1(3))* Karnac Bks. GBR. Dist: Stylus Publishing, LLC.

Schaefer, Charles E. Play Therapy for Preschool Children. 2009. (Illus.). 333p. 59.95 *(978-1-4338-0566-0(9))* American Psychological Assn.

Schaefer, Charles E. & Briesmeister, James M., eds. Handbook of Parent Training: Helping Parents Prevent & Solve Problem Behaviors. 3rd rev. ed. 2007. (ENG., Illus.). 576p. 95.00 *(978-0-471-78997-0(6)*, Wiley) Wiley, John & Sons, Inc.

Schmidt Neven, Ruth. Core Principles of Assesement & Therapeutic Communication with Children: Towards the Promotion of Child & Family Wellbeing. 2010. (ENG., Illus.). 192p. (C). pap. 39.95 *(978-0-415-55243-1(5))* Routledge.

—Core Principles of Assesement & Therapeutic Communication with Children, Parents & Families: Towards the Promotion of Child & Family Wellbeing. 2010. (ENG., Illus.). 192p. (C). 100.00 *(978-0-415-55242-4(7))* Routledge.

Schmukler, Anita G. Ethical Practice in Child & Adolescent Analysis & Psychotherapy: Protecting Safety in a Therapeutic Environment. 2011. xv, 124p. ***(978-0-7657-0820-5(5)***, Aronson, Jason) Rowman & Littlefield Publishers, Inc.

Schmukler, Anita G., et al. Ethical Practice in Child & Adolescent Analysis & Psychotherapy: Protecting Safety in a Therapeutic Environment. 2011. (ENG.). 132p. (gr. 17). 55.00 ***(978-0-7657-0818-2(3)***, Aronson, Jason) Rowman & Littlefield Publishers, Inc.

Shechtman, Zipora. Group Counseling & Psychotherapy with Children & Adolescents: Theory, Research, & Practice. 2006. (ENG., Illus.). 312p. 135.00 *(978-0-8058-5685-9(4))*; per. 44.95 *(978-0-8058-5686-6(2))* Routledge.

Sheppard, Tony/L. Group Psychotherapy with Children. 2008. 73p. ring bd. 100.00 *(978-0-9774879-7-4(0))* American Group Psychotherapy Assn.

Shriver, Mark D. & Allen, Keith D. Working with Parents of Noncompliant Children: A Guide to Evidence-Based Parent Training for Practitioners & Students. 2008. (School Psychology Book Ser.). (Illus.). 304p. 49.95 *(978-1-4338-0344-4(5))* American Psychological Assn.

Silverman, Wendy K. & Field, Andy, eds. Anxiety Disorders in Children & Adolescents. 2nd ed. 2011. (Cambridge Child & Adolescent Psychiatry Ser.). (ENG., Illus.). 436p. pap. 80.00 *(978-0-521-72148-6(2))* Cambridge Univ. Pr.

Slivinske, Johanna & Slivinske, Lee R. Storytelling & Other Activities for Children in Therapy. 2011. (ENG., Illus.). 346p. pap. 52.00 *(978-0-470-91998-9(1)*, Wiley) Wiley, John & Sons, Inc.

Smith, Steven R. & Handler, Leonard, eds. The Clinical Assessment of Children & Adolescents: A Practitioner's Handbook. 2006. (ENG., Illus.). 648p. 257.95 *(978-0-8058-5791-7(5))* Routledge.

Sommers-Flanagan, John & Sommers-Flanagan, Rita. How to Listen So Parents Will Talk & Talk So Parents Will Listen. 2011. (ENG.). 304p. pap. 40.00 *(978-1-118-01296-3(8)*, Wiley) Wiley, John & Sons, Inc.

Sori, Catherine Ford & Hecker, Lorna L. The Therapist's Notebook Vol. 3: More Homework, Handouts, & Activities for Use in Psychotherapy. 2008. (ENG., Illus.). 248p. 54.50 *(978-0-7890-3522-6(7))* Routledge.

Steele, Ric G., et al, eds. Handbook of Evidence-Based Therapies for Children & Adolescents: Bridging Science & Practice. (Issues in Clinical Child Psychology Ser.). 2010. x, 585p. pap. 114.00 *(978-1-4419-4469-6(9)*, 1441944699) 2007. (Illus.). 585p. 114.00 *(978-0-387-73690-7(5))* Springer.

Steele, William & Malchiodi, Cathy A. Trauma-Informed Practices with Children & Adolescents. 2011. (ENG., Illus.). 279p. pap. 39.95 *(978-0-415-89052-6(7))* Routledge.

Stern, Marcia B. Child-Friendly Therapy: Biopsychosocial Innovations for Children & Families. 2008. (ENG., Illus.). 384p. pap. 29.00 *(978-0-393-70564-5(1)*, 70564) Norton, W. W. & Co., Inc.

Terr, Lenore. Magical Moments of Change: How Psychotherapy Turns Kids Around. 2007. (ENG.). 224p. 30.00 *(978-0-393-70530-0(7)*, 70530) Norton, W. W. & Co., Inc.

Trowell. Childhood Depression: A Place for Psychotherapy. 2011. (Tavistock Clinic Ser.). 320p. pap. 32.95 ***(978-1-78049-004-5(6))*** Karnac Bks. GBR. Dist: Stylus Publishing, LLC.

Tuber, Steven & Caflisch, Jane M. Beginning Treatment with Children & Adolescents: A Process-Oriented Guide for Therapists. 2011. (ENG.). 324p. 130.00 *(978-0-415-88557-7(4))* Routledge.

—Beginning Treatment with Children & Adolescents: The Clinician's Guide to Psychodynamic Approaches. 2011. (ENG.). 324p. pap. 34.95 *(978-0-415-88558-4(2))* Routledge.

Urwin, Cathy. Psychotherapy & Infancy: Models of Mental Development in Psychoanalytic Theories. Scott, Ann, ed. 2011. (Palgrave Psychotherapy Ser.). (ENG.). 208p. (C). 89.95 *(978-0-333-76328-5(9))*; pap. 29.95 *(978-0-333-76329-2(7))* Palgrave Macmillan.

Ventling, C. D., ed. Childhood Psychotherapy: A Bioenergetic Approach. (Illus.). *(978-3-8055-7149-4(6))* Karger, S. AG.

Vernon, Ann. More What Works When with Children & Adolescents (Book & CD) 2009. pap. 44.95 *(978-0-87822-614-6(1))* Research Pr.

Wagner, William G. Counseling, Psychology, & Children. 2nd ed. 2007. (ENG.). 456p. (C). 119.40 *(978-0-13-170277-6(7)*, Prentice Hall) Prentice Hall PTR.

Wedge, Marilyn. Suffer the Children: The Case Against Labeling & Medicating & an Effective Alternative. 2011. (ENG.). 243p. 26.95 *(978-0-393-07159-7(6)*, 7159) Norton, W. W. & Co., Inc.

Weisz, John R. & Kazdin, Alan E., eds. Evidence-Based Psychotherapies for Children & Adolescents. 2nd ed. 2010. (ENG., Illus.). 602p. 75.00 *(978-1-59385-974-9(0))* Guilford Pubns., Inc.

Winnicott. Psycho-Analytic Explorations. 2010. 614p. pap. 57.95 *(978-1-85575-853-7(9))* Karnac Bks. GBR. Dist: Stylus Publishing, LLC.

Wood, Jeffrey J. & McLeod, Bryce D. Child Anxiety Disorders: A Family-Based Treatment Manual for Practitioners. 2008. (ENG., Illus.). 272p. 32.00 *(978-0-393-70540-9(4)*, 70540) Norton, W. W. & Co., Inc.

Zarichansky, Mark, et al. Overcoming Resistance: Engaging Parents in Play Therapy - a DVD Workshop. 2007. DVD 60.00 *(978-1-930557-11-6(6))* Play Therapy Pr.

Ziegler, Dave. Traumatic Experience & the Brain: A Handbook for Understanding & Treating Those Traumatized as Children. 2nd ed. 2011. (ENG., Illus.). 255p. pap. 24.95 ***(978-1-935089-42-1(0))*** Acacia Publishing, Inc.

Zucker, Bonnie. Anxiety-Free Kids: An Interactive Guide for Parents & Children. 2008. (ENG.). 250p. pap. 16.95 *(978-1-59363-343-1(2))* Prufrock Pr.

CHILD PSYCHOTHERAPY—RESIDENTIAL TREATMENT

Barton, Susan, et al. Therapeutic Residential Care for Children & Young People: An Attachment & Trauma-Informed Model for Practice. 2011. (ENG., Illus.). 288p. pap. ***(978-1-84905-255-9(7))*** Kingsley, Jessica Ltd.

Bettelheim, Bruno & Sylvester, Emmy. Delinquency & Morality. 2011. 20p. pap. 35.95 ***(978-1-258-01448-3(3))*** Literary Licensing, LLC.

Ellis, Rodney A. Best Practices in Residential Treatment. 2008. (Illus.). 168p. (C). 150.00 *(978-0-7890-3788-6(2))*; 41.95 *(978-0-7890-3789-3(0))* Routledge.

Goldstein, Stanley. Troubled Children/Troubled Parents: The Way Out: Sound advice & some case histories to make you a more understanding & effective parent in coping with your children's problems. 2nd ed. 2011. 9.95 ***(978-0-9717705-8-4(1))*** Wyston Bks., Inc.

McGlinn, Christopher. Reducing the Use of Physical Restraints - the Effect of Federal Legislation. 2008. 92p. pap. *(978-3-639-10401-1(3))* VDM Verlag Dr. Mueller e.K.

C

Redford, Roberta Carly. Crazy: My Seven Years at Bruno Bettelheim's Orthogenic School. 2010. 364p. 30.33 *(978-1-4251-9176-4(2))*; pap. 20.33 *(978-1-4251-9175-7(4))* Trafford Publishing.

Rodenhiser, Roy W. Assessment in Residential Care for Children & Youth. 2008. 228p. 45.95 *(978-0-7890-3839-5(0))*; 150.00 *(978-0-7890-3838-8(2))* Routledge.

Whittaker, James & Trieschman, Albert, eds. Children Away from Home: A Sourcebook of Residential Treatment. 2009. (ENG.). 463p. pap. 49.95 *(978-0-202-36274-8(4))* Aldine Transaction.

Winnicott, D. W. Deprivation & Delinquency. Winnicott, Clare et al, eds. 2011. (Routledge Classics Ser.). (ENG., Illus.). 288p. pap. 26.95 *(978-0-415-67373-0(9))* Routledge.

CHILD REARING

Here are entered works on the principles and techniques of raising children. Works on the psycho-social interaction between parents and their minor children are entered under Parent and Child. Works on the skills, attributes and attitudes needed for parenthood are entered under Parenting.

see also Child Abuse; Child Development; Child Psychology; Children—Health and Hygiene; Discipline of Children; Domestic Education; Moral Education; Parenting; Socialization; Toilet Training

Aaron, Jane E. & Riley, Kathryn. Developmental Exercises for the Little. 7th ed. 2009. (ENG.). 110p. (C). pap. 19.20 *(978-0-205-70197-1(3))* Longman Publishing Group.

Abbott, Jacob. Gentle Measures in the Management & Training of the Young by Jacob Abbott. 2006. 336p. per. 23.99 *(978-1-4255-3343-4(4))* MPublishing.

Acosta, Judith & Prager, Judith Simon. Verbal First Aid: Help Your Kids Heal from Fear & Pain — and Come Out Strong. 2010. (ENG.). 336p. (gr. 12). 15.00 *(978-0-425-23427-3(4)*, Berkley Trade) Penguin Group (USA) Inc.

Acredolo, Linda & Goodwyn, Susan. Baby Signs Program Kit: Everything You Need to Get Started Signing with Your Baby. 2006. (ENG.). (J). 39.95 *(978-1-933877-00-6(6))* Baby Signs, Inc.

—Baby Smarts Deck: 50 Brain-Building Games Your Baby Will Love. 2010. 108p. 14.99 *(978-0-307-71862-4(X)*, Potter Style) Crown Publishing Group.

Acredolo, Linda, et al. Baby Signs: How to Talk with Your Baby Before Your Baby Can Talk. 3rd ed. 2009. (ENG., Illus.). 208p. pap. 16.95 *(978-0-07-161503-7(2)*, 0071615032) McGraw-Hill Cos., The.

Adams, Bobbie. Unsolicited Advice from a Mother to Her Son about Child Rearing. 2011. pap. 8.95 ***(978-0-7414-6515-3(9))*** Infinity Publishing.

Adams, Eric L. Don't Let It Happen. 2009. 152p. pap. 14.99 *(978-1-60791-985-8(0))* Xulon Pr., Inc.

Akanda, Md. Zahir Uddin & Akanda, Zahir Uddin. Father's Role in Enhancing Children's Development. 2011. 60p. pap. ***(978-3-8454-1886-5(9))*** Lambert Academic Publishing.

Al-Araimi, Saif & Al-Rawahi, Thuria. Smart Parents Meet Mr. Motivation. 2010. 85p. pap. 38.50 *(978-0-557-19609-8(4))* Lulu Enterprises Inc.

Alexander-Roberts, Colleen. The AD/HD Parenting Handbook: Practical Advice for Parents from Parents. 2nd rev. ed. 2006. (ENG., Illus.). 320p. per. 15.95 *(978-1-58979-283-8(1))* Taylor Trade Publishing.

Allred, Lynnae. Piggyback Rides & Slippery Slides: How to Have Fun Raising First-Rate Children. 2007. 231p. per. 14.99 *(978-1-59955-053-4(9))* Cedar Fort, Inc./CFI Distribution.

Alvy, Kerby T. Postive Parent: Raising Healthy, Happpy, & Successful Children, Birth - Adolescence. 2007. (ENG., Illus.). 264p. pap. 22.95 *(978-0-8077-4808-4(0))* Teachers College Pr., Teachers College, Columbia Univ.

Amaya & Prado. Puppet Master or Pawn? Raising Successful, Happy, & Resilient Childrens with Needs, Failures, Self-Discipline. 2009. 110p. pap. 10.15 *(978-1-60860-790-7(9)*, Eloquent Bks.) AEG Literary Publishing Services, Inc.

American Academy of Pediatrics. ADHD: A Complete & Authoritative Guide. Reiff, Michael I., ed. 2nd ed. 2011. (ENG.). 350p. pap. 16.95 *(978-1-58110-451-6(0))* American Academy of Pediatrics.

American Academy of Pediatrics. Patient Education for Children, Teens, & Parents: Patient Education Compendium. 4th ed. 2011. (ENG.). 464p. pap. 119.95 ***(978-1-58110-566-7(5))*** American Academy of Pediatrics.

American Academy of Pediatrics Staff, contrib. by. Patient Education for Children, Teens, & Parents. 3rd ed. 2007. (Illus.). xii, 436p. *(978-1-58110-231-4(3))* American Academy of Pediatrics.

American Girl (Firm) Staff, contrib. by. Raising an American Girl: Parenting Advice for the Real World. 2009. 9.95 *(978-1-59369-618-4(3)*, American Girl) American Girl Publishing, Inc.

Anderson, Patricia Nan. Parenting: A Field Guide: 150 Key Ideas for Raising Successful, Well-Adjusted & Confident Kids. 2009. (Illus.). 325p. 24.95 *(978-1-890427-55-9(1))* Aviva Publishing.

Anderson Sheckels, Ceetee. What your children need from you — & Why. 2009. 87p. pap. 20.49 *(978-0-557-15782-2(X))* Lulu Enterprises Inc.

Appelbaum, Maryln. No More Battles with Strong Willed Kids. 2007. (Illus.). 76p. per. 8.00 *(978-0-9777189-7-9(2))* Appelbaum Publishing Co.

Arinoldo, Carl Guy & Arinoldo, Linda D. Essentials of Smart Parenting: Learning the Fine Art of Managing Your Children. 2006. 168p. pap. 47.00 *(978-1-60021-420-2(7))* Nova Science Pubs., Inc.

Armagost-Harding, Barbara. Baby Talks~the Inside Story. 2011. (ENG.). 178p. 24.95 ***(978-1-4327-8023-4(9))***; pap. 12.95 ***(978-1-4327-7805-7(6))*** Outskirts Pr., Inc.

Arnall, Judy. Discipline Without Distress: 135 Tools for Raising Caring, Responsible Children Without Time-Out, Spanking, Punishment, or Bribery. 2007. (SPA, KOR & CHI., Illus.). 440p. pap. 19.95 *(978-0-9780509-0-0(8))* Professional Parenting Canada CAN. Dist: Partners Pubs. Group, Inc.

Arnall, Judy. The Last Word on Parenting Advice. 2011. (Illus.). 128p. 9.95 ***(978-0-9780509-2-4(4))*** Professional Parenting Canada CAN. Dist: Partners Pubs. Group, Inc.

Arnstein, Helene S. What to Tell Your Child about Birth, Death, Illness, Divorce, & Other Family Crises. 2011. 202p. 44.95 ***(978-1-258-08200-0(4))*** Literary Licensing, LLC.

Arthur, Maurice. A Black Man Thinking Vol. 1: Raising Children. 2007. 147p. spiral bd. 19.95 *(978-0-9788340-0-5(3))* Black Man Thing, LLC, A.

Arthur, T. S. The Mothers Rule; or the Right Way & the Wrong Way. 2007. 312p. per. 19.95 *(978-1-60466-004-3(X))* Capricorn Hse. Publishing.

Ashton, Kelly & Weinberg, Pamela. City Baby New York: The Ultimate Guide for New York City Parents, from Pregnancy to Preschool. 4th ed. 2010. (ENG.). 304p. pap. 19.95 *(978-0-7893-2030-8(4))* Universe Publishing.

Atkins, Lucy. First-Time Parent: The Honest Guide to Coping Brilliantly & Staying Sane in Your Baby's First Year. 2009. (ENG., Illus.). 240p. pap. 22.95 *(978-0-00-726944-0(7))* HarperCollins Pubs. Ltd. GBR. Dist: Independent Pubs. Group.

Atkins, Sue. Raising Happy Children for Dummies(r). 2012. (ENG., Illus.). 378p. pap. 29.99 ***(978-0-470-05978-4(8)***, For Dummies) Wiley, John & Sons, Inc.

Atlantic Publishing Group. A Parent's Guide to Effectively Communicating with Your Child: How to Speak So Your Toddler & Preschooler Will Listen & Do What You Say. 2012. (ENG.). 288p. pap. 24.95 *(978-1-60138-570-3(6))* Atlantic Publishing Co.

Au, Sara & Stavinoha, Peter. Stress-Free Potty Training: A Commonsense Guide to Finding the Right Approach for Your Child. 2008. (ENG.). 192p. pap. 12.95 *(978-0-8144-0162-0(7))* Amacom.

Aunos, Marjorie & Feldman, Maurice. Comprehensive, Competence-Based Parenting Assessment for Parents with Learning Difficulties & Their Children. 2011. (ENG.). 170p. pap. 44.95 *(978-1-57256-146-5(7))* National Assn. For The Dually Diagnosed.

Austin, Michael W. Conceptions of Parenthood: Ethics & the Family. 2007. (Ashgate Studies in Applied Ethics Ser.). 148p. 99.95 *(978-0-7546-5838-2(4))* Ashgate Publishing Co.

Avraham-Krehwinkel, Carmelite & Aldridge, David. Happy Families: A Parents' Guide to the Non-Violent Resistance Approach. 2010. (ENG., Illus.). 96p. pap. *(978-1-84905-084-5(8))* Kingsley, Jessica Ltd.

Baicker-McKee, Carol. The Preschooler Problem Solver: Tackling Tough & Tricky Times with Your Three- To Four-Year-Old. 2009. (ENG.). 256p. pap. 16.95 *(978-1-56145-445-7(1))* Peachtree Pubs.

Baird, Craig. A Complete Guide for Single Dads: Everything You Need to Know about Raising Healthy, Happy Children on Your Own. 2011. (ENG.). 336p. pap. 24.95 *(978-1-60138-396-9(7))* Atlantic Publishing Co.

Baird, David. Now That You're... a Dad. 2008. (ENG., Illus.). 256p. pap. 9.95 *(978-1-84601-263-1(5)*, Spruce) Octopus Publishing Group GBR. Dist: Hachette Bk. Group.

Baird, Nicola. Homemade Kids: Thrifty, Creative & Eco-Friendly Ways to Raise Your Child. 2010. (ENG.). 278p. pap. 19.95 ***(978-0-09-192989-3(X))*** Random Hse. GBR. Dist: Independent Pubs. Group.

Balardo, Sharon L. Midnight Sailor. 2010. 20p. pap. 12.49 *(978-1-4490-9611-3(5))* AuthorHouse.

Baldock, Carole. How to Raise Confident Children. 2007. 140p. reprint ed. pap. 17.00 *(978-1-4223-6817-6(3))* DIANE Publishing Co.

Bancroft Symanski, Barbara. Successful Children: One Teacher's Viewpoint: Step by Step. 2010. (Illus.). 98p. pap. 17.95 *(978-1-936198-07-8(X))* Hillcrest Publishing Group, Inc.

Barker, Richard, ed. Making Sense of Every Child Matters: Multi-Professional Practice Guidance. 2008. (Illus.). 224p. pap. 35.95 *(978-1-84742-011-4(7))* Policy Pr. GBR. Dist: Chicago Distribution Ctr.

Barnes, Christie. The Paranoid Parents Guide: Worry Less, Parent Better, & Raise a Resilient Child. 2010. (ENG.). 264p. pap. 14.95 *(978-0-7573-1505-3(4))* Health Communications, Inc.

Barnett, Edith A. The Training of Girls for Work. reprint ed. 150.00 *(978-0-7222-1587-6(8))* Library Reprints, Inc.

Barron, Lisa. Precious in His Sight: A Mother's Journey of Faith with Her Special Needs Child. 2008. 184p. pap. 15.95 *(978-0-595-48487-4(5))* iUniverse, Inc.

Bartell, Susan. Fit & Fun Family Action Plan: 301 Things You Can Do Today. 2009. (ENG.). 384p. pap. 11.99 *(978-1-4022-2949-7(6))* Sourcebooks, Inc.

Bartkowiak, Judy. Be a Happier Parent with NLP: A Teach Yourself Guide. 2011. (Teach Yourself: General Reference Ser.). (ENG.). 256p. pap. 15.00 *(978-0-07-176955-6(2)*, 0071769552) McGraw-Hill Cos., The.

Batts, Brenda. Ready, Set, Potty! Toilet Training for Children with Autism & Other Developmental Disorders. 2010. (ENG., Illus.). 144p. pap. *(978-1-84905-833-9(4))* Kingsley, Jessica Ltd.

Bauer, William W. Stop Annoying Your Children. 2011. 272p. 47.95 ***(978-1-258-07699-3(3))*** Literary Licensing, LLC.

Bayley, Ros, et al. Help Your Young Child to Succeed: The Essential Guide for Parents of 3-5 Year Olds. 2007. (Help Your Child to Succeed Ser.). (ENG., Illus.). 96p. per. 19.95 *(978-1-85539-214-4(3)*, Network Continuum Education) Continuum International Publishing Group, Ltd. GBR. Dist: National Bk. Network.

Beach & Tyers, Alan. Gin & Juice: The Victorian Guide to Parenting. 2012. (ENG., Illus.). 160p. 14.99 ***(978-1-4088-2434-4(5)***, 109238) A & C Black GBR. Dist: Macmillan.

Bean, Shawn. Show Dad How: The Brand-New Dad's Guide to Baby's First Year. Dougherty, Elizabeth, ed. 2011. (ENG.). 144p. pap. 14.95 *(978-1-61628-111-3(1))* Weldon Owen, Inc.

Beaudet, Denyse. Dreamguider: Open the Door to Your Child's Dreams, 1 vol. 2008. (ENG., Illus.). 208p. pap. 16.95 *(978-1-57174-593-4(9))* Hampton Roads Publishing Co., Inc.

Bellamy, Richard. Catch Them after They Fall. Date not set. pap. 8.95 *(978-1-929293-03-2(8))* Whole Child Institute - WCI.

Benson, Peter L. All Kids Are Our Kids: What Communities Must Do to Raise Caring & Responsible Children & Adolescents. 2nd rev. ed. 2006. (ENG., Illus.). 448p. per. 24.95 *(978-0-7879-8518-9(X)*, Jossey-Bass) Wiley, John & Sons, Inc.

Benson, Peter L., et al. What Kids Need to Succeed: Proven, Practical Ways to Raise Good Kids (Revised & Updated 3rd Edition) 3rd ed. 2012. (ENG.). 256p. pap. 9.99 ***(978-1-57542-397-5(9))*** Free Spirit Publishing, Inc.

Bentz, Virginia. Quick Guide to Good Kids. 2007. 141p. per. 11.95 *(978-0-88391-153-2(1))* Fell, Frederick Pubs., Inc.

Berk, Brett. The Gay Uncle's Guide to Parenting: Candid Counsel from the Depths of the Daycare Trenches. 2008. (ENG., Illus.). 256p. per. 13.95 *(978-0-307-38138-5(2)*, Three Rivers Pr.) Crown Publishing Group.

Berman, Jenn. The A to Z Guide to Raising Happy, Confident Kids. 2007. (ENG.). 256p. per. 15.95 *(978-1-57731-563-6(4))* New World Library.

—SuperBaby: 12 Ways to Give Your Child a Head Start in the First 3 Years. 2011. (ENG., Illus.). 432p. pap. 16.95 *(978-1-4027-8953-3(X))* Sterling Publishing Co., Inc.

Berman, Laura & Dorling Kindersley Publishing Staff. Talking to Your Kids about Sex: Turning the Talk into a Conversation for Life. 2009. (ENG.). 1p. (gr. 12). pap. 16.95 *(978-0-7566-5738-3(5))* Dorling Kindersley Publishing, Inc.

Bernard Blue Rowell. Son I Got Your Back. 2010. 48p. pap. 9.95 *(978-1-4502-1111-6(9))* iUniverse, Inc.

Berrick, Jill Duerr & Gilbert, Neil, eds. Raising Children: Emerging Needs, Modern Risks, & Social Responses. 2008. (ENG., Illus.). 336p. pap. 24.95 *(978-0-19-531012-2(8))* Oxford Univ. Pr., Inc.

Bertelli, Yantra, et al, eds. My Baby Rides the Short Bus: The Unabashedly Human Experience of Raising Kids with Disabilities. 2009. (ENG.). 336p. pap. 20.00 *(978-1-60486-109-9(6))* PM Pr.

Best-Boss, Angie. The Everything Parent's Guide to Eating Disorders: The information plan you need to see the warning signs, help promote positive body image, & develop a recovery plan for your child. 2012. (ENG.). 288p. pap. 14.95 ***(978-1-4405-2785-2(7))*** Adams Media Corp.

Best, Frederick Ronzell. They Said I Wouldn't Make It: Born to lose but did he? Born handicapped but Is He? 2008. 336p. 34.95 *(978-1-4343-5820-2(8))* AuthorHouse.

—They Said I Wouldn't Make It: Born to Lose, but Did He? Born Handicapped, but Is He? 2008. 336p. pap. 24.95 *(978-1-4343-5821-9(6))* AuthorHouse.

Beswick, Kelly. Managing Your Toddler's Behaviour. 2009. (Teach Yourself: Relationships & Self-Help Ser.). (ENG.). 192p. pap. 14.95 *(978-0-07-159843-9(X)*, 007159843X) McGraw-Hill Cos., The.

—Tackle Your Toddler's Behaviour. 2011. (Teach Yourself Ser.). (ENG.). 284p. pap. 15.95 *(978-1-4441-0748-7(6)*, Hodder & Stoughton) Hodder General Publishing Div. GBR. Dist: Independent Pubs. Group.

Beth, Chew, Ai Mei. Siblings' Conflict in Play: How Siblings Manage Conflicts in Play. 2011. 132p. pap. ***(978-3-639-23030-7(2))*** VDM Verlag Dr. Mueller e.K.

Bialik, Mayim. Beyond the Sling: A Real-Life Guide to Raising Confident, Loving Children the Attachment Parenting Way. 2012. pap. ***(978-1-4516-6218-4(1))*** Simon & Schuster.

—Beyond the Sling: A Real-Life Guide to Raising Confident, Loving Children the Attachment Parenting Way. 2012. (ENG.). 272p. 23.99 ***(978-1-4516-1800-6(X)***, Touchstone) Touchstone.

Biddulph, Steve. The Complete Secrets of Happy Children. 2007. *(978-0-7322-8129-8(6))* HarperCollins Pubs. Australia.

—Raising Boys: Why Boys Are Different - & How to Help Them Become Happy & Well-Balanced Men. 2nd rev. ed. 2008. (ENG., Illus.). 224p. pap. 14.99 *(978-1-58761-328-9(X)*, Celestial Arts) Ten Speed Pr.

Biel, Lindsey & Peske, Nancy. Raising a Sensory Smart Child: The Definitive Handbook for Helping Your Child with Sensory Processing Issues. rev. ed. 2009. (ENG.). 464p. (gr. 12-18). 16.00 *(978-0-14-311534-2(0)*, Penguin (Non-Classics)) Penguin Group (USA) Inc.

Blaine, Kimberley. The Go-to Mom's Parents' Guide to Emotion Coaching Young Children. 2010. (ENG.). 240p. pap. 16.95 *(978-0-470-58497-2(1)*, Jossey-Bass) Wiley, John & Sons, Inc.

Block, James E. The Crucible of Consent: American Child Rearing & the Forging of Liberal Society. 2012. (ENG.). 420p. 45.00 *(978-0-674-05194-2(7))* Harvard Univ. Pr.

Blue, Ron, et al. Your Kids Can Master Their Money: Fun Ways to Help Them Learn How. 2006. (ENG., Illus.). 272p. per. 13.99 *(978-1-58997-191-2(4))* Tyndale Hse. Pubs.

Blyth, Myrna & Winston, Chriss. How to Raise an American: 1776 Fun & Easy Tools, Tips, & Activities to Help Your Child Love This Country. 2008. (ENG.). 320p. pap. 13.95 *(978-0-307-33922-5(X)*, Three Rivers Pr.) Crown Publishing Group.

Boland, Mary L. Child Support Made Easy: Your Complete Guide to Collecting, Enforcing or Terminating the Court's Order. 2nd rev. ed. 2006. (Child Support Made Easy Ser.). (ENG.). 320p. per. 18.95 *(978-1-57248-571-6(X)*, Sphinx Publishing) Sourcebooks, Inc.

Borba, Michele. The Big Book of Parenting Solutions: 101 Answers to Your Everyday Challenges & Wildest Worries. 2009. (Child Development Ser.: 1). (ENG., Illus.). 694p. pap. 19.95 *(978-0-7879-8831-9(6)*, Jossey-Bass) Wiley, John & Sons, Inc.

Borden, Marian Edelman & Schonwald, Alison D. The Everything Baby's First Year Book: The Advice You Need to Get You & Baby Through the First Twelve Months. 2nd ed. 2010. (ENG., Illus.). 304p. pap. 15.95 *(978-1-60550-368-4(1))* Adams Media Corp.

Borsellino, Chuck. Pinocchio Parenting: 21 Outrageous Lies We Tell Our Kids. 2006. (ENG.). 288p. 17.99 *(978-1-58229-572-5(7)*, Howard Bks.) Howard Books.

Bowen, Debbie. From Pampered to Productive: Raising Children Who Know How to Work. 2012. pap. 11.99 ***(978-1-4621-1019-3(3)***, Horizon Pubs.) Cedar Fort, Inc./CFI Distribution.

Bowen Shea, Sarah & Schlosberg, Suzanne. The Essential Breastfeeding Log: A Feedings Tracker & Baby-Care Organizer for Nursing Moms. 2009. (ENG.). 240p. pap. 15.00 *(978-0-345-50649-8(9)*, Ballantine Bks.) Random House Publishing Group.

Bowers, Ellen. The Everything Guide to Raising a Toddler: All You Need to Raise a Happy, Healthy, & Confident Toddler. 2011. (ENG.). 304p. pap. 15.95 *(978-1-4405-2585-8(4))* Adams Media Corp.

Bowers, Ellen. The Everything Parent's Guide to the Strong-Willed Child: A positive approach to increase self-control, improve communication, & reduce Conflict. 2nd ed. 2012. (ENG.). 304p. pap. 15.95 ***(978-1-4405-3342-6(3))*** Adams Media Corp.

Bowers, Ellen & Pickhardt, Carl E. The Everything Parent's Guide to the Strong-Willed Child. 2nd ed. 2012. E-Book ***(978-1-4405-3848-3(4))*** Adams Media Corp.

Bowkett, Steve, et al. Happy Families: Insights into the Art of Parenting. 2008. (ENG., Illus.). 152p. 19.95 *(978-1-85539-447-6(2)*, Network Continuum Education) Continuum International Publishing Group, Ltd. GBR. Dist: National Bk. Network.

Bowley, Agatha. Guiding the Normal Child. *(978-0-8022-0164-5(4))* Philosophical Library, Inc.

Bradley, Elizabeth & Emanuel, Louise. "What Can the Matter Be?" Therapeutic Interventions with Parents, Infants, & Young Children: The Work of the Tavistock Clinic under Fives Service. Bradley, Elizabeth & Emanuel, Louise, eds. 2008. (Tavistock Clinic Ser.). 320p. pap. 38.95 *(978-1-85575-340-2(5))* Karnac Bks. GBR. Dist: Stylus Publishing, LLC.

Bradshaw, Chloe. Life as a Child: Teaches us how to raise our children & re-raise ourselves to live a balanced & enlightened & joyful Life. 2008. (Illus.). 216p. pap. 19.95 *(978-0-9712271-2-5(8))* Olivia Shakespeare Publishing.

Brantley, Jamie & Duffey, Gary. Lullaby Tune: A Mother's Wish for Her Little One. 2007. (ENG., Illus.). 24p. 14.99 *(978-0-8249-5902-9(7))* Ideals Pubns.

Brawner, Jim and Suzette. Taming the Family Zoo. 2007. 172p. per. 13.99 *(978-1-60266-178-3(2))* Xulon Pr., Inc.

Breakey, Beverly M. The Blessings of Love: Wisdom for New Parents. 2009. (Illus.). 86p. pap., wbk. ed. 24.95 *(978-0-9674738-2-6(9))* Ashar Pr.

Brechter, Henry G. 101 Things to Do with Your Kids: Practical Tips for Raising Small Children. 2006. 124p. pap. 19.95 *(978-1-4241-3565-3(6))* PublishAmerica, Inc.

Brennan, Samantha & Noggle, Robert, eds. Taking Responsibility for Children. 2007. (Studies in Childhood & Family in Canada Ser.). (ENG.). 210p. pap. 42.95 *(978-1-55458-015-6(3))* Wilfrid Laurier Univ. Pr. CAN. Dist: Univ. of Toronto Pr.

Brenneman, Simone. The Castle We Called Home. 2011. 296p. 25.99 ***(978-1-4520-9856-2(5))***; pap. 16.99 ***(978-1-4520-9857-9(3))*** AuthorHouse.

Briant, Monta Z. Baby Sign Language Basics: Early Communication for Hearing Babies & Toddlers. rev. exp. ed. 2009. (ENG.). 496p. 19.95 *(978-1-4019-2159-0(0))*; (Illus.). pap. 11.95 *(978-1-4019-2160-6(4))* Hay Hse., Inc.

Bried, Erin. How to Rock Your Baby: And Other Timeless Tips for Modern Moms. 2012. (ENG., Illus.). 304p. pap. 14.99 ***(978-1-4013-2459-9(2))*** Hyperion Pr.

Briers, Stephen. How Your Child Thinks: Give Your Child the Superpowers to Be a Happy, Healthy Person. 2009. (ENG., Illus.). 272p. pap. 18.99 *(978-0-13-815674-9(3))* FT Press.

Bright Reich, Jennifer. The Babyproofing Bible: The Exceedingly Thorough Guide to Keeping Your Child Safe from Crib to Kitchen to Car to Yard. 2007. (ENG., Illus.). 240p. 14.95 *(978-1-59233-248-9(X)*, 159233248X, Fair Winds Press) Quayside.

Bristow, Jennie. Standing up to Supernanny. 2009. (ENG.). 118p. pap. 17.90 *(978-1-84540-170-2(0))* Imprint Academic GBR. Dist: Ingram Pub. Services.

Bromfield, Richard. How to Unspoil Your Child Fast: A Speedy, Complete Guide to Contented Children & Happy Parents. 2010. (ENG.). 256p. pap. 14.99 *(978-1-4022-4206-9(9))* Sourcebooks, Inc.

Bronson, Po & Merryman, Ashley. NurtureShock: New Thinking about Children. (ENG.). 352p. 2011. pap. 14.99 *(978-0-446-50413-3(0))* 2009. 24.99 *(978-0-446-50412-6(2))* Grand Central Publishing. (Twelve).

Brooks, Robert & Goldstein, Sam. Nurturing Resilience in Our Children. 2011. (ENG.). 288p. pap. 18.00 ***(978-0-07-138522-0(3)***, 0071385223) McGraw-Hill Cos., The.

Brooks, Robert & Goldstein, Sam. Raising a Self-Disciplined Child: Help Your Child Become More Responsible, Confident, & Resilient. (ENG.). 2009. 304p. pap. 15.95 *(978-0-07-162711-5(1)*, 0071627111) 2007. 288p. 22.95 *(978-0-07-141196-7(8)*, 0071411968) McGraw-Hill Cos., The.

Brooks, Yvonne. Intellectual Parenting Skills: An Instructional Guide for Parents. 2009. 224p. pap. 18.95 *(978-1-4401-5484-3(8))* iUniverse, Inc.

Browne-Miller, Angela. Raising Thinking Children & Teens: Guiding Mental & Moral Development. 1 vol. 2009. (Illus.). 204p. 39.95 *(978-0-313-35876-0(1), C35876, Praeger Pubs.)* Greenwood Publishing Group, Inc.

Brozovich, Richard. Say Goodbye to Being Shy: A Workbook to Help Kids Overcome Shyness. 2008. (Instant Help Ser.). (ENG.). 120p. (J). pap. 24.95 *(978-1-57224-668-3(5))* Play2Grow.

Bruce, Tina, et al. Child Care & Education. 5th ed. 2010. (ENG., Illus.). 696p. pap. 49.95 *(978-1-4441-1798-1(X))* Hodder Arnold Pubs.

Bruett, Terrill L. If Parenting Was Easy it Wouldn't Begin with Labor: A Practical, Common Sense Approach to Parenting. 2010. (Illus.). 209p. pap. 17.95 *(978-1-4327-5200-2(6))* Outskirts Pr., Inc.

—If Parenting was Easy it Wouldn't Begin with Labor: A Practical, Common Sense Approach to Parenting. 2010. 209p. 24.95 *(978-1-4327-5267-5(7))* Outskirts Pr., Inc.

Brundell Dc, Edmund C. Think Safe — Stay Safe: Secrets to Increase the Situational Awareness of You & Your Children. 2009. 146p. pap. 24.95 *(978-1-60836-999-7(4))* PublishAmerica, Inc.

Bullen, June P. Me! A Baby's Guide to Parenting. 2007. 88p. per. 11.95 *(978-0-595-42051-3(6))* iUniverse, Inc.

Bullivant, Jane. Skydiving for Parents: Raising Amazing Kids Without Going into Free Fall. 2007. 144p. pap. 11.99 *(978-0-8254-6124-8(3)*, Monarch Bks.) Lion Hudson PLC GBR. Dist: Kregel Pubns.

Burke, Ray, et al. Common Sense Parenting: Using Your Head as Well as Your Heart to Raise School-Aged Children. 3rd ed. 2006. (Illus.). 289p. per. 14.95 *(978-1-889322-70-4(9))* Boys Town Pr.

Burt, Sandra & Perlis, Linda. Raising a Successful Child: Discover & Nurture Your Child's Talents. 2006. (ENG., Illus.). 272p. per. 14.95 *(978-1-56975-564-8(7))* Ulysses Pr.

Byrd, Sophia A. Mommy & Daddy, Why! 2011. 58p. pap. 15.99 ***(978-1-4568-5226-9(4))*** Xlibris Corp.

Byron, Tanya. The House of Tiny Tearaways. 2006. (ENG., Illus.). 160p. (C). pap. *(978-0-563-52036-8(1))* Pearson Education Canada.

—Your Toddler Month by Month: Your Essential Guide to the First 4 Years. 2008. (ENG., Illus.). 320p. (gr. 12). pap. 19.95 *(978-0-7566-3360-8(5))* Dorling Kindersley Publishing, Inc.

Calhoun, Ada. Instinctive Parenting: Trusting Ourselves to Raise Good Kids. 2010. (ENG.). 288p. pap. 15.00 *(978-1-4391-9580-2(3))*; (Illus.). 23.00 *(978-1-4391-5729-9(4))* Gallery Pr., The IRL. Dist: Simon & Schuster, Inc.

Call Essert, Priscilla. MY LIFE AS A PANCREAS: Reflections on Raising a Child with Diabetes. 2007. 72p. pap. 15.00 *(978-1-4303-0521-7(5))* Lulu Enterprises Inc.

Callahan Iii, Joseph J. Parenting for Crisis Avoidance: Discover 22 Powerful, Practical, Parenting Tips & 101 Tools Used to Rear Responsible Children. 2011. 250p. 29.99 ***(978-1-4500-6852-9(9))***; pap. 19.99 ***(978-1-4500-6851-2(0))*** Xlibris Corp.

Cammilleri, Oona Elisabeth. 101 Things I Wish I Had Known about Raising a Baby. 2009. 130p. pap. 10.95 *(978-1-60860-599-6(X)*, Eloquent Bks.) AEG Literary Publishing Services, Inc.

Carey, Seamus. Growing up with Your Children: 7 Turning Points in the Lives of Parents. 2009. (ENG.). 176p. 40.00 *(978-1-4422-0096-8(0))* Rowman & Littlefield Publishers, Inc.

Carey, Tanith. How to Be an Amazing Mum When You Just Don't Have the Time: The Ultimate Handbook for Hassled Mothers. 2009. (ENG., Illus.). 192p. pap. 14.95 *(978-0-7459-5375-5(1))* Lion Hudson PLC GBR. Dist: Independent Pubs. Group.

Carey, Tanith. Where Has My Little Girl Gone? How to Protect Your Daughter from Growing up Too Soon. 2011. (ENG.). 192p. pap. 14.95 ***(978-0-7459-5542-1(8))*** Lion Hudson PLC GBR. Dist: Independent Pubs. Group.

Carlsson-Paige, Nancy. Taking Back Childhood: A Proven Roadmap for Raising Confident, Creative, Compassionate Kids. 2009. (ENG.). 304p. (gr. 12-18). 16.00 *(978-0-452-29029-9(0)*, Plume) Penguin Group (USA) Inc.

Carter, Christine. Raising Happiness: 10 Simple Steps for More Joyful Kids & Happier Parents. 2011. (ENG., Illus.). 256p. pap. 15.00 *(978-0-345-51562-9(5)*, Ballantine Bks.) Random House Publishing Group.

Carter, William Lee. Putting Humpty Dumpty Back Together: Parenting a Distressed Child. 2009. 176p. pap. 15.00 *(978-0-9841080-0-8(9))* Restoration Pubns.

Cattanach, Lynoa. Be a Greener Parent. 2011. (Teach Yourself Ser.). (ENG.). 240p. pap. 19.95 *(978-1-4441-0386-1(5)*, Hodder & Stoughton) Hodder General Publishing Div. GBR. Dist: Independent Pubs. Group.

Causland, Gladys E. Five Generations of Life, Strife, Spice. 2011. 248p. 46.95 ***(978-1-258-06996-4(2))*** Literary Licensing, LLC.

Chand, Elise Gaston. A Parent's Guide to Riding Lessons: Everything You Need to Know to Survive & Thrive with a Horse-Loving Kid. 2009. (ENG., Illus.). 179p. pap. 14.95 *(978-1-60342-447-9(4)*, 1603424474) Workman Publishing Co., Inc.

Chansky, Tamar E. Freeing Your Child from Negative Thinking: Powerful, Practical Strategies to Build a Lifetime of Resilience, Flexibility, & Happiness. 2008. (ENG.). 336p. pap. 15.95 *(978-0-7382-1185-5(0))* Da Capo Pr., Inc.

Chiem, David Phu An, et al. Pre-School Parenting Secrets: Talking with the Sky. 2010. (Illus.). 200p. (J). 28.00 *(978-981-4317-09-2(8))* World Scientific Publishing Co., Inc.

Child, Lydia Maria. Mothers Book. 2006. 180p. per. *(978-1-4067-9578-3(X)*, Pierides Pr.) Read Bks.

Christian, Christina. Re-Engaging the Village. 2009. 100p. pap. 15.99 *(978-1-4363-7140-7(6))* Xlibris Corp.

Chua, Amy. Battle Hymn of the Tiger Mother. 2011. (ENG.). 256p. (gr. 12). 16.00 ***(978-0-14-312058-2(1)***, Penguin (Non-Classics)); (Illus.). 25.95 *(978-1-59420-284-1(2)*, Penguin Pr. HC, The) Penguin Group (USA) Inc.

Clark, Megan. Today's Toddler: Things We Worry about (but Probably Shouldn't) 2009. pap. 9.99 *(978-1-60799-451-0(8))* Tate Publishing & Enterprises, LLC.

Clawson, Susan. Parent/Teen Stories. 2009. 324p. 29.50 *(978-1-60693-671-9(9)*, Strategic Bk. Publishing) AEG Literary Publishing Services, Inc.

Colburn, Kerry & Sorensen, Rob. Mama's Big Book of Little Lifesavers: 398 Ways to Save Your Time, Money & Sanity. 2011. (ENG., Illus.). 224p. 14.95 *(978-0-8118-7854-7(3))* Chronicle Bks. LLC.

Coles, Roberta. Best Kept Secret: Single Black. 2010. (ENG.). 180p. pap. 24.95 *(978-0-7425-6426-8(6))* Rowman & Littlefield Publishers, Inc.

Coles, Roberta L. The Best Kept Secret: Single Black Fathers. 2009. (ENG.). 180p. 37.50 *(978-0-7425-6425-1(8))* Rowman & Littlefield Publishers, Inc.

Connole, Marika Lee. Out of the Mouths of Babes: A Little Book of Sunshine. 2010. 165p. pap. 12.95 *(978-1-4357-3074-8(7))* Lulu Enterprises Inc.

Contey, Carrie & Takikawa DC, Debby. Calms: A Guide to Soothing Your Baby. 2007. (Illus.). 96p. pap. 12.00 *(978-0-9768735-2-5(4))* Hana Peace Works.

Converse, Judy. Special-Needs Kids Eat Right: Strategies to Help Kids on the Autism Spectrum Focus, Learn, & Thrive. 2009. (ENG.). 304p. (gr. 12-18). pap. 15.95 *(978-0-399-53488-1(1)*, Perigee Trade) Penguin Group (USA) Inc.

Cooper, Aaron & Keitel, Eric. I Just Want My Kids to Be Happy! Why You Shouldn't Say It, Why You Shouldn't Think It, What You Should Embrace Instead. 2007. (Illus.). 173p. per. *(978-0-9797926-0-1(6)*, Late August Pr.) Ace Coupay Publishing.

Cooper, Carol. Baby & Toddles Essentials. 2008. (ENG., Illus.). 112p *(978-1-84597-604-0(5))* CICO Bks.

Cooper, Colin. A Dad's Guide to Babycare. 2011. (ENG., Illus.). 128p. pap. 18.95 *(978-1-904760-56-6(2))* Carroll & Brown Pubs., Ltd. GBR. Dist: Independent Pubs. Group.

Corkhill, Melissa. Green Parenting: Healthy Choices for Your Family & the Planet. 2009. (Green Essentials Ser.). (Illus.). 128p. pap. 12.95 *(978-1-4027-4892-9(2))* Sterling Publishing Co., Inc.

Cosby, Bill & Poussaint, Alvin F. Come on People: On the Path from Victims to Victors, 0 vols. 2009. 288p. pap. 14.99 *(978-1-59555-186-3(7))* Nelson, Thomas Inc.

Coulthard, Sally. The Parents' Book of Checklists: From Pregnancy to Toddlers. 2006. (ENG.). 208p. (C). pap. *(978-1-4066-1205-9(7))* Pearson Education Canada.

—The Parents' Book of Checklists: From Toddlers to Teenagers. 2007. (ENG.). 192p. pap. 33.50 *(978-0-273-71279-4(9))* Pearson Education, Ltd. GBR. Dist: Trans-Atlantic Pubns., Inc.

Couser, Tom. Parenting Without Guilt: AVOIDING 7 Things Parents Do to Screw-up Their Kids. 2009. 144p. pap. 14.95 *(978-1-4327-4031-3(8))* Outskirts Pr., Inc.

Cox, Martyn. New Father's Survival Guide. 2010. (ENG., Illus.). 112p. *(978-1-84597-955-3(9))* Ryland Peters & Small.

Craker, Lorilee. Loving Life with Your Preschooler. 2008. 208p. 5.99 *(978-0-8007-8776-9(5))* Revell.

Cram101 Textbook Reviews. Outlines & Highlights for Child in the Family, School & Community: The Teachers Working with Families by Janet Gonzalez-Mena, ISBN. 2011. 98p. pap. 27.95 ***(978-1-61812-325-1(4))*** Cram101 Inc.

Cram101 Textbook Reviews. Outlines & Highlights for Parent & Child Relations by Heath, Isbn: 0131596764. 2010. 140p. pap. 28.95 *(978-1-61698-854-8(1))* Cram101 Inc.

Cram101 Textbook Reviews & Cram101 Textbook Reviews. Outlines & Highlights for Positive Child Guidance by Darla Ferris Miller, Isbn: 9781435418592. 2011. 218p. pap. 30.95 ***(978-1-61744-290-2(9))*** Cram101 Inc.

Cram101 Textbook Reviews Staff. Outlines & Highlights for Child's World: Infancy through Adolescence by Papalia, ISBN. 2008. 316p. per. 15.95 *(978-1-4288-5781-0(8))* Cram101 Inc.

—Outlines & Highlights for Parent & Child Relations by Heath, Isbn: 0131596764. 2009. 112p. pap. 24.95 *(978-1-4288-6696-6(5))* Cram101 Inc.

Crawford, Catherine. The Highly Intuitive Child: A Guide to Understanding & Parenting Unusually Sensitive & Empathic Children. 2009. (ENG.). 264p. pap. 15.95 *(978-0-89793-509-8(8))* Hunter Hse., Inc.

Crawford, Kelinda. Supermom. 2007. 106p. pap. 16.95 *(978-1-4241-9389-9(3))* PublishAmerica, Inc.

Crittenden, Patricia McKinsey. Raising Parents: Attachment, Parenting & Child Safety. 2011. (ENG., Illus.). 400p. pap. 53.95 *(978-1-84392-498-2(6))* Routledge.

Curtis, Steven E. Understanding Your Child's Puzzling Behavior: A Guide for Parents of Children with Behavioral, Social, & Learning Challenges. 2008. (Illus.). 160p. per. 14.95 *(978-0-9794982-0-6(1))* Lifespan Pr.

Damon, William. The Path to Purpose: How Young People Find Their Calling in Life. 2009. (ENG.). 240p. pap. 15.99 *(978-1-4165-3724-3(4)*, Free Pr.) Free Pr.

Dathan A. Paterno, Psy. D. Desperately Seeking Parents: Why Your Child Needs a Parent in Charge & How to Become One. 2010. 172p. 30.95 *(978-1-4497-0018-8(7))*; pap. 13.95 *(978-1-4497-0017-1(9))* Author Solutions, Inc. (WestBow Pr.).

DAversa, Oreste. Empowering Your Children in the New Millennium: Practical Tools for Children, Parents & Teachers. 2007. (YA). ring bd. *(978-0-9762561-0-6(X))* Cutting Edge Technology Publishing.

Davidson, Kimberly. Torn Between Two Masters: Encouraging Teens to Live Authentically in a Celebrity-Obsessed World. 2011. pap. 21.99 ***(978-1-61777-348-8(4))*** Tate Publishing & Enterprises, LLC.

Davies, Kim. Caring for Your Toddler: Raising Your Child the Way Nature Intended. 2008. (ENG., Illus.). 96p. pap. 14.99 *(978-1-84476-482-2(5))* Anness Publishing GBR. Dist: National Bk. Network.

—Natural Baby Care: Raising Your Child the Way Nature Intended. 2008. (ENG., Illus.). 160p. pap. 18.99 *(978-1-84476-365-8(X))* Anness Publishing GBR. Dist: National Bk. Network.

Davis, Susan & Eppler-Wolff, Nancy Jo. Raising Children Who Soar: A Guide to Healthy Risk-Taking in an Uncertain World. (ENG., Illus.). 208p. 2010. 52.00 *(978-0-8077-4998-2(2))* 2009. pap. 21.95 *(978-0-8077-4997-5(4))* Teachers College Pr., Teachers College, Columbia Univ.

Davis, Susan Elisabeth, et al. Play & Learn: 1001 Fun Activities for Your Baby & Child. 2008. (Gymboree Play & Music Ser.). (ENG., Illus.). 240p. pap. 24.95 *(978-1-55470-033-2(7))* Key Porter Bks. CAN. Dist: Perseus-PGW.

Day, Jerry. How to Raise Kids You Want to Keep: The Proven Discipline Program Your Kids Will Love (and That Really Works!) 2006. (ENG., Illus.). 320p. per. 14.95 *(978-1-4022-0745-7(X))* Sourcebooks, Inc.

Deacon, Caroline. Boost Your Baby's Development. 2011. (Teach Yourself Ser.). (ENG.). 250p. pap. 14.95 *(978-1-4441-0304-5(0)*, Hodder & Stoughton) Hodder General Publishing Div. GBR. Dist: Independent Pubs. Group.

—Teach Yourself Your Baby's Development. 2008. (Teach Yourself Ser.). (ENG.). 192p. pap. 16.00 *(978-0-07-154501-3(8)*, 0071545018) McGraw-Hill Cos., The.

—Your Toddler's Development. 2008. (Teach Yourself: Parenting Ser.). (ENG.). 192p. pap. 12.95 *(978-0-07-158314-5(9)*, 0071583149) McGraw-Hill Cos., The.

Deerwester, Karen. The Entitlement-Free Child: Positive Parenting Solutions for Raising Confident & Respectful Kids. 2009. (ENG.). 224p. pap. 14.99 *(978-1-4022-1510-0(X))* Sourcebooks, Inc.

Dehrer, Gary P. Building a Championship Family: Coaching Kids Values & Instilling Character. 2007. (ENG., Illus.). 224p. per. 15.95 *(978-0-88282-299-0(3))*; 234p. per. 15.95 *(978-0-88282-285-3(3))* New Horizon Pr. Pubs., Inc.

Dimerman, Sara. Character Is the Key: How to Unlock the Best in Our Children & Ourselves. 2009. (ENG.). 272p. pap. 19.95 *(978-0-470-15560-8(4)*, Wiley) Wiley, John & Sons, Inc.

Discovery House Publishers Staff, et al. Cherish: Quiet Moments for Moms - Strength for the Soul from Our Daily Bread. 2007. (Strength for the Soul from Our Daily Bread Ser.). (ENG.). 128p. pec. 5.99 *(978-1-57293-260-9(0))* Discovery Hse. Pubs.

Dobbins, Amanda. The Baby File: All the Lists, Forms, & Practical Information You Need Before-And After-Baby's Arrival. 2008. (ENG., Illus.). 224p. 17.95 *(978-0-7624-2735-2(3)*, Running Pr.) Running Pr. Bk. Pubs.

Dobson, James C. The New Strong-Willed Child. rev. ed. 2007. (ENG., Illus.). 288p. per. 14.99 *(978-1-4143-1363-4(2))* Tyndale Hse. Pubs.

—Parenting Isn't for Cowards: The "You Can Do It" Guide for Hassled Parents. 2007. (ENG.). 240p. per. 14.99 *(978-1-4143-1746-5(8))* Tyndale Hse. Pubs.

Doman, Glenn & Doman, Janet. How to Teach Your Baby to Read: The Gentle Revolution. 2006. (How to Teach Your Baby to Read Ser.). (ENG., Illus.). 288p. pap. 13.95 *(978-0-7570-0185-7(8))* Square One Pubs.

Dorling Kindersley Publishing Staff. Baby & Child Healthcare Everything You Need to Know. 2012. (ENG., Illus.). 224p. 14.95 *(978-0-7566-8975-9(9))* Dorling Kindersley Publishing, Inc.

—Baby Day by Day. 2012. (ENG.). 432p. 40.00 ***(978-0-7566-8985-8(6))*** Dorling Kindersley Publishing, Inc.

Dougherty, Dale. Discipline of Yesteryear: The Way America Used to Raise Its Children... & Should Again. 2007. per. *(978-0-9791893-2-6(2))*, Wooden Spoon Publishing.

Dowokpor, Irene B. (Nee' Tettey). My Child. 2010. 78p. 24.99 *(978-1-4535-3076-4(2))*; pap. 15.99 *(978-1-4535-3075-7(4))* Xlibris Corp.

Druckerman, Pamela. Bringing up Bébé: One American Mother Discovers the Wisdom of French Parenting. 2012. (ENG.). 304p. (gr. 12). 25.95 ***(978-1-59420-333-6(4)***, Penguin Pr. HC, The) Penguin Group (USA) Inc.

Duggar, Michelle & Duggar, Jim Bob. A Love That Multiplies: An Up-Close View of How They Make It Work. 2011. (ENG., Illus.). 288p. 19.99 *(978-1-4391-8381-6(3)*, Howard Bks.) Howard Books.

Dupanloup, F. T. lix. The Child Tr by Kate Anderson. 2006. 300p. per. 23.99 *(978-1-4255-2828-7(7))* MPublishing.

Eden, Alvin. Positive Parenting: Raising Healthy Children from Birth to Three Years. 2007. (ENG., Illus.). 288p. pap. 15.95 *(978-1-57826-252-6(6)*, Hatherleigh Pr.) Hatherleigh Co., Ltd., The.

Edwards, Carol. Why Jeffrey? Why Us? 2010. pap. 8.99 *(978-1-61663-113-0(9))* Tate Publishing & Enterprises, LLC.

Ehrensaft, Diane. Gender Born, Gender Made: Raising Healthy Gender-Nonconforming Children. 2011. (ENG.). 304p. pap. 16.95 *(978-1-61519-001-0(5)*, 1615190015) Experiment LLC, The.

Eisen, Andrew R. & Engler, Linda B. Helping Your Child Overcome Separation Anxiety or School Refusal: A Step-by-Step Guide for Parents. 2006. (ENG.). 216p. per. 16.95 *(978-1-57224-431-3(3))* New Harbinger Pubns.

Eisenberg, Arlene, et al. El Primer Ano del Bebe. (SPA.). pap. 20.00 *(978-958-04-3438-2(7)*, NR9004) Norma S.A. COL. Dist: Distribuidora Norma, Inc.

Elkind, David. Hurried Child: Growing up Too Fast Too Soon. 25th anniv. ed. 2006. (ENG.). 288p. pap. 16.95 *(978-0-7382-1082-7(X))* Da Capo Pr., Inc.

Ellis, Maria. Night Song for a Firstborn. 2011. 96p. pap. 9.99 ***(978-1-4520-6826-8(7))*** AuthorHouse.

Emery, Betty. Respect, Responsibility & Reverence. 2010. 28p. pap. 13.95 *(978-1-4497-0150-5(7)*, WestBow Pr.) Author Solutions, Inc.

Enrique G. Macias. Abc's = about Basic Child Care: A Parent's Handbook of Pediatric Information. 2009. 88p. pap. 19.00 *(978-1-4389-3556-0(0))* AuthorHouse.

Ensher, Gail L. & Clark, David A. Relationship-Centered Practices in Early Childhood: Working with Families, Infants, & Young Children at Risk. 2011. (Illus.). 248p. pap. 34.95 ***(978-1-59857-059-5(5))*** Brookes, Paul H. Publishing Co.

Envision-U. You're Having A Wonderful Childhood: The Stressed Parents Guide to Raising Great Children. 2007. (Illus.). 146p. pap. 16.99 *(978-0-9792620-2-9(X))* Invictus International.

Erwin, Cheryl L. The Everything Parent's Guide to Raising Boys: A Complete Handbook to Develop Confidence, Promote Self-Esteem, & Improve Communication. 2nd ed. 2010. (ENG.). 304p. pap. 14.95 *(978-1-4405-0689-5(2))* Adams Media Corp.

Esolen, Anthony. Ten ways to destroy the imagination of your Child. 2010. (ENG.). 320p. 26.95 *(978-1-935191-88-9(8))* ISI Bks.

Esquith, Rafe. Lighting Their Fires: How Parents & Teachers Can Raise Extraordinary Kids in a Mixed-Up, Muddled-Up, Shook-Up World. 2010. (ENG.). 208p. (gr. 12). 15.00 *(978-0-14-311766-7(1)*, Penguin (Non-Classics)) Penguin Group (USA) Inc.

Etelson, Erica. For Our Own Good: the Politics of Parenting in an Ailing Society. 2010. 377p. pap. 19.99 *(978-0-557-27780-3(9))* Lulu Enterprises Inc.

Eugene N. Smith. Songs of Life. 2010. 112p. 22.95 *(978-1-4502-1603-6(X))*; pap. 12.95 *(978-1-4502-1601-2(3))* iUniverse, Inc.

Everly, George S., Jr. The Resilient Child: Seven Essential Lessons for Your Child's Happiness & Success. 2008. (ENG.). 160p. pap. 14.95 *(978-0-9793564-5-2(8))* DiaMed, LLC.

Ewing, Baylisia. I Am American: From the I AM Collection of Books. 2011. 24p. pap. 11.99 ***(978-1-4634-0422-2(0))*** AuthorHouse.

Eybergen, Dyan. Out of the Mouths of Babes: Parenting from a Child's Perspective. 2011. 148p. pap. 12.95 ***(978-1-936236-57-2(5))*** iUniverse, Inc.

Eyre, Linda & Eyre, Richard. The Entitlement Trap: How to Rescue Your Child with a New Family System of Choosing, Earning, & Ownership. 2011. (ENG.). 256p. (gr. 12). pap. 18.00 *(978-1-58333-415-7(7)*, Avery) Penguin Group (USA) Inc.

Eyre, Richard & Eyre, Linda. 5 Spiritual Solutions for Everyday Parenting Challenges. 2011. 208p. 19.99 *(978-1-60641-933-5(1))* Deseret Bk. Co.

Ezzo, Gary. On Becoming Babywise: Giving Your Infant the Gift of Nighttime Sleep. 5th ed. 2012. (Illus.). 280p. pap. 13.95 ***(978-1-932740-13-4(9))*** Parent-Wise Solutions, Inc.

Ezzo, Gary & Bucknam, Robert. On Becoming Baby Wise: Giving Your Infant the Gift of Nighttime Sleep. 2006. (On Becoming... Ser.). (Illus.). 252p. per. 13.95 *(978-1-932740-08-0(2))* Parent-Wise Solutions, Inc.

Fabiano, Jennifer L. Savor the Love: Capturing the Moments that Matter Most. 2010. 108p. pap. 11.95 *(978-1-4497-0162-8(0)*, WestBow Pr.) Author Solutions, Inc.

Fairchild, Penelope. Tips from a British Nanny: Tried & Tested Advice. 2009. (ENG., Illus.). 96p. 9.95 *(978-1-57324-416-9(3)*, Conari Pr.) Red Wheel/Weiser.

Fassa, Lynda. Green Kids, Sage Families: The Ultimate Guide to Raising Your Organic Kids. 2009. (ENG.). 272p. (gr. 12-18). 15.00 *(978-0-451-22581-8(3)*, N A L Trade) Penguin Group (USA) Inc.

Faull, Jan & McLean Oliver, Jennifer. Amazing Minds: The Science of Nurturing Your Child's Developing Mind with Games, Activites & More. 2010. (ENG.). 368p. (gr. 12). 15.00 *(978-0-425-23224-8(7)*, Berkley Trade) Penguin Group (USA) Inc.

Favaro, Peter J. Smart Parenting During & after Divorce: The Essential Guide to Making Divorce Easier on Your Child. 2008. (ENG.). 256p. pap. 16.95 *(978-0-07-159755-5(7)*, 0071597557) McGraw-Hill Cos., The.

Fay, Charles. From Bad Grades to a Great Life! Unlocking the Mystery of Achievement for Your Child. 2011. xiv, 146p. pap. 17.95 ***(978-1-935326-08-3(2))*** Love & Logic Institute, Inc.

Fay, Charles. Parenting Kids - To Become the People Employers Really Want and... America Desperately Needs! 2008. pap. 17.95 *(978-1-930429-96-3(7))* Love & Logic Institute, Inc.

Fay, Jim & Billings, Dawn L. From Innocence to Entitlement: A Love & Logic Cure for the Tragedy of Entitlement. 2010. 140p. per. 17.95 *(978-1-930429-74-1(6))* Love & Logic Institute, Inc.

Fay, Jim & Fay, Charles. Love & Logic Powder Room Reader. 2009. pap. 11.95 *(978-1-935326-05-2(8))* Love & Logic Institute, Inc.

Fay, Jim & Leatherman, Kristan. Love & Logic Money-Isms: Wise Words about Raising Money-Smart Kids. 2009. 144p. pap. 6.95 *(978-1-935326-01-4(5))* Love & Logic Institute, Inc.

—Millionaire Babies or Bankrupt Brats? Love & Logic Solutions to Teaching Kids about Money. 2008. 480p. pap. 24.95 *(978-1-930429-95-6(9))* Love & Logic Institute, Inc.

Ferre, Whitney. 33 Things to Know about Raising Creative Kids. 2010. (Good Things to Know Ser.). (ENG.). 148p. pap. 9.99 *(978-1-59652-562-7(2))* Turner Publishing Co.

Fertig, Carol. Raising a Gifted Child: A Parenting Success Handbook. 2008. (ENG.). 225p. pap. 16.95 *(978-1-59363-344-8(0))* Prufrock Pr.

C

Fields, Denise & Brown, Ari. Baby 411: Clear Answers & Smart Advice for Your Baby's First Year. 5th rev. ed. 2011. (ENG.). 576p. pap. 14.95 (978-1-889392-41-7(3)) Windsor Peak Pr.

—Toddler 411: Clear Answers & Smart Advice for Your Toddler. 3rd rev. ed. 2010. (ENG.). 576p. pap. 14.95 (978-1-889392-38-7(3)) Windsor Peak Pr.

Fine, Jeffrey L. The Art of Conscious Parenting. 2009. (ENG.). 1p. pap. 16.95 (978-1-59477-322-8(X), Healing Arts Pr.) Inner Traditions International, Ltd.

Fisher, Kay. Early Years Daily Diary. 2011. 428p. pap. 23.95 (978-1-4389-4160-8(9)) AuthorHouse.

Fishman, Nancy. Raising Happy Children after Divorce: What to Do When Children Have Divorce Stress. 2010. (ENG.). 96p. pap. 9.95 (978-1-879094-89-5(4)) Momentum Bks., LLC.

Fister, Jeff. Counting Chickens: Raising 8 kids & 4 hens in the City. 2009. 168p. pap. 13.95 (978-1-891442-50-6(3)) Virginia Publishing Corp.

Fitness (Adam Shafran) and the Fat Guy (Lee Kantor). 35 Things to Know to Raise Active Kids. 2010. (Good Things to Know Ser.). (ENG.). 144p. pap. 9.99 (978-1-59652-587-0(8)) Turner Publishing Co.

Flais, Shelly Vaziri. Raising Twins: From Pregnancy to Preschool, Advice from a Pediatrician-Mom of Twins. 2009. 200p. pap. 14.95 (978-1-58110-344-1(1)) American Academy of Pediatrics.

Fletcher, Janice M. Grooming for Greatness: Preparing Children for Academic Excellence. 2009. 100p. pap. 10.49 (978-1-4389-0618-8(8)) AuthorHouse.

Fletcher, Kale Pearl. The Waiting Room. 2009. 348p. 29.99 (978-1-4415-4523-7(9)); pap. 19.99 (978-1-4415-4522-0(0)) Xlibris Corp.

Folbre, Nancy. Valuing Children: Rethinking the Economics of the Family. 2010. (Family & Public Policy Ser.). (Illus.). 248p. pap. 21.95 (978-0-674-04727-3(3)) Harvard Univ. Pr.

Fontana, Gina. Child Growth & Development. rev. ed. 2007. (ENG.). 86p. spiral bd. 60.00 (978-0-7575-4686-0(2)) Kendall Hunt Publishing Co.

Ford, Patricia, creator. Your First Year. 2006. 26.00 (978-0-8059-7034-0(7)) Dorrance Publishing Co., Inc.

Forehand, Rex & Long, Nicholas. Parenting the Strong-Willed Child: The Clinically Proven Five-Week Program for Parents of Two- To Six-Year-Olds. 3rd ed. 2010. (ENG., Illus.). 288p. pap. 16.95 (978-0-07-166782-1(2), 0071667822) McGraw-Hill Cos., The.

Fox, Jenifer. Your Child's Strengths: A Guide for Parents & Teachers. 2009. (ENG.). 368p. (gr. 12-18). 16.00 (978-0-14-311517-5(0), Penguin (Non-Classics)) Penguin Group (USA) Inc.

Fox, Louisa Lane. Love to the Little Ones: The Trials & Triumphs of Parents Through the Ages in Letters, Diaries, Memoirs & Essays. 2009. (ENG., Illus.). 304p. 24.95 (978-0-7112-2940-2(6)) Lincoln, Frances Ltd. GBR. Dist: Perseus-PGW.

Fraker, Cheri, et al. Food Chaining: The Proven 6-Step Plan to Stop Picky Eating, Solve Feeding Problems, & Expand Your Child's Diet. 2007. (ENG.). 416p. pap. 15.95 (978-1-60094-016-3(1)) Da Capo Pr., Inc.

Frankenstein, Diane W. Reading Together: Everything You Need to Know to Raise a Child Who Loves to Read. 2009. (ENG., Illus.). 288p. (gr. 12-18). 15.00 (978-0-399-53524-6(1), Perigee Trade) Penguin Group (USA) Inc.

Frantz, Rodgers & Frantz, Marc. The Yes Child. 2009. 104p. pap. 14.95 (978-1-59858-966-5(0)) Dog Ear Publishing, LLC.

Fraser, Bonnie Beth. Consider This Before Having a Child: Child Rearing Seeds for Thought. 2008. (ENG., Illus.). 139p. pap. 12.00 (978-0-9777851-0-0(6)) Publishing God'S Way.

Fried-Buchalter, Sharon. Children Are People Too: Unlocking the Secrets to a Happier Child & a Happier You. 2007. 408p. 24.95 (978-0-9791202-0-6(9)) People Too Unlimited.

Friedman, Jeremy. The Toddler Care Book: A Complete Guide from 1 to 5 Years Old. 2009. (ENG., Illus.). 448p. pap. 29.95 (978-0-7788-0214-3(0)) Rose, Robert Inc. CAN. Dist: Firefly Bks., Ltd.

Frost, Jo. Jo Frost's Confident Baby Care: What You Need to Know for the First Year from America's Most Trusted Nanny. 2008. (Illus.). 256p. pap. 15.95 (978-1-4013-0906-0(2)) Hyperion Pr.

Gallagher, Rosina & Webb, James. Educando Hijos Exitosos. 2009. (SPA.). 48p. 9.95 (978-0-910707-91-6(X)) Great Potential Pr., Inc.

Gans, Joshua. Parentonomics: An Economist Dad Looks at Parenting. (ENG.). 256p. (gr. 17). 2010. pap. 12.95 (978-0-262-51497-2(4)) 2009. 22.95 (978-0-262-01278-2(2)) MIT Pr.

Gao, Minghui. The Ethical Discourse of Chinese Children: A Narrative Approach to the Social & Moral Intricacy of Lying about Good Deeds. 2010. (Illus.). iv, 174p. 99.95 (978-0-7734-3632-9(4)) Mellen, Edwin Pr., The.

Gedeon-Gaude, R. Felice. Raising the Future: Practical Parenting for Practicing Parents. 2011. 108p. 22.95 (978-1-4502-4587-6(0)); pap. 12.95 (978-1-4502-4586-9(2)) iUniverse, Inc.

Gerard, Robert V. Icon Power for Kids: Quick-Fix Resolution of Problems for Kids Ages 8-10 Years. 2009. (J). pap. (978-1-880666-17-3(0)) Oughten Hse. Foundation, Inc.

Gibson, Andrew D. Got an Angry Kid? Parenting Spike, a Seriously Difficult Child. 2009. 188p. pap. (978-1-932690-89-7(1)) Loving Healing Pr., Inc.

Gillman, Claire. Green Guide to Bringing Up Your Baby. 2009. (ENG., Illus.). 160p. (978-1-906525-97-2(8)) Ryland Peters & Small.

Gilman, Charlotte Perkins. Concerning Children. 2009. 316p. 36.99 (978-1-113-66552-2(1)) 2009. 316p. 32.99 (978-1-113-66551-5(3)) 2009. 316p. pap. 29.75 (978-1-113-66547-8(5)) 2009. 308p. 32.99 (978-1-110-27102-3(6)) 2009. 308p. pap. 28.75 (978-1-110-27095-8(X)) 2008. 308p. 28.99 (978-0-559-25498-7(9)) 2008. 308p. pap. 28.75 (978-0-559-25496-3(2)) BiblioBazaar.

—Concerning Children. 2009. 120p. pap. (978-0-217-91859-6(X)) Books LLC.

—Concerning Children. 2007. (ENG.). 304p. 43.95 (978-0-548-33408-9(0)); 308p. per. 28.95 (978-1-4326-9309-1(3)) Kessinger Publishing, LLC.

Gimre, Amy. If I Could. 2009. 20p. pap. 12.99 (978-1-4389-7018-9(8)) AuthorHouse.

Ginott, Haim G. Entre Padres E Hijos: Un Clásico Que Revoluciono la Comunicacion con Nuestros Hijos. 2007. (Vintage Espanol Ser.). (ENG & SPA.). 288p. pap. 13.95 (978-0-307-27890-6(5), Vintage) Knopf Doubleday Publishing Group.

Ginsburg, Kenneth R. Building Resilience in Children & Teens: Giving Kids Roots & Wings. 2nd ed. 2011. (ENG.). 358p. (J). pap. 15.95 (978-1-58110-551-3(7)) American Academy of Pediatrics.

Giordani, Tania. All Children Are Our Children. 2009. 188p. pap. (978-3-639-02154-7(1)) VDM Verlag Dr. Mueller e.K.

Gipson, Cynthia. Parenting Practices of Lesbian Mothers. 2009. 190p. pap. (978-3-639-11714-1(X)) VDM Verlag Dr. Mueller e.K.

Glass, Cathy. Happy Kids: The Secrets to Raising Well-Behaved, Contented Children. 2010. (ENG.). 288p. (J). 12.95 (978-0-00-733925-9(9)) HarperCollins Pubs. Ltd. GBR. Dist: Independent Pubs. Group.

Gloden, Lynn "Raynee". Raising Kids by the Book. 2008. 156p. pap. 14.95 (978-0-9790221-3-5(4)) YAV.

Glover, Leland E. How to Give Your Child a Good Start in Life. 2011. 224p. 44.95 (978-1-258-07953-6(4)) Literary Licensing, LLC.

Godfrey, Neale S. & Edwards, Carolina. Money Doesn't Grow on Trees: A Parent's Guide to Raising Financially Responsible Children. rev. ed. 2006. (ENG., Illus.). 192p. pap. 14.99 (978-0-7432-8780-7(0), Touchstone) Touchstone.

Gold, Claudia M. Keeping Your Child in Mind: Overcoming Defiance, Tantrums, & Other Everyday Behavior Problems by Seeing the World Through Your Child's Eyes. 2011. (Merloyd Lawrence Book Ser.). (ENG.). 240p. pap. 15.00 (978-0-7382-1485-6(X)) Da Capo Pr., Inc.

Goldstein, Robin S. New Baby Answer Book: From Birth to Kindergarten, Answers to the Top 150 Questions about Raising a Young Child. 2nd ed. 2009. (ENG.). 288p. pap. 14.99 (978-1-4022-1827-9(3)) Sourcebooks, Inc.

Gonzalez-Mena, Janet. Child, Family, & Community: Family-Centered Early Care & Education. 5th ed. 2011. (ENG.). pap. 77.33 (978-0-558-85223-8(8)) Pearson Learning Solutions.

—Child, Family, & Community: Family-Centered Early Care & Education. 6th rev. ed. 2012. (ENG., Illus.). 432p. (C). pap. 80.20 (978-0-13-265714-3(7), Prentice Hall) Prentice Hall PTR.

Goodall, B. C. Mom Jail: A Teenager's Nightmare, 1 vol. 2010. 68p. pap. 19.95 (978-1-4489-3872-8(4)) PublishAmerica, Inc.

Goodell, Nancy & Garrett, Ann. TLC for Frazzled Kids. 2010. 123p. pap. 14.95 (978-0-557-56041-7(1)) Lulu Enterprises Inc.

Gordon, Mary. Roots of Empathy: Changing the World Child by Child. 2009. (ENG.). 312p. pap. 15.95 (978-1-61519-007-2(4), 161519007X) Experiment LLC, The.

Grace, Janey Lee & Grace, Janey L. Imperfectly Natural Baby & Toddler: How to Be a Green Parent in Today's Busy World. 2008. (Illus.). 256p. pap. 19.95 (978-0-7528-8589-6(8)) Orion Bks. Ltd. GBR. Dist: Sterling Publishing Co., Inc.

Grandizio, Joan M. Parenting 101: Notes to a Friend. 2009. 68p. pap. 26.49 (978-1-4490-1896-2(3)) AuthorHouse.

Green, Fiona Joy. Practicing Feminist Mothering. 2012. (ENG., Illus.). 200p. pap. 21.95 (978-1-894037-54-9(5)) Arbeiter Ring Publishing CAN. Dist: AK Pr. Distribution.

Green, Joanne. To My Child Concerning Your Birth Mother. 2008. 60p. pap. (978-1-897512-13-5(9)) Saga Bks.

Greene, Ross W. The Explosive Child: A New Approach for Understanding & Parenting Easily Frustrated, Chronically Inflexible Children. 2010. (ENG.). 336p. pap. 14.99 (978-0-06-190619-0(0), HarperPerennial) HarperCollins Pubs.

Greenspan, Stanley I. & Glovinsky, Cindy. Children & Babies with Mood Swings: New Insights for Parents & Professionals. 2007. (ENG.). 120p. pap. 24.95 (978-0-9767758-5-0(9)) Interdisciplinary Council on Developmental & Learning Disorders.

Greenspon, Thomas S. Moving Past Perfect: How Perfectionism May Be Holding Back Your Kids (and You!) & What You Can Do about It. 2012. (ENG.). 128p. pap. 15.99 (978-1-57542-387-6(1)) Free Spirit Publishing, Inc.

Gregory, Carol. Power from Within: Voices of Jamaican Female Leaders. 2010. 168p. pap. (978-3-8383-7031-6(7)) Lambert Academic Publishing.

Grille, Robin. Heart to Heart Parenting: Empower Your Child Empower Yourself. 2011. (ENG.). 352p. pap. 17.95 (978-0-9823975-0-3(X)) LifeTime Media, Inc.

—Parenting for a Peaceful World. 2009. (ENG.). 442p. pap. 29.95 (978-1-921004-14-8(2)) Longueville Media AUS. Dist: Consortium Bk. Sales & Distribution.

Grosshans, Beth A. & Burton, Janet H. Beyond Time-Out: From Chaos to Calm. (ENG.). 336p. 2010. pap. 14.95 (978-1-4027-7764-6(7)) 2008. 19.95 (978-1-4027-5297-1(0)) Sterling Publishing Co., Inc.

Guerney, Louise F. Ser Padres: Manual de Estrategias para la Crianza de los Hijos. 2008.Tr. of Parenting: A Skills Training Manual. (SPA., Illus.). 151p. spiral bd. (978-0-932990-07-5(X)) Institute for the Development of Emotional And Life Skills (IDEALS).

Guldberg, Helene. Reclaiming Childhood: Freedom & Play in an Age of Fear. 2009. 206p. 150.00 (978-0-415-47722-2(0)); (ENG.). 216p. pap. 31.95 (978-0-415-47723-9(9)) Routledge.

Gunnoe, Jennifer. Mommy Goes to Work: A Gabriella Story. 2009. 24p. pap. 11.49 (978-1-4389-5111-9(6)) AuthorHouse.

Gunter, Jennifer. The Preemie Primer: A Complete Guide for Parents of Premature Babies — from Birth through the Toddler Years & Beyond. 2010. (ENG.). 352p. pap. 16.95 (978-0-7382-1393-4(4)) Da Capo Pr., Inc.

Gurian, Michael. Nurture the Nature: Understanding & Supporting Your Child's Unique Core Personality. 2007. (ENG.). 368p. 24.95 (978-0-7879-8633-9(X), Jossey-Bass) Wiley, John & Sons, Inc.

—The Wonder of Boys: What Parents, Mentors & Educators Can Do to Shape Boys into Exceptional Men. 20th anniv. ed. 2006. (ENG.). 320p. (gr. 12-18). 15.95 (978-1-58542-528-0(1), Tarcher) Penguin Group (USA) Inc.

Gurian, Michael & Gurian. Nurture the Nature: Understanding & Supporting Your Child's Unique Core Personality. 2009. (ENG.). 368p. pap. 16.95 (978-0-470-32252-9(7), Jossey-Bass) Wiley, John & Sons, Inc.

Gursten, Steven M. How to Keep Your Children Safe. 2010. 60p. pap. 10.99 (978-0-557-51392-5(8)) Lulu Enterprises Inc.

Guthrie, Stephen. Practical Parenting a Counselor's Guide to Raising the Difficult Child: A counselor's Guide to Raising the Difficult Child. 2011. 74p. pap. 15.99 (978-1-4628-8671-5(X)) Xlibris Corp.

Haddad, Douglas. Save Your Kids Now! The Revolutionary Guide to Helping Youth Conquer Today's Challenges. 2009. 252p. 29.95 (978-1-4401-5305-1(1)); pap. 19.95 (978-1-4401-5303-7(5)) iUniverse, Inc.

Hairston, Julie. You're Having A Wonderful Childhood: The Stressed Parents Guide to Raising Great Children. 2011. 160p. 28.59 (978-1-4634-5306-0(X)); pap. 15.04 (978-1-4634-5305-3(1)) AuthorHouse.

Hale, Elnader. Parenting Solo. 2009. 81p. pap. 16.24 (978-0-557-06252-2(7)) Lulu Enterprises Inc.

Hall, Mosiah. Parent & Child. 2008. 148p. 24.99 (978-0-554-23469-4(6)); 21.99 (978-0-554-32772-3(4)) BiblioBazaar.

—Parent & Child. 2007. 112p. per. (978-1-4068-1657-0(4)) Echo Library.

Hall, Sharon & Hall, Sharon K. Raising Kids in the 21st Century: The Science of Psychological Health for Children. 2008. (ENG., Illus.). 192p. pap. 29.95 (978-1-4051-5806-0(9), Wiley-Blackwell) Wiley, John & Sons, Inc.

Hall, Sharon K. Raising Kids in the 21st Century: The Science of Psychological Health for Children. 2008. (ENG., Illus.). 192p. 89.95 (978-1-4051-5805-3(0), Wiley-Blackwell) Wiley, John & Sons, Inc.

Haller, Thomas & Moorman, Chick. Teaching the Attraction Principle to Children: Practical Strategies for Parents & Teachers to Help Children Manifest a Better World. 2008. (Illus.). 184p. 24.95 (978-0-9772321-6-1(6)) Personal Power Pr.

Hamburg, Jean. Cooperation Counts! Life-Saving Strategies for Parenting Toddlers to Teens. 2011. 203p. pap. 13.95 (978-1-4327-6255-1(9)) Outskirts Pr., Inc.

Hamm, Amanda. Double Take: My First Year as a Mother of Twins. 2010. 148p. pap. 11.39 (978-0-557-68182-2(0)) Lulu Enterprises Inc.

Hancock, Jonathan. Help Your Child to Succeed at School: A Teach Yourself Guide. 2010. (ENG.). 224p. pap. 14.95 (978-0-07-174004-3(X), 007174004X) McGraw-Hill Cos., The.

Hanessian, Lu. Let the Baby Drive: Navigating the Road of New Motherhood. Date not set. mass mkt. (978-0-312-99624-6(1), St. Martin's Paperbacks) St. Martin's Pr.

Hanna, Janet, et al, adapted by. Fun to Play, Ready to Learn: Activity Guide. 2007. (Illus.). 96p. spiral bd. (978-0-9616828-7-3(6)) Univ. of Nebraska, Institute of Agriculture & Natural Resources.

Hansen, Hank. Baby Management for Men: The Handy Guide for Dads. van Bakel, Rogier, tr. 2009.Tr. of Babymanagement voor Mannen. (Illus.). 200p. pap. 14.95 (978-90-8885-032-5(1)) Saga-Whyte Pr. NLD. Dist: AtlasBooks Distribution.

Hanser, Christina. The Law of Attraction for Children. 2010. 32p. pap. 12.99 (978-1-4520-0996-4(1)) AuthorHouse.

Harland. A Will of His Own Reflections on Parenting a Child with Autism - Revised Edition. 2007. (ENG.). 176p. pap. (978-1-84310-869-6(0)) Kingsley, Jessica Ltd.

Harris. Thinking about Infants Young Children. 2011. (Harris Meltzer Trust Ser.). (Illus.). 130p. 32.95 (978-1-78049-010-6(0)) Karnac Bks. GBR. Dist: Stylus Publishing, LLC.

Harris, Bonnie. Confident Parents, Remarkable Kids: 8 Principles for Raising Kids You'll Love to Live With. 2008. (ENG.). 256p. pap. 12.95 (978-1-59869-471-0(5)) Adams Media Corp.

Harris, Judith Rich. The Nurture Assumption: Why Children Turn Out the Way They Do. 2nd rev. ed. 2009. (ENG., Illus.). 480p. pap. 16.95 (978-1-4391-0165-0(5), Free Pr.) Free Pr.

Hart, Roger. The Changing City of Childhood: Implications for Play & Learning. (Catherine Molony Memorial Lectures). (Illus.). 23p. (C). pap. 5.00 (978-0-918374-22-6(7)) City College Workshop Ctr.

Hart, Sura & Kindle-Hodson, Victoria. Respectful Parents, Respectful Kids: 7 Keys to Turn Family Conflict into Co-Operation. 2006. (ENG., Illus.). 208p. per. 17.95 (978-1-892005-22-9(0)) Puddledancer Pr.

Harvey, Pat & Penzo, Jeanine A. Parenting a Child Who Has Intense Emotions: Dialectical Behavior Therapy Skills to Help Your Child Regulate Emotional Outbursts & Aggressive Behaviors. 2009. (ENG.). 224p. pap. 18.95 (978-1-57224-649-2(9)) New Harbinger Pubns.

Hatherleigh Press Staff. Why Save Africa? Voices from Around the World. Eding, June, ed. 2011. (Little Book. Big Idea Ser.). (ENG.). 176p. pap. 12.00 (978-1-57826-308-0(5)) Hatherleigh Co., Ltd., The.

Haywood, Robin & Sellers Publishing Inc. Editors, eds. Life Is Poop: And Other Diaper Dramas. 2010. (Illus.). 64p. 9.95 (978-1-4162-0569-2(1)) Sellers Publishing, Inc.

Healy, Maureen. Growing Happy Kids: How to Foster Inner Confidence, Success, & Happiness. 2012. (ENG.). 264p. pap. 14.95 (978-0-7573-1612-8(3)) Health Communications, Inc.

Heaphy, Cheryl. What's That? 2009. 32p. pap. 12.95 (978-1-4327-2135-0(6)) Outskirts Pr., Inc.

Hearron, Patricia F. & Hildebrand, Verna. Guiding Young Children. (ENG., Illus.). (C). 8th ed. 2008. 400p. pap. 82.80 (978-0-13-515164-8(3)) 9th rev. ed. 2012. 384p. pap. 82.80 (978-0-13-265713-6(9)) Prentice Hall PTR. (Prentice Hall).

Heath, Phyllis. Parent-Child Relations: Context, Research, & Application. (ENG., Illus.). (C). 2nd ed. 2008. 416p. per. 105.00 (978-0-13-159676-4(4)) 3rd rev. ed. 2011. 464p. pap. 105.00 (978-0-13-265712-9(0)) Prentice Hall PTR. (Prentice Hall).

Heath, Samuel D. G. To Kill a Mockingbird: A critique on behalf of Children. 2007. 80p. per. 10.95 (978-0-595-44369-7(9)) iUniverse, Inc.

Heim, Susan M. It's Twins: Parent-to-Parent Advice from Infancy Through Adolescence. 2007. (ENG., Illus.). 328p. per. 18.95 (978-1-57174-531-6(9)) Hampton Roads Publishing Co., Inc.

Heimann, Charlotte & Pearson, Betsy. How to Amuse & Outwit Important People Under. 2011. 82p. 37.95 (978-1-258-08264-2(0)) Literary Licensing, LLC.

Heller, Lora. All Day Long: Teaching Your Baby to Sign. 2008. (Baby Fingers Ser.). (ENG., Illus.). 24p. (J). (gr. -1). bds. 4.95 (978-1-4027-5395-4(0)) Sterling Publishing Co., Inc.

—Baby Fingers: Hello, Goodbye: Teaching Your Baby to Sign. 2008. (Baby Fingers Ser.). (ENG., Illus.). 24p. (J). (gr. -1). bds. 4.95 (978-1-4027-5394-7(2)) Sterling Publishing Co., Inc.

Herzig, Helene. A Father's Dream Through a Daughter's Eyes: How to Raise a Wonderful Family. 2008. 248p. 29.95 (978-0-595-51209-6(7)); pap. 19.95 (978-0-595-45244-6(2)) iUniverse, Inc.

Hibbard Willett, Jean. Dear Mom: Why Raising Four Boys Was Neither Boring nor Monotonous. 2008. 242p. per. 19.95 (978-0-9765872-2-4(X)) Caseys World Bks.

Hicks, Marybeth. Bringing up Geeks: How to Protect Your Kid's Childhood in a Grow-up-Too-Fast World. 2008. (ENG.). 336p. (gr. 12-18). 14.00 (978-0-425-22156-3(3), Berkley Trade) Penguin Group (USA) Inc.

Hill, E. D. I'm Not Your Friend, I'm Your Parent: Helping Your Children Set the Boundaries They Need... & Really Want, 0 vols. 2008. 256p. 24.99 (978-0-7852-2810-3(1)) Nelson, Thomas Inc.

Hill, Natasha. Parent Survival Kit: Divorce Edition. 2008. 56p. pap. 21.95 (978-1-59858-552-0(5)) Dog Ear Publishing, LLC.

Hines, Gill & Baverstock, Alison. It's Not Fair! Parenting the Bright & Challenging Child. 2012. (ENG.). 304p. pap. 14.95 (978-0-7499-5248-8(2)) Piatkus Bks. GBR. Dist: Independent Pubs. Group.

Hines, Gill, et al. It's Not Fair! Parenting the Bright & Challenging Child. 2009. (ENG.). 304p. pap. 19.95 (978-0-7499-4046-1(8)) Piatkus Bks. GBR. Dist: Independent Pubs. Group.

Hines, Jerry. Be the Dad You Wish You Had! 52 Lessons My Kids Made Me Learn. 2011. 120p. pap. 11.95 (978-1-4497-1230-3(4), WestBow Pr.) Author Solutions, Inc.

Hirsch, Alan. How to Tell If Your Teenager Is Lying. 2010. (ENG.). 177p. pap. 17.95 (978-0-9800649-0-2(2)) Hilton Publishing Co.

Hodgkinson, Tom. The Idle Parent: Why Less Means More When Raising Kids. 2010. (ENG.). 272p. (gr. 12). 15.95 (978-1-58542-800-7(0), Tarcher) Penguin Group (USA) Inc.

Hoffman, Rosalyn. Smart Mama, Smart Money: Raising Happy, Healthy Kids Without Breaking the Bank. 2012. (ENG.). 320p. (gr. 12). 15.00 (978-0-451-23559-6(2), N A L Trade) Penguin Group (USA) Inc.

Hoffman, Susan. Grand Wishes: Advocating to Preserve the Grandparent Grandchild Bond. 2007. 176p. per. 13.50 (978-0-9799168-0-9(1)) Collegare Pr.

Holmes, Joe. How to Raise Successful Children (Love Is the Key) 2009. 48p. pap. 11.97 (978-0-557-22629-0(5)) Lulu Enterprises Inc.

Honore, Carl. Under Pressure: Putting the Child Back in Childhood. 2009. 304p. pap. 14.99 (978-0-06-112881-3(3), HarperOne) HarperCollins Pubs.

—Under Pressure: Putting the Child Back in Childhood. 2009. (ENG.). 304p. pap. (978-0-676-97843-8(6), Vintage Canada) Random Hse. of Canada, Ltd. CAN. Dist: Random Hse., Inc.

Hopkins, Christal D. Shattering of Myths & Fears: Raising a Healthy Happy Disabled Child, 1 vol. 2009. 53p. pap. 16.95 (978-1-61546-951-2(6)) PublishAmerica, Inc.

Hrdy, Sarah Blaffer. Mothers & Others: The Evolutionary Origins of Mutual Understanding. 2011. (ENG., Illus.). 432p. pap. 19.95 (978-0-674-06032-6(6), Belknap Pr.) Harvard Univ. Pr.

Hummel, Katherine & Darragh Lantry, Noreen. Building Baby's Brain Power: Hundreds of One-Minute Brain Stimulating Activities for Baby's First Years. 2007. (Illus.). 229p. per. 14.95 (978-0-9671289-1-7(9)) B E T A Ctr., Inc.

—Fortaleciendo la Facultad Cerebral del Bebe: Hundreds of One-Minute Brain Stimulating Activities for Baby's First Years. 2007. (Illus.). 230p. per. 14.95 (978-0-9671289-3-1(5)) B E T A Ctr., Inc.

Humphries, Qwin. PC-Mommy; 123 Ideas to Run Your Family with Microsoft Office(r) & Get A Promotion. 2007. 149p. pap. 24.95 (978-0-615-17382-5(9)) Humphries, Qwin.

Hungrywolf, Adolf. Tribal Childhood: Growing up in Traditional Native America. 2008. (ENG., Illus.). 224p. pap. (978-1-57067-213-2(X)) Book Publishing Co.

Hunt, Mary. Debt-Proof Your Kids. annot. ed. 2007. 215p. per. 14.99 (978-0-9760791-4-9(3)) DPL Pr.

Hunter, Julie D. The ABCs of Positive Parenting: A Creative Approach to Raising Children. 2011. pap. 7.99 *(978-1-61777-840-7(0))* Tate Publishing & Enterprises, LLC.

Hurley, Kathy. Mommy, Why Do Bad Things Happen? 2009. 16p. pap. 8.49 *(978-1-4490-2630-1(3))* AuthorHouse.

Iorio, Alice. Champion Parenting: Giving Your Child a Competitive Edge. 2010. 112p. 28.95 *(978-1-4497-0048-5(9))*; pap. 11.95 *(978-1-4497-0047-8(0))* Author Solutions, Inc. (WestBow Pr.).

Jacobelli, Frank & Watson, Lynn Ann. SmartHelp for Good 'n' Angry Kids: Teaching Children to Manage Anger. 2009. (ENG., Illus.). 222p. pap. 33.95 *(978-0-470-75802-1(3)*, Wiley) Wiley, John & Sons, Inc.

Jacobs, Miriam. My Name Is NOT Monkey Girl. 2007. (Illus.). 52p. (J). pap. 13.97 *(978-0-9798217-3-8(8))* Candalyse Publishing.

Jacobson, Arminta & Keim, Robert, eds. Wisdom for Parents: Key Ideas from Parent Educators. 2011. 286p. pap. 24.95 *(978-1-897160-57-2(7))* de Sitter Pubns. CAN. Dist: International Specialized Bk. Services.

James, Stephen & Thomas, David S. Wild Things: The Art of Nurturing Boys. 2009. (ENG.). 368p. pap. 14.99 *(978-1-4143-2227-8(5))* Tyndale Hse. Pubs.

Jamieson, Wendell. Father Knows Less: One Dad's Quest to Answer His Son's Most Baffling Questions. 2008. (ENG.). 320p. (gr. 12-18). 13.95 *(978-0-399-53458-4(X)*, Perigee Trade) Penguin Group (USA) Inc.

—Father Knows Less or, Can I Cook My Sister? One Dad's Quest to Answer His Son's Most Baffling Questions. l.t. ed. 2008. (Laugh Lines Ser.). (Illus.). 365p. 29.95 *(978-1-4104-0495-4(1))* Thorndike Pr.

Jantz, Gregory. The Molding of a Champion: Helping Your Child Shape a Winning Destiny. 2006. (Illus.). 239p. per. 12.99 *(978-0-89221-643-2(4))* New Leaf Pr., Inc.

Jarrell, Jane & Ladd, Karol. The Frazzled Factor: Relief for Working Moms, 0 vols. 2008. 224p. pap. 14.99 *(978-0-7852-9655-3(7))* Nelson, Thomas Inc.

Jay, Roni. Nobody Told Me That! 10 Tools for Parenting a Happy, Healthy Children. 2009. (ENG.). 208p. pap. 18.99 *(978-0-13-815573-2(5))* FT Press.

Jele, Cynthia. So You Wanna Be an Au Pair in the Usa. 2006. pap. *(978-1-904623-50-2(6))* WritersPrintShop.

Jennings, Isaac. A Sermon for the Times; Preached to the First Church & Society in Stamford, Conn , April 24th 1853. 2011. 18p. pap. 11.99 *(978-1-4181-9080-4(2))* MPublishing.

Johnson, Matthew. Positive Parenting with a Plan. 2009. ix, 282p. pap. 24.95 *(978-0-9819682-7-8(9))* Intermedia Publishing Group.

Jones, Charles. To Be a Single Father. 2009. 184p. 27.99 *(978-1-4389-4244-5(3))*; pap. 21.49 *(978-1-4389-4245-2(1))* AuthorHouse.

Jones, Cinde R. Young Man Multimillionaire: 5 Steps to Make Your Child A Millionaire. 2010. 124p. (ENG.). 32.50 *(978-1-4490-9335-8(3))*; pap. 25.50 *(978-1-4490-9334-1(5))* AuthorHouse.

Jones, Deborah. Men in the Lives of Young Children: An International Perspective. Jones, Deborah & Evans, Roy, eds. 2009. (ENG., Illus.). 210p. 125.00 *(978-0-415-49704-6(3))* Routledge.

Jones, Katina Z. & Iannelli, Vincent. Bottles, Budgets, & Birthplans: What You Really Need to Know to Get Ready for Baby. 2009. (ENG.). 256p. pap. 9.95 *(978-1-60550-097-3(6))* Adams Media Corp.

Jones, Sandy & Jones, Marcie. Great Expectations: the Toddler Years: Everything You Need to Know about Your 1- To 3-Year-Old. 2011. (Great Expectations Ser.). (ENG., Illus.). 296p. pap. 14.95 *(978-1-4027-5816-4(2))* Sterling Publishing Co., Inc.

Jordan, Sarah. Teen Owner's Manual: Operating Instructions, Trouble-Shooting Tips, & Advice on Adolescent Maintenance. 2009. (Owner's & Instruction Manual Ser.). (ENG.). 224p. pap. 16.95 *(978-1-59474-417-4(3))* Quirk Bks.

Juarez, Patricia. Padres buenos, padres Malos. 2009. (SPA.). 240p. pap. 16.95 *(978-0-307-39277-0(5))* Grijalbo Mondadori, S.A.-Junior ESP. Dist: Random Hse., Inc.

Juffer, F., et al. Promoting Positive Parenting. 2007. (Monographs in Parenting). (ENG., Illus.). 256p. pap. 41.95 *(978-0-8058-6352-9(4)*, Routledge) Taylor & Francis Group GBR. Dist: Taylor & Francis Group.

Juffer, Femmie & Van Ijzendoorn, Marinus, eds. Promoting Positive Parenting: An Attachment-Based Intervention. 2007. (Monographs in Parenting). (ENG., Illus.). 256p. 90.95 *(978-0-8058-6351-2(6)*, Routledge) Taylor & Francis Group GBR. Dist: Taylor & Francis Group.

Karem-Gramig, Pat. Don't Look Now, but Your Kid Is Showing: A Memoir. 2011. pap. 10.99 *(978-1-61777-339-6(5))* Tate Publishing & Enterprises, LLC.

Karp, Harvey. Happiest Toddler on the Block: How to Eliminate Tantrums & Raise a Patient, Respectful & Cooperative One-to Four-Year-Old. rev. ed. 2008. (ENG., Illus.). 336p. 24.00 *(978-0-553-80521-5(5)*, Bantam) Random House Publishing Group.

—The Happiest Toddler on the Block: How to Eliminate Tantrums & Raise a Patient, Respectful, & Cooperative One-To Four-Year-Old. rev. ed. 2008. (ENG., Illus.). 336p. pap. 15.00 *(978-0-553-38442-0(2)*, Bantam) Random House Publishing Group.

Kaweblum, Y. Aaron. Crystoppers: A Play by Play Guide Book for Wise Parenting. 2011. 132p. 21.23 *(978-1-4567-3104-5(1))*; pap. 14.99 *(978-1-4567-3102-1(5))* AuthorHouse.

Kazdin, Alan E. The Kazdin Method for Parenting the Defiant Child: With No Pills, No Therapy, No Contest of Wills. (ENG.). 304p. 2009. pap. 14.95 *(978-0-547-09582-1(6))* 2008. (Illus.). 26.00 *(978-0-618-77367-1(3))* Houghton Mifflin Harcourt Trade & Reference Pubs.

Kearney, Christopher A. Silence Is Not Golden: Strategies for Helping the Shy Child, 1 vol. 2010. (ENG., Illus.). 144p. pap. 19.95 *(978-0-19-532662-8(8))* Oxford Univ. Pr., Inc.

Kellam, Theresa. The Parent Survival Guide: From Chaos to Harmony in Ten Weeks or Less. 2008. (ENG., Illus.). 264p. 19.95 *(978-0-415-98934-3(5))* Routledge.

Kelly, Matthew. Building Better Families: A Practical Guide to Raising Amazing Children. 2008. (ENG.). 208p. 23.00 *(978-0-345-49453-5(9)*, Ballantine Bks.) Random House Publishing Group.

Kendall, Anne & DeGangi, Georgia A. Effective Parenting for the Hard-to-Manage Child: A Skills-Based Book. 2007. (ENG., Illus.). 304p. per. 24.95 *(978-0-415-95546-1(7))* Routledge.

Kenny, Cathy. Becoming A Successful Parent in Ten Step. 2006. pap. 10.00 *(978-1-4257-2096-4(X))* Xlibris Corp.

Kenny, Cedric M. Love Without Spoiling, Discipline Without Nagging: Toddlers to Teens. 2007. (Illus.). 397p. pap. 14.95 *(978-81-86685-86-0(3))* Wisdom Tree IND. Dist: SCB Distributors.

Keys, Dalen. The Mess. Halter, Pam, ed. 2011. (Illus.). 32p. (J). 16.00 *(978-1-886068-50-6(X))* Fruitbearer Publishing, LLC.

Khonsari, Terri A. Raising a Superstar: Simple Strategies to Bring Out the Brilliance in Every Child. 2007. (ENG., Illus.). 137p. per. 14.99 *(978-1-59932-046-5(0)*, Advantage) Advantage Media Group.

—Raising a Superstar: Simple Strategies to Bring Out the Brilliance in Every Child. 2008. (ENG.). pap. 14.99 *(978-1-60037-356-5(9))* Morgan James Publishing.

Kidder, Rushworth M. Good Kids, Tough Choices: How Parents Can Help Their Children Do the Right Thing. 2010. (ENG., Illus.). 272p. pap. 16.95 *(978-0-470-54762-5(6)*, Jossey-Bass) Wiley, John & Sons, Inc.

Kielburger, Craig, et al. The World Needs Your Kid: Raising Children Who Care & Contribute, 1 vol. 2nd rev. ed. 2010. (ENG., Illus.). 304p. pap. 19.95 *(978-1-55365-586-2(9)*, Greystone Bks.) D&M Pubs. Inc. CAN. Dist: Perseus-PGW.

Kilson, Marion & Ladd, Florence. Is That Your Child? Mothers Talk about Rearing Biracial Children. 2008. (ENG., Illus.). 146p. 57.99 *(978-0-7391-2763-6(2))*; pap. 24.50 *(978-0-7391-2764-3(0))* Lexington Bks.

Kimmel, Tim. Raising Kids Who Turn Out Right. annot. ed. 2006. (ENG.). 234p. per. 14.99 *(978-0-9747683-9-7(1))* Family Matters (R).

Knight, Jan. Help! I'm A Parent! A Collection of Tips & Information on Being an Affective Parent in Today's World. 2011. 336p. pap. 22.95 *(978-1-4620-5739-9(X))* iUniverse, Inc.

Koch, Molly Brown. 27 Secrets to Raising Amazing Children. 2007. (Illus.). 202p. per. *(978-1-886968-20-2(9))* Sidran Institute Pr.

Komarek, Pierrette L. Camps. Musings from the Past: While I am still Standing!, 1 vol. 2009. 88p. pap. 16.95 *(978-1-4489-9996-5(0))* PublishAmerica, Inc.

Koocher, Gerald & La Greca, Annette. The Parents' Guide to Psychological First Aid, 1 vol. 2010. (ENG., Illus.). 496p. pap. 27.95 *(978-0-19-538191-7(2))* Oxford Univ. Pr., Inc.

Kuman, Maria. The Fun (& Wisdom) of Raising a Child. Date not set. pap. *(978-1-893637-26-9(3))* Health & Happiness Bks.

Kurcinka, Mary Sheedy. Sleepless in America: Is Your Child Misbehaving or Missing Sleep? 2007. 331p. 25.00 *(978-1-4223-6698-1(7))* DIANE Publishing Co.

Kurcinka, Mary Sheedy & Kurcinka, Mary S. Raising Your Spirited Child: A Guide for Parents Whose Child Is More Intense, Sensitive, Perceptive, Persistent, & Energetic. rev. ed. 2006. (ENG.). 320p. pap. 14.99 *(978-0-06-073966-9(5)*, William Morrow Paperbacks) HarperCollins Pubs.

—Sleepless in America: Is Your Child Misbehaving... or Missing Sleep? 2007. (ENG.). 352p. pap. 13.99 *(978-0-06-073602-6(X)*, HarperPerennial) HarperCollins Pubs.

Kuriansky, Judy & Hand, Edie. 31 Things to Raise a Child's Self-Esteem. 2010. (Good Things to Know Ser.). (ENG.). 174p. pap. 9.99 *(978-1-59652-582-5(7))* Turner Publishing Co.

Lancaster, Evelyn. Poo Soup for the Lousy Mother's Soul: A How NOT to Guide. 2008. 64p. pap. 9.95 *(978-0-595-52195-1(9))* iUniverse, Inc.

Landau, Erika, et al. The Essential Guide to Baby's First Year. 2011. (ENG.). 400p. (gr. 12). 16.95 *(978-1-61564-086-7(X)*, Alpha Bks.) Penguin Group (USA) Inc.

Landy, Sarah. Pathways to Competence: Encouraging Healthy Social & Emotional Development in Young Children. 2nd ed. 2009. 672p. pap. 59.95 *(978-1-55766-891-2(4))* Brookes, Paul H. Publishing Co.

LaRowe, Michelle. A Mom's Ultimate Book of Lists: 100+ Lists to Save You Time, Money, & Sanity, 1 vol. 2010. (ENG.). 336p. pap. 13.99 *(978-0-8007-3382-7(7))* Revell.

—Nanny to the Rescue Again!, 0 vols. 2006. (Illus.). 256p. pap. 15.99 *(978-0-8499-1244-3(X))* Nelson, Thomas Inc.

Larroudt, Bettina. The Hispanic Family: Language & Learning at Home. 2009. 140p. pap. *(978-3-639-14185-6(7))* VDM Verlag Dr. Mueller e.K.

Lashlie, Celia. He'll Be OK: Growing Gorgeous Boys into Good Men. 2007. 224p. *(978-0-7322-8450-3(3))* HarperCollins Pubs. Australia.

Lavis, Rose Brenda. The Girl Who Tamed Her Wonder Worm. 2009. 44p. pap. 16.99 *(978-1-4389-9323-2(4))* AuthorHouse.

Law, Stephen. The War for Children's Minds. 2007. (Illus.). 198p. per. 22.95 *(978-0-415-42768-5(1))* Routledge.

—The War for Children's Minds: Liberal Values & Why We Should Defend Them. 2006. (Illus.). 198p. 31.95 *(978-0-415-37855-0(9)*, RU8559X) Routledge.

Le Messurier, Mark. Parenting Tough Kids: Simple Proven Strategies to Help Kids Succeed. 2007. (Illus.). 160p. (gr. k-12). per. 27.95 *(978-1-890455-06-4(7)*, B55064P) Corwin Pr.

Leach, Penelope. Your Baby & Child. 2010. (ENG., Illus.). 560p. pap. 23.95 *(978-0-375-71203-6(8)*, Knopf) Knopf Doubleday Publishing Group.

Lederer, Aaron. Taming the Wild Child: From Living Hell to Living Well. 2008. 176p. pap. 15.95 *(978-1-4401-0142-7(6))* iUniverse, Inc.

Lee, Allison. How to Grow Great Kids: The Good Parents' Guide to Rearing Sociable, Confident & Healthy Children. 2010. 285p. pap. 22.00 *(978-1-84528-288-2(4))* How To Books GBR. Dist: Parkwest Pubns., Inc.

Lee, Ilchi. Power Brain Kids: 12 Easy Lessons to Ignite Your Child's Potential. 2010. 118p. pap. 16.95 *(978-1-935127-35-2(7))* BEST Life Media.

—Power Brain Kids: 12 Easy Lessons to Ignite Your Child's Potential. 2007. (Illus.). 118p. per. 18.95 *(978-1-932843-19-4(1))* Healing Society, Inc.

Leman, Kevin. Have a New Kid by Friday: How to Change Your Child's Attitude, Behavior & Character in 5 Days. 2012. pap. 14.99 *(978-0-8007-3218-9(9))* 2008. 208p. pap. 12.99 *(978-0-8007-3276-9(6))* 2008. 304p. 17.99 *(978-0-8007-1902-9(6))* Revell.

Lerner, Ben & Mercola, Joseph. Generation XL: Raising Healthy, Intelligent Kids in a High-Tech, Junk-Food World, 0 vols. 2007. 272p. 21.99 *(978-0-7852-2186-9(7))* Nelson, Thomas Inc.

Levene, Alysa. Childcare, Health & Mortality at the London Foundling Hospital, 1741-1800. 2007. (ENG., Illus.). 224p. 79.00 *(978-0-7190-7354-0(5))* Manchester Univ. Pr. GBR. Dist: Macmillan.

Levine, Madeline. The Price of Privilege: How Parental Pressure & Material Advantage Are Creating a Generation of Disconnected & Unhappy Kids. (ENG.). 256p. 2008. pap. 13.99 *(978-0-06-059585-2(X)*, HarperPerennial) 2006. 25.95 *(978-0-06-059584-5(1))* HarperCollins Pubs.

Liamputtong, Pranee. Childrearing & Infant Care Issues: A Cross-Cultural Perspective. 2007. 291p. (C). 89.00 *(978-1-60021-610-7(2))* Nova Science Pubs., Inc.

Licata, Alice. It's Not Rocket Science: down-to-Earth Advice on Raising Stellar Kids. 2009. 134p. pap. 13.50 *(978-0-557-10354-6(1))* Lulu Enterprises Inc.

Lincoln, Michael J. Honey, I Blew up the Kids. 2007. spiral bd. 34.00 *(978-0-9772069-2-6(0))* Talking Hearts.

Linder, Beverly. A Never-Give-up Heart. 2010. 140p. pap. 12.99 *(978-0-557-31809-4(2))* Lulu Enterprises Inc.

Lindsay, Jeanne Warren. The P. A. R. E. N. T Approach: How to Teach Young Moms & Dads the Art & Skills of Parenting. 2008. (ENG., Illus.). 160p. per. 12.95 *(978-1-932538-85-4(2))* Morning Glory Pr., Inc.

Lindsay, Jeanne Warren, et al. Imami, Tengo Hambre! Buena Alimentación para los Pequeños. 2008. (Teen Pregnancy & Parenting Ser.). (ENG & SPA., Illus.). 176p. (J). (gr. 7). pap. 12.95 *(978-1-932538-75-5(5))* Morning Glory Pr., Inc.

Lipman, Blythe. Help! My Baby Came Without Instructions: How to Survive (And Enjoy) Your Baby's First Year. 2010. (ENG.). 176p. pap. 14.95 *(978-1-57344-390-6(5)*, Viva Editions) Cleis Pr.

Lipps, Brian & Allison, Cyndi. Playskool Guide to Raising Boys: Essential Information & Practical Advice for Raising Happy, Confident Boys. 2008. (Playskool Ser.). 304p. pap. 14.95 *(978-1-4022-1446-2(4))* Sourcebooks, Inc.

Lisa Marie Anderson. Rhythm of the Spirit: One child's inner strength to overcome illness & multiple Disabilities. 2010. 296p. pap. 18.49 *(978-1-4269-2280-0(9))* Trafford Publishing.

Livingstone, Tessa. Child of Our Time: Early Learning. 2008. (ENG., Illus.). 224p. pap. 29.95 *(978-0-593-05927-2(1))* Transworld Publishers Ltd. GBR. Dist: Independent Pubs. Group.

Lluch, Alex A. & Lluch, Elizabeth. The Ultimate Baby Journal. 2010. (ENG.). 100p. 26.95 *(978-1-936061-12-9(0))* WS Publishing.

Loehr, Jamie & Meyers, Jennifer. Playskool Guide to Baby's First Year. 2007. (ENG.). 304p. pap. 14.95 *(978-1-4022-0931-4(2))* Sourcebooks, Inc.

Lombardo, Gregory T. Understanding the Mind of Your Bipolar Child: The Complete Guide to the Development, Treatment, & Parenting of Children with Bipolar Disorder. 2008. (ENG., Illus.). 384p. pap. 14.99 *(978-0-312-35890-7(3)*, St. Martin's Griffin) St. Martin's Pr.

Longford, Elizabeth. All in the Family: Parenting the 50s Way. 2008. (ENG.). 240p. pap. 22.95 *(978-0-7509-5066-4(8))* History Pr. Ltd.,The GBR. Dist: Independent Pubs. Group.

Lord, Daniel. Some Notes for the Guidance of Parents. 2007. 252p. per. 23.95 *(978-0-9783198-3-0(4))* Catholic Authors Pr.

Lord Nelson. Celebrating You & Me: A Journal for Children & their Parents. 2009. 132p. pap. 39.99 *(978-1-4389-8226-7(7))* AuthorHouse.

Lord, Udis. Raising a Child As a Single Parent. *(978-0-937571-07-1(5))* Philippine-American Educational Pr.

Loreman, Tim & Loreman. Respecting Childhood. 2009. (ENG., Illus.). 152p. 39.95 *(978-0-8264-3244-5(1))* Continuum International Publishing Group, Ltd. GBR. Dist: National Bk. Network.

Loveland-Coen, Victoria & Myers, Sarah. You've Earned It Kid! A Positive Reward Systems for Children, 3. 2007. (Give a Little Love Ser.: 3). (Illus.). 62p. pap. 5.95 *(978-0-9644765-9-2(2))* Love & Blessings.

Lowe, Fergus & Lowe, Brigid. Brain Training for Babies: A Teach Yourself Guide. 2011. (Teach Yourself: General Reference Ser.). (ENG.). 224p. pap. 15.00 *(978-0-07-176980-8(3)*, 0071769803) McGraw-Hill Cos., The.

Lozowick, Lee. Conscious Parenting. rev. ed. 2010. (ENG.). 336p. (Orig.). pap. 19.95 *(978-1-935387-16-9(2))* Hohm Pr.

Ludman, Batya L. Life's Journey: Exploring Relationships, Resolving Conflicts. 2011. (ENG.). 368p. pap. 24.95 *(978-1-934440-57-5(4)*, Devora Publishing) Simcha Media Group.

Ma, Lan. You Can Have It All Baby Career & Plan. 2006. pap. 15.95 *(978-0-7414-3174-5(2))* Infinity Publishing.

Macdonald, Cameron Lynne. Shadow Mothers: Nannies, au Pairs, & the Micropolitics of Mothering. 2011. (ENG., Illus.). 292p. pap. 22.95 *(978-0-520-26697-1(8))* Univ. of California Pr.

MacLaughlin, Sarah. What Not to Say: Tools for Talking with Young Children. 2010. (Illus.). 96p. 12.00 *(978-0-9654694-2-5(5))* Bay Island Bks.

Maffini, Helen & Bahman, Shahnaz. Developing Children's Emotional Intelligence. 2008. (ENG., Illus.). 144p. 34.95 *(978-0-8264-9974-5(0))* Continuum International Publishing Group, Ltd. GBR. Dist: National Bk. Network.

Mah, Ronald. The One-Minute Temper Tantrum Solution: Strategies for Responding to Children's Challenging Behaviors. 2008. 160p. 71.95 *(978-1-4129-5720-5(6)*, B57206C); pap. 29.95 *(978-1-4129-5721-2(4)*, B57206P) Corwin Pr.

Mahammed, Cidi. Parent Guide & Childlike Behavior. 2011. 48p. pap. 23.51 *(978-1-4343-5926-1(3))* AuthorHouse.

Manukul. I Luv Myself. 2010. 215p. pap. *(978-81-223-1119-8(9))* Mahal, Pustak Pubs., Booksellers & Order Suppliers.

Marascia, Paul. Son Shine: A Divorced Father Establishes Principles for the Fulfillment & Growth of His Sons. 2008. 107p. pap. 16.95 *(978-1-60563-426-5(3))* PublishAmerica, Inc.

Marci Psalmonds. Still Alive: After raising 400+ children & Counting... ... 2010. 60p. pap. 9.95 *(978-1-4502-1171-0(2))* iUniverse, Inc.

Mariani, Anna Marina. Parenting: A Necessity & a Utopia. Buonanno, Elda, tr. 2008. 192p. pap. *(978-88-95145-30-3(5))* Italian Paths of Culture.

Marion, Marian C. Guidance of Young Children. 8th ed. 2010. (ENG.). 416p. (C). pap. 82.80 *(978-0-13-703402-4(4)*, Prentice Hall) Prentice Hall PTR.

—Guidance of Young Children (with MyEducationLab) 8th ed. 2010. (ENG.). 416p. (C). pap. 89.47 *(978-0-13-138119-3(9)*, Prentice Hall) Prentice Hall PTR.

Markway, Barbara G. & Markway, Gregory P. Nurturing the Shy Child: Practical Help for Raising Confident & Socially Skilled Kids & Teens. 2006. (ENG., Illus.). 240p. pap. 13.95 *(978-0-312-32978-5(4)*, St. Martin's Griffin) St. Martin's Pr.

Maroni, Lesley. Understanding 4-5-Year-Olds. 2007. (Understanding Your Child (Jessica Kingsley Publishers) Ser.). (ENG.). 8p. per. *(978-1-84310-534-3(9))* Kingsley, Jessica Ltd.

Marsh, Monica Miller & Turner-Vorveck, Tammy. (Mis)Understanding Families: Learning from Real Families in Our Schools. 2010. (ENG.). 224p. pap. 31.95 *(978-0-8077-5037-7(9))* Teachers College Pr., Teachers College, Columbia Univ.

Marshall, Marvin. Parenting without Stress: How to Raise Responsible Kids While Keeping a Life of Your Own, unabr. ed. 2010. (Illus.). 288p. 29.97 *(978-0-9700606-6-2(1))* Piper Pr.

Martin, Stephen & Costello, Victoria. The Everything Parent's Guide to Children with OCD: Professional, Reassuring Advice for Raising a Happy, Well-Adjusted Child. 2008. (ENG.). 304p. pap. 14.95 *(978-1-59869-685-1(8))* Adams Media Corp.

Martyn, Suzy. Enjoy the Ride: Tools, Tips, & Inspiration for the Most Common Parenting Challenges. 2009. (ENG.). 142p. pap. 12.95 *(978-0-578-00951-3(X))* Mothers Friend Publishing.

—Enjoying the Ride: The Parenting Journey from Birth to Ten. 2008. (Illus.). 93p. pap. 15.99 incl. cd-rom *(978-0-615-16672-8(5))* Mother's Friend.

Mason, Charlotte. Home Education [Charlotte Mason's Homeschooling Series]. 2011. 210p. pap. 6.85 *(978-1-61427-093-5(7))* Martino Publishing.

McCaffrey, Kitty. Raising Charlie: A Self Help Book for Single Mothers. 2010. 188p. pap. 13.95 *(978-1-4497-0611-1(8)*, WestBow Pr.) Author Solutions, Inc.

McCarthy, Jenna. Parent Trip: From High Heels & Parties to Highchairs & Potties. 2008. (ENG.). 200p. pap. *(978-0-9799135-6-3(X))* Bella Luna Pr.

McClelland, Audrey & Padilla, Colleen. The Digital Mom Handbook: How to Blog, Vlog, Tweet, & Facebook Your Way to a Dream Career at Home. 2011. (ENG.). 256p. pap. 15.99 *(978-0-06-204827-1(9)*, Harper Paperbacks) HarperCollins Pubs.

McClelland, Kylie. Extreme Parenting: Raising children who have Disabilities. 2011. 300p. 29.99 *(978-1-4568-3761-7(3))*; pap. 19.99 *(978-1-4568-3760-0(5))* Xlibris Corp.

McClure, Robin. The Playskool Guide to Baby Play: More Than 300 Games & Activities to Play & Learn with Your Baby. 2007. (ENG.). 224p. per. 14.95 *(978-1-4022-1069-3(8))* Sourcebooks, Inc.

McClure, Robin & Iannelli, Vincent. Baby's First Year: Your Child's First Twelve Months. 2009. (Knack: Make It Easy Ser.). (ENG., Illus.). 256p. pap. 19.95 *(978-1-59921-503-7(9)*, Knack) Globe Pequot Pr., The.

—Knack Parenting a Preschooler: A Complete Illustrated Guide to Preparing Your Child for School — Ages Three to Five. 2010. (Knack: Make It Easy Ser.). (ENG., Illus.). 256p. pap. 19.95 *(978-1-59921-875-5(5)*, Knack) Globe Pequot Pr., The.

McClure, Robin, et al. Raising Your Toddler: A Complete Illustrated Guide from First Steps to Preschool. 2010. (Knack: Make It Easy Ser.). (ENG., Illus.). 256p. pap. 19.95 *(978-1-59921-620-1(5)*, Knack) Globe Pequot Pr., The.

McCord, Alex & van Kempen, Simon. Little Kids, Big City: Tales from a Real House in New York City (with Lessons on Life & Love for Your Own Concrete Jungle) 2010. (ENG.). 224p. pap. 14.95 *(978-0-9821392-2-6(5))* Sterling & Ross Pubs.

McCready, Amy. If I Have to Tell You One More Time... The Revolutionary Program That Gets Your Kids to Listen Without Nagging, Reminding, or Yelling. (ENG., 320p. (gr. 12). 2012. Illus.). pap. 15.95 *(978-0-399-16059-2(0))* 2011. 24.95 *(978-1-58542-864-9(7))* Penguin Group (USA) Inc. (Tarcher).

McGivern, Patricia Seaver. Angel Babies: Messages from Miscarried & Other Lost Babies. 2009. 168p. pap. 15.95 *(978-0-595-53542-2(9))* iUniverse, Inc.

C

McGowan, Dale, et al. Raising Freethinkers: A Practical Guide for Parenting Beyond Belief. 2009. (ENG., Illus.). 288p. pap. 17.95 (978-0-8144-1096-7(0)) Amacom.

McGrail, Anna, et al. The Babycenter Essential Guide to Your Baby's First Year: Expert Advice & Mom-to-Mom Wisdom from the World's Most Popular Parenting Website. 2007. (ENG., Illus.). 480p. pap. 19.99 (978-1-59486-411-7(X)) Rodale Pr., Inc.

McGuire, Sr. Raising Doctors on a Patient's Salary. 2010. 244p. 25.99 (978-1-4490-7699-3(8)); pap. 15.95 (978-1-4490-7698-6(X)) AuthorHouse.

McKenna, James J. Sleeping with Your Baby: A Parent's Guide to Cosleeping. Michels, Dia, ed. 2007. (ENG.). 128p. pap. 14.95 (978-1-930775-34-3(2)) Platypus Media, L.L.C.

McKenzie, Clancy D. "Babies Need Mothers" 2009. 304p. 29.99 (978-1-4363-4308-4(9)); pap. 19.99 (978-1-4363-4307-7(0)) Xlibris Corp.

McLean, William A. Women Helping Boys to Become Men. 2009. 60p. pap. 11.00 (978-1-4389-9664-6(0)) AuthorHouse.

McMillan, Susan & Heren, Louise. Nanny in a Book: The Common-Sense Guide to Childcare. 2012. (ENG., Illus.). 278p. pap. 19.95 (978-0-09-193546-7(6)) Random Hse. GBR. Dist: Independent Pubs. Group.

McNair, Tom. Guiding Parents, Succeeding Children: Reflections on Raising Children in 79 Articles by a Parent, Therapist, Teacher, Coach. 2007. 253p. per. 14.95 (978-0-9786261-3-6(3)) SP & A Pr.

McVey-Noble, Merry, et al. When Your Child Is Cutting: A Parent's Guide to Helping Children Overcome Self-Injury. 2006. (ENG.). 184p. per. 17.95 (978-1-57224-437-5(2)) New Harbinger Pubns.

Meadow, Linda & Rocchio, Lisa. City Baby L. A: The Ultimate Guide for Los Angeles Parents, from Pregnancy to Preschool. 3rd ed. 2011. (Illus.). 272p. pap. 19.95 (978-0-7893-2092-6(4)) Universe Publishing.

Medina, John. Brain Rules for Baby: How to Raise a Smart & Happy Child from Zero to Five. 2011. (ENG.). 294p. pap. 15.00 (978-0-9832633-0-2(2)) Pear Pr.

Meeker, Meg. Boys Should Be Boys: 7 Secrets to Raising Healthy Sons. 2009. (ENG.). 304p. pap. 15.00 (978-0-345-51369-4(X), Ballantine Bks.) Random House Publishing Group.

—Boys Should Be Boys: 7 Secrets to Raising Healthy Sons. 2008. (ENG.). 287p. 24.95 (978-1-59698-057-0(5)) Regnery Publishing, Inc., An Eagle Publishing Co.

Mendelson, Robert A. Oh, Baby! Loving (And Surviving!) Your Newborn's First Year. 2007. (Hundreds of Heads Survival Guides). (ENG., Illus.). 240p. per. 14.95 (978-1-933512-12-9(1)) Hundreds of Heads Bks., Inc.

Mercogliano, Chris. In Defense of Childhood: Protecting Kids' Inner Wildness. 2008. (ENG.). 224p. pap. 16.00 (978-0-8070-3287-9(5)) Beacon Pr.

Miller, Betsy. The Parents' Guide to Hip Dysplasi. 2008. 156p. pap. 17.95 (978-1-59858-744-9(7)) Dog Ear Publishing, LLC.

Miller Marsh, Monica & Turner-Vorveck, Tammy. (Mis)Understanding Families: Learning from Real Families in Our Schools. 2010. (ENG.). 224p. 58.00 (978-0-8077-5038-4(7)) Teachers College Pr., Teachers College, Columbia Univ.

Miller, Sue. Supporting Parents. 2010. (ENG., Illus.). 184p. (C). pap. 43.00 (978-0-335-24176-7(X), 033524176X) McGraw-Hill Education GBR. Dist: McGraw-Hill Cos., The.

Miller, Toby & Miller, Darla Ferris. Guidance & Behavior Management PET. 5th ed. 2006. (ENG.). 128p. (C). pap. 23.95 (978-1-4180-3098-8(8)) Wadsworth.

Mills, Jessica. My Mother Wears Combat Boots: A Parenting Guide for the Rest of Us. 2007. (ENG.). 260p. per. 16.95 (978-1-904859-72-7(0)) AK Pr. GBR. Dist: Consortium Bk. Sales & Distribution.

Miss Gwen's Do's & Don'ts for Parents. 2008. (ENG.). 32p. pap. 16.49 (978-1-4389-1778-8(3)) AuthorHouse.

Mitchell, A. Manic Mums Guide Magnificent Pare. 2008. (Illus.). 272p. (978-1-84850-010-5(6), 779) Hay Hse. UK, Ltd. GBR. Dist: Grantham Bk. Services.

Mitchell, Lorelei. Corporal Punishment & Low-Income Mothers: The Role of Family Structure, Race, & Class in America. 2008. xx, 245p. (C). 104.95 (978-1-60497-531-4(8)) Cambria Pr.

Mock, Melanie Springer. Just Moms. Mock, Melanie Springer & Schneiter, Rebekah D., eds. 2011. 216p. pap. 20.00 (978-1-59498-022-0(5)) Barclay Pr., Inc.

Mondragon, Dona M. Parents Companion. 2006. 23p. 8.00 (978-0-9746644-2-2(1)) Debu, Inc.

Montgomery, Douglas C. & Montgomery, Heather. An Introduction to Childhood: Anthropological Perspectives on Children's Lives. 2008. (ENG.). 296p. 99.95 (978-1-4051-2591-8(8), Wiley-Blackwell) Wiley, John & Sons, Inc.

Montgomery, Heather. An Introduction to Childhood: Anthropological Perspectives on Children's Lives. 2008. (ENG.). 296p. pap. 38.95 (978-1-4051-2590-1(X), Wiley-Blackwell) Wiley, John & Sons, Inc.

Moore, Lynn. The Everything Parent's Guide to Children with Special Needs: A Reassuring, Informative Guide to Your Child's Well-Being & Happiness. 2009. (ENG.). 320p. pap. 14.95 (978-1-60550-163-5(8)) Adams Media Corp.

Moorman, Chick & Haller, Thomas. The Only Three Discipline Strategies You Will Ever Need: Essential Tools for Busy Parents. 2007. (Illus.). 110p. per. (978-0-9772321-4-7(X)) Personal Power Pr.

—Parent Talk Essentials: How to Talk to Kids about Divorce, Sex, Money, School & Being Responsible in Today's World. 2010. (Illus.). 350p. pap. (978-0-9821568-3-4(9)) Personal Power Pr.

Morgan, Druanne. Parenting with LOLLIPOPS. 2008. (Illus.). 128p. pap. 14.95 (978-0-9800402-0-3(5)) Patio Publishing.

Morgan, Jay. Fingerpainting in Psych Class: Artfully Applying Science to Better Work with Children & Teens. 2010. 352p. pap. 23.95 (978-1-4401-6751-5(6)) iUniverse, Inc.

Morgan, Linda. Beyond Smart: Boosting Your Child's Social, Emotional, & Academic Potential. 2010. (ENG.). 148p. pap. 14.95 (978-0-9823454-2-9(9)) ParentMap.

Morris, Desmond. Child: How Children Think, Learn & Grow in the Early Years. 2010. (ENG., Illus.). 192p. 29.99 (978-0-600-61994-9(X), Hamlyn) Octopus Publishing Group GBR. Dist: Hachette Bk. Group.

Morrison, Donald L. Growing Children. 2010. 120p. 21.49 (978-1-4520-7934-9(X)); pap. 10.99 (978-1-4520-7935-6(8)) AuthorHouse.

Morse, Jennifer Roback. Love & Economics: It Takes a Family to Raise a Village. 2008. xviii, 306p. pap. (978-0-9816059-0-6(7)) Ruth Institute Bks.

Morse, Wendy. Beyond the Lines. 2011. pap. 11.99 (978-1-61566-964-6(7)) Tate Publishing & Enterprises, LLC.

Moss, Ted D. Look Out, I'm Parenting Here: A Survival Guide for the Single Parent. 2011. 216p. 27.95 (978-1-4620-1665-5(0)); pap. 17.95 (978-1-4620-1664-8(2)) iUniverse, Inc.

Mother's Associ. 1001 T.I.P.S. Timely Tips & Parenting Strategies. 2009. 190p. 21.99 (978-1-59826-316-9(1)) Feldheim Pubs.

Mounts, Nina S. & Brown, B. Bradford, eds. Linking Parents & Family to Adolescent Peer Relations: Ethnic & Cultural Considerations - New Directions for Child & Adolescent Development. 2007. (J-B CAD Single Issue Child & Adolescent Development Ser.: 86). (ENG., Illus.). 120p. per. 29.00 (978-0-470-17801-0(9), Jossey-Bass) Wiley, John & Sons, Inc.

Mueller, Linda S. How I Raised Three Damn Good Kids. 2009. 80p. pap. 15.99 (978-1-4415-6522-8(1)) Xlibris Corp.

Mulholland, Siobhan. Coping with Crying & Colic: An Easy-to-Follow Guide. 2008. (Easy-to-Follow Guides). (ENG., Illus.). 64p. pap. 12.95 (978-0-09-192344-0(1)) Random Hse. GBR. Dist: Independent Pubs. Group.

—Helping Your Baby to Sleep: An Easy-To-Follow Guide. 2008. (Easy-to-Follow Guides). (ENG., Illus.). 64p. pap. 12.95 (978-0-09-192345-7(X)) Random Hse. GBR. Dist: Independent Pubs. Group.

Muller, Treion. Dad Rules: A Simple Manual for a Complex Job. 2012. pap. 9.99 (978-1-4621-1031-5(2), Plain Sight Publishing) Cedar Fort, Inc./CFI Distribution.

Murkoff, Heidi. What to Expect the First Year. 2008. (ENG.). 832p. pap. 16.95 (978-0-7611-5212-5(1), 0761152121) Workman Publishing Co., Inc.

—What to Expect: the Second Year: From 12 to 24 Months. 2011. (ENG., Illus.). 540p. 24.95 (978-0-7611-6364-0(6), 0761163646) Workman Publishing Co., Inc.

Murkoff, Heidi & Eisenberg, Arlene. What to Expect the First Year. rev. ed. 2009. (ENG.). 832p. 28.95 (978-0-7611-5213-2(X)) Workman Publishing Co., Inc.

Murphy, Eileen M. Childhood in the Past (2008) 2008. (Childhood in the Past Ser.). (C). pap. 50.00 (978-1-84217-346-6(4)) Oxbow Bks., Ltd. GBR. Dist: Brown, David Bk. Co., The.

—Childhood in the Past 3 (2010) 2010. (Childhood in the Past Ser.). (ENG.). 139p. (C). pap. 50.00 (978-1-84217-995-6(0)) Oxbow Bks., Ltd. GBR. Dist: Brown, David Bk. Co., The.

Murray, Andrew. God's Best Secrets. 2011. 66p. pap. 5.95 (978-1-61427-155-0(0)) Martino Publishing.

Myers, Thomas J. Jr. Pick up the Phone & Listen. 2010. 322p. 32.99 (978-1-4415-6776-5(3)); pap. 22.99 (978-1-4415-6667-6(8)) Xlibris Corp.

Nandi, Christine A. The Abc's of Raising a Successful Student: A Meaningful Companion for Parents, Students & Educators. 2009. 324p. pap. 17.99 (978-1-4389-3216-3(2)) AuthorHouse.

National Center for Health Statistics (U.S.) Staff, contrib. by. Adoption Experiences of Women & Men, & Demand for Children to Adopt by Women Ages 18-44 in the United States: Data from Cycle 6 (2002) of the National Survey of Family Growth. 2008. (DHHS Publication Ser.: Nos. 2008-1979). (Illus.). v, 36p. (978-0-8406-0624-2(9)) National Ctr. for Health Statistics.

Naughton Kendall, Keri. The Mommy Manual. 2010. 131p. pap. 14.49 (978-0-557-58782-7(4)) Lulu Enterprises Inc.

Needlman, Robert. Dr. Spock's Baby Basics: Take Charge Parenting Guides. 2009. (ENG.). 304p. pap. 20.95 (978-1-4391-6941-4(1)) Pocket Books.

Neel, Ruby. The Gift of Giving. 2010. 32p. pap. 14.49 (978-1-4490-7069-4(8)) AuthorHouse.

Neely, Alexis Martin. Wear Clean Underwear! A Fast, Fun, Friendly & Essential Guide to Legal Planning for Busy Parents. 2008. (ENG.). 152p. pap. 16.95 (978-1-60037-441-8(7)) Morgan James Publishing.

Nelsen, Jane, et al. Positive Discipline - The First Three Years: From Infant to Toddler — Laying the Foundation for Raising a Capable, Confident Child. 2nd ed. 2007. (Positive Discipline Library). (ENG., Illus.). 304p. pap. 16.99 (978-0-307-34159-4(3), Three Rivers Pr.) Crown Publishing Group.

—Preschoolers: For Their Early Years — Raising Children Who Are Responsible, Respectful, & Resourceful. 3rd ed. 2007. (Positive Discipline Library). (ENG., Illus.). 368p. per. 16.99 (978-0-307-34160-0(7), Three Rivers Pr.) Crown Publishing Group.

Nelson, Gerald E. The One-Minute Scolding: The Amazingly Effective Approach to Child Discipline. 2009. 160p. 29.99 (978-1-4363-9555-7(0)); pap. 19.99 (978-1-4363-9554-0(2)) Xlibris Corp.

Netmums Cookery Book Staff, et al. Toddling to Ten: Your Common Parenting Problems Solved - The Netmums Guide to the Challenges of Childhood. 2008. (ENG.). 416p. pap. 25.95 (978-0-7553-1607-6(X)) Headline Bk. Publishing GBR. Dist: Independent Pubs. Group.

Neville, Helen F. Is This a Phase? Child Development & Parent Strategies, Birth to 6 Years. 2006. (ENG., Illus.). 220p. pap. 22.95 (978-1-884734-63-2(4)) Parenting Pr., Inc.

Neville, Helen Fowler. Is This a Phase? Child Development & Parent Strategies, Birth to 6 Years. 2006. (ENG., Illus.). 220p. lib. bdg. 42.95 (978-1-884734-64-9(2)) Parenting Pr., Inc.

Newmark, Gerald. How to Raise Emotionally Healthy Children: Meeting the Five Critical Needs of Children - And Parents Too! 2007. Orig. Title: Parents, Expectant Parents, All Persons Concerned with Childcare. 184p. pap. (978-0-932767-13-4(3)) NMI Pubs.

Newsom, Emery. The Parent's Guide for Raising Safer K-12 Students, 2 vols., Vol. 2. 2nd ed. 2007. 120p. pap. 8.99 (978-0-9787143-6-9(9)) Carrington Bks.

Newson, Elizabeth & Newsom, John. Four Years Old in & Urban Community. 2007. 605p. 190.00 (978-0-415-41755-6(4)) Routledge.

Newson, John & Newson, Elizabeth. Four Years Old in an Urban Community. 2007. (ENG.). 570p. (gr. 11). pap. 49.95 (978-0-202-36164-2(0)) Aldine Transaction.

Newton, Ruth P. The Attachment Connection: Parenting a Secure & Confident Child Using the Science of Attachment Theory. 2008. (ENG., Illus.). 240p. pap. 16.95 (978-1-57224-520-4(4)) New Harbinger Pubns.

Nicholasen, Michelle & O'Neal, Barbara. I Brake for Meltdowns: How to Handle the Most Exasperating Behavior of Your 2- To 5-Year-Old. 2008. (ENG.). 336p. pap. 14.95 (978-0-7382-1167-1(2)) Da Capo Pr., Inc.

Nichols, Clay, et al. Dadlabs' Guide to Fatherhood: Pregnancy & Year One. 2009. (ENG., Illus.). 192p. pap. 16.95 (978-1-59474-318-4(5)) Quirk Bks.

Nicholson, Barbara & Parker, Lysa. Attached at the Heart: 8 Proven Parenting Principles for Raising Connected & Compassionate Children. 2009. 380p. pap. 23.95 (978-1-935278-86-3(X), iUniverse Star) iUniverse, Inc.

Nilsen, Barbara Ann. Week by Week: Plans for Documenting Children's Development, Reprint. 4th ed. 2009. (ENG.). 416p. (C). pap. 112.95 (978-1-4390-4376-9(0)) Delmar Cengage Learning.

Nixon, Caroline. A Mom's Guide to Sanity: The Journey of a Metaphysical Mama - How to Stay Calm, Cool & Collected While Living in a Sea of Chaos Known as Child Rearing. 2008. 155p. pap. 24.95 (978-1-60672-778-2(8)) PublishAmerica, Inc.

Nolan, Coleen. Mum to Mum: Happy Memories & Honest Advice, from a Real Mum. 2010. (ENG., Illus.). 336p. 19.95 (978-0-283-07107-2(9)); 342p. pap. 19.95 (978-0-283-07122-5(2)) Macmillan Pubs., Ltd. GBR. Dist: Independent Pubs. Group.

Nordine, Ray & Vettrus, Linda. Parenting with C. A. R. E. Credibility, Assertiveness, Responsibility, Esteem-Building. Date not set. 128p. pap. 9.95 (978-1-929293-02-5(X)) Whole Child Institute - WCI.

Nowicki, Stephen, et al. Starting Kids off Right: How to Raise Confident Children Who Can Make Friends & Build Healthy Relationships, 1 vol. 2008. (ENG., Illus.). 224p. pap. 16.95 (978-1-56145-447-1(8)) Peachtree Pubs.

Nyagah, Lucy. Who Is Watching Your Child? A Step-by Step Guide for Families & Nannies. 2010. 110p. 29.99 (978-1-4363-5505-6(2)); pap. 19.99 (978-1-4363-5504-9(4)) Xlibris Corp.

Oddo, Jeffrey B. The 10 Kidmandments: Ten Principles for Raising Successful Children. 2011. (Illus.). 89p. 19.95 (978-1-928782-27-8(2), Strong Bks.) Publishing Directions, LLC.

O'Donohue, Mary. The When You Say Thank You, Mean It: And 11 Other Lessons for Instilling Lifelong Values in Your Children. 2010. (ENG.). 256p. pap. 16.95 (978-1-4405-0377-1(X)) Adams Media Corp.

O'Dwyer, Starbuck. How to Raise A Good Kid: A Guide to Growing up for Parents & Children. 2011. (ENG.). 188p. pap. 11.99 (978-0-615-48532-4(4)) Green Chair Publishing.

Offen, Rita. The Chilled Parent - Effective Parenting - Peacefully & Powerfully. 2007. (Illus.). 144p. per. (978-1-905823-19-2(3)) Academy Pr. Ltd.

Okwany, Auma, et al. The Role of Local Knowledge & Culture in Child Care in Africa: A Sociological Study of Several Ethnic Groups in Kenya & Uganda. 2011. 168p. (978-0-7734-1583-6(1)) Mellen, Edwin Pr., The.

Oliver, Christopher. Baby Sleepytime: The CD Scientifically Proven to Put Your Baby to Sleep — Fast. 2007. (ENG., Illus.). 48p. 19.95 (978-1-57826-260-1(7), Hatherleigh Pr.) Hatherleigh Co., Ltd., The.

O'Loughlin, Michael. The Subject of Childhood. 2008. (Rethinking Childhood Ser.). 99.95 (978-1-4331-0347-6(8)); pap. 32.95 (978-1-4331-0120-5(3)) Lang, Peter Publishing, Inc.

Olusola, Lily. God, I Want My Baby! A source of hope & encouragement for those who Wait. 2011. 116p. pap. 15.66 (978-1-4567-7107-2(8)) AuthorHouse.

Omer, Haim. The New Authority: Family, School, & Community. Herbsman, Michal & Sappir, Shoshana London, trs. from HEB. 2010. (ENG.). 270p. pap. 29.99 (978-0-521-13776-8(4)); (Illus.). 296p. 90.00 (978-0-521-76137-6(9)) Cambridge Univ. Pr.

Oppenheimer, Sharifa. Heaven on Earth: A Handbook for Parents of Young Children. 2006. (Illus.). 235p. per. 25.00 (978-0-88010-566-8(6)) SteinerBooks, Inc.

Orange & O'Flynn. How to Stop Your Kids Watching Tv. 2007. (Illus.). xv, 180p. (978-1-4019-1547-6(7), 466) Hay Hse. UK, Ltd. GBR. Dist: Grantham Bk. Services.

Orlans, Michael & Levy, Terry M. Healing Parents: Helping Wounded Children Learn to Trust & Love. 2006. (Illus.). 304p. per. (978-1-58760-096-8(X), CWLA Pr.) Child Welfare League of America, Inc.

Orlowek, Noach, contrib. by. Raising Roses among the Thorns: Bringing up Spiritually Healthy Children in Today's Society. 371p. 25.99 (978-1-58330-519-5(X)) Feldheim Pubs.

Orr, Brian & Raskin, Donna. The Everything Guide to Raising a Two-Year-Old: From Personality & Behavior to Nutrition & Health — A Complete Handbook. 2006. (ENG.). 288p. per. 12.95 (978-1-59337-728-1(2)) Adams Media Corp.

O'Sullivan, June. Leadership Skills in the Early Years: Making a Difference. 2009. (ENG.). 176p. 39.95 (978-1-85539-470-4(7), Network Continuum Education) Continuum International Publishing Group, Ltd. GBR. Dist: National Bk. Network.

Ozkaptan, Halim. Love Is Not Enough - to Prepare Your Child for Life's Challenges. 2010. 143p. pap. 18.84 (978-0-557-18647-1(1)) Lulu Enterprises Inc.

Paciorek, Karen Menke. Annual Editions: Early Childhood Education 12/13. 33rd ed. 2012. (Annual Editions Ser.). (ENG., Illus.). 240p. (C). pap. 44.00 (978-0-07-805126-5(6), 0078051266, McGraw-Hill/Dushkin) McGraw-Hill Higher Education.

Palka, Joe. Positive Penelope & Friends. 2010. 16p. 11.99 (978-1-4520-1855-3(3)) AuthorHouse.

Palm Beach Community College & Children and Families Research Group Staff. Special Needs Appropriate Practices. rev. ed. 2009. (ENG.). 222p. pap. 24.15 (978-0-7575-5482-7(2)) Kendall Hunt Publishing Co.

Palmer, Sue. Detoxing Childhood: What Parents Need to Know to Raise Happy, Successful Children. 2008. (ENG., Illus.). 176p. pap. 14.95 (978-0-7528-9010-4(7)) Orion Bks. Ltd. GBR. Dist: Sterling Publishing Co., Inc.

Pantley, Elizabeth & Pantley. The No-Cry Nap Solution: Guaranteed Gentle Ways to Solve All Your Naptime Problems. 2008. (Pantley Ser.). (ENG., Illus.). 256p. pap. 15.95 (978-0-07-159695-4(X), 007159695X) McGraw-Hill Cos., The.

Papalia, Olds & Cram101 Textbook Reviews Staff. A Child's World: Infancy Through Adolescence. 2007. 280p. per. 15.95 (978-1-4288-2700-4(5)) Cram101 Inc.

Parens, Henri. Taming Aggression in Your Child: How to Avoid Raising Bullies, Delinquents, or Trouble-Makers. 2012. (978-0-7657-0898-4(1)) 2011. (ENG.). 240p. (gr. 17). 70.00 (978-0-7657-0896-0(5)) 2011. (ENG.). 240p. (gr. 17). pap. 29.99 (978-0-7657-0897-7(3)) Rowman & Littlefield Publishers, Inc. (Aronson, Jason).

Parr, Daryl O'Brien. Molested Mommies When Incest Survivors Become Parents: A Qualitative Study. 2010. 138p. pap. 19.99 (978-1-4500-1605-6(7)) Xlibris Corp.

Paschal, Angelia M. Voices of African-American Teen Fathers: I'm Doing What I Got to Do. 2006. (ENG.). 246p. per. 54.95 (978-0-7890-2738-2(0)); (Illus.). 128.00 (978-0-7890-2737-5(2)) Routledge.

Pascoe, Robin. Raising Global Nomads: Parenting Abroad in an On-Demand World. 2006. 248p. per. (978-0-9686760-3-5(0)) Expatriate Pr.

Paszkowska-Rogacz, Anna. Parents As Career Counsellors of Their Children. 2010. 168p. pap. (978-3-8383-8632-4(9)) Lambert Academic Publishing.

Payne, Kim John & Ross, Lisa M. Simplicity Parenting: Using the Extraordinary Power of Less to Raise Calmer, Happier, & More Secure Kids. 2010. (ENG.). 256p. pap. 15.00 (978-0-345-50798-3(3), Ballantine Bks.) Random House Publishing Group.

Pearce, John. Baby & Toddler Sleep Programme. 160p. pap. 17.95 (978-0-09-181571-4(1)) Random Hse. GBR. Dist: Trafalgar Square Publishing.

Pearman, Christopher B & Newhem, Ian Blake. Dream So Big: A Parent's Guide to Helping Your Child Believe & Achieve. 2010. (ENG.). 256p. 19.95 (978-1-4405-0402-0(4)) Adams Media Corp.

Peele, Amy S. Aunt Mary's Guide to Raising Children the Old-Fashioned Way. 2009. 184p. pap. 15.95 (978-0-557-08442-5(3)) Lulu Enterprises Inc.

Pendleton McClain. The Intentional Parenting Plan: Tipp. 2009. 172p. pap. 20.99 (978-1-4389-9740-7(X)) AuthorHouse.

Penn, Frederick. 111 Wonderful Ways to Build Children's Self Esteem & Confidence Everyday. 2009. 228p. 24.99 (978-1-4389-9136-8(3)); pap. 19.95 (978-1-4389-9135-1(5)) AuthorHouse.

Percy, Bernard, et al. How to Grow a Child: A Child's Advice to Parents. 2009. 134p. pap. 15.95 (978-1-888045-24-6(8)) Action Publishing, LLC.

Pereira, Hilary. Raise a Confident Child: A Teach Yourself Guide. 2011. (Teach Yourself: General Reference Ser.). (ENG.). 224p. pap. 15.00 (978-0-07-176946-4(3), 0071769463) McGraw-Hill Cos., The.

Perry, R. Scott. Making Sense of Your Child's Hearing Loss: A Guide for Parents. 2007. pap. 14.95 (978-0-9795997-1-2(7)) Parchment Hill.

Phelan, Thomas W. Surviving Your Adolescents: How to Manage & Let Go of Your 13-18 Year Olds. 3rd ed. 2012. (ENG.). 192p. pap. 14.95 (978-1-889140-60-5(0)) ParentMagic, Inc.

Phelan, Thomas W. 1-2-3 Magic: Effective Discipline for Children 2-12. 4th ed. 2010. (ENG., Illus.). 224p. pap. 14.95 (978-1-889140-43-8(0)) ParentMagic, Inc.

Pickhardt, Carl E. The Future of Your Only Child: How to Guide Your Child to a Happy & Successful Life. 2008. (ENG.). 256p. pap. 15.00 (978-1-4039-8417-3(4)) Palgrave Macmillan.

—Stop the Screaming: How to Turn Angry Conflict with Your Child into Positive Communication. 2009. (ENG.). 240p. pap. 14.95 (978-0-230-60645-6(8)) Palgrave Macmillan.

Pierce, Anne. Ships without a Shore: America's Undernurtured Children. 2009. (ENG., Illus.). 276p. pap. 29.95 (978-1-4128-1090-6(6)) Transaction Pubs.

Piette, Linda. Just Two More Bites! Helping Picky Eaters Say Yes to Food. 2006. (ENG., Illus.). 304p. per. 13.95 (978-1-4000-8109-7(2), Three Rivers Pr.) Crown Publishing Group.

Placone, Pilar. Mindful Parent Happy Child: A Guide to Raising Joyful & Resilient Children. 2011. 299p. pap. 15.95 (978-0-615-35878-9(0)) Alaya Pr., Pili Enterprises, Inc.

Player, Corrie Lynn, et al. The Everything Parent's Guide to Raising Your Adopted Child: A Complete Handbook to Welcoming Your Adopted Child into Your Heart & Home. 2008. (ENG., Illus.). 304p. pap. 14.95 *(978-1-59869-606-6(8))* Adams Media Corp.

Plott, Kathryn. Can You Do What I Can Do? 2010. 36p. pap. 15.49 *(978-1-4520-1620-7(8))* AuthorHouse.

Pollack, Neal. Alternadad: The True Story of One Family's Struggle to Raise a Cool Kid in America. 2008. (ENG., Illus.). 368p. pap. 14.95 *(978-1-4000-9558-2(1),* Anchor) Knopf Doubleday Publishing Group.

Pollack, William. Real Boys: Rescuing Our Sons from the Myths of Boyhood. 480p. pap. 35.00 *(978-0-908011-42-1(3))* Scribe Pubns. AUS. Dist: Independent Pubs. Group.

Pope, Liz. Love at Home: Embracing the Divine Call of Full-Time Motherhood. 2009. 144p. pap. 24.95 *(978-1-60749-020-3(X))* PublishAmerica, Inc.

Popiel, Jennifer J. Rousseau's Daughters: Domesticity, Education, & Autonomy in Modern France. 2008. (Becoming Modern: New Nineteenth-Century Studies). (ENG., Illus.). 284p. lib. bdg. 35.00 *(978-1-58465-732-3(4),* University of New Hampshire Press) Univ. Pr. of New England.

Popkin, Michael H. Active Parenting of Teens, 3rd Edition. 3rd ed. 2009. (ENG.). 232p. pap. 14.95 *(978-1-59723-231-9(9))* Active Parenting Pubs.

Preston, Koko. Organic Parenting: The Prevention of Parent Deficit Disorder. 2009. (ENG.). 144p. pap. 14.95 *(978-1-935359-03-6(7))* Book Pubs. Network.

Publications International Staff, ed. 500 Things to Do with Your Children Before They Grow Up. 2010. 320p. 15.98 *(978-1-60553-481-7(1),* PIL Kids) Publications International, Ltd.

Raet, Iya. Holistic Parenting: From the pan-Afrikan Perspective. 2007. pap. 15.00 *(978-1-56411-500-3(3),* YBBG#490, United Sisters Bks.) UBUS Communications Systems.

Raguenaud, Virginie. Bilingual by Choice: The Family Guide for Raising Kids in Two (or More!) Languages. 2009. (ENG., Illus.). 240p. 19.95 *(978-1-85788-526-2(0))* Ebsco Publishing.

Rainn, Elizabeth. Let the Children Speak, 1 vol. 2009. 104p. pap. 16.95 *(978-1-61546-083-0(7))* PublishAmerica, Inc.

Randol, Susan. Mom's Survival Guide: Save Time, Money, & Your Sanity. Redbook Magazine Editors, ed. 2010. (ENG., Illus.). 240p. pap. 16.95 *(978-1-58816-804-7(2))* Hearst Communications, Inc.

Reasoner, Robert W. & Lane, Marilyn L. Parenting with Purpose: Five Keys to Raising Children with Values & Vision. 2007. (ENG., Illus.). 240p. pap. 14.95 *(978-1-932181-25-8(3))* Personhood Pr.

Recipes from Parenting. 2nd ed. 164p. reprint ed. pap. 12.95 *(978-0-9626359-1-5(X))* McDaniel, Sandy Spurgeon Inc.

Reed, Lori. Life Lessons for Little Ones: A Parental Guide Teaching Tiny Babies about Their New World. 2009. 72p. pap. 24.99 *(978-1-4389-5763-0(7))* AuthorHouse.

Reed, Pam L. Taming Your Toddler (& Yourself) 2006. 172p. pap. 14.95 *(978-0-7414-3672-6(8))* Infinity Publishing.

Regan-Loomis, Meghan. Juggling Twins: The Best Tips, Tricks, & Strategies from Pregnancy to the Toddler Years. 2008. (ENG.). 336p. pap. 16.95 *(978-1-4022-1405-9(7))* Sourcebooks, Inc.

Reid, Erica. The Thriving Child: Parenting Successfully through Allergies, Asthma & Other Common Challenges. 2012. (ENG.). 272p. 19.99 *(978-0-89296-864-0(8))* Center St.

Reimers, Thomas. Help! There's a Toddler in the House! 2011. (ENG.). 220p. pap. 14.95 *(978-1-934490-19-8(9))* Boys Town Pr.

Reisser, Paul C. Baby & Child Care: From Pre-Birth Through the Teen Years. rev. ed. 2007. (ENG., Illus.). 928p. 29.97 *(978-1-4143-1305-4(5))* Tyndale Hse. Pubs.

Reith, Judy. Be a Great Mum. 2010. (Teach Yourself Ser.). (ENG., Illus.). 224p. pap. 18.95 *(978-1-4441-0380-9(6),* Hodder & Stoughton) Hodder General Publishing Div. GBR. Dist: Independent Pubs. Group.

Renzulli, Joseph S., et al. Light up Your Child's Mind: Finding a Unique Pathway to Happiness & Success. 2009. (ENG.). 304p. 25.99 *(978-0-316-00398-8(0))* Little Brown & Co.

Rhodes, Alison. Honey, I Lost the Baby in the Produce Aisle! Safety Mom's Guide to Childproofing Your Life. 2011. (ENG.). 240p. pap. 16.99 *(978-1-4354-5970-0(9))* Course Technology.

Rice, Joan. Parenting Solutions: Encouragement for Everyday Parenting. 2009. (ENG., Illus.). 208p. pap. 18.95 *(978-1-55778-879-5(0))* Paragon Hse. Pubs.

Rich, Dorothy. Megaskills: Building Our Children's Character & Achievement for School & Life. 2nd ed. 2008. (ENG.). 384p. pap. 16.99 *(978-1-4022-1215-4(1))* Sourcebooks, Inc.

Rich, Dorothy & Mattox, Beverly. Megaskills for Babies, Toddlers & Beyond: Building Your Child's Happiness & Success in School & Life. 2009. (ENG.). 304p. pap. 14.95 *(978-1-4022-1214-7(3))* Sourcebooks, Inc.

Rich, Joe. Parenting: The Long Journey. 2007. (ENG., Illus.). 256p. pap. 21.95 *(978-0-470-83923-2(6),* Wiley) Wiley, John & Sons, Inc.

Richardson, Rhonda A. & Pevec, A. Margaret. What Kids Really Want to Ask: Using Movies to Start Meaningful Conversations. 2007. (Illus.). 192p. per. 12.95 *(978-1-889242-31-6(4))* VanderWyk & Burnham.

Ricks, Marie. The Children You Want with the Kids You Have. 2010. 24p. pap. 17.99 *(978-1-60641-665-5(0))* Deseret Bk. Co.

Riekerk, Marjon. How to Give Children an Emotional Head Start. Karlsen, Torill E., tr. Date not set. (Illus.). 13p. pap. 2.00 *(978-82-91816-27-2(1))* Rational Island Pubs.

Rigby, Jill. Raising Respectful Children in a Disrespectful World. 2006. (ENG., Illus.). 208p. pap. 14.99 *(978-1-58229-574-9(3),* Howard Bks.) Howard Books.

—Raising Unselfish Children in a Self-Absorbed World. 2008. (ENG.). 288p. pap. 14.99 *(978-1-4165-5842-2(X),* Howard Bks.) Howard Books.

Riley, Douglas. Dr. Riley's Box of Tricks: 80 Uncommon Solutions for Everyday Parenting Problems. 2011. (ENG.). 240p. pap. 15.00 *(978-0-7382-1428-3(0))* Da Capo Pr., Inc.

Riley, Tim. First the Broccoli, Then the Ice Cream: A Parent's Guide to Deliberate Discipline. 2010. 208p. pap. 15.95 *(978-0-9841423-1-6(2))* Two Fish, Inc.

Rimm, Sylvia B. How to Parent So Children Will Learn: Strategies for Raising Happy, Achieving Children. 3rd ed. 2008. (Illus.). 318p. pap. 24.95 *(978-0-910707-86-2(3))* Great Potential Pr., Inc.

Ripudaman, Singh, et al. Rearing a Child: Prenatal & Natal Care. 2011. 112p. pap. *(978-3-639-33142-4(7))* VDM Verlag Dr. Mueller e.K.

Roberts, Theresa. ABC's of Bumps & Bruises, a guide to home & herbal remedies for Children. 2008. 188p. pap. 19.95 *(978-1-4357-0922-5(5))* Lulu Enterprises Inc.

Robinson, Barbara M. Tangled Webs. 2009. 144p. (ENG.). 28.96 *(978-0-557-09128-7(4));* pap. 13.48 *(978-0-557-07893-6(8))* Lulu Enterprises Inc.

Robinson, Devin A. Raising a Rebel Son: What's Really Wrong with Him & How to Tackle It! 2008. 151p. pap. *(978-978-8174-78-3(7))* Loretta Davis.

Rock, Rose & Graham, Valerie. Mama Rock's Rules: Ten Lessons for Raising a Houseful of Successful Children. 256p. 2009. pap. 16.99 *(978-0-06-153611-3(3),* Harper Paperbacks) 2008. (ENG.). 22.95 *(978-0-06-153612-0(1),* Morrow, William & Co.) HarperCollins Pubs.

Rodinsky, Katie. Mummy. 2009. (Illus.). 204p. pap. 14.49 *(978-1-4490-3309-5(1))* AuthorHouse.

Roehlkepartain, Jolene L. Parenting Preschoolers with a Purpose: Caring for Your Kids & Yourself. 2006. (ENG., Illus.). 232p. pap. 13.95 *(978-1-57482-239-7(X))* Search Institute.

Rogers, Russ. The 17 Laws of Parenting. 2006. (ENG.). 24.99 *(978-1-60034-744-3(4));* pap. 14.99 *(978-1-60034-743-6(6))* Xulon Pr., Inc.

Roizen, Michael F. & Oz, Mehmet C. You - Raising Your Child: The Owner's Manual from First Breath to First Grade. 2010. (ENG., Illus.). 496p. 24.99 *(978-1-4391-0948-9(6),* Free Pr.) Free Pr.

Roper, Jane. Double Time: How I Survived — -and Mostly Thrived — -Through the First Three Years of Mothering Twins. 2012. (ENG.). 272p. 24.99 *(978-0-312-55223-7(8))* St. Martin's Pr.

Rosemond, John. The Well-Behaved Child: Discipline That Really Works! 2011. 240p. pap. 15.99 *(978-0-8499-4715-5(4))* Nelson, Thomas Inc.

Rosenthal, S. L. Childology: Are You Ready for the Truth?, 1 vol. 2010. 328p. pap. 29.95 *(978-1-4512-9355-5(0))* PublishAmerica, Inc.

Ross, Julie A. How to Hug a Porcupine: Negotiating the Prickly Points of the Tween Years. 2008. (ENG., Illus.). 224p. pap. 15.95 *(978-0-07-154589-1(1),* 0071545891) McGraw-Hill Cos., The.

Rowe, Marcus. Goodnight Fingers Goodnight Toes. 2011. (Illus.). 56p. 9.95 *(978-1-60755-269-7(8))* Willow Creek Pr., Inc.

Rozman, Deborah. Meditation for Children: Pathways to Happiness, Harmony, Creativity & Fun for the Family. 3rd ed. 2008. (ENG.). 153p. pap. 14.95 *(978-0-932040-62-6(4))* Integral Yoga Pubns.

Rudd, Betty. Help Your Child Develop Emotional Literacy: The Parents' Guide to Happy Children. 2009. (Help Your Child to Succeed Ser.). (ENG., Illus.). 128p. 24.95 *(978-1-85539-467-4(7),* Network Continuum Education) Continuum International Publishing Group, Ltd. GBR. Dist: National Bk. Network.

Runkel, Hal Edward. ScreamFree Parenting: The Revolutionary Approach to Raising Your Kids by Keeping Your Cool. 2008. (ENG.). 240p. pap. 13.99 *(978-0-7679-2743-7(5))* Broadway Bks.

—ScreamFree Parenting: The Revolutionary Approach to Raising Your Kids by Keeping Your Cool. 2008. (ENG.). 256p. pap. 13.99 *(978-1-4000-7373-3(1))* Doubleday Religious Publishing Group, The.

Rutherford, Markella B. Adult Supervision Required: Private Freedom & Public Constraints for Parents & Children. 2011. (Families in Focus Ser.). (ENG.). 208p. 45.95 *(978-0-8135-5149-4(8))* Rutgers Univ. Pr.

Rutledge, Rebecca. Playskool Guide to Raising Girls: Essential Information & Practical Advice for Raising Happy, Confident Girls. 2008. (Playskool Ser.). 304p. pap. 14.95 *(978-1-4022-1444-8(8))* Sourcebooks, Inc.

Rutten, Owner/Designer Kristin. Baby's First Year Memory Logbook. 2010. 344p. pap. 34.95 *(978-0-557-41026-2(6))* Lulu Enterprises Inc.

Saban, Cheryl. New Mother's Survival Guide. 2008. (Illus.). 112p. *(978-1-84597-713-9(0))* Ryland Peters & Small.

Sabatello, Maya. Children's Bioethics: The International Biopolitical Discourse on Harmful Traditional Practices & the Right of the Child to Cultural Identity. 2009. 250p. *(978-90-04-17341-5(2))* BRILL.

Sadler, Katharine. What Adults Need to Know about Kids & Substance Use: Dealing with Alcohol, Tobacco, & Other Drugs. 2011. (ENG., Illus.). 118p. pap. 29.95 *(978-1-57482-495-7(3))* Search Institute.

Sam Goldstein. A Different Kind of Resilience: Collected Essays, 1999-2009. 2010. 300p. pap. 21.95 *(978-1-4502-0672-3(7))* iUniverse, Inc.

Samuel, John. Parenting for Tomorrow. 2008. (ENG.). 123p. pap. 10.95 *(978-0-533-15839-3(7))* Vantage Pr., Inc.

Sanderson, Catherine A. Slow & Steady Parenting: Active Child-Raising for the Long Haul, Birth to Age 3: Avoiding the Short-Term Solutions That Lead to Long-Term Problems. 2007. (ENG.). 224p. per. 15.95 *(978-1-59077-045-0(5))* Evans, M. & Co., Inc.

Sargent, Emma. Flying Start: Coaching Your Children for Life. 2007. (ENG., Illus.). 224p. per. 17.95 *(978-1-904879-67-1(5))* Cyan Communications GBR. Dist: Independent Pubs. Group.

—Parent: What the Best Parents Know, Do & Say. 2009. (ENG.). 200p. (C). pap. 19.99 *(978-0-273-72493-3(2))* FT Press.

Sarles, Sharon. Faith Family Learing: Great Shalom at Home. 2008. pap. *(978-0-9657770-5-6(7))* Organizational Strategies Pub.

Schafer, Alyson. Ain't Misbehavin' Tactics for Tantrums, Meltdowns, Bedtime Blues & Other Perfectly Normal Kid Behaviors. 2011. (ENG.). 288p. pap. 14.95 *(978-0-470-67909-8(3),* Wiley) Wiley, John & Sons, Inc.

—Honey, I Wrecked the Kids: When Yelling, Screaming, Threats, Bribes, Time-Outs, Sticker Charts & Removing Privileges All Don't Work. 2009. (ENG.). 256p. pap. 18.95 *(978-0-470-15603-2(1),* Wiley) Wiley, John & Sons, Inc.

Schroeder, Ruth Knott. Coach Yourself Through the Autism Spectrum. 2009. (ENG., Illus.). 240p. pap. *(978-1-84905-801-8(6))* Kingsley, Jessica Ltd.

Schwarz Faacap Difapa, Eitan. Kids, Parents, & Technology: An Instruction Manual for Young Families. 2010. 244p. pap. 26.95 *(978-0-557-19482-7(2))* Lulu Enterprises Inc.

Schwarz, Jay. 21 Simple Things Every New Father Must Know. 2008. 27p. 29.95 *(978-1-4357-2140-1(3))* Lulu Enterprises Inc.

Schweiger, Ingrid. Self-Esteem for A Lifetime. 2008. 132p. pap. 15.99 *(978-1-4343-7225-3(1))* AuthorHouse.

Sebrey, Leann. The Parents' Guide to Baby Signs: Early Communication with Your Infant. 2009. (ENG., Illus.). 128p. (gr. k — 1). pap. 19.95 *(978-1-56368-398-5(9))* Gallaudet Univ. Pr.

Sedor, Daniel L. Model Coach: A Common Sense Guide for Coaches of Youth Sports. 2008. 108p. 22.95 *(978-0-595-50186-1(9))* iUniverse, Inc.

Seidenfaden, Kirsten. The Vibrant Family: A Handbook for Parents & Professionals. Draiby, Pat, ed. 2011. (Systemic Thinking & Practice Ser.). 240p. pap. 34.95 *(978-1-85575-818-6(0))* Karnac Bks. GBR. Dist: Stylus Publishing, LLC.

Seldin, Tim. How to Raise an Amazing Child the Montessori Way. 2006. (ENG., Illus.). 192p. pap. 20.00 *(978-0-7566-2505-4(X))* Dorling Kindersley Publishing, Inc.

Sells, Scott. Parenting the Extreme Teenager. Date not set. *(978-0-312-27781-9(4))* St. Martin's Pr.

Seti, Candice. Parenting Boot Camp: A Survival Guide for New Parents. 2009. 98p. pap. 17.00 *(978-0-557-03432-1(9))* Lulu Enterprises Inc.

Shapiro, Lawrence. A Parent's Guide to Getting Kids Out of the Family Bed: A Twenty-One Day Program. 2008. (Instant Help Ser.). 110p. pap. 16.95 *(978-1-931704-29-8(5))* Play2Grow.

Shapiro, Lawrence E., et al. The Baby Emergency Handbook: Lifesaving Information Every Parent Needs to Know. 2008. (ENG., Illus.). 192p. pap. 14.95 *(978-1-57224-566-2(2))* New Harbinger Pubns.

Sharry, John. Positive Parenting: Bringing up Responsible, Well-behaved & Happy Children. 2008. (ENG., Illus.). 175p. pap. 13.95 *(978-1-84730-077-5(4))* Veritas Pubns. IRL. Dist: Dufour Editions, Inc.

Shearin Karres, Erika V. The Everything Parent's Guide to Raising Girls: All you need to help your daughter develop confidence, achieve self-esteem, & improve Communication. 2nd ed. 2011. (ENG.). 320p. pap. 14.95 *(978-1-4405-1098-4(9))* Adams Media Corp.

Shelly, Pamela. 9 Steps to Conscious Parenting: Raising Healthy, Happy, & Confident Children. 2011. 96p. pap. 14.95 *(978-1-4575-0490-7(1))* Dog Ear Publishing, LLC.

Shiller, Virginia M. Recompensas para niños Por Buen Comportamiento. 2006. Orig. Title: Rewards for Kids!: Ready-to-Use Charts & Activities for Positive Parenting. (SPA.). per. 23.95 *(978-0-9774724-4-4(2))* American Psychological Assn.

Shockney, E. A. Delusional Entitlement Disorder: The Unofficial Disease That Is Destroying America's Spirit. 2009. 156p. pap. 19.95 *(978-1-4401-8887-9(4))* iUniverse, Inc.

Siegel, Daniel J. & Bryson, Tina Payne. The Whole-Brain Child: 12 Revolutionary Strategies to Nurture Your Child's Developing Mind, Survive Everyday Parenting Struggles, & Help Your Family Thrive. 2011. (ENG.). 192p. 24.00 *(978-0-553-80791-2(9),* Delacorte Pr) Random House Publishing Group.

Silber, Julie. A Little Treasure or a Monster in the Making! 2008. 106p. pap. 16.95 *(978-1-60563-716-7(5))* PublishAmerica, Inc.

Silberg, J. & Silberg, Jackie. Juegos para Hacer Pensar a los Ninos de 1 a 3 Anos. (SPA.). 140p. *(978-84-95456-45-8(1),* 87125) Ediciones Oniro S.A.

Silverman, Phyllis R. & Kelly, Madelyn. A Parent's Guide to Raising Grieving Children: Rebuilding Your Family after the Death of a Loved One. 2009. (ENG., Illus.). 272p. (YA). pap. 17.95 *(978-0-19-532884-4(1))* Oxford Univ. Pr., Inc.

Simmons, Justine, et al. Take Back Your Family: How to Raise Respectful & Loving Kids in a Dysfunctional World. 2009. (ENG.). 288p. (gr. 12-18). 15.00 *(978-1-59240-501-5(0),* Gotham) Penguin Group (USA) Inc.

Simpson, Teresa R. Everything Baby Sign Language Book: Get an Early Start Communicating with Your Baby! 2008. (ENG., Illus.). 256p. pap. 14.95 *(978-1-59869-564-9(9))* Adams Media Corp.

Singer, Jen. Stop Second-Guessing Yourself — The Preschool Years: The Field-Tested Guide to Confident Parenting. 2009. (Momma Said Ser.). (ENG.). 264p. pap. 14.95 *(978-0-7573-1417-9(1))* Health Communications, Inc.

—Stop Second-Guessing Yourself — The Toddler Years: A Field-Tested Guide to Confident Parenting. 2009. (Momma Said Ser.). (ENG.). 264p. pap. 14.95 *(978-0-7573-0653-2(5))* Health Communications, Inc.

Skallerup, Susan, ed. Bebes con Sindrome de Down: Nueva Guia para Padres. 3rd ed. 2008. (SPA.). 352p. pap. 21.95 *(978-1-890627-99-7(2))* Woodbine Hse.

Skenazy, Lenore. Free-Range Kids: How to Raise Safe, Self-Reliant Children. 2010. (ENG.). 256p. pap. 14.95 *(978-0-470-57475-1(5),* Jossey-Bass) Wiley, John & Sons, Inc.

Skiles, Madalyn. 1001 Natural Logical Consequences: Specific Solutions to Help Kids Behave. 2006. 238p. pap. 24.95 *(978-1-4241-5696-2(3))* PublishAmerica, Inc.

Skinner, Wendy. Infinity & Zebra Stripes: Life with Gifted Children. 2007. 169p. per. 16.95 net. *(978-0-910707-81-7(2))* Great Potential Pr., Inc.

Smith, Julie K. & Lake, Kelly O. Child Family & Community. rev. ed. 2010. (ENG.). 154p. pap. 59.95 *(978-0-7575-7978-3(7))* Kendall Hunt Publishing Co.

Smith, Lynton. The Journey of a Child: The Beginning. 2008. (Illus.). 256p. (J). per. 19.95 *(978-0-9700939-2-9(6))* Parent 2 Child Bks., LLC.

Smith, Ray B. The Child in the Voting Booth: When Grown People Elect Parents into Political Office. 2009. 231p. pap. 14.99 *(978-1-60696-538-2(7))* Tate Publishing & Enterprises, LLC.

Smuts, Alice. Science in the Service of Children, 1893-1935. 2008. (ENG., Illus.). 398p. pap. 32.00 *(978-0-300-14435-2(0))* Yale Univ. Pr.

Solomon, Lewis D. Bratproofing Your Children: How to Teach Your Kids Social & Financial Responsibility. 2008. 200p. pap. 15.95 *(978-1-56980-345-5(5))* Barricade Bks., Inc.

Sone, John. My Three Sons: The Birth of a New Family. 2009. 208p. 27.95 *(978-1-4401-3420-3(0));* pap. 17.95 *(978-1-4401-3418-0(9))* iUniverse, Inc.

Sonthalia, Sweta & Dasgupta, Subrata. Creativity & Relationship. 2010. 60p. pap. *(978-3-639-26926-0(8))* VDM Verlag Dr. Mueller e.K.

Speak Softly, Love Loudly: Uncommon Sense for Raising Healthy & Successful Kids. 2007. 274p. per. 20.99 *(978-1-60247-087-3(1))* Tate Publishing & Enterprises, LLC.

Spencer, R. Separated Dad Syndrome: A Dad's Perspective (A Guide for Dads Who Don't Know What to Expect) 2007. 73p. pap. 16.95 *(978-1-60441-437-0(5))* PublishAmerica, Inc.

Spizman, Robyn Freedman & Sacks, Evelyn. Eat, Nap, Play: How to Get Even More Out of Your Child's Day for Less. 2010. (ENG.). 240p. pap. 14.95 *(978-0-7573-1361-5(2))* Health Communications, Inc.

Spock, M.D., Benjamin & Needlman, Robert. Dr. Spock's Baby & Child Care: 9th Edition. 9th ed. 2011. (ENG., Illus.). 1168p. mass mkt. 8.99 *(978-1-4391-8929-0(3))* Pocket Books.

Spock, Benjamin M. & Needlman, Robert. Dr. Spock's Baby & Child Care: 9th Edition. 9th ed. 2012. (ENG., Illus.). 1152p. pap. 19.99 *(978-1-4391-8928-3(5))* Gallery Pr., The. IRL. Dist: Simon & Schuster, Inc.

Spungin, Pat. Silent Nights: How to develop a peaceful sleeping Routine. 2007. (ENG.). 224p. (C). pap. *(978-0-273-71479-8(1))* Pearson Education Canada.

St. John, Robin. Love Coupons for Kids. 2007. (ENG., Illus.). 112p. pap. 6.99 *(978-0-7407-6566-7(3))* Andrews McMeel Publishing.

Stahl, Cathleen & Boyle, Christina. Twin Set: Moms of Multiples Share Survive & Thrive Secrets. 2008. (ENG., Illus.). 304p. pap. 13.95 *(978-0-307-39352-4(6),* Three Rivers Pr.) Crown Publishing Group.

Stamm, Jill. Bright from the Start: The Simple, Science-Backed Way to Nurture Your Child's Developing Mindfrom Birth to Age 3. 2008. (ENG.). 368p. (gr. 12-18). 17.00 *(978-1-59240-362-2(X),* Gotham) Penguin Group (USA) Inc.

Stauffenger, Len. Getting over It! Wisdom for Divorced Parents. 2009. 192p. pap. 12.95 *(978-0-9796836-0-2(2))* Stauffenger, Leonard W.

Stawar, Diane E. & Stawar, Terry L. How to Be a Responsible Mother: A Workbook for Offenders. 2008. (Illus.). 229p. pap. 30.00 *(978-1-56991-300-0(5))* American Correctional Assn.

Stiffelman, Susan. Parenting Without Power Struggles: Raising Joyful, Resilient Kids While Staying Cool, Calm, & Connected. 2012. (ENG., Illus.). 320p. pap. 16.00 *(978-1-4516-6766-0(3),* Beyond Words/Atria Bks.) Atria Bks.

Stoner, Jodi & Weiner, Lori. Good Manners are Contagious. 2009. 137p. pap. 15.00 *(978-0-615-25388-6(1))* Spinner Pr.

Stuart, Carol. Foundations of Child & Youth Care. rev. ed. 2010. (ENG., Illus.). 408p. pap. 65.60 *(978-0-7575-6744-5(4))* Kendall Hunt Publishing Co.

Sturges, Tom. Grow the Tree You Got: And 99 Other Ideas for Raising Amazing Adolescents & Teenagers. 2011. (ENG.). 288p. (gr. 12). 15.95 *(978-1-58542-860-1(4),* Tarcher) Penguin Group (USA) Inc.

—Parking Lot Rules & 75 Other Ideas for Raising Amazing Children. 2009. (ENG.). 224p. pap. 15.00 *(978-0-345-50378-7(3),* Ballantine Bks.) Random House Publishing Group.

Sullivan, Bobbi. Help to Help Your Child. 2011. 192p. 29.99 *(978-1-4568-4746-3(5));* pap. 19.99 *(978-1-4568-4745-6(7))* Xlibris Corp.

Sullivan, Mike. Online Predators: A Parent's Guide for the Virtual Playground. 2008. 312p. pap. 17.99 *(978-1-60647-741-0(2))* Xulon Pr., Inc.

Sutton, James D. What Parents Need to Know about ODD, Revised: Up-to-Date Insights & Ideas for Managing Oppositional Disorder & Other Defiant Behaviors. I.t. rev. ed. 2006. (Illus.). 140p. per. 21.95 *(978-1-878878-73-1(5))* Friendly Oaks Pubns.

Sykes, Charles J. 50 Rules Kids Won't Learn in School: Real-World Antidotes to Feel-Good Education. rev. ed. 2007. (ENG.). 192p. 21.99 *(978-0-312-36038-2(X))* St. Martin's Pr.

Taffel, Ron. Childhood Unbound: Saving Our Kids' Best Selves - Confident Parenting in a World of Change. 2009. (ENG.). 336p. 26.00 *(978-1-4165-5927-6(2),* Free Pr.) Free Pr.

—Childhood Unbound: The Powerful New Parenting Approach That Gives Our 21st Century Kids the Authority, Love, & Listening They Need to Thrive. 2010. (ENG.). 336p. pap. 16.00 *(978-1-4165-5928-3(0)*, Free Pr.) Free Pr.

Talbot, James C. The Road to Positive Discipline: A Parent's Guide. 2009. 165p. pap. 14.95 *(978-0-578-01058-8(5))* TNT Publishing.

Tavangar, Homa Sabet. Growing up Global: Raising Children to Be at Home in the World. 2009. (ENG., Illus.). 304p. pap. 16.00 *(978-0-345-50654-2(5)*, Ballantine Bks.) Random House Publishing Group.

Taylor, Jennifer Poss. Forfeiting All Sanity: A Mother's Story of Raising A Child with Fetal Alcohol Syndrome. 2010. pap. 10.99 *(978-1-61566-812-0(8))* Tate Publishing & Enterprises, LLC.

Taylor, Katharine Whiteside. Understanding & Guiding the Adolescent Child: Do Adolescents Need Parents? 2011. 390p. 53.95 ***(978-1-258-10227-2(7))*** Literary Licensing, LLC.

Taylor, LaMar H. The Actual Parent Handbook. 2009. pap. 14.99 *(978-1-60696-945-8(5))* Tate Publishing & Enterprises, LLC.

Teach Children to Succeed: At Home, in School & Life. *(978-0-937571-06-4(7))* Philippine-American Educational Pr.

Tekin, Ali. Psychological Factors of Parent Involvement. 2009. 216p. pap. *(978-3-639-10935-1(X))* VDM Verlag Dr. Mueller e.K.

The Honorable Hubert L. Grimes. How to Keep Your Child from Going to Jail: Restoring Parental Authority & Developing Successful Youth. 2010. 140p. pap. 13.95 *(978-1-4502-0539-9(9))* iUniverse, Inc.

Thicke, Alan. How to Raise Kids Who Won't Hate You: Bringing up Rockstars & Other Forms of Children. 2009. (ENG.). 192p. pap. 14.95 *(978-0-9814535-3-8(8))* Sterling & Ross Pubs.

Thomas, Margaret, et al. Love & Limits in & Out of Child Care: What Your Child Care Provider & Your Pediatrician Want You to Know. 2008. (ENG., Illus.). 224p. 40.00 *(978-0-8018-8797-0(6))*; pap. 16.95 *(978-0-8018-8798-7(4))* Johns Hopkins Univ. Pr.

Thompson, Charlotte & Tilton, Adelle Jameson. The Everything Parent's Guide to Children with Autism: Expert, reassuring advice to help your child at home, at school, & at Play. 2nd ed. 2010. (ENG.). 304p. pap. 14.95 *(978-1-4405-0392-4(3))* Adams Media Corp.

Thompson, Michael & Barker, Teresa. It's a Boy! Your Son's Development from Birth to Age 18. 2009. (ENG., Illus.). 480p. pap. 17.00 *(978-0-345-49396-5(6)*, Ballantine Bks.) Random House Publishing Group.

Tinglof, Christina Baglivi & Tinglof, Christina. Double Duty: The Parents' Guide to Raising Twins, from Pregnancy Through the School Years. 2nd ed. 2009. (ENG., Illus.). 224p. pap. 16.95 *(978-0-07-161344-6(7)*, 0071613447) McGraw-Hill Cos., The.

Tiraphatna, Jet. Raising Child Prodigies. 2011. 108p. 24.99 ***(978-1-4628-9573-1(5))***; pap. 15.99 ***(978-1-4628-9572-4(7))*** Xlibris Corp.

Tomlin, Tonia. Chaos 2 Calm. 2008. 204p. pap. 17.95 *(978-0-9801548-0-1(4))* Sorted Out.

Trachtenberg, Jennifer. Good Kids, Bad Habits: The RealAge Guide to Raising Healthy Children. 2007. (RealAge Ser.). (Illus.). 352p. per. 21.95 *(978-0-06-112775-5(2)*, Harper Paperbacks) HarperCollins Pubs.

Trahan, Arita & Eckroate, Norma. The Santa Story Revisited: How to Give Your Children a Santa They Will Never Outgrow. 2009. (Illus.). 176p. pap. 16.95 *(978-0-9825328-0-5(6))* Downstream Enterprises LLC.

Train, Alan. The Bullying Problem: How to Deal with Difficult Children. 2nd ed. 2009. (ENG.). 208p. pap. 19.95 *(978-0-285-63829-7(7))* Souvenir Pr. Ltd. GBR. Dist: Independent Pubs. Group.

Tsabary, Shefali. The Conscious Parent: Transforming Ourselves, Empowering Our Children. 2010. (ENG.). 300p. pap. 19.95 *(978-1-897238-45-5(2))* Namaste Publishing, Inc. CAN. Dist: Perseus-PGW.

Tudge, Jonathan. The Everyday Lives of Young Children: Culture, Class, & Child Rearing in Diverse Societies. 2010. (ENG., Illus.). 326p. pap. 32.99 *(978-0-521-14848-1(0))* Cambridge Univ. Pr.

Turecki, Stanley & Tonner, Leslie. El Nino Dificil de Criar.Tr. of Difficult Child. (SPA.). 14.00 *(978-958-04-4140-3(5))* Norma S.A. COL. Dist: Distribuidora Norma, Inc.

The Ultimate Recipe Book for Raising Great Kids. 2007. 99p. pap. 16.95 *(978-1-4241-8543-6(2))* PublishAmerica, Inc.

Ulton, M. Paulette. A Study of Parent-Child Relationships. 2007. (ENG.). 208p. 39.95 *(978-0-548-14604-0(7))* 2006. pap. 24.95 *(978-1-4286-5929-2(3))* Kessinger Publishing, LLC.

Unell, Barbara C. & Unell, Bob. Uncle Dan's Report Card: From Toddlers to Teenagers, Helping Our Children Build Strength of Character with Healthy Habits & Values Every Day. 2011. (ENG., Illus.). 192p. (gr. 12). 14.00 *(978-0-399-53677-9(9)*, Perigee Trade) Penguin Group (USA) Inc.

Unruh, Gary M. Unleashing the Power of Parental Love: 4 Steps to Raising Joyful & Self-Confident Kids. 2010. (ENG., Illus.). 280p. pap. 17.95 *(978-0-9824204-4-7(7))* Lighthouse Love Productions, LLC.

Vachon, Marc & Vachon, Amy. Equally Shared Parenting: Rewriting the Rules for a New Generation of Parents. 2011. (ENG.). 304p. (gr. 12). 15.00 *(978-0-399-53651-9(5)*, Perigee Trade) Penguin Group (USA) Inc.

Valinejad, Carol. How to Have a Happy Toddler: Responding to Your Child's Emotional Needs From 0 - 4. 2006. (ENG., Illus.). 144p. pap. 14.95 *(978-0-600-61601-6(0)*, Hamlyn) Octopus Publishing Group GBR. Dist: Hachette Bk. Group.

Venuto, Peter Anthony. Are You Sure You Want to Marry That Person? 2nd ed. 2006. (IND, POL & JPN.). per. 19.95 *(978-0-615-13020-0(8))* Life Experiences.

Vernon Sigmon. Parenting with a Plan: Building Blocks & Raising Children. 2010. 108p. 22.95 *(978-1-4401-9776-5(8))*; pap. 12.95 *(978-1-4401-9774-1(1))* iUniverse, Inc.

Vettrus, Linda & Vettrus, Gregory S. Family Dynamics & the Challenging Child. Date not set. pap. *(978-1-929293-04-9(6))* Whole Child Institute - WCI.

Vitale, Judi. Babystrology: The Astrological Guide to Your Little Star. 2012. (ENG.). 224p. 15.95 ***(978-1-4405-3888-9(3))*** Adams Media Corp.

Vitali, Keith & Brouillard, Adam. Bullyproof Your Child: An Expert's Advice on Teaching Children to Defend Themselves. 2007. (Illus.). 176p. pap. 14.95 *(978-1-60239-076-8(2))* Skyhorse Publishing Co., Inc.

Volles, Sandy. Grandma's Two Cents. 2010. 52p. pap. 15.99 *(978-1-4500-5607-6(5))* Xlibris Corp.

Volpe, Richard. The Secure Child: Timeless Lessons in Parenting. 2010. 250p. *(978-1-60752-390-1(6))*; pap. *(978-1-60752-389-5(2))* Information Age Publishing, Inc.

Wachtel, Suzanne & Le Vine, Blake. Like Mother, Like Son: A Mom's Guide to Raising Healthy Children. 2007. 129p. per. 14.95 *(978-0-9768733-2-7(X))* Sb Pubs.

Waddilove, Rachel. The Toddler Book How to Enjoy Your Growing Child. 2008. (Illus.). 192p. pap. 14.95 *(978-0-7459-5296-3(8))* Lion Hudson PLC GBR. Dist: Independent Pubs. Group.

Wahlgren, Anna. For the Love of Children: Childcare & Child Rearing 0-16 Years. 2009. 726p. 39.95 *(978-91-977736-2-1(X))* Wahlgren, Anna AB SWE. Dist: AtlasBooks Distribution.

Wakeling, Ben. Goodbye, Pert Breasts: the Diary of a Newborn Dad. 2010. 274p. pap. 18.95 *(978-1-4461-7134-9(5))* Lulu Enterprises Inc.

Waldfogel, Jane. What Children Need. 2010. (Family & Public Policy Ser.). (Illus.). 288p. pap. 19.95 *(978-0-674-04640-5(4))* Harvard Univ. Pr.

Wallace, Charlton. Parenting the Black Male: An African American Male's Opinionated View of How It Should Be Done, 1 vol. 2010. 122p. pap. 19.95 *(978-1-4489-4620-4(4))* PublishAmerica, Inc.

Walsh, David. No: Why Kids — of All Ages — Need to Hear It & Ways Parents Can Say It. 2007. (ENG.). 336p. pap. 15.00 *(978-0-7432-8920-7(X)*, Free Pr.) Free Pr.

Walsh, David. Smart Parenting, Smarter Kids: The One Brain Book You Need to Help Your Child Grow Brighter, Healthier, & Happier. (ENG.). 304p. 2012. pap. 15.00 ***(978-1-4391-2119-1(2))*** 2011. lib. bdg. 25.00 *(978-1-4391-2117-7(6))* Free Pr. (Free Pr.).

Warner, P. Tu Bebe Juega y Aprende. (SPA.). 192p. *(978-84-95456-25-0(7)*, 87118) Ediciones Oniro S.A.

Warner, Penny, contrib. by. Baby Play & Learn. (Illus.). ix, 181p. *(978-0-88166-328-0(X))* Meadowbrook Pr.

Webb, James T., et al. A Parent's Guide to Gifted Children. 2007. (Illus.). 390p. 32.95 *(978-0-910707-79-4(0))*; per. 24.95 *(978-0-910707-52-7(9))* Great Potential Pr., Inc.

Weil, Glenda & Marden, Doro. Bringing up Happy Children. 2009. (Teach Yourself: Parenting Ser.). (ENG.). 192p. pap. 14.95 *(978-0-07-162582-1(8)*, 0071625828) McGraw-Hill Cos., The.

Weiner, Andrea Goodman. More Than Saying I Love You: 4 Powerful Steps That Help Children Love Themselves. 2011. (ENG.). 160p. pap. 12.95 *(978-0-9826387-8-1(7)*, 0982638787) Franklin Green Publishing.

Weisenberger, Gary J., et al. The Complete Idiot's Guide to Raising Girls. 2009. (Complete Idiot's Guide Ser.). (ENG.). 320p. (gr. 12-18). pap. 14.95 *(978-1-59257-881-8(0)*, Alpha Bks.) Penguin Group (USA) Inc.

Weissbourd, Richard. The Parents We Mean to Be: How Well-Intentioned Adults Undermine Children's Moral & Emotional Development. (ENG.). 256p. 2010. pap. 14.95 *(978-0-547-24803-5(2)*, Mariner Bks.) 2009. 25.00 *(978-0-618-62617-5(4))* Houghton Mifflin Harcourt Trade & Reference Pubs.

Well, Glenda & Marden, Doro. Raise Happy Children. 2011. (Teach Yourself Ser.). (ENG.). 324p. pap. 15.95 *(978-1-4441-0383-0(0)*, Hodder & Stoughton) Hodder General Publishing Div. GBR. Dist: Independent Pubs. Group.

Wesley, Ravey D. Government Program. 2011. 176p. 29.99 ***(978-1-4628-4576-7(2))***; pap. 19.99 ***(978-1-4628-4575-0(4))*** Xlibris Corp.

Western Schools. Treating Explosive Kids: Behavioral Health Series. 2007. wbk. ed. 54.95 *(978-1-57801-205-3(8))* Western Schls.

—Treating Explosive Kids: Nursing Series. 2007. wbk. ed. 54.95 *(978-1-57801-204-6(X))* Western Schls.

Wheeler, Hayley Nicole. Please Grow Up. 2010. 70p. pap. 12.97 *(978-0-557-13351-2(3))* Lulu Enterprises Inc.

White, Charles. A Handbook for Raising Children in the 21st Century. 2007. (ENG.). 84p. per. 10.95 *(978-1-4327-0028-7(6))* Outskirts Pr., Inc.

White-Hill, Carol. Footsteps. 2009. 12p. pap. 12.99 *(978-1-4490-4213-4(9))* AuthorHouse.

White, Jean. Finding A Quality Child Care Center Can Be Difficult ... Let Me Help. 2010. 66p. pap. 15.99 *(978-1-4500-5903-9(1))* Xlibris Corp.

White, Jon. Hey Kidz! Your Entrepreneur Is Showing! A Parenting Guide to the American Dream. 2007. 215p. per. 15.95 *(978-0-9793251-0-6(2))* Prevail Pr.

White, Melody Hiatt. By My Side: Parenting from a Higher Consciousness. 2008. 108p. pap. 24.95 *(978-1-59858-644-2(0))* Dog Ear Publishing, LLC.

Wickens, Paul. Handbook for Parents. Date not set. (Illus.). 43p. pap. 7.00 *(978-0-911845-10-5(0))* Neumann Pr., The.

Wilber, Adelbert L. Co-Teaching for High School: Lessons Learned & Considerations for Future Applications. 2009. 120p. pap. 21.95 *(978-1-4327-2193-0(3))* Outskirts Pr., Inc.

Wild, Ingrid. BALANCED PARENTS Create Global Peace. 2010. 265p. pap. 15.95 *(978-0-557-47883-5(9))* Lulu Enterprises Inc.

Wiley, Gordon. Where's Uncle Gordo? 2011. 20p. pap. 12.99 ***(978-1-4634-0214-3(7))*** AuthorHouse.

Williams, Pat, et al. The Takeaway: 20 Unforgettable Life Lessons That Every Father Should Pass on to His Children. 2009. (ENG.). 248p. pap. 14.95 *(978-0-7573-1389-9(2))* Health Communications, Inc.

Wilson, Gary. Help Your Boys Succeed. 2008. (Help Your Child to Succeed Ser.). (ENG., Illus.). 112p. 19.95 *(978-1-85539-449-0(9)*, Network Continuum Education) Continuum International Publishing Group, Ltd. GBR. Dist: National Bk. Network.

Winget, Larry. Your Kids Are Your Own Fault: A Fix-the-Way-You-Parent Guide for Raising Responsible, Productive Adults. 2011. (ENG.). 272p. (gr. 12). 16.00 *(978-1-59240-605-0(X)*, Gotham) Penguin Group (USA) Inc.

—Your Kids Are Your Own Fault: A Guide for Raising Responsible, Productive Adults. 2009. 256p. 26.00 *(978-1-59240-496-4(0))* Penguin Group (USA) Inc.

Winn, Ralph B. Encyclopedia of Child Guidance. *(978-0-8022-1903-9(9))* Philosophical Library, Inc.

Wipfler, Patty. Parenting Builds Leadership. 2.00 *(978-1-885357-35-9(4))* Rational Island Pubs.

Wiseman, Ann S. Nightmare Help: A Guide for Adults & Children. (Dream Exploration Ser.). (Illus.). pap. 9.95 *(978-0-937369-05-0(5))* Ansayre Pr.

Wissel, Megan & Smith. Simply Baby: An invaluable quick reference to Infants. 2010. 116p. pap. 13.95 *(978-1-60844-445-8(7))* Dog Ear Publishing, LLC.

Wong, Alice, ed. Mom's Book of Lists: 100 Practical Lists for Raising Your Kids. 2011. (Code Busters Club Ser.). (Illus.). 160p. 17.95 *(978-1-59962-097-8(9)*, Welcome Bks.) Welcome Enterprises, Inc.

Wright, Caffee Lawrence Med Lpc Ncc. When Touching Hurts. 2011. 28p. pap. 15.99 ***(978-1-4628-6454-6(6))*** Xlibris Corp.

Wright-Lee, Linda D. Oops!!! I'm a Parent. No One Told Me it Would be Hard Work: Learn Effective Parenting. Lee, David J., ed. pap. 23.95 *(978-0-9673754-6-5(0))* Wright On Time Publishing Co.

Wynn, Cynthia. Parenting Styles Among Substance: Parenting Styles, Substance Abuse & Its Impact on Child Rearing. 2008. 132p. pap. *(978-3-639-09275-2(9))* VDM Verlag Dr. Mueller e.K.

Yantis-Grube, Sally D. Raised by my Child: Reflections on Raising a Child with Special Needs. 2011. 88p. pap. 14.95 ***(978-1-4327-7392-2(5))*** Outskirts Pr., Inc.

Yarber, Annice & Sharp, Paul M., eds. Focus on Single-Parent Families: Past, Present, & Future. 2010. 298p. 54.95 *(978-0-313-37950-5(5)*, A2021C, Praeger Pubs.) Greenwood Publishing Group, Inc.

Yee, Albert H. Raising & Teaching Children for their Tomorrows. 2011. pap. 16.99 *(978-1-61739-212-2(X))* Tate Publishing & Enterprises, LLC.

Young, Caroline. Babies & Toddlers. 2009. (Parent's Guides). 128p. 12.99 *(978-0-7945-1727-4(7)*, Usborne) EDC Publishing.

Young, Leslie. The Everything Parent's Guide to Vaccines: Balanced, professional advice to help you make the best decision for your Child. 2009. (ENG.). 304p. pap. 14.95 *(978-1-60550-366-0(5))* Adams Media Corp.

Young, Savannah M. & Philpott, Susan B. Parenting: A Handbook with Ideas for Doing Your Best. 2009. 100p. pap. 15.95 *(978-1-4259-8807-4(5))* AuthorHouse.

Zandonella, Catherine & Green Guide Editors. Families: A Complete Reference for Eco-Friendly Parents. 2010. (ENG., Illus.). 400p. pap. 21.95 *(978-1-4262-0542-2(2)*, National Geographic) National Geographic Society.

Zimin, I. V. Povsednevnaia Zhizn Rossiiskogo Imperatorskogo Dvora: Detskii Mir Imperatorskikh Rezidentsii: Byt Monarkhov I Ikh Okruzhenie. 2010. (RUS., Illus.). 571p. *(978-5-227-02410-7(3))* Centropoligraf, AO zakrytogo tipa, torgovo-izdatel'skoe obedinenie.

Zindler, Adelaide. Fearless Parenting: Raising Your Child with Confidence & Purpose. 2008. 157p. per. 14.95 *(978-0-9797119-0-9(8))* David Bauer Pr.

CHILD REARING—BIBLICAL TEACHING

Parenting among Christian Immigrants in the United States. 2009. 64p. pap. 15.99 *(978-1-4415-7098-7(5))* Xlibris Corp.

Pastor Jerry L. Macon, Jr. Solution to a Fatherless Nation. 2010. 72p. pap. 10.95 *(978-1-4502-1423-0(1))* iUniverse, Inc.

Peace, Martha & Scott, Stuart. The Faithful Parent: A Biblical Guide to Raising a Family. 2010. pap. *(978-1-59638-201-5(5))* P & R Publishing.

Wegner, Paul, et al. Wise Parenting: Guidelines from the Book of Proverbs. 2009. (ENG.). 144p. pap. 11.99 *(978-1-57293-352-1(6))* Discovery Hse. Pubs.

CHILD REARING—BIOGRAPHY

Ambrus, Julian L. & Ambrus, Clara M. Babel: Review of 60 years of life in Medicine. 2011. 312p. pap. 21.12 *(978-1-4251-8727-9(7))* Trafford Publishing.

Casey, David R. Bad Boy, 1 vol. 2009. 235p. pap. 24.95 *(978-1-60836-001-7(6))* PublishAmerica, Inc.

Frederick Mizer, Caroline's Wish Kelly. Summer of the Pigeon. 2009. 171p. 32.99 *(978-0-615-26414-1(X))* Mizer, Kelly Federick.

Oliver, Jools. The Diary of an Honest Mum. 2006. (ENG., Illus.). 320p. 23.95 *(978-1-4013-0270-2(X))* Hyperion Pr.

Schusteff, Arlene, compiled by. Special Gifts: Women Writers on the Heartache, the Happiness & the Hope of Raising a Special Needs Child. 2007. 228p. per. 15.00 *(978-1-932279-59-7(8))* Wyatt-MacKenzie Publishing.

Wright, Roberta. Blessings in the Storm: Samuel Wesley Gathing: A Closer Look. 2011. 100p. pap. 11.65 ***(978-1-4269-3770-5(9))*** Trafford Publishing.

CHILD REARING—RELIGIOUS ASPECTS

Abbott, Jacob. Gentle Measures in the Management & Training of the Young. 2008. 292p. 28.99 *(978-0-554-24001-5(7))* 2008. 292p. 25.99 *(978-0-554-33304-5(X))* 2006. (ENG.). 256p. pap. 21.99 *(978-1-4264-0115-2(9))* 2006. (ENG.). 252p. pap. 23.99 *(978-1-4264-0244-9(9))* BiblioBazaar.

—Gentle Measures in the Management & Training of the Young: Or, the Principles on Which a Firm Parental Authority May Be Established & Maintained, Without Violence or Anger, & the Right Development of the Moral & Mental Capacities Be Promoted by Methods in Harmony with the Structure & the Characteristics of the Juvenile Mind. 2007. (ENG.). 258p. pap. 21.99 *(978-1-4264-5567-4(4))*; 290p. pap. 23.99 *(978-1-4264-5615-2(8))* BiblioBazaar.

Baker, Maureen. Choices & Constraints in Family Life. (Themes in Canadian Sociology Ser.). (ENG., Illus.). 2007. 216p. pap. 45.00 *(978-0-19-542105-7(1))* 2nd ed. 2010. 264p. 39.95 *(978-0-19-543159-9(6))* Oxford Univ. Pr., Inc.

Barclay, Jim. Lessons for Parents from a Perfect Parent. 2006. 212p. pap. 17.99 *(978-1-4141-0669-4(6))* Pleasant Word.

Battistelli, Kate. Growing Great Kids: Partner with God to Cultivate His Purpose in Your Child's Life. 2012. E-Book ***(978-1-61638-655-9(X))***; (ENG.). 240p. pap. 14.99 ***(978-1-61638-654-2(1))*** Charisma Media. (Charisma Hse.).

Beeke, Joel R. Parenting by God's Promises: How to Raise Children in the Covenant of Grace. 2011. ***(978-1-56769-266-2(4))*** Reformation Pubs.

Beshir, Mohamed Rida. When Muslim Teens Rebel: Causes & Solutions. 2008. *(978-1-59008-055-9(6))* amana pubns.

Boa, Kenneth & Turner, John Alan. Hearts & Minds: Raising Your Child with a Christian View of the World. 2006. (ENG.). 256p. pap. 14.99 *(978-1-4143-0164-8(2))* Tyndale Hse. Pubs.

Bogear, Jim. Faith Legacy: Six Values to Shape Your Child's Journey. 2009. 224p. 16.99 *(978-0-89827-427-1(3))* Wesleyan Publishing Hse.

Bostrom, Kathleen Long. 99 Ways to Raise Spiritually Healthy Children. 2010. (ENG.). 208p. pap. 15.00 *(978-0-664-23536-9(0))* Westminster John Knox Pr.

Boykin, Caroline. The Well-Versed Family: Raising Kids of Faith Through Do-Able Scripture Memory. 2007. 145p. pap. 12.99 *(978-1-59886-768-8(7))* Tate Publishing & Enterprises, LLC.

Brandt, Henry & Skinner, Kerry L. I Want to Enjoy My Children (workbook) 2011. 198p. pap. 14.99 ***(978-1-931080-04-0(6)***, KLS LifeChange Ministries) Skinner, Kerry L.

Brazelton, Katie. How Your Teenager Is Wired: Discovering Who God Made Your Teenager to Be. 2011. pap. *(978-0-7644-4705-1(X))* Group Publishing, Inc.

Brown, Carolyn C. Raising Children to Love Their Neighbors: Practical Resources for Congregations. 2008. (Illus.). 114p. per. 17.00 *(978-0-687-65142-9(5))* Abingdon Pr.

Bruner, Olivia. The Minivan Years: Celebrating the Hectic Joys of Motherhood. 2008. (ENG.). 208p. pap. 18.99 *(978-1-931722-76-6(5))* Center St.

Caldwell, Elizabeth F. & Caldwell, Elizabeth. God's Big Table: Nurturing Children in a Diverse World. 2011. *(978-0-8298-1814-7(6))* Pilgrim Pr., The/United Church Pr.

Chandler, Phyllis, et al. Sharing the Faith with Your Child: From Birth to Age Four. 2006. 112p. per. 5.95 *(978-0-7648-1523-2(7))* Liguori Pubns.

Chisholm, Dana S. Single Moms Raising Sons: Preparing Boys to Be Men When There's No Man Around. 2006. (ENG.). 192p. pap. 14.99 *(978-0-8341-2308-3(8)*, 083-412-3088) Beacon Hill Pr. of Kansas City.

Clerk-Cole, Tammy. Heirloom of Wisdom, 1 vol. 2009. 95p. pap. 16.95 *(978-1-60813-357-4(5))* PublishAmerica, Inc.

Cole, Maria Covey. Contentment: Inspiring Insights for LDS Mothers. 2009. 87p. *(978-1-59811-777-6(7))* Covenant Communications.

Colopy, Elsa Kok. The Single Mom's Guide to Keeping It All Together, 1 vol. 2010. (ENG.). 192p. 5.99 *(978-0-8007-8782-0(X))* Revell.

Cooke, Shae. Single Parent's Guide to Raising Godly Children. 2010. (ENG.). pap. 14.99 *(978-0-7684-3198-8(0))* Destiny Image Pubs.

Cooper, Scott. I Don't Want to Go to Church! Practical Ways to Deal with Kids & Religion, Whether You're Religious or Not. 2006. 108p. per. 12.95 *(978-0-8091-4398-6(4)*, 4398-4) Paulist Pr.

Cox, Michael H. Creative Devotions with Dad. 2010. 110p. pap. 13.99 *(978-1-60957-526-7(1))* Xulon Pr., Inc.

Crum, Carlene. Something of Value: A Mother's Spiritual Journey with a Special-Needs Child. 2008. 160p. pap. 13.99 *(978-1-60647-192-0(9))* Xulon Pr., Inc.

Curry, Cyndi Lamb. Keeping Your Kids Afloat When It Feels Like You're Sinking. 158p. (Orig.). pap. 9.99 *(978-0-8307-3453-5(8)*, Gospel Light) Gospel Light Pubns.

Day, Juanita. Shh Shh Mothers Are Hurting. 2008. 49p. pap. 16.95 *(978-1-60441-959-7(8))* PublishAmerica, Inc.

Dear, Lisa. The Roller Coaster Ride of Raising Teens. 2011. 160p. 30.95 ***(978-1-4497-1971-5(6))***; pap. 13.95 ***(978-1-4497-1970-8(8))*** Author Solutions, Inc. (WestBow Pr.).

DeBoer, Karen. Home Grown Handbook for Christian Parenting: 111 Real-Life Questions & Answers. 2010. 215p. *(978-1-59255-491-1(1))* Faith Alive Christian Resources.

Diamant, Anita & Kushner, Karen. How to Raise a Jewish Child: A Practical Handbook for Family Life. 2008. (ENG.). 320p. pap. 15.95 *(978-0-8052-1221-1(3)*, Schocken) Knopf Doubleday Publishing Group.

Dickow, Cheryl. Raising Christian Children in a Secular World: Christian Parenting. 2nd rev. ed. 2007. (ENG.). 204p. per. 9.99 *(978-0-9794976-0-5(4))* Bezalel Bks.

Doades, Joanne. Parenting Jewish Teens: A Guide for the Perplexed. 2006. (Illus.). 149p. per. 16.99 *(978-1-58023-305-7(8))* Jewish Lights Publishing.

Dobson, James C. Respuestas Confiables.Tr. of Solid Answers. (SPA.). 13.99 *(978-0-7899-0431-7(4),* 495016) Editorial Unilit.

Dornacher, Kara. Heaven Sent Baby: A Bundle of Blessings for the New Mom, 0 vols. 2007. (Illus.). 80p. 12.99 *(978-1-4041-0441-9(0))* Nelson, Thomas Inc.

Doster, Lenore Lawson. Rock Solid Parenting. 2008. 116p. 18.99 *(978-1-60477-894-6(6));* pap. 10.99 *(978-1-60477-893-9(8))* Xulon Pr., Inc.

Elliott, Sharon Norris. Raising Boys to Be Like Jesus. 2009. 192p. pap. 16.00 *(978-0-8170-1541-1(8))* Judson Pr.

Emlet, Michael R. Angry Children: Understanding & Helping Your Child Regain Control. 2008. (ENG.). 24p. 3.99 *(978-1-934885-26-0(6))* New Growth Pr.

Estroff, Sharon Duke. Can I Have a Cell Phone for Hanukkah? The Essential Scoop on Raising Modern Jewish Kids. 2007. (ENG.). 304p. pap. 13.99 *(978-0-7679-2544-0(0),* Broadway) Broadway Bks.

Eyre, Linda & Pothier, Shawni Eyre. A Mother's Book of Secrets. 2009. xiv, 154p. *(978-1-60641-070-7(9))* Deseret Bk. Co.

Fabre, Linda. Full Potential. 2008. 116p. pap. 14.99 *(978-1-4343-9003-5(9))* AuthorHouse.

Families. (Early Intervention Levels Ser.). 32.22 *(978-0-7362-1050-8(4));* 5.37 *(978-0-7362-0957-1(3))* Hampton-Brown Bks.

Feldhahn, Shaunti & Rice, Lisa A. For Parents Only: Getting Inside the Head of Your Kid. 2007. (ENG., Illus.). 192p. 14.99 *(978-1-59052-932-4(4),* Multnomah) Doubleday Religious Publishing Group, The.

Flynn, DeAnne. The Mother's Mite: Why Even Our Smallest Efforts Matter. 2011. (Illus.). 128p. pap. 18.99 *(978-1-60641-937-3(4))* Deseret Bk. Co.

Fowler, Anna. From a Child's Perception, 1 vol. 2010. 386p. pap. 29.95 *(978-1-4512-1434-5(0))* PublishAmerica, Inc.

Fowler, Larry. Raising a Modern-Day Joseph: A Timeless Strategy for Growing Great Kids, 1 vol. 2009. (ENG.). 144p. pap. 12.99 *(978-1-4347-6705-9(1))* Cook, David C.

Frances, Dee. Golden Rules of Child Rearing. Date not set. pap. 6.00 *(978-1-885519-47-4(8))* DDDD Pubns.

—52 Ways to Make Your Child Feel Special. Date not set. 6.00 *(978-1-885519-48-1(6))* DDDD Pubns.

Gilbert, Greg. If Your Baby Could Talk Would You Listen? 2008. 88p. per. 9.99 *(978-1-60477-579-2(3))* Xulon Pr., Inc.

Ginsberg, Binyomin. A Principal's Principles: Encouraging Messages for Parents from a Noted Mechanech. 2009. (Artscroll Ser.). (Illus.). 351p. 23.99 *(978-1-4226-0903-3(0))* Mesorah Pubns., Ltd.

Glickman, Elaine Rose. Sacred Parenting: Jewish Wisdom for Your Family's First Years. 2009. *(978-0-8074-1089-9(6))* URJ Pr.

Goodwin, Debbie Salter. Raising Kids to Extraordinary Faith: Helping Parents & Teachers Disciple the Next Generation. 2008. (ENG.). 192p. pap. 14.99 *(978-0-8341-2391-5(6),* 9780834123915) Beacon Hill Pr. of Kansas City.

Group Publishing. Trust Us — They'll Ask: Answers to Your Kids' Toughest & Most Awkward Questions. 2010. pap. *(978-0-7644-4911-6(7))* Group Publishing, Inc.

Group Publishing Staff, contrib. by. Comforting Those in Crisis for Children. 2008. pap. *(978-0-7644-3829-5(8),* Group) Group Publishing, Inc.

—Comforting Those in Crisis for Teens. 2008. pap. *(978-0-7644-3830-1(1),* Group) Group Publishing, Inc.

—The Quick Guide to Discipline for Children's Ministry: 101 Good Ideas for Bad Behavior. 2009. pap. *(978-0-7644-4004-5(7))* Group Publishing, Inc.

Groves, Laura Lee. I'm Outnumbered! One Mom's Lessons in the Lively Art of Raising Boys, 1 vol. 2010. 192p. pap. 12.99 *(978-0-8254-2739-8(8))* Kregel Pubns.

Guarendi, Ray. Good Discipline, Great Teens. 2007. 172p. per. 13.99 *(978-0-86716-835-8(8),* Servant Bks.) Franciscan Media.

Gurian, Michael. The Soul of the Child: Nurturing the Divine Identity of Our Children. 2007. (ENG.). 256p. pap. 17.95 *(978-1-4165-7041-7(1),* Beyond Words/Atria Bks.) Atria Bks.

Hall, Amy Laura. Conceiving Parenthood: American Protestantism & the Spirit of Reproduction. 2007. (Illus.). 452p. 32.00 *(978-0-8028-3936-7(3))* Eerdmans, William B. Publishing Co.

Harris, Joseph. God's Relationship with Man. 2008. 128p. 10.99 *(978-1-60604-520-6(2))* Tate Publishing & Enterprises, LLC.

Haynes, Cathy. Train up a Child: Pouring New Wine into New Wine Skins. 2006. per. 13.95 *(978-0-9787788-1-1(2))* LUMEN-US Pubns.

Heinsohn, Laura Lee. Cracking the Parenting Code: 6 Clues to Solving the Mystery of Meeting Your Child's Needs. 2008. (ENG.). 192p. pap. 12.99 *(978-1-59669-207-7(3))* New Hope Pubs.

Hinckley, Kevin. Parenting the Strong-Willed Child: Fortifying Our Youth & Healing Our Prodigals. 2008. *(978-1-59038-917-1(4))* Deseret Bk. Co.

Hoffhines, Emily. Bible Lessons with Babies. 2007. 80p. pap. 12.95 *(978-0-615-17178-4(8))* Hoffhines, Emily.

Hollies, Linda H. Pilgrim Prayers for Grandmothers Raising Grandchildren. 2010. 128p. pap. 16.00 *(978-1-60899-190-7(3),* Wipf and Stock) Wipf & Stock Pubs.

Holmen, Mark. Faith Begins @ Home Dad. 2010. (Faith @ Home Ser.). (ENG.). 80p. pap. 6.99 *(978-0-8307-5230-0(7))* Gospel Light Pubns.

—Faith Begins @ Home Mom. 2010. (Faith @ Home Ser.). (ENG., Illus.). 80p. pap. 6.99 *(978-0-8307-5231-7(5))* Gospel Light Pubns.

Housman, Brian. Engaging Your Teen's World: Become a Culturally Savvy Parent. 2009. (Illus.). 203p. pap. 14.99 *(978-1-58743-254-5(4))* Brazos Pr.

Hughes, Barbara & Hughes, R. Kent. Disciplines of a Godly Family. annot. ed. 2007. 256p. pap. 15.99 *(978-1-58134-941-2(6))* Crossway.

Hutchcraft, Ron. Cinco Necesidades Que Deben Suplirse al Nino...Tr. of Five Needs Your Child Must Have Met at Home. (SPA.). 7.99 *(978-0-7899-0138-5(2),* 497274) Editorial Unilit.

Ingram, Chip. Effective Parenting in a Defective World: How to Raise Kids Who Stand Out from the Crowd. 2007. (ENG., Illus.). 208p. per. 13.99 *(978-1-4143-0384-0(X))* Tyndale Hse. Pubs.

Jacks, Noreen. Promises from the Olive Tree. 2008. (Illus.). 117p. pap. 17.99 *(978-0-9799116-0-6(5))* LifeSong Pubs.

Jackson, Timothy P. The Best Love of the Child: Being Loved & Being Taught to Love As the First Human Right. 2011. pap. 28.00 *(978-0-8028-6539-7(9))* Eerdmans, William B. Publishing Co.

Jamison, Rita. Parenting Your ADHD Child: Biblical Guidance for Your Child's Diagnosis. 2011. (ENG.). 24p. 3.99 ***(978-1-936768-43-1(7))*** New Growth Pr.

Jankovic, Rachel. Loving the Little Years: Mothering in the Trenches. 2010. pap. *(978-1-59128-081-1(8))* Canon Pr.

Jensen, David H. Parenting. 2011. (Compass: Christian Explorations of Daily Living Ser.). 128p. (C). pap. 15.00 *(978-0-8006-9848-5(7),* Fortress Pr.) Augsburg Fortress, Pubs.

Joiner, Reggie & Nieuwhof, Carey. Parenting Beyond Your Capacity: Connect Your Family to a Wider Community. 2010. (Orange Ser.). (ENG.). 208p. pap. 14.99 *(978-1-4347-6481-2(8))* Cook, David C.

Jones, Timothy. Nurturing Your Child's Soul: 10 Keys to Helping Your Child Grow in Faith, 0 vols. 2006. 272p. per. 13.99 *(978-0-8499-1403-4(5))* Nelson, Thomas Inc.

Jungreis-Wolff, Slovie. Raising a Child with Soul: How Time-Tested Jewish Wisdom Can Shape Your Child's Character. 2009. (ENG.). 288p. pap. 15.99 *(978-0-312-54196-5(1),* St. Martin's Griffin) St. Martin's Pr.

Kasl, Charlotte. If the Buddha Had Kids: Raising Children to Create a More Peaceful World. 2012. (ENG.). 320p. (gr. 12-18). 14.00 *(978-0-14-311631-8(2),* Penguin (Non-Classics)) Penguin Group (USA) Inc.

Keen, Jim. Inside Intermarriage: A Christian Partner's Perspective on Raising a Jewish Family. 2006. 144p. per. 15.95 *(978-0-8074-0966-4(9))* URJ Pr.

Ken & Phillips, Dottie. No Problems Only Situations! 2010. 204p. pap. 15.99 *(978-1-60957-879-4(1))* Xulon Pr., Inc.

Kendall, Peggy. Connected: Christian Parenting in an Age of IM & Myspace. 2007. 144p. pap. 12.00 *(978-0-8170-1516-9(7))* Judson Pr.

Kitch, Anne E. Taking the Plunge: Baptism & Parenting. 2006. 144p. per. 15.00 *(978-0-8192-2185-8(6),* Morehouse Publishing) Church Publishing, Inc.

Koelman, Jacobus. The Duties of Parents. Osterhaven, M. Eugene, ed. Vriend, John, tr. from DUT. 2009.Tr. of Pligten der Ouders. (ENG., Illus.). 173p. pap. 15.00 *(978-1-60178-060-7(5))* Reformation Heritage Bks.

Kornoluth, Doron. Raising Kids to Love Being Jewish. 2009. 189p. 21.99 *(978-1-60204-015-1(X))* K'hal Publishing.

Krueger, L. Elizabeth. Raising Godly Tomatoes. 2007. ix, 260p. pap. *(978-1-60530-330-7(5))* Independent Pub.

Labosh, Kathy. The Child with Autism Learns about Faith: 15 Ready-to-Use Scripture Lessons, from the Garden of Eden to the Parting of the Red Sea. 2011. (ENG.). 97p. pap. 14.95 *(978-1-935274-19-3(8))* Future Horizons, Inc.

Larson, Susie. Growing Grateful Kids: Teaching Them to Appreciate an Extraordinary God in Ordinary Places, 1 vol. 2010. (ENG.). 256p. pap. 12.99 *(978-0-8024-5282-5(5))* Moody Pubs.

Lasher, Cynthia Long. Death Is No Stranger: Helping Children Grieve. 2008. 93p. per. *(978-0-7880-2505-1(8))* CSS Publishing Co.

Lewis, Robert. Raising a Modern-Day Knight: A Father's Role in Guiding His Son to Authentic Manhood. 2007. (ENG., Illus.). 208p. per. 14.99 *(978-1-58997-309-1(7))* Tyndale Hse. Pubs.

Life Teen, creator. Rocking the Cradle Catholic. 2009. pap. 11.95 *(978-0-9802362-7-9(4))* Life Teen.

Lovelace, Lygia. Time Travels & Pirate Telescopes. 2010. 292p. 35.95 *(978-1-61507-265-1(9));* pap. 19.95 *(978-1-61507-260-6(8))* Cross Bks. Publishing.

Lucado, Max. God Thinks You're Wonderful, Mom!, 0 vols. 2008. (Illus.). 128p. 13.99 *(978-1-4041-0506-5(9))* Nelson, Thomas Inc.

Marty, Martin E. The Mystery of the Child. 2007. (Religion, Marriage, & Family Ser.). 257p. 24.00 *(978-0-8028-1766-2(1))* Eerdmans, William B. Publishing Co.

Masin, Valerie. Hidden in Their Hearts. 2011. 100p. pap. 16.95 ***(978-1-4497-1877-0(9),*** WestBow Pr.) Author Solutions, Inc.

Mata, Daya. Skilled Profession of Child Rearing. 48p. 2.00 *(978-0-87612-415-4(5))* Self-Realization Fellowship Pubs.

Matlock, Mark. Raising Wise Children. 2012. (ENG.). 176p. pap. 12.99 ***(978-0-310-66937-1(5))*** Zondervan.

McDowell, Josh. The Father Connection: How You Can Make the Difference in Your Child's Self-Esteem & Sense of Purpose. 2008. (ENG.). 208p. pap. 12.99 *(978-0-8054-4742-2(3),* B&H Bks.) B&H Publishing Group.

Meyer, Nancy Sebastian. Spiritually Single Moms: Raising Godly Kids When Dad Doesn't Believe. 2007. (Living the Questions Ser.). (ENG.). 192p. pap. 12.99 *(978-1-57683-874-7(9))* NavPress Publishing Group.

Michelle, Latesha. Mothers Milk. 2008. (Illus.). 208p. 26.99 *(978-1-4343-8555-0(8));* pap. 19.99 *(978-1-4343-8554-3(X))* AuthorHouse.

Mogel, Wendy. The Blessing of a B Minus: Using Jewish Teachings to Raise Resilient Teenagers. (ENG.). 2011. 224p. pap. 15.00 *(978-1-4165-4204-9(3))* 2010. 208p. 24.00 *(978-1-4165-4203-2(5))* Scribner. (Scribner).

—The Blessing of A Skinned Knee: Using Jewish Teachings to Raise Self-Reliant Children. 2008. (ENG.). 304p. pap. 15.00 *(978-1-4165-9306-5(3),* Scribner) Scribner.

Moore, Walker. Rite of Passage Parenting Workbook, 0 vols. 2007. 256p. per. 15.99 *(978-1-4185-1973-5(1))* Nelson, Thomas Inc.

Mueller, Walt. 99 Thoughts for Parents of Teenagers: The Truth on Raising Teenagers from Parents Who Have Been There. 2011. pap. *(978-0-7644-4869-0(2))* Group Publishing, Inc.

Myers, Jimmy. Toe to Toe with Your Teen: Successfully Parenting a Defiant Teenager Without Giving up or Giving In. 2009. (ENG.). 224p. pap. 14.99 *(978-0-8307-4901-0(2))* Gospel Light Pubns.

Nowak, Jennifer. Families. 2006. (Rosen Real Readers Big Bookstm Ser.). (ENG.). 8p. (gr. k-1). 29.95 *(978-1-4042-6212-6(1))* Rosen Publishing Group, Inc., The.

Obeng, Rex. What Manner of Child Shall This Be? How to Influence Your Child's Destiny. 2007. 122p. pap. *(978-88-89127-48-3(1))* Destiny Image Europe.

Obunge, Adesola. Daily Devotions for 2 to 6 Year Olds: Hidden Treasure for Little Minds(r). 2011. 64p. pap. 30.44 *(978-1-4490-5372-7(6))* AuthorHouse.

Peace, Martha & Scott, Stuart. The Faithful Parent: A Biblical Guide to Raising a Family. 2010. pap. *(978-1-59638-201-5(5))* P & R Publishing.

Phelan, Thomas W. & Webb, Chris. 1-2-3 Magic for Christian Parents: Effective Discipline for Children 2-12. 2nd ed. 2011. (ENG., Illus.). 256p. pap. 14.95 *(978-1-889140-59-9(7))* ParentMagic, Inc.

Pollard, Prudence LaBeach. How to Raise a Leader — God's Way. 2012. ***(978-0-8280-2636-9(X))*** Review & Herald Publishing Assn.

Priolo, Lou. Workbook for the Heart of Anger: Practical Help for the Prevention & Cure of Anger in Children. 2007. 79p. pap. 16.99 *(978-1-879737-51-8(5))* Calvary Pr.

Priolo, Louis Paul & Payne, Brenda. Teach Them Diligently: How to Use the Scriptures in Child Training. 2008. 100p. pap. 11.50 *(978-1-889032-60-3(3))* Timeless Texts, Inc.

Raising Purity. 2008. 163p. per. 12.99 *(978-0-9773892-0-9(0))* Ryver Media.

Rayne, Paul & Rayne, Carolyn. The Connected Family: Simple Steps to Positive Parenting. 2011. pap. 14.99 *(978-0-8163-2457-6(3))* Pacific Pr. Publishing Assn.

Rogers, Rich. Next Level Parenting: Raising authentic, independent, spiritually healthy children with God's Help. 2009. (ENG.). 224p. pap. 14.99 *(978-1-59979-473-0(X))* Charisma Media.

Rosemond, John. Parenting by the Book: Biblical Wisdom for Raising Your Child. 2007. (ENG.). 288p. 19.99 *(978-1-4165-4484-5(4),* Howard Bks.) Howard Books.

Sandford, Paula & Sandford, John Loren. Growing Pains: How to Overcome Life's Earliest Experiences to Become All God Wants You to Be. 2008. (Transformation Ser.). (ENG.). 240p. pap. 14.99 *(978-1-59979-278-1(8),* Charisma Hse.) Charisma Media.

Sanford, Timothy L. Losing Control & Liking It: How to Set Your Teen (and Yourself) Free. 2008. (ENG.). 192p. pap. 13.99 *(978-1-58997-481-4(6))* Tyndale Hse. Pubs.

Schweikert, Gigi. There's A Perfect Little Angel in Every Child: Guiding Your Children to a Bright Future. 2010. (ENG.). 144p. pap. 10.99 *(978-1-4391-9620-5(6),* Howard Bks.) Howard Books.

Simmons, Tricia. Intentional Parenting. 2008. pap. 10.99 *(978-1-60477-945-5(4))* Xulon Pr., Inc.

Smiley, Kendra, et al. Journey of a Strong-Willed Child 2009. (ENG.). 144p. pap. 13.99 *(978-0-8024-4353-3(2))* Moody Pubs.

Smith, William P. How to Talk to Your Kid about Sex: Honesty & Openness for a Sensitive Subject. 2011. (ENG.). 24p. 3.99 ***(978-1-936768-44-8(5))*** New Growth Pr.

—When Your Kid's in Trouble: How to Intervene Constructively. 2011. (ENG.). 24p. 3.99 ***(978-1-936768-46-2(1))*** New Growth Pr.

Smith, William P. & Smith, Winston P. How Do I Stop Losing It with My Kids? Getting to the Heart of Your Discipline Problems. 2008. (ENG.). 24p. 3.99 *(978-1-934885-28-4(2))* New Growth Pr.

St John Taylor, Jennie. Culture-Proof Kids: Building Character in Your Children. 2007. 333p. per. 14.99 *(978-0-89957-116-4(6))* AMG Pubs.

Stafford, Wess. Too Small to Ignore: Why the Least of These Matters Most. 2007. (ENG.). 304p. pap. 14.99 *(978-1-4000-7392-4(8),* WaterBrook Pr.) Doubleday Religious Publishing Group, The.

Strom, Kay Marshall. Quiet Moments for Grandmothers: Scriptures, Meditations, & Prayers. 2006. (ENG.). 192p. per. 14.99 *(978-0-8341-2278-9(2),* 083-412-2782) Beacon Hill Pr. of Kansas City.

Stubna, Kris D. & Aquilina, Mike. Talking to Youth about Sexuality: A Parents' Guide. 2006. 63p. per. *(978-1-59276-310-8(3))* Our Sunday Visitor, Publishing Div.

Sumrall, Abner C. Correcting Your Child in Love: A Christian Parent's Manual - A Biblical Guide for Loving Discipline. 2009. (Illus.). 124p. pap. 11.99 *(978-1-61579-262-7(7))* Xulon Pr., Inc.

Tassi, Peter & Tassi, Filomena. Greatness in Our Teenagers: A 10 Step Guide for Parents & Educators. 2009. (Illus.). 104p. pap. 9.95 *(978-0-8091-4604-8(5))* Paulist Pr.

Trevathan, Melissa, et al. Raising Girls, 1 vol. annot. ed. 2007. (ENG.). 256p. pap. 12.99 *(978-0-310-27289-2(0))* Zondervan.

Viars, Stephen. Your Special Needs Child: Help for Weary Parents. 2011. (ENG.). 24p. 3.99 ***(978-1-936768-45-5(3))*** New Growth Pr.

Washam, Michele & Mooty, Tom. Protecting Those You Love in an X-Rated World: Blocking Harmful Media & Online Influences. 2007. x, 238p. pap. *(978-0-88270-443-2(5))* Bridge-Logos Foundation.

Watkins, Don & Watkins, Ann. Reclaiming the Art of Child Training:Toward a Biblical Approach. 2009. 154p. pap. 12.95 *(978-0-557-08905-5(0))* Lulu Enterprises Inc.

Weddle, Linda Massey. How to Raise a Modern-Day Joseph: A Practical Guide for Growing Great Kids, 1 vol. 2009. (ENG.). 224p. pap. 16.99 *(978-1-4347-6531-4(8))* Cook, David C.

—How to Raise a Modern-Day Joseph: A Practical Guide for Growing Great Kids. 2009. 220p. E-Book *(978-1-4347-0027-8(5))* Kingsway Pubns.

Wegner, Paul, et al. Wise Parenting: Guidelines from the Book of Proverbs. 2009. (ENG.). 144p. pap. 11.99 *(978-1-57293-352-1(6))* Discovery Hse. Pubs.

Wertheimer, Jack, ed. Family Matters: Jewish Education in an Age of Choice. 2007. (Brandeis Series in American Jewish History, Culture & Life Ser.). (Illus.). 312p. pap. 29.95 *(978-1-58465-636-4(0))* Univ. Pr. of New England.

White, Andrew. Suffer the Children: Dispatches to & from the Front Line. 2010. (ENG., Illus.). 128p. pap. 19.95 *(978-1-84706-374-8(8))* Continuum International Publishing Group, Ltd. GBR. Dist: National Bk. Network.

Wilcox, S. Michael. What the Scriptures Teach Us about Raising a Child. 2009. 18.95 *(978-1-60641-130-8(6))* Deseret Bk. Co.

Wilson, Rodney & Wilson, Selma. The Parent Adventure: Preparing Your Kid for a Life with God. 2008. pap. 97.25 *(978-1-4158-6511-8(6))* LifeWay Christian Resources.

Wright, H. Norman. Cómo Ayudar a Sus Hijos a Enfrentar el Enojo, el Miedo y la Tristeza, 1 vol. 2008.Tr. of Helping Your Kids Deal with Anger, Fear, & Sadness. (SPA., Illus.). 192p. pap. 9.99 *(978-0-8254-1878-5(X),* Editorial Portavoz) Kregel Pubns.

Yates, Susan Alexander. And Then I Had Teenagers, 1 vol. 2010. (ENG.). 208p. 5.99 *(978-0-8007-8791-2(9))* Revell.

Youngblood, Pastor Larry. Biblical Principles for Parenting. 2011. 166p. pap. 14.99 ***(978-1-61379-235-3(2))*** Xulon Pr., Inc.

Ziegler, Tom & Zeigler, Lori. As for Me & My House Vol. 2: 50 Easy-to-Use Devotionals for Preteens & Young Teens, Vol. 2. 2008. 151p. (J). pap. 12.00 *(978-1-57782-231-8(5))* Discipleship Pubns. International.

CHILD REARING—STUDY AND TEACHING

Craig, Lyn. Contemporary Motherhood: The Impact of Children upon Adult Time. 2007. (Illus.). 198p. 114.95 *(978-0-7546-4998-4(9))* Ashgate Publishing Co.

Kuzma, Kay. Parenting Boot Camp: Basic Training for Raising Responsible Kids. 2010. pap. 15.99 *(978-0-8163-2377-7(1))* Pacific Pr. Publishing Assn.

CHILD SEXUAL ABUSE

Akal, Matthew Jordan. Non-Supportive Disclosure in Child Sexual Abuse. 2011. 68p. pap. ***(978-3-8454-0673-2(9))*** Lambert Academic Publishing.

Akdeniz, Yaman. Internet Child Pornography & the Law: National & International Responses. 2008. (Illus.). 326p. 124.95 *(978-0-7546-2297-0(5))* Ashgate Publishing Co.

Alberter, Caroline Cannon. Cheated: A True Story of Child Sexual Abuse, Promiscuity & Bi-Polar Disorder. 2011. 82p. pap. 19.95 ***(978-1-4626-4255-7(1))*** PublishAmerica, Inc.

Alberts, Amy. Burnt Cookies: A Quest for Closure. 2010. 244p. pap. 17.95 *(978-1-60594-210-0(3),* Llumina Pr.) Aeon Publishing Inc.

Allen, Alan. I Missed Me after the Terror, During the Years of Unbearable Sorrow: Trafficking the Holy Spirit. 2010. 740p. pap. 33.08 *(978-1-4269-2746-1(0))* Trafford Publishing.

Allender, Dan B. The Wounded Heart: A Companion Workbook for Personal or Group Use. 2008. (Maranatha Novels Ser.). (ENG.). 208p. pap., wbk. ed. 16.99 *(978-1-60006-308-4(X))* NavPress Publishing Group.

—The Wounded Heart: Hope for Adult Victims of Childhood Sexual Abuse. 2008. (Real Life Stuff for Women Ser.). (ENG.). 272p. pap. 16.99 *(978-1-60006-307-7(1))* NavPress Publishing Group.

ANEP, et al. Mapa de ruta en el ámbito escolar para las situaciones de maltrato y abuso sexual que viven niños, niñas y Adolescentes. 2007.Tr. of Roadmap in school environment for situations of child abuse & sexual abuse suffered by children & Adolescents. (SPA.). 60p. per. *(978-92-806-4176-9(X))* United Nations Children's Fund, The (UNICEF).

Aprile, Anna & Ranzato, Cristina. Child Sexual Abuse: Pitfalls in the Substantiation Process. 2009. pap. 43.00 *(978-1-60741-427-8(9))* Nova Science Pubs., Inc.

Bailey, Charles, Jr. In the Shadow of the Cross. 2006. 204p. per. 17.95 *(978-0-595-40578-7(9))* iUniverse, Inc.

Balboni, Jennifer M. Clergy Sexual Abuse Litigation: Survivors Seeking Justice. 2011. 170p. 59.95 *(978-1-935049-37-1(2))* FirstForumPress.

Bange, Dirk & Enders, Ursula. Auch Indianer kennen Schmerz. Sexuelle Gewalt gegen Jungen. (GER.). 386p. pap. *(978-3-462-02467-8(1))* Kiepenheuer & Witsch GmbH & Company KG DEU. Dist: International Bk. Import Service, Inc.

Bass, Ellen & Davis, Laura. The Courage to Heal: A Guide for Women Survivors of Child Sexual Abuse. 4th anniv. ed. 2008. (ENG.). 640p. pap. 22.99 *(978-0-06-128433-5(5),* HarperPerennial) HarperCollins Pubs.

Bergquist, Patrick. The Long Dark Winter's Night: Reflections of a Priest in a Time of Pain & Privilege. 2010. 144p. pap. 16.95 *(978-0-8146-3301-4(3))* Liturgical Pr.

Berry, Jason & Renner, Gerald. Vows of Silence: The Abuse of Power in the Papacy of John Paul II. 2010. (ENG.). 368p. pap. 16.00 *(978-0-7432-8706-7(1),* Free Pr.) Free Pr.

Beverly, R. Devin. Influence of Child Molestation Tendencies & Antisocial Behavior. 2009. 152p. pap. *(978-3-639-18092-3(5))* VDM Verlag Dr. Mueller e.K.

Bonnie Lis Norris &. John Norris, Lis No & Bonnie Lis Norris & John Norris. Keeper of Secrets: My story of childhood sexual Abuse. 2009. 92p. pap. 11.95 *(978-1-4401-8111-5(X))* iUniverse, Inc.

C

Book, Lauren. It's OK to Tell: A Story of Hope & Recovery. 2011. (ENG.). 224p. 19.95 (978-1-935212-43-0(5)) Easton Studio Pr., LLC.

Bowens, DeShannon. Hush Hush: An African American Family Breaks Their Silence on Sexuality & Sexual Abuse - A Collection. 2007. 200p. pap. (978-0-9796619-0-7(0)) ILERA, LLC.

Bramham, Daphne. The Secret Lives of Saints: Child Brides & Lost Boys in a Polygamous Mormon Sect. 2009. (ENG., Illus.). 496p. pap. 18.00 (978-0-307-35589-8(6), Vintage Canada) Random Hse. of Canada, Ltd. CAN. Dist: Random Hse., Inc.

Bromley, Nicole Braddock. Breathe: Finding Freedom to Thrive in Relationships after Childhood Sexual Abuse, 1 vol. 2009. (ENG.). 192p. pap. 12.99 (978-0-8024-4865-1(8)) Moody Pubs.

—Hush: Moving from Silence to Healing after Childhood Sexual Abuse. 2007. (ENG.). 192p. per. 12.99 (978-0-8024-4864-4(X)) Moody Pubs.

Buess, Terese & Darby, Darin. Investigation & Prosecution of Child Sexual Abuse. 2011. 292p. pap. 40.00 (978-1-934973-35-6(1)) Texas District & County Attorneys Assn.

Burch, Cynthia. You'll See Jesus on My Face. 2011. 144p. pap. 12.95 (978-1-60920-014-5(4)) Ajoyin Publishing, Inc.

Cafardi, Nicholas P. Before Dallas: The U. S. Bishops' Response to Clergy Sexual Abuse of Children. 2008. 255p. 27.95 (978-0-8091-0580-9(2), 0580-9) Paulist Pr.

Calder, Martin, ed. Sexual Abuse Assessments: Using & Developing Frameworks for Practice. 2nd rev. ed. 2009. (Illus.). 437p. pap. 65.00 (978-1-905541-28-7(7)) Russell Hse. Publishing Ltd. GBR. Dist: International Specialized Bk. Services.

Calder, Martin C., ed. The Carrot or the Stick? Towards Effective Practice with Involuntary Clients in Safeguarding Children Work. 2008. (Illus.). 320p. pap. 65.00 (978-1-905541-22-5(8)) Russell Hse. Publishing Ltd. GBR. Dist: International Specialized Bk. Services.

Camden, Laura Beth. Molested — Why Me? I Thought These Things Only Happened to Bad Girls. 2008. 152p. pap. 14.95 (978-0-595-52176-0(2)) iUniverse, Inc.

Catholic Church, contrib. by. Promise to Protect, Pledge to Heal: Charter for the Protection of Children & Young People: Essential Norms: Statement of Episcopal Commitment. 2006. 35p. (978-1-57455-721-3(1)) United States Conference of Catholic Bishops.

Cavicante, Michael. A Father's Double Life: (New Edited Edition) 2011. 236p. 24.95 (978-1-4634-0646-2(0)); pap. 14.95 (978-1-4634-0648-6(7)) AuthorHouse.

Cheung, Monit. Child Sexual Abuse: Best Practices for Interviewing & Treatment. 2012. pap. 49.95 (978-1-933478-43-2(8)) Lyceum Bks., Inc.

Chinnici, Joseph P. When Values Collide: The Catholic Church, Sexual Abuse & the Challenges of Leadership. 2009. 240p. pap. 25.00 (978-1-57075-873-7(5)) Orbis Bks.

Claire, Maggie. As If It Didn't Happen: A memoir of abuse, multiple personalities, & Hope. 2009. 334p. pap. 21.32 (978-0-557-15501-9(0)) Lulu Enterprises Inc.

Clancy, Susan A. The Trauma Myth: The Truth about the Sexual Abuse of Children - And Its Aftermath. 2011. (ENG.). 256p. (gr. 9). pap. 16.99 (978-0-465-02211-3(1)) Basic Bks.

Colarusso, Calvin A. The Long Shadow of Sexual Abuse: Developmental Effects Across the Life Cycle. 2010. (ENG.). 202p. 55.00 (978-0-7657-0766-6(7), Aronson, Jason) Rowman & Littlefield Publishers, Inc.

Cooper, Sharon W., et al. Child Sexual Exploitation Quick Reference: For Healthcare, Social Service, & Law Enforcement Professionals. 2007. (ENG., Illus.). 384p. spiral bd. 52.00 (978-1-878060-21-1(X)) STM Learning, Inc.

Cram101 Textbook Reviews & Cram101 Textbook Reviews. Outlines & Highlights for Introduction to Working with Adult Survivors of Childhood Traum: Technique by Carolyn Knight, ISBN. 2011. 60p. pap. 26.95 (978-1-4288-7924-9(2)) Cram101 Inc.

Dank, Meredith L. The Commercial Sexual Exploitation of Children. 2011. 166p. 65.00 (978-1-59332-409-4(X)) LFB Scholarly Publishing LLC.

Daugherty, Lynn B. Why Me? Help for Victims of Child Sexual Abuse (Even if they are adults now), Fourth Edition. 4th rev. ed. 2007. 128p. per. 12.95 (978-0-9771614-3-0(9)) Cleanan Pr., Inc.

Davidson Julia. Child Sexual Abuse: Media Representations & Government Reactions. 2008. XIV, 178p. 150.00 (978-1-904385-69-1(9)) 2007. 176p. 57.95 (978-1-904385-68-4(0)) Taylor & Francis Group GBR. (Routledge Cavendish). Dist: Taylor & Francis Group.

Davies, Sara. Running from the Devil. 2006. (ENG.). 288p. 29.95 (978-1-84454-284-0(X)) Blake, John Publishing, Ltd. GBR. Dist: Independent Pubs. Group.

—Running from the Devil: How I Survived a Stolen Childhood. 2007. (ENG.). 257p. per. 14.95 (978-1-84454-413-4(3)) Blake, John Publishing, Ltd. GBR. Dist: Independent Pubs. Group.

Davis, Gail. Not Afraid to Tell Who I Was Because I Know Who I Am. 2011. 92p. pap. 14.99 (978-1-4634-1208-1(8)) AuthorHouse.

Davis, Lisa. The Sins of Brother Curtis: A Story of Betrayal, Conviction, & the Mormon Church. 2011. (ENG., Illus.). 368p. 27.00 (978-1-4165-9103-0(6), Scribner) Scribner.

Dias, Maria Berenice & Kristensen, Christian Haag. Incesto e Alienação Parental: Realidades Que a Justiça Insiste Em Não Ver. 2nd ed. 2010. (POR.). 207p. (978-85-203-3147-7(5)) Revista dos Tribunais, Editora.

Dimond, Diane. Be Careful Who You Love: Inside the Michael Jackson Case. 2009. (ENG.). 352p. pap. 22.95 (978-0-7432-7092-2(4), Beyond Words/Atria Bks.) Atria Bks.

Djata, Empress. Disturbed. 2009. 220p. pap. 24.95 (978-0-615-16480-9(3)) Djata, Empress.

Dorais, Michel. Don't Tell: The Sexual Abuse of Boys. Meyer, Isabel Denholm, tr. from FRE. 2nd ed. 2008. (ENG.). 240p. (C). (978-0-7735-3471-1(7)); pap. (978-0-7735-3472-8(5)) McGill-Queen's Univ. Pr.

Dorn, Michael & Dorn, Chris. Sexual Monsters - What Every Parent, Educator & Youth Service Professional Must Know about Child Molesters. 2006. 156p. 19.95 (978-0-9741240-4-9(4)) Safe Havens International, Inc.

Dudek, Wanda. Touch My Soul No Longer. 2007. pap. 14.99 (978-1-60034-918-8(8)) Xulon Pr., Inc.

Duncan, Karen A. Healing from the Trauma of Childhood Sexual Abuse: The Journey for Women, 1 vol. 2008. (Illus.). 264p. pap. 19.95 (978-0-313-36321-4(8), B36321, Praeger Trade) Greenwood Publishing Group, Inc.

Dunn, Munita. Hands Off! 2010. 388p. pap. (978-3-8383-5048-6(0)) Lambert Academic Publishing.

Egan, Kevin. Remaining a Catholic after the Murphy Report. 2011. (ENG.). 168p. pap. 25.95 (978-1-85607-740-8(3)) Columba Pr. IRL. Dist: Dufour Editions, Inc.

Ellison, Randy. Boys Don't Tell: Ending the Silence of Abuse. 2011. (ENG.). 150p. pap. 16.95 (978-1-61448-046-4(X)) Morgan James Publishing.

Erickson, Al & Malloy, Patricia. Parents Arise! Grandparents Arise! Book. 2011. 212p. pap. 15.95 (978-1-880292-39-6(4)) LangMarc Publishing.

Erickson, Alvin & Malloy, Patricia. Parents Arise! Grandparents Arise! Book 2 Ten Actions to Take to Safeguard Our Children. 2011. 230p. pap. 15.95 (978-1-880292-40-2(8)) LangMarc Publishing.

Evans, Maurice. Why Didn't I Ask Why: Sexual Abuse. 2010. 100p. pap. 19.95 (978-1-4327-5919-3(1)) Outskirts Pr., Inc.

Faller, Kathleen Coulborn. Interviewing Children about Sexual Abuse: Controversies & Best Practice. 2007. (ENG., Illus.). 328p. 39.95 (978-0-19-531177-8(9)) Oxford Univ. Pr., Inc.

Fanning, Tim. The Fethard-on-Sea Boycott. 2010. (ENG., Illus.). 240p. pap. 26.95 (978-1-84889-032-9(X)) Collins Pr., The IRL. Dist: Dufour Editions, Inc.

Flannery, Tony, ed. Responding to the Ryan Report. 2010. (ENG.). 233p. pap. 27.95 (978-1-85607-673-9(3)) Columba Pr. IRL. Dist: Dufour Editions, Inc.

Floric, Marylee & Broyles, Matthew. Sexual Abuse. 2011. (Girls' Health Ser.). (Illus.). 48p. (YA). (gr. 5-9). lib. bdg. 27.95 (978-1-4488-4572-9(6)) Rosen Publishing Group, Inc., The.

Fortune, Marie M. & Poling, James N. Sexual Abuse by Clergy: A Crisis for the Church. 2008. 76p. pap. 11.00 (978-1-55635-686-5(2)) Wipf & Stock Pubs.

Foster, Chrissie. Hell on the Way to Heaven: An Australian Mother's Love - The Power of the Catholic Church, & a Fight for Justice over Child Sexual Abuse. 2010. (ENG., Illus.). 391p. 27.95 (978-1-74166-952-7(9)) Random Hse. Australia AUS. Dist: Independent Pubs. Group.

Fowler, Jeff. A Practitioners' Tool for the Assessment of Adults Who Sexually Abuse Children. 2008. (ENG.). 160p. pap. (978-1-84310-639-5(6)) Kingsley, Jessica Ltd.

Frost, Sasha. The Letting Go. 2011. 144p. pap. 13.14 (978-1-4269-6309-4(2)) Trafford Publishing.

Fuller, Joseph. Vivere: (to Live) 2011. 338p. pap. 29.95 (978-1-4560-5552-3(6)) PublishAmerica, Inc.

Galasso, Carmine. Crosses: Portraits of Clergy Abuse. 2007. (Illus.). 200p. 50.00 (978-1-904563-59-4(7)) Trolley GBR. Dist: Prestel Publishing.

Gardner, Yun. Affective Responses of Counselors to Child Sexual Abuse Disclosure. 2009. 120p. pap. (978-3-639-14343-0(4)) VDM Verlag Dr. Mueller e.K.

Garris, Grant. Under the Red Velvet Cover: Conquering Victimhood & Breaking the Silence of Abuse, Corruption & Family Secrets - My Life Journey. 2010. 252p. 24.99 (978-1-4490-6911-7(8)) AuthorHouse.

Geesey, Janet. Cry of the Innocent: The Illusion of a Happy Family. 2008. 162p. pap. 24.95 (978-1-60474-629-7(7)) PublishAmerica, Inc.

Gerber, Doris. Makin' Do. 2011. pap. 15.95 (978-0-7414-6411-8(X)) Infinity Publishing.

Glatt, John. Secrets in the Cellar. 2009. (ENG., Illus.). 256p. 7.99 (978-0-312-94786-6(0), St. Martin's True Crime) St. Martin's Pr.

Gledhill, Debbie. Growing up Small: The Diary Memoirs of a Woman Seeing the World Through the Eyes of a Sexually Abused Child. 2011. 80p. pap. 19.95 (978-1-4560-5268-3(3)) PublishAmerica, Inc.

Goldner, Virginia & Frawley-O'Dea, Mary G., eds. Predatory Priests, Silenced Victims: The Sexual Abuse Crisis & the Catholic Church. 2007. (ENG.). 259p. 44.50 (978-0-88163-424-2(7)) Routledge.

Goode, Sarah D. Paedophiles in Society: Reflecting on Sexuality, Abuse & Hope. 2011. (ENG., Illus.). 248p. 85.00 (978-0-230-27188-3(X)) Palgrave Macmillan.

Grey, William. The Devil Within. 2011. (Illus.). 107p. pap. 39.17 (978-1-4567-8589-5(3)) AuthorHouse.

Haaken, Jan, et al. Memory Matters: Contexts for Understanding Sexual Abuse Recollections. Haaken, Jan, ed. 2009. (ENG., Illus.). 248p. 79.95 (978-0-415-44491-0(8)) Routledge.

Hambke, Paul M. & Calder, Martin C. What I Did on My Summer Vacation: Surviving & Helping Others Learn from a Boyhood of Sexual Abuse. 2010. (Illus.). 142p. pap. 39.95 (978-1-905541-59-1(7)) Russell Hse. Publishing Ltd. GBR. Dist: International Specialized Bk. Services.

Hamilton, Marci. Justice Denied: What America Must Do to Protect Its Children. 2008. (ENG.). 168p. 26.00 (978-0-521-88621-5(X)) Cambridge Univ. Pr.

Hamilton, Marci A. Justice Denied: What America Must Do to Protect Its Children. 2012. (ENG.). 176p. pap. 18.99 (978-1-107-67312-0(7)) Cambridge Univ. Pr.

Harbeck, Bill. Shattered: One Man's Journey from Sexual Abuse. 2009. 148p. pap. 14.99 (978-1-61579-191-0(4)) Xulon Pr., Inc.

Harper, Sarah. Life & Survival As a Destitute: My Own True Story. 2011. 208p. pap. 21.29 (978-1-4567-8945-9(7)) AuthorHouse.

Harris, Cory B. The Child/Adult Safety Bible. 2011. 140p. pap. 18.70 (978-1-4567-4107-5(1)) AuthorHouse.

Hawkins, David B. When Your Child Has Been Molested. Date not set. (Illus.). pap. (978-1-930195-08-0(7)) Your Pocket Therapist.

Hedgepeth, Donnie. He Heard My Cry. 2009. 48p. pap. 11.95 (978-0-9841899-3-9(9)) PearlStone Publishing, Inc.

Henderson, Crystal. When My Father Preys. 2010. 256p. pap. 13.99 (978-1-60844-477-9(5)) Dog Ear Publishing, LLC.

Hennecy, Carolyn S. Orange Blossom Wishes: Child Molested, Woman Abused — Her Victorious Journey to Freedom. 2008. 176p. 25.95 (978-0-595-49211-4(8)); pap. 15.95 (978-0-595-46148-6(4)) iUniverse, Inc.

Herrera, Teresa. Finding Little Girl Lost: A journey of healing through child sexual Abuse. 2011. 88p. pap. 19.95 (978-1-4560-7044-1(4)) PublishAmerica, Inc.

Hidalgo, Myra L. Sexual Abuse & Catholicism: How Priests & Nuns Become Perpetrators. 2007. (ENG., Illus.). 164p. 125.00 (978-0-7890-2955-3(3)) Routledge.

—Sexual Abuse & the Culture of Catholicism: How Priests & Nuns Become Perpetrators. 2007. (ENG., Illus.). 164p. per. 18.95 (978-0-7890-2956-0(1)) Routledge.

Higgins, Martina & Swain, John. Disability & Child Sexual Abuse: Lessons from Survivors' Narratives for Effective Protection, Prevention & Treatment. 2009. (ENG.). 256p. pap. (978-1-84310-563-3(2)) Kingsley, Jessica Ltd.

Higgins, Michael W. & Kavanagh, Peter. Suffer the Children unto Me: An Enquiry into Canada's Clerical Abuse Scandal. 2010. 256p. (978-2-89646-233-9(3)) Novalis Publishing.

Hilarski, Carolyn, et al. Handbook of Social Work in Child & Adolescent Sexual Abuse. 2008. (ENG.). 288p. 104.95 (978-0-7890-3201-0(5)); 302p. pap. 57.95 (978-0-7890-3202-7(3)) Routledge.

Hood, Lynley. A City Possessed: The Christchurch Civic Creche Case. 672p. (978-1-877135-62-0(3), Longacre Pr.) Random Hse. New Zealand.

Hughes, Bruce D. The Snare Is Broken. 2011. 364p. pap. 20.99 (978-1-61215-474-9(3)) Xulon Pr., Inc.

HULBERT, JOAN F. The Shake-up. 2007. 56p. per. 10.95 (978-1-4327-0750-7(7)) Outskirts Pr., Inc.

Hynes, Lauren E. Sexual Abuse: Types, Signs & Treatments. 2011. (Psychology of Emotions, Motivations & Actions Ser.). 221p. 129.00 (978-1-61209-611-7(5)) Nova Science Pubs., Inc.

Jackson, D. M. Secrets: A Story of Innocence Lost. 2007. 52p. pap. 9.00 (978-0-8059-7486-7(5)) Dorrance Publishing Co., Inc.

Jackson, Denise. Grace for the Pilgrimage: Your travelogue to Healing from Childhood Sexual Abuse. 2010. 56p. spiral bd. 25.00 (978-0-9842171-1-3(8)) Masterpiece Creations Graphics & Publishing.

—I'm Special... I'm a Survivor: A Journal for Older Adolescents. Weller, Mary, ed. 2010. 36p. spiral bd. 22.00 (978-0-9842171-5-1(0)) Masterpiece Creations Graphics & Publishing.

Jameel, Issam. Iraq Through a Bullet Hole: A Civilian Returns Home. 2008. 212p. pap. 19.95 (978-1-932690-70-5(0), Modern History Pr.) Loving Healing Pr., Inc.

Jessop, Flora & Brown, Paul T. Church of Lies. (ENG.). 328p. 2010. pap. 14.95 (978-0-470-56546-9(2)) 2009. (Illus.). 25.95 (978-0-7879-9462-4(6)) Wiley, John & Sons, Inc. (Jossey-Bass).

Jones, Kris. How Do I Escape When I'm Trapped in My Own Mind? 2011. 116p. 22.95 (978-1-4620-3566-3(3)); pap. 12.95 (978-1-4620-3564-9(7)) iUniverse, Inc.

Joseph, Arthur S. The 'Pedophile' Sham: Undermining the Torah Matrix. 2008. 188p. pap. 14.49 (978-1-4389-0222-7(0)) AuthorHouse.

Kaplan, Rich, et al. Medical Response to Child Sexual Abuse with CD-ROM: A Resource for Clinicians & Other Professionals. 2011. (ENG., Illus.). 440p. 85.00 (978-1-878060-12-9(0)) STM Learning, Inc.

Keane, Terence, et al. Survivors of Clergy Sexual Abuse. 2008. 285p. 130.00 (978-0-7890-3599-8(5)); 45.95 (978-0-7890-3600-1(2)) Routledge.

Keenan, Caroline & Hoyano, Laura. Child Abuse: Law & Policy Across Boundaries. 2007. (ENG.). 1080p. 250.00 (978-0-19-829946-2(X)) Oxford Univ. Pr., Inc.

Keenan, Marie. Child Sexual Abuse & the Catholic Church: Gender, Power, & Organizational Culture. 2011. (ENG.). 400p. 59.95 (978-0-19-989567-0(8)) Oxford Univ. Pr., Inc.

Kelso, Chandrika. Domestic Violence & Problem Behaviors among Children. 2009. 140p. pap. (978-3-639-19213-1(3)) VDM Verlag Dr. Mueller e.K.

King, Gary C. Stolen in the Night: The True Story of a Family's Murder, a Kidnapping & the Child Who Survived. 2007. (ENG., Illus.). 256p. mass mkt. 7.99 (978-0-312-94205-2(2), St. Martin's Paperbacks) St. Martin's Pr.

Kirkengen, A. L. Inscribed Bodies: Health Impact of Childhood Sexual Abuse. 2010. 472p. pap. 239.00 (978-90-481-5718-1(8), 9048157188) Springer.

Kleinleder, Peggy Ellen & Evensen, Kimber. The Thursday Group: A Story & Information for Girls Healing from Sexual Abuse. 2009. (Illus.). 272p. pap. 25.00 (978-1-929657-44-5(7)) Neari Pr.

Kuehnle, Kathryn & Connell, Mary A. The Evaluation of Child Sexual Abuse Allegations: A Comprehensive Guide to Assessment & Testimony. 2008. (ENG., Illus.). 600p. 100.00 (978-0-470-28860-3(4), Wiley) Wiley, John & Sons, Inc.

Kuehnle, Kathryn & Drozd, Leslie M., eds. Child Custody Litigation: Allegations of Child Sexual Abuse. 2006. (Illus.). 145p. per. 54.95 (978-0-7890-3134-1(5)); 175.00 (978-0-7890-3133-4(7)) Routledge.

Lamb, Michael E., et al, eds. Child Sexual Abuse: Disclosure, Delay, & Denial. 2007. (ENG., Illus.). 328p. 105.95 (978-0-8058-5284-4(0), Psychology Press) Taylor & Francis Group GBR. Dist: Taylor & Francis Group.

Lee, Jason. Celebrity, Pedophilia, & Ideology in American Culture. 2009. 464p. 29.99 (978-1-60497-599-4(7)) Cambria Pr.

Lee, Sheri Nelson. Feel Your Way Home. 2011. 124p. pap. 19.95 (978-1-4560-6955-1(1)) PublishAmerica, Inc.

Legrand, Daniel & Vattier, Youki. Histoire Commune. 2008. (FRE.). 354p. (978-2-234-06148-4(2)) Stock, Editions.

Levenkron, Steven. Stolen Tomorrows: Understanding & Treating Women's Childhood Sexual Abuse. 2007. (ENG.). 224p. 25.95 (978-0-393-06086-7(1), 6086) Norton, W. W. & Co., Inc.

Levenkron, Steven & Levenkron, Abby. Stolen Tomorrows: Understanding & Treating Women's Childhood Sexual Abuse. 2008. (ENG.). 288p. pap. 15.95 (978-0-393-33201-8(2), 33201) Norton, W. W. & Co., Inc.

Lewis, Michael. Handbook of Child Sexual Abuse: Identification, Assessment, & Treatment. Goodyear-Brown, Paris, ed. movie tie-in ed. 2011. (ENG., Illus.). 616p. 75.00 (978-0-470-87729-6(4), Wiley) Wiley, John & Sons, Inc.

Lewis, Sophie. Catching up to Tulsi. 2008. 72p. pap. 14.00 (978-0-8059-7651-9(5)) Dorrance Publishing Co., Inc.

Loiselle, Mindy B. & Wright, Leslie Bailey. Rewind, Rebound: A teenage guy's book for dealing with sexual Abuse. 2010. (ENG.). x, 123p. (YA). 20.00 (978-1-884444-84-5(9)) Safer Society Pr.

Lytton, Timothy D. Holding Bishops Accountable: How Lawsuits Helped the Catholic Church Confront Clergy Sexual Abuse. 2008. (Illus.). 304p. 38.50 (978-0-674-02810-4(4)) Harvard Univ. Pr.

Madden, Amy. Stolen Beauty: Healing the Scars of Child Abuse: One Woman's Journey. 2007. 196p. per. 14.95 (978-0-929636-74-0(0)) Syren Bk. Co.

Maher, Eamon & Littleton, John, eds. The Dublin/Murphy Report: A Watershed for Irish Catholicism? 2010. (ENG.). 174p. pap. 24.95 (978-1-85607-697-5(0)) Columba Pr. IRL. Dist: Dufour Editions, Inc.

Mallon, Chris. Light at the End of the Tunnel. 2012. (ENG.). 122p. pap. (978-1-904444-81-7(4)) Apex Publishing Ltd., Essex.

Mam, Somaly. The Road of Lost Innocence: The True Story of a Cambodian Heroine. 2009. (ENG.). 224p. pap. 15.00 (978-0-385-52622-7(9)) Spiegel & Grau.

Mandel, David & Pelcovitz, David A. Breaking the Silence: Sexual Abuse in the Jewish Community. 2010. (978-1-60280-165-3(7)) Ktav Publishing Hse., Inc.

Margel, Ellen. Loving & Leaving an Abuser: A Mother's Struggle to Save Her Child from Sexual Abuse. 2011. 172p. 23.95 (978-1-4620-1962-5(5)); pap. 13.95 (978-1-4620-1960-1(9)) iUniverse, Inc.

Marsh, Stefanie & Pancevski, Bojan. I'm No Monster: The Horrifying True Story of Josef Fritzl. 2011. (ENG.). 336p. (gr. 12). 9.99 (978-0-425-24452-4(0), Berkley) Penguin Group (USA) Inc.

Martellozzo, Elena. Online Child Sexual Abuse: Grooming, Policing & Child Protection in a Multi-Media World. 2012. (ENG., Illus.). 184p. 125.00 (978-0-415-61821-2(5)) Routledge.

Martínez, Sanjuana. Prueba de Fe: La Red de Cardenales y Obispos en la Pederastia Clerical. 2009. (SPA.). 273p. 18.95 (978-970-37-0713-3(0)) Editorial Planeta, S. A. ESP. Dist: Giron Bks.

McCall, Catherine. When the Piano Stops: A Memoir of Healing from Sexual Abuse. 2009. (ENG.). 280p. pap. 16.95 (978-1-58005-267-2(3)) Seal Pr.

McCarthy, Justine. Deep Deception: Ireland's Swimming Scandals. 2010. (ENG.). 304p. pap. 18.95 (978-1-84717-204-4(0)) O'Brien Pr., Ltd., The IRL. Dist: Dufour Editions, Inc.

McColgan, Maria D., et al. Child Sexual Abuse Training Curriculum: A Training Curriculum. 2012. (ENG., Illus.). 250p. spiral bd. 200.00 incl. cd-rom (978-1-878060-93-8(7)) STM Learning, Inc.

McGregor, Kim. Surviving & Moving On: Self-Help for Survivors of Childhood Sexual Abuse. 2010. (ENG.). 464p. pap. 38.00 (978-1-84392-507-1(9)) Willan Publishing GBR. Dist: Taylor & Francis Group.

McIntyre, Mike. Devil among Us: How Canada Failed to Stop a Pedophile. 2008. (ENG.). 320p. mass mkt. 11.95 (978-1-894283-80-9(5)) Great Plains Pubns. CAN. Dist: Univ. of Toronto Pr.

McMillian, Myi-Shanka. The Little Girl Inside of Me. 2010. 106p. pap. 14.95 (978-0-9841899-2-2(0)) PearlStone Publishing, Inc.

Medina, Sarah. Abuse & Neglect. 2008. (Emotional Health Issues Ser.). (Illus.). 48p. (YA). (gr. 7-12). lib. bdg. 31.00 (978-0-8368-9198-0(8)) Stevens, Gareth Publishing LLLP.

Méndez-Negrete, Josie. Las Hijas de Juan: Daughters Betrayed. 2006. (Latin America Otherwise Ser.). (ENG.). 224p. 79.95 (978-0-8223-3880-2(7)) Duke Univ. Pr.

—Las Hijas de Juan: Daughters Betrayed. 2006. (Latin America Otherwise Ser.). (ENG.). 224p. per. 22.95 (978-0-8223-3896-3(3)) Duke Univ. Pr.

Meyer, Anneke. The Child at Risk: Paedophiles, Media Responses & Public Opinion. 2007. (ENG., Illus.). 192p. 95.00 (978-0-7190-7344-1(8)) Manchester Univ. Pr. GBR. Dist: Macmillan.

Michael J. Rodgers Jr. Mercy. 2010. 152p. pap. 13.99 (978-1-4269-2507-8(7)) Trafford Publishing.

Miletski, Hani G. Mother-Son Incest: An updated & Revised Overview of Findings: the Unthinkable Broken Taboo Persists. 2007. 120p. per. 20.00 net. (978-0-9716917-3-5(8)) East-West Publishing, LLC.

Montgomery, Christina V. Crying Out Loud. 2009. 82p. pap. 15.99 *(978-1-4500-0584-5(5))* Xlibris Corp.
Montgomery, Lyman A. Shattered Masks: 7 Masks We Wear. 2011. 172p. pap. 17.00 ***(978-1-4634-0316-4(X))*** AuthorHouse.
Mooney, Tom. All the Bishops' Men: Clerical Abuse in an Irish Diocese. 2011. (ENG., Illus.). 288p. pap. 23.95 *(978-1-84889-099-2(0))* Collins Pr., The IRL. Dist: Dufour Editions, Inc.
Mosgofian, Peter T. & Chischlager, George W. Sexual Misconduct in Counseling & Ministry. 2009. 366p. pap. 43.00 *(978-1-60608-506-6(9)*, Wipf and Stock) Wipf & Stock Pubs.
Moushey, Bill, et al. Game Over: Jerry Sandusky, Penn State, & the Culture of Silence. 2012. (ENG.). 256p. 26.99 ***(978-0-06-220113-3(1)***, Morrow, William & Co.) HarperCollins Pubs.
—Game Over: Penn State, Jerry Sandusky, & the Culture of Silence. Lt. ed. 2012. (ENG.). 336p. pap. 26.99 ***(978-0-06-220134-8(4)***, HarperLuxe) HarperCollins Pubs.
Muntarbhorn, Vitit. Sexual Exploitation & Sexual Abuse of Children. Alen, André et al, eds. 2006. (Commentary on the United Nations Convention on the Rights of the Child Ser.). (FRE & ENG.). 41p. pap. *(978-90-04-14884-0(1))* BRILL.
Neustein, Amy, ed. Tempest in the Temple: Jewish Communities & Child Sex Scandals. 2009. (Brandeis Series in American Jewish History, Culture & Life Ser.). (ENG.). 308p. 35.00 *(978-1-58465-671-5(9)*, Brandeis University Press) Univ. Pr. of New England.
O'Donnell, Ian & Milner, Claire. Child Pornography: Crime, Computers & Society. 2007. (Illus.). 259p. (C). pap. *(978-1-84392-356-5(4))* Willan Publishing.
Owensby, J. Jackson, told to. My Sister & I: We Are Survivors. 2008. per. 16.95 *(978-0-9801555-3-2(3))* Argus Enterprises Internationa, Inc.
Oz, Sheri & Ogiers, Sarah-Jane. Overcoming Childhood Sexual Trauma: A Guide to Breaking Through the Wall of Fear for Practitioners & Survivors. 2006. (ENG., Illus.). 338p. 145.00 *(978-0-7890-2979-9(0))*; per. 44.95 *(978-0-7890-2980-5(4))* Routledge.
Palmer, Simon. Losing the Hate. 2011. 210p. pap. ***(978-1-908481-64-1(1))*** YouWriteOn.
Pearce, Jennifer & Pearce, Jenny. Young People & Sexual Exploitation: 'It's Not Hidden, You Just Aren't Looking' 2009. (ENG., Illus.). VIII, 184p. 44.95 *(978-0-415-40716-8(8))*; 140.00 *(978-0-415-40715-1(X))* Routledge.
Pennington, Lucinda. They Meant it for Evil. 2011. pap. 11.99 ***(978-1-61346-093-1(7))*** Tate Publishing & Enterprises, LLC.
Phelps, Shirley Itim Melo. We Women of Many Shades & Hues: Daily Common Ground for Survivors of Childhood Sexual Abuse, Incest, & Rape. 2008. 404p. pap. 25.00 *(978-0-9798633-8-7(4))* Robertson Publishing.
Philpot, Terry. Understanding Child Abuse: The Partners of Child Sex Offenders Tell Their Stories. 2009. X, 150p. pap. 43.95 *(978-0-415-45600-5(2))* 2008. 150p. 140.00 *(978-0-415-40949-0(7))* Routledge.
Pierre, Jimmie. The Courage of a Crusader. 2011. 222p. 30.00 ***(978-1-257-09579-7(X))*** Lulu Enterprises Inc.
Pipe, Margaret-Ellen, et al, eds. Child Sexual Abuse: Disclosure, Delay, & Denial. 2007. (ENG., Illus.). 328p. per. 52.95 *(978-0-8058-6317-8(6)*, Psychology Press) Taylor & Francis Group GBR. Dist: Taylor & Francis Group.
Plach, Tom. Investigating Allegations of Child & Adolescent Sexual Abuse: An Overview for Professionals. 2008. 192p. *(978-0-398-07794-5(0))*; pap. *(978-0-398-07795-2(9))* Thomas, Charles C. Pub., Ltd.
Pollock, Philip H. The Paedophilic Killer: Clinical Insights, Forensic Psychotherapy & Case Management. 2009. 200p. *(978-0-470-01804-0(6)*, Wiley-Blackwell) Wiley, John & Sons, Ltd.
Potts, Anthony & O'Donoghue, T. A. Schools As Dangerous Places: Historical Perspectives. 2007. 119.95 *(978-1-934043-76-9(1))* Cambria Pr.
Powa Women's Writing Competition Staff. Breaking the Silence: Murmurs of the Girl in Me. 2009. (ENG.). 116p. pap. 15.00 *(978-1-920196-04-2(8))* Jacana Media ZAF. Dist: Independent Pubs. Group.
Preventing Child Abuse & Improving Responses to Families in Crisis: Hearing Before the Subcommittee on Healthy Families & Communities, Committee on Education & Labor, U.S. House of Representatives, One Hundred Eleventh Congress, First Session, Hearing Held in Washington, DC, November 5, 2009. 2010. (Illus.). iii, 123p. *(978-0-16-086315-8(5)*, 552-070-41402-9) United States Government Printing Office.
Quayle, Ethel & Ribisl, Kurt M., eds. Internet Child Pornography. 2012. (ENG., Illus.). 296p. (C). 150.00 ***(978-0-415-68940-3(6))***; pap. 53.95 ***(978-0-415-68941-0(4))*** Routledge.
Rae, Carla. There's Healing in the Garden: Journaling Home to Abba Father. 2011. 112p. 24.95 ***(978-1-4567-1534-2(8))***; pap. 14.95 ***(978-1-4567-1532-8(1))*** AuthorHouse.
Rauch, Mikele. Healing the Soul after Religious Abuse: The Dark Heaven of Recovery, 1 vol. 2009. (Religion, Health, & Healing Ser.). 189p. 44.95 *(978-0-313-34670-5(4)*, C34670, Praeger Pubs.) Greenwood Publishing Group, Inc.
Rice, Pum. Child Abuse, My Story. 2011. 58p. pap. 21.49 ***(978-1-4583-4688-9(9))*** Lulu Enterprises Inc.
Richardson, Myra K. The Innocent Molester. 2007. (Illus.). 296p. per. 23.50 *(978-1-4251-1084-0(3))* Trafford Publishing.
Richardson, W. The Presumption of Innocence in Canonical Trials of Clerics Accused of Child Sexual Abuse: An Historical Analysis of the Current Law. 2011. (Canon Law Monograph Ser.). (ENG.). 324p. (C). pap. 66.00 *(978-90-429-2549-9(5))* Peeters Pubs. & Booksellers BEL. Dist: Brown, David Bk. Co., The.
Ricker, Audrey. The Ultimate Betrayal: The Enabling Mother, Incest & Sexual Abuse. 2006. (ENG.). 200p. per. 12.95 *(978-1-884365-40-9(X))* See Sharp Pr.
Riegel, David L. We were NOT Abused! 2007. 96p. pap. *(978-0-9676997-3-8(8))* SafeHaven Foundation Pr.
Rikoff, C. Ann. Bears Don't Tell: A Story for Grownups. 2011. 60p. pap. 10.49 ***(978-1-4567-4438-0(0))*** AuthorHouse.
Robbins, Sidney & Robbins, Shirley. Slavery Unmasked: Arousing the Conscience of Churches & Society. 2010. (DUT.). 108p. pap. 19.75 *(978-1-177-02009-1(2))* BiblioBazaar.
Robertson, Geoffrey. The Case of the Pope: Vatican Accountability for Human Rights Abuse. 2010. (ENG., Illus.). 240p. pap. 9.99 *(978-0-241-95384-6(7)*, Penguin Global) Penguin Group (USA) Inc.
Robinson, Geoffrey. Confronting Power & Sex in the Catholic Church: Reclaiming the Spirit of Jesus. 2008. 307p. (Orig.). pap. *(978-1-920721-47-3(9))* Liturgical Pr.
Ronquillo, Victor. Los NiNtilde;Os de Nadie. 2007. (SPA.). 200p. pap. 18.95 *(978-970-710-262-0(4))* B. Mexico, Ediciones, S.A. de C.V. MEX. Dist: Ediciones Urano S. A.
Rostagnol, Susana & Grabino, Valeria. Historias en el Silencio: Prostitución infantil y adolescente en Montevideo y área Metropolitana. 2007.Tr. of Stories of silence: child & adolescent prostitution in Montevideo & metropolitan Area. (SPA.). 120p. per. *(978-92-806-4236-0(7))* United Nations Children's Fund, The (UNICEF).
Sacco, Lynn. Unspeakable: Father-Daughter Incest in American History. 2009. (ENG.). 368p. (gr. 17). 52.00 *(978-0-8018-9300-1(3))* Johns Hopkins Univ. Pr.
Salter, Michael. Organised Child Sexual Abuse. 2012. (ENG.). 224p. 125.00 *(978-0-415-68977-9(5))* Routledge.
Savirimuthu, Joseph. Online Child Safety: Law, Technology & Governance. 2012. (ENG., Illus.). 376p. 90.00 ***(978-0-230-24152-7(2))*** Palgrave Macmillan.
Sax, Robin. It Happens Every Day: Inside the World of a Sex Crimes DA. 2009. (ENG., Illus.). 300p. 26.00 *(978-1-59102-758-4(6))* Prometheus Bks., Pubs.
—Predators & Child Molesters: What Every Parent Needs to Know to Keep Kids Safe. 2009. (ENG.). 224p. pap. 17.98 *(978-1-59102-712-6(8))* Prometheus Bks., Pubs.
Scharff, David & Scharff, Jill. Object Relations Therapy of Physical & Sexual Trauma. 2008. (Library of Object Relations Ser.). (ENG.). 390p. pap. 41.99 *(978-0-7657-0406-1(4)*, Aronson, Jason) Rowman & Littlefield Publishers, Inc.
Schinaia. On Paedophilia. 2010. 352p. pap. 41.95 *(978-1-85575-589-5(0))* Karnac Bks. GBR. Dist: Stylus Publishing, LLC.
Schmutzer, Andrew J., ed. The Long Journey Home: Understanding & Ministering to the Sexually Abused. 2011. 524p. pap. 57.00 ***(978-1-60899-395-6(7)***, Wipf and Stock) Wipf & Stock Pubs.
Seto, Michael C. Pedophilia & Sexual Offending Against Children: Theory, Assessment, & Intervention. 2007. 303p. 49.95 *(978-1-4338-0114-3(0))* American Psychological Assn.
Sherrie Watkins. Touching Temptation. 2010. 468p. pap. 28.95 *(978-1-4502-0220-6(9))* iUniverse, Inc.
Shuy, Roger W. The Language of Sexual Misconduct Cases, 1 vol. 2012. (ENG.). 256p. 65.00 ***(978-0-19-992696-1(4))*** Oxford Univ. Pr., Inc.
Simari. Maltrato y Abuso Sexual de Ninos. (Serie Actualidades - Actualities Ser.).Tr. of Mistreatment & Sexual Abuse of Children. (SPA.). 2.29 *(978-1-56063-661-8(0)*, 496252) Editorial Unilit.
Skarbek/Parrish. What You Dont Know Will Hurt You: Sexual Abuse in Schools. 2009. (ENG.). 120p. pap. 27.95 *(978-1-60709-269-8(7))* Rowman & Littlefield Education.
Smith, Megan J. Child Sexual Abuse: Issues & Challenges. 2008. (Illus.). (C). 89.00 *(978-1-60021-999-3(3))* Nova Science Pubs., Inc.
Spiro, Colleen. The Third Floor Window: A True Story of Secrets, Survival & Hope. 2008. 120p. pap. 12.95 *(978-1-60145-574-1(7))* Booklocker.com Inc.
Staller, Karen M. & Faller, Kathleen Coulborn, eds. Seeking Justice in Child Sexual Abuse: Shifting Burdens & Sharing Responsibilities. 2009. (ENG., Illus.). 288p. (gr. 17). 50.00 *(978-0-231-14614-2(0))* Columbia Univ. Pr.
Tennyson, Philip, et al. The Missing Girls: A Shocking True Story of Abduction & Murder. 2007. (ENG., Illus.). 384p. mass mkt. 7.99 *(978-0-312-94161-1(7)*, St. Martin's True Crime) St. Martin's Pr.
Tracy, Steven R. Mending the Soul: Understanding & Healing Abuse. 2008. (ENG., Illus.). 272p. pap. 16.99 *(978-0-310-28529-8(1))* Zondervan.
Trent, Michael E. & Buess, Terese M. Investigation & Prosecution of Child Sexual Abuse. 2007. 304p. pap. 40.00 *(978-0-9796993-6-8(3))* Texas District & County Attorneys Assn.
Trotter, Joy. No-One's Listening: Mothers, Fathers, & Child Sexual Abuse. 156p. *(978-1-86177-023-3(5))* Whiting & Birch, Ltd.
Turton, Jackie. Child Abuse Gender & Society. 2010. (ENG.). 160p. pap. 39.95 *(978-0-415-88294-1(X))* Routledge.
United Nations, Economic and Social Commission for Asia and the Pacific Staff. Pacific perspectives on the commercial sexual exploitation & sexual abuse of children & Youth. 2009. 132p. pap. 15.00 *(978-92-1-120552-7(2))* United Nations Pubns.
Vermeulen, Gert, ed. EU Quality Standards in Support of the Fight against Trafficking in Human Beings & Sexual Exploitation of Children: Exploratory Study of the Potential & Feasibility of Self-Regulation or Public-Private Co-operation. 2007. 443p. pap. 81.25 *(978-90-466-0116-7(1))* Maklu Uitgevers N.V. BEL. Dist: International Specialized Bk. Services.
Wallace, Sharon. A House Full of Whispers. 2010. pap. *(978-1-61599-065-8(8)*, Modern History Pr.) Loving Healing Pr., Inc.
—Surviving a House Full of Whispers. 2009. 168p. pap. *(978-1-932690-90-3(5)*, Modern History Pr.) Loving Healing Pr., Inc.
Warner, Sam. Understanding the Effects of Child Sexual Abuse: Feminist Revolutions in Theory, Research & Practice. Warner, Sam, ed. 2009. (Women & Psychology Ser.). (ENG., Illus.). 304p. 34.95 *(978-0-415-36028-9(5)*, RU60285) Routledge.
—Understanding the Effects of Child Sexual Abuse: Feminist Revolutions in Theory, Research & Practice. 2009. (Women & Psychology Ser.). (ENG., Illus.). 304p. 95.00 *(978-0-415-36027-2(7)*, RU60277) Routledge.
Watkins, Audrey Lee. On the Way Here: The Path That Chose Me. 2009. 206p. pap. 19.95 *(978-1-60703-241-0(4))* PublishAmerica, Inc.
Watkins, Tiffany. The Sexual Abuse of Youth Within the Church. 2008. 72p. per. 13.95 *(978-1-4327-1897-8(5))* Outskirts Pr., Inc.
Wedlake, Nick. Eat the Pretty Ones: A Testament. 2009. 236p. pap. 14.49 *(978-1-4389-8106-2(6))* AuthorHouse.
Whelan, David. No More Silence: He Thought He'D Got Away with It - But One Day Little David Would Find the Strength to Speak Out. McBeth, Jim & Scott, Marion, eds. 2011. (ENG.). 304p. 11.95 *(978-0-00-738890-5(X))* HarperCollins Pubs. Ltd. GBR. Dist: Independent Pubs. Group.
Whittier, Nancy. The Politics of Child Sexual Abuse: Emotion, Social Movements, & the State. 2011. (ENG., Illus.). 272p. pap. 21.95 *(978-0-19-978331-1(4))* Oxford Univ. Pr., Inc.
Wiersma, Noelle S. Perceived Impact of Childhood Sexual Abuse on Adult Relationship Partners. 2008. pap. 29.00 *(978-1-60456-938-4(7))* Nova Science Pubs., Inc.
Williams, Dan. Above His Shoulders: A True Account of Sexual Abuse,Its Impact on Relationships, & the Emotional Survival & Healing. 2009. (Illus.). 242p. pap. 15.95 *(978-1-4327-3749-8(X))* Outskirts Pr., Inc.
Wills, Laurie, ed. Sexual Predators. 2008. (Social Issues Firsthand Ser.). (ENG., Illus.). 127p. (J). (gr. 4-7). lib. bdg. 31.80 *(978-0-7377-4032-5(9)*, Greenhaven Pr., Inc.) Cengage Gale.
Wilmer, Graham. Conspiracy of Faith: Fighting for Justice after Child Abuse. 2007. (ENG.). 160p. per. 28.00 *(978-0-7188-3058-8(X))* Lutherworth Pr., The GBR. Dist: Brown, David Bk. Co., The.
Wolff, Larry. Paolina's Innocence: Child Abuse in Casanova's Venice. 2012. (ENG.). 328p. 90.00 ***(978-0-8047-6261-8(9))***; pap. 29.95 ***(978-0-8047-6262-5(7))*** Stanford Univ. Pr.
Woodiwiss, Jo. Contesting Stories of Childhood Sexual Abuse. 2009. (ENG.). 256p. 95.00 *(978-0-230-57404-5(1))* Palgrave Macmillan.

CHILD SEXUAL ABUSE—LAW AND LEGISLATION

see Child Sexual Abuse

CHILD SEXUAL ABUSE—PREVENTION

Aspatore Books Staff, compiled by. Strategies for Defending Internet Pornography Cases: Leading Lawyers on Analyzing Electronic Documents, Utilizing Expert Witnesses, & Explaining Technological Evidence. 2008. (Inside the Minds Ser.). 236p. pap. 90.00 *(978-0-314-19999-7(3))* Aspatore Bks.
Benson, Edmund F. & Benson, Susan. Life Skills Curriculum: ARISE Work in Progress, Book 3. 2011. (Work in Progress Ser.). (Illus.). 102p. (YA). pap., wbk. ed. 14.95 *(978-1-58614-019-9(1))* Arise Foundation.
Combating the Sexual Exploitation of Children: Hearing Before the Commission on Security & Cooperation in Europe, One Hundred Ninth Congress, Second Session, September 27, 2006. 2007. iii, 98p. *(978-0-16-079402-5(1)*, 552-070-36414-5) United States Government Printing Office.
Conflict Minerals Trade ACT; International Megan's Law of 2010; Extending Immunities to the Office of the High Representative & the International Civilian Office in Kosovo ACT of 2010; Lord's Resistance Army Disarmament & Northern Uganda Recovery ACT of 2009; & Global Science Program for Security, Competitiveness, & Diplomacy ACT of 2010: Markup Before the Committee on Foreign Affairs, House of Representatives, One Hundred Eleventh Congress, Second Session, on H.R. 4128, H.R. 5138, H.R. 5139, S. 1067, & H.R. 4801, April 28, 2010. 2010. iii, 214p. *(978-0-16-086281-6(7)*, 552-070-41372-3) United States Government Printing Office.
Council of Europe. Protecting Children from Sexual Violence: A Comprehensive Approach. 2010. 325p. pap. 50.00 *(978-92-871-6972-3(1))* Council of Europe FRA. Dist: Manhattan Publishing Co.
Crimes Associated with Polygamy: The Need for a Coordinated State & Federal Response: Hearing Before the Committee on the Judiciary, United States Senate, One Hundred Tenth Congress, Second Session, July 24, 2008. 2008. (Illus.). iii, 185p. *(978-0-16-081993-3(8)*, 552-070-38165-1) United States Government Printing Office.
Davidson, Julia & Gottschalk, Petter, eds. Internet Child Abuse: Current Research & Policy. 2011. (ENG., Illus.). 216p. pap. 44.95 ***(978-0-415-69780-4(8)***, Routledge Cavendish) Taylor & Francis Group GBR. Dist: Taylor & Francis Group.
Delgatto, Laurie. Creating Safe & Sacred Places for Young Adolescents: Sexual Abuse Educational Sessions for 5th to 8th Graders. 2007. 84p. per. 20.95 *(978-0-88489-983-9(7))* St. Mary's Pr.
Domestic Minor Sex Trafficking: Hearing Before the Subcommittee on Crime, Terrorism, & Homeland Security of the Committee on the Judiciary, House of Representatives, One Hundred Eleventh Congress, Second Session, September 15, 2010. 2011. (Illus.). iv, 407p. ***(978-0-16-087958-6(2)***, 552-070-42390-7) United States Government Printing Office.
Gillespie, Alisdair A. & Gillespie, Alisdair. Child Exploitation & Communication Technologies. 2008. (Illus.). 160p. (C). pap. 39.95 *(978-1-905541-23-2(6))* Russell Hse. Publishing Ltd. GBR. Dist: International Specialized Bk. Services.
Hall, Scott. Unforgivable Sins: Protecting Our Children from Predators, 1 vol. Davie, Michael B., ed. 2009. (ENG.). 336p. pap. 17.95 *(978-1-897453-06-3(X))* Manor Hse. Publishing, Inc. CAN. Dist: APG Sales & Distribution Services.
Jasper, Margaret C. Missing & Exploited Children: How to Protect Your Child. 2006. (Legal Almanac Ser.). 232p. 47.00 *(978-0-19-532157-9(X))* Oxford Univ. Pr., Inc.
Johnson, Victoria. Children & Sexual Abuse. 2007. (IVP Booklets Ser.). (ENG.). 32p. 1.50 *(978-0-87784-040-4(7)*, IVP Bks.) InterVarsity Pr.
Johnstone, Debra Anne. TaleTime Trauma: Keeping Kids Safe from Sexual Abuse. 2008. 52p. pap. 12.95 *(978-1-4092-3513-2(0))* Lulu Enterprises Inc.
Jones, Preston & Jackson, Joyce. How to Protect My Child from Sexual Predators. 2007. 196p. *(978-0-9796939-0-8(X))* Keeping Kids Safe.
Kamatz, Elisabeth. Sexualerziehung im Kindergarten als Prävention von sexuellem Missbrauch. 2009. (GER.). 154p. pap. 38.95 *(978-3-631-58304-3(4))* Lang, Peter GmbH, Europäischer Verlag der Wissenschaften DEU. Dist: Lang, Peter.
Kinnear, Karen L. Childhood Sexual Abuse. 2nd rev. ed. 2007. (Contemporary World Issues Ser.). 343p. 55.00 *(978-1-85109-905-4(0)*, CHSEAB2C) ABC-CLIO, LLC.
Langwith, Jacqueline, ed. Child Abuse. 2011. (Introducing Issues with Opposing Viewpoints Ser.). (Illus.). 144p. (YA). (gr. 9-12). 35.75 *(978-0-7377-5672-2(1))* Cengage Gale.
Maeseele, Thomas. Reality & Rhetoric in European Policy on Child Sex Tourism. 2009. 124p. pap. *(978-3-639-15966-0(7))* VDM Verlag Dr. Mueller e.K.
McDonald, Stephen & McDonald, Po Chu. The Mind of a Child: Thoughts of a Predator, Prevention for a Parent. 2008. 106p. pap. 14.95 *(978-0-7414-4749-4(5))* Infinity Publishing.
Milner, Claire & O'Donnell, Ian. Child Pornography: Crime, Computers & Society. 2011. (ENG., Illus.). 240p. (C). 84.95 *(978-1-84392-357-2(2))* Willan Publishing GBR. Dist: Taylor & Francis Group.
Morgan, Marcia. SafeTOUCH: Child Sexual Abuse Prevention Curriculum. 2010. spiral bd. 59.95 *(978-0-930413-02-6(4))* Migima Designs.
Reauthorization of the Adam Walsh ACT: Hearing Before the Subcommittee on Crime, Terrorism, & Homeland Security of the Committee on the Judiciary, House of Representatives, One Hundred Twelfth Congress, First Session, February 15, 2011. 2011. iii, 94p. ***(978-0-16-088615-7(5)***, 552-070-42784-3) United States Government Printing Office.
Sandoval, Terrell G. Adam Walsh Child Protection & Safety Act: Analysis & Law. 2010. (Children's Issues, Laws & Programs Ser.). 166p. 115.00 *(978-1-61668-808-0(4))* Nova Science Pubs., Inc.
Sax, Robin. Predators & Child Molesters: What Every Parent Needs to Know to Keep Kids Safe. 2009. (ENG.). 224p. pap. 17.98 *(978-1-59102-712-6(8))* Prometheus Bks., Pubs.
Sexual Exploitation of Children over the Internet: A Staff Report Prepared for the Use of the Committee on Energy & Commerce, U.S. House of Representatives, 109th Congress. 2007. v, 33p. *(978-0-16-078078-3(0)*, 552-070-35491-3) United States Government Printing Office.
Sher, Julian. Caught in the Web: Inside the Police Hunt to Rescue Children from Online Predators. 2008. (ENG.). 336p. pap. 15.95 *(978-0-7382-1171-8(0))* Da Capo Pr., Inc.
Skarbek, Denise & Parrish, Patricia A. What You Don't Know Will Hurt You: Sexual Abuse in the Schools. 2009. (ENG.). 120p. 65.00 *(978-1-60709-268-1(9))* Rowman & Littlefield Education.
Smallbone, Stephen, et al. Preventing Child Sexual Abuse: Evidence, Policy & Practice. 2008. (Crime Science Ser.). 272p. (C). pap. 49.95 *(978-1-84392-222-3(3))*; 89.95 *(978-1-84392-221-6(5))* Willan Publishing GBR. Dist: Taylor & Francis Group.
Turton, Jackie. Child Abuse, Gender & Society. 2007. (Routledge Research in Gender & Society Ser.). 152p. 143.00 *(978-0-415-36505-5(8))* Routledge.
United Nations Staff, contrib. by. Toolkit for Implementing & Monitoring the East Asia & Pacific Regional Commitment & Action Plan Against Commercial Sexual Exploitation of Children. 2006. (ENG.). 184p. pap. 28.00 *(978-92-1-120470-4(4))* United Nations Pubns.
United States Congress Senate Committee, creator. Challenges & Solutions for Protecting Our Children from Violence & Exploitation in the 21st Century. 2010. (ENG.). 154p. pap. 21.75 ***(978-1-240-54986-3(5)***, BiblioGov) BiblioBazaar.
Weisz, Arlene N. & Black, Beverly M. Programs to Reduce Teen Dating Violence & Sexual Assault: Perspectives on What Works. 2009. (ENG.). 336p. (gr. 17). pap. 35.00 *(978-0-231-13453-8(3))*; (Illus.). 89.50 *(978-0-231-13452-1(5))* Columbia Univ. Pr.
Wortley, Richard & Smallbone, Stephen, eds. Situational Prevention of Child Sexual Abuse. 2006. (Crime Prevention Studies: 19). (Illus.). 276p. (C). *(978-1-881798-60-6(7))* Rienner, Lynne Pubs.
Wurtele, Sandy K. Out of Harm's Way: A Parent's Guide to Protecting Young Children from Sexual Abuse. 2010. (ENG.). 32p. pap. 9.95 *(978-1-884734-97-7(9))*; lib. bdg. 19.95 *(978-1-884734-98-4(7))* Parenting Pr., Inc.
Wurtele, Sandy K. Safe Connections: A Parent's Guide to Protecting Young Teens from Sexual Exploitation. 2011. ***(978-1-936903-02-3(4))***; pap. ***(978-1-936903-00-9(8))*** Parenting Pr., Inc.
Wurtele, Sandy K. & Berkower, Feather. Off Limits: A Parent's Guide to Keeping Kids Safe from Sexual Abuse. 2010. (Illus.). xiv, 176p. *(978-1-884444-83-8(0))* Safer Society Pr.

C

CHILD SEXUAL ABUSE VICTIMS
see Sexually Abused Children

CHILD SEXUAL ABUSE VICTIMS, ADULT
see Adult Child Sexual Abuse Victims

CHILD SNATCHING BY PARENTS
see Parental Kidnapping

CHILD STUDY
see Child Development; Child Psychology

CHILD SUPPORT

Clarke, Rebecca B., ed. Child Support Enforcement: Trends, Tribal Programs & License Suspension. 2012. (Children's Issues, Laws & Programs Social Issues, Justice & Status Ser.). 169p. 95.00 ***(978-1-62100-495-0(3))*** Nova Science Pubs., Inc.

Donovan, Sherri. Hit Him Where It Hurts: The Take-No Prisoners Guide to Divorce — Alimony, Child Support, Custody, & More. 2006. (ENG., Illus.). 304p. per. 16.95 *(978-1-59337-739-7(8))* Adams Media Corp.

Gentile, M. B. A. 100 Effective Ways to Collect Child Support. 2009. 48p. pap. 12.95 *(978-1-4389-8320-2(4))* AuthorHouse.

Greenberg, Ann Core. How to Keep Your Child Out of Special Education. 2010. 154p. pap. *(978-1-905823-76-5(2))* Ecademy Pr. Ltd.

Lund, Francie. Changing Social Policy: The Child Support Grant in South Africa. 2008. (ENG.). 168p. pap. 26.95 *(978-0-7969-2200-7(4))* Human Sciences Research Council ZAF. Dist: Independent Pubs. Group.

Parkinson, Patrick & Cashmore, Judy. The Voice of a Child in Family Law Disputes. 2009. (ENG.). 200p. 99.00 *(978-0-19-923779-1(4))* Oxford Univ. Pr., Inc.

Rudman, Jack. Support Collection Supervisor. (Career Examination Ser.: C-3753). pap. 29.95 *(978-0-8373-3753-1(4))* National Learning Corp.

Shaw, Vernal. Child Support Vendetta. Gerst, LeAnn, ed. 2010. 159p. (YA). lib. bdg. 20.00 ***(978-0-9799904-1-0(6))*** Hood Estate, LLC.

Speight, Willie. Your Child Support Check Ruined Our Child's Life. 2010. 56p. pap. 10.49 *(978-1-4520-3619-9(5))* AuthorHouse.

Travers Simon, Joan. Mind the Gap? 2010. 312p. pap. *(978-3-8383-5924-3(0))* Lambert Academic Publishing.

CHILD SUPPORT—LAW AND LEGISLATION

Anosike, Benjamin. How to Legally Collect Your Child's Fair Support Dues, or to Fight Payment When You Need To: The National Child Support Collection Enforcement Manual. 2007. 164p. per. 26.95 *(978-0-932704-91-7(3))* Do-It-Yourself Legal Pubs.

Bazley, Janet, et al. Applications under Schedule 1 of the Children Act 1989. 2010. (ENG., Illus.). 392p. pap. *(978-1-84661-214-5(4))* Jordan Publishing, Ltd.

Bird, Roger & Burrows, David. Child Maintenance. 2009. (ENG.). 512p. pap. *(978-1-84661-130-8(X))* Jordan Publishing, Ltd.

Boland, Mary L. Como Recibir Manutencion de Ninos: Su Guia Practica para Cobrar y Hacer Cumplir la Orden Judicial. 2007. (SPA & ENG., Illus.). 128p. per. 9.95 *(978-1-57248-585-3(X)*, Sphinx Publishing) Sourcebooks, Inc.

—Your Right to Child Custody, Visitation, & Support. 4th rev. ed. 2007. (Legal Survival Guides). (ENG., Illus.). 272p. per. 31.99 *(978-1-57248-582-2(5)*, Sphinx Publishing) Sourcebooks, Inc.

Buttone, Gavin J. Healthy Marriage & Responsible Fatherhood Initiative. 2009. (Family Issues in the 21st Century Ser.). 43.00 *(978-1-60741-754-5(5))* Nova Science Pubs., Inc.

Connel, Linda. Child Custody, Visitation, & Support in Illinois. 2nd ed. 2008. (ENG.). 304p. pap. 24.95 *(978-1-57248-683-6(X)*, Sphinx Publishing) Sourcebooks, Inc.

Crowley, Jocelyn Elise. Defiant Dads: Fathers' Rights Activists in America. 2008. (Illus.). 288p. 29.95 *(978-0-8014-4690-0(2))* Cornell Univ. Pr.

Dawes, Mark & Jones, Deborah. Understanding Unreasonable Force. 2007. 180p. per. *(978-1-84667-030-5(6))* Derwent Pr., The.

Dijksterhuis, Bregje. Rechters normeren de Alimentatiehoogte: Een empirisch onderzoek naar rechterlijke samenwerking in de Werkgroep Alimentatienormen (1975-2007) 2008. (LUP Meijersreeks Ser.). (DUT.). 260p. pap. *(978-90-8728-045-1(9)*, Leiden Univ. Pr.) Amsterdam Univ. Pr.

Florida Bar, Continuing Legal Education Staff, contrib. by. Florida Proceedings after Dissolution of Marriage. (Illus.). 8th ed. 2007. 115.00 *(978-0-8205-7322-9(1))* 9th ed. 2009. *(978-1-4224-5391-9(X))* 10th ed. 2011. ***(978-1-4224-6688-9(4))*** Florida Bar Continuing Legal Education Pubns., The.

Glenn, Donald A., et al. Family Law Services Handbook: The Role of the Financial Expert. 2010. (ENG., Illus.). 429p. 175.00 *(978-0-470-57253-5(1)*, Wiley) Wiley, John & Sons, Inc.

Haman, Edward. Child Custody Visitation & S. 2008. 360p. pap. 27.95 *(978-1-57248-679-9(1)*, Sphinx Publishing) Sourcebooks, Inc.

Isaacs, Ronald L. The Comprehensive Guide to Fathers Rights. 2007. 157p. *(978-0-9741095-3-4(3))* Fathers' Rights Foundation.

Jensen, Geraldine. How to Collect Child Support, 3rd Edition. 2008. 98p. pap. 14.95 *(978-0-615-16765-7(9))* Smarter Changers, LLC.

Khodeir, Lucien. Children with 2 Homes. 2008. 88p. pap. 39.95 *(978-1-4357-1265-2(X))* Lulu Enterprises Inc.

Millar, Paul. The Best Interests of Children: An Evidence-Based Approach. 2009. (Illus.). (ENG.). 140p. *(978-0-8020-9890-0(8))*; xiv, 139p. pap. *(978-0-8020-9593-0(3))* Univ. of Toronto Pr.

Payne, Julien D. & Payne, Marilyn A. Child Support Guidelines in Canada. 2006th rev. ed. 2006. (Illus.). 840p. pap. *(978-1-55221-126-7(6))* Irwin Law, Inc.

Richey, Verkisserous. Child Support 101: What Every Man Should Know. 2007. 196p. per. 24.95 *(978-1-4241-7365-5(5))* PublishAmerica, Inc.

Smith, T. J. Child Support Enforcement Kit, Do-It-Yourself. 14.95 *(978-1-880398-09-8(5))* S.J.T. Enterprises, Inc.

Spence, Simone. Deadbeats: What Responsible Parents Need to Know about Collecting Child Support. 2007. per. 19.98 *(978-1-4276-2112-2(8))* Aardvark Global Publishing.

Thomas, Ralph D. A Study of the Child Support Collection Business. 45p. (C). pap. 29.95 *(978-0-918487-68-1(4))* Thomas Investigative Pubns., Inc.

Truly, Traci. Child Custody, Visitation & Support in Texas. 2nd ed. 2008. (Legal Survival Guides). (ENG.). 368p. pap. 22.99 *(978-1-57248-656-0(2)*, Sphinx Publishing) Sourcebooks, Inc.

Wikeley, Nick. Child Support: Law & Policy. 2006. (Illus.). 525p. (C). pap. 80.00 *(978-1-84113-532-8(1))* Hart Publishing Ltd. GBR. Dist: International Specialized Bk. Services.

CHILD VAGRANTS
see Vagrant Children

CHILD VERBAL ABUSE
see Psychological Child Abuse

CHILD WELFARE
see also Charity-Schools; Child Abuse; Child Health Services; Child Support; Children—Institutional Care; Day Care Centers; Foster Home Care; Maternal and Infant Welfare

ABA Center on Children and the Law Staff & Center for Children, Law & Policy Staff, contrib. by. Children, Law, & Disasters: What Have We Learned from the Hurricanes of 2005? 2008. *(978-1-60442-249-8(1))* American Bar Assn.

Adams, Christine. Poverty, Charity, & Motherhood: Maternal Societies in Nineteenth-Century France. 2010. (ENG.). 280p. 45.00 *(978-0-252-03547-0(X))* Univ. of Illinois Pr.

Adams, Harry. Justice for Children: Autonomy Development & the State. 2009. 264p. pap. 29.95 *(978-0-7914-7332-0(5))* 2008. 254p. 70.00 *(978-0-7914-7331-3(7))* State Univ. of New York Pr.

Adroher Biosca, Salomé, et al. Infancia en España: Nuevos Desafíos Sociales, Nuevas Respuestas Jurídicas. 2009. (SPA., Illus.). 589p. *(978-84-8468-259-2(5))* Universidad Pontificia Comillas de Madrid.

Alwon, Floyd J., et al. On the Job in Child Welfare: Recruiting, Retaining, & Supporting a Competent Workforce. 2009. pap. *(978-1-58760-124-8(9)*, CWLA Pr.) Child Welfare League of America, Inc.

Ame, Robert. Children's Rights in Ghana: Reality or Rhetoric? 2011. (ENG., Illus.). 310p. 75.00 *(978-0-7391-4800-6(1))* Lexington Bks.

Andrews, William D. America's Secret Children's Prisons. 2011. 180p. pap. 14.23 *(978-1-4269-5127-5(2))* Trafford Publishing.

Anning, Angela, et al. Developing Multi-Professional Teamwork for Integrated Children's Services: Research, Policy & Practice. 2006. (Illus.). 156p. (C). pap. 57.00 *(978-0-335-21978-0(0)*, 0335219780, Open University Pr.) McGraw-Hill Education GBR. Dist: McGraw-Hill Cos., The.

—Developing Multiprofessional Teamwork for Integrated Children's Services. 2006. (ENG., Illus.). 156p. (C). 162.00 *(978-0-335-21979-7(9)*, 0335219799, Open University Pr.) McGraw-Hill Education GBR. Dist: McGraw-Hill Cos., The.

Ansell, Nicola. Children, Youth & Development. 2nd rev. ed. 2013. (Routledge Perspectives on Development Ser.). (ENG., Illus.). 336p. (C). 128.00 *(978-0-415-61719-2(7))*; pap. 44.95 *(978-0-415-61720-8(0))* Routledge.

Arrighi, Barbara A. & Maume, David J. Child Poverty in America Today, 4 vols. 2007. (Praeger Perspectives Ser.). (Illus.). *(978-0-275-98927-9(5)*, Praeger Pubs.) Greenwood Publishing Group, Inc.

Arrighi, Barbara A. & Maume, David J., eds. Child Poverty in America Today, 4 vols. 2007. (Praeger Perspectives Ser.). (Illus.). 792p. 300.00 *(978-0-275-98926-2(7)*, C8926, Praeger Pubs.) Greenwood Publishing Group, Inc.

Austin, Michael J., ed. Evidence for Child Welfare Practice. 2009. (ENG., Illus.). 125.00 *(978-0-7890-3814-2(5))*; pap. 45.95 *(978-0-7890-3815-9(3))* Routledge.

Axford, Nick. Exploring Concepts of Child Well-Being: Implications for Children's Services. 2008. (Policy Press - Studies in Poverty, Inequality & Social Exclusion Ser.). 272p. (C). 125.00 *(978-1-84742-065-7(6))* Policy Pr. GBR. Dist: Chicago Distribution Ctr.

Bailey, Judith A. & Cottom, Robert I. Programs & Interventions for Maltreated Children & Families at Risk. Rubin, Allen, ed. 2011. (Clinician's Guide to Evidence-Based Practice Ser.: 5). (ENG.). 354p. pap. 55.00 *(978-0-470-89063-9(0)*, Wiley) Wiley, John & Sons, Inc.

Bakan, Joel. Childhood under Siege. 2012. (ENG.). 288p. pap. 15.00 *(978-1-4391-2122-1(2)*, Free Pr.) Free Pr.

—Childhood under Siege: How Big Business Targets Children. 2011. (ENG.). 288p. lib. bdg. 26.00 *(978-1-4391-2120-7(6)*, Free Pr.) Free Pr.

Bamba, Sachiko & Haight, Wendy. Child Welfare & Development: A Japanese Case Study. 2011. (ENG., Illus.). 224p. 80.00 ***(978-1-107-00284-5(2))*** Cambridge Univ. Pr.

Barker, Richard, ed. Making Sense of Every Child Matters: Multi-Professional Practice Guidance. 2008. (Illus.). 224p. pap. 35.95 *(978-1-84742-011-4(7))* Policy Pr. GBR. Dist: Chicago Distribution Ctr.

Barkman, Frieda & Barkman, Paul. Lad with Summer Eyes: A Story of the Grace Children's Home. 2011. 130p. 40.95 ***(978-1-258-08973-3(4))*** Literary Licensing, LLC.

Barth, Richard P., et al. From Child Abuse to Foster Care: Child Welfare Services Pathways & Placements. 2010. (ENG., Illus.). 310p. pap. 29.95 *(978-0-202-36397-4(X))* Transaction Pubs.

Beckett, Chris. Child Protection: An Introduction. 2nd ed. 2007. 240p. (C). 125.00 *(978-1-4129-2091-9(4)*, B20914C); per. 49.00 *(978-1-4129-2092-6(2)*, B20914P) SAGE Pubns., Ltd. GBR. Dist: SAGE Pubns., Inc.

Belanger, Kathleen & Brooks, Susan. Guidelines for Cultural Competence in Rural Child Welfare. 2010. *(978-1-58760-127-9(3)*, CWLA Pr.) Child Welfare League of America, Inc.

Bell, Erica, et al. Climate Change & Rural Child Health. 2011. (Series: Health & Human Development Ser.). 129.00 *(978-1-61122-640-9(6))* Nova Science Pubs., Inc.

Ben-Arieh, Asher, et al. Measuring & Monitoring Children's Well-Being. 2010. (Social Indicators Research Ser.). 184p. pap. 139.00 *(978-90-481-5642-9(4)*, 9048156424) Springer.

Berman, Stephen. Getting It Right for Children: Stories of Pediatric Care & Advocacy. 2007. (ENG., Illus.). 256p. per. 30.00 *(978-1-58110-286-4(0))* American Academy of Pediatrics.

Bernini, Stefania. Family Life & Individual Welfare in Post-War Europe: Britain & Italy Compared. 2007. (ENG.). 256p. 95.00 *(978-1-4039-8795-2(5))* Palgrave Macmillan.

Berrick, Jill Duerr. Take Me Home: Protecting America's Vulnerable Children & Families. 2008. (ENG., Illus.). 208p. 24.95 *(978-0-19-532262-0(2))* Oxford Univ. Pr., Inc.

Biggeri, Mario, et al, eds. Children & the Capability Approach. 2011. (Studies in Childhood & Youth Ser.). (ENG., Illus.). 392p. 90.00 *(978-0-230-28481-4(7))* Palgrave Macmillan.

Bishop-Josef, Sandra J., et al, eds. Child Development & Social Policy: Knowledge for Action. 2006. (Decade of Behavior Ser.). (Illus.). 311p. 39.95 *(978-1-59147-425-8(6))* American Psychological Assn.

Blum, Ann S. Domestic Economies: Family, Work, & Welfare in Mexico City, 1884-1943. 2010. (Engendering Latin America Ser.). (ENG., Illus.). 396p. pap. 30.00 *(978-0-8032-1359-3(X))* Univ. of Nebraska Pr.

Boendermaker, Leonieke. Implementeren Is Reflecteren: Evidence based werken en de implementatie van interventies in de Jeugdzorg. 2011. (HvA Openbare Lessen Ser.). (DUT.). 44p. pap. ***(978-90-5629-686-5(8)***, Vossiupers UvA) Amsterdam Univ. Pr.

Bonke, Jens & Esping-Andersen, Gosta. Family Investments in Children: What Drives the Social Gap in Parenting? (Study Paper No. 26) 2009. 36p. pap. 12.00 *(978-87-90199-29-6(4))* Univ. Pr. of Southern Denmark DNK. Dist: International Specialized Bk. Services.

Borkowski, John G. & Weaver, Chelsea M., eds. Prevention: The Science & Art of Promoting Health Child & Adolescent Development. 2006. 298p. per. 39.95 *(978-1-55766-868-4(X)*, 868X) Brookes, Paul H. Publishing Co.

Branche, C., et al. World Report on Child Injury Prevention. 2009. (Nonserial Publication Ser.). 228p. pap. 48.00 *(978-92-4-156357-4(5))* World Health Organization.

Brennan, Samantha & Noggle, Robert, eds. Taking Responsibility for Children. 2007. (Studies in Childhood & Family in Canada Ser.). (ENG.). 210p. pap. 42.95 *(978-1-55458-015-6(3))* Wilfrid Laurier Univ. Pr. CAN. Dist: Univ. of Toronto Pr.

Briggs, Laura. Somebody's Children: The Politics of Transracial & Transnational Adoption. 2012. (ENG., Illus.). 384p. 94.95 ***(978-0-8223-5147-4(1))***; pap. 25.95 ***(978-0-8223-5161-0(7))*** Duke Univ. Pr.

Brouwer, Thomas P. Parents with Substance Use Disorders & Child Protection Issues. 2011. (Children's Issues, Laws & Programs Ser.). viii, 280p. 195.00 *(978-1-60692-400-6(1))* Nova Science Pubs., Inc.

Budd, Karen S., et al. Evaluation of Parenting Capacity in Child Protection. 2011. (Guides to Best Practices for Forensic Mental Health Assessments Ser.). (ENG.). 224p. pap. 39.95 *(978-0-19-533360-2(8))* Oxford Univ. Pr., Inc.

Calder, Martin C., ed. Contemporary Risk Assessment in Safeguarding Children. 2008. (Illus.). 290p. pap. 65.00 *(978-1-905541-20-1(1))* Russell Hse. Publishing Ltd. GBR. Dist: International Specialized Bk. Services.

Cameron, Gary, et al, eds. Moving Toward Positive Systems of Child & Family Welfare: Current Issues & Future Directions. 2007. (ENG., Illus.). 408p. (C). pap. 44.95 *(978-0-88920-518-5(3))* Wilfrid Laurier Univ. Pr. CAN. Dist: Univ. of Toronto Pr.

Capul, Maurice & David, Monique. L'invention de L'enfance Inadaptée: L'exemple de Toulouse Saint-Simon, 1950-1975. 2010. (FRE.). 588p. *(978-2-7492-1289-0(8))* Eres Editions.

Caring for Children in Out-of-Home Placement. 23p. pap. 30.00 *(978-0-7881-4180-5(5))* DIANE Publishing Co.

Challenges Facing the Child Welfare System: Hearing Before the Subcommittee on Income Security & Family Support of the Committee on Ways & Means, U.S. House of Representatives, One Hundred Tenth Congress, First Session, May 15, 2007. 2008. (Illus.). iii, 136p. *(978-0-16-081803-5(6)*, 552-070-38009-4) United States Government Printing Office.

Chambers, Ruth. Child Neglect & Service Integration in a Child Welfare System: A Comprehensive Examination of Family Needs, Services & Outcomes. 2008. 116p. pap. *(978-3-639-08552-5(3))* VDM Verlag Dr. Mueller e.K.

Chapman, Vernon & Burton, Allan, eds. Child Fatalities Due to Maltreatment: The Role of Quality Data. 2012. 230p. pap. ***(978-1-61942-342-8(1))*** Nova Science Pubs., Inc.

Cheng, Shirley. Parental Rights in Children's Medical Care - Where Is Our Freedom to Say No? A Look at the Injustice of the American Medical System. 2008. 161p. pap. 14.97 *(978-0-615-14994-3(4))* Dance With Your Heart! Publishing.

Chesaina, Ciarunji. The Significance of Oral Literature in Children's Development. 2010. 48p. pap. *(978-3-8383-0121-1(8))* Lambert Academic Publishing.

Child Labor Enforcement: Are We Adequately Protecting Our Children?: Hearing Before the Subcommittee on Workforce Protections, Committee on Education & Labor, U.S. House of Representatives, One Hundred Tenth Congress, Second Session, Hearing Held in Washington, DC, September 23, 2008. 2008. iii, 34p. *(978-0-16-082280-3(7)*, 552-070-38344-1) United States Government Printing Office.

Children Who Age Out of the Foster Care System: Hearing Before the Subcommittee on Income Security & Family Support of the Committee on Ways & Means, U.S. House of Representatives, One Hundred Tenth Congress, First Session, July 12, 2007. 2008. iii, 123p. *(978-0-16-081923-0(7)*, 552-070-38096-5) United States Government Printing Office.

Cigno, Alessandro & Werding, Martin. Children & Pensions. 2007. (CESifo Book Ser.). (ENG., Illus.). 232p. (gr. 17). 35.00 *(978-0-262-03369-5(0))* MIT Pr.

Cleaver, Hedy. Safeguarding Children: A Shared Responsibility. Gorin, Sarah et al, eds. 2009. (Wiley Child Protection & Policy Ser.: 21). (ENG., Illus.). 300p. 115.95 *(978-0-470-51873-1(1)*, Wiley) Wiley, John & Sons, Inc.

Clinton, Hillary Rodham & Clinton, Hillary Rodham. It Takes a Village: And Other Lessons Children Teach Us. 2006. (ENG., Illus.). 352p. 25.00 *(978-1-4165-4064-9(4))* Simon & Schuster.

Cockburn, John & Kabubo-Mariara, Jane. Child Welfare in Developing Countries. 2010. (Illus.). (ENG.). 350p. 139.00 *(978-1-4419-6337-6(5)*, 1441963375); x, 298p. pap. 15.00 ***(978-1-4419-6274-4(3))***; x, 298p. E-Book ***(978-1-4419-6275-1(1))*** Springer.

Concern Worldwide. Dear President Obama... The Concern Worldwide 2009 Writing Competition. 2010. (ENG., Illus.). 256p. pap. 25.95 *(978-1-905785-65-0(8))* Liffey Pr., The IRL. Dist: Dufour Editions, Inc.

Connolly, Marie & Morris, Kate. Understanding Child & Family Welfare: Statutory Responses to Children at Risk. 2012. (ENG., Illus.). 200p. (C). pap. 30.00 ***(978-0-230-25019-2(X))*** Palgrave Macmillan.

Contexo/Media, creator. National Directory of Children, Youth & Families Services. 2007. (National Directory of Children, Youth & Families Services Ser.). (Illus.). 1616p. per. 219.50 *(978-1-885461-19-3(4))* National Directory CYF.

Contosta, David R. Philadelphia's Progressive Orphanage: The Carson Valley School. 2007. (ENG.). 276p. per. 25.95 *(978-0-271-02771-5(1))* Pennsylvania State Univ. Pr.

Cope, Pam, et al. Jantsen's Gift: A True Story of Grief, Rescue, & Grace. 2009. (ENG., Illus.). 320p. 24.99 *(978-0-446-19969-8(9))* Grand Central Publishing.

Council of Europe. Protecting Children from Sexual Violence: A Comprehensive Approach. 2010. 325p. pap. 50.00 *(978-92-871-6972-3(1))* Council of Europe FRA. Dist: Manhattan Publishing Co.

Cousins, Lynn. Shaping Children's Behaviour in the Early Years. 2010. (ENG., Illus.). 235p. pap. 45.00 *(978-1-4082-2502-8(6))* Longman Publishing Group.

Couture, Pamela. Child Poverty: Love, Justice, & Social Responsibility. 2008. 235p. per. 29.99 *(978-0-8272-0509-3(0))* Chalice Pr.

Crabbere, Edina Dookie. Bill of Rights. Crabberg, Edna Dookie, ed. (Illus.). (C). spiral bd. *(978-0-9667830-6-3(9))* Early Learning Institute.

Cram101 Textbook Reviews. Outlines & Highlights for Child Protection by Eileen Munro, Isbn: 9781412911788. 2011. 56p. pap. 26.95 ***(978-1-61461-888-1(7))*** Cram101 Inc.

Cram101 Textbook Reviews. Outlines & Highlights for Social Welfare: History of the American Response to Need by June Axinn, ISBN. 2010. 244p. pap. 31.95 *(978-1-61654-171-2(7))* Cram101 Inc.

Cram101 Textbook Reviews & Cram101 Textbook Reviews. Outlines & Highlights for Child Protection: An Introduction by Chris Beckett, ISBN. 2011. 106p. pap. 28.95 ***(978-1-61461-101-1(7))*** Cram101 Inc.

—Outlines & Highlights for Childhood Programs & Practices in the First Decade of Life: A Human Capital Integration by Arthur Reynolds, ISBN. 2011. 198p. pap. 30.95 ***(978-1-61461-092-2(4))*** Cram101 Inc.

—Outlines & Highlights for Effective Child Protection by Eileen Munro, Isbn: 9781412946940. 2011. 86p. pap. 27.95 ***(978-1-61461-076-2(2))*** Cram101 Inc.

—Outlines & Highlights for Gender & Child Welfare in Society by Brid Featherstone, Isbn: 9780470681862. 2011. 98p. pap. 27.95 ***(978-1-61461-102-8(5))*** Cram101 Inc.

Crosson-Tower, Cynthia. Exploring Child Welfare: A Practice Perspective. 5th ed. 2008. (ENG.). 480p. (C). 120.20 *(978-0-205-67276-9(0))* Allyn & Bacon, Inc.

Crouse, Janice. Children at Risk: The Precarious State of Children's Well-Being in America. 2009. (ENG.). 224p. 34.95 *(978-1-4128-1076-0(0))* Transaction Pubs.

Danielson, Caroline & Lee, Helen. Foster Care in California: Achievements & Challenges. 2010. *(978-1-58213-139-9(2))* Public Policy Institute of California.

Daro, Deborah, ed. World Perspectives on Child Abuse: Eighth Edition (2008) 8th ed. 2008. (Illus.). vi, 242p. pap. 35.00 *(978-0-9787530-1-6(1))* ISPCAN.

Davies, Liz & Duckett, Nora. Proactive Child Protection & Social Work. 2008. (Illus.). 184p. (C). pap. *(978-1-84445-131-9(3))* Learning Matters Ltd.

Del Campo, Diana, et al. Taking Sides: Clashing Views in Childhood & Society. (Taking Sides Ser.). (ENG.). 416p. (C). 8th ed. 2009. pap. 48.00 *(978-0-07-812757-1(2)*, 0078127572) 9th ed. 2011. pap. 48.00 ***(978-0-07-805021-3(9)***, 0078050219) McGraw-Hill Higher Education. (McGraw-Hill/Dushkin).

DelCampo, Diana S. Taking Sides: Childhood & Society. 5th ed. 2006. pap. 9.95 *(978-1-4288-1720-3(4))* Cram101 Inc.

Dettlaff, Alan & Fong, Rowena, eds. Child Welfare Practice with Immigrant Children & Families. 2011. (ENG.). 176p. (C). 125.00 *(978-0-415-68469-9(2))* Routledge.

Devine, Dympna, et al, eds. Flexible Childhood? Exploring Children's Welfare in Time & Space. 2007. 238p. pap. 34.99 (978-87-7674-202-7(4)) Univ. Pr. of Southern Denmark DNK. Dist: International Specialized Bk. Services.

Dicker, Sheryl. Reversing the Odds: Improving Outcomes for Babies in the Child Welfare System. 2009. 216p. pap. 29.95 (978-1-55766-961-2(9)) Brookes, Paul H. Publishing Co.

Dorland Health, creator. The National Directory of Children, Youth & Families Services: The Professionals' Reference. 2008. (National Directory of Children, Youth & Families Services Ser.). 1036p. pap. 199.00 (978-1-885461-26-1(7)) Contexo Media.

Douglas, Emily M. Innovations in Child & Family Policy: Multidisciplinary Research & Perspectives on Strengthening Children & Their Families. 2010. (ENG., Illus.). 292p. 73.50 (978-0-7391-3790-1(5)) Lexington Bks.

Downs, Susan Whitelaw, et al. Child Welfare & Family Services: Policies & Practice. 8th ed. 2007. (ENG., Illus.). 512p. (C). 133.40 (978-0-205-57190-1(5)) Allyn & Bacon, Inc.

Dubowitz, Howard & Merrick, Joav. International Aspects of Child Abuse & Neglect. 2011. (Series: Health & Human Development Ser.). xxii, 286p. pap. 69.00 (978-1-61122-049-0(1)) Nova Science Pubs., Inc.

Dubowitz, Howard & Merrick, Joav, eds. International Aspects of Child Abuse & Neglect. 2010. (Health & Human Development (Joav Merrick - Series Editor - National Institute of Child Health & Human Development, Ministry of Social Affairs, Jerusalem Ser.). (Illus.). xxii, 286p. 125.00 (978-1-60876-703-8(5)) Nova Science Pubs., Inc.

Dueger, Caroline & O'Callahan, Cliff. Working in International Child Health. 2nd ed. 2008. (ENG., Illus.). 275p. pap. 39.95 (978-1-58110-332-8(8)) American Academy of Pediatrics.

Dunhill, Ally, et al, eds. Effective Communication & Engagement with Children & Young People, their Families & Carers. 2009. (Illus.). 118p. pap. (978-1-84445-265-1(4)) Learning Matters Ltd.

Eddy, J. Mark & Poehlmann, Julie, eds. Children of Incarcerated Parents: A Handbook for Researchers & Practitioners. 2010. 364p. pap. (978-0-87766-768-1(3)) Urban Institute Pr.

Edelman, Marian Wright & Edelman, Marian W. The Sea Is So Wide & My Boat Is So Small: Charting a Course for the Next Generation. 2008. 176p. 19.95 (978-1-4013-2333-2(2)) Hyperion Pr.

Escobari de Querejazu, Laura. Mentalidad Social y Niñez Abandonada: La Paz, 1900-1948. 2009. (SPA., Illus.). 281p. (978-99954-1-241-8(1)) Instituto Francés de Estudios Andinos, IFEA.

Featherstone, Brid. Contemporary Fathering: Theory, Policy & Practice. 2009. 232p. pap. 34.95 (978-1-86134-987-3(4)) Policy Pr. GBR. Dist: Chicago Distribution Ctr.

Featherstone, Brid, et al, eds. Gender & Child Welfare in Society. 2010. (ENG.). 320p. 120.95 (978-0-470-68186-2(1), Wiley) Wiley, John & Sons, Inc.

Federal Foster Care Financing: Hearing Before the Subcommittee on Human Resources of the Committee on Ways & Means, U.S. House of Representatives, One Hundred Ninth Congress, First Session, June 9, 2005. 2007. (Illus.). iii, 122p. (978-0-16-079242-7(8), 552-070-36339-4) United States Government Printing Office.

Fernandes, Laura M., ed. Child Well-Being & Nonresident Parents. 2011. (Children's Issues, Laws & Programs Ser.). (Illus.). 262p. 195.00 (978-1-60692-382-5(X)) Nova Science Pubs., Inc.

Forbes, Juliana. The Moment: A calendar & guide for advocating on behalf of the world's children. 2008. (Illus.). 147p. spiral bd. 20.00 (978-0-9788759-2-3(3)) Mothers Acting Up.

Forrester, Donald & Harwin, Judith. Parents Who Misuse Drugs & Alcohol: Effective Interventions in Social Work & Child Protection. 2011. (Wiley Child Protection & Policy Ser.). (ENG., Illus.). 262p. pap. 47.95 (978-0-470-87151-5(2)); 110.95 (978-0-470-87150-8(4)) Wiley, John & Sons, Inc. (Wiley).

Forsberg, Hannele & Kröger, Teppo, eds. Social work & child welfare Politics: Through Nordic Lenses. 2009. 216p. 99.00 (978-1-84742-406-8(6)) Policy Pr. GBR. Dist: Chicago Distribution Ctr.

—Social Work & Child Welfare Politics: Through Nordic Lenses. 2011. 216p. pap. 42.95 (978-1-84742-900-1(9)) Policy Pr. GBR. Dist: Chicago Distribution Ctr.

Fraser, Mark W. & Jenson, Jeffrey M., eds. Social Policy for Children & Families: A Risk & Resilience Perspective. 2nd ed. 2010. (Illus.). 416p. (C). pap. 64.00 (978-1-4129-8139-2(5), B81392P) SAGE Pubns., Inc.

Fyfe, Alec & International Labour Office, International Labour Standards Dept Staff. The Worldwide Movement Agaist Child Labour: Progress & Future Directions. 2008. (ENG., Illus.). 94p. pap. 14.00 (978-92-2-120017-8(5)) International Labour Office.

Gainsborough, Juliet F. Scandalous Politics: Child Welfare Policy in the States. 2010. (American Governance & Public Policy Ser.). (ENG., Illus.). 216p. pap. 26.95 (978-1-58901-707-8(2)) Georgetown Univ. Pr.

Gal, Tali. Child Victims & Restorative Justice: A Needs-Rights Model, 1 vol. 2011. (Interpersonal Violence Ser.). (ENG., Illus.). 264p. 49.95 (978-0-19-974471-8(8)) Oxford Univ. Pr., Inc.

Galano. Healthy Families America Initiative: Integrating Research, Theor. 2007. (ENG.). 256p. 125.00 (978-0-7890-3680-3(0)) Routledge.

Garbarino, James. Children & the Dark Side of Human Experience: Confronting Global Realities & Rethinking Child Development. 2008. (ENG.). viii, 157p. pap. 39.95 (978-0-387-75625-7(6), 0387756256) Springer London, Ltd. GBR. Dist: Springer.

Garcia-Coll, C. The Impact of Immigration on Children's Development. 2011. (Contributions to Human Development Ser.). (ENG., Illus.). 154p. pap. **(978-3-8055-9798-2(3))** Karger, S. AG.

Garfoot, Jill. Inside Child Welfare: A Caseworker's Story, 1 vol. 2010. 196p. pap. 24.95 (978-1-4489-3982-4(8)) PublishAmerica, Inc.

Giardino, Angelo P., et al. Child Safety: A Pediatric Guide for Parents, Teachers, Nurses, & Caregivers. 2007. (ENG., Illus.). 341p. 33.00 (978-1-878060-67-9(8)) STM Learning, Inc.

Gibbs, Robert. Imminent Risk: The Child Welfare State. 2006. 64p. pap. 10.95 (978-1-59800-736-7(X)) Outskirts Pr., Inc.

Gilbert, Neil, et al, eds. Child Protection Systems: International Trends & Orientations, 1 vol. 2011. (International Policy Exchange Ser.). (ENG., Illus.). 288p. 55.00 (978-0-19-979335-8(2)) Oxford Univ. Pr., Inc.

Gleeson, Brendan & Sipe, Neil, eds. Creating Child Friendly Cities: Reinstating Kids in the City. 2006. (Illus.). 164p. 155.00 (978-0-415-39160-3(1)) Routledge.

Golden, Olivia. Reforming Child Welfare. 2009. 312p. pap. 29.50 (978-0-87766-759-9(4)) Urban Institute Pr.

Gonzales, Gizela M. Where the Children Are. 2011. (ENG.). 167p. pap. 50.00 (978-971-94292-6-5(7)) Artpostasia Inc. PHL. Dist: National Bk. Network.

Gorin, Sarah, et al, eds. Safeguarding Children: A Shared Responsibility. 2009. (Wiley Child Protection & Policy Ser.). (ENG., Illus.). 300p. pap. 47.95 (978-0-470-51874-8(X), Wiley) Wiley, John & Sons, Inc.

Grafton, Gordon J., compiled by. Lost Children of the Ohio Valley. 2008. (Illus.). vii, 175p. pap. (978-1-55856-492-3(6)) Closson Pr.

Green, Deborah. Challenging Racial Disproportionality in Child Welfare: Research, Policy, & Practice. 2011. **(978-1-58760-144-6(3)**, CWLA Pr.) Child Welfare League of America, Inc.

Groark, Christina J., et al, eds. Early Childhood Intervention: Shaping the Future for Children with Special Needs & Their Families, 3 vols. 2011. (Illus.). 876p. 154.95 (978-0-313-37793-8(6), C37793) Greenwood Publishing Group, Inc.

Hagemann, Karen, et al, eds. Children, Families, & States: Time Policies of Childcare, Preschool & Primary Education in Europe. 2011. (CEH Ser.). (Illus.). 456p. 95.00 (978-0-85745-096-8(4)) Berghahn Bks., Inc.

Hagger, Lynn. The Child as Vulnerable Patient: Protection & Empowerment. 2009. (Medical Law & Ethics Ser.). 268p. 124.95 (978-0-7546-7252-4(2)) Ashgate Publishing Co.

Harden, Brenda Jones. Infants in the Child Welfare System: A Developmental Framework for Policy & Practice. 2007. 34.95 (978-0-943657-97-4(0), Zero To Three Pr.

Harrison, Paul. Managing Child Welfare & Protection Services. 2009. 113p. pap. 33.95 (978-1-905541-52-2(X)) Russell Hse. Publishing Ltd. GBR. Dist: International Specialized Bk. Services.

Haskins, Ron & Sawhill, Isabel, eds. The Next Generation of Antipoverty Politics. 2007. (Future of Children Ser.). (ENG.). 200p. pap. 24.95 (978-0-8157-5565-4(1)) Brookings Institution Pr.

Health Care for Children in Foster Care: Hearing Before the Subcommittee on Income Security & Family Support of the Committee on Ways & Means, U.S. House of Representatives, One Hundred Tenth Congress, First Session, July 19, 2007. 2008. (Illus.). iii, 89p. (978-0-16-082173-8(8), 552-070-38308-5) United States Government Printing Office.

Heller, Sherryl Scott & Gilkerson, Linda. A Practical Guide to Reflective Supervision. 2009. (978-1-934019-36-8(4)) Zero To Three Pr.

Heymann, Jody, et al, eds. Protecting Childhood in the AIDS Pandemic: Finding Solutions that Work, 1 vol. 2012. (ENG., Illus.). 336p. 55.00 **(978-0-19-976512-6(X))** Oxford Univ. Pr., Inc.

Higgs, Jacqueline. Corporate Parenting: The Contribution of Designated Teachers. 2009. 220p. pap. (978-3-639-12975-5(X)) VDM Verlag Dr. Mueller e.K.

Hill, Malcolm, et al. Children's Services: Working Together. 2012. (ENG.). 416p. pap. **(978-1-4082-3725-0(3))** Addison-Wesley Longman, Inc.

Holzscheiter, Anna. Children's Rights in International Politics: The Transformative Power of Discourse. 2010. (Transformations of the State Ser.). (ENG., Illus.). 288p. 95.00 (978-0-230-24180-0(8)) Palgrave Macmillan.

Improving the Child Welfare System: Hearing Before the Subcommittee on Income Security & Family Support of the Committee on Ways & Means, U.S. House of Representatives, One Hundred Tenth Congress, Second Session, February 27, 2008. 2009. iii, 185p. (978-0-16-082947-5(X), 552-070-38859-1) United States Government Printing Office.

Innocenti Research Centre. General Comments of the Committee on the Rights of the Child. 2010. (FRE.). 76p. pap. 25.00 (978-88-89129-40-1(9)) United Nations Children's Fund, The (UNICEF).

Jaycox, Lisa H. National Evaluation of Safe Start Promising Approaches: Assessing Program Outcomes, 1 vol. 2011. (ENG.). 82p. pap. 24.50 **(978-0-8330-5822-5(3))** RAND Corp., The.

John, Jaiya. Reflection Pond. 2007. (ENG.). 228p. per. 17.00 (978-0-9713306-2-5(4)) Soul Water Rising.

Jolly, Richard. UNICEF (United Nations Children's Fund) 2011. (Global Institutions Ser.). (ENG.). 176p. 27.95 (978-0-415-49117-4(7)); 125.00 (978-0-415-49116-7(9)) Routledge.

Jones, Jenny L. & Sundet, Paul, eds. Developing an Empirically Based Practice Initiative: A Case Study in CPS Supervision. 2007. (ENG., Illus.). 210p. pap. 54.95 (978-0-7890-3346-8(1)) Routledge.

Kamerman, Sheila, et al, eds. From Child Welfare to Child Well-Being: An International Perspective on Knowledge in the Service of Policy Making. 2009. (Childrenâ€(tm)s Well-Being: Indicators & Research Ser.). (Illus.). xx, 440p. 269.00 (978-90-481-3376-5(9), 9048133769) Springer.

Katz, Lynne F., et al. Child-Centered Practices for the Courtroom & Community: A Guide to Working Effectively with Young Children & Their Families in the Child Welfare System. 2010. (Illus.). 240p. 34.95 (978-1-59857-073-1(0)) Brookes, Paul H. Publishing Co.

Kendrick, Andrew, ed. Residental Child Care: Prospects & Challenges. 2007. (Research Highlights in Social Work Ser.). 248p. per. (978-1-84310-526-8(8)) Kingsley, Jessica Ltd.

Kerman, B. Achieving Permanence for Older Children & Youth in Foster Care Kerman, Benjamin et al, eds. 2009. (ENG., Illus.). 416p. (gr. 17). pap. 32.50 (978-0-231-14689-0(2)) Columbia Univ. Pr.

Kerman, Benjamin, et al, eds. Achieving Permanence for Older Children & Youth in Foster Care. 2009. (ENG., Illus.). 416p. (gr. 17). 90.00 (978-0-231-14688-3(4)) Columbia Univ. Pr.

Kim, Chong Sun. Sahoe Kujo Ui Pyonhwa e Taeung Han Chanyo Yangyuk Kwallyon Popche Kaeson Pangan Yon'gu. 2007. (KOR.). 165p. (978-89-8323-347-9(8)) Korea Legislation Research Institute.

Krabacher, Susan Scott. Angels of a Lower Flight: One Woman's Mission to Save a Country... One Child at a Time. 2008. (ENG., Illus.). 336p. pap. 20.99 (978-1-4165-3516-4(0), Touchstone) Touchstone.

La Fontaine, Jean De. The Devil's Children: From Spirit Possession to Witchcraft: New Allegations That Affect Children. 2009. (Illus.). 220p. 89.95 (978-0-7546-6733-9(2)) Ashgate Publishing Co.

Lager, Patricia B., et al. Child Welfare: Policies & Best Practices. 2nd rev. ed. 2006. (Children & Adolescents Ser.). (ENG., Illus.). 352p. (C). per. 108.95 (978-0-495-00484-4(7)) Wadsworth.

Land, Kenneth C., ed. The Well-Being of America's Children: Developing & Improving the Child & Youth Well-Being Index. 2012. (Childrenrsquo;s Well-Being: Indicators & Research Ser.). (ENG., Illus.). x, 262p. 129.00 **(978-94-007-4091-4(3)**, 9400740913) Springer.

Langely, Terrance R., ed. Child Protection, the Courts & Social Workers. 2010. (Children's Issues, Laws & Programs Ser.). (Illus.). 356p. 195.00 (978-1-60741-279-3(9)) Nova Science Pubs., Inc.

Lau, Kenneth J., et al. Mandated Reporting of Child Abuse & Neglect: A Practical Guide for Social Workers. 2008. 224p. 45.00 (978-0-8261-1098-5(3)) Springer Publishing Co., Inc.

Levine, Phillip B. & Zimmerman, David J., eds. Targeting Investments in Children: Fighting Poverty When Resources Are Limited. 2010. (National Bureau of Economic Research Conference Report). (ENG., Illus.). 408p. 99.00 (978-0-226-47581-3(6)) Univ. of Chicago Pr.

Levitt, Emily. Malnutrition in Afghanistan: Scale, Scope, Causes, & Potential Response. 2011. (Illus.). xxi, 210p. (978-0-8213-8442-8(2)) World Bank Pubns.

Levitt, Emily, et al. Malnutrition in Afghanistan: Scale, Scope, Causes, & Potential Reponse. 2010. (Directions in Development Ser.). (ENG., Illus.). 236p. pap. 25.00 (978-0-8213-8441-1(4), 9780821384411) World Bank Pubns.

Lewis, Jane, ed. Children, Changing Families & Welfare States. 2008. (Illus.). 328p. pap. 50.00 (978-1-84720-987-0(4)) Elgar, Edward Publishing, Inc.

Lieten, G. K. Children Structure & Agency. 2012. (ENG., Illus.). 172p. pap. 39.95 **(978-0-415-53665-3(0))** Routledge.

Lieten, Kristoff, et al. Children, Structure, & Agency: Realities Across the Developing World. 2008. (Routledge Studies in Development & Society). (ENG., Illus.). 172p. 125.00 (978-0-415-98973-2(6)) Routledge.

Lindsey, Duncan, ed. Child Poverty & Inequality: Securing a Better Future for America's Children. 2008. (ENG., Illus.). 208p. 31.99 (978-0-19-530544-9(2)) Oxford Univ. Pr., Inc.

Lonne, Bob. Reforming Child Protection. 2007. (Illus.). 224p. 150.00 (978-0-415-42905-4(6)) Routledge.

Lonne, Bob, et al. Reforming Child Protection. 2007. (Illus.). 224p. 45.95 (978-0-415-42906-1(4)) Routledge.

López-Calva, Luis Felipe. Trabajo Infantil: Teoría y Lecciones de la América Latina. 2006. (Lecturas de el Trimestre Económico Ser.). (SPA., Illus.). 461p. pap. (978-968-16-8120-3(7)) Fondo de Cultura Economica.

Louis, David. Scars That Can Heal: Does every life have Value? 2006. 420p. pap. 24.95 (978-1-60145-053-1(2)) Booklocker.com, Inc.

Machel, Graca. The Impact of War on Children: A Review of Progress since the 1996 United Nations Report on the Impact of Armed Conflict on Children. (ENG., Illus.). 176p. (978-0-7748-0867-5(5)) Univ. of British Columbia Pr.

Mapp, Susan C. Global Child Welfare & Well-Being, 1 vol. 2010. (ENG., Illus.). 272p. pap. 37.95 (978-0-19-533971-0(1)) Oxford Univ. Pr., Inc.

Markova, Galina. Parents, Children, Institutions in a Post-Totalitarian Context. 2010. 128p. pap. (978-3-639-22270-8(9)) VDM Verlag Dr. Mueller e.K.

Marten, James, ed. Children & Youth in a New Nation. 2009. (ENG., Illus.). 320p. pap. 24.00 (978-0-8147-5749-9(9)) New York Univ. Pr.

Matthews, Sherry. We Were Not Orphans: Stories from the Waco State Home. 2011. (ENG., Illus.). 234p. 29.95 (978-0-292-72559-1(0)) Univ. of Texas Pr.

Maweu, Christine. Children at Risk. 2010. 80p. pap. (978-3-639-23392-6(1)) VDM Verlag Dr. Mueller e.K.

McAuley, Colette, et al, eds. Child Well-Being: Understanding Children's Lives. 2010. (ENG., Illus.). 256p. pap. (978-1-84310-925-9(5)) Kingsley, Jessica Ltd.

McDonald, Stephen & McDonald, Po Chu. The Mind of a Child: Thoughts of a Predator, Prevention for a Parent. 2008. 106p. pap. 14.95 (978-0-7414-4749-4(5)) Infinity Publishing.

McElwee, Niall. At-Risk Children & Youth: Resiliency Explored. 2007. (ENG.). 334p. pap. 56.95 (978-0-7890-3382-6(8)) Routledge.

Mcfall, Michael. Licensing Parents: Family, State, & Child Maltreatment. 2010. (ENG.). 248p. pap. 32.95 (978-0-7391-2914-2(7)) Lexington Bks.

McFall, Michael T. Licensing Parents: Family, State, & Child Maltreatment. 2009. (ENG.). 248p. 78.99 (978-0-7391-2913-5(9)) Lexington Bks.

McLanahan, Sara, ed. Opportunity in America: Number 2, Fall 2006. 2006. (Future of Children Ser.). (Illus.). 196p. per. 24.95 (978-0-8157-5563-0(5)) Brookings Institution Pr.

Merrick, Joav, ed. Child & Adolescent Health Yearbook 2008. 2009. 145.00 (978-1-60692-866-0(X)) Nova Science Pubs., Inc.

Meuwese, Stan, et al, eds. 100 Years of Child Protection. 2007. 276p. 75.00 (978-90-5850-293-3(7)) Wolf Legal Pubs., W.L.P. NLD. Dist: Gaunt, Inc.

Michaelian, Britt. Secrets of the Safety Goddess: A Modern Safety Guide for Busy Parents. 2009. (Illus.). x, 230p. pap. (978-0-9794245-5-7(0)) Bush Street Pr.

Moody, Iain & Fearnley, Barry. Nursing & Health - Child Protection: Survival Guide. rev. ed. 2011. (ENG.). 50p. spiral bd. 14.95 **(978-0-273-75071-0(2))** Pearson Education, Ltd. GBR. Dist: Trans-Atlantic Pubns., Inc.

Morris, Kate, et al. Children, Families & Social Exclusion: New Approaches to Prevention. 2009. 168p. 99.00 (978-1-86134-966-8(1)); pap. 36.95 (978-1-86134-965-1(3)) Policy Pr. GBR. Dist: Chicago Distribution Ctr.

Multiple Indicator Cluster Survey Manual 2005: Monitoring the Situation of Women & Children. 2006. 400p. (SPA.). spiral bd. (978-92-806-3955-1(2)); (RUS.). spiral bd. (978-92-806-4115-8(8)) United Nations Children's Fund, The (UNICEF).

Munch, Donna G., et al. A Chance for Every Child: A History of the el Paso Center for Children. 2009. (Illus.). 288p. 25.00 (978-0-9749823-1-1(8)); pap. 15.00 (978-0-9749823-2-8(6)) Trego-Hill Pubns.

Munro, Eileen. Child Protection. 2007. (SAGE Course Companions Ser.). (Illus.). 200p. (C). 89.00 (978-1-4129-1178-8(8), B11788C); per. 34.00 (978-1-4129-1179-5(6), B11788P) SAGE Pubns., Ltd. GBR. Dist: SAGE Pubns., Inc.

—Effective Child Protection. 2nd ed. 2008. (Illus.). 192p. (C). 116.00 (978-1-4129-4694-0(8), B46940C); pap. 49.00 (978-1-4129-4695-7(6), B46940P) SAGE Pubns., Ltd. GBR. Dist: SAGE Pubns., Inc.

Myers, John E. B., ed. Child Maltreatment: A Collection of Readings. 2011. (Illus.). 384p. (C). pap. 36.00 (978-1-4129-9506-1(X), B95061P) SAGE Pubns., Inc.

National Center for Health Statistics (U.S.) Staff & National Health Interview Survey (U.S.) Staff, contrib. by. Family Structure & Children's Health in the United States: Findings from the National Health Interview Survey, 2001-2007. 2010. (978-0-8406-0642-6(7)) National Ctr. for Health Statistics.

National Directory of Children Youth & Families Services, creator. The National Directory of Children, Youth, & Families Services: The Professionals Reference. 2007. (National Directory of Children, Youth & Families Services Ser.). 1438p. per. 179.00 (978-1-885461-18-6(6)) National Directory CYF.

Naudeau, Sophie. Investing in Young Children: An Early Childhood Development Guide for Policy Dialogue & Project Preparation. 2010. (Directions in Development Ser.). (Illus.). (ENG.). 320p. pap. 30.00 (978-0-8213-8526-5(7), 9780821385265); xix, 294p. (978-0-8213-8528-9(3)) World Bank Pubns.

, Neighbor To Family, Inc., Inc., Neighbor To Family. One Family at A Time. 2009. 70p. pap. 15.00 (978-0-557-11778-9(X)) Lulu Enterprises Inc.

Nybell, Lynn M., et al, eds. Childhood, Youth, & Social Work in Transformation: Implications for Policy & Practice. 2009. (ENG., Illus.). 480p. (gr. 17). 60.00 (978-0-231-14140-6(8)) Columbia Univ. Pr.

Oliver, Christine M. & Dalrymple, Jane, eds. Developing Advocacy for Children & Young People: Current Issues in Research, Policy & Practice. 2008. 224p. pap. (978-1-84310-596-1(9)) Kingsley, Jessica Ltd.

Olson, Diane & Friedrich, Laura Dean. Weaving A Just Future for Children. 2008. 160p. pap. 15.00 (978-0-88177-547-1(9)) Upper Room Bks.

Oneka, Angelo. How to Protect Your Child from Harm & Dangers. 2011. 86p. pap. 19.95 **(978-1-4560-6582-9(3))** PublishAmerica, Inc.

Organisation for Economic Co-operation and Development Staff. Doing Better for Children. 2009. (Illus.). 160p. pap. 63.00 (978-92-64-05933-7(4)) Organization for Economic Cooperation & Development.

Ostler, Teresa. Assessment of Parenting Competency in Mothers with Mental Illness. 2007. (Illus.). 188p. per. 32.95 (978-1-55766-665-9(2)) Brookes, Paul H. Publishing Co.

Otto, Hans-Uwe & Flösser, Gaby, eds. How to Organize Prevention: Political, Organizational, & Professional Challenges to Social Services. (Prevention & Intervention in Childhood & Adolescence Ser.). (ENG., Illus.). XVI, 424p. 252.00 **(978-3-11-187943-7(7))** De Gruyter, Walter Inc.

Owusu-Bempah, Kwame. The Wellbeing of Children in Care: A New Approach for Improving Developmental Outcomes. 2010. (ENG.). 192p. (C). 125.00 (978-0-415-47939-4(8)); pap. 39.95 (978-0-415-47940-0(1)) Routledge.

Paciorek, Karen Menke. Annual Editions: Early Childhood Education 12/13. 33rd ed. 2012. (Annual Editions Ser.). (ENG., Illus.). 240p. (C). pap. 44.00 **(978-0-07-805126-5(6)**, 0078051266, McGraw-Hill/Dushkin) McGraw-Hill Higher Education.

Palfrey, Judith S. Child Health in America: Making a Difference Through Advocacy. 2006. (ENG., Illus.). 312p. (gr. 17). per. 32.00 (978-0-8018-8453-5(5)) Johns Hopkins Univ. Pr.

—Child Health in America: Making a Difference Through Advocacy. 2006. (ENG., Illus.). 312p. (gr. 17). 67.00 (978-0-8018-8452-8(7)) Johns Hopkins Univ. Pr.

Papatheodorou, Theodora, ed. International Debates on Early Childhood Practices & Policies: Global Snapshots of Pedagogical Thinking & Encounters. 2012. (ENG., Illus.). 256p. (C). pap. 48.95 **(978-0-415-69101-7(X))**; 155.00 **(978-0-415-69100-0(1))** Routledge.

Patterson, Kasi G. Children in Foster Care - the Effects of Foster Parent Characteristics on Anxiety Levels of Children Placed in the Foster Care System. 2008. 96p. pap. (978-3-639-01753-3(6)) VDM Verlag Dr. Mueller e.K.

C

Pearce, Jennifer & Pearce, Jenny. Young People & Sexual Exploitation: 'It's Not Hidden, You Just Aren't Looking' 2009. (ENG., Illus.). VIII, 184p. 44.95 (978-0-415-40716-8(8)); 140.00 (978-0-415-40715-1(X)) Routledge.

Pearson, Susan J. The Rights of the Defenseless: Protecting Animals & Children in Gilded Age America. 2011. (ENG., Illus.). 280p. 45.00 (978-0-226-65201-6(7)) Univ. of Chicago Pr.

Pecora, . Child Welfare Challenge. 2006. pap. 9.95 (978-1-4288-1650-3(X)) Cram101 Inc.

Pecora, Peter, et al. The Child Welfare Challenge: Policy, Practice, & Research. 3rd ed. 2009. (ENG., Illus.). 458p. 59.95 (978-0-202-36306-6(6)); pap. 39.95 (978-0-202-36314-1(7)) Aldine Transaction.

Peirce, Bradford Kinney. A Half Century with Juvenile Delinquents; 2006. 412p. per. 26.99 (978-1-4255-4408-9(8)) MPublishing.

Perez-Escamilla, Rafael. At Risk: Latino Children's Health. Melgar-Quinonez, Hugo, ed. 2011. 25.95 (978-1-55885-708-7(7)) Arte Publico Pr.

Peters, Friedhelm, ed. Residential Child Care & Its Alternatives: International Perspectives. 2008. (Illus.). 184p. per. 32.95 (978-1-85856-409-8(3)) Trentham Bks. Ltd. GBR. Dist: Stylus Publishing, LLC.

Peters, Ray D., et al, eds. Resilience in Children, Families, & Communities: Linking Context to Practice & Policy. 2010. xviii, 201p. pap. 109.00 (978-1-4419-3463-5(4), 1441934634) Springer.

Peterson, Mary J. Jason: Ward of the State. 2007. xi, 130p. (978-0-9761235-5-2(X)) Ampersand, Inc.

Piper, Christine. Investing in Children: Policy, Law & Practice in Context. 2008. 256p. (C). 89.95 (978-1-84392-325-1(4)) Willan Publishing GBR. Dist: Taylor & Francis Group.

—Investing in Children: Rights, Law & Practice in Context. 2008. 256p. (C). pap. 45.00 (978-1-84392-324-4(6)) Willan Publishing GBR. Dist: Taylor & Francis Group.

Potter, Cathryn C., et al, eds. Child Welfare Supervision: A Practical Guide for Supervisors, Managers, & Administrators. 2009. (ENG., Illus.). 432p. pap. 36.99 (978-0-19-532676-5(8)) Oxford Univ. Pr., Inc.

Prosser, Carol L. From the Trenches: Advice to Parent's Raising a Child with Special Needs. 2006. pap. 14.95 (978-0-9777764-6-7(8)) Arbor Bks.

Protections for Foster Children Enrolled in Clinical Trials: Hearing Before the Subcommittee on Human Resources of the Committee on Ways & Means, U.S. House of Representatives, One Hundred Ninth Congress, First Session, May 18, 2005. 2007. iii, 71p. (978-0-16-079306-6(8), 552-070-36384-0) United States Government Printing Office.

Quintero, Steven J., ed. Child Welfare Issues & Perspectives. 2008. 171p. 89.00 (978-1-60692-659-8(4)) Nova Science Pubs., Inc.

Radford, Lorraine & Hester, Marianne. Mothering Through Domestic Violence. 2006. (ENG., Illus.). 176p. per. (978-1-84310-473-5(3)) Kingsley, Jessica Ltd.

Researcher, C. Q. Childhood & Adolescence in Society: Selections from CQ Researcher. 2011. (Illus.). 336p. (C). pap. 36.00 (978-1-4129-9434-7(9), B94347P) SAGE Pubns., Inc.

Researcher, C. Q., ed. Issues for Debate in Family Violence: Selections from CQ Researcher. 2010. (Illus.). 200p. (C). pap. 37.00 (978-1-4129-9032-5(7), B90325P) SAGE Pubns., Inc.

Reynolds, Arthur J., et al, eds. Childhood Programs & Practices in the First Decade of Life: A Human Capital Integration. 2010. (ENG., Illus.). 542p. 95.00 (978-0-521-19846-2(1)); 544p. pap. 36.99 (978-0-521-13233-6(9)) Cambridge Univ. Pr.

Richardson, Tom I. & Williams, Marsha V. Child Abuse & Violence. 2008. (C). 90.00 (978-1-60456-128-9(9)) Nova Science Pubs., Inc.

Riley, Tom. Orphan Train Riders: Entrance Records from the American Female Guardian Society's Home for the Friendless in New York, Vol. 2. 2008. (Illus.). 274p. per. 32.50 (978-0-7884-3644-4(9)) Heritage Bks.

Roberts, Rosemary. Wellbeing from Birth. 2010. (Illus.). 224p. (C). 108.00 (978-1-84860-720-0(2), B07200C); pap. 43.00 (978-1-84860-721-7(0), B07200P) SAGE Pubns., Ltd. GBR. Dist: SAGE Pubns., Inc.

Robison, Susan. Delivering on the Promise: Promoting Court Capacity to Improve Outcomes for Abused & Neglected Children. 2007. (Illus.). 62p. (978-1-58024-480-0(7)) National Conference of State Legislatures.

Rondeau, Christina. Power Parent: How to Keep Your Kids Safe. 2007. (ENG.). 92p. per. 11.95 (978-1-58736-557-7(X)) Wheatmark.

Rosenwald, Mitchell & Riley, Beth N. Advocating for Children in Foster & Kinship Care: A Guide to Getting the Best Out of the System for Caregivers & Practitioners. 2010. (ENG., Illus.). 272p. (gr. 17). pap. 24.50 (978-0-231-14687-6(6)) Columbia Univ. Pr.

—Advocating for Children in Foster & Kinship Care: A Guide to Getting the Best out of the System for Caregivers & Practitioners. 2010. (ENG., Illus.). 272p. (gr. 17). 79.50 (978-0-231-14686-9(8)) Columbia Univ. Pr.

Ross, Timothy. Child Welfare: The Challenges of Collaboration. 2009. (978-0-87766-756-8(X)) Urban Institute Pr.

Ruck, Martin & Horn, Stacey. Young People's Perspectives on the Rights of the Child: Implications for Theory, Research & Practice. 2008. (Journal of Social Issues Ser.). (ENG., Illus.). 200p. pap. 47.95 (978-1-4051-9434-1(0), Wiley-Blackwell) Wiley, John & Sons, Inc.

Sanborn, Robert, et al, eds. Growing up in Houston 2006-2008: Assessing the Quality of Life of Our Children. 2006. (978-0-9789952-0-1(1)) Children At Risk.

Scaife, Joyce. Deciding Children's Futures: Assessments for Safeguarding & Promoting Children's Welfare. 2012. (ENG., Illus.). 392p. (C). 150.00 (978-0-415-59635-0(1)); pap. 47.95 (978-0-415-59634-3(3)) Routledge.

Schaefer, Judith. Seen, but Not Heard: Placing Children & Youth on the Security Governance Agenda. Nosworthy, David, ed. 2009. (ENG.). 336p. pap. 44.95 (978-3-8258-1398-7(3)) Lit Verlag DEU. Dist: Transaction Pubs.

Schlaack, Holly. Invisible Kids: Marcus Fiesel's Legacy: One Short Life, One Terrible Death & 12 Things YOU Can Do to Improve the Lives of Foster Children. 2009. 201p. pap. 18.95 (978-0-615-22976-8(X)) Advocacy Publishing.

Schultz, Dana, et al. National Evaluation of Safe Start: Promising Approaches - Assessing Program Implementation. 2010. (ENG.). 290p. pap. 35.00 (978-0-8330-4968-1(2), tr-750) RAND Corp., The.

Scourfield, Jonathan, et al, eds. Gender & Child Welfare in Society. 2010. (ENG.). 320p. pap. 55.95 (978-0-470-68187-9(X), Wiley) Wiley, John & Sons, Inc.

Shaheen, Amira. Child Injury. 2010. 260p. pap. (978-3-639-22833-5(2)) VDM Verlag Dr. Mueller e.K.

Sheehan, Rosemary, et al, eds. Vulnerable Children & the Law: International Evidence for Improving Child Welfare, Child Protection & Children's Rights. 2012. (ENG., Illus.). 304p. pap. (978-1-84905-868-1(7)) Kingsley, Jessica Ltd.

Shultz, William J. Humane Movement in the United States, 1910-1922. (Columbia University, Studies in the Social Sciences: No. 252). reprint ed. 21.00 (978-0-404-51252-1(6)) AMS Pr., Inc.

Singer, Jana, et al. Resolving Family Conflicts. 2008. (Family, Law & Society Ser.). 594p. 325.00 (978-0-7546-2659-6(8)) Ashgate Publishing Co.

Smuts, Alice. Science in the Service of Children, 1893-1935. 2008. (ENG., Illus.). 398p. pap. 32.00 (978-0-300-14435-2(0)) Yale Univ. Pr.

Song, Minkyoung. Termination of Parental Rights & Adoption in Foster Care - a Foster Care Decision on Child Maltreatment. 2007. 180p. per. (978-3-8364-2728-9(1)) VDM Verlag Dr. Mueller e.K.

Sorte, Joanne, et al. Nutrition, Health, & Safety for Young Children: Promoting Wellness. 2010. (ENG.). 696p. (C). pap. 109.20 (978-0-13-234941-3(8), Prentice Hall) Prentice Hall PTR.

—Nutrition, Health, & Safety for Young Children: Promoting Wellness (with MyEducationLab) 2010. (ENG.). 544p. (C). pap. 115.87 (978-0-13-138120-9(2), Prentice Hall) Prentice Hall PTR.

Spargo, John. The Bitter Cry of the Children. 2009. 148p. pap. 19.99 (978-1-150-60309-9(7)) General Bks. LLC.

—The Bitter Cry of the Children. 2008. 428p. 51.95 (978-1-4365-6792-3(0)) 2007. (ENG.). 432p. per. 36.95 (978-0-548-77060-3(3)) Kessinger Publishing, LLC.

Stahl, Philip M. Conducting Child Custody Evaluations: From Basic to Complex Issues. 2010. 368p. (C). 99.95 (978-1-4129-7433-2(X), B74332C) SAGE Pubns., Inc.

Stahl, Philip M. & Stahl, Philip A. Conducting Child Custody Evaluations: From Basic to Complex Issues. 2010. 368p. (C). pap. 54.95 (978-1-4129-7434-9(8), B74332P) SAGE Pubns., Inc.

The State of the World's Children 2007: Executive Summary. 2006. (State of the World's Children Ser.). 40p. (978-92-806-4064-9(X)) United Nations Children's Fund, The (UNICEF).

Stecher, Brian M., et al. Pain & Gain: Implementing No Child Left Behind in Three States, 2004-2006. 2008. 168p. pap. 31.50 (978-0-8330-4610-9(1), mg-784) RAND Corp., The.

Stein, Mike. Quality Matters in Children's Services: Messages from Research. 2009. (ENG., Illus.). 144p. pap. (978-1-84310-926-6(3)) Kingsley, Jessica Ltd.

Steinzor, Rena I. Mother Earth & Uncle Sam: How Pollution & Hollow Government Hurt Our Kids. 2007. (ENG., Illus.). 280p. pap. 24.95 (978-0-292-71690-2(7)) Univ. of Texas Pr.

Stepenoff, Bonnie. The Dead End Kids of St. Louis: Homeless Boys & the People Who Tried to Save Them. 2010. (ENG., Illus.). 192p. (C). 29.95 (978-0-8262-1888-9(1)) Univ. of Missouri Pr.

Stern, Mark & Axinn, June. Social Welfare: A History of the American Response to Need. 8th ed. 2011. (ENG.). 384p. (C). 82.67 (978-0-205-82748-0(9), Prentice Hall) Prentice Hall PTR.

—Social Welfare: A History to the American Response to Need. 8th ed. 2011. (ENG.). (C). 46.67 (978-0-205-82746-6(2), Prentice Hall) Prentice Hall PTR.

Stern, Mark J. & Axinn, June. Social Welfare: A History of the American Response to Need. 8th rev. ed. 2011. (MySocialWorkLab Ser.). (ENG.). 384p. (C). pap. 101.80 (978-0-205-00191-0(2), Prentice Hall) Prentice Hall PTR.

Stern, Mark J. & Axinn, June. Social Welfare: A History of the American Response to Need, Books a la Carte Plus MySocialWorkLab. 8th ed. 2011. (ENG.). (C). ring bd. 73.33 (978-0-205-00330-3(3), Prentice Hall) Prentice Hall PTR.

Stern, Mark J. & Axinn, June J. Social Welfare: A History of the American Response to Need, Books a la Carte Edition. 8th ed. 2011. (ENG.). 384p. (C). ring bd. 66.67 (978-0-205-00329-7(X), Prentice Hall) Prentice Hall PTR.

Strega, Susan. The Case of the Missing Perpetrator. 2009. 312p. pap. (978-3-639-15179-4(8)) VDM Verlag Dr. Mueller e.K.

Taking to Scale Imci Implementation in Mongolia 2000-2008: Lessons Learnts. 2011. (WPRO Nonserial Publication Ser.). (ENG.). 57p. cd-rom 12.00 (978-92-9061-477-7(3)) WHO Regional Office for the Western Pacific PHL. Dist: World Health Organization.

Taylor, Fred. Roll Away the Stone: Saving America's Children. 2nd ed. 2007. (ENG.). 266p. pap. 15.95 (978-1-882480-15-9(5)) Information International.

Testa, Mark. Fostering Accountability: Using Evidence to Guide & Improve Child Welfare Policy. Poertner, John, ed. 2010. (ENG., Illus.). 400p. 49.95 (978-0-19-532130-2(8)) Oxford Univ. Pr., Inc.

Thoburn, June & Courtney, Mark. Children in Need & Child Welfare. 2009. (Library of Essays in Child Welfare & Development Ser.). (Illus.). 572p. 325.00 (978-0-7546-2587-2(7)) Ashgate Publishing Co.

Thompson, Richard H. The Handbook of Child Life: A Guide for Pediatric Psychosocial Care. 2009. 378p. 79.95 (978-0-398-07831-7(9)); pap. 55.95 (978-0-398-07832-4(7)) Thomas, Charles C. Pub., Ltd.

Tilmouth, Tina. Diploma in Leadership for Health & Social Care & Children & Young People's Services. 2012. (ENG.). 256p. pap. 59.95 (978-1-4441-5608-9(X)) Hodder Arnold Pubs.

Tregeagle, Susan. Harnessing Information & Communication Technology in Child Welfare. 2010. 336p. pap. (978-3-8383-5485-9(0)) Lambert Academic Publishing.

Trodd & Chivers. Interprofessional Working in Practice: Learning & Working Together for Children & Families. 2011. (ENG., Illus.). 200p. (C). pap. 45.00 (978-0-335-24447-8(5), 0335244475) McGraw-Hill Education GBR. Dist: McGraw-Hill Cos., The.

Tubbs, David Lewis. Freedom's Orphans: Contemporary Liberalism & the Fate of American Children. 2007. (New Forum Bks.). (ENG.). 248p. (C). per. 32.95 (978-0-691-13470-3(7)) Princeton Univ. Pr.

UNICEF Uruguay. Discurso y Realidad: Segundo informe de aplicación del Código de la niñez y la Adolescencia en Maldonado, Montevideo y Salto 2006. 2009.Tr. of Speech & reality: second report on the application of the Code on Childhood & Adolescence in Maldonado, Montevideo & Salto. (SPA.). 256p. pap. (978-92-806-4488-3(2)) United Nations Children's Fund, The (UNICEF).

UNICEF: Innocenti Research Centre. General comments of the Committee on the Rights of the Child. 2008. 90p. pap. 25.00 (978-88-89129-51-7(4)) United Nations Children's Fund, The (UNICEF).

United Nations Children', et al. Progress for Children: A Report Card on Child Protection, No. 8. 2009. (Illus.). 48p. pap. 15.00 (978-92-806-4439-5(4)) United Nations Children's Fund, The (UNICEF).

van Nijnatten, Carolus. Children's agency, children's Welfare: A dialogical approach to child development, policy & Practice. 2010. 168p. 99.00 (978-1-84742-489-1(9)) Policy Pr. GBR. Dist: Chicago Distribution Ctr.

Vincent-Lum, Sharon. Children Experiencing Domestic Abuse. Stafford, Anne, ed. 2010. 110p. pap. 26.95 (978-1-903765-97-5(8)) Dunedin Academic Pr. GBR. Dist: International Specialized Bk. Services.

Wade, Jim, et al. Caring for Abused & Neglected Children: Making the Right Decisions for Reunification or Long-Term Care. 2011. (ENG., Illus.). 240p. pap. (978-1-84905-207-8(7)) Kingsley, Jessica Ltd.

Walker, Eric S. Children & Disasters: Preparedness, Response & Recovery. 2011. (Children's Issues, Laws & Programs Ser.). 171p. 185.00 (978-1-61470-697-7(2)) Nova Science Pubs., Inc.

Wall, John. Ethics in Light of Childhood. 2010. (ENG.). 216p. pap. 34.95 (978-1-58901-692-7(0)) Georgetown Univ. Pr.

Ward, Harriet. Understanding Child Welfare Interventions: The Provision of Services for Children in Need. Becker, Saul, ed. 2007. (Understanding Welfare Ser.). 276p. 80.00 (978-1-86134-454-0(6)); pap. 36.95 (978-1-86134-453-3(8)) Policy Pr. GBR. Dist: International Specialized Bk. Services.

Webb, Mary Bruce, et al, eds. Child Welfare & Child Well-Being: New Perspectives from the National Survey of Child & Adolescent Well-Being, 1 vol. 2009. (ENG., Illus.). 448p. 74.95 (978-0-19-539846-5(7)) Oxford Univ. Pr., Inc.

Weinberg, Lois A. The Systematic Mistreatment of Children in the Foster Care System: Through the Cracks. 2007. (ENG.). 358p. (C). 125.00 (978-0-7890-2392-6(X)); 354p. per. 60.50 (978-0-7890-2393-3(8)) Routledge.

Weiss, Heather & Jacobs, Francine, eds. Evaluating Family Programs: Current Issues in Theory & Policy. 2008. (ENG., Illus.). 588p. pap. 49.95 (978-0-202-36215-1(9)) Aldine Transaction.

White, Andrew. Suffer the Children: Dispatches to & from the Front Line. 2010. (ENG., Illus.). 128p. pap. 19.95 (978-1-84706-374-8(8)) Continuum International Publishing Group, Ltd. GBR. Dist: National Bk. Network.

WHO Regional Office for the Western Pacific. Child Survival Profile: Cambodia. 2007. (WPRO Publication). 35p. pap. 12.00 (978-92-9061-224-7(X)) World Health Organization.

Willemsen, Jan. Children's Rights & Human Development. 2010. (Illus.). 964p. pap. 189.00 (978-94-000-0032-2(4)) Intersentia Uitgevers N.V. BEL. Dist: International Specialized Bk. Services.

Williams, Betty. The Madness in My Country & the Welfare of Children. Darst, David H., ed. (International Albert Schweitzer Lecture Ser. at Yale University). (Illus.). 12p. (Orig.). pap. 3.50 (978-1-885007-03-2(5)) Schweitzer, Albert Institute-Quinnipiac College Pr.

Williams, Samuel M. Poverty in the U. S. Trends, Issues & Measurements. 2011. (Economic Issues, Problems & Perspectives Ser.). 115.00 (978-1-61209-119-8(9)) Nova Science Pubs., Inc.

Wilson, Aubrey D. & Ryan, Sally G., eds. Child Welfare System: Transitions. 2011. (Series: Children's Issues, Laws & Programs Ser.). (Illus.). viii, 318p. 215.00 (978-1-61324-713-6(3)) Nova Science Pubs., Inc.

Wilson, Kate & James, Adrian L. The Child Protection Handbook. 3rd rev. ed. 2007. (ENG., Illus.). 632p. (C). pap. 65.95 (978-0-7020-2829-8(0), Bailliere Tindall) Elsevier - Health Sciences Div.

Wilson, Rowena Grice & Crewe, Sandra Edmonds. Tradition & Policy Perspectives in Kinship Care. 2007. (ENG., Illus.). 268p. 125.00 (978-0-7890-3551-6(0)); per. 54.50 (978-0-7890-3552-3(9)) Routledge.

Winrock International Staff, contrib. by. Child Labor Through Education: Drawn from Winrock Global CIRCLE Projects: Community-Based Innovations to Reduce Child Labor Through Education. 2008. (978-1-57360-070-5(9)) Winrock International Institute for Agricultural Development.

World Bank Group Staff, et al. The Promise of Early Childhood Development in Latin America & the Caribbean. 2009. (Latin American Development Forum Ser.). (ENG., Illus.). 220p. pap. 40.00 (978-0-8213-7759-8(0), 9780821377598) World Bank Pubns.

A World Fit for Children. 2006. 108p. per. (978-92-806-4087-8(9)) United Nations Children's Fund, The (UNICEF).

Wright, Josephine-Joy, ed. Celebrating Children: Equipping People Working with Children & Young People Living in Difficult Circumstances Around the World. 2006. (ENG., Illus.). 442p. per. 34.99 (978-1-84227-060-8(5), Paternoster) Authentic Media.

Wulczyn, Fred & Webb, Mary Bruce, eds. Child Protection: Using Research to Improve Policy & Practice. 2007. (ENG., Illus.). 268p. 54.95 (978-0-8157-3514-4(6)); per. 24.95 (978-0-8157-3513-7(8)) Brookings Institution Pr.

Yanes, Kelly. Reunification Efforts with Methamphetamine Abusing Families. 2009. 80p. pap. (978-3-639-14570-0(4)) VDM Verlag Dr. Mueller e.K.

Young, Mary E. Early Child Development from Measurement to Action: A Priority for Growth & Equity. Young, Mary Eming & Richardson, Linda, eds. 2007. (Stand Alone Ser.). (ENG., Illus.). 324p. per. 35.00 (978-0-8213-7086-5(3), 9780821370865) World Bank Pubns.

Zigler, Edward F., et al. The Tragedy of Child Care in America. 2011. 240p. pap. 26.00 (978-0-300-17211-9(7)) Yale Univ. Pr.

1946-2006 Sixty Years for Children. 2006. (Illus.). 36p. 15.00 (978-92-806-4053-3(4)) United Nations Children's Fund, The (UNICEF).

CHILD WELFARE—FEDERAL AID

see Federal Aid to Child Welfare

CHILD WELFARE—LAW AND LEGISLATION

see Children—Legal Status, Laws, etc.

CHILD WELFARE—RESEARCH

Axford, Nick. Exploring Concepts of Child Well-Being: Implications for Children's Services. 2012. (Policy Press - Studies in Poverty, Inequality & Social Exclusion Ser.). 272p. pap. 42.95 (978-1-4473-0585-9(X)) Policy Pr. GBR. Dist: Chicago Distribution Ctr.

Baker, Amy J. L. & Charvat, Benjamin S. Research Methods in Child Welfare. 2008. (Illus.). xii, 448p. pap. (978-0-231-14131-4(9)); (ENG., 464p. (gr. 17). 55.00 (978-0-231-14130-7(0)) Columbia Univ. Pr.

Ben-Arieh, Asher & Goerge, Robert M., eds. Indicators of Children's Well-Being: Understanding Their Role, Usage & Policy Influence. 2010. (Social Indicators Research Ser.). xi, 204p. pap. 169.00 (978-90-481-7081-4(8), 9048170818) Springer.

Ben-Aryeh, Asher & Frones, Ivar. Indicators of Children's Well-Being: Theory & Practice in a Multi-Cultural Perspective. 2008. (Social Indicators Research Ser.). (ENG., Illus.). xii, 592p. 239.00 (978-1-4020-9303-6(9), 1402093039) Springer.

Fleming, Jennie & Boeck, Thilo, eds. Involving Children & Young People in Health & Social Care Research. 2012. (ENG.). 272p. (C). 145.00 (978-0-415-66349-6(0)) Routledge.

Jones, Nick & Sundet. Developing an Empirically Based Practice Initiative: A Case Stud. 2007. (ENG., Illus.). 210p. 150.00 (978-0-7890-3345-1(3)) Routledge.

Lindsey, Duncan & Shlonsky, Aron, eds. Child Welfare Research: Advances for Practice & Policy. 2008. (ENG., Illus.). 448p. 42.99 (978-0-19-530496-1(9)) Oxford Univ. Pr., Inc.

CHILD WELFARE—AFRICA

Alozie I. Ikonne. Blame Not the Child. 2010. 108p. pap. 14.85 (978-1-4269-1141-5(6)) Trafford Publishing.

Amantana, Vivian. A Sociological Study of Street Children in Ghana: Victims of Kinship Breakdown & Rural-Urban Migration. 2011. (Illus.). 186p. 119.95 (978-0-7734-1606-2(4)) Mellen, Edwin Pr., The.

Bray, Rachel, et al. Growing up in the New South Africa: Childhood & Adolescence in Post-Apartheid Cape Town. 2010. (ENG.). 448p. pap. 34.95 (978-0-7969-2313-4(2)) Human Sciences Research Council ZAF. Dist: Independent Pubs. Group.

DoeK, Jaap, et al, eds. Child Poverty: African & International Perspectives. 2009. 310p. pap. 91.00 (978-90-5095-929-2(6)) Intersentia Uitgevers N.V. BEL. Dist: International Specialized Bk. Services.

Falola, Toyin & Heaton, Matthew M. Endangered Bodies: Women, Children, & Health in Africa. 2008. (Illus.). 300p. pap. (978-1-59221-501-0(7)) Africa World Pr.

Grannis, Susanna W. Hope Amidst Despair: HIV/AIDS-Affected Children in Sub-Saharan Africa, 1 vol. 2011. (ENG.). 200p. 25.00 (978-0-7453-3153-9(X)); lib. bdg. 75.00 (978-0-7453-3154-6(8)) Pluto Pr. GBR. Dist: Macmillan.

Handa, Sudhanshu, et al, eds. Social Protection for Africas Children. 2010. (Routledge Studies in Development Economics Ser.). (ENG., Illus.). 272p. (C). 140.00 (978-0-415-58333-6(0), Routledge) Taylor & Francis Group GBR. Dist: Taylor & Francis Group.

Nakazibwe, Faustine. The Hiv/Aids Orphan Crisis. 2009. 90p. pap. (978-3-639-18236-1(7)) VDM Verlag Dr. Mueller e.K.

Obeng, Cecilia. Children's Health in a Traditional Society. 2009. 87.00 (978-1-60692-769-4(8)) Nova Science Pubs., Inc.

Sharp, Maryaane & Kruse, Ioana. Health, Nutrition & Population Outcomes in Madagascar 2000-2009: A Country Status Report. 2011. (World Bank Working Papers: 216). (ENG.). 176p. pap. 15.00 (978-0-8213-8538-8(0), 9780821385388) World Bank Pubns.

Staunton, Irene, et al. Our Broken Dreams: Child Migration in Southern Africa. 2008. (Illus.). 114p. pap. (978-1-77922-070-7(7)) Weaver Pr. ZWE. Dist: Michigan State Univ. Pr.

World Bank Center Staff. Africa's Future, Africa's Challenge: Early Childhood Care & Development in Sub-Saharan Africa. Garcia, Marito et al, eds. 2008. (Directions in Development Ser.). (ENG., Illus.). 556p. per. 25.00 *(978-0-8213-6886-2(9)*, 9780821368862) World Bank Pubns.

CHILD WELFARE—AUSTRALIA

Hunter, Nicole & Topfer, Alex. Educational Outcomes of Children on Guardianship or Custody Orders: A Pilot Study, Stage 2. 2011. (Illus.). vii, 70p. *(978-1-74249-069-4(7))* Australian Institute of Health & Welfare.

Penglase, Joanna. Orphans of the Living. 2007. (ENG.). 384p. pap. 18.00 *(978-1-920731-66-3(0))* Fremantle Pr. AUS. Dist: Independent Pubs. Group.

Swain, Hillel, et al. Child, Nation, Race & Empire: Child Rescue Discourse, England, Canada & Australia, 1850-1915. 2010. (Studies in Imperialism Ser.). (ENG., Illus.). 224p. 89.95 *(978-0-7190-7894-1(6))* Manchester Univ. Pr. GBR. Dist: Macmillan.

CHILD WELFARE—CANADA

Brown, Ivan, et al, eds. Awakening the Spirit: Moving Child Welfare Forward. 2012. (Fpws Ser.: 4). (ENG.). 600p. 39.95 ***(978-0-88977-278-6(9))*** Canadian Plains Research Ctr. CAN. Dist: Univ. of Toronto Pr.

Brown, Ivan, et al. Passion for Action in Child & Family Services: Voices from the Prairies. 2009. (University of Regina Publications(UR) Ser.). (ENG.). 288p. pap. 35.00 *(978-0-88977-213-7(4))* Canadian Plains Research Ctr. CAN. Dist: Univ. of Toronto Pr.

Chandler, Karen. Administering for Quality: Canadian Early Childhood Development Programs, Third Edition. 3rd ed. 2008. (ENG.). 295p. (C). pap. *(978-0-13-205175-0(3))* Pearson Education Canada.

Foster, Leslie T. & Wharf, Brian, eds. People, Politics, & Child Welfare in British Columbia. 2007. (ENG., Illus.). 304p. *(978-0-7748-1372-3(5))* Univ. of British Columbia Pr.

Friendly, Martha & Prentice, Susan. Childcare. 2009. (About Canada Ser.). (ENG.). 150p. pap. 17.95 *(978-1-55266-291-5(8))* Fernwood Publishing Co., Ltd. CAN. Dist: Independent Pubs. Group.

Howe, R. Brian & Covell, Katherine, eds. A Question of Commitment: Children's Rights in Canada. 2007. (Studies in Childhood & Family in Canada). (ENG.). 456p. (C). pap. 48.95 *(978-1-55458-003-3(X))* Wilfrid Laurier Univ. Pr. CAN. Dist: Univ. of Toronto Pr.

Kufeldt, Kathleen & McKenzie, Brad, eds. Child Welfare: Connecting Research, Policy, & Practice. 2nd ed. 2011. (ENG., Illus.). 696p. (C). pap. 54.95 *(978-1-55458-330-0(6))* Wilfrid Laurier Univ. Pr. CAN. Dist: Univ. of Toronto Pr.

Lemay, Raymond A., et al. Looking after Children: A Practitioner's Guide. 2007. (ENG., Illus.). 136p. pap. *(978-0-7766-0643-9(3))* Univ. of Ottawa Pr./Presses de l'Université d'Ottawa.

Payne, Julien D. & Payne, Marilyn A. Child Support Guidelines in Canada. 2006th rev. ed. 2006. (Illus.). 840p. pap. *(978-1-55221-126-7(6))* Irwin Law, Inc.

Strong-Boag, Veronica. Fostering Nation? Canada Confronts Its History of Childhood Disadvantage. 2011. (Studies in Childhood & Family in Canada Ser.). (ENG.). 318p. (C). pap. 38.95 ***(978-1-55458-337-9(3))*** Wilfrid Laurier Univ. Pr. CAN. Dist: Univ. of Toronto Pr.

Swain, Hillel, et al. Child, Nation, Race & Empire: Child Rescue Discourse, England, Canada & Australia, 1850-1915. 2010. (Studies in Imperialism Ser.). (ENG., Illus.). 224p. 89.95 *(978-0-7190-7894-1(6))* Manchester Univ. Pr. GBR. Dist: Macmillan.

Swift, Karen & Callahan, Marilyn. At Risk: Social Justice in Child Welfare & Other Human Services. 2009. (Illus.). 259p. *(978-0-8020-9331-8(0))*; (ENG., pap. *(978-0-8020-9499-5(6))* Univ. of Toronto Pr.

CHILD WELFARE—CHINA

Chan, Edward Ko Ling, ed. Child Protection in Chinese Societies: Challenges & Policies. 2012. ***(978-1-61942-879-9(2))*** Nova Science Pubs., Inc.

CHILD WELFARE—GREAT BRITAIN

Arthur, Raymond. Family Life & Youth Offending: Home Is Where the Hurt Is. (Routledge Advances in Criminology Ser.). (ENG.). 240p. (C). 2012. pap. 42.95 ***(978-0-415-51454-5(1))*** 2008. (Illus.). 180.00 *(978-0-415-40844-8(X))* Routledge.

Axford, Nick. Exploring Concepts of Child Well-Being: Implications for Children's Services. 2012. (Policy Press - Studies in Poverty, Inequality & Social Exclusion Ser.). 272p. pap. 42.95 ***(978-1-4473-0585-9(X))*** Policy Pr. GBR. Dist: Chicago Distribution Ctr.

Bamfield, Louise. Born Unequal: Why We Need a Progressive Pre-Birth Agenda. 2007. 91p. *(978-0-7163-3061-5(X))* Fabian Society.

Barker, Judy & Hodes, Deborah. The Child in Mind. 3rd rev. ed. 2007. (Illus.). 128p. 31.95 *(978-0-415-42602-2(2))* Routledge.

—The Child in Mind: A Child Protection Handbook. 4th rev. ed. 2012. (ENG.). 136p. 115.00 *(978-0-415-60995-1(X))*; pap. 31.95 *(978-0-415-60996-8(8))* Routledge.

Beaty, Carole. Integrated Children's Centres: Overcoming Barriers to Truly Integrated Services. 2010. (Illus.). 256p. 36.95 *(978-0-415-47915-8(0))*; 112.00 *(978-0-415-47914-1(2))* Taylor & Francis Group.

Bedingfield, David. Child in Need. 2nd rev. ed. 2010. 500p. pap. 120.00 *(978-1-84661-027-1(3))* Jordan Publishing, Ltd. GBR. Dist: International Specialized Bk. Services.

Blair, Mitch, et al. Child Public Health. 2nd ed. 2010. (ENG., Illus.). 310p. (Orig.). pap. 59.95 *(978-0-19-954750-0(5))* Oxford Univ. Pr., Inc.

Blyth, Maggie & Solomon, Enver, eds. Effective Safeguarding for Children & Young People: What Next after Munro? 2012. 165p. pap. 28.95 ***(978-1-4473-0490-6(X))*** Policy Pr. GBR. Dist: Chicago Distribution Ctr.

Blythe, Maggie et al, eds. Young People & Risk. 2007. (Illus.). 128p. (C). pap. 29.95 *(978-1-84742-000-8(1))* Policy Pr. GBR. Dist: Chicago Distribution Ctr.

Bradshaw, Jonathan, ed. The Well-Being of Children in the UK. 3rd rev. ed. 2011. (Illus.). 315p. 99.00 *(978-1-84742-837-0(1))*; 336p. pap. 42.95 *(978-1-84742-836-3(3))* Policy Pr. GBR. Dist: Chicago Distribution Ctr.

Broadhurst, Karen, et al, eds. Critical Perspectives on Safeguarding Children. 2009. (ENG.). 300p. 120.95 *(978-0-470-68232-6(9))*; pap. 57.95 *(978-0-470-69756-6(3))* Wiley, John & Sons, Inc. (Wiley).

Collins, Janet. Promoting Children's Wellbeing: Policy & Practice. Foley, Pam, ed. 2008. (Illus.). 312p. pap. 35.95 *(978-1-84742-059-6(1))* Policy Pr. GBR. Dist: Chicago Distribution Ctr.

Cram101 Textbook Reviews & Cram101 Textbook Reviews. Outlines & Highlights for Parents Who Misuse Drugs & Alcohol: Effective Interventions in Social Work & Child Protection by Donald Forrester. 2011. 162p. pap. 29.95 ***(978-1-61830-566-4(2))*** Cram101 Inc.

Davies, Carolyn & Ward, Harriet. Safeguarding Children Across Services: Messages from Research. 2011. (Illus.). 224p. pap. ***(978-1-84905-124-8(0))*** Kingsley, Jessica Ltd.

Denisoff, Dennis. Nineteenth-Century Childhood & the Rise of Consumer Culture. 2008. (Ashgate Studies in Childhood, 1700 to the Present Ser.). (Illus.). 252p. 114.95 *(978-0-7546-6156-6(3))* Ashgate Publishing Co.

Eisenstadt, Naomi. Providing a Sure Start: How Government Discovered Early Childhood. 192p. 2012. pap. 36.95 *(978-1-84742-729-8(4))* 2011. 89.95 *(978-1-84742-730-4(8))* Policy Pr. GBR. Dist: Chicago Distribution Ctr.

Ferguson, Harry. Child Protection Practice. 2011. (ENG., Illus.). 208p. pap. 30.00 *(978-0-230-24283-8(9))* Palgrave Macmillan.

Flegel, Monica. Creating Cruelty to Children in Nineteenth-Century England: Literature, Representation, & the NSPCC. 2009. (Ashgate Studies in Childhood, 1700 to the Present Ser.). 214p. 99.95 *(978-0-7546-6456-7(2))* Ashgate Publishing Co.

Frankel, Jill & Hobart, Christine. Good Practice in Childminding: A Handbook for the Diploma in Home-Based Childcare. Walker, Miranda, ed. 4th rev. ed. 2009. (ENG., Illus.). 336p. pap. 57.50 ***(978-1-4085-0493-2(6))*** Nelson Thornes Ltd. GBR. Dist: Trans-Atlantic Pubns., Inc.

Füredi, Frank & Bristow, Jennie. Licensed to Hug: How Child Protection Policies Are Poisoning the Relationship Between the Generations & Damaging the Voluntary Sector. 2nd ed. 2010. 68p. pap. 13.50 *(978-1-906837-16-7(3))* Civitas:Institute for the Study of Civil Society GBR. Dist: Coronet Bks.

Garrett, Paul Michael. Transforming Children's Services? Social Work, Children & Families in a Modern World. 2009. (ENG.). 200p. (C). pap. 49.00 *(978-0-335-23425-7(9)*, 0335234259) McGraw-Hill Education GBR. Dist: McGraw-Hill Cos., The.

—Transforming Children's Services? Social Work, Neoliberalism & the 'Modern' World. 2009. (ENG.). 200p. (C). 127.00 *(978-0-335-23424-0(0)*, 0335234240) McGraw-Hill Education GBR. Dist: McGraw-Hill Cos., The.

Harbour, Anthony & Mitchell, Mary. Children with Mental Disorder & the Law: A Guide to Law & Practice. 2008. (ENG.). 224p. pap. *(978-1-84310-576-3(4))* Kingsley, Jessica Ltd.

Hester, Marianne, et al. Making an Impact: Children & Domestic Violence - A Reader. 2nd ed. 2006. (ENG.). 288p. per. *(978-1-84310-157-4(2))* Kingsley, Jessica Ltd.

Holmes, Lisa & McDermid, Samantha. Understanding Costs & Outcomes in Child Welfare Services: A Comprehensive Costing Approach to Managing Your Resources. 2012. (ENG.). 240p. pap. ***(978-1-84905-214-6(X))*** Kingsley, Jessica Ltd.

Horner, Nigel & Krawczyk, Steve. Social Work in Education & Children's Services. 2006. (Illus.). 130p. pap. *(978-1-84445-045-9(7))* Learning Matters Ltd.

Hothersall, Steve. Social Work with Children, Young People & their Families in Scotland. 2nd rev. ed. 2008. (Illus.). 200p. pap. *(978-1-84445-156-2(9))* Learning Matters Ltd.

Iwaniec, Dorota, ed. The Child's Journey Through Care: Placement Stability, Care Planning, & Achieving Permanency. 2006. (ENG., Illus.). 304p. 164.95 *(978-0-470-01137-9(8))*; per. 65.00 *(978-0-470-01138-6(6))* Wiley, John & Sons, Inc. (Wiley).

Kay, Janet. Protecting Children. pap. *(978-0-8264-5802-5(5))* Continuum International Publishing Group, Ltd.

Kellett, Mary. Children's Perspectives on Integrated Services: Every Child Matters in Policy & Practice. 2011. (Interagency Working in Health & Social Care Ser.). (ENG., Illus.). 256p. (C). pap. 32.95 *(978-0-230-23039-2(3))* Palgrave Macmillan.

Lee, Allison. How to Be an Outstanding Childminder. 2009. (ENG., Illus.). 152p. 24.95 *(978-1-84706-496-7(5))* Continuum International Publishing Group, Ltd. GBR. Dist: National Bk. Network.

—The Parent's Guide to Childcare: How to Choose & Manage the Right Care for Your Child. 2008. 166p. pap. *(978-1-84528-220-2(5))* How To Books.

—Working Mum's Guide to Childcare: How to Choose & Manage the Right Childcare for Your Child. 2nd ed. 2010. (Illus.). 179p. pap. 26.00 *(978-1-84528-378-0(3))* How To Books GBR. Dist: Parkwest Pubns., Inc.

Levene, Alysa. The Childhood of the Poor: Welfare in Eighteenth-Century London. 2012. (ENG., Illus.). 264p. 85.00 ***(978-0-230-35480-7(7))*** Palgrave Macmillan.

Lindon, Jennie. Safeguarding Children - 0-8 Years. 4th rev. ed. 2012. (ENG., Illus.). 224p. pap. 45.00 ***(978-1-4441-4548-9(7))*** Hodder Arnold Pubs.

Martin, Lucy. The Childcare Bible: The Ultimate Guide to All Forms of Childcare. 2009. (ENG.). 352p. 27.95 *(978-0-09-192426-3(X))* Random Hse. GBR. Dist: Independent Pubs. Group.

Masson, Judith. Protecting Powers: Emergency Intervention for Children's Protection. 2007. (Wiley Child Protection & Policy Ser.: 13). (ENG., Illus.) 260p. 159.95 *(978-0-470-01602-2(7))*; per. 59.95 *(978-0-470-01603-9(5))* Wiley, John & Sons, Inc. (Wiley).

McShane, John. It Must Never Happen Again: The Lessons Learned from the Short Life & Terrible Death of Baby P. 2009. (ENG., Illus.). 288p. pap. 14.95 *(978-1-84454-789-0(2))* Blake, John Publishing, Ltd. GBR. Dist: Independent Pubs. Group.

Mulley, Clare. The Woman Who Saved the Children: A Biography of Eglantyne Jebb - Founder of Save the Children. 2010. (ENG., Illus.). 416p. pap. 16.95 *(978-1-85168-722-0(X))* Oneworld Pubns. GBR. Dist: National Bk. Network.

Pearl, David. Care Standards Legislation Handbook. 7th rev. ed. 2009. (ENG.). 808p. pap. *(978-1-84661-165-0(2))* Jordan Publishing, Ltd.

Pomerantz, Kathryn Anne, et al. How to Reach 'Hard to Reach' Children: Improving Access, Participation & Outcomes. 2007. (ENG.). 282p. per. 62.95 *(978-0-470-05884-8(6)*, Wiley) Wiley, John & Sons, Inc.

Read, Veronica. Developing Attachment in Early Years Settings: Nurturing Secure Relationships from Birth to Five Years. 2009. (ENG., Illus.). 144p. 33.95 *(978-0-415-49164-8(9))*; XII, 132p. 105.00 *(978-0-415-49163-1(0))* Fulton, David Pubs. GBR. Dist: Taylor & Francis Group.

Smith, Mark. Rethinking Residential Child Care: Positive Perspectives. 2009. 224p. pap. 37.95 *(978-1-86134-908-8(4))* Policy Pr. GBR. Dist: Chicago Distribution Ctr.

Southworth, Kate & Hope, Becky. I'll Never Give up on You: No Child Should Ever Be Forgotten. 2011. (ENG.). 288p. pap. 10.95 ***(978-1-4447-2329-8(4)***, Hodder & Stoughton) Hodder General Publishing Div. GBR. Dist: Independent Pubs. Group.

Stafford, Anne & Vincent, Sharon. Safeguarding & Protecting Children & Young People. Stafford, Anne & Vincent-Lum, Sharon, eds. 2008. 96p. pap. 26.95 *(978-1-903765-69-2(2))* Dunedin Academic Pr. GBR. Dist: International Specialized Bk. Services.

Stafford, Anne, et al. Child Protection Systems in the United Kingdom: A Comparative Analysis. 2011. (ENG., Illus.). 256p. pap. ***(978-1-84905-067-8(8))*** Kingsley, Jessica Ltd.

Stevenson, Olive. Neglected Children & Their Families. 2nd rev. ed. 2007. (ENG., Illus.). 200p. per. 49.95 *(978-1-4051-5171-9(4)*, Wiley-Blackwell) Wiley, John & Sons, Inc.

Swain, Hillel, et al. Child, Nation, Race & Empire: Child Rescue Discourse, England, Canada & Australia, 1850-1915. 2010. (Studies in Imperialism Ser.). (ENG., Illus.). 224p. 89.95 *(978-0-7190-7894-1(6))* Manchester Univ. Pr. GBR. Dist: Macmillan.

Thom, Betsy, et al, eds. Growing up with Risk. 2007. (Illus.). 296p. 99.00 *(978-1-86134-732-9(4))*; pap. 35.00 *(978-1-86134-731-2(6))* Policy Pr. GBR. Dist: Chicago Distribution Ctr.

Tisdall, Kay, et al. Children, Young People & Social Inclusion: Participation for What? 2006. (Illus.). 272p. (C). pap. 39.95 *(978-1-86134-662-9(X))* Policy Pr. GBR. Dist: Chicago Distribution Ctr.

Turney, Danielle, et al. Improving Child & Family Assessments: Turning Research into Practice. 2011. (ENG., Illus.). 256p. pap. ***(978-1-84905-256-6(5))*** Kingsley, Jessica Ltd.

Waldfogel. Britains War on Poverty. 2010. (Illus.). x, 270p. *(978-0-87154-897-9(6))* Russell Sage Foundation.

Walker, Gary & Walker. Working Together for Children: A Critical Introduction to Multi-Agency Working. 2009. (ENG.). 216p. 39.95 *(978-0-8264-9817-5(5))* Continuum International Publishing Group, Ltd. GBR. Dist: National Bk. Network.

Warren-Adamson, Chris. Post-Qualifying Child Care Social Work: Developing Reflective Practice. Ruch, Gillian, ed. 2008. (Illus.). 176p. (C). pap. 49.00 *(978-1-4129-2826-7(5)*, B28257P) SAGE Pubns., Ltd. GBR. Dist: SAGE Pubns., Inc.

—Post-Qualifying Child Care Social Work: Developing Reflective Practice. Ruch, Gillian, ed. 2008. (Illus.). 176p. (C). 98.00 *(978-1-4129-2825-0(7)*, B28257C) SAGE Pubns., Ltd. GBR. Dist: SAGE Pubns., Inc.

Whitney, Ben. Social Inclusion in Schools: Improving Outcomes, Raising Standards. 2007. (David Fulton Bks.). (Illus.). 112p. per. 37.50 *(978-1-84312-474-0(2))* Routledge.

CHILD WELFARE—ITALY

Chamley, Jean. An American Social Worker in Italy. 2009. (ENG.). 336p. pap. 60.00 *(978-0-8166-5723-0(8))* Univ. of Minnesota Pr.

CHILD WITNESSES

Bottoms, Bette L., et al, eds. Children as Victims, Witnesses, & Offenders: Psychological Science & the Law. 2009. (ENG.). 412p. 50.00 *(978-1-60623-332-0(7))* Guilford Pubns., Inc.

Bourg Carter, Sherrie. Children in the Courtroom: Challenges for Lawyers & Judges. 2nd ed. 2009. *(978-1-60156-071-1(0))* National Institute for Trial Advocacy.

Cram101 Textbook Reviews & Cram101 Textbook Reviews. Outlines & Highlights for Tell Me What Happened: Structured Investigative Interviews of Child Victims & Witnesses by Michael E. Lamb (University Of. 2011. 220p. pap. 30.95 ***(978-1-4288-4717-0(0))*** Cram101 Inc.

Hall, Susan R. & Sales, Bruce Dennis. Courtroom Modifications for Child Witnesses: Law & Science in Forensic Evaluations. 2008. (Law & Public Policy Ser.). 368p. 49.95 *(978-1-4338-0354-3(2))* American Psychological Assn.

King, Julie Adair. Children's Testimony: A Handbook of Psychological Research & Forensic Practice. Katz, Carmit et al, eds. 2nd ed. 2011. (Wiley Series in Psychology of Crime, Policing & Law Ser.: 51). (ENG., Illus.). 480p. pap. 54.95 *(978-0-470-68678-2(2)*, Wiley-Blackwell) Wiley, John & Sons, Inc.

Lamb, Michael E., et al. Tell Me What Happened: Structured Investigative Interviews of Child Victims & Witnesses. 2008. (Wiley Series in Psychology of Crime, Policing & Law Ser.). (ENG.). 386p. pap. 71.95 *(978-0-470-51866-3(9))*; 172.95 *(978-0-470-51865-6(0))* Wiley, John & Sons, Inc. (Wiley).

Mather, J. Children's Testimony: A Handbook of Psychological Research & Forensic Practice. Katz, Carmit et al, eds. 2nd ed. 2011. (Wiley Series in Psychology of Crime, Policing & Law Ser.). (ENG., Illus.). 480p. 119.95 *(978-0-470-68677-5(4)*, Wiley-Blackwell) Wiley, John & Sons, Inc.

Smith, Kevin & Tilney, Steve. Vulnerable Adult & Child Witnesses. 2007. (Blackstone's Practical Policing Ser.). (ENG.). 256p. 80.00 *(978-0-19-921410-5(7)*, Blackstone Pr.) Oxford Univ. Pr. GBR. Dist: Oxford Univ. Pr., Inc.

Spencer, John & Lamb, Michael, eds. Children & Cross-Examination: Time to Change the Rules? 2012. (ENG.). 158p. pap. 60.00 ***(978-1-84946-307-2(7))*** Hart Publishing Ltd. GBR. Dist: International Specialized Bk. Services.

CHILDBED FEVER

see Puerperal Septicemia

CHILDBIRTH

see also Birth Customs; Labor (Obstetrics); Multiple Birth; Natural Childbirth

Achiron, Deborah "The Momma". What Not to Expect, When You Are Expecting. 2006. 17.00 *(978-0-8059-9078-2(X))* Dorrance Publishing Co., Inc.

Al-Zirqi, Iqbal. Severe Obstetric Haemorrhage. 2011. 112p. pap. ***(978-3-8443-8707-0(2))*** Lambert Academic Publishing.

Alleyne-Ho, Dale. The Ultimate Guide to Labour & Birth. 2009. (Illus.). 88p. pap. *(978-1-84903-011-3(1))* Schiel & Denver Publishing Ltd.

American Dietetic Association Staff & Ward, Elizabeth M. Expect the Best: Your Guide to Healthy Eating Before, During, & after Pregnancy. 2009. (ENG.). 272p. pap. 15.95 *(978-0-470-29076-7(5)*, Wiley) Wiley, John & Sons, Inc.

Armstrong, Penny & Feldman, Sheryl. A Wise Birth: Bringing Together the Best of Natural Childbirth & Modern Medicine. 2007. (ENG.). 240p. per. 17.95 *(978-1-905177-03-5(8))* Pinter & Martin Ltd. GBR. Dist: National Bk. Network.

Arons, Harry. Hypnotic Conditioning for Childbirth. 2011. 12p. pap. 35.95 ***(978-1-258-02449-2(9))*** Literary Licensing, LLC.

Arsenault, Carole Kramer. The Baby Nurse Bible: Secrets Only a Baby Nurse Can Tell You about Having & Caring for Your Baby. 2011. (ENG., Illus.). 352p. pap. 15.95 *(978-1-61519-014-0(7)*, 1615190147) Experiment LLC, The.

Barrett, Joyce & Pitman, Teresa. Pregnancy & Birth: A Guide to Making Decisions That Are Right for You & Your Baby. 2nd rev. ed. 2008. (ENG., Illus.). 320p. pap. 21.95 *(978-1-55263-791-3(3))* Key Porter Bks. CAN. Dist: Perseus-PGW.

Baxendale, Martin. Your New Baby's First Birthday. pap. *(978-0-9522032-2-3(7))* Silent But Deadly Pubns. GBR. Dist: Vine Hse. Distribution.

Bedell, Debby. Raising Triplets: Our Journey from Surrogacy Through Two Years. 2011. 157p. pap. 36.95 *(978-1-4327-5974-2(4))* Outskirts Pr., Inc.

Behrens, Carolyn. Parenting: It's Your Decision. Johnson, Judy & Wright, Becky, eds. 2008. *(978-0-9776782-9-7(6))* J & B Products, Inc.

Bhakare, Shilpa. Rituals & Practices Attendant to Pregnancy & Childbirth. 2011. 204p. pap. ***(978-3-8383-8289-0(7))*** Lambert Academic Publishing.

Bohn, Yvonne, et al. The Mommy Docs' Ultimate Guide to Pregnancy & Birth. 2011. (ENG.). 544p. pap., instr.'s gde. ed. 15.95 *(978-0-7382-1460-3(4))* Da Capo Pr., Inc.

Brodsky, Phyllis L. The Control of Childbirth: Women Versus Medicine Through the Ages. 2008. (ENG.). 222p. per. 35.00 *(978-0-7864-3362-9(0))* McFarland & Co., Inc. Pubs.

Bullard, Julia. How to Raise a Child. 2011. 84p. pap. 11.11 ***(978-1-4269-6582-1(6))*** Trafford Publishing.

Calais-Germain, Blandine & Pares, Nuria Vives. Preparing for a Gentle Birth. 2011. (ENG.). 1p. pap. 19.95 ***(978-1-59477-388-4(2))*** Inner Traditions International, Ltd.

Caldwell, Holly Morse. City Baby D. C. The Ultimate Guide for DC Metro Parents from Pregnancy to Preschool. 2008. (City & Company Ser.). (ENG.). 208p. 19.95 *(978-0-7893-1686-8(2))* Universe Publishing.

Canfield, Jack, et al. Chicken Soup for the Soul: New Moms: 101 Inspirational Stories of Joy, Love, & Wonder. 2011. (ENG.). 416p. pap. 14.95 *(978-1-935096-63-4(X))* Chicken Soup for the Soul Publishing, LLC.

Cassidy, Tina. Birth: The Surprising History of How We Are Born. 2007. (ENG., Illus.). 320p. per. 14.00 *(978-0-8021-4324-2(5)*, Grove Pr.) Grove/Atlantic, Inc.

Chapman, D. The Midwife's Labour & Birth Handbook. Chapman, Vicky & Charles, Cathy, eds. 2nd ed. 2008. (ENG., Illus.). 368p. pap. 54.99 *(978-1-4051-6105-3(1)*, Wiley-Blackwell) Wiley, John & Sons, Inc.

Chye, Tan Thiam, et al. The Art & Science of Pregnancy & Childbirth: What You Want to Know from Your Obstetrician. 2008. 81.00 *(978-981-277-939-7(6))* World Scientific Publishing Co., Inc.

—The New Art & Science of Pregnancy & Childbirth: What You Want to Know from Your Obstetrician. 2008. (Illus.). 314p. pap. 52.00 *(978-981-277-940-3(X))* World Scientific Publishing Co., Inc.

Ciccone, Tiziana. Wake up, the Baby's Coming. 2010. 24p. pap. 10.95 *(978-1-60860-685-6(6)*, Strategic Bk. Publishing) AEG Literary Publishing Services, Inc.

Cobb, Janice Reed. A Perfect Dwelling Place. 2011. 296p. 37.95 ***(978-1-4497-2160-2(5))***; pap. 22.95 ***(978-1-4497-2159-6(1))*** Author Solutions, Inc. (WestBow Pr.)

Cody, Lisa Forman. Birthing the Nation: Sex, Science, & the Conception of Eighteenth-Century Britons. 2008. (ENG., Illus.). 374p. pap. 45.00 *(978-0-19-954140-9(X))* Oxford Univ. Pr., Inc.

C

Cohen, Harlan. Dad's Pregnant Too! Expectant Fathers, Expectant Mothers, New Dads & New Moms Share Advice, Tips & Stories about All the Surprises, Questions & Joys Ahead... 2008. (ENG., Illus.). 560p. pap. 13.99 *(978-1-4022-1133-1(3))* Sourcebooks, Inc.

Colburn, Kerry, et al. How to Have Your Second Child First: 100 Things That Are Good to Know... the First Time Around. 2010. (ENG.). 176p. pap. 18.95 *(978-0-8118-6988-1(1))* Chronicle Bks. LLC.

Common Knowledge Trust, prod. The Pink Kit Method for Birthing Better(r): Effective skills for a positive birth experience for men & Women. 2008. (ENG.). *(978-0-473-15360-1(2))* Common Knowledge Trust.

Cooper, Carol. Pregnancy Week by Week. 2008. (ENG., Illus.). 112p. *(978-1-84597-602-6(9))* CICO Bks.

Crane, Dede & Moore, Lisa. Great Expectations: Twenty-Four True Stories about Childbirth, 1 vol. 2008. (ENG.). 400p. pap. 18.95 *(978-0-88784-778-3(1))* House of Anansi Pr. CAN. Dist: Perseus-PGW.

Cunningham, Darren. Joseph's Life Story: Seeking Justice. 2011. 292p. pap. 63.99 ***(978-1-4389-2356-7(2))*** AuthorHouse.

Curtis, Glade B. & Schuler, Judith. Your Pregnancy Week by Week. 7th ed. 2011. (ENG.). 688p. 23.00 *(978-0-7382-1463-4(9))*; pap. 15.95 *(978-0-7382-1464-1(7))* Da Capo Pr., Inc.

—Your Pregnancy Week by Week (Health Mgt Corp custom Cover) 2008. 664p. pap. 15.95 *(978-0-7382-1321-7(7))* Da Capo Pr., Inc.

Cushman-Dowdee, Heather. Simply Give Birth. 2010. 164p. pap. 14.99 *(978-0-557-13810-4(8))* Lulu Enterprises Inc.

Davis-Floyd, Robbie. Birth Models That Work. Davis-Floyd, Robbie E. et al, eds. 2009. (ENG., Illus.). 320p. pap. 29.95 *(978-0-520-25891-4(6))* Univ. of California Pr.

Davis-Floyd, Robbie E., et al, eds. Birth Models That Work. 2009. (ENG., Illus.). 320p. 65.00 *(978-0-520-24863-2(5))* Univ. of California Pr.

Deen-Ellis, Sherie. Firstborn. 2007. 164p. pap. 21.50 *(978-1-84753-438-5(4))* Lulu Enterprises Inc.

Doblhammer, Gabriele. The Late Life Legacy of Very Early Life. 2010. (Demographic Research Monographs). (Illus.). xiv, 204p. pap. 129.00 *(978-3-642-06046-5(3)*, 3642060463) Springer.

Donegan, Tracy. The Better Birth Book: Taking the Mystery (and Fear) Out of Childbirth. 2006. (ENG., Illus.). 266p. per. 21.95 *(978-1-904148-87-6(5))* Liffey Pr., The IRL. Dist: Dufour Editions, Inc.

Donna, Sylvie. Preparing for a Healthy Birth: 10 steps to take so you & your baby can have the best possible Birth. 2009. (Illus.). 580p. pap. 30.00 *(978-1-906619-01-5(8))* Fresh Heart Publishing GBR. Dist: Lightning Source, Inc.

—Surprising, Inspiring Birth! Accounts of Birth to Inform, Amuse & Reassure. 2009. (Illus.). 156p. pap. 30.00 *(978-1-906619-12-1(3))* Fresh Heart Publishing GBR. Dist: Lightning Source, Inc.

Dorling Kindersley Publishing Staff & Greaves, Steen. Everything You Need to Know Pregnancy & Birth. 2011. (ENG.). 192p. 14.95 *(978-0-7566-7169-3(8))* Dorling Kindersley Publishing, Inc.

Douglas, Ann. The Mother of All Pregnancy Books: An All-Canadian Guide to Conception, Birth & Everything in Between. 2nd ed. 2011. (ENG.). 608p. pap. 29.95 *(978-1-118-03468-2(6)*, Wiley) Wiley, John & Sons, Inc.

Drinker, Elizabeth Sandwith. The Diary of Elizabeth Drinker: The Life Cycle of an Eighteenth-Century Woman. Crane, Elaine Forman, ed. abr. ed. 2010. 352p. (C). pap. 22.50 *(978-0-8122-2077-3(3))* Univ. of Pennsylvania Pr.

Du Plessis, Diana. Juta's Clinical Guide for Midwives. 2007. (ENG., Illus.). 300p. per. 51.95 *(978-0-7021-7284-7(7))* Juta Academic ZAF. Dist: Independent Pubs. Group.

Duke, Wendy. The Grace by Which We Stand. 2008. 132p. pap. 19.99 *(978-1-4363-7178-0(3))* Xlibris Corp.

Duong, Dat. Childbirth & Infant Feeding. 2010. 236p. pap. *(978-3-639-24364-2(1))* VDM Verlag Dr. Mueller e.K.

Elwins, Dannie. How Men Can Be A Great Help in the Delivery Room. 2009. 40p. pap. 16.99 *(978-0-557-15615-3(7))* Lulu Enterprises Inc.

Epstein, Randi Hutter. Get Me Out: A History of Childbirth from the Garden of Eden to the Sperm Bank. (ENG., Illus.). 2011. 336p. pap. 15.95 *(978-0-393-33906-2(8)*, 33906) 2010. 302p. 24.95 *(978-0-393-06458-2(1)*, 6458) Norton, W. W. & Co., Inc.

Erdrich, Louise. The Blue Jay's Dance: A Memoir of Early Motherhood. 2010. (P.S. Ser.). (ENG.). 240p. pap. 13.99 *(978-0-06-176797-5(2)*, HarperPerennial) HarperCollins Pubs.

Fahy, Kathleen, et al. Birth Territory & Midwifery Guardianship: Theory for Practice, Education & Research. 2008. (ENG., Illus.). 198p. (C). pap. 45.95 *(978-0-7506-8870-3(X)*, Books for Midwives) Elsevier - Health Sciences Div.

Feinbloom, Richard I. Pregnancy, Birth, & the Early Months. 3rd ed. Date not set. 366p. pap. *(978-0-201-36099-8(3))* Addison-Wesley Longman, Inc.

Fine, Jeffrey L. The Art of Conscious Parenting. 2009. (ENG.). 1p. pap. 16.95 *(978-1-59477-322-8(X)*, Healing Arts Pr.) Inner Traditions International, Ltd.

Ford-Martin, Paula. The Everything Pregnancy Organizer: Monthly Calendars, Charts, Checklists, & Schedules. 2nd ed. 2006. (ENG., Illus.). 304p. pap. 16.95 *(978-1-59337-639-0(1))* Adams Media Corp.

Ford-Martin, Paula. The Everything Pregnancy Organizer, 3rd Edition: A month-by-month guide to a stress-free Pregnancy. 3rd ed. 2011. (ENG.). 304p. pap. 16.95 ***(978-1-4405-2676-3(1))*** Adams Media Corp.

Fordyce, Lauren & Maraesa, Aminata, eds. Risk, Reproduction, & Narratives of Experience. 2012. (ENG.). 256p. 69.95 ***(978-0-8265-1819-4(2))***; pap. 29.95 ***(978-0-8265-1820-0(6))*** Vanderbilt Univ. Pr.

Franklin, Emily & Swain, Heather, eds. After: Stories of Childbirth & Infancy from Our Top Writers. 2007. 432p. 23.95 *(978-1-58567-892-1(9))* Overlook Pr., The.

Fullick, Ann. Pregnancy & Birth. 2009. (Why Science Matters Ser.). (ENG.). 56p. (gr. 6-9). 33.50 *(978-1-4329-2479-9(6))*; 2nd ed. pap. 9.49 *(978-1-4329-2486-7(9))* Heinemann-Raintree. (NA-h).

Galvez, Alyshia. Patient Citizens, Immigrant Mothers: Mexican Women, Public Prenatal Care, & the Birth Weight Paradox. 2011. (Critical Issues in Health & Medicine Ser.). (ENG., Illus.). 240p. 72.00 *(978-0-8135-5141-8(2))* Rutgers Univ. Pr.

Gálvez, Alyshia. Patient Citizens, Immigrant Mothers: Mexican Women, Public Prenatal Care, & the Birth Weight Paradox. 2011. (Critical Issues in Health & Medicine Ser.). (ENG., Illus.). 230p. (C). pap. 24.95 *(978-0-8135-5142-5(0))* Rutgers Univ. Pr.

Garland, Dianne. Revisiting Waterbirth: An Attitude to Care. 3rd ed. 2010. (ENG., Illus.). 240p. pap. 32.00 *(978-0-230-27357-3(2))* Palgrave Macmillan.

Gliksman, Michele Isaacs & DiGeronimo, Theresa Foy. Pregnancy & Childbirth. 3rd rev. ed. 2010. (Complete Idiot's Guide Ser.). (ENG.). 352p. (gr. 12). 16.95 *(978-1-61564-030-0(4)*, Alpha Bks.) Penguin Group (USA) Inc.

Goldberg, Linda. Pea in a Pod: Your Complete Guide to Pregnancy, Childbirth & Beyond. 2nd ed. 2011. (ENG.). 496p. pap. *(978-0-7570-0347-9(8))* Square One Pubs.

Goldstein, Robin S. New Baby Answer Book: From Birth to Kindergarten, Answers to the Top 150 Questions about Raising a Young Child. 2nd ed. 2009. (ENG.). 288p. pap. 14.99 *(978-1-4022-1827-9(3))* Sourcebooks, Inc.

Greene, Alan. Feeding Baby Green: The Earth-Friendly Program for Healthy, Safe Nutrition During Pregnancy, Childhood, & Beyond. 2009. (ENG., Illus.). 312p. pap. 16.95 *(978-0-470-42524-4(5)*, Jossey-Bass) Wiley, John & Sons, Inc.

Greenwell, Penelope A. Birthing the Babes of the Light. 17.00 *(978-0-9648147-8-3(1))* Pentangle Pr.

Grumbling, Amy. Only for a Season: The Baby in Bed No1. 2009. 252p. pap. 15.99 *(978-1-60696-681-5(2))* Tate Publishing & Enterprises, LLC.

Guyer, Ruth Levy. Baby at Risk: The Uncertain Legacies of Medical Miracles for Babies, Families & Society. 2006. (Capital Currents Ser.). (Illus.). 256p. 10.00 *(978-1-933102-26-9(8))* Capital Bks., Inc.

Halvorsen, Theresa & Halvorsen, Brad. The Dad's Playbook to Labor & Birth: A Practical & Strategic Guide to Preparing for the Big Day. 2012. (ENG., Illus.). 192p. pap. 14.95 ***(978-1-55832-672-9(3))*** Harvard Common Pr.

Hamel, Lois. Planning for a Healthier Birth & Beyond: Strategies Women Use to Manage Gestational Diabetes. 2008. 284p. pap. *(978-3-639-04734-9(6))* VDM Verlag Dr. Mueller e.K.

Herring, Jonathan. Birth Rites & Rights. Ebtehaj, Fatemeh et al, eds. Johnson, Martin et al, eds. 2011. (ENG., Illus.). 306p. pap. 80.00 *(978-1-84946-188-7(0))* Hart Publishing Ltd. GBR. Dist: International Specialized Bk. Services.

Hill, Thomas, et al. What to Expect When Your Wife Is Expanding: A Reassuring Month-by-Month Guide for the Father-to-Be, Whether He Wants Advice or Not. 2nd ed. 2007. (ENG., Illus.). 160p. pap. 12.99 *(978-0-7407-6752-4(6))* Andrews McMeel Publishing.

Hillard, Paula J. Adams, ed. The 5-Minute Obstetrics & Gynecology Consult. 2008. (5-Minute Consult Ser.). (ENG., Illus.). 752p. 108.99 *(978-0-7817-6942-6(6))* Lippincott Williams & Wilkins.

Hofmeyr, G. Justus, et al. Pregnancy & Childbirth. 2008. (Wiley Cochrane Series?? Ser.). (ENG.). 446p. pap. 72.00 *(978-0-470-51845-8(6)*, Wiley) Wiley, John & Sons, Inc.

Hubbell Maiden, Anne, et al. The Tibetan Art of Parenting: From Before Conception Through Early Childhood. rev. ed. 2008. (ENG., Illus.). 204p. pap. 16.95 *(978-0-86171-579-4(9))* Wisdom Pubns.

Hux, Charles. Nine Healthy Months: All You Need to Know. 2009. 320p. pap. 15.95 *(978-1-4401-3985-7(7))* iUniverse, Inc.

Inkeles, Gordon. Massage for a Peaceful Pregnancy: A Daily Book for New Mothers & Fathers. rev. ed. 2007. (Illus.). 142p. pap. 19.95 *(978-0-9748535-4-3(2))* Arcata Arts.

Jackson, Deborah. A Gift for New Mothers: Traditional Wisdom of Pregnancy, Birth, & Motherhood. 2006. (ENG., Illus.). 128p. pap. 12.95 *(978-1-84483-133-3(7))* Duncan Baird Pubs. GBR. Dist: Sterling Publishing Co., Inc.

Johnson, Psyd. Wombology: Healing the primordial memories & wounds your grandmother's daughter gave to You. 2009. 124p. 23.95 *(978-0-595-49427-9(7))*; pap. 13.95 *(978-0-595-49692-1(X))* iUniverse, Inc.

Johnson, Tina. Childbirth in Republican China: Delivering Modernity. 2011. (ENG., Illus.). 268p. 65.00 *(978-0-7391-6440-2(6))* Lexington Bks.

Johnson, Tina Phillips. Childbirth in Republican China: Delivering Modernity. 2011. (Illus.). xliv, 223p. E-Book ***(978-0-7391-6442-6(2))*** Lexington Bks.

Jones, Marcie & Jones, Sandy. Great Expectations: Pregnancy Journal & Planner, Revised Edition. 2010. (Great Expectations Ser.). (ENG., Illus.). 224p. spiral bd. 14.95 *(978-1-4027-7705-9(1))* Sterling Publishing Co., Inc.

Jones, Sandy, et al. Baby's First Year. 2007. (Great Expectations Ser.). (ENG., Illus.). 656p. per. 14.95 *(978-1-4027-3646-9(0))* Sterling Publishing Co., Inc.

Jordan, Sarah. The Pregnancy Instruction Manual: Essential Information, Troubleshooting Tips, & Advice for Parents-to-Be. 2008. (Owner's & Instruction Manual Ser.). (ENG., Illus.). 224p. pap. 16.95 *(978-1-59474-245-3(6))* Quirk Bks.

Kalef, Mia. The Secret Life of Babies. 2009. 300p. pap. 26.50 *(978-0-557-00793-6(3))* Lulu Enterprises Inc.

Kate Breding. The Revolution of Cool. 2010. 108p. pap. 10.95 *(978-1-4401-8811-4(4))* iUniverse, Inc.

Kaye, Philippa. Your Pregnancy Week by Week: Practical & Reassuring Advice from Conception to Birth. 2010. (ENG., Illus.). 340p. pap. 22.95 *(978-0-09-192930-5(X))* Random Hse. GBR. Dist: Independent Pubs. Group.

Kennedy, V. Lynn. Born Southern: Childbirth, Motherhood, & Social Networks in the Old South. (ENG.). 288p. (gr. 17). 2012. pap. 30.00 ***(978-1-4214-0580-3(6))*** 2009. 65.00 *(978-0-8018-9417-6(4))* Johns Hopkins Univ. Pr.

Kerner, Ian & Raykeil, Heidi. Love in the Time of Colic: The New Parents' Guide to Getting It on Again. 2009. (ENG.). 240p. pap. 16.99 *(978-0-06-146512-3(7)*, Harper Paperbacks) HarperCollins Pubs.

King, Thomas. 59 Tips for Pregnant Men. 2007. 116p. pap. 10.99 *(978-0-944372-14-2(7))* Nissi Publishing, Inc.

Kitzinger, Sheila. Birth Your Way - Choosing birth at home or in a birth Centre: A guide for pregnant women. 2011. (Illus.). 344p. pap. 50.00 ***(978-1-906619-18-3(2))*** Fresh Heart Publishing GBR. Dist: Lightning Source, Inc.

Kitzinger, Sheila. Rediscovering Birth. 2nd ed. 2011. (ENG.). 300p. pap. 15.95 *(978-1-905177-38-7(0))* Pinter & Martin Ltd. GBR. Dist: National Bk. Network.

Klein, Susan, et al. Un Libro para Parteras: Atención Del Embarazo, el Parto y la Salud de la Mujer. 2007.Tr. of Book for Midwives: Care for Pregnancy, Birth, & Women's Health. (SPA.). pap. *(978-0-942364-29-3(5))* Hesperian Foundation, The.

Knickerbocker-Silva, Heather. The Chronicles of an Inexperienced Mommy. 2006. 124p. per. 10.95 *(978-1-59858-253-6(4))* Dog Ear Publishing, LLC.

Kroelinger, Charlan. Biological & Psychosocial Determinants of Problematic Birth Outcomes. 2008. 252p. pap. *(978-3-639-03158-4(X))* VDM Verlag Dr. Mueller e.K.

Lanfer, Stefan. The Faith of a Child. 2009. 162p. pap. 14.92 *(978-0-557-13452-6(8))* Lulu Enterprises Inc.

Leavitt, Judith Walzer. Make Room for Daddy: The Journey from Waiting Room to Birthing Room. (ENG., Illus.). 2010. 400p. pap. 22.95 *(978-0-8078-7168-3(0))* 2009. 448p. 36.95 *(978-0-8078-3255-4(3))* Univ. of North Carolina Pr.

Leboyer, Frédérick. Birth Without Violence. 2009. (ENG.). 1p. pap. 14.95 *(978-1-59477-297-9(5)*, Healing Arts Pr.) Inner Traditions International, Ltd.

Lees, Christoph. Pregnancy & Birth: Your Questions Answered: Your Questions Answered. 2012. (ENG.). 264p. 19.95 ***(978-0-7566-9265-0(2))*** Dorling Kindersley Publishing, Inc.

Lees, Christoph, et al. Pregnancy & Birth. 2007. (ENG., Illus.). 264p. pap. 20.00 *(978-0-7566-2610-5(2))* Dorling Kindersley Publishing, Inc.

Liamputtong, Pranee. The Journey of Becoming a Mother among Women in Northern Thailand. 2007. (ENG., Illus.). 238p. 62.99 *(978-0-7391-2005-7(0))*; per. 30.50 *(978-0-7391-2006-4(9))* Lexington Bks.

Liamputtong, Pranee, ed. Reproduction, Childbearing & Motherhood: A Cross-Cultural Perspective. 2007. 284p. (C). 89.00 *(978-1-60021-606-0(4))* Nova Science Pubs., Inc.

Lintott, Sheila & Sander-Staudt, Maureen, eds. Maternal Subjects: Philosophical Inquiry into Pregnancy, Childbirth, & Mothering. 2011. (Routledge Studies in Contemporary Philosophy Ser.). (ENG., Illus.). 284p. (C). 125.00 *(978-0-415-89187-5(6))* Routledge.

Lisa Marie Anderson. Rhythm of the Spirit: One child's inner strength to overcome illness & multiple Disabilities. 2010. 296p. pap. 18.49 *(978-1-4269-2280-0(9))* Trafford Publishing.

Liu, David T. Y., ed. Labour Ward Manual. 4th rev. ed. 2007. (ENG., Illus.). 236p. pap. 65.95 *(978-0-443-10252-3(X)*, Churchill Livingstone) Elsevier - Health Sciences Div.

Lutgen, Edward. Expecting Dads Now What. 2009. 70p. pap. 12.99 *(978-0-578-03674-8(6))* Lulu Enterprises Inc.

Lynch, Sheri. Hello My Name Is Mommy. Date not set. pap. *(978-0-312-31833-8(2)*, St. Martin's Paperbacks) St. Martin's Pr.

—Hello, My Name Is Mommy. Date not set. mass mkt. *(978-0-312-99179-1(7)*, St. Martin's Paperbacks) St. Martin's Pr.

Lyon, Erica. The Big Book of Birth. 2007. (ENG., Illus.). 352p. (gr. 12-18). 15.00 *(978-0-452-28768-6(5)*, Plume) Penguin Group (USA) Inc.

Maffi, Irene. Women, Health & the State in the Middle East: The Politics & Culture of Childbirth in Jordan. 2012. (Library of Modern Middle East Studies). (ENG., Illus.). 288p. 96.00 ***(978-1-84885-757-5(8))*** I. B. Tauris & Co., Ltd. GBR. Dist: Macmillan.

Mander, Rosemary. Pain in Childbearing & Its Control: Key Issues for Midwives & Women. 2nd ed. 2011. (ENG., Illus.). 216p. pap. 46.99 *(978-1-4051-9568-3(1)*, Wiley-Blackwell) Wiley, John & Sons, Inc.

Mangels, Reed. The Everything Vegan Pregnancy Book: All you need to know for a healthy pregnancy that fits your Lifestyle. 2011. (ENG.). 304p. pap. 16.95 *(978-1-4405-2551-3(X))* Adams Media Corp.

Mann, Jennifer. Belly Button Bliss: A Small Collection of Happy Birth Stories. 2010. (ENG.). 120p. 16.95 *(978-1-57749-230-6(7))* Taylor Trade Publishing.

McCarthy, Jenna. Parent Trip: From High Heels & Parties to Highchairs & Potties. 2008. (ENG.). 200p. pap. *(978-0-9799135-6-3(X))* Bella Luna Pr.

McCourt, Christine, ed. Childbirth, Midwifery & Concepts of Time. (FRS Ser.). (Illus.). 272p. 2010. 32.95 *(978-1-84545-294-0(1))* 2009. 90.00 *(978-1-84545-586-6(X))* Berghahn Bks., Inc.

McIntosh, Tania. A Social History of Maternity & Childbirth. 2012. (ENG., Illus.). 200p. (C). 125.00 *(978-0-415-56162-4(0))*; pap. 44.95 ***(978-0-415-56163-1(9))*** Routledge.

McIntosh, Tania. A Social History of Maternity & Childbirth: Key Themes in Maternity Care. 2012. E-Book ***(978-0-203-12422-2(7))*** Routledge.

Mckay-Moffat, Stella. Disability in Pregnancy & Childbirth. 2007. (ENG., Illus.). 240p. pap. 55.95 *(978-0-443-10318-6(6)*, Churchill Livingstone) Elsevier - Health Sciences Div.

McMeekan-Cates, LaNita. The Day My Baby Was Born: The Joys, Wonders, & Surprises of the Day You'll Never Forget. 2009. (ENG.). 272p. pap. 14.99 *(978-1-4022-1675-6(0))* Sourcebooks, Inc.

McMoyler, Sarah & Brott, Armin. The Best Birth: Your Guide to the Safest, Healthiest, Most Satisfying Labor & Delivery. 2008. (ENG., Illus.). 256p. pap. 18.95 *(978-0-7382-1121-3(4))* Da Capo Pr., Inc.

Meehan, Dawn. You'll Lose the Baby Weight: (and Other Lies about Pregnancy & Childbirth) 2010. (ENG.). 272p. pap. 14.99 *(978-1-4391-8380-9(5)*, Howard Bks.) Howard Books.

Murkoff, Heidi. Before You're Expecting. 2009. (ENG., Illus.). 256p. 23.95 *(978-0-7611-5552-2(X)*, 076115552X) Workman Publishing Co., Inc.

—The Welcome Baby! Gift Set. 2011. (ENG.). 1370p. pap. 32.90 ***(978-0-7611-6680-1(7))*** Workman Publishing Co., Inc.

—What to Expect Before You're Expecting. 2009. (ENG., Illus.). 275p. pap. 12.95 *(978-0-7611-5276-7(8)*, 0761152768) Workman Publishing Co., Inc.

—The What to Expect Pregnancy Journal & Organizer. rev. ed. 2007. (ENG., Illus.). 288p. pap. 12.95 *(978-0-7611-4212-6(6)*, 0761142126) Workman Publishing Co., Inc.

Murkoff, Heidi & Mazel, Sharon. What to Expect When You're Expecting. 4th ed. 2008. (ENG., Illus.). 656p. 24.95 *(978-0-7611-5079-4(X)*, 076115079X); 616p. pap. 14.95 *(978-0-7611-4857-9(4)*, 0761148574) Workman Publishing Co., Inc.

Murkoff, Heidi, et al. Que Puedes Esperar Cuando Se Esta Esperando. 4th ed. 2010. (SPA & ENG., Illus.). 676p. pap. 15.95 *(978-0-7611-5738-0(7)*, 0761157387) Workman Publishing Co., Inc.

Mysko, Claire & Amadeï, Magali. Does This Pregnancy Make Me Look Fat? The Essential Guide to Loving Your Body Before & after Baby. 2009. (ENG., Illus.). 256p. pap. 15.95 *(978-0-7573-0792-8(2))* Health Communications, Inc.

Navascues, Berta, illus. Happy mami (una mama Feliz) Un libro para las que acaban de ser mamas o estan a punto de Serlo. 2011. (Libro Amigo Ser.). (SPA.). 128p. 9.95 *(978-84-96708-45-7(4))* Robinbk., Ediciones S.L. ESP. Dist: Independent Pubs. Group.

Nelson, Kevin. The Everything Father-To-Be Book: A Survival Guide for Men. 2nd ed. 2010. xii, 272p. ***(978-1-4405-0461-7(X))*** Adams Media Corp.

Neupane, Subas. Rural Woman's Health: Work During Pregnancy & Birth Outcome. 2011. 96p. pap. ***(978-3-8433-9092-7(4))*** Lambert Academic Publishing.

Odent, Michel. Childbirth in the Age of Plastics. 2011. 208p. pap. 17.95 *(978-1-905177-54-7(2))* Pinter & Martin Ltd. GBR. Dist: National Bk. Network.

O'Neill, Kim. Bond with Your Baby Before Birth: How to Communicate with Your Unborn Child. 2009. (ENG.). 278p. pap. 14.95 *(978-0-7573-0743-0(4))* Health Communications, Inc.

Otte, Tina. Pregnancy & Birth: Your Complete Guide from Conception to Birth. 2007. (ENG., Illus.). 160p. pap. 17.95 *(978-1-84537-029-9(5))* New Holland Pubs., Ltd. GBR. Dist: Sterling Publishing Co., Inc.

Petrone, Elaine. Miracle Ball Method for Pregnancy: Relieve Back Pain & Labor Pain, Regain a Flat Belly, & More. 2011. (ENG., Illus.). 288p. pap. 19.95 *(978-0-7611-6097-7(3)*, 0761160973) Workman Publishing Co., Inc.

Pincott, Jena. Do Chocolate Lovers Have Sweeter Babies? The Surprising Science of Pregnancy. 2011. (ENG.). 288p. pap. 15.00 *(978-1-4391-8334-2(1)*, Free Pr.) Free Pr.

Pinto, Sarah. Where There Is No Midwife: Birth & Loss in Rural India. (Fertility, Reproduction & Sexuality Ser.). 342p. 2011. (ENG.). pap. 37.95 ***(978-0-85745-153-8(7))*** 2007. (C). 90.00 *(978-1-84545-310-7(7))* Berghahn Bks., Inc.

Posey, Julie & Blumanhourst, Eric. I Called Him Jeremy. 2010. 154p. pap. 24.99 *(978-0-557-45348-1(8))* Lulu Enterprises Inc.

Pukui, Mary Kawena. Hawaiian Beliefs & Customs During Birth, Infancy, & Childhood. 2011. 28p. 35.95 ***(978-1-258-10128-2(9))*** Literary Licensing, LLC.

Punger Faafp Ibclc, Denise. Permission to Mother: Going Beyond the Standard-of-Care to Nurture our Children. 2008. 272p. per. 29.95 *(978-1-4327-0385-1(4))* Outskirts Pr., Inc.

Puryear, Lucy J. & Puryear, Lucy. Understanding Your Moods When You're Expecting: Emotions, Mental Health, & Happiness - Before, During, & after Pregnancy. 2008. (ENG.). 256p. pap. 14.95 *(978-0-547-05362-2(2))* Houghton Mifflin Harcourt Trade & Reference Pubs.

Rasmussen, Dani & Perez, Antoinette. The Essential Pregnancy Organizer: 40 Weeks + 2nd rev. ed. 2008. (ENG.). 138p. spiral bd. 19.95 *(978-0-9766479-1-1(5))* Mango Media, Inc.

Roizen, Michael F. & Oz, Mehmet C. YOU: Having a Baby: The Owner's Manual to a Happy & Healthy Pregnancy. 2010. (ENG.). 464p. pap. 14.99 *(978-1-4165-7237-4(6)*, Free Pr.) Free Pr.

Roud, Steve & Roud, Stephen. Monday's Child Is Fair of Face: And Other Traditional Beliefs about Babies & Motherhood. 2008. (ENG., Illus.). 224p. 18.95 *(978-1-905211-52-4(X))* Random Hse. GBR. Dist: Independent Pubs. Group.

Sagady Leslie. Promoting & Preserving Physiological Childbirth: A Systems Approach for Midwives, Physicians, & Nurses. rev. ed. 2010. pap. 69.95 *(978-0-7637-7239-0(9))* Jones & Bartlett Learning, LLC.

Schatz, Howard. With Child. 2011. (ENG., Illus.). 176p. 95.00 *(978-0-9823799-3-6(5))* Glitterati, Inc.

Schlenzka, Peter F. Safety of Alternative Approaches to Childbirth. 2010. 188p. pap. *(978-3-8383-2419-7(6))* Lambert Academic Publishing.

Schmid, Verena. Birth Pain: A guide for pregnant women. 2011.Tr. of Geburtsschmerz. (Illus.). 192p. pap. ***(978-1-906619-21-3(2))*** Fresh Heart Publishing GBR. Dist: Lightning Source, Inc.

Schott, Robin May, ed. Birth, Death, & Femininity: Philosophies of Embodiment. 2010. (ENG.). 280p. 70.00 *(978-0-253-35535-5(4)*, 0253355354); pap. 24.95 *(978-0-253-22237-4(0)*, 0253222370) Indiana Univ. Pr.

Schuurmans, Nan & Lalonde, Andre. Healthy Beginnings: Giving Your Baby the Best Start, from Preconception to Birth. 4th ed. 2009. (ENG., Illus.). 192p. pap. 14.95 *(978-0-470-16024-4(1)*, Wiley) Wiley, John & Sons, Inc.

Schwartz, Marie Jenkins. Birthing a Slave: Motherhood & Medicine in the Antebellum South. 2010. 416p. pap. 20.00 *(978-0-674-03492-1(9))* Harvard Univ. Pr.

Selin, Helaine, ed. Childbirth Across Cultures: Ideas & Practices of Pregnancy, Childbirth & the Postpartum. 2009. (Science Across Cultures: the History of Non-Western Science Ser.). (ENG., Illus.). xvii, 314p. 219.00 *(978-90-481-2598-2(7)*, 9048125987) Springer.

Sieber, Samanta Christine Schwaningerr. Lebendiges Glück: Leben beginnt vor der Zeugung. 2011. 86p. pap. 12.80 ***(978-1-257-06551-6(3))*** Lulu Enterprises Inc.

Simkin, Penny. Pregnancy, Childbirth, & the Newborn: The Complete Guide. 4th ed. 2010. (Illus.). 544p. *(978-0-88166-531-4(2))* Meadowbrook Pr.

Simkin, Penny, et al. Pregnancy,Childbirth, & the Newborn. McGinnis, Megan & Ester, Alicia, eds. 4th rev. exp. ed. 2010. (ENG., Illus.). 512p. pap. 16.00 *(978-1-4391-7511-8(X))* Meadowbrook Pr.

—The Simple Guide to Having a Baby-Spanish Edition (Guia Sencilla para Tender un Bebe: What You Need to Know. McGinnis, Megan & Ester, Alicia, eds. 2010. (ENG & SPA.). 288p. pap. 12.00 *(978-1-4516-0065-0(8))* Meadowbrook Pr.

Smith, Linda J. & Kroeger, Mary. Impact of Birthing Practices on Breastfeeding: Protecting the Mother & Baby Continuum. 2nd rev. ed. 2009. (Illus.). 248p. pap. 61.95 *(978-0-7637-6374-9(8))* Jones & Bartlett Learning, LLC.

Smysniuk, Fredrick. Holy Crap, I'm a Dad! 2008. 64p. pap. 16.00 *(978-1-4251-6545-1(1))* Trafford Publishing.

Spencer, Nancy. Heaven in My Hands: A Midwife's Stories of Birth & Life. 2010. pap. 12.99 *(978-1-61663-298-4(4))* Tate Publishing & Enterprises, LLC.

Stewart, Deborah D. Mi Bebe y Yo: Una Guia Esencial para el Embarazo y el Cuidado de Tu Recien Nacido. 4th ed. 2008. (SPA., Illus.). 248p. pap. 12.95 *(978-1-933503-11-0(4))* Bull Publishing Co.

Stone, Joanne & Eddleman, Keith, eds. The Pregnancy Bible: Your Complete Guide to Pregnancy & Early Parenthood. 2nd rev. ed. 2008. (ENG., Illus.). 392p. pap. 29.95 *(978-1-55407-380-1(4)*, 9781554073801) Firefly Bks., Ltd.

Stone, Joanne, et al. Pregnancy for Canadians for Dummies. 2007. (ENG., Illus.). 416p. pap. 29.99 *(978-0-470-83945-4(7)*, For Dummies) Wiley, John & Sons, Inc.

—Pregnancy for Dummies. 3rd ed. 2009. (ENG.). 408p. pap. 19.99 *(978-0-470-38767-2(X)*, For Dummies) Wiley, John & Sons, Inc.

Stoppard, Miriam. Trusted Advice Preparing for Childbirth. 2012. (ENG.). 96p. 9.95 *(978-0-7566-8973-5(2))* Dorling Kindersley Publishing, Inc.

Strasser, Teresa. Exploiting My Baby: Because It's Exploiting Me. 2011. (ENG.). 304p. (gr. 12). 15.00 *(978-0-451-23207-6(0)*, N A L Trade) Penguin Group (USA) Inc.

Stratton, M. L. The Little Book of Boys. 2011. (ENG.). 128p. 10.95 ***(978-1-4405-2895-8(0))*** Adams Media Corp.

—The Little Book of Girls. 2011. (ENG.). 128p. 10.95 ***(978-1-4405-2896-5(9))*** Adams Media Corp.

Sullivan, Karen. Pregnancy & Birth: The Essential Checklists. 2009. (ENG.). 192p. 12.95 *(978-0-7566-5583-9(8))* Dorling Kindersley Publishing, Inc.

Sutton, Amy, ed. Pregnancy & Birth Sourcebook. 3rd rev. ed. 2009. (Health Reference Ser.). xx, 677p. lib. bdg. 93.00 *(978-0-7808-1074-7(0))* Omnigraphics, Inc.

Thomson, Gill, et al, eds. Qualitative Research in Midwifery & Childbirth: Phenomenological Approaches. 2011. (ENG., Illus.). 264p. (C). 145.00 *(978-0-415-57501-0(X))* Routledge.

Trevathan, Wenda R. Human Birth: An Evolutionary Perspective. 2011. (Illus.). 286p. pap. 29.95 ***(978-1-4128-1502-4(9))*** Transaction Pubs.

van Rooij, Riet. Pregnant with Heart & Soul: With Exercises & Visualizations on CD. 2009. (ENG., Illus.). 1p. 16.90 *(978-90-78302-24-7(0))* Binkey Kok NLD. Dist: Red Wheel/Weiser.

Van-Zeller, Teresa L. Birthing as Nature Intended (B. A. N. I.) A Guide to Achieving the Birth You Envision. 2010. 168p. 27.95 *(978-1-4269-4278-5(8))*; pap. 17.95 *(978-1-4269-4260-0(5))* Trafford Publishing.

Vaughan, J. L. The Pregnancy Mask. 2009. 88p. pap. 14.95 *(978-1-61546-141-7(8))* PublishAmerica, Inc.

Verrilli. Take Care in the Childbearing Years. Date not set. pap. 8.95 *(978-0-312-25427-8(X))* St. Martin's Pr.

—Take Care in the Middle & Beyond. Date not set. pap. 8.95 *(978-0-312-24331-9(6))* St. Martin's Pr.

Vetter, Blake. Dreams. 2008. 20p. pap. 9.95 *(978-1-4327-2213-5(1))* Outskirts Pr., Inc.

Wagner, Marsden. Born in the USA: How a Broken Maternity System Must Be Fixed to Put Women & Infants First. 2008. (Illus.). 295p. pap. 24.95 *(978-0-520-25633-0(6))* Univ. of California Pr.

Walsh, Denis. Evidence-Based Care for Normal Labour & Birth. 2nd rev. ed. (ENG., Illus.). 224p. 2012. 135.00 ***(978-0-415-57731-1(4))*** 2011. pap. 44.95 *(978-0-415-57732-8(2))* Routledge.

—Evidence-Based Care for Normal Labour & Birth: A Guide for Midwives. 2007. (ENG., Illus.). 200p. 150.00 ***(978-0-415-41890-4(9))*** Routledge.

Warren, Richard & Arulkumaran, Sabaratnam, eds. Best Practice in Labour & Delivery. 2009. (ENG., Illus.). 374p. pap. 105.00 *(978-0-521-72068-7(0))* Cambridge Univ. Pr.

Wesson, Nicky. Home Birth. 4th ed. 2006. (ENG., Illus.). 256p. (Orig.). per., instr.'s gde. ed. 17.95 *(978-1-905177-06-6(2))* Pinter & Martin Ltd. GBR. Dist: National Bk. Network.

West, Jennifer L. & Romaine, Deborah S. The Complete Idiot's Guide to Natural Childbirth. 2009. (Complete Idiot's Guide Ser.). (ENG.). 336p. (gr. 12-18). 16.95 *(978-1-59257-937-2(X)*, Alpha Bks.) Penguin Group (USA) Inc.

West, Zita. Acupuncture in Pregnancy & Childbirth. Isaacs, Lyndsey, ed. 2nd ed. 2008. (ENG., Illus.). 272p. 89.95 *(978-0-443-10371-1(2)*, Churchill Livingstone) Elsevier - Health Sciences Div.

Whalley, Janet. The Simple Guide to Having a Baby: What You Need to Know. 2011. (Illus.). 208p. ***(978-0-88166-574-1(6))*** Meadowbrook Pr.

Wharton, Wiz. How to Have a Baby on EBay: Your One-Stop Shopping Guide to Pregnancy, Birth & Beyond. 2007. (ENG., Illus.). 356p. per. 18.00 *(978-1-905641-16-1(8))* Harriman Hse. Publishing GBR. Dist: Ingram Pub. Services.

Wheatley Philip, Monét & Lareesa M. Ferdinand, Preface by. Fifteen Steps to the Best Childbirth Experience of Your Life. 2007. 56p. pap. 15.95 *(978-1-4303-2458-4(9))* Lulu Enterprises Inc.

Williams, Zoe. Bring It On, Baby: How to Have a Dudelike Pregnancy. 2010. (ENG.). 216p. pap. 18.99 *(978-0-85265-205-3(4))* Random Hse. GBR. Dist: Independent Pubs. Group.

Willis, Melisse. The Basket Case Files. 2010. (Illus.). 240p. pap. *(978-1-55452-552-2(7)*, Epic Pr.) Essence Publishing.

Willis, Melisse, concept. The Basket Case Files. 2010. (Illus.). 240p. 19.95 *(978-1-55452-553-9(5))* Epic Pr.

Willis, Renae. 101 Most Important Things You Need to Know Before You Have a Baby: Life Lessons You're Going to Learn Sooner or Later... 2009. (ENG., Illus.). 112p. pap. 9.99 *(978-1-4165-5012-9(7)*, Howard Bks.) Howard Books.

Wolf, Jacqueline H. Deliver Me from Pain: Anesthesia & Birth in America. 2012. (ENG., Illus.). 296p. (gr. 17). pap. 30.00 ***(978-1-4214-0572-8(5))*** Johns Hopkins Univ. Pr.

Wolf, Jacqueline H. & Wolf, J. H. Deliver Me from Pain: Anesthesia & Birth in America. 2009. (ENG., Illus.). 296p. (gr. 17). 52.00 *(978-0-8018-9110-6(3))* Johns Hopkins Univ. Pr.

Wolk, Claudine. It Gets Easier! ... & Other Lies We Tell New Mothers: A Fun, Practical Guide to Becoming a Mom, 1 vol. 2009. (ENG.). 192p. pap. 14.00 *(978-0-8144-1502-3(4))* Amacom.

World Health Organization: Department of Making Pregnancy Safer. Midwifery education Modules: Education for safe Motherhood. 2007. 5p. cd-rom 60.00 *(978-92-4-154706-2(5))* World Health Organization.

Wu, Yi-Li. Reproducing Women: Medicine, Metaphor, & Childbirth in Late Imperial China. 2010. (ENG., Illus.). 378p. 49.95 *(978-0-520-26068-9(6))* Univ. of California Pr.

Wylie, Linda & Bryce, Helen. The Midwives' Guide to Key Medical Conditions: Pregnancy & Childbirth. 2008. (ENG., Illus.). 188p. pap. 42.95 *(978-0-443-10387-2(9)*, Churchill Livingstone) Elsevier - Health Sciences Div.

Zimmerman, Rachel & Lowe, Ananda. The Doula Guide to Birth: Secrets Every Pregnant Woman Should Know. 2009. (ENG.). 304p. pap. 17.00 *(978-0-553-38526-7(7))* Random House Publishing Group.

CHILDBIRTH—JUVENILE LITERATURE

Bhandari, D. Journey to Remember. 2010. 36p. 18.99 *(978-1-4520-1212-4(1))* AuthorHouse.

CHILDBIRTH—PSYCHOLOGICAL ASPECTS

Bardacke, Nancy. Mindful Birthing: Training the Mind, Body, & Heart for Childbirth & Beyond. 2012. (ENG.). 384p. pap. 19.99 ***(978-0-06-196395-7(X)***, HarperOne) HarperCollins Pubs.

Figes, Kate. Life after Birth. 2009. (ENG.). 320p. pap. 17.95 *(978-1-84408-466-1(3)*, Virago Press) Little, Brown Bk. Group Ltd. GBR. Dist: Independent Pubs. Group.

Hamilton, Loralyn. Pixie Dust: Magical Insights for Childbirth & Life with Little One. 2010. pap. 11.99 *(978-1-61566-267-8(7))* Tate Publishing & Enterprises, LLC.

Hayton, A. M., ed. A Silent Cry: Wombtwin Survivors Tell Their Stories. 2008. 236p. pap. *(978-0-9557808-0-6(2))* Wren Pubns.

Kitzinger, Sheila. Birth Crisis. 2006. (Illus.). (ENG.). 160p. 150.00 *(978-0-415-37265-7(8))*; 191p. per. 33.95 *(978-0-415-37266-4(6))* Routledge.

Kleiman, Karen & Wenzel, Amy. Dropping the Baby & Other Scary Thoughts: Breaking the Cycle of Unwanted Thoughts in Motherhood. 2010. (ENG., Illus.). 268p. 26.95 *(978-0-415-87700-8(8))* Routledge.

Raynor, Maureen D. & England, Carole. Psychology for Midwives. 2010. (ENG., Illus.). 208p. (C). pap. 49.00 *(978-0-335-23433-2(X)*, 033523433X) McGraw-Hill Education GBR. Dist: McGraw-Hill Cos., The.

Riecher-Rössler, Anita & Steiner, Meir. Perinatal Stress, Mood & Anxiety Disorders: From Bench to Bedside, Vol. 173. (Bibliotheca Psychiatrica Ser.: No. 173). (Illus.). *(978-3-8055-7865-3(2))* Karger, S. AG.

Soliday, Elizabeth. Childbirth in a Technocratic Age: The Documentation of Women's Expectations & Experiences. 2012. ***(978-1-60497-798-1(1))*** Cambria Pr.

Wenzel, Amy. Anxiety in Childbearing Women: Diagnosis & Treatment. 2010 (Illus.). viii, 273p. E-Book *(978-1-4338-0901-9(X))*; 264p. 59.95 *(978-1-4338-0900-2(1))* American Psychological Assn.

Wheeldon, Shirley. Pocket Size Handbook for Dads Who Don't Have a Clue! 2008. 48p. pap. 8.95 *(978-0-595-50999-7(1))* iUniverse, Inc.

CHILDBIRTH—RELIGIOUS ASPECTS

see also Virgin Birth

Baumgarten, Elisheva. Mothers & Children: Jewish Family Life in Medieval Europe. 2007. (Jews, Christians, & Muslims from the Ancient to the Modern World Ser.). (ENG., Illus.). 296p. (C). per. 28.95 *(978-0-691-13029-3(9))* Princeton Univ. Pr.

Bergmann, Claudia D. Childbirth As a Metaphor for Crisis: Evidence from the Ancient near East, the Hebrew Bible, & 1QH XI, 1-18. 2008. (Beihefte zur Zeitschrift für die alttestamentliche Wissenschaft Ser.). (ENG.). X, 267p. 119.00 *(978-3-11-020042-3(2))* De Gruyter, Walter Inc.

Bergmann, Claudia D. Childbirth as a Metaphor for Crisis: Evidence from the Ancient near East, the Hebrew Bible, & 1QH XI, 1-18. 2008. (Beihefte zur Zeitschrift far die alttestamentliche Wissenschaft Ser.). (ENG.). X, 267p. 182.00 ***(978-3-11-173517-7(6))*** De Gruyter, Walter Inc.

Brown, Juanita. Mommies Pajamas: An Inspirational Story of How God Heals from Within. 2010. 112p. (ENG.). 27.49 *(978-1-4490-8110-2(X))*; pap. 16.49 *(978-1-4490-8108-9(8))* AuthorHouse.

Connole, Marika. Childbirth: Preparing for the Miracle. 2009. 121p. pap. 11.96 *(978-1-4357-2427-3(5))* Lulu Enterprises Inc.

Daub, Cathy. Birthing in the Spirit. 2007. 380p. per. *(978-0-9724616-2-7(0))* Livingstone Corp.

England, Pam. The Labyrinth of Birth: Creating a Map, Meditations & Rituals for Your Childbearing Year. 2010. 140p. pap. 13.95 *(978-1-61623-037-1(1))* Birthing From Within.

Hannon, Ruth & Hoagland, Victor, eds. Catholic Baby's First Bible-Nab. 2008. (Illus.). 93p. 10.95 *(978-0-88271-147-8(4))* Regina Pr., Malhame & Co.

Henson, Belinda C. The Veil of Flesh. 2008. 128p. pap. 11.95 *(978-1-4327-2313-2(8))* Outskirts Pr., Inc.

Mitchell, Shirley. From Conception to Birth of a Vision. 2007. 200p. per. 14.99 *(978-1-60034-540-1(9))* Xulon Pr., Inc.

Nadav, Pamela. L' Mazeltov. 2008. (Illus.). 280p. pap. 18.00 *(978-0-9778661-0-6(6))* L'Mazeltov, Inc.

Owoputi, Morolayo Anne. The Blessing of Sarah. 2009. 176p. pap. 11.99 *(978-1-4389-1804-4(6))* AuthorHouse.

Russell, Janet. Benjamin! 2008. 152p. pap. 14.99 *(978-1-60647-576-8(2))* Xulon Pr., Inc.

Smith Ph. D, Rosalynn M. A Prayer for Baby: A 40-Week Pregnancy Daily Devotional. 2011. 204p. 33.95 ***(978-1-4627-0602-0(9))*** Cross Bks. Publishing.

Stockton, Adela. Birth Space, Safe Place: Emotional Well-Being Through Pregnancy & Birth. 2009. (ENG.). 112p. pap. 14.95 *(978-1-84409-165-2(1))* Findhorn Pr. GBR. Dist: Independent Pubs. Group.

Stubbs, David. Our Birth on Earth. 2009. 100p. pap. 14.99 *(978-1-4251-8588-6(6))* Trafford Publishing.

Tarpley, R. Michael. Be Fruitful & Multiply: Spiritual Pregnancy. 2009. 156p. 22.99 *(978-1-4490-5205-8(3))*; pap. 12.99 *(978-1-4490-5204-1(5))* AuthorHouse.

Vanderlaan, Jennifer. The Christian Childbirth Handbook. 2008. (Illus.). 428p. pap. 19.95 *(978-0-9765541-2-7(7))* Birthing Naturally.

Verret, Kristie. Unforgotten Children: A Testimony of God's Healing through Miscarriage. 2009. pap. 10.99 *(978-1-60799-937-9(4))* Tate Publishing & Enterprises, LLC.

CHILDBIRTH—STATISTICS

New Strategist Editors. American Sexual Behavior: Demographics of Sexual Activity, Fertility, & Childbearing. 2006. 424p. 89.95 *(978-1-933588-09-4(8))* New Strategist Pubns., Inc.

CHILDBIRTH, NATURAL

see Natural Childbirth

CHILDBIRTH AT HOME

Cheyney, Melissa. Born at Home: The Biological, Cultural & Political Dimensions of Maternity Care in the United States. 2010. (ENG.). 160p. (C). pap. 37.95 *(978-0-495-79366-3(3))* Wadsworth.

Craven, Christa. Pushing for Midwives: Homebirth Mothers & the Reproductive Rights Movement. 2010. (ENG.). 232p. 81.50 *(978-1-4399-0219-6(4))* Temple Univ. Pr.

—Pushing for Midwives: Reproductive Rights in a Consumer Era. 2010. (ENG.). 208p. pap. 26.95 *(978-1-4399-0220-2(8))* Temple Univ. Pr.

Nolan, Mary. Home Birth. 2010. (ENG., Illus.). 160p. 120.00 *(978-0-415-55754-2(2))*; pap. 37.95 *(978-0-415-55755-9(0))* Routledge.

Punger Faafp Ibclc, Denise. Permission to Mother: Going Beyond the Standard-of-Care to Nurture our Children. 2008. 272p. per. 29.95 *(978-1-4327-0385-1(4))* Outskirts Pr., Inc.

Sheldon, Robyn. The Mama Bamba Way: Discover the Power & Pleasure of Childbirth. 2010. (ENG., Illus.). 272p. pap. 19.95 *(978-1-84409-185-0(9))* Findhorn Pr. GBR. Dist: Independent Pubs. Group.

Spatafora, Denise & Spatafora. Better Birth: The Ultimate Guide to Childbirth from Home Births to Hospitals. 2009. (ENG., Illus.). 288p. pap. 15.95 *(978-0-470-25561-2(7)*, Wiley) Wiley, John & Sons, Inc.

Steen, Mary, ed. Supporting Women to Give Birth at Home. 2011. (ENG., Illus.). 288p. 135.00 *(978-0-415-56029-0(2))*; pap. 42.95 *(978-0-415-56030-6(6))* Routledge.

Worth, Jennifer. The Midwife: A Memoir of Birth, Joy, & Hard Times. 2009. (ENG.). 352p. (gr. 12-18). 15.00 *(978-0-14-311623-3(1)*, Penguin (Non-Classics)) Penguin Group (USA) Inc.

CHILDBIRTH IN LITERATURE

Crawford, Julie. Marvelous Protestantism: Monstrous Births in Post-Reformation England. 2011. (ENG., Illus.). 282p. (gr. 17). pap. 35.00 ***(978-1-4214-0586-5(5))*** Johns Hopkins Univ. Pr.

Dodson, Sandra & Haden, Rosamund, eds. Just Keep Breathing: South African Birth Stories. 2009. (ENG.). 224p. pap. 22.00 *(978-1-77009-576-2(4))* Jacana Media ZAF. Dist: Independent Pubs. Group.

Kipp, Julie. Romanticism, Maternity, & the Body Politic. 2007. (Cambridge Studies in Romanticism Ser.). (ENG.). 260p. pap. 50.00 *(978-0-521-03626-9(7))* Cambridge Univ. Pr.

Laoutaris, Chris. Shakespearean Maternities: Crises of Conception in Early Modern England. 2008. (ENG., Illus.). 256p. (gr. 17). 125.00 *(978-0-7486-2436-2(8))* Edinburgh Univ. Pr. GBR. Dist: Columbia Univ. Pr.

Lock, Charles, ed. Cultures of Childhood: Literary & Historical Studies in Memory of Julia Briggs (Angles on the English-Speaking World, Vol. 8) 2008. 132p. pap. 23.00 *(978-87-635-2522-0(4))* Museum Tusculanum Pr. DNK. Dist: Chicago Distribution Ctr.

Mossman, Carol A. Politics & Narratives of Birth: Gynocolonization from Rousseau to Zola. 2006. (Cambridge Studies in French Ser.). (ENG.). 272p. pap. 53.00 *(978-0-521-03098-4(6))* Cambridge Univ. Pr.

Praetorius, Johannes & Scholz Williams, Gerhild. Mothering Baby: On Being a Woman in Early Modern Germany: Johannes Praetorius's Apocalypsis Mysteriorum Cybeles, das Ist eine Schnakische Wochen- Comedie (1662) 2010. *(978-0-86698-419-5(4))* ACMRS.

Read, Kirk D. Birthing Bodies in Early Modern France: Stories of Gender & Reproduction. 2011. (Women & Gender in the Early Modern World Ser.). (Illus.). 220p. 99.95 *(978-0-7546-6632-5(8))* Ashgate Publishing Co.

CHILDBIRTH IN MIDDLE AGE

see also Pregnancy in Middle Age

Carolan, Mary. Doing It Properly. 2010. 296p. pap. *(978-3-8383-7599-1(8))* Lambert Academic Publishing.

Paulson, Richard J. & Sachs, Judith. Rewinding Your Biological Clock: Motherhood Late in Life. 2011. 356p. pap. 22.95 ***(978-1-4502-9599-4(1))*** iUniverse, Inc.

Sweet, Corinne. Birth Begins at Forty. x, 193p. pap. 13.95 *(978-0-340-75696-6(9)*, Hodder & Stoughton) Hodder General Publishing Div. GBR. Dist: Trafalgar Square Publishing.

CHILDHOOD

see Children

CHILDLESSNESS

see also Infertility

Brooks Hansen. The Brotherhood of Joseph: A Father's Memoir of Infertility & Adoption in the 21st Century. 2008. 17.50 *(978-1-60529-923-5(5)*, Modern Times) Rodale Pr., Inc.

Gallup, Caroline. Making Babies the Hard Way: Living with Infertility & Treatment. 2007. (ENG., Illus.). 224p. per. *(978-1-84310-463-6(6))* Kingsley, Jessica Ltd.

Grubb, Bobbi. Masterpiece of Joy: From the Despair of Infertility to the Joy of Adoption. 2007. 256p. per. 14.95 *(978-1-4327-1614-1(X))* Outskirts Pr., Inc.

Hansen, Brooks. The Brotherhood of Joseph: A Father's Memoir of Infertility & Adoption in the 21st Century. 2008. (ENG.). 288p. 24.95 *(978-1-59486-827-6(1)*, Modern Times) Rodale Pr., Inc.

Jaffe, Janet & Diamond, Martha Ourieff. Reproductive Trauma: Psychotherapy with Infertility & Pregnancy Loss Clients. 2010. ix, 275p. 59.95 *(978-1-4338-0841-8(2))* American Psychological Assn.

Leibovich, Lori. Maybe Baby: 28 Writers Tell the Truth about Skepticism, Infertility, Baby Lust, Childlessness, Ambivalence, & How They Made the Biggest Decision of Their Lives. 2007. (ENG.). 304p. pap. 13.95 *(978-0-06-073732-5(4)*, HarperPerennial) HarperCollins Pubs.

Lievore, Denise. What If We're the Special Ones? 2010. 260p. pap. *(978-3-8383-4770-7(6))* Lambert Academic Publishing.

Maier, Corinne. No Kids: 40 Good Reasons Not to Have Children. 2009. (ENG.). 136p. pap. 12.95 *(978-0-7710-5477-8(7))* McClelland & Stewart CAN. Dist: Random Hse., Inc.

Moulet, Christine. Neither 'Less' Nor 'Free' 2010. 304p. pap. *(978-3-8383-3906-1(1))* Lambert Academic Publishing.

Scott, Laura S. Two is Enough: A Couple's Guide to Living Childless by Choice. 2009. (ENG.). 254p. pap. 16.95 *(978-1-58005-263-4(0))* Seal Pr.

Sedaka, Marc. What He Can Expect When She's Not Expecting: How to Support Your Wife, Save Your Marriage, & Conquer Infertility! 2011. (ENG.). 208p. pap. 12.95 *(978-1-61608-058-7(2)*, 608058) Skyhorse Publishing Co., Inc.

Van Luven, Lynne. Nobody's Mother: Life Without Kids, 1 vol. 2010. (ENG.). 240p. per. *(978-1-894898-40-9(0))* TouchWood Editions.

Van Luven, Lynne & Gillespie, Bruce. Nobody's Father: Life Without Kids, 1 vol. rev. ed. 2009. (ENG.). 256p. pap. *(978-1-894898-74-4(5))* TouchWood Editions.

Walker, Ellen. Content Without Kids: An Insider's Guide to Childfree Living by Choice or by Chance. 2011. 168p. pap. 14.95 *(978-1-60832-073-8(1))* Greenleaf Book Group.

Weston Woods Staff, creator. The Rainbabies. 2011. 18.95 ***(978-0-439-72945-1(9))***; 38.75 ***(978-0-439-72947-5(5))*** Weston Woods Studios, Inc.

Wyatt, Randall C. & Seid, Erika L. Couples & Infertility (Instructor's Version) 2007. 149.00 *(978-1-60124-055-2(4))* Psychotherapy.net.

CHILDREN

Here are entered works on people from birth through twelve years of age.

C

see also Abused Children; Adopted Children; Adult Children; Bilingualism in Children; Birth Order; Boys; Child Development; Children—Asia; Church Work with Children; City Children; Comic Books and Children; Computers and Children; Dance for Children; Etiquette for Children and Teenagers; Exceptional Children; Foster Children; Girls; Homeless Children; Indian Children; Infants; Jewish Children; Missing Children; Motion Pictures and Children; Orphans; Poor Children; Prenatal Influences; Preschool Children; Problem Children; School Children; Social Work with Children; Stepchildren; Television and Children; Toddlers; Vagrant Children; Video Recordings for Children

also subdivision Children under individual wars, e.g. World War, 1939-1945—Children; and headings beginning with the word Child

Adler-Tapia, Robbie & Settle, Carolyn. EMDR & the Art of Psychotherapy with Children. 2008. (Illus.). 360p. 55.00 *(978-0-8261-1117-3(3))* Springer Publishing Co., Inc.

Ai, Jiabing. Guan Er Dai. 2011. (CHI., Illus.). 316p. ***(978-1-935981-23-7(4))*** Mirror Bks. USA.

Allen, Jen, et al. Helping Your Pupils to Be Resilient. 2007. (Illus.). VI, 66p. 21.95 *(978-0-415-44728-7(3))* Fulton, David Pubs. GBR. Dist: Taylor & Francis Group.

Andresen, Sabine, et al, eds. Children & the Good Life: New Challenges for Research on Children. 2010. (Childrenâ€(tm)s Well-Being: Indicators & Research Ser.). (Illus.). viii, 205p. 159.00 *(978-90-481-9218-2(8),* 9048192188) Springer.

Bailey, Judith A. & Cottom, Robert I. Programs & Interventions for Maltreated Children & Families at Risk. Rubin, Allen, ed. 2011. (Clinician's Guide to Evidence-Based Practice Ser.: 5). (ENG.). 354p. pap. 55.00 *(978-0-470-89063-9(0),* Wiley) Wiley, John & Sons, Inc.

Bass, Loretta E. & Kinney, David A., eds. The Well-Being, Peer Cultures & Rights of Children. 2011. (Sociological Studies of Children & Youth Ser.). (Illus.). 352p. *(978-1-78052-074-2(3))* Emerald Group Publishing Ltd.

Beidel, Deborah C. & Alfano, Candice. Child Anxiety Disorders: Research & Treatment. 2nd rev. ed. 2011. (ENG., Illus.). 544p. instr.'s gde. ed. 52.95 *(978-0-415-87373-4(8))* Routledge.

Berryman, Jerome W. Children & the Theologians: Clearing the Way for Grace. 2009. 288p. 35.00 *(978-0-8192-2347-0(6),* Morehouse Publishing) Church Publishing, Inc.

Blerk, Lorraine van & Kesby, Mike, eds. Doing Children's Geographies: Methodological Issues in Research with Young People. 2009. (ENG., Illus.). 240p. (C). 140.00 *(978-0-415-44820-8(4))* Routledge.

Brennan, Patrick McKinely. The Vocation of the Child. 2008. 432p. (C). pap. 36.00 *(978-0-8028-6240-2(3))* Eerdmans, William B. Publishing Co.

Bucholtz, Mary. White Kids: Language, Race & Styles of Youth Identity. 2010. (ENG., Illus.). 296p. 99.00 *(978-0-521-87149-5(2));* pap. 33.99 *(978-0-521-69204-5(0))* Cambridge Univ. Pr.

Bunge, Marcia J., ed. Children, Adults, & Shared Responsibilities: Jewish, Christian & Muslim Perspectives. 2012. (ENG.). 320p. 95.00 ***(978-1-107-01114-4(0))*** Cambridge Univ. Pr.

Cahill. Children & Society: Sociology Childre. 2006. 372p. pap. *(978-1-933220-40-6(6))* Roxbury Publishing Co.

Canada, Geoffrey & Nicholas, Jamar. Fist Stick Knife Gun: A Personal History of Violence. 2010. (ENG.). 192p. pap. 14.00 *(978-0-8070-4461-2(X))* Beacon Pr.

Caplan, Bryan. Selfish Reasons to Have More Kids: Why Being a Great Parent Is Less Work & More Fun Than You Think. (ENG.). 240p. (gr. 9). 2012. pap. 15.99 ***(978-0-465-02861-0(6))*** 2011. 24.99 *(978-0-465-01867-3(X))* Basic Bks.

Carter, Laura V. Child Nutrition Research Advances. 2007. 225.00 *(978-1-60021-849-1(0))* Nova Science Pubs., Inc.

Cassidy, Claire. Thinking Children: The Concept of 'Child' from a Philosophical Perspective. 2008. (ENG.). 208p. 140.00 *(978-0-8264-9818-2(3))* Continuum International Publishing Group, Ltd. GBR. Dist: National Bk. Network.

Chau, Tom & Fairley, Jillian, eds. Pediatric Rehabilitation Engineering: From Disability to Possibility. 2010. (CRC Press Series in Rehabilitation Science in Practice Ser.). (ENG., Illus.). 366p. 145.95 *(978-1-4398-0842-9(2),* CRC Press) Taylor & Francis Group GBR. Dist: Taylor & Francis Group.

Chigier, E., ed. Looking up at down Syndrome. *(978-965-294-084-1(4))* Freund Publishing Hse., Ltd.

Children. (DUT.). 5.00 *(978-1-4031-3084-6(1));* (POR.). 5.00 *(978-1-4031-3065-5(5));* (SPA.). 5.00 *(978-0-88404-963-0(9))* Bridge Pubns., Inc.

Cook, Joan Littlefield & Cook, Greg. The World of Children. 2nd ed. 2009. (ENG.). 656p. (C). 154.40 *(978-0-205-68592-9(7),* Prentice Hall) Prentice Hall PTR.

—World of Children. 2nd ed. 2010. (ENG.). 656p. (C). 109.33 *(978-0-205-80589-1(2),* Prentice Hall) Prentice Hall PTR.

Corsaro, William A. The Sociology of Childhood. 3rd ed. 2010. (Sociology for a New Century Ser.). (Illus.). 456p. (C). pap. 40.00 *(978-1-4129-7943-6(9),* B79436P) SAGE Pubns., Inc.

Cram101 Textbook Reviews Staff. Outlines & Highlights for the World of Children by Cook, Isbn: 0205447430. 2008. 224p. pap. 13.95 *(978-1-4288-6281-4(1))* Cram101 Inc.

Delgado, Anthony. Children of Thunder. 2006. 69p. per. 8.99 *(978-1-59886-453-3(X))* Tate Publishing & Enterprises, LLC.

DuRocher, Kristina. Raising Racists: The Socialization of White Children in the Jim Crow South. 2011. (New Directions in Southern History Ser.). (ENG., Illus.). 248p. 40.00 *(978-0-8131-3001-9(8))* Univ. Pr. of Kentucky.

Dwyer, James G. Moral Status & Human Life: The Case for Children's Superiority. 2010. (ENG.). 220p. 90.00 *(978-0-521-76691-3(5))* Cambridge Univ. Pr.

Erwitt, Elliott. Kids. 2012. (ENG., Illus.). 128p. 29.95 ***(978-1-59372-049-0(1),*** 372049) Quantuck Lane Pr. & The Mill Road Collaborative, The.

Ettlin, Tony. Blätterteig und Völkerball: Eine Kindheit Im Schatten des Stanserhorns. 2007. (GER., Illus.). 252p. *(978-3-85791-532-1(3))* Limmat Verlag.

Exley, Peter & Exley, Sharon. Design for Kids. 2007. (ENG., Illus.). 224p. 60.00 *(978-1-86470-180-7(3))* Images Publishing Group AUS. Dist: National Bk. Network.

Feigin, Ralph D., et al. Feigin & Cherry's Textbook of Pediatric Infectious Diseases: Expert Consult - Online & Print, 2-Volume Set, 2 vols., Set. Cherry, James et al, eds. 6th ed. 2009. (ENG., Illus.). 3856p. 455.00 *(978-1-4160-4044-6(7),* Saunders) Elsevier - Health Sciences Div.

Five Year Olds. Date not set. 96p. 7.98 *(978-0-7525-8711-0(0))* Parragon, Inc.

Frances, Dee. Kids Chores: What Chores? What Age? Date not set. pap. 3.00 *(978-1-885519-61-0(3))* DDDD Pubns.

Frost, Nick. Rethinking Children & Families: The Relationship Between the Child, the Family & the State. 2011. (New Childhoods Ser.). (ENG., Illus.). 144p. 120.00 *(978-1-4411-6292-2(5))* Continuum International Publishing Group, Ltd. GBR. Dist: National Bk. Network.

Gardner, Hilary & Forrester, Michael, eds. Analysing Interactions in Childhood: Insights from Conversation Analysis. 2010. (ENG., Illus.). 294p. pap. 67.99 *(978-0-470-76034-5(6),* Wiley) Wiley, John & Sons, Inc.

Gershman, George & Thomson, Mike. Practical Pediatric Gastrointestinal Endoscopy. 2nd ed. 2012. (ENG., Illus.). 254p. 124.95 ***(978-1-4443-3649-8(5),*** Wiley-Blackwell) Wiley, John & Sons, Inc.

Gilman, Charlotte Perkins. Families, Marriages, & Children. Hill, Michael, ed. 2011. (ENG.). 136p. 39.95 *(978-1-4128-1485-0(5))* Transaction Pubs.

Gingko Press, creator. Play! Indoor & Outdoor. 2011. (ENG., Illus.). 313p. 49.95 ***(978-1-58423-436-4(9))*** Gingko Pr., Inc.

Godinho, Sally & Wilson, Jeni. Helping Your Pupils to Ask Questions. 2008. (Little books of life Skills Ser.). (ENG., Illus.). 72p. per. 21.95 *(978-0-415-44727-0(5))* Fulton, David Pubs. GBR. Dist: Taylor & Francis Group.

Greig, Anne D., et al. Doing Research with Children. 2nd ed. 2007. (Illus.). 216p. (C). per. 53.00 *(978-1-4129-1845-9(6),* B18448P) SAGE Pubns., Ltd. GBR. Dist: SAGE Pubns., Inc.

Gruenberg, Sidonie Matzner. Your Child: Today & Tomorrow. 2008. 172p. 22.99 *(978-0-554-32445-6(8))* 2008. 172p. 25.99 *(978-0-554-23142-6(5))* 2007. (ENG.). 154p. pap. 19.99 *(978-1-4264-3793-9(5))* 2007. (ENG.). 304p. pap. 24.99 *(978-1-4264-3863-9(X))* BiblioBazaar.

—Your Child: Today & Tomorrow. 2008. 144p. pap. *(978-1-4099-4723-3(8))* Dodo Pr.

—Your Child: Today & Tomorrow. 2007. 112p. per. *(978-1-4068-6264-5(9))* Echo Library.

Guindani, Stefano. Haiti: Through the Eye of Stefano Guindani. 2010. (ENG.). 164p. 75.00 *(978-88-370-7453-1(0),* Mondadori Electa (Acc)) Antique Collectors' Club GBR. Dist: National Bk. Network.

Handal, Gilbert, et al. Pediatric Imaging: Rapid-Fire Questions & Answers. Quattromani, Frank, ed. 2007. (ENG.). 468p. pap. 49.99 *(978-1-58890-658-8(2))* Thieme Medical Pubs., Inc.

Handel, Gerald, et al. Children & Society: The Sociology of Children & Childhood Socialization. 2006. (ENG., Illus.). 372p. (C). per. 54.95 *(978-0-19-533078-6(1))* Oxford Univ. Pr., Inc.

Harris, Paul L. Trusting What You're Told: How Children Learn from Others. 2012. (ENG., Illus.). 272p. 26.95 ***(978-0-674-06572-7(7),*** Belknap Pr.) Harvard Univ. Pr.

Harrison, Elgloria A. Neonatal Respiratory Care Handbook. rev. ed. 2009. (Illus.). 272p. spiral bd. 37.95 *(978-0-7637-5546-1(X))* Jones & Bartlett Learning, LLC.

Haukanes, Haldis & Thelen, Tatjana, eds. Parenting after the Century of the Child: Travelling Ideals Institutional Negotiations & Individual Responses. 2010. 246p. 99.95 *(978-1-4094-0111-7(1))* Ashgate Publishing Co.

Hegde, M. N. & Pomaville, Frances. Assessment of Communication Disorders in Children: Resources & Protocols. 2008. (Illus.). 514p. pap. 97.95 *(978-1-59756-291-1(2))* Plural Publishing, Inc.

Hills, Andrew P., et al, eds. Children, Obesity & Exercise. 2007. (Routledge Studies in Physical Education & Youth Sport Ser.). (ENG., Illus.). 184p. (C). 170.00 *(978-0-415-40883-7(0))* Routledge.

—Children, Obesity & Exercise: Prevention, Treatment & Management of Childhood & Adolescent Obesity. 2007. (International Studies in Physical Education & Youth Sport Ser.). (ENG., Illus.). 184p. (C). per. 47.95 *(978-0-415-40884-4(9))* Routledge.

Hoffman, Julian I. E. & Moller, James H., eds. Pediatric Cardiovascular Medicine. 2nd ed. 2012. (ENG.). 1094p. 324.95 ***(978-1-4443-3589-7(8),*** Wiley-Blackwell) Wiley, John & Sons, Inc.

Holt, Louise, ed. Geographies of Children Youth & Families. 2011. (ENG., Illus.). 320p. (C). 130.00 *(978-0-415-56383-3(6))* Routledge.

—Geographies of Children Youth & Families. 2011. (ENG., Illus.). 320p. (C). 45.95 *(978-0-415-56384-0(4),* Routledge) Taylor & Francis Group GBR. Dist: Taylor & Francis Group.

Hosin, Amer A. Autism, ADHD, & Anorexia Nervosa: Essays on Three Childhood Disorders. (Illus.). 120p. 89.95 *(978-0-7734-5163-6(3))* Mellen, Edwin Pr., The.

Infancia y violencia en los Medios: Monitoreo de medios de Difusión. 2007. (SPA.). 64p. *(978-92-806-4159-2(X))* United Nations Children's Fund, The (UNICEF).

Jamail, Michael L. The Best Childhood Ever: (the Best Part about Growing up Is Getting to Know Yourself Better) 2008. 96p. pap. 16.95 *(978-1-60672-011-0(2))* PublishAmerica, Inc.

Jeub, Chris & Jeub, Wendy. Love Another Child: Children. They're blessings. Always. 2011. 148p. 30.95 *(978-1-4497-1065-1(4));* pap. 13.95 *(978-1-4497-1063-7(8))* Author Solutions, Inc. (WestBow Pr.).

Jones, Mark. Children as Treasures: Childhood & the Middle Class in Early Twentieth Century Japan. 2010. (Harvard East Asian Monographs: 328). 275p. 45.00 *(978-0-674-05334-2(6))* Harvard Univ., Asia Ctr.

Kampmark, Binoy. Sacred Child: The Politics of Child Abuse & Abusers in the Twenty-First Century. 2011. ix, 114p. ***(978-1-61324-155-4(0))*** Nova Science Pubs., Inc.

Kendon, Frank. The Small Years. 2010. (ENG.). 232p. pap. 22.99 *(978-0-521-15547-2(9))* Cambridge Univ. Pr.

Laoprasert, Pramote. Atlas of Pediatric EEG. 2011. (Atlas Ser.). (ENG., Illus.). 904p. 176.00 *(978-0-07-162334-6(5),* 0071623345) McGraw-Hill Professional Publishing.

Linn, Susan. The Case for Make Believe: Saving Play in a Commercialized World. 2009. (ENG.). 272p. pap. 17.95 *(978-1-59558-449-6(8),* 955449) New Pr., The.

Litman, Ronald S., ed. Pediatric Anesthesia Practice. 2007. (Cambridge Pocket Clinicians Ser.). (ENG.). 228p. per. 55.00 *(978-0-521-70937-8(7))* Cambridge Univ. Pr.

Longaretti, Lynette & English, Robyn. Helping Your Pupils to Communicate Effectively & Manage Conflict. 2007. (Little books of life Skills Ser.). (Illus.). VI, 66p. 21.95 *(978-0-415-44729-4(1))* Fulton, David Pubs. GBR. Dist: Taylor & Francis Group.

Loreman, Tim & Loreman. Respecting Childhood. 2009. (ENG., Illus.). 152p. 39.95 *(978-0-8264-3244-5(1))* Continuum International Publishing Group, Ltd. GBR. Dist: National Bk. Network.

Mac Naughton, Glenda & Hughes, Patrick. Doing Action Research in Early Childhood Studies. 2008. (ENG., Illus.). 208p. (C). pap. 45.00 *(978-0-335-22862-1(3),* 0335228623) McGraw-Hill Education GBR. Dist: McGraw-Hill Cos., The.

Macnaughton, Glenda & Hughes, Patrick. Doing Action Research in Early Childhood Studies. 2008. (Illus.). 208p. (C). 126.95 *(978-0-335-22861-4(5),* 0335228615, Open University Pr.) McGraw-Hill Education GBR. Dist: McGraw-Hill Cos., The.

Madell, Jane Reger & Flexer, Carol Ann. Pediatric Audiology: Diagnosis, Technology, & Management. 2008. 84.95 *(978-1-60406-002-7(6))* Thieme Medical Pubs., Inc.

Madell, Jane Reger & Flexer, Carol Ann, eds. Pediatric Audiology: Diagnosis, Technology, & Management. 2008. (ENG., Illus.). 352p. 89.99 *(978-1-60406-001-0(8))* Thieme Medical Pubs., Inc.

McCarthy, Dennis. "If You Turned into a Monster" Transformation Through Play: A Body-Centered Approach to Play Therapy. 2007. (ENG., Illus.). 16p. pap. *(978-1-84310-529-9(2))* Kingsley, Jessica Ltd.

McClary, LaShawn M. Can I Be Frank: About the Childhood I've Never Revealed. 2010. 162p. pap. 19.95 *(978-1-4327-6261-2(3))* Outskirts Pr., Inc.

McCracken, Elizabeth. The American Child. 2008. 247p. 24.99 *(978-0-554-88404-2(6))* 2008. 124p. 21.99 *(978-0-554-35814-7(X))* 2008. 247p. 27.99 *(978-0-554-88396-0(1))* 2008. 124p. 24.99 *(978-0-554-26511-7(7))* 2008. 247p. pap. 26.75 *(978-0-554-88398-4(8))* 2008. 253p. pap. 25.75 *(978-0-554-88402-8(X))* 2007. 108p. pap. 18.99 *(978-1-4346-1327-1(5))* 2007. (ENG.). 120p. pap. 19.99 *(978-1-4346-1329-5(1))* BiblioBazaar.

—The American Child. 2009. 118p. pap. *(978-1-4099-8009-4(X))* Dodo Pr.

—The American Child. 2010. (Illus.). 70p. pap. 20.00 *(978-1-153-69173-4(6))* 2009. 76p. pap. 20.00 *(978-1-151-42792-2(6))* General Bks. LLC.

—The American Child. 2010. 94p. pap. *(978-1-4076-0772-6(3))* HardPr.

McLeod, Alison. Listening to Children: A Practitioner's Guide. 2008. (Illus.). 224p. pap. *(978-1-84310-549-7(7))* Kingsley, Jessica Ltd.

McMahon, Linnet. Play Therapy & Therapeutic Play. 2nd rev. ed. 2009. (ENG., Illus.). 296p. (C). pap., instr.'s hndbk. ed. 36.95 *(978-0-415-43942-8(6))* Routledge.

Meeks, Robert J. Childhood Revisited. 2010. pap. 10.99 *(978-1-61663-880-1(X))* Tate Publishing & Enterprises, LLC.

Michaels, Sheila. 7 Reasons to Be Grateful You're the Mother of a Tweenager. 2007. (Mom2Mom Ser.). (Illus.). 70p. *(978-0-89221-651-2(4))* New Leaf Pr., Inc.

Miller, Scott A. Theory of Mind: Beyond the Preschool Years. 2012. (ENG.). 264p. 94.95 *(978-1-84872-927-8(8));* pap. 45.95 *(978-1-84872-928-5(6))* Taylor & Francis Group GBR. (Psychology Press). Dist: Taylor & Francis Group.

Mohr, Angie. Piggy Banks to Paychecks: Helping Kids Understand the Value of a Dollar. 2012. (ENG., Illus.). 260p. pap. 19.95 ***(978-1-55455-210-8(9))*** Fitzhenry & Whiteside, Ltd. CAN. Dist: Ingram Pub. Services.

Montgomery, Douglas C. & Montgomery, Heather. An Introduction to Childhood: Anthropological Perspectives on Children's Lives. 2008. (ENG.). 296p. 99.95 *(978-1-4051-2591-8(8),* Wiley-Blackwell) Wiley, John & Sons, Inc.

Montgomery, Heather. An Introduction to Childhood: Anthropological Perspectives on Children's Lives. 2008. (ENG.). 296p. pap. 38.95 *(978-1-4051-2590-1(X),* Wiley-Blackwell) Wiley, John & Sons, Inc.

Muris, Peter. Normal & Abnormal Fear & Anxiety in Children & Adolescents. 2007. (BRAT Series in Clinical Psychology Ser.). (ENG., Illus.). 400p. 109.00 *(978-0-08-045073-5(3),* Elsevier Science) Elsevier Science & Technology Bks.

O'Driscoll, Denis. 100 Physical Education Activities. 2009. (Illus.). 62p. pap. *(978-1-84748-612-7(6))* Athena Pr.

Opdyke, Jeff D. Piggybanking: Preparing Your Financial Life for Kids & Your Kids for a Financial Life. 2010. (ENG.). 224p. pap. 15.99 *(978-0-06-135819-7(3),* Harper Paperbacks) HarperCollins Pubs.

Parkstone Press Staff. Dogs. 2010. (Art for Kids Ser.). (ENG., Illus.). 12p. (gr. k-5). 14.95 *(978-1-84484-752-5(7))* Parkstone International GBR. Dist: Ingram Pub. Services.

Perry, Deborah F., et al, eds. Social & Emotional Health in Early Childhood: Building Bridges Between Services & Systems. 2007. (Systems of Care for Children's Mental Health Ser.: 7). (Illus.). 404p. per. 39.95 *(978-1-55766-782-3(9))* Brookes, Paul H. Publishing Co.

Quattromani, Frank, et al. Pediatric Imaging: Rapid-Fire Questions & Answers. 2007. 49.95 *(978-3-13-148021-7(1))* Thieme Medical Pubs., Inc.

Raffensperger, John G. Children's Surgery: A Worldwide History. 2012. (ENG., Illus.). 347p. pap. 55.00 ***(978-0-7864-6825-6(4))*** McFarland & Co., Inc. Pubs.

Riley, James Whitcomb. A Child-World. 2008. 104p. pap. *(978-1-4065-2438-3(7))* Dodo Pr.

—A Child-World. 2008. 164p. pap. *(978-1-4097-9881-1(X))* Read Bks.

Roberts-Holmes, Guy. Doing Your Early Research Project. 2nd ed. 2011. (Illus.). 232p. (C). 104.00 *(978-1-84920-519-1(1),* B05191C); pap. 45.00 *(978-1-84920-520-7(5),* B05191P) SAGE Pubns., Ltd. GBR. Dist: SAGE Pubns., Inc.

Rosenberg, David & Gershon, Samuel, eds. Pharmacotherapy of Child & Adolescent Psychiatric Disorders. 3rd ed. 2012. (ENG.). 474p. 100.00 ***(978-0-470-97376-9(5),*** Wiley-Blackwell) Wiley, John & Sons, Inc.

Ross, Julie A. How to Hug a Porcupine: Negotiating the Prickly Points of the Tween Years. 2008. (ENG., Illus.). 224p. pap. 15.95 *(978-0-07-154589-1(1),* 0071545891) McGraw-Hill Cos., The.

Rotenberg, Ken J., ed. Interpersonal Trust During Childhood & Adolescence. 2010. (ENG., Illus.). 344p. 104.00 *(978-0-521-88799-1(2))* Cambridge Univ. Pr.

Shaddy, Robert, et al. Pediatric Practice Cardiology. 2012. (Pediatric Practice Ser.). (ENG., Illus.). 400p. 89.00 ***(978-0-07-176320-2(1),*** 0071763201) McGraw-Hill Professional Publishing.

Shaw, George Bernard. A Treatise on Parents & Children. 2008. (ENG.). per. 6.99 *(978-1-60450-157-5(X))* Arc Manor.

—A Treatise on Parents & Children. 2008. 160p. 22.99 *(978-0-554-37583-0(4))* 2008. 160p. 25.99 *(978-0-554-28280-0(1))* 2007. (ENG.). 142p. per. 18.99 *(978-1-4346-5053-5(7))* 2007. (ENG.). 158p. per. 21.99 *(978-1-4346-5054-2(5))* BiblioBazaar.

—A Treatise on Parents & Children. 2006. (ENG.). pap. *(978-1-4068-0534-5(3))* Echo Library.

Smidt, Sandra. The Developing Child in the 21st Century: A Global Perspective on Child Development. 2006. (Illus.). 150p. 160.00 *(978-0-415-38569-5(5));* per. 34.95 *(978-0-415-38570-1(9))* Routledge.

Soldin, Steven J., et al. Pediatric Reference Intervals. 6th ed. 2007. x, 271p. *(978-1-59425-067-5(7),* AACC Pr.) American Assn. for Clinical Chemistry, Inc.

Steppe, Erma. I'm Nobody: My Mother Said It; I No Longer Believe It. 2010. 176p. 25.95 *(978-1-4502-7399-2(8));* pap. 15.95 *(978-1-4502-7398-5(X))* iUniverse, Inc.

Stewart, Sheila. My Feelings Have Names. 2009. (Kids Have Troubles Too Ser.). 48p. (YA). (gr. 5-18). pap. 7.95 *(978-1-4222-1910-2(0))* Mason Crest Pubs.

Sully, James. Studies of Childhood. 2009. 350p. pap. *(978-0-217-56355-0(4));* 120p. pap. *(978-0-217-56358-1(9))* Books LLC.

Taylor, Jayne, et al. Doing Research with Children. 2nd ed. 2007. (Illus.). 216p. (C). 125.00 *(978-1-4129-1844-2(8),* B18448C) SAGE Pubns., Ltd. GBR. Dist: SAGE Pubns., Inc.

Tecklin, Jan Stephen, ed. Pediatric Physical Therapy. 4th rev. ed. 2007. (ENG., Illus.). 680p. 83.99 *(978-0-7817-5399-9(6))* Lippincott Williams & Wilkins.

Thomas, Claire. Growing up with Languages: Reflections on Multilingual Childhoods. 2012. (Parents' & Teachers' Guides). (ENG., Illus.). 256p. 99.95 ***(978-1-84769-715-8(1));*** pap. 29.95 ***(978-1-84769-714-1(3))*** Multilingual Matters GBR. Dist: Univ. of Toronto Pr.

Thomas, Susan Gregory. Buy, Buy Baby: How Consumer Culture Manipulates Parents & Harms Young Minds. 2007. (ENG., Illus.). 288p. 25.00 *(978-0-618-46351-0(8))* Houghton Mifflin Harcourt Publishing Co.

Timberlake, Lloyd & Thomas, Laura. When the Bough Breaks... Our Children, Our Environment. 2nd ed. 2009. (Environmentalism & Politics Set Ser.). (ENG.). 276p. 110.00 *(978-1-84971-002-2(3))* Routledge.

Turmel, André. A Historical Sociology of Childhood: Developmental Thinking, Categorization, & Graphic Visualization. 2008. (ENG., Illus.). 376p. 121.00 *(978-0-521-87977-4(9));* pap. 38.00 *(978-0-521-70563-9(0))* Cambridge Univ. Pr.

Twycross. Managing Pain in Children: A Clinical Guide. Twycross, Alison et al, eds. 2009. (ENG., Illus.). 256p. pap., instr.'s gde. ed. 56.99 *(978-1-4051-6894-6(3),* Wiley-Blackwell) Wiley, John & Sons, Inc.

Wall, John. Ethics in Light of Childhood. 2010. (ENG.). 216p. pap. 34.95 *(978-1-58901-692-7(0))* Georgetown Univ. Pr.

Ward, Robin & Frost, Nick. Rethinking Children & Families: The Relationship Between Childhood, Families & the State. 2011. (New Childhoods Ser.). (ENG., Illus.). 144p. pap. 34.95 *(978-1-84706-080-8(3))* Continuum International Publishing Group, Ltd. GBR. Dist: National Bk. Network.

Wells, Karen. Childhood in Global Perspective. 2009. (ENG.). 220p. pap. 24.95 *(978-0-7456-3837-9(6))* Polity Pr. GBR. Dist: Wiley, John & Sons, Inc.

Wiggin, Kate Douglas. Children's Rights & Others: A Book of Nursery Logic. 2007. (ENG.). 120p. per. 18.99 *(978-1-4346-1747-7(5))*; 132p. per. 19.99 *(978-1-4346-1753-8(X))* BiblioBazaar.

Wilson, Jeni. Helping Your Pupils to Think for Themselves. 2007. (Little books of life Skills Ser.). (Illus.). vi, 66p. 21.95 *(978-0-415-44730-0(5))* Fulton, David Pubs. GBR. Dist: Taylor & Francis Group.

Wurtele, Sandy K. Out of Harm's Way: A Parent's Guide to Protecting Young Children from Sexual Abuse. 2010. (ENG.). 32p. pap. 9.95 *(978-1-884734-97-7(9))*; lib. bdg. 19.95 *(978-1-884734-98-4(7))* Parenting Pr., Inc.

Wurtele, Sandy K. & Berkower, Feather. Off Limits: A Parent's Guide to Keeping Kids Safe from Sexual Abuse. 2010. (Illus.). xiv, 176p. *(978-1-884444-83-8(0))* Safer Society Pr.

Yarborough, Pamela A. & Yarborough, Robert T. Children's Reiki Handbook: A Guide to Energy Healing for Kids. 2nd ed. 2007. (Illus.). xii, 83p. *(978-0-9774181-5-2(4))* Andborough Publishing.

Young-Bruehl, Elisabeth. Childism: Confronting Prejudice Against Children. 2012. (ENG.). 368p. 28.00 *(978-0-300-17311-6(3))* Yale Univ. Pr.

Zentai, László & Nunez, Jesús Reyes, eds. Maps for the Future: Children, Education & Internet. 2012. (Lecture Notes in Geoinformation & Cartography / Publications of the International Cartographic Association (ICA) Ser.). (ENG., Illus.). vii, 316p. 129.00 *(978-3-642-19521-1(0)*, 3642195210) Springer.

CHILDREN—AMUSEMENTS

see Amusements

CHILDREN—ANECDOTES AND SAYINGS

see also Wit and Humor, Juvenile

Battles, Louise P. From the Mouths of Babes: Wee Wisdom from Little Ones. Date not set. (Illus.). 95p. pap. 5.95 *(978-1-885055-00-2(5))* Aiken-Argo Publishing Co.

Connole, Marika Lee. Out of the Mouths of Babes: A Little Book of Sunshine. 2010. 165p. pap. 12.95 *(978-1-4357-3074-8(7))* Lulu Enterprises Inc.

Lebowski, Kathleen. What about Me?, 1 vol. 2009. 178p. pap. 19.95 *(978-1-4489-9046-7(7))* PublishAmerica, Inc.

CHILDREN—ASYLUMS

see Children—Institutional Care

CHILDREN—BIBLICAL TEACHING

see Children in the Bible

CHILDREN—BIOGRAPHY

see also Children in the Bible

Aas, Martha Andrea. Pearls on a String: One Woman's Journey to the Past. 2007. (Illus.). vi, 214p. pap. *(978-1-887317-78-8(3))* X-communication.

Alberts, Amy. Burnt Cookies: A Quest for Closure. 2010. 244p. pap. 17.95 *(978-1-60594-210-0(3)*, Llumina Pr.) Aeon Publishing Inc.

B., Rita. Life Is Just a Dance! 2008. 136p. 29.99 *(978-1-4257-9068-4(2))*; per. 19.99 *(978-1-4257-9067-7(4))* Xlibris Corp.

Bailey, Carolyn Sherwin. Boys & Girls of Discovery Days. 2011. 222p. 44.95 ***(978-1-258-07220-9(3))*** Literary Licensing, LLC.

Booth, John. Collect All 21! Memoirs of a Star Wars Geek - the First 30 Years. 2008. 122p. pap. 14.95 *(978-1-4357-4376-2(8))* Lulu Enterprises Inc.

Braun, Helga. The Survival of Helga Braun. 2010. 172p. 22.49 *(978-1-4520-2246-8(1))*; pap. 11.99 *(978-1-4520-2245-1(3))* AuthorHouse.

Brenneman, Simone. Effervescence: A True-Life Tale of Autism & of Courage. 2009. 196p. 25.50 *(978-1-4389-7753-9(0))*; pap. 15.99 *(978-1-4389-7754-6(9))* AuthorHouse.

Brenner, Norm. Wanker. 2011. 136p. 29.99 ***(978-1-4628-8807-8(0))*** Xlibris Corp.

Bridge, Andrew. Hope's Boy. 2009. (ENG.). 336p. pap. 14.99 *(978-1-4013-0974-9(7))* Hyperion Pr.

Cameron & Cameron, Theresa. Learning to Live: A Black Woman's Journey Beyond Foster Care. 2009. x, 278p. pap. *(978-1-59194-108-8(3))* Townsend Pr.

Chambers, Eric. No Bed for Me. 2007. 272p. per. *(978-1-906210-11-3(X))* Grosvenor Hse. Publishing Ltd.

Chandler, Charlene Roberson. Childhood Memories: 1930s And 1940s. 2011. 48p. pap. 31.99 ***(978-1-4568-9616-4(4))*** Xlibris Corp.

Conde, Gloria & Bailey, Trish. Audrey: The True Story of One Child's Heroic Journey of Faith. 2008. *(978-1-933271-18-7(3))* Circle Pr.

D'Argan, Tanua LaSon. A Shelter in the Midst of a Storm: A True Life's Testimony, 1 vol. 2010. 395p. pap. 29.95 *(978-1-60703-302-8(X))* PublishAmerica, Inc.

de Werth Neu, Sabina. A Long Silence: Memories of a German Refugee Child, 1941-1958. 2011. (ENG., Illus.). 300p. 19.00 *(978-1-61614-256-8(1))* Prometheus Bks., Pubs.

Derbyshire, Georgina J. Stand up for Autism: A Boy, a Dog, & a Prescription for Laughter. 2010. (ENG., Illus.). 144p. pap. *(978-1-84905-099-9(6))* Kingsley, Jessica Ltd.

Elkin, S. E. Cabrini's Child. 2007. 108p. per. 19.95 *(978-1-4241-7956-5(4))* PublishAmerica, Inc.

Finn, Janet L. Mining Childhood: Growing up in Butte, 1900 - 1960. 2012. (ENG., Illus.). 256p. 34.95 ***(978-0-9801292-4-3(9))*** Montana Historical Society Pr.

—Mining Childhood: Growing up in Butte, 1900-1960. 2012. (ENG., Illus.). 256p. pap. 24.95 ***(978-0-9801292-5-0(7))*** Montana Historical Society Pr.

Fiorillo, Jure. Great Bastards of History: True & Riveting Accounts of the Most Famous Illegitimate Children Who Went on to Achieve Greatness. 2010. (ENG., Illus.). 272p. pap. 19.99 *(978-1-59233-401-8(6)*, 1592334016, Fair Winds Press) Quayside.

Forster, Annette. Journey: Reminders from A Guardian Angel Memoir. 2011. (Illus.). 144p. pap. 17.23 *(978-1-4520-7923-3(4))* AuthorHouse.

Fragoso, Margaux. Tiger, Tiger: A Memoir. 2011. (ENG.). 336p. 26.00 *(978-0-374-27762-8(1))* Farrar, Straus & Giroux.

Fraser, Eugenie. The House by the Dvina: A Russian Childhood. 2011. (ENG., Illus.). 368p. pap. 14.95 *(978-1-84596-573-0(6))* Mainstream Publishing Co., Ltd. GBR. Dist: Independent Pubs. Group.

Gangel, Alison. The Sun Hasn't Fallen from the Sky. 2012. (ENG.). 256p. pap. 18.50 *(978-1-4088-2205-0(9))* Bloomsbury Publishing.

Greenfield, Stephen. We wish you a retro Christmas. 2008. 196p. pap. 18.95 *(978-1-4092-4675-6(2))* Lulu Enterprises Inc.

Hall, Elaine & Hall, Neal. Now I See the Moon: A Mother, a Son, & the Miracle of Autism. 2011. (ENG.). 304p. pap. 14.99 *(978-0-06-174381-8(X)*, Harper Paperbacks) HarperCollins Pubs.

Harris, Robert M. Pieces of Bob. 2007. 84p. per. 16.95 *(978-1-4241-8092-9(9))* PublishAmerica, Inc.

Higgott, Albert. Teddy's War. 2009. 88p. pap. 12.99 *(978-1-4389-4411-1(X))* AuthorHouse.

Iliescu, Antonie. Broken Gates. 2011. 120p. 29.99 ***(978-1-4568-6760-7(1))*** Xlibris Corp.

Ilyn, Vanya & Ilyn, Peter. Out of the Far Corners: An Epic Tale of Rejection, Grace, & Deliverance. 2011. *(978-1-57658-545-0(X))* YWAM Publishing.

Juan. 2009. 252p. pap. *(978-0-217-85761-1(2))* Books LLC.

Kakmi, Dmetri. Mother Land. 2010. (ENG., Illus.). 231p. 39.95 *(978-1-906011-39-0(7))* Eland Bks. GBR. Dist: Dufour Editions, Inc.

Kierner, Cynthia A. Martha Jefferson Randolph, Daughter of Monticello: Her Life & Times. 2012. (ENG., Illus.). 400p. 35.00 ***(978-0-8078-3552-4(8))*** Univ. of North Carolina Pr.

Lauck, Jennifer. Found: A Memoir. (ENG.). 2012. 280p. pap. 17.00 ***(978-1-58005-395-2(5))*** 2011. 272p. 24.95 *(978-1-58005-367-9(X))* Seal Pr.

Lee, Cesar. Zamboanga Remembered. 2007. (Illus.). 148p. per. 14.95 *(978-0-9799341-1-7(7))* Imago Pr.

Leone, Marianne. Knowing Jesse: A Mother's Story of Grief, Grace, & Everyday Bliss. 2010. (ENG., Illus.). 272p. 25.00 *(978-1-4391-8392-2(9))* Simon & Schuster.

Lindenmeyer, Kriste. The Greatest Generation Grows Up: American Childhood in The 1930s. 2007. (American Childhoods Ser.). (ENG., Illus.). 320p. per. 18.95 *(978-1-56663-730-5(9))* Dee, Ivan R. Pub.

Long, Al. Alone in a Crowd: One Mentor, One Child, One Journey. 2007. (Illus.). 184p. pap. 14.95 *(978-0-9787268-9-8(8))* Power Publishing.

Long, Jeffrey E. Remembered Childhoods: A Guide to Autobiography & Memoirs of Childhood & Youth, 1 vol. 2007. (Illus.). 524p. 75.00 *(978-1-59158-174-1(5)*, LU1745) Libraries Unlimited, Inc.

Luchs, Lewis. Children of the Manse. 2009. 306p. pap., pap. 18.99 *(978-0-578-03523-9(5))* Luchs, Lewis.

Martin, James E. Life Aboard the Monkey Bus. 2006. 152p. pap. 14.00 *(978-1-4259-5364-5(6))* AuthorHouse.

McGill, Jerry. Dear Marcus: A Letter to the Man Who Shot Me. 2012. (ENG., Illus.). 192p. 22.00 ***(978-0-8129-9307-3(1))***; E-Book ***(978-0-679-64460-6(1))*** Spiegel & Grau.

Meeks, George & Buchanan, James Malcolm. Why Did It Happen? 2010. 252p. pap. 14.49 *(978-1-4490-1337-0(6))* AuthorHouse.

Mehrban, Shaida. Blossom & I: Tears Behind Closed Doors. 2010. 174p. pap. *(978-1-84748-702-5(5))* Athena Pr.

Meier, Peg. Wishing for a Snow Day: Growing up in Minnesota. 2010. (ENG., Illus.). 264p. pap. 29.95 *(978-0-87351-640-2(0))* Minnesota Historical Society Pr.

Melton, Diane. James' Journey. 2007. 76p. per. 16.95 *(978-1-4241-6747-0(7))* PublishAmerica, Inc.

Mondy, Tim. Memoirs of Miracles. 2008. 232p. pap. 22.33 *(978-0-615-19877-4(5))* Mondy, Tim.

Montouris, Georgia D., et al. Epilepsy on Our Terms: Stories by Children with Seizures & Their Parents. 2007. (Brainstorms Ser.). (ENG., Illus.). 192p. pap. 22.99 *(978-0-19-533090-8(0))* Oxford Univ. Pr., Inc.

Mussolum, Patricia. Wilted Bouquets. 2011. 172p. pap. 24.95 ***(978-1-4626-3650-1(0))*** PublishAmerica, Inc.

Nelson, Lane. Orphan Child. 2007. 116p. 25.49 *(978-1-4303-2123-1(7))* Lulu Enterprises Inc.

Nolet, Kasara. The Spiritual Diary of a Nine-Year-Old Child: True Stories. 2010. (Illus.). 184p. pap. *(978-2-923097-66-4(1))* Universe/City Mikael (UCM) Publishing, Inc.

O'Keeffe, Toni. Those Who Trespass Against Us. 2007. 252p. 29.95 *(978-1-4251-6734-9(9))* Trafford Publishing.

Paris, Gloria. A Child of Sanitariums: A Memoir of Tuberculosis Survival & Lifelong Disability. 2010. (ENG., Illus.). 212p. pap. 29.95 *(978-0-7864-5939-1(5))* McFarland & Co., Inc. Pubs.

Pike, Donna. Bradley's Journey Home. 2008. 188p. pap. 14.49 *(978-1-4389-2609-4(X))* AuthorHouse.

Ringgold, Timothy. Bella's Blessings: a Humble Story of Providence. 2010. 264p. pap. 22.28 *(978-0-557-25657-0(7))* Lulu Enterprises Inc.

Rosen, Michael. What Else but Home: Seven Boys & an American Journey Between the Projects & the Penthouse. 2010. (ENG., Illus.). 384p. pap. 15.95 *(978-1-58648-894-9(5))* PublicAffairs.

Ross, Tracy. The Source of All Things: A Memoir. (ENG.). 2012. 320p. pap. 15.00 ***(978-1-4391-7298-8(6))*** 2011. 304p. 26.00 *(978-1-4391-7297-1(8))* Free Pr. (Free Pr.).

Sarah Dreams of Pitchipoi: A Hidden Child's Memoir of the Holocaust in France. 2008. per. 17.95 *(978-0-9793771-4-3(5))* ComteQ Publishing.

Scott, Elizabeth Burton. Raindrops on Roman: Overcoming Autism: A Message of Hope. Rakini, Kate, ed. 2009. 160p. pap. 14.95 *(978-1-934759-24-0(4))* Reed, Robert D. Pubs.

shavers isbn 978-1-4357-4540-7, shante. Tay's unlocked Journal. 2008. 132p. 28.28 *(978-1-4357-4540-7(X))* Lulu Enterprises Inc.

Shute, Henry Augustus. The Real Diary of a Real Boy. 2009. 202p. 28.99 *(978-1-116-80755-4(6))*; 32.99 *(978-1-116-80754-7(8))*; pap. 24.75 *(978-1-116-80756-1(4))*; pap. 23.75 *(978-1-116-80757-8(2))* BiblioBazaar.

Spry, Christopher. Child C: Surviving a Foster Mother's Reign of Terror. 2008. (ENG.). 320p. pap. 12.95 *(978-1-84739-189-6(3))* Simon & Schuster, Ltd. GBR. Dist: Independent Pubs. Group.

Starr, David. From Bombs to Books: Refugee children, their families, & an exceptional Canadian School. 2011. (ENG., Illus.). 192p. pap. 22.95 ***(978-1-55277-860-9(6))*** Lorimer, James & Co., Ltd., Pubs. CAN. Dist: Casemate Pubs. & Bk. Distributors, LLC.

Stepanek, Jeni. Messenger: The Legacy of Mattie J. T. Stepanek & Heartsongs. 2010. (ENG.). 336p. (gr. 12). 15.00 *(978-0-451-23114-7(7)*, N A L Trade) Penguin Group (USA) Inc.

Stepanek, Jeni & Lindner, Larry. Messenger: The Legacy of Mattie J. T. Stepanek & Heartsongs. 2009. (ENG.). 336p. (gr. 12). 25.95 *(978-0-525-95142-1(3)*, Dutton Adult) Penguin Group (USA) Inc.

Swaim, Theresa P. Children of the Reverend. 2008. 156p. pap. 14.95 *(978-0-595-52664-2(0))* iUniverse, Inc.

Swan, Anna. Statues Without Shadows: A Daughter's Search for the Truth about the Parents She Never Knew. 2006. (ENG., Illus.). 288p. per. 13.95 *(978-0-340-83539-5(7))* Hodder General Publishing Div. GBR. Dist: Independent Pubs. Group.

Taylor, Kennesaw. Informally Educated: A True Tale of Child Abuse, Survival, & Murder. 2010. 256p. pap. 14.99 *(978-0-9844183-4-3(2))* Lemon Pr. LLC.

Thomson, David. Try to Tell the Story. 2010. (Vintage Ser.). (ENG.). 224p. pap. 15.00 *(978-0-307-47317-2(1)*, Vintage) Knopf Doubleday Publishing Group.

Titley, Harry. A Staffordshire Lad. 2009. (Illus.). 240p. pap. 14.49 *(978-1-4389-4179-0(X))* AuthorHouse.

Trujillo, Olga R. The Sum of My Parts: A Survivor's Story of Dissociative Identity Disorder. 2011. (ENG.). 256p. pap. 18.95 *(978-1-57224-991-2(9))* New Harbinger Pubns.

Williamson-Taylor, James. They Can't Touch Him Now. 2007. pap. *(978-0-9554101-0-9(X))* Anodyne Pubs.

Zoppi, Thelma Ward. The Childhood Adventures of Bobbie, Ivan, & Thumper: A Childhood Autobiography. 2011. 20p. pap. 12.95 ***(978-1-4560-3466-5(9))*** PublishAmerica, Inc.

CHILDREN—BOOKS AND READING

Here are entered works on the reading interests of children, and-or lists of books read by or recommended for children. Collections of literary works or individual literary works written by children under 15 years of age are entered under Children's Writings. Works on child authors and-or discussions of their works are entered under Child Authors. Collections of works published for children are entered under Children's Literature.

see also Children's Reference Books; Comic Books and Children; Youth—Books and Reading

Ada, Alma Flor. Alma Flor Ada & YOU, 1 vol., Vol. 2. 2nd ed. 2008. (Author & YOU Ser.). (Illus.). 128p. pap. 35.00 *(978-1-59158-228-1(8)*, LU2288) Libraries Unlimited, Inc.

Alcubierre Moya, Beatriz. Ciudadanos del Futuro: Una Historia de las Publicaciones para niños en el Siglo Xix Mexicano. 2010. (Estudios Históricos Ser.). 224p. pap. 26.00 *(978-607-462-114-3(4))* El Colegio de México, A.C., Biblioteca Miguel Cosío Villegas MEX. Dist: Fondo de Cultura Economica USA.

American Library Association Staff, ed. The Newbery & Caldecott Awards: A Guide to the Medal Honor Books, 2008. 2008. 192p. pap. 19.00 *(978-0-8389-3574-3(5))* American Library Assn.

Anderson, Nancy. What Should I Read Aloud? A Guide to 200 Best-Selling Picture Books. 2007. 168p. (gr. 17). pap. 22.95 *(978-0-87207-679-2(2))* International Reading Assn.

Anderson, Nancy A. Elementary Children's Literature: Infancy through Age 13. 3rd ed. 2009. (ENG.). 408p. (C). pap. 78.67 *(978-0-13-715143-1(8))* Allyn & Bacon, Inc.

Applebaum, Noga. Representations of Technology in Science Fiction for Young People. 2009. xv, 198p. (C). 110.00 *(978-0-203-87389-2(0))* Routledge.

Association for Library Service to Children (ALSC). The Newbery & Caldecott Awards: A Guide to the Medal & Honor Books. 2007. (Newbery & Caldecott Awards Ser.). 186p. per. 19.00 *(978-0-8389-3567-5(2))* American Library Assn.

Balina, Marina & Rudova, Larissa, eds. Russian Children's Literature & Culture. 2007. (Children's Literature & Culture Ser.). (ENG., Illus.). 352p. 125.00 *(978-0-415-97864-4(5))* Routledge.

Barone, Diane M. Children's Literature in the Classroom: Engaging Lifelong Readers. 2010. (Solving Problems in the Teaching of Literacy Ser.). (ENG., Illus.). 242p. (gr. k-6). 50.00 *(978-1-60623-939-1(2))*; pap. 28.00 *(978-1-60623-938-4(4))* Guilford Pubns., Inc.

Barstow, Barbara, et al. Beyond Picture Books: Subject Access to Best Books for Beginning Readers, 1 vol. 3rd rev. ed. 2007. (Children's & Young Adult Literature Reference Ser.). 668p. 75.00 *(978-1-59158-545-9(7)*, LU5545) Libraries Unlimited, Inc.

Baxter, Kathleen A. & Kochel, Marcia Agness. Gotcha Good! Nonfiction Books to Get Kids Excited about Reading, 1 vol. 2008. (Illus.). 268p. pap. 35.00 *(978-1-59158-654-8(2)*, LU8654) Libraries Unlimited, Inc.

Becford, April Whatley & Albright, Lettie K., eds. A Master Class in Children's Literature: Trends & Issues in an Evolving Field. 2011. pap *(978-0-8141-3082-7(8))* National Council of Teachers of English.

Bell, Luke. Baptizing Harry Potter: A Christian Reading of J. K. Rowling. 2010. (Illus.). 240p. pap. 16.00 *(978-1-58768-058-8(0)*, HiddenSpring) Paulist Pr.

Berndt, Valerie. Reading Made Easy: A Guide to Teach Your Child to Read. 2008. (ENG., Illus.). 312p. pap. 49.95 *(978-1-882514-70-0(X))* Greenleaf Pr.

Bilton, Helen. Playing Outside: Activities, Ideas & Inspiration for the Early Years. 2nd rev. ed. 2012. (ENG.). 112p. (C). pap. 31.95 *(978-0-415-60480-2(X))* Routledge.

Birch, Elizabeth. Children's Literature Gems: Choosing & Using Them in Your Library Career. 2009. 125p. 45.00 *(978-0-8389-0995-9(7))* American Library Assn.

Blass, Rosanne J. Windows on the World: International Books for Elementary & Middle Grade Readers, 1 vol. 2010. 214p. pap. 40.00 *(978-1-59158-830-6(8)*, LU8830) Libraries Unlimited, Inc.

Boland, Dagny D. Ready, Willing, & Able: Teaching English to Gifted, Talented, & Exceptionally Conscientious Adolescents. 2006. (ENG., Illus.). 208p. pap. 31.25 *(978-0-325-01000-7(5)*, E01000) Heinemann.

Bornhold, Catharine R., et al. Twice upon a Time: A Guide to Fractured, Altered, & Retold Folk & Fairy Tales, 1 vol. 2008. (Children's & Young Adult Literature Reference Ser.). 224p. 45.00 *(978-1-59158-390-5(X)*, LU390X) Libraries Unlimited, Inc.

Bosmajian. Sparing the Child. 2010. (Children's Literature & Culture Ser.). (ENG.). 304p. pap. 29.95 *(978-0-8153-3857-4(0))* Routledge.

Bouttsis, Suzanne & Williamson, Noelle. The Fiction Gateway. Williamson, Noelle & Eberle, Suzanne, eds. 2009. 162p. pap. 39.95 *(978-0-86431-880-0(4))* ACER Pr. AUS. Dist: International Specialized Bk. Services.

Bradbury, Judy, ed. Children's Book Corner: A Read-Aloud Resource with Tips, Techniques, & Plans for Teachers, Librarians, & Parents Grades 5 And 6, 1 vol. 2006. (Illus.). 488p. per. 32.00 *(978-1-59158-045-4(5)*, LU0455) Libraries Unlimited, Inc.

—Children's Book Corner Set. Bk. 4: A Read-Aloud Resource with Tips, Techniques & Plans for Teachers, Their Students & Their Parents, 4 vols. 2006. pap. 99.95 *(978-1-59158-459-9(0)*, LU4590) Libraries Unlimited, Inc.

Bramwell, Peter. Pagan Themes in Modern Children's Fiction: Green Man, Shamanism, Earth Mysteries. 2009. (ENG., Illus.). 256p. 89.00 *(978-0-230-21839-0(3))* Palgrave Macmillan.

Bressell, Danny. 75+ Reading Strategies: Boost Achievement & Build a Life-Long Love of Reading. 2009. *(978-1-934026-95-3(6)*, Crystal Springs Bks.) Staff Development for Educators.

Brown, Penelope E. A Critical History of French Children's Literature. 2009. 312p. pap. 39.95 *(978-0-415-87670-4(2))*; 368p. pap. 39.95 *(978-0-415-87671-1(0))* Routledge.

Bryant, Sara Cone. How to Tell Stories to Children. 2009. 112p. pap. *(978-1-150-55974-7(8))* Books LLC.

—How to Tell Stories to Children. 2008. 316p. pap. 17.95 *(978-1-933184-34-0(5))* Sophia Institute Pr.

Buckner, Aimee E. Notebook Connections: Strategies for the Reader's Notebook. 2009. (ENG.). 152p. (C). (gr. 3-8). pap. 17.50 *(978-1-57110-782-4(7))* Stenhouse Pubs.

Butler, Dorothy & Clay, Marie M. Reading Begins at Home, Second Edition: Preparing Children Before They Go to School. 2nd ed. 2008. (Illus.). 56p. pap. 20.00 *(978-0-325-01714-3(X)*, E01714) Heinemann.

Calkins, Lucy McCormick & Ehrenworth, Mary. Tackling Complex Texts: Historical Fiction in Book Clubs. 2010. *(978-0-325-03068-5(5))* Heinemann.

Carpan, Carolyn. Sisters, Schoolgirls, & Sleuths: Girls' Series Books in America. 2008. (Scarecrow Studies in Young Adult Literature Ser.). (ENG.). 184p. 45.00 *(978-0-8108-5756-8(1))* Scarecrow Pr., Inc.

Carroll, Julia M., et al. Developing Language & Literacy: Effective Intervention in the Early Years. 2011. (ENG., Illus.). 190p. 110.00 *(978-0-470-71166-6(6)*, Wiley-Blackwell); pap. 49.95 *(978-0-470-71185-9(X)*, Wiley) Wiley, John & Sons, Inc.

Cheh, Oksana. Literature Preferences of Multilingual Children- a Study of Children's Reading. 2007. 112p. per. *(978-3-8364-2113-3(5))* VDM Verlag Dr. Mueller e.K.

Clark, M. A. Ready, Set, Read: Reading Program. 2010. 294p. pap. 34.95 *(978-1-60844-669-8(7))* Dog Ear Publishing, LLC.

Cleonan, Kathryn L. Sing Me a Story, Read Me a Song Bk. 1: Patterns: Ideas for Making Great Books from Favorite Children's Songs. (Illus.). 56p. 10.00 *(978-1-87983-00-7(9))* Rhythm & Reading Resources.

—Sing Me a Story, Read Me a Song Bk. 2: Patterns: Ideas for Making Great Books from Favorite Children's Songs. (Illus.). 66p. 10.00 *(978-1-87983-04-5(1))* Rhythm & Reading Resources.

Collingwood, Stuart Dodgson. The Life & Letters of Lewis Carroll. 2009. 396p. 31.99 *(978-0-559-12569-0(0))*; 29.99 *(978-0-559-12579-9(8))*; pap. 32.75 *(978-0-559-12577-5(1))*; pap. 26.99 *(978-0-559-12572-0(7))* BiblioBazaar.

—The Life & Letters of Lewis Carroll. 2007. (ENG.). 232p. per. *(978-1-4068-4707-9(0))* Echo Library.

Collins, Joan. Motivating Readers in the Middle Grades, 1 vol. 2008. 112p. pap. 36.95 *(978-1-58683-297-1(2)*, A2276P) Linworth Publishing, Inc.

C

Compton-Lilly, Catherine. Re-Reading Families: The Literate Lives of Urban Children, Four Years Later. 2007. (Practitioner Inquiry Ser.). (ENG.). 160p. 56.00 (978-0-8077-4792-6(0)); pap. 25.95 (978-0-8077-4791-9(2)) Teachers College Pr., Teachers College, Columbia Univ.

Cram101 Textbook Reviews & Cram101 Textbook Reviews. Outlines & Highlights for Through the Eyes of a Child by Donna E Norton. 2011. 250p. pap. 31.95 (978-1-61830-898-6(X)) Cram101 Inc.

Darton, Frederick Joseph Harvey. Children's Books in England: Five Centuries of Social Life. 2011. (Cambridge Library Collection - Literary Studies). (ENG., Illus.). 394p. pap. 29.99 (978-1-108-03381-7(4)) Cambridge Univ. Pr.

Davies, Alison. Reading to Your Baby: Techniques That Bring Language Alive for Your Little Ones. 2011. (ENG., Illus.). 96p. pap. 14.95 (978-1-904760-78-8(3)) Carroll & Brown Pubs., Ltd. GBR. Dist: Independent Pubs. Group.

Desmet, Mieke K. T. Babysitting the Reader: Translating English Narrative Fiction for Girls into Dutch (1946-1995) (European Literature for Children & Young Adults in an Ser.: Vol. 1). 352p. pap. 74.95 (978-3-03911-147-3(7)) Lang, Peter CHE. Dist: Lang, Peter Publishing, Inc.

Dewan, Pauline. The Art of Place in Literature for Children & Young Adults: How Locale Shapes a Story. 2010. 412p. 129.95 (978-0-7734-3762-3(2)) Mellen, Edwin Pr., The.

Dollins, Cynthia. The ABCs of Literacy: Preparing Our Children for Lifelong Learning. 2008. (ENG.). 332p. pap. 16.95 (978-1-58182-652-4(4)) Turner Publishing Co.

Donohue, Lisa. Independent Reading Inside the Box: How to Organize, Observe, & Assess Reading Strategies That Promote Deeper Thinking & Improve Comprehension. 2008. (ENG.). 160p. (C). (gr. k-6). pap. 21.00 (978-1-55138-225-8(3)) Stenhouse Pubs.

Dusinberre, Juliet, contrib. by. Alice to the Lighthouse: Children's Books & Radical Experiments in Art. 2nd ed. (Illus.). xxi, 352p. 24.95 (978-0-333-75984-4(2)) Macmillan Pubs., Ltd. GBR. Dist: Trans-Atlantic Pubns., Inc.

Edwards, Owen Dudley. British Children's Fiction in the Second World War. (Illus.). 2009. (ENG.). 752p. pap. 55.00 (978-0-7486-1650-3(0)) 2007. 544p. 300.00 (978-0-7486-1651-0(9)) Edinburgh Univ. Pr. GBR. Dist: Columbia Univ. Pr.

Ehrenworth, Mary. A Quick Guide to Teaching Reading Through Fantasy Novels. Calkins, Lucy, ed. 2011. (Workshop Help Desk Ser.). 104p. pap. 10.00 (978-0-325-04281-7(0), E04281, Firsthand) Heinemann.

Elbert, Monika M., ed. Enterprising Youth: Social Values & Acculturation in Nineteenth-Century American Children's Literature. 2009. 286p. pap. 39.95 (978-0-415-87667-4(2)) Routledge.

Falconer, Rachel. The Crossover Novel. 2009. 264p. pap. 39.95 (978-0-415-87937-8(X)) Routledge.

Farren, Donald & Imholtz, August A., eds. The Baltimore Bibliophiles at Fifty, 1954-2004. 2009. 55.00 (978-1-58456-251-1(X)) Oak Knoll Pr.

Flippo, Rona F., ed. Reading Researchers in Search of Common Ground. 2nd rev. ed. 2011. (ENG., Illus.). 392p. 135.00 (978-0-415-80112-6(5)); pap. 54.95 (978-0-415-80111-9(7)) Routledge.

Fountas, Irene C. & Pinnell, Gay Su. The Fountas & Pinnell Leveled Book List, K-8+ 2009-2011 Edition, Print Version. 2009. (F & P Professional Books & Multimedia Ser.). 736p. pap. 62.50 (978-0-325-02608-4(4), E02608) Heinemann.

Fox, Mem. Reading Magic: Why Reading Aloud to Our Children Will Change Their Lives Forever. 2nd ed. 2008. (ENG., Illus.). 208p. pap. 12.00 (978-0-15-603510-1(3), Mariner Bks.) Houghton Mifflin Harcourt Trade & Reference Pubs.

Freeman, Judy. Books Kids Will Sit Still For, 1 vol., Set. 2nd ed. 2006. (Children's & Young Adult Literature Reference Ser.). (Illus.). 126.00 (978-1-59158-477-3(9), LU4779) Libraries Unlimited, Inc.

—The WINNERS! Handbook: A Closer Look at Judy Freeman's Top-Rated Children's Books of 2006, 1 vol. 2007. 244p. per. 35.00 (978-1-59158-510-7(4), LU5104) Libraries Unlimited, Inc.

Freeman, Marcia S. & Koehler, Susan. Models for Teaching Writing-Craft Target Skills. 2nd ed. 2010. pap. 19.95 (978-1-934338-81-0(8)) Maupin Hse. Publishing.

Frith, Margaret & Rock, Victoria, eds. Once upon a Time: Celebrating the Magic of Children's Books in Honor of the Twentieth Anniversary of Reading Is Fundamental. 2006. (Illus.). 64p. (J). (gr. 4-8). reprint ed. pap. 7.00 (978-1-4223-5726-2(0)) DIANE Publishing Co.

Gillespie, John & Barr, Catherine. Best Books for Children: Preschool Through Grade 6, 1 vol. 9th ed. 2010. (Children's & Young Adult Literature Reference Ser.). 1901p. 95.00 (978-1-59158-575-6(9), LU8575) Libraries Unlimited, Inc.

Giorgis, Cyndi & Glazer, Joan I. Literature for Young Children: Supporting Emergent Literacy, Ages 0-8. 6th ed. 2008. (ENG.). 312p. (C). pap. 73.40 (978-0-13-240504-1(0), Prentice Hall) Prentice Hall PTR.

Gollub, Matthew. Give the Gift! 10 Fulfilling Ways to Raise a Lifetime Reader, 1. 2007. (Illus.). 32p. 15.95 (978-1-889910-41-3(4)); per. 6.95 (978-1-889910-42-0(2)) Tortuga Pr.

Gooch, C. Kay & Massey, Charlotte. Camp Summer Read: How to Create Your Own Summer Reading Camp, 1 vol. 2010. (Illus.). 108p. pap. 30.00 (978-1-59884-447-4(4), A2901P) Libraries Unlimited, Inc.

Goodwin, Prue, ed. Understanding Children's Books: A Guide for Education Professionals. 2008. (Illus.). 144p. (C). 103.00 (978-1-84787-031-5(7), B70315C); pap. 42.00 (978-1-84787-032-2(5), B70315P) SAGE Pubns., Ltd. GBR. Dist: SAGE Pubns., Inc.

Great Books Foundation (U.S.) Staff, contrib. by. Great Books Roundtable Planner: Using Shared Inquiry with Your Students. 2010. (978-1-933147-58-1(X)); (978-1-933147-56-7(3)); (978-1-933147-57-4(1)) Great Bks. Foundation.

Great Books Roundtable. 2010. (978-1-933147-52-9(0)) Great Bks. Foundation.

Grenby, M. O. The Child Reader, 1700-1840. 2011. (ENG., Illus.). 336p. 90.00 (978-0-521-19644-4(2)) Cambridge Univ. Pr.

Grover, Sharon & Hannegan, Lizette D. Listening to Learn: Audiobooks Supporting Literacy. 2011. 208p. pap. (978-0-8389-1107-5(2)) American Library Assn.

Gupta, Suman. Re-Reading Harry Potter. 2nd rev. ed. 2009. (ENG.). 240p. 95.00 (978-0-230-21957-1(8)); pap. 28.00 (978-0-230-21958-8(6)) Palgrave Macmillan.

Halsey, Rosalie Vrylina. Forgotten Books of the American Nursery: A History of the Development of the American Story. 2007. (ENG.). 202p. per. 20.99 (978-1-4346-2875-6(2)); 224p. per. 22.99 (978-1-4346-2910-4(4)) BiblioBazaar.

Hamilton, Emma Walton. Raising Bookworms: Getting Kids Reading for Pleasure & Empowerment. 2008. 189p. pap. 14.95 (978-0-9815833-0-3(X)) Beech Tree Bks.

Hancock, Marjorie R. A Celebration of Literature & Response: Children, Books, & Teachers in K-8 Classrooms. 3rd ed. 2007. (ENG.). 544p. (C). pap. 94.20 (978-0-13-613394-0(0), Prentice Hall) Prentice Hall PTR.

Harvey, Stephanie & Goudvis, Anne. Strategies That Work: Teaching Comprehension for Understanding & Engagement. 2nd ed. 2007. (ENG., Illus.). 344p. (C). (gr. k-8). pap. 32.00 (978-1-57110-481-6(X)) Stenhouse Pubs.

Hateley, Erica. Shakespeare in Children's Literature. 2011. 218p. pap. 39.95 (978-0-415-88888-2(3)) Routledge.

Heilman, Elizabeth. Critical Perspectives on Harry Potter. 2nd rev. ed. 2008. (ENG.). 368p. 39.95 (978-0-415-96484-5(9)) Routledge.

Herald, Nathan. Graphic Novels for Young Readers: A Genre Guide for Ages 4-14, 1 vol. 2011. (Genreflecting Advisory Ser.). 188p. 40.00 (978-1-59884-395-8(8), A2724C) Libraries Unlimited, Inc.

Hesperides. Books to Read - a Classified & Annotated Catalogue Being a Guide for Young Readers. 2007. 600p. per. (978-1-4067-5565-7(6), Hesperides Pr.) Read Bks.

Hindley, Charles. History of the Catnach Press: At Berwick-upon-Tweed, Alnwick & Newcastle-upon-Tyne, in Northumberland, & Seven Dials, London. 2010. (Cambridge Library Collection - Printing & Publishing History Ser.). (Illus.). 360p. pap. 29.99 (978-1-108-00909-6(3)) Cambridge Univ. Pr.

Hintz, Carrie. Utopian & Dystopian Writing for Children & Young Adults. 2009. 252p. 39.95 (978-0-415-80364-9(0)) Routledge.

Hobbs, Nancy, et al. It's a Piece of PIE: Personalized Reading. 2010. E-Book (978-1-59884-523-5(3)) Libraries Unlimited, Inc.

—Personalized Reading: It's a Piece of PIE, 1 vol. 2010. (Illus.). 135p. pap. 35.00 (978-1-59884-522-8(5), A3021P) Libraries Unlimited, Inc.

Hobsbaum, Angela, et al. Bridging Bands for Guided Reading: Resourcing for Diversity into Key Stage 2. 2006. (Guided Reading Ser.). (ENG., Illus.). 170p. spiral bd. 48.95 (978-0-85473-690-4(5)) Institute of Education GBR. Dist: Stylus Publishing, LLC.

Hodaie, Nazli. Der Orient in der deutschen Kinder- und Jugendliteratur: Fallstudien aus drei Jahrhunderten. 2008. (Kinder- und Jugendkultur, -literatur und -medien. Theorie - Geschichte - Didaktik Ser.). 344p. pap. 81.95 (978-3-631-56144-7(X)) Lang, Peter GmbH, Europaischer Verlag der Wissenschaften DEU. Dist: Lang, Peter.

Hohmann, Mary & Adams, Kate. Storybook Talk: Conversations for Comprehension. 2008. (978-1-57379-353-7(1)) High/Scope Pr.

Hooper, Walter. Past Watchful Dragons: The Origin, Interpretation, & Appreciation of the Chronicles of Narnia. 2007. (C. S. Lewis Secondary Studies Ser.). 156p. pap. 17.00 (978-1-55635-548-6(3)) Wipf & Stock Pubs.

Horne, Jackie C. History & the Construction of the Child in Early British Children's Literature. 2011. (Ashgate Studies in Childhood, 1700 to the Present Ser.). (Illus.). 298p. 99.95 (978-1-4094-0788-1(8)) Ashgate Publishing Co.

Horning, Kathleen T. From Cover to Cover: Evaluating & Reviewing Children's Books. rev. ed. 2010. (ENG.). 240p. pap. 14.99 (978-0-06-077757-9(5), Collins) HarperCollins Pubs.

Hoyt, Linda. Revisit, Reflect, Retell, Updated Edition: Time-Tested Strategies for Teaching Reading Comprehension. rev. ed. 2008. (Illus.). 256p. pap. 35.63 (978-0-325-02579-7(7), E02579) Heinemann.

Hoyt, Linda. Solutions for Reading Comprehension: Strategic Interventions for Striving Students, K-6. 2011. 224p. pap. 30.00 (978-0-325-02967-2(9), E02967) Heinemann.

Hunt, Peter. Chidren's Literature, 4 vols., Set. 2006. (Critical Concepts in Literary & Cultural Studies). (ENG.). 1712p. (C). 1350.00 (978-0-415-37228-2(3)) Routledge.

Hynes-Berry, Mary. Don't Leave the Story in the Book: Using Literature to Guide Inquiry in Early Childhood Classrooms. 2011. (Early Childhood Education Ser.). (ENG.). 216p. 64.00 (978-0-8077-5288-3(6)); pap. 29.95 (978-0-8077-5287-6(8)) Teachers College Pr., Teachers College, Columbia Univ.

Immel, Andrea. Childhood & Children's Books in Early Modern Europe, 1550-1800. 2009. 346p. 39.95 (978-0-415-80363-2(2)) Routledge.

Irving, Jan. Story Celebrations: A Program Guide for Schools & Libraries, 1 vol. 2008. (Illus.). 216p. per. 35.00 (978-1-59158-432-2(9), LU4329) Libraries Unlimited, Inc.

Jacobs, George M. & Farrell, Thomas S. C. Teachers Sourcebook for Extensive Reading. 2012. (978-1-61735-778-7(2)); pap. (978-1-61735-777-0(4)) Information Age Publishing, Inc.

Jenkins, Carol Brennan, et al. Nonfiction Author Studies in the Elementary Classroom. 2007. (Illus.). 160p. pap. 26.25 (978-0-325-00855-4(8), E00855) Heinemann.

Johnson, Denise. The Joy of Children's Literature. 2nd ed. 2011. (Whatâ€(tm)s New in Education Ser.). (ENG.). 512p. (C). pap. 93.95 (978-1-111-29836-4(X)) Wadsworth.

Johnson, Nancy J. & Giorgis, Cyndi. The Wonder of It All: When Literature & Literacy Intersect. 2007. (Illus.). 224p. pap. 32.50 (978-0-325-00973-5(2), E00973) Heinemann.

Jones, V. C. Catch the Reading Bug. 2009. 32p. pap. 14.49 (978-1-4389-6628-1(8)) AuthorHouse.

Keane, Nancy J. 101 Great, Ready-to-Use Book Lists for Children, 1 vol. 2012. 130p. pap. 40.00 (978-1-61069-083-6(4), A3769P) Pearson Education GBR. Dist: ABC-CLIO, LLC.

Kelley, Michelle & Clausen-Grace, Nicki. Comprehension Shouldn't Be Silent: From Strategy Instruction to Student Independence. 2007. 248p. 25.95 (978-0-87207-620-4(2)) International Reading Assn.

Kelley, Michelle J. & Clausen-Grace, Nicki. R5 in Your Classroom: A Guide to Differentiating Independent Reading & Developing Avid Readers. 2008. (ENG.). 184p. pap. 24.95 (978-0-87207-684-6(9)) International Reading Assn.

Kempton, Susan L. The Literate Kindergarten: Where Wonder & Discovery Thrive. 2007. (Illus.). 208p. pap. 28.75 (978-0-325-00833-2(7), E00833) Heinemann.

Killinger, John. The Life, Death, & Resurrection of Harry Potter. 2009. 192p. pap. 17.00 (978-0-88146-162-6(8)) Mercer Univ. Pr.

Kliewer, Ursula & Kliewer, Heinz-Jurgen, eds. Nur das Denken, das wir leben, hat einen Wert: Zur Erinnerung an den Literaturdidaktiker und Kinder- und Jugendliteraturforscher Malte Dahrendorf (1928-2008) 2009. (Kinder- und Jugendkultur, -literatur und -medien. Theorie - Geschichte - Didaktik Ser.). (GER.). 270p. 67.95 (978-3-631-58974-8(3)) Lang, Peter GmbH, Europaischer Verlag der Wissenschaften DEU. Dist: Lang, Peter.

Knowles, Elizabeth. Differentiating Reading Instruction through Children's Literature, 1 vol. 2009. 153p. pap. 35.00 (978-1-59158-787-3(5), LU8787) Libraries Unlimited, Inc.

Kogure, Keisuke. Onara Rori: Kyo Mo Genki ni II Onara. 2011. (JPN., Illus.). 32p. (J). (gr. -1-3). (978-4-05-203374-2(4)) Gakushu Kenkyu-Sha.

Kohl, Herbert R. & Kohl, Herbert. Should We Burn Babar? Essays on Children's Literature & the Power of Stories. rev. ed. 2007. (ENG.). 224p. pap. 14.95 (978-1-59558-130-3(8)) New Pr., The.

Kokkola, Lydia. Representing the Holocaust in Children's Literature. 2009. 206p. pap. 39.95 (978-0-415-80365-6(9)) Routledge.

Kokusai Kodomo Toshokan (Japan) Staff, contrib. by. Itsu, Nani to Deau Ka: Akachan Ehon Kara Yangu Adaruto Bungaku Made. 2010. (JPN., Illus.). 116p. (978-4-87582-701-6(6)) National Diet Library.

Kolencik, Patricia Liotta & Bernadowski, Carianne. Teaching with Books That Heal: Authentic Literature & Literacy Strategies to Help Children Cope with Everyday Problems, 1 vol. 2007. (Illus.). 184p. per. 36.95 (978-1-58683-220-9(4), A2463P) Linworth Publishing, Inc.

Kosman, Gary. Bonding While Learning. 2007. 183p. pap. 15.95 (978-0-615-13829-9(2)) America Learns, LLC.

Kotaman, Hüseyin. Children's Vocabulary Development Through Dialogical Reading. 2009. 192p. pap. (978-3-639-19014-4(9)) VDM Verlag Dr. Mueller e.K.

Krashen, Stephen D. Free Voluntary Reading. 2011. (Illus.). viii, 90p. E-Book (978-1-59884-845-8(3)) Libraries Unlimited, Inc.

—Free Voluntary Reading: Power 2010, 1 vol. (Illus.). 90p. pap. 25.00 (978-1-59884-844-1(5), A3456P) Libraries Unlimited, Inc.

Krim, Geri & Mittelman, Sandy, compiled by. Choices: A Core Collection for Young Reluctant Readers, Vol. 6. 2006. 237p. 50.00 (978-0-934272-87-2(5)) Burke, John Gordon Pub., Inc.

Lanes, Selma G. Through the Looking Glass: Further Adventures & Misadventures in the Realm of Children's Literature. 2006. (ENG., Illus.). 247p. pap. 18.95 (978-1-56792-318-6(6)) Godine, David R. Pub.

Lehman, Barbara A. Children's Literature & Learning: Literary Study Across the Curriculum. 2007. (Language & Literacy Ser.). (ENG.). 168p. 50.00 (978-0-8077-4824-4(2)); (Illus.). pap. 23.95 (978-0-8077-4823-7(4)) Teachers College Pr., Teachers College, Columbia Univ.

Lester, Neal A. Once upon a Time in a Different World: Issues & Ideas in African American Children's Literature. 2007. (Children's Literature & Culture Ser.). 304p. 131.00 (978-0-415-98019-7(4)) Routledge.

Lockwood, Michael. Promoting Reading for Pleasure in the Primary School. 2008. (Illus.). 168p. 117.00 (978-1-4129-2966-0(0), B29660C); pap. 36.00 (978-1-4129-2967-7(9), B29660P) SAGE Pubns., Ltd. GBR. Dist: SAGE Pubns., Inc.

Long, Greg. Today I Found God. 2010. (Illus.). 32p. (J). (978-1-935268-23-9(6)) Halo Publishing International.

Lowe, Virginia. Stories, Pictures & Reality. 2006. (Illus.). XVIII, 190p. 190.00 (978-0-415-39723-0(5)) Routledge.

—Stories, Pictures & Reality: Young Children's Understanding of Reality & Pretence. 2006. (ENG., Illus.). 208p. (C). 46.95 (978-0-415-39724-7(3)) Routledge.

Lurie, Alison. Boys & Girls Forever: Children's Classics from Cinderella to Harry Potter. 2006. 219p. reprint ed. 25.00 (978-1-4223-5774-3(0)) DIANE Publishing Co.

Lusardi, Donna M. & Kent, Rosemarie. The New Book of Knowledge. 2008. 266p. (978-0-7172-0589-9(4), Grolier) Scholastic Library Publishing.

Mallan, Kerry & Bradford, Clare, eds. Contemporary Children's Literature & Film: Engaging with Theory. 2011. (ENG., Illus.). 240p. pap. 28.00 (978-0-230-23150-4(0)) Palgrave Macmillan.

Mallett, Margaret. Choosing & Using Fiction & Non-Fiction 3-11. 2010. (ENG., Illus.). 416p. 155.00 (978-0-415-48458-9(8)) Routledge.

Marcus, Leonard S. Minders of Make-Believe: Idealists, Entrepreneurs, & the Shaping of American Children's Literature. 2008. (ENG.). 416p. (gr. 17). 28.00 (978-0-395-67407-9(7)) Houghton Mifflin Harcourt Trade & Reference Pubs.

—Pass It Down: Five Picture Book Families Make Their Mark. 2006. (ENG., Illus.). 64p. (J). (gr. 2-7). 19.95 (978-0-8027-9600-4(1)); lib. bdg. 20.85 (978-0-8027-9601-1(X)) Walker & Co.

Matthew, Kathryn I. & Lowe, Joy L. Neal-Schuman Guide to Recommended Children's Books & Media for Use with Every Elementary Subject. 2nd ed. 2010. 400p. 80.00 (978-1-55570-688-3(6)) Neal-Schuman Pubs., Inc.

McCallum, Elizabeth & Scott, Jane. The Book Tree: A Christian Reference for Children's Literature. 2nd ed. 2008. (ENG.). 19.00 (978-1-59128-050-7(8)) Canon Pr.

McDaniel, Deanna J. Gentle Reads: Great Books to Warm Hearts & Lift Spirits, Grades 5-9, 1 vol. 2007. (Children's & Young Adult Literature Reference Ser.). 328p. 45.00 (978-1-59158-491-9(4), LU4914) Libraries Unlimited, Inc.

McGavran, James Holt, ed. Romanticism & Children's Literature in Nineteenth-Century England. 2009. (ENG.). 272p. pap. 24.95 (978-0-8203-3487-5(1)) Univ. of Georgia Pr.

McGuire, Beth. Active Reading: Activities for Librarians & Teachers, 1 vol. 2008. (Illus.). 184p. pap. 35.00 (978-1-59158-666-1(6), LU8666) Libraries Unlimited, Inc.

Meier, Daniel R. & Meier, Daniel, eds. Here's the Story: Using Narrative to Promote Young Children's Language & Literacy Learning. 2009. (ENG., Illus.). 176p. pap. 26.95 (978-0-8077-4979-1(6)); (978-0-8077-4980-7(X)) Teachers College Pr., Teachers College, Columbia Univ.

Melrose, Andrew. Here Comes the Bogeyman: Exploring Contemporary Issues in Writing for Children. 2012. (ENG., Illus.). 152p. (C). 130.00 (978-0-415-61752-9(9)); pap. 31.95 (978-0-415-61753-6(7)) Routledge.

Mendlesohn, Farah. The Inter-Galactic Playground: A Critical Study of Children's & Teens' Science Fiction. Palumbo, Donald E. & Sullivan, C. W., III, eds. 2009. (Critical Explorations in Science Fiction & Fantasy Ser.). (ENG., Illus.). 283p. pap. 45.00 (978-0-7864-3503-6(8)) McFarland & Co., Inc. Pubs.

Mesmer, Heidi Anne E. Tools for Matching Readers to Texts: Research-Based Practices. 2007. (Solving Problems in Teaching of Literacy Ser.). (ENG.). 180p. (gr. k-6). 50.00 (978-1-59385-598-7(2)) Guilford Pubns., Inc.

Messner, Patricia A. & Copeland, Brenda S. Every Day Reading Incentives, 1 vol. 2009. 190p. pap. 35.00 (978-1-59158-755-2(7), LU8755) Libraries Unlimited, Inc.

Miller, Cathy Puett. Anytime Reading Readiness: Fun & Easy Family Activities That Prepare Your Child to Read. 2009. 96p. pap. 11.95 (978-1-934338-74-2(5)) Maupin Hse. Publishing.

Miller, Donalyn & Miller. The Book Whisperer: Awakening the Inner Reader in Every Child. 2009. (ENG., Illus.). 240p. pap. 23.95 (978-0-470-37227-2(3), Jossey-Bass) Wiley, John & Sons, Inc.

Miller, Pat. Stretchy Lesson Plans: August/September. 2007. (Illus.). 77p. per. 15.95 (978-1-932146-92-9(X), Upstart Bks.) Highsmith Inc.

Mogilner, Alijandra & Mogilner, Tayopa. Children's Writer's Word Book. 2nd ed. 2006. (ENG., Illus.). 352p. per. 16.99 (978-1-58297-413-2(6), 11031) F&W Media, Inc.

Morgenstern, John. Playing with Books: A Study of the Reader as Child. 2009. (ENG.). 240p. pap. 39.95 (978-0-7864-4295-9(6)) McFarland & Co., Inc. Pubs.

Morrow, Lesley Mandel, et al. Using Children's Literature in Preschool to Develop Comprehension: Understanding & Enjoying Books. 2nd ed. 2009. (ENG.). 144p. pap. 19.95 (978-0-87207-474-3(9)) International Reading Assn.

Moses, Montrose J. Children's Books & Reading. 2008. 284p. 42.95 (978-1-4369-5125-8(9)); pap. 27.95 (978-1-4367-9127-4(8)) Kessinger Publishing, LLC.

Murphy, Barbara Thrash & Murphy, Deborah. Black Authors & Illustrators of Books for Children & Young Adults: A Biographical Dictionary. Murphy, Barbara T. & Murphy, Deborah L., eds. 4th rev. ed. 2006. (Illus.). 568p. 110.00 (978-0-415-97219-2(1)) Routledge.

Nash, Jennie. Curious George Gets Away with Murder: How I Passed on My Passion, ARK. (Illus.). mass mkt. (978-0-312-99012-1(X), St. Martin's Paperbacks) St. Martin's Pr.

Neal, Connie. The Gospel According to Harry Potter: The Spritual Journey of the World's Greatest Seeker. rev. exp. ed. 2008. (Gospel according To... Ser.). (ENG.). 305p. pap. 17.00 (978-0-664-23123-1(3)) Westminster John Knox Pr.

Nodelman, Perry. The Hidden Adult: Defining Children's Literature. 2008. (ENG.). 408p. (C). (gr. 13-17). 72.00 (978-0-8018-8979-0(0)); pap. 37.00 (978-0-8018-8980-6(4)) Johns Hopkins Univ. Pr.

Norcia, Megan A. X Marks the Spot: Women Writers Map the Empire for British Children, 1790-1895. 2010. (ENG.). 304p. 49.95 (978-0-8214-1907-6(2)) Ohio Univ. Pr.

Northrup, Mary. Picture Books for Children. 2012. 202p. pap. 50.00 (978-0-8389-1144-0(7)) American Library Assn.

Norton, Donna E. Multicultural Children's Literature: Through the Eyes of Many Children. 3rd ed. 2008. (ENG., Illus.). 368p. (C). pap. 53.80 (978-0-13-514528-9(7), Prentice Hall) Prentice Hall PTR.

—Through the Eyes of a Child: An Introduction to Children's Literature. 7th ed. 2006. 124.20 (978-0-13-240155-5(X)) Prentice Hall PTR.

Norton, Donna E. & Norton, Saundra. Through the Eyes of a Child: An Introduction to Children's Literature. 8th ed. 2010. (MyEducationKit Ser.). (ENG., Illus.). 640p. (C). 155.60 *(978-0-13-702875-7(X))* Allyn & Bacon, Inc.

—Through the Eyes of a Child: An Introduction to Children's Literature (with MyEducationKit) 8th ed. 2010. (ENG.). (C). 159.60 *(978-0-13-707401-3(8),* Prentice Hall) Prentice Hall PTR.

Nunes, Terezinha & Bryant, Peter. Children's Reading & Spelling: Beyond the First Steps. 2009. (Understanding Children's Worlds Ser.). (ENG., Illus.). 320p. pap. 44.95 *(978-0-631-23403-6(9))*; 116.95 *(978-0-631-23402-9(0))* Wiley, John & Sons, Inc. (Wiley-Blackwell).

O'Callaghan, Catherine M., et al. Using Children's Literature Across the Curriculum: A Handbook of Instructional Strategies. 2010. (ENG.). 264p. (C). pap. 35.00 *(978-0-13-171191-4(1),* Allyn & Bacon) Pearson Education Canada CAN. Dist: Pearson Education.

O'Dell, Felicity Ann. Socialisation through Children's Literature: The Soviet Example. 2010. (Cambridge Russian, Soviet & Post-Soviet Studies). (ENG.). 290p. pap. 23.99 *(978-0-521-14437-7(X))* Cambridge Univ. Pr.

O'Sullivan, Emer. Comparative Children's Literature. 2009. 210p. pap. 40.00 *(978-0-415-56412-0(3))* Routledge.

O'Sullivan, Keith & Coghlan, Valerie, eds. Irish Children's Literature & Culture: New Perspectives on Contemporary Writing. 2012. (ENG.). (C). pap. 39.95 ***(978-0-415-62355-1(3))*** Routledge.

Pantaleo, Sylvia. Exploring Student Response to Contemporary Picturebooks. 2009. (Illus.). 264p. pap. *(978-1-4426-1095-8(6))* Univ. of Toronto Pr.

Parsons, Stephanie. First Grade Readers: Units of Study to Help Children See Themselves As Readers & Meaning Makers. 2010. 168p. pap. 23.75 *(978-0-325-01728-0(X),* E01728) Heinemann.

Paul, Lissa. The Children's Book Business: Lessons from the Long Eighteenth Century. 2012. (ENG.). 208p. (C). pap. 39.95 ***(978-0-415-62826-6(1))*** Routledge.

Pavonetti, Linda. Bridges to Understanding: Envisioning the World through Children's Books. 2011. (ENG.). 534p. (gr. 17). pap. 55.00 *(978-0-8108-8106-8(3))* Scarecrow Pr., Inc.

Pavonetti, Linda M. Bridges to Understanding: Envisioning the World Through Children's Books. 2011. E-Book ***(978-0-8108-8107-5(1))*** Scarecrow Pr., Inc.

The Pearl. 8.97 *(978-0-673-58331-4(7))* Addison-Wesley Longman, Inc.

Peck, Penny. Readers' Advisory for Children And 'Tweens, 1 vol. 2010. 190p. pap. 36.00 *(978-1-59884-387-3(7),* A2717P) Libraries Unlimited, Inc.

Peterson, Shelley Stagg & Swartz, Larry. Good Books Matter: How to Choose & Use Children's Literature to Help Students Grow as Readers. 2008. (ENG.). 160p. (C). (gr. k-8). pap. 21.00 *(978-1-55138-232-6(6))* Pembroke Pubs., Ltd. CAN. Dist: Stenhouse Pubs.

Petzold, Dieter. Das englische Kunstmärchen im neunzehnten Jahrhundert. (Buchreihe der Anglia Ser.). (GER.). X, 362p. 140.00 ***(978-3-11-127768-4(2))*** De Gruyter, Mouton DEU. Dist: de Gruyter, Walter GmbH & Co. KG.

Polette, Nancy. Reading the World with Picture Books. 2010. E-Book *(978-1-59884-589-4(8))* Libraries Unlimited, Inc.

Polette, Nancy J. Find Someone Who: Introducing 200 Favorite Picture Books, 1 vol. 2006. 220p. per. 35.00 *(978-1-59158-465-0(5),* LU4655) Libraries Unlimited, Inc.

—Reading the World with Picture Books, 1 vol. 2010. 348p. pap. 35.00 *(978-1-59884-587-7(X),* A3100P) Libraries Unlimited, Inc.

Potts-Klement, Edina. Harry Potter As a Fairy Tale. 2008. 80p. pap. *(978-3-639-01915-5(6))* VDM Verlag Dr. Mueller e.K.

Price, Anne & Rowland, Marguerita. Children's Core Collection. 20th ed. 2010. 1700p. 210.00 *(978-0-8242-1106-6(5))* Wilson, H.W.

Raines, Shirley C. & Smith, Brian Scott. Story Stretchers for the Primary Grades: Activities to Expand Children's Books. 2011. (Story S-t-r-e-t-c-h-e-r-s Ser.). (ENG., Illus.). 256p. (gr. k-4). pap. 29.95 ***(978-0-87659-309-7(0))*** Gryphon Hse., Inc.

Reid, Rob. Reid's Read-Alouds: Selections for Children & Teens. 2009. 208p. 45.00 *(978-0-8389-0980-5(9))* American Library Assn.

—Reid's Read-Alouds 2: Modern-Day Classics from C. S. Lewis to Lemony Snicket. 2010. pap. *(978-0-8389-1072-6(6))* American Library Assn.

—Shake & Shout: 16 Noisy, Lively Story Programs. 2008. (Illus.). 110p. pap. 17.95 *(978-1-60213-006-7(X),* Upstart Bks.) Highsmith Inc.

—Something Musical Happened at the Library: Adding Song & Dance to Children's Story Programs. 2007. (Illus.). 158p. per. 35.00 *(978-0-8389-0942-3(6))* American Library Assn.

Reis, Sally M. & Reis. The Joyful Reading Resource Kit: Teaching Tools, Hands-On Activities, & Enrichment Resources. 2009. (ENG., Illus.). 320p. pap. 29.95 *(978-0-470-39188-4(X),* Jossey-Bass) Wiley, John & Sons, Inc.

Reuter, Kara. Children Selecting Books in a Library. 2008. 240p. per. *(978-3-8364-5728-6(8))* VDM Verlag Dr. Mueller e.K.

Reynolds, Kimberley. Children's Literature: A Very Short Introduction. 2011. (Very Short Introductions Ser.). (ENG., Illus.). 168p. pap. 11.95 *(978-0-19-956024-0(2))* Oxford Univ. Pr., Inc.

Richmond, Velma Bourgeois. Shakespeare as Children's Literature: Edwardian Retellings in Words & Pictures. 2008. (ENG., Illus.). 371p. pap. 35.00 *(978-0-7864-3781-8(2))* McFarland & Co., Inc. Pubs.

Roberts, Dave. The Twilight Gospel: The Spiritual Roots of the Stephenie Meyer Vampire Saga, 1 vol. 2009. (ENG., Illus.). 160p. pap. 12.99 *(978-1-85424-976-0(2),* Monarch Bks.) Lion Hudson PLC GBR. Dist: Kregel Pubns.

Rockman, Connie C. Tenth Book of Junior Authors & Illustrators. 2008. 803p. 120.00 *(978-0-8242-1066-3(2))* Wilson, H.W.

Rollin, Lucy & West, Mark I. Psychoanalytic Responses to Children's Literature. alt. ed. 2008. (ENG.). 190p. pap. 29.95 *(978-0-7864-3764-1(2))* McFarland & Co., Inc. Pubs.

Rudd, David. Children's Literature. 2010. (Routledge Companions Ser.). (ENG., Illus.). 336p. 115.00 *(978-0-415-47270-8(9))*; pap. 32.95 *(978-0-415-47271-5(7))* Routledge.

Russell, David L. Literature for Children: A Short Introduction. 7th ed. 2011. (ENG., Illus.). 360p. (C). pap. 78.67 *(978-0-13-217379-7(4))* Allyn & Bacon, Inc.

Saccardi, Marianne. Books That Teach Kids to Write. 2011. E-Book *(978-1-59884-452-8(0))* Libraries Unlimited, Inc.

Saccardi, Marianne C. Books That Teach Kids to Write, 1 vol. 2011. (Illus.). 178p. pap. 30.00 *(978-1-59884-451-1(2),* A2903P) Pearson Education GBR. Dist: ABC-CLIO, LLC.

Sawyer, Walter. Growing up with Literature. 6th ed. 2011. (Whatsrquo;s New in Early Childhood Ser.). (ENG.). 400p. (C). pap. 95.95 *(978-1-111-34265-4(2))* Wadsworth.

Schakel, Peter J. The Longing for a Form: Essays on the Fiction of C. S. Lewis. Schakel, Peter J., ed. 2008. (C. S. Lewis Secondary Studies Ser.). 256p. pap. 28.00 *(978-1-55635-588-2(2),* Wipf and Stock) Wipf & Stock Pubs.

Schakel, Peter J. & Huttar, Charles A., eds. Word & Story in C. S. Lewis: Language & Narrative in Theory & Practice. 2008. (C. S. Lewis Secondary Studies Ser.). 330p. pap. 36.00 *(978-1-55635-587-5(4))* Wipf & Stock Pubs.

Schiller, Pam & Phipps, Pat. Starting with Stories: Engaging Multiple Intelligences Through Children's Books. 2006. (ENG., Illus.). 256p. per. 24.95 *(978-0-87659-297-7(3))* Gryphon Hse., Inc.

Scholastic, Inc. Staff, contrib. by. Core Knowledge Library: Teacher's Guide PreK. 2008. (Illus.). 32p. *(978-0-545-06680-8(8))* Scholastic, Inc.

Schon, Isabel. Recommended Books in Spanish for Children & Young Adults, 2004-2008. 2008. (ENG.). 424p. 65.00 *(978-0-8108-6386-6(3))* Scarecrow Pr., Inc.

Schulman, Mary Browning. Guided Reading: Everything You Need to Make Small-Group Reading Instruction Work in Your Classroom. 2006. (Scholastic Teaching Strategies Ser.). (ENG., Illus.). 176p. (gr. 3-6). per. 21.99 *(978-0-439-44397-5(0),* Teaching Strategies) Scholastic, Inc.

Schwebel, Sara L. Child-Sized History: Fictions of the Past in U. S. Classrooms. 2011. (ENG.). 272p. 69.95 *(978-0-8265-1792-0(7))*; pap. 34.95 *(978-0-8265-1793-7(5))* Vanderbilt Univ. Pr.

Schwedt, Rachel & DeLong, Janice. Core Collection for Children & Young Adults. 2008. (ENG.). 218p. 60.00 *(978-0-8108-6115-2(1))* Scarecrow Pr., Inc.

Serchay, David S. The Librarian's Guide to Graphic Novels for Children & Tweens. 2008. (Illus.). 272p. pap. 55.00 *(978-1-55570-626-5(6))* Neal-Schuman Pubs., Inc.

Shedlock, Marie L. The Art of the Story-Teller. I.t. ed. 2007. (ENG.). 220p. pap. 22.99 *(978-1-4264-2817-3(0))* BiblioBazaar.

Silver, Linda. The Jewish Values Finder: A Guide to Values in Jewish Children's Literature. 2008. 290p. pap. 55.00 *(978-1-55570-624-1(X))* Neal-Schuman Pubs., Inc.

Silvers, Penny & Shorey, Mary C. Many Texts, Many Voices: Teaching Literacy & Social Justice to Young Learners in the Digital Age. 2012. pap. ***(978-1-57110-875-3(0))*** Stenhouse Pubs.

Smart, Lizzie. A More Complex View of Reading. 2012. 160p. 130.00 *(978-0-415-58601-6(1))*; pap. 41.95 *(978-0-415-58602-3(X))* Routledge.

Smith, Henrietta M. The Coretta Scott King Awards, 1970-2009. 4th ed. 2009. (Illus.). xii, 131p. *(978-0-8389-3584-2(2))* American Library Assn.

Soltan, Rita. Summer Reading Renaissance: An Interactive Exhibits Approach, 1 vol. 2008. (Illus.). 264p. pap. 45.00 *(978-1-59158-572-5(4),* LU8572) Libraries Unlimited, Inc.

Spiegel, Carol. Book by Book: An Annotated Guide to Young People's Literature with Peacemaking & Conflict Resolution Themes. 2010. 186p. pap. 35.00 *(978-0-942349-93-1(8))* Educators for Social Responsibility.

Stephens, John, ed. Ways of Being Male: Representing Masculinities in Children's Literature. 2008. (Illus.). 304p. 39.95 *(978-0-415-99515-3(9))* Routledge.

Stipek, Deborah J., et al. Motivated Minds: Raising Children to Love Learning. (ENG.). pap. 14.00 *(978-0-8050-6396-7(X),* Owl Bks.) Holt, Henry & Co.

Stoodt-Hill, Barbara D. & Amspaugh-Corson, Linda B. Children's Literature: Discovery for a Lifetime. 4th ed. 2008. (ENG., Illus.). 412p. (C). pap. 102.20 *(978-0-13-158939-1(3),* Prentice Hall) Prentice Hall PTR.

Styles, Morag & Arizpe, Evelyn, eds. Acts of Reading: Teachers, Texts & Childhood. 2009. (Illus.). 256p. pap. 34.95 *(978-1-85856-438-8(7))* Trentham Bks. Ltd. GBR. Dist: Stylus Publishing, LLC.

Sutton, Roger & Parravano, Martha, eds. A Family of Readers: The Book Lover's Guide to Children's & Young Adult Literature. 2011. (ENG., Illus.). 368p. pap. 14.99 *(978-0-7636-5755-0(7))* Candlewick Pr.

Sutton, Roger & Parravano, Martha V., eds. A Family of Readers: The Book Lover's Guide to Children's & Young Adult Literature. 2010. (ENG., Illus.). 368p. 22.00 *(978-0-7636-3280-9(5))* Candlewick Pr.

Szymusiak, Karen, et al. Beyond Leveled Books, Second Edition. 2nd ed. 2008. (ENG.). 272p. (C). (gr. k-5). pap. 21.00 *(978-1-57110-714-5(2))* Stenhouse Pubs.

Tatar, Maria. Enchanted Hunters: The Power of Stories in Childhood. 2009. (ENG., Illus.). 304p. 26.95 *(978-0-393-06601-2(0),* 6601) Norton, W. W. & Co., Inc.

Teacher Created Materials Staff & Hart, Melissa. Using Graphic Novels in Classr. 2010. 48p. pap. 8.99 *(978-1-4206-2363-5(X))* Teacher Created Resources, Inc.

Thomas, Joseph T. Poetry's Playground: The Culture of Contemporary American Children's Poetry. 2007. (Landscapes of Childhood Ser.). (Illus.). 180p. per. 24.95 *(978-0-8143-3296-2(X))* Wayne State Univ. Pr.

Thomas, Rebecca L. & Barr, Catherine. Popular Series Fiction for K-6 Readers: A Reading & Selection Guide, 1 vol. 2nd ed. 2008. (Children's & Young Adult Literature Reference Ser.). 1016p. 65.00 *(978-1-59158-659-3(3),* LU8659) Libraries Unlimited, Inc.

Thompson, Deborah L. Multicultural Children's Literature. 2009. (ENG.). 304p. (C). pap. 30.00 *(978-0-13-199413-3(1),* Prentice Hall) Prentice Hall PTR.

Thomson-Wohlgem & Thomson-wohlgemuth, Gaby. Translation under State Control: Books for Young People in the German Democratic Republic. 2009. (Children's Literature & Culture Ser.). (Illus.). 260p. 136.00 *(978-0-415-99580-1(9))* Routledge.

Thorpe, Dina. Reading for Fun: A Study of How Parents & Libraries Encouraged Children Aged 9-12 to Read for Enjoyment. (Illus.). x, 202p. 34.95 *(978-0-947767-91-4(6))* Cranfield Univ. GBR. Dist: Paul & Co. Pubs. Consortium, Inc.

Totten, Kathryn. Let's Read! Storytime Crafts, Grade PreK-1: Literacy Activities for Little Learners. 2007. (Illus.). 107p. per. 12.99 *(978-1-56472-236-2(8),* Upstart Bks.) Highsmith Inc.

Travers, John F. & Travers, Barbara E. Children's Literature: A Developmental Perspective. 2008. (ENG., Illus.). 440p. (C). per. 138.95 *(978-0-470-11104-8(6),* Wiley) Wiley, John & Sons, Inc.

Treviño, Rose Zertuche. Read Me a Rhyme in Spanish & English: Léame una Rima en Español e Inglés. 2009. (SPA & ENG.). 160p. 45.00 *(978-0-8389-0982-9(5))* American Library Assn.

Underdown, Harold D. Publishing Children's Books - Complete Idiot's Guide. 3rd ed. 2008. (Complete Idiot's Guide Ser.). (ENG., Illus.). 384p. (gr. 12-18). 18.95 *(978-1-59257-750-7(4),* Alpha Bks.) Penguin Group (USA) Inc.

van Kleeck, Anne. Sharing Books & Stories to Promote Language & Literacy. 2006. (Emergent & Early Literacy Ser.). (Illus.). 356p. per. 57.95 *(978-1-59756-091-7(X))* Plural Publishing, Inc.

Van Orden, Phyllis J., et al. Children's Books: A Practical Guide to Selection. 2007. (Illus.). pap. 59.95 *(978-1-55570-584-8(7))* Neal-Schuman Pubs., Inc.

Vardell, Sylvia. Children's Literature in Action: A Librarian's Guide, 1 vol. 2008. (Library & Information Science Text Ser.). (Illus.). 323p. pap. 50.00 *(978-1-59158-557-2(0),* LU8557) Libraries Unlimited, Inc.

Vardell, Sylvia M. Children's Literature in Action: A Librarian's Guide, 1 vol. 2008. (Library & Information Science Text Ser.). (Illus.). 340p. 65.00 *(978-1-59158-657-9(7),* LU6579) Libraries Unlimited, Inc.

Vasquez, Vivian. Getting Beyond I Like the Book: Creating Space for Critical Literacy in K-6 Classrooms. 2nd ed. 2010. (ENG., Illus.). ix, 148p. pap. 21.95 *(978-0-87207-505-4(2))* International Reading Assn.

Welsh, Charles. A Bookseller of the Last Century. 2010. (Cambridge Library Collection - Printing & Publishing History Ser.). (ENG., Illus.). 404p. pap. 31.99 *(978-1-108-01279-9(5))* Cambridge Univ. Pr.

Wilson, Nicole L. From Formula to Solid Food: How Media Nourishes Children's Literature. 2011. 236p. pap. ***(978-3-8433-8982-2(9))*** Lambert Academic Publishing.

Wunderlich, Richard & Morrissey, Thomas J. Pinocchio Goes Postmodern: Perils of a Puppet in the United States. 2008. (Illus.). 304p. 39.95 *(978-0-415-99324-1(5))* Routledge.

Yellin, David G. & DeVries, Beverly A. Sharing the Journey: Literature for Young Children. 2011. *(978-1-934432-07-5(5))* Holcomb Hathaway, Inc.

Zipes, Jack. Fairy Tales & the Art of Subversion. 2nd ed. 2011. (Routledge Classics Ser.). (ENG.). 288p. pap. 24.95 *(978-0-415-61025-4(7))* Routledge.

Zipes, Jack D. Relentless Progress: The Reconfiguration of Children's Literature, Fairy Tales, & Storytelling. 2008. (ENG., Illus.). 208p. (C). 125.00 *(978-0-415-99063-9(7))* Routledge.

Zipes, Jack D., et al. Relentless Progress: The Reconfiguration of Children's Literature, Fairy Tales, & Storytelling. 2008. (Illus.). 208p. pap. 34.95 *(978-0-415-99064-6(5))* Routledge.

Zvirin, Stephanie. Read with Me: Best Books for Preschoolers. 2012. (ENG.). 184p. pap. 18.95 ***(978-1-937589-03-5(X)***, Huron Street Pr.) American Library Assn.

CHILDREN—CARE

see Child Care

CHILDREN—CARE AND HYGIENE

see Child Care; Children—Health and Hygiene

CHILDREN—CHARITIES

see Child Welfare

CHILDREN—CLOTHING

see Children's Clothing

CHILDREN—CLUBS

see Children's Clubs

CHILDREN—CONDUCT OF LIFE

Allen, Hazel. A Journey of Love: The Special Children Who Inspired Me to Find & Follow My Passion. 2009. 100p. pap. 15.00 *(978-1-4269-0595-7(5))* Trafford Publishing.

Amaya & Prado. Puppet Master or Pawn? Raising Successful, Happy, & Resilient Childrens with Needs, Failures, Self-Discipline. 2009. 110p. pap. 10.15 *(978-1-60860-790-7(9),* Eloquent Bks.) AEG Literary Publishing Services, Inc.

Atlantic Publishing Group. The Complete Guide to Discussing Difficult Subjects with Children & Teens: Alcohol, Drugs, Sex, Relationships & Other Hard Topics Made Easy. 2012. (ENG.). 288p. pap. 24.95 *(978-1-60138-574-1(9))* Atlantic Publishing Co.

Becker, David. 50 Life Skills to Ensure Kids Stay in School, off Drugs & Out of Trouble. 2008. (ENG., Illus.). 152p. 44.95 *(978-1-85539-461-2(8),* Network Continuum Education) Continuum International Publishing Group, Ltd. GBR. Dist: National Bk. Network.

Bokoff, Cathy G., ed. Helping Children Thrive: A Handbook for Grassroots Regional Collaboration. 2007. 104p. pap. 49.50 *(978-1-879979-04-8(7))* Lifescape Enterprises.

Brower, Robert & Keller, Amy. Empowering Students: Seven Strategies for a Smart Start in School & Life. 2006. (ENG.). 164p. 55.00 *(978-1-57886-491-1(7))*; per. 27.95 *(978-1-57886-492-8(5))* Rowman & Littlefield Education.

Canfield, Jack, et al. Chicken Soup for the Soul: Just for Preteens - 101 Stories of Inspiration & Support for Tweens. 2011. (ENG.). 400p. pap. 14.95 *(978-1-935096-73-3(7))* Chicken Soup for the Soul Publishing, LLC.

Chatelle, Melody. Journeys of Heartache & Grace: Conversations & Life Lessons from Young People with Serious Illnesses. 2008. 256p. pap. 16.95 *(978-1-880292-35-8(1))* LangMarc Publishing.

Child, Lydia Maria. Mothers Book. 2006. 180p. per. *(978-1-4067-9578-3(X),* Pierides Pr.) Read Bks.

Cook, Wanda. Guidance for the Gourmet: 23 recipes to teach children lifeskill Lessons. 2005. pap. 25.95 *(978-1-57543-142-0(4))* MAR*CO Products, Inc.

Cooper, Terry T. Protecting Our Children. 2006. pap. 10.00 *(978-1-4257-1471-0(4))* Xlibris Corp.

Corlett, Ian James. E Is for Ethics: How to Talk to Kids about Morals, Values, & What Matters Most. 2011. (ENG., Illus.). 128p. pap. 14.00 *(978-1-4165-9655-4(0),* Beyond Words/Atria Bks.) Atria Bks.

Crossen, Jan. 9 Lives, Cat Tales. 2008. 168p. pap. 12.25 *(978-0-9798686-3-4(7))* Dragonpublishing.net.

Csoti, Marianna. Developing Children's Social, Emotional & Behavioural Skills. 2009. (ENG.). 152p. 35.95 *(978-1-85539-471-1(5))* Continuum International Publishing Group, Ltd. GBR. Dist: National Bk. Network.

David Gudgeon. 1001 Things Every Child Should Try to Do, Before Childhood Is Through! 2010. 72p. pap. 10.95 *(978-1-4401-9884-7(5))* iUniverse, Inc.

Drew, Naomi. No Kidding about Bullying: 125 Ready-to-Use Activities to Help Kids Manage Anger, Resolve Conflicts, Build Empathy, & Get Along. 2010. (Bully Free Classroom Ser.). (ENG.). 288p. (gr. 3-6). 39.99 *(978-1-57542-349-4(9))* Free Spirit Publishing, Inc.

Eiderzen, Doug. The Metaphysics of the Model: Values within/toward the Attitude & Approach of Life. 2009. 92p. pap. 14.49 *(978-1-4490-5430-9(3))* AuthorHouse.

Fletcher, Tricia. The Wonderful World of Jacob & Juli. 2009. 16p. pap. 12.99 *(978-1-4490-3751-2(8))* AuthorHouse.

Frankel, Sam. Children, Morality & Society. 2012. (Studies in Childhood & Youth Ser.). (ENG., Illus.). 240p. 85.00 ***(978-0-230-28426-5(4))*** Palgrave Macmillan.

Fried, Suellen. Banishing Bullying Behavior: Transforming the Culture of Peer Abuse. 2nd ed. 2011. (ENG.). 192p. pap. 19.95 ***(978-1-61048-433-6(9))*** Rowman & Littlefield Education.

Fried, Suellen & Sosland, Blanch. Banishing Bullying Behavior: Transforming the Culture of Pain, Rage, & Revenge. 2009. (ENG., Illus.). 196p. pap. 31.95 *(978-1-60709-221-6(2))* Rowman & Littlefield Publishers, Inc.

Fried, Suellen & Sosland, Blanche E. Banishing Bullying Behavior: Exploring the Culture of Pain, Rage & Revenge. 2009. (ENG., Illus.). 196p. 90.00 *(978-1-60709-220-9(4))* Rowman & Littlefield Education.

Fried, Suellen & Sosland, Blanche E. Banishing Bullying Behavior: Transforming the Culture of Peer Abuse. 2nd ed. 2011. ***(978-1-61048-434-3(7))*** Rowman & Littlefield Publishers, Inc.

Garrett, Joan. The Journey Continues: Life's Travel Guide for Teens & Young Adults. 2010. 196p. pap. 16.95 *(978-1-4401-9653-9(2))* iUniverse, Inc.

Ginsberg, Binyomin. A Principal's Principles: Encouraging Messages for Parents from a Noted Mechanech. 2009. (Artscroll Ser.). (Illus.). 35p. 23.99 *(978-1-4226-0903-3(0))* Mesorah Pubns., Ltd.

Goba, Fairhope Dumile. Trends in Relation to the Involvement of Family in Children in Care. 2011. 216p. pap. ***(978-3-8443-9823-6(6))*** Lambert Academic Publishing.

Hooker, Horace. The Child's Book on the Sabbath. 2008. 208p. 24.99 *(978-0-559-22390-7(0))*; pap. 17.99 *(978-0-559-22387-7(0))* BiblioBazaar.

Hunter-King, Clara, et al. This Is Not Cool: Legal Lessons for Youth & Their Parents. 2007. per. 12.00 *(978-0-9792016-2-2(4))* Milligan Bks.

Jelleberg, Susan. Jellybean Jamboree: 6 Lifeskill Units for Young Children. 2006. pap. 22.95 *(978-1-57543-145-1(9))* MAR*CO Products, Inc.

Jones, Charles. To Be a Single Father. 2009. 184p. 27.99 *(978-1-4389-4244-5(3))*; pap. 21.49 *(978-1-4389-4245-2(1))* AuthorHouse.

Lamb, Pat. Let the Children Come. 2009. 175p. pap. 12.99 *(978-1-60696-397-5(X))* Tate Publishing & Enterprises, LLC.

Leanoria Johnson. Lillie Dillie Start Wealthy: Early Wealth Management for Kids. 2009. 156p. pap. 20.00 *(978-1-4251-8167-3(8))* Trafford Publishing.

Margitics, Ferenc, et al, eds. New Perspectives in the Examination of School Bullying. 2012. (Psychology of Emotions Ser.). 187p. pap. 47.00 ***(978-1-61324-931-4(4))*** Nova Science Pubs., Inc.

Marsico, Katie. Be on Time! 2012. (21st Century Basic Skills Library). (ENG.). 24p. (gr. k-3). 22.79 ***(978-1-61080-435-6(X)***, 202045); pap. 12.79 ***(978-1-61080-609-1(3)***, 202219) Cherry Lake Publishing.

C

O'Donohue, Mary. The When You Say Thank You, Mean It: And 11 Other Lessons for Instilling Lifelong Values in Your Children. 2010. (ENG.). 256p. pap. 16.95 *(978-1-4405-0377-1(X))* Adams Media Corp.

Osborne, Mike. Filbert the Flea: Joins the Circus. 2010. 36p. pap. 17.99 *(978-1-4490-4180-9(9))* AuthorHouse.

Owen, David. The First National Bank of Dad: A Foolproof Method for Teaching Your Kids the Value of Money. 2007. (ENG.). 208p. pap. 13.00 *(978-1-4165-3425-9(3))* Simon & Schuster.

Robbins, Alexandra. The Overachievers: The Secret Lives of Driven Kids. 2006. 448p. 24.95 *(978-1-4013-0201-6(7))* Hyperion Pr.

Roehlkepartain, Jolene L., ed. Pass It On! Ready-to-Use Handouts for Asset Builders. 2nd ed. 2006. (ENG., Illus.). 176p. pap. 29.95 *(978-1-57482-243-4(8))* Search Institute.

Ronald Parton. Memos: To Kids. 2010. 164p. pap. 17.99 *(978-1-4269-2227-5(2))* Trafford Publishing.

Rosson - Tumblacer. The Good Manners Workbook: Tadpole Dreams Etiquette Program, 1. 2006. (Illus.). 67p. (J). ring bd. 19.95 *(978-0-9769320-3-1(2))* Smith, S. Pubns.

Schleifer, Michael & Martiny, Cynthia. Talking to Children about Responsibility & Emotions. 2006. (Illus.). 190p. 28.95 *(978-1-55059-321-1(8))* Detselig Enterprises, Ltd. CAN. Dist: Temeron Bks., Inc.

Senning, Cindy Post & Post, Peggy. Emily Post's Table Manners for Kids. 2009. (ENG.). 96p. (J). (gr. 3-7). 15.99 *(978-0-06-111709-1(9),* Collins) HarperCollins Pubs.

—Emily Post's the Guide to Good Table Manners for Kids. 2009. (J). lib. bdg. *(978-0-06-111711-4(0),* Collins) HarperCollins Pubs. Ltd.

Shapiro, Lawrence & Corcoran, Judy. The Self-Motivated Kid: Helping Children Develop Good Homework Habits & Reach Their Potential. 2008. (Instant Help Ser.). 130p. pap. 16.95 *(978-1-931704-32-8(5))* Play2Grow.

Smith, Maggie & Dukes, Chris. Building Better Behaviour in the Early Years. 2009. (Hands on Guides). (Illus.). 120p. 112.00 *(978-1-84787-519-8(X),* B75198C); pap. 45.00 *(978-1-84787-520-4(3),* B75198P) SAGE Pubns., Ltd. GBR. Dist: SAGE Pubns., Inc.

Sommer, Carl. t for Success Guidebook. 2009. (Quest for Success Ser.). (ENG.). 48p. pap. 14.95 *(978-1-57537-643-1(1))* Advance Publishing, Inc.

Sykes, Charles J. 50 Rules Kids Won't Learn in School: Real-World Antidotes to Feel-Good Education. rev. ed. 2007. (ENG.). 192p. 21.99 *(978-0-312-36038-2(X))* St. Martin's Pr.

Sze, Susan & Cowden, Peter. What about my Child? 2009. 152p. pap. 47.95 *(978-1-4269-0594-0(7))* Trafford Publishing.

Tateo, Christopher. A Child's First Play Book: 40 Practices to Help a Child Succeed in the Game of Life. 2010. (Illus.). 64p. pap. 25.49 *(978-1-4490-6567-6(8))* AuthorHouse.

Taylor, Daniel. Letters to My Children: A Father Passes on His Values. 2010. 177p. per. 14.95 *(978-0-9706511-2-9(0))* Bog Walk Pr.

Taylor, Kenneth Nathaniel. Big Thoughts for Little People: ABC's to Help You Grow. 2009. (ENG.). 64p. (J). 14.99 *(978-1-4143-3310-6(2),* Tyndale Kids) Tyndale Hse. Pubs.

Unell, Barbara C. & Unell, Bob. Uncle Dan's Report Card: From Toddlers to Teenagers, Helping Our Children Build Strength of Character with Healthy Habits & Values Every Day. 2011. (ENG., Illus.). 192p. (gr. 12). 14.00 *(978-0-399-53677-9(9),* Perigee Trade) Penguin Group (USA) Inc.

Wolf, Joanne, et al. Teaching Kids to Care: Nurturing Character & Compassion. 2007. (ENG., Illus.). 248p. per. 16.95 *(978-1-57174-548-4(3))* Hampton Roads Publishing Co., Inc.

Zirpoli, Thomas J. Behavior Management: Positive Applications for Teachers. 6th rev. ed. 2010. (ENG.). 480p. (C). pap. 120.20 *(978-0-13-706320-8(2),* Prentice Hall) Prentice Hall PTR.

CHILDREN—COSTUME

see Children's Costumes

CHILDREN—COUNSELING OF

Benson, Peter L. Parent, Teacher, Mentor, Friend: How Every Adult Can Change Kids' Lives. 2010. (ENG., Illus.). 256p. pap. 7.95 *(978-1-57482-283-0(7))* Search Institute.

Billington, Tom. Working with Children: Assessment, Representation & Intervention. 2006. (Illus.). 192p. (C). 124.00 *(978-1-4129-0869-6(8),* B08698C); per. 46.00 *(978-1-4129-0870-2(1),* B08698P) SAGE Pubns., Ltd. GBR. Dist: SAGE Pubns., Inc.

Coutellier, Connie. Camp Is for the Camper: A Counselor's Guide to Youth Development. 2nd ed. 2007. (Illus.). 69p. per. 9.95 *(978-1-58518-041-7(6),* Healthy Learning) Coaches Choice.

Cram101 Textbook Reviews & Cram101 Textbook Reviews. Outlines & Highlights for Counseling & Psychotherapy with Children & Adolescents: Theory & Practice for School & Clinical Settings by H. Thom. 2011. 112p. pap. 28.95 ***(978-1-61744-885-0(0))*** Cram101 Inc.

Crompton, Margaret. Children & Counselling. (Illus.). 272p. pap. *(978-0-340-55435-7(5),* Hodder Arnold) Hodder Education.

Doka, Kenneth J. & Tucci, Amy S., eds. Living with Grief: Children & Adolescents. 2008. 360p. pap. 24.95 *(978-1-893349-09-4(8))* Hospice Foundation of America.

Field, Evelyn M. Bully Blocking: Six Secrets to Help Children Deal with Teasing & Bullying. 2nd ed. 2007. Orig. Title: Bullybusting. (ENG., Illus.). 176p. per. *(978-1-84310-554-1(3))* Kingsley, Jessica Ltd.

Geldard, David & Geldard, Kathryn. Counselling Children: A Practical Introduction. 3rd ed. 2008. (Illus.). 328p. (C). 121.00 *(978-1-4129-4833-3(9),* B48333C) SAGE Pubns., Ltd. GBR. Dist: SAGE Pubns., Inc.

—Counselling Children: A Practical Introduction. 3rd ed. 2008. (Illus.). 328p. (C). per. 59.00 *(978-1-4129-4834-0(7),* B48333P) SAGE Pubns., Ltd. GBR. Dist: SAGE Pubns., Inc.

Geldard, Kathryn & Geldard, David. Relationship Counselling for Children, Young People & Families. 2008. (Illus.). 272p. (C). 121.00 *(978-1-84787-550-1(5),* B75501C); pap. 51.00 *(978-1-84787-551-8(3),* B75501P) SAGE Pubns., Ltd. GBR. Dist: SAGE Pubns., Inc.

Gerali, Steven. What Do I Do When Teenagers Are Victims of Abuse?, 1 vol. 2009. (What Do I Do When Ser.). (ENG.). 128p. pap. 6.99 *(978-0-310-29195-4(X))* Zondervan.

Hague, Gill, et al. The Experiences of Adult Survivors of Domestic Violence in Childhood: Strategies for Recovery for Children & Adults. 2012. (ENG.). 160p. pap. ***(978-1-84905-096-8(1))*** Kingsley, Jessica Ltd.

Halstead, Richard W., et al. Counseling Children: A Core Issues Approach. 2011. *(978-1-55620-283-4(0))* American Counseling Assn.

Kaduson, Heidi Gerard & Schaefer, Charles E., eds. Short-Term Play Therapy for Children. 2nd rev. ed. 2006. (ENG., Illus.). 388p. 60.00 *(978-1-59385-330-3(0))* Guilford Pubns., Inc.

Martenz, Arden. Groups to Go Grades K-3: 14 Ready-to-Use Small-Group Counseling Plans. 2007. 240p. pap. 24.95 *(978-1-57543-148-2(3))* MAR*CO Products, Inc.

Murray, Amy R. Mending Hearts: When a School Grieves: Grades Pre-K Thru 6. 2006. (Illus.). 64p. per. 19.95 *(978-1-931636-71-1(0))* National Ctr. For Youth Issues.

Prever, Mark. Counselling & Supporting Children & Young People: A Person-Centred Approach. 2010. 208p. (C). 112.00 *(978-1-84787-934-9(9),* B79349C); pap. 39.00 *(978-1-84787-935-6(7),* B79349P) SAGE Pubns., Ltd. GBR. Dist: SAGE Pubns., Inc.

Prout, H. Thompson & Brown, Douglas T., eds. Counseling & Psychotherapy with Children & Adolescents: Theory & Practice for School & Clinical Settings. 4th rev. ed. 2007. (ENG., Illus.). 480p. 152.00 *(978-0-471-77091-6(4),* Wiley) Wiley, John & Sons, Inc.

Rivero, Lisa. A Parent's Guide to Gifted Teens: Living with Intense & Creative Adolescents. 2010. pap. 24.95 *(978-0-910707-99-2(5))* Great Potential Pr., Inc.

Rubin, Lawrence C. Using Superheroes in Counseling & Play Therapy. 2007. (Illus.). 333p. 60.00 *(978-0-8261-0269-0(7))* Springer Publishing Co., Inc.

Schaefer, Dan, et al. How Do We Tell the Children? 4th ed. 2010. (ENG.). 224p. pap. 16.95 *(978-1-55704-911-7(4),* William Morrow Paperbacks) HarperCollins Pubs.

Sommers-Flanagan, John & Sommers-Flanagan, Rita. How to Listen So Parents Will Talk & Talk So Parents Will Listen. 2011. (ENG.). 304p. pap. 40.00 *(978-1-118-01296-3(8),* Wiley) Wiley, John & Sons, Inc.

Strong, Judy. A Child's Grief: Surviving the Death of a Parent. 2009. 80p. pap. 16.95 *(978-1-59298-308-7(1))* Beaver's Pond Pr., Inc.

Thompson, Charles L. & Henderson, Donna A. Counseling Children. 8th ed. 2010. (SW 360K Child Abuse & Neglect Ser.). (ENG.). 768p. (C). 167.95 *(978-0-495-90338-3(8))* Brooks/Cole.

Vernon, Ann. Counseling Children & Adolescents. 4th ed. 2009. 528p. (C). 90.00 *(978-0-89108-340-5(5))* Love Publishing Co.

—More What Works When with Children & Adolescents (Book & CD) 2009. pap. 44.95 *(978-0-87822-614-6(1))* Research Pr.

Webb, Nancy Boyd, ed. Helping Bereaved Children: A Handbook for Practitioners. 3rd ed. 2010. (Social Work Practice with Children & Families Ser.). (ENG., Illus.). 408p. instr.'s hndbk. ed. 50.00 *(978-1-60623-597-3(4))* Guilford Pubns., Inc.

Webb, Nancy Boyd, ed. Helping Bereaved Children, Third Edition: A Handbook for Practitioners. 3rd rev. ed. 2011. (Social Work Practice with Children & Families Ser.). (ENG., Illus.). 408p. pap. 30.00 ***(978-1-4625-0451-0(5))*** Guilford Pubns., Inc.

Wicks-Nelson, Rita & Israel, Allen C. Abnormal Child & Adolescent Psychology. 7th ed. 2008. (ENG., Illus.). 576p. (C). 167.00 *(978-0-13-235978-6(2),* Prentice Hall) Prentice Hall PTR.

Wolfelt, Alan D. Companioning the Bereaved Child: A Soulful Guide for Counselors & Caregivers. 2012. (Companioning Ser.). (ENG.). 176p. 29.95 ***(978-1-61722-158-3(9))*** Companion Pr.

CHILDREN—CRIMES AGAINST

see also Child Abuse; Incest

Alt, Betty L. & Wells, Sandra. When Caregivers Kill: Understanding Child Murder by Parents & Other Guardians. 2010. (ENG.). 160p. 44.95 *(978-1-4422-0077-7(4))* Rowman & Littlefield Publishers, Inc.

Beaudin, Karen. A Child Is Missing: A True Story. 2010. pap. 15.99 *(978-1-61566-725-3(3))* Tate Publishing & Enterprises, LLC.

Berry-Dee, Christopher & Morris, Steven. How to Make a Serial Killer: The Twisted Development of Innocent Children into the World's Most Sadistic Murderers. 2008. (ENG., Illus.). 276p. pap. 14.95 *(978-1-56975-654-6(6))* Ulysses Pr.

Bottoms, Bette L., et al, eds. Children as Victims, Witnesses, & Offenders: Psychological Science & the Law. 2009. (ENG.). 412p. 50.00 *(978-1-60623-332-0(7))* Guilford Pubns., Inc.

Cacho, Lydia. Esclavas del Poder. 2010. pap. 27.95 *(978-84-8306-857-1(5))* Random House Mondadori ESP. Dist: Random Hse., Inc.

Cekic, Smail. Zlocini Nad Djecom Sarajeva U Opsadi. 2010. (Illus.). 867p. *(978-9958-740-63-3(X))* Institut Za Istrazivanje Zlocina Protiv Covjecnosti I Medunarodnog Prava.

Das, Dilip K. & Ebbe, Obi N. I., eds. Global Trafficking in Women & Children. 2007. (ENG., Illus.). 272p. 113.95 *(978-1-4200-5943-4(2),* CRC Press) Taylor & Francis Group GBR. Dist: Taylor & Francis Group.

Davidson, Julia & Hamerton, Christopher. International Perspectives on Child Victimisation. 2012. (ENG.). 208p. 125.00 *(978-0-415-57957-5(0))* Routledge.

DePino, Catherine. Real Life Bully Prevention for Real Kids: 50 Ways to Help Elementary & Middle School Students. 2009. (ENG.). 150p. 33.00 *(978-1-57886-965-7(X))* Rowman & Littlefield Education.

Eliminating Violence against Children: A Handbook for Parliamentarians. 2007. 84p. *(978-92-806-4158-5(1))* United Nations Children's Fund, The (UNICEF).

Eliminating Violence against Children: Handbook of Korean parliamentarians to deal with VAC. 2007. (KOR.). 84p. *(978-92-806-4170-7(0))* United Nations Children's Fund, The (UNICEF).

Finkelhor, David. Childhood Victimization: Violence, Crime & Abuse in the Lives of Young People. 2008. (Interpersonal Violence Ser.). (ENG., Illus.). 256p. 39.99 *(978-0-19-534285-7(2))* Oxford Univ. Pr., Inc.

Gal, Tali. Child Victims & Restorative Justice: A Needs-Rights Model, 1 vol. 2011. (Interpersonal Violence Ser.). (ENG., Illus.). 264p. 49.95 *(978-0-19-974471-8(8))* Oxford Univ. Pr., Inc.

Garbarino, James. Children & the Dark Side of Human Experience: Confronting Global Realities & Rethinking Child Development. 2008. (ENG.). viii, 157p. pap. 39.95 *(978-0-387-75625-7(6),* 0387756256) Springer London, Ltd. GBR. Dist: Springer.

Green, David A. & Green, David. When Children Kill Children: Penal Populism & Political Culture. 2008. (Clarendon Studies in Criminology Ser.). (ENG., Illus.). 200p. 121.00 *(978-0-19-923096-9(X))* Oxford Univ. Pr., Inc.

Hall, Allan & Leidig, Michael. Girl in the Cellar: The Natascha Kampusch Story. 288p. 2010. mass mkt. 7.99 *(978-0-06-194529-8(3))* 2007. (Illus.). 24.95 *(978-0-06-134510-4(5))* HarperCollins Pubs.

Higgins, Jeff V. & Brady, Christopher M. Child Sex Trafficking in the United States. 2012. pap. ***(978-1-62100-266-6(7))*** Nova Science Pubs., Inc.

Jasper, Margaret C. Missing & Exploited Children: How to Protect Your Child. 2006. (Legal Almanac Ser.). 232p. 47.00 *(978-0-19-532157-9(X))* Oxford Univ. Pr., Inc.

Koss, Mary P., et al, eds. Violence Against Women & Children Vol. 2: Navigating Solutions, 2 vols. 2010. (Illus.). 304p. 69.95 *(978-1-4338-0914-9(1))* American Psychological Assn.

Malarek, Victor. The Johns: Sex for Sale & the Men Who Buy It. 2011. (ENG.). 328p. pap. 14.95 *(978-1-61145-012-5(8),* 611012, Arcade Publishing) Skyhorse Publishing Co., Inc.

Mam, Somaly. The Road of Lost Innocence: The True Story of a Cambodian Heroine. 2009. (ENG.). 224p. pap. 15.00 *(978-0-385-52622-7(9))* Spiegel & Grau.

Marcum, Catherine Davis. Adolescent Online Victimization: A Test of Routine Activities Theory. 2009. (Criminal Justice). 284p. 75.00 *(978-1-59332-345-5(X))* LFB Scholarly Publishing LLC.

McDonagh, Josephine. Child Murder & British Culture, 1720-1900. 2008. (ENG.). 296p. pap. 34.99 *(978-0-521-05456-0(7))* Cambridge Univ. Pr.

Muller, Mary Margaret. The Guardians of Innocence. 2011. pap. 14.99 *(978-0-88290-979-0(7))* Cedar Fort, Inc./CFI Distribution.

Obokata, Tomoya. Trafficking of Human Beings from a Human Rights Perspective: Towards a Holistic Approach. 2006. (International Studies in Human Rights: Vol. 89). xviii, 250p. *(978-90-04-15405-6(1))* BRILL.

O'Donnell, Ian & Milner, Claire. Child Pornography: Crime, Computers & Society. 2007. (Illus.). 259p. (C). pap. *(978-1-84392-356-5(4))* Willan Publishing.

Orozco, Michael. Investigating the Death of Innocents. 2010. (Illus.). 224p. pap. 15.00 *(978-1-935437-22-2(4))* Imago Pr.

Phillips, Timothy. Beslan. 2008. (ENG., Illus.). 304p. pap. 15.95 *(978-1-86207-993-9(5))* Granta Bks. GBR. Dist: Independent Pubs. Group.

Priyadarsini, S. & Hartjen, Clayton A. The Global Victimization of Children: Problems & Solutions. 2011. (ENG., Illus.). xiii, 402p. 169.00 ***(978-1-4614-2178-8(0),*** 1461421780) Springer.

Rape As a Weapon of War: Accountability for Sexual Violence in Conflict: Hearing Before the Subcommittee on Human Rights & the Law of the Committee on the Judiciary, United States Senate, One Hundred Tenth Congress, Second Session, April 1, 2008. 2008. iii, 158p. *(978-0-16-082119-6(3),* 552-070-38266-6) United States Government Printing Office.

Rochester, Julia. Candelaria Massacre: How Wagner dos Santos Survived the Street Children's Killing That Shook Brazil. 2008. (ENG.). 288p. pap. 17.95 *(978-1-905745-26-5(5))* Vision Paperbacks GBR. Dist: Independent Pubs. Group.

Rostagnol, Susana & Grabino, Valeria. Historias en el Silencio: Prostitución infantil y adolescente en Montevideo y área Metropolitana. 2007.Tr. of Stories of silence: child & adolescent prostitution in Montevideo & metropolitan Area. (SPA.). 120p. per. *(978-92-806-4236-0(7))* United Nations Children's Fund, The (UNICEF).

Roy, Norman Jean & Pearl, Mariane. Traffik. 2008. (ENG.). 224p. 50.00 *(978-1-57687-474-5(5))* powerHouse Cultural Entertainment, Inc.

Sexual Exploitation of Children over the Internet: A Staff Report Prepared for the Use of the Committee on Energy & Commerce, U.S. House of Representatives, 109th Congress. 2007. v, 33p. *(978-0-16-078078-3(0),* 552-070-35491-3) United States Government Printing Office.

Sher, Julian. Caught in the Web: Inside the Police Hunt to Rescue Children from Online Predators. 2008. (ENG.). 336p. pap. 15.95 *(978-0-7382-1171-8(0))* Da Capo Pr., Inc.

Snow, Robert L. Child Abduction: Prevention, Investigation, & Recovery, 1 vol. 2008. 192p. 44.95 *(978-0-313-34786-3(7),* C34786, Praeger Pubs.) Greenwood Publishing Group, Inc.

Stout, David. The Boy in the Box: The Unsolved Case of America's Unknown Child. 2008. (ENG., Illus.). 272p. pap. 16.95 *(978-1-59921-269-2(2),* Lyons Pr.) Globe Pequot Pr., The.

Territo, Leonard & Kirkham, George. International Sex Trafficking of Women & Children: Understanding the Global Epidemic. 2009. 536p. pap. 39.95 *(978-1-932777-86-4(5),* LLP) Looseleaf Law Pubns., Inc.

Thomson, June, et al. Beyond All Evil: Two Monsters Two Mothers a Love That Will Last Forever. 2012. (ENG.). 304p. 11.95 ***(978-0-00-743851-8(6))*** HarperCollins Pubs. Ltd. GBR. Dist: Independent Pubs. Group.

UNICEF: Innocenti Research Centre. Child trafficking in Europe: A broad vision to put children first; summary Report. 2009. (ENG., Illus.). 68p. pap. 20.00 incl. cd-rom *(978-88-89129-62-3(X))* United Nations Pubns.

United Nations Children's Fund. Un Human Rights Standards & Mechanisms to Combat Violence against Children - A Contribution to the un Secretary General's Study on Violence against Children. 2009. 54p. pap. 15.00 *(978-88-89129-23-4(9))* United Nations Children's Fund, The (UNICEF).

—South Asia in Action: Preventing & Responding to Child Trafficking - Child Rights-based Programme Practices. 2009. (Insight Innocenti Ser.). 42p. pap. 20.00 *(978-88-89129-77-7(8))* United Nations Children's Fund, The (UNICEF).

Valentine, Suzie Q. My Twisted Life: Memoirs of Randolph Douglas Hopkins. 2009. 348p. pap. 22.99 *(978-1-4389-7784-3(0))* AuthorHouse.

White, Jacquelyn W., et al, eds. Violence Against Women & Children Vol. 1: Mapping the Terrain, 2 vols. 2010. (Illus.). 296p. 69.95 *(978-1-4338-0912-5(5))* American Psychological Assn.

Whitney, Ben. Social Inclusion in Schools: Improving Outcomes, Raising Standards. 2007. (David Fulton Bks.). (Illus.). 112p. per. 37.50 *(978-1-84312-474-0(2))* Routledge.

CHILDREN—CUSTODY

see Custody of Children

CHILDREN—DEATH

Here are entered works on the death of children. Works on children's experiences with, conceptions of, and reactions to death are entered under Children and Death. Works on children's death rates and causes are entered under Children—Mortality.

see also Terminally Ill Children

ABBE Scientist Research Division Staff. Children's Toys with Occurrence of Injuries, Disability & Death: Index, Reference & Medical Analysis of New Clinical & Research Information. 2008. (Illus.). 160p. ring bd. 69.95 *(978-0-7883-4678-1(4))* ABBE Pubs. Assn. of Washington, D.C.

Alexander, Randell & Case, Mary E. Child Fatality Review Guide/Atlas with Supplementary CD-ROM: An Interdisciplinary Guide & Photographic Reference & Supplementary CD-ROM. 2008. (ENG., Illus.). 832p. 275.00 incl. cd-rom *(978-1-878060-75-4(9))* STM Learning, Inc.

Amoroso, Angela. Surrounded by Angels. 2008. 112p. 22.95 *(978-0-595-48833-9(1));* pap. 12.95 *(978-0-595-48779-0(3))* iUniverse, Inc.

Apple, Dennis L. Life after the Death of My Son: What I'm Learning. 2008. (ENG.). 192p. pap. 14.99 *(978-0-8341-2365-6(7),* 083-412-3657) Beacon Hill Pr. of Kansas City.

Atlantic Publishing Group. How to Endure the Loss of a Child: A Parent's Guide to Mourning & Moving Forward. 2012. (ENG.). 288p. pap. 24.95 *(978-1-60138-571-0(4))* Atlantic Publishing Co.

Bacvarov, Krum, ed. Babies Reborn: Infant/Child Burials in Pre- & Protohistory, Vol. 24. 2008. (Bar S Ser.). (FRE & ENG., Illus.). 213p. (C). pap. 95.00 *(978-1-4073-0316-1(3))* British Archaeological Reports Ltd. GBR. Dist: Brown, David Bk. Co., The.

Barker, Amettia S. The Deep Distress of Losing a Child: My 1st Son. 2011. 64p. pap. 15.99 ***(978-1-4653-4571-4(X))*** Xlibris Corp.

Bazan, Alma. Para Siempre Navidad. 2006. (SPA.). 140p. per. 13.48 *(978-1-4251-0432-0(0))* Trafford Publishing.

Beaulieu, Joyce. From a Father's Heart: (Heartfelt Sharings of the Loss of a Child) 2008. 154p. pap. 24.95 *(978-1-60610-699-0(6))* PublishAmerica, Inc.

—From a Mother's Heart. 2007. 132p. per. 19.95 *(978-1-4241-9555-8(1))* PublishAmerica, Inc.

Brown, Elizabeth B. Surviving the Loss of a Child: Support for Grieving Parents, 1 vol. 2010. (ENG.). 176p. pap. 12.99 *(978-0-8007-3356-8(8))* Revell.

Buckle, Jennifer. Parenting after the Death of a Child: A Practitioner's Guide. 2010. (Series in Death, Dying & Bereavement Ser.). (ENG., Illus.). 226p. 41.95 *(978-0-415-99573-3(6))* Routledge.

Bulen, Shirley. Forever Remembered: When Your Baby Is in Heaven. 2009. 100p. pap. 13.99 *(978-1-4343-8008-1(4))* AuthorHouse.

Butterfield, Edna. Golden Bubbles: Learning Through Loss: A Grandmother's Insight into Childhood Cancer. 2007. (Illus.). 96p. *(978-0-929540-64-1(6))* Publishing Designs, Inc.

Caldwell, Frank. A Parent's Journey into Darkness: In Loving Tribute to Our Son, Eric. 2011. 64p. pap. 14.99 ***(978-1-4634-0080-4(2))*** AuthorHouse.

Carson, Stephanie A. Why My Child? A Clinical Guide for Helping Parents Survive the Sudden Death of a Child. 2009. 144p. pap. 11.99 *(978-1-60799-057-4(1))* Tate Publishing & Enterprises, LLC.

Claussen, Cindy. Born to Fly: An Infant's Journey to God. 2007. (Illus.). per. 9.95 *(978-0-9650848-5-7(X))* ACTA Pubns.

Coleman, Melissa. This Life Is in Your Hands: One Dream, Sixty Acres, & a Family Undone. 2011. (ENG.). 352p. 25.99 (978-0-06-195832-8(8)) HarperCollins Pubs.

Coleman, Melissa. This Life Is in Your Hands: One Dream, Sixty Acres, & a Family's Heartbreak. 2012. (P. S. Ser.). (ENG.). 352p. pap. 15.99 **(978-0-06-195833-5(6)**, HarperPerennial) HarperCollins Pubs.

Cunningham, Darren. Joseph's Life Story: Seeking Justice. 2009. (Illus.). 292p. pap. 16.99 (978-1-4389-7486-6(8)) AuthorHouse.

D'Arcy, Paula. Song for Sarah: A Mother's Journey Through Grief & Beyond. 2009. (ENG.). 144p. pap. 12.95 (978-0-8245-2523-1(X)) Crossroad Publishing Co., The.

Forbes, Patricia. Healing Life's Broken Dreams , a Son's Tragedy, a Mother's Grief, a Miracle Recovery. 2009. 190p. 23.50 (978-1-60693-641-2(7), Eloquent Bks.) AEG Literary Publishing Services, Inc.

Frenette, Karen. Lost in Grief: A Mom's Story. 2011. 188p. 23.95 **(978-1-4620-2097-3(6))**; pap. 13.95 **(978-1-4620-2096-6(8))** iUniverse, Inc.

Geesey, Barbara. A Child's First Christmas in Heaven. 2009. 108p. 19.99 (978-1-61579-199-6(X)) Xulon Pr., Inc.

Green, Reg. The Nicholas Effect: A Boy's Gift to the World. 2009. 270p. pap. 14.49 (978-1-4490-0841-3(0)) AuthorHouse.

Haddix-Fisher, Kimberly. Foreshadow. 2010. pap. 8.99 (978-1-61663-180-2(5)) Tate Publishing & Enterprises, LLC.

Haley, Renee & Jack. The Austin Haley Story: A Family Confronting Unthinkable Tragedy. 2010. pap. 16.99 (978-1-61566-992-9(2)) Tate Publishing & Enterprises, LLC.

Hamilton, Gavin. The Nurses Are Innocent: The Digoxin Poisoning Fallacy. 2011. (ENG., Illus.). 240p. pap. 25.99 (978-1-4597-0057-4(0)) Dundurn CAN. Dist: Ingram Pub. Services.

Harris, Paul Nigel & Crisman, Chris. Mothers in Charge: Faces of Courage. 2009. 96p. 35.00 (978-0-915180-43-1(X)) Harrowood Bks.

Holcombe, William H. (William Henry). Our Children in Heaven / [by Wm H Holcombe]. 2006. 328p. per. 23.99 (978-1-4255-3248-2(9)) MPublishing.

—Our Children in Heaven by Wm H Holcombe, M D. 2006. 328p. per. 23.99 (978-1-4255-3281-9(0)) MPublishing.

Hood, Ann. Comfort: A Journey Through Grief. (ENG.). 192p. 2009. pap. 12.95 (978-0-393-33659-7(X), 33659) 2008. 19.95 (978-0-393-06456-8(5), 6456) Norton, W. W. & Co., Inc.

Killian, Wendy. To Have Loved. 2009. 116p. pap. 10.99 (978-1-60799-032-1(6)) Tate Publishing & Enterprises, LLC.

Komppa, De Anna. Better, Not Bitter: The Tiffany Miller Story. 2011. 124p. 23.95 **(978-1-4634-4299-6(8))** AuthorHouse.

Korbon, Gregg. Beyond Reason: Lessons from the Loss of a Gifted Child. 2009. 136p. 23.95 (978-1-4401-2399-3(3)); pap. 13.95 (978-1-4401-2397-9(7)) iUniverse, Inc.

Labno, Jeannie. Commemorating the Polish Renaissance Child: Funeral Monuments & Their European Context. 2011. (Illus.). 472p. 134.95 (978-0-7546-6825-1(8)) Ashgate Publishing Co.

Larson, Beth. Shirley's Garden. 2009. 64p. pap. 19.50 (978-1-60693-095-3(8), Eloquent Bks.) AEG Literary Publishing Services, Inc.

Licht, Chaim. In the Grip of Bereavement An. 2009. 272p. pap. 18.95 (978-965-229-446-3(2)) Gefen Publishing Hse., Ltd ISR. Dist: Strauss Consultants.

Lightner, Robert P. A Donde van los Que Mueren Sin Poder Creer: Safe in the Arms of Jesus. 2008. (SPA.). 96p. pap. 6.99 (978-0-8254-1381-0(8), Editorial Portavoz) Kregel Pubns.

Madill, Betty. One Step at a Time: Mourning a Child, 1 vol. (ENG., Illus.). 128p. 12.95 (978-0-86315-338-9(0)) Floris Bks. GBR. Dist: SteinerBooks, Inc.

Maritz, Jeanette. Until Death Do Us Part. 2010. 124p. pap. (978-3-8383-6504-6(6)) Lambert Academic Publishing.

Mayer, Donald E. Letters to Peter: On the Journey from Grief to Wholeness. 2010. 194p. pap. 22.00 (978-1-60899-104-4(0), Cascade Bks.) Wipf & Stock Pubs.

Mayhew, Lisa. Child Death Investigations: Interdisciplinary Techniques from Cradle to Court. 2007. 20.00 (978-1-59460-209-2(3)) Carolina Academic Pr.

Mazzola, Lori E. The Lori Story. 2011. 74p. pap. 19.95 **(978-1-4560-0387-6(9))** PublishAmerica, Inc.

McGivern, Patricia Seaver. Angel Babies: Messages from Miscarried & Other Lost Babies. 2009. 168p. 25.95 (978-1-4401-2522-5(8)) iUniverse, Inc.

Miller, Jeri Rae. Heartfelt: A Companion for Bereaved Parents. 2007. 62p. per. 10.00 (978-1-879384-74-3(4)) Cypress Hse.

Nold, Deanna. The Best Is yet to Be! 2010. 48p. pap. 5.99 (978-1-58169-348-5(6), Axiom Pr.) Genesis Communications, Inc.

Notman, Andrea. Remembering You: A practical guide for bereaved Parents. 2011. 108p. 24.99 **(978-1-4653-0004-1(X))**; pap. 15.99 **(978-1-4653-0003-4(1))** Xlibris Corp.

O'Neal, Bobbi Jo. Investigating Infant Deaths. 2007. (ENG., Illus.). 256p. 99.95 (978-0-8493-8204-8(1), CRC Press) Taylor & Francis Group GBR. Dist: Taylor & Francis Group.

O'Shea, Jim. When a Child Dies: Footsteps of a Grieving Family. 2009. (ENG.). 144p. pap. 16.95 (978-1-84730-078-2(2)) Veritas Pubns. IRL. Dist: Dufour Editions, Inc.

Parrish, Preston & Parrish, Glenda. Finding Hope in Times of Grief. 2011. 192p. pap. 10.99 (978-0-7369-3075-8(2)) Harvest Hse. Pubs.

Peinkofer, James. Lilacs in the Rain: The Shocking Story of Conneticut's Shaken-Baby Serial Killer. 2007. (Illus.). 253p. per. 19.95 (978-1-60008-073-9(1), Rooftop Publishing) AuthorHouse.

Pieterse, Anne. What If I Whispered Your Name? 2011. 96p. pap. 15.99 **(978-1-4628-5741-8(8))** Xlibris Corp.

Prime, Samuel Iren- us. Thoughts on the Death of Little Children by Samuel Irenaeus Prime with an App Selected from Various Authors. 2006. 184p. per. 18.99 (978-1-4255-1461-7(8)) MPublishing.

Rand, Hollister. I'M Not Dead, I'm Different: Kids in Spirit Teach Us about Living a Better Life on Earth. 2011. (ENG.). 288p. pap. 14.99 (978-0-06-195906-6(5)) HarperCollins Pubs.

Redfern, Suzanne & Gilbert, Susan K. The Grieving Garden: Living with the Death of a Child - Twenty Two Parents Share Their Stories. 2008. 304p. 24.95 (978-1-57174-569-9(6)); (ENG., Illus.). per. 18.95 (978-1-57174-581-1(5)) Hampton Roads Publishing Co., Inc.

Repczynski, Barbara. Anatomy of Grief: An Inspirational Guide to Surviving the Death of Your Child. 2010. 92p. pap. 11.95 (978-1-4502-5505-9(1)) iUniverse, Inc.

Samson, Peter & Crow, Alan. Dunblane: Our Year of Tears. (Illus.). 174p. 27.50 (978-1-85158-975-3(9)) Mainstream Publishing Co., Ltd. GBR. Dist: Trafalgar Square Publishing.

Schenck, William Edward. Children in Heaven or, the Infant Dead Redeemed by the Blood Of. 2007. pap. 31.95 (978-1-4304-5121-1(1)) Kessinger Publishing, LLC.

[Schenck, William Edward]. Children in Heaven; or, the Infant Dead Redeemed by the Blood of Jesus. 2006. 356p. per. 26.99 (978-1-4255-3596-4(8)) MPublishing.

Schrock, Julie Burget. Missing Max. 2011. 100p. pap. 13.00 **(978-1-59755-269-1(0)**, Advantage Inspirational) Advantage Bks.

Schroedel, Jenny. Naming the Child: Hope-Filled Reflections on Miscarriage, Stillbirth, & Infant Death. 2009. (ENG.). 168p. (gr. 13). pap. 16.99 (978-1-55725-585-3(7)) Paraclete Pr., Inc.

Schuette, Janice. Awakening by Departure. 2006. (ENG.). 84p. per. 16.95 (978-1-4241-5231-5(3)) PublishAmerica, Inc.

Schulz, Gregory. The Problem of Suffering: A Father's Hope. 2nd ed. 2011. pap. **(978-0-7586-2661-5(4))** Concordia Publishing Hse.

Short, Susan Austin. Emma's Hope: A Grieving Mother's Spiritual Journey. 2010. 224p. pap. 18.95 (978-1-4401-9126-8(3)) iUniverse, Inc.

Sidebotham, Peter & Fleming, Peter, eds. Unexpected Death in Childhood: A Handbook for Practitioners. 2008. (Wiley Child Protection & Policy Ser.: 16). (ENG.). 368p. 149.95 (978-0-470-06095-7(6)); pap. 57.95 (978-0-470-06096-4(4)) Wiley, John & Sons, Inc. (Wiley-Interscience).

Stanford, Peter. The Death of a Child. Stanford, Peter, ed. 2011. (ENG., Illus.). 184p. 22.95 (978-1-4411-8303-3(5)) Continuum International Publishing Group, Ltd. GBR. Dist: National Bk. Network.

Stoller, Galen. My Life after Life: A Posthumous Memoir. Stoller, Kenneth, ed. 2011. 174p. 19.95 (978-0-615-38307-1(6)) Dream Treader Pr.

Susan Austin Short. Emma's Hope: A Grieving Mother's Spiritual Journey. 2010. 224p. 28.95 (978-1-4401-9124-4(7)) iUniverse, Inc.

Triplett, Wayne. The Sun Will Come Out Tomorrow: Beginning Again after the Death of A Child. 2010. 440p. 36.95 (978-1-4502-5100-6(5)); pap. 26.95 (978-1-4502-5099-3(8)) iUniverse, Inc.

Vincent, Sharon. Learning from Child Deaths & Serious Abuse. 2010. 133p. pap. 26.95 (978-1-903765-96-8(X)) Dunedin Academic Pr. GBR. Dist: International Specialized Bk. Services.

Walsh, John. Tears of Rage. 2008. (ENG.). 432p. pap. 27.95 (978-1-4391-3634-8(3)) Pocket Books.

Werth, Jean. There's Someone in Your Kingdom, Lord. 2006. 156p. pap. 15.99 (978-1-4141-0679-3(3)) Pleasant Word.

Wiersbe, David W. Gone but Not Lost: Grieving the Death of a Child. rev. ed. 2011. 128p. pap. 11.99 (978-0-8010-1381-2(X)) Baker Bks.

Wilkerson, Sandra. Memoirs of a Teenage Angel. 2009. 128p. pap. (978-1-55452-357-3(5), Guardian Bks.) Essence Publishing.

Young, Rebecca J. Losing Jenny: A Walk Through the Valley: Lessons from a Mother's Broken Heart. 2009. pap. 10.99 (978-1-60799-335-3(X)) Tate Publishing & Enterprises, LLC.

Zuniga, Michael A. & Zuniga, Micha'El A. A Special Vow: To Care for & Love Forever. 2009. 72p. pap. 10.99 (978-1-61579-179-8(5)) Xulon Pr., Inc.

CHILDREN—DEVELOPMENT

see Child Development

CHILDREN—DEVELOPMENT AND GUIDANCE

see Child Rearing

CHILDREN—DISCIPLINE

see Discipline of Children

CHILDREN—DISEASES

see also Allergy in Children; Chronic Diseases in Children; Cystic Fibrosis in Children; Dentition; Infants—Diseases; Minimal Brain Dysfunction in Children; Pediatric Emergencies; Pediatric Hematology; Pediatric Otolaryngology; Syndromes in Children; Tumors in Children

also individual diseases that occur primarily in childhood, e.g. Chickenpox; and headings of the type Cystic Fibrosis in Children

Abrams, Steven A. & Hawthorne, Keli M. Bone Health in Children. 2012. (ENG., Illus.). 241p. 119.95 **(978-1-4398-4926-2(9)**, CRC Press) Taylor & Francis Group GBR. Dist: Taylor & Francis Group.

Acquarone, Stella, ed. Signs of Autism in Infants: Recognition & Early Intervention. 2007. (Illus.). 298p. per. 43.95 (978-1-85575-486-7(X)) Karnac Bks. GBR. Dist: Stylus Publishing, LLC.

Aicardi, Jean. Diseases of the Nervous System in Childhood. 3rd ed. 2009 (Clinics in Developmental Medicine Ser.: 3). (ENG., Illus.). 912p. 350.00 (978-1-898683-59-9(X)) Mac Keith Pr. GBR. Dist: Wiley, John & Sons, Inc.

Alaki, Sumer. Children's Risk for Dental Caries- the Most Common Chronic Childhood Illness. 2007. pap. (978-3-8364-2985-6(3)) VDM Verlag Dr. Mueller e.K.

Alexander, June & Le Grange, Daniel. My Kid Is Back. 2010. (ENG.). 272p. pap. 17.95 (978-0-415-58115-8(X)) Routledge.

American Academy of Pediatrics. Pediatric Environmental Health. Etzel, MD, PhD, FAAP, Ruth A, ed. 3rd ed. 2011. (ENG.). 934p. (C). pap. 49.95 **(978-1-58110-313-7(1))** American Academy of Pediatrics.

American Academy of Pediatrics, creator. Autism: Caring for Children with Autism Spectrum Disorders: A Resource Toolkit for Clinicians. 2007. cd-rom 79.95 (978-1-58110-276-5(3)) American Academy of Pediatrics.

American Heart Association, creator. Heartsaver Child & Infant CPR AED Wallet Card. 2011. (ENG., Illus.). ring bd. 17.50 **(978-1-61669-064-9(X))** American Heart Assn., Inc.

Anand, Geeta. The Cure: How a Father Raised $100 Million — And Bucked the Medical Establishment — in a Quest to Save His Children. 2009. (ENG.). 352p. pap. 15.99 (978-0-06-073440-4(X), William Morrow Paperbacks) HarperCollins Pubs.

Appleton, Peter. Children's Anxiety: A Contextual Approach. Appleton, Peter A., ed. 2008. (ENG., Illus.). 200p. (C). 47.50 (978-0-415-45944-0(3)) Routledge.

Austin, Glenn, et al. The Parents' Medical Manual. (Illus.). 426p. 11.95 (978-0-13-650317-0(9)) Prentice Hall PTR.

Barton, Leslie L. & Friedman, Neil R., eds. The Neurological Manifestations of Pediatric Infectious Diseases & Immunodeficiency Syndromes. 2010. (Infectious Disease Ser.). (Illus.). xviii, 421p. pap. 189.00 (978-1-61737-858-4(5), 1617378585) Humana Pr.

Belson, Martin, et al. Risk Factors for Acute Leukemia in Children: A Review: A Reprint from the Journal, Environmental Health Perspectives. 2007. (Illus.). 33p. (C). pap. 15.00 (978-1-4223-1394-7(8)) DIANE Publishing Co.

Bergersen, Lisa. Congenital Heart Disease: The Catheterization Manual. 2008. (ENG., Illus.). viii, 200p. pap. 69.95 (978-0-387-77291-2(X), 038777291X) Springer.

Birch, Stephen. Shonishin: Japanese Pediatric Acupuncture. 2011. (ENG., Illus.). 272p. 79.99 (978-3-13-150061-8(1)) Thieme Medical Pubs., Inc.

Bimkrant, Jonathan & Alario, Anthony J. Pediatrics. 2007. (Crash Course Ser.). (ENG., Illus.). 320p. pap. 54.95 (978-0-323-04735-1(5), Mosby) Elsevier - Health Sciences Div.

Bishop, Warren P. Gastroenterology. 2010. (Pediatric Practice Ser.). (ENG., Illus.). 472p. 93.00 (978-0-07-163379-6(0), 0071633790) McGraw-Hill Professional Publishing.

Blair, Karen. Medicines Management in Children's Nursing. 2011. (ENG., Illus.). 224p. pap. (978-1-84445-470-9(3)) Learning Matters Ltd.

Blizzard, Merlon. Help! My Child Has Cancer: My Angel on Loan. 2009. 136p. 22.49 (978-1-4389-4286-5(9)); pap. 11.99 (978-1-4389-4285-8(0)) AuthorHouse.

Bluestone, Charles D. & Klein, Jerome O. Otitis Media in Infants & Children. 4th rev. ed. 2007. (Otitis Media in Infants & Children (BlueStone/Klein) Ser.). (Illus.). 462p. incl. cd-rom (978-1-55009-335-3(5)) Decker Publishing.

Bradley, John S. & Nelson, John D. 2010-2011 Nelson's Pocket Book of Pediatric Antimicrobial Therapy. 18th ed. 2010. (Nelson's Pocket Book of Pediatric Antimicrobial Therapy Ser.). (ENG., Illus.). 168p. pap. 34.95 (978-1-58110-373-1(5)) American Academy of Pediatrics.

Brom, Danny, et al. Treating Traumatized Children: Risk, Resilience, & Recovery. Ford, Julian D. & Pat-Horenczyk, Ruth, eds. 2010. (ENG., Illus.). 304p. (C). pap. 47.50 (978-0-415-47150-3(8)) Routledge.

Campbell, Ralph & Saul, Andrew W. The Vitamin Cure for Children's Health: Problems Prevent & Treat Children's Health Problems Using Nutrition & Vitamin Supplementation, 1 vol. 2011. (ENG.). 192p. pap. **(978-1-59120-294-3(9))** Basic Health Pubns., Inc.

Cañadell, José & San-Julian, Mikel, eds. Pediatric Bone Sarcomas: Epiphysiolysis before Excision. 2011. (Illus.). ix, 152p. pap. 69.95 (978-0-85729-517-0(9), 0857295179) Springer.

Carr, Michele M. & Hayward, Geoffrey. Pediatric Obstructive Sleep Apnea. 2007. pap. (978-1-56772-109-6(5)) American Academy of Otolaryngology-Head & Neck Surgery Foundation, Inc.

Carreiro, Jane Elizabeth. Osteopathic Approach to Children. 2nd ed. 2009. (ENG., Illus.). 310p. 90.95 (978-0-443-06738-9(4), Churchill Livingstone) Elsevier - Health Sciences Div.

—Pediatric Manual Medicine: An Osteopathic Approach. 2009. (ENG., Illus.). 380p. (C). 74.95 (978-0-443-10308-7(9), Churchill Livingstone) Elsevier - Health Sciences Div.

Cartwright-Hatton, Samantha. From Timid to Tiger: A Treatment Manual for Parenting the Anxious Child. 2010. (ENG., Illus.). 186p. pap. 41.95 (978-0-470-68310-1(4), Wiley) Wiley, John & Sons, Inc.

Cataltepe, Oguz & Jallo, George I., eds. Pediatric Epilepsy Surgery: Preoperative Assessment & Surgical Treatment. 2010. (ENG., Illus.). 400p. 259.99 (978-1-60406-254-0(1)) Thieme Medical Pubs., Inc.

Chapman, Kevin, et al, eds. Pediatric Epilepsy Case Studies: From Infancy & Childhood Through Adolescence. 2008. (ENG., Illus.). 296p. 89.95 (978-1-4200-8342-2(2), CRC Press) Taylor & Francis Group GBR. Dist: Taylor & Francis Group.

Chatelle, Melody. Journeys of Heartache & Grace: Conversations & Life Lessons from Young People with Serious Illnesses. 2008. 256p. pap. 16.95 (978-1-880292-35-8(1)) LangMarc Publishing.

Cheryl Nineff D'Ambrosio. Pooling Blood: A journey of two girls with hemophilia & their parents' struggle to keep them Alive. 2010. 316p. 32.95 (978-0-595-51786-2(2)); pap. 22.95 (978-0-595-53055-7(9)) iUniverse, Inc.

Chesterton, Carrie M., ed. Food Allergies: New Research. 2008. 89.00 (978-1-60456-978-0(6)) Nova Science Pubs., Inc.

Christophersen, Edward R. & Friman, Patrick C. Elimination Disorders in Children & Adolescents, Vol. 16. 2010. (Illus.). 88p. pap. 29.80 (978-0-88937-334-1(5)) Hogrefe Publishing.

Clark, Demetria. Herbal Healing for Children: A Parent's Guide to Treatments for Common Childhood Illnesses. 2011. 224p. pap. 14.95 (978-1-57067-214-9(8), Healthy Living) Book Publishing Co.

Claxton, Rosie & Harrison, Tony, eds. Caring for Children with HIV & AIDS. (Illus.). 224p. pap. (978-0-340-55256-8(5), Hodder Arnold) Hodder Education.

Clements, John, et al. Transition or Transformation? Helping Young People with Autistic Spectrum Disorder Set Out on a Hopeful Road Towards Their Adult Lives. 2010. (Illus.). 177p. pap. (978-1-84310-964-8(6)) Kingsley, Jessica Ltd.

Comacchio, Cynthia R., et al. Healing the World's Children: Interdisciplinary Perspectives on Child Health in the Twentieth Century. 2008. (McGill-Queen's/Associated Medical Services Studies in the History of Medicine, H Ser.). (ENG., Illus.). 324p. (978-0-7735-3399-8(0)) McGill-Queen's Univ. Pr.

Committee on Blue Water Navy Vietnam Veterans and Agent Orange Exposure & Institute of Medicine. Blue Water Navy Vietnam Veterans & Agent Orange Exposure. 2011. (ENG.). 158p. pap. 37.50 **(978-0-309-16247-0(5))** National Academies Pr.

Connolly, Cynthia A. Saving Sickly Children: The Tuberculosis Preventorium in American Life, 1909-1970. 2008. (Critical Issues in Health & Medicine Ser.). (ENG., Illus.). 200p. 39.95 (978-0-8135-4267-6(7)) Rutgers Univ. Pr.

Coplan, James. Making Sense of Autistic Spectrum Disorders: Create the Brightest Future for Your Child with the Best Treatment Options. 2010. (Illus.). 448p. 25.00 (978-0-553-80581-6(5)) Random House Publishing Group.

Cottingham, Sandra & Cerazy, Joanna. Lead Babies: How Heavy Metals Are Causing Our Children's Autism, ADHD, Learning Disabilities, Low IQ & Behavior Problems. 2010. 224p. pap. 19.95 (978-1-4401-8807-7(6)) iUniverse, Inc.

Cram101 Textbook Reviews & Cram101 Textbook Reviews. Outlines & Highlights for Well Child Assessment for Primary Care Providers by Colyar, Isbn: 9780803610057 080361005x. 2011. 278p. pap. 32.95 **(978-1-61490-518-9(5))** Cram101 Inc.

Crockett, Bettye. Fighting the Dragon. 2006. 90p. per. 8.95 (978-1-59824-320-8(9)) E-BookTime LLC.

Czemichow, P. & Dannecker, G., eds. Juvenile Idiopathic Arthritis: Clinical Picture, Mechanisms of Disease & Effects of Growth Hormone Treatment: Experts Conference, Chantilly, May 2008. 2009. (Illus.). 70p. pap. (978-3-8055-9292-5(2)) Karger, S. AG.

Delaney, Tara. Sensory Processing Disorder: Practical Answers to the Top 275 Questions Parents Ask. 2008. (ENG., Illus.). 240p. pap. 14.95 (978-1-4022-1123-2(6)) Sourcebooks, Inc.

Densmore, Ann E. Helping Children with Autism Become More Social: 76 Ways to Use Narrative Play, 1 vol. 2007. (Illus.). 272p. 49.95 (978-0-275-99702-1(2), C9702, Praeger Pubs.) Greenwood Publishing Group, Inc.

Dishion, Thomas J., et al. Everyday Parenting: A Professional's Guide to Building Family Management Skills. 2011. pap. 18.95 **(978-0-87822-658-0(3))** Research Pr.

Ditchek, Stuart H., et al. Healthy Child, Whole Child: Integrating the Best of Conventional & Alternative Medicine to Keep Your Kids Healthy. 2009. (ENG.). 352p. pap. 17.99 (978-0-06-168598-9(4), William Morrow Paperbacks) HarperCollins Pubs.

Dlamini, Thomas. Morbidity & Mortality Patterns. 2011. 92p. pap. **(978-3-8443-9746-8(9))** Lambert Academic Publishing.

Donoghue, Elaine A. & Kraft, Colleen A. Managing Chronic Health Needs in Child Care & Schools: A Quick Reference Guide. 2009. (ENG.). 214p. pap. 47.00 (978-1-58110-299-4(2)) American Academy of Pediatrics.

Duncan, Tami & Rosner, Bryan. The Lyme-Autism Connection: Unveiling the Shocking Link Between Lyme Disease & Childhood Developmental Disorders. 2008. 288p. pap. 25.95 (978-0-9763797-5-1(9)) BioMed Publishing Group.

Edwards, Laurie. A Life Disrupted: Getting Real about Chronic Illness in Your Twenties & Thirties. 2008. (ENG.). 288p. pap. 14.99 (978-0-8027-1649-1(0)) Walker & Co.

Ehrlich, Fred. You Can't Take Your Body to a Repair Shop: A Book about What Makes You Sick. 2011. (Illus.). 40p. (J). (gr. k-5). 15.95 **(978-1-60905-148-8(3))** Blue Apple Bks.

El-Khayat, Zakarya, et al. Cd95 & Bcl-2 As a New Markers in Acute Lymphocytic Leukemi. 2011. 132p. pap. **(978-3-8443-3015-1(1))** Lambert Academic Publishing.

Engel Fisher, Jennifer & Price, Janet. Take Control of Asperger's Syndrome: The Official Strategy Guide for Teens with Asperger's Syndrome & Nonverbal Learning Disorder. 2010. (ENG.). 200p. (gr. 5-10). pap. 16.95 (978-1-59363-405-6(6)) Prufrock Pr.

Fatima, Iram & Suhail, Kausar. Belief in a Just World & Subjective Well-Being. 2011. 148p. pap. **(978-3-8443-3267-4(7))** Lambert Academic Publishing.

Feld, Leonard G. & Kaskel, Frederick. Fluid & Electrolytes in Pediatrics: A Comprehensive Handbook. 2010. (Nutrition & Health Ser.). (ENG., Illus.). xvi, 411p. 119.00 (978-1-60327-224-7(0), 1603272240) Humana Pr.

Feld, Leonard G. & Kaskel, Frederick J. Fluid & Electrolytes in Pediatrics: A Comprehensive Handbook. 2010. (Illus.). xviii, 408p. E-Book (978-1-60327-225-4(9)) Humana Pr.

Feld, Leonard G. & Kaskel, Frederick J., eds. Fluid & Electrolytes in Pediatrics: A Comprehensive Handbook. 2011. (Nutrition & Health Ser.). (ENG., Illus.). xviii, 411p. pap. 49.95 (978-1-61779-410-0(4), 1617794104) Humana Pr.

Finn, Adam, et al, eds. Hot Topics in Infection & Immunity in Children 6. 2009. (Advances in Experimental Medicine & Biology Ser.). (ENG., Illus.). xiii, 205p. 209.00 (978-1-4419-0980-0(X), 144190980X) Springer.

Finn, Adam & Pollard, Andrew J., eds. Hot Topics in Infection & Immunity in Children IV. (Advances in Experimental Medicine & Biology Ser.). (Illus.). 2010. xii, 238p. pap. 159.00 (978-1-4419-2540-4(6), 1441925406) 2007. 238p. 159.00 (978-0-387-73959-5(9)) Springer.

Florin, Todd, et al. Netter's Pediatrics. 2011. (Netter Clinical Science Ser.). (ENG., Illus.). 864p. (C). 79.95 (978-1-4377-1155-4(3), Saunders) Elsevier - Health Sciences Div.

—Pediatrics. 2011. (Netter Clinical Science Ser.). (ENG., Illus.). 880p. (C). 140.00 (978-1-4377-1156-1(1), Saunders) Elsevier - Health Sciences Div.

Frank, Robert & Livingston, Kathryn E. The Secret Life of the Dyslexic Child: How She Thinks, How He Feels, How They Can Succeed. 2007. 260p. reprint ed. pap. 16.00 (978-1-4223-6796-4(7)) DIANE Publishing Co.

Freeman, Sabrina Karen. The Complete Guide to Autism Treatments: A Parent's Handbook: Make Sure Your Child Gets What Works! 2007. viii, 509p. pap. 29.95 (978-0-9657565-6-3(4)) SKF Bks., Inc.

Gage, James R., et al, eds. The Identification & Treatment of Gait Problems in Cerebral Palsy. 2nd ed. 2009. (Clinics in Developmental Medicine Ser.: 4). (ENG., Illus.). 660p. 209.00 (978-1-898683-65-0(4)) Mac Keith Pr. GBR. Dist: Wiley, John & Sons, Inc.

Galant, Stanley P. What to Do for Kids with Asthma: Easy to Read, Easy to Use. 2011. (Illus.). ix, 145p. pap. (978-0-9720148-6-1(1)) Institute for Healthcare Advancement.

Ghizzoni, L., et al, eds. Pediatric Adrenal Diseases: Workshop, Turin, May 2010. 2010. (Endocrine Development Ser.). (Illus.). 218p. (978-3-8055-9643-5(X)) Karger, S. AG.

Glover, Mark. Application & Review of Pediatric Pharmacotherapy. 2nd ed. 2011. 224p. pap. 49.99 (978-0-85369-941-5(0)) Pharmaceutical Pr. GBR. Dist: Smith Fulfillment Services.

Golden, Janet & Weisz, George. Healing the World's Children: Interdisciplinary Perspectives on Child Health in the Twentieth Century. Comacchio, Cynthia, ed. 2008. (McGill-Queen's/Associated Medical Services Studies in the History of Medicine, H Ser.). (ENG., Illus.). 324p. pap. (978-0-7735-3400-1(8)) McGill-Queen's Univ. Pr.

Goodheart, Kristin, et al, eds. Eating Disorders in Women & Children: Prevention, Stress Management, & Treatment. 2nd rev. ed. 2011. (ENG., Illus.). 456p. 129.95 (978-1-4398-2481-8(9), CRC Press) Taylor & Francis Group GBR. Dist: Taylor & Francis Group.

Graef, John W., ed. Manual of Pediatric Therapeutics. 7th rev. ed. 2007. (Lippincott Manual Series (Formerly Known As the Spiral Manual Series) Ser.). (ENG., Illus.). 736p. pap. 63.99 (978-0-7817-7166-5(8)) Lippincott Williams & Wilkins.

Griffin, Simone Wyn & Sandler, Dianne. Motivate to Communicate! 300 Games & Activities for Your Child with Autism. 2009. (ENG.). 240p. pap. (978-1-84905-041-8(4)) Kingsley, Jessica Ltd.

Gupta Mandal, Ujjwala. Diarrhoeal Diseases in Children. 2011. 88p. pap. (978-3-8433-7851-2(7)) Lambert Academic Publishing.

Hartmann, Franz. Dr Franz Hartmann's Diseases of Children & Their Homeopathic. Hempel, Charles J., tr. 2007. pap. 40.95 (978-1-4304-5123-5(8)) Kessinger Publishing, LLC.

Hartnick, Christopher & Boseley, Mark, eds. Clinical Management of Children's Voice Disorders. 2010. (Illus.). 300p. pap. 98.00 (978-1-59756-354-3(4)) Plural Publishing, Inc.

Hartnick, Christopher J. & Boseley, Mark. Pediatric Voice Disorders: Diagnosis & Treatment. 2008. (Illus.). 300p. 189.95 incl. DVD (978-1-59756-178-5(9)) Plural Publishing, Inc.

Horry, Keva DeVelle. Glamorous Sacrifice. 2010. (978-1-935052-32-6(2)); pap. (978-1-935052-34-0(9)) White River Pr.

Hoss, Phoebe. All Eyes: A Mother's Struggle to Save Her Schizophrenic Son. 2010. 300p. pap. 15.95 (978-0-932112-01-9(3)) Carolina Wren Pr.

Hughes-Lynch, Claire E. Children with High-Functioning Autism: A Parent's Guide. 2010. (ENG.). 225p. pap. 17.95 (978-1-59363-402-5(1)) Prufrock Pr.

Hutson, John M., et al, eds. Disorders of Sex Development: An Integrated Approach to Management. 2012. (ENG., Illus.). xv, 311p. 219.00 (978-3-642-22963-3(8), 3642229638) Springer.

Infectious Diseases in the Pediatric Intensive Care Unit. 2008. (Illus.). 580p. 219.00 (978-1-84628-916-3(5)) Springer.

Jacobi, Abraham. Therapeutics of Infancy & Childhood. 2009. 542p. pap. (978-0-217-30545-7(8)) Books LLC.

—Therapeutics of Infancy & Childhood. 2007. (ENG.). 578p. 58.95 (978-0-548-04466-7(X)) Kessinger Publishing, LLC.

Janice & Dietert, Rodney R. Strategies for Protecting Your Child's Immune System: Tools for Parents & Parents-to-Be. 2010. (Illus.). 300p. pap. 19.95 (978-981-4287-09-8(1)) World Scientific Publishing Co., Inc.

Janzen, Janice, et al. Autism Encyclopedia: The Complete Guide to Autism Spectrum Disorders. 2009. (ENG.). 300p. pap. 22.95 (978-1-59363-360-8(2)) Prufrock Pr.

Jelliffe, D., ed. Child Health in the Tropics. 5th rev. ed. (ENG., Illus.). 304p. (978-0-7131-4438-3(6), Hodder Arnold) Hodder Education.

Jelliffe, D. B., et al. Diseases of Children in the Subtropics & Tropics. Brueton, Martin J. et al, eds. 4th rev. ed. (ENG., Illus.). 1104p. (978-0-340-50633-2(4), Hodder Arnold) Hodder Education.

Johns Hopkins Hospital, et al. Harriet Lane Handbook & Harriet Lane Handbook of Pediatric Antimicrobial Therapy Package. 2nd ed. 2011. (Mobile Medicine Ser.). (ENG.). pap. 79.95 (978-0-323-08723-0(X), Mosby) Elsevier - Health Sciences Div.

Judd, Sandra J., ed. Childhood Diseases Sourcebook. 2nd rev. ed. 2009. (Health Reference Ser.). 93.00 (978-0-7808-1031-0(7)) Omnigraphics, Inc.

Kane, Kay Shou-Mei. Color Atlas & Synopsis of Pediatric Dermatology. 2nd ed. 2009. (Illus.). xiv, 497p. (978-0-07-163855-5(5)) McGraw-Hill Medical Publishing Div.

Kang, Y. James & Gad, Shayne C., eds. Pediatric Drugs & Medical Devices: Safety Evaluation & Development. (Methods in Pharmacology & Toxicology Ser.). 250p. 2008. 135.00 (978-1-58829-582-8(6), 1588295826) 2006. 135.00 (978-1-59745-307-3(2)) Humana Pr.

Kearney, Christopher. Social Anxiety & Social Phobia in Youth: Characteristics, Assessment, & Psychological Treatment. 2010. (Series in Anxiety & Related Disorders Ser.). (Illus.). x, 220p. pap. 84.95 (978-1-4419-3552-6(5), 1441935525) Springer.

Keen, Deb & Rodger, Sylvia. Working with Parents of a Newly Diagnosed Child with Autism Spectrum Disorder: A Guide for Professionals. 2012. (ENG., Illus.). 288p. pap. (978-1-84905-120-0(8)) Kingsley, Jessica Ltd.

Keene, Nancy. Childhood Leukemia. 4th ed. 2010. (Patient Centered Guides). (ENG., Illus.). 528p. pap., instr.'s gde. ed. 29.95 (978-1-4493-8043-4(3)) O'Reilly Media, Inc.

Kessick, Rosemary. Autism & Gastrointestinal Complaints: What You Need to Know. 2009. (ENG., Illus.). 80p. pap. (978-1-84310-984-6(0)) Kingsley, Jessica Ltd.

Kibel, Maurice, et al. Child Health for All. 4th ed. 2008. (ENG., Illus.). 576p. pap. 69.50 (978-0-19-576495-6(1)) Oxford Univ. Pr., Inc.

Kirkham, Fenella & Ganesan, Vijeya, eds. Stroke & Cerebrovascular Disease in Childhood. 2011. (ENG., Illus.). 248p. 199.95 (978-1-898683-34-6(4)) Mac Keith Pr. GBR. Dist: Wiley, John & Sons, Inc.

Klimo, Paul, Jr., et al. Pediatric Vascular Neurosurgery, an Issue of Neurosurgery Clinics. 2010. (Clinics: Surgery Ser.: 21-3). (ENG., Illus.). xiv, 400p. 105.00 (978-1-4377-1840-9(X), Saunders) Elsevier - Health Sciences Div.

Korn, Danna. Gluten-Free Kids: Raising Happy, Healthy Children with Celiac Disease, Autism & Other Conditions. 2010. 280p. pap. (978-1-60613-006-3(4)) Woodbine Hse.

Krassas, G. E., et al, eds. Diseases of the Thyroid in Childhood & Adolescence [Bibliography & Price not Definite.]. (Pediatric & Adolescent Medicine Ser.: Vol. 11). (Illus.). 320p. (978-3-8055-8205-6(6)) Karger, S. AG.

Krejcirova, Inka & Autrata, Rudolf. Pediatric Glaucoma & Use of Drainage Implants. 2011. 112p. pap. (978-3-8433-8947-1(0)) Lambert Academic Publishing.

Kuttner, Leora. A Child in Pain: What Health Professionals Can Do to Help. 2010. (Illus.). 416p. pap. (978-1-84590-436-4(2)) Crown Hse. Publishing.

Langston, Kelly. Autism's Hidden Blessings: Discovering God's Promises for Autistic Children & Their Families, 1 vol. 2009. 208p. pap. 13.99 (978-0-8254-2977-4(3)) Kregel Pubns.

Lee, Peter N. & Forey, Barbara. Exacerbation of Asthma: Epidemiological Evidence in Children. 2008. pap. 35.00 (978-1-60692-083-1(9)) Nova Science Pubs., Inc.

Leeland, Jeff. A Thousand Small Sparrows: Amazing Stories of Kids Helping Kids. 2007. (ENG.). 256p. per. 13.99 (978-1-59052-933-1(2), Multnomah) Doubleday Religious Publishing Group, The.

Lehman, Thomas J. A. A Parent's Guide to Rheumatic Disease in Children. 2008. (ENG., Illus.). 228p. pap. 16.95 (978-0-19-534189-8(9)) Oxford Univ. Pr., Inc.

Levin, Alex V. & Wilson, Thomas W., eds. The Hospital for Sick Children's Atlas of Pediatric Ophthalmology & Strabismus. 2006. (Illus.). 320p. 198.99 (978-0-7817-4309-9(5)) Lippincott Williams & Wilkins.

Li, Huijun, et al. Identifying, Assessing, & Treating Early Onset Schizophrenia at School. 2010. (Developmental Psychopathology at School Ser.). (ENG.). xii, 148p. 149.00 (978-1-4419-6271-3(9), 1441962719) Springer.

Loar, Roberto N. Sugar Bugs. 2009. 24p. pap. 13.50 (978-1-4389-7192-6(3)) AuthorHouse.

Long, Sarah S., et al. Principles & Practice of Pediatric Infectious Disease. 4th ed. 2012. (ENG., Illus.). 1633p. 279.00 (978-1-4377-2702-9(6), Churchill Livingstone) Elsevier - Health Sciences Div.

Long, Sarah S., et al. Principles & Practice of Pediatric Infectious Diseases. 3rd rev. ed. 2008. (Principles & Practice of Pediatric Infectious Diseases Ser.). (Illus.). 1618p. 249.00 incl. cd-rom (978-0-443-06687-0(6), Churchill Livingstone) Elsevier - Health Sciences Div.

Longe, Jacqueline L. Gale Encyclopedia of Children's Health: Infancy Through Adolescence. 2nd ed. 2011. (978-1-4144-8645-1(6)); (978-1-4144-8642-0(1)); (978-1-4144-8643-7(X)); (978-1-4144-8644-4(8)); 748.00 (978-1-4144-8641-3(3)) Cengage Gale.

Lucan, Dawn. Practical Asperger Syndrome Manual. 2010. 80p. pap. 16.95 (978-0-557-72875-6(4)) Lulu Enterprises Inc.

—Practical down Syndrome Manual. 2010. (ENG.). 60p. pap. 12.95 (978-0-557-45967-4(2)); 60p. pap. 12.95 (978-0-557-47631-2(3)); 76p. pap. 16.95 (978-0-557-47754-8(9)) Lulu Enterprises Inc.

Macintyre, Christine. Dyspraxia 5-14: Identifying & Supporting Young People with Movement Difficulties. 2nd ed. 2009. (David Fulton / Nasen Ser.). (ENG., Illus.). 132p. 37.95 (978-0-415-54396-5(7)); 105.00 (978-0-415-54397-2(5)) Routledge.

Mars, Laura, ed. Complete Directory for Pediatric Disorders. 2011. 2500p. pap. 165.00 (978-1-59237-742-8(4)) Grey Hse. Publishing.

Mars-Proietti, Laura, ed. Complete Directory for Pediatric Disorders 2010. 5th rev. ed. 2009. 1000p. pap. 165.00 (978-1-59237-430-4(1)) Grey Hse. Publishing.

Massey, Rachel & Ackerman, Frank. Costs of Preventable Childhood Illness: The Price We Pay for Pollution (in Massachusetts) 2006. (Illus.). 51p. (C). reprint ed. pap. 15.00 (978-1-4223-0606-2(2)) DIANE Publishing Co.

May Loo Staff & Loo, May. Integrative Medicine for Children. 2008. (ENG., Illus.). 536p. 75.95 (978-1-4160-2299-2(6), Saunders) Elsevier - Health Sciences Div.

Mayville, Erik A. & Mulick, James A. Behavioral Foundations of Effective Autism Treatment. 2010. (978-1-59738-031-7(8)) Sloan Publishing.

McClain, Brenda C. & Suresh, Santhanam, eds. Handbook of Pediatric Chronic Pain: Current Science & Integrative Practice. 2011. (Perspectives on Pain in Psychology Ser.). (ENG., Illus.). xv, 418p. 169.00 (978-1-4419-0349-5(6), 1441903496) Springer.

Melillo, Robert. Disconnected Kids: The Groundbreaking Brain Balance Program for Children with Autism, ADHD, Dyslexia, & Other Neurological Disorders. 2010. (ENG.). 288p. (gr. 12-18). 15.95 (978-0-399-53560-4(8), Perigee Trade) Penguin Group (USA) Inc.

Merrick, Joav. Child & Adolescent Health Yearbook 2009. 2012. (Health & Human Development (Joav Merrick - Ser. Editor - National Institute of Child Health & Human Development, Ministry of Social Affairs, Jerusalem) Ser.). 733p. 295.00 (978-1-61668-913-1(7)) Nova Science Pubs., Inc.

Minns. Problems Intracranial Children. (Illus.). 458p. (C). (978-0-901260-82-6(7)) Cambridge Univ. Pr.

Mitchell, Ron B., et al, eds. Pediatric Otolaryngology for the Clinician. 2009. (ENG., Illus.). xiii, 228p. 109.00 (978-1-58829-542-2(7), 1588295427) Humana Pr.

Mokra, Daniela & Mokry, Juraj, eds. Meconium Aspiration Syndrome: from Pathomechanisms to Treatment. 2010. (Pregnancy & Infants: Medical, Psychological & Social Issues Ser.). pap. 43.00 (978-1-60876-944-5(5), Nova Biomedical Bks.) Nova Science Pubs., Inc.

Mondy, Tim. Memoirs of Miracles. 2008. 232p. pap. 22.33 (978-0-615-19877-4(5)) Mondy, Tim.

Montouris, Georgia D., et al. Epilepsy on Our Terms: Stories by Children with Seizures & Their Parents. 2007. (Brainstorms Ser.). (ENG., Illus.). 192p. pap. 22.99 (978-0-19-533090-8(0)) Oxford Univ. Pr., Inc.

Mosley, W. Henry & Chen, Lincoln C. Child Survival: Strategies for Research. 2008. (ENG., Illus.). 412p. pap. 50.00 (978-0-521-07297-7(2)) Cambridge Univ. Pr.

Munoz, Ricardo, et al, eds. Critical Care of Children with Heart Disease: Basic Medical & Surgical Concepts. 2010. (ENG., Illus.). xxx, 700p. 199.00 (978-1-84882-261-0(8), 1848822618) Springer.

Nakamura, Hiroto, ed. Congenital Heart Defects: Etiology, Diagnosis & Treatment. 2008. (Illus.). 368p. 129.00 (978-1-60692-559-1(8)) Nova Science Pubs., Inc.

Neustaedter, Randall. The Holistic Baby Guide: Alternative Care for Common Health Problems. 2010. (New Harbinger Whole-Body Healing Ser.). (ENG., Illus.). 240p. pap. 18.95 (978-1-57224-693-5(6)) New Harbinger Pubns.

Norall, Cynthia La Brie & Brust, Beth Wagner. Quirky, Yes - Hopeless, No: Practical Tips to Help Your Child with Asperger's Syndrome Be More Socially Accepted. 2009. (ENG.). 384p. pap. 16.99 (978-0-312-55849-9(X), St. Martin's Griffin) St. Martin's Pr.

Olness, Karen & Culbert, Timothy. Integrative Pediatrics. 2009. (Weil Integrative Medicine Library). (ENG., Illus.). 720p. 49.95 (978-0-19-538472-7(5)) Oxford Univ. Pr., Inc.

O'Toole, Jennifer Cook. Asperkids: An Insider's Guide to Loving, Understanding, & Teaching Children with Asperger Syndrome. 2012. (ENG., Illus.). 192p. pap. (978-1-84905-902-2(0)) Kingsley, Jessica Ltd.

Panayiotopoulos, C. P. Benign Childhood Focal Seizures & Related Epileptic Syndromes. 2010. (Illus.). ix, 61p. pap. 24.95 (978-1-84996-476-0(9), 1849964769) Springer.

Patel, Dilip R. & Greydanus, Donald E. Autism Spectrum Disorders: Practical Overview for Pediatricians, an Issue of Pediatric Clinics. 2012. (Clinics: Internal Medicine Ser.: 59-1). (ENG., Illus.). xvii, 224p. 92.00 (978-1-4557-3908-0(1), Saunders) Elsevier - Health Sciences Div.

Peirsman, Etienne & Peirsman, Neeto. Craniosacral Therapy for Babies & Small Children. 2006. (ENG., Illus.). 120p. pap. 24.95 (978-1-55643-597-3(5)) North Atlantic Bks.

Perkins, C. Gale. The Baby's Cross: A Tuberculosis Survivor's Memoir. 3rd ed. 2012. (ENG., Illus.). 186p. pap. (978-1-927360-14-9(5), CCB Publishing) CCB Publishing.

Petrone, Joe. Can't Hold Me Down. 2009. 162p. pap. 19.96 (978-0-557-09051-8(2)) Lulu Enterprises Inc.

Phiri, Kamija. Iron Deficiency & Malari. 2010. 228p. pap. (978-3-639-23935-5(0)) VDM Verlag Dr. Mueller e.K.

Phuka, John. Efficacy of Complementary Food Supplementation with Lipid-Based Nutrient Supplements on Growth of Malawian Children. 2009. (Acta Universitatis Tamperensis Ser.). 176p. pap. 82.50 (978-951-44-7832-1(0)) Tampere Univ. Pr. FIN. Dist: Coronet Bks.

Piccoli, David A. & Liacouras, Chris A. Pediatric Gastroenterology. 2007. (Requisites in Pediatrics Ser.). (ENG., Illus.). 576p. 82.95 (978-0-323-03280-3(X), Mosby) Elsevier - Health Sciences Div.

Platt, Allan F., et al. Hope & Destiny: The Patient & Parent's Guide to Sickle Cell Disease & Sickle Cell Trait. 3rd rev. ed. 2011. (ENG.). 276p. pap. 16.95 (978-0-9841447-0-9(6)) Hilton Publishing Co.

Pollard, Andrew J., et al, eds. Hot Topics in Infection & Immunity in Children VIII. 2011. (Advances in Experimental Medicine & Biology Ser.). (ENG., Illus.). xiii, 212p. 189.00 (978-1-4614-0203-9(4), 1461402034) Springer.

Pollard, Andrew J. & Finn, Adam. Hot Topics in Infection & Immunity in Children V. 2008. (Advances in Experimental Medicine & Biology Ser.). (Illus.). 208p. 159.00 (978-0-387-79837-0(4)) Springer.

Pollard, Andrew J. & Finn, Adam, eds. Hot Topics in Infection & Immunity in Children III. 2010. (Advances in Experimental Medicine & Biology Ser.). (Illus.). xxviii, 276p. pap. 159.00 (978-1-4419-4067-4(7), 1441940677) Springer.

Prasad, Kaushal K, et al. Project of Gurbakhshish Singh - Growth Retardation in Ehpvo. 2010. 72p. pap. (978-3-8383-6478-0(3)) Lambert Academic Publishing.

Programs Affecting Safety & Innovation in Pediatric Therapies: Hearing Before the Subcommittee on Health of the Committee on Energy & Commerce, House of Representatives, One Hundred Tenth Congress, First Session, May 22, 2007. 2008. (Illus.). v, 153p. (978-0-16-081926-1(1), 552-070-38099-0) United States Government Printing Office.

Puri, Prem, ed. Vesicoureteral Reflux. 2009. (Illus.). 256p. 159.00 (978-3-540-69503-5(6)) Springer.

Raal, Nadine. Mending a Broken Heart. 2011. (ENG.). 213p. pap. 29.95 (978-1-77009-909-8(3)) Jacana Media ZAF. Dist: Independent Pubs. Group.

Raue, Charles S. Diseases of Children. 473p. reprint ed. 98.00 (978-0-7222-9870-1(6)) Library Reprints, Inc.

Rogers, Sally J. & Dawson, Geraldine. Early Start Denver Model for Young Children with Autism: Promoting Language, Learning, & Engagement. 2009. (ENG., Illus.). 297p. pap. 50.00 (978-1-60623-631-4(8)) Guilford Pubns., Inc.

Roseff, Susan D. Pediatric Transfusion: A Physician's Handbook. 3rd ed. 2009. (Illus.). viii, 228p. (978-1-56395-291-3(2), AABB Pr.) American Assn. of Blood Banks.

Rubin, Jerry, et al. Naturally Healthy Kids: Integrating Conventional & Holistic Treatments for Common Illnesses of Children. 2007. 328p. spiral bd. 24.95 (978-0-9773949-2-0(1)) Partners in Pediatrics.

Ruddock, Edward H. The Diseases of Infants & Children & their Homeopathic & General Treatment. 240p. reprint ed. 98.00 (978-0-7222-9871-8(4)) Library Reprints, Inc.

Rustoen, Riitta A. & Ziegler, Serena R. Child Exposure to Elemental Mercury. 2011. (Public Health in the 21st Century Ser.). pap. 47.00 (978-1-61470-941-1(6)) Nova Science Pubs., Inc.

Sadeh, Avi. Sleeping Like a Baby: A Sensitive & Sensible Approach to Solving Your Child's Sleep Problem. 2011. (ENG., Illus.). 220p. pap. 24.00 (978-0-300-17698-8(8)) Yale Univ. Pr.

Sampaolesi, Roberto. The Glaucomas. 2008. (Illus.). xxii, 486p. 279.00 (978-3-540-69144-0(8)) Springer.

Saunders, Len. Keeping Kids Fit: A Family Plan for Raising Active, Healthy Children. 2010. (ENG., Illus.). 225p. pap. 15.95 (978-1-934184-26-4(8)) Lachance Publishing LLC.

Schauer, Maggie, et al. Narrative Exposure Therapy: A Short-Term Treatment for Traumatic Stress Disorders. 2nd ed. 2011. (Illus.). 112p. pap. 49.00 (978-0-88937-388-4(4)) Hogrefe Publishing.

Schmitt, Barton D. My Child Is Sick! Expert Advice for Managing Common Illnesses & Injuries. 2011. (ENG.). 315p. (J). pap. 14.95 (978-1-58110-552-0(5)) American Academy of Pediatrics.

Schmitz, J., ed. Cholestatic Disease in Childhood. 2008. (Illus.). 48p. pap. (978-3-8055-8965-9(4)) Karger, S. AG.

Schultz, Stephen. Autism Risk. 2008. 132p. pap. (978-3-639-06790-3(8)) VDM Verlag Dr. Mueller e.K.

Sears, William, et al. The Portable Pediatrician: Everything You Need to Know about Your Child's Health. 2011. (ENG., Illus.). 592p. pap. 21.99 (978-0-316-01748-0(5)) Little Brown & Co.

Semple, Randye J. & Lee, Jennifer. Mindfulness-Based Cognitive Therapy for Anxious Children: A Manual for Treating Childhood Anxiety. 2011. (Professional Ser.). (ENG.). 394p. 59.95 (978-1-57224-719-2(3)) New Harbinger Pubns.

Shah, Samir S. Infectious Disease. 2009. (Pediatric Practice Ser.). (ENG., Illus.). 808p. 89.00 (978-0-07-148924-9(X), 007148924X) McGraw-Hill Professional Publishing.

Shaw, Steven R. & McCabe, Paul C. Genetic & Acquired Disorders: Current Topics & Interventions for Educators. Shaw, Steven R. & McCabe, Paul C., eds. 2010. 192p. pap. 36.95 (978-1-4129-6872-0(0), B6713P) Corwin Pr.

—Pediatric Disorders: Current Topics & Interventions for Educators. Shaw, Steven R. & McCabe, Paul C., eds. 2010. 184p. pap. 36.95 (978-1-4129-6874-4(7), B68737P) Corwin Pr.

—Psychiatric Disorders: Current Topics & Interventions for Educators. Shaw, Steven R. & McCabe, Paul C., eds. 2010. 184p. pap. 36.95 (978-1-4129-6876-8(3), B68751P) Corwin Pr.

Sheillah, Simiyu & Augustine, Afullo. Effects of Interventions on Childhood Diarrhoeal Morbidity in Kenya: Water, Sanitation & Health Education Interventions on Diarrhoeal Morbidity in Children under Five Years in Mandera, Kenya. 2011. 112p. pap. (978-3-639-32524-9(9)) VDM Verlag Dr. Mueller e.K.

Siegel, Bryna. Getting the Best for Your Child with Autism: An Expert's Guide to Treatment. 2008. (ENG.). 280p. (gr. -1-7). 40.00 *(978-1-59385-601-4(6))*; per. 16.95 *(978-1-59385-317-4(3))* Guilford Pubns., Inc.

Skowron, Jared M. 100 Natural Remedies for Your Child: The Complete Guide to Safe, Effective Treatments for Childhood's Most Common Ailments, from Allergies to Weight Loss. 2011. (ENG., Illus.). 368p. pap. 19.99 *(978-1-60961-115-6(2))* Rodale Pr., Inc.

Smith Roley, Susanne, et al. Understanding the Nature of Sensory Integration with Diverse Populations. 2007. 73.00 *(978-1-4164-0332-6(9))* PRO-ED, Inc.

Solomons, N. W., ed. Emerging Infectious Diseases in Children. 2009. (Illus.). 48p. pap. *(978-3-8055-9269-7(3))* Karger, S. AG.

Spurlock, Stacy. Not by Chance. 2008. 212p. pap. 15.50 *(978-1-4343-7484-4(X))* AuthorHouse.

Stanley, Barry. Rebreathing. 2009. 120p. pap. 13.99 *(978-1-4389-7923-6(1))* AuthorHouse.

Stecklein, Hilary Pert. Recognizing Common Illnesses in Early Childhood Settings. 2009. (Redleaf Quick Guides). (ENG.). 50p. pap. 14.95 *(978-1-933653-67-9(1))* Redleaf Pr.

Steele, Russell W. Clinical Handbook of Pediatric Infectious Disease. 3rd rev. ed. 2007. (ENG., Illus.). 336p. 200.00 *(978-1-4200-5150-6(4)*, Informa Healthcare) Taylor & Francis Group GBR. Dist: Taylor & Francis Group.

Steingraber, Sandra. Raising Elijah: Protecting Our Children in an Age of Environmental Crisis. 2011. (Merloyd Lawrence Book Ser.). (ENG.). 368p. 26.00 *(978-0-7382-1399-6(3))* Da Capo Pr., Inc.

Stores, Gregory. Sleep problems in Children & Adolescents. 2009. (Facts Ser.). (ENG., Illus.). 154p. pap. 19.95 *(978-0-19-929614-9(6))* Oxford Univ. Pr., Inc.

Taketomo, Carol K., et al. Pediatric Dosage Handbook: Including Neonatal Dosing, Drug Administration, & Extemporaneous Preparations. 14th ed. 2007. (Pediatric Dosage Handbook Ser.). 2003p. per. 51.95 *(978-1-59195-215-2(8))* Lexi-Comp, Inc.

—Pediatric Dosage Handbook with International Trade Names Index. 14th ed. 2007. (Lexi-Comp's Drug Reference Handbooks Ser.). (Illus.). 2153p. per. 55.95 *(978-1-59195-216-9(6))* Lexi-Comp, Inc.

Taylor, Edith Meyer. Psychological Appraisal of Children with Cerebral Defects. 2011. 516p. 60.95 ***(978-1-258-09635-0(8))*** Literary Licensing, LLC.

Thompson, Travis. Freedom from Meltdowns: Dr. Thompson's Solutions for Children with Autism. 2008. 304p. *(978-1-55766-986-5(4))* Brookes, Paul H. Publishing Co.

—Individualized Autism Intervention for Young Children: Blending Discrete Trial & Naturalistic Strategies. 2011. (Illus.). 208p. pap. 29.95 *(978-1-59857-173-8(7))* Brookes, Paul H. Publishing Co.

Thomson, Kate, et al, eds. Paediatric Handbook. 8th ed. 2009. (ENG., Illus.). 656p. pap. 62.95 *(978-1-4051-7400-8(5))* Wiley, John & Sons, Inc.

Towbin, Jeffrey. Heart Failure in Children, an Issue of Heart Failure Clinics. 2010. (Clinics: Internal Medicine Ser.: 6-4). (ENG., Illus.). xviii, 402p. 94.00 *(978-1-4377-2457-8(4)*, Saunders) Elsevier - Health Sciences Div.

UNICEF Staff. Malaria & Children: Progress in Intervention Coverage. 2007. (Illus.). 73p. pap. 20.00 *(978-92-806-4184-4(0))* United Nations Children's Fund, The (UNICEF).

van der Vinne, Fredah Kagiso & Van Der Vinne, Fredah Kagiso. Back into Society; de-Institunalising Hiv Positive CHildren. 2010. 100p. pap. *(978-3-8383-3873-6(1))* Lambert Academic Publishing.

Van Dorp, S., et al. Child Health. 2007. (Oxford GP Library Ser.). (Illus.). 192p. pap. 27.50 *(978-0-19-921568-3(5))* Oxford Univ. Pr., Inc.

Volpe, Joseph J., frwd. The Neurological Manifestations of Pediatric Infectious Diseases & Immunodeficiency Syndromes. 2008. (Infectious Disease Ser.). (Illus.). 421p. 189.00 *(978-1-58829-567-3(8))* Springer.

Waghela, Priti. The Homeopathic Treatment for Children's Disease. 2009. 116p. pap. 19.99 *(978-1-4363-6047-0(1))* Xlibris Corp.

Wagner, Aureen, Sr. Treatment of OCD in Children & Adolescents: Professional's Kit. 2007. (YA). per. *(978-0-9795392-2-0(6))* Lighthouse Pr., Inc.

Wakefield, Andrew. Callous Disregard: Autism & Vaccines - The Truth Behind a Tragedy. 2010. pap. *(978-1-4507-1187-6(1))* Independent Pub.

—Callous Disregard: Autism & Vaccines - The Truth Behind a Tragedy. 2010. (ENG.). 288p. 26.95 *(978-1-61608-169-0(4)*, 608169) Skyhorse Publishing Co., Inc.

Walco, Gary A. & Goldschneider, Kenneth R., eds. Pain in Children: A Practical Guide for Primary Care. (ENG., Illus.). xxi, 279p. 2010. pap. 99.00 *(978-1-61737-929-1(8)*, 1617379298) 2008. 99.00 *(978-1-934115-31-2(2)*, 1934115312) Humana Pr.

Webber, Steven. Paediatric Heart Disease: A Practical Guide. Daubeney, Piers et al, eds. 2007. (ENG., Illus.). 384p. 108.95 *(978-0-7279-1861-1(3))* Wiley, John & Sons, Inc.

Weber, Doron. Immortal Bird: A Family Memoir. 2012. 358p. pap. ***(978-1-4516-1807-5(7))***; (ENG.). 368p. 25.00 ***(978-1-4516-1806-8(9))*** Simon & Schuster.

—Immortal Bird: A Family Memoir. Lt. ed. 2012. (ENG.). 623p. 31.99 ***(978-1-4104-4541-4(0))*** Thorndike Pr.

Wetmore, Ralph, et al, eds. Pediatric Otolaryngology: Principles & Practice Pathways. 2nd ed. 2012. (ENG., Illus.). 976p. 229.99 ***(978-1-60406-413-1(7))*** Thieme Medical Pubs., Inc.

Wetmore, Ralph F. Pediatric Otolaryngology. 2007. (Requisites in Pediatrics Ser.). (ENG., Illus.). 256p. 84.95 *(978-0-323-04855-2(2)*, Mosby) Elsevier - Health Sciences Div.

Whitehouse, Beth. The Match: Savior Siblings & One Family's Battle to Heal Their Daughter. 2010. (ENG.). 272p. 24.95 *(978-0-8070-7286-8(9))* Beacon Pr.

Whitlock, Evelyn P. Effectiveness of Weight Management Programs in Children & Adolescents. 2008. (Illus.). x, 99p. pap. *(978-1-58763-364-5(7))* Agency for Healthcare Research & Quality.

Wilmott, Robert W., et al. Kendig & Chernick's Disorders of the Respiratory Tract in Children: Expert Consult - Online & Print. 8th ed. 2012. (ENG., Illus.). 1168p. 289.00 ***(978-1-4377-1984-0(8)***, Saunders) Elsevier - Health Sciences Div.

Wittenberg, D. F. Paediatrics & Child Health. 6th ed. 2010. (ENG., Illus.). 816p. pap. 79.95 *(978-0-19-598843-7(4))* Oxford Univ. Pr., Inc.

World Health Organization. Helminth Control in School-Age Children. Second Edition: A Guide for Managers of Control Programmes. 2nd rev. ed. 2012. (Nonserial Publication Ser.). (ENG.). 100p. pap. 36.00 ***(978-92-4-154826-7(6))*** World Health Organization.

Wren, Christopher. Concise Guide to Pediatric Arrhythmias. 2011. (ENG., Illus.). 198p. pap. 64.95 ***(978-0-470-65855-0(X)***, Wiley-Blackwell) Wiley, John & Sons, Inc.

Yaffe, Sumner J. & Aranda, Jacob V., eds. Neonatal & Pediatric Pharmacology: Therapeutic Principles in Practice. 4th rev. ed. 2010. (ENG., Illus.). 1072p. 256.99 *(978-0-7817-9538-8(9))* Lippincott Williams & Wilkins.

Younis, R., ed. Tonsillectomy in Children [Bibliography & Price not Definite.]. 2007. (Illus.). 58p. pap. *(978-3-8055-8436-4(9))* Karger, S. AG.

Zarbock, Sarah, ed. The Complete Directory for Pediatric Disorders. 4th ed. 2007. (Complete Directory for Pediatric Disorders Ser.). 1131p. per. 165.00 *(978-1-59237-150-1(7))* Grey Hse. Publishing.

Zuniga, Cecilia. Ad/Hd Generation: Holistic Ways to Support Children. 2010. 296p. pap. 22.50 *(978-1-4251-8114-7(7))* Trafford Publishing.

CHILDREN—DISEASES—DIAGNOSIS

see also Pediatric Radiology

Abu-Arafeh, Ishaq. Childhood Headache. 2007. (Clinics in Developmental Medicine Ser.: No. 158). (ENG., Illus.). 208p. 87.95 *(978-1-898683-26-1(3))* Mac Keith Pr. GBR. Dist: Wiley, John & Sons, Inc.

Anton, Christopher G., et al. Pediatrics. 2009. (EXPERTddx™ Ser.). (ENG.). 700p. 299.00 *(978-1-931884-13-6(7))* Lippincott Williams & Wilkins.

Baily, Mary Ann & Murray, Thomas H., eds. Ethics & Newborn Genetic Screening: New Technologies, New Challenges. 2009. (ENG., Illus.). 376p. (gr. 17). 52.00 *(978-0-8018-9151-9(5))* Johns Hopkins Univ. Pr.

Barness, Lewis A. & Gilbert-Barness, Enid. Handbook of Pediatric Physical & Clinical Diagnosis. 2nd ed. 2008. (ENG., Illus.). 568p. pap. 34.95 *(978-0-19-537325-7(1))* Oxford Univ. Pr., Inc.

Bourgarit, R. Medicina Natural para Ninos (Natural Medicine for Children) (SPA.). pap. *(978-84-305-8885-5(X))* Susaeta Ediciones, S.A.

Chiocca, Ellen M. Advanced Pediatric Assessment. 2010. (ENG., Illus.). 560p. 76.99 *(978-0-7817-9165-6(0))* Lippincott Williams & Wilkins.

Coley, Brian D. Pediatric Ultrasound - An Issue of Ultrasound Clinics Pt. 2. 2010. (Clinics: Radiology Ser.: 5-1). (ENG., Illus.). 79.00 *(978-1-4377-1945-1(7)*, Saunders) Elsevier - Health Sciences Div.

Cram101 Textbook Reviews & Cram101 Textbook Reviews. Outlines & Highlights for Pediatric Clinical Skills by Richard Goldbloom, Isbn: 9781437713978. 2011. 464p. pap. 36.95 ***(978-1-61451-215-5(3))*** Cram101 Inc.

de Bruyn, Rose, ed. Pediatric Ultrasound: How, Why & When. 2nd ed. 2010. (How, Why & When Ser.). (ENG., Illus.). 404p. (C). 92.95 *(978-0-443-06917-8(4)*, Churchill Livingstone) Elsevier - Health Sciences Div.

Deterding, Robin R., et al. CURRENT Diagnosis & Treatment Pediatrics 2011. 20th ed. 2010. (LANGE CURRENT Ser.). (ENG., Illus.). 1328p. pap. 78.00 incl. cd-rom *(978-0-07-166444-8(0)*, 0071664440) McGraw-Hill Professional Publishing.

Dick, Macdonald, ed. Clinical Cardiac Electrophysiology in the Young. 2010. (Developments in Cardiovascular Medicine Ser.). (Illus.). 320p. pap. 229.00 *(978-1-4419-3973-9(3)*, 1441939733) Springer.

DiMario, Francis J., Jr. Non-Epileptic Childhood Paroxysmal Disorders. 2009. (ENG., Illus.). 400p. 59.95 *(978-0-19-533537-8(6))* Oxford Univ. Pr., Inc.

Garfunkel, Lynn C., et al. Pediatric Clinical Advisor: Instant Diagnosis & Treatment. 2nd rev. ed. 2007. (Clinical Advisor Ser.). (ENG., Illus.). 864p. 110.00 *(978-0-323-03506-4(X)*, Mosby) Elsevier - Health Sciences Div.

Goldbloom, Richard B. Pediatric Clinical Skills: With STUDENT CONSULT Online Access. 4th ed. 2010. (ENG., Illus.). 360p. (C). pap. 64.95 *(978-1-4377-1397-8(1)*, Saunders) Elsevier - Health Sciences Div.

Greydanus, Donald E. The Pediatric Diagnostic Examination. 2008. (Illus.). xviii, 813p. *(978-0-07-128727-2(2))* McGraw-Hill Medical Publishing Div.

Hill, Robert W. & Castro, Eduardo. Healing Young Brains: The Neurofeedback Solution. 2009. (ENG., Illus.). 386p. pap. 16.95 *(978-1-57174-603-0(X))* Hampton Roads Publishing Co., Inc.

Jonas, Nico. The Adenoid in Children. 2010. 64p. pap. *(978-3-8383-2125-7(1))* Lambert Academic Publishing.

Lucaya, Javier & Strife, Janet L., eds. Pediatric Chest Imaging: Chest Imaging in Infants & Children. 2nd ed. 2011. (Medical Radiology / Diagnostic Imaging Ser.). (ENG., Illus.). x, 450p. pap. 319.00 *(978-3-642-06917-8(7)*, 3642069177) Springer.

McCarthy, James. The Child's Foot & Ankle. Drennan, James C., ed. 2nd rev. ed. 2009. (ENG., Illus.). 576p. 248.99 *(978-0-7817-7847-3(6))* Lippincott Williams & Wilkins.

Murasko, Maria. Jacob's Journal - My Journey Home. 2007. 81p. pap. 16.95 *(978-1-4303-1152-2(5))* Lulu Enterprises Inc.

Orkin, Stuart H., et al. Oncology of Infancy & Childhood. 2009. (ENG., Illus.). 1392p. 228.00 *(978-1-4160-3431-5(5)*, Saunders) Elsevier - Health Sciences Div.

Proytcheva, Maria, ed. Diagnostic Pediatric Hematopathology. 2011. (ENG., Illus.). 588p. 225.00 *(978-0-521-88160-9(9))* Cambridge Univ. Pr.

Sawyer. Pediatric Physical Exam & Health Assesment. rev. ed. 2011. 672p. pap. 78.95 *(978-0-7637-7438-7(3))* Jones & Bartlett Learning, LLC.

Schroten, Horst & Wirth, Stefan. Pediatric Infectious Diseases Revisited. 2007. (Birkhauser Advances in Infectious Diseases Ser.). (Illus.). 503p. 239.00 *(978-3-7643-7997-1(9))* Birkhauser Boston.

Siegel, Marilyn J., ed. Pediatric Sonography. 4th rev. ed. 2010. (ENG., Illus.). 736p. 245.99 *(978-1-60547-665-0(X))* Lippincott Williams & Wilkins.

Slovis, Thomas L. High Yield Imaging: Pediatrics: Expert Radiology Series. 2010. (HIGH YIELD in Radiology Ser.). (ENG., Illus.). 768p. 199.00 *(978-1-4160-6180-9(0)*, Saunders) Elsevier - Health Sciences Div.

Soldin, Steven J. Pediatric Reference Intervals. 7th ed. 2011. ***(978-1-59425-101-6(0))*** American Assn. for Clinical Chemistry, Inc.

Soldin, Steven J., et al. Pediatric Reference Intervals. 6th ed. 2007. x, 271p. *(978-1-59425-067-5(7)*, AACC Pr.) American Assn. for Clinical Chemistry, Inc.

Toy, Eugene, et al. Case Files Pediatrics, Fourth Edition. 4th ed. 2012. (LANGE Case Files Ser.). (ENG.). 512p. (C). pap. 34.00 ***(978-0-07-176698-2(7)***, 0071766987) McGraw-Hill Medical Publishing Div.

Valman, Bernard, et al. Children's Medical Guide. 3rd ed. 2008. (ENG., Illus.). 216p. (gr. 12). pap. 20.00 *(978-0-7566-3399-8(0))* Dorling Kindersley Publishing, Inc.

Wolff, Johannes. HIT-GBM-A Studien Protokoll. 2. Ausgabe. 2010. 73p. pap. 17.66 *(978-0-557-31469-0(0))* Lulu Enterprises Inc.

—HIT-GBM-B Studienprotokoll 2. Ausgabe. 2010. 122p. pap. 20.10 *(978-0-557-31778-3(9))* Lulu Enterprises Inc.

—HIT-GBM C Studien-Protokoll 2. Ausgabe. 2010. 162p. pap. 22.10 *(978-0-557-31405-8(4))* Lulu Enterprises Inc.

—HIT-GBM-D (Deutsch) Studien Protokoll 2. Ausgabe. 2010. 161p. pap. 22.06 *(978-0-557-31797-4(5))* Lulu Enterprises Inc.

CHILDREN—DISEASES—NUTRITIONAL ASPECTS

Herbert, Martha & Weintraub, Karen. The Autism Revolution: Whole-Body Strategies for Making Life All It Can Be. 2012. (ENG.). 320p. 26.00 ***(978-0-345-52719-6(4)***, Ballantine Bks.) Random House Publishing Group.

Kirk, Sally. Hope for the Autism Spectrum: A Mother & Son Journey of Insight & Biomedical Intervention. 2008. (ENG., Illus.). 320p. *(978-1-84310-894-8(1))* Kingsley, Jessica Ltd.

Kossoff, Eric, et al. Ketogenic Diets: Treatments for Epilepsy & Other Disorders. 5th ed. 2011. (ENG., Illus.). 300p. pap. 29.95 *(978-1-936303-10-6(8))* Demos Medical Publishing, LLC.

Samour. Pediatric Nutrition 4E. 4th rev. ed. 2010. (Illus.). 538p. pap. 101.95 *(978-0-7637-8450-8(8))* Jones & Bartlett Learning, LLC.

Shaw, Vanessa & Lawson, Margaret, eds. Clinical Paediatric Dietetics. 3rd rev. ed. 2007. (ENG., Illus.). 632p. 146.99 *(978-1-4051-3493-4(3)*, Wiley-Blackwell) Wiley, John & Sons, Inc.

Suskind, David & Lenssen, Polly, eds. Pediatric Nutrition Handbook: An Algorithm Approach. 2011. (ENG.). 204p. pap. 46.99 ***(978-0-470-65995-3(5)***, Wiley-Blackwell) Wiley, John & Sons, Inc.

World Bank Staff. Environmental Health & Child Survival: Epidemiology, Economics, Experiences. 2008. (Environment & Development Ser.). (ENG.). 224p. pap. 18.00 *(978-0-8213-7236-4(X)*, 9780821372364) World Bank Pubns.

CHILDREN—DISEASES—PSYCHOSOMATIC ASPECTS

see Pediatrics—Psychosomatic Aspects

CHILDREN—EDUCATION

see Education

CHILDREN—EMPLOYMENT

see Child Labor

CHILDREN—ETIQUETTE

see Etiquette for Children and Teenagers

CHILDREN—FOLKLORE

Here are entered works on folklore produced by or for children and works on children as a theme in folklore.

Chamber, Alexander F. The Child & Childhood in Folk-Thought: Studies of the Activities & Influences of the Child among Primitive Peoples, Their Analogues & Survivals in the Civilization of To-Day. 2006. 632p. pap. 33.99 *(978-1-4264-2742-8(5))* 2007. (ENG.). 548p. pap. 30.99 *(978-1-4264-2685-8(2))* BiblioBazaar.

Chamberlain, Alexander Francis. The Child & Childhood in Folk Thought. 2009. 540p. pap. *(978-1-4589-1260-2(4))*; 542p. pap. *(978-1-4588-6658-5(0))*; 538p. pap. *(978-0-217-75164-3(4))* Books LLC.

—The Child & Childhood in Folk Thought. 2007. (ENG.). 472p. 52.95 *(978-0-548-01352-6(7))* Kessinger Publishing, LLC.

Delamar, Gloria T. Children's Counting-Out Rhymes, Fingerplays, Jump-Rope & Bounce-Ball Chants & Other Rhythms: A Comprehensive English-Language Reference. alt. ed. 2006. (ENG., Illus.). 224p. per. 39.95 *(978-0-7864-2833-5(3))* McFarland & Co., Inc. Pubs.

Tucker, Elizabeth. Children's Folklore: A Handbook, 1 vol. 2008. (Greenwood Folklore Handbooks Ser.). (Illus.). 172p. 55.00 *(978-0-313-34189-2(3)*, GR4189, Greenwood Pr.) Greenwood Publishing Group, Inc.

CHILDREN—FOOD

see Children—Nutrition

CHILDREN—GROWTH

Benson, Michael K. D., et al, eds. General Principles of Children's Orthopaedic Disease. 2011. (ENG., Illus.). xii, 226p. pap. 49.95 *(978-0-85729-548-4(9)*, 0857295489) Springer.

Cooper, Linda & Doherty, Jonathan. Physical Development. 2011. (Supporting Development in the Early Years Foundation Stage Ser.). (ENG., Illus.). 144p. 90.00 *(978-1-4411-2400-5(4))* Continuum International Publishing Group, Ltd. GBR. Dist: National Bk. Network.

Cram101 Textbook Reviews. Outlines & Highlights for Infants & Toddlers: Development & Curriculum Planning by Penny Deiner. ISBN. 2010. 66p. pap. 27.95 *(978-1-61698-667-4(0))* Cram101 Inc.

Cram101 Textbook Reviews Staff. Outlines & Highlights for Infants & Toddlers: Development & Curriculum Planning by Penny Deiner, ISBN. 2009. 64p. pap. 27.95 *(978-1-4288-8077-1(1))* Cram101 Inc.

Deiner, Penny Low. Infants & Toddlers: Development & Curriculum Planning. 2nd rev. ed. 2008. (ENG., Illus.). 784p. (C). pap. 133.95 *(978-1-4283-1824-3(0))* Delmar Cengage Learning.

Domellöf, Erik. Development of Functional Asymmetries in Young Infants - a Sensory-Motor Approach. 2008. 60p. pap. *(978-3-639-04422-5(3))* VDM Verlag Dr. Mueller e.K.

Formosa, Pamela. Fraid Not! Empowering Kids with Learning Differences. 2009. 92p. pap. 11.95 *(978-1-4401-5224-5(1))* iUniverse, Inc.

Hochberg, Ze'ev. Evo-Devo of Child Growth: Treatise on Child Growth & Human Evolution. 2012. (ENG., Illus.). 240p. 139.95 ***(978-1-118-02716-5(7)***, Wiley-Blackwell) Wiley, John & Sons, Inc.

Hochberger, Nan Landis. Parenting by the Steps. 2007. 128p. pap. 11.95 *(978-0-7414-3969-7(7))* Infinity Publishing.

Hoffhines, Emily. Bible Lessons with Babies. 2007. 80p. pap. 12.95 *(978-0-615-17178-4(8))* Hoffhines, Emily.

Holt, Pat & Ketterman, Grace. Don't Give in, Give Choices: Winning Your Child's Cooperation. 2010. pap. 11.99 *(978-1-61579-829-2(3))* Xulon Pr., Inc.

Hyndman, Robert. Connecting School Culture to Boys' Learning. 2008. 116p. pap. *(978-3-639-03358-8(2))* VDM Verlag Dr. Mueller e.K.

Johnston, Jane, et al. Physical Development. Nahmad-Williams, Lindy, ed. 2011. (Supporting Development in the Early Years Foundation Stage Ser.). (ENG., Illus.). 144p. 27.95 *(978-1-4411-9244-8(1))* Continuum International Publishing Group, Ltd. GBR. Dist: National Bk. Network.

Junn, Ellen & Boyatzis, Chris. Annual Editions: Child Growth & Development 12/13. 19th ed. 2011. (Annual Editions Ser.). (ENG., Illus.). 224p. (C). pap. 44.00 *(978-0-07-805107-4(X)*, 007805107X, McGraw-Hill/Dushkin) McGraw-Hill Higher Education.

—Child Growth & Development 11/12. annuals 18th ed. 2010. (Annual Editions Ser.). (ENG., Illus.). 224p. (C). pap. 44.00 *(978-0-07-805075-6(8)*, 0078050758, McGraw-Hill/Dushkin) McGraw-Hill Higher Education.

Junn, Ellen, et al. Child Growth & Development 10/11. 17th ed. 2009. (Annual Editions Ser.). (ENG., Illus.). 176p. (C). pap. 44.00 *(978-0-07-812784-7(X)*, 007812784X, McGraw-Hill/Dushkin) McGraw-Hill Higher Education.

Lentze, M. J., ed. Growth in Children - A Global Perspective. 2008. (Illus.). 48p. pap. *(978-3-8055-8493-7(8))* Karger, S. AG.

Lucas, A., et al, eds. Importance of Growth for Health & Development: 65th Nestlé Nutrition Institute Workshop, Pediatric Program, Kuala Lumpur, March 2009. 2010. (Nestlé Nutrition Institute Workshop Series: Clinical & Performance Program Ser.). (ENG., Illus.). 252p. *(978-3-8055-9304-5(X))* Karger, S. AG.

Morris, Desmond. Amazing Baby. 2008. (ENG., Illus.). 208p. pap. 24.95 *(978-1-55407-743-4(5))* Firefly Bks., Ltd.

Raikes, Helen H., et al. Extending the Dance in Infant & Toddler Caregiving: Enhancing Attachment & Relationships. 2009. (Illus.). 224p. pap. 29.95 *(978-1-55766-859-2(0))* Brookes, Paul H. Publishing Co.

S. H. Jacob. Your Baby's Mind: How to Make the Most of the Critical First Two Years. 2009. 332p. pap. 19.99 *(978-1-4343-6936-9(6))* AuthorHouse.

Sheridan, Mary D., et al. From Birth to Five Years: Children's Developmental Progress. 3rd rev. ed. 2007. (ENG., Illus.). 112p. pap. 19.95 *(978-0-415-42365-6(1))* Routledge.

Snow, McGaha & Cram101 Textbook Reviews Staff. Infant Development. 2007. 156p. per. 12.95 *(978-1-4288-2064-7(7))* Cram101 Inc.

Squires, Jane. ASQ-3 User's Guide. 2009. *(978-1-59857-004-5(8))* Brookes, Paul H. Publishing Co.

Squires, Jane & Bricker, Diane D. Ages & Stages Questionnaires in Spanish: A Parent-Completed Child Monitoring System. 3rd ed. 2009. (SPA.). 225.00 *(978-1-59857-003-8(X))* Brookes, Paul H. Publishing Co.

Sweetser, Stan. Growing up Cape Cod. 2009. 120p. pap. 12.95 *(978-1-4327-3694-1(9))* Outskirts Pr., Inc.

Wittmer, Donna S. & Petersen, Sandy. Infant & Toddler Development & Responsive Program Planning: A Relationship-Based Approach. 2nd ed. 2009. (ENG.). 432p. (C). pap. 85.60 *(978-0-13-715263-6(9)*, Prentice Hall) Prentice Hall PTR.

World Health Organization. WHO Child Growth Standards: Growth Velocity Based on Weight Length & Head Circumference - Methods & Development. 2009. (Nonserial Publication Ser.). (ENG., Illus.). 261p. pap. 60.00 *(978-92-4-154763-5(4))* World Health Organization.

World Health Organization Staff & World Health Organization, Nutrition for Health and Development Staff, contrib. by. Who Child Growth Standards: Head Circumference-for-Age, Arm Circumference-For Age, Triceps Skinfold-for-Age & Subscapular Skinfold-For Age. 2007. (Nonseria Publication). (ENG.). 234p. pap. 48.00 *(978-92-4-154718-5(9))* World Health Organization.

C

CHILDREN—HEALTH AND HYGIENE

see also Babysitters; Babysitting; Child Health Services; Children—Diseases; Children—Nutrition; Children—Preparation for Dental Care; Children—Preparation for Medical Care; Health Education; Infants—Care and Hygiene; Pediatric Nursing; Physical Education for Children; School Children—Food; School Nursing; Toilet Training

ABBE Scientist Research Division Staff. AIDS & HIV in Children: Index & Medical Analysis of New Clinical & Research Information. 2007. (ENG., Illus.). 160p. ring bd. 69.95 *(978-0-7883-4779-5(9))* ABBE Pubs. Assn. of Washington, D.C.

—Emotional Pain in Babies, Romance, War & the Dying: Index, Reference & Medical Analysis of New Research Information. 2008. (Illus.). 160p. ring bd. 69.95 *(978-0-7883-4661-3(X))* ABBE Pubs. Assn. of Washington, D.C.

Acevedo-Nieves, Rose. Influence of Acculturation on Asthma Outcomes in Hispanic Children - the Influence of Acculturation & Other Family Characteristics on Asthma Outcome. 2008. 108p. pap. *(978-3-639-04228-3(X))* VDM Verlag Dr. Mueller e.K.

Acid Reflux in Infants & Children: A practical guide for parents, caregivers, & health Professionals. 2007. per. 19.95 *(978-0-9745945-2-1(0))* SportWork.

Adams, Amanda Rose. Heart Warriors: A Family Faces Congenital Heart Disease. 2012. (ENG.). 300p. pap. 16.95 ***(978-1-933016-80-1(9))*** Behler Pubns., LLC.

Adibe, Maxwell. Quinine & Artemether in the Treatment of Severe Malaria in Children. 2010. 88p. pap. *(978-3-8383-9205-9(1))* Lambert Academic Publishing.

Ahmadi, Homayun. Sport & Children Go Together! Creating a better future life for Children. 2011. 100p. pap. 15.99 ***(978-1-4628-7112-4(7))*** Xlibris Corp.

Ajala, Aderemi S. Dyeing from the Womb. 2009. 148p. pap. *(978-3-639-18048-0(8))* VDM Verlag Dr. Mueller e.K.

Alcott, William A. The Young Mother: Management of Children in Regard to Health. 2007. (ENG.). 202p. pap. 20.99 *(978-1-4346-2153-5(7))*; 226p. pap. 22.99 *(978-1-4346-2213-6(4))* BiblioBazaar.

Alcott, William A. The Young Mother: Management of Children in Regard to Health. 2007. (ENG.). 210p. pap. 20.99 *(978-1-4264-0877-9(3))* 2006. 194p. pap. 21.99 *(978-1-4264-0858-8(7))* BiblioBazaar.

American Academy of Pediatrics. Patient Education for Children, Teens, & Parents: Patient Education Compendium. 4th ed. 2011. (ENG.). 464p. pap. 119.95 ***(978-1-58110-566-7(5))*** American Academy of Pediatrics.

American Academy of Pediatrics Staff, contrib. by. Patient Education for Children, Teens, & Parents. 3rd ed. 2007. (Illus.). xii, 436p. *(978-1-58110-231-4(3))* American Academy of Pediatrics.

Andolini, Laura. Secrets of a Toddler: Diet, Energy & Success. 2010. 100p. pap. 12.99 *(978-1-60911-445-9(0)*, Eloquent Bks.) AEG Literary Publishing Services, Inc.

Andrzejewski, Catherine. Education, Health Knowledge & Child Health in Coastal Ghana - What Do People Know, How Do They Know It, & Does It Matter? 2008. 144p. per. *(978-3-8364-5854-2(3))* VDM Verlag Dr. Mueller e.K.

Antidepressants, Antipsychotics, & Stimulants: Dangerous Drugs on Trial. 2007. (Soaring Heights Ser.). per. 24.95 *(978-0-9772703-2-3(7))* Soaring Heights Publishing.

Armstrong, Neil & Williams, Craig, eds. Children & Exercise Xxvi. 2011. (ENG., Illus.). 352p. (C). 160.00 *(978-0-415-57859-2(0))* Routledge.

Atter, Elizabeth & Drew, Sharon. Can't Play Won't Play: Simply Sizzling Ideals to Getting the Ball Rolling for Children with Dyspraxia. 2008. (ENG., Illus.). 200p. per. *(978-1-84310-601-2(9))* Kingsley, Jessica Ltd.

Austin, Glenn, et al. The Parents' Medical Manual. (Illus.). 426p. 11.95 *(978-0-13-650317-0(9))* Prentice Hall PTR.

Bammann, Karin & Ahrens, Wolfgang, eds. Measurement Tools for a Health Survey on Nutrition, Physical Activity & Lifestyle in Children: The European IDEFICS Study. 2012. (Springer Series on Epidemiology & Health Ser.). (ENG.). 370p. 159.00 *(978-1-4419-1382-1(3)*, 1441913823) Springer.

Bangura, Umaru & Mohamed Koroma, Bashiru. Morbidity & Mortality among Children under Five Years in Freetown. 2010. 164p. pap. *(978-3-8383-8683-6(3))* Lambert Academic Publishing.

Barker, Judy & Hodes, Deborah. The Child in Mind. 3rd rev. ed. 2007. (Illus.). 128p. 31.95 *(978-0-415-42602-2(2))* Routledge.

Barkley, Russell A. Barkley Deficits in Executive Functioning Scale — Children & Adolescents (BDEFS-CA) 2012. (ENG.). 184p. pap. 149.00 ***(978-1-4625-0394-0(2))*** Guilford Pubns., Inc.

Bartell, Susan. Fit & Fun Family Action Plan: 301 Things You Can Do Today. 2009. (ENG.). 384p. pap. 11.99 *(978-1-4022-2949-7(6))* Sourcebooks, Inc.

Bell, Erica, ed. Rural Child Health: International Aspects. 2010. (Health & Human Development (Joav Merrick - Series Editor - National Institute of Child Health & Human Development, Ministry of Social Ser.). (Illus.). xv, 269p. 125.00 *(978-1-60876-357-3(9)*, Nova Biomedical Bks.) Nova Science Pubs., Inc.

Benaroch, Roy. A Guide to Getting the Best Health Care for Your Child, 1 vol. 2007. (Praeger Series on Contemporary Health & Living Ser.). 192p. 44.95 *(978-0-275-99346-7(9)*, C9346, Praeger Pubs.) Greenwood Publishing Group, Inc.

—Solving Health & Behavioral Problems from Birth Through Preschool: A Parent's Guide. 2007. (Praeger Series on Contemporary Health & Living Ser.). (Illus.). 208p. 44.95 *(978-0-275-99347-4(7)*, C9347, Praeger Pubs.) Greenwood Publishing Group, Inc.

The Benefits of Physical & Health Education for Our Nation's Children: Hearing Before the Committee on Education & Labor, U.S. House of Representatives, One Hundred Tenth Congress, Second Session, Hearing Held in Washington, DC, July 24, 2008. 2008. iii, 71p. *(978-0-16-081825-7(7)*, 552-070-38023-0) United States Government Printing Office.

Berthoin, Serge & Baquet, Georges, eds. Children & Exercise Xxv. 2010. (ENG., Illus.). 280p. (C). 140.00 *(978-0-415-57514-0(1))* Routledge.

Bhavani Sankar, Rema. Assessment of Health Status of Children: Impact of External Factors. 2011. 80p. pap. ***(978-3-8443-9803-8(1))*** Lambert Academic Publishing.

Bilt Boockvar, M. S. How Austin Got His Muscles. 2009. 32p. pap. 12.99 *(978-1-4389-8054-6(X))* AuthorHouse.

Black, Christina. Starting School with a Food Allergy: Tips for a Peanut Allergic Kid. 2007. per. *(978-1-59872-763-0(X))* Instant Pub.

Blair, Mitch, et al. Child Public Health. 2nd ed. 2010. (ENG., Illus.). 310p. (Orig.). pap. 59.95 *(978-0-19-954750-0(5))* Oxford Univ. Pr., Inc.

Boise, Phil. Go Green Rating Scale for Early Childhood Settings. 2009. (ENG.). 88p. pap. 19.95 *(978-1-60554-006-1(4))* Redleaf Pr.

Bradford, Helen. The Well Being of Children Under 3. 2012. (Supporting Children from Birth to Three Ser.). (ENG., Illus.). 120p. 105.00 *(978-0-415-61270-8(5))*; pap. 28.95 *(978-0-415-61272-2(1))* Routledge.

Bridgeman, Jo. Parental Responsibility, Young Children & Healthcare Law. 2007. (ENG.). 282p. 115.00 *(978-0-521-86312-4(0))* Cambridge Univ. Pr.

Brisch, Karl Heinz. Treating Attachment Disorders, Second Edition: From Theory to Therapy. Kronenberg, Kenneth, tr. from GER. 2nd rev. ed. 2012. (ENG.). 369p. 40.00 ***(978-1-4625-0483-1(3))*** Guilford Pubns., Inc.

Brown, Brett V., ed. Key Indicators of Child & Youth Well-Being: Completing the Picture. 2007. (ENG., Illus.). 485p. 175.00 *(978-0-8058-4809-0(6))*; per. 60.00 *(978-0-8058-6313-0(3))* Taylor & Francis Group GBR. (Psychology Press). Dist: Taylor & Francis Group.

Bull, Thomas. The Maternal Management of Children, in Health & Disease. 2009. 176p. 22.99 *(978-0-559-09581-8(3))*; 25.99 *(978-0-559-09566-5(X))*; pap. 16.99 *(978-0-559-09576-4(7))*; pap. 21.99 *(978-0-559-09570-2(8))* BiblioBazaar.

—The Maternal Management of Children, in Health, & Disease. 2009. 244p. pap. *(978-1-4588-8735-1(9))* Books LLC.

Cameron, R. J. (Seàn), et al. Achieving Positive Outcomes for Children in Care. 2009. (Lucky Duck Bks.). (Illus.). 176p. 57.00 *(978-1-84787-448-1(7)*, B74487C); pap. 27.00 *(978-1-84787-449-8(5)*, B74487P) SAGE Pubns., Ltd. GBR. Dist: SAGE Pubns., Inc.

Campos, David. Jump Start Health! Practical Ideas to Promote Wellness in Kids of All Ages. 2011. (ENG., Illus.). 240p. 66.00 *(978-0-8077-5179-4(0))*; pap. 29.95 *(978-0-8077-5178-7(2))* Teachers College Pr., Teachers College, Columbia Univ.

Cartlidge, Patrick H. T., ed. Ethical, Legal & Social Aspects of Child Healthcare. 2007. (ENG., Illus.). 224p. pap. 69.95 *(978-0-08-044682-0(5)*, Elsevier) Elsevier - Health Sciences Div.

Chandra, Anita & Gresenz, Carole Roan. Health & Health Care among District of Columbia Youth. 2009. (Illus.). 216p. pap. 46.00 *(978-0-8330-4805-9(8)*, tr-751) RAND Corp., The.

Chavasse, Pye Henry. Advice to A Mother on the Management of. 2007. pap. *(978-1-4065-1438-4(1))* Dodo Pr.

Cheryl Nineff D'Ambrosio. Pooling Blood: A journey of two girls with hemophilia & their parents' struggle to keep them Alive. 2010. 316p. 32.95 *(978-0-595-51786-2(2))*; pap. 22.95 *(978-0-595-53055-7(9))* iUniverse, Inc.

Chideme-Munodawafa, Auxilia. Family Functioning in Childhood Cancer among Zimbabwean Families. 2009. 176p. pap. *(978-3-639-11184-2(2))* VDM Verlag Dr. Mueller e.K.

Chua, Philip S. Facs Fpcs. Let's Stop "Killing" Our Children: Disease Prevention Starting From the Crib A Simplified Survival Guide for Parents & Society to Save Our Children. 2011. 796p. 34.99 ***(978-1-4628-7754-6(0))***; pap. 23.99 ***(978-1-4628-7753-9(2))*** Xlibris Corp.

Cinar, Ayse Basak. Oral & General Health Promotion for Children: A Holistic Approach. 2009. 108p. pap. *(978-3-639-14938-8(6))* VDM Verlag Dr. Mueller e.K.

Clark, Demetria. Herbal Healing for Children: A Parent's Guide to Treatments for Common Childhood Illnesses. 2011. 224p. pap. 14.95 *(978-1-57067-214-9(8)*, Healthy Living) Book Publishing Co.

Clendon, Jill. Intergenerational Connections & Motherhood. 2010. 272p. pap. *(978-3-8383-7809-1(1))* Lambert Academic Publishing.

Cohn, Anthony. Constipation, Withholding & Your Child: A Family Guide to Soiling & Wetting. 2006. (ENG., Illus.). 8p. per. *(978-1-84310-491-9(1))* Kingsley, Jessica Ltd.

Comacchio, Cynthia R., et al. Healing the World's Children: Interdisciplinary Perspectives on Child Health in the Twentieth Century. 2008. (McGill-Queen's/Associated Medical Services Studies in the History of Medicine, H Ser.). (ENG., Illus.). 324p. *(978-0-7735-3399-8(0))* McGill-Queen's Univ. Pr.

Converse, Judy. Special-Needs Kids Go Pharm-Free: Nutrition-Focused Tools to Help Minimize Meds & Maximize Health & Well-Being. 2010. (ENG.). 288p. (gr. 12). 15.95 *(978-0-399-53622-9(1)*, Perigee Trade) Penguin Group (USA) Inc.

Cooking Light Magazine Staff. Cooking Light: First Foods - Baby Steps to a Lifetime of Healthy Eating. 2010. (ENG., Illus.). 144p. spiral bd. 19.95 *(978-0-8487-3321-6(5))* Oxmoor Hse., Inc.

Corbin, Charles, et al. Fitness for Life Elementary School Program Package. 2010. (gr. k-6). 599.00 *(978-0-7360-8387-4(1))* Human Kinetics Pubs.

Corbin, Charles B., et al. Fitness for Life: Elementary School Guide for Wellness Coordinators. 2010. (Illus.). 136p. (gr. k-6). pap. 39.00 *(978-0-7360-8718-6(4))* Human Kinetics Pubs.

Cram101 Textbook Reviews. Outlines & Highlights for Health, Safety, & Nutrition for the Young Child by Lynn R Marotz, Isbn: 9781428320703. 2010. 82p. pap. 27.95 *(978-1-61698-190-7(3))* Cram101 Inc.

Cram101 Textbook Reviews. Outlines & Highlights for Safety, Nutrition & Health in Early Education by Cathie Robertson. 2011. 220p. pap. 30.95 ***(978-1-61905-643-5(7))*** Cram101 Inc.

Cram101 Textbook Reviews & Cram101 Textbook Reviews. Outlines & Highlights for Nutrition, Health, & Safety for Young Children: Promoting Wellness by Joanne Sorte, ISBN. 2011. 502p. pap. 37.95 ***(978-1-61461-717-4(1))*** Cram101 Inc.

Cram101 Textbook Reviews Staff. Outlines & Highlights for Health, Safety, & Nutrition for the Young Child by Lynn R Marotz, Isbn: 9781428320703. 2009. 70p. pap. 27.95 *(978-1-4288-8621-6(4))* Cram101 Inc.

Croser, Natarsha. Obesogenicity of the Home Environment. 2010. 116p. pap. *(978-3-8383-4355-6(7))* Lambert Academic Publishing.

Davenport, Randi. The Boy Who Loved Tornadoes. 2010. (ENG.). 384p. 23.95 *(978-1-56512-611-4(4)*, 1565126114) Algonquin Bks. of Chapel Hill.

Davies, Andrew. When I Were a Lad- Snapshots from a Time That Health & Safety Forgot. 2010. (ENG., Illus.). 144p. 14.95 *(978-1-907554-00-1(9))* Anova Bks. GBR. Dist: Independent Pubs. Group.

Davies, Hywel. The Child & Coronary Heart Disease: Environment, Nutritional & Medical Issues. 2006. (Illus.). 328p. (C). 119.95 *(978-0-7734-5702-7(X))* Mellen, Edwin Pr., The.

Davies, Kim. Baby & Childcare the Pure & Natural Way: Raising Your Baby & Child the Way Nature Intended, from Birth Right Through to the Age Of 5. 2007. (ENG., Illus.). 256p. 29.99 *(978-0-7548-1672-0(9))* Anness Publishing GBR. Dist: National Bk. Network.

Dawes, Andrew, et al, eds. Monitoring Child Well-Being: A South African Rights-Based Approach. 2008. (Child Indicators Ser.). (ENG., Illus.). 640p. pap. 40.00 *(978-0-7969-2177-2(6))* Human Sciences Research Council ZAF. Dist: Independent Pubs. Group.

De Marzo, Jenine, et al. Healthy & Sustainable Fundraising Activities: Mobilizing Your Community Toward Social Responsibility. 2012. (Illus.). 184p. pap. 20.00 ***(978-1-4504-1281-0(5))*** Human Kinetics Pubs.

Dean, Michael. Empty Cribs: The Impact of Smoking on Child Health. 2007. (Illus.). 160p. per. 11.95 *(978-0-9786907-0-0(2))* Arts & Sciences Publishing.

Ditchek, Stuart H., et al. Healthy Child, Whole Child: Integrating the Best of Conventional & Alternative Medicine to Keep Your Kids Healthy. 2009. (ENG.). 352p. pap. 17.99 *(978-0-06-168598-9(4)*, William Morrow Paperbacks) HarperCollins Pubs.

Docter, Melinda & Naqvi, Syed. Asperger's Syndrome: A Guide to Helping Your Child Thrive at Home & at School. 2010. (ENG., Illus.). 224p. pap. 16.95 *(978-0-470-14014-7(3)*, Wiley) Wiley, John & Sons, Inc.

Doctor Me Book- Adolescents thru Pediatrics: Adolescents Thru Pediatrics. 2nd exp. ed. 2008. 241p. pap. 19.99 *(978-0-9799695-1-5(4))* DoctoRx Me, Inc.

Dorfman, Kelly. What's Eating Your Child? The Hidden Connection Between Food & Your Child's Well-Being. 2011. (ENG.). 334p. pap. 13.95 *(978-0-7611-6119-6(8)*, 0761161198) Workman Publishing Co., Inc.

Dorling Kindersley Publishing Staff. Baby & Child Healthcare Everything You Need to Know. 2012. (ENG., Illus.). 224p. 14.95 ***(978-0-7566-8975-9(9))*** Dorling Kindersley Publishing, Inc.

—Baby Day by Day. 2012. (ENG.). 432p. 40.00 ***(978-0-7566-8985-8(6))*** Dorling Kindersley Publishing, Inc.

Dunnett, Kathy, et al, eds. Health of Looked after Children. 2006. (Illus.). 174p. pap. 49.95 *(978-1-903855-83-6(7))* Russell Hse. Publishing Ltd. GBR. Dist: International Specialized Bk. Services.

Ehiri, John, ed. Maternal & Child Health: Global Challenges, Programs, & Policies. 2009. (ENG., Illus.). xii, 688p. 99.00 *(978-0-387-89244-3(3)*, 0387892443) Springer.

Ehrlich, Fred. You Can't Take Your Body to a Repair Shop: A Book about What Makes You Sick. 2011. (Illus.). 40p. (J). (gr. k-5). 15.95 ***(978-1-60905-148-8(3))*** Blue Apple Bks.

El-Metwally, Ashraf. Musculoskeletal Pain in Schoolchildren. 2009. (Acta Universitatis Tamperensis Ser.). 163p. pap. 82.50 *(978-951-44-7762-1(6))* Tampere Univ. Pr. FIN. Dist: Coronet Bks.

Enrique G. Macias. Abc's = about Basic Child Care: A Parent's Handbook of Pediatric Information. 2009. 88p. pap. 19.00 *(978-1-4389-3556-0(0))* AuthorHouse.

Etherington, Natasha. Gardening for Children with Autism Spectrum Disorders & Special Educational Needs: Engaging with Nature to Combat Anxiety, Promote Sensory Integration & Build Social Skills. 2012. (ENG., Illus.). 160p. pap. ***(978-1-84905-278-8(6))*** Kingsley, Jessica Ltd.

Eticha, Kebede. Prevalence & Determinants of Child Malnutrition. 2009. 68p. pap. *(978-3-639-17264-5(7))* VDM Verlag Dr. Mueller e.K.

Evans, Kate. The Food of Love: The Easier Way to Breastfeed Your Baby. 2009. (ENG., Illus.). 192p. pap. 16.95 *(978-1-59376-217-9(8)*, Soft Skull Pr.) Counterpoint LLC.

Faigenbaum, Avery D. & Westcott, Wayne L. Youth Strength Training: Programs for Health, Fitness & Sport. 2nd ed. 2009. (ENG., Illus.). 248p. (gr. k-12). pap. 24.95 *(978-0-7360-6792-8(2))* Human Kinetics Pubs.

Falola, Toyin & Heaton, Matthew M. Endangered Bodies: Women, Children, & Health in Africa. 2008. (Illus.). xii, 291p. *(978-1-59221-500-3(9))*; 300p. pap. *(978-1-59221-501-0(7))* Africa World Pr.

Florence, Tyler. Start Fresh: Your Child's Jump Start to Lifelong Healthy Eating. 2011. (ENG., Illus.). 160p. 19.99 *(978-1-60961-194-1(2))* Rodale Pr., Inc.

Franz, S. Cornelia. Common Sense Pediatrics: Combining Alternative & Traditional Medicine in Everyday Practice. 2008. 224p. pap. 19.99 *(978-1-4343-6910-9(2))* AuthorHouse.

Fuhrman, Joel. Disease-Proof Your Child: Feeding Kids Right. 2006. (ENG., Illus.). 288p. pap. 15.99 *(978-0-312-33808-4(2)*, St. Martin's Griffin) St. Martin's Pr.

Garabedian, Helen. Itsy Bitsy Yoga for Toddlers & Preschoolers: 8-Minute Routines to Help Your Child Grow Smarter, Be Happier, & Behave Better. 2008. (ENG., Illus.). 240p. pap. 16.95 *(978-1-60094-008-8(0))* Da Capo Pr., Inc.

Garbarino, James & Sigman, Garry. A Child's Right to a Healthy Environment. 2010. (Illus.). xii, 254p. ***(978-1-4419-6805-0(9))*** Springer.

Gaspar, Tania. Health-Related Quality of Life in Children & Adolescents. 2010. 128p. pap. *(978-3-8383-8494-8(6))* Lambert Academic Publishing.

Gavigan, Christopher. Healthy Child Healthy World: Creating a Cleaner, Greener, Safer Home. 2009. (ENG.). 336p. (gr. 12-18). pap. 16.00 *(978-0-452-29019-8(8)*, Plume) Penguin Group (USA) Inc.

Geary, Natalie & Garcia, Oz. The Food Cure for Kids: A Nutritional Approach to Your Child's Wellness. 2010. (ENG.). 288p. pap. 16.95 *(978-0-7627-5886-9(4)*, Lyons Pr.) Globe Pequot Pr., The.

Giordano, Simona, ed. Children with Gender Identity Disorder: An Ethical, Clinical, & Legal Analysis. 2012. (Routledge Studies in Health & Social Welfare Ser.). (ENG., Illus.). 208p. (C). 125.00 ***(978-0-415-50271-9(3))*** Routledge.

God's Creative Power for Babies & Toddlers. 2007. 33p. (J). pap. 0.00 *(978-0-9747513-8-2(3))* Capps Publishing.

Goebel, Wolfgang & Glockler, Michaela. A Guide to Child Health. Creeger, Catherine, tr. from GER. 3rd rev. ed. 2007. (Illus.). 477p. pap. *(978-0-86315-606-9(1))* Floris Bks.

Golden, Janet & Weisz, George. Healing the World's Children: Interdisciplinary Perspectives on Child Health in the Twentieth Century. Comacchio, Cynthia, ed. 2008. (McGill-Queen's/Associated Medical Services Studies in the History of Medicine, H Ser.). (ENG., Illus.). 324p. pap. *(978-0-7735-3400-1(8))* McGill-Queen's Univ. Pr.

Gotlin, Robert S. & Wyse, Lois. Dr. Rob's Guide to Raising Fit Kids: A Family-Centered Approach to Achieving Optimal Health. 2008. (ENG., Illus.). 208p. pap. 16.95 *(978-0-9793564-3-8(1))* DiaMed, LLC.

Gotovou, Marianna. Investigating the effects of a brief preoperative psychological intervention on children's postoperative adjustment & Recovery. 2010. 180p. pap. *(978-3-8325-2440-1(1))* Logos Verlag Berlin.

Gow, Melanie. Toasters Don't Roast Chickens: The Story of an Ordinary Mum Who Challenged Conventional Medical Thinking & Transformed the Health of Her Chronically-Ill Child. 2008. 224p. pap. 20.00 *(978-1-905862-17-7(2))* How To Books GBR. Dist: Parkwest Pubns., Inc.

Grady, Brian & Nelson, Eve-lynn. Telepsychiatry & Telemental Health - An Issue of Child & Adolescent Psychiatric Clinics of North America. 2010. (Clinics: Internal Medicine Ser.: 20-1). (ENG., Illus.). 200p. 110.00 *(978-1-4557-0427-9(X)*, Saunders) Elsevier - Health Sciences Div.

Gray, Terri. Helpful Hints. 2011. 24p. pap. 15.99 ***(978-1-4535-7787-5(4))*** Xlibris Corp.

Green Buildings: Benefits to Health, the Environment, & the Bottom Line: Hearing Before the Committee on Environment & Public Works, United States Senate, One Hundred Tenth Congress, First Session, May 15, 2007. 2011. (Illus.). iii, 228p. ***(978-0-16-087998-2(1)***, 552-070-42408-3) United States Government Printing Office.

Gullotta, Thomas P. & Blau, Gary. Handbook of Childhood Behavioral Issues: Evidence-Based Approaches to Prevention & Treatment. 2007. (ENG., Illus.). 432p. 125.00 *(978-0-415-95461-7(4))* Routledge.

Hall, G. Stanley. Youth: Its Education, Regimen, & Hygiene. 2006. 332p. pap. 23.99 *(978-1-4264-3414-3(6))* 2007. (ENG.). 366p. pap. 26.99 *(978-1-4264-3464-8(2))* BiblioBazaar.

—Youth Its Education Regimen & Hygiene. 2006. pap. *(978-1-4068-1090-5(8))* Echo Library.

—Youth: Its Education, Regimen, & Hygiene. 2007. (ENG.). 312p. per. *(978-1-4065-1591-6(4))* Dodo Pr.

Harel-Raviv, Milli. Nicole Goes to Dr. Milli - The Dentist. 2008. (ENG., Illus.). 32p. pap. 19.80 *(978-1-4343-9700-3(9))* AuthorHouse.

Heimann, Charlotte & Pearson, Betsy. How to Amuse & Outwit Important People Under. 2011. 82p. 37.95 ***(978-1-258-08264-2(0))*** Literary Licensing, LLC.

Hermann, Luke & Summers Hermann, Tara. Baby Medbasics: Lifesaving Action Steps at Your Fingertips - Birth to One Year. 2011. (ENG.). 64p. 12.00 *(978-0-7624-4108-2(9))* Running Pr. Bk. Pubs.

—Toddler Medbasics: Lifesaving Action Steps at Your Fingertips: Ages 1-5. 2011. (ENG.). 64p. 12.00 *(978-0-7624-4205-8(0))* Running Pr. Bk. Pubs.

Hirschfeld, A. James. Our Children Deserve Better Health Care: A Pediatrician's Forty Year Experience & Observations. 2007. (ENG.). 98p. pap. 9.95 *(978-0-533-15579-8(7))* Vantage Pr., Inc.

Horwath, Jan. Child Neglect: Identificatoin & Assesment. 2007. (ENG.). 232p. pap. 39.00 *(978-1-4039-3346-1(4))* Palgrave Macmillan.

Hutchinson, Woods. Childs Day. 2006. pap. *(978-1-4068-1409-5(1))* Echo Library.

Hyman, Bill. Current Issues in Child & Adolescent Health. 2nd rev. ed. 2009. (ENG.). 194p. pap. 64.15 *(978-0-7575-0360-3(8))* Kendall Hunt Publishing Co.

Jarvis, Sarah & Holland, Katy, eds. Children's Health for Dummies. 2006. (ENG., Illus.). 258p. per. 27.50 *(978-0-470-02735-6(5)*, For Dummies) Wiley, John & Sons, Inc.

Jelliffe, D., ed. Child Health in the Tropics. 5th rev. ed. (ENG., Illus.). 304p. *(978-0-7131-4438-3(6)*, Hodder Arnold) Hodder Education.

Johnson, Christopher. How Your Child Heals: An Inside Look at Common Childhood Ailments. 2010. (ENG.). 220p. 34.95 *(978-1-4422-0203-0(3))* Rowman & Littlefield Publishers, Inc.

Johnson, Christopher M. How Your Child Heals: An Inside Look at Common Childhood Ailments. 2011. (ENG.). 220p. pap. 19.95 ***(978-1-4422-0204-7(1))*** Rowman & Littlefield Publishers, Inc.

Jordan, Amy B., ed. Overweight & Obesity in America's Children: Causes, Consequences, Solutions. 2008. (ANNALS of the American Academy of Political & Social Science Ser.: 615). 244p. (C). 52.95 *(978-1-4129-6684-9(1),* 295615C) SAGE Pubns., Inc.

Jordan, Amy B. & Kaniss, Phyllis, eds. Overweight & Obesity in America's Children: Causes, Consequences, Solutions. 2008. (ANNALS of the American Academy of Political & Social Science Ser.: 615). (Illus.). 244p. (C). pap. 37.95 *(978-1-4129-5685-6(X),* 295615P) SAGE Pubns., Inc.

Judd, Sandra J., ed. Childhood Diseases Sourcebook. 2nd rev. ed. 2009. (Health Reference Ser.). 93.00 *(978-0-7808-1031-0(7))* Omnigraphics, Inc.

Kaplan, Stuart L. Your Child Does Not Have Bipolar Disorder: How Bad Science & Good Public Relations Created the Diagnosis. 2011. E-Book *(978-0-313-38135-5(6),* Praeger Pubs.) Greenwood Publishing Group, Inc.

Kaplan, Stuart L., ed. Your Child Does Not Have Bipolar Disorder: How Bad Science & Good Public Relations Created the Diagnosis, 1 vol. 2011. (Childhood in America Ser.). (Illus.). 184p. 34.95 *(978-0-313-38134-8(8),* A2574C, Praeger Pubs.) Greenwood Publishing Group, Inc.

Keeling, Knute & Block, Melissa L. Family Fun & Fitness: Getting Healthy & Staying Healthy - Together. 2009. 288p. pap. 18.95 *(978-1-59120-255-4(8))* Basic Health Pubns., Inc.

Klain, Eva J. & Sandt, Claire. Healthy Beginnings, Healthy Futures: A Judge's Guide. 2009. *(978-1-60442-611-3(X))* American Bar Assn.

Klein, Nigel, et al, eds. Clinical Manual of Fever in Children. 2008. (ENG., Illus.). xx, 318p. 109.00 *(978-3-540-78597-2(3),* 3540785973) Springer.

Kuttner, Leora. A Child in Pain: How to Help, What to Do. 2008. (Illus.). 271p. pap. *(978-1-84590-119-6(3))* Crown House Publishing, Whaley Bridge.

Lambdin, Dolly, et al. Fitness for Life: Classroom Guide First Grade. 2010. (ENG., Illus.). (gr. 1-1). spiral bd. 49.00 *(978-0-7360-8601-1(3))* Human Kinetics Pubs.

—Fitness for Life: Elementary School Classroom Guide. 2010. (ENG., Illus.). (gr. 2-2). spiral bd. 49.00 *(978-0-7360-8602-8(1))*; 168p. (gr. 3-3). spiral bd. 49.00 *(978-0-7360-8603-5(X))*; 168p. (gr. 4-4). 49.00 *(978-0-7360-8604-2(8))*; 168p. (gr. 5-5). spiral bd. 49.00 *(978-0-7360-8505-9(6))*; 176p. (gr. 6-6). spiral bd. 49.00 *(978-0-7360-8506-6(4))* Human Kinetics Pubs.

—Fitness for Life: Elementary School Classroom Guide - Kindergarten. 2010. (ENG., Illus.). 160p. (gr. k-k). spiral bd. 49.00 *(978-0-7360-8600-4(5))* Human Kinetics Pubs.

Langone, Melissa. The Health Plan for Overweight Children: A Parent's Guide to Raising a Healthier Child. 2007. 120p. 22.95 *(978-0-595-69099-2(8))*; per. 12.95 *(978-0-595-44939-2(5))* iUniverse, Inc.

Lapine, Missy Chase & Didio, Larysa. Sneaky Fitness: Fun, Foolproof Ways to Slip Fitness into Your Child's Everyday Life. 2009. (ENG.). 296p. pap. 19.95 *(978-0-7624-3795-5(2))* Running Pr. Bk. Pubs.

Le Masurier, Guy C., et al. Fitness for Life: Elementary School Physical Education Lesson Plans. 2010. (Illus.). 272p. (gr. k-6). 299.00 *(978-0-7360-8719-3(2))* Human Kinetics Pubs.

Leach, Melissa & Fairhead, James. Vaccine Anxieties: Global Science, Child Health & Society. 2007. (Science in Society Ser.). (ENG., Illus.). 216p. (C). 140.00 *(978-1-84407-416-7(1))*; pap. 38.95 *(978-1-84407-370-2(X))* Routledge.

Lee, Allison & Lee, Rachel. Childminder's Guide to Health & Safety & Child Protection. 2008. (ENG., Illus.). 124p. 29.95 *(978-1-84706-086-0(2))* Continuum International Publishing Group, Ltd. GBR. Dist: National Bk. Network.

Levene, Alysa. Childcare, Health & Mortality at the London Foundling Hospital, 1741-1800. 2007. (ENG., Illus.). 224p. 79.00 *(978-0-7190-7354-0(5))* Manchester Univ. Pr. GBR. Dist: Macmillan.

Levy, Maurice. Baby & Toddler: A Complete, Practical Guide for Feeding & Nutritional Health. 2009. 29.95 *(978-1-897456-00-2(X),* White Knight Bks.) Black Cross Pr.

Lieberman, Alexis & Merrick, Joav. Poverty & Children: A Public Health Concern. 2009. pap. 79.00 *(978-1-60741-140-6(7))* Nova Science Pubs., Inc.

Lim, Hayoung A. Developmental Speech-Language Training Through Music for Children with Autism Spectrum Disorders: Theoretical Orientation & Clinical Application. 2011. (ENG., Illus.). 208p. pap. *(978-1-84905-849-0(0))* Kingsley, Jessica Ltd.

Loar, Roberto N. Sugar Bugs. 2009. 24p. pap. 13.50 *(978-1-4389-7192-6(3))* AuthorHouse.

Loehr, Jamie. The Vaccine Answer Book: 200 Essential Answers to Help You Make the Right Decisions for Your Child. 2009. (ENG.). 320p. pap. 11.99 *(978-1-4022-1826-2(5))* Sourcebooks, Inc.

Lohrmann, David K., et al. Creating a Healthy School: Using the Healthy School Report Card. 2nd rev. ed. 2011. 208p. pap. 79.00 ***(978-1-4166-1428-9(1))*** Assn. for Supervision & Curriculum Development.

Longe, Jacqueline L. Gale Encyclopedia of Children's Health: Infancy Through Adolescence. 2nd ed. 2011. *(978-1-4144-8642-0(1))*; *(978-1-4144-8643-7(X))*; *(978-1-4144-8645-1(6))*; ***(978-1-4144-8644-4(8))*** 748.00 *(978-1-4144-8641-3(3))* Cengage Gale.

Luckenbill, W. Bernard & Immroth, Barbara Froling. Health Information in a Changing World: Practical Approaches for Teachers, Schools, & School Librarians, 1 vol. 2010. 244p. pap. 45.00 *(978-1-59884-398-9(2),* A2832P) Libraries Unlimited, Inc.

Lukenbill, W. Bernard & Immroth, Barbara Froling. Health Information for Youth: The Public Library & School Library Media Center Role, 1 vol. 2007. (Illus.). 236p. 45.00 *(978-1-59158-508-4(2),* LU5082) Libraries Unlimited, Inc.

—Health Information in a Changing World: Practical Approaches for Teachers, Schools, & School Librarians. 2010. E-Book *(978-1-59884-399-6(0))* Libraries Unlimited, Inc.

Mahbub ul Haq Human Development Centre Staff, ed. Human Development in South Asia 2009: Trade & Human Development in South Asia. 2010. (ENG.). 348p. 24.95 *(978-0-19-906020-7(7))* Oxford Univ. Pr., Inc.

Markel, Susan. What Your Pediatrician Doesn't Know Can Hurt Your Child: A More Natural Approach to Raising Your Child. 2010. (ENG.). 300p. pap. 14.95 *(978-1-935618-10-2(5))* BenBella Bks.

Marotz, Lynn R. Cengage Advantage Books: Health, Safety, & Nutrition for the Young Child. 8th ed. 2011. (ENG.). 576p. (C). ring bd. 121.95 *(978-1-111-35580-7(0))* Wadsworth.

—Health, Safety, & Nutrition for the Young Child. 8th ed. 2011. (Whatrsquo;s New in Early Childhood Ser.). (ENG.). 576p. (C). pap. 165.95 *(978-1-111-29837-1(8))* Wadsworth.

Matricardi, Joanne & McLarty, Jeanne. Health, Safety, & Nutrition Activities A to Z. 2007. (ENG., Illus.). 208p. per. 30.95 *(978-1-4180-4850-1(X))* Delmar Cengage Learning.

May Loo Staff & Loo, May. Integrative Medicine for Children. 2008. (ENG., Illus.). 536p. 75.95 *(978-1-4160-2299-2(6),* Saunders) Elsevier - Health Sciences Div.

McCarthy, Moira. Everything Parent's Guide to Children with Juvenile Diabetes: Reassuring Advice for Managing Symptoms & Raising a Healthy, Happy Child. 2007. (ENG.). 304p. per. 14.95 *(978-1-59869-246-4(1))* Adams Media Corp.

Mccoy, Colette. Aspergers & the Infant Child: How to Recognise the Signs; Starting School & Problems Encountered; Practical Advice for Parents/Teachers. 2011. 80p. pap. 16.83 ***(978-1-4567-8975-6(9))*** AuthorHouse.

McDonald, Libby. The Toxic Sandbox: The Truth about Environmental Toxins & Our Children's Health. 2007. (ENG., Illus.). 224p. (gr. 12-18). 14.00 *(978-0-399-53363-1(X),* Perigee Trade) Penguin Group (USA) Inc.

Meinert, Lotte. Hopes in Friction: Schooling, Health, & Everyday Life in Uganda. 2009. 204p. *(978-1-60752-005-4(2))*; pap. *(978-1-60752-004-7(4))* Information Age Publishing, Inc.

Merrick, Joav. Child & Adolescent Health Yearbook 2009. 2012. (Health & Human Development (Joav Merrick - Ser. Editor - National Institute of Child Health & Human Development, Ministry of Social Affairs, Jerusalem) Ser.). 733p. 295.00 *(978-1-61668-913-1(7))* Nova Science Pubs., Inc.

Merrick, Joav, ed. Child & Adolescent Health Yearbook 2008. 2009. 145.00 *(978-1-60692-866-0(X))* Nova Science Pubs., Inc.

—Child Health & Human Development Yearbook 2008. 2009. 145.00 *(978-1-60692-979-7(8))* Nova Science Pubs., Inc.

Mindell, Jodi A. & Owens, Judith A. A Clinical Guide to Pediatric Sleep: Diagnosis & Management of Sleep Problems. 2nd rev. ed. 2009. (ENG., Illus.). 352p. pap. 73.99 *(978-1-60547-389-5(6))* Lippincott Williams & Wilkins.

Mohanty, Sanjay. Multidimensional Poverty & Reproductive & Child Health in Incl 2011. 100p. pap. ***(978-3-8443-2953-7(6))*** Lambert Academic Publishing.

Mosley, W. Henry & Chen, Lincoln C. Child Survival: Strategies for Research. 2008. (ENG., Illus.). 412p. pap. 50.00 *(978-0-521-07297-7(2))* Cambridge Univ. Pr.

Mulholland, Siobhan. Helping Your Baby to Sleep: An Easy-To-Follow Guide. 2008. (Easy-to-Follow Guides). (ENG., Illus.). 64p. pap. 12.95 *(978-0-09-192345-7(X))* Random Hse. GBR. Dist: Independent Pubs. Group.

National Center for Health Statistics (U.S.) Staff & National Health Interview Survey (U.S.) Staff, contrib. by. Family Structure & Children's Health in the United States: Findings from the National Health Interview Survey, 2001-2007. 2010. *(978-0-8406-0642-6(7))* National Ctr. for Health Statistics.

Natterson, Cara. Worry Proof: A Pediatrician (And Mom) Explains Which Foods, Medicines, & Chemicals to Avoid to Have Safe & Healthy Children. 2010. (ENG.). 304p. (gr. 12). 16.00 *(978-0-452-29659-6(5),* Plume) Penguin Group (USA) Inc.

Newton, Hannah. The Sick Child in Early Modern England, 1580-1720. 2012. (ENG., Illus.). 272p. 110.00 ***(978-0-19-965049-1(7))*** Oxford Univ. Pr., Inc.

Nyagetiria Daniel, Akungah, et al. Burden of Childhood Diarrhea from Water, Sanitation & Hygiene. 2010. 116p. pap. *(978-3-639-27847-7(X))* VDM Verlag Dr. Mueller e.K.

Obeng, Cecilia. Children's Health in a Traditional Society. 2009. 87.00 *(978-1-60692-769-4(8))* Nova Science Pubs., Inc.

Offit, Paul A. Deadly Choices: How the Anti-Vaccine Movement Threatens Us All. 2010. (ENG., Illus.). 288p. (gr. 9). 27.50 *(978-0-465-02149-9(2))* Basic Bks.

Olfman, Sharna, ed. The Sexualization of Childhood, 1 vol. 2008. (Childhood in America Ser.). 224p. 44.95 *(978-0-275-99985-8(8),* C9985, Praeger Pubs.) Greenwood Publishing Group, Inc.

Opitz, Michael F. & Davis-Duerr, Jennifer. Literacy Lessons to Help Kids Get Fit & Healthy. 2010. (ENG.). 144p. (gr. k-6). pap. 19.99 *(978-0-545-16324-8(2)* Teaching Resources) Scholastic, Inc.

Oria, Maria & Sawyer, Kristin. Joint U. S. -Mexico Workshop on Preventing Obesity in Children & Youth of Mexican Origin: Summary. 2007. (ENG., Illus.). 210p. pap. 46.25 *(978-0-309-10325-1(8))* National Academies Pr.

Panel to Review the National Children's Study Research Plan, et al. The National Children's Study Research Plan: A Review. 2008. (ENG.). 166p. pap. 38.75 *(978-0-309-12056-2(X))* National Academies Pr.

Parham, Phil & Parham, Amy. The Awesome Fitness Adventure for Your Kids: 90 Days to Raising Healthy Children. 2011. 235p. (YA). pap. 12.99 *(978-0-7369-3921-8(0))* Harvest Hse. Pubs.

Parish, Betsy. Legacy: 50 Years of Loving Care, Texas Children's Hospital, 1954-2004, 1. (Illus.). ltd. ed. 2006. 716p. 45.50 *(978-0-9786200-5-9(4))* ltd. ed. 2006. xiii, 699p. pap. 32.95 *(978-0-9786200-4-2(6))* 2nd exp. ed. 2008. (ENG., 762p. 45.50 *(978-0-9786200-6-6(2))* Elisha Freeman Publishing.

Parizkova, Jana. Nutrition, Physical Activity, & Health in Early Life. 2nd rev. ed. 2009. (ENG., Illus.). 428p. 144.95 *(978-1-4200-8231-9(0),* CRC Press) Taylor & Francis Group GBR. Dist: Taylor & Francis Group.

Parker, Lynn. Health & Safety in Early Years Settings. 2nd rev. ed. 2012. (ENG., Illus.). 112p. (C). pap. 35.95 *(978-0-415-67532-1(4))* Routledge.

Paul, Bobby & Saha, Indranil. Physical Growth Pattern & Morbidity of Low Babies in a Slum of Kolkat. 2010. 236p. pap. *(978-3-8383-6188-8(1))* Lambert Academic Publishing.

Pediatrists. The Baby Care Book: Absolutely Everything You Need to Know about Your Fabulous Baby. 2010. 99p. pap. 19.95 *(978-1-4327-5783-0(0))* Outskirts Pr., Inc.

Perfect Helpers. Minding Your Child's Health: A Health & Symptom Diary for Kids. 2007. spiral bd. 9.95 *(978-0-9798005-1-1(X))* Perfect Helpers, Inc.

Petaja, Paivi. Post Traumatic Stress Disorder in Children & the Role of Ot. 2010. 92p. pap. *(978-3-8383-7269-3(7))* Lambert Academic Publishing.

Phillipson-Webb, Lianne. Sprout Right: Nutrition from Tummy to Toddler. 2010. (ENG., Illus.). 292p. pap. 20.00 *(978-0-14-317350-2(2),* Penguin Global) Penguin Group (USA) Inc.

R&S Information LLC Staff. Healthy Baby, Happy Home; Create a Safe Green Home for Your Baby. 2009. 182p. pap. 17.95 *(978-1-935097-38-9(5))* Hillcrest Publishing Group, Inc.

Rapoff, Michael A. Adherence to Pediatric Medical Regimens. 2nd ed. 2010. (Issues in Clinical Child Psychology Ser.). (Illus.). xii, 232p. pap. 49.95 *(978-1-4419-8143-1(8),* 1441981438) Springer.

Reid, Erica. The Thriving Child: Parenting Successfully through Allergies, Asthma & Other Common Challenges. 2012. (ENG.). 272p. 19.99 ***(978-0-89296-864-0(8))*** Center St.

Reno, Tosca. Eat-Clean Diet for Family & Kids. 2008. (ENG.). 348p. pap. 19.95 *(978-1-55210-050-9(2))* Kennedy, Robert Publishing CAN. Dist: National Bk. Network.

Roberts, Ceri. Boost Your Child's Fitness. 2011. (Teach Yourself Ser.). (ENG., Illus.). 192p. pap. 15.95 *(978-1-4441-0750-0(X),* Hodder & Stoughton) Hodder General Publishing Div. GBR. Dist: Independent Pubs. Group.

—Helping Your Child to Get Fit. 2009. (Teach Yourself: Parenting Ser.). (ENG.). 192p. pap. 14.95 *(978-0-07-162587-6(9),* 0071625879) McGraw-Hill Cos., The.

Roberts, Theresa. ABC's of Bumps & Bruises, a guide to home & herbal remedies for Children. 2008. 188p. pap. 19.95 *(978-1-4357-0922-5(5))* Lulu Enterprises Inc.

Robinson, Gary, et al, eds. Contexts of Child Development: Culture, policy & Intervention. 2008. (Illus.). 290p. pap. *(978-0-9803846-8-0(0))* Darwin, Charles Univ. Pr.

Rodríguez, Pablo & Mannarelli, María Emma. Historia de la Infancia en América Latina. 2007. (SPA., Illus.). 673p. pap. 33.00 *(978-958-710-218-5(5))* Universidad Externado de Colombia COL. Dist: Siglo del Hombre.

Rogers, Sally J., et al. An Early Start for Your Child with Autism: Using Everyday Activities to Help Kids Connect, Communicate, & Learn. 2012. (ENG.). 326p. 45.00 ***(978-1-4625-0389-6(6))***; pap. 16.95 ***(978-1-60918-470-4(X))*** Guilford Pubns., Inc.

Ronney, Karen. Proud Parents' Guide to Raising Athletic, Balanced, & Coordinated Kids: A Lifetime of Benefit in Just 10 Minutes a Day, 0 vols. 2008. 320p. pap. 16.99 *(978-0-7852-2822-6(5))* Nelson, Thomas Inc.

Rosemond, John & Ravenel, M.D., Bose. The Diseasing of America's Children: Exposing the ADHD Fiasco & Empowering Parents to Take Back Control, 0 vols. 2009. 272p. pap. 15.99 *(978-0-7852-9747-5(2))* Nelson, Thomas Inc.

Roulstone. Prioritising Child Health. 2006. (Illus.). 136p. 49.95 *(978-0-415-37634-1(3))* Routledge.

Roulstone, Sue. Prioritising Child Health. 2006. (Illus.). 136p. 160.00 *(978-0-415-37633-4(5))* Routledge.

Rowe, Stuart H. Physical Nature of the Child & How to. 2006. pap. 26.95 *(978-1-4286-3534-0(3))* Kessinger Publishing, LLC.

Roy, Niloy. Usage of R H Services by Adolescents in Two Government Hospitals. 2011. 76p. pap. ***(978-3-8443-0755-9(9))*** Lambert Academic Publishing.

Roy, Runa & KUMAR KURI, Pravat. Child Health & Mortality in Indi. 2011. 120p. pap. ***(978-3-8443-1101-3(7))*** Lambert Academic Publishing.

Rubin, Jerry, et al. Naturally Healthy Kids: Integrating Conventional & Holistic Treatments for Common Illnesses of Children. 2007. 328p. spiral bd. 24.95 *(978-0-9773949-2-0(1))* Partners in Pediatrics.

Rubin, Jordan S. The Great Physician's RX for Children's Health, 0 vols. 2008. 256p. 24.99 *(978-0-7852-1902-6(1))* Nelson, Thomas Inc.

Rubin, Jordan S. & Rubin, Nicki. The Great Physician's Rx for Children's Health. 2008. 256p. pap. 14.99 ***(978-1-4016-0398-4(X))*** Nelson, Thomas Inc.

Rudolf, Mary, et al. Paediatrics & Child Health. 3rd ed. 2011. (ENG., Illus.). 496p. pap. 61.95 *(978-1-4051-9474-7(X),* Wiley-Blackwell) Wiley, John & Sons, Inc.

Ruffman, Jill V. & Sladek, Marjorie B. Now, What Do We Do? How to Manage Your Child's Critical Medical Needs: A Guided Journal for Parents & Child Advocates, 1. 2006. (Illus.). 179p. spiral bd. 19.95 *(978-0-9766323-0-6(6))* Ruffman, Sladek Publishing Co.

Sabatello, Maya. Children's Bioethics: The International Biopolitical Discourse on Harmful Traditional Practices & the Right of the Child to Cultural Identity. 2009. 250p. *(978-90-04-17341-5(2))* BRILL.

Sach, Penelope. Natural Children's Health. 2007. (ENG.). 176p. (gr. 12-18). 14.00 *(978-0-14-300265-9(1),* Penguin Global) Penguin Group (USA) Inc.

Saunders, Len. Keeping Kids Fit: A Family Plan for Raising Active, Healthy Children. 2010. (ENG., Illus.). 225p. pap. 15.95 *(978-1-934184-26-4(8))* Lachance Publishing LLC.

Schaefer-McDaniel, Nicole. Children Talk about Their New York City Neighborhoods - the Role of Subjective & Objective Neighborhood Evaluations in Understanding Child Health. 2007. 208p. per. *(978-3-8364-2708-1(7))* VDM Verlag Dr. Mueller e.K.

Schmitt, Barton D. My Child Is Sick! Expert Advice for Managing Common Illnesses & Injuries. 2011. (ENG.). 315p. (J). pap. 14.95 *(978-1-58110-552-0(5))* American Academy of Pediatrics.

Sears, Robert W. HappyBaby: The Organic Guide to Baby's First 24 Months. 2009. (ENG.). 464p. pap. 16.99 *(978-0-06-171136-7(5),* Harper Paperbacks) HarperCollins Pubs.

Sears, William, et al. The Portable Pediatrician: Everything You Need to Know about Your Child's Health. 2011. (ENG., Illus.). 592p. pap. 21.99 *(978-0-316-01748-0(5))* Little Brown & Co.

Seiler, Laurie. Cool Connections with Cognitive Behavioural Therapy: Encouraging Self-Esteem, Resilience & Well-Being in Children & Young People Using CBT Approaches. 2008. (ENG., Illus.). 96p. pap. *(978-1-84310-618-0(3))* Kingsley, Jessica Ltd.

Shilstone, MacKie. Mackie Shilstone's Body Plan for Kids: A Weight-Loss Resource for Parents & Kids from One of America's Leading Health-and-fitness Dynamos, 1 vol. 2009. (ENG.). 324p. pap. 18.95 *(978-1-59120-249-3(3))* Basic Health Pubns., Inc.

Shipps, Shannon. Children s Miracles. 2010. 36p. pap. 24.99 *(978-1-60957-540-3(7))* Xulon Pr., Inc.

Simmons, Janice C. Everything Parent's Guide to Children with Asthma: Professional Advice to Help Your Child Manage Symptoms, Be More Active, & Breathe Better. 2008. (ENG.). 304p. pap. 14.95 *(978-1-59869-430-7(8))* Adams Media Corp.

Siren, Auli. Childhood Absence Epilepsy: An Epidemiological, Neuropsychological & Molecular Genetic Study. 2011. (Acta Universitatis Tamperensis Ser.). 89p. pap. 82.50 ***(978-951-44-8384-4(7))*** Tampere Univ. Pr. FIN. Dist: Coronet Bks.

Smith, Laura M. Mommy What's This? Mommy Where Are We Going? 2010. 36p. pap. 16.99 *(978-1-4490-6182-1(6))* AuthorHouse.

Snyder, Deborah. Keto Kid: Helping Your Child Succeed on the Ketogenic Diet. 2006. (ENG., Illus.). 144p. per. 16.95 *(978-1-932603-29-3(8))* Demos Medical Publishing, LLC.

Solis, Sydney. The Treasure in Your Heart: Yoga & Stories for Peaceful Children. 2008. (Storytime Yoga Ser.). (ENG., Illus.). 117p. pap. *(978-0-9777063-1-0(1))* Mythic Yoga Studio, The.

Sorte, Joanne, et al. Nutrition, Health, & Safety for Young Children: Promoting Wellness. 2010. (ENG.). 696p. (C). pap. 109.20 *(978-0-13-234941-3(8),* Prentice Hall) Prentice Hall PTR.

—Nutrition, Health, & Safety for Young Children: Promoting Wellness (with MyEducationLab) 2010. (ENG.). 544p. (C). pap. 115.87 *(978-0-13-138120-9(2),* Prentice Hall) Prentice Hall PTR.

Stanescu, Dan Florin. Children of Parents with Acute Central Nervous System Injuries. 2010. 120p. pap. *(978-3-8383-0381-9(4))* Lambert Academic Publishing.

Steingraber, Sandra. Raising Elijah: Protecting Our Children in an Age of Environmental Crisis. 2011. (Merloyd Lawrence Book Ser.). (ENG.). 368p. 26.00 *(978-0-7382-1399-6(3))* Da Capo Pr., Inc.

Sugumar, V. Raji & Meena, K. Peak Expiratory Flow Rate among School Going Children: A Study. 2011. 88p. pap. ***(978-3-639-33379-4(9))*** VDM Verlag Dr. Mueller e.K.

Tally, James E. One for the Kids: Creating Children's Healthcare of Atlanta. 2008. (Illus.). 141p. *(978-1-934144-31-2(2))* Indigo.

Tamanini, Kara T. Understanding My Attention-Deficit/Hyperactivity Disorder. 2008. 28p. pap. 14.50 *(978-1-60693-170-7(9),* Eloquent Bks.) AEG Literary Publishing Services, Inc.

Taylor, Roger, et al. Practical Paediatric Radiotherapy. (Illus.). 416p. pap. 65.00 ***(978-0-340-81016-3(5),*** Hodder Arnold) Hodder Education GBR. Dist: Oxford Univ. Pr., Inc.

Telfer, Kevin. The Remarkable Story of Great Ormond Street Hospital. 2007. (ENG., Illus.). 208p. 37.95 *(978-1-84737-113-3(2))* Simon & Schuster, Ltd. GBR. Dist: Independent Pubs. Group.

Tewari, Suruchi. Child Health & Health Care in Indi. 2008. 160p. per. *(978-3-8364-3580-2(2))* VDM Verlag Dr. Mueller e.K.

Tornoe, Birte. Supine Head Lift & Stabilisation in Children from Five to Seven Yrs. 2010. 72p. pap. *(978-3-639-23734-4(X))* VDM Verlag Dr. Mueller e.K.

Trachtenberg, Jennifer. The Smart Parent's Guide: To Getting Your Kids Through Checkups, Illnesses, & Accidents. 2010. (ENG., Illus.). 336p. pap. 16.00 *(978-1-4391-5291-1(8),* Free Pr.) Free Pr.

Turner, Deborah. Monday's Child. 2010. 233p. pap. 14.99 *(978-0-557-51099-3(6))* Lulu Enterprises Inc.

Underdown, Angela. Health & Well-Being in Early Childhood. 2006. (ENG.). 216p. (C). 162.00 *(978-0-335-21907-0(1),* 0335219071, Open University Pr.) McGraw-Hill Education GBR. Dist: McGraw-Hill Cos., The.

C

—Health & Well Being in Early Childhood. 2006. (ENG., Illus.). 216p. (C). pap. 45.00 (978-0-335-21906-3(3), 0335219063) McGraw-Hill Education GBR. Dist: McGraw-Hill Cos., The.

Ungar, Wendy. Economic Evaluation in Child Health. 2010. (ENG., Illus.). 328p. pap. 65.00 (978-0-19-954749-4(1)) Oxford Univ. Pr., Inc.

UNICEF Staff. The State of Africa's Children 2008: Child Survival. 2008. (Illus.). 56p. (978-92-806-4247-6(2)) United Nations Children's Fund, The (UNICEF).

Van Der Meulen Staff & Rodgers, Y. Labor Standards & Globalisation in Asia. 2011. (Illus.). 224p. 99.95 **(978-1-84720-510-0(0))** Elgar, Edward Publishing, Inc.

Vance, Peggy. 1000 Top Tips for Moms & Dads: How to Keep Your Kids Healthy, Safe & Smiling. 2007. (ENG., Illus.). 232p. pap. 9.95 (978-1-84483-408-2(5)) Duncan Baird Pubs. GBR. Dist: Sterling Publishing Co., Inc.

Vicker, Beverly. Sharing Information about Your Child with Autism Spectrum Disorder: What Do Respite or Alternative Caregivers Need to Know? 2007. (Illus.). 228p. pap. 24.95 incl. cd-rom (978-1-931282-40-6(4)) Autism Asperger Publishing Co.

Vickery, Donald M., et al. Taking Care of Your Child: A Parent's Illustrated Guide to Complete Medical Care. 2006. (ENG., Illus.). 448p. per. 7.99 (978-0-7382-1071-1(4), Da Capo Lifelong) Da Capo Pr., Inc.

Villepigue, James. Combat Fat for Kids: A Whole-Family Approach to Optimal Health. 2012. (ENG.). 224p. pap. 15.00 (978-1-57826-396-7(4)) Hatherleigh Co., Ltd., The.

Wachtel, Suzanne & Le Vine, Blake. Like Mother, Like Son: A Mom's Guide to Raising Healthy Children. 2007. 129p. per. 14.95 (978-0-9768733-2-7(X)) Sb Pubs.

Wahlgren, Anna. Gns: A Good Night's Sleep. 2009. 260p. pap. 22.35 (978-91-977736-1-4(1)) Wahlgren, Anna AB SWE. Dist: AtlasBooks Distribution.

Walker, Mishara S. A Gift for Life: A Complete Record of Your Child's Health History. 2008. 209p. spiral bd. 18.00 (978-0-9770493-0-1(2)) Kadon Publishing, LLC.

Wells, Chris & Johnson, Kurtis. Hip-Hop Health: Learning Concepts Through Physical Activity. 2009. (ENG.). (gr. k-6). 22.95 (978-0-7360-8171-9(2)) Human Kinetics Pubs.

Whitlatch, Shelley. Fitplay: Building Healthy Lifestyles for Kids. 3rd ed. 2007. spiral bd. 99.00 (978-0-9790787-3-6(3)) Desert Southwest Fitness, Inc.

WHO Regional Office for the Eastern Mediterranean. A Practical Guide to Developing & Implementing School Policy on Diet & Physical Activity. 2011. (Who Regional Office for the Eastern Mediterranean Ser.). 26p. pap. 18.00 (978-92-9021-694-0(8)) World Health Organization.

WHO Regional Office for the Western Pacific. Child Survival Profile: Cambodia. 2007. (WPRO Publication). 35p. pap. 12.00 (978-92-9061-224-7(X)) World Health Organization.

—Reaching the Poor. 2007. (WPRO Publication). 72p. pap. 12.00 (978-92-9061-246-9(0)) World Health Organization.

Winterfeld, Amy, et al. Promoting Healthy Communities & Reducing Childhood Obesity: Legislative Options. 2009. (Illus.). iii, 50p. pap. **(978-1-58024-543-2(9))** National Conference of State Legislatures.

World Health Organization Regional Office For Europe Staff. Protecting Children's Health in a Changing Environment: Report of the Fifth Ministerial Conference on Environment & Health. 2011. (Euro Non Serial Publications). (Illus.). 90p. pap. 24.00 (978-92-890-1419-9(9)) World Health Organization.

Wright, Jan & MacDonald, Doune, eds. Young People Physical Activity & the Everyday: Living Physical Activity. 2010. (International Studies in Physical Education & Youth Sport Ser.). (ENG., Illus.). 232p. (C). 133.00 (978-0-415-49313-0(7), Routledge) Taylor & Francis Group GBR. Dist: Taylor & Francis Group.

Yarborough, Pamela A. & Yarborough, Robert T. Children's Reiki Handbook: A Guide to Energy Healing for Kids. 2nd exp. rev. ed. 2007. (Illus.). 81p. (YA). per. 17.95 (978-0-9774181-0-7(3)) Andborough Publishing.

You, Wen. Time Well Spent: How Watching Time can Reduce the Chances of Having Overweight Children. 2008. 152p. pap. (978-3-8364-3926-8(3)) VDM Verlag Dr. Mueller e.K.

Zolezzi, Anthony, et al. Chemical-Free Kids. 2008. pap. 12.99 (978-0-9753157-5-0(7)) ASM Bks.

Zurawski, Elizabeth. Ian's Guide: Information for Children with Special Medical Needs. 2008. 73p. pap. 16.95 (978-1-60672-014-1(7)) PublishAmerica, Inc.

CHILDREN—HISTORY

Ariantzi, Despoina. Kindheit in Byzanz: Emotionale, geistige und materielle Entwicklung im familiären Umfeld vom 6. bis zum 11. Jahrhundert. 2012. (Millennium-Studien / Millennium Studies).Tr. of Childhood in Byzantium. Emotional, Intellectual & Economic Development in Family Structures from the 6th to the 11th Century. (GER.). VIII, 384p. (gr. 17). 154.00 **(978-3-11-026568-2(0))** De Gruyter, Walter Inc.

Crawford, Sally & Shepherd, Gillian, eds. Children, Childhood & Society. 2007. (Bar S Ser.). (Illus.). 106p. (C). 70.00 (978-1-4073-0138-9(1)) British Archaeological Reports Ltd. GBR. Dist: Brown, David Bk. Co., The.

Davies, Andrew. When I Were a Lad- Snapshots from a Time That Health & Safety Forgot. 2010. (ENG., Illus.). 144p. 14.95 (978-1-907554-00-1(9)) Anova Bks. GBR. Dist: Independent Pubs. Group.

Fass, Paula S. Children of a New World: Society, Culture, & Globalization. 2006. (ENG.). 304p. 75.00 (978-0-8147-2756-0(5)); per. 24.00 (978-0-8147-2757-7(3)) New York Univ. Pr.

Fleming, Laurence. Last Children of the Raj. 55.00 (978-1-85043-624-9(X)); pap. 55.00 (978-1-85043-663-8(0)) I. B. Tauris & Co., Ltd. GBR. Dist: Palgrave Macmillan.

Foyster, Elizabeth A., et al. A Cultural History of Childhood & Family in the Age of Empire, 6 vols. 2012. (ENG., Illus.). 254p. (C). 99.95 **(978-1-84788-798-6(8))**; 99.95 **(978-1-84788-799-3(6))**; 99.95 **(978-1-84788-794-8(5))**; 99.95 **(978-1-84788-795-5(3))**; 99.95 **(978-1-84788-796-2(1))**; 99.95 **(978-1-84788-797-9(X))** Berg Pubs. GBR. Dist: Macmillan.

Greven, Philip J. Children in Colonial America. Marten, James, ed. 2006. (ENG., Illus.). 288p. pap. 24.00 (978-0-8147-5716-1(2)) New York Univ. Pr.

Gutman, Marta, ed. Designing Modern Childhoods: History, Space, & the Material Culture of Children. 2008. (Rutgers Series in Childhood Studies). (ENG., Illus.). 368p. 70.00 (978-0-8135-4195-2(6)) Rutgers Univ. Pr.

Gutman, Marta & de Coninck-Smith, Ning, eds. Designing Modern Childhoods: History, Space, & the Material Culture of Children. 2008. (Rutgers Series in Childhood Studies). (ENG., Illus.). 368p. per. 24.95 (978-0-8135-4196-9(4)) Rutgers Univ. Pr.

Horn, Cornelia B. & Martens, John W. Let the Little Children Come to Me: Childhood & Children in Early Christianity. 2009. 440p. pap. 44.95 (978-0-8132-1674-4(5)) Catholic Univ. of America Pr.

Laes, Christian & Mustakallio, Katariina, eds. The Dark Sides of Childhood: In Late Antiquity & the Middle Ages. 2011. (Childhood in Archaeology Ser.). (ENG.). 130p. (C). pap. 56.00 (978-1-84217-417-3(7)) Oxbow Bks., Ltd. GBR. Dist: Brown, David Bk. Co., The.

Leonard, Amy & Nelson, Karen L. Masculinities, Childhood, Violence: Attending to Early Modern Women — And Men: Proceedings of the 2006 Symposium. 2011. (978-0-87413-098-0(0)) 2010. (ENG.). 400p. 85.00 (978-1-61149-018-3(9)) Univ. of Delaware Pr.

Lindquist, Heather C., ed. Children of Manzanar. 2012. (Illus.). xi, 145p. pap. 17.95 **(978-1-59714-160-4(7))** Heyday.

Montgomery, Douglas C. & Montgomery, Heather. An Introduction to Childhood: Anthropological Perspectives on Children's Lives. 2008. (ENG.). 296p. 99.95 (978-1-4051-2591-8(8), Wiley-Blackwell) Wiley, John & Sons, Inc.

Montgomery, Heather. An Introduction to Childhood: Anthropological Perspectives on Children's Lives. 2008. (ENG.). 296p. pap. 38.95 (978-1-4051-2590-1(X), Wiley-Blackwell) Wiley, John & Sons, Inc.

Morrison, Heidi, ed. The Global History of Childhood Reader. 2012. (Routledge Readers in History Ser.). (ENG.). 496p. (C). 135.00 **(978-0-415-78248-7(1))** Routledge.

Murphy, Eileen, ed. Childhood in the Past Volume 2 (2009) 2009. (Childhood in the Past Ser.). (ENG.). 192p. (C). pap. 50.00 (978-1-84217-378-7(2)) Oxbow Bks., Ltd. GBR. Dist: Brown, David Bk. Co., The.

Papaconstantinou, Arietta, et al, eds. Becoming Byzantine: Children & Childhood in Byzantium. 2009. (Dumbarton Oaks Byzantine Symposia & Colloquia Ser.). (Illus.). 336p. 55.00 (978-0-88402-356-2(7)) Dumbarton Oaks.

Stearns, Peter N. Childhood in World History. 2nd rev. ed. 2010. (Themes in World History Ser.). (ENG.). 192p. (C). 115.00 (978-0-415-59808-8(7)); pap. 29.95 (978-0-415-59809-5(5)) Routledge.

CHILDREN—HOSPITALS

see also names of individual hospitals for children

Arooj Butt, Saniya. Feedback of Attendants of Patients on Services. 2011. 184p. pap. **(978-3-8443-0987-4(X))** Lambert Academic Publishing.

Bice, Wendy Rose. Children's Hospital of Michigan: 125 Years: Always There Just for Them. 2012. **(978-1-57864-749-1(5))** Donning Co. Pubs.

Bishop, Kate. Through Children's Eyes. 2009. 202p. pap. (978-3-639-18394-8(0)) VDM Verlag Dr. Mueller e.K.

Boyer, Edward W., et al. Pediatric Hospital Surge Capacity in Public Health Emergencies. 2009. (Illus.). iii, 32p. (978-1-58763-377-5(9)) Agency for Healthcare Research & Quality.

Connolly, Cynthia A. Saving Sickly Children: The Tuberculosis Preventorium in American Life, 1909-1970. 2008. (Critical Issues in Health & Medicine Ser.). (ENG., Illus.). 200p. 39.95 (978-0-8135-4267-6(7)) Rutgers Univ. Pr.

Crowley, Walt, et al. Hope on the Hill: The First Century of Seattle Children's Hospital. 2010. (ENG., Illus.). 192p. 40.00 (978-0-295-98956-3(4)) Univ. of Washington Pr.

DuBois, Lisa A. More Than a Place: The Origins of a Children's Hospital at Vanderbilt. 2007. (Illus.). 274p. 26.95 net. (978-1-57736-387-3(6)) Providence Hse Pubs.

Homan, Sidney R. A Fish in the Moonlight: Growing up in the Bone Marrow Unit. 2008. 226p. 24.95 (978-1-55753-486-6(1)) Purdue Univ. Pr.

Katz, Beatrice. Cincinnati Children¿s Hospital Medical Center. 2008. (Images of America Ser.). (ENG., Illus.). 128p. pap. 21.99 (978-0-7385-6196-7(7)) Arcadia Publishing.

Komiske, Bruce King, ed. Designing the World's Best Children's Hospital Volume 3: The Quest Continues. 2012. (ENG., Illus.). 224p. 70.00 **(978-1-86470-339-9(3))** Images Publishing Group AUS. Dist: National Bk. Network.

Komiske, Bruce King, ed. Heroes: The Story of Hasbro Children's Hospital. 2010. (ENG., Illus.). 124p. 30.00 (978-1-86470-346-7(6)) Images Publishing Group AUS. Dist: National Bk. Network.

Komiski, Bruce. Children's Hospitals Vol. 2: The Future of Healing Environments. 2nd ed. 2006. (Designing the World's Best Ser.). (ENG., Illus.). 160p. 70.00 (978-1-920744-32-8(0)) Images Publishing Group AUS. Dist: National Bk. Network.

Lanzkowsky, Philip. How It All Began: The History of a Children's Hospital. 2008. (978-1-57864-522-0(0)) Donning Co. Pubs.

Parish, Betsy. Legacy: 50 Years of Loving Care, Texas Children's Hospital, 1954-2004, 1. (Illus.). ltd. ed. 2006. 716p. 45.50 (978-0-9786200-5-9(4)) ltd. ed. 2006. xiii, 699p. pap. 32.95 (978-0-9786200-4-2(6)) 2nd exp. ed. 2008. (ENG., 762p. 45.50 (978-0-9786200-6-6(2)) Elisha Freeman Publishing.

Shipps, Shannon. Children s Miracles. 2010. 36p. pap. 24.99 (978-1-60957-540-3(7)) Xulon Pr., Inc.

Weir, Meghan. Between Expectations: Lessons from a Pediatric Residency. 2011. (ENG.). 288p. 25.00 (978-1-4391-8907-8(2), Free Pr.) Free Pr.

Zaoutis, Lisa B. & Chiang, Vincent. Comprehensive Pediatric Hospital Medicine. 2007. (ENG., Illus.). 1384p. 172.00 (978-0-323-03004-5(1), Mosby) Elsevier - Health Sciences Div.

CHILDREN—HOURS OF LABOR

see Hours of Labor

CHILDREN—HYGIENE

see Children—Health and Hygiene

CHILDREN—INSTITUTIONAL CARE

see also Charity-Schools; Child Psychotherapy—Residential Treatment; Day Care Centers; Foster Home Care; Housemothers; Orphans; Reformatories

Andersen, Signe. A Good Place to Live: On How Municipality Level Characteristics Explain Municipality Level Variation in Children's Placement Risk (Study Paper No. 29) 2010. 32p. pap. 9.75 (978-87-90199-41-8(3)) Univ. Pr. of Southern Denmark DNK. Dist: International Specialized Bk. Services.

Andersen, Signe & Fallesen, Peter. Disentangling the Heterogeneous Relationship between Background Characteristics & a Child's Placement Risk. 2010. 27p. pap. 9.75 (978-87-90199-45-6(6)) Univ. Pr. of Southern Denmark DNK. Dist: International Specialized Bk. Services.

Bamba, Sachiko & Haight, Wendy. Child Welfare & Development: A Japanese Case Study. 2011. (ENG., Illus.). 224p. 80.00 **(978-1-107-00284-5(2))** Cambridge Univ. Pr.

Barkman, Frieda & Barkman, Paul. Lad with Summer Eyes: A Story of the Grace Children's Home. 2011. 130p. 40.95 **(978-1-258-08973-3(4))** Literary Licensing, LLC.

Bloom, Debra. Foster Care. 2009. (At ISSUE Ser.). (ENG.). 128p. pap. 22.50 (978-0-7377-4515-3(0)); (Illus.). pap. 31.80 (978-0-7377-4514-6(2)) Cengage Gale. (Greenhaven Pr., Inc.).

Brogan, Irene & Brogan, Alan A. Not Without You: Some People Are Just Destined to Be Together. 2009. (ENG.). 288p. pap. 24.95 (978-0-340-97639-5(X), Hodder & Stoughton) Hodder General Publishing Div. GBR. Dist: Independent Pubs. Group.

Broten, Alton M. Houseparents in Children's Institutions: A Discussion Guide. 2011. (ENG.). 96p. pap. 25.00 **(978-0-8078-7826-2(X))** Univ. of North Carolina Pr.

Chandler, Caroline, et al. Early Child Care: The New Perspectives. Dittmann, Laura, ed. 2008. (ENG.). 395p. pap. 34.95 (978-0-202-36218-2(3)) Aldine Transaction.

Council of Europe Staff. Rights of children at risk & in Care (2007) 2007. 80p. pap. 18.00 (978-92-871-6039-3(2)) Council of Europe FRA. Dist: Manhattan Publishing Co.

Courtney, Mark E. & Iwaniec, Dorota, eds. Residential Care of Children. 2009. (ENG., Illus.). 224p. 39.95 (978-0-19-530918-8(9)) Oxford Univ. Pr., Inc.

Daubert, Thomas. Your House Their House: The Best & Worst of Residential Child Care. 2011. 156p. pap. 11.70 **(978-1-4634-3487-8(1))** AuthorHouse.

Enrique G. Macias. Abc's = about Basic Child Care: A Parent's Handbook of Pediatric Information. 2009. 88p. pap. 19.00 (978-1-4389-3556-0(0)) AuthorHouse.

Fulcher, Leon C. & Ainsworth, Frank, eds. Group Care Practice with Children & Young People Revisited, 2 vols. 2006. (ENG., Illus.). 346p. 175.00 (978-0-7890-3279-9(1)); pap. 56.95 (978-0-7890-3280-5(5)) Routledge.

Goba, Fairhope Dumile. Trends in Relation to the Involvement of Family in Children in Care. 2011. 216p. pap. **(978-3-8443-9823-6(5))** Lambert Academic Publishing.

Goswami, Namrata. Psycho-Social Profile of Institutionalized Children. 2011. 100p. pap. **(978-3-8433-9186-3(6))** Lambert Academic Publishing.

Higgs, Jacqueline. Corporate Parenting: The Contribution of Designated Teachers. 2009. 220p. pap. (978-3-639-12975-5(X)) VDM Verlag Dr. Mueller e.K.

Hobry, Jack. Lost Boys. 2010. 255p. pap. 17.95 (978-1-58241-373-0(8)) Harbor Directories, Inc.

Holden, Martha J. Children & Residential Experiences: Creating Conditions for Change. 2nd ed. 2009. pap. (978-1-58760-126-2(5)) Child Welfare League of America, Inc.

Hudson, Raymond L. Family after All: Alaska's Jesse Lee Home, Vol. I, Unalaska 1889-1925. 2007. (Illus.). 400p. pap. 33.00 (978-0-9789979-0-8(5)) Hardscratch Pr.

Humphreys, Margaret. Oranges & Sunshine: Empty Cradles. 2011. (ENG., Illus.). 382p. pap. 12.95 **(978-0-552-16335-4(X))** Transworld Publishers Ltd. GBR. Dist: Independent Pubs. Group.

Jacobs, Margaret D. White Mother to a Dark Race: Settler Colonialism, Maternalism, & the Removal of Indigenous Children in the American West & Australia, 1880-1940. 2011. (ENG., Illus.). 592p. pap. 30.00 (978-0-8032-3516-8(X)) Univ. of Nebraska Pr.

Keith-Lucas, Alan. Group Child Care as a Family Service. 2011. (ENG.). 283p. pap. 40.00 (978-0-8078-9696-9(9)) Univ. of North Carolina Pr.

Kendrick, Andrew, ed. Residential Child Care: Prospects & Challenges. 2007. (Research Highlights in Social Work Ser.). 248p. per. (978-1-84310-526-8(8)) Kingsley, Jessica Ltd.

Kim, Chong Sun. Sahoe Kujo Ui Pyonhwa e Taeung Han Chanyo Yangyuk Kwallyon Popche Kaeson Pangan Yon'gu. 2007. (KOR.). 165p. (978-89-8323-347-9(8)) Korea Legislation Research Institute.

Laurie, Annie & Richardson, Brian. The Gathering: One Family's Adoption Story. 2010. pap. 24.99 (978-1-61566-458-0(0)) Tate Publishing & Enterprises, LLC.

Lechner-Kreidl, Christina, et al, eds. When Knowledge Sparks a Flame: Knowledge Communication in the International Non-Profit Organisation SOS Children's Villages. 2007. (Illus.). 214p. pap. 29.95 (978-3-631-56578-0(X)) Lang, Peter GmbH, Europaischer Verlag der Wissenschaften DEU. Dist: Lang, Peter Publishing, Inc.

Lemay, Raymond A., et al. Looking after Children: A Practitioner's Guide. 2007. (ENG., Illus.). 136p. pap. (978-0-7766-0643-9(3)) Univ. of Ottawa Pr./Presses de l'Universite d'Ottawa.

Lindsey, Duncan & Shlonsky, Aron, eds. Child Welfare Research: Advances for Practice & Policy. 2008. (ENG., Illus.). 448p. 42.99 (978-0-19-530496-1(9)) Oxford Univ. Pr., Inc.

Markova, Galina. Parents, Children, Institutions in a Post-Totalitarian Context. 2010. 128p. pap. (978-3-639-22270-8(9)) VDM Verlag Dr. Mueller e.K.

Matthews, Sherry. We Were Not Orphans: Stories from the Waco State Home. 2011. (ENG., Illus.). 234p. 29.95 (978-0-292-72559-1(0)) Univ. of Texas Pr.

Meeks, George & Buchanan, James Malcolm. Why Did It Happen? 2010. 252p. pap. 14.49 (978-1-4490-1337-0(6)) AuthorHouse.

Merva, Monika, et al. The City of Children. 2011. (ENG., Illus.). 112p. 45.00 **(978-3-86828-174-3(6))** Kehrer Verlag Heidelberg, Klaus Kehrer DEU. Dist: Consortium Bk. Sales & Distribution.

Mitchell, R. B. Castaway Kid: One Man's Search for Hope & Home. 2007. (ENG., Illus.). 272p. per. 13.99 (978-1-58997-434-0(4)) Tyndale Hse. Pubs.

National Foster Parents Association Staff, et al. Success As a Foster Parent: Everything You Need to Know about Foster Care. 2009. (ENG.). 272p. (gr. 12-18). pap. 16.95 (978-1-59257-747-7(4), Alpha Bks.) Penguin Group (USA) Inc.

Ó Ris, Pádraig. Dare to Dream. 2009. (Illus.). 240p. pap. 14.49 (978-1-4490-4624-8(X)) AuthorHouse.

Office of Management and Budget (U.S.), compiled by. Cases of Child Neglect & Abuse at Private Residential Treatment Facilities: Hearing Before the Committee on Education & Labor, U. S. House of Representatives, One Hundred Tenth Congress, First Session, Hearing Held in Washington, DC, October 10, 2007. 2008. (ENG., Illus.). iii, 138p. pap. 102.00 (978-0-16-080875-3(8), 552-070-37425-6, Office of Management & Budget) United States Government Printing Office.

O'Malley, Kathleen. Childhood Interrupted: Growing up Unaer the Cruel Regime of the Sisters of Mercy. 2006. 244p. reprint ed. pap. 22.00 (978-1-4223-5723-1(6)) DIANE Publishing Co.

Owusu-Bempah, Kwame. The Wellbeing of Children in Care: A New Approach for Improving Developmental Outcomes. 2010. (ENG.). 192p. (C). 125.00 (978-0-415-47939-4(8)); pap. 39.95 (978-0-415-47940-0(1)) Routledge.

Penglase, Joanna. Orphans of the Living. 2007. (ENG.). 384p. pap. 18.00 (978-1-920731-66-3(0)) Fremantle Pr. AUS. Dist: Independent Pubs. Group.

Peters, Friedhelm, ed. Residential Child Care & Its Alternatives: International Perspectives. 2008. (Illus.). 184p. per. 32.95 (978-1-85856-409-8(3)) Trentham Bks. Ltd. GBR. Dist: Stylus Publishing, LLC.

Petrie, Pat, et al. Working with Children in Care: European Perspectives. 2006. (Illus.). 208p. (ENG.). 183.95 (978-0-335-21635-2(8), 0335216358); pap. 67.00 (978-0-335-21634-5(X), 033521634X) McGraw-Hill Cos., The.

Ramey, Jessie B. Child Care in Black & White: Working Parents & the History of Orphanages. 2012. (Working Class in American History Ser.). (ENG., Illus.). 296p. 55.00 **(978-0-252-03690-3(5))** Univ. of Illinois Pr.

Rockhill, Elena Khlinovskaya. Lost to the State: Family Discontinuity, Social Orphanhood & Residential Care in the Russian Far East. 2010. (Illus.). 336p. 90.00 (978-1-84545-738-9(2)) Berghahn Bks., Inc.

Rohs, Edward & Estrine, Judith. Raised by the Church: Growing up in New York City's Catholic Orphanages. 2011. (ENG., Illus.). 240p. 22.95 **(978-0-8232-4022-7(3))** Fordham Univ. Pr.

Sachs, Isaac. The Universal Daycare System. 2009. 376p. pap. 27.99 (978-1-4490-4173-1(6)) AuthorHouse.

Schroeder, Jenna. Simply Knowing, Trusting, Obeying, Doing, Living, & Serving God's Word. 2007. 88p. per. 16.95 (978-1-4241-9841-2(0)) PublishAmerica, Inc.

Tolevski, Amelia. Virtual Predators. 2007. per. (978-1-59916-257-7(1)) Printing Systems.

Whelan, David. No More Silence: He Thought He'D Got Away with It - But One Day Little David Would Find the Strength to Speak Out. McBeth, Jim & Scott, Marion, eds. 2011. (ENG.). 304p. 11.95 (978-0-00-738890-5(X)) HarperCollins Pubs. Ltd. GBR. Dist: Independent Pubs. Group.

Williams, Andrew. Working with Street Children: An Approach Explored. 2011. (Illus.). 176p. pap. 29.95 **(978-1-905541-80-5(5))** Russell Hse. Publishing Ltd. GBR. Dist: International Specialized Bk. Services.

Wolins, Martin, ed. Successful Group Care: Explorations in the Powerful Environment. 2008. (ENG., Illus.). 472p. pap. 49.95 (978-0-202-36258-8(2)) Aldine Transaction.

Wright, Orville, Jr. 'Twas a Hard Knock Life: The Tabor Home Story. 2007. 206p. pap. 19.95 (978-0-7414-3775-4(9)) Infinity Publishing.

Zero to Three (Organization) Staff, contrib. by. Preventing Child Abuse & Neglect: Parent-Provider Partnerships in Child Care. 2006. (978-0-943657-98-1(9)) Zero To Three Pr.

CHILDREN—INSTITUTIONAL CARE—GREAT BRITAIN

Allain, Lucille & Cocker, Christine. Social Work with Looked after Children. 2008. (Illus.). 214p. (C). pap. *(978-1-84445-103-6(8))* Learning Matters Ltd.

Brogan, Alan & Brogan, Irene. Not Without You: Some People Are Just Destined to Be Together. 2009. (ENG.). 288p. 24.95 *(978-0-340-97638-8(1))*, Hodder & Stoughton) Hodder General Publishing Div. GBR. Dist: Independent Pubs. Group.

Brogan, Irene & Brogan, Alan. Not Without You: The Two Children Who Could Survive Anything - Except Being Apart. 2009. (ENG.). 288p. 12.95 *(978-0-340-97640-1(3))*, Hodder & Stoughton) Hodder General Publishing Div. GBR. Dist: Independent Pubs. Group.

Chivell, Rachel & Chapel, Alix. The Throwaway Boy. 2008. (ENG.). 288p. 29.95 *(978-1-84454-565-0(2))* Blake, John Publishing, Ltd. GBR. Dist: Independent Pubs. Group.

Connelly, Graham & Milligan, Ian. Residential Child Care: Between Home & Family (Practice & Policy in Health & Social Care, 17) 2012. 112p. pap., pap. 29.99 ***(978-1-78046-000-0(7))*** Dunedin Academic Pr. GBR. Dist: International Specialized Bk. Services.

Connolly, Paul. Against All Odds. 2010. (ENG.). 278p. pap. 12.95 *(978-1-84454-905-4(4))* Blake, John Publishing, Ltd. GBR. Dist: Independent Pubs. Group.

Cooper, Teresa. Trust No One. (ENG., Illus.). 2008. 312p. pap. 14.95 *(978-0-7528-9330-3(0))* 2007. 300p. 24.95 *(978-0-7528-8611-4(8))* Orion Publishing Group, Ltd. GBR. Dist: Independent Pubs. Group.

Cram101 Textbook Reviews. Outlines & Highlights for Residential Child Care: Collaborative Practice by Ian Milligan. 2011. 58p. pap. 26.95 ***(978-1-61905-371-7(3))*** Cram101 Inc.

Hicks, Leslie, et al. Managing Children's Homes: Developing Effective Leadership in Small Organisations. 2007. (Illus.). 224p. pap. *(978-1-84310-542-8(X))* Kingsley, Jessica Ltd.

Holland, Jimmy. Lost in Care: The True Story of a Forgotten Child. 2007. (Illus.). 288p. per. 14.95 *(978-1-84454-361-8(7))* Blake, John Publishing, Ltd. GBR. Dist: Independent Pubs. Group.

Hylands, Ivy. My Life as a Blue Coat Girl. 2007. (Illus.). 60p. per. *(978-1-84401-935-9(7))* Athena Pr.

Jackson, Sonia. Education for Social Exclusion: Can We Change the Future for Children in Care? 2010. (IOE Inaugural Professional Lectures). (ENG., Illus.). 30p. pap. 9.95 *(978-0-85473-906-6(8))* Institute of Education GBR. Dist: Stylus Publishing, LLC.

Landler, Christine & Martin, Sue. No Way Home: The Terrifying Story of Life in a Children's Home & a Little Girl's Struggle to Survive. 2007. (ENG.). 288p. pap. 14.95 *(978-0-09-191737-1(9))* Random Hse. GBR. Dist: Independent Pubs. Group.

Punch, et al, eds. Childrenrsquo;s Food Practices in Families & Institutions. 2012. (ENG.). 98p. (C). pap. 42.95 ***(978-0-415-63226-3(9))*** Routledge.

Swain, Hillel, et al. Child, Nation, Race & Empire: Child Rescue Discourse, England, Canada & Australia, 1850-1915. 2010. (Studies in Imperialism Ser.). (ENG., Illus.). 224p. 89.95 *(978-0-7190-7894-1(6))* Manchester Univ. Pr. GBR. Dist: Macmillan.

CHILDREN—INSTITUTIONAL CARE—ITALY

Charnley, Jean. An American Social Worker in Italy. 2009. (ENG.). 336p. pap. 60.00 *(978-0-8166-5723-0(8))* Univ. of Minnesota Pr.

CHILDREN—JUVENILE LITERATURE

Brundage, George. Oraciones Diarias. 2006. (Illus.). 16p. bds. 4.75 *(978-0-89942-849-9(5))* Catholic Bk. Publishing Corp.

Goyette, Linda. Kidmonton: True Stories of River City Kids, 1 vol. (ENG., Illus.). 128p. pap. 6.95 *(978-0-9732481-7-3(3))* Brindle & Glass Publishing CAN. Dist: Literary Pr. Group of Canada.

Yonge, Charlotte M. Little Lucy's Wonderful Globe. 2009. (Illus.). 74p. pap. *(978-1-4099-4027-2(6))* Dodo Pr.

—Little Lucy's Wonderful Globe. 2009. 72p. pap. *(978-1-84830-172-6(3))*, Wildhern Pr.) Echo Library.

CHILDREN—LANGUAGE

Here are entered works which discuss child language in general or within an educational framework, including general characteristics and usage. Works which discuss from the linguistic or psycholinguistic viewpoint the process of the acquisition of the native language in children are entered under the heading Language Acquisition.

see also Language Disorders in Children

Adone, Dany. The Acquisition of Creole Languages: How Children Surpass their Input. 2012. (ENG., Illus.). 248p. 99.00 ***(978-0-521-19965-0(4))*** Cambridge Univ. Pr.

Bardige, Betty S. Talk to Me, Baby! How You Can Support Young Children's Language Development. 2009. 312p. pap. 24.95 *(978-1-55766-977-3(5))* Brookes, Paul H. Publishing Co.

Bavin, Edith L., ed. The Cambridge Handbook of Child Language. 2012. (ENG.). 608p. pap. 50.00 ***(978-1-107-60542-8(3))*** Cambridge Univ. Pr.

Bavin, Edith Laura. The Cambridge Handbook of Child Language. Bavin, Edith L., ed. 2009. (Cambridge Handbooks in Language & Linguistics Ser.). (ENG., Illus.). 608p. 160.00 *(978-0-521-88337-5(7))* Cambridge Univ. Pr.

Bayer, Tedi. My Child Speaks Ten Languages. 2009. 279p. pap. 20.00 *(978-0-9801270-6-5(8))* Seven Locks Pr.

Benson, Janette B. & Haith, Marshall M., eds. Language, Memory, & Cognition in Infancy & Early Childhood. 2009. (ENG., Illus.). 552p. 103.00 *(978-0-12-375069-3(5))*, Academic Pr.) Elsevier Science & Technology Bks.

Bernstein, Basil. Theoretical Studies Towards a Sociology of Language, 4 vols. 2008. (Illus.). 256p. 39.95 *(978-0-415-48856-3(7))* Routledge.

Between the Lions Staff. Wild about Group Time: Simple Literacy Plans for Preschool. 2010. (ENG., Illus.). 256p. pap. 24.95 *(978-0-87659-305-9(8))* Gryphon Hse., Inc.

Beyer, Monica. Teach Your Baby to Sign: An Illustrated Guide to Simple Sign Language for Babies. 2007. (ENG., Illus.). 176p. pap. 17.95 *(978-1-59233-273-1(0))*, 1592332730) Quayside.

Bloom, Lois. One Word at a Time: The Use of Single Word Utterances before Syntax. (Janua Linguarum. Series Minor Ser.). (ENG.). 264p. 196.00 ***(978-3-11-174790-3(5))*** De Gruyter, Mouton DEU. Dist: de Gruyter, Walter GmbH & Co. KG.

Bradford, Helen. Communication, Language & Literacy in the Early Years Foundation Stage. 2009. (Practical Guidance in the EYFS Ser.). (ENG.). 144p. 120.00 *(978-0-415-47835-9(9))* Fulton, David Pubs. GBR. Dist: Taylor & Francis Group.

—Communication, Language & Literacy in the Early Years Foundation Stage: Supporting the Framework Through the Use of Story, 7 vols. 2009. (Practical Guidance in the EYFS Ser.). (Illus.). 96p. pap. 31.95 *(978-0-415-47427-6(2))*, Fulton, David Pubs. GBR. Dist: Taylor & Francis Group.

Briant, Monta Z. Baby Sign Language Basics: Early Communication for Hearing Babies & Toddlers. rev. exp. ed. 2009. (ENG., Illus.). 496p. pap. 11.95 *(978-1-4019-2160-6(4))* Hay Hse., Inc.

Bruner, Jerome S. & Haste, Helen, eds. Making Sense: The Child's Construction of the World. 2010. (Routledge Revivals Ser.). (ENG., Illus.). 216p. 95.00 *(978-0-415-58099-1(4))* Routledge.

Burman, Lisa. Are You Listening? Fostering Conversations That Help Young Children Learn. 2008. (ENG., Illus.). 200p. pap. 27.95 *(978-1-933653-46-4(9))* Redleaf Pr.

Butler, Carly W. Talk & Social Interaction in the Playground. 2008. (Directions in Ethnomethodology & Conversation Analysis Ser.). 230p. 114.95 *(978-0-7546-7416-0(9))* Ashgate Publishing Co.

Callander, Nichola & Nahmad-Williams, Lindy. Communication, Language & Literacy. 2011. (Supporting Development in the Early Years Foundation Stage Ser.). (ENG., Illus.). 160p. 100.00 *(978-1-4411-0355-0(4))*; pap. 29.95 *(978-1-4411-2898-0(0))* Continuum International Publishing Group, Ltd. GBR. Dist: National Bk. Network.

Cattell, Ray & Cattell. Children's Language: Consensus & Controversy. 2nd ed. 2007. (ENG., Illus.). 304p. 60.00 *(978-0-8264-8880-0(3))*; 180.00 *(978-0-8264-8879-4(X))* Continuum International Publishing Group, Ltd. GBR. Dist: National Bk. Network.

Chamberlain, Catherine. Basic Concept Pictures. 2007. (J). 89.95 *(978-0-7606-9970-6(4))* LinguiSystems, Inc.

Chandlee, Jane, et al, eds. Proceedings of the 33rd annual Boston University Conference on Language Development: Bucld 33. 2009. (Illus.). 657p. pap. 60.00 *(978-1-57473-094-4(0))* Cascadilla Pr.

Cheng, Li-Rong Lily & Butler, Katharine G., eds. Child Language Update: Folia Phoniatrica et Logopaedia. (Illus.). 58p. *(978-3-8055-7430-3(4))* Karger, S AG.

Christie, Frances. Language Education Throughout the School Years: A Functional Perspective. 2012. (Language Learning Monograph Ser.: 4). (ENG.). 300p. pap. 39.95 ***(978-1-118-29200-6(6))***, Wiley-Blackwell) Wiley, John & Sons, Inc.

Christie, Frances & Derewianka, Beverly. School Discourse: Learning to Write Across the Years of Schooling. 2010. (Continuum Discourse Ser.). (ENG.). 280p. 49.95 *(978-1-4411-3131-7(0))* Continuum International Publishing Group, Ltd. GBR. Dist: National Bk. Network.

Christie, Frances, et al. School Discourse: Learning to Write Across the Years of Schooling. 2009. (Continuum Discourse Ser.). (ENG., Illus.). 280p. 150.00 *(978-0-8264-9992-9(9))* Continuum International Publishing Group, Ltd. GBR. Dist: National Bk. Network.

Clay, Jenny, compiled by. Memories of Marie: Reflections on the Life & Work of Marie Clay. 2009. (Illus.). 259p. pap. 31.25 *(978-0-325-02675-6(0))* Heinemann.

Clay, Marie M. Biks & Gutches: New Edition. 2007. 56p. pap. 21.25 *(978-0-325-01293-3(8))*, E01293) Heinemann.

—Record of Oral Language: New Edition. 2007. 56p. pap. 21.25 *(978-0-325-01292-6(X))*, E01292) Heinemann.

Colombo/McCardle. Infant Pathways to Language. 2008. (ENG., Illus.). 336p. 94.95 *(978-0-8058-6063-4(0))*, Psychology Press) Taylor & Francis Group GBR. Dist: Taylor & Francis Group.

Cram101 Textbook Reviews & Cram101 Textbook Reviews. Outlines & Highlights for Language Development in Early Childhood by Beverly W Otto, Isbn: 9780135019696 0135019699. 2011. 348p. pap. 33.95 ***(978-1-61490-836-4(2))*** Cram101 Inc.

Cram101 Textbook Reviews Staff. Outlines & Highlights for Infants & Toddlers: Development & Curriculum Planning by Penny Deiner, ISBN. 2009. 64p. pap. 27.95 *(978-1-4288-8077-1(1))* Cram101 Inc.

Cross, Melanie. Children with Social, Emotional & Behavioural Difficulties & Communication Problems: There Is Always a Reason. 2nd rev. ed. 2011. (ENG., Illus.). 208p. pap. ***(978-1-84905-129-3(1))*** Kingsley, Jessica Ltd.

Danis, Nick, et al, eds. Proceedings of the 35th annual Boston University Conference on Language Development: Bucld 35. 2011. (Illus.). 677p. pap. 60.00 ***(978-1-57473-065-4(7))***; lib. bdg. 125.00 ***(978-1-57473-165-1(3))*** Cascadilla Pr.

DeBruin-Parecki, Andrea, ed. Effective Early Literacy in Practice: Here's How, Here's Why. 2008. (Illus.). 168p. per. 24.95 *(978-1-55766-940-7(6))* Brookes, Paul H. Publishing Co.

Deiner, Penny Low. Infants & Toddlers: Development & Curriculum Planning. 2nd rev. ed. 2008. (ENG., Illus.). 784p. (C). pap. 133.95 *(978-1-4283-1824-3(0))* Delmar Cengage Learning.

Dickinson, David K. & Neuman, Susan B., eds. Handbook of Early Literacy Research, Volume 2. 2nd rev. ed. 2007. (ENG., Illus.). 468p. (gr. k-2). pap. 50.00 *(978-1-59385-577-2(X))* Guilford Pubns., Inc.

Diessel, Holger. The Acquisition of Complex Sentences. 2009. (Cambridge Studies in Linguistics Ser.). (ENG., Illus.). 244p. pap. 34.99 *(978-0-521-10748-8(2))* Cambridge Univ. Pr.

Evans, Roy. Metacognitive Approaches to Developing Oracy: Developing Speaking & Listening with Young Children. 2008. pap. 40.00 *(978-0-415-49555-4(5))* Routledge.

Feilke, Helmuth, et al, eds. Grammatikalisierung, Spracherwerb und Schriftlichkeit. (Linguistische Arbeiten Ser.).Tr. of Grammaticalization, Language Acquisition & the Medium of Writing. (GER.). VIII, 181p. 150.00 ***(978-3-11-186452-5(9))*** De Gruyter, Walter Inc.

Fields, Marjorie V., et al. Let's Begin Reading Right: A Developmental Approach to Emergent Literacy. 6th ed. 2007. (ENG., Illus.). 448p. (C). per. 83.80 *(978-0-13-159502-6(4))*, Prentice Hall PTR) Prentice Hall PTR.

Fisher, Ros, et al. Using Talk to Support Writing. 2010. (Illus.). 200p. (C). 112.00 *(978-1-84920-143-8(9))*, B01438C); pap. 43.00 *(978-1-84920-144-5(7))*, B01438P) SAGE Pubns., Ltd. GBR. Dist: SAGE Pubns., Inc.

Galasso, Joseph. Minimum of English Grammar: An Introduction to Feature Theory with a special note on the nature of early child grammars of English. 2009. (Illus.). 600p. (C). pap. 133.95 *(978-1-934269-41-1(7))* Univ. Readers.

Genishi, Celia & Dyson, Anne Haas. Children, Language, & Literacy: Diverse Learners in Diverse Times. 2009. (ENG., Illus.). 176p. pap. 21.95 *(978-0-8077-4974-6(5))*; *(978-0-8077-4975-3(3))* Teachers College Pr., Teachers College, Columbia Univ.

Gerngross, Günter & Puchta, Herbert. Playway to English Level 1 Pupil's Book. 2nd ed. 2009. (ENG.). 84p. pap. 19.66 *(978-0-521-12996-1(6))* Cambridge Univ. Pr.

Gerngross, Günter, et al. Playway to English Level 1 Activity Book with CD-ROM. 2nd ed. 2009. (ENG.). 64p. pap. 24.15 incl. cd-rom *(978-0-521-12993-0(1))* Cambridge Univ. Pr.

Goodacre, Elizabeth. Children & Learning to Read (RLE Edu I) 2012. (Routledge Library Editions: Education Ser.). (ENG.). 132p. 100.00 ***(978-0-415-69449-0(3))*** Routledge.

Goodman, Yetta M. & Martens, Prisca, eds. Critical Issues in Early Literacy: Research & Pedagogy. 2007. (Illus.). 302p. 110.00 *(978-0-8058-5899-0(7))*; per. 45.95 *(978-0-8058-5900-3(4))* Erlbaum, Lawrence Assocs., Inc.

Grimm, Angela, et al, eds. Production-Comprehension Asymmetries in Child Language. 2011. (Studies on Language Acquisition [SOLA] Ser.). (ENG., VIII, 274p. Illus.). 210.00 ***(978-3-11-220423-8(9))***; 140.00 ***(978-3-11-023872-3(1))*** De Gruyter, Mouton DEU. Dist: de Gruyter, Walter GmbH & Co. KG.

Grinstead, John. Hispanic Child Languages: Typical & Impaired Development. 2009. *(978-90-272-5311-8(0))* Benjamins, John Publishing Co.

Hallissy, Jennifer. The Write Start: A Guide to Nurturing Writing at Every Stage, from Scribbling to Forming Letters & Writing Stories. 2010. (ENG., Illus.). 160p. pap. 17.95 *(978-1-59030-837-0(9))*, Trumpeter) Shambhala Pubns., Inc.

Hicks, Deborah, ed. Discourse, Learning, & Schooling. 2008. (ENG., Illus.). 304p. pap. 38.99 *(978-0-521-02792-6(9))* Cambridge Univ. Pr.

Hoff, Erika, ed. Research Methods in Child Language: A Practical Guide. 2011. (GMLZ - Guides to Research Methods in Language & Linguistics Ser.: 3). (ENG., Illus.). 384p. pap. 99.95 *(978-1-4443-3125-7(6))*; 99.95 *(978-1-4443-3124-0(8))* Wiley, John & Sons, Inc. (Wiley-Blackwell).

Honsa, Vladimir & Hardman-de-Bautista, M. J., eds. Papers on Linguistics & Child Language: Ruth Hirsch Weir Memorial Volume. (Janua Linguarum. Series Maior Ser.). (ENG.). VIII, 298p. 210.00 ***(978-3-11-185829-6(4))*** De Gruyter, Mouton DEU. Dist: de Gruyter, Walter GmbH & Co. KG.

Jakobson, Roman. Child Language, Aphasia & Phonological Universals. Keiler, Allan R., tr. (Janua Linguarum. Series Minor Ser.). (ENG.). 101p. 60.00 ***(978-3-11-179541-6(1))*** De Gruyter, Mouton DEU. Dist: de Gruyter, Walter GmbH & Co. KG.

—Child language, aphasia & phonological universals. Keiler, Allan R., ed. (Janua Linguarum. Series Minor Ser.). (ENG.). 101p. 210.00 ***(978-3-11-219353-2(9))***; 135.00 ***(978-3-11-099831-3(9))*** De Gruyter, Mouton DEU. Dist: de Gruyter Walter GmbH & Co. KG.

Johnston, Peter H. & Power, Brenda Miller. Opening Minds: Using Language to Change Lives. 2012. (Illus.). viii, 152p. E-Book ***(978-1-57110-953-8(6))***; (ENG., (C). pap. 14.00 ***(978-1-57110-816-6(5))*** Stenhouse Pubs.

Kamhi, Alan G. & Catts, Hugh W. Language & Reading Disabilities. 3rd ed. 2011. (ENG., Illus.). 320p. (C). pap. 86.67 *(978-0-13-707277-4(5))* Allyn & Bacon, Inc.

Kaper, Willem. Child Language: A Language which Does Not Exist? (ENG.). VIII, 148p. 210.00 ***(978-3-11-178041-2(4))*** De Gruyter, Mouton DEU. Dist: de Gruyter, Walter GmbH & Co. KG.

Kayser, Hortencia. Educating Latino Preschool Children. 2007. (Illus.). 232p. per. 55.00 *(978-1-59756-121-1(5))* Plural Publishing, Inc.

Levey, Sandra & Polirstok, Susan. Language Development: Understanding Language Diversity in the Classroom. 2010. (Illus.). 384p. (C). pap. 81.00 *(978-1-4129-7407-3(0))*, B74073P) SAGE Pubns., Inc.

Lines, Katrina & Cottrell, David. Children's Language Ability. 2008. 216p. pap. *(978-3-8364-9066-5(8))* VDM Verlag Dr. Mueller e.K.

Luckevich, Diana. Verbal Behavior Targets: A Tool to Teach Mands, Tacts & Intraverbals. 2008. 160p. pap. 24.95 *(978-0-9755859-4-8(0))* DRL Bk., Inc.

Lybolt, John, et al. Building Language Throughout the Year: The Preschool Early Literacy Curriculum. 2007. (Illus.). 436p. spiral bd. 49.95 *(978-1-55766-780-9(2))* Brookes, Paul H. Publishing Co.

Matuszak, Mel E. Helping Your Child with Speech. 2008. (ENG.). 48p. pap. 12.95 *(978-1-886057-14-2(1))* Warren Publishing, Inc.

Maybin, Janet. Children's Voices: Talk, Knowledge & Identity. 2008. (ENG.). 208p. pap. 39.00 *(978-1-4039-3331-7(6))* Palgrave Macmillan.

McLeod, Sharynne. The International Guide to Speech Acquisition. 2007. (ENG., Illus.). 656p. (C). per. 74.95 *(978-1-4180-5360-4(0))* Delmar Cengage Learning.

Meece, Judith L., et al. Child & Adolescent Development for Educators. 3rd rev. ed. 2007. (ENG., Illus.). 340p. (C). per. 107.67 *(978-0-07-352576-1(5))*, 0073525766) McGraw-Hill Cos., The.

Mercer, Neil & Hodgkinson, Steve, eds. Exploring Talk in School: Inspired by the Work of Douglas Barnes. 2008. (Illus.). 208p. (C). 121.00 *(978-1-84787-378-1(2))*, B73781C); pap. 51.00 *(978-1-84787-379-8(0))*, B73781P) SAGE Pubns., Ltd. GBR. Dist: SAGE Pubns., Inc.

Moginer, Alijandra & Mogilner, Tayopa. Children's Writer's Word Book. 2nd ed. 2006. (ENG., Illus.). 352p. per. 16.99 *(978-1-58297-413-2(6))*, 11031) F&W Media, Inc.

Murphy Buckley, Eileen. 360 Degrees of Text: Using Poetry to Teach Close Reading & Powerful Writing. 2011. pap. ***(978-0-8141-6023-7(9))*** National Council of Teachers of English.

Nash, Marion, et al. Developing Language & Communication Skills Through Effective Small Group Work. 3rd rev. ed. 2010. (ENG., Illus.). 144p. pap. 36.95 *(978-0-415-57689-5(X))* Routledge.

Nelson, Katherine, ed. Narratives from the Crib. 2006. (Illus.). 368p. per. 25.00 *(978-0-674-02363-5(3))* Harvard Univ. Pr.

Neuman, Susan B. & Dickinson, David K., eds. Handbook of Early Literacy Research Vol. 3, Vol. 3. 2011. (ENG.). 467p. (gr. -1-3). pap. 40.00 ***(978-1-4625-0335-3(7))*** Guilford Pubns., Inc.

Neuman, Susan B., et al. User's Guide to the Child/Home Early Language & Literacy Observation (CHELLO) Tool. 2007. pap. *(978-1-55766-920-9(1))* Brookes, Paul H. Publishing Co.

Pena-Brooks, Adriana & Hedge, M. N. Assessment & Treatment of Articulation & Phonological Disorders in Children, Complete Kit. 2nd ed. 2007. 624p. 102.00 *(978-1-4164-0229-9(2))*, PRO-ED, Inc.

Peña-Brooks, Adriana & Hegde, M. N. Assessment & Treatment of Articulation & Phonological Disorders in Children. 2nd ed. 2006. (Illus.). xix, 624p. 75.00 *(978-1-4164-0230-5(6))* PRO-ED, Inc.

Piaget, Jean. The Language & Thought of the Child. 2007. (ENG., Illus.). 272p. per. *(978-1-4067-2832-3(2))* Read Bks.

Rauter, Lisa. Acquisition of Grammar in Children. 2010. 136p. pap. *(978-3-639-27223-9(4))* VDM Verlag Dr. Mueller e.K.

Reed, Michael A. Children & Language: Development, Impairment & Training. 2009. 89.00 *(978-1-60692-395-5(1))* Nova Science Pubs., Inc.

Rhyner, Paula M. Emergent Literacy & Language Development: Promoting Learning in Early Childhood. Rhyner, Paula M., ed. 2009. (Challenges in Language & Literacy Ser.). (ENG.). 240p. 35.00 *(978-1-60623-300-9(9))*, Guilford Pubns., Inc.

Richards, Jill. Classroom Language: What Sort (Rle Edu O) 2012. (Routledge Library Editions: Education Ser.). (ENG.). 160p. 100.00 ***(978-0-415-68984-7(8))*** Routledge.

Roberts, Anthony David. The Role of Metalinguistic Awareness in the Effective Teaching of Foreign Languages. 2011. (Rethinking Education Ser.). (Illus.). 417p. pap. 82.95 ***(978-3-0343-0280-7(0))*** Lang, Peter AG GBR. Dist: Lang, Peter.

Roskos, Kathleen A., et al. Oral Language & Early Literacy in Preschool: Talking, Reading, & Writing. 2nd ed. 2009. (ENG.). 144p. pap. 19.95 *(978-0-87207-693-8(8))* International Reading Assn.

Saxton, Matthew. Child Language: Acquisition & Development. 2010. (Illus.). 344p. (C). 112.00 *(978-1-4129-0231-1(2))*, B02312C); pap. 56.00 *(978-1-4129-0232-8(0))*, B02312P) SAGE Pubns., Ltd. GBR. Dist: SAGE Pubns., Inc.

Schaerlaekens, A. M. The Two-Word Sentence in Child Language Development: A Study Based on Evidence Provided by Dutch-speaking Triplets. (Janua Linguarum. Series Maior Ser.). (ENG.). 196p. 210.00 ***(978-3-11-186987-2(3))*** De Gruyter, Mouton DEU. Dist: de Gruyter, Walter GmbH & Co. KG.

Schlemmer, Phil & Schlemmer, Dori. Teaching Kids to Be Confident, Effective Communicators: Differentiated Projects to Get All Students Writing, Speaking, & Presenting. rev. ed. 2011. (ENG.). 240p. (gr. k-6). 35.99 *(978-1-57542-371-5(5))* Free Spirit Publishing, Inc.

Slama-Cazacu, Tatiana. Dialogue in Children. (Janua Linguarum. Series Minor Ser.). (ENG.). 157p. 210.00 ***(978-3-11-175207-5(0))*** De Gruyter, Mouton DEU. Dist: de Gruyter, Walter GmbH & Co. KG.

Smith, Neilson V. The Acquisition of Phonology: A Case Study. 2010. (ENG.). 284p. pap. 24.99 *(978-0-521-13433-0(1))* Cambridge Univ. Pr.

Spector, Cecile Cyrul. Sounds Like Fun: Activities for Developing Phonological Awareness, Revised Edition. 2009. 128p. 29.95 *(978-1-59857-049-9(X))* Brookes, Paul H. Publishing Co.

Steiner, Erich. A Functional Perspective on Language, Action, & Interpretation: An Initial Approach with a View to Computational Modeling. (Natural Language Processing Ser.). (ENG.). VII, 289p. 196.00 ***(978-3-11-178713-8(3))*** De Gruyter, Mouton DEU. Dist: de Gruyter, Walter GmbH & Co. KG.

Sugarman, Susan. Children's Early Thought: Developments in Classification. 2011. (ENG., Illus.). 248p. pap. 31.99 *(978-0-521-17631-6(X))* Cambridge Univ. Pr.

Tanz, Christine. Studies in the Acquisition of Deictic Terms. 2009. (Cambridge Studies in Linguistics Ser.). (ENG.). 196p. pap. 31.99 *(978-0-521-10323-7(1))* Cambridge Univ. Pr.

Tough, Joan. The Development of Meaning (Rle Edu I) 2012. (Routledge Library Editions: Education Ser.). (ENG.). 216p. 115.00 ***(978-0-415-69485-8(X))*** Routledge.

Vukelich, Carol, et al. Helping Young Children Learn Language & Literacy: Birth Through Kindergarten. 3rd ed. 2011. (ENG., Illus.). 288p. (C). pap. 92.00 *(978-0-13-231636-1(6))* Allyn & Bacon, Inc.

Wall, Carol. Predication: A Study of its Development. (Janua Linguarum. Series Minor Ser.). (ENG.). 258p. 210.00 ***(978-3-11-174877-1(4))*** De Gruyter, Mouton DEU. Dist: de Gruyter, Walter GmbH & Co. KG.

Wang, Yalien. Explorations in the Development of Young Children's Speech Act of Threatening in Mandarin Chinese. 2008. 120p. pap. *(978-3-639-00302-4(0))* VDM Verlag Dr. Mueller e.K.

Ward, Robert. Natural Language, Computer-Assisted Learning & Language-Impaired Children. 2010. 368p. pap. 37.95 *(978-1-4452-7751-6(4))* Lulu Enterprises Inc.

Watts, A. F. Language & Mental Development of Child. 2006. 356p. per. *(978-1-4067-3333-4(4),* Hesperides Pr.) Read Bks.

Wells, Gordon. The Meaning Makers: Learning to Talk & Talking to Learn. 2nd ed. 2009. (New Perspectives on Language & Education Ser.). (ENG., Illus.). 344p. 29.95 *(978-1-84769-198-9(6));* 119.95 *(978-1-84769-199-6(4))* Multilingual Matters GBR. Dist: Univ. of Toronto Pr.

Wells Lindfors, Judith. Children's Language: Connecting Reading, Writing, & Talk. 2008. (Language & Literacy Ser.). (ENG., Illus.). 144p. 56.00 *(978-0-8077-4886-2(2));* pap. 23.95 *(978-0-8077-4885-5(4))* Teachers College Pr., Teachers College, Columbia Univ.

Willes, Mary. Children into Pupils (Rle Edu I) 2012. (Routledge Library Editions: Education Ser.). (ENG.). 220p. 115.00 ***(978-0-415-69429-2(9))*** Routledge.

Wintergerst, Ann C. & McVeigh, Joe. Tips for Teaching Culture: Practical Approaches to Intercultural Communication. 2010. (ENG., Illus.). 232p. (C). pap. 49.47 *(978-0-13-245822-1(5))* Prentice Hall, ESL Dept.

CHILDREN—LEGAL STATUS, LAWS, ETC.

see also Adoption; Children's Rights; Custody of Children; Guardian and Ward; Illegitimacy; Juvenile Courts; Juvenile Delinquency; Legal Assistance to Children; Parent and Child (Law); Stepchildren

ABA Center on Children and the Law Staff & Center for Children, Law & Policy Staff, contrib. by. Children, Law, & Disasters: What Have We Learned from the Hurricanes of 2005? 2008. *(978-1-60442-249-8(1))* American Bar Assn.

Abrams, et al. Children & the Law: Doctrine, Policy & Practice, 4th. 4th rev. ed. 2010. 1242p. 183.00 *(978-0-314-90576-5(6),* West Legalworks) West.

Abrams, Douglas E. & Ramsey, Sarah H. Children & the Law: Doctrine, Policy, & Practice. 3rd rev. ed. 2007. (American Casebook Ser.). 1196p. 142.00 *(978-0-314-16951-8(2),* West Legalworks) West.

—Children & the Law: Doctrine, Policy, & Practice. 3rd ed. 2007. xlix, 1196p. pap. *(978-0-314-16950-1(4))* 4th ed. 2010. xlvi, 1192p. *(978-0-314-20722-7(8))* West Publishing Co., College & Schl. Div.

Abramson, Bruce. Article 2: Non-Discrimination. 2008. (Commentary on the United Nations Convention on the Rights of the Child Ser.). 100p. (C). pap. *(978-90-04-14917-5(1))* BRILL.

Abril Stoffels, Ruth & Stoffels, Ruth María Abril. La Protección de Los Niños en Los Conflictos Armados. 2007. (SPA.). 126p. *(978-84-8456-656-4(0))* Tirant lo Blanch.

Achilihu, Stephen Nmeregini. Do African Children Have Rights? A Comparative & Legal Analysis of the United Nations Convention on the Rights of the Child. 2010. 280p. pap. 25.95 *(978-1-59942-853-6(9))* Universal Pubs.

Adroher Biosca, Salomé, et al. Infancia en España: Nuevos Desafíos Sociales, Nuevas Respuestas Jurídicas. 2009. (SPA., Illus.). 589p. *(978-84-8468-259-2(5))* Universidad Pontificia Comillas de Madrid.

Agaltsova, Marina. Elimination of Child Labor. 2010. 100p. pap. *(978-3-8383-8313-2(3))* Lambert Academic Publishing.

Alen, Andre, et al, eds. The UN Children's Rights Convention Vol. 1: Theory Meets Practice. 2007. (Illus.). 658p. pap. 154.00 *(978-90-5095-640-6(8))* Intersentia Uitgevers N.V. BEL. Dist: International Specialized Bk. Services.

Ali, Shaheen Sardar, et al. Protecting the World's Children: Impact of the Convention on the Rights of the Child in Diverse Legal Systems. 2008. (ENG.). 286p. pap. 29.00 *(978-0-521-73291-8(3))* Cambridge Univ. Pr.

Alschuler, Joan N. The Guardian Ad Litem Handbook. 3rd ed. 2007. *(978-1-57862-182-8(8))* State Bar of Wisconsin.

Arthur, Raymond. Family Life & Youth Offending: Home Is Where the Hurt Is. (Routledge Advances in Criminology Ser.). (ENG.). 240p. (C). 2012. pap. 42.95 ***(978-0-415-51454-5(1))*** 2006. (Illus.). 180.00 *(978-0-415-40844-8(X))* Routledge.

Atwood, Barbara Ann. Children, Tribes, & States: Adoption & Custody Conflicts over American Indian Children. 2010. pap. 42.00 *(978-1-59460-522-2(X))* Carolina Academic Pr.

Bainham, Andrew. Parents & Children. 2008. (Family, Law & Society Ser.). 638p. 350.00 *(978-0-7546-2645-9(8))* Ashgate Publishing Co.

Bajpai, Asha. Child Rights in India: Law, Policy, & Practice. 2nd ed. 2006. (ENG., Illus.). 496p. pap. 42.00 *(978-0-19-567082-0(5))* Oxford Univ. Pr., Inc.

Balboni, Jennifer M. Clergy Sexual Abuse Litigation: Survivors Seeking Justice. 2011. 170p. 59.95 *(978-1-935049-37-1(2))* FirstForumPress.

Bazley, Janet, et al. Applications under Schedule 1 of the Children Act 1989. 2010. (ENG., Illus.). 392p. pap. *(978-1-84661-214-5(4))* Jordan Publishing, Ltd.

Bedingfield, David. Child in Need. 2nd rev. ed. 2010. 500p. pap. 120.00 *(978-1-84661-027-1(3))* Jordan Publishing, Ltd. GBR. Dist: International Specialized Bk. Services.

Blane, Mark C. Justice for the Injured Child: A Parent's Complete Legal Survival Guide for Their Child's California Injury Case. 2011. 176p. 29.99 ***(978-1-4583-9674-7(6))*** Lulu Enterprises Inc.

Boezaart, Trynie. Child Law in South Africa. 2010. 772p. pap. 74.50 *(978-0-7021-8212-9(5))* Gaunt, Inc.

Bottoms, Bette L., et al, eds. Children as Victims, Witnesses, & Offenders: Psychological Science & the Law. 2009. (ENG.). 412p. 50.00 *(978-1-60623-332-0(7))* Guilford Pubns., Inc.

Brewer, Holly. By Birth or Consent: Children, Law, & the Anglo-American Revolution in Authority. 2007. (Published for the Omohundro Institute of Early American History & Culture, Williamsburg, Virginia Ser.). (ENG., Illus.). 408p. per. 27.95 *(978-0-8078-5832-5(3))* Univ. of North Carolina Pr.

Bridgeman, Jo. Parental Responsibility, Young Children & Healthcare Law. 2007. (ENG.). 282p. 115.00 *(978-0-521-86312-4(0))* Cambridge Univ. Pr.

Brookfield, Tarah. Cold War Comforts: Canadian Women, Child Safety, & Global Insecurity. 2012. (Studies in Childhood & Family in Canada Ser.). (ENG., Illus.). 270p. (C). pap. 39.95 ***(978-1-55458-623-3(2))*** Wilfrid Laurier Univ. Pr. CAN. Dist: Univ. of Toronto Pr.

Buck, Trevor. International Child Law. 2nd rev. ed. 2010. (ENG., Illus.). 376p. (C). 69.95 *(978-0-415-48717-7(X));* 180.00 *(978-0-415-48716-0(1))* Taylor & Francis Group GBR. (Routledge). Dist: Taylor & Francis Group.

Butler, Clark W., ed. Child Rights: The Movement, International Law, & Opposition. 2012. (ENG.). 260p. pap. 35.00 *(978-1-55753-549-8(3))* Purdue Univ. Pr.

Butler, Ian & Drakeford, Mark. Social Work on Trial: The Colwell Inquiry & the State of Welfare. 2011. 248p. 110.00 *(978-1-84742-868-4(1))* Policy Pr. GBR. Dist: Chicago Distribution Ctr.

Cantwell, Nigel & Holzscheiter, Anna. A Commentary on the United Nations Convention on the Rights of the Child, Article 20: Children Without Parental Care. 2007. (Commentary on the United Nations Convention on the Rights of the Child Ser.). 51p. pap. *(978-90-04-14873-4(6))* BRILL.

Carter, Samuel. The Infants Lawyer, or, the Law (Ancient & Modern) Relating to Infants. 2007. 431p. 135.00 *(978-1-58477-833-2(4))* Lawbook Exchange, Ltd., The.

Casualties of War: Child Soldiers & the Law: Hearing Before the Subcommittee on Human Rights & the Law of the Committee on the Judiciary, United States Senate, One Hundred Tenth Congress, First Session, April 24, 2007. 2007. iii, 105p. *(978-0-16-079848-1(5),* 552-070-36742-0) United States Government Printing Office.

Chadwick, David L. The Child Abuse Doctors. 2010. (Illus.). 192p. lib. bdg. 35.00 *(978-1-878060-69-3(4))* STM Learning, Inc.

Chan, Edward Ko Ling, ed. Child Protection in Chinese Societies: Challenges & Policies. 2012. ***(978-1-61942-879-9(2))*** Nova Science Pubs., Inc.

Child Labor Enforcement: Are We Adequately Protecting Our Children?: Hearing Before the Subcommittee on Workforce Protections, Committee on Education & Labor, U.S. House of Representatives, One Hundred Tenth Congress, Second Session, Hearing Held in Washington, DC, September 23, 2008. 2008. iii, 34p. *(978-0-16-082280-3(7),* 552-070-38344-1) United States Government Printing Office.

Child Soldiers Accountability ACT of 2007: Hearing Before the Subcommittee on Crime, Terrorism, & Homeland Security of the Committee on the Judiciary, House of Representatives, One Hundred Tenth Congress, Second Session, on S. 2135, April 8, 2008. 2008. (Illus.). iii, 186p. *(978-0-16-082522-4(9),* 552-070-38557-6) United States Government Printing Office.

Children, Families & the State, 2001. rev. ed. *(978-1-57589-201-6(4))* Massachusetts Continuing Legal Education, Inc.

Cipriani, Don. Children's Rights & the Minimum Age of Criminal Responsibility: A Global Perspective. 2009. (Advances in Criminology Ser.). (Illus.). 252p. 124.95 *(978-0-7546-7730-7(3))* Ashgate Publishing Co.

Cobley, Cathy & Sanders, Tom, eds. Non-Accidental Head Injury in Young Children: Medical, Legal & Social Responses. 2006. (ENG., Illus.). 192p. per. *(978-1-84310-360-8(5))* Kingsley, Jessica Ltd.

Cotter, Anne-Marie Mooney. Little Angels: An International Legal Perspective on Child Discrimination. 2012. 320p. 124.95 ***(978-1-4094-2980-7(6))*** Ashgate Publishing Co.

Crabbere, Edina Dookie. Bill of Rights. Crabberg, Edna Dookie, ed. (Illus.). (C). spiral bd. *(978-0-9667830-6-3(9))* Early Learning Institute.

Davel, C. J. & Skelton, A. M., eds. Commentary on the Children's Act. 2007. 110.00 *(978-0-7021-7883-2(7))* Juta & Co., Ltd. ZAF. Dist: Gaunt, Inc.

D'Aversa, Carmina Y. Tax, Estate, & Lifetime Planning for Minors. 2006. (ENG., Illus.). xi, 371p. pap. 139.95 incl. lp *(978-1-59031-683-2(5))* American Bar Assn.

David, Paulo. The Right to Leisure, Play & Culture: Article 31. 2006. (Commentary on the United Nations Convention on the Rights of the Child Ser.). 33p. pap. *(978-90-04-14882-6(5))* BRILL.

Davidson, Julia & Hamerton, Christopher. International Perspectives on Child Victimisation. 2012. (ENG.). 208p. 125.00 *(978-0-415-57957-5(0))* Routledge.

Davis, Lynn. The Social Worker's Guide to Children & Families Law. 2008. (ENG.). 240p. pap. *(978-1-84310-653-1(1))* Kingsley, Jessica Ltd.

Davis, Samuel M. Children in the Legal System: Cases & Materials. 4th ed. 2009. (University Casebook Ser.). xiv, 1233p. pap. *(978-1-59941-624-3(7))* West.

—Children's Rights under & the Law. 2011. (ENG.). 474p. 95.00 *(978-0-19-979548-2(7))* Oxford Univ. Pr., Inc.

De Boyser, Katrien, et al, eds. Why Care? Children's Rights & Child Poverty. 2010. 209p. pap. 54.75 *(978-94-000-0025-4(1))* Intersentia Uitgevers N.V. BEL. Dist: International Specialized Bk. Services.

Devon, Raymond T., ed. Working with the Courts in Child Protection. 2010. (Children's Issues, Laws & Programs Ser.). (Illus.). 185p. 69.00 *(978-1-61668-303-0(1))* Nova Science Pubs., Inc.

Doek, Jaap. Commentary on the United Nations Convention on the Rights of the Child , Volume 8 Articles 8-9: The Right to Preservation of Identity & the Right Not to Be Separated from His or Her Parents. 2006. (Commentary on the United Nations Convention on the Rights of the Child Ser.). xiv, 34p. *(978-90-04-14864-2(7))* BRILL.

Du Preez, Nicolien & Luyt, Willem. Fundamentals & Developmental Psychology in Youth Corrections: Second Edition. 2nd ed. 2011. 266p. pap. 25.00 *(978-1-86888-603-6(4))* Unisa Press / Uitgewers GBR. Dist: International Specialized Bk. Services.

Duquette, Donald N. & Haralambie, Ann M. Child Welfare Law & Practice: Representing Children, Parents, & State Agencies in Abuse, Neglect, & Dependency Cases. 2nd ed. 2010. *(978-1-932779-96-7(5))* Bradford Publishing Co.

Dwyer, James G. The Relationship Rights of Children. 2011. (ENG.). 380p. pap. 50.00 ***(978-1-107-40233-1(6))*** Cambridge Univ. Pr.

Effertz, Tobias. Kindermarketing: Analyse und rechtliche Empfehlungen. 2008. (Schriftenreihe Ökonomische Analyse des Rechts. Law & Economics Ser.). 596p. pap. 124.95 *(978-3-631-57849-0(0))* Lang, Peter GmbH, Europaischer Verlag der Wissenschaften DEU. Dist: Lang, Peter.

Eide, Asbjo. Commentary on the United Nations Convention on the Rights of the Child , Volume 27 Article 27: The Right to an Adequate Standard of Living. 2006. 30p. pap. *(978-90-04-14878-9(7))* BRILL.

Eliminating Violence against Children: A Handbook for Parliamentarians. 2007. 84p. *(978-92-806-4158-5(1))* United Nations Children's Fund, The (UNICEF).

Eliminating Violence against Children: Handbook of Korean parliamentarians to deal with VAC. 2007. (KOR.). 84p. *(978-92-806-4170-7(0))* United Nations Children's Fund, The (UNICEF).

Elliston, Sarah. Best Interests of the Child in Healthcare. 2006. (Biomedical Law & Ethics Library). 328p. 200.00 *(978-1-84472-043-9(8),* Routledge) Taylor & Francis Group GBR. Dist: Taylor & Francis Group.

—The Best Interests of the Child in Healthcare. 2007. (Biomedical Law & Ethics Library). 308p. per. 57.50 *(978-1-84472-042-2(X),* Routledge) Taylor & Francis Group GBR. Dist: Taylor & Francis Group.

Epstein, Irving, ed. The Greenwood Encyclopedia of Children's Issues Worldwide, 6 vols. 2007. (Illus.). 3048p. 599.95 *(978-0-313-33614-0(8),* GR3614, Greenwood Pr.) Greenwood Publishing Group, Inc.

Erichsen, Hans-Uwe. Verstaatlichung der Kindeswohlentscheidung? Zur verfassungsrechtlichen Bestimmung des schulischen Erziehungsrechts; Vortrag gehalten vor der Berliner Juristischen Gesellschaft am 27. September 1978. (Schriftenreihe der Juristischen Gesellschaft zu Berlin Ser.). (GER., Illus.). 27p. 135.00 ***(978-3-11-007951-7(8))*** De Gruyter, Walter Inc.

Farmer, Elaine & Moyers, Sue. Kinship Care: Fostering Effective Family & Friends Placements. 2008. (Quality Matters in Children's Services Ser.). (ENG.). 288p. (C). pap. *(978-1-84310-631-9(0))* Kingsley, Jessica Ltd.

Fellmeth, Robert C. Child Rights & Remedies. 3rd enl. ed. 2011. (ENG.). 840p. pap. 49.95 ***(978-0-9833539-1-1(3))*** Clarity Pr., Inc.

Feria Tinta, Mónica. The Landmark Rulings of the Inter-American Court of Human Rights on the Rights of the Child: Protecting the Most Vulnerable at the Edge. 2008. (International Studies in Human Rights Ser.). 692p. *(978-90-04-16513-7(4))* BRILL.

Fernández Molina, Esther & Molina, Esther Fernández. Entre la Educación y el Castigo: Una Análisis de la Justicia de Menores en España. 2008. (SPA.). 430p. *(978-84-9876-002-6(X))* Tirant lo Blanch.

Ferreira, Nuno. Fundamental Rights & Tort Law in the European Union: The Case of Children's Liability in Tort. 2011. (ENG., Illus.). 304p. (C). 150.00 *(978-0-415-57945-2(7))* Routledge.

Fineman, Martha & Worthington, Karen. What Is Right for Children? The Competing Paradigms of Religion & Human Rights. 2009. 462p. 124.95 *(978-0-7546-7419-1(3))* Ashgate Publishing Co.

Flannery, James L. The Glass House Boys of Pittsburgh: Law, Technology, & Child Labor. 2009. (ENG., Illus.). 240p. (C). 35.00 *(978-0-8229-4377-8(8))* Univ. of Pittsburgh Pr.

Fortin, Jane. Children's Rights & the Developing Law. 3rd rev. ed. 2009. (Law in Context Ser.). (ENG.). 878p. (C). pap. 103.00 *(978-0-521-69801-6(4))* Cambridge Univ. Pr.

Freeman, Michael, ed. Law & Childhood Studies: Current Legal Issues Volume 14. 2012. (ENG., Illus.). 450p. 170.00 ***(978-0-19-965250-1(3))*** Oxford Univ. Pr., Inc.

Freeman, Michael A. A Commentary on the United Nations Convention on the Rights of the Child: Article 3: the Best Interests of the Child. 2007. (Commentary on the United Nations Convention on the Rights of the Child Ser.: Vol. 3). 79p. pap. *(978-90-04-14861-1(2))* BRILL.

Freeman, Michael D. A. Children's Rights: Progress & Perspectives: Essays from the International Journal of Children's Rights. 2011. 525p. *(978-90-04-19049-8(X))* BRILL.

Friedberg, Fredric J. Turning Eighteen & the Law: A Complete Guide to your New Rights & Responsibilities. 2010. (Illus.). 128p. pap. 24.99 *(978-0-7643-3608-9(8))* Schiffer Publishing, Ltd.

Gardner, Martin R. Understanding Juvenile Law. 3rd ed. 2009. pap. *(978-1-4224-2955-6(5))* LexisNexis Matthew Bender.

Goldrein. Child Case Management Practice. 2009. 858p. pap. 194.00 *(978-1-84661-031-8(1))* Jordan Publishing, Ltd. GBR. Dist: International Specialized Bk. Services.

Gondolf, Yvonne. Die Vormundschaft und Pflegschaft für Minderjährige: Ist eine Reform notwendig und wie sollte sie Aussehen? 2008. (Familienrechtliche Untersuchungen Ser.). 252p. pap. 65.95 *(978-3-631-57455-3(X))* Lang, Peter GmbH, Europaischer Verlag der Wissenschaften DEU. Dist: Lang, Peter.

Gore, Sally. Children Act 1989: Local Authority Support for Children & Families. 2011. (ENG., Illus.). 304p. pap. *(978-1-84661-248-0(9))* Jordan Publishing, Ltd.

Grossman, Joanna L. & Friedman, Lawrence Meir. Inside the Castle: Law & the Family in 20th Century America. 2011. (ENG.). 448p. (C). 35.00 *(978-0-691-14982-0(8))* Princeton Univ. Pr.

Guggenheim, Martin. What's Wrong with Children's Rights. 2007. (Illus.). 320p. pap. 22.50 *(978-0-674-02546-2(6))* Harvard Univ. Pr.

Gultom, Maidin. Perlindungan Hukum Terhadap Anak Dalam Sistem Peradilan Pidana Anak Di Indonesia. 2008. (IND.). ix, 170p. *(978-979-1073-56-1(2))* Refika Aditama.

Hame, Lynne. Violent Fathering & the Risks to Children: The Need for Change. 2011. (Illus.). 216p. 85.00 *(978-1-84742-917-9(3))* Policy Pr. GBR. Dist: Chicago Distribution Ctr.

Harris, P. Instructing Expert Witnesses in Children Cases. 2010. pap. 80.00 *(978-0-85308-872-1(1))* Jordan Publishing, Ltd. GBR. Dist: International Specialized Bk. Services.

Harris-Short, Sonia. Aboriginal Child Welfare Self-Government & the Rights of Indigenous Children: Protecting the Vulnerable under International Law. 2012. 342p. 124.95 ***(978-1-4094-1954-9(1))*** Ashgate Publishing Co.

Hartson, John & Payne, Brenda. Creating Effective Parenting Plans: A Developmental Approach for Lawyers & Divorce Professionals. 2006. (ENG., Illus.). 237p. pap. 64.95 incl. lp *(978-1-59031-610-8(X))* American Bar Assn.

Hearing on the Implementation of the Fostering Connections to Success & Increasing Adoptions ACT: Hearing Before the Subcommittee on Income Security & Family Support of the Committee on Ways & Means, U.S. House of Representatives, One Hundred Eleventh Congress, First Session, September 15, 2009. 2010. (Illus.). iii, 103p. *(978-0-16-085205-3(6),* 552-070-40558-5) United States Government Printing Office.

Herring, David J. Everyday Law for Children. 2007. (Everyday Law Ser.). (ENG.). 256p. per. 39.95 *(978-1-59451-252-0(3))* Paradigm Pubs.

Hilwig, E. & Tofan, C., eds. Children's Rights: Selected Documents, 2 vols. 2008. 1500p. 250.00 *(978-90-5887-005-6(7))* Gaunt, Inc.

Hoyano, Laura & Keenan, Caroline. Child Abuse: Law & Policy Across Boundaries. 2010. 1,080p. pap. 99.00 *(978-0-19-957156-7(2))* Oxford Univ. Pr., Inc.

H.R. 5504: Improving Nutrition for America's Children ACT: Hearing Before the Committee on Education & Labor, U.S. House of Representatives, One Hundred Eleventh Congress, Second Session, Hearing Held in Washington, DC, July 1, 2010. 2010. (Illus.). iii, 126p. ***(978-0-16-087135-1(2),*** 552-070-41980-2) United States Government Printing Office.

Improving the Child Welfare System: Hearing Before the Subcommittee on Income Security & Family Support of the Committee on Ways & Means, U.S. House of Representatives, One Hundred Tenth Congress, Second Session, February 27, 2008. 2009. iii, 185p. *(978-0-16-082947-5(X),* 552-070-38859-1) United States Government Printing Office.

Innocenti Research Centre. General Comments of the Committee on the Rights of the Child. 2010. (FRE.). 76p. pap. 25.00 *(978-88-89129-40-1(9))* United Nations Children's Fund, The (UNICEF).

Ito, Shuhei. Hoiku Seido Kaikaku to Jido Fukushiho No Yukue. 2010. (JPN., Illus.). 207p. *(978-4-7803-0336-0(2))* Kamogawa Shuppan.

It's time to listen to Us! Youth response to the Report of the Expert Group Meeting on the Elimination of all forms of discrimination & violence against the girl Child. 2007. 28p. (FRE.). *(978-92-806-4142-4(5)); (978-92-806-4141-7(7))* United Nations Children's Fund, The (UNICEF).

Jolly, Richard. UNICEF (United Nations Children's Fund) 2011. (Global Institutions Ser.). (ENG.). 176p. 27.95 *(978-0-415-49117-4(7));* 125.00 *(978-0-415-49116-7(9))* Routledge.

Jones, B. J., et al. The Indian Child Welfare ACT Handbook: A Legal Guide to the Custody & Adoption of Native American Children. 2nd ed. 2008. (ENG.). pap. 79.95 incl. lp *(978-1-59031-858-4(7))* American Bar Assn.

Juta Staff. Juta Legislation Service Vol. 1: Family Law Legislation I: Children. Date not set. ring bd. 37.50 *(978-0-7021-2276-7(9))* Juta & Co., Ltd. ZAF. Dist: Gaunt, Inc.

Kantrowitz, R. Marc, et al, eds. Massachusetts Juvenile Delinquency & Child Welfare Law Sourcebook & Citator 2007. 2007. pap. 125.00 *(978-1-57589-440-9(8))* Massachusetts Continuing Legal Education, Inc.

Kauble, Phil, ed. California Laws Relating to Minors. 2007. per. 46.95 *(978-1-933408-10-1(3))* LBD Pubs.

Kauble, Phil D. California Laws Relating to Minors. 2009. (ENG.). 885p. (C). pap. 48.95 *(978-1-933408-17-0(0))* LBD Pubs.

Kay, Janet. Protecting Children. pap. *(978-0-8264-5802-5(5))* Continuum International Publishing Group, Ltd.

Kedrowski, Karen M. & Lipscomb, Michael E. Breastfeeding Rights in the United States, 1 vol. 2007. (Reproductive Rights & Policy Ser.). (Illus.). 192p. 44.95

(978-0-275-99136-4(9), C9136, Praeger Pubs.) Greenwood Publishing Group, Inc.

Kilbourne, Susan. Children Behind Bars: Youth Who Are Detained, Incarcerated & Executed. Barnitz, Laura A., ed. Date not set. 42p. pap. 6.00 *(978-0-9663709-5-9(3))* Youth Advocate Program International.

Kilkelly, Ursula. Children's Rights in Ireland: Law, Policy & Practice. 2008. 601p. 240.00 *(978-1-84592-157-6(7),* Bloomsbury Professional) Bloomsbury Publishing Plc GBR. Dist: International Specialized Bk. Services.

Klain, Eva J. & Sandt, Claire. Healthy Beginnings, Healthy Futures: A Judge's Guide. 2009. *(978-1-60442-611-3(X))* American Bar Assn.

Kruger, Marie E. & Spies, G. M. The Recognition & Protection of Children S Rights. 2008. 492p. per. *(978-3-8364-3428-7(8))* VDM Verlag Dr. Mueller e.K.

Kumari, Ved. The Juvenile Justice System in India: From Welfare to Rights. 2nd ed. 2011. (ENG.). 440p. 40.00 *(978-0-19-806577-7(9))* Oxford Univ. Pr., Inc.

Langely, Terrance R., ed. Child Protection, the Courts & Social Workers. 2010. (Children's Issues, Laws & Programs Ser.). (Illus.). 356p. 195.00 *(978-1-60741-279-3(9))* Nova Science Pubs., Inc.

Laver, Mimi & Khoury, Andrea. Opening Doors for LGBTQ Youth in Foster Care: A Guide for Lawyers & Judges. 2008. pap. *(978-1-60442-073-9(1))* American Bar Assn.

Lewis, Browne. The Inheritance Rights of Children in the United States: Cases & Materials. 2010. 342p. pap. 40.00 *(978-1-59460-457-7(6))* Carolina Academic Pr.

Lievens, Eva. Protecting Children in the Digital Era: The Use of Alternative Regulatory Instruments. 2010. (International Studies in Human Rights Ser.). 330p. *(978-90-04-18477-0(5))* BRILL.

Liu, Huawen. Er Tong Quan Li Yu Fa Lü Bao Hu: Rights of the Child & Legal Protection. 2009. (CHI., Illus.). *(978-7-208-08744-6(X))* Shanghai People's Publishing Hse.

Looseleaf Law Publications, suppl. Legal References for Child Wellfare Cases. 2010. 160p. pap. 9.95 *(978-1-932777-61-1(X),* LLP) Looseleaf Law Pubns., Inc.

Lucero, Killian. Federal Programs for Troubled Youth. 2009. (Children's Issues, Laws & Programs Ser.). (Illus.). 263p. 79.00 *(978-1-60692-318-4(8))* Nova Science Pubs., Inc.

Lund, Therese Roe & Renne, Jennifer L. Child Safety: A Guide for Judges & Attorneys. 2009. *(978-1-59031-914-7(1))* American Bar Assn.

MacDonald, Alistair. Rights of the Child: The Law & Practice. 2011. (ENG.). 1232p. *(978-1-84661-210-7(1))* Jordan Publishing, Ltd.

Manful, Esmeranda. The Development of Children's Rights in Africa & Europe: Comparing Legislation in Ghana & Northern Ireland. 2010. (Illus.). xi, 355p. 119.95 *(978-0-7734-3746-3(0))* Mellen, Edwin Pr., The.

Mangion, Ann Marie. Competency & Best Interests of the Child Relating to Health Issues. 2010. 180p. pap. *(978-3-639-23252-3(6))* VDM Verlag Dr. Mueller e.K.

Marrus, Ellen & Rosenberg, Irene Merker. Children & Juvenile Justice. 2007. (Carolina Academic Press Law Casebook Ser.). 594p. 65.00 *(978-1-59460-062-3(7))* Carolina Academic Pr.

Marsh, Toni. Juvenile Law. 2006. (ENG., Illus.). 304p. (C). per. 73.95 *(978-1-4018-4019-8(1))* Delmar Cengage Learning.

Martín-Casals, Miquel, ed. Children in Tort Law, Pts. 1&2. 2007. (Tort & Insurance Law Ser.). (Illus.). XIX, 796p. 239.00 *(978-3-211-32211-6(6),* 3211322116) Springer.

—Children in Tort Law Pt. 2: Children As Victims. 2006. (Tort & Insurance Law Ser.). (Illus.). x, 320p. pap. 149.00 *(978-3-211-31130-1(0),* 3211311300) Springer.

Masson, Judith. Protecting Powers: Emergency Intervention for Children's Protection. 2007. (Wiley Child Protection & Policy Ser.: 13). (ENG., Illus.). 260p. 159.95 *(978-0-470-01602-2(7))*; per. 59.95 *(978-0-470-01603-9(5))* Wiley, John & Sons, Inc. (Wiley).

Mcfarlane, Andrew. Hershman & Mcfarlane Children Act Handbook 2011/2012. 2011. (ENG.). 772p. pap. ***(978-1-84661-285-5(3))*** Jordan Publishing, Ltd.

McWhirter, Robert James. The Citizenship Flowchart & Boxnotes. 2007. *(978-1-59031-921-5(4))* American Bar Assn.

Mitchell, John. Child Law: Essential Court Materials. 2010. (ENG.). 200p. pap. *(978-1-84661-230-5(6))* Jordan Publishing, Ltd.

—Children Act Prvate Law Proceedings: A Handbook. 3rd rev. ed. 2012. (ENG.). 600p. pap. *(978-1-84661-238-1(1))* Jordan Publishing, Ltd.

Mitchels, Barbara & James, Helen. Child Care & Protection: Law & Practice, Vol. 1. 4th rev. ed. 2009. (Illus.). 189p. pap. 48.50 *(978-0-85490-038-1(1))* Gaunt, Inc.

Mnookin, Robert H. Child Family & State: Problems & Materials on Children & the Law. 6th rev. ed. 2009. xxxv, 915p. 149.00 *(978-0-7355-7926-2(1))* Wolters Kluwer Law & Business.

Montgomery, Heather & Kellett, Mary, eds. Children & Young People's Worlds: Developing Frameworks for Integrated Practice. 2009. 272p. 85.00 *(978-1-84742-388-7(4))* Policy Pr. GBR. Dist: Chicago Distribution Ctr.

—Children's & Young People's Worlds: Developing Frameworks for Integrated Practice. 2009. 272p. pap. 32.95 *(978-1-84742-387-0(6))* Policy Pr. GBR. Dist: Chicago Distribution Ctr.

Mullally, Maureen. Law & the Family in the UK. 2nd ed. 2007. 192p. pap. 17.00 *(978-1-901657-53-1(1))* Blackhall Publishing IRL. Dist: Gaunt, Inc.

Muntarbhorn, Vitt. Sexual Exploitation & Sexual Abuse of Children. Alen, André et al, eds. 2006. (Commentary on the United Nations Convention on the Rights of the Child Ser.). (FRE & ENG.). 41p. pap. *(978-90-04-14884-0(1))* BRILL.

Muratbekova, S. M. Mekhanizm Realizatsii Konstitutsionnykh Garantii Prav I Zakonnykh Interesov Nesovershennoletnikh V Kyrgyzskoi Respublike. 2010. (RUS.). 213p. *(978-9967-08-199-4(6))* SAM, Publishing House, Izdatel'stvo.

National Association of Social Workers Staff, contrib. by. Legal Rights of Children. 2009. *(978-0-87101-396-5(7),* NASW Pr.) National Assn. of Social Workers/NASW Pr.

Native American Rights Fund. A Practical Guide to the Indian Child Welfare Act. 2007. pap. 20.00 net. *(978-0-9794099-1-2(8))* Native American Rights Fund.

Nolan, Aoife. Children's Socio-Economic Rights, Democracy & the Courts, 0 vols. 2011. (ENG.). 336p. 110.00 *(978-1-84113-769-8(3))* Hart Publishing Ltd. GBR. Dist: International Specialized Bk. Services.

Oliver, Christine M. & Dalrymple, Jane, eds. Developing Advocacy for Children & Young People: Current Issues in Research, Policy & Practice. 2008. 224p. pap. *(978-1-84310-596-1(9))* Kingsley, Jessica Ltd.

Pearl, David. Care Standards Legislation Handbook. 7th rev. ed. 2009. (ENG.). 808p. pap. *(978-1-84661-165-0(2))* Jordan Publishing, Ltd.

Pervall, Henry J. Child Abuse & Neglect: Aspects & Summaries of State Laws. 2011. (Children's Issues, Laws & Programs Ser.). 253p. 185.00 ***(978-1-62100-157-7(1))*** Nova Science Pubs., Inc.

Popovski, Vesselin & Arts, Karin, eds. International Criminal Accountability & the Rights of Children. 2006. (From Peace to Justice Ser.). (ENG.). 206p. 69.95 *(978-90-6704-227-7(7),* 9067042277) T.M.C. Asser Pr. NLD. Dist: Springer.

Prest, Charles & Wildblood, Stephen, eds. Family Law Case Library: Children. 2nd rev. ed. 2011. (ENG.). 800p. pap. incl. cd-rom *(978-1-84661-277-0(2))* Jordan Publishing, Ltd.

Qvortrup, Jens & Kjorholt, Anne-Trine, eds. The Modern Child & the Flexible Labour Market: Early Childhood Education & Care. 2011. (Studies in Childhood & Youth Ser.). (ENG., Illus.). 272p. (C). 85.00 *(978-0-230-57932-3(9))* Palgrave Macmillan.

Ramsey, Sarah H. & Abrams, Douglas E. Children & the Law. 3rd rev. ed. 2008. (Nutshell Ser.). 628p. 35.00 *(978-0-314-18451-1(1),* West Legalworks) West.

—Children & the Law in a Nutshell: 4th Edition. 4th rev. ed. 2011. (Nutshell Ser.). 690p. 38.00 *(978-0-314-26290-5(3),* West Legalworks) West.

Raposo, Miguel G. & Carroca, Danielle M., eds. Child Welfare: Federal Role in Assistance & Improvement. 2011. (Children's Issues, Laws & Programs Ser.). pap. 43.00 *(978-1-61209-704-6(9))* Nova Science Pubs., Inc.

Rathman, David. As Good As A Dog: The Custody Trial. 2011. 380p. pap. 17.33 *(978-1-4269-5804-5(8))* Trafford Publishing.

Robison, Susan. Delivering on the Promise: Promoting Court Capacity to Improve Outcomes for Abused & Neglected Children. 2007. (Illus.). 62p. *(978-1-58024-480-0(7))* National Conference of State Legislatures.

Rodríguez Arias, Miguel Ángel & Arias, Miguel Ángel Rodríguez. El Caso de Los Niños Perdidos Del Franquismo: Crimen Contra la Humanidad. 2008. (SPA.). 436p. *(978-84-9876-303-4(7))* Tirant lo Blanch.

Rodríguez, Pablo & Mannarelli, María Emma. Historia de la Infancia en América Latina. 2007. (SPA., Illus.). 673p. pap. 33.00 *(978-958-710-218-5(5))* Universidad Externado de Colombia COL. Dist: Siglo del Hombre.

Roman, Victor. Should Child Soldiers Be Punished for War Crimes? 2011. 76p. pap. ***(978-3-8454-1247-4(X))*** Lambert Academic Publishing.

Rosenwald, Mitchell & Riley, Beth N. Advocating for Children in Foster & Kinship Care: A Guide to Getting the Best out of the System for Caregivers & Practitioners. 2010. (ENG., Illus.). 272p. (gr. 17). 79.50 *(978-0-231-14686-9(8))* Columbia Univ. Pr.

Ross, Lainie Friedman. Children in Medical Research: Access versus Protection. 2008. (Issues in Biomedical Ethics Ser.). (ENG.). 280p. pap. 45.00 *(978-0-19-923042-6(0))* Oxford Univ. Pr., Inc.

Ryder, Justice & Goldrein, Iain, eds. Child Case Management Practice. 2nd rev. ed. 2012. (ENG.). 900p. pap. 250.00 *(978-1-84661-264-0(0))* Jordan Publishing, Ltd. GBR. Dist: International Specialized Bk. Services.

Sabatello, Maya. Children's Bioethics: The International Biopolitical Discourse on Harmful Traditional Practices & the Right of the Child to Cultural Identity. 2009. 250p. *(978-90-04-17341-5(2))* BRILL.

Schorlemer, Sabine von & Schulte-Herbrüggen, Elena, eds. 1989-2009: 20 Jahre Un-Kinderrechtskonvention: Erfahrungen und Perspektiven. 2010. (Dresdner Schriften zu Recht und Politik der Vereinten Nationen. Dresden Papers on Law & Policy of the United Nations Ser.). (GER.). 240p. 57.95 *(978-3-631-60253-9(7))* Lang, Peter GmbH, Europaischer Verlag der Wissenschaften DEU. Dist: Lang, Peter.

Schwartz Lita Linzer & Isser Natalie K. Child Homicide: Parents Who Kill. 2nd ed. 2006. (ENG., Illus.). 297p. 99.95 *(978-0-8493-9366-2(3),* CRC Press) Taylor & Francis Group GBR. Dist: Taylor & Francis Group.

Sheehan, Rosemary, et al, eds. Vulnerable Children & the Law: International Evidence for Improving Child Welfare, Child Protection & Children's Rights. 2012. (ENG., Illus.). 304p. pap. ***(978-1-84905-868-1(7))*** Kingsley, Jessica Ltd.

Shilling, Dana. Legal Issues of Dependent & Incapacitated People. 2007. *(978-1-887554-56-5(4))* Civic Research Institute, Inc.

Shultz, William J. Humane Movement in the United States, 1910-1922. (Columbia University, Studies in the Social Sciences: No. 252). reprint ed. 21.00 *(978-0-404-51252-1(6))* AMS Pr., Inc.

Silverstein, Helena. Girls on the Stand: How Courts Fail Pregnant Minors. 2009. (ENG.). 256p. pap. 23.00 *(978-0-8147-4073-6(1))* New York Univ. Pr.

Singel, Wenona T. & Fort, Kathryn E. Facing the Future: The Indian Child Welfare ACT at 30. Fletcher, Matthew L. M., ed. 2009. (American Indian Studies). (ENG.). 299p. pap. 39.95 *(978-0-87013-860-7(X))* Michigan State Univ. Pr.

Sloth-Nielsen, Julia & Toit, Zenobia du, eds. Trials & Tribulations, Trends & Triumphs: Developments in International, African & South African Child & Family Law. 2008. (Illus.). 288p. pap. 49.00 *(978-0-7021-7948-8(5))* Juta & Co., Ltd. ZAF. Dist: Gaunt, Inc.

Stalford, Helen. Children & the European Union: Rights, Welfare & Accountability. 2012. (ENG.). 326p. pap. 55.00 *(978-1-84113-765-0(0))* Hart Publishing Ltd. GBR. Dist: International Specialized Bk. Services.

Standing Committee on Childhood Obesity Prevention Staff & Institute of Medicine. Legal Strategies in Childhood Obesity Prevention: Workshop Summary. 2011. (ENG., Illus.). 104p. pap. 33.00 ***(978-0-309-21019-5(4))*** National Academies Pr.

Stein, Theodore J. Child Welfare & the Law. 3rd ed. 2007. 539p. per. *(978-1-58760-042-5(0),* CWLA Pr.) Child Welfare League of America, Inc.

Tanenhaus, David Spinoza. The Constitutional Rights of Children: In Re Gault & Juvenile Justice. 2011. xviii, 152p. 29.95 ***(978-0-7006-1813-2(9))***; pap. 16 95 ***(978-0-7006-1814-9(7))*** Univ. Pr. of Kansas.

Te One, Sarah. Perceptions of Children's Rights. 2010. 344p. pap. *(978-3-8383-4198-9(8))* Lambert Academic Publishing.

Thorgeirsdóttir, Herdís. Commentary on the United Nations Convention on the Rights of the Child , Volume 13 Article 13: The Right to Freedom of Expression. 2006. (Commentary on the United Nations Convention on the Rights of the Child Ser.). 30p. pap. *(978-90-04-14868-0(X))* BRILL.

Todd, David. Texas Child Injury Guide: What You Should Know Before You Call a Lawyer. 2009. 63p. pap. 14.95 *(978-0-557-14804-2(9))* Lulu Enterprises Inc.

Ton, Liefaard. Deprivation of Liberty of Children in Light of International Human Rights Law & Standards. 2008. 696p. pap. 124.75 *(978-90-5095-838-7(9))* Intersentia Uitgevers N.V. BEL. Dist: International Specialized Bk. Services.

Troller, Simone. Lost in Transit: Insufficient Protection for Unaccompanied Migrant Children at Roissy Charles de Gaulle Airport. 2009. (Illus.). 60p. ***(978-1-56432-557-0(1))*** Human Rights Watch.

UNICEF Staff. Implementation Handbook for the Convention on the Rights of the Child. 3rd rev. ed. 2007. (Illus.). 812p. 50.00 *(978-92-806-4183-7(2))* United Nations Children's Fund, The (UNICEF).

—Protecting the World's Children: Impact of the Convention on the Rights of the Child in Diverse Legal Systems. 2007. (ENG.). 288p. 79.00 *(978-0-521-87513-4(7))* Cambridge Univ. Pr.

UNICEF: Innocenti Research Centre. General comments of the Committee on the Rights of the Child. 2008. 90p. pap. 25.00 *(978-88-89129-51-7(4))* United Nations Children's Fund, The (UNICEF).

United Nations Children's Fund. Law Reform & the Implementation of the Convention on the Rights of the Child. 2009. 148p. pap. 25.00 *(978-88-89129-66-1(2))* United Nations Children's Fund, The (UNICEF).

United Nations, Office of the High Commissioner for Human Rights Staff, contrib. by. Legislative History of the Convention on the Rights of the Child, 2 vols. 2007. (ENG.). 1012p. pap. 50 00 *(978-92-1-154177-9(8))* United Nations Pubns.

Van Crombrugge, Hans, et al, eds. Shared Pedagogical Responsibility. 2008. 118p. pap. 40.75 *(978-90-5095-813-4(3))* Intersentia Uitgevers N.V. BEL. Dist: International Specialized Bk. Services.

Vandenhole, Wouter. Article 26: the Right to Benefit from Social Security. Alen, André et al, eds. 2007. (Commentary on the United Nations Convention on the Rights of the Child Ser.). 44p. per. *(978-90-04-14879-6(5))* BRILL.

Ventrell, Marvin R. Trial Advocacy for the Child Welfare Lawyer: Telling the Story of the Family. 2011. *(978-1-60156-149-7(0))* National Institute for Trial Advocacy.

Wabwile, Michael. Legal Protection of Social & Economic Rights of Children in Developing Countries: Reassessing International Cooperation & Responsibility. 2010. 272p. pap. 89.75 *(978-94-000-0107-7(X))* Intersentia Uitgevers N.V. BEL. Dist: International Specialized Bk. Services.

Wall, Lord Justice, et al. A Handbook for Expert Witnesses in Children ACT Cases. 2nd rev. ed. 2007. (ENG., Illus.). 244p. pap., pap. incl. cd-rom *(978-1-84661-034-9(6))* Jordan Publishing, Ltd.

Walsh, Elizabeth. Working in the Family Justice System: The Official Handbook of the Family Justice Council. 3rd rev. ed. 2010. (ENG.). 488p. pap. *(978-1-84661-112-4(1))* Jordan Publishing, Ltd.

Weiner, Myron, et al. Born Unfree - Child Labour, Education, & the State in India: An Omnibus - The Child & the State in India, Born to Work, & Child Rights in India (Extract) 2007. (ENG., Illus.). 740p. 65.00 *(978-0-19-567990-8(3))* Oxford Univ. Pr., Inc.

Willems, Jan, ed. Developmental & Autonomy Rights of Children: Empowering Children, Caregivers & Communities. 2nd ed. 2007. 211p. (C). pap. 63.00 *(978-90-5095-726-7(9))* Intersentia Uitgevers N.V. BEL. Dist: International Specialized Bk. Services.

Willemsen, Jan. Children's Rights & Human Development. 2010. (Illus.). 964p. pap. 189.00 *(978-94-000-0032-2(4))* Intersentia Uitgevers N.V. BEL. Dist: International Specialized Bk. Services.

Williams, Jane. Child Law for Social Work. 2008. (Illus.). 288p. (C). 121.00 *(978-1-4129-0803-0(5),* B08035C); pap. 47.00 *(978-1-4129-0804-7(3),* B08035P) SAGE Pubns., Ltd. GBR. Dist: SAGE Pubns., Inc.

Williams, Jane & Invernizzi, Antonella, eds. Children's Rights: Revisiting Visions, Assessing Progress, Rethinking Implementation. 2011. (Illus.). 372p. 134.95 *(978-1-4094-0531-3(1))* Ashgate Publishing Co.

Wilson, Melanie H., ed. Child Abduction Resources. 2010. (Children's Issues, Laws & Programs Ser.). 195.00 *(978-1-61668-247-7(7))* Nova Science Pubs., Inc.

Witte, Jr., John, John. The Sins of the Fathers: The Law & Theology of Illegitimacy Reconsidered. 2009. (ENG., Illus.). 226p. 85.00 *(978-0-521-83941-9(6))*; pap. 30.00 *(978-0-521-54824-3(1))* Cambridge Univ. Pr.

Woodhouse, Barbara Bennett. Hidden in Plain Sight: The Tragedy of Children's Rights from Ben Franklin to Lionel Tate. (Public Square Ser.). (ENG., Illus.). 384p. (C). 2010. pap. 19.95 *(978-0-691-14621-8(7))* 2008. 27.95 *(978-0-691-12690-6(9))* Princeton Univ. Pr.

A World Fit for Children. 2006. 108p. per. *(978-92-806-4087-8(9))* United Nations Children's Fund, The (UNICEF).

Ziemele, Ineta. A Commentary on the United Nations Convention on the Rights of the Child, Volume 7 Article 7: The Right to Birth Registration, Name & Nationality, & the Right to Know & Be Cared for by Parents. 2007. 40p. pap. *(978-90-04-14863-5(9))* BRILL.

CHILDREN—MANAGEMENT

see Child Rearing

CHILDREN—MEDICAL CARE

see Child Health Services

CHILDREN—MEDICAL EXAMINATIONS

Athreya, Balu H. & Zitelli, Basil. Pediatric Physical Diagnosis. 2nd ed. 2008. (Illus.). 368p. pap. 70.00 *(978-1-84829-014-3(4))* Anshan GBR. Dist: Publishers Storage & Shipping.

Barness, Lewis A. & Gilbert-Barness, Enid. Handbook of Pediatric Physical & Clinical Diagnosis. 2nd ed. 2008. (ENG., Illus.). 568p. pap. 34.95 *(978-0-19-537325-7(1))* Oxford Univ. Pr., Inc.

Chiocca, Ellen M. Advanced Pediatric Assessment. 2010. (ENG., Illus.). 560p. 76.99 *(978-0-7817-9165-6(0))* Lippincott Williams & Wilkins.

Colyar, Margaret R. Assessment of the School-Age Child & Adolescent. 2011. (Illus.). 352p. pap. 44.95 *(978-0-8036-2334-7(8))* Davis, F. A. Co.

Cram101 Textbook Reviews & Cram101 Textbook Reviews. Outlines & Highlights for Pediatric Clinical Skills by Richard Goldbloom, Isbn: 9781437713978. 2011. 464p. pap. 36.95 ***(978-1-61461-215-5(3))*** Cram101 Inc.

—Outlines & Highlights for Well Child Assessment for Primary Care Providers by Colyar, Isbn: 9780803610057 080361005x. 2011. 278p. pap. 32.95 ***(978-1-61490-518-9(5))*** Cram101 Inc.

Franklin, Cynthia, et al, eds. The School Practitioner's Concise Companion to Mental Health. 2008. (ENG., Illus.). 272p. pap. 17.95 *(978-0-19-537058-4(9))* Oxford Univ. Pr., Inc.

Gill, Denis & O'Brien, Niall. Paediatric Clinical Examination Made Easy. 5th ed. 2007. *(978-0-443-10393-3(3))* 2006. (ENG., Illus.). 288p. (C). pap. 44.95 *(978-0-443-10395-7(X))* Elsevier - Health Sciences Div. (Churchill Livingstone).

Goldbloom, Richard B. Pediatric Clinical Skills: With STUDENT CONSULT Online Access. 4th ed. 2010. (ENG., Illus.). 360p. (C). pap. 64.95 *(978-1-4377-1397-8(1),* Saunders) Elsevier - Health Sciences Div.

Greydanus, Donald E. The Pediatric Diagnostic Examination. 2008. (Illus.). xviii, 813p. *(978-0-07-128727-2(2))* McGraw-Hill Medical Publishing Div.

Millan, Luiz Roberto. Medical Career Choice: A Gender Study. 2009. (Illus.). xvii, 171p. 59.00 *(978-1-60692-884-4(8))* Nova Science Pubs., Inc.

Osinowo, T. O., et al. BMAT & UKCAT Uncovered: A Guide to Medical School Entrance Exams. 2008. (ENG., Illus.). 344p. pap. 40.95 *(978-1-4051-6918-9(4),* Wiley-Blackwell) Wiley, John & Sons, Inc.

Passing the Nevada High School Proficiency Exam in Science. 2007. per. 23.00 *(978-1-59807-121-4(1))* American Bk. Co.

Peterson, John. Children in Practice. 2012. (ENG.). 236p. pap. 35.00 ***(978-1-107-69523-8(6))*** Cambridge Univ. Pr.

Sawyer. Pediatric Physical Exam & Health Assesment. rev. ed. 2011. 672p. pap. 78.95 *(978-0-7637-7438-7(3))* Jones & Bartlett Learning, LLC.

CHILDREN—MENTAL DISORDERS

see Child Psychiatry; Child Psychopathology

CHILDREN—MENTAL HEALTH

see Child Mental Health

CHILDREN—MORTALITY

Here are entered works on children's death rates and causes. Works on children's experiences with, conceptions of, and reactions to death are entered under Children and Death. Works on the death of children are entered under Children—Death.

see also Infants—Mortality

Alexander, Randell. Child Fatality Review Guide/Atlas Set: An Interdisciplinary Guide & Photographic Reference. 2007. (ENG., Illus.). 832p. 175.00 *(978-1-878060-58-7(9))* STM Learning, Inc.

Alexander, Randell & Case, Mary E. Child Fatality Review Quick-Reference: For Health Care, Social Service, & Law Enforcement Professionals. 2011. (ENG., Illus.). 400p. spiral bd. 55.00 *(978-1-878060-59-4(7))* STM Learning, Inc.

—Child Fatality Review Supplementary CD-ROM: An Interdisciplinary Guide & Photographic Reference, 1 disc. 2008. (ENG., Illus.). suppl. ed. 215.00 incl. cd-rom *(978-1-878060-65-5(1))* STM Learning, Inc.

Antobam, Samuel Kojo. Sex Differentials in Child Mortality. 2010. 68p. pap. *(978-3-639-28140-8(3))* VDM Verlag Dr. Mueller e.K.

Bettelheim, Bruno & Sylvester, Emmy. Delinquency & Morality. 2011. 20p. pap. 35.95 ***(978-1-258-01448-3(3))*** Literary Licensing, LLC.

Byard, Roger W. Sudden Death in the Young. 3rd ed. 2010. (ENG., Illus.). 700p. 275.00 *(978-0-521-51661-7(7))* Cambridge Univ. Pr.

Chapman, Vernon & Burton, Allan, eds. Child Fatalities Due to Maltreatment: The Role of Quality Data. 2012. 230p. pap. ***(978-1-61942-342-8(1))*** Nova Science Pubs., Inc.

Hossain, Zakir. Development of Some Demographic Models & Implementation in Bangladesh. 2010. 164p. pap. *(978-3-8383-9328-5(7))* Lambert Academic Publishing.

Keshri, Kunal & Bhagat, Ram B. Rural-Urban Migration & Child Survival in Indi. 2011. 88p. pap. ***(978-3-8443-8979-1(2))*** Lambert Academic Publishing.

Mark, Kiptui. Effects of Maternal Education: A Study of Infant & Child Mortality in Rural Kenya. 2011. 96p. pap. ***(978-3-639-34235-2(6))*** VDM Verlag Dr. Mueller e.K.

Misselhorn, Mark. Measurement of Poverty, Undernutrition & Child Mortality. 2008. (Göttinger Studien zur Entwicklungsökonomik. Göttingen Studies in Development Economics Ser.). (Illus.). 156p. pap. 49.95 *(978-3-631-57659-5(5))* Lang, Peter GmbH, Europaischer Verlag der Wissenschaften DEU. Dist: Lang, Peter.

Mosley, W. Henry & Chen, Lincoln C. Child Survival: Strategies for Research. 2008. (ENG., Illus.). 412p. pap. 50.00 *(978-0-521-07297-7(2))* Cambridge Univ. Pr.

Pradhan, Jalandhar. Clustering of Child Mortality. 2011. 76p. pap. ***(978-3-8433-9434-5(2))*** Lambert Academic Publishing.

Roy, Runa & KUMAR KURI, Pravat. Child Health & Mortality in Indi. 2011. 120p. pap. ***(978-3-8443-1101-3(7))*** Lambert Academic Publishing.

Sarda, Prasad. Ailing & Hospitalization in India: An Analysis of NSS 52nd & 60th Round. 2011. 164p. pap. ***(978-3-639-34212-3(7))*** VDM Verlag Dr. Mueller e.K.

Shepherd, Mary E. Sex-Selective Abortion in India: The Impact on Child Mortality. 2007. (C). 109.95 *(978-1-934043-69-1(9))* Cambria Pr.

Sifat, Sharmin. Child Mortality Risk Factors with Associated Socio-Economic Inequality: A Case Study of Bangladeshi Children. 2011. 72p. pap. ***(978-3-639-32449-5(8))*** VDM Verlag Dr. Mueller e.K.

UNICEF Staff. The State of Africa's Children 2008: Child Survival. 2008. (Illus.). 56p. *(978-92-806-4247-6(2))* United Nations Children's Fund, The (UNICEF).

WHO Regional Office for the Western Pacific. Child Survival Profile: Cambodia. 2007. (WPRO Publication). 35p. pap. 12.00 *(978-92-9061-224-7(X))* World Health Organization.

CHILDREN—NUTRITION

see also Children—Diseases—Nutritional Aspects; Infants—Nutrition; School Children—Food

Aaron, Fanae. What Chefs Feed Their Kids: Recipes & Techniques for Cultivating a Love of Good Food. 2011. (ENG., Illus.). 224p. 24.95 *(978-0-7627-6095-4(8),* Lyons Pr.) Globe Pequot Pr., The.

Abt, Issac. The Baby's Food. 2008. (Cooking in America Ser.). (ENG.). 156p. pap. 11.95 *(978-1-4290-1184-6(X))* Applewood Bks.

Adjei Frempong, Augusta. Food Operation in Senior High Schools. 2010. 88p. pap. *(978-3-8383-0845-6(X))* Lambert Academic Publishing.

Aina, Tade Akin, et al, eds. Beyond Benign Neglect: Early Childhood Care, Development & Nutrition in Metropolitan Lagos, Nigeria. 2008. 220p. pap. *(978-978-023-205-4(2))* Malthouse Press Ltd, Nigeria NGA. Dist: Michigan State Univ. Pr.

Albon, Deborah & Mukherji, Penny. Food & Health in Early Childhood: A Holistic Approach. 2008. (Illus.). 184p. (C). 104.00 *(978-1-4129-4721-3(9),* B47213C); pap. 39.00 *(978-1-4129-4722-0(7),* B47213P) SAGE Pubns., Ltd. GBR. Dist: SAGE Pubns., Inc.

Allen, Terese & Malone, Bobbie. The Flavor of Wisconsin for Kids: A Feast of History, with Stories & Recipes Celebrating the Land & People of Our State. 2012. (ENG., Illus.). 192p. (J). 18.95 ***(978-0-87020-493-7(9))*** Wisconsin Historical Society.

Altamirano, Wendy, et al. A Mother S Decision Making Process. 2008. 96p. pap. *(978-3-639-06517-6(4))* VDM Verlag Dr. Mueller e.K.

Amster-Burton, Matthew. Hungry Monkey: A Food-Loving Father's Quest to Raise an Adventurous Eater. (ENG.). 272p. 2010. pap. 14.95 *(978-0-547-33689-3(6),* Mariner Bks.) 2009. 23.00 *(978-0-15-101324-1(1))* Houghton Mifflin Harcourt Trade & Reference Pubs.

Antine, Stacey. Appetite for Life: The Thumbs up, No Yucks Guide to Getting Your Kid to Be a Great Eater-Including over 100 Kid-Approved Recipes. 2012. (ENG.). 256p. 26.99 ***(978-0-06-210370-3(9),*** HarperOne) HarperCollins Pubs.

Atkinson, Catherine. Healthy Meals for Healthy Kids: 80 Delicious Recipes for Kids of All Ages. 2008. (ENG., Illus.). 160p. pap. 14.95 *(978-1-84537-991-9(8))* New Holland Pubs., Ltd. GBR. Dist: Sterling Publishing Co., Inc.

—Quick & Easy Lunch Box Planner: Great Eating They Won't Want to Swap at School. 2007. (ENG., Illus.). 1p. per. 11.95 *(978-0-572-03262-3(5))* Foulsham, W. Co., Ltd. GBR. Dist: APG Sales & Distribution Services.

Bader, Elizabeth, et al. The Cleaner Plate Club: Raising Healthy Eaters One Meal at a Time. 2011. (ENG., Illus.). 305p. pap. 16.95 *(978-1-60342-585-8(3),* 1603425853) Storey Publishing, LLC.

Bailey, Christine. The Top 100 Recipes for Brainy Kids: Great Ways to Maximize Your Child's Potential. 2009. (Top 100 Recipes Ser.). (ENG., Illus.). 144p. pap. 9.95 *(978-1-84483-852-3(8))* Duncan Baird Pubs. GBR. Dist: Sterling Publishing Co., Inc.

Baker, Susan S., et al. Pediatric Nutrition Support. 2006. (Illus.). 612p. pap. 165.95 *(978-0-7637-3154-0(4),* 0763731544) Jones & Bartlett Learning, LLC.

Bammann, Karin & Ahrens, Wolfgang, eds. Measurement Tools for a Health Survey on Nutrition, Physical Activity & Lifestyle in Children: The European IDEFICS Study. 2012. (Springer Series on Epidemiology & Health Ser.). (ENG.). 370p. 159.00 *(978-1-4419-1382-1(3),* 1441913823) Springer.

Barnes, Lisa. Cooking for Baby: Wholesome, Homemade, Delicious Foods for 6 to 18 Months. 2009. (ENG., Illus.). 128p. 19.99 *(978-1-4165-9918-0(5),* Touchstone) Touchstone.

—Petit Appetit: Eat, Drink, & Be Merry - Easy, Organic Snacks, Beverages, & Party Foods for Kids of All Ages. 2009. (ENG., Illus.). 288p. (gr. 12-18). 17.95 *(978-0-399-53489-8(X),* Perigee Trade) Penguin Group (USA) Inc.

Bartell, Susan. Fit & Fun Family Action Plan: 301 Things You Can Do Today. 2009. (ENG.). 384p. pap. 11.99 *(978-1-4022-2949-7(6))* Sourcebooks, Inc.

Bauer, Dottie, et al. Early Sprouts: Cultivating Healthy Food Choices in Young Children. 2009. (ENG.). 224p. pap. 24.95 *(978-1-933653-72-3(8))* Redleaf Pr.

Baxter, Thomas J., ed. School Nutrition & Children. 2009. 69.00 *(978-1-60692-891-2(0))* Nova Science Pubs., Inc.

Beckett, Fiona. Healthy Lunchbox. 2008. (Illus.). 64p. 22.95 *(978-1-904943-23-5(3))* Grub Street GBR. Dist: Casemate Pubs. & Bk. Distributors, LLC.

Benefits of Farm-To-School Projects: Healthy Eating & Physical Activity for School Children: Field Hearing Before the Committee on Agriculture, Nutrition, & Forestry, United States Senate, One Hundred Eleventh Congress, First Session, May 15, 2009. 2010. (Illus.). iii, 299p. *(978-0-16-085702-7(3),* 552-070-40934-3) United States Government Printing Office.

Beseler, Lucille & BarCharts Inc., Staff. Children's Nutrition. 2007. (Quickstudy: Health Ser.). (ENG., Illus.). 6p. 5.95 *(978-1-4232-0277-6(5))* Barcharts, Inc.

Bhutta, Zulfiqar Ahmed. Nutrition Interventions for Maternal & Child Health & Survival. 2011. (Illus.). 320p. 37.99 *(978-0-19-547360-5(4))* Oxford Univ. Pr., Inc.

Bier, Dennis M., et al. Personalized Nutrition for the Diverse Needs of Infants & Children: 62nd Nestlé Nutrition Workshop, Pediatric Program, Helsinki, September 2007. German, J. Bruce, ed. 2008. (Nestlé Nutrition Workshop Series: Pediatric Program Ser.). (Illus.). 262p. *(978-3-8055-8553-8(5))* Karger, S. AG.

Bradshaw, Brenda & Mutch, Cheryl. Good Food to Go: Healthy Lunches Your Kids Will Love. 2011. (ENG., Illus.). 240p. pap. 19.95 *(978-0-307-35897-4(6),* Random Hse CAN) Random Hse. of Canada, Ltd. CAN. Dist: Random Hse., Inc.

Brand-Miller, Jennie, et al. The New Glucose Revolution Kids' Low GI Eating Made Easy: The Busy Family's Guide to Eating with the Glycemic Index. 2008. (Glucose Revolution Ser.). (ENG.). 224p. pap. 13.95 *(978-1-56924-288-9(7))* Da Capo Pr., Inc.

Brown, Judith E. Nutrition Through the Life Cycle. 2006. (ENG.). pap. 17.95 *(978-1-4288-1836-1(7))* Cram101 Inc.

—Nutrition Through the Life Cycle. 3rd ed. 2007. (ENG., Illus.). 576p. (C). per. 173.95 *(978-0-495-11637-0(8))* Wadsworth.

Brown, Judith E., et al. Nutrition Through the Life Cycle. 4th ed. 2010. (Available Titles CourseMate Ser.). (ENG.). 624p. (C). pap. 195.95 *(978-0-538-73341-0(1))* Wadsworth.

Brug, J., et al, eds. Promoting Fruit & Vegetable Consumption in Children across Europe - the Pro Children Project, Vol. 49. (Annals of Nutrition & Metabolism 2005, Vol. 49, No. 4 Ser.). (Illus.). 78p. *(978-3-8055-8018-2(5))* Karger, S. AG.

Building a Foundation for Families: Fighting Hunger, Investing in Children: Hearing Before the Committee on the Budget, House of Representatives, One Hundred Eleventh Congress, First Session, Hearing Held in Washington, DC, February 12, 2009. 2009. (Illus.). iii, 97p. *(978-0-16-083077-8(X),* 552-070-39071-7) United States Government Printing Office.

Bundy, Donald, et al. Rethinking School Feeding: Social Safety Nets, Child Development, & the Education Sector. 2009. (Directions in Development Ser.). (ENG., Illus.). 184p. pap. 22.00 *(978-0-8213-7974-5(7),* 9780821379745) World Bank Pubns.

Caballero, B., ed. Improving Childhood Nutrition for Optimal Growth & Development: Workshop of the 17th International Congress of Nutrition, Vienna, August 2001: Proceedings, Vol. 46. (Annals of Nutrition & Metabolism Ser.). (Illus.). *(978-3-8055-7493-8(2))* Karger, S. AG.

Campos, David. Expanding Waistlines: An Educator's Guide to Childhood Obesity. 2007. 208p. per. *(978-90-8790-206-3(9))* Sense Pubs.

Carter, Laura V. Child Nutrition Research Advances. 2007. 225.00 *(978-1-60021-849-1(0))* Nova Science Pubs., Inc.

Caruana, Vicki Guercia & Hammer, Kelly Guercia. Brain Food: Recipes for Success for School, Sports, & Life. 2007. (ENG., Illus.). 256p. per. 15.95 *(978-1-59077-100-6(1))* Evans, M. & Co., Inc.

Cavin, Molly O'Hearn. Well-fed. 2009. 240p. pap. 24.95 *(978-0-557-05138-0(X))* Lulu Enterprises Inc.

Child Nutrition & the School Setting: Hearing Before the Committee on Agriculture, Nutrition, & Forestry, United States Senate, One Hundred Tenth Congress, First Session, March 6, 2007. 2007. iii, 128p. *(978-0-16-078890-1(0),* 552-070-36022-1) United States Government Printing Office.

Clowes, Gina. One of the Gang: Nurturing the Souls of Children with Food Allergies. 2008. 44p. pap. 16.99 *(978-1-4343-6997-0(8))* AuthorHouse.

Committee on Nutrition Standards for National School Lunch and Breakfast Programs & Institute of Medicine. School Meals: Building Blocks for Healthy Children. 2010. (ENG.). 252p. pap. 55.00 *(978-0-309-14436-0(1))* National Academies Pr.

Committee to Review Child and Adult Care Food Program Meal Requirements & Institute of Medicine Staff. Child & Adult Care Food Program: Aligning Dietary Guidance for All. Yaktine, Ann L., ed. 2011. (ENG.). 208p. pap. 48.00 *(978-0-309-15845-9(1))* National Academies Pr.

Converse, Judy. Special-Needs Kids Eat Right: Strategies to Help Kids on the Autism Spectrum Focus, Learn, & Thrive. 2009. (ENG.). 304p. (gr. 12-18). pap. 15.95 *(978-0-399-53488-1(1),* Perigee Trade) Penguin Group (USA) Inc.

—Special-Needs Kids Go Pharm-Free: Nutrition-Focused Tools to Help Minimize Meds & Maximize Health & Well-Being. 2010. (ENG.). 288p. (gr. 12). 15.95 *(978-0-399-53622-9(1),* Perigee Trade) Penguin Group (USA) Inc.

Conway, Rana. Meals Without Tears: How to Get Your Child to Eat Healthily & Happily. 2007. (ENG.). 224p. pap. 33.50 *(978-0-273-71268-8(3))* Pearson Education, Ltd. GBR. Dist: Trans-Atlantic Pubns., Inc.

Cooking Light Magazine Editors. Cooking Light the Ultimate Kid-Approved Cookbook: Delicious Food Kids Will Eat, Nutritious Meals Mom Will Love. 2011. (ENG., Illus.). 144p. spiral bd. 19.95 *(978-0-8487-3453-4(X))* Oxmoor Hse., Inc.

Cram101 Textbook Reviews. Outlines & Highlights for Health, Safety, & Nutrition for the Young Child by Lynn R Marotz, Isbn: 9781428320703. 2010. 82p. pap. 27.95 *(978-1-61698-190-7(3))* Cram101 Inc.

Cram101 Textbook Reviews & Cram101 Textbook Reviews. Outlines & Highlights for Childhood Programs & Practices in the First Decade of Life: A Human Capital Integration by Arthur Reynolds, ISBN. 2011. 198p. pap. 30.95 ***(978-1-61461-092-2(4))*** Cram101 Inc.

—Outlines & Highlights for Nutrition, Health, & Safety for Young Children: Promoting Wellness by Joanne Sorte, ISBN. 2011. 502p. pap. 37.95 ***(978-1-61461-717-4(1))*** Cram101 Inc.

Cram101 Textbook Reviews Staff. Outlines & Highlights for Health, Safety, & Nutrition for the Young Child by Lynn R Marotz, Isbn: 9781428320703. 2009. 70p. pap. 27.95 *(978-1-4288-8621-6(4))* Cram101 Inc.

Daly, Robin M. & Petit, Moira A. Optimizing Bone Mass & Strength: The Role of Physical Activity & Nutrition During Growth. 2007. (Medicine & Sport Science Ser.: Vol. 51). (Illus.). 162p. *(978-3-8055-8275-9(7))* Karger, S. AG.

de Belloy, Marisa. French Children Don't Get Fat. 2007. 90p. pap. 12.99 *(978-0-615-13765-0(2))* MDB Publishing.

Denny, Roz. Vegetarian Kids' Cookbook: Fresh, fun food show in 350 step-by-step Photographs. 2010. (ENG., Illus.). 96p. 9.99 *(978-0-7548-2258-5(3))* Anness Publishing GBR. Dist: National Bk. Network.

Dietz, William H. & Stern, Loraine, eds. Your Child's Nutrition: The American Academy of Pediatrics Guide to Making Peace at the Table & Building Healthy Eating Habits for Life. 2nd ed. 2011. (ENG.). 300p. (J). pap. 14.95 *(978-1-58110-321-2(2))* American Academy of Pediatrics.

Dolgoff, Joanna. Red Light, Green Light, Eat Right: The Food Solution That Lets Kids Be Kids. 2009. (ENG., Illus.). 272p. pap. 21.99 *(978-1-60529-484-1(5))* Rodale Pr., Inc.

Dorfman, Kelly. What's Eating Your Child? The Hidden Connection Between Food & Your Child's Well-Being. 2011. (ENG.). 334p. pap. 13.95 *(978-0-7611-6119-6(8),* 0761161198) Workman Publishing Co., Inc.

Drewett, Robert. The Nutritional Psychology of Childhood. 2007. (ENG., Illus.). 298p. (C). 119.00 *(978-0-521-82787-4(6));* per. 44.00 *(978-0-521-53510-6(7))* Cambridge Univ. Pr.

Erena, Temesgen Woyessa. Communication in Child Feeding. 2010. 80p. pap. *(978-3-639-23043-7(4))* VDM Verlag Dr. Mueller e.K.

Eticha, Kebede. Prevalence & Determinants of Child Malnutrition. 2009. 68p. pap. *(978-3-639-17264-5(7))* VDM Verlag Dr. Mueller e.K.

Examining Innovative Practices to Improve Child Nutrition: Hearing Before the Subcommittee on Healthy Families & Communities, Committee on Education & Labor, U.S. House of Representatives, One Hundred Eleventh Congress, First Session, Hearing Held in Washington, DC, October 8, 2009. 2010. iii, 50p. *(978-0-16-085109-4(2),* 552-070-40465-1) United States Government Printing Office.

Finnie-Chapin, Corinne. Inspired Sprouts Kindergarten Nutrition. 2009. 146p. pap. 31.60 *(978-0-557-03443-7(4))* Lulu Enterprises Inc.

Ford, Gina. Top Tips for Fussy Eaters. 2011. (ENG.). 176p. pap. 11.95 *(978-0-09-193515-3(6))* Random Hse. GBR. Dist: Independent Pubs. Group.

Fraker, Cheri, et al. Food Chaining: The Proven 6-Step Plan to Stop Picky Eating, Solve Feeding Problems, & Expand Your Child's Diet. 2007. (ENG.). 416p. pap. 15.95 *(978-1-60094-016-3(1))* Da Capo Pr., Inc.

Frost, Emma Jane. 200 Recipes for Kids. 2010. (ENG., Illus.). 240p. pap. 7.99 *(978-0-600-62089-1(1),* Hamlyn) Octopus Publishing Group GBR. Dist: Hachette Bk. Group.

Fuhrman, Joel. Disease-Proof Your Child: Feeding Kids Right. 2006. (ENG., Illus.). 288p. pap. 15.99 *(978-0-312-33808-4(2),* St. Martin's Griffin) St. Martin's Pr.

Galloway, Jeff. Fit Kids, Smarter Kids. 2006. (Illus.). 216p. pap. 16.95 *(978-1-84126-193-5(9))* Meyer & Meyer Sport, Ltd. GBR. Dist: Cardinal Pubs. Group.

Garvey, Hugh, et al. The Gastrokid Cookbook: Feeding a Foodie Family in a Fast-Food World. 2009. (ENG., Illus.). 160p. 22.95 *(978-0-470-28645-6(8),* Wiley) Wiley, John & Sons, Inc.

Geary, Natalie & Garcia, Oz. The Food Cure for Kids: A Nutritional Approach to Your Child's Wellness. 2010. (ENG.). 288p. pap. 16.95 *(978-0-7627-5886-9(4),* Lyons Pr.) Globe Pequot Pr., The.

Goday, Praveen S. & Sentongo, Timothy S. Nutritional Deficiencies, an Issue of Pediatric Clinics. 2009. (Clinics: Internal Medicine Ser.: 56-5). (ENG.). xiv, 1036p. 78.00 *(978-1-4377-1257-5(6),* Saunders) Elsevier - Health Sciences Div.

Goldman, Herbert I. Baby Knows Best: How to Prevent Childhood Obesity from Day One. 2011. (ENG.). 128p. 15.95 *(978-0-9814536-1-3(9),* Cambridge House Pr.) Sterling & Ross Pubs.

Graimes, Nicola. Great Healthy Food for Vegetarian Kids. (Illus.). 128p. pap. 24.00 *(978-1-903258-31-6(6))* Carroll & Brown Pubs., Ltd. GBR. Dist: Trafalgar Square Publishing.

—The Top 100 Recipes for a Healthy Lunchbox: Easy & Exciting Ideas for Your Child's Lunches. 2007. (Top 100 Recipes Ser.). (ENG., Illus.). 144p. pap. 9.95 *(978-1-84483-507-2(3))* Duncan Baird Pubs. GBR. Dist: Sterling Publishing Co., Inc.

Grant, Amanda. Healthy Lunchboxes for Kids. 2008. (ENG., Illus.). 128p. *(978-1-84597-706-1(8))* Ryland Peters & Small.

Graves, Hillary. The Little Dish Favourites Cookbook: Over 60 Simple Recipes from Weaning Onwards. 2010. (ENG., Illus.). 160p. 23.95 *(978-1-4447-0417-4(6),* Hodder & Stoughton) Hodder General Publishing Div. GBR. Dist: Independent Pubs. Group.

Guzman, Rosentra, et al. Time for Dinner: Strategies, Inspiration, & Recipes for Family Meals Every Night of the Week. 2010. (ENG., Illus.). 264p. pap. 24.95 *(978-0-8118-7742-8(6))* Chronicle Bks. LLC.

Halileh, Samia. Developing Screening Tools for Palestinian Children. 2010. 196p. pap. *(978-3-639-24550-9(4))* VDM Verlag Dr. Mueller e.K.

Halliday, Judy & Jack, Joani. Raising Fit Kids in a Fat World. 2008. (ENG., Illus.). 224p. 19.99 *(978-0-8307-4534-0(3))* Gospel Light Pubns.

Hart, Megan & Lutz, Kim. The Everything Guide to Cooking for Children with Autism: From Everyday Meals to Holiday Treats - 200 Tasty Recipes Your Child Will Love to Eat. 2010. (ENG., Illus.). 304p. pap. 15.95 *(978-1-4405-0021-3(5))* Adams Media Corp.

Hernell, O., ed. Vaccination. 2008. (Illus.). 54p. pap. *(978-3-8055-8630-6(2))* Karger, S. AG.

Hernell, Olle & Schmitz, J., eds. Feeding During Late Infancy & Early Childhood Vol. 56: Impact on Health. (Nestle Nutrition Workshop Ser.: Vol. 56). (Illus.). *(978-3-8055-7906-3(3))* Karger, S. AG.

Herrin, Marcia & Matsumoto, Nancy. The Parent's Guide to Eating Disorders: Supporting Self-Esteem, Healthy Eating, & Positive Body Image at Home. 2nd ed. 2007. (ENG.). 324p. per. 18.95 *(978-0-936077-03-1(4))* Gurze Bks.

Hill, Rachael Anne. Baby & Toddler Cookbook. 2008. (ENG., Illus.). 144p. *(978-1-84597-588-3(X))* CICO Bks.

Hillis, Anne & Stone, Penelope. Breast, Bottle, Bowl: Fuss-Free Recipes & Nutrition for Babies & Young Children. 2008. (Illus.). 320p. *(978-0-7322-8565-4(8))* HarperCollins Pubs. Australia.

Hobday, Cara. Kids' Healthy Lunchbox: Over 50 Delicious & Nutritious Recipes for Children of All Ages. 2010. (ENG., Illus.). 96p. pap. 12.95 *(978-1-55285-880-6(4))* Whitecap Bks., Ltd. CAN. Dist: Midpoint Trade Bks., Inc.

Holford, Patrick & Colson, Deborah. Optimum Nutrition for Your Child's Mind: Maximize Your Child's Potential. 2008. (ENG., Illus.). 592p. pap. 14.95 *(978-1-58761-332-6(8),* Celestial Arts) Ten Speed Pr.

Holford, Patrick & Joyce, Fiona McDonald. Smart Food for Smart Kids: Easy Recipes to Boost Your Child's Health & IQ. 2010. (ENG., Illus.). 160p. pap. 22.95 *(978-0-7499-5345-4(4))* Piatkus Bks. GBR. Dist: Independent Pubs. Group.

Holt, Katrina. Bright Futures. 3rd ed. 2011. (Bright Futures Ser.). (ENG., Illus.). 90p. spiral bd. 14.95 ***(978-1-58110-555-1(X))*** American Academy of Pediatrics.

Holt, Katrina & Sofka, Denise. Nutrition. Wooldridge, Nancy & Story, Mary, eds. 3rd ed. 2011. (Bright Futures Ser.). (ENG., Illus.). 296p. pap. 54.95 ***(978-1-58110-554-4(1))*** American Academy of Pediatrics.

Hopper, Chris, et al. Physical Activity & Nutrition for Health. 2008. (ENG., Illus.). 392p. (gr. k-6). 39.00 *(978-0-7360-6538-2(5))* Human Kinetics Pubs.

H.R. 5504: Improving Nutrition for America's Children ACT: Hearing Before the Committee on Education & Labor, U.S. House of Representatives, One Hundred Eleventh Congress, Second Session, Hearing Held in Washington, DC, July 1, 2010. 2010. (Illus.). iii, 126p. ***(978-0-16-087135-1(2),*** 552-070-41980-2) United States Government Printing Office.

HURST. Fit Not Fat. 2006. 128p. pap. *(978-0-85969-934-1(X),* Sheldon Press) SPCK Publishing.

Improving Children's Health: Strengthening Federal Child Nutrition Programs: Hearing Before the Committee on Education & Labor, U.S. House of Representatives, One Hundred Eleventh Congress, Second Session, Hearing Held in Washington, DC, March 2, 2010. 2010. (Illus.). iii, 57p. ***(978-0-16-087126-9(3),*** 552-070-41971-3) United States Government Printing Office.

Improving Nutrition for America's Children in Difficult Economic Times: Hearing Before the Committee on Agriculture, Nutrition, & Forestry, United States Senate, One Hundred Eleventh Congress, First Session, March 4, 2009. 2009. (Illus.). iv, 169p. *(978-0-16-085633-4(7),* 552-070-40875-4) United States Government Printing Office.

Inna Tauglich. Elephant Zee & the Magic Pyramid. 2009. 36p. pap. 15.49 *(978-1-4389-4884-3(0))* AuthorHouse.

Institute of Medicine. Childhood Obesity Prevention in Texas: Workshop Summary. 2009. (ENG.). 86p. pap. 21.00 *(978-0-309-14417-9(5))* National Academies Pr.

—Planning a WIC Research Agenda: Workshop Summary. 2011. (ENG.). 176p. pap. 40.50 *(978-0-309-16179-4(7))* National Academies Pr.

Jana, Laura A. & Shu, Jennifer. Food Fights: Winning the Nutritional Challenges of Parenthood Armed with Insight, Humor, & a Bottle of Ketchup. 2012. (ENG.). 345p. pap. 14.95 ***(978-1-58110-585-8(1))*** American Academy of Pediatrics.

Jones, Lisa D. A Guide to Inexpensive Health for You & Baby, 1 vol. 2010. 52p. pap. 16.95 *(978-1-4489-5891-7(1))* PublishAmerica, Inc.

Jukes, Matthew C. H., et al. School Health, Nutrition, & Education for All: Levelling the Playing Field. 2007. (Illus.). 160p. pap. 55.00 *(978-1-84593-311-1(7))* CABI GBR. Dist: Stylus Publishing, LLC.

Kalafa, Amy. Lunch Wars: How to Start a School Food Revolution & Win the Battle for Our Children's Health. 2011. (ENG.). 384p. (gr. 12). 17.95 *(978-1-58542-862-5(0),* Tarcher) Penguin Group (USA) Inc.

Karmel, Annabel. The Fussy Eaters' Recipe Book: 135 Quick, Tasty & Healthy Recipes that Your Kids Will Actually Eat. 2008. (ENG., Illus.). 224p. 23.00 *(978-1-4165-7876-5(5),* Beyond Words/Atria Bks.) Atria Bks.

Kenton, Leslie. Nature's Child. 150p. 13.95 *(978-0-09-177836-1(0))* Random Hse. GBR. Dist: Trafalgar Square Publishing.

Kilcast, D. & Angus, F., eds. Developing Children¿s Food Products. 2011. (Woodhead Publishing Series in Food Science, Technology & Nutrition Ser.). (ENG., Illus.). 264p. 210.00 *(978-1-84569-431-9(7))* Woodhead Publishing Ltd. GBR. Dist: Ingram Pub. Services.

Kinderernaehrung. (GER.). 387p. pap. *(978-3-462-02468-5(X))* Kiepenheuer & Witsch GmbH & Company KG DEU. Dist: International Bk. Import Service, Inc.

Kingham, Karen. Eat Well, Live Well with Growing Children: Healthy Kids' Recipes & Tips. 2008. (Eat Well, Live Well Ser.). (ENG., Illus.). 192p. pap. 19.95 *(978-1-55285-886-8(3))* Whitecap Bks., Ltd. CAN. Dist: Midpoint Trade Bks., Inc.

Kirschenbaum, Daniel. Sierras Weight Loss for Teens & Kids. 2007. (ENG.). 256p. (gr. 8). pap. 16.95 *(978-0-14-305535-8(6),* Putnam Adult) Penguin Group (USA) Inc.

Koletzko, B., et al, eds. Drivers of Innovation in Pediatric Nutrition: 66th Nestlé Nutrition Institute Workshop, Pediatric Program, Sanya, November 2009. 2010. (Nestlé Nutrition Institute Workshop Series: Clinical & Performance Program Ser.). (ENG., Illus.). 228p. *(978-3-8055-9454-7(2))* Karger, S. AG.

—Pediatric Nutrition in Practice. 2008. (Illus.). 306p. pap. *(978-3-8055-8477-7(6))* Karger, S. AG.

La Leche League International. Feed Yourself, Feed Your Family: Good Nutrition & Healthy Cooking for New Moms & Growing Families. 2012. (ENG., Illus.). 288p. pap. 20.00 *(978-0-345-51846-0(2),* Ballantine Bks.) Random House Publishing Group.

Langone, Melissa. The Health Plan for Overweight Children: A Parent's Guide to Raising a Healthier Child. 2007. 120p. 22.95 *(978-0-595-69099-2(8));* per. 12.95 *(978-0-595-44939-2(5))* iUniverse, Inc.

Lapine, Missy Chase. The Sneaky Chef: Simple Strategies for Hiding Healthy Foods in Kids' Favorite Meals. 2007. (ENG., Illus.). 272p. per. 17.95 *(978-0-7624-3075-8(3))* Running Pr. Bk. Pubs.

Le Billon, Karen. French Kids Eat Everything: How Our Family Moved to France, Cured Picky Eating, Banned Snacking, & Discovered 10 Simple Rules for Raising Happy, Healthy Eaters. 2012. 320p. 24.99 ***(978-0-06-210329-1(6),*** Morrow, William & Co.) HarperCollins Pubs.

Lee, Allison, et al. How to Live & Work in the UK. 2010. 280p. pap. 26.00 *(978-1-84528-382-7(1))* How To Books GBR. Dist: Parkwest Pubns., Inc.

Leonberg, Beth L. ADA Pocket Guide to Pediatric Nutrition Assessment. 2007. *(978-0-88091-367-6(3))* Academy of Nutrition & Dietetics.

Lemer, Ben & Mercola, Joseph. Generation XL: Raising Healthy, Intelligent Kids in a High-Tech, Junk-Food World, 0 vols. 2007. 272p. 21.99 *(978-0-7852-2186-9(7))* Nelson, Thomas Inc.

Levine, Susan. School Lunch Politics: The Surprising History of America's Favorite Welfare Program. (Politics & Society in Twentieth Century America Ser.). (ENG., Illus.). 272p. (C). 2010. pap. 25.95 *(978-0-691-14619-5(5))* 2008. 46.95 *(978-0-691-05068-1(0))* Princeton Univ. Pr.

Lewis, Sara. Cooking for Toddlers. 2009. (ENG., Illus.). 96p. pap. 14.99 *(978-1-84476-629-1(2))* Anness Publishing GBR. Dist: National Bk. Network.

Lindsay, Jeanne Warren, et al. Mommy, I'm Hungry! Good Eating for Little Ones from Pregnancy to Age 5. 2007. (Teen Pregnancy & Parenting Ser.). (ENG., Illus.). 160p. (J). 18.95 *(978-1-932538-54-0(2));* per. 12.95 *(978-1-932538-51-9(8))* Morning Glory Pr., Inc.

Lipski, Elizabeth. Digestive Wellness for Children: How to Stengthen the Immune System & Prevent Disease Through Healthy Digestion. 2006. (ENG., Illus.). 320p. pap. 18.95 *(978-1-59120-151-5(9))* Basic Health Pubns., Inc.

Litz Julien, Ronni. The Everything Cooking for Kids Cookbook. 2010. (ENG.). 304p. pap. 15.95 *(978-1-60550-665-4(6))* Adams Media Corp.

Lombardi, Dominic J. Child Nutrition & the WIC Program. 2011. (Children's Issues, Laws & Programs Ser.). 115.00 *(978-1-61209-142-6(3))* Nova Science Pubs., Inc.

Lucas, A., et al, eds. Importance of Growth for Health & Development: 65th Nestlé Nutrition Institute Workshop, Pediatric Program, Kuala Lumpur, March 2009. 2010. (Nestlé Nutrition Institute Workshop Series: Clinical & Performance Program Ser.). (ENG., Illus.). 252p. *(978-3-8055-9304-5(X))* Karger, S. AG.

Makrides, M., ed. Mother & Child Nutrition. 2010. (Illus.). 40p. pap. *(978-3-8055-9507-0(7))* Karger, S. AG.

Marcus, Susan Archibald & Augustine, Susan. The Hungry Brain: The Nutrition/Cognition Connection. 2007. (In a Nutshell Ser.). (Illus.). 168p. per. 27.95 *(978-0-9763426-3-2(4),* B51755P) Corwin Pr.

Marotz, Lynn R. Cengage Advantage Books: Health, Safety, & Nutrition for the Young Child. 8th ed. 2011. (ENG.). 573p. (C). ring bd. 121.95 *(978-1-111-35580-7(0))* Wadsworth.

—Health, Safety, & Nutrition for the Young Child. 8th ed. 2011. (Whatrsquo;s New in Early Childhood Ser.). (ENG.). 576p. (C). pap. 165.95 *(978-1-111-29837-1(8))* Wadsworth.

Martin, Josephine & Oakley, Charlotte. Managing Child Nutrition Programs: Leadership for Excellence. 2nd rev. ec. 2007. 860p. (C). 136.95 *(978-0-7637-3390-2(3))* Jones & Bartlett Learning, LLC.

Matricardi, Joanne & McLarty, Jeanne. Health, Safety, & Nutrition Activities A to Z. 2007. (ENG., Illus.). 208p. per. 30.95 *(978-1-4180-4850-1(X))* Delmar Cengage Learning.

McDougall, Nancy. Healthy Kid's Cookbook: Fantastic Recipes for Children to Cook That Are Good for You Too! 60 Tasty Dishes Made Easy, Shown in 300 Easy-to-Follow Photographs. 2012. (ENG., Illus.). 96p. pap. 16.99 *(978-1-84476-983-4(6))* Anness Publishing GBR. Dist: National Bk. Network.

Michalka, Dayna A. & Monroy, Christopher J. Meals in School: Issues & Impacts. 2011. (Food & Beverage Consumption & Health Ser.). 89.00 *(978-1-61209-127-3(X))* Nova Science Pubs., Inc.

Miller-Kovach, Karen & Weight Watchers International, Inc. Staff. Weight Watchers Family Power: 5 Simple Rules for a Healthy-Weight Home. 2006. (ENG., Illus.). 256p. per. 12.95 *(978-0-470-05133-7(7),* Wiley) Wiley, John & Sons, Inc.

Mistry, Dilaawar J. & Kirk, Susan E. Obesity & Diabetes in Sports Medicine: Clinics in Sports Medicine. 2009. (Clinics: Orthopedics Ser.: 28-3). (ENG.). 99.00 *(978-1-4377-1275-9(4),* Saunders) Elsevier - Health Sciences Div.

More, Judy. Infant, Child & Adolescent Nutrition: A Practical Handbook. 2012. 320p. pap. 37.95 ***(978-1-4441-1185-9(X))*** Hodder Arnold Pubs.

Morgan, Kevin & Sonnino, Roberta. The School Food Revolution: Public Food & the Challenge of Sustainable Development. 2008. (ENG., Illus.). 256p. 140.00 *(978-1-84407-482-2(X))* Routledge.

Mullen, Mary Catherine & Shield, Jo Ellen. ADA Pocket Guide to Pediatric Weight Management. 2009. *(978-0-88091-435-2(1))* Academy of Nutrition & Dietetics.

Mulvany, Sandra. Healthy Cooking for Secondary Schools, 5 vols. 2009. (Illus.). 88p. pap. *(978-1-905780-25-9(7))* Brilliant Pubns.

—Healthy Cooking for Secondary Schools - Book, 5 vols. 2009. (Illus.). 88p. pap. *(978-1-905780-27-3(3))* Brilliant Pubns.

—Healthy Cooking for Secondary Schools-Book 1, 5 vols. 2009. (Illus.). 88p. pap. ***(978-1-905780-24-2(9))*** Brilliant Pubns.

—Healthy Cooking for Secondary Schools-Book 3, 5 vols. 2009. (Illus.). 88p. (YA). pap. *(978-1-905780-26-6(5))* Brilliant Pubns.

—Healthy Cooking for Secondary Schools-Book 5, 5 vols. 2009. (Illus.). 88p. (YA). pap. *(978-1-905780-28-0(1))* Brilliant Pubns.

Netmums Cookery Book Staff & Wills, Judith. Feeding Kids: The Netmums Cookery Book. 2009. (ENG., Illus.). 224p. pap. 19.95 *(978-0-7553-1605-2(3))* Headline Bk. Publishing GBR. Dist: Independent Pubs. Group.

Neufeld, Naomi & Nelson, Pete. KidShape: A Practical Prescription for Raising Healthy, Fit Children. 2007. (Illus.). 262p. reprint ed. pap. 17.00 *(978-1-4223-9049-8(7))* DIANE Publishing Co.

Nilsen, Angela & Wright, Jeni. 101 Recipes for Kids: Tried-and-Tested Ideas. 2008. (Good Food 101 Ser.). (ENG., Illus.). 216p. (J). pap. 9.95 *(978-1-84607-424-0(X))* BBC Worldwide GBR. Dist: Independent Pubs. Group.

Nitzke, , RD, RD, Susan, Susan, et al. Rethinking Nutrition: Connecting Science & Practice in Early Childhood Settings. 2010. (Redleaf Professional Library). (ENG.). 168p. pap. 27.95 *(978-1-60554-031-3(5))* Redleaf Pr.

Northeast, Mark. Funky Lunch: Happy Food for Happy Children. 2010. (ENG., Illus.). 112p. 12.95 *(978-1-906650-30-8(6))* Absolute Pr. GBR. Dist: Independent Pubs. Group.

O'Donohue, William T., et al. Handbook of Pediatric & Adolescent Obesity Treatment. O'Donohue, William T. et al, eds. 2007. (ENG.). 360p. 136.95 *(978-0-415-95432-7(0))* Routledge.

Ojeda, Linda. Safe Dieting for Teens. 2nd ed. 2007. (ENG., Illus.). 144p. (Orig.). pap. 14.95 *(978-0-89793-502-9(0))* Hunter Hse., Inc.

Olivier, Suzannah. Healthy Foods for Happy Kids: An A-Z Nutritional Know-How. 2007. 264p. pap. 16.95 *(978-1-58054-392-7(8))* Woodland Publishing, Inc.

Opitz, Michael F. & Davis-Duerr, Jennifer. Literacy Lessons to Help Kids Get Fit & Healthy. 2010. (ENG.). 144p. (gr. k-6). pap. 19.99 *(978-0-545-16324-8(2),* Teaching Resources) Scholastic, Inc.

Overton, Linda T. & Ewente, Monica R., eds. Child Nutrition Physiology. 2008. (Illus.). 326p. 120.00 *(978-1-60456-302-3(8))* Nova Science Pubs., Inc.

Paleo Parents Staff. Eat Like a Dinosaur: Recipe & Guidebook for Gluten-free Kids. 2012. (ENG., Illus.). 288p. pap. 29.95 ***(978-1-936608-87-4(1))*** Victory Belt Publishing.

Palmer, Gabrielle. Complementary Feeding: Nutrition, Culture & Politics. 2011. (ENG.). 128p. pap. 14.95 *(978-1-905177-42-4(9))* Pinter & Martin Ltd. GBR. Dist: National Bk. Network.

Pandit, Apoorvaa. Watershed Development Inputs & Social Change: Understanding the Changing Culture of Child Nutrition. 2010. (Illus.). 186p. 35.00 *(978-81-316-0342-0(3))* Rawat Pubns. IND. Dist: International Specialized Bk. Services.

Pantley, Elizabeth. The No-Cry Picky Eater Solution: Gentle Ways to Encourage Your Child to Eat-And Eat Healthy. 2011. (ENG., Illus.). 208p. pap. 17.00 ***(978-0-07-174436-2(3),*** 007174436З) McGraw-Hill Cos., The.

Parenting Magazine Staff & Chronicle Books Staff. Love in Spoonfuls. 2010. (ENG.). 160p. pap. 19.95 *(978-0-8118-7131-0(2))* Chronicle Bks. LLC.

Parents Editors. Parents Quick & Easy Kid-Friendly Meals: 125 Dishes the Whole Family Will Love. 2012. (ENG.). 224p. pap. 19.99 ***(978-1-118-17360-2(0),*** Wiley) Wiley, John & Sons, Inc.

Parizkova, Jana. Nutrition, Physical Activity, & Health in Early Life. 2nd rev. ed. 2009. (ENG., Illus.). 428p. 144.95 *(978-1-4200-8231-9(0),* CRC Press) Taylor & Francis Group GBR. Dist: Taylor & Francis Group.

Parker, Calvin G., ed. Diet Quality of American Young Children. 2009. 79.00 *(978-1-60692-771-7(X))* Nova Science Pubs., Inc.

Phuka, John. Efficacy of Complementary Food Supplementation with Lipid-Based Nutrient Supplements on Growth of Malawian Children. 2009. (Acta Universitatis Tamperensis Ser.). 176p. pap. 82.50 *(978-951-44-7832-1(0))* Tampere Univ. Pr. FIN. Dist: Coronet Bks.

Piehl, Norah. Should Junk Food Be Sold in Schools? 2011. (At Issue Ser.). 128p. pap. 22.50 *(978-0-7377-5164-2(9));* lib. bdg. 31.80 *(978-0-7377-5163-5(0))* Cengage Gale. (Greenhaven Pr., Inc.).

Piette, Linda. Just Two More Bites! Helping Picky Eaters Say Yes to Food. 2006. (ENG., Illus.). 304p. per. 13.95 *(978-1-4000-8109-7(2),* Three Rivers Pr.) Crown Publishing Group.

Piho, Nancy Tringali. My Two-Year-Old Eats Octopus: Raising Children Who Love to Eat Everything. 2009. (ENG.). 224p. pap. 16.95 *(978-1-933503-17-2(3))* Bull Publishing Co.

Pillsbury Company Staff. Pillsbury Fast & Healthy Meals for Kids. 2010. (ENG., Illus.). 192p. 19.95 *(978-0-470-64725-7(6),* Wiley) Wiley, John & Sons, Inc.

Poppendieck, Janet. Free for All: Fixing School Food in America. (California Studies in Food & Culture Ser.). 2011. (ENG.). 368p. pap. 17.95 *(978-0-520-26988-0(8))* 2010. 340p. 45.00 *(978-0-520-24370-5(6))* Univ. of California Pr.

Promoting Health, Preventing Chronic Disease, & Fighting Hunger: Assessment of USDA Food Assistance & Child Nutrition Programs in the Economic Downturn: Hearing Before the Committee on Agriculture, Nutrition, & Forestry, United States Senate, One Hundred Tenth Congress, Second Session, December 8, 2008. 2009. iv, 80p. *(978-0-16-084116-3(X),* 552-070-39723-0) United States Government Printing Office.

Punch, et al, eds. Childrenrsquo;s Food Practices in Families & Institutions. 2012. (ENG.). 98p. (C). pap. 42.95 ***(978-0-415-63226-3(9))*** Routledge.

Punch, Samantha, et al, eds. Children's Food Practices in Families & Institutions. 2011. (ENG., Illus.). 104p. (C). 125.00 *(978-0-415-59455-4(3))* Routledge.

Queen, J. Allen & Schumacher, Donald. Overcoming Obesity in Childhood & Adolescence: A Guide for School Leaders. 2006. (Illus.). 168p. 66.95 *(978-1-4129-1665-3(8),* B16658C) per. 27.95 *(978-1-4129-1666-0(6),* B16658P) Corwin Pr.

Rabinovich, Adriana. The Gluten-Free Cookbook for Kids: 101 Exciting & Delicious Recipes. 2009. (ENG., Illus.). 224p. pap. 22.95 *(978-0-09-192389-1(1))* Random Hse. GBR. Dist: Independent Pubs. Group.

Reavely, Dave. Healthy Eating & Pollution Protection for Kids: Parents' Guide. 2011. (ENG.). 213p. pap. 22.95 *(978-1-84694-621-9(2))* Hunt, John Publishing Ltd. GBR. Dist: National Bk. Network.

Reno, Tosca. Eat-Clean Diet for Family & Kids. 2008. (ENG.). 348p. pap. 19.95 *(978-1-55210-050-9(2))* Kennedy, Robert Publishing CAN. Dist: National Bk. Network.

Review the Federal Food Stamp Program & Its Impact on Children's Health: Hearing Before the Subcommittee on Department Operations, Oversight, Nutrition, & Forestry of the Committee on Agriculture, House of Representatives, One Hundred Tenth Congress, First Session, March 13, 2007. 2007. (Illus.). iv, 143p. *(978-0-16-079650-0(4),* 552-070-36601-6) United States Government Printing Office.

Reynolds, Arthur J., et al, eds. Childhood Programs & Practices in the First Decade of Life: A Human Capital Integration. 2010. (ENG., Illus.). 542p. 95.00 *(978-0-521-19846-2(1));* 544p. pap. 36.99 *(978-0-521-13233-6(9))* Cambridge Univ. Pr.

Rigal, Natalie. Winning the Food Fight: How to Introduce Variety into Your Child's Diet. Gladding, Jody, tr. from FRE. 2006. (ENG., Illus.). 1p. per. 14.95 *(978-1-59477-097-5(2))* Inner Traditions International, Ltd.

Rigo, Jacques & Ziegler, Ekhard E. Protein & Energy Requirements in Infancy & Childhood, Vol. 58. (Nestlé Nutrition Workshop Series: Pediatric Program Ser.). (Illus.). *(978-3-8055-8081-6(5))* Karger, S. AG.

The Rising Cost of Food & Its Impact on Federal Child Nutrition Programs: Hearing Before the Committee on Education & Labor, U.S. House of Representatives, One Hundred Tenth Congress, Second Session, Hearing Held in Washington, DC, July 9, 2008. 2008. (Illus.). iv, 95p. *(978-0-16-082198-1(3),* 552-070-38332-8) United States Government Printing Office.

Roberts, Ceri. Boost Your Child's Fitness. 2011. (Teach Yourself Ser.). (ENG., Illus.). 192p. pap. 15.95 *(978-1-4441-0750-0(X),* Hodder & Stoughton) Hodder General Publishing Div. GBR. Dist: Independent Pubs. Group.

—Helping Your Child to Get Fit. 2009. (Teach Yourself: Parenting Ser.). (ENG.). 192p. pap. 14.95 *(978-0-07-162587-6(9),* 0071625879) McGraw-Hill Cos., The.

Rock, Chef. 44 Things Parents Should Know about Healthy Cooking for Kids. 2010. (Good Things to Know Ser.). (ENG.). 249p. pap. 9.99 *(978-1-59652-744-7(7))* Turner Publishing Co.

Rodriguez, Barbara. The Organic Nanny's Guide to Raising Healthy Kids: How to Create a Well-Balanced Diet & Lifestyle for Your Child — From Toddlers to Tweens. 2012. (ENG.). 272p. pap. 16.00 *(978-0-7382-1489-4(2))* Da Capo Pr., Inc.

Rodriguez, Barbara & Adamson, Eve. The Organic Nanny's Guide to Raising Healthy Kids: How to Create a Well-Balanced Diet & Lifestyle for Your Child — From Toddlers to Tweens. 2012. x, 259p. E-Book ***(978-0-7382-1530-3(9),*** Da Capo Lifelong) Da Capo Pr., Inc.

Roskelley, Amy. 201 Healthy Smoothies & Juices for Kids. 2012. E-Book ***(978-1-4405-3612-0(0))*** Adams Media Corp.

—201 Healthy Smoothies & Juices for Kids: Fresh, Wholesome No-Sugar Added Drinks Your Child Will Love. 2012. (ENG.). 240p. pap. 15.95 ***(978-1-4405-3364-8(4))*** Adams Media Corp.

Saab, Joanne & Kalnins, Daina. Better Food for Kids: Your Essential Guide to Nutrition for All Children from Age 2 To 10. 2nd exp. enl. rev. ed. 2010. (ENG., Illus.). 352p. pap. 24.95 *(978-0-7788-0251-8(5))* Rose, Robert Inc. CAN. Dist: Firefly Bks., Ltd.

Salyers, Christopher D. The Face Food Bento Book. 2012. (ENG.). 144p. pap. 19.95 ***(978-1-935613-49-7(9))*** Batty, Mark Pub., LLC.

Samour. Pediatric Nutrition 4E. 4th rev. ed. 2010. (Illus.). 538p. pap. 101.95 *(978-0-7637-8450-8(8))* Jones & Bartlett Learning, LLC.

Sarros, Connie. Wheat-Free, Gluten-Free Cookbook for Kids & Busy Adults. 2nd ed. 2009. (ENG., Illus.). 224p. pap. 16.95 *(978-0-07-162747-4(2),* 0071627472) McGraw-Hill Cos., The.

Satter, Ellyn. Secrets of Feeding a Healthy Family: How to Eat, How to Raise Good Eaters, How to Cook. 2nd ed. 2008. (ENG., Illus.). 256p. pap. 19.95 *(978-0-9671189-2-5(1))* Kelcy Pr.

Saunders, Len. Keeping Kids Fit: A Family Plan for Raising Active, Healthy Children. 2010. (ENG., Illus.). 225p. pap. 15.95 *(978-1-934184-26-4(8))* Lachance Publishing LLC.

Savona, Natalie. Wonderfoods for Kids: Keep Your Child Healthy & Happy. 2009. (Illus.). 320p. pap. 16.95 *(978-1-84400-673-1(5))* Quadrille Publishing, Ltd. GBR. Dist: Ingram Pub. Services.

Schmidt, Christina. The Toddler Bistro: Toddler-Approved Recipes & Expert Nutrition Advice. 2009. (ENG., Illus.). 144p. pap. 16.95 *(978-1-933503-19-6(X))* Bull Publishing Co.

Sears, William. The N. D. D. Book: How Nutrition Deficit Disorder Affects Your Child's Learning, Behavior, & Health, & What You Can Do about It — Without Drugs. 2009. (ENG.). 224p. pap. 12.99 *(978-0-316-04344-1(3))* Little Brown & Co.

Seinfeld, Jessica. Deceptively Delicious: Simple Secrets to Get Your Kids Eating Good Food. 2008. (ENG.). 208p. 12.95 *(978-0-06-176793-7(X),* Morrow, William & Co.) HarperCollins Pubs.

—Delicioso y Sano: Secretos Simples para que Sus Hijos Coman Bien. 2008. (SPA.). 208p. pap. 16.95 *(978-0-06-165578-4(3),* Rayo) HarperCollins Pubs.

Seinfeld, Jessica & Seinfeld. Deceptively Delicious: Simple Secrets to Get Your Kids Eating Good Food. 2007. (ENG., Illus.). 208p. 24.95 *(978-0-06-125134-4(8))* HarperCollins Pubs.

Seti, Candice. Parenting Boot Camp: A Survival Guide for New Parents. 2009. 98p. pap. 17.00 *(978-0-557-03432-1(9))* Lulu Enterprises Inc.

Shino, Mika. Smart Bites for Baby: 300 Easy-to-Make, Easy-to-Love Meals that Boost Your Baby & Toddler's Brain. 2012. (ENG.). 288p. pap. 18.00 ***(978-0-7382-1555-6(4))*** Da Capo Pr., Inc.

Sinnott, Ann. Breastfeeding Older Children. 2010. 294p. pap. 34.50 *(978-1-85343-939-1(8))* Free Assn. Bks. Ltd. GBR. Dist: International Specialized Bk. Services.

Sorte, Joanne, et al. Nutrition, Health, & Safety for Young Children: Promoting Wellness. 2010. (ENG.). 696p. (C). pap. 109.20 *(978-0-13-234941-3(8),* Prentice Hall) Prentice Hall PTR.

—Nutrition, Health, & Safety for Young Children: Promoting Wellness (with MyEducationLab) 2010. (ENG.). 544p. (C). pap. 115.87 *(978-0-13-138120-9(2),* Prentice Hall) Prentice Hall PTR.

Standing Committee on Childhood Obesity Prevention Staff & Institute of Medicine. Legal Strategies in Childhood Obesity Prevention: Workshop Summary. 2011. (ENG., Illus.). 104p. pap. 33.00 ***(978-0-309-21019-5(4))*** National Academies Pr.

Steel, Tanya Wenman & Seaman, Tracey. Real Food for Healthy Kids: 200+ Easy, Wholesome Recipes. 2008. (ENG., Illus.) 384p. 29.95 *(978-0-06-085791-2(9),* Morrow, William Cookbooks) HarperCollins Pubs.

Stern, Michelle. The Whole Family Cookbook: Celebrate the goodness of locally grown Foods. 2011. (ENG., Illus.). 192p. pap. 17.95 *(978-1-4405-1120-2(9))* Adams Media Corp.

Strickland, Elizabeth. Eating for Autism: The 10-Step Nutrition Plan to Help Treat Your Child's Autism, Asperger's, or ADHD. 2009. (ENG.). 304p. pap. 17.95 *(978-0-7382-1243-2(1))* Da Capo Pr., Inc.

Sullivan, Peter B., ed. Feeding & Nutrition in Children with Neurodevelopmental Disability. 2009. (ENG., Illus.). 144p. pap. 43.00 *(978-1-898683-60-5(3))* Mac Keith Pr. GBR. Dist: Wiley, John & Sons, Inc.

Suskind, David & Lenssen, Polly, eds. Pediatric Nutrition Handbook: An Algorithm Approach. 2011. (ENG.). 204p. pap. 46.99 ***(978-0-470-65995-3(5),*** Wiley-Blackwell) Wiley, John & Sons, Inc.

Sweetser, Wendy. Healthy Juices for Healthy Kids. 2010. (ENG., Illus.). 160p. pap. 12.95 *(978-1-84773-612-3(2))* New Holland Pubs., Ltd. GBR. Dist: Sterling Publishing Co., Inc.

Taylor, Eleanor P., et al. Feeding the Kids: The Flexible, No-Battles, Healthy Eating System for the Whole Family. 2007. (Fork & Spoon Field Guides). (Illus.). 248p. per. 16.95 *(978-0-9789385-4-3(2))* Mancala Publishing.

The World Bank. What Can We Learn from Nutrition Impact Evaluations? Lessons from a Review of Interventions to Reduce Child Malnutrition in Developing Countries. 2010. (Independent Evaluation Group Studies). (ENG., Illus.). 168p. pap. 25.00 *(978-0-8213-8406-0(6),* 9780821384060) World Bank Pubns.

Thompson, Colleen A., et al. Overcoming Childhood Obesity. 2006. (ENG., Illus.). 232p. pap. 16.95 *(978-0-923521-78-3(X))* Bull Publishing Co.

van Goudoever, H., et al, eds. Early Nutrition: Impact on Short- & Long-Term Health: 68th Nestlé Nutrition Institute Workshop, Pediatric Program, Washington, DC, October 2010. 2011. (Nestlé Nutrition Institute Workshop Ser.). (ENG., Illus.). 262p. ***(978-3-8055-9745-6(2))*** Karger, S. AG.

C

Van Straten, Michael. Superjuice for Kids. 2007. (ENG., Illus.). 128p. pap. 19.95 *(978-1-55285-870-7(7))* Whitecap Bks., Ltd. CAN. Dist: Midpoint Trade Bks., Inc.

Vartabedian, Brian. Feeding Your Child. Date not set. *(978-0-312-28078-9(5))* St. Martin's Pr.

Villa, Jimena Gomez. Lo Que Los Ninos Si Comen. 2008. (SPA., Illus.). 194p. pap. 14.95 *(978-958-709-252-3(X))* Circulo de Lectores S.A. COL. Dist: Random Hse., Inc.

Villamagna, Dana & Villamagna, Andrew. The Complete Idiot's Guide to Vegan Eating for Kids. 2010. (Complete Idiot's Guide Ser.). (ENG.). 256p. (gr. 12-18). 14.95 *(978-1-59257-978-5(7)*, Alpha Bks.) Penguin Group (USA) Inc.

Volkarsky, Kelly B. Diet Quality of American School-Age Children. 2010. (Children's Issues, Laws & Programs Ser.). 314p. 79.00 *(978-1-60692-776-2(0))* Nova Science Pubs., Inc.

Wahn, U., et al. Nutrition Support for Infants & Children at Risk. (Nestlé Nutrition Workshop Series: Pediatric Program Ser.). *(978-3-8055-8194-3(7))* Karger, S. AG.

Warner, Penny. New Healthy Snacks for Kids. 2007. (ENG.). 160p. pap. 8.95 *(978-1-55867-336-6(9)*, Bristol Cookbooks) Bristol Publishing Enterprises.

Watts, Charlotte & Adams, Gemini. The Top 100 Recipes for Happy Kids: Keep Your Child Alert, Focused, Active, & Healthy. 2008. (Top 100 Recipes For... Ser.) (ENG., Illus.). 144p. pap. 9.95 *(978-1-84483-603-1(7))* Duncan Baird Pubs. GBR. Dist: Sterling Publishing Co., Inc.

Weight Watchers International, Inc. Staff, contrib. by. Eat! Move! Play! A Parent's Guide for Raising Healthy, Happy Kids. 2010. (ENG., Illus.). 240p. pap. 19.95 *(978-0-470-47420-4(3)*, Wiley) Wiley, John & Sons, Inc.

Weiss, Liz & Bissex, Janice Newell. No Whine with Dinner: 150 Healthy, Kid-Tested Recipes from the Meal Makeover Moms. 2010. (ENG., Illus.). 224p. pap. 24.95 *(978-0-615-38122-0(7))* M3 Pr.

Whiting, Mary. The Nursery Food Book. (Illus.). viii, 177p. pap. *(978-0-340-55935-2(7)*, Hodder Arnold) Hodder Education.

WHO Regional Office for the Eastern Mediterranean. A Practical Guide to Developing & Implementing School Policy on Diet & Physical Activity. 2011. (Who Regional Office for the Eastern Mediterranean Ser.). 26p. pap. 18.00 *(978-92-9021-694-0(8))* World Health Organization.

Wollenberg, Brenda. Overweight Kids in a Toothpick World: Easy Weight Loss for Teens & Children or a Nutritionist's Step-by-Step Plan to Keep Childhood Obesity Facts from Making Your Kid a Childhood Obesity Statistic. 2010. (ENG., Illus.). 264p. pap. *(978-0-9866365-0-9(9))* Choices Lifestyle Pubns.

Wolterman, Jan, et al. Treasure Hunt with the Munch Crunch Bunch. 2006. (J). 12.95 *(978-0-9789542-0-8(3))* Kid Well Enterprise.

Wu, Sarah. Fed up with Lunch: How One Anonymous Teacher Survived a Year of School Lunches. 2011. (ENG.). 208p. 22.95 *(978-1-4521-0228-3(7))* Chronicle Bks. LLC.

You, Wen. Time Well Spent: How Watching Time can Reduce the Chances of Having Overweight Children. 2008. 152p. pap. *(978-3-8364-3926-8(3))* VDM Verlag Dr. Mueller e.K.

Zinczenko, David & Goulding, Matt. Eat This Not That! for Kids! Be the Leanest, Fittest Family on the Block! 2008. pap. 16.50 *(978-1-60529-799-6(2))* Rodale Pr., Inc.

—Eat This Not That! For Kids: Thousands of Simple Food Swaps That Can Save Your Child from Obesity. 2008. (ENG., Illus.). 320p. pap. 19.95 *(978-1-60529-943-3(X))* Rodale Pr., Inc.

CHILDREN—PHOTOGRAPHY

see Photography of Children and Youth

CHILDREN—PICTORIAL WORKS

Asael, Anthony & Rabemiafara, Stephanie. Children of the World: How We Live, Learn, & Play in Poems, Drawings, & Photographs. 2011. (ENG., Illus.). 416p. 29.95 *(978-0-7893-2267-8(6))* Universe Publishing.

Carter, Keith, photos by. Fireflies: Photographs of Children. 2009. (ENG., Illus.). 168p. 50.00 *(978-0-292-72182-1(X))* Univ. of Texas Pr.

Chard, Sylvia C. & Kogan, Yvonne. From My Side: Being a Child. 2009. (ENG.). 136p. 29.95 *(978-0-87659-074-4(1))* Gryphon Hse., Inc.

Colbert, Gregory, photos by. Ashes & Snow One Thousand Rivers. 2008. (Ashes & Snow Bks.). (ENG., Illus.). 60p. pap. 30.00 *(978-1-933632-35-3(6))* Flying Elephants Pr.

Davies, Andrew. When I Were a Nipper- Snapshots from a Time Before Indoor Plumbing. 2011. (ENG., Illus.). 144p. 14.95 *(978-1-907554-36-0(X))* Anova Bks. GBR. Dist: Independent Pubs. Group.

De Fabianis, Valeria M., ed. Children. 2011. (MiniCube Ser.). (ENG., Illus.). 768p. 6.95 *(978-88-544-0316-1(4))* White Star ITA. Dist: Random Hse., Inc.

Dover Publications Inc. Staff, creator. Old-Fashioned Children's Photos CD-ROM & Book. 2006. (Dover Electronic Clip Art Ser.). (ENG., Illus.). 48p. pap. 14.95 *(978-0-486-99764-3(2))* Dover Pubns., Inc.

Dromgoole, Glenn. What Grandchildren Do. 2007. (ENG., Illus.). 96p. 15.95 *(978-1-59543-454-8(2))* Willow Creek Pr., Inc.

Hale, Rachael, photos by. The Happy Baby Book: 50 Things Every New Mother Should Know. 2009. (ENG., Illus.). 160p. pap. 17.99 *(978-0-7407-8512-2(5))* Andrews McMeel Publishing.

Helnwein, Gottfried, photos by. Gottfried Helnwein: I Was a Child. 2011. (ENG., Illus.). 80p. 50.00 ***(978-0-9829112-0-4(3))*** Friedman Benda.

Henrich, Karen. The Wonder of Babies: The World Through the Eyes of a Child. 2007. (ENG., Illus.). 128p. 14.95 *(978-1-58182-585-5(4))* Turner Publishing Co.

—The Wonder of Boys: The World Through a Boy's Eyes. 2007. (ENG., Illus.). 128p. 14.95 *(978-1-58182-612-8(5))* Turner Publishing Co.

Horn, Susan K. Life's BIG Little Moments: Grandfathers & Grandchildren. 2008. (Life's BIG Little Moments Ser.). (ENG., Illus.). 96p. 9.95 *(978-1-4027-5839-3(1))* Sterling Publishing Co., Inc.

Imagine... Amazing Me! 2008. 28p. 12.95 *(978-0-9797429-3-4(5))* Halo Publishing International.

Jan, Reynolds. Vanishing Cultures Series. 2007. (J). 118.65 *(978-1-60060-149-1(9))* Lee & Low Bks., Inc.

Joyce, Denise & Watkins, Nancy. Scared of Santa: Scenes of Terror in Toyland. 2012. (ENG.). 288p. pap. 12.99 ***(978-0-06-220458-5(0)***, William Morrow Paperbacks) HarperCollins Pubs.

Kennedy, Jayne. My baby record Book. 2010. 32p. pap. 31.50 *(978-1-4452-8183-4(X))* Lulu Enterprises Inc.

Kienitz, Michael. Small Arms — Children of Conflict: Photographs by Michael Kienitz. 2007. (Illus.). 96p. pap. 25.00 *(978-0-9798091-0-1(X))* Small Arms Productions.

Kouwenhoven, Bill. Little Adults. 2011. (ENG & GER., Illus.). 112p. 50.00 ***(978-3-86828-192-7(4))*** Kehrer Verlag Heidelberg, Klaus Kehrer DEU. Dist: Consortium Bk. Sales & Distribution.

Kyte, Sarah-Jayne. Telling Tales: An Investigation into How Children Perceive Pictorial Imagery. 2011. 36p. pap. ***(978-3-639-32330-6(0))*** VDM Verlag Dr. Mueller e.K.

Lerner, Loren, ed. Depicting Canada's Children. 2009. (Studies in Childhood & Family in Canada Ser.). (ENG., Illus.). 468p. 95.00 *(978-1-55458-050-7(1))* Wilfrid Laurier Univ. Pr. CAN. Dist: Univ. of Toronto Pr.

Manferto De Fabianis, Valeria. Children. Ponting, Sarah, tr. 2006. (Cube Book Ser.). (ENG., Illus.). 736p. 19.95 *(978-88-544-0153-2(6)*, White Star) Rizzoli International Pubns., Inc.

Meene, Hellen van. Neue Photographien. 2009. (GER & ENG., Illus.). 80p. *(978-3-8296-0417-8(3))* Schirmer/Mosel Verlag GmbH.

Merva, Monika, et al. The City of Children. 2011. (ENG., Illus.). 112p. 45.00 ***(978-3-86828-174-3(6))*** Kehrer Verlag Heidelberg, Klaus Kehrer DEU. Dist: Consortium Bk. Sales & Distribution.

Mollison, James, photos by. Where Children Sleep. 2010. (ENG., Illus.). 120p. 30.00 *(978-1-905712-16-8(2))* Boot, Chris GBR. Dist: D.A.P./Distributed Art Pubs.

O'Donnell, E. E., ed. All Our Yesterdays: Father Browne's Photographs of Children & their Favourite Poems. 2008. (ENG.). 132p. pap. 29.95 *(978-1-85607-968-6(6))* Currach Pr. IRL. Dist: Dufour Editions, Inc.

Parker, David L. & Parker, David. Before Their Time: The World of Child Labor. 2007. (ENG., Illus.). 160p. 35.00 *(978-1-59372-024-7(6)*, 372024) Quantuck Lane Pr. & The Mill Road Collaborative, The.

Rand McNally Staff. Rand Mcnally Children Around the World Big Book: People, Spaces, & Places. 2010. 29.00 *(978-0-528-67725-0(X))* Rand McNally.

Toro, Beatrice & Des Fabianis, Valeria Manferto. Ninos. Vila, J. Castillo, tr. 2007. (Cube Bks.). (Illus.). 735p. 19.95 *(978-970-718-439-8(6)*, Numen) Advanced Marketing, S. de R. L. de C. V. MEX. Dist: Perseus-PGW.

Von Zitzewitz, Vanessa. Slaughterhouse Angels. 2008. (Illus.). 180p. 95.00 *(978-3-8327-9246-6(5))* teNeues Publishing Co.

Wilson, Christine K. Faces of Hope: A Family Album. 2011. pap. 12.99 *(978-1-61739-082-1(8))* Tate Publishing & Enterprises, LLC.

CHILDREN—POETRY

Childhood in the Third Reich: World War II & its Aftermath, 1 bk. 2nd ed. 2006. 75p. per. 14.95 net. *(978-0-9760053-2-2(8))* Westlake Publishing Partners.

Kutchins, Laurie. Slope of the Child Everlasting. 2007. (American Poets Continuum Ser.). (ENG.). 88p. pap. 15.50 *(978-1-929918-91-1(7))* BOA Editions, Ltd.

CHILDREN—PORTRAITS

see Children in Art

CHILDREN—PRAYERS AND DEVOTIONS

Abdu'l-Baha. First Prayers: For Tender Plants: Prayers. 2011. ***(978-0-87743-715-4(7))*** Baha'i Publishing Trust, U.S.

Blanchard, Eliza & Baviera, Rocco. A Child's Book of Blessings & Prayers. 2008. (ENG., Illus.). 1p. (J). 12.00 *(978-1-55896-535-5(1)*, Skinner Hse. Bks.) Unitarian Universalist Assn.

Bleck, Linda, illus. A Children's Treasury of Prayers. 2006. (ENG.). 24p. (J). (gr. -1-k). bds. 12.95 *(978-1-4027-2982-9(0))* Sterling Publishing Co., Inc.

Blecker, Lisa. Blessed Is the Spot: A Prayer, 1 vol., 1 DVD. 2007. (Illus.). bds. 14.95 incl. DVD *(978-1-931492-08-9(5))* Discover Writing Pr.

Bostrom, Kathleen Long. Como Es el Cielo? 2006. (Little Hearts Ser.). (Illus.). 73p. (J). 8.99 *(978-0-7899-1002-8(0))* Editorial Unilit.

Bradley, Stella Duncan. Psst! Pass It On! A Devotional. 2011. (J). *(978-0-8280-2518-8(5))* Review & Herald Publishing Assn.

Columba Press, ed. The Columba Lectionary for the Masses with Children. 2009. (ENG.). 192p. pap. 34.95 *(978-1-85607-648-7(2))* Columba Pr. IRL. Dist: Dufour Editions, Inc.

Costello, Gwen. Praying with Children. 2007. (Jump Starts for Catechists Ser.). 41p. (J). (gr. 2). pap. 4.95 *(978-1-58595-635-7(X))* Twenty-Third Pubns./Bayard.

Creations for Children International Belgium, creator. A Child's Book of Psalms. 2007. (Illus.). 61p. (J). (gr. -1-7). 12.95 *(978-1-58087-124-2(0)*, Stampley) Stampley, C. D. Enterprises, Inc.

Cullen-Skowronski, Fiona. Charismatic Liturgy of the Word with Children. 2009. 112p. pap. *(978-1-84923-796-3(4))* YouWriteOn.

—The Spirit-Filled Liturgy of the World. 2008. 72p. pap. *(978-1-84923-055-1(2))* YouWriteOn.

Daughters of St Paul. Novena O L of Guadalupe. 22p. pap. *(978-0-8198-5119-2(1)*, 332-231) Pauline Bks. & Media.

DeStefano, Anthony. This Little Prayer of Mine. 2010. (ENG., Illus.). 40p. (J). (gr. k-k). 12.99 *(978-0-307-45804-9(0)*, WaterBrook Pr.) Doubleday Religious Publishing Group, The.

Evans, Dale. Dale Evans Prayer Book for Children. 2011. 32p. pap. 35.95 ***(978-1-258-01762-0(8))*** Literary Licensing, LLC.

Group Publishing, creator. On the Spot: No-Prep Devotions for Children's Ministry. 2008. 24p. pap. 5.99 *(978-0-7644-3869-1(7))* Group Publishing, Inc.

Hilton, Todd. Expecting A Miracle: A Devotional Journal of Faith & Anticipation. 2006. (ENG.). 264p. per. 21.99 *(978-1-4141-0394-5(8))* Pleasant Word.

Humphrey, Sandra McLeod. Me, Myself, & I: Youth Meditations for Grades 5-8. 2008. (J). *(978-0-7880-2560-0(0))* CSS Publishing Co.

Iskowitz, Yaakov Yosef, tr. from HEB. Aneni: Special Prayers for Special Occasions. 208p. 15.99 *(978-1-58330-440-2(1))* Feldheim Pubs.

Jahsmann, Allan Hart & Simon, Martin P. Little Visits with God. 50th anniv. ed. 2007. (Little Visits Ser.). (ENG., Illus.). 413p. (J). (gr. 2). 12.99 *(978-0-7586-1374-5(1))* Concordia Publishing Hse.

Kangas, Juli. A Child's Book of Prayers. 2008. (ENG., Illus.). 32p. (J). (gr. -1-18). 12.99 *(978-0-8037-3054-0(3)*, Dial) Penguin Group (USA) Inc.

Kuzma, Kay & Walsh, Brenda. Prayer Promises for Kids: More Than 100 Promises to Pray, Claim, & Believe. 2009. (J). 11.99 *(978-0-8163-2343-2(7))* Pacific Pr. Publishing Assn.

Mountain, Vivienne. Research into Children's Perception of Prayer. 2008. 224p. pap. *(978-3-639-05656-3(6))* VDM Verlag Dr. Mueller e.K.

Munoz, Hector. Oraciones Para Ninos. (SPA.). 160p. 4.95 *(978-958-607-533-6(8))* Sociedad de San Pablo ESP. Dist: St Pauls/Alba Hse. Pubs.

Mupanduki, Stellah. God's Little Flock Healed: They will rise on wings like Eagles. 2010. 220p. pap. 24.00 *(978-1-4520-1984-0(3))* AuthorHouse.

Novena O L Perpetual Help. 14p. pap. *(978-0-8198-5118-5(3)*, 332-230) Pauline Bks. & Media.

Omartian, Stormie. The Power of Praying for Your Adult Children. l.t. ed. 2010. (ENG.). 420p. pap. 17.99 *(978-1-59415-317-4(5))* Cengage Gale.

—Prayers & Promises for My Little Boy. 2008. 48p. 15.99 *(978-0-7369-2159-6(1))* Harvest Hse. Pubs.

—Prayers & Promises for My Little Girl. 2008. 48p. 15.99 *(978-0-7369-2158-9(3))* Harvest Hse. Pubs.

Power, Amanda Steadman. Barnyard Talk: Let's Talk about Jesus. 2010. 40p. pap. 18.49 *(978-1-4389-6476-8(5))* AuthorHouse.

Preski, Jeanne. Praying for Christmas: Children's Advent Wreath Devotions. 2011. 36p. pap. 16.86 *(978-1-4567-3848-8(8))* AuthorHouse.

Rock Lois. Lion Book of 1000 Prayers for Children. 2010. (ENG., Illus.). 544p. (J). (gr. k-2). 16.99 *(978-0-7459-6231-3(9))* Lion Hudson PLC GBR. Dist: Independent Pubs. Group.

Schneider, M. Valerie. 10 Wise & Wonderful Stories for Children: Celebrating Holidays & Holy Days. 2007. (Illus.). 60p. per. 14.95 *(978-1-58595-614-2(7))* Twenty-Third Pubns./Bayard.

Shea, Chris. Goodnight Blessings for My Child, 0 vols. 2007. (Illus.). 64p. 9.99 *(978-1-4041-0374-0(0))* Nelson, Thomas Inc.

Smith Msw, Jennifer Janine. This Little Light of Mine. 2011. 20p. pap. 12.99 ***(978-1-4634-3907-1(5))*** AuthorHouse.

Sorenson, Jane. Five Minutes with God. 2011. (J). *(978-0-87239-893-1(5))* Standard Publishing.

Trent, John. Bedtime Blessings 1. 2009. (ENG.). 224p. (J). pap. 9.99 *(978-1-58997-551-4(0))* Tyndale Hse. Pubs.

Wheeler, Penny Estes, ed. Elasti-Brain: 365 Devotions to Stretch Your Mind & Shape Your Faith: A Daily Devotional for Juniors & Earliteens. 2008. 381p. (J). 14.99 *(978-0-8280-2339-9(5))* Review & Herald Publishing Assn.

Winn, Tina. Secrets of Worship: Teaching Children How to Worship. 2011. 76p. pap. 13.99 ***(978-1-4520-2576-6(2))*** AuthorHouse.

Wolfe, Jaymie Stuart. Praying with the Holy Father. 2011. (J). pap. 9.95 ***(978-0-8198-5973-0(7))*** Pauline Bks. & Media.

CHILDREN—PREPARATION FOR DENTAL CARE

Necessary Reform to Pediatric Dental Care under Medicaid: Hearing Before the Subcommittee on Domestic Policy of the Committee on Oversight & Government Reform, House of Representatives, One Hundred Tenth Congress, Second Session, September 23, 2008. 2009. (Illus.). iii, 210p. *(978-0-16-084314-3(6)*, 552-070-39869-4) United States Government Printing Office.

One Year Later: Medicaid's Response to Systemic Problems by the Death of Deamonte Driver: Hearing Before the Subcommittee on Domestic Policy of the Committee on Oversight & Government Reform, House of Representatives, One Hundred Tenth Congress, Second Session, February 14, 2008. 2009. (Illus.). iii, 109p. *(978-0-16-083519-3(4)*, 552-070-39242-4) United States Government Printing Office.

Yoonis, Eiman, et al. Esthetical Dental Materials in Primary Dentition. 2011. 140p. pap. ***(978-3-8433-9258-7(7))*** Lambert Academic Publishing.

CHILDREN—PREPARATION FOR MEDICAL CARE

see also Children—Preparation for Dental Care

Crompton, Margaret. Attending to Children. 128p. pap. *(978-0-340-52741-2(2)*, Hodder Arnold) Hodder Education.

Ditkoff, Beth Ann. Why Don't Your Eyelashes Grow? 2008. (ENG.). 192p. (gr. 12-18). 14.95 *(978-1-58333-323-5(1)*, Avery) Penguin Group (USA) Inc.

Snyder, Leigh. Stars in the Sand: Finding the Light of the Lord in Unexpected Places. 2011. (ENG.). 128p. pap. 11.95 ***(978-1-4620-2731-6(8))*** iUniverse, Inc.

CHILDREN—PROTECTION

see Child Welfare

CHILDREN—PSYCHOLOGY

see Child Psychology

CHILDREN—PSYCHIC ABILITY

Boyd, Beckah. Raising Indigo, Crystal, & Psychic Kids. 2010. (Illus.). 144p. pap. 12.99 *(978-0-7643-3391-0(7))* Schiffer Publishing, Ltd.

Brocas, Joanne. Psychic Children. 2010. (ENG.). 156p. pap. 16.95 *(978-1-84694-367-6(1))* Hunt, John Publishing Ltd. GBR. Dist: National Bk. Network.

Browne, Sylvia. Psychic Children: Revealing the Intuitive Gifts & Hidden Abilities of Boys & Girls. l.t. ed. 2007. (Thorndike Basic Ser.). 397p. 31.95 *(978-1-4104-0278-3(9))* Thorndike Pr.

Browne, Sylvia & Harrison, Lindsay. Psychic Children: Revealing the Intuitive Gifts & Hidden Abilities of Boys & Girls. 2008. (ENG.). 288p. (gr. 12-18). 15.00 *(978-0-451-22404-0(3)*, N A L Trade) Penguin Group (USA) Inc.

Covington, Frederick B. Things I Know. 2010. 23p. (J). pap. 15.95 *(978-1-4327-5352-8(5))* Outskirts Pr., Inc.

Dosick, Wayne D., et al. Empowering Your Indigo Child: A Handbook for Parents of Children of Spirit. 2009. (ENG., Illus.). 1p. pap., instr.'s hndbk. ed. 15.95 *(978-1-57863-444-6(X)*, Weiser Bks.) Red Wheel/Weiser.

Gallagher, Lynne. Psychic Kids. 2008. (ENG.). 315p. pap. 20.95 *(978-1-85635-551-3(9))* Mercier Pr., Ltd., The IRL. Dist: Dufour Editions, Inc.

Goode, Caron B. Kids Who See Ghosts: How to Guide Them Through Fear. 2010. (ENG.). 1p. pap. 16.95 *(978-1-57863-472-9(5)*, Weiser Bks.) Red Wheel/Weiser.

Losey, Meg Blackburn. Conversations with the Children of Now: Crystal, Indigo, & Star Kids Speak about the World, Life, & the Coming 2012 Shift. 2008. (ENG., Illus.). 1p. pap. 15.99 *(978-1-56414-978-7(1)*, New Page Bks.) Career Pr., Inc.

Losey, Meg Blackburn & Losey, Meg. The Children of Now: Crystalline Children, Indigo Children, Star Kids, Angels on Earth, & the Phenomenon of Transitional Children. 2006. (ENG., Illus.). 1p. pap. 15.99 *(978-1-56414-948-0(X))* Career Pr., Inc.

Newcomb, Jacky. Angel Kids: Die medialen Erfahrungen unserer Kinder. 2008. xvi, 253p. *(978-1-84850-016-7(5)*, 785) Hay Hse. UK, Ltd. GBR. Dist: Grantham Bk. Services.

—Angel Kids: Enchanting Stories of True-Life Guardian Angels & 'Sixth Sense' Abilities in Children. 2009. (ENG.). xvi, 256p. pap. 17.95 *(978-1-4019-2285-6(6))* Hay Hse., Inc.

Pierson, Christina A. A Knowing: Living with Psychic Children. 2010. 204p. 24.99 *(978-1-4490-4939-3(7))* AuthorHouse.

Soto, Ramon, tr. Mas Alla de los Ninos Indigo: Los Nuevos Ninos y la Llegada del Quinto Mundo. 2008. (ENG., Illus.). 1p. per. 16.00 *(978-1-59477-215-3(0))* Inner Traditions International, Ltd.

Talty, Janine. Indigo Awakening: A Doctor's Memoir of Forging an Authentic Life in a Turbulent World. 2009. (Illus.). 368p. pap. 17.95 *(978-1-60070-063-7(2)*, Elite Bks.) Author's Publishing Cooperative.

Tanous, Alex & Donnelly, Katherine Fair. Is Your Child Psychic? A Guide to Developing Your Child's Innate Abilities. 2009. (ENG.). 224p. (gr. 12-18). 15.95 *(978-1-58542-738-3(1)*, Tarcher) Penguin Group (USA) Inc.

Thompson, Bruce & Subotnik, Rena Faye. Methodologies for Conducting Research on Giftedness. 2010. (Illus.). 280p. 69.95 *(978-1-4338-0714-5(9))* American Psychological Assn.

Thompson, D. Carr. How to Grow Science & Math Kids. 2010. 58p. pap. 12.00 *(978-0-557-28910-3(6))* Lulu Enterprises Inc.

Twyman, James. Psychic Children Speak to the World: How Love Creates Miracles. 2011. 176p. pap. 16.95 *(978-1-57174-652-8(8))* Hampton Roads Publishing Co., Inc.

Virtue, Doreen. The Care & Feeding of Indigo Chil. 2006. 256p. *(978-1-4019-1164-5(1)*, 412) Hay Hse. UK, Ltd. GBR. Dist: Grantham Bk. Services.

Wiseman, Sara. Your Psychic Child: How to Raise Intuitive & Spiritually Gifted Kids of All Ages. 2010. (ENG.). 312p. pap. 17.95 *(978-0-7387-2061-6(5))* Llewellyn Pubns.

CHILDREN—RECREATION

see Amusements; Creative Activities and Seat Work; Games

CHILDREN—RELATIONSHIP WITH ADULTS

see Children and Adults

CHILDREN—RELIGIOUS LIFE

see also Children—Prayers and Devotions

Adams, Kate, et al. The Spiritual Dimension of Childhood. 2008. 160p. pap. *(978-1-84310-602-9(7))* Kingsley, Jessica Ltd.

Allen, Holly Catterton, ed. Nurturing Children's Spirituality: Christian Perspectives & Best Practices. 2008. (Illus.). 416p. pap. 46.00 *(978-1-55635-558-5(0))* Wipf & Stock Pubs.

Anderson, Joan Wester. An Angel to Watch over Me: True Stories of Children's Encounters with Angels. 2012. (ENG.). 144p. pap. 14.95 ***(978-0-8294-3654-9(5))*** Loyola Pr.

Angel, Jessica. The Princess & Her King: A Special Mission- A Personalized Children's Book. 2011. 37p. (J). pap. 17.95 ***(978-1-4327-6876-8(X))*** Outskirts Pr., Inc.

Anthony, Michael, ed. Perspectives on Children's Spiritual Formation. 2007. (Perspectives Ser.). (ENG.). 352p. pap. 24.99 *(978-0-8054-4186-4(7),* B&H Academic) B&H Publishing Group.
Auditor, Chantel. Butterfly Kisses. 2008. 58p. pap. 22.78 *(978-0-557-01263-3(5))* Lulu Enterprises Inc.
Bacon, Richard. Revealed to Babes: Children in the Worship of God. 75p. pap. 7.95 *(978-0-9632557-3-0(8))* Old Paths Pubns., Inc.
Barrett, Justin L. Born Believers: The Science of Children's Religious Belief. 2012. (ENG.). 320p. 26.00 ***(978-1-4391-9654-0(0),*** Free Pr.) Free Pr.
becker, ellen c. & barnes, mary t. Advent in the Home: Activities for Families. 2008. (Illus.). 120p. pap. 14.95 *(978-1-59276-430-3(4))* Our Sunday Visitor, Publishing Div.
Berryman, Renee C. Children Are Gifts from God, Disabled or Not! A Mother's Personal Journey of Hope & Inspiration. 2009. 336p. 28.99 *(978-1-60791-636-9(3));* pap. 18.99 *(978-1-60791-635-2(5))* Xulon Pr., Inc.
Blinston, Irene. When Children Witness the Sacred. 2011. 224p. pap. ***(978-3-8443-2617-8(0))*** Lambert Academic Publishing.
Broadberry, Richard E. The Kingdom Within: The Ark of Spirituality in a Secular Sea. 2010. 140p. pap. 11.99 *(978-1-4490-6338-2(1))* AuthorHouse.
Brown, Joyce. Discovering Together. 2007. 16p. 2.00 *(978-0-687-49186-5(X))* Abingdon Pr.
Browning, Don S. & Bunge, Marcia J., eds. Children & Childhood in World Religions: Primary Sources & Texts. (Rutgers Series in Childhood Studies). (ENG.). 412p. 2011. pap. 32.95 ***(978-0-8135-5176-0(5))*** 2009. 62.00 *(978-0-8135-4517-2(X))* Rutgers Univ. Pr.
Bullock, Monica. 50 Ideas for Kids Church. 2009. 71p. pap. 15.84 *(978-0-557-17263-4(2))* Lulu Enterprises Inc.
Burns, Irene. A Light Shines in God's Country: Hilarious & Heartwarming Stories from Our Home to Yours. 2007. (ENG.). 224p. per. 13.99 *(978-1-59979-242-2(7),* Creation Hse.) Charisma Media.
Bushnell, Horace, abr. Views of Christian Nurture. 2009. (Amer Philosophy, Religion Ser.). (ENG.). 256p. pap. 17.95 *(978-1-4290-1936-1(0))* Applewood Bks.
Butt, Christian. Kindertheologische Untersuchungen zu Auferstehungsvorstellungen von Grundschulerinnen und Grundschulern. 2009. (Arbeiten zur Religionspadagogik Ser.). (GER., Illus.). 307p. (C). 54.00 *(978-3-89971-720-4(1))* Vandenhoeck & Ruprecht GmbH & Co. KG DEU. Dist: ISD.
Byrne, Brendan. Coping with Bullying in Schools. (Illus.). 96p. (Orig.). pap. *(978-0-304-33071-3(X),* Burns & Oates) Continuum International Publishing Group, Ltd.
Caldwell, Elizabeth F. Making a Home for Faith: Nurturing the Spiritual Life of Your Children. 2007. 139p. per. *(978-0-8298-1769-0(7))* Pilgrim Pr., The/United Church Pr.
Capps, Beverly. God's Creative Power for Kids. 2008. (ENG.). 54p. (J). pap. 10.00 *(978-0-9747513-5-8(7))* Capps Publishing.
, CFP Staff., C. F. P. Staff. CF4K Children's Resources Catalogue 2009/10: Because you're never too young to know Jesus! 2009. (ENG.). 32p. *(978-1-84550-515-8(8))* Christian Focus Pubns. GBR. Dist: STL Distribution North America.
A Childs Beattitudes Anthem. 1.25 *(978-0-687-05195-3(9))* Abingdon Pr.
Cooper, Scott. I Don't Want to Go to Church! Practical Ways to Deal with Kids & Religion, Whether You're Religious or Not. 2006. 108p. per. 12.95 *(978-0-8091-4398-6(4),* 4398-4) Paulist Pr.
Croom, Tina L. Diary of a Bullied Child: The Aftermath I. 2011. 108p. pap. 11.95 ***(978-1-4497-1847-3(7),*** WestBow Pr.) Author Solutions, Inc.
Csinos, David M. ChildrenÕs Ministry That Fits: Beyond One-Size-Fits-All Approaches to Nuturing ChildrenÕs Spirituality. 2011. 188p. pap. 22.00 *(978-1-61097-121-8(3),* Wipf and Stock) Wipf & Stock Pubs.
Cullen-Skowronski, Fiona. Charismatic Liturgy of the Word with Children. 2009. 112p. pap. *(978-1-84923-796-3(4))* YouWriteOn.
Dewey, Simon, et al. Blessed Are the Children: The Miracle & Beauty of Childhood. 2007. (Illus.). *(978-1-59811-390-7(9))* Covenant Communications.
Dillen, A. & Pollefeyt, D., eds. Children's Voices: Children's Perspectives in Ethics, Theology & Religious Education. 2010. (Bibliotheca Ephemeridum Theologicarum Lovaniensium Ser.). (ENG.). 450p. (C). pap. 105.00 *(978-90-429-2247-1(8))* Peeters Pubs. & Booksellers BEL. Dist: Brown, David Bk. Co., The.
Dobson, James C. Como Criar a un Nino Dificil.Tr. of Strong-Willed Child. (SPA.). 256p. *(978-84-7228-456-2(5),* 220168) Clie, Editorial.
Dockray, Lydia. The G. O. D. Adventure. 2008. 142p. pap. 39.95 *(978-1-4092-1326-0(9))* Lulu Enterprises Inc.
Domencic, Peter. Watching Children Follow the Spirit. 2008. 172p. 22.99 *(978-1-60647-923-0(7))* Xulon Pr., Inc.
Durbin, Kara G. Parenting with Scripture: A Topical Guide for Teachable Moments. 2012. (ENG.). 256p. pap. 14.99 ***(978-0-8024-0849-5(4))*** Moody Pubs.
Edwards, Grant. Passing the Baton: Guide Your Child to Follow Jesus. 2009. (ENG.). 143p. pap. 14.99 *(978-0-7644-3875-2(1))* Group Publishing, Inc.
Edwards, Luna. Luna's Thanksgiving Prayer. 2009. 20p. pap. 12.49 *(978-1-4490-1240-3(X))* AuthorHouse.
Ford, Aundria H. Hawkins. From the Pastor's Daughter: A testimony of life in the ministry through the eyes of the Pastor's Child. 2010. pap. 12.99 *(978-1-60799-803-7(3))* Tate Publishing & Enterprises, LLC.
Furman, Richard. The Children of Church Members. 15p. pap. 2.99 *(978-0-9652883-4-7(X))* Audubon Pr. & Christian Bk. Service.
God's Creative Power for PreSchoolers. 2007. 34p. (J). pap. 8.00 *(978-0-9747513-7-5(5))* Capps Publishing.
Gomez, Michelle Mannette. Memoir to Grandma. 2006. (ENG.). 80p. per. 11.99 *(978-1-4141-0659-5(9))* Pleasant Word.
Goodwin, Debbie Salter. Raising Kids to Extraordinary Faith: Helping Parents & Teachers Disciple the Next Generation. 2008. (ENG.). 192p. pap. 14.99 *(978-0-8341-2391-5(6),* 9780834123915) Beacon Hill Pr. of Kansas City.
Gospel Light Publications Staff. Baby Beginnings Nursery Smart Pages. 2008. (ENG.). 272p. 39.99 *(978-0-8307-4498-5(3))* Gospel Light Pubns.
—Rock-Solid Followers: Helping Kids Discover Jesus' Love for Them & the World. 2008. (ENG.). 256p. (J). (gr. -1-7). 49.99 *(978-0-8307-5114-3(9))* Gospel Light Pubns.
Greenwood, Rebecca. Let Our Children Go. 2011. E-Book ***(978-1-61638-568-2(5),*** Charisma Hse.) Charisma Media.
Group Publishing. Children's Ministry Pocket Guide to Special Needs: Quick Tips to Reach Every Child. 2008. 16p. pap. 12.99 *(978-0-7644-3701-4(1))* Group Publishing, Inc.
Group Publishing, creator. Devotions: 110 Eye-Popping, Jaw-Dropping Children's Messages. 2006. (Illus.). 128p. per. 17.99 *(978-0-7644-3440-2(3))* Group Publishing, Inc.
Gurian, Michael. The Soul of the Child: Nurturing the Divine Identity of Our Children. 2007. (ENG.). 256p. pap. 17.95 *(978-1-4165-7041-7(1),* Beyond Words/Atria Bks.) Atria Bks.
Halliday, Judy & Jack, Joani. Raising Fit Kids in a Fat World. 2008. (ENG., Illus.). 224p. 19.99 *(978-0-8307-4534-0(3))* Gospel Light Pubns.
Hanks, Scott. Take Heed to Thyself for Kids. 2007. (J). spiral bd. 7.00 *(978-0-9799518-7-9(9))* Hanks, Scott.
Harding, Leander S. Reverence for the Heart of the Child. 2011. 178p. pap. 20.00 ***(978-1-61097-398-4(4),*** Wipf and Stock) Wipf & Stock Pubs.
Harris, Unice. What's Ailing You Child? 2010. 34p. pap. 19.95 *(978-0-557-66850-2(6))* Lulu Enterprises Inc.
—What's Ailing You Child? Bullying. 2010. 32p. pap. 19.95 *(978-0-557-67305-6(4))* Lulu Enterprises Inc.
—What's Ailing You Child? Overweight! 2010. 33p. pap. 19.95 *(978-0-557-68281-2(9))* Lulu Enterprises Inc.
Hartshorne, Hugh. Childhood & Character an Introduction. 2006. pap. 28.95 *(978-1-4286-3643-9(9))* Kessinger Publishing, LLC.
Hayes, Norvel. Stand in the Gap for Your Children. rev. ed. 2011. 64p. (Orig.). pap. 6.99 *(978-0-89274-886-0(9),* HH886) Harrison House Pubs.
Hays, Rita B. The Children's Minister. 2008. 127p. per. 13.00 *(978-0-88177-527-3(4))* Discipleship Resources.
—Most Important Space in the Ch. 2009. 128p. pap. 14.00 *(978-0-88177-568-6(1))* Discipleship Resources.
Henry, Matthew. Family Religion: Principles for Raising a Godly Family. 2008. (ENG.). 272p. pap. 14.99 *(978-1-84550-313-0(9),* Christian Heritage) Christian Focus Pubns. GBR. Dist: STL Distribution North America.
Hoagland, Victor, ed. A Catholic Child's First Prayer Book. 2008. (Illus.). 37p. (J). (gr. -1-2). 9.95 *(978-0-88271-148-5(2))* Regina Pr., Malhame & Co.
Hoffman, Sharon. A Car Seat in My Convertible? Giving Your Grandkids the Spiritual Ride of Their Lives. 2008. (ENG., Illus.). 176p. pap. 12.99 *(978-1-59669-208-4(1))* New Hope Pubs.
Holloway, Elnora & Lamb, Connie. Shaping Little Minds for the Future. 2009. 72p. pap. 15.49 *(978-1-4389-7277-0(6))* AuthorHouse.
Horn, Cornelia & Phenix, Robert, eds. Children in Late Ancient Christianity. 2009. 497p. pap. 167.50 *(978-3-16-150235-4(3))* Mohr Siebeck GmbH & Co. KG DEU. Dist: Coronet Bks.
Horst, Tamyra. Praying Like Crazy for Your Kids. 2009. 12.99 *(978-0-8163-2345-6(3))* Pacific Pr. Publishing Assn.
Hughes, Barbara & Hughes, R. Kent. Disciplines of a Godly Family. annot. ed. 2007. 256p. pap. 15.99 *(978-1-58134-941-2(6))* Crossway.
Humphrey, Sandra McLeod. Me, Myself, & I: Youth Meditations for Grades 5-8. 2008. (J). *(978-0-7880-2560-0(0))* CSS Publishing Co.
Hutchcraft, Ron. Cinco Necesidades Que Deben Suplirse al Nino...Tr. of Five Needs Your Child Must Have Met at Home. (SPA.). 7.99 *(978-0-7899-0138-5(2),* 497274) Editorial Unilit.
Hyde, Brendan. Children & Spirituality: Searching for Meaning & Connectedness. 2008. (ENG.). 192p. per. *(978-1-84310-589-3(6))* Kingsley, Jessica Ltd.
I Am Somebody! Je Quelqu'un Suis! 2007.Tr. of French. (J). 15.95 *(978-0-9768828-1-7(7))* Parker, Kimberly.
Israel, Vanessa. From Mother's Womb to God & from Mommy's Womb to God. 2007. 9.00 *(978-0-8059-8882-6(3))* Dorrance Publishing Co., Inc.
Jean-Francois, Charmaine. Broken by God to Be Blessed. 2010. 90p. pap. 8.00 *(978-0-88144-397-4(2),* Thorncrown Publishing) Yorkshire Publishing Group.
Johnson, Lois Walfrid & Walfrid Johnson, Lois. Girl Talk: 52 Weekly Devotions, 1 vol. 2009. (Faithgirlz! Ser.). (ENG.). 432p. (J). pap. 12.99 *(978-0-310-71449-1(4))* Zonderkidz.
Johnson, Victoria. Children & Sexual Abuse. 2007. (IVP Booklets Ser.). (ENG.). 32p. 1.50 *(978-0-87784-040-4(7),* IVP Bks.) InterVarsity Pr.
Jones, Timothy. Nurturing Your Child's Soul: 10 Keys to Helping Your Child Grow in Faith, 0 vols. 2006. 272p. per. 13.99 *(978-0-8499-1403-4(5))* Nelson, Thomas Inc.
Kawasaki, Shauna. My Eternal Family: 2009 Activities for Children. 2008. 64p. 14.95 *(978-1-60641-002-8(4))* Deseret Bk. Co.
Kingswood, Jeff. From the Lips of Little Ones. 2008. 164p. (J). pap. 10.00 *(978-1-884527-24-1(8))* Crown & Covenant Pubns.
Knight, Gavin & Knight, Joanna. Called by Mind & Spirit: Crossing the Borderlands of Childhood. 2010. (ENG.). 184p. pap. 24.95 *(978-1-4411-3761-6(0))* Mowbray, A. R. & Co., Ltd. GBR. Dist: National Bk. Network.
Lamb, Pat. Children, Come to Me: Weekly Mini Lessons for Children. 2011. pap. 12.99 ***(978-1-61777-199-6(6))*** Tate Publishing & Enterprises, LLC.
Lamb, Winifred Wing Han & de Souza, Marian, eds. Children, Adolescents & Spirituality. 2008. (Interface: A Forum for Theology in the World Ser.). (ENG.). 168p. (C). pap. 10.00 *(978-1-920691-90-5(1))* ATF Pr. AUS. Dist: Brown, David Bk. Co., The.
Lenton, Sarah. Creative Ideas for Children's Worship: Based on the Sunday Gospels. 2012. 384p. pap. 39.99 ***(978-1-84825-112-0(2),*** Canterbury Pr. Norwich) Hymns Ancient & Modern Ltd GBR. Dist: Westminster John Knox Pr.
Lightner, Robert P. A Donde van los Que Mueren Sin Poder Creer: Safe in the Arms of Jesus. 2008. (SPA.). 96p. pap. 6.99 *(978-0-8254-1381-0(8),* Editorial Portavoz) Kregel Pubns.
Macaulay, Susan Schaeffer. For the Children's Sake: Foundations of Education for Home & School. 2009. 166p. pap. 14.99 *(978-1-4335-0695-6(5))* Crossway.
Mackenzie, Carine. Nuestro Bebe (Our Baby Book) (SPA.). 10.99 *(978-1-56063-613-7(0),* 494014) Editorial Unilit.
Maweu, Christine. Children at Risk. 2010. 80p. pap. *(978-3-639-23392-6(1))* VDM Verlag Dr. Mueller e.K.
Mayer-Whittington, Nancy. For the Love of Angela. 2007. 93p. pap. *(978-0-9762284-7-9(5))* St. Catherine of Siena Pr.
McMaster, Jenica. Prayerwithpurpose: Passionate Prayers for Children. 2011. 164p. pap. 13.95 ***(978-1-61507-800-4(2))*** Cross Bks. Publishing.
Miller, Sally & Mueller, Cheri. Play with Me: Two Friends on a Spiritual Journey with Kids. 2006. 210p. per. *(978-1-932902-61-7(9))* FaithWalk Publishing.
Moore, Mary Elizabeth & Wright, Almeda. Children, Youth, & Spirituality in a Troubling World. Moore-Keish, Martha L., ed. 2008. 288p. pap. 29.99 *(978-0-8272-0513-0(9))* Chalice Pr.
Mow, Anna B. Tu Hijo, del Nacimiento Al Nuevo: Your Child: From Birth to Rebirth. (SPA.). *(978-84-7228-140-0(X),* 220912) Clie, Editorial.
Nelson, Carl Ellis. Growing up Christian: A Congregational Strategy for Nurturing Disciples. 2008. pap. 16.00 *(978-1-57312-523-9(7))* Smyth & Helwys Publishing, Inc.
Not One Should Perish: Devotional Inspired True Stories of Children. 9.99 *(978-1-55976-418-6(X))* CEF Pr.
Nunn, Rhonda. Created in Seven Days. 2011. 20p. pap. 24.95 ***(978-1-4626-2218-4(6))*** PublishAmerica, Inc.
Nye, Rebecca. Children's Spirituality: What It Is & Why It Matters. 2009. (ENG., Illus.). 128p. pap. 16.99 *(978-0-7151-4027-7(2))* Church Hse. Publishing GBR. Dist: Westminster John Knox Pr.
Odiwo, Edith Lamira. Blessings for My Child. 2009. 156p. 24.49 *(978-1-4490-1324-0(4));* pap. 18.99 *(978-1-4490-1323-3(6))* AuthorHouse.
Omartian, Stormie. The Power of Praying for Your Adult Children. Lt. ed. 2010. (ENG.). 420p. pap. 17.99 *(978-1-59415-317-4(5))* Cengage Gale.
—The Power of Praying for Your Adult Children. 2009. 160p. pap., pupil's gde. ed. 8.99 *(978-0-7369-2536-5(8));* 240p. pap. 13.99 *(978-0-7369-2086-5(2))* Harvest Hse. Pubs.
Orr, William. Como Llevar Ninos a Cristo: How to Lead Young Kids to Christ. (SPA.). 80p. *(978-84-7228-707-5(6),* 220218) Clie, Editorial.
Ota, Cathy & Chater, Mark. Spiritual Education in a Divided World. 2007. (Illus.). 216p. 140.00 *(978-0-415-39191-7(1))* Routledge.
Pearson, Eric P. Ryan's Stories: God's Perfect Child. 2007. pap. 14.95 *(978-0-9799461-0-3(7))* California Dreamer Publishing, LLC.
Penick, Starla. Comparison of Children's God-Concepts & Logical Thinking Ability. 2008. 120p. pap. *(978-3-639-08516-7(1))* VDM Verlag Dr. Mueller e.K.
Pratney, Winkie. Devil Take the Youngest. 2009. 273p. pap. 18.97 *(978-0-557-21791-5(1))* Lulu Enterprises Inc.
Ratcliff, Donald & Ratcliff, Brenda. ChildFaith: Experiencing God & Spiritual Growth with Your Children. 2009. 194p. pap. 22.00 *(978-1-60608-552-3(2),* Cascade Bks.) Wipf & Stock Pubs.
Reid, Kathryn Goering & Hawkley, Ken. Children Together: Teaching Girls & Boys to Value Themselves & Each Other. 2010. 128p. pap. 16.00 *(978-1-60899-183-9(0),* Resource Pubns.) Wipf & Stock Pubs.
Reyes, Keith. Filicide As Child Sacrifice in the Judeo-Christian Worldview. 2009. 62p. pap. *(978-3-639-16119-9(X))* VDM Verlag Dr. Mueller e.K.
Ridgely, Susan, ed. The Study of Children in Religions: A Methods Handbook. 2011. (ENG., Illus.). 325p. 39.00 ***(978-0-8147-7646-9(9))*** New York Univ. Pr.
Ridgely, Susan B. The Study of Children in Religion: A Methods Handbook. 2011. E-Book ***(978-0-8147-7747-3(3));*** E-Book ***(978-0-8147-7746-6(5))*** New York Univ. Pr.
Roche, Maite. My First Prayers with Mary. 2011. (Illus.). 14p. bds. 6.99 ***(978-1-58617-506-1(8))*** Ignatius Pr.
Royer, Katherine. Nursery Stories of Jesus. 2009. 52p. pap. 12.00 *(978-1-60899-140-2(7),* Resource Pubns.) Wipf & Stock Pubs.
Rubin, Jordan S. The Great Physician's RX for Children's Health, 0 vols. 2008. 256p. 24.99 *(978-0-7852-1902-6(1))* Nelson, Thomas Inc.
Rubin, Jordan S. & Rubin, Nicki. The Great Physician's Rx for Children's Health. 2008. 256p. pap. 14.99 ***(978-1-4016-0398-4(X))*** Nelson, Thomas Inc.
Rundell, Simon. Creative Ideas for Sacramental Worship with Children. 2011. (Creative Ideas Ser.). 128p. pap. 28.99 ***(978-1-84825-092-5(4),*** Canterbury Pr. Norwich) Hymns Ancient & Modern Ltd GBR. Dist: Westminster John Knox Pr.
Ruthruff, Ron. The Least of These: Lessons Learned from Kids on the Street. 2010. (ENG.). 208p. 19.99 *(978-1-59669-272-5(3))* New Hope Pubs.
Sasson, Vanessa R. Little Buddhas: Children & Childhoods in Buddhist Texts & Traditions. 2012. ***(978-0-19-986026-5(2))*** Oxford Univ. Pr., Inc.
Seamands, David. Dejando a un Lado lo Que Es de Nino: Putting Away Childish Things. (SPA.). *(978-84-7645-136-6(9),* 223185) Clie, Editorial.
Shoemaker, Tim. Mashed Potatoes, Paint Balls: And Other Indoor/Outdoor Devotionals You Can Do with Your Kids. 2007. (Illus.). 165p. pap. 12.99 *(978-1-60066-135-8(1))* WingSpread Publishers.
Sims, David A. The Child in American Evangelicalism & the Problem of Affluence: A Theological Anthropology of the Affluent American-Evangelical Child in Late Modernity. 2009. 346p. pap. 38.00 *(978-1-55635-957-6(8),* Pickwick Pubns.) Wipf & Stock Pubs.
Sisemore, Timothy A. Our Covenant with Kids: Biblical Nurture in Home & Church. 2008. (ENG.). 208p. pap. 12.99 *(978-1-84550-350-5(3))* Christian Focus Pubns. GBR. Dist: STL Distribution North America.
Smallman, Stephen. How Our Children Come to Faith. 2007. (Basics of the Reformed Faith Ser.). 32p. pap. 3.50 *(978-1-59638-053-0(5))* P & R Publishing.
Smith, Dorothy. How to Be a Successful Christian in Today's Troublesome Schools. 2007. 112p. per. 12.95 *(978-0-595-46190-5(5))* iUniverse, Inc.
Spindle, Blair. Fuel: In Depth Discipleship Bible Study. 2007. 48p. 3.99 *(978-0-8341-5016-4(6))* Beacon Hill Pr. of Kansas City.
Staal, David. Words Kids Need to Hear, 1 vol. 2008. (ENG.). 144p. pap. 12.99 *(978-0-310-28098-9(2))* Zondervan.
Stanley, Charles F. When Your Children Hurt, 0 vols. 2008. 160p. per. 7.99 *(978-1-4002-0098-6(9))* Nelson, Thomas Inc.
Stapf, Irvin F., Jr. Not for This Life Only: A Study for Growth into Maturity as the Children of God. 2009. (J). pap. 11.99 *(978-1-60799-753-5(3))* Tate Publishing & Enterprises, LLC.
Stephens, Myrtice Walters. On My Mother's Prayers: Save the Children. 2011. 48p. pap. 9.95 ***(978-1-4620-3068-2(8))*** iUniverse, Inc.
Stonehouse, Catherine & May, Scottie. Listening to Children on the Spiritual Journey: Guidance for Those Who Teach & Nurture, 1 vol. 2010. (ENG., Illus.). 192p. (C). pap. 20.00 *(978-0-8010-3236-3(9))* Baker Academic.
Stoner, Marcia J., ed. Live It! Living Positively in a Media Age for Tweens: Building Skills for Christian Living. 2006. (Live It! Ser.). (Illus.). 63p. 15.95 *(978-0-687-49785-0(X))* Abingdon Pr.
Taylor, Kenneth Nathaniel. Big Thoughts for Little People: ABC's to Help You Grow. 2009. (ENG.). 64p. (J). 14.99 *(978-1-4143-3310-6(2),* Tyndale Kids) Tyndale Hse. Pubs.
Titus, Devi. The Table Experience: Discover What Creates Deeper, More Meaningful Relationships. 2009. 208p. 21.99 *(978-1-935245-13-1(9))* HigherLife Development Services, Inc.
Tolbert, La Verne. Keeping You & Your Kids Sexually Pure. 2009. 188p. 30.99 *(978-1-4415-1415-8(5));* pap. 20.99 *(978-1-4415-1414-1(7))* Xlibris Corp.
Unilit Staff. Guia Diaria: Jovenes-Acuerdate de Tu Creador.Tr. of Agenda: Youth - Remember Your Creator. (SPA.). 1.99 *(978-1-56063-551-2(7),* 491409) Editorial Unilit.
Van Bronkhorst, Kathie. Vertical Truths for Kids: (of all Ages) 2009. 48p. pap. 20.49 *(978-1-4389-9731-5(0))* AuthorHouse.
Wapnick, Kenneth. Parents & Children: Our Most Difficult Classroom, 2 vols. 2007. 215p. pap. 14.00 *(978-1-59142-205-1(1),* B22) Foundation for "A Course in Miracles".
Williams, Jeri. Raising Prophetic Kids. 2009. (J). pap. *(978-1-61584-372-5(8))* Independent Pub.
Williams, Joseph L. & Staples, Melina H. Feed the Hunger: Do something that will outlive you / A 31-day devotional journey about children around the World. 2010. 148p. pap. 14.95 *(978-1-4327-6525-6(5))* Outskirts Pr., Inc.
Wolfe, Jaymie Stuart. Honoring Mary with the Holy Father. 2011. (J). pap. 9.95 ***(978-0-8198-3409-6(2))*** Pauline Bks. & Media.
Wright, H. Norman. It's Okay to Cry: A Parents' Guide to Helping Children through the Losses of Life: an Interactive Recovery Work Book. 2006. 133p. reprint ed. pap. 11.00 *(978-1-4223-5487-2(3))* DIANE Publishing Co.
Wright, Una. For Children Only, Volume II: A Book of Object Lessons for Young Children. 2009. 100p. pap. 12.85 *(978-1-4269-1622-9(1))* Trafford Publishing.
Wuthnow, Robert. After the Baby Boomers: How Twenty - And Thirty - Somethings Are Shaping the Future of American Religion. 2010. (ENG., Illus.). 320p. (C). pap. 25.95 *(978-0-691-14614-0(4))* Princeton Univ. Pr.
Wyller, Trygve & Nayar, Usha S. The Given Child: The Religions' Contributions to Children's Citizenship. 2007. (Research in Contemporary Religion Ser.). (ENG., Illus.). 199p. (C). 59.00 *(978-3-525-60436-6(X))* Vandenhoeck & Ruprecht GmbH & Co. KG DEU. Dist: ISD.
Zacharias, Ravi. Vuelva A Maravillarse: Como Recuperar el Regalo Divino de Asombramos Que Tuvimos de Ninos. Varisco, Marta, tr. 2006. 191p. 9.00 *(978-0-311-46029-8(1),* Editorial Mundo Hispano) Casa Bautista de Publicaciones.

CHILDREN—RESIDENTIAL CARE

see Children—Institutional Care

CHILDREN—SERVICES FOR

see also Child Care Services; Child Health Services

Adams, Christine. Poverty, Charity, & Motherhood: Maternal Societies in Nineteenth-Century France. 2010. (ENG.). 280p. 45.00 *(978-0-252-03547-0(X))* Univ. of Illinois Pr.
Albert, Isabel. Innerfamiliäre Gewalt gegen Kinder: Eine kriminologische und rechtliche Betrachtung der Erscheinungsformen, Ursachen und Möglichkeiten der Bekämpfung. 2008. (Würzburger Schriften zur Kriminalwissenschaft Ser.).

C

292p. pap. 74.95 *(978-3-631-57862-9(8))* Lang, Peter GmbH, Europaischer Verlag der Wissenschaften DEU. Dist: Lang, Peter.

Anning, Angela & Ball, Mog, eds. Improving Services for Young Children: From Sure Start to Children's Centres. 2008. (Illus.). 192p. (C). 116.00 *(978-1-4129-4821-0(5)*, B48210C); pap. 55.00 *(978-1-4129-4822-7(3)*, B48210P) SAGE Pubns., Ltd. GBR. Dist: SAGE Pubns., Inc.

Anning, Angela, et al. Developing Multiprofessional Teamwork for Integrated Children's Services. 2nd ed. 2010. (ENG., Illus.). 168p. (C). pap. 43.00 *(978-0-335-23811-8(4)*, 0335238114) McGraw-Hill Education GBR. Dist: McGraw-Hill Cos., The.

Ashton, Kelly & Weinberg, Pamela. City Baby New York: The Ultimate Guide for New York City Parents, from Pregnancy to Preschool. 4th ed. 2010. (ENG.). 304p. pap. 19.95 *(978-0-7893-2030-8(4))* Universe Publishing.

Axford, Nick. Defining & Classifying Children in Need. 2009. (Library of Essays in Child Welfare & Development Ser.). (Illus.). 436p. 225.00 *(978-0-7546-2556-8(7))* Ashgate Publishing Co.

—Exploring Concepts of Child Well-Being: Implications for Children's Services. (Policy Press - Studies in Poverty, Inequality & Social Exclusion Ser.). 272p. 2012. pap. 42.95 ***(978-1-4473-0585-9(X))*** 2008. (C). 125.00 *(978-1-84742-065-7(6))* Policy Pr. GBR. Dist: Chicago Distribution Ctr.

Barker, Judy & Hodes, Deborah. The Child in Mind. 3rd rev. ed. 2007. (Illus.). 128p. 31.95 *(978-0-415-42602-2(2))* Routledge.

Beaty, Carole. Integrated Children's Centres: Overcoming Barriers to Truly Integrated Services. 2010. (Illus.). 256p. 36.95 *(978-0-415-47915-8(0))*; 112.00 *(978-0-415-47914-1(2))* Taylor & Francis Group.

Beecham, Jennifer & Sinclair, Ian. Costs & Outcomes in Children's Social Care: Messages from Research. 2006. (ENG., Illus.). 144p. per. *(978-1-84310-496-4(2))* Kingsley, Jessica Ltd.

Belanger, Kathleen & Brooks, Susan. Guidelines for Cultural Competence in Rural Child Welfare. 2010. *(978-1-58760-127-9(3)*, CWLA Pr.) Child Welfare League of America, Inc.

Belton, Brian, et al. Supervision: Praxis & Purpose: Developing A Critical Model of Practice for Those Working with Children & Young People Post Munro. 2011. (Illus.). 144p. pap. 33.95 ***(978-1-905541-78-2(3))*** Russell Hse. Publishing Ltd. GBR. Dist: International Specialized Bk. Services.

Ben-Arieh, Asher & Goerge, Robert M., eds. Indicators of Children's Well-Being: Understanding Their Role, Usage & Policy Influence. 2010. (Social Indicators Research Ser.). xi, 204p. pap. 169.00 *(978-90-481-7081-4(8)*, 9048170818) Springer.

Ben-Aryeh, Asher & Frones, Ivar. Indicators of Children's Well-Being: Theory & Practice in a Multi-Cultural Perspective. 2008. (Social Indicators Research Ser.). (ENG., Illus.). xii, 592p. 239.00 *(978-1-4020-9303-6(9)*, 1402093039) Springer.

Bishop-Josef, Sandra J., et al, eds. Child Development & Social Policy: Knowledge for Action. 2006. (Decade of Behavior Ser.). (Illus.). 311p. 39.95 *(978-1-59147-425-8(6))* American Psychological Assn.

Borkowski, John G. & Weaver, Chelsea M., eds. Prevention: The Science & Art of Promoting Health Child & Adolescent Development. 2006. 298p. per. 39.95 *(978-1-55766-868-4(X)*, 868X) Brookes, Paul H. Publishing Co.

Briggs, Mary & Briggs, Ian. Developing Your Leadership in the Early Years. 2009. (ENG., Illus.). 168p. 39.95 *(978-1-84706-233-8(4))* Continuum International Publishing Group, Ltd. GBR. Dist: National Bk. Network.

Burnier-Smith, Dennis. Thomas John Barnardo, His Life, Homes & Orphanages: A Short History. 2010. (Illus.). 76p. pap. 11.49 *(978-1-4490-9042-5(7))* AuthorHouse.

Caring for Special Needs During Disasters: What's Being Done for Vulnerable Populations?: Hearing Before the Subcommittee on Emergency Communications, Preparedness, & Response of the Committee on Homeland Security, House of Representatives, One Hundred Eleventh Congress, Second Session, June 15, 2010. 2011. iii, 82p. ***(978-0-16-088709-3(7)***, 552-070-42867-4) United States Government Printing Office.

Causton-Theoharis, Julie. The Paraprofessional's Handbook for Effective Support in Inclusive Classrooms. 2009. 144p. pap. 26.95 *(978-1-55766-899-8(X))* Brookes, Paul H. Publishing Co.

Challenges Facing the Child Welfare System: Hearing Before the Subcommittee on Income Security & Family Support of the Committee on Ways & Means, U.S. House of Representatives, One Hundred Tenth Congress, First Session, May 15, 2007. 2008. (Illus.). iii, 136p. *(978-0-16-081803-5(6)*, 552-070-38009-4) United States Government Printing Office.

Cheminais, Rita. Effective Multi-Agency Partnerships: Putting Every Child Matters into Practice. 2009. 160p. 125.00 *(978-1-84860-138-3(7)*, B01383C); pap. 51.00 *(978-1-84860-139-0(5)*, B01383P) SAGE Pubns., Ltd. GBR. Dist: SAGE Pubns., Inc.

—The Pocket Guide to Every Child Matters: An at the glance overview for the busy Teacher. 2009. (ENG., Illus.). 102p. 26.95 *(978-0-415-47917-2(7))* Taylor & Francis Group.

Cram101 Textbook Reviews & Cram101 Textbook Reviews. Outlines & Highlights for Ensuring Every Child Matters: A Critical Approach by Gianna Knowles, ISBN. 2011. 116p. pap. 28.95 ***(978-1-61461-070-0(3))*** Cram101 Inc.

—Outlines & Highlights for Understanding Child Abuse & Neglect by Cynthia Crosson-Tower, Isbn: 9780205769155 0205769152. 2011. 170p. pap. 29.95 ***(978-1-4288-9068-8(8))*** Cram101 Inc.

Dabir, Neela. From Street to Hope: Faith Based & Secular Programmes in Los Angeles, Mumbai & Nairobi for Street-living Children. 2011. (Illus.). 336p. (C). 40.00 ***(978-81-321-0513-8(3)***, B05138C) SAGE Pubns., Inc.

Danielson, Caroline & Lee, Helen. Foster Care in California: Achievements & Challenges. 2010. *(978-1-58213-139-9(2))* Public Policy Institute of California.

Davies, Carolyn & Ward, Harriet. Safeguarding Children Across Services: Messages from Research. 2011. (Illus.). 224p. pap. ***(978-1-84905-124-8(0))*** Kingsley, Jessica Ltd.

Davies, Liz. Protecting Children: A resource Book. 2nd ed. 2010. (ENG., Illus.). 136p. pap. *(978-1-905179-07-7(3)*, Lonely Scribe) Armadillo Design Ltd.

Davis, John B. Integrated Children's Services. 2011. 160p. (C). 104.00 *(978-1-84920-730-0(5)*, B07300C); pap. 45.00 *(978-1-84920-731-7(3)*, B07300P) SAGE Pubns., Ltd. GBR. Dist: SAGE Pubns., Inc.

De Carvalho, Sarah. The Street Children of Brazil: One Woman's Remarkable Story. 2009. (ENG.). 256p. 14.95 *(978-0-340-98008-8(7)*, Hodder & Stoughton) Hodder General Publishing Div. GBR. Dist: Independent Pubs. Group.

Delgado Fuentes, Marco Antonio. Community Involvement in Services for Children, Families. 2009. 252p. pap. *(978-3-639-16039-0(8))* VDM Verlag Dr. Mueller e.K.

Dennison, Wally. For the Love of God's Kids. 2007. (ENG.). 384p. per. *(978-1-55452-110-4(6))* Essence Publishing.

Depaul, Aldrick, ed. Youth with Disabilities in the Foster Care System: Solutions for Barriers to Success. 2010. (Disability & the Disabled - Issues, Laws & Programs Ser.). 137.00 *(978-1-60741-530-5(5))* Nova Science Pubs., Inc.

Dicker, Sheryl. Reversing the Odds: Improving Outcomes for Babies in the Child Welfare System. 2009. 216p. pap. 29.95 *(978-1-55766-961-2(9))* Brookes, Paul H. Publishing Co.

Dodge, Kenneth A. Preventing Child Maltreatment: Community Approaches. Dodge, Kenneth A. & Coleman, Doriane Lambelet, eds. 2009. (Duke Series in Child Development & Public Policy Ser.). (ENG., Illus.). 203p. 45.00 *(978-1-59385-973-2(2))* Guilford Pubns., Inc.

Dorland Health, creator. The National Directory of Children, Youth & Families Services: The Professionals' Reference. 2008. (National Directory of Children, Youth & Families Services Ser.). 1036p. pap. 199.00 *(978-1-885461-26-1(7))* Contexo Media.

Douglas, Jo, et al. A Community Health Approach to the Assessment of Infants & Their Parents: The CARE Programme. 2006. (ENG., Illus.). 234p. per. 60.95 *(978-0-470-09252-1(1)*, Wiley) Wiley, John & Sons, Inc.

D'Souza, Barnabe. From Ecstasy to Agony & Back: Journeying with Adolescents on the Street. 2011. (Illus.). 252p. (C). pap. 40.00 ***(978-81-321-0703-3(9)***, B07033C) SAGE Pubns., Inc.

Dunhill, Ally, et al, eds. Effective Communication & Engagement with Children & Young People, their Families & Carers. 2009. (Illus.). 118p. pap. *(978-1-84445-265-1(4))* Learning Matters Ltd.

Edwards, Anne, et al. Improving Inter-Professional Collaborations: Learning to Do Multi-Agency Work. 2009. (Improving Learning Ser.). (ENG., Illus.). 222p. pap. 41.95 *(978-0-415-46870-1(1))*; 150.00 *(978-0-415-46869-5(8))* Routledge.

Eyal, Gil. The Autism Matrix: The Social Origins of the Autism Epidemic. 2010. (ENG., Illus.). 240p. 69.95 *(978-0-7456-4399-1(X))*; pap. 24.95 *(978-0-7456-4400-4(7))* Polity Pr. GBR. Dist: Wiley, John & Sons, Inc.

Fellmeth, Robert C. Child Rights & Remedies. 3rd enl. ed. 2011. (ENG.). 840p. pap. 49.95 ***(978-0-9833539-1-1(3))*** Clarity Pr., Inc.

Fiedler, Craig R. & Clark, Denise M. Making a Difference: Advocacy Competencies for Special Education Professionals. 2nd ed. 2008. 41.00 *(978-1-4164-0377-7(9))* PRO-ED, Inc.

Foley, Pam. Changing Children's Services: Working & Learning Together. Rixon, Andy, ed. 2008. (Illus.). 312p. pap. 35.95 *(978-1-84742-060-2(5))* Policy Pr. GBR. Dist: Chicago Distribution Ctr.

—Children & Young People's Spaces: Developing Practice. Leverett, Steve, ed. 2010. (ENG., Illus.). 240p. pap. 35.00 *(978-0-230-28009-0(9))* Palgrave Macmillan.

Foley, Pam & Leverett, Stephen. Connecting with Children: Developing Working Relationships. 2008. (Illus.). 312p. (C). pap. 35.95 *(978-1-84742-058-9(3))* Policy Pr. GBR. Dist: Chicago Distribution Ctr.

Forbes, Joan & Watson, Cate, eds. The Transformation of Childrens Services. 2011. (ENG., Illus.). 216p. (C). 144.00 *(978-0-415-61847-2(9))*; pap. 51.95 *(978-0-415-61849-6(5))* Routledge.

Garrett, Paul Michael. Transforming Children's Services? Social Work, Children & Families in a Modern World. 2009. (ENG.). 200p. (C). pap. 49.00 *(978-0-335-23425-7(9)*, 0335234259) McGraw-Hill Education GBR. Dist: McGraw-Hill Cos., The.

—Transforming Children's Services? Social Work, Neoliberalism & the 'Modern' World. 2009. (ENG.). 200p. (C). 127.00 *(978-0-335-23424-0(0)*, 0335234240) McGraw-Hill Education GBR. Dist: McGraw-Hill Cos., The.

Gharabaghi, Kiaras. Professional Issues in Child & Youth Care Practice. 2010. (ENG.). 248p. (C). 125.00 *(978-0-415-58297-1(0))* Routledge.

Gonzalez-Mena, Janet. 50 Strategies for Communicating & Working with Diverse Families. 2nd ed. 2009. (ENG.). 144p. (C). pap. 27.60 *(978-0-13-700231-3(9)*, Prentice Hall) Prentice Hall PTR.

Haight, Wendy L., et al. Children of Methamphetamine-Involved Families: The Case of Rural Illinois. 2008. (ENG., Illus.). 288p. 35.00 *(978-0-19-532605-5(9))* Oxford Univ. Pr., Inc.

Harrison, Roger, et al, eds. Leading Work with Young People. 2007. (Published in Association with the Open University Ser.). (Illus.). 312p. (C). 120.00 *(978-1-4129-4603-2(4)*, B46032C); per. 44.00 *(978-1-4129-4604-9(2)*, B46032P) SAGE Pubns., Ltd. GBR. Dist: SAGE Pubns., Inc.

Health Care for Children in Foster Care: Hearing Before the Subcommittee on Income Security & Family Support of the Committee on Ways & Means, U.S. House of Representatives, One Hundred Tenth Congress, First Session, July 19, 2007. 2008. (Illus.). iii, 89p. *(978-0-16-082173-8(8)*, 552-070-38308-5) United States Government Printing Office.

Higgs, Jacqueline. Corporate Parenting: The Contribution of Designated Teachers. 2009. 220p. pap. *(978-3-639-12975-5(X))* VDM Verlag Dr. Mueller e.K.

Hill, Malcolm, et al. Children's Services: Working Together. 2012. (ENG.). 416p. pap. ***(978-1-4082-3725-0(3))*** Addison-Wesley Longman, Inc.

Hoggarth, Liz, et al. Managing Modern Youth Work. 2009. (Empowering Youth & Community Work Practice Ser.). (Illus.). 146p. pap. *(978-1-84445-206-4(9))* Learning Matters Ltd.

Holmes, Lisa & McDermid, Samantha. Understanding Costs & Outcomes in Child Welfare Services: A Comprehensive Costing Approach to Managing Your Resources. 2012. (ENG.). 240p. pap. ***(978-1-84905-214-6(X))*** Kingsley, Jessica Ltd.

Hunter, William. Through Our Eyes: A Foster Family Shares Their Secret World. 2010. (ENG.). 274p. pap. 38.99 *(978-0-7618-5067-0(8))* Hamilton Bks.

Improving the Child Welfare System: Hearing Before the Subcommittee on Income Security & Family Support of the Committee on Ways & Means, U.S. House of Representatives, One Hundred Tenth Congress, Second Session, February 27, 2008. 2009. iii, 185p. *(978-0-16-082947-5(X)*, 552-070-38859-1) United States Government Printing Office.

Iwaniec, Dorota, ed. The Child's Journey Through Care: Placement Stability, Care Planning, & Achieving Permanency. 2006. (ENG., Illus.). 304p. 164.95 *(978-0-470-01137-9(8))*; per. 65.00 *(978-0-470-01138-6(6))* Wiley, John & Sons, Inc. (Wiley).

Jaycox, Lisa H. National Evaluation of Safe Start Promising Approaches: Assessing Program Outcomes, 1 vol. 2011. (ENG.). 82p. pap. 24.50 ***(978-0-8330-5822-5(3))*** RAND Corp., The.

Jones, Phil & Walker, Gary, eds. Children's Rights in Practice. 2011. 256p. (C). 104.00 *(978-1-84920-379-1(2)*, B03791C); pap. 45.00 *(978-1-84920-380-7(6)*, B03791P) SAGE Pubns., Ltd. GBR. Dist: SAGE Pubns., Inc.

Kaoukji, Dwan & M'Jid, Najat. Children's Services in the Developing World. 2009. (Library of Essays in Child Welfare & Development Ser.). (Illus.). 412p. 225.00 *(978-0-7546-2779-1(9))* Ashgate Publishing Co.

Kay, Janet & Fitzgerald, Damien. Working Together in Children's Services. 2007. (Illus.). VI, 146p. 37.50 *(978-1-84312-467-2(X))* Fulton, David Pubs. GBR. Dist: Taylor & Francis Group.

Keen, Shellie, et al. Why Me? A Programme for Children & Young People Who Have Experienced Victimization. 2010. (ENG., Illus.). 128p. pap. *(978-1-84905-097-5(X))* Kingsley, Jessica Ltd.

Kelly, Emma & Bokhari, Farhat, eds. Safeguarding Children from Abroad: Refugee, Asylum Seeking & Trafficked Children in the UK. 2012. (ENG., Illus.). 160p. pap. ***(978-1-84905-157-6(7))*** Kingsley, Jessica Ltd.

Knowles, Gianna. Ensuring Every Child Matters: A Critical Approach. 2009. 176p. (C). 112.00 *(978-1-84860-136-9(0)*, B01369C); pap. 47.00 *(978-1-84860-137-6(9)*, B01369P) SAGE Pubns., Ltd. GBR. Dist: SAGE Pubns., Inc.

Kohli, Ravi. Social Work with Unaccompanied Asylum Seeking Children. 2007. (ENG., Illus.). 240p. 130.00 *(978-1-4039-8965-9(6))* Palgrave Macmillan.

Kraftl, Peter, et al, eds. Critical Geographies of Childhood & Youth: Contemporary Policy & Practice. 2012. 304p. 110.00 ***(978-1-84742-846-2(0))*** Policy Pr. GBR. Dist: Chicago Distribution Ctr.

Lancaster, Y. Penny & Kirby, Perpetua. Listening to Young Children. 2nd ed. 2010. (ENG., Illus.). 254p. 345.95 *(978-0-335-24127-9(1)*, 0335241271) McGraw-Hill Education GBR. Dist: McGraw-Hill Cos., The.

Leeland, Jeff. A Thousand Small Sparrows: Amazing Stories of Kids Helping Kids. 2007. (ENG.). 256p. per. 13.99 *(978-1-59052-933-1(2)*, Multnomah) Doubleday Religious Publishing Group, The.

Levine, Phillip B. & Zimmerman, David J., eds. Targeting Investments in Children: Fighting Poverty When Resources Are Limited. 2010. (National Bureau of Economic Research Conference Report). (ENG., Illus.). 408p. 99.00 *(978-0-226-47581-3(6))* Univ. of Chicago Pr.

Lieten, G. K. Children Structure & Agency. 2012. (ENG., Illus.). 172p. pap. 39.95 ***(978-0-415-53665-3(0))*** Routledge.

Lieten, Kristoff, et al. Children, Structure, & Agency: Realities Across the Developing World. 2008. (Routledge Studies in Development & Society). (ENG., Illus.). 172p. 125.00 *(978-0-415-98973-2(6))* Routledge.

Lowenstein, Alison. City Kid New York: The Ultimate Guide for NYC Parents. 2010. (ENG.). 224p. pap. 18.95 *(978-0-7893-1878-7(4))* Universe Publishing.

McEwen, Irene, ed. Providing Physical Therapy Services under Parts B&C of IDEA (2nd Edition) 2009. 200p. pap. 70.00 *(978-0-9702105-1-7(5))* Section on Pediatrics, APTA.

Mcfarlane, Andrew. Hershman & Mcfarlane Children Act Handbook 2011/2012. 2011. (ENG.). 772p. pap. ***(978-1-84661-285-5(3))*** Jordan Publishing, Ltd.

McGillivray, Gillian, et al, eds. Working with Children, Young People & Families. 2010. 208p. (C). 108.00 *(978-1-84860-988-4(4)*, B09884C); pap. 41.00 *(978-1-84860-989-1(2)*, B09884P) SAGE Pubns., Ltd. GBR. Dist: SAGE Pubns., Inc.

Miller, Linda, et al. Supporting Children's Learning in the Early Years. Miller, Linda et al, eds. 2nd ed. 2009. (ENG., Illus.). (C). 246p. 37.95 *(978-0-415-49697-1(7))*; 256p. 130.00 *(978-0-415-49696-4(9))* Routledge.

Morton Palter, Elisa & Wert, Shari. Help!.. We've Got Kids: GTA's Complete Childrens Resource Directory Covering Oakville Topickering & Newmarket to the Lake. 15th ed. 2008. (Help... We've Got Kids Ser.). (Illus.). 342p. pap. *(978-1-896208-24-4(X))* Help...We've Got Kids.

Mulvey, Janet D. & Cooper, Bruce S. Intersections of Children's Health, Education, & Welfare. 2012. (Education Policy Ser.). (ENG., Illus.). 256p. 85.00 ***(978-0-230-34014-5(8))*** Palgrave Macmillan.

Nolan, Aoife. Children's Socio-Economic Rights, Democracy & the Courts, 0 vols. 2011. (ENG.). 336p. 110.00 *(978-1-84113-769-8(3))* Hart Publishing Ltd. GBR. Dist: International Specialized Bk. Services.

Oliver, Christine M. & Dalrymple, Jane, eds. Developing Advocacy for Children & Young People: Current Issues in Research, Policy & Practice. 2008. 224p. pap. *(978-1-84310-596-1(9))* Kingsley, Jessica Ltd.

O'Sullivan, June. Leadership Skills in the Early Years: Making a Difference. 2009. (ENG.). 176p. 39.95 *(978-1-85539-470-4(7)*, Network Continuum Education) Continuum International Publishing Group, Ltd. GBR. Dist: National Bk. Network.

Parton, Nigel & Frost, Nick P. Understanding Children's Social Care: Politics, Policy & Practice. 2009. (Illus.). 224p. (C). 108.00 *(978-1-4129-2349-1(2)*, B23492C); pap. 43.00 *(978-1-4129-2350-7(6)*, B23492P) SAGE Pubns., Ltd. GBR. Dist: SAGE Pubns., Inc.

Payne, Ruby K. & Slocumb, Paul D. Boys in Poverty: A Framework for Understanding Dropout. 2010. 44.95 *(978-1-935249-86-3(X))*; 160p. pap. 24.95 *(978-1-935542-22-3(2))* Solution Tree Pr.

Peck, Penny. Crash Course in Children's Services, 1 vol. 2006. (Crash Course Ser.). 136p. per. 25.00 *(978-1-59158-352-3(7)*, LU3527) Libraries Unlimited, Inc.

Percy-Smith, Barry. A Handbook of Children & Young People's Participation: Perspectives from Theory & Practice. Percy-smith, Barry & Thomas, Nigel, eds. 2009. (ENG., Illus.). 400p. (C). 160.00 *(978-0-415-46851-0(5))* Routledge.

Piper, Christine. Investing in Children: Policy, Law & Practice in Context. 2008. 256p. (C). 89.95 *(978-1-84392-325-1(4))* Willan Publishing GBR. Dist: Taylor & Francis Group.

—Investing in Children: Rights, Law & Practice in Context. 2008. 256p. (C). pap. 45.00 *(978-1-84392-324-4(6))* Willan Publishing GBR. Dist: Taylor & Francis Group.

Plimley, Lynn, et al. Autistic Spectrum Disorders in the Early Years. 2007. (Autistic Spectrum Disorder Support Kit Ser.). (Illus.). 112p. 94.00 *(978-1-4129-2314-9(X)*, B2314XC); per. 29.00 *(978-1-4129-2315-6(8)*, B2314XP) SAGE Pubns., Ltd. GBR. Dist: SAGE Pubns., Inc.

Pomerantz, Kathryn Anne, et al. How to Reach 'Hard to Reach' Children: Improving Access, Participation & Outcomes. 2007. (ENG.). 282p. per. 62.95 *(978-0-470-05884-8(6)*, Wiley) Wiley, John & Sons, Inc.

Preston-Shoot, Michael. Children's Services at the Crossroads: A Critical Evaluation of Contemporary Policy for Practice. Ayre, Patrick, ed. 2010. 144p. pap. 39.95 *(978-1-905541-64-5(3))* Russell Hse. Publishing Ltd. GBR. Dist: International Specialized Bk. Services.

Price, Margaret "Peg". Divorce & the Special Needs Child: A Guide for Parents. 2010. (ENG., Illus.). 256p. pap. *(978-1-84905-825-4(3))* Kingsley, Jessica Ltd.

Puddefoot, Ginny & Foster, Lisa K. Keeping Children Safe When Their Parents Are Arrested: Local Approaches That Work. 2007. iv, 93p. *(978-1-58703-223-3(6))* California Research Bureau.

Rapoport, Robert Norman, ed. Children, Youth, & Families: The Action-Research Relationship. 2010. (ENG.). 332p. (C). pap. 34.99 *(978-0-521-14369-1(1))* Cambridge Univ. Pr.

Reid, Gavin. Dyslexia: A Complete Guide for Parents & Those Who Help Them. 2nd ed. 2011. (ENG., Illus.). 280p. 84.95 *(978-0-470-97374-5(9))*; pap. 29.95 *(978-0-470-97373-8(0))* Wiley, John & Sons, Inc. (Wiley).

Schlaack, Holly. Invisible Kids: Marcus Fiesel's Legacy: One Short Life, One Terrible Death & 12 Things YOU Can Do to Improve the Lives of Foster Children. 2009. 201p. pap. 18.95 *(978-0-615-22976-8(X))* Advocacy Publishing.

Schroeder, Jenna. Simply Knowing, Trusting, Obeying, Doing, Living, & Serving God's Word. 2007. 88p. per. 16.95 *(978-1-4241-9841-2(0))* PublishAmerica, Inc.

Schultz, Dana, et al. National Evaluation of Safe Start: Promising Approaches - Assessing Program Implementation. 2010. (ENG.). 290p. pap. 35.00 *(978-0-8330-4968-1(2)*, tr-750) RAND Corp., The.

Sinclair, Ian, et al. The Pursuit of Permanence: A Study of the English Child Care System. 2007. (ENG.). 320p. (C). pap. *(978-1-84310-595-4(0))* Kingsley, Jessica Ltd.

Siraj-Blatchford, Iram, et al, eds. The Team Around the Child: Multi-Agency Working in the Early Years. 3rd ed. 2008. (Illus.). 192p. reprint ed. pap. 32.95 *(978-1-85856-418-0(2))* Trentham Bks. Ltd. GBR. Dist: Stylus Publishing, LLC.

Stein, Mike. Quality Matters in Children's Services: Messages from Research. 2009. (ENG., Illus.). 144p. pap. *(978-1-84310-926-6(3))* Kingsley, Jessica Ltd.

Tisdall, Kay, et al. Children, Young People & Social Inclusion: Participation for What? 2006. (Illus.). 272p. (C). pap. 39.95 *(978-1-86134-662-9(X))* Policy Pr. GBR. Dist: Chicago Distribution Ctr.

Tomlinson, Pat, et al. Childhood, Services & Provision for Children. 2008. (Illus.). 304p. pap. 55.00 *(978-1-4058-3257-1(6)*, Prentice Hall) Pearson Education, Ltd. GBR. Dist: Trans-Atlantic Pubns., Inc.

Vissing, Yvonne Marie & Vissing, Yvonne. How to Keep Your Children Safe: A Guide for Parents. 2007. (ENG., Illus.). 216p. pap. 12.95 *(978-1-58465-529-9(1))* Univ. Pr. of New England.

Wagman, Tracie. Help! . We've Got Kids. 18th ed. 2011. (Help!.. We've Got Kids Ser.). (ENG., Illus.). 278p. pap. ***(978-1-896208-27-5(4))*** Help...We've Got Kids.

Watters, Charles. Refugee Children in the Industrialised World. 2007. (ENG., Illus.). 224p. (C). 45.95 *(978-0-415-38305-6(4))* Routledge.

Westwater, Judy. Nowhere to Run: Where Do You Go When There's Nowhere Left to Hide? 2008. (ENG.). 280p. pap. 15.95 *(978-0-00-726664-7(2))* HarperCollins Pubs. Ltd. GBR. Dist: Independent Pubs. Group.

Willemsen, Jan. Children's Rights & Human Development. 2010. (Illus.). 964p. pap. 189.00 *(978-94-000-0032-2(4))* Intersentia Uitgevers N.V. BEL. Dist: International Specialized Bk. Services.

Williams, Andrew. Working with Street Children: An Approach Explored. 2011. (Illus.). 176p. pap. 29.95 ***(978-1-905541-80-5(5))*** Russell Hse. Publishing Ltd. GBR. Dist: International Specialized Bk. Services.

Woody, Robert H. Helping Children & Adolescents: Evidence-Based Strategies from Developmental & Social Psychology. 2011. 206p. 39.80 *(978-0-88937-397-6(3))* Hogrefe Publishing.

Young, Mary E. Early Child Development from Measurement to Action: A Priority for Growth & Equity. Young, Mary Eming & Richardson, Linda, eds. 2007. (Stand Alone Ser.). (ENG., Illus.). 324p. per. 35.00 *(978-0-8213-7086-5(3)*, 9780821370865) World Bank Pubns.

Zaslow, Martha, et al, eds. Quality Measurement in Early Childhood Settings. 2011. (Illus.). 456p. pap. 44.95 *(978-1-59857-161-5(3))* Brookes, Paul H. Publishing Co.

Zigler, Edward F., et al. The Tragedy of Child Care in America. 2011. 240p. pap. 26.00 *(978-0-300-17211-9(7))* Yale Univ. Pr.

Zimmermann, Carol Rapp. Desktop Guide to Reentry for Juvenile Confinement Facilities. 2007. *(978-1-56991-249-2(1))* American Correctional Assn.

CHILDREN—SLEEP

Carskadon, Mary A., ed. Adolescent Sleep Patterns: Biological, Social, & Psychological Influences. 2010. (ENG.). 318p. pap. 39.99 *(978-0-521-16869-4(4))* Cambridge Univ. Pr.

Daymond, Kate. Parenttalk Guide to Sleep. (Illus.). 176p. pap. 11.99 *(978-0-340-78541-6(1)*, Hodder & Stoughton) Hodder General Publishing Div. GBR. Dist: Trafalgar Square Publishing.

Durand, V. Mark. When Children Don't Sleep Well: Interventions for Pediatric Sleep Disorders. 2008. (Treatments That Work Ser.). (ENG., Illus.). 112p. pap., wbk. ed. 27.95 *(978-0-19-532948-3(1))* Oxford Univ. Pr., Inc.

Durand, V. Mark & Durand, Vincent Mark. When Children Don't Sleep Well: Interventions for Pediatric Sleep Disorders. 2008. (Treatments That Work Ser.). (ENG., Illus.). 160p. (C). pap., instr.'s gde. ed. 37.95 *(978-0-19-532947-6(3))* Oxford Univ. Pr., Inc.

El-Sheikh, Mona, ed. Sleep & Development: Familial & Socio-Cultural Considerations. 2011. (ENG.). 432p. 59.95 *(978-0-19-539575-4(1))* Oxford Univ. Pr., Inc.

Estivill, Eduard. 5 Days to a Perfect Night's Sleep for Your Child: The Secrets to Making Bedtime a Dream. Lethem, Mara Faye, tr. from SPA. 2008. (ENG., Illus.). 96p. per. 10.00 *(978-0-345-50180-6(2)*, Ballantine Bks.) Random House Publishing Group.

Ezzo, Gary. On Becoming Babywise: Giving Your Infant the Gift of Nighttime Sleep. 5th ed. 2012. (Illus.). 280p. pap. 13.95 ***(978-1-932740-13-4(9))*** Parent-Wise Solutions, Inc.

Ezzo, Gary & Bucknam, Robert. On Becoming Baby Wise: Giving Your Infant the Gift of Nighttime Sleep. 2006. (On Becoming... Ser.). (Illus.). 252p. per. 13.95 *(978-1-932740-08-0(2))* Parent-Wise Solutions, Inc.

Gethin, Anni & Macgregor, Beth. Helping Baby Sleep. 2009. (ENG., Illus.). 224p. pap. 15.99 *(978-1-58761-340-1(9)*, Celestial Arts) Ten Speed Pr.

—Sleep Solutions: Essential Information & Practical Advice to Soothe Crying & Help Your Child Sleep Through the Night. 2008. (ENG.). 304p. pap. 14.95 *(978-1-4022-1188-1(0))* Sourcebooks, Inc.

Hollyer, Beatrice. Sleep: The Easy Way to Peaceful Nights. 2006. (ENG., Illus.). 64p. per. 9.95 *(978-1-84188-185-0(6)*, Cassell Illustrated) Octopus Publishing Group GBR. Dist: Hachette Bk. Group.

Jordan, Laurie. Yawning Yoga: A goodnight book for a good night's Sleep. 2011. (ENG., Illus.). 64p. (J). 17.95 *(978-0-9844406-5-5(6))* 4th Street Media.

Kelmanson, Igor A. Sleep & Breathing in Infants & Young Children. 2006. (Illus.). 226p. 89.00 *(978-1-60021-279-6(4))* Nova Science Pubs., Inc.

Kheirandish-Gozal, Leila & Gozal, David, eds. Sleep Disordered Breathing in Children: A Comprehensive Clinical Guide to Evaluation & Treatment. 2012. (Respiratory Medicine Ser.). (ENG., Illus.). iv, 1062p. 279.00 ***(978-1-60761-724-2(2)***, 1607617242) Humana Pr.

Krahn, Lois E., et al, eds. Atlas of Sleep & Sleep Medicine. 2009. (Illus.). CLXp. 199.95 *(978-0-415-45008-9(X)*, Informa Healthcare) Taylor & Francis Group.

Kurcinka, Mary Sheedy. Sleepless in America: Is Your Child Misbehaving or Missing Sleep? 2007. 331p. 25.00 *(978-1-4223-6698-1(7))* DIANE Publishing Co.

Kurcinka, Mary Sheedy & Kurcinka, Mary S. Sleepless in America: Is Your Child Misbehaving... or Missing Sleep? 2007. (ENG.). 352p. pap. 13.99 *(978-0-06-073602-6(X)*, HarperPerennial) HarperCollins Pubs.

Lavin, Arthur & Glaser, Susan. Baby & Toddler Sleep Solutions for Dummies. 2007. (ENG., Illus.). 265p. per. 16.99 *(978-0-470-11794-1(X)*, For Dummies) Wiley, John & Sons, Inc.

Levine, Valerie & Levine, Valerie J. Break the Co-Sleeping Habit: How to Set Bedtime Boundaries - And Raise a Secure, Happy, Well-Adjusted Child. 2009. (ENG.). 240p. pap. 14.95 *(978-1-59869-901-2(6))* Adams Media Corp.

Lewis, Marc & Granic, Isabela. Bedtiming: The Parent's Guide to Getting Your Child to Sleep at Just the Right Age. 2010. (ENG., Illus.). 244p. pap. 14.95 *(978-1-61519-015-7(5)*, 1615190155) Experiment LLC, The.

Loughlin, Gerald M., et al, eds. Sleep & Breathing in Children: Developmental Changes in Breathing During Sleep. 2nd rev. ed. 2008. (Lung Biology in Health & Disease Ser.). (ENG., Illus.). 648p. 200.00 *(978-1-4200-6082-9(1)*, Informa Healthcare) Taylor & Francis Group GBR. Dist: Taylor & Francis Group.

Loughlin, Gerald M. & Marcus, Carole, eds. Sleep in Children Set: Developmental Changes in Sleep Patterns, 2 vols. 2nd rev. ed. 2008. (ENG., Illus.). 1080p. 370.00 *(978-1-4200-8001-8(6)*, Informa Healthcare) Taylor & Francis Group GBR. Dist: Taylor & Francis Group.

Marcus, Carole, et al, eds. Sleep in Children: Developmental Changes in Sleep Patterns. 2nd rev. ed. 2008. (ENG., Illus.). 432p. 200.00 *(978-1-4200-6080-5(5))* CRC Pr. LLC.

Mindell, Jodi A. Sleep Deprived No More: From Pregnancy to Early Motherhood-Helping You & Your Baby Sleep Through the Night. 2007. (ENG.). 304p. per. 14.95 *(978-1-56924-255-1(0))* Da Capo Pr., Inc.

Moore, Polly. The 90-Minute Baby Sleep Program: Follow Your Child's Natural Sleep Rhythms for Better Nights & Naps. 2008. (ENG., Illus.). 184p. pap. 9.95 *(978-0-7611-4311-6(4)*, 0761143114) Workman Publishing Co., Inc.

Oliver, Christopher. Baby Sleepytime: The CD Scientifically Proven to Put Your Baby to Sleep — Fast. 2007. (ENG., Illus.). 48p. 19.95 *(978-1-57826-260-1(7)*, Hatherleigh Pr.) Hatherleigh Co., Ltd., The.

Pantley, Elizabeth & Pantley. The No-Cry Nap Solution: Guaranteed Gentle Ways to Solve All Your Naptime Problems. 2008. (Pantley Ser.). (ENG., Illus.). 256p. pap. 15.95 *(978-0-07-159695-4(X)*, 007159695X) McGraw-Hill Cos., The.

Pearce, John. Baby & Toddler Sleep Programme. 160p. pap. 17.95 *(978-0-09-181571-4(1))* Random Hse. GBR. Dist: Trafalgar Square Publishing.

Sadeh, Avi. Sleeping Like a Baby: A Sensitive & Sensible Approach to Solving Your Child's Sleep Problems. 2006. 204p. reprint ed. 20.00 *(978-1-4223-5361-5(3))* DIANE Publishing Co.

Shapiro, Lawrence. It's Time to Sleep in Your Own Bed. 2008. (Transition Times Ser.). (ENG., Illus.). 32p. (J). (gr. -1). 7.95 *(978-1-57224-586-0(7))* New Harbinger Pubns.

—A Parent's Guide to Getting Kids Out of the Family Bed: A 21-Day Program. 2008. (Instant Help Ser.). (ENG., Illus.). 110p. (J). pap. 24.95 *(978-1-57224-667-6(7))* Play2Grow.

—A Parent's Guide to Getting Kids Out of the Family Bed: A Twenty-One Day Program. 2008. (Instant Help Ser.). 110p. pap. 16.95 *(978-1-931704-29-8(5))* Play2Grow.

Spungin, Pat. Silent Nights: How to develop a peaceful sleeping Routine. 2007. (ENG.). 224p. (C). pap. *(978-0-273-71479-8(1))* Pearson Education Canada.

St James-Roberts, Ian. The Origins, Prevention & Treatment of Infant Crying & Sleeping Problems: An Evidence-Based Guide to Preventing & Managing Problems for Healthcare Professionals & the Families They Support. 2012. (ENG., Illus.). 280p. (C). 120.00 *(978-0-415-60116-0(9))*; pap. 36.95 *(978-0-415-60117-7(7))* Routledge.

Tobin, M.D., Cathryn. The Lull-A-Baby Sleep Plan: The Soothing, Superfast Way to Help Your New Baby Sleep Through the Night... & Prevent Sleep Problems Before They Develop. 2006. (ENG., Illus.). 288p. per. 14.95 *(978-1-59486-222-9(2))* Rodale Pr., Inc.

Wahlgren, Anna. Gns: A Good Night's Sleep. 2009. 260p. pap. 22.35 *(978-91-977736-1-4(1))* Wahlgren, Anna AB SWE. Dist: AtlasBooks Distribution.

Waldburger, Jennifer & Spivack, Jill. The Sleepeasy Solution: The Exhausted Parent's Guide to Getting Your Child to Sleep from Birth to Age 5. 2007. (ENG., Illus.). 308p. pap. 14.95 *(978-0-7573-0560-3(1))* Health Communications, Inc.

Watson, Harriett Madayo. Good Night, Baby, Good Night: Sleep Train Your Infant or Older Baby for Nighttime Sleep. 2007. 56p. per. 9.95 *(978-0-595-41769-8(8))* iUniverse, Inc.

West, Kim. The Good Night, Sleep Tight: The Sleep Lady's Gentle Step-by-Step Guide for Tired Parents. Rhodes, Maura, ed. 2010. (ENG., Illus.). 120p. pap., wbk. ed. 13.95 *(978-0-9798248-6-9(9))* Easton Studio Pr., LLC.

—The Sleep Lady's Good Night, Sleep Tight: Gentle Proven Solutions to Help Your Child Sleep Well & Wake up Happy. 2009. (ENG.). 440p. pap. 15.95 *(978-1-59315-558-2(1))* Vanguard Pr.

—52 Sleep Secrets for Babies. 2008. (ENG.). 79p. pap. 9.95 *(978-0-9798248-4-5(2))* Easton Studio Pr., LLC.

CHILDREN—SOCIAL CONDITIONS

see also Ethnicity in Children

Adroher Biosca, Salomé, et al. Infancia en España: Nuevos Desafíos Sociales, Nuevas Respuestas Jurídicas. 2009. (SPA., Illus.). 589p. *(978-84-8468-259-2(5))* Universidad Pontificia Comillas de Madrid.

Africa's Orphaned & Vulnerable Generations: Children Affected by AIDS. 2006. (Illus.). 12p. *(978-92-806-4034-2(8))* United Nations Children's Fund, The (UNICEF).

Agger, Ben & Shelton, Beth Anne. Fast Families, Virtual Children: A Critical Sociology of Families & Schooling. 2007. (ENG.). 208p. 125.00 *(978-1-59451-339-8(2))*; per. 37.95 ***(978-1-59451-340-4(6))*** Paradigm Pubs.

Aitken, Stuart, et al, eds. Border Spaces & Revolutionary Imaginations. 2011. (ENG., Illus.). 120p. (C). 133.00 *(978-0-415-61946-2(7))* Routledge.

Ajmera, Maya, et al. Children of the U. S. A. 2008. (Illus.). 128p. (J). (gr. 3-6). 23.95 *(978-1-57091-615-1(2))* Charlesbridge Publishing, Inc.

Alozie I. Ikonne. Blame Not the Child. 2010. 108p. pap. 14.85 *(978-1-4269-1141-5(6))* Trafford Publishing.

Ame, Robert. Children's Rights in Ghana: Reality or Rhetoric? 2011. (ENG., Illus.). 310p. 75.00 *(978-0-7391-4800-6(1))* Lexington Bks.

Anderson, Vicki & Beauchamp, Miriam H., eds. Developmental Social Neuroscience & Childhood Brain Insult: Theory & Practice. 2012. (ENG.). 400p. 75.00 ***(978-1-4625-0429-9(9))*** Guilford Pubns., Inc.

Ansell, Nicola. Children, Youth & Development. 2nd rev. ed. 2013. (Routledge Perspectives on Development Ser.). (ENG., Illus.). 336p. (C). 128.00 *(978-0-415-61719-2(7))*; pap. 44.95 *(978-0-415-61720-8(0))* Routledge.

Ariantzi, Despoina. Kindheit in Byzanz: Emotionale, geistige und materielle Entwicklung im familiären Umfeld vom 6. bis zum 11. Jahrhundert. 2012. (Millennium-Studien / Millennium Studies).Tr. of Childhood in Byzantium. Emotional, Intellectual & Economic Development in Family Structures from the 6th to the 11th Century. (GER.). VIII, 384p. (gr. 17). 154.00 ***(978-3-11-026568-2(0))*** De Gruyter, Walter Inc.

Arrighi, Barbara A. & Maume, David J. Child Poverty in America Today, 4 vols. 2007. (Praeger Perspectives Ser.). (Illus.). *(978-0-275-98927-9(5)*, Praeger Pubs.) Greenwood Publishing Group, Inc.

Arrighi, Barbara A. & Maume, David J., eds. Child Poverty in America Today, 4 vols. 2007. (Praeger Perspectives Ser.). (Illus.). 792p. 300.00 *(978-0-275-98926-2(7)*, C8926, Praeger Pubs.) Greenwood Publishing Group, Inc.

Aves, Corinne. Understanding 6-7-Year-Olds. 2006. (Understanding Your Child Ser.). (ENG.). 80p. per. *(978-1-84310-467-4(9))* Kingsley, Jessica Ltd.

Axford, Nick. Defining & Classifying Children in Need. 2009. (Library of Essays in Child Welfare & Development Ser.). (Illus.). 436p. 225.00 *(978-0-7546-2556-8(7))* Ashgate Publishing Co.

Axford, Nick. Exploring Concepts of Child Well-Being: Implications for Children's Services. 2012. (Policy Press - Studies in Poverty, Inequality & Social Exclusion Ser.). 272p. pap. 42.95 ***(978-1-4473-0585-9(X))*** Policy Pr. GBR. Dist: Chicago Distribution Ctr.

Barrett, Damon, ed. Children of the Drug War. 2011. 288p. pap. 25.95 *(978-1-61770-018-7(5))* International Debate Education Assn.

Basile, Frank & Basile, Katrina, frwds. The Scenic Route: Stories from the Heartland. 2007. (Illus.). 112p. pap. *(978-0-87195-259-2(9))* Indiana Historical Society.

Belanger, Kathleen & Brooks, Susan. Guidelines for Cultural Competence in Rural Child Welfare. 2010. *(978-1-58760-127-3(3)*, CWLA Pr.) Child Welfare League of America, Inc.

Ben-Arieh, Asher & Goerge, Robert M., eds. Indicators of Children's Well-Being: Understanding Their Role, Usage & Policy Influence. 2010. (Social Indicators Research Ser.). xi, 204p. pap. 169.00 *(978-90-481-7081-4(8)*, 9048170818) Springer.

Ben-Aryeh, Asher & Frones, Ivar. Indicators of Children's Well-Being: Theory & Practice in a Multi-Cultural Perspective. 2008. (Social Indicators Research Ser.). (ENG., Illus.). xii, 592p. 239.00 *(978-1-4020-9303-6(9)*, 1402093039) Springer.

Ben-Ishai, Anat. The Prickly Pear: A Sabra in Two Worlds. 2008. 363p. pap. 17.95 *(978-1-934938-07-2(6))*, Langdon Street Pr.) Hillcrest Publishing Group, Inc.

Boyer, Rick & Boyer, Marilyn. What about Socialization: Answering the Questions about Homeschool & Social Interaction. Date not set. 150p. lib. bdg. 10.99 *(978-0-9645396-2-4(4)*, Home School Pr.) Holly Hall Pubns., Inc.

Bradford, Helen. The Well Being of Children Under 3. 2012. (Supporting Children from Birth to Three Ser.). (ENG., Illus.). 120p. 105.00 *(978-0-415-61270-8(5))*; pap. 28.95 *(978-0-415-61272-2(1))* Routledge.

Brown, Brett V., ed. Key Indicators of Child & Youth Well-Being: Completing the Picture. 2007. (ENG., Illus.). 485p. 175.00 *(978-0-8058-4809-0(6))*; per. 50.00 *(978-0-8058-6313-0(3))* Taylor & Francis Group GBR. (Psychology Press). Dist: Taylor & Francis Group.

Cadet, Jean-Robert. My Stone of Hope: From Haitian Slave Child to Abolitionist. 2011. (ENG., Illus.). 224p. 29.95 *(978-0-292-72853-0(0))*; pap. 21.95 *(978-0-292-72529-2(4))* Univ. of Texas Pr.

Canada, Geoffrey. Fist Stick Knife Gun. 2011. 14.05 *(978-0-7848-3397-1(4)*, Everbind) Marco Bk. Co.

—Fist Stick Knife Gun: A Personal History of Violence. 2010. (Illus.). 144p. pap. 14.00 *(978-0-8070-4449-0(0))* Beacon Pr.

—Fist Stick Knife Gun: A Personal of Violence. 2011. 14.05 *(978-0-7848-3590-6(X)*, Everbind) Marco Bk. Co.

—Fist Stick Knife Gun: Graphic Novel. 2011. 14.05 *(978-0-7848-3579-1(9)*, Everbind) Marco Bk. Co.

Casey. Child of Stone. 2011. 68p. pap. 10.99 ***(978-1-4670-4418-9(0))*** AuthorHouse.

Chelpi-den Hamer, Magali. Youngest Recruits: Pre-War, War & Post-War Experiences in Western Côte D'Ivoire. 2011. 79p. pap. *(978-90-8555-028-0(9)*, Pallas Publications) Amsterdam Univ. Pr.

Chery, Rene. Women & Children's Tribulation in Haiti. 2011. 260p. 29.99 ***(978-1-4628-8813-9(5))***; pap. 19.99 ***(978-1-4628-8812-2(7))*** Xlibris Corp.

Clark, Rory McDowall. Childhood in Society for Early Childhood Studies. 2010. (ENG., Illus.). 144p. pap. *(978-1-84445-384-9(7))* Learning Matters Ltd.

Cole, Jennifer & Durham, Deborah Lynn, eds. Figuring the Future: Globalization & the Temporalities of Children & Youth. 2008. (School for Advanced Research Advanced Seminar Ser.). (Illus.). 320p. pap. 29.95 *(978-1-934691-05-2(4))* School for Advanced Research Pr./SAR Pr.

Committee on the Impact of Mobility and Change on the Lives of Young Children, Schools, and Neighborhoods, et al. Student Mobility: Exploring the Impact of Frequent Moves on Achievement: Summary of a Workshop. 2010. (ENG.). 92p. pap. 21.00 *(978-0-309-15013-2(2))* National Academies Pr.

Crawford, Sally & Shepherd, Gillian, eds. Children, Childhood & Society. 2007. (Bar S Ser.). (Illus.). 106p. (C). 70.00 *(978-1-4073-0138-9(1))* British Archaeological Reports Ltd. GBR. Dist: Brown, David Bk. Co., The.

Crouse, Janice. Children at Risk: The Precarious State of Children's Well-Being in America. 2009. (ENG.). 224p. 34.95 *(978-1-4128-1076-0(0))* Transaction Pubs.

Dabir, Neela. From Street to Hope: Faith Based & Secular Programmes in Los Angeles, Mumbai & Nairobi for Street-living Children. 2011. (Illus.). 336p. (C). 40.00 ***(978-81-321-0513-8(3)***, B05138C) SAGE Pubns., Inc.

Dannerbeck, Anne, et al, eds. Quality-of-Life Research on Children & Adolescents. 2010. (Social Indicators Research Ser.). 200p. pap. 219.00 *(978-90-481-6635-0(7)*, 9048166357) Springer.

Davies, Andrew. When I Were a Lad — School Days: Snapshots from a Time When They Taught the Three 'R's. 2011. (ENG., Illus.). 144p. 14.95 *(978-1-907554-14-8(9))* Anova Bks. GBR. Dist: Independent Pubs. Group.

de Salazar, Maria. Children & Adolescents Need to Be Accepted by Society. 2007. 100p. pap. 10.00 *(978-0-8059-7452-2(0))* Dorrance Publishing Co., Inc.

Del Campo, Diana, et al. Taking Sides: Clashing Views in Childhood & Society. (Taking Sides Ser.). (ENG.). 416p. (C). 8th ed. 2009. pap. 48.00 *(978-0-07-812757-1(2)*, 0078127572) 9th ed. 2011. pap. 48.00 ***(978-0-07-805021-3(9)***, 0078050219) McGraw-Hill Higher Education. (McGraw-Hill/Dushkin).

DelCampo, Diana S. Taking Sides: Childhood & Society. 5th ed. 2006. pap. 9.95 *(978-1-4288-1720-3(4))* Cram101 Inc.

Devine, Dympna, et al, eds. Flexible Childhood? Exploring Children's Welfare in Time & Space. 2007. 238p. pap. 34.99 *(978-87-7674-202-7(4))* Univ. Pr. of Southern Denmark DNK. Dist: International Specialized Bk. Services.

Dickson, Foster, ed. Children of the Changing South: Accounts of Growing up During & after Integration. 2011. (ENG.). 196p. pap. 35.00 ***(978-0-7864-6048-9(2))*** McFarland & Co., Inc. Pubs.

D'Souza, Barnabe. From Ecstasy to Agony & Back: Journeying with Adolescents on the Street. 2011. (Illus.). 252p. (C). pap. 40.00 ***(978-81-321-0703-3(9)***, B07033C) SAGE Pubns., Inc.

Duane, Anna Mae. Suffering Childhood in Early America: Violence, Race, & the Making of the Child Victim. 2011. (ENG., Illus.). 224p. pap. 24.95 ***(978-0-8203-4058-6(8))*** Univ. of Georgia Pr.

Ejigu, Addisu Birhanu. Livelihood. 2009. 112p. pap. *(978-3-639-21383-6(1))* VDM Verlag Dr. Mueller e.K.

Epstein, Irving, ed. The Greenwood Encyclopedia of Children's Issues Worldwide, 6 vols. 2007. (Illus.). 3048p. 599.95 *(978-0-313-33614-0(8)*, GR3614, Greenwood Pr.) Greenwood Publishing Group, Inc.

Fass, Paula S. Children of a New World: Society, Culture, & Globalization. 2006. (ENG.). 304p. 75.00 *(978-0-8147-2756-0(5))*; per. 24.00 *(978-0-8147-2757-7(3))* New York Univ. Pr.

Fass, Paula S. & Grossberg, Michael, eds. Reinventing Childhood after World War II. 2011. 200p. (C). 42.50 ***(978-0-8122-4367-3(6))*** Univ. of Pennsylvania Pr.

Fernandes, Laura M., ed. Child Well-Being & Nonresident Parents. 2011. (Children's Issues, Laws & Programs Ser.). (Illus.). 262p. 195.00 *(978-1-60692-382-5(X))* Nova Science Pubs., Inc.

Fiedler, Anselm & Kuester, Isidor, eds. Child Development & Child Poverty. 2010. (Children's Issues, Laws & Programs Ser.). (Illus.). xii, 304p. 129.00 *(978-1-60741-816-0(9))* Nova Science Pubs., Inc.

Francis, Becky, et al. The Identities & Practices of High Achieving Pupils: Negotiating Achievement & Peer Cultures. 2012. (ENG., Illus.). 216p. 140.00 *(978-1-4411-5719-5(0))*; pap. 44.95 *(978-1-4411-2156-1(0))* Continuum International Publishing Group, Ltd. GBR. Dist: National Bk. Network.

Francis, Becky, et al. The Identities & Practices of High-Achieving Pupils: Negotiating Achievement & Peer Cultures. 2012. 256p. E-Book ***(978-1-4411-9923-2(3))***; E-Book ***(978-0-8264-2177-7(6))*** Continuum International Publishing Group, Ltd.

Frost, Ginger S. Victorian Childhoods, 1 vol. 2008. (Victorian Life & Times Ser.). (Illus.). 208p. 44.95 *(978-0-275-98966-8(6)*, C8966, Praeger Pubs.) Greenwood Publishing Group, Inc.

Gale Editor, ed. Information Plus Growing Up: Issues Affecting America's Youth. 2011. pap. 58.00 *(978-1-4144-4862-6(7))* Cengage Gale.

Ganaway, Bryan. Toys, Consumption, & Middle-Class Childhood in Imperial Germany, 1871-1918. 2009. (Illus.). 292p. pap. 55.95 *(978-3-03911-548-8(0))* Lang, Peter AG GBR. Dist: Lang, Peter.

Garbarino, James. Children & the Dark Side of Human Experience: Confronting Global Realities & Rethinking Child Development. 2008. (ENG.). viii, 157p. pap. 39.95 *(978-0-387-75625-7(6)*, 0387756256) Springer London, Ltd. GBR. Dist: Springer.

Garcia-Coll, C. The Impact of Immigration on Children's Development. 2011. (Contributions to Human Development Ser.). (ENG., Illus.). 154p. pap. ***(978-3-8055-9798-2(3))*** Karger, S. AG.

Garrett, Paul Michael. Transforming Children's Services? Social Work, Neoliberalism & the 'Modern' World. 2009. (ENG.). 200p. (C). 127.00 *(978-0-335-23424-0(0)*, 0335234240) McGraw-Hill Education GBR. Dist: McGraw-Hill Cos., The.

C

Gebre-Egziabher, Kinfe Abraha. The Existing Situation of Street Children in Mekelle City, Ethiopi. 2010. 96p. pap. *(978-3-639-25431-0(7))* VDM Verlag Dr. Mueller e.K.

Gee, Martha Bettis. Piece Work / Peace Work: Working Together for Peace & Sudan: 2009-2010 Mission Study for Children (Teacher's Guide) 2009. (ENG.). 100p. (J). pap. 7.00 *(978-1-933663-34-0(0)*, WD/GBGM Bks.) General Board of Global Ministries, The United Methodist Church.

Geitz, Elizabeth Rankin. I Am That Child: Changing Hearts & Changing the World. 2012. E-Book ***(978-0-8192-2779-9(X)***, Morehouse Publishing); 176p. pap. 18.00 ***(978-0-8192-2778-2(1))*** Church Publishing, Inc.

Gonzales, Gizela M. Where the Children Are. 2011. (ENG.). 167p. pap. 50.00 *(978-971-94292-6-5(7))* Artpostasia Inc. PHL. Dist: National Bk. Network.

Goodenough, Elizabeth N. A Place for Play: A Companion Volume to the Michigan Television Film Where Do the Children Play? 2008. (ENG., Illus.). 284p. pap. 32.50 *(978-0-615-20282-2(9))* National Institute for Play.

Graham, Paul, ed. Inheriting Poverty? the Link Between Children's Wellbeing & Unemployment in South Afric. 2007. 144p. pap. *(978-1-920118-24-2(1))* IDASA Pubs. ZAF. Dist: Michigan State Univ. Pr.

Gutman, Marta, ed. Designing Modern Childhoods: History, Space, & the Material Culture of Children. 2008. (Rutgers Series in Childhood Studies). (ENG., Illus.). 368p. 70.00 *(978-0-8135-4195-2(6))* Rutgers Univ. Pr.

Gutman, Marta & de Coninck-Smith, Ning, eds. Designing Modern Childhoods: History, Space, & the Material Culture of Children. 2008. (Rutgers Series in Childhood Studies). (ENG., Illus.). 368p. per. 24.95 *(978-0-8135-4196-9(4))* Rutgers Univ. Pr.

Haider, Syed Imran. Life of Afghan Scavenger Children in Pakistan. 2010. 100p. pap. *(978-3-639-28681-6(2))* VDM Verlag Dr. Mueller e.K.

Handa, Sudhanshu, et al, eds. Social Protection for Africas Children. 2010. (Routledge Studies in Development Economics Ser.). (ENG., Illus.). 272p. (C). 140.00 *(978-0-415-58333-6(0)*, Routledge) Taylor & Francis Group GBR. Dist: Taylor & Francis Group.

Harding, Lorraine Fox & Smith, Roger. A Universal Child? 2009. (ENG.). 208p. pap. 29.00 *(978-1-4039-0785-1(4))* Palgrave Macmillan.

—A Universal Child? 2009. (ENG.). 208p. 90.00 *(978-1-4039-0784-4(6))* Palgrave Macmillan.

Harper, Caroline, et al, eds. Children in Crisis: Seeking Child-Sensitive Policy Responses. 2012. (Rethinking International Development Ser.). (ENG., Illus.). 256p. 85.00 ***(978-0-230-31397-2(3))*** Palgrave Macmillan.

Hartas, Dimitra. Right to Childhoods: Critical Perspectives on Rights, Difference & Knowledge in a Transient World. 2010. (ENG.). 232p. 49.95 *(978-1-4411-7642-4(X))* Continuum International Publishing Group, Ltd. GBR. Dist: National Bk. Network.

Hartas, Dimitra & Hartas. Right to Childhoods: Critical Perspectives on Rights, Difference & Knowledge in a Transient World. 2008. (ENG.). 232p. 150.00 *(978-0-8264-9568-6(0))* Continuum International Publishing Group, Ltd. GBR. Dist: National Bk. Network.

Heath, Samuel D. G. To Kill a Mockingbird: A critique on behalf of Children. 2007. 80p. per. 10.95 *(978-0-595-44369-7(9))* iUniverse, Inc.

Helander, Einar. Children & Violence: The World of the Defenceless. 2008. (ENG., Illus.). 288p. 105.00 *(978-0-230-57394-9(0))* Palgrave Macmillan.

Hoffman, Deborah. The Littlest Enemies: Children in the Shadow of the Gulag. 2009. 189p. *(978-0-89357-366-9(3))* Slavica Pubs.

Hörschelmann, Kathrin & Colls, Rachel, eds. Contested Bodies of Childhood & Youth. 2009. (ENG., Illus.). 288p. 100.00 *(978-0-230-20138-5(5))* Palgrave Macmillan.

Humphries, Jane. Childhood & Child Labour in the British Industrial Revolution. 2011. (Cambridge Studies in Economic History - Second Ser.). (ENG., Illus.). 454p. pap. 34.99 ***(978-0-521-24896-9(5))*** Cambridge Univ. Pr.

Hungerland, Beatrice, et al, eds. Working to Be Someone: Child Focused Research & Practice with Working Children. 2007. (ENG., Illus.). 272p. per. *(978-1-84310-523-7(3))* Kingsley, Jessica Ltd.

James, Allison & James, Adrian L. Key Concepts in Childhood Studies. 2008. (SAGE Key Concepts Ser.). 160p. (C). 98.00 *(978-1-4129-0878-8(7)*, B08787C); pap. 36.00 *(978-1-4129-0879-5(5)*, B08787P) SAGE Pubns., Ltd. GBR. Dist: SAGE Pubns., Inc.

James, Allison & James, Adrian L., eds. European Childhoods: Cultures, Politics & Childhoods in the European Union. 2008. (ENG.). 272p. 100.00 *(978-1-4039-9750-0(0))* Palgrave Macmillan.

Johnson, Heather Beth. Children & Youth Speak for Themselves. 2010. (Illus.). 493p. 164.95 *(978-1-84950-734-9(1))* Emerald Group Publishing Ltd. GBR. Dist: Turpin Distribution Services Ltd.

Kassem, Derek. Childhood & Youth Studies: Critical Issues. Murphy, Lisa & Taylor, Elizabeth, eds. 2009. (ENG., Illus.). 240p. (C). pap. 39.95 *(978-0-415-46889-3(2))* Routledge.

—Key Issues in Childhood & Youth Studies. Murphy, Lisa & Taylor, Elizabeth, eds. 2009. (ENG., Illus.). 240p. (C). 125.00 *(978-0-415-46888-6(4))* Routledge.

Kovats-Bernat, J. Christopher. Sleeping Rough in Port-au-Prince: An Ethnography of Street Children & Violence in Haiti. 2008. (ENG.). 256p. pap. 29.95 *(978-0-8130-3302-0(0))* Univ. Pr. of Florida.

Krinsky, Charles. Moral Panics over Contemporary Children & Youth. 2008. 270p. 114.95 *(978-0-7546-7465-8(7))* Ashgate Publishing Co.

Kuppuswamy, Jayashree. Development Intervention: The Rational of a Pro-Poor State. 2010. 144p. pap. *(978-3-639-24672-8(1))* VDM Verlag Dr. Mueller e.K.

Lareau, Annette. Unequal Childhoods: Class, Race, & Family Life, Second Edition with an Update a Decade Later. 2nd rev. ed. 2011. (ENG., Illus.). 480p. pap. 24.95 *(978-0-520-27142-5(4))* Univ. of California Pr.

Lerner, Loren, ed. Depicting Canada's Children. 2009. (Studies in Childhood & Family in Canada Ser.). (ENG., Illus.). 468p. 95.00 *(978-1-55458-050-7(1))* Wilfrid Laurier Univ. Pr. CAN. Dist: Univ. of Toronto Pr.

LeVine, Robert A. & New, Rebecca S., eds. Anthropology & Child Development: A Cross-Cultural Reader. 2008. (Wiley-Blackwell Anthologies in Social & Cultural Anthropology Ser.: 3). (ENG., Illus.). 336p. pap. 49.95 *(978-0-631-22976-6(0)*, Wiley-Blackwell) Wiley, John & Sons, Inc.

Lindsey, Duncan, ed. Child Poverty & Inequality: Securing a Better Future for America's Children. 2008. (ENG., Illus.). 208p. 31.99 *(978-0-19-530544-9(2))* Oxford Univ. Pr., Inc.

Loreman, Tim & Loreman. Respecting Childhood. 2009. (ENG., Illus.). 152p. 130.00 *(978-0-8264-3370-1(7))* Continuum International Publishing Group, Ltd. GBR. Dist: National Bk. Network.

Mayers, Lynne. A Dangerous Place to Work! 2008. (Illus.). 108p. pap. 16.95 *(978-0-9556896-0-4(0))* Blaize Bailey Bks. GBR. Dist: Lulu Enterprises Inc.

McLanahan, Sara, ed. Opportunity in America: Number 2, Fall 2006. 2006. (Future of Children Ser.). (Illus.). 196p. per. 24.95 *(978-0-8157-5563-0(5))* Brookings Institution Pr.

McNamee, Abigail. Being Puerto Rican & American, Nuyorican Children's Voices. 2009. 116p. 22.50 *(978-1-60693-920-8(3)*, Eloquent Bks.) AEG Literary Publishing Services, Inc.

Menezes, Edirle. Children S Play & the Socio-Cultural Nature of Subjectivity. 2008. 156p. pap. *(978-3-639-08771-0(2))* VDM Verlag Dr. Mueller e.K.

Milanich, Nara B. Children of Fate: Childhood, Class, & the State in Chile, 1850-1930. 2009. (ENG., Illus.). 376p. 94.95 *(978-0-8223-4557-2(9))*; pap. 25.95 *(978-0-8223-4574-9(9))* Duke Univ. Pr.

Minujin, Alberto & Nandy, Shailen, eds. Global Child Poverty & Well-Being: Measurement, Concepts, Policy & Action. 2012. (Studies in Poverty, Inequality & Social Exclusion). (Illus.). 320p. 110.00 *(978-1-84742-482-2(1))*; pap. 42.95 *(978-1-84742-481-5(3))* Policy Pr. GBR. Dist: Chicago Distribution Ctr.

Mitchell, Fiona, et al. Working with Unaccompanied Asylum Seeking Children: Issues for Policy & Practice. 2007. (ENG.). 208p. pap. 39.00 *(978-1-4039-9755-5(1))* Palgrave Macmillan.

Mitchell, W. R. & Buckton, Henry. The Children's Front: The Impact of the Second World War on British Children. 2009. (ENG., Illus.). 160p. pap. 29.95 *(978-1-86077-571-0(3))* History Pr. Ltd.,The GBR. Dist: Independent Pubs. Group.

Modin, Bitte. Setting the Scene for Life - Longitudinal Studies of Early Social Disadvantage & Later Life Chances. 2008. 144p. pap. *(978-3-639-05166-7(1))* VDM Verlag Dr. Mueller e.K.

Molinas, Jose R. Do Our Children Have a Chance? The Human Opportunity Report for Latin America & the Caribbean. 2012. (Illus.). xv, 154p. ***(978-0-8213-8902-7(5))*** World Bank Pubns.

Montgomery, Douglas C. & Montgomery, Heather. An Introduction to Childhood: Anthropological Perspectives on Children's Lives. 2008. (ENG.). 296p. 99.95 *(978-1-4051-2591-8(8)*, Wiley-Blackwell) Wiley, John & Sons, Inc.

Montgomery, Heather. An Introduction to Childhood: Anthropological Perspectives on Children's Lives. 2008. (ENG.). 296p. pap. 38.95 *(978-1-4051-2590-1(X)*, Wiley-Blackwell) Wiley, John & Sons, Inc.

Morrison, Heidi, ed. The Global History of Childhood Reader. 2012. (Routledge Readers in History Ser.). (ENG.). 496p. (C). 135.00 ***(978-0-415-78248-7(1))*** Routledge.

Moss, Dorothy. Children & Social Change: Memories of Diverse Childhoods. 2011. (ENG.). 240p. 140.00 *(978-0-8264-3531-6(9))* Continuum International Publishing Group, Ltd. GBR. Dist: National Bk. Network.

Murphy, Eileen, ed. Childhood in the Past Volume 2 (2009) 2009. (Childhood in the Past Ser.). (ENG.). 192p. (C). pap. 50.00 *(978-1-84217-378-7(2))* Oxbow Bks., Ltd. GBR. Dist: Brown, David Bk. Co., The.

Murray, Angela. Through the Eyes of a Street Child: Amazing Stories of Hope. 2007. (Illus.). 160p. pap. 12.99 *(978-0-8254-6136-1(7)*, Monarch Bks.) Lion Hudson PLC GBR. Dist: Kregel Pubns.

Neustadter, Roger. Obvious Child: Studies in the Significance of Childhood. 2008. (ENG.). 152p. 62.99 *(978-0-7618-4365-8(5))* Univ. Pr. of America, Inc.

Neustadter, Roger & Neustadter, Roger M. The Obvious Child: Studies in the Significance of Childhood. 2008. (ENG.). 152p. pap. 33.99 *(978-0-7618-4366-5(3))* Univ. Pr. of America, Inc.

New, Rebecca S. & LeVine, Robert A., eds. Anthropology of Child Development: A Cross-Cultural Reader. 2008. (Wiley-Blackwell Anthologies in Social & Cultural Anthropology Ser.: 4). (ENG., Illus.). 336p. 116.95 *(978-0-631-22975-9(2)*, Wiley-Blackwell) Wiley, John & Sons, Inc.

Nolan, Aoife. Children's Socio-Economic Rights, Democracy & the Courts, 0 vols. 2011. (ENG.). 336p. 110.00 *(978-1-84113-769-8(3))* Hart Publishing Ltd. GBR. Dist: International Specialized Bk. Services.

Olfman, Sharna, ed. The Sexualization of Childhood, 1 vol. 2008. (Childhood in America Ser.). 224p. 44.95 *(978-0-275-99985-8(8)*, C9985, Praeger Pubs.) Greenwood Publishing Group, Inc.

Organisation for Economic Co-operation and Development Staff. Doing Better for Children. 2009. (Illus.). 160p. pap. 63.00 *(978-92-64-05933-7(4))* Organization for Economic Cooperation & Development.

Panelli, Ruth. Global Perspectives on Rural Childhood & Youth. 2010. (ENG., Illus.). 288p. pap. 39.95 *(978-0-415-88296-5(6))* Routledge.

Panelli, Ruth, et al, eds. Global Perspectives on Rural Childhood & Youth. 2007. (Routledge Studies in Human Geography Ser.). (Illus.). 320p. 148.00 *(978-0-415-39703-2(0))* Routledge.

Paris, Catherine. Modern Day Slavery: Human Trafficking Revealed. 2007. 34.95 *(978-0-9795213-0-0(0)*, Claddagh, Ltd.) Claddagh Limited Publishing Hse.

Park, Hyu-Yong. Raising Ambi-Lingual Children. 2008. 176p. pap. *(978-3-639-11255-9(5))* VDM Verlag Dr. Mueller e.K.

Parker, Roy. Uprooted: The shipment of poor children. 2008. 416p. 110.00 *(978-1-84742-014-5(1))* Policy Pr. GBR. Dist: International Specialized Bk. Services.

Qvortrup, Jens, et al, eds. The Palgrave Handbook of Childhood Studies. (ENG., Illus.). 500p. 2011. pap. 60.00 *(978-0-230-53261-8(6))* 2009. 231.00 *(978-0-230-53260-1(8))* Palgrave Macmillan.

Ragazzi, Rossella. Walking on Uneven Paths: The Transcultural Experience of Children Entering Europe in the Years 2000. 2009. 240p. pap. *(978-3-0343-0042-1(5))* Lang, Peter.

Rawlinson, Regenia Mitchum. A Mind Shaped by Poverty: Ten Things Educators Should Know. 2011. 56p. pap. 8.95 ***(978-1-936236-71-8(0))*** iUniverse, Inc.

Rawson, Harve E. Captain English's Legacy: The Englishton Park Children's Program. 2010. 256p. pap. 17.49 *(978-1-4520-8073-4(9))* AuthorHouse.

Roberts, Rosemary. Wellbeing from Birth. 2010. (Illus.). 224p. (C). 108.00 *(978-1-84860-720-0(2)*, B07200C); pap. 43.00 *(978-1-84860-721-7(0)*, B07200P) SAGE Pubns., Ltd. GBR. Dist: SAGE Pubns., Inc.

Rodríguez, Pablo & Mannarelli, Maria Emma. Historia de la Infancia en América Latina. 2007. (SPA., Illus.). 673p. pap. 33.00 *(978-958-710-218-5(5))* Universidad Externado de Colombia COL. Dist: Siglo del Hombre.

Ruparanganda, Watch. Children with Adult Hearts? 2011. 56p. pap. ***(978-3-8443-8174-0(0))*** Lambert Academic Publishing.

Sarma, Santanu. Street Children of Developing World & Their Experiences. 2011. 68p. pap. ***(978-3-8433-9483-3(0))*** Lambert Academic Publishing.

Scarre, Geoffrey, ed. Children, Parents & Politics. 2010. (ENG.). 224p. pap. 27.99 *(978-0-521-36935-0(5))* Cambridge Univ. Pr.

Schmidt, Ella. The Dream Fields of Florida: Mexican Farmworkers & the Myth of Belonging. 2009. (ENG.). 160p. 62.99 *(978-0-7391-3872-4(3))* Lexington Bks.

Schumann, Dirk, ed. Raising Citizens in the Century of the Child: The United States & German Central Europe in Comparative Perspective. 2010. (SGH Ser.). (Illus.). 280p. 85.00 *(978-1-84545-696-2(3))* Berghahn Bks., Inc.

Schweizer, Sally. Well, I Wonder: Childhood in the Modern World: A Handbook for Parents, Carers & Teachers. 2007. (Bringing Spirit to Life Ser.). (Illus.). 224p. per. *(978-1-85584-124-6(X))* Steiner, Rudolf Pr.

Sheikh, Fazal, photos by. Ladli, 1 vol. 2008. (ENG., Illus.). 180p. 45.00 *(978-3-86521-381-5(2))* Steidl, Gerhard Druckerei und Verlag DEU. Dist: Innovative Logistics.

Shirley, Lindsey. Leadership & the Family & Consumer Sciences Classroom. 2010. 220p. pap. *(978-3-8383-5242-8(4))* Lambert Academic Publishing.

Silbereisen, Rainer K. & Eye, Alexander von, eds. Growing up in Times of Social Change. (International Studies on Childhood & Adolescence Ser.). (ENG.). XVI, 344p. 210.00 ***(978-3-11-182665-3(1))*** De Gruyter, Walter Inc.

Sisk, Dorothy, ed. Making Great Kids Greater: Easing the Burden of Being Gifted. 2008. (Illus.). 176p. 72.95 *(978-1-4129-5871-4(7)*, B58714C); pap. 31.95 *(978-1-4129-5872-1(5)*, B58714P) Corwin Pr.

Sosenski, Susana. Niños en Acción: El Trabajo Infantil en la Ciudad de México (1920-1934) 2010. (Estudios Históricos Ser.). (SPA., Illus.). 365p. pap. 48.99 *(978-607-462-053-5(9))* El Colegio de México, A.C., Biblioteca Miguel Cosio Villegas MEX. Dist: Fondo de Cultura Economica USA.

Stearns, Peter N. Childhood in World History. 2nd rev. ed. 2010. (Themes in World History Ser.). (ENG.). 192p. (C). 115.00 *(978-0-415-59808-8(7))*; pap. 29.95 *(978-0-415-59809-5(5))* Routledge.

Teves, Ryan. In Defense of the American Teen: An insider's commentary on the state of our secondary Schools. 2010. 220p. 24.99 *(978-1-4520-1918-5(5))* AuthorHouse.

Thomas, Susan Gregory. Buy, Buy Baby: How Consumer Culture Manipulates Parents & Harms Young Minds. 2009. (ENG.). 288p. pap. 14.95 *(978-0-547-23795-4(2)*, Mariner Bks.) Houghton Mifflin Harcourt Trade & Reference Pubs.

Tingstad, Vebjrg & Buckingham, David, eds. Childhood & Consumer Culture. 2010. (Studies in Childhood & Youth Ser.). (ENG., Illus.). 272p. 89.00 *(978-0-230-22783-5(X))* Palgrave Macmillan.

Trawick, Margaret. Enemy Lines: Childhood, Warfare, & Play in Batticaloa. 2007. 307p. 60.00 *(978-0-520-24515-0(6))*; per. 26.95 *(978-0-520-24516-7(4))* Univ. of California Pr.

Tudge, Jonathan. The Everyday Lives of Young Children: Culture, Class, & Child Rearing in Diverse Societies. 2008. (ENG., Illus.). 328p. 90.00 *(978-0-521-80384-7(5))* Cambridge Univ. Pr.

UNICEF Botswana & University of Botswana. Thari ya Bana: Reflections on Children in Botswana 2011. 2011. (Illus.). 100p. ***(978-92-806-4594-1(3))*** United Nations Children's Fund, The (UNICEF).

UNICEF Staff. Africa's Orphaned & Vulnerable Generations: Children Affected by AIDS. 2006. (Illus.). 48p. pap. 15.00 *(978-92-806-4035-9(6))* United Nations Children's Fund, The (UNICEF).

United Nations Children', et al. Progress for Children: A Report Card on Child Protection, No. 8. 2009. (Illus.). 48p. pap. 15.00 *(978-92-806-4439-5(4))* United Nations Children's Fund, The (UNICEF).

Vale, Allison & Rattle, Alison. The Woman Who Murdered Babies for Money: The Story of Amelia Dyer. 2011. (ENG., Illus.). 264p. pap. 14.95 *(978-0-233-00316-0(9))* Andre Deutsch GBR. Dist: Independent Pubs. Group.

Watson, Debbie, et al. Children's Social & Emotional Wellbeing in Schools: A Critical Perspective. 2012. 274p. 110.00 ***(978-1-84742-523-2(2))***; (Illus.). 256p. pap. 42.95 ***(978-1-84742-513-3(5))*** Policy Pr. GBR. Dist: Chicago Distribution Ctr.

Weiner, Myron, et al. Born Unfree - Child Labour, Education, & the State in India: An Omnibus - The Child & the State in India, Born to Work, & Child Rights in India (Extract) 2007. (ENG., Illus.). 740p. 65.00 *(978-0-19-567990-8(3))* Oxford Univ. Pr., Inc.

Weld, Nicki. Making Sure Children Get 'HELD' Ideas & Resources to Help Workers Place Hope, Empathy, Love & Dignity at the Heart of Child Protection & Support. 2009. (Illus.). 61p. spiral bd. 39.95 *(978-1-905541-55-3(4))* Russell Hse. Publishing Ltd. GBR. Dist: International Specialized Bk. Services.

Werner, Emmy E. Passages to America: Oral Histories of Child Immigrants from Ellis Island & Angel Island. 2009. 208p. 29.95 *(978-1-59797-296-3(7))* Potomac Bks., Inc.

West, Mark I. The Japanification of Children's Popular Culture: From Godzilla to Miyazaki. West, Mark I., ed. 2008. (ENG.). 306p. pap. 55.00 *(978-0-8108-5121-4(0))* Scarecrow Pr., Inc.

Williams, Andrew. Working with Street Children: An Approach Explored. 2011. (Illus.). 176p. pap. 29.95 ***(978-1-905541-80-5(5))*** Russell Hse. Publishing Ltd. GBR. Dist: International Specialized Bk. Services.

Wilson, Diane. Beloved Child: A Dakota Way of Life. 2011. (ENG., Illus.). 195p. 24.95 ***(978-0-87351-826-0(8)***, Borealis Bk.) Minnesota Historical Society Pr.

World Bank Group Staff, et al. The Promise of Early Childhood Development in Latin America & the Caribbean. 2009. (Latin American Development Forum Ser.). (ENG., Illus.). 220p. pap. 40.00 *(978-0-8213-7759-8(0)*, 9780821377598) World Bank Pubns.

Wright, J. E. The Sexualization of America's Kids: And How to Stop It. 2011. 176p. pap. 15.95 ***(978-1-4620-0846-9(1))*** iUniverse, Inc.

Wyness, Michael. Childhood & Society. 2nd rev. ed. 2011. (ENG., Illus.). 344p. (C). pap. 35.00 *(978-0-230-24182-4(4))* Palgrave Macmillan.

Zinia, Josinta. The Forbidden Future. 2010. 296p. pap. *(978-3-639-26688-7(9))* VDM Verlag Dr. Mueller e.K.

2006 UNICEF Botswana Annual Report. 2007. (Illus.). 44p. *(978-92-806-4173-8(5))* United Nations Children's Fund, The (UNICEF).

CHILDREN—SOCIETIES AND CLUBS

see Children's Clubs

CHILDREN—SPEECH

see Children—Language

CHILDREN—SUBSTANCE USE

Pagliaro, Ann Marie & Pagliaro, Louis A. The Handbook of Child & Adolescent Drug & Substance Abuse: Pharmacological, Developmental, & Clinical Considerations. 2nd ed. 2011. (ENG., Illus.). 528p. 65.00 ***(978-0-470-63906-1(7)***, Wiley) Wiley, John & Sons, Inc.

Peele, Stanton. Addiction Proof Your Child: A Realistic Approach to Preventing Drug, Alcohol, & Other Dependencies. 2007. (ENG.). 272p. per. 14.95 *(978-0-307-23757-6(5)*, Three Rivers Pr.) Crown Publishing Group.

Sadler, Katharine. What Adults Need to Know about Kids & Substance Use: Dealing with Alcohol, Tobacco, & Other Drugs. 2011. (ENG., Illus.). 118p. pap. 29.95 *(978-1-57482-495-7(3))* Search Institute.

United Nations. Preventing Amphetamine-type Stimulant Use among Young People: A Policy & Programming Guide. 2007. (RUS.). 36p. pap. 25.00 *(978-92-1-448029-7(X))* United Nations Pubns.

United Nations: Office on Drugs and Crime. Preventing amphetamine-type stimulant use among young People: A policy & programming Guide. 2007. (ENG.). 36p. pap. 25.00 *(978-92-1-148223-2(2))* United Nations Pubns.

Your Child & Substance Abuse. 12.00 *(978-0-687-09552-0(2))* Abingdon Pr.

CHILDREN—SURGERY

see also Infants (Newborn)—Surgery; Pediatric Orthopedics

Albright, A. Leland, et al. Principles & Practice of Pediatric Neurosurgery. 2nd ed. 2007. (ENG.). 1296p. 349.99 *(978-1-58890-395-2(8))*; 329.95 *(978-3-13-114692-2(3))* Thieme Medical Pubs., Inc.

American Pediatric Surgical Nurses Association, creator. Pocket Guide to Pediatric Surgical Nursing. 2007. (ENG., Illus.). 644p. spiral bd. 60.95 *(978-0-7637-5107-4(3))* Jones & Bartlett Learning, LLC.

Arensman, Robert M., et al, eds. Pediatric Surgery: Second Edition. 2009. (Vademecom Ser.). pap. *(978-1-57059-704-6(9))* Landes Bioscience.

Ashok, Garg. Pediatric Opthalmic Surgery. 2011. 630p. 99.00 ***(978-93-5025-148-5(5))*** Jaypee Brothers, Medical Pubs. IND. Dist: BookMasters Distribution Services (BDS).

Bax, N. M. A., et al, eds. Endoscopic Surgery in Infants & Children. 2008. (Illus.). XXVIII, 834p. 529.00 *(978-3-540-00115-7(8)*, 3540001158) Springer.

Bentz, Michael L., et al. Principles & Practice of Pediatric Plastic Surgery. 2007. *(978-1-57626-225-2(1))* Quality Medical Publishing, Inc.

Borden Institute, Walter Reed Army Medical Center, et al, eds. Pediatric Surgery & Medicine for Hostile Environments. 2011. (ENG., Illus.). 588p. 67.00 *(978-0-16-086980-8(3)*, Dept. of the Army) United States Government Printing Office.

Browne, Nancy Tcakz, et al. Nursing Care of the Pediatric Surgical Patient. 2nd rev. ed. 2006. (Illus.). 531p. (C). 163.95 *(978-0-7637-4052-8(7))* Jones & Bartlett Learning, LLC.

Carachi. A History of Surgical Pediatrics. 2009. 134.00 *(978-981-277-226-8(X))* World Scientific Publishing Co., Inc.

Carachi, Robert, et al, eds. Basic Techniques in Pediatric Surgery: An Operative Manual. 2012. (ENG., Illus.). 700p. 249.00 *(978-3-642-20640-5(9)*, 3642206409) Springer.

Cartwright, Cathy & Wallace, Donna C., eds. Nursing Care of the Pediatric Neurosurgery Patient. 2010. (Illus.). xviii, 284p. pap. 139.00 *(978-3-642-06744-0(1)*, 3642067441) Springer.

Caty, Michael G. Complications in Pediatric Surgery. Caty, Michael G. & Glick, Philip L, eds. 2008. (ENG., Illus.). 400p. 250.00 *(978-0-8247-2836-6(X)*, Informa Healthcare) Taylor & Francis Group GBR. Dist: Taylor & Francis Group.

Chung, Dai H. & Chen, Mike. Atlas of Pediatric Surgical Techniques. 2010. (ENG., Illus.). 408p. 274.00 *(978-1-4160-4689-9(5)*, Saunders) Elsevier - Health Sciences Div.

Coppes, Max J., et al. Hematopoietic Stem Cell Transplantation: Pediatric Clinics of North America. 2010. (Clinics: Internal Medicine Ser.: 57-1). (ENG., Illus.). xix, 352p. 84.00 *(978-1-4377-1852-2(3)*, Saunders) Elsevier - Health Sciences Div.

Coran, Arnold G., et al. Pediatric Surgery, 2-Volume Set: Expert Consult - Online & Print, 2 vols. 7th ed. 2012. (ENG., Illus.). 848p. 395.00 ***(978-0-323-07255-7(0)***, Mosby) Elsevier - Health Sciences Div.

Davenport, Mark & Pierro, Agostino, eds. Paediatric Surgery. 2009. (ENG., Illus.). 476p. pap. 79.95 *(978-0-19-920880-7(8))* Oxford Univ. Pr., Inc.

Esposito, Ciro & Esposito, Giovanni. Pediatric Surgical Diseases: A Radiologic Surgical Case Study Approach. 2008. (Illus.). 400p. 249.00 *(978-3-540-71515-3(0))* Springer.

Fundamentals of Pediatric Surgery. 2011. (ENG., Illus.). xxviii, 956p. 219.00 *(978-1-4419-6642-1(0)*, 1441966420) Springer.

Godbole, Prasad P., et al, eds. Guide to Pediatric Urology & Surgery in Clinical Practice. 2010. (Illus.). xv, 282p. pap. 39.95 *(978-1-84996-365-7(7)*, 1849963657) Springer.

Goodrich, James T. Pediatric Neurosurgery. 2008. 269.95 *(978-3-13-144191-1(7))* Thieme Medical Pubs., Inc.

Goodrich, James Tait, ed. Pediatric Neurosurgery. 2008. (Neurosurgical Operative Atlas Ser.). (ENG.). 336p. 269.99 *(978-1-58890-510-9(1))* Thieme Medical Pubs., Inc.

Grosfeld, Jay L., et al, eds. The Surgery of Childhood Tumors. 2nd ed. 2008. (Illus.). 626p. 379.00 *(978-3-540-29733-8(2))* Springer.

Gundeti, Mohan S., ed. Pediatric Robotic & Reconstructive Urology: A Comprehensive Guide. 2012. (ENG.). 364p. 249.95 ***(978-1-4443-3553-8(7)***, Wiley-Blackwell) Wiley, John & Sons, Inc.

Gupta, Devendra, et al. Pediatric Surgery, 2 vols. 2010. (ENG., Illus.). 1616p. 324.00 *(978-0-07-171987-2(3)*, 0071719873) McGraw-Hill Professional Publishing.

Hadidi, Ahmed T. & Azmy, A. F., eds. Hypospadias Surgery. 2010. 299.00 *(978-3-540-72058-4(8)*, 3540720588) Springer.

Hinman, Frank & Baskin, Laurence S. Pediatric Urologic Surgery. 2nd ed. 2008. (ENG., Illus.). 992p. 350.00 *(978-0-7216-0645-3(8)*, Saunders) Elsevier - Health Sciences Div.

Holcomb, George W. III & Murphy, J. Patrick. Ashcraft's Pediatric Surgery. 5th ed. 2009. (ENG., Illus.). 1128p. 329.00 *(978-1-4160-6127-4(4)*, Saunders) Elsevier - Health Sciences Div.

Holcomb, George W., et al. Atlas of Pediatric Laparoscopy & Thoracoscopy. 2008. (ENG., Illus.). 336p. 218.00 *(978-1-4160-3373-8(4)*, Saunders) Elsevier - Health Sciences Div.

Hutson, John M., et al, eds. Jones' Clinical Paediatric Surgery: Diagnosis & Management. 6th rev. ed. 2008. (ENG., Illus.). 336p. pap. 128.95 *(978-1-4051-6267-8(8)*, Wiley-Blackwell) Wiley, John & Sons, Inc.

Jallo, George I., et al, eds. Controversies in Pediatric Neurosurgery. 2010. (ENG., Illus.). 288p. 139.99 *(978-1-60406-074-4(3))* Thieme Medical Pubs., Inc.

Katowitz, James A., ed. Pediatric Oculoplastic Surgery. 2012. (ENG., Illus.). xxi, 694p. pap. 569.00 *(978-1-4419-2858-0(8)*, 1441928588) Springer.

Kicher, Minindra S. MPHPediatrics: Sports Surgery of Children & Adolescents. 2011. pap. 199.00 ***(978-0-89203-758-2(X))*** American Academy of Orthopaedic Surgeons.

Kilborn, Tracy & Daneman, Alan. ABC of Pediatric Surgical Imaging. Andronikou, Savvas et al, eds. 2009. (ENG., Illus.). xx, 170p. pap. 99.00 *(978-3-540-89384-4(9)*, 3540893849) Springer.

Ladd. Pediatric Surgical Patient Care. 2011. 181.00 *(978-981-4287-88-3(1))* World Scientific Publishing Co., Inc.

Lewis Spitz Staff, et al. Operative Pediatric Surgery. 6th rev. ed. 2007. (ENG., Illus.). 800p. 375.00 *(978-0-340-81340-9(7))* Hodder Arnold Pubs.

Lobe. Pediatric Laparoscopy. (Handbooks Ser.). (Illus.). 45.00 *(978-1-57059-636-4(7))* Landes Bioscience.

Loukanov, Tsvetomir. Surgery of Congenital Tracheal & Cardiac Anomalies- in Infants & Children. 2007. 84p. per. *(978-3-8364-1310-7(8))* VDM Verlag Dr. Mueller e.K.

Monnier, Philippe. Pediatric Airway Surgery: Management of Laryngotracheal Stenosis in Infants & Children. Monnier, Philippe, ed. 2010. (Illus.). xvii, 371p. 219.00 *(978-3-642-13534-7(X)*, 364213534X) Springer.

Parens, Erik, ed. Surgically Shaping Children: Technology, Ethics, & the Pursuit of Normality. 2008. (ENG., Illus.). 304p. (gr. 17). pap. 25.00 *(978-0-8018-9090-1(X))* Johns Hopkins Univ. Pr.

Parikh, Dakshesh, et al, eds. Pediatric Thoracic Surgery. 2009. (ENG., Illus.). xvi, 614p. 299.00 *(978-1-84800-902-8(X))* Springer.

Paul, Arun Kumar. Fundamentals of Paediatric Anaesthesia. 2006. (Illus.). 262p. (C). pap. 29.95 *(978-1-904798-88-0(8))* Anshan GBR. Dist: Publishers Storage & Shipping.

Puri, Prem & Höllwarth, Michael E. Pediatric Surgery. 2010. (Springer Surgery Atlas Ser.). (ENG., Illus.). xiv, 634p. pap. 519.00 *(978-3-642-07387-8(5)*, 3642073875) Springer.

Puri, Prem & Höllwarth, Michael, eds. Pediatric Surgery. 2008. (Illus.). 544p. 239.00 *(978-3-540-69559-2(1))* Springer.

Saxena, Amulya K. & Höllwarth, Michael E., eds. Essentials of Pediatric Endoscopic Surgery. 2010. (ENG., Illus.). xxxiv, 538p. pap. 229.00 *(978-3-642-09711-9(1)*, 3642097111) Springer.

Saxena, Amulya K. & Höllwarth, M. E. Essentials of Pediatric Endoscopic Surgery. 2008. (ENG., Illus.). xxxiv, 538p. 229.00 *(978-3-540-78385-2(5)*, 3540783865) Springer.

Scherl, Susan, ed. Surgical Management of the Pediatric Long Bone. 2008. per. 55.00 *(978-0-89203-456-7(4))* American Academy of Orthopaedic Surgeons.

Schier, Felix. Laparoscopy in Children. 2010. (ENG., Illus.). v, 147p. pap. 115.00 *(978-3-642-07694-7(7)*, 3642076947) Springer.

Sinha, Chandrasen K. & Davenport, Mark, eds. Handbook of Pediatric Surgery. 2010. (ENG., Illus.). xxi, 256p. pap. 69.95 *(978-1-84882-131-6(X)*, 184882131X) Springer.

Smith, Richard G. Paediatric Neurosurgery for Nurses: Evidence-Based Care for Children & Their Families. 2008. (ENG., Illus.). 288p. (C). pap. 53.95 *(978-0-415-44620-4(1))* Routledge.

Teich, Steven & Caniano, Donna A., eds. Reoperative Pediatric Surgery. 2010. (ENG., Illus.). xvi, 554p. pap. 179.00 *(978-1-61737-762-4(7)*, 1617377627) Humana Pr.

—Reoperative Pediatric Surgery. 2008. (ENG., Illus.). xvi, 554p. 179.00 *(978-1-58829-761-7(6)*, 1588297616) Humana Pr.

Zachariou, Zacharias, ed. Pediatric Surgery Digest. 2006. (Illus.). 500p. pap. 129.00 *(978-3-540-34032-4(7)*, 3540340327) Springer.

Zelinger, Laurie. The O, My in Tonsillectomy & Adenoidectomy: How to prepare your child for surgery, a parent's manual, 2nd Edition. 2010. 32p. pap. 19.95 *(978-1-61599-053-6(4))* Loving Healing Pr., Inc.

Zelinger, Laurie E. The "O, My" in Tonsillectomy & Adenoidectomy: How to Prepare Your Child for Surgery, a Parent's Manual. 2008. pap. *(978-1-932690-74-3(3))* Loving Healing Pr., Inc.

CHILDREN—TRAINING

see Child Rearing

CHILDREN—TRANSPORTATION

see School Children—Transportation

CHILDREN—TRAVEL

Bond, M. Mamas Valientes. (Rosa de Los Vientos Ser.). (SPA.). 140p. *(978-84-9754-002-5(6)*, 88102) Ediciones Oniro S.A.

Brown, Jacqueline. Fodor's Around London with Kids, 4th Edition. 2008. (Around the City with Kids Ser.). 160p. pap. 11.00 *(978-1-4000-0744-8(5)*, Fodor's) Fodor's Travel Pubns.

Buckner, Sharry & Kimball, Allan C. Fun with the Family Texas: Hundreds of Ideas for Day Trips with the Kids. 7th ed. 2009. (Fun with the Family Ser.). (ENG.). 256p. pap. 14.95 *(978-0-7627-5340-6(4))* Globe Pequot Pr., The.

Carrier, Rhonda. London. 3rd ed. 2009. (Frommer's with Kids Ser.: 47). (ENG., Illus.). 288p. pap. 17.99 *(978-0-470-50467-3(6)*, Frommers) Wiley, John & Sons, Inc.

Catron, Ingrid Roper. Washington D. C. 50 Adventures on Foot. 2007. (ENG., Illus.). 50p. 14.95 *(978-0-8118-6169-4(4))* Chronicle Bks. LLC.

Chan, Christina. LifeTips 101 Baby Travel Tips. 2007. 9.99 *(978-1-60275-007-4(6))* LifeTips.

Chronicle Books Staff, et al. San Francisco: 50 Adventures on Foot. 2007. (City Walks Ser.: CITY). (ENG., Illus.). 50p. 14.95 *(978-0-8118-6006-2(X))* Chronicle Bks. LLC.

Chronicle Gift Staff & Baker, Emily Laurence. London: 50 Adventures on Foot. 2009. (City Walks Ser.: CITY). (ENG.). 50p. 14.95 *(978-0-8118-6451-0(0))* Chronicle Bks. LLC.

Clowers, Anya. Jet with Kids: Taking the Fear Out of Flying... with Your Kids! 2006. 164p. per. 19.95 *(978-0-615-13757-5(1))* Jet Seven, Inc.

Copeland, Cynthia, et al. Vermont, New Hampshire & Maine. 3rd ed. 2007. (Best Hikes with Kids Ser.). (ENG., Illus.). 285p. per. 17.95 *(978-0-89886-644-5(8))* Mountaineers Bks., The.

Edwards, Natasha. Paris: 50 Adventures on Foot. 2008. (ENG., Illus.). 50p. 14.95 *(978-0-8118-6170-0(8))* Chronicle Bks. LLC.

FamilyTravelForum.com Staff & McCarthy, Kyle. The Complete Idiot's Guide to the Best Family Destinations. 2011. (Complete Idiot's Guide Ser.). (ENG.). 416p. (gr. 12). 18.95 *(978-1-61564-047-8(9)*, Alpha Bks.) Penguin Group (USA) Inc.

Field, Ellyce. Michigan Family Field Trips: Fun Sites for Kids. 2008. (ENG., Illus.). 144p. pap. 14.95 *(978-0-472-03271-6(2))* Univ. of Michigan Pr.

Fienberg, Stephen. The Art of Vacationing with Grandkids. 2007. per. 12.95 *(978-1-59872-827-9(X))* Instant Pub.

Flippin, Alexis Lipsitz. New York City with Kids. 12th ed. 2011. (Frommer's with Kids Ser.: 52). (ENG., Illus.). 320p. pap. 16.99 *(978-0-470-63100-3(7)*, Frommers) Wiley, John & Sons, Inc.

Forsberg, Leslie & Duffy, Michelle. Traveling with Kids. 2009. (Wanderlust & Lipstick Ser.). (ENG., Illus.). 368p. pap. 15.95 *(978-0-9787280-7-6(6))* Dispatch Travels.

Franklin, Sarah, ed. How to Fit a Car Seat on a Camel: And Other Misadventures Traveling with Kids. 2008. (ENG.). 280p. pap. 15.95 *(978-1-58005-242-9(8))* Westview Pr.

Gray, William. Footprint Travel with Kids. 2008. (Footprint - Lifestyle Guides). (ENG., Illus.). 384p. pap. 29.95 *(978-1-906098-03-2(4))* Footprint Handbooks GBR. Dist: Globe Pequot Pr., The.

Gray, William. Travel with Kids, 2nd. 2nd ed. 2012. (Footprint - Activity Guides). (ENG., Illus.). 352p. pap. 29.95 ***(978-1-907263-56-9(X))*** Footprint Handbooks GBR. Dist: Globe Pequot Pr., The.

Harriman, Cynthia W. Take Your Kids to Europe: How to Travel Safely (and Sanely) in Europe with Your Children. 8th ed. 2007. (Take Your Kids to Europe Ser.). (ENG., Illus.). 352p. per. 16.95 *(978-0-7627-4563-0(0))* Globe Pequot Pr., The.

Hartford, Michael. Dad's Eye View: 52 Family Adventures in the Twin Cities. 2011. (ENG., Illus.). 144p. pap. 15.95 *(978-0-87351-818-5(7))* Minnesota Historical Society Pr.

Johnston, Rebecca & Detering, Julia Rader. Bringing Out Baby: Places to Take Babies & Toddlers: Seattle, the Eastside, & South Snohomish County. 2nd ed. 2006. (Illus.). 172p. pap. *(978-1-881409-32-8(5))* JASI.

Jordon, Dorothy. Great Cruise Vacations with Your Kids. 208p. (C). pap. 11.95 *(978-0-915009-50-3(1))* World Leisure Marketing Ltd GBR. Dist: Midpoint Trade Bks., Inc.

—Great Sports Vacations with Your Kids. 208p. (C). pap. 11.95 *(978-0-915009-49-7(8))* World Leisure Marketing Ltd GBR. Dist: Midpoint Trade Bks., Inc.

—Great Vacations with Your Kids: America's Top Family Resorts & Activities. Date not set. 500p. pap. 24.95 *(978-0-915009-68-8(4))* World Leisure Corp.

Labosh, Kathy. The Child with Autism Goes to Florida: Hundreds of practical tips, with reviews of theme parks, rides, resorts, & More! 2011. (ENG.). 125p. pap. 14.95 *(978-1-935274-24-7(4))* Future Horizons, Inc.

Lain, Larry. Florida for Families. 2008. (Illus.). 320p. pap. 22.00 *(978-1-56656-695-7(9)*, Interlink Bks.) Interlink Publishing Group, Inc.

Lonely Planet Staff & Barta, Brigitte. Travel with Children: From Short Breaks to Round-the-World Adventures. 5th ed. 2009. (How To Ser.). (ENG., Illus.). 288p. pap. 19.99 *(978-1-74059-502-5(5))* Lonely Planet Pubns.

Marsh, Terry & Kelsall, Dennis. Frommer's Ireland with Your Family: From Vibrant Towns to Picnic Perfect Countryside. 2008. (Frommers with Your Family Ser.: 7). (ENG., Illus.). 256p. pap. 18.99 *(978-0-470-51878-6(2)*, Frommers) Wiley, John & Sons, Inc.

Michaels, Joanne. Let's Take the Kids! Great Places to Go in New York's Hudson Valley. 4th ed. 2011. (ENG., Illus.). 328p. pap. 18.95 *(978-0-88150-938-0(8)*, 150938) Countryman Pr.

Morrill, Stephen & Woodyard, Adele. Fun with the Family Florida: Hundreds of Ideas for Day Trips with the Kids. 7th ed. 2009. (Fun with the Family Ser.). (ENG., Illus.). 256p. pap. 14.95 *(978-0-7627-5338-3(2))* Globe Pequot Pr., The.

Nitkin, Karen. Fun with the Family Maryland: Hundreds of Ideas for Day Trips with the Kids. 2nd ed. 2009. (Fun with the Family Ser.). (ENG., Illus.). 200p. pap. 13.95 *(978-0-7627-5068-9(5))* Globe Pequot Pr., The.

Pape, Barbara & Calabrese, Michael. Open Road's Washington DC with Kids. 3rd ed. 2008. (ENG., Illus.). 208p. pap. 14.95 *(978-1-59360-098-3(4))* Open Road Publishing.

Pasquesi, J. M. Rome with Kids: An Insider's Guide. 2007. (Illus.). 244p. pap. 19.95 *(978-1-933538-47-1(3))* Synergy Bks.

Permenter, Paris & Bigley, John. Caribbean with Kids. 5th ed. 2008. (ENG., Illus.). 248p. pap. 14.95 *(978-1-59360-109-6(3))* Open Road Publishing.

—Open Road's Best National Parks with Kids. 2007. (ENG., Illus.). 176p. pap. 12.95 *(978-1-59360-097-6(6))* Open Road Publishing.

Peterson, Chris. Boy Wonder & the Big Bums: A Photographer, His Autistic Son & their Most Fascinating Journey Through the Wildfires of Glacier National Park. 2006. 14.95 *(978-0-9785354-0-7(5))* Glacier Geographic Bks.

Promise, Mama Val. The Home & Away Guide to Traveling with Kids. 2008. (Illus.). 192p. 18.95 *(978-1-933754-16-1(8))* Waterside Publishing.

Publications International Staff. Amazing Places to Take Your Kids in NA. 2007. (Illus.). 320p. 15.98 *(978-1-4127-1320-7(X)*, PIL Kids) Publications International, Ltd.

Rivoli, Shelly. Travels with Baby: The Ultimate Guide for Planning Trips with Babies, Toddlers, & Preschool-Age Children. 2007. (ENG.). 316p. pap. 21.95 *(978-0-615-15925-6(7))* Travels with Baby Bks.

Rogan, Helen & Gingold, Alfred. The Cool Parent's Guide to All of New York, 4th Edition: Excursion & Activities in & around our city that your children will love & you won't think are too bad Either. 2nd rev. ed. 2008. (ENG., Illus.). 144p. pap. 15.95 *(978-0-7893-1687-5(0))* Universe Publishing.

Ryder, Christopher S. Take Your Pediatrician with You: Keeping Your Child Healthy at Home & on the Road. 2007. (Johns Hopkins Press Health Book Ser.). (ENG., Illus.). 648p. per. 17.00 *(978-0-8018-8601-0(5))* Johns Hopkins Univ. Pr.

Sarver, Patrick. New Jersey for Kids. 2012. (ENG.). 240p. pap. 17.95 *(978-0-8135-5165-4(X)*, Rivergate Bks.) Rutgers Univ. Pr.

Semion, Bill. Michigan: Hundreds of Ideas for Day Trips with the Kids. 7th ed. 2009. (Fun with the Family Ser.). (ENG., Illus.). 296p. pap. 14.95 *(978-0-7627-5069-6(3))* Globe Pequot Pr., The.

Stein, Elissa. New York: 50 Adventures on Foot. 2007. (City Walks Ser.: CITY). (ENG., Illus.). 50p. 14.95 *(978-0-8118-5729-1(8))* Chronicle Bks. LLC.

Swimow, Linda. Take on Utah! A PhotoPhonicsÕ¬ Reader. 2009. 32p. pap. 12.99 *(978-1-4389-8177-2(5))* AuthorHouse.

Villarreal Bishop, Sara S. Born Expatriated. 2008. 262p. pap. 16.95 *(978-0-615-20165-8(2))* Bishop, Sara S. Villarreal.

Zavatsky, George & Zavatsky, Michele. Kids Love Florida: A Family Travel Guide to Exploring Kid-Tested Places in Florida ... Year Round! 2007. 288p. (J). per. 14.95 *(978-0-9774434-1-3(8))* Kids Love Pubns.

—Kids Love Tennessee: A Family Travel Guide to Exploring Kid-Tested Places in Tennessee... Year Round! 2nd rev. ed. 2007. (Kids Love... Ser.). (Illus.). 223p. per. 14.95 *(978-0-9774434-4-4(2))* Kids Love Pubns.

Zoer, Martine. The Kids' Guide to Living Abroad. 2007. pap. *(978-0-9658538-4-2(5))* Foreign Service Youth Foundation.

CHILDREN—VOCABULARY

see Children—Language

CHILDREN—WOUNDS AND INJURIES

see also Battered Child Syndrome

ABBE Scientist Research Division Staff. Children's Toys with Occurrence of Injuries, Disability & Death: Index, Reference & Medical Analysis of New Clinical & Research Information. 2008. (Illus.). 160p. ring bd. 69.95 *(978-0-7883-4678-1(4))* ABBE Pubs. Assn. of Washington, D.C.

Beaty, James H. & Kasser, James R., eds. Fractures in Children: Text Plus Integrated Content Website. 7th rev. ed. 2009. (ENG., Illus.). 1096p. 285.99 *(978-1-58255-784-7(5))* Lippincott Williams & Wilkins.

Benson, Michael, et al. Children's Orthopaedics & Fractures. Parsch, Klausdieter, ed. 3rd ed. 2010. (ENG., Illus.). xii, 869p. 199.00 *(978-1-84882-610-6(9)*, 1848826109) Springer.

Blane, Mark C. Justice for the Injured Child: A Parent's Complete Legal Survival Guide for Their Child's California Injury Case. 2011. 176p. 29.99 ***(978-1-4583-9674-7(6))*** Lulu Enterprises Inc.

Branche, C., et al. World Report on Child Injury Prevention. 2009. (Nonserial Publication Ser.). 228p. pap. 48.00 *(978-92-4-156357-4(5))* World Health Organization.

Brandenburg. Baby Safe: The Practical Guide for Preventing Infant & Toddler Injures. 2012. 242p. pap. 14.00 ***(978-0-578-09275-1(1))*** Child Safe Strategies.

Chadwick, David L., et al. Child Maltreatment 4E; Set with CD-ROM: A Clinical Guide & Reference & A Comprehensive Photographic Reference Identifying Potential Child Abuse, 2 vols. 4th ed. 2012. (Illus.). 375.00 incl. cd-rom *(978-1-878060-94-5(5))* STM Learning, Inc.

Davies, Ffion, et al. Emergency Care & Minor Injuries in Children: A Practical Handbook. 2011. (ENG., Illus.). 232p. pap. 42.95 *(978-1-4441-2014-1(X))* Hodder Arnold Pubs.

Frasier, Lori, et al. Abusive Head Trauma in Infants & Children; A Clinical Guide/Color Atlas: A Medical, Legal, & Forensic Reference. 2006. (Illus.). 630p. 175.00 *(978-1-878060-68-6(6))* STM Learning, Inc.

—Abusive Head Trauma in Infants & Children Guide/Atlas, & Supplementary CD-ROM: A Medical, Legal, & Forensic Reference. 2007. (ENG., Illus.). 630p. 275.00 incl. cd-rom *(978-1-878060-74-7(0))* STM Learning, Inc.

—Abusive Head Trauma Quick Reference: For Health Care, Social Service, & Law Enforcement Professionals. 2007. (ENG., Illus.). 355p. spiral bd. 52.00 *(978-1-878060-57-0(0))* STM Learning, Inc.

Frasier, Lori D. Abusive Head Trauma Pocket Atlas. 2012. (Illus.). pap. 60.00 *(978-1-878060-40-2(6))* STM Learning, Inc.

Frasier, Lori D., et al. Abusive Head Trauma in Infants & Children; Supplementary CD-ROM: A Medical, Legal, & Forensic Reference Supplementary CD-ROM, 1 disc. 2007. (ENG., Illus.). cd-rom 215.00 *(978-1-878060-64-8(3))* STM Learning, Inc.

Giardino, Angelo P. & Alexander, Randell. Child Abuse Quick Reference 2E: For Healthcare, Social Service, & Law Enforcement Professionals. 2nd rev. ed. 2006. (ENG., Illus.). 448p. spiral bd. 52.00 *(978-1-878060-60-0(0))* STM Learning, Inc.

Hebestreit, Helge. The Young Athlete. Bar-Or, Oded, ed. 2007. (Encyclopaedia of Sports Medicine Ser.: Vol. 13). (ENG., Illus.). 512p. 188.95 *(978-1-4051-5647-9(3)*, Wiley-Blackwell) Wiley, John & Sons, Inc.

Johnson, Karl J. & Bache, E. Imaging in Pediatric Skeletal Trauma: Techniques & Applications. 2010. (Medical Radiology / Diagnostic Imaging Ser.). (Illus.). x, 364p. pap. 219.00 *(978-3-642-08545-1(8)*, 3642085458) Springer.

Kapoor, Tanya. Child Occupant Protection in Vehicles. 2009. 364p. pap. *(978-3-639-14776-6(6))* VDM Verlag Dr. Mueller e.K.

Karantanas, Apostolos H., ed. Sports Injuries in Children & Adolescents. 2010. (Medical Radiology / Diagnostic Imaging Ser.). (Illus.). 300p. 319.00 *(978-3-540-88589-4(7)*, 3540885897) Springer.

Keenan, Don C., ed. Closing Arguments: Child Injury Child Wrongful Death, 2 vols., Vol. II. 2008. (Illus.). 400p. pap. *(978-0-9774425-4-6(3))* Balloon Pr.

Keeping America's Children Safe: Preventing Childhood Injury: Hearing of the Committee on Health, Education, Labor, & Pensions, United States Senate, One Hundred Tenth Congress, Second Session, on Examining Preventing Childhood Accidental Injury, May 1, 2008. 2009. iii, 43p. *(978-0-16-084831-5(8)*, 552-070-40232-2) United States Government Printing Office.

Martino, Fabio, et al, eds. Imaging of Pediatric Bone & Joint Trauma. 2010. (Illus.). 200p. 139.00 *(978-88-470-1654-5(1)*, 8847016541) Springer.

Mikrogianakis, Angelo, et al, eds. The Hospital for Sick Children Manual of Pediatric Trauma. 2007. (SickKids Ser.). (ENG., Illus.). 304p. 61.95 *(978-0-7817-7816-5(6))* Lippincott Williams & Wilkins.

Moore, Charles E. Diagnosis & Treatment of Traumatic Injuries to the Pediatric Craniofacial Skeleton. 2007. (Illus.). 87p. *(978-1-59756-140-2(1))* Plural Publishing, Inc.

Nath, Rahul. Obstetric Brachial Plexus Injuries. 2006. (ENG., Illus.). 116p. per. 24.95 *(978-1-58939-970-9(6))* Virtualbookworm.com Publishing, Inc.

Protecting Our Children: Current Issues in Children's Product Safety: Hearing Before the Subcommittee on Commerce, Trade, & Consumer Protection of the Committee on Energy & Commerce, House of Representatives, One

C

Hundred Tenth Congress, First Session, May 15, 2007. 2008. vi, 236p. (978-0-16-082680-1(2), 552-070-38697-1) United States Government Printing Office.

Schaefer-Wilson, Jamie & Consumer Reports Editors. Childproofing & Safety: Tips to Protect Your Baby & Child from Injury at Home & on the Go. 2008. (ENG., Illus.). 199p. pap. 12.95 (978-1-933524-17-7(0)) Consumers Union of U. S., Inc.

Sethi, Dinesh & World Health Organization: Regional Office for Europe. European Report on Child Injury Prevention. 2009. (EURO Nonserial Publication Ser.). (ENG., Illus.). 113p. pap. 24.00 (978-92-890-4295-6(8)) World Health Organization.

Stone, David. Injury Prevention in Children: A Primer for Students & Professionals. 2011. (Illus.). 224p. pap. 45.00 (978-1-906716-25-7(0)) Dunedin Academic Pr. GBR. Dist: International Specialized Bk. Services.

Ward Platt, M. P. & Little, R. A., eds. Injury in the Young. 2007. (ENG., Illus.). 332p. pap. 69.00 (978-0-521-03737-2(9)) Cambridge Univ. Pr.

WHO Regional Office for South-East Asia. Profile of Child Injuries: Selected Member States in the Asia-Pacific Region. 2010. (SEARO Publication). 62p. pap. 12.00 (978-92-9022-376-4(6)) World Health Organization.

Wootton-Gorges, Sandra L. Pediatric Musculoskeletal Imaging: Magnetic Resonance Imaging Clinics. 2009. (Clinics: Radiology Ser.: 17-3). (ENG.). 575p. 99.00 (978-1-4377-1238-4(X), Saunders) Elsevier - Health Sciences Div.

Zibners, Lara. If Your Kid Eats This Book, Everything Will Still Be Okay: How to Know If Your Child's Injury or Illness Is Really an Emergency. 2009. (ENG.). 320p. pap. 14.99 (978-0-446-50880-3(2)) Grand Central Publishing.

CHILDREN—WRITING

Here are entered works on the process or result of children recording language in the form of conventionalized visible marks or graphic signs on a surface.

Crebbin, Jennifer. Soul Development Through Handwriting: The Waldorf Approach to the Vimala Alphabet. 2007. (Illus.). 115p. per. 20.00 (978-0-88010-587-3(9)) SteinerBooks, Inc.

Free Spirit Publishing. Early Story Starters in a Jar. 2009. (In A Jar Ser.). (ENG.). (J). 9.95 (978-1-57542-956-4(X)) Free Spirit Publishing, Inc.

Hallissy, Jennifer. The Write Start: A Guide to Nurturing Writing at Every Stage, from Scribbling to Forming Letters & Writing Stories. 2010. (ENG., Illus.). 160p. pap. 17.95 (978-1-59030-837-0(9), Trumpeter) Shambhala Pubns., Inc.

Lancaster, Lesley. The Multimodality of Mark-making in Early Childhood. 2012. (Routledge Studies in Multimodality Ser.). (ENG.). 192p. (C). 125.00 (978-0-415-87231-7(6)) Routledge.

Meier, Daniel. Teaching Children to Write: Constructing Meaning & Mastering Mechanics. 2011. (ENG., Illus.). 176p. 27.95 (978-0-8077-5239-5(8)); pap. 27.95 (978-0-8077-5238-8(X)) Teachers College Pr., Teachers College, Columbia Univ.

Tunks, Karyn Wellhousen & Giles, Rebecca McMahon. Write Now! Publishing with Young Authors, PreK-Grade 2. 2007. (Illus.). 112p. pap. 20.00 (978-0-325-00911-7(2), E00911) Heinemann.

CHILDREN—AFRICA

Achilihu, Stephen Nmeregini. Do African Children Have Rights? A Comparative & Legal Analysis of the United Nations Convention on the Rights of the Child. 2010. 280p. pap. 25.95 (978-1-59942-853-6(9)) Universal Pubs.

Awoke, Tadesse. Psychological Problems of Physically Abused Children. 2011. 88p. pap. **(978-3-639-32341-2(6))** VDM Verlag Dr. Mueller e.K.

Belizaire, J. C. Cutting the Shackles of Mental Occupation. 2008. 136p. 26.95 (978-1-59858-588-9(6)) Dog Ear Publishing, LLC.

Berre, Kjersti. For When the Guests Come. 2009. 148p. pap. (978-3-639-16141-0(6)) VDM Verlag Dr. Mueller e.K.

Brewer, Vernon & Yeatts, Noel. Children of Hope: Be touched. Be inspired. Be Changed. 2007. per. 14.99 (978-0-9788041-2-1(0)) World Help Inc.

Chadamoyo, Patrick & Dumbu, Emmanuel. The Effect of Socio-Economic Factors on Maternal & Infant Behaviours. 2011. 84p. pap. **(978-3-8443-0267-7(0))** Lambert Academic Publishing.

Ejigu, Gardachew Tiruneh. The Destiny of Orphans & Vulnerable Children in Ethiopia: Situational Analysis of Orphans & Vulnerable Children in Bahir Dar Town, Northwest Ethiopia. 2011. 88p. pap. **(978-3-639-22771-0(9))** VDM Verlag Dr. Mueller e.K.

Eshetu, Genaye. Awareness Creation of Children on Child Right. 2009. 68p. pap. (978-3-639-20887-0(0)) VDM Verlag Dr. Mueller e.K.

Eticha, Kebede. Prevalence & Determinants of Child Malnutrition. 2009. 68p. pap. (978-3-639-17264-5(7)) VDM Verlag Dr. Mueller e.K.

Evers, Sandra, et al. Not Just a Victim: The Child As Catalyst & Witness of Contemporary Africa. 2011. (Illus.). 272p. pap. **(978-90-04-20400-3(8))** BRILL.

Falola, Toyin & Heaton, Matthew M. Endangered Bodies: Women, Children, & Health in Africa. 2008. (Illus.). 300p. pap. (978-1-59221-501-0(7)) Africa World Pr.

Garcia, Marito, et al. Africa's Future, Africa's Challenge: Early Childhood Care & Development in Sub Saharan Africa. 2007. (Directions in Development Ser.). 40.00 (978-0-8213-7054-4(5)) World Bank Pubns.

Gebre-Egziabher, Kinfe Abraha. The Existing Situation of Street Children in Mekelle City, Ethiopi. 2010. 96p. pap. (978-3-639-25431-0(7)) VDM Verlag Dr. Mueller e.K.

Gee, Martha Bettis. Piece Work / Peace Work: Working Together for Peace & Sudan: 2009-2010 Mission Study for Children (Teacher's Guide) 2009. (ENG.). 100p. (J). pap. 7.00 (978-1-933663-34-0(0), WD/GBGM Bks.) General Board of Global Ministries, The United Methodist Church.

Geitz, Elizabeth Rankin. I Am That Child: Changing Hearts & Changing the World. 2012. E-Book **(978-0-8192-2779-9(X)**, Morehouse Publishing); 176p. pap. 18.00 **(978-0-8192-2778-2(1))** Church Publishing, Inc.

Handa, Sudhanshu, et al, eds. Social Protection for Africas Children. 2010. (Routledge Studies in Development Economics Ser.). (ENG., Illus.). 272p. (C). 140.00 (978-0-415-58333-6(0), Routledge) Taylor & Francis Group GBR. Dist: Taylor & Francis Group.

Hashim, Iman & Thorsen, Dorte. Child Migration in Africa. 2011. (Africa Now Ser.). (ENG., Illus.). 160p. (C). pap. 39.95 (978-1-84813-456-0(8)); 240p. 125.95 (978-1-84813-455-3(X)) Zed Bks., Ltd. GBR. Dist: Palgrave Macmillan, Macmillan.

Hinton, Samuel. Street Children in Sierra Leone Who Forgive Those Who Physically & Sexually Abuse Them: A Quantitative & Qualitative Analysis. 2009. 180p. 99.95 (978-0-7734-4955-8(8)) Mellen, Edwin Pr., The.

Honwana, Alcinda. Child Soldiers in Africa. 2007. (Ethnography of Political Violence Ser.). (Illus.). 216p. (C). per. 24.95 (978-0-8122-1987-6(2)) Univ. of Pennsylvania Pr.

Kibel, Maurice, et al. Child Health for All. 4th ed. 2008. (ENG., Illus.). 576p. pap. 69.50 (978-0-19-576495-6(1)) Oxford Univ. Pr., Inc.

Kimaro, Marine. Cerebral Palsy: Case control study of risk factors (ohangwena Namibia) 2011. 60p. pap. **(978-3-8383-7642-4(0))** Lambert Academic Publishing.

Lloyd, Harvey. Through My Eyes: The Remarkable Children of Senegal. 2010. (ENG.). 256p. 45.00 incl. DVD (978-1-932646-42-9(6)) Ruder-Finn Pr.

Matimba, Peter. Analysis of Impact of Hiv on Children's Education in Zambi. 2009. 116p. pap. (978-3-639-21049-1(2)) VDM Verlag Dr. Mueller e.K.

Messay, Gebremariam Kotecho. The Psychological & Social Adjustment of Orphaned Children: The Case of Wolaita Soddo. 2011. 68p. pap. **(978-3-639-32795-3(0))** VDM Verlag Dr. Mueller e.K.

Musonye, Miriam. Narrating the Self in a Global Context. 2011. 64p. pap. **(978-3-8443-1169-3(6))** Lambert Academic Publishing.

Nguka, Gordon & Odebero, Stephen O. The Crisis of Acute Malnutrition among Children in Southern Sudan. 2011. 136p. pap. **(978-3-8454-1475-1(8))** Lambert Academic Publishing.

Oduasi, Geoffrey, et al. Malaria & Nutritional Status among Under-Fives. 2011. 120p. pap. **(978-3-8443-1363-5(X))** Lambert Academic Publishing.

Okwany, Auma, et al. The Role of Local Knowledge & Culture in Child Care in Africa: A Sociological Study of Several Ethnic Groups in Kenya & Uganda. 2011. 168p. **(978-0-7734-1583-6(1))** Mellen, Edwin Pr., The.

Pecora, Norma, ed. African Media, African Children: Yearbook 2008. 2008. (International Clearinghouse on Children, Youth & Media Ser.). 243p. pap. 87.50 (978-91-89471-68-9(7)) International Clearinghouse on Childrennordicom SWE. Dist: Coronet Bks.

Rajkumar, Andrew Sunil, et al. Malnutrition in Ethiopia: Current Interventions, Cost-Benefit Analysis, & the Way Forward. 2011. (Africa Human Development Ser.). (ENG.). 222p. pap. 25.00 (978-0-8213-8765-8(0), 9780821387658); **(978-0-8213-8766-5(9))** World Bank Pubns.

Rowe, Salome G. Opened Vistas: Building Minds One Brain at the Time. 2010. 40p. pap. 24.99 (978-1-4520-8636-1(2)) AuthorHouse.

Ruparanganda, Watch. Children with Adult Hearts? 2011. 56p. pap. **(978-3-8443-8174-0(0))** Lambert Academic Publishing.

Ryan, Christine. The Children of War: Child Soldiers As Victims & Participants in the Sudan Civil War. 2012. (International Library of African Studies). (ENG., Illus.). 320p. 95.00 **(978-1-78076-017-9(5))** I. B. Tauris & Co., Ltd. GBR. Dist: Macmillan.

Sajiwandani, Jonathan. Road to Emancipation: From Slavery to Happiness. 2007. (ENG.). 342p. per. (978-1-85756-587-4(8)) Janus Publishing Co.

Sloth-Nielsen, Julia. Children's Rights in Africa: A Legal Perspective. 2008. 362p. 124.95 (978-0-7546-4887-1(7)) Ashgate Publishing Co.

Sloth-Nielsen, Julia & Tolt, Zenobia du, eds. Trials & Tribulations, Trends & Triumphs: Developments in International, African & South African Child & Family Law. 2008. (Illus.). 288p. pap. 49.00 (978-0-7021-7948-8(5)) Juta & Co., Ltd. ZAF. Dist: Gaunt, Inc.

Starting Over: Child Camel Jockeys Return Home. 2006. (Illus.). 20p. (ARA.). (978-92-806-4068-7(2)); (978-92-806-4067-0(4)) United Nations Children's Fund, The (UNICEF).

Turney, Denise. Long Walk Up. 2007. pap. 6.95 (978-0-9663539-3-8(5)) Chistell Publishing.

UNICEF Botswana & University of Botswana. Thari ya Bana: Reflections on Children in Botswana 2011. 2011. (Illus.). 100p. **(978-92-806-4594-1(3))** United Nations Children's Fund, The (UNICEF).

UNICEF Staff. The State of Africa's Children 2008: Child Survival. 2008. (Illus.). 56p. (978-92-806-4247-6(2)) United Nations Children's Fund, The (UNICEF).

Winlow, Clara Vostrovsky. Our Little Carthaginian Cousin of Long Ago. 2010. 96p. pap. 7.95 (978-1-59915-286-8(X)) Yesterday's Classics.

CHILDREN—AFRICA, WEST

Casualties of War: Child Soldiers & the Law: Hearing Before the Subcommittee on Human Rights & the Law of the Committee on the Judiciary, United States Senate, One Hundred Tenth Congress, First Session, April 24, 2007. 2007. iii, 105p. (978-0-16-079848-1(5), 552-070-36742-0) United States Government Printing Office.

Davis, Marvin Garbeh, et al. Brave New Child: Liberating the Children of Liberia — & the World: Lessons in Peace Education from a War Torn Country. 2007. (Illus.). 231p. 24.95 (978-1-4251-1947-8(6)) Trafford Publishing.

CHILDREN—ASIA

Taking to Scale Imci Implementation in Mongolia 2000-2008: Lessons Learnts. 2011. (WPRO Nonserial Publication Ser.). (ENG.). 57p. cd-rom 12.00 **(978-92-9061-477-7(3))** WHO Regional Office for the Western Pacific PHL. Dist: World Health Organization.

Zinia, Josinta. The Forbidden Future. 2010. 296p. pap. (978-3-639-26688-7(9)) VDM Verlag Dr. Mueller e.K.

CHILDREN—AUSTRALIA

Brogan, Irene & Brogan, Alan A. Not Without You: Some People Are Just Destined to Be Together. 2009. (ENG.). 288p. pap. 24.95 (978-0-340-97639-5(X), Hodder & Stoughton) Hodder General Publishing Div. GBR. Dist: Independent Pubs. Group.

Faulkner, Joanne. The Importance of Being Innocent: Why We Worry about Children, 1 vol. 2010. 176p. pap. 32.99 (978-0-521-14697-5(6)) Cambridge Univ. Pr.

Gill, Judith, et al. Knowing Our Place: Children Talking about Power, Identity & Citizenship. 2009. 186p. pap. 49.95 (978-0-86431-872-5(3)) ACER Pr. AUS. Dist: International Specialized Bk. Services.

Humphreys, Margaret. Oranges & Sunshine: Empty Cradles. 2011. (ENG., Illus.). 382p. pap. 12.95 **(978-0-552-16335-4(X))** Transworld Publishers Ltd. GBR. Dist: Independent Pubs. Group.

Nowak, Madeleine. Beliefs Behaviours & Concerns of Adolescents about Food & Weight. 2010. 296p. pap. (978-3-8383-2138-7(3)) Lambert Academic Publishing.

Robinson, Gary, et al, eds. Contexts of Child Development: Culture, policy & Intervention. 2008. (Illus.). 290p. pap. (978-0-9803846-8-0(0)) Darwin, Charles Univ. Pr.

CHILDREN—BOSNIA AND HERCEGOVINA

Carpenter, Charli. Forgetting Children Born of War: Setting the Human Rights Agenda in Bosnia & Beyond. 2010. (ENG., Illus.). 304p. (gr. 17). 35.00 (978-0-231-15130-6(6)) Columbia Univ. Pr.

Cekic, Smail. Zlocini Nad Djecom Sarajeva U Opsadi. 2010. (Illus.). 867p. (978-9958-740-63-3(X)) Institut Za Istrazivanje Zlocina Protiv Covjecnosti I Medunarodnog Prava.

CHILDREN—BRAZIL

De Carvalho, Sarah. The Street Children of Brazil: One Woman's Remarkable Story. 2009. (ENG.). 256p. 14.95 (978-0-340-98008-8(7), Hodder & Stoughton) Hodder General Publishing Div. GBR. Dist: Independent Pubs. Group.

Dias, Maria Berenice & Kristensen, Christian Haag. Incesto e Alienação Parental: Realidades Que a Justiça Insiste Em Não Ver. 2nd ed. 2010. (POR.). 207p. (978-85-203-3147-7(5)) Revista dos Tribunais, Editora.

Mcafee, Steven D. Please God, Be with Us. 2011. 270p. pap. 16.99 **(978-1-61379-153-0(4))** Xulon Pr., Inc.

Mesquita, Mônica, et al. Asphalt Children & City Streets: A Life, a City, & a Case Study of History, Culture, & Ethnomathematics in São Paulo. 2011. 172p. **(978-94-6091-632-8(5))**; pap. **(978-94-6091-631-1(7))** Sense Pubs.

CHILDREN—CANADA

Backhouse, Frances. Children of the Klondike. 2010. (Illus.). 224p. pap. 19.95 (978-1-55285-950-6(9)) Whitecap Bks., Ltd. CAN. Dist: Midpoint Trade Bks., Inc.

Brookfield, Tarah. Cold War Comforts: Canadian Women, Child Safety, & Global Insecurity. 2012. (Studies in Childhood & Family in Canada Ser.). (ENG., Illus.). 270p. (C). pap. 39.95 **(978-1-55458-623-3(2))** Wilfrid Laurier Univ. Pr. CAN. Dist: Univ. of Toronto Pr.

Cleghorn, A. & Prochner, L. Shades of Globalization in Three Early Childhood Settings. 2010. 178p. pap. (978-94-6091-099-9(8)) Sense Pubs.

Fisher, Susan. Boys & Girls in No Man's Land: Canadian Children & the First World War. 2010. (Illus.). x, 311p. (ENG.). (978-1-4426-4224-9(6)); pap. (978-1-4426-1123-8(5)) Univ. of Toronto Pr.

Golden, Janet & Weisz, George. Healing the World's Children: Interdisciplinary Perspectives on Child Health in the Twentieth Century. Comacchio, Cynthia, ed. 2008. (McGill-Queen's/Associated Medical Services Studies in the History of Medicine, H Ser.). (ENG., Illus.). 324p. pap. (978-0-7735-3400-1(8)) McGill-Queen's Univ. Pr.

Hamilton, Gavin. The Nurses Are Innocent: The Digoxin Poisoning Fallacy. 2011. (ENG., Illus.). 240p. pap. 25.99 (978-1-4597-0057-4(0)) Dundurn CAN. Dist: Ingram Pub. Services.

Kayum, Azeem. Wrestling with the Goddess: A Personal Odyssey. 2008. (ENG.). 176p. 25.95 (978-0-595-71957-0(0)); pap. 15.95 (978-0-595-48564-2(2)) iUniverse, Inc.

Lerner, Loren, ed. Depicting Canada's Children. 2009. (Studies in Childhood & Family in Canada Ser.). (ENG., Illus.). 468p. 95.00 (978-1-55458-050-7(1)) Wilfrid Laurier Univ. Pr. CAN. Dist: Univ. of Toronto Pr.

Millar, Paul. The Best Interests of Children: An Evidence-Based Approach. 2009. (Illus.). (ENG.). 140p. (978-0-8020-9890-0(8)); xiv, 139p. pap. (978-0-8020-9593-0(3)) Univ. of Toronto Pr.

Remington, Robert & Zickefoose, Sherri. Runaway Devil: How Forbidden Love Drove a 12-Year-Old to Murder Her Family. 2010. (ENG., Illus.). 296p. pap. 17.95 (978-0-7710-7361-8(5), McClelland & Stewart) McClelland & Stewart CAN. Dist: Random Hse., Inc.

Schissel, Bernard. About Canada - Youth & Children. 2011. (About Canada Ser.). (ENG.). 144p. pap. 17.95 **(978-1-55266-412-4(0))** Fernwood Publishing Co., Ltd. CAN. Dist: Independent Pubs. Group.

Stewart, Jan. Between Two Worlds: Supporting Refugee Children & Youth. 2011. (Illus.). xxiv, 348p. pap. (978-1-4426-0030-0(6)) Univ. of Toronto Pr.

Strong-Wilson, Teresa. Bringing Memory Forward: Storied Remembrance in Social Justice Education with Teachers. 2007. (Complicated Conversation: A Book Ser. of Curriculum Studies: Vol. 23). 200p. (C). pap. 29.95 (978-0-8204-8874-5(7)) Lang, Peter Publishing, Inc.

Thomson, Donna. The Four Walls of My Freedom. 2012. (ENG., Illus.). 262p. pap. 18.95 **(978-1-55278-986-5(1))** McArthur & Co. CAN. Dist: National Bk. Network.

Williamson, Janice. Omar Khadr, Oh Canada. 2012. (ENG., Illus.). 400p. (C). pap. **(978-0-7735-4022-4(9))** McGill-Queen's Univ. Pr.

CHILDREN—CHINA

Bi, Lijun. Chinese Children's Literature in the 20th Century. 2010. 260p. pap. (978-3-8383-7082-8(1)) Lambert Academic Publishing.

Droeger, Linda. Bound by Love: The Journey of Lily Nie & Thousands of China's Forsaken Children. 2010. (978-0-615-34737-0(1)) Meriwether Publishing, Ltd.

Gao, Minghui. The Ethical Discourse of Chinese Children: A Narrative Approach to the Social & Moral Intricacy of Lying about Good Deeds. 2010. (Illus.). iv, 174p. 99.95 (978-0-7734-3632-9(4)) Mellen, Edwin Pr., The.

Haner, Jean. The Wisdom of Your Child's Face: Discover Your Child's True Nature with Chinese Face Reading. 2010. (ENG., Illus.). 336p. pap. 15.95 (978-1-4019-2534-5(0)) Hay Hse., Inc.

Headland, Isaac Taylor. The Chinese Boy & Girl. 2008. 112p. 21.99 (978-0-554-31995-7(0)) 2008. 112p. 24.99 (978-0-554-22692-7(8)) 2007. 584p. pap. 19.99 (978-1-4264-2902-6(9)) 2007. 522p. pap. 16.99 (978-1-4264-2865-4(0)) BiblioBazaar.

—The Chinese Boy & Girl. 2010. 62p. pap. (978-1-151-96800-5(5)) Books LLC.

—The Chinese Boy & Girl. 2008. 96p. pap. (978-1-4099-1809-7(2)) Dodo Pr.

Hsiung, Ping-Chen. A Tender Voyage: Children & Childhood in Late Imperial China. 2007. (ENG., Illus.). 378p. per. 30.95 (978-0-8047-5754-6(2)) Stanford Univ. Pr.

Liu, Huawen. Er Tong Quan Li Yu Fa Lü Bao Hu: Rights of the Child & Legal Protection. 2009. (CHI., Illus.). (978-7-208-08744-6(X)) Shanghai People's Publishing Hse.

Yu, Jie. Bu Yao Zuo Zhong Guo Ren de Hai Zi. 2008. (CHI.). 349p. pap. 18.00 (978-1-931550-22-2(0)) Laogai Research Foundation, The.

CHILDREN—DEVELOPING COUNTRIES

Ahmad, Ali. Iodine Status of Childern Aged 8-11 Year. 2010. 56p. pap. (978-3-639-25241-5(1)) VDM Verlag Dr. Mueller e.K.

Alderman, Harold. No Small Matter. 2011. (978-0-8213-8678-1(6)) World Bank Pubns.

Alderman, Harold H., ed. No Small Matter: The Impact of Poverty, Shocks, & Human Capital Investments in Early Childhood Development. 2011. (Human Development Perspectives Ser.). (ENG., Illus.). 208p. pap. 35.00 (978-0-8213-8677-4(8), 9780821386774) World Bank Pubns.

Beier, J. Marshall, ed. The Militarization of Childhood: Thinking Beyond the Global South. 2011. (ENG., Illus.). 320p. 90.00 (978-0-230-11576-7(4)) Palgrave Macmillan.

Bhutta, Zulfiqar Ahmed. Nutrition Interventions for Maternal & Child Health & Survival. 2011. (Illus.). 320p. 37.99 (978-0-19-547360-5(4)) Oxford Univ. Pr., Inc.

Denov, Myriam & Maclure, Richard, eds. Children's Rights & International Development. 2011. (ENG., Illus.). 320p. 90.00 (978-0-230-60682-1(2)) Palgrave Macmillan.

Jukes, Matthew C. H., et al. School Health, Nutrition, & Education for All: Levelling the Playing Field. 2007. (Illus.). 160p. pap. 55.00 (978-1-84593-311-1(7)) CABI GBR. Dist: Stylus Publishing, LLC.

Kaoukji, Dwan & M'Jid, Najat. Children's Services in the Developing World. 2009. (Library of Essays in Child Welfare & Development Ser.). (Illus.). 412p. 225.00 (978-0-7546-2779-1(9)) Ashgate Publishing Co.

Mosley, W. Henry & Chen, Lincoln C. Child Survival: Strategies for Research. 2008. (ENG., Illus.). 412p. pap. 50.00 (978-0-521-07297-7(2)) Cambridge Univ. Pr.

Sarma, Santanu. Street Children of Developing World & Their Experiences. 2011. 68p. pap. **(978-3-8433-9483-3(0))** Lambert Academic Publishing.

The State of the World's Children 2007: Executive Summary. 2006. (State of the World's Children Ser.). 40p. (978-92-806-4064-9(X)) United Nations Children's Fund, The (UNICEF).

Valencia, Lance K. & Hahn, Bryson J., eds. Employment & Labor Issues: Unemployment, Youth Employment & Child Labor. 2010. (Economic Issues, Problems & Perspectives Ser.). (Illus.). 243p. 129.00 (978-1-60876-282-8(3)) Nova Science Pubs., Inc.

Wabwile, Michael. Legal Protection of Social & Economic Rights of Children in Developing Countries: Reassessing International Cooperation & Responsibility. 2010. 272p. pap. 89.75 (978-94-000-0107-7(X)) Intersentia Uitgevers N.V. BEL. Dist: International Specialized Bk. Services.

Wittenberg, D. F. Paediatrics & Child Health. 6th ed. 2010. (ENG., Illus.). 816p. pap. 79.95 (978-0-19-598843-7(4)) Oxford Univ. Pr., Inc.

CHILDREN—EGYPT

Fahmi, Kamal. Beyond the Victim: The Politics & Ethics of Empowering Cairo's Street Children. 2007. (ENG., Illus.). 272p. 29.95 (978-977-416-063-9(0)) American Univ. in Cairo Pr. EGY. Dist: Oxford Univ. Pr., Inc.

Janssen, Rosalind M. & Janssen, Jac J. Growing up & Getting Old in Ancient Egypt. 2007. (Illus.). 320p. (C). 50.00 (978-0-9550256-9-3(9)) Golden Hse. Pubns. GBR. Dist: Brown, David Bk. Co., The.

CHILDREN—EUROPE

Andersen, Signe. A Good Place to Live: On How Municipality Level Characteristics Explain Municipality Level Variation in Children's Placement Risk (Study Paper No. 29) 2010. 32p. pap. 9.75 *(978-87-90199-41-8(3))* Univ. Pr. of Southern Denmark DNK. Dist: International Specialized Bk. Services.

Andersen, Signe & Fallesen, Peter. Disentangling the Heterogeneous Relationship between Background Characteristics & a Child's Placement Risk. 2010. 27p. pap. 9.75 *(978-87-90199-45-6(6))* Univ. Pr. of Southern Denmark DNK. Dist: International Specialized Bk. Services.

Bailey, Bernadine. Little Greta of Denmark. 2011. 192p. 42.95 ***(978-1-258-09312-9(X))*** Literary Licensing, LLC.

Belizaire, J. C. Cutting the Shackles of Mental Occupation. 2008. 136p. 26.95 *(978-1-59858-588-9(6))* Dog Ear Publishing, LLC.

Bove, Isabel & Cerruti, Florencia. Encuesta de lactancia, estado nutricional y alimentación complementaria en niños menores de 24 meses atendidos por servicios públicos y mutuales de Montevideo y el interior del País. 2007.Tr. of Survey on lactation, nutricional status & complementary feeding on children under 24 months cared by public & private health services in Montevideo & interior of the Country. (SPA.). 72p. per. *(978-92-806-4186-8(7))* United Nations Children's Fund, The (UNICEF).

Brug, J., et al, eds. Promoting Fruit & Vegetable Consumption in Children across Europe - the Pro Children Project, Vol. 49. (Annals of Nutrition & Metabolism 2005, Vol. 49, No. 4 Ser.). (Illus.). 78p. *(978-3-8055-8018-2(5))* Karger, S. AG.

Collins, Danny. The Truth about the Disappearance of Madeleine McCann. 2008. (ENG., Illus.). 288p. pap. 15.95 *(978-1-84454-614-5(4))* Blake, John Publishing, Ltd. GBR. Dist: Independent Pubs. Group.

Council of Europe Staff. Rights of children at risk & in Care (2007) 2007. 80p. pap. 18.00 *(978-92-871-6039-3(2))* Council of Europe FRA. Dist: Manhattan Publishing Co.

Cowles, Julia Darrow. Our Little Macedonian Cousin of Long Ago. 2010. 88p. pap. 7.95 *(978-1-59915-287-5(8))* Yesterday's Classics.

Danforth, Loring M. & Van Boeschoten, Riki. Children of the Greek Civil War: Refugees & the Politics of Memory. 2011. (ENG., Illus.). 352p. 80.00 *(978-0-226-13598-4(5))* Univ. of Chicago Pr.

De Boyser, Katrien, et al, eds. Why Care? Children's Rights & Child Poverty. 2010. 209p. pap. 54.75 *(978-94-000-0025-4(1))* Intersentia Uitgevers N.V. BEL. Dist: International Specialized Bk. Services.

Devine, Dympna, et al, eds. Flexible Childhood? Exploring Children's Welfare in Time & Space. 2007. 238p. pap. 34.99 *(978-87-7674-202-7(4))* Univ. Pr. of Southern Denmark DNK. Dist: International Specialized Bk. Services.

Dooly, Melinda. Their Hopes, Fears & Reality: Working with Children & Youth for the Future. 2010. (Illus.). 256p. pap. *(978-3-0343-0441-2(2))* Lang, Peter GmbH, Europaischer Verlag der Wissenschaften.

Hall, Allan & Leidig, Michael. Girl in the Cellar: The Natascha Kampusch Story. 288p. 2010. mass mkt. 7.99 *(978-0-06-194529-8(3))* 2007. (Illus.). 24.95 *(978-0-06-134510-4(5))* HarperCollins Pubs.

Hennessy, Cecily. Images of Children in Byzantium. 2008. (Illus.). 296p. 124.95 *(978-0-7546-5631-9(4))* Ashgate Publishing Co.

Heywood, Colin. Childhood & Youth in Modern Europe. 2008. 280p. (C). 70.00 *(978-0-521-86623-1(5))*; pap. 34.99 *(978-0-521-68525-2(7))* Cambridge Univ. Pr.

James, Allison & James, Adrian L., eds. European Childhoods: Cultures, Politics & Childhoods in the European Union. 2008. (ENG.). 272p. 100.00 *(978-1-4039-9750-0(0))* Palgrave Macmillan.

Kaniasty, Krzysztof, et al, eds. Stress & Psychosocial Resources: Coping with life changes, occupational demands, educational challenges, & threats to physical & emotional Well-being. 2008. 160p. pap. *(978-3-8325-1971-1(8))* Logos Verlag Berlin.

Kelnar, C., ed. European Society for Paediatric Endocrinology (ESPE) Vol. 76: 50th Annual Meeting, Glasgow, September 2011- Abstracts. Supplement Issue - 'Hormone Research in Paediatrics 2011, Suppl. 2' 2011. (ENG., Illus.). 356p. pap. ***(978-3-8055-9835-4(1))*** Karger, S. AG.

Kristoffersen, Eva M. Hans Christian of Elsinore. 2011. 82p. 37.95 ***(978-1-258-02484-0(5))*** Literary Licensing, LLC.

Laes, Christian. Children in the Roman Empire: Outsiders Within. 2011. (ENG., Illus.). 350p. 105.00 *(978-0-521-89746-4(7))* Cambridge Univ. Pr.

Leira, Arnlaug & Saraceno, Chiara, eds. Childhood: Changing Contexts. 2008. (Comparative Social Research Ser.). (Illus.). 430p. 99.95 *(978-0-7623-1419-5(2))* Emerald Group Publishing Ltd. GBR. Dist: Turpin Distribution Services Ltd.

Liegeois, Jean-Pierre & Commission of the European Communities, contrib. by. School Provision for Gypsy & Traveller Children: Report on the Implementation of Measures Envisaged in the Resolution of the Council & of the Ministers of Education Meeting with the Council, 22nd May 1989 (89/C 153/02) 94p. *(978-92-827-9446-3(6))* European Commission BEL. Dist: Balogh International, Inc.

Markova, Galina. Parents, Children, Institutions in a Post-Totalitarian Context. 2010. 128p. pap. *(978-3-639-22270-8(9))* VDM Verlag Dr. Mueller e.K.

Newman, Paul B. Growing up in the Middle Ages. 2007. (ENG., Illus.). 311p. per. 39.95 *(978-0-7864-3084-0(2))* McFarland & Co., Inc. Pubs.

Olcott, Virginia. Adventures in Switzerland: The Story of Anton & Trini. 2011. 162p. 41.95 ***(978-1-258-06369-6(7))*** Literary Licensing, LLC.

Paolo, Rocko. Gallivanting Through Europe with Young Children. 2011. 176p. pap. 24.95 ***(978-1-4626-1296-3(2))*** PublishAmerica, Inc.

Parruca, Etion. Eu & Member States Facing Modern-Day Slavery in Children. 2011. 112p. pap. ***(978-3-8433-8901-3(2))*** Lambert Academic Publishing.

Petrie, Pat, et al. Working with Children in Care: European Perspectives. 2006. (Illus.). 208p. (ENG.). 183.95 *(978-0-335-21635-2(8))*, 0335216358); pap. 67.00 *(978-0-335-21634-5(X))*, 033521634X) McGraw-Hill Cos., The.

Sethi, Dinesh & World Health Organization: Regional Office for Europe. European Report on Child Injury Prevention. 2009. (EURO Nonserial Publication Ser.). (ENG., Illus.). 113p. pap. 24.00 *(978-92-890-4295-6(8))* World Health Organization.

Sippell, W. G., ed. ESPE - the First 50 Years: A History of the European Society for Paediatric Endocrinology. 2011. (ENG., Illus.). 220p. ***(978-3-8055-9868-2(8))*** Karger, S. AG.

UNICEF: Innocenti Research Centre. Child trafficking in Europe: A broad vision to put children first; summary Report. 2009. (ENG., Illus.). 68p. pap. 20.00 incl. cd-rom *(978-88-89129-62-3(X))* United Nations Pubns.

Venturini, Gian Lorenzo. The Unacceptable Threat. 2010. 84p. pap. *(978-3-8383-4809-4(5))* Lambert Academic Publishing.

Vockel, Gabriel. The Protection of Children's Human Rights in Europe. 2007. 64p. per. *(978-3-8364-0993-3(3))* VDM Verlag Dr. Mueller e.K.

Yavneh, Naomi & Miller, Naomi. Gender & Early Modern Constructions of Childhood. 2011. (Women & Gender in the Early Modern World Ser.). (Illus.). 264p. 99.95 ***(978-1-4094-2997-5(0))*** Ashgate Publishing Co.

Zych, Marta. The Ability of Orphanages to Meet Child Development Needs. 2011. 100p. pap. ***(978-3-8433-8335-6(9))*** Lambert Academic Publishing.

CHILDREN—EUROPE—HISTORY

Immel, Andrea. Childhood & Children's Books in Early Modern Europe, 1550-1800. 2009. 346p. 39.95 *(978-0-415-80363-2(2))* Routledge.

Tallis, Raymond, et al. A Tender Age: Cultural Anxieties over the Child in the Twelfth & Thirteenth Centuries. Buttigieg, Joseph A., tr. 2009. (Gutenberg-E Ser.). (ENG.). 264p. (gr. 17). 60.00 *(978-0-231-14256-4(0))* Columbia Univ. Pr.

CHILDREN—FRANCE

Adams, Christine. Poverty, Charity, & Motherhood: Maternal Societies in Nineteenth-Century France. 2010. (ENG.). 280p. 45.00 *(978-0-252-03547-0(X))* Univ. of Illinois Pr.

Bouyer, Rene-Jean. Les Mémoires D'un Bébé: Un Siècle D'éducation de L'enfant de Pasteur à Dolto. 2010. (FRE., Illus.). 221p. *(978-2-35013-232-7(3))* Gawsewitch, Jean-Claude.

Capul, Maurice & David, Monique. L'invention de L'enfance Inadaptée: L'exemple de Toulouse Saint-Simon, 1950-1975. 2010. (FRE.). 588p. *(978-2-7492-1289-0(8))* Eres Editions.

Druckerman, Pamela. Bringing up Bébé: One American Mother Discovers the Wisdom of French Parenting. 2012. (ENG.). 304p. (gr. 12). 25.95 ***(978-1-59420-333-6(4))***, Penguin Pr. HC, The) Penguin Group (USA) Inc.

Heywood, Colin. Growing up in France: From the Ancien Régime to the Third Republic. 2009. (ENG., Illus.). 328p. pap. 45.00 *(978-0-521-12311-2(9))* Cambridge Univ. Pr.

Le Billon, Karen. French Kids Eat Everything: How Our Family Moved to France, Cured Picky Eating, Banned Snacking, & Discovered 10 Simple Rules for Raising Happy, Healthy Eaters. 2012. 320p. 24.99 ***(978-0-06-210329-1(6))***, Morrow, William & Co.) HarperCollins Pubs.

Olcott, Virginia. Adventures in France: The Story of Jean & Fanchon. 2011. 180p. 42.95 ***(978-1-258-06351-1(4))*** Literary Licensing, LLC.

Power, Angie. Moving to France with Your Children. 2007. (Illus.). 182p. per. 22.00 *(978-1-84528-166-3(7))* How To Books GBR. Dist: Parkwest Pubns., Inc.

Troller, Simone. Lost in Transit: Insufficient Protection for Unaccompanied Migrant Children at Roissy Charles de Gaulle Airport. 2009. (Illus.). 60p. ***(978-1-56432-557-0(1))*** Human Rights Watch.

CHILDREN—GERMANY

Albert, Isabel. Innerfamiliäre Gewalt gegen Kinder: Eine kriminologische und rechtliche Betrachtung der Erscheinungsformen, Ursachen und Möglichkeiten der Bekämpfung. 2008. (Würzburger Schriften zur Kriminalwissenschaft Ser.). 292p. pap. 74.95 *(978-3-631-57862-9(8))* Lang, Peter GmbH, Europaischer Verlag der Wissenschaften DEU. Dist: Lang, Peter.

Braun, Helga. The Survival of Helga Braun. 2010. 172p. 22.49 *(978-1-4520-2246-8(1))*; pap. 11.99 *(978-1-4520-2245-1(3))* AuthorHouse.

DuBois-Reymond, Manuela, et al, eds. Childhood & Youth in Germany & the Netherlands: Transitions & Coping Strategies of Adolescents. (International Studies on Childhood & Adolescence Ser.) (ENG.). XII, 351p. 196.00 ***(978-3-11-178028-3(7))*** De Gruyter, Walter Inc.

Ganaway, Bryan. Toys, Consumption, & Middle-Class Childhood in Imperial Germany, 1871-1918. 2009. (Illus.). 292p. pap. 55.95 *(978-3-03911-548-8(0))* Lang, Peter AG GBR. Dist: Lang, Peter.

Gondolf, Yvonne. Die Vormundschaft und Pflegschaft für Minderjährige: Ist eine Reform notwendig und wie sollte sie Aussehen? 2008. (Familienrechtliche Untersuchungen Ser.). 252p. pap. 65.95 *(978-3-631-57455-3(X))* Lang, Peter GmbH, Europaischer Verlag der Wissenschaften DEU. Dist: Lang, Peter.

Harrington, Joel F. The Unwanted Child: The Fate of Foundlings, Orphans, & Juvenile Criminals in Early Modern Germany. 2009. (ENG., Illus.). 456p. 45.00 *(978-0-226-31727-4(7))* Univ. of Chicago Pr.

Kollmeier, Kathrin. Ordnung und Ausgrenzung: Die Disziplinarpolitik der Hitler-Jugend. 2007. (Kritische Studien Zur Geschichtswissenschaft Ser.). (GER., Illus.). 368p. (C). pap. 63.00 *(978-3-525-35158-1(5))* Vandenhoeck & Ruprecht GmbH & Co. KG DEU. Dist: ISD.

Ocker, Christa Holder. Auf Wiedersehen. 2009. 148p. pap. 14.95 *(978-1-935514-27-5(X))* Plain View Pr.

Otto, Hans-Uwe. Sozialarbeit zwischen Routine und Innovation: Professionelles Handeln in Sozialadministrationen. (Prevention & Intervention in Childhood & Adolescence Ser.). (GER.). IX, 204p. 210.00 ***(978-3-11-187698-6(5))*** De Gruyter, Walter Inc.

Schumann, Dirk, ed. Raising Citizens in the Century of the Child: The United States & German Central Europe in Comparative Perspective. 2010. (SGH Ser.). (Illus.). 280p. 85.00 *(978-1-84545-696-2(3))* Berghahn Bks., Inc.

Stargardt, Nicholas. Witnesses of War: Children's Lives under the Nazis. 2007. (Vintage Ser.). (ENG., Illus.). 528p. pap. 16.95 *(978-1-4000-3379-9(9))*, Vintage) Knopf Doubleday Publishing Group.

Willmann, Silke. Kleidungspraktiken aus Sicht von Kindern im Vorschulalter: Eine Studie zur kulturellen Identität vor differentem kulturellem Hintergrund. 2008. (Europäische Hochschulschriften. Reihe 22: Soziologie Ser.). 220p. pap. 56.95 *(978-3-631-57691-5(9))* Lang, Peter GmbH, Europaischer Verlag der Wissenschaften DEU. Dist: Lang, Peter.

Würzbach, Natascha & Whitinger, Raleigh. The Green Sofa. 2011. (Life Writing Ser.). (Illus.). 256p. (C). pap. 24.95 *(978-1-55458-334-8(9))* Wilfrid Laurier Univ. Pr. CAN. Dist: Univ. of Toronto Pr.

CHILDREN—GERMANY (WEST)

Erichsen, Hans-Uwe. Verstaatlichung der Kindeswohlentscheidung? Zur verfassungsrechtlichen Bestimmung des schulischen Erziehungsrechts; Vortrag gehalten vor der Berliner Juristischen Gesellschaft am 27. September 1978. (Schriftenreihe der Juristischen Gesellschaft zu Berlin Ser.). (GER., Illus.). 27p. 135.00 ***(978-3-11-007951-7(8))*** De Gruyter, Walter Inc.

CHILDREN—GHANA

Adjei Frempong, Augusta. Food Operation in Senior High Schools. 2010. 88p. pap. *(978-3-8383-0845-6(X))* Lambert Academic Publishing.

Amantana, Vivian. A Sociological Study of Street Children in Ghana: Victims of Kinship Breakdown & Rural-Urban Migration. 2011. (Illus.). 186p. 119.95 ***(978-0-7734-1606-2(4))*** Mellen, Edwin Pr., The.

Ame, Robert. Children's Rights in Ghana: Reality or Rhetoric? 2011. (ENG., Illus.). 310p. 75.00 *(978-0-7391-4800-6(1))* Lexington Bks.

Boakye-Boaten, Agya. Understanding the Street Children Phenomenon. 2008. 256p. per. *(978-3-8364-3734-9(1))* VDM Verlag Dr. Mueller e.K.

Bosman, Ineke. To Be a Man Is Not Easy: Stories from Ghanaian Emigrants. 2007. 124p. pap. 22.00 *(978-90-5170-850-9(5))* Purdue Univ. Pr.

Manful, Esmeranda. The Development of Children's Rights in Africa & Europe: Comparing Legislation in Ghana & Northern Ireland. 2010. (Illus.). xi, 355p. 119.95 *(978-0-7734-3746-3(0))* Mellen, Edwin Pr., The.

Opare-Henaku, Annabella. What Is Worrying Children in Ghana? 2009. 68p. pap. *(978-3-639-19898-0(0))* VDM Verlag Dr. Mueller e.K.

CHILDREN—GREAT BRITAIN

Alexander, Christine & McMaster, Juliet, eds. The Child Writer from Austen to Woolf. 2010. (Cambridge Studies in Nineteenth-Century Literature & Culture Ser.). (ENG., Illus.). 336p. pap. 45.00 *(978-0-521-12838-4(2))* Cambridge Univ. Pr.

Alexander, Robin J. Children, Their World, Their Education: The Final Report & Recommendations of the Cambridge Primary Review. 2009. (ENG., Illus.). 608p. pap. 58.95 *(978-0-415-54871-7(3))* Routledge.

Alexander, Robin J., et al. Children, Their World, Their Education: The Final Report & Recommendations of the Cambridge Primary Review. 2009. (ENG., Illus.). 608p. 160.00 *(978-0-415-54870-0(5))* Routledge.

Anning, Angela & Ball, Mog, eds. Improving Services for Young Children: From Sure Start to Children's Centres. 2008. (Illus.). 192p. (C). 116.00 *(978-1-4129-4821-0(5)*, B48210C); pap. 55.00 *(978-1-4129-4822-7(3)*, B48210P) SAGE Pubns., Ltd. GBR. Dist: SAGE Pubns., Inc.

Arthur, Raymond. Family Life & Youth Offending: Home Is Where the Hurt Is. (Routledge Advances in Criminology Ser.). (ENG.). 240p. (C). 2012. pap. 42.95 ***(978-0-415-51454-5(1))*** 2006. (Illus.). 180.00 *(978-0-415-40644-8(X))* Routledge.

Ashbee, Felicity. Child in Jerusalem. 2008. (Middle East Studies). (Illus.). 166p. *(978-0-8156-0872-1(1))* Syracuse Univ. Pr.

Atkins, Liz & Reason, Matthew. The Young Audience: Exploring & Enhancing Children's Experiences of Theatre. 2010. (Illus.). 192p. pap. 34.95 *(978-1-85856-450-0(6))* Trentham Bks. Ltd. GBR. Dist: Stylus Publishing LLC.

Avery, J.Gordon & Jackson, R.Hugh. Children & Their Accidents. (Illus.). 192p. pap. *(978-0-340-37001-8(7)*, Hodder Arnold) Hodder Education.

Bazley, Janet, et al. Applications under Schedule 1 of the Children Act 1989. 2010. (ENG., Illus.). 392p. pap. *(978-1-84661-214-5(4))* Jordan Publishing, Ltd.

Beecham, Jennifer & Sinclair, Ian. Costs & Outcomes in Children's Social Care: Messages from Research. 2006. (ENG., Illus.). 144p. per. *(978-1-84310-496-4(2))* Kingsley, Jessica Ltd.

Beem, Charles, ed. The Royal Minorities of Medieval & Early Modern England. 2008. (ENG., Illus.). 272p. 95.00 *(978-0-230-60866-5(3))* Palgrave Macmillan.

Bell, Margaret. Promoting Children's Rights in Social Work & Social Care: A Guide to Participatory Practice. 2011. (ENG., Illus.). 224p. pap. ***(978-1-84310-607-4(8))*** Kingsley, Jessica Ltd.

Benziman, Galia. Narratives of Child Neglect in Romantic & Victorian Culture. 2011. (ENG., Illus.). 272p. 85.00 ***(978-0-230-29392-2(1))*** Palgrave Macmillan.

Brannigan, Tim. Where Are You Really From? 2010. (ENG.). 208p. pap. 20.95 *(978-0-85640-853-3(0))* Blackstaff Pr., Ltd. GBR. Dist: Dufour Editions, Inc.

Bridgeman, Jo. Parental Responsibility, Young Children & Healthcare Law. 2007. (ENG.). 282p. 115.00 *(978-0-521-86312-4(0))* Cambridge Univ. Pr.

Broadhurst, Karen, et al, eds. Critical Perspectives on Safeguarding Children. 2009. (ENG.). 300p. 120.95 *(978-0-470-68232-6(9))*; pap. 57.95 *(978-0-470-69756-6(3))* Wiley, John & Sons, Inc. (Wiley).

Brown, Mike. A Child's War: Growing up on the Home Front, 1939-45. 2011. (ENG., Illus.). 128p. pap. 17.95 *(978-0-7524-5858-8(2))* History Pr. Ltd., The GBR. Dist: Independent Pubs. Group.

Bruce, Tina, ed. Early Childhood: A Guide for Students. (Illus.). (C). 2006. 344p. 116.00 *(978-1-4129-2075-9(2)*, B20752C) 2006. 344p. per. 47.95 *(978-1-4129-2076-6(0)*, B20752P) 2nd ed. 2010. 440p. 112.00 *(978-1-84860-223-6(5)*, B02236C) 2nd ed. 2010. 440p. pap. 46.00 *(978-1-84860-224-3(3)*, B02236P) SAGE Pubns., Ltd. GBR. Dist: SAGE Pubns., Inc.

Butler, Ian & Drakeford, Mark. Social Work on Trial: The Colwell Inquiry & the State of Welfare. 2011. 248p. 110.00 *(978-1-84742-868-4(1))* Policy Pr. GBR. Dist: Chicago Distribution Ctr.

Cheminais, Rita. Effective Multi-Agency Partnerships: Putting Every Child Matters into Practice. 2009. 160p. 125.00 *(978-1-84860-138-3(7)*, B01383C); pap. 51.00 *(978-1-84860-139-0(5)*, B01383P) SAGE Pubns., Ltd. GBR. Dist: SAGE Pubns., Inc.

—The Pocket Guide to Every Child Matters: An at-a-Glance Overview for the Busy Teacher. 2009. (ENG., Illus.). 102p. 120.00 *(978-0-415-47916-5(9))* Taylor & Francis Group.

Collingwood, Stuart Dodgson. The Life & Letters of Lewis Carroll. 2009. 396p. 29.99 *(978-0-559-12579-9(8))*; 31.99 *(978-0-559-12569-0(0))*; pap. 32.75 *(978-0-559-12577-5(1))*; pap. 26.99 *(978-0-559-12572-0(0))* BiblioBazaar.

—The Life & Letters of Lewis Carroll. 2007. (ENG.). 232p. per. *(978-1-4068-4707-9(0))* Echo Library.

Cram101 Textbook Reviews & Cram101 Textbook Reviews. Outlines & Highlights for Early Childhood: A Guide for Students by Tina Bruce, ISBN. 2011. 62p. pap. 27.95 ***(978-1-61461-115-8(7))***; pap. 27.95 ***(978-1-61461-069-4(X))*** Cram101 Inc.

—Outlines & Highlights for Early Childhood Education & Care: Policy & Practice by Margaret Clark, ISBN. 2011. 56p. pap. 26.95 ***(978-1-61461-117-2(3))*** Cram101 Inc.

—Outlines & Highlights for Ensuring Every Child Matters: A Critical Approach by Gianna Knowles, ISBN. 2011. 116p. pap. 28.95 ***(978-1-61461-070-0(3))*** Cram101 Inc.

Darton, Frederick Joseph Harvey. Children's Books in England: Five Centuries of Social Life. 2011. (Cambridge Library Collection - Literary Studies). (ENG., Illus.). 394p. pap. 29.99 ***(978-1-108-03381-7(4))*** Cambridge Univ. Pr.

Dash, P. African Caribbean Pupils in Art Education. 2010. 242p. *(978-94-6091-049-4(1))*; (Illus.). pap. *(978-94-6091-048-7(3))* Sense Pubs.

Davies, Andrew. When I Were a Lad — School Days: Snapshots from a Time When They Taught the Three 'R's. 2011. (ENG., Illus.). 144p. 14.95 *(978-1-907554-14-8(9))* Anova Bks. GBR. Dist: Independent Pubs. Group.

—When I Were a Nipper- Snapshots from a Time Before Indoor Plumbing. 2011. (ENG., Illus.). 144p. 14.95 *(978-1-907554-36-0(X))* Anova Bks. GBR. Dist: Independent Pubs. Group.

Davies, Hywel. Fleeing Franco: How Wales Gave Shelter to Refugee Children from the Basque Country During the Spanish Civil War. 2011. (Illus.). 169p. pap. 25.00 *(978-0-7083-2336-6(7))* Univ. of Wales Pr. GBR. Dist: Chicago Distribution Ctr.

Davies, Liz. Protecting Children: A resource Book. 2nd ed. 2010. (ENG., Illus.). 136p. pap. *(978-1-905179-07-7(3)*, Lonely Scribe) Armadillo Design Ltd.

Davis, Lynn. The Social Worker's Guide to Children & Families Law. 2008. (ENG.). 240p. pap. *(978-1-84310-653-1(1))* Kingsley, Jessica Ltd.

Day, David. The Bevin Boy: A History of the Use of Young Boys in British Mines During WWII. Lt. ed. 192p. 21.95 *(978-1-85695-162-3(6))* ISIS Large Print Bks. GBR. Dist: Transaction Pubs.

Dex, Shirley, et al, eds. Children of the 21st Century: The first five Years. 2010. (Illus.). 320p. 85.00 *(978-1-84742-476-1(7))* Policy Pr. GBR. Dist: Chicago Distribution Ctr.

—Children of the 21st Century: The First Five Years. 2010. (Illus.). 320p. pap. 39.95 *(978-1-84742-475-4(9))* Policy Pr. GBR. Dist: Chicago Distribution Ctr.

Doncaster, Sheila. To Be the Same. 2008. 72p. per. *(978-1-84748-235-8(X))* Athena Pr.

Doyle, Celia. Working with Abused Children: Focus on Child. 4th rev. ed. 2012. (Practical Social Work Ser.). (ENG., Illus.). 304p. (C). pap. 31.00 ***(978-0-230-29794-4(3))*** Palgrave Macmillan.

Ferrall, Charles & Jackson, Anna. Juvenile Literature & British Society, 1850-1950: The Age of Adolescence. 2012. (ENG., Illus.). 194p. pap. 39.95 ***(978-0-415-63422-9(9))*** Routledge.

Fletcher, Anthony. Growing up in England: The Experience of Childhood, 1600-1914. 2010. (ENG., Illus.). 456p. pap. 35.00 *(978-0-300-16396-4(7))* Yale Univ. Pr.

Foley, Pam. Changing Children's Services: Working & Learning Together. Rixon, Andy, ed. 2008. (Illus.). 312p. pap. 35.95 *(978-1-84742-060-2(5))* Policy Pr. GBR. Dist: Chicago Distribution Ctr.

Foley, Pam & Leverett, Stephen. Connecting with Children: Developing Working Relationships. 2008. (Illus.). 312p. (C). pap. 35.95 *(978-1-84742-058-9(3))* Policy Pr. GBR. Dist: Chicago Distribution Ctr.

Forbes, Joan & Watson, Cate, eds. The Transformation of Childrens Services. 2011. (ENG., Illus.). 216p. (C). 144.00 *(978-0-415-61847-2(9))*; pap. 51.95 *(978-0-415-61849-6(5))* Routledge.

Frost, Ginger S. Victorian Childhoods, 1 vol. 2008. (Victorian Life & Times Ser.). (Illus.). 208p. 44.95 *(978-0-275-98966-8(6)*, C8966, Praeger Pubs.) Greenwood Publishing Group, Inc.

C

Gibson, Clare. Army Childhood: British Army Children's Lives & Times. 2012. (Shire Library). (ENG., Illus.). 56p. pap. 12.95 (978-0-7478-1099-5(0)) Shire Pubns., Ltd. GBR. Dist: Random Hse., Inc.

Godfrey, Elizabeth. English Children in the Olden Time. 2010. 468p. pap. 37.75 (978-1-142-59801-3(2)) BiblioBazaar.

—English Children in the Olden Time. 2009. 286p. pap. (978-1-4590-6973-2(0)) Books LLC.

Godfrey, Elizabeth & Bedford, Jessie. English Children in the Olden Time. 2010. 430p. pap. 35.75 (978-1-143-67261-3(5)) BiblioBazaar.

Goodyer, Annabel. Child-Centred Foster Care: A Rights-Based Model for Practice. 2011. (ENG., Illus.). 208p. pap. (978-1-84905-174-3(7)) Kingsley, Jessica Ltd.

Gore, Sally. Children Act 1989: Local Authority Support for Children & Families. 2011. (ENG., Illus.). 304p. pap. (978-1-84661-248-0(9)) Jordan Publishing, Ltd.

Green, David A. & Green, David. When Children Kill Children: Penal Populism & Political Culture. 2008. (Clarendon Studies in Criminology Ser.). (ENG., Illus.). 200p. 121.00 (978-0-19-923096-9(X)) Oxford Univ. Pr., Inc.

Guishard-Pine, Jeune, ed. Psychology, Race Equality & Working with Children. 2010. (Illus.). 228p. pap. 36.95 (978-1-85856-474-6(3)) Trentham Bks. Ltd. GBR. Dist: Stylus Publishing, LLC.

Hindley, Charles. History of the Catnach Press: At Berwick-upon-Tweed, Alnwick & Newcastle-upon-Tyne, in Northumberland, & Seven Dials, London. 2010. (Cambridge Library Collection - Printing & Publishing History Ser.). (Illus.). 360p. pap. 29.99 (978-1-108-00909-6(3)) Cambridge Univ. Pr.

Hobart, Christine & Frankel, Jill. Good Practice in Childminding: A Handbook for the Diploma in Home-Based Childcare. Walker, Miranda, ed. 4th ed. 2006. (ENG., Illus.). 272p. pap. 52.50 (978-0-7487-9764-6(5)) Nelson Thornes Ltd. GBR. Dist: Trans-Atlantic Pubns., Inc.

Hollingsworth, Kathryn. Rights & Responsibilities of Children in Youth Crime. 2013. 364p. pap. 70.00 (978-1-84946-006-4(X)) Hart Publishing Ltd. GBR. Dist: International Specialized Bk. Services.

Holmes, Lisa & McDermid, Samantha. Understanding Costs & Outcomes in Child Welfare Services: A Comprehensive Costing Approach to Managing Your Resources. 2012. (ENG.). 240p. pap. (978-1-84905-214-6(X)) Kingsley, Jessica Ltd.

Hooper, Walter. Past Watchful Dragons: The Origin, Interpretation, & Appreciation of the Chronicles of Narnia. 2007. (C. S. Lewis Secondary Studies Ser.). 156p. pap. 17.00 (978-1-55635-548-6(3)) Wipf & Stock Pubs.

Horne, Jackie C. History & the Construction of the Child in Early British Children's Literature. 2011. (Ashgate Studies in Childhood, 1700 to the Present Ser.). (Illus.). 298p. 99.95 (978-1-4094-0788-1(8)) Ashgate Publishing Co.

Humphries, Jane. Childhood & Child Labour in the British Industrial Revolution. (Cambridge Studies in Economic History - Second Ser.). (ENG., Illus.). 2011. 454p. pap. 34.99 (978-0-521-24896-9(5)) 2010. 456p. 110.00 (978-0-521-84756-8(7)) Cambridge Univ. Pr.

Hymer, Barry. Gifted & Talented Pocketbook. 2009. (Illus.). 128p. pap. (978-1-906610-01-2(0), Teachers' Pocketbooks) Management Pocketbooks GBR. Dist: Ware-Pak, Inc.

Isles-Buck, Emma & Newstead, Shelly. Essential Skills for Managers of Child-Centred Settings. 2nd rev. ed. 2011. (ENG., Illus.). 104p. 112.00 (978-0-415-58553-8(8)); pap. 30.95 (978-0-415-58554-5(6)) Routledge.

Kantola, Johanna. Feminists Theorize the State. annot. ed. 2006. (ENG.). 256p. 95.00 (978-0-230-00025-4(8)) Palgrave Macmillan.

Kay, Janet & Fitzgerald, Damien. Working Together in Children's Services. 2007. (Illus.). VI, 146p. 37.50 (978-0-84312-467-2(X)) Fulton, David Pubs. GBR. Dist: Taylor & Francis Group.

Kelly, Emma & Bokhari, Farhat, eds. Safeguarding Children from Abroad: Refugee, Asylum Seeking & Trafficked Children in the UK. 2012. (ENG., Illus.). 160p. pap. (978-1-84905-157-6(7)) Kingsley, Jessica Ltd.

Kershaw, Roger & Sacks, Janet. New Lives for Old: The Story of Britain's Child Migrants. 2007. (Illus.). 240p. 34.95 (978-1-905615-17-9(5)) National Archives (PRO), The GBR. Dist: International Publishers Marketing.

Lancaster, Y. Penny & Kirby, Perpetua. Listening to Young Children. 2nd ed. 2010. (ENG., Illus.). 254p. 345.95 (978-0-335-24127-9(1), 0335241271) McGraw-Hill Education GBR. Dist: McGraw-Hill Cos., The.

Lapotaire, Jane. Everybody's Daughter, Nobody's Child. 2007. (ENG.). 384p. pap. 13.95 (978-1-84408-416-6(7), Virago Press) Little, Brown Bk. Group Ltd. GBR. Dist: Independent Pubs. Group.

Lee, Allison & Lee, Rachel. Childminder's Guide to Health & Safety & Child Protection. 2008. (ENG., Illus.). 124p. 29.95 (978-1-84706-086-0(2)) Continuum International Publishing Group, Ltd. GBR. Dist: National Bk. Network.

MacDonald, Alistair. Rights of the Child: The Law & Practice. 2011. (ENG.). 1232p. (978-1-84661-210-7(1)) Jordan Publishing, Ltd.

MacIntyre, Christine. Gifted & Talented Children 4-11: Understanding & supporting their Development. 2008. (Illus.). XIV, 98p. 37.50 (978-0-415-46492-5(7)) Routledge.

Mallett. Choosing Using Childrens Fiction. 2010. (ENG., Illus.). 416p. pap. 47.95 (978-1-84312-322-4(3)) Routledge.

Manful, Esmeranda. The Development of Children's Rights in Africa & Europe: Comparing Legislation in Ghana & Northern Ireland. 2010. (Illus.). xi, 355p. 119.95 (978-0-7734-3746-3(0)) Mellen, Edwin Pr., The.

Marr, Neil & Field, Tim. Bullycide: Death at Playtime. 2nd ed. 2011. (Illus.). 273p. pap. (978-1-906609-97-9(7)) BeWrite Bks.

Masson, Judith. Protecting Powers: Emergency Intervention for Children's Protection. 2007. (Wiley Child Protection & Policy Ser.: 13). (ENG., Illus.). 260p. 159.95 (978-0-470-01602-2(7)); per. 59.95 (978-0-470-01603-9(5)) Wiley, John & Sons, Inc. (Wiley).

Mathieson, Kay. Identifying Special Needs in the Early Years. 2007. (Illus.). 112p. 81.00 (978-1-4129-2906-6(7), B29067C); per. 34.00 (978-1-4129-2907-3(5), B29067P) SAGE Pubns., Ltd. GBR. Dist: SAGE Pubns., Inc.

McDonough, Rich. A Cincinnati Private Eye Protecting Princess Di: A Fascinating Footnote in History. 2011. 132p. pap. 10.68 (978-1-4567-5721-2(0)) AuthorHouse.

Mcfarlane, Andrew. Hershman & Mcfarlane Children Act Handbook 2011/2012. 2011. (ENG.). 772p. pap. (978-1-84661-285-5(3)) Jordan Publishing, Ltd.

McGavran, James Holt, ed. Romanticism & Children's Literature in Nineteenth-Century England. 2009. (ENG.). 272p. pap. 24.95 (978-0-8203-3487-5(1)) Univ. of Georgia Pr.

McLaughlin, Janice, et al. Families Raising Disabled Children: Enabling Care & Social Justice. 2008. (ENG., Illus.). 248p. 100.00 (978-0-230-55145-9(9)) Palgrave Macmillan.

Meggitt, Carolyn, et al. Cache Level 3 Child Care & Education. 2nd ed. 2012. (Illus.). 624p. pap. 49.95 (978-1-4441-7099-3(6)) Hodder Arnold Pubs.

Mitchell, John. Children Act Private Law Proceedings: A Handbook. 3rd rev. ed. 2012. (ENG.). 600p. pap. (978-1-84661-238-1(1)) Jordan Publishing, Ltd.

Mitchell, W. R. & Buckton, Henry. The Children's Front: The Impact of the Second World War on British Children. 2009. (ENG., Illus.). 160p. pap. 29.95 (978-1-86077-571-0(3)) History Pr. Ltd., The GBR. Dist: Independent Pubs. Group.

Mitchels, Barbara & James, Helen. Child Care & Protection: Law & Practice, Vol. 1. 4th rev. ed. 2009. (Illus.). 189p. pap. 48.50 (978-0-85490-038-1(1)) Gaunt, Inc.

Mowat, Ashley McCabe. Brilliant Activities for Stretching Gifted & Talented Children. 2008. (Illus.). 104p. pap. (978-1-905780-17-4(6)) Brilliant Pubns.

Mowat, Joan. Using Support Groups to Improve Behaviour. 2007. (Illus.). 128p. 69.00 (978-1-4129-2914-1(8), B29148C); pap. 32.95 (978-1-4129-2915-8(6), B29148P) SAGE Pubns., Ltd. GBR. Dist: SAGE Pubns., Inc.

Mullally, Maureen. Law & the Family in the UK. 2nd ed. 2007. 192p. pap. 17.00 (978-1-901657-53-1(1)) Blackhall Publishing IRL. Dist: Gaunt, Inc.

Müller, Anja. Framing Childhood in Eighteenth-Century English Periodicals & Prints, 1689-1789. 2009. (Ashgate Studies in Childhood, 1700 to the Present Ser.). (Illus.). 276p. 114.95 (978-0-7546-6503-8(8)) Ashgate Publishing Co.

Neumeister, Mirjam, ed. The Changing Face of Childhood: British Children's Portraits & Their Influence in Europe. 2007. (Illus.). 214p. (978-3-8321-7793-5(0)) DuMont.

Newson, Elizabeth & Newsom, John. Four Years Old in & Urban Community. 2007. 605p. 190.00 (978-0-415-41755-6(4)) Routledge.

Newson, John & Newson, Elizabeth. Four Years Old in an Urban Community. 2007. (ENG.). 570p. (gr. 11). pap. 49.95 (978-0-202-36164-2(0)) Aldine Transaction.

—Infant Care & Motherhood in an Urban Community. 2008. (ENG., Illus.). 288p. pap. 29.95 (978-0-202-36229-8(9)) Aldine Transaction.

Norwich, Brahm. Dilemmas of Difference, Inclusion & Disability: International Perspectives & Future Directions. 2007. (Illus.). X, 230p. 44.95 (978-0-415-39847-3(9)); 145.00 (978-0-415-39846-6(0)) Taylor & Francis Group.

Oliphant, John. The Early Education of the Blind in Britain C. 1790-1900: Institutional Experience in England & Scotland. 2007. 200p. (978-0-7734-5247-3(8)) Mellen, Edwin Pr., The.

Osborne, Mary Pope & Boyce, Natalie Pope. Rags & Riches: Kids in the Time of Charles Dickens. 2010. (Stepping Stone Book(TM) Ser.: No. 22). (ENG.). 128p. (J). (gr. 2-6). 5.99 (978-0-375-86010-2(X)); lib. bdg. 12.99 (978-0-375-96010-9(4)) Random Hse. Children's Bks. (Random Hse. Bks. for Young Readers).

Parton, Nigel & Frost, Nick P. Understanding Children's Social Care: Politics, Policy & Practice. 2009. (Illus.). 224p. (C). 108.00 (978-1-4129-2349-1(2), B23492C); pap. 43.00 (978-1-4129-2350-7(6), B23492P) SAGE Pubns., Ltd. GBR. Dist: SAGE Pubns., Inc.

Pati, Jagannath, ed. Adoption: Global Perspectives & Ethical Issues. 2007. 314p. (978-81-8069-442-4(9)) Concept Publishing Co.

Pinson, Halleli, et al. Education, Asylum & the 'Non-Citizen' Child: The Politics of Compassion & Belonging. 2010. (ENG., Illus.). 224p. 84.00 (978-0-230-52468-2(0)) Palgrave Macmillan.

Plimley, Lynn, et al. Autistic Spectrum Disorders in the Early Years. 2007. (Autistic Spectrum Disorder Support Kit Ser.). (Illus.). 112p. 94.00 (978-1-4129-2314-9(X), B2314XC); per. 29.00 (978-1-4129-2315-6(8), B2314XP) SAGE Pubns., Ltd. GBR. Dist: SAGE Pubns., Inc.

Power, Anne. City Survivors: Bringing up Children in Disadvantaged Neighbourhoods. 2007. (Case Studies on Poverty, Place & Policy Ser.). 226p. (C). 110.00 (978-1-84742-050-3(8)) Policy Pr. GBR. Dist: International Specialized Bk. Services.

Radford, Lorraine. Rethinking Children, Violence & Safeguarding: Attitudes in Contemporary Society. 2012. (New Childhoods Ser.). (ENG., Illus.). 184p. 120.00 (978-1-4411-6890-0(7)); pap. 34.95 (978-1-84706-558-2(9)) Continuum International Publishing Group, Ltd. GBR. Dist: National Bk. Network.

Reid, Gavin. Dyslexia. 3rd ed. 2011. (Special Educational Needs Ser.). (ENG., Illus.). 256p. pap. 34.95 (978-1-4411-6585-5(1)) Continuum International Publishing Group, Ltd. GBR. Dist: National Bk. Network.

Rhamie, Jasmine. Eagles Who Soar: How Black Learners Find the Path to Success. 2008. (Illus.). 140p. per. 31.95 (978-1-85856-394-7(1)) Trentham Bks. Ltd. GBR. Dist: Stylus Publishing, LLC.

Robb, Martin & Thomson, Rachel, eds. Critical Practice with Children & Young People. 2010. (Illus.). 312p. pap. 34.95 (978-1-84742-681-9(6)) Policy Pr. GBR. Dist: Chicago Distribution Ctr.

Rodgon, Maris Monitz. Single-Word Usage, Cognitive Development, & the Beginnings of Combinatorial Speech: A study of ten English-speaking Children. 2009. (ENG.). 176p. (C). pap. 28.99 (978-0-521-11114-0(5)) Cambridge Univ. Pr.

Roud, Steve. The Lore of the Playground: One Hundred Years of Children's Games, Rhymes & Traditions. 2010. (ENG., Illus.). 576p. 39.95 (978-1-905211-51-7(1)) Random Hse. GBR. Dist: Independent Pubs. Group.

Roulstone. Prioritising Child Health. 2006. (Illus.). 136p. 49.95 (978-0-415-37634-1(3)) Routledge.

Roulstone, Sue. Prioritising Child Health. 2006. (Illus.). 136p. 160.00 (978-0-415-37633-4(5)) Routledge.

Schakel, Peter J. The Longing for a Form: Essays on the Fiction of C. S. Lewis. Schakel, Peter J., ed. 2008. (C. S. Lewis Secondary Studies Ser.). 256p. pap. 28.00 (978-1-55635-588-2(2), Wipf and Stock) Wipf & Stock Pubs.

Schakel, Peter J. & Huttar, Charles A., eds. Word & Story in C. S. Lewis: Language & Narrative in Theory & Practice. 2008. (C. S. Lewis Secondary Studies Ser.). 330p. pap. 36.00 (978-1-55635-587-5(4)) Wipf & Stock Pubs.

Sinclair, Skye. Runaway. 2008. (ENG.). 320p. 25.95 (978-0-340-95336-5(5), Hodder & Stoughton) Hodder General Publishing Div. GBR. Dist: Independent Pubs. Group.

Smith, Emma. The Great Western Beach: A Memoir of a Cornish Childhood Between the Wars. 2008. (ENG., Illus.). 384p. 29.95 (978-0-7475-9591-5(7)) Bloomsbury Publishing Plc GBR. Dist: Independent Pubs. Group.

Spooner, Wendy. The SEN Handbook for Trainee Teachers, NQTs & Teaching Assistants. 2nd rev. ed. 2010. (David Fulton / Nasen Ser.). (ENG., Illus.). 136p. 36.95 (978-0-415-56771-8(8)) Routledge.

Spry, Christopher. Child C: Surviving a Foster Mother's Reign of Terror. 2008. (ENG.). 320p. pap. 12.95 (978-1-84739-189-6(3)) Simon & Schuster, Ltd. GBR. Dist: Independent Pubs. Group.

Steemers, Jeanette. Creating Preschool Television: A Story of Commerce, Creativity & Curriculum. 2010. (ENG., Illus.). 256p. 95.00 (978-0-230-57440-3(8)) Palgrave Macmillan.

Stiller, Charles, ed. Childhood Cancer in Britain: Incidence, Survival & Mortality. 2007. (ENG., Illus.). 288p. 185.00 (978-0-19-852070-2(0)) Oxford Univ. Pr., Inc.

Stubbs, Michael. Language Schools & Classrooms (Rle Edu L Sociology of Education) 2012. (Routledge Library Editions: Education Ser.). (ENG.). 168p. 115.00 (978-0-415-50104-0(0)) Routledge.

Swan, Anna. Statues Without Shadows: A Daughter's Search for the Truth about the Parents She Never Knew. 2006. (ENG., Illus.). 288p. per. 13.95 (978-0-340-83539-5(7)) Hodder General Publishing Div. GBR. Dist: Independent Pubs. Group.

Taylor, D. J. Bright Young People: The Lost Generation of London's Jazz Age. 2010. (ENG., Illus.). 384p. pap. 17.00 (978-0-374-53211-6(7)) Farrar, Straus & Giroux.

Thomson, Rachel. Critical Practice with Children & Young People. Robb, Martin, ed. 2010. (Illus.). 312p. 89.95 (978-1-84742-682-6(4)) Policy Pr. GBR. Dist: Chicago Distribution Ctr.

Tomlinson, Jo, et al, eds. Music Therapy in Schools: Working with Children of All Ages in Mainstream & Special Education. 2011. (ENG., Illus.). 256p. pap. (978-1-84905-000-5(7)) Kingsley, Jessica Ltd.

Tomlinson, Pat, et al. Childhood, Services & Provision for Children. 2008. (Illus.). 304p. pap. 55.00 (978-1-4058-3257-1(6), Prentice Hall) Pearson Education, Ltd. GBR. Dist: Trans-Atlantic Pubns., Inc.

Tunnicliffe, Clive. Teaching Able, Gifted & Talented Children: Strategies, Activities & Resources. 2010. 144p. 127.00 (978-1-4129-4766-4(9), B47664C) SAGE Pubns., Ltd. GBR. Dist: SAGE Pubns., Inc.

Vale, Allison & Rattle, Alison. The Woman Who Murdered Babies for Money: The Story of Amelia Dyer. 2011. (ENG., Illus.). 264p. pap. 14.95 (978-0-233-00316-0(9)) Andre Deutsch GBR. Dist: Independent Pubs. Group.

Wallace, Eileen. Children of the Labouring Poor: The Working Lives of Children in Nineteenth-Century Hertfordshire. 2010. (ENG., Illus.). 256p. pap. 33.95 (978-1-905313-49-5(7)) Univ. of Hertfordshire Pr. GBR. Dist: Independent Pubs. Group.

Watson, Casey. Crying for Help: The Shocking True Story of a Damaged Girl with a Dark Past. 2012. (ENG.). 304p. 12.95 (978-0-00-743658-3(0)) HarperCollins Pubs. Ltd. GBR. Dist: Independent Pubs. Group.

White, John. Exploring Well-Being in Schools: A Guide to Making Children's Lives More Fulfilling. 2011. (ENG.). 160p. 120.00 (978-0-415-60347-8(1)); pap. 35.99 (978-0-415-60348-5(X)) Routledge.

Whitney, Ben. Social Inclusion in Schools: Improving Outcomes, Raising Standards. 2007. (David Fulton Bks.). (Illus.). 112p. per. 37.50 (978-1-84312-474-0(2)) Routledge.

Witmore, Michael. Pretty Creatures: Children & Fiction in the English Renaissance. 2007. (Illus.). 233p. 43.95 (978-0-8014-4399-2(7)) Cornell Univ. Pr.

Zairi, Alweena. Raising Children's Learning & Performance. 2010. 336p. pap. (978-3-8383-8657-7(4)) Lambert Academic Publishing.

CHILDREN—GREECE

Cowles, Julia Darrow. Our Little Athenian Cousin of Long Ago. 2008. (Illus.). 104p. pap. 7.95 (978-1-59915-283-7(5)) Yesterday's Classics.

—Our Little Spartan Cousin of Long Ago. 2008. 120p. pap. 8.95 (978-1-59915-284-4(3)) Yesterday's Classics.

Danforth, Loring M. & Van Boeschoten, Riki. Children of the Greek Civil War: Refugees & the Politics of Memory. 2011. (ENG., Illus.). 352p. pap. 25.00 (978-0-226-13599-1(3)) Univ. of Chicago Pr.

Deissler, Johannes & Heinen, Heinz, eds. Kindersklaven - Sklavenkinder: Schicksale zwischen Zuneigung und Ausbeutung in der Antike und im interkulturellen Vergleich. Beiträge zur Tagung des Akademievorhabens Forschungen zur antiken Sklaverei (Mainz, 14. Oktober 2008) 2012. (Forschungen Zur Antiken Sklaverei - Beiheft Ser.: 39). (GER., Illus.). 327p. (C). pap. 78.00 (978-3-515-09414-6(8)) Steiner, Franz Verlag Wiesbaden GmbH DEU. Dist: Brown, David Bk. Co., The.

Kakmi, Dmetri. Mother Land. 2010. (ENG., Illus.). 231p. 39.95 (978-1-906011-39-0(7)) Eland Bks. GBR. Dist: Dufour Editions, Inc.

Karavasilis, Niki. The Abducted Greek Children of the Communists: Paidomazoma. 2006. 23.00 (978-0-8059-7320-4(6)) Dorrance Publishing Co., Inc.

Schlegelmilch, Sabine. Bürger, Gott und Götterschützling: Kinderbilder der hellenistischen Kunst und Literatur. 2009. (Beiträge zur Altertumskunde Ser.).Tr. of Citizens, God & God's Chosen Ones. Portrayals of Children in Hellenistic Art & Literature. (GER., Illus.). VIII, 311p. 140.00 (978-3-11-021765-0(1)) De Gruyter, Walter Inc.

CHILDREN—HUNGARY

Merva, Monika, et al. The City of Children. 2011. (ENG., Illus.). 112p. 45.00 (978-3-86828-174-3(6)) Kehrer Verlag Heidelberg, Klaus Kehrer DEU. Dist: Consortium Bk. Sales & Distribution.

The Hungarian Hidden Children. Remember Us: A collection of memories from Hungarian Hidden Children of the Holocaust. 2009. 304p. pap. 25.00 (978-1-4389-2905-7(6)) AuthorHouse.

CHILDREN—INDIA

Anandalakshmy, S., et al. Researching Families & Children: Culturally Appropriate Methods. Anandalakshmy, S. et al, eds. 2008. (Illus.). 252p. (C). pap. 29.95 (978-81-7829-872-6(4), B98726P) SAGE Pubns., Inc.

Arokiasamy, P. & Pradhan, J. Demand & Supply Aspects: Of Maternal & Child Health Care Services Utilization in India. 2011. 104p. pap. (978-3-639-32621-5(0)) VDM Verlag Dr. Mueller e.K.

Baru, Rama V., ed. School Health Services in India: The Social & Economic Contexts. 2009. (Illus.). 228p. (C). 39.95 (978-81-7829-873-3(2), B98733C) SAGE Pubns., Inc.

Cleghorn, A. & Prochner, L. Shades of Globalization in Three Early Childhood Settings. 2010. 178p. (978-94-6091-100-2(5)); pap. (978-94-6091-099-9(8)) Sense Pubs.

Dabir, Neela. From Street to Hope: Faith Based & Secular Programmes in Los Angeles, Mumbai & Nairobi for Street-living Children. 2011. (Illus.). 336p. (C). 40.00 (978-81-321-0513-8(3), B05138C) SAGE Pubns., Inc.

Ganga, R. & Supputhai, M. Children's Rights as Basic Human Rights: Sensitization of Stakeholders. 2007. 370p. 46.00 (978-81-8405-039-4(9), Reference Pr.) Ess Ess Pubns. IND. Dist: International Specialized Bk. Services.

Gupta Mandal, Ujjwala. Diarrhoeal Diseases in Children. 2011. 88p. pap. (978-3-8433-7851-2(7)) Lambert Academic Publishing.

Keshri, Kunal & Bhagat, Ram B. Rural-Urban Migration & Child Survival in Indi. 2011. 88p. pap. (978-3-8443-8979-1(2)) Lambert Academic Publishing.

Mohanty, Sanjay. Multidimensional Poverty & Reproductive & Child Health in Indi. 2011. 100p. pap. (978-3-8443-2953-7(6)) Lambert Academic Publishing.

Mukherjee, Dipa. Child Workers in Indi. 2011. 100p. pap. (978-3-8443-0648-4(X)) Lambert Academic Publishing.

Naqshbandi, M. Mudasir. Child Labor in Kashmir. 2011. 100p. pap. (978-3-8443-0637-8(4)) Lambert Academic Publishing.

Nieuwenhuizen, Patricia. Street Children in Bangalore (India) Their Dreams & Their Future. 2008. (ENG.). 160p. pap. 29.95 (978-90-5589-269-3(6)) Het Spinhuis NLD. Dist: Transaction Pubs.

Pandey, Janak, et al, eds. Perspectives on Learning Disabilities in India: Current Practices & Prospects. 2008. 304p. (C). 60.00 (978-81-7829-825-2(2), B98252C) SAGE Pubns., Inc.

Pandit, Apoorvaa. Watershed Development Inputs & Social Change: Understanding the Changing Culture of Child Nutrition. 2010. (Illus.). 186p. 35.00 (978-81-316-0342-0(3)) Rawat Pubns. IND. Dist: International Specialized Bk. Services.

Pradhan, Jalandhar. Clustering of Child Mortality. 2011. 76p. pap. (978-3-8433-9434-5(2)) Lambert Academic Publishing.

Roy, Runa & KUMAR KURI, Pravat. Child Health & Mortality in Indi. 2011. 120p. pap. (978-3-8443-1101-3(7)) Lambert Academic Publishing.

Seale, Shelley. The Weight of Silence: Invisible Children of India. 2009. (ENG.). 334p. pap. 16.95 (978-0-9802323-7-0(6)) Dog's Eye View Media.

Seth, Veenu, et al. Nutrition Issues in Children with Disabilities. 2011. 496p. pap. (978-3-8443-2917-9(0)) Lambert Academic Publishing.

Sheikh, Fazal, photos by. Ladli, 1 vol. 2008. (ENG., Illus.). 180p. 45.00 (978-3-86521-381-5(2)) Steidl, Gerhard Druckerei und Verlag DEU. Dist: Innovative Logistics.

Shepherd, Mary E. Sex-Selective Abortion in India: The Impact on Child Mortality. 2007. (C). 109.95 (978-1-934043-69-1(9)) Cambria Pr.

Weiner, Myron, et al. Born Unfree - Child Labour, Education, & the State in India: An Omnibus - The Child & the State in India, Born to Work, & Child Rights in India (Extract) 2007. (ENG., Illus.). 740p. 65.00 (978-0-19-567990-8(3)) Oxford Univ. Pr., Inc.

CHILDREN—INDONESIA

Atwell, Alison. The Impact of a School Leadership Training Program in Indonesi. 2009. 308p. pap. *(978-3-639-03709-8(X))* VDM Verlag Dr. Mueller e.K.

CHILDREN—IRELAND

Laoire, Caitriona Ní, et al. Childhood & Migration in Europe: Portraits from Contemporary Ireland. 2011. (Studies in Migration & Diaspora Ser.). (Illus.). 212p. 99.95 *(978-1-4094-0109-4(X))* Ashgate Publishing Co.

Mcelwee. At-Risk Children & Youth: Resiliency Explored. 2007. (ENG.). 334p. 125.00 *(978-0-7890-3381-9(X))* Routledge.

O'Donnell, E. E., ed. All Our Yesterdays: Father Browne's Photgraphs of Children & Their Favorite Poems. 2007. (ENG., Illus.). 132p. 44.95 *(978-1-85607-952-5(X))* Columba Pr. IRL. Dist: Dufour Editions, Inc.

—All Our Yesterdays: Father Browne's Photographs of Children & their Favourite Poems. 2008. (ENG.). 132p. pap. 29.95 *(978-1-85607-968-6(6))* Currach Pr. IRL. Dist: Dufour Editions, Inc.

O'Malley, Kathleen. Childhood Interrupted: Growing up Unaer the Cruel Regime of the Sisters of Mercy. 2006. 244p. reprint ed. pap. 22.00 *(978-1-4223-5723-1(6))* DIANE Publishing Co.

O'Sullivan, Keith & Coghlan, Valerie, eds. Irish Children's Literature & Culture. 2010. (Children's Literature & Culture Ser.). (ENG.). 228p. (C). 125.00 *(978-0-415-87789-3(X))* Routledge.

Sixsmith, Martin. The Lost Child of Philomena Lee: A Mother, Her Son & a Fifty Year Search. 2009. (Illus.). 464p. pap. 28.50 *(978-0-230-74427-1(3),* Macmillan) Pan Macmillan GBR. Dist: Trans-Atlantic Pubns., Inc.

Stein, Evaleen. Our Little Celtic Cousin of Long Ago. 2008. (Illus.). 72p. pap. *(978-1-4099-1695-6(2))* Dodo Pr.

—Our Little Celtic Cousin of Long Ago. 2007. 104p. per. 8.95 *(978-1-59915-242-4(8))* Yesterday's Classics.

Van Erwegen, Luck. Quis Custodiet Ipsas Custodies ? 2010. 68p. pap. *(978-3-8383-6470-4(8))* Lambert Academic Publishing.

CHILDREN—ISRAEL

Ashbee, Felicity. Child in Jerusalem. 2008. (Middle East Studies). (Illus.). 166p. *(978-0-8156-0872-1(1))* Syracuse Univ. Pr.

CHILDREN—ITALY

Cowles, Julia Darrow. Our Little Roman Cousin of Long Ago. 2010. 98p. pap. 7.95 *(978-1-59915-285-1(1))* Yesterday's Classics.

Deissler, Johannes & Heinen, Heinz, eds. Kindersklaven - Sklavenkinder: Schicksale zwischen Zuneigung und Ausbeutung in der Antike und im interkulturellen Vergleich. Beiträge zur Tagung des Akademievorhabens Forschungen zur antiken Sklaverei (Mainz, 14. Oktober 2008) 2012. (Forschungen Zur Antiken Sklaverei - Beiheft Ser.: 39). (GER., Illus.). 327p. (C). pap. 78.00 ***(978-3-515-09414-6(8))*** Steiner, Franz Verlag Wiesbaden GmbH DEU. Dist: Brown, David Bk. Co., The.

Ferraro, Joanne Marie. Nefarious Crimes, Contested Justice: Illicit Sex & Infanticide in the Republic of Venice, 1557-1789. 2008. (ENG., Illus.). 272p. (gr. 17). 49.00 *(978-0-8018-8987-5(1))* Johns Hopkins Univ. Pr.

Stawoska-Jundzi, Bozena. Vixit Cum Parentibus: Dzieci W Wieku Do Siedmiu Lat W Rodzinach Chrzescijan Z Rzymu III-VI Wieku. 2008. (LAT & POL., Illus.). 616p. *(978-83-7096-668-3(3))* Wydawnictwo Uczelniane.

CHILDREN—JAPAN

Bamba, Sachiko & Haight, Wendy. Child Welfare & Development: A Japanese Case Study. 2011. (ENG., Illus.). 224p. 80.00 ***(978-1-107-00284-5(2))*** Cambridge Univ. Pr.

Kamada, Laurel. Hybrid Identities & Adolescent Girls: Being 'Half' in Japan. 2009. (Critical Language & Literacy Studies). (ENG., Illus.). 272p. 119.95 *(978-1-84769-233-7(8))*; pap. 49.95 *(978-1-84769-232-0(X))* Multilingual Matters GBR. Dist: Univ. of Toronto Pr.

Kaneko, Masa & Yamamoto, Kikuo. Nurie: The Fascination of Coloring. 2009. *(978-0-935047-68-4(9))* Americas Group, The.

Kokusai Kodomo Toshokan (Japan) Staff, contrib. by. Itsu, Nani to Deau Ka: Akachan Ehon Kara Yangu Adaruto Bungaku Made. 2010. (JPN., Illus.). 116p. *(978-4-87582-701-6(6))* National Diet Library.

United Nations Children's Fund. Trafficking for Sexual Exploitation & other Exploitative Purposes. 2009. 24p. pap. 15.00 *(978-88-89129-21-0(2))* United Nations Children's Fund, The (UNICEF).

Ushijima, Yoshitomo & Ando, Nobuo. Seishonen, 2 vols. 2010. (JPN., Illus.). *(978-4-87733-528-1(5))*; *(978-4-87733-529-8(3))* Kross Shuppan.

CHILDREN—KENYA

Charles, Nyangara Asaka & Odago, Adhiambo Donata. Psychosocial Support & Care Projects: A Managerial View of Orphaned & Vulnerable Children (OVC)Situation in Bumala, Kenya. 2011. 184p. pap. ***(978-3-639-34390-8(5))*** VDM Verlag Dr. Mueller e.K.

Koech, Peter. Parent-Teacher Partnerships. 2010. 156p. pap. *(978-3-639-26624-5(2))* VDM Verlag Dr. Mueller e.K.

Mwelu Foundation and Africalia Staff. Julius Mwelu & the Mwelu Foundation/Nairobi. 2012. (ENG., Illus.). 148p. 55.50 ***(978-90-5856-403-0(7))*** Stichting Kunstboek Bvba BEL. Dist: Antique Collectors' Club.

Njoroge, Martin. Aspirations & Educational Challenges of Kenya's Street Children. 2009. 92p. pap. *(978-3-639-16427-5(X))* VDM Verlag Dr. Mueller e.K.

Oketch, Patricia & Patricia, Oketch. Support for the Adolescents: The Effects of Urbanisation on the Kenyan Adolescents. 2011. 56p. pap. ***(978-3-639-32082-4(4))*** VDM Verlag Dr. Mueller e.K.

Okoronkwo, Stella. Effective Communication with Children & Youth: A Guide for Parents & Youth Workers. 2011. 124p. 43.89 *(978-1-4520-2026-6(4))*; pap. 31.35 *(978-1-4520-2023-5(X))* AuthorHouse.

CHILDREN—KOREA

Hong, Sung-A. Ch'wiop Pumo Ui Chanyo Yangyuk Chiwon Sobisu Hyoyurhwa Pangan. 2010. (KOR., Illus.). xxi, 272p. *(978-89-8491-346-2(4))* Korean Women's Development Institute.

Sohn, Byoungduk. Juvenile Delinquency in Korea & Korean Social Policy: A Critical Examination of Korean Youth Aged 12-15 in Correctional Institutions in Korea with a View to Societal Betterment. 2006. (Hermit Kingdom Studies in Identity & Society: Vol. 2). *(978-1-59689-065-7(7))*; pap. *(978-1-59689-066-4(5))* Hermit Kingdom Pr., The.

Tuan, Mia & Shiao, Jiannbin Lee. Choosing Ethnicity, Negotiating Race: Korean Adoptees in America. 2011. 213p. 35.00 *(978-0-87154-875-7(5))* Russell Sage Foundation.

CHILDREN—LATIN AMERICA

Barros, Ricardo Paes de, et al. Measuring Inequality of Opportunities in Latin America & the Caribbean. 2008. (Latin American Development Forum Ser.). (ENG., Illus.). 220p. pap. 30.00 *(978-0-8213-7745-1(0),* 9780821377451) World Bank Pubns.

Gonzalez, Ondina E. & Premo, Bianca, eds. Raising an Empire: Children in Early Modern Iberia & Colonial Latin America. 2007. (Dialogos Ser.). (ENG., Illus.). 270p. (C). pap. 29.95 *(978-0-8263-3441-1(5))* Univ. of New Mexico Pr.

López-Calva, Luis Felipe. Trabajo Infantil: Teoría y Lecciones de la América Latina. 2006. (Lecturas de el Trimestre Económico Ser.). (SPA., Illus.). 461p. pap. *(978-968-16-8120-3(7))* Fondo de Cultura Economica.

Molinas, Jose R. Do Our Children Have a Chance? The Human Opportunity Report for Latin America & the Caribbean. 2012. (Illus.). xv, 154p. ***(978-0-8213-8902-7(5))*** World Bank Pubns.

Molinas Vega, Jose R., et al. Do Our Children Have a Chance? The 2010 Human Opportunity Report for Latin America & the Caribbean. 2011. (Directions in Development Ser.). (ENG., Illus.). 170p. pap. 25.00 ***(978-0-8213-8699-6(9),*** 9780821386996) World Bank Pubns.

Ngozika Ihewulezi, Cajetan. Forward March to Professionalism: Starting Early to Help Latino American Children Develop a Vision of Their Dream Careers. 2009. pap. 10.99 *(978-1-60799-025-3(3))* Tate Publishing & Enterprises, LLC.

Rodríguez, Pablo & Mannarelli, Maria Emma. Historia de la Infancia en América Latina. 2007. (SPA., Illus.). 673p. pap. 33.00 *(978-958-710-218-5(5))* Universidad Externado de Colombia COL. Dist: Siglo del Hombre.

World Bank Group Staff, et al. The Promise of Early Childhood Development in Latin America & the Caribbean. 2009. (Latin American Development Forum Ser.). (ENG., Illus.). 220p. pap. 40.00 *(978-0-8213-7759-8(0),* 9780821377598) World Bank Pubns.

CHILDREN—LEBANON

Matar, Rania & Shadid, Anthony. Ordinary Lives. 2009. (ENG., Illus.). 128p. 39.95 *(978-1-59372-037-7(8),* 372037) Quantuck Lane Pr. & The Mill Road Collaborative, The.

Wilson, Anna, ed. Lebanon, Lebanon. 2006. (ENG., Illus.). 256p. per. 18.95 *(978-0-86356-641-7(3))* Saqi Bks. GBR. Dist: Consortium Bk. Sales & Distribution.

CHILDREN—MALAYSIA

Peow, See Hoon. Law & Child Labour in Malaysia: Case Study in a Chinese New Village. 2007. 168p. (C). pap. 28.50 *(978-967-978-937-9(3))* Pelanduk Pubns. Malaysia Sdn. Bhd MYS. Dist: Coronet Bks.

CHILDREN—MEXICO

Fielding, Jed. Look at Me: Photographs from Mexico City by Jed Fielding. 2009. (ENG., Illus.). 144p. 55.00 *(978-0-226-24852-3(6))* Univ. of Chicago Pr.

Oria, Maria & Sawyer, Kristin. Joint U. S. -Mexico Workshop on Preventing Obesity in Children & Youth of Mexican Origin: Summary. 2007. (ENG., Illus.). 210p. pap. 46.25 *(978-0-309-10325-1(8))* National Academies Pr.

Ronquillo, Victor. Los NiNtilde;Os de Nadie. 2007. (SPA.). 200p. pap. 18.95 *(978-970-710-262-0(4))* B. Mexico, Ediciones, S.A. de C.V. MEX. Dist: Ediciones Urano S. A.

Sosenski, Susana. Niños en Acción: El Trabajo Infantil en la Ciudad de México (1920-1934) 2010. (Estudios Históricos Ser.). (SPA., Illus.). 365p. pap. 48.99 *(978-607-452-053-5(9))* El Colegio de México, A.C., Biblioteca Miguel Cosio Villegas MEX. Dist: Fondo de Cultura Economica USA.

CHILDREN—MIDDLE EAST

Hentschel, Jesko S., et al. Life Chances in Turkey: Expanding Opportunities for the Next Generation. 2010. (Directions in Development Ser.). (ENG.). 112p. pap. 20.00 *(978-0-8213-8400-8(7),* 9780821384008) World Bank Pubns.

Pimentel, David. What Are Children Learning about Islam & the Middle East in Public Schools? Are the Students Also Being Taught to Hate America? 2011. 84p. 22.00 ***(978-1-4269-7470-0(1))***; pap. 12.00 ***(978-1-4269-7469-4(8))*** Trafford Publishing.

Safarinejad, Mohammad Reza. Epidemiology of Nocturnal Enuresis in Iranian School Children. 2009. 96p. pap. *(978-3-639-20541-1(3))* VDM Verlag Dr. Mueller e.K.

Saleem, Kamal. The Blood of Lambs: A Former Terrorist's Memoir of Death & Redemption. 2009. (ENG.). 352p. 24.99 *(978-1-4165-7780-5(7),* Howard Bks.) Howard Books.

Somçelik-Köksa, Aysegül. Working & Non-Working Children in Turkey. 2010. 80p. pap. *(978-3-8383-8003-2(7))* Lambert Academic Publishing.

CHILDREN—NETHERLANDS

Olcott, Virginia. Adventures in Holland: The Story of Klaas & Jansje. 2011. 162p. 41.95 ***(978-1-258-06352-8(2))*** Literary Licensing, LLC.

CHILDREN—NEW ZEALAND

Clendon, Jill. Intergenerational Connections & Motherhood. 2010. 272p. pap. *(978-3-8383-7809-1(1))* Lambert Academic Publishing.

Sawicki, Nina. Listening Through Deaf Ears. 2010. 192p. pap. *(978-3-8383-4278-8(X))* Lambert Academic Publishing.

Taylor, Nicola J. & Smith, Anne B., eds. Children as Citizens? International Voices. 2009. (Illus.). 221p. pap. 45.00 *(978-1-877372-62-9(5))* Otago University Pr. NZL. Dist: International Specialized Bk. Services.

CHILDREN—NIGERIA

Adibe, Maxwell. Quinine & Artemether in the Treatment of Severe Malaria in Children. 2010. 88p. pap. *(978-3-8383-9205-9(1))* Lambert Academic Publishing.

Oladipo, Gabriel. Craniofacial Measurements of Nigerian Ikwerre Children. 2010. 116p. pap. *(978-3-8383-7614-1(5))* Lambert Academic Publishing.

CHILDREN—NORWAY

Olcott, Virginia. Adventures in Norway: The Story of Olaf & Ane. 2011. 180p. 42.95 ***(978-1-258-01278-6(2))*** Literary Licensing, LLC.

CHILDREN—PALESTINE

Halileh, Samia. Developing Screening Tools for Palestinian Children. 2010. 196p. pap. *(978-3-639-24550-9(4))* VDM Verlag Dr. Mueller e.K.

CHILDREN—PHILIPPINES

Gonzales, Gizela M. Where the Children Are. 2011. (ENG.). 167p. pap. 50.00 *(978-971-94292-6-5(7))* Artpostasia Inc. PHL. Dist: National Bk. Network.

Lee, Cesar. Zamboanga Remembered. 2007. (Illus.). 148p. per. 14.95 *(978-0-9799341-1-7(7))* Imago Pr.

CHILDREN—PUERTO RICO

McNamee, Abigail. Being Puerto Rican & American, Nuyorican Children's Voices. 2009. 116p. 22.50 *(978-1-60693-920-8(3),* Eloquent Bks.) AEG Literary Publishing Services, Inc.

CHILDREN—RUSSIA (FEDERATION)

Balina, Marina & Rudova, Larissa, eds. Russian Children's Literature & Culture. 2007. (Children's Literature & Culture Ser.). (ENG., Illus.). 352p. 125.00 *(978-0-415-97864-4(5))* Routledge.

Fraser, Eugenie. The House by the Dvina: A Russian Childhood. 2011. (ENG., Illus.). 368p. pap. 14.95 *(978-1-84596-573-0(6))* Mainstream Publishing Co., Ltd. GBR. Dist: Independent Pubs. Group.

Gorshkov, Boris B. Russia's Factory Children: State, Society, & Law, 1800-1917. 2009. (Pitt Russian East European Ser.). (ENG., Illus.). 228p. (C). 60.00 *(978-0-8229-4383-9(2))*; pap. 25.95 *(978-0-8229-6048-5(6))* Univ. of Pittsburgh Pr.

Kouwenhoven, Bill. Little Adults. 2011. (ENG & GER., Illus.). 112p. 50.00 ***(978-3-86828-192-7(4))*** Kehrer Verlag Heidelberg, Klaus Kehrer DEU. Dist: Consortium Bk. Sales & Distribution.

Rockhill, Elena Khlinovskaya. Lost to the State: Family Discontinuity, Social Orphanhood & Residential Care in the Russian Far East. 2010. (Illus.). 336p. 90.00 *(978-1-84545-738-9(2))* Berghahn Bks., Inc.

Zimin, I. V. Povsednevnaia Zhizn Rossiiskogo Imperatorskogo Dvora: Detskii Mir Imperatorskikh Rezidentsii: Byt Monarkhov I Ikh Okruzhenie. 2010. (RUS., Illus.). 571p. *(978-5-227-02410-7(3))* Centropoligraf, AO zakrytogo tipa, torgovo-izdatel'skoe obedinenie.

CHILDREN—SCOTLAND

Charles, Emma. How Could He Do It? 2009. (ENG.). 352p. pap. 13.95 *(978-1-84809-000-2(5))* Random Hse. GBR. Dist: Independent Pubs. Group.

Gangel, Alison. The Sun Hasn't Fallen from the Sky. 2012. (ENG.). 256p. pap. 18.50 *(978-1-4088-2205-0(9))* Bloomsbury Publishing.

Sprange, H. Kingdom Kids. 319p. 13.50 *(978-1-85792-096-3(1))* Christian Focus Pubns. GBR. Dist: Spring Arbor Distributors, Inc.

Thomson, June, et al. Beyond All Evil: Two Monsters Two Mothers a Love That Will Last Forever. 2012. (ENG.). 304p. 11.95 ***(978-0-00-743851-8(6))*** HarperCollins Pubs. Ltd. GBR. Dist: Independent Pubs. Group.

CHILDREN—SOUTH AFRICA

Bieber, Jodi, photos by. Between Dogs & Wolves: Growing up with South Africa. 2007. (ENG., Illus.). 144p. 30.00 *(978-1-904587-32-3(1))* Lewis, Dewi Publishing GBR. Dist: Consortium Bk. Sales & Distribution

Boezaart, Trynie. Child Law in South Africa. 2010. 772p. pap. 74.50 *(978-0-7021-8212-9(5))* Gaunt, Inc.

Cleghorn, A. & Prochner, L. Shades of Globalization in Three Early Childhooc Settings. 2010. 178p. pap. *(978-94-6091-099-9(8))* Sense Pubs.

Crause, Ewald. The Occupational Aspirations & Perceptions of South African Children. 2010. 148p. pap. *(978-3-639-23891-4(5))* VDM Verlag Dr. Mueller e.K.

Davel, C. J. & Skelton, A. M., eds. Commentary on the Children's Act. 2007. 110.00 *(978-0-7021-7863-2(7))* Juta & Co., Ltd. ZAF. Dist: Gaunt, Inc.

Dawes, Andrew, et al, eds. Monitoring Child Well-Being: A South African Rights-Based Approach. 2008. (Child Indicators Ser.). (ENG., Illus.). 640p. pap. 40.00 *(978-0-7969-2177-2(6))* Human Sciences Research Council ZAF. Dist: Independent Pubs. Group.

Deacon, Harriet & Stephney, Inez. HIV/AIDS, Stigma & Children: A Literature Review. 2008. (ENG., Illus.). 88p. pap. 16.95 *(978-0-7969-2188-8(1))* Human Sciences Research Council ZAF. Dist: Independent Pubs. Group.

Kidd, Dudley. Savage Childhood: A Study of Kafir Children. 2010. 402p. pap. 34.75 *(978-1-144-53428-6(3))*; 396p. pap. 33.75 *(978-1-142-10719-2(1))* BiblioBazaar.

—Savage Childhood A Study of Kafir Children. 2007. (ENG.). 318p. 45.95 *(978-0-548-15670-4(0))*; 320p. per. 30.95 *(978-1-4304-5139-6(4))* Kessinger Publishing, LLC.

Mentis, M. T. Bridging Learning: Unlocking Cognitive Potential in & Out of the Classroom. Mentis, Martene et al, eds. 2nd ed. 2009. (Illus.). 152p. pap. 31.95 *(978-1-4129-6995-6(6),* B69949P) Corwin Pr.

Mentis, Martene, et al, eds. Bridging Learning: Unlocking Cognitve Potential in & Out of the Classroom. 2nd ed. 2009. (Illus.). 152p. 72.95 *(978-1-4129-6994-9(8),* B69949C) Corwin Pr.

Miller, Kirsten. Children on the Bridge: A Story of Autism in South Africa. 2007. (ENG.). 240p. per. 21.00 *(978-1-77009-218-1(8))* Jacana Media ZAF. Dist: Independent Pubs. Group.

Stranger, Kgamphe. Physical Measurements: Chronic Impact of Apartheid in Black Children: Physical Growth & Development of Rural South African Black Children Using Anthropometric Techniques. 2011. 528p. pap. ***(978-3-639-28650-2(2))*** VDM Verlag Dr. Mueller e.K.

United Nations Children's Fund. South Asia in Action: Preventing & Responding to Child Trafficking - Child Rights-based Programme Practices. 2009. (Insight Innocenti Ser.). 42p. pap. 20.00 *(978-88-89129-77-7(8))* United Nations Children's Fund, The (UNICEF).

Varughese, Sara. A Situation Analysis of Retinopathy of Prematurity in South Afric. 2010. 64p. pap. *(978-3-8383-6793-4(6))* Lambert Academic Publishing.

CHILDREN—SOVIET UNION

Balina, Marina & Rudova, Larissa, eds. Russian Children's Literature & Culture. 2007. (Children's Literature & Culture Ser.). (ENG., Illus.). 352p. 125.00 *(978-0-415-97864-4(5))* Routledge.

Bird, Robert & Jackson, Matthew Jesse, eds. Adventures in the Soviet Imaginary: Soviet Children's Books & Graphic Art. 2011. (ENG., Illus.). 48p. pap. 12.00 *(978-0-943056-40-1(3))* Univ. of Chicago, Library, The.

Frierson, Cathy A. & Vilensky, Semyon Samuilovich. Children of the Gulag. 2010. (Annals of Communism Ser.). (ENG., Illus.). 480p. (C). 55.00 *(978-0-300-12293-0(4))* Yale Univ. Pr.

Hoffman, Deborah. The Littlest Enemies: Children in the Shadow of the Gulag. 2009. 189p. *(978-0-89357-366-9(3))* Slavica Pubs.

Rockhill, Elena Khlinovskaya. Lost to the State: Family Discontinuity, Social Orphanhood & Residential Care in the Russian Far East. 2010. (Illus.). 336p. 90.00 *(978-1-84545-738-9(2))* Berghahn Bks., Inc.

CHILDREN—SPAIN

Fernández Molina, Esther & Molina, Esther Fernández. Entre la Educación y el Castigo: Una Análisis de la Justicia de Menores en España. 2008. (SPA.). 430p. *(978-84-9876-002-6(X))* Tirant lo Blanch.

García Pérez, Octavio, et al. La Delincuencia Juvenil Ante Los Juzgados de Menores. 2008. (Tirant "Criminología y Educación Socialquot Ser.). (SPA.). 261p. *(978-84-9876-004-0(6))* Tirant lo Blanch.

CHILDREN—SRI LANKA

Trawick, Margaret. Enemy Lines: Childhood, Warfare, & Play in Batticaloa. 2007. 307p. 60.00 *(978-0-520-24515-0(6))*; per. 26.95 *(978-0-520-24516-7(4))* Univ. of California Pr.

CHILDREN—SWEDEN

Fass, Paula S. & Grossberg, Michael, eds. Reinventing Childhood after World War II. 2011. 200p. (C). 42.50 ***(978-0-8122-4367-3(6))*** Univ. of Pennsylvania Pr.

Olcott, Virginia. Adventures in Sweden: The Story of Erik & Britta. 2011. 180p. 42.95 ***(978-1-258-06164-7(3))*** Literary Licensing, LLC.

CHILDREN—UGANDA

Bwengye-Kahororo, Edward. Child Labour in Solid Waste Scavenging. 2011. 152p. pap. ***(978-3-8433-8793-5(4))*** Lambert Academic Publishing.

Dunson, Donald H. Child, Victim, Soldier: The Loss of Innocence in Uganda. 2008. (Illus.). 160p. pap. 16.00 *(978-1-57075-799-0(2))* Orbis Bks.

The Forgotten Children: Hungry. Hopeless. Running for their Lives. 2006. per. 14.95 *(978-0-9788041-0-7(4))* World Help Inc.

Jagielski, Wojciech. The Night Wanderers: Uganda's Children & the Lord's Resistance Army. Lloyd-Jones, Antonia, tr. from POL. 2012. (ENG., Illus.). 288p. pap. 18.95 ***(978-1-60980-350-6(7))*** Seven Stories Pr.

McClintock, Heather, photos by. The Innocent: Casualties of the Civil War in Northern Uganda. 2010. (ENG., Illus.). 120p. 40.00 *(978-90-5330-697-0(8))* Mets en Schilt Uitgevers NLD. Dist: Ingram Pub. Services.

McDonnell, Faith J. H. & Akallo, Grace. Girl Soldier: A Story of Hope for Northern Uganda's Children. 2007. (Illus.). 240p. pap. 14.99 *(978-0-8007-9421-7(4))* Chosen Bks.

Mæland, Bård. Culture, Religion, & the Reintegration of Female Child Soldiers in Northern Uganda. 2010. (Bible & Theology in Africa Ser.). 332p. (C). 84.95 *(978-1-4331-0951-5(4))* Lang, Peter Publishing, Inc.

CHILDREN—UNITED STATES

see also Mexican American Children

ABA Center on Children and the Law Staff & Center for Children, Law & Policy Staff, contrib. by. Children, Law, & Disasters: What Have We Learned from the Hurricanes of 2005? 2008. *(978-1-60442-249-8(1))* American Bar Assn.

Abrams, et al. Children & the Law: Doctrine, Policy & Practice, 4th. 4th rev. ed. 2010. 1242p. 183.00 *(978-0-314-90576-5(6),* West Legalworks) West.

Abrams, Douglas E. & Ramsey, Sarah H. Children & the Law: Doctrine, Policy, & Practice. 3rd rev. ed. 2007. (American Casebook Ser.). 1196p. 142.00 *(978-0-314-16951-8(2),* West Legalworks) West.

—Children & the Law: Doctrine, Policy & Practice. 3rd ed. 2007. xlix, 1196p. pap. *(978-0-314-16950-1(4))* West Publishing Co., College & Schl. Div.

C

Ada, Alma Flor. Alma Flor Ada & YOU, 1 vol., Vol. 2. 2nd ed. 2008. (Author & YOU Ser.). (Illus.). 128p. pap. 35.00 *(978-1-59158-228-1(8),* LU2288) Libraries Unlimited, Inc.

Adger, Carolyn Temple, et al. Dialects in Schools & Communities. 2nd rev. ed. 2007. 226p. 95.00 *(978-0-8058-4315-6(9));* (Illus.). per. 37.95 *(978-0-8058-4316-3(7))* Erlbaum, Lawrence Assocs., Inc.

Aitken, Stuart, et al, eds. Border Spaces & Revolutionary Imaginations. 2011. (ENG., Illus.). 120p. (C). 133.00 *(978-0-415-61946-2(7))* Routledge.

Ajmera, Maya, et al. Children of the U. S. A. 2008. (Illus.). 128p. (J). (gr. 3-6). 23.95 *(978-1-57091-615-1(2))* Charlesbridge Publishing, Inc.

Al-Qubbaj, Kholoud. Acculturation among Arabic Children & Their Families in the U S. 2010. 136p. pap. *(978-3-8383-7498-7(3))* Lambert Academic Publishing.

American Library Association Staff, ed. The Newbery & Caldecott Awards: A Guide to the Medal Honor Books, 2008. 2008. 192p. pap. 19.00 *(978-0-8389-3574-3(5))* American Library Assn.

Anderegg, David. Nerds: How Dorks, Dweebs, Techies, & Trekkies Can Save America & Why They Might Be Our Last Hope. 2011. (ENG.). 304p. (gr. 12). 14.95 *(978-1-58542-852-6(3),* Tarcher) Penguin Group (USA) Inc.

Arditti, Joyce. Parental Incarceration & the Family: Psychological & Social Effects of Imprisonment on Children, Parents, & Caregivers. 2012. (ENG.). 240p. 39.00 ***(978-0-8147-0512-4(X))*** New York Univ. Pr.

Aron, Laudan Y. & Loprest, Pamela J. Meeting the Needs of Children with Disabilities. 2007. (Illus.). 138p. pap. 26.50 *(978-0-87766-746-9(2))* Urban Institute Pr.

Arrighi, Barbara A. & Maume, David J. Child Poverty in America Today, 4 vols. 2007. (Praeger Perspectives Ser.). (Illus.). *(978-0-275-98927-9(5),* Praeger Pubs.) Greenwood Publishing Group, Inc.

Arrighi, Barbara A. & Maume, David J., eds. Child Poverty in America Today, 4 vols. 2007. (Praeger Perspectives Ser.). (Illus.). 792p. 300.00 *(978-0-275-98926-2(7),* C8926, Praeger Pubs.) Greenwood Publishing Group, Inc.

Association for Library Service to Children, compiled by. In the Words of the Winners: The Newbery & Caldecott Medals, 2001-2010. 2010. pap. *(978-0-8389-3586-6(9))* American Library Assn.

Barry, Tammy. An Introduction to Children with Autism. 2009. (ENG.). pap. 12.95 *(978-1-59363-370-7(X))* Prufrock Pr.

Barstow, Barbara, et al. Beyond Picture Books: Subject Access to Best Books for Beginning Readers, 1 vol. 3rd rev. ed. 2007. (Children's & Young Adult Literature Reference Ser.). 668p. 75.00 *(978-1-59158-545-9(7),* LU8545) Libraries Unlimited, Inc.

Belanger, Kathleen & Brooks, Susan. Guidelines for Cultural Competence in Rural Child Welfare. 2010. *(978-1-58760-127-9(3),* CWLA Pr.) Child Welfare League of America, Inc.

The Benefits of Physical & Health Education for Our Nation's Children: Hearing Before the Committee on Health Education & Labor, U.S. House of Representatives, One Hundred Tenth Congress, Second Session, Hearing Held in Washington, DC, July 24, 2008. 2008. iii, 71p. *(978-0-16-081825-7(7),* 552-070-38023-0) United States Government Printing Office.

Berman, Stephen. Getting It Right for Children: Stories of Pediatric Care & Advocacy. 2007. (ENG., Illus.). 256p. per. 30.00 *(978-1-58110-286-4(0))* American Academy of Pediatrics.

Bernet, William & Ash, Don R. Children of Divorce: A Practical Guide for Parents, Therapists, Attorneys, & Judges. 2nd ed. 2007. 196p. 31.50 *(978-1-57524-288-0(5))* Krieger Publishing Co.

Berrick, Jill Duerr. Take Me Home: Protecting America's Vulnerable Children & Families. 2008. (ENG., Illus.). 208p. 24.95 *(978-0-19-532262-0(2))* Oxford Univ. Pr., Inc.

Birsch, Judith R. Multisensory Teaching Basic Language Skills, Third Edition. 3rd ed. 2011. (Illus.). 816p. 79.95 *(978-1-59857-093-9(5))* Brookes, Paul H. Publishing Co.

Bishop-Josef, Sandra J., et al, eds. Child Development & Social Policy: Knowledge for Action. 2006. (Decade of Behavior Ser.). (Illus.). 311p. 39.95 *(978-1-59147-425-8(6))* American Psychological Assn.

Bishop, Ronald. When Play Was Play: Why Pick-Up Games Matter. 2009. (Excelsior Editions Ser.). 208p. 65.00 *(978-1-4384-2603-7(8));* pap. 24.94 *(978-1-4384-2604-4(6))* State Univ. of New York Pr.

Blane, Mark C. Justice for the Injured Child: A Parent's Complete Legal Survival Guide for Their Child's California Injury Case. 2011. 176p. 29.99 ***(978-1-4583-9674-7(6))*** Lulu Enterprises Inc.

Blosser, Jean L. School Programs in Speech-Language Pathology: Organization & Service Delivery. 5th rev. ed. 2011. (Illus.). 480p. pap. 55.00 *(978-1-59756-403-8(6))* Plural Publishing, Inc.

Boland, Mary L. Como Recibir Manutencion de Ninos: Su Guia Practica para Cobrar y Hacer Cumplir la Orden Judicial. 2007. (SPA & ENG., Illus.). 128p. per. 9.95 *(978-1-57248-585-3(X),* Sphinx Publishing) Sourcebooks, Inc.

Borkowski, John G., et al, eds. Risk & Resilience: Adolescent Mothers & Their Children Grow Up. 2007. (ENG., Illus.). 312p. 105.95 *(978-0-8058-5054-3(6));* per. 49.95 *(978-0-8058-5055-0(4))* Taylor & Francis Group GBR. (Psychology Press). Dist: Taylor & Francis Group.

Bridges, Dennie. Kids Don't Bat Rocks Anymore. 2006. per. 10.00 *(978-0-9788101-0-8(4))* Bridges, Dennie.

Browning, Don S. & Miller-McLemore, Bonnie J. Children & Childhood in American Religions: Primary Sources & Texts. Browning, Don S. & Miller-McLemore, Bonnie, eds. 2009. (Rutgers Series in Childhood Studies). (ENG.). 224p. (C). pap. 23.95 *(978-0-8135-4481-6(5))* Rutgers Univ. Pr.

Browning, Don S. & Miller-McLemore, Bonnie J., eds. Children & Childhood in American Religions: Primary Sources & Texts. 2009. (Rutgers Series in Childhood Studies). (ENG.). 224p. (C). 72.00 *(978-0-8135-4480-9(7))* Rutgers Univ. Pr.

Bryant, Nick. The Franklin Scandal: A Story of Powerbrokers, Child Abuse & Betrayal. 2012. (Illus.). 656p. pap. 19.95 *(978-1-936296-07-1(1))* Trine Day.

Bullock, Jane A., et al. Managing Children in Disasters: Planning for Their Unique Needs. 2010. (ENG., Illus.). 394p. 79.95 *(978-1-4398-3766-5(X),* CRC Press) Taylor & Francis Group GBR. Dist: Taylor & Francis Group.

Canada, Geoffrey. Fist Stick Knife Gun. 2011. 14.05 *(978-0-7848-3397-1(4),* Everbind) Marco Bk. Co.

—Fist Stick Knife Gun: A Personal History of Violence. 2010. (Illus.). 144p. pap. 14.00 *(978-0-8070-4449-0(0))* Beacon Pr.

—Fist Stick Knife Gun: A Personal of Violence. 2011. 14.05 *(978-0-7848-3590-6(X),* Everbind) Marco Bk. Co.

—Fist Stick Knife Gun: Graphic Novel. 2011. 14.05 *(978-0-7848-3579-1(9),* Everbind) Marco Bk. Co.

Carini, Patricia F. & Himley, Margaret. Jenny's Story: Taking the Long View of the Child - Prospect's Philosophy in Action. 2010. (ENG.). 216p. 62.00 *(978-0-8077-5052-0(2));* pap. 29.95 *(978-0-8077-5051-3(4))* Teachers College Pr., Teachers College, Columbia Univ.

Chandra, Anita & Gresenz, Carole Roan. Health & Health Care among District of Columbia Youth. 2009. (Illus.). 216p. pap. 46.00 *(978-0-8330-4805-9(8),* tr-751) RAND Corp., The.

Child Nutrition & the School Setting: Hearing Before the Committee on Agriculture, Nutrition, & Forestry, United States Senate, One Hundred Tenth Congress, First Session, March 6, 2007. 2007. iii, 128p. *(978-0-16-078890-1(0),* 552-070-36022-1) United States Government Printing Office.

Children & Disasters: A Progress Report on Addressing Needs: Hearing Before the Ad Hoc Subcommittee on Disaster Recovery of the Committee on Homeland Security & Governmental Affairs, United States Senate, One Hundred Eleventh Congress, First Session, De[c]ember 10, 2009. 2010. (Illus.). iv, 217p. *(978-0-16-086377-6(5),* 552-070-41456-8) United States Government Printing Office.

Chudacoff, Howard & Chudacoff, Howard P. Children at Play: An American History. 2008. (ENG., Illus.). 288p. pap. 22.00 *(978-0-8147-1665-6(2))* New York Univ. Pr.

Chudacoff, Howard P. Children at Play: An American History. 2007. (ENG., Illus.). 288p. 65.00 *(978-0-8147-1664-9(4))* New York Univ. Pr.

Clincy, Sekou. The Socialization of the African American Child: In Contemporary America. 2010. 192p. 24.99 *(978-1-4490-8788-3(4));* pap. 14.49 *(978-1-4490-8787-6(6))* AuthorHouse.

Coleman, Melissa. This Life Is in Your Hands: One Dream, Sixty Acres, & a Family's Heartbreak. 2012. (P. S. Ser.). (ENG.). 352p. pap. 15.99 ***(978-0-06-195833-5(6),*** HarperPerennial) HarperCollins Pubs.

Committee on Nutrition Standards for National School Lunch and Breakfast Programs & National Research Council. Nutrition Standards & Meal Requirements for National School Lunch & Breakfast Programs: Phase I. Proposed Approach for Recommending Revisions. Stallings, Virginia A. & Taylor, Christine L., eds. 2008. (ENG.). 192p. pap. 43.25 *(978-0-309-12795-0(5))* National Academies Pr.

Conley, Dalton. Honky. 2009. 13.32 *(978-0-7848-1482-6(1),* Everbind) Marco Bk. Co.

Connolly, Cynthia A. Saving Sickly Children: The Tuberculosis Preventorium in American Life, 1909-1970. 2008. (Critical Issues in Health & Medicine Ser.). (ENG., Illus.). 200p. 39.95 *(978-0-8135-4267-6(7))* Rutgers Univ. Pr.

Corporal Punishment in Schools & Its Effect on Academic Success: Hearing Before the Subcommittee on Healthy Families & Communities, Committee on Education & Labor, U.S. House of Representatives, One Hundred Eleventh Congress, Second Session, Hearing Held in Washington, D.C., April 15, 2010. 2010. iii, 65p. ***(978-0-16-087673-8(7),*** 552-070-42225-1) United States Government Printing Office.

Covering Uninsured Children: The Impact of the August 17th CHIP Directive: Hearing Before the Subcommittee on Health Care of the Committee on Finance, United States Senate, One Hundred Tenth Congress, Second Session, April 9, 2008. 2008. (Illus.). iii, 146p. *(978-0-16-085855-0(0),* 552-070-41067-8) United States Government Printing Office.

Covering Uninsured Kids: Missed Opportunities for Moving Forward: Hearing Before the Subcommittee on Health of the Committee on Energy & Commerce, House of Representatives, One Hundred Tenth Congress, Second Session, January 29, 2008. 2008. (Illus.). vi, 134p. ***(978-0-16-087074-3(7),*** 552-070-41931-4) United States Government Printing Office.

Cram101 Textbook Reviews & Cram101 Textbook Reviews. Outlines & Highlights for Through the Eyes of a Child by Donna E Norton. 2011. 250p. pap. 31.95 ***(978-1-61830-898-6(X))*** Cram101 Inc.

—Outlines & Highlights for Understanding Child Abuse & Neglect by Cynthia Crosson-Tower, Isbn: 9780205769155 0205769152. 2011. 170p. pap. 29.95 ***(978-1-4288-9068-8(8))*** Cram101 Inc.

Dabir, Neela. From Street to Hope: Faith Based & Secular Programmes in Los Angeles, Mumbai & Nairobi for Street-living Children. 2011. (Illus.). 336p. (C). 40.00 ***(978-81-321-0513-8(3),*** B05138C) SAGE Pubns., Inc.

Danielson, Caroline & Lee, Helen. Foster Care in California: Achievements & Challenges. 2010. *(978-1-58213-139-9(2))* Public Policy Institute of California.

Danzig, Robert J. Conversations with Bobby: From Foster Child to Corporate Executive. 2007. *(978-1-58760-108-8(7),* CWLA Pr.) Child Welfare League of America, Inc.

D'Aversa, Carmina Y. Tax, Estate, & Lifetime Planning for Minors. 2006. (ENG., Illus.). xi, 371p. pap. 139.95 incl. lp *(978-1-59031-683-2(5))* American Bar Assn.

Davies, H. Dele & Fitzgerald, Hiram E., eds. Obesity in Childhood & Adolescence, 2 vols. 2007. (Child Psychology & Mental Health Ser.). (Illus.). 676p. 200.00 *(978-0-275-99615-4(8),* C9615, Praeger Pubs.) Greenwood Publishing Group, Inc.

Davis, Samuel M. Children in the Legal System: Cases & Materials. 4th ed. 2009. (University Casebook Ser.). xiv, 1233p. pap. *(978-1-59941-624-3(7))* West.

De Marzo, Jenine, et al. Healthy & Sustainable Fundraising Activities: Mobilizing Your Community Toward Social Responsibility. 2012. (Illus.). 184p. pap. 20.00 ***(978-1-4504-1281-0(5))*** Human Kinetics Pubs.

de Schweinitz, Rebecca. If We Could Change the World: Young People & America's Long Struggle for Racial Equality. 2011. (ENG., Illus.). 400p. pap. 24.95 *(978-0-8078-7215-4(6))* Univ. of North Carolina Pr.

Dettlaff, Alan & Fong, Rowena, eds. Child Welfare Practice with Immigrant Children & Families. 2011. (ENG.). 176p. (C). 125.00 *(978-0-415-68469-9(2))* Routledge.

Diamant-Cohen, Betsy. Crash Course in Library Services to Preschool Children, 1 vol. 2010. (Crash Course Ser.). 137p. pap. 30.00 *(978-1-59884-688-1(4),* A3268P) Libraries Unlimited, Inc.

Douglas, Emily M. Innovations in Child & Family Policy: Multidisciplinary Research & Perspectives on Strengthening Children & Their Families. 2010. (ENG., Illus.). 292p. 73.50 *(978-0-7391-3790-1(5))* Lexington Bks.

Drago, Edmund L. Confederate Phoenix: Rebel Children & Their Families in South Carolina. 3rd ed. 2008. (Reconstructing America Ser.). (ENG., Illus.). 224p. 70.00 *(978-0-8232-2937-6(8))* Fordham Univ. Pr.

Drozd, Leslie M., ed. Relocation Issues in Child Custody Cases. 2007. (ENG., Illus.). 198p. per. 54.95 *(978-0-7890-3534-9(0))* Routledge.

Druckerman, Pamela. Bringing up Bébé: One American Mother Discovers the Wisdom of French Parenting. 2012. (ENG.). 304p. (gr. 12). 25.95 ***(978-1-59420-333-6(4),*** Penguin Pr. HC, The) Penguin Group (USA) Inc.

Duane, Anna Mae. Suffering Childhood in Early America: Violence, Race, & the Making of the Child Victim. 2011. (ENG., Illus.). 224p. pap. 24.95 ***(978-0-8203-4058-6(8))*** Univ. of Georgia Pr.

Dupont, Arthur T. & Peeters, Sarah L. Medicaid, Children's Health Insurance, & the Patient Protection & Affordable Care Act. 2011. (Health Care Issues, Costs & Access Ser.). 176p. 79.00 *(978-1-61122-903-5(0))* Nova Science Pubs., Inc.

Dwyer, James G. The Relationship Rights of Children. 2011. (ENG.). 380p. pap. 50.00 ***(978-1-107-40233-1(6))*** Cambridge Univ. Pr.

Dyson, Maurice R. & Weddle, Daniel B. Our Promise: Achieving Educational Equity for America's Children. 2009. 636p. pap. 65.00 *(978-1-59460-127-9(5))* Carolina Academic Pr.

Earle, Alice Morse. Child Life in Colonial Days. 2009. 250p. pap. *(978-1-4590-4088-5(0))* Books LLC.

—Child Life in Colonial Days. 2007. (ENG.). 556p. per. *(978-1-4067-5823-8(X))* Read Bks.

Elbert, Monika M., ed. Enterprising Youth: Social Values & Acculturation in Nineteenth-Century American Children's Literature. 2009. 286p. pap. 39.95 *(978-0-415-87667-4(2))* Routledge.

EPM Communications. Tween Spending & Influence. 2010th ed. 2010. (ENG.). 199.00 *(978-1-935521-15-0(2))* EPM Communications, Inc.

An Examination of Children's Privacy: New Technologies & the Children's Online Privacy Protection ACT: Hearing Before the Subcommittee on Consumer Protection, Product Safety, & Insurance of the Committee on Commerce, Science, & Transportation, United States Senate, One Hundred Eleventh Congress, Second Session, April 29, 2010. 2011. (Illus.). iii, 134p. ***(978-0-16-088859-5(X),*** 552-070-42979-4) United States Government Printing Office.

Examining Innovative Practices to Improve Child Nutrition: Hearing Before the Subcommittee on Healthy Families & Communities, Committee on Education & Labor, U.S. House of Representatives, One Hundred Eleventh Congress, First Session, Hearing Held in Washington, DC, October 8, 2009. 2010. iii, 50p. *(978-0-16-085109-4(2),* 552-070-40465-1) United States Government Printing Office.

Faller, Kathleen Coulborn. Interviewing Children about Sexual Abuse: Controversies & Best Practice. 2007. (ENG., Illus.). 328p. 39.95 *(978-0-19-531177-8(9))* Oxford Univ. Pr., Inc.

Fass, Paula S. Children of a New World: Society, Culture, & Globalization. 2006. (ENG.). 304p. 75.00 *(978-0-8147-2756-0(5));* per. 24.00 *(978-0-8147-2757-7(3))* New York Univ. Pr.

Fass, Paula S. & Grossberg, Michael, eds. Reinventing Childhood after World War II. 2011. 200p. (C). 42.50 ***(978-0-8122-4367-3(6))*** Univ. of Pennsylvania Pr.

Fernandes, Laura M., ed. Child Well-Being & Nonresident Parents. 2011. (Children's Issues, Laws & Programs Ser.). (Illus.). 262p. 195.00 *(978-1-60692-382-5(X))* Nova Science Pubs., Inc.

Ferrara, Jeannie. The Fatherless American: The Growing Minority That Is Changing America, 1 vol. 2009. 73p. pap. 16.95 *(978-1-4489-2551-3(7))* PublishAmerica, Inc.

Finn, Janet L. Mining Childhood: Growing up in Butte, 1900-1960. 2012. (ENG., Illus.). 256p. pap. 24.95 ***(978-0-9801292-5-0(7))*** Montana Historical Society Pr.

Flowers, R. Barri. Street Kids: The Lives of Runaway & Thrownaway Teens. 2010. (ENG., Illus.). 244p. pap. 45.00 *(978-0-7864-4137-2(2))* McFarland & Co., Inc. Pubs.

Forbes, Joan & Watson, Cate, eds. The Transformation of Childrens Services. 2011. (ENG., Illus.). 216p. (C). 144.00 *(978-0-415-61847-2(9));* pap. 51.95 *(978-0-415-61849-6(5))* Routledge.

Fraser, Mark W. & Jenson, Jeffrey M., eds. Social Policy for Children & Families: A Risk & Resilience Perspective. 2nd ed. 2010. (Illus.). 416p. (C). pap. 64.00 *(978-1-4129-8139-2(5),* B81392P) SAGE Pubns., Inc.

Freiberg, Karen & Freiberg, Karen L. Annual Editions: Educating Children with Exceptionalities 10/11. 20th ed. 2009. (Annual Editions Ser.). (ENG., Illus.). 192p. (C). pap. 44.00 *(978-0-07-813587-3(7),* 0078135877, McGraw-Hill/Dushkin) McGraw-Hill Higher Education.

Galda, Lee, et al. Literature & the Child. 7th ed. 2009. (ENG.). 528p. (C). 198.95 *(978-0-495-60239-2(6));* pap. 139.95 *(978-0-495-80997-5(7))* Wadsworth.

Gale Editor, ed. Information Plus Growing Up: Issues Affecting America's Youth. 2011. pap. 58.00 *(978-1-4144-4862-6(7))* Cengage Gale.

Giroux, Henry A. Politics after Hope: Obama & the Crisis of Youth, Race, & Democracy. 2010. (Radical Imagination Ser.). 240p. 104.00 *(978-1-59451-852-2(1));* pap. 27.95 *(978-1-59451-853-9(X))* Paradigm Pubs.

Goodenough, Elizabeth N. A Place for Play: A Companion Volume to the Michigan Television Film Where Do the Children Play? 2008. (ENG., Illus.). 284p. pap. 32.50 *(978-0-615-20282-2(9))* National Institute for Play.

Graham, George, et al. Children Moving: Becoming a Reflective Teacher. 9th ed. 2012. ***(978-0-07-802259-3(2))*** McGraw-Hill Cos., The.

Great Books Foundation (U.S.) Staff, contrib. by. Great Books Roundtable Planner: Using Shared Inquiry with Your Students. 2010. *(978-1-933147-57-4(1))* Great Bks. Foundation.

Great Books Roundtable. 2010. *(978-1-933147-52-9(0))* Great Bks. Foundation.

Greven, Philip J. Children in Colonial America. Marten, James, ed. 2006. (ENG., Illus.). 288p. pap. 24.00 *(978-0-8147-5716-1(2))* New York Univ. Pr.

Haight, Wendy L., et al. Children of Methamphetamine-Involved Families: The Case of Rural Illinois. 2008. (ENG., Illus.). 288p. 35.00 *(978-0-19-532605-5(9))* Oxford Univ. Pr., Inc.

Hale, Liisa & Copenhagen Bainer, Claire. Second Home: A Day in the Life of a Model Early Childhood Program. 2007. (ENG., Illus.). 280p. (J). 49.95 *(978-1-929610-92-1(0))* Redleaf Pr.

Halliday, Judy & Jack, Joani. Raising Fit Kids in a Fat World. 2008. (ENG., Illus.). 224p. 19.99 *(978-0-8307-4534-0(3))* Gospel Light Pubns.

Harmon, Judson A. Be Home by Dark: Humorous Stories of Youthful Misadventure. 2008. (Illus.). 78p. pap. 15.00 *(978-0-9799963-8-2(4))* IGI Pr.

Harris, Leslie J. & Teitelbaum, Lee E. Children, Parents, & the Law: Public & Private Authority in the Home, Schools, & Juvenile Courts. 2nd ed. 2007. xxxi, 769p. *(978-0-7355-6365-0(9),* Aspen Pubs.) Wolters Kluwer Law & Business.

Hartson, John & Payne, Brenda. Creating Effective Parenting Plans: A Developmental Approach for Lawyers & Divorce Professionals. 2006. (ENG., Illus.). 237p. pap. 64.95 incl. lp *(978-1-59031-610-8(X))* American Bar Assn.

Heath, Samuel D. G. To Kill a Mockingbird: A critique on behalf of Children. 2007. 80p. per. 10.95 *(978-0-595-44369-7(9))* iUniverse, Inc.

Heinberg, Leslie J. & Thompson, J. Kevin. Obesity in Youth: Causes, Consequences, & Cures. 2009. (Illus.). 240p. 59.95 *(978-1-4338-0427-4(1))* American Psychological Assn.

Helmreich, Joseph & Marcus, Paul. Warring Parents, Wounded Children, & the Wretched World of Child Custody: Cautionary Tales, 1 vol. 2007. 144p. 39.95 *(978-0-313-34973-7(8),* C34973, Praeger Pubs.) Greenwood Publishing Group, Inc.

Hill, Janelle. Special Needs Families in the Military: A Resource Guide. 2011. (Military Life Ser.). (ENG.). 280p. 34.95 *(978-1-60590-715-4(4))* Government Institutes.

Hill, Nancy E., et al, eds. African American Children & Mental Health Vols. 1 & 2: Development & Context. 2011. (Child Psychology & Mental Health Ser.). (Illus.). 498p. 104.95 *(978-0-313-38302-1(2),* A2699C, Praeger Pubs.) Greenwood Publishing Group, Inc.

Holden, Martha J. Children & Residential Experiences: Creating Conditions for Change. 2nd ed. 2009. pap. *(978-1-58760-126-2(5))* Child Welfare League of America, Inc.

Hoog, Mark, ed. Letters from Katrina: Stories of Hope & Inspiration. 2007. (Illus.). 96p. 24.95 *(978-0-9770391-9-7(6))* Growing Field Bks.

Howitt, Rene. Whose Best Interest? A Fight to Save Two American Kids. 2007. 255p. per. 14.99 *(978-1-59886-822-7(5))* Tate Publishing & Enterprises, LLC.

H.R. 5504: Improving Nutrition for America's Children ACT: Hearing Before the Committee on Education & Labor, U.S. House of Representatives, One Hundred Eleventh Congress, Second Session, Hearing Held in Washington, DC, July 1, 2010. 2010. (Illus.). iii, 126p. ***(978-0-16-087135-1(2),*** 552-070-41980-2) United States Government Printing Office.

Hutchison, Bobby. Annual Editions: Gender 10/11. 2009. (Annual Editions Ser.). (ENG., Illus.). 272p. (C). pap. 44.00 *(978-0-07-805052-7(9),* 0078050529, McGraw-Hill/Dushkin) McGraw-Hill Higher Education.

Institute of Medicine. Planning a WIC Research Agenda: Workshop Summary. 2011. (ENG.). 176p. pap. 40.50 *(978-0-309-16179-4(7))* National Academies Pr.

Irwin, Catherine. Twice Orphaned: Voices from the Children's Village of Manzanar. 2008. pap. *(978-0-930046-24-8(2))* California State Univ. Fullerton, Ctr. for Oral & Public History.

Israel, Susan E., et al. Collaborative Literacy: Using Gifted Strategies to Enrich Learning for Every Student. 2006. (Illus.). 256p. per. 41.95 *(978-1-4129-1698-1(4),* B16976P) Corwin Pr.

Jacobson, Lisa. Children & Consumer in American Society: A Historical Handbook & Guide. 2007. (Children & Youth: History & Culture Ser.). (Illus.). 216p. 49.95

(978-0-313-33140-4(5), GR3140, Praeger Pubs.) Greenwood Publishing Group, Inc.

Jensen, Eric. Teaching with Poverty in Mind: What Being Poor Does to Kids' Brains & What Schools Can Do about It. 2009. pap. 23.95 (978-1-4166-0884-4(2)) Assn. for Supervision & Curriculum Development.

Johnson, Nancy J. & Giorgis, Cyndi. The Wonder of It All: When Literature & Literacy Intersect. 2007. (Illus.). 224p. pap. 32.50 (978-0-325-00973-5(2), E00973) Heinemann.

Jones, Phil. Rethinking Childhood: Attitudes in Contemporary Society. 2009. (New Childhoods Ser.). (ENG., Illus.). 208p. 39.95 (978-0-8264-9936-3(8)) Continuum International Publishing Group, Ltd. GBR. Dist: National Bk. Network.

Jordan, Amy B., ed. Overweight & Obesity in America's Children: Causes, Consequences, Solutions. 2008. (ANNALS of the American Academy of Political & Social Science Ser.: 615). 244p. (C). 52.95 (978-1-4129-6684-9(1), 295615C) SAGE Pubns., Inc.

Jordan, Amy B. & Kaniss, Phyllis, eds. Overweight & Obesity in America's Children: Causes, Consequences, Solutions. 2008. (ANNALS of the American Academy of Political & Social Science Ser.: 615). (Illus.). 244p. (C). pap. 37.95 (978-1-4129-6685-6(X), 295615P) SAGE Pubns., Inc.

Joyce, Denise & Watkins, Nancy. Scared of Santa: Scenes of Terror in Toyland. 2012. (ENG.). 288p. pap. 12.99 **(978-0-06-220458-5(0)**, William Morrow Paperbacks) HarperCollins Pubs.

Kamhi, Alan G. & Catts, Hugh W. Language & Reading Disabilities. 3rd ed. 2011. (ENG., Illus.). 320p. (C). pap. 86.67 (978-0-13-707277-4(5)) Allyn & Bacon, Inc.

Kauffman, James. Working with Troubled Children. 2009. 158p. pap. 19.00 (978-1-57861-678-7(6)) Attainment Co., Inc.

Kay, Janet & Kay. Behavioural, Emotional & Social Difficulties: A Guide for the Early Years. 2007. (Sen in the Early Years Ser.). (ENG.). 160p. 21.95 (978-0-8264-8469-7(7)) Continuum International Publishing Group, Ltd. GBR. Dist: National Bk. Network.

Keane, Nancy J. 101 Great Ready-to-Use Book Lists for Children, 1 vol. 2012. 130p. pap. 40.00 **(978-1-61069-083-6(4)**, A3769P) Pearson Education GBR. Dist: ABC-CLIO, LLC.

Keehn, Kelley. The Prosperity Factor for Kids: A Comprehensive Parent's Guide to Developing Positive Saving, Spending, & Credit Habits. 2007. (ENG., Illus.). 208p. per. (978-1-897178-42-3(5)) Insomniac Pr.

Keith-Lucas, Alan. Group Child Care as a Family Service. 2011. (ENG.). 283p. pap. 40.00 (978-0-8078-9696-9(9)) Univ. of North Carolina Pr.

Kennedy, V. Lynn. Born Southern: Childbirth, Motherhood, & Social Networks in the Old South. 2009. (ENG.). 288p. (gr. 17). 65.00 (978-0-8018-9417-6(4)) Johns Hopkins Univ. Pr.

Keyser, Donna, et al. Improving Childhood Blood Lead Level Screening, Reporting, & Surveillance in Allegheny County, Pennsylvania. 2006. (Illus.). 98p. per. 20.00 (978-0-8330-3945-3(8), MG-423) RAND Corp., The.

Klain, Eva J. & Sandt, Claire. Healthy Beginnings, Healthy Futures: A Judge's Guide. 2009. (978-1-60442-611-3(X)) American Bar Assn.

Kline, Kathleen Kovner, ed. Authoritative Communities: The Scientific Case for Nurturing the Whole Child. 2007. (Search Institute Series on Developmentally Attentive Community & Society Ser.). (Illus.). 386p. 79.95 (978-0-387-72720-2(5), 0387727205) Springer.

Kolencik, Patricia Liotta & Bernadowski, Carianne. Teaching with Books That Heal: Authentic Literature & Literacy Strategies to Help Children Cope with Everyday Problems, 1 vol. 2007. (Illus.). 184p. per. 36.95 (978-1-58683-220-9(4), A2463P) Linworth Publishing, Inc.

Koplow, Lesley, ed. Unsmiling Faces: How Preschools Can Heal. 2nd rev. ed. 2007. (ENG., Illus.). 288p. 56.00 (978-0-8077-4804-6(8)) Teachers College Pr., Teachers College, Columbia Univ.

Koss, Mary P., et al, eds. Violence Against Women & Children Vol. 2: Navigating Solutions, 2 vols. 2010. (Illus.). 304p. 69.95 (978-1-4338-0914-9(1)) American Psychological Assn.

Krueger, Gretchen. Hope & Suffering: Children, Cancer, & the Paradox of Experimental Medicine. 2008. (ENG., Illus.). 232p. (gr. 17). 35.00 (978-0-8018-8831-1(X)) Johns Hopkins Univ. Pr.

Lally, J. Ronald, et al, eds. Concepts for Care: 20 Essays on Infant/Toddler Development & Learning. 2006. (ENG., Illus.). 144p. pap. 21.95 (978-0-914409-39-7(5)) WestEd.

Langely, Terrance R., ed. Child Protection, the Courts & Social Workers. 2010. (Children's Issues, Laws & Programs Ser.). (Illus.). 356p. 195.00 (978-1-60741-279-3(9)) Nova Science Pubs., Inc.

Larson, Scott. At Risk: Bringing Hope to Hurting Teenagers. 2006. 144p. per. 12.99 (978-0-9754305-8-3(0)) Praxis Pr., Inc.

Layton, Stanford J., ed. The Skeleton in Grandpa's Barn: And Other Stories of Growing up in Utah. 2008. (Favorite Readings from the Utah Historical Quarterly Ser.). (Illus.). 282p. pap. 23.95 (978-1-56085-160-8(0)) Signature Bks., LLC.

Leone, Marianne. Knowing Jesse: A Mother's Story of Grief, Grace, & Everyday Bliss. 2010. (ENG., Illus.). 272p. 25.00 (978-1-4391-8392-2(9)) Simon & Schuster.

Levin, Diane E. & Kilbourne, Jean. So Sexy So Soon: The New Sexualized Childhood & What Parents Can Do to Protect Their Kids. 2009. (ENG.). 240p. pap. 15.00 (978-0-345-50507-1(7), Ballantine Bks.) Random House Publishing Group.

Levine, Susan. School Lunch Politics: The Surprising History of America's Favorite Welfare Program. 2010. (Politics & Society in Twentieth Century America Ser.). (ENG., Illus.). 272p. (C). pap. 25.95 (978-0-691-14619-5(5)) Princeton Univ. Pr.

Lindenmeyer, Kriste. The Greatest Generation Grows Up: American Childhood in The 1930s. 2007. (American Childhoods Ser.). (ENG., Illus.). 320p. per. 18.95 (978-1-56663-730-5(9)) Dee, Ivan R. Pub.

Lindquist, Heather C., ed. Children of Manzanar. 2012. (Illus.). xi, 145p. pap. 17.95 **(978-1-59714-160-4(7))** Heyday.

Lindsey, Duncan, ed. Child Poverty & Inequality: Securing a Better Future for America's Children. 2008. (ENG., Illus.). 208p. 31.99 (978-0-19-530544-9(2)) Oxford Univ. Pr., Inc.

Longo, Laura M. The Youngest Survivors. 2006. 51p. per. 8.95 (978-1-59824-325-3(X)) E-BookTime LLC.

Manson, Tony J. Ways Teachers Cope with the Physical, Psychological, & Social Disabilities of Their Students: Diabetes, Autism, ADHD, Hunger, Anger, & Other Infirmites. Manson, Tony J., ed. 220p. 109.95 (978-0-7734-4976-3(0)) Mellen, Edwin Pr., The.

Marten, James, ed. Children & Youth in a New Nation. 2009. (ENG., Illus.). 320p. pap. 24.00 (978-0-8147-5749-9(9)) New York Univ. Pr.

Martin, James E. Life Aboard the Monkey Bus. 2006. 152p. pap. 14.00 (978-1-4259-5364-5(6)) AuthorHouse.

Martin, W. C. Small Town, Big Miracle: How Love Came to the Least of These. 2007. (ENG., Illus.). 168p. pap. 13.99 (978-1-58997-443-2(3)) Tyndale Hse. Pubs.

Matthews, Sherry. We Were Not Orphans: Stories from the Waco State Home. 2011. (ENG., Illus.). 234p. 29.95 (978-0-292-72559-1(0)) Univ. of Texas Pr.

Mattingly, Cheryl. The Paradox of Hope: Journeys Through a Clinical Borderland. 2010. (ENG.). 291p. 60.00 (978-0-520-26734-3(6)); pap. 26.95 (978-0-520-26735-0(4)) Univ. of California Pr.

McEwen, Irene, ed. Providing Physical Therapy Services under Parts B&C of IDEA (2nd Edition) 2009. 200p. pap. 70.00 (978-0-9702105-1-7(5)) Section on Pediatrics, APTA.

McIntosh, Alex. Parental Time & Obesity. 2006. (Illus.). 222p. 125.00 (978-1-60021-341-0(3)) Nova Science Pubs., Inc.

McLanahan, Sara, ed. Opportunity in America: Number 2, Fall 2006. 2006. (Future of Children Ser.). (Illus.). 196p. per. 24.95 (978-0-8157-5563-0(5)) Brookings Institution Pr.

Meier, Peg. Wishing for a Snow Day: Growing up in Minnesota. 2010. (ENG., Illus.). 264p. pap. 29.95 (978-0-87351-640-2(0)) Minnesota Historical Society Pr.

Mesmer, Heidi Anne E. Tools for Matching Readers to Texts: Research-Based Practices. 2007. (Solving Problems in Teaching of Literacy Ser.). (ENG.). 180p. (gr. k-6). 50.00 (978-1-59385-598-7(2)) Guilford Pubns., Inc.

Morgan, Terrence B., ed. Missing Children: Family Survival Guide & Federal Programs. 2012. **(978-1-62100-523-0(2))** Nova Science Pubs., Inc.

Morris, C. A Child's Story of America. reprint ed. 150.00 (978-0-7222-7253-4(7)) Library Reprints, Inc.

Nagle, Ami & Jacobs, Victoria. Illinois Kids Count 1995: Building the Future. 65p. (C). pap. 15.00 (978-1-886008-02-1(7)) Voices for Illinois Children.

National Research Council. Databases for Estimating Health Insurance Coverage for Children: A Workshop Summary. 2010. (ENG.). 204p. pap. 45.25 (978-0-309-16240-1(8)) National Academies Pr.

Necessary Reform to Pediatric Dental Care under Medicaid: Hearing Before the Subcommittee on Domestic Policy of the Committee on Oversight & Government Reform, House of Representatives, One Hundred Tenth Congress, Second Session, September 23, 2008. 2009. (Illus.). iii, 210p. (978-0-16-084314-3(6), 552-070-39869-4) United States Government Printing Office.

Office of Management and Budget (U.S.), compiled by. Cases of Child Neglect & Abuse at Private Residential Treatment Facilities: Hearing Before the Committee on Education & Labor, U. S. House of Representatives, One Hundred Tenth Congress, First Session, Hearing Held in Washington, DC, October 10, 2007. 2008. (ENG., Illus.). iii, 138p. pap. 102.00 (978-0-16-080875-3(8), 552-070-37425-6, Office of Management & Budget) United States Government Printing Office.

O'Kelley, Sarah, et al. Diagnosis & Treatment of Children with Autism Spectrum Disorders. 2009. (ENG.). pap. 12.95 (978-1-59363-372-1(6)) Prufrock Pr.

Olfman, Sharna, ed. The Sexualization of Childhood, 1 vol. 2008. (Childhood in America Ser.). 224p. 44.95 (978-0-275-99985-8(8), C9985, Praeger Pubs.) Greenwood Publishing Group, Inc.

Olivas, Michael. No Undocumented Child Left Behind: Plyler V. Doe & the Education of Undocumented Schoolchildren. 2012. (ENG.). 208p. 35.00 **(978-0-8147-6244-8(1))** New York Univ. Pr.

Olivas, Michael A. No Undocumented Child Left Behind: Plyler V. Doe & the Education of Undocumented Schoolchildren. 2011. E-Book **(978-0-8147-6267-7(0))**; E-Book **(978-0-8147-6245-5(X))** New York Univ. Pr.

Ollhoff, Laurie & Ollhoff, Jim. Giving Children Their Childhood Back: Relearning the Purpose of Out-Of-School Time. 2006. (978-0-9786018-0-5(7)) Sparrow Media Group, Inc.

One Year Later: Medicaid's Response to Systemic Problems by the Death of Deamonte Driver: Hearing Before the Subcommittee on Domestic Policy of the Committee on Oversight & Government Reform, House of Representatives, One Hundred Tenth Congress, Second Session, February 14, 2008. 2009. (Illus.). iii, 109p. (978-0-16-083519-3(4), 552-070-39242-4) United States Government Printing Office.

O'Reilly, Bill & Flowers, Charles. Kids Are Americans Too. 2008. (ENG.). 160p. 14.95 (978-0-06-084677-0(1), Morrow, William & Co.) HarperCollins Pubs.

Ossian, Lisa L. The Forgotten Generation: American Children & World War II. 2011. (ENG., Illus.). 192p. (gr. 8). 29.95 (978-0-8262-1919-0(5)) Univ. of Missouri Pr.

Owens, Derek. Memory's Wake. 2011. **(978-1-933132-86-0(8))** Spuyten Duyvil.

Pangrazi, Robert P., et al. Promoting Physical Activity & Health in the Classroom. 2008. (ENG., Illus.). 600p. (C). pap., pap. 97.67 (978-0-321-54762-0(4)) Benjamin-Cummings Publishing Co.

Paris, Leslie. Children's Nature: The Rise of the American Summer Camp. (ENG.). 368p. 2010. pap. 23.00 (978-0-8147-6782-5(6)) 2008. (Illus.). 60.00 (978-0-8147-6707-8(9)) New York Univ. Pr.

Pastor, Patricia N. & Reuben, Cynthia A. Diagnosed Attention Deficit Hyperactivity Disorder & Learning Disability, United States, 2004-2006: Data from the National Health Interview Survey. 2008. (DHHS Publication Ser.: Nos. 2008-1565). (978-0-8406-0623-5(0)) National Ctr. for Health Statistics.

Pecora, Peter, et al. The Child Welfare Challenge: Policy, Practice, & Research. 3rd ed. 2009. (ENG., Illus.). 458p. pap. 39.95 (978-0-202-36314-1(7)) Aldine Transaction.

Pelzer, Hilderbrand. Unlocking Potential: Organizing A School Inside A Prison. 2011. 113p. pap. 15.95 **(978-1-4327-7027-3(6))** Outskirts Pr., Inc.

Perry, Claire. Young America: Childhood in Nineteenth-Century Art & Culture. 2006. (Illus.). xii, 236p. pap. (978-0-937031-27-8(5)) Cantor, Iris & B. Gerald Ctr. for Visual Arts at Stanford Univ.

Peterson, Wendy D. Your Special Soldier. 2011. 56p. pap. 21.68 (978-1-4490-9076-0(1)) AuthorHouse.

Petite, Mary Deborah. The Women Will Howl: The Union Army Capture of Roswell & New Manchester, Georgia, & the Forced Relocation of Mill Workers. alt. ed. 2010. (ENG., Illus.). 197p. pap. 35.00 (978-0-7864-6114-1(4)) McFarland & Co., Inc. Pubs.

Petty, Karen. Deployment: Strategies for Working with Kids in Military Families. 2009. (ENG., Illus.). 180p. pap. 24.95 (978-1-933653-74-7(4)) Redleaf Pr.

Polakow, Valerie. Who Cares for Our Children? The Child Care Crisis in the Other America. 2007. (ENG., Illus.). 240p. 46.00 (978-0-8077-4775-9(0)); pap. 21.95 (978-0-8077-4774-2(2)) Teachers College Pr., Teachers College, Columbia Univ.

Poovey, Tony. We Always Lived From: The Story of the Gas Camp Kids. 2011. 94p. pap. 19.95 **(978-1-4626-1985-6(1))** PublishAmerica, Inc.

Poppendieck, Janet. Free for All: Fixing School Food in America. (California Studies in Food & Culture Ser.). 2011. (ENG.). 368p. pap. 17.95 (978-0-520-26988-0(8)) 2010. 340p. 45.00 (978-0-520-24370-5(6)) Univ. of California Pr.

Powell, Lynn. Framing Innocence: A Mother's Photographs, a Prosecutor's Zeal, & a Small Town's Response. 2011. (ENG., Illus.). 320p. pap. 17.95 (978-1-59558-714-5(4)) New Pr., The.

Protecting Our Children: Current Issues in Children's Product Safety: Hearing Before the Subcommittee on Commerce, Trade, & Consumer Protection of the Committee on Energy & Commerce, House of Representatives, One Hundred Tenth Congress, First Session, May 15, 2007. 2008. vi, 236p. (978-0-16-082680-1(2), 552-070-38697-1) United States Government Printing Office.

Pukui, Mary Kawena. Hawaiian Beliefs & Customs During Birth, Infancy, & Childhood. 2011. 28p. 35.95 **(978-1-258-10128-2(9))** Literary Licensing, LLC.

Queen, J. Allen & Schumacher, Donald. Overcoming Obesity in Childhood & Adolescence: A Guide for School Leaders. 2006. (Illus.). 168p. 66.95 (978-1-4129-1565-3(8), B16658C); per. 27.95 (978-1-4129-1666-0(6), B16658P) Corwin Pr.

Quinn, Karen. Testing for Kindergarten: Simple Strategies to Help Your Child Ace the Tests for: Public School Placement, Private School Admissions, Gifted Program Qualification. 2010. (ENG., Illus.). 272p. pap. 15.99 (978-1-4165-9107-8(9), Touchstone) Touchstone.

Rains, Prudence Mors & Rains, Prudence. Becoming an Unwed Mother: A Sociological Account. 2007. (ENG.). 215p. pap. 19.95 (978-0-202-30955-2(X)) Aldine Transaction.

Ramsey, Sarah H. & Abrams, Douglas E. Children & the Law in a Nutshell: 4th Edition. 4th rev. ed. 2011. (Nutshell Ser.). 690p. 38.00 (978-0-314-26296-5(3), West Legalworks) West.

Raphael, Lev. My Germany: A Jewish Writer Returns to the World His Parents Escaped. 2011. (ENG., Illus.). 236p. pap. 19.95 **(978-0-299-23154-5(2))** Univ. of Wisconsin Pr.

Rawson, Harve E. Captain English's Legacy: The Englishton Park Children's Program. 2010. 256p. pap. 17.49 (978-1-4520-8073-4(9)) AuthorHouse.

Rayes, Gilberto dela, ed. Nonmarital Childbearing: Trends, Reasons & Policy. 2010. (Pregnancy & Infants: Medical, Psychological & Social Issues Ser.). 160p. pap. 43.00 (978-1-60741-756-9(1)) Nova Science Pubs., Inc.

Reed, Matthew P. & Klinich, Kathleen D. Child Anthropometry for Improved Vehicle Occupant Safety. 2010. (Illus.). vii, 416p. pap. (978-0-7680-2172-1(3)) SAE Intl.

Reed, Ruth. Negro Illegitimacy in New York City / by Ruth Reed. 2006. 156p. per. 18.99 (978-1-4255-1160-9(0)) MPublishing.

Reid, Rob. Reid's Read-Alouds 2: Modern-Day Classics from C. S. Lewis to Lemony Snicket. 2010. pap. (978-0-8389-1072-6(6)) American Library Assn.

Review the Federal Food Stamp Program & Its Impact on Children's Health: Hearing Before the Subcommittee on Department Operations, Oversight, Nutrition, & Forestry of the Committee on Agriculture, House of Representatives, One Hundred Tenth Congress, First Session, March 13 2007. 2007. (Illus.). iv, 143p. (978-0-16-079650-0(4), 552-070-36601-6) United States Government Printing Office.

Rich, Dorothy. Megaskills: Building Our Children's Character & Achievement for School & Life. 2nd ed. 2008. (ENG.). 384p. pap. 16.99 (978-1-4022-1215-4(1)) Sourcebooks, Inc.

Richardson, Rhonda A. & Pevec, A. Margaret. What Kids Really Want to Ask: Using Movies to Start Meaningful Conversations. 2007. (Illus.). 192p. per. 12.95 (978-1-889242-31-6(4)) VanderWyk & Burnham.

Rivers, Mary V. & Shurman, Dvora. Deaf Lives in Contrast: Two Women's Stories. 2008. (Gallaudet New Deaf Lives Ser.). (ENG., Illus.). 272p. pap. 34.95 (978-1-56368-394-7(6)) Gallaudet Univ. Pr.

Rodenborg, Benjamin H. The History of Child Abduction in the United States & an Analysis of Today's AMBER Alert System. 2010. 46p. pap. 6.75 (978-0-557-45107-4(8)) Lulu Enterprises Inc.

Rosemond, John & Ravenel, M.D., Bose. The Diseasing of America's Children: Exposing the ADHD Fiasco & Empowering Parents to Take Back Control, 0 vols. 2009. 272p. pap. 15.99 (978-0-7852-9747-5(2)) Nelson, Thomas Inc.

Rothenberg, Mira. The Children of Raquette Lake: One Summer That Helped Change the Course of Treatment for Autism. 2012. (ENG.). 256p. pap. 19.95 **(978-1-58394-467-7(2))** North Atlantic Bks.

Russell, Michael K. & Kavanaugh, Maureen. Assessing Students in the Margin: Challenges, Strategies, & Techniques. 2011. (978-1-61735-315-4(9)); pap. (978-1-61735-314-7(0)); E-Book (978-1-61735-316-1(7)) Information Age Publishing, Inc.

R4 Educated Solutions Staff. Making Math Accessible to Students with Special Needs: Practical Tips & Suggestions, Grades 3-5. 2010. (ENG.). 224p. 64.95 (978-1-935249-07-8(X)) Solution Tree Pr.

—Making Math Accessible to Students with Special Needs: Practical Tips & Suggestions (Grades 6-8) 2010. (ENG.). 192p. pap. 29.95 (978-1-934009-68-0(7)) Solution Tree Pr.

R4 Educated Solutions Staff, contrib. by. Making Math Accessible to Students with Special Needs: Practical Tips & Suggestions (Grades 6-8) 2010. (ENG.). 192p. lib. bdg. 64.95 (978-1-935249-08-5(8)) Solution Tree Pr.

Sanborn, Robert, et al, eds. Growing up in Houston 2006-2008: Assessing the Quality of Life of Our Children. 2006. (978-0-9789952-0-1(1), Children At Risk.

Savarese, Ralph James. Reasonable People: A Memoir of Autism & Adoption: on the Meaning of Family & the Politics of Neurological Difference. annot. ed. 2007. (ENG.). 496p. 25.95 (978-1-59051-129-9(8)) Other Pr., LLC.

Schabecoff, Philip & Schabecoff, Alice. Poisoned for Profit: How Toxins Are Making Our Children Chronically Ill — With New Information on What We Can Do. 2010. (ENG.). 368p. pap. 17.95 (978-1-60358-256-8(8)) Chelsea Green Publishing.

Schmidt, Ella. The Dream Fields of Florida: Mexican Farmworkers & the Myth of Belonging. 2009. (ENG.). 160p. 62.99 (978-0-7391-3872-4(3)) Lexington Bks.

Scholastic, Inc. Staff, contrib. by. Core Knowledge Library: Teacher's Guide PreK. 2008. (Illus.). 32p. (978-0-545-06680-8(8)) Scholastic, Inc.

Schultz, Dana & Barnes-Proby, Dionne. Toolkit for Adapting Cognitive Behavioral Intervention for Trauma in Schools (CBITS) or Supporting Students Exposed to Trauma (SSET) for Implementation with Youth in Foster Care. 2010. 44p. pap. 20.00 (978-0-8330-4924-7(0), tr-772) RAND Corp., The.

Schultz, Dana, et al. National Evaluation of Safe Start: Promising Approaches - Assessing Program Implementation. 2010. (ENG.). 290p. pap. 35.00 (978-0-8330-4968-1(2), tr-750) RAND Corp., The.

Schumann, Dirk, ed. Raising Citizens in the Century of the Child: The United States & German Central Europe in Comparative Perspective. 2010. (SGH Ser.). (Illus.). 280p. 85.00 (978-1-84545-696-2(3)) Berghahn Bks., Inc.

Sheff, David. Beautiful Boy: A Father's Journey Through His Son's Addiction. lt. ed. 2008. 464p. lib. bdg. 32.95 (978-1-60285-294-5(4)) Ctr. Point Large Print.

Shepard, Judy. The Meaning of Matthew: My Son's Murder in Laramie, & a World Transformed. 2010. (ENG.). 288p. (gr. 12). 15.00 (978-0-452-29638-1(2), Plume) Penguin Group (USA) Inc.

Singer, Dorothy G. & Singer, Jerome L., eds. Handbook of Children & the Media. 2nd ed. 2011. (Illus.). 824p. 150.00 (978-1-4129-8242-9(1), B82429C) SAGE Pubns., Inc.

Siraj-Blatchford, Iram. Early Childhood Matters: Evidence from the Effective Pre-school & Primary Education Project. Melhuish, Edward C. et al, eds. 2009. (Illus.). 176p. 140.00 (978-0-415-48242-4(9)) Routledge.

Siraj-Blatchford, Iram, et al, eds. Early Childhood Matters: Evidence from the Effective Pre-school & Primary Education Project. 2009. (Illus.). 176p. pap. 47.95 (978-0-415-48243-1(7)) Routledge.

Smith, David G. The Child Health Insurance Program: Past & Future. 2011. (ENG.). 121p. 34.95 (978-1-4128-1869-8(9)) Transaction Pubs.

Smuts, Alice. Science in the Service of Children, 1893-1935. 2008. (ENG., Illus.). 393p. pap. 32.00 (978-0-300-14435-2(0)) Yale Univ. Pr.

Snow, Robert L. Child Abduction: Prevention, Investigation, & Recovery, 1 vol. 2008. 192p. 44.95 (978-0-313-34786-3(7), C34786, Praeger Pubs.) Greenwood Publishing Group, Inc.

St. John, Warren. Outcasts United: The Story of a Refugee Soccer Team That Changed a Town. 2012. (ENG.). 240p. (YA). (gr. 7). 16.99 **(978-0-385-74194-1(4))**; lib. bdg. 19.99 **(978-0-375-99033-5(X))** Random Hse. Children's Bks. (Delacorte Bks. for Young Readers).

Stahl, Philip M. & Drozd, Leslie M., eds. Relocation Issues in Child Custody Cases. 2007. (Illus.). 181p. 175.00 (978-0-7890-3533-2(2)) Routledge.

Steemers, Jeanette. Creating Preschool Television: A Story of Commerce, Creativity & Curriculum. 2010. (ENG., Illus.). 256p. 95.00 (978-0-230-57440-3(8)) Palgrave Macmillan.

Stein, Theodore J. Child Welfare & the Law. 3rd ed. 2007. 539p. per. (978-1-58760-042-5(0), CWLA Pr.) Child Welfare League of America, Inc.

Stepenoff, Bonnie. The Dead End Kids of St. Louis: Homeless Boys & the People Who Tried to Save Them. 2010. (ENG., Illus.). 192p. (C). 29.95 (978-0-8262-1888-9(1)) Univ. of Missouri Pr.

Stroul, Beth A. & Blau, Gary M. The System of Care Handbook: Transforming Mental Health Services for Children, Youth, & Families. 2008. (Systems of Care for Children's Mental Health Ser.). (Illus.). 760p. 74.95 (978-1-55766-962-9(7)) Brookes, Paul H. Publishing Co.

Szekely. Art Teaching. 2011. (ENG., Illus.). 456p. pap. 89.95 (978-0-415-99058-5(0)) Routledge.

Taylor, Fred. Roll Away the Stone: Saving America's Children. 2nd ed. 2007. (ENG.). 266p. pap. 15.95 (978-1-882480-15-9(5)) Information International.

Teves, Ryan. In Defense of the American Teen: An insider's commentary on the state of our secondary Schools. 2010. 220p. 24.99 (978-1-4520-1918-5(5)) AuthorHouse.

—In Defense of the American Teen: An Insider's Commentary on the State of Our Secondary Schools. 2010. 220p. pap. 14.99 (978-1-4520-1917-8(7)) AuthorHouse.

Thomas, Joseph T. Poetry's Playground: The Culture of Contemporary American Children's Poetry. 2007. (Landscapes of Childhood Ser.). (Illus.). 180p. per. 24.95 (978-0-8143-3296-2(X)) Wayne State Univ. Pr.

Thomas, Nancy Pickering, et al. Information Literacy & Information Skills Instruction: Applying Research to Practice in the 21st Century School Library, 1 vol. 3rd rev. ed. 2011. 261p. pap. 40.00 (978-1-59884-490-0(3), A2995P) Libraries Unlimited, Inc.

Trowell, Melody. Linguistic Stereotypes in Children's Animated Film: A Language Attitude Study. 2008. 60p. pap. (978-3-639-11002-9(1)) VDM Verlag Dr. Mueller e.K.

Uhlberg, Myron. Hands of My Father: A Hearing Boy, His Deaf Parents, & the Language of Love. 2009. (ENG., Illus.). 256p. 24.00 (978-0-553-80688-5(2)) Random House Publishing Group.

Van Orden, Phyllis J., et al. Children's Books: A Practical Guide to Selection. 2007. (Illus.). pap. 59.95 (978-1-55570-584-8(7)) Neal-Schuman Pubs., Inc.

Ventrell, Marvin R. Trial Advocacy for the Child Welfare Lawyer: Telling the Story of the Family. 2011. (978-1-60156-149-7(0)) National Institute for Trial Advocacy.

Vissing, Yvonne Marie & Vissing, Yvonne. How to Keep Your Children Safe: A Guide for Parents. 2007. (ENG., Illus.). 216p. pap. 12.95 (978-1-58465-529-9(1)) Univ. Pr. of New England.

Wakefield, Andrew J. Waging War on the Autistic Child: The Legacy of Baron von Munchausen. 2012. (ENG.). 272p. 26.95 **(978-1-61608-614-5(9)**, 608614) Skyhorse Publishing Co., Inc.

Waldfogel, Jane. What Children Need. 2010. (Family & Public Policy Ser.). (Illus.). 288p. pap. 19.95 (978-0-674-04640-5(4)) Harvard Univ. Pr.

Walker, Eric S. Children & Disasters: Preparedness, Response & Recovery. 2011. (Children's Issues, Laws & Programs Ser.). 171p. 185.00 **(978-1-61470-697-7(2))** Nova Science Pubs., Inc.

Ward, Gordon Thomas. Bit of Earth in the Somerset Hills. 2007. 192p. pap. 19.99 (978-1-59629-382-3(9)) History Pr., The.

Watkins, Audrey Lee. On the Way Here: The Path That Chose Me. 2009. 206p. pap. 19.95 (978-1-60703-241-0(4)) PublishAmerica, Inc.

Werner, Emmy E. In Pursuit of Liberty: Coming of Age in the American Revolution, 1 vol. 2006. (Illus.). 208p. 49.95 (978-0-275-99306-1(X), C9306, Praeger Pubs.) Greenwood Publishing Group, Inc.

—In Pursuit of Liberty: Coming of Age in the American Revolution. 2009. (Illus.). 192p. pap. 17.95 (978-1-59797-268-0(1)) Potomac Bks., Inc.

West, Mark I. The Japanification of Children's Popular Culture: From Godzilla to Miyazaki. West, Mark I., ed. 2008. (ENG.). 306p. pap. 55.00 (978-0-8108-5121-4(0)) Scarecrow Pr., Inc.

White, Jacquelyn W., et al, eds. Violence Against Women & Children Vol. 1: Mapping the Terrain, 2 vols. 2010. (Illus.). 296p. 69.95 (978-1-4338-0912-5(5)) American Psychological Assn.

White, Jacquelyn W., et al. Violence Against Women & Children. 2011. (Illus.). xxi, 330p. E-Book **(978-1-4338-0913-2(3))** American Psychological Assn.

Wiggins, Jim. Florida & World War II: A Personal Recollection. 2008. (Illus.). 206p. pap. 23.00 (978-0-7884-4545-3(6)) Heritage Bks.

Williams, Randy & Williams, Betty. Effective Programs for the Treatment of Autism: Applied Behavior Analysis Models. 2010. (ENG.). 304p. 160.00 (978-0-415-99931-1(6)) Routledge.

—Effective Programs for Treating Autism Spectrum Disorder: Applied Behavior Analysis Models. 2010. (ENG.). 304p. pap. 59.95 (978-0-415-99932-8(4)) Routledge.

Wilson, Aubrey D. & Ryan, Sally G., eds. Child Welfare System: Transitions. 2011. (Series: Children's Issues, Laws & Programs Ser.). (Illus.). viii, 318p. 215.00 (978-1-61324-713-6(3)) Nova Science Pubs., Inc.

Winterfeld, Amy, et al. Promoting Healthy Communities & Preventing Childhood Obesity: Trends in Recent Legislation. 2010. (Illus.). iii, 34p. pap. **(978-1-58024-587-6(0))** National Conference of State Legislatures.

—Reversing the Trend in Childhood Obesity: Policies to Promote Healthy Kids & Communities. 2011. (Illus.). iii, 37p. pap. **(978-1-58024-617-0(6))** National Conference of State Legislatures.

Woodhouse, Barbara Bennett. Hidden in Plain Sight: The Tragedy of Children's Rights from Ben Franklin to Lionel Tate. 2010. (Public Square Ser.). (ENG., Illus.). 384p. (C). pap. 19.95 (978-0-691-14621-8(7)) Princeton Univ. Pr.

Wright, J. E. The Sexualization of America's Kids: And How to Stop It. 2011. 176p. pap. 15.95 **(978-1-4620-0846-9(1))** iUniverse, Inc.

Wu, Sarah. Fed up with Lunch: How One Anonymous Teacher Survived a Year of School Lunches. 2011. (ENG.). 208p. 22.95 (978-1-4521-0228-3(7)) Chronicle Bks. LLC.

Yang, Weidong & Wen, Xiaoying. Child Health Care Support Programs for Deafness, Dental Services & down Syndrome. 2012. (Children's Issues, Laws & Programs Ser.). 161p. 125.00 **(978-1-61470-970-1(X))** Nova Science Pubs., Inc.

Zigler, Edward F., et al. The Tragedy of Child Care in America. 2009. (ENG.). 240p. 40.00 (978-0-300-12233-6(0)) Yale Univ. Pr.

Zirpoli, Thomas J. Behavior Management: Positive Applications for Teachers. 6th rev. ed. 2010. (ENG.). 480p. (C). pap. 120.20 (978-0-13-706320-8(2), Prentice Hall) Prentice Hall PTR.

CHILDREN—WALES

Mullally, Maureen. Law & the Family in the UK. 2nd ed. 2007. 192p. pap. 17.00 (978-1-901657-53-1(1)) Blackhall Publishing IRL. Dist: Gaunt, Inc.

Trevor, Alun. The Songbird Is Singing: Scenes from a Welsh Childhood in the 1920's. 2010. (ENG.). 120p. pap. 14.95 (978-1-906998-06-6(X)) Parthian Bks. GBR. Dist: Independent Pubs. Group.

CHILDREN, ABANDONED
see Abandoned Children

CHILDREN, ABNORMAL AND BACKWARDS
see Exceptional Children

CHILDREN, ADOPTED
see Adopted Children

CHILDREN, AFRICAN AMERICAN
see African American Children

CHILDREN, APHASIC
see Aphasia

CHILDREN, AUTISTIC
see Autistic Children

CHILDREN, BLIND
see also Blind—Education

Cutter, Joseph. Promoting Independent Movement & Travel in Blind Children: A Developmental Orientation & Mobility Approach. 2007. (ENG., Illus.). 356p. (978-1-59311-604-0(7)); per. (978-1-59311-603-3(9)) Information Age Publishing, Inc.

Ferrell, Kay Alicyn. Reach Out & Teach: Helping Your Child Who Is Visually Impaired Learn & Grow. 2nd ed. 2011. **(978-0-89128-457-4(5)); (978-0-89128-484-0(2))** American Foundation for the Blind Pr.

Fielding, Jed. Look at Me: Photographs from Mexico City by Jed Fielding. 2009. (ENG., Illus.). 144p. 55.00 (978-0-226-24852-3(6)) Univ. of Chicago Pr.

Junefelt, Karen. Rethinking Egocentric Speech: Towards a New Hypothesis. 2007. 169.00 (978-1-60021-724-1(9)) Nova Science Pubs., Inc.

Kolaschinsky, Doreen. Selbstwertgefühl Sehbehinderter und Blinder Kinder und Jugendlicher in Sozialen Interaktionen: Theorie und Empirische Untersuchung. 2011. (Europäische Hochschulschriften. Reihe 11: Pädagogik Ser.). (GER.). 380p. pap. 76.95 **(978-3-631-62029-8(2))** Lang, Peter GmbH, Europaischer Verlag der Wissenschaften DEU. Dist: Lang, Peter.

Oliphant, John. The Early Education of the Blind in Britain C. 1790-1900: Institutional Experience in England & Scotland. 2007. 200p. (978-0-7734-5247-3(8)) Mellen, Edwin Pr., The.

Sullivan, Tom. Adventures in Darkness: Memoirs of an Eleven-Year-Old Blind Boy, 0 vols. 2008. 224p. pap. 14.99 (978-0-8499-2910-6(5)) 2007. 240p. 24.99 (978-0-7852-2081-7(X)) Nelson, Thomas Inc.

Tenberken, Sabriye. My Path Leads to Tibet: The Inspiring Story of How One Young Blind Woman Brought Hope to the Blind Children of Tibet. l.t. ed. 2007. 368p. 32.50 (978-1-84617-941-9(6)) Ulverscroft Large Print Bks., Ltd.

CHILDREN, BLIND—EDUCATION

Castellano, Carol. Getting Ready for College Begins in Third Grade: Working Toward an Independent Future for Your Blind/Visually Impaired Child. 2010. E-Book (978-1-61735-072-6(9)); (Illus.). 120p. (978-1-61735-071-9(0)); (Illus.). 120p. pap. (978-1-61735-070-2(2)) Information Age Publishing, Inc.

French, Sally, et al. An Oral History of the Education of Visually Impaired People: Telling Stories for Inclusive Futures. 2006. (Illus.). 448p. 129.95 (978-0-7734-5706-5(2)) Mellen, Edwin Pr., The.

Tenberken, Sabriye. My Path Leads to Tibet: The Inspiring Story of How One Young Blind Woman Brought Hope to the Blind Children of Tibet. l.t. ed. 2007. 368p. 32.50 (978-1-84617-941-9(6)) Ulverscroft Large Print Bks., Ltd.

CHILDREN, BOOKS AND READING FOR
see Children—Books and Reading

CHILDREN, CUSTODY OF
see Custody of Children

CHILDREN, DEAF
see Deaf Children

CHILDREN, EXCEPTIONAL
see Exceptional Children

CHILDREN, FIRST-BORN

Bambolo, Jr. The Firstborn Son: A Curse, a Gift, or a Calling. 2011. 200p. pap. 15.99 **(978-1-4575-0369-6(7))** Dog Ear Publishing, LLC.

Gong, Ginny. From Ironing Board to Corporate Board: My Chinese Laundry Experience in America. 2008. pap. (978-1-931907-50-7(1)) Homa & Sekey Bks.

Hensel, Benedikt. Die Vertauschung des Erstgeburtssegens in der Genesis: Eine Analyse der Narrativ-Theologischen Grundstruktur des Ersten Buches der Tora. 2011. (Beihefte zur Zeitschrift für die alttestamentliche Wissenschaft Ser.). (GER.). XIV, 387p. 182.00 **(978-3-11-024792-3(5))** De Gruyter, Walter Inc.

Leman, Kevin. Born to Win: Keeping Your Firstborn Edge Without Losing Your Balance. 2009. 288p. pap. 13.99 (978-0-8007-3262-2(6)) Revell.

—The First Born Advantage: Making Your Birth Order Work for You. 2008. 288p. pap. 12.99 (978-0-8007-3337-7(1)) Baker Publishing Group.

—The Firstborn Advantage: Making Your Birth Order Work for You. 2008. 288p. 19.99 (978-0-8007-1911-1(5)) Revell.

CHILDREN, FOLKLORE OF
see Children—Folklore

CHILDREN, HEARING IMPAIRED
see Hearing Impaired Children

CHILDREN, HOMELESS
see Homeless Children

CHILDREN, INDIAN
see Indian Children

CHILDREN, JEWISH
see Jewish Children

CHILDREN, LATE-BORN
see Children of Older Parents

CHILDREN, MEXICAN AMERICAN
see Mexican American Children

CHILDREN, MISSING
see Missing Children

CHILDREN, ORIENTAL
see Children—Asia

CHILDREN, PHOTOGRAPHY OF
see Photography of Children and Youth

CHILDREN, POOR
see Poor Children

CHILDREN, PRESCHOOL
see Preschool Children

CHILDREN, RETARDED
see Slow Learning Children

CHILDREN, RUNAWAY
see Runaway Children

CHILDREN, VAGRANT
see Vagrant Children

CHILDREN AND ADULTS
see also Children and Older People; Parent and Child; Teacher-Student Relationships

Benson, Peter L. Parent, Teacher, Mentor, Friend: How Every Adult Can Change Kids' Lives. 2010. (ENG., Illus.). 256p. pap. 7.95 (978-1-57482-283-0(7)) Search Institute.

Bowen, Chris. Our Kids: Building Relationships in the Classroom. 2008. 148p. pap. 14.95 (978-1-4327-2453-5(3)) Outskirts Pr., Inc.

Bowes, Jennifer & Grace, Rebekah, eds. Children, Families & Communities: Context & Consequences. 3rd rev. ed. 2008. (ENG.). xviii, 267p. 65.00 (978-0-19-555154-9(0)) Oxford Univ. Pr., Inc.

Broadhead, Pat, et al. Children, Families & Communities: Creating & Sustaining Integrated Services. 2007. (ENG.). 136p. 134.00 (978-0-335-22094-6(0), 0335220940); pap. 58.00 (978-0-335-22093-9(2), 0335220932) McGraw-Hill Education GBR. (Open University Pr.). Dist: McGraw-Hill Cos., The.

Burke, Ruth Marie. Six Pieces of Pie: Dealing with elderly parents as an adult Child. 2009. 144p. pap. 12.99 (978-1-4389-9814-5(7)) AuthorHouse.

Burns, Kristie. The Temperaments & the Adult-Child Relationship. 2010. 239p. pap. 35.00 (978-0-557-42069-8(5)) Lulu Enterprises Inc.

Cassidy, Claire. Thinking Children. 2009. (ENG.). 208p. 44.95 (978-1-4411-8754-3(5)) Continuum International Publishing Group, Ltd. GBR. Dist: National Bk. Network.

—Thinking Children: The Concept of 'Child' from a Philosophical Perspective. 2008. (ENG.). 208p. 140.00 (978-0-8264-9818-2(3)) Continuum International Publishing Group, Ltd. GBR. Dist: National Bk. Network.

Fletcher, Anthony. Growing up in England: The Experience of Childhood, 1600-1914. 2010. (ENG., Illus.). 456p. pap. 35.00 (978-0-300-16396-4(7)) Yale Univ. Pr.

Foley, Pam & Leverett, Stephen. Connecting with Children: Developing Working Relationships. 2008. (Illus.). 312p. (C). pap. 35.95 (978-1-84742-058-9(3)) Policy Pr. GBR. Dist: Chicago Distribution Ctr.

Füredi, Frank & Bristow, Jennie. Licensed to Hug: How Child Protection Policies Are Poisoning the Relationship Between the Generations & Damaging the Voluntary Sector. 2nd ed. 2010. 68p. pap. 13.50 (978-1-906837-16-7(3)) Civitas:Institute for the Study of Civil Society GBR. Dist: Coronet Bks.

Gerhardt, Sue. The Selfish Society: How We All Forgot to Love One Another & Made Money Instead. (ENG.). 2011. 400p. pap. 16.95 **(978-1-84739-676-1(3))** 2010. 390p. pap. 22.95 **(978-1-84737-571-1(5))** Simon & Schuster, Ltd. GBR. Dist: Independent Pubs. Group.

Gutman, Marta, ed. Designing Modern Childhoods: History, Space, & the Material Culture of Children. 2008. (Rutgers Series in Childhood Studies). (ENG., Illus.). 368p. 70.00 (978-0-8135-4195-2(6)) Rutgers Univ. Pr.

Gutman, Marta & de Coninck-Smith, Ning, eds. Designing Modern Childhoods: History, Space, & the Material Culture of Children. 2008. (Rutgers Series in Childhood Studies). (ENG., Illus.). 368p. per. 24.95 (978-0-8135-4196-9(4)) Rutgers Univ. Pr.

Henley, Karyn. Communicating with Young Children. (Children's Ministry Folders). tchr. ed. 2.99 (978-0-7847-0686-2(7), 42236) Standard Publishing.

Hohmann, Mary, et al. Educating Young Children: Active Learning Practices for Preschool & Child Care Programs. 3rd ed. 2008. (978-1-57379-354-4(X)) High/Scope Pr.

Joseph, Sandra & Korczak, Janusz. Loving Every Child: Wisdom for Parents. Joseph, Sandra & Korczak, Janusz, eds. 2007. (ENG., Illus.). 84p. 10.95 (978-1-56512-489-9(8), 1565124898) Algonquin Bks. of Chapel Hill.

Kennedy, David. The Well of Being: Childhood, Subjectivity, & Education. 2006. (SUNY Series, Early Childhood Education). xii, 235p. (C). 71.50 (978-0-7914-6825-8(9)); 235p. per. 29.95 (978-0-7914-6826-5(7)) State Univ. of New York Pr.

Kiel-Hinrichsen, Monika. Why Children Don't Listen: A Guide for Parents & Teachers. 2006. (Illus.). 185p. per. (978-0-86315-574-1(X)) Floris Bks.

Kotre, John. Make It Count: How to Generate a Legacy That Gives Meaning to You. 2011. (ENG.). 256p. pap. 16.99 **(978-1-4516-8236-6(0)**, Free Pr.) Free Pr.

Marsiglio, William. Men on a Mission: Valuing Youth Work in Our Communities. 2008. (ENG.). 416p. (gr. 17). 60.00 (978-0-8018-8829-8(8)); pap. 32.00 (978-0-8018-8830-4(1)) Johns Hopkins Univ. Pr.

Moyles, Janet & Papatheodorou, Theodora, eds. Learning Together in the Early Years: Exploring Relational Pedagogy. 2008. (Illus.). XVIII, 238p. 44.95 (978-0-415-46933-3(3)) Routledge.

Notkin, Melanie. Savvy Auntie: The Ultimate Guide for Cool Aunts, Great-Aunts, Godmothers, & All Women Who Love Kids. 2011. (ENG.). 384p. 24.99 (978-0-06-199997-0(0), Morrow, William & Co.) HarperCollins Pubs.

Papatheordorou, Theodora. Learning Together in the Early Years: Exploring Relational Pedagogy. Moyles, Janet, ed. 2008. (Illus.). XVIII, 238p. 170.00 (978-0-415-46932-6(5)) Routledge.

Schroff, Laura & Tresniowski, Alex. An Invisible Thread: The True Story of an 11-Year-Old Panhandler, a Busy Sales Executive, & an Unlikely Meeting with Destiny. l.t. ed. 2012. (ENG.). 335p. 31.99 **(978-1-4104-4786-9(3)**, Wheeler Publishing, Inc.) Cengage Gale.

Schroff, Laura L. & Tresniowski, Alex. An Invisible Thread: The True Story of an 11-Year-Old Panhandler, a Busy Sales Executive, & an Unlikely Meeting with Destiny. (ENG., Illus.). 272p. 2012. pap. 14.99 **(978-1-4516-4897-3(9))** 2011. 25.00 (978-1-4516-4251-3(2)) Howard Books. (Howard Bks.).

Te One, Sarah. Perceptions of Children's Rights. 2010. 344p. pap. (978-3-8383-4198-9(8)) Lambert Academic Publishing.

Vissing, Yvonne Marie & Vissing, Yvonne. How to Keep Your Children Safe: A Guide for Parents. 2007. (ENG., Illus.). 216p. pap. 12.95 (978-1-58465-529-9(1)) Univ. Pr. of New England.

Walsh, Richard J. True Jersey City Story: Super Proud Dad 14 Years of Motivational Letters. 2009. 208p. 24.99 (978-1-4389-5378-6(X)); pap. 14.49 (978-1-4389-5377-9(1)) AuthorHouse.

Wheless, James. Adult Epilepsy. Cascino, Gregory & Sirven, Joseph, eds. 2011. (ENG., Illus.). 326p. 169.00 (978-0-470-74122-1(8), Wiley) Wiley, John & Sons, Inc.

CHILDREN AND COMIC BOOKS
see Comic Books and Children

CHILDREN AND COMPUTERS
see Computers and Children

CHILDREN AND DEATH
Here are entered works on children's experiences with, conceptions of, and reactions to death. Works on the death of children are entered under Children—Death. Works on children's death rates and causes are entered under Children—Mortality.

Akhtar, Salman. Three Faces of Mourning: Melancholia, Manic Defense, & Moving On. 2006. (Margaret S. Mahler Ser.). (ENG.). 280p. pap. 39.99 (978-0-7657-0516-7(8), Aronson, Jason) Rowman & Littlefield Publishers, Inc.

Berber, Beth. My Life by Me: A Kid's Forever Book. 2011. 64p. (J). pap. 14.95 **(978-1-4338-1036-7(0)**, Magination Pr.) American Psychological Assn.

Brown, Brenda Fewtrell. Lollipops, Bubblegum, Death & Lies: A Young Life Scarred by a Culture of Silence. 2011. (Illus.). 396p. pap. 21.14 (978-1-4520-5316-5(2)) AuthorHouse.

Chatelle, Melody. Journeys of Heartache & Grace: Conversations & Life Lessons from Young People with Serious Illnesses. 2008. xxix, 221p. (978-1-880292-34-1(3)) LangMarc Publishing.

Corr, Charles A. & Balk, David E. Children's Encounters with Death, Bereavement, & Coping. 2010. (Illus.). 488p. 70.00 (978-0-8261-3422-6(X)) Springer Publishing Co., Inc.

Dann, Patty. The Goldfish Went on Vacation: A Memoir of Loss (and Learning to Tell the Truth about It) 2007. (ENG.). 176p. per. 11.95 (978-1-59030-564-5(7), Trumpeter) Shambhala Pubns., Inc.

Di Ciacco, Janis A. The Colors of Grief: Understanding a Child's Journey Through Loss from Birth to Adulthood. 2008. (ENG., Illus.). 176p. pap. (978-1-84310-886-3(0)) Kingsley, Jessica Ltd.

Doka, Kenneth J. & Tucci, Amy S., eds. Living with Grief: Children & Adolescents. 2008. 360p. pap. 24.95 *(978-1-893349-09-4(8))* Hospice Foundation of America.

Dyregrov, Atle. Grief in Young Children: A Handbook for Adults. 2008. (ENG.). 96p. pap. *(978-1-84310-650-0(7))* Kingsley, Jessica Ltd.

Goldman, Linda. Great Answers to Difficult Questions about Death: What Children Need to Know. 2009. (ENG., Illus.). 96p. pap. *(978-1-84905-805-6(9))* Kingsley, Jessica Ltd.

Goldring, Ellen & Leeuwenburgh, Erika. Why Did You Die? Activities to Help Children Cope with Grief & Loss. 2008. (Instant Help Ser.). (ENG., Illus.). 136p. (J). per. 16.95 *(978-1-57224-604-1(9))* Play2Grow.

Helping Children Cope with Death (In Spanish: 35 Maneras de Ayudar aun Niño Angustiado o Apenado. 2007. (SPA.). pap. 9.95 *(978-1-890534-09-7(9))* Dougy Ctr.

Jones, Susan. Until We Meet Again. 2007. 64p. lib. bdg. 24.95 *(978-1-59298-157-1(7))* Beaver's Pond Pr., Inc.

Kampmann, Jennifer. The Well Being of Children: As Viewed through Their Conceptions of Death. 2008. 88p. pap. *(978-3-639-09416-9(6))* VDM Verlag Dr. Mueller e.K.

Lasher, Cynthia Long. Death Is No Stranger: Helping Children Grieve. 2008. 93p. per. *(978-0-7880-2505-1(8))* CSS Publishing Co.

Lawrence, Don Harold. Glimpses into Grief. 2010. (Illus.). xviii, 300p. pap. ***(978-0-9827848-0-8(5))*** Monument Pr.

Lawson, John Edward, et al. A Child's Guide to Prison. 2011. (Illus.). 40p. pap. 11.95 ***(978-1-935738-18-3(6))*** Raw Dog Screaming Pr.

Monahan, Pat. To Thee We Do Cry: A Grandmother's Journey Through Grief. 2010. 112p. 22.95 *(978-1-4502-7173-8(1))*; pap. 12.95 *(978-1-4502-7172-1(3))* iUniverse, Inc.

Schaefer, Dan, et al. How Do We Tell the Children? 4th ed. 2010. (ENG.). 224p. pap. 16.95 *(978-1-55704-911-7(4),* William Morrow Paperbacks) HarperCollins Pubs.

Stickney, Doris. Water Bugs & Dragonflies: Explaining Death to Young Children. 2009. *(978-0-8298-1858-1(8))* Pilgrim Pr., The/United Church Pr.

Strong, Judy. A Child's Grief: Surviving the Death of a Parent. 2009. 80p. pap. 16.95 *(978-1-59298-308-7(1))* Beaver's Pond Pr., Inc.

Struthers, Marilyn F. Butterflies & Beyond: Preparing A Young Child to Cope with Grief or Loss. 2011. 44p. pap. 20.95 *(978-1-4497-1098-9(0),* WestBow Pr.) Author Solutions, Inc.

Talwar, Victoria, et al, eds. Children's Understanding of Death: From Biological to Religious Conceptions. 2011. (ENG., Illus.). 202p. 90.00 *(978-0-521-19459-4(8))* Cambridge Univ. Pr.

Turner, Mary. Talking with Children & Young People about Death & Dying. 2nd ed. 2006. (ENG., Illus.). 16p. per. *(978-1-84310-441-4(5))* Kingsley, Jessica Ltd.

Walukonis, Jodi Ann. Grappling with Grief, a Child's Navigation Through the Loss of a Loved. 2007. 40p. pap. 14.95 *(978-1-934246-35-1(2))* Peppertree Pr., The.

Webb, Nancy Boyd, ed. Helping Bereaved Children: A Handbook for Practitioners. 3rd ed. 2010. (Social Work Practice with Children & Families Ser.). (ENG., Illus.). 408p. instr.'s hndbk. ed. 50.00 *(978-1-60623-597-3(4))* Guilford Pubns., Inc.

Webb, Nancy Boyd, ed. Helping Bereaved Children, Third Edition: A Handbook for Practitioners. 3rd rev. ed. 2011. (Social Work Practice with Children & Families Ser.). (ENG., Illus.). 408p. pap. 30.00 ***(978-1-4625-0451-0(5))*** Guilford Pubns., Inc.

Wilson, Shirley Butts. Light in the Darkest Hours: The Autobiographical Writings of a Parent of a Murdered Child. 2010. 120p. 24.95 *(978-1-4490-7232-2(1))* AuthorHouse.

35 Ways to Help a Grieving Child: Como Ayudar a un Niño a Sobrellevar una Muerte. 2007. pap. 9.95 *(978-1-890534-08-0(0))* Dougy Ctr.

CHILDREN AND GRANDPARENTS
see Grandparent and Child

CHILDREN AND MASS MEDIA
see Mass Media and Children

CHILDREN AND MOTION PICTURES
see Motion Pictures and Children

CHILDREN AND OLDER PEOPLE
Here are entered works on relationships between children and elderly people.
see also Grandparent and Child

Carter, Lois. Boundless Grace: Devotions from a Caregiver's Heart. 2010. pap. 8.99 *(978-1-61663-500-8(2))* Tate Publishing & Enterprises, LLC.

Hyams, Jacky. Time to Help Your Parents: A Practical Guide to Recognising Problems & Providing Support. 2011. (ENG.). 288p. pap. 14.95 *(978-0-7499-4065-2(4))* Piatkus Bks. GBR. Dist: Independent Pubs. Group.

CHILDREN AND POLITICS

Block, James E. The Crucible of Consent: American Child Rearing & the Forging of Liberal Society. 2012. (ENG.). 420p. 45.00 *(978-0-674-05194-2(7))* Harvard Univ. Pr.

Bond, Helen, et al. Through Children's Eyes: President Obama & the Future Generation. 2012. (ENG.). 250p. pap. 27.99 ***(978-1-926780-06-1(X))*** Key Publishing Hse., Inc., The CAN. Dist: AtlasBooks Distribution.

Earls, Felton J., ed. The Child as Citizen. 2011. (ANNALS of the American Academy of Political & Social Science Ser.: 633). (Illus.). 264p. (C). 47.00 *(978-1-4129-9586-3(8),* 295633C); pap. 34.00 *(978-1-4129-9585-6(X),* 295633P) SAGE Pubns., Inc.

Harris, Nonie. Comparing Child Care Subsidy Policies in California & Australi. 2010. 224p. pap. *(978-3-8383-2009-0(3))* Lambert Academic Publishing.

Hayward, Bronwyn. Children As Ecological Citizens: Nurturing a Democratic Imagination in a Changing World. 2012. (ENG., Illus.). 208p. 145.00 ***(978-1-84971-436-5(3))***; pap. 42.95 ***(978-1-84971-437-2(1))*** Routledge.

Krüger, Hans-Peter. Politische Partizipation Jugendlicher in der Gemeinde: Ein internationaler Vergleich: Leipzig - Lyon. 2008. (Europäische Hochschulschriften. Reihe 31: Politikwissenschaft Ser.). 362p. pap. 81.95 *(978-3-631-58253-4(6))* Lang, Peter GmbH, Europaischer Verlag der Wissenschaften DEU. Dist: Lang, Peter.

Nel, Philip & Zipes, Jack. Tales for Little Rebels: A Collection of Radical Children's Literature. Mickenberg, Julia L., ed. 2008. (ENG., Illus.). 313p. 65.00 *(978-0-8147-5720-8(0))* New York Univ. Pr.

—Tales for Little Rebels: A Collection of Radical Children's Literature. Mickenberg, Julia, ed. 2010. (ENG., Illus.). 313p. pap. 26.00 *(978-0-8147-5721-5(9))* New York Univ. Pr.

Sugarman, Sally. If Kids Could Vote: Children, Democracy, & the Media. 2006. (ENG.). 144p. 68.50 *(978-0-7391-1395-0(X))*; per. 26.50 *(978-0-7391-1396-7(8))* Lexington Bks.

Thomas, Nigel Patrick & Thomas, Nigel, eds. Children, Politics & Communication: Participation at the Margins. 2009. (Illus.). 216p. 85.00 *(978-1-84742-184-5(9))*; pap. 39.95 *(978-1-84742-183-8(0))* Policy Pr. GBR. Dist: Chicago Distribution Ctr.

Zahra, Tara. Kidnapped Souls: National Indifference & the Battle for Children in the Bohemian Lands, 1900-1948. (Illus.). 2011. 304p. pap. 24.95 ***(978-0-8014-7760-7(3))*** 2008. 279p. 39.95 *(978-0-8014-4628-3(7))* Cornell Univ. Pr.

CHILDREN AND PROSTITUTION
see Child Prostitution

CHILDREN AND STRANGERS

Hall, Scott. Unforgivable Sins: Protecting Our Children from Predators, 1 vol. Davie, Michael B., ed. 2009. (ENG.). 336p. pap. 17.95 *(978-1-897453-06-3(X))* Manor Hse. Publishing, Inc. CAN. Dist: APG Sales & Distribution Services.

CHILDREN AND TELEVISION
see Television and Children

CHILDREN AND THE AGED
see Children and Older People

CHILDREN AND THE INTERNET
see Internet and Children

CHILDREN AND VIOLENCE

Barter, Christine & Berridge, David, eds. Children Behaving Badly: Peer Violence Between Children & Young People. 2011. (Wiley Child Protection & Policy Ser.). (ENG., Illus.). 262p. pap. 47.95 *(978-0-470-72705-8(5),* Wiley); 110.95 *(978-0-470-69440-4(8),* Wiley-Blackwell) Wiley, John & Sons, Inc.

Brockliss, Laurence & Montgomery, Heather. Childhood & Violence in the Western Tradition. 2010. (Children in Archaeology Ser.). (ENG., Illus.). 352p. (C). 80.00 *(978-1-84217-978-9(0))* Oxbow Bks., Ltd. GBR. Dist: Brown, David Bk. Co., The.

Canada, Geoffrey. Fist Stick Knife Gun. 2011. 14.05 *(978-0-7848-3397-1(4),* Everbind) Marco Bk. Co.

—Fist Stick Knife Gun: A Personal History of Violence. 2010. (Illus.). 144p. pap. 14.00 *(978-0-8070-4449-0(0))* Beacon Pr.

—Fist Stick Knife Gun: A Personal of Violence. 2011. 14.05 *(978-0-7848-3590-6(X),* Everbind) Marco Bk. Co.

—Fist Stick Knife Gun: Graphic Novel. 2011. 14.05 *(978-0-7848-3579-1(9),* Everbind) Marco Bk. Co.

Canada, Geoffrey & Nicholas, Jamar. Fist Stick Knife Gun: A Personal History of Violence. 2010. (ENG.). 192p. pap. 14.00 *(978-0-8070-4461-2(X))* Beacon Pr.

Chelpi-den Hamer, Magali. Youngest Recruits: Pre-War, War & Post-War Experiences in Western Côte D'Ivoire. 2011. 79p. pap. *(978-90-8555-028-0(9),* Pallas Publications) Amsterdam Univ. Pr.

Children & Media Violence. *(978-91-630-6358-9(1))* Bindu Pubs.

Cram101 Textbook Reviews. Outlines & Highlights for Media & the American Child by George Comstock. 2011. 60p. pap. 26.95 ***(978-1-61905-826-2(X))*** Cram101 Inc.

Duhon-Sells, Rose, et al, eds. Youth Violence in American Schools: How Can It Be Alleviated. 2009. (Illus.). 204p. 109.95 *(978-0-7734-4917-6(5))* Mellen, Edwin Pr., The.

Dunson, Donald H. Child, Victim, Soldier: The Loss of Innocence in Uganda. 2008. (Illus.). 160p. pap. 16.00 *(978-1-57075-799-0(2))* Orbis Bks.

Eliminating Violence against Children: A Handbook for Parliamentarians. 2007. 84p. *(978-92-806-4158-5(1))* United Nations Children's Fund, The (UNICEF).

Eliminating Violence against Children: Handbook of Korean parliamentarians to deal with VAC. 2007. (KOR.). 84p. *(978-92-806-4170-7(0))* United Nations Children's Fund, The (UNICEF).

Garbarino, James. Children & the Dark Side of Human Experience: Confronting Global Realities & Rethinking Child Development. 2008. (ENG.). viii, 157p. pap. 39.95 *(978-0-387-75625-7(6),* 0387756256) Springer London, Ltd. GBR. Dist: Springer.

Gentile, Douglas A., et al. Violent Video Game Effects on Children & Adolescents: Theory, Research, & Public Policy. 2007. (ENG., Illus.). 200p. 37.99 *(978-0-19-530983-6(9))* Oxford Univ. Pr., Inc.

Godsi, Elie. Violence in Society. 235p. *(978-0-09-478140-5(0),* Constable & Co. Ltd.) Constable & Robinson Ltd.

Graham-Bermann, Sandra A. & Levendosky, Alytia A. How Intimate Partner Violence Affects Children: Developmental Research, Case Studies, & Evidence-Based Intervention. 2011. xi, 314p. 69.95 *(978-1-4338-0930-9(3))* American Psychological Assn.

Hatch, David. Violence & Teachers. 2009. 176p. pap. *(978-3-639-14952-4(1))* VDM Verlag Dr. Mueller e.K.

Haugen, David M. Is Media Violence a Problem? 2006. (At Issue Ser.). (ENG.). 114p. (J). pap. 31.80 *(978-0-7377-2398-4(X),* Greenhaven Pr., Inc.) Cengage Gale.

Hester, Marianne, et al. Making an Impact: Children & Domestic Violence - A Reader. 2nd ed. 2006. (ENG.). 288p. per. *(978-1-84310-157-4(2))* Kingsley, Jessica Ltd.

Honwana, Alcinda. Child Soldiers in Africa. 2007. (Ethnography of Political Violence Ser.). (Illus.). 216p. (C). per. 24.95 *(978-0-8122-1987-6(2))* Univ. of Pennsylvania Pr.

It's time to listen to Us! Youth response to the Report of the Expert Group Meeting on the Elimination of all forms of discrimination & violence against the girl Child. 2007. 28p. *(978-92-806-4141-7(7))*; (FRE.). *(978-92-806-4142-4(5))* United Nations Children's Fund, The (UNICEF).

Jaffe, Peter G., et al. Growing up with Domestic Violence. 2011. (Illus.). 78p. pap. 29.80 *(978-0-88937-336-5(1))* Hogrefe Publishing.

Jaycox, Lisa H. National Evaluation of Safe Start Promising Approaches: Assessing Program Outcomes, 1 vol. 2011. (ENG.). 82p. pap. 24.50 ***(978-0-8330-5822-5(3))*** RAND Corp., The.

Jeyarajah-Dent, Renuka & Hagell, Ann, eds. Children Who Commit Acts of Serious Interpersonal Violence: Messages for Practice. 2006. (ENG., Illus.). 256p. per. *(978-1-84310-384-4(2))* Kingsley, Jessica Ltd.

Jones, Nikki. Between Good & Ghetto: African American Girls & Inner City Violence. 2009. (Rutgers Series in Childhood Studies). (ENG.). (C). 224p. 72.00 *(978-0-8135-4614-8(1))*; 228p. pap. 22.95 *(978-0-8135-4615-5(X))* Rutgers Univ. Pr.

Jones, Russell O. Marketing Violent Entertainment to Children. 2007. (Illus.). 132p. pap. 73.00 *(978-1-59454-787-4(4))* Nova Science Pubs., Inc.

Kahn, Leora, ed. Child Soldiers. 2008. (Illus.). 120p. 45.00 *(978-1-57687-455-4(9))* powerHouse Cultural Entertainment, Inc.

Kinnell, Gretchen. No Biting: Policy & Practice for Toddler Programs. 2nd ed. 2008. (ENG.). 120p. pap. 15.95 *(978-1-933653-56-3(6))* Redleaf Pr.

Kirsh, Steven J. Children, Adolescents, & Media Violence: A Critical Look at the Research. 2nd ed. 2011. (Illus.). 408p. (C). 100.00 *(978-1-4129-9643-3(0),* B96433C); pap. 56.00 *(978-1-4129-9642-6(2),* B96433P) SAGE Pubns., Inc.

Lampinen, James M. & Sexton-radek, Kathleen J., eds. Protecting Children from Violence: Evidence Based Interventions. 2010. (ENG., Illus.). 392p. 36.95 *(978-1-84872-841-7(7))*; 78.95 *(978-1-84872-840-0(9))* Taylor & Francis Group GBR. (Psychology Press). Dist: Taylor & Francis Group.

Lebrun, Marcel. Children in Crisis: Violence, Victims, & Victories. 2011. (ENG.). 212p. 60.00 ***(978-1-61048-020-8(1))***; pap. 29.95 ***(978-1-61048-021-5(X))*** Rowman & Littlefield Education.

—Children in Crisis: Violence, Victims, & Victories. 2011. ***(978-1-61048-022-2(8))*** Rowman & Littlefield Publishers, Inc.

Lewis, James, III & Griffin, Dawn. Children Exposed to Violence: Current Issues, Interventions & Research. Zellner, Jennifer, ed. 2009. 266p. pap. 45.95 *(978-0-7890-3828-9(5))* Routledge.

—Children Exposed to Violence: Current Issues, Interventions & Research. Geffner, Bob & Zellner, Jennifer, eds. 2009. 266p. 130.00 *(978-0-7890-3827-2(7))* Routledge.

Lund, Therese Roe & Renne, Jennifer L. Child Safety: A Guide for Judges & Attorneys. 2009. *(978-1-59031-914-7(1))* American Bar Assn.

Marcovitz, Hal. Are Video Games Harmful? 2010. (In Controversy Ser.). (YA). (gr. 7-12). 26.95 *(978-1-60152-125-5(1))* ReferencePoint Pr., Inc.

Martin, Kevin J. Violent Television Programming & Its Impact on Children: Statements before the Federal Communications Commission. 2007. 39p. (C). pap. 15.00 *(978-1-4223-1516-3(9))* DIANE Publishing Co.

Paludi, Michele A., ed. The Psychology of Teen Violence & Victimization, 2 vols. 2011. (Illus.). 557p. 110.00 *(978-0-313-39375-4(3),* A3389C) Greenwood Publishing Group, Inc.

Paludi, Michele Antoinette. The Psychology of Teen Violence & Victimization. 2011. E-Book ***(978-0-313-39376-1(1),*** Praeger Pubs.) Greenwood Publishing Group, Inc.

Peltonen, Kirsi. Children & Violence: Nature, Consequences & Interventions. 2011. (Acta Universitatis Tamperensis Ser.). 102p. pap. 82.50 ***(978-951-44-8470-4(3))*** Tampere Univ. Pr. FIN. Dist: Coronet Bks.

Racford, Lorraine. Rethinking Children, Violence & Safeguarding: Attitudes in Contemporary Society. 2012. (New Childhoods Ser.). (ENG., Illus.). 184p. 120.00 *(978-1-4411-6890-0(7))*; pap. 34.95 *(978-1-84706-558-2(9))* Continuum International Publishing Group, Ltd. GBR. Dist: National Bk. Network.

Researcher, C. Q. Childhood & Adolescence in Society: Selections from CQ Researcher. 2011. (Illus.). 336p. (C). pap. 36.00 *(978-1-4129-9434-7(9),* B94347P) SAGE Pubns., Inc.

Richardson, Tom I. & Williams, Marsha V. Child Abuse & Violence. 2008. (C). 90.00 *(978-1-60456-128-9(9))* Nova Science Pubs., Inc.

Roman, Victor. Should Child Soldiers Be Punished for War Crimes? 2011. 76p. pap. ***(978-3-8454-1247-4(X))*** Lambert Academic Publishing.

Saffell, Christina. Voyeur to Violence. 2008. 196p. pap. 15.99 *(978-1-4343-5045-9(2))* AuthorHouse.

Schultz, Dana, et al. National Evaluation of Safe Start: Promising Approaches - Assessing Program Implementation. 2010. (ENG.). 290p. pap. 35.00 *(978-0-8330-4968-1(2),* tr-750) RAND Corp., The.

Seifert, Kathryn. How Children Become Violent: Keeping Your Kids Out of Gangs, Terrorist Organizations, & Cults. 2006. (Illus.). 269p. per. 19.95 *(978-1-933631-48-6(1))* Acanthus Publishing.

Seifert, Kathryn & Kohl, Ben. Youth Violence: Theory, Prevention, & Interventions. 2011. ***(978-0-8261-0740-4(0))***; E-Book ***(978-0-8261-0741-1(9))*** Springer Publishing Co., Inc.

Thomas, Donald. Freedom's Frontier: Censorship in Modern Britain. 2007. (ENG.). 1p. 59.95 *(978-0-7195-5733-0(X))* Murray, John GBR. Dist: Independent Pubs. Group.

Trawick, Margaret. Enemy Lines: Childhood, Warfare, & Play in Batticaloa. 2007. 307p. per. 26.95 *(978-0-520-24516-7(4))* Univ. of California Pr.

United States Congress Senate Committee, creator. Challenges & Solutions for Protecting Our Children from Violence & Exploitation in the 21st Century. 2010. (ENG.). 154p. pap. 21.75 ***(978-1-240-54986-3(5),*** BiblioGov) BiblioBazaar.

Your Child & Violence. 12.00 *(978-0-687-03404-8(3))* Abingdon Pr.

Your Child & Violent Play. 12.00 *(978-0-687-04423-8(5))* Abingdon Pr.

CHILDREN AND WAR

Abril Stoffels, Ruth & Stoffels, Ruth María Abril. La Protección de Los Niños en Los Conflictos Armados. 2007. (SPA.). 126p. *(978-84-8456-656-4(0))* Tirant lo Blanch.

Alvarez, Eduardo Manuel & Escobar, Arturo José, eds. Psychology of War. 2012. 230p. ***(978-1-61942-312-1(X))*** Nova Science Pubs., Inc.

Arya, Sanjaya. Use of Child Soldiers in Nepal. 2011. 116p. pap. ***(978-3-8433-9438-3(5))*** Lambert Academic Publishing.

Beier, J. Marshall, ed. The Militarization of Childhood: Thinking Beyond the Global South. 2011. (ENG., Illus.). 320p. 90.00 *(978-0-230-11576-7(4))* Palgrave Macmillan.

Bol, Aher. Lost Boy. 2010. pap. 16.95 *(978-0-7957-0278-5(7))* International Publishers Marketing.

Boothby, Neil, et al, eds. A World Turned Upside DOwn: Social Ecological Approaches to Children in War Zones. 2006. (Illus.). 288p. 69.95 *(978-1-56549-226-4(9))*; pap. 27.95 *(978-1-56549-225-7(0))* Stylus Publishing, LLC.

Carpenter, Charli. Forgetting Children Born of War: Setting the Human Rights Agenda in Bosnia & Beyond. 2010. (ENG., Illus.). 304p. (gr. 17). 35.00 *(978-0-231-15130-6(6))* Columbia Univ. Pr.

Carpenter, Charli, ed. Born of War: Protecting Children of Sexual Violence Survivors in Conflict Zones. 2007. (Illus.). 288p. pap. 24.95 *(978-1-56549-237-0(4))* Stylus Publishing, LLC.

Casualties of War: Child Soldiers & the Law: Hearing Before the Subcommittee on Human Rights & the Law of the Committee on the Judiciary, United States Senate, One Hundred Tenth Congress, First Session, April 24, 2007. 2007. iii, 105p. *(978-0-16-079848-1(5),* 552-070-36742-0) United States Government Printing Office.

Cook, Daniel Thomas & Wall, John, eds. Children & Armed Conflict: Cross-disciplinary Investigations. 2011. (Studies in Childhood & Youth Ser.) (ENG., Illus.). 240p. 85.00 *(978-0-230-27443-3(9))* Palgrave Macmillan.

Dallaire, Roméo A. They Fight Like Soldiers, They Die Like Children: The Global Quest to Eradicate the Use of Child Soldiers. 2010. (ENG.). 320p. 28.95 *(978-0-307-35577-5(2),* Random Hse CAN) Random Hse. of Canada, Ltd. CAN. Dist: Random Hse., Inc.

de Werth Neu, Sabina. A Long Silence: Memories of a German Refugee Child, 1941-1958. 2011. (ENG., Illus.). 300p. 19.00 *(978-1-61614-256-8(1))* Prometheus Bks., Pubs.

Dix, Paul. Nicaragua: Surviving the Legacy of US Policy. Just Sharing Press, ed. 2011. Tr. of Nicaragua: Sobreviviendo el Legado de la Política de los EE. UU. (ENG & SPA., Illus.). 220p. pap. 34.95 *(978-0-615-37409-3(3))* Just Sharing Pr.

Dunson, Donald H. Child, Victim, Soldier: The Loss of Innocence in Uganda. 2008. (Illus.). 160p. pap. 16.00 *(978-1-57075-799-0(2))* Orbis Bks.

Dupuy, Kendra E. & Peters, Krijn. War & Children: A Reference Handbook, 1 vol. 2009. (Contemporary Military, Strategic, & Security Issues Ser.). (Illus.). 204p. 44.95 *(978-0-313-36208-8(4),* C36208, Praeger Pubs.) Greenwood Publishing Group, Inc.

Eichstaedt, Peter. First Kill Your Family: Child Soldiers of Uganda & the Lord's Resistance Army. 2009. (ENG., Illus.). 336p. 24.95 *(978-1-55652-799-9(3),* Hill, Lawrence Bks.) Chicago Review Pr., Inc.

Filipovic, Zlata & Challenger, Melanie, eds. Stolen Voices: Young People's War Diaries, from World War I to Iraq. 2006. (ENG., Illus.). 320p. (gr. 12-18). 15.00 *(978-0-14-303871-9(0),* Penguin (Non-Classics)) Penguin Group (USA) Inc.

Fuller, Alexandra. Don't Let's Go to the Dogs Tonight. Lt. ed. 2011. lib. bdg. 33.95 *(978-1-61173-112-5(7))* Ctr. Point Large Print.

Gates, Scott & Reich, Simon, eds. Child Soldiers in the Age of Fractured States. 2010. (Security Continuum Ser.). (ENG.). 352p. (C). pap. 27.95 *(978-0-8229-6029-4(X))* Univ. of Pittsburgh Pr.

Giroux, Henry A. Hearts of Darkness: Torturing Children in the War on Terror, 1 vol. 2010. (Radical Imagination Ser.). 128p. (ENG.). pap. 19.95 *(978-1-59451-826-3(2))*; 94.00 *(978-1-59451-825-6(4))* Paradigm Pubs.

Goodyear-Brown, Paris. Play Therapy with Traumatized Children: A Prescriptive Approach. 2009. (ENG., Illus.). 378p. pap. 49.95 *(978-0-470-39524-0(9),* Wiley) Wiley, John & Sons, Inc.

C

Holland, Emily & Kamara-Umunna, Agnes. And Still Peace Did Not Come: A Memoir of Reconciliation. 2011. (ENG.). 320p. 22.99 *(978-1-4013-2357-8(X))* Hyperion Pr.

Honwana, Alcinda. Child Soldiers in Africa. 2007. (Ethnography of Political Violence Ser.). (Illus.). 216p. (C). per. 24.95 *(978-0-8122-1987-6(2))* Univ. of Pennsylvania Pr.

Jabour, Anya. Topsy-Turvy: How the Civil War Turned the World Upside down for Southern Children. 2010. (ENG., Illus.). 272p. 28.95 *(978-1-56663-632-2(9))* Dee, Ivan R. Pub.

Jagielski, Wojciech. The Night Wanderers: Uganda's Children & the Lord's Resistance Army. Lloyd-Jones, Antonia, tr. from POL. 2012. (ENG., Illus.). 288p. pap. 18.95 ***(978-1-60980-350-6(7))*** Seven Stories Pr.

Kahn, Leora, ed. Child Soldiers. 2008. (Illus.). 120p. 45.00 *(978-1-57687-455-4(9))* powerHouse Cultural Entertainment, Inc.

Lamish, Dafnah & Götz, Maya. Children & Media at Times of Conflict & War. 2007. (Hampton Press Communication Ser.). (C). *(978-1-57273-749-5(2))*; *(978-1-57273-748-8(4))* Hampton Pr., Inc.

London, Charles. One Day the Soldiers Came: Voices of Children in War. 2007. (P. S. Ser.). (Illus.). 304p. pap. 14.95 *(978-0-06-124047-8(8)*, HarperPerennial) HarperCollins Pubs.

Machel, Graca. The Impact of War on Children: A Review of Progress since the 1996 United Nations Report on the Impact of Armed Conflict on Children. (ENG., Illus.). 176p. *(978-0-7748-0867-5(5))* Univ. of British Columbia Pr.

Marten, James, ed. Children & Youth during the Civil War Era. 2012. (Children & Youth in America Ser.). (ENG., Illus.). 282p. 75.00 ***(978-0-8147-9607-8(9))***; pap. 25.00 *(978-0-8147-9608-5(7))* New York Univ. Pr.

Marten, James Alan. Children & Youth During the Civil War ERA. 2011. (Children & Youth in America Ser.). E-Book ***(978-0-8147-6339-1(1))*** New York Univ. Pr.

Montanti, Elissa & Haupt, Jennifer. I'll Stand by You: One Woman's Mission to Heal the Children of the World. 2012. (ENG., Illus.). 288p. (gr. 12). 25.95 ***(978-0-525-95295-4(0)**, Dutton Adult)* Penguin Group (USA) Inc.

Mæland, Bård. Culture, Religion, & the Reintegration of Female Child Soldiers in Northern Uganda. 2010. (Bible & Theology in Africa Ser.). 332p. (C). 84.95 *(978-1-4331-0951-5(4))* Lang, Peter Publishing, Inc.

Nutt, Samantha. Damned Nations: Greed, Guns, Armies, & Aid. (ENG.). 240p. 2012. pap. 17.99 ***(978-0-7710-5146-3(8))*** 2011. 27.95 *(978-0-7710-5145-6(X))* McClelland & Stewart CAN. (McClelland & Stewart). Dist: Random Hse., Inc.

Ossian, Lisa L. The Forgotten Generation: American Children & World War II. 2011. (ENG., Illus.). 192p. (gr. 8). 29.95 *(978-0-8262-1919-0(5))* Univ. of Missouri Pr.

Özerdem, Alpaslan & Podder, Sukanya, eds. Child Soldiers: from Recruitment to Reintegration. 2011. (ENG., Illus.). 352p. 95.00 *(978-0-230-24196-1(4))* Palgrave Macmillan.

Parsons, Martin. War Child: History Children Conflict. 2008. (ENG., Illus.). 288p. 36.95 *(978-0-7524-4293-8(7))* History Pr. Ltd., The GBR. Dist: Independent Pubs. Group.

Peters, Krijn. War & the Crisis of Youth in Sierra Leone. 2011. (International African Library). (ENG., Illus.). 296p. 90.00 ***(978-1-107-00419-1(5))*** Cambridge Univ. Pr.

Pflugfelder, Reinhold. World War II Through the Eyes of a German Child. 2011. 176p. 29.99 ***(978-1-4653-4489-2(6))***; pap. 19.99 ***(978-1-4653-4488-5(8))*** Xlibris Corp.

Powers, J. L., ed. That Mad Game: Growing up in a Warzone: an Anthology of Essays from Around the Globe. 2012. (ENG.). 300p. pap. 16.95 ***(978-1-935955-22-1(5))*** Cinco Puntos Pr.

Roman, Victor. Should Child Soldiers Be Punished for War Crimes? 2011. 76p. pap. ***(978-3-8454-1247-4(X))*** Lambert Academic Publishing.

Rosen, Ph.D., David M. Child Soldiers: A Reference Handbook, 1 vol. 2012. (Contemporary World Issues Ser.). 322p. 58.00 ***(978-1-59884-526-6(8)**,* A3024C) ABC-CLIO, LLC.

Sachs, Dana. The Life We Were Given: Operation Babylift, International Adoption, & the Children of War in Vietnam. (ENG.). 2011. 280p. pap. 20.00 *(978-0-8070-0124-0(4))* 2010. 288p. 25.95 *(978-0-8070-4241-0(2))* Beacon Pr.

Sanchez, Gervasio, photos by. Gervasio Sanchez: PHotoBolsillo. 2011. (ENG & SPA., Illus.). 112p. pap. 20.00 *(978-84-92841-15-8(X))* La Fabrica ESP. Dist: D.A.P./Distributed Art Pubs.

Schorlemer, Sabine von. Kindersoldaten und bewaffneter Konflikt: Nukleus eines umfassenden Schutzregimes der Vereinten Nationen. 2009. (Dresdner Schriften zu Recht und Politik der Vereinten Nationen. Papers on Law & Policy of the United Nations Ser.). (GER.). 426p. 86.95 *(978-3-631-58798-0(8))* Lang, Peter GmbH, Europaischer Verlag der Wissenschaften DEU. Dist: Lang, Peter.

Sheriff, Moriken. Women, Children & War. 2010. 128p. pap. *(978-3-8383-8368-2(0))* Lambert Academic Publishing.

Soto, Carlos Rodriguez. Tall Grass: Stories of Suffering & Peace in Northern Uganda. (Illus.). 286p. pap. 29.95 *(978-9970-02-733-0(6))* Michigan State Univ. Pr.

Trawick, Margaret. Enemy Lines: Childhood, Warfare, & Play in Batticaloa. 2007. 307p. 60.00 *(978-0-520-24515-0(6))*; per. 26.95 *(978-0-520-24516-7(4))* Univ. of California Pr.

UNICEF Staff & Office of the Special Representative of the Secretary- for Children and Armed Conflict. Machel Study 10-Year Strategic Review: Children & Conflict in a Changing World. 2009. (Illus.). 232p. pap. 35.00 incl. cd-rom *(978-92-806-4363-3(0))* United Nations Children's Fund, The (UNICEF).

United Nations, Office for Disarmament Affairs Staff. Conflict of Interests: Children & Guns in Zones of Instability; Panel Discussion at the United Nations; 15 July 2008, New York. 2009. (ENG., Illus.). 36p. pap. 10.00 *(978-92-1-142265-8(5))* United Nations Pubns.

Walters, Eric & Bradbury, Adrian. When Elephants Fight: The Lives of Children in Conflict in Afghanistan, Bosnia, Sri Lanka, Sudan & Uganda, 1 vol. 2012. (ENG., Illus.). 96p. (J). (gr. 5-12). pap. 14.00 ***(978-1-55469-355-9(1))*** Orca Bk. Pubs. USA.

CHILDREN AS ACTORS

see Child Actors

CHILDREN AS ARTISTS

see Child Artists

CHILDREN AS AUTHORS

see Child Authors

CHILDREN AS MUSICIANS

see Child Musicians

CHILDREN AS WITNESSES

see Child Witnesses

CHILDREN IN ADVERTISING

Clark, Eric. The Real Toy Story: Inside the Ruthless Battle for America's Youngest Consumers. 2007. (ENG.). 272p. 26.00 *(978-0-7432-4765-8(5)*, Free Pr.) Free Pr.

Faulkner, Joanne. The Importance of Being Innocent: Why We Worry about Children, 1 vol. 2010. 176p. pap. 32.99 *(978-0-521-14697-5(6))* Cambridge Univ. Pr.

Grafton, Carol Belanger, ed. Children in Old-Time Trade Cards CD-ROM & Book. 2008. (Dover Electronic Clip Art Ser.). (ENG., Illus.). 48p. pap. 22.95 *(978-0-486-99897-8(5))* Dover Pubns., Inc.

Manning, Steven. Kids for Sale. Date not set. *(978-0-312-28457-2(8))* St. Martin's Pr.

CHILDREN IN ART

see also Photography of Children and Youth

Cornacchio, Cynthia R., et al. Healing the World's Children: Interdisciplinary Perspectives on Child Health in the Twentieth Century. 2008. (McGill-Queen's/Associated Medical Services Studies in the History of Medicine, H Ser.). (ENG., Illus.). 324p. *(978-0-7735-3399-8(0))* McGill-Queen's Univ. Pr.

Daly, Jim. Our Furry Friends: Delighting in the Pets We Love. 2007. 48p. 15.99 *(978-0-7369-1913-5(9))* Harvest Hse. Pubs.

Daly, Jim, illus. Grandpa, Do You Remember When? Sharing a Lifetime of Loving Memories — A Keepsake Journal. 2007. 48p. 15.99 *(978-0-7369-1051-4(4))* Harvest Hse. Pubs.

Dewey, Simon, et al. Blessed Are the Children: The Miracle & Beauty of Childhood. 2007. (Illus.). *(978-1-59811-390-7(9))* Covenant Communications.

Golden, Janet & Weisz, George. Healing the World's Children: Interdisciplinary Perspectives on Child Health in the Twentieth Century. Comacchio, Cynthia, ed. 2008. (McGill-Queen's/Associated Medical Services Studies in the History of Medicine, H Ser.). (ENG., Illus.). 324p. pap. *(978-0-7735-3400-1(8))* McGill-Queen's Univ. Pr.

Grafton, Carol Belanger, ed. Children in Old-Time Trade Cards CD-ROM & Book. 2008. (Dover Electronic Clip Art Ser.). (ENG., Illus.). 48p. pap. 22.95 *(978-0-486-99897-8(5))* Dover Pubns., Inc.

Kames, Andrea. Pretty Baby: February 23-May 27, 2007. 2007. *(978-0-929865-26-3(X))* Modern Art Museum of Fort Worth.

Langmuir, Erika. Imagining Childhood. 2006. (ENG., Illus.). 256p. 65.00 *(978-0-300-10131-7(7))* Yale Univ. Pr.

Lee, Bev. Painting Children: Secrets to Capturing Childhood Moments. 2008. (ENG., Illus.). 128p. 29.99 *(978-1-60061-038-7(2)*, North Light Bks.) F&W Media, Inc.

Leppanen-Guerra, Analisa. Children's Stories & 'Child-Time' in the Works of Joseph Cornell & the Trans-Atlantic Avant-Garde. 2011. (Ashgate Studies in Surrealism Ser.). (Illus.). 286p. 99.95 ***(978-1-4094-0156-8(1))*** Ashgate Publishing Co.

Lerner, Loren, ed. Depicting Canada's Children. 2009. (Studies in Childhood & Family in Canada Ser.). (ENG., Illus.). 468p. 95.00 *(978-1-55458-050-7(1))* Wilfrid Laurier Univ. Pr. CAN. Dist: Univ. of Toronto Pr.

L'Estrange, Elizabeth. Holy Motherhood: Gender, Dynasty & Visual Culture in the Later Middle Ages. 2008. (Manchester Medieval Studies). (ENG., Illus.). 320p. 88.00 *(978-0-7190-7543-8(2))* Manchester Univ. Pr. GBR. Dist: Macmillan.

Lisi, Victoria. Vibrant Children's Portraits: Painting Beautiful Hair & Skin Tones with Oils. 2010. (ENG., Illus.). 128p. pap. 24.99 *(978-1-60061-314-2(4)*, North Light Bks.) F&W Media, Inc.

Ma, Yuan. Yuan M: Childhood Memories. 2011. 88p. pap. 51.99 ***(978-1-4628-9635-6(9))*** Xlibris Corp.

McRae Books. Children. 2010. (Magnet Art Bks.). (ENG.). 24p. 5.95 *(978-88-6098-164-6(6))* McRae Bks. Srl ITA. Dist: Independent Pubs. Group.

Neumeister, Mirjam, ed. The Changing Face of Childhood: British Children's Portraits & Their Influence in Europe. 2007. (Illus.). 214p. *(978-3-8321-7793-5(0))* DuMont.

Pearson, Fiona & Stevenson, Sara. Joan Eardley. 2008. (ENG., Illus.). 96p. pap. *(978-1-906270-04-9(X))* National Galleries of Scotland.

Perry, Claire. Young America: Childhood in Nineteenth-Century Art & Culture. 2006. (Illus.). xii, 236p. pap. *(978-0-937031-27-8(5))* Cantor, Iris & B. Gerald Ctr. for Visual Arts at Stanford Univ.

Schlegelmilch, Sabine. Bürger, Gott und Götterschützling: Kinderbilder der hellenistischen Kunst und Literatur. 2009. (Beiträge zur Altertumskunde Ser.).Tr. of Citizens, God & God's Chosen Ones. Portrayals of Children in Hellenistic Art & Literature. (GER., Illus.). VIII, 311p. 140.00 *(978-3-11-021765-0(1))* De Gruyter, Walter Inc.

Scudder, Horace E. Childhood in Literature & Art with Som. 2006. pap. 27.95 *(978-1-4286-3822-8(9))* Kessinger Publishing, LLC.

Snoijink, Eva. Down's Upside: A Positive View of down's Syndrome. 2008. (ENG., Illus.). 216p. 65.00 *(978-90-491-0683-6(8))* Lannoo Pubs./Racine.

Stuart Parks, Carrie & Parks, Rick. Secrets to Drawing Realistic Children. 2008. (ENG., Illus.). 128p. pap. 24.99 *(978-1-58180-963-3(8)*, North Light Bks.) F&W Media, Inc.

Thomas, Greg M. Impressionist Children: Childhood, Family, & Modern Identity in French Art. 2011. (ENG., Illus.). 240p. 65.00 *(978-0-300-11285-6(8))* Yale Univ. Pr.

Uzzi, Jeannine Diddle. Children in the Visual Arts of Imperial Rome. 2011. (ENG.). 268p. pap. 35.99 ***(978-1-107-40337-6(5))*** Cambridge Univ. Pr.

Van der Vinde, Lea. Children in the Mauritshuis. 2008. (ENG., Illus.). 72p. 29.95 *(978-90-400-8430-0(0))* Waanders B.V., Uitgeverij NLD. Dist: National Bk. Network.

Varty, Anne. Children & Theatre in Victorian Britain: All Work, No Play. 2008. (ENG., Illus.). 272p. 89.00 *(978-0-230-55155-8(6))* Palgrave Macmillan.

Zolan, Donald, illus. Puppy Love: Wiggles & Wags to Warm Your Heart. 2007. 32p. 14.99 *(978-0-7369-1802-2(7))* Harvest Hse. Pubs.

CHILDREN IN CITIES

see City Children

CHILDREN IN LITERATURE

Bernstein, Robin. Racial Innocence: Performing American Childhood & Race from Slavery to Civil Rights. 2011. E-Book ***(978-0-8147-8709-0(6))***; E-Book ***(978-0-8147-8978-0(1))*** New York Univ. Pr.

—Racial Innocence: Performing American Childhood from Slavery to Civil Rights. 2011. (ENG., Illus.). 318p. 75.00 ***(978-0-8147-8707-6(X))*** New York Univ. Pr.

—Racial Innocence: Performing Childhood & Race from Slavery to Civil Rights. 2011. (ENG., Illus.). 318p. pap. 24.00 ***(978-0-8147-8708-3(8))*** New York Univ. Pr.

Blume, Svenja & Kümmerling-Meibauer, Bettina, eds. Astrid Lindgren - Werk und Wirkung: Internationale und interkulturelle Aspekte. 2008. (Kinder- und Jugendkultur, -literatur und -medien. Theorie - Geschichte - Didaktik Ser.). (GER & ENG., Illus.). 328p. pap. 81.95 *(978-3-631-57028-9(7))* Lang, Peter GmbH, Europaischer Verlag der Wissenschaften DEU. Dist: Lang, Peter.

Chedgzoy, Kate, et al, eds. Shakespeare & Childhood. (ENG.). 2011. 298p. pap. 36.99 *(978-0-521-18284-3(0))* 2007. 296p. 110.00 *(978-0-521-87125-9(5))* Cambridge Univ. Pr.

Flegel, Monica. Creating Cruelty to Children in Nineteenth-Century England: Literature, Representation, & the NSPCC. 2009. (Ashgate Studies in Childhood, 1700 to the Present Ser.). 214p. 99.95 *(978-0-7546-6456-7(2))* Ashgate Publishing Co.

Fraser, Jennifer. Be A Good Soldier. 2011. ***(978-1-4426-4313-0(7))*** Univ. of Toronto Pr.

Fusso, Susanne. Discovering Sexuality in Dostoevsky. 2008. (Srit Ser.). (ENG.). 240p. per. 29.95 *(978-0-8101-5190-1(1))* Northwestern Univ. Pr.

Gaffney, Phyllis. Constructions of Youth in Old French Narrative: Writing the Medieval Child. 2011. 244p. 99.95 *(978-0-7546-6920-3(3))* Ashgate Publishing Co.

Gargano, Elizabeth. Reading Victorian Schoolrooms. 2012. (ENG.). 216p. pap. 39.95 ***(978-0-415-69946-4(0))*** Routledge.

Gargano, Elizabeth. Reading Victorian Schoolrooms: Childhood & Education in Nineteenth-Century Fiction. 2007. (Children's Literature & Culture Ser.). (ENG., Illus.). 216p. 125.00 *(978-0-415-98034-0(8))* Routledge.

Gavin, Adrienne E., ed. The Child in British Literature: Literary Constructions of Childhood, Medieval to Contemporary. 2012. (ENG., Illus.). 280p. 85.00 ***(978-0-230-34827-1(0))*** Palgrave Macmillan.

Gavin, Adrienne E. & Humphries, Andrew F., eds. Childhood in Edwardian Fiction: Worlds Enough & Time. 2009. (ENG., Illus.). 248p. 89.00 *(978-0-230-22161-1(0))* Palgrave Macmillan.

Gubar, Marah. Artful Dodgers: Reconceiving the Golden Age of Children's Literature, 1 vol. 2010. (ENG., Illus.). 272p. pap. 24.95 *(978-0-19-975674-2(0))* Oxford Univ. Pr., Inc.

Hancock, Susan. The Child That Haunts Us: Symbols & Images in Fairytale & Miniature Literature. 2008. (ENG., Illus.). 168p. (C). 110.00 *(978-0-415-44775-1(5))*; pap. 34.95 *(978-0-415-44776-8(3))* Routledge.

Honeyman. Consumption & Agency in Fairy Tales & Folkliterature. 2009. (Routledge Studies in Folklore & Fairy Tales Ser.). (ENG., Illus.). 246p. (C). 125.00 *(978-0-415-80614-5(3))* Routledge.

Horne, Jackie C. History & the Construction of the Child in Early British Children's Literature. 2011. (Ashgate Studies in Childhood, 1700 to the Present Ser.). (Illus.). 298p. 99.95 *(978-1-4094-0788-1(8))* Ashgate Publishing Co.

Immel, Andrea. Childhood & Children's Books in Early Modern Europe, 1550-1800. 2009. 346p. 39.95 *(978-0-415-80363-2(2))* Routledge.

Kidd, Kenneth B. Freud in OZ: At the Inter - Sections of Psychoanalysis & Children's Literature. 2011. (ENG.). 336p. pap. 25.00 ***(978-0-8166-7583-8(X))*** Univ. of Minnesota Pr.

—Freud in Oz: At the Intersections of Psychoanalysis & Children's Literature. 2011. (ENG.). 336p. 75.00 ***(978-0-8166-7582-1(1))*** Univ. of Minnesota Pr.

Lesnik-Oberstein, Karin, ed. Children in Culture, Revisited: Further Approaches to Childhood. 2011. (ENG., Illus.). 248p. 85.00 *(978-0-230-27554-6(0))* Palgrave Macmillan.

Levander, Caroline F. Cradle of Liberty: Race, the Child, & National Belonging from Thomas Jefferson to W. E. B. du Bois. 2006. (New Americanists Ser.). (ENG., Illus.). 264p. (C). 84.95 *(978-0-8223-3856-7(4))* Duke Univ. Pr.

Levander, Caroline Field. Cradle of Liberty: Race, the Child, & National Belonging from Thomas Jefferson to W. E. B. du Bois. 2006. (New Americanists Ser.). (ENG., Illus.). 264p. per. 23.95 *(978-0-8223-3872-7(6))* Duke Univ. Pr.

Locke, Richard. Critical Children: The Use of Childhood in Ten Great Novels. 2011. (Illus.). (ENG.). 232p. (gr. 17). 29.50 *(978-0-231-15782-7(7))*; 218p. E-Book *(978-0-231-52799-6(3))* Columbia Univ. Pr.

Lomax, Elaine. The Writings of Hesba Stretton: Reclaiming the Outcast. 2009. (Ashgate Studies in Childhood, 1700 to the Present Ser.). (Illus.). 252p. 114.95 *(978-0-7546-5576-3(8))* Ashgate Publishing Co.

Mallan, Kerry & Bradford, Clare, eds. Contemporary Children's Literature & Film: Engaging with Theory. 2011. (ENG., Illus.). 240p. 82.00 *(978-0-230-23149-8(7))* Palgrave Macmillan.

McGavran, James Holt, Jr., ed. Time of Beauty, Time of Fear: The Romantic Legacy in the Literature of Childhood. 2012. (ENG., Illus.). pap. 39.95 ***(978-1-60938-100-4(9))*** Univ. of Iowa Pr.

Müller, Anja. Framing Childhood in Eighteenth-Century English Periodicals & Prints, 1689-1789. 2009. (Ashgate Studies in Childhood, 1700 to the Present Ser.). (Illus.). 276p. 114.95 *(978-0-7546-6503-8(8))* Ashgate Publishing Co.

Nelson, Claudia. Precocious Children & Childish Adults: Age Inversion in Victorian Literature. 2012. (ENG.). 224p. (gr. 17). 50.00 ***(978-1-4214-0534-6(2))*** Johns Hopkins Univ. Pr.

Olga, Yazbec. Image of the Child in Fiction: Child Characters in Selected British & American Novels: A Psychoanalytic Approach. 2011. 384p. pap. ***(978-3-639-31702-2(5))*** VDM Verlag Dr. Mueller e.K.

Parille, Ken. Boys at Home: Discipline, Masculinity, & the Boy-Problem in Nineteenth-Century American Literature. 2011. (ENG.). 184p. pap. 21.00 *(978-1-57233-787-9(7))* Univ. of Tennessee Pr.

Pattison, Robert. The Child Figure in English Literature. 2008. (ENG.). 208p. pap. 24.95 *(978-0-8203-3247-5(X))* Univ. of Georgia Pr.

Pemberton, Marilyn, ed. & compiled by. Enchanted Ideologies: A Collection of Rediscovered Ninetennth-Century English Moral Fairy Tales. 2010. (ENG., Illus.). 307p. 45.00 *(978-0-9791116-5-5(X))* True Bill Pr., The.

Peters, Laura. Dickens & Childhood. 2012. (Library of Essays on Charles Dickens Ser.). 590p. 275.00 ***(978-1-4094-3041-4(3))*** Ashgate Publishing Co.

Raynard, Sophie, ed. The Teller's Tale: Lives of the Classic Fairy Tale Writers. 2012. (ENG.). 160p. 75.00 ***(978-1-4384-4355-3(2))*** State Univ. of New York Pr.

Rutter, Carol Chillington. Shakespeare & Child's-Play: Performing Lost Boys on Stage & Screen. 2007. (ENG., Illus.). 272p. 36.95 *(978-0-415-36519-2(8))*; 125.00 *(978-0-415-36518-5(X))* Routledge.

Sadrin, Anny. Parentage & Inheritance in the Novels of Charles Dickens. 2010. (European Studies in English Literature Ser.). (ENG.). 184p. pap. 26.99 *(978-0-521-17232-5(2))* Cambridge Univ. Pr.

Salvodon, Marjorie Attignol. Fictions of Childhood: The Roots of Identity in Contemporary French Narratives. 2008. (After the Empire: The Francophone World & Postcolonial France Ser.). (ENG.). 126p. 57.99 *(978-0-7391-1829-0(3))* Rowman & Littlefield Publishers, Inc.

Schlegelmilch, Sabine. Bürger, Gott und Götterschützling: Kinderbilder der hellenistischen Kunst und Literatur. 2009. (Beiträge zur Altertumskunde Ser.).Tr. of Citizens, God & God's Chosen Ones. Portrayals of Children in Hellenistic Art & Literature. (GER., Illus.). VIII, 311p. 140.00 *(978-3-11-021765-0(1))* De Gruyter, Walter Inc.

Scudder, Horace E. Childhood in Literature & Art with Som. 2006. pap. 27.95 *(978-1-4286-3822-8(9))* Kessinger Publishing, LLC.

Selwyn, David. Jane Austen & Children. 2010. (ENG., Illus.). 256p. 39.95 *(978-1-84725-041-4(6))* Continuum International Publishing Group, Ltd. GBR. Dist: National Bk. Network.

Singley, Carol J. Adopting America: Childhood, Kinship, & National Identity in Literature. 2011. (ENG.). 304p. 65.00 *(978-0-19-977939-0(2))* Oxford Univ. Pr., Inc.

Spitz, Ellen Handler. Illuminating Childhood: Portraits in Fiction, Film, & Drama. (ENG., Illus.). 214p. 2012. pap. 24.95 ***(978-0-472-03507-6(X))*** 2010. 35.00 *(978-0-472-11754-3(8))* Univ. of Michigan Pr.

Tichelaar, Tyler. King Arthur's Children: A Study in Fiction & Tradition. 2011. *(978-1-61599-067-2(4))*; pap. *(978-1-61599-066-5(6))* Loving Healing Pr., Inc. (Modern History Pr.).

Wierda Rowland, Ann. Romanticism & Childhood: The Infantilization of British Literary Culture. 2012. (Cambridge Studies in Romanticism Ser.: 93). (ENG.). 300p. 90.00 ***(978-0-521-76814-6(4))*** Cambridge Univ. Pr.

Witmore, Michael. Pretty Creatures: Children & Fiction in the English Renaissance. 2007. (Illus.). 233p. 43.95 *(978-0-8014-4399-2(7))* Cornell Univ. Pr.

CHILDREN IN POETRY

see Children in Literature

CHILDREN IN PORNOGRAPHY

see Child Pornography

CHILDREN IN THE BIBLE

Bunge, Marcia J., et al. The Child in the Bible. Bunge, Marcia J. & Gaventa, Beverly Roberts, eds. 2008. 392p. pap. 30.00 *(978-0-8028-4835-2(4))* Eerdmans, William B. Publishing Co.

Enns, Peter. Telling God's Story: A Parents' Guide to Teaching the Bible. 2011. (Telling God's Story Ser.). (ENG., Illus.). 140p. pap. 11.95 *(978-1-933339-46-7(2),* 333946) Peace Hill Pr.

Francis, James M. M. Adults as Children Vol. 17: Images of Childhood in the Ancient World & the New Testament. 2006. (Religions & Discourse Ser.: Vol. 17). 346p. pap. 68.95 *(978-0-8204-6289-9(6))* Lang, Peter Publishing, Inc.

Hensel, Benedikt. Die Vertauschung des Erstgeburtssegens in der Genesis: Eine Analyse der Narrativ-Theologischen Grundstruktur des Ersten Buches der Tora. 2011. (Beihefte zur Zeitschrift für die alttestamentliche Wissenschaft Ser.). (GER.). XIV, 387p. 182.00 **(978-3-11-024792-3(5))** De Gruyter, Walter Inc.

Mackenzie, Carine. Children of the Bible. 2009. (ENG.). 48p. 11.99 *(978-1-84550-450-2(X))* Christian Focus Pubns. GBR. Dist: STL Distribution North America.

Ninos y Mujeres en la Biblia (Children & Women in the Bible) Quarter 2, Level 2. (Caminando con Jesus (Walking with Jesus) Series A). (SPA.). tchr. ed. 3.50 *(978-0-570-05127-5(4),* 16-2802) Concordia Publishing Hse.

Rushton, Kathleen P. The Parable of the Woman in Childbirth of John 16: A Metaphor for the Death & Glorification of Jesus. 2011. 404p. 139.95 *(978-0-7734-1500-3(9))* Mellen, Edwin Pr., The.

CHILDREN OF ABUSED WIVES

Abrahams, Hilary. Rebuilding Lives after Domestic Violence: Understanding Long-Term Outcomes. 2010. (Illus.). 176p. pap. *(978-1-84310-961-7(1))* Kingsley, Jessica Ltd.

Crenshaw, Arlene R. Twelve Roses for Uretta. 2010. 64p. pap. 15.99 *(978-0-557-30920-7(4),* Lulu Enterprises Inc.

Graham-Bermann, Sandra A. & Levendosky, Alytia A. How Intimate Partner Violence Affects Children: Developmental Research, Case Studies, & Evidence-Based Intervention. 2011. xi, 314p. 69.95 *(978-1-4338-0930-9(3))* American Psychological Assn.

McCollum, Linda Ann. Every Damn Day. 2007. 80p. per. 16.95 *(978-1-4241-8161-2(5))* PublishAmerica, Inc.

Radford, Lorraine & Hester, Marianne. Mothering Through Domestic Violence. 2006. (ENG., Illus.). 176p. per. *(978-1-84310-473-5(3))* Kingsley, Jessica Ltd.

CHILDREN OF AGING PARENTS

see Adult Children

CHILDREN OF AIDS PATIENTS

Africa's Orphaned & Vulnerable Generations: Children Affected by AIDS. 2006. (Illus.). 12p. *(978-92-806-4034-2(8))* United Nations Children's Fund, The (UNICEF).

Ande, Karen & Richter, Ruthann. Face to Face: Children of the AIDS Crisis in Africa. 2010. 128p. pap. 39.95 *(978-1-932717-20-4(X))* Hope Publishing Hse.

Arogo, Grace & Mweru, Maureen. Psychosocial Impact of Hiv/Aids on Orphaned & Affected Children. 2010. 80p. pap. *(978-3-639-24790-9(6))* VDM Verlag Dr. Mueller e.K.

Ashburn, Kristen, photos by. I Am Because We Are. 2009. (ENG., Illus.). 180p. 49.95 *(978-1-57687-482-0(6))* powerHouse Cultural Entertainment, Inc.

Bukuluki, Paul. Succession Planning for Vulnerable Children. 2010. 396p. pap. *(978-3-639-24044-3(8))* VDM Verlag Dr. Mueller e.K.

Deacon, Harriet & Stephney, Inez. HIV/AIDS, Stigma & Children: A Literature Review. 2008. (ENG., Illus.). 88p. pap. 16.95 *(978-0-7969-2188-8(1))* Human Sciences Research Council ZAF. Dist: Independent Pubs. Group.

Ebersöhn, Liesel, ed. From Microscope to Kaleidoscope: Reconsidering Educational Aspects Related to Children in the HIV & AIDS Pandemic. 2008. 220p. *(978-90-8790-563-7(7));* pap. *(978-90-8790-562-0(9))* Sense Pubs.

Evans, Ruth & Becker, Saul. Children Caring for Parents with HIV & AIDS: Global Issues & Policy Responses. 2009. (Illus.). 368p. 85.00 *(978-1-84742-022-0(2));* pap. 39.95 *(978-1-84742-021-3(4))* Policy Pr. GBR. Dist: Chicago Distribution Ctr.

Greene, Melissa Fay. There Is No Me Without You: One Woman's Odyssey to Rescue Africa's Children. 2006. (ENG., Illus.). 480p. 25.95 *(978-1-59691-116-1(6))* Bloomsbury Publishing.

—There Is No Me Without You: One Woman's Odyssey to Rescue Her Country's Children. 2007. (ENG., Illus.). 480p. per. 17.00 *(978-1-59691-293-9(6))* Bloomsbury Publishing.

Kaguri, Twesigye Jackson. The Price of Stones: Building a School for My Village. 2010. lib. bdg. *(978-1-60285-836-7(5))* Ctr. Point Large Print.

Kaguri, Twesigye Jackson & Linville, Susan Urbanek. The Price of Stones: Building a School for My Village. 2010. (ENG., Illus.). 288p. (gr. 12). 25.95 *(978-0-670-02184-0(9),* Viking Adult) Penguin Group (USA) Inc.

Lloyd, Mary Elizabeth. AIDS Orphans Rising: What You Should Know & What You Can Do to Help Them Succeed. 2008. 120p. per. *(978-1-932690-47-7(6))* Loving Healing Pr., Inc.

Lloyd, Sister Mary Elizabeth. Aids Orphans Rising. 2008. 132p. 27.95 *(978-1-932690-61-3(1))* Loving Healing Pr., Inc.

Maxwell, Janine. It's Not Okay with Me. 2009. 208p. per. 14.99 *(978-1-57921-885-0(7))* WinePress Publishing.

Menuez, Douglas. Transcendent Spirit: The Orphans of Uganda. 2008. (Illus.). 156p. 35.00 *(978-0-8253-0585-6(3))* Beaufort Bks., Inc.

UNICEF Staff. Africa's Orphaned & Vulnerable Generations: Children Affected by AIDS. 2006. (Illus.). 48p. pap. 15.00 *(978-92-806-4035-9(6))* United Nations Children's Fund, The (UNICEF).

United Nations Children's Fund. Caring for Children Affected by HIV & AIDS. 2008. (Insight Innocenti Ser.). (Illus.). 56p. pap. 20.00 *(978-88-89129-48-7(4))* United Nations Children's Fund, The (UNICEF).

CHILDREN OF ALCOHOLICS

see also Adult Children of Alcoholics

Al-Anon Family Group Headquarters, Inc Staff, contrib. by. Opening Our Hearts: Transforming Our Losses. 2007. x, 193p. pap. *(978-0-910034-47-0(8))* Al-Anon Family Group Headquarters, Inc.

Barry, Nicola. Mother's Ruin. 2008. (ENG.). 304p. pap. 13.95 *(978-0-7553-1674-8(6))* Headline Bk. Publishing GBR. Dist: Independent Pubs. Group.

Blackburn, Julia. The Three of Us: A Family Story. 2009. (Vintage Ser.). (ENG., Illus.). 320p. pap. 16.00 *(978-0-307-27893-7(X),* Vintage) Knopf Doubleday Publishing Group.

Blow, Simon. No Time to Grow Shattered Childhood. (Illus.). 262p. 35.00 *(978-0-7195-5442-1(X))* Murray, John GBR. Dist: Trafalgar Square Publishing.

Centre For Addiction And Mental Health. Wishes & Worries: Coping with a Parent Who Drinks Too Much Alcohol. 2011. (Coping Ser.). (ENG., Illus.). 32p. (J). (gr. k-3). 17.95 *(978-1-77049-238-7(0))* Tundra Bks., Inc./Livres Toundra, Inc. CAN. Dist: Random Hse., Inc.

Cooley, Michael G. Rock Bottom: From the Streets to Success. 2011. pap. 16.99 *(978-1-61739-738-7(5))* Tate Publishing & Enterprises, LLC.

Cram101 Textbook Reviews & Cram101 Textbook Reviews. Outlines & Highlights for Parents Who Misuse Drugs & Alcohol: Effective Interventions in Social Work & Child Protection by Donald Forrester. 2011. 162p. pap. 29.95 **(978-1-61830-566-4(2))** Cram101 Inc.

Curtis, Patricia. Legends of the Plastic Chairs. 2007. 204p. per. 19.95 *(978-1-59858-463-9(4))* Dog Ear Publishing, LLC.

Encyclopaedia Britannica, Inc., compiled by. When Your Parents Drink. 2008. 49.95 *(978-1-59339-635-0(X))* Encyclopaedia Britannica, Inc.

Hammond, Adam. Alcohol in the Home: What Should the Church Do? 2010. 124p. pap. 11.95 *(978-1-61507-297-2(7))* Cross Bks. Publishing.

Heaps, Emelyn. Heaps of Trouble. 2011. (ENG.). 248p. pap. 23.95 *(978-1-84889-041-1(9))* Collins Pr., The IRL. Dist: Dufour Editions, Inc.

Helget, Nicole Lea. The Summer of Ordinary Ways. 2007. 182p. per. 14.95 *(978-0-87351-588-7(9),* Borealis Bk.) Minnesota Historical Society Pr.

Long, Al. Alone in a Crowd: One Mentor, One Child, One Journey. 2007. (Illus.). 184p. pap. 14.95 *(978-0-9787268-9-8(8))* Power Publishing.

Lowe, Anna. Wake Up, Mummy: An Abused Little Girl - A Mother Too Drunk to Notice. 2011. (ENG.). 320p. pap. 12.95 **(978-0-09-194051-5(6))** Ebury Publishing GBR. Dist: Independent Pubs. Group.

McCall, Catherine. Lifeguarding: A Memoir of Secrets, Swimming, & the South. 2006. (Illus.). 272p. 23.00 *(978-1-4000-9818-7(1),* Harmony) Crown Publishing Group.

Munro, Eileen. If I Should Die Before I Wake. 2012. (ENG.). 272p. pap. 14.95 **(978-1-84596-616-4(3))** Mainstream Publishing Co., Ltd. GBR. Dist: Independent Pubs. Group.

O'Connor, Ed. D. I Can Be Me: A Helping Book for Children of Alcoholic Parents. 2009. 184p. pap. 14.95 *(978-1-4259-9899-8(2))* AuthorHouse.

Schaffer, Lesley Ann. Pet People: Surviving the Alcoholic Home. 2006. (ENG.). 23.50 *(978-1-59330-426-3(9));* pap. 10.95 *(978-1-59330-425-6(0))* Aventine Pr.

Schulz, Pat J. Making Sweet Lemonade. 2007. (ENG.). 160p. per. 21.95 *(978-0-9654899-6-6(5))* ENHEART Publishing.

Walls, Jeannette. The Glass Castle: A Memoir. lt. ed. 2009. lib. bdg. 33.95 *(978-1-60285-557-1(9))* Ctr. Point Large Print.

—The Glass Castle: A Memoir. 2009. 14.45 *(978-0-7848-1813-8(4),* Everbind) Marco Bk. Co.

—The Glass Castle: A Memoir. 2009. (ENG.). 304p. 30.00 *(978-1-4391-5696-4(4),* Scribner) Scribner.

CHILDREN OF DIVORCED PARENTS

see also Adult Children of Divorced Parents; Children of Single Parents

Ackerman, Marc J. "Does Wednesday Mean Mom's House or Dad's?" Parenting Together While Living Apart. 2nd ed. 2008. (ENG.). 245p. per. 24.95 *(978-0-470-12753-7(8),* Wiley) Wiley, John & Sons, Inc.

Andrews, Julian. Parental-Alienation Playbook & Three-Quarters Custody: A Father Speaks Out. 2011. 80p. 18.95 **(978-1-4620-6343-7(8));** pap. 8.95 **(978-1-4620-6341-3(1))** iUniverse, Inc.

Arterburn, Cheri. The Perfect Divorce II: Children, Cheaters, Choices. 2006. pap. 16.95 *(978-0-9753049-1-4(7))* BCC Publishing.

Atlantic Publishing Group. The Complete Guide to Shared Parenting after Divorce: What You Need to Know to Co-Raise Your Children Successfully. 2012. (ENG.). 288p. pap. 24.95 *(978-1-60138-576-5(5))* Atlantic Publishing Co.

Azzopardi, Charlie. Talking about Separation. 2008. (ENG & MLT.). 48p. (C). pap. 9.95 *(978-99932-7-238-0(8))* Midsea Bks. Ltd. MLT. Dist: Brown, David Bk. Co., The.

—Telling your child about Separation. 2008. (ENG & MLT.). 79p. (C). pap. 10.00 *(978-99932-7-240-3(X))* Midsea Bks. Ltd. MLT. Dist: Brown, David Bk. Co., The.

—Will They Still Love Me? 2008. (ENG & MLT.). 16p. (C). pap. 9.00 *(978-99932-7-242-7(6))* Midsea Bks. Ltd. MLT. Dist: Brown, David Bk. Co., The.

Baksh, Nadir & Murphy, Laurie. In the Best Interest of the Child: A Manual for Divorcing Parents. 2007. 132p. per. 16.95 *(978-1-890772-73-4(9))* Hohm Pr.

Bernet, William & Ash, Don R. Children of Divorce: A Practical Guide for Parents, Therapists, Attorneys, & Judges. 2nd ed. 2007. 196p. 31.50 *(978-1-57524-288-0(5))* Krieger Publishing Co.

Bertram, Anita Gee. Relationships: Divorced Grandparents & their Grandchildren. 2008. 88p. pap. *(978-3-639-03628-2(X))* VDM Verlag Dr. Mueller e.K.

Blackstone-Ford, Jann & Jupe, Sharyl. Ex-Etiquette for Holidays & Other Family Celebrations. 2007. (ENG.). 144p. pap. 12.95 *(978-1-55652-719-7(5))* Chicago Review Pr., Inc.

Burrett, Jill, et al. Shared Parenting: Raising Your Children Cooperatively after Separation. 2009. (ENG., Illus.). 160p. pap. 15.99 *(978-1-58761-346-3(9),* Celestial Arts) Ten Speed Pr.

Cantelo, Anne. It's No Big Deal Really: A Parent's Guide to Making Divorce Easy for Children. 2008. (ENG.). 256p. pap. 19.95 *(978-1-905745-24-1(9))* Vision Paperbacks GBR. Dist: Independent Pubs. Group.

Castro, Joy. Island of Bones: Essays. 2012. (American Lives Ser.). (ENG.). 144p. pap. 16.95 **(978-0-8032-7142-5(5),** Bison Bks.) Univ. of Nebraska Pr.

Cochran, Cate. Reconcilable Differences: Marriages End, Families Don't. 2007. (ENG., Illus.). 288p. pap. 19.95 *(978-1-897187-29-6(7))* Second Story Pr. CAN. Dist: Univ. of Toronto Pr.

Corcoran, Ross, et al. Joint Custody with a Jerk: Raising a Child with an Uncooperative Ex - A Hands-On, Practical Guide to Communicating with a Difficult Ex-Spouse. rev. ed. 2011. (ENG., Illus.). 304p. pap. 15.99 *(978-0-312-58420-7(2),* St. Martin's Griffin) St. Martin's Pr.

Daisley, Errol. Marriage vs. Katrina, the Spirit of Divorce. 2007. (ENG.). 140p. per. 11.95 *(978-0-7414-3767-9(8))* Infinity Publishing.

Darnall, Doug. Divorce Casualties, Second Edition: Keeping Your Children Close While You're Breaking Apart. 2nd ed. 2008. (ENG.). 304p. pap. 16.95 *(978-1-58979-376-7(5))* Taylor Trade Publishing.

Darnall, Douglas. Beyond Divorce Casualties: Reunifying the Alienated Family. 2010. (ENG.). 224p. pap. 16.95 *(978-1-58979-415-3(X))* Taylor Trade Publishing.

Drozd, Leslie M., ed. Relocation Issues in Child Custody Cases. 2007. (ENG., Illus.). 198p. per. 54.95 *(978-0-7890-3534-9(0))* Routledge.

Encyclopaedia Britannica, Inc., compiled by. When Your Parents Divorce. 2008. 49.95 *(978-1-59339-650-3(3))* Encyclopaedia Britannica, Inc.

Favaro, Peter J. Smart Parenting During & after Divorce: The Essential Guide to Making Divorce Easier on Your Child. 2008. (ENG.). 256p. pap. 16.95 *(978-0-07-159755-5(7),* 0071597557) McGraw-Hill Cos., The.

Fidler, Barbara Jo, et al. Children Who Resist Post-Separation Parental Contact: A Differential Approach for Legal & Mental Health Professionals, 1 vol. 2012. (American Psychology-Law Society Ser.). (ENG.). 328p. pap. 75.00 **(978-0-19-989549-6(X))** Oxford Univ. Pr., Inc.

Fishman, Nancy. Raising Happy Children after Divorce: What to Do When Children Have Divorce Stress. 2010. (ENG.). 96p. pap. 9.95 *(978-1-879094-89-5(4))* Momentum Bks., LLC.

—Two Homes, One World: Divorce & the Reconstituted Family. 2010. (ENG.) 112p. pap. 9.95 *(978-1-879094-88-8(6))* Momentum Bks., LLC.

Flesberg, Evon O. The Switching Hour: Kids of Divorce Say Good-Bye Again. 2008. (Illus.). 119p. 14.00 *(978-0-687-64976-1(5))* Abingdon Pr.

Garber, Benjamin D. Keeping Kids Out of the Middle: Child-Centered Parenting in the Midst of Conflict, Separation, & Divorce. 2008. (ENG.). 292p. pap. 14.95 *(978-0-7573-0711-9(6))* Health Communications, Inc.

Grant, Emma S. Divorced, Now What? A Recovery Plan for Divorced Women with Children. 2011. 48p. pap. 13.99 **(978-1-4567-6572-9(8))** AuthorHouse.

Hannibal, Mary Ellen. Good Parenting Through Your Divorce: The Essential Guidebook to Helping Your Children Adjust & Thrive — Based on the Leading National Program. 2nd ed. 2006. (ENG.). 304p. per. 18.00 *(978-1-56924-257-5(7))* Da Capo Pr., Inc.

Harvey, John H. Children of Divorce: Stories of Loss & Growth. 2nd rev. ed. 2010. (ENG., Illus.). 192p. pap. 31.95 *(978-0-415-87258-4(8),* Routledge) Taylor & Francis Group GBR. Dist: Taylor & Francis Group.

Harvey, John H. & Fine, Mark A. Children of Divorce: Stories of Loss & Growth. 2nd rev. ed. 2010. (ENG., Illus.). 192p. 52.95 *(978-0-415-87256-0(1),* Routledge) Taylor & Francis Group GBR. Dist: Taylor & Francis Group.

Heard-Martin, Lcsw. When Families Change: All about Stepfamilies. 2008. 96p. pap. 28.99 *(978-1-4343-2005-6(7))* AuthorHouse.

Hemreich, Joseph & Marcus, Paul. Warring Parents, Wounded Children, & the Wretched World of Child Custody: Cautionary Tales, 1 vol. 2007. 144p. 39.95 *(978-0-313-34973-7(8),* C34973, Praeger Pubs.) Greenwood Publishing Group, Inc.

Henley, Joy. Off the Papers: What the Family Court Drama Taught, 1 vol. 2009. 196p. pap. 24.95 *(978-1-61546-711-2(4))* PublishAmerica, Inc.

Hill, Kim & Harper, Lisa. Hope No Matter What: Helping Your Children Heal after Divorce. 2008. (ENG., Illus.). 80p. per. 14.99 *(978-0-8307-4515-9(7))* Gospel Light Pubns.

Hill, Natasha. Parent Survival Kit: Divorce Edition. 2008. 56p. pap. 21.95 *(978-1-59858-552-0(5))* Dog Ear Publishing, LLC.

Hutchby, Ian. The Discourse of Child Counselling. 2007. 114.00 *(978-90-272-1859-9(5));* xi, 144p. pap. 39.95 *(978-90-272-1860-5(9))* Benjamins, John Publishing Co.

Irvine, Holli. Bittersweet Mayfair Memories. 2011. 160p. pap. 14.95 **(978-1-4620-2146-8(8))** Universe, Inc.

Johnston, Janet R., et al. In the Name of the Child: A Developmental Approach to Understanding & Helping Children of Conflicted & Violent Divorce. 2nd ed. 2009. (Illus.). 400p. *(978-0-8261-1127-2(0))* Springer.

Just, Marjorie. Divorce Decisions: Practical Ways to Protect Yourself, Your Children, & Your Wallet. 2009. 176p. pap. 10.00 *(978-1-932102-84-9(5))* Capital Bks., Inc.

Kellner, Ellen. The Pro-Child Way: Parenting with an Ex. 2010. 128p. pap. 15.00 *(978-0-9820834-3-7(2))* UnTapped Talent LLC.

Kids First. Kids First: What Kids Want Adults to Know about Separation & Divorce. 2008. 142p. per. 14.95 *(978-1-932056-73-0(4),* Towers Maguire Publishing) Local History Co., The.

Klein, Manuela. Die Bedeutung von Trennung und Scheidung für die Bindung des Kindes. 2010. (Europäische Hochschulschriften. Reihe 6: Psychologie Ser.). (GER.). 122p. pap. 28.95 *(978-3-631-60004-7(6))* Lang, Peter GmbH, Europäischer Verlag der Wissenschaften DEU. Dist: Lang, Peter.

Kuehnle, Kathryn & Drozd, Leslie, eds. Parenting Plan Evaluations: Applied Research for the Family Court, 1 vol. 2012. (ENG., Illus.). 640p. 79.99 **(978-0-19-975402-1(0))** Oxford Univ. Pr., Inc.

LaMotte, Elisabeth Joy. Overcoming Your Parents' Divorce: 5 Steps to a Happy Relationship. 2008. (ENG.) 224p. (gr. 8-12). pap. 14.95 *(978-0-88282-329-4(9))* New Horizon Pr. Pubs., Inc.

Lippman, Jessica G. & Lewis, Paddy Greenwall. Divorcing with Children: Expert Answers to Tough Questions from Parents & Children, 1 vol. 2008. 184p. 39.95 *(978-0-275-99311-5(6),* C9311, Praeger Pubs.) Greenwood Publishing Group, Inc.

Lowenstein, L. F. Parental Alienation: How to Understand & Address Parental Alienation Resulting from Acrimonious Divorce or Separation. 2007. 232p. (C). pap. 69.95 *(978-1-905541-10-2(4))* Russell Hse. Publishing Ltd. GBR. Dist: International Specialized Bk. Services.

Lowenstein, Liana. Creative Interventions for Children of Divorce. 2006. (Illus.). 175p. *(978-0-9685199-3-6(8))* Champion Pr.

Maclean, Mavis, ed. Parenting after Partnering: Containing Conflict after Separation. 2007. (ENG.). 240p. 100.00 *(978-1-84113-781-0(2));* 229p. pap. 48.00 *(978-1-84113-782-7(0))* Hart Publishing Ltd. GBR. Dist: International Specialized Bk. Services.

Margerum, Judith, et al. Take Control of Your Divorce: Strategies to Stop Fighting & Start Co-Parenting. 2010. pap. 18.95 *(978-1-886230-97-2(5))* Impact Pubs., Inc.

Marquardt, Elizabeth. Between Two Worlds: The Inner Lives of Children of Divorce. 2006. (ENG.). 288p. pap. 13.95 *(978-0-307-23711-5(7),* Three Rivers Pr.) Crown Publishing Group.

Marsolini, Maxine. Raising Children in Blended Families: Helpful Insights, Expert Opinions, & True Stories. 2006. 176p. pap. 11.99 *(978-0-8254-3355-9(X))* Kregel Pubns.

McWilliams, Joan H. Parenting Plans for Families after Divorce. 2011. 153p. pap. 15.00 **(978-0-9768663-0-5(7))** McWilliams Mediation Group Ltd.

Millar, Paul. The Best Interests of Children: An Evidence-Based Approach. 2009 (Illus.). (ENG.). 140p. *(978-0-8020-9890-0(8));* xiv, 139p. pap. *(978-0-8020-9593-0(3))* Univ. of Toronto Pr.

Nowinski, Joseph. The Divorced Child: Strengthening Your Family through the First Three Years of Separation. 2010. (ENG.). 240p. pap. 17.00 *(978-0-230-61772-8(7))* Palgrave Macmillan.

Oates, Elizabeth. Dealing with Divorce Leader's Guide, 1 vol. 2008. (ENG.). 160p. pap. 14.99 *(978-0-310-27887-0(2))* Zondervan.

—Dealing with Divorce Student's Guide, 1 vol. 2008. (ENG.). 128p. pap. 9.99 *(978-0-310-27886-3(4))* Zondervan.

Pedro-Carroll, JoAnne. Putting Children First: Proven Parenting Strategies for Helping Children Thrive Through Divorce. 2010. (ENG.). 352p. (gr. 12). 16.00 *(978-1-58333-401-0(7),* Avery) Penguin Group (USA) Inc.

Price, Margaret "Pegi". Divorce & the Special Needs Child: A Guide for Parents. 2010. (ENG., Illus.). 256p. pap. *(978-1-84905-825-4(3))* Kingsley, Jessica Ltd.

Reynolds, Lisa René. Parenting Through Divorce: Helping Your Children Thrive During & after the Split. 2011. (ENG.). 288p. pap. 15.95 *(978-1-61608-442-4(1),* 608442) Skyhorse Publishing Co., Inc.

Ricker, Muriel M. When the Walls Come Tumbling Down. 2011. 108p. 24.99 **(978-1-4568-5027-2(X));** pap. 15.99 **(978-1-4568-5026-5(1))** Xlibris Corp.

Robinson, Joyce A. I was a waif & child Servant... No Regrets. 2008. 492p. 30.99 *(978-1-4343-4730-5(3))* AuthorHouse.

Ross, Melanie. Fractured Families - Pathways to Sex Work in Nairobi, Keny. 2009. 84p. pap. *(978-3-639-10748-7(9))* VDM Verlag Dr. Mueller e.K.

Schab, Lisa. The Divorce Workbook for Children: Help for Kids to Overcome Difficult Family Changes & Grow up Happy. 2008. (Instant Help Ser.). (ENG.) 152p. (J). pap. 32.95 *(978-1-57224-659-1(6))* Play2Grow.

Schab, Lisa & New Harbinger Publications Staff. Divorce Workbook for Children: Activities to Help Kids Grow up Happy & Healthy Despite Difficult Family Changes. 2008. (Instant Help Ser.). 138p. pap. 16.95 *(978-1-931704-42-7(2),* Play2Grow.

Schab, Lisa M. & Schab, Lisa. The Divorce Workbook for Children: Help for Kids to Overcome Difficult Family Changes & Grow up Happy. 2008. (Instant Help Ser.). (ENG., Illus.). 152p. (J). (gr. 4-7). pap. 16.95 *(978-1-57224-601-0(4))* Play2Grow.

Scott, Phillip. A Voice for the Children, 1 vol. 2009. 57p. pap. 16.95 *(978-1-61582-538-7(X))* PublishAmerica, Inc.

Shaker, Ellen. Children are Not Chess Pieces: The Game of Divorce. 2011. 104p. pap. 14.99 **(978-1-4634-1465-3(X))** AuthorHouse.

Sheff, David. Beautiful Boy: A Father's Journey Through His Son's Addiction. lt. ed. 2008. 464p. lib. bdg. 32.95 *(978-1-60285-294-5(4))* Ctr. Point Large Print.

C

—Beautiful Boy: A Father's Journey Through His Son's Addiction. 2009. (ENG.). 336p. pap. 14.95 *(978-0-547-20388-1(8))* Houghton Mifflin Harcourt Publishing Co.

—Mi hijo Precioso: El viaje de un padre a través de la adicción de su Hijo. 2009. (Vintage Espanol Ser.). (SPA.). 400p. pap. 14.95 *(978-0-307-45568-0(8),* Vintage) Knopf Doubleday Publishing Group.

Sindell, Max. The Bright Side: Surviving Your Parents' Divorce. 2007. (ENG.). 128p. (J). (gr. 4-7). pap. 12.95 *(978-0-7573-0625-9(X))* Health Communications, Inc.

Spencer, Madeline A. A Shattered Life an Amazing God: When Fear Collides with Love. 2009. 364p. pap. 20.99 *(978-1-61579-259-7(7))* Xulon Pr., Inc.

Stahl, Philip M. & Drozd, Leslie M., eds. Relocation Issues in Child Custody Cases. 2007. (Illus.). 181p. pap. 175.00 *(978-0-7890-3533-2(2))* Routledge.

Steakley, Kristine. Child of Divorce, Child of God: A Journey of Hope & Healing. 2008. (ENG.). 181p. pap. 15.00 *(978-0-8308-3471-6(0),* IVP Bks.) InterVarsity Pr.

Suggs, Lisa. Choices: When Divorce Happens to You & Your Children. 2010. pap. 10.99 *(978-1-61566-829-8(2))* Tate Publishing & Enterprises, LLC.

Tessman, Lora Heims. Children of Parting Parents. 2nd ed. *(978-1-56821-055-1(8),* Aronson, Jason) Rowman & Littlefield Publishers, Inc.

Warshak, Richard A. Divorce Poison: How to Protect Your Family from Bad-Mouthing & Brainwashing. rev. ed. 2010. (ENG.). 336p. pap. 14.99 *(978-0-06-186326-4(2),* William Morrow Paperbacks) HarperCollins Pubs.

Weaver, Nancy. What? My Parents Are Getting a Divorce? 2008. 108p. 21.49 *(978-1-4389-1043-7(6));* pap. 15.49 *(978-1-4389-1042-0(8))* AuthorHouse.

Wells, Rosemary. Helping Children Cope with Divorce. 3rd ed. 128p. *(978-0-85969-901-3(3),* Sheldon Press) SPCK Publishing.

Whitepen, Baldy. Horsefeathers, Chaos, & Tragedy. 2010. 156p. 19.95 *(978-1-4269-2957-1(9));* pap. 9.95 *(978-1-4269-2956-4(0))* Trafford Publishing.

Wolfelt, Alan D. & Maloney, RaeLynn. Healing a Child's Heart after Divorce: 100 Practical Ideas for Families, Friends, & Caregivers. 2011. (Healing a Grieving Heart Ser.). (ENG.). 128p. pap. 11.95 *(978-1-61722-142-2(2))* Companion Pr.

Woodall, Karen & Woodall, Nick. Putting Children First: A Handbook for Separated Parents. 2009. (ENG., Illus.). 256p. pap. 17.95 *(978-0-7499-2804-9(2))* Piatkus Bks. GBR. Dist: Independent Pubs. Group.

Woodall, Karen & Woodall, Nick. The Guide for Separated Parents: Putting Your Children First. 2010. (ENG.). 288p. pap. 15.95 *(978-0-7499-4000-3(X))* Piatkus Bks. GBR. Dist: Independent Pubs. Group.

CHILDREN OF DRUG ADDICTS

see also Adult Children of Drug Addicts

Boyce, Lucas Daniel. Living Proof: From Foster Care to the White House & the NBA. 2011. (ENG.). 228p. pap. 16.99 *(978-1-59932-257-5(9))* Advantage Media Group.

Brouwer, Thomas P. Parents with Substance Use Disorders & Child Protection Issues. 2011. (Children's Issues, Laws & Programs Ser.). viii, 280p. 195.00 *(978-1-60692-400-6(1))* Nova Science Pubs., Inc.

Finnegan, Loretta P. & Kandall, Stephen R., eds. Women, Children, & Addiction. 2011. (ENG.). 176p. (C). 125.00 *(978-0-415-60103-0(7))* Routledge.

Haight, Wendy L., et al. Children of Methamphetamine-Involved Families: The Case of Rural Illinois. 2008. (ENG., Illus.). 288p. 35.00 *(978-0-19-532605-5(9))* Oxford Univ. Pr., Inc.

Itzkoff, Dave. Cocaine's Son: A Memoir. 2011. (ENG.). 240p. 24.00 *(978-1-4000-6572-1(0),* Villard Bks.) Random House Publishing Group.

Krochta, Denise. Sweat: A Practical Plan for Keeping Your Heart Intact While Loving an Addict. 2010. 120p. pap. 12.95 *(978-1-60844-346-8(9))* Dog Ear Publishing, LLC.

Marcum, Ryan. The Diary of a Three-Year-Old, & Life Thereafter. 2007. 76p. per. 16.95 *(978-1-4137-4381-4(1))* PublishAmerica, Inc.

Murray, Liz. Breaking Night: A Memoir of Forgiveness, Survival, & My Journey from Homeless to Harvard. (ENG.). 352p. 2011. pap. 14.99 *(978-1-4013-1059-2(1))* 2010. 24.99 *(978-0-7868-6891-9(0))* Hyperion Pr.

—Breaking Night: A Memoir of Forgiveness, Survival, & My Journey from Homeless to Harvard. l.t. ed. 2011. 625p. 31.99 *(978-1-4104-3340-4(4))* Thorndike Pr.

Rebecca Diamond. Saving the Kids a Grandmother's Story. 2010. 128p. 23.95 *(978-1-4502-0050-9(8));* pap. 13.95 *(978-1-4502-0049-3(4))* iUniverse, Inc.

Salter, Shane. When a Child Becomes the Four-Year-Old Parent... Trouble Don't Last Always. 2006. 217p. pap. 13.95 *(978-0-7414-3695-5(7))* Infinity Publishing.

CHILDREN OF GAY PARENTS

Andrews, Helena. Bitch Is the New Black: A Memoir. 2011. 256p. pap. 14.99 *(978-0-06-177884-1(2),* Harper Paperbacks) HarperCollins Pubs.

Cahill, Sean & Tobias, Sarah. Policy Issues Affecting Lesbian, Gay, Bisexual, & Transgender Families. 2006. (ENG., Illus.). 184p. pap. 22.95 *(978-0-472-03061-3(2))* Univ. of Michigan Pr.

Foster, Deborah. The Experiences of Planned Two-Mother Families. 2008. 160p. pap. *(978-3-639-08140-4(4))* VDM Verlag Dr. Mueller e.K.

Hayden, A., et al. Children & Same Sex Families: A Legal Handbook. 2012. 400p. pap. 110.00 ***(978-1-84661-319-7(1))*** Jordan Publishing, Ltd. GBR. Dist: International Specialized Bk. Services.

Sember, Brette McWhorter. Gay & Lesbian Medical Rights: How to Protect Yourself, Your Partner, & Your Family. 2006. (Illus.). 219p. per. 14.99 *(978-1-56414-896-4(3))* Career Pr., Inc.

Stefanowicz, Dawn. Out from Under: The Impact of Homosexual Parenting. 2007. 245p. per. 14.95 *(978-1-59977-011-6(3))* Annotation Pr.

Tasker. Lesbian & Gay Parenting: New Directions. 2007. 130.00 *(978-0-7890-3106-8(X))* Routledge.

Tasker, Fiona L. & Bigner, Jerry J. Gay & Lesbian Parenting: New Directions. 2007. pap. 78.95 *(978-0-7890-3107-5(8))* Routledge.

Taylor, Yvette. Lesbian & Gay Parenting: Securing Social & Educational Capital. 2009. (ENG.). 224p. 95.00 *(978-0-230-20272-6(1))* Palgrave Macmillan.

Thomas-Jones, Deborah & Shinew, Dawn. Redefining Family- an in-Depth Exploration of Youth with Lesbian Parents. 2007. 180p. per. *(978-3-8364-2714-2(1))* VDM Verlag Dr. Mueller e.K.

CHILDREN OF GOD

see also God—Fatherhood

Burke, Trevor J. The Message of Sonship. 2011. (Bible Speaks Today Bible Themes Ser.). (ENG.). 244p. pap. 20.00 ***(978-0-8308-2413-7(8),*** IVP Acad.) InterVarsity Pr.

Marshall, Timothy. Where Have All the Stars Gone? Man's Light Working Hard to Hide God's Light. 2009. 120p. pap. 11.49 *(978-1-4490-4573-9(1))* AuthorHouse.

Wilsenach, Louis. Journal of Blessings. 2009. 60p. pap. 23.99 *(978-1-4490-3266-1(4))* AuthorHouse.

Yeary, Clifford M. Pilgrim People: A Scriptural Commentary. 2010. 11.95 *(978-0-8146-3333-5(1));* E-Book 7.95 *(978-0-8146-3926-9(7))* Liturgical Pr.

CHILDREN OF GOD (MOVEMENT)

Lattin, Don. Jesus Freaks: A True Story of Murder & Madness on the Evangelical Edge. 2008. 256p. pap. 13.95 *(978-0-06-111806-7(0),* HarperOne) HarperCollins Pubs.

Shepherd, Gordon & Shepherd, Gary. Talking with the Children of God: Prophecy & Transformation in a Radical Religious Group. 2010. (ENG., Illus.). 272p. 85.00 *(978-0-252-03534-0(8));* pap. 28.00 *(978-0-252-07721-0(0))* Univ. of Illinois Pr.

CHILDREN OF HANDICAPPED PARENTS

see Children of Parents with Disabilities

CHILDREN OF HOLOCAUST SURVIVORS

Adorján, Johanna. An Exclusive Love: A Memoir. Bell, Anthea, tr. 2012. (ENG.). 192p. pap. 14.95 ***(978-0-393-34055-6(4),*** 34055) Norton, W. W. & Co., Inc.

Bar-On, Dan. Tell Your Life Story: Creating Dialogue among Jews & Germans, Israelis & Palestinians. 2006. 250p. 41.95 *(978-963-7326-70-7(7))* Central European Univ. Pr.

Brysk, Miriam. Amidst the Shadows of Trees: A Holocaust Child's Survival in the Partisans. 2006. (Illus.). 183p. pap. 14.95 *(978-0-9788747-0-4(6))* Yellow Star Pr.

Danieli, Yael, ed. International Handbook of Multigenerational Legacies of Trauma. 2010. (Springer Series on Stress & Coping Ser.). 734p. pap. 209.00 *(978-1-4419-3287-7(9),* 1441932879) Springer.

Ehrenreich, Jake. A Jew Grows in Brooklyn: The Curious Reflections of a First-Generation American. 2010. (ENG.). 264p. pap. 14.95 *(978-0-7573-1466-7(X))* Health Communications, Inc.

Einhorn, Erin. The Pages in Between: A Holocaust Legacy of Two Families, One Home. 2009. (ENG.). 288p. pap. 16.00 *(978-1-4165-5831-6(4),* Touchstone) Touchstone.

Eisenstein, Bernice. I Was a Child of Holocaust Survivors. 2007. (ENG., Illus.). 192p. pap. 19.99 *(978-0-7710-3064-2(9),* McClelland & Stewart) McClelland & Stewart CAN. Dist: Random Hse., Inc.

Fass, Paula. Inheriting the Holocaust: A Second-Generation Memoir. 2011. (ENG., Illus.). 210p. (C). pap. 22.95 ***(978-0-8135-5193-7(5))*** Rutgers Univ. Pr.

Fass, Paula S. Inheriting the Holocaust: A Second-Generation Memoir. 2008. (ENG.). 210p. 35.95 *(978-0-8135-4458-8(0))* Rutgers Univ. Pr.

Grimwood, Marita & Le, Grimwood. Holocaust Literature of the Second Generation. 2007. (ENG.). 192p. 84.00 *(978-1-4039-7980-3(4))* Palgrave Macmillan.

Hirsch, Marianne. The Generation of Postmemory: Writing & Visual Culture after the Holocaust. 2012. (Gender & Culture Ser.). (ENG., Illus.). 320p. (gr. 17). 89.50 ***(978-0-231-15652-3(9))*** Columbia Univ. Pr.

—The Generation of Postmemory: Writing & Visual Cultures after the Holocaust. 2012. (Gender & Culture Ser.). (ENG., Illus.). 320p. (gr. 17). pap. 27.50 ***(978-0-231-15653-0(7))*** Columbia Univ. Pr.

Kliot, Rasia & Mitsios, Helen. Waltzing with the Enemy: A Mother & Daughter Confront the Aftermath of the Holocaust. 2011. (Illus.). 287p. pap. 19.95 ***(978-1-936068-21-0(4),*** Penina Pr.) Urim Pubns. ISR. Dist: Coronet Bks.

Kogan, Ilany. The Struggle Against Mourning. 2007. (ENG., Illus.). 282p. 78.99 *(978-0-7657-0508-2(7));* per. 41.99 *(978-0-7657-0507-5(9))* Rowman & Littlefield Publishers, Inc. (Aronson, Jason).

Lemelman, Martin. Two Cents Plain: My Brooklyn Boyhood. 2010. (ENG.). 320p. 26.00 *(978-1-60819-004-1(8))* Bloomsbury Publishing.

Lev-Wiesel, Rachel. Hell Within Hell: Sexually Abused Child Holocaust Survivors. 2011. (ENG.). 96p. pap. 18.50 *(978-0-7618-5477-7(0))* Univ. Pr. of America, Inc.

Magal, Alicia Fleissig. From Miracle to Miracle: A Story of Survival. 2011. 167p. pap. 19.95 *(978-1-4327-6058-8(0))* Outskirts Pr., Inc.

McGlothlin, Erin. Second-Generation Holocaust Literature: Legacies of Survival & Perpetration. 2006. (Studies in German Literature Linguistics & Culture Ser.). (Illus.). 264p. 80.00 *(978-1-57113-352-6(6))* Camden Hse.

Meyerhoff, Marianne. Four Girls from Berlin: A True Story of a Friendship That Defied the Holocaust. 2007. (ENG., Illus.). 256p. 24.95 *(978-0-471-22405-1(7),* Wiley) Wiley, John & Sons, Inc.

Raphael, Lev. My Germany: A Jewish Writer Returns to the World His Parents Escaped. (ENG., Illus.). 2011. 236p. pap. 19.95 ***(978-0-299-23154-5(2))*** 2009. 224p. 26.95 *(978-0-299-23150-7(X))* Univ. of Wisconsin Pr.

Rosenthal, Gabriele. The Holocaust in Three Generations: Families of Victims & Perpetrators of the Nazi Regime. 2nd rev. ed. 2010. 389p. pap. 58.00 *(978-3-86649-282-0(0))* Budrich-Esser, Barbara DEU. Dist: International Specialized Bk. Services.

Rudavsky, Oren & Daum, Menachem. Hiding & Seeking. 2011. 320p. 13.99 *(978-0-06-076085-4(0),* HarperPerennial) HarperCollins Pubs.

Schwab, Gabriele. Haunting Legacies: Violent Histories & Transgenerational Trauma. 2010. (ENG.). 256p. (gr. 17). 79.50 *(978-0-231-15256-3(6));* pap. 26.50 *(978-0-231-15257-0(4))* Columbia Univ. Pr.

Sontag, Eleanor. Second Generation. 2011. 84p. 24.99 ***(978-1-4568-2366-5(3));*** pap. 15.99 ***(978-1-4568-2365-8(5))*** Xlibris Corp.

Spiegelman, Art. Gift. 2009. (SPA.). 168p. pap. 15.95 *(978-607-07-0205-1(0))* Editorial Seix Barral ESP. Dist: Perseus Distribution.

—Gift. 2009. 14.72 *(978-0-7848-0772-9(8),* Everbind) Marco Bk. Co.

—Maus: A Survivor's Tale. tchr.'s training gde. ed. *(978-0-394-26528-5(9),* Vintage) Knopf Doubleday Publishing Group.

—Maus II: A Survivor's Tale: And Here My Troubles Began. 2010. (SPA.). 144p. pap. 15.95 *(978-950-04-1423-4(6))* Editorial Planeta, S. A. ESP. Dist: Perseus Distribution.

—Maus II: A Survivor's Tale: And Here My Troubles Began. 2009. 14.72 *(978-0-7848-0773-6(6),* Everbind) Marco Bk. Co.

Weisz, Mischa & Hemsworth, Wade. I Choose to Live: A Self-Made Millionaire Faces Cancer. 2009. (ENG., Illus.). 168p. 35.00 *(978-1-55488-718-7(6))* Dundurn CAN. Dist: Ingram Pub. Services.

CHILDREN OF HOMOSEXUAL PARENTS

see Children of Gay Parents

CHILDREN OF IMMIGRANTS

Adams, Leah D., ed. Global Migration & Education: Schools, Children, & Families. 2006. (Illus.). 349p. 145.00 *(978-0-8058-5837-2(7));* per. 47.95 *(978-0-8058-5838-9(5))* Erlbaum, Lawrence Assocs., Inc.

Agbese, Ajeori. The Role of Intercultural Communication in Conflict Resolution. 2010. 84p. pap. *(978-3-8383-2159-2(6))* Lambert Academic Publishing.

Alam, M. Y., ed. The Invisible Village: Small World, Big Society. 2011. (ENG.). 288p. pap. 18.95 ***(978-1-901927-46-7(6))*** Route GBR. Dist: Dufour Editions, Inc.

Alba, Richard D. The Next Generation: Immigrant Youth in a Comparative Perspective. Waters, Mary C. & Alba, Richard, eds. 2011. (ENG., Illus.). 382p. 75.00 *(978-0-8147-0742-5(4))* New York Univ. Pr.

Alba, Richard D. & Waters, Mary C. The Next Generation: Immigrant Youth in a Comparative Perspective. 2011. E-Book *(978-0-8147-0762-3(9))* New York Univ. Pr.

Alba, Richard D. & Waters, Mary C., eds. The Next Generation: Immigrant Youth in a Comparative Perspective. 2011. (ENG., Illus.). 382p. pap. 25.00 *(978-0-8147-0743-2(2))* New York Univ. Pr.

Areepattamannil, Shaljan. Self-Determination & Achievement. 2010. 192p. pap. *(978-3-639-18816-5(0))* VDM Verlag Dr. Mueller e.K.

Ascher, Carol. Afterimages: A Family Memoir. 2008. (Illus.). 240p. 24.00 *(978-0-8419-1449-0(4))* Holmes & Meier Pubs., Inc.

Ballenger, Cynthia. Puzzling Moments, Teachable Moments: Practicing Teacher Research in Urban Classrooms. 2010. (Practitioners Inquiry Ser.). (ENG., Illus.). 160p. 58.00 *(978-0-8077-4994-4(X));* pap. 24.95 *(978-0-8077-4993-7(1))* Teachers College Pr., Teachers College, Columbia Univ.

Bennett, Jo. Care & Advocacy Narratives from a School for Adolescent Immigrants. 2012. 85.99 ***(978-1-61735-660-5(3));*** pap. 45.99 ***(978-1-61735-659-9(X));*** E-Book ***(978-1-61735-661-2(1))*** Information Age Publishing, Inc.

Bhabha, Jacqueline, ed. Children Without a State: A Global Human Rights Challenge. 2011. (ENG., Illus.). 392p. (gr. 17). 32.00 *(978-0-262-01527-1(7))* MIT Pr.

Bhalla, A. S. & McCormick, Peter. Poverty among Immigrant Children in Europe. 2009. (ENG., Illus.). 248p. 105.00 *(978-0-230-22104-8(1))* Palgrave Macmillan.

Bogomolny, Abby, ed. New to North America: Writing by U. S. Immigrants, Their Children & Grandchildren, Second Edition. 2nd ed. 2007. (ENG.). 358p. 29.95 *(978-0-9650665-6-3(8))* Burning Bush Pubns.

Campano, Gerald. Immigrant Students & Literacy: Reading, Writing, & Remembering. (Practitioner Inquiry Ser.). (ENG., Illus.). 160p. 2007. pap. 23.95 *(978-0-8077-4732-2(7))* 2006. 50.00 *(978-0-8077-4733-9(5))* Teachers College Pr., Teachers College, Columbia Univ.

Campbell, Sean. Irish Blood English Heart: Second Generation Irish Musicians in England. 2011. (Illus.). 280p. 55.00 *(978-1-85918-461-5(8))* Cork Univ. Pr. IRL. Dist: Stylus Publishing, LLC.

Campbell, Sean. Irish Blood, English Heart: Second Generation Irish Musicians in England. 2011. (Illus.). 280p. pap. 34.95 ***(978-1-85918-490-5(1))*** Cork Univ. Pr. IRL. Dist: Stylus Publishing, LLC.

Cejudo, Henry & Plaschke, Bill. American Victory: Wrestling, Dreams & a Journey Toward Home. 2011. (ENG.). 240p. (gr. 12). 15.00 *(978-0-451-23203-8(8),* Celebra) Penguin Group (USA) Inc.

Chang-Muy, Fernando & Congress, Elaine Piller. Social Work with Immigrants & Refugees: Legal Issues, Clinical Skills, & Advocacy. 2008. 336p. 60.00 *(978-0-8261-3335-9(5))* Springer Publishing Co., Inc.

Chinn, Sarah E. Inventing Modern Adolescence: The Children of Immigrants in Turn-of-the-Century America. 2008. (Rutgers Series in Childhood Studies). (ENG., Illus.). 216p. (C). 70.00 *(978-0-8135-4309-3(6));* pap. 25.95 *(978-0-8135-4310-9(X))* Rutgers Univ. Pr.

Choi, Ye Ri. Chinese Immigrant Children's Social Relationships. 2010. 84p. pap. *(978-3-8383-4341-9(7))* Lambert Academic Publishing.

Chuang, Susan & Moreno, Robert P. Immigrant Children: Change, Adaptation, & Cultural Transformation. 2011. (ENG., Illus.). 330p. 75.00 *(978-0-7391-2390-4(4))* Lexington Bks.

Chuang, Susan S. & Moreno, Robert P. Immigrant Children: Change, Adaptation, & Cultural Transformation. 2011. *(978-0-7391-6706-9(5))* Lexington Bks.

Chung, Angie. Legacies of Struggle: Conflict & Cooperation in Korean American Politics. 2007. (ENG., Illus.). 344p. 65.00 *(978-0-8047-5657-0(0))* Stanford Univ. Pr.

Chung, Angie Y. Legacies of Struggle: Conflict & Cooperation in Korean American Politics. 2007. (ENG., Illus.). 344p. per. 24.95 *(978-0-8047-5658-7(9))* Stanford Univ. Pr.

Coe, Cati, et al, eds. Everyday Ruptures: Children, Youth, & Migration in Global Perspective. 2011. (ENG.). 240p. 59.95 *(978-0-8265-1747-0(1));* pap. 27.95 *(978-0-8265-1748-7(X))* Vanderbilt Univ. Pr.

Conde-Frazier, Elizabeth. Listen to the Children/Escuchemos a los Ninos: Conversations with Immigrant Families/Conversaciones con familias Inmigrantes. 2011. (ENG & SPA.). 160p. pap. 13.99 *(978-0-8170-1661-6(9))* Judson Pr.

Cressey, Gill. Diaspora Youth & Ancestral Homeland: British Pakistani /Kashmiri Youth Visiting Kin in Pakistan & Kashmir. 2006. (Muslim Minorities Ser.: Vol. 5). 221p. *(978-90-04-15346-2(2))* BRILL.

Dettlaff, Alan & Fong, Rowena, eds. Child Welfare Practice with Immigrant Children & Families. 2011. (ENG.). 176p. (C). 125.00 *(978-0-415-68469-9(2))* Routledge.

Dicketmnller, Yvonne. Being Left Behind. 2008. 104p. pap. *(978-3-8364-4620-4(0))* VDM Verlag Dr. Mueller e.K.

Dimitrova, Radosveta. The Immigrant Child. 2009. 116p. pap. *(978-3-639-17614-8(6))* VDM Verlag Dr. Mueller e.K.

Don-Yihya, Eliezer. Mashber U-Temurah Bi-Medinah Hadashah: Hinukh, Dat U-Politikah Ba-Maavak Al Ha-Aliyah Ha-Gedolah. 2008. (HEB.). 515p. *(978-965-217-280-8(4))* Yad Izhak Ben-Zvi.

Donato, Ruben. Mexicans & Hispanos in Colorado Schools & Communities, 1920-1960. (Illus.). 180p. 2008. per. 24.95 *(978-0-7914-6968-2(9))* 2007. 55.00 *(978-0-7914-6967-5(0))* State Univ. of New York Pr.

Dong Jie. Discourse, Identity, & China's Internal Migration: The Long March to the City. 2011. (Encounters Ser.). (Illus.). 176p. (ENG.). 119.95 *(978-1-84769-420-1(9));* pap. 39.95 *(978-1-84769-419-5(5))* Multilingual Matters GBR. Dist: Univ. of Toronto Pr.

Duque-Paramo, Maria Claudia. Food as a Function of Cultural Identity among Immigrant Children: An Ethnographic Study. 2009. (Illus.). 360p. 119.95 *(978-0-7734-4696-0(6))* Mellen, Edwin Pr., The.

Dyrness, Andrea. Mothers United: An Immigrant Struggle for Socially Just Education. 2011. 264p. 69.00 *(978-0-8166-7466-4(3));* pap. 22.95 *(978-0-8166-7467-1(1))* Univ. of Minnesota Pr.

Ehrenreich, Jake. A Jew Grows in Brooklyn: The Curious Reflections of a First-Generation American. 2010. (ENG.). 264p. pap. 14.95 *(978-0-7573-1466-7(X))* Health Communications, Inc.

Eijgu, Addisu Birhanu. Livelihood. 2009. 112p. pap. *(978-3-639-21383-6(1))* VDM Verlag Dr. Mueller e.K.

Ensor, Marisa O. & Gozdziak, Elzbieta M., eds. Children & Migration: At the Crossroads of Resiliency & Vulnerability. 2010. (ENG., Illus.). 272p. 95.00 *(978-0-230-27253-8(3))* Palgrave Macmillan.

Faulkner, Caroline L. Economic Mobility & Cultural Assimilation among Children of Immigrants. 2011. 67.00 ***(978-1-59332-472-8(3))*** LFB Scholarly Publishing LLC.

Feliciano, Cynthia. Unequal Origins: Immigrant Selection & the Education of the Second Generation. 2006. (New Americans). (Illus.). 190p. lib. bdg. 55.00 *(978-1-59332-087-4(6))* LFB Scholarly Publishing LLC.

Fereidooni, Karim. Schule - Migration - Diskriminierung: Ursachen der Benachteiligung von Kindern mit Migrationshintergrund im deutschen Schulwesen. 2011. (GER., Illus.). 176p. pap. *(978-3-531-17635-2(8))* Westdeutscher Verlag GmbH.

Fujiwara, Lynn. Mothers Without Citizenship: Asian Immigrant Families & the Consequences of Welfare Reform. 2008. (Illus.). 272p. 67.50 *(978-0-8166-5075-0(6));* pap. 22.50 *(978-0-8166-5076-7(4))* Univ. of Minnesota Pr.

Garcia-Coll, C. The Impact of Immigration on Children's Development. 2011. (Contributions to Human Development Ser.). (ENG., Illus.). 154p. pap. ***(978-3-8055-9798-2(3))*** Karger, S. AG.

García Coll, Cynthia T. & Marks, Amy Kerivan. The Immigrant Paradox in Children & Adolescents: Is Becoming American a Developmental Risk? 2011. 69.95 ***(978-1-4338-1053-4(0))*** American Psychological Assn.

García Coll, Cynthia T. & Marks, Amy Kerivan. Immigrant Stories: Ethnicity & Academics in Middle Childhood. 2009. (Child Development in Cultural Context Ser.). (Illus.). 304p. 39.95 *(978-0-19-517459-5(3))* Oxford Univ. Pr., Inc.

Georgescu, Simona Adriana. Immigrant Children in Norwegian Kindergartens. 2011. 104p. pap. ***(978-3-8433-9460-4(1))*** Lambert Academic Publishing.

Gerngross, Günter & Puchta, Herbert. Playway to English Level 1 Pupil's Book. 2nd ed. 2009. (ENG.). 84p. pap. 19.66 *(978-0-521-12996-1(6))* Cambridge Univ. Pr.

—Playway to English Level 1 Teacher's Book. 2nd ed. 2009. (ENG.). 176p. pap. 38.22 *(978-0-521-12990-9(7))* Cambridge Univ. Pr.

Gerngross, Günter, et al. Playway to English Level 1 Activity Book with CD-ROM. 2nd ed. 2009. (ENG.). 84p. pap. 24.15 incl. cd-rom *(978-0-521-12993-0(1))* Cambridge Univ. Pr.

—Playway to English Level 1 Teacher's Resource Pack with Audio CD. 2nd ed. 2009. (ENG.). 80p. pap. 39.31 incl. audio compact disk *(978-0-521-12987-9(7))* Cambridge Univ. Pr.

Gowens, Judith, ed. Migrant Education 2009. 2nd rev. ed. 2010. (gr. 4-6). 145.00 *(978-1-59237-293-5(7))* Grey Hse. Publishing.

Grigorenko, Elena. Immigration, Diversity, & Education. Grigorenko, Elena L. & Takanishi, Ruby, eds. 2009. (ENG., Illus.). 320p. 145.00 *(978-0-415-45627-2(4))* Routledge.

Hajratwala, Minal. Leaving India: My Family's Journey from Five Villages to Five Continents. 2009. (ENG., Illus.). 352p. 26.00 *(978-0-618-25129-2(4))* Houghton Mifflin Harcourt Trade & Reference Pubs.

Hariton, Leon. The Making of an American. 2009. 308p. pap. 21.95 *(978-0-595-50948-5(7))* iUniverse, Inc.

Harris, Yvette R. & Bergen, Doris. Children & Families of African Origin: A Guide for Educators & Service Providers. 2008. pap. *(978-0-87173-173-9(8))* Assn. for Childhood Education International.

Hashim, Iman & Thorsen, Dorte. Child Migration in Africa. 2011. (Africa Now Ser.). (ENG., Illus.). 160p. (C). pap. 39.95 *(978-1-84813-456-0(8))*; 240p. 125.95 *(978-1-84813-455-3(X))* Zed Bks., Ltd. GBR. Dist: Palgrave Macmillan, Macmillan.

Hauser, Brooke. The New Kids: Big Dreams & Brave Journeys at a High School for Immigrant Teens. 2011. (ENG.). 320p. 26.00 *(978-1-4391-6328-3(6))*, Free Pr.) Free Pr.

Haynes, Judie. Getting Started with English Language Learners: How Educators Can Meet the Challenge. 2007. (Illus.). 163p. per. 23.95 *(978-1-4166-0519-5(3))* Assn. for Supervision & Curriculum Development.

Holton, Gerald & Sonnert, Gerhard, eds. Helping Young Refugees & Immigrants Succeed: Public Policy, Aid, & Education. 2010. (ENG.). 328p. 95.00 *(978-0-230-62196-1(1))* Palgrave Macmillan.

Housel, Teresa Heinz & Harvey, Vickie L. The Invisibility Factor: Administrators & Faculty Reach Out to First-Generation College Students. 2009. 158p. pap. 25.95 *(978-1-59942-523-8(8))*, Brown Walker Pr.) Universal Pubs.

Hugger, Kai-Uwe. Junge Migranten online: Suche nach sozialer Anerkennung und Vergewisserung von Zugehörigkeit. 2009. (GER., Illus.). 321p. pap. *(978-3-531-16151-8(2))* Westdeutscher Verlag GmbH.

Human Rights Watch (Organization) Staff, contrib. by. Denied Status, Denied Education: Children of North Korean Women in China. 2008. (Illus.). 21p. *(978-1-56432-304-0(8))* Human Rights Watch.

ICE Workplace Raids: Their Impact on U.S. Children, Families, & Communities: Hearing Before the Subcommittee on Workforce Protections, Committee on Education & Labor, U.S. House of Representatives, One Hundred Tenth Congress, Second Session, Hearing Held in Washington, DC, May 20, 2008. 2008. (Illus.). iv, 96p. *(978-0-16-082752-5(3)*, 552-070-38757-9) United States Government Printing Office.

Irby, Caroline, photos by. A Child from Everywhere: Photographs & Interviews of Children from 185 Countries in the UK. 2010. (ENG., Illus.). 160p. pap. 24.95 *(978-1-906155-93-3(3))* Black Dog Publishing Ltd. GBR. Dist: Perseus Distribution.

Jaramillo, Nathalia E. Immigration & the Challenge of Education: A Social Drama Analysis in South Central Los Angeles. 2011. (Education, Politics & Public Life Ser.). (ENG & SPA., Illus.). 194p. 85.00 ***(978-0-230-33826-5(7))***; pap. 28.00 ***(978-0-230-33827-2(5))*** Palgrave Macmillan.

Jensen, Peter & Rasmussen, Astrid Wurtz. Immigrant & Native Children's Cognitive Outcomes & the Effect of Ethnic Concentration in Danish Schools Num. 20: Study Paper. 2008. 47p. pap. 13.00 *(978-87-7674-369-7(1))* Univ. Pr. of Southern Denmark DNK. Dist: International Specialized Bk. Services.

Kasinitz, Philip. Becoming New Yorkers: Ethnographies of the New Second Generation. Mollenkopf, John H. & Waters, Mary, eds. 2006. 432p. pap. 24.95 *(978-0-87154-437-7(7))* Russell Sage Foundation.

Kasinitz, Philip, et al. Inheriting the City: The Children of Immigrants Come of Age. 2008. (Russell Sage Foundation Books at Harvard University Press Ser.). (Illus.). 432p. 52.50 *(978-0-674-02803-6(1))* Harvard Univ. Pr.

Kearney, George R. More Than a Dream: The Cristo Rey Story: How One School's Vision Is Changing the World. 2008. (ENG., Illus.). 424p. 22.95 *(978-0-8294-2576-5(4))* Loyola Pr.

Klapper, Melissa R., ed. Small Strangers: The Experiences of Immigrant Children in America, 1880-1925. 2007. (American Childhoods Ser.). (ENG., Illus.). 256p. 27.50 *(978-1-56663-733-6(3))* Dee, Ivan R. Pub.

Klinker, Sonja. Maghrebiner in Frankreich, Türken in Deutschland: Eine vergleichende Untersuchung zu Identität und Integration muslimischer Einwanderergruppen in europäische Mehrheitsgesellschaften. 2010. (Hildesheimer Schriften zur Interkulturellen Kommunikation Ser.). (GER.). 358p. 86.95 *(978-3-631-59940-2(4))* Lang, Peter GmbH, Europaischer Verlag der Wissenschaften DEU. Dist: Lang, Peter.

Kugler, Eileen. Innovative Voices in Education: Engaging Diverse Communities. 2012. (ENG.). 308p. (gr. 17). pap. 38.95 ***(978-1-61048-540-1(8))*** Rowman & Littlefield Education.

Kugler, Eileen, et al. Innovative Voices in Education: Engaging Diverse Communities. 2012. (ENG.). 308p. (gr. 17). 80.00 ***(978-1-61048-539-5(4))*** Rowman & Littlefield Education.

Kugler, Eileen Gale. Innovative Voices in Education: What It Takes to Engage Diverse Communities. 2011. E-Book ***(978-1-61048-541-8(6))*** Rowman & Littlefield Education.

Kupe, Tawana & Worby, Eric, eds. Go Home or Die Here: Violence, Xenophobia & the Reinvention of Difference in South Africa. 2009. (ENG.). 272p. pap. 34.95 *(978-1-86814-487-7(9))*; Witwatersrand Univ. Pr. Pubns. ZAF. Dist: Transaction Pubs.

Landale, Nancy, et al, eds. Growing up Hispanic: Health & Development of Children of Immigrants. 2010. 368p. pap. 32.50 *(978-0-87766-763-6(2))* Urban Institute Pr.

Laurino, Maria. Old World Daughter, New World Mother: An Education in Love & Freedom. 2009. (ENG.). 224p. 23.95 *(978-0-393-05728-7(3)*, 5728) Norton, W. W. & Co., Inc.

Legendary Publications. Extra! Extra! the Orphan Trains & Newsboys of New York, Vol. 1. 2010. (ENG., Illus.). 180p. 29.95 *(978-0-615-29755-2(2))* Legendary Pubns.

—Extra! Extra! the Orphan Trains & Newsboys of New York, Vol. 1. 2009. (Illus.). 180p. pap. 29.95 *(978-0-615-30930-9(5))* Legendary Pubns.

Li, Guofang. Multicultural Families, Home Literacies, & Mainstream Schooling. 2009. 312p. *(978-1-60752-036-8(2))*; pap. *(978-1-60752-035-1(4))* Information Age Publishing, Inc.

Li, Minhui. A Heart-to-Heart Talk with Parents & Students. 2010. (ENG & CHI., Illus.). 148p. pap. 16.50 *(978-0-9788198-2-8(9))* Chang, Joyce.

Lin, Jun. Parental Expectations of Chinese Immigrants for Children's School Achievement: Sociocultural Context, Psychological Adjustment, & Educational Consequences. 2009. 232p. 109.95 *(978-0-7734-4837-7(3))* Mellen, Edwin Pr., The.

Lopez/Lopez. Persistent Inequality: Contemporary Realities in the Education of Undocumented. 2009. (ENG., Illus.). 224p. pap. 39.95 *(978-0-415-95794-6(X))* Routledge.

Madmoni-Gerber, Shoshana & Madmoni-gerber, Shoshana. Israeli Media & the Framing of Internal Conflict: The Yemenite Babies Affair. 2009. (ENG., Illus.). 240p. 89.00 *(978-0-230-61346-1(2))* Palgrave Macmillan.

Mounsi. Territoire D'outre-Ville. (FRE.). 124p. *(978-2-234-04411-1(1))* Stock, Editions.

Nasaw, David. Children of the City: At Work & at Play. 2012. (ENG., Illus.). 256p. pap. 15.95 ***(978-0-345-80297-2(7)***, Anchor) Knopf Doubleday Publishing Group.

Nazario, Sonia. Enrique's Journey. 2007. (Illus.). 299p. 22.60 *(978-0-7569-9042-8(4))* Perfection Learning Corp.

—Enrique's Journey. 2007. (ENG., Illus.). 336p. pap. 16.00 *(978-0-8129-7178-1(7)*, Random Hse. Trade Paperbacks) Random House Publishing Group.

Ogbu, John U. Minority Status, Oppositional Culture & Schooling. 2008. (Sociocultural, Political, & Historical Studies in Education). (ENG., Illus.). 688p. 56.95 *(978-0-8058-5104-5(6))* Routledge.

Ogbu, John U., ed. Minority Status, Oppositional Culture & Schooling. 2008. (Sociocultural, Political, & Historical Studies in Education). (ENG., Illus.). 688p. 170.00 *(978-0-8058-5103-8(8))* Routledge.

Olsen, Laurie. Made in America: Immigrant Students in Our Public Schools. 10th rev. anniv. ed. 2008. (ENG.). 276p. pap. 18.95 *(978-1-59558-349-9(1))* New Pr., The.

Orellana, Marjorie Faulstich. Translating Childhoods: Immigrant Youth, Language, & Culture. 2009. (Rutgers Series in Childhood Studies). (ENG.). 224p. (C). 68.00 *(978-0-8135-4522-6(6))*; pap. 22.95 *(978-0-8135-4523-3(4))* Rutgers Univ. Pr.

Organisation for Economic Co-operation and Development. Equal Opportunities? The labour market integration of the children of Immigrants. 2010. (Illus.). 258p. pap. 5.00 *(978-92-64-08239-7(5))* Organization for Economic Cooperation & Development.

Parenting among Christian Immigrants in the United States. 2009. 64p. pap. 15.99 *(978-1-4415-7098-7(5))* Xlibris Corp.

Park, Clara C., et al, eds. New Perspectives on Asian American Parents, Students, & Teacher Recruitment. 2009. (Illus.). 236p. 85.99 *(978-1-60752-092-4(3))*; pap. 45.99 *(978-1-60752-091-7(5))* Information Age Publishing, Inc.

Park, Hyu-Yong. Raising Ambi-Lingual Children. 2008. 176p. pap. *(978-3-639-11255-9(5))* VDM Verlag Dr. Mueller e.K.

Parker, Roy. Uprooted: The Shipment of Poor Children to Canada, 1867-1917. 2010. (Illus.). 376p. pap. 34.95 *(978-1-84742-668-0(9))* Policy Pr. GBR. Dist: Chicago Distribution Ctr.

Penn, Roger D., et al. Children of International Migrants in Europe: Comparative Perspectives. 2009. (ENG., Illus.). 256p. 84.00 *(978-0-230-01879-2(3))* Palgrave Macmillan.

Peréa, Flavia C. Language, Gender, & Academic Performance: A Study of the Children of Dominican Immigrants. 2011. 168p. 65.00 *(978-1-59332-390-5(5))* LFB Scholarly Publishing LLC.

Philip, Cheri L. Asian American Identity: Racial & Ethnic Identity Issues in the Twenty-First Century. 2007. (ENG.). 236p. (C). 99.95 *(978-1-934043-62-2(1))* Cambria Pr.

Phillion, JoAnn, et al, eds. Minority Students in East Asia: Government Policies, School Practices & Teacher Responses. 2011. (Routledge Series on Schools & Schooling in Asia Ser.). (ENG., Illus.). 280p. (C). 125.00 *(978-0-415-88839-4(5))* Routledge.

Pirinen, Maija. In Place, Out of Place: Meaning of Place & Question of Belonging for Adult Third Culture Kids. 2008. 88p. pap. *(978-3-639-09863-1(3))* VDM Verlag Dr. Mueller e.K.

Poon-McBrayer, Kim Fong. Partnership Challenges with Asian Immigrant Parents. 2011. 68p. pap. ***(978-3-8443-1461-8(X))*** Lambert Academic Publishing.

Preissle, Judith & Rong, Xue Lan. Educating Immigrant Students in the 21st Century: What Educators Need to Know. 2nd ed. 2008. (Illus.). 344p. pap. 41.95 *(978-1-4129-4095-5(8)*, B4094XP) Corwin Pr.

—Educating Immigrant Students in the 21st Century: What Educators Need to Know. 2nd ed. 2008. (Illus.). 344p. 90.95 *(978-1-4129-4094-8(X)*, B4094XC) Corwin Pr.

Pung, Alice. Unpolished Gem: My Mother, My Grandmother, & Me. 2009. (ENG.). 304p. (gr. 12-18). 16.00 *(978-0-452-29000-6(7)*, Plume) Penguin Group (USA) Inc.

Ragazzi, Rossella. Walking on Uneven Paths: The Transcultural Experience of Children Entering Europe in the Years 2000. 2009. 240p. pap. *(978-3-0343-0042-1(5))* Lang, Peter.

Reyes-Cruz, Mariolga. Mexican Immigrant Parents Advocating for School Reform. 2008. (New Americans). 208p. 60.00 *(978-1-59332-236-6(4))* LFB Scholarly Publishing LLC.

Rodriguez, Nora. Educar Desde el Locutorio: Ayuda a Que Tus Hijos Sigan Creciendo Contigo. 2008. (Plataforma Actual Ser.). (SPA.). 135p. pap. 21.00 ***(978-84-96981-03-4(7))*** Plataforma Editorial SL ESP. Dist: Independent Pubs. Group.

Rutter, Jill. Worlds on the Move: Educational Responses to Changing Migration Patterns. 2011. 220p. pap. 36.95 *(978-1-85856-375-6(5))* Trentham Bks. Ltd. GBR. Dist: Stylus Publishing, LLC.

Saran, Rupam & Diaz, Rosalina, eds. Beyond Stereotypes: Minority Children of Immigrants in Urban Schools. 2010. 248p. *(978-94-6091-079-1(3))*; pap. *(978-94-6091-078-4(5))* Sense Pubs.

Sardar, Ziauddin. Balti Britain: A Journey Through the British Asian Experience. 2009. (ENG.). 392p. pap. 16.95 *(978-1-84708-082-0(0))* Granta Bks. GBR. Dist: Independent Pubs. Group.

—Balti Britain: Journeys Through the British Asian Experience. 2008. (ENG.). 416p. 37.95 *(978-1-86207-931-1(5))* Granta Bks. GBR. Dist: Independent Pubs. Group.

Schmid, Stefan. Integration als Ideal - Assimilation als Realitat: Vorstellungen von jungen Deutschen und turkischstammigen Migranten uber ein Leben in Deutschland. 2010. (GER.). 310p. (C). 63.00 *(978-3-89971-783-9(X)*, Vandenhoeck & Ruprecht GmbH & Co. KG DEU. Dist: ISD.

Schneider, Jens & Crul, Maurice, eds. Theorising Integration & Assimilation. 2012. (Ethnic & Racial Studies). (ENG., Illus.). 144p. (C). 125.00 *(978-0-415-68002-8(6))* Routledge.

Shah, Bindi V. Laotian Daughters: Working toward Community, Belonging, & Environmental Justice. 2011. (Asian American History & Culture Ser.). (ENG.). 216p. 87.50 *(978-1-4399-0813-6(3))*; pap. 28.95 *(978-1-4399-0815-0(X))* Temple Univ. Pr.

Shah, Bindi V. Laotian Daughters: Working Toward Community, Belonging, & Environmental Justice. 2011. E-Book ***(978-1-4399-0816-7(8))*** Temple Univ. Pr.

Smidt, Sandra. Supporting Multilingual Learners in the Early Years: Many languages - many Children. 2008. (Nursery World/Routledge Essential Guides for Early Years Practitioners Ser.). (Illus.). VIII, 152p. 32.50 *(978-0-415-43801-8(2))* Routledge.

—Supporting Multilingual Learners in the Early Years: Many Languages, Many Children. 2007. (Nursery World/Routledge Essential Guides for Early Years Practitioners Ser.). (Illus.). VIII, 152p. 130.00 *(978-0-415-43800-1(4))* Routledge.

Sorondo, Marcelo Sanchez & Pierre, Lena, eds. Globalization & Education. 2007. (ENG., Illus.). XXI, 285p. 112.00 *(978-3-11-019113-4(X))* De Gruyter, Walter Inc.

Street, Chris, et al. English Language Learners in Your Classroom: Strategies That Work. 3rd ed. 2007. (Illus.). 216p. 76.95 *(978-1-4129-5816-5(4)*, B58165C); per. 33.95 *(978-1-4129-5817-2(2)*, B58165P) Corwin Pr.

Suarez-Orozco, Carola, et al. Learning a New Land: Immigrant Students in American Society. 2010. (Illus.). 440p. pap. 19.95 *(978-0-674-04580-4(7)*, Belknap Pr.) Harvard Univ. Pr.

Suzuki, Taku. Embodying Belonging: Racializing Okinawan Diaspora in Bolivia & Japan. 2010. 256p. (C). 47.00 *(978-0-8248-3344-2(9))* Univ. of Hawaii Pr.

Tabors, Patton O. & Terrill, Dawn. A Parent's Guide to Helping Your Child Learn Two Languages. 2011. ***(978-1-60617-494-4(0))*** Teaching Strategies, Inc.

—Pasos para Ayudar a Su Niño a Aprender DOS Idiomas: Una Guía para Los Padres. 2011. (SPA & ENG.). ***(978-1-60617-495-1(9))*** Teaching Strategies, Inc.

Tapia, Ricardo Wahby. Memories of Alexandria: From A Void to Nothingness. 2011. (Illus.). 232p. pap. 17.09 ***(978-1-4567-8359-4(9))*** AuthorHouse.

Terrio, Susan J. Judging Mohammed: Juvenile Delinquency, Immigration, & Exclusion at the Paris Palace of Justice. 2009. (ENG.). 368p. pap. 24.95 *(978-0-8047-5960-1(X))* Stanford Univ. Pr.

Terrio, Susan J. & Terrio, Susan. Judging Mohammed: Juvenile Delinquency, Immigration, & Exclusion at the Paris Palace of Justice. 2009. (ENG.). 368p. 75.00 *(978-0-8047-5959-5(6))* Stanford Univ. Pr.

Thomas, Liz & Quinn, Jocey. First Generation Entry into Higher Education. 168p. 2007. 119.95 *(978-0-335-21791-5(5))* 2006. (ENG.). (C). pap. 78.00 *(978-0-335-21790-8(7)*, 0335217907) McGraw-Hill Professional Publishing.

Trias, Mary. Crisis of Identity II. 2007. 156p. per. 24.95 *(978-1-4241-6368-7(4))* PublishAmerica, Inc.

Troller, Simone. Lost in Transit: Insufficient Protection for Unaccompanied Migrant Children at Roissy Charles de Gaulle Airport. 2009. (Illus.). 60p. ***(978-1-56432-557-0(1))*** Human Rights Watch.

Tyrrell, Naomi, et al, eds. Transnational Migration & Childhood. 2012. (ENG.). 160p. (C). 135.00 ***(978-0-415-53935-7(8))*** Routledge.

Uhing, Brad & Gonzales, Jorge. Comprehensive Language-Intensive Research. 2008. 116p. pap. *(978-3-639-08396-5(2))* VDM Verlag Dr. Mueller e.K.

UNICEF Innocenti Research Centre Staff. Children in Immigrant Families in Eight Affluent Countries: Their Family, National & International Context. 2009. (Insight Innocenti Ser.). 112p. pap. 20.00 *(978-88-89129-93-7(X))* UNICEF Innocenti Research Centre, UNICEF-IRC ITA. Dist: United Nations Pubns.

Vargas, Lucila. Latina Teens, Migration, & Popular Culture. 2009. (Intersections in Communications & Culture: Global Approaches & Transdisciplinary Perspectives Ser.). pap. 99.95 *(978-0-8204-8845-5(3))* Lang, Peter Publishing, Inc.

Vocke, Karen S. Where Do I Go from Here? Meeting the Unique Educational Needs of Migrant Students. 2007. (Illus.). 128p. pap. 21.25 *(978-0-325-00888-2(4)*, E00888) Heinemann.

Warikoo, Natasha Kumar. Balancing Acts: Youth Culture in the Global City. 2011. (ENG.). 296p. 55.00 *(978-0-520-26210-2(7))*; pap. 21.95 *(978-0-520-26211-9(5))* Univ. of California Pr.

Weinberg, Paul. My Word Is My Bond: A Memoir. 2008. 168p. 24.95 *(978-0-595-69579-9(5))*; pap. 14.95 *(978-0-595-44625-4(6))* iUniverse, Inc.

Yeh, Lily. Awakening Creativity: Dandelion School Blossoms. 2011. (ENG., Illus.). 224p. 34.95 *(978-0-9815593-7-7(9))* New Village Pr.

Yoshikawa, Hirokazu. Immigrants Raising Citizens: Undocumented Parents & Their Young Children. 2011. *(978-0-87154-986-0(7))* Russell Sage Foundation.

CHILDREN OF INTERRACIAL MARRIAGE

Patel, Tina & Patel, Tina G. Mixed-Up Kids? Race, Identity & Social Order. 2009. 159p. pap. 37.95 *(978-1-905541-38-6(4))* Russell Hse. Publishing Ltd. GBR. Dist: International Specialized Bk. Services.

CHILDREN OF MIDDLE-AGED PARENTS

see Children of Older Parents

CHILDREN OF MILITARY PERSONNEL

Atkinson, William. Military Brat: Volume 1 (the Red Book) Sons of Man. 2008. 432p. pap. 29.95 *(978-1-60672-138-4(0))* PublishAmerica, Inc.

Bagby, Gloria Rowland. Corregidor: Has Anyone Seen My Father? Last Known Address Was the Oryoku Maru. 2010. 156p. pap. 14.99 *(978-1-4520-2943-6(1))* AuthorHouse.

Chandra, Anita, et al. Views from the Homefront: The Experiences of Youth & Spouses from Military Families. 2011. 122p. pap. 28.00 *(978-0-8330-5127-1(X)*, tr-913) RAND Corp., The.

Doell, Sandy. Mom's Field Guide: What You Need to Know to Make It Through Your Loved One's Military Deployment. 2006. pap. 19.95 *(978-1-932311-20-4(3)*, Warrior Angel Pr.) Hartsough, Marian Assocs.

Gibson, Clare. Army Childhood: British Army Children's Lives & Times. 2012. (Shire Library). (ENG., Illus.). 56p. pap. 12.95 ***(978-0-7478-1099-5(0))*** Shire Pubns., Ltd. GBR. Dist: Random Hse., Inc.

Hair, Tanya Davenport. Remember When: My Life as a Military Child. 2011. 92p. pap. 32.95 ***(978-1-4567-6360-3(0))*** AuthorHouse.

Harris-Morrow, Verna. My Mommy Wears Army Boots. 2007. 33p. per. 17.95 *(978-1-58961-465-9(8))* PageFree Publishing, Inc.

Hill, Janelle. Special Needs Families in the Military: A Resource Guide. 2011. (Military Life Ser.). (ENG.). 280p. 34.95 *(978-1-60590-715-4(4))* Government Institutes.

Hill, Janelle & Philpott, Don. Special Needs Families in the Military: A Resource Guide. 2011. (ENG.). 280p. pap. 19.95 *(978-1-60590-767-3(7))* Government Institutes.

Leitman, Richard & Hollander, Michael. Dear Roz: Finding the Truth about My Father in his Wartime Love Letters to My Mother. 2009. 332p. 32.95 *(978-1-4401-7116-1(5))*; pap. 22.95 *(978-1-4401-7114-7(9))* iUniverse, Inc.

Miller, Laura L., et al. A New Approach for Assessing the Needs of Service Members & Their Families. 2011. (ENG.). 158p. pap. 29.50 ***(978-0-8330-5874-4(6))*** RAND Corp., The.

Moini, Joy S., et al. Providing Child Care to Military Families: The Role of the Demand Formula in Defining Need & Informing Policy. 2005. (Illus.). 138p. per. 25.00 *(978-0-8330-3927-9(X)*, MG-387) RAND Corp., The.

O'Neill, Joy. Service Children: A Guide for Education & Welfare Professionals. 2011. 80p. pap. ***(978-0-7552-1350-4(5))*** Authors OnLine, Ltd.

Oversight of Family Support Programs: Hearing Before the Military Personnel Subcommittee of the Committee on Armed Services, House of Representatives, One Hundred Eleventh Congress, First Session, Hearing Held, July 22, 2009. 2010. (Illus.). iv, 162p. *(978-0-16-085179-7(3)*, 552-070-40533-0) United States Government Printing Office.

Peggy Logue. Skin in the Game: Journey of a Mother & Her Marine Son. 2010. 392p. 35.00 *(978-1-4269-2434-7(8))* Trafford Publishing.

Petty, Karen. Deployment: Strategies for Working with Kids in Military Families. 2009. (ENG., Illus.). 180p. pap. 24.95 *(978-1-933653-74-7(4))* Redleaf Pr.

Recent Studies on the Effects of Deployment on Military Children: Hearing Before the Military Personnel Subcommittee of the Committee on Armed Services, House of Representatives, One Hundred Eleventh Congress, Second Session, Hearing Held March 9, 2010. 2010. (Illus.). iii, 46p. ***(978-0-16-086449-0(6))***, 552-070-41506-8) United States Government Printing Office.

C

Richardson, Amy, et al. Effects of Soldiers Deployment on Children. 2011. (Illus.). 176p. pap. 28.00 (978-0-8330-5181-3(4)) Royal Pavilion, Art Gallery & Museums GBR. Dist: National Bk. Network.

Wizelman, Leah. When the War Never Ends: The Voices of Military Members with PTSD & Their Families. 2011. (ENG.). 176p. 37.00 (978-1-4422-1207-7(1)) Rowman & Littlefield Publishers, Inc.

Wong, Leonard & Gerras, Stephen. The Effects of Multiple Deployments on Army Adolescents. 2010. (Illus.). vii, 39p. (978-1-58487-423-2(6)) Strategic Studies Institute, U.S. Army War College Commandant (AWCC-DSI/Pubns.).

Yarborough, Trin. Surviving Twice: Amerasian Children of the Vietnam War. 2006. (Illus.). 336p. per. 16.95 (978-1-57488-865-2(X)) Potomac Bks., Inc.

Zellman, Gail. Options for Improving the Military Child Care System. 2008. 76p. pap. 26.50 (978-0-8330-4414-3(1)) RAND Corp., The.

CHILDREN OF MINORITIES

Bireda, Martha. Schooling Poor Minority Children: New Segregation in the Post-Brown Era. 2011. (ENG.). 146p. 40.00 (978-1-60709-882-9(2)); pap. 19.95 (978-1-60709-883-6(0)) Rowman & Littlefield Education.

Bireda, Martha R. Schooling Poor Minority Children: New Segregation in the Post-Brown ERA. 2011. xi, 133p. (978-1-60709-884-3(9)) Rowman & Littlefield Education.

Castro, Dina C., et al. New Voices ~ Nuevas Voces: A Handbook on Cultural & Linguistic Diversity in Early Childhood. 2010. (Illus.). 184p. pap. 34.95 (978-1-59857-046-5(3)) Brookes, Paul H. Publishing Co.

Darling, Sandra K. & Tileston, Donna E. Walker, eds. Closing the Poverty & Culture Gap: Strategies to Reach Every Student. 2009. (Illus.). 120p. pap. 27.95 (978-1-4129-5531-7(9), B55300P) Corwin Pr.

Darmody, Merike, et al, eds. The Changing Faces of Ireland: Exploring the Lives of Immigrant & Ethnic Minority Children. 2011. 288p. (978-94-6091-474-4(8)); pap. (978-94-6091-473-7(X)) Sense Pubs.

Dyrness, Andrea. Mothers United: An Immigrant Struggle for Socially Just Education. 2011. 264p. 69.00 (978-0-8166-7466-4(3)); pap. 22.95 (978-0-8166-7467-1(1)) Univ. of Minnesota Pr.

Etim, James S., ed. Essays in Helping Diverse Students Attain Educational Success: When the Classroom Isn't White & Middle Class. 2011. 252p. 109.95 (978-0-7734-3936-8(6)) Mellen, Edwin Pr., The.

Gallagher-Geurtsen, Tricia. (Un)knowing Diversity: Researching Narratives of Neocolonial Classrooms Through Youth's Testimonios. 2012. viii, 178p. (978-1-4331-1007-8(5)); pap. (978-1-4331-1006-1(7)); E-Book (978-1-4539-0213-4(9)) Lang, Peter GmbH, Europaischer Verlag der Wissenschaften.

Gilton, Donna L. Multicultural & Ethnic Children's Literature in the United States. 2007. (ENG.). 244p. per. 55.00 (978-0-8108-5672-1(7)) Scarecrow Pr., Inc.

Guggisberg, Manuela & Guggisberg, Marika. Can Children from Minority Backgrounds Be Gifted? 2010. 84p. pap. (978-3-8383-9266-0(3)) Lambert Academic Publishing.

Haji-Kella, Mohamed. What's Culture Got to Do with It? 2009. 76p. pap. (978-3-639-14815-2(0)) VDM Verlag Dr. Mueller e.K.

Hands, Catherine M. & Hubbard, Lea. Including Families & Communities in Urban Education. 2011. 85.99 (978-1-61735-400-7(7)); pap. (978-1-61735-399-4(X)); E-Book (978-1-61735-401-4(5)) Information Age Publishing, Inc.

Herrera, Socorro G., et al. Assessment Accommodations for Classroom Teachers of Culturally & Linguistically Diverse Students. 2nd rev. ed. 2012. (ENG.). 336p. (C). pap. 68.40 (978-0-13-285335-4(3)) Allyn & Bacon, Inc.

Hollins, Etta R. Learning to Teach in Urban Schools: The Transition from Preparation to Practice. 2011. (ENG., Illus.). 120p. 135.00 (978-0-415-89385-5(2)); pap. 39.95 (978-0-415-89386-2(0)) Routledge.

Kirklighter, Cristina, et al. Teaching Writing with Latino/A Students: Lessons Learned at Hispanic-Serving Institutions. Kirklighter, Cristina & Murphy, Susan Wolff, eds. 2007. (Illus.). 240p. 74.50 (978-0-7914-7193-7(4)) State Univ. of New York Pr.

—Teaching Writing with Latino/A Students: Lessons Learned at Hispanic-Serving Institutions. Kirklighter, Cristina et al, eds. 2007. (Illus.). 240p. per. 29.95 (978-0-7914-7194-4(2)) State Univ. of New York Pr.

Knowles, Gianna & Lander, Vini. Diversity, Equality & Achievement in Education. 2011. (Illus.). 192p. (C). 104.00 (978-1-84920-600-6(7), B06006C); pap. 42.00 (978-1-84920-601-3(5), B06006P) SAGE Pubns., Ltd. GBR. Dist: SAGE Pubns., Inc.

Kugler, Eileen. Innovative Voices in Education: Engaging Diverse Communities. 2012. (ENG.). 308p. (gr. 17). pap. 38.95 (978-1-61048-540-1(8)) Rowman & Littlefield Education.

Kugler, Eileen, et al. Innovative Voices in Education: Engaging Diverse Communities. 2012. (ENG.). 308p. (gr. 17). 80.00 (978-1-61048-539-5(4)) Rowman & Littlefield Education.

Kugler, Eileen Gale. Innovative Voices in Education: What It Takes to Engage Diverse Communities. 2011. E-Book (978-1-61048-541-8(6)) Rowman & Littlefield Education.

Li, Guofang. Multicultural Families, Home Literacies, & Mainstream Schooling. 2009. 312p. (978-1-60752-036-8(2)); pap. (978-1-60752-035-1(4)) Information Age Publishing, Inc.

Lindon, Jennie. Equality & Inclusion in Early Years: Linking Theory & Practice. 2nd ed. 2012. (ENG., Illus.). 224p. pap. 45.00 (978-1-4441-4550-2(9)) Hodder Arnold Pubs.

Lytra, Vally. Play Frames & Social Identities: Contact Encounters in a Greek Primary School. 2007. (C). (978-90-272-5407-8(9)) Benjamins, John Publishing Co.

Margolis, Jane. Stuck in the Shallow End: Education, Race, & Computing. 2010. (ENG., Illus.). 216p. (gr. 17). pap. 16.95 (978-0-262-51404-0(4)) MIT Pr.

McAninch/Books. Guest Editor's Introduction. 2006. 120p. 45.95 (978-0-8058-9352-6(0)) Erlbaum, Lawrence Assocs., Inc.

McNaughton, Stuart. Designing Better Schools for Culturally & Linguistically Diverse Children: A Science of Performance Model for Research. 2011. (ENG., Illus.). 200p. 135.00 (978-0-415-88659-8(7)); pap. 39.95 (978-0-415-88660-4(0)) Routledge.

Morrow, Lesley Mandel, et al, eds. Handbook of Research on Literacy & Diversity. (ENG.). 464p. (gr. k-12). 2010. pap. 50.00 (978-1-60918-145-1(X)) 2009. (Illus.). 75.00 (978-1-60623-246-0(0)) Guilford Pubns., Inc.

National Education Association of the United States Staff & National Association of School Psychologists Staff, contrib. by. Truth in Labeling: Disproportionality in Special Education. 2007. (978-0-8106-2040-7(5), NEA Professional Library) National Education Assn.

Nieto, Sonia. The Light in Their Eyes: Creating Multicultural Learning Communities. 10th ed. 2010. (ENG.). 272p. pap. 26.95 (978-0-8077-5054-4(9)) Teachers College Pr., Teachers College, Columbia Univ.

Noltemeyer, Amity/Lynn & Mcloughlin, Caven S., eds. Disproportionality in Education & Special Education: A Guide to Creating More Equitable Learning Environments. 2012. (978-0-398-08800-2(4)); pap. (978-0-398-08801-9(2)) Thomas, Charles C. Pub., Ltd.

Norton, Donna E. Multicultural Children's Literature: Through the Eyes of Many Children. 3rd ed. 2008. (ENG.). 368p. (C). pap. 53.80 (978-0-13-514528-9(7), Prentice Hall) Prentice Hall PTR.

Parker-Jenkins, Marie, et al. Aiming High: Raising Attainment of Pupils from Culturally-Diverse Backgrounds. 2007. 128p. 65.00 (978-1-4129-2938-7(5), B29387C) SAGE Pubns., Ltd. GBR. Dist: SAGE Pubns., Inc.

—Aiming High: Raising Attainment of Pupils from Culturally Diverse Backgrounds. 2007. (Illus.). 128p. per. 30.00 (978-1-4129-2939-4(3), B29387P) SAGE Pubns., Ltd. GBR. Dist: SAGE Pubns., Inc.

Phillion, JoAnn, et al, eds. Minority Students in East Asia: Government Policies, School Practices & Teacher Responses. 2011. (Routledge Series on Schools & Schooling in Asia Ser.). (ENG., Illus.). 280p. (C). 125.00 (978-0-415-88839-4(5)) Routledge.

Saran, Rupam & Diaz, Rosalina, eds. Beyond Stereotypes: Minority Children of Immigrants in Urban Schools. 2010. 248p. (978-94-6091-079-1(3)); pap. (978-94-6091-078-4(5)) Sense Pubs.

Sentilles, Sarah. Taught by America: A Story of Struggle & Hope in Compton. 2006. (ENG.). 216p. per. 16.00 (978-0-8070-3273-2(5)) Beacon Pr.

Sleeter, Christine E. & Grant, Carl A. Making Choices for Multicultural Education: Five Approaches to Race, Class, & Gender. 6th ed. 2008. (ENG., Illus.). 252p. (C). pap. 131.95 (978-0-470-38369-8(0), Wiley) Wiley, John & Sons, Inc.

Stambaugh, Tamra & Chandler, Kimberley. Effective Curriculum for Underserved Gifted Students: A Cec-Tag Educational Resource. 2011. (ENG.). 100p. pap. 24.95 (978-1-59363-842-9(6)) Prufrock Pr.

Tsuneyoshi, Ryoko, et al, eds. Minorities & Multiculturalism in Japanese Education. 2010. (Asia's Transformations Ser.). (ENG., Illus.). 288p. (C). 130.00 (978-0-415-55938-6(3)) Routledge.

Williams, Gary & Obiakor, Festus E. The State of Education of Urban Learners & Possible Solutions: The Milwaukee Experience. rev. ed. 2009. (ENG.). 112p. pap. 45.41 (978-0-7575-7104-6(2)) Kendall Hunt Publishing Co.

CHILDREN OF NARCOTIC ADDICTS

see Children of Drug Addicts

CHILDREN OF OLDER PARENTS

Here are entered works on children born to, or adopted by, middle aged or older parents.

Sandell, Diane & Hudson, Lois. Ending Elder Abuse: A Family Guide. 2010. 160p. pap. 16.95 (978-0-936609-43-0(5)) QED Pr.

Winakur, Jerald. Memory Lessons: A Doctor's Story. 2008. 304p. 24.95 (978-1-4013-0302-0(1)) Hyperion Pr.

CHILDREN OF PARENTS WITH DISABILITIES

Cleaver, Hedy & Nicholson, Don. Parental Learning Disability & Children's Needs: Family Experiences & Effective Practice. 2008. (ENG., Illus.). 144p. per. (978-1-84310-632-6(9)) Kingsley, Jessica Ltd.

Crews, Kambri. Burn down the Ground: A Memoir. 2012. (ENG., Illus.). 352p. 25.00 (978-0-345-51602-2(8), Villard Bks.) Random House Publishing Group.

Davis, Lennard J. My Sense of Silence: Memoirs of a Childhood with Deafness. 2008. (ENG., Illus.). 176p. pap. 25.00 (978-0-252-07577-3(3)) Univ. of Illinois Pr.

Eckerman, Carol O. Lessons in Simply Being: Finding the Peace within Tumult. 2012. (ENG.). 224p. pap. 16.95 (978-1-84694-723-0(5)) Hunt, John Publishing Ltd. GBR. Dist: National Bk. Network.

Faulkner, Mara. Going Blind: A Memoir. 2009. 226p. 60.00 (978-1-4384-2667-9(4)); pap. 19.95 (978-1-4384-2668-6(2)) State Univ. of New York Pr.

Flynn, Laura M. Swallow the Ocean: A Memoir. 2009. (ENG.). 288p. pap. 15.95 (978-1-58243-461-2(1), Counterpoint Pr.) Basic Bks. GBR. Dist: Perseus-PGW.

Straussner, S. Lala Ashenberg et al. Children of Substance Abusing Parents H/C: Dynamics & Treatment. 2011. 320p. (978-0-8261-6507-7(9)) Springer.

Straussner, Shulamith Lala Ashenberg & Fewell, Christine Huff. Children of Substance-Abusing Parents: Dynamics & Treatment. 2011. xv, 288p. (978-0-8261-6508-4(7)) Springer.

Uhlberg, Myron. Hands of My Father: A Hearing Boy, His Deaf Parents, & the Language of Love. 2009. (ENG., Illus.). 256p. 24.00 (978-0-553-80688-5(2)) Random House Publishing Group.

Van Dernoot, Peter. Helping Your Children Cope with Your Cancer: A Guide for Parents & Families. 2nd ed. 2006. (ENG., Illus.). 176p. pe. 15.95 (978-1-57826-231-1(3), Hatherleigh Pr.) Hatherleigh Co., Ltd., The.

CHILDREN OF PRENATAL ALCOHOL ABUSE

Alters, Sandra. Fetal Alcohol Disorders. 2011. (Compact Research Ser.). (ENG.). 96p. (YA). (gr. 7-12). lib. bdg. 27.95 (978-1-60152-159-0(6)) ReferencePoint Pr., Inc.

Crowe, Jody Allen. The Fatal Link: The Connection Between School Shooters & the Brain Damage from Prenatal Exposure to Alcohol. 2008. 224p. pap. 17.95 (978-1-4327-2917-2(9)) Outskirts Pr., Inc.

Neafcy, Stephen James. The Long Way to Success: 50 Years of ideas to live, love & laugh as a person with FASD. Kulp, Jodee, ed. 2008. (ENG.). 96p. (YA). pap. 12.95 (978-0-9637072-8-4(0)) Better Endings New Beginnings.

Snow, M. Elizabeth. Effects on Prenatal Alcohol Exposure on Long Bone Development. 2008. 176p. pap. (978-3-639-04892-6(X)) VDM Verlag Dr. Mueller e.K.

CHILDREN OF PRESIDENTS

Roosevelt, Theodore. Letters to His Children. 2009. 152p. 21.99 (978-0-559-10818-1(4)); 24.99 (978-0-559-10808-2(7)); pap. 15.99 (978-0-559-10815-0(X)); pap. 21.75 (978-0-559-10810-5(9)) BiblioBazaar.

—Letters to His Children. Bishop, Joseph Bucklin, ed. 2007. (ENG.). 136p. per. (978-1-4065-6312-2(9)) Dodo Pr.

—Letters to His Children. 2006. pap. (978-1-4068-0157-6(7)) Echo Library.

CHILDREN OF PRESIDENTS—UNITED STATES

Angelo, Bonnie. First Families: The Impact of the White House on Their Lives. 2007. (Illus.). 368p. pap. 15.99 (978-0-06-056358-5(3), William Morrow Paperbacks) HarperCollins Pubs.

Bishop, Joseph, ed. Theodore Roosevelt's Letters to His Children. 2010. 260p. pap. 16.95 (978-1-4290-4550-6(7)) Applewood Bks.

Bishop, Joseph Bucklin. Theodore Roosevelt's Letters to His Children. 2007. 260p. 29.95 (978-1-4344-8395-9(9)); per. 17.95 (978-1-4344-8394-2(0)) Wildside Pr., LLC.

Emerson, Jason. Giant in the Shadows: The Life of Robert T. Lincoln. 2012. (ENG., Illus.). 640p. 39.95 (978-0-8093-3055-3(5)) 2011. E-Book 39.95 (978-0-8093-9071-7(X)) Southern Illinois Univ. Pr.

Federal Bureau Of Investigation & Kennedy, John F., Jr. John F Kennedy, Jr: The FBI Files. 2007. 184p. per. 22.99 (978-1-59986-247-7(6), Filibust) Filiquarian Publishing, LLC.

Heymann, C. David. American Legacy: The Story of John & Caroline Kennedy. 2008. (ENG., Illus.). 608p. pap. 34.99 (978-0-7434-9739-8(2), Beyond Words/Atria Bks.) Atria Bks.

Kierner, Cynthia A. Martha Jefferson Randolph, Daughter of Monticello: Her Life & Times. 2012. (ENG., Illus.). 400p. 35.00 (978-0-8078-3552-4(8)) Univ. of North Carolina Pr.

Koch, Doro Bush. My Father, My President: A Personal Account of the Life of George H. W. Bush. 2006. (ENG., Illus.). 608p. 33.99 (978-0-446-57990-2(4)) Grand Central Publishing.

Kroeber, Theodora. Ishi in Two Worlds A Biography of the Last Wild Indian in North America. 2011. (Illus.). 308p. per. 25.95 (978-0-923891-01-5(3)) Ishi Pr. International.

Lewis, Nelly Custis, et al. George Washington's Beautiful Nelly: The Letters of Eleanor Parke Custis Lewis to Elizabeth Bordley Gibson, 1794-1851: With a New Guide to Nelly Custis Lewis & Her Family's Homes. 2006. (Illus.). xxvi, 287p. pap. (978-1-57003-631-6(4)) Univ. of South Carolina Pr.

Packard, Jerrold M. The Lincolns in the White House: Four Years That Shattered a Family. 2006. (ENG., Illus.). 304p. pap. 15.95 (978-0-312-31303-6(9), St. Martin's Paperbacks) St. Martin's Pr.

Roosevelt, Theodore. Theodore Roosevelt's Letters to His Children. 2009. 252p. 24.99 (978-1-103-65275-4(3)); 252p. pap. 18.99 (978-1-103-65272-3(9)); 260p. 24.99 (978-0-559-97491-5(4)); 260p. pap. 18.99 (978-0-559-97489-2(2)) BiblioBazaar.

—Theodore Roosevelt's Letters to His Children. 2009. 90p. pap. (978-1-151-60369-2(4)) Books LLC.

—Theodore Roosevelt's Letters to His Children. Bishop, Joseph Bucklin, ed. 2007. (ENG.). 254p. 42.95 (978-0-548-15663-6(8)); pap. 27.95 (978-1-4304-5128-0(9)) Kessinger Publishing, LLC.

—Theodore Roosevelt's Letters to His Children. 240p. reprint ed. 98.00 (978-0-7222-8868-9(9)) Library Reprints, Inc.

—Theodore Roosevelt's Letters to His Children. 2007. 260p. 29.95 (978-1-4344-9624-9(4)); per. 19.95 (978-1-4344-9623-2(6)) Wildside Pr., LLC.

Roosevelt, Theodore, IV & Roosevelt, Theodore. Theodore Roosevelt's Letters to His Children. 2009. 260p. 24.99 (978-1-103-89310-2(6)); pap. 18.99 (978-1-103-89299-0(1)) BiblioBazaar.

Wead, Doug. All the President's Children: Triumph & Tragedy in the Lives of America's First Families. 2006. (Illus.). 456p. reprint ed. 26.00 (978-0-7567-8994-7(X)) DIANE Publishing Co.

CHILDREN OF SINGLE PARENTS

see also Children of Divorced Parents

Covington, Zadora. A Fatherless Generation. 2011. pap. 9.99 (978-1-61346-106-8(2)) Tate Publishing & Enterprises, LLC.

Joseph.Shipp. Momma's Only Son: An Urban Autobiography. 2011. 334p. pap. 29.95 (978-1-4560-9130-9(1)) PublishAmerica, Inc.

Kowaleski-Jones, Lori & Wolfinger, Nicholas H., eds. Fragile families & the marriage Agenda. 2007. 256p. per. 49.95 (978-0-387-68172-6(8)) Springer.

Leman, Kevin. Single Parenting That Works: Six Keys to Raising Happy, Healthy Children in a Single-Parent Home. 2006. (ENG., Illus.). 288p. per. 14.99 (978-1-4143-0335-2(1)) Tyndale Hse. Pubs.

McGill, Jerry. Dear Marcus: A Letter to the Man Who Shot Me. 2012. (ENG., Illus.). 192p. 22.00 (978-0-8129-9307-3(1)); E-Book (978-0-679-64460-6(1)) Spiegel & Grau.

Miller, Lynda Mahan. Looking for My Father. 2009. 36p. pap. 15.49 (978-1-4389-8699-9(8)) AuthorHouse.

Popenoe, David. Families Without Fathers: Fathers, Marriage & Children in American Society. 2009. (ENG.). 287p. pap. 24.95 (978-1-4128-1038-8(8)) Transaction Pubs.

Turner, Janine. Holding Her Head High: 12 Single Mothers Who Championed Their Children & Changed History, 0 vols. 2008. (Illus.). 240p. 22.99 (978-0-7852-2324-5(X)) Nelson, Thomas Inc.

Woodall, Karen & Woodall, Nick. Putting Children First: A Handbook for Separated Parents. 2009. (ENG., Illus.). 256p. pap. 17.95 (978-0-7499-2804-9(2)) Piatkus Bks. GBR. Dist: Independent Pubs. Group.

CHILDREN OF THE MENTALLY ILL

Bartok, Mira. The Memory Palace: A Memoir. 2011. (ENG.). 336p. pap. 15.00 (978-1-4391-8332-8(5)); (Illus.). 320p. 25.00 (978-1-4391-8331-1(7)) Free Pr. (Free Pr.).

Casey, Ingeborg Gubler. The Heart Moves in a Circular Direction: A Story of Healing. 2007. 228p. (ENG.). 28.95 (978-0-595-67881-5(5)); per. 18.95 (978-0-595-41227-3(0)) iUniverse, Inc.

Curtis, Patricia. Legends of the Plastic Chairs. 2007. 204p. per. 19.95 (978-1-59856-463-9(4)) Dog Ear Publishing, LLC.

Davis, Tom. A Legacy of Madness: Recovering My Family from Generations of Mental Illness. 2011. (ENG.). 288p. pap. 14.95 (978-1-61649-121-5(3)) Hazelden Publishing & Educational Services.

Nathiel, Susan. Daughters of Madness: Growing up & Older with a Mentally Ill Mother, 1 vol. annot. ed. 2007. (Women's Psychology Ser.). 224p. 49.95 (978-0-275-99042-8(7), C9042, Praeger Pubs.) Greenwood Publishing Group, Inc.

Ostler, Teresa. Assessment of Parenting Competency in Mothers with Mental Illness. 2007. (Illus.). 188p. per. 32.95 (978-1-55766-665-9(2)) Brookes, Paul H. Publishing Co.

Stevens, Katrina & Davis, Tina. Daddy's Little Secret: Pregnant at 14 & There's Only Man Who Can Be the Father. 2011. (ENG.). 336p. pap. 12.95 (978-0-09-194100-0(8)) Ebury Publishing GBR. Dist: Independent Pubs. Group.

CHILDREN OF THE POOR

see Poor Children

CHILDREN OF WORKING PARENTS

Agger, Ben & Shelton, Beth Anne. Fast Families, Virtual Children: A Critical Sociology of Families & Schooling. 2007. (ENG.). 208p. 125.00 (978-1-59451-339-8(2)); per. 37.95 (978-1-59451-340-4(6)) Paradigm Pubs.

Chambliss, Catherine. Maternal Employment: Marvel or Menace - the Views of Children, Young Adults, & Parents. 2009. (Illus.). xvii, 475p. 89.00 (978-1-60741-365-3(5)) Nova Science Pubs., Inc.

Cusworth, Linda. The Impact of Parental Employment: Young People Well-Being & Educational Achievement. 2009. (Studies in Cash & Care Ser.). (Illus.). 260p. 114.95 (978-0-7546-7559-4(9)) Ashgate Publishing Co.

Dobinson, Tee. The Mummy Glue: Keeping Mums & Kids Connected. 2010. 40p. 17.23 (978-1-4567-0108-6(8)) AuthorHouse.

Emlen, Arthur. Solving the Childcare & Flexibility Puzzle: How Working Parents Make the Best Feasible Choices & What That Means for Public Policy. 2010. 122p. pap. 25.95 (978-1-59942-868-0(7)) Universal Pubs.

Gunnoe, Jennifer. Mommy Goes to Work: A Gabriella Story. 2009. 24p. pap. 11.49 (978-1-4389-5111-9(6)) AuthorHouse.

Heymann, Jody. Forgotten Families: Ending the Growing Crisis Confronting Children & Working Parents in the Global Economy. 2007. (ENG., Illus.). 336p. per. 20.00 (978-0-19-533524-8(4)) Oxford Univ. Pr., Inc.

Hilbrecht, Margo. Living in Real Time. 2009. 288p. pap. (978-3-639-17419-9(4)) VDM Verlag Dr. Mueller e.K.

Hong, Sung-A. Ch'wiop Pumo Ui Chanyo Yangyuk Chiwon Sobisu Hyoyurhwa Pangan. 2010. (KOR., Illus.). xxi, 272p. (978-89-8491-346-2(4)) Korean Women's Development Institute.

LaRowe, Michelle. Working Mom's 411: How to Manage Kids, Career & Home. 2009. (ENG.). 224p. pap. 14.99 (978-0-8307-4608-8(0)) Gospel Light Pubns.

Van Der Meulen Staff & Rodgers, Y. Labor Standards & Globalisation in Asia. 2011. (Illus.). 224p. 99.95 (978-1-84720-510-0(0)) Elgar, Edward Publishing, Inc.

Waldfogel, Jane. What Children Need. 2010. (Family & Public Policy Ser.). (Illus.). 288p. pap. 19.95 (978-0-674-04640-5(4)) Harvard Univ. Pr.

CHILDREN WITH DISABILITIES

see also Children with Mental Disabilities; Children with Social Disabilities; Children with Visual Disabilities; Developmentally Disabled Children; Parents of Children with Disabilities; Physical Education for Children with Disabilities; Teachers of Children with Disabilities

Acharya-Koirala, Pushpa. Humanitarian Impact of Resettlement of Idps: A Case of Northern Iraq. 2009. 184p. pap. *(978-3-639-13820-7(1))* VDM Verlag Dr. Mueller e.K.

Aron, Laudan Y. & Loprest, Pamela J. Meeting the Needs of Children with Disabilities. 2007. (Illus.). 138p. pap. 26.50 *(978-0-87766-746-9(2))* Urban Institute Pr.

Askham, Suzanne. Coping with Your Child's Special Needs. xii, 116p. *(978-0-85969-825-2(4)*, Sheldon Press) SPCK Publishing.

Baditoi, Barbara & Brott, Pamelia E. What School Counselors Need to Know about Special Education & Students with Disabilities. 2011. 206p. spiral bd. 39.95 ***(978-0-86586-461-0(6))*** Council for Exceptional Children.

Bakken, Jeffrey & Rotatori, Anthony, eds. Current Issues & Trends in Special Education: Identification, Assessment & Instruction. 2009. 252p. 124.95 *(978-1-84855-668-3(3))* Emerald Group Publishing Ltd. GBR. Dist: Turpin Distribution Services Ltd.

Bartram, Pamela. Understanding Your Young Child with Special Needs. 2007. (Understanding Your Child (Jessica Kingsley Publishers) Ser.). (ENG.). 88p. per. *(978-1-84310-533-6(0))* Kingsley, Jessica Ltd.

Beckerleg, Tracey. Fun with Messy Play: Ideas & Activities for Children with Special Needs. 2008. (ENG., Illus.). 160p. pap. *(978-1-84310-641-8(8))* Kingsley, Jessica Ltd.

Berry, Judy O. Lifespan Perspectives on the Family & Disability. 2nd ed. 2008. pap. 73.00 *(978-1-4164-0379-1(5))* PRO-ED, Inc.

Bertelli, Yantra, et al, eds. My Baby Rides the Short Bus: The Unabashedly Human Experience of Raising Kids with Disabilities. 2009. (ENG.). 336p. pap. 20.00 *(978-1-60486-109-9(6))* PM Pr.

Betz, Cecily L. & Nehring, Wendy M., eds. Promoting Health Care Transitions for Adolescents with Special Health Care Needs & Disabilities. 2007. (Illus.). 311p. per. 34.95 *(978-1-55766-860-8(4))* Brookes, Paul H. Publishing Co.

Biel, Lindsey & Peske, Nancy. Raising a Sensory Smart Child: The Definitive Handbook for Helping Your Child with Sensory Processing Issues. rev. ed. 2009. (ENG.). 464p. (gr. 12-18). 16.00 *(978-0-14-311534-2(0)*, Penguin (Non-Classics)) Penguin Group (USA) Inc.

Bjarnason, Dora. Parents & Exceptionality: Social Policy & Social Capital. Experiences of Having a Disabled Child in Ocelandic Familes 1974-2007. 2011. (Series: Children's Issues, Laws & Programs Ser.). 59.00 *(978-1-61122-643-0(0))* Nova Science Pubs., Inc.

Boy Scouts Of America. Scouting with Handicapped Boys. 2011. 68p. 36.95 ***(978-1-258-03596-9(0))*** Literary Licensing, LLC.

Brodey, Denise. The Elephant in the Playroom: Ordinary Parents Write Intimately & Honestly about Raising Kids with Special Needs. 2008. (ENG.). 256p. (gr. 12-18). 14.00 *(978-0-452-28908-6(4)*, Plume) Penguin Group (USA) Inc.

Broggi, Joan. Bursting with Joy: Discovering Universal Truths Through Our Special Son. 2010. (ENG.). 144p. pap. 12.95 *(978-1-933916-53-8(2)*, Ferne Pr.) Nelson Publishing & Marketing.

Brown, Lawauna. Loving a Disabled Child, 1 vol. 2009. 101p. pap. 14.95 *(978-1-60749-794-3(8))* PublishAmerica, Inc.

Brown, William H., et al. Social Competence of Young Children: Risk, Disability, & Intervention. Brown, William H. et al, eds. 2007. (Illus.). 341p. per. 39.95 *(978-1-55766-923-0(6))* Brookes, Paul H. Publishing Co.

Burke, Peter C. Disability & Impairment: Working with Children & Families. 2008. (Illus.). 168p. per. *(978-1-84310-396-7(6))* Kingsley, Jessica Ltd.

Burns, Daniel. Disabled Children Living Away from Home in Foster Care & Resident Settings. Burns, Claire E., ed. 2009. (PGMKP - a Practical Guide from MKP Ser.: 1). (ENG.). 144p. pap. 36.95 *(978-1-898683-58-2(1))* Mac Keith Pr. GBR. Dist: Wiley, John & Sons, Inc.

Butler, Darnell. Aaron's Special Sunday. 2007. (ENG., Illus.). 28p. pap. 16.95 *(978-1-59299-279-9(X))* Inkwater Pr.

Campbell, Jonathan M. Psychological Assessment & Treatment of Children with Autism Spectrum Disorders: An Integrated Action Guide to Diagnosis, Treatment, & Educational Planning. 2009. (ENG.). 336p. 60.00 *(978-0-470-17568-2(0)*, Wiley) Wiley, John & Sons, Inc.

Care for the Disabled in Romania: Hearing Before the Commission on Security & Cooperation in Europe, One Hundred Ninth Congress, Second Session, September 13, 2006. 2008. iii, 58p. *(978-0-16-081495-2(2)*, 552-070-37854-5) United States Government Printing Office.

Chabon, Shelly S. & Cohn, Ellen R. The Communication Disorders Casebook: Learning by Example. 2010. (ENG.). 576p. (C). pap. 88.40 *(978-0-205-61012-9(9))* Allyn & Bacon, Inc.

Chen, Jih-Yuan & Instone, Susan L. Family Resilience & Functioning in Child with Dmd. 2008. 272p. pap. *(978-3-639-06661-6(8))* VDM Verlag Dr. Mueller e.K.

Cheng, Shirley. The Revelation of a Star's Endless Shine: A Young Woman's Autobiography of 20-Year Victories over Victimization. 2008. 700p. pap. 36.97 *(978-0-615-15044-4(6))* Dance With Your Heart! Publishing.

Christie, Philip, et al. First Steps in Intervention with Your Child with Autism: Frameworks for Communication. 2009. (ENG., Illus.). 238p. pap. *(978-1-84905-011-1(2))* Kingsley, Jessica Ltd.

Cline, Foster & Greene, Lisa C. Parenting Children with Health Issues & Special Needs: Love & Logic Essentials for Raising Happy, Healthier Kids. 2010. 105p. pap. 7.95 *(978-1-935326-04-5(X))* Love & Logic Institute, Inc.

Cline, Foster W. & Greene, Lisa C. Parenting Children with Health Issues: Essential Tools, Tips, & Tactics for Raising Kids with Chronic Illness, Medical Conditions & Special Healthcare Needs. 2007. (Illus.). 384p. per. 24.95 *(978-1-930429-89-5(4))* Love & Logic Institute, Inc.

Committee on Strengthening Benefit-Cost Methodology for the Evaluation of Early Childhood Interventions, et al. Benefit-Cost Analysis for Early Childhood Interventions: Workshop Summary. 2009. (ENG.). 88p. pap. 21.00 *(978-0-309-14563-3(5))* National Academies Pr.

Compart, Pamela & Laake, Dana. The Kid-Friendly ADHD & Autism Cookbook, Updated & Revised: The Ultimate Guide to the Gluten-Free, Casein-Free Diet. 2012. (ENG., Illus.). 352p. pap. 18.99 *(978-1-59233-472-8(5)*, 1592334725) Quayside.

Compton Ollenberger, Naomi. Wanted: Someone Who Cares. 2010. pap. 9.95 *(978-0-7414-5993-0(0))* Infinity Publishing.

Conners, Susan. The Tourette Syndrome & OCD Checklist: A Practical Reference for Parents & Teachers. 2011. (J-B Ed: Checklist Ser.: 5). (ENG., Illus.). 192p. pap. 18.95 *(978-0-470-62333-6(0)*, Jossey-Bass) Wiley, John & Sons, Inc.

Cook, Ruth E. & Sparks, Shirley N. The Art & Practice of Home Visiting: Early Intervention for Children with Special Needs & Their Families. 2008. 224p. 34.95 *(978-1-55766-885-1(X))* Brookes, Paul H. Publishing Co.

Cowden, Jo E. & Torrey, Carol C. Motor Development & Movement Activities for Preschoolers & Infants with Delays: A Multisensory Approach for Professionals & Families. 2nd ed. 2007. *(978-0-398-07764-8(9))*; 348p. pap. *(978-0-398-07765-5(7))* Thomas, Charles C. Pub., Ltd.

Cronin, Mary E., et al. Life Skills Instruction: A Practical Guide for Integrating Real-Life Content into the Curriculum at the Elementary & Secondary Levels for Students with Special Needs or Who Are Placed at Risk. 2nd ed. 2006. (Illus.). xi, 201p. 44.00 *(978-1-4164-0142-1(3))* PRO-ED, Inc.

Cuddy, Andrew. The Special Education Battlefield. 2007. per. 40.00 *(978-0-9787113-4-4(3)*, Ithaca Pr.) Authors & Artists Publishers of New York, Inc.

Cullen, Kairen. The Inner Lives of Professionals Working with Children with Special Needs. 2007. 160p. pap. 35.00 *(978-0-470-01947-4(6)*, Wiley) Wiley, John & Sons, Inc.

Depaul, Aldrick, ed. Youth with Disabilities in the Foster Care System: Solutions for Barriers to Success. 2010. (Disability & the Disabled - Issues, Laws & Programs Ser.). 137.00 *(978-1-60741-530-5(5))* Nova Science Pubs., Inc.

Digman, Carmel & Soan, Sue. Working with Parents: A Guide for Education Professionals. 2008. 152p. 122.00 *(978-1-4129-4758-9(8)*, B47589C); pap. 36.00 *(978-1-4129-4759-6(6)*, B47589P) SAGE Pubns., Ltd. GBR. Dist: SAGE Pubns., Inc.

Doo, DooLee. I think you know what that, that was... that Bbbuuuzzzz! 2009. 34p. pap. 17.95 *(978-0-557-04807-6(9))* Lulu Enterprises Inc.

Dóra S. Bjarnason. Social Policy & Social Capital: Parents & Exceptionality, 1974-2007. 2011. pap. *(978-1-61122-758-1(5))* Nova Science Pubs., Inc.

Douglas, Nancy. Freedom. 2008. 227p. pap. 19.95 *(978-0-615-18822-5(2))* Douglas, Nancy.

Draper, Sharon. How Mothers Cope with Their Adolescent Child's Disability. 2011. 108p. pap. ***(978-3-8443-1476-2(8))*** Lambert Academic Publishing.

Elias, Stephen & Urbatsch, Kevin. Special Needs Trusts: Protect Your Child's Financial Future, 2 vols. 4th rev. ed. 2011. (ENG.). 296p. pap. 34.99 *(978-1-4133-1384-0(1))* NOLO.

Elvikyte, Raimonda. Mothering a Disabled Child in Lithuania - Personal Experiences Revealed. 2008. 72p. pap. *(978-3-639-06257-1(4))* VDM Verlag Dr. Mueller e.K.

Ensher, Gail L., et al. Families, Infants, & Young Children at Risk: Pathways to Best Practice. 2008. (Illus.). 480p. pap. 54.95 *(978-1-55766-806-6(X))* Brookes, Paul H. Publishing Co.

Enzer & Goin. 1st Chance-Social Emotions. pap. 15.95 *(978-0-8027-7263-3(3))* Walker & Co.

Ferguson, Danyelle & Parsons, Lynn. (Dis)Abilities & the Gospel: How to Bring People with Special Needs Closer to Christ. 2011. pap. 16.90 *(978-1-59955-820-2(3))* Cedar Fort, Inc./CFI Distribution.

Fitzgerald, Hayley, ed. Disability & Youth Sport. 2008. (Illus.). XII, 180p. 130.00 *(978-0-415-47041-4(2))* Routledge.

Gallagher, Gina & Konjoian, Patricia. Shut up about Your Perfect Kid: A Survival Guide for Ordinary Parents of Special Children. 2010. (ENG.). 288p. pap. 15.00 *(978-0-307-58748-0(7)*, Three Rivers Pr.) Crown Publishing Group.

Gallagher, Peggy A., et al. Brothers & Sisters: An Special Part of Exceptional Families. 3rd ed. 2006. (Illus.). 367p. per. 24.95 *(978-1-55766-719-9(5)*, 7195) Brookes, Paul H. Publishing Co.

Geesey, Barbara. A Child's First Christmas in Heaven. 2009. 108p. 19.99 *(978-1-61579-199-6(X))* Xulon Pr., Inc.

Glicken, Morley D. Evidence-Based Practice with Emotionally Troubled Children & Adolescents. 2009. (Practical Resources for the Mental Health Professional Ser.). (ENG.). 664p. 72.95 *(978-0-12-374523-1(3)*, Academic Pr.) Elsevier Science & Technology Bks.

Gomez, Joan. How to Cope with Bulimia. (Illus.). 128p. *(978-0-85969-694-4(4)*, Sheldon Press) SPCK Publishing.

Greene, Melissa L. Children's Social Competence: Theory & Intervention. 2010. (Children's Issues, Laws & Programs Ser.). pap. 43.00 *(978-1-61668-861-5(0)*, Nova Novinka) Nova Science Pubs., Inc.

Hadders-Algra, Mijna & Carlberg, Eva Brogen. Postural Control: A Key Issue in Developmental Disorders. 2008. (Clinics in Developmental Medicine Ser.: 2). (ENG., Illus.). 352p. pap. 83.99 *(978-1-898683-57-5(3)*, Wiley-Blackwell) Wiley, John & Sons, Inc.

Hamm, Regie. Angels & Idols: The Rise, Fall, & Redemption of a Would-Be Pop Star. 2010. pap. 14.99 *(978-1-61663-440-7(5))* Tate Publishing & Enterprises, LLC.

Hansen, Mark Victor, et al. Chicken Soup for the Soul: Children with Special Needs: Stories of Love & Understanding for Those Who Care for Children with Disabilities. 2007. (Chicken Soup for the Soul Ser.). (ENG., Illus.). 288p pap. 14.95 *(978-0-7573-0620-4(9))* Health Communications, Inc.

Harbour, Anthony & Mitchell, Mary. Children with Mental Disorder & the Law: A Guide to Law & Practice. 2008. (ENG.). 224p. pap. *(978-1-84310-576-3(4))* Kingsley, Jessica Ltd.

Harrison, Jill. Different Dads: Fathers' Stories of Parenting Disabled Children. Henderson, Matthew & Leonard, Rob, eds. 2007. (ENG.). 16p. pap. *(978-1-84310-454-4(7))* Kingsley, Jessica Ltd.

Helander, Einar. Children & Violence: The World of the Defenceless. 2008. (ENG., Illus.). 288p. 105.00 *(978-0-230-57394-9(0))* Palgrave Macmillan.

Hewitt-Taylor, Jaquelina. Providing Support at Home for Children & Young People Who Have Complex Health Needs. 2008. (ENG.). 216p. pap. 60.99 *(978-0-470-51731-4(X)*, Wiley) Wiley, John & Sons, Inc.

Heymann, Lois Kam. The Sound of Hope: Recognizing, Coping with, & Treating Your Child's Auditory Processing Disorder. 2010. (ENG.). 256p. 25.00 *(978-0-345-51218-5(9)*, Ballantine Bks.) Random House Publishing Group.

Higgins, Martina & Swain, John. Disability & Child Sexual Abuse: Lessons from Survivors' Narratives for Effective Protection, Prevention & Treatment. 2009. (ENG.). 256p. pap. *(978-1-84310-563-3(2))* Kingsley, Jessica Ltd.

Hill, Janelle. Special Needs Families in the Military: A Resource Guide. 2011. (Military Life Ser.). (ENG.). 280p. 34.95 *(978-1-60590-715-4(4))* Government Institutes.

Hill, Janelle & Philpott, Don. Special Needs Families in the Military: A Resource Guide. 2011. (ENG.). 280p. pap. 19.95 *(978-1-60590-767-3(7))* Government Institutes.

Hogan, Dennis. Family Consequences of Children's Disabilities. 2012. pap. ***(978-0-87154-457-5(1))*** Russell Sage Foundation.

Human Kinetics Staff. Brockport Physical Fitness Test CD- Win/Video Update. 2008. cd-rom 149.00 *(978-0-7360-7898-6(3))* Human Kinetics Pubs.

Institute of Psycho-Analysis Staff, contrib. by. Psychoanalytic Study of the Child. viii, 544p. *(978-0-7012-0401-3(X)*, Hogarth Pr.) Random Hse.

Jones, Carroll J. Social & Emotional Development of Exceptional Students: Disabled & Gifted 2nd Edition. 2009. 268p. pap. 72.50 *(978-0-9822229-1-1(2))* Omdee Omnimedia, Inc.

Kalyva, Efrosini. Peer Interpersonal Conflict Resolution in Children with & Without Disabilities. 2011. (Series: Psychology Research Progress Ser.). 90p. pap. 47.00 *(978-1-61209-942-2(4))* Nova Science Pubs., Inc.

Kamata, Suzanne, ed. Love You to Pieces: Creative Writers on Raising a Child with Special Needs. 2008. (ENG.). 272p. pap. 16.00 *(978-0-8070-0030-4(2))* Beacon Pr.

Kay, Janet & Kay. Behavioural, Emotional & Social Difficulties: A Guide for the Early Years. 2007. (Sen in the Early Years Ser.). (ENG.). 160p. 21.95 *(978-0-8264-8469-7(7))* Continuum International Publishing Group, Ltd. GBR. Dist: National Bk. Network.

Kayum, Azeem. Wrestling with the Goddess: A Personal Odyssey. 2008. (ENG.). 176p. 25.95 *(978-0-595-71957-0(0))*; pap. 15.95 *(978-0-595-48564-2(2))* iUniverse, Inc.

Kennedy, Diane M. & Banks, Rebecca S. Bright Not Broken: Gifted Kids, ADHD, & Autism - Why Twice Exceptional Kids Who They Are, Why They're Stuck, & How to Help Them. 2011. (ENG., Illus.). 320p. 24.95 *(978-0-470-62332-9(2)*, Jossey-Bass) Wiley, John & Sons, Inc.

Kleinert, Harold L. & Kearns, Jacqui Farmer. Alternate Assessment for Students with Significant Cognitive Disabilities: An Educator's Guide. 2010. (Illus.). 376p. pap. 39.95 *(978-1-59857-076-2(5))* Brookes, Paul H. Publishing Co.

Korpi, Mary. Guiding Your Teenager with Special Needs Through the Transition from School to Adult Life: Tools for Parents. 2007. (ENG.). 112p. per. *(978-1-84310-874-0(7))* Kingsley, Jessica Ltd.

Kritikos, Effie P., et al. Foundations of Assessment in Early Childhood Special Education. 2011. (ENG., Illus.). 288p. (C). pap. 73.33 *(978-0-13-606423-7(X)*, Prentice Hall) Prentice Hall PTR.

Laes, Christian & Mustakallio, Katariina, eds. The Dark Sides of Childhood: In Late Antiquity & the Middle Ages. 2011. (Childhood in Archaeology Ser.). (ENG.). 130p. (C). pap. 56.00 *(978-1-84217-417-3(7))* Oxbow Bks., Ltd. GBR. Dist: Brown, David Bk. Co., The.

Lane, Sharon E. Green Is the Cure: Everything You Wanted to Know about 504 Plans, IEPs, Learning Disabilities & What the Hell Is in the Food. 2007. 136p. per. 13.95 *(978-0-595-44775-6(9))* iUniverse, Inc.

Lee, April. Let Them Be Free the Tyler Geiger Story. 2009. 84p. pap. 10.49 *(978-1-4389-7866-6(9))* AuthorHouse.

Leicester, Mal. Special Stories for Disability Awareness: Stories & Activities for Teachers, Parents & Professionals. 2006. (ENG., Illus.). 123p. per. *(978-1-84310-390-5(7))* Kingsley, Jessica Ltd.

Levasheff, Christina Adelseck. Eyes that See: Judson's Story of Hope in Suffering. 2010. pap. 16.99 *(978-1-60799-993-5(5))* Tate Publishing & Enterprises, LLC.

Levine, Kathryn. Against All Odds: Resilience in Single Mothers of Children with Disabilities. 2008. 172p. pap. *(978-3-639-07986-9(8))* VDM Verlag Dr. Mueller e.K.

Lewiecki-Wilson, Cynthia & Cellio, Jen. Disability & Mothering: Liminal Spaces of Embodied Knowledge. 2011. ***(978-0-8156-3284-9(3))*** Syracuse Univ. Pr.

Lucan, Dawn. Practical Rare Syndrome Manual. 2010. 76p. pap. 14.95 *(978-0-557-54588-6(5))* Lulu Enterprises Inc.

Malian, Freda. How We Survived Our 'Difficult' Child & Learned to Thrive. 2009. 244p. pap. *(978-1-84747-941-9(3))* Chipmunkapublishing.

Mathieson, Kay. Identifying Special Needs in the Early Years. 2007. (Illus.). 112p. 81.00 *(978-1-4129-2906-6(7)*, B29067C); per. 34.00 *(978-1-4129-2907-3(5)*, B29067P) SAGE Pubns., Ltd. GBR. Dist: SAGE Pubns., Inc.

Matson, Johnny L., ed. Social Behavior & Skills in Children. 2009. (ENG.). x, 334p. 149.95 *(978-1-4419-0233-7(3)*, 1441902333) Springer.

McLaughlin, Janice, et al. Families Raising Disabled Children: Enabling Care & Social Justice. 2008. (ENG., Illus.). 248p. 100.00 *(978-0-230-55145-9(9))* Palgrave Macmillan.

McWilliam, R. A. Routines-Based Early Intervention: Supporting Young Children & Their Families. 2010. (Illus.). 288p. pap. 34.95 *(978-1-59857-062-5(5))* Brookes, Paul H. Publishing Co.

Meyer, Diana J. Chad's Triumph: The Story of the Life of Chad Green. 2007. (Illus.). 221p. per. 17.99 *(978-1-60247-091-0(X))* Tate Publishing & Enterprises, LLC.

Mikita, Steve. I Sit All Amazed: The Extraordinary Power of a Mother's Love. 2011. (Illus.). 128p. pap. 15.99 *(978-1-60641-938-0(2))* Deseret Bk. Co.

Miller, Julie. For Jason a Mother's Story. 2009. 152p. pap. 11.99 *(978-1-4490-1856-6(4))* AuthorHouse.

Mucklow, Nancy. More Comic Sense: More comics & cartoons on common sense & social skills for young People. 2011. (Illus.). 195p. (YA). pap. ***(978-0-9811439-6-5(2))*** Grass, Michael Hse.

Mueller, Kathleen. Facing Autism: A Parent's Guide to a Difficult Journey. 2008. 96p. pap. 11.95 *(978-0-595-48698-4(3))* iUniverse, Inc.

Muir, Kristy. Family Resilience Where Families Have a Child (0-8 years) with Disability: Final Report. 2008. spiral bd. *(978-0-7334-2655-1(7))* Social Policy Research Ctr.

Nadworny, John & Haddad, Cynthia. The Special Needs Planning Guide: How to Prepare for Every Stage in Your Child's Life. 2007. 310p. pap. 29.95 incl. cd-rom *(978-1-55766-802-8(7))* Brookes, Paul H. Publishing Co.

Naidoo, Pravani. The Experiences of Children with Disabilities in Therapeutic Riding. 2010. 308p. pap. *(978-3-8383-6474-2(0))* Lambert Academic Publishing.

Norwich, Brahm. Dilemmas of Difference, Inclusion & Disability: International Perspectives & Future Directions. 2007. (Illus.). X, 230p. 44.95 *(978-0-415-39847-3(9))*; 145.00 *(978-0-415-39846-6(0))* Taylor & Francis Group.

Palm Beach Community College & Children and Families Research Group Staff. Special Needs Appropriate Practices. rev. ed. 2009. (ENG.). 222p. pap. 24.15 *(978-0-7575-5482-7(2))* Kendall Hunt Publishing Co.

Parritz, Robin Hornik & Troy, Michael F. Disorders of Childhood: Development & Psychopathology. 2010. (ENG.). 488p. (C). 106.95 *(978-0-534-59274-5(0))* Wadsworth.

Patton, Sally. Don't Fix Me; I'm Not Broken: Changing Our Minds about Ourselves & Our Children. 2011. (ENG.). 168p. pap. 19.95 *(978-1-84694-466-6(X))* Hunt, John Publishing Ltd. GBR. Dist: National Bk. Network.

Paun, Margaret Voysey. A Constant Burden: The Reconstitution of Family Life. 2nd rev. ed. 2006. (Ashgate Classics in Sociology Ser.). 254p. 120.00 *(978-0-7546-4470-5(7))* Ashgate Publishing Co.

Pearson, Eric P. Ryan's Stories: God's Perfect Child. 2007. pap. 14.95 *(978-0-9799461-0-3(7))* California Dreamer Publishing, LLC.

Pepin, Ricki. God's Health Plan - the Audacious Journey to a Better Life. 2007. 308p. per. 17.99 *(978-1-60266-698-6(9))* Xulon Pr., Inc.

Peterson, Carla, et al, eds. Young Exceptional Children Monograph Series No. 9: Linking Curriculum to Child & Family Outcomes. 2007. (Young Exceptional Children Ser.). 100p. per. 15.00 *(978-0-9773772-7-5(X))* Division for Early Childhood.

Pike, Donna. Bradley's Journey Home. 2008. 188p. pap. 14.49 *(978-1-4389-2609-4(X))* AuthorHouse.

A Practical Guide to Estate Planning for a Family with a Special Needs Child. 2009. pap. *(978-0-8318-9992-9(1))* American Law Institute.

Price, Margaret "Pegi". Divorce & the Special Needs Child: A Guide for Parents. 2010. (ENG., Illus.). 256p. pap. *(978-1-84905-825-4(3))* Kingsley, Jessica Ltd.

Price, Margaret S. Special Needs Children & Divorce: A Practical Guide to Handling & Evaluating Cases. 12th ed. 2010. (ENG., Illus.). xiv, 343p. pap. 99.95 incl. cd-rom *(978-1-60442-492-8(3))* American Bar Assn.

Remembering Alexis: Finding Perspective in Love & Loss. 2009. (ENG., Illus.). 216p. lib. bdg. 24.99 *(978-0-9822357-0-6(4))* Strider International.

Reston, James Jr. Fragile Innocence: A Father's Memoir of His Daughter's Courageous Journey. 2007. (ENG.). 272p. pap. 13.95 *(978-1-4000-8244-5(7)*, Three Rivers Pr.) Crown Publishing Group.

Riddick-Grisham, Susan & Deming, Laura, eds. Pediatric Life Care Planning & Case Management, Second Edition. 2nd rev. ed. 2011. (ENG., Illus.). 1051p. 159.95 *(978-1-4398-0358-5(7)*, CRC Press) Taylor & Francis Group GBR. Dist: Taylor & Francis Group.

Rizzo, David. Faith, Family, & Children with Special Needs: How Catholic Parents & Their Kids with Special Needs Can Develop a Richer Spiritual Life. 2012. (ENG.). 112p. pap. 12.95 ***(978-0-8294-3651-8(0))*** Loyola Pr.

Roberts, Laura. By Faith: A family's search for meaning in Suffering. 2009. pap. 12.99 *(978-1-60799-836-5(X))* Tate Publishing & Enterprises, LLC.

Roozeboom, Bev. Unlocking the Treasure: A Bible Study for Moms Entrusted with Special-Needs Children. 2011. 132p. pap. 16.95 ***(978-1-4497-1599-1(0)***, WestBow Pr.) Author Solutions, Inc.

Ross, Ruth Herron & Roberts-Pacchione, Beth. Making Friends, PreK-3: A Social Skills Program for Inclusive Settings. 2nd ed. 2011. (Illus.). 232p. pap. 33.95 *(978-1-4129-8113-2(1)*, B81132P) Corwin Pr.

Ryals, Tammy. Meet the Challenge: One Family's Journey Raising a Child with Multiple Severe Disabilities. 2009. pap. 10.99 *(978-1-60799-868-6(8))* Tate Publishing & Enterprises, LLC.

Seligman, Milton & Darling, Rosalyn Benjamin. Ordinary Families, Special Children: A Systems Approach to Childhood Disability. 3rd rev. ed. 2007. (ENG., Illus.). 434p. 65.00 *(978-1-59385-362-4(9))* Guilford Pubns., Inc.

—Ordinary Families, Special Children, Third Edition: A Systems Approach to Childhood Disability. 3rd ed. 2009. (ENG.). 434p. pap. 40.00 *(978-1-60623-317-7(3))* Guilford Pubns., Inc.

Shapiro, Lawerence. Learning to Listen, Learning to Care: A Workbook to Help Kids Learn Self-Control & Empathy. 2008. (Instant Help Ser.). 130p. pap. 16.95 *(978-1-931704-37-3(6))* Play2Grow.

Sher, Barbara. Early Intervention Games: Fun, Joyful Ways to Develop Social & Motor Skills in Children with Autism Spectrum or Sensory Processing Disorders. 2009. (ENG., Illus.). 252p. pap. 16.95 *(978-0-470-39126-6(X),* Jossey-Bass) Wiley, John & Sons, Inc.

Smerglia, Pamela. Tourette's Syndrome: Our Story, Everything We Wish We Were Told, & Hints We Learned along the Way. 2007. 48p. pap. 16.95 *(978-1-60441-275-8(5))* PublishAmerica, Inc.

Smith, Traci. In Our Skin. 2010. 16p. 12.99 *(978-1-4520-6594-6(2))* AuthorHouse.

Soper, Kathryn. The Year My Son & I Were Born: A Story of down Syndrome, Motherhood, & Self-Discovery. 2010. (ENG.). 336p. pap. 12.95 *(978-0-7627-6034-3(6))* Globe Pequot Pr., The.

Soper, Kathryn L., ed. Gifts: Mothers Reflect on How Children with down Syndrome Enrich Their Lives. 2007. (Illus.). 292p. per. 18.95 *(978-1-890627-85-0(2))* Woodbine Hse.

Stepanek, Jeni. Messenger: The Legacy of Mattie J. T. Stepanek & Heartsongs. 2010. (ENG.). 336p. (gr. 12). 15.00 *(978-0-451-23114-7(7),* N A L Trade) Penguin Group (USA) Inc.

Stepanek, Jeni & Lindner, Larry. Messenger: The Legacy of Mattie J. T. Stepanek & Heartsongs. 2009. (ENG.). 336p. (gr. 12). 25.95 *(978-0-525-95142-1(3),* Dutton Adult) Penguin Group (USA) Inc.

Stephenson, Karen. Let Them Fly: A Mother's Account of Twins & Disabilities. 2008. 80p. pap. 14.99 *(978-1-4389-0505-1(X))* AuthorHouse.

Strauss & Begley, Thomas D. Special Needs Trusts Handbook. 2008. ring bd. 260.00 *(978-0-7355-7288-1(7))* Wolters Kluwer Law & Business.

Strohm, Kate. Being the Other One: Growing up with a Brother or Sister Who Has Special Needs. 2009. (ENG.). 249p. pap. 15.00 *(978-1-4379-6612-1(8))* DIANE Publishing Co.

Teare, Jean, ed. Caring for Children with Complex Needs in the Community. 2008. (ENG., Illus.). 208p. pap. 62.99 *(978-1-4051-5177-1(3),* Wiley-Blackwell) Wiley, John & Sons, Inc.

Thambirajah, M. S. Developmental Assessment of the School-Aged Child with Developmental Disabilities: A Clinician's Guide. 2011. (ENG., Illus.). 336p. pap. *(978-1-84905-181-1(X))* Kingsley, Jessica Ltd.

Thompson, Charlotte E. Grandparenting a Child with Special Needs. 2009. (ENG.). 224p. pap. *(978-1-84310-906-8(9))* Kingsley, Jessica Ltd.

Thomson, Donna. The Four Walls of My Freedom. (ENG., Illus.). 2012. 262p. pap. 18.95 ***(978-1-55278-986-5(1))*** 2010. 200p. 29.95 *(978-1-55278-890-5(3))* McArthur & Co. CAN. Dist: National Bk. Network.

Trail, Beverly & Prufrock Press Inc. Staff. Twice-Exceptional Gifted Children: Understanding, Teaching, & Counseling Gifted Students. 2010. (ENG.). 275p. pap. 24.95 *(978-1-59363-489-6(7))* Prufrock Pr.

Turnbull, Jackie & Stewart, Trudy. Helping Children Cope with Stammering. (Illus.). 115p. *(978-0-85969-728-6(2),* Sheldon Press) SPCK Publishing.

UNICEF: Innocenti Research Centre. Promoting the rights of children with Disabilities. 2008. (ENG., Illus.). 76p. pap. 18.00 *(978-88-89129-60-9(3))* United Nations Pubns.

United Nations Children's Fund. Children & Disability in Transition in CEE/CIS & Baltic States. 2009. (Insight Innocenti Ser.). 84p. pap. 20.00 *(978-88-89129-20-3(4))* United Nations Children's Fund, The (UNICEF).

Viscardi Jr., Henry. A Letter to Jimmy: A Book of Hope & Encouragement. 2011. 174p. 42.95 ***(978-1-258-06523-2(1))*** Literary Licensing, LLC.

Von Ende, Teri. Decoding the Special Needs Child: With a Comprehensive Resource Guide for Parents. 2007. 324p. per. 29.95 *(978-1-4241-9043-0(6))* PublishAmerica, Inc.

Welch, Debra. Son of My Soul - the Adoption of Christopher. 2007. 140p. per. *(978-1-894936-93-4(0))* Saga Bks.

West, Tricia. DiGeorge & Sean. 2010. 48p. pap. 9.95 *(978-1-4502-3497-9(6))* iUniverse, Inc.

Wilder, Lynn K. & King-Peery, Karolyn. Family HOPE Program Guide: Positive Behavior Support for Families of Children with Challenging Behaviors. 2011. pap. 18.95 ***(978-0-87822-610-8(9))*** Research Pr.

Winslet, Kate & Ericsdottir, Margret. The Golden Hat: Talking Back to Autism. 2012. (ENG., Illus.). 256p. 29.95 *(978-1-4516-4543-9(0))* Simon & Schuster.

Wise, Alicia L. My Angel Kiss: Overcoming Disfigurement through the Transforming Power of Love. 2010. pap. 8.99 *(978-1-61663-597-8(5))* Tate Publishing & Enterprises, LLC.

Wise, Paul H., et al. A Critical Analysis of Care Coordination Strategies for Children with Special Health Care Needs. 2007. v, 35p. *(978-1-58763-262-4(4))* Agency for Healthcare Research & Quality.

Wood, Karren/Ikeda & Youcha, Victoria. The ABCs of the ADA: Your Early Childhood Program's Guide to the Americans with Disabilities Act. 2nd ed. 2008. (Illus.). 256p. 29.95 *(978-1-55766-933-9(3))* Brookes, Paul H. Publishing Co.

CHILDREN WITH DISABILITIES—BIBLIOGRAPHY

Lierow, Diane, et al. Dani's Story: A Journey from Neglect to Love. 2011. (ENG., Illus.). 272p. 24.95 *(978-0-470-59133-8(1),* Wiley) Wiley, John & Sons, Inc.

CHILDREN WITH DISABILITIES—EDUCATION

Ackerman, Beth & Quigley, Katherine, eds. Life Skills Instruction in a Time of Accountability. 2010. (Disability & the Disabled - Issues, Laws & Programs Ser.). pap. 43.00 *(978-1-61668-780-9(0))* Nova Science Pubs., Inc.

Aguoji, Josephine Uzoamaka. Retention of Culture As Inequity. 2008. 48p. pap. 15.99 *(978-1-4363-5994-8(5))* Xlibris Corp.

Allan, Julie. Rethinking Inclusive Education: The Philosophers of Difference in Practice. 2007. (Inclusive Education: Cross Cultural Perspectives Ser.). 186p. 149.00 *(978-1-4020-6092-2(0))* Springer.

—Rethinking Inclusive Education: the Philosophers of Difference in Practice: The Philosophers of Difference in Practice. 2010. (Inclusive Education: Cross Cultural Perspectives Ser.). ix, 186p. pap. 149.00 *(978-90-481-7532-1(1),* 9048175321) Springer.

Allen, Eileen K. & Cowdery, Glynnis Edwards. Exceptional Child: Inclusion in Early Childhood Education. 6th ed. 2008. (ENG.). 126p. (C). 23.95 *(978-1-4180-7404-3(7))* Wadsworth.

—The Exceptional Child: Inclusion in Early Childhood Education. 7th ed. 2011. (PSY 683 Psychology of the Exceptional Child Ser.). (ENG.). 648p. (C). pap. 157.95 *(978-1-111-34210-4(5))* Wadsworth.

Ambrose, Mary. Kindergarten Fun. 2009. pap. 134.67 *(978-0-13-515403-8(0))* Pearson Education.

Anderson, Susan. In Pursuit of Excellence. 2010. 512p. pap. *(978-3-639-26304-6(9))* VDM Verlag Dr. Mueller e.K.

Angermeier, Patricia, et al. Learning in Motion: 101+ Sensory Activities for the Classroom. 2nd ed. 2009. (ENG., Illus.). 350p. pap. 39.95 *(978-1-932565-90-4(6))* Future Horizons, Inc.

Appelbaum, Maryln. How to Handle Hard-to-Handle Preschoolers: A Guide for Early Childhood Educators. 2009. (Illus.). 136p. pap. 24.95 *(978-1-4129-7003-7(2),* B00720P) Corwin Pr.

—How to Handle the Hard-to-Handle Student, K-5. 2008. 136p. 66.95 *(978-1-4129-6438-8(5),* B64385C); pap. 27.95 *(978-1-4129-6439-5(3),* B64385P) Corwin Pr.

Archer, Anita L. & Hughes, Charles A. Explicit Instruction: Effective & Efficient Teaching. 2010. (What Works for Special-Needs Learners Ser.). (ENG.). 290p. (gr. k-12). pap. 40.00 *(978-1-60918-041-6(0))* Guilford Pubns., Inc.

Ashbaker, Betty Y. & Minney, R. Brent. Planning Your Paraprofessional's Path: An Administrator's Legal Compliance & Training Guide. 2007. *(978-1-57834-078-1(0))* LRP Pubns.

Aune, Beth, et al. Behavior Solutions for the Inclusive Classroom: See a Behavior? Look It Up! 2010. (ENG., Illus.). 120p. pap. 14.95 *(978-1-935274-08-7(2))* Future Horizons, Inc.

Auxter, David & Pyfer, Jean. Gross Motor Activities for Small Children with Special Needs to accompany Principals & Methods of Adapted PE & Recreation. 2009. 96p. pap. 22.00 *(978-0-07-335831-4(2))* McGraw-Hill Professional Publishing.

Baca, Jimmy Santiago. Stories from the Edge. 2010. 112p. pap. 12.44 *(978-0-325-02948-1(2),* E02948) Heinemann.

Bagnato, Stephen J. Authentic Assessment for Early Childhood Intervention: Best Practices. 2007. (Guilford School Practitioner Ser.). (ENG., Illus.). 315p. 55.00 *(978-1-59385-474-4(9))* Guilford Pubns., Inc.

Bailey, Craig. Into the Darkness: Children behind Bars. 2008. 256p. pap. *(978-3-639-06138-3(1))* VDM Verlag Dr. Mueller e.K.

Bakken, Jeffrey/P & Obiakor, Festus E. Transition Planning for Students with Disabilities: What Educators & Service Providers Can Do. 2008. 214p. (Illus.). *(978-0-398-07788-4(6));* pap. *(978-0-398-07789-1(4))* Thomas, Charles C. Pub., Ltd.

Barnett, David. Privileged Thinking in Today's Schools: The Implications for Social Justice. 2010. (ENG.). 125p. 49.95 *(978-1-60709-969-7(1))* Rowman & Littlefield Education.

Barratt, Sarah J. The Special Educator's Tool Kit. 2008. (Illus.). 220p. (C). pap. 31.00 *(978-81-7829-897-9(X),* B98979P) SAGE Pubns., Inc.

Barry, Tammy. An Introduction to Children with Autism. 2009. (ENG.). pap. 12.95 *(978-1-59363-370-7(X))* Prufrock Pr.

Barry, Tammy D. Enhancing Communication in Children with Autism Spectrum Disorders. 2010. (ENG.). 72p. pap. 12.95 *(978-1-59363-409-4(9))* Prufrock Pr.

Bartlett, Larry D., et al. Special Education Law & Practice in Public Schools. 2nd rev. ed. 2006. (ENG., Illus.). 400p. (C). pap. 89.20 *(978-0-13-220714-0(1),* Prentice Hall) Prentice Hall PTR.

Baumberger, Julie P. & Harper, Ruth E. Assisting Students with Disabilities: A Handbook for School Counselors. 2nd rev. ed. 2006. 160p. pap. 27.95 *(978-1-4129-4182-2(2),* B41814P) Corwin Pr.

Beard, Lawrence A., et al. Assistive Technology: Access for All Students. 2nd ed. 2010. (ENG.). 208p. (C). pap. 44.60 *(978-0-13-705641-5(9),* Prentice Hall) Prentice Hall PTR.

Bender, Michael. A Functional Assessment & Curriculum for Teaching Students with Disabilities, 4 vols. 4th ed. 2008. (Illus.). 53.00 *(978-1-4164-0221-3(7));* 53.00 *(978-1-4164-0222-0(5));* 53.00 *(978-1-4164-0223-7(3))* PRO-ED, Inc.

—A Functional Curriculum for Teaching Students with Disabilities. 4th ed. 2007. 53.00 *(978-1-4164-0220-6(9))* PRO-ED, Inc.

Benner, Susan M. & Grim, Joan. Assessment of Young Children with Special Needs. 2nd rev. ed. 2012. (ENG., Illus.). 288p. 150.00 ***(978-0-415-88568-3(X))***; pap. 55.95 ***(978-0-415-88569-0(8))*** Routledge.

Benoliel, Jennifer. Autism & PDD Photo Cards Wh Questions. 2007. (J). 89.95 *(978-0-7606-9994-2(1))* LinguiSystems, Inc.

Berninger, Virginia W. & Wolf, Beverly J. Helping Students with Dyslexia & Dysgraphia Make Connections: Differentiated Instruction Lesson Plans in Reading & Writing. 2009. 424p. spiral bd. 64.95 *(978-1-59857-021-2(8))* Brookes, Paul H. Publishing Co.

Best, Sherwood, et al. Teaching Individuals with Physical & Multiple Disabilities. 6th ed. 2009. (ENG.). 576p. (C). pap. 142.20 *(978-0-13-159012-0(X),* Prentice Hall) Prentice Hall PTR.

Birnbaum, Barry W. English Language Learners with Disbilities: A Resource Guide for Educators. 2008. 120p. 89.95 *(978-0-7734-4991-6(4))* Mellen, Edwin Pr., The.

Birnbaum, Ruth. Choosing a School for a Child with Special Needs. 2009. (ENG., Illus.). 304p. pap. *(978-1-84310-987-7(5))* Kingsley, Jessica Ltd.

Bore, Julie Chelagat. Voices. 2011. 216p. pap. 23.99 ***(978-1-4634-8756-0(8))*** AuthorHouse.

Boutot, E. Amanda & Myles, Brenda Smith. Autism Spectrum Disorders: Foundations, Characteristics, & Effective Strategies. 2010. (ENG.). 320p. (C). pap. 52.60 *(978-0-205-54575-9(0),* Prentice Hall) Prentice Hall PTR.

Bowe & Cram101 Textbook Reviews Staff. Birth To: Early Childhood Special Education. 2007. 120p. per. 11.95 *(978-1-4288-1982-5(7))* Cram101 Inc.

Bowe, Frank G. Early Childhood Special Education: Birth to Eight. 4th rev. ed. 2007. (ENG.). 496p. (C). pap. 189.95 *(978-1-4180-4810-5(0))* Delmar Cengage Learning.

Boyle, Joseph & Scanlon, David. Methods & Strategies for Teaching Students with Mild Disabilities: A Case-Based Approach. 2009. (ENG.). 576p. (C). pap. 134.95 *(978-0-618-39689-4(6),* 305361) Wadsworth.

Brajkovic, Reanna. Socialization of Children with Disabilities. 2010. 88p. pap. *(978-3-8383-8624-9(8))* Lambert Academic Publishing.

Breitenbach, Marlene. Basic Skills Checklists: Teacher-Friendly Assessment for Students with Autism or Special Needs. 2008. (ENG., Illus.). 53p. spiral bd. 19.95 *(978-1-932565-75-1(2))* Future Horizons, Inc.

Brock, Stephen E., et al. Identifying, Assessing, & Treating ADHD at School. 2009. (Developmental Psychopathology at School Ser.). (Illus.). xi, 168p. pap. 49.95 *(978-1-4419-5990-4(4),* 1441959904) Springer.

Broun, Leslie & Oelwein, Patricia. Literacy Skill Development for Students with Special Learning Needs: A Strengths-Based Approach. 2007. pap. 29.95 *(978-1-934032-07-7(7),* Dude Publishing) National Professional Resources, Inc.

Browder, Diane M. & Spooner, Fred. Teaching Students with Moderate & Severe Disabilities. 2011. (ENG.). 429p. (gr. k-12). 75.00 *(978-1-60623-991-9(0))* Guilford Pubns., Inc.

Brower, Francine. 100 Ideas for Supporting Pupils on the Autistic Spectrum. 2007. (Continuum One Hundreds Ser.). (ENG., Illus.). 128p. 20.95 *(978-0-8264-9421-4(8))* Continuum International Publishing Group, Ltd. GBR. Dist: National Bk. Network.

Brueggemann, Brenda Jo & Lewiecki-Wilson, Cynthia. Disability & the Teaching of Writing: A Critical Sourcebook. 2007. (ENG.). 320p. (C). per. 43.95 *(978-0-312-44725-0(6))* Bedford/Saint Martin's.

Brunswick. Reading & Dyslexia in Different Orthographies. 2010. (ENG., Illus.). 336p. 69.95 *(978-1-84169-712-3(5),* Psychology Press) Taylor & Francis Group GBR. Dist: Taylor & Francis Group.

Brustein & Manasevit. Idea: New Expectations for Schools & Students. 3rd ed. 2007. 565p. per. *(978-1-933807-22-5(9))* Thompson Media Group LLC.

Bryant, Brian R., et al. Teaching Students with Special Needs in Inclusive Classrooms. 2007. (ENG., Illus.). 656p. (C). per. 139.40 *(978-0-205-43092-5(9))* Allyn & Bacon, Inc.

Bugaj, Christopher R. & Norton-Darr, Sally. The Practical (And Fun) Guide to Assistive Technology in Public Schools. 2010. (Illus.). 200p. pap. *(978-1-56484-263-3(0))* International Society for Technology in Education.

Burns, Edward. The Essential SPECIAL EDUCATION GUIDE for the Regular Education Teacher. 2007. 326p. *(978-0-398-07754-9(1))*; pap. *(978-0-398-07755-6(X))* Thomas, Charles C. Pub., Ltd.

Buron, Kari Dunn. A 5 Is Against the Law! Social Boundaries - Straight Up! - An Honest Guide to Teens & Young Adults. 2007. (Illus.). 48p. (YA). (gr. 7-14). per. 20.95 *(978-1-931282-35-2(8))* Autism Asperger Publishing Co.

Capul, Maurice & David, Monique. L'invention de L'enfance Inadaptée: L'exemple de Toulouse Saint-Simon, 1950-1975. 2010. (FRE.). 588p. *(978-2-7492-1289-0(8))* Eres Editions.

Carter, Nari J., et al. What Every Teacher Should Know About: Adaptations & Accommodations for Students with Mild to Moderate Disabilities. 2008. (What Every Teacher Should Know about... (WETSKA Series) Ser.). (ENG.). 176p. (C). pap. 20.00 *(978-0-205-60836-2(1))* Allyn & Bacon, Inc.

Castelli, Perry Anthony & Castelli, Vivian Lois. Exploring the Foundations of American Education. 2007. ring bd. *(978-0-9714972-1-4(4))* Sheepdog Publishing of Lakeland.

Castillo, Christine L. Children with Complex Medical Issues in Schools: Neuropsychological Descriptions & Interventions. 2008. (Illus.). 79.00 *(978-0-8261-2472-2(0))* Springer Publishing Co., Inc.

Causton-Theoharis, Julie. The Paraprofessional's Handbook for Effective Support in Inclusive Classrooms. 2009. 144p. pap. 26.95 *(978-1-55766-899-8(X))* Brookes, Paul H. Publishing Co.

Chafouleas, Sandra, et al. School-Based Behavioral Assessment: Informing Intervention & Instruction. 2007. (Guilford Practical Intervention in the Schools Ser.). (ENG.). 148p. (gr. k-12). pap. 35.00 *(978-1-59385-494-2(3))* Guilford Pubns., Inc.

Chapman, Randy. The Everyday Guide to Special Education Law: A Handbook for Parents, Teachers & Other Professionals. 2nd ed. 2008. 140p. per. 24.95 *(978-0-9770179-3-5(1))* Legal Ctr. for People with Disabilities, The.

Charema, John. Counseling Parents of Pupils with Special Educational Needs. 2010. 260p. pap. *(978-3-8383-4465-2(0))* Lambert Academic Publishing.

Chopra, Ritu. Parent-Paraeducator Collaboration in Inclusive Classrooms. 2009. 224p. pap. *(978-3-639-15793-2(1))* VDM Verlag Dr. Mueller e.K.

Cochrane, Katrina & Wood, Tracey. Understanding & Managing Dyslexia for Dummies. 2009. (ENG., Illus.). 388p. pap. 27.95 ***(978-0-470-74132-0(5),*** For Dummies) Wiley, John & Sons, Inc.

Cohen, Libby G. & Spenciner, Loraine J. Teaching Students with Mild & Moderate Disabilities: Research-Based Practices. 2nd ed. 2008. (ENG.). 576p. (C). pap. 129.80 *(978-0-13-233138-8(1),* Prentice Hall) Prentice Hall PTR.

Cohen, Matthew. A Guide to Special Education Advocacy: What Parents, Clinicians & Advocates Need to Know. 2009. (ENG., Illus.). 304p. *(978-1-84310-893-1(3))* Kingsley, Jessica Ltd.

Colker, Ruth & Waterstone, Julie K. Special Education Advocacy. 2011. *(978-1-4224-7958-2(7))* LexisNexis Matthew Bender.

Cook, Ruth E., et al. Adapting Early Childhood Curricula for Children with Special Needs. 8th rev. ed. 2011. (ENG., Illus.). 528p. (C). pap. 112.00 ***(978-0-13-259678-7(4),*** Prentice Hall) Prentice Hall PTR.

Coombs, Norman. Making Online Teaching Accessible: Inclusive Course Design for Students with Disabilities. 2010. (Jossey-Bass Guides to Online Teaching & Learning Ser.: 17). (ENG., Illus.). 192p. pap. 29.00 *(978-0-470-49904-7(4),* Jossey-Bass) Wiley, John & Sons, Inc.

Cooper, Paul & Jacobs, Barbara. From Inclusion to Engagement: Helping Students Engage with Schooling Through Policy & Practice. 2011. (ENG., Illus.). 258p. 99.95 *(978-0-470-66484-1(3),* Wiley) Wiley, John & Sons, Inc.

Copeland, Susan & Keefe, Elizabeth. Effective Literacy Instruction for Students with Moderate or Severe Disabilities. 2007. 197p. per. 27.95 *(978-1-55766-837-0(X))* Brookes, Paul H. Publishing Co.

Corrigan, Joshua J., ed. Individuals with Disabilities Education Act: Developments. 2010. (Education in a Competitive & Globalizing World Ser.). x, 202p. 130.00 *(978-1-61728-272-0(3))* Nova Science Pubs., Inc.

Courter, Margo Kinzer. Here's How Children Learn Speech & Language: A Text on Different Learning Strategies. 2011. 185p. pap. 79.95 *(978-1-59756-366-6(8))* Plural Publishing, Inc.

Cram101 Textbook Reviews. Outlines & Highlights for Assessment of Exceptional Students by Ronald L Taylor. 2011. 130p. pap. 28.95 ***(978-1-61906-031-9(0))*** Cram101 Inc.

—Outlines & Highlights for Elementary Classroom Management: Lessons from Research & Practice by Carol Simon Weinstein. 2011. 94p. pap. 27.95 ***(978-1-61830-723-1(1))*** Cram101 Inc.

Cram101 Textbook Reviews. Outlines & Highlights for the Exceptional Child: Inclusion in Early Childhood Education by Eileen K. Allen, Glynnis Edwards Cowdery, ISBN. 2010. 72p. pap. 27.95 *(978-1-61698-709-1(X))* Cram101 Inc.

Cram101 Textbook Reviews & Cram101 Textbook Reviews. Outlines & Highlights for Characteristics of & Strategies for Teaching Students with Mild Disabilities by Martin R Henley, Isbn: 9780205608386. 2011. 182p. pap. 29.95 ***(978-1-61744-949-9(0))*** Cram101 Inc.

—Outlines & Highlights for Creating Inclusive Learning Environments for Young Children: What to Do on Monday Morning by Clarissa Ann Willis, ISBN. 2011. 96p. pap. 27.95 ***(978-1-4288-3352-4(8))*** Cram101 Inc.

—Outlines & Highlights for Early Childhood Special Education: Birth to Eight by Frank G. Bowe, ISBN. 2011. 126p. pap. 28.95 ***(978-1-61744-896-6(6))*** Cram101 Inc.

—Outlines & Highlights for Every Child Can Learn: Using Learning Tools & Play to Help Children with Developmental Delay by Katrin Stroh, ISBN. 2011. 60p. pap. 26.95 ***(978-1-4288-6133-6(5))*** Cram101 Inc.

—Outlines & Highlights for Exceptional Lives by Ann P Turnbull, Isbn: 0135026962 9780135026960 9780136101413 0136101410. 2011. 230p. pap. 31.95 ***(978-1-4288-8908-8(6))*** Cram101 Inc.

—Outlines & Highlights for Inclusion Strategies for Young Children: A Resource Guide for Teachers, Child Care Providers, & Parents by Lorraine Moore. 2011. 90p. pap. 27.95 ***(978-1-61461-096-0(7))*** Cram101 Inc.

—Outlines & Highlights for the Exceptional Child: Inclusion in Early Childhood Education by Eileen Allen, ISBN. 2011. 128p. pap. 28.95 ***(978-1-61461-104-2(1))*** Cram101 Inc.

—Outlines & Highlights for Understanding Physical, Health, & Multiple Disabilities by Kathryn Wolff Heller, Paul a Alberto, Paula E Forney, Isbn. 2011. 268p. pap. 31.95 ***(978-1-61490-535-6(5))*** Cram101 Inc.

—Outlines & Highlights for Young Children with Special Needs by Stephen R Hooper, Isbn: 9780131590144. 2011. 88p. pap. 27.95 ***(978-1-61698-392-5(2))*** Cram101 Inc.

Crick, Wendy Anne. From Learning Disabled to Enabled: A Mother's Journey to Find an Effective Way to Teach Reading to Her Daughter & the Children She Teaches. 2010. 112p. pap. 12.80 *(978-1-4269-0178-2(X))* Trafford Publishing.

Curriculum, Assessment & Instruction for Students with Disabilities: Instructor's Manual. pap. *(978-0-534-16771-4(3))* Wadsworth.

Davies, Christopher. Creating Multi-Sensory Environments. 2012. (David Fulton / Nasen Ser.). (ENG., Illus.). 176p. 155.00 ***(978-0-415-57329-0(7))***; pap. 33.95 ***(978-0-415-57330-6(0))*** Routledge.

Davis, E. Ann. Physical Activities in the Wheelchair & Out: An Illustrated Guide to Personalizing Participation. 2011. (Illus.). 136p. pap. 24.00 ***(978-1-4504-0199-9(6))*** Human Kinetics Pubs.

Davis, Kim & Dixon, Susan D. When Actions Speak Louder Than Words: Understanding the Challenging Behaviors of Young Children & Students with Disabilities. 2009. pap. 29.95 *(978-1-934009-60-4(1))*; lib. bdg. 64.95 *(978-1-935249-13-9(4))* Solution Tree Pr.

Dettmer, Peggy, et al. Collaboration, Consultation & Teamwork for Students with Special Needs. 7th rev. ed. 2012. (ENG.). 480p. (C). pap. 124.20 *(978-0-13-265967-3(0))*, Prentice Hall) Prentice Hall PTR.

Dewis, Pam & Dewis. Medical Conditions: A Guide for the Early Years. 2007. (Sen in the Early Years Ser.). (ENG., Illus.). 144p. 21.95 *(978-0-8264-8475-8(1))* Continuum International Publishing Group, Ltd. GBR. Dist: National Bk. Network.

Dinnebeil, Laurie A. & McInerney, William F. A Guide to Itinerant Early Childhood Services. 2011. (Illus.). xi, 243p. pap. *(978-1-557-6696-5(9))* Brookes, Paul H. Publishing Co.

Dittrich, Winand H. & Tutt, Rona. Educating Children with Complex Conditions: Understanding Overlapping & Co-existing Developmental Disorders. 2008. (Illus.). 128p. pap. 33.00 *(978-1-84787-316-7(9)*, B73170P) SAGE Pubns., Ltd. GBR. Dist: SAGE Pubns., Inc.

—Educating Children with Complex Conditions: Understanding Overlapping & Co-Existing Developmental Disorders. 2008. (Illus.). 128p. 76.00 *(978-1-84787-317-0(0)*, B73170C) SAGE Pubns., Ltd. GBR. Dist: SAGE Pubns., Inc.

Dowling, Jan Lavenger & Mitchell, Terri. I Belong: Active Learning for Children with Special Needs. 2007. *(978-1-57379-322-3(1))* High/Scope Pr.

Downing, June E. Including Students with Severe & Multiple Disabilities in Typical Classrooms: Practical Strategies for Teachers. 3rd ed. 2008. (Illus.). 352p. pap. 44.95 *(978-1-55766-908-7(2))* Brookes, Paul H. Publishing Co.

Doyle, Mary Beth, ed. Quick Guides to Inclusion: Ideas for Educating Students with Disabilities. 2nd ed. 2007. (Illus.). 324p. per. 39.95 *(978-1-55766-897-4(3))* Brookes, Paul H. Publishing Co.

Dunn, Rita Stafford & Honigsfeld, Andrea. Differentiating Instruction for At-Risk Students: What to Do & How to Do It. 2009. (ENG.). 202p. 74.95 *(978-1-57886-982-4(X))*; pap. 28.95 *(978-1-57886-983-1(8))* Rowman & Littlefield Education.

Duran, Elva. Teaching English Learners in Inclusive Classrooms. 3rd ed. 2006. (Illus.). 506p. 92.95 *(978-0-398-07674-0(X))*; pap. 67.95 *(978-0-398-07675-7(8))* Thomas, Charles C. Pub., Ltd.

Edwards, Sylvia. The Senco Survival Guide. 2011. (David Fulton / Nasen Ser.). (ENG., Illus.). 192p. pap. 28.95 *(978-0-415-59281-9(X))* Routledge.

Enoch, Jessica. Refiguring Rhetorical Education: Women Teaching African American, Native American, & Chicano/A Students, 1865-1911. 2008. (ENG., Illus.). 240p. pap. 35.00 *(978-0-8093-2835-2(6))* Southern Illinois Univ. Pr.

Evans, Linda. Senco at a Glance: A Toolkit for Success. 2008. (ENG., Illus.). 80p. 34.95 *(978-0-8264-9564-8(8))* Continuum International Publishing Group, Ltd. GBR. Dist: National Bk. Network.

Evans, Linda & East, Viv. At a Glance. 2nd ed. 2006. (ENG., Illus.). 80p. 31.95 *(978-0-8264-9151-0(0))* Continuum International Publishing Group, Ltd. GBR. Dist: National Bk. Network.

Fagen, Friedman & Fulfrost Staff, contrib. by. IDEA Due Process Survival Guide: A Step-By-Step Companion for Administrators & Attorneys. 2008. *(978-1-57834-105-4(1))* LRP Pubns.

Farrell. The Special Needs Handbook. 2007. (David Fulton / Nasen Ser.). (Illus.). 184p. 47.50 *(978-0-415-41586-3(8))*; 160.00 *(978-0-415-41685-6(X))* Routledge.

Farrell, Michael. Educating Special Children. 2nd rev. ed. 2012. (ENG., Illus.). 344p. 180.00 ***(978-0-415-52369-1(9))***; pap. 51.95 ***(978-0-415-52370-7(2))*** Routledge.

—The Effective Teacher's Guide to Sensory & Physical Impairments. 2nd rev. ed. 2011. (Effective Teacher's Guides). (ENG., Illus.). 144p. pap. 31.95 *(978-0-415-56565-3(0))* Routledge.

—The Effective Teacher's Guide to Sensory & Physical Impairments: Sensory, Orthopaedic, Motor & Health Impairments, & Traumatic Brain Injury. 2nd rev. ed. 2011. (Effective Teacher's Guides). (ENG., Illus.). 144p. 112.00 *(978-0-415-56567-7(7))* Routledge.

Fernley, Sheila, et al. What Do I Do When- The Answer Book on RTI. 2007. *(978-1-57834-089-7(6))* LRP Pubns.

Ficová, et al. Integration of Pupils with Disabilities from the View of Schoolmates. 2011. 60p. pap. ***(978-3-8433-9397-3(4))*** Lambert Academic Publishing.

Fiedler, Craig R. & Clark, Denise M. Making a Difference: Advocacy Competencies for Special Education Professionals. 2nd ed. 2008. 41.00 *(978-1-4164-0377-7(9))* PRO-ED, Inc.

Fitzgerald, Damien & Fitzgerald. Coordinating Special Educational Needs: A Guide for the Early Years. 2007. (Sen in the Early Years Ser.). (ENG.). 136p. 21.95 *(978-0-8264-8476-5(X))* Continuum International Publishing Group, Ltd. GBR. Dist: National Bk. Network.

Flexer, Robert W., et al. Transition Planning for Secondary Students with Disabilities. 3rd ed. 2007. (ENG., Illus.). 480p. (C). per. 113.33 *(978-0-13-238763-7(8)*, Prentice Hall) Prentice Hall PTR.

Flick, Grad L., ed. Managing ADHD in the K-8 Classroom: A Teacher's Guide. 2010. (Illus.). 248p. pap. 38.95 *(978-1-4129-6910-9(7)*, B69093P) Corwin Pr.

Flora, Sherrill B. Famous #34;Wonder#34; Women. 2010. (Real-Life Ser.). (ENG.). 8p. (gr. 3-8). 16.99 *(978-1-60268-089-0(2)*, Key Education Publishing Company, LLC) Carson-Dellosa Publishing, LLC.

Florian, Lani. Disability Classification in Education: Issues & Perspectives. McLaughlin, Margaret, ed. 2008. (Illus.). 296p. pap. 39.95 *(978-1-4129-3877-8(5)*, B38767P) Corwin Pr.

Forlin, Christine & Lian, Ming-Gon John, eds. Reform, Inclusion & Teacher Education: Towards a New Era of Special & Inclusive Education in the Asia-Pacific Region. 2008. (Illus.). XXII, 250p. 47.50 *(978-0-415-46447-5(1))*; (ENG., 272p. 170.00 *(978-0-415-46448-2(X))* Routledge

Frankel, Fred & Wood, Jeffrey J. Social Skills Success for Students with Autism/Asperger's: How to Teach Conversation Skills, Prevent Meltdowns, & Help Kids Fit In. 2011. (ENG., Illus.). 256p. pap. 29.95 ***(978-0-470-95238-2(5)***, Jossey-Bass) Wiley, John & Sons, Inc.

Frederick, Carrie. Put Learning to Work. 2010. 136p. pap. *(978-3-639-22626-3(7))* VDM Verlag Dr. Mueller e.K.

Freiberg, Karen. Annual Editions: Educating Children with Exceptionalities 12/13. 21st ed. 2011. (Annual Editions Ser.). (ENG., Illus.). 224p. (C). pap. 44.00 *(978-0-07-805108-1(8)*, 0078051088, McGraw-Hill/Dushkin) McGraw-Hill Higher Education.

Freiberg, Karen & Freiberg, Karen L. Annual Editions: Educating Children with Exceptionalities 10/11. 20th ed. 2009. (Annual Editions Ser.). (ENG., Illus.). 192p. (C). pap. 44.00 *(978-0-07-813587-3(7)*, 0078135877, McGraw-Hill/Dushkin) McGraw-Hill Higher Education.

Friend, Marilyn & Bursuck, William D. Including Students with Special Needs: A Practical Guide for Classroom Teachers. 6th ed. 2011. (ENG.). 504p. (C). 107.60 ***(978-0-13-273007-0(0))***; (Illus.). pap. 134.67 *(978-0-13-217972-0(5))* Prentice Hall PTR. (Prentice Hall).

—Including Students with Special Needs: A Practical Guide for Classroom Teachers, Student Value Edition. 6th ed. 2011. (ENG.). 504p. (C). ring bd. 87.53 ***(978-0-13-276813-9(5)***, Prentice Hall) Prentice Hall PTR.

Gargiulo, Richard & Kilgo, Jennifer. Young Children with Special Needs. 3rd ed. 2011. 432p. pap. ***(978-0-8400-3177-8(7))*** Wadsworth.

Gargiulo, Richard & Kilgo, Jennifer L. An Introduction to Young Children with Special Needs: Birth Through Age Eight. 3rd ed. 2010. (Available Titles CourseMate Ser.). (ENG.). 408p. (C). pap. 184.95 *(978-0-495-81315-6(X))* Wadsworth.

George, Jack E. The Autism Handbook: Easy to Understand Information, Insight, Perspectives & Case Studies from a Special Education Teacher. 2009. 178p. pap. *(978-1-926585-50-5(X)*, No.1 Bk. Pubs.) CCB Publishing.

Giangreco, Michael F., et al. Choosing Outcomes & Accommodations for Children (COACH) A Guide to Educational Planning for Students with Disabilities, Third Edition. 3rd ed. 2011. (Illus.). 232p. pap. 44.95 *(978-1-59857-187-5(7))* Brookes, Paul H. Publishing Co.

Gibb, Gordon S. & Dyches, Tina Taylor. Guide to Writing Quality Individualized Education Programs. 2nd rev. ed. 2006. (ENG.). 112p. (C). pap. 40.00 *(978-0-205-49545-0(1))* Allyn & Bacon, Inc.

Giles, Ellie. Paraprofessionals' Perceptions of Training & Efficacy. 2010. 192p. pap. *(978-3-639-26919-2(5))* VDM Verlag Dr. Mueller e.K.

Giuliani, George. Understanding Assessment in the Special Education Process: A Step-by-Step Guide for Educators. Pierangelo, Roger, ed. 2007. (Illus.). 136p. 66.95 *(978-1-4129-5424-2(X)*, B17913C); per. 27.95 *(978-1-4129-1791-9(3)*, B17913P) Corwin Pr.

Giuliani, George A. The Comprehensive Guide to Special Education Law: Answering over 400 Frequently Asked Questions about the Legal Rights of Exceptional Children & Their Parents. 2012. (ENG.). 288p. pap. ***(978-1-84905-882-7(2))*** Kingsley, Jessica Ltd.

Gleckel, Evie K. & Koretz, Ellen S. Collaborative Individualized Education Process: RSVP to IDEA. 2007. (ENG., Illus.). 320p. (C). per. 59.00 *(978-0-13-112593-3(1)*, Prentice Hall) Prentice Hall PTR.

Golden, Cindy. The Special Educator's Toolkit: Everything You Need to Organize, Manage, & Monitor Your Classroom. 2012. 240p. pap. 39.95 ***(978-1-59857-097-7(8))*** Brookes, Paul H. Publishing Co.

Gore, Mildred C., ed. Inclusion Strategies for Secondary Classrooms: Keys for Struggling Learners. 2nd ed. 2010. (Illus.). 248p. pap. 38.95 *(978-1-4129-7544-5(1)*, B75445P) Corwin Pr.

Gosden-Kitchen, Suzanne. Perceptions of Students with Disabilities. 2008. 84p. pap. *(978-3-639-07300-3(2))* VDM Verlag Dr. Mueller e.K.

Gragl, Paul. Wrongful Life: Gibt es ein Recht, nicht geboren zu werden? 2010. 112p. pap. *(978-3-639-09181-6(7))* VDM Verlag Dr. Mueller e.K.

Greenspan, Stanley I. & Wieder, Serena. Engaging Autism: Using the Floortime Approach to Help Children Relate, Communicate & Think. 2009. (Merloyd Lawrence Book Ser.). (ENG.). 448p. pap. 18.00 *(978-0-7382-1094-0(3))* Perseus Bks. Group.

Grigorenko, Elena L. Educating Individuals with Disabilities: IDEIA 2004 & Beyond. 2008. (Illus.). 494p. 65.00 *(978-0-8261-0356-7(1))* Springer Publishing Co., Inc.

Groark, Christina J., et al, eds. Early Childhood Intervention: Shaping the Future for Children with Special Needs & Their Families, 3 vols. 2011. (Illus.). 876p. 154.95 *(978-0-313-37793-8(6)*, C37793) Greenwood Publishing Group, Inc.

Gruenberg, Ann M. & Miller, Regina. A Practical Guide to Early Childhood Inclusion: Effective Reflection. 2010. (ENG.). 288p. (C). pap. 43.20 *(978-0-13-240279-8(3)*, Prentice Hall) Prentice Hall PTR.

Guernsey, Thomas & Klare, Kathe. Special Education Law. 3rd ed. 2008. 65.00 *(978-1-59460-250-4(6))* Carolina Academic Pr.

Hammeken, Peggy A. The Paraprofessional's Essential Guide to Inclusive Education. 3rd ed. 2008. 248p. 39.95 *(978-1-4129-6611-5(6)*, B66108P); instr.'s gde. ed. 88.95 *(978-1-4129-6610-8(8)*, B66108C) Corwin Pr.

Hammeken, Peggy A., ed. The Teacher's Guide to Inclusive Education: 750 Strategies for Success! 2007. (Illus.). 352p. pap. 39.95 *(978-1-890455-10-1(5)*, B55101P) Corwin Pr.

Hammel, Alice & Hourigan, Ryan M. Teaching Music to Students with Special Needs: A Label-Free Approach, 1 vol. 2011. (ENG.). 288p. pap. 24.95 *(978-0-19-539541-9(7))* Oxford Univ. Pr., Inc.

Hanley-Maxwell, Cheryl & Collet-Klingenberg, Lana. Education. 2011. (SAGE Reference Series on Disability: Key Issues & Future Directions Ser.: 2). 360p. 75.00 *(978-1-4129-8690-8(7)*, B86903C) SAGE Pubns., Inc.

Hannell, Glynis. Success with Inclusion: 1001 Teaching Strategies & Activities That Really Work. 2007. (Illus.). 184p. 44.95 *(978-0-415-44534-4(5))* Routledge.

Harry, Beth, et al. Case Studies of Minority Student Placement in Special Education. 2007. (ENG.). 144p. per. 20.95 *(978-0-8077-4761-2(0))* Teachers College Pr., Teachers College, Columbia Univ.

Hayden, Sue & Jordan, Emma. Language for Learning: A Practical Guide for Supporting Pupils with Language & Communication Difficulties Across the Curriculum. 2007. (David Fulton Bks.). (ENG., Illus.). 136p. pap. 52.95 *(978-1-84312-468-9(8))* Fulton, David Pubs. GBR. Dist: Taylor & Francis Group.

Helman, Lori, et al. Words Their Way: Letter-Name Alphabetic Sorts for Spanish-Speaking English Learners. 5th ed. 2008. (Words Their Way Ser.). (SPA & ENG., Illus.). 160p. (C). pap. 24.99 *(978-0-13-242103-4(8)*, Prentice Hall) Prentice Hall PTR.

Henderson, Anne. Maths for the Dyslexic Learner. 2nd rev. ed. 2012. (ENG., Illus.). 160p. pap. 42.95 *(978-0-415-68311-1(4))* Routledge.

Heward, Et Al. & Cram101 Textbook Reviews Staff. Focus on Behavior Analysis in Education. 2007. 136p. per. 11.95 *(978-1-4288-2062-3(0))* Cram101 Inc.

Hills, Geraldine. The Equality Act Made Simple for Education Professionals. 2012. (David Fulton / Nasen Ser.). (ENG., Illus.). 96p. (C). pap. 53.95 ***(978-0-415-68768-3(3))*** Routledge.

Hippel-Laabs, Natalie. Johan Kvandal - Leben und Werk: Eine Biografisch-Analytische Studie Unter Besonderer Berücksichtigung Sonderpädagogischer Umsetzung. 2011. (Beiträge zur europäischen Musikgeschichte Ser.). (GER.). 246p. 64.95 *(978-3-631-61162-3(5))* Lang, Peter GmbH, Europaischer Verlag der Wissenschaften DEU. Dist: Lang, Peter.

Hodge, Samuel R., et al. Essentials of Teaching Adapted Physical Education: Diversity, Culture, & Inclusion. 2012. ***(978-1-934432-37-2(7))*** Holcomb Hathaway, Inc.

Hooper, Stephen & Umansky, Warren. Young Children with Special Needs. 5th ed. 2008. (ENG., Illus.). 544p. (C). pap. 116.00 *(978-0-13-159014-4(6)*, Prentice Hall) Prentice Hall PTR.

How NCLB Affects Students with Disabilities: Hearing Before the Subcommittee on Early Childhood, Elementary & Secondary Education, Committee on Education & Labor, U.S. House of Representatives, One Hundred Tenth Congress, First Session, Hearing Held in Washington, D.C., March 29, 2007. 2007. (Illus.). iii, 91p. *(978-0-16-079753-8(5)*, 552-070-36671-7) United States Government Printing Office.

Howard, Vikki F., et al. Very Young Children with Special Needs: A Foundation for Educators, Families, & Service Providers. 4th ed. 2009. (ENG.). 544p. (C). pap. 116.00 *(978-0-13-208088-0(5)*, Prentice Hall) Prentice Hall PTR.

Howlin, Patricia, et al. Teaching Children with Autism to Mind-Read. 2nd ed. 2013. (ENG.). 160p. pap., wbk. ed. 34.95 *(978-0-470-09324-5(2)*, Wiley) Wiley, John & Sons, Inc.

Huck, Kelly. A Case Study of One Family's Experience with Assistive Technology. 2009. 162p. pap. *(978-3-639-16318-6(4))* VDM Verlag Dr. Mueller e.K.

Huerta, Nancy, et al. The Individuals with Disabilities Education Act as Amended in 2004. 2nd ed. 2008. (What Every Student Should Know about... (WESSKA Series) Ser.). (ENG.). 112p. (C). pap. 8.00 *(978-0-13-714911-7(5))* Prentice Hall Higher Education.

Hutchison, Bobby. Annual Editions: Gender 10/11. 2009. (Annual Editions Ser.). (ENG., Illus.). 272p. (C). pap. 44.00 *(978-0-07-805052-7(9)*, 0078050529, McGraw-Hill/Dushkin) McGraw-Hill Higher Education.

Iannacci, Luigi & Heydon, Rachel M. Early Childhood Curricula & the de-pathologizing of Childhood. 2008. (ENG.). 208p. *(978-0-8020-9768-2(5))* Univ. of Toronto Pr.

Irick, Angela. Sampson to the Rescue. 2011. 20p. pap. 13.00 ***(978-1-4634-4836-3(8))*** AuthorHouse.

Isbell, Christy & Isbell, Rebecca. Sensory Integration: A Guide for Preschool Teachers. 2007. (ENG., Illus.). 144p. pap. 19.95 *(978-0-87659-060-7(1))* Gryphon Hse., Inc.

Isbell, Christy & Isbell, Rebecca T. The Inclusive Learning Centers Book: For Preschool Children with Special Needs. 2007. (ENG., Illus.). 320p. pap. 29.95 *(978-0-87659-294-6(9))* Gryphon Hse., Inc.

Iseman, Jacqueline S., et al. 101 School Success Tools for Students with ADHD. 2010. (ENG., Illus.). 200p. pap. 16.95 *(978-1-59363-403-2(X)*, 1311348) Prufrock Pr.

Izzo, Margo & Guider, Sarah K. Inclusion in the Consumer Classroom. 2008. (Illus.). 143p. pap. *(978-0-07-876789-0(X))* Glencoe/McGraw-Hill.

Jaeger, Paul T., et al. Disability Matters. 2009. 216p. pap. 45.99 *(978-1-60752-070-2(2))* Information Age Publishing, Inc.

Jeanette D. Harmon. The Other Normal: Understanding Asperger's. 2011. 216p. pap. 24.95 ***(978-1-4560-6048-0(1))*** PublishAmerica, Inc.

Jennifer, Greening. Opening Doors, Opening Lives: Creating Awareness of Advocacy, Inclusion, & Education for Our Children. 2009. (ENG.). 136p. pap. 12.95 *(978-1-933916-42-2(7)*, Ferne Pr.) Nelson Publishing & Marketing.

Jennings, Matthew. Before the Special Education Referral: Leading Intervention Teams. 2008. (Illus.). 168p. 66.95 *(978-1-4129-6690-0(6)*, B66900C); pap. 27.95 *(978-1-4129-6691-7(4)*, B66900P) Corwin Pr.

—Negotiating Individualized Education Plans: A Guide for School Administrators. 2009. (ENG.). 97p. 70.00 *(978-1-57886-993-0(5))*; 140p. pap. 27.95 *(978-1-60709-017-5(1))* Rowman & Littlefield Education.

Johnston, Linda, et al. Assistive Technology: Access for All Students. 2006. (ENG., Illus.). 224p. (C). per. 41.33 *(978-0-13-117569-3(6))* Pearson Education.

Jones, Carroll J., ed. Curriculum Development for Students with Mild Disabilities: Academic & Social Skills for RTI Planning & Inclusion IEPs. 2nd ed. 2010. 454p. spiral bd. 63.95 *(978-0-398-07911-6(0))* Thomas, Charles C. Pub., Ltd.

Jones, Phyllis, et al, eds. Leading for Inclusion: How Schools Can Build on the Strengths of All Learners. 2011. (ENG., Illus.). 256p. 70.00 ***(978-0-8077-5259-3(2))***; pap. 31.95 ***(978-0-8077-5258-6(4))*** Teachers College Pr., Teachers College, Columbia Univ.

Karten, Toby J. Inclusion Activities That Work! Grades 3-5. 2007. (Illus.). 96p. per. 16.95 *(978-1-4129-5235-4(2)*, B52352P) Corwin Pr.

—Inclusion Activities That Work! Grades 6-8. 2007. (Illus.). 96p. per. 16.95 *(978-1-4129-5234-7(4)*, B52344P) Corwin Pr.

—Inclusion Activities That Work! Grades K-2. 2007. (Illus.). 96p. per. 16.95 *(978-1-4129-5233-0(6)*, B52336P) Corwin Pr.

—Inclusion Strategies That Work! Research-Based Methods for the Classroom. 2nd ed. 2010. (Illus.). 408p. pap. 39.95 *(978-1-4129-7937-5(4)*, B79375P) Corwin Pr.

Karten, Toby J., ed. Embracing Disabilities in the Classroom: Strategies to Maximize Students' Assets. 2008. (Illus.). 296p. 90.95 *(978-1-4129-5769-4(9)*, B57694C); pap. 41.95 *(978-1-4129-5770-0(2)*, B57694P) Corwin Pr.

—More Inclusion Strategies That Work! Aligning Student Strengths with Standards. 2007. (Illus.). 336p. 90.95 *(978-1-4129-4115-0(6)*, B41156C); per. 39.95 *(978-1-4129-4116-7(4)*, B41156P) Corwin Pr.

Katz, Lynne F., et al. Child-Centered Practices for the Courtroom & Community: A Guide to Working Effectively with Young Children & Their Families in the Child Welfare System. 2010. (Illus.). 240p. 34.95 *(978-1-59857-073-1(0))* Brookes, Paul H. Publishing Co.

Kauffman, James M., et al. An Introduction to Students with High-Incidence Disabilities. 2007. (ENG., Illus.). 400p. (C). per. 119.40 *(978-0-13-117802-1(4)*, Prentice Hall) Prentice Hall PTR.

Kempe, Andy. Drama, Disability & Education: A critical exploration for students & Practitioners. 2012. (ENG.). 208p. (C). 155.00 *(978-0-415-67503-1(0))*; pap. 31.95 *(978-0-415-67504-8(9))* Routledge.

Kerzner Lipsky, Dorothy & Gartner, Alan. Inclusion A Service Not A Place. 2007. per. 29.99 *(978-1-934032-00-8(X)*, Dude Publishing) National Professional Resources, Inc.

Kewley, Geoff D., et al. 100 Ideas for Supporting Pupils with ADHD. 2008. (Continuum One Hundreds Ser.). (ENG.). 168p. 19.95 *(978-0-8264-9660-7(1))* Continuum International Publishing Group, Ltd. GBR. Dist: National Bk. Network.

Killion, William K. Tackle Box: The Training Companion for the Functional Independence Skills Handbook or F. I. S. H. 2007. per. 29.95 *(978-1-59872-750-0(8))* Instant Pub.

Kirby, Amanda & Peters, Lynne. 100 Ideas for Supporting Pupils with Dyspraxia & DCD. 2007. (Continuums One Hundreds Ser.). (ENG.). 128p. 20.95 *(978-0-8264-9440-5(4))* Continuum International Publishing Group, Ltd. GBR. Dist: National Bk. Network.

Kirk. Educating Exceptional Children: Testbank, 8 vols. Date not set. (C). pap., suppl. ed. 11.96 *(978-0-395-82842-7(2))* CENGAGE Learning.

Kirk, Samuel, et al. Cengage Advantage: Educating Exceptional Children. 13th ed. 2011. (ENG.). 544p. (C). ring bd. 113.95 *(978-1-111-35611-8(4))* Wadsworth.

Klein & Cook & Richardson-Gibbs & Cram101 Textbook Reviews Staff. Strategies for Including Children with Special Needs in Early Childhood Settings. 2007. 60p. per. 9.95 *(978-1-4288-2032-6(9))* Cram101 Inc.

Kliewer, Christopher. Seeing All Kids as Readers: A New Vision for Literacy in the Inclusive Early Childhood Classroom. 2008. (Illus.). 160p. per. 28.95 *(978-1-55766-901-8(5))* Brookes, Paul H. Publishing Co.

Klor, Gerry. Leading Successful IEP Teams: A Guide to Managing the People & the Process. 2007. *(978-1-57834-091-0(8))* LRP Pubns.

Kloskowski, Vincent J. Pedagogy Plain & Fancy: Historical Analysis: The Amish & the Disadvantaged Student. 2009. (Illus.). x, 166p. *(978-1-4389-9941-8(0))* AuthorHouse.

Kosnitsky, Carol. IEP Goals That Make a Difference: An Administrator's Guide to Improving the Process. 2008. *(978-1-57834-101-6(9))* LRP Pubns.

Kuder, S. Jay. Teaching Students with Language & Communication Disabilities. 4th rev. ed. 2012. (ENG.). 432p. (C). 133.33 ***(978-0-13-265666-5(3))*** Allyn & Bacon, Inc.

Kukathas, Uma. Disability Rights. 2009. (EXAMINING ISS COURT DECSNS Ser.). (ENG., Illus.). 240p. 39.70 *(978-0-7377-4488-0(X)*, Greenhaven Pr., Inc.) Cengage Gale.

Kutscher, Martin L. & Moran, Marcella. Organizing the Disorganized Child: Simple Strategies to Succeed in School. 2009. (ENG.). 160p. pap. 12.99 *(978-0-06-179741-5(3)*, William Morrow Paperbacks) HarperCollins Pubs.

Lake, Steven E. What Do I Do When: The Answer Book on Special Education Practice & Procedure. 2007. *(978-1-57834-083-5(7))* LRP Pubns.

Lancaster, Gwen. Phoneme Factory. 2008. (ENG., Illus.). 176p. 41.95 *(978-1-84312-382-8(7))* Fulton, David Pubs. GBR. Dist: Taylor & Francis Group.

Larkey, Sue. Practical Sensory Programmes for Students with Autism Spectrum Disorder & Other Special Needs. 2006. (ENG., Illus.). 12p. per. *(978-1-84310-479-7(2))* Kingsley, Jessica Ltd.

Lerner & Cram101 Textbook Reviews Staff. Learning Disabilities. 2007. 120p. per. 11.95 *(978-1-4288-2046-3(9))* Cram101 Inc.

Levine, James E. Learning from Behavior: How to Understand & Help Challenging Children in School, 1 vol. 2007. (Child Psychology & Mental Health Ser.). 168p. 44.95 (978-0-275-99040-4(0), C9040, Praeger Pubs.) Greenwood Publishing Group, Inc.

—Learning from Behavior: How to Understand & Help Challenging Children in School. 2009. (ENG.). 150p. pap. 27.95 (978-1-57886-804-9(1)) Rowman & Littlefield Publishers, Inc.

Libert, Rodney A. Practice of Education in Trinidad & Tobago: Does it Infringe on the Human Rights of Disabled Students? 2007. 130p. pap. 16.95 (978-0-615-17133-3(8)) Libert, Rodney A.

Lindberg, Jill A., et al. Common-Sense Classroom Management for Special Education Teachers, Grades 6-12. 2007. (Illus.). 160p. 76.95 (978-1-4129-4038-2(9), B40389C); per. 33.95 (978-1-4129-4039-9(7), B40389P) Corwin Pr.

Linsenbach, Sherri. The Everything Homeschooling Book: All you need to create the best curriculum & learning environment for your Child. 2nd ed. 2010. (ENG.). 304p. pap. 15.95 (978-1-60550-135-2(2)) Adams Media Corp.

Lordi, Viola S. IDEA 2004 Guidebook: A Comprehensive Guide to the Individuals with Disabilities Education ACT. 2nd ed. 2007. (978-1-57834-079-8(9)) LRP Pubns.

Lucan, Dawn. Practical Teacher's Autism Manual. 2010. (ENG.). 56p. pap. 24.95 (978-0-557-47438-7(8)); 52p. pap. 24.95 (978-0-557-46483-8(8)) Lulu Enterprises Inc.

—Practical Teacher's I. E. P. Manual. 2010. 64p. pap. 24.95 (978-0-557-48430-0(8)) Lulu Enterprises Inc.

Maanum, Jody L., ed. The General Educator's Guide to Special Education. 3rd ed. 2009. (Illus.). 256p. 90.95 (978-1-4129-7136-2(5), B71362C); pap. 41.95 (978-1-4129-7137-9(3), B71362P) Corwin Pr.

MacIntyre, Christine. Dyspraxia in the Early Years: Identifying & Supporting Children with Movement Difficulties. 2nd rev. ed. 2008. (Illus.). 136p. 110.00 (978-0-415-47889-2(8)) Routledge.

Macomber, Phyl T. The Power of T. H. E. P. A. C. T. The Solution to Adapting the Curriculum. 2010. (Illus.). 232p. 75.00 (978-0-9844401-7-7(8)) Make A Differnece, Inc.

Magyar, Caroline I. Developing & Evaluating Educational Programs for Students with Autism. 2010. (ENG., Illus.). xxiv, 297p. 129.00 (978-1-4419-6302-4(2), 1441963022) Springer.

Mahoney, Gerald & MacDonald, James D. Autism & Developmental Delays in Young Children: The Responsive Teaching Curriculum for Parents & Professionals: Curriculum Guide. 2007. (Illus.). xiii, 337p. 87.00 (978-1-4164-0236-7(5)) PRO-ED, Inc.

Manasevit, Leigh. IDEA: New Expectations for Schools & Students. 4th ed. 2008. (Illus.). vi, 568p. (978-1-933807-52-2(0)) Thompson Media Group LLC.

Mandlawitz, Myrna. What Every Teacher Should Know about IDEA 2004 Laws & Regulations. 2006. (ENG.). 176p. per. 8.00 (978-0-205-50568-5(6)) Allyn & Bacon, Inc.

Mannix, Darlene. Life Skills Activities for Special Children. 2nd ed. 2009. (ENG., Illus.). 400p. pap. 29.95 (978-0-470-25937-5(X), Jossey-Bass) Wiley, John & Sons, Inc.

Manson, Tony J. Ways Teachers Cope with the Physical, Psychological, & Social Disabilities of Their Students: Diabetes, Autism, ADHD, Hunger, Anger, & Other Infirmities. Manson, Tony J., ed. 220p. 109.95 (978-0-7734-4976-3(0)) Mellen, Edwin Pr., The.

Manzo, David & Peters, Elizabeth Campbell. Cotting School. 2008. (Campus History Ser.). (ENG., Illus.). 128p. pap. 21.99 (978-0-7385-5765-6(X)) Arcadia Publishing.

Marcus, Lee M., et al. Families of Children with Autism: What Educational Professionals Should Know. 2010. (ENG.). 72p. pap. 12.95 (978-1-59363-408-7(0)) Prufrock Pr.

Marshak, Laura E., et al. The School Counselor's Guide to Helping Students with Disabilities. 2009. (ENG., Illus.). 384p. pap. 32.95 (978-0-470-17579-8(6), Jossey-Bass) Wiley, John & Sons, Inc.

Maschke, Thomas. Integrative Aspekte der anthroposophischen Heilpädagogik in Theorie und schulischer Praxis: Eine Studie unter besonderer Berücksichtigung der Unterrichtspraxis an der Kaspar Hauser Schule Überlingen. 2008. (Europäische Hochschulschriften. Reihe 11: Pädagogik Ser.). 142p. pap. 39.95 (978-3-631-58517-7(9)) Lang, Peter GmbH, Europaischer Verlag der Wissenschaften DEU. Dist: Lang, Peter.

Mauro, Terri. 50 Ways to Support Your Child's Special Education: From IEPs to Assorted Therapies, an Empowering Guide to Taking Action, Every Day. 2009. (ENG.). 224p. pap. 12.95 (978-1-60550-112-3(3)) Adams Media Corp.

McBride, Guy, et al. Essentials of Idea for Assessment Professionals. 2011. (Essentials of Psychological Assessment Ser.: 86). (ENG.). 290p. pap. 48.95 (978-0-470-87392-2(2), Wiley) Wiley, John & Sons, Inc.

McCoy, Kathleen M. Strategies for Teaching Students with Special Needs: Methods & Techniques for Classroom Instruction. 2008. 572p. pap. 86.00 (978-0-89108-328-3(6)) Love Publishing Co.

McEwen, Irene, ed. Providing Physical Therapy Services under Parts B&C of IDEA (2nd Edition) 2009. 200p. pap. 70.00 (978-0-9702105-1-7(5)) Section on Pediatrics, APTA.

McGrath, Constance. The Inclusion-Classroom Problem Solver: Structures & Supports to Serve All Learners. 2007. 144p. pap. 23.13 (978-0-325-01270-4(9), E01270) Heinemann.

McGrath, Mary Z. & Johns, Beverley H. Reaching Students with Diverse Disabilities: Cross Categorical Ideas & Activities. 2008. (ENG.). 160p. 80.00 (978-1-57886-811-7(4)); pap. 29.95 (978-1-57886-812-4(2)) Rowman & Littlefield Education.

McLaughlin, Margaret J., ed. What Every Principal Needs to Know about Special Education. 2nd ed. 2008. (Illus.). 120p. 62.95 (978-1-4129-6415-9(6), B64159C); pap. 25.95 (978-1-4129-6416-6(4), B64159P) Corwin Pr.

McLaughlin, Margaret J. & Florian, Lani. Disability Classification in Education: Issues & Perspectives. 2008. (Illus.). 296p. 86.95 (978-1-4129-3876-1(7), B38767C) Corwin Pr.

McLeskey, James, et al. Inclusion: Highly Effective Practices for all Students (with MyEducationLab) 2009. (ENG.). 480p. (C). pap. 141.33 (978-0-13-610132-1(1), Prentice Hall) Prentice Hall PTR.

McLoughlin, James A. & Lewis, Rena B. Assessing Students with Special Needs. 7th ed. 2007. (ENG.). 648p. (C). 143.60 (978-0-13-196191-3(8), Prentice Hall) Prentice Hall PTR.

McManus, Jennifer. Inclusion & Art Education at Second Level. 2011. 100p. pap. (978-3-8443-1441-0(5)) Lambert Academic Publishing.

McWilliam, R. A., ed. Working with Families of Young Children with Special Needs. 2010. (What Works for Special-Needs Learners Ser.). (ENG., Illus.). 265p. (gr. -1-1). pap. 35.00 (978-1-60623-539-3(7)) Guilford Pubns., Inc.

Mednick, Michael & Mednick. Supporting Children with Multiple Disabilities. 2nd rev. ed. 2007. (Supporting Children Ser.). (ENG., Illus.). 205p. 49.95 (978-0-8264-9298-2(3)) Continuum International Publishing Group, Ltd. GBR. Dist: National Bk. Network.

Meehan, Margaret, et al. Dyslexia-Friendly Further & Higher Education. 2010. (Illus.). 136p. (C). 108.00 (978-1-84787-585-3(8), B75853C); pap. 51.00 (978-1-84787-586-0(6), B75853P) SAGE Pubns., Ltd. GBR. Dist: SAGE Pubns., Inc.

Mendelsohn, James. A Parent's Guide to Tutors & Tutoring: How to Support the Unique Needs of Your Child. 2008. (ENG.). 208p. pap., instr.'s gde. ed. 16.95 (978-0-470-25383-0(5), Jossey-Bass) Wiley, John & Sons, Inc.

Miller, Helen. The Educator's Guide to Teaching Students with Autism Spectrum Disorders. Ben-Arieh, Josefa & Miller, Helen J., eds. 2009. (Illus.). 176p. pap. 31.95 (978-1-4129-5776-2(1), B57755P) Corwin Pr.

Mitchell, David, ed. Contextualizing Inclusive Education: Evaluating Old & New International Paradigms. 2008. 312p. pap. 44.95 (978-0-415-47882-3(0)) Routledge.

Montgomery, D. Bruce. Able, Gifted & Talented Underachievers. Montgomery, Diane L., ed. 2nd ed. 2009. (ENG., Illus.). 370p. pap. 65.00 (978-0-470-77940-8(3), Wiley) Wiley, John & Sons, Inc.

Montgomery, Diane L., et al. Able, Gifted & Talented Underachievers. Montgomery, Diane, ed. 2nd ed. 2009. (ENG., Illus.). 370p. 105.00 (978-0-470-74097-2(3), Wiley) Wiley, John & Sons, Inc.

Moore, Barbara J. & Montgomery, Judy K. Making a Difference for America's Children: Speech-Language Pathologists in Public Schools. 2nd ed. 2007. (978-1-58650-855-5(5)) Super Duper Pubns.

Moore, Lorraine O., ed. Inclusion Strategies for Young Children: A Resource Guide for Teachers, Child Care Providers, & Parents. 2nd ed. 2009. (Illus.). 152p. 72.95 (978-1-4129-7107-2(1), B71072C); pap. 29.95 (978-1-4129-7108-9(X), B71072P) Corwin Pr.

Mutua, Kagendo & Sunal, Cynthia S. Advances in Research & Praxis in Special Education in Africa, Caribbean, & the Middle East. 2012. 246p. 85.99 (978-1-61735-772-5(3)); pap. 45.99 (978-1-61735-771-8(5)) Information Age Publishing, Inc.

Naparstek, Nathan & Greenwood. Successful Educators. 2009. 204p. pap. 45.99 (978-1-60752-072-6(9)) Information Age Publishing, Inc.

Ndaji, Francis & Tymms, Peter. The P Scales: Assessing the Progress of Children with Special Educational Needs. 2010. (ENG., Illus.). 212p. pap. 55.00 (978-0-470-51898-4(7), Wiley) Wiley, John & Sons, Inc.

Nelsen, Jane, et al. Positive Discipline for Children with Special Needs: Raising & Teaching All Children to Become Resilient, Responsible, & Respectful. 2011. (ENG.). 256p. pap. 17.00 (978-0-307-58982-8(X), Three Rivers Pr.) Crown Publishing Group.

Newman, Sarah. Small Steps Forward: Using Games & Activities to Help Your Pre-School Child with Special Needs. 2nd ed. 2008. (ENG., Illus.). 272p. pap. (978-1-84310-693-7(0)) Kingsley, Jessica Ltd.

Nielsen, Lee Brattland. Brief Reference of Student Disabilites: With Strategies for the Classroom. 2nd ed. 2008. (Illus.). 272p. 86.95 (978-1-4129-6632-0(9), B66320C); pap. 39.95 (978-1-4129-6633-7(7), B66320P) Corwin Pr.

Nierengarten, Geraldine (Gerry). What Matters Most in Co-teaching in High School: Views from Administration, General Educators andSpecial Educators. 2008. 116p. pap. (978-3-639-10069-3(7)) VDM Verlag Dr. Mueller e.K.

Norlin, John W. & Gorn, Susan. What Do I Do When- The Answer Book on Section 504. 3rd ed. 2008. (978-1-57834-096-5(9)) LRP Pubns.

Nyman, Terri R. Key Characteristics of Effective Middle Schools. 2008. 84p. pap. (978-3-639-07828-2(4)) VDM Verlag Dr. Mueller e.K.

Ockelford, Adam. Music for Children & Young People with Complex Needs. 2008. (Oxford Music Education Ser.). (ENG., Illus.). 320p. pap. 25.95 (978-0-19-322301-1(5)) Oxford Univ. Pr., Inc.

O'Donovan, Margaret & Dare, Angela. Good Practice in Caring for Young Children with Special Needs. Walker, Miranda, ed. 3rd rev. ed. 2009. (ENG., Illus.). 432p. pap. 57.50 (978-1-4085-0490-1(1)) Nelson Thornes Ltd. GBR. Dist: Trans-Atlantic Pubns., Inc.

O'Kelley, Sarah, et al. Diagnosis & Treatment of Children with Autism Spectrum Disorders. 2009. (ENG.). pap. 12.95 (978-1-59363-372-1(6)) Prufrock Pr.

Ong-Dean, Colin. Distinguishing Disability: Parents, Privilege, & Special Education. 2009. (ENG., Illus.). 216p. 54.00 (978-0-226-63000-7(5)); pap. 19.00 (978-0-226-63001-4(3)) Univ. of Chicago Pr.

Osgood, Robert L. The History of Special Education: A Struggle for Equality in American Public Schools, 1 vol. 2007. (Growing up: History of Children & Youth Ser.). 184p. 39.95 (978-0-275-98913-2(5), C8913, Praeger Pubs.) Greenwood Publishing Group, Inc.

Packer, Leslie E. & Pruitt, Sheryl K. Challenging Kids, Challenged Teachers: Teaching Students with Tourette's, Bipolar Disorder, Executive Dysfuction, OCD, AD/HD & More. 2010. (Illus.). 330p. 29.95 (978-1-890627-82-9(8)) Woodbine Hse.

Palm Beach Community College & Children and Families Research Group Staff. Developmentally Appropriate Practices for School-Age Children (5-12 Years) rev. ed. 2009. (ENG.). 160p. pap. 18.30 (978-0-7575-5480-3(6)) Kendall Hunt Publishing Co.

Palm Beach Community Staff & Children and Families Research Group Staff. Developmentally Appropriate Practices for Infants & Toddlers. rev. ed. 2010. (ENG.). 126p. pap. 15.97 (978-0-7575-5475-9(X)) Kendall Hunt Publishing Co.

—Developmentally Appropriate Practices for Young Children (3-5 Years) rev. ed. 2010. (ENG.). 132p. pap. 17.14 (978-0-7575-5477-3(6)) Kendall Hunt Publishing Co.

Paul, Peter V. & Whitelaw, Gail M. Hearing & Deafness. rev. ed. 2010. (Illus.). 308p. pap. 73.95 (978-0-7637-5732-8(2)) Jones & Bartlett Learning, LLC.

Pavey, Barbara. The Dyslexia-Friendly Primary School: A Practical Guide for Teachers. 2007. (Illus.). 120p. 81.00 (978-1-4129-1029-3(3), B10293C); per. 34.00 (978-1-4129-1030-9(7), B10293P) SAGE Pubns., Ltd. GBR. Dist: SAGE Pubns., Inc.

Pedriana, Anthony. Leaving Johnny Behind: Overcoming Barrier to Literacy & Reclaiming At-Risk Readers. 2nd ed. 2010. (Illus.). xxv, 175p. 32.95 (978-1-60709-914-7(4)) Rowman & Littlefield Publishers, Inc.

—Leaving Johnny Behind: Overcoming Barriers to Literacy & Reclaiming at-Risk Readers. 2nd ed. 2010. (ENG., Illus.). 202p. 80.00 (978-1-60709-912-3(8)) Rowman & Littlefield Publishers, Inc.

—Leaving Johnny Behind: Overcoming Barriers to Literacy & Reclaiming At-Risk Readers. 2nd ed. 2010. (ENG., Illus.). 202p. pap. 32.95 (978-1-60709-913-0(6)) Rowman & Littlefield Publishers, Inc.

Peer, Lindsay & Reid, Gavin, eds. Special Educational Needs: A Guide for Inclusive Practice. 2011. (Illus.). 328p. (C). 115.00 (978-0-85702-162-5(1), B21625C); pap. 50.00 (978-0-85702-163-2(X), B21625P) SAGE Pubns., Ltd. GBR. Dist: SAGE Pubns., Inc.

Phillips, Nicky & Beavan, Liz. Teaching Play to Children with Autism: Practical Interventions Using Identiplay. 2007. (Lucky Duck Bks.). (Illus.). 80p. pap. 25.95 (978-1-4129-2894-6(X), B2894XP) SAGE Pubns., Ltd. GBR. Dist: SAGE Pubns., Inc.

Phillips, Nicky & Beavan, Liz. Teaching Play to Children with Autism: Practical Interventions using Identiplay. 2nd ed. 2012. (Lucky Duck Bks.). 136p. pap. 50.00 (978-1-4462-0766-6(8), B07666P) SAGE Pubns., Ltd. GBR. Dist: SAGE Pubns., Inc.

Pickard, K. E. Square Peg Round Hole: A Family's survival of Developmental Dispraxia & Dyslexia. 2011. 128p. pap. 15.66 (978-1-4567-7996-2(6)) AuthorHouse.

Pierangelo, Roger & Giuliani, George. The Educator's Diagnostic Manual of Disabilities & Disorders. 2007. (ENG., Illus.). 576p. per. 49.95 (978-0-7879-7812-9(4), Jossey-Bass) Wiley, John & Sons, Inc.

—Understanding, Developing, & Writing Effective IEPs: A Step-by-Step Guide for Educators. 2007. 176p. per. 31.95 (978-1-4129-1786-5(7), B17867P); (Illus.). 72.95 (978-1-4129-5421-1(5), B17867C) Corwin Pr.

Pierangelo, Roger & Giuliani, George A. Assessment in Special Education: A Practical Approach. 3rd ed. 2008. (ENG.). 432p. (C). pap. 125.33 (978-0-205-60835-5(3)) Allyn & Bacon, Inc.

—The Special Educator's Comprehensive Guide to 301 Diagnostic Tests. rev. exp. ed. 2006. (ENG., Illus.). 504p. per. 39.95 (978-0-7879-7813-6(2), Jossey-Bass) Wiley, John & Sons, Inc.

—Teaching in a Special Education Classroom: A Step-by-Step Guide for Educators. 2008. 120p. 62.95 (978-1-4129-5425-9(8), B17840C); pap. 25.95 (978-1-4129-1784-1(0), B17840P) Corwin Pr.

Pierangelo, Roger A. & Giuliani, George A. Assessment in Special Education: A Practical Approach. 4th rev. ed. 2012. (ENG.). 400p. (C). pap. 118.80 (978-0-13-261326-2(3), Prentice Hall) Prentice Hall PTR.

—Assessment in Special Education: A Practical Approach, Student Value Edition. 4th ed. 2012. (ENG.). 448p. (C). ring bd. 77.27 (978-0-13-300786-2(3), Prentice Hall) Prentice Hall PTR.

Pillay, Sarosha. Sensory Compatibility of Children with Autism & Their Mothers. 2011. 172p. pap. (978-3-8443-0811-2(3)) Lambert Academic Publishing.

Polloway, Edward A., et al. Language Instruction for Students with Disabilities. 4th ed. 2011. 528p. 92.00 (978-0-89108-351-1(0), Wiley-Blackwell) Love Publishing Co.

Prechotko, Carol. Autonomy & Children with Disabilities in the Classroom. 2010. 144p. pap. (978-3-8383-3881-1(2)) Lambert Academic Publishing.

Rapoport, Esta M. Adhd & Social Skills: A Step-by-Step Guide for Teachers & Parents. 2009. (ENG.). 250p. 85.00 (978-1-60709-280-3(8)); pap. 34.95 (978-1-60709-281-0(6)) Rowman & Littlefield Education.

Rapp, Whitney H. & Arndt, Katrina L. Teaching Everyone: An Introduction to Inclusive Education. 2012. (ENG.). 400p. pap. 59.95 (978-1-59857-212-4(1)) Brookes, Paul H. Publishing Co.

Raver, Sharon A. Early Childhood Special Education-0 to 8 Years: Strategies for Positive Outcomes. 2008. (ENG., Illus.). 412p. (C). pap. 74.60 (978-0-13-174598-8(0), Prentice Hall) Prentice Hall PTR.

Ready to Use Professional Development: Focusing on LRE & Inclusion. 2007. (978-1-57834-080-4(2)) LRP Pubns.

Reid, Gavin. Dyslexia. 3rd ed. 2011. (Special Educational Needs Ser.). (ENG., Illus.). 256p. pap. 34.95 (978-1-4411-6585-5(1)) Continuum International Publishing Group, Ltd. GBR. Dist: National Bk. Network.

—Dyslexia. 4th ed. 2009. (ENG., Illus.). 408p. pap. 55.00 (978-0-470-76040-6(0), Wiley) Wiley, John & Sons, Inc.

Reid, Gavin & Green, Shannon. 100+ Ideas for Supporting Children with Dyslexia. 2nd ed. 2011. (Illus.). xii, 166p. (978-1-4411-3093-8(4)); (978-1-4411-7406-2(0)) Continuum International Publishing Group, Ltd.

—100+ Ideas for Supporting Children with Dyslexia. 2nd ed. 2011. (Continuums One Hundreds Ser.). (ENG., Illus.). 184p. pap. 19.95 (978-0-8264-3416-6(9)) Continuum International Publishing Group, Ltd. GBR. Dist: National Bk. Network.

Research and Education Association Staff. FTCE: Exceptional Student Education. 2010. (Test Preps Ser.). (ENG.). 300p. (C). pap. 39.95 (978-0-7386-0831-0(9)) Research & Education Assn.

Resources for Children with Special Needs. The Comprehensive Directory, 2nd Edition: Programs & Services for Children & Youth with Disabilities & Special Needs & Their Families in the Metro New York Area. 2007. 1p. per. 75.00 (978-0-9755116-3-3(7)) Resources for Children with Special Needs, Inc.

Rieser, Richard. Implementing Inclusive Education: A Commonwealth Guide to Implementing Article 24 of the un Convention on the Rights of People with Disabilities. 2008. (ENG., Illus.). 200p. pap. 38.95 (978-0-85092-885-3(0)) Commonwealth Secretariat GBR. Dist: Stylus Publishing, LLC.

Riffel, Laura A. Writing A Behavioral Intervention Plan Using Functional Behavior Assessment Data. 2009. 90p. pap. 18.70 (978-0-578-00796-0(7)) Behavior Doctor Seminars.

Robinson, A. Helene. Reading Achievement of Ninth Grade Students with Disabilities. 2009. 80p. pap. (978-3-639-17343-7(0)) VDM Verlag Dr. Mueller e.K.

Rockwell, Robert E., et al. Families & Educators as Partners: Issues & Challenges. 2nd ed. 2009. (ENG., Illus.). 416p. (C). pap. 104.95 (978-1-4283-1828-1(3)) Delmar Cengage Learning.

Roffey, Sue & Parry, John. Special Needs in the Early Years: Supporting collaboration, communication & Co-ordination. 3rd rev. ed. 2012. (ENG.). 160p. (C). 155.00 (978-0-415-50475-1(9)); pap. 35.95 (978-0-415-50476-8(7)) Routledge.

Rose, David H. & Meyer, Anne, eds. A Practical Reader in Universal Design for Learning. 2006. (Illus.). 180p. pap. 26.95 (978-1-891792-29-8(6), 888-437-1437); lib. bdg. (978-1-891792-30-4(X), 888-437-1437) Harvard Education Publishing Group (HEPG). (Harvard Education Pr.).

Rosenberg, Michael S., et al. Special Education for Today's Teachers: An Introduction. (ENG., (C). 2007. Illus.). 552p. pap. 140.00 (978-0-13-118560-9(8)) 2nd ed. 2010. 544p. pap. 146.00 (978-0-13-703397-3(4)) Prentice Hall PTR. (Prentice Hall).

—Special Education for Today's Teachers: An Introduction (with MyEducationLab) 2nd ed. 2010. (ENG.). 544p. (C). pap. 152.67 (978-0-13-138122-3(9), Prentice Hall) Prentice Hall PTR.

Ruble, Kim. Facilitator Supplement for Tutor Training for Disabilities. 25p. 19.95 (978-0-940287-31-0(5)) Academic Success Pr., Inc.

Russo, Charles J., ed. The Legal Rights of Students with Disabilities: International Perspectives. 2011. (ENG.). 266p. (gr. 17). 70.00 (978-1-4422-1083-7(4)) Rowman & Littlefield Publishers, Inc.

Russo, Charles J. & Osborne, Allan G., Jr. Section 504 & the ADA. 2008. (Illus.). 152p. 68.95 (978-1-4129-5508-9(4), B55084C); pap. 28.95 (978-1-4129-5509-6(2), B55084P) Corwin Pr.

r4 Educated Solutions. Making Math Accessible to Students with Special Needs: Practical Tips & Suggestions, Grades 9-12. 2010. (ENG.). 192p. pap. 29.95 (978-1-934009-69-7(5)) Solution Tree Pr.

—Making Math Accessible to Students with Special Needs: Practical Tips & Suggestions, Grades K-2. 2010. 232p. pap. 29.95 (978-1-934009-66-6(0)); lib. bdg. 64.95 (978-1-935249-06-1(1)) Solution Tree.

R4 Educated Solutions Staff. Making Math Accessible to Students with Special Needs: Practical Tips & Suggestions, Grades 3-5. 2010. (ENG.). 224p. 64.95 (978-1-935249-07-8(X)) Solution Tree Pr.

—Making Math Accessible to Students with Special Needs: Practical Tips & Suggestions (Grades 6-8) 2010. (ENG.). 192p. pap. 29.95 (978-1-934009-68-0(7)) Solution Tree Pr.

R4 Educated Solutions Staff, contrib. by. Making Math Accessible to Students with Special Needs: Practical Tips & Suggestions, Grades 3-5. 2010. (ENG.). 224p. pap. 29.95 (978-1-934009-67-3(9)) Solution Tree Pr.

—Making Math Accessible to Students with Special Needs: Practical Tips & Suggestions (Grades 6-8) 2010. (ENG.). 192p. lib. bdg. 64.95 (978-1-935249-08-5(8)) Solution Tree Pr.

—Making Math Accessible to Students with Special Needs: Practical Tips & Suggestions, Grades 9-12. 2010. lib. bdg. 64.95 (978-1-935249-09-2(6)) Solution Tree Pr.

Sadao, Kathleen & Robinson, Nancy B. Assistive Technology for Young Children: Creating Inclusive Learning Environments W/CD. 2010. 256p. pap. 39.95 (978-1-59857-091-5(9)) Brookes, Paul H. Publishing Co.

Salend, Spencer J. Creating Inclusive Classrooms: Effective & Reflective Practices. 7th ed. 2010. (ENG.). 560p. (C). pap. 134.67 (978-0-13-703074-3(6), Prentice Hall) Prentice Hall PTR.

—Creating Inclusive Classrooms: Effective & Reflective Practices, Student Value Edition. 7th ed. 2010. (ENG.). (C). ring bd. 90.40 (978-0-13-258217-9(1), Prentice Hall) Prentice Hall PTR.

—Creating Inclusive Classrooms: Effective & Reflective Practices (with MyEducationLab) 7th ed. 2010. (ENG.). (C). pap. 141.33 (978-0-13-138123-0(7), Prentice Hall) Prentice Hall PTR.

Sandall, Susan R. & Schwartz, Ilene S. Building Blocks for Teaching Preschoolers with Special Needs. 2nd ed. 2008. (Illus.). 237p. pap. 36.95 incl. cd-rom (978-1-55766-967-4(8)) Brookes, Paul H. Publishing Co.

Sansosti, Frank J., et al. High-Functioning Autism - Asperger Syndrome in Schools: Assessment & Intervention. 2010. (Guilford Practical Intervention in Schools Ser.). (ENG., Illus.). 257p. (gr. k-12). pap. 40.00 (978-1-60623-670-3(9)) Guilford Pubns., Inc.

Sarathy, Padmaja. Striking a Balance Between IDEA & NCLB for Students with Significant Disabilities: Techniques & Tools for Aligning Standards- Based Instruction, Alternate Assessments, & IEPs. 2008. (978-1-57834-103-0(5)) LRP Pubns.

Schafer, William D. & Lissitz, Robert W. Alternate Assessments Based on Alternate Achievement Standards: Policy, Practice, & Potential. 2009. 408p. pap. 44.95 (978-1-59857-037-3(4)) Brookes, Paul H. Publishing Co.

Schleder, Mary. With Open Arms: Creating School Communities of Support for Kids with Social Challenges Using Circle of Friends, Extracurricular Activities, & Leawrning Teams. 2007. pap. 19.95 (978-1-934575-00-0(3)) Autism Asperger Publishing Co.

Schmidt, Stuart M., et al. All Children Can Learn: Effectively Educating the Under-Resourced Child. rev. ed. 2009. 98p. pap. 57.65 (978-0-7575-6593-9(X)) Kendall Hunt Publishing Co.

Schneider, Cornelia. Une etude comparative de l-education inclusive des enfants avec besoins particuliers en France et en Allemagne: Recherches dans onze salles de closse/Case Studies of Eleven Classrooms. 2011.Tr. of Comparative Study of the Inclusion of Children with Special Needs in Mainstream Schools in France & Germany. (FRE., Illus.). 252p. 119.95 (978-0-7734-1534-7(9)) Mellen, Edwin Pr., The.

Seale, Jane. E-Learning & Disability in Higher Education. 2006. (ENG., Illus.). 248p. (C). 175.00 (978-0-415-38309-7(9)) Routledge.

Seale, Jane K. E-Learning & Disability in Higher Education. Accessibility Research & Practice. 2006. (Illus.). 240p. per. 52.95 (978-0-415-38310-3(2)) Routledge.

Siebert, Birger, ed. Integrative Pädagogik und die Kulturhistorische Theorie. 2009. (Behindertenpädagogik und Integration Ser.). (GER.). 338p. pap. 49.95 (978-3-631-55520-0(2)) Lang, Peter GmbH, Europaischer Verlag der Wissenschaften DEU. Dist: Lang, Peter.

Siegel, Lawrence. The Complete IEP Guide: How to Advocate for Your Special Ed Child. 7th rev. ed. 2011. (ENG.). 402p. pap. 34.99 (978-1-4133-1313-0(2)) NOLO.

Siegel, Lawrence M. The Complete IEP Guide: How to Advocate for Your Special Ed Child. 7th ed. 2011. E-Book (978-1-4133-1336-9(1)) NOLO.

Sigafoos, Jeff, et al. How to Use Video Modeling & Video Prompting. 2006. (PRO-ED Series on Autism Spectrum Disorders). 14.00 (978-1-4164-0152-0(0)) PRO-ED, Inc.

Simon, Sara Rubinow & Forrest, Linda, eds. V'khol Banayikh. 2010. 574p. pap. 59.95 (978-1-934527-20-7(3)) Torah Aura Productions.

Simpson, Cynthia & Bakken, Jeffrey. Collaboration: A Multidisciplinary Approach to Educating Students with Disabilities. 2011. (ENG.). 450p. pap. 45.00 (978-1-59363-716-3(0)) Prufrock Pr.

Simpson, Cynthia G. & Warner, Laverne. Inclusive Strategies for Early Childhood Teachers: Helping Children with Special Needs Succeed. 2009. 140p. pap. 19.95 (978-0-87659-073-7(3)) Gryphon Hse., Inc.

Sitlington, Patricia L., et al. Transition Education & Services for Students with Disabilities. 5th ed. 2009. (ENG.). 352p. (C). 138.00 (978-0-13-505608-0(X), Prentice Hall) Prentice Hall PTR.

Skrtic, Thomas M., et al. Taking Stock of Special Education, Policy & Practice: A Retrospective Commentary. 2009. (Illus.). x, 486p. (978-0-89108-337-5(5)) Love Pubs.

Smith, Tom E., et al. Teaching Students with Special Needs in Inclusive Settings. 6th ed. 2011. (ENG., Illus.). 608p. (C). pap. 134.67 (978-0-13-800783-6(7), Prentice Hall) Prentice Hall PTR.

Smith, Tom E., et al. Teaching Students with Special Needs in Inclusive Settings, Student Value Edition. 2011. (ENG.). 608p. (C). ring bd. 90.60 **(978-0-13-276812-2(7)**, Prentice Hall) Prentice Hall PTR.

Smith, Tom E. C. & Patton, James R. Section 504 & Public Schools: A Practical Guide for Determining Eligibility, Developing Accommodation Plans, & Documenting Compliance. 2nd ed. 2007. (Illus.). vii, 107p. 40.00 (978-1-4164-0253-4(5)) PRO-ED, Inc.

Smith, Tom E. C., et al. Teaching Students with Special Needs in Inclusive Settings, Third Canadian Edition. 3rd ed. 2008. 496p. (C). pap. (978-0-205-55417-1(2)) Pearson Education Canada.

Sobol, Elise S. & Hammel, Alice M. An Attitude & Approach for Teaching Music to Special Learners. 2nd ed. 2008. (ENG., Illus.). 148p. pap. 36.95 incl. cd-rom (978-1-57886-856-8(4)) Rowman & Littlefield Education.

Solomon, Walter, et al. Autism & Understanding: The Waldon Approach to Child Development. 2012. 240p. 115.00 **(978-1-4462-0923-3(7)**, B09233C) SAGE Pubns., Ltd. GBR. Dist: SAGE Pubns., Inc.

Soto, Gloria & Zangari, Carole. Practically Speaking: Language, Literacy, & Academic Development for Students with AAC Needs. 2009. 400p. pap. 39.95 (978-1-55766-951-3(1)) Brookes, Paul H. Publishing Co.

Spinelli, Cathleen G. Classroom Assessment for Students in Special & General Education. 3rd ed. 2011. (ENG., Illus.). 528p. (C). pap. 124.20 (978-0-13-705013-0(5), Prentice Hall) Prentice Hall PTR.

Spooner, Wendy. The SEN Handbook for Trainee Teachers, NQTs & Teaching Assistants. 2nd rev. ed. 2010. (David Fulton / Nasen Ser.) (ENG., Illus.). 136p. 36.95 (978-0-415-56771-8(8)) Routledge.

Strax, Marshall, et al. Kids in the Middle: The Micro Politics of Special Education. 2012. (ENG.). 244p. 85.00 **(978-1-60709-846-1(6))**; pap. 39.95 **(978-1-60709-847-8(4))** Rowman & Littlefield Education.

Sulzer-Azaroff, Beth. Applying Behavior Analysis Across the Autism Spectrum: A Guide for Practitioners. 2007. (C). pap. 30.00 net. (978-1-59738-009-6(1)) Sloan Publishing.

Tarr, Jane & Tsokova, Diana. Diverse Perspectives on Inclusive School Communities. 2012. (ENG., Illus.). 144p. (C). 155.00 **(978-0-415-59457-8(X))**; pap. 44.95 **(978-0-415-59458-5(8))** Routledge.

Taylor, Ronald L. Assessment of Exceptional Students. 8th ed. 2008. (ENG.). 480p. (C). pap. 129.80 (978-0-205-60839-3(6)) Allyn & Bacon, Inc.

Thomson, Michael. The Psychology of Dyslexia: A Handbook for Teachers with Case Studies. 2nd ed. 2009. (ENG., Illus.). 250p. pap., tchr. ed., instr.'s hndbk. ed. 49.95 (978-0-470-69954-6(X), Wiley) Wiley, John & Sons, Inc.

Trawick-Smith, Jeffrey W. & Trawick-Smith, Jeffrey. Early Childhood Development: A Multicultural Perspective. 5th ed. 2008. (ENG., Illus.). 576p. (C). pap. 105.00 (978-0-13-501546-6(0), Prentice Hall) Prentice Hall PTR.

Turnbull, Ann, et al. Exceptional Lives: Special Education in Today's Schools. 7th rev. ed. 2011. (ENG., Illus.). 512p. (C). pap. 146.00 **(978-0-13-282177-3(X)**, Prentice Hall) Prentice Hall PTR.

Turnbull, Ann, et al. Exceptional Lives: Special Education in Today's Schools, Student Value Edition. (ENG.). 544p. (C). 6th ed. 2010. ring bd. 98.20 (978-0-13-258215-5(5)) 7th ed. 2012. ring bd. 94.93 **(978-0-13-289303-9(7))** Prentice Hall PTR. (Prentice Hall).

Turnbull, Ann P., et al. Exceptional Lives: Special Education in Today's Schools. 4th ed. pap. 98.60 incl. cd-rom (978-0-13-153395-8(1)) 6th ed. 2008. (ENG.). 576p. (C). pap. 146.00 (978-0-13-502696-0(2)) Prentice Hall PTR. (Prentice Hall).

—Exceptional Lives: Special Education in Today's Schools (with MyEducationLab) 6th ed. 2008. (ENG.). 576p. (C). pap. 152.67 (978-0-13-610141-3(0), Prentice Hall) Prentice Hall PTR.

Turnbull III, H. Rutherford, et al. Free Appropriate Public Education: The Law & Children with Disabilities. 7th ed. 2007. 448p. (C). 80.00 (978-0-89108-325-2(1)) Love Publishing Co.

Twachtman-Cullen, Diane & Twachtman-Bassett, Jennifer. The IEP from A to Z: How to Create Meaningful & Measurable Goals & Objectives. 2nd ed. 2011. (ENG.). 224p. pap. 29.95 (978-0-470-56234-5(X), Jossey-Bass) Wiley, John & Sons, Inc.

Tymchuk, Alexander J. The Health & Wellness Program: A Parenting Curriculum for Families at Risk. 2006. (Illus.). 213p. spiral bd. 69.95 incl. cd-rom (978-1-55766-817-2(5)) Brookes, Paul H. Publishing Co.

Understanding IDEA: What it Means for Preschoolers with Disabilities & Their Families. 2007. per. 20.00 (978-0-9773772-5-1(3)) Division for Early Childhood.

Underwood, Kathryn. The Construction of Disability in Our Schools: Teacher & Parent perspectives on the experience of labelled Students. 2008. 208p. (978-90-8790-221-6(2)); pap. (978-90-8790-220-9(4)) Sense Pubs.

University of Florida Staff. Teachers & Learners in Inclusive Schools. 3rd rev. ed. 2008. (ENG.). 654p. spiral bd. 142.47 (978-0-7575-2658-9(6)) Kendall Hunt Publishing Co.

van Kleeck, Anne. Sharing Books & Stories to Promote Language & Literacy. 2006. (Emergent & Early Literacy Ser.). (Illus.). 356p. per. 57.95 (978-1-59756-091-7(X)) Plural Publishing, Inc.

Vaughn, Sharon R., et al. Teaching Students Who are Exceptional, Diverse, & at Risk in the General Education Classroom. 5th ed. 2010. (ENG., Illus.). 576p. (C). pap. 134.67 (978-0-13-715179-0(9), Prentice Hall) Prentice Hall PTR.

—Teaching Students Who are Exceptional, Diverse, & at Risk in the General Education Classroom, Student Value Edition. 5th ed. 2010. (ENG.). 576p. (C). ring bd. 90.40 (978-0-13-258216-2(3), Prentice Hall) Prentice Hall PTR.

—Teaching Students Who are Exceptional, Diverse, & at Risk in the General Education Classroom (with MyEducationLab) 5th ed. 2010. (ENG.). 576p. (C). pap. 141.33 (978-0-13-138125-4(3), Prentice Hall) Prentice Hall PTR.

Visser, John. Diversity & Personalised Learning. 2009. 80p. 35.95 (978-0-415-46752-0(7)) Routledge.

Wagner, Vicki. Did They Teach Me This in College?: & Other Life Lessons Learned. 2007. (ENG.). 76p. per. 16.95 (978-1-4241-3455-7(2)) PublishAmerica, Inc.

Wandberg, Robert. Powerful Practices for High-Performing Special Educators. Kaufman, Roberta C., ed. 2010. (Illus.). 200p. pap. 34.95 (978-1-4129-6807-2(0), B68065P) Corwin Pr.

Wanerman, Todd & Roffman, Leslie. Including One, Including All: A Guide to Relationship-Based Early Childhood Inclusion. 2010. (ENG.). 304p. pap. 39.95 (978-1-60554-013-9(7)) Redleaf Pr.

Wappett, Matthew. Preparing Teachers for Inclusion. 2008. 104p. pap. (978-3-639-04985-5(3)) VDM Verlag Dr. Mueller e.K.

Wearmouth, Janice. Special Educational Needs: The Basics. 2011. (Basics Ser.). (ENG., Illus.). 232p. 90.00 **(978-0-415-59223-9(2))**; pap. 19.95 **(978-0-415-59224-6(0))** Routledge.

Webber, Jo & Scheuermann, Brenda. Educating Students with Autism: A Quick Start Manual. 2008. 51.00 (978-1-4164-0255-8(1)) PRO-ED, Inc.

Weber, et al. Special Education Law: Statutes & Regulations. 2nd ed. 2008. xxxi, 538p. pap. (978-1-4224-2073-7(6)) 3rd ed. 2010. xxi, 609p. pap. (978-1-4224-9351-9(2)) LexisNexis Matthew Bender.

Weber, Mark C. Special Education Law & Litigation Treatise. 3rd ed. 2008. (978-1-57834-099-6(3)) LRP Pubns.

Weber, Mark C., et al. Special Education Law: Cases & Materials. 2nd ed. 2007. xv, 636p. (978-1-4224-2603-6(3)) 2nd ed. 2007. 97.00 (978-1-4224-2072-0(8)) 3rd ed. 2010. (978-1-4224-7774-8(6)) LexisNexis Matthew Bender.

Weishaar, Mary Konya. Case Studies in Special Education Law: No Child Left Behind Act & Individuals with Disabilities Education Improvement Act. 2006. (ENG., Illus.). 160p. (C). per. 24.00 (978-0-13-218628-5(4), Prentice Hall) Prentice Hall PTR.

Weiss, Mary Jane. Practical Solutions for Educating Young Children with High Functioning Autism & Asperger Syndrome. 2007. (Illus.). 242p. pap. 21.95 (978-1-934575-14-7(3)) Autism Asperger Publishing Co.

WEST-E Exam Secrets Test Prep Staff, ed. WEST-E Early Childhood Special Education (071) Secrets Study Guide: WEST-E Test Review for the Washington Educator Skills Tests-Endorsements. 2011. (C). 62.99 (978-1-61403-764-4(7)) Mometrix Media LLC.

Westling, David L. & Fox, Lise. Teaching Students with Severe Disabilities. 4th ed. 2008. (ENG., Illus.). 624p. (C). 142.20 (978-0-13-241444-9(9), Prentice Hall) Prentice Hall PTR.

Westwood, Peter. Commonsense Methods for Children with Special Educational Needs. 6th rev. ed. 2010. (ENG.). 240p. (C). 120.00 (978-0-415-58376-3(4)); pap. 36.95 (978-0-415-58375-6(6)) Routledge.

—A Parent's Guide to Learning Difficulties. 2008. 120p. pap. 32.95 (978-0-86431-840-4(5)) ACER Pr. AUS. Dist: International Specialized Bk. Services.

—What Teachers Need to Know About Students With Disabilities. 2009. 146p. pap. 34.95 (978-0-86431-869-5(3)) ACER Pr. AUS. Dist: International Specialized Bk. Services.

Wexler, Alice & Wexler, Alice J. Art & Disability: The Social & Political Struggles Facing Education. 2009. (ENG., Illus.). 272p. 89.00 (978-0-230-60629-6(6)) Palgrave Macmillan.

Wexler, Alice J. Art & Disability: The Social & Political Struggles Facing Education. 2011. (ENG., Illus.). 266p. pap. 28.00 (978-0-230-11485-2(7)) Palgrave Macmillan.

Williams, Regena. A Study of Inclusion of Students with Disabilities. 2008. 88p. pap. (978-3-639-01963-6(6)) VDM Verlag Dr. Mueller e.K.

Willis, Clarissa. Creating Inclusive Learning Environments for Young Children: What to Do on Monday Morning. 2008. (Illus.). 240p. 76.95 (978-1-4129-5718-2(4), B57184C) Corwin Pr.

—Teaching Infants, Toddlers, & Twos with Special Needs. 2009. (ENG., Illus.). 160p. pap. 19.95 (978-0-87659-069-0(5)) Gryphon Hse., Inc.

—Teaching Young Children with Autism Spectrum Disorder. 2008. (ENG., Illus.). 224p. per. 24.95 (978-0-87659-008-9(3)) Gryphon Hse., Inc.

Wilson, Vicki A., et al. Building on Student Diversity: Profiles & Activities. 2006. (Illus.). 248p. (C). per. 41.00 (978-1-4129-3693-4(4), B36934P) SAGE Pubns., Inc.

Winton, Pamela J., et al. Practical Approaches to Early Childhood Professional Development: Evidence, Strategies, & Resources. 2007. (978-1-934019-19-1(4)) Zero To Three Pr.

Wright, Jim. RTI Toolkit: A Practical Guide for Schools. 2007. pap. 34.95 (978-1-934032-05-3(0), Dude Publishing) National Professional Resources, Inc.

Yell, Mitchell L. The Law & Special Education. 3rd ed. 2011. (ENG., Illus.). 448p. (C). pap. 101.33 (978-0-13-137609-0(8), Prentice Hall) Prentice Hall PTR.

Ziegler, Michele Flasch, et al. Common-Sense Classroom Management Techniques for Working with Students with Significant Disabilities. 2008. (Illus.). 144p. pap. 31.95 (978-1-4129-5819-6(9), B58189P) Corwin Pr.

CHILDREN WITH DISABILITIES—JUVENILE LITERATURE

McDonnell, Kathleen. Emily Included. 1 vol. 2012. (ENG., Illus.). 126p. (J). (gr. 3-7). mass mkt. 8.95 **(978-1-926920-33-7(3))** Second Story Pr. CAN. Dist: Orca Bk. Pubs. USA.

CHILDREN WITH DISABILITIES—REHABILITATION

Alexander, Michael A. & Matthews, Dennis J. Pediatric Rehabilitation: Principles & Practice. 4th ed. 2009. (Illus.). 500p. 449.00 (978-1-933864-37-2(0)) Demos Medical Publishing, LLC.

Anderson, Vicki & Yeates, Keith Owen, eds. Pediatric Traumatic Brain Injury: New Frontiers in Clinical & Translational Research. 2010. (ENG., Illus.). 244p. 105.00 (978-0-521-76332-5(0)) Cambridge Univ. Pr.

Chen, Deborah. Early Interactions: Parent Professional Perspectives in Early Intervention. 2007. 89.95 (978-1-55766-919-3(8)) Brookes, Paul H. Publishing Co.

Drnach, Mark. The Clinical Practice of Pediatric Physical Therapy: From the NICU to Independent Living. 2007. (Point (Lippincott Williams & Wilkins) Ser.). (ENG., Illus.). 379p. 65.99 (978-0-7817-9063-5(8)) Lippincott Williams & Wilkins.

Goodman, Karen D. Music therapy groupwork with special needs Children: The Evolving Process. 2007. 318p. (978-0-398-07739-6(8)); (978-0-398-07740-2(1)) Thomas, Charles C. Pub., Ltd.

Gutstein, Steven, ed. The Relationship Development Intervention Program & Education. 2007. 259p. per. 22.50 (978-0-9777186-1-0(1)) Connections Center.

Hanft, Barbara E. & Shepherd, Jayne. Collaborating for Student Success: A Guide for School-Based Occupational Therapy. 2008. (978-1-56900-247-6(9)) American Occupational Therapy Assn., Inc.

Hewitt-Taylor, Jaqui. Children with Complex & Continuing Health Needs: The Experiences of Children, Families & Care Staff. 2007. (ENG.). 240p. pap. (978-1-84310-502-2(0)) Kingsley, Jessica Ltd.

Jackson, Leslie L. Occupational Therapy Services for Children & Youth under IDEA. 3rd ed. 2007. pap. (978-1-56900-237-7(1)) American Occupational Therapy Assn., Inc.

Kirk, Sally. Hope for the Autism Spectrum: A Mother & Son Journey of Insight & Biomedical Intervention. 2008. (ENG., Illus.). 320p. (978-1-84310-894-8(1)) Kingsley, Jessica Ltd.

Kohan, Darius, et al. Evaluation & Rehabilitation of the Hearing Impaired Child. 2nd ed. 2006. (SIPac Ser.). (Illus.). 104p. pap. (978-1-56772-104-1(4)) American Academy of Otolaryngology-Head & Neck Surgery Foundation, Inc.

Kuhaneck, Heather Miller, et al. Activity Analysis, Creativity & Playfulness in Pediatric Occupational Therapy: Making Play Just Right. 2009. (Illus.). 208p. pap. 68.95 (978-0-7637-5606-2(7)) Jones & Bartlett Learning, LLC.

LeComer, Laurie. The Socially Included Child: A Parent's Guide to Successful Playdates, Recreation, & Family Events for Children with Autism. 2009. (ENG.). 256p. (gr. 12-18). pap. 14.00 (978-0-425-22965-1(3), Berkley Trade) Penguin Group (USA) Inc.

Miller, Frederic P., et al, eds. Cerebral Palsy. 2010. 104p. pap. **(978-613-0-72913-4(8))** VDM Verlag Dr. Mueller e.K.

Nelson, Maureen R. Pediatrics. 2010. 240p. 79.00 (978-1-933864-60-0(5)) Demos Medical Publishing, LLC.

Ohnabe, H. & Kubo, M., eds. Selected Papers from the Japanese Conference on the Advancement of Assistive & Rehabilitation Technology: 23rd JCAART 2008, Niigata - Assistive Technology Research Series. 2011. 224p. 160.00 **(978-1-60750-757-4(9))** IOS Pr., Inc.

Padula, William V., et al. Neuro-Visual Processing Rehabilitation: An Interdisciplinary Approach. 2012. **(978-0-929780-31-3(0))** Optometric Extension Program Foundation.

Rasore-Quartino, Alberto & Rondal, Jean-Adolphe, eds. Therapies & Rehabilitation in down Syndrome. 2007. (ENG., Illus.). 228p. per. 82.95 (978-0-470-06006-3(9), Wiley) Wiley, John & Sons, Inc.

Riddick-Grisham, Susan & Deming, Laura, eds. Pediatric Life Care Planning & Case Management, Second Edition. 2nd rev. ed. 2011. (ENG., Illus.). 1051p. 159.95 (978-1-4398-0358-5(7), CRC Press) Taylor & Francis Group GBR. Dist: Taylor & Francis Group.

Seth, Veenu, et al. Nutrition Issues in Children with Disabilities. 2011. 496p. pap. **(978-3-8443-2917-9(X))** Lambert Academic Publishing.

Sobo, Elisa J. & Kurtin, Paul S., eds. Optimizing Care for Young Children with Special Health Care Needs: Knowledge & Strategies for Navigating the System. 2007. (Illus.). 291p. per. 39.95 (978-1-55766-854-7(X)) Brookes, Paul H. Publishing Co.

Trief, Ellen & Shaw, Rona. Everyday Activities to Promote Visual Efficiency: A Handbook for Working with Young Children with Visual Impairments. 2009. (978-0-89128-836-7(8)); (978-0-89128-453-6(2)); (978-0-89128-835-0(X)) American Foundation for the Blind Pr.

Williams, Nancy. Yoga Therapy for Every Special Child: Meeting Needs in a Natural Setting. 2010. (ENG., Illus.). 224p. pap. (978-1-84819-027-6(1)) Kingsley, Jessica Ltd.

Woodward, Bob. Spiritual Healing with Children with Special Needs. 2007. (ENG.). 192p. per. (978-1-84310-545-9(4)) Kingsley, Jessica Ltd.

Yeadon, Helen. When Sophie Met Darcy Day: A Neglected Racehorse, a Troubled Child, a Friendship That Would Change Lives Forver. 2011. (ENG.). 320p. 13.95 (978-0-00-735424-5(X)) HarperCollins Pubs. Ltd. GBR. Dist: Independent Pubs. Group.

CHILDREN WITH MENTAL DISABILITIES

see also Learning Disabled Children; Religious Education of Children with Mental Disabilities

Bagnato, Stephen J. Authentic Assessment for Early Childhood Intervention: Best Practices. 2008. (Guilford School Practitioner Ser.). (ENG.). 315p. pap. 30.00 (978-1-60623-250-7(9)) Guilford Pubns., Inc.

Bagnato, Stephen J., et al. LINKing Authentic Assessment & Early Childhood Intervention: Best Measures for Best Practices, Second Edition. 2nd ed. 2010. (Illus.). 400p. pap. 49.95 (978-1-59857-047-2(1)) Brookes, Paul H. Publishing Co.

Baniel, Anat. Kids Beyond Limits: The Anat Baniel Method for Awakening the Brain & Transforming the Life of Your Child with Special Needs. 2012. (ENG.). 288p. (gr. 12). 16.00 **(978-0-399-53736-3(8)**, Perigee Trade) Penguin Group (USA) Inc.

Berryman, Renee C. Children Are Gifts from God, Disabled or Not! A Mother's Personal Journey of Hope & Inspiration. 2009. 336p. 28.99 (978-1-60791-636-9(3)); pap. 18.99 (978-1-60791-635-2(5)) Xulon Pr., Inc.

Bosman, Ineke. To Be a Man Is Not Easy: Stories from Ghanaian Emigrants. 2007. 124p. pap. 22.00 (978-90-5170-350-9(5)) Purdue Univ. Pr.

Bursztyn, Alberto. Childhood Psychological Disorders: Current Controversies. 2011. E-Book (978-0-313-06406-7(7), Praeger Pubs.) Greenwood Publishing Group, Inc.

Hale, Natalie. Down Syndrome Parenting 101: Must-Have Advice for Making Your Life Easier. 2011. 240p. pap. **(978-1-60613-020-9(X))** Woodbine Hse.

Heinks, Julie K. Andrew's Story: One Boy's Journey Back from Autism. 2008. 134p. pap. 24.95 (978-1-60610-943-4(X)) PublishAmerica, Inc.

Hill, Robert W. & Castro, Eduardo. Healing Young Brains: The Neurofeedback Solution. 2009. (ENG., Illus.). 386p. pap. 16.95 (978-1-57174-603-0(X)) Hampton Roads Publishing Co., Inc.

Hiner, Danielle. Growing with Joe. 2007. (ENG.). 216p. per. 24.95 (978-1-4241-4561-4(9)) PublishAmerica, Inc.

C

Holzhauser-Peters, Leslie & True, Leslie. Making Sense of Children's Thinking & Behavior. 2008. (ENG., Illus.). 192p. pap. (978-1-84310-888-7(7)) Kingsley, Jessica Ltd.

Hudson, Jill & Coffin, Amy Bixler. Out & About: Preparing Children with Autism Spectrum Disorders to Participate in Their Communities. 2007. (Illus.). 78p. per. 19.95 (978-1-931282-48-2(X)) Autism Asperger Publishing Co.

Jones, Anne. By His Hand. 2007. 124p. per. 10.99 (978-1-60034-872-3(6)) Xulon Pr., Inc.

Kober, Ralph. Enhancing the Quality of Life of People with Intellectual Disabilities: From Theory to Practice. Kober, Ralph, ed. 2010. (Social Indicators Research Ser.). (Illus.). xxiii, 400p. 189.00 (978-90-481-9649-4(3), 9048196493) Springer.

Kopetzky, Ulrike. Kinder mit Down-Syndrom: Lerntheoretische und verhaltenspsychologische Aspekte. 2009. 180p. pap. (978-3-639-18880-6(2)) VDM Verlag Dr. Mueller e.K.

Ling, John. I Can't Do That! My Social Stories to Help with Communication, Self-Care & Personal Skills. 2nd ed. 2010. (Lucky Duck Bks.). (Illus.). 120p. pap. 38.00 (978-0-85702-044-4(7), B20444P) SAGE Pubns., Ltd. GBR. Dist: SAGE Pubns., Inc.

Mathewson, Judith. Down Syndrome, Raising a Child Like Kimmy. 2009. 82p. pap. 11.95 (978-1-60860-193-6(5), Strategic Bk. Publishing) AEG Literary Publishing Services, Inc.

Matson, Johnny L., et al, eds. Assessing Childhood Psychopathology & Developmental Disabilities. 2010. x, 506p. pap. 89.95 (978-1-4419-8137-0(3), 1441981373) Springer.

McConnell, David. Disability. 2009. 200p. pap. (978-3-639-19483-8(7)) VDM Verlag Dr. Mueller e.K.

Meyer, Don, ed. Thicker Than Water. 2008. 212p. pap. 21.95 (978-1-890627-91-1(7)) Woodbine Hse.

Rasore-Quartino, Alberto & Rondal, Jean-Adolphe, eds. Therapies & Rehabilitation in down Syndrome. 2007. (ENG., Illus.). 228p. per. 82.95 (978-0-470-06006-3(9), Wiley) Wiley, John & Sons, Inc.

Regan, Kathy. Opening Our Arms: Helping Troubled Kids Do Well. 2006. (ENG., Illus.). 224p. pap. 16.95 (978-0-923521-94-3(1)) Bull Publishing Co.

Reynolds, Kate E. Party Planning for Children & Teens on the Autism Spectrum: How to Avoid Meltdowns & Have Fun! 2012. (ENG., Illus.). 128p. pap. **(978-1-84905-277-1(8))** Kingsley, Jessica Ltd.

Rondal, Jean-Adolphe, et al, eds. Neurocognitive Rehabilitation of down Syndrome: Early Years. 2011. (ENG., Illus.). 252p. pap. 65.00 (978-1-107-40043-6(0)) Cambridge Univ. Pr.

Routh, Donald K. & Routh, Donald, eds. The Experimental Psychology of Mental Retardation. 2006. (ENG., Illus.). 363p. (gr. 11). pap. 32.95 (978-0-202-30888-3(X)) Aldine Transaction.

Schermerhorn, William. Kids with Down Syndrome: Staying Healthy & Making Friends. 2007. DVD 29.99 (978-0-9748071-3-3(3)) Blueberry Shoes Productions LLC.

Shagufta, Wahab, et al. Transcranial Doppler in Hydrocephalus: Relevance of Transcranial Doppler (TCD) Sonography in Children with Hydrocephalus. 2011. 96p. pap. **(978-3-639-32647-5(4))** VDM Verlag Dr. Mueller e.K.

Simons, Jo Ann. The down Syndrome Transition Handbook: Charting Your Child's Course to Adulthood. 2010. (978-1-890627-87-4(9)) Woodbine Hse.

Skallerup, Susan J., ed. Babies with Down Syndrome: A New Parents' Guide. 3rd ed. 2008. (Illus.). 358p. pap. 18.95 (978-1-890627-55-3(0)) Woodbine Hse.

Smith, Veronica & Patterson, Stephanie Y. Getting into the Game: Sports Programs for Kids with Autism. 2012. (ENG.). 256p. pap. **(978-1-84905-249-8(2))** Kingsley, Jessica Ltd.

Tawfig, Nada & Ibrahim Ghandour, Prof. Periodontal Health of Mentally Retarded Children. 2010. 124p. pap. (978-3-639-25107-4(5)) VDM Verlag Dr. Mueller e.K.

Woolston, Joseph, et al. IICAPS: A Home-Based Psychiatric Treatment for Children & Adolescents. 2007. (ENG., Illus.). 186p. 55.00 (978-0-300-11249-8(1)) Yale Univ. Pr.

CHILDREN WITH MENTAL DISABILITIES—BIOGRAPHY

Buck, Pearl S. The Child Who Never Grew. 24.95 (978-0-8488-1250-8(6)) Amereon LTD.

Calinescu, Matei. Matthew's Enigma: A Father's Portrait of His Autistic Son. Jianu, Angela, tr. from ROM. 2009. (ENG., Illus.). 224p. 50.00 (978-0-253-35297-2(5), 0253352975); pap. 19.95 (978-0-253-22066-0(1), 0253220661) Indiana Univ. Pr.

Johnson, Myrtle. God Is My Witness. 2007. per. (978-1-59581-368-8(3), Brentwood Christian Pr.) Brentwood Communications Group.

Knol, Faye. Receiving David: The Gift of a Son Who Taught Us How to Live & Love. 2010. (Illus.). 176p. pap. 15.00 (978-0-8028-6543-4(7)) Eerdmans, William B. Publishing Co.

Moultry, Christopher Lamar. Don't Judge a Book by Its Cover. 2010. 112p. pap. 14.99 (978-1-4490-3369-9(5)) AuthorHouse.

Rubinyi, Susan. Natural Genius: The Gift of Aspreger's Syndrome. 2007. (ENG.). 12p. per. (978-1-84310-784-2(8)) Kingsley, Jessica Ltd.

Simpson, Wallis A. My Andrew: Day-to-Day Living with a Child with an Autism Spectrum Disorder. 2007. 163p. per. 19.95 (978-1-931282-30-7(7)) Autism Asperger Publishing Co.

Soucy, Jean-Charles. Of Granite & Tigers: The Parenting of Thomas. 2008. 89p. pap. 16.95 (978-1-60441-094-5(9)) PublishAmerica, Inc.

Stallings, Gene & Cook, Sally. Another Season: A Coach's Story of Raising an Exceptional Son. 2009. (ENG., Illus.). 240p. pap. 18.99 (978-0-316-05652-6(9), Back Bay Bks.) Little Brown & Co.

Talty, Janine. Indigo Awakening: A Doctor's Memoir of Forging an Authentic Life in a Turbulent World. 2009. (Illus.). 368p. pap. 17.95 (978-1-60070-063-7(2), Elite Bks.) Author's Publishing Cooperative.

Unger, Frank James. Cymbals in the Sanctuary: The story of an other kind of Love. 2011. 144p. pap. 19.99 **(978-1-4653-3970-6(1))** Xlibris Corp.

CHILDREN WITH MENTAL DISABILITIES—EDUCATION

Aune, Beth, et al. More Behavior Solutions in & Beyond the Inclusive Classroom. 2011. (ENG.). 110p. pap. 14.95 (978-1-935274-48-3(1)) Future Horizons, Inc.

Bakken, Jeffrey/P, et al, eds. Behavioral Disorders: Identification, Assessment, & Instruction of Students with EBD, Vol. 22. 2012. (Advances in Special Education Ser.). 231p. 124.95 **(978-1-78052-504-4(4))** Emerald Group Publishing Ltd. GBR. Dist: Turpin Distribution Services Ltd.

Bambara, Linda M. & Knoster, Tim. Designing Positive Behavior Support Plans. 2nd ed. 2009. (978-1-935304-03-6(8)) American Assn. on Intellectual & Developmental Disabilities.

Barone, John. A Place for All: Ministry for Youth with Special Needs. 2008. (Illus.). 131p. pap. 26.25 (978-0-88489-972-3(1)) St. Mary's Pr.

Betts, Dion E., et al. Hints & Tips for Helping Children with Autism Spectrum Disorders: Useful Strategies for Home, School, & the Community. 2008. (ENG.). 192p. pap. (978-1-84310-896-2(8)) Kingsley, Jessica Ltd.

Betts, Stacey W. Asperger Syndrome in the Inclusive Classroom: Advice & Strategies for Teachers. 2007. (ENG.). 16p. per. (978-1-84310-840-5(2)) Kingsley, Jessica Ltd.

Christo, Catherine. Identifying, Assessing, & Treating Dyslexia at School. 2009. (Developmental Psychopathology at School Ser.). 49.95 (978-0-387-88599-5(4)) Springer.

Christo, Catherine, et al. Identifying, Assessing, & Treating Dyslexia at School. 2010. (Developmental Psychopathology at School Ser.). (ENG., Illus.). xii, 152p. pap. 49.95 (978-1-4419-4696-6(9), 1441946969) Springer.

Cooley, Myles L. Teaching Kids with Mental Health & Learning Disorders in the Regular Classroom: How to Recognize, Understand, & Help Challenged (and Challenging) Students Succeed. 2007. (ENG.). 224p. (gr. k-12). pap. 35.99 (978-1-57542-242-8(5)) Free Spirit Publishing, Inc.

Cram101 Textbook Reviews. Outlines & Highlights for Strategies for Teaching Learners with Special Needs by Cram101. 2011. 176p. pap. 30.95 **(978-1-61744-114-1(7))** Cram101 Inc.

Cram101 Textbook Reviews & Cram101 Textbook Reviews. Outlines & Highlights for Learners with Mild Disabilities by Eileen B Raymond, Isbn: 9780205519149 0205519148. 2011. 80p. pap. 27.95 **(978-1-61654-109-5(1))** Cram101 Inc.

Cumine, Val, et al. Asperger Syndrome: A Practical Guide for Teachers. 2nd ed. 2009. (Illus.). (ENG.). 116p. 37.95 (978-0-415-48371-1(9)); xi, 112p. 37.95 **(978-0-203-86486-9(7))** Routledge.

Dallmann-Jones, Anthony. Shadow Children: Understanding Education's #1 Problem. 2006. (Illus.). xvii, 188p. per. 24.95 (978-0-9787610-0-4(6)) RLD Pubns., Inc.

Davis, Ronald D. & Braun, Eldon M. The Gift of Dyslexia: Why Some of the Smartest People Can't Read... & How They Can Learn. rev. exp. ed. 2010. (ENG.). 304p. (gr. 12-18). 15.95 (978-0-399-53566-6(7), Perigee Trade) Penguin Group (USA) Inc.

Dixon, Janet. ISPEEK at Home: Over 1300 Visual Communication Images. 2007. (Ispeek Ser.). (ENG.). cd-rom (978-1-84310-510-7(1)) Kingsley, Jessica Ltd.

Dyrbjerg, Pernille & Vedel, Maria. Everyday Education: Visual Support for Children with a Autism. 2006. (ENG., Illus.). 128p. (978-1-84310-457-5(1)) Kingsley, Jessica Ltd.

Feifer, Steven. Emotional Disorders: A Neuropsychological, Psychopharmacological, & Educational Perspective. Rattan, Gurmal, ed. 2010. (ENG., Illus.). 320p. pap. 49.95 (978-0-9703337-5-9(7), 970335) Norton, W. W. & Co., Inc.

Fennell, Francis M. Achieving Fluency: Special Education & Mathematics. 2011. (978-0-87353-654-7(1)) National Council of Teachers of Mathematics.

Fertig, Beth. Why Cant U Teach Me 2 Read? Three Students & a Mayor Put Our Schools to the Test. 2009. (ENG., Illus.). 368p. 27.00 (978-0-374-29905-7(6)) Farrar, Straus & Giroux.

Foreman, Phil. Education of Students with an Intellectual Disability: Research & Practice (HC) 2009. 254p. 85.99 (978-1-60752-215-7(2)) Information Age Publishing, Inc.

—Education of Students with an Intellectual Disability: Research & Practice (PB) 2009. 254p. pap. 45.99 (978-1-60752-214-0(4)) Information Age Publishing, Inc.

Gallegos, Elena M. & Shallenberger, Jill M. Autism Methodology Cases to Live By: Legal Guidance for Practical Program Strategies. 2008. (978-1-57834-100-9(0)) LRP Pubns.

Gallenstein, Nancy L. & Hodges, Dodi. Mathematics for All: Instructional Strategies to Assist Students with Learning Challenges. 2011. pap. (978-0-87173-178-4(9)) Assn. for Childhood Education International.

Grossberg, Blythe. Asperger's Rules! How to Make Sense of School & Friends. 2012. 14.95 **(978-1-4338-1128-9(6))**; pap. 9.95 **(978-1-4338-1127-2(8))** American Psychological Assn. (Magination Pr.).

Hanbury, Martin. Educating Students on the Autistic Spectrum: A Practical Guide. 2nd ed. 2012. (Illus.). 144p. 100.00 **(978-0-85702-893-8(6)**, B28938C); pap. 40.00 **(978-0-85702-894-5(4)**, B28938P) SAGE Pubns., Ltd. GBR. Dist: SAGE Pubns., Inc.

Hanbury, Martin. Positive Behaviour Strategies to Support Children & Young People with Autism. 2007. (Illus.). 120p. 65.00 (978-1-4129-2910-3(5), B29105C); per. 30.00 (978-1-4129-2911-0(3), B29105P) SAGE Pubns., Ltd. GBR. Dist: SAGE Pubns., Inc.

Hanft, Barbara E. & Shepherd, Jayne. Collaborating for Student Success: A Guide for School-Based Occupational Therapy. 2008. (978-1-56900-247-6(9)) American Occupational Therapy Assn., Inc.

Hoffman, Anne, et al. Discrimination Training Alternatives: Module 1. 2007. DVD 35.00 (978-1-928598-12-1(9)) Pyramid Educational Products, Inc.

Ingersoll, Brooke & Dvortcsak, Anna. Teaching Social Communication to Children with Autism: A Manual for Parents. 2010. (ENG., Illus.). 144p. pap. 25.00 (978-1-60623-440-2(4)) Guilford Pubns., Inc.

—Teaching Social Communication to Children with Autism Set: A Practitioner's Guide to Parent Training & A Manual for Parents, 2 bks. 2010. (ENG.). pap. 85.00 (978-1-60623-442-6(0)) Guilford Pubns., Inc.

Kapur, Malavika. Learning from Children What to Teach Them. 2007. (Illus.). 200p. (C). 45.00 (978-0-7619-3611-4(4), B36114C) SAGE Pubns., Inc.

Kumin, Libby. Helping Children with Down Syndrome Communicate Better: Speech & Language Skills for Ages 6 - 14. 2008. (Illus.). 393p. pap. 24.95 (978-1-890627-54-6(2)) Woodbine Hse.

Labosh, Kathy. The Child with Autism Learns about Faith: 15 Ready-to-Use Scripture Lessons, from the Garden of Eden to the Parting of the Red Sea. 2011. (ENG.). 97p. pap. 14.95 (978-1-935274-19-3(8)) Future Horizons, Inc.

Lawrence, Clare. Autism & Flexischooling: A Shared Classroom & Homeschooling Approach. 2012. (ENG.). 160p. pap. **(978-1-84905-279-5(4))** Kingsley, Jessica Ltd.

Lickey, Deborah C. & Powers, Denise J. Starting with Their Strengths: Using the Project Approach in Early Childhood Special Education. 2011. (Early Childhood Education Ser.). (Illus.). 176p. (ENG.). 29.95 (978-0-8077-5235-7(5)); pap. 29.95 (978-0-8077-5234-0(7)) Teachers College Pr., Teachers College, Columbia Univ.

Massey, June. Meeting the Needs of Students with Dyslexia. 2008. (Meeting the Needs Ser.). (ENG., Illus.). 144p. 39.95 (978-1-85539-445-2(6), Network Continuum Education) Continuum International Publishing Group, Ltd. GBR. Dist: National Bk. Network.

Miller, Kirsten. Children on the Bridge: A Story of Autism in South Africa. 2007. (ENG.). 240p. per. 21.00 (978-1-77009-218-1(8)) Jacana Media ZAF. Dist: Independent Pubs. Group.

Morgan, Angela. Constructing & Maintaining Disability. 2011. 240p. pap. **(978-3-8443-3181-3(6))** Lambert Academic Publishing.

Myles, Brenda Smith. The Comprehensive Autism Planning System [CAPS] for Individuals with Asperger Syndrome, Autism, & Related Disabilities: Integrating Best Practices Throughout the Student's Day. 2007. pap. 29.95 (978-1-934575-03-1(8)) Autism Asperger Publishing Co.

Notbohm, Ellen. Ten Things Your Student with Autism Wishes You Knew. 2006. (ENG., Illus.). 117p. per. 14.95 (978-1-932565-36-2(1)) Future Horizons, Inc.

O'Brien, et al. Teaching Students with Special Needs: A Guide for Future Educators. rev. ed. 2011. (ENG.). 362p. pap. 52.00 (978-0-7575-8752-8(6)) Kendall Hunt Publishing Co.

O'Donovan, Margaret & Dare, Angela. Good Practice in Caring for Young Children with Special Needs. Walker, Miranda, ed. 3rd rev. ed. 2009. (ENG., Illus.). 432p. pap. 57.50 **(978-1-4085-0490-1(1))** Nelson Thornes Ltd. GBR. Dist: Trans-Atlantic Pubns., Inc.

Okech, John Baptist. Special Needs Education in Ugand. 2011. 352p. pap. **(978-3-8443-8262-4(3))** Lambert Academic Publishing.

O'Regan, Fintan J. & O'Regan. Adhd. 2nd ed. 2007. (SEN (Continuum) Ser.). (ENG., Illus.). 136p. 29.95 (978-0-8264-9234-0(7)) Continuum International Publishing Group, Ltd. GBR. Dist: National Bk. Network.

Otten, Kaye & Tuttle, Jodie. How to Reach & Teach Children with Challenging Behavior: Practical, Ready-to-Use Interventions That Work. 2010. (J-B Ed: Reach & Teach Ser.: 7). (ENG., Illus.). 336p. pap. 29.95 (978-0-470-50516-8(8), Jossey-Bass) Wiley, John & Sons, Inc.

Ramaswamy, Sudha & Greer, R. Douglas. An Establishing Operation for Academic ResponseAcquisition: Testing the Effects of an Establishing Operation onResponse Acquisition & its Differential Effect onPerformance Tasks of Children with Autism. 2008. 88p. pap. (978-3-639-09942-3(7)) VDM Verlag Dr. Mueller e.K.

Reid, Gavin, et al. Assessing Children with Specific Learning Difficulties. 2012. (David Fulton / Nasen Ser.). 160p. pap. 42.95 **(978-0-415-67027-2(6))**; 140.00 **(978-0-415-59759-3(5))** Routledge.

Rosner, D. M. The China Doll. 2008. (ENG., Illus.). 28p. (J). 8.99 (978-1-934340-98-1(7)) Jigsaw Pr.

Schneider, Cindy B. Acting Antics: A Theatrical Approach to Teaching Social Understanding to Kids & Teens with Asperger Syndrome. 2007. (ENG., Illus.). 224p. per. (978-1-84310-845-0(3)) Kingsley, Jessica Ltd.

Seguin, Edward. Report on Education. 2010. (ENG.). 220p. pap. 24.75 (978-1-176-57822-7(7)) 2010. 230p. pap. 25.75 (978-1-175-99006-8(X)) 2010. 218p. pap. 24.75 (978-1-143-09524-5(3)) 2009. 220p. 28.99 (978-1-115-51301-2(X)) 2009. 220p. pap. 23.75 (978-1-115-51303-6(6)) 2009. 220p. pap. 24.75 (978-1-115-51302-9(8)) 2009. (ENG.). 218p. pap. 22.99 (978-1-115-51304-3(4), BiblioLife) 2009. (ENG.). 218p. pap. 20.99 (978-1-115-51305-0(2), BiblioLife) 2009. 220p. 23.99 (978-1-103-30662-6(6)) 2009. 220p. pap. 17.99 (978-1-103-30658-9(8)) BiblioBazaar.

Sheehan, Martin R., et al. Managing the Cycle of Meltdowns for Students with Autism Spectrum Disorder. 2012. 240p. pap. 27.16 **(978-1-4129-9403-3(9)**, B94033P) Corwin Pr.

Thomson, Michael, et al. The Psychology of Dyslexia: A Handbook for Teachers with Case Studies. 2nd ed. 2009. (ENG., Illus.). 250p. tchr. ed. 105.00 (978-0-470-74096-5(5), Wiley) Wiley, John & Sons, Inc.

UC Davis Mind Institute Staff. Educational Interventions for Students with Autism. Mundy, Peter & Mastergeorge, Ann, eds. 2012. (ENG.). 336p. pap. 30.00 **(978-0-470-58486-6(6)**, Jossey-Bass) Wiley, John & Sons, Inc.

Vadasy, Patricia F. & Nelson, J. Ron. Vocabulary Instruction for Struggling Students. 2012. (What Works for Special-Needs Learners Ser.). (ENG.). 190p. (gr. -1-8). pap. 27.00 **(978-1-4625-0282-0(2))** Guilford Pubns., Inc.

Whalen, Christina. Real Life, Real Progress for Children with Autism Spectrum Disorders: Strategies for Successful Generalization in Natural Environments. 2009. (Illus.). 256p. pap. 29.95 (978-1-55766-954-4(6)) Brookes, Paul H. Publishing Co.

Winner, Michelle Garcia. A Politically Incorrect Look at Evidence-based Practices & Teaching Social Skills: A literature review & Discussion. 2008. pap. 20.00 (978-0-9792922-5-5(5)) Think Social Publishing, Inc.

CHILDREN WITH MENTAL DISABILITIES—GREAT BRITAIN

Cumine, Val, et al. Asperger Syndrome: A Practical Guide for Teachers. 2nd ed. 2009. (Illus.). (ENG.). 116p. 37.95 (978-0-415-48371-1(9)); xi, 112p. 37.95 **(978-0-203-86486-9(7))** Routledge.

Cunningham, Cliff. Down Syndrome: An Introduction for Parents & Carers. 3rd ed. 2010. (Human Horizons Ser.). (ENG., Illus.). 480p. pap. 24.95 (978-0-285-63697-2(9)) Souvenir Pr. Ltd. GBR. Dist: Independent Pubs. Group.

Kennedy, Anna. Not Stupid. 2009. (ENG., Illus.). 288p. pap. 14.95 (978-1-84454-784-5(1)) Blake, John Publishing, Ltd. GBR. Dist: Independent Pubs. Group.

O'Regan, Fintan J. & O'Regan. Adhd. 2nd ed. 2007. (SEN (Continuum) Ser.). (ENG., Illus.). 136p. 29.95 (978-0-8264-9234-0(7)) Continuum International Publishing Group, Ltd. GBR. Dist: National Bk. Network.

CHILDREN WITH SOCIAL DISABILITIES

see also Teachers of Children with Social Disabilities

Acker-Hocevar, Michele, et al. Leadership from the Ground Up: Effective Schooling in Traditionally Low Performing Schools. 2012. pap. **(978-1-61735-650-6(6))**; E-Book **(978-1-61735-652-0(2))** Information Age Publishing, Inc.

Anderegg, David. Nerds: How Dorks, Dweebs, Techies, & Trekkies Can Save America & Why They Might Be Our Last Hope. 2011. (ENG.). 304p. (gr. 12). 14.95 (978-1-58542-852-6(3), Tarcher) Penguin Group (USA) Inc.

Bishop-Josef, Sandra J., et al, eds. Child Development & Social Policy: Knowledge for Action. 2006. (Decade of Behavior Ser.). (Illus.). 311p. 39.95 (978-1-59147-425-8(6)) American Psychological Assn.

Breaux, Chrissy. Angel Wings for Jenny. 2007. 484p. per. 29.95 (978-1-4241-8978-6(0)) PublishAmerica, Inc.

Cheney, Douglas, ed. Transition of Secondary Students with Emotional or Behavioral Disorders (Second Edition) Current Approaches for Positive Outcomes. 2nd ed. 2010. (ENG.). 464p. pap. 35.95 (978-0-87822-626-9(5)) Research Pr.

Clabeaux, M. My First Year in Purgatory. 2007. 219p. pap. 14.94 (978-1-4303-1198-0(3)) Lulu Enterprises Inc.

Curwin, Richard L. Meeting Students Where They Live: Motivation in Urban Schools. 2010. 181p. pap. 23.95 (978-1-4166-0956-8(3)) Assn. for Supervision & Curriculum Development.

Dallmann-Jones, Anthony. Shadow Children: Understanding Education's #1 Problem. 2006. (Illus.). xvii, 188p. per. 24.95 (978-0-9787610-0-4(6)) RLD Pubns., Inc.

Ejigu, Gardachew Tiruneh. The Destiny of Orphans & Vulnerable Children in Ethiopia: Situational Analysis of Orphans & Vulnerable Children in Bahir Dar Town, Northwest Ethiopia. 2011. 88p. pap. **(978-3-639-22771-0(9))** VDM Verlag Dr. Mueller e.K.

Gill, Owen & Jack, Gordon. The Child & Family in Context: Developing Ecological Pratice in Disadvantaged Communities. 2007. (Illus.). 176p. pap. 37.95 (978-1-905541-15-7(5)) Russell Hse. Publishing Ltd. GBR. Dist: International Specialized Bk. Services.

Ginsberg, Alice E. Embracing Risk in Urban Education: Curiosity, Creativity, & Courage in the Era of No Excuses & Relay Race Reform. 2012. (ENG.). 144p. pap. 21.95 **(978-1-60709-949-9(7))**; 40.00 **(978-1-60709-948-2(9))** Rowman & Littlefield Education.

—Embracing Risk in Urban Education: Curiosity, Creativity, & Courage in the ERA of "No Excuses" & Relay Race Reform. 2012. **(978-1-60709-950-5(0))** Rowman & Littlefield Education.

Gleason, Mona, et al, eds. Lost Kids: Vulnerable Children & Youth in Twentieth-Century Canada & the United States. 2010. (ENG., Illus.). 272p. (C). pap. 37.95 (978-0-7748-1687-8(2)) UBC Pr. CAN. Dist: Univ. of Washington Pr.

Johnson, Dale D., et al. Stop High-Stakes Testing: An Appeal to America's Conscience. 2007. (ENG., Illus.). 192p. 70.00 (978-0-7425-5937-0(8)); per. 24.95 (978-0-7425-5938-7(6)) Rowman & Littlefield Publishers, Inc.

Kershaw, Roger & Sacks, Janet. New Lives for Old: The Story of Britain's Child Migrants. 2007. (Illus.). 240p. 34.95 (978-1-905615-17-9(5)) National Archives (PRO), The GBR. Dist: International Publishers Marketing.

Kramer, Paula & Kramer, Paula. Frames of Reference for Pediatric Occupational Therapy. Hinojosa, Jim, ed. 3rd rev. ed. 2009. (ENG., Illus.). 602p. 84.99 (978-0-7817-6826-9(8)) Lippincott Williams & Wilkins.

Kurfi, Mustapha Hashim. Societal Responses to the State of Orphans & Vulnerable Children. 2011. 136p. pap. **(978-3-8443-3099-1(2))** Lambert Academic Publishing.
Ling, John. I Can't Do That! My Social Stories to Help with Communication, Self-Care & Personal Skills. 2nd ed. 2010. (Lucky Duck Bks.). (Illus.). 120p. pap. 38.00 *(978-0-85702-044-4(7)*, B20444P) SAGE Pubns., Ltd. GBR. Dist: SAGE Pubns., Inc.
Maguire, Moira J. Precarious Childhood in Post-Independence Ireland. 2012. (ENG.). 272p. pap. 28.95 **(978-0-7190-8774-5(0))** Manchester Univ. Pr. GBR. Dist: Macmillan.
Mathews, Jay. Work Hard. Be Nice: How Two Inspired Teachers Created the Most Promising Schools in America. 2009. (ENG.). 329p. pap. 14.95 *(978-1-56512-516-2(9)*, 1565125169) Algonquin Bks. of Chapel Hill.
Neal, Gerald W. Quiet Desperation: The Effects of Competition in School on Abused & Neglected Children. 2008. (ENG.). 136p. pap. 29.50 *(978-0-7618-3993-4(3))* Hamilton Bks.
Ntakirutimana, Niyiguha Vestine. Faith Based Organizations Empowering Vulnerable Children, South Afric. 2011. 132p. pap. **(978-3-639-32189-0(8))** VDM Verlag Dr. Mueller e.K.
Ostovar, Roya. The Ultimate Guide to Sensory Processing in Children: Easy, Everyday Solutions to Sensory Challenges. 2010. (ENG.). 340p. pap. 19.95 *(978-1-935274-07-0(4))* Future Horizons, Inc.
Phillips, Norma Kolko & Straussner, Shulamith Lala Ashenberg. Children in the Urban Environment: Linking Social Policy & Clinical Practice. 2nd ed. 2006. 300p. 67.95 *(978-0-398-07669-6(3))*; pap. 47.95 *(978-0-398-07670-2(7))* Thomas, Charles C. Pub., Ltd.
Polakow, Valerie. Who Cares for Our Children? The Child Care Crisis in the Other America. 2007. (ENG., Illus.). 240p. 46.00 *(978-0-8077-4775-9(0))*; pap. 21.95 *(978-0-8077-4774-2(2))* Teachers College Pr., Teachers College, Columbia Univ.
Power, Anne. City Survivors: Bringing up Children in Disadvantaged Neighbourhoods. 2007. 232p. (C). pap. 39.95 *(978-1-84742-049-7(4))* Policy Pr. GBR. Dist: Chicago Distribution Ctr.
Roberts, Helen. What Works in Reducing Inequalities in Child Health. 2nd rev. ed. 2012. 208p. pap. 32.95 **(978-1-84742-996-4(3))** Policy Pr. GBR. Dist: Chicago Distribution Ctr.
—What Works in Reducing Inequalities in Child Health? 2nd rev. ed. 2012. 208p. 89.95 **(978-1-84742-997-1(1))** Policy Pr. GBR. Dist: Chicago Distribution Ctr.
Ross, Ruth Herron & Roberts-Pacchione, Beth. Making Friends, Prek-3: A Social Skills Program for Inclusive Settings. 2nd ed. 2011. (Illus.). 232p. pap. 33.95 *(978-1-4129-8113-2(1)*, B81132P) Corwin Pr.
Schneider, Justine, et al, eds. Supporting Children & Families: Lessons from Sure Start for Evidence-Based Practice in Health, Social Care & Education. 2007. (Illus.). 287p. per. *(978-1-84310-506-0(3))* Kingsley, Jessica Ltd.
Yisrael, Sean. Classroom Management: A Guide for Urban School Teachers. 2012. (ENG.). 100p. 32.00 **(978-1-61048-762-7(1))**; pap. 16.95 **(978-1-61048-763-4(X))** Rowman & Littlefield Education.

CHILDREN WITH SOCIAL DISABILITIES—EDUCATION

see also Head Start Programs

Acker-Hocevar, Michele, et al. Leadership from the Ground Up: Effective Schooling in Traditionally Low Performing Schools. 2012. **(978-1-61735-651-3(4))** Information Age Publishing, Inc.
Akhavan, Nancy. Teaching Writing in Title I Schools, K-3. 2009. 192p. pap. 27.50 *(978-0-325-01388-6(8)*, E01388) Heinemann.
—The Title I Teacher's Guide to Teaching Reading, K-3. 2008. (Illus.). 240p. pap. 31.25 *(978-0-325-01083-0(8)*, E01083) Heinemann.
Akhavan, Nancy L. Teaching Reading in a Title I School, K-3. 2010. pap. 31.25 *(978-0-325-03724-0(8))* Heinemann.
Allington, Richard L. & Walmsley, Sean A., eds. No Quick Fix: Rethinking Literacy Programs in America's Elementary Schools. 2007. (Language & Literacy Ser.). (ENG., Illus.). 192p. per. 26.95 *(978-0-8077-4844-2(7))* Teachers College Pr., Teachers College, Columbia Univ.
Ansalone, George. Exploring Unequal Achievement in the Schools: The Social Construction of Failure. 2010. (ENG.). 256p. pap. 29.95 *(978-0-7391-2469-7(2))* Lexington Bks.
Ansalone, George Edward. Exploring Unequal Achievement in the Schools: The Social Construction of Failure. 2009. (ENG.). 256p. 78.99 *(978-0-7391-2468-0(4))* Lexington Bks.
Ayers, William, et al, eds. City Kids, City Schools: More Reports from the Front Row. 2008. (ENG.). 346p. pap. 24.95 *(978-1-59558-338-3(6))* New Pr., The.
Baca, Jimmy Santiago. Stories from the Edge. 2010. 112p. pap. 12.44 *(978-0-325-02945-1(2)*, E02948) Heinemann.
Barnett, David. Privileged Thinking in Today's Schools: The Implications for Social Justice. 2010. ix, 124p. *(978-1-60709-971-0(3))*; (ENG.). 125p. pap. 18.95 *(978-1-60709-970-3(5))* Rowman & Littlefield Education.
Barr, Robert D. & Parrett, William Hays. Saving Our Students, Saving Our Schools: 50 Proven Strategies for Helping Underachieving Students & Improving Schools. 2nd ed. 2007. 432p. 90.95 *(978-1-4129-5792-2(3)*, B57922C); (Illus.). per. 44.95 **(978-1-4129-5793-9(1)**, B57922P) Corwin Pr.
Bireda, Martha. Schooling Poor Minority Children: New Segregation in the Post-Brown Era. 2011. (ENG.). 146p. 40.00 *(978-1-60709-882-9(2))*; pap. 19.95 *(978-1-60709-883-6(0))* Rowman & Littlefield Education.
Bireda, Martha R. Schooling Poor Minority Children: New Segregation in the Post-Brown ERA. 2011. xi, 133p. **(978-1-60709-884-3(9))** Rowman & Littlefield Education.
Bitz, Michael. Manga High: Literacy, Identity, & Coming of Age in an Urban High School. 2009. (ENG.). 206p. pap. 29.95 *(978-1-934742-18-1(X))*; lib. bdg. 54.95 *(978-1-934742-19-8(8))* Harvard Education Publishing Group (HEPG). (Harvard Education Pr.).
Boswell, Cecelia & Adams, Cheryll M. Effective Program Practices for Underserved Gifted Students: A CEC-TAG Educational Resource. 2011. (ENG.). 125p. pap. 24.95 *(978-1-59363-843-6(4))* Prufrock Pr.
Bradshaw, Alison J., et al. The Better Beginnings, Better Futures Project: Findings from Grade 3 to Grade 9. 2010. (Monographs of the Society for Research in Child Development Ser.: 1). (ENG., Illus.). 200p. pap. 41.95 *(978-1-4443-3976-5(1)*, Wiley-Blackwell) Wiley, John & Sons, Inc.
Brown, William H., et al. Social Competence of Young Children: Risk, Disability, & Intervention. Brown, William H. et al, eds. 2007. (Illus.). 341p. per. 39.95 *(978-1-55766-923-0(6))* Brookes, Paul H. Publishing Co.
Brustein and Manasevit. The Administrator's Guide to Federal Programs for English Learners. 2010. pap. 229.00 *(978-1-933807-91-1(1))* Thompson Media Group LLC.
Chapman, Christopher. Structural Solutions for Educational Improvement. 2012. (ENG.). 272p. (C). 120.00 *(978-0-415-55848-8(4))*; pap. 36.95 *(978-0-415-55849-5(2))* Routledge.
Chavous, Kevin P. Voices of Determination: Children that Defy the Odds. 2011. (ENG.). 204p. 34.95 **(978-1-4128-4267-9(0))** Transaction Pubs.
Cheminais. Every Child Matters in Extended Schools & Children's Centres. 2007. (Illus.). 176p. 37.95 *(978-1-84312-475-7(0))* Routledge.
Cheminais, Rita. The Pocket Guide to Every Child Matters: An at-a-Glance Overview for the Busy Teacher. 2009. (ENG., Illus.). 102p. 120.00 *(978-0-415-47916-5(9))* Taylor & Francis Group.
—The Pocket Guide to Every Child Matters: An at the glance overview for the busy Teacher. 2009. (ENG., Illus.). 102p. 26.95 *(978-0-415-47917-2(7))* Taylor & Francis Group.
Chenoweth, Karin. How It's Being Done: Urgent Lessons from Unexpected Schools. 2009. 220p. pap. 28.95 *(978-1-934742-28-0(7))*; (ENG.). lib. bdg. 54.95 *(978-1-934742-29-7(5))* Harvard Education Publishing Group (HEPG). (Harvard Education Pr.).
Cohen, David K. & Moffitt, Susan L. The Ordeal of Equality: Did Federal Regulation Fix the Schools? 2009. (Illus.). 336p. 37.00 *(978-0-674-03546-1(1))* Harvard Univ. Pr.
Cole, Robert W., ed. Educating Everybody's Children: Diverse Teaching Strategies for Diverse Learners, Revised & Expanded 2nd Edition. 2nd ed. 2008. 295p. pap. 29.95 *(978-1-4166-0674-1(2))* Assn. for Supervision & Curriculum Development.
Corwin, Miles. And Still We Rise: The Trials & Triumphs of Twelve Gifted Inner-City Students. 2008. (P. S. Ser.). 448p. pap. 14.95 *(978-0-06-157218-0(7)*, HarperPerennial) HarperCollins Pubs.
Craig, Susan E. Reaching & Teaching Children Who Hurt: Strategies for Your Classroom. 2008. 208p. pap. 26.95 *(978-1-55766-974-2(0))* Brookes, Paul H. Publishing Co.
Cullen, Jane, et al. Schools on the Edge: Responding to Challenging Circumstances. 2006. (Illus.). 168p. pap. 34.00 *(978-1-4129-2971-4(7)*, B29709P) SAGE Pubns., Ltd. GBR. Dist: SAGE Pubns., Inc.
Dallmann-Jones, Anthony S. Shadow Children: Understanding Education's #1 Problem. 2nd ed. 2011. (Illus.). xxv, 208p. **(978-0-9787610-3-5(0))** RLD Pubns., Inc.
Darling, Sandra K. & Tileston, Donna E. Walker, eds. Closing the Poverty & Culture Gap: Strategies to Reach Every Student. 2009. (Illus.). 120p. pap. 27.95 *(978-1-4129-5531-7(9)*, B55300P) Corwin Pr.
Davis, Donna M. Resiliency Reconsidered Policy Implications of the Resiliency Movement. 2007. (Educational Policy in the 21st Century Ser.). (ENG.). 164p. *(978-1-59311-755-9(8))*; per. *(978-1-59311-754-2(X))* Information Age Publishing, Inc.
Dekker, Jeroen J. H. Educational Ambitions in History: Childhood & Education in an Expanding Educational Space from the Seventeenth to the Twentieth Century. 2010. 228p. pap. 57.95 *(978-3-631-59501-5(8))* Lang, Peter GmbH. Europaischer Verlag der Wissenschaften DEU. Dist: Lang, Peter.
DeVitis, Joseph L. & Irwin-DeVitis, Linda. Adolescent Education: A Reader. 2010. (Adolescent Cultures, School & Society Ser.). 520p. (C). 169.95 *(978-1-4331-0505-0(5))*; pap. 54.95 *(978-1-4331-0504-3(7))* Lang, Peter Publishing, Inc.
Dixon-Román, Ezekiel & Gordon, Edmund W. Thinking Comprehensively about Education: Spaces of Educative Possibility & Their Implications for Public Policy. 2012. **(978-0-203-12001-9(9))** Routledge.
Duncan, Greg J. & Murnane, Richard J. Whither Opportunity? Rising Inequality & the Uncertain Life Chances of Low-Income Children. 2011. **(978-0-87154-324-0(9))**; pap. **(978-0-87154-372-1(9))** Russell Sage Foundation.
Dunn, Rita Stafford & Honigsfeld, Andrea. Differentiating Instruction for At-Risk Students: What to Do & How to Do It. 2009. (ENG.). 202p. 74.95 *(978-1-57886-982-4(X))*; pap. 28.95 *(978-1-57886-983-1(8))* Rowman & Littlefield Education.
Dye, Angela. Empowerment Starts Here. 2011. (ENG.). 182p. 60.00 **(978-1-61048-581-4(5))**; pap. 29.95 **(978-1-61048-582-1(3))** Rowman & Littlefield Education.
—Empowerment Starts Here: The Seven Principles to Empowering Urban Youth. 2011. xxxiv, 147p. **(978-1-61048-583-8(1))** Rowman & Littlefield Education.
Edwards, John. Language Diversity in the Classroom. 2009. (Bilingual Education & Bilingualism Ser.). (ENG.). 312p. 159.95 *(978-1-84769-226-9(5))*; pap. 49.95 *(978-1-84769-225-2(7))* Multilingual Matters GBR. Dist: Univ. of Toronto Pr.
Etim, James S., ed. Essays in Helping Diverse Students Attain Educational Success: When the Classroom Isn't White & Middle Class. 2011. 252p. 109.95 **(978-0-7734-3936-8(6))** Mellen, Edwin Pr., The.
Evans, Gillian. Educational Failure & White Working Class Children in Britain. 2008. (ENG.). 224p. pap. 33.00 *(978-0-230-55303-3(6))* Palgrave Macmillan.
—Educational Failure & Working Class White Children in Britain. 2006. (ENG., Illus.). 224p. 114.00 *(978-1-4039-9216-1(9))* Palgrave Macmillan.
Feifer, Steven. Emotional Disorders: A Neuropsychological, Psychopharmacological, & Educational Perspective. Rattan, Gurmal, ed. 2010. (ENG., Illus.). 320p. pap. 49.95 *(978-0-9703337-5-9(7)*, 970335) Norton, W. W. & Co., Inc.
Feiler, Anthony. Engaging 'Hard to Reach' Parents: Teacher-Parent Collaboration to Promote Children's Learning. 2010. (ENG., Illus.). 186p. 105.00 *(978-0-470-68229-6(9))*; pap. 44.95 *(978-0-470-51632-4(1))* Wiley, John & Sons, Inc. (Wiley).
Flaxman, Erwin, ed. School Year, 1971-1972, Vol. 4. 498p. 47.50 *(978-0-404-10104-6(6))* AMS Pr., Inc.
Garcia Winner, Michelle & Crooke, Pamela. You Are A Social Detective: Explaining Social Thinking to Kids. 2010. (Illus.). (J). pap. 20.00 *(978-0-98427-200-7(1))* North River Pr. Publishing Corp., The.
Gordon, Edmund W. & Bridglall, Beatrice L. Affirmative Development: Cultivating Academic Ability. 2006. (Critical Issues in Contemporary American Education Ser.). (ENG., Illus.). 310p. 97.00 *(978-0-7425-1658-8(X))* Rowman & Littlefield Publishers, Inc.
Gordon, Edmund W. & Bridglall, Beatrice L., eds. Affirmative Development: Cultivating Academic Ability. 2006. (Critical Issues in Contemporary American Education Ser.). (ENG., Illus.). 310p. per. 31.95 *(978-0-7425-1659-5(8))* Rowman & Littlefield Publishers, Inc.
Gorlewski, Julie A. Power, Resistance, & Literacy: Writing for Social Justice. 2011. **(978-1-61735-406-9(6))**; pap. **(978-1-61735-405-2(8))**; E-Book **(978-1-61735-407-6(4))** Information Age Publishing, Inc.
Green, Connie. The Lydia Year: Learning from Pre-Kindergarten Children in Rural Appalachia. 2009. pap. *(978-0-87173-175-3(4))* Assn. for Childhood Education International.
Hanft, Barbara E. & Shepherd, Jayne. Collaborating for Student Success: A Guide for School-Based Occupational Therapy. 2008. *(978-1-56900-247-6(9))* American Occupational Therapy Assn., Inc.
Hanley-Maxwell, Cheryl & Collet-Klingenberg, Lana. Education. 2011. (SAGE Reference Series on Disability: Key Issues & Future Directions Ser.: 2). 360p. 75.00 *(978-1-4129-8690-8(7)*, B8690EC) SAGE Pubns., Inc.
Heishman, Angela. Effective Collaboration for Educating the Whole Child. Kochhar-Bryant, Carol A., ed. 2010. (Illus.). 280p. pap. 39.95 *(978-1-4129-6527-9(6)*, B65262P) Corwin Pr.
Heydon, Rachel & Iannacci, Luigi. Early Childhood Curricula & the De-Pathologizing of Childhood. 2009. (ENG.). 208p. pap. *(978-1-4426-1026-2(3))* Univ. of Toronto Pr.
Hollowell, Mary. The Forgotten Room: Inside a Public Alternative School for At-Risk Youth. 2009. (ENG.). 190p. 68.50 *(978-0-7391-3495-5(7))* Rowman & Littlefield Publishers, Inc.
Hollowell, Mary. Forgotten Room: Inside A Public Alternative School for At-Risk Youth. 2011. (ENG.). 230p. pap. 29.95 **(978-0-7391-3496-2(5))** Lexington Bks.
Hornbeck, David & Hornbeck/Conner. Where There's a Will: Choosing Educational Excellence for All Children. 2009. (New Frontiers in Education Ser.). (ENG.). 300p. 90.00 *(978-1-60709-154-7(2))*; pap. 43.95 *(978-1-60709-155-4(0))* Rowman & Littlefield Education.
Howard, Lizette, et al. Poverty Is NOT a Learning Disability: Equalizing Opportunities for Low SES Students. Dunklee, Dennis R., ed. 2009. 160p. pap. 31.95 *(978-1-4129-6904-8(2)*, B69031P) Corwin Pr.
Hughes, Pat. Breaking Barriers to Learning in Primary Schools: An Integrated Children's Services Approach. 2009. (ENG., Illus.). 288p. pap. 41.95 *(978-0-415-47944-8(4))* Fulton, David Pubs. GBR. Dist: Taylor & Francis Group.
—Breaking Barriers to Learning in Primary Schools: An Integrated Children's Services Approach. 2009. (Illus.). 288p. 140.00 *(978-0-415-47943-1(6))* Taylor & Francis Group.
Iannacci, Luigi & Heydon, Rachel M. Early Childhood Curricula & the de-pathologizing of Childhood. 2008. (ENG.). 208p. *(978-0-8020-9768-2(5))* Univ. of Toronto Pr.
Jackson, Sonia. Education for Social Exclusion: Can We Change the Future for Children in Care? 2010. (IOE Inaugural Professional Lectures). (ENG., Illus.). 30p. pap. 9.95 *(978-0-85473-906-6(8))* Institute of Education GBR. Dist: Stylus Publishing, LLC.
Jackson, Yvette. The Pedagogy of Confidence: Inspiring High Intellectual Performance in Urban Schools. 2011. (ENG., Illus.). 208p. 27.95 *(978-0-8077-5224-1(X))*; pap. 27.95 *(978-0-8077-5223-4(1))* Teachers College Pr., Teachers College, Columbia Univ.
Jenlink, Patrick M. Equity Issues for Today's Educational Leaders: Meeting the Challenge of Creating Equitable Schools for All. 2009. (ENG.). 190p. 85.00 *(978-1-60709-139-4(9))*; pap. 31.95 *(978-1-60709-140-0(2))* Rowman & Littlefield Education.
Jensen, Arthur. Educational Differences (Rle Edu L) 2011. (Routledge Library Editions: Education Ser.). (ENG.). 472p. 150.00 **(978-0-415-50624-3(7))** Routledge.
Jones, Jami Biles & Zambone, Alana M. The Power of Media Specialists to Raise Academic Achievement & Strengthen At-Risk Youth. 2007. 108p. pap. 44.95 *(978-1-58683-229-2(8))* Linworth Publishing, Inc.
Jones, Lori. Outside the School Day Programs in High Poverty Elementary Schools. 2010. 60p. pap. *(978-3-639-23239-4(9))* VDM Verlag Dr. Mueller e.K.
Kane, Jean. Social Class, Gender & Exclusion from School. 2010. (ENG., Illus.). 168p. (C). pap. 38.95 *(978-0-415-55302-5(4))* Routledge.
—Social Class, Gender & Exclusion from School. 2010. (ENG., Illus.). 168p. (C). 120.00 *(978-0-415-55301-8(6)*, Routledge) Taylor & Francis Group GBR. Dist: Taylor & Francis Group.
Karns, Michelle S., et al. Culturally Proficient Education: An Asset-Based Response to Conditions of Poverty. 2010. (Illus.). 176p. pap. 31.95 *(978-1-4129-7086-0(5)*, B70853P) Corwin Pr.
Knowles, Gianna & Lander, Vini. Diversity, Equality & Achievement in Education. 2011. (Illus.). 192p. (C). 104.00 *(978-1-84920-600-6(7)*, B06006C); pap. 42.00 *(978-1-84920-601-3(5)*, B06006P) SAGE Pubns., Ltd. GBR. Dist: SAGE Pubns., Inc.
Lamb, Darel. Academic Remediation for Adolescents with Ebd. 2009. 212p. pap. *(978-3-639-16100-7(9))* VDM Verlag Dr. Mueller e.K.
LeBlanc-Esparza, Ricardo & Roulston, William S. Breaking the Poverty Barrier: Changing Student Lives with Passion, Perseverance, & Performance. 2011. 216p. pap. **(978-1-935543-14-5(8))**; (ENG.). lib. bdg. **(978-1-935543-15-2(6))** Solution Tree Pr.
Leiding/Brown. Winds of Change: Declaring War on Education. 2012. pap. **(978-1-61048-822-8(9))**; (ENG.). 140p. 60.00 **(978-1-61048-821-1(0))** Rowman & Littlefield Education.
Lent, Releah Cossett & Baca, Jimmy Santiago. Adolescents on the Edge: Stories & Lessons to Transform Learning. 2010. 192p. pap. 31.25 *(978-0-325-02691-6(2)*, E02691) Heinemann.
MacBeath, John E. C., et al. Schools on the Edge: Responding to Challenging Circumstances. 2006. (Illus.). 168p. 81.00 *(978-1-4129-2970-7(9)*, B29709C) SAGE Pubns., Ltd. GBR. Dist: SAGE Pubns., Inc.
Manson, Tony J. Ways Teachers Cope with the Physical, Psychological, & Social Disabilities of Their Students: Diabetes, Autism, ADHD, Hunger, Anger, & Other Infirmities. Manson, Tony J., ed. 220p. 109.95 *(978-0-7734-4976-3(0))* Mellen, Edwin Pr., The.
Marrah, Charissa. Emotionally/Behaviorally Disabled & Gifted. 2009. 200p. pap. *(978-3-639-04384-6(7))* VDM Verlag Dr. Mueller e.K.
Marsh, John. Class Dismissed: Why We Cannot Teach or Learn Our Way Out of Inequality. 2011. (ENG.). 328p. 85.00 *(978-1-58367-244-0(3))*; pap. 19.95 *(978-1-58367-243-3(5))* Monthly Review Pr.
McAninch/Books. Guest Editor's Introduction. 2006. 120p. 45.95 *(978-0-8058-9352-6(0))* Erlbaum, Lawrence Assocs., Inc.
Messiou, Kyriaki. Confronting Marginalisation in Education: A Framework for Promoting Inclusion. 2012. (ENG., Illus.). 168p. (C). 155.00 *(978-0-415-60350-8(1))*; pap. 44.95 *(978-0-415-60351-5(X))* Routledge.
Meyer, Richard J. Official Portraits & Unofficial Counterportraits of at Risk Students: Writing Spaces in Hard Times. 2009. (ENG., Illus.). 294p. 145.00 *(978-0-415-87123-5(9))*; pap. 50.95 *(978-0-415-87124-2(7))* Routledge.
Michie, Gregory. Holler If You Hear Me: The Education of a Teacher & His Students. 2nd rev. ed. 2009. (Teaching for Social Justice Ser.). (ENG.). 240p. pap. 19.95 *(978-0-8077-4958-6(3))* Teachers College Pr., Teachers College, Columbia Univ.
Neuman, Susan B. Educating the Other America: Top Experts Tackle Poverty, Literacy, & Achievement in Our Schools. Neuman, Susan B., ed. 2008. (Illus.). 416p. pap. 39.95 *(978-1-55766-906-3(6))* Brookes, Paul H. Publishing Co.
Nolterneyer, Amity/Lynn & Mcloughlin, Caven S., eds. Disproportionality in Education & Special Education: A Guide to Creating More Equitable Learning Environments. 2012. **(978-0-398-08800-2(4))**; pap. **(978-0-398-08801-9(2))** Thomas, Charles C. Pub., Ltd.
Padilla, Raymon, ed. Student Success Modeling. 2008. 236p. pap. 29.95 *(978-1-57922-327-4(3))* Stylus Publishing, LLC.
Padilla, Raymond V., ed. Student Success Modeling: Elementary School to College. 2008. (Illus.). 236p. 75.00 *(978-1-57922-326-7(5))* Stylus Publishing LLC.
Pappas, Sophia. Good Morning, Children: My First Years in Early Childhood Education. 2009. (ENG., Illus.). 192p. pap. 14.95 *(978-0-87659-078-2(4))* Gryphon Hse., Inc.
Parrett, William H. & Budge, Kathleen M. Turning High-Poverty Schools into High-Performing Schools. 2012. 221p. pap. 30.95 **(978-1-4166-1313-8(7))** Assn. for Supervision & Curriculum Development.
Peak, Martha H. Rewriting the Future: Cooperative for Education's Quest to Transform How a Nation Learns. 2010. (Illus.). xiii, 100p. **(978-1-4415-6346-0(6))** Xlibris Corp.
Pearlstein, Mitch. Female Political Leadership & Athletics: The Educational, Economic, & Social Costs of Family Fragmentation. 2011. (New Frontiers in Education Ser.). (ENG.). 165p. pap. 24.95 *(978-1-60709-352-6(6))* Rowman & Littlefield Education.
—From Family Collapse to America's Decline: The Educational, Economic, & Social Costs of Family Fragmentation. 2011. (New Frontiers in Education Ser.). (ENG.). 165p. 50.00 *(978-1-60709-361-9(8))* Rowman & Littlefield Education.

C

Pearlstein, Mitchell B. Shortchanging Student Achievement: The Educational, Economic, & Social Costs of Family Fragmentation. 2011. xxv, 165p. **(978-1-60709-363-3(4))** Rowman & Littlefield Education.

Pink, William T. Schools for Marginalized Youth: An International Perspective. 2011. **(978-1-61289-069-2(5))**; **(978-1-61289-068-5(7))** Hampton Pr., Inc.

Pomerantz, Kathryn Anne, et al. How to Reach 'Hard to Reach' Children: Improving Access, Participation & Outcomes. 2007. (ENG.). 282p. per. 62.95 (978-0-470-05884-8(6), Wiley) Wiley, John & Sons, Inc.

Raffo, Carlo, ed. Education & Poverty in Affluent Countries. 2009. (Routledge Research in Education Ser.). (ENG., Illus.). 270p. 125.00 (978-0-415-99880-2(8)) Routledge.

Raffo, Carlo, et al, eds. Education & Poverty in Affluent Countries. 2011. (Illus.). 270p. pap. 39.95 **(978-0-415-89729-7(7))** Routledge.

Robinson, Philip. Education & Poverty (RLE Edu L) 2011. (Routledge Library Editions: Education Ser.). (ENG.). 128p. 100.00 **(978-0-415-50510-9(0))** Routledge.

Sandall, Susan R. & Schwartz, Ilene S. Building Blocks for Teaching Preschoolers with Special Needs. 2nd ed. 2008. (Illus.). 237p. pap. 36.95 incl. cd-rom (978-1-55766-967-4(8)) Brookes, Paul H. Publishing Co.

Seidel, Samuel Stein. Hip Hop Genius: Remixing High School Education. 2012. (ENG.). 140p. pap. 18.95 (978-1-61048-027-7(9)) Rowman & Littlefield Education.

Slavin, Robert E., et al. 2 Million Children: Success for All. 2nd ed. 2008. (Illus.). 408p. 95.95 (978-1-4129-5307-8(3), B53073C); pap. 44.95 (978-1-4129-5308-5(1), B53073P) Corwin Pr.

Smyth, John. From Silent Witnesses to Active Agents: Student Voice in Re-Engaging with Learning. 2012. (C). pap. 139.95 **(978-1-4331-1374-1(0))**; pap. 34.95 **(978-1-4331-1373-4(2))** Lang, Peter Publishing, Inc.

Soto, Ivannia. ELL Shadowing as a Catalyst for Change. 2012. 160p. pap. 33.95 **(978-1-4129-9206-0(0)**, B92060P) Corwin Pr.

St. John, Edward P. Readings on Equal Education: Confronting Educational Inequality; Reframing, Building Understanding, & Making Change. Stillman, Phyllis Kreger, ed. 2008. 410p. 137.50 **(978-0-404-10122-0(4))** AMS Pr., Inc.

Stambaugh, Tamra & Chandler, Kimberley. Effective Curriculum for Underserved Gifted Students: A Cec-Tag Educational Resource. 2011. (ENG.). 100p. pap. 24.95 (978-1-59363-842-9(6)) Prufrock Pr.

Strickland, Melinda. More Than a Test Score: Strategies for Empowering At-Risk Youth. 2012. (ENG.). 118p. (gr. 17). pap. 19.95 **(978-1-61048-706-1(0))** Rowman & Littlefield Education.

—More Than a Test Score: Strategies for Empowering at-Risk Youth. 2012. (ENG.). 118p. (gr. 17). 50.00 **(978-1-61048-705-4(2))** Rowman & Littlefield Education.

Supovitz, Jonathan A. & Weinbaum, Elliot H., eds. Implementation Gap: Understanding Reform in High Schools. 2007. (ENG., Illus.). 208p. (C). 56.00 (978-0-8077-4845-9(5)) Teachers College Pr., Teachers College, Columbia Univ.

Sweeney, Jeanne. What Do I Do When — The Answer Book on Title I. 2007. (978-1-57834-087-3(X)) LRP Pubns.

Tileston, Donna Walker & Darling, Sandra K. Why Culture Counts: Teaching Children of Poverty. 2008. 216p. pap. 32.95 (978-1-934009-24-6(5)) Solution Tree.

Tobias, Randolf. Ensuring Success in Math & Science: Curriculum & Teaching Strategies for at-Risk Learners. 2006. 208p. per. 21.95 (978-1-932127-88-1(7)) Solution Tree.

Tully, Matthew. Searching for Hope: Life at a Failing School in the Heart of America. 2012. (Illus.). xv, 261p. **(978-0-253-00597-7(3))**; (ENG., 288p. 28.00 **(978-0-253-00593-9(0)**, 0253005930) Indiana Univ. Pr.

Van Hemel, Susan B. Early Childhood Assessment: Why, What, & How. Snow, Catherine E., ed. 2008. (ENG., Illus.). 520p. 59.95 (978-0-309-12465-2(4)) National Academies Pr.

VanTassel-Baska, Joyce. Patterns & Profiles of Promising Learners from Poverty. 2009. (ENG.). 296p. pap. 34.95 (978-1-59363-396-7(3)) Prufrock Pr.

Vaughn, Sharon R., et al. Teaching Students Who are Exceptional, Diverse, & at Risk in the General Education Classroom. 5th ed. 2010. (ENG., Illus.). 576p. (C). pap. 134.67 (978-0-13-715179-0(9), Prentice Hall) Prentice Hall PTR.

—Teaching Students Who are Exceptional, Diverse, & at Risk in the General Education Classroom, Student Value Edition. 5th ed. 2010. (ENG.). 576p. (C). ring bd. 90.40 (978-0-13-258216-2(3), Prentice Hall) Prentice Hall PTR.

—Teaching Students Who are Exceptional, Diverse, & at Risk in the General Education Classroom (with MyEducationLab) 5th ed. 2010. (ENG.). 576p. (C). pap. 141.33 (978-0-13-138125-4(3), Prentice Hall) Prentice Hall PTR.

Veltri, Barbara Torre. Learning on Other People's Kids: Becoming a Teach for America Teacher. 2010. (978-1-60752-443-4(0)); pap. (978-1-60752-442-7(2)) Information Age Publishing, Inc.

Vizard, Dave. Disaffected Students: Engaging Students with Social, Emotional & Behavioural Difficulties. 2009. (Meeting the Needs Ser.). (ENG., Illus.). 136p. 34.95 (978-0-8264-3465-4(7), Network Continuum Education) Continuum International Publishing Group, Ltd. GBR. Dist: National Bk. Network.

Vogel, Robert & Galbraith, Michael. Voices of Teens: In Their Own Words. 2008. (978-1-56090-220-1(5)) National Middle Schl. Assn.

—Voices of Teens: Writers Matter. 2008. (978-1-56090-218-8(3)) National Middle Schl. Assn.

Wargo, Michael J. & Green, Donald R., eds. Achievement Testing of Disadvantaged & Minority Students for Educational Program Evaluation. Date not set. (Orig.). pap. 8.95 (978-0-07-068282-5(8), 99814) McGraw-Hill Cos., The.

Warring, William H., Jr. Leaving No Child Behind: A Teacher's Model for Meeting the Challenges of the No Child Left Behind. 2008. 196p. pap. 27.95 (978-0-9815414-0-2(2)) Warring & Assocs. Pubs.

Weis, Lois & Dolby, Nadine, eds. Social Class & Education: Global Perspectives. 2012. (ENG., Illus.). 236p. 135.00 (978-0-415-88695-6(3)); pap. 46.95 (978-0-415-88696-3(1)) Routledge.

Winner, Michelle Garcia. Thinking About You Thinking About Me. 2nd rev. ed. 2007. (978-0-9701320-1-7(8), Social Cognitive Deficits) Think Social Publishing, Inc.

Wong, Ovid K. High Poverty, High Performing Schools. 2011. (ENG.). 116p. 55.00 **(978-1-60709-789-1(3))** Rowman & Littlefield Education.

—High Poverty High Performing Schools. 2011. (ENG.). 116p. pap. 22.95 **(978-1-60709-790-7(7))** Rowman & Littlefield Education.

—High-Poverty, High-Performing Schools: Foundations for Real Student Success. 2011. **(978-1-60709-791-4(5))** Rowman & Littlefield Education.

Wood, Mary M., et al. Teaching Responsible Behavior: Developmental Therapy-Developmental Teaching for Troubled Children & Adolescents. 4th ed. 2006. (Illus.). xxx, 316p. pap. 87.00 (978-1-4164-0134-6(2)) PRO-ED, Inc.

CHILDREN WITH VISUAL DISABILITIES

see also Children, Blind

Ek, Ulla. Children with Visual Disorders - Cognitive Development, Developmental Disorders & Consequences for Treatment & Counselling. 2008. 72p. pap. (978-3-639-05867-3(4)) VDM Verlag Dr. Mueller e.K.

Ferrell, Kay Alicyn. Reach Out & Teach: Helping Your Child Who Is Visually Impaired Learn & Grow. 2nd ed. 2011. **(978-0-89128-457-4(5))**; **(978-0-89128-484-0(2))** American Foundation for the Blind Pr.

Holbrook, M. Cay, ed. Children with Visual Impairments: A Parents' Guide. 2nd ed. 2006. (Illus.). 434p. per. 18.95 (978-1-890627-40-9(2)) Woodbine Hse.

Kolaschinsky, Doreen. Selbstwertgefühl Sehbehinderter und Blinder Kinder und Jugendlicher in Sozialen Interaktionen: Theorie und Empirische Untersuchung. 2011. (Europäische Hochschulschriften. Reihe 11: Pädagogik Ser.). (GER.). 380p. pap. 76.95 **(978-3-631-62029-8(2))** Lang, Peter GmbH, Europaischer Verlag der Wissenschaften DEU. Dist: Lang, Peter.

Tomaszewski, Ellen. My Blindy Girl: A Mother's journey through Achromatopsia. 2008. (ENG., Illus.). 280p. pap., pap. 16.99 (978-0-9785160-3-1(6)) Etcetera Press.

CHILDREN WITH VISUAL DISABILITIES—EDUCATION

Bridgeo, Wendy, et al. School to Work: Developing Transition Portfolios for Students with Significant Disabilites. 2007. ring bd. 29.95 (978-0-9743510-9-4(1)) Perkins Schl. for the Blind.

Castellano, Carol. Getting Ready for College Begins in Third Grade: Working Toward an Independent Future for Your Blind/Visually Impaired Child. 2010. E-Book (978-1-61735-072-6(9)); (Illus.). 120p. (978-1-61735-071-9(0)); (Illus.). 120p. pap. (978-1-61735-070-2(2)) Information Age Publishing, Inc.

chieve Publications, Addie. Visual Discrimination: Noting Differences in Frequently Misperceived Words. 2007. (ENG.). 67p. (J). 15.00 (978-0-9727762-2-6(2)) Achieve Pubns.

Cleveland, Jeri. Empowered: An Activity Based Self-Determination Curriculum for Students with Visual Impairments. 2007. (978-1-880366-39-4(8)) Texas Schl. for the Blind & Visually Impaired.

Fairbrother, Kenneth R. A Vision of School. 2010. (Illus.). 250p. pap. (978-1-84748-712-4(2)) Athena Pr.

French, Sally, et al. An Oral History of the Education of Visually Impaired People: Telling Stories for Inclusive Futures. 2006. (Illus.). 448p. 129.95 (978-0-7734-5706-5(2)) Mellen, Edwin Pr., The.

Hagood, Linda. Better Together: Building Relationships with People Who Have Visual Impairment & Autism Spectrum Disorder (or Atypical Social Development) 2008. (Illus.). vi, 418p. (978-1-880366-40-0(1)) Texas Schl. for the Blind & Visually Impaired.

LaVenture, Susan. A Parents' Guide to Special Education for Children with Visual Impairments. 2007. (978-0-89128-893-0(7)); pap. (978-0-89128-892-3(9)) American Foundation for the Blind Pr.

Oliphant, John. The Early Education of the Blind in Britain C. 1790-1900: Institutional Experience in England & Scotland. 2007. 200p. (978-0-7734-5247-3(8)) Mellen, Edwin Pr., The.

Region IV Education Service Center. Technology Tips for Teachers of Students with Visual Impairments. 2007. spiral bd. (978-1-933521-73-2(2)) Region IV Education Service Ctr.

Roman-Lantzy, Christine. Cortical Visual Impairment: An Approach to Assessment & Intervention. 2007. (978-0-89128-830-5(9)); 211p. pap. 49.95 (978-0-89128-829-9(5)) American Foundation for the Blind Pr.

Salisbury, Ruth, ed. Teaching Pupils with Visual Impairment: A Guide to Making the School Curriculum Accessible. 2007. (David Fulton Bks.). (ENG., Illus.). 176p. pap. 57.50 (978-1-84312-395-8(9)) Fulton, David Pubs. GBR. Dist: Taylor & Francis Group.

Schlachter, Gail & Weber, R. David. Funding for Persons with Visual Impairments. l.t. ed. 2007. (Funding for Persons with Visual Impairments Ser.). pap. 30.00 (978-1-58841-168-6(0)) Reference Service Pr.

Trief, Ellen & Shaw, Rona. Everyday Activities to Promote Visual Efficiency: A Handbook for Working with Young Children with Visual Impairments. 2009. (978-0-89128-835-0(X)); (978-0-89128-453-6(2)); (978-0-89128-836-7(8)) American Foundation for the Blind Pr.

Welcoming Students with Visual Impairment to Your School: A guide for training public school personnel & families about the needs of students with vision Loss. 2006. ring bd. (978-0-9743510-8-7(3)) Perkins Schl. for the Blind.

CHILDREN'S ACCIDENTS

see also Children—Wounds and Injuries

American Academy of Pediatrics, creator. Car Safety Seats: A Guide for Families. 2011. pap. 22.00 **(978-0-04-463701-1(2))** American Academy of Pediatrics.

Avery, J.Gordon & Jackson, R.Hugh. Children & Their Accidents. (Illus.). 192p. pap. (978-0-340-37001-8(7), Hodder Arnold) Hodder Education.

Bright Reich, Jennifer. The Babyproofing Bible: The Exceedingly Thorough Guide to Keeping Your Child Safe from Crib to Kitchen to Car to Yard. 2007. (ENG., Illus.). 240p. 14.95 (978-1-59233-248-9(X), 159233248X, Fair Winds Press) Quayside.

Comprehensive Children's Product Safety Commission Reform Legislation: Hearing Before the Subcommittee on Commerce, Trade, & Consumer Protection of the Committee on Energy & Commerce, House of Representatives, One Hundred Tenth Congress, First Session, November 6, 2007. 2008. v, 115p. (978-0-16-082620-7(9), 552-070-38638-6) United States Government Printing Office.

Consumer Product Safety Commission, ed. Think Toy Safety Coloring Book for Kids Sake. 2009.Tr. of Piense en Juguetes Seguros Libro de Colorear: por el Bien de los Ninos. (ENG & SPA., Illus.). 11p. 5.00 (978-0-16-084101-9(1), Consumer Product Safety Commission) United States Government Printing Office.

Cram101 Textbook Reviews. Outlines & Highlights for Health, Safety, & Nutrition for the Young Child by Lynn R Marotz, Isbn: 9781428320703. 2010. 82p. pap. 27.95 (978-1-61698-190-7(3)) Cram101 Inc.

Cram101 Textbook Reviews & Cram101 Textbook Reviews. Outlines & Highlights for Ergonomics for Children: Designing Products & Places for Toddlers to Teens by Rani Lueder (Editor) 2011. 172p. pap. 29.95 **(978-1-61830-359-2(7))** Cram101 Inc.

Cram101 Textbook Reviews Staff. Outlines & Highlights for Health, Safety, & Nutrition for the Young Child by Lynn R Marotz, Isbn: 9781428320703. 2009. 70p. pap. 27.95 (978-1-4288-8621-6(4)) Cram101 Inc.

Drago, Dorothy A. From Crib to Kindergarten: The Essential Child Safety Guide. 2007. (ENG., Illus.). 208p. 46.00 (978-0-8018-8569-3(8)); per. 16.00 (978-0-8018-8570-9(1)) Johns Hopkins Univ. Pr.

Giardino, Angelo P., et al. Child Safety: A Pediatric Guide for Parents, Teachers, Nurses, & Caregivers. 2007. (ENG., Illus.). 341p. 33.00 (978-1-878060-67-9(8)) STM Learning, Inc.

Hoffmann, Arthur W., ed. Precious Cargo: Promote Child Safety. 2011. 124p. pap. 10.95 **(978-1-4620-1453-8(4))** iUniverse, Inc.

Lee, Allison. How to Keep Your Child Safe. 2009. 208p. 20.00 (978-1-84528-236-3(1)) How To Books GBR. Dist: Parkwest Pubns., Inc.

Legislation to Improve Consumer Product Safety for Children: Hearing Before the Subcommittee on Commerce, Trade, & Consumer Protection of the Committee on Energy & Commerce, House of Representatives, One Hundred Tenth Congress, First Session, on H.R. 2474, H.R. 1699, H.R. 814, H.R. 1721, June 6, 2007. 2008. (Illus.). v, 110p. (978-0-16-082549-1(0), 552-070-38578-9) United States Government Printing Office.

Marotz, Lynn R. Cengage Advantage Books: Health, Safety, & Nutrition for the Young Child. 8th ed. 2011. (ENG.). 576p. (C). ring bd. 121.95 (978-1-111-35580-7(0)) Wadsworth.

—Health, Safety, & Nutrition for the Young Child. 8th ed. 2011. (Whatrsquo;s New in Early Childhood Ser.). (ENG.). 576p. (C). pap. 165.95 (978-1-111-29837-1(8)) Wadsworth.

Matricardi, Joanne & McLarty, Jeanne. Health, Safety, & Nutrition Activities A to Z. 2007. (ENG., Illus.). 208p. per. 30.95 (978-1-4180-4850-1(X)) Delmar Cengage Learning.

Mayhew, Lisa. Child Death Investigations: Interdisciplinary Techniques from Cradle to Court. 2007. 20.00 (978-1-59460-209-2(3)) Carolina Academic Pr.

Michaelian, Britt. Secrets of the Safety Goddess: A Modern Safety Guide for Busy Parents. 2009. (Illus.). x, 230p. pap. (978-0-9794245-5-7(0)) Bush Street Pr.

Protecting the Playroom: Holding Foreign Manufacturers Accountable for Defective Products: Hearing Before the Subcommittee on Commercial & Administrative Law of the Committee on the Judiciary, House of Representatives, One Hundred Tenth Congress, First Session, November 15, 2007. 2009. (Illus.). iv, 86p. (978-0-16-082488-3(5), 552-070-38525-8) United States Government Printing Office.

Rhodes, Alison. Honey, I Lost the Baby in the Produce Aisle! Safety Mom's Guide to Childproofing Your Life. 2011. (ENG.). 240p. pap. 16.99 (978-1-4354-5970-0(9)) Course Technology.

Sethi, Dinesh & World Health Organization: Regional Office for Europe. European Report on Child Injury Prevention. 2009. (EURO Nonserial Publication Ser.). (ENG., Illus.). 113p. pap. 24.00 (978-92-890-4295-6(8)) World Health Organization.

Subcommittee on Investigations & Oversight Hearing on the Consumer Product Safety Improvement ACT & Small Business: Hearing Before the Committee on Small Business, United States House of Representatives, One Hundred Eleventh Congress, First Session, Hearing Held May 14, 2009. 2009. (Illus.). v, 160p. (978-0-16-083946-7(7), 552-070-39635-7) United States Government Printing Office.

Tucci, J., et al. Children's sense of Safety: Children¿s experiences of childhood in contemporary Australia. 2008. 39p. spiral bd. (978-0-9775355-3-8(3)) Australian Childhood Foundation.

Williams, Kimberly & Lebrun, Marcel. Keeping Kids Safe, Healthy, & Smart: An Educator's Guide to Child Health & Safety. 2009. (ENG.). 304p. 45.00 (978-1-57886-971-8(4)) Rowman & Littlefield Education.

CHILDREN'S AID SOCIETY (NEW YORK, N.Y.)

Virag, Bonnie E. The Stovepipe. 2011. (ENG.). 440p. pap. 17.95 **(978-1-936782-30-7(8)**, Langdon Street Pr.) Hillcrest Publishing Group, Inc.

CHILDREN'S ART

Here are entered collections of art produced by children under fifteen years of age and-or below the ninth grade in school.

Cobb, Benjamin & Linn, Susan. Kids Design Glass. 2009. (ENG., Illus.). 132p. 40.00 (978-0-295-98937-2(8)) Univ. of Washington Pr.

Fineberg, Jonathan, ed. When We Were Young: New Perspectives on the Art of the Child. 2006. (Illus.). 289p. 65.00 (978-0-520-25042-0(7)); pap. 39.95 (978-0-520-25043-7(5)) Univ. of California Pr.

Goodman, Robin F. & Fahnestock, Andrea Henderson. The Day Our World Changed: Children's Art Of 9/11. 2006. (Illus.). 128p. reprint ed. 20.00 (978-1-4223-5685-2(X)) DIANE Publishing Co.

Kalin, Nadine M. Children's Perspectives on Drawing. 2008. 128p. pap. (978-3-639-07183-2(2)) VDM Verlag Dr. Mueller e.K.

Milbrath, Constance. Patterns of Artistic Development in Children: Comparative Studies of Talent. 2010. (ENG.). 438p. pap. 39.99 (978-0-521-15562-5(2)) Cambridge Univ. Pr.

Milbrath, Constance & Trautner, Hanns M., eds. Children's Understanding & Production of Pictures, Drawings, & Art: Theoretical & Empirical Approaches. 2007. (Illus.). 352p. pap. 44.00 (978-0-88937-350-1(7)) Hogrefe Publishing.

Stivers, Janet B. & Schudel, Donna. Dream-Makers Early Childhood: Building Creativity & Confidence. Stivers, Janet B. & Schudel, Donna, eds. 2008. 104p. spiral bd. 19.99 (978-0-86696-331-2(6)) Binney & Smith, Inc.

Strauss, Michaela. Understanding Children's Drawings: Tracing the Path of Incarnation. Wehrle, Pauline, tr. from GER. 2008. (Illus.). 96p. (978-1-85584-199-4(1)) Steiner, Rudolf Pr.

Williams, Susan L., ed. Children's Vision of the Future: 2007/2008 Crayola Juried Art Exhibition. 2008. (Illus.). 92p. per. 24.99 incl. audio (978-0-86696-330-5(8)) Binney & Smith, Inc.

CHILDREN'S ATLASES

Encyclopaedia Britannica, Inc, ed. Britannica's Student Atlas. 2009. (Illus.). 132p. lib. bdg. 29.95 (978-1-61535-335-4(6)) Encyclopaedia Britannica, Inc.

Hammond World Atlas Corporation Staff. Historical World Atlas. 5th ed. 2007. (Atlas Ser.). (Illus.). 72p. (gr. 9-12). tchr. ed. 16.95 (978-0-8437-1390-9(9), 713909) Langenscheidt Publishing Group.

Meyers Neuer Weltatlas: Unser Planet in Karten, Fakten und Bildern. (978-3-411-07494-5(9)) Bibliographisches Institut & F. A. Brockhaus AG DEU. Dist: i. b. d., Ltd.

National Geographic Society Staff. National Geographic Atlas of the World. 9th ed. 2010. (ENG., Illus.). 424p. 175.00 (978-1-4262-0634-4(8), National Geographic) National Geographic Society.

Wiegand, Patrick. Oxford First Atlas. 2010. (ENG., Illus.). 48p. 80.00 (978-0-19-830000-7(X)) Oxford Univ. Pr., Inc.

World Atlas. (978-0-8160-4379-8(5)) Facts On File, Inc.

CHILDREN'S BOOKS

see Children—Books and Reading; Children's Literature

CHILDREN'S CHOIRS

Childrens Choir. 2.95 (978-0-7673-6200-9(4)); 4.98 (978-0-7673-6228-3(4)) LifeWay Christian Resources.

Children's Choir. (978-0-7673-8478-0(4)) LifeWay Christian Resources.

CHILDREN'S CHRISTIAN LITERATURE

see Christian Literature for Children

CHILDREN'S CLOTHING

see also Children's Costumes

Abreu, Mary. Little Girls, Big Style: Sew a Boutique Wardrobe from 4 Easy Patterns. 2010. (Illus.). 160p. pap. 25.95 (978-1-60705-188-6(5)) C & T Publishing.

Adel, Jean. Knitted Critters for Kids to Wear: More Than 40 Animal-Themed Accessories. 2008. (ENG., Illus.). 96p. pap. 19.95 (978-0-307-39466-8(2), Potter Craft) Crown Publishing Group.

Aldrich, Winifred. Metric Pattern Cutting for Children's Wear & Babywear. 4th ed. 2009. (ENG., Illus.). 216p. 52.99 (978-1-4051-8292-8(X), Wiley) Wiley, John & Sons, Inc.

Alexander, Karla. Baby Wraps: Quick, Cuddly Quilts. 2008. (That Patchwork Place Ser.). (ENG., Illus.). 32p. pap. 19.95 (978-1-56477-839-0(8), That Patchwork Place) Martingale & Co.

Beer, Randi. Designer's Guide to Girls' & Junior Apparel. 2009. (Illus.). 272p. pap. 86.00 (978-1-56367-692-5(3)) Fairchild Bks.

Bell, Fiona. Sewn with Love: Classic Patterns for Children's Clothes & Accessories. 2010. (ENG., Illus.). 144p. 26.95 (978-1-59668-349-5(X)) Interweave Pr., LLC.

Better Homes and Gardens Editors, ed. Knitting for Babies & Kids: Better Homes & Gardens. 2006. (ENG.). 48p. pap. 10.95 (978-1-60140-095-6(0)) Leisure Arts, Inc.

Bonnette, Mary Helene & Murchland, Jo Lynne. Simply Knits for Kids: 20 Knitting Projects. 2011. (Simply Pamphlet Ser.). (ENG., Illus.). 64p. 9.95 (978-1-4547-0019-7(X)) Lark Bks.

Cooper, Emmanuel. Contemporary Ceramics. 2009. (ENG., Illus.). 304p. 45.00 (978-0-500-51487-0(9), 551487) Thames & Hudson.

Cousineau, Susan. Sewing for Tiny Tots: Sweet & Simple Clothes, Toys & Room Accents. 2007. (ENG., Illus.). 136p. pap. 12.95 (978-1-60059-028-3(4)) Lark Bks.

Crazy for Baby: Four Fast & Fun Quilts. 2006. 40p. 10.95 *(978-1-60140-077-2(2))* Leisure Arts, Inc.

DAAB Media Staff, ed. Kids Fashion Designers, 1 vol. 2009. (ITA, FRE, GER, SPA & ENG., Illus.). 381p. 37.95 *(978-3-86554-048-4(5))* DAAB Media Gmbh DEU. Dist: Innovative Logistics.

de Hugo, Caroline. Baby Booties: Eighteen Pretty Pairs to Knit. 2012. (Made in France Ser.). (ENG., Illus.). 64p. pap. 24.95 ***(978-1-74196-971-9(9))*** Murdoch Bks. Pty Ltd. AUS. Dist: Independent Pubs. Group.

Eaton, Jil. Pipsqueak Knits: 12 Deluxe QuickKnits for Your Baby & Toddler. 2009. (ENG., Illus.). 96p. 14.95 *(978-1-933308-23-4(0))* Breckling Pr.

England, Diane. Cute Crochet for Kids. 2006. (Illus.). 80p. per. 24.95 *(978-1-56477-707-2(3))* Martingale & Co.

Gaughan, Norah & Berroco Design Team. Comfort Knitting & Crochet - Babies & Toddlers: 50 Knit & Crochet Designs Using Berroco's Comfort & Vintage Yarns. 2012. (ENG., Illus.). 160p. pap. 19.95 ***(978-1-58479-987-0(0))*** Stewart, Tabori & Chang.

Gibson, Liesl & Liesl Rockchild Arts Management and Design Staff. Oliver + S Little Things to Sew: 20 Classic Accessories & Toys for Children. 2011. (ENG., Illus.). 136p. 27.50 *(978-1-58479-910-8(2))* Stewart, Tabori & Chang.

Givens, Tina. Sew Tina! 30 Cute Projects & Adorable Decor Items for Kidsgs. 2010. (ENG., Illus.). 144p. spiral bd. 24.95 *(978-1-60059-425-0(5))* Lark Bks.

Ham, Catherine. Nifty Knits for Kids: Fun Wearables for Kids on the Go. 2007. (ENG., Illus.). 112p. 24.95 *(978-1-57990-851-5(9))* Lark Bks.

Henry, Simon. The Little Best Dress: Make the Perfect Little Dress for a BIG Occasion. 2010. (ENG., Illus.). 176p. pap. 19.95 *(978-1-86108-687-7(3))* Guild of Master Craftsman Pubns., Ltd. GBR. Dist: Sterling Publishing Co., Inc.

Hewitt, Sally & Rowe, Jane. The Clothes We Wear. 2010. (Look Around You Ser.). (ENG., Illus.). 32p. (J). (gr. -1). pap. 10.99 *(978-0-237-53131-7(3),* Evans Brothers, Limited) Evans Publishing Group GBR. Dist: Independent Pubs. Group.

Hoffman, Rosalyn. Smart Mama, Smart Money: Raising Happy, Healthy Kids Without Breaking the Bank. 2012. (ENG.). 320p. (gr. 12). 15.00 ***(978-0-451-23559-6(2),*** N A L Trade) Penguin Group (USA) Inc.

House of White Birches, creator. Tickle-Me Knits for Toddlers: 12 adorable hand knits for babies & Toddlers. 2006. 24p. 7.95 *(978-1-60140-307-0(0))* Leisure Arts, Inc.

Hubert, Margaret. Hooked for Toddlers: 20 Easy Crochet Projects. 2007. (ENG., Illus.). 96p. pap. 19.95 *(978-1-58923-297-6(6),* 1589232976, Creative Publishing International) Quayside.

Langdon, Nancy & Pollehn, Sabine. Sewing Clothes Kids Love: Sewing Patterns & Instructions for Boys' & Girls' Outfits. 2010. (ENG., Illus.). 144p. 24.99 *(978-1-58923-473-4(1),* 1589234731) Quayside.

Leach Staff. Leach's Dainty Dresses & Jumpers in Knitting & Crochet No. 21. 2007. spiral bd. 9.95 *(978-1-934268-21-6(6))* Bramcost Pubns., LLC.

Marquart, Doreen L. Grammy's Favorite Knits for Baby. 2011. (ENG., Illus.). 64p. pap. *(978-1-60468-030-0(X))* Martingale & Co.

Marshall, Noreen. Dictionary of Children's Clothes: 1700s to Present. 2008. (ENG., Illus.). 280p. 60.00 *(978-1-85177-547-7(1))* V & A Pubns. GBR. Dist: Hachette Bk. Group.

Mason, Lorine. Hand Me-Ups: Recrafting Kid's Clothes with Easy Techniques & Fun Designs. 2010. (ENG.). 128p. pap. 22.99 *(978-1-4402-0243-8(5))* Krause Pubns.

McElwee, Meg. Growing up Sew Liberated: Making Handmade Clothes & Projects for Your Creative Child. 2011. (ENG., Illus.). 160p. pap. 24.95 *(978-1-59668-162-0(4))* Interweave Pr., LLC.

Merrett, Robert. Making Baby's Clothes. 2006. (ENG., Illus.). 128p. pap. 19.95 *(978-1-907030-70-3(0))* CICO Bks. GBR. Dist: Ryland Peters & Small.

Montgomerie, Claire. Easy Baby Knits: Clothes & Accessories for 0-3 Year-Olds. 2007. (ENG., Illus.). 128p. pap. *(978-1-84597-355-1(0))* Ryland Peters & Small.

—Easy Kids Knits: Clothes & Accessories for 3-10-Year-Olds. 2009. (Illus.). 128p. pap. *(978-1-84597-882-2(X))* Ryland Peters & Small.

More, Judith. Pretty Little Things to Make: 25 Heirloom Projects for Babies & Toddlers. 2009. (ENG., Illus.). 144p. 19.95 *(978-1-84340-504-7(0),* Collins & Brown) Anova Bks. GBR. Dist: Sterling Publishing Co., Inc.

Options: Baby - Knit Fashions for Tots. 2006. (ENG.). 48p. pap. 11.95 *(978-1-60140-100-7(0))* Leisure Arts, Inc.

Peacock, John. Children's Costume: The Complete Historical Sourcebook. 2009. (ENG., Illus.). 160p. 40.00 *(978-0-500-51488-7(7),* 551488) Thames & Hudson.

Porter, Kristi. More Knitting in the Sun: 32 Patterns to Knit for Kids. 2011. (ENG., Illus.). 192p. pap. 22.99 *(978-0-470-87448-6(1),* Wiley) Wiley, John & Sons, Inc.

Rob Merrett. Cute Clothes for Kids. 2011. (ENG., Illus.). 128p. pap. 19.95 *(978-1-907563-83-6(0))* CICO Bks. GBR. Dist: Ryland Peters & Small.

Rose, Clare. Making, Selling & Wearing Boys' Clothes in Late-Victorian England. 2010. (History of Retailing & Consumption Ser.). (Illus.). 294p. 124.95 *(978-0-7546-6444-4(9))* Ashgate Publishing Co.

Rosner, Sandi. Not Just Socks for Kids. 2007. (Illus.). 75p. pap. 18.95 *(978-1-893063-20-4(8))* Unicorn Bks. & Crafts, Inc.

Ware, Debby Scrumptious Toppers for Tots & Toddlers: 30 Hats & Caps from Debby Ware. 2008. (ENG., Illus.). 137p. pap. 19.95 *(978-1-56158-998-2(5),* Taunton) Taunton Pr., Inc.

Whiting, Sue. Easy to Crochet Cute Clothes for Kids: A Gorgeous Collection of 25 Quick & Easy Designs. 2007. (ENG., Illus.). 128p. 19.99 *(978-0-89689-588-1(2))* Krause Pubns.

Willmann, Silke. Kleidungspraktiken aus Sicht von Kindern im Vorschulalter: Eine Studie zur kulturellen Identität vor differentem kulturellem Hintergrund. 2008. (Europäische Hochschulschriften. Reihe 22: Soziologie Ser.). 220p. pap. 56.95 *(978-3-631-57691-5(9))* Lang, Peter GmbH, Europäischer Verlag der Wissenschaften DEU. Dist: Lang, Peter.

Zoob, Caroline. Childhood Treasures: Handmade Gifts for Babies & Children. 2006. (ENG., Illus.). 128p. pap. *(978-1-84597-216-5(3))* Ryland Peters & Small.

CHILDREN'S CLUBS

see also Girls—Societies and Clubs

Meybohm, Ivonne. Erziehung zum Zionismus: Der jüdische Wanderbund Blau-Weiss als Versuch einer praktischen Umsetzung des Programms der jüdischen Renaissance. 2009. (Zivilisationen & Geschichte Ser.). (GRE.). 132p. 39.95 *(978-3-631-58481-1(4))* Lang, Peter GmbH, Europäischer Verlag der Wissenschaften DEU. Dist: Lang, Peter.

Moore, Theresa. Writing from a Vygotskian Perspective. 2009. 112p. pap. *(978-3-639-18244-6(8))* VDM Verlag Dr. Mueller e.K.

CHILDREN'S COSTUMES

Hardy, Emma. Cute & Easy Costumes for Kids. 2006. (ENG., Illus.). 128p. pap. 19.95 *(978-1-907030-54-3(9))* CICO Bks. GBR. Dist: Ryland Peters & Small.

Jones, Nic. Marketing Brands to Children - Ethically. 2009. 96p. pap. 19.95 *(978-1-60860-256-8(7),* Strategic Bk. Publishing) AEG Literary Publishing Services, Inc.

CHILDREN'S COURTS

see Juvenile Courts

CHILDREN'S CRUSADE, 1212

Bell, Charlie. Phillip's Crusade: The True Story of the Children's Crusade. 2006. 320p. per. 11.99 *(978-0-9766243-6-3(2))* 21st Century Pr.

Dickson, Gary. The Children's Crusade Medieval History, Modern Mythistory. 2010. (ENG., Illus.). 264p. pap. 23.00 *(978-0-230-24887-8(X))* Palgrave Macmillan.

Gray, George Zabriskie. The Children's Crusade; an Episode of the Thirteenth Century by George Zabriskie Gray. 2006. 256p. per. 23.99 *(978-1-4255-2276-6(9))* MPublishing.

CHILDREN'S DANCES

see Dance for Children

CHILDREN'S DISEASES

see Children—Diseases

CHILDREN'S DRAMA

see Children's Plays

CHILDREN'S ENCYCLOPEDIAS AND DICTIONARIES

Arnett, Jeffrey Jensen, ed. Encyclopedia of Children, Adolescents, & the Media, 2 vols., Set. 2006. (Illus.). 1104p. 370.00 *(978-1-4129-0530-5(3),* B05303C) SAGE Pubns., Inc.

Big Book of Knowledge. 224p. *(978-1-4075-2425-2(9))* Parragon, Inc.

Children's Illustrated Dictionary. (Children's Reference Ser.). 256p. *(978-1-4054-5121-5(1))* Parragon, Inc.

Cram101 Textbook Reviews & Cram101 Textbook Reviews. Outlines & Highlights for the Child: An Encyclopedic Companion by Richard Shweder, ISBN. 2011. 474p. pap. 36.95 ***(978-1-61461-030-4(4))*** Cram101 Inc.

Encyclopaedia Britannica, compiled by. Britannica Student Encyclopedia 2010, 16 vols. 2010. (Illus.). 2900p. 399.00 *(978-1-61535-321-7(6))* Encyclopaedia Britannica, Inc.

Johnson, Steve. Encyclopedia for Boys & Girls. *(978-0-8022-0807-1(X))* Philosophical Library, Inc.

Knowles, Elizabeth, ed. The Dictionary of Modern Quotations. 3rd ed. 2008. (Oxford Paperback Reference Ser.). (ENG.). 496p. pap. 18.95 *(978-0-19-954746-3(7))* Oxford Univ. Pr., Inc.

—Oxford Dictionary of Modern Quotations. 3rd ed. 2007. (ENG.). 512p. 39.95 *(978-0-19-920895-1(6))* Oxford Univ. Pr., Inc.

Lusardi, Donna M. & Kent, Rosemarie. The New Book of Knowledge. 2008. 266p. *(978-0-7172-0589-9(4),* Grolier) Scholastic Library Publishing.

Maple Tree Press Editors. Smart-Opedia Junior: The Amazing Book about Everything. Meland, Sheba, tr. from FRE. 2008. (ENG., Illus.). 192p. (J). (gr. k-3). 24.95 *(978-1-897349-30-4(0),* Maple Tree Pr.) Owlkids Bks. Inc. CAN. Dist: Perseus-PGW.

Massey, Gerald. A Book of the Beginnings. 2007. (ENG.). 700p. per. 29.95 *(978-1-60206-830-8(5));* 516p. per. 26.95 *(978-1-60206-829-2(1));* 516p. 36.95 *(978-1-60206-082-1(7));* 700p. 39.95 *(978-1-60206-083-8(5))* Cosimo, Inc.

Morales, C. Sanchez. Larousse Practicas con el Diccionario. (SPA., Illus.). 108p. pap., wbk. ed. 5.95 *(978-968-6147-48-3(9),* LA489) Larousse, Ediciones, S. A. de C. V. MEX. Dist: Continental Bk. Co., Inc.

The Real Deal Set, 15-Volumes. 2008. (Real Deal Ser.). (gr. 4-6). 207.00 *(978-0-7910-9874-5(5),* Chelsea Clubhouse) Facts On File, Inc.

Shweder, Richard A., et al, eds. The Child: An Encyclopedic Companion. 2009. (ENG., Illus.). 1144p. 75.00 *(978-0-226-47539-4(5))* Univ. of Chicago Pr.

Truesdell, Ann. Find the Facts with Encyclopedias. 2012. (Explorer Junior Library: Information Explorer Junior Ser.). (ENG.). 24p. (gr. 1-4). lib. bdg. 28.50 ***(978-1-61080-367-0(1),*** 201268) Cherry Lake Publishing.

World Book, contrib. by. The World Book Student Discovery Encyclopedia, 13 vols. 2nd ed. 2007. (Illus.). (J). (gr. 2-6). *(978-0-7166-7414-6(9),* SKU20194) World Bk., Inc.

World Book, Inc. Staff. World Book Discovery Encyclopedia, 8 vols. 2008. (Illus.). (J). (gr. 2-5). 389.00 *(978-0-7166-7415-3(7))* World Bk., Inc.

CHILDREN'S ETIQUETTE

see Etiquette for Children and Teenagers

CHILDREN'S FILMS

This heading is used as a topical heading for works about films produced especially for children.

Aardman and Sony Pictures Animation Staff. The Art & Making of Arthur Christmas: An Inside Look at Behind-the-Scenes Artwork with Filmmaker Commentary. Sunshine, Linda, ed. 2011. (ENG., Illus.). 160p. 40.00 ***(978-1-55704-997-1(1))*** Newmarket Pr.

Arendt, Kathleen & Rössler, Patrick. Children's Film in Europe: A Literature Review. 2010. 176p. 50.95 *(978-3-631-60454-0(8))* Lang, Peter GmbH, Europäischer Verlag der Wissenschaften DEU. Dist: Lang, Peter.

Berry, Jo. The Parents' Guide to Kids' Movies. 2006. (Illus.). 324p. per. 12.95 *(978-0-7528-7487-6(X))* Orion Bks. Ltd. GBR. Dist: Sterling Publishing Co., Inc.

Burr, Ty. The Best Old Movies for Families: A Guide to Watching Together. 2007. (ENG.). 384p. pap. 18.00 *(978-1-4000-9686-2(3),* Anchor) Knopf Doubleday Publishing Group.

Mallan, Kerry & Bradford, Clare, eds. Contemporary Children's Literature & Film: Engaging with Theory. 2011. (ENG., Illus.). 240p. 82.00 *(978-0-230-23149-8(7));* pap. 28.00 *(978-0-230-23150-4(0))* Palgrave Macmillan.

Martín-Rodríguez, Manuel. Latinos - As in Children's Films: Imagines of an In-Visible Minority. 2013. (ENG.). 256p. 80.00 *(978-1-4039-6615-5(X))* Palgrave Macmillan.

Martín-Rodríguez, Manuel M. Latinos - As in Children's Films: Images of an in-Visible Minority. 2013. (ENG.). 256p. pap. 25.00 *(978-1-4039-6616-2(8))* Palgrave Macmillan.

Metzdorf, Ragna. Stilwandel des Kinderfilms: 1960er Bis 1980er Jahre. 2011. (Kinder- und Jugendkultur, -literatur und -medien. Theorie - Geschichte - Didaktik Ser.). (GER.). 196p. 57.95 *(978-3-631-60988-0(4))* Lang, Peter GmbH, Europäischer Verlag der Wissenschaften DEU. Dist: Lang, Peter.

Neighbors, R. C. & Rankin, Sandy, eds. The Galaxy Is Rated G: Essays on Children's Science Fiction Film & Television. 2011. (ENG.). 292p. pap. 40.00 ***(978-0-7864-5875-2(5))*** McFarland & Co., Inc. Pubs.

Polette, Nancy. Fairy Tale Fun! 2011. ***(978-1-55570-773-6(4))*** Neal-Schuman Pubs., Inc.

Rupprecht, Hosea M. How to Watch Movies with Kids: A Values-Based Strategy. 2011. 108p. pap. *(978-0-8198-3398-3(3))* Pauline Bks. & Media.

CHILDREN'S FURNITURE

Christian, Vicki & Marshall, Paula, eds. Great Kids' Rooms Collection. 2006. (Better Homes & Gardens Decorating Ser.: 8). (ENG., Illus.). 288p. pap. 19.95 *(978-0-696-22972-5(2),* Wiley) Wiley, John & Sons, Inc.

Kooler Desing Studio, des. Painted Chairs for Tiny Tots. 2007. 52p. 11.95 *(978-1-60140-427-5(1))* Leisure Arts, Inc.

Wilson, Judith. Children's Spaces: From Zero to Ten. 2008. (ENG., Illus.). 144p. *(978-1-84597-591-3(X))* CICO Bks.

Zoob, Caroline. Childhood Treasures: Handmade Gifts for Babies & Children. 2006. (ENG., Illus.). 128p. pap. *(978-1-84597-216-5(3))* Ryland Peters & Small.

CHILDREN'S GARDENS

Here are entered works on gardens planted and cultivated with the participation of children. General works on gardening written for children are entered under Gardening—Juvenile Literature.

Atkins, Patricia. Container Gardening for Schools. 2009. 65p. pap. 14.50 *(978-1-4452-2163-2(2))* Lulu Enterprises Inc.

Bucklin-Sporer, Arden & Pringle, Rachel. How to Grow a School Garden: A Complete Guide for Parents & Teachers. 2010. (ENG., Illus.). 224p. pap. 24.95 *(978-1-60469-000-2(3),* 1604690003) Timber Pr., Inc.

Dannenmaier, Molly. A Child's Garden: 60 Ideas to Make Any Garden Come Alive for Children. 2008. (ENG., Illus.). 180p. pap. 19.95 *(978-0-88192-843-3(7),* 0881928437) Timber Pr., Inc.

Gaylie, Veronica. The Learning Garden: Ecology, Teaching, & Transformation. 2009. (Illus.). x, 219p. *(978-1-4331-0471-8(7))* Lang, Peter Publishing, Inc.

Lockie, Beatrys. Gardening with Young Children. 2007. (Hawthorn Press Early Years Ser.). (Illus.). 140p. per. *(978-1-903458-38-9(2))* Hawthorn Pr.

Sunset Magazine Editors. Sunset Outdoor Design & Build - Backyards for Kids: Fresh Ideas for Outdoor Living. 2012. (ENG., Illus.). 176p. pap. 19.95 *(978-0-376-01436-8(9))* Oxmoor Hse., Inc.

Watts, Ann. Every Nursery Needs a Garden. 2011. (ENG., Illus.). 144p. pap. 31.95 *(978-0-415-59131-7(7))* Routledge.

—Every Nursery Needs A Garden. 2011. (ENG., Illus.). 144p. 104.00 *(978-0-415-59130-0(9))* Routledge.

CHILDREN'S HOMES

see Children—Institutional Care

CHILDREN'S HOSPITALS

see Children—Hospitals

CHILDREN'S LIBRARIES

see also Libraries and Schools

Alire, Camila A. & Ayala, Jacqueline. Serving Latino Communities: A How-To-Do-It Manual. 2nd ed. 2007. (Illus.). 59.95 *(978-1-55570-606-7(1))* Neal-Schuman Pubs., Inc.

Balkin, Alfred. Tune up to Literacy: Original Songs & Activities for Kids. 2009. 45.00 *(978-0-8389-0996-0(1))* American Library Assn.

Bane, Rebecca C. Let's Pretend: 50 Start-To-Finish Preschooler Programs for the Busy Librarian That Foster Imagination. 2010. 143p. 55.00 *(978-1-55570-728-6(9))* Neal-Schuman Pubs., Inc.

Barstow, Barbara, et al. Beyond Picture Books: Subject Access to Best Books for Beginning Readers, 1 vol. 3rd rev. ed. 2007. (Children's & Young Adult Literature Reference Ser.). 668p. 75.00 *(978-1-59158-545-9(7),* LU8545) Libraries Unlimited, Inc.

Bird, Elizabeth. Children's Literature Gems: Choosing & Using Them in Your Library Career. 2009. 125p. 45.00 *(978-0-8389-0995-9(7))* American Library Assn.

Bon, Ingrid, et al, eds. Designing Library Space for Children. 2012. (IFLA Publications). (ENG., Illus.). vi, 150p. (gr. 17). E-Book 196.00 ***(978-3-11-175212-9(7))*** De Gruyter, Walter Inc.

Bromann, Jennifer. More Storytime Action! 2,000+ More Ideas for Making 500+ Picture Books Interactive. 2009. 253p. 55.00 *(978-1-55570-675-3(4))* Neal-Schuman Pubs., Inc.

Cerny, Rosanne, et al. Outstanding Library Service to Children: Putting the Core Competencies to Work. 2006. (Illus.). 94p. per. 30.00 *(978-0-8389-0922-5(1))* American Library Assn.

Cobb, Jane. What'll I Do with the Baby-O? Nursery Rhymes, Songs, & Stories for Babies. 2007. (ENG., Illus.). 256p. (J). (gr. k — 1). pap. 39.95 *(978-0-9698666-1-9(5))* Black Sheep Pr.

Cranfield, Andrew, et al, eds. Designing Library Space for Children. 2011. (IFLA Publications). (ENG.). vi, 150p. *(978-3-11-023216-5(2))* Saur, K. G. Verlag GmbH & Co.

Cullum, Carolyn N. The Storytime Sourcebook II. 2007. 489p. 95.30 *(978-1-4177-8205-5(6),* Turtleback) Turtleback Bks.

—The Storytime Sourcebook II: A Compendium of 3500+ New Ideas & Resources for Storytellers. 2007. xvi, 489p. pap. 75.00 *(978-1-55570-589-3(8))* Neal-Schuman Pubs., Inc.

Dailey, Susan M. Sing a Song of Storytime. 2007. (Illus.). 199p. pap. 59.95 *(978-1-55570-576-3(6))* Neal-Schuman Pubs., Inc.

de Las Casas, Dianne. Tell along Tales! Playing with Participation Stories, 1 vol. 125p. pap. 30.00 *(978-1-59884-635-5(3),* A3168P) Libraries Unlimited, Inc.

De las Casas, Dianne. Tell along Tales! Playing with Participation Stories. 2011. E-Book *(978-1-59884-636-2(1))* Libraries Unlimited, Inc.

Diamant-Cohen, Betsy. Children's Services: Partnerships for Success. 2010. (Illus.). 128p. 50.00 *(978-0-8389-1044-3(0))* American Library Assn.

—Early Literacy Programming en Español: Mother Goose on the Loose Programs for Bilingual Learners. 2010. (ENG & SPA.). 180p. 65.00 *(978-1-55570-691-3(6))* Neal-Schuman Pubs., Inc.

Ernst, Linda L. Baby Rhyming Time. 2007. 235p. pap. 59.95 incl. cd-rom *(978-1-55570-540-4(5))* Neal-Schuman Pubs., Inc.

Essential Guide to Spanish Reading for Children & Young Adults. 2009. 206p. pap. *(978-0-9821418-8-5(2))* TRIALTEA USA, LLC.

Fasick, Adele M. From Boardbook to Facebook: Children's Services in an Interactive Age, 1 vol. 157p. pap. 30.00 *(978-1-59884-468-9(7),* A2940P) Libraries Unlimited, Inc.

Fasick, Adele M. & Holt, Leslie E. Managing Children's Services in the Public Library, 1 vol. 3rd ed. 2007. (Illus.). 264p. per. 45.00 *(978-1-59158-412-4(4),* LU4124) Libraries Unlimited, Inc.

Faurot, Kimberly K. Storytime Around the Year. 2008. (Illus.). 217p. (J). pap. 17.95 *(978-1-932146-50-9(4),* Upstart Bks.) Highsmith Inc.

Feinberg, Sandra & Keller, James R. Designing Space for Children & Teens in Libraries & Public Places. 2010. *(978-0-8389-1020-7(3))* American Library Assn.

Gooch, C. Kay & Massey, Charlotte. Camp Summer Read: How to Create Your Own Summer Reading Camp, 1 vol. 2010. (Illus.). 108p. pap. 30.00 *(978-1-59884-447-4(4),* A2901P) Libraries Unlimited, Inc.

Harper, Meghan. Reference Sources & Services for Youth. 2011. (Illus.). 250p. 65.00 *(978-1-55570-641-8(X))* Neal-Schuman Pubs., Inc.

Hazeltine, Alice. Library Work with Children. 2008. 380p. 31.99 *(978-0-554-21456-6(3))* 2008. 380p. 29.99 *(978-0-554-30759-6(6))* 2006. (ENG.). 486p. pap. 18.99 *(978-1-4264-0190-9(6))* 2006. (ENG.). 396p. pap. 25.99 *(978-1-4264-0061-2(6))* BiblioBazaar.

Hysell, Shannon Graff, ed. Index to American Reference Books Annual 2005-2009: A Cumulative Index to Subjects, Authors, & Titles, 1 vol. 2009. 281p. 85.00 *(978-1-59158-858-0(8),* LU8858) Libraries Unlimited, Inc.

Irving, Jan. Story Celebrations: A Program Guide for Schools & Libraries, 1 vol. 2008. (Illus.). 216p. per. 35.00 *(978-1-59158-432-2(9),* LU4329) Libraries Unlimited, Inc.

Keane, Nancy J. 101 Great, Ready-to-Use Book Lists for Children, 1 vol. 2012. 130p. pap. 40.00 ***(978-1-61069-083-6(4),*** A3769P) Pearson Education GBR. Dist: ABC-CLIO, LLC.

Larsen, Stephanie & Bauman, Stephanie G. Storytimes for Children, 1 vol. 2010. (Illus.). 252p. pap. 30.00 *(978-1-59884-565-5(9),* A3076P) Libraries Unlimited, Inc.

Larson, Jeanette. El Día de los Niños/el Día de los Libros: Building a Culture of Literacy in Your Community. 2011. (Illus.). xii, 123p. pap. *(978-0-8389-3599-6(0))* American Library Assn.

C

Lincycomb, Kay. Storytimes... Plus! 2006. (Illus.). 201p. 45.00 *(978-1-55570-583-1(9))* Neal-Schuman Pubs., Inc.

—Storytimes... Plus! 2007. (Illus.). 201p. 60.50 *(978-1-4177-8206-2(4), Turtleback)* Turtleback Bks.

Lowe, Joy L. & Matthew, Kathryn I. Puppet Magic. 2008. (Illus.). 146p. pap. 45.00 *(978-1-55570-599-2(5))* Neal-Schuman Pubs., Inc.

Lushington, Nolan. Libraries Designed for Kids. 2008. 150p. 85.00 *(978-1-55570-631-9(2))* Neal-Schuman Pubs., Inc.

MacMillan, Kathy. A Box Full of Tales: Easy Ways to Share Library Resources Through Story Boxes. 2008. (Illus.). 45.00 *(978-0-8389-0960-7(4))* American Library Assn.

MacMillan, Kathy & Kirker, Christine. Multicultural Storytime Magic. 2012. 160p. ***(978-0-8389-1142-6(0))*** American Library Assn.

MacMillan, Kathy & Kirker, Christine. Storytime Magic: 500+ Fingerplays, Flannelboards, & Other Activities. 2008. 200p. 45.00 *(978-0-8389-0977-5(9))* American Library Assn.

Miller, Pat. Reaching Every Reader: Instructional Strategies in the Library for Grades K-5, 1 vol. 2nd ed. 2007. (Illus.). 160p. pap. 39.95 *(978-1-58683-284-1(0),* A2472P) Linworth Publishing, Inc.

Miller, Teresa. Holiday Stories All Year Round: Audience Participation Stories & More, 1 vol. 2008. (Illus.). 256p. pap. 35.00 *(978-1-59158-675-3(5),* LU8675) Libraries Unlimited, Inc.

Naidoo, Jamie Campbell, ed. Celebrating Cuentos: Promoting Latino Children's Literature & Literacy in Classrooms & Libraries, 1 vol. (Children's & Young Adult Literature Reference Ser.). (Illus.). 381p. 55.00 *(978-1-59158-904-4(5),* A2244C) Libraries Unlimited, Inc.

Nelson, Jennifer & Braafladt, Keith. Technology & Literacy: 21st Century Library Programming for Children & Teens. 2011. ***(978-0-8389-1108-2(0))*** American Library Assn.

Nichols, Judy. Storytimes for Two-Year-Olds. 3rd ed. 2007. (Illus.). 252p. per. 40.00 *(978-0-8389-0925-6(6))* American Library Assn.

Peck, Penny. Crash Course in Storytime Fundamentals, 1 vol. 2008. (Crash Course Ser.). 172p. pap. 30.00 *(978-1-59158-715-6(8),* LU8715) Libraries Unlimited, Inc.

—Readers' Advisory for Children And 'Tweens, 1 vol. 2010. 190p. pap. 36.00 *(978-1-59884-387-3(7),* A2717P) Libraries Unlimited, Inc.

Polette, Nancy. Fairy Tale Fun! 2011. ***(978-1-55570-773-6(4))*** Neal-Schuman Pubs., Inc.

Polette, Nancy J. The Library Film Party: Activities with Children's Classic Films, 1 vol. 231p. pap. 35.00 *(978-1-59884-820-5(8),* A3440P) Libraries Unlimited, Inc.

Preddy, Leslie B. Social Readers: Promoting Reading in the 21st Century, 1 vol. 2010. (Illus.). 223p. pap. 35.00 *(978-1-59158-869-6(3),* LU8869) Libraries Unlimited, Inc.

Price, Anne & Rowland, Marguerita. Children's Core Collection. 20th ed. 2010. 1700p. 210.00 *(978-0-8242-1106-6(5))* Wilson, H.W.

Reid, Rob. More Family Storytimes: Twenty-Four Creative Programs for All Ages. 2008. 181p. 45.00 *(978-0-8389-0973-7(6))* American Library Assn.

—Shake & Shout: 16 Noisy, Lively Story Programs. 2008. (Illus.). 110p. pap. 17.95 *(978-1-60213-006-7(X),* Upstart Bks.) Highsmith Inc.

—Something Musical Happened at the Library: Adding Song & Dance to Children's Story Programs. 2007. (Illus.). 158p. per. 35.00 *(978-0-8389-0942-3(6))* American Library Assn.

Reid, Rob. What's Black & White & Reid All Over? Something Hilarious Happened at the Library. 2012. ***(978-0-8389-1147-1(1))*** American Library Assn.

Reuter, Kara. Children Selecting Books in a Library. 2008. 240p. per. *(978-3-8364-5728-6(8))* VDM Verlag Dr. Mueller e.K.

Schon, Isabel. Recommended Books in Spanish for Children & Young Adults, 2004-2008. 2008. (ENG.). 424p. 65.00 *(978-0-8108-6386-6(3))* Scarecrow Pr., Inc.

Schwedt, Rachel & DeLong, Janice. Core Collection for Children & Young Adults. 2008. (ENG.). 218p. 60.00 *(978-0-8108-6115-2(1))* Scarecrow Pr., Inc.

Scott, Barbara A. 1,000 Fingerplays & Action Rhymes: A Sourcebook & DVD. 2010. 400p. 65.00 *(978-1-55570-695-1(9))* Neal-Schuman Pubs., Inc.

Simpson, Martha Seif & Duwel, Lucretia I. Bringing Classes into the Public Library: A Handbook for Librarians. 2007. (ENG., Illus.). 183p. per. 49.95 *(978-0-7864-2806-9(6))* McFarland & Co., Inc. Pubs.

Skinner, Tina, et al. Children's Rooms: From Newborns to Teens. 2007. (Schiffer Design Book Ser.). (Illus.). 144p. pap. 24.95 *(978-0-7643-2147-4(1))* Schiffer Publishing, Ltd.

Soltan, Rita. Summer Reading Renaissance: An Interactive Exhibits Approach, 1 vol. 2008. (Illus.). 264p. pap. 45.00 *(978-1-59158-572-5(4),* LU8572) Libraries Unlimited, Inc.

Struckmeyer, Amanda Moss & Hetzler, Svetha. DIY Programming & Book Displays: How to Stretch Your Programming without Stretching Your Budget & Staff, 1 vol. 213p. pap. 36.00 *(978-1-59884-472-6(5),* A2942P) Libraries Unlimited, Inc.

—DIY Programming & Book Displays: How to Stretch Your Programming Without Stretching Your Budget & Staff. 2010. E-Book *(978-1-59884-473-3(3))* Libraries Unlimited, Inc.

Sullivan, Michael. Connecting Boys with Books 2: Closing the Reading Gap. 2009. 136p. 40.00 *(978-0-8389-0979-9(5))* American Library Assn.

Taylor-Dileva, Kimberly. Once upon a Sign: Using American Sign Language to Engage, Entertain, & Teach All Children, 1 vol. 2011. (Illus.). 270p. pap. 38.00 *(978-1-59884-476-4(8),* A2946P) Libraries Unlimited, Inc.

Thomas, Rebecca L. & Barr, Catherine. Popular Series Fiction for Middle School & Teen Readers: A Reading & Selection Guide, 1 vol. 2nd ed. 2008. (Children's & Young Adult Literature Reference Ser.). 724p. 65.00 *(978-1-59158-660-9(7),* LU8660) Libraries Unlimited, Inc.

Totten, Herman L. & Brown, Risa W. Culturally Diverse Library Collections, 2 vols., Set. Incl. Culturally Diverse Library Collections for Children. 299p. 1994. 49.95 *(978-1-55570-140-6(X));* Culturally Diverse Library Collections for Youth. Garner, Carolyn. 220p. 1996. 49.95 *(978-1-55570-141-3(8));* Set pap. 60.00 *(978-1-55570-300-4(3))* Neal-Schuman Pubs., Inc.

Totten, Kathryn. Family Literacy Storytimes: Readymade Storytimes Suitable for the Whole Family. 2009. (Illus.). 169p. 59.95 *(978-1-55570-671-5(1))* Neal-Schuman Pubs., Inc.

Treviño, Rose Zertuche. Read Me a Rhyme in Spanish & English: Léame una Rima en Español e Inglés. 2009. (SPA & ENG.). 160p. 45.00 *(978-0-8389-0982-9(5))* American Library Assn.

Van Orden, Phyllis J., et al. Children's Books: A Practical Guide to Selection. 2007. (Illus.). pap. 59.95 *(978-1-55570-584-8(7))* Neal-Schuman Pubs., Inc.

Vardell, Sylvia. Children's Literature in Action: A Librarian's Guide, 1 vol. 2008. (Library & Information Science Text Ser.). (Illus.). 323p. pap. 50.00 *(978-1-59158-557-2(0),* LU8557) Libraries Unlimited, Inc.

Vardell, Sylvia M. Children's Literature in Action: A Librarian's Guide, 1 vol. 2008. (Library & Information Science Text Ser.). (Illus.). 340p. 65.00 *(978-1-59158-657-9(7),* LU6579) Libraries Unlimited, Inc.

Walter, Virginia A. Twenty-First-Century Kids, Twenty-First-Century Librarians. 2009. (ENG.). 112p. pap. *(978-0-8389-1007-8(6))* American Library Assn.

Yousha, LaDonna. Teddy Bear Storytimes: Ready-To-Go Flannel & Magnetic Storyboard Programs That Captivate Children. 2009. 55.00 *(978-1-55570-677-7(0))* Neal-Schuman Pubs., Inc.

CHILDREN'S LIBRARIES—EUROPE

Farmer, Lesley S. J., et al. Youth-Serving Libraries in Japan, Russia, & the United States. 2012. (Illus.). vi, 372p. E-Book ***(978-0-8108-8226-3(4))*** Scarecrow Pr., Inc.

Farmer/Gendina/Nakam. Youth-Serving Libraries in Japan, Russia, & the United States. 2011. (ENG., Illus.). 378p. (gr. 17). pap. 65.00 ***(978-0-8108-8225-6(6))*** Scarecrow Pr., Inc.

CHILDREN'S LITERATURE

Here are entered collections of works published for children. Works on the reading interests of children, and-or lists of books read by or recommended for children, are entered under Children—Books and Reading. Collections of literary works or individual literary works written by children under 15 years of age are entered under Children's Writings. Works on child authors and-or discussions of their works are entered under Child Authors.

see also Children's Encyclopedias and Dictionaries; Children's Plays; Children's Poetry; Children's Stories; Christian Literature for Children; Fairy Tales; Newbery Medal Books; Picture Books for Children; Readers

also subdivision Juvenile Literature under particular subjects for works of nonfiction, e.g. Astronomy—Juvenile Literature

Abington-Pitre, Albertaeve. Native Americans in Children's Literature. 2010. 116p. pap. *(978-3-8383-5799-7(X))* Lambert Academic Publishing.

Arnold, Arnold & Dover. Pictures & Stories from Vintage Children's Books. 2012. (Dover Pictorial Archive Ser.). (ENG.). 176p. pap. 19.95 ***(978-0-486-48843-1(8))*** Dover Pubns., Inc.

Aronson, Marc & Campbell, Patty, eds. War Is... Soldiers, Survivors, & Storytellers Talk about War. 2009. (ENG.). 288p. (YA). (gr. 9). mass mkt. 6.99 *(978-0-7636-4231-0(2))* Candlewick Pr.

Arthur, T. S. (Timothy Shay). Our Little Harry, & Other Poems & Stories with Illus from Original Designs by Croome. 2006. 156p. per. 18.99 *(978-1-4255-1166-1(X))* MPublishing.

Asael, Anthony & Rabemiafara, Stephanie. Children of the World: How We Live, Learn, & Play in Poems, Drawings, & Photographs. 2011. (ENG., Illus.). 416p. 29.95 *(978-0-7893-2267-8(6))* Universe Publishing.

Association for Library Service to Children (ALSC), creator. The Newbery & Caldecott Awards: A Guide to the Medal & Honor Books. 2011. 172p. 28.00 ***(978-0-8389-8569-4(6))*** American Library Assn.

Baden-Powell, Robert, et al. The Second Trail. 2011. 288p. 48.95 ***(978-1-258-05949-1(5))*** Literary Licensing, LLC.

Bader, Simone. Ômagicö As a Phenomenon in Childrenæs Books. 2008. 100p. pap. *(978-3-639-09092-5(6))* VDM Verlag Dr. Mueller e.K.

Bailey, Carolyn Sherwin. For the Children's Hour. 2008. 356p. 29.99 *(978-0-559-25124-5(6));* pap. 31.75 *(978-0-559-25122-1(X))* BiblioBazaar.

Barr, Catherine. Best Books for Middle School & Junior High Readers, Grades 6-9: Supplement to the Second Edition, 1 vol. (Children's & Young Adult Literature Reference Ser.). 238p. 45.00 *(978-1-59884-783-3(X),* A3400C) Libraries Unlimited, Inc.

Baxter, Kathleen A. & Kochel, Marcia Agness. Gotcha Again for Guys! More Nonfiction Books to Get Boys Excited about Reading. 2010. (Illus.). xiii, 248p. E-Book *(978-1-59884-377-4(X))* Libraries Unlimited, Inc.

Baxter, Nicola. My Treasury of Stories & Rhymes: An Enchanting Collection of 145 Classis Tales. 2012. (ENG., Illus.). 256p. (J). (gr. k-4). 18.99 ***(978-1-84322-818-9(1))*** Anness Publishing GBR. Dist: National Bk. Network.

Carroll, Lewis, pseud. Lewis Carroll & the House of Macmillan. Cohen, Morton N. & Gandolfo, Anita, eds. 2007. (Cambridge Studies in Publishing & Printing History Ser.). (ENG., Illus.). 396p. pap. 79.00 *(978-0-521-04471-4(5))* Cambridge Univ. Pr.

Cheh, Oksana. Literature Preferences of Multilingual Children- a Study of Children's Reading. 2007. 112p. per. *(978-3-8364-2113-3(5))* VDM Verlag Dr. Mueller e.K.

Christelow and others. Family Bedtime Treasury with CD. 2012. (ENG., Illus.). 288p. (J). (gr. -1-3). 18.99 ***(978-0-547-85786-2(1),*** Houghton Mifflin Harcourt) Houghton Mifflin Harcourt Trade & Reference Pubs.

Clifton, Sasha, contrib. by. Little Folks World. 2007. 136p. per. 16.95 *(978-1-60466-011-1(2))* Capricorn Hse. Publishing.

Coats, Karen. Looking Glasses & Neverlands: Lacan, Desire, & Subjectivity in Children's Literature. 2007. 202p. per. 19.95 *(978-1-58729-586-7(5))* Univ. of Iowa Pr.

Coffin, Rebecca J., et al, eds. Tabby & the Boat Fire. 2011. 50p. 35.95 ***(978-1-258-09863-6(6))*** Literary Licensing, LLC.

Collie, Jan van. Children's Literature in Translation: Challenges & Strategies. 2006. (Illus.). ix, 190p. *(978-1-900650-88-5(6))* St. Jerome Publishing.

Collingwood, Stuart Dodgson. The Life & Letters of Lewis Carroll. 2009. 396p. 29.99 *(978-0-559-12579-9(8));* 31.99 *(978-0-559-12569-0(0));* pap. 32.75 *(978-0-559-12577-5(1));* pap. 26.99 *(978-0-559-12572-0(0))* BiblioBazaar.

—The Life & Letters of Lewis Carroll. 2007. (ENG.). 232p. per. *(978-1-4068-4707-9(0))* Echo Library.

Collins, Fiona M. & Ridgman, Jeremy. Turning the Page: Children's Literature in Performance & the Media. 2006. 297p. 59.95 *(978-0-8204-7184-6(4))* Lang, Peter Publishing, Inc.

Cowan, C. C. Amanda's Amazing Advenutes: The Case of the Missing Pooch. 2007. (Illus.). (J). 12.95 *(978-0-9800655-7-2(7))* CCP Publishing & Entertainment.

Davis, Doug "Hollywood". Franks & Beans: Stories, Poems, & Tongue Twisters, 1 vol. 2009. 93p. pap. 16.95 *(978-1-4489-2129-4(5))* PublishAmerica, Inc.

Dean, Susan H. The Tree of the Child. 2007. 56p. pap. 27.99 *(978-1-4257-7965-8(4))* Xlibris Corp.

Eleanor H. Porter & Eleanor H. Porter. Oh, Money! Money! 2011. (Illus.). 248p. pap. 5.89 ***(978-1-60386-407-7(5),*** Merchant Bks.) Rough Draft Printing.

Epstein, B. J. Translating Expressive Language in Children's Literature: Problems & Solutions. 2012. (ENG.). 269p. 93.95 ***(978-3-0343-0796-3(9))*** Lang, Peter AG GBR. Dist: Lang, Peter.

Evans, Janet. Talking Beyond the Page: Reading & Responding to Picturebooks. Evans, Janet, ed. 2009. (Illus.). 194p. (ENG.). 150.00 *(978-0-415-47695-9(X));* pap. 42.95 *(978-0-415-47696-6(8))* Routledge.

Ewers, Hans-Heino. Fundamental Concepts of Children's Literature Research: Literary & Sociological Approaches. 2009. (Children's Literature & Culture Ser.). (ENG., Illus.). 196p. (C). 125.00 *(978-0-415-80019-8(6))* Routledge.

Ferguson, Dana. Children's Book Review 2008: Annual Cumlation. 2008th rev. ed. 2008. (Children's Book Review Index Ser.). (ENG.). 624p. 267.00 *(978-0-7876-9545-3(9))* Cengage Gale.

Ford, Robert. Children's Rhymes, Children's Games, Children's Songs, Children's Stories. 2009. 184p. pap. *(978-0-217-69500-8(0))* Books LLC.

Francis, Pauline, selected by. World Book Day - Primary Anthology. 2011. (World Book Day Ser.). 112p. pap. 3.99 *(978-0-237-54444-3(1))* Evans Publishing Group GBR. Dist: CENGAGE Learning.

—World Book Day - Secondary Anthology. 2011. (World Book Day Ser.). 112p. pap. 3.99 *(978-0-237-54444-7(X))* Evans Publishing Group GBR. Dist: CENGAGE Learning.

Fredericks, Anthony D. MORE Science Adventures with Children's Literature: Reading Comprehension & Inquiry-Based Science, 1 vol. 2008. (Through Children's Literature Ser.). (Illus.). 456p. pap. 35.00 *(978-1-59158-619-7(4),* TIP8619, Teacher Ideas Pr.) Libraries Unlimited, Inc.

Freeman, Judy. The WINNERS! Handbook: A Closer Look at Judy Freeman's Top-Rated Children's Books Of 2008, 1 vol. 2008. (Illus.). 190p. pap. 35.00 *(978-1-59158-859-7(6),* LU8859) Libraries Unlimited, Inc.

Frimmelova, Katerina. Translating Children's Literature. 2010. 96p. pap. *(978-3-8383-6387-5(6))* Lambert Academic Publishing.

Gale Editor, ed. Children's Book Review Index. 2011th ed. 2011. 909p. lib. bdg. 267.00 *(978-1-4144-6185-4(2))* Cengage Gale.

Galway, Elizabeth. From Nursery Rhymes to Nationhood. 2011. (ENG.). 202p. pap. 34.95 ***(978-0-415-69941-9(X))*** Routledge.

Garfield High School Staff. Sheep Can't Fly. 2009. (ENG.). 352p. pap. 15.00 *(978-1-934750-12-4(3))* 826 Valencia.

Green, Connie R. & Oldendorf, Sandra Brenneman. Religious Diversity & Children's Literature: Strategies & Resources. 2011. (Illus.). 250p. *(978-1-61735-397-0(3));* pap. *(978-1-61735-396-3(5))* Information Age Publishing, Inc.

Grenby, M. O. & Immel, Andrea, eds. The Cambridge Companion to Children's Literature. 2009. (Cambridge Companions to Literature Ser.). (ENG., Illus.). 324p. (C). 89.00 *(978-0-521-86819-8(X))* Cambridge Univ. Pr.

Hancock, Susan. The Child That Haunts Us: Symbols & Images in Fairytale & Miniature Literature. 2008. (ENG., Illus.). 168p. (C). 110.00 *(978-0-415-44775-1(5));* pap. 34.95 *(978-0-415-44776-8(3))* Routledge.

Harbor, Missy. Missy Harbor's Collection of Children's Stories & Poems, 1 vol. 2010. 71p. pap. 16.95 *(978-1-4489-6862-6(3))* PublishAmerica, Inc.

Havill, Juanita, ed. Booklove: Creating Good Books for Children in an Age that Values Neither. 12.95 *(978-0-9657557-1-9(1),* E&L Bks.) Phoenix College Pr.

Hawthorne, Nathaniel. A Wonder Book for Girls & Boys. 2006. (ENG.). 156p. (gr. 4-7). per. 12.95 *(978-1-59818-883-7(6))* Aegypan.

—A Wonder Book for Girls & Boys. 2009. (Illus.). 240p. (gr. 4-7). pap. 10.95 *(978-1-59915-092-5(1))* Yesterday's Classics.

Hilbun, Janet W. & Claes, Jane H. Coast to Coast: Exploring State Book Awards, 1 vol. 249p. pap. 40.00 *(978-1-59158-735-4(2),* LU8735) Libraries Unlimited, Inc.

Howells, William Dean & Alden, Henry Mills, eds. The Heart of Childhood. 2007. (ENG.). 292p. 43.95 *(978-0-548-02541-3(X))* Kessinger Publishing, LLC.

Hysell, Shannon Graff, ed. Index to American Reference Books Annual 2005-2009: A Cumulative Index to Subjects, Authors, & Titles, 1 vol. 2009. 281p. 85.00 *(978-1-59158-858-0(8),* LU8858) Libraries Unlimited, Inc.

Impelsys Staff, ed. Sesame Street ebookstore subscription. 2011. (SPA & ENG.). 2563p. E-Book ***(978-1-61831-158-0(1))*** Sesame Workshop.

Intner, Sheila I., et al. Cataloging Correctly for Kids: An Introduction to the Tools. 5th ed. 2010. (Illus.). 232p. *(978-0-8389-3589-7(3))* American Library Assn.

Jones, Beth Felker. Touched by a Vampire: Discovering the Hidden Messages in the Twilight Saga. 2009. (ENG.). 192p. pap. 13.99 *(978-1-60142-278-1(4),* Multnomah) Doubleday Religious Publishing Group, The.

Karwath, Ingo. Hort auf zu Lesen, Kinder! Die Philanthropische Rezeptionserziehung. (Europaische Hochschulschriften Ser.: Vol. 852). (GER.). 308p. 39.95 *(978-3-631-37890-8(4))* Lang, Peter Publishing, Inc.

Larousse Mexico Staff, ed. Historias para Dormir. 2008.Tr. of Bedtime Stories. (SPA & ENG., Illus.). 35p. 19.95 *(978-970-22-1632-2(X))* Larousse, Ediciones, S. A. de C. V. MEX. Dist: Houghton Mifflin Harcourt Trade & Reference Pubs.

Levithnan, David. This Is Push. 2011. 8.44 *(978-0-7848-3577-7(2),* Everbind) Marco Bk. Co.

Lydia Maria Francis Child (ES 4-vol. Set) 2011. 1125.00 *(978-4-86166-114-3(5))* Synapse, Edition JPN. Dist: Taylor & Francis Group.

McNicol, Sarah. Forbidden Fruit: The Censorship of Literature & Information for Young People - Conference Proceedings. 2008. 128p. pap. 25.95 *(978-1-59942-480-4(0),* Brown Walker Pr.) Universal Pubs.

Menges, Jeff A., ed. Once upon a Time ... A Treasury of Classic Fairy Tale Illustrations. 2008. (Dover Fine Art, History of Art Ser.). (ENG.). 192p. pap. 19.95 *(978-0-486-46830-3(5))* Dover Pubns., Inc.

Metzdorf, Ragna. Stilwandel des Kinderfilms: 1960er Bis 1980er Jahre. 2011. (Kinder- und Jugendkultur, -literatur und -medien. Theorie - Geschichte - Didaktik Ser.). (GER.). 196p. 57.95 *(978-3-631-60988-0(4))* Lang, Peter GmbH, Europaischer Verlag der Wissenschaften DEU. Dist: Lang, Peter.

Mills, Alice, ed. Classic Children's Stories: Nursery Rhymes, Bedtime Stories, Nonsense Poems, & Much More. 2011. (ENG., Illus.). 304p. (J). (gr. k-2). 19.95 *(978-1-61608-468-4(5),* 608468, Sky Pony Pr.) Skyhorse Publishing Co., Inc.

Moore-Broyles, Toya. Chicken & Chocolate. 2008. 36p. pap. 19.98 *(978-0-557-01534-4(0))* Lulu Enterprises Inc.

Muhle, Eva-Maria. History in Irish Historical Fiction for Children & Young Adults. 2011. (Europäische Bildung im Dialog. Region - Sprache - Identität Ser.). 274p. 64.95 ***(978-3-631-61116-6(1))*** Lang, Peter GmbH, Europaischer Verlag der Wissenschaften DEU. Dist: Lang, Peter.

Munro, Roxie, illus. Great American Landmarks Adventure. 2008. (ENG.). 45p. pap. 9.00 *(978-0-16-081138-8(4))* National Park Service Div. of Pubns.

Naidoo, Jamie Campbell, ed. Celebrating Cuentos: Promoting Latino Children's Literature & Literacy in Classrooms & Libraries, 1 vol. (Children's & Young Adult Literature Reference Ser.). (Illus.). 381p. 55.00 *(978-1-59158-904-4(5),* A2244C) Libraries Unlimited, Inc.

Napoli, Mary. Selling the Perfect Girl: Girls as Consumers, Girls as Commodities. 2012. (Children's Literature & Culture Ser.). (ENG.). 256p. 125.00 *(978-0-415-97953-5(6))* Routledge.

Nel, Philip & Zipes, Jack. Tales for Little Rebels: A Collection of Radical Children's Literature. Mickenberg, Julia L., ed. 2008. (ENG., Illus.). 313p. 65.00 *(978-0-8147-5720-8(0))* New York Univ. Pr.

—Tales for Little Rebels: A Collection of Radical Children's Literature. Mickenberg, Julia, ed. 2010. (ENG., Illus.). 313p. pap. 26.00 *(978-0-8147-5721-5(9))* New York Univ. Pr.

Ngugi, Pamela. Language & Literary Education. 2011. 356p. pap. ***(978-3-8433-9327-0(3))*** Lambert Academic Publishing.

Nichols, Walter H. Cowboy Hugh: The Odyssey of A Boy. 2011. 298p. 48.95 ***(978-1-258-08668-8(9))*** Literary Licensing, LLC.

O'Hara, Virginia. Flights into Fantasy: The Kendra & Allan Daniel Collection of Children's Illustration. 2007. (Illus.). 80p. pap. 24.95 *(978-0-9795872-2-1(0))* Brandywine River Museum.

Olson, Marilynn. Children's Culture & the Avant-Garde. 2012. (Children's Literature & Culture Ser.). (ENG., Illus.). 240p. (C). 125.00 *(978-0-415-87268-3(5))* Routledge.

O'Sullivan, Sheryl. A Festival of Talent: Wisdom from the First Decade of the Charlotte S. Huck Children's Literature Festival. rev. ed. 2007. (ENG.). 204p. pap. 53.51 *(978-0-7575-3906-0(8))* Kendall Hunt Publishing Co.

Pale Hecates Team Vol. 2: Briggs. 2011. (ENG.). 302p. pap. 45.95 ***(978-0-415-60691-2(8))*** Routledge.

Parsons, Adam. The Valley of Rhyme. 2007. (J). *(978-0-9794773-0-0(1))* Worldwide Interactive Network.

Patten, William. The Junior Classics. 2008. 432p. 32.99 *(978-0-554-22535-7(2))* 2008. 432p. 30.99 *(978-0-554-31838-7(5))* 2008. 404p. 30.99 *(978-0-554-32993-2(X))* 2008. 380p. 29.99 *(978-0-554-32991-8(3))* 2008. 416p. 30.99 *(978-0-554-33020-4(2))* 2008. 416p. 32.99 *(978-0-554-23717-6(2))* 2008. 380p. 31.99 *(978-0-554-23688-9(5))* 2008. 404p. 32.99 *(978-0-554-23690-2(7))* Vol. 8. 2007. (ENG.). 382p. pap. 25.99 *(978-1-4264-2565-3(1))* Vol. 8. 2007. (ENG.). 430p. pap. 28.99 *(978-1-4264-2606-3(2))* BiblioBazaar.

—The Junior Classics: Volume 6 Old-Fashioned Tales. 2007. (ENG.). 374p. pap. 25.99 (978-1-4264-4950-5(X)); 412p. pap. 28.99 (978-1-4264-5251-2(9)) BiblioBazaar.

—The Junior Classics, Volume 4. 2007. (ENG.). 334p. pap. 23.99 (978-1-4264-4920-8(8)); 376p. pap. 26.99 (978-1-4264-5221-5(7)) BiblioBazaar.

—TheJunior Classics, Volume 5. 2007. (ENG.). 360p. pap. 25.99 (978-1-4264-4922-2(4)); 402p. pap. 28.99 (978-1-4264-5223-9(3)) BiblioBazaar.

Plesse, Amanda & Shine Thompson, Mary, eds. Young Irelands: Studies in Children's Literature. 2011. 198p. 65.00 (978-1-84682-141-7(X)) Four Courts Pr. IRL. Dist: International Specialized Bk. Services.

Pizzi, Katia, ed. Pinocchio, Puppets, & Modernity: The Mechanical Body. 2011. (Children's Literature & Culture Ser.). (ENG., Illus.). 246p. (C). 125.00 (978-0-415-89096-0(9)) Routledge.

Rackham, Arthur, illus. English Fairy Tales. 2011. (Calla Editions Ser.). (ENG.). 408p. 40.00 (978-1-60660-018-4(4)) Dover Pubns., Inc.

Rathmell, Donna, et al. All-Title Set (Paperback) 2011. (J). pap. 537.00 (978-1-60718-347-1(1)) Sylvan Dell Pubng.

Reynolds, Kimberley & Grenby, M. O. Children's Literature Studies: A Research Handbook. 2011. (ENG., Illus.). 272p. 80.00 (978-0-230-52553-5(9)); pap. 27.95 (978-0-230-52554-2(7)) Palgrave Macmillan.

Rosenthal, Amy Krouse. The Wonder Book. 2010. 80p. (J). lib. bdg. 18.89 (978-0-06-142975-0(9)) HarperCollins Pubs.

Rubatino, Michele. The Origin of the Wonderful Wizard of Oz. 2010. 108p. 22.95 (978-1-4502-2801-5(1)); pap. 12.95 (978-1-4502-2800-8(3)) iUniverse, Inc.

Rudman, Kabakow & Botelho, Maria José Rondon Régis. Critical Multicultural Analysis of Children's Literature: Mirrors, Windows, & Doors. 2009. (Language, Culture, & Teaching Ser.). (ENG., Illus.). 376p. 51.95 (978-0-8058-3711-7(6)) Routledge.

School, Isaac Crary Elementary. Young Authors Leaving Their Mark. 2007. 52p. per. 10.00 (978-1-4257-3625-5(4)) Xlibris Corp.

Scieszka, Jon. Guys Write for Guys Read: Boys' Favorite Authors Write about Being Boys. 2008. (J). (gr. 6). 16.99 (978-0-670-01143-8(6)); (ENG., Illus.). 272p. 11.99 (978-0-670-01144-5(4)) Penguin Group (USA) Inc. (Viking Juvenile).

Shanks, Danny L. Poeantasy III: A Book of Poetry & Fantasy. 2007. 72p. per. 8.95 (978-0-595-45711-3(8)) iUniverse, Inc.

Shirley Jerideau. A Unique Children's Book of Stories & Poetry. 2010. (Illus.). 72p. pap. 24.27 (978-1-4269-2456-9(9)) Trafford Publishing.

St. John, Raymond A. Explorations in Literature. 3rd ed. 2007. (Illus.). xxiii, 623p. pap. (978-1-59166-502-1(7)) BJU Pr.

Stephens, John, ed. Subjectivity in Asian Children's Literature & Film: Global Theories & Implications. 2012. (Children's Literature & Culture Ser.). (ENG.). 228p. (C). 125.00 (978-0-415-80688-6(7)) Routledge.

Stirling, Kirsten. Peter Pan's Shadows in the Literary Imagination. 2011. (Children's Literature & Culture Ser.). (ENG.). 188p. (C). 125.00 (978-0-415-88864-6(6)) Routledge.

Stout, William. William Stout: Hallucinations. 2010. (ENG., Illus.). 48p. pap. 19.95 (978-1-933865-25-6(3)) Flesk Pubns.

Students Of St. Joseph'S. St Joseph's Catholic School Presents Knight Writers 2007-2008. 2008. (Illus.). 128p. pap. 11.95 (978-0-595-52715-1(9)) iUniverse, Inc.

Sylvester, Charles H. Journeys Through Bookland. 2009. 452p. 32.99 (978-0-559-07830-9(7)) 2009. 452p. 27.99 (978-0-559-07847-7(1)) 2009. 452p. pap. 36.75 (978-0-559-07835-4(3)) 2009. 452p. pap. 35.75 (978-0-559-07842-2(0)) 2008. 360p. 31.99 (978-0-554-22331-5(7)) 2008. 340p. 29.99 (978-0-554-22325-4(2)) 2008. 384p. 31.99 (978-0-554-22640-8(5)) 2008. 384p. 29.99 (978-0-554-31943-8(8)) 2008. 360p. 29.99 (978-0-554-31634-5(X)) 2008. 340p. 28.99 (978-0-554-31628-4(5)) 2007. (ENG.). 344p. pap. 23.99 (978-1-4264-2006-1(4)) 2007. (ENG.). 356p. pap. 26.99 (978-1-4264-2191-4(5)) Vol. 2. 2006. 338p. pap. 24.99 (978-1-4264-2117-4(6)) BiblioBazaar.

—Journeys Through Bookland. 2009. 340p. pap. (978-0-217-85757-4(4)); 278p. pap. (978-1-4590-9318-8(6)) Books LLC.

—Journeys Through Bookland. 2008. 340p. pap. (978-1-4099-1279-8(5)); (Illus.). 428p. pap. (978-1-4099-1282-8(5)) Dodo Pr.

—Journeys Through Bookland. 2008. 552p. 29.95 (978-1-4344-7790-3(8)); 528p. 29.95 (978-1-4344-7794-1(0)); 528p. 29.95 (978-1-4344-7792-7(4)); 512p. 29.95 (978-1-4344-7810-8(6)); 528p. 29.95 (978-1-4344-7796-5(7)); 520p. 29.95 (978-1-4344-7803-0(3)); 520p. 29.95 (978-1-4344-7804-7(1)); 516p. 29.95 (978-1-4344-7807-8(6)); 512p. 29.95 (978-1-4344-7808-5(4)); 520p. 29.95 (978-1-4344-7800-9(9)); 524p. 29.95 (978-1-4344-7798-9(3)); 552p. pap. 14.95 (978-1-4344-7789-7(4)); 528p. pap. 14.95 (978-1-4344-7791-0(6)); 528p. pap. 14.95 (978-1-4344-7795-8(9)); 528p. pap. 14.95 (978-1-4344-7793-4(2)); 524p. pap. 14.95 (978-1-4344-7797-2(5)); 516p. pap. 14.95 (978-1-4344-7805-4(X)); 512p. pap. 14.95 (978-1-4344-7809-2(2)); 520p. pap. 14.95 (978-1-4344-7801-6(7)); 520p. pap. 14.95 (978-1-4344-7802-3(5)); 520p. pap. 14.95 (978-1-4344-7799-6(1)); 494p. pap. 14.95 (978-1-4344-7806-1(8)) Wildside Pr., LLC.

—Journeys Through Bookland, Volume 3. 2007. (ENG.). 338p. pap. 23.99 (978-1-4264-2774-9(3)); 380p. pap. 26.99 (978-1-4264-2812-8(X)) BiblioBazaar.

—Journeys Through Bookland, Volume 4. 2006. 368p. pap. 25.99 (978-1-4264-2123-5(0)) BiblioBazaar.

Sylvester, Charles Herbert. Journeys Through Bookland. 2008. 416p. 32.99 (978-0-554-23636-0(2)) 2008. 416p. 30.99 (978-0-554-32939-0(5)) 2007. (ENG.). 356p. pap. 25.99 (978-1-4264-4825-6(2)) Vol. 5. 2007. (ENG.). 414p. pap. 28.99 (978-1-4264-4868-3(6)) BiblioBazaar.

Tabori, Lena. Moms. Wong, Alice, ed. 10th anniv. ed. 2010. (ENG., Illus.). 352p. 24.95 (978-1-59962-075-5(8), Welcome Bks.) Welcome Enterprises, Inc.

Thomas, Rebecca L. & Barr, Catherine. Popular Series Fiction for Middle School & Teen Readers: A Reading & Selection Guide, 1 vol. 2nd ed. 2008. (Children's & Young Adult Literature Reference Ser.). 724p. 65.00 (978-1-59158-660-9(7), LU8660) Libraries Unlimited, Inc.

Tuer, Andrew W. Stories from Old-Fashioned Children's Books. 456p. 2010. pap. 30.36 (978-1-163-79828-7(2)) 2007. 52.95 (978-0-548-55730-3(6)) 2007. (ENG.). per. 37.95 (978-0-548-48825-6(3)) Kessinger Publishing, LLC.

Waldrep, Mary Carolyn, ed. Classic Children's Book Illustrations CD-ROM & Book. 2008. (Dover Electronic Clip Art Ser.). (ENG., Illus.). 48p. pap. 22.95 (978-0-486-99862-6(2)) Dover Pubns., Inc.

Wannamaker, Annette & Abate, Michelle Ann, eds. Global Perspectives on Tarzan: From King of the Jungle to International Icon. 2012. (Routledge Research in Cultural & Media Studies). (ENG., Illus.). 226p. (C). 125.00 (978-0-415-89724-2(6)) Routledge.

Watson, Nancy. The Politics & Poetics of Irish Children's Literature. 2009. 187p. 74.95 (978-0-7165-3003-9(1)) Irish Academic Pr. IRL. Dist: International Specialized Bk. Services.

Wolf. Handbook of Research on Children's & Young Adult Literature. 2010. (ENG., Illus.). 568p. 305.00 (978-0-415-96505-7(5)); pap. 119.95 (978-0-415-96506-4(3)) Routledge.

Zellman, Gail L., et al. Identifying Arabic-Language Materials for Children That Promote Tolerance & Critical Thinking, 1 vol. 2011. (ENG., Illus.). 84p. (C). pap. 20.00 (978-0-8330-5174-5(1), RAND Corp., The.

Zhang, Jie. She Knocked at the Door. 2010. 194p. pap. 11.95 (978-1-60220-909-1(X)) BetterLink Pr., Inc.

CHILDREN'S LITERATURE—AUTHORSHIP

Ambrosek, Renee. E. L. Konigsburg. 2009. (Library of Author Biographies Ser.). 112p. (gr. 5-8). 63.90 (978-1-60853-532-3(0), Rosen Central) Rosen Publishing Group, Inc., The.

—E.L. Konigsburg. 2006. (Library of Author Biographies). (ENG., Illus.). 112p. (gr. 5-8). pap. 12.95 (978-1-4042-0648-9(5)) Rosen Publishing Group, Inc., The.

Belpré, Pura & Sánchez González, Lisa. The Stories I Read to the Children: The Life & Writing of Pura Belpré. 2011. pap. 28.00 (978-1-936117-15-4(0), Library Juice Pr.) Litwin Bks., LLC.

Cadden, Michael, ed. Telling Children's Stories: Narrative Theory & Children's Literature. 2011. (Frontiers of Narrative Ser.). (ENG., Illus.). 344p. pap. 35.00 (978-0-8032-1568-9(1)) Univ. of Nebraska Pr.

Carver, Peter. So You Want to Write a Children's Book: An Insider's Handbook for Children's Writers & Illustrators Who Want to Get Published, 1 vol. 2011. (ENG.). 124p. pap. 12.95 (978-0-88995-456-4(9)) Red Deer Pr. CAN. Dist: Ingram Pub. Services.

Casil, Amy Sterling. Lois Duncan. 2009. (Library of Author Biographies Ser.). 112p. (gr. 5-8). 63.90 (978-1-60853-543-9(6), Rosen Central) Rosen Publishing Group, Inc., The.

Cleaver, Pamela. Writing for Children. 4th ed. 2010. (ENG., Illus.). 199p. pap. 22.00 (978-1-84528-330-8(9)) How To Books GBR. Dist: Parkwest Pubns., Inc.

Cowley, Joy. Writing from the Heart: How to Write for Children. 2011. (ENG.). 128p. 19.95 (978-1-59078-871-4(0)) Boyds Mills Pr.

Crook, Marion. Writing Books for Children & Young Adults. 2nd ed. 2007. (ENG., Illus.). 208p. pap. 18.95 (978-1-55180-813-0(7)) Self-Counsel Pr., Inc. CAN. Dist: Midpoint Trade Bks., Inc.

Daniels, Susana. Lois Lowry. 2009. (Library of Author Biographies Ser.). 112p. (gr. 5-8). 63.90 (978-1-60853-544-6(4), Rosen Central) Rosen Publishing Group, Inc., The.

Dils, Tracey E. You Can Write Children's Books. 2nd ed. 2009. (ENG., Illus.). 176p. pap. 14.99 (978-1-58297-573-3(6), Writer's Digest Bks.) F&W Media, Inc.

Hopkinson, Deborah. Deborah Hopkinson & YOU, 1 vol. 2007. (Author & YOU Ser.). (Illus.). 112p. pap. 35.00 (978-1-59158-278-6(4), LU2784) Libraries Unlimited, Inc.

Jordan, Louise. How to Write for Children - And Get Published. AS, ed. 2007. (ENG.). 192p. pap. 19.95 (978-0-7499-2772-1(0)) Piatkus Bks. GBR. Dist: Independent Pubs. Group.

Lomax, Elaine. The Writings of Hesba Stretton: Reclaiming the Outcast. 2009. (Ashgate Studies in Childhood, 1700 to the Present Ser.). (Illus.). 252p. 114.95 (978-0-7546-5576-3(8)) Ashgate Publishing Co.

Martin, Salisbury. Children's Picturebooks: The Art of Visual Storytelling. 2012. (ENG., Illus.). 192p. pap. 35.00 (978-1-85669-738-5(X)) King, Laurence Publishing GBR. Dist: Hachette Bk. Group.

McCannon, Desdemona, et al. The Encyclopedia of Writing & Illustrating Children's Books: From Creating Characters to Developing Stories, a Step-by-Step Guide to Making Magical Picture Books. 2008. (ENG.). 160p. 27.95 (978-0-7624-3148-9(2)) Perseus Bks. Group.

McElmeel, Sharron L. & McElmeel, Deborah L. Authors in the Pantry: Recipes, Stories, & More, 1 vol. 2006. (Illus.). 280p. pap. 32.00 (978-1-59158-321-9(7), LU3217) Libraries Unlimited, Inc.

Melrose, Andrew. Here Comes the Bogeyman: Exploring Contemporary Issues in Writing for Children. 2012. (ENG., Illus.). 152p. (C). 130.00 (978-0-415-61752-9(9)); pap. 31.95 (978-0-415-61753-6(7)) Routledge.

Melrose, Andrew & Knight, Karenanne. Monsters under the Bed: Critically investigating early years Writing. 2012. (ENG., Illus.). 168p. (C). 155.00 (978-0-415-61749-9(9)); pap. 31.95 (978-0-415-61750-5(2)) Routledge.

Mogilner, Alijandra & Mogilner, Tayopa. Children's Writer's Word Book. 2nd ed. 2006. (ENG., Illus.). 352p. per. 16.99 (978-1-58297-413-2(6), 11031) F&W Media, Inc.

Payment, Simone. Scott O'Dell. (Library of Author Biographies Ser.). 112p. (gr. 5-8). 2009. 63.90 (978-1-60853-554-5(1), Rosen Central) 2006. (Illus.). pap. 12.95 (978-1-4042-0651-9(5)) Rosen Publishing Group, Inc., The.

Pollinger, Lesley & Jones, Allan Frewin. Write a Children's Book - And Get It Published. 2010. (Teach Yourself Ser.). (ENG., Illus.). 346p. pap. 23.95 (978-1-4441-0320-5(2), Hodder & Stoughton) Hodder General Publishing Div. GBR. Dist: Independent Pubs. Group.

Pope, Alice. 2010 Children's Writer's & Illustrator's Market. 21st ed. 2009. (ENG.). 448p. pap. 29.99 (978-1-58297-587-0(6), Writer's Digest Bks.) F&W Media, Inc.

Pope, Alice, ed. 2011 Children's Writer's & Illustrator's Market. 23rd ed. 2010. (ENG., Illus.). 440p. pap. 29.99 (978-1-58297-952-6(9), Writer's Digest Bks.) F&W Media, Inc.

Ray, Katie Wood. Teaching the Qualities of Good Writing Through Illustration Study. 2010. 280p. pap. 31.25 (978-0-325-02855-2(9), E02855) Heinemann.

Reeser, Cynthia. How to Write & Publish a Successful Children's Book: Everything You Need to Know Explained Simply. 2010. (ENG.). 288p. pap. 24.95 (978-1-60138-407-2(6)) Atlantic Publishing Co.

Sambuchino, Chuck, ed. 2012 Children's Writer's & Illustrator's Market. 24th ed. 2011. (ENG.). 448p. pap. 29.99 (978-1-59963-231-5(4), Writer's Digest Bks.) F&W Media, Inc.

Sampson, Brent. Adventures in Publishing: How to Publish Color Children¿s Books with Original Illustrations, & Other Books in Full-Color for Self-Publishing Writers. 2008. (Illus.). 24p. pap. 9.95 (978-1-932672-33-6(8)) Outskirts Pr., Inc.

Small, David. Stitches: A Memoir. 2010. (ENG., Illus.). 329p. pap. 16.95 (978-0-393-33896-6(7), 33896) Norton, W. W. & Co., Inc.

Sturrock, Donald. Storyteller: The Authorized Biography of Roald Dahl. (ENG., Illus.). 672p. 2011. pap. 18.99 (978-1-4391-8976-4(5)) 2010. 30.00 (978-1-4165-5082-2(8)) Simon & Schuster.

Tracy, Kathleen. Judy Blume: A Biography, 1 vol. 2007. (Greenwood Biographies Ser.). (Illus.). 152p. (gr. 4-8). 35.00 (978-0-313-34272-1(5), GR4272, Greenwood Pr.) Greenwood Publishing Group, Inc.

Underdown, Harold D. Publishing Children's Books - Complete Idiot's Guide. 3rd ed. 2008. (Complete Idiot's Guide Ser.). (ENG., Illus.). 384p. (gr. 12-18). 18.95 (978-1-59257-750-7(4), Alpha Bks.) Penguin Group (USA) Inc.

Wallin, Luke & Gordon, Eva. The Everything Guide to Writing Children's Books: How to write, publish, & promote books for children of all Ages! 2nd ed. 2011. (ENG.). 304p. pap. 15.95 (978-1-4405-0549-2(7)) Adams Media Corp.

CHILDREN'S LITERATURE—BIBLIOGRAPHY

Association for Library Service to Children, compiled by. In the Words of the Winners: The Newbery & Caldecott Medals, 2001-2010. 2010. pap. (978-0-8389-3586-6(9)) American Library Assn.

Association for Library Service to Children Staff. The Newbery & Caldecott Awards: A Guide to the Medal Honor Books. 2009. 168p. pap. 25.00 (978-0-8389-3585-9(0)) American Library Assn.

Bank Street College of Education, Children's Book Committee. The Best Children's Books of the Year. 100th anniv. ed. 2009. (ENG., Illus.). 96p. pap. 8.95 (978-0-8077-5014-8(X)) Teachers College Pr., Teachers College, Columbia Univ.

Bank Street College of Education Editors, ed. Best Children's Books of the Year 2008. 2008. (ENG.). 64p. pap. 8.95 (978-0-8077-4891-6(9)) Teachers College Pr., Teachers College, Columbia Univ.

Barstow, Barbara, et al. Beyond Picture Books: Subject Access to Best Books for Beginning Readers, 1 vol. 3rd rev. ed. 2007. (Children's & Young Adult Literature Reference Ser.). 668p. 75.00 (978-1-59158-545-9(7), LU8545) Libraries Unlimited, Inc.

Baxter, Kathleen A. & Kochel, Marcia Agness. Gotcha Again for Guys! More Nonfiction Books to Get Boys Excited about Reading, 1 vol. 2010. (Illus.). 248p. pap. 35.00 (978-1-59884-376-7(1), A2702P) Libraries Unlimited, Inc.

—Gotcha Good! Nonfiction Books to Get Kids Excited about Reading, 1 vol. 2008. (Illus.). 268p. pap. 35.00 (978-1-59158-654-8(2), LU8654) Libraries Unlimited, Inc.

Bird, Elizabeth. Children's Literature Gems: Choosing & Using Them in Your Library Career. 2009. 125p. 45.00 (978-0-8389-0995-9(7)) American Library Assn.

Bomhold, Catharine R., et al. Twice upon a Time: A Guide to Fractured, Altered, & Retold Folk & Fairy Tales, 1 vol. 2008. (Children's & Young Adult Literature Reference Ser.). 224p. 45.00 (978-1-59158-390-5(X), LU390X) Libraries Unlimited, Inc.

Bowker Staff, ed. Children's Books in Print, 2 vols. 2011. 530.00 (978-1-59237-734-3(3)) 2011. 530.00 (978-1-59237-733-6(5)) 2010. 505.00 (978-1-59237-656-8(8)) 2010. 505.00 (978-1-59237-655-1(X)) Grey Hse. Publishing.

—Children's Books In Print 2010: Author, Title, & Illustrator Index to Books for Children & Young Adults, 2 vols., Set. 2009. 455.00 (978-0-8352-5025-2(3)) Bowker LLC, R. R.

—Children's Books In Print 2011: Author, Title, & Illustrator Index to Books for Children & Young Adults, 2 vols. 2010. 505.00 (978-1-59237-654-4(1)) Grey Hse. Publishing.

—Children's Books in Print 2012, 2 vols. 43rd ed. 2011. 530.00 (978-1-59237-732-9(7)) Grey Hse. Publishing.

—Subject Guide to Children's Books In Print, 2010. 2009. 345.00 (978-0-8352-5028-3(8)) Bowker LLC, R. R.

—Subject Guide to Children's Books In Print, 2011. 2010. 385.00 (978-1-59237-657-5(6)) Grey Hse. Publishing.

—Subject Guide to Children's Books in Print 2012. 2011. 405.00 (978-1-59237-735-0(1)) Grey Hse. Publishing.

Casement, Rose. Black History in the Pages of Children's Literature. 2007. (ENG.). 336p. 70.00 (978-0-8108-5843-5(6)) Scarecrow Pr., Inc.

Cerrillo, Pedro C. & Martínez Soria, Carlos Julián, eds. Lectura, Infancia y Escuela: 25 Años de Libro Escolar en España, 1931-1956. 2009. (Illus.). 124p. (978-84-8427-706-4(2)) Ediciones de la Universidad de Castilla-La Mancha.

Dunwell, Anna. Guide to the 400 Best Children's & Adult's Multicultural Books about Immigration & Moving. spiral bd. 42.95 (978-1-891657-29-0(1), S2990) Lift Every Voice.

Essential Guide to Spanish Reading for Children & Young Adults. 2009. 206p. pap. (978-0-9821418-8-5(2)) TRIALTEA USA, LLC.

Farren, Donald & Imholtz, August A., eds. The Baltimore Bibliophiles at Fifty, 1954-2004. 2009. 55.00 (978-1-58456-251-1(X)) Oak Knoll Pr.

Fearrington, Ann. Teacher & Librarian Guide to the Little Green Book. Date not set. tchr. ed. (978-0-935400-71-7(0)) News & Observer, The.

Freeman, Judy. Books Kids Will Sit Still For, 1 vol., Set. 2nd ed. 2006. (Children's & Young Adult Literature Reference Ser.). (Illus.). 126.00 (978-1-59158-477-3(9), LU4779) Libraries Unlimited, Inc.

—The WINNERS! Handbook: A Closer Look at Judy Freeman's Top-Rated Children's Books of 2006, 1 vol. 2007. 244p. per. 35.00 (978-1-59158-510-7(4), LU5104) Libraries Unlimited, Inc.

—The Winners! Handbook: A Closer Look at Judy Freeman's Top-Rated Children's Books of 2007, 1 vol. 2008. 244p. pap. 35.00 (978-1-59158-712-5(3), LU8712) Libraries Unlimited, Inc.

Freeman, Marcia S. & Koehler, Susan. Models for Teaching Writing-Craft Target Skills. 2nd ed. 2010. pap. 19.95 (978-1-934338-81-0(8)) Maupin Hse. Publishing.

Galda, Lee, et al. Literature & the Child. 7th ed. 2009. (ENG.). 528p. (C). 198.95 (978-0-495-60239-2(6)); pap. 139.95 (978-0-495-80997-5(7)) Wadsworth.

Gale Cengage Publishing, creator. Something about the Author: Facts & Pictures about Authors & Illustrators of Books for Young People. 2008. (Something about the Author Ser.: Vol. 186). (ENG., Illus.). 240p. (J). 202.00 (978-0-7876-9935-2(7)) Cengage Gale.

—Something about the Author: Facts & Pictures about Authors & Illustrators of Books of Young People. 2008. (Something about the Author Ser.). (ENG., Illus.). 384p. 202.00 (978-0-7876-9934-5(9)) Cengage Gale.

—Something about the Author Volume 184: Facts & Pictures about Authors & Illustrators of Books for Young People. 2008. (Something about the Author Ser.: Vol. 184). (ENG., Illus.). 240p. 202.00 (978-0-7876-9933-8(0)) Cengage Gale.

Gale Editors, ed. Something about the Author, Vol. 171. 2006. (Something about the Author Ser.). (ENG.). 352p. 202.00 (978-0-7876-8795-3(2)) Cengage Gale.

Gillespie, John & Barr, Catherine. Best Books for Children: Preschool Through Grade 6, 1 vol. 9th ed. 2010. (Children's & Young Adult Literature Reference Ser.). 1901p. 95.00 (978-1-59158-575-6(9), LU8575) Libraries Unlimited, Inc.

H. W. Wilson Company Staff. Children's Catalog. 19th ed. 2006. 195.00 (978-0-8242-1073-1(5)) Wilson, H.W.

Halsted, Judith Wynn. Some of My Best Friends Are Books: Guiding Gifted Readers. 3rd ed. 2009. pap. 29.95 (978-0-910707-96-1(0)) Great Potential Pr., Inc.

Hesperides. Books to Read - a Classified & Annotated Catalogue Being a Guide for Young Readers. 2007. 600p. per. (978-1-4067-5565-7(6), Hesperides Pr.) Read Bks.

Hilbun, Janet W. & Claes, Jane H. Coast to Coast: Exploring State Book Awards. 2010. E-Book (978-1-59884-656-0(6)) Libraries Unlimited, Inc.

Hindley, Charles. History of the Catnach Press: At Berwick-upon-Tweed, Alnwick & Newcastle-upon-Tyne, in Northumberland, & Seven Dials, London. 2010. (Cambridge Library Collection - Printing & Publishing History Ser.). (Illus.). 360p. pap. 29.99 (978-1-108-00909-6(3)) Cambridge Univ. Pr.

Howell, Julie Ann, compiled by. Children's Book Catalog, Peppertree Press. 2009. 20p. pap. 12.95 (978-1-936051-06-9(0)) Peppertree Pr., The.

Keane, Nancy J. 101 Great, Ready-to-Use Book Lists for Children, 1 vol. 2012. 130p. pap. 40.00 (978-1-61069-083-6(4), A3769P) Pearson Education GBR. Dist: ABC-CLIO, LLC.

Krim, Geri & Mittelman, Sandy, compiled by. Choices: A Core Collection for Young Reluctant Readers, Vol. 6. 2006. 237p. 50.00 (978-0-934272-87-2(5)) Burke, John Gordon Pub., Inc.

Kumar, Lisa. Something about the Author. 2008. (Something about the Author Ser.). (ENG.). 384p. 202.00 (978-0-7876-9938-3(1)); 368p. 202.00 (978-0-7876-9936-9(5)); 224p. 202.00 (978-0-7876-9937-6(3)) Cengage Gale.

Kumar, Lisa, ed. Something about the Author. 2008. (Something about the Author Ser.). (ENG.). 368p. 202.00 (978-0-7876-8807-3(X)) Cengage Gale.

C

Lima, Carolyn W. & Thomas, Rebecca L. A to Zoo: Subject Access to Children's Picture Books, 1 vol. 7th ed. 2008. (Children's & Young Adult Literature Reference Ser.). (Illus.). 208p. suppl. ed. 45.00 *(978-1-59158-672-2(0)*, LU8672) Libraries Unlimited, Inc.

Lusardi, Donna M. & Kent, Rosemarie. The New Book of Knowledge. 2008. 266p. *(978-0-7172-0589-9(4)*, Grolier) Scholastic Library Publishing.

Lynch-Brown, Carol & Tomlinson, Carl M. Essentials of Children's Literature. 6th ed. 2007. (ENG., Illus.). 432p. (C). per. 71.33 *(978-0-205-52032-9(4))* Allyn & Bacon, Inc.

—Essentials of Children's Literature (with MyEducationKit) 7th ed. 2010. (ENG.). (C). pap. 82.67 *(978-0-13-707402-0(6))* Allyn & Bacon, Inc.

Lynch-Brown, Carol, et al. Essentials of Children's Literature. 7th ed. 2010. (MyEducationKit Ser.). (ENG., Illus.). 432p. (C). pap. 78.67 *(978-0-13-704884-7(X))* Allyn & Bacon, Inc.

Matthew, Kathryn I. & Lowe, Joy L. Neal-Schuman Guide to Recommended Children's Books & Media for Use with Every Elementary Subject. 2nd ed. 2010. 400p. 80.00 *(978-1-55570-688-3(6))* Neal-Schuman Pubs., Inc.

McCallum, Elizabeth & Scott, Jane. The Book Tree: A Christian Reference for Children's Literature. 2nd ed. 2008. (ENG.). 19.00 *(978-1-59128-050-7(8))* Canon Pr.

Moses, Montrose J. Children's Books & Reading. 2008. 284p. 42.95 *(978-1-4369-5125-8(9))*; pap. 27.95 *(978-1-4367-9127-4(8))* Kessinger Publishing, LLC.

Price, Anne & Rowland, Marguerita. Children's Core Collection. 20th ed. 2010. 1700p. 210.00 *(978-0-8242-1106-6(5))* Wilson, H.W.

Reid, Rob. Reid's Read-Alouds: Selections for Children & Teens. 2009. 208p. 45.00 *(978-0-8389-0980-5(9))* American Library Assn.

—Reid's Read-Alouds 2: Modern-Day Classics from C. S. Lewis to Lemony Snicket. 2010. pap. *(978-0-8389-1072-6(6))* American Library Assn.

Schon, Isabel. Recommended Books in Spanish for Children & Young Adults, 2004-2008. 2008. (ENG.). 424p. 65.00 *(978-0-8108-6386-6(3))* Scarecrow Pr., Inc.

Schwedt, Rachel & DeLong, Janice. Core Collection for Children & Young Adults. 2008. (ENG.). 218p. 60.00 *(978-0-8108-6115-2(1))* Scarecrow Pr., Inc.

Shedlock, Marie L. The Art of the Story-Teller. 2010. (ENG.). 316p. pap. 30.75 *(978-1-147-83956-2(5))* 2010. (ENG.). 312p. pap. 29.75 *(978-1-177-41728-0(6))* 2010. (ENG.). 312p. pap. 29.75 *(978-1-176-44238-2(4))* 2010. 318p. pap. 30.75 *(978-1-143-98766-3(7))* 2008. 224p. 24.99 *(978-0-554-31948-3(9))* 2008. 224p. 27.99 *(978-0-554-22645-3(6))* 2006. 208p. pap. 20.99 *(978-1-4264-2779-4(4))* 2007. (ENG.). 220p. pap. 22.99 *(978-1-4264-2817-3(0))* BiblioBazaar.

—The Art of the Story-Teller. 2008. 220p. pap. *(978-1-4099-1729-8(0))* Dodo Pr.

—The Art of the Story-Teller. 2007. (ENG.). 160p. per. *(978-1-4068-1522-1(5))* Echo Library.

—The Art of the Story-Teller. 2010. (Illus.). 124p. pap. 21.33 *(978-1-153-69267-0(8))* General Bks. LLC.

Smith, Henrietta M. The Coretta Scott King Awards, 1970-2009. 4th ed. 2009. (Illus.). xiii, 131p. *(978-0-8389-3584-2(2))* American Library Assn.

Smith, Martha & Knowles, Liz, eds. Understanding Diversity Through Novels & Picture Books, 1 vol. 2007. (Illus.). 156p. per. 39.00 *(978-1-59158-440-7(X)*, LU440X) Libraries Unlimited, Inc.

Something about the Author. (ENG.). 2011. 202.00 *(978-1-4144-6127-4(5))* 2011. 202.00 *(978-1-4144-6126-7(7))* 2011. 202.00 *(978-1-4144-6125-0(9))* 2011. 202.00 *(978-1-4144-6124-3(0))* 2011. 202.00 *(978-1-4144-6123-6(2))* 2008. 240p. 202.00 *(978-1-4144-2162-9(1))* 2008. 368p. 202.00 *(978-1-4144-2163-6(X))*193. 2008. 400p. 202.00 *(978-1-4144-2165-0(6))*194. 2009. 240p. 202.00 *(978-1-4144-2166-7(4))*195. 2009. 400p. 202.00 *(978-1-4144-2167-4(2))*196. 2009. 240p. 202.00 *(978-1-4144-2168-1(0))*197. 2009. 368p. 202.00 *(978-1-4144-2169-8(9))* Vol. 205. 2010. 202.00 *(978-1-4144-4218-1(1))* Vol. 206. 2010. 202.00 *(978-1-4144-4219-8(X))* Vol. 207. 2010. 202.00 *(978-1-4144-4220-4(3))* Vol. 208. 2010. 202.00 *(978-1-4144-4221-1(1))* Vol. 210. 2010. 202.00 *(978-1-4144-4223-5(8))* Vol. 211. 2010. 202.00 *(978-1-4144-4224-2(6))* Vol. 212. 2010. 202.00 *(978-1-4144-4225-9(4))* Cengage Gale.

Thomas, Rebecca L. & Barr, Catherine. Popular Series Fiction for K-6 Readers: A Reading & Selection Guide, 1 vol. 2nd ed. 2008. (Children's & Young Adult Literature Reference Ser.). 1016p. 65.00 *(978-1-59158-659-3(3)*, LU8659) Libraries Unlimited, Inc.

Thomson Gale, creator. Something about the Author: Facts & Pictures about Authors & Illustrators of Books for Young People, Vol. 170. 2006. (Something about the Author Ser.). (ENG., Illus.). 224p. 202.00 *(978-0-7876-8794-6(4))* Cengage Gale.

—Something about the Author: Volume 169, Vol. 169. 2006. (Something about the Author Ser.). (ENG., Illus.). 336p. 202.00 *(978-0-7876-8793-9(6))* Cengage Gale.

Treviño, Rose Zertuche. Read Me a Rhyme in Spanish & English: Léame una Rima en Español e Inglés. 2009. (SPA & ENG.). 160p. 45.00 *(978-0-8389-0982-9(5))* American Library Assn.

Van Orden, Phyllis J., et al. Children's Books: A Practical Guide to Selection. 2007. (Illus.). pap. 59.95 *(978-1-55570-584-8(7))* Neal-Schuman Pubs., Inc.

Wadham, Tim. Libros Esenciales: Building, Marketing, & Programming a Core Collection of Spanish-Language Children's Materials. 2006. xiv, 322p. pap. 65.00 *(978-1-55570-575-6(8))* Neal-Schuman Pubs., Inc.

Wedwick, Linda & Wutz, Jessica Ann. Bookmatch: How to Scaffold Student Book Selection for Independent Reading. 2008. (ENG.). 144p. pap. 22.95 *(978-0-87207-619-8(9))* International Reading Assn.

Welsh, Charles. A Bookseller of the Last Century. 2010. (Cambridge Library Collection - Printing & Publishing History Ser.). (ENG., Illus.). 404p. pap. 31.99 *(978-1-108-01279-9(5))* Cambridge Univ. Pr.

Zbaracki, Matthew D. Best Books for Boys: A Resource for Educators, 1 vol. 2008. (Children's & Young Adult Literature Reference Ser.). (Illus.). 204p. 45.00 *(978-1-59158-599-2(6)*, LU8599) Libraries Unlimited, Inc.

CHILDREN'S LITERATURE—BIO-BIBLIOGRAPHY

Kumar, Lisa, ed. Something about the Author: Facts & Pictures about Authors & Illustrators of Books for Young People. 2007. (Something about the Author Ser.). (ENG., Illus.). 352p. 202.00 *(978-0-7876-8799-1(5))*; Vol. 173. 336p. 202.00 *(978-0-7876-8797-7(9))* Cengage Gale.

McDaniel, Deanna J. Gentle Reads: Great Books to Warm Hearts & Lift Spirits, Grades 5-9, 1 vol. 2007. (Children's & Young Adult Literature Reference Ser.). 328p. 45.00 *(978-1-59158-491-9(4)*, LU4914) Libraries Unlimited, Inc.

Murphy, Barbara Thrash & Murphy, Deborah. Black Authors & Illustrators of Books for Children & Young Adults: A Biographical Dictionary. Murphy, Barbara T. & Murphy, Deborah L., eds. 4th rev. ed. 2006. (Illus.). 568p. 110.00 *(978-0-415-97219-2(1))* Routledge.

O'Sullivan, Emer. Historical Dictionary of Children's Literature. 2010. (Historical Dictionaries of Literature & the Arts Ser.). (ENG.). 372p. 80.00 *(978-0-8108-6080-3(5))*; E-Book *(978-0-8108-7496-1(2))* Scarecrow Pr., Inc.

Rockman, Connie C. Tenth Book of Junior Authors & Illustrators. 2008. 803p. 120.00 *(978-0-8242-1066-3(2))* Wilson, H.W.

Smthng about Auth. 2008. (Something about the Author Ser.). (ENG.). 272p. 202.00 *(978-1-4144-2164-3(8))* Cengage Gale.

Something about the Author Something about the Author, Vol. 209. 2010. (Something about the Author Ser.). (ENG.). 202.00 *(978-1-4144-4222-8(X))* Cengage Gale.

Thomson Gale, creator. Something about the Author. (Something about the Author Ser.). (ENG., Illus.). 2007. 256p. 202.00 *(978-0-7876-8802-8(9))* Vol. 172. 2006. 224p. 202.00 *(978-0-7876-8796-0(0))* Cengage Gale.

—Something about the Author: Facts & Pictures about Authors & Illustrators of Books for Young People. 2007. (Something about the Author Ser.: Vol. 182). (ENG., Illus.). 224p. 202.00 *(978-0-7876-8806-6(1))* Cengage Gale.

—Something about the Author: Volume 176. 2007. (Something about the Author Ser.). (ENG., Illus.). 240p. 202.00 *(978-0-7876-8800-4(2))* Cengage Gale.

—Something about the Author: Volume 177. 2007. (Something about the Author Ser.). (ENG., Illus.). 368p. 202.00 *(978-0-7876-8801-1(0))* Cengage Gale.

—Something about the Author: Volume 179. 2007. (Something about the Author Ser.: Vol. 179). (ENG., Illus.). 368p. 202.00 *(978-0-7876-8803-5(7))* Cengage Gale.

—Something about the Author: Volume 180. 2007. (Something about the Author Ser.: Vol. 180). (ENG., Illus.). 272p. 202.00 *(978-0-7876-8804-2(5))* Cengage Gale.

Thomson Gale Staff. Something about the Author Vol 174. 2007. (Something about the Author Ser.). (ENG.). 224p. 202.00 *(978-0-7876-8798-4(7))* Cengage Gale.

CHILDREN'S LITERATURE—HISTORY AND CRITICISM

Abate, Michelle Ann. Raising Your Kids Right: Children's Literature & American Political Conservatism. (Rutgers Series in Childhood Studies). (ENG., Illus.). 260p. 2011. pap. 24.95 ***(978-0-8135-5173-9(0))*** 2010. 42.95 *(978-0-8135-4798-5(9))* Rutgers Univ. Pr.

Alcubierre Moya, Beatriz. Ciudadanos del Futuro: Una Historia de las Publicaciones para niños en el Siglo Xix Mexicano. 2010. (Estudios Históricos Ser.). 224p. pap. 26.00 *(978-607-462-114-3(4))* El Colegio de México, A.C., Biblioteca Miguel Cosío Villegas MEX. Dist: Fondo de Cultura Economica USA.

Alston, Ann. The Family in English Children's Literature. 2008. (Children's Literature & Culture Ser.). (ENG.). 176p. 125.00 *(978-0-415-98885-8(3))* Routledge.

Alston, Ann. The Family in English Childrens Literature. 2011. (ENG.). 162p. pap. 37.95 ***(978-0-415-69961-7(4))*** Routledge.

Ambrosek, Renee. E. L. Konigsburg. 2009. (Library of Author Biographies Ser.). 112p. (gr. 5-8). 63.90 *(978-1-60853-532-3(0)*, Rosen Central) Rosen Publishing Group, Inc., The.

—E.L. Konigsburg. 2006. (Library of Author Biographies). (ENG., Illus.). 112p. (gr. 5-8). pap. 12.95 *(978-1-4042-0648-9(5))* Rosen Publishing Group, Inc., The.

Anderson, Nancy A. Elementary Children's Literature: Infancy through Age 13. 3rd ed. 2009. (ENG.). 408p. (C). pap. 78.67 *(978-0-13-715143-1(8))* Allyn & Bacon, Inc.

Ark, Steve Vander. The Lexicon: An Unauthorized Guide to Harry Potter Fiction & Related Materials. 2009. (Illus.). 364p. pap. 24.95 *(978-1-57143-174-5(8))* RDR Bks.

Balina, Marina & Rudova, Larissa, eds. Russian Children's Literature & Culture. 2007. (Children's Literature & Culture Ser.). (ENG., Illus.). 352p. 125.00 *(978-0-415-97864-4(5))* Routledge.

Barnes, Walter. Types of Children's Literature. 2009. 366p. pap. *(978-1-150-41433-6(2))* Books LLC.

—Types of Children's Literature. 2010. (Illus.). 340p. pap. 41.39 *(978-1-153-72979-6(2))* General Bks. LLC.

—Types of Children's Literature. 2010. 510p. 44.76 *(978-1-169-35323-7(1))*; pap. 32.76 *(978-1-162-71511-7(1))*; 55.95 *(978-1-161-48375-8(6))* Kessinger Publishing, LLC.

Barry, Florence V. A Century of Children's Books. 2010. 156p. pap. 24.39 *(978-1-152-63194-6(2))* General Bks. LLC.

Beahm, George. Muggles & Magic: An Unofficial Guide to J. K. Rowling & the Harry Potter Phenomenon. 3rd rev. ed. 2007. (ENG., Illus.). 400p. (YA). (gr. 4-7). per. 17.95 *(978-1-57174-542-2(4))* Hampton Roads Publishing Co., Inc.

Beckett, Sandra L. & Nikolajeva, Maria. Beyond Babar: The European Tradition in Children's Literature. 2006. (ENG.). 336p. per. 60.00 *(978-0-8108-5415-4(5))* Scarecrow Pr., Inc.

Bishop, Rudine Sims. Free Within Ourselves: The Development of African American Children's Literature. 2007. (Illus.). 320p. 65.00 *(978-0-313-34093-2(5)*, GR4093, Greenwood Pr.) Greenwood Publishing Group, Inc.

—Free Within Ourselves: The Development of African American Children's Literature. 2007. 352p. pap. 31.25 *(978-0-325-07135-0(7)*, E07135) Heinemann.

Black Dog Publishing Staff, ed. Illustrated Children's Books. 2009. (ENG., Illus.). 240p. 39.95 *(978-1-906155-81-0(X))* Black Dog Publishing Ltd. GBR. Dist: Perseus Distribution.

Blake, Andrew. The Irresistible Rise of Harry Potter: Kid-Lit in a Globalised World. 2006. 118p. reprint ed. 20.00 *(978-1-4223-5877-1(1))* DIANE Publishing Co.

Bodger, Joan. How the Heather Looks: A Joyous Journey to the British Sources of Children's Books. 2010. (ENG., Illus.). 264p. pap. 16.50 *(978-0-7710-1129-0(6)*, Emblem Edns) McClelland & Stewart CAN. Dist: Random Hse., Inc.

Bosmajian. Sparing the Child. 2010. (Children's Literature & Culture Ser.). (ENG.). 304p. pap. 29.95 *(978-0-8153-3857-4(0))* Routledge.

Botelho, Maria J., et al. Critical Multicultural Analysis of Children's Literature: Mirrors, Windows, & Doors. 2009. (Language, Culture, & Teaching Ser.). (ENG., Illus.). 376p. 145.00 *(978-0-415-99666-2(X))* Routledge.

Bowen, John P. The Spirituality of Narnia: The Deeper Magic of C.S. Lewis. 2007. (ENG.). 148p. per. *(978-1-57383-402-5(5)*, Regent College Publishing) Regent College Publishing.

Bradford, Clare, et al. New World Orders in Contemporary Children's Literature: Utopian Transformations. (ENG.). 2011. 216p. pap. 28.95 *(978-0-230-30856-5(2))* 2008. 256p. 84.00 *(978-0-230-02005-4(4))* Palgrave Macmillan.

Brennan, Herbie. Through the Wardrobe: Your Favorite Authors on C. S. Lewis' Chronicles of Narnia. 2010. (ENG.). 200p. (J). (gr. 6-11). pap. 12.95 *(978-1-935251-68-2(6))* BenBella Bks.

Brennan, Herbie & Wilson, Leah. Through the Wardrobe: Your Favorite Authors on C. S. Lewis's Chronicles of Narnia. 2008. x, 187p. pap. *(978-0-9792331-3-5(5))* BenBella Bks.

Brooks, Wanda M. Embracing, Evaluating, & Examining African American Children's & Young Adult Literature. McNair, Jonda C., ed. 2007. (ENG., Illus.). 262p. per. 55.00 *(978-0-8108-6027-8(9))* Scarecrow Pr., Inc.

Brown, Kate. Critical Hist of French Chl, 1600-1830, 2 vols., Vol. 1. 2007. (Children's Literature & Culture Ser.). 304p. 131.00 *(978-0-415-97326-7(0))* Routledge.

Brown, Penelope E. A Critical History of French Children's Literature. 2009. 368p. pap. 39.95 *(978-0-415-87671-1(0))*; 312p. pap. 39.95 *(978-0-415-87670-4(2))* Routledge.

Brown, Penny. A Critical History of French Children's Literature: Volume Two: 1830-Present, 2 vols., Vol. 2. 2007. (Children's Literature & Culture Ser.). 368p. 131.00 *(978-0-415-97327-4(9))* Routledge.

Bryfonski, Dedria. Peer Pressure in Robert Cormier's the Chocolate War. 2009. (Social Issues in Literature Ser.). (ENG.). 224p. (gr. 10-12). 26.50 *(978-0-7377-4621-1(1))*; (Illus.). pap. 38.45 *(978-0-7377-4620-4(3))* Cengage Gale. (Greenhaven Pr., Inc.).

Burns, Tom. Children's Literature Review. (Children's Literature Review Ser.: Vol. 137). (ENG.). 2008. 256p. 313.00 *(978-0-7876-9612-2(9))* 2008. 256p. 313.00 *(978-0-7876-9611-5(0))* 2008. 256p. 313.00 *(978-0-7876-9609-2(9))* 2008. 256p. 313.00 *(978-0-7876-9610-8(2))* 2008. 272p. 313.00 *(978-0-7876-9607-8(2))* 2008. 272p. 313.00 *(978-0-7876-9608-5(0))* 2008. 256p. 313.00 *(978-0-7876-9606-1(4))* Vol. 124. 2007. 288p. 313.00 *(978-0-7876-8055-8(9))* Cengage Gale.

—Chld Lit Rvw. (Children's Literature Review Ser.). (ENG.). 2009. 256p. 313.00 *(978-1-4144-1970-1(8))* 2008. 272p. 313.00 *(978-1-4144-1969-5(4))* 2008. 256p. 313.00 *(978-1-4144-1968-8(6))* Cengage Gale.

Burns, Tom, ed. Children's Literature Review: Excerpts from Reviews, Criticism, & Commentary on Books for Children & Young People. (Children's Literature Review Ser.: Vol. 127). (ENG.). 2007. 272p. 313.00 *(978-0-7876-8058-9(3))* 2007. 256p. 313.00 *(978-0-7876-8057-2(5))* Vol. 117. 2006. (Illus.). 256p. 313.00 *(978-0-7876-8048-0(6))* Vol. 118. 2006. (Illus.). 272p. 313.00 *(978-0-7876-8049-7(4))* Vol. 119. 2006. 256p. 313.00 *(978-0-7876-8050-3(8))* Vol. 120. 2007. (Illus.). 272p. 313.00 *(978-0-7876-8051-0(6))* Vol. 122. 2007. (Illus.). 256p. 313.00 *(978-0-7876-8053-4(2))* Vol. 123. 2007. 256p. 313.00 *(978-0-7876-8054-1(0))* Cengage Gale.

—Children's Literature Review: Volume 129. 2007. (Children's Literature Review Ser.: Vol. 129). (ENG.). 256p. 313.00 *(978-0-7876-9604-7(8))* Cengage Gale.

—Children's Literature Review: Volume 130. 2008. (Children's Literature Review Ser.). (ENG.). 256p. 313.00 *(978-0-7876-9605-4(6))* Cengage Gale.

—Children's Literature Review, Volume 115: Excerpts from Reviews, Criticism, & Commentary on Books for Children & Young People, Vol. 115. 2006. (Children's Literature Review Ser.). (ENG., Illus.). 232p. 313.00 *(978-0-7876-8046-6(X))* Cengage Gale.

—Children's Literature Review, Volume 121: Excerpts from Reviews, Criticism, & Commentary on Books for Children & Young People, Vol. 121. 2007. (Children's Literature Review Ser.). (ENG., Illus.). 256p. 313.00 *(978-0-7876-8052-7(4))* Cengage Gale.

—Children's Literature Review, Volume 125: Excerpts from Reviews, Criticism, & Commentary on Books for Children & Young People, Vol. 125. 2007. (Children's Literature Review Ser.). (ENG.). 256p. 313.00 *(978-0-7876-8056-5(7))* Cengage Gale.

—Children's Literature Review, Volume 128: Excerpts from Reviews, Criticism, & Commentary on Books for Children & Young People. 2007. (Children's Literature Review Ser.: Vol. 128). (ENG.). 272p. 313.00 *(978-0-7876-9603-0(X))* Cengage Gale.

Butts, Dennis. Children's Literature & Social Change: Some Case Studies from Barbara Hofland to Philip Pullman. 2010. 207p. (C). pap. 53.00 *(978-0-7188-9208-1(9))* Lutherworth Pr., The GBR. Dist: Brown, David Bk. Co., The.

Butts, Dennis, et al. Popular Children's Literature in Britain. 2008. (Illus.). 356p. 124.95 *(978-1-84014-242-6(1))* Ashgate Publishing Co.

Cadden, Michael, ed. Telling Children's Stories: Narrative Theory & Children's Literature. 2011. (Frontiers of Narrative Ser.). (ENG., Illus.). 344p. pap. 35.00 *(978-0-8032-1568-9(1))* Univ. of Nebraska Pr.

Carpan, Carolyn. Sisters, Schoolgirls, & Sleuths: Girls' Series Books in America. 2008. (Scarecrow Studies in Young Adult Literature Ser.). (ENG.). 184p. 45.00 *(978-0-8108-5756-8(1))* Scarecrow Pr., Inc.

Casement, Rose. Black History in the Pages of Children's Literature. 2007. (ENG.). 336p. 70.00 *(978-0-8108-5843-5(6))* Scarecrow Pr., Inc.

Cazanave, Caroline & Houssais, Yvon. Grands Textes du Moyen Age à L'usage des Petits. 2010. (FRE., Illus.). 332p. pap. *(978-2-84867-294-6(3))* Presses Universitaires Franc-Comtoises.

Children's Literature. 2008. 96p. pap. *(978-1-4097-9833-0(X))* Read Bks.

Children's Literature Review. 2010. (Children's Literature Review Ser.). (ENG.). Vol. 148. 313.00 *(978-1-4144-3915-0(6))* Vol. 149. 313.00 *(978-1-4144-3916-7(4))* Vol. 150. 313.00 *(978-1-4144-3917-4(2))* Vol. 151. 313.00 *(978-1-4144-3918-1(0))* Vol. 152. 313.00 *(978-1-4144-3919-8(9))* Vol. 153. 313.00 *(978-1-4144-3920-4(2))* Cengage Gale.

Children's Literature Review: Excerpts from Reviews, Criticism, & Commentary on Books for Children & Young People. 2011. (ENG.). 313.00 *(978-1-4144-7052-8(5))*; (ENG.). 313.00 *(978-1-4144-7051-1(7))*; (ENG.). 313.00 *(978-1-4144-7050-4(9))*; 313.00 *(978-1-4144-7049-8(5))*; 313.00 *(978-1-4144-4924-1(0))* Cengage Gale.

Chld Lit Rvw. 2009. (Children's Literature Review Ser.). (ENG.). 272p. 313.00 *(978-1-4144-3914-3(8))*; 272p. 313.00 *(978-1-4144-1976-3(7))*; 256p. 313.00 *(978-1-4144-1975-6(9))*; 256p. 313.00 *(978-1-4144-1974-9(0))*; 256p. 313.00 *(978-1-4144-1972-5(4))*; 256p. 313.00 *(978-1-4144-1973-2(2))*; 256p. 313.00 *(978-1-4144-1971-8(6))* Cengage Gale.

Colomer, Teresa, et al, eds. New Directions in Picturebook Research. 2012. (ENG., Illus.). 262p. (C). pap. 39.95 ***(978-0-415-63416-8(4))*** Routledge.

Cornelius, Michael G., ed. The Boy Detectives: Essays on the Hardy Boys & Others. 2010. (ENG., Illus.). 220p. pap. 35.00 *(978-0-7864-6033-5(4))* McFarland & Co., Inc. Pubs.

Costello, Peter R. Philosophy in Children's Literature. 2012. ***(978-0-7391-6824-0(X))*** 2011. (ENG.). 354p. (gr. 17). 80.00 ***(978-0-7391-6823-3(1))*** Lexington Bks.

Cram101 Textbook Reviews & Cram101 Textbook Reviews. Outlines & Highlights for Through the Eyes of a Child by Donna E Norton. 2011. 250p. pap. 31.95 ***(978-1-61830-898-6(X))*** Cram101 Inc.

Cross, Julie. Humor in Contemporary Junior Literature. 2010. (Children's Literature & Culture Ser.). (ENG., Illus.). 264p. (C). 125.00 *(978-0-415-88267-5(2))* Routledge.

Cutter-Mackenzie, Amy, et al, eds. Experiencing Environment & Place Through Children's Literature. 2011. (Illus.). 232p. (C). 125.00 *(978-0-415-67286-3(4))* Routledge.

Daniel, Carolyn. Voracious Children: Who Eats Whom in Children's Literature. 2009. 266p. 39.95 *(978-0-415-80366-3(7))* Routledge.

Darton, Frederick Joseph Harvey. Children's Books in England: Five Centuries of Social Life. 2011. (Cambridge Library Collection - Literary Studies). (ENG., Illus.). 394p. pap. 29.99 ***(978-1-108-03381-7(4))*** Cambridge Univ. Pr.

de Mylius, Johan, et al, eds. Hans Christian Andersen: Between Children's Literature & Adult Literature. 2008. (Illus.). 639p. (C). 62.00 *(978-87-7674-256-0(3))* Univ. Pr. of Southern Denmark DNK. Dist: International Specialized Bk. Services.

Desmet, Mieke K. T. Babysitting the Reader: Translating English Narrative Fiction for Girls into Dutch (1946-1995) (European Literature for Children & Young Adults in an Ser.: Vol. 1). 352p. pap. 74.95 *(978-3-03911-147-3(7))* Lang, Peter CHE. Dist: Lang, Peter Publishing, Inc.

Dewan, Pauline. The Art of Place in Literature for Children & Young Adults: How Locale Shapes a Story. 2010. 412p. 129.95 *(978-0-7734-3762-3(2))* Mellen, Edwin Pr., The.

Díaz, Lidia. Introducción a la Literatura Infantil en Español. 2008. 188p. pap. 35.00 *(978-1-930879-54-6(7)*, Academic Press ENE) Ediciones Nuevo Espacio-AcademicPressENE.

Downing, David C. Into the Wardrobe: C. S. Lewis & the Narnia Chronicles. 2008. (ENG., Illus.). 256p. pap. 14.95 *(978-0-470-24839-3(4)*, Jossey-Bass) Wiley, John & Sons, Inc.

Durand, Kevin K. J. & Leigh, Mary K., eds. The Universe of Oz: Essays on Baum's Series & Its Progeny. 2010. (ENG., Illus.). 258p. pap. 35.00 *(978-0-7864-4628-5(5))* McFarland & Co., Inc. Pubs.

Dusinberre, Juliet, contrib. by. Alice to the Lighthouse: Children's Books & Radical Experiments in Art. 2nd ed. (Illus.). xxi, 352p. 24.95 *(978-0-333-75984-4(2))* Macmillan Pubs., Ltd. GBR. Dist: Trans-Atlantic Pubns., Inc.

Eddy, Jacalyn. Bookwomen: Creating an Empire in Children's Book Publishing, 1919-1939. 2006. (Print Culture History in Modern America Ser.). (Illus.). 224p. per. 29.95 *(978-0-299-21794-5(9))* Univ. of Wisconsin Pr.

Engelen, Bernhard. Aufsatze Zur Kinderliteratur: Geschichte - Rezeption - Sprache. (GER.). 197p. pap. 37.95 *(978-3-631-51702-4(5))* Lang, Peter GmbH, Europaischer Verlag der Wissenschaften DEU. Dist: Lang, Peter Publishing, Inc.

Erisman, Fred. Boys' Books, Boys' Dreams, & the Mystique of Flight. 2006. (ENG., Illus.). 300p. 29.95 *(978-0-87565-330-3(8))* Texas Christian Univ. Pr.

Erzse-Boitor, Kinga. Das Bild des Anderen in der rumäniendeutschen Kinder- und Jugendliteratur. 2008. (Kinder- und Jugendkultur, -literatur und -medien. Theorie - Geschichte - Didaktik Ser.). (GER.). 188p. pap. 56.95 *(978-3-631-58437-8(7))* Lang, Peter GmbH, Europaischer Verlag der Wissenschaften DEU. Dist: Lang, Peter.

Ferrall, Charles & Jackson, Anna. Juvenile Literature & British Society, 1850-1950: The Age of Adolescence. (ENG., Illus.). 2012. 194p. pap. 39.95 ***(978-0-415-63422-9(9))*** 2009. 210p. 125.00 *(978-0-415-96476-0(8))* Routledge.

Flanagan, Victoria. Into the Closet: Cross-Dressing & the Gendered Body in Children's Literature & Film. 2007. (Children's Literature & Culture Ser.). (ENG., Illus.). 296p. 125.00 *(978-0-415-98008-1(9))* Routledge.

Frank, Helen T. Cultural Encounters in Translated Children's Literature: Images of Australia in French Translation. 2007. (Illus.). 262p. pap. *(978-1-905763-03-0(4))* St. Jerome Publishing.

Frith, Margaret & Rock, Victoria, eds. Once upon a Time: Celebrating the Magic of Children's Books in Honor of the Twentieth Anniversary of Reading Is Fundamental. 2006. (Illus.). 64p. (J). (gr. 4-8). reprint ed. pap. 7.00 *(978-1-4223-5726-2(0))* DIANE Publishing Co.

Galda, Lee, et al. Literature & the Child. 7th ed. 2009. (ENG.). 528p. (C). 198.95 *(978-0-495-60239-2(6))* pap. 139.95 *(978-0-495-80997-5(7))* Wadsworth.

Gale Editor, ed. Children's Literature Review: Excerpts from Reviews, Criticism, & Commentary on Books for Children & Young People. 2011. (ENG.). lib. bdg. 313.00 *(978-1-4144-7058-0(4))*; (ENG.). lib. bdg. 313.00 *(978-1-4144-7057-3(6))*; (ENG.). lib. bdg. 313.00 *(978-1-4144-7056-6(8))*; lib. bdg. 313.00 *(978-1-4144-7055-9(X))*; (ENG.). lib. bdg. 313.00 *(978-1-4144-7054-2(1))*; (ENG.). 485p. 313.00 *(978-1-4144-7053-5(3))* Cengage Gale.

Gale Editors, ed. Children's Literature Review, Vol. 116. 2006. (Children's Literature Review Ser.). (ENG.). 256p. 313.00 *(978-0-7876-8047-3(8))* Cengage Gale.

Galway, Elizabeth. From Nursery Rhymes to Nationhood: Children's Literature & the Construction of Canadian Identity. 2008. (Children's Literature & Culture Ser.). (ENG., Illus.). 216p. 131.00 *(978-0-415-95848-6(2))* Routledge.

Gansel, Carsten & Korte, Hermann, eds. Kinder- und Jugendliteratur und Narratologie. 2009. (Deutschsprachige Gegenwartsliteratur und Medien Ser.). (GER.). 241p. (C). 54.00 *(978-3-89971-726-6(0))* Vandenhoeck & Ruprecht GmbH & Co. KG DEU. Dist: ISD.

Gargano, Elizabeth. Reading Victorian Schoolrooms. 2012. (ENG.). 216p. pap. 39.95 ***(978-0-415-69946-4(0))*** Routledge.

Garrett, Greg. One Fine Potion: The Literary Magic of Harry Potter. 2010. (ENG.). 160p. pap. 19.95 *(978-1-60258-198-2(3))* Baylor Univ. Pr.

Gates, Pamela S. & Mark, Dianne L. Hall. Cultural Journeys: Multicultural Literature for Children & Young Adults. annot. ed. 2006. (ENG.). 272p. 60.00 *(978-0-8108-5079-8(6))* Scarecrow Pr., Inc.

Gates/Hall Mark. Cultural Journeys: Multicultural Literature for Elementary & Middle School Students. 2010. (ENG.). 258p. pap. 27.50 *(978-1-4422-0687-8(X))* Rowman & Littlefield Publishers, Inc.

Gavin, Adrienne E. & Humphries, Andrew F., eds. Childhood in Edwardian Fiction: Worlds Enough & Time. 2009. (ENG., Illus.). 248p. 89.00 *(978-0-230-22161-1(0))* Palgrave Macmillan.

Gillespie, John T. The Family in Literature for Young Readers: A Resource Guide for Use with Grades 4 To 9, 1 vol. (Children's & Young Adult Literature Reference Ser.). 470p. 60.00 *(978-1-59158-915-0(0),* A2251C) Libraries Unlimited, Inc.

Gillespie, John Thomas. The Family in Literature for Young Readers: A Resource Guide for Use with Grades 4 to 9. 2011. E-Book *(978-1-59158-916-7(9))* Libraries Unlimited, Inc.

Gilton, Donna L. Multicultural & Ethnic Children's Literature in the United States. 2007. (ENG.). 244p. per. 55.00 *(978-0-8108-5672-1(7))* Scarecrow Pr., Inc.

Glasenapp, Gabriele von & Ewers, Hans-Heino, eds. Kriegs- und Nachkriegskindheiten: Studien zur literarischen Erinnerungskultur für junge Leser. 2008. (Kinder- und Jugendkultur, -literatur und -medien. Theorie - Geschichte - Didaktik Ser.). 520p. pap. 99.95 *(978-3-631-57456-0(8))* Lang, Peter GmbH, Europaischer Verlag der Wissenschaften DEU. Dist: Lang, Peter.

Golden, Joanne M. The Narrative Symbol in Childhood Literature: Explorations in the Construction of Text. (Approaches to Semiotics [AS] Ser.). (ENG.). XVI, 270p. 196.00 ***(978-3-11-180383-8(X))*** De Gruyter, Mouton DEU. Dist: de Gruyter, Walter GmbH & Co. KG.

González, Ann. Resistance & Survival: Children's Narrative from Central America & the Caribbean. 2009. (ENG., Illus.). 196p. 45.00 *(978-0-8165-2824-0(1))* Univ. of Arizona Pr.

Goodenough, Elizabeth & Immel, Andrea. Under Fire: Childhood in the Shadow of War. 2008. (Landscapes of Childhood Ser.). (Illus.). x, 289p. pap. *(978-0-8143-3361-7(3))*; pap. *(978-81-433-4040-5(6))* Wayne State Univ. Pr.

Goodenough, Elizabeth & Immel, Andrea, eds. Under Fire: Childhood in the Shadow of War. 2008. (Landscapes of Childhood Ser.). 289p. pap. 27.95 *(978-0-8143-3404-1(0))* Wayne State Univ. Pr.

Gopalakrishnan, Ambika. Multicultural Children's Literature: A Critical Issues Approach. 2010. 238p. (C). pap. 51.00 *(978-1-4129-5522-5(X),* B55211P) SAGE Pubns., Inc.

Goswami, Supriya. Colonial India in Children's Literature. 2012. (Children's Literature & Culture Ser.). (ENG., Illus.). 224p. (C). 125.00 *(978-0-415-88636-9(8))* Routledge.

Granger, John. How Harry Cast His Spell: The Meaning Behind the Mania for J. K. Rowling's Bestselling Books. 3rd ed. 2008. (ENG.). 304p. pap. 14.99 *(978-1-4143-2188-2(0),* SaltRiver) Tyndale Hse. Pubs.

—Unlocking Harry Potter: Five Keys for the Serious Reader. 2007. 312p. per. 18.99 *(978-0-9723221-2-6(4))* Zossima Pr.

Grenby, M. O. The Child Reader, 1700-1840. 2011. (ENG., Illus.). 336p. 90.00 *(978-0-521-19644-4(2))* Cambridge Univ. Pr.

Grenby, M. O. & Immel, Andrea, eds. The Cambridge Companion to Children's Literature. 2009. (Cambridge Companions to Literature Ser.). (ENG., Illus.). 324p. (C). pap. 29.99 *(978-0-521-68782-9(9))* Cambridge Univ. Pr.

Grenby, Matthew. Children's Literature. 2008. (Edinburgh Critical Guides to Literature Ser.). (ENG., Illus.). 224p. (gr. 17). 90.00 *(978-0-7486-2273-3(X))*; pap. 29.50 *(978-0-7486-2274-0(8))* Edinburgh Univ. Pr. GBR. Dist: Columbia Univ. Pr.

Grilli, Giorgia. Myth, Symbol & Meaning in Mary Poppins: The Governess as Provocateur. Varney, Jennifer, tr. from ITA. 2006. (Children's Literature & Culture Ser.). (ENG.). 224p. 125.00 *(978-0-415-97767-8(3))* Routledge.

Griswold, Jerry. Feeling Like a Kid: Childhood & Children's Literature. 2006. (ENG., Illus.). 160p. 23.00 *(978-0-8018-8517-4(5))* Johns Hopkins Univ. Pr.

Gubar, Marah. Artful Dodgers: Reconceiving the Golden Age of Children's Literature, 1 vol. 2010. (ENG., Illus.). 272p. pap. 24.95 *(978-0-19-975674-2(0))* Oxford Univ. Pr., Inc.

Gupta, Suman. Re-Reading Harry Potter. 2nd rev. ed. 2009. (ENG.). 240p. 95.00 *(978-0-230-21957-1(8))*; pap. 28.00 *(978-0-230-21958-8(6))* Palgrave Macmillan.

Hadaway, Nancy L. Breaking Boundaries with Global Literature: Celebrating Diversity in K-12 Classrooms (Explorations of the Notable Books for a Global Society Booklists) 2007. 232p. pap. 29.95 *(978-0-87207-616-7(4))* International Reading Assn.

Halsey, Rosalie V. Forgotten Books of the American Nursery. 2007. (ENG.). 204p. per. *(978-1-4065-1953-2(7))* Dodo Pr.

—Forgotten Books of the American Nursery. 2006. (ENG.). pap. *(978-1-84702-538-8(2))* Echo Library.

Halsey, Rosalie Vrylina. Forgotten Books of the American Nursery: A History of the Development of the American Story. 2007. (ENG.). 202p. per. 20.99 *(978-1-4346-2875-6(2))*; 224p. per. 22.99 *(978-1-4346-2910-4(4))* BiblioBazaar.

Hateley, Erica. Shakespeare in Children's Literature. 2011. 218p. pap. 39.95 ***(978-0-415-88888-2(3))*** Routledge.

Hateley, Erica. Shakespeare in Children's Literature: Gender & Cultural Capital. 2008. (Illus.). 192p. 118.00 *(978-0-415-96492-0(X))* Routledge.

Heath, P. M. The Works of Mrs Trimmer. 2010. 344p. pap. *(978-3-8383-2458-6(7))* Lambert Academic Publishing.

Heilman, Elizabeth. Critical Perspectives on Harry Potter. 2nd rev. ed. 2008. (ENG.). 368p. 39.95 *(978-0-415-96484-5(9))* Routledge.

Henky, Daniele & Hurley, Robert, eds. Traces de spiritualité en littérature de Jeunesse. 2009. (Recherches en littérature et spiritualité Ser.: Vol. 16). (FRE, GER & ENG., Illus.). 213p. pap. *(978-3-0343-0018-6(2))* Lang, Peter.

Heywood. Catholicism & Children's Lit: Catholicism & Children's Literature in France. 2012. (Studies in Modern French History Ser.). (ENG., Illus.). 240p. 95.00 ***(978-0-7190-8466-9(0))*** Manchester Univ. Pr. GBR. Dist: Macmillan.

Higgins, James E. Little Prince. Date not set. 136p. 17.95 *(978-0-8488-2801-1(1))* Amereon LTD.

Hilton, Mary & Nikolajeva, Maria. Contemporary Adolescent Literature & Culture: The Emergent Adult. 2012. ***(978-1-4094-3989-9(5))*** Ashgate Publishing, Ltd.

Hintz, Carrie. Utopian & Dystopian Writing for Children & Young Adults. 2009. 252p. 39.95 *(978-0-415-80364-9(0))* Routledge.

Hodaie, Nazli. Der Orient in der deutschen Kinder- und Jugendliteratur: Fallstudien aus drei Jahrhunderten. 2008. (Kinder- und Jugendkultur, -literatur und -medien. Theorie - Geschichte - Didaktik Ser.). 344p. pap. 81.95 *(978-3-631-56144-7(X))* Lang, Peter GmbH, Europaischer Verlag der Wissenschaften DEU. Dist: Lang, Peter.

Honeyman. Consumption & Agency in Fairy Tales & Folkliterature. 2009. (Routledge Studies in Folklore & Fairy Tales Ser.). (ENG., Illus.). 246p. (C). 125.00 *(978-0-415-80614-5(3))* Routledge.

Horne, Jackie C. History & the Construction of the Child in Early British Children's Literature. 2011. (Ashgate Studies in Childhood, 1700 to the Present Ser.). (Illus.). 298p. 99.95 *(978-1-4094-0738-1(8))* Ashgate Publishing Co.

Horne, Jackie C. & White, Donna R. The Wind in the Willows: A Children's Classic at 100. 2009. (Children's Literature Association Centennial Studies). (ENG.). 302p. 60.00 *(978-0-8108-7258-5(7),* Scarecrow Pr., Inc.

Horning, Kathleen T. From Cover to Cover: Evaluating & Reviewing Children's Books. rev. ed. 2010. (ENG.). 240p. pap. 14.99 *(978-0-06-077757-9(5),* Collins) HarperCollins Pubs.

Humphrey, Judith. The English Girls' School Story: Subversion & Challenge in a Traditional Conservative Literary Genre. 2009. (Illus.). xviii, 273p. lib. bdg. *(978-1-933146-50-8(6))* Academica Pr., LLC.

Humphrey, Judith. The English Girls' School Story: Subversion & Challenge in a Traditional Conservative Literary Genre. 2010. (Illus.). 292p. pap. *(978-1-933146-98-0(2))* Academica Pr., LLC.

Hunt, Peter. Children's Literature, 4 vols., Set. 2006. (Critical Concepts in Literary & Cultural Studies). (ENG.). 1712p. (C). 1350.00 *(978-0-415-37228-2(3))* Routledge.

Hunt, Peter & Ray, Sheila G., eds. International Companion Encyclopedia of Children's Literature. 2011. 944p. pap. 34.95 *(978-0-415-28559-9(3))* Routledge.

Immel, Andrea. Childhood & Children's Books in Early Modern Europe, 1550-1800. 2009. 346p. 39.95 *(978-0-415-80363-2(2))* Routledge.

Irwin, William & Bassham, Gregory, eds. The Ultimate Harry Potter & Philosophy: Hogwarts for Muggles. 2010. (Blackwell Philosophy & Pop Culture Ser.: 7). (ENG., Illus.). 304p. pap. 17.95 *(978-0-470-39825-8(6),* Wiley) Wiley, John & Sons, Inc.

Jaffe, Charlotte & Roberts, Barbara. Call It Courage: L-I-T Guide. (L-I-T Guides: Literature in Teaching Ser.). tchr. ed. 3.95 *(978-0-910857-82-6(2))* Educational Impressions.

Jenkins, Elwyn. National Character in South African English Children's Literature. 2006. (Children's Literature & Culture Ser.). (ENG., Illus.). 240p. 125.00 *(978-0-415-97676-3(6))* Routledge.

Johansen, K. V. Beyond Window Dressing? Canadian Children's Fantasy at the Millennium. 2007. 147p. pap. 20.00 *(978-0-9688024-5-8(1))* Sybertooth Inc. CAN. Dist: Lightning Source, Inc.

Johnson, Denise. The Joy of Children's Literature. 2nd ed. 2011. (Whatâ€(tm)s New in Education Ser.). (ENG.). 512p. (C). pap. 93.95 *(978-1-111-29836-4(X))* Wadsworth.

Kavey, Allison. Second Star to the Right: Peter Pan in the Popular Imagination. Friedman, Lester D., ed. 2008. (ENG., Illus.). xii, 277p. (C). pap. 25.95 *(978-0-8135-4437-3(8))* Rutgers Univ. Pr.

Kavey, Allison & Friedman, Lester D. Second Star to the Right: Peter Pan in the Popular Imagination. 2008. (ENG., Illus.). 288p. (C). 68.00 *(978-0-8135-4436-6(X))* Rutgers Univ. Pr.

Keeling, Kara K. & Pollard, Scott T. Critical Approaches to Food in Children's Literature. Keeling, Kara & Pollard, Scott, eds. 2008. (Children's Literature & Culture Ser.). (Illus.). XIV, 276p. 126.00 *(978-0-415-96366-4(4))* Routledge.

Kelen, Christopher & Sundmark, Bjorn, eds. The Nation in Childrenrsquo;s Literature: Nations of Childhood. 2012. (Children's Literature & Culture Ser.). (ENG., Illus.). 272p. (C). 125.00 ***(978-0-415-62479-4(7))*** Routledge.

Kenfel, Veljka Ruzicka, ed. Diálogos intertextuales 2: Bambi: Estudios de literatura infantil y juvenil alemana e inglesa: trasvases Semióticos. 2009. (SPA.). 150p. pap. 43.95 *(978-3-631-59186-4(1))* Lang, Peter GmbH, Europaischer Verlag der Wissenschaften DEU. Dist: Lang, Peter.

Kenfel, Veljka Ruzicka & Ewers, Hans-Heino, contrib. by. Kulturelle Regionalisierung in Spanien und Literarische Übersetzung: Studien zur Rezeption Deutschsprachiger Kinder- und Jugendliteratur in den Zweisprachigen Autonomen Regionen Baskenland, Galicien und Katalonien. (Kinder- und Jugendkultur, -Literatur und -Medien Ser.: Vol. 21). (GER., Illus.). 253 S.p. 35.95 *(978-3-631-50336-2(9))* Lang, Peter Publishing, Inc.

Kidd, Kenneth B. Freud in OZ: At the Inter - Sections of Psychoanalysis & Children's Literature. 2011. (ENG.). 336p. pap. 25.00 ***(978-0-8166-7583-8(X))*** Univ. of Minnesota Pr.

—Freud in OZ: At the Intersections of Psychoanalysis & Children's Literature. 2011. (ENG.). 336p. 75.00 ***(978-0-8166-7582-1(1))*** Univ. of Minnesota Pr.

Kilian, Heinke. Von Hexen, Zauberern und magischen Gestalten: Hexenverfolgung in der Jugendliteratur der Gegenwart - ein Thema mit aktuellen Bezügen. 2009. (Kinder- und Jugendkultur, -literatur und -medien. Theorie - Geschichte - Didaktik Ser.). (GER.). 166p. 47.95 *(978-3-631-59627-2(8))* Lang, Peter GmbH, Europaischer Verlag der Wissenschaften DEU. Dist: Lang, Peter.

Killeen, Jarlath. The Fairy Tales of Oscar Wilde. 2007. 202p. 99.95 *(978-0-7546-5813-9(9))* Ashgate Publishing Co.

Killinger, John. The Life, Death, & Resurrection of Harry Potter. 2009. 192p. pap. 17.00 *(978-0-88146-162-6(8))* Mercer Univ. Pr.

Kohl, Herbert R. & Kohl, Herbert. Should We Burn Babar? Essays on Children's Literature & the Power of Stories. rev. ed. 2007. (ENG.). 224p. pap. 14.95 *(978-1-59558-130-3(8))* New Pr., The.

Kromp, Ilona. Eigennamen in der deutschen und polnischen Kinderliteratur unter textlinguistischem und translatorischem Aspekt. 2008. (Danziger Beiträge zur Germanistik Ser.). 162p. pap. 49.95 *(978-3-631-57625-0(0))* Lang, Peter GmbH, Europaischer Verlag der Wissenschaften DEU. Dist: Lang, Peter.

Kronzek, Allan Zola & Kronzek, Elizabeth. The Sorcerer's Companion: A Guide to the Magical World of Harry Potter. 3rd ed. 2010. (ENG.). 384p. pap. 16.99 *(978-0-307-88513-5(5))* Broadway Bks.

Kümmerling-Meibauer, Bettina, et al, eds. New Directions in Picturebook Research. 2010. (Children's Literature & Culture Ser.). (Illus.). 280p. (C). 125.00 *(978-0-415-87690-2(7))* Routledge.

Kunzel, Bonnie & Fichtelberg, Susan. Tamora Pierce, 1 vol. 2007. (Teen Reads: Student Companions to Young Adult Literature Ser.). 296p. 45.00 *(978-0-313-33660-7(1),* GR3660, Greenwood Pr.) Greenwood Publishing Group, Inc.

Lanes, Selma G. Through the Looking Glass: Further Adventures & Misadventures in the Realm of Children's Literature. 2006. (ENG., Illus.). 247p. pap. 18.95 *(978-1-56792-318-6(6))* Godine, David R. Pub.

Lathey, Gillian. The Role of Translators in Children's Literature: Invisible Storytellers of English-Language Works. 2010. (Children's Literature & Culture Ser.). (ENG., Illus.). 258p. (C). 125.00 *(978-0-415-98952-7(3))* Routledge.

—The Translation of Children's Literature: A Reader. 2006. (ENG., Illus.). 264p (C). pap. 44.95 *(978-1-85359-905-7(0))* Multilingual Matters GBR. Dist: Univ. of Toronto Pr.

Lathey, Gillian, ed. The Translation of Children's Literature: A Reader a Reader. 2006. (Topics in Translation Ser.: Vol. 31). (ENG., Illus.). 272p. (C). 109.95 *(978-1-85359-906-4(9))* Multilingual Matters GBR. Dist: Univ. of Toronto Pr.

Lefebvre, Benjamin, ed. Transforming the Text in Childrens Literature. 2012. (Children's Literature & Culture Ser.). (ENG.). 228p. (C). 125.00 ***(978-0-415-50971-8(8))*** Routledge.

Lehr, Susan S. Shattering the Looking Glass: Challenge, Risk, & Controversy in Children's Literature. 2008. (Illus.). 480p. 24.95 *(978-1-933760-12-4(5))* Christopher-Gordon Pubs., Inc.

Lerer, Seth. Children's Literature: A Reader's History, from Aesop to Harry Potter. (Illus.). 2009. (ENG.). 400p. pap. 19.00 *(978-0-226-47301-7(5))* 2008. 385p. 30.00 *(978-0-226-47300-0(7))* Univ. of Chicago Pr.

Lester, Neal A. Once upon a Time in a Different World: Issues & Ideas in African American Children's Literature. 2007. (Children's Literature & Culture Ser.). 304p. 131.00 *(978-0-415-98019-7(4))* Routledge.

Loncraine, Rebecca. The Real Wizard of Oz: The Life & Times of L. Frank Baum. 2010. (ENG.). 352p. (gr. 12). 18.00 *(978-1-59240-558-9(4),* Gotham) Penguin Group (USA) Inc.

Luebke, Alexandra. The Pilgrim's Progress in American Juvenile Literature 1860-1900. 2007. 84p. per. *(978-3-8364-2300-7(6))* VDM Verlag Dr. Mueller e.K.

Lukens, Rebecca J., et al. Lukens: Critic Handbo Childr Liter_9. 9th rev. ed. 2012. (ENG.). 408p. (C). pap. 89.80 ***(978-0-13-705638-5(9))*** Allyn & Bacon, Inc.

Lurie, Alison. Boys & Girls Forever: Children's Classics from Cinderella to Harry Potter. 2006. 219p. reprint ed. 25.00 *(978-1-4223-5774-3(0))* DIANE Publishing Co.

Lynch-Brown, Carol & Tomlinson, Carl M. Essentials of Children's Literature. 6th ed. 2007. (ENG., Illus.). 432p. (C). per. 71.33 *(978-0-205-52032-9(4))* Allyn & Bacon, Inc.

—Essentials of Children's Literature (with MyEducationKit) 7th ed. 2010. (ENG.). (C). pap. 82.67 *(978-0-13-707402-0(6))* Allyn & Bacon, Inc.

Lynch-Brown, Carol, et al. Essentials of Children's Literature. 7th ed. 2010. (MyEducationKit Ser.). (ENG., Illus.). 432p. (C). pap. 78.67 *(978-0-13-704884-7(X))* Allyn & Bacon, Inc.

MacCann, Donnarae & Maddy, Yulisa Amadu. Neo-Imperialism in Children's Literature about Africa: A Study of Contemporary Fiction. 2008. (Children's Literature & Culture Ser.). (ENG.). 190p. (C). 125.00 *(978-0-415-99390-6(3))* Routledge.

MACK, Robert. The Arabian Nights in Children's Literature. 2009. 244p. 110.00 *(978-0-415-99816-1(6))* Routledge.

MacKenzie-Bowie, Ewen. The Wolf in Children's Literature. 2011. 104p. pap. ***(978-3-8443-9235-7(1))*** Lambert Academic Publishing.

Mallan, Kerry & Bradford, Clare, eds. Contemporary Children's Literature & Film: Engaging with Theory. 2011. (ENG., Illus.). 240p. pap. 28.00 *(978-0-230-23150-4(0))* Palgrave Macmillan.

Maltese, Racheline. The Book of Harry Potter Trifles, Trivias, & Particularities. 2007. (ENG.). 300p. (J). (gr. 3). pap. 14.95 *(978-0-9779545-2-0(8))* Sterling & Ross Pubs.

Marcus, Leonard S. Minders of Make-Believe: Idealists, Entrepreneurs, & the Shaping of American Children's Literature. 2008. (ENG.). 416p. (gr. 17). 28.00 *(978-0-395-67407-9(7))* Houghton Mifflin Harcourt Trade & Reference Pubs.

Martin, Marie-Claire & Martin, Serge. Quelle Littérature Pour la Jeunesse. 2009. (FRE.). 197p. *(978-2-252-03709-6(1))* Klincksieck, Editions.

Maybin, Janet & Watson, Nicola J. Approaches & Territories. Maybin, Janet & Watson, Nicola J., eds. 2009. (ENG., Illus.). 432p. pap. 40.00 *(978-0-230-22713-2(9))* Palgrave Macmillan.

Mayes-Elma, Ruthann. Females & Harry Potter: Not All That Empowering. 2006. (Reverberations: Contemporary Curriculum & Pedagogy Ser.). (ENG., Illus.). 184p. per. 22.95 *(978-0-7425-3779-8(X))* Rowman & Littlefield Publishers, Inc.

McCulloch, Fiona. Children's Literature in Context. 2011. (Texts & Contexts Ser.). (ENG.). 192p. 90.00 *(978-1-84706-486-8(8))* Continuum International Publishing Group, Ltd. GBR. Dist: National Bk. Network.

McCulloch, Margery Palmer. Children's Literature in Context. 2011. (Texts & Contexts Ser.). (ENG.). 192p. pap. 27.95 *(978-1-84706-487-5(6))* Continuum International Publishing Group, Ltd. GBR. Dist: National Bk. Network.

McDowall, Stephen. Qian Qianyi's Reflections on Yellow Mountain: Traces of a Late-Ming Hatchet & Chisel. 2009. (ENG., Illus.). 236p. (gr. 17). 50.00 *(978-962-209-084-2(2))* Hong Kong Univ. Pr. HKG. Dist: Columbia Univ. Pr.

McGavran, James Holt, ed. Romanticism & Children's Literature in Nineteenth-Century England. 2009. (ENG.). 272p. pap. 24.95 *(978-0-8203-3487-5(1))* Univ. of Georgia Pr.

Mendlesohn, Farah. The Inter-Galactic Playground: A Critical Study of Children's & Teens' Science Fiction. Palumbo, Donald E. & Sullivan, C. W., III, eds. 2009. (Critical Explorations in Science Fiction & Fantasy Ser.). (ENG., Illus.). 283p. pap. 45.00 *(978-0-7864-3503-6(8))* McFarland & Co., Inc. Pubs.

C

Mickenberg, Julia L. & Vallone, Lynne, eds. The Oxford Handbook of Children's Literature, 1 vol. 2011. (Oxford Handbooks Ser.). (ENG., Illus.). 608p. 150.00 *(978-0-19-537978-5(0))* Oxford Univ. Pr., Inc.

Miller, Laura. The Magician's Book: A Skeptic's Adventures in Narnia. 2009. (ENG.). 336p. pap. 14.99 *(978-0-316-01765-7(5)*, Back Bay Bks.) Little Brown & Co.

Montgomery, Heather & Watson, Nicola J. Children's Literature - Classic Texts & Contemporary Trends. Montgomery, Heather & Watson, Nicola J., eds. 2009. (ENG., Illus.). 432p. pap. 40.00 *(978-0-230-22714-9(7))* Palgrave Macmillan.

Morgenstern, John. Playing with Books: A Study of the Reader as Child. 2009. (ENG.). 240p. pap. 39.95 *(978-0-7864-4295-9(6))* McFarland & Co., Inc. Pubs.

Mulholland, Neil. The Psychology of Harry Potter: An Unauthorized Examination of the Boy Who Lived. Mulholland, Neil, ed. 2007. (Smart Pop Ser.). (ENG.). 326p. pap. 17.95 *(978-1-932100-88-4(1))* BenBella Bks.

Myers, Lindsay. Making the Italians: Poetics & Politics of Italian Children's Fantasy. 2011. (ENG.). 251p. pap. 58.95 ***(978-3-03911-361-3(5))*** Lang, Peter AG GBR. Dist: Lang, Peter.

Napoli, Donna Jo. Alligator Bayou. 2010. lib. bdg. 19.65 *(978-0-606-14501-5(X)*, Turtleback) Turtleback Bks.

Nel, Philip. Crockett Johnson & Ruth Krauss: How an Unlikely Couple Found Love, Dodged the FBI, & Transformed Children's Literature. 2012. (Children's Literature Association Ser.). (ENG., Illus.). 368p. 70.00 ***(978-1-61703-624-8(2))***; pap. 40.00 ***(978-1-61703-636-1(6))*** Univ. Pr. of Mississippi.

Nel, Philip & Paul, Lissa. Keywords for Children's Literature. 2011. (ENG.). 293p. 79.00 *(978-0-8147-5854-0(1))*; (ENG.). 293p. pap. 25.00 *(978-0-8147-5855-7(X))*; 288p. E-Book *(978-0-8147-5889-2(4))* New York Univ. Pr.

Nikolajeva, Maria. Power, Voice & Subjectivity in Literature for Young Readers. 2009. (Children's Literature & Culture Ser.). (ENG.). 232p. (C). 125.00 *(978-0-415-80215-4(6))* Routledge.

Nilsen, Alleen Pace. Joan Bauer, 1 vol. 2007. (Teen Reads: Student Companions to Young Adult Literature Ser.). (Illus.). 176p. 45.00 *(978-0-313-33550-1(8)*, GR3550, Greenwood Pr.) Greenwood Publishing Group, Inc.

Nodelman, Perry. The Hidden Adult: Defining Children's Literature. 2008. (ENG.). 408p. (C). (gr. 13-17). 72.00 *(978-0-8018-8979-0(0))*; pap. 37.00 *(978-0-8018-8980-6(4))* Johns Hopkins Univ. Pr.

Norcia, Megan A. X Marks the Spot: Women Writers Map the Empire for British Children, 1790-1895. 2010. (ENG.). 304p. 49.95 *(978-0-8214-1907-6(2))* Ohio Univ. Pr.

Norton, Donna E. Multicultural Children's Literature: Through the Eyes of Many Children. 4th rev. ed. 2012. (ENG.). 360p. (C). pap. 53.80 ***(978-0-13-268576-4(0))*** Allyn & Bacon, Inc.

Norton, Donna E. Through the Eyes of a Child: An Introduction to Children's Literature. 7th ed. 2006. 124.20 *(978-0-13-240155-5(X))* Prentice Hall PTR.

Norton, Donna E. & Norton, Saundra. Through the Eyes of a Child: An Introduction to Children's Literature. 8th ed. 2010. (MyEducationKit Ser.). (ENG., Illus.). 640p. (C). 155.60 *(978-0-13-702875-7(X))* Allyn & Bacon, Inc.

—Through the Eyes of a Child: An Introduction to Children's Literature (with MyEducationKit) 8th ed. 2010. (ENG.). (C). 159.60 *(978-0-13-707401-3(8)*, Prentice Hall) Prentice Hall PTR.

Novel Units, Inc. Staff, creator. The Invention of Hugo Cabret Student Packet. 2010. (J). *(978-1-60878-107-2(0))* Novel Units, Inc.

O'Dell, Felicity Ann. Socialisation through Children's Literature: The Soviet Example. 2010. (Cambridge Russian, Soviet & Post-Soviet Studies). (ENG.). 290p. pap. 23.99 *(978-0-521-14437-7(X))* Cambridge Univ. Pr.

Olich, Jacqueline. Competing Ideologies & Children's Literature in Russia, 1918-1935. 2009. 280p. pap. *(978-3-639-13431-5(1))* VDM Verlag Dr. Mueller e.K.

op de Beeck, Nathalie. Suspended Animation: Children's Picture Books & the Fairy Tale of Modernity. 2010. (ENG., Illus.). 288p. 82.50 *(978-0-8166-6573-0(7))*; pap. 27.50 *(978-0-8166-6574-7(5))* Univ. of Minnesota Pr.

O'Sullivan, Emer. Comparative Children's Literature. 2009. 210p. pap. 40.00 *(978-0-415-56412-0(3))* Routledge.

—Historical Dictionary of Children's Literature. 2010. (Historical Dictionaries of Literature & the Arts Ser.). (ENG.). 372p. 80.00 *(978-0-8108-6080-3(5))*; E-Book *(978-0-8108-7496-1(2))* Scarecrow Pr., Inc.

O'Sullivan, Keith & Coghlan, Valerie, eds. Irish Children's Literature & Culture. 2010. (Children's Literature & Culture Ser.). (ENG.). 228p. (C). 125.00 *(978-0-415-87789-3(X))* Routledge.

O'Sullivan, Keith & Coghlan, Valerie, eds. Irish Children's Literature & Culture: New Perspectives on Contemporary Writing. 2012. (ENG.). (C). pap. 39.95 ***(978-0-415-62355-1(3))*** Routledge.

Pantaleo, Sylvia. Exploring Student Response to Contemporary Picturebooks. 2009. (Illus.). 264p. pap. *(978-1-4426-1095-8(6))* Univ. of Toronto Pr.

Parille, Ken. Boys at Home: Discipline, Masculinity, & the Boy-Problem in Nineteenth-Century American Literature. 2011. (ENG.). 184p. pap. 21.00 *(978-1-57233-787-9(7))* Univ. of Tennessee Pr.

Paruolo, Elena, ed. Brave New Worlds: Old & New Classics of Children's Literatures. 2011. (Recherches comparatives sur les livres et le multimédia d'enfance Ser.). 231p. pap. 48.95 *(978-90-5201-710-5(7))* PIE - Peter Lang BEL. Dist: Lang, Peter.

Paul, Clayton R. Children's Book Business. 2010. (Children's Literature & Culture Ser.). (ENG., Illus.). 234p. (C). 125.00 *(978-0-415-93789-4(2))* Routledge.

Paul, Lissa. The Children's Book Business: Lessons from the Long Eighteenth Century. 2012. (ENG.). 208p. (C). pap. 39.95 ***(978-0-415-62826-6(1))*** Routledge.

Pavonetti, Linda. Bridges to Understanding: Envisioning the World through Children's Books. 2011. (ENG.). 534p. (gr. 17). pap. 55.00 *(978-0-8108-8106-8(3))* Scarecrow Pr., Inc.

Pavonetti, Linda M. Bridges to Understanding: Envisioning the World Through Children's Books. 2011. E-Book ***(978-0-8108-8107-5(1))*** Scarecrow Pr., Inc.

Pearson, Lucy & Hunt, Peter, eds. Children's Literature. 2011. (York Notes Companions Ser.). 338p. pap. 33.95 ***(978-1-4082-6662-5(8))*** Longman Publishing Group.

Pederzoli, Roberta. Écrire et Traduire Pour les Enfants: Voix, Images et Mots: Writing & Translating for Children: Voices, Images & Texts. Elefante, Chiara & Di Giovanni, Elena, eds. 2010. (FRE, ITA & ENG.). 343p. pap. 55.95 *(978-90-5201-660-3(7))* PIE - Peter Lang BEL. Dist: Lang, Peter.

Pemberton, Marilyn, ed. & compiled by. Enchanted Ideologies: A Collection of Rediscovered Ninetenth-Century English Moral Fairy Tales. 2010. (ENG., Illus.). 307p. 45.00 *(978-0-9791116-5-5(X))* True Bill Pr., The.

Pepetone, Gregory G. Hogwarts & All: Gothic Perspectives on Children's Literature. 2012. 248p. (C). pap. 29.95 ***(978-1-4331-0060-4(6))*** Lang, Peter Publishing, Inc.

Peterson, Shelley Stagg & Swartz, Larry. Good Books Matter: How to Choose & Use Children's Literature to Help Students Grow as Readers. 2008. (ENG.). 160p. (C). (gr. k-8). pap. 21.00 *(978-1-55138-232-6(6))* Pembroke Pubs., Ltd. CAN. Dist: Stenhouse Pubs.

Petzold, Dieter. Das englische Kunstmärchen im neunzehnten Jahrhundert. (Buchreihe der Anglia Ser.). (GER.). X, 362p. 140.00 ***(978-3-11-127768-4(2))*** De Gruyter, Mouton DEU. Dist: de Gruyter, Walter GmbH & Co. KG.

Plastow, Jenny, ed. Owners of the Means of Instruction? Children's Literature - Some Marxist Perspectives. 2010. (Children's Literature Annual Ser.). (ENG., Illus.). 152p. pap. 19.95 *(978-1-902806-65-5(4))* Univ. of Hertfordshire Pr. GBR. Dist: Independent Pubs. Group.

—The Story & the Self: Children's Literature - Some Psychoanalytic Perspectives. 2010. (Children's Literature Annual Ser.). (ENG., Illus.). 264p. pap. 19.95 *(978-1-905313-52-5(7))* Univ. of Hertfordshire Pr. GBR. Dist: Independent Pubs. Group.

Plastow, Jenny & Hillel, Margot, eds. The Sands of Time: Children's Literature Culture, Politics & Identity. 2010. (Children's Literature Annual Ser.). (ENG., Illus.). 176p. pap. 19.95 *(978-1-905313-80-8(2))* Univ. of Hertfordshire Pr. GBR. Dist: Independent Pubs. Group.

Poole, L. M. Maurice Sendak: And the Art of Children's Book Illustration. 2007. (Illus.). 250p. 24.00 *(978-1-86171-061-1(5))* 2nd ed. 60.00 *(978-1-86171-191-5(3))* Crescent Moon Publishing GBR. Dist: NACSCORP, Inc.

Prater, Mary Anne & Dyches, Tina Taylor. Teaching about Disabilities Through Children's Literature, 1 vol. 2008. (Through Children's Literature Ser.). (Illus.). 148p. per. 38.00 *(978-1-59158-541-1(4)*, TIP5414, Teacher Ideas Pr.) Libraries Unlimited, Inc.

Pugh, Tison. Innocence, Heterosexuality, & the Queerness of Children's Literature. 2010. (Children's Literature & Culture Ser.). (ENG.). 222p. (C). 125.00 *(978-0-415-88633-8(3))* Routledge.

Reimer, Mavis. Home Words: Discourses of Children's Literature in Canada. Reimer, Mavis, ed. 2008. (Studies in Childhood & Family in Canada Ser.). (ENG., Illus.). 308p. 85.00 *(978-1-55458-016-3(1))* Wilfrid Laurier Univ. Pr. CAN. Dist: Univ. of Toronto Pr.

Reynolds, Kimberley. Children's Literature: From the fin de siecle to the new Millennium. 2012. (Writers & Their Work Ser.). (ENG.). 128p. (C). pap. 26.00 ***(978-0-7463-1218-6(0))*** Northcote Hse. Publishers, Ltd. GBR. Dist: Brown, David Bk. Co., The.

—Children's Literature: A Very Short Introduction. 2011. (Very Short Introductions Ser.). (ENG., Illus.). 168p. pap. 11.95 *(978-0-19-956024-0(2))* Oxford Univ. Pr., Inc.

—Radical Children's Literature: Future Visions & Aesthetic Transformations in Juvenile Fiction. (ENG., Illus.). 2010. 232p. pap. 30.00 *(978-0-230-23937-1(4))* 2007. 248p. 95.00 *(978-1-4039-8561-3(8))* Palgrave Macmillan.

Richmond, Velma Bourgeois. Shakespeare as Children's Literature: Edwardian Retellings in Words & Pictures. 2008. (ENG., Illus.). 371p. pap. 35.00 *(978-0-7864-3781-8(2))* McFarland & Co., Inc. Pubs.

Richter-Vapaatalo, Ulrike. Da Batte Das Pferd Die Nustern Voll: Gebrauch und Funktion Von Phraseologie Im Kinderbuch. (GER.). 333p. pap. 68.95 *(978-3-631-57082-1(1))* Lang, Peter GmbH, Europaischer Verlag der Wissenschaften DEU. Dist: Lang, Peter Publishing, Inc.

Riordan, Rick & Wilson, Leah. Demigods & Monsters: Your Favorite Authors on Rick Riordan's Percy Jackson & the Olympians Series. 2008. *(978-0-9792331-4-2(3))* BenBella Bks.

Rollin, Lucy & West, Mark I. Psychoanalytic Responses to Children's Literature. alt. ed. 2008. (ENG.). 190p. pap. 29.95 *(978-0-7864-3764-1(2))* McFarland & Co., Inc. Pubs.

Rossi, Melanie. Das Mittelalter in Romanen für Jugendliche: Historische Jugendliteratur und Identitätsbildung. 2009. (Kinder- und Jugendkultur, -literatur und -medien. Theorie - Geschichte - Didaktik Ser.). (GER.). 340p. 79.95 *(978-3-631-59735-4(5))* Lang, Peter GmbH, Europaischer Verlag der Wissenschaften DEU. Dist: Lang, Peter.

Rudd, David. Children's Literature. 2010. (Routledge Companions Ser.). (ENG., Illus.). 336p. 115.00 *(978-0-415-47270-8(9))*; pap. 32.95 *(978-0-415-47271-5(7))* Routledge.

Russell, David L. Literature for Children: A Short Introduction. 7th ed. 2011. (ENG., Illus.). 360p. (C). pap. 78.67 *(978-0-13-217379-7(4))* Allyn & Bacon, Inc.

Ruthann, Mayes-Elma. Harry Potter: Feminist Friend or Foe? 2008. 160p. *(978-90-8790-082-3(1))* Sense Pubs.

Sands, Karen. Soon Come Home to This Island: West Indians in British Children's Literature. 2007. (Children's Literature & Culture Ser.). (ENG., Illus.). 256p. 131.00 *(978-0-415-97630-5(8))* Routledge.

Sands-O'Connor, Karen. Soon Come Home to This Island: West Indians in British Children's Literature. 2012. (Children's Literature & Culture Ser.). (ENG., Illus.). 256p. pap. 42.95 ***(978-0-415-54221-0(9))*** Routledge.

Sawers, Naarah. Critical Ficions. 2008. 168p. pap. *(978-3-639-08308-8(3))* VDM Verlag Dr. Mueller e.K.

Shavit, Zohar. Poetics of Children's Literature. 2009. (ENG.). 216p. pap. 24.95 *(978-0-8203-3481-3(2))* Univ. of Georgia Pr.

Shimada. Books on Children in 16th-18th Century Britain Series I. Engetsu, Yuko, ed. 2008. 1910p. 1040.00 *(978-4-902454-31-4(9))* Synapse, Edition JPN. Dist: Taylor & Francis Group.

Silvey, Anita, ed. Everything I Need to Know I Learned from a Children's Book: Life Lessons from Notable People from All Walks of Life. 2009. (ENG., Illus.). 240p. 29.99 *(978-1-59643-395-3(7))* Roaring Brook Pr.

Sipe, Lawrence R. & Pantaleo, Sylvia. Postmodern Picturebooks: Play, Parody, & Self-Referentiality. 2012. (Routledge Research in Education Ser.). (ENG., Illus.). 280p. pap. 42.95 ***(978-0-415-54305-7(3))*** Routledge.

Smith, Katharine Capshaw. Children's Literature of the Harlem Renaissance. 2006. (Blacks in the Diaspora Ser.). (ENG., Illus.). 368p. pap. 21.95 *(978-0-253-21888-9(8)*, 0253218888) Indiana Univ. Pr.

Smith, Michelle J. Empire in British Girls' Literature & Culture: Imperial Girls, 1880-1915. 2011. (ENG., Illus.). 240p. 85.00 *(978-0-230-27286-6(X))* Palgrave Macmillan.

Smith, Robert B. Hogwarts, Narnia, & Middle Earth: Places upon a Time. 2007. 124p. per. 10.95 *(978-0-9785165-6-7(7))* Drinian Pr., LLC.

Springman, Luke. Carpe Mundum: German Youth Culture of the Weimar Republic. 2007. (Kinder- und Jugendkultur, -Literatur und -Medien Ser.: Vol. 50). 299p. (C). pap. 62.95 *(978-3-631-56244-4(6))* Lang, Peter Publishing, Inc.

Stahl, J. D., et al, eds. Crosscurrents of Children's Literature: An Anthology of Texts & Criticism. 2006. (ENG., Illus.). 1080p. (C). pap. 84.95 *(978-0-19-513493-3(1))* Oxford Univ. Pr., Inc.

Stephens, John, ed. Ways of Being Male: Representing Masculinities in Children's Literature. 2008. (Illus.). 304p. 39.95 *(978-0-415-99515-3(9))* Routledge.

Stewart, Michelle Pagni & Atkinson, Yvonne, eds. Ethnic Literary Traditions in American Children's Literature. 2009. (ENG.). 268p. 89.00 *(978-0-230-61875-6(8))* Palgrave Macmillan.

Stoneley, Peter. Consumerism & American Girls' Literature, 1860-1940. 2007. (Cambridge Studies in American Literature & Culture Ser.). (ENG., Illus.). 180p. pap. 44.00 *(978-0-521-03575-0(9))* Cambridge Univ. Pr.

Styles, Morag & Arizpe, Evelyn, eds. Acts of Reading: Teachers, Texts & Childhood. 2009. (Illus.). 256p. pap. 34.95 *(978-1-85856-438-8(7))* Trentham Bks. Ltd. GBR. Dist: Stylus Publishing, LLC.

Sutton, Roger & Parravano, Martha, eds. A Family of Readers: The Book Lover's Guide to Children's & Young Adult Literature. 2011. (ENG., Illus.). 368p. pap. 14.99 *(978-0-7636-5755-0(7))* Candlewick Pr.

Sutton, Roger & Parravano, Martha V., eds. A Family of Readers: The Book Lover's Guide to Children's & Young Adult Literature. 2010. (ENG., Illus.). 368p. 22.00 *(978-0-7636-3280-9(5))* Candlewick Pr.

Swartz, Larry. The Picture Book Experience: Choosing & Using Picture Books in the Classroom. 2009. (ENG.). 32p. (C). (gr. k-12). 13.00 *(978-1-55138-235-7(0))* Stenhouse Pubs.

Temple, Charles A., et al. Children's Books in Children's Hands: An Introduction to Their Literature (with MyEducationKit) 4th ed. 2010. (ENG.). (C). pap. 155.20 *(978-0-13-707403-7(4))* Allyn & Bacon, Inc.

The Students of June Jordan School for Equity Staff & San Francisco Bay Area Students Staff. Beyond Stolen Flames, Forbidden Fruit, & Telephone Booths: Our Own Myths, Our Own Futures. Hosseini, Khaled, ed. 2011. (ENG.). 304p. 22.00 *(978-1-934750-22-3(0))* 826 Valencia.

Thiel, Elizabeth. The Fantasy of Family: Nineteenth-Century Children's Literature & the Myth of the Domestic Ideal. 2007. (Children's Literature & Culture Ser.). (Illus.). XIV, 202p. 126.00 *(978-0-415-98035-7(6))* Routledge.

Thompson, Deborah L. Multicultural Children's Literature. 2009. (ENG.). 304p. (C). pap. 30.00 *(978-0-13-199413-3(1)*, Prentice Hall) Prentice Hall PTR.

Thompson, Mary Shine & Coghlan, Valerie, eds. Divided Worlds: Studies in Children's Literature. 2007. 223p. (C). 74.50 *(978-1-84682-011-3(1))* Four Courts Pr. IRL. Dist: International Specialized Bk. Services.

Thomson-Wohlgem & Thomson-wohlgemuth, Gaby. Translation under State Control: Books for Young People in the German Democratic Republic. 2009. (Children's Literature & Culture Ser.). (Illus.). 260p. 136.00 *(978-0-415-99580-1(9))* Routledge.

Tolson, Nancy. Black Children's Literature Got de Blues: The Creativity of Black Writers & Illustrators. 2008. (Illus.). xi, 116p. pap. 24.95 *(978-0-8204-6332-2(9))* Lang, Peter Publishing, Inc.

Trevarthen, Geo Athena. The Seeker's Guide to Harry Potter: The Unauthorized Course. 2008. (ENG., Illus.). 261p. per. 24.95 *(978-1-84694-093-4(1))* Hunt, John Publishing Ltd. GBR. Dist: National Bk. Network.

Tuerk, Richard. Oz in Perspective: Magic & Myth in the L. Frank Baum Books. 2007. (ENG., Illus.). 241p. per. 35.00 *(978-0-7864-2899-1(6))* McFarland & Co., Inc. Pubs.

Tunnell, Michael O., et al. Children's Literature, Briefly. 5th ed. 2011. (ENG.). 336p. (C). pap. 78.67 *(978-0-13-248056-7(5))* Allyn & Bacon, Inc.

Vaclavik, Kiera. Uncharted Depths: Descent Narratives in English & French Children's Literature. 2010. (Legenda Main Ser.). (ENG., Illus.). 139p. (C). 89.50 *(978-1-906540-39-5(X))* European Humanities Research Ctr. GBR. Dist: Brown, David Bk. Co., The.

Velarde, Robert. The Heart of Narnia: Wisdom, Virtue, & Life Lessons from the Classic Chronicles. 2008. (Living the Letters Ser.). (ENG.). 208p. per. 12.99 *(978-1-60006-238-4(5))* NavPress Publishing Group.

Villaluz, Nancy Solon. Does Harry Potter Tickle Sleeping Dragons? 2008. (Illus.). 352p. 24.95 *(978-0-9794229-8-0(1))* Ramance Pr.

Waller, Alison. Constructing Adolescence in Fantastic Realism. 2008. (Children's Literature & Culture Ser.). (ENG., Illus.). 240p. 126.00 *(978-0-415-95832-5(6))* Routledge.

Walsh, Sue. Re-Reading Kipling His Critics & Constructions of Childhood. 2010. (Ashgate Studies in Childhood, 1700 to the Present Ser.). (Illus.). 186p. 99.95 *(978-0-7546-5596-1(2))* Ashgate Publishing Co.

Wannamaker, Annette. Boys in Children's Literature & Popular Culture: Masculinity, Abjection, & the Fictional Child. 2007. (Children's Literature & Culture Ser.). 200p. 131.00 *(978-0-415-97469-1(0))* Routledge.

Watts, Irene N. Munsch at Play Act 2: Eight More Stage Adaptations. 2011. (ENG., Illus.). 108p. (J). (gr. 1-4). 24.95 *(978-1-55451-358-1(8))* Annick Pr., Ltd. CAN. Dist: Firefly Bks., Ltd.

White, Gleeson. Children's Books & Their Illustrators. 2010. (ENG.). 77p. pap. 17.75 *(978-1-176-54597-7(3))* BiblioBazaar.

—Children's Books & Their Illustrators. 2010. (Illus.). 62p. pap. 20.00 *(978-1-153-80232-1(5))*; 52p. pap. 17.50 *(978-1-152-75170-5(0))* General Bks. LLC.

Wilkie-Stibbs, Christine. The Outside Child, in & Out of the Book. 2007. (Children's Literature & Culture Ser.). (ENG.). 216p. 125.00 *(978-0-415-97800-2(9))* Routledge.

Wilkin, Binnie Tate. African & African American Images in Newbery Award Winning Titles: Progress in Portrayals. 2009. (ENG.). 210p. pap. 45.00 *(978-0-8108-6959-2(4))* Scarecrow Pr., Inc.

Williams, Thomas. Following Prince Caspian: Further Encounters with the Lion of Narnia, 0 vols. 2008. 64p. pap. 2.99 *(978-0-8499-1997-8(5))* Nelson, Thomas Inc.

Wills, Ashley. Beyond Binaries. 2007. 88p. per. *(978-3-8364-2609-1(9))* VDM Verlag Dr. Mueller e.K.

Wilson, Kim. Re-visioning Historical Fiction for Young Readers: The Past through Modern Eyes. 2011. (Children's Literature & Culture Ser.). (ENG., Illus.). 228p. (C). 125.00 *(978-0-415-89007-6(1))* Routledge.

Wilson, Nicole L. From Formula to Solid Food: How Media Nourishes Children's Literature. 2011. 236p. pap. ***(978-3-8433-8982-2(9))*** Lambert Academic Publishing.

Wolosky, Shira. The Riddles of Harry Potter: Secret Passages & Interpretive Quests. 2010. (ENG.). 238p. 84.00 *(978-0-230-10929-2(2))* Palgrave Macmillan.

Yarbrough, Wynn William. Masculinity in Children's Animal Stories, 1888-1928: A Critical Study of Anthropomorphic Tales by Wilde, Kipling, Potter, Grahame & Milne. 2011. (ENG., Illus.). 195p. pap. 40.00 *(978-0-7864-5943-8(3))* McFarland & Co., Inc. Pubs.

Yellin, David G. & DeVries, Beverly A. Sharing the Journey: Literature for Young Children. 2011. *(978-1-934432-07-5(5))* Holcomb Hathaway, Inc.

Yenika-Agbaw, Vivian. Representing Africa in Children's Literature. 2011. (ENG.). 168p. pap. 34.95 ***(978-0-415-69956-3(8))*** Routledge.

Yenika-Agbaw, Vivian S. Representing Africa in Children's Literature: Old & New Ways of Seeing. 2007. (Children's Literature & Culture Ser.). (ENG.). 168p. 125.00 *(978-0-415-97468-4(2))* Routledge.

Zipes, Jack D. Relentless Progress: The Reconfiguration of Children's Literature, Fairy Tales, & Storytelling. 2008. (ENG., Illus.). 208p. (C). 125.00 *(978-0-415-99063-9(7))* Routledge.

Zipes, Jack D. Relentless Progress: The Reconfiguration of Children's Literature, Fairy Tales, & Storytelling. 2008. (Illus.). 208p. pap. 34.95 *(978-0-415-99064-6(5))* Routledge.

CHILDREN'S LITERATURE—PROHIBITED BOOKS

see Prohibited Books

CHILDREN'S LITERATURE—STORIES, PLOTS, ETC.

Fletcher, Stella & Birt. Storylines. Date not set. (Illus.). 47p. pap. 9.95 *(978-0-582-79103-9(0))* Addison-Wesley Longman, Ltd. GBR. Dist: Trans-Atlantic Pubns., Inc.

Ms. Keown'S Class. Hot Baked Cheetos & Other Things We Like about Indianapolis. 2009. 56p. pap. 13.50 *(978-1-4389-4787-7(9))* AuthorHouse.

Roetzheim, William, ed. The Giant Book of Bedtime Stories: Classic Nursery Rhymes, Bible Stories, Fables, Proverbs, & Stories. 2007. (Illus.). 800p. (J). 14.95 *(978-1-933769-20-2(3))* Level 4 Press, Inc.

CHILDREN'S LITERATURE—STUDY AND TEACHING

Across Five Aprils Guide: Study Guide for Novel. 16.47 *(978-0-13-437501-4(7))* Prentice Hall PTR.

Anderson, Nancy. What Should I Read Aloud? A Guide to 200 Best-Selling Picture Books. 2007. 168p. (gr. 17). pap. 22.95 *(978-0-87207-679-2(2))* International Reading Assn.

Anderson, Nancy A. Elementary Children's Literature: Infancy through Age 13. 3rd ed. 2009. (ENG.). 408p. (C). pap. 78.67 *(978-0-13-715143-1(8))* Allyn & Bacon, Inc.

Appelbaum, Peter. Children's Books for Grown-up Teachers: Reading & Writing Curriculum Theory. 2007. (Studies in Curriculum Theory). (ENG., Illus.). 288p. 45.95 *(978-0-415-96463-8(0))* Routledge.

—Children's Books for Grown-Up Teachers: Reading & Writing Curriculum Theory. 2007. (Studies in Curriculum Theory). (ENG., Illus.). 288p. 150.00 *(978-0-8058-4928-8(9))* Routledge.

Appelbaum, Peter Michael. Children's Literature for Grown-Up Teachers: Curriculum Theorizing for a Pedagogy of Response to Global Consumer Culture. 2007. (Studies in Curriculum Theory). (Illus.). xix, 268p. 41.95 *(978-1-4106-1812-2(9))* Routledge.

Barone, Diane M. Children's Literature in the Classroom: Engaging Lifelong Readers. 2010. (Solving Problems in the Teaching of Literacy Ser.). (ENG., Illus.). 242p. (gr. k-6). 50.00 *(978-1-60623-939-1(2))*; pap. 28.00 *(978-1-60623-938-4(4))* Guilford Pubns., Inc.

Bedford, April Whatley & Albright, Lettie K., eds. A Master Class in Children's Literature: Trends & Issues in an Evolving Field. 2011. pap. *(978-0-8141-3032-7(8))* National Council of Teachers of English.

Blass, Rosanne J. Windows on the World: International Books for Elementary & Middle Grade Readers, 1 vol. 2010. 214p. pap. 40.00 *(978-1-59158-830-6(8),* LU8830) Libraries Unlimited, Inc.

Blume, Judy. Tales of a Fourth Grade Nothing. 2007. (ENG.). 128p. (J). (gr. 2-18). 5.99 *(978-0-14-240881-0(6),* Puffin) Penguin Group (USA) Inc.

Boutsis, Suzanne & Williamson, Noelle. The Fiction Gateway. Williamson, Noelle & Eberle, Suzanne, eds. 2009. 162p. pap. 39.95 *(978-0-86431-880-0(4))* ACER Pr. AUS. Dist: International Specialized Bk. Services.

Butler, Charles, Jr., ed. Teaching Children's Fiction. 2006. (Teaching the New English Ser.). (ENG., Illus.). 192p. pap. 39.00 *(978-1-4039-4495-5(4))* Palgrave Macmillan.

Butler, Charles, ed. Teaching Children's Fiction. 2006. (Teaching New English Ser.). (ENG., Illus.). 232p. 116.00 *(978-1-4039-4494-8(6))* Palgrave Macmillan.

Cappelli, Rose & Dorfman, Lynne R. Nonfiction Mentor Texts: Teaching Informational Writing Through Children's Literature, K-8. 2009. (ENG., Illus.). 304p. (C). (gr. k-8). pap. 24.00 *(978-1-57110-496-0(8))* Stenhouse Pubs.

Casanova, Mary. Mary Casanova & You, 1 vol. 2006. (Author & YOU Ser.). (Illus.). 156p. per. 35.00 *(978-1-59158-405-6(1),* LU4051) Libraries Unlimited, Inc.

Collins, Suzanne. The Hunger Games: Downloadable Teaching Unit. 2011. (Hunger Games Trilogy: Bk. 1). 29.99 ***(978-1-935468-75-2(8))*** Prestwick Hse., Inc.

—The Hunger Games: Teaching Unit (Reproducible) 2011. (Hunger Games Trilogy: Bk. 1). ring bd. 29.99 ***(978-1-935468-74-5(X))*** Prestwick Hse., Inc.

Crowe, Chris. Teaching the Selected Works of Mildred D. Taylor. 2007. (Young Adult Novels in the Classroom Ser.). 112p. pap. 21.25 *(978-0-325-00789-2(6),* E00789) Heinemann.

Dorfman, Lynne R. & Cappelli, Rose. Mentor Texts: Teaching Writing Through Children's Literature, K-6. 2007. (ENG., Illus.). 328p. (C). (gr. k-6). pap., per. 24.00 *(978-1-57110-433-5(X))* Stenhouse Pubs.

Duncan, Diane. Teaching Children's Literature: Making Stories Work in the Classroom. 2008. (Illus.). (ENG.). 232p. 180.00 *(978-0-415-42100-3(4))*; XII, 220p. pap. 46.95 *(978-0-415-42101-0(2))* Routledge.

Ehmann, Susan & Gayer, Kellyann. I Can Write Like That! A Guide to Mentor Texts & Craft Studies for Writers' Workshop, K-6. 2009. (ENG.). 176p. pap. 26.95 *(978-0-87207-708-9(X))* International Reading Assn.

Forsten, Charlene. The Wish Giver. Friedland, Joyce & Kessler, Rikki, eds. 2007. (Novel-Ties Ser.). 25p. (J). pap. 16.95 *(978-1-56982-195-4(X))* Learning Links Inc.

Fredericks, Anthony D. Much More Social Studies Through Children's Literature: A Collaborative Approach, 1 vol. 2007. (Through Children's Literature Ser.). (Illus.). 276p. per. 35.00 *(978-1-59158-445-2(0),* TIP4450, Teacher Ideas Pr.) Libraries Unlimited, Inc.

Garner, Joan. Wings of Fancy: Using Readers Theatre to Study Fantasy Genre, 1 vol. 2006. (Readers Theatre Ser.). (Illus.). 256p. pap. 30.00 *(978-1-59158-342-4(X),* LU342X, Teacher Ideas Pr.) Libraries Unlimited, Inc.

Gibson, Karen A. & Wise, Sheila L. If You Give a Teacher a Book: Using Picture Books to Teach the Traits of Writing. 2008. (Illus.). 124p. pap. 17.95 *(978-1-60213-005-0(1),* Upstart Bks.) Highsmith Inc.

Giorgis, Cyndi & Glazer, Joan I. Literature for Young Children: Supporting Emergent Literacy, Ages 0-8. 6th ed. 2008. (ENG.). 312p. (C). pap. 73.40 *(978-0-13-240504-1(0),* Prentice Hall) Prentice Hall PTR.

Gopalakrishnan, Ambika. Multicultural Children's Literature: A Critical Issues Approach. 2010. 288p. (C). pap. 51.00 *(978-1-4129-5522-5(X),* B55211P) SAGE Pubns., Inc.

Hadaway, Nancy L. Breaking Boundaries with Global Literature: Celebrating Diversity in K-12 Classrooms (Explorations of the Notable Books for a Global Society Booklists) 2007. 232p. pap. 29.95 *(978-0-87207-616-7(4))* International Reading Assn.

Hancock, Marjorie R. A Celebration of Literature & Response: Children, Books, & Teachers in K-8 Classrooms. 3rd ed. 2007. (ENG.). 544p. (C). pap. 94.20 *(978-0-13-613394-0(0),* Prentice Hall) Prentice Hall PTR.

Hatchet. 8.97 *(978-0-673-58329-1(5))* Addison-Wesley Longman, Inc.

House of Dies Drear Reproducible. (J). pap. 3.95 *(978-0-439-04471-4(5))* Scholastic, Inc.

Humphrey, Mary. Bounce Back! Resiliency Strategies Through Children's Literature, 1 vol. 2008. (Illus.). 100p. pap. 35.00 *(978-1-59158-400-1(0),* LU4000) Libraries Unlimited, Inc.

Irving, Jan. Story Celebrations: A Program Guide for Schools & Libraries, 1 vol. 2008. (Illus.). 216p. per. 35.00 *(978-1-59158-432-2(9),* LU4329) Libraries Unlimited, Inc.

Jaffe, Charlotte & Roberts, Barbara. Call It Courage: L-I-T Guide. (L-I-T Guides: Literature in Teaching Ser.). tchr. ed. 8.95 *(978-0-910857-82-6(2))* Educational Impressions.

—A Wrinkle in Time: L-I-T Guide. (L-I-T Guides: Literature in Teaching Ser.). tchr. ed. 8.95 *(978-0-910857-84-0(9))* Educational Impressions.

Jenkins, Carol Brennan, et al. Nonfiction Author Studies in the Elementary Classroom. 2007. (Illus.). 160p. pap. 26.25 *(978-0-325-00855-4(8),* E00855) Heinemann.

Johnson, Nancy J. & Giorgis, Cyndi. The Wonder of It All: When Literature & Literacy Intersect. 2007. (Illus.). 224p. pap. 32.50 *(978-0-325-00973-5(2),* E00973) Heinemann.

Jordan, Louise. How to Write for Children & Get Published. 2010. (ENG., Illus.). 192p. pap. 15.95 *(978-0-7499-4061-4(1))* Piatkus Bks. GBR. Dist: Independent Pubs. Group.

Kerr, Judith. When Hitler Stole Pink Rabbit. 2009.Tr. of Cuando Hitler Robo el Conejo Rosa. (ENG.). 192p. (J). (gr. 4-6). 6.99 *(978-0-14-241408-8(5),* Puffin) Penguin Group (USA) Inc.

Kiefer, Barbara. Charlotte Huck's Children's Literature. 10th ed. 2009. (ENG.). 688p. (C). 165.00 *(978-0-07-337856-5(9),* 0073378569) McGraw-Hill Cos., The.

Kiefer, Barbara Zulandt, et al. Children's Literature: A Brief Guide. 2009. (ENG., Illus.). 368p. (C). pap., instr.'s gde. ed. 85.00 *(978-0-07-340383-0(0),* 0073403830) McGraw-Hill Cos., The.

Leland, Christine, et al. Teaching Children's Literature. 2012. (ENG., Illus.). 240p. 140.00 ***(978-0-415-50866-7(5))***; pap. 49.95 ***(978-0-415-50868-1(1))*** Routledge.

Lewis, C. S. The Lion, the Witch & the Wardrobe. 2009. (Narnia Ser.). (ENG.). 176p. (J). (gr. 3). 20.00 *(978-0-06-171505-1(0))* HarperCollins Pubs.

Lynch-Brown, Carol & Tomlinson, Carl M. Essentials of Children's Literature. 6th ed. 2007. (ENG., Illus.). 432p. (C). per. 71.33 *(978-0-205-52032-9(4))* Allyn & Bacon, Inc.

—Essentials of Children's Literature (with MyEducationKit) 7th ed. 2010. (ENG.). (C). pap. 82.67 *(978-0-13-707402-0(6))* Allyn & Bacon, Inc.

Lynch-Brown, Carol, et al. Essentials of Children's Literature. 7th ed. 2010. (MyEducationKit Ser.). (ENG., Illus.). 432p. (C). pap. 78.67 *(978-0-13-704884-7(X))* Allyn & Bacon, Inc.

Mariana, Cortez. Through Lines & Words. 2010. 348p. pap. *(978-3-639-25861-5(4))* VDM Verlag Dr. Mueller e.K.

Matthew, Kathryn I. & Lowe, Joy L. Neal-Schuman Guide to Recommended Children's Books & Media for Use with Every Elementary Subject. 2nd ed. 2010. 400p. 80.00 *(978-1-55570-688-3(6))* Neal-Schuman Pubs., Inc.

Miller, Pat. Stretchy Lesson Plans: August/September. 2007. (Illus.). 77p. per. 15.95 *(978-1-932146-92-9(X),* Upstart Bks.) Highsmith Inc.

Monseau, Virginia R. Teaching the Selected Works of Robert Cormier. 2007. (Young Adult Novels in the Classroom Ser.). (Illus.). 96p. pap. 21.25 *(978-0-325-00745-8(4),* E00745) Heinemann.

Novel Units, Inc. Staff, creator. Cloudy with a Chance of Meatballs Teacher Guide. 2010. (J). *(978-1-56137-977-4(8))* Novel Units, Inc.

—The Invention of Hugo Cabret Teacher Guide. 2010. (J). *(978-1-60878-106-5(2))* Novel Units, Inc.

Nyberg, Judy. Charts for Children 2E. 2007. 176p. pap. 19.95 *(978-1-59647-135-1(2))* Good Year Bks.

O'Callaghan, Catherine M., et al. Using Children's Literature Across the Curriculum: A Handbook of Instructional Strategies. 2010. (ENG.). 264p. (C). pap. 35.00 *(978-0-13-171191-4(1),* Allyn & Bacon) Pearson Education Canada CAN. Dist: Pearson Education.

Olness, Rebecca. Using Literature to Enhance Content Area Instruction: A Guide for K-5 Teachers. 2007. 218p. (gr. 17). 24.95 *(978-0-87207-600-6(8))* International Reading Assn.

Paterson, Katherine. La Gran Gilly Hopkins.Tr. of Great Gilly Hopkins. (SPA.). (J). (gr. 6-8). 9.95 *(978-970-29-0434-2(X),* AF0939) Santillana, S.A. de C.V., Editorial MEX. Dist: Santillana USA Publishing Co., Inc.

The Pearl. 8.97 *(978-0-673-58331-4(7))* Addison-Wesley Longman, Inc.

Polette, Keith & Polette, Nancy. Spoofing & Proofing the Classics: Literature-Based Activities to Develop Critical Reading Skills & Grammatical Knowledge, 1 vol. 2007. 116p. per. 25.00 *(978-1-59158-518-3(X),* TIP518X, Teacher Ideas Pr.) Libraries Unlimited, Inc.

Polette, Nancy. Get up & Move with Nonfiction Grades 4-8, 1 vol. 2007. (Illus.). 176p. per. 30.00 *(978-1-59158-661-6(5),* TIP6661, Teacher Ideas Pr.) Libraries Unlimited, Inc.

Prentice-Hall Staff & Hamilton, Virginia. The House of Dies Drear. 2nd ed. stu. ed. *(978-0-13-717083-8(1))* Prentice Hall (Schl. Div.).

Raines, Shirley C. & Smith, Brian Scott. Story Stretchers for the Primary Grades: Activities to Expand Children's Books. 2011. (Story S-t-r-e-t-c-h-e-r-s Ser.). (ENG., Illus.). 256p. (gr. k-4). pap. 29.95 ***(978-0-87659-309-7(0))*** Gryphon Hse., Inc.

Reid, Rob. Shake & Shout: 16 Noisy, Lively Story Programs. 2008. (Illus.). 110p. pap. 17.95 *(978-1-60213-006-7(X),* Upstart Bks.) Highsmith Inc.

—Something Musical Happened at the Library: Adding Song & Dance to Children's Story Programs. 2007. (Illus.). 158p. per. 35.00 *(978-0-8389-0942-3(6))* American Library Assn.

Rende, Thomas. Novel Ideas: Judy Blume's Fudge Series: Tales of a Fourth Grade Nothing/Otherwise Known as Sheila the Great/Super Fudge/Fudge-A-Mania/Double Fudge. 2007. (Illus.). 136p. per. 19.99 *(978-0-9793576-0-2(8))* New Learning Publishing.

—Novel Ideas: Roald Dahl Classics: Charlie & the Chocolate Factory/Charlie & the Great Glass Elevator/James & the Giant Peach. 2007. (Novel Ideas Ser.). (Illus.). 81p. spiral bd. 12.99 *(978-0-9793576-7-1(5))* New Learning Publishing.

—Novel Ideas: the Magic Tree House Series: Books 1-4. 2007. 79p. spiral bd. 12.99 *(978-0-9793576-4-0(0))* New Learning Publishing.

Rende, Thomas & Rende, Crystal. Novel Ideas: The Magic Tree House Series Books 5 - 8. 2007. (Novel Ideas Ser.). 79p. spiral bd. 12.99 *(978-0-9793576-5-7(9))* New Learning Publishing.

—Novel Ideas: The Magic Tree House Series Books 9 - 12. 2007. (Novel Ideas Ser.). 79p. spiral bd. 12.99 *(978-0-9793576-6-4(7))* New Learning Publishing.

Rende, Thomas, et al. Novel Ideas: Prequel Series to Peter Pan: Peter & the Starcatchers/Peter & the Shadow Thieves. 2007. (Novel Ideas Ser.). (Illus.). 89p. spiral bd. 12.99 *(978-0-9793576-9-5(1))* New Learning Publishing.

Rogers, Linda K. Shaped by the Standards: Geographic Literacy Through Children's Literature, 1 vol. 2008. (Through Children's Literature Ser.). (Illus.). 200p. pap. 35.00 *(978-1-59158-462-9(0),* TIP4620, Teacher Ideas Pr.) Libraries Unlimited, Inc.

Sawyer, Walter. Growing up with Literature. 6th ed. 2011. (Whatrsquo;s New in Early Childhood Ser.). (ENG.). 400p. (C). pap. 95.95 *(978-1-111-34265-4(2))* Wadsworth.

Smolen, Lynn Atkinson & Oswald, Ruth A. Multicultural Literature & Response: Affirming Diverse Voices. 2010. E-Book *(978-1-59884-475-7(X))* Libraries Unlimited, Inc.

Stoodt-Hill, Barbara D. & Amspaugh-Corson, Linda B. Children's Literature: Discovery for a Lifetime. 4th ed. 2008. (ENG., Illus.). 412p. (C). pap. 102.20 *(978-0-13-158939-1(3),* Prentice Hall) Prentice Hall PTR.

Towell & Towell, Janet. Hooked on Books: Language Arts & Literature in Elementary Classrooms Prek-Grade 8. rev. ed. 2011. (ENG.). 464p. pap. 100.17 *(978-0-7575-7320-0(7))* Kendall Hunt Publishing Co.

Travers, John F. & Travers, Barbara E. Children's Literature: A Developmental Perspective. 2008. (ENG., Illus.). 440p. (C). per. 138.95 *(978-0-470-11104-8(6),* Wiley) Wiley, John & Sons, Inc.

Tunnell, Michael O., et al. Children's Literature, Briefly. 5th ed. 2011. (ENG.). 336p. (C). pap. 78.67 *(978-0-13-248056-7(5))* Allyn & Bacon, Inc.

Wanamaker, Karen A. Farmer. Instant Library Lessons: Fall Fun. 2008. (Instant Library Lessons Ser.). (Illus.). 181p. (J). (gr. -1-3). pap. 17.95 *(978-1-932146-78-3(4),* Upstart Bks.) Highsmith Inc.

Wartenberg, Thomas E. Big Ideas for Little Kids: Teaching Philosophy through Children's Literature. 2009. (ENG.). 164p. pap. 25.95 *(978-1-60709-335-0(9))* Rowman & Littlefield Education.

—Big Ideas for Little Kids: Teaching Philosophy Through Children's Literature. 2009. (ENG.). 164p. 65.00 *(978-1-60709-334-3(0))* Rowman & Littlefield Education.

Wrich, Gordon, et al. Literacy: Reading, Writing & Children's Literature. 4th rev. ed. 2010. (ENG., Illus.). xlvi, 748p. (Orig.). pap. 89.95 *(978-0-19-556563-8(0))* Oxford Univ. Pr., Inc.

Wooten, Deborah A. & Cullinan, Bernice E., eds. Children's Literature in the Reading Program: An Invitation to Read. 3rd ed. 2009. (ENG.). 200p. pap. 27.95 *(978-0-87207-699-0(7))* International Reading Assn.

Yellin, David G. & DeVries, Beverly A. Sharing the Journey: Literature for Young Children. 2011. *(978-1-934432-07-5(5))* Holcomb Hathaway, Inc.

Yenika-Agbaw, Vivian. African & African-American Children's & Adolescent Literature in the Classroom: A Critical Guide. 2011. (Black Studies & Critical Thinking Ser.). 318p. (C). 129.95 ***(978-1-4331-1196-9(9))*** Lang, Peter Publishing, Inc.

—African & African American Children's & Adolescent Literature in the Classroom: A Critical Guide. 2011. (Black Studies & Critical Thinking Ser.). 320p. (C). pap. 32.95 ***(978-1-4331-1195-2(0))*** Lang, Peter Publishing, Inc.

Zitlow, Connie S. Teaching the Selected Works of Walter Dean Myers. 2007. (Young Adult Novels in the Classroom Ser.). 96p. pap. 21.25 *(978-0-325-00886-8(8),* E00886) Heinemann.

CHILDREN'S LITERATURE—TECHNIQUE

see also New Literates, Writing for

Cowley, Joy. Writing from the Heart: How to Write for Children. 2011. (ENG.). 128p. 19.95 ***(978-1-59078-871-4(0))*** Boyds Mills Pr.

Crook, Marion. Writing Books for Children & Young Adults. 2nd ed. 2007. (ENG., Illus.). 208p. pap. 18.95 *(978-1-55180-813-0(7))* Self-Counsel Pr., Inc. CAN. Dist: Midpoint Trade Bks., Inc.

Dils, Tracey E. You Can Write Children's Books. 2nd ed. 2009. (ENG., Illus.). 176p. pap. 14.99 *(978-1-58297-573-3(6),* Writer's Digest Bks.) F&W Media, Inc.

Gordon Smith, A. Writing Best Selling Children?'s Boo. 2007. (52 brilliant ideas Ser.). (Illus.). n/ap. pap. 9.99 *(978-1-905940-07-3(6))* Infinite Ideas GBR. Dist: Sony Electronics.

Jordan, Louise. How to Write for Children - And Get Published. AS, ed. 2007. (ENG.). 192p. pap. 19.95 *(978-0-7499-2772-1(0))* Piatkus Bks. GBR. Dist: Independent Pubs. Group.

—How to Write for Children & Get Published. 2010. (ENG., Illus.). 192p. pap. 15.95 *(978-0-7499-4061-4(1))* Piatkus Bks. GBR. Dist: Independent Pubs. Group.

Melrose, Andrew. Here Comes the Bogeyman: Exploring Contemporary Issues in Writing for Children. 2012. (ENG., Illus.). 152p. (C). 130.00 *(978-0-415-61752-9(9))*; pap. 31.95 *(978-0-415-61753-6(7))* Routledge.

Strachan, Linda. Writing for Children. 2008. (Writing Handbooks Ser.). (ENG.). 192p. pap. 19.95 *(978-0-7136-8774-3(6),* Methuen Drama) A & C Black GBR. Dist: Macmillan.

CHILDREN'S MUSEUMS

see also Museums and Schools

Leikop, Epp. Starting a Children'S Museum. 2010. 80p. pap. *(978-3-8383-6101-7(6))* Lambert Academic Publishing.

Norris, Joann. Children's Museums: An American Guidebook. 2nd rev. ed. 2009. (ENG., Illus.). 235p. pap. 39.95 *(978-0-7864-4000-9(7))* McFarland & Co., Inc. Pubs.

CHILDREN'S PARAPHERNALIA

see also Children's Clothing; Children's Furniture; Children's Playhouses; Toys

Anderson, Susan B. Itty-Bitty Nursery: Sweet, Adorable Knits for the Baby & Beyond. 2007. (ENG., Illus.). 164p. (J). pap. 17.95 *(978-1-57965-334-7(0),* 1579653340) Artisan.

Baird, Nicola. Homemade Kids: Thrifty, Creative & Eco-Friendly Ways to Raise Your Child. 2010. (ENG.). 278p. pap. 19.95 ***(978-0-09-192989-3(X))*** Random Hse. GBR. Dist: Independent Pubs. Group.

Christian, Vicki & Marshall, Paula, eds. Great Kids' Rooms Collection. 2006. (Better Homes & Gardens Decorating Ser.: 8). (ENG., Illus.). 288p. pap. 19.95 *(978-0-696-22972-5(2),* Wiley) Wiley, John & Sons, Inc.

Consumer Reports Editors & Gordon, Sandra. Best Baby Products. 10th ed. 2009. (Consumer Reports Best Baby Products Ser.). (ENG.). 368p. pap. 16.95 *(978-1-933524-24-5(3))* Consumer Reports Bks.

Cram101 Textbook Reviews & Cram101 Textbook Reviews. Outlines & Highlights for Ergonomics for Children: Designing Products & Places for Toddlers to Teens by Rani Lueder (Editor) 2011. 172p. pap. 29.95 ***(978-1-61830-359-2(7))*** Cram101 Inc.

Danger, Kimberly. COMPL BK of Baby Bargains. 2nd ed. 2010. (ENG.). 432p. pap. 12.99 *(978-1-4022-3717-1(0))* Sourcebooks, Inc.

Fields, Denise & Fields, Alan. Baby Bargains: Secrets to Saving 20% to 50% on baby furniture, gear, clothes, toys, maternity wear & much, much More! 9th rev. ed. 2011. (ENG.). 608p. pap. 17.95 *(978-1-889392-40-0(5))* Windsor Peak Pr.

Fierlinger, Hadley. Vintage Knits for Modern Babies. 2009. (ENG., Illus.). 104p. pap. 19.99 *(978-1-58008-960-9(7))* Ten Speed Pr.

Givens, Tina. Sew Tina! 30 Cute Projects & Adorable Decor Items for Kidscs. 2010. (ENG., Illus.). 144p. spiral bd. 24.95 *(978-1-60059-425-0(5))* Lark Bks.

Gott Warner, Kara, ed. Baby Nouveau: Stylish Blankets for Baby. 2011. (ENG., Illus.). 48p. pap. 12.95 ***(978-1-59217-339-6(X),*** House of White Birches, Inc.) Annie's Publishing, LLC.

Gutman, Marta, ed. Designing Modern Childhoods: History, Space, & the Material Culture of Children. 2008. (Rutgers Series in Childhood Studies). (ENG., Illus.). 368p. 70.00 *(978-0-8135-4195-2(6))* Rutgers Univ. Pr.

Gutman, Marta & de Coninck-Smith, Ning, eds. Designing Modern Childhoods: History, Space, & the Material Culture of Children. 2008. (Rutgers Series in Childhood Studies). (ENG., Illus.). 368p. per. 24.95 *(978-0-8135-4196-9(4))* Rutgers Univ. Pr.

Hoffman, Rosalyn. Smart Mama, Smart Money: Raising Happy, Healthy Kids Without Breaking the Bank. 2012. (ENG.). 320p. (gr. 12). 15.00 ***(978-0-451-23559-6(2),*** N A L Trade) Penguin Group (USA) Inc.

Lamb, Sharon & Brown, Lyn Mikel. Packaging Girlhood: Rescuing Our Daughters from Marketers' Schemes. annot. ed. 2007. (ENG., Illus.). 336p. pap. 14.95 *(978-0-312-37005-3(9),* St. Martin's Griffin) St. Martin's Pr.

Lamb, Sharon, et al. Packaging Boyhood: Saving Our Sons from Superheroes, Slackers, & Other Media Stereotypes. 2009. (ENG.). 320p. 25.99 *(978-0-312-37939-1(0))* St. Martin's Pr.

Lowenstein, Alison. City Kid New York: The Ultimate Guide for NYC Parents. 2010. (ENG.). 224p. pap. 18.95 *(978-0-7893-1878-7(4))* Universe Publishing.

McElwee, Meg. Growing up Sew Liberated: Making Handmade Clothes & Projects for Your Creative Child. 2011. (ENG., Illus.). 160p. pap. 24.95 *(978-1-59668-162-0(4))* Interweave Pr., LLC.

Minguet, Eva & Minguet, Josep M. Kids Design. 2010. (SPA & ENG., Illus.). 256p. 49.50 *(978-84-96096-98-1(0))* Instituto Monsa de Ediciones, S.A. ESP. Dist: Trans-Atlantic Pubns., Inc.

Morton Palter, Elisa & Wert, Shari. Help!.. We've Got Kids: GTA's Complete Childrens Resource Directory Covering Oakville Topickering & Newmarket to the Lake. 15th ed. 2008. (Help... We've Got Kids Ser.). (Illus.). 342p. pap. *(978-1-896208-24-4(X))* Help...We've Got Kids.

Protecting Children from Lead-Tainted Imports: Hearings Before the Subcommittee on Commerce, Trade, & Consumer Protection of the Committee on Energy & Commerce, House of Representatives, One Hundred Tenth Congress, First Session, September 19 & 20, 2007. 2008. (Illus.). vi, 281p. *(978-0-16-082649-8(7),* 552-070-38668-8) United States Government Printing Office.

Protecting Our Children: Current Issues in Children's Product Safety: Hearing Before the Subcommittee on Commerce, Trade, & Consumer Protection of the Committee on Energy & Commerce, House of Representatives, One Hundred Tenth Congress, First Session, May 15, 2007. 2008. vi, 236p. *(978-0-16-082680-1(2),* 552-070-38697-1) United States Government Printing Office.

C

Richardson, Phyllis. Designed for Kids: A Complete Sourcebook of Stylish Products for the Modern Family. 2008. (ENG., Illus.). 256p. 34.95 *(978-0-500-51413-9(5))* Thames & Hudson.

Shreeve, Rebecca. Nursery Stitch: 20 Projects to Make. 2010. (ENG.). 112p. pap. 14.99 *(978-0-7641-4469-1(3))* Barron's Educational Series, Inc.

Thoren Turner, Krista. Start Your Own Kid-Focused Business & More: Party Planning, Gift & Bath Products, Educational Toys & Games, Plus-Size Clothing, Cooking Classes. 2008. (ENG.). 250p. pap. 17.95 *(978-1-59918-258-2(0),* 1599182580) Entrepreneur Pr. dba Entrepreneur Media, Inc.

Turner, Krista Thoren. Kids-Focused Businesses. 2008. (Illus.). 264p. pap. 69.00 *(978-1-59918-226-1(2))* Entrepreneur Pr. dba Entrepreneur Media, Inc.

Wagman, Tracie. Help! . We've Got Kids. 18th ed. 2011. (Help!., We've Got Kids Ser.). (ENG., Illus.). 278p. pap. ***(978-1-896208-27-5(4))*** Help...We've Got Kids.

Wolk, Bruce H. Made Here, Baby! The Essential Guide to Finding the Best American-Made Products for Your Kids, 1 vol. 2009. (ENG.). 304p. pap. 17.95 *(978-0-8144-1388-3(9))* Amacom.

Woram, Catherine. Gifts for Baby: 25 Simple Projects to Welcome the New Arrival. 2007. (ENG., Illus.). 128p. pap. *(978-1-84597-458-9(1))* Ryland Peters & Small.

CHILDREN'S PARTIES

Alexiadou, Alexia. Cooking a Fairytale: 400 Recipes & Ideas for Children's Parties. 2007. (Illus.). 240p. 69.95 *(978-960-85875-1-9(4))* Alexia Alexiadou, Greece GRC. Dist: Perseus-PGW.

Amos, Janell Shride. Entertaining Children: Theme Parties, Activities, Games & Fun Ideas for Groups. alt. ed. 2011. (ENG.). 144p. pap. 25.00 ***(978-0-7864-6702-0(9))*** McFarland & Co., Inc. Pubs.

Dodd, Jenny. Party Fun! Themes, Cakes, Invitations, Treat Bags, Food, Games. 2007. (ENG., Illus.). 168p. pap. 17.95 *(978-1-77007-399-9(X))* New Holland Pubs., Ltd. GBR. Dist: Sterling Publishing Co., Inc.

Gabriel, Annette S. Children's Parties & How to Plan Them. Lowrie, Drucella, ed. 2011. 128p. 40.95 ***(978-1-258-07221-6(1))*** Literary Licensing, LLC.

Hylton, Dawn, et al, texts. Taking Tea with Alice: Looking Glass Tea Parties. 2008. (ENG., Illus.). 85p. (J). 19.95 *(978-0-9793431-4-8(3))* Benjamin Pr.

Kothari, Lisa. Dear Peppers & Pollywogs... What Parents Want to Know about Planning Their Kids' Parties. 2007. per. 9.95 *(978-0-9794968-0-6(2))* Peppers & Pollywogs Pr.

Lynette, Rachel. Let's Throw a Halloween Party! 2011. 49.50 *(978-1-4488-2728-2(0))*; pap. 8.25 *(978-1-4488-2727-5(2))*; lib. bdg. 21.25 *(978-1-4488-2569-1(5))* Rosen Publishing Group, Inc., The. (PowerKids Pr.).

Marson, Caroline. Party Food for Kids. 2007. (ENG., Illus.). 64p. *(978-1-84597-477-0(8))* Ryland Peters & Small.

Mullaney, Colleen. Presbool Parties: Easy Ideas for Princesses, Pirates & Other Little People. 2011. (ENG., Illus.). 144p. pap. 17.95 *(978-1-936096-17-6(X))* Sixth&Spring Bks.

Mullaney, Colleen & Chronicle Books Staff. Fairy Parties: Recipes, Crafts, & Games for Enchanting Celebrations. 2010. (ENG., Illus.). 144p. 19.95 *(978-0-8118-6731-3(5))* Chronicle Bks. LLC.

Peters, Amy Jean. How to Start a Home-Based Children's Birthday Party Business. 2008. (Home-Based Business Ser.). (Illus.). 192p. pap. 18.95 *(978-0-7627-4938-6(5))* Globe Pequot Pr., The.

Reynolds, Kate E. Party Planning for Children & Teens on the Autism Spectrum: How to Avoid Meltdowns & Have Fun! 2012. (ENG., Illus.). 128p. pap. ***(978-1-84905-277-1(8))*** Kingsley, Jessica Ltd.

Ryland Peters & Small Staff, creator. Birthdays. 2007. (ENG., Illus.). 112p. *(978-1-84597-407-7(7))* Ryland Peters & Small.

Wolgemuth, Bobbie. Tea Parties with a Purpose: 10 Simple & Fun Party Ideas for Kids of All Ages. 2009. (ENG., Illus.). 128p. 14.99 *(978-1-4165-7294-7(5),* Howard Bks.) Howard Books.

CHILDREN'S PERIODICALS

Brewer, Susan. A History of Girls' Comics. 2010. (Illus.). 240p. 39.95 *(978-1-84468-072-6(X))* Pen & Sword Bks. Ltd. GBR. Dist: Casemate Pubs. & Bk. Distributors, LLC.

Kawabata. The Girls' Own Paper, -4 (1880-1883), Victorian Periodicals, Vol. 1. 2007. 3200p. 1295.00 *(978-4-902454-17-8(3))* Synapse, Edition JPN. Dist: Taylor & Francis Group.

CHILDREN'S PLAYHOUSES

see also Tree Houses

Al Khalaileh, Eyyad. UNDERSTANDING CHILDREN'S ENVIRONMENTS: Where To Go, Where To Play: Growing up in Cities: Are Their Any Places For Us In The City. 2008. 244p. pap. *(978-3-639-10104-1(9))* VDM Verlag Dr. Mueller e.K.

Kashef, Ziba & Sunset Books Staff. Backyards for Kids: Playhouses, Sandboxes, Tree Forts, Swing Sets, Sports Areas, & More. 2008. (ENG., Illus.). 144p. pap. 16.95 *(978-0-376-01060-5(6),* Sunset Bks./Sunset Publishing Corp.) Oxmoor Hse., Inc.

Stiles, Jeanie & Stiles, David. Treehouses & Playhouses You Can Build, 1 vol. 2006. (ENG., Illus.). 144p. pap. 19.99 *(978-1-58685-780-6(0))* Gibbs Smith, Publisher.

Sunset Magazine Editors. Sunset Outdoor Design & Build - Backyards for Kids: Fresh Ideas for Outdoor Living. 2012. (ENG., Illus.). 176p. pap. 19.95 *(978-0-376-01436-8(9))* Oxmoor Hse., Inc.

Zander, Jean-Paul Deridder City of Children, Berlin: City of Transience. 2009. (ENG.). 104p. 60.00 *(978-3-7757-2286-5(6))* Hatje Cantz Verlag GmbH & Co KG DEU. Dist: D.A.P./Distributed Art Pubs.

CHILDREN'S PLAYS

see also Bible Plays; College and School Drama

Abingdon Press, creator. A Rooster's Tale: Easter Dramas, Speeches, & Recitations for Children. 2007. 48p. pap. 7.50 *(978-0-687-46500-2(1))* Abingdon Pr.

Antologia de Dramas para Ninos.Tr. of Anthology of Dramas for Children. (SPA.). pap. 4.50 *(978-0-311-07013-8(2))* Casa Bautista de Publicaciones.

Bany-Winters. On Stage: Theater Games & Activities for Kids. 2nd ed. 2012. (ENG.). 208p. (J). (gr. 2-6). pap. 16.95 *(978-1-61374-073-6(5))* Chicago Review Pr., Inc.

Beck, Andy & Fisher, Brian. The Nightingale: An Enchanting Imperial Tale for Unison & 2-Part Voices, Based on a Story by Hans Christian Andersen (Director's Score) 2007. (ENG.). 76p. pap. 19.95 *(978-0-7390-4748-4(5))* Alfred Publishing Co., Inc.

Black, Ann N. Readers Theatre for Middle School Boys: Investigating the Strange & Mysterious, 1 vol. 2008. (Readers Theatre Ser.). (Illus.). 204p. (gr. 4-7). per. 30.00 *(978-1-59158-535-0(X),* TIP8535, Teacher Ideas Pr.) Libraries Unlimited, Inc.

Black, Kathryn A. & Black, Ann N. More Readers Theatre for Middle School Boys: Adventures with Mythical Creatures, 1 vol. 2009. (Readers Theatre Ser.). 153p. pap. 28.00 *(978-1-59158-757-6(3),* TIP8757) Libraries Unlimited, Inc.

Brennan, Kit, ed. Things That Go Bump: Volume 2, Plays for Young Audiences. 2009. 312p. pap. 22.95 *(978-1-897109-41-0(5))* Signature Editions CAN. Dist: Univ. of Toronto Pr.

Bufano, Ariel. La Bella y la Bestia.Tr. of Beauty & the Beast. (SPA., Illus.). 55p. 10.95 *(978-950-9732-31-5(1))* Coquena Grupo Editor, Libros del Quirquincho ARG. Dist: AIMS International Bks., Inc.

Come Rack! Come Rope! 17.00 *(978-1-931555-13-5(3))* Our Lady of Victory Schl.

Dabrowski, K. Ult Aud BK Teens, Vol. 10. 2006. 128p. pap. 11.95 *(978-1-57525-528-6(6))* Smith & Kraus Pubs., Inc.

Dabrowski, Kristen. 111 One-Minute Monologues by Type. 2007. (Ultimate Audition Book for Teens Ser.). (ENG.). 117p. pap. *(978-1-57525-529-3(4))* Smith & Kraus Pubs., Inc.

Dahl, Roald. The Twits: A Set of Plays. 2007. (ENG., Illus.). 128p. (J). (gr. 2-18). 5.99 *(978-0-14-240793-6(3),* Puffin) Penguin Group (USA) Inc.

—The Witches: A Set of Plays. 2007. (ENG., Illus.). 128p. (J). (gr. 2-18). 5.99 *(978-0-14-240794-3(1),* Puffin) Penguin Group (USA) Inc.

Edgeworth, Maria. The Parent's Assistant. 2008. 496p. (gr. 4-7). 31.99 *(978-0-554-38253-1(9))*; 33.99 *(978-0-554-28950-2(4))* BiblioBazaar.

—The Parent's Assistant. 2011. 552p. (gr. 4-7). pap. 42.75 ***(978-1-173-85986-2(1))*** BiblioBazaar.

—The Parent's Assistant. 2009. 332p. pap. *(978-1-4068-5153-3(1))* Echo Library.

—The Parent's Assistant. 2010. (Illus.). 292p. (gr. 4-7). pap. 36.93 *(978-1-153-71583-6(X))*; 158p. pap. 21.43 *(978-1-151-77354-8(9))* General Bks. LLC.

Figley, Marty Rhodes. President Lincoln, Willie Kettles, & the Telegraph Machine. 2010. (History Speaks: Picture Books Plus Reader's Theater Ser.). (Illus.). 48p. (J). (gr. 2-4). lib. bdg. 27.93 *(978-1-58013-671-6(0),* Millbrook Pr.) Lerner Publishing Group.

Foon, Dennis. New Canadian Kid/Invisible Kid. 2007. (ENG.). 96p. per. 15.95 *(978-0-88754-830-7(X))* Theatre Communications Group, Inc.

Fredericks, Anthony D. Mother Goose Readers Theatre for Beginning Readers, 1 vol. 2007. (Readers Theatre Ser.). (SPA & ENG., Illus.). 188p. per. 25.00 *(978-1-59158-500-8(7),* TIP5007, Teacher Ideas Pr.) Libraries Unlimited, Inc.

Garner, Joan. Wings of Fancy: Using Readers Theatre to Study Fantasy Genre, 1 vol. 2006. (Readers Theatre Ser.). (Illus.). 256p. pap. 30.00 *(978-1-59158-342-4(X),* LU342X, Teacher Ideas Pr.) Libraries Unlimited, Inc.

González, José Cruz. Nine Plays by José Cruz González: Magical Realism & Mature Themes in Theatre for Young Audiences. Jennings, Coleman A., ed. 2008. (Louann Atkins Temple Women & Culture Ser.). (ENG., Illus.). 347p. pap. 24.95 *(978-0-292-71855-5(1))* Univ. of Texas Pr.

Gurley, Gregory. Drama & Moral Education. 2008. 180p. pap. *(978-3-639-05380-7(X))* VDM Verlag Dr. Mueller e.K.

Jagendorf, M. 25 Non Royalty Holiday Plays. 2007. (ENG.). 288p. 43.95 *(978-0-548-05694-3(3))* Kessinger Publishing, LLC.

Johnson, Neil. Childrens Plays. 182p. pap. 24.95 *(978-1-56861-020-7(3))* Swift Learning Resources.

Jordan, Pat. Nursery Rhyme Plays: From Every Teacher's Friend Classroom Plays Vol. 5: Nursery Rhyme Plays. 2011. 40p. pap. 5.00 *(978-0-88734-066-6(0))* Players Pr., Inc.

—Plays from Around the World: From Every Teacher's Friend Classroom Plays Vol. 3: Plays from Around the World. 2011. (Illus.). 80p. (J). pap. 7.00 *(978-0-88734-064-2(4))* Players Pr., Inc.

Korba, Joanna. Next!, Observing the Ants. 2011. (Readers' & Writers' Genre Workshop Ser.). (YA). pap. *(978-1-4509-3014-7(X))* Benchmark Education Co.

Lewis, Mack. Read-Aloud Plays: Classic Short Stories. 2011. (Illus.). 72p. (J). ***(978-0-439-20456-9(9),*** Teaching Resources) Scholastic, Inc.

Lewis, Mack. Read-Aloud Plays - Classic Short Stories: 8 Fluency-Boosting Plays with Easy Activities That Teach Key Literary Elements. 2011. (ENG.). 72p. (gr. 4-8). pap. 11.99 *(978-0-545-20456-9(9),* Teaching Resources) Scholastic, Inc.

MacHardy, Dilan. Mothello, the Butterfly of Venus: A High-Flying Introduction to Shakespeare for Kids (Phakespeare's Animal Shakespeare for Children Series) 2008. (Illus.). 176p. (YA). pap. 15.00 *(978-0-9785237-0-1(9))* Phakespeare Prodns.

Pujado, Lynda. A Night in Shining Darkness. 5.95 *(978-1-55673-656-8(8))* CSS Publishing Co.

Russell, Mary M. Dramatized Bible Stories for Young People. 2007. (ENG.). 108p. (gr. 4-7). 33.95 *(978-0-548-06015-5(0))* Kessinger Publishing, LLC.

Shaw, George Bernard. Androcles & the Lion. 2008. 108p. 21.99 *(978-1-60512-073-7(1))*; pap. 10.99 *(978-1-60512-173-4(8))* Akasha Publishing, LLC. (Akasha Classics).

—Androcles & the Lion. 2008. 56p. pap. 7.95 *(978-1-4385-0490-2(X),* Book Jungle) Standard Pubns., Inc.

Smith, Carrie. Old Mother Hubbard's Hungry Family. 2008. (Reader's Theater Nursery Rhymes & Songs Ser.). (Illus.). 48p. (J). (gr. k-1). pap. *(978-1-60437-959-4(6))* Benchmark Education Co.

Sodaro, Craig. Make It Mystery: An Anthology of Short Mystery Plays. 2006. 223p. per. 19.95 *(978-1-56608-115-3(7))* Meriwether Publishing, Ltd.

Sole, Mia & Haycock, Jeff. Theatre Games for Elementary School Children Ages 7-12. 2009. pap. 24.95 *(978-0-578-01219-3(7))* Play-Ground Theatre Co.

—Theatre Games for Preschool Children Ages 3-6. 2009. pap. 24.95 *(978-0-578-01175-2(1))* Play-Ground Theatre Co.

Stevenson, Augusta. Children's Classics in Dramatic Form. 2009. 228p. 23.99 *(978-1-103-58677-6(7))* 2009. 228p. pap. 17.99 *(978-1-103-58675-2(0))* 2008. 228p. pap. 24.99 *(978-0-559-25009-5(6))* 2008. 228p. pap. 24.75 *(978-0-559-25007-1(X))* 2008. 202p. 24.99 *(978-0-554-83157-2(0))* 2008. 200p. 22.99 *(978-0-554-32639-9(6))* 2008. 200p. 25.99 *(978-0-554-23336-9(3))* 2008. 202p. 21.99 *(978-0-554-83164-0(3))* 2008. 259p. pap. 20.75 *(978-0-554-83160-2(0))* 2008. 263p. pap. 21.75 *(978-0-554-83158-9(9))* 2007. (ENG.). 162p. pap. 19.99 *(978-1-4264-4180-6(0))* 2006. 196p. pap. 21.99 *(978-1-4264-4221-6(1))* BiblioBazaar.

—Children's Classics in Dramatic Form. 2009. 118p. pap. *(978-0-217-45936-5(6))* Books LLC.

Weinstein, Elizabeth. Shakespeare with Children: Six Scripts for Young Players. 2008. (Illus.). 240p. pap. 19.95 *(978-1-57525-573-6(1))* Smith & Kraus Pubs., Inc.

Wilson, Jacqueline. Bad Girls. 2006. (Nick Hern Bks.). (ENG.). 96p. (gr. 7-12). per. 16.95 *(978-1-85459-910-0(0))* Hern, Nick Bks., Ltd. GBR. Dist: Consortium Bk. Sales & Distribution.

—The Lottie Project. 2006. (ENG.). 96p. (gr. 7-12). per. 16.95 *(978-1-85459-911-7(9))* Hern, Nick Bks., Ltd. GBR. Dist: Consortium Bk. Sales & Distribution.

—The Lottie Project. 14.35 *(978-0-7569-0427-2(7))* Perfection Learning Corp.

—Midnight. 2006. (Nick Hern Bks.). (ENG.). 96p. (gr. 4-7). per. 18.95 *(978-1-85459-909-4(7))* Hern, Nick Bks., Ltd. GBR. Dist: Consortium Bk. Sales & Distribution.

Yavneh, Naomi & Miller, Naomi. Gender & Early Modern Constructions of Childhood. 2011. (Women & Gender in the Early Modern World Ser.). (Illus.). 264p. 99.95 ***(978-1-4094-2997-5(0))*** Ashgate Publishing Co.

Young, Rebecca. 10-Minute Plays for Middle School Performers: Plays for a variety of cast Sizes. 2008. 130p. (YA). pap. 17.95 *(978-1-56608-158-0(0))* Meriwether Publishing, Ltd.

CHILDREN'S PLAYS—PRESENTATION, ETC.

see Children's Theater

CHILDREN'S POETRY

see also Children's Songs; Nursery Rhymes

Alford, Gene. Busy Little Feet. 2007. (ENG.). 108p. (gr. 4-7). 34.95 *(978-0-548-05887-9(3))* Kessinger Publishing, LLC.

Appelt, Kathi. Poems from Homeroom. 2010. (ENG.). 128p. (J). pap. 14.95 *(978-0-8050-7596-0(8),* Holt, Henry & Co. Bks. For Young Readers) Holt, Henry & Co.

Barker, Charles Ferguson, illus. From the Outside Looking In. 2011. pap. ***(978-0-8137-6033-9(X))*** Geological Society of America, Inc.

Barner, Bob. Bob Barner & You, 1 vol. 2006. (Author & YOU Ser.). (Illus.). 136p. per. 35.00 *(978-1-59158-262-5(8),* LU2628) Libraries Unlimited, Inc.

Belloc, Hilaire. Cautionary Tales & Bad Child's Book of Beasts. 2008. (Dover Children's Classics Ser.). (ENG.). 128p. pap. 7.99 *(978-0-486-46785-6(6))* Dover Pubns., Inc.

Black Jack the Bold & the Other Verse: Level O, 6 vols. (Wonder Worldtm Ser.). 48p. 39.95 *(978-0-7802-2954-9(1))* Wright Group, The.

Bleck, Linda, illus. A Children's Treasury of Nursery Rhymes. 2006. (ENG.). 24p. (J). (gr. -1-k). bds. 12.95 *(978-1-4027-2980-5(4))* Sterling Publishing Co., Inc.

Brown, Margaret Wise. Nibble Nibble. 2007. (Illus.). 32p. (J). (gr. -1-3). lib. bdg. 17.89 *(978-0-06-059209-7(5))* HarperCollins Pubs.

Carleton, Will. Young Folks' Centennial Rhymes by Will Carleton. 2006. 128p. per. 16.99 *(978-1-4255-0855-5(3))* MPublishing.

Cary, Alice. Ballads for Little Folk. 2009. 104p. pap. *(978-1-151-34470-0(2))* Books LLC.

—Ballads for Little Folk. 2010. (Illus.). 62p. pap. 15.81 *(978-1-154-63490-7(6))* General Bks. LLC.

Cary, Alice & Cary, Phoebe. Ballads for Little Folk. Ames, Mary Clemmer, ed. 202p. 2010. 31.96 *(978-1-166-51182-1(0))* 2009. 39.95 *(978-1-120-22722-5(4))* 2009. pap. 24.95 *(978-1-120-16133-8(9))* Kessinger Publishing, LLC.

Crane, Thomas. London Town: A Facsimile. 2011. (Illus.). 56p. 19.95 *(978-0-7123-5814-9(5))* British Library, The GBR. Dist: Chicago Distribution Ctr.

Creative Communication, ed. Celebrating What Is Important to Me - East 4-6 Spring 2006. 2006. (J). 21.95 *(978-1-60050-017-6(X))* Creative Communication.

Dafad, Cyfres Pen & Lolfa, Y. Cawl Lloerig. 2008. (Nofelau A Storiau I'R Arddegau Novels & Stories for Young Adults Ser.). (WEL., Illus.). 64p. pap. *(978-0-86243-702-2(4))* Y Lolfa.

Davenport, E. Story Poems for Young & Old. 2007. 460p. per. *(978-1-4067-6980-5(1),* Pierides Pr.) Read Bks.

Desnos, Robert. Chantefables et Chantefleurs. (FRE., Illus.). 7.95 *(978-0-8288-9579-8(1),* F98094) French & European Pubns., Inc.

Dumad, Philippe. Comptines Francaises. (FRE.). pap. *(978-2-08-162862-5(7))* Flammarion et Cie.

Dyan, Penelope. Fairies & Stuff. 2007. 108p. 17.95 *(978-0-9794006-4-3(3))*; 108p. 16.95 *(978-0-9794006-3-6(5))*; 104p. per. 8.95 *(978-0-9794006-2-9(7))* Bellissima Publishing, LLC.

—Stuff & Nonsense. 2007. 108p. 16.95 *(978-0-9793358-8-4(4))*; 108p. 17.95 *(978-0-9793358-9-1(2))*; 104p. per. 8.95 *(978-0-9793358-7-7(6))* Bellissima Publishing, LLC.

Feldman, Jody. Golfer's Night Before Christmas. 59.50 *(978-0-87905-724-4(6))* Gibbs Smith, Publisher.

Field, Eugene. Second Book of Verse. 2009. 88p. pap. *(978-0-217-28966-5(5))* Books LLC.

—Second Book of Verse. 2009. 152p. pap. 14.14 *(978-1-4589-6957-6(6))* General Bks. LLC.

—Second Book of Verse. 2007. 268p. 42.95 *(978-0-548-01783-8(2))* Kessinger Publishing, LLC.

—Second Book of Verse. 2006. 272p. per. 23.99 *(978-1-4255-2414-2(1))* MPublishing.

—Second Book of Verse. 2008. 272p. pap. *(978-1-4097-3205-1(3))* Read Bks.

—With Trumpet & Drum. 2008. 140p. 21.99 *(978-0-559-52908-5(2))*; pap. 19.75 *(978-0-559-52905-4(8))* BiblioBazaar.

—With Trumpet & Drum. 2007. (ENG.). 138p. 35.95 *(978-0-548-00867-6(1))* Kessinger Publishing, LLC.

—With Trumpet & Drum. 2007. (ENG.). 136p. per. *(978-1-4067-7666-9(1))* Read Bks.

Fitzmaurice, Gabriel. Really Rotten Rhymes. 2008. (ENG., Illus.). 96p. (J). (gr. -1). per. 12.95 *(978-1-85635-544-5(6))* Mercier Pr., Ltd., The IRL. Dist: Dufour Editions, Inc.

Fitzmaurice, Gabriel & MacDonald, Stella. Do Teachers Go to the Toilet? 2010. (ENG.). 96p. (J). pap. 12.95 *(978-1-85635-657-2(4))* Mercier Pr., Ltd., The IRL. Dist: Dufour Editions, Inc.

FLH Students & Lutz, Suzanne. Many Voices: Where Dreams Take Flight III: Audio CD. 2008. 149p. pap. 19.95 *(978-0-7414-4570-4(0))* Infinity Publishing.

Florian, Douglas. Dinothesaurus: Prehistoric Poems & Paintings. 2009. (ENG., Illus.). 56p. (J). (gr. 1-4). 16.00 *(978-0-15-216496-6(0),* Houghton Mifflin Bks. for Children) Houghton Mifflin Harcourt Trade & Reference Pubs.

Foster, John. My First Oxford Book of Poems. 2007. (ENG., Illus.). 96p. (YA). (gr. 4-7). pap. 14.99 *(978-0-19-276339-6(3))* Oxford Univ. Pr., Inc.

Franco, Betsy, ed. Falling Hard: 100 Love Poems by Teenagers. 2008. (ENG., Illus.). 160p. (YA). (gr. 9). 15.99 *(978-0-7636-3437-7(9))* Candlewick Pr.

Fusek Peters, Andrew, compiled by. Poems about Air. 2007. (Elements in Poetry Ser.). (Illus.). 30p. (J). 18.95 *(978-0-237-52888-1(6),* Evans Brothers, Limited) Evans Publishing Group GBR. Dist: Independent Pubs. Group.

Giovanni, Nikki. Hip Hop Speaks to Children: A Celebration of Poetry with a Beat. 2008. (ENG., Illus.). 80p. (J). (gr. 1-3). 19.99 *(978-1-4022-1048-8(5),* Sourcebooks Jabberwocky) Sourcebooks, Inc.

Gould, Hannah Flagg. The Youth's Coronal. 2008. 168p. 25.99 *(978-0-554-26973-3(2))* 2008. 168p. 22.99 *(978-0-554-36276-2(7))* 2007. (ENG.). 140p. pap. 18.99 *(978-1-4346-2209-9(6))* 2007. (ENG.). 166p. pap. 21.99 *(978-1-4346-2269-3(X))* BiblioBazaar.

—The Youth's Coronal. 2009. 140p. pap. *(978-1-4099-7481-9(2))* Dodo Pr.

Griffin, Jennifer. Humpty Who? A Crash Course in 80 Nursery Rhymes for Clueless Moms & Dads. 2007. (ENG., Illus.). 224p. (J). 11.95 *(978-0-7611-4368-0(8),* 0761143688) Workman Publishing Co., Inc.

Guest, Edgar A. Rhymes of Childhood. 190p. 20.95 *(978-0-8488-2547-8(0))* Amereon LTD.

Harrison, David. Bugs: Poems about Creeping Things. 2007. (ENG., Illus.). 55p. (J). (gr. -1-3). 16.95 *(978-1-59078-451-8(0))* Boyds Mills Pr.

Harrison, David L. Sounds of Rain: Poems of the Amazon. 2006. (ENG., Illus.). 32p. (J). (gr. -1-3). 16.95 *(978-1-59078-442-6(1))* Boyds Mills Pr.

Hawkins, Wendy. Living on My Farm. 2010. (Illus.). 20p. pap. 13.99 *(978-1-4389-7462-0(0))* AuthorHouse.

Hazard, Bertha. Three Years with the Poets. 2009. 176p. pap. *(978-0-217-30627-0(6))*; 172p. pap. *(978-0-217-80527-8(2))* Books LLC.

Heine, Heinrich. Gedichte. pap. 26.95 *(978-3-257-20383-7(7))* Diogenes Verlag AG CHE. Dist: Distribooks, Inc.

Hernández, Miguel & Aguilar, José. 4 Poemas de Miguel Hernández y una Canción de Cuna. 2008. (SPA., Illus.). 32p. pap. *(978-84-934160-6-5(1))* Atalante.

Hillert, Margaret. Come Play with Me. 2008. (ENG., Illus.). 32p. (J). pap. *(978-1-59577-058-5(5))* Starfall Education.

Hirsch, Edward. How to Read a Poem: And Fall in Love with Poetry. 2010. (ENG.). 354p. pap. 15.00 *(978-1-4379-7372-3(8))* DIANE Publishing Co.

Hughes, Ted. Collected Poems for Children. 2007. (ENG., Illus.). 272p. (J). (gr. 3-18). 18.00 *(978-0-374-31429-3(2),* Farrar, Straus & Giroux (BYR)) Farrar, Straus & Giroux.

Hugo, Victor. Chanson pour faire danser En. (FRE.). pap. 20.95 *(978-2-07-053914-7(8))* Gallimard, Editions FRA. Dist: Distribooks, Inc.

Janeczko, Paul B. Dirty Laundry Pile: Poems in Different Voices. 2007. (Illus.). 40p. (J). (gr. k-5). pap. 6.99 *(978-0-06-113613-9(1)*, Harper Trophy) HarperCollins Pubs.

Karapetkova, Holly. Shapes. 2006. (Poetry (Rourke) Ser.). (Illus.). 16p. (J). pap. 6.95 *(978-1-59515-972-4(X))* Rourke Publishing, LLC.

Katz, Bobbi. Trailblazers: Poems of Exploration. 2007. (Illus.). 208p. (J). (gr. 5-9). lib. bdg. 19.89 *(978-0-688-16534-5(6))* HarperCollins Pubs.

Kids Express Series, 6 bks., Set. 128.21 *(978-0-7614-1503-9(3)*, Benchmark Bks.) Marshall Cavendish Corp.

Lamb, Charles. Poetry for Children, 2 Vols. reprint ed. lib. bdg. 196.00 *(978-0-7426-2088-9(3))* Classic Bks.

—Poetry for Children. 2008. 128p. pap. *(978-1-4065-4906-5(1))* Dodo Pr.

Lansky, Bruce. My Teacher's in Detention: Kids' Favorite Funny School Poems. 2006. (Illus.). 73p. (J). *(978-0-88166-514-7(2))* Meadowbrook Pr.

Lear, Edward. The Owl & the Pussycat. Manhoff, Bill, ed. 2011. pap. 8.95 ***(978-0-573-61354-8(0))*** French, Samuel Inc.

Letria, Jose, et al. The Moon Has Written You a Poem. Riordan, Maurice, tr. from POR. & adapted by by. 2006. (Picture books from around the World Seri Ser.). (ENG., Illus.). 60p. (J). (gr. 2-4). 22.95 *(978-1-905341-00-9(8))* WingedChariot Pr. GBR. Dist: Independent Pubs. Group.

Lewis, J. Patrick. Black Cat Bone: The Life of Blues Legend Robert Johnson. 2006. (ENG., Illus.). 48p. (J). (gr. 5-17). 24.95 *(978-1-56846-194-6(1)*, Creative Editions) Creative Co., The.

Longfellow, Henry Wadsworth. The Song of Hiawatha. 2008. 188p. 23.99 *(978-1-60512-046-1(4))*; pap. 12.99 *(978-1-60512-146-8(0))* Akasha Publishing, LLC. (Akasha Classics).

—The Song of Hiawatha. 2009. 324p. 36.99 *(978-1-113-75453-0(2))* 2009. 324p. 32.99 *(978-1-113-75451-6(6))* 2009. 324p. pap. 30.75 *(978-1-113-75449-3(4))* 2009. 324p. pap. 29.75 *(978-1-113-75448-6(6))* 2008. 228p. 27.99 *(978-0-554-23431-1(9))* 2007. (ENG.). 186p. pap. 19.99 *(978-1-4264-4385-5(4))* BiblioBazaar.

—The Song of Hiawatha. 2009. 124p. pap. *(978-1-151-12820-1(1))*; 154p. pap. *(978-0-217-39762-9(X))* Books LLC.

—The Song of Hiawatha. 2009. 124p. pap. 5.99 *(978-1-4209-3248-5(9))* Digireads.com.

—The Song of Hiawatha. (ENG.). 2008. 200p. pap. 13.95 *(978-1-60597-313-5(0))* 2007. 212p. per. 7.45 *(978-1-60424-085-6(7))* Standard Pubns., Inc. (Book Jungle).

Longfellow, Henry Wadsworth & Jordan, Elizabeth. The Song of Hiawatha. 2007. (ENG.). 226p. pap. 22.99 *(978-1-4264-4423-4(0))* BiblioBazaar.

Low, Elizabeth Cothen. Big Book of Animal Rhymes, Fingerplays, & Songs, 1 vol. 2009. (Illus.). 300p. pap. 40.00 *(978-1-59158-630-2(5)*, LU8630) Libraries Unlimited, Inc.

Miles Kelly Publishing, creator. Great Poems. 2007. (Illus.). 511p. pap. *(978-1-84236-576-2(2))* Miles Kelly Publishing, Ltd.

Minkova, Milena & Tunberg, Terence. Mater Anserina: Poems in Latin for Children. 2006. (LAT., Illus.). 68p. pap. 19.95 *(978-1-58510-193-1(1))* Focus Publishing/R. Pullins Co., Inc.

Miranda, Anne. To Market, to Market. 2007. (ENG., Illus.). 34p. (J). (gr. k — 1). bds. 11.99 *(978-0-15-205903-3(2)*, Houghton Mifflin Harcourt) Houghton Mifflin Harcourt Trade & Reference Pubs.

Montoney, Jeanette. Silly Animal Poems: Crocodile; the Donkey; the Elephant Who Jumped a Fence; Little Bird; A Horse & a Flea & Three Blind Mice; I Never Had a Dog That Could Talk; Five Little Froggies; Quincy, 8 bks., Set. 2006. (ENG.). 8p. (J). pap. 120.00 *(978-1-893986-31-2(4))* Keep Bks.

Moore, Clement. T'was the Night Before Christmas. 2010. (ENG.). pap. 12.95 *(978-1-937004-13-2(9))* Old Line Publishing, LLC.

Moore, Clement C. The Night Before Christmas. 2006. (Dover Coloring Bks.). (ENG., Illus.). 32p. (J). pap. 4.99 *(978-0-486-45211-1(5))* Dover Pubns., Inc.

—The Night Before Christmas. (Live Oak Readalong Ser.). pap. 18.95 incl. audio compact disk *(978-1-59519-331-5(6))* Live Oak Media.

—Twas the Night Before Christmas. 2008. (ENG., Illus.). 34p. (J). 15.00 *(978-0-9800285-7-7(4))* O'More Publishing.

Moore, Clement Clarke. The Night Before Christmas. 2006. (ENG., Illus.). 40p. (J). (gr. -1-18). 17.99 *(978-0-399-23745-4(3)*, Philomel) Penguin Group (USA) Inc.

Morley, Amanda. Going & Doing Poems: Zoom, Zoom, Zoom; Lunar Lars; I Have a Little Wagon; Chickery, Chickery, Cranny, Crow; Here Is the Sea; Hippity Hop; Window Watching; This Is the Way We Go to School, 8 bks., Set. 2006. (ENG.). 8p. (J). pap. 120.00 *(978-1-893986-28-2(4))* Keep Bks.

Morpurgo, Ida Bohatta, illus. The Gnome's Almanack. 2011. 28p. 35.95 ***(978-1-258-04782-5(9))*** Literary Licensing, LLC.

Nelson, Marilyn. A Wreath for Emmett Till. 2009. 9.68 *(978-0-7848-3207-3(2)*, Everbind) Marco Bk. Co.

Nesbitt, Ken. Revege of the Lunch Ladies. Lansky, Bruce, ed. 2007. (ENG., Illus.). 80p. (J). pap. 8.95 *(978-1-4169-4364-8(1))* Meadowbrook Pr.

Nesbitt, Kenn & Knaus, Linda. Santa Got Stuck in the Chimney: 20 Funny Poems Full of Christmas Cheer. 2006. (Illus.). 30p. *(978-0-88166-515-4(0))* Meadowbrook Pr.

Nursery Songs. 2006. (J). *(978-1-884270-09-3(3))* Hall, Nancy Inc.

Nystrom, Marty & Bjorkman, Steve. Don't Mess with Moses! Peculiar Poems & Rib-Tickling Rhymes. 2010. (ENG., Illus.). 192p. (J). (gr. 1). 17.99 *(978-0-7847-1833-9(4))* Standard Publishing.

O'Donnell, E. E., ed. All Our Yesterdays: Father Browne's Photgraphs of Children & Their Favorite Poems. 2007. (ENG., Illus.). 132p. 44.95 *(978-1-85607-952-5(X))* Columba Pr. IRL. Dist: Dufour Editions, Inc.

Peters, Andrew Fusek, compiled by. Poems about Fire. 2006. (Elements in Poetry Ser.). (Illus.). 30p. (J). 19.95 *(978-0-237-52885-0(1)*, Evans Brothers, Limited) Evans Publishing Group GBR. Dist: Independent Pubs. Group.

Phinn, Gervase. What I Like! Poems for the Very Young. 2007. (Poetry Ser.). (ENG., Illus.). 32p. (J). (gr. -1-3). pap. incl. audio compact disk *(978-1-84643-028-2(3))* Child's Play International Ltd.

Pottle, Robert. I'm Allergic to School! Funny Poems & Songs about School. 2007. (ENG., Illus.). 32p. (J). (gr. k-7). 11.95 *(978-1-4169-2947-5(9))* Meadowbrook Pr.

Prelutsky, Jack. It's Christmas! 2008. (I Can Read Book 3 Ser.). (ENG., Illus.). 48p. (J). (gr. k-3). 16.99 *(978-0-06-053706-7(X))* HarperCollins Pubs.

—It's Snowing! It's Snowing! Winter Poems. 2006. (I Can Read Bks.). (ENG., Illus.). 48p. (J). (gr. k-3). per. 3.99 *(978-0-06-053717-3(5))* HarperCollins Pubs.

—It's Thanksgiving. 2007. (I Can Read Bks.). (Illus.). 44p. (J). (gr. -1-3). lib. bdg. 17.89 *(978-0-06-053709-8(4)*, Greenwillow Bks.) HarperCollins Pubs.

—It's Valentine's Day. 2008. (I Can Read Book 3 Ser.). 48p. (J). 16.99 *(978-0-06-053712-8(4)*, Greenwillow Bks.) HarperCollins Pubs.

Ramirez, Claudia. Mandaderos de la Lluvia. Lee, Claudia M., ed. 2011. Tr. of Messengers of Rain. (SPA & ENG., Illus.). 160p. (J). (gr. 6). pap. 14.95 *(978-1-55498-114-4(X))* Groundwood Bks. CAN. Dist: Perseus-PGW.

Rat de ville et le rat des Champs. 13.95 *(978-2-09-202113-2(3))* Nathan, Fernand FRA. Dist: Distribooks, Inc.

Rehg, Paul A. Critter Poems: The Elephant Goes Like This; Baby Mice; Gray Squirrel; Here Is a Bunny; Little Snail; Hickety Pickety; If I Were a Bird; My Dog Rags, 8 bks., Set. 2006. (ENG.). 8p. (J). pap. 120.00 *(978-1-893985-29-9(2))* Keep Bks.

Richards, Laura E. Mrs Tree. 2010. 290p. 35.16 *(978-1-163-32320-5(9))* 2010. 290p. pap. 23.16 *(978-1-162-78555-4(1))* 2007. (ENG.). 288p. 43.95 *(978-0-548-01098-3(6))* Kessinger Publishing, LLC.

Richards, Laura Elizabeth Howe. Mrs Tree. 2011. 294p. pap. 28.75 ***(978-1-179-67169-7(4))*** BiblioBazaar.

—Mrs Tree. 2009. 86p. pap. *(978-1-151-35846-2(0))* Books LLC.

—Mrs Tree. 2010. 74p. pap. 20.00 *(978-1-153-82636-5(4))* General Bks. LLC.

Riley, James Whitcomb. Riley Child-Rhymes. 2008. 72p. pap. *(978-1-4065-2445-1(X))* Dodo Pr.

—Riley Child-Rhymes. 2008. 184p. (gr. -1-3). pap. *(978-1-4086-7921-0(3))* Read Bks.

—Riley Child-Rhymes. 2008. 188p. 24.95 *(978-1-4344-7542-8(5))*; pap. 14.95 *(978-1-4344-7541-1(7))* Wildside Pr., LLC.

Rylant, Cynthia. Boris. 2006. (ENG., Illus.). 80p. (J). (gr. 9-12). pap. 7.95 *(978-0-15-205809-8(5)*, Sandpiper) Houghton Mifflin Harcourt Trade & Reference Pubs.

—Boris. 14.80 *(978-0-7569-6893-9(3))* Perfection Learning Corp.

Schertle, Alice. Teddy Bear, Teddy Bear. 2006. (Illus.). 28p. (J). (gr. k-4). reprint ed. 16.00 *(978-1-4223-5554-1(3))* DIANE Publishing Co.

Shakespeare, William. Winter Song. 2006. (ENG., Illus.). 32p. (J). (gr. k-4). 15.95 *(978-1-59078-275-0(5))* Boyds Mills Pr.

Shapiro, Karen Jo. I Must Go down to the Beach Again: And Other Poems. 2007. (Illus.). 48p. (J). (gr. 4-7). 14.95 *(978-1-58089-143-1(8))* Charlesbridge Publishing, Inc.

Smith, H. Allen. Write Me a Poem, Baby. 16.95 *(978-0-8488-0149-6(0))* Amereon LTD.

Stevenson, Robert Louis. A Child's Garden of Verses. Stevenson, Robert Louis, ed. reprint ed. lib. bdg. 48.00 *(978-0-7426-1048-4(9))* Classic Bks.

Stone, Tiffany. Baaaad Animals, 1 vol. 2007. (ENG., Illus.). 64p. (J). (gr. k-4). per. 7.95 *(978-1-896580-36-4(X))* Tradewind Bks. CAN. Dist: Orca Bk. Pubs. USA.

Thompson, Blanche J. Silver Pennies. 16.95 *(978-0-8488-1487-8(8))* Amereon LTD.

Twin Sister Produtions Staff & Galvin, Laura Gates. Sesame Street Abby Cadabby's Nursery Rhymes. 2010. (J). (gr. k-2). 14.99 *(978-1-59922-527-2(1))* Twin Sisters Productions, LLC.

Waldman, K. D Is for Dog Team - D Is for Denali. 2010. 15.00 *(978-0-9816758-2-4(4))* Nomadic Pr.

Wells, Rosemary. Twinkle, Twinkle Little Star. 2006. (ENG., Illus.). 18p. (J). (gr. k — 1). bds. 6.99 *(978-0-439-87886-9(1)*, Scholastic Pr.) Scholastic, Inc.

Wiggin, Kate Douglas & Smith, Nora Archibald. The Posy Ring: A Book of Verse for Children. 2008. (ENG.). 224p. pap. 20.99 *(978-1-4346-9251-1(5))*; 268p. pap. 23.99 *(978-1-4346-9252-8(3))* BiblioBazaar.

Yolen, Jane. The Emily Sonnets: The Life of Emily Dickinson in Verse. 2012. (ENG.). 40p. (J). (gr. 6-17). 19.99 ***(978-1-56846-215-8(8)***, Creative Editions) Creative Co., The.

Zook, Miriam. We Want to Learn about Zoo Animals. 2007. (Little Learners Ser.). (Illus.). 48p. (J). (gr. 2). 4.55 *(978-0-7399-2387-0(0))* Rod & Staff Pubs., Inc.

CHILDREN'S POETRY—HISTORY AND CRITICISM

Blanchard, Mary Loving & Falcetti, Cara. Poets for Young Adults: Their Lives & Works, 1 vol. 2006. (Illus.). 304p. 59.95 *(978-0-313-32884-8(6)*, GR2884, Greenwood Pr.) Greenwood Publishing Group, Inc.

Kreller, Susan. Englischsprachige Kinderlyrik: Deutsche Ubersetzungen Im 20. Jahrhundert. (GER.). XII, 365p. pap. 68.95 *(978-3-631-56544-5(5))* Lang, Peter GmbH, Europaischer Verlag der Wissenschaften DEU. Dist: Lang, Peter Publishing, Inc.

Thomas, Joseph T. Poetry's Playground: The Culture of Contemporary American Children's Poetry. 2007. (Landscapes of Childhood Ser.). (Illus.). 180p. per. 24.95 *(978-0-8143-3296-2(X))* Wayne State Univ. Pr.

Winstanley, Carrie. Poetry & Childhood. 2010. (Illus.). 270p. pap. 37.95 *(978-1-85856-472-2(7))* Trentham Bks. Ltd. GBR. Dist: Stylus Publishing, LLC.

CHILDREN'S POETRY—STUDY AND TEACHING

Carlow, Regina. Exploring the Connection Between Children's Literature & Music, 1 vol. 2008. (Illus.). 132p. pap. 30.00 *(978-1-59158-439-1(6)*, LU4396) Libraries Unlimited, Inc.

CHILDREN'S PORTRAITS

see Children in Art

CHILDREN'S PRAYERS

see Children—Prayers and Devotions

CHILDREN'S QUESTIONS AND ANSWERS

Arnstein, Helene S. What to Tell Your Child about Birth, Death, Illness, Divorce, & Other Family Crises. 2011. 202p. 44.95 ***(978-1-258-08200-0(4))*** Literary Licensing, LLC.

Bartell, Susan. Top 50 Questions Kids Ask (3rd through 5th Grade) 2010. (ENG.). 256p. pap. 10.99 *(978-1-4022-1916-0(4))* Sourcebooks, Inc.

—Top 50 Questions Kids Ask (Pre-K through 2nd Grade) 2010. (ENG.). 240p. pap. 10.99 *(978-1-4022-1915-3(6))* Sourcebooks, Inc.

Berger, Melvin. Do Tarantulas Have Teeth? Questions & Answers about Poisonous Creatures. 15.85 *(978-0-7569-1739-5(5))* Perfection Learning Corp.

—Do Tornadoes Really Twist? Questions & Answers about Tornadoes & Hurricanes. 15.85 *(978-0-7569-1740-1(9))* Perfection Learning Corp.

Bild Buch Staff. Warum? Warum? Was Kinder wissen Wollen. (GER.). 128p. pap. *(978-3-548-42007-3(9))* Ullstein-Taschenbuch-Verlag DEU. Dist: International Bk. Import Service, Inc.

Bostrom, Kathleen Long. Existen los Angeles? 2006. (Little Hearts Ser.). (SPA., Illus.). 73p. (J). 8.99 *(978-0-7899-1005-9(5))* Editorial Unilit.

Burchett, Author Walter, BA. Christian children's questions & answers walk of christ Volume 6. 2009. (ENG.). 32p. pap. 14.28 *(978-0-557-08155-4(6))* Lulu Enterprises Inc.

Charman, Andy, et al. My First Book of Knowledge: 1001 Fantastic Facts & 801 Great Pictures. 2008. (ENG., Illus.). 128p. (J). pap. 16.99 *(978-1-84476-461-7(3))* Anness Publishing GBR. Dist: National Bk. Network.

Galens, Judy & Pear, Nancy. The Handy Answer Book for Kids: and Parents. (Illus.). 382p. pap. *(978-1-57859-181-7(3))* Visible Ink Pr.

Group Publishing. Trust Us — They'll Ask: Answers to Your Kids' Toughest & Most Awkward Questions. 2010. pap. *(978-0-7644-4911-6(7))* Group Publishing, Inc.

Jamieson, Wendell. Father Knows Less: One Dad's Quest to Answer His Son's Most Baffling Questions. 2008. (ENG.). 320p. (gr. 12-18). 13.95 *(978-0-399-53458-4(X)*, Perigee Trade) Penguin Group (USA) Inc.

—Father Knows Less or, Can I Cook My Sister? One Dad's Quest to Answer His Son's Most Baffling Questions. l.t. ed. 2008. (Laugh Lines Ser.). (Illus.). 365p. 29.95 *(978-1-4104-0495-4(1))* Thorndike Pr.

Payne, Jan. Liar! Liar! Pants on Fire! 2012. (ENG.). 144p. (gr. 12-18). 9.99 ***(978-1-60652-476-3(3)***, Reader's Digest Juvenile) Penguin Group (USA) Inc.

—Liar! Liar! Pants on Fire! Can You Spot the Truth among the Lies? 2012. (J). ***(978-1-60652-477-0(1))*** Reader's Digest Assn., Inc., The.

Richardson, Rhonda A. & Pevec, A. Margaret. What Kids Really Want to Ask: Using Movies to Start Meaningful Conversations. 2007. (Illus.). 192p. per. 12.95 *(978-1-889242-31-6(4))* VanderWyk & Burnham.

Ripley, Catherine. How? The Most Awesome Question & Answer Book about Nature, Animals, People, Places — And You! 2012. (ENG., Illus.). 192p. (J). (gr. -1-2). 19.95 ***(978-1-926973-24-1(0))*** Owlkids Bks. Inc. CAN. Dist: Perseus-PGW.

Shields, Amy. National Geographic Little Kids First Big Book of Why. 2011. (ENG., Illus.). 128p. (J). (gr. -1-1). 14.95 *(978-1-4263-0793-5(4)*, National Geographic Children's Bks.) National Geographic Society.

Tîrnauca, Cristina. Formal Language Learning with Correction Queries. 2009. 152p. pap. *(978-3-639-17698-8(7))* VDM Verlag Dr. Mueller e.K.

CHILDREN'S REFERENCE BOOKS

see also Children's Encyclopedias and Dictionaries

Batra, Arjun. Make Your Kid Smarter Than Other Kids. 2010. 76p. pap. 27.49 *(978-1-4490-6350-4(0))* AuthorHouse.

Harper, Meghan. Reference Sources & Services for Youth. 2011. (Illus.). 250p. 65.00 *(978-1-55570-641-8(X))* Neal-Schuman Pubs., Inc.

Muldavin, Peter. The Complete Guide to Vintage Children's Records. 2006. (ENG., Illus.). 432p. per. 24.95 *(978-1-57432-509-6(4)*, 1574325094) Collector Bks.

CHILDREN'S REFERENCE BOOKS—BIBLIOGRAPHY

Safford, Barbara Ripp. Guide to Reference Materials for School Library Media Centers, 1 vol. 6th rev. ed. 2010. 236p. 60.00 *(978-1-59158-277-9(6)*, LU2776) Libraries Unlimited, Inc.

CHILDREN'S RIGHTS

see also Children—Legal Status, Laws, etc.

Abiad, Nisrine & Mansoor, Farkhanda. Criminal Law & the Rights of the Child in Muslim States: A Comparative & Analytical Perspective. 2010. 395p. pap. 90.00 *(978-1-905221-45-5(2))* British Institute of International & Comparative Law GBR. Dist: International Specialized Bk. Services.

Abramson, Bruce. Article 2: Non-Discrimination. 2008. (Commentary on the United Nations Convention on the Rights of the Child Ser.). 100p. (C). pap. *(978-90-04-14917-5(1))* BRILL.

Achilihu, Stephen Nmeregini. Do African Children Have Rights? A Comparative & Legal Analysis of the United Nations Convention on the Rights of the Child. 2010. 280p. pap. 25.95 *(978-1-59942-853-6(9))* Universal Pubs.

Agaltsova, Marina. Elimination of Child Labor. 2010. 100p. pap. *(978-3-8383-8313-2(3))* Lambert Academic Publishing.

Alderson, Priscilla. Young Children's Rights: Exploring Beliefs, Principles & Practice. 2nd ed. 2008. (ENG., Illus.). 192p. pap. *(978-1-84310-599-2(3))* Kingsley, Jessica Ltd.

Alen, Andre, et al, eds. The UN Children's Rights Convention Vol. 1: Theory Meets Practice. 2007. (Illus.). 658p. pap. 154.00 *(978-90-5095-640-6(8))* Intersentia Uitgevers N.V. BEL. Dist: International Specialized Bk. Services.

Arne, Robert. Children's Rights in Ghana: Reality or Rhetoric? 2011. (ENG., Illus.). 310p. 75.00 *(978-0-7391-4800-6(1))* Lexington Bks.

Apodaca, Clair. Child Hunger & Human Rights: International Governance. 2010. (Routledge Research in Human Rights Ser.). (ENG., Illus.). 192p. (C). 128.00 *(978-0-415-55269-1(9))* Routledge.

Awaleh, Mahad. Child Labor & Access to Education. 2008. 128p. pap. *(978-3-639-09403-9(4))* VDM Verlag Dr. Mueller e.K.

Balakrishnan, Vijayalakshmi. Growing up & Away: Narratives of Indian Childhoods Memory, History, Identity. 2011. (ENG.). 288p. 65.00 ***(978-0-19-807126-6(4))*** Oxford Univ. Pr., Inc.

Bell, Margaret. Promoting Children's Rights in Social Work & Social Care: A Guide to Participatory Practice. 2011. (ENG., Illus.). 224p. pap. ***(978-1-84310-607-4(8))*** Kingsley, Jessica Ltd.

Ben-Arieh, Asher, et al. Measuring & Monitoring Children's Well-Being. 2010. (Social Indicators Research Ser.). 184p. pap. 139.00 *(978-90-481-5642-9(4)*, 9048156424) Springer.

Billet, Bret L. Cultural Relativism in the Face of the West: The Plight of Women & Female Children. rev. ed. 2007. (ENG., Illus.). 240p. 89.00 *(978-0-312-22131-7(2))* Palgrave Macmillan.

Brennan, Samantha & Noggle, Robert, eds. Taking Responsibility for Children. 2007. (Studies in Childhood & Family in Canada Ser.). (ENG.). 210p. pap. 42.95 *(978-1-55458-015-6(3))* Wilfrid Laurier Univ. Pr. CAN. Dist: Univ. of Toronto Pr.

Brocklehurst, Helen. Who's Afraid of Children? Children Conflict & International Relations. 2006. (Ethics & Global Politics Ser.). (Illus.). 204p. 120.00 *(978-0-7546-4171-1(6))* Ashgate Publishing Co.

Bromdal, Annette. Intersex. 2008. 136p. pap. *(978-3-639-05882-6(8))* VDM Verlag Dr. Mueller e.K.

Burns, Lynch. Children's Rights & Child Protection: Critical Times, Critical Issues In Ireland. Burns, Kenneth & Lynch, Deborah, eds. 2012. (ENG., Illus.). 256p. 100.00 ***(978-0-7190-8627-4(2))*** Manchester Univ. Pr. GBR. Dist: Macmillan.

Butler, Clark W., ed. Child Rights: The Movement, International Law, & Opposition. 2012. (ENG.). 260p. pap. 35.00 *(978-1-55753-549-8(3))* Purdue Univ. Pr.

Cantwell, Nigel & Holzscheiter, Anna. A Commentary on the United Nations Convention on the Rights of the Child, Article 20: Children Without Parental Care. 2007. (Commentary on the United Nations Convention on the Rights of the Child Ser.). 51p. pap. *(978-90-04-14873-4(6))* BRILL.

Carpenter, Charli. Forgetting Children Born of War: Setting the Human Rights Agenda in Bosnia & Beyond. 2010. (ENG., Illus.). 304p. (gr. 17). 35.00 *(978-0-231-15130-6(6))* Columbia Univ. Pr.

Carpenter, Charli, ed. Born of War: Protecting Children of Sexual Violence Survivors in Conflict Zones. 2007. (Illus.). 288p. pap. 24.95 *(978-1-56549-237-0(4))* Stylus Publishing, LLC.

Cassidy, Claire. Thinking Children. 2009. (ENG.). 208p. 44.95 *(978-1-4411-8754-3(5))* Continuum International Publishing Group, Ltd. GBR. Dist: National Bk. Network.

—Thinking Children: The Concept of 'Child' from a Philosophical Perspective. 2008. (ENG.). 208p. 140.00 *(978-0-8264-9818-2(3))* Continuum International Publishing Group, Ltd. GBR. Dist: National Bk. Network.

Casualties of War: Child Soldiers & the Law: Hearing Before the Subcommittee on Human Rights & the Law of the Committee on the Judiciary, United States Senate, One Hundred Tenth Congress, First Session, April 24, 2007. 2007. ii, 105p. *(978-0-16-079848-1(5)*, 552-070-36742-0) United States Government Printing Office.

Chan, Edward Ko Ling, ed. Child Protection in Chinese Societies: Challenges & Policies. 2012. ***(978-1-61942-879-9(2))*** Nova Science Pubs., Inc.

Cohen, C.P. The Negotiations for a New Agreement on Agriculture. 2011. (Nijhoff International Trade Law Ser.). (ENG.). XIV, 322p. ***(978-1-57105-375-6(1))*** BRILL.

Council of Europe Staff. Rights of children at risk & in Care (2007) 2007. 80p. pap. 18.00 *(978-92-871-6039-3(2))* Council of Europe FRA. Dist: Manhattan Publishing Co.

Council of Europe Staff, compiled by. Abolishing corporal punishment of Children: Questions & Answers. 2007. (Illus.). 52p. pap. 18.00 *(978-92-871-6310-3(3))* Council of Europe FRA. Dist: Manhattan Publishing Co.

—Eliminating corporal punishment 2nd Edition: A human rights imperative for Europe's Childres. 2nd ed. 2007. 133p. pap. 29.00 *(978-92-871-6182-6(8))* Council of Europe FRA. Dist: Manhattan Publishing Co.

Covell, Katherine & Howe, R. Brian. Empowering Children: Children's Rights Education as a Pathway to Citizenship. 2007. 252p. pap. *(978-0-8020-9523-7(2))* Univ. of Toronto Pr.

Covell, Katherine & Howe, Robert Brian. Children, Families & Violence: Challenges for Children's Rights. Covell, Katherine et al, eds. 2008. (ENG.). 288p. pap. *(978-1-84310-698-2(1))* Kingsley, Jessica Ltd.

Crosson-Tower, Cynthia. A Clergy Guide to Child Abuse & Neglect. 2006. 256p. per. *(978-0-8298-1595-5(3))* Pilgrim Pr., The/United Church Pr.

David, Paulo. The Right to Leisure, Play & Culture: Article 31. 2006. (Commentary on the United Nations Convention on the Rights of the Child Ser.). 33p. pap. *(978-90-04-14882-6(5))* BRILL.

Davidson, Julia & Hamerton, Christopher. International Perspectives on Child Victimisation. 2012. (ENG.). 208p. 125.00 *(978-0-415-57957-5(0))* Routledge.

Davis, Samuel M. Children's Rights under & the Law. 2011. (ENG.). 474p. 95.00 *(978-0-19-979548-2(7))* Oxford Univ. Pr., Inc.

De Boyser, Katrien, et al, eds. Why Care? Children's Rights & Child Poverty. 2010. 209p. pap. 54.75 *(978-94-000-0025-4(1))* Intersentia Uitgevers N.V. BEL. Dist: International Specialized Bk. Services.

Denov, Myriam & Maclure, Richard, eds. Children's Rights & International Development. 2011. (ENG., Illus.). 320p. 90.00 *(978-0-230-60682-1(2))* Palgrave Macmillan.

Derluyn, Ilse, et al, eds. Re-Member: Rehabilitation, Reintegration & Reconciliation of War-Affected Children. 2012. 602p. 140.00 *(978-94-000-0027-8(8))* Intersentia Uitgevers N.V. BEL. Dist: International Specialized Bk. Services.

Du Preez, Nicolien & Luyt, Willem. Fundamentals & Developmental Psychology in Youth Corrections: Second Edition. 2nd ed. 2011. 266p. pap. 25.00 *(978-1-86888-603-6(4))* Unisa Press / Uitgewers GBR. Dist: International Specialized Bk. Services.

Earls, Felton J., ed. The Child as Citizen. 2011. (ANNALS of the American Academy of Political & Social Science Ser.: 633). (Illus.). 264p. (C). 47.00 *(978-1-4129-9586-3(8),* 295633C); pap. 34.00 *(978-1-4129-9585-6(X),* 295633P) SAGE Pubns., Inc.

Edelman, Marian Wright & Edelman, Marian W. The Sea Is So Wide & My Boat Is So Small: Charting a Course for the Next Generation. 2008. 176p. 19.95 *(978-1-4013-2333-2(2))* Hyperion Pr.

Eide, Asbjo. Commentary on the United Nations Convention on the Rights of the Child , Volume 27 Article 27: The Right to an Adequate Standard of Living. 2006. 30p. pap. *(978-90-04-14878-9(7))* BRILL.

Eshetu, Genaye. Awareness Creation of Children on Child Right. 2009. 68p. pap. *(978-3-639-20887-0(0))* VDM Verlag Dr. Mueller e.K.

Fedorov, Alexander. Children & Media Violence. 2010. 164p. pap. *(978-3-8383-2580-4(X))* Lambert Academic Publishing.

Fellmeth, Robert C. Child Rights & Remedies. 3rd enl. ed. 2011. (ENG.). 840p. pap. 49.95 ***(978-0-9833539-1-1(3))*** Clarity Pr., Inc.

Fennimore, Beatrice S. & Goodwin, A. Lin, eds. Promoting Social Justice for Young Children. 2011. (Educating the Young Child Ser.). (ENG., Illus.). xv, 179p. 139.00 *(978-94-007-0569-2(7),* 9400705697) Springer.

Feria Tinta, Mónica. The Landmark Rulings of the Inter-American Court of Human Rights on the Rights of the Child: Protecting the Most Vulnerable at the Edge. 2008. (International Studies in Human Rights Ser.). 692p. *(978-90-04-16513-7(4))* BRILL.

Fineman, Martha & Worthington, Karen. What Is Right for Children? The Competing Paradigms of Religion & Human Rights. 2009. 462p. 124.95 *(978-0-7546-7419-1(3))* Ashgate Publishing Co.

Fleming, Jennie & Boeck, Thilo, eds. Involving Children & Young People in Health & Social Care Research. 2012. (ENG.). 272p. (C). 145.00 *(978-0-415-66349-6(0))* Routledge.

Flowers, Charles & O'Reilly, Bill. Kids Are Americans Too. 2007. (ENG., Illus.). 160p. (gr. 4-7). 24.95 *(978-0-06-084676-3(3),* Morrow, William & Co.) HarperCollins Pubs.

Fortin, Jane. Children's Rights & the Developing Law. 3rd rev. ed. 2009. (Law in Context Ser.). (ENG.). 878p. (C). pap. 103.00 *(978-0-521-69801-6(4))* Cambridge Univ. Pr.

Freeman, Michael A. A Commentary on the United Nations Convention on the Rights of the Child: Article 3: the Best Interests of the Child. 2007. (Commentary on the United Nations Convention on the Rights of the Child Ser.: Vol. 3). 79p. pap. *(978-90-04-14861-1(2))* BRILL.

Freeman, Michael D. A. Children's Rights: Progress & Perspectives: Essays from the International Journal of Children's Rights. 2011. 525p. *(978-90-04-19049-8(X))* BRILL.

Gal, Tali. Child Victims & Restorative Justice: A Needs-Rights Model, 1 vol. 2011. (Interpersonal Violence Ser.). (ENG., Illus.). 264p. 49.95 *(978-0-19-974471-8(8))* Oxford Univ. Pr., Inc.

Ganga, R. & Supputhai, M. Children's Rights as Basic Human Rights: Sensitization of Stakeholders. 2007. 370p. 46.00 *(978-81-8405-039-4(9),* Reference Pr.) Ess Ess Pubns. IND. Dist: International Specialized Bk. Services.

Ganguly Thukral, Enakshi, ed. Children, Citizenship & Governance: Holding States Accountable. 2011. (ENG.). 196p. 95.00 *(978-0-415-67837-7(4),* Routledge India) Taylor & Francis Group GBR. Dist: Taylor & Francis Group.

Garbarino, James & Sigman, Garry. A Child's Right to a Healthy Environment. 2010. (Illus.). xii, 254p. ***(978-1-4419-6805-0(9))*** Springer.

Garbarino, James & Sigman, Garry, eds. A Child's Right to a Healthy Environment. 2010. (Loyola University Symposium on the Human Rights of Children Ser.). (Illus.). xii, 235p. 129.00 *(978-1-4419-6789-3(3),* 1441967893) Springer.

Gerber, Paula. From Convention to Classroom: The Long Road to Human Rights Education. 2008. 408p. pap. *(978-3-639-09629-3(0))* VDM Verlag Dr. Mueller e.K.

Gleason, Mona, et al, eds. Lost Kids: Vulnerable Children & Youth in Twentieth-Century Canada & the United States. 2010. (ENG., Illus.). 272p. (C). pap. 37.95 *(978-0-7748-1687-8(2))* UBC Pr. CAN. Dist: Univ. of Washington Pr.

Greenbaum, Charles & Ronen, Ya'ir, eds. The Case for the Child: Towards A New Agenda. 2008. 334p. (C). pap. 77.00 *(978-90-5095-406-8(5))* Intersentia Uitgevers N.V. BEL. Dist: International Specialized Bk. Services.

Guggenheim, Martin. What's Wrong with Children's Rights. 2007. (Illus.). 320p. pap. 22.50 *(978-0-674-02546-2(6))* Harvard Univ. Pr.

Hall, Ellen Lynn & Rudkin, Jennifer Kofkin. Seen & Heard: Children's Rights in Early Childhood Education. 2011. (Early Childhood Education Ser.). 144p. (ENG.). 57.00 *(978-0-8077-5161-9(8));* (Illus.). pap. 24.95 *(978-0-8077-5160-2(X))* Teachers College Pr., Teachers College, Columbia Univ.

Harrison, Don. Regardless of Frontiers: Children's Rights & Global Learning. 2008. (Illus.). 110p. pap. 27.00 *(978-1-85856-400-5(X))* Trentham Bks. Ltd. GBR. Dist: Stylus Publishing, LLC.

Hartas, Dimitra. Right to Childhoods: Critical Perspectives on Rights, Difference & Knowledge in a Transient World. 2010. (ENG.). 232p. 49.95 *(978-1-4411-7642-4(X))* Continuum International Publishing Group, Ltd. GBR. Dist: National Bk. Network.

Hartas, Dimitra & Hartas. Right to Childhoods: Critical Perspectives on Rights, Difference & Knowledge in a Transient World. 2008. (ENG.). 232p. 150.00 *(978-0-8264-9568-6(0))* Continuum International Publishing Group, Ltd. GBR. Dist: National Bk. Network.

Helander, Einar. Children & Violence: The World of the Defenceless. 2008. (ENG., Illus.). 288p. 105.00 *(978-0-230-57394-9(0))* Palgrave Macmillan.

Hilwig, E. & Tofan, C., eds. Children's Rights: Selected Documents, 2 vols. 2008. 1500p. 250.00 *(978-90-5887-005-6(7))* Gaunt, Inc.

Hollingsworth, Kathryn. Rights & Responsibilities of Children in Youth Crime. 2013. 364p. pap. 70.00 *(978-1-84946-006-4(X))* Hart Publishing Ltd. GBR. Dist: International Specialized Bk. Services.

Holzscheiter, Anna. Children's Rights in International Politics: The Transformative Power of Discourse. 2010. (Transformations of the State Ser.). (ENG., Illus.). 288p. 95.00 *(978-0-230-24180-0(8))* Palgrave Macmillan.

Howe, R. Brian & Covell, Katherine, eds. A Question of Commitment: Children's Rights in Canada. 2007. (Studies in Childhood & Family in Canada). (ENG.). 456p. (C). pap. 48.95 *(978-1-55458-003-3(X))* Wilfrid Laurier Univ. Pr. CAN. Dist: Univ. of Toronto Pr.

Humbert, Franziska. The Challenge of Child Labour in International Law. 2009. (Cambridge Studies in International & Comparative Law Ser.). (ENG.). 458p. 113.00 *(978-0-521-76490-2(4))* Cambridge Univ. Pr. GBR. Dist: Cambridge Univ. Pr.

Innocenti Research Centre. General Comments of the Committee on the Rights of the Child. 2010. (FRE.). 76p. pap. 25.00 *(978-88-89129-40-1(9))* United Nations Children's Fund, The (UNICEF).

It's time to listen to Us! Youth response to the Report of the Expert Group Meeting on the Elimination of all forms of discrimination & violence against the girl Child. 2007. 28p. (FRE.). *(978-92-806-4142-4(5)); (978-92-806-4141-7(7))* United Nations Children's Fund, The (UNICEF).

James, Allison & James, Adrian L., eds. European Childhoods: Cultures, Politics & Childhoods in the European Union. 2008. (ENG.). 272p. 100.00 *(978-1-4039-9750-0(0))* Palgrave Macmillan.

Jensen, Eric & Jepsen, Jorgen, eds. Juvenile Law Violators, Human Rights, & the Development of New Juvenile Justice Systems. 2006. (Oñati International Series in Law & Society). (ENG., Illus.). (C). 496p. 116.00 *(978-1-84113-637-0(9));* 478p. pap. 52.00 *(978-1-84113-636-3(0))* Hart Publishing Ltd. GBR. Dist: International Specialized Bk. Services.

Jolly, Richard. UNICEF (United Nations Children's Fund) 2011. (Global Institutions Ser.). (ENG.). 176p. 27.95 *(978-0-415-49117-4(7));* 125.00 *(978-0-415-49116-7(9))* Routledge.

Jones, Phil & Walker, Gary, eds. Children's Rights in Practice. 2011. 256p. (C). 104.00 *(978-1-84920-379-1(2),* B03791C); pap. 45.00 *(978-1-84920-380-7(6),* B03791P) SAGE Pubns., Ltd. GBR. Dist: SAGE Pubns., Inc.

Jones, Phil & Welch, Sue. Rethinking Children's Rights: Attitudes in Contemporary Society. 2010. (New Childhoods Ser.). (ENG., Illus.). 208p. 120.00 *(978-1-4411-9540-1(8))* Continuum International Publishing Group, Ltd. GBR. Dist: National Bk. Network.

Joseph, Sandra & Korczak, Janusz. Loving Every Child: Wisdom for Parents. Joseph, Sandra & Korczak, Janusz, eds. 2007. (ENG., Illus.). 84p. 10.95 *(978-1-56512-489-9(8),* 1565124898) Algonquin Bks. of Chapel Hill.

Kaime, Thoko. The Convention on the Rights of the Child: A Cultural Legitimacy Critique. 2011. 228p. pap. 75.00 ***(978-90-8952-113-2(5))*** Europa Law Publishing, Netherlands NLD. Dist: International Specialized Bk. Services.

Kauffmann, Heiko & Riedelsheimer, Albert. Kindeswohl oder Ausgrenzung? Flüchtlingskinder in Deutschland nach der Rücknahme der Vorbehalte. 2010. (GER., Illus.). 269p. *(978-3-86059-432-2(X))* Loeper, Angelika von.

Kaushal, Lata. Child Labour & Human Rights: A Social Dimension. 2009. 335p. 62.50 *(978-81-7533-219-5(0))* M. D. Pubns. Pvt. Ltd. IND. Dist: Coronet Bks.

Kilkelly, Ursula. Children's Rights in Ireland: Law, Policy & Practice. 2008. 601p. 240.00 *(978-1-84592-157-6(7),* Bloomsbury Professional) Bloomsbury Publishing Plc GBR. Dist: International Specialized Bk. Services.

Kruger, Marie E. & Spies, G. M. The Recognition & Protection of Children S Rights. 2008. 492p. per. *(978-3-8364-3428-7(8))* VDM Verlag Dr. Mueller e.K.

Kumari, Ved. The Juvenile Justice System in India: From Welfare to Rights. 2nd ed. 2011. (ENG.). 440p. 40.00 *(978-0-19-806577-7(9))* Oxford Univ. Pr., Inc.

Langlaude, Sylvie. The Right of the Child to Religious Freedom in International Law. 2007. (International Studies in Human Rights Ser.). 291p. *(978-90-04-16266-2(6))* BRILL.

Levander, Caroline F. Cradle of Liberty: Race, the Child, & National Belonging from Thomas Jefferson to W. E. B. du Bois. 2006. (New Americanists Ser.). (ENG., Illus.). 264p. (C). 84.95 *(978-0-8223-3856-7(4))* Duke Univ. Pr.

Levander, Caroline Field. Cradle of Liberty: Race, the Child, & National Belonging from Thomas Jefferson to W. E. B. du Bois. 2006. (New Americanists Ser.). (ENG., Illus.). 264p. per. 23.95 *(978-0-8223-3872-7(6))* Duke Univ. Pr.

Liebel, Manfred & Saadi, Iven. Children's Rights from Below: Cross-Cultural Perspectives. 2012. (Studies in Childhood & Youth Ser.). (ENG., Illus.). 288p. 85.00 ***(978-0-230-30251-8(3))*** Palgrave Macmillan.

Liu, Huawen. Er Tong Quan Li Yu Fa Lü Bao Hu: Rights of the Child & Legal Protection. 2009. (CHI., Illus.). *(978-7-208-08744-6(X))* Shanghai People's Publishing Hse.

Lucero, Kilian. Federal Programs for Troubled Youth. 2009. (Children's Issues, Laws & Programs Ser.). (Illus.). 263p. 79.00 *(978-1-60692-318-4(8))* Nova Science Pubs., Inc.

Mahood, Linda. Feminism & Voluntary Action: Eglantyne Jebb & Save the Children, 1876-1928. 2009. (ENG., Illus.). 256p. 95.00 *(978-0-230-52560-3(1))* Palgrave Macmillan.

Mapp, Susan C. Global Child Welfare & Well-Being, 1 vol. 2010. (ENG., Illus.). 272p. pap. 37.95 *(978-0-19-533971-0(1))* Oxford Univ. Pr., Inc.

Meuwese, Stan, et al, eds. 100 Years of Child Protection. 2007. 276p. 75.00 *(978-90-5850-293-3(7))* Wolf Legal Pubs., W.L.P. NLD. Dist: Gaunt, Inc.

Minujin, Alberto, et al. Human Rights & Social Policies for Children & Women: The Multiple Indicator Cluster Survey (MICS) in Practice. 2006. 352p. pap. 14.95 *(978-0-9766252-0-9(2))* New Schl. Univ., The.

Montgomery, Heather & Kellett, Mary, eds. Children & Young People's Worlds: Developing Frameworks for Integrated Practice. 2009. 272p. 85.00 *(978-1-84742-388-7(4))* Policy Pr. GBR. Dist: Chicago Distribution Ctr.

—Children's & Young People's Worlds: Developing Frameworks for Integrated Practice. 2009. 272p. pap. 32.95 *(978-1-84742-387-0(6))* Policy Pr. GBR. Dist: Chicago Distribution Ctr.

Muratbekova, S. M. Mekhanizm Realizatsii Konstitutsionnykh Garantii Prav I Zakonnykh Interesov Nesovershennoletnikh V Kyrgyzskoi Respublike. 2010. (RUS.). 213p. *(978-9967-08-199-4(6))* SAM, Publishing House, Izdatel'stvo.

Nolan, Aoife. Children's Socio-Economic Rights, Democracy & the Courts, 0 vols. 2011. (ENG.). 336p. 110.00 *(978-1-84113-769-8(3))* Hart Publishing Ltd. GBR. Dist: International Specialized Bk. Services.

Oliver, Christine M. & Dalrymple, Jane, eds. Developing Advocacy for Children & Young People: Current Issues in Research, Policy & Practice. 2008. 224p. pap. *(978-1-84310-596-1(9))* Kingsley, Jessica Ltd.

Olson, Diane & Friedrich, Laura Dean. Weaving A Just Future for Children. 2008. 160p. pap. 15.00 *(978-0-88177-547-1(9))* Upper Room Bks.

O'Neill, Tom & Zinga, Dawn, eds. Children's Rights: Multidisciplinary Approaches to Participation & Protection. 2008. (ENG.). 384p. *(978-0-8020-9785-9(5))* Univ. of Toronto Pr.

O'Reilly, Bill & Flowers, Charles. Kids Are Americans Too. 2008. (ENG.). 160p. 14.95 *(978-0-06-084677-0(1),* Morrow, William & Co.) HarperCollins Pubs.

Parkes, Aisling. Children & International Human Rights Law: The Right of the Child to be Heard. 2012. (Routledge Research in Human Rights Law Ser.). (ENG.). 320p. 140.00 *(978-0-415-45836-8(6))* Routledge.

Pati, Jagannath, ed. Adoption: Global Perspectives & Ethical Issues. 2007. 314p. *(978-81-8069-442-4(9))* Concept Publishing Co.

Piper, Heather & Stronach, Ian. Don't Touch! The Educational Story of a Panic. 2008. (ENG.). 184p. 170.00 *(978-0-415-42007-5(5));* pap. 39.95 *(978-0-415-42008-2(3))* Routledge.

Rafiq, Usman. Financial Rights of the Children in Uncrc 1989 & Islamic Law. 2011. 120p. pap. ***(978-3-8443-9428-3(1))*** Lambert Academic Publishing.

Ruck, Martin & Horn, Stacey. Young People's Perspectives on the Rights of the Child: Implications for Theory, Research & Practice. 2008. (Journal of Social Issues Ser.). (ENG., Illus.). 200p. pap. 47.95 *(978-1-4051-9434-1(0),* Wiley-Blackwell) Wiley, John & Sons, Inc.

Rutgers, Catherine, ed. Creating a World Fit for Children: Understanding the un Convention on the Rights of the Child. 2010. 256p. pap. 24.95 *(978-1-932716-82-5(3))* International Debate Education Assn.

Saunders, Bernadette J. & Goddard, Christopher Rex. Physical Punishment in Childhood: The Rights of the Child. 2010. (ENG., Illus.). 284p. pap. 54.95 *(978-0-470-72706-5(3),* Wiley) Wiley, John & Sons, Inc.

Scarre, Geoffrey, ed. Children, Parents & Politics. 2010. (ENG.). 224p. pap. 27.99 *(978-0-521-36935-0(5))* Cambridge Univ. Pr.

Schaefer, Judith. Seen, but Not Heard: Placing Children & Youth on the Security Governance Agenda. Nosworthy, David, ed. 2009. (ENG.). 336p. pap. 44.95 *(978-3-8258-1398-7(3))* Lit Verlag DEU. Dist: Transaction Pubs.

Schissel, Bernard. About Canada - Youth & Children. 2011. (About Canada Ser.). (ENG.). 144p. pap. 17.95 ***(978-1-55266-412-4(0))*** Fernwood Publishing Co., Ltd. CAN. Dist: Independent Pubs. Group.

Schorlemer, Sabine von & Schulte-Herbrüggen, Elena, eds. 1989-2009: 20 Jahre Un-Kinderrechtskonvention: Erfahrungen und Perspektiven. 2010. (Dresdner Schriften zu Recht und Politik der Vereinten Nationen. Dresden Papers on Law & Policy of the United Nations Ser.). (GER.). 240p. 57.95 *(978-3-631-60253-9(7))* Lang, Peter GmbH, Europaischer Verlag der Wissenschaften DEU. Dist: Lang, Peter.

Scott, John A. The Child's Bill of Rights: A Beginner's Guide to Parenting: A Primer for Parents of Children from Birth Through Six Years Old. 2007. 260p. per. 18.95 *(978-1-4251-0001-8(5))* Trafford Publishing.

Sen, Purna, ed. Child Rights in the Commonwealth: 20 Years of the Convention on the Rights of the Child. 2010. (ENG., Illus.). 68p. pap. 17.95 *(978-1-84929-011-1(3))* Commonwealth Secretariat GBR. Dist: Stylus Publishing, LLC.

Sloth-Nielsen, Julia. Children's Rights in Africa: A Legal Perspective. 2008. 362p. 124.95 *(978-0-7546-4887-1(7))* Ashgate Publishing Co.

Smith, Anne B. & Durrant, Joan E., eds. Global Pathways to Abolishing Physical Punishment: Realizing the Rights of Children. 2010. (Routledge Research in Education Ser.). (ENG., Illus.). 374p. (C). 125.00 *(978-0-415-87920-0(5))* Routledge.

Sokoine Martine, Jackson. International Children's Rights Law Versus Maasai Traditional Culture: A Case of Loitokitok District, Kenya. 2011. 136p. pap. ***(978-3-639-33260-5(1))*** VDM Verlag Dr. Mueller e.K.

Taylor, Nicola J. & Smith, Anne B., eds. Children as Citizens? International Voices. 2009. (Illus.). 221p. pap. 45.00 *(978-1-877372-62-9(5))* Otago University Pr. NZL. Dist: International Specialized Bk. Services.

Te One, Sarah. Perceptions of Children's Rights. 2010. 344p. pap. *(978-3-8383-4198-9(8))* Lambert Academic Publishing.

Teele, Dawn L. If ratification does not affect compliance, why docountries bother? An investigation into child labor & the minimum age to work convention. 2008. 112p. pap. *(978-3-639-09369-8(0))* VDM Verlag Dr. Mueller e.K.

Thomas, R. Murray. What Schools Ban & Why, 1 vol. 2008. 292p. 49.95 *(978-0-313-35298-0(4),* C35298, Praeger Pubs.) Greenwood Publishing Group, Inc.

Thorgeirsdóttir, Herdís. Commentary on the United Nations Convention on the Rights of the Child , Volume 13 Article 13: The Right to Freedom of Expression. 2006. (Commentary on the United Nations Convention on the Rights of the Child Ser.). 30p. pap. *(978-90-04-14868-0(X))* BRILL.

Ton, Liefaard. Deprivation of Liberty of Children in Light of International Human Rights Law & Standards. 2008. 696p. pap. 124.75 *(978-90-5095-838-7(9))* Intersentia Uitgevers N.V. BEL. Dist: International Specialized Bk. Services.

Tuttle, Cheryl Gerson & Silva, Joann Augeri. Self-Advocacy: The Ultimate Teen Guide. 2007. (It Happened to Me Ser.). (ENG., Illus.). 232p. 55.00 *(978-0-8108-5646-2(8))* Scarecrow Pr., Inc.

UNICEF Staff. Implementation Handbook for the Convention on the Rights of the Child. 3rd rev. ed. 2007. (Illus.). 812p. 50.00 *(978-92-806-4183-7(2))* United Nations Children's Fund, The (UNICEF).

UNICEF Staff & United Nations Children's Fund Staff. The State of the World's Children: Celebrating 20 Years on the Convention on the Rights of the Child. 2009. (ENG., Illus.). 94p. pap. 15.00 *(978-92-806-4442-5(4))* United Nations Children's Fund, The (UNICEF).

UNICEF: Innocenti Research Centre. General comments of the Committee on the Rights of the Child. 2008. 90p. pap. 25.00 *(978-88-89129-51-7(4))* United Nations Children's Fund, The (UNICEF).

—Promoting the rights of children with Disabilities. 2008. (ENG., Illus.). 76p. pap. 18.00 *(978-88-89129-60-9(3))* United Nations Pubns.

United Nations Children's Fund. Law Reform & the Implementation of the Convention on the Rights of the Child. 2009. 148p. pap. 25.00 *(978-88-89129-66-1(2))* United Nations Children's Fund, The (UNICEF).

United Nations, Office of the High Commissioner for Human Rights Staff, contrib. by. Legislative History of the Convention on the Rights of the Child, 2 vols. 2007. (ENG.). 1012p. pap. 50.00 *(978-92-1-154177-9(8))* United Nations Pubns.

Van Bueren, Geraldine. Child rights in Europe (2008) Europeans & their Rights. 2008. 200p. pap. 26.00 *(978-92-871-6269-4(7))* Council of Europe FRA. Dist: Manhattan Publishing Co.

Van Crombrugge, Hans, et al, eds. Shared Pedagogical Responsibility. 2008. 118p. pap. 40.75 *(978-90-5095-813-4(3))* Intersentia Uitgevers N.V. BEL. Dist: International Specialized Bk. Services.

van Oudenhoven, Nico & Wazir, Rekha. Newly Emerging Needs of Children: An Exploration. 2006. 171p. (C). pap. 42.50 *(978-90-441-1913-8(3))* Garant Uitgevers N.V. BEL. Dist: Coronet Bks.

Vandenhole, Wouter. Article 26: the Right to Benefit from Social Security. Alen, André et al, eds. 2007. (Commentary on the United Nations Convention on the Rights of the Child Ser.). 44p. per. *(978-90-04-14879-6(5))* BRILL.

Vité, Sylvain & Boéchat, Hervé. Commentary on the United Nations Convention on the Rights of the Child, Volume 21 Article 21: Adoption. 2008. (Commentary on the United Nations Convention on the Rights of the Child Ser.). (ENG & FRE.). 49p. pap. *(978-90-04-14874-1(4))* BRILL.

Vockel, Gabriel. The Protection of Children's Human Rights in Europe. 2007. 64p. per. *(978-3-8364-0993-3(3))* VDM Verlag Dr. Mueller e.K.

Wabwile, Michael. Legal Protection of Social & Economic Rights of Children in Developing Countries: Reassessing International Cooperation & Responsibility. 2010. 272p. pap. 89.75 *(978-94-000-0107-7(X))* Intersentia Uitgevers N.V. BEL. Dist: International Specialized Bk. Services.

Welch, Sue & Jones, Phil. Rethinking Children's Rights: Attitudes in Contemporary Society. 2010. (New Childhoods Ser.). (ENG., Illus.). 208p. 34.95 *(978-1-84706-324-3(1))* Continuum International Publishing Group, Ltd. GBR. Dist: National Bk. Network.

Wiggin, Kate Douglas & Smith, Nora. Children's Rights & Others. 2008. 84p. pap. *(978-1-84830-117-7(0))* Echo Library.

Willems, Jan, ed. Developmental & Autonomy Rights of Children: Empowering Children, Caregivers & Communities. 2nd ed. 2007. 211p. (C). pap. 63.00

(978-90-5095-726-7(9)) Intersentia Uitgevers N.V. BEL. Dist: International Specialized Bk. Services.

Willemsen, Jan. Children's Rights & Human Development. 2010. (Illus.). 964p. pap. 189.00 (978-94-000-0032-2(4)) Intersentia Uitgevers N.V. BEL. Dist: International Specialized Bk. Services.

Williams, Jane & Invernizzi, Antonella, eds. Children & Citizenship. 2007. 216p. (C). per. 53.00 (978-1-4129-3538-8(5), B35377P); (Illus.). 112.00 (978-1-4129-3537-1(7), B35377C) SAGE Pubns., Ltd. GBR. Dist: SAGE Pubns., Inc.

—Children's Rights: Revisiting Visions, Assessing Progress, Rethinking Implementation. 2011. (Illus.). 372p. 134.95 (978-1-4094-0531-3(1)) Ashgate Publishing Co.

Woodhouse, Barbara Bennett. Hidden in Plain Sight: The Tragedy of Children's Rights from Ben Franklin to Lionel Tate. (Public Square Ser.). (ENG., Illus.). 384p. (C). 2010. pap. 19.95 (978-0-691-14621-8(7)) 2008. 27.95 (978-0-691-12690-6(9)) Princeton Univ. Pr.

A World Fit for Children. 2005. 108p. per. (978-92-806-4087-8(9)) United Nations Children's Fund, The (UNICEF).

Wyller, Trygve & Nayar, Usha S. The Given Child: The Religions' Contributions to Children's Citizenship. 2007. (Research in Contemporary Religion Ser.). (ENG., Illus.). 199p. (C). 59.00 (978-3-525-60436-6(X)) Vandenhoeck & Ruprecht GmbH & Co. KG DEU. Dist: ISD.

Ziemele, Ineta. A Commentary on the United Nations Convention on the Rights of the Child, Volume 7 Article 7: The Right to Birth Registration, Name & Nationality, & the Right to Know & Be Cared for by Parents. 2007. 40p. pap. (978-90-04-14863-5(9)) BRILL.

Zinga, Dawn & O'Neill, Tom. Children's Rights: Multidisciplinary Approaches to Participation & Protection. 2008. (ENG.). 384p. pap. (978-0-8020-9540-4(2)) Univ. of Toronto Pr.

CHILDREN'S SAYINGS

see Children—Anecdotes and Sayings

CHILDREN'S SERMONS

see also Object-Teaching

Baker, Brant D., ed. The Abingdon Children's Sermon Library, Vol. 3. 2008. (Abingdon Children's Sermon Library). 124p. per. 16.00 (978-0-687-65152-8(2)) Abingdon Pr.

Bowie, Walter Russell. Sunny Windows & Other Sermons for Children. 2007. (ENG.). 188p. (gr. 4-7). 37.95 (978-0-548-03259-6(9)) Kessinger Publishing, LLC.

Evans, Karen. The Abingdon Children's Sermon Library, Vol. 2. Baker, Brant D., ed. 2007. 122p. per. 16.00 (978-0-687-33397-4(0)) Abingdon Pr.

Greenwood, F. W. P. (Francis William Pit. Sermons to Children. 2006. 412p. per. 26.99 (978-1-4255-4413-3(4)) MPublishing.

Hammer, Randy. The Shining Light: 26 Children Sermons with Activities. 2010. (978-0-8298-1868-0(5)) Pilgrim Pr., The/United Church Pr.

—The Singing Bowl: 26 Children Sermons with Activities. 2009. (978-0-8298-1851-2(0)) Pilgrim Pr., The/United Church Pr.

—The Talking Stick: 40 Children's Sermons with Activities. 2007. (New Brown Bag Ser.). (Illus.). 110p. per. (978-0-8298-1761-4(1)) Pilgrim Pr., The/United Church Pr.

Hastings, James. The Children's Great Texts of the Bible. 2009. 334p. 36.99 (978-1-115-66770-8(X)); 334p. pap. 30.75 (978-1-115-66773-9(4)); 342p. (gr. 4-7). 32.99 (978-1-110-34485-7(6)); 342p. (gr. 4-7). pap. 31.75 (978-1-110-34480-2(5)); 332p. (gr. 4-7). 25.99 (978-1-103-43995-9(2)); 332p. (gr. 4-7). pap. 19.99 (978-1-103-43992-8(8)) BiblioBazaar.

—The Children's Great Texts of the Bible. 2009. 214p. pap. (978-0-217-62078-9(7)) Books LLC.

Helme, Janet S. The Children's Sermon: Moments with God. 2010. 144p. pap. 16.99 (978-0-8272-0522-2(8)) Chalice Pr.

Suddarth, Marti Kramer. Ping-Pong Words: And 30 More Children's Sermon Stories. 2007. (978-0-7880-2484-9(1)) CSS Publishing Co.

Svanoe, Rolf. Bread for the Journey: A High-Carb, Multi-Sensory Lenten Worship Series. 2007. (Illus.). 84p. per. 9.95 (978-0-7880-2507-5(4)) CSS Publishing Co.

Wimberly, Anne Streaty. Children's Sermons. 2010. 96p. pap. 12.00 (978-1-4267-0650-9(2)) Abingdon Pr.

CHILDREN'S SONGS

see also Games with Music; Kindergarten—Music; Nursery Rhymes

Ada, Alma Flor & Campoy, F. Isabel. Merry Navidad! Villancicos en Español E Ingles/Christmas Carols in Spanish & English. 2007. (ENG & SPA., Illus.). 63p. (J). (gr. k-5). lib. bdg. 17.89 (978-0-06-058435-1(1), Rayo) HarperCollins Pubs.

Ada, Alma Flor, et al. Merry Navidad! Villancicos en Español E Inglés - Christmas Carols in Spanish & English. 2007. (ENG & SPA., Illus.). 64p. (J). (gr. k-5). 16.99 (978-0-06-058434-4(3), Rayo) HarperCollins Pubs.

Alfred Publishing Staff. Farm Songs & the Sounds of Moo-sic! Book & CD. 2009. (ENG.). 96p. pap. 29.99 (978-0-7390-6255-5(7)) Alfred Publishing Co., Inc.

Allen, Amy. This Little Piggy Went to Prada: Nursery Rhymes for the Blahnik Brigade. 2006. (ENG., Illus.). 88p. 19.99 (978-0-06-113885-0(1)) HarperCollins Pubs.

Amsco Publications, creator. The Piano Treasury of Children's Songs. 2006. (Illus.). 400p. pap. 29.95 incl. audio compact disk (978-0-8256-3481-9(4), Amsco Music) Music Sales Corp.

Andriasov, Iosif. Five Children's Songs: For Soloists, Children's Choir, & Piano. 2011. (Illus.). 28p. spiral bd. 19.95 (978-1-931815-35-2(6)) IMMA Publishing Co.

Balkin, Alfred. Tune up to Literacy: Original Songs & Activities for Kids. 2009. 45.00 (978-0-8389-0998-0(1)) American Library Assn.

Bance, Linda. Musical Ideas for Early Learning. 2012. (ENG., Illus.). 112p. pap. 48.95 (978-0-415-67921-3(4)) Routledge.

Beall, Pamela Conn & Nipp, Susan Hagen. Wee Sing for Halloween, 1 vol. 2006. (Wee Sing Ser.). (ENG., Illus.). 64p. (J). (gr. -1-2). 10.99 (978-0-8431-1644-1(7), Price Stern Sloan) Penguin Group (USA) Inc.

—Wee Sing Fun 'n' Folk, 1 vol. 2006. (Wee Sing Ser.). (ENG.). 64p. (J). (gr. -1-2). 9.99 (978-0-8431-2098-1(3), Price Stern Sloan) Penguin Group (USA) Inc.

—Wee Sing More Bible Songs, 1 vol. 2006. (Wee Sing Ser.). (ENG.). 64p. (J). (gr. -1-2). 9.99 (978-0-8431-2100-1(9), Price Stern Sloan) Penguin Group (USA) Inc.

Beall, Pamela Conn, et al. Wee Sing Animals, 1 vol. 2006. (Wee Sing Ser.). (ENG., Illus.). 64p. (J). (gr. -1-2). 10.99 (978-0-8431-2034-9(7), Price Stern Sloan) Penguin Group (USA) Inc.

Bleck, Linda, illus. A Children's Treasury of Songs. 2006. (ENG.). 24p. (J). (gr. -1-k). bds. 12.95 (978-1-4027-2981-2(2)) Sterling Publishing Co., Inc.

Brantley, Jamie & Duffey, Gary. Lullaby Tune: A Mother's Wish for Her Little One. 2007. (ENG., Illus.). 24p. 14.99 (978-0-8249-5902-9(7)) Ideals Pubns.

Brentwood-Benson Music Publishing Staff, creator. The Ultimate Kids Songbook: Over 300 Worship Songs in Lead Sheet Format. 2006. (AFR & ENG., Illus.). 470p. pap. 34.99 (978-1-59802-067-0(6), 1598020676) Brentwood Music, Inc.

Buchanan, Colin. Practice being Godly. 2008. (ENG.). 32p. 14.99 (978-1-84550-385-7(6)) Christian Focus Pubns. GBR. Dist: STL Distribution North America.

Cabrera, Jane. Wheels on the Bus. 2011. (ENG., Illus.). 32p. (YA). 16.95 (978-0-8234-2350-7(6)) Holiday Hse., Inc.

Canto y Cuento. (SPA & ENG.). 10.00 net. (978-1-57417-039-9(2), AC30088) Arcoiris Records, Inc.

Carle, Eric. Today Is Monday. 2007. (World of Eric Carle Ser.). (ENG., Illus.). 16p. (J). (gr. -1-1). bds. 9.99 (978-0-448-44492-5(5), Grosset & Dunlap) Penguin Group (USA) Inc.

Carmona, Macarena & Lunansky, Isabel. Armonia: Musica E Imagenes para Estimular y Relajar A Tu Bebe. 2010. (SPA., Illus.). 32p. (J). incl. audio compact disk (978-84-7942-434-3(6)) Heinemann Iberia, S.A.

Carpenter, Stephen, illus. Oh My Darling, Porcupine: And Other Silly Sing-A-Long Songs. 2006. 32p. (978-0-88166-496-6(0)) Meadowbrook Pr.

A Child's Gift of Lullabyes. rev. abr. ed. 2006. (ENG.). (J). (gr. -1). 12.95 (978-0-8249-5541-0(2)) Ideals Pubns.

Coates, Dan. Top 50 Children's Songs: Easy Piano. 2011. (Top 50 Ser.). (ENG.). 88p. pap. 16.99 (978-0-7390-7787-0(2)) Alfred Publishing Co., Inc.

Dailey, Susan M. Sing a Song of Storytime. 2007. (Illus.). 199p. pap. 59.95 (978-1-55570-576-3(6)) Neal-Schuman Pubs., Inc.

DeSpain, Lisa, ed. Broadway Presents! Kids' Musical Theatre Anthology: A Treasury of Songs from Stage & Film, Specially Designed for Young Singers!, Book & CD. 2008. (ENG.). 128p. pap. 22.95 (978-0-7390-5571-7(2)) Alfred Publishing Co., Inc.

Diaz, David. De Colores, 1 vol. 2011. (ENG.). 32p. pap. (978-0-7614-5934-7(0)) Marshall Cavendish.

—De Colores - Bright with Colors, 1 vol. 2008. (ENG & SPA., Illus.). 32p. (J). (gr. 3-7). 16.99 (978-0-7614-5431-1(4)) Marshall Cavendish Corp.

Field, Trixi. Jazzicle Pops! 2008. 206p. pap. 41.95 (978-0-9559805-0-3(X)) Voice Confidence GBR. Dist: Lulu Enterprises Inc.

Ford, Robert. Children's Rhymes, Children's Games, Children's Songs, Children's Stories. 2009. 184p. pap. (978-0-217-69500-8(0)) Books LLC.

Fox, Daniel. World's Greatest Children's Songs: 88 of the World's Most Popular & Best Loved Traditional & Contemporary Children's Songs. rev. ed. 2008. (World's Greatest Ser.). (ENG.). 144p. pap. 17.95 (978-0-7390-5206-8(3)) Alfred Publishing Co., Inc.

Frawley, Ken & Frawley, Georgia. Play-along Songs Volume 2: Fun Children's Activity Songs. 2011. (ENG.). 80p. (J). pap. 19.95 (978-1-887120-19-7(X)) Production Assocs., Inc.

Fredericks, Anthony D. Songs & Rhymes Readers Theatre for Beginning Readers, 1 vol. 2007. (Readers Theatre Ser.). (Illus.). 176p. pap. 25.00 (978-1-59158-627-2(5), TIP8627, Teacher Ideas Pr.) Libraries Unlimited, Inc.

George, Susie. Peppa Pig: Nursery Rhyme Time! 2007. (Peppa Pig Ser.). 24p. (J). pap. 3.99 (978-0-06-117362-2(2), Harper Entertainment) HarperCollins Pubs.

Gilpin, Greg. How to Be a Pirate in Seven Easy Songs: A Mini-Musical for the Pirate in Us All. 2008. (ENG., Illus.). 92p. pap. 49.95 incl. audio compact disk (978-1-59235-242-5(1), 1592352421) Shawnee Pr., Inc.

Graham, Patricia Kelsey. We Shall Make Music: Stories of the Primary Songs & How They Came to Be. 2007. (Illus.). 285p. per. 19.99 (978-0-88290-818-2(9)) Cedar Fort, Inc./CFI Distribution.

Guaraldi, Vince. Peanuts: Clarinet. 2010. (ENG.). 24p. pap. 12.99 incl. audio compact disk (978-1-4234-8687-9(0), 1423486870) Leonard, Hal Corp.

Hal Leonard Corp. Anthology of Children's Songs - Gold Edition. 2011. (ENG.). 368p. pap. 24.99 (978-1-61780-568-4(8), 1617805688) Leonard, Hal Corp.

—Children's Songs: Ukulele Play-along Volume 4. 2011. (ENG.). 32p. pap. 12.99 incl. audio compact disk (978-1-4234-9072-2(X), 142349072X) Leonard, Hal Corp.

Hal Leonard Corp., creator. The Best Children's Songs Ever. 2012. (ENG.). 210p. pap. 14.99 (978-1-4584-1217-1(2), 1458412172) Leonard, Hal Corp.

—Broadway Songs for Kids: Songs Originally Sung on Stage by Children. 2011. (ENG.). 154p. pap. 17.99 (978-1-61774-043-5(8), 1617740438) Leonard, Hal Corp.

—Children's Songs for Guitar Strummers: 38 Fun Songs for Singing, Playing & Listening. 2010. (ENG.). 56p. pap. 14.99 incl. audio compact disk (978-1-4234-9153-8(X), 142349153X) Leonard, Hal Corp.

—Collected Disney Kids' Solos. 2011. (ENG.). 136p. pap. 29.99 incl. audio compact disk (978-1-61774-105-0(1), 1617741051) Leonard, Hal Corp.

—Scripture Songs for Kids. 2010. (ENG.). 48p. pap. 9.99 (978-1-4234-9296-2(X), 142349296X) Leonard, Hal Corp.

Hal Leonard Corp., creator. 4 the Best Broadway Songs Ever. 2012. (ENG.). 288p. pap. 14.99 (978-1-4584-1218-8(0), 1458412180) Leonard, Hal Corp.

Hal Leonard Corporation Staff. Children's Piano Songs for Dummies, 1 vol. 2010. (ENG.). 200p. pap. 19.99 (978-1-4234-7388-6(4), 1423473884) Leonard, Hal Corp.

Hal Leonard Corporation Staff, creator. Alvin & the Chipmunks. 2008. (ENG., Illus.). 80p. pap. 14.95 (978-1-4234-5522-6(3), 1423455223) Leonard, Hal Corp.

—Children's Classic Songs, 1 vol. 2009. (ENG.). 256p. pap. 7.99 (978-1-4234-3568-6(0), 1423435680) Leonard, Hal Corp.

—Children's Songs. 2010. (ENG.). 152p. pap. 12.99 (978-1-4234-9059-3(2), 1423490592) Leonard, Hal Corp.

—Children's Songs: Essential Songs Series. 2009. (ENG.). 360p. pap. 24.99 (978-1-4234-6472-3(9), 1423464729) Leonard, Hal Corp.

—The Christian Children's Songbook. 2008. (ENG.). 136p. pap. 14.95 (978-1-4234-3507-5(9), 1423435079) Leonard, Hal Corp.

—Disney Classics: Easy Piano CD Play-along Volume 23. 2009. (ENG.). 32p. pap. 14.99 incl. audio compact disk (978-1-4234-6720-5(5), 1423467205) Leonard, Hal Corp.

—Disney Favorites: Jazz Play-along Volume 93. 2009. (ENG.). 88p. pap. 14.99 incl. audio compact disk (978-1-4234-5908-8(3), 1423459083) Leonard, Hal Corp.

—Easy Songs. 2009. (ENG.). 56p. pap. 12.99 incl. audio compact disk (978-1-4234-3083-4(2), 1423430832) Leonard, Hal Corp.

—Lullabyes: Pro Vocal Women's Edition Volume 53. 2010. (ENG.). 32p. pap. 14.99 incl. audio compact disk (978-1-4234-8744-9(3), 1423487443) Leonard, Hal Corp.

—Teaching Little Fingers to Play More Children's Songs. 2009. (ENG.). 40p. pap. 6.99 (978-1-4234-6757-1(4), 1423467574); pap. 12.99 incl. audio compact disk (978-1-4234-6758-8(2), 1423467582) Willis Music Co.

Hal Leonard Publications Staff. Disney's My First Songbook Vol. 3: A Treasury of Favorite Songs to Sing & Play. 2009. (ENG.). 64p. pap. 12.99 (978-1-4234-5629-2(7), 1423456297) Leonard, Hal Corp.

Hammerstein II, Oscar & Hal Leonard Music Books Staff. Rodgers & Hammerstein Solos for Kids: 14 Classic Songs Voice & Piano with a CD of Performances by Kids & Accompaniments, 1 vol. 2010. (ENG.). 64p. pap. 19.99 incl. audio compact disk (978-1-4234-8329-8(4), 1423483294) Leonard, Hal Corp.

Hart, Sybil. Lullaby Massage: Rhyme & Touch Massage for Infants & Children. 2009. 44p. spiral bd. 14.95 (978-0-9823379-2-9(2)) Hale Publishing.

Higgins, John. Festivals & Folksongs Around the World: Multicultural Resource of Songs, Celebrations & Fun Facts. 2011. (ENG.). 64p. pap. 29.99 incl. audio compact disk (978-1-61774-162-3(0), 1617741620) Leonard, Hal Corp.

Hill, Helen, et al. The Saintons Go to Bethlehem. 2011. 66p. 36.95 (978-1-258-08557-5(7)) Literary Licensing, LLC.

Krasnow, Judy Gail. Rudolph, Frosty, & Captain Kangaroo: The Musical Life of Hecky Krasnow - Producer of the World's Most Beloved Children's Songs. 2007. (ENG., Illus.). 424p. 24.95 (978-1-59580-026-8(3)) Santa Monica Pr.

Lacoursiere, Patrick. Dream Songs Night Songs: From Belgium to Brazil. 2008. (ENG.). 36p. (J). (gr. -1-2). 16.95 (978-2-923163-32-1(X)) La Montagne Secrete CAN. Dist: Independent Pubs. Group.

Lansky, Bruce & Pottle, Robert. Tinkle, Tinkle, Little Tot: Songs & Rhymes for Toilet Training. 2006. (ENG., Illus.). 32p. (J). (gr. -1). 12.95 (978-1-4169-2365-7(9)) Meadowbrook Pr.

Lee / Sinonexus, Emma / Fung-Ing. Learn Mandarin Chinese through Children's Songs from Around the World. 2007. (CHI & ENG., Illus.). 192p. (J). 49.95 incl. audio compact disk (978-0-9787664-2-9(3)) Sinonexus Publishing Co.

Lee/ Sinonexus, Emma/ Fung-Ing. Learn Mandarin Chinese through Chinese Children's Songs. 2007. (CHI & ENG., Illus.). 192p. (J). 49.95 incl. audio compact disk (978-0-9787664-1-2(5)) Sinonexus Publishing Co.

Lomba, Ana. Hop, Skip, & Sing Spanish for Kids: An Interactive Audio Program for Kids. 2006. (ENG.). 24p. 12.95 (978-0-07-147451-1(X), 007147451X) McGraw-Hill Cos., The.

Lomba, Ana & Wenzel, Dominique. Hop, Skip, & Sing French for Kids. 2006. (J). 12.95 (978-0-07-147456-6(0), 9780071474566) McGraw-Hill Cos., The.

Low, Elizabeth Cothen. Big Book of Animal Rhymes, Fingerplays, & Songs, 1 vol. 2009. (Illus.). 300p. pap. 40.00 (978-1-59158-630-2(5), LU8330) Libraries Unlimited, Inc.

Lyden, Clara. Children Come & Sing: Seasons & Such. 2011. 26p. 35.95 (978-1-258-07060-1(X)) Literary Licensing, LLC.

Mahoney, Anna Maria. Feliz Navidad - Learning Songs & Traditions in Spanish. 2006. (Teach Me Ser.). (SPA & ENG., Illus.). 32p. (gr. k-6). 13.95 incl. audio compact disk (978-1-59972-060-9(4), Teach Me...) Teach Me Tapes, Inc.

Mahoney, Judy. Joyeux Noel - Learning Songs & Traditions in French. 2006. (FRE., Illus.). 32p. (gr. k-4). lib. bdg. 19.95 incl. audio compact disk (978-1-59972-061-6(2), Teach Me...) Teach Me Tapes, Inc.

McMaster, Clara. Whenever I Hear. 2007. 32p. 16.95 (978-1-59592-062-7(X)) Leatherwood Pr.

McQueen, Lucinda, illus. Albuquerque Turkey. 2006. (ENG.). 36p. (J). (gr. -1-k). 6.95 (978-1-4027-2039-0(4)) Sterling Publishing Co., Inc.

Miller, Cristi Cary. Sound Stories (Digital) For Interactive Listening & Reading Fun. 2011. (ENG.). 4p. cd-rom 24.99 (978-1-61780-712-1(5), 1617807125) Leonard, Hal Corp.

Newell, William Wells, ed. Games & Songs of American Children. 2007. (ENG.). pap. 27.95 (978-1-4304-5118-1(1)) Kessinger Publishing, LLC.

Nursery Rhymes. 2006. (ENG.). (J). (978-1-884270-08-6(5)) Hall, Nancy Inc.

Nursery Rhymes. (Pop up a Page Ser.). 6p. (978-1-4054-6636-3(7)); 2008. 48p. (978-1-4075-3202-8(2)) Parragon, Inc.

Palmer, Alison. Sharing Through Song: My Eternal Family. 2008. 128p. (J). pap. 14.99 (978-0-88290-953-0(3)) Cedar Fort, Inc./CFI Distribution.

Perry, Dave & Perry, Jean. The Hundred-Year Snooze: The Story of Sleeping Beauty. 2008. (ENG.). 48p. pap. 34.95 (978-1-59235-241-8(3), 1592352413); 80p. pap. 29.95 (978-1-59235-240-1(5), 1592352405) Shawnee Pr., Inc.

Read, Howard. Little Howard's Unpleasant Lullaby. 2007. (ENG., Illus.). 24p. (J). (gr. -1-k). 8.99 (978-1-905548-74-3(5)) HarperCollins Pubs. Ltd. GBR. Dist: Independent Pubs. Group.

Reid, Rob. Children's Jukebox: The Select Subject Guide to Children's Musical Recordings. 2nd ed. 2007. 55.00 (978-0-8389-0940-9(X)) American Library Assn.

—Shake & Shout: 16 Noisy, Lively Story Programs. 2008. (Illus.). 110p. pap. 17.95 (978-1-60213-006-7(X), Upstart Bks.) Highsmith Inc.

—Something Musical Happened at the Library: Adding Song & Dance to Children's Story Programs. 2007. (Illus.). 158p. per. 35.00 (978-0-8389-0942-3(6)) American Library Assn.

Rodriguez, Robert Xavier. Three Lullabies. 2007. (ENG.). 6p. pap. 4.95 (978-1-4234-1956-3(1), 1423419561, G Schirmer, Inc.) Leonard, Hal Corp.

Rollins, Jack & Nelson, Steve. Frosty the Snowman. 2006. (ENG., Illus.). 24p. (J). (gr. -1-k). bds. 12.99 (978-0-8249-6671-3(6), Candy Cane Pr.) Ideals Pubns.

Rowsell, Cyrilla. Music Handbook. 2009. (Illus.). 139p. (J). spiral bd. (978-1-84414-112-8(8)) Jolly Learning, Ltd.

—Music Handbook Level 1. 2009. (Illus.). 192p. (J). pap. (978-1-84414-143-2(8), Jolly Learning, Ltd.

Schram, Ruth Elaine & Hayden, Tim. Gather 'Round & Sing: 6 Rounds for 2-Part & 3-Part Children's Choirs. 2008. (ENG.). 48p. pap. 19.95 (978-0-7390-5034-7(6)) Alfred Publishing Co., Inc.

—Gather 'Round & Sing: 6 Rounds for 2-Part & 3-Part Children's Choirs, Book & CD. 2008. (ENG.). 48p. pap. 44.95 (978-0-7390-5035-4(4)) Alfred Publishing Co., Inc.

Silberg, Jackie & Schiller, Pam. The Complete Book of Rhymes, Songs, Poems, Fingerplays & Chants: Over 700 Selections. 2006. (Complete Book Ser.). (ENG., Illus.). 512p. 44.95 (978-0-87659-053-9(9)) Gryphon Hse., Inc.

Song at the Scaffold. 12.00 (978-1-931555-26-5(5)) Our Lady of Victory Schl.

Songs for God & Country: Song Book. pap. 5.00 (978-1-931555-30-2(3)) Our Lady of Victory Schl.

Tom Glazer's Treasury of Songs for Children. (Style Collections). 256p. 14.95 (978-0-9643258-0-7(2), HL00310968) Songs Music, Inc.

Trapani, Iza. Jingle Bells. 2008. (ENG.). 30p. (J). 16.00 (978-1-4379-6328-1(5)) DIANE Publishing Co.

Trapani, Iza, illus. & as told by. Here We Go 'Round the Mulberry Bush. 2006. 32p. (J). (gr. -1-3). lib. bdg. 16.95 (978-1-57091-663-2(2)) Charlesbridge Publishing, Inc.

Treviño, Rose Zertuche. Read Me a Rhyme in Spanish & English: Léame una Rima en Español e Inglés. 2009. (SPA & ENG.). 160p. 45.00 (978-0-8389-0982-9(5)) American Library Assn.

Turner, Barrie C. Best of Childrens Songs. 2007. (ENG.). 88p. pap. 19.95 (978-1-902455-83-9(5), 1902455835) Schott Music Corp.

Twin Sisters Productions. Ten in the Bed. 2010. (J). (gr. k-1). 14.99 (978-1-59922-628-6(6)) Twin Sisters Productions, LLC.

Twin Sisters Productions Staff. The Christmas Story Box Set-2 books. 2009. 12.99 (978-1-59922-151-9(9)) Twin Sisters Productions, LLC.

Verney, Candy. The Singing Year. 2006. (Festivals Ser.). (Illus.). 136p. pap. 28.95 incl. audio compact disk (978-1-903458-39-6(0)) Hawthorn Pr. GBR. Dist: SteinerBooks, Inc.

Ward, Jennifer. There Was a Coyote Who Swallowed a Flea. 2007. (ENG., Illus.). 32p. (J). (gr. -1-3). 15.95 (978-0-87358-898-0(3)) Cooper Square Publishing Llc.

Warner, Anna Bartlett. Jesus Loves Me. 2007. (Illus.). (J). (978-1-60261-266-2(8)) Cliff Road Bks.

Wilson, LuVal. Old School Classic Play Songs: Song Book. 2011. 40p. pap. 19.57 (978-1-4269-7031-3(5)) Trafford Publishing.

Witchipoo. l.t. ed. 2006. (Illus.). 24p. (J). (gr. -1-3). per. 11.99 (978-1-59879-206-5(7)) Lifevest Publishing, Inc.

Wiz, Bob & Lande, Aubrey. Songames for Sensory Integration: 25 Therapist Created Musical Activities for Improving Fine & Gross Motor Skills, Muscle Strength, & Rhythmicity. 2011. (ENG.). 80p. pap. 24.95 (978-1-935567-07-3(1)) Sensory Resources.

Wright, Vicki Hancock & Reeves, Jeff. Can't Wait to Sing: Anthems & Fun Songs to Sing All Year. Reeves, Jeff ed. 2007. pap. 29.95 (978-1-929187-18-8(1)) Choristers Guild.

Wyckoff, Marjorie M. A Book of Cradle Songs. 2011. 40p. pap. 35.95 (978-1-258-06262-0(3)) Literary Licensing, LLC.

CHILDREN'S STORIES

see also Fairy Tales; Missionary Stories; Science Fiction—Juvenile Literature; Storytelling

Adoff, Arnold & Cook, Kacy. Virginia Hamilton: Speeches, Essays, & Conversations. 2010. (ENG.). 368p. (J). (gr. 5-18). 29.99 (978-0-439-27193-6(2), Blue Sky Pr., The) Scholastic, Inc.

Alexander, Lloyd. The Chronicles of Prydain Set, 4 vols. 2011. (Chronicles of Prydain Ser.). (ENG.). (J). pap. 34.95 (978-1-250-00093-4(9)) Square Fish.

Ambrosek, Renee. E. L. Konigsburg. 2009. (Library of Author Biographies Ser.). 112p. (gr. 5-8). 63.90 (978-1-60853-532-3(0), Rosen Central) Rosen Publishing Group, Inc., The.

Andrews, Jane. The Seven Little Sisters Who Live on the Round Ball That Floats in the Air. 2009. 116p. 21.99 (978-1-103-57297-7(0)); pap. 15.99 (978-1-103-57294-6(6)) BiblioBazaar.

—The Seven Little Sisters Who Live on the Round Ball That Floats in the Air. 2009. 78p. (gr. -1-7). pap. (978-1-4589-3529-8(9)) Books LLC.

—The Seven Little Sisters Who Live on the Round Ball That Floats in the Air. 2007. 160p. (gr. -1-7). 36.95 (978-0-548-01880-4(4)) Kessinger Publishing, LLC.

—The Seven Little Sisters Who Live on the Round Ball That Floats in the Air. 2009. (Illus.). 124p. (gr. -1-7). pap. 8.95 (978-1-59915-307-0(6)) Yesterday's Classics.

Animal Treasury. 2007. (ENG.). 240p. 9.99 (978-1-4037-3368-9(6)) Dalmatian Pr.

Applebaum, Noga. Representations of Technology in Science Fiction for Young People. 2009. xv, 198p. (C). 110.00 (978-0-203-87389-2(0)) Routledge.

Armstrong, Ari. Values of Harry Potter: Lessons for Muggles. 2008. 112p. pap. 12.95 (978-0-9818030-0-5(8)) Ember Publishing.

Auchet, Marc. (Re)lire Andersen: Modernité de L'oeuvre. 2007. (FRE., Illus.). 300p. (C). pap. 39.00 **(978-2-252-03636-5(2))** Klincksieck, Editions FRA. Dist: ISD.

Bambi. 2008. 96p. 24.99 (978-1-4037-4749-5(0)) Dalmatian Pr.

Bambi. (Disney Book of Film Bilingual Ser.). 32p. (978-1-4054-8503-6(5)); 9p. bds. (978-1-4054-8480-0(2)) Parragon, Inc.

Beckett, Sandra. Crossover Fiction. 2009. 346p. pap. 39.95 (978-0-415-87936-1(1)) Routledge.

Beckett, Sandra L. Crossover Fiction: Global & Historical Perspectives. 2008. (Children's Literature & Culture Ser.). XIV, 346p. 136.00 (978-0-415-98033-3(X)) Routledge.

Bramwell, Peter. Pagan Themes in Modern Children's Fiction: Green Man, Shamanism, Earth Mysteries. 2009. (ENG., Illus.). 256p. 89.00 (978-0-230-21839-0(3)) Palgrave Macmillan.

Brezina, Corona. Johnny Tremain & the American Revolution. 2009. (Looking at Literature Through Primary Sources Ser.). 64p. (gr. 5-8). 58.50 (978-1-61514-304-7(1)) Rosen Publishing Group, Inc., The.

Briggs, Dianne. Toddler Storytimes II. 2008. (ENG.). 178p. pap. 55.00 (978-0-8108-6057-5(0)) Scarecrow Pr., Inc.

Briggs, Thomas, illus. Preschool Favorites: 35 Storytimes Kids Love. 2007. 227p. per. 45.00 (978-0-8389-0938-6(8)) American Library Assn.

Bryant, Sara Cone. Stories to Tell Children. 2008. 208p. 27.99 (978-0-554-26028-0(X)); 24.99 (978-0-554-35331-9(8)) BiblioBazaar.

Burkart, Gina. Finding Purpose in Narnia: A Journey with Prince Caspian. 2008. 163p. pap. 16.00 (978-1-58768-028-1(9), HiddenSpring) Paulist Pr.

Burt, Mary E. Stories from Plato & Other Classic Writers. 2009. (Illus.). 144p. pap. 8.95 (978-1-59915-309-4(2)) Yesterday's Classics.

Cadden, Mike. Ursula K. le Guin Beyond Genre: Fiction for Children & Adults. 2008. 224p. 39.95 (978-0-415-99527-6(2)) Routledge.

Carpentier Brown, Nancy. The Mystery of Harry Potter: A Catholic Family Guide. 2007. (Illus.). 175p. per. 12.95 (978-1-59276-398-6(7)) Our Sunday Visitor, Publishing Div.

Carroll, Jane Suzanne. Landscape in Children's Literature. 2012. (Children's Literature & Culture Ser.). (ENG., Illus.). 256p. (C). 125.00 **(978-0-415-80814-9(6))** Routledge.

Carroll, Lewis, pseud. Alice au Pays des Merveilles.Tr. of Alice in Wonderland. (FRE.). pap. 16.95 (978-2-07-051366-6(1)) Gallimard, Editions FRA. Dist: Distribooks, Inc.

—Alice au Pays des Merveilles.Tr. of Alice in Wonderland. pap. 17.95 (978-2-266-09945-5(0)) Presses Pocket FRA. Dist: Distribooks, Inc.

Carroll, Sheila, ed. Living Books Press Aesop's Fables. Jones, V. S., tr. 2007. 236p. 22.00 (978-0-9790876-8-4(6)) Living Bks. Pr.

Chapin, Patricia. A Rock Concert for India. 2009. (Readers for Teens Ser.). (ENG.). 24p. pap. 6.00 (978-0-521-73691-6(9)) Cambridge Univ. Pr.

Crump, Irving, ed. Boys' Life Book of Scout Stories. 2011. 216p. 44.95 **(978-1-258-07140-0(1))** Literary Licensing, LLC.

Dalmatian Press Staff, creator. Bambi. 2006. (ENG., Illus.). 48p. (J). 3.99 (978-1-4037-2385-7(0)) Dalmatian Pr.

Dalmatian Press Staff, ed. Lion King. (ENG.). 48p. 3.99 (978-1-4037-2386-4(9)) Dalmatian Pr.

Davis, Graeme. Re-Read Harry Potter & the Sorcerer's Stone Today! an Unauthorized Guide. 2008. 84p. pap. 15.21 (978-1-934840-57-3(2)) Nimble Bks. LLC.

Ditchfield, Christin. A Family Guide to Prince Caspian. 2008. (Illus.). 128p. pap. 8.99 (978-1-58134-844-6(4)) Crossway.

Dizer, John T. Readings in American Juvenile Literature: The Collected Essays of John T. Dizer. Terryberry, Karl J., ed. 2006. (Illus.). 320p. (978-0-7734-5601-3(5)) Mellen, Edwin Pr., The.

Duriez, Colin. Field Guide to Harry Potter. 2007. (ENG.). 301p. per. 16.00 (978-0-8308-3430-3(3), IVP Bks.) InterVarsity Pr.

Eaton, Erica, Editor. Outside the Box. 2007. 37p. 15.10 (978-0-615-15071-0(3)) Evolutionary Girls.

Ediciones, Susaeta, et al. Cuentos Clasicos: Para Todos. 2010. (Duende de los Cuentos Ser.). (SPA.). 356p. (J). (gr. k-2). pap. 15.95 (978-84-305-6204-6(4)) Susaeta Ediciones, S.A. ESP. Dist: Independent Pubs. Group.

Erisman, Fred. From Birdwomen to Skygirls: American Girls' Aviation Stories. 2009. (ENG., Illus.). 192p. 29.95 (978-0-87565-397-6(9)) Texas Christian Univ. Pr.

Fairytale Num. 58, 1 vol. 2011. (ENG., Illus.). 168p. 195.00 (978-1-888645-81-1(4)) Visionaire Publishing.

Falconer, Rachel. The Crossover Novel. 2009. 264p. pap. 39.95 (978-0-415-87937-8(X)) Routledge.

Famous Stories Every Child Should Know. 2008. 280p. 28.99 (978-0-554-25551-4(0)) 2008. 280p. 25.99 (978-0-554-34854-4(3)) 2007. (ENG.). 248p. pap. 20.99 (978-1-4264-9239-6(1)) BiblioBazaar.

Gargano, Elizabeth. Reading Victorian Schoolrooms: Childhood & Education in Nineteenth-Century Fiction. 2007. (Children's Literature & Culture Ser.). (ENG., Illus.). 216p. 125.00 (978-0-415-98034-0(8)) Routledge.

Geye, Susan, et al. Orca Currents Resource Guide, 1 vol. 2009. (Orca Currents Ser.). (ENG.). 300p. spiral bd. 45.00 (978-1-55143-956-3(5)) Orca Bk. Pubs. USA.

Goetz, Sharon K. Phoenix Rising: Collected Papers on Harry Potter, 17-21 May 2007. 2008. 564p. pap. 27.99 (978-0-615-19524-7(5)) Narrate Conferences, Inc.

Grahame, Kenneth. Dream Days. 2011. (Hesperus Classics Ser.). (ENG.). 136p. pap. 14.95 (978-1-84391-195-1(7)) Hesperus Pr. GBR. Dist: Independent Pubs. Group.

HarperCollins Children's Books. Puss in Boots. 2007. (Play along Fairy Tales Ser.). (ENG., Illus.). 14p. (J). (gr. -1-k). bds. 9.95 (978-0-00-721443-3(X)) HarperCollins Pubs. Ltd. GBR. Dist: Independent Pubs. Group.

—Snow White. 2007. (Play along Fairy Tales Ser.). (ENG., Illus.). 14p. (J). (gr. -1-k). bds. 9.95 (978-0-00-721442-6(1)) HarperCollins Pubs. Ltd. GBR. Dist: Independent Pubs. Group.

—The Three Little Pigs. 2007. (Play along Fairy Tales Ser.). (ENG., Illus.). 14p. (J). (gr. -1-k). bds. 9.95 (978-0-00-721444-0(8)) HarperCollins Pubs. Ltd. GBR. Dist: Independent Pubs. Group.

Heilman, Elizabeth. Critical Perspectives on Harry Potter. 2nd rev. ed. 2008. (ENG.). 368p. 39.95 (978-0-415-96484-5(9)) Routledge.

Held, Jacob M. Dr. Seuss & Philosophy: Oh, the Thinks You Can Think! 2011. (ENG.). 288p. pap. 18.95 (978-1-4422-0311-2(0)) Rowman & Littlefield Publishers, Inc.

Hollingsworth, Cristopher, ed. Alice beyond Wonderland: Essays for the Twenty-first Century. 2009. (ENG., Illus.). 256p. 42.95 (978-1-58729-819-6(8)) Univ. of Iowa Pr.

Horne, Jackie C. & Sanders, Joe Sutliff. Frances Hodgson Burnett's The Secret Garden: A Children's Classic at 100. 2011. (Children's Literature Association Centennial Studies). (ENG.). 312p. 65.00 (978-0-8108-8187-7(X)) Scarecrow Pr., Inc.

Jackson, Anna, ed. The Gothic in Children's Literature. 2009. (Illus.). 264p. pap. 39.95 (978-0-415-87574-5(9)) Routledge.

Jones, Diana Wynne. The Tough Guide to Fantasyland: The Essential Guide to Fantasy Travel. 2006. (ENG., Illus.). 256p. (YA). (gr. 7-18). 9.99 (978-0-14-240722-6(4), Puffin) Penguin Group (USA) Inc.

Kidd, Kenneth B. & Abate, Michelle Ann. Over the Rainbow: Queer Children's & Young Adult Literature. 2011. (ENG., Illus.). 420p. (C). 95.00 (978-0-472-07146-3(7)); pap. 45.00 (978-0-472-05146-5(6)) Univ. of Michigan Pr.

Kronzek, Allan Zola & Kronzek, Elizabeth. The Sorcerer's Companion: A Guide to the Magical World of Harry Potter. 3rd ed. 2010. (ENG.). 384p. pap. 16.99 (978-0-307-88513-5(5)) Broadway Bks.

Lampert, Jo. Children's Fiction About 9/11: Ethnic, National & Heroic Identities. 2009. (Children's Literature & Culture Ser.). (ENG., Illus.). 204p. 126.00 (978-0-415-99630-3(9)) Routledge.

Lear, Linda. Beatrix Potter: A Life in Nature. 2007. (ENG., Illus.). 608p. 30.00 (978-0-312-36934-7(4)) St. Martin's Pr.

Lewis, C. S. Le Monde de Narnia: le Lion, la Sorciere Blanche et L'Armoire Magique. Dalmais, Anne-Marie, tr. 2008. (Folio Junior Ser.). (Illus.). 195p. (J). (gr. 4-7). pap. (978-2-07-061901-6(X)) Gallimard, Editions.

Lucas. Forgotten Tales of Long Ago. 2010. 206p. pap. 28.66 (978-1-152-46911-2(8)) General Bks. LLC.

Lucas, E. V. Forgotten Tales of Long Ago. 2010. (Illus.). 202p. pap. 28.66 (978-1-153-81442-3(0)) General Bks. LLC.

Lucas, E. 1868-1938. Forgotten Tales of Long Ago. 2010. 458p. pap. 36.75 (978-1-171-84228-6(7)) BiblioBazaar.

Lucas, E. 1868-1938 & Bedford, F. D. Forgotten Tales of Long Ago. 2010. (ENG.). 456p. pap. 36.75 (978-1-176-60874-0(6)) BiblioBazaar.

Lucas, Edward Verall, ed. Forgotten Tales of Long Ago. 448p. 2010. 41.56 (978-1-163-40052-4(1)) 2010. pap. 29.56 (978-1-162-92918-7(9)) 2007. (ENG.). 51.95 (978-0-548-09246-0(X)) Kessinger Publishing, LLC.

Mabie, Hamilton Wright. Famous Stories Every Child Should Know. 2009. 178p. (gr. -1-7). pap. (978-0-217-21117-8(8)) Books LLC.

Mabie, Hamilton Wright, ed. Famous Stories Every Child Should Know. 2007. (ENG.). 252p. (gr. -1-7). per. (978-1-4065-2958-6(3)) Dodo Pr.

Mallan, Kerry. Gender Dilemmas in Children's Fiction. 2009. (ENG., Illus.). 240p. 89.00 (978-0-230-20251-1(9)) Palgrave Macmillan.

Margulies, Leo. Wings over the World. 2007. (ENG.). 442p. 51.95 (978-0-548-07374-2(0)) Kessinger Publishing, LLC.

Markey, Anne, ed. Children's Fiction, 1765-1808. 2011. (Illus.). 189p. 60.00 (978-1-84682-287-2(4)) Four Courts Pr. IRL. Dist: International Specialized Bk. Services.

—Children's Fiction, 1765-1808: By John Carey - Margaret King Moore - Lady Mount Cashell & Henry Brooke. 2011. (Illus.). 189p. pap. 29.95 (978-1-84682-288-9(2)) Four Courts Pr. IRL. Dist: International Specialized Bk. Services.

Martens, Frederick Herman & Wilhelm, Richard. The Chinese fairy Book. 2010. (ENG.). 358p. pap. 32.75 **(978-1-176-54309-6(1))** BiblioBazaar.

McDaniel, Lurlene. Reaching Through Time: Three Novellas. 2012. (ENG.). 240p. (YA). (gr. 7). pap. 8.99 **(978-0-440-24018-1(2**, Ember) Random Hse. Children's Bks.

McKissack, Patricia C., et al. The Clone Codes. 2010. (Clone Codes Ser.). (ENG.). 192p. (J). (gr. 7-7). 16.99 (978-0-439-92983-7(0), Scholastic Pr.) Scholastic, Inc.

McLaren, Duncan. Looking for Enid: The Mysterious & Inventive Life of Enid Blyton. 2007. (ENG., Illus.). 336p. 29.95 (978-1-84708-115-5(0)) Granta Bks. GBR. Dist: Independent Pubs. Group.

Meeker, Ezra. Uncle Ezra's Short Stories for Children. 2010. 106p. pap. 18.75 (978-1-178-15973-8(6)) BiblioBazaar.

—Uncle Ezra's Short Stories for Children. 100p. reprint ed. pap. 10.00 (978-0-8466-0242-2(3), S242) Shorey's Bookstore.

Menges, Jeff A., ed. Alice Illustrated: 110 Images from the Classic Tales of Lewis Carroll. 2012. (Dover Fine Art, History of Art Ser.). (ENG., Illus.). 128p. pap. 19.95 (978-0-486-48204-0(9)) Dover Pubns., Inc.

Neal, Connie. The Gospel According to Harry Potter: The Spritual Journey of the World's Greatest Seeker. rev. exp. ed. 2008. (Gospel according to... Ser.). (ENG.). 305p. pap. 17.00 (978-0-664-23123-1(3)) Westminster John Knox Pr.

Nelson, Christine. Drawing Babar: Early Drafts & Watercolors. 2008. (Illus.). xi, 150p. (978-0-87598-151-2(8)); pap. (978-0-87598-152-9(6)) Pierpont Morgan Library.

Nelson, Claudia. Precocious Children & Childish Adults: Age Inversion in Victorian Literature. 2012. (ENG.). 224p. (gr. 17). 50.00 **(978-1-4214-0534-6(2))** Johns Hopkins Univ. Pr.

Perrault, Charles & Doré, Gustave. The Complete Fairy Tales. Betts, Christopher, tr. from FRE. 2009. (Oxford World's Classics Hardcovers Ser.). (ENG., Illus.). 256p. 29.95 (978-0-19-923683-1(6)) Oxford Univ. Pr., Inc.

Publications International Staff, ed. Treasury of Christmas Tales. 2007. (J). pap. 15.98 (978-1-4127-8375-0(5)) Publications International, Ltd.

Riordan, Rick & Wilson, Leah, eds. Demigods & Monsters: Your Favorite Authors on Rick Riordan's Percy Jackson & the Olympians Series. 2009. (ENG.). 196p. (J). (gr. 6-11). pap. 14.95 (978-1-933771-83-0(6)) BenBella Bks.

Roper, Denise. The Lord of the Hallows: Christian Symbolism & Themes in J. K. Rowling's Harry Potter. 2009. (Illus.). 117p. pap. 14.95 (978-1-4327-4112-9(8)) Outskirts Pr., Inc.

Ryken, Leland & Mead, Marjorie Lamp. A Reader's Guide to Caspian: A Journey into C. S. Lewis's Narnia. 2008. (ENG., Illus.). 172p. pap. 15.00 (978-0-8308-3499-0(0), IVP Bks.) InterVarsity Pr.

Sanders, Joe Sutliff. Disciplining Girls: Understanding the Origins of the Classic Orphan Girl Story. 2011. (ENG.). 240p. (gr. 17). 60.00 (978-1-4214-0318-2(8)) Johns Hopkins Univ. Pr.

Schakel, Peter J. Imagination & the Arts in C. S. Lewis: Journeying to Narnia & Other Worlds. 2011. (ENG., Illus.). 232p. (C). (gr. 13). pap. 30.00 (978-0-8262-1937-4(3)) Univ. of Missouri Pr.

—The Longing for a Form: Essays on the Fiction of C. S. Lewis. Schakel, Peter J., ed. 2008. (C. S. Lewis Secondary Studies Ser.). 256p. pap. 28.00 (978-1-55635-588-2(2), Wipf and Stock) Wipf & Stock Pubs.

Schakel, Peter J. & Huttar, Charles A., eds. Word & Story in C. S. Lewis: Language & Narrative in Theory & Practice. 2008. (C. S. Lewis Secondary Studies Ser.). 330p. pap. 36.00 (978-1-55635-587-5(4)) Wipf & Stock Pubs.

Sebag-Montefiore, Mary. Women Writers of Children's Classics. 2007. (Writers & Their Work Ser.). (ENG.). 154p. (C). pap. 26.00 (978-0-7463-1157-8(5)) Northcote Hse. Publishers, Ltd. GBR. Dist: Brown, David Bk. Co., The.

Shedlock, Marie L. The Art of the Story-Teller. 2010. (ENG.). 316p. pap. 30.75 (978-1-147-83956-2(5)) 2010. (ENG.). 312p. pap. 29.75 (978-1-177-41728-0(6)) 2010. (ENG.). 312p. pap. 29.75 (978-1-176-44238-2(4)) 2010. 318p. pap. 30.75 (978-1-143-98766-3(7)) 2008. 224p. 27.99 (978-0-554-22645-3(6)) 2008. 224p. 24.99 (978-0-554-31948-3(9)) 2006. 208p. pap. 20.99 (978-1-4264-2779-4(4)) BiblioBazaar.

—The Art of the Story-Teller. 2008. 220p. pap. (978-1-4099-1729-8(0)) Dodo Pr.

—The Art of the Story-Teller. 2007. (ENG.). 160p. per. (978-1-4068-1522-1(5)) Echo Library.

—The Art of the Story-Teller. 2010. (Illus.). 124p. pap. 21.33 (978-1-153-69267-0(8)) General Bks. LLC.

Sims, Michael. The Story of Charlotte's Web: E. B. White's Eccentric Life in Nature & the Birth of an American Classic. 2011. (ENG., Illus.). 320p. 25.00 (978-0-8027-7754-6(6)) Walker & Co.

Smidt, Sandra. Reading the World. 2012. (Illus.). 186p. pap. 34.95 **(978-1-85856-505-7(7))** Trentham Bks. Ltd. GBR. Dist: Stylus Publishing, LLC.

Sunderland, Jane. Language, Gender & Children's Fiction. 2011. (ENG., Illus.). 272p. 150.00 (978-0-8264-4613-8(2)) Continuum International Publishing Group, Ltd. GBR. Dist: National Bk. Network.

Superle, Michelle. Contemporary English-Language Indian Children's Literature: Representations of Nation, Culture, & the New Indian Girl. 2011. (Children's Literature & Culture Ser.). (ENG.). 214p. (C). 125.00 (978-0-415-88634-5(1)) Routledge.

Sydney, Margaret. Twilight Stories. 2008. 144p. 21.99 (978-0-554-31003-9(1)); 24.99 (978-0-554-21700-0(7)) BiblioBazaar.

Sydney, Margaret, et al. Twilight Stories. 2006. (ENG.). 138p. pap. 18.99 (978-1-4264-0745-1(9)); 140p. pap. 19.99 (978-1-4264-0729-1(7)) BiblioBazaar.

Talairach-Vielmas, Laurence. Moulding the Female Body in Victorian Fairy Tales & Sensation Novels. 2007. (Illus.). 198p. 99.95 (978-0-7546-6034-7(6)) Ashgate Publishing Co.

Taylor, C. J. All the Stars in the Sky: Native Stories from the Heavens. 2006. (ENG., Illus.). 40p. (J). (gr. 3). 17.95 (978-0-88776-759-3(1)) Tundra Bks., Inc./Livres Toundra, Inc. CAN. Dist: Random Hse., Inc.

Toy Story. (Disney Book of Film Bilingual Ser.). 32p. (978-1-4054-7658-4(3)); 56p. (978-1-4054-9275-1(9)) Parragon, Inc.

Treadwell, Harriette Taylor, et al. Kensa Lyver Redya. 2009. (COR., Illus.). 121p. pap. (978-1-904808-24-4(7)) Evertype.

Tribunella, Eric L. Melancholia & Maturation: The Use of Trauma in American Children's Literature. 2009. (ENG.). 42.00 (978-1-57233-681-0(1)) Univ. of Tennessee Pr.

Wannamaker, Annette. Boys in Children's Literature & Popular Culture: Masculinity, Abjection, & the Fictional Child. 2007. (Children's Literature & Culture Ser.). 200p. 131.00 (978-0-415-97469-1(0)) Routledge.

Winnie the Pooh. (Disney Sticker Activity Ser.). 16p. pap. (978-1-4054-7680-5(X)); 5p. bds. (978-1-4054-9414-4(X)); 9p. bds. (978-1-4054-8481-7(0)) Parragon, Inc.

Yousha, LaDonna. Teddy Bear Storytimes: Ready-To-Go Flannel & Magnetic Storyboard Programs That Captivate Children. 2009. 55.00 (978-1-55570-677-7(0)) Neal-Schuman Pubs., Inc.

Zhang, Jie. She Knocked at the Door. 2010. 194p. pap. 11.95 (978-1-60220-909-1(X)) BetterLink Pr., Inc.

CHILDREN'S STORIES—BIBLIOGRAPHY

Bienvenue, Paul R. The Book Collector's Guide to L. Frank Baum & Oz. 2009. (Illus.). 408p. 75.00 (978-0-615-24725-0(3)) March Hare Bks.

Gillespie, John T. The Family in Literature for Young Readers: A Resource Guide for Use with Grades 4 To 9, 1 vol. (Children's & Young Adult Literature Reference Ser.). 470p. 60.00 (978-1-59158-915-0(0), A2251C) Libraries Unlimited, Inc.

Gillespie, John Thomas. The Family in Literature for Young Readers: A Resource Guide for Use with Grades 4 to 9. 2011. E-Book (978-1-59158-916-7(9)) Libraries Unlimited, Inc.

Gross, Melissa. HIV/AIDS in Young Adult Novels: An Annotated Bibliography. 2010. (ENG., Illus.). 246p. (gr. 17). 49.95 (978-0-8108-7443-5(1)) Scarecrow Pr., Inc.

Gross, Melissa, et al. HIV/AIDS in Young Adult Novels: An Annotated Bibliography. 2010. E-Book 49.95 (978-0-8108-7444-2(X)) Scarecrow Pr., Inc.

Shedlock, Marie L. The Art of the Story-Teller. l.t. ed. 2007. (ENG.). 220p. pap. 22.99 (978-1-4264-2817-3(0)) BiblioBazaar.

Thomas, Rebecca L. & Barr, Catherine. Popular Series Fiction for K-6 Readers: A Reading & Selection Guide, 1 vol. 2nd ed. 2008. (Children's & Young Adult Literature Reference Ser.). 1016p. 65.00 (978-1-59158-659-3(3), LU8659) Libraries Unlimited, Inc.

—Popular Series Fiction for Middle School & Teen Readers: A Reading & Selection Guide, 1 vol. 2nd ed. 2008. (Children's & Young Adult Literature Reference Ser.). 724p. 65.00 (978-1-59158-660-9(7), LU8660) Libraries Unlimited, Inc.

Wadham, Rachel L. This Is My Life: A Guide to Realistic Fiction for Teens, 1 vol. 2010. (Genreflecting Advisory Ser.). 431p. 55.00 (978-1-59158-942-6(8), A2627C) Libraries Unlimited, Inc.

Young, Timothy G. My Heart in Company: The Work of J. M. Barrie & the Birth of Peter Pan. 2007. (Illus.). 89p. per. 20.00 (978-0-300-13403-2(7)) Yale Univ. Pr.

CHILDREN'S STORIES—TECHNIQUE

Clark, Elizabeth. Stories to Tell & How to Tell Them. 2008. 164p. pap. 27.45 (978-1-4437-0462-5(8)) Audubon Pr. & Christian Bk. Service.

CHILDREN'S TELEVISION PROGRAMS

Banet-Weiser, Sarah. Kids Rule! Nickelodeon & Consumer Citizenship. 2007. (Console-Ing Passions: Television & Cultural Power Ser.). (ENG., Illus.). 296p. 89.95 (978-0-8223-3976-2(5)); per. 24.95 (978-0-8223-3993-9(5)) Duke Univ. Pr.

Bryant, J. Alison. The Children's Television Community. 2006. (LEA's Communication Ser.). (Illus.). 304p. per. 42.95 (978-0-8058-4997-4(1)) Erlbaum, Lawrence Assocs., Inc.

—The Children's Television Community. 2006. (LEA's Communication Ser.). (ENG., Illus.). 320p. 125.00 (978-0-8058-4996-7(3)) Routledge.

Calloway, Alexander. All That about All That. 2007. 84p. pap. 11.95 (978-1-60145-140-8(7)) Booklocker.com, Inc.

Colliver, Tim. Good Morning World. 2008. 116p. per. 14.95 (978-1-59393-135-3(2)) BearManor Media.

Davis, Jeffery. Children's Television, 1947-1990: Over 200 Series, Game & Variety Shows, Cartoons, Educational Programs & Specials. alt. ed. 2011. (ENG., Illus.). 295p. pap. 25.00 **(978-0-7864-6726-6(6))** McFarland & Co., Inc. Pubs.

Erickson, Hal. Sid & Marty Krofft: A Critical Study of Saturday Morning Children's Television, 1969-1993. alt. ed. 2007. (ENG., Illus.). 303p. per. 35.00 *(978-0-7864-3093-2(1))* McFarland & Co., Inc. Pubs.

Guernsey, Lisa. Into the Minds of Babes: How Screen Time Affects Children from Birth to Age Five. 2007. (ENG.). 304p. (gr. 9). 25.00 *(978-0-465-02798-9(9))* Basic Bks.

Hamlett, Tiffany, et al. Content Analysis of Aggression in Television Programs for Preschoolers. 2010. 76p. pap. *(978-3-639-18648-2(6))* VDM Verlag Dr. Mueller e.K.

Hayes, Dade. Anytime Playdate: Inside the Preschool Entertainment Boom, or, How Television Became My Baby's Best Friend. (ENG.). 256p. 2011. pap. 16.99 ***(978-1-4165-4684-9(7))*** 2008. (Illus.). 25.00 *(978-1-4165-4683-2(9))* Free Pr. (Free Pr.).

Hollingsworth, Amy. The Simple Faith of Mister Rogers: Spiritual Insights from the World's Most Beloved Neighbor, 0 vols. 2007. 224p. per. 14.99 *(978-0-8499-1894-0(4))* Nelson, Thomas Inc.

Matthews, Julian. Producing Serious News for Citizen Children: A Study of the BBC's Children's Program Newsround. 2010. xii, 193p. 109.95 *(978-0-7734-3653-4(7))* Mellen, Edwin Pr., The.

May, David. Views from Behind the Sof. 2007. 640p. per. 46.50 *(978-1-84753-851-2(7))* Lulu Enterprises Inc.

Neighbors, R. C. & Rankin, Sandy, eds. The Galaxy Is Rated G: Essays on Children's Science Fiction Film & Television. 2011. (ENG.). 292p. pap. 40.00 ***(978-0-7864-5875-2(5))*** McFarland & Co., Inc. Pubs.

Nevins, Francis M. & Keller, Gary D. The Cisco Kid: American Hero, Hispanic Roots. 2008. 50.00 *(978-1-931010-48-1(X))*; pap. 35.00 *(978-1-931010-49-8(8))* Bilingual Pr./Editorial Bilingue.

Potter, Anna. Internationalising Australian Children's Television Dram. 2008. 108p. pap. *(978-3-639-05326-5(5))* VDM Verlag Dr. Mueller e.K.

Ross, Sharon Marie & Stein, Louisa Ellen, eds. Teen Television: Essays on Programming & Fandom. 2008. (ENG.). 259p. pap. 35.00 *(978-0-7864-3589-0(5))* McFarland & Co., Inc. Pubs.

Ruelas, Richard. Thanks for Tuning In. 2006. (ENG., Illus.). 198p. pap. 16.95 *(978-0-9752822-1-2(2))* Boffo Bks.

Steemers, Jeanette. Creating Preschool Television: A Story of Commerce, Creativity & Curriculum. 2010. (ENG., Illus.). 256p. 95.00 *(978-0-230-57440-3(8))* Palgrave Macmillan.

CHILDREN'S THEATER

Atkins, Liz & Reason, Matthew. The Young Audience: Exploring & Enhancing Children's Experiences of Theatre. 2010. (Illus.). 192p. pap. 34.95 *(978-1-85856-450-0(6))* Trentham Bks. Ltd. GBR. Dist: Stylus Publishing, LLC.

Chamblin, Thomas M. Children's Theatre. 2009. 132p. pap. *(978-3-639-17871-5(8))* VDM Verlag Dr. Mueller e.K.

Chevarie, Pascal, et al. Traces: Théâtre Bouches Décousues, 25 Ans. 2010. (FRE., Illus.). 125p. pap. *(978-2-89637-036-8(6))* Dramaturge Editeurs.

de Las Casas, Dianne. Handmade Tales: Stories to Make & Take, 1 vol. 2007. (Illus.). 112p. per. 30.00 *(978-1-59158-536-7(8)*, LU8536) Libraries Unlimited, Inc.

Eggers, Kelly. Children's Theater: A Paradigm, Primer, & Resource. 2010. (ENG.). 236p. (gr. 17). 55.00 *(978-0-8108-5988-3(2))* Scarecrow Pr., Inc.

Gold, Muriel. The Dramatic Legacy of Dorothy Davis & Violet Walters: The Montreal Children's Theatre, 1933-2009. 2010. 272p. pap. 20.95 *(978-1-4502-6070-1(5))* iUniverse, Inc.

Greig, Noel. Young People, New Theatre: A Practical Guide to an Intercultural Process. 2008. (Illus.). XVIII, 214p. 110.00 *(978-0-415-45250-2(3))* Routledge.

Greig, Noël. Young People, New Theatre: A Practical Guide to an Intercultural Process. 2008. (Illus.). XVIII, 214p. 32.95 *(978-0-415-45251-9(1))* Routledge.

Lantolf, James P. & Poehner, Matthew E. Young People, New Theatre: A Practical Guide to an Intercultural Process. 2012. (ESL & Applied Linguistics Professional Ser.). (ENG.). 224p. pap. 42.95 *(978-0-415-89418-0(2))* Routledge.

Lewis, Mack. Read-Aloud Plays: Classic Short Stories. 2011. (Illus.). 72p. (J). ***(978-0-439-20456-9(9)***, Teaching Resources) Scholastic, Inc.

Lewis, Mack. Read-Aloud Plays - Classic Short Stories: 8 Fluency-Boosting Plays with Easy Activities That Teach Key Literary Elements. 2011. (ENG.). 72p. (gr. 4-8). pap. 11.99 *(978-0-545-20456-9(9)*, Teaching Resources) Scholastic, Inc.

Marcus, Cindy. PLAYdate: A Parent's & Teacher's Guide to Putting on a Play. 2009. (Illus.). 124p. pap. 19.95 *(978-1-56608-160-3(2))* Meriwether Publishing, Ltd.

McGowan, Tara. The Kamishibai Classroom: Engaging Multiple Literacies Through the Art of "Paper Theater", 1 vol. 2010. (Illus.). 99p. pap. 40.00 *(978-1-59158-873-3(1)*, LU8873) Libraries Unlimited, Inc.

Nash, Eric Peter. Manga Kamishibai: The Art of Japanese Paper Theater. 2009. (ENG., Illus.). 304p. 35.00 *(978-0-8109-5303-1(X))* Abrams.

Ross, Beverly B. & Durgin, Jean P. Junior Broadway: How to Produce Musicals with Children 9 to 13, 2d Ed. 2nd rev. alt. ed. 2011. (ENG., Illus.). 223p. pap. 25.00 ***(978-0-7864-6704-4(5))*** McFarland & Co., Inc. Pubs.

Rubin, Janet & Merrion, Margaret Dee. Creative Drama & Music Methods: Activities for the Classroom. 3rd ed. 2010. (Illus.). xv, 130p. *(978-1-4422-0463-8(X))* Rowman & Littlefield Publishers, Inc.

Rubin, Janet E. Creative Drama & Music Methods: Activities for the Classroom. 3rd ed. 2011. (ENG., Illus.). 148p. 75.00 *(978-1-4422-0461-4(3))* Rowman & Littlefield Publishers, Inc.

—Creative Drama & Music Methods: Activities for the Classroom. 3rd ed. 2011. (ENG., Illus.). 148p. pap. 39.95 *(978-1-4422-0462-1(1))* Rowman & Littlefield Publishers, Inc.

Schneider, Wolfgang, ed. Theatre for Early Years: Research in Performing Arts for Children from Birth to Three. 2009. (Kinder-, Schul- und Jugendtheater - Beiträge zu Theorie und Praxis Ser.). (Illus.). 200p. 43.95 *(978-3-631-59259-5(0))* Lang, Peter GmbH, Europäischer Verlag der Wissenschaften DEU. Dist: Lang, Peter.

CHILDREN'S VILLAGES

see Children—Institutional Care

CHILDREN'S WIT AND HUMOR

see Children—Anecdotes and Sayings; Wit and Humor, Juvenile

CHILDREN'S WRITINGS

Here are entered collections of literary works or individual literary works written by children under 15 years of age. Works on child authors and-or discussions of their works are entered under Child Authors. Collections of works published for children are entered under Children's Literature. Works on the reading interests of children, and-or lists of books read by or recommended for children are entered under Children—Books and Reading.

see also School Prose; School Verse

Alexander, Christine & McMaster, Juliet, eds. The Child Writer from Austen to Woolf. 2010. (Cambridge Studies in Nineteenth-Century Literature & Culture Ser.). (ENG., Illus.). 336p. pap. 45.00 *(978-0-521-12838-4(2))* Cambridge Univ. Pr.

Baldwin, Barbara. Dear Soldier, 0 vols. 2009. 12.99 *(978-1-59555-213-6(8))* Nelson, Thomas Inc.

Ball, Marshall S. A Good Kiss: The Wisdom of a Listening Child. 2007. (ENG.). 224p. pap. 16.95 *(978-1-4165-7365-4(8)*, Beyond Words/Atria Bks.) Atria Bks.

Creative Communication, ed. Celebrating What Is Important to Me - East 7-12 Spring 2006. 2006. (YA). 21.95 *(978-1-60050-022-0(6))* Creative Communication.

—Celebrating What Is Important to Me - Great Lakes 7-12 Spring 2006. 2006. (YA). 21.95 *(978-1-60050-023-7(4))* Creative Communication.

—Celebrating What Is Important to Me - South 4-6 Spring 2006. 2006. (J). 21.95 *(978-1-60050-018-3(8))* Creative Communication.

Falvey, David. Letters to a Soldier. 2009. (J). *(978-0-7614-5635-3(X))* Marshall Cavendish Corp.

Hall, Sharon J., ed. Ridgeway Middle School Anthology: Changes. 2009. 200p. pap. 16.95 *(978-1-4401-4773-9(6))* iUniverse, Inc.

Hoog, Mark, ed. Letters from Katrina: Stories of Hope & Inspiration. 2007. (Illus.). 96p. 24.95 *(978-0-9770391-9-7(6))* Growing Field Bks.

Mavers, Diane. Children¿s Writing & Drawing as Design. 2010. (Routledge Research in Education Ser.). (ENG., Illus.). 162p. 125.00 *(978-0-415-96155-4(6))* Routledge.

Mitchell, Margaret. Before Scarlett: Girlhood Writings of Margaret Mitchell. Eskridge, Jane, ed. 2010. pap. 24.95 *(978-1-57003-938-6(0))* Univ. of South Carolina Pr.

Mukhopadhyay, Tito Rajarshi. The Mind Tree: A Miraculous Child Breaks the Silence of Autism. 2011. (ENG.). 176p. pap. 14.95 *(978-1-61145-002-6(0)*, 611002, Arcade Publishing) Skyhorse Publishing Co., Inc.

New Writers Uk. Nottinghamshire Children Tell Tales. 2010. (Illus.). 116p. pap. 10.99 *(978-1-4490-5780-0(2))* AuthorHouse.

Ogburn-Thompson, Gina, et al, eds. Urban Dreams: Stories of Hope, Resilience, & Character. 2007. (ENG.). 130p. per. 26.50 *(978-0-7618-3843-2(0))* Hamilton Bks.

Ooligan Press Staff. Classroom Publishing: A Practical Guide for Teachers. 2nd rev. ed. 2010. (OpenBook Ser.). (ENG.). 300p. pap. 34.95 *(978-1-932010-28-2(9))* Ooligan Pr.

Smit, Teresa, et al, eds. Lit Kids: Mama Bird & the Electric Rabbit. 2007. 244p. pap. 12.95 *(978-1-934248-34-8(7))* Mill City Pr., Inc.

Werner, Emmy E. In Pursuit of Liberty: Coming of Age in the American Revolution, 1 vol. 2006. (Illus.). 208p. 49.95 *(978-0-275-99306-1(X)*, C9306, Praeger Pubs.) Greenwood Publishing Group, Inc.

—In Pursuit of Liberty: Coming of Age in the American Revolution. 2009. (Illus.). 192p. pap. 17.95 *(978-1-59797-268-0(1))* Potomac Bks., Inc.

Williams, Reno. Reno's World, Presenting Autism & Related Disabilities to Youth. 2009. 20p. pap. 10.95 *(978-1-936051-67-0(2))* Peppertree Pr., The.

CHILE

Chile mit Osterinsel. pap. 10.00 *(978-0-85345-700-8(X))* Monthly Review Pr.

Elliott, L. E. Chile Today & Tomorrow. 2009. (ENG.). 404p. 41.99 *(978-1-117-53370-4(0))*; 406p. pap. 33.75 *(978-1-117-53371-1(9))* BiblioBazaar.

Elliott, L. E. & The. Chile Today & Tomorrow. 2009. (ENG.). 404p. pap. 26.99 *(978-1-117-53372-8(7)*, BiblioLife) BiblioBazaar.

Miers, John. Travels in Chile & la Plata: Including Accounts Respecting the Geography, Geology, Statistics, Government, Finances, Agriculture, Manners & Customs, & the Mining Operations in Chile. 2011. (Cambridge Library Collection - Travel & Exploration Ser.). (ENG.). 572p. pap. 39.99 *(978-1-108-07296-0(8))*; (Illus.). 554p. pap. 39.99 *(978-1-108-07295-3(X))* Cambridge Univ. Pr.

Organisation for Economic Co-operation and Development Staff. Chile. 2009. 221p. pap. 63.00 *(978-92-64-06074-6(X))* Organization for Economic Cooperation & Development.

CHILE—BIOGRAPHY

Allende, Isabel. La Suma de los Días. (SPA & ENG.). 2009. 352p. pap. 14.99 *(978-0-06-155188-8(0))* 2007. 368p. 26.95 *(978-0-06-155187-1(2))* HarperCollins Pubs. (Rayo).

Bolaño, Roberto. Roberto Bolano: the Last Interview: And Other Conversations. Perez, Sybil, tr. 2011. (ENG.). 128p. pap. 15.95 ***(978-1-61219-095-2(2))*** Melville Hse. Publishing.

Donoso, Julio. The Why of Things. 2006. 316p. pap. *(978-1-84401-808-6(3))* Athena Pr.

Dorfman, Ariel. Feeding on Dreams: Confessions of an Unrepentant Exile. (ENG.). 352p. 2012. pap. 14.95 ***(978-0-547-84418-3(2)***, Mariner Bks.) 2011. 27.00 *(978-0-547-54946-0(6))* Houghton Mifflin Harcourt Trade & Reference Pubs.

Edmundson, William. The Nitrate King: A Biography of Colonel John Thomas North. 2011. (Studies of the Americas Ser.). (ENG., Illus.). 218p. 85.00 *(978-0-230-11280-3(3))* Palgrave Macmillan.

Franklin, Jonathan. 33 Men: Inside the Miraculous Survival & Dramatic Rescue of the Chilean Miners. 2011. (ENG.). 320p. (gr. 12). 9.99 *(978-0-425-24686-3(8)*, Berkley); 25.95 *(978-0-399-15777-6(8)*, Putnam Adult) Penguin Group (USA) Inc.

—33 Men: Inside the Miraculous Survival & Dramatic Rescue of the Chilean Miners. Lt. ed. 2011. 31.99 *(978-1-4104-3662-7(4))* Thorndike Pr.

García Márquez, Gabriel. Clandestine in Chile: The Adventures of Miguel Littín. Zatz, Asa, tr. from SPA. 2010. (Illus.). 160p. pap. 14.00 *(978-1-59017-340-4(6)*, NYRB Classics) New York Review of Bks., Inc., The.

Kerschen, Karen. Violeta Parra: At the Whim of the Wind. 2010.Tr. of 285. (Illus.). pap. 15.95 *(978-0-9843024-1-3(7)*, ABQ Pr.) ABQ Bks., Inc.

Mills, George J. Chile. 2009. 176p. pap. *(978-0-217-18735-0(8))* Books LLC.

—Chile. 193p. reprint ed. 88.00 *(978-0-7222-9606-6(1))* Library Reprints, Inc.

Moorcroft, Jennifer. God Is All Joy: Life of Saint Teresa of the Andes. 2009. (ENG.). 170p. pap. 12.95 *(978-0-935216-42-4(1))* I C S Pubns.

Neruda, Pablo. Confieso Que He Vivido. (SPA.). 464p. 39.50 *(978-84-322-2001-2(9)*, SB3658) Editorial Seix Barral ESP. Dist: Continental Bk. Co., Inc.

Parker, William B. Chileans of Today. (Hispanic Notes & Monographs). 633p. reprint ed. 128.00 *(978-0-7222-9603-5(7))* Library Reprints, Inc.

Peña y Lillo, Josefa de los Dolores. Epistolario de Sor Dolores Peña y Lillo (Chile, 1763-1769) Kordic Riquelme, Raissa, ed. & prologue by by. 2008. (SPA.). 518p. pap. 44.00 *(978-84-8489-328-8(6))* Iberoamericana Vervuert Publishing Corp.

Pino Toro, Manuel. Buried Alive: The True Story of the Chilean Mining Disaster & the Extraordinary Rescue at Camp Hope. 2011. (ENG., Illus.). 240p. 25.00 *(978-0-230-11515-6(2))* Palgrave Macmillan.

Reed, Lawrence E. A Garden of Paradise: A History of el Vergel. 2008. 568p. pap. 23.99 *(978-1-4389-1425-1(3))* AuthorHouse.

Toro, Manuel Pino. Vivos Bajo Tierra: La Historia Verdadera de los 33 Mineros Chilenos. 2011.Tr. of Alive under Ground. (SPA.). 272p. (gr. 12). pap. 16.95 *(978-0-9831390-0-3(8))* C.A.R. Pr.

Worth, Richard. Michelle Bachelet. 2007. (Modern World Leaders Ser.). (Illus.). 112p. (YA). (gr. 7-12). lib. bdg. 30.00 *(978-0-7910-9500-3(2))* Facts On File, Inc.

CHILE—DESCRIPTION AND TRAVEL

Abraham, Rudolf. Torres del Paine: Trekking in Chile's Premier National Park. 2010. (Illus.). 224p. pap. 24.95 *(978-1-85284-593-3(7))* Cicerone Pr. GBR. Dist: Midpoint Trade Bks., Inc.

Agosín, Marjorie & Gordenstein, Roberta. Of Earth & Sea: A Chilean Memoir. 2009. *(978-0-8165-2665-9(6))* 2008. (ENG., Illus.). 176p. pap. 16.95 *(978-0-8165-2666-6(4))* Univ. of Arizona Pr.

Andrews, Joseph D. Journey from Buenos Ayres Undertaken on Behalf of the Chilian & Peruvian Mining Assn., 1825-26, 2 vols. reprint ed. 82.50 *(978-0-404-00410-1(5))* AMS Pr., Inc.

Bernhardson, Wayne. Chilean Lake District. 2009. (Moon Spotlight Ser.). (ENG., Illus.). 95p. pap. 7.95 *(978-1-59880-330-3(1))* Avalon Travel Publishing.

—Moon Chile: Including Easter Island. 2009. (Moon Handbooks). (ENG., Illus.). 720p. pap. 22.95 *(978-1-59880-181-1(3))* Avalon Travel Publishing.

—Moon Patagonia: Including the Falkland Islands. 2011. (Moon Handbooks Ser.). (ENG., Illus.). 636p. pap. 21.99 *(978-1-59880-932-9(6))* Avalon Travel Publishing.

Bishop, Nathaniel Holmes. The Pampas & Andes a Thousand Miles' Walk Across South America by Nathaniel H Bishop with an Introduction by Edward a Samuels. 2006. 332p. per. 23.99 *(978-1-4255-3307-6(8))* MPublishing.

Bourne, Benjamin Franklin. The Captive in Patagonia; or, Life among the Giants a Personal Narrative. 2006. 252p. per. 20.99 *(978-1-4255-2131-8(2))* MPublishing.

Buford, Tim. Chile Highlights. 2012. (ENG., Illus.). 272p. pap. 24.99 ***(978-1-84162-408-2(X))*** Bradt Travel Guides GBR. Dist: Globe Pequot Pr., The.

Callcott, Maria. Journal of a Residence in Chile, during the Year 1822. 2011. (Cambridge Library Collection - Women's Writing Ser.). (ENG., Illus.). 552p. pap. 39.99 ***(978-1-108-03378-7(4))*** Cambridge Univ. Pr.

Chester, Sharon. A Wildlife Guide to Chile: Continental Chile, Chilean Antarctica, Easter Island, & Juan Fernandez Archipelago. 2008. (ENG.). 400p. pap. 19.95 *(978-0-691-12976-1(2))*; (Illus.). (C). 46.95 *(978-0-691-12975-4(4))* Princeton Univ. Pr.

de la Harpe, Jean Paul. Chile, Shelter of Life. 2007. 157p. *(978-956-310-766-1(7))* Abtao Ediciones.

Dorling Kindersley Publishing Staff. Eyewitness Travel Guides - Chile & Easter Island. 2011. (Eyewitness Travel Guides). (ENG., Illus.). 352p. pap. 25.00 *(978-0-7566-6951-5(0))* Dorling Kindersley Publishing, Inc.

Everton, Macduff. Patagonia, la Última Esperanza. 2012. (ENG & SPA., Illus.). 235p. 65.00 ***(978-0-938531-02-9(6))*** Txcacalcupul Pr.

Fodor's Travel Publications, Inc. Staff. Chile: Including Easter Island & Argentine Patagonia. 5th ed. 2010. (Fodor's Gold Guides). (ENG., Illus.). 480p. pap. 22.99 *(978-1-4000-0434-8(9)*, Fodor's) Fodor's Travel Pubns.

—Patagonia. 2008. (Fodor's Gold Guides). (ENG., Illus.). 416p. pap. 21.95 *(978-1-4000-0684-7(8)*, Fodor's) Fodor's Travel Pubns.

Gill, Nicholas, et al. Frommer's Chile & Easter Island. 3rd ed. 2011. (Frommer's Complete Guides: 989). (ENG., Illus.). 480p. pap. 23.99 *(978-0-470-95139-2(7)*, Frommers) Wiley, John & Sons, Inc.

Graham, Melissa & Benson, Andrew. Chile. 4th ed. 2009. (Rough Guide Travel Guides). (ENG., Illus.). 640p. (gr. 12). pap. 24.99 *(978-1-84836-175-1(0))* Rough Guides, Ltd. GBR. Dist: Dorling Kindersley Publishing, Inc.

Heller, Ingrid. Footprints in the Andes: The True Story of A Woman Who Chose to Follow Her Inner Guidance to Move to South America. 2010. 180p. pap. 16.95 *(978-1-4269-4295-2(8))* Trafford Publishing.

Hill, S. S. Travels in Peru & Mexico. 2008. 328p. 28.99 *(978-0-559-69706-7(6))*; pap. 30.75 *(978-0-559-69703-6(1))*; 28.99 *(978-0-559-56374-4(4))*; pap. 30.75 *(978-0-559-56372-0(8))* BiblioBazaar.

—Travels in Peru & Mexico. 2009. 220p. pap. *(978-1-151-29613-9(9))* Books LLC.

Hudson, W. H. Idle Days in Patagonia. 2008. 152p. pap. *(978-1-4099-0534-9(9))* Dodo Pr.

—Idle Days in Patagonia. 2007. (ENG.). 268p. per. 27.95 *(978-1-4325-2148-6(9))* Kessinger Publishing, LLC.

Jani, Janak. Chile. 6th ed. 2010. (ENG., Illus.). 592p. instr.'s hndbk. ed. 24.95 *(978-1-906098-78-0(6))* Footprint Handbooks GBR. Dist: Globe Pequot Pr., The.

Koebel, William H. Modern Chile. 278p. reprint ed. 98.00 *(978-0-7222-9604-2(5))* Library Reprints, Inc.

Lawrence, Rachel. Chile. 5th ed. 2009. (Insight Guides). (ENG., Illus.). 368p. pap. 23.99 *(978-981-282-062-4(0))* APA Publications Services SGP. Dist: Ingram Pub. Services.

Locken, E. Travel Journal Chile. 2010. 192p. pap. 19.99 *(978-0-557-43455-8(6))*, Lulu Enterprises Inc.

McCarthy, Carolyn & Lonely Planet Staff. Chile & Easter Island. 8th rev. ed. 2009. (Country Guide Ser.). (ENG., Illus.). 528p. pap. 24.99 *(978-1-74104-779-0(X))* Lonely Planet Pubns.

Moss, Chris. Patagonia: A Cultural History. 2008. (Landscapes of the Imagination Ser.). (ENG., Illus.). 256p. 25.00 *(978-0-19-534249-9(6))* Oxford Univ. Pr., Inc.

Perrone, Caterina. Chile. 2007. (Culture Smart! A Quick Guide to Customs & Etiquette Ser.). (ENG., Illus.). 168p. pap. 9.95 *(978-1-85733-341-1(1))* Kuperard Pubs. GBR. Dist: Random Hse., Inc.

Rakemustieto Publishing. Jose Cruz Ovalle Spirit of Nature Wood Architecture Award 2008. 2009. (ENG.). 176p. pap. 76.00 *(978-951-682-896-4(5)*, Art Stock Bks. Ltd/Csi) Continental Sales, Inc.

Roraff, Susan. Cultureshock Chile, 1 vol. 2011. (ENG.). 240p. pap. 15.95 *(978-0-7614-6053-4(5))* Marshall Cavendish Corp.

Roraff, Susan, et al. Cultureshock! Chile: A Survival Guide to Customs & Etiquette, 1 vol. 2007. (Cultureshock Chile: A Survival Guide to Customs & Etiquette Ser.). (ENG., Illus.). 32p. pap. 15.95 *(978-0-7614-5401-4(2))* Marshall Cavendish Corp.

Rushenberger, William, abr. Three Years in the Pacific. 2009. (Military History Ser.). (ENG.). 463p. pap. 27.95 *(978-1-4290-2192-0(6))* Applewood Bks.

Sahm, Reiner, photos by. Patagonia. 2007. (Illus.). 186p. 59.95 *(978-1-877339-60-8(1))* NZVP Bks. & Calendars Ltd. NZL. Dist: Perseus-PGW.

Schultes, Richard Evans & Ruiz, Hipólito. The Journals of Hipolito Ruiz. 2009. (ENG.). 368p. pap. 44.95 *(978-1-60469-082-8(8)*, 1604690828) Timber Pr., Inc.

Smith, Edmond Reuel. The Araucanians; or, Notes of a Tour among the Indian Tribes of Southern Chili. 2006. 340p. per. 23.99 *(978-1-4255-3468-4(6))* MPublishing.

Solís V, Paula & Barros C, Macarena. Testimonio de una Captura en Valparaíso, Chile. 2007. (ENG & SPA., Illus.). *(978-956-16-0445-2(0))*; pap. *(978-956-16-0444-5(2))* Pehuén Editores Ltda.

Stevenson, W. B. A Historical & Descriptive Narrative of Twenty Years' Residence in South America. 2011. (Cambridge Library Collection - History Ser.). (ENG.). 462p. pap. 32.99 ***(978-1-108-03364-0(4))***; 454p. pap. 34.99 ***(978-1-108-03365-7(2))***; (Illus.). 486p. pap. 35.99 ***(978-1-108-03366-4(0))*** Cambridge Univ. Pr.

Terreehorst, Pauline & Ladd, Jeffrey, texts. Koen Wessing: Chili, September 1973. 2010. (ENG., Illus.). 64p. 39.95 *(978-1-935004-14-1(X))* Errata Editions.

Thomas Cook Publishing Staff & Gill, Nicholas. Chile. 2nd ed. 2009. (Travellers - Thomas Cook Ser.). (ENG., Illus.). 176p. pap. 16.95 *(978-1-84848-185-5(3))* Cook, Thomas Publishing GBR. Dist: Globe Pequot Pr., The.

van Baerle, Caspar. The History of Brazil under the Governorship of Count Johan Maurits of Nassau, 1636-1644. 2011. (ENG., Illus.). 448p. 79.95 *(978-0-8130-3664-9(X))* Univ. Pr. of Florida.

Wallpaper Magazine Editors, ed. Santiago 2011 - Wallpaper City Guides. 2011. (ENG.). 128p. pap. 9.95 *(978-0-7148-5937-8(0))* Phaidon Pr., Inc.

Weale, B. L. Putnam. Manchu & Muscovite. 2007. (ENG.). 632p. 60.95 *(978-0-548-03632-7(2))* Kessinger Publishing, LLC.

CHILE—ECONOMIC CONDITIONS

Alexander, Kjirsten. The Costs of Profit Priorities. 2008. 60p. pap. *(978-3-639-00672-8(0))* VDM Verlag Dr. Mueller e.K.

Alexander, William. Lost in the Long Transition: Struggles for Social Justice in Neoliberal Chile. 2009. (ENG., Illus.). 216p. 73.50 *(978-0-7391-1864-1(1))*; pap. 31.50 *(978-0-7391-1865-8(X))* Lexington Bks.

Aroca, Patricio A. Structure & Structural Change in the Chilean Economy. Hewings, Geoffrey J. D., ed. 2006. (ENG., Illus.). 304p. 110.00 *(978-0-230-00496-2(2))* Palgrave Macmillan.

Bernan Press Staff & World Trade Organization Staff. Tpr: Chile 2009. 2010. (ENG.). 192p. pap. 75.00 *(978-1-59888-375-6(5))* Bernan Assocs.

Castillo, Juan C. The Legitimacy of Economic Inequality: An Empirical Approach to the Case of Chile. 2011. 282p. pap. 25.95 ***(978-1-59942-376-0(6)***, Dissertation.com) Universal Pubs.

Claudia, Cerda. Valuing Biological Diversity in Chile: A Choice Experiment Approach. 2011. 208p. pap. ***(978-3-639-34026-6(4))*** VDM Verlag Dr. Mueller e.K.

de Vylder, Stefan. Allende's Chile: The Political Economy of the Rise & Fall of the Unidad Popular. 2009. (Cambridge Latin American Studies). (ENG.). 264p. pap. 36.99 *(978-0-521-10757-0(1))* Cambridge Univ. Pr.

Doing Business in Chile. Date not set. (Doing Business in Regions & Countries Around the World Ser.). 80p. *(978-1-882390-55-7(5))* Training Management Corp.

Edmundson, William. The Nitrate King: A Biography of Colonel John Thomas North. 2011. (Studies of the Americas Ser.). (ENG., Illus.). 218p. 85.00 *(978-0-230-11280-3(3))* Palgrave Macmillan.

Ffrench-Davis, Ricardo. Economic Reforms in Chile: From Dictatorship to Democracy. 2nd rev. ed. 2010. (ENG., Illus.). 320p. 110.00 *(978-0-230-57738-1(5))* Palgrave Macmillan.

Fleischer, Belton M., et al, eds. Market Development in China: Spillovers, Growth & Inequality. 2007. (Advances in Chinese Economic Studies). (Illus.). 288p. (C). 127.00 *(978-1-84542-851-8(X))* Elgar, Edward Publishing, Inc.

Halabi, Claudia. A Productivity Analysis in the Electricity Generation Industry. 2010. 164p. pap. *(978-3-639-15891-5(1))* VDM Verlag Dr. Mueller e.K.

Han, Clara. Life in Debt: Times of Care & Violence in Neoliberal Chile. 2012. (ENG.). 265p. 65.00 ***(978-0-520-27209-5(9))***; pap. 26.95 ***(978-0-520-27210-1(2))*** Univ. of California Pr.

Icon Group International, Inc. Staff, compiled by. The 2006 Economic & Product Market Databook for Antofagasta, Chile. 2006. 618p. ring bd. 95.00 *(978-0-497-80064-2(0))* Icon Group International, Inc.

—The 2006 Economic & Product Market Databook for Arica, Chile. 2006. 618p. ring bd. 95.00 *(978-0-497-80082-6(9))* Icon Group International, Inc.

—The 2006 Economic & Product Market Databook for Concepcion, Chile. 2006. 618p. ring bd. 95.00 *(978-0-497-80402-2(6))* Icon Group International, Inc.

—The 2006 Economic & Product Market Databook for Puerto Montt, Chile. 2006. 618p. ring bd. 95.00 *(978-0-497-81296-6(7))* Icon Group International, Inc.

—The 2006 Economic & Product Market Databook for Punta Arenas, Chile. 2006. 618p. ring bd. 95.00 *(978-0-497-81302-4(5))* Icon Group International, Inc.

—The 2006 Economic & Product Market Databook for Rancagua, Chile. 2006. 618p. ring bd. 95.00 *(978-0-497-81330-7(0))* Icon Group International, Inc.

—The 2006 Economic & Product Market Databook for Santiago, Chile. 2006. 618p. ring bd. 95.00 *(978-0-497-81457-1(9))* Icon Group International, Inc.

—The 2006 Economic & Product Market Databook for Talca, Chile. 2006. 618p. ring bd. 95.00 *(978-0-497-81630-8(X))* Icon Group International, Inc.

—The 2006 Economic & Product Market Databook for Talcahuano, Chile. 2006. 618p. ring bd. 95.00 *(978-0-497-81629-2(6))* Icon Group International, Inc.

—The 2006 Economic & Product Market Databook for Temuco, Chile. 2006. 618p. ring bd. 95.00 *(978-0-497-81661-2(X))* Icon Group International, Inc.

—The 2006 Economic & Product Market Databook for Valparaiso, Chile. 2006. 618p. ring bd. 95.00 *(978-0-497-81775-6(6))* Icon Group International, Inc.

—The 2006 Economic & Product Market Databook for Viña del Mar, Chile. 2006. 618p. ring bd. 95.00 *(978-0-497-81800-5(0))* Icon Group International, Inc.

Keller, William W. & Rawski, Thomas G., eds. China's Rise & the Balance of Influence in Asia. 2007. (Pitt Security Continuum Ser.). (Illus.). 328p. (C). per. 27.95 *(978-0-8229-5967-0(4))* Univ. of Pittsburgh Pr.

Lagos, Ricardo, et al. The Southern Tiger: Chile's Fight for a Democratic & Prosperous Future. 2012. (ENG., Illus.). 272p. 28.00 ***(978-0-230-33816-6(X))*** Palgrave Macmillan.

Medina, Eden. Cybernetic Revolutionaries: Technology & Politics in Allende's Chile. 2011. (ENG & ACE., Illus.). 312p. (gr. 17). 32.00 ***(978-0-262-01649-0(4))*** MIT Pr.

Meyer, Jasmin. Subprime Crisis & Its Impacts on the Economies of Chile & Austri. 2009. 72p. pap. *(978-3-639-21920-3(1))* VDM Verlag Dr. Mueller e.K.

Oecd Publishing. Maintaining Momentum: OECD Perspectives on Policy Challenges in Chile. 2011. 256p. pap. 42.00 ***(978-92-64-09275-4(7))*** Organization for Economic Cooperation & Development.

—Mejores Políticas para el Desarrollo: Perspectivas OCDE sobre Chile. 2011. 268p. pap. 42.00 ***(978-92-64-09574-8(8))*** Organization for Economic Cooperation & Development.

Oppenheim, Lois Hecht. Politics in Chile: Socialism, Authoritarianism, & Market Democracy. 3rd rev. ed. 2007. (ENG., Illus.). 336p. per. 40.00 *(978-0-8133-4227-6(9))* Westview Pr.

Organisation for Economic Co-operation and Development. Chile. 2010. (Illus.). 146p. pap. 63.00 *(978-92-64-07575-7(5))* Organization for Economic Cooperation & Development.

Organisation for Economic Co-operation and Development Staff. An Appraisal of the Chilean Fisheries Sector. 2009. 142p. pap. 63.00 *(978-92-64-07394-4(9))* Organization for Economic Cooperation & Development.

—Chile. 2007. 182p. pap. 63.00 *(978-92-64-04006-9(4))* Organization for Economic Cooperation & Development.

—Oecd Review of Agricultural Policies Chile. 2008. (Illus.). 153p. pap. 63.00 *(978-92-64-04223-0(7))* Organization for Economic Cooperation & Development.

Posner, Paul W. State, Market, & Democracy in Chile: The Constraint of Popular Participation. 2008. (ENG.). 272p. 95.00 *(978-0-230-60595-4(8))* Palgrave Macmillan.

Sanchez, Omar. Mobilizing Resources in Latin America: The Political Economy of Tax Reform in Chile & Argentina. 2011. (ENG.). 258p. 85.00 *(978-0-230-11446-3(6))* Palgrave Macmillan.

Shambaugh, David. China's Communist Party: Atrophy & Adaptation. 2009. (ENG.). 256p. pap. 24.95 *(978-0-520-26007-8(4))* Univ. of California Pr.

Solimano, Andrés. Chile & the Neoliberal Trap: The Post-Pinochet Era. 2012. (ENG., Illus.). 192p. 90.00 ***(978-1-107-00354-5(7))*** Cambridge Univ. Pr.

Sorensen, Lene Mette. Re-Thinking Corporate Social Responsibility. 2011. 76p. pap. ***(978-3-8433-9363-8(X))*** Lambert Academic Publishing.

Turner, Robert C., ed. Chile & Argentina: South American Neighbors. 2010. (Illus.). x, 158p. 98.00 ***(978-1-61728-881-4(0))*** Nova Science Pubs., Inc.

United Nations Development Programme. Assessment of Development Results: Chile. 2010. (ENG.). 104p. pap. 23.00 ***(978-92-1-126289-6(5))*** United Nations Pubns.

Valdes, Juan Gabriel. Pinochet's Economists: The Chicago School of Economics in Chile. 2008. (Historical Perspectives on Modern Economics Ser.). (ENG.). 352p. pap. 39.99 *(978-0-521-06440-8(6))* Cambridge Univ. Pr.

CHILE—FOREIGN RELATIONS

Cox, Eric W. Why Enduring Rivalries Do¿or Don¿t¿End. 2010. 210p. 65.00 *(978-1-935049-24-1(0))* FirstForumPress.

Edmundson, William. A History of the British Presence in Chile: From Bloody Mary to Charles Darwin & the Decline of British Influence. 2011. (ENG., Illus.). 288p. pap. 32.00 *(978-0-230-11483-8(0))* Palgrave Macmillan.

Garcia, Maria J. The Path to the 2002 Association Agreement Between the European Union & Chile: A Case Study in Successful Political Negotiation. 2009. (Illus.). 340p. 119.95 *(978-0-7734-4833-9(0))* Mellen, Edwin Pr., The.

Geldenhuys, Deon. Isolated States: A Comparative Analysis. 2011. (Cambridge Studies in International Relations Ser.). (ENG.). 782p. pap. 90.00 *(978-0-521-28326-7(4))* Cambridge Univ. Pr.

Harmer, Tanya. Allende's Chile & the Inter-American Cold War. 2011. (New Cold War History Ser.). (ENG., Illus.). 384p. 45.00 *(978-0-8078-3495-4(5))* Univ. of North Carolina Pr.

Hua, Shiping & Guo, Sujian, eds. China in the Twenty-First Century: Challenges & Opportunities. 2007. (ENG.). 280p. 89.00 *(978-1-4039-7975-9(8))* Palgrave Macmillan.

Mani, Kristina. Democratization & Military Transformation in Argentina & Chile: Rethinking Rivalry. 2011. (Illus.). 240p. 65.00 *(978-1-935049-40-1(2))* FirstForumPress.

Mullins, Martin. In the Shadow of Generals: Foreign Policy Formation in Argentina Brazil & Chile. 2006. (Illus.). 178p. 120.00 *(978-0-7546-4736-2(6))* Ashgate Publishing Co.

Turner, Robert C., ed. Chile & Argentina: South American Neighbors. 2010. (Illus.). x, 158p. 98.00 ***(978-1-61728-881-4(0))*** Nova Science Pubs., Inc.

Yang, Jian. The Pacific Islands in China's Grand Strategy: Small States, Big Games. 2011. (ENG., Illus.). 288p. 85.00 *(978-0-230-11323-7(0))* Palgrave Macmillan.

CHILE—HISTORY

Barros Arana, Diego. Historia General de Chile I. 2011. (SPA.). 534p. per. 21.95 *(978-84-9816-733-7(7))* Linkgua Ediciones, S.L. ESP. Dist: AtlasBooks Distribution.

—Historia General de Chile II. 2011. (SPA.). 564p. per. 20.95 *(978-84-9816-792-4(2))* Linkgua Ediciones, S.L. ESP. Dist: AtlasBooks Distribution.

—Historia General de Chile III. 2011. (SPA.). 596p. per. 21.95 *(978-84-9816-793-1(0))* Linkgua Ediciones, S.L. ESP. Dist: AtlasBooks Distribution.

—Historia General de Chile Iv. 2011. (SPA.). 440p. per. 24.95 *(978-84-9816-794-8(9))* Linkgua Ediciones, S.L. ESP. Dist: AtlasBooks Distribution.

Borja-Villel, Manuel J. Drifts & Derivations: Experiences, Journeys & Morphologies. 2011. (ENG.). 301p. pap. 54.95 *(978-84-8026-425-9(X))* Museo Nacional Centro de Arte Reina Sofia ESP. Dist: Actar Birkhauser Distribution.

Chapman, Anne. European Encounters with the Yamana People of Cape Horn, Before & after Darwin. 2010. (ENG., Illus.). 744p. 120.00 *(978-0-521-51379-1(0))* Cambridge Univ. Pr.

Childress, Diana. Augusto Pinochet's Chile. 2008. (Dictatorships Ser.). (YA). (gr. 7-12). lib. bdg. 38.60 *(978-0-8225-8667-8(3))* Twenty First Century Bks.

Cruz, Josefina. Chile. (Biblioteca Iberoamericana Ser.). (SPA., Illus.). 126p. pap. *(978-84-207-3067-7(X)*, BI-2031) Grupo Anaya, S.A.

Dolores Luna Guinot. Conspiracy in Mendoz. 2009. 340p. pap. 25.00 *(978-1-4269-2185-8(3))* Trafford Publishing.

Dorfman, Ariel. Chile: El Otro 11 de Septiembre: Una Antología Acerca Del Golpe de Estado En 1973. 2006. (Ocean Sur Ser.). (SPA & ENG.). 100p. pap. 11.95 *(978-1-920888-81-7(0))* Ocean Pr. AUS. Dist: Consortium Bk. Sales & Distribution.

Edmundson, William. A History of the British Presence in Chile: From Bloody Mary to Charles Darwin & the Decline of British Influence. (ENG., Illus.). 288p. 2011. pap. 32.00 *(978-0-230-11483-8(0))* 2009. 89.00 *(978-0-230-61849-7(9))* Palgrave Macmillan.

Elsey, Brenda. Citizens & Sportsmen: Fútbol & Politics in Twentieth-Century Chile. (ENG., Illus.). 2012. 327p. pap. 30.00 ***(978-0-292-74393-9(9))*** 2011. 294p. 55.00 *(978-0-292-72630-7(9))* Univ. of Texas Pr.

Ette, Ottmar & Nitschack, Horst. Trans*Chile: Cultura-Historia-Itinerarios-Literatura-Educación: Un Acercamiento Transareal. 2010. (SPA.). 204p. pap. 29.80 *(978-84-8489-524-4(6))* Iberoamericana Vervuert Publishing Corp.

Evans, Robley D. A Sailor's Log: Recollections of Forty Years of Naval Life. 2010. 506p. pap. 31.16 *(978-1-163-24993-2(9))* 2007. (ENG.). 504p. 53.95 *(978-0-548-22586-8(9))* 2007. (ENG.). 508p. per. 38.95 *(978-1-4325-4794-3(1))* Kessinger Publishing, LLC.

Evans, Robley Dunglison. A Sailor's Log. 467p. reprint ed. 98.00 *(978-0-7222-9411-6(5))* Library Reprints, Inc.

Franklin, Jonathan. 33 Men: Inside the Miraculous Survival & Dramatic Rescue of the Chilean Miners. 2011. (ENG.). 320p. (gr. 12). 25.95 *(978-0-399-15777-6(8)*, Putnam Adult) Penguin Group (USA) Inc.

Gomez-Barris, Macarena. Where Memory Dwells: Culture & State Violence in Chile. 2008. (Illus.). 224p. 60.00 *(978-0-520-25583-8(6))*; 240p. pap. 26.95 *(978-0-520-25584-5(4))* Univ. of California Pr.

Góngora Marmolejo, Alonso de. Historia de Todas Las Cosas Que Han Acaecido en el Reino de Chile y de Los Que Han Gobernado. Donoso Rodríguez, Miguel, ed. 2010. (SPA.). 638p. pap. 56.00 *(978-84-8489-508-4(4))* Iberoamericana Vervuert Publishing Corp.

Gustafson, Kristian. Hostile Intent: U. S. Covert Operations in Chile, 1964-1974. 2007. (Illus.). 288p. 29.95 *(978-1-59797-097-6(2))* Potomac Bks., Inc.

Julian, Beatrice, et al. The A to Z of the Dirty Wars. 2009. (A to Z Guide Ser.: No. 29). (ENG.). 250p. pap. 34.45 *(978-0-8108-6812-0(1))* Scarecrow Pr., Inc.

Kohut, David R. & Vilella, Olga. Historical Dictionary of the Dirty Wars. 2nd ed. 2010. (Historical Dictionaries of War, Revolution, & Civil Unrest Ser.). (ENG., Illus.). 432p. 111.00 *(978-0-8108-5839-8(8))* Scarecrow Pr., Inc.

Lazzara, Michael J. Chile in Transition: The Poetics & Politics of Memory. (ENG., Illus.). 224p. 2011. pap. 25.95 *(978-0-8130-3568-0(6))* 2006. 59.95 *(978-0-8130-3008-1(0))* Univ. Pr. of Florida.

—Luz Arce & Pinochet's Chile: Testimony in the Aftermath of State Violence. Lazzara, Michael J., ed. Fischer, Carl, tr. 2011. (ENG., Illus.). 218p. 90.00 *(978-0-230-62275-3(5))* Palgrave Macmillan.

Lisle, Gerard de. The Royal Navy & the Peruvian-Chilean War 1879 - 1881: Rudolf de Lisle's Diaries & Watercolours. 2008. (Illus.). 192p. 50.00 *(978-1-84415-652-8(4))* Pen & Sword Bks. Ltd. GBR. Dist: Casemate Pubs. & Bk. Distributors, LLC.

Lledo, Haroldo. Experimental Studies on the Origin of Iron Deposits. 2010. 292p. pap. *(978-3-8383-0405-2(5))* Lambert Academic Publishing.

Mansfield, Robert E. Progressive Chile. 2009. 256p. 34.99 *(978-1-115-37148-3(7))*; 30.99 *(978-1-115-37146-9(0))*; pap. 26.75 *(978-1-115-37144-5(4))* BiblioBazaar.

—Progressive Chile. 2009. 132p. pap. *(978-0-217-25179-2(X))* Books LLC.

—Progressive Chile. 254p. reprint ed. 98.00 *(978-0-7222-9605-9(3))* Library Reprints, Inc.

Mariani, Jafeth. Chilean Miners. 2010. (Illus.). 78p. pap. 17.95 *(978-1-4466-4409-6(X))* Lulu Enterprises Inc.

Markham, Clements R. The War Between Peru & Chile, 1879-1882. 2009. 216p. pap. *(978-1-150-73722-0(0))* Books LLC.

Moss, Chris. Patagonia: A Cultural History. 2008. (Landscapes of the Imagination Ser.). (ENG., Illus.). 256p. 25.00 *(978-0-19-534249-9(6))* Oxford Univ. Pr., Inc.

Museo Nacional Centro de Arte Reina Sofía Staff, contrib. by. Desvíos de la Deriva: Experiencias, Travesías y Morfologías. 2010. (SPA., Illus.). 301p. *(978-84-8026-424-2(1))* Museo Nacional Centro de Arte Reina Sofia.

Nahuelpan, Elicura Chihuailaf. Message to Chileans. 2009. 260p. pap. 28.00 *(978-1-4251-8650-0(5))* Trafford Publishing.

Oyarzún, Fernando Pérez, et al. Chilean Modern Architecture since 1950. Quantrill, Malcolm, ed. 2010. (Studies in Architecture & Culture Ser.). (ENG., Illus.). 192p. 45.00 *(978-1-60344-135-3(2))* Texas A&M Univ. Pr.

Policzer, Pablo. The Rise & Fall of Repression in Chile. 2009. (ND Kellogg Inst Int'l Studies). (ENG., Illus.). 272p. pap. 30.00 *(978-0-268-03835-9(X))* Univ. of Notre Dame Pr.

Qureshi, Lubna Z. Nixon, Kissinger, & Allende: U. S. Involvement in the 1973 Coup in Chile. 2008. (ENG.). 192p. 68.50 *(978-0-7391-2655-4(5))* Lexington Bks.

Qureshi, Lubna Zakia. Nixon, Kissinger, & Allende: U. S. Involvement in the 1973 Coup in Chile. 2009. (ENG.). 192p. pap. 29.50 *(978-0-7391-2656-1(3))* Lexington Bks.

Rabassa, J., ed. The Late Cenozoic of Patagonia & Tierra del Fuego. 2008. (Developments in Quaternary Science Ser.: 11). (ENG., Illus.). 524p. 205.00 *(978-0-444-52954-1(3)*, Elsevier Science) Elsevier Science & Technology Bks.

Ros, Ana. The Post-Dictatorship Generation in Argentina, Chile, & Uruguay: Collective Memory & Cultural Production. 2012. (ENG., Illus.). 256p. 85.00 ***(978-0-230-12060-0(1))*** Palgrave Macmillan.

Sater, William F. Andean Tragedy: Fighting the War of the Pacific, 1879-1884. 2009. (Studies in War, Society, & the Militar Ser.). (ENG., Illus.). 456p. pap. 29.95 *(978-0-8032-2799-6(X))* Univ. of Nebraska Pr.

Scott, Harry. Pensando el Chile Nuevo: Las Ideas de la Revolución de Los Tenientes y el Primer Gobierno de Ibáñez, 1924-1931. 2009. (Illus.). 347p. *(978-956-8147-74-7(8))* Centro de Estudios Bicentenario.

Serrano, Sol. Qué Hacer con Dios en la República? Política y Secularización en Chile (1845-1885) 2008. (Historia Ser.). (SPA.). 375p. pap. *(978-956-289-064-9(3))* Fondo de Cultura Economica.

Stern, Steve. Reckoning with Pinochet: The Memory Question in Democratic Chile, 1989-2006. 2010. (Latin America Otherwise Ser.). (ENG., Illus.). 584p. 99.95 *(978-0-8223-4712-5(1))*; pap. 29.95 *(978-0-8223-4729-3(6))* Duke Univ. Pr.

Stern, Steve J. Battling for Hearts & Minds: Memory Struggles in Pinochet's Chile, 1973-1988. 2006. (Latin America Otherwise Ser.). (ENG., Illus.). 576p. 99.95 *(978-0-8223-3827-7(0))*; per. 29.95 *(978-0-8223-3841-3(6))* Duke Univ. Pr.

—Remembering Pinochet's Chile: On the Eve of London 1998. 2006. (Latin America Otherwise Ser.). (ENG., Illus.). 280p. per. 23.95 *(978-0-8223-3816-1(5))* Duke Univ. Pr.

Thomas Cochrane. Narrative of Services in the Liberation of Chili Peru & Brazil. l.t. ed. 2007. 260p. pap. 23.99 *(978-1-4264-8275-5(2))*; (ENG.). 298p. pap. 23.99 *(978-1-4264-8312-7(0))* BiblioBazaar.

Timossi, Jorge, ed. Fascismos Paralelos: El Golpe del Estado en Chile. 2007. (ENG & SPA.). 250p. per. 17.95 *(978-1-921235-11-5(X))* Ocean Pr. AUS. Dist: Consortium Bk. Sales & Distribution.

Vale, Brian. Cochrane in the Pacific: Fortune & Freedom in Spanish America. 2007. (ENG., Illus.). 256p. 47.00 *(978-1-84511-446-6(9))* I. B. Tauris & Co., Ltd. GBR. Dist: Macmillan.

Von Kleist, Heinrich. Die Marquise von O... Das Erdbeben in Chili. (GER.). cd-rom *(978-3-15-120004-8(4))* Reclam, Philip jun., Verlag GmbH DEU. Dist: International Bk. Import Service, Inc.

Wood, James A. The Society of Equality: Popular Republicanism & Democracy in Santiago de Chile, 1818-1851. 2011. (ENG., Illus.). 344p. (C). pap. 29.95 *(978-0-8263-4941-5(2))* Univ. of New Mexico Pr.

CHILE—POLITICS AND GOVERNMENT

Agosín, Marjorie. Tapestries of Hope, Threads of Love: The Arpillera Movement in Chile. 2nd ed. 2007. (ENG., Illus.). 240p. 70.00 *(978-0-7425-4002-6(2))* Rowman & Littlefield Publishers, Inc.

—Tapestries of Hope, Threads of Love: The Arpillera Movement in Chile. 2nd ed. 2007. (ENG., Illus.). 240p. pap. 24.95 *(978-0-7425-4003-3(0))* Rowman & Littlefield Publishers, Inc.

Aguilar, Mario I. A Social History of the Catholic Church in Chile: The Second Period of the Pinochet Government 1980-1990. 2006. 282p. (C). 109.95 *(978-0-7734-5653-2(8))* Mellen, Edwin Pr., The.

Alexander, Kjirsten. The Costs of Profit Priorities. 2008. 60p. pap. *(978-3-639-00672-8(0))* VDM Verlag Dr. Mueller e.K.

Angell, Alan. Democracy after Pinochet: Politics, Parties & Elections in Chile. 2007. (ENG., Illus.). 200p. per. 24.95 *(978-1-900039-71-0(0))* Institute of Latin American Studies GBR. Dist: Brookings Institution Pr.

Autores Varios Staff. Constituciones Fundacionales de Chile. 2010. (SPA.). 84p. per. 10.00 *(978-84-9816-133-5(9))* Linkgua Ediciones, S.L. ESP. Dist: AtlasBooks Distribution.

Backhouse, Edmund Trelawny. Decadence Mandchoue: The China Memoirs of Sir Edmund Trelawny Backhouse. Sandhaus, Derek, ed. 2011. (ENG.). 336p. 39.99 *(978-988-19445-1-1(1))* Earnshaw Bks. HKG. Dist: Independent Pubs. Group.

Baur, Patrick. Rethinking Sustainable Development. 2011. 100p. pap. ***(978-3-8443-9779-6(5))*** Lambert Academic Publishing.

Borzutzky, Silvia & Weeks, Gregory B., eds. The Bachelet Government: Conflict & Consensus in Post-Pinochet Chile. 2010. (ENG., Illus.). 224p. 69.95 *(978-0-8130-3475-1(2))* Univ. Pr. of Florida.

Chovanec, Donna M. Between Hope & Despair: Women Learning Politics. 2009. (ENG., Illus.). 128p. pap. 15.95 *(978-1-55266-299-1(3))* Fernwood Publishing Co., Ltd. CAN. Dist: Independent Pubs. Group.

Collier, Simon. Chile: the Making of a Republic, 1830-1865: Politics & Ideas. 2007. (Cambridge Latin American Studies). (ENG., Illus.). 296p. pap. 45.00 *(978-0-521-03312-1(8))* Cambridge Univ. Pr.

—Ideas & Politics of Chilean Independence 1808-1833. 2008. (Cambridge Latin American Studies). (ENG.). 416p. pap. 53.00 *(978-0-521-10169-1(7))* Cambridge Univ. Pr.

Cram101 Textbook Reviews & Cram101 Textbook Reviews. Outlines & Highlights for Economic Openness & Territorial Politics in China by Yumin Sheng. 2011. 212p. pap. 30.95 ***(978-1-61830-592-3(1))*** Cram101 Inc.

De La Barra, Ximena, ed. Neoliberalism's Fractured Showcase: Another Chile Is Possible. 2010. (Studies in Critical Social Sciences Ser.). 272p. *(978-90-04-18895-2(9))* BRILL.

de Vylder, Stefan. Allende's Chile: The Political Economy of the Rise & Fall of the Unidad Popular. 2009. (Cambridge Latin American Studies). (ENG.). 264p. pap. 36.99 *(978-0-521-10757-0(1))* Cambridge Univ. Pr.

Donoso, Julio. The Why of Things. 2006. 316p. pap. *(978-1-84401-808-6(3))* Athena Pr.

Faundez, Julio. Democratization, Development, & Legality: Chile, 1831-1973. 2007. (Studies of the Americas Ser.). (ENG.). 296p. 95.00 *(978-1-4039-8406-7(9))* Palgrave Macmillan.

Fernández Jilberto, Alex E. Dictadura militar y oposicion politica en Chile: 1973 - 1981. (Latin America Studies). (SPA.). 455p. 171.00 ***(978-3-11-126461-5(0))*** De Gruyter, Mouton DEU. Dist: De Gruyter, Walter GmbH & Co. KG.
Fernández Jilberto, Alex E. Dictadura militar y oposicion politica en Chile: 1973 - 1981. (Latin America Studies). (SPA.). 455p. 255.00 ***(978-3-11-205053-8(3))*** De Gruyter, Mouton DEU. Dist: de Gruyter, Walter GmbH & Co. KG.
Ffrench-Davis, Ricardo. Economic Reforms in Chile: From Dictatorship to Democracy. 2nd rev. ed. 2010. (ENG., Illus.). 320p. 110.00 *(978-0-230-57738-1(5))* Palgrave Macmillan.
Frazier, Lessie Jo. Salt in the Sand: Memory, Violence, & the Nation-State in Chile, 1890 to the Present. 2007. (Politics, History, & Culture Ser.). (ENG., Illus.). 408p. 94.95 *(978-0-8223-3986-1(2))*; per. 26.95 *(978-0-8223-4003-4(8))* Duke Univ. Pr.
García-Corales, Guillermo & Pino, Mirian. El neopolicial latinoamericano y la crónica del Chile actual en las novelas de Ramón Díaz Eterovic. 2008. (SPA.). 160p. 99.95 *(978-0-7734-5189-6(7))* Mellen, Edwin Pr., The.
González, Francisco E. Dual Transitions from Authoritarian Rule: Institutionalized Regimes in Chile & Mexico, 1970-2000. 2008. (ENG., Illus.). 304p. (C). (gr. 13-17). pap. 27.00 *(978-0-8018-8800-7(X))* Johns Hopkins Univ. Pr.
González, Francisco E. & González González, Francisco Enrique. Dual Transitions from Authoritarian Rule: Institutionalized Regimes in Chile & Mexico, 1970-2000. 2008. (ENG., Illus.). 304p. (C). (gr. 13-17). 60.00 *(978-0-8018-8799-4(2))* Johns Hopkins Univ. Pr.
Kurtz, Marcus J. (Ohio State University). Free Market Democracy & the Chilean & Mexican Countryside. 2006. (ENG., Illus.). 264p. pap. 55.00 *(978-0-521-53474-1(7))* Cambridge Univ. Pr.
Lagos, Ricardo, et al. The Southern Tiger: Chile's Fight for a Democratic & Prosperous Future. 2012. (ENG., Illus.). 272p. 28.00 ***(978-0-230-33816-6(X))*** Palgrave Macmillan.
Lazzara, Michael J. Luz Arce & Pinochet's Chile: Testimony in the Aftermath of State Violence. Lazzara, Michael J., ed. Fischer, Carl, tr. 2011. (ENG., Illus.). 218p. 90.00 *(978-0-230-62275-3(5))* Palgrave Macmillan.
Lazzara, Michael J., ed. Luz Arce & Pinochet's Chile: Testimony in the Aftermath of State Violence. 2011. (ENG., Illus.). 218p. pap. 30.00 *(978-0-230-62276-0(3))* Palgrave Macmillan.
Londregan, John B. Legislative Institutions & Ideology in Chile. 2007. (Political Economy of Institutions & Decisions Ser.). (ENG., Illus.). 292p. pap. 60.00 *(978-0-521-03726-6(3))* Cambridge Univ. Pr.
Macaulay, Fiona. Gender Politics in Brazil & Chile. 2006. (St. Antony's Ser.). (ENG.). 256p. 116.00 *(978-0-333-73614-2(1))* Palgrave Macmillan.
Medina, Eden. Cybernetic Revolutionaries: Technology & Politics in Allende's Chile. 2011. (ENG & ACE., Illus.). 312p. (gr. 17). 32.00 ***(978-0-262-01649-0(4))*** MIT Pr.
Muñoz, Heraldo. The Dictator's Shadow: Life under Augusto Pinochet. 2008. (ENG., Illus.). 376p. 27.50 *(978-0-465-00250-4(1))* Perseus Bks. Group.
Oecd Publishing. Maintaining Momentum: OECD Perspectives on Policy Challenges in Chile. 2011. 256p. pap. 42.00 ***(978-92-64-09275-4(7))*** Organization for Economic Cooperation & Development.
Oppenheim, Lois Hecht. Politics in Chile: Socialism, Authoritarianism, & Market Democracy. 3rd rev. ed. 2007. (ENG., Illus.). 336p. per. 40.00 *(978-0-8133-4227-6(9))* Westview Pr.
Organisation for Economic Co-operation and Development Staff. Web Participatif: Contenu Créé Par L'Utilisateur. 2007. pap. 45.00 *(978-92-64-03751-9(9))* Organization for Economic Cooperation & Development.
Oxhorn, Philip. Sustaining Civil Society: Economic Change, Democracy, & the Social Construction of Citizenship in Latin America. 2011. (ENG.). 280p. 74.95 *(978-0-271-04894-9(8))* Pennsylvania State Univ. Pr.
Pavilack, Jody. Mining for the Nation: The Politics of Chile's Coal Communities from the Popular Front to the Cold War. 2011. 376p. 84.95 *(978-0-271-03769-1(5))* Pennsylvania State Univ. Pr.
Pieper Mooney, Jadwiga E. The Politics of Motherhood: Maternity & Women's Rights in Twentieth-Century Chile. 2009. (Pitt Latin American Studies). (ENG., Illus.). 320p. (C). pap. 27.95 *(978-0-8229-6043-0(5))* Univ. of Pittsburgh Pr.
Policzer, Pablo. The Rise & Fall of Repression in Chile. 2009. (ND Kellogg Inst Int'l Studies). (ENG., Illus.). 272p. pap. 30.00 *(978-0-268-03835-9(X))* Univ. of Notre Dame Pr.
Posner, Paul W. State, Market, & Democracy in Chile: The Constraint of Popular Participation. 2008. (ENG.). 272p. 95.00 *(978-0-230-60595-4(8))* Palgrave Macmillan.
Ray, Leslie. Language of the Land: The Mapuche in Argentina & Chile. 2008. (Illus.). 291p. pap. 29.95 *(978-87-91563-37-9(2))* IWGIA DNK. Dist: Transaction Pubs.
Rosales Herrera, Eduardo Alfonso. El Juicio Del Siglo: Augusto Pinochet Frente Al Derecho y la Política Internacional. 2009. (SPA.). 211p. 20.00 *(978-970-722-675-3(7))* Plaza y Valdes, S.A. de C.V. MEX. Dist: Sony Electronics.
Rowe, Walker. Wine Communism Volcanoes A Story of Chi. 2006. 296p. per. 16.95 *(978-1-934074-03-9(9))* Apprentice Hse.
Scott, Harry. Pensando el Chile Nuevo: Las Ideas de la Revolución de Los Tenientes y el Primer Gobierno de Ibáñez, 1924-1931. 2009. (Illus.). 347p. *(978-956-8147-74-7(8))* Centro de Estudios Bicentenario.
Serrano, Sol. Qué Hacer con Dios en la República? Política y Secularización en Chile (1845-1885) 2008. (Historia Ser.). (SPA.). 375p. pap. *(978-956-289-064-9(3))* Fondo de Cultura Economica.
Shayne, Julie. They Used to Call Us Witches: Chilean Exiles, Culture, & Feminism. 2009. (ENG., Illus.). 320p. 89.50 *(978-0-7391-1849-8(8))* Lexington Bks.
Silva, Patricio. Estado, neoliberalismo y politica agraria en Chile 1973 - 1981. (Latin America Studies). (GER.). 389p. 225.00 ***(978-3-11-209982-7(6))***; 146.00 ***(978-3-11-122900-3(9))*** De Gruyter, Mouton DEU. Dist: de Gruyter, Walter GmbH & Co. KG.
Silva, Patricio. In the Name of Reason: Technocrats & Politics in Chile. 2009. (ENG.). 256p. 65.00 *(978-0-271-03453-9(X))* Pennsylvania State Univ. Pr.
Silva, Patricio & Cleuren, Herwig. Widening Democracy: Citizens & Participatory Schemes in Brazil & Chile. 2009. *(978-90-04-17763-3(3))* BRILL.
Solimano, Andrés. Chile & the Neoliberal Trap: The Post-Pinochet Era. 2012. (ENG., Illus.). 192p. 90.00 ***(978-1-107-00354-5(7))*** Cambridge Univ. Pr.
Sorensen, Kristin. Media, Memory, & Human Rights in Chile. 2009. (ENG.). 196p. 89.00 *(978-0-230-61283-9(0))* Palgrave Macmillan.
Spooner, Mary Helen. The General's Slow Retreat: Chile after Pinochet. 2011. (ENG., Illus.). 300p. 60.00 *(978-0-520-25613-2(1))*; pap. 26.95 *(978-0-520-26680-3(3))* Univ. of California Pr.
Sweetman, Arthur & Zhang, Jun. Economic Transitions with Chinese Characteristics Vol. 2: Social Change During Thirty Years of Reform. 2009. (ENG.). 216p. (C). pap. *(978-1-55339-234-7(5))* McGill-Queen's Univ. Pr.
Thomas, Gwynn. Contesting Legitimacy in Chile: Familial Ideals, Citizenship, & Political Struggle, 1970-1990. 2011. (Illus.). 280p. 71.95 *(978-0-271-04848-2(4))* Pennsylvania State Univ. Pr.
Timossi, Jorge, ed. Fascismos Paralelos: El Golpe del Estado en Chile. 2007. (ENG & SPA.). 250p. per. 17.95 *(978-1-921235-11-5(X))* Ocean Pr. AUS. Dist: Consortium Bk. Sales & Distribution.
Turner, Robert C., ed. Chile & Argentina: South American Neighbors. 2010. (Illus.). x, 158p. 98.00 ***(978-1-61728-881-4(0))*** Nova Science Pubs., Inc.
United Nations Conference on Trade and Development Staff. Best practices in investment for Development: How to utilise FDI to improve infrastructure - electricity - lessons from Chile & New Zealand. 2009. (ENG., Illus.). 108p. pap. 15.00 *(978-92-1-112773-7(4))* United Nations Pubns.
United Nations Development Programme. Assessment of Development Results: Chile. 2010. (ENG.). 104p. pap. 23.00 *(978-92-1-126289-6(5))* United Nations Pubns.
Vergara, Angela. Copper Workers, International Business, & Domestic Politics in Cold War Chile. 2008. (ENG., Illus.). 208p. (C). 60.00 *(978-0-271-03334-1(7))* Pennsylvania State Univ. Pr.
What Democracy Means in China after 30 Years of Reform: Roundtable Before the Congressional-Executive Commission on China, One Hundred Eleventh Congress, First Session, May 22, 2009. 2009. (Illus.). ii, 51p. *(978-0-16-084471-3(1)*, 552-070-39994-1) United States Government Printing Office.
Worth, Richard. Michelle Bachelet. 2007. (Modern World Leaders Ser.). (Illus.). 112p. (YA). (gr. 7-12). lib. bdg. 30.00 *(978-0-7910-9500-3(2))* Facts On File, Inc.

CHILE—RELIGION

Lindhardt, Martin. Power in Powerlessness: A Study of Pentecostal Life Worlds in Urban Chile. 2012. (Religion in the Americas Ser.). (ENG., Illus.). 273p ***(978-90-04-21600-6(6))*** BRILL.
Maggiore, Jacqueline Hansen & Vint, Catherine McDermott. Vessel of Clay: The Inspirational Journey of Sister Carla. 2010. (University of Scranton Press - Peace, Justice, Human Rights, & Freedom in Lati Ser.). (Illus.). 171p. pap. 18.00 *(978-1-58966-217-9(2))* Univ. of Scranton Pr.

CHILE—SOCIAL CONDITIONS

Agosín, Marjorie & Gordenstein, Roberta. Of Earth & Sea: A Chilean Memoir. 2009. *(978-0-8165-2665-9(6))* 2008. (ENG., Illus.). 176p. pap. 16.95 *(978-0-8165-2666-6(4))* Univ. of Arizona Pr.
Alexander, Kjirsten. The Costs of Profit Priorities. 2008. 60p. pap. *(978-3-639-00672-8(0))* VDM Verlag Dr. Mueller e.K.
Alexander, William. Lost in the Long Transition: Struggles for Social Justice in Neoliberal Chile. 2009. (ENG., Illus.). 216p. 73.50 *(978-0-7391-1864-1(1))*; pap. 31.50 *(978-0-7391-1865-8(X))* Lexington Bks.
Alexander, William L. Resiliency In Hostile Environments: A Comunidad Agricola in Chile's Norte Chico. 2008. (Illus.). 260p. (C). 55.00 *(978-0-934223-89-8(0))* Lehigh Univ. Pr.
Bacigalupo, Ana Mariella. Shamans of the Foye Tree: Gender, Power, & Healing among Chilean Mapuche. 2007. (ENG., Illus.). 335p. pap. 26.95 *(978-0-292-71659-9(1))* Univ. of Texas Pr.
Bauer, Arnold J. Chilean Rural Society: From the Spanish Conquest To 1930. 2008. (Cambridge Latin American Studies). (ENG.). 288p. pap. 38.99 *(978-0-521-10175-2(1))* Cambridge Univ. Pr.
Burton, Guy. Policy-Making & Education Reform in the Development of Latin American Social Democracy: The Role of the Left in Brazil & Chile. 2011. (Illus.). 432p. 139.95 *(978-0-7734-1433-4(9))* Mellen, Edwin Pr., The.
Earthquake Preparedness: What the United States Can Learn from the 2010 Chilean & Haitian Earthquakes: Hearing Before the Ad Hoc Subcommittee on State, Local, & Private Sector Preparedness & Integration of the Committee on Homeland Security & Governmental Affairs, United States Senate, One Hundred Eleventh Congress, Second Session, September 20, 2010. 2011. (Illus.). iii, 196p. ***(978-0-16-089210-3(4)***, 552-070-43207-8) United States Government Printing Office.
Finkelstein, Rodrigo. The Constitutive Role of Occupational Safety in Chile. 2009. 128p. pap. *(978-3-639-16637-8(X))* VDM Verlag Dr. Mueller e.K.
Han, Clara. Life in Debt: Times of Care & Violence in Neoliberal Chile. 2012. (ENG.). 265p. 65.00 ***(978-0-520-27209-5(9))***; pap. 26.95 ***(978-0-520-27210-1(2))*** Univ. of California Pr.
Heberlein, Regine I. Writing a National Colony: The Hostility of Inscription in the German Settlement of Lake Llanquihue. 2008. 109.95 *(978-1-60497-554-3(7))* Cambria Pr.
Jones, Phil. Rethinking Childhood: Attitudes in Contemporary Society. 2009. (New Childhoods Ser.). (ENG., Illus.). 208p. 39.95 *(978-0-8264-9936-3(8))* Continuum International Publishing Group, Ltd. GBR. Dist: National Bk. Network.
Lagos, Ricardo, et al. The Southern Tiger: Chile's Fight for a Democratic & Prosperous Future. 2012. (ENG., Illus.). 272p. 28.00 ***(978-0-230-33816-6(X))*** Palgrave Macmillan.
Macaulay, Fiona. Gender Politics in Brazil & Chile. 2006. (St. Antony's Ser.). (ENG.). 256p. 116.00 *(978-0-333-73614-2(1))* Palgrave Macmillan.
Mansfield, Robert E. Progressive Chile. 2009. 256p. 34.99 *(978-1-115-37148-3(7))*; 30.99 *(978-1-115-37146-9(0))*; pap. 26.75 *(978-1-115-37144-5(4))* BiblioBazaar.
—Progressive Chile. 2009. 132p. pap. *(978-0-217-25179-2(X))* Books LLC.
—Progressive Chile. 254p. reprint ed. 98.00 *(978-0-7222-9605-9(3))* Library Reprints, Inc.
Perrone, Caterina. Chile. 2007. (Culture Smart! A Quick Guide to Customs & Etiquette Ser.). (ENG., Illus.). 168p. pap. 9.95 *(978-1-85733-341-1(1))* Kuperard Pubs. GBR. Dist: Random Hse., Inc.
Perry, Claire. Young America: Childhood in Nineteenth-Century Art & Culture. 2006. (Illus.). xii, 236p. pap. *(978-0-937031-27-8(5))* Cantor, Iris & B. Gerald Ctr. for Visual Arts at Stanford Univ.
Posner, Paul W. State, Market, & Democracy in Chile: The Constraint of Popular Participation. 2008. (ENG.). 272p. 95.00 *(978-0-230-60595-4(8))* Palgrave Macmillan.
Ray, Leslie. Language of the Land: The Mapuche in Argentina & Chile. 2008. (Illus.). 291p. pap. 29.95 *(978-87-91563-37-9(2))* IWGIA DNK. Dist: Transaction Pubs.
Reifenberg, Steve. Santiago's Children: What I Learned about Life at an Orphanage in Chile. 2008. (ENG., Illus.). 250p. 55.00 *(978-0-292-71741-1(5))*; pap. 24.95 *(978-0-292-71742-8(3))* Univ. of Texas Pr.
Rowe, Walker. Wine Communism Volcanoes A Story of Chi. 2006. 296p. per. 16.95 *(978-1-934074-03-9(9))* Apprentice Hse.
Scarpaci, Joseph L. Primary Medical Care in Chile: Accessibility under Military Rule. 2009. (Pitt Latin American Studies). (ENG.). 208p. (C). pap. 25.95 *(978-0-8229-8570-9(5))* Univ. of Pittsburgh Pr.
Teichman, Judith A. Social Forces & States: Poverty & Distributional Outcomes in South Korea, Chile, & Mexico. 2012. (ENG.). 272p. 80.00 ***(978-0-8047-7825-1(6))***; pap. 24.95 ***(978-0-8047-7826-8(4))*** Stanford Univ. Pr.
United Nations Development Programme. Assessment of Development Results: Chile. 2010. (ENG.). 104p. pap. 23.00 *(978-92-1-126289-6(5))* United Nations Pubns.

CHILE—SOCIAL LIFE AND CUSTOMS

Course, Magnus. Becoming Mapuche: Person & Ritual in Indigenous Chile. 2011. (Interp Culture New Millennium Ser.). (ENG., Illus.). 224p. 75.00 ***(978-0-252-03647-7(6))***; pap. 25.00 ***(978-0-252-07823-1(3))*** Univ. of Illinois Pr.
Edmundson, William. A History of the British Presence in Chile: From Bloody Mary to Charles Darwin & the Decline of British Influence. 2011. (ENG., Illus.). 288p. pap. 32.00 *(978-0-230-11483-8(0))* Palgrave Macmillan.
Lindhardt, Martin. Power in Powerlessness: A Study of Pentecostal Life Worlds in Urban Chile. 2012. (Religion in the Americas Ser.). (ENG., Illus.). 273p. ***(978-90-04-21600-6(6))*** BRILL.
Roraff, Susan. Cultureshock Chile, 1 vol. 2011. (ENG.). 240p. pap. 15.95 *(978-0-7614-6053-4(5))* Marshall Cavendish Corp.
Winter, Nevin O. Chile & Her People of Today. 2009. 190p. pap. *(978-1-4590-4103-5(8))* Books LLC.
—Chile & Her People of Today. 411p. reprint ed. 98.00 *(978-0-7222-9607-3(X))* Library Reprints, Inc.

CHILEAN ART

see Art, Chilean

CHILEAN CLOVER

see Alfalfa

CHILEAN LITERATURE

Bolaño, Roberto. Between Parentheses: Essays, Articles & Speeches, 1998-2003. Echevarria, Ignacio, ed. Wimmer, Natasha, tr. from SPA. 2011. (ENG.). 352p. 24.95 *(978-0-8112-1814-6(7)*, 21814) New Directions Publishing Corp.
Bolaño, Roberto. The Secret of Evil. Andrews, Chris, tr. from SPA. 2012. (ENG.). 192p. 22.95 ***(978-0-8112-1815-3(5)***, 21815) New Directions Publishing Corp.
Canaparo, Claudio. El Imaginario Patagonia: Ensayo Acerca de la Evolución Conceptual Del Espacio. 2012. (Hispanic Studies: Culture & Ideas Ser.). (SPA., Illus.). 554p. pap. 85.95 ***(978-3-0343-0287-6(8))*** Lang, Peter AG GBR. Dist: Lang, Peter.
Ette, Ottmar & Nitschack, Horst. Trans*Chile: Cultura-Historia-Itinerarios-Literatura-Educación: Un Acercamiento Transareal. 2010. (SPA.). 204p. pap. 29.80 *(978-84-8489-524-4(6))* Iberoamericana Vervuert Publishing Corp.
Fischer, Emilio Rivano. Dictionary of Chilean Slang: Your Key to Chilean Language & Culture. 2010. 656p. pap. 25.99 *(978-1-4520-6115-1(8))* AuthorHouse.
Jodorowsky, Alejandro. Albina y los Hombres-Perro.Tr. of Albina & the Dog-Men. (SPA., Illus.). 135p. *(978-970-05-1207-5(X))* Grijalbo, Editorial.
Lizama, Patricio & Zaldívar, María Inés. Las Vanguardias Literarias en Chile: Bibliografía y Antología Crítica. 2009. (SPA., Illus.). 731p. pap. 36.00 *(978-84-8489-389-9(8))* Iberoamericana Vervuert Publishing Corp.
Llanos M, Bernardita. Passionate Subjects/Split Subjects in Twentieth-Century Literature in Chile: Brunet, Bombal, & Eltit. 2009. 58.50 *(978-0-8387-5733-8(2))* Bucknell Univ. Pr.
Mistral, Gabriela. Madwomen: The Locas Mujeres Poems of Gabriela Mistral. Couch, Randall, tr. 2009. (ENG & SPA.). 184p. pap. 18.00 *(978-0-226-53191-5(0))* Univ. of Chicago Pr.
Sarabia, Rosa. La Poética Visual de Vicente Huidobro. 2007. (SPA.). 212p. pap. 29.80 *(978-84-8489-311-0(1))* Iberoamericana Vervuert Publishing Corp.

CHILEAN PAINTING

see Art, Chilean

CHILES (HOT PEPPERS)

see Hot Peppers

CHILES (PEPPERS)

see Peppers

CHILI

see Chili Con Carne

CHILI CON CARNE

August Home Publishing, compiled by. Soups, Stews, Chilies: (Cuisine at Home) 2008. 9.95 *(978-0-9801045-3-9(7))* August Home Publishing Co.
Butel, Jane. Chili Madness: A Passionate Cookbook. 95.40 *(978-0-89480-436-6(7)*, 9436); 2nd ed. 2008. (ENG., Illus.). 204p. pap. 12.95 *(978-0-7611-4761-9(6)*, 0761147616) Workman Publishing Co., Inc.
Carriere, Kathryn Marie. 74 Great-Tasting Chili Recipes. 2007. 164p. per. 14.57 *(978-1-4251-1556-2(X))* Trafford Publishing.
Kong, Beth. Big Book of Soup: Over 500 Home-Cooked Favorites for Soup, Chowder, Chili, Stew & More! 2008. (Illus.). 320p. *(978-0-89821-610-3(9))* Reiman Pubns., L.P.

CHILIASM

see Millennium

CHILLIDA, EDUARDO, 1924-2002

Chillida, Eduardo. Eduardo Chillida: Writings. 2011. (ENG., Illus.). 160p. 40.00 *(978-3-941263-07-9(2))* Richter Verlag DEU. Dist: D.A.P./Distributed Art Pubs.
Chillida, Eduardo & Koelen, Martin van der. Eduardo Chillida: Opus II: Catalog Raisonne of the Original Prints, 4 vols. (GER, ENG & SPA., Illus.). 400p. *(978-3-931876-12-8(8))* Koelen OHG DEU. Dist: Gingko Pr., Inc.
Van Der Koelen, Martin. Eduardo Chillida: Opus I: Catalog Raisonne of the Original Prints. 4 vols. (GER, ENG & SPA., Illus.). 400p. *(978-3-931876-11-1(X))* San Francisco Museum of Modern Art.

CHILLINGWORTH, WILLIAM, 1602-1644

George, Edward Augustus. Seventeenth Century Men of Latitude: Forerunners of the New. 2007. (ENG.). 220p. per. 24.95 *(978-1-4304-4705-4(2))* Kessinger Publishing, LLC.

CHILLS AND FEVER

see Malaria

CHILOPODA

see Centipedes

CHIMERA (GENETICS)

see Mosaicism

CHIMNEYS

see also Fireplaces

American Society of Civil Engineers Staff, contrib. by. Design of Fiberglass-Reinforced Plastic (FRP) Stacks: Asce/sei 52-10. 2010. (ENG.). 58p. pap. 75.00 *(978-0-7844-1056-1(9))* American Society of Civil Engineers.
American Society of Mechanical Engineers Staff, ed. Steel Stacks. 104p. 72.00 *(978-0-7918-2210-4(9))* ASME Pr.
Baumgarten, Lothar. Lothar Baumgarten: Air, 1 vol. 2006. (ENG., Illus.). 152p. lthr. 40.00 *(978-3-933807-46-5(8))* Richter Verlag DEU. Dist: D.A.P./Distributed Art Pubs.
Cullingford, Benita. Chimneys & Chimney Sweeps. 2008. (Shire Library). (ENG., Illus.). 32p. pap. 11.95 *(978-0-7478-0553-3(9))* Shire Pubns., Ltd. GBR. Dist: Random Hse., Inc.
Padgitt, Margaret. The Chimney & Hearth Pro's Resource Book. 2010. 191p. pap. 29.95 *(978-0-557-31583-3(2))* Lulu Enterprises Inc.
Perridge, Madeleine. Decorative Indi. 2010. 72p. pap. *(978-3-8383-3378-6(0))* Lambert Academic Publishing.
Taylor, A. D. Camstoves, Fireplaces & Chimneys. (Shorey Lost Arts Ser.). (Illus.). 112p. reprint ed. pap. 10.00 *(978-0-8466-6055-2(5)*, U-55) Shorey's Bookstore.
Van Lemmen, Hans. Ceramic Roofware. 2008. (Shire Library). (ENG., Illus.). 40p. pap. 11.95 *(978-0-7478-0569-4(5))* Shire Pubns., Ltd. GBR. Dist: Random Hse., Inc.

CHIMPANZEE, PYGMY

see Bonobo

CHIMPANZEES

Boesch, Christophe. Real Chimpanzee: Sex Strategies in the Forest. 2009. (ENG., Illus.). 196p. (C). 120.00 *(978-0-521-11008-2(4))*; pap. 52.00 *(978-0-521-12513-0(8))* Cambridge Univ. Pr.

C

Bubbles. My Secret Diary: From Swaziland to Neverland. 2010. (ENG., Illus.). 228p. pap. 13.95 *(978-1-84454-913-9(5))* Blake, John Publishing, Ltd. GBR. Dist: Independent Pubs. Group.

Cohen, Jon. Almost Chimpanzee: Redrawing the Line That Separates Us from Them. 2011. (ENG., Illus.). 384p. pap. 15.99 *(978-0-312-61176-7(5)*, St. Martin's Griffin) St. Martin's Pr.

—Almost Chimpanzee: Searching for What Makes Us Human, in Rainforests, Labs, Sanctuaries, & Zoos. 2010. (ENG., Illus.). 384p. 27.50 *(978-0-8050-8307-1(3)*, Times Bks.) Holt, Henry & Co.

Cussons, Eugene. Saving Chimpanzees: A Man on A Rescue Mission. 2012. (ENG.). 256p. (gr. 12). pap. 35.00 ***(978-0-14-352813-5(0)***, Penguin Global) Penguin Group (USA) Inc.

de Waal, Frans. Chimpanzee Politics: Power & Sex among Apes. 25th ed. 2007. (ENG., Illus.). 256p. per. 26.95 *(978-0-8018-8656-0(2))* Johns Hopkins Univ. Pr.

De Waal, Frans B. M. Our Inner Ape: A Leading Primatologist Explains Why We Are Who We Are. 2006. (ENG., Illus.). 304p. (gr. 12-18). 16.00 *(978-1-59448-196-3(2)*, Riverhead Trade (Paperbacks)) Penguin Group (USA) Inc.

—Our Inner Ape: The Best & Worst of Human Nature. 2008. 272p. 35.00 *(978-1-4223-9513-4(8))* DIANE Publishing Co.

Garner, R. Gorillas & Chimpanzees. 2007. 192p. per. *(978-1-4068-2337-0(6))* Echo Library.

Goodall, Jane. The Chimpanzee: The Living Link Between "Man" & "Beast" Darst, David H., ed. (International Albert Schweitzer Lecture Ser. at Yale University). (Illus.). 12p. (C). pap. 3.50 *(978-1-885007-02-5(7))* Schweitzer, Albert Institute-Quinnipiac College Pr.

—In the Shadow of Man. 2010. (ENG., Illus.). 400p. pap. 15.95 *(978-0-547-33416-5(8)*, Mariner Bks.) Houghton Mifflin Harcourt Trade & Reference Pubs.

—Jane Goodall: 50 Years at Gombe. 2010. (ENG., Illus.). 144p. 29.95 *(978-1-58479-878-1(5))* Stewart, Tabori & Chang.

—Through a Window: My Thirty Years with the Chimpanzees of Gombe. 2010. (ENG., Illus.). 400p. pap. 15.95 *(978-0-547-33695-4(0)*, Mariner Bks.) Houghton Mifflin Harcourt Trade & Reference Pubs.

Goodall, Jane & Adams, Janine. Jane Goodall's Return to Gombe: Reflections on a Life's Work in Africa. 2007. 24.95 *(978-0-525-94995-4(X)*, Dutton Adult) Penguin Group (USA) Inc.

Halloran, Andrew R. The Song of the Ape: Understanding the Languages of Chimpanzees. 2012. (ENG., Illus.). 288p. 25.99 ***(978-0-312-56311-0(6))*** St. Martin's Pr.

Hess, Elizabeth. Nim Chimpsky: The Chimp Who Would Be Human. 2009. (CHI., Illus.). 346p. pap. *(978-986-6651-65-6(7))* Business Weekly Pubns., A Division of Cite Publishing, Ltd.

—Nim Chimpsky: The Chimp Who Would Be Human. 2008. (ENG., Illus.). 384p. 15.00 *(978-0-553-38277-8(2))* Random House Publishing Group.

—Nim Chimpsky: The Chimp Who Would Be Human. l.t. ed. 2008. (Thorndike Nonfiction Ser.). (Illus.). 571p. 30.95 *(978-1-4104-0686-6(5))* Thorndike Pr.

Lemon, Tess. Chimpanzees. (Illus.). 112p. 19.95 *(978-1-873580-04-2(5))* Whittet Bks., Ltd. GBR. Dist: Diamond Farm Bk. Pubs.

Lonsdorf, Elizabeth V., et al, eds. The Mind of the Chimpanzee: Ecological & Experimental Perspectives. 2010. (ENG., Illus.). 464p. 125.00 *(978-0-226-49278-0(8))*; pap. 49.00 *(978-0-226-49279-7(6))* Univ. of Chicago Pr.

Lovrien, Everett Winslow. Doctor Guilt? 2010. 500p. 39.95 *(978-1-4502-1684-5(6))*; pap. 29.95 *(978-1-4502-1682-1(X))* iUniverse, Inc.

Matsuzawa, Tetsuro, et al, eds. The Chimpanzees of Bossou & Nimba. 2011. (Primatology Monographs). (Illus.). 490p. 209.00 *(978-4-431-53920-9(4)*, 4431539204) Springer.

—Cognitive Development in Chimpanzees. 2011. (Illus.). xxvi, 522p. pap. 69.95 *(978-4-431-53991-9(3)*, 4431539913) Springer.

Nishida, Toshisada. The Chimpanzees of the Lakeshore: Natural History & Culture at Mahale. 2011. (ENG., Illus.). 340p. 125.00 ***(978-1-107-01578-4(2))***; pap. 50.00 ***(978-1-107-60178-9(9))*** Cambridge Univ. Pr.

Nishida, Toshisada, et al. Chimpanzee Behavior in the Wild: An Audio-Visual Encyclopedia. 2010. (Illus.). 255p. 189.00 *(978-4-431-53894-3(1)*, 4431538941) Springer.

Peterson, Dale. Jane Goodall: The Woman Who Redefined Man. 2006. (ENG., Illus.). 752p. 35.00 *(978-0-395-85405-1(9))* Houghton Mifflin Harcourt Publishing Co.

—Jane Goodall: The Woman Who Redefined Man. 2008. (ENG., Illus.). 768p. pap. 17.95 *(978-0-547-05356-1(8)*, Mariner Bks.) Houghton Mifflin Harcourt Trade & Reference Pubs.

Siebert, Charles. The Wauchula Woods Accord: Toward a New Understanding of Animals. 2009. (ENG., Illus.). 224p. 25.00 *(978-0-7432-9586-4(2)*, Scribner) Scribner.

Stanford, Craig. Apes of the Impenetrable Forest: The Behavioral Ecology of Sympatric Chimpanzees & Gorillas. 2007. (ENG., Illus.). 160p. (C). per. 30.20 *(978-0-13-243260-3(9)*, Prentice Hall) Prentice Hall PTR.

Taylor, Jeremy. Not a Chimp: The Hunt to Find the Genes That Make Us Human. (ENG., Illus.). 2010. 368p. pap. 14.95 *(978-0-19-922779-2(9))* 2009. 256p. (J). 27.95 *(978-0-19-922778-5(0))* Oxford Univ. Pr., Inc.

Westoll, Andrew. The Chimps of Fauna Sanctuary: A True Story of Resilience & Recovery. (ENG.). 288p. 2012. pap. 14.95 ***(978-0-547-73738-6(6)***, Mariner Bks.) 2011. (Illus.). 25.00 *(978-0-547-32780-8(3))* Houghton Mifflin Harcourt Trade & Reference Pubs.

CHIN

Fraser, David W. & Fraser, Barbara G. Mantles of Merit: Chin Textiles from Myanmar, India & Bangladesh. 2006. (ENG., Illus.). *(978-974-9863-01-5(1)*, River Bks. Pr. Dist A C) Antique Collectors' Club.

CHIN LANGUAGES

Oxford Chinese Desk Dictionary Book & CD-ROM. 4th ed. 2009. 1136p. 39.95 *(978-0-19-800596-4(2))* Oxford Univ. Pr., Inc.

CH'IN SHIH-HUANG, EMPEROR OF CHINA, 259-210 B.C.

see Qin shi huang, Emperor of China, 259-210 B.C.

CHINA

Balfour, Frederic Henry. Leaves from My Chinese Scrapbook. 2008. 224p. pap. *(978-1-4437-0357-4(5))* Read Bks.

Bolton, Kingsley. Chinese Englishes: A Sociolinguistic History. 2006. (Studies in English Language Ser.). (ENG., Illus.). 360p. pap. 48.00 *(978-0-521-03001-4(3))* Cambridge Univ. Pr.

Cummins, J. S., ed. The Travels & Controversies of Friar Domingo Navarrete, 1616-1686. 2010. (Hakluyt Society, Second Ser.). 284p. 69.95 *(978-1-4094-1484-1(1))*; 322p. 69.95 *(978-1-4094-1485-8(X))* Hakluyt Society GBR. Dist: Ashgate Publishing Co.

—The Travels & Controversies of Friar Domingo Naveatrete 1616-1686. 2010. (Hakluyt Society, Second Ser.). 606p. 120.00 *(978-1-4094-2493-2(6))* Hakluyt Society GBR. Dist: Ashgate Publishing Co.

Donald, Stephanie Hemelryk & Benewick, Robert. Pocket China Atlas: Maps & Facts at Your Fingertips. 2007. (Illus.). 64p. pap. 15.95 *(978-0-520-25468-8(6))* Univ. of California Pr.

Fallows, James. Postcards from Tomorrow Square: Reports from China. 2008. (Vintage Ser.). (ENG., Illus.). 288p. pap. 15.00 *(978-0-307-45624-3(2)*, Vintage) Knopf Doubleday Publishing Group.

Gamer, Robert E., ed. Understanding Contemporary China. 3rd ed. 2008. (Illus.). 300p. (C). pap. 26.50 *(978-1-58826-594-4(3))* Rienner, Lynne Pubs.

Griffis, William Elliot. China's Story in Myth, Legend, & Art & Annals. 2009. 206p. pap. *(978-0-217-69559-6(0))*; pap. *(978-0-217-33850-9(X))* Books LLC.

Lindqvist, Cecilia. China: Empire of Living Symbols: Empire of Living Symbols. Tate, Joan, tr. from SWE. 2008. (ENG., Illus.). 448p. pap. 25.00 *(978-0-306-81609-3(1))* Da Capo Pr., Inc.

Shi, Wei. Intellectual Property in the Global Trading System: EU-China Perspective. 2010. (ENG., Illus.). xvi, 324p. pap. 139.00 *(978-3-642-09648-8(4)*, 3642096484) Springer.

Wilcox, Joseph. China Primer for Students. 2007. (ENG., Illus.). 102p. 49.95 *(978-1-57886-624-3(3))* Rowman & Littlefield Education.

Wilcox, Joseph D. A China Primer for Students. 2007. (ENG., Illus.). 203p. per. 17.95 *(978-1-57886-625-0(1))* Rowman & Littlefield Education.

CHINA—ANTIQUITIES

Aczel, Amir D. The Jesuit & the Skull: Teilhard de Chardin, Evolution, & the Search for Peking Man. 2008. (ENG.). 320p. (gr. 12-18). 16.00 *(978-1-59448-335-6(3)*, Riverhead Trade (Paperbacks)) Penguin Group (USA) Inc.

An, Zhimin, et al. Recent Archaeological Discoveries in the People's Republic of China. (Illus.). xi, 103p. *(978-4-89656-401-3(4))* Bow Historical Bks.

Bagley, Robert W., et al. Max Loehr & the Study of Chinese Bronzes: Style & Classification in the History of Art. 2008. (Illus.). 199p. 55.00 *(978-1-933947-41-9(1))* Cornell Univ. East Asia Program.

Barthoux, Jules L. The Excavations of Hadda. 2006. (ENG.). 228p. 80.00 *(978-1-878529-41-1(2))* Orchid Pr. THA. Dist: National Bk. Network.

Bellezza, John Vincent. Zhang Zhung: Foundations of Civilization in Tibet: A Historical & Ethnoarchaeological Study of the Monuments, Rock Art, Texts, & Oral Tradition of the Ancient Tibetan Upland. 2008. (Denkschriften der Phil.-Hist. Klasse Ser.). (ENG & CHI., Illus.). 842p. (C). pap. 194.00 *(978-3-7001-6046-5(1))* Austrian Academy of Sciences Press AUT. Dist: Brown, David Bk. Co., The.

Cao, Bingwu & Li, Wei. Fa Xian Zhongguo: 2008 Nian 100 Ge Zhong Yao Kao Gu Xin Fa Xian. 2009. (Zhongguo Wen Wu Bao Shu Xi Ser.). (CHI., Illus.). 427p. *(978-7-5077-3444-7(7))* Xueyuan Press.

Chang, Kwang-Chih. Kao Gu Xue Zhuan Ti Liu Jiang. 2010. (CHI., Illus.). *(978-7-108-03330-7(5))* SDX Joint Publishing, Co.

Chi, Li. Ch'eng-Tzu-Yai: The Black Pottery Culture Site at Lung-Shan-Chen in Li-Ch'eng-Hsien, Shantung Province. Chi, Li & Rouse, Irving, eds. Starr, Kenneth, tr. 2011. 294p. 48.95 ***(978-1-258-06946-9(6))*** Literary Licensing, LLC.

Chinese University of Hong Kong Staff. Archaeological Finds from Pre-Qin Sites in Guangdong. (CHI & ENG., Illus.). 300p. pap. 37.50 *(978-962-7101-02-4(8))* Art Museum Chinese Univ. of Hong Kong DEU. Dist: Art Media Resources, Inc.

—Archaeological Finds from the Five Dynasties to the Qing Periods in Guangdong. (CHI & ENG., Illus.). 206p. pap. 50.00 *(978-962-7101-13-0(3))* Art Museum Chinese Univ. of Hong Kong DEU. Dist: Art Media Resources, Inc.

Dai, Xiangming. Pottery Production, Settlement Patterns & Development of Social Complexity in the Yuanqu Basin, North Central China. 2006. (Bar S Ser.). (Illus.). viii,129p. (C). 75.00 *(978-1-84171-939-9(0))* British Archaeological Reports Ltd. GBR. Dist: Brown, David Bk. Co., The.

De Luca, Araldo, photos by. The Eternal Army: The Terracotta Soldiers of the First Emperor. 2012. (ENG., Illus.). 288p. 24.95 ***(978-88-544-0627-8(9))*** White Star ITA. Dist: Sterling Publishing Co., Inc.

Delgado, James P. Khubilai Khan's Lost Fleet: In Search of a Legendary Armada. 2009. (ENG.). 240p. 40.00 *(978-0-520-25976-8(9))* Univ. of California Pr.

Deng, Honghai. The Co-Evolution of Human Culture & Spherical Artifacts. 2011. 240p. pap. ***(978-3-8443-2555-3(7))*** Lambert Academic Publishing.

Ebrey, Patricia Buckley. Accumulating Culture: The Collections of Emperor Huizong. 2008. (ENG., Illus.). 576p. 65.00 *(978-0-295-98778-1(2))* Univ. of Washington Pr.

Falkenhausen, Lothar von. Chinese Society in the Age of Confucius. 2006. (Ideas, Debates, & Perspectives Ser.). (ENG., Illus.). 557p. (C). 69.00 *(978-1-931745-31-4(5))* Cotsen Institute of Archaeology at UCLA.

Fan, Jinshi & Zhao, Shengliang. The Art of Mogao Grottoes in Dunhuang: A Journey into China's Buddhist Shrine. 2009. 29.95 *(978-1-931907-53-8(6))* Homa & Sekey Bks.

Fang, Gu, ed. The Complete Collection of Jades Unearthed in China. 2006. 3600p. *(978-7-03-016009-6(6))* BRILL.

Fengshi, Luan, et al, eds. Archaologie in China: Prehistory at the Lower Reaches of the Yellow River: the Haidai Region. 2009. (Archaologie in China Ser.: 2). (ENG & GER., Illus.). 215p. (C). pap. 42.00 *(978-3-8053-4116-5(4))* Zabern, Philipp von Verlag, GmbH DEU. Dist: Brown, David Bk. Co., The.

Hu, Kemin. Modern Chinese Scholars' Rocks: A Guide for Collectors. 2006. (ENG., Illus.). 128p. per. 29.95 *(978-1-891640-34-6(8))* Floating World Editions.

Hui, Humphrey K. F. & Lam, Peter Y. K. Elegance & Radiance: Grandeur in Qing Glass. Yee, Lai Suk, ed. (CHI & ENG., Illus.). 384p. 135.00 *(978-962-7101-51-2(6))* Art Museum Chinese Univ. of Hong Kong DEU. Dist: Art Media Resources, Inc.

Jeon, Ho-tae. Goguryeo: In Search of Its Culture & History. 2008. (Illus.). 288p. 69.50 *(978-1-56591-282-3(9))* Hollym International Corp.

Jiao, Tianlong. The Neolithic of Southeast China: Cultural Transformation & Regional Interaction on the Coast. 2007. (ENG.). 324p. (C). 99.95 *(978-1-934043-16-5(8))* Cambria Pr.

Juliano, Annette. Unearthed: Recent Archaeological Discoveries from Northern China. 2012. (ENG., Illus.). 288p. 65.00 ***(978-0-300-17967-5(7))*** Yale Univ. Pr.

Kaliff, Anders. Archaeology in the East & the West: Papers Presented at the Sino-Sweden Archaeology Forum, Beijing, in September 2005. Kaliff, Anders, ed. 2007. (ENG., Illus.). 302p. (C). pap. 36.00 *(978-91-7209-469-7(9))* Riksantikvarieambetet och Statens historiska museer SWE. Dist: Brown, David Bk. Co., The.

Laufer, Berthold. Jade: A Study in Chinese Archaeology & Religion. 2009. 466p. 52.95 *(978-1-104-84195-9(9))* 2007. (ENG.). 464p. per. 37.95 *(978-0-548-44548-8(6))* Kessinger Publishing, LLC.

—Jade: A Study in Chinese Archaeology & Religion. (Field Museum of Natural History Ser.: Vol. 10). (Illus.). 50.00 *(978-0-527-01870-2(8))* Periodicals Service Co.

Li, Li. China's Cultural Relics. 3rd ed. 2011. (Introductions to Chinese Culture Ser.). (ENG., Illus.). 168p. pap. 19.99 ***(978-0-521-18656-8(0))*** Cambridge Univ. Pr.

Li, Xinwei. Development of Social Complexity in the Liaoxi Area, Northeast China. 2008. (Bar S Ser.). (Illus.). viii, 155p. (C). pap. 87.50 *(978-1-4073-0307-9(4))* British Archaeological Reports Ltd. GBR. Dist: Brown, David Bk. Co., The.

Liang, Ssu Yung. New Stone Age Pottery from the Prehistoric Site at Hsi-Yin Tsun, Shansi, Chin: Memoirs of the American Anthropological Association, No. 37 1930. 2011. 98p. 38.95 ***(978-1-258-08824-8(X))*** Literary Licensing, LLC.

Lim, Patricia. Forgotten Souls: A Social History of the Hong Kong Cemetery. 2011. (Royal Asiatic Society Hong Kong Studies). (CHI., Illus.). 624p. ***(978-988-220-771-4(5))***; ***(978-988-8053-74-2(4))*** Hong Kong Univ. Pr.

Liu, Qingzhu. Zhongguo Kao Gu Fa Xian Yu Yan Jiu, 1949-2009: Zhongguo Kaogu Faxian Yu Yanjiu. 2010. (CHI., Illus.). 7p. *(978-7-01-008539-5(0))* People's Publishing Hse., The.

Man, John. The Terra Cotta Army: China's First Emperor & the Birth of a Nation. 2009. (ENG.). 336p. pap. 16.95 *(978-0-306-81840-0(X))* Da Capo Pr., Inc.

Ming Jia, Wei. Transition from Foraging to Farming in Northeast China. 2007. (Bar S Ser.). (Illus.). 211p. (C). pap. 90.00 *(978-1-4073-0043-6(1))* Archaeopress GBR. Dist: Brown, David Bk. Co., The.

Mooney, Paul, et al. Xi'an, Shaanxi & the Terracotta Army. 2nd ed. 2009. (Odyssey Illustrated Guides). (ENG., Illus.). 336p. pap. 24.95 *(978-962-217-800-7(6)*, 217800) Airphoto International/Odyssey HKG. Dist: Norton, W. W. & Co., Inc.

Nelson, N. C. Archaeological Research in North China. 2011. 83.12 *(978-1-61143-909-0(4))* Gorgias Pr., LLC.

Nickel, Lukas. Gräber der Han-Zeit in Luoyang. 2010. (Munchener Ostasiatische Studien Ser.). (GER., Illus.). 325p. (C). pap. 90.00 *(978-3-515-09698-0(1))* Steiner, Franz Verlag Wiesbaden GmbH DEU. Dist: Brown, David Bk. Co., The.

Nylan, Michael & Loewe, Michael, eds. China's Early Empires: A Re-appraisal. 2010. (University of Cambridge Oriental Publications). (ENG., Illus.). 654p. 135.00 *(978-0-521-85297-5(8))* Cambridge Univ. Pr.

Portal, Jane. Terra Cotta Warriors: Guardians of China's First Emperor. 2008. (ENG., Illus.). 96p. 14.95 *(978-1-4262-0380-0(2)*, National Geographic) National Geographic Society.

Portal, Jane, ed. The First Emperor: China's Terracotta Army. adapted ed. 2008. Orig. Title: First Emperor. 45.00 *(978-1-932543-25-4(2))*; pap. 35.00 *(978-1-932543-26-1(0))* High Museum of Art.

Rukang, Wu & Olsen, John W., eds. Paleoanthropology & Paleolithic Archaeology in the People's Republic of China. 2009. (ENG., Illus.). 322p. pap. 49.95 *(978-1-59874-458-3(5))* Left Coast Pr., Inc.

Salmony, Alfred. Sino-Siberian Art in the Collection of C. T. Loo. 2006. (ENG., Illus.). 119p. 70.00 *(978-1-878529-36-7(6))* Orchid Pr. THA. Dist: National Bk. Network.

Shang, Hong & Trinkaus, Erik. The Early Modern Human from Tianyuan Cave, China. 2010. (Texas A&M University Anthropology Ser.). (ENG., Illus.). 272p. 45.00 *(978-1-60344-177-3(8))* Texas A&M Univ. Pr.

Shelach, Gideon. Leadership Strategies, Economic Activity, & Interregional Interaction: Social Complexity in Northeast China. 2010. (Fundamental Issues in Archaeology Ser.). 278p. pap. 129.00 *(978-1-4419-3314-0(X)*, 144193314X) Springer.

Shen, Chen. The Warrior Emperor & China's Terracotta Army. 2010. (ENG.). 80p. pap. 5.00 *(978-0-88854-478-0(2))* Royal Ontario Museum CAN. Dist: Univ. of Toronto Pr.

Stein, M. Aurel. Ancient Khotan: Detailed Report of Archaeological Explorations in Chinese Turkestan Carried Out & Described under the Orders of H. M. Indian Government. 2006. (ENG.). 621p. 160.00 *(978-1-878529-42-8(0))* Orchid Pr. THA. Dist: National Bk. Network.

Su, Xiaobo & Teo, Peggy. The Politics of Heritage Tourism in China. 2011. (ENG., Illus.). 224p. pap. 42.95 ***(978-0-415-66625-1(2))*** Routledge.

Sun, Zhouyong. Craft Production in the Western Zhou Dynasty (1046-771 BC) A Case Study of a Jue-Earrings Workshop at the Predynastic Capital Site, Zhouyuan, China. 2008. (Bar S Ser.). (Illus.). 127p. (C). 70.00 *(978-1-4073-0265-2(5))* British Archaeological Reports Ltd. GBR. Dist: Brown, David Bk. Co., The.

Sylwan, Vivi. Investigation of Silk from Edsen-Gol & Lop-nor: A Survey of Wool & Vegetable Materials. 2006. (Reports from the Scientific Expedition to the North-Western Ser.). (ENG., Illus.). 180p. 60.00 *(978-1-878529-43-5(9))* Orchid Pr. THA. Dist: National Bk. Network.

Thorp, Robert L. Visiting China's Past: A Guide to Sites & Resources. 2006. (ENG., Illus.). 240p. per. 24.95 *(978-1-891640-33-9(X))* Floating World Editions.

Tsuen-hsuin, Tsien. Collected Writings on Chinese Culture. 2011. (ENG., Illus.). 430p. (gr. 17). 55.00 *(978-962-996-422-1(8))* Chinese Univ. of Hong Kong, The HKG. Dist: Columbia Univ. Pr.

Tythacott, Louise. The Lives of Chinese Objects: Buddhism, Imperialism & Display. 2011. (MD Ser.). (Illus.). 288p. 120.00 *(978-0-85745-238-2(X))* Berghahn Bks., Inc.

Underhill, Anne P. A Companion to Chinese Archaeology. 2013. (Wiley-Blackwell Companions to Anthropology Ser.). (ENG.). 576p. 199.95 ***(978-1-4443-3529-3(4)***, Wiley-Blackwell) Wiley, John & Sons, Inc.

Von Falkenhausen, Lothar. Chinese Society in the Age of Confucius (1000-250 BC) The Archaeological Evidence. 2006. (Ideas, Debates, & Perspectives Ser.). (ENG., Illus.). 557p. (C). per. 32.95 *(978-1-931745-30-7(7))* Cotsen Institute of Archaeology at UCLA.

White Star, et al. China. 2010. (Treasures Ancient Civilization Ser.). (ENG., Illus.). 208p. 35.00 *(978-88-544-0330-7(X))* White Star ITA. Dist: Random Hse., Inc.

Ye, Yincong. Wei Dang Xia Huai Jiu: Wen Hua Bao Yu de Qian Shi Jin Sheng. 2010. (CHI., Illus.). xix, 116p. *(978-962-441-584-1(6))* Chinese Univ. of Hong Kong - Hong Kong Institute of Asia-Pacific Studies, The.

CHINA—ARMED FORCES

Blasko, Dennis J. The Chinese Army Today: Tradition & Transformation for the 21st Century. 2nd rev. ed. 2012. (Asian Security Studies). (ENG., Illus.). 312p. (C). 150.00 *(978-0-415-78321-7(6))*; pap. 39.95 *(978-0-415-78322-4(4))* Routledge.

Bowers, William T. & Greenwood, John T., eds. Passing the Test: Combat in Korea, April-June 1951. 2011. (Battles & Campaigns Ser.). (ENG., Illus.). 488p. 40.00 *(978-0-8131-3452-9(8))* Univ. Pr. of Kentucky.

Cliff, Roger, et al. New Opportunities & Challenges for Taiwan's Security. 2011. (ENG.). 172p. (C). pap. 23.50 *(978-0-8330-5149-3(0))* RAND Corp., The.

Conti, Ryan. Mass Destruction vol. 3 Fallen Eagle. 2009. 293p. pap. 19.72 *(978-0-557-25461-3(2))* Lulu Enterprises Inc.

Cordesman, Anthony H. & Kleiber, Martin. Chinese Military Modernization: Force Development & Strategic Capabilities. 2007. (Significant Issues Ser.: No. 29). (Illus.). (C). pap. *(978-0-89206-496-0(X)*, CSIS Pr., The) Ctr. for Strategic & International Studies.

Fisher, Richard D. China's Military Modernization: Building for Regional & Global Reach, 1 vol. 2008. (Praeger Security International Ser.). (Illus.). 344p. 75.00 *(978-0-275-99486-0(4)*, C9486, Praeger Security International) Greenwood Publishing Group, Inc.

—China's Military Modernization: Building for Regional & Global Reach. 2010. (Illus.). xxii, 309p. *(978-0-8047-7194-8(4))*; (ENG.). 344p. pap. 25.95 *(978-0-8047-7195-5(2))* Stanford Univ. Pr.

Fleischer, Samuel E., ed. Measuring China's Military Might. 2010. (China in the 21st Century Ser.). 69.00 *(978-1-60876-846-2(5))* Nova Science Pubs., Inc.

Goldstein, Lyle. Five Dragons Stirring up the Sea: Challenges & Opportunities in China's Improving Maritime Enforcement Capabilities. 2010. (Illus.). 39p. *(978-1-884733-76-5(X))* Naval War College Pr.

Holslag, Jonathan. Trapped Giant. 2011. (Adelphi Ser.). (ENG., Illus.). 160p. (C). pap. 19.95 *(978-0-415-66989-4(8))* Routledge.

Kamphausen, Roy, et al, eds. Beyond the Strait: PLA Missions Other Than Taiwan. 2009. pap. *(978-1-58487-382-2(5))* Strategic Studies Institute, U.S. Army War College Commandant (AWCC-DSI/Pubns.).

King, Dean. Unbound: A True Story of War, Love, & Survival. 2010. (ENG., Illus.). 432p. 25.99 *(978-0-316-16708-6(8))* Little Brown & Co.

Leehy, Anthony G., et al. Military & Security Developments in China. 2012. ***(978-1-61942-009-0(0))*** Nova Science Pubs., Inc.

Lewis, John Wilson & Xue, Litai. Zhongguo Jun Shi Jue Ce Ji Zhi Ji Taiwan Chong Tu. 2007. ("Zhongguo Ju Shi " Xi Lie Ser.: Vol. 47). (CHI., Illus.). 7p. pap. *(978-1-932138-57-3(9))* Mirror Bks. USA.

Li, Xiaobing. A History of the Modern Chinese Army. 2009. (ENG.). 432p. pap. 27.95 *(978-0-8131-9240-6(4))* Univ. Pr. of Kentucky.

Military Power of the People's Republic of China: Hearing Before the Committee on Armed Services, House of Representatives, One Hundred Ninth Congress, Second Session, Hearing Held, June 22, 2006. 2007. iii, 69p. *(978-0-16-079305-9(X)*, 552-070-36383-1) United States Government Printing Office.

Scobell, Andrew & Wortzel, Larry M. Shaping China's Security Environment: The Role of the People's Liberation Army. 2006. vi, 314p. pap. *(978-1-58487-251-1(9))* Strategic Studies Institute, U.S. Army War College Commandant (AWCC-DSI/Pubns.).

United States, Congress House Committee on Armed Services Staff, contrib. by. China's Military Power: Hearing Before the Committee on Armed Services, House of Representatives, One Hundred Ninth Congress, First Session, Hearing Held July 27, 2005. 2007. iii, 98p. *(978-0-16-077923-7(5)*, 552-070-35358-5) United States Government Printing Office.

CHINA—BIBLIOGRAPHY

Selby, Thomas G. As the Chinese See Us. 2009. (ENG.). 258p. 34.99 *(978-1-117-30691-9(7))* BiblioBazaar.

Takagi, Seiichiro, et al, eds. China Watching: Perspectives from Europe, Japan & the United States. 2006. (ENG.). 272p. (C). 190.00 *(978-0-415-41396-1(6))* Routledge.

—China Watching: Perspectives from Europe, Japan & the United States. 2006. (Routledge Contemporary China Ser.). 261p. per. 43.95 *(978-0-415-41397-8(4)*, Routledge) Taylor & Francis Group GBR. Dist: Taylor & Francis Group.

Yuan, Tung-Li. Russian Works on China, 1918-1960, in American Libraries. 2011. 178p. 42.95 ***(978-1-258-08352-6(3))*** Literary Licensing, LLC.

CHINA—BIBLIOGRAPHY—1949-

Tai-Pei National Central Library. Chung-Yang T'u-S. A Selected & Annotated Bibliography of the Republic of China, 1958-59, & 1959-60, 2 vols. in 1. (China Classic & Contemporary Works in Reprint Ser.). reprint ed. 64.50 *(978-0-404-56921-1(8))*, AMS Pr., Inc.

CHINA—BIOGRAPHY

Abels, Janet Jiryu. Making Zen Your Own: Giving Life to Twelve Key Golden Age Ancestors. 2012. (ENG., Illus.). 200p. pap. 16.95 ***(978-0-86171-702-6(3))*** Wisdom Pubns.

Acker, Peter. Liu Chuxuan (1147-1203) & His Commentary on the Daoist Scripture Huangdi Yinfu Jing. 2007. (Asien- und Afrika-Studien der Humboldt-Universität Zu Berlin Ser.: Vol. 23). (CHI & ENG., Illus.). 125p. pap. 58.00 *(978-3-447-05241-2(4))* Harrassowitz, Otto Verlag DEU. Dist: Ahura Pubs.

Adams, Clarence. An American Dream: The Life of an African American Soldier & POW Who Spent Twelve Years in Communist China. Adams, Della & Carlson, Lewis H., eds. 2007. (Illus.). 155p. 22.95 *(978-1-55849-594-4(0))*; per. 22.95 *(978-1-55849-595-1(9))* Univ. of Massachusetts Pr.

Ai, Yanghua & Chen, Xiaoming. Gong Qing Tuan Shi Li. 2009. (CHI., Illus.). 431p. pap. *(978-962-8744-08-4(9))* Mirror Bks. USA.

Alon, Ilan & Zhang, Wenxian, eds. Biographical Dictionary of New Chinese Entrepreneurs & Business Leaders. 2009. (Elgar Original Reference Ser.). 296p. 182.00 *(978-1-84720-636-7(0))* Elgar, Edward Publishing, Inc.

Avery, Kevin & Long, John. Where Strangers Cross. 2010. 300p. pap. 18.99 *(978-1-60957-845-9(7))* Xulon Pr., Inc.

Avis, Yu-Jung L., et al, trs. from CHI. A Sixty-Year Spiritual Voyage on the Ocean of Dharma. 2008. pap. 10.00 *(978-0-9818531-0-9(2))* Noble Path Buddhist Education Fellowship.

Ayi, Bamo, et al. Fieldwork Connections: The Fabric of Ethnographic Collaboration in China & America. 2007. (ENG., Illus.). 384p. per. 30.00 *(978-0-295-98668-5(9))* Univ. of Washington Pr.

Bai, Zhide. Zhang Wang Zhi Lai: Fu Qin Bai Shouyi de Jiu Shi Yi Nian. 2008. (CHI., Illus.). *(978-7-5008-4038-1(1))* Worker Publishing Hse., The.

Barnouin, Barbara, et al. Zhou Enlai: A Political Life. 2007. (ENG.). 404p. (gr. 17). pap. 25.00 *(978-962-996-280-7(2))* Chinese Univ. of Hong Kong, The HKG. Dist: Columbia Univ. Pr.

Benge, Janet & Benge, Geoff. Christian Heroes - Then & Now - Isobel Kuhn: An Adding up of Days. 2009. 208p. (J). pap. 8.99 *(978-1-57658-497-2(6))* YWAM Publishing.

Bentley, Lisa Misraje. Saving Levi: Left to Die ... Destined to Live. 2006. (ENG., Illus.). 176p. per. 13.99 *(978-1-58997-449-4(2))* Tyndale Hse. Pubs.

Benton, Gregor & Lin, Chun. Was Mao Really a Monster? The Academic Response to Chang & Halliday's Mao: the Unknown Story. Benton, Gregor & Chun, Lin, eds. 2009. (ENG.). 208p. 145.00 *(978-0-415-49329-1(3))*; pap. 42.95 *(978-0-415-49330-7(7))* Routledge.

Berold, Robert. Meanwhile Don't Push & Squeeze: A Year of Life in China. 2008. (ENG.). 246p. pap. 23.95 *(978-1-77009-385-0(0))* Jacana Media ZAF. Dist: Independent Pubs. Group.

Biao, Zhong. Zhong Biao. 2011. (ENG., Illus.). 336p. pap. 50.00 *(978-988-18906-5-8(9))* Timezone 8 Ltd. HKG. Dist: D.A.P./Distributed Art Pubs.

Biographiq. Mao Zedong - the Great Helmsman. 2008. 76p. pap. 9.99 *(978-1-59986-036-7(8)*, Biographiq) Filiquarian Publishing, LLC.

Blair, Margaret. Gudao, Lone Islet: The War Years in Shanghai: A Childhood Memoir. 2008. (Illus.). 220p. pap. 19.05 *(978-1-4251-1142-7(4))* Trafford Publishing.

Blo-gros-rgya-Mtsho & Don-grub-phun-Tshogs. Slob Dpon Sans Rgyas Gñis Pa Padma-Byun-Gnas Kyi Rnam Thar Yid Kyi Mun Sel Zes Bya Ba Bzugs So. 2010. (TIB., Illus.). 17p. *(978-7-223-02606-2(5))* Tibetan People's Publishing Hse.

Boerop, Joy K. Joy in Living: A Memoir of an MK, an MW & an MM. 2010. 340p. 37.99 *(978-1-4141-1644-0(6))*; pap. 19.99 *(978-1-4141-1569-6(5))* Pleasant Word.

Bolin, Liu, photos by. Liu Bolin: Hiding in the City. 2011. (ENG., Illus.). 150p. 60.00 ***(978-988-15-0633-7(6))*** Timezone 8 Ltd. HKG. Dist: D.A.P./Distributed Art Pubs.

Bratt, Kay. Silent Tears: A Journey of Hope in a Chinese Orphanage. 2011. (ENG.). 352p. pap. 15.95 ***(978-0-547-74496-4(X)***, Mariner Bks.) Houghton Mifflin Harcourt Trade & Reference Pubs.

Brauen, Yangzom. Across Many Mountains: A Tibetan Family's Epic Journey from Oppression to Freedom. Derbyshire, Katy, tr. from GER. 2011. (ENG., Illus.). 320p. 26.99 ***(978-0-312-60013-6(5))*** St. Martin's Pr.

Brewer, S. Grey. The Rabbit in the Moon. 2009. 232p. 25.99 *(978-1-60791-311-5(9))*; pap. 15.99 *(978-1-60791-388-7(7))* Xulon Pr., Inc.

Brown, Kerry. Hu Jintao: China's Silent Ruler. 2012. 256p. 45.00 ***(978-981-4350-02-0(8))*** World Scientific Publishing Co., Inc.

Brown, Patrick. Butterfly Mind: Revolution, Recovery, & One Reporter's Road to Understanding China, 1 vol. 2009. (ENG.). 264p. pap. 15.95 *(978-0-88784-830-8(3))* House of Anansi Pr. CAN. Dist: Perseus-PGW.

Burton, Margaret E. Notable Women of Modern China. lt. ed. 2007. (ENG.). 194p. pap. 21.99 *(978-1-4264-8081-2(4))* BiblioBazaar.

Cai Yuanpei yan jiu hui Staff, contrib. by. Cai Yuanpei Yu Xian Dai Zhongguo. 2010. (CHI.). *(978-7-301-16501-0(3))* Beijing University Pr.

Cai, Zheng. Yi Ge Jie Fang Jun de 1989. 2009. (Zhen Xiang Xi Lie Ser.: Vol. 54). (CHI., Illus.). 244p. *(978-1-932138-90-0(0))* Mirror Bks. USA.

Cannon, Isidore Cyril. Public Success, Private Sorrow: The Life & Times of Charles Henry Brewitt-Taylor (1857-1938), China Customs Commissioner. 2009. (Royal Asiatic Society Hong Kong Studies Ser.). (ENG., Illus.). 288p. (gr. 17). 45.00 *(978-962-209-961-6(0))* Hong Kong Univ. Pr. HKG. Dist: Columbia Univ. Pr.

Carter, James. Heart of Buddha, Heart of China: The Life & Times of a 20th-Century Chinese Monk, 1 vol. 2010. (ENG., Illus.). 256p. 29.95 *(978-0-19-539885-4(8))* Oxford Univ. Pr., Inc.

Chan, Hok-lam. Ming Taizu (R. 1368-98)and the Foundation of the Ming Dynasty in China. 2011. (Variorum Collected Studies). (Illus.). 374p. 165.00 ***(978-1-4094-3128-2(2))*** Ashgate Publishing Co.

Chan, Loi. To Bank, or Not to Bank: From Pauper to Millionaire, from Hopeless to Hopeful. 2010. pap. 22.99 *(978-1-61566-815-1(2))* Tate Publishing & Enterprises, LLC.

Chang, David Wen-Wei & Carter, Alden R. The Scholar & the Tiger: A Memoir of Famine & War in Revolutionary China. 2009. (ENG., Illus.). 200p. 39.95 *(978-0-7425-5761-1(8))* Rowman & Littlefield Publishers, Inc.

Chen, Bilan. Zao Qi Zhong Gong Yu Tuo Pai: Wo de Ge Ming Sheng Ya Hui Yi. 2010. (CHI., Illus.). 540p. *(978-988-219-157-0(6))* Cosmos Bks. Ltd.

Chen, Da. Colors of the Mountain. pap. *(978-0-385-72864-5(6))* Knopf Doubleday Publishing Group.

Chen, Jinhua. Philosopher, Practitioner, Politician: The Many Lives of Fazang (643-712) 2007. (Sinica Leidensia Ser.). 550p. *(978-90-04-15613-5(5))* BRILL.

Chen, Pingao. Zhui Yi Yu Gan Huai: "Bo Lan Qun Shu" Za Zhi Jing Xuan Ji = Zhuiyi Yu Ganhuai. 2008. (CHI.). *(978-7-01-007213-5(2))* People's Publishing Hse., The.

Chen, Stephen. Red Circle: China & Me 1949-2009. 2009. (ENG.). 552p. pap. 19.95 *(978-1-4490-3365-1(2))* AuthorHouse.

Cheng, Chi & Maxwell, Alexander J. Grassland Journal: Nomads & the Red Sun. 2007. (Illus.). viii, 777p. *(978-0-9723807-3-7(6))* Cheng, Charlie.

Cheng, Xin'guo. Hai Shang Da Shi: Zhongguo Xian Dai Ke Xue Dian Ji Zhe Ping Zong. 2007. (CHI., Illus.). *(978-7-5427-3672-7(8))* Shanghai Popular Science Pr.

Chin, Annping & Simon and Schuster Staff. Confucius: A Life of Thought & Politics. 2009. (ENG., Illus.). 288p. pap. 14.95 *(978-0-300-15118-3(7)*, Yale Univ. Pr.

Ching, Frank. Ancestors: The Story of China Told Through the Lives of an Extraordinary Family. 2010. (ENG., Illus.). 544p. pap. 14.95 *(978-1-84604-177-8(5))* Random Hse. GBR. Dist: Independent Pubs. Group.

Ching-Shing Chan, Alex. Intellectual Narratives: Theory, History, & Self-Characterization of Social Margins in Public Writings. 2011. (ENG.). 240p. pap. ***(978-3-0343-0695-9(4))*** Lang, Peter.

Ch'o, Su. Biography of Su Ch'o: Chinese Dynastic Histories Translations, No. 3. Goodrich, Chauncey S., tr. 2011. 160p. 41.95 ***(978-1-258-06791-5(9))*** Literary Licensing, LLC.

Chong, Denise. Egg on Mao: The Story of an Ordinary Man Who Defaced an Icon & Unmasked a Dictatorship. 2009. (ENG.). 256p. 26.00 *(978-1-58243-547-3(2)*, Counterpoint Pr.) Basic Bks. GBR. Dist: Perseus-PGW.

Christie, Vance. Hudson Taylor: Gospel Pioneer to China. 2011. pap. ***(978-1-59638-236-7(8))*** P & R Publishing.

Clarkson, Adrienne. Norman Bethune. 2011. (ENG.). 204p. (gr. 12). 19.95 ***(978-0-670-06731-2(8)***, Penguin Global) Penguin Group (USA) Inc.

Clements, Jonathan. Wellington Koo? China. 2008. (Haus Histories Ser.). (ENG., Illus.). 176p. 19.95 *(978-1-905791-69-9(0))* Haus Publishing GBR. Dist: Consortium Bk. Sales & Distribution.

Coleman, Inabelle Graves & Kelly, Willie Hayes. One of Us: The Story of the Life of Willie Hayes Kelly. 2011. 140p. 40.95 ***(978-1-258-09344-0(8))*** Literary Licensing, LLC.

Conley, Susan. The Foremost Good Fortune. (Vintage Ser.). (ENG., 2012. Illus.). 368p. pap. 15.00 ***(978-0-307-73986-5(4)***, Vintage) 2011. 288p. 25.95 *(978-0-307-59406-8(8)*, Knopf) Knopf Doubleday Publishing Group.

Cromarty, Jim. It Is Not Death to Die: A New Biography of Hudson Taylor. 2008. (ENG.). 514p. pap. 17.99 *(978-1-84550-367-3(8))* Christian Focus Pubns. GBR. Dist: STL Distribution North America.

Cunningham, Philip. Tiananmen Moon: Inside the Chinese Student Uprising Of 1989. 2010. (Asian Voices Ser.). (ENG.). 320p. pap. 19.95 *(978-0-7425-6673-6(0))* Rowman & Littlefield Publishers, Inc.

Cunningham, Philip J. Tiananmen Moon: Inside the Chinese Student Uprising of 1989. 2009. (Asian Voices Ser.). (ENG.). 320p. 39.95 *(978-0-7425-6672-9(2))* Rowman & Littlefield Publishers, Inc.

Davis, Daniel K. Hu Jintao. 2007. (Modern World Leaders Ser.). (Illus.). 128p. (YA). (gr. 7-12). lib. bdg. 30.00 *(978-0-7910-9518-8(5))* Facts On File, Inc.

de Crespigny, Rafe. A Biographical Dictionary of Later Han to the Three Kingdoms (23-220 AD) 2006. (Handbook of Oriental Studies. Section 4 China Ser.). (Illus.). 1306p. *(978-90-04-15605-0(4))* BRILL.

DeLong, Thomas A. Madame Chiang Kai-Shek & Miss Emma Mills: China's First Lady & Her American Friend. 2007. (ENG., Illus.). 264p. per. 39.95 *(978-0-7864-2980-6(1))* McFarland & Co., Inc. Pubs.

Deng, Zhanyun. Qing Dai de Yi Bai Ge Lao Bai Xing. 2009. (CHI.). *(978-7-5034-2259-1(9))* China Culture and History Pr.

Der Ling, Princess. Two Years in the Forbidden City. 2010. (ENG.). 436p. pap. 35.75 *(978-1-171-82430-5(0))* BiblioBazaar.

—Two Years in the Forbidden City. 2010. (Illus.). 140p. pap. 22.91 *(978-1-153-72975-8(X))* General Bks. LLC.

Der Ling, The Princess. Two Years in the Forbidden City. 2008. 244p. 24.99 *(978-1-60512-017-1(0))*; pap. 13.99 *(978-1-60512-117-8(7))* Akasha Publishing, LLC. (Akasha Classics).

—Two Years in the Forbidden City. 2008. 224p. pap. *(978-1-4099-2921-5(3))* Dodo Pr.

Designwallas, creator. Chairman Cool. 2009. (ICONoclastic Ser.). (ENG.). 128p. 12.95 *(978-81-7436-668-9(7))* Roli Bks. Private, Ltd. IND. Dist: Ingram Pub. Services.

Ding, Kaiwen. Bai Nian Lin Biao. 2007. (CHI., Illus.). 642p. *(978-1-932138-54-2(4))* Mirror Bks. USA.

Du, Weiyun. Han Mo Sheng Ya. 2010. (CHI., Illus.). 16p. *(978-957-41-7394-5(1))* San Min Bk. Co., Ltd.

Dunlop, Fuchsia. Shark's Fin & Sichuan Pepper: A Sweet-Sour Memoir of Eating in China. 2009. (ENG.). 336p. pap. 17.95 *(978-0-393-33288-9(8)*, 33288) Norton, W. W. & Co., Inc.

Egle, Rene D. Hotel: Untold Stories II. 2009. 324p. 37.95 *(978-1-60594-192-9(1))*; pap. 17.95 *(978-1-60594-191-2(3))* Aeon Publishing Inc. (Llumina Pr.).

Eng, Tak Wah. Journey of a Martial Art Master. 2007. per. 22.95 *(978-0-9755201-5-4(6))* Bo Law Kung Fu Federation.

Evans, Brian L. Pursuing China: Memoir of a Beaver Liaison Officer. 2012. (ENG., Illus.). 312p. pap. 34.95 *(978-0-88864-600-2(3))* Univ. of Alberta Pr. CAN. Dist: Michigan State Univ. Pr.

Fairbank, Wilma. Liang & Lin: Partners in Exploring China's Architectural Past. 2009. 256p. (C). pap. 21.95 *(978-0-8122-2040-7(4))* Univ. of Pennsylvania Pr.

Fang, Zhijin. Jiang Jieshi de Wang Pai Chong Jiang Chen Cheng Zhuan. 2010. (CHI., Illus.). 301p. *(978-7-5108-0235-5(0))* Jiuzhou Publishing Hse.

Feng, Jin. The Making of a Family Saga. 2010. 326p. pap. 26.95 *(978-1-4384-2912-0(6)*, Suny Pr.) State Univ. of New York Pr.

Ferguson, Andrew. Zen's Chinese Heritage: The Masters & Their Teachings. 2011. (ENG.). 568p. pap. 26.95 *(978-0-86171-617-3(5))* Wisdom Pubns.

Fleming, Ann Marie. The Magical Life of Long Tack Sam. 2007. (Illus.). 170p. 24.50 *(978-1-4178-1269-1(9)*, Turtleback) Turtleback Bks.

Fleming, Ann Marie & Fleming, Ann. The Magical Life of Long Tack Sam. 2007. (ENG., Illus.). 176p. (gr. 12-18). 16.00 *(978-1-59448-264-9(0)*, Riverhead Trade (Paperbacks)) Penguin Group (USA) Inc.

Fontana, Michela. Matteo Ricci: A Jesuit in the Ming Court. 2011. (ENG.). 336p. 44.95 *(978-1-4422-0586-4(5))* Rowman & Littlefield Publishers, Inc.

Ford, James Ishmael & Blacker, Melissa, eds. The Book of Mu: Essential Writings on Zen's Most Important Koan. 2011. (ENG.). 352p. pap. 17.95 *(978-0-86171-643-2(4))* Wisdom Pubns.

Fraguas, Jose M. Jeet Kune Do Conversations. 2006. (Illus.). 305p. per. *(978-1-933901-18-3(7))* Empire Bks.

Fu, Zhiying. Bright Star, Luminous Cloud: The Life of a Simple Monk. Smitheram, Robert, tr. from CHI. 2008. 472p. pap. 15.00 *(978-1-932293-29-6(9))* Buddha's Light Publishing.

Gao, Hongman. Secrets from My Money-Smart Brother: Modern Strategies for Attaining Wealth, Health, & Happiness. 2011. (ENG., Illus.). 122p. pap. 15.00 ***(978-0-9814756-8-4(X))*** Soar With Eagles.

Gao, Xiao. Ta Jiang Ling Dao Zhongguo: Xi Jinping Zhuan. 2010. ("Zhongguo Zhang Quan Zhe" Xi Lie Ser.). (Illus.). 570p. pap. ***(978-962-8744-44-2(5))*** Mirror Bks. USA.

Gibson, Jody Babydol. Seduced: Diary of a Double Dealing Spy. 2008. 156p. 24.95 *(978-0-9792202-6-5(2))* Corona Bks. & Music.

Gifford, Elisabeth. The House of Hope: A Story of God's Love & Provision for the Abandoned Orphans of China, 1 vol. 2011. (Illus.). 224p. pap. 13.99 ***(978-0-85721-059-3(9)***, Monarch Bks.) Lion Hudson PLC GBR. Dist: Kregel Pubns.

Goossaert, Vincent. The Taoists of Peking, 1800-1949: A Social History of Urban Clerics. 2007. (Harvard East Asian Monographs: 284). (Illus.). 395p. 49.95 *(978-0-674-02505-9(9))* Harvard Univ., Asia Ctr.

Graefe, Nils. Liu Guitang (1892-1943) Einer der Gröten Banditen der Chinesischen Republikzeit. 2008. (Illus.). xvi, 488p. *(978-3-447-05824-7(2))* Harrassowitz, Otto Verlag.

Graf, Ellen. The Natural Laws of Good Luck: A Memoir of an Unlikely Marriage. 2011. (ENG.). 272p. pap. 15.95 *(978-1-59030-833-2(6)*, Trumpeter) Shambhala Pubns., Inc.

Grant, Beata. Eminent Nuns: Women Chan Masters of Seventeenth-Century China. 2008. (Illus.). 241p. (C). 48.00 *(978-0-8248-3202-5(7))* Univ. of Hawaii Pr.

Gu Chang-Sheng. Awaken: Memoirs of a Chinese Historian. 2009. 228p. 25.99 *(978-1-4490-0618-1(3))*; pap. 14.99 *(978-1-4490-0617-4(5))* AuthorHouse.

Guo, Jianlin & Guo, Hui. Han Lin Zong Tong Xu Shichang. 2010. (CHI., Illus.). 483p. *(978-7-80214-904-5(5))* Unitp Publishing Hse.

Guo, Jiulin. Zhongguo Er Shi Shi Ji Zhuan Ji Wen Xue Shi. 2009. (CHI., Illus.). *(978-7-203-06439-8(5))* Shaanxi People's Publishing Hse.

Hall, Kenneth E. John Woo's The Killer. 2009. (New Hong Kong Cinema Ser.). (ENG., Illus.). 140p. (gr. 17). pap. 18.00 *(978-962-209-956-2(4))* Hong Kong Univ. Pr. HKG. Dist: Columbia Univ. Pr.

Hammond, Kenneth J. Pepper Mountain: The Life, Death & Posthumous Career of Yang Jisheng. 2007. (ENG., Illus.). 256p. 160.00 *(978-0-7103-1280-8(5))* Routledge.

Hammond, Kenneth J. & Stapleton, Kristin, eds. The Human Tradition in Modern China. 2007. (Human Tradition Around the World Ser.). (ENG.). 216p. per. 24.95 *(978-0-7425-5466-5(X))*; (Illus.). 70.00 *(978-0-7425-5465-8(1))* Rowman & Littlefield Publishers, Inc.

Hammonds, Max W. The Indomitable Gertrude Green. 2010. 701p. pap. 24.99 *(978-0-8280-2499-0(5))* Review & Herald Publishing Assn

Hancock, Christopher. Robert Morrison & the Birth of Chinese Protestantism. 2008. (ENG.). 272p. 130.00 *(978-0-567-03177-8(2)*, T&T Clark Int'l) Continuum International Publishing Group, Ltd. GBR. Dist: National Bk. Network.

Hancock, Christopher & Hancock. Robert Morrison & the Birth of Chinese Protestantism. 2008. (T&T Clark Theology Ser.). (ENG., Illus.). 280p. 39.95 *(978-0-567-03178-5(0)*, T&T Clark Int'l) Continuum International Publishing Group, Ltd. GBR. Dist: National Bk. Network.

Harris, J. T. China Jim Being Incidents & Adventures in the Life of an Indian Mutiny Veteran. 2011. 234p. pap. ***(978-1-84574-846-3(8))*** Naval & Military Pr., The.

Hayhoe, Ruth. Portraits of Influential Chinese Educators. (CERC Studies in Comparative Education Ser.). 2010. xvii, 399p. pap. 239.00 *(978-90-481-7396-9(5)*, 9048173965) 2007. (Illus.). 420p. 239.00 *(978-1-4020-5567-6(6))* Springer.

Hayter-Menzies, Grant. The Empress & Mrs. Conger: The Uncommon Friendship of Two Women & Two Worlds. 2011. (ENG., Illus.). 364p. (gr. 17). 35.00 *(978-988-8033-00-8(7))* Hong Kong Univ. Pr. HKG. Dist: Columbia Univ. Pr.

—Imperial Masquerade: The Legend of Princess der Ling. 2008. (ENG., Illus.). 444p. (gr. 17). 35.00 *(978-962-209-881-7(9))* Hong Kong Univ. Pr. HKG. Dist: Columbia Univ. Pr.

Heinze, Ruth-Inge. The Biography of Ahjan Man. (Asian Folklore & Social Life Monographs: No. 89). 12.00 *(978-0-89986-296-5(9))* Bluffton Bks.

Hirst, Bamboo. Blue China. Rose, Sue, tr. from ITA. 2008. 336p. pap. 30.00 *(978-0-9529426-8-9(2))* Loki Books Ltd. GBR. Dist: Central Bks. Ltd.

Hong, Qing. Ta Jiang Shi Zhongguo Da Guan Jia: Li Keqiang Zhuan. 2010. ("Zhongguo Zhang Quan Zhe" Xi Lie Ser.: Vol. 42). (Illus.). 524p. ***(978-962-8744-47-3(X))*** Mirror Bks. USA.

Hsia, R. Po-chia. A Jesuit in the Forbidden City: Matteo Ricci 1552-1610. 2012. (ENG., Illus.). 384p. pap. 35.00 ***(978-0-19-965653-0(3))*** Oxford Univ. Pr., Inc.

Hsieh, Ming Tung. A Lost Tribe. 2011. 252p. pap. 63.01 ***(978-1-4567-7338-0(0))*** AuthorHouse.

Hsu, Andrew. Winning Principles: Wisdom from Conversations with 11 Distinguished Chinese American Scientists. 2006. (YA). pap. 19.95 *(978-0-9752778-0-5(4))* Ovo Pr.

Hsu, Andrew & Hsu, Patrick. Life of Science: Lessons from 11 Successful Chinese Scientists. 2007. pap. *(978-0-9752778-1-2(2))* Ovo Pr.

Hua, Hsuan. A Pictorial Biography of the Venerable Master Hsu Yun, 2 vols., Set. Buddhist Text Translation Society Staff, tr. Incl. Vol. 1. Pictorial Biography of the Venerable Hsu Yun. 1983. pap. *(978-0-88139-008-7(9))*; Vol. 2. Pictorial Biography of the Venerable Hsu Yun. 1985. pap. *(978-0-88139-116-9(6))*; (Illus.). 208p. Set pap. 16.00 *(978-0-917512-40-7(5))* Buddhist Text Translation Society.

Huang, Weican. Mo Nian de Ri Zi. 2009. (CHI., Illus.). *(978-7-5426-2981-4(6))* SDX Joint Publishing, Co.

Hummel, Arthur A. Eminent Chinese of the Ching Period, 2 vols. 1116p. *(978-1-906876-06-7(1))* BRILL.

Hung, Hing Ming. The Road to the Throne: How Liu Bang Founded China's Han Dynasty. 2011. pap. 22.95 *(978-0-87586-837-0(1))*; pap. 32.95 *(978-0-87586-838-7(X))* Algora Publishing.

Iliyn, Vanya & Iliyn, Peter. Out of the Far Corners: An Epic Tale of Rejection, Grace, & Deliverance. 2011. *(978-1-57658-545-0(X))* YWAM Publishing.

Jacob, Ellis. The Shanghai I Knew: A Foreign Native in Pre-Revolutionary China. 2007. per. 18.95 *(978-0-9793771-0-5(2))* ComteQ Publishing.

Jiang, Caijian & Chiang, Tsai-Chien. Madame Chien-Shiung Wu: The First Lady of Physics Research. 2012. 300p. 98.00 (978-981-4374-84-2(9)); pap. 48.00 (978-981-4368-92-6(X)) World Scientific Publishing Co., Inc.

Jiang, Qisheng. Yi Sheng Shuo Zhen Hua. 2009. (CHI., Illus.). 466p. (978-1-931550-32-1(8)) Laogai Research Foundation, The.

Johnston, Reginald F. Twilight in the Forbidden City. 2011. (Cambridge Library Collection - History Ser.). (ENG., Illus.). 572p. pap. 43.00 (978-1-108-02965-0(5)) Cambridge Univ. Pr.

Johnston, Reginald Fleming. Twilight in the Forbidden City. 2008. (Illus.). 488p. per. 28.95 (978-0-9680459-5-4(2)) Soul Care Publishing CAN. Dist: Ingram Bk. Co.

Joy, Joe. The Year of My Returning Home: Tell You the True China. 2011. 88p. pap. 15.99 (978-1-4568-8059-0(4)) Xlibris Corp.

Kafalas, Philip A. In Limpid Dream: Nostalgia & Zhang Dai's Reminiscences of the Ming. 2006. 288p. pap. 29.95 (978-1-891936-63-0(8), Signature Bks.) EastBridge.

Kang, Jim. Study in China (Chinese Version) 2008. 213p. pap. 39.99 (978-1-4357-5985-5(0)) Lulu Enterprises Inc.

Kang, Zhengguo. Confessions: An Innocent Life in Communist China. Wilf, Susan, tr. from CHI. 2008. (ENG., Illus.). 480p. pap. 15.95 (978-0-393-33200-1(4), 33200) Norton, W. W. & Co., Inc.

Kaplan, Lawrence M. Homer Lea: American Soldier of Fortune. 2010. (American Warriors Ser.). (ENG., Illus.). 312p. 40.00 (978-0-8131-2616-6(9)) Univ. Pr. of Kentucky.

Karl, Rebecca E. Mao Zedong & China in the Twentieth-Century World: A Concise History. 2010. (Asia-Pacific: Culture, Politics, & Society Ser.). (ENG.). 216p. 74.95 (978-0-8223-4780-4(6)); pap. 21.95 (978-0-8223-4795-8(4)) Duke Univ. Pr.

Karsen, Wendell P. The Church under the Cross: Mission in Asia in Times of Turmoil: A Missionary Memoir. 2010. pap. 36.00 (978-0-8028-6614-1(X)) Eerdmans, William B. Publishing Co.

Kei, Shu. Ann Hui's "The Secret" 2009. (ENG., Illus.). (gr. 17). 212p. pap. 29.95 (978-962-209-586-1(0)); 172p. 50.00 (978-962-209-587-8(9)) Hong Kong Univ. Pr. HKG. Dist: Columbia Univ. Pr.

Keith, Zak. My Life as a Squint-eyed Chink. 2009. 328p. pap. 24.95 (978-1-4092-5314-3(7)) Lulu Enterprises Inc.

Khoo, Salma Nasution. Sun Yat Sen in Penang. 2008. (Illus.). 130p. (978-983-42834-8-3(2)) Starain Educational (M) Sdn Bhd.

Kidd, David. Peking Story. 2009. (ENG.). 164p. pap. 29.95 (978-1-906011-00-0(1)) Eland Bks. GBR. Dist: Dufour Editions, Inc.

Kim, Ki Ho. Hometryless. 2007. 16.00 (978-0-8059-8924-3(2)) Dorrance Publishing Co., Inc.

Kitto, Mark. Chasing China: How I Went to China in Search of a Fortune & Found a Life. 2009. (ENG.). 304p. 22.95 (978-1-60239-657-9(4), 239657) Skyhorse Publishing Co., Inc.

Kon-sprul Blo-gros-mtha-Yas. Zab Moi Gter Dan Gter Ston Grub Thob Ji Ltar Byon Pai lo Rgyus Mdor Bsdus Su Bkod Pa Rin Chen Baiduryai Phren Ba Zes Bya Ba Bzugs So. 2007. (TIB., Illus.). 527p. (978-7-223-02119-7(5)) Tibetan People's Publishing Hse.

Kong, Rudy. Dragons, Donkeys & Dust: Memoirs from a Decade in China. 2010. (978-0-9813003-2-0(4)) Bing Long Bks.

Koo, Hui-Lan. Hui-Lan Koo, Madame Wellington Koo: An Autobiography. Thayer, Mary Van Rensselaer, ed. 2011. 370p. 53.95 (978-1-258-03410-8(7)) Literary Licensing, LLC.

Krebs, Sylvia H. How Am I to Touch with You? Encounters with China. 2010. 273p. pap. 16.00 (978-0-557-16708-1(6)) Lulu Enterprises Inc.

Kuo, Gioetta. China My Other Country. 2010. 244p. pap. 15.95 (978-1-4520-6709-4(0)) AuthorHouse.

Lee, William Poy. The Eighth Promise: An American Son's Tribute to His Toisanese Mother. 2007. (ENG.). 336p. pap. 14.95 (978-1-59486-811-5(5)) Rodale Pr., Inc.

Lei, Fengxing. Zhan Tianyou Zhi Lu. 2009. (CHI., Illus.). (978-7-113-10745-1(1)) China Railway Publishing Hse.

Levy, Michael. Kosher Chinese: Living, Teaching, & Eating with China's Other Billion. 2011. (ENG.). 256p. pap. 15.00 (978-0-8050-9196-0(3), Holt Paperback) Holt, Henry & Co.

Lew, Yu-Tang Daniel. The Best of Two Worlds: Notes of my spiritual Pilgrimage. 2008. 248p. pap. 19.95 (978-0-595-50960-7(6)) iUniverse, Inc.

Li. Journey Across the Four Seas. 2006. 250p. pap. (978-1-931907-43-9(9)) Homa & Sekey Bks.

Li, Ling. Constructing Teacher's Professional Identity in China & Canada: Life Stories in Context. 2008. 280p. pap. (978-3-639-09503-6(0)) VDM Verlag Dr. Mueller e.K.

Liang, Diane Wei. Lake with No Name: A True Story of Love & Conflict in Modern China. 2009. (ENG., Illus.). 320p. pap. 14.00 (978-1-4391-3686-7(6)) Simon & Schuster.

Liao, Gailong & Luo, Zhufeng, eds. Who's Who in China: Current Leaders. 2nd ed. 1037p. (978-7-119-00725-0(4)) Bow Historical Bks.

Lighte, Peter. Pieces of China. 2009. 127p. pap. 18.00 (978-0-557-15652-8(1)) Lulu Enterprises Inc.

Lin, Biao, et al. Lin Biao Ri Ji, 2 vols. 2nd ed. 2009. (CHI.). 1229p. (978-1-932138-98-6(6)) Mirror Bks. USA.

Lin, Paul. In the Eye of the China Storm: A Life Between East & West. 2011. (Illus.). 256p. (C). (978-0-7735-3857-3(7)) McGill-Queen's Univ. Pr.

Ling, Der. Two Years in the Forbidden City. 2010. 442p. pap. 35.75 (978-1-142-63531-2(7)); 436p. pap. 35.75 (978-1-142-11899-0(1)); 444p. pap. 36.75 (978-1-143-21032-7(8)) BiblioBazaar.

—Two Years in the Forbidden City. 2009. 164p. pap. (978-1-150-52685-5(8)) Books LLC.

Ling, Princess Der. Two Years in the Forbidden City. 2007. (ENG.). 270p. pap. 19.99 (978-988-17149-9-2(0)) Earnshaw Bks. HKG. Dist: Independent Pubs. Group.

—Two Years in the Forbidden City. 2010. 170p. pap. (978-1-4076-5076-0(9)) HardPr.

Ling, Rich. Old Buddha. 2007. 190.00 (978-0-7103-1111-5(7)) Taylor & Francis Group.

—Two Years in the Forbidden City. 2007. 190.00 (978-0-7103-1112-2(5)) Taylor & Francis Group.

Ling, The Princess Der. Two Years in the Forbidden City. 2010. 180p. pap. 18.36 (978-1-162-71509-4(X)); 30.36 (978-1-169-27745-8(4)); 37.95 (978-1-161-48373-4(X)) Kessinger Publishing, LLC.

Ling, Zhu, compiled by. Building Wealth in China: 36 True Stories of Chinese Millionaires & How They Made Their Fortunes. 2010. (ENG.). 320p. pap. 15.00 (978-0-307-59162-3(X), Crown) Crown Publishing Group.

Littell, Joe. Adventures & Misadventures of a Mishkid. 2007. 256p. per. 15.95 (978-0-615-13306-5(1)) New World Publishing Co.

Liu, Xiuwu R., creator. Wandering form China to America: An Autobiography. 2006. per. 19.95 (978-0-9778102-2-2(4)) Zip Publishing.

Liu, Yongzhi. Jun Lü Sheng Ya Wu Shi Nian: Junlushengya50nian. 2009. (CHI., Illus.). (978-7-5065-6008-5(9)) P.L.A. Publishing Hse., The.

Lu, Di. Mao Zedong de Jin Chen He Nü Ren: Ling Xiu Men Liu Xia de Mi Tuan. 2010. 360p. pap. (978-962-8744-22-0(4)) Mirror Bks. USA.

Lu-Shan, An. Biography of an Lu-Shan: Chinese Dynastic Histories Translations No. 8. Levy, Howard S., tr. 2011. 136p. 40.95 (978-1-258-07044-1(8)) Literary Licensing, LLC.

Lung, Rachel. Interpreters in Early Imperial China. 2011. 128.00 (978-90-272-2444-6(7)); (978-90-272-8418-1(0)) Benjamins, John Publishing Co.

MacFarquhar, Roderick. Prisoner of the State: The Secret Journal of Premier Zhao Ziyang. 2009. (CHI., Illus.). 382p. pap. (978-957-13-5052-3(4)) China Times Publishing Co.

MacManus, James. Ocean Devil: The Life & Legend of George Hogg. 2008. (ENG., Illus.). 288p. 12.95 (978-0-00-727075-0(5)) HarperCollins Pubs. Ltd. GBR. Dist: Independent Pubs. Group.

Malherbe, Braam. The Great Run: Conquering the Sleeping Dragon Within: Life's Lessons on the Run. 2010. 200p. pap. 25.00 (978-1-920289-05-8(4)) Ball, Jonathan Pubs. ZAF. Dist: International Publishers Marketing.

Martin, Barry S. Forgotten Aviator: The Adventures of Royal Leonard. 2011. 256p. pap. 15.95 (978-1-60844-929-3(7)) Dog Ear Publishing, LLC.

Mather, Richard B. William Arnot Mather, American Missionary to China & Richard Burroughs Mather, Professor of Chinese: The Biography & Autobiography of a Father & a Son. 2010. (Illus.). xiv, 61p. 89.95 (978-0-7734-1314-6(6)) Mellen, Edwin Pr., The.

Mazur, Mary. Wu Han, Historian: Son of China's Times. 2009. (ENG.). 530p. 115.50 (978-0-7391-2456-7(0)) Lexington Bks.

Mertz, Henriette. Pale Ink: Two Ancient Records of Chinese Exploration in America. 2008. (ENG.). 158p. pap. 20.75 (978-1-4375-1907-5(5)); 174p. pap. 22.75 (978-1-4375-1908-2(3)) BiblioBazaar.

Meynard, Thierry. The Religious Philosophy of Liang Shuming: The Hidden Buddhist. 2010. (Modern Chinese Philosophy Ser.). 226p. (978-90-04-17151-0(7)) BRILL.

Mielke, Joy. An Ordinary Man - A Great God: The life of Missionary Knute Hjalmar Ekblad to North China. 2011. 120p. pap. 11.99 (978-1-4567-1638-7(7)) AuthorHouse.

Milkon, Phyllis A. Earthly Angels [Special Reprint for David's 100th Birthday]: David Chen's Survival of Famine & Persecution. 2007. (Illus.). 160p. pap. 14.00 (978-0-9630025-3-2(8)) Burgess Creative Ventures.

Mullin, Glenn H. The Fourteen Dalai Lamas: A Sacred Legacy of Reincarnation. Shepherd, Valerie, ed. 2008. (Illus.). 554p. pap. 34.95 (978-1-57416-092-5(3)) Clear Light Pubs.

Ong, Connie. Letta in China. 2006. pap. 15.99 (978-1-60034-543-2(3)) Xulon Pr., Inc.

Otie, Philippe. A Chinese Life. 2012. (Illus.). 720p. pap. 27.50 (978-1-906838-55-3(0), SelfMadeHero) Metro Media Ltd. GBR. Dist: Abrams.

Pakula, Hannah. The Last Empress: Madame Chiang Kai-shek & the Birth of Modern China. 2010. (ENG., Illus.). 816p. pap. 20.00 (978-1-4391-4894-5(5)) Simon & Schuster.

Pantsov, Alexander & Levine, Steven I. Mao: The Real Story. 2012. (ENG., Illus.). 736p. 35.00 (978-1-4516-5447-9(2)) Simon & Schuster.

Park, No-Yong. Chinaman's Chance: An Autobiography. 2011. 180p. 42.95 (978-1-258-01837-5(3)) Literary Licensing, LLC.

Pearson, Stuart & Raben, Remco. Bittersweet: The Memoir of a Chinese Indonesian Family in the Twentieth Century. Shaffer, Wendie, tr. 2008. (Ohio RIS Southeast Asia Ser.). (ENG., Illus.). 352p. pap. 28.00 (978-0-89680-264-3(7)) Ohio Univ. Pr.

Peili, Zhang. Zhang Peili: Chinese Contemporary Art Awards 2010. 2012. (ENG., Illus.). 160p. 40.00 (978-988-19912-7-0(7)) Timezone 8 Ltd. HKG. Dist: D.A.P./Distributed Art Pubs.

Peng, Sen & Chen, Li. Reforming China: Major Events (1978-1991), 5 vols., Vol. 3. Li, Tieying, ed. 2010. (Enrich Series on China's Economic Reform Ser.). (ENG.). 400p. 138.00 (978-981-4298-04-9(2)) Enrich Professional Publishing (S)., Ltd. SGP. Dist: Independent Pubs. Group.

Peterson, E. W. Shanghai Policeman. 2012. (ENG.). 256p. pap. 19.99 (978-988-19983-8-5(7)) Earnshaw Bks. HKG. Dist: Independent Pubs. Group.

Peverelli, Peter J. & Song, Jiwen. Chinese Entrepreneurship: A Social Capital Approach. 2012. (ENG., Illus.). xiv, 170p. 129.00 (978-3-642-28205-8(9), 3642282059) Springer.

Phemister, Mary Anne. Lessons from a Broken Chopstick. 2009. 160p. pap. 14.95 (978-1-934749-62-3(1)) Hannibal Bks.

Pollock, John. The Cambridge Seven. 2006. (History Makers Ser.). (ENG.). 128p. per. 11.99 (978-1-84550-177-8(2)) Christian Focus Pubns. GBR. Dist: STL Distribution North America.

Pomfret, John. Chinese Lessons: Five Classmates & the Story of the New China. 2007. (ENG., Illus.). 336p. pap. 16.99 (978-0-8050-8664-5(1), Holt Paperback) Holt, Henry & Co.

Porter, Bill & Pine, Red. Road to Heaven: Encounters with Chinese Hermits. 2009. (ENG.). 240p. pap. 15.95 (978-1-58243-523-7(5), Counterpoint Pr.) Basic Bks. GBR. Dist: Perseus-PGW.

Poulsen, Else. Smiling Bears: A Zookeeper Explores the Behavior & Emotional Life of Bears, 1 vol. 2011. (ENG.). 264p. pap. 17.95 (978-1-55365-805-4(1), Greystone Bks.) D&M Pubs. Inc. CAN. Dist: Perseus-PGW.

Qin, Huasun. Chu Shi Lian He Guo: Ambassador's Memoir: Representing China in the UN. 2010. (CHI., Illus.). pap. (978-7-5011-9136-9(0)) Xinhua Publishing Hse.

Qingqiuzi. Zhongguo Ren Neng Zuo Dao: Minguo Shi Ye Jia Lu Zuofu. 2010. (CHI.). 315p. (978-7-80729-647-8(X)) Phoenix Publishing House.

Qunying, Li & Han, Louis. The Doctor Who Was Followed by Ghosts: The Family Saga of a Chinese Woman Doctor. 2007. (ENG., Illus.). 300p. 25.95 (978-1-55022-781-9(5)) ECW Pr. CAN. Dist: Independent Pubs. Group.

"Ren wu" bian ji bu Staff, contrib. by. Zhongguo Ke Xue de Chen Xi: Zhongguo Kexue Dechenxi. 2009. (CHI., Illus.). 280p. (978-7-5060-3722-8(X)) Ori Pr, The.

Rhodes, Bill. Hillbilly in China. 2008. 80p. pap. 16.95 (978-1-60672-344-9(8)) PublishAmerica, Inc.

Richard, Bako, contrib. by. Who Is Who. 2007. pap. (978-0-9791826-0-0(3)) Valley Graphics Printing Inc.

Roloff, Carola. Red mda' ba. Buddhist Yogi-Scholar of the Fourteenth Century: The Forgotten Reviver of Madhyamaka Philosophy in Tibet. 2010. (Contributions to Tibetan Studies). 500p. (C). 168.00 (978-3-89500-693-7(9)) Reichert, Ludwig Dr. DEU. Dist: Brown, David Bk. Co., The.

Rossabi, Morris & Rossabi, M. Khubilai Khan: His Life & Times. 20th anniv. ed. 2009. (ENG., Illus.). 348p. pap. 24.95 (978-0-520-26132-7(1)) Univ. of California Pr.

Sam-Tio Chung, Husain. God the Therapist: A True Story of a Man's Search for His Soul. 2011. 156p. 24.95 (978-1-4620-0691-5(4)); pap. 14.95 (978-1-4620-0687-8(6)) iUniverse, Inc.

Sanborn, James G. Shanghai Remembered: Growing up in a Japanese Concentration Camp. 2009. (ENG.). 53p. pap. 8.95 (978-0-533-16106-5(1)) Vantage Pr., Inc.

Scocca, Tom. Beijing Welcomes You: Unveiling the Capital City of the Future. 2011. (ENG., Illus.). 384p. (gr. 12). 26.95 (978-1-59448-784-2(7), Riverhead Bks. (Hardcover)) Penguin Group (USA) Inc.

Shemilt, Wei Wei. The Girl with Complicated Thoughts. 2007. 320p. pap. 21.50 (978-1-84799-843-9(7)) Lulu Enterprises Inc.

Shemo, Connie. The Chinese Medical Ministries of Kang Cheng & Shi Meiyu, 1872-1937: On a Cross-Cultural Frontier of Gender, Race, & Nation. 2011. (Studies in Missionaries & Christianity in China Ser.). (ENG.). 304p. 80.00 (978-1-61146-085-8(9)) Lehigh Univ. Pr.

Short, Philip. Mao. Robles, David Martinez, tr. 2007. (Biblioteca de Bolsillo Ser.). (Illus.). 1046p. pap. 19.95 (978-84-8432-858-2(9)) Critica Editorial ESP. Dist: Planeta Publishing Corp.

Shu, Jingnan. Zhu Xi Yan Jiu. (CHI.). 40p. (978-7-01-007171-8(3)) People's Publishing Hse., The.

Sidenvall, E. O. L & Sidenvall, Erik. The Making of Manhood among Swedish Missionaries in China & Mongolia, C.1890-C.1914. 2009. (Studies in Christian Mission Ser.). (Illus.). xi, 189p. (978-90-04-17408-5(7)) BRILL.

Smith, Karen, ed. Nine Lives: the Birth of Avant-Garde Art in New China. 2008. (ENG., Illus.). 473p. pap. 50.00 (978-988-17143-3-6(8)) Timezone 8 Ltd. HKG. Dist: D.A.P./Distributed Art Pubs.

Song, Sonia J. Donkey Baby: From Beijing to Berkeley & Beyond. 2008. 292p. pap. 15.49 (978-1-4343-9150-6(7)) AuthorHouse.

Ssu-Ma, Ch'ien. Statesman, Patriot, & General in Ancient Chin: Three Shih Chi Biographies of the Ch'in Dynasty, 255-206 B. C. Bodde, Derk, tr. 2011. 90p. 38.95 (978-1-258-10339-2(7)) Literary Licensing, LLC.

Stewart, Sharon & Stewart, Roderick. Phoenix: The Life of Norman Bethune. 2011. (Illus.). 488p. (C). (978-0-7735-3819-1(4)) McGill-Queen's Univ. Pr.

Su, Tongbing. Ming Dai Shi Shi Yu Ren Wu. 2010. (CHI.). pap. (978-7-80047-922-9(6)) Forbidden City Publishing Hse.

—Qing Dai Shi Shi Yu Ren Wu. 2010. (CHI.). (978-7-80047-921-2(8)) Forbidden City Publishing Hse.

Suzhou da xue, Tu shu guan Staff, contrib. by. Qi Xian Xie Zhen: Suzhou Da Xue Tu Shu Guan Cang Qing Dai Ren Wu Tu Xiang Xuan. 2008. (Illus.). (978-7-300-09168-6(7)) China Renmin Univ.Pr.

Swann, Nancy Lee. Pan Chao: Foremost Woman Scholar of China, First Century A. D. 2008. 208p. pap. 20.00 (978-1-59740-684-0(8)) ACLS Humanities E-Book.

Sydes, Stephanie. Journey for Julie: Witnessing God's Glory Through Toddler Adoption in China. 2011. 140p. pap. 15.99 (978-1-4567-3574-6(8)) AuthorHouse.

Tan, Pamela. The Chinese Factor: An Australian Chinese Woman's Life in China from 1950 to 1979. 2008. (Illus.). 272p. pap. 29.95 (978-1-877058-74-5(2)) Rosenberg Publishing Pty, Ltd. AUS. Dist: International Specialized Bk. Services.

Tan, Yuci. An American-Spy Father & His Daughter in Communist China: The Hopes of Two Generations. 2008. (ENG., Illus.). 272p. pap. 17.95 (978-1-57733-207-7(5)) Blue Dolphin Publishing, Inc.

Taylor, Jay. The Generalissimo: Chiang Kai-Shek & the Struggle for Modern China. 2011. (ENG., Illus.). 752p. pap. 19.95 (978-0-674-06049-4(0), Belknap Pr.) Harvard Univ. Pr.

Tian, Min, ed. China's Greatest Operatic Male Actor of Female Roles: Documenting the Life & Art of Mei Lanfang 1894-1961. 2010. 428p. (978-0-7734-3777-7(0)) Mellen, Edwin Pr., The.

Timothy, Cheek, ed. A Critical Introduction to Mao. 2010. (ENG., Illus.). 392p. (C). pap. 27.99 (978-0-521-71154-8(1)) Cambridge Univ. Pr.

Tobias, Sigmund. Strange Haven: A Jewish Childhood in Wartime Shanghai. 2008. (ENG.). 208p. pap. 20.95 (978-0-252-07624-4(9)) Univ. of Illinois Pr.

Todd, Martha Sue. Never Too Old to Climb Walls. 2007. 456p. per. 27.85 (978-1-4251-0936-3(5)) Trafford Publishing.

Transplanting Life: From mainland China to Taiwan to American. 2009. pap. (978-1-61584-115-8(6)) Independent Pub.

Tse, Helen. Sweet Mandarin: The Courageous True Story of Three Generations of Chinese Women & Their Journey from East to West. 2009. (ENG., Illus.). 304p. pap. 16.99 (978-0-312-60481-3(5), St. Martin's Griffin) St. Martin's Pr.

Tyson Li, Laura, et al. Madame Chiang Kai-Shek: China's Eternal First Lady. 2007. (ENG., Illus.). 576p. per. 17.00 (978-0-8021-4322-8(9), Grove Pr.) Grove/Atlantic, Inc.

Vautrin, Minnie. Terror in Minnie Vautrin's Nanjing: Diaries & Correspondence, 1937-38. Lu, Suping, ed. 2008. (ENG., Illus.). 312p. 47.00 (978-0-252-03332-2(9)) Univ. of Illinois Pr.

Vautrin, Minnie, et al. The Undaunted Women of Nanking: The Wartime Diaries of Minnie Vautrin & Tsen Shui-Fang. Hu, Hualing, ed. 2010. (ENG., Illus.). 264p. 29.95 (978-0-8093-2963-2(8)) Southern Illinois Univ. Pr.

Vincer, Alex. The ChinaMerr Blog (or, How I Went to China with a Dream & Returned with a Cat) 2009. 111p. pap. 8.50 (978-0-557-07205-7(0)) Lulu Enterprises Inc.

Wang, Chenghong. Wei le Hong Se Zhongguo: Zhongguo Gong Chan Dang Ying Lie Zhuan Lüe. 2009. (Illus.). (978-7-207-08486-6(2)) Heilongjiang People's Publishing Hse.

Wang, Chi. A Compelling Journey from Peking to Washington: Building a New Life in America. 2011. (ENG.). 210p. pap. 30.00 (978-0-7618-5385-5(5)) Hamilton Bks.

Wang, Fuyi. Jin Kan Xiang Ying. 2009. (CHI., Illus.). (978-7-5098-0340-0(3)) Chinese Communist Party History Pr.

Wang, Guangyuan. Jiang Jieshi Yu Xin Jun Fa Hun Zhan. 2010. (CHI., Illus.). (978-7-5034-2560-8(1)) China Culture and History Pr.

Wang, Ping. Guo Min Dang Gao Ji Jiang Ling de Zi Nü Men. 2009. (CHI., Illus.). pap. (978-7-80141-647-6(3)) Taihai Publishing House.

Wang, Weiling. Sui Yue Chuan Zhen: Wo He Dang Dai Zuo Jia. 2009. (CHI., Illus.). (978-7-81119-534-7(8)) Capital Normal Univ. Pr.

Wang, Xiangkun. Du Dong Liu Shaoqi: Dudong Liiu Shaoqi. 2010. (978-7-220-07989-4(3)) Sichuan Renmin Chubanshe.

Wang, Yupin. Manchurian American: A Memoir. 2009. (Illus.). vii, 156p. E-Book (978-1-4401-8677-6(4)) iUniverse, Inc.

Weatherley, Robert. Mao's Forgotten Successor: The Political Career of Hua Guofeng. 2010. (ENG., Illus.). 224p. 89.00 (978-0-230-54247-1(6)) Palgrave Macmillan.

Wei, Betty Peh-T'i. Ruan Yuan, 1764-1849: The Life & Work of a Major Scholar-Official in Nineteenth-Century China Before the Opium War. 2006. (ENG., Illus.). 416p. (gr. 17). 60.00 (978-962-209-785-8(5)) Hong Kong Univ. Pr. HKG. Dist: Columbia Univ. Pr.

Wei, Cho-min. The Political Principles of Mencius. 2010. 62p. pap. (978-1-152-06022-7(8)) Books LLC.

Weigand, Jerrine. Knowing Miss Chen. 2006. (Illus.). 352p. 32.95 (978-1-4122-0176-6(4)) Trafford Publishing.

Weishan & Wu, Weishan. The Poetry of Sculpture. 2008. (Illus.). 250p. (C). 99.00 (978-981-279-007-1(1)) World Scientific Publishing Co., Inc.

Wells, Matthew V. To Die & Not Decay: Autobiography & the Pursuit of Immortality in Early China. 2009. (978-0-924304-58-3(8)) Assn. for Asian Studies, Inc.

Wen, Siyong & Ren, Zhichu. Ta Ling Dao Zhongguo: Hu Jintao Xin Zhuan. 2010. (CHI., Illus.). 649p. pap. (978-962-8744-33-6(X)) Mirror Bks. USA.

Weng, Wenhao & Li, Xuetong. Weng Wenhao Ri Ji. 2010. (CHI.). (978-7-101-05979-3(1)) Zhonghua Bk. Co.

Who Was LS Chang? Character-the Key to China. 2006. (Illus.). 140p. per. 11.99 (978-1-59886-558-5(7)) Tate Publishing & Enterprises, LLC.

Wiles, Sue & Hong Lee, Lily Xiao, eds. Biographical Dictionary of Chinese Women: Antiquity Through Sui, 1600 B. C. E. — 618 C. E. 2007. (University of Hong Kong Libraries Publications). (ENG.). 440p. 122.95 (978-0-7656-1750-7(1), East Gate Bk.) Sharpe, M.E. Inc.

William Poy Lee. The Eighth Promise: An American Son's Tribute to His Toisanese Mother. 2007. pap. 12.50 (978-0-61529-854-2(9)) Rodale Pr., Inc.

Williams, Tony. John Woo's Bullet in the Head. 2009. (New Hong Kong Cinema Ser.). (ENG., Illus.). 144p. (gr. 17). pap. 18.00 (978-962-209-968-5(8)) Hong Kong Univ. Pr. HKG. Dist: Columbia Univ. Pr.

Wong, Flora & Decker, Tom. Long Way Home: Journeys of a Chinese Montanan. 2011. (Illus.). 248p. pap. 18.00 **(978-1-59152-083-2(5))** Farcountry Pr.

Woo, X. L. Empress Wu the Great. 2008. 31.95 *(978-0-87586-661-1(1))*; pap. 21.95 *(978-0-87586-660-4(3))* Algora Publishing.

Wu, Banqiu. Zou Chu Nuo Ruo. 2008. (CHI.). 316p. pap. *(978-0-9766906-1-0(6))* William Publishing Co.

Wu, Carlton C. From Yellow River to Lake Champlain. 2007. 9.00 *(978-0-8059-8936-6(6))* Dorrance Publishing Co., Inc.

Wu, Grace. Lang Lang: Chinese Biographies: Graded Readers = [Lang Lang: Gu Dian Yin Yue de Qi Cai: Ren Wu Zhuan Ji: Zhong Wen Pin Yin Fu Zhu du Ben]. 2010. (C). pap., stu. ed. 15.95 *(978-0-88727-758-0(6))* Cheng & Tsui Co.

—Yao Ming: Chinese Biographies: Graded Readers = [Yao Ming: Lan Qiu de Ju Xing: Ren Wu Zhuan Ji: Zhong Wen Pin Yin Fu Zhu du Ben]. 2010. (CHI & ENG.). (C). pap. 15.95 *(978-0-88727-759-7(4))* Cheng & Tsui Co.

Wu, Guo. Zheng Guanying, Merchant Reformer of Late Qing China & His Influence on Economics, Politics, & Society. 2010. *(978-1-60497-705-9(1))* Cambria Pr.

Wu, Kangmin. Fu You Shi Shu Qi Zi Hua: Wu Kangmin Xin du Shu Bi Ji. 2009. (CHI., Illus.). 373p. *(978-988-219-123-5(1))* Cosmos Bks. Ltd.

Wu, Nanying & Cheng, Yuxia. Zhongguo Xin Quan Gui Zhi Guan Fu Ren. 2009. ("Zhongguo Zhang Quan Zhe" Xi Lie Ser.: Vol. 24). (CHI., Illus.). 414p. *(978-1-932138-81-8(1))* Mirror Bks. USA.

Xinran, Xinran. China Witness. 2010. (ENG., Illus.). 464p. pap. 16.95 *(978-0-307-38853-7(0)*, Anchor) Knopf Doubleday Publishing Group.

Xiong, Shihui, et al. Hai Sang Ji: Xiong Shihui Hui Yi Lu, 1907-1949. 2nd ed. 2008. (CHI., Illus.). 710p. pap. *(978-1-932138-70-2(6))* Mirror Bks. USA.

Xu, Shoushang. Zhang Bing in Zhuan. 2009. (CHI., Illus.). *(978-7-5060-3396-1(8))* Ori Pr, The.

Yamashita, Michael. Zheng He. 2006. (ENG., Illus.). 504p. 39.95 *(978-88-544-0164-8(1)*, White Star) Rizzoli International Pubns., Inc.

Yang, Qingxi & Xia, Fei. Shi Ba Da: Zhu Hou Jin Jing. 2010. (CHI., Illus.). 586p. pap. *(978-962-8744-42-8(9))* Mirror Bks. USA.

Yang, Shengqun, et al. Deng Xiaoping Nian Pu: Yi Jiu Ling Si — Yi Jiu Qi Si, 3 vols. 2009. (CHI.). *(978-7-5073-2768-7(X))*; *(978-7-5073-2767-0(1))* Central Party Literature Audio & Video Publishing Hse.

Yang, Shubiao & Yang, Jing. Song Meiling Zhuan. 2010. (CHI.). 256p. *(978-7-308-06772-0(6))* Zhejiang Univ. Electronic & Audio-Video Pr.

Yang, Yun & Fang, Yanhong. Nei Ge Xin San Jiao: Wen Jiabao, Li Keqiang, Wang Qishan Ying Zhan Wei Ji. 2nd ed. 2008. ("Zhongguo Zhang Quan Zhe" Xi Lie Ser.: Vol. 21). (CHI., Illus.). 539p. *(978-1-932138-67-2(6))* Mirror Bks. USA.

—Wen Jiabao Bian Ge. 2008. ("Zhongguo Ju Shi" Xi Lie Ser.: Vol. 50). (CHI., Illus.). 341p. *(978-1-932138-62-7(5))* Mirror Bks. USA.

Ying, Esther Cheo. Black Country to Red China: One Girl's Journey from War-Torn England to Revolutionary China. 2009. (ENG., Illus.). 190p. pap. 14.95 *(978-0-09-953603-1(X))* Random Hse. GBR. Dist: Independent Pubs. Group.

Young, Gordon. Journey from Bann: My Life, Times, & Adventures. 2011. 328p. 29.99 **(978-1-4568-6855-0(1))**; pap. 19.99 **(978-1-4568-6854-3(3))** Xlibris Corp.

Yu, Le, et al. Wan Qing Hong Ru Zhu Yixin, 2 vols. 2011. (CHI., Illus.). xi, 658p. *(978-1-59343-124-2(4))* Cozy Graphics Corp.

Yu, Shiping. Xin Tai Zi Shang. 2010. (CHI., Illus.). 517p. *(978-962-8744-32-9(1))* Mirror Bks. USA.

Zha, Jianguo. Tie Gu Rou Qing: Zha Jianguo Wen Xuan. 2010. (CHI.). xiii, 346p. *(978-1-931550-08-6(5))* Laogai Research Foundation, The.

Zhang, Fengbo. A Chinese Economist's Journey. 2008. 100p. pap. 19.95 *(978-1-4357-5451-5(4))* Lulu Enterprises Inc.

Zhang, Lijia. Socialism Is Great: A Worker's Memoir of the New China. 2008. (ENG.). 320p. 24.00 *(978-0-9777433-7-7(3)*, 977747) Atlas & Co.

Zhang, Wenxian & Alon, Ilan, eds. Biographical Dictionary of New Chinese Entrepreneurs & Business Leaders. 2011. (Elgar Original Reference Ser.). 296p. pap. 49.95 *(978-1-84980-130-0(4))* Elgar, Edward Publishing, Inc.

Zhao, Jianhua. Zhen Shi de Kongzi. 2010. (CHI., Illus.). *(978-7-80257-104-4(9))* ET Pr.

Zhou, Qibo. Bai Ban Wei Qu Nan Qiu Quan. 2010. (CHI., Illus.). 262p. **(978-1-183-43122-5(8))** Cozy Graphics Corp.

Zhou, Shaochang. Xing Xing Chong Xing Xing: "Fan You Yun Dong" Ji. 2008. ("Wen Hua Qing Li" Xi Lie Ser.: Vol. 24). (CHI.). 322p. *(978-1-932138-69-6(2))* Mirror Bks. USA.

Zhou, Xinghua. Ningbo Bang Zhi. 2009. (CHI., Illus.). *(978-7-5004-8104-1(7))* China Social Sciences Pr.

Zhou, Yiliang. Tian Di Yi Shu Sheng: Zhou Yiliang Zi Zhuan. 2010. (CHI., Illus.). 265p. *(978-7-301-16252-1(9))* Beijing University Pr.

Zhu, Zhu, et al, eds. Thirty Years of Adventures: Art & Artists From 1979. 2011. (ENG., Illus.). 792p. 75.00 **(978-988-19912-4-9(2))** Timezone 8 Ltd. HKG. Dist: D.A.P./Distributed Art Pubs.

CHINA—BOUNDARIES

Breuker. Pre-Modern States on China's North-Eastern Frontier: The Liao, 916-1125, & the Koryo, 918-1392. 2012. (Asian States & Empires Ser.). (ENG.). 240p. (C). 135.00 *(978-0-415-77620-2(1))* Routledge.

Fravel, M. Taylor. Strong Borders, Secure Nation: Cooperation & Conflict in China's Territorial Disputes. 2008. (Princeton Studies in International History & Politics Ser.). (ENG., Illus.). 408p. (C). 72.50 *(978-0-691-13608-0(4))*; pap. 32.50 *(978-0-691-13609-7(2))* Princeton Univ. Pr.

Lin, Hsiao-Ting. Modern China's Ethnic Frontiers: A Journey to the West. 2010. (Routledge Studies in the Modern History of Asia Ser.). (ENG., Illus.). 224p. (C). 125.00 *(978-0-415-58264-3(4))* Routledge.

Liu, Li & Chen, Xingcan. State Formation in Early China. 2010. (Duckworth Debates in Archaeology Ser.). (Illus.). 148p. pap. 24.95 *(978-0-7156-3224-6(8))* Duckworth Publishers GBR. Dist: International Publishers Marketing.

Myint-U, Thant. Where China Meets India: Burma & the New Crossroads of Asia, 1 vol. 2012. (ENG., Illus.). 384p. pap. 16.00 **(978-0-374-53352-6(0))** Farrar, Straus & Giroux.

Noorani, A. G. India-China Boundary Problem, 1846-1947: History & Diplomacy, 1 vol. 2011. (ENG., Illus.). 360p. 65.00 *(978-0-19-807068-9(3))* Oxford Univ. Pr., Inc.

Pan, Junwu. Toward a New Framework for Peaceful Settlement of China's Territorial & Boundary Disputes. 2009. *(978-90-04-17428-3(1))* BRILL.

Shin, Leo K. The Making of the Chinese State: Ethnicity & Expansion on the Ming Borderlands. 2011. (ENG.). 270p. pap. 50.00 *(978-0-521-18989-7(6))* Cambridge Univ. Pr.

Standen, Naomi. Unbounded Loyalty: Frontier Crossing in Liao China. 2007. (Illus.). 279p. 55.00 *(978-0-8248-2983-4(2))* Univ. of Hawaii Pr.

CHINA—CHURCH HISTORY

Bays, Daniel H. A New History of Christianity in China. 2011. (Blackwell Guides to Global Christianity Ser.). (ENG., Illus.). 256p. pap. 39.95 *(978-1-4051-5955-5(3))*; 89.95 *(978-1-4051-5954-8(5))* Wiley, John & Sons, Inc. (Wiley-Blackwell).

Brockey, Liam Matthew. Journey to the East: The Jesuit Mission to China, 1579-1724. 2008. (Illus.). 512p. pap. 22.50 *(978-0-674-03036-7(2)*, Belknap Pr.) Harvard Univ. Pr.

Brother, Yun. Living Water, 1 vol. 2008. (ENG.). 240p. pap. 14.99 *(978-0-310-28554-0(2))* Zondervan.

Butcher, Beverly J. Chinese & Chinese American Ancestor Veneration in the Catholic Church, 635 A.D. to the Present. 2010. (CHI & ENG., Illus.). viii 447p. 129.95 *(978-0-7734-3624-4(3))* Mellen, Edwin Pr., The.

Cao, Nanlai. Constructing China's Jerusalem: Christians, Power, & Place in Contemporary Wenzhou. 2010. (Contemporary Issues in Asia & Pacific Ser.). (ENG., Illus.). 232p. 55.00 *(978-0-8047-7060-4(8))*; pap. 21.95 *(978-0-8047-7360-7(2))* Stanford Univ. Pr.

Charbonnier, Jean. Christians in China. 2006. 700p. pap. 24.95 *(978-0-89870-916-2(4))* Ignatius Pr.

Chu, Cindy Yik-Yi. The Diaries of the Maryknoll Sisters in Hong Kong, 1921-1966. 2007. (ENG., Illus.). 256p. 89.00 *(978-1-4039-7668-0(6))* Palgrave Macmillan.

Church Of Rock. Unveil the Chinese Official Church. 2009. pap. *(978-1-61584-214-8(4))* Independent Pub.

Clark, Anthony E. Chinas Saints: Catholic Martyrdom During the Qing (1644-1911) 2011. (Studies in Missionaries & Christianity in China Ser.). (ENG.). 286p. 75.00 *(978-1-61146-016-2(6))* Fairleigh Dickinson Univ. Pr.

Cook, Richard R. & Pao, David W., eds. After Imperialism: Christian Identity in China & the Global Evangelical Movement. 2012. (ENG.). 256p. pap. 35.00 **(978-0-7188-9257-9(7))** Lutherworth Pr., The GBR. Dist: Brown, David Bk. Co., The.

Crofts, Daniel W. Upstream Odyssey: An American in China, 1895-1944. 2008. (ENG., Illus.). 263p. pap. 29.95 *(978-1-59988-004-4(0)*, Missionary Experience in Asia, The) EastBridge.

Desideri, Ippolito. Mission to Tibet: The Extraordinary Eighteenth-Century Account of Father Ippolito Desideri S. J. Sweet, Michael, tr. from ITA. 2010. (ENG., Illus.). 832p. pap. 34.95 *(978-0-86171-676-0(C))* Wisdom Pubns.

Falkenstine, Mike. The Chinese Puzzle: Putting the Pieces Together for a Deeper Understanding of China & Her Church. 2008. pap. 13.99 *(978-1-60647-143-2(0))* Xulon Pr., Inc.

Guillen-Nuñez, Cesar. Macao's Church of Saint Paul: A Glimmer of the Baroque in China. 2008. (ENG., Illus.). 196p. (gr. 17). 45.00 *(978-962-209-922-7(X))* Hong Kong Univ. Pr. HKG. Dist: Columbia Univ. Pr.

Hamrin, Carol Lee & Bieler, Stacey, eds. Salt & Light, Three Volume Set: More Lives of Faith That Shaped Modern China. 2011. (Studies in Chinese Christianity: Ser.). 782p. pap. 80.00 **(978-1-61097-690-9(8)**, Pickwick Pubns.) Wipf & Stock Pubs.

—Salt & Light, Volume 2: More Lives of Faith That Shaped Modern China. 2010. (Studies in Chinese Christianity Ser.). 252p. pap. 28.00 *(978-1-60608-955-2(2)*, Pickwick Pubns.) Wipf & Stock Pubs.

Hamrin, Carol Lee & Bieler, Stacey, eds. Salt & Light, Volume 3: More Lives of Faith That Shaped Modern China. 2011. (Studies in Chinese Christianity: Ser.). 278p. pap. 31.00 **(978-1-61097-158-4(2)**, Pickwick Pubns.) Wipf & Stock Pubs.

Hattaway, Paul & Yun, Brother. Yun: The Illustrated Story of the Heavenly Man. 2006. (Illus.). 128p. pap. 11.99 *(978-0-8254-6128-6(6)*, Monarch Bks.) Lion Hudson PLC GBR. Dist: Kregel Pubns.

Ho Dmin, Mdiv. The Dragon & the Cross. 2009. 260p. pap. 16.99 *(978-1-60791-259-0(7))* Xulon Pr., Inc.

Hogan, Brian Patrick. There's a Sheep in my Bathtub: Birth of a Church Planting Movement in Mongolia. 2007. (ENG., Illus.). 272p. pap. 15.95 *(978-0-9799056-0-5(5))* Asteroidea Bks.

Keating, John Craig William. A Protestant Church in Communist China: Moore Memorial Church Shanghai, 1949-1989. 2012. (ENG.). 330p. 85.00 **(978-1-61146-090-2(5))** Lehigh Univ. Pr.

Leatherwood, Rick. Mongolia & the Christ. 2006. *(978-0-87808-368-8(5))* Carey, William Library Pubs.

Leung, Beatrice. Sino-Vatican Relations: Problems in Conflicting Authority, 1976-1986. 2009. (LSE Monographs in International Studies). (ENG.). 440p. pap. 57.00 *(978-0-521-12256-6(2))* Cambridge Univ. Pr.

Lutz, Jessie G. Pioneer Chinese Christian Women: Gender, Christianity, & Social Mobility. 2010. (ENG.). 1p. 85.00 *(978-1-61146-061-2(1))* Lehigh Univ. Pr.

Lutz, Jessie Gregory. Pioneer Chinese Christian Women: Gender, Christianity, & Social Mobility. 2010. (Illus.). 444p. 85.00 *(978-0-9801496-8-5(1))* Lehigh Univ. Pr.

Mariani, Paul P. Church Militant: Bishop Kung & Catholic Resistance in Communist Shanghai. 2011. (ENG., Illus.). 310p. 39.95 *(978-0-674-06153-8(5))* Harvard Univ. Pr.

Mather, Richard B. William Arnot Mather, American Missionary to China & Richard Burroughs Mather, Professor of Chinese: The Biography & Autobiography of a Father & a Son. 2010. (Illus.). xiv, 61p. 89.95 *(978-0-7734-1314-6(6))* Mellen, Edwin Pr., The.

Menegon, Eugenio. Ancestors, Virgins, & Friars: Christianity As a Local Religion in Late Imperial China. 2010. (Harvard-Yenching Institute Monograph Ser.: 69). (Illus.). 450p. 49.95 *(978-0-674-03596-6(8))* Harvard Univ., Asia Ctr.

Moule, A. C. Christians in China. 2010. pap. 60.40 *(978-1-61143-605-1(2))* Gorgias Pr., LLC.

Pavey, Stephen. Theologies of Power & Crisis: Envisioning / Embodying Christianity in Hong Kong. 2011. (American Society of Missiology Monograph Ser.). 148p. pap. 18.00 **(978-1-60899-513-4(5)**, Pickwick Pubns.) Wipf & Stock Pubs.

Rule, Paul, ed. The Church in China. 2010. (Interface Ser.). (ENG.). 128p. (C). pap. 20.00 **(978-1-921511-96-7(6))** ATF Theology AUS. Dist: Brown, David Bk. Co., The.

Selles, Kurt D. A New Way of Belonging: Covenant Theology, China, & the Christian Reformed Church, 1921-1951. 2010. pap. 28.00 *(978-0-8028-6662-2(X))* Eerdmans, William B. Publishing Co.

Wang, Aiming. Church in China: Faith, Ethics, Structure: The Heritage of the Reformation for the Future of the Church in China. 2009. 590p. pap. *(978-3-03911-814-4(5))* Lang, Peter.

Wickeri, Philip L. Reconstructing Christianity in China: K. H. Ting & the Chinese Church. 2007. (American Society of Missiology Ser.). (Illus.). 516p. per. 50.00 *(978-1-57075-751-8(8))* Orbis Bks.

Wickeri, Philip L. Seeking the Common Ground: Protestant Christianity the Three-Self Movement, & China's United Front. 2011. 384p. pap. 46.00 **(978-1-61097-529-2(4)**, Wipf and Stock) Wipf & Stock Pubs.

Wu, Xiaoxin, ed. Christianity in China: A Scholars' Guide to Resources in the Libraries & Archives of the United States. 2nd ed. 2006. (East Gate Book Ser.). 1800p. 249.95 *(978-1-56324-337-0(7)*, East Gate Bk.) Sharpe, M.E. Inc.

Xin, Yalin. Inside China's House Church Networke Postmodern City: The Word of Life Movement & Its Renewing Dynamic. 2009. (ENG., Illus.). 212p. 42.00 *(978-0-9819582-2-4(2))* Emeth Pr.

Ying-Ki, Ignatius & O'Toole, Barry, trs. The Nestorian Tablet at Sianfu. 2010. pap. 18.88 *(978-1-61143-584-9(6))* Gorgias Pr., LLC.

Yiwu, Liao. God Is Red: The Secret Story of How Christianity Survived & Flourished in Communist China. (ENG.). 256p. 2012. pap. 14.99 **(978-0-06-207847-6(X))** 2011. 25.99 *(978-0-06-207846-9(1))* HarperCollins Pubs. (HarperOne).

Yun, Brother & Hattaway, Paul. The Heavenly Man: The Remarkable True Story of Chinese Christian Brother Yun. 2009. (Illus.). 351p. 19.95 *(978-1-59856-392-4(0))* Hendrickson Pubs. Marketing, LLC.

CHINA—CIVILIZATION

Baker, Hugh. Ancestral Images: A Hong Kong Collection. 2011. (Royal Asiatic Society Hong Kong Studies Ser.). (ENG., Illus.). 404p. (gr. 17). 50.00 *(978-988-8083-09-1(0))* Hong Kong Univ. Pr. HKG. Dist: Columbia Univ. Pr.

Bao, Yuheng. A Handbook of Chinese Art, Crafts, & Culture. 2009. (Illus.). 436p. 129.95 *(978-0-7734-4897-1(7))* Mellen, Edwin Pr., The.

Barondes, R. De Rohan. Chin: Lore, Legend & Lyrics. 2011. 286p. 48.95 **(978-1-258-07291-9(2))** Literary Licensing, LLC.

Barr, Michael. Who's Afraid of China? 2011. (Asian Arguments Ser.). (ENG.). 144p. 125.95 *(978-1-84813-589-5(0))*; pap. 29.95 *(978-1-84813-590-1(4))* Zed Bks., Ltd. GBR. Dist: Macmillan.

Beck, Sanderson. China, Korea & Japan to 1800. 2007. xi, 667p. *(978-0-9792532-0-1(9))* World Peace Communications.

Bellezza, John Vincent. Zhang Zhung: Foundations of Civilization in Tibet: A Historical & Ethnoarchaeological Study of the Monuments, Rock Art, Texts, & Oral Tradition of the Ancient Tibetan Upland. 2008. (Denkschriften der Phil.-Hist. Klasse Ser.). (ENG & CHI., Illus.). 842p. (C). pap. 194.00 *(978-3-7001-6046-5(1))* Austrian Academy of Sciences Press AUT. Dist: Brown, David Bk. Co., The.

Bieler, Stacey. 'Patriots' Or 'Traitors'? A History of American-Educated Chinese Students. 2009. (ENG.). 544p. pap. 42.95 *(978-0-7656-1187-1(2)*, East Gate Bk.) Sharpe, M.E. Inc.

Brown, Miranda & Schirokauer, Conrad. A Brief History of Chinese Civilization. 4th ed. 2012. (ENG.). 448p. (C). pap. 111.95 **(978-0-495-91323-8(5))** Wadsworth.

Cao, Tianyu, et al. Culture & Social Transformations in Reform ERA China. 2010. 450p. *(978-90-04-17516-7(4))* BRILL.

Carter, Alden R. China: From the First Chinese to the Olympics. 2008. 216p. pap. 26.95 *(978-1-60145-455-3(4))* Booklocker.com, Inc.

Chan, Thomas & Moser v. Filseck, Karin. Perceptions & Images of China. Assmann, Heinz-Dieter, ed. 2008. 298p. pap. 49.00 *(978-3-8329-3459-0(6))* Nomos Verlagsgesellschaft DEU. Dist: International Specialized Bk. Services.

Chang, Kwang-Chih. Kao Gu Xue Zhuan Ti Liu Jiang. 2010. (CHI., Illus.). *(978-7-108-03330-7(5))* SDX Joint Publishing, Co.

Chee-beng, Tan. Southern Fujian: Reproduction of Traditions in Post-Mao China. Chee-Beng, Tan, ed. 2006. (ENG., Illus.). 300p. (gr. 17). 42.00 *(978-962-996-233-3(0))* Chinese Univ. of Hong Kong, The HKG. Dist: Columbia Univ. Pr.

Chen, Lai. Tradition & Modernity: A Humanist View. Ryden, E., tr. from CHI. 2009. (Brill's Humanities in China Library). x, 386p. *(978-90-04-16578-6(9))* BRILL.

Chen, Pingyuan. Dang Dai Zhongguo Ren Wen Guan Cha. 2010. (CHI.). *(978-7-301-16490-7(4))* Beijing University Pr.

Chey, Ong Siew. China Condensed: 5000 Years of History & Culture, 1 vol. 2009. (ENG.). 176p. pap. 12.00 *(978-981-261-619-7(5))* Marshall Cavendish International (Asia) Private Ltd. SGP. Dist: Marshall Cavendish Corp.

Chow, Kai-wing. Beyond the May Fourth Paradigm: In Search of Chinese Modernity. Hon/Price/Chow/Ip, ed. 2008. (ENG., Illus.). 352p. 83.99 *(978-0-7391-1122-2(1))* Lexington Bks.

—Publishing, Culture, & Power in Early Modern China. 2007. (ENG., Illus.). 416p. per. 24.95 *(978-0-8047-3368-7(6))* Stanford Univ. Pr.

Clunas, Craig. Empire of Great Brightness: Visual & Material Cultures of Ming China, 1368-1644. 2012. (ENG., Illus.). 256p. pap. 55.00 **(978-1-86189-360-4(4))** Reaktion Bks., Ltd. GBR. Dist: Chicago Distribution Ctr.

—Empire of Great Brightness: Visual & Material Cultures of Ming China, 1368-1644. 2007. (Illus.). 288p. 61.00 *(978-0-8248-3149-3(7))* Univ. of Hawaii Pr.

Cochran, Sherman & Pickowicz, Paul G. China on the Margins. 2010. (ENG.). 336p. 50.00 *(978-1-933947-16-7(0))*; pap. 25.00 *(978-1-933947-46-4(2))* Cornell Univ. East Asia Program.

Cornaby, W. Arthur. China under the Search-Light. 2010. (Cambridge Library Collection - Travel & Exploration Ser.). 268p. pap. 23.99 *(978-1-108-01411-3(9))* Cambridge Univ. Pr.

Cram101 Textbook Reviews Staff. Outlines & Highlights for Cambridge Illustrated History of China by Patricia Buckley Ebrey, Isbn: 9780521669917. 2009. (Illus.). 90p. pap. 27.95 *(978-1-4288-9602-4(3))* Cram101 Inc.

Damm, Jens & Steen, Andreas, eds. Postmodern China. 2011. (ENG., Illus.). 176p. pap. 44.95 *(978-3-8258-1705-3(9))* Lit Verlag DEU. Dist: Transaction Pubs.

Davis, Edward L. Encyclopedia of Contemporary Chinese Culture. 2008. XXXII, 800p. pap. 80.00 *(978-0-415-77716-2(X))* Routledge.

De Bary, William Theodore. Self & Society in Ming Thought. 2008. 576p. pap. 57.00 *(978-1-59740-593-5(0))* ACLS Humanities E-Book.

De Mente, Boye Lafayette. The Chinese Mind: Understanding Traditional Chinese Beliefs & Their Influence on Contemporary Culture. 2009. (ENG.). 192p. pap. 16.95 *(978-0-8048-4011-8(3))* Tuttle Publishing.

Dickinson, G. Lowes. An Essay on the Civilisations of India, China & Japan. 2010. (ENG., Illus.). 86p. 80.00 *(978-0-415-58533-0(3))* Routledge.

Dickinson, Goldsworthy Lowes. An Essay on the Civilisations of India, China & Japan. 2009. (ENG.). 87p. pap. 18.75 *(978-1-116-96968-9(8))*; pap. 18.75 *(978-1-116-96967-2(X))* BiblioBazaar.

—An essay on the civilisations of India, China & Japan. 2009. (ENG.). 87p. pap. 18.99 *(978-1-116-96969-6(6))*; pap. 16.99 *(978-1-116-96970-2(X))* BiblioBazaar. (BiblioLife).

Egan, Ronald. The Problem of Beauty: Aesthetic Thought & Pursuits in Northern Song Dynasty China. 2006. (Harvard East Asian Monographs: 271). (Illus.). 382p. 49.95 *(978-0-674-02264-5(5))* Harvard Univ., Asia Ctr.

Fallows, Deborah. Dreaming in Chinese: Mandarin Lessons in Life, Love, & Language. (ENG.). 208p. 2011. pap. 13.00 *(978-0-8027-7914-4(X))* 2010. (Illus.). 22.00 *(978-0-8027-7913-7(1))* Walker & Co.

Fang, Xiangshu. The Rise of Ancient Chin. 2011. 328p. pap. **(978-3-8443-2282-8(5))** Lambert Academic Publishing.

Fenby, Jonathan. The Seventy Wonders of China. 2007. (ENG., Illus.). 304p. 40.00 *(978-0-500-25137-9(1))* Thames & Hudson.

Fiero, Gloria. The Humanistic Tradition Bk. 2: Medieval Europe & the World Beyond. 6th ed. 2010. (ENG., Illus.). 192p. (C). pap. 45.67 *(978-0-07-734618-8(1)* 0077346181) McGraw-Hill Cos., The.

Fitzgerald, C. P. Ancient China. 2007. (ENG.). 415p. per. 16.00 *(978-1-59687-302-5(7))* IBks., Inc.

Fogel, Joshua A., ed. Crossing the Yellow Sea: Sino-Japanese Cultural Contacts, 1600-1950. 2007. 346p. pap. 29.95 *(978-1-891936-90-6(5)*, Signature Bks.) EastBridge.

Fu, Hua. Beijing Xicheng Wen Hua Shi. 2007. (CHI., Illus.). 8p. *(978-7-5402-1923-9(8))* Beijing Yanshan Pr.

Fürlus, Eckhard, ed. Varianto logy 3. 2008. (ENG., Illus.). 476p. pap. 98.00 *(978-3-86560-366-1(1))* Verlag der Buchhandlung Walther Konig DEU. Dist: D.A.P./Distributed Art Pubs.

Giles, Herbert A. The Civilization of China. 2007. (ENG.). 128p. per. *(978-1-4065-4457-2(4))* Dodo Pr.

Giles, Herbert Allen. The Civilization of China. 2009. (ENG.). 257p. pap. 21.99 *(978-1-116-83694-3(7))*; pap. 23.99 *(978-1-116-83693-6(9))* BiblioBazaar. (BiblioLife).

Gong, Haomin. Uneven Modernity: Literature, Film & Intellectual Discourse in Postsocialist China. 2012. (Illus.). 224p. 47.00 **(978-0-8248-3531-6(X))** Univ. of Hawaii Pr.

Goodrich, L. Carrington. A Short History of the Chinese People. 2007. (ENG.). 332p. per. *(978-1-4067-6976-0(2))* Read Bks.
Han, Zechun. Zhongguo Xian Dai Wen Hua Fa Zhan Lun Gang. 2010. (CHI.). *(978-7-5087-2700-4(2))* China Society Pr.
He, Xirong. Cultural Tradition & Social Progress. 2009. *(978-1-56518-266-0(9))* Council for Research in Values & Philosophy.
Henderson, John B. The Development & Decline of Chinese Cosmology. 2011. (ENG & CHI., Illus.). 292p. pap. 29.99 *(978-0-9823212-4-9(4))* Windstone Press.
Herbert A. Giles, LL.D., MA. The Civilization of China. 2006. (ENG.). 148p. pap. 18.99 *(978-1-4264-0094-0(2))*; 138p. pap. 13.99 *(978-1-4264-0223-4(6))* BiblioBazaar.
Hessler, Peter. Oracle Bones: A Journey Through Time in China. 2007. (P. S. Ser.). (ENG., Illus.). 528p. pap. 15.99 *(978-0-06-082659-8(2),* HarperPerennial) HarperCollins Pubs.
Ho, Clara Wing-chung. Windows on the Chinese World: Reflections by Five Historians. 2008. (AsiaWorld Ser.). (ENG., Illus.). 156p. 52.50 *(978-0-7391-2769-8(1))* Lexington Bks.
Hua, Yu. China in Ten Words. Barr, Allan H., tr. from CHI. 2011. (ENG.). 240p. 25.95 *(978-0-307-37935-1(3),* Pantheon) Knopf Doubleday Publishing Group.
Huang, Chun-chieh. Taiwan in Transformation, 1895-2005: The Challenge of a New Democracy to an Old Civilization. 2007. (ENG.). 260p. (gr. 11). pap. 29.95 *(978-1-4128-0727-2(1))* Transaction Pubs.
Huang, Pei. Reorienting the Manchus. 2011. (Illus.). 376p. 65.00 ***(978-1-933947-22-8(5))***; (ENG., xxiv, 374p. 45.00 ***(978-1-933947-52-5(7))*** Cornell Univ. East Asia Program.
Ingham, Michael. Hong Kong: A Cultural History. 2007. (Cityscapes Ser.). (ENG., Illus.). 256p. 75.00 *(978-0-19-531496-0(4))* Oxford Univ. Pr., Inc.
Jami, Catherine. The Emperor's New Mathematics: Western Learning & Imperial Authority During the Kangxi Reign (1662-1722) 2012. (ENG., Illus.). 464p. 135.00 ***(978-0-19-960140-0(2))*** Oxford Univ. Pr., Inc.
Jankowiak, William R. Sex, Death, & Hierarchy in a Chinese City: An Anthropological Account. 2nd ed. 368p. pap. 27.50 *(978-0-231-13183-4(6))* Columbia Univ. Pr.
Jankowiak, William R., et al. Sex & World Peace. 2nd ed. 2012. (ENG.). 304p. (gr. 17). 26.50 *(978-0-231-13182-7(8))* Columbia Univ. Pr.
Johansson, Perry. Saluting the Yellow Emperor: A Case of Swedish Sinography. 2012. (ENG.). VIII, 244p. ***(978-90-04-22097-3(6))*** BRILL.
Johnston, Reginald Fleming. Confucianism & Modern China. 2008. (Illus.). 208p. per. 22.95 *(978-0-9680459-4-7(4))* Soul Care Publishing CAN. Dist: Ingram Bk. Co.
Katzenstein, Peter J., ed. Sinicization & the Rise of China. 2012. (ENG., Illus.). 312p. (C). 135.00 ***(978-0-415-80953-5(0))***; pap. 29.95 ***(978-0-415-80952-8(5))*** Routledge.
Khoo, James C. M. Art & Archaeology of Funan: Pre-Khmer Kingdom of the Lower Mekong Valley. 2006. (ENG., Illus.). 45.00 *(978-974-524-035-3(4))* Orchid Pr. THA. Dist: National Bk. Network.
Kuiper, Kathleen, ed. The Culture of China. 2010. (Understanding China Ser.). (Illus.). 304p. (YA). 106.00 *(978-1-61530-186-7(0))*; lib. bdg. 53.00 *(978-1-61530-140-9(2))* Rosen Publishing Group, Inc., The.
Lai, Eric C. The Music of Chou Wen-Chung. 2009. (Illus.). 174p. 99.95 *(978-0-7546-6500-7(3))* Ashgate Publishing Co.
Law, Wing Sang. Collaborative Colonial Power: The Making of the Hong Kong Chinese. 2009. (Hong Kong Culture & Society Ser.). (ENG.). 276p. (gr. 17). 50.00 *(978-962-209-929-6(7))*; pap. 28.00 *(978-962-209-930-2(0))* Hong Kong Univ. Pr. HKG. Dist: Columbia Univ. Pr.
Leese, Daniel, ed. Brill's Encyclopedia of China: Edited by Daniel Leese. 2008. (Handbook of Oriental Studies. Section 4 China Ser.). (Illus.). (C). *(978-90-04-16863-3(X))* BRILL.
Lehner, Georg. China in European Encyclopedias, 1700-1850. 2011. 387p. *(978-90-04-20150-7(5))* BRILL.
Levenson, Joseph R. Confucian China & Its Modern Fate: A Trilogy. 2008. 644p. pap. 22.00 *(978-1-59740-592-8(2))* ACLS Humanities E-Book.
—Confucian China & its Modern Fate Vol. 14: The Problem of Intellectual Continuity, 3 vols. 2008. 248p. 190.00 *(978-0-415-36158-3(3))* Routledge.
Levenson, Joseph R. Liang Ch'i Ch'ao & the Mind of Modern Chin. 2011. 272p. 47.95 ***(978-1-258-02837-4(9))*** Literary Licensing, LLC.
Li, Kay. Bernard Shaw & China: Cross-Cultural Encounters. Dietrich, Richard F., ed. 2007. (Florida Bernard Shaw Ser.). (ENG., Illus.). 320p. 59.95 *(978-0-8130-3085-2(4))* Univ. Pr. of Florida.
Li, Shulan. Jing Wei Wen Hua Shi Lun. 2009. (CHI., Illus.). *(978-7-81119-325-1(6))* Capital Normal Univ. Pr.
Li, Xinwei. Development of Social Complexity in the Liaoxi Area, Northeast China. 2008. (Bar S Ser.). (Illus.). viii, 155p. (C). pap. 87.50 *(978-1-4073-0307-9(4))* British Archaeological Reports Ltd. GBR. Dist: Brown, David Bk. Co., The.
Liang, Shuming. Les Idées Maîtresses de la Culture Chinoise. 2010. (FRE.). 421p. *(978-2-204-09060-5(3))* Editions du Cerf.
Lin, Man-Houng. China Upside Down: Currency, Society, & Ideologies, 1808-1856. 2007. (Harvard East Asian Monographs: 270). (Illus.). 450p. 49.95 *(978-0-674-02268-3(8))* Harvard Univ., Asia Ctr.
Lin, Yi-Chieh Jessica. Mcounterfeiting Inc: China & the Rise of Counterfeit Goods. 2011. (Routledge Series for Creative Teaching & Learning Ser.). (ENG., Illus.). 104p. 125.00 *(978-0-415-88302-3(4))*; pap. 19.95 *(978-0-415-88303-0(2))* Routledge.
Liu, Li. The Chinese Neolithic: Trajectories to Early States. 2007. (New Studies in Archaeology). (ENG.). 332p. pap. 72.00 *(978-0-521-01064-1(0))* Cambridge Univ. Pr.
Lo, Kwai-Cheung. Excess & Masculinity in Asian Cultural Productions. 2011. 251p. pap. 24.95 ***(978-1-4384-3208-3(9)***, Suny Pr.) State Univ. of New York Pr.
Louie, Kam, ed. The Cambridge Companion to Modern Chinese Culture. 2008. (Cambridge Companions to Culture Ser.). (ENG., Illus.). 424p. 81.00 *(978-0-521-86322-3(8))*; pap. 29.99 *(978-0-521-68190-2(1))* Cambridge Univ. Pr.
—Hong Kong Culture: Word & Image. 2010. (ENG., Illus.). 324p. (gr. 17). pap. 30.00 *(978-988-8028-41-2(3))* Hong Kong Univ. Pr. HKG. Dist: Columbia Univ. Pr.
Lu, Jie, ed. China's Literary & Cultural Scenes at the Turn of the 21st Century. 2008. (ENG., Illus.). 304p. 140.00 *(978-0-415-42078-5(4))* Routledge.
Luo, Shen. Zhuan Zhi Wen Hua Xia de Zhongguo. 2009. ("Wen Hua Qing Li" Xi Lie Ser.: Vol. 26). (CHI.). 338p. *(978-7-932138-82-5(X))* Mirror Bks. USA.
Lupke, Christopher. The Cultural State of Contemporary Taiwan. 2009. (ENG., Illus.). 222p. pap. 14.00 *(978-0-8223-6708-6(4))* Duke Univ. Pr.
Mackinnon, Alex & Powell, Barnaby. China Counting: How the West Was Lost. 2009. (ENG., Illus.). 272p. 49.00 *(978-0-230-23403-1(8))* Palgrave Macmillan.
Mathieu, Christine & Ho, Cindy, eds. Ancestral Realms of the Naxi: Quentin Roosevelt's China. 2011. (ENG., Illus.). 200p. 70.00 *(978-3-89790-343-2(1))* Arnoldsche Art Pubs. DEU. Dist: Antique Collectors' Club.
Meng, Fanhua. The Phenomenon of Chinese Culture at the Turn of the 21st Century. 2011. 344p. 178.00 *(978-981-4332-35-4(6),* Silkroad Pr.) Enrich Professional Publishing (S)., Ltd. SGP. Dist: Independent Pubs. Group.
Mittler, Barbara. A Continuous Revolution: Making Sense of Cultural Revolution Culture. 2012. (Harvard East Asian Monographs: 343). (ENG., Illus.). 500p. 59.95 ***(978-0-674-06581-9(6))*** Harvard Univ., Asia Ctr.
Mungello, David E. The Great Encounter of China & the West, 1500-1800. 3rd ed. 2009. (Critical Issues in World & International History Ser.). (ENG., Illus.). 184p. 79.00 *(978-0-7425-5797-0(9))*; pap. 24.95 *(978-0-7425-5798-7(7))* Rowman & Littlefield Publishers, Inc.
Nahuelpan, Elicura Chihuailaf. Message to Chileans. 2009. 260p. pap. 28.00 *(978-1-4251-8650-0(5))* Trafford Publishing.
Nietupski, Paul Kocot. Labrang Monastery: A Tibetan Buddhist Community on the Inner Asian Borderlands, 1709-1958. (Illus.). 2011. xxxi, 273p. E-Book *(978-0-7391-6445-7(7))* 2010. (ENG., 306p. 80.00 *(978-0-7391-6443-3(0))* Lexington Bks.
Parfitt, Troy. Why China Will Never Rule the World: Travels in the Two Chinas. 2011. (CHI & ENG.). 416p. pap. 20.95 *(978-0-9868035-0-5(2))* Western Hemisphere Pr. CAN. Dist: AtlasBooks Distribution.
Pierre, Ostrowski. It's All Chinese to Me: An Illustrated Overview of Culture & Etiquette in China. 2008. (Illus.). 208p. pap. 17.95 *(978-0-9784409-4-7(3))* All Out Pr. CAN. Dist: Independent Pubs. Group.
Polizzi, Kristina. Dragons Behind Glasses. 2008. 92p. pap. *(978-3-8364-7108-4(6))* VDM Verlag Dr. Mueller e.K.
Pong, David. Encyclopedia of Modern China. 2009. *(978-0-684-31570-6(X))*; *(978-0-684-31569-0(6))*; *(978-0-684-31567-6(X))*; *(978-0-684-31568-3(8))*; 568.00 *(978-0-684-31566-9(1))* Cengage Gale. (Charles Scribner's Sons).
Qiu, Zhengbao, et al. Long Nan Baima Ren Min Su Wen Hua Yan Jiu: Longnan Baimaren Minzu Wenhua Yanjiu, 2 vols. 2009. (CHI., Illus.). *(978-7-226-03854-3(4))* Gansu People's Publishing Hse.
Qu, Jinliang. Zhongguo Hai Yang Wen Hua Guan de Chong Jian: Zhongguo Haiyang Wenhuaguan de Chongjian. 2009. (CHI.). *(978-7-5004-8200-0(0))* China Social Sciences Pr.
Reed, Marcia & Dematte, Paola, eds. China on Paper: European & Chinese Works from the Late Sixteenth to the Early Nineteenth Century. 2011. (ENG., Illus.). 248p. pap. 30.00 *(978-1-60606-068-1(6))* Getty Pubns.
Reed, Marcia & Demattè, Paola, eds. China on Paper: European & Chinese Works from the Late Sixteenth to the Early Nineteenth Century. 2007. (Illus.). 280p. 45.00 *(978-0-89236-869-3(1))* Oxford Univ. Pr., Inc.
Roberts, J. A. G. Life in Early China. 2008. (ENG.). 96p. (YA). (gr. 7). pap. 11.95 *(978-0-7509-4729-9(2))* History Pr. Ltd., The GBR. Dist: Independent Pubs. Group.
Rojas, Carlos. Rethinking Chinese Popular Culture: Cannibalizations of the Canon. Chow, Eileen, ed. 2009. (Routledge Contemporary China Ser.). (ENG.). 304p. (C). 160.00 *(978-0-415-46880-0(9))* Routledge.
Ropp, Paul. China in World History, 1 vol. 2010. (New Oxford World History Ser.). (ENG., Illus.). 208p. pap. 19.95 *(978-0-19-538195-5(5))* Oxford Univ. Pr., Inc.
Ruan, Wei. Zhong Wai Wen Ming Shi Wu Lun: 15 Lectures on Civilizations. 2008. (CHI.). *(978-7-301-13114-5(3))* Beijing University Pr.
Russell, Bertrand. The Problem of China. 2008. 220p. 27.99 *(978-0-554-24817-2(4))* 2006. (ENG.). 196p. pap. 19.99 *(978-1-4264-7458-3(X))* 2007. 218p. pap. 22.99 *(978-1-4264-7535-1(7))* BiblioBazaar.
—The Problem of China. 2008. 188p. pap. *(978-1-4099-0103-7(3))* Dodo Pr.
—The Problem of China. 2007. (ENG.). 152p. per. *(978-1-4068-4109-1(9))* Echo Library.
—The Problem of China. 2009. (ENG.). 204p. pap. 13.95 *(978-1-4385-1290-7(2),* Book Jungle) Standard Pubns., Inc.
Sa, Shana. Empress. 2009. (P. S. Ser.). (ENG., Illus.). 352p. pap. 14.99 *(978-0-06-182960-4(9),* HarperPerennial) HarperCollins Pubs.
Santangelo. Materials for an Anatomy of Personality in Late Imperial China. 2010. (Emotions & States of Mind in East Asia Ser.). 640p. *(978-90-04-17753-6(1))* BRILL.
Santangelo, Paolo, ed. Love, Hatred, & Other Passions: Questions & Themes on Emotions in Chinese Civilization. 2006. (CHI & ENG.). 424p. pap. *(978-90-04-15544-2(9))* BRILL.
Schaeffer, Kurtis R., et al. Sources of Tibetan Tradition. (Introduction to Asian Civilizations Ser.). 2013. (ENG., Illus.). 832p. (gr. 17). 120.00 *(978-0-231-13598-6(X))* 2013. (ENG., Illus.). 832p. (gr. 17). pap. 40.00 ***(978-0-231-13599-3(8))*** 2012. ***(978-0-231-50978-7(2))*** Columbia Univ. Pr.
Schafer, Edward H. The Vermilion Bird: T'Ang Images of the South. 2008. (ENG., Illus.). 392p. per. 50.00 *(978-1-891640-37-7(2))* Floating World Editions.
Schirokauer, Conrad & Brown, Miranda. A Brief Histroy of Chinese Civilisation. 2nd ed. 2006. (ENG.). 448p. (C). pap. 111.95 *(978-0-618-91506-4(0))* CENGAGE Learning.
Sen, Tansen & Mair, Victor H. Traditional China in Asian & World History. 2011. pap. ***(978-0-924304-65-1(0))*** Assn. for Asian Studies, Inc.
Shanghai Daily. Snapshots Lifestyl. 2010. 132p. pap. 16.95 *(978-1-60220-402-7(0))* BetterLink Pr., Inc.
Shelach, Gideon. Leadership Strategies, Economic Activity, & Interregional Interaction: Social Complexity in Northeast China. 2010. (Fundamental Issues in Archaeology Ser.). 278p. pap. 129.00 *(978-1-4419-3314-0(X),* 144193314X) Springer.
Sherman, Edward D. America Through the Eyes of China & India: Television, Identity, & Intercultural Communication in a Changing World. 2010. (ENG.). 184p. 80.00 *(978-0-8264-2270-5(5))*; pap. 24.95 *(978-0-8264-3092-2(9))* Continuum International Publishing Group, Ltd. GBR. Dist: National Bk. Network.
Shih, Chih-Yu. Civilization Nation & Modernity in East Asia. 2012. (Routledge Advances in Asia-Pacific Studies). (ENG., Illus.). 256p. (C). 155.00 ***(978-0-415-52426-1(1))*** Routledge.
Shih, Fang-Long, et al, eds. Re-Writing Culture in Taiwan. 2011. (ENG.). 234p. (C). pap. 44.95 ***(978-0-415-60293-8(9))*** Routledge.
Simcox, Edith Jemima. Primitive Civilizations: Or, Outlines of the History of Ownership in Archaic Communities. 2010. (Cambridge Library Collection - Women's Writing Ser.). 592p. pap. 43.00 *(978-1-108-02184-5(0))*; (ENG.). 566p. pap. 39.99 *(978-1-108-02185-2(9))* Cambridge Univ. Pr.
Smith, Richard J. Mapping China & Managing the World: Culture, Cartography & Cosmology in Late Imperial Times. 2012. (Asia's Transformations/Critical Asian Scholarship Ser.). (ENG., Illus.). 304p. (C). 150.00 *(978-0-415-68509-2(5))*; pap. 49.95 *(978-0-415-68510-8(9))* Routledge.
Stunkel, Kenneth R. Ideas & Art in Asian Civilizations: India, China, & Japan. 2011. (ENG., Illus.). 320p. (C). 99.95 *(978-0-7656-2540-3(7),* East Gate Bk.) Sharpe, M.E. Inc.
Su, Shuyang. A Reader on China. 2010. 174p. pap. 9.95 *(978-1-60220-901-5(4))* BetterLink Pr., Inc.
Sun, Weilin. Min Zhu Yu Ke Xue Wen Ji. 2009. (CHI., Illus.). 8p. *(978-7-5077-3277-1(0))* Xueyuan Press.
Tao, Zhijian. Drawing the Dragon: Western European Reinvention of China. 2009. (Illus.). 233p. pap. *(978-3-03911-812-0(9))* Lang, Peter.
Tarocco, Francesca. The Cultural Practices of Modern Chinese Buddhism. 2010. (ENG.). pap. 39.95 ***(978-0-415-59617-6(3))*** Routledge.
Temple, Robert. The Genius of China: 3,000 Years of Science, Discovery, & Invention. 2007. (Illus.). 288p. pap. 29.95 *(978-1-59477-217-7(7))* Inner Traditions International, Ltd.
Templeman, David, ed. New views of Tibetan Culture. 2010. 196p. pap. 32.95 *(978-1-876924-77-5(2),* Monash Univ. Pr.) Monash Univ. Publishing AUS. Dist: International Specialized Bk. Services.
Thibourney, Arion. Crazy English. 2010. 108p. pap. *(978-3-8383-0474-8(8))* Lambert Academic Publishing.
Thompson, Sandy. One in a Billion: Xploring the New World of China. 2006. (ENG., Illus.). 144p. 8.99 *(978-1-57687-296-3(3),* powerHouse Bks.) powerHouse Cultural Entertainment, Inc.
Tian, Xiaofei. Visionary Journeys: Travel Writings from Early Medieval & Nineteenth-Century China. 2012. (Harvard-Yenching Institute Monograph Ser.: 78). (ENG.). 398p. 39.95 *(978-0-674-06252-8(3))* Harvard Univ., Asia Ctr.
Tong, Junie Therese. Finance & Society in 21st Century China: Chinese Culture Versus Western Markets. 2011. (Transformation & Innovation Ser.). (Illus.). 234p. 114.95 *(978-1-4094-0129-2(4),* Gower Publishing Co., Ltd.) Ashgate Publishing, Ltd. GBR. Dist: Ashgate Publishing Co.
University of Pittsburgh Chinese Studies Faculty Staff & University of Pittsburgh Chinese Studies Faculty, eds. Contemporary Chinese Societies: Continuity & Change, CD for Windows and Macintosh. 2nd ed. 2007. (Edinburgh Edition of the Waverley Novels Ser.). (ENG.). (gr. 17). 51.50 *(978-0-231-13982-3(9))* Columbia Univ. Pr.
Vukovich, Daniel, ed. China & Orientalism: Western Knowledge Production & the P. R. C. 2011. (Postcolonial Politics Ser.). (ENG.). 208p. (C). 130.00 *(978-0-415-59220-8(8))* Routledge.
Wagner, Donald B. Science & Civilisation in China Vol. 5, Pt. 11: Chemistry & Chemical Technology Ferrous Metallurgy. 2008. (Science & Civilisation in China Ser.). (ENG., Illus.). 512p. 195.00 *(978-0-521-87566-0(8))* Cambridge Univ. Pr.
Wang. A Billion Voices: Languages & Peoples of China. 2011. 52.00 *(978-981-4287-72-2(5))* World Scientific Publishing Co., Inc.
Wang, Jun & Li, Shaojun. The Rhetoric & Reality of Culture-Led Urban Regeneration: A Comparison of Beijing & Shanghai, China. 2011. (China in the 21st Century Ser.). 60p. pap. 43.00 *(978-1-61668-683-3(9))* Nova Science Pubs., Inc.
Wang, Luxiang. Wo Men de Chuan Tong: Wang Luxiang Wen Hua Fang Tan Lu. 2009. (CHI., Illus.). 222p. *(978-7-5057-2603-1(X))* China Friendship Publishing Hse.
Wang, Zhongwen. Zhongguo Wen Hua Shi. 2010. (CHI., Illus.). 412p. *(978-986-236-222-8(7))* New Wun Ching Developmental Publishing Co., Ltd.
Wasserstrom, Jeffrey N. China's Brave New World: And Other Tales for Global Times. 2007. (Illus.). 210p. 55.00 *(978-0-253-34889-0(7))* Indiana Univ. Pr.
—China's Brave New World: — and Other Tales for Global Times. 2007. (ENG., Illus.). 240p. pap. 21.95 *(978-0-253-21908-4(6),* 0253219086) Indiana Univ. Pr.
Weiming, Tu. Global Significance of Concrete Humanity: Essays on the Confucian Discourse in Cultural China. 2010. 411p. 57.50 *(978-81-215-1220-6(4))* Munshiram Manoharial Pubs. Private, Ltd. IND. Dist: Coronet Bks.
Wheeler, Norton. The Role of American NGOs in China's Modernization: Invited Influence. 2012. (Asia's Transformations Ser.). (ENG., Illus.). 240p. (C). 135.00 ***(978-0-415-50657-1(3))*** Routledge.
Williams, S. Wells. The Middle Kingdom: A Survey of the Geography, Government, Literature, Social Life, Arts & History of the Chinese Empire & Its in Habitants, 2 vols. 2006. (Kegan Paul China Library). (Illus.). 892p. 500.00 *(978-0-7103-1167-2(2))* Taylor & Francis Group.
Wong, Sin Kiong. Confucianism, Chinese History & Society. 2012. 300p. pap. 48.00 ***(978-981-4374-47-7(4))*** World Scientific Publishing Co., Inc.
Wu, Guang. China: Has the Last Opportunity Passed By?! 2009. (China in the 21st Century Ser.). xiii, 88p. pap. 43.00 *(978-1-60741-538-1(0))* Nova Science Pubs., Inc.
Wu, Xiaogang. An Introduction to Chinese Sociology. 2012. (ENG., Illus.). 224p. (C). 150.00 *(978-0-415-58916-1(9))*; pap. 45.95 *(978-0-415-58917-8(7))* Routledge.
Xia, Xingzhen. Liu Shi Nian Guo Shi Ji Yao. 2009. (CHI.). *(978-7-5438-6027-8(9))* Hunan Publishing Hse.
Xu, Zhuoyun. Rivers in Time: A Cultural History of China. 2012. 576p. ***(978-0-231-52818-4(3))*** Columbia Univ. Pr.
Xu, Zhuoyun & Hsu, Cho-Yun. China: A New Cultural History. Baker, Timothy D. & Duke, Michael S., trs. from CHI. 2012. (Masters of Chinese Studies). (ENG., Illus.). 632p. (gr. 17). 120.00 ***(978-0-231-15920-3(X))*** Columbia Univ. Pr.
Xu, Zhuoyun & Hsu, Cho-yun. China: A New Cultural History. Baker, Timothy D. & Duke, Michael S., trs. from CHI. 2012. (Masters of Chinese Studies). (ENG., Illus.). 632p. (gr. 17). pap. 40.00 ***(978-0-231-15921-0(8))*** Columbia Univ. Pr.
Yajun, Zhang. A Kaleidoscope of Chinese Culture. 2008. (CHI.). 256p. pap. 19.95 *(978-7-80200-400-9(4))* Sinolingua CHN. Dist: China Bks. & Periodicals, Inc.
Yanaka, Shinichi. Seichi No Shiso Bunka No Tenkai to Kodai Chugoku No Keisei. 2008. (Illus.). 10p. *(978-4-7629-2575-7(6))* Kyuko Shoin.
Yang, Chi-Ming. Performing China: Virtue, Commerce, & Orientalism in Eighteenth-Century England, 1660-1760. 2011. (ENG., Illus.). 288p. (gr. 17). 70.00 *(978-1-4214-0216-1(5))* Johns Hopkins Univ. Pr.
Yang, Mayfair Mei-Hui. Chinese Religiosities: Afflictions of Modernity & State Formation. 2008. (Global, Area, & International Archive Ser.). (Illus.). 360p. pap. 39.95 *(978-0-520-09864-0(1))* Univ. of California Pr.
Yanne, Andrew & Heller, Gillis. Signs of a Colonial ERA. 2009. (ENG., Illus.). 208p. (gr. 17). pap. 25.00 *(978-962-209-944-9(0))* Hong Kong Univ. Pr. HKG. Dist: Columbia Univ. Pr.
Yi, Dai. A Concise History of the Qing Dynasty, Vol. 4. 2012. (Concise History of the Qing Dynasty Ser.). (ENG.). 352p. 128.00 ***(978-981-4332-21-7(6),*** Silkroad Pr.) Enrich Professional Publishing (S)., Ltd. SGP. Dist: Independent Pubs. Group.
Yong, Jin & Ikeda, Daisaku. Compassionate Light in Asia: A Dialogue. 2012. (Echoes & Reflections Ser.). (ENG.). 256p. 50.00 *(978-1-84885-198-6(7))* I. B. Tauris & Co., Ltd. GBR. Dist: Macmillan.
Yu, Xiaorong, et al. Han Yu Shi Zhong de Yu Yan Jie Chu Wen Ti Yan Jiu. 2010. (CHI., Illus.). *(978-7-80241-106-7(8))* Language Publishing Hse.
Yuan, Xingpei, ed. The History of Chinese Civilisation 4 Volume Set, 4 vols. 2012. (Cambridge China Library). (ENG., Illus.). 2000p. 350.00 ***(978-1-107-01309-4(7))*** Cambridge Univ. Pr.
Zhang, Ji. Zhongguo Wen Hua an Quan Yu Yi Shi Xing Tai Zhan Lüe: The Strategy of Chinese Cultural Security & Ideology. 2010. (CHI.). *(978-7-01-008540-1(4))* People's Publishing Hse., The.
Zhang, Qizhi, ed. Sourcebook of Traditional Chinese Culture. 2012. (ENG.). 300p. pap. 22.95 ***(978-1-59265-125-2(9))*** Long River Pr.
Zhang, Wei-Bin. The Rise & Fall of China's Last Dynasty: The Deepening of the Chinese Servility. 2011. (Focus on Civilizations & Cultures Ser.). ix, 237p. 85.00 *(978-1-61209-510-3(0))* Nova Science Pubs., Inc.
Zhao, Weimin & Guo, Junling. Bei Da Shi Ye: Xin Zhongguo 60 Nian Xue Shu Liu Bian Ji. 2010. (CHI., Illus.). *(978-7-301-16032-9(1))* Beijing University Pr.
Zheng, Biao. Zhongguo Ruan Shi Li: Jue Ding Zhongguo Ming Yun de Liang Zhong Si Lu. 2010. (CHI.). *(978-7-5117-0165-7(5))* Cetial Compilation & Fanslation Pr.
Zhou, Jianchao. Jin Dai Zhongguo "Ren de Xian Dai Hua Si Xiang" Yan Jiu. 2010. (CHI.). *(978-7-5097-1216-0(5))* China Social Science Documentation Publishing Hse.
Zhou, Xinghua. Ningbo Bang Zhi. 2009. (CHI., Illus.). *(978-7-5004-8104-1(7))* China Social Sciences Pr.
Zhou, Yiqun. Festivals, Feasts, & Gender Relations in Ancient China & Greece. 2010. (ENG.). 373p. 90.00 *(978-0-521-19762-5(7))* Cambridge Univ. Pr.

CHINA—COMMERCE

Agarwala, Rina & Herring, Ronald J., eds. Whatever Happened to Class? Reflections from South Asia. 2008. (Illus.). 240p. 140.00 *(978-0-415-45468-1(9))* Routledge.

Allen, Wilfred J. & Young, Alex, eds. In China We Trust: The Impacts of Chinese Economic Policies. 2012. ***(978-1-61942-828-7(8))*** Nova Science Pubs., Inc.

Alon, Ilan & Zhang, Wenxian. Top 100 Companies in China. 2010. 340p. pap., instr.'s gde. ed. 38.00 *(978-981-4291-46-0(3))* World Scientific Publishing Co., Inc.

Arrighi, Giovanni. Adam Smith in Beijing: Lineages of the Twenty-First Century. 2007. (ENG., Illus.). 416p. 35.00 *(978-1-84467-104-5(6)*, 844104) Verso Bks. GBR. Dist: Norton, W. W. & Co., Inc.

Arthur Judson Brown. New Forces in Old China: An Inevitable Awakening. l.t. ed. 2006. (ENG.). 364p. pap. 18.99 *(978-1-4264-0145-9(0))* BiblioBazaar.

Austin, Denise. Kingdom-Minded People: Christian Identity & the Contributions of Chinese Business Christians: Christian Identity & the Contributions of Chinese Business Christians. 2011. (Global Pentecostal & Charismatic Studies). (Illus.). 249p. ***(978-90-04-20402-7(4))*** BRILL.

Baird, Christina. Liverpool China Traders. 2007. (Illus.). 224p. pap. 59.95 *(978-0-8204-8321-4(4))* Lang, Peter Publishing, Inc.

Barnett, S. A. & Sladkovskii, M. I. History of Economic Relations Between Russia & China: From Modernization to Maoism. 2007. (ENG.). 311p. (gr. 11). pap. 49.95 *(978-1-4128-0639-8(9))* Transaction Pubs.

Basu, Parikshit K. & Bandara, Yapa, eds. WTO Accession & Socio-Economic Development in China. 2009. (Chandos Asian Studies). (ENG., Illus.). 234p. 110.00 *(978-1-84334-547-3(1)*, Chandos Publishing) Woodhead Publishing Ltd. GBR. Dist: Ingram Pub. Services.

Baumler, Alan. The Chinese & Opium under the Republic: Worse Than Floods & Wild Beasts. 2007. (Illus.). 298p. 80.00 *(978-0-7914-6953-8(0))* State Univ. of New York Pr.

Bell, Sandra. International Brand Management of Chinese Companies: Case Studies on the Chinese Household Appliances & Consumer Electronics Industry Entering Us An. 2008. (Contributions to Economics Ser.). (Illus.). X, 370p. (C). 179.00 *(978-3-7908-2029-4(6)*, 3790820296) Springer.

—International Brand Management of Chinese Companies: Case Studies on the Chinese Household Appliances & Consumer Electronics Industry Entering US & Western European Markets. 2010. (Contributions to Economics Ser.). (ENG., Illus.). x, 370p. pap. 179.00 *(978-3-7908-2549-7(2)*, 3790825492) Physica-Verlag DEU. Dist: Springer.

Bennett, Joe. Where Underpants Come From: From Cotton Fields to Checkout Counters — Travels Through the New China & into the New Global Economy. 2009. (ENG., Illus.). 368p. (gr. 12-18). 25.95 *(978-1-59020-228-9(7))* Overlook Pr., The.

BIA. Essential Chinese Manufacturers: Food, Textile, Clothing, & Chemical Companies. 6th rev. ed. 2006. 450p. (J). pap. 249.00 *(978-1-4187-4194-5(9))* Business Information Agency.

—Major Wholesalers of China. 6th rev. ed. 2006. 250p. (J). pap. 249.00 *(978-1-4187-4296-6(1))* Business Information Agency.

Blackford, Mansel G. The Rise of Modern Business: Great Britain, the United States, Germany, Japan, & China. 3rd ed. 2008. (ENG., Illus.). 296p. 66.50 *(978-0-8078-3210-3(3))*; pap. 27.95 *(978-0-8078-5886-8(2))* Univ. of North Carolina Pr.

Block, Carson & Collins, Robert. Doing Business in China for Dummies. 2007. (ENG., Illus.). 384p. per. 21.99 *(978-0-470-04929-7(4)*, For Dummies) Wiley, John & Sons, Inc.

Boden, Jeanne. Wall Behind China's Open Door: Towards Efficient Intercultural Management in China. 2008. (ENG.). 300p. pap. 38.00 *(978-90-5487-464-5(3))* VUB Univ. Pr. BEL. Dist: Independent Pubs. Group.

Broadman, Harry G. Africa's Silk Road: China & India's New Economic Frontier. 2006. (Stand Alones Ser.). (ENG., Illus.). 384p. per. 25.00 *(978-0-8213-6835-0(4)*, 9780821368350) World Bank Pubns.

Buderi, Robert & Huang, Gregory T. Guanxi (the Art of Relationships) Microsoft, China, & Bill Gates's Plan to Win the Road Ahead. 2007. (ENG., Illus.). 320p. pap. 19.99 *(978-0-7432-7323-7(0))* Simon & Schuster.

Celone, Barton V. China-United States Trade: Inextricably Intertwined? Celone, Barton V., ed. 2008. (Illus.). 151p. (C). 69.00 *(978-1-60456-198-2(X))* Nova Science Pubs., Inc.

CER Publishing, ed. China Business Guide 2008. 2007. 706p. pap. 54.00 *(978-988-17149-3-0(1))* China Economic Review Publishing HKG. Dist: Trans-Atlantic Pubns., Inc.

Chambers, Sam T. & French, Paul. Oil on Water: Tankers, Pirates & the Rise of China. 2010. (ENG., Illus.). 224p. 125.95 *(978-1-84813-468-3(1))*; pap. 29.95 *(978-1-84813-469-0(X))* Zed Bks., Ltd. GBR. Dist: Macmillan.

Chan, Kai Yiu. Business Expansion & Structural Change in Pre-War China: Liu Hongsheng & His Enterprises, 1920-1937. 2006. (Business, Innovation, & Society in Asia Ser.). (ENG., Illus.). 324p. (gr. 17). 60.00 *(978-962-209-764-3(2))* Hong Kong Univ. Pr. HKG. Dist: Columbia Univ. Pr.

Chaston, Ian. Strategy for Sustainable Competitive Advantage. 2012. (Routledge Research in Organizational Behavior & Strategy Ser.). (ENG., Illus.). 314p. (C). 125.00 ***(978-0-415-52274-8(9))*** Routledge.

Cheung, Yin-Wong & Ma, Guonan. Asia & China in the Global Economy. 2011. 300p. 84.00 ***(978-981-4335-26-3(6))*** World Scientific Publishing Co., Inc.

Child, John, et al. The Dynamics of Co-Evolution: A Case Study of the Development of China's Port Industry. 2012. (Organisation & Strategy: Case Studies in their Context Ser.). 180p. 110.00 ***(978-1-84980-743-2(4))*** Elgar, Edward Publishing, Inc.

China Knowledge Press Pte Ltd. Branding in China. 2007. (Illus.). 355p. pap. 59.00 *(978-981-4163-05-7(8))* China Knowledge Press Pte Ltd SGP. Dist: Independent Pubs. Group.

China Telecom - 2000 Reports Vol. 5: Data & Market Opportunities. Date not set. pap. 2995.00 *(978-1-56851-132-0(9)*, IGIC38) Information Gatekeepers, Inc.

China Trade Handbook: Companies-Products-Services. (Orig.). 450p. pap. 750.00 *(978-0-7605-1866-3(1))*; (Illus.). 600p. pap. *(978-0-7605-0672-1(8))* Rector Pr., Ltd.

Coxe, William. Account of the Russian Discoveries Between Asia & America. 2008. 536p. 57.95 *(978-1-4370-1154-8(3))*; pap. 42.95 *(978-1-4367-2209-4(8))* Kessinger Publishing, LLC.

Crick, Monique. Chinese Trade Ceramics for Southeast Asia, I-XVII Centuries: Collection of Ambassador & Mrs. Charles Muller. 2010. (ENG., Illus.). 416p. 150.00 *(978-88-7439-463-0(2))* 5 Continents ITA. Dist: Hachette Bk. Group.

Curtis, Emily Byrne. Glass Exchange Between Europe & China, 1550-1800: Diplomatic, Mercantile & Technological Interactions. 2009. (Transculturalisms 1400-1700 Ser.). (Illus.). 174p. 114.95 *(978-0-7546-6316-4(7))* Ashgate Publishing Co.

Dinello, Natalia & Shaoguang, Wang, eds. China, India & Beyond: Development Drivers & Limitations. 2009. (Global Development Network Ser.). (Illus.). 296p. 127.00 *(978-1-84720-595-4(6))* Elgar, Edward Publishing, Inc.

Doing Business in China. Date not set. (Doing Business in Regions & Countries Around the World Ser.). 80p. *(978-1-882390-56-4(3))* Training Management Corp.

Elwell, Craig K., et al. Is China a Threat to the U. S. Economy? 2008. (Illus.). 88p. pap. 29.00 *(978-1-60456-843-1(7))* Nova Science Pubs., Inc.

Farooki, Masuma & Kaplinsky, Raphael. The Impact of China on Global Commodity Prices. 2012. (Routledge Studies in the Modern World Economy Ser.). (ENG., Illus.). 232p. (C). 140.00 *(978-0-415-59789-0(7))* Routledge.

Feenstra, Robert C. & Wei, Shang-Jin, eds. China's Growing Role in World Trade. (National Bureau of Economic Research Conference Report). (ENG., Illus.). 608p. 2012. pap. 85.00 ***(978-0-226-23974-3(8))*** 2010. 110.00 *(978-0-226-23971-2(3))* Univ. of Chicago Pr.

Feng, Lei. Hai Xia Liang an Jing Ji He Zuo Mo Shi Yan Jiu: Study on Cross-Straits Economic & Trade Cooperation Pattern. 2009. (CHI., Illus.). *(978-7-5097-0775-3(7))* China Social Science Documentation Publishing Hse.

Fernandez, Juan Antonio & Underwood, Laurie. China Entrepreneur: Voices of Experience from 40 International Business Pioneers. 2009. (ENG., Illus.). 250p. pap. 27.95 *(978-0-470-82321-7(6)*, Wiley) Wiley, John & Sons, Inc.

Finn, Lisa & EPM Communications, Inc Staff, eds. The Research Alert Consumer Segmentation Survey. 2007. 75p. pap. 395.00 *(978-1-885747-87-7(X))* EPM Communications, Inc.

Forest Products Trade Between Russia & China (Synthesis Report) Potential Production, Processing, Consumption & Trade Scenarios. 2007. 0.00 net. *(978-1-932928-25-9(1))* Forest Trends.

Fornés, Gastón & Butt-Philip, Alan. The Chinese-Latin American Axis: Emerging Markets & the Future of Globalisation. 2012. (ENG., Illus.). 200p. 95.00 ***(978-0-230-57487-8(4))*** Palgrave Macmillan.

Frank, Caroline. Objectifying China, Imagining America. 2012. (ENG., Illus.). 272p. 75.00 *(978-0-226-26027-3(5))* Univ. of Chicago Pr.

—Objectifying China, Imagining America: Chinese Commodities in Early America. 2012. (ENG., Illus.). 280p. pap. 25.00 *(978-0-226-26028-0(3))* Univ. of Chicago Pr.

Gallagher, Kevin & Porzecanski, Roberto. The Dragon in the Room: China & the Future of Latin American Industrialization. 2010. (ENG., Illus.). 200p. 55.00 *(978-0-8047-7187-0(1))*; pap. 19.95 *(978-0-8047-7188-7(X))* Stanford Univ. Pr.

Ganse, Shirley H. Chinese Export Porcelain: East to West. 2009. (ENG.). 180p. pap. 22.95 *(978-1-59265-080-4(5))* Long River Pr.

Gao, Yuning. China as the Workshop of the World. 2011. (Routledge Studies on the Chinese Economy Ser.). (ENG., Illus.). 256p. (C). 155.00 *(978-0-415-60405-5(2))* Routledge.

Gerth, Karl. As China Goes, So Goes the World: How Chinese Consumers Are Transforming Everything. 2010. (ENG., Illus.). 272p. 26.00 *(978-0-8090-3429-1(8)*, Hill & Wang) Farrar, Straus & Giroux.

Gipouloux, François. The Asian Mediterranean: Port Cities & Trading Networks in China, Japan & South Asia, 13th-21st Century. 2011. (Illus.). 400p. 160.00 ***(978-0-85793-426-0(0))*** Elgar, Edward Publishing, Inc.

Goldstein, Jonathan. Stephen Girard's Trade with China, 1787-1824: The Norms Versus the Profits of Trade. 2010. *(978-1-878282-82-8(4))*; pap. *(978-1-878282-93-4(X))* St. Johann Pr.

Goodwin, Jason. A Time for Tea. 2009. (ENG.). 410p. pap. 29.95 *(978-1-4128-1307-5(7))* Transaction Pubs.

Greenberg, Michael. British Trade & the Opening of China 1800-42. 2008 (Cambridge Studies in Economic History Ser.). (ENG.). 252p. pap. 34.99 *(978-0-521-07916-7(0))* Cambridge Univ. Pr.

Grunor, Jerry A. Enough to Make You Sick: Tainted & Counterfeit Imports! 2009. 372p. 34.95 *(978-1-4401-4742-5(6))*; pap. 24.95 *(978-1-4401-4740-1(X))* iUniverse, Inc.

Guo, Li'an & Zong, Fai. Business, Finance & Economics of China. 2010. (China in the 21st Century Ser.). 145.00 *(978-1-60741-299-1(3))* Nova Science Pubs., Inc.

Hamilton, Stewart & Zhang, Jinxuan. Doing Business with China: Avoiding the Pitfalls. 2012. (ENG., Illus.). 208p. 40.00 *(978-0-230-22265-6(X))* Palgrave Macmillan.

Harney, Alexandra. The China Price: The True Cost of Chinese Competitive Advantage. 2009. (ENG., Illus.). 352p. (gr. 12-18). 16.00 *(978-0-14-311486-4(7)*, Penguin (Non-Classics)) Penguin Group (USA) Inc.

Hearing on H.R. 1229: The Nonmarket Economy Trade Remedy ACT of 2007: Hearing Before the Subcommittee on Trade of the Committee on Ways & Means, U.S. House of Representatives, U.S. House of Representatives, One Hundred Tenth Congress, First Session, March 15, 2007. 2009. iii, 77p. ***(978-0-16-087456-7(4)***, 552-070-42148-3) United States Government Printing Office.

Heshmati, Almas. Recent Developments in the Chinese Economy. 2006. 232p. (C). 169.00 *(978-1-60021-449-3(5))* Nova Science Pubs., Inc.

Hodder, R. N. W. Overseas Chinese & Trade Between the Philippines & China: The Intertwining of Family, Social, & Business Interests in Promoting Trade. 2006. (Illus.). 328p. 119.95 *(978-0-7734-5793-5(3))* Mellen, Edwin Pr., The.

Hoffmann, W. John, et al. China into the Future: Making Sense of the World's Most Dynamic Economy. 2007. (ENG., Illus.). 220p. 34.95 *(978-0-470-82244-9(9)*, Wiley) Wiley, John & Sons, Inc.

Hufbauer, Gary Clyde, et al. US-China Trade Disputes: Rising Tide, Rising Stakes. 2006. (Policy Analyses in International Economics Ser.: 78). (Illus.). 111p. per. 21.95 *(978-0-88132-394-8(2))* Peterson Institute for International Economics.

Impacts of the Chinese Hardwood Plywood Trade: Hearing Before the Subcommittee on Public Lands & Forests of the Committee on Energy & Natural Resources, One Hundred Tenth Congress, First Session, to Receive Testimony on the Impacts of the Chinese Hardwood Plywood Trade on the National Forest System & Other Public Lands, & the Communities That Depend on Them, Medford, or, May 30, 2007. 2007. iii, 51p. *(978-0-16-079294-6(0)*, 552-070-36372-6) United States Government Printing Office.

Isik, Hakime. Cross Cultural Guide- How to Do Business in China, Russia, Spain & Columbi. 2007. 112p. per. *(978-3-8364-1659-6(7))* VDM Verlag Dr. Mueller e.K.

Jin, Zhesong & Li, Jun. Foreign Trade Growth & Economic Development in China: Enrich Series on China's Edonomic Issues: Retrospective & Future Prospects, 5 vols., Vol. 3. 2011. (Enrich Series on China's Economic Issues Ser.). (ENG.). 296p. 98.00 *(978-981-4298-22-3(0))* Enrich Professional Publishing (S)., Ltd. SGP. Dist: Independent Pubs. Group.

Kang, Yuanfei. Performance & Network Governance in International Joint Ventures. 2010. 348p. pap. *(978-3-639-10623-7(7))* VDM Verlag Dr. Mueller e.K.

Kastner, Scott L. Political Conflict & Economic Interdependence Across the Taiwan Strait & Beyond. 2009. (Studies in Asian Security Ser.). (ENG., Illus.). 256p. 70.00 *(978-0-8047-6203-8(1))* Stanford Univ. Pr.

Kastner, Scott L. & Kastner, Scott. Political Conflict & Economic Interdependence Across the Taiwan Strait & Beyond. 2009. (Studies in Asian Security). (ENG., Illus.). 256p. pap. 24.95 *(978-0-8047-6204-5(X))* Stanford Univ. Pr.

Kauz, Ralph, ed. Aspects of the Maritime Silk Road: From the Persian Gulf to the East China Sea. 2010. (East Asian Economic & Socio-Cultural Studies). (ENG.). 193p. (C). 72.00 *(978-3-447-06103-2(0))* Harrassowitz, Otto Verlag DEU. Dist: ISD.

Kayser, Pedro. The Brazilian Shoe Industry - Competing in International Markets. 2009. 152p. pap. *(978-3-639-16644-6(2))* VDM Verlag Dr. Mueller e.K.

Khanna, Tarun. Billions of Entrepreneurs: How China & India Are Reshaping Their Futures — and Yours. 2011. (ENG.). 368p. pap. 16.95 *(978-1-4221-5728-2(8))* Harvard Business Review Pr.

—Billions of Entrepreneurs: How China & India Are Reshaping Their Futures & Yours. 2007. (ENG.). 353p. 29.95 *(978-1-4221-0383-8(8))* Harvard Business Review Pr.

Kong, Bo. China's International Petroleum Policy, 1 vol. 2009. (Energy & Security Ser.). 229p. 44.95 *(978-0-313-37791-4(X)*, C37791, Praeger Pubs.) Greenwood Publishing Group, Inc.

Kraft, Christian. Joining the WTO: The Impact of Trade, Competition & Redistributive Conflicts on China's Accession to the World Trade Organization. 2007. (European University Studies 31 Ser.: Vol. 550). (Illus.). 174p. pap. *(978-3-631-56773-9(1))* Lang, Peter AG.

Kudaisya, Malik & Ng, Chin-Keong, eds. Chinese & Indian Business: Historical Antecedents. 2009. (Social Sciences in Asia Ser.). 200p. pap. *(978-90-04-17279-1(3))* BRILL.

Kuhns, John D. China Fortunes: A Tale of Business in the New World. 2011. (ENG.). 592p. 34.95 *(978-0-470-92804-2(2)*, Wiley) Wiley, John & Sons, Inc.

Kuo Jane C. M. Open for Business 2 2nd Edition, 2 vols. 2nd rev. ed. 2007. (C). pap. 52.95 incl. audio compact disk *(978-0-88727-626-2(1))* Cheng & Tsui Co.

Kynge, James. China Shakes the World: A Titan's Rise & Troubled Future — & the Challenge for America. 2006. (Edition 001 Ser.). (ENG.). 288p. 25.00 *(978-0-618-70564-1(3))* Houghton Mifflin Harcourt Trade & Reference Pubs.

Lacity, Mary C., et al, eds. China's Emerging Outsourcing Capabilities: The Services Challenge. 2010. (Technology, Work & Globalization Ser.). (ENG., Illus.). 256p. 100.00 *(978-0-230-23844-2(0))* Palgrave Macmillan.

Lam, N. Mark & Graham, John L. China Now: Doing Business in the World's Most Dynamic Market. 2006. (ENG., Illus.). 385p. 27.95 *(978-0-07-147254-8(1)*, 0071472541) McGraw-Hill Cos., The.

Larcon. Chinese Multinationals. 2008. (Illus.). xxx, 269p. pap. 32.00 *(978-981-283-559-8(8))* World Scientific Publishing Co., Inc

Le Pichon, Alain, ed. China Trade & Empire: Jardine, Matheson & Co. & the Origins of British Rule in Hong Kong, 1827-1843. 2006. (Records of Social & Economic History, New Ser.: Vol. 38). (ENG., Illus.). 592p. 150.00 *(978-0-19-726337-2(2))* Oxford Univ. Pr., Inc.

Li, Chunling. Kong Gu Gu Dong Yu Shang Shi Gong Si Gu Li Zheng Ce: Controlling Shareholders & the Listed Companies' Dividend Policies. 2009. (CHI., Illus.). *(978-7-01-008512-8(9))* People's Publishing Hse., The.

Lim Jason. Linking an Asian Trans-Regional Commerce in Tea Overseas Chinese Merchants in the Fujian-Singapore Trade, 1920-1960. 2010. (Illus.). 280p. *(978-90-04-18243-1(8))* BRILL.

Lin, Man-Houng. China Upside Down: Currency, Society, & Ideologies, 1808-1856. 2007. (Harvard East Asian Monographs: 270). (Illus.). 450p. 49.95 *(978-0-674-02268-3(8))* Harvard Univ., Asia Ctr.

Litzenburg, Thomas V., Jr. Chinese Export Porcelain: In the Reeves Center Collection at Washington & Lee University. 2006. (ENG., Illus.). 65.00 *(978-1-903942-19-2(5)*, Third Millenium Pub Ltd) Antique Collectors' Club GBR. Dist: National Bk. Network.

Liu, Chunhang. Multinationals, Globalisation & Indigenous Firms in China. 2009. (Routledge Studies on the Chinese Economy Ser.). (Illus.). 208p. 160.00 *(978-0-415-45190-1(6))* Routledge.

Longlong, Ma. Evolution & Growth of China's Wholesale Industry Since 1978. 2011. (ENG.). 504p. 158.00 ***(978-981-4298-40-7(9))*** Enrich Professional Publishing (S)., Ltd. SGP. Dist: Independent Pubs. Group.

Martin, Steven. The Art of Opium Antiques. 2007. (ENG., Illus.). 128p. pap. 29.95 *(978-974-9511-22-0(0))* Silkworm Bks. THA. Dist: Univ. of Washington Pr.

Miller, Debra A. Importing from China. 2009. (Current Controversies Ser.). (ENG.). 240p. (gr. 10-12). pap. 27.50 *(978-0-7377-4321-0(2))*; pap. 39.70 *(978-0-7377-4322-7(0))* Cengage Gale. (Greenhaven Pr., Inc.).

Miller, Debra A., ed. Importing from China. 2012. (Current Controversies Ser.). (ENG.). 240p. (gr. 10-12). pap. 28.35 ***(978-0-7377-6234-1(3))***; lib. bdg. 40.90 ***(978-0-7377-6233-4(0))*** Cengage Gale. (Greenhaven Pr., Inc.).

Min, Dai, et al. New China Business Strategies: Chinese & American Companies As Global Partners. 2009. (ENG., Illus.). 351p. 32.95 *(978-1-56171-820-7(3))* SPI Bks.

Morse, Hosea Ballou. The Chronicles of the East India Company, Trading to China 1635-1834, 5 vols., Set. reprint ed. 625.00 *(978-0-7222-2749-7(3))* Library Reprints, Inc.

—The Chronicles of the East India Company, Trading to China 1635-1834, 5 vols. 2008. 395.00 *(978-1-57898-666-8(4))* Martino Publishing.

—The Gilds of China with an Account of the Gild Merchant or Co Hong of Canton. 2007. (ENG.). 108p. 34.95 *(978-0-548-03054-7(5))* Kessinger Publishing LLC.

Müller, Gerhard Friedrich & Pallas, Peter Simon. Conquest of Siberia: And the History of the Transactions, Wars, Commerce, etc. Carried on between Russia & China, from the Earliest Period. 2010. (Cambridge Library Collection - History Ser.). (ENG.). 163p. pap. 19.99 *(978-1-108-02383-2(5))* Cambridge Univ. Pr.

Nassimbeni, Guido & Sartor, Marco. Sourcing in China: Strategies, Methods & Experiences. 2006. (ENG., Illus.). 320p. 126.00 *(978-1-4039-9855-2(8))* Palgrave Macmillan.

Navarro, Peter W. & Autry, Gregory W. Death by China: Confronting the Dragon - A Global Call to Action. 2011. (ENG.). 300p. 25.99 *(978-0-13-218023-8(5))* Wharton Schl. Publishing.

Nocker, Elisabeth. How to Negotiate in China. 2008. 136p. pap. *(978-3-639-01498-3(7))* VDM Verlag Dr. Mueller e.K.

Organization, World Trade. Trade Policy Review: Separate Customs Territory of Taiwan, Penghu, Kinmen, & Matsu 2010. 2010. (ENG.). 164p. pap. 75.00 *(978-1-59888-450-0(6))* Bernan Assocs.

—Trade Policy Review - China 2010. 2010. (ENG.). 182p. pap 75.00 *(978-1-59888-441-8(7))* Bernan Assocs.

Overton, Rachel H. China's Trade with the United States & the World. Overton, Rachel H., ed. 2008. (Illus.). viii, 71p. pap. 37.00 *(978-1-60692-126-5(6))* Nova Science Pubs., Inc.

Pecht, Michael. China's Electronics Industry: The Definitive Guide for Companies & Policy Makers with Interest in China. 2006. (ENG., Illus.). 265p. pap., instr.'s gde. ed. 405.00 *(978-0-8155-1536-4(7))* William Andrew, Inc.

Peng, Songlan. Chinese Accounting Standards. 2007. 184p. per. *(978-3-8364-3433-1(4))* VDM Verlag Dr. Mueller e.K.

Petersen, Kasper Brandi. Luxury Consumption in Chin. 2011. 92p. pap. ***(978-3-8443-9557-0(1))*** Lambert Academic Publishing.

Plafker, Ted. Doing Business in China: How to Profit in the World's Fastest Growing Market. 2008. (ENG.). 304p. pap. 16.99 *(978-0-446-69696-8(X))* 2007. 302p. pap. 16.00 *(978-0-446-69863-4(6))* Grand Central Publishing. (Business Plus).

Ptak, Roderich. Birds & Beasts in Chinese Texts & Trade: Lectures Related to South China & the Overseas World. 2011. (Maritime Asia Ser.). (ENG., Illus.). 140p. (C). 57.00 ***(978-3-447-06449-1(8))*** Harrassowitz, Otto Verlag DEU. Dist: ISD.

Qingjiang. China-Eu Trade Disputes & Their Management. 2011. 250p. 88.00 *(978-981-4273-40-4(6))* World Scientific Publishing Co., Inc.

Reuvid, Jonathan. China: Practical Advice on Operational Strategy & Risk Management. 2nd ed. 2011. (Business Insights Ser.). (ENG., Illus.). 328p. pap. 49.95 *(978-0-7494-5991-8(3))* Kogan Page, Ltd. GBR. Dist: Ingram Pub. Services.

Saee, John, ed. China & the Global Economy in the 21st Century. 2011. (Routledge Studies in the Growth Economies of Asia Ser.). (ENG., Illus.) 224p. (C). 130.00 *(978-0-415-67051-7(9))* Routledge.

Sandrey, Ron & Edinger, Hannah. Examining the South African-China Agricultural Trading Relationship. 2009. (NAI Discussion Papers). 50p. pap. 12.95

C

(978-91-7106-643-5(8)) Nordiska Afrikainstitutet SWE. Dist: Stylus Publishing, LLC.

Santiso, Javier, ed. The Visible Hand of China in Latin America. 2007. (ENG., Illus.). 200p. per. 45.00 (978-92-64-02796-1(3)) Organization for Economic Cooperation & Development.

Scheiwein, Lin. Die Auslandmesse in China: Theorie und Praxis für die Messeteilnahme im asiatischen Raum, speziell in der Volksrepublik China. 2009. 114p. pap. (978-3-639-18421-1(1)) VDM Verlag Dr. Mueller e.K.

Schulz, Andrea. Chinese Business Culture- Theories, Examples, Figures. 2007. 136p. per. (978-3-8364-0487-7(7)) VDM Verlag Dr. Mueller e.K.

Shang, Huping. Evaluations to Chinese Public. 2009. 108p. pap. (978-3-639-15752-9(4)) VDM Verlag Dr. Mueller e.K.

Shaw, Samuel. The Journals of Major Samuel Shaw. 2009. (Revolutionary War Ser.). (ENG.). 380p. pap. 23.95 (978-1-4290-1696-4(5)) Applewood Bks.

Shi, Wei. Intellectual Property in the Global Trading System: EU-China Perspective. 2010. (ENG., Illus.). xvi, 324p. pap. 139.00 (978-3-642-09648-8(4), 3642096484) Springer.

Shi Wei Staff. Intellectual Property in Global Trading System: EU-China Perspective. 2008. (ENG., Illus.). xvi, 324p. 139.00 (978-3-540-77736-6(9), 3540777369) Springer.

Simpfendorfer, Ben. The New Silk Road: How a Rising Arab World Is Turning Away from the West & Rediscovering China. 2009. (ENG.). 256p. 46.00 (978-0-230-58026-8(2)) Palgrave Macmillan.

—The New Silk Road - Revised & Updated: How a Rising Arab World Is Turning Away from the West & Rediscovering China. rev. ed. 2011. (ENG., Illus.). 224p. pap. 22.00 (978-0-230-28485-2(X)) Palgrave Macmillan.

Singla, S. K. India & China: Comparative Economic Performance. 2011. 274p. 45.25 (978-81-7708-280-7(9)) New Century Publications IND. Dist: International Specialized Bk. Services.

Song, Baohui. Empirical Study of China's Soybean Import Market. 2008. 140p. per. (978-3-8364-3713-4(9)) VDM Verlag Dr. Mueller e.K.

Song, Weiming, et al. Russian Logs in China: The Softwood Commodity Chain & Economic Development in China. 2007. pap. (978-1-932928-24-2(3)) Forest Trends.

SPANOTES Mathematics - Bilingual CD: A bilingual study aid for secondary school Mathematics. 2009. (SPA & ENG., Illus.). 146p. cd-rom 24.95 (978-1-884730-02-3(7)) InterLingua.com, Inc.

Story, Jonathan. China Uncovered: What You Need to Know to Do Business in China. 2010. (Financial Times Ser.). (ENG., Illus.). 248p. (C). pap. 29.99 (978-0-273-70827-8(9)) FT Press.

Su, Jiang & Myers, Ramon Hawley. The Treaty Port Economy in Modern China: Empirical Studies of Institutional Change & Economic Performance. 2011. (978-1-55729-099-1(7)) Univ. of California, Institute of East Asian Studies.

Tagliacozzo, Eric & Chang, Wen-Chin, eds. Chinese Circulations: Capital, Commodities, & Networks in Southeast Asia. 2011. (ENG., Illus.). 552p. 99.95 (978-0-8223-4881-8(0)); pap. 27.95 (978-0-8223-4903-7(5)) Duke Univ. Pr.

Tannert, Norman. Produkt- und Markenpiraterie in der VR China: Nationale und lokale Interessenmuster bei der Durchsetzung geistiger Eigentumsrechte. (GER., Illus.). 127p. pap. 32.95 (978-3-631-56849-1(5)) Lang, Peter GmbH, Europaischer Verlag der Wissenschaften DEU. Dist: Lang, Peter Publishing, Inc.

Tong, Joy Kooi-Chin. Overseas Chinese Christian Entrepreneurs in Modern China: A Case Study of the Influence of Christian Ethics on Business Life. 2012. (Key Issues in Modern Sociology Ser.). (Illus.). 180p. 99.00 (978-0-85728-353-5(7)) Anthem Pr. GBR. Dist: Books International, Inc.

Torrens, Christopher. Doing Business in China: A Guide to the Risks & the Rewards. 2010. (Economist Bks.). (ENG., Illus.). 256p. 29.95 (978-1-84668-281-0(9), Wiley) Wiley, John & Sons, Inc.

Turley, Joan. Connecting with China: Business Success Through Mutual Benefit & Respect. 2010. (ENG.). 278p. 35.00 (978-0-470-74841-1(9), Wiley) Wiley, John & Sons, Inc.

Vodicka, Matthias. Guideline for the Development of Chinese Suppliers. 2007. 100p. per. (978-3-8364-0732-8(9)) VDM Verlag Dr. Mueller e.K.

Wan, Changxuan. ICMeCG 2009: 2009 International Conference on Management of E-Commerce & E-Government: Proceedings, 16-19 September 2009, Nanchang, China. 2009. (Illus.). xxiii, 567p. (978-0-7695-3778-8(2)) IEEE Computer Society Pr.

Wang, Chenglu. Handbook of Contemporary Marketing in China: Theories & Practices. 2010. 175.00 (978-1-61761-689-1(3)) Nova Science Pubs., Inc.

Wang, Jing. Brand New China: Advertising, Media, & Commercial Culture. 2010. (Illus.). 432p. pap. 18.95 (978-0-674-04708-2(7)) Harvard Univ. Pr.

Wang, Junmin. State-Market Interactions in China's Reform Era: Local State Competition & Global Market Building in the Tobacco Industry. 2012. (Routledge Contemporary China Ser.). (ENG., Illus.). 160p. (C). 125.00 (978-0-415-50694-6(8)) Routledge.

Wang, Yonggui & Li-Hua, Richard. Marketing Competences & Strategic Flexibility in China. 2007. (ENG., Illus.). 288p. 110.00 (978-0-230-01350-6(3)) Palgrave Macmillan.

Warner, Malcolm, ed. Society & Hrm in China. 2012. (ENG.). 240p. (C). 125.00 (978-0-415-69744-6(1)) Routledge.

Warner, Malcolm & Rowley, Chris, eds. Chinese Management in the 'Harmonious Society' Managers, Markets & the Globalized Economy. 2011. (ENG.). 240p. (C). 125.00 (978-0-415-57242-2(8)) Routledge.

Wills, John E., Jr. China & Maritime Europe, 1500-1800: Trade, Settlement, Diplomacy, & Missions. 2010. (ENG., Illus.). 312p. (C). pap. 28.99 (978-0-521-17945-4(9)) Cambridge Univ. Pr.

Wong, Raymond Sin-kwo, ed. Chinese Entrepreneurship in A Global Era. 2009. (ENG.). 236p. (C). pap. 44.95 (978-0-415-57425-9(0)) Routledge.

Wood, Frances. No Dogs & Not Many Chinese. (Illus.). xii, 368p. 50.00 (978-0-7195-5758-3(5)) Murray, John GBR. Dist: Trafalgar Square Publishing.

Xia, Chunyu. Zhongguo Nong Cun Liu Tong Ti Zhi Gai Ge Yan Jiu. 2009. (CHI., Illus.). (978-7-5058-8882-1(X)) Jingji Kexue Chubanshe.

Xu, Jijun. Nan Song Lin'an Gong Shang Ye. 2009. (CHI.). 40p. (978-7-01-008449-7(1)) People's Publishing Hse., The.

Yager, Loren. World Trade Organization: Limited Progress at Hong Kong Ministerial Clouds Prospects for Doha Agreement. 2006. (Illus.). 51p. (C). pap. 20.00 (978-1-4223-0724-3(7)) DIANE Publishing Co.

Yi, Si-Uk. Tae Chungguk Kyoyok Kujo Ui Pyonhwa Ch'ui Wa Kosi Kyongjejok Sisachom. 2008. (KOR., Illus.). 86p. (978-89-8063-368-5(8)) KDI.

Yuansheng, Zhong. Management of E-Commerce & E-Government. 2006. (Illus.). 238p. (C). 225.00 (978-1-60021-324-3(3)) Nova Science Pubs., Inc.

Zaigui, Li. Traditional Chinese Foods: Production & Research Progress. 2009. (Illus.). ix, 342p. 79.00 (978-1-60692-902-5(X)) Nova Science Pubs., Inc.

Zelin, Madeleine. The Merchants of Zigong: Industrial Entrepreneurship in Early Modern China. 2008. (Studies of the Weatherhead East Asian Institute, Columbia University Ser.). (ENG., Illus.). 432p. (gr. 17). pap. 26.00 (978-0-231-13597-9(1)) Columbia Univ. Pr.

Zeng, Ka. China's Foreign Trade Policy: The New Constituencies. 2007. (Routledge Contemporary China Ser.). (Illus.). XII, 196p. 160.00 (978-0-415-77086-6(6)) Routledge.

Zhang, Marina Yue. China 2.0: The Transformation of an Emerging Superpower... & the New Opportunities. 2010. (ENG.). 256p. 34.95 (978-0-470-82423-8(9), Wiley) Wiley, John & Sons, Inc.

Zhang, Shouguang. Ningbo Bang Zhi. 2009. (CHI.). (978-7-5004-8105-8(5)) China Social Sciences Pr.

Zheng, Yangwen. China on the Sea. 2011. (MUL., Illus.). 362p. (978-90-04-19477-9(0)) BRILL.

CHINA—COMMERCIAL POLICY

Celone, Barton V. China-United States Trade: Inextricably Intertwined? Celone, Barton V., ed. 2008. (Illus.). 151p. (C). 69.00 (978-1-60456-198-2(X)) Nova Science Pubs., Inc.

CER Publishing, ed. China Business Guide 2008. 2007. 706p. pap. 54.00 (978-988-17149-3-0(1)) China Economic Review Publishing HKG. Dist: Trans-Atlantic Pubns., Inc.

Chu. China's Accession to the Wto & Its Impact on Asian Economies. 2007. 304p. (978-1-84542-842-6(0)) Elgar, Edward Publishing, Inc.

Dyke, Paul A. Van. Merchants of Hong Kong & Macau: Vol. 1: Politics & Strategies in Eighteenth Century Trade. 2011. (Illus.). 656p. (978-988-8053-77-3(9)) Hong Kong Univ. Pr.

Fleischer, Belton M., et al, eds. Market Development in China: Spillovers, Growth & Inequality. 2007. (Advances in Chinese Economic Studies). (Illus.). 288p. (C). 127.00 (978-1-84542-851-8(X)) Elgar, Edward Publishing, Inc.

Gallagher, Mary Elizabeth. Contagious Capitalism: Globalization & the Politics of Labor in China. 2007. (ENG., Illus.). 256p. (C). per. 24.95 (978-0-691-13036-1(1)) Princeton Univ. Pr.

Isett, Christopher M. State, Peasant, & Merchant in Qing Manchuria, 1644-1862. 2006. (ENG., Illus.). 440p. 65.00 (978-0-8047-5271-8(0)) Stanford Univ. Pr.

Johnson, Kendall, ed. Narratives of Free Trade & the Commercial Cultures of Early US-China Relations. 2011. (Illus.). 212p. (978-988-8053-90-2(6)) Hong Kong Univ. Pr.

Kelley, Lane & Shenkar. International Business in China. pap. (978-0-415-11881-1(6)) CENGAGE Learning.

Kessler, Martha B. Trade Barriers & China. 2008. 132p. pap. 50.00 (978-1-60456-686-4(8)) Nova Science Pubs., Inc.

Li, Kangying. The Ming Maritime Policy in Transition, 1367 To 1568. 2010. (East Asian Economic & Socio-Cultural Studies). (ENG., Illus.). 211p. (C). 72.00 (978-3-447-06172-8(3)) Harrassowitz, Otto Verlag DEU. Dist: ISD.

Lieberthal, Kenneth G. Managing the China Challenge: How to Achieve Corporate Success in the People's Republic. 2011. (ENG., Illus.). 149p. 26.95 (978-0-8157-2204-5(4)) Brookings Institution Pr.

McGregor, James. One Billion Customers: Lessons from the Front Lines of Doing Business in China. 2007. (ENG.). 352p. pap. 15.99 (978-0-7432-5841-8(X), Free Pr.) Free Pr.

Navarro, Peter. The Coming China Wars: Where They Will Be Fought & How They Can Be Won. 2nd exp. ed. 2008. (ENG.). 240p. pap. 15.99 (978-0-13-235982-5(0)) FT Press.

—The Coming China Wars: Where They Will Be Fought & How They Can Be Won. 2006. (ENG., Illus.). 288p. 24.99 (978-0-13-228128-7(7)) Prentice Hall PTR.

Nolan, Peter. Integrating China: Towards the Coordinated Market Economy. 2007. (Anthem Studies in Development & Globalization Ser.). (ENG., Illus.). 281p. 80.00 (978-1-84331-237-6(9)) Anthem Pr. GBR. Dist: Books International, Inc.

Organisation for Economic Co-operation and Development Staff. China: Defining the Boundary Between the Market & the State. 2009. (OECD Reviews of Regulatory Reform Ser.). (Illus.). 320p. pap. 63.00 (978-92-64-05939-9(3)) Organization for Economic Cooperation & Development.

Organization, World Trade. Trade Policy Review: Separate Customs Territory of Taiwan, Penghu, Kinmen, & Matsu 2010. 2010. (ENG.). 164p. pap. 75.00 (978-1-59888-450-0(6)) Bernan Assocs.

—Trade Policy Review - China 2010. 2010. (ENG.). 182p. pap. 75.00 (978-1-59888-441-8(7)) Bernan Assocs.

Reuvid, Jonathan & Yong, Li. Doing Business with China. 5th rev. ed. 2006. (Doing Business with China Ser.). (ENG., Illus.). 702p. 230.00 (978-1-905050-08-6(9), GMB Publishing Ltd.) Blue Ibex Ltd. GBR. Dist: Ingram Pub. Services.

Somarajah, Muthucumaraswamy & Wang, Jiangyu, eds. China, India & the International Economic Order. 2010. (ENG., Illus.). 660p. 125.00 (978-0-521-11057-0(2)) Cambridge Univ. Pr.

Williams, Alan. Contemporary Issues Shaping China's Civil Aviation Policy: Balancing International with Domestic Priorities. 2009. 258p. 124.95 (978-0-7546-7140-4(2)) Ashgate Publishing Co.

Zeng, Ka. China's Foreign Trade Policy: The New Constituencies. 2009. 186p. pap. 39.95 (978-0-415-54709-3(1)) Routledge.

CHINA—CONSTITUTIONAL HISTORY

see Constitutional History—China

CHINA—CONSTITUTIONAL LAW

see Constitutional Law—China

CHINA—COURT AND COURTIERS

Der Ling, Princess. Two Years in the Forbidden City. 2010. (ENG.). 436p. pap. 35.75 (978-1-171-82430-5(0)) BiblioBazaar.

—Two Years in the Forbidden City. 2010. (Illus.). 140p. pap. 22.91 (978-1-153-72975-8(X)) General Bks. LLC.

Der Ling, The Princess. Two Years in the Forbidden City. 2008. 244p. 24.99 (978-1-60512-017-1(0)); pap. 13.99 (978-1-60512-117-8(7)) Akasha Publishing, LLC. (Akasha Classics).

—Two Years in the Forbidden City. 2008. 224p. pap. (978-1-4099-2921-5(3)) Dodo Pr.

Goh, Meow. Sound & Sight: Poetry & Courtier Culture in the Yongming Era (483-493) 2010. (ENG.). 208p. 50.00 (978-0-8047-6859-7(5)) Stanford Univ. Pr.

Hayter-Menzies, Grant. Imperial Masquerade: The Legend of Princess der Ling. 2008. (ENG., Illus.). 444p. (gr. 17). 35.00 (978-962-209-881-7(9)) Hong Kong Univ. Pr. HKG. Dist: Columbia Univ. Pr.

Headland, Isaac Taylor. Court Life in China. 2008. 224p. 27.99 (978-0-554-29444-5(3)) BiblioBazaar.

—Court Life in China. 2007. (ENG.). 196p. per. (978-1-4065-4425-1(6)) Dodo Pr.

—Court Life in China. 2007. (ENG.). 144p. per. (978-1-4068-1605-1(1)) Echo Library.

Holdsworth, May & Courtauld, Caroline. Forbidden City: The Great Within. 2nd ed. 2008. (ENG.). 152p. pap. 24.95 (978-962-217-792-5(1), 217792) Airphoto International/Odyssey HKG. Dist: Norton, W. W. & Co., Inc.

Jin, Xingyao. Qing Dai Gong Ting Zheng Bian. 2010. (CHI.). (978-7-80047-926-7(9)) Forbidden City Publishing Hse.

Ling, Der. Two Years in the Forbidden City. 2010. 442p. pap. 35.75 (978-1-142-63531-2(7)); 436p. pap. 35.75 (978-1-142-11899-0(1)); 444p. pap. 36.75 (978-1-143-21032-7(8)) BiblioBazaar.

—Two Years in the Forbidden City. 2009. 164p. pap. (978-1-150-52685-5(8)) Books LLC.

Ling, Princess Der. Two Years in the Forbidden City. 2007. (ENG.). 270p. pap. 19.99 (978-988-17149-9-2(0)) Earnshaw Bks. HKG. Dist: Independent Pubs. Group.

—Two Years in the Forbidden City. 2010. 170p. pap. (978-1-4076-5076-0(9)) HardPr.

Ling, Rich. Two Years in the Forbidden City. 2007. 190.00 (978-0-7103-1112-2(5)) Taylor & Francis Group.

Ling, The Princess Der. Two Years in the Forbidden City. 2010. 180p. pap. 18.36 (978-1-162-71509-4(X)); 30.36 (978-1-169-27745-8(4)); 37.95 (978-1-161-48373-4(X)) Kessinger Publishing, LLC.

CHINA—DEFENSES

Cheung, Tai Ming. Fortifying China: The Struggle to Build a Modern Defense Economy. 2008. (Illus.). 272p. 39.95 (978-0-8014-4692-4(9)) Cornell Univ. Pr.

Fleischer, Samuel E., ed. Measuring China's Military Might. 2010. (China in the 21st Century Ser.). 69.00 (978-1-60876-846-2(5)) Nova Science Pubs., Inc.

Fruhling, Stephan. Preparing for the Next Asia-Pacific War: Defence Planning in the Twenty-First Century. 2012. (Routledge Security in Asia Pacific Ser.). (ENG.). (C). 130.00 (978-0-415-60573-1(3)) Routledge.

Garrett, Richard J. The Defences of Macau: Forts, Ships, & Weapons over 450 Years. 2010. (ENG.). 288p. (gr. 17). 60.00 (978-962-209-993-7(9)) Hong Kong Univ. Pr. HKG. Dist: Columbia Univ. Pr.

—The Defences of Macau: Forts, Ships & Weapons over 450 Years. 2010. (Illus.). 288p. (978-988-220-680-9(8)) Hong Kong Univ. Pr.

—The Defences of Macau: Forts, Ships & Weapons over 450 Years. 2010. (ENG., Illus.). 288p. (gr. 17). pap. 30.00 (978-988-8028-49-8(9)) Hong Kong Univ. Pr. HKG. Dist: Columbia Univ. Pr.

Military Power of the People's Republic of China: Hearing Before the Committee on Armed Services, House of Representatives, One Hundred Ninth Congress, Second Session, Hearing Held, June 22, 2006. 2007. iii, 69p. (978-0-16-079305-9(X), 552-070-36383-1) United States Government Printing Office.

United States, Congress House Committee on Armed Services Staff, contrib. by. China's Military Power: Hearing Before the Committee on Armed Services, House of Representatives, One Hundred Ninth Congress, First Session, Hearing Held July 27, 2005. 2007. iii, 98p. (978-0-16-077923-7(5), 552-070-35358-5) United States Government Printing Office.

CHINA—DESCRIPTION AND TRAVEL

Airey, David & Chong, King. Tourism in China: Policy & Development since 1949. 2011. (Contemporary Geographies of Leisure, Tourism & Mobility Ser.). (ENG., Illus.). 352p. (C). 158.00 (978-0-415-54809-0(8)) Routledge.

Alford, Jeffrey & Duguid, Naomi. Beyond the Great Wall: Recipes & Travels in the Other China. 2008. (ENG., Illus.). 376p. 40.00 (978-1-57965-301-9(4), 1579653014) Artisan.

Anderson, John. Mandalay to Momien: A Narrative of the Two Expeditions to Western China of 1868 & 1875, under Colonel Edward B. Sladen & Colonel Horace Browne. 2007. (978-1-57898-673-6(7)) Martino Publishing.

Andrews, Roy Chapman. The New Conquest of Central Asia: A Narrative of the Explorations of the Central Asiatic Expeditions in Mongolia & China, 1921-1930. 2007. (978-1-57898-684-2(2)) Martino Publishing.

Angel, Heather. Exploring Natural China. 2010. (ENG., Illus.). 192p. 24.95 (978-1-901268-41-6(1), 1901268411) Evans Mitchell Bks. GBR. Dist: MBI Distribution Services/Quayside Distribution.

Archibald, Alicia E. Neva. In the Land of the Blue Gown. 2010. (Cambridge Library Collection - Travel & Exploration Ser.). (ENG.). 396p. pap. 31.99 (978-1-108-01386-4(4)) Cambridge Univ. Pr.

Arlt, Wolfgang Georg. China's Outbound Tourism. 2006. (Routledge Studies in Contemporary Geographies of Leisure, Tourism, & Mobility). (Illus.). 300p. 180.00 (978-0-415-36536-9(8)) Routledge.

Ashraf, Lubna & Syed, M. N. Wedding Cry ~ Death Dance: An Insight into Chinese Culture: an Ethnographic Study of Xuan'en, Hubei with Special Emphasis on Tujia Rites of Passage. 2008. (ENG.). 252p. pap. 39.50 (978-0-9801675-8-0(2)) Robertson Publishing.

Astrada, Carlos. Hacia la Revolución: Viajeros Argentinos de Izquierda. 2007. (Tierra Firme Ser.). (SPA.). 347p. pap. (978-950-557-731-6(1)) Fondo de Cultura Economica.

August, Oliver. Inside the Red Mansion: On the Trail of China's Most Wanted Man. 2007. (ENG., Illus.). 288p. 26.00 (978-0-618-71498-8(7)) Houghton Mifflin Harcourt Publishing Co.

—Inside the Red Mansion: On the Trail of China's Most Wanted Man. 2008. (ENG., Illus.). 288p. pap. 14.95 (978-0-547-05350-9(9), Mariner Bks.) Houghton Mifflin Harcourt Trade & Reference Pubs.

Ayres, Gene. A Billion To: An American Insider in the New China. Strozier, M. Stefan & Torke, Kyle, eds. 2009. 264p. pap. 20.00 (978-1-935444-06-0(9)) World Audience Pubs.

—Inside the New China: An Ethnographic Memoir. 2010. (ENG.). 260p. pap. 29.95 (978-1-4128-1350-1(6)) Transaction Pubs.

Bagg, Mary, ed. Berkshire Encyclopedia of China, 5 vols., Set. 2008. (Illus.). 2500p. lib. bdg. 525.00 (978-0-9770159-4-8(7)) Berkshire Publishing Group.

Barnett, Robert. Lhasa: Streets with Memories. 2010. (Asia Perspectives: History, Society, & Culture Ser.). (ENG., Illus.). 244p. (gr. 17). pap. 19.50 (978-0-231-13681-5(1)) Columbia Univ. Pr.

Barrow, John. Travels in China: Containing Descriptions, Observations & Comparisons, Made & Collected in the Course of a Short Residence at the Imperial Palace of Yuen-Min-Yuen. 2010. (Cambridge Library Collection - Travel & Exploration Ser.). (ENG., Illus.). 672p. pap. 45.00 (978-1-108-01362-8(7)) Cambridge Univ. Pr.

Barrow, John & Macartney, George. The Public Life of the Earl of Macartney. 2011. (Cambridge Library Collection - Travel & Exploration Ser.). (Illus.). 626p. pap. 43.00 (978-1-108-02619-2(2)) Cambridge Univ. Pr.

—Some Account of the Public Life, & a Selection from the Unpublished Writings, of the Earl of Macartney. 2011. (Cambridge Library Collection - Travel & Exploration Ser.). 540p. pap. 39.99 (978-1-108-02620-8(6)) Cambridge Univ. Pr.

Barthes, Roland. Travels in China. 2012. (ENG.). 240p. 19.95 (978-0-7456-5080-7(5)) Polity Pr. GBR. Dist: Wiley, John & Sons, Inc.

Barzini, Luigi. Peking to Paris. 2007. (Illus.). 416p. per. 24.95 (978-0-9789563-1-8(1)) Demontreville Pr., Inc.

Beauvoir, Simone de. The Long March: An Account of Modern China. 2006. 513p. reprint ed. pap. 22.00 (978-1-4223-5385-1(0)) DIANE Publishing Co.

Bennett, Joe. Where Underpants Come From. 2011. (ENG., Illus.). 256p. (gr. 12). 14.95 (978-1-59020-336-1(4)) Overlook Pr., The.

—Where Underpants Come From: From Cotton Fields to Checkout Counters—Travels Through the New China & into the New Global Economy. 2009. (ENG., Illus.). 368p. (gr. 12-18). 25.95 (978-1-59020-228-9(7)) Overlook Pr., The.

Berg, Cecilie Gamst. Don't Joke on the Stairs: How I Learned to Navigate China by Breaking Most of the Rules. 2012. (ENG.). 356p. pap. 16.95 (978-988-19002-0-3(4)) Blacksmith Bks. HKG. Dist: National Bk. Network.

Biderman, Stan. Bullet Trains to Yaks: Glimpses into Art, Politics, & Culture in China & Tibet. 2011. 144p. pap. 24.95 (978-0-9832636-0-9(4)) Irony Pr.

Bird, Isabella. The Golden Chersonese & the Way Thither. 2011. (Stanfords Travel Classics Ser.). 312p. pap. 16.95 (978-1-906780-38-8(2)) Beaufoy, John Publishing GBR. Dist: Midpoint Trade Bks., Inc.

—The Yangtze Valley & Beyond. 2008. (ENG.). 500p. pap. 21.99 (978-988-17326-2-0(X)) Earnshaw Bks. HKG. Dist: Independent Pubs. Group.

—The Yangtze Valley & Beyond: An Account of Journeys in China, Chiefly in the Province of Sze Chuan & among the Man-tze of the Somo Territory. 2010. (Cambridge Library Collection - Travel & Exploration Ser.). (Illus.). 584p. pap. 43.00 (978-1-108-01389-5(9)) Cambridge Univ. Pr.

Bird, Isabella L. The Golden Chersonese: A 19th-Century Englishwoman's Travels in Singapore & the Malay Peninsula. 2011. (Illus.). 352p. pap. 15.95 (978-981-08-4484-4(0)) Monsoon Bks. Pte. Ltd.

—The Golden Chersonese & the Way Thither. 2008. (Illus.). 344p. pap. *(978-1-4099-4232-0(5))* Dodo Pr.

Blackmore, Charles. Conquering the Desert of Death: Across the Taklamakan. 2008. (ENG., Illus.). 288p. pap. 16.95 *(978-1-84511-582-1(1),* Tauris Parke Paperbacks) I. B. Tauris & Co., Ltd. GBR. Dist: Macmillan.

Blakiston, Thomas Wright. Five Months on the Yang-Tsze: With a Narrative of the Exploration of its Upper Waters & Notices of the Present Rebellions in China. 2010. (Cambridge Library Collection - Travel & Exploration Ser.). (ENG., Illus.). 436p. pap. 34.99 *(978-1-108-01361-1(9))* Cambridge Univ. Pr.

Bland, J. O. P. Houseboat Days in China. 2008. (ENG.). 250p. pap. 19.99 *(978-988-17621-2-2(X))* Earnshaw Bks. HKG. Dist: Independent Pubs. Group.

Blofeld, John. My Journey in Mystic China: Old Pu's Travel Diary. Reid, Daniel, tr. from CHI. 2008. (ENG., Illus.). 1p. 24.95 *(978-1-59477-157-6(X))* Inner Traditions International, Ltd.

Boutilier Kendall, Karen. Berkeley to Beijing: The journey of a young Activist. 2009. 212p. 27.95 *(978-1-4401-4131-7(2))*; pap. 17.95 *(978-1-4401-4130-0(4))* iUniverse, Inc.

Boxer, C. R., ed. South China in the Sixteenth Century (1550-1575) Being the narratives of Galeote Pereira, Fr. Gaspar da Cruz, O. P. , Fr. Martin de Rada, O. E. S. A. , (1550-1575) 2010. (Hakluyt Society, Second Ser.). 480p. 69.95 *(978-1-4094-1472-8(8))* Hakluyt Society GBR. Dist: Ashgate Publishing Co.

Braam, André Everard van & de Saint-Méry, M. L. E. Moreau. An Authentic Account of the Embassy of the Dutch East-India Company, to the Court of the Emperor of China, in the Years 1794 & 1795 2 Volume Set. 2011. (Cambridge Library Collection - History Ser.). (ENG., Illus.). 682p. pap., pap. 57.00 *(978-1-108-02907-0(8))* Cambridge Univ. Pr.

Braam Houckgeest, André Everard van. An Authentic Account of the Embassy of the Dutch East-India Company, to the Court of the Emperor of China, in the Years 1794 and 1795. 2011. (Cambridge Library Collection - History Ser.). (ENG.). 332p. pap. 28.99 *(978-1-108-02906-3(X))*; (Illus.). 352p. pap. 29.99 *(978-1-108-02905-6(1))* Cambridge Univ. Pr.

Bradford, Ruth & Leith, Katherine Dunham. Maskee! the Journal & Letters of Ruth Bradford, 1861-1872. 2011. 176p. 42.95 ***(978-1-258-03238-8(4))*** Literary Licensing, LLC.

Buffington, Lois Gamblin. The China Miracle. 2008. 84p. pap. 16.95 *(978-1-60563-638-2(X))* PublishAmerica, Inc.

Burkett, Glenda R. No Blue Sky: An American Traveler's Glimpse of China. 2011. 96p. pap. 24.79 ***(978-1-4567-5897-4(7))*** AuthorHouse.

Bush, Charles Peck. Five Years in China; or, the Factory Boy Made a Missionary the Life & Observations of Rev W Aitchison by Rev Charles P Bush, a M. 2006. 312p. per. 23.99 *(978-1-4255-2942-0(9))* MPublishing.

Candler, Edmund. The Unveiling of Lhasa. 2011. (ENG.). 248p. pap. 19.99 *(978-988-19090-8-4(2))* Earnshaw Bks. HKG. Dist: Independent Pubs. Group.

Carter, Tom. China: Portrait of a People. 2010. (ENG.). 638p. pap. 24.95 *(978-988-99799-4-2(2))* Blacksmith Bks. HKG. Dist: National Bk. Network.

CER Publishing, ed. Hangzhou Business Eats. 2007. 100p. pap. 19.95 *(978-988-99874-9-7(X))* China Economic Review Publishing HKG. Dist: Trans-Atlantic Pubns., Inc.

Chang, Elizabeth H., ed. British Travel Writing from China, 1798-1901, 5 vols., Set. 2009. (ENG.). 1600p. 795.00 *(978-1-85196-625-7(0))* Pickering & Chatto Pubs., Ltd. GBR. Dist: Ashgate Publishing Co.

Chen, Sonia M. China Changing in My Eyes: People, Schools & Landscapes. 2010. 260p. pap. 14.99 *(978-1-4490-5060-3(3))* AuthorHouse.

Chiwoon, Pak. The Jehol Diary, 1 vol. 2010. (ENG., Illus.). 240p. *(978-1-906876-17-3(7))* BRILL.

Clark, Steve & Smethurst, Paul. Asian Crossings: Travel Writing on China, Japan & Southeast Asia. 2008. (ENG., Illus.). 288p. (gr. 17). 60.00 *(978-962-209-914-2(9))*; pap. 30.00 *(978-962-209-915-9(7))* Hong Kong Univ. Pr. HKG. Dist: Columbia Univ. Pr.

Cordier, Henri, ed. Cathay & the Way Thither - Being a Collection of Medieval Notices of China. 2010. (Hakluyt Society, Second Ser.). 376p. 69.95 *(978-1-4094-1408-7(6))*; 392p. 69.95 *(978-1-4094-1404-9(3))* Hakluyt Society GBR. Dist: Ashgate Publishing Co.

—Cathay & the Way Thither - Being a Collection of Medieval Notices of China: Odoric of Pordenone. 2010. (Hakluyt Society, Second Ser.). 384p. 69.95 *(978-1-4094-1400-1(0))* Hakluyt Society GBR. Dist: Ashgate Publishing Co.

—Cathay & the Way Thither Being a Collection of Medieval Notices of China. 2010. (Hakluyt Society, Second Ser.). 1416p. 240.00 *(978-1-4094-2480-2(4))* Hakluyt Society GBR. Dist: Ashgate Publishing Co.

—Migrants & Cities: The Accommodation of Migrant Organizations in Europe. 2010. (Hakluyt Society, Second Ser.). 296p. 69.95 *(978-1-4094-1405-6(1))* Hakluyt Society GBR. Dist: Ashgate Publishing Co.

Czech, Kenneth P. Hunting Trips in the Land of the Dragon: Anglo & American Sportsmen Afield in Old China, 1870-1940. 2009. (ENG., Illus.). 242p. 34.95 *(978-1-57157-303-2(8))* Safari Pr., Inc.

Daguan, Zhou. A Record of Cambodia: The Land & Its People. Harris, Peter, tr. from CHI. 2007. (ENG., Illus.). 184p. (C). pap. 26.95 *(976-974-9511-24-4(7))* Silkworm Bks. THA. Dist: Univ. of Washington Pr.

Dajani, Adel & Man, Wong How. Islamic Frontiers of China: Peoples of the Silk Road. 2010. (ENG., Illus.). 160p. 50.00 *(978-1-84885-702-5(0))* I. B. Tauris & Co., Ltd. GBR. Dist: Macmillan.

Danis, Jean-Francois. Eternal Shanghai. (Illus.). 96p. 24.95 *(978-2-911589-32-4(7),* Weatherhill, Inc.) Shambhala Pubns., Inc.

D'Arcy-Brown, Liam. The Emperor's River: Travels to the Heart of a Resurgent China. 2010. (ENG.). 288p. pap. 12.95 *(978-1-903070-70-3(8))* Eye Bks. GBR. Dist: Independent Pubs. Group.

Davidson, Robert J. & Mason, Isaac. Life in West China: Described by Two Residents in the Province of Sz-Chwan. 2007. (ENG.). 272p. per. 27.95 *(978-1-4326-6146-5(9))* Kessinger Publishing, LLC.

Davies, Hannah & Bird, Isabella. Among Hills & Valleys in Western China: Incidents of Missionary Work. 2010. (Cambridge Library Collection - Travel & Exploration Ser.). (ENG., Illus.). 332p. pap. 28.99 *(978-1-108-01388-8(0))* Cambridge Univ. Pr.

Davies, Henry Rodolph. Yün-nan: The Link Between India & the Yangtze. 2010. (Cambridge Library Collection - Travel & Exploration Ser.). (ENG., Illus.). 618p. pap. 43.00 *(978-1-108-01079-5(2))* Cambridge Univ. Pr.

—Yun-Nan: The Link Between India & the Yangtze. 2008. 95.00 *(978-1-57898-555-5(2))* Martino Publishing.

De Windt, Harry. From Pekin to Calais by Land. 2008. 408p. 49.95 *(978-1-4372-6468-5(9))*; 406p. pap. 34.95 *(978-1-4371-3807-8(1))* Kessinger Publishing, LLC.

DeFrancis, John. In the Footsteps of Genghis Khan. 2008. (ENG.). 284p. 26.00 *(978-1-4223-9269-0(4))* DIANE Publishing Co.

Deluxe...Spirit of China. 2008. 256p. *(978-1-4075-3953-9(1))* Parragon, Inc.

Dev, Amiya, et al. Tagore & China. 2011. (Illus.). 504p. (C). 50.00 ***(978-81-321-0637-1(7),*** B06371C) SAGE Pubns., Inc.

Dingle, Edwin. Across China on Foot. 2007. 300p. (ENG.). 98.99 *(978-1-4280-7717-1(0))*; per. 91.99 *(978-1-4280-7715-7(4))* IndyPublish.com.

Dingle, Edwin John. Across China on Foot. 2009. 368p. 31.99 *(978-0-559-10338-4(7))*; 29.99 *(978-0-559-10350-6(6))*; pap. 20.99 *(978-0-559-10348-3(4))*; pap. 32.75 *(978-0-559-10342-1(5))* BiblioBazaar.

—Across China on Foot. 2009. 336p. pap. *(978-0-217-16344-6(0))* Books LLC.

—Across China on Foot. 2007. (ENG.). 476p. pap. 21.95 *(978-988-99874-4-2(9))* Earnshaw Bks. HKG. Dist: Independent Pubs. Group.

—Across China on Foot. 2010. (Illus.). 192p. pap. 9.89 *(978-1-77045-554-2(X))* General Bks. LLC.

—Across China on Foot: One Man's Incredible Quest. 2007. (ENG.). 276p. per. 19.99 *(978-0-9794154-5-6(4))* Arc Manor.

Dobsons, Richard P. China Cycle. 2006. 236p. per. *(978-1-4067-3378-5(4),* Hesperides Pr.) Read Bks.

Donald, Stephanie Hemelryk & Gammack, John G. Tourism & the Branded City: Film & Identity on the Pacific Rim. 2007. (New Directions in Tourism Analysis Ser.). (Illus.). 234p. 114.95 *(978-0-7546-4829-1(X))* Ashgate Publishing Co.

Donnelly, Phillip. China. 2009. 180p. pap. 16.95 *(978-1-4092-5679-3(0))* Lulu Enterprises Inc.

D'Orleans, Pierre Joseph & Witsen, Nicholaas. History of the Two Tartar Conquerors of China: Including the Two Journeys into Tartary of Father Ferdinand Verbiest, in the Suite of the Emperor Kanh-Hi. Ellesmere, Earl of, tr. 2010. (Cambridge Library Collection - Travel & Exploration Ser.). (ENG.). 188p. pap. 19.99 *(978-1-108-00812-9(7))* Cambridge Univ. Pr.

Dunlop, Fuchsia. Shark's Fin & Sichuan Pepper: A Sweet-Sour Memoir of Eating in China. (ENG.). 2009. 336p. pap. 17.95 *(978-0-393-33288-9(8)* 33288) 2008. (Illus.). 320p. 24.95 *(978-0-393-06657-9(6),* 6657) Norton, W. W. & Co., Inc.

Dwyer, John. High Road to Tibet. 2009. 201p. pap. 18.50 *(978-1-4452-4614-7(7))* Lulu Enterprises Inc.

EAR Books, creator. Shanghai: City Between Cultures. 2007. (Ear Books Mini Ser.). (ENG., Illus.). 80p. 14.95 incl. lp *(978-3-937406-69-5(7))* Edel Classica Gmbh.

Earnshaw, Graham. The Great Walk of China: Travels on Foot from Shanghai to Tibet. 2010. (ENG.). 344p. pap. 16.95 *(978-988-19002-1-0(2))* Blacksmith Bks. HKG. Dist: National Bk. Network.

Edkins, Joseph. Religion in China: Containing a Brief Account of the Three Religions. 2007. (ENG.). 284p. per. 27.95 *(978-1-4304-4274-5(3))* Kessinger Publishing, LLC.

Evans, Polly. Fried Eggs with Chopsticks: One Woman's Hilarious Adventure into a Country & a Culture Not Her Own. 2006. (ENG., Illus.). 320p. pap. 14.00 *(978-0-385-33993-3(3),* Delta) Random House Publishing Group.

Falson, Seth. South of the Clouds: Exploring the Hidden Realms of China. Date not set. pap. *(978-0-312-30641-0(5),* St. Martin's Griffin); mass mkt. *(978-0-312-98539-4(8),* St. Martin's Paperbacks) St. Martin's Pr.

Fan, Chengda. Treatises of the Supervisor & Guardian of the Cinnamon Sea: The Natural World & Material Culture of Twelfth-Century China. Hargett, James M., tr. from CHI. 2011. (ENG., Illus.). 368p. (C). 80.00 *(978-0-295-99078-1(3))*; pap. 40.00 *(978-0-295-99079-8(1))* Univ. of Washington Pr.

Flanagan, Cheryn & Kolowich, Benjamin. Me No Speak China: China. 2nd ed. 2008. (ENG & CHI., Illus.). 96p. pap. 9.95 *(978-0-9787680-1-0(9),* Me No Speak.

Flanagan, Mark & Kirkham, Tony. Wilson's China: A Century On. 2010. (Illus.). 256p. 46.00 *(978-1-84246-394-9(2))* Kew Publishing GBR. Dist: Chicago Distribution Ctr.

Fleming, George. Travels on Horseback in Mantchu Tartary: Being a Summer's Ride Beyond the Great Wall of China. 2010. (Cambridge Library Collection - Travel & Exploration Ser.). (Illus.). 608p. pap. 43.00 *(978-1-108-01426-7(7))* Cambridge Univ. Pr.

Fleming, Peter. To Peking: A Forgotten Journey from Moscow to Manchuria. 2009. (ENG., Illus.). 200p. pap. 16.00 *(978-1-84511-996-6(7),* Tauris Parke Paperbacks) I. B. Tauris & Co., Ltd. GBR. Dist: Macmillan.

Fortune, Robert. Three Years' Wanderings in the Northern Provinces of China. 2009. 238p. pap. *(978-0-217-90214-4(6))* Books LLC.

—Two Visits to the Tea Countries of China & the British Tea Plantations in the Himalaya: With a Narrative of Adventures, & a Full Description of the Culture of the Tea Plant, the Agriculture, Horticulture & Botany of China. 2007. *(978-1-57898-672-9(9))* Martino Publishing.

Friend, James. China Journal: A World of Difference. 2008. (Illus.). 400p. pap. 30.00 *(978-0-9669525-2-0(9))* Friend, Beverly.

Gifford, Rob. China Road. 2008. (Playaway Adult Nonfiction Ser.). 74.99 *(978-1-60514-772-7(9))* Findaway World, LLC.

—China Road: A Journey into the Future of a Rising Power. (ENG., Illus.). 352p. 2008. pap. 17.00 *(978-0-8129-7524-6(3),* Random Hse. Trade Paperbacks) 2007. 26.95 *(978-1-4000-6467-0(8),* Random House) Random House Publishing Group.

Gilman, Susan Jane. Undress Me in the Temple of Heaven. 2010. (ENG.). 320p pap. 13.99 *(978-0-446-69693-7(5))* Grand Central Publishing.

Glover, Denise M., et al, eds. Explorers & Scientists in China's Borderlands, 1880-1950. 2011. (ENG., Illus.). 320p. (C). 75.00 *(978-0-295-99117-7(8),*; pap. 35.00 *(978-0-295-99118-4(6))* Univ. of Washington Pr.

Gonzflez de Mendoza, Juan. History of the Great & Mighty Kingdom of China & the Situation Thereof Set: Compiled by the Padre Juan Gonzflez de Mendoza & Now Reprinted from the Early Translation of R. Parke. Staunton, George, ed. Parke, R., tr. 2010. (Cambridge Library Collection - Travel & Exploration Ser.). (ENG.). 626p. pap. 52.00 *(978-1-108-00820-4(8))* Cambridge Univ. Pr.

—History of the Great & Mighty Kingdome of China & the Situation Thereof: Compiled by the Padre Juan Gonzflez de Mendoza. Staunton, George, ed. Parke, R., tr. 2010. (Cambridge Library Collection - Travel & Exploration Ser.). (ENG.). 364p. pap. 29.99 *(978-1-108-00819-8(4))*; 272p. pap. 23.99 *(978-1-108-00810-5(0))* Cambridge Univ. Pr.

Goodman, Jim. Yunnan: China South of the Clouds. 2009. (Odyssey Guides). (ENG., Illus.). 624p. pap. 29.95 *(978-962-217-775-8(1),* 217775) Airphoto International/Odyssey HKG. Dist: Norton, W. W. & Co., Inc.

Grande, Alison. Unpacking the Baggage. 2008. 104p. pap. *(978-3-639-01852-3(4))* VDM Verlag Dr. Mueller e.K.

Gray, Nathan Hoturoa & Gray, Nathan. First Pass under Heaven: One Man's 4,000-Kilometre Walk along the Great Wall of China. 2006. (ENG., Illus.). 240p. (gr. 12-18). 22.00 *(978-0-14-302067-7(6),* Penguin Global) Penguin Group (USA) Inc.

Green, Jen. China. 2009. (Changing World Ser.). (YA). (gr. 5-9). 34.25 *(978-1-84837-005-0(9))* Arcturus Pubs., Inc.

Haddad, John Rogers. The Romance of China: Excursions to China in U. S. Culture, 1776-1876. 2008. (Gutenberg-E Ser.). (ENG.). 348p. (gr. 17). 60.00 *(978-0-231-13094-3(5))* Columbia Univ. Pr.

Haedecke, Friederike. Luxury Trains. 2008. (ENG.). 24.95 *(978-3-8327-9251-0(1))* teNeues Publishing Co.

Hammond, Sally. Playing Chopsticks: Travels Through China. 2007. (ENG., Illus.). 224p. per. 14.95 *(978-1-74110-397-7(5))* New Holland Pubs. Pty, Ltd. AUS. Dist: Tuttle Publishing.

Hare, John. Mysteries of the Gobi: Searching for Wild Camels & Lost Cities in the Heart of Asia. 2008. (ENG., Illus.). 256p. 37.00 *(978-1-84511-512-8(0))* I. B. Tauris & Co., Ltd. GBR. Dist: Macmillan.

Hargett, James M. & Huang, Xiyi. Riding the River Home: A Complete & Annotated Translation of Fan Chengda's (1126 — 1193) Travel Diary Record of a Boat Trip to Wu (Wuchuan Lu) 2008. (ENG., Illus.). 400p. (gr. 17). 55.00 *(978-962-996-302-6(7))* Chinese Univ. of Hong Kong, The HKG. Dist: Columbia Univ. Pr.

Hebert, Jacques, et al. Two Innocents in Red China, 1 vol. Owen, I M, tr. 2007. (ENG., Illus.). 224p. 27.95 *(978-1-55365-254-0(1))* D&M Pubs. Inc. CAN. Dist: Perseus-PGW.

Hedin, Sven. The Trail of War: On the Track of Big Horse in Central Asia. 2009. (ENG., Illus.). 272p. pap. 15.95 *(978-1-84511-702-3(6),* Tauris Parke Paperbacks) I. B. Tauris & Co., Ltd. GBR. Dist: Macmillan.

—The Wandering Lake: Into the Heart of Asia. 2010. (ENG., Illus.). 312p. pap. 19.00 *(978-1-84885-022-4(0),* Tauris Parke Paperbacks) I. B. Tauris & Co., Ltd. GBR. Dist: Macmillan.

Hemmingsen, John & Hemmingsen, Cherie. 2000 Days in Chin: China 1998-2009. 2010. 250p. pap. 14.95 *(978-1-60264-538-7(8),* Virtualbookworm.com Publishing, Inc.

Henley, Mark, photos by. China (Sur)real, 1 vol. 2007. (ENG., Illus.). 135p. 40.00 *(978-988-99265-6-4(3))* Timezone 8 Ltd. HKG. Dist: D.A.P./Distributed Art Pubs.

Hessler, Peter. Country Driving: A Chinese Road Trip. 2011. (P. S. Ser.). (ENG.). 480p. pap. 15.99 *(978-0-06-180410-6(X),* HarperPerennial) HarperCollins Pubs.

—Country Driving: A Journey Through China from Farm to Factory. 2010. (ENG.). 416p. 27.99 *(978-0-06-180409-0(6))* HarperCollins Pubs.

—Oracle Bones: A Journey Through Time in China. 2007. (P. S. Ser.). (ENG., Illus.). 528p. pap. 15.99 *(978-0-06-082659-8(2),* HarperPerennial) HarperCollins Pubs.

Hlavacek, John. Letters Home: An American Reporter in China, 1939-1944. 2009. 272p. pap. 19.95 *(978-0-9819034-5-3(2),* Hlucky Bks.) Concierge Marketing, Inc.

Hobson, Michael W. The Year I Smelled Like Milk: Stories from Beijing & Beyond. 2010. 248p. 32.97 *(978-0-557-21684-0(2))*; pap. 15.97 *(978-0-557-21691-8(5))* Lulu Enterprises Inc.

Holmes, Samuel. The Journal of Mr Samuel Holmes, Serjeant-Major of the XIth Light Dragoons, During his Attendance, as One of the Guard on Lord Macartney's Embassy to China & Tartary. 2010. (Cambridge Library Collection - Travel & Exploration Ser.). (ENG.). 272p. pap. 23.99 *(978-1-108-01378-9(3))* Cambridge Univ. Pr.

Huai, Dong. 50 Amazing Places in China. 2010. (ENG., Illus.). 158p. 14.95 *(978-1-60220-122-4(6))* BetterLink Pr., Inc.

Huberman, Hari. Off the Great Wall. 2007. 274p. pap. 15.95 *(978-0-7414-4245-1(0))* Infinity Publishing.

Huggins-Cooper, Lynn. China. 2008. (Travel Through (QEB) Ser.). (Illus.). 32p. (J). (gr. 3-6). lib. bdg. 18.95 *(978-1-59566-359-7(2))* QEB Publishing Inc.

Jackson, Mark. An Intrepid Traveller: Breaking China with the Idiots Abroad. 2011. 220p. pap. 18.70 ***(978-1-4269-9487-6(7))*** Trafford Publishing.

Johnston, Reginald Fleming. From Peking to Mandalay: A Journey from North China to Burma through Tibetan Ssuch'uan & Yunnan. 2008. (Illus.). 428p. pap. 26.95 *(978-0-9680459-7-8(9))* Soul Care Publishing CAN. Dist: Ingram Bk. Co.

Kerr, Douglas & Kuehn, Julia. A Century of Travels in China. 2007. (ENG., Illus.). 248p. (gr. 17). pap. 27.95 *(978-962-209-846-6(0))* Hong Kong Univ. Pr. HKG. Dist: Columbia Univ. Pr.

—A Century of Travels in China: Critical Essays on Travel Writing from the 1840s to The 1940s. 2007. (Illus.). 248p. *(978-962-209-845-9(2))* Hong Kong Univ. Pr.

Kitto, Mark. Chasing China: How I Went to China in Search of a Fortune & Found a Life. 2009. (ENG.). 304p. 22.95 *(978-1-60239-657-9(4),* 239657) Skyhorse Publishing Co., Inc.

Kusamori, Shinichi. Moji No Tairiku, Owai No Miyako: Meijjin Shinkoku Kenbunroku. 2010. (JPN.). 439p. *(978-4-469-23260-8(2))* Taishukan Publishing Co., Ltd.

Kwong, Kylie. My China: A Feast for all the Senses. 2007. (ENG., Illus.). 496p. (gr. 12-18). 55.00 *(978-0-670-01879-6(1),* Studio) Penguin Group (USA) Inc.

Lancaster, Roy. Plantsman's Paradise: Travels in China. 2006. (ENG., Illus.). 512p. *(978-1-85149-515-3(0),* Antique Collectors Club Dist) Antique Collectors' Club.

Landor, A. Henry Savage. In the Forbidden Land: An Account of a Journey in Tibet, Capture by the Tibetan Authorities Imprisonment, Torture & Ultimate Release (Volumes I And. 2011. 512p. pap. ***(978-1-84902-210-1(0))*** Benediction Classics.

—In the Forbidden Land: An Account of a Journey in Tibet, Capture by the Tibetan Authorities Imprisonment, Torture, & Ultimate Release (Volumes I & I. 2011. 512p. ***(978-1-84902-209-5(7))*** Benediction Classics.

Lansdell, Henry. Chinese Central Asia; a Ride to Little Tibet. 2009. 304p. pap. *(978-1-4590-4130-1(5))* Books LLC.

Lau, Grace. Picturing the Chinese: Early Western Photographs & Postcards of China. 2009. (ENG.). 180p. pap. 24.95 *(978-1-59265-081-1(3))* Long River Pr.

Lee, Stephen. Faraway Faces: The Vanishing World of Southwest China, 1 vol. 2007. (Discover Ser.). (ENG., Illus.). 144p. 32.00 *(978-981-261-212-0(2))* Marshall Cavendish International (Asia) Private Ltd. SGP. Dist: Marshall Cavendish Corp.

Legerton, Colin & Rawson, Jacob. Invisible China: A Journey Through Ethnic Borderlands. 2009. (ENG., Illus.). 256p. 24.95 *(978-1-55652-814-9(0),* Chicago Review Pr., Inc.

Letts, Janis. A Glimpse of the Dragon - Beyond the Great Wall. 2008. 300p. pap. 24.95 *(978-1-4092-0273-8(9),)* Lulu Enterprises Inc.

Lewis, Cecil. Sagittarius Rising. 2009. 344p. pap. 29.99 *(978-1-84832-519-7(3),* Frontline) Pen & Sword Bks. Ltd. GBR. Dist: Casemate Pubs. & Bk. Distributors, LLC.

Li, Mimi & Bihu, Wu, eds. Urban Tourism in China. 2012. (ENG.). 224p. 140.00 ***(978-0-415-62382-7(0))*** Routledge.

Life, Jean M. Life in Chin: My Story. 2011. 302p. 29.99 ***(978-1-4568-9868-7(X))***; pap. 19.99 ***(978-1-4568-9867-0(1))*** Xlibris Corp.

Liguolli. They like it Loud! 2008. 104p. pap. 12.95 *(978-1-4357-4820-0(4))* Lulu Enterprises Inc.

Lindqvist, Cecilia. China: Empire of Living Symbols: Empire of Living Symbols. Tate, Joan, tr. from SWE. 2008. (ENG., Illus.). 448p. pap. 25.00 *(978-0-306-81609-3(1))* Da Capo Pr., Inc.

Little, Alicia E. Neva. Intimate China: The Chinese as I Have Seen Them. 2010. (Cambridge Library Collection - Travel & Exploration Ser.). (ENG., Illus.). 636p. pap. 43.00 *(978-1-108-01427-4(5))* Cambridge Univ. Pr.

Little, Archibald John. Across Yunnan: A Journey of Surprises. Little, Alicia, ed. 2010. (Cambridge Library Collection - Travel & Exploration Ser.). (ENG.). 196p. pap. 19.99 *(978-1-108-01409-0(7))* Cambridge Univ. Pr.

—Gleanings from Fifty Years in China. Little, Alicia, ed. 2010. (Cambridge Library Collection - Travel & Exploration Ser.). (ENG., Illus.). 384p. pap. 31.99 *(978-1-108-01408-3(9))* Cambridge Univ. Pr.

—Through the Yang-tse Gorges: Or, Trade & Travel in Western China. 2010. (Cambridge Library Collection - Travel & Exploration Ser.). (ENG., Illus.). 396p. pap. 31.99 *(978-1-108-01384-0(8))* Cambridge Univ. Pr.

Live ABC. Chinese on the Go. 2011. (ENG., Illus.). 160p. pap. 18.00 incl. audio compact disk *(978-0-07-176891-7(2),* 0071768912) McGraw-Hill Cos., The.

Lloyd, Barbara. China: Travels Between the Yangtze & Yellow Rivers. 2007. (ENG., Illus.). 152p. 48.00 *(978-88-7624-938-9(9))* Skira Editore ITA. Dist: Random Hse., Inc.

Locken, E. Travel Journal Shanghai - China. 2010. 192p. pap. 19.99 *(978-0-557-42208-1(6))* Lulu Enterprises Inc.

Lu, Hua. Wutai Shan Wen Hua Bao Dian. 2010. (CHI.). 24p. *(978-7-5087-2726-4(6))* China Society Pr.

C

Lyon, Danny, photos by. Deep Sea Diver: An American Photographer's Journey in Shanxi, China. 2011. (ENG., Illus.). 136p. 200.00 *(978-0-7148-6104-3(9))* Phaidon Pr., Inc.

Maclay, Robert Samuel. Life among the Chinese: With Characteristic Sketches & incidents of Missionary Operations & Prospects in China. by Rev. R. S. Maclay ... 2006. 404p. per. 26.99 *(978-1-4255-4311-2(1))* MPublishing.

Man, John. The Great Wall: The Extraordinary Story of China's Wonder of the World. 2008. (ENG., Illus.). 352p. 26.00 *(978-0-306-81767-0(5))* Da Capo Pr., Inc.

Mandeville, John. The Book of Marvels & Travels. Bale, Anthony, tr. 2012. (ENG., Illus.). 224p. pap. 14.95 ***(978-0-19-960060-1(0))*** Oxford Univ. Pr., Inc.

Margary, Augustus Raymond. Notes of a Journey from Hankow to Ta-li Fu. 2010. (Cambridge Library Collection - Travel & Exploration Ser.). (ENG.). 64p. pap. 19.99 *(978-1-108-01519-6(0))* Cambridge Univ. Pr.

Maugham, W. Somerset. On a Chinese Screen. 2008. 238p. 41.95 *(978-1-4365-8138-7(9))* 2007. (ENG.). 240p. per. 26.95 *(978-0-548-78979-7(7))* Kessinger Publishing, LLC.

McCabe, Nancy. Crossing the Blue Willow Bridge: A Journey to My Daughter's Birthplace in China. 2nd ed. 2011. (ENG.). 216p. (gr. 3). pap. 19.95 *(978-0-8262-1942-8(X))* Univ. of Missouri Pr.

McKee, Susan Edwards. Days Like Floating Water: A Story of Modern China. 2008. (ENG., Illus.). 440p. pap. *(978-0-9799306-0-7(X))* Oak Leaf Impressions Pr.

Medhurst, Walter Henry. The Foreigner in Far Cathay. 2010. (Cambridge Library Collection - Travel & Exploration Ser.). (ENG., Illus.). 208p. pap. 22.99 *(978-1-108-01468-7(2))* Cambridge Univ. Pr.

Messmer, Matthias. Jewish Wayfarers in Modern China: Tragedy & Splendor. 2012. (ENG.). 272p. (gr. 17). 65.00 ***(978-0-7391-6938-4(6))*** 2011. E-Book ***(978-0-7391-6939-1(4))*** Lexington Bks.

Metford, Beatrix. Where China Meets Burma: Life & Travel in the Burma-China Border Lands. reprint ed. 29.50 *(978-0-404-16844-5(2))* AMS Pr., Inc.

Mexico, Zachary. China Underground. 2009. (ENG.). 320p. pap. 16.95 *(978-1-59376-223-0(2),* Soft Skull Pr.) Counterpoint LLC.

Michell, George, et al. Kashgar: Oasis City on China's Old Silk Road. 2008. (ENG., Illus.). 160p. 50.00 *(978-0-7112-2913-6(9))* Lincoln, Frances Ltd. GBR. Dist: Perseus-PGW.

Morris-Suzuki, Tessa. To the Diamond Mountains: A Hundred-Year Journey Through China & Korea. 2010. (Illus.). xiii, 201p. ***(978-1-4422-0505-5(9))*** Rowman & Littlefield Publishers, Inc.

Morris-Suzuki, Tessa, ed. To the Diamond Mountains: A Hundred-Year Journey through China & Korea. 2010. (Asia/Pacific/Perspectives Ser.). (ENG., Illus.). 216p. 37.50 *(978-1-4422-0503-1(2))* Rowman & Littlefield Publishers, Inc.

Morris, T. M. & Glover, Richard. A Winter in North China. 2010. (Cambridge Library Collection - Travel & Exploration Ser.). (Illus.). 264p. pap. 23.99 *(978-1-108-01382-6(1))* Cambridge Univ. Pr.

Morrison, G. E. An Australian in China. 2009. (ENG.). 351p. pap. 25.99 *(978-1-117-51246-4(0),* BiblioLife) BiblioBazaar.

Morrison, George. An Australian in China. 2010. 300p. pap. 19.99 *(978-988-17621-8-4(9))* Earnshaw Bks. HKG. Dist: Independent Pubs. Group.

Morrison, George Ernest. An Australian in China. 2008. 276p. 28.99 *(978-0-554-29123-9(1))* BiblioBazaar.

—An Australian in China. 2008. (Illus.). 256p. pap. *(978-1-4065-7703-7(0))* Dodo Pr.

Mote, Frederick W. China & the Vocation of History in the Twentieth Century: A Personal Memoir. 2010. (ENG., Illus.). 360p. (C). 29.95 *(978-0-691-14463-4(X))* Princeton Univ. Pr.

Mueggler, Erik. The Paper Road: Archive & Experience in the Botanical Exploration of West China & Tibet. 2011. (ENG., Illus.). 346p. 70.00 *(978-0-520-26902-6(0));* pap. 29.95 *(978-0-520-26903-3(9))* Univ. of California Pr.

Nichols, Francis. Through Hidden Shensi. 2007. (ENG.). 464p. 52.95 *(978-0-548-05321-8(9))* Kessinger Publishing, LLC.

Notar, Beth E. Displacing Desire: Travel & Popular Culture in China. 2007. (Illus.). 193p. per. 23.00 *(978-0-8248-3071-7(7))* Univ. of Hawaii Pr.

Nunn, Darrell & Russett, Donna. Faces of China: From Mao to Now. 2007. 308p. per. 21.95 *(978-0-595-44456-4(3))* iUniverse, Inc.

Ono, Katsutoshi, et al. Ru Tang Qiu Fa Xun Li Xing Ji Jiao Zhu. 2007. (Riben Ru Hua Qiu Fa Seng Ren Xing Ji Jiao Zhu Cong Kan Ser.: Vol. 1). (CHI., Illus.). *(978-7-80755-145-4(3))* Huashan Arts and Literature Publishing Hse.

Ortman, Blanche Sellers. New York to Peking. 2011. 154p. pap. 27.45 ***(978-1-4460-7336-0(X))*** Thorndike Pr.

Pao, Basil. China Revealed: An Extraordinary Journey of Rediscovery. 2007. (ENG., Illus.). 373p. 60.00 *(978-0-7892-0947-4(0))* Abbeville Pr., Inc.

Parfitt, Troy. Why China Will Never Rule the World: Travels in the Two Chinas. 2011. (CHI & ENG.). 416p. pap. 20.95 *(978-0-9868035-0-5(2))* Western Hemisphere Pr. CAN. Dist: AtlasBooks Distribution.

Paulding, James Kirke. A Book of Vagaries; Comprising the New Mirror for Travelers & Other Whim-Whams: Being Selections from the Papers of A Retired Common-Councilman, Ere. 2006. 436p. per. 26.99 *(978-1-4255-4800-1(8))* MPublishing.

Peck, Graham. Two Kinds of Time. (Illus.). reprint ed. 67.50 *(978-0-404-20198-2(9))* AMS Pr., Inc.

—Two Kinds of Time. 2008. (ENG., Illus.). 734p. pap. 28.95 *(978-0-295-98852-8(5))* Univ. of Washington Pr.

Percival, William Spencer. Land of the Dragon: My Boating & Shooting Excursions to the Gorges of the Upper Yangtze. 2010. (Cambridge Library Collection - Travel & Exploration Ser.). (ENG., Illus.). 360p. pap. 29.99 *(978-1-108-01381-9(3))* Cambridge Univ. Pr.

Pineda, Carlos. Honor Thy Daughters: A Father's Story of a China Adoption. 2008. 128p. 23.99 *(978-1-4343-8831-5(X));* pap. 13.99 *(978-1-4343-8830-8(1))* AuthorHouse.

Porter, Bill & Pine, Red. Road to Heaven: Encounters with Chinese Hermits. 2009. (ENG.). 240p. pap. 15.95 *(978-1-58243-523-7(5),* Counterpoint Pr.) Basic Bks. GBR. Dist: Perseus-PGW.

Prinsep, Henry Thoby. Tibet, Tartary & Mongolia: Their Social & Political Condition, & the Religion of Boodh, as There Existing. 2011. (Cambridge Library Collection - History Ser.). (ENG., Illus.). 184p. pap. 19.99 *(978-1-108-02873-8(X))* Cambridge Univ. Pr.

Purini, Franco, ed. Competition Ideas for the Italian Pavilion at Expo Shanghai 2010: The Future of Cities Is 'Made in Italy' 2011. 208p. pap. 38.95 *(978-88-492-1934-0(2))* Gangemi ITA. Dist: International Publishers Marketing.

Pyke, Richard. Green Edge of Asia. 2006. 168p. per. *(978-1-4067-2155-3(7),* Hesperides Pr.) Read Bks.

Qin, Xiu Yan & Sunderman, Stuart Alan. Learning English Through Phonetics. 2011. 208p. 29.99 ***(978-1-4535-8727-0(6))***; pap. 19.99 ***(978-1-4535-8726-3(8))*** Xlibris Corp.

Renouf, Alice & Ryan-Maher, Mary Beth. Yin-Yang: American Perspectives on Living in China. 2011. ***(978-1-4422-1271-8(3))*** Rowman & Littlefield Publishers, Inc.

Renouf/Ryan-Maher. China Survival Guide: American Perspectives on Living in China. 2011. (ENG.). 246p. 70.00 ***(978-1-4422-1269-5(1))*** Rowman & Littlefield Publishers, Inc.

—Yin-Yang: American Perspectives on Living in China. 2011. (ENG.). 246p. pap. 22.95 ***(978-1-4422-1270-1(5))*** Rowman & Littlefield Publishers, Inc.

Robbins, Helen Henrietta Macartney & Macartney, George. Our First Ambassador to China: An Account of the Life of George, Earl of Macartney, with Extracts from His Letters, & the Narrative of His Experiences in China, as Told by Himself, 1737¿1806. 2011. (Cambridge Library Collection - Travel & Exploration Ser.). (Illus.). 540p. pap. 37.99 *(978-1-108-02625-3(7))* Cambridge Univ. Pr.

Rockhill, W. Woodville. The Land of the Lamas: Notes of a Journey Through China, Mongolia & Tibet. 2007. (ENG.). 416p. 49.95 *(978-0-548-03607-5(1))* Kessinger Publishing, LLC.

Rose, Sarah. For All the Tea in China: How England Stole the World's Favorite Drink & Changed History. (ENG.). 272p. (gr. 12). 2011. 15.00 *(978-0-14-311874-9(9),* Penguin (Non-Classics)) 2010. 25.95 *(978-0-670-02152-9(0),* Viking Adult) Penguin Group (USA) Inc.

Ryan, Chris & Gu, Huimin. Tourism in China: Destination, Cultures & Communities. Huimin, Gu, ed. 2008. (Routledge Advances in Tourism Ser.). (ENG., Illus.). 418p. 125.00 *(978-0-415-99189-6(7))* Routledge.

Salzman, Mark. Iron & Silk. 2009. (ENG.). 197p. pap. 29.95 *(978-1-4128-1269-6(0))* Transaction Pubs.

Schafer, Edward H. The Vermilion Bird: T'Ang Images of the South. 2008. (ENG., Illus.). 392p. per. 50.00 *(978-1-891640-37-7(2))* Floating World Editions.

Shaw, Samuel. The Journals of Major Samuel Shaw. 2009. (Revolutionary War Ser.). (ENG.). 380p. pap. 23.95 *(978-1-4290-1696-4(5))* Applewood Bks.

Smith, Jennifer L. Under the Mosquito Net. 2008. 139p. pap. 11.95 *(978-0-7414-4565-0(4))* Infinity Publishing.

Spirit of China. 2008. 240p. *(978-1-4075-2515-0(8))* Parragon, Inc.

Stein, M. Aurel. Ancient Khotan: Detailed Report of Archaeological Explorations in Chinese Turkestan Carried Out & Described under the Orders of H. M. Indian Government. 2006. (ENG.). 621p. 160.00 *(978-1-878529-42-8(0))* Orchid Pr. THA. Dist: National Bk. Network.

Stone, Laura. I Give Seven Chicken. 2007. 215p. pap. 16.95 *(978-1-4303-1001-3(4))* Lulu Enterprises Inc.

Strittmatter, Kai. China: An Introduction to the Culture & People. 2012. (Armchair Traveller Ser.). (ENG.). 171p. pap. 11.95 ***(978-1-907973-17-8(6))*** Haus Publishing GBR. Dist: Consortium Bk. Sales & Distribution.

Strittmatter, Kai. China A-Z. Tobler, Stefan, tr. from GER. 2006. (Armchair Traveller Ser.). (ENG., Illus.). 316p. 19.95 *(978-1-904950-80-6(9))* Haus Publishing GBR. Dist: Consortium Bk. Sales & Distribution.

Su, Xiaobo & Teo, Peggy. The Politics of Heritage Tourism in China: A View from Lijiang. 2009. (Routledge Contemporary China Ser.). (ENG., Illus.). 224p. 150.00 *(978-0-415-47808-3(1))* Routledge.

Tamm, Eric Enno. The Horse That Leaps Through Clouds: A Tale of Espionage, the Silk Road, & the Rise of Modern China. 2011. (ENG.). 512p. 30.00 *(978-1-58243-734-7(3),* Counterpoint) Counterpoint LLC.

Tamm, Eric Enno. The Horse That Leaps Through Clouds: A Tale of Espionage, the Silk Road, & the Rise of Modern China. 2012. (ENG.). 512p. pap. 21.95 ***(978-1-58243-817-7(X),*** Counterpoint) Counterpoint LLC.

Tate, Mary Kate, et al. Feeding the Dragon: A Culinary Travelogue Through China with Recipes. 2011. (ENG., Illus.). 304p. pap. 24.99 *(978-1-4494-0111-5(2))* Andrews McMeel Publishing.

Thayer, Helen. Walking the Gobi: A 1600-Mile Trek Across a Desert of Hope & Despair. 2007. (ENG., Illus.). 272p. 23.95 *(978-1-59485-064-6(X))* Mountaineers Bks., The.

Theroux, Paul. Riding the Iron Rooster: By Train Through China. 2006. (ENG., Illus.). 480p. pap. 15.95 *(978-0-618-65897-8(1),* Mariner Bks.) Houghton Mifflin Harcourt Trade & Reference Pubs.

Thomson, J. (John). The Straits of Malacca, Indo-China, & China; or, Ten Years' Travels, Adventures, & Residence Abroad by J Thomson Illustrated with Upward Of. 2006. (Illus.). 624p. per. 34.99 *(978-1-4255-6564-0(6))* MPublishing.

Todd, Martha Sue. Never Too Old to Climb Walls. 2007. 456p. 35.40 *(978-1-4251-2770-1(3))* Trafford Publishing.

TRAVELMAG Das Reisemagazin Westfalen, Ruhrgebiet. 2008. (Country Explorers Ser.). (J). pap. 8.95 *(978-0-8225-8507-7(3))* Lerner Publishing Group.

Tredinnick, Jeremy, et al. Xinjiang: China's Central Asia. 2012. (Odyssey Illustrated Guides). (ENG., Illus.). 480p. pap. 29.95 *(978-962-217-790-1(5),* 217790) Airphoto International/Odyssey HKG. Dist: Norton, W. W. & Co., Inc.

Troost, J. Maarten. Lost on Planet China: One Man's Attempt to Understand the World's Most Mystifying Nation. 2009. (ENG.). 400p. pap. 14.95 *(978-0-7679-2201-2(8))* Broadway Bks.

Truman, Sarah. Searching for Guan Yin. 2011. (Companions for the Journey Ser.). (ENG.). 220p. pap. 16.00 ***(978-1-935210-28-3(9))*** White Pine Pr.

Tuan, Yi-Fu. Coming Home to China. 2007. (Illus.). 184p. 55.50 *(978-0-8166-4991-4(X));* per. 18.50 *(978-0-8166-4992-1(8))* Univ. of Minnesota Pr.

UC Publishing Staff & Newburn, Denny. Action Literacy: China. 2008. 32p. pap. 10.95 *(978-0-86431-695-0(X))* ACER Pr. AUS. Dist: International Specialized Bk. Services.

Van Braam Houckgeest, André Everard Van. An Authentic Account of the Embassy of the Dutch East-India Company, to the Court of the Emperor of China, in the Years 1794 & 1795; Taken From. 2010. 348p. pap. 32.75 *(978-1-140-72809-2(1));* 336p. pap. 31.75 *(978-1-140-72808-5(3))* BiblioBazaar. (Gale ECCO, Print Editions).

Wagner, David. Unpaved Roads. 2007. 190p. per. 15.95 *(978-0-9766340-8-9(2))* Inkwell Productions, LLC.

Walker, William. Where There's a Will There's a Way. 2009. (Illus.). 88p. pap. 30.49 *(978-1-4389-6789-9(6))* AuthorHouse.

Walters, Martin. Chinese Wildlife: A Visitor's Guide. 2008. (Bradt Travel Guide Chinese Wildlife Ser.). (ENG., Illus.). 208p. pap. 26.99 *(978-1-84162-220-0(6))* Bradt Travel Guides GBR. Dist: Globe Pequot Pr., The.

Wang, Leslie Kim, et al, eds. From Home to Homeland: What Adoptive Families Need to Know Before Making a Return Trip to China. 2010. 363p. pap. 18.95 *(978-1-59743-003-6(X))* Yeong & Yeong Bk. Co.

Wang, Lin & Wei, Xiaohao. Living in China: How to Feel at Home, Make Friends & Enjoy Everyday Life. 2008. (Illus.). 84p. pap. 12.50 *(978-0-86647-267-8(3))* Hood, Alan C. & Co., Inc.

Ward, Kirwan. Willow Pattern Walkabout. 2011. (ENG.). 152p. 49.99 *(978-988-18667-1-4(5))* Earnshaw Bks. HKG. Dist: Independent Pubs. Group.

Weale, B. L. Putnam. Manchu & Muscovite: Being Letters from Manchuria Written During. 2006. (ENG.). 636p. per. 45.95 *(978-1-4286-5915-5(3))* Kessinger Publishing, LLC.

Weäyling, Bernhard. Here I Am Laowei. 2011. 224p. pap. 80.50 ***(978-3-8448-7273-6(6))*** Bks. on Demand.

Weiner, Rebecca, et al. China: CultureShock!, 1 vol. 2nd ed. 2007. (Cultureshock China: A Survival Guide to Customs & Etiquette Ser.). (ENG., Illus.). 32p. pap. 15.95 *(978-0-7614-5403-8(9))* Marshall Cavendish Corp.

Weiss, Linn. China Readies for Its Close-Up: As the Countryprepares to Face the Klieg Lights of the 2008 Olympics: A Look at Tibet, China's Classic Cities, & Hong Kong/Macao. 2008. (Illus.). 79p. ***(978-1-4363-1523-4(9))*** Xlibris Corp.

West, James. Beijing Blur: A Head-Spinning Journey into Modern China. 2008. 230p. pap. 14.95 *(978-0-9788259-6-6(9))* Chilmark Pr., The.

Westwell, Ian. Timeless China. 2007. (Timeless Ser.). (Illus.). 160p. 12.99 *(978-0-7858-2318-6(2),* Chartwell) Book Sales, Inc.

Williams, S. Wells. The Middle Kingdom: A Survey of the Geography, Government, Literature, Social Life, Arts & History of the Chinese Empire & Its in Habitants, 2 vols. 2006. (Kegan Paul China Library). (Illus.). 892p. 500.00 *(978-0-7103-1167-2(2))* Taylor & Francis Group.

Williamson, Isabelle. Old Highways in China. 2010. (Cambridge Library Collection - Travel & Exploration Ser.). (ENG., Illus.). 236p. pap. 22.99 *(978-1-108-01518-9(2))* Cambridge Univ. Pr.

Wilson, Ernest Henry. A Naturalist in Western China with Vasculum, Camera & Gun: Being Some Account of Eleven Years' Travel. 2011. (Cambridge Library Collection - Life Sciences Ser.). (ENG.). 344p. pap. 28.99 *(978-1-108-03046-5(7));* (Illus.). 408p. pap. 31.99 *(978-1-108-03045-8(9))* Cambridge Univ. Pr.

Winter, Dave. Footprint Karakoram Highway Handbook: The Travel Guide. Date not set. (Illus.). 408p. pap. *(978-1-903471-26-5(5))* Footprint Handbooks.

Wong, Jan. A Comrade Lost & Found: A Beijing Memoir. 2010. (ENG.). 336p. pap. 14.95 *(978-0-547-24789-2(3),* Mariner Bks.) Houghton Mifflin Harcourt Trade & Reference Pubs.

—A Comrade Lost & Found: A Beijing Story. 2009. (ENG., Illus.). 336p. 25.00 *(978-0-15-101342-5(X))* Houghton Mifflin Harcourt Trade & Reference Pubs.

Wood, Frances. The Lure of China: History & Literature from Marco Polo to J. G. Ballard. 2009. (ENG.). 330p. pap. 24.95 *(978-1-59265-082-8(1))* Long River Pr.

Wright, Patrick. Passport to Peking: A Very British Mission to Mao's China. 2010. (ENG., Illus.). 352p. 34.95 *(978-0-19-954193-5(0))* Oxford Univ. Pr., Inc.

Wu, Xiaozhen. Chinese Landscapes (Essays) 2010. 156p. pap. 9.95 *(978-1-60220-903-9(0))* BetterLink Pr., Inc.

Xi'an Qujiang Da ming gong yi zhi qu bao hu gai zao ban gong shi Staff, contrib. by. Da Ming Gong Guo Jia Yi Zhi Gong Yuan: Daming Palace National Heritage Park. 2009. (Illus.). *(978-7-01-008396-4(7))* People's Publishing Hse., The.

Xiao, Honggen, ed. Contemporary Perspectives on China Tourism. 2011. (ENG.). 224p. (C). 125.00 ***(978-0-415-69753-8(0))*** Routledge.

Xie, Philip Feifan. Authenticating Ethnic Tourism. 2010. (Tourism & Cultural Change Ser.). (ENG., Illus.). 288p. 149.95 *(978-1-84541-158-9(7));* pap. 54.95 *(978-1-84541-157-2(9))* Channel View Pubns., Ltd. GBR. Dist: Univ. of Toronto Pr.

Yang, Jun. Impact Analysis of the Olympic Games Host City - Specially Focused on Sports Tourism Development in Qingdao, the Sailing Events Host City of 2008 Beij. 2008. 112p. pap. *(978-3-639-10832-3(9))* VDM Verlag Dr. Mueller e.K.

Yardley, Jim. Brave Dragons: A Chinese Basketball Team, an American Coach, & Two Cultures Clashing. 2012. (ENG., Illus.). 320p. 26.95 ***(978-0-307-27221-8(4),*** Knopf) Knopf Doubleday Publishing Group.

Yule, Henry, ed. Cathay & the Way Thither: Being a Collection of Medieval Notices of China. 2010. (Cambridge Library Collection - Hakluyt First Ser.). (Illus.). 524p. pap. 39.99 *(978-1-108-01036-8(9))* Cambridge Univ. Pr.

Yule, Henry, tr. Cathay & the Way Thither: Being a Collection of Medieval Notices of China. 2010. (Cambridge Library Collection - Hakluyt First Ser.). (ENG.). 456p. pap. 34.99 *(978-1-108-01037-5(7))* Cambridge Univ. Pr.

Zhaitian, Yang, et al, eds. Chinese Tourism Geography. 2nd rev. ed. 2012. (ENG.). 416p. 129.95 *(978-1-4398-6036-6(X),* CRC Press) Taylor & Francis Group GBR. Dist: Taylor & Francis Group.

Zhaoming, Yang. Tour of Qufu: The Hometown of Confucius. 2010. (Illus.). 176p. pap. 24.95 *(978-1-60220-305-1(9))* BetterLink Pr., Inc.

Zhu, Judy. Modern Chinese Cultural Encounters: Volume I Studying & traveling in China. 2009. 128p. pap. 13.95 *(978-1-4401-3323-7(9))* iUniverse, Inc.

Zola, Alberto. China: A Land of Age-Old Culture. 2008. (Exploring Countries of the Wor Ser.). (ENG., Illus.). 128p. 9.95 *(978-88-544-0293-5(1))* White Star ITA. Dist: Random Hse., Inc.

CHINA—DIRECTORIES

CER Publishing, ed. China Financial Services Directory 2007. 2007. 728p. pap. 57.50 *(978-988-99114-7-8(7))* China Economic Review Publishing HKG. Dist: Trans-Atlantic Pubns., Inc.

—China Hotel Directory 2007. 2007. 738p. pap. 57.50 *(978-988-99633-5-4(3))* China Economic Review Publishing HKG. Dist: Trans-Atlantic Pubns., Inc.

—China Logistics Directory 2007/2008. 2007. 804p. pap. 57.50 *(978-988-99633-7-8(X))* China Economic Review Publishing HKG. Dist: Trans-Atlantic Pubns., Inc.

—China Media Directory 2008. 2007. 540p. pap. 57.50 *(978-988-99874-0-4(6))* China Economic Review Publishing HKG. Dist: Trans-Atlantic Pubns., Inc.

—China Stock Directory 2007/2008. 5th ed. 2007. 1004p. pap. 97.50 *(978-988-99874-6-6(5))* China Economic Review Publishing HKG. Dist: Trans-Atlantic Pubns., Inc.

—Shanghai Business Eats. 2007. 100p. pap. 19.95 *(978-988-99633-1-6(0))* China Economic Review Publishing HKG. Dist: Trans-Atlantic Pubns., Inc.

Djordjevic, Nenad. Old Shanghai Clubs & Associations: A Directory of the Rich Life of Foreigners in Shanghai from the 1840s to the 1950s. 2010. (ENG., Illus.). 340p. 29.99 *(978-988-17621-9-1(7))* Earnshaw Bks. HKG. Dist: Independent Pubs. Group.

CHINA—ECONOMIC CONDITIONS

"Aba Zangzu Qiangzu Zizhizhou gai kuang" bian xie zu Staff & "Aba Zangzu Qiangzu Zizhizhou gai kuang" xiu ding ben bian xie zu Staff, contrib. by. Aba Zangzu Qiangzu Zizhizhou Gai Kuang: AbaZangzuQiangzuZizhizhougaikuang. 2009. (CHI., Illus.). *(978-7-105-08670-2(X))* Nationalities Publishing Hse, The.

Agarwala, Rina & Herring, Ronald J., eds. Whatever Happened to Class? Reflections from South Asia. 2008. (Illus.). 240p. 140.00 *(978-0-415-45468-1(9))* Routledge.

Alas, Ruth & Gao, Junhong. Crisis Management in Chinese Organizations: Benefiting from the Changes. 2012. (ENG., Illus.). 216p. 90.00 ***(978-0-230-27334-4(3))*** Palgrave Macmillan.

Allen, Wilfred J. & Young, Alex, eds. In China We Trust: The Impacts of Chinese Economic Policies. 2012. ***(978-1-61942-828-7(8))*** Nova Science Pubs., Inc.

Anderson, Eric C. China Restored: The Middle Kingdom Looks to 2020 & Beyond, 1 vol. 2010. 323p. 44.95 *(978-0-313-38517-9(3),* A2975C, Praeger Pubs.) Greenwood Publishing Group, Inc.

Arrighi, Giovanni. Adam Smith in Beijing: Lineages of the Twenty-First Century. 2007. (ENG., Illus.). 418p. 35.00 *(978-1-84467-104-5(6),* 844104) Verso Bks. GBR. Dist: Norton, W. W. & Co., Inc.

Arrighi, Giovanni & Smith, Adam. Adam Smith in Beijing: Lineages of the Twenty-First Century. 2009. (ENG., Illus.). 418p. pap. 26.95 *(978-1-84467-298-1(0),* 844298) Verso Bks. GBR. Dist: Norton, W. W. & Co., Inc.

Atzberger, Craig. Will Peak Oil Fuel the Aids Epidemic? 2008. 412p. pap. *(978-3-8364-8737-5(3))* VDM Verlag Dr. Mueller e.K.

Austin, Denise. Kingdom-Minded People: Christian Identity & the Contributions of Chinese Business Christians: Christian Identity & the Contributions of Chinese Business Christians. 2011. (Global Pentecostal & Charismatic Studies). (Illus.). 249p. ***(978-90-04-20402-7(4))*** BRILL.

Bagge, John & Schou, Kristoffer. Effectiveness of an Interactive Marketing Platform in Taipei. 2011. 156p. pap. ***(978-3-8443-0576-0(9))*** Lambert Academic Publishing.

Bahl, Raghav. Superpower? The Amazing Race Between China's Hare & India's Tortoise. 2010. (ENG., Illus.). 272p. (gr. 12). 26.95 *(978-1-59184-396-2(0)*, Portfolio (Hardcover)) Penguin Group (USA) Inc.

"Baoting Lizu Miaozu Zizhixian gai kuang" bian xie zu Staff, contrib. by. Baoting Lizu Miaozu Zizhixian Gai Kuang: BaotingLizuMiaozuZ zhixiangaikuang. 2008. (CHI., Illus.). *(978-7-105-08617-7(3))* Nationalities Publishing Hse, The.

Barth, James R., et al, eds. China's Emerging Financial Markets: Challenges & Opportunities. 2009. (Milken Institute Series on Financial Innovation & Economic Growth Ser.). (ENG., Illus.). xxii, 658p. 179.00 *(978-0-387-93768-7(4)*, 0387937684) Springer.

Barton, Dominic. China Vignettes: An Inside Look at China. Yelin, Meir, ed. 2008. (CHI & ENG., Illus.). 336p. pap. 25.00 *(978-981-05-8091-9(6))* Thorogood GBR. Dist: Stylus Publishing, LLC.

Basu, Jisnu. Technology Transfer & Assimilation in Rural Industrial Clusters. 2010. 204p. pap. *(978-3-8383-7506-9(8))* Lambert Academic Publishing.

Basu, Parikshit K. & Bandara, Yapa, eds. WTO Accession & Socio-Economic Development in China. 2009. (Chandos Asian Studies). (ENG., Illus.). 234p. 110.00 *(978-1-84334-547-3(1)*, Chandos Publishing) Woodhead Publishing Ltd. GBR. Dist: Ingram Pub. Services.

Bennett, Joe. Where Underpants Come From. 2011. (ENG., Illus.). 256p. (gr. 12). 14.95 *(978-1-59020-336-1(4))* Overlook Pr., The.

—Where Underpants Come From: From Cotton Fields to Checkout Counters — Travels Through the New China & into the New Global Economy. 2009. (ENG., Illus.). 368p. (gr. 12-18). 25.95 *(978-1-59020-228-9(7))* Overlook Pr., The.

Bergère, Marie-Claire. The Golden Age of the Chinese Bourgeoisie, 1911-1937. 2009. (Studies in Modern Capitalism Ser.). (ENG.). 372p. pap. 38.99 *(978-0-521-11071-6(8))* Cambridge Univ. Pr.

Bergsten, C. Fred, et al. China: The Balance Sheet - What the World Needs to Know Now about the Emerging Superpower. 2007. (ENG., Illus.). 224p. per. 13.95 *(978-1-58648-435-4(4))* PublicAffairs.

—China's Rise: Challenges & Opportunities. (Illus.). 2009. 280p. pap. 13.95 *(978-0-88132-434-1(5))* 2008. 256p. 26.95 *(978-0-88132-417-4(5))* Peterson Institute for International Economics.

Berik, Günseli, et al, eds. Gender, China & the World Trade Organization: Essays from Feminist Economics. 2012. (ENG.). 344p. (C). pap. 42.95 ***(978-0-415-62335-3(9))*** Routledge.

Berkshire Encyclopedia of Sustainability Vol. 7: China & India: Assessing Sustainability. 2010. 512p. lib. bdg. 150.00 *(978-1-933782-69-0(2))* Berkshire Publishing Group.

Bhaumik, T. K. Old China's New Economy: The Conquest of a Billion Paupers. 2009. (Illus.). 328p. (C). pap. 32.95 *(978-81-7829-862-7(7)*, B98627P) SAGE Pubns., Inc.

BIA. Essential Chinese Manufacturers: Food, Textile, Clothing, & Chemical Companies. 6th rev. ed. 2006. 450p. (J). pap. 249.00 *(978-1-4187-4194-5(9))* Business Information Agency.

—Major Wholesalers of China. 6th rev. ed. 2006. 250p. (J). pap. 249.00 *(978-1-4187-4296-6(1))* Business Information Agency.

Blankert. China Rising: Will the West Be Able to. . 2009. 28.00 *(978-981-283-795-0(7))* World Scientific Publishing Co., Inc.

Boden, Jeanne. Wall Behind China's Open Door: Towards Efficient Intercultural Management in China. 2008. (ENG.). 300p. pap. 38.00 *(978-90-5487-464-5(3))* VUB Univ. Pr. BEL. Dist: Independent Pubs. Group.

Borysevicz, Mathieu. Learning from Hangzhou. 2009. (ENG., Illus.). 330p. pap. 45.00 *(978-988-18033-6-8(5))* Timezone 8 Ltd. HKG. Dist: D.A.P./Distributed Art Pubs.

Brady, Anne-Marie & Brown, Douglas, eds. Foreigners & Foreign Institutions in Republican China. 2012. (Chinese Worlds Ser.). (ENG., Illus.). 320p. (C). 135.00 ***(978-0-415-52865-8(8))*** Routledge.

BRAMALL. Chinese Economic Development. 2008. (Illus.). 640p. pap. 68.95 *(978-0-415-37348-7(4))* Routledge.

Bramall, Chris. Chinese Economic Development. 2008. (ENG., Illus.). 640p. (C). 190.00 *(978-0-415-37347-0(6))* Routledge.

Brandt, Loren & Rawski, Thomas G., eds. China's Great Economic Transformation. 2008. (ENG., Illus.). 928p. 183.99 *(978-0-521-88557-7(4))*; pap. 85.00 *(978-0-521-71290-3(4))* Cambridge Univ. Pr.

Breslin, Shaun. China & the Global Political Economy. 2009. (ENG.). 246p. pap. 37.00 *(978-0-230-57793-0(8))* Palgrave Macmillan.

Breslin, Shaun & Shaw, Timothy M. China & the Global Political Economy. 2007. (International Political Economy Ser.). (ENG., Illus.). 256p. 106.00 *(978-1-4039-8647-4(9))* Palgrave Macmillan.

Brodsgaard, Kjeld Erik. Hainan - State, Society, & Business in a Chinese Province. 2012. (China Policy Ser.). (ENG., Illus.). 208p. (C). pap. 42.95 ***(978-0-415-54138-1(7))*** Routledge.

Brown, Jeremy. City Versus Countryside in Mao's China: Negotiating the Divide. 2012. (ENG., Illus.). 264p. 99.00 ***(978-1-107-02404-5(8))*** Cambridge Univ. Pr.

Brown, Kerry. The Rise of the Dragon: Inward & Outward Investment in China in the Reform Period. 2008. (Illus.). 244p. *(978-1-84334-351-6(7)*, Chandos Publishing) Woodhead Publishing Ltd.

—The Rise of the Dragon: Inward & Outward Investment in China in the Reform Period,1978-2007. 2008. (Chandos Asian Studies). (ENG., Illus.). 242p. per. 50.00 *(978-1-84334-481-0(5)*, Chandos Publishing) Woodhead Publishing Ltd. GBR. Dist: Ingram Pub. Services.

Buoye, Thomas M. Manslaughter, Markets, & Moral Economy: Violent Disputes over Property Rights in Eighteenth-Century China. 2006. (Cambridge Studies in Chinese History, Literature & Institutions Ser.). (ENG., Illus.). 300p. pap. 58.00 *(978-0-521-02781-6(0))* Cambridge Univ. Pr.

Cabestan, Jean-Pierre, et al, eds. China & the Global Economic Crisis. 2012. (Routledge Studies on the Chinese Economy Ser.). (ENG., Illus.). 192p. (C). 150.00 *(978-0-415-67514-7(6))* Routledge.

Calomiris, Charles W., ed. China's Financial Transition at a Crossroads. 2007. (ENG., Illus.). 432p. (gr. 17). 45.00 *(978-0-231-14192-5(0))* Columbia Univ. Pr.

CER Publishing, ed. China by Numbers 2008. 2007. 272p. 32.50 *(978-988-17149-2-3(3))* China Economic Review Publishing HKG. Dist: Trans-Atlantic Pubns., Inc.

Chai, J. C. H. An Economic History of Modern China. 2011. (Illus.). 288p. 110.00 ***(978-1-84720-937-5(8))*** Elgar, Edward Publishing, Inc.

Chan, Anita, et al. Chen Village: Revolution to Globalization. 3rd ed. 2009. (Illus.). 400p. pap. 26.95 *(978-0-520-25931-7(9))* Univ. of California Pr.

Chan, Kai Yiu. Business Expansion & Structural Change in Pre-War China: Liu Hongsheng & His Enterprises, 1920-1937. 2006. (Business, Innovation, & Society in Asia Ser.). (ENG., Illus.). 324p. (gr. 17). 60.00 *(978-962-209-764-3(2))* Hong Kong Univ. Pr. HKG. Dist: Columbia Univ. Pr.

Chan, Thomas & Moser v. Filseck, Karin. Perceptions & Images of China. Assmann, Heinz-Dieter, ed. 2008. 298p. pap. 49.00 *(978-3-8329-3459-0(6))* Nomos Verlagsgesellschaft DEU. Dist: International Specialized Bk. Services.

Chang, Julian & Goldstein, Steven M., eds. Economic Reform & Cross-Strait Relations: Taiwan & China in the WTO. 2007. (Ser. on Contemporary China Ser.). (Illus.). 377p. 113.00 *(978-981-256-854-0(9))* World Scientific Publishing Co., Inc.

Changzheng, Zhang, ed. Manipulation Effect of Managerial Discretion on Managerial Compensation: Evidence from Listed Firms in China. 2010. (Management Science - Theory & Applications Ser.). (Illus.). x, 213p. 89.00 *(978-1-60876-460-0(5))* Nova Science Pubs., Inc.

Chee, Harold. Myths about Doing Business in China. 2nd rev. ed. 2007. (ENG., Illus.). 176p. pap. 43.00 *(978-0-230-55118-3(1))* Palgrave Macmillan.

Chen, Binlin. Environmental Impacts of the Tves Law of Chin. 2010. 64p. pap. *(978-3-639-26177-6(1))* VDM Verlag Dr. Mueller e.K.

Chen, Hesheng, ed. Large Research Infrastructures Development in China: A Roadmap To 2050: A Roadmap To 2050. 2011. (ENG., Illus.). 170p. pap. 99.00 *(978-3-642-19367-5(6)*, 3642193676) Springer.

Chen, J., ed. The China Economy Yearbook, Volume 3: Analysis & Forecast of China's Economy (2008) 2009. (Chinese Academy of Social Sciences Yearbooks: Society Ser.). *(978-90-04-17351-4(X))* BRILL.

Chen, Nai-Ruenn, ed. Chinese Economic Statistics in the Maoist Era: 1949-1965. 2008. (ENG.). 570p. pap. 95.00 *(978-0-202-36281-6(7))* Aldine Transaction.

Chen, Yang. Ownership in China's Transitional Economy: The Limitations of Conventional Property Rights Theory. 2007. 340p. *(978-0-7734-5265-7(6))* Mellen, Edwin Pr., The.

Chen, Yong, ed. Energy Science & Technology in China: A Roadmap To 2050: A Roadmap To 2050. 2010. (Illus.). 103p. pap. 99.00 *(978-3-642-05319-1(X)*, 364205319X) Springer.

Cheng. A Guideline to Investment in the Chinese Currency (Cny) & Interest Rates Markets: Opportunities & Risks. 2011. 58.00 *(978-981-4287-68-5(7))* World Scientific Publishing Co., Inc.

Cheng, Chih-Peng. Deciphering a Global Industry. 2007. 256p. per. *(978-3-8364-1772-3(3))* VDM Verlag Dr. Mueller e.K.

Cheng, Shi. China's Rural Industrialization Policy: Growing under Orders Since 1949. 2006. (ENG., Illus.). 368p. 137.00 *(978-1-4039-9615-2(6))* Palgrave Macmillan.

Cheng, Siwei. Economic Reforms & Development in China, 3 vols., Vol. 1. 2011. (Selected Works of Cheng Siwei Ser.). (ENG.). 432p. 138.00 *(978-981-4332-16-3(X))* Enrich Professional Publishing (S)., Ltd. SGP. Dist: Independent Pubs. Group.

Cheung, Gordon C. K. & Cheung, Gordon. China Factors: Political Perspectives & Economic Interactions. 2007. (ENG.). 177p. (gr. 11). 49.95 *(978-0-7658-0342-9(9))* Transaction Pubs.

Cheung, Yin-Wong, et al. The Economic Integration of Greater China: Real & Financial Linkages & the Prospects for Currency Union. 2007. (ENG., Illus.). 172p. (gr. 17). 59.50 *(978-962-209-822-0(3))* Hong Kong Univ. Pr. HKG. Dist: Columbia Univ. Pr.

Chevalier, Michel & Lu, Pierre Xiao. Luxury China: Market Opportunities & Potential. 2009. (ENG., Illus.). 300p. 34.95 *(978-0-470-82341-5(0)*, Wiley) Wiley, John & Sons, Inc.

Chiang Kai-Shek Staff. China's Dest & Chinese Eco Theory. 2009. 348p. *(978-1-905246-81-6(1))* BRILL.

China Development Research Foundation. Thirty Years of China's Reform. 2012. (Routledge Studies on the Chinese Economy Ser.). (ENG., Illus.). 632p. (C). 215.00 ***(978-0-415-68999-1(6))*** Routledge.

China Employment Handbook: Companies-Products-Services, 3 vols. (Illus.). 1800p. *(978-0-7605-0668-4(X))* Rector Pr., Ltd.

China Knowledge Press, creator. Financial Services in China: The Past, Present & Future of a Changing Industry. 2007. (Illus.). 547p. pap. 90.00 *(978-981-4163-26-2(0)*, CKP3260) China Knowledge Press Pte Ltd SGP. Dist: Independent Pubs. Group.

China Knowledge Press Pte Ltd. Branding in China. 2007. (Illus.). 355p. pap. 59.00 *(978-981-4163-05-7(8))* China Knowledge Press Pte Ltd SGP. Dist: Independent Pubs. Group.

—Chengdu Business Guide. Wang, Julia, ed. 2007. 352p. pap. *(978-981-4163-45-3(7))* China Knowledge Press Pte Ltd.

China's Financial Policy Research Center Staff. Growth Without Crisis: China's Modern Financial System. 2011. (ENG.). 448p. 128.00 *(978-981-4298-32-2(8))* Enrich Professional Publishing (S)., Ltd. SGP. Dist: Independent Pubs. Group.

Chow, Peter. The One China Dilemma. 2008. (ENG., Illus.). 336p. 105.00 *(978-1-4039-8394-7(1))* Palgrave Macmillan.

Chu. China's Accession to the Wto & Its Impact on Asian Economies. 2007. 304p. *(978-1-84542-842-6(0))* Elgar, Edward Publishing, Inc.

Chu, Ming-Chin Monique. The East Asian Computer Chip War. 2012. (Routledge Studies on the Chinese Economy Ser.). (ENG.). 192p. (C). 130.00 *(978-0-415-56552-3(9))* Routledge.

Clegg. China's Global Strategy: Towards a Multipolar World. 2009. (ENG.). 288p. pap. 34.00 *(978-0-7453-2518-7(1))* Pluto Pr. GBR. Dist: Macmillan.

Clegg, Stewart R., et al. Business Networks & Strategic Alliances in China. 2007. 352p. (C). 150.00 *(978-1-84542-306-3(2))* Elgar, Edward Publishing, Inc.

Coates, Rosemary. 42 Rules for Sourcing & Manufacturing in China: A practical handbook for doing business in China, special economic zones, factory tours & Manufact. Lowell, Laura, ed. 2009. 134p. pap. 19.95 *(978-1-60773-050-7(2)*, Super Star Pr.) Happy About.

Cousin, Violaine. Banking in China. 2nd rev. ed. 2011. (ENG., Illus.). 352p. 105.00 *(978-0-230-27269-9(X))* Palgrave Macmillan.

Crow, Carl. 400 Million Customers: The Experiences -Some Happy, Some Sad of an American in China, & What They Taught Him. 2008. (Illus.). 276p. pap. *(978-0-9680459-0-9(1))* Soul Care Publishing.

Crow, Carl & Ayer, A. J. Four Hundred Million Customers. 2007. (ENG., Illus.). 256p. pap. 250.00 *(978-0-7103-1212-9(1))* Routledge.

Dahlman, Carl. The World under Pressure: How China & India Are Influencing the Global Economy & Environment. 2011. (ENG., Illus.). 326p. 65.00 ***(978-0-8047-7713-1(6)***, Stanford Economics & Finance) Stanford Univ. Pr.

Dai, Jianzhong. Bank Restructuring & Economic Growth. 2011. 96p. pap. ***(978-3-8454-0905-4(3))*** Lambert Academic Publishing.

"Daozhen Gelaozu Miaozu Zizhixian gai kuang" bian xie zu Staff & "Daozhen Gelaozu Miaozu Zizhixian gai kuang" xiu ding ben bian xie zu Staff, contrib. by. Daozhen Gelaozu Miaozu Zizhixian Gai Kuang: DaozhenGelaozuMiaozuZizhixiangaikuang. 2007. (Zhongguo Shao Shu Min Zu Zi Zhi Di Fang Gai Kuang Cong Shu (Xiu Ding Ben) Ser.). (CHI., Illus.). *(978-7-105-08537-8(1))* Nationalities Publishing Hse, The.

Das, Dilip K. China & India: A Tale of Two Economies. 2009. 182p. pap. 39.95 *(978-0-415-54449-8(1))* 2006. (Routledge Studies in the Growth Economies of Asia: Vol. 66). (ENG., Illus.). 224p. 160.00 *(978-0-415-40629-1(3))* Routledge.

—The Chinese Economic Renaissance: Apocalypse or Cornucopia? 2008. (ENG., Illus.). 288p. 105.00 *(978-0-230-21840-6(7))* Palgrave Macmillan.

De Pablos, Patricia Ordóñez & Lytras, Miltiadis D. The China Information Technology Handbook. 2008. (ENG., Illus.). xvii, 433p. 199.00 *(978-0-387-77742-9(3)*, 0387777423) Springer.

Deng. The Premodern Chinese Economy. 2007. (Illus.). 440p. 43.95 *(978-0-415-45864-1(1))* Routledge.

Deng, Kent G. China's Political Economy in Modern Times. 2011. (Routledge Studies in the Modern History of Asia Ser.). (ENG., Illus.). 320p. (C). 140.00 *(978-0-415-67405-8(0))* Routledge.

Deng, Yingtao. A New Development Model & China's Future. 2012. (Routledge Studies on the Chinese Economy Ser.). (ENG.). 240p. (C). 140.00 *(978-0-415-61092-6(3))* Routledge.

Deng, Ziliang. Foreign Direct Investment in China: Spillover Effects on Domestic Enterprises. 2011. (Routledge Studies in the Modern World Economy Ser.). (ENG., Illus.). 288p. (C). 180.00 *(978-0-415-59142-3(2))* Routledge.

Developing China. 2011. pap. 42.95 ***(978-0-415-66613-8(9))*** Routledge.

Dezan Shira & Associates, et al, eds. China's Neighbors: Who Is Influencing China & Who China Is Influencing in the New Emerging Asia. 3rd ed. 2012. (China Briefing Ser.). (ENG., Illus.). viii, 87p. pap. 49.95 ***(978-3-642-27614-9(8)***, 3642276148) Springer.

—The Yangtze River Delta: Business Guide to the Shanghai Region. 5th ed. 2012. (China Briefing Ser.). (ENG., Illus.). vi, 131p. pap. 59.95 ***(978-3-642-27623-1(7)***, 3642276237) Springer.

Dillon. Key Papers on Chinese Economic History in the second half of the Twentieth Century up to the Present Day. 2 vols. 2010. (Key Papers). 676p. *(978-1-905246-54-0(4))* BRILL.

Dillon, Michael. Key Papers on Chinese Economic History. 2008. (Key Papers). 700p. *(978-1-905246-52-6(8))* BRILL.

Dillon, Mike. Contemporary China: An Introduction. 2007. (Illus.). 256p. 150.00 *(978-0-415-34320-6(8))*; pap. 44.95 *(978-0-415-34319-0(4))* Routledge.

Ding, Sheng. The Dragon's Hidden Wings: How China Rises with Its Soft Power. 2008. (Challenges Facing Chinese Political Development Ser.). (ENG., Illus.). 210p. 73.50 *(978-0-7391-2392-8(0))* Lexington Bks.

Dionne, JoAnn. Little Emperors: A Year with the Future of China. 2008. (ENG., Illus.). 256p. pap. 24.99 *(978-1-55002-756-3(5)*, Dundurn Pr.) Dundurn CAN. Dist: Ingram Pub. Services.

Dobson, Wendy. Gravity Shift. 2010. (Illus.). 254p. pap. *(978-1-4426-1165-8(0))*, Univ. of Toronto Pr.

Doctoroff, Tom. What Chinese Want: Culture, Communism & the Modern Chinese Consumer. 2012. (ENG., Illus.). 272p. 27.00 ***(978-0-230-34030-5(X))*** Palgrave Macmillan.

Dodson, Bill. China Inside Out: 10 Irreversible Trends Reshaping China & Its Relationship with the World. 2011. (ENG.). 200p. 29.95 *(978-0-470-82643-0(6)*, Wiley) Wiley, John & Sons, Inc.

Donaldson, John A. Small Works: Poverty & Economic Development in Southwestern China. 2011. (Illus.). 240p. 45.00 *(978-0-8014-4968-0(5))* Cornell Univ. Pr.

du Cros, Hilary & Lee, Yok-Shiu F., eds. Cultural Heritage Management in China: Preserving the Cities of the Pearl River Delta. 2011. (ENG., Illus.). 192p. pap. 42.95 ***(978-0-415-66642-8(2))*** Routledge.

Economic Research Centre Staff, et al. Almanac of China's Economy, 1949-1981. Muqiao, Xue, ed. 155.00 *(978-0-88410-894-8(5))* Eurasia Pr.

Edkins, Joseph. The Revenue & Taxation of the Chinese Empire. 2010. (ENG.). 258p. pap. 26.75 *(978-1-171-74680-5(6))* 2010. 258p. pap. 26.75 *(978-1-177-78000-1(3))* 2010. (ENG.). 260p. pap. 26.75 *(978-1-175-35228-6(4))* 2010. 260p. pap. 26.75 *(978-1-148-08741-2(9))* 2010. 254p. pap. 26.75 *(978-1-141-55518-5(2))* 2008. 256p. 25.99 *(978-0-559-25944-9(1))* 2008. 256p. pap. 25.75 *(978-0-559-25941-8(7))* BiblioBazaar.

—The Revenue & Taxation of the Chinese Empire. 2010. (Illus.). 148p. pap. 19.82 *(978-1-152-70785-6(X))* General Bks. LLC.

—The Revenue & Taxation of the Chinese Empire. 2008. 256p. 42.95 *(978-1-4374-3234-3(4))*; pap. 27.95 *(978-1-4373-3869-0(0))* Kessinger Publishing, LLC.

Ehebruster, Marianne. Economic Boom - Blessing or Curse? Linking Economic Performance with Environmental Development by Analysing China's Water Resources. 2008. 116p. pap. *(978-3-639-10339-7(4))* VDM Verlag Dr. Mueller e.K.

Elleman, Bruce & Kotkin, Stephen, eds. Manchurian Railways & the Opening of China: An International History. 2009. 256p. pap. 34.95 *(978-0-7656-2515-1(6))*; (ENG., Illus.). 89.95 *(978-0-7656-2514-4(8))* Sharpe, M.E. Inc.

Engardio, Pete. Chindia: How China & India Are Revolutionizing Global Business. 2006. (ENG.). 224p. per. 19.95 *(978-0-07-147657-7(1)*, 0071476571) McGraw-Hill Cos., The.

Espinosa De Godas, Eusebio. China 2008. 2008. (Illus.). 208p. pap. *(978-0-7552-0410-6(7))* Authors OnLine, Ltd.

Eyferth, Jacob. Eating Rice from Bamboo Roots: The Social History of a Community of Handicraft Papermakers in Rural Sichuan, 1920-2000. 2009. (Harvard East Asian Monographs: 314). (Illus.). 335p. 45.00 *(978-0-674-03288-0(8))* Harvard Univ., Asia Ctr.

Fan, Joseph P. H. & Morck, Randall, eds. Capitalizing China. 2012. (National Bureau of Economic Research Conference Report). (Illus.). 368p. 110.00 ***(978-0-226-23724-4(9))*** Univ. of Chicago Pr.

Fan, Zhiyong, et al. Enrich Series on China's Economic Issues, vols. 5, Vols. 1-5, set. 2011. (Enrich Series on China's Economic Issues Ser.). 1552p. 448.00 *(978-981-4298-28-5(X))* Enrich Professional Publishing (S)., Ltd. SGP. Dist: Independent Pubs. Group.

Fang, Ning. Cao Gen Jing Ji Yu Min Zhu Zheng Zhi: She Hui Zhu Yi Shi Chang Jing Ji Yu She Hui Zhu Yi Min Zhu Zheng Zhi Xie Tong Fa Zhan de Taizhou Mo Shi Yan Jiu = Grassroots Economy & Democratic Politics. 2008. (CHI.). 9p. *(978-7-5097-0434-9(0))* China Social Science Documentation Publishing Hse.

Farah, Hosh. Energy Security & Sustainable Development. 2011. 136p. pap. ***(978-3-8443-0807-5(5))*** Lambert Academic Publishing.

Fei, Yiwen. The Institutional Approach to Mergers. 2009. 256p. pap. *(978-3-639-08781-9(X))* VDM Verlag Dr. Mueller e.K.

Feng, Lianyong & Yan, Hu. The Chinese Oil Industry: History & Trends To 2030. 2012. (SpringerBriefs in Energy / SpringerBriefs in Energy Analysis Ser.). (ENG., Illus.). 80p. pap. 49.95 *(978-1-4419-9409-7(2)*, 1441994092) Springer.

Feng, Liling. Saving, Growth & Financial Market Imperfections in Transitional Chin. 2007. 112p. per. *(978-3-8364-2992-4(6))* VDM Verlag Dr. Mueller e.K.

Feng, Wang. Boundaries & Categories: Rising Inequality in Post-Socialist Urban China. 2007. (Studies in Social Inequality Ser.). (ENG., Illus.). 254p. 55.00 *(978-0-8047-5794-2(1))* Stanford Univ. Pr.

Fernandez, Juan Antonio & Fernandez. China's State-Owned Enterprise Reforms: An Industrial & CEO Approach. 2006. (Routledge Studies in the Growth Economies of Asia). (Illus.). 307p. 160.00 *(978-0-415-40268-2(9))* Routledge.

Fernandez-Stembridge, Leila & Fisac, Taciana, eds. China Today. 2010. (Illus.). 286p. pap. 39.95 ***(978-0-415-60016-3(2))*** Routledge.

The Financial Crisis & the Changing Role of Workers in China: Roundtable Before the Congressional-Executive Commission on China, One Hundred Eleventh Congress, First Session, June 19, 2009. 2009. ii, 36p. *(978-0-16-084977-0(2)*, 552-070-40356-6) United States Government Printing Office.

Fleisher, Belton M., et al, eds. Policy Reform & Chinese Markets: Progress & Challenges. 2008. (Advances in Chinese Economic Studies). 352p. (C). 150.00 *(978-1-84720-396-0(5))* Elgar, Edward Publishing, Inc.

Flynn, Dennis O. & Giraldez, Arturo. China & the Birth of Globalization in the 16th Century. 2010. (Variorum Collected Studies). (Illus.). 298p. 134.95 *(978-0-7546-6858-9(4))* Ashgate Publishing Co.

Freidhof, Jan. The Dilemma of Cash Management in China. 2007. 52p. per. *(978-3-8364-0841-7(4))* VDM Verlag Dr. Mueller e.K.

Friedman, Edward & Gilley, Bruce. Asia's Giants: Comparing China & India. Friedman, Edward & Gilley, Bruce, eds. 2008. (ENG.). 264p. pap. 34.00 *(978-0-230-60616-6(4))* Palgrave Macmillan.

Fu, Xiaolan, ed. Chinas Role in Global Economic Recovery. 2011. (Routledge Studies on the Chinese Economy Ser.). (ENG., Illus.). 336p. (C). 155.00 *(978-0-415-67034-0(9))* Routledge.

C

Gale, William & Elmendorf, Douglas W., eds. Brookings Papers on Economic Activity 2. 2008. (Brookings Papers on Economic Activity Ser.). (ENG., Illus.). 240p. pap. 36.00 *(978-0-8157-1356-2(8))* Brookings Institution Pr.

Gao, Xuan. The Proliferation of Anti-Dumping & Poor Governance in Emerging Economies: Case Studies of China & South Africa. 2009. (NAI Discussion Papers). 30p. pap. 12.95 *(978-91-7106-644-2(6))* Nordiska Afrikainstitutet SWE. Dist: Stylus Publishing, LLC.

Garnaut, Ross & Song, Ligang, eds. The Turning Point in China's Economic Development. 2006. (Illus.). 390p. (C). pap. *(978-0-7315-3763-1(7))* Asia Pacific Pr.

Gerth, Karl. As China Goes, So Goes the World: How Chinese Consumers Are Transforming Everything, 1 vol. 2011. (ENG., Illus.). 272p. pap. 16.00 *(978-0-8090-2689-0(9),* Hill & Wang) Farrar, Straus & Giroux.

Global China. 2012. (C). 41.95 ***(978-0-203-87739-5(X))*** Routledge.

Golley, Jane. The Dynamics of Chinese Regional Development: Market Nature, State Nurture. 2007. (Advances in Chinese Economic Studies). (Illus.). 208p. (C). 119.00 *(978-1-84720-145-4(8))* Elgar, Edward Publishing, Inc.

Gong, Gang. Contemporary Chinese Economy. 2012. (Illus.). x, 210p. ***(978-0-203-12486-4(3))***; (ENG., 224p. (C). 168.00 *(978-0-415-61690-4(5))* Routledge.

Goodstadt, Leo F. Reluctant Regulators: How the West Created & How China Survived the Global Financial Crisis. 2011. (ENG.). 224p. (gr. 17). 40.00 *(978-988-8083-25-1(2))* Hong Kong Univ. Pr. HKG. Dist: Columbia Univ. Pr.

Graff, Michael. Growth of the International Economy 1820-2010. 2012. (ENG., Illus.). 352p. (C). 150.00 *(978-0-415-47609-6(7))* Routledge.

Graff, Michael, et al. Growth of the International Economy 1820-2010. 5th rev. ed. 2012. (ENG., Illus.). 352p. (C). 70.00 *(978-0-415-47610-2(0))* Routledge.

Grivoyannis, Elias C., ed. The New Chinese Economy: Dynamic Transitions into the Future. 2012. (ENG., Illus.). 206p. 105.00 ***(978-0-230-11567-5(5))***; pap. 29.00 ***(978-0-230-11568-2(3))*** Palgrave Macmillan.

Groenewold, Nicolaas, et al. Linkages Between China's Regions: Measurement & Policy. 2008. (Advances in Chinese Economic Studies). (Illus.). 192p. (C). 119.00 *(978-1-84720-242-0(X))* Elgar, Edward Publishing, Inc.

Grove, Linda. A Chinese Economic Revolution: Rural Entrepreneurship in the Twentieth Century. 2006. (State & Society in East Asia Ser.). (ENG., Illus.). 320p. 74.00 *(978-0-7425-5354-5(X))* Rowman & Littlefield Publishers, Inc.

Grumbine, R. Edward. Where the Dragon Meets the Angry River: Nature & Power in the People's Republic of China. (Illus.). 256p. 2011. pap. 21.95 *(978-1-61091-160-3(1))* 2010. (ENG., 27.50 *(978-1-59726-551-5(9))* Island Pr.

Guerra Vio, Jose. China's Calculus in Asia-Pacific. 2010. 88p. pap. *(978-3-639-25430-3(9))* VDM Verlag Dr. Mueller e.K.

Gungwu, Wang & Wong, John, eds. Interpreting China's Development. 2007. 265p. 104.00 *(978-981-270-802-1(2))*; (Illus.). per. 62.00 *(978-981-270-806-9(5))* World Scientific Publishing Co., Inc.

Guo, Baogang & Li, He, eds. The Chinese Labyrinth: Exploring China's Model of Development. 2011. (Challenges Facing Chinese Political Development Ser.). (ENG.). 230p. (gr. 17). 65.00 ***(978-0-7391-6575-1(5))*** Lexington Bks.

Guo, Li'an & Zong, Fai. Business, Finance & Economics of China. 2010. (China in the 21st Century Ser.). 145.00 *(978-1-60741-299-1(3))* Nova Science Pubs., Inc.

Guo, Rongxing. How the Chinese Economy Works. (ENG., Illus.). 2nd rev. ed. 2007. 280p. 126.00 *(978-0-230-54274-7(3))* 3rd rev. ed. 2009. 368p. 121.00 *(978-0-230-58100-5(5))* Palgrave Macmillan.

Guo, Rongxing. Understanding the Chinese Economies. 2012. (ENG.). 352p. 59.95 ***(978-0-12-397826-4(2),*** Academic Pr.) Elsevier Science & Technology Bks.

Guruswamy, Mohan & Singh, Zorawar Daulet. Chasing the Dragon: Will India Catch up with China? 2010. (ENG., Illus.). 204p. (C). 34.99 *(978-81-317-2411-8(5))* FT Press.

Han, Zheng. Managing Foreign Research & Development in the People's Republic of China: The New Think Tank of the World. 2008. (Chandos Asian Studies). (ENG., Illus.). 260p. 110.00 *(978-1-84334-153-6(0),* Chandos Publishing) Woodhead Publishing Ltd. GBR. Dist: Ingram Pub. Services.

Hao, Yufan. Macau & U. S. -China Relations. 2010. (ENG., Illus.). 330p. 80.00 *(978-0-7391-4367-4(0))* Lexington Bks.

Hao, Yufan & Wang, Jianwei. Macao & Sino-U.S. Relations. 2010. (Illus.). vii, 360p. *(978-0-7391-4369-8(7))* Lexington Bks.

Hao, Zhidong. Macau History & Society. 2011. (ENG., Illus.). 328p. (gr. 17). pap. 38.00 *(978-988-8028-54-2(5))* Hong Kong Univ. Pr. HKG. Dist: Columbia Univ. Pr.

Hasmath, Reza & Hsu, Jennifer, eds. China in an Era of Transition: Understanding Contemporary State & Society Actors. 2009. (ENG., Illus.). 244p. 100.00 *(978-0-230-61350-8(0))* Palgrave Macmillan.

He, Xin. He Xin: Fan Zhu Liu Jing Ji Xue = He Xin: Fan Zhuliu Jingji Xue, 2 vols. 2010. (CHI., Illus.). *(978-7-80232-326-1(6))* Current Affairs Publishing Hes.

Heberer, Thomas. Doing Business in Rural China: Liangshan's New Ethnic Entrepreneurs. 2007. (Studies on Ethnic Groups in China). (ENG., Illus.). 280p. 50.00 *(978-0-295-98729-3(4))* Univ. of Washington Pr.

Heng, Derek. Sino-Malay Trade & Diplomacy from the Tenth through the Fourteenth Century. 2009. (Ohio RIS Southeast Asia Ser.). (ENG., Illus.). 304p. pap. 28.00 *(978-0-89680-271-1(X))* Ohio Univ. Pr.

Hill, Emily M. Smokeless Sugar: The Death of a Provincial Bureaucrat & the Construction of China's National Economy. 2011. (Contemporary Chinese Studies Ser.). (ENG., Illus.). 336p. pap. 35.95 *(978-0-7748-1654-0(6))* UBC Pr. CAN. Dist: Univ. of Washington Pr.

Ho, ChyeKok & Koh, ChinSeng. HR Due Diligence: Mergers & Acquisitions in China. 2012. (Chandos Asian Studies). (ENG.). 190p. 120.00 *(978-0-85709-153-6(0),* Chandos Publishing) Woodhead Publishing Ltd. GBR. Dist: Ingram Pub. Services.

Ho, Peter. Developmental Dilemmas: Land Reform & Institutional Change in China. 2009. 348p. pap. 39.95 *(978-0-415-49737-4(X))* Routledge.

Hofer, Markus B. & Ebel, Bernhard, eds. Business Success in China. 2006. (ENG., Illus.). viii, 275p. 74.95 *(978-3-540-34614-2(7),* 3540346147) Springer.

Hoffman, Lisa M. Patriotic Professionalism in Urban China: Fostering Talent. 2010. (Urban Life, Landscape & Policy Ser.). (ENG., Illus.). 216p. 71.50 *(978-1-4399-0034-5(5))*; pap. 26.95 *(978-1-4399-0035-2(3))* Temple Univ. Pr.

Horn, Sharon & Mosher, Stacy, eds. Challenging China: Struggle & Hope in an Era of Change. 2008. (ENG.). 313p. pap. 17.95 *(978-1-59558-416-8(1))* New Pr., The.

Hongyi, Lai. The Domestic Sources of China's Foreign Policy. 2011. (ENG., Illus.). 202p. (C). pap. 42.95 ***(978-0-415-69721-7(2))*** Routledge.

Howie, Fraser J. T. & Howie, Fraser J. T. Privatizing China: Inside China's Stock Markets. 2nd rev. ed. 2006. (ENG., Illus.). 290p. pap. 60.00 *(978-0-470-82214-2(7),* Wiley) Wiley, John & Sons, Inc.

Hsing, You-tien. The Great Urban Transformation: Politics of Land & Property in China. 2012. (ENG., Illus.). 272p. pap. 40.00 ***(978-0-19-964459-9(4))*** Oxford Univ. Pr., Inc.

Hsing, You-tien & Lee, Ching Kwan. Reclaiming Chinese Society: The New Social Activism. Hsing, You-tien & Lee, Ching Kwan, eds. 2009. (Asia's Transformations Ser.). (ENG., Illus.). 272p. 170.00 *(978-0-415-49137-2(1))* Routledge.

Hsing, You-tien & Lee, Ching Kwan, eds. Reclaiming Chinese Society: The New Social Activism. 2009. (Asia's Transformations Ser.). (ENG., Illus.). 272p. (C). pap. 42.95 *(978-0-415-49139-6(8))* Routledge.

Hsu, Robert. China Fireworks: How to Make Dramatic Wealth from the Fastest-Growing Economy in the World. 2008. (ENG., Illus.). 276p. 27.95 *(978-0-470-27677-8(0),* Wiley) Wiley, John & Sons, Inc.

Hu, Angang, ed. Economic & Social Transformation in China: Challenges & Opportunities. 2006. (Routledge Studies on the Chinese Economy). (Illus.). 276p. 170.00 *(978-0-415-38067-6(7))* Routledge.

Hu, Angang & Hu, An'gang. Road Map of China's Rise. 2010. (Routledge Studies on the Chinese Economy Ser.). (ENG., Illus.). 512p. 150.00 *(978-0-415-47992-9(4))* Routledge.

Hu, An'gang & Hu, Guangyu. Achievement Evaluation of IFI Assistance Loans to China (1981-2002) 2007. (Illus.). 280p. 259.00 *(978-3-540-45888-3(3))* Springer.

Hu, Shuli & Yang, Zheyu. Shuli Guan Cha: Zhongguo Shi Nian Zhi Zhen Wen Ti. 2010. (CHI.). 9p. *(978-7-306-03602-5(5))* Zhongshan Univ. Pr.

Hu, Xinying. China's New Underclass: Paid Domestic Labour. 2011. (Routledge Contemporary China Ser.). (ENG., Illus.). 208p. (C). 140.00 *(978-0-415-61765-9(0))* Routledge.

Huang, Xiaoming. The Institutional Dynamics of China's Great Transformation. 2011. (China Policy Ser.). (ENG., Illus.). 272p. (C). 140.00 *(978-0-415-58058-8(7))* Routledge.

Huang, Xiaoming, et al, eds. China & India & the End of Development Models. 2012. (Rethinking International Development Ser.). (ENG., Illus.). 312p. 95.00 ***(978-0-230-30158-0(4))*** Palgrave Macmillan.

Huchet, Jean-Francois, et al. Globalisation in China, India, & Russia: Emergence of National Groups & Global Strategies of Firms. Huchet, Jean-Francois et al, eds. 2007. (ENG., Illus.). 346p. 67.95 *(978-81-7188-582-4(9))* Academic Foundation IND. Dist: Independent Pubs. Group.

Hutton, Will. The Writing on the Wall: Why We Must Embrace China as a Partner or Face It as an Enemy. 2006. (ENG., Illus.). 432p. 28.00 *(978-0-7432-7528-6(4),* Free Pr.) Free Pr.

Icon Group International, Inc. Staff, compiled by. The 2006 Economic & Product Market Databook for Beijing, China. 2006. 618p. ring bd. 95.00 *(978-0-497-80170-0(1))* Icon Group International, Inc.

—The 2006 Economic & Product Market Databook for Changchun, China. 2006. 618p. ring bd. 95.00 *(978-0-497-80335-3(6))* Icon Group International, Inc.

—The 2006 Economic & Product Market Databook for Chengdu, China. 2006. 618p. ring bd. 95.00 *(978-0-497-80349-0(6))* Icon Group International, Inc.

—The 2006 Economic & Product Market Databook for Chongqing, China. 2006. 618p. ring bd. 95.00 *(978-0-497-79972-4(3))* Icon Group International, Inc.

—The 2006 Economic & Product Market Databook for Dalian, China. 2006. 618p. ring bd. 95.00 *(978-0-497-80437-4(9))* Icon Group International, Inc.

—The 2006 Economic & Product Market Databook for Guangzhou, China. 2006. 618p. ring bd. 95.00 *(978-0-497-80624-8(X))* Icon Group International, Inc.

—The 2006 Economic & Product Market Databook for Harbin, China. 2006. 618p. ring bd. 95.00 *(978-0-497-81886-9(8))* Icon Group International, Inc.

—The 2006 Economic & Product Market Databook for Macau, Macau. 2006. 618p. ring bd. 95.00 *(978-0-497-80901-0(X))* Icon Group International, Inc.

—The 2006 Economic & Product Market Databook for Nanjing, China. 2006. 618p. ring bd. 95.00 *(978-0-497-81093-1(X))* Icon Group International, Inc.

—The 2006 Economic & Product Market Databook for Shanghai, China. 2006. 618p. ring bd. 95.00 *(978-0-497-81516-5(8))* Icon Group International, Inc.

—The 2006 Economic & Product Market Databook for Shenyang, China. 2006. 618p. ring bd. 95.00 *(978-0-497-81521-9(4))* Icon Group International, Inc.

—The 2006 Economic & Product Market Databook for Shenzhen, China. 2006. 618p. ring bd. 95.00 *(978-0-497-81522-6(2))* Icon Group International, Inc.

—The 2006 Economic & Product Market Databook for Taipa, Macau. 2006. 618p. ring bd. 95.00 *(978-0-497-81619-3(9))* Icon Group International, Inc.

—The 2006 Economic & Product Market Databook for Taiyuan, China. 2006. 618p. ring bd. 95.00 *(978-0-497-81623-0(7))* Icon Group International, Inc.

—The 2006 Economic & Product Market Databook for Tianjin, China. 2006. 618p. ring bd. 95.00 *(978-0-497-81678-0(4))* Icon Group International, Inc.

—The 2006 Economic & Product Market Databook for Wuhan, China. 2006. 618p. ring bd. 95.00 *(978-0-497-81831-9(0))* Icon Group International, Inc.

—The 2006 Economic & Product Market Databook for Xi'an, China. 2006. 618p. ring bd. 95.00 *(978-0-497-81833-3(7))* Icon Group International, Inc.

Ine, et al. Supertrends of Future China: Billion Dollar Business Opportunities for China's Olympic Decade. 2008. xxii, 286p. 27.95 *(978-981-281-439-5(6))* World Scientific Publishing Co., Inc.

International Organization for Migration. Migration & Poverty Alleviation in China. 2007. (IOM Migration Research Ser.). 40p. pap. 16.00 *(978-92-1-103651-0(8))* International Organization for Migration (IOM) CHE. Dist: United Nations Pubns.

Islam, Nazrul, ed. Resurgent China: Issues for the Future. 2009. (ENG., Illus.). 264p. 131.00 *(978-0-230-53807-8(X))* Palgrave Macmillan.

Jeffries, Ian. China: A Guide to Economic & Political Developments. 2006. (Guides to Economic & Political Developments in Asia Ser.: Vol. 3). (Illus.). 673p. 210.00 *(978-0-415-38223-6(8),* RU238X) Routledge.

—China: A Guide to Economic & Political Developments. 2012. (Guides to Economic & Political Developments in Asia Ser.). (ENG., Illus.). 592p. pap. 44.95 ***(978-0-415-51422-4(3))*** Routledge.

Jeffries, Ian. Economic Development in Contemporary China. 2010. (Guides to Economic & Political Developments in Asia Ser.). (ENG., Illus.). 736p. (C). 200.00 *(978-0-415-47866-3(9),* Routledge) Taylor & Francis Group GBR. Dist: Taylor & Francis Group.

Jha, Prem Shankar. Crouching Dragon, Hidden Tiger: Can China & India Dominate the West? 2009. (ENG.). 256p. pap. 16.95 *(978-1-59376-248-3(8),* Soft Skull Pr.) Counterpoint LLC.

Jia, Xiangping. Credit Rationing & Institutional Constraint: Evidence from Rural China. 2008. (Development Economics & Policy Ser.). (Illus.). 162p. pap. 49.95 *(978-3-631-58285-5(4))* Lang, Peter GmbH, Europaischer Verlag der Wissenschaften DEU. Dist: Lang, Peter.

Jiao, Jian & Xuan, Guo. Do Chinese Underwriters Grandstand to Attract More Firms. 2010. 88p. pap. *(978-3-8383-8451-1(2))* Lambert Academic Publishing.

Junbo, Xiang. Structural Economics in China: A Three-Dimensional Framework for Balanced Growth. 2012. (ENG.). 360p. 118.00 ***(978-981-4298-38-4(7))*** Enrich Professional Publishing (S)., Ltd. SGP. Dist: Independent Pubs. Group.

Karabell, Zachary. Superfusion: How China & America Became One Economy & Why the World's Prosperity Depends on It. 2009. (ENG.). 352p. 26.00 *(978-1-4165-8370-7(X))* Simon & Schuster.

Keane, Michael. China's New Creative Clusters: Governance, Human Capital & Investment. 2011. (Media, Culture & Social Change in Asia Ser.). (ENG., Illus.). 216p. (C). 145.00 *(978-0-415-60396-6(X))* Routledge.

Kee, Tan Teng & Xiaofang, Fu, eds. Proceedings of the International Conference on Chinese Enterprise Research 2007. 2008. 548p. pap. 99.00 *(978-981-283-471-3(0))* World Scientific Publishing Co., Inc.

Kennedy, Scott, ed. Beyond the Middle Kingdom: Comparative Perspectives on China's Capitalist Transformation. 2011. (Contemporary Issues in Asia & Pacific Ser.). (ENG.). 280p. 65.00 *(978-0-8047-6957-0(5))*; pap. 22.95 *(978-0-8047-6958-7(3))* Stanford Univ. Pr.

Kim, Jaeyoon. Ethnicity, Local Conflicts & the Qing State. 2010. 212p. pap. *(978-3-639-25419-8(8))* VDM Verlag Dr. Mueller e.K.

Kipnis, Andrew. Contemporary Chinese Society & Politics, 4 vols. Tomba, Luigi & Unger, Jonathan, eds. 2009. (Critical Concepts in Asian Studies). (ENG., Illus.). 1872p. 1430.00 *(978-0-415-45748-4(3))* Routledge.

Kirby, William C., et al. The People's Republic of China at 60: An International Assessment. 2011. (CHI & ENG., Illus.). 432p. pap. 29.95 *(978-0-674-06064-7(4))* Harvard Univ., Asia Ctr.

Knight, John & Ding, Sai. China's Remarkable Economic Growth. 2012. (ENG., Illus.). 424p. 45.00 ***(978-0-19-969869-1(4))*** Oxford Univ. Pr., Inc.

Koenen, Gerd. Was war der Kommunismus? 2010. (FRIAS Rote Reihe Ser.). (GER.). 143p. (C). pap. 18.00 *(978-3-525-32301-4(8))* Vandenhoeck & Ruprecht GmbH & Co. KG DEU. Dist: ISD.

Krug, Barbara & Hendrischke, Hans, eds. The Chinese Economy in the 21st Century: Enterprise & Business Behaviour. 2009. (Illus.). 264p. pap. 58.00 *(978-1-84844-458-4(3))* Elgar, Edward Publishing, Inc.

Kuhn, Robert Lawrence. How China's Leaders Think: The Inside Story of China's Past, Current & Future Leaders. rev. ed. 2011. (ENG., Illus.). 576p. pap. 29.95 *(978-1-118-08590-5(6),* Wiley) Wiley, John & Sons, Inc.

Kwok-bun, Chan & Wai-wan, Chan. Mobile Chinese Entrepreneurs. 2011. (International Series on Consumer Science Ser.). (ENG., Illus.). xii, 200p. 129.00 *(978-1-4419-9642-8(7),* 1441996427) Springer.

Kynge, James. China Shakes the World: A Titan's Rise & Troubled Future — & the Challenge for America. 2006. (Edition 001 Ser.). (ENG.). 288p. 25.00 *(978-0-618-70564-1(3))* Houghton Mifflin Harcourt Trade & Reference Pubs.

—China Shakes the World: A Titan's Rise & Troubled Future - And the Challenge for America. 2007. (Edition 001 Ser.). (ENG.). 288p. per. 14.95 *(978-0-618-91906-2(6),* Mariner Bks.) Houghton Mifflin Harcourt Trade & Reference Pubs.

Laliberte, Andre & Lanteigne, Marc, eds. The Chinese Party-State in the 21st Century. 2011. (Illus.). 204p. pap. 42.95 ***(978-0-415-69218-2(0))*** Routledge.

Lam, N. Mark & Graham, John L. China Now: Doing Business in the World's Most Dynamic Market. 2006. (ENG., Illus.). 385p. 27.95 *(978-0-07-147254-8(1),* 0071472541) McGraw-Hill Cos., The.

Lanqing, Li. Breaking Through: The Birth of China's Opening-Up Policy. 2010. (ENG., Illus.). 480p. 35.00 *(978-0-19-801692-2(1))* Oxford Univ. Pr., Inc.

Lardy, Nicholas. Sustaining China's Economic Growth after the Global Financial Crisis. 2012. (Illus.). 200p. pap. 21.95 ***(978-0-88132-626-0(7))*** Peterson Institute for International Economics.

Lardy, Nicholas R. Economic Growth & Distribution in China. 2006. (ENG.). 260p. pap. 53.00 *(978-0-521-03463-0(9))* Cambridge Univ. Pr.

Law, Alice, et al. Leadership Success in China: An Expatriate's Guide. 2008. pap. 30.00 *(978-0-9761514-4-9(8))* Development Dimensions International, Inc.

Le Pichon, Alain, ed. China Trade & Empire: Jardine, Matheson & Co. & the Origins of British Rule in Hong Kong, 1827-1843. 2006. (Records of Social & Economic History, New Ser.: Vol. 38). (ENG., Illus.). 592p. 150.00 *(978-0-19-726337-2(2))* Oxford Univ. Pr., Inc.

Lee, Grace O. M. & Warner, Malcolm, eds. Unemployment in China: Economy, Human Resources & Labour Markets. 2006. (Routledge Contemporary China Ser.). (ENG., Illus.). 288p. (C). 168.00 *(978-0-415-37171-1(6))* Routledge.

Lee, John Chi-Kin, et al. Schooling for Sustainable Development in Chinese Communities: Experience with Younger Children. Lee, John Chi-Kin & Williams, Michael, eds. 2009. (Schooling for Sustainable Development Ser.). (ENG., Illus.). 300p. 189.00 *(978-1-4020-9685-3(2),* 1402096852) Springer.

Lee, Keun. Power & Sustainability of the Chinese State. Kim, Joon-Han & Woo, Wing Thye, eds. 2009. (China Policy Ser.). (Illus.). 240p. 160.00 *(978-0-415-46939-5(2))* Routledge.

Lee, Mabel P. Economic History of China. (Columbia University, Studies in the Social Sciences: No. 225). reprint ed. 39.50 *(978-0-404-51225-5(9))* AMS Pr., Inc.

Lee, Yok-Shiu F. & Du Cros, Hilary, eds. Cultural Heritage Management in China: Preserving the Cities of the Pearl River Delta. 2007. (Routledge Contemporary China Ser.). (ENG., Illus.). 192p. (C). 180.00 *(978-0-415-39719-3(7))* Routledge.

Leeb, Stephen. Red Alert: How China's Growing Prosperity Threatens the American Way of Life. 2011. 272p. pap. 17.99 ***(978-0-446-57624-6(7),*** Business Plus) Grand Central Publishing.

Lei, Chun Kwok & Yao, Shujie. Economic Convergence in Greater China: Mainland China, Hong Kong, Macau & Taiwan. 2009. (Routledge Studies on the Chinese Economy Ser.). (ENG., Illus.). 272p. (C). 170.00 *(978-0-415-43581-9(1))* Routledge.

Lei, Un Tong. World Expo 2010 Shanghai Chin. 2011. 120p. pap. ***(978-3-8443-8565-6(7))*** Lambert Academic Publishing.

Leng, Jing. Corporate Governance & Financial Reform in China's Transition Economy. 2009. (Hong Kong University Press Law Ser.). (ENG.). 328p. (gr. 17). 60.00 *(978-962-209-931-9(9))*; pap. 30.00 *(978-962-209-932-6(7))* Hong Kong Univ. Pr. HKG. Dist: Columbia Univ. Pr.

Leonard, Mark. What Does China Think? 2008. (ENG., Illus.). 176p. 22.95 *(978-1-58648-484-2(2))* PublicAffairs.

Li. Wealth Doesn't Last 3 Generations: How... 2008. (Illus.). xx, 364p. 65.00 *(978-981-279-751-3(3))* World Scientific Publishing Co., Inc.

Li, Cheng, ed. China's Emerging Middle Class: Beyond Economic Transformation. 2010. (ENG., Illus.). 396p. pap. 34.95 *(978-0-8157-0405-8(4))* Brookings Institution Pr.

Li, Lillian. Fighting Famine in North China: State, Market, & Environmental Decline, 1690s-1990s. 2010. (ENG., Illus.). 544p. pap. 34.95 *(978-0-8047-7181-8(2))* Stanford Univ. Pr.

Li, Minqi. The Rise of China & the Demise of the Capitalist World Economy, 1 vol. 2008. (Illus.). 240p. 29.95 *(978-0-7453-2772-3(9))*; 192p. 95.00 *(978-0-7453-2773-0(7))* Pluto Pr. GBR. Dist: Univ. of Michigan Pr.

Li, Qianpin. Consumer Boycotts in Contemporary Chin. 2010. 280p. pap. *(978-3-8383-8082-7(7))* Lambert Academic Publishing.

Li, Tieying, ed. Enrich Series on China's Economic Reform: Five-Volume Set, 5 vols., Vols. 1-5, set. 2010. (Enrich Series on China's Economic Reform Ser.). 1632p. 528.00 *(978-981-4298-08-7(5))* Enrich Professional Publishing (S)., Ltd. SGP. Dist: Independent Pubs. Group.

Li, Wei. China's Early Industrialization. 2008. 192p. pap. *(978-3-639-06824-5(6))* VDM Verlag Dr. Mueller e.K.

Li, Xiaoxi, ed. Assessing the Extent of China's Marketization. 2006. (Chinese Trade & Industry Ser.). (Illus.). 350p. 130.00 *(978-0-7546-4878-9(8))* Ashgate Publishing Co.

Li, Yi. Zhongguo Xin Xi Chan Ye Ji Qun Fa Zhan Yan Jiu: Research on China's Information Industry Cluster Development. 2010. (Illus.). *(978-7-80745-627-8(2))* Shanghai Academy of Social Sciences Pr.

Li, Zhe. Melamine Milk Bomb Landing in Chin. 2011. 56p. pap. ***(978-3-8443-1809-8(7))*** Lambert Academic Publishing.

Liao, Chun. The Governance Structures of Chinese Firms: Innovation, Competitiveness, & Growth in a Dual Economy. 2009. (Innovation, Technology, & Knowledge Management Ser.). (ENG., Illus.). xxvi, 205p. 159.00 *(978-1-4419-0035-7(7),* 1441900357) Springer.

Lin, Cheng, et al, eds. The History of Ancient Chinese Economic Thought. 2013. (Routledge Studies in the History of Economics Ser.). (ENG.). 256p. (C). 140.00 ***(978-0-415-50014-2(1))*** Routledge.

Lin, Chun. Reorienting Chinese Development in the Twenty-First Century: Is Xiaokang Socialism Possible? 2008. 192p. 150.00 *(978-0-415-38069-0(3))* Routledge.

Liu, Chang. Peasants & Revolution in Rural China: Rural Political Change in the North China Plain & the Yangzi Delta, 1850-1949. 2009. 262p. pap. 39.95 *(978-0-415-54422-1(X))* 2007. (Illus.). 258p. 160.00 *(978-0-415-42176-8(4))* Routledge.

Liu, Chunhang. Multinationals, Globalisation & Indigenous Firms in China. 2012. (Routledge Studies on the Chinese Economy Ser.). (ENG., Illus.). 208p. (C). pap. 42.95 **(978-0-415-54177-0(8))** Routledge.
Liu, Fang & Peters, Bill. Beat Chinese Stock Market with Statistics. 2011. 108p. pap. **(978-3-8433-9041-5(X))** Lambert Academic Publishing.
—Green Trade Barriers. 2011. 100p. pap. **(978-3-8443-0977-5(2))** Lambert Academic Publishing.
Liu, Guoguang, et al, eds. The China Economy Yearbook, Volume 1: Analysis & Forecast of China's Economy. 2008. (Chinese Academy of Social Sciences Yearbooks: Society Ser.). (Illus.). 451p. *(978-90-04-15638-8(0))* BRILL.
Liu, Hong. Chinese Business: Landscapes & Strategies. 2008. xvii, 206p. (C). 54.95 **(978-0-203-89084-4(1))**; (Illus.). XVIII, 206p. 165.00 *(978-0-415-40308-5(1))*; (Illus.). XVIII, 206p. pap. 54.95 *(978-0-415-40309-2(X))* Routledge.
Liu, Manhong Mannie, et al, eds. The Green Economy & Its Implementation in China. 2011. (ENG.). 400p. 128.00 **(978-981-4298-95-7(6))** Enrich Professional Publishing (S)., Ltd. SGP. Dist: Independent Pubs. Group.
Liu, Ming & Lin, Z. Jun. Corporate Governance, Auditor Choice & Auditor Switch - Evidence from Chin. 2009. 108p. pap. *(978-3-639-10868-2(X))* VDM Verlag Dr. Mueller e.K.
Liu, Mingfu. Zhongguo Meng: Zhong Mei Shi Ji Dui Jue, Jun Ren Yao Fa Yan. 2010. (CHI.). x, 288p. *(973-962-231-062-9(1))* Chung Hwa Bk. Co., Ltd.
Liu, Xiaohui & Zhang, Wei. China's Three Decades of Economic Reforms. Liu, Xiaohui & Zhang, Wei, eds. 2009. (ENG., Illus.). 302p. 160.00 *(978-0-415-49600-1(4))* Routledge.
Liu, Xin. The Mirage of China: Anti-Humanism, Narcissism, & Corporeality of the Contemporary World. 2009. 222p. 90.00 *(978-1-84545-545-3(2))* Berghahn Bks., Inc.
Liu, Xiuli. Some Advance of Input-Output Analysis. 2009. 90p. pap. *(978-3-639-18136-4(0))* VDM Verlag Dr. Mueller e.K.
Liu, Zhibiao & Zheng, Jianghuai. Growth of the Service Sector in the Yangtze River Delta: Enrich Series on China's Economic Issues, 5 vols., Vol. 2. 2011. (Enrich Series on China's Economic Issues Ser.). (ENG.). 512p. 148.00 *(978-981-4298-20-9(4))* Enrich Professional Publishing (S)., Ltd. SGP. Dist: Independent Pubs. Group.
Lo, Chi. Understanding China's Growth: Forces That Drive China's Economic Future. 2007. (ENG., Illus.). 272p. 110.00 *(978-0-230-51557-4(6))* Palgrave Macmillan.
Logan, John R., ed. Urban China in Transition. 2008. (Studies in Urban & Social Change Ser.: 12). (ENG., Illus.). 384p. 94.95 *(978-1-4051-6145-9(0))*; pap. 39.95 *(978-1-4051-6146-6(9))* Wiley, John & Sons, Inc. (Wiley-Blackwell).
Lu. The Great Urbanization of China. 2011. 118.00 *(978-981-4287-80-7(6))* World Scientific Publishing Co., Inc.
Ma, Junya. Bei Xi Sheng de "Ju Bu" Huai Bei She Hui Sheng Tai Bian Qian Yan Jiu (1680-1949) 2010. (CHI., Illus.). 646p. *(978-986-02-2875-5(2))* Academia Sinica.
Ma, Rong. Population & Society in Contemporary Tibet. 2011. (CHI., Illus.). 408p. **(978-988-8053-76-6(0))**; **(978-988-220-728-8(6))**; **(978-988-220-656-4(5))** Hong Kong Univ. Pr.
MacDonald, Scott B. & Lemco, Jonathan. Asia's Rise in the 21st Century, 1 vol. 2011. 200p. 37.00 *(978-0-313-39370-9(2)*, A3372C); E-Book **(978-0-313-39371-6(0)**, Praeger Pubs.) Greenwood Publishing Group, Inc.
Maddison, Angus. Chinese Economic Performance in the Long Run: 960-2030 Ad. 2nd ed. 2007. (ENG., Illus.). 196p. pap. 50.00 *(978-92-64-03762-5(4))* Organization for Economic Cooperation & Development.
Malik, Khalid. Why Has China Grown So Fast for So Long? 2012. (ENG.). 254p. 45.00 **(978-0-19-807883-8(8))** Oxford Univ. Pr., Inc.
Malkiel, Burton G. & Taylor, Patricia A. From Wall Street to the Great Wall: How Investor's Can Profit from China's Booming Economy. 2008. (ENG., Illus.). 320p. pap. 18.95 *(978-0-393-33358-9(2)*, 33358) Norton, W. W. & Co., Inc.
Maluste, Rajiv G. Endogenous Origins of Economic Reforms in India & Chin: The Role of Attitudinal Changes. 2011. 368p. pap. 29.95 **(978-1-61233-753-1(8)**, Dissertation.com) Universal Pubs.
Marks, Robert. Tigers, Rice, Silk, & Silt: Environment & Economy in Late Imperial South China. 2006. (Studies in Environment & History). (ENG., Illus.). 408p. pap. 58.00 *(978-0-521-02776-2(4))* Cambridge Univ. Pr.
McGregor, James. One Billion Customers: Lessons from the Front Lines of Doing Business in China. 2007. (ENG.). 352p. pap. 15.99 *(978-0-7432-5841-8(X)*, Free Pr.) Free Pr.
McManus, John, et al. China & India: Opportunities & Threats for the Global Software Industry. 2007. (Chandos Asian Studies). (ENG.). 188p. 110.00 *(978-1-84334-158-1(1)*, Chandos Publishing) Woodhead Publishing Ltd. GBR. Dist: Ingram Pub. Services.
McNally, Christopher A. China's Emergent Political Economy: Capitalism in the Dragon's Lair. 2009. 262p. pap. 39.95 *(978-0-415-49718-3(3))* 2007. (Illus.). XXVI, 262p. 170.00 *(978-0-415-42572-8(7))* Routledge.
Meng, Erika C. H. & Brennan, John P. Economic Analysis of Diversity in Modern Wheat. 2009. (ENG., Illus.). 204p. 99.95 *(978-1-57808-575-0(6))* BIOS Scientific Publishers Ltd. GBR. Dist: Taylor & Francis Group.
Mengkui, Wang. China in the Wake of Asia's Financial Crisis. 2008. (Illus.). 320p. 180.00 *(978-0-415-46469-7(2))* Routledge.
Meredith, Robyn. The Elephant & the Dragon: The Rise of India & China & What It Means for All of Us. 2007. (ENG., Illus.). 256p. 25.95 *(978-0-393-06236-6(8)*, 6236) Norton, W. W. & Co., Inc.
Meyer, Claude. China or Japan: Who Will Lead Asia? 2012. (Columbia/Hurst Ser.). (ENG.). 176p. (gr. 17). 35.00 **(978-0-231-70286-7(8))** Columbia Univ. Pr.
Meyer, Susanne. Informal Modes of Governance in Customer Producer Relations: The Electronic Industry in the Greater Pearl River Delta (China) 2011. (Megacities & Global Change / Megastadte und globaler Wandel Ser.). (Illus.). 222p. (C). pap. 64.00 *(978-3-515-09849-6(6))* Steiner, Franz Verlag Wiesbaden GmbH DEU. Dist: Brown, David Bk. Co., The.
Min, Dong. Political & Economic Reform. 2010. 224p. pap. *(978-3-8383-3766-1(2))* Lambert Academic Publishing.
Moh, Feng-Yuan & Lin, Bing-Huei. Risk Issues on Banking Industry in Taiwan & Mainland Chin. 2011. 64p. pap. **(978-3-8443-2715-1(0))** Lambert Academic Publishing.
Moore, Davon R. Russia, China & Eurasia: Social, Historical & Cultural Issues. 2010. (Russia, China & Eurasia: Social, Historical & Cultural Issues Ser.). 188p. 89.00 *(978-1-61668-016-9(4))* Nova Science Pubs., Inc.
Morita, Ken & Chen, Yun. Transition, Regional Development & Globalization. 2008. (Illus.). 300p. 111.00 *(978-981-283-344-0(7))* World Scientific Publishing Co., Inc.
Mosk, Carl. Traps Embraced or Escaped: Elites in the Economic Development of Modern Japan & China. 2010. 350p. 87.00 *(978-981-4287-52-4(0))* World Scientific Publishing Co., Inc.
Moyo, Dambisa. Winner Take All: China's Push for Resources & What It Means for the World. 2012. (ENG.). 240p. (gr. 9). 26.99 **(978-0-465-02828-3(4))** Basic Bks.
Mukhopadhaya, Pundarik, et al. Economic Growth & Income Inequality in China, India & Singapore: Trends & Policy Implications. 2011. (Routledge Studies in the Modern World Economy Ser.). (ENG., Illus.). 208p. (C). 152.00 *(978-0-415-61646-1(8))* Routledge.
Murphy, Rachel. Media, Identity & Struggle in Twenty-First-Century China. Fong, Vanessa L., ed. 2008. (ENG.). 184p. (C). 150.00 *(978-0-415-46058-3(1))* Routledge.

Naisbitt, John & Naisbitt, Doris. Chinas Megatrends: Die 8 Säulen Einer Neuen Gesellschaft. 2010. 272p. 27.99 *(978-0-06-185944-1(3)*, Collins) HarperCollins Pubs.
Naughton, Barry J. The Chinese Economy: Transitions & Growth. 2006. (ENG., Illus.). 544p. per. 28.00 *(978-0-262-64064-0(3))* MIT Pr.
Nearing, Scott. Whither China? an Economic Interpretation of Recent Events in the Far East. 2011. 224p. 44.95 **(978-1-258-06124-1(4))** Literary Licensing, LLC.
Neftci, Salih N. & Yuan Menager-Xu, Michelle, eds. China's Financial Markets: An Insider's Guide to How the Markets Work. 2006. (ENG., Illus.). 416p. 86.95 *(978-0-12-088580-0(8)*, Academic Pr.) Elsevier Science & Technology Bks.
Newman, Frank N. Six Myths That Hold Back America: And What America Can Learn from the Growth of China's Economy. 2011. (ENG.). 192p. 25.95 **(978-0-9839885-1-9(X))** Diversion Bks.
Ngo, Tak-Wing & Wu, Yongping, eds. Rent Seeking in China. 2012. (Routledge Contemporary China Ser.). (ENG., Illus.). 336p. (C). pap. 42.95 **(978-0-415-54205-0(7))** Routledge.
Ni, Pengfei. Dongguan Cheng Shi Guo Ji Jing Zheng Li Bao Gao: Kua Yue Shi Fa Zhan de Quan Qiu Yang Ban Report on Dongguan's Global Urban Competitiveness. 2010. (CHI., Illus.). 215p. *(978-7-5097-1331-0(5))* China Social Science Documentation Publishing Hse.
Nolan, Ernest P. China in Focus: Economic, Political & Educational Issues. 2008. 150.00 *(978-1-60021-543-8(2))* Nova Science Pubs., Inc.
Nolan, Peter. China in the Asian Financial Crisis. 2008. (Routledge Studies on the Chinese Economy Ser.). 320p. 130.00 *(978-0-415-30372-9(9))* Routledge.
Oecd Publishing. Growth & Sustainability in Brazil, China, India, Indonesia & South Afric. 2010. 190p. pap. 75.00 *(978-92-64-09019-4(3))* Organization for Economic Cooperation & Development.
Ong, Aihwa. Neoliberalism as Exception: Mutations in Citizenship & Sovereignty. 2006. (ENG., Illus.). 304p. per. 24.95 *(978-0-8223-3748-5(7))* Duke Univ. Pr.
Orcutt, John & Shen, Hong. Shaping China's Innovation Future: University Technology Transfer in Transition. 2011. (Illus.). 320p. 135.00 *(978-1-84980-358-8(7))* Elgar, Edward Publishing, Inc.
Organisation for Economic Co-operation and Development. China. 2010. (Illus.). 234p. pap. 63.00 *(978-92-64-07667-9(0))* Organization for Economic Cooperation & Development.
Orlik, Thomas. Understanding China's Economic Indicators: Translating the Data into Investment Opportunities. rev. ed. 2011. (ENG., Illus.). 272p. 49.99 *(978-0-13-262019-2(7))* FT Press.
Oxfeld, Ellen. Drink Water, but Remember the Source: Moral Discourse in a Chinese Village. 2010. (ENG., Illus.). 312p. 60.00 *(978-0-520-26094-8(5))*; pap. 24.95 *(978-0-520-26095-5(3))* Univ. of California Pr.
Pang, Laikwan. Creativity & Its Discontents: China's Creative Industries & Intellectual Property Rights Offenses. 2012. (ENG., Illus.). 320p. 89.95 **(978-0-8223-5065-1(3))**; pap. 24.95 **(978-0-8223-5082-8(3))** Duke Univ. Pr.
Pant, Harsh. China's Rising Global Profile: The Great Power Tradition. 2012. (ENG.). 132p. pap. 24.95 **(978-1-84519-517-5(5))** Sussex Academic Pr. GBR. Dist: International Specialized Bk. Services.
Pant, Harsh V. China's Rising Global Profile: The Great Power Tradition. 2011. 132p. 45.00 *(978-1-84519-457-4(8))* Sussex Academic Pr. GBR. Dist: International Specialized Bk. Services.
Paus, Eva, et al. Global Giant: Is China Changing the Rules of the Game? 2009. (ENG.). 288p. 100.00 *(978-0-230-61588-5(0))*; pap. 44.00 *(978-0-230-61589-2(9))* Palgrave Macmillan.
Peerenboom, Randall. China Modernizes: Threat to the West or Model for the Rest? 2007. (ENG., Illus.). 432p. 50.00 *(978-0-19-920834-0(4))* Oxford Univ. Pr., Inc.
—China Modernizes: Threat to the West or Model for the Rest? 2008. (ENG., Illus.). 432p. pap. 21.95 *(978-0-19-922612-2(1))* Oxford Univ. Pr., Inc.
Peng, Sen & Chen, Li. Reforming China: Major Events (1978-1991), 5 vols., Vol. 3. Li, Tieying, ed. 2010. (Enrich Series on China's Economic Reform Ser.). (ENG.). 400p. 138.00 *(978-981-4298-04-9(2))* Enrich Professional Publishing (S)., Ltd. SGP. Dist: Independent Pubs. Group.
Perkins, Dwight H. The Challenges of China's Growth. 2007. (Henry Wendt Lecture Ser.). (ENG., Illus.). 62p. per. 15.00 *(978-0-8447-7195-3(3)*, AEI Pr.) American Enterprise Institute for Public Policy Research.
Phillips, Jack M. & Moore, Logan J., eds. China: Economics, Political & Social Issues. 2008. (Illus.). xi, 307p. 98.00 *(978-1-60456-727-4(9))* Nova Science Pubs., Inc.
Plafker, Ted. Doing Business in China: How to Profit in the World's Fastest Growing Market. 2008. (ENG.). 304p. pap. 16.99 *(978-0-446-69696-8(X))* 2007. 302p. pap. 16.00 *(978-0-446-69863-4(6))* Grand Central Publishing. (Business Plus).
Powell, Jason L. China, Aging, & Theory. 2012. pap. **(978-1-62100-915-3(7))** Nova Science Pubs., Inc.
Qi, Shouhua. China Complex: U. S.-China Relations in the 21st Century: Crossroads or Collision Course. 2009. (ENG.). 224p. pap. 18.95 *(978-1-59265-079-8(1))* Long River Pr.
Qiang, Christine Zhen-Wei. China's Information Revolution: Managing the Economic & Social Transformation. 2007. (Books Ser.). (ENG., Illus.). 156p. per. 29.95 *(978-0-8213-6720-9(X)*, 9780821367209) World Bank Pubns.
"Qinglong Manzu Zizhixian gai kuang" bian xie zu Staff & "Qinglong Manzu Zizhixian gai kuang" xiu ding ben bian xie zu Staff, contrib. by. Qinglong Manzu Zizhixian Gai Kuang: Qinglongmanzuzizhixiangaikuang. 2009. (CHI., Illus.). *(978-7-105-08672-6(6))* Nationalities Publishing Hse, The.
Qiu, Jack Linchuan. Working-Class Network Society: Communication Technology & the Information Have-Less in Urban China. 2009. (Information Revolution & Global Politics Ser.). (ENG., Illus.). 320p. (gr. 17). 37.00 *(978-0-262-17006-2(X))* MIT Pr.
Rahman, Rita Dulci & Andreu, Jose Miguel. China & India: Towards Global Economic Supremacy? 2006. (ENG.). 249p. 49.95 *(978-81-7188-424-7(5))* Academic Foundation IND. Dist: Independent Pubs. Group.
Realizing Rational Exuberance: An Appreciation of the Mundell-Huang Da Lectures. 2011. 106.00 *(978-981-4295-32-1(9))* World Scientific Publishing Co., Inc.
Ren, Jia. Financial-Growth Nexus in China. 2007. pap. *(978-3-8364-1643-6(3))* VDM Verlag Dr. Mueller e.K.
Riedel, James, et al. How China Grows: Investment, Finance, & Reform. 2007. (ENG., Illus.). 222p. (C). 55.00 *(978-0-691-12562-6(7))* Princeton Univ. Pr.
Roraback, Amanda. China in a Nutshell. 2009. (Nutshell Notes Ser.). (ENG., Illus.). 108p. pap. 9.95 *(978-0-9763079-2-0(2))* Enisen Publishing.
Rose, Axel & Grupe, Claudia. China - Indien: Wettbewerbsfähigkeit im Vergleich. 2009. (GER.). 182p. pap. 43.95 *(978-3-631-58522-1(5))* Lang, Peter GmbH, Europaischer Verlag der Wissenschaften DEU. Dist: Lang, Peter.
Rosen, Daniel & Whang, Zhi. The Implications of China-Taiwan Economic Liberalization. 2010. pap. 21.95 *(978-0-88132-501-0(5))* Peterson Institute for International Economics.
Rosenthal, Jean-Laurent & Wong, Roy Bin. Before & Beyond Divergence: The Politics of Economic Change in China & Europe. 2011. (Illus.). 290p. 45.00 *(978-0-674-05791-3(0))* Harvard Univ. Pr.
Rowen, Henry S., et al, eds. Greater China's Quest for Innovation. 2008. (ENG.). 432p. pap. 24.95 *(978-1-931368-12-4(0))* Shorenstein, Walter H. Asia-Pacific Research Ctr.

Rubinfien, Leo, intro. Phantom Shanghai. 2007. (FRE & ENG., Illus.). 240p. 50.00 *(978-0-9739739-1-4(9))* Magenta Publishing for the Arts CAN. Dist: Consortium Bk. Sales & Distribution.
Rui, Mingjie. Zhongguo Chan Ye Fa Zhan de Zhan Lüe Xuan Ze. 2010. (CHI., Illus.). *(978-7-5432-1706-9(2))* Chinese Dictionary Publishing House.
Ryan, Chris & Gu, Huimin. Tourism in China: Destination, Cultures & Communities. Huimin, Gu, ed. 2008. (Routledge Advances in Tourism Ser.). (ENG., Illus.). 418p. 125.00 *(978-0-415-99189-6(7))* Routledge.
Sajaniemi, Pietari. Tourism As a Socially Sustainable Tool for Rural Development. 2010. 124p. pap. *(978-3-8383-6251-9(9))* Lambert Academic Publishing.
Sanders, Richard & Yang, Chen C., eds. China's Post-Reform Economy - Achieving Harmony, Sustaining Growth. 2008. (Routledge Studies on the Chinese Economy Ser.). (Illus.). XVI, 256p. 170.00 *(978-0-415-43432-4(7))* Routledge.
"Sanjiang Dongzu Zizhixian gai kuang" bian xie zu Staff & "Sanjiang Dongzu Zizhixian gai kuang" xiu ding ben bian xie zu Staff, contrib. by. Sanjiang Dongzu Zizhixian Gai Kuang: SanjiangDongzuZizhixiangaikuang. 2008. (CHI., Illus.). *(978-7-105-08612-2(2))* Nationalities Publishing Hse, The.
Schiere, Richard. China's Development Challenges: Public Sector Reform & Vulnerability to Poverty. 2008. (Routledge Studies on the Chinese Economy Ser.). (Illus.). 192p. 130.00 *(978-0-415-47865-6(0))* Routledge.
Schwartz, Jonathan. State & Society Responses to Social Welfare Needs in China: Serving the People. Schwartz, Jonathan & Shieh, Shawn, eds. 2009. (Routledge Contemporary China Ser.). (ENG., Illus.). 224p. 130.00 *(978-0-415-45224-3(4))* Routledge.
Scott Lash, et al. Global China. 2012. (International Library of Sociology Ser.). (ENG.). 256p. (C). 120.00 *(978-0-415-49705-3(1))*; pap. 41.95 *(978-0-415-49706-0(X))* Routledge.
Selvanathan, E. Antony, et al. China's Economic Miracle: Does FDI Matter? 2012. 224p. 110.00 **(978-0-85793-680-6(8))** Elgar, Edward Publishing, Inc.
Seng. Global Financial Crisis & Challenges for China. 2011. 54.00 *(978-981-4282-27-7(8))* World Scientific Publishing Co., Inc.
Shambaugh, David, ed. Charting China's Future: Domestic & International Challenges. 2011. (ENG., Illus.). 208p. (C). pap. 51.95 **(978-0-415-61955-4(6))** Routledge.
Shek, Daniel T.L., ed. Quality of Life of Chinese People in a Changing World. 2010. (Social Indicators Research Ser.). (Illus.). vi, 198p. 79.95 *(978-94-007-0223-3(X)*, 940070223X) Springer.
Shen, Raphael & Mantzopoulos, Victoria. Political Economy of China's Systemic Transformation: 1979 to the Present. 2011. (ENG., Illus.). 250p. 85.00 *(978-0-230-10303-0(0))* Palgrave Macmillan.
Sherman, So & Westland, J. Christopher. Red Wired: China's Internet Revolution. 2009. (Illus.). 256p. pap. 16.95 *(978-0-462-09967-5(9))* Marshall Cavendish GBR. Dist: Midpoint Trade Bks., Inc.
Shi, Lai. The Balanced Scorecard & Its Applications in Chin. 2008. 68p. pap. *(978-3-639-07881-7(0))* VDM Verlag Dr. Mueller e.K.
Shi, Li, et al. Eliminating Poverty Through Development in China. 2008. (Illus.). 280p. 180.00 *(978-0-415-46277-8(0))* Routledge.
Shirk, Susan L. China: Fragile Superpower. 2008. (ENG., Illus.). 336p. pap. 16.95 *(978-0-19-537319-6(7))* Oxford Univ. Pr., Inc.
Shiroyama, Tomoko. China During the Great Depression: Market, State, & the World Economy, 1929-1937. (Harvard East Asian Monographs: 294). (Illus.). 350p. 2009. pap. 24.95 *(978-0-674-03617-8(4))* 2008. 45.00 *(978-0-674-02831-9(7))* Harvard Univ., Asia Ctr.
Shue, Vivienne & Wong, Christine, eds. Paying for Progress in China: Public Finance, Human Welfare & Changing Patterns of Inequality. 2008. 39.95 *(978-0-415-48779-5(X))* 2007. (Illus.). 195p. 160.00 *(978-0-415-42254-3(X))* Routledge.
Sieren, Frank. The China Code: What's Left for Us. Rede, Thomas, tr. from GER. 2007. (ENG.). 320p. 59.00 *(978-0-230-00135-0(1))* Palgrave Macmillan.
Sluglett, Peter & Huang, Xiyi. Power, Entitlement & Social Practice: Resource Distribution in North China Village. 2007. (ENG., Illus.). 220p. (gr. 17). 39.00 *(978-962-996-315-6(9))* Chinese Univ. of Hong Kong, The HKG. Dist: Columbia Univ. Pr.
Smith, David. Growling Tiger, Roaring Dragon: India, China, & the New World Order, 1 vol. 2008. (ENG.). 272p. 27.95 *(978-1-55365-334-9(3))* D&M Pubs Inc. CAN. Dist: Perseus-PGW.
Smith, S. A. Revolution & the People in Russia & China: A Comparative History. 2008. (Wiles Lectures). (ENG.). (C). 258p. 84.00 *(978-0-521-88637-6(6))*; 264p. pap. 30.99 *(978-0-521-71396-2(X))* Cambridge Univ. Pr.
So, Billy, ed. Economic History of Lower Yangzi Delta in Late Imperial China. 2012. (Academia Sinica on East Asia Ser.). (ENG., Illus.). 336p. (C). 135.00 **(978-0-415-50896-4(7))** Routledge.
Solomon & Adler, Solomon. Chinese Economy V1. 2008. (Illus.). 304p. 200.00 *(978-0-415-36145-3(1)*, Routledge Cavendish) Taylor & Francis Group GBR. Dist: Taylor & Francis Group.
Son, Joonmo. Social Capital & Institutional Constraints. 2012. (Routledge Contemporary China Ser.). (ENG., Illus.). 192p. (C). 135.00 **(978-0-415-59522-3(3))** Routledge.
Song, Guiwu. Peng Zhuang Zhongguo She Hui Jing Ji Wen Ti: Mian Zi, Xue Yuan, Quan Li = Pengzhuang Zhongguoshehui Jingjiwenti. 2010. (CHI., Illus.). *(978-7-5017-8787-6(5))* China Economics Publishing Hse.
Song, Liang & Woo, Wing Thye, eds. China's Dilemma: Economic Growth, the Environment & Climate Change. 2008. (Illus.). pap. *(978-0-7315-3819-5(6))* Asia Pacific Pr.
Song, Weiming, et al. Russian Logs in China: The Softwood Commodity Chain & Economic Development in China. 2007. pap. *(978-1-932928-24-2(3))* Forest Trends.
Springborg, Robert. Development Models in Muslim Contexts: Chinese, 'Islamic' & Neo-Liberal Alternatives. 2010. (Exploring Muslim Contexts Ser.). (ENG., Illus.). 280p. (gr. 17). 105.00 *(978-0-7486-3968-7(3))* Edinburgh Univ. Pr. GBR. Dist: Columbia Univ. Pr.
Steinfeld, Edward S. Playing Our Game: Why China's Rise Doesn't Threaten the West. 2012. (ENG., Illus.). 280p. pap. 21.95 **(978-0-19-983708-3(2))** Oxford Univ. Pr., Inc.
Storey, Ian. Asean & the Rise of China. 2011. (Routledge Security in Asia Ser.). (ENG., Illus.). 384p. 145.00 *(978-0-415-32621-6(4))* Routledge.
Stou. Entrepreneurship & Economic Growth in China. 2011. 96.00 *(978-981-4273-36-7(8))* World Scientific Publishing Co., Inc.
Street, Nancy Lynch & Matelski, Marilyn J. American Businesses in China: Balancing Culture & Communication. 2nd rev. ed. 2008. (ENG.). 359p. pap. 39.95 *(978-0-7864-3592-0(5))* McFarland & Co., Inc. Pubs.
Su, Jilang & Myers, Ramon Hawley. The Treaty Port Economy in Modern China: Empirical Studies of Institutional Change & Economic Performance. 2011. *(978-1-55729-099-1(7))* Univ. of California, Institute of East Asian Studies.
Subramanian, Arvind. Eclipse: Living in the Shadow of China's Economic Dominance. 2011. (Illus.). xvii, 216p. pap. 21.95 *(978-0-88132-606-2(2))* Peterson Institute for International Economics.
Sun, Hongzhi. She Hui Zhu Yi Xin Nong Cun Jian She Shi Jian Yan Jiu. 2008. (CHI., Illus.). *(978-7-5035-3952-7(6))* Party Schl. Pr. of the Central Committee of CPC, The.
Sun, Kang. Disciplinary Identity of Technical Communication. 2009. 72p. pap. *(978-3-639-18210-1(3))* VDM Verlag Dr. Mueller e.K.
Sutherland, Dylan. Hiv/Aids in China. 2011. (Routledge Contemporary China Ser.). (ENG., Illus.). 184p. (C). 145.00 *(978-0-415-41875-1(5))* Routledge.

C

Sweetman, Arthur & Zhang, Jun. Economic Transitions with Chinese Characteristics Vol. 1: Thirty Years of Reform & Opening Up. 2009. (ENG.). 232p. (C). (978-1-55339-226-2(4)); pap. (978-1-55339-225-5(6)) McGill-Queen's Univ. Pr.

—Economic Transitions with Chinese Characteristics Vol. 2: Social Change During Thirty Years of Reform. 2009. (ENG.). 216p. (C). (978-1-55339-235-4(3)); pap. (978-1-55339-234-7(5)) McGill-Queen's Univ. Pr.

Sykes, Geoffrey, ed. Courting the Media: Contemporary Perspectives on Media & Law. 2010. (Media & Communications - Technologies, Policies & Challenges Ser.). vi, 182p. 145.00 (978-1-61668-784-7(3)) Nova Science Pubs., Inc.

Takagi, Seiichiro, et al, eds. China Watching: Perspectives from Europe, Japan & the United States. 2006. (ENG.). 272p. (C). 190.00 (978-0-415-41396-1(6)) Routledge.

—China Watching: Perspectives from Europe, Japan & the United States. 2006. (Routledge Contemporary China Ser.). 261p. per. 43.95 (978-0-415-41397-8(4), Routledge) Taylor & Francis Group GBR. Dist: Taylor & Francis Group.

Tan, Yinglan. Chinnovation: How Chinese Innovators Are Changing the World. 2011. (ENG., Illus.). 288p. 29.95 (978-0-470-82796-3(3), Wiley) Wiley, John & Sons, Inc.

Tang, Lei. The Chinese Consumer Market: Opportunities & Risks. 2009. (Chandos Asian Studies). (ENG., Illus.). 250p. 110.00 (978-1-84334-332-5(0), Chandos Publishing) Woodhead Publishing Ltd. GBR. Dist: Ingram Pub. Services.

Tang, Wenfang & Holzner, Burkart, eds. Social Change in Contemporary China: C. K. Yang & the Concept of Institutional Diffusion. 2006. (Illus.). 336p. 65.00 (978-0-8229-4297-9(6)); per. 26.95 (978-0-8229-5933-5(X)) Univ. of Pittsburgh Pr.

Tanzi, Vito. Peoples, Places & Policies: China, Japan & Southeast Asia. 2007. per. 19.95 (978-0-9795576-5-1(8)) Pinto, Jorge Bks.

Tao, Julia Lai Po-Wah. China: Bioethics, Trust, & the Challenge of the Market. 2008. (Philosophy & Medicine / Asian Studies in Bioethics & the Philosophy of Medicine Ser.). xi, 212p. (C). 159.00 (978-1-4020-6756-3(9)) Springer.

Taylor, Robert, ed. International Business in China: Understanding the Global Economic Crisis. 2012. (ENG.). 152p. (C). 125.00 (978-0-415-67483-6(2)) Routledge.

Tézenas, Ambroise, photos by. Beijing: Theatre of the People. 2007. (ENG., Illus.). 120p. 45.00 (978-1-904587-36-1(4)) Lewis, Dewi Publishing GBR. Dist: Consortium Bk. Sales & Distribution.

Thargyal, Rinzin. Nomads of Eastern Tibet: Social Organization & Economy of a Pastoral Estate in the Kingdom of Dege. Huber, Toni, ed. 2007. (Brill's Tibetan Studies Library). (Illus.). 222p. (978-90-04-15813-9(8)) BRILL.

Thaxton, Ralph A., Jr. Catastrophe & Contention in Rural China: Mao's Great Leap Famine & the Origins of Righteous Resistance in Da Fo Village. 2008. (Cambridge Studies in Contentious Politics Ser.). (ENG., Illus.). 406p. 82.00 (978-0-521-89749-5(1)) Cambridge Univ. Pr.

The Institute of Economic Research of Renmin University of China. Vol. 1 China's Economy 2009: Enrich Annual Economic Review Series, 3 vols., Vol. 1. 2011. (Enrich Annual Economic Review Ser.). (ENG.). 312p. 98.00 (978-981-4298-67-4(0)) Enrich Professional Publishing (S)., Ltd. SGP. Dist: Independent Pubs. Group.

Thompson, Sandy. One in a Billion: Xploring the New World of China. 2006. (ENG., Illus.). 144p. 8.99 (978-1-57687-296-3(3), powerHouse Bks.) powerHouse Cultural Entertainment, Inc.

Tian, Rumiao. Nong Min Zeng Shou Zhi Fu de Cou Shi Yu Ji Shu. 2008. (CHI., Illus.). (978-7-80233-752-7(6)) China Agricultural Scientech Pr.

"Tianzhu Zangzu Zizhixian gai kuang" bian xie zu Staff & "Tianzhu Zangzu Zizhixian gai kuang" xiu ding ben bian xie zu Staff, contrib. by. Tianzhu Zangzu Zizhixian Gai Kuang: TianzhuZangzuZizhixiangaikuang. 2009. (CHI., Illus.). (978-7-105-08624-5(6)) Nationalities Publishing Hse, The.

Tong, Junie Therese. Finance & Society in 21st Century China: Chinese Culture Versus Western Markets. 2011. (Transformation & Innovation Ser.). (Illus.). 234p. 114.95 (978-1-4094-0129-2(4), Gower Publishing Co., Ltd.) Ashgate Publishing, Ltd. GBR. Dist: Ashgate Publishing Co.

Tong, Yanqi & Lei, Shaohua. Social Protest in Contemporary China. 2012. (China Policy Ser.). (ENG.). 192p. (C). 130.00 (978-0-415-60569-4(5)) Routledge.

"Tongdao Dongzu Zizhixian gai kuang" bian xie zu Staff & "Tongdao Dongzu Zizhixian" xiu ding ben bian xie zu Staff, contrib. by. Tongdao Dongzu Zizhixian Gai Kuang: TongdaoDongzuZizhixiangaikuang. 2008. (CHI., Illus.). (978-7-105-08608-5(4)) Nationalities Publishing Hse, The.

Trippon, James. Becoming Your Own China Stock Guru: The Ultimate Investor's Guide to Profiting from China's Economic Boom. 2008. (ENG., Illus.). 204p. 34.95 (978-0-470-22312-3(X), Wiley) Wiley, John & Sons, Inc.

Tselichtchev, Ivan. China Versus the West: The Global Power Shift of the 21st Century. 2012. (ENG.). 224p. 29.95 (978-0-470-82972-1(9), Wiley) Wiley, John & Sons, Inc.

Tseng, Wanda S. India's & China's Recent Experience with Reform & Growth. Tseng, Wanda S. & Cowen, David G., eds. 2007. (ENG., Illus.). 336p. pap. 47.00 (978-0-230-54281-5(6)) Palgrave Macmillan.

Tsui, Anne S., et al, eds. China's Domestic Private Firms: Multidisciplinary Perspectives on Management & Performance. 2006. (Illus.). 342p. per. 39.95 (978-0-7656-1383-7(2)) Sharpe, M.E. Inc.

Tubilewicz, Czeslaw. Critical Issues in Contemporary China. 2006. (ENG., Illus.). 288p. (C). 180.00 (978-0-415-39584-7(4)); per. 43.95 (978-0-415-39585-4(2)) Routledge.

United Nations. Eco-Efficiency: A Practical Path to Sustainable Development - A Reference for Eco-efficiency Partnership in North-East Asia. 2008. (ENG.). 80p. pap. 28.00 (978-92-1-120525-1(5)) United Nations Pubns.

Urio, Paolo. Reconciling State Market & Civil Society in China: The Long March Towards Prosperity. 2010. (Routledge Contemporary China Ser.). (Illus.). 304p. (C). 135.00 (978-0-415-56446-5(8)) Routledge.

Usui, Chikako, ed. Comparative Entrepreneurship Initiatives: Studies in China, Japan & the USA. 2011. (Palgrave Macmillan Asian Business Ser.). (ENG., Illus.). 328p. 105.00 (978-0-230-29881-1(8)) Palgrave Macmillan.

Vermeer, Eduard B. & Ho, Peter, eds. China's Limits to Growth: Greening State & Society. 2006. (Development & Change Special Issues Ser.). (ENG., Illus.). 288p. per. 39.95 (978-1-4051-5390-4(3), Wiley-Blackwell) Wiley, John & Sons, Inc.

Vermeer, Eduard B. & Vermeer, E. B. Economic Development in Provincial China: The Central Shaanxi since 1930. 2009. (Contemporary China Institute Publications). (ENG.). 552p. pap. 56.00 (978-0-521-11543-8(4)) Cambridge Univ. Pr.

Walter, Carl & Howie, Fraser. Red Capitalism: The Fragile Financial Foundation of China's Extraordinary Rise. 2nd rev. ed. 2012. (ENG.). 260p. 29.95 (978-1-118-25510-0(0), Wiley) Wiley, John & Sons, Inc.

Wan, Guanghua. Understanding Inequality & Poverty in China: Methods & Applications. Wan, Guanghua, ed. 2008. (Studies in Development Economics & Policy Ser.). (ENG., Illus.). 320p. 110.00 (978-0-230-53804-7(5)) Palgrave Macmillan.

Wang, Henry. Successful Business with China Oil Companies. 2012. (Routledge Studies in the Modern World Economy Ser.). (ENG.). 256p. (C). 152.00 (978-0-415-66956-6(1)) Routledge.

Wang, Lei. Foreign Direct Investment & Urban Growth in China. 2011. (Illus.). 152p. 99.95 (978-1-4094-0685-3(7)) Ashgate Publishing Co.

Wang, Mei-Ling, et al. WTO, Globalization, & China's Health Care System. 2007. (ENG.). 384p. 137.00 (978-1-4039-4326-2(5)) Palgrave Macmillan.

Wang, Ping. Public Procurement in China: A Long March Towards Integration into the Global Trading System. 2012. (China Policy Ser.). (ENG.). 208p. (C). 145.00 (978-0-415-46276-1(2)) Routledge.

Wang, Shengzhe. True Sale Securitization: Germany & China. 2007. 84p. per. (978-3-86550-950-5(9)) VDM Verlag Dr. Mueller e.K.

Wang, Shifen. Huo Bi Jia Zhi Lun: Cong Hui Lü Sheng Cheng Ji Zhi Kan Ren Min Bi Sheng Zhi Qian Jing = a Study on the Prospects of the Exchange Rates Between RMB & USD. 2009. (CHI., Illus.). (978-7-5096-0595-0(4)) Economic Management Publishing Hse.

Warner, Malcolm, ed. Making Sense of Chinese Human Resource Management in China: Economy, Enterprises & Workers. 2010. (ENG.). 272p. (C). 125.00 (978-0-415-56537-0(5), Routledge) Taylor & Francis Group GBR. Dist: Taylor & Francis Group.

Webber, M. Making Capitalism in Rural China. 2012. (Illus.). 336p. 150.00 (978-0-85793-409-3(0)) Elgar, Edward Publishing, Inc.

Wedeman, Andrew H. From Mao to Market: Rent Seeking, Local Protectionism, & Marketization in China. 2009. (Cambridge Modern China Ser.). (ENG., Illus.). 300p. pap. 38.99 (978-0-521-10015-1(1)) Cambridge Univ. Pr.

Wei, Sen. Shi Chang, Fa Zhi Yu Min Zhu: Yi Ge Jing Ji Xue Jia de Ri Chang Si Kao = Market Economy, Rule of Law & Constitutional Democracy. 2008. (CHI.). 312p. (978-7-208-08147-5(6)) Shanghai People's Publishing Hse.

Wei, Shulin. Zhongguo Shi Chang Jing Ji Fa Zhan de Zhi du Zhang Ai Tan Yuan: Wang Yanan Jing Ji Si Xiang de Qi Shi. 2009. (CHI., Illus.). (978-7-218-05866-5(3)) Guangdong Peoples Publishing Hse.

Wei, Yuwa. Securities Markets & Corporate Governance: A Chinese Experience. 2009. 304p. 134.95 (978-0-7546-7177-0(1)) Ashgate Publishing Co.

Wemheuer, Felix. Steinnudeln: Landliche Erinnerungen und staatliche Vergangenheitsbewaltigung der <GroBen Sprung>-Hungersnot in der chinesischen Provinz Henan. (GER., Illus.). 294p. pap. 62.95 (978-3-631-56279-6(9)) Lang, Peter GmbH, Europaischer Verlag der Wissenschaften DEU. Dist: Lang, Peter Publishing, Inc.

Weston, Timothy B. & Jensen, Lionel M. China in & Beyond the Headlines. 2011. (978-1-4422-0906-0(2)) Rowman & Littlefield Publishers, Inc.

Westra, Richard. The Evil Axis of Finance: The US-Japan-China Stranglehold on the Global Future. 2012. (ENG.). 244p. pap. 24.95 (978-0-932863-90-4(6)) Clarity Pr., Inc.

Whalley, John. China's Integration into the World Economy. 2010. (Illus.). 300p. 120.00 (978-981-4304-78-8(6)) World Scientific Publishing Co., Inc.

Whyte, Martin King. Myth of the Social Volcano: Perceptions of Inequality & Distributive Injustice in Contemporary China. 2010. (ENG., Illus.). 264p. 80.00 (978-0-8047-6941-9(9)); pap. 27.95 (978-0-8047-6942-6(7)) Stanford Univ. Pr.

Winters, Alan & Yusuf, Shahid, eds. Dancing with Giants: China, India, & the Global Economy. 2007. (Stand Alones Ser.). (ENG., Illus.). 288p. per. 24.95 (978-0-8213-6749-0(8), 9780821367490) World Bank Pubns.

Wong, Raymond Sin-kwo, ed. Chinese Entrepreneurship in A Global Era. 2009. (ENG.). 236p. (C). pap. 44.95 (978-0-415-57425-9(0)) Routledge.

Woo, Wing Thye & Song, Ligang. China's Dilemma: Economic Growth, the Environment & Climate Change. Song, Liang & Woo, Wing Thye, eds. 2008. (ENG., Illus.). 428p. pap. 32.95 (978-0-8157-3123-8(X)) Brookings Institution Pr.

Worm, Verner, ed. China: Business Opportunities in a Globalizing Economy. 2008. 195p. pap. 36.00 (978-87-630-0214-1(0)) Copenhagen Business Schl. Pr. DNK. Dist: International Specialized Bk. Services.

Worrall, Jonathan & O'Shea, Peter. From Wall Street to the Great Wall: How to Invest in China. 2006. (ENG., Illus.). 224p. 27.95 (978-0-470-10911-3(4), Wiley) Wiley, John & Sons, Inc.

Wright, Tim. The Coal Industry in China's Political Economy. 2011. (Routledge Studies on the Chinese Economy Ser.). (ENG., Illus.). 272p. (C). 150.00 (978-0-415-49328-4(5)) Routledge.

Wu. Understanding Economic Growth in China & India: A Comparative Study of Selected Issues. 2011. 180p. 73.00 (978-981-4287-78-4(4)) World Scientific Publishing Co., Inc.

Wu, Bin, et al, eds. China's Development & Harmonization: Towards a balance with nature, society & the international Community. 2012. (Routledge Studies on the Chinese Economy Ser.). (ENG.). 320p. (C). 155.00 (978-0-415-66567-4(1)) Routledge.

Wu, Bin & Flynn, Andrew. Marginalisation in China: Perspectives on Transition & Globalisation. Zhang, Heather Xiaoquan & Sanders, Richard, eds. 2007. (Marginal Regions (and in Association with IGU - Dynamics of Marginal & Critical Regions) Ser.). (Illus.). 280p. 124.95 (978-0-7546-4427-9(8)) Ashgate Publishing Co.

Wu, Bingxin. Consumption & Management: New Discovery & Applications. 2011. (Illus.). 510p. 132.00 (978-1-907568-07-7(7), Chandos Publishing) Woodhead Publishing Ltd. GBR. Dist: Neal-Schuman Pubs., Inc.

Wu, Fulong. Marginalization in Urban China: Comparative Perspectives. Webster, C. J., ed. 2010. (International Political Economy Ser.). (ENG., Illus.). 336p. 95.00 (978-0-230-23772-8(X)) Palgrave Macmillan.

Wu, Guoguang. Socialist China, Capitalist China: Social Tension & Political Transition under Economic Globalisation. Wu, Guoguang & Lansdowne, Helen, eds. 2009. (China Policy Ser.). (ENG., Illus.). 240p. 160.00 (978-0-415-48226-4(7)) Routledge.

Wu, Xiaobo. Die Dang Yi Bai Nian: Zhongguo Qi Ye, 1870-1977, 2 vols. 2009. (CHI., Illus.). (978-7-5086-1342-0(2)) CITIC Publishing Hse.

Wu, Zhongmin. China in the World Economy. Wu, Zhongmin, ed. 2009. (Routledge Studies on the Chinese Economy Ser.). (ENG., Illus.). 344p. (C). 190.00 (978-0-415-47002-5(1)) Routledge.

Xia, Donglin, ed. Case Studies on Chinese Enterprises. 2012. (Routledge Studies in the Modern World Economy Ser.). (ENG., Illus.). 328p. (C). 152.00 (978-0-415-66811-8(5)) Routledge.

Xiaoxi, Li, et al. Emerging Markets Reform & Development in China. 2010. (Illus.). ix, 49p. pap. 49.00 (978-1-61668-769-4(X)) Nova Science Pubs., Inc.

Xin, Ru, et al, eds. The China Society Yearbook: China's Social Development; Analysis & Forecast. 2007. (Chinese Academy of Social Sciences Yearbooks: Society Ser.). (Illus.). 343p. (978-90-04-15637-1(2)) BRILL.

"Xinbin Manzu Zizhixian gai kuang" bian xie zu Staff & "Xinbin Manzu Zizhixian gai kuang" xiu ding ben bian xie zu Staff, contrib. by. Xinbin Manzu Zizhixian Gai Kuang: XinbinManzuZizhixiangaikuang. 2009. (CHI., Illus.). (978-7-105-08661-0(0)) Nationalities Publishing Hse, The.

Yan, Li. The Effects of Transnational Corporations in the Era of Globalisation: The Case of China. 2011. 60p. pap. (978-3-639-31512-7(X)) VDM Verlag Dr. Mueller e.K.

"Yanbian Chaoxianzu Zizhizhou gai kuang" bian xie zu Staff & "Yanbian Chaoxianzu Zizhizhou gai kuang" xiu ding ben bian xie zu Staff, contrib. by. Yanbian Chaoxianzu Zizhizhou Gai Kuang: YanbianChaoxianzuZizhizhougaikuang. 2009. (CHI., Illus.). (978-7-105-08642-9(4)) Nationalities Publishing Hse, The.

Yang, Dali L., ed. Discontented Miracle: Growth, Conflict, & Institutional Adaptations in China. 2007. (Ser. on Contemporary China ndash; Vol. 10 Ser.). (Illus.). 311p. 113.00 (978-981-270-354-5(3)) World Scientific Publishing Co., Inc.

Yang, Dali L., ed. The Global Recession & China's Political Economy. 2012. (China in Transformation Ser.). (ENG., Illus.). 282p. 95.00 (978-0-230-34085-5(7)) Palgrave Macmillan.

Yang, Jisheng. Tombstone: The Great Chinese Famine, 1958-1962, 1 vol. Mosher, Stacy & Guo, Jian, trs. from CHI. 2012. (ENG., Illus.). 752p. 35.00 (978-0-374-27793-2(1)) Farrar, Straus & Giroux.

Yang, Jun. Impact Analysis of the Olympic Games Host City - Specially Focused on Sports Tourism Development in Qingdao, the Sailing Events Host City of 2008 Beij. 2008. 112p. pap. (978-3-639-10832-3(9)) VDM Verlag Dr. Mueller e.K.

Yao, Shujie, et al. Sustainable Reform & Development in Post-Olympic China. 2010. (Routledge Studies on the Chinese Economy Ser.). (ENG., Illus.). 240p. 140.00 (978-0-415-55956-0(1), Routledge) Taylor & Francis Group GBR. Dist: Taylor & Francis Group.

Yeung, Y. M. & Jianfa, Shen. The Pan-Pearl River Delta: An Emerging Regional Economy in a Globalizing China. 2008. (ENG.). 640p. (gr. 17). 59.00 (978-962-996-376-7(0)) Chinese Univ. of Hong Kong, The HKG. Dist: Columbia Univ. Pr.

Yi, Jingtao. China's Exchange Rates & Exchange Rate Regimes. 2010. 232p. pap. (978-3-8383-8861-8(5)) Lambert Academic Publishing.

Yi, Si-Uk. Tae Chunggguk Kyoyok Kujo Ui Pyonhwa Ch'ui Wa Kosi Kyongjejok Sisachom. 2008. (KOR., Illus.). 86p. (978-89-8063-368-5(8)) KDI.

Yingming, Zhu. Analysis on Industrial Clusters in China. 2009. (ENG., Illus.). 248p. 133.95 (978-1-4200-8919-6(6), CRC Press) Taylor & Francis Group GBR. Dist: Taylor & Francis Group.

Yip, Paul Sau-Leung. China's Exchange Rate System Reform: Lessons from Its Latest Macroeconomic & Financial Experiences. 2011. 400p. 118.00 (978-981-4289-10-8(8)) World Scientific Publishing Co., Inc.

Yiwu, Liao. The Corpse Walker: Real Life Stories: China from the Bottom Up. 2009. (ENG.). 352p. pap. 15.95 (978-0-307-38837-7(9), Anchor) Knopf Doubleday Publishing Group.

Yong, Kwek Ping. Private Equity in China: Challenges & Opportunities. 2012. (ENG.). 256p. 150.00 (978-0-470-82651-5(7), Wiley) Wiley, John & Sons, Inc.

Yongqin, Wang. China's Miracle. 2013. (Routledge Studies in the Modern World Economy Ser.). (ENG.). 256p. (C). 152.00 (978-0-415-68107-0(3)) Routledge.

Yu, Guanghua. Comparative Corporate Governance in China: Political Economy & Legal Infrastructure. 2007. (ENG.). 208p. (C). 175.00 (978-0-415-40306-1(5)); per. 63.95 (978-0-415-40307-8(3)) Routledge.

Yu, Hong. Economic Development & Inequality in China: The Case of Guangdong. 2010. (Illus.). xviii, 252p. (978-0-203-83950-8(1)) Routledge.

Yu, Hong & Yang, Mu. China's Industrial Development in the 21st Century. 2011. (Illus.). 268p. 78.00 (978-981-4324-74-8(4)) World Scientific Publishing Co., Inc.

Yuan, Zaijun. Failure of Chinas Democratic Reforms. 2011. (Challenges Facing Chinese Political Development Ser.). (ENG.). 195p. 60.00 (978-0-7391-6694-9(8)) Lexington Bks.

Yueh, Linda. The Economy of China. 2010. (Illus.). 264p. 112.00 (978-1-84542-194-6(9)) Elgar, Edward Publishing, Inc.

Yueh, Linda Y. The Economy of China. 2012. (Illus.). 264p. pap. 39.95 (978-1-78100-398-5(X)) Elgar, Edward Publishing, Inc.

Yuhua, Fu, et al, eds. Cultural Advantages in China / Tale of Six Cities. 2008. mass mkt. (978-1-59973-068-4(5)) Multimedia Larga.

Zanasi, Margherita. Saving the Nation: Economic Modernity in Republican China. 2006. (ENG.). 336p. 60.00 (978-0-226-97873-4(7)) Univ. of Chicago Pr.

Zeng, Peiyan. Xi Bu Da Kai Fa Jue Ce Hui Gu. 2010. (Illus.). (978-7-5098-0595-4(3)) Chinese Communist Party History Pr.

Zha, Jianying. Tide Players: The Movers & Shakers of a Rising China. 2011. (ENG.). 224p. 24.95 (978-1-59558-620-9(2)) New Pr., The.

Zhang, Fengbo. Economic Analysis of Chinese Transportation. 2009. (Illus.). 200p. pap. 19.75 (978-0-557-09490-5(9)) Lulu Enterprises Inc.

Zhang, Li & Ong, Aihwa, eds. Privatizing China: Socialism from Afar. 2008. (Illus.). 296p. 75.50 (978-0-8014-4596-5(5)); 282p. per. 22.95 (978-0-8014-7378-4(0)) Cornell Univ. Pr.

Zhang, Marina Yue. China 2.0: The Transformation of an Emerging Superpower... & the New Opportunities. 2010. (ENG.). 256p. 34.95 (978-0-470-82423-8(9), Wiley) Wiley, John & Sons, Inc.

Zhang, Si & Pearce, Robert. Multinationals in China: Business Strategy, Technology & Economic Development. 2012. (ENG.). 168p. 105.00 (978-0-230-57741-1(5)) Palgrave Macmillan.

Zhang, Wei. Economic Reform in Modern China V1, 4 vols. 2011. (Illus.). (978-0-415-56945-3(1)) Routledge.

—Economic Reform in Modern China V2, 4 vols. 2011. (Illus.). (978-0-415-56944-6(3)) Routledge.

—Economic Reform in Modern China V3, 4 vols. 2011. (Illus.). (978-0-415-56942-2(7)) Routledge.

—Economic Reform in Modern China V4, 4 vols. 2011. (Illus.). (978-0-415-56941-5(9)) Routledge.

Zhang, Wenxian, et al, eds. Entrepreneurial & Business Elites of China: The Chinese Returnees who have Shaped Modern China. 2011. 325p. (978-0-85724-089-7(7)) Emerald Group Publishing Ltd.

Zhang, Xiaobo. Narratives of Chinese Economic Reforms: How Does China Cross the River? 2010. 200p. 88.00 (978-981-4293-30-3(X)) World Scientific Publishing Co., Inc.

Zhang, Yong. Large Chinese State-Owned Enterprises: Corporatisation & Strategic Development. 2008. (ENG., Illus.). 288p. 100.00 (978-0-230-54293-8(X)) Palgrave Macmillan.

Zhang, Youde. Fan Zui She Hui Xue Li Lun Yu Zhuan Xing Qi de Fan Zui Wen Ti Yan Jiu. 2008. (CHI.). 7p. (978-7-5633-7913-2(4)) Guangxi Teachers Univ. Pr.

Zhao, Litao. Paths to Private Entrepreneurship. 2008. 160p. pap. (978-3-639-05170-4(X)) VDM Verlag Dr. Mueller e.K.

Zhenglai, Deng. China's Economy Vol. 1: Rural Reform & Agricultural Development. 2009. 432p. 111.00 (978-981-4291-85-9(4)) World Scientific Publishing Co., Inc.

Zhong gong zhong yang wen xian yan jiu shi, Deng Xiaoping yan jiu zu Staff, contrib. by. Kai Chuang: Deng Xiaoping Jue Ce Gai Ge Kai Fang Shi Hua. 2008. (CHI., Illus.). 297p. (978-7-5340-2557-0(5)) Zehjiang People's Fine Arts Publishing Hse.

Zhou, Yunbo & Qin, Yan. Empirical Analysis on Income Inequality of Chinese Residents. 2012. (ENG., Illus.). xv, 202p. 139.00 (978-3-642-24951-8(5), 3642249515) Springer.

Zhu, Xiaodong, ed. Private Enterprises & China's Economic Development. 2007. (Routledgecurzon Studies in the Growth Economics of Asia Ser.). (ENG., Illus.). 304p. (C). 180.00 (978-0-415-77147-4(1)) Routledge.

Zhu, Ying. The Everyday Impact of Economic Reform in China: Management Change, Enterprise Performance & Daily Life. 2010. (Routledge Studies in the Growth Economies of Asia Ser.). (ENG., Illus.). 224p. (C). 150.00 (978-0-415-42841-5(6)) Routledge.

CHINA—ECONOMIC CONDITIONS—1949-

Al. Investing in Human Capital for Economi. . 2009. (Illus.). xx, 401p. 135.00 (978-981-281-441-8(8)) World Scientific Publishing Co., Inc.

Ambler, Tim, et al. Doing Business in China. 3rd rev. ed. 2008. (ENG., Illus.). 304p. (C). pap. 39.95 (978-0-415-43632-8(X)) Routledge.

Bardhan, Pranab K. Awakening Giants, Feet of Clay: Assessing the Economic Rise of China & India. 2010. (ENG., Illus.). 192p. (C). 25.95 (978-0-691-12994-5(0)) Princeton Univ. Pr.

Benewick, Robert, et al. The State of China Atlas: Mapping the World's Fastest-Growing Economy. 2nd rev. ed. 2009. (ENG., Illus.). 128p. pap. 19.95 (978-0-520-25610-1(7)) Univ. of California Pr.

Brodsgaard, Kjeld Erik. The Chinese Communist Party in Reform. 2009. 272p. pap. 39.95 (978-0-415-54576-1(5)) Routledge.

Brugger, Bill & Brugger, William E. Democracy & Organisation in the Chinese Industrial Enterprise (1948-1953) 2010. (Contemporary China Institute Publications). (ENG.). 384p. pap. 31.99 (978-0-521-13429-3(3)) Cambridge Univ. Pr.

Cai, Fang. Transforming the Chinese Economy. 2010. (Social Scientific Studies in Reform Era China Ser.). (Illus.). l 360p. (978-90-04-18421-3(X)) BRILL.

—Zhongguo Jing Ji Zhuan Xing 30 Nian, 1978-2008: Transforming the Chinese Economy, 1978-2008. 2009. (CHI., Illus.). (978-7-5097-0807-1(9)) China Social Science Documentation Publishing Hse.

Chan, Lai-Ha. China At 60: Global-Local Interactions. 2011. 352p. 98.00 (978-981-4299-29-9(4)) World Scientific Publishing Co., Inc.

Chance, Giles. China & the Credit Crisis: Emergence of a New World Order. 2010. (ENG., Illus.). 228p. pap. 24.95 (978-0-470-82507-5(3), Wiley) Wiley, John & Sons, Inc.

Chen, Chunlai, ed. China's Integration with the Global Economy: WTO Accession, Foreign Direct Investment & International Trade. 2009. (Advances in Chinese Economic Studies). (Illus.). 240p. 119.00 (978-1-84844-214-6(9)) Elgar, Edward Publishing, Inc.

Chen, Jiagui. The China Economy Yearbook, Vol. 4. 2010. 225p. (978-90-04-18240-0(3)) BRILL.

Chen, Nai-Ruenn & Galenson, Walter. The Chinese Economy under Maoism: The Early Years, 1949-1969. 2011. 260p. pap. 29.95 (978-1-4128-4274-7(3)) Aldine Transaction.

Chow, Gregory C. China As a Leader of the World Economy. 2011. 54.00 (978-981-4368-79-7(2)); pap. 28.00 (978-981-4368-80-3(6)) World Scientific Publishing Co., Inc.

—China's Economic Transformation. 2nd rev. ed. 2007. (ENG., Illus.). 464p. per. 62.95 (978-1-4051-5624-0(4), Wiley-Blackwell) Wiley, John & Sons, Inc.

—Interpreting China's Economy. 2010. (Illus.). 300p. 54.00 (978-981-4317-94-8(2)); pap. 28.00 (978-981-4317-95-5(0)) World Scientific Publishing Co., Inc.

Chu, Yun-han & Leng, Tse-Kang. Dynamics of Local Governance in China During the Reform Era. 2009. (Challenges Facing Chinese Political Development Ser.). (ENG., Illus.). 326p. 83.99 (978-0-7391-2688-2(1)) Lexington Bks.

Clegg. China & the Reshaping of the World Order. 2009. (ENG.). 288p. 100.00 (978-0-7453-2519-4(X)) Pluto Pr. GBR. Dist: Macmillan.

Coase, Ronald & Wang, Ning. How China Became Capitalist. 2012. (International Economic Association Ser.). (ENG., Illus.). 272p. 100.00 (978-1-137-01936-3(0)) Palgrave Macmillan.

Cousin, Volaine. Banking in China. Molyneux, Philip, ed. 2007. (Palgrave Macmillan Studies in Banking & Financial Institutions Ser.). (ENG.). 288p. 110.00 (978-0-230-00695-9(7)) Palgrave Macmillan.

Dallas, Nick. How to Do Business in China: 24 Lessons to Make Working in China More Profitable. 2008. (ENG., Illus.). 128p. 12.95 (978-0-07-159723-4(9), 0071597239) McGraw-Hill Cos., The.

Di, Yansheng. Li Shi de Hui Mou: Mao Zedong Yu Zhongguo Jing Ji. 2010. (CHI., Illus.). (978-7-5011-9010-2(0)) Xinhua Publishing Hse.

Dobson, Wendy. Gravity Shift: How Asia's New Economic Powerhouses Will Shape the Twenty-First Century. 2009. (Illus.). 224p. (978-1-4426-4052-8(9)) Univ. of Toronto Pr.

Donnithorne, Audrey G. China's Economic System, Vol. 3. 2008. (Illus.). 600p. 200.00 (978-0-415-36147-7(8)) Routledge.

D'Sylva, Dalton. Jewels in the Australian Crown. 2009. pap. (978-1-921578-74-8(2)) BookPal.

Duckett, Jane. The Chinese State's Retreat from Health: Policy & the Politics of Retrenchment. 2010. (Routledge Studies on China in Transition Ser.). (ENG., Illus.). 160p. (C). 130.00 (978-0-415-57389-4(0), Routledge) Taylor & Francis Group GBR. Dist: Taylor & Francis Group.

Eichengreen, Barry, et al, eds. Emerging Giants: China & India in the World Economy. 2010. (ENG., Illus.). 256p. 99.00 (978-0-19-957507-7(X)) Oxford Univ. Pr., Inc.

El Karouni, Ilyess. Les Rtformes Tconomiques en Chine Depuis 1978. 2009. 260p. pap. (978-3-639-16986-7(7)) VDM Verlag Dr. Mueller e.K.

Er. The Rise of China & India. 2009. viii, 169p. 90.00 (978-981-4280-33-4(X)) World Scientific Publishing Co., Inc.

Fallows, James. China Airborne. 2012. (ENG., Illus.). 288p. 25.95 (978-0-375-42211-9(0), Pantheon) Knopf Doubleday Publishing Group.

Fan, Shenggen. Regional Inequality in China: Trends, Explanations & Policy Responses. Kanbur, Ravi & Zhang, Xiaobo, eds. 2009. (Routledge Studies in the Modern World Economy Ser.). (ENG., Illus.). 272p. (C). 145.00 (978-0-415-77588-5(4)) Routledge.

Fan, Zhiyong. China's Opening Up: The Impact of Monetary Policy Choice, 5 vols., Vol. 1. 2011. (Enrich Series on China's Economic Issues Ser.). (ENG.). 288p. 108.00 (978-981-4298-18-6(2)) Enrich Professional Publishing (S)., Ltd. SGP. Dist: Independent Pubs. Group.

Farndon, John. China Rises: How China's Astonishing Growth Will Change the World. 2008. (ENG., Illus.). 240p. pap. 14.95 (978-0-7535-1349-1(8)) Virgin Bks. Ltd. GBR. Dist: Independent Pubs. Group.

Fewsmith, Joseph. China Today, China Tomorrow: Domestic Politics, Economy, & Society. 2010. (Illus.). (ENG.). 344p. 89.00 (978-0-7425-6706-1(0)); (ENG., 344p. pap. 34.95 (978-0-7425-6707-8(9),; ix, 334p. (978-0-7425-6708-5(7)) Rowman & Littlefield Publishers, Inc.

Gittings, John. The Changing Face of China: From Mao to Market. 2006. (ENG., Illus.). 384p. per. 19.95 (978-0-19-280734-2(X)) Oxford Univ. Pr., Inc.

Gomel, Giorgio, et al, eds. The Chinese Economy: Recent Trends & Policy Issues. 2012. (ENG., Illus.). vi, 300p. 179.00 (978-3-642-28637-7(2), 3642286372) Springer.

Gommans, Jos & Zurndorfer, Hariet, eds. Roots & Routes of Development in China & India: Highlights of Fifty Years of the Journal of the Economic & Social History of the Orient (1957-2007) 2008. xl, 456p. (978-90-04-17060-5(X)) BRILL.

Gore, Lance. The Chinese Communist Party & China's Capitalist Revolution: The Political Impact of Market. 2010. (Routledge Contemporary China Ser.). (ENG., Illus.). 200p. (C). 125.00 (978-0-415-58744-0(1)) Routledge.

Greenaway, David, et al, eds. China & the World Economy. 2010. (ENG., Illus.). 304p. 105.00 (978-0-230-52152-0(5)) Palgrave Macmillan.

Greenhalgh, Susan. Cultivating Global Citizens: Population in the Rise of China. 2010. (Edwin O. Reischauer Lectures: 2008). (ENG., Illus.). 156p. 29.95 (978-0-674-05571-1(3)) Harvard Univ. Pr.

Gries, Peter & Rosen, Stanley, eds. Chinese Politics: State, Society & the Market. 2010. (Asia's Transformations Ser.). (ENG., Illus.). 304p. (C). 44.95 (978-0-415-56403-8(4)); 153.00 (978-0-415-56402-1(6)) Routledge.

Gu, George Zhibin. China's Global Reach: (Revised & Updated Edition) rev. ed. 2006. 252p. (978-1-59682-094-4(2), Fultus Publishing) Fultus Corp.

Gu, Kejian & Yu, Jian. China's Exchange Rate Variation: Impact on Industrial Restructuring. 2012. (ENG.). 272p. 98.00 (978-981-4298-34-6(4)) Enrich Professional Publishing (S). Ltd. SGP. Dist: Independent Pubs. Group.

Gul, Ferdinand Akthar & Lu, Haitian. Truths & Half Truths: China's Socio-Economic Reforms From, 1979-2009. 2011. (Chandos Asian Studies). (ENG.). 282p. 135.00 (978-0-85709-170-3(0), Chandos Publishing) Woodhead Publishing Ltd. GBR. Dist: Ingram Pub. Services.

Guo, Baogang & Hickey, Dennis. Toward Better Governance in China: An Unconventional Pathway of Political Reform. 2009. (Challenges Facing Chinese Political Development Ser.). (ENG., Illus.). 226p. 73.50 (978-0-7391-4027-7(2)) Lexington Bks.

Guo, Rongxing. Introduction to the Chinese Economy: The Driving Forces Behind Modern Day China. 2010. (ENG., Illus.). 256p. 29.95 (978-0-470-82604-1(5), Wiley) Wiley, John & Sons, Inc.

Guthrie, Doug. China & Globalization. 3rd rev. ed. 2012. (ENG., Illus.). 360p. 130.00 (978-0-415-50400-3(7)) Routledge.

—China & Globalization: The Social, Economic & Political Transformation of Chinese Society. 3rd rev. ed. 2012. (ENG., Illus.). 360p. pap. 39.95 (978-0-415-50401-0(5)) Routledge.

Han, Yan. FDI Dui Zhongguo Jing Ji Zeng Zhang Ying Xiang de Cha Yi Xing Yan Jiu. 2008. (Illus.). (978-7-80706-857-0(4)) Shanghai Far East Publishing Ctr.

Hanser, Amy. Service Encounters: Class, Gender, & the Market for Social Distinction in Urban China. 2008. (ENG., Illus.). 256p. 55.00 (978-0-8047-5836-9(0)); per. 21.95 (978-0-8047-5837-6(9)) Stanford Univ. Pr.

Hauser, Gunther & Kernic, Franz, eds. China: The Rising Power. 2009. 216p. pap. 56.95 (978-3-631-58269-5(2)) Lang, Peter GmbH, Europaischer Verlag der Wissenschaften DEU. Dist: Lang, Peter.

He, Xiongfei. Xin Yang Yu Wei Ji: Youtai Si Xiang He Zhongguo Wen Ti. 2010. (CHI., Illus.). (978-7-80178-694-4(7)) Hua Ling Pr.

He, Yaomin & Wu, Li. Liu Shi Nian Guo Shi Ji Yao. 2009. (CHI.). (978-7-5438-6026-1(0)) Hunan Publishing Hse.

Herberer, Thomas, et al. Regime Legitimacy in Contemporary China: Institutional Change & Stability. Schubert, Gunter, ed. 2008. (Routledge Contemporary China Ser.). (ENG., Illus.). 320p. (C). 150.00 (978-0-415-46664-6(4)) Routledge.

Ho, Lok Sang & Wong, John. Apec & the Rise of China. 2011. 248p. 85.00 (978-981-4329-40-8(1)) World Scientific Publishing Co., Inc.

Hofer, Markus B. & Ebel, Bernhard, eds. Business Success in China. 2010. (ENG., Illus.). viii, 275p. pap. 74.95 (978-3-642-07098-3(1), 3642070981) Springer.

Hua, Yu. China in Ten Words. Barr, Allan H., tr. from CHI. 2011. (ENG.). 240p. 25.95 (978-0-307-37935-1(3), Pantheon) Knopf Doubleday Publishing Group.

Huang, Yasheng. Capitalism with Chinese Characteristics: Entrepreneurship & the State. 2008. (ENG., Illus.). 366p. (C). 40.00 (978-0-521-89810-2(2)) Cambridge Univ. Pr.

Hung, Ho-Fung, ed. China & the Transformation of Global Capitalism. 2009. (Themes in Global Social Change Ser.). (ENG., Illus.). 224p. 50.00 (978-0-8018-9307-0(0)); (C). (gr. 13-17). pap. 27.00 (978-0-8018-9308-7(9)) Johns Hopkins Univ. Pr.

Ichimura, Shinichi, et al, eds. Transition from Socialist to Market Economies: Comparison of European & Asian Experiences. 2009. (ENG., Illus.). 320p. 116.00 (978-0-230-22803-0(8)) Palgrave Macmillan.

Icon Group International, Inc. Staff, compiled by. The 2006 Economic & Product Market Databook for Coloane, Macau. 2006. 618p. ring bd. 95.00 (978-0-497-80393-3(3)) Icon Group International, Inc.

—The 2006 Economic & Product Market Databook for Jinan, China. 2006. 618p. ring bd. 95.00 (978-0-497-81949-1(X)) Icon Group International, Inc.

Ito, Takatoshi & Hahn, Chin Hee. The Rise of China & Structural Changes in Korea & Asia. Ito, Takatoshi & Hahn, Chin Hee, eds. 2010. (Illus.). 352p. 155.00 (978-1-84844-855-1(4)) Elgar, Edward Publishing, Inc.

Jacques, Martin. When China Rules the World: The End of the Western World & the Birth of a New Global Order. (ENG.). (gr. 12). 2009. 576p. 29.95 (978-1-59420-185-1(4), Penguin Pr. HC, The) 2012. 848p. 20.00 (978-0-14-311800-8(5), Penguin (Non-Classics)) Penguin Group (USA) Inc.

Jensen, Lionel M. & Weston, Timothy B. China's Transformations: The Stories Beyond the Headlines. 2006. (ENG., Illus.). 378p. 97.00 (978-0-7425-3862-7(1)); per. 34.95 (978-0-7425-3863-4(X)) Rowman & Littlefield Publishers, Inc.

Kanbur, Ravi. Governing Rapid Growth in China: Equity & Institutions. Zhang, Xiaobo, ed. 2009. (Routledge Studies in the Modern World Economy Ser.). (ENG., Illus.). 400p. (C). 160.00 (978-0-415-77587-8(6)) Routledge.

Keith, Ronald C. China as a Rising World Power & Its Response To 'Globalization' 2008. 256p. pap. 39.95 (978-0-415-46417-8(X)) Routledge.

Keping, Yu. Democracy & Rule of Law in China. 2010. (Issues in Contemporary Chinese Thought & Culture Ser.). (ENG.). 300p. (978-90-04-18212-7(8)) BRILL.

Knight, Nick. Imagining Globalisation in China: Debates on Ideology, Politics, & Culture. 2008. 256p. (C). 125.00 (978-1-84720-210-9(1)) Elgar, Edward Publishing, Inc.

Kueh, Y. Y. China's New Industrialization Strategy: Was Chairman Mao Really Necessary? 2008. (Illus.). 296p. 135.00 (978-1-84720-232-1(2)) Elgar, Edward Publishing, Inc.

Lanteigne, Marc & Laliberte, Andre, eds. The Chinese Party-State in the 21st Century: Adaptation & the Reinvention of Legitimacy. 2008. (Routledge Contemporary China Ser.). (ENG., Illus.). 208p. (C). 160.00 (978-0-415-45056-0(X)) Routledge.

Lardy, Nicholas R. Economic Growth & Distribution in China. 2006. (ENG.). 260p. pap. 53.00 (978-0-521-03463-0(9)) Cambridge Univ. Pr.

Larus, Elizabeth Freund. Politics & Society in Contemporary China. 2012. (C). 275p. pap. 32.50 (978-1-58826-825-9(X)); (Illus.). 75.00 (978-1-58826-800-6(4)) Rienner, Lynne Pubs.

Le, Son. Total Factor Productivity of Vietnam & Chin. 2011. 64p. pap. (978-3-8443-1450-2(4)) Lambert Academic Publishing.

Lee, Chun-Yi. Taiwanese Business or Chinese Security Asset: A Changing Pattern of Interaction Between Taiwanese Businesses & Chinese Governments. 2011. (Routledge/Leiden Series in Modern East Asian Politics & History Ser.). (ENG., Illus.). 184p. (C). 125.00 (978-0-415-57593-5(1)) Routledge.

Lee, Grace O. M. & Warner, Malcolm, eds. Unemployment in China: Economy, Human Resources & Labour Markets. 2012. (Routledge Contemporary China Ser.). (ENG., Illus.). 288p. (C). pap. 44.95 (978-0-415-51159-9(3)) Routledge.

Lei, Chun Kwok & Yao, Shujie. Economic Convergence in Greater China. 2011. (ENG., Illus.). 248p. (C). pap. 44.95 (978-0-415-67390-7(9)) Routledge.

Leutner, Mechthild, ed. Rethinking China in the 1950s. 2008. (Chinese History & Society Ser.). (GER & ENG.). 184p. pap. 36.95 (978-3-8258-0291-2(4)) Lit Verlag DEU. Dist: Transaction Pubs.

Li, Minqi. The Rise of China & the Demise of the Capitalist World Economy. 2009. (ENG.). 240p. 75.00 (978-1-58367-183-2(8)); pap. 16.95 (978-1-58367-182-5(X)) Monthly Review Pr.

Li, Xiaoxi & Hu, Biliang. China's New Deal: Economic Development under International Financial Crisis. 2011. (Global Economic Studies). (Illus.). 407p. 89.00 (978-1-61668-486-0(0)) Nova Science Pubs., Inc.

Li, Yanhui. Zheng Zhi Jing Ji de Hu Dong Yu Zhong Mei Guan Xi: Yi Zhong Makesi Zhu Yi Guo Ji Zheng Zhi Jing J Xue de Fen Xi = Mutual-Drive of Politics & Economy on Sino-US Relations. 2009. (CHI.). (978-7-80745-579-0(9)) Shanghai Academy of Social Sciences Pr.

Li, Yining. Economic Reform & Development in China. 2012. (Cambridge China Library). (ENG.). 368p. 115.00 (978-1-107-02405-2(6)) Cambridge Univ. Pr.

Lin, Justin Yifu. Demystifying the Chinese Economy. 2011. (ENG., Illus.). 330p. 75.00 (978-0-521-19180-7(7)); pap. 27.99 (978-0-521-18174-7(7)) Cambridge Univ. Pr.

Lin, Shuanglin & Zhu, Xiaodong, eds. Private Enterprises & China's Economic Development. 2011. (ENG., Illus.). 300p. pap. 42.95 (978-0-415-66644-2(9)) Routledge.

Lin, Yi-Chieh Jessica. Mccounterfeiting Inc: China & the Rise of Counterfeit Goods. 2011. (Routledge Series for Creative Teaching & Learning Ser.). (ENG., Illus.). 104p. 125.00 (978-0-415-88302-3(4)); pap. 19.95 (978-0-415-88303-0(2)) Routledge.

Lo, Chi. China after the Subprime Crisis: Opportunities in the New Economic Landscape. 2010. (ENG., Illus.). 204p. 95.00 (978-0-230-28196-7(6)) Palgrave Macmillan.

—Phantom of the China Economic Threat: Shadow of the Next Asian Crisis DISTRIBUTION CANCELLED. 2008. (ENG.). 204p. pap. 42.50 (978-0-230-51544-4(4)) Palgrave Macmillan.

Long, Norman, et al, eds. Rural Transformations & Development in China: Policy Interventions for the 21st Century. 2010. (Illus.). 408p. 139.00 (978-1-84980-093-8(6)) Elgar, Edward Publishing, Inc.

Longlong, Ma. Evolution & Growth of China's Wholesale Industry Since 1978. 2011. (ENG.). 504p. 158.00 (978-981-4298-40-7(9)) Enrich Professional Publishing (S)., Ltd. SGP. Dist: Independent Pubs. Group.

Lu, Caizhen. Poverty & Development in China: Alternative Approaches to Poverty Assessment. 2011. (Routledge Contemporary China Ser.). (ENG., Illus.). 304p. (C). 140.00 (978-0-415-61822-9(3)) Routledge.

Lu, M., et al. China's Economic Development: Institutions, Growth & Imbalances. 2012. 224p. 110.00 (978-0-85793-508-3(9)) Elgar, Edward Publishing, Inc.

McFaul, Thomas R. The Future of Peace & Justice in the Global Village: The Role of the World Religions in the Twenty-First Century. 2006. 240p. 49.95 (978-0-275-99313-9(2), C9313, Praeger Pubs.) Greenwood Publishing Group, Inc.

Meredith, Robyn. The Elephant & the Dragon: The Rise of India & China & What It Means for All of Us. 2008. (ENG., Illus.). 256p. pap. 16.95 (978-0-393-33193-6(8), 33193) Norton, W. W. & Co., Inc.

Mexico, Zachary. China Underground. 2009. (ENG.). 320p. pap. 16.95 (978-1-59376-223-0(2), Soft Skull Pr.) Counterpoint LLC.

Napoleoni, Loretta. Maonomics: Why Chinese Communists Make Better Capitalists Than We Do. Twilley, Stephen, tr. from ITA. 2011. (ENG., Illus.). 384p. 26.95 (978-1-60980-341-4(8)) Seven Stories Pr.

Ngo, Tak-Wing, ed. Contemporary China Studies 2: Economy & Society, 8 vols. 2011. (Illus.). 1624p. 995.00 (978-1-4129-4883-8(5), B48838C) SAGE Pubns., Ltd. GBR. Dist: SAGE Pubns., Inc.

Nolan, Jane. Western Bankers in China. 2012. (Routledge Contemporary China Ser.). (ENG.). (C). 150.00 (978-0-415-58464-7(7)) Routledge.

Oi, Jean C., et al, eds. Growing Pains: Tensions & Opportunity in China's Transformation. 2010. (ENG., Illus.). 380p. pap. 28.95 (978-1-931368-18-6(X)) Shorenstein, Walter H. Asia-Pacific Research Ctr.

Pearce, Robert R., ed. China & the Multinationals: International Business & the Entry of China into the Global Economy. 2012. (New Horizons in International Business Ser.). (Illus.). 224p. 110.00 (978-1-84844-668-7(3)) Elgar, Edward Publishing, Inc.

Pekkanen, Saadia & Tsai, Kellee, eds. Japan & China in the World Political Economy. 2009. 248p. pap. 39.95 (978-0-415-54675-1(3)) Routledge.

Peng, Long, et al. Zhongguo Jing Ji Zhuan Xing de Duo Wei Shi Jiao: Zhongguo Jingji Zhuanxing de Duowei Shijiao. 2009. (CHI., Illus.). (978-7-5017-9241-2(0)) China Economics Publishing Hse.

Peng, Sen & Chen, Li. Reforming China: Major Events, 1992-2004, 5 vols., Vol. 4. Tieying, Li, ed. 2010. (Enrich Series on China's Economic Reform Ser.). (ENG.). 400p. 138.00 (978-981-4298-42-1(5)) Enrich Professional Publishing (S)., Ltd. SGP. Dist: Independent Pubs. Group.

Peng, Sen, et al. Reforming China: International Comparisons & Reference, 5 vols., Vol. 5. Li, Tieying, ed. 2010. (Enrich Series on China's Economic Reform Ser.). (ENG.). 400p. 118.00 (978-981-4298-06-3(9)) Enrich Professional Publishing (S)., Ltd. SGP. Dist: Independent Pubs. Group.

Porter, Robin. From Mao to Market: China Reconfigured. 2011. (Columbia/Hurst Ser.). (ENG.). 288p. (gr. 17). 35.00 (978-0-231-70190-7(X)) Columbia Univ. Pr.

Rein, Shaun. The End of Cheap China: Economic & Cultural Trends That Will Disrupt the World. 2012. (ENG.). 240p. 24.95 (978-1-118-17206-3(X), Wiley) Wiley, John & Sons, Inc.

Ren, Hai. Neoliberalism & Culture in China & Hong Kong. 2010. (Routledge Contemporary China Ser.). (ENG., Illus.). 256p. (C). 130.00 (978-0-415-58262-9(8), Routledge) Taylor & Francis Group GBR. Dist: Taylor & Francis Group.

Sanders, Richard & Yang, Chen, eds. China's Post-Reform Economy - Achieving Harmony, Sustaining Growth. 2012. (Routledge Studies on the Chinese Economy Ser.). (ENG., Illus.). 272p. (C). pap. 42.95 (978-0-415-54261-6(8)) Routledge.

Santos-Paulino, Amelia U. & Wan, Guanghua, eds. The Rise of China & India: Impacts, Prospects & Implications. 2010. (Studies in Development Economics & Policy Ser.). (ENG., Illus.). 336p. 110.00 (978-0-230-25273-8(7)) Palgrave Macmillan.

Saw, Swee-Hock & Wong, John. Regional Economic Development in China. 2009. (Illus.). xviii, 332p. (978-981-230-941-9(1)) Institute of Southeast Asian Studies.

Schiere, Richard. China's Development Challenges: Economic Vulnerability & Public Sector Reform. 2012. (ENG., Illus.). 176p. (C). pap. 44.95 (978-0-415-62494-7(0)) Routledge.

Shambaugh, David, ed. Charting China's Future: Domestic & International Challenges. 2011. (ENG., Illus.). 208p. (C). 150.00 (978-0-415-61954-7(8)) Routledge.

Sharma, Shalendra D. China & India in the Age of Globalization. 2009. (ENG., Illus.). 336p. (C). 99.00 (978-0-521-51571-9(8)); pap. 30.00 (978-0-521-73136-2(4)) Cambridge Univ. Pr.

Sheng, Yuming. Economic Openness & Territorial Politics in China. 2010. (ENG., Illus.). 312p. 85.00 (978-0-521-19538-6(1)) Cambridge Univ. Pr.

Shi, Zhongquan & Yu, Jingsong. Ji Nian Gai Ge Kai Fang 30 Zhou Nian Lun Ji: Jinian Gaige Kaifang Sanshi Zhounian Lunji. 2010. (CHI.). (978-7-5098-0444-5(2)) Chinese Communist Party History Pr.

Shu, Fumin. Zhongguo Quan Mian Xiao Kang Fa Zhan Bao Gao: Zhongguo Quanmian Xiaokang Fazhan Baogao. 2nd ed. 2008. (CHI.). (978-7-5097-0447-9(2)) China Social Science Documentation Publishing Hse.

Soares de Oliveira, Ricardo, et al. China Returns to Africa: A Rising Power & a Continent Embrace. 2008. (Columbia/Hurst Ser.). (ENG., Illus.). 400p. (gr. 17). 75.00 (978-0-231-70098-6(9)) Columbia Univ. Pr.

Someren, Taco C. R. van & Someren-Wang, Shuhua van. Green China. 2012. (Management for Professionals Ser.). (ENG., Illus.). 210p. 69.95 (978-3-642-28809-8(X), 364228809X) Springer.

Starr, John Bryan. Understanding China: A Guide to China's Economy, History, & Political Culture. 3rd rev. ed. 2010. (ENG., Illus.). 448p. pap. 17.95 (978-0-8090-1651-8(6), Hill & Wang) Farrar, Straus & Giroux.

Steinfeld, Edward S. Playing Our Game: Why China's Rise Doesn't Threaten the West, 1 vol. 2010. (ENG., Illus.). 280p. 27.95 (978-0-19-539065-0(2)) Oxford Univ. Pr., Inc.

Suryadinata, ed. Southeast Asia's Chinese Businesses in an Era of Globalization. 2006. 384p. *(978-981-230-401-8(0))* Institute of Southeast Asian Studies.

Tong, Sarah Y. & Zheng, Yongnian. China & the Global Economic Crisis. 2010. (Illus.). 308p. 85.00 *(978-981-4287-70-8(9))* World Scientific Publishing Co., Inc.

Tyler, Benjamin A. The Chinese Economy. 2010. (China in the 21st Century Ser.). 146p. 69.00 *(978-1-60876-937-7(2))* Nova Science Pubs., Inc.

Wan, Guanghua, ed. Inequality & Growth in Modern China. 2008. (WIDER Studies in Development Economics Ser.). (ENG., Illus.). 256p. 74.00 *(978-0-19-953519-4(1))* Oxford Univ. Pr., Inc.

Wang, Yuan, et al. China Business Culture: Strategies for Success. 2008. 280p. pap. 35.00 *(978-981-04-8704-1(5))* Thorogood GBR. Dist: Stylus Publishing, LLC.

Wang, Yuanhong. Zhongguo Jing Ji Nei Wai Jun Heng Wen Ti Yan Jiu: A Research on Internal & External Balance of China Economy. 2009. (CHI., Illus.). *(978-7-5096-0833-3(3))* Economic Management Publishing Hse.

Watts, Jonathan. When a Billion Chinese Jump: How China Will Save Mankind — Or Destroy It. 2010. (ENG., Illus.). 448p. pap. 17.00 *(978-1-4165-8076-8(X)*, Scribner) Scribner.

Wedeman, Andrew Hall. Double Paradox: Rapid Growth & Rising Corruption in China. 2012. (ENG., Illus.). 280p. pap. 26.95 ***(978-0-8014-7776-8(X))*** Cornell Univ. Pr.

—The Double Paradox of Rapid Growth & Intensifying Corruption in Contemporary China. 2012. (ENG., Illus.). 280p. 75.00 ***(978-0-8014-5046-4(2))*** Cornell Univ. Pr.

Wei, Dazhi. Zhong Xin Cheng Shi Zong Bu Jing Ji Cheng Zhang Lun: Zhongxin Chengshi Zongbu Jingji Chengzhanglun. 2010. (CHI., Illus.). *(978-7-5074-2242-9(9))* China City Publishing Hse.

Weston, Timothy B. China in & Beyond the Headlines. 3rd ed. 2012. (ENG.). 384p. pap. 35.00 ***(978-1-4422-0905-3(4))*** Rowman & Littlefield Publishers, Inc.

Weston, Timothy B. & Jensen, Lionel M., eds. China in & Beyond the Headlines. 3rd ed. 2012. (ENG.). 384p. 99.00 ***(978-1-4422-0904-6(6))*** Rowman & Littlefield Publishers, Inc.

Witzel, Morgen, et al. Doing Business in China. 3rd rev. ed. 2008. (ENG., Illus.). 304p. (C). 170.00 *(978-0-415-43631-1(1))* Routledge.

Wong, John & Liu, Wei, eds. China's Surging Economy: Adjusting for More Balanced Development. 2007. (Ser. on Contemporary China Ser.). (Illus.). 380p. 99.00 *(978-981-270-627-0(5))* World Scientific Publishing Co., Inc.

Wright, Teresa. Accepting Authoritarianism: State-Society Relations in China's Reform Era. 2010. (ENG.). 264p. pap. 24.95 *(978-0-8047-6904-4(4))*; (Illus.). 70.00 *(978-0-8047-6903-7(6))* Stanford Univ. Pr.

Wu, Chengming & Dong, Zhikai. Zhonghua Renmin Gongheguo Jing Ji Shi, 1949-1952: The Economic History of the People's Republic of China. 2010. *(978-7-5097-1010-4(3))* China Social Science Documentation Publishing Hse.

Wu, Guang. China: Has the Last Opportunity Passed By?! 2009. (China in the 21st Century Ser.). xiii, 88p. pap. 43.00 *(978-1-60741-538-1(0))* Nova Science Pubs., Inc.

Wu, Jinglian. China's Long March Toward A. 2010. 316p. pap. 25.95 *(978-1-59265-063-7(5))* BetterLink Pr., Inc.

Wuwei, Li. How Creativity Is Changing China. 2011. (ENG., Illus.). 160p. 75.00 *(978-1-84966-619-0(9))*; pap. 25.95 *(978-1-84966-616-9(4))* Bloomsbury Publishing.

Xing, Li. The Rise of China & Its Implication on World Order. 2010. (International Political Economy of New Regionalisms Ser.). (Illus.). 222p. 99.95 *(978-0-7546-7913-4(6))* Ashgate Publishing Co.

Xu, L. China's Economy in the Post-WTO Environment: Stock Markets, FDI & Challenges of Sustainability. 2011. (Advances in Chinese Economic Studies Ser.). (Illus.). 288p. 135.00 ***(978-1-84980-934-4(8))*** Elgar, Edward Publishing, Inc.

Xue, Muqiao. Chinese Economists on Economic Reform - Xue Muqiao. 2011. (Routledge Studies on the Chinese Economy Ser.). (Illus.). 224p. (C). 140.00 *(978-0-415-59821-7(4))* Routledge.

Yan, Xuyang. Zhongguo Nong Cun Xiao Fei Shi Chang Fa Zhan Gai Lun. 2010. (CHI., Illus.). *(978-7-01-008690-3(7))* People's Publishing Hse., The.

Yang, Keming. Entrepreneurship in China. 2007. 260p. 114.95 *(978-0-7546-4668-6(8))* Ashgate Publishing Co.

Yang, Qixian & Shi, Xiaomin. Reforming China: Theoretical Framework, vols. 5, Vol. 1. Li, Tiyeng, ed. 2010. (Enrich Series on China's Economic Reform Ser.). (ENG.). 272p. 88.00 ***(978-981-4298-00-1(X))*** Enrich Professional Publishing (S)., Ltd. SGP. Dist: Independent Pubs. Group.

Yang, Shangguang. Zhongguo Da Cheng Shi Jing Ji Kong Jian de Yan Hua. 2009. (CHI., Illus.). *(978-7-208-08973-0(6))* Shanghai People's Publishing Hse.

Yao, Yang & Yueh, Linda, eds. Globalisation & Economic Growth in China. 2006. (Series on Economic Development & Growth). (Illus.). 289p. 96.00 *(978-981-256-855-7(7))* World Scientific Publishing Co., Inc.

Ye, Feiwen. Zhongguo Jing Ji Qu Bi Jiao. 2010. (CHI., Illus.). *(978-7-5097-1276-4(9))* China Social Science Documentation Publishing Hse.

Yu, Hong. Economic Development & Inequality in China. 2010. (Routledge Studies in the Growth Economies of Asia Ser.). (ENG., Illus.). 272p. (C). 125.00 *(978-0-415-59658-9(0))* Routledge.

Yueh, Linda. Enterprising China: Business, Economic, & Legal Developments Since 1979. 2011. (ENG., Illus.). 336p. 110.00 *(978-0-19-920583-7(3))*; pap. 45.00 *(978-0-19-920582-0(5))* Oxford Univ. Pr., Inc.

Zhang, Wei. Economic Reform in Modern China, 4 vols. 2011. (Critical Concepts in Economics Ser.). (ENG., Illus.). 1736p. 1250.00 *(978-0-415-56068-9(3))* Routledge.

Zhang, Xiaohuan. Npd in Indigenous Chinese Companies and. 2006. 272p. per. 25.95 *(978-1-58112-340-1(X)*, Dissertation.com) Universal Pubs.

Zhao, Quansheng. Managing the China Challenge: Global Perspectives. Liu, Guoli, ed. 2008. (Asian Security Studies). (Illus.). XVI, 264p. 160.00 *(978-0-415-46573-1(7))* Routledge.

Zheng, Yongnian. Zhongguo Mo Shi: Jing Yan Yu Kun Ju. 2010. (CHI., Illus.). *(978-7-213-04190-7(8))* Zhejiang People's Publishing Hse.

Zhou, Dongtao. Reforming China: Experiences & Lessons, vols. 5, vol. 2. Tiyeng, Li, ed. 2010. (Enrich Series on China's Economic Reform Ser.). (ENG.). 464p. 138.00 *(978-981-4298-02-5(6))* Enrich Professional Publishing (S)., Ltd. SGP. Dist: Independent Pubs. Group.

CHINA—ECONOMIC POLICY

Aglietta, Michel & Bai, Guo. China's Development: Capitalism & Empire. 2012. (Rethinking Globalizations Ser.). (ENG., Illus.). 320p. (C). 135.00 ***(978-0-415-53502-1(6))*** Routledge.

Allen, Wilfred J. & Young, Alex, eds. In China We Trust: The Impacts of Chinese Economic Policies. 2012. ***(978-1-61942-828-7(8))*** Nova Science Pubs., Inc.

Alpermann, Björn. China's Cotton Industry: Economic Transformation & State Capacity. 2010. (Routledge Studies on China in Transition Ser.). (ENG., Illus.). 272p. (C). 130.00 *(978-0-415-55237-0(0))* Routledge.

Ambler, Tim, et al. Doing Business in China. 3rd rev. ed. 2008. (ENG., Illus.). 304p. (C). pap. 39.95 ***(978-0-415-43632-8(X))*** Routledge.

Amitendu, Palit. China-India Economics. 2011. (Routledge Studies in the Growth Economies of Asia Ser.). (ENG., Illus.). 216p. (C). 136.00 *(978-0-415-59831-6(1))* Routledge.

Anderson, Eric C. China Restored: The Middle Kingdom Looks to 2020 & Beyond. 2010. xxiii, 323p. E-Book *(978-0-313-38518-6(1)*, Praeger Pubs.) Greenwood Publishing Group, Inc.

Bachman, David. Bureaucracy, Economy, & Leadership in China: The Institutional Origins of the Great Leap Forward. 2006. (ENG.). 288p. (C). pap. 42.00 *(978-0-521-03233-9(4))* Cambridge Univ. Pr.

Bandelj, Nina & Solinger, Dorothy J., eds. Socialism Vanquished, Socialism Challenged: Eastern Europe & China, 1989-2009. 2012. (ENG.). 288p. 99.00 ***(978-0-19-989597-7(X))***; pap. 27.95 ***(978-0-19-989596-0(1))*** Oxford Univ. Pr., Inc.

Bardhan, Pranab K. Awakening Giants, Feet of Clay: Assessing the Economic Rise of China & India. 2010. (ENG., Illus.). 192p. (C). 25.95 *(978-0-691-12994-5(0))* Princeton Univ. Pr.

Bhaumik, T. K. Old China's New Economy: The Conquest of a Billion Paupers. 2009. (Illus.). 328p. (C). pap. 32.95 *(978-81-7829-862-7(7)*, B98627P) SAGE Pubns., Inc.

Bijian, Zheng. China's Road to Peaceful Development. 2011. (Routledge Studies on the Chinese Economy Ser.). (ENG.). 352p. (C). 145.00 *(978-0-415-55271-4(0))* Routledge.

Blecher, Marc J. China Against the Tides: Restructuring Through Revolution, Radicalism & Reform. 3rd ed. 2009. (ENG., Illus.). 256p. 120.00 *(978-0-8264-2725-0(1))*; pap. 34.95 *(978-0-8264-2698-7(0))* Continuum International Publishing Group, Ltd. GBR. Dist: National Bk. Network.

Bo, Zhiyue & Wong, John. China's Reform in Global Perspective. 2010. (Illus.). 400p. 96.00 *(978-981-4289-24-5(8))* World Scientific Publishing Co., Inc.

Borowy, Iris, ed. Uneasy Encounters: The Politics of Medicine & Health in China 1900-1937. 2009. 230p. pap. 61.95 *(978-3-631-57803-2(2))* Lang, Peter GmbH, Europaischer Verlag der Wissenschaften DEU. Dist: Lang, Peter.

BRAMALL. Chinese Economic Development. 2008. (Illus.). 640p. pap. 68.95 *(978-0-415-37348-7(4))* Routledge.

Bramall, Chris. The Industrialization of Rural China. 2007. (Illus.). 436p. 135.00 *(978-0-19-927593-9(9))* Oxford Univ. Pr., Inc.

Breznitz, Dan & Murphree, Michael. Run of the Red Queen: Government, Innovation, Globalization, & Economic Growth in China. 2011. (ENG., Illus.). 278p. 35.00 *(978-0-300-15271-5(X))* Yale Univ. Pr.

Brodsgaard, Kjeld Erik. Hainan - State, Society, & Business in a Chinese Province. 2012. (China Policy Ser.). (ENG., Illus.). 208p. (C). pap. 42.95 ***(978-0-415-54138-1(7))*** Routledge.

Brodsgaard, Kjeld Erik & Brodsgaard, Kjeld Erik. Hainan: State, Society, & Business in a Chinese Province. 2008. (China Policy Ser.). (ENG., Illus.). 208p. (C). 168.00 *(978-0-415-46033-0(6))* Routledge.

Brooks, Lucy M. & Watson, Julie E. China's Currency: Economic Issues & Background. 2011. (China in the 21st Century Ser.). 115.00 *(978-1-61209-300-0(0))* Nova Science Pubs., Inc.

Büchelhofer, Christian. Corporate Control & Enterprise Reform in China: An Econometric Analysis of Block Share Trades. 2010. (Contributions to Economics Ser.). (ENG., Illus.). xii, 115p. pap. 109.00 *(978-3-7908-2546-6(8)*, 3790825468) Physica-Verlag DEU. Dist: Springer.

—Corporate Control & Enterprise Reform in China: An Econometric Analysis of Block Share Trades. 2007. (Contributions to Economics Ser.). 128p. (C). 109.00 *(978-3-7908-2019-5(9))* Springer.

Burman, Edward. China & Iran: Parallel History, Future Threat? 2009. (ENG., Illus.). 224p. pap. 24.95 *(978-0-7524-4854-1(4))* History Pr. Ltd.,The GBR. Dist: Independent Pubs. Group.

Cai, Fang. Transforming the Chinese Economy. 2010. (Social Scientific Studies in Reform Era China Ser.). (Illus.). l 360p. *(978-90-04-18421-3(X))* BRILL.

—Zhongguo Jing Ji Zhuan Xing 30 Nian, 1978-2008: Transforming the Chinese Economy, 1978-2008. 2009. (CHI., Illus.). *(978-7-5097-0807-1(9))* China Social Science Documentation Publishing Hse.

Cao, Tian Yu. The Chinese Model of Modern Development. 2009. 324p. 41.95 *(978-0-415-55525-8(6))* Routledge.

Chan, Chak. Social Security Policy in Hong Kong: From British Colony to Special Administrative Region of China. 2011. (ENG.). 260p. 70.00 ***(978-0-7391-4954-6(7))*** Lexington Bks.

Chan, Chak Kwan. Social Security Policy in Hong Kong: From British Colony to China's Special Administrative Region. 2011. xiii, 216p. ***(978-0-7391-4956-0(3))*** Lexington Bks.

Chance, Giles. China & the Credit Crisis: Emergence of a New World Order. 2010. (ENG., Illus.). 228p. pap. 24.95 *(978-0-470-82507-5(3)*, Wiley) Wiley, John & Sons, Inc.

Chang, Julian & Goldstein, Steven M., eds. Economic Reform & Cross-Strait Relations: Taiwan & China in the WTO. 2007. (Ser. on Contemporary China Ser.). (Illus.). 377p. 113.00 *(978-981-256-854-0(9))* World Scientific Publishing Co., Inc.

Chen, Calvin. Some Assembly Required: Work, Community, & Politics in China's Rural Enterprises. 2008. (Harvard East Asian Monographs: 302). (Illus.). 224p. 39.95 *(978-0-674-02783-1(3))* Harvard Univ., Asia Ctr.

Chen, Chien-Hsun & Shih, Hui-Tzu. Mergers & Acquisitions in China: Impacts of WTO Accession. 2008. (Advances in Chinese Economic Studies). (Illus.). 192p. (C). 119.00 *(978-1-84720-802-6(9))* Elgar, Edward Publishing, Inc.

Chen, Jiagui. The China Economy Yearbook, Vol. 4. 2010. 225p. *(978-90-04-18240-0(3))* BRILL.

Chen, Lanyan. Gender & Chinese Development: Towards an Equitable Society. 2008. (Routledge IAFFE Advances in Feminist Economics Ser.). (Illus.). X, 182p. 44.95 *(978-0-415-46723-0(3))*; 160.00 *(978-0-415-46722-3(5))* Routledge.

Cheng. A Guideline to Investment in the Chinese Currency (Cny) & Interest Rates Markets: Opportunities & Risks. 2011. 58.00 *(978-981-4287-68-5(7))* World Scientific Publishing Co., Inc.

Cheng, J. I. Economics & Foreign Investment in China. 2006. (Illus.). 229p. (C). 79.00 *(978-1-60021-238-3(7))* Nova Science Pubs., Inc.

Cheng, Siwei. Economic Reforms & Development in China, 3 vols. (Selected Works of Cheng Siwei Ser.). (ENG.). 432p. Vol. 1. 2011. 138.00 *(978-981-4332-16-3(X))* Vol. 2. 2012. 138.00 *(978-981-4298-30-8(1))* Enrich Professional Publishing (S)., Ltd. SGP. Dist: Independent Pubs. Group.

Cheung, Yin-Wong & Ma, Guonan. Asia & China in the Global Economy. 2011. 300p. 84.00 ***(978-981-4335-26-3(6))*** World Scientific Publishing Co., Inc.

China Development Bank Staff, contrib. by. Development Finance in China: Bond Market Innovation, 3 vols. 2010. (Enrich Series on Developmental Finance in China Ser.). (ENG.). 280p. 108.00 *(978-981-4298-14-8(X))* Enrich Professional Publishing (S)., Ltd. SGP. Dist: Independent Pubs. Group.

China Development Research Foundation. Thirty Years of China's Reform. 2012. (Routledge Studies on the Chinese Economy Ser.). (ENG., Illus.). 632p. (C). 215.00 ***(978-0-415-68999-1(6))*** Routledge.

China Photographers' Association Staff, et al. China's Thirty Years. 2011. (CHI & ENG., Illus.). 372p. 65.00 *(978-0-19-800897-2(X))* Oxford Univ. Pr., Inc.

China Trade Institute. Customs Tariff Schedule of the People's Republic of China, 2008 Edition. 2008. 644p. pap. 199.95 *(978-1-84799-462-2(8))* Lulu Enterprises Inc.

China's Financial Policy Research Center Staff. Growth Without Crisis: China's Modern Financial System. 2011. (ENG.). 448p. 128.00 *(978-981-4298-32-2(8))* Enrich Professional Publishing (S)., Ltd. SGP. Dist: Independent Pubs. Group.

Chou, Bill K. P. Government & Policy-Making Reform in China: The Implications of Governing Capacity. 2009. (Comparative Development & Policy in Asia Ser.). (ENG., Illus.). 178p. 130.00 *(978-0-415-43704-2(0))* Routledge.

Chow, Gregory C. China As a Leader of the World Economy. 2011. 54.00 ***(978-981-4368-79-7(2))***; pap. 28.00 ***(978-981-4368-80-3(6))*** World Scientific Publishing Co., Inc.

—China's Economic Transformation. 2nd rev. ed. 2007. (ENG., Illus.). 464p. per. 62.95 *(978-1-4051-5624-0(4)*, Wiley-Blackwell) Wiley, John & Sons, Inc.

—Interpreting China's Economy. 2010. (Illus.). 300p. 54.00 *(978-981-4317-94-8(2))*; pap. 28.00 *(978-981-4317-95-5(0))* World Scientific Publishing Co., Inc.

Chung, Mona. Doing Business Successfully in China. 2011. (Chandos Asian Studies). 246p. 120.00 ***(978-0-85709-155-0(7)***, Chandos Publishing) Woodhead Publishing Ltd. GBR. Dist: Ingram Pub. Services.

Chung, Tan & Uberoi, Patricia. Rise of the Asian Giants: The Dragon-Elephant Tango. 2009. (Anthem Press India Ser.). (ENG.). 250p. 100.00 *(978-81-905835-9-6(X))* Anthem Pr. GBR. Dist: Books International, Inc.

Coase, Ronald & Wang, Ning. How China Became Capitalist. 2012. (International Economic Association Ser.). (ENG., Illus.). 272p. 100.00 ***(978-1-137-01936-3(0))*** Palgrave Macmillan.

Committee on the Competitiveness and Workforce Needs of U.S. Industry & National Research Council. The Dragon & the Elephant: Understanding the Development of Innovation Capacity in China & India: Summary of a Conference. 2010. (ENG.). 78p. pap. 21.00 *(978-0-309-15160-3(0))* National Academies Pr.

Conklin, Lisa. Chinese E-Commerce: A Guide to Selling Online in China. 2008. 84p. pap. *(978-3-639-10617-6(2))* VDM Verlag Dr. Mueller e.K.

Cooke, Fang Lee. Human Rescource Management in China. 2011. (ENG., Illus.). 264p. (C). 145.00 *(978-0-415-55379-7(2))* Routledge.

Cram101 Textbook Reviews & Cram101 Textbook Reviews. Outlines & Highlights for Economic Openness & Territorial Politics in China by Yumin Sheng. 2011. 212p. pap. 30.95 ***(978-1-61830-592-3(1))*** Cram101 Inc.

Csaba, Laszlo. The New Political Economy of Emerging Europe. 2nd ed. 396p. (C). *(978-963-05-8459-3(X))* Akademiai Kiado.

Dallas, Nick. How to Do Business in China: 24 Lessons to Make Working in China More Profitable. 2008. (ENG., Illus.). 128p. 12.95 *(978-0-07-159723-4(9)*, 0071597239) McGraw-Hill Cos., The.

Das, Dilip K. China & India: A Tale of Two Economies. 2009. 182p. pap. 39.95 *(978-0-415-54449-8(1))* 2006. (Routledge Studies in the Growth Economies of Asia: Vol. 66). (ENG., Illus.). 224p. 160.00 *(978-0-415-40629-1(3))* Routledge.

Das, Geeta. Special Economic Zones (SEZs) in India: Lessons from China. 2009. 248p. 42.50 *(978-81-7708-202-9(7))* New Century Publications IND. Dist: International Specialized Bk. Services.

Denoon, David B. H. The Economic & Strategic Rise of China & India: Asian Realignments after the 1997 Financial Crisis. 2009. (ENG.). 228p. pap. 31.00 *(978-0-230-61404-8(3))* Palgrave Macmillan.

Denoon, David B. H. & Denoon, David B. The Economic & Strategic Rise of China & India: Asian Realignments after the 1997 Financial Crisis. 2007. (ENG., Illus.). 228p. 95.00 *(978-1-4039-8200-1(7))* Palgrave Macmillan.

Devaland, Mary Jo. China's Economic Policy Impact on the United States. 2008. (Illus.). viii, 251p. 69.00 *(978-1-60692-194-4(0))* Nova Science Pubs., Inc.

Di, Yansheng. Li Shi de Hui Mou: Mao Zedong Yu Zhongguo Jing Ji. 2010. (CHI., Illus.). *(978-7-5011-9010-2(0))* Xinhua Publishing Hse.

Dickson, Bruce. Wealth & Power in Contemporary China: The Communist Party's Embrace of the Private Sector. 2008. (ENG., Illus.). 292p. pap. 28.00 *(978-0-521-70270-6(4))* Cambridge Univ. Pr.

—Wealth into Power: The Communist Party's Embrace of China's Private Sector. 2008. (ENG., Illus.). 292p. 80.00 *(978-0-521-87845-6(4))* Cambridge Univ. Pr.

Dikötter, Frank. Mao's Great Famine: The History of China's Most Devastating Catastrophe, 1958-62. (ENG., Illus.). 448p. 2011. pap. 20.00 *(978-0-8027-7923-6(9))* 2010. 30.00 *(978-0-8027-7768-3(6))* Walker & Co.

Dumas, Charles & Choyleva, Diana. The American Phoenix. 2011. (ENG., Illus.). 224p. pap. 22.95 ***(978-1-84668-564-4(8))*** Profile Bks. Ltd. GBR. Dist: Consortium Bk. Sales & Distribution.

Dumas, Charles-. China & America: A Time of Reckoning. 2009. (ENG., Illus.). 224p. pap. 22.95 *(978-1-84668-155-4(3))* Profile Bks. Ltd. GBR. Dist: Consortium Bk. Sales & Distribution.

Dunstan, Helen. State or Merchant? Political Economy & Political Process in 1740s China. 2006. (Harvard East Asian Monographs: 273). (Illus.). 523p. 54.95 *(978-0-674-02262-1(9))* Harvard Univ., Asia Ctr.

Elleman, Bruce. International Competition in China 1899-1949. 2010. 192p. 130.00 *(978-0-415-56393-2(3))* Routledge.

Elwell, Craig K., et al. Is China a Threat to the U. S. Economy? 2008. (Illus.). 88p. pap. 29.00 *(978-1-60456-843-1(7))* Nova Science Pubs., Inc.

Eyferth, Jacob. How China Works: Perspectives on the Twentieth-Century Industrial Workplace. 2009. 168p. pap. 39.95 *(978-0-415-49744-2(2))* Routledge.

Fan, Joseph P. H. & Morck, Randall, eds. Capitalizing China. 2012. (National Bureau of Economic Research Conference Report). (Illus.). 368p. 110.00 ***(978-0-226-23724-4(9))*** Univ. of Chicago Pr.

Fan, Qimiao, et al, eds. Innovation for Development & the Role of Government: A Perspective from the East Asia & Pacific Region. 2008. (ENG., Illus.). 224p. pap. 35.00 *(978-0-8213-7672-0(1)*, 9780821376720) World Bank Pubns.

Fan, Zhiyong, et al. Enrich Series on China's Economic Issues, vols. 5, Vols. 1-5, set. 2011. (Enrich Series on China's Economic Issues Ser.). 1552p. 448.00 *(978-981-4298-28-5(X))* Enrich Professional Publishing (S)., Ltd. SGP. Dist: Independent Pubs. Group.

Feng, Lingqin. Effects of Policy Shifts on Marital Relations. 2010. 168p. pap. *(978-3-8383-1350-4(X))* Lambert Academic Publishing.

Fewsmith, Joseph. China since Tiananmen: From Deng Xiaoping to Hu Jintao. 2nd rev. ed. 2008. (Cambridge Modern China Ser.). (ENG., Illus.). 352p. (C). 75.00 *(978-0-521-86693-4(6))*; pap. 25.99 *(978-0-521-68605-1(9))* Cambridge Univ. Pr.

Financial Reforms & Development in China. 2011. 111.00 *(978-981-4317-54-2(3))* World Scientific Publishing Co., Inc.

Fleisher, Belton M., et al, eds. Policy Reform & Chinese Markets: Progress & Challenges. 2008. (Advances in Chinese Economic Studies). 352p. (C). 150.00 *(978-1-84720-396-0(5))* Elgar, Edward Publishing, Inc.

Fu, Xiaolan, ed. Chinas Role in Global Economic Recovery. 2011. (Routledge Studies on the Chinese Economy Ser.). (ENG., Illus.). 336p. (C). 155.00 *(978-0-415-67034-0(9))* Routledge.

Gale, William & Elmendorf, Douglas W., eds. Brookings Papers on Economic Activity 2. 2008. (Brookings Papers on Economic Activity Ser.). (ENG., Illus.). 240p. pap. 36.00 *(978-0-8157-1356-2(8))* Brookings Institution Pr.

Garibaldo, Francesco, et al, eds. Is China a Risk or an Opportunity for Europe? An Assessment of the Automobile, Steel & Shipbuilding Sectors. 2007. (Illus.). 125p. pap. 32.95 *(978-3-631-57474-4(6))* Lang, Peter Publishing, Inc.

Glaeser, Bernhard, ed. Learning from China? Development & Environment in Third World Countries. 2011. (ENG., Illus.). 312p. 115.00 *(978-0-415-59296-3(8))* Routledge.

Gong, Gang. Contemporary Chinese Economy. 2012. (Illus.). x, 210p. (978-0-203-12486-4(3)); (ENG., 224p. (C). 168.00 (978-0-415-61690-4(5)) Routledge.

GOODMAN. Chinas Regional Development V8. 2008. 224p. 200.00 (978-0-415-36152-1(4)) Routledge.

Goodstadt, Leo F. Reluctant Regulators: How the West Created & China Survived the Global Financial Crisis. 2011. 224p. (978-988-220-648-9(4)); (978-988-8053-58-2(2)) Hong Kong Univ. Pr.

—Reluctant Regulators: How the West Created & How China Survived the Global Financial Crisis. 2011. 224p. (978-988-220-734-9(0)) Hong Kong Univ. Pr.

Gore, Lance. The Chinese Communist Party & China's Capitalist Revolution: The Political Impact of Market. 2010. (Routledge Contemporary China Ser.). (ENG., Ilus.). 200p. (C). 125.00 (978-0-415-58744-0(1)) Routledge.

Greenaway, David, et al, eds. China & the World Economy. 2010. (ENG., Illus.). 304p. 105.00 (978-0-230-52152-0(5)) Palgrave Macmillan.

Groenewold, Nicolaas, et al. Linkages Between China's Regions: Measurement & Policy. 2008. (Advances in Chinese Economic Studies). (Illus.). 192p. (C). 119.00 (978-1-84720-242-0(X)) Elgar, Edward Publishing, Inc.

Gungwu, Wang & Wong, John, eds. Interpreting China's Development. 2007. 265p. 104.00 (978-981-270-802-1(2),; (Illus.). per. 62.00 (978-981-270-806-9(5)) World Scientific Publishing Co., Inc.

Guo, Kaijun, et al. Understanding Organizational Fitness: The Case of China. 2011. 278p. pap. (978-1-61735-375-8(2)); (Illus.). xxix, 247p. E-Book (978-1-61735-377-2(9)) Information Age Publishing, Inc.

—Understanding Organizational Fitness: The Case of China (HC) 2011. 278p. (978-1-61735-376-5(0)) Information Age Publishing, Inc.

Guo, Rongxing. How the Chinese Economy Works. (ENG., Illus.). 2nd rev. ed. 2007. 280p. 126.00 (978-0-230-54274-7(3)) 3rd rev. ed. 2009. 368p. 121.00 (978-0-230-58100-5(5)) Palgrave Macmillan.

—Introduction to the Chinese Economy: The Driving Forces Behind Modern Day China. 2010. (ENG., Illus.). 256p. 29.95 (978-0-470-82604-1(5), Wiley) Wiley, John & Sons, Inc.

Guo, Rongxing. Understanding the Chinese Economies. 2012. (ENG.). 352p. 59.95 (978-0-12-397826-4(2), Academic Pr.) Elsevier Science & Technology Bks.

Guo, Rongxing, ed. China's Political & Economic Transformation: Theory & Case Studies. 2010. (China in the 21st Century Ser.). pap. 43.00 (978-1-60876-321-4(8)) Nova Science Pubs., Inc.

Guruswamy, Mohan & Singh, Zorawar Daulet. Chasing the Dragon: Will India Catch up with China? 2010. (ENG., Illus.). 204p. (C). 34.99 (978-81-317-2411-8(5), FT Press.

Gustafsson, Bj_rn A., et al, eds. Inequality & Public Policy in China. 2010. (ENG.). 384p. pap. 36.99 (978-0-521-15905-0(9)) Cambridge Univ. Pr.

Hallding, Karl, et al, eds. The Economics of Climate Change in China: Towards a Low Carbon Economy. 2011. (ENG., Illus.). 480p. 125.00 (978-1-84971-174-6(7)) Routledge.

Hassard, John. China's State Enterprise Reform: From Marx to the Market. 2010. (ENG.). pap. 39.95 (978-0-415-59053-2(1)) Routledge.

Hassard, John, et al. China's State Enterprise Reform: From Marx to the Market. 2007. (Routledge Contemporary China Ser.). (ENG., Illus.). 288p. (C). 158.00 (978-0-415-37172-8(4)) Routledge.

He, Xiangzhou. Zheng Fu Jue Ce de Ji Hui Cheng Ben Wen Ti Yan Jiu. 2010. (CHI., Illus.). xiii, 235p. (978-7-03-026983-6(7)) Science Pr.

He, Xin. He Xin: Fan Zhu Liu Jing Ji Xue = He Xin: Fan Zhuliu Jingji Xue, 2 vols. 2010. (CHI., Illus.). (978-7-80232-326-1(6)) Current Affairs Publishing Hes.

Heshmati, Almas. Recent Developments in the Chinese Economy. 2006. 232p. (C). 169.00 (978-1-60021-449-3(5)) Nova Science Pubs., Inc.

Hoffmann, W. John, et al. China into the Future: Making Sense of the World's Most Dynamic Economy. 2007. (ENG., Illus.). 220p. 34.95 (978-0-470-82244-9(9), Wiley) Wiley, John & Sons, Inc.

Hongyi, Lai, ed. China into the Hu-Wen Era: Policy Initiatives & Challenges. 2006. (Series on Contemporary China: Vol. 5). (Illus.). 565p. 150.00 (978-981-256-732-1(1)) World Scientific Publishing Co., Inc.

Horesh, Niv & Horesh, N. Shanghai's Bund & Beyond: British Banks, Banknote Issuance, & Monetary Policy in China, 1842-1937. 2009. (Yale Series in Economic & Financial History Ser.). (ENG., Illus.). 256p. 48.00 (978-0-300-14356-0(7)) Yale Univ. Pr.

Hsu, Carolyn L. Creating Market Socialism: How Ordinary People Are Shaping Class & Status in China. 2007. (Politics, History, & Culture Ser.). (ENG., Illus.). 240p. (C). 79.95 (978-0-8223-4017-1(3)); per. 22.95 (978-0-8223-4036-2(4)) Duke Univ. Pr.

Hu, Angang. Economic & Social Transformation in China: Challenges & Opportunities. 2009. 282p. pap. 39.95 (978-0-415-54557-0(9)) Routledge.

Hu, Angang, ed. Economic & Social Transformation in China: Challenges & Opportunities. 2006. (Routledge Studies on the Chinese Economy). (Illus.). 276p. 170.00 (978-0-415-38067-6(7)) Routledge.

Hu, Angang & Hu, An'gang. Road Map of China's Rise. 2010. (Routledge Studies on the Chinese Economy Ser.). (ENG., Illus.). 512p. 150.00 (978-0-415-47992-9(4)) Routledge.

Hu, An'gang & Yan, Yilong. Zhongguo: Zou Xiang 2015: Zhonguo Zouxiang 2015. 2010. (Illus.). (978-7-213-04219-5(X)) Zhejiang People's Publishing Hse.

Hu, Ping & Song, Airu. Gai Ge Kai Fang Qin Li Ji: Hu Ping Fang Tan Lu. 2010. 20p. (978-7-5073-2908-7(9)) Central Party Literature Audio & Video Publishing Hse.

Hua, Shiping. Chinese Utopianism: A Comparative Study of Reformist Thought with Japan & Russia, 1898-1997. 2006. (ENG.). 208p. 35.00 (978-0-8047-6161-1(2)) Stanford Univ. Pr.

Hua, Shiping & Guo, Sujian, eds. China in the Twenty-First Century: Challenges & Opportunities. (ENG., 2011. Illus.). 296p. pap. 30.00 (978-0-230-12072-3(5)) 2007. 280p. 89.00 (978-1-4039-7975-9(8)) Palgrave Macmillan.

Huang, Yasheng. Capitalism with Chinese Characteristics: Entrepreneurship & the State. 2008. (ENG., Illus.). 366p. (C). 40.00 (978-0-521-89810-2(2)) Cambridge Univ. Pr.

Hung, Ho-Fung, ed. China & the Transformation of Global Capitalism. 2009. (Themes in Global Social Change Ser.). (ENG., Illus.). 224p. 50.00 (978-0-8018-9307-0(0)); (C). (gr. 13-17). pap. 27.00 (978-0-8018-9308-7(9)) Johns Hopkins Univ. Pr.

Ine, et al. Supertrends of Future China: Billion Dollar Business Opportunities for China's Olympic Decade. 2008. xxii, 256p. 27.95 (978-981-281-439-5(6)) World Scientific Publishing Co., Inc.

Ito, Takatoshi & Hahn, Chin Hee. The Rise of China & Structural Changes in Korea & Asia. Ito, Takatoshi & Hahn, Chin Hee, eds. 2010. (Illus.). 352p. 155.00 (978-1-84844-855-1(4)) Elgar, Edward Publishing, Inc.

Jha, Prem Shankar. Managed Chaos: The Fragility of the Chinese Miracle. 2009. 204p. (C). 34.95 (978-81-321-0076-8(X), B00768C) SAGE Pubns., Inc.

Jin, Zhesong & Li, Jun. Foreign Trade Growth & Economic Development in China: Enrich Series on China's Edonomic Issues: Retrospective & Future Prospects, 5 vols., Vol. 3. 2011. (Enrich Series on China's Economic Issues Ser.). (ENG.). 296p. 98.00 (978-981-4298-22-3(0)) Enrich Professional Publishing (S)., Ltd. SGP. Dist: Independent Pubs. Group.

Jones, Handel. Chinamerica: The Uneasy Partnership That Will Change the World. 2010. (ENG., Illus.). 304p. 27.95 (978-0-07-174242-9(5), 0071742425) McGraw-Hill Cos., The.

Junbo, Xiang. Structural Economics in China: A Three-Dimensional Framework for Balanced Growth. 2012. (ENG.). 360p. 118.00 (978-981-4298-38-4(7)) Enrich Professional Publishing (S)., Ltd. SGP. Dist: Independent Pubs. Group.

Kanbur, Ravi. Governing Rapid Growth in China: Equity & Institutions. Zhang, Xiaobo, ed. 2009. (Routledge Studies in the Modern World Economy Ser.). (ENG., Illus.). 400p. (C). 160.00 (978-0-415-77587-8(6)) Routledge.

Kastner, Scott L. Political Conflict & Economic Interdependence Across the Taiwan Strait & Beyond. 2009. (Studies in Asian Security Ser.). (ENG., Illus.). 256p. 70.00 (978-0-8047-6203-8(1)) Stanford Univ. Pr.

Kastner, Scott L. & Kastner, Scott. Political Conflict & Economic Interdependence Across the Taiwan Strait & Beyond. 2009. (Studies in Asian Security). (ENG., Illus.). 256p. pap. 24.95 (978-0-8047-6204-5(X)) Stanford Univ. Pr.

Kee, Tan Teng & Xiaofang, Fu, eds. Proceedings of the International Conference on Chinese Enterprise Research 2007. 2008. 548p. pap. 99.00 (978-981-283-471-3(0)) World Scientific Publishing Co., Inc.

Keller, William W. & Rawski, Thomas G., eds. China's Rise & the Balance of Influence in Asia. 2007. (Pitt Security Continuum Ser.). (Illus.). 328p. (C). per. 27.95 (978-0-8229-5967-0(4)); 284p. 65.00 (978-0-8229-4312-9(3)) Univ. of Pittsburgh Pr.

Kennedy, Scott, ed. Beyond the Middle Kingdom: Comparative Perspectives on China's Capitalist Transformation. 2011. (Contemporary Issues in Asia & Pacific Ser.). (ENG.). 280p. 65.00 (978-0-8047-6957-0(5)); pap. 22.95 (978-0-8047-6958-7(3)) Stanford Univ. Pr.

Khanna, Tarun. Billions of Entrepreneurs: How China & India Are Reshaping Their Futures — and Yours. 2011. (ENG.). 368p. pap. 16.95 (978-1-4221-5728-2(8)) Harvard Business Review Pr.

—Billions of Entrepreneurs: How China & India Are Reshaping Their Futures & Yours. 2007. (ENG.). 353p. 29.95 (978-1-4221-0383-8(8)) Harvard Business Review Pr

Killion, Ulric, ed. Modern Chinese Rules of Order: Paradox of Law & Economics. 2007. 79.00 (978-1-60021-837-8(7)) Nova Science Pubs., Inc.

Knight, John & Ding, Sai. China's Remarkable Economic Growth. 2012. (ENG., Illus.). 424p. 45.00 (978-0-19-969869-1(4)) Oxford Univ. Pr., Inc.

Krug, Barbara & Hendrischke, Hans, eds. The Chinese Economy in the 21st Century: Enterprise & Business Behaviour. 2007. (Illus.). 264p. (C). 119.00 (978-1-84542-750-4(5)) Elgar, Edward Publishing, Inc.

Kueh, Y. Y. China's New Industrialization Strategy: Was Chairman Mao Really Necessary? 2008. (Illus.). 296p. 135.00 (978-1-84720-232-1(2)) Elgar, Edward Publishing, Inc.

Kuhn, Robert Lawrence. How China's Leaders Think: The Inside Story of China's Past, Current & Future Leaders. rev. ed. 2011. (ENG., Illus.). 576p. pap. 29.95 (978-1-118-08590-5(6), Wiley) Wiley, John & Sons, Inc.

Kumar, Rajesh & Worm, Verner. International Negotiation in China & India: A Comparison of the Emerging Business Giants. 2011. (ENG., Illus.). 200p. 85.00 (978-0-230-24594-5(3)) Palgrave Macmillan.

LaFleur, Robert André. China, 1 vol. 2009. (Asia in Focus Ser.). (Illus.). 504p. 85.00 (978-1-59884-166-4(1), CHINAS1C) ABC-CLIO, LLC.

Lai, Hongyi Harry & Lai, Hongyi. Reform & the Non-State Economy in China: The Political Economy of Liberalization Strategies. 2006. (ENG., Illus.). 312p. 95.00 (978-1-4039-7418-1(7)) Palgrave Macmillan.

Lam, Lai Sing. The International Environment & China's Twin Models of Development. 287p. pap. 69.95 (978-3-03911-030-8(6)); 2007. pap. 69.95 (978-0-8204-9319-0(8)) Lang, Peter Publishing, Inc.

Lampton, David M. The Three Faces of Chinese Power: Might, Money, & Minds. 2008. (Illus.). 361p. pap. 26.95 (978-0-520-25442-8(2)) Univ. of California Pr.

Lanqing, Li. Breaking Through: The Birth of China's Opening-Up Policy. 2010. (ENG., Illus.). 480p. 35.00 (978-0-19-801692-2(1)) Oxford Univ. Pr., Inc.

Lardy, Nicholas R. Agriculture in China's Modern Economic Development. 2008. (ENG., Illus.). 300p. pap. 42.00 (978-0-521-07170-3(4)) Cambridge Univ. Pr.

Leeb, Stephen. Red Alert: How China's Growing Prosperity Threatens the American Way of Life. 2011. 272p. (ENG.). 27.99 (978-0-446-57623-9(9)); pap. 17.99 (978-0-446-57624-6(7)) Grand Central Publishing. (Business Plus).

Li, Minqi. The Rise of China & the Demise of the Capitalist World Economy. 2008. (Illus.). 192p. 95.00 (978-0-7453-2773-0(7)) Pluto Pr. GBR. Dist: Univ. of Michigan Pr.

Li, Tieying, ed. Enrich Series on China's Economic Reform: Five-Volume Set, 5 vols., Vols. 1-5, set. 2010. (Enrich Series on China's Economic Reform Ser.). 1632p. 528.00 (978-981-4298-08-7(5)) Enrich Professional Publishing (S)., Ltd. SGP. Dist: Independent Pubs. Group.

Li, Xiao & Takao, Kamikawa. Cooperation Between the Renminbi & the Yen, 3 vols., Vol. 3. 2011. (Enrich Series on Chinese Currency Reform Ser.). (ENG.). 360p. 118.00 (978-981-4339-05-6(9)) Enrich Professional Publishing (S)., Ltd. SGP. Dist: Independent Pubs. Group.

Li, Xiaoxi, ed. Assessing the Extent of China's Marketization. 2006. (Chinese Trade & Industry Ser.). (Illus.). 350p. 130.00 (978-0-7546-4878-9(8)) Ashgate Publishing Co.

Li, Xiaoxi & Hu, Biliang. China's New Deal: Economic Development under International Financial Crisis. 2011. (Global Economic Studies/China in the 21st Century Ser.). 407p. pap. 89.00 (978-1-61470-815-5(0)); (Illus.). 89.00 (978-1-61668-486-0(0)) Nova Science Pubs., Inc.

Li, Yining. Economic Reform & Development in China. 2012. (Cambridge China Library). (ENG.). 368p. 115.00 (978-1-107-02405-2(6)) Cambridge Univ. Pr.

Liang, Bin. The Changing Chinese Legal System, 1978 ndash; Present: Centralization of Power & Rationalization of the Legal System. 2012. (East Asia: History, Politics, Sociology & Culture Ser.). (ENG., Illus.). 266p. pap. 42.95 (978-0-415-54103-9(4)) Routledge.

Liang, Bin. The Changing Chinese Legal System, 1978-Present: Centralization of Power & Rationalization of the Legal System. 2007. (East Asia: History, Politics, Sociology & Culture Ser.). (ENG., Illus.). 266p. 125.00 (978-0-415-95859-2(8)) Routledge.

Lieberthal, Kenneth G. Managing the China Challenge: How to Achieve Corporate Success in the People's Republic. 2011. (ENG., Illus.). 149p. 26.95 (978-0-8157-2204-5(4)) Brookings Institution Pr.

Liew, Leong H. & Wu, Harry X. The Making of China's Exchange Rate Policy: From Plan to WTO Entry. 2008. (Illus.). 264p. 119.00 (978-1-84376-008-5(8)) Elgar, Edward Publishing, Inc.

Lin, Lanceral, et al. The Marketization of Higher Education in Taiwan. 2008. 144p. pap. (978-3-639-10576-6(1)) VDM Verlag Dr. Mueller e.K.

Lin, Man-Houng. China Upside Down: Currency, Society, & Ideologies, 1808-1856. 2007. (Harvard East Asian Monographs: 270). (Illus.). 450p. 49.95 (978-0-674-02268-3(8)) Harvard Univ., Asia Ctr.

Lin, Shuanglin & Song, Shunfeng, eds. The Revival of Private Enterprise in China. 2007. (Chinese Trade & Industry Ser.). (Illus.). 306p. 124.95 (978-0-7546-4892-5(3)) Ashgate Publishing Co.

Lin, Shuanglin & Zhu, Xiaodong, eds. Private Enterprises & China's Economic Development. 2011. (ENG., Illus.). 300p. pap. 42.95 (978-0-415-66644-2(9)) Routledge.

Lin, Shuanglin, et al. Chinese Economy after WTO Accession. 2006. (Chinese Economy Ser.). (Illus.). 374p. 130.00 (978-0-7546-4482-8(0)) Ashgate Publishing Co.

Liu, Manhong Mannie, et al, eds. The Green Economy & Its Implementation in China. 2011. (ENG.). 400p. 128.00 (978-981-4298-95-7(6)) Enrich Professional Publishing (S)., Ltd. SGP. Dist: Independent Pubs. Group.

Liu, Xiaohui & Zhang, Wei. China's Three Decades of Economic Reforms. Liu, Xiaohui & Zhang, Wei, eds. 2009. (ENG., Illus.). 302p. 160.00 (978-0-415-49600-1(4)) Routledge.

Lo, Chi. China after the Subprime Crisis: Opportunities in the New Economic Landscape. 2010. (ENG., Illus.). 204p. 95.00 (978-0-230-28196-7(6)) Palgrave Macmillan.

—Phantom of the China Economic Threat: Shadow of the Next Asian Crisis DISTRIBUTION CANCELLED. 2008. (ENG.). 204p. pap. 42.50 (978-0-230-51544-4(4)) Palgrave Macmillan.

—Understanding China's Growth: Forces That Drive China's Economic Future. 2007. (ENG., Illus.). 272p. 110.00 (978-0-230-51557-4(6)) Palgrave Macmillan.

Lu, M., et al. China's Economic Development: Institutions, Growth & Imbalances. 2012. 224p. 110.00 (978-0-85793-508-3(9)) Elgar, Edward Publishing, Inc.

Lumetsberger, Sigrid. China's Challenge on the Yuan. 2009. 156p. pap. (978-3-639-11185-9(0)) VDM Verlag Dr. Mueller e.K.

Luo, Jing. Business & Technology in China, 1 vol. 2010. (Understanding China Today Ser.). (Illus.). 234p. 35.00 (978-0-313-35732-9(3), GR5732, Greenwood Pr.) Greenwood Publishing Group, Inc.

Ma, Shu-Yun. Shareholding System Reform in China: Privatizing by Groping for Stones. 2010. 176p. 112.00 (978-1-84844-051-7(0)) Elgar, Edward Publishing, Inc.

McGee, Robert W. & Preobragenskaya, Galina G. Accounting & Financial System Reform in a Transition Economy: A Case Study of Russia: A Case Study of Russia. 2010. (ENG.). vii, 182p. pap. 139.00 (978-1-4419-3667-7(X), 144193667X) Springer.

—Accounting & Financial System Reform in Eastern Europe & Asia. 2010. (ENG.). vii, 352p. pap. 159.00 (978-1-4419-3822-0(2), 1441938222) Springer.

McGee, Terry, et al. China's Urban Space: Development under Market Socialism. (Illus.). 288p. 2011. (ENG.). pap. 42.95 (978-0-415-66647-3(3)) 2007. 160.00 (978-0-415-43805-6(5)) Routledge.

McGregor, Richard. The Party: The Secret World of China's Communist Rulers. 2012. (ENG.). 336p. pap. 16.99 (978-0-06-170876-3(3), HarperPerennial) HarperCollins Pubs.

McNally, Christopher A. China's Emergent Political Economy: Capitalism in the Dragon's Lair. 2009. 262p. pap. 39.95 (978-0-415-49718-3(3)) Routledge.

Medeiros, Evan S. China's International Behavior: Activism, Opportunism, & Diversification. 2009. 278p. pap. 34.00 (978-0-8330-4709-0(4), mg-850) RAND Corp., The.

Meier, Nicola. China - the New Developmental State? An Empirical Analysis of the Automotive Industry. 2009. (Hohenheimer volkswirtschaftliche Schriften Ser.). 362p. pap. 81.95 (978-3-631-58284-8(6)) Lang, Peter GmbH, Europaischer Verlag der Wissenschaften DEU. Dist: Lang, Peter.

Meng, Xin. Labour Market Reform in China. 2009. (Trade & Development Ser.). (ENG.). 240p. pap. 36.99 (978-0-521-12111-8(6)) Cambridge Univ. Pr.

Moosa, Imad. The USndash;China Trade Dispute: Facts, Figures & Myths. 2012. 328p. 145.00 (978-1-78100-154-7(5)) Elgar, Edward Publishing, Inc.

Morita, Ken & Chen, Yun. Comparative Analyses of Transition & Development in China & Central Europe. 2009. (Transition & Development Ser.). (Illus.). 426p. 144.95 (978-0-7546-4834-5(6)) Ashgate Publishing Co.

Moyo, Dambisa. Winner Take All: China's Push for Resources & What It Means for the World. 2012. (ENG.). 240p. (gr. 9). 26.99 (978-0-465-02828-3(4)) Basic Bks.

Naughton, Barry. Holding China Together: Diversity & National Integration in the Post-Deng ERA. Yang, Dali L., ed. 2010. (ENG.). 318p. pap. 39.99 (978-0-521-16858-8(9)) Cambridge Univ. Pr.

Naughton, Barry J. The Chinese Economy: Transitions & Growth. 2006. (ENG., Illus.). 544p. per. 28.00 (978-0-262-64064-0(3)) MIT Pr.

Nee, Victor & Opper, Sonja. Capitalism from Below: Markets & Institutional Change in China. 2012. (ENG., Illus.). 456p. 45.00 (978-0-674-05020-4(7)) Harvard Univ. Pr.

Neftci, Salih N. & Yuan Menager-Xu, Michelle, eds. China's Financial Markets: An Insider's Guide to How the Markets Work. 2006. (ENG., Illus.). 416p. 86.95 (978-0-12-088580-0(8), Academic Pr.) Elsevier Science & Technology Bks.

Nicolas, Francoise. Korea in the New Asia: East Asian Integration & the China Factor. 2009. 176p. pap. 39.95 (978-0-415-54706-2(7)) Routledge.

Ning, Lutao. China's Rise in the World ICT Industry: Industrial Strategies & the Catch-up Development Model. 2009. (China Policy Ser.). (ENG., Illus.). 254p. 145.00 (978-0-415-48224-0(0)) Routledge.

Nolan, Peter. China in the Asian Financial Crisis. 2008. (Routledge Studies on the Chinese Economy Ser.). 320p. 130.00 (978-0-415-30372-9(9)) Routledge.

Organisation for Economic Co-operation and Development. China. 2010. (Illus.). 234p. pap. 63.00 (978-92-64-07667-9(0)) Organization for Economic Cooperation & Development.

Organisation for Economic Co-operation and Development Staff. China: Defining the Boundary Between the Market & the State. 2009. (OECD Reviews of Regulatory Reform Ser.). (Illus.). 320p. pap. 63.00 (978-92-64-05939-9(3)) Organization for Economic Cooperation & Development.

—China: Encouraging Responsible Business Conduct. 2008. 286p. pap. 63.00 (978-92-64-05366-3(2)) Organization for Economic Cooperation & Development.

Overton, Rachel H. China's Trade with the United States & the World. Overton, Rachel H., ed. 2008. (Illus.). viii, 71p. pap. 37.00 (978-1-60692-126-5(6)) Nova Science Pubs., Inc.

Pei, Minxin. China's Trapped Transition: The Limits of Developmental Autocracy. 2008. (Illus.). 308p. per. 22.50 (978-0-674-02754-1(X)) Harvard Univ. Pr.

Pekkanen, Saadia & Tsai, Kellee, eds. Japan & China in the World Political Economy. 2009. 248p. pap. 39.95 (978-0-415-54675-1(3)) Routledge.

Peng, Long, et al. Zhongguo Jing Ji Zhuan Xing de Duo Wei Shi Jiao: Zhongguo Jingji Zhuanxing de Duowei Shijiao. 2009. (CHI., Illus.). (978-7-5017-9241-2(0)) China Economics Publishing Hse.

Peng, Sen & Chen, Li. Reforming China: Major Events, 1992-2004, 5 vols., Vol. 4. Tieying, Li, ed. 2010. (Enrich Series on China's Economic Reform Ser.). (ENG.). 400p. 138.00 (978-981-4298-42-1(5)) Enrich Professional Publishing (S)., Ltd. SGP. Dist: Independent Pubs. Group.

Peng, Sen, et al. Reforming China: International Comparisons & Reference, 5 vols., Vol. 5. Li, Tieying, ed. 2010. (Enrich Series on China's Economic Reform Ser.). (ENG.). 400p. 118.00 (978-981-4298-06-3(9)) Enrich Professional Publishing (S)., Ltd. SGP. Dist: Independent Pubs. Group.

Perkins, Dwight H. The Challenges of China's Growth. 2007. (Henry Wendt Lecture Ser.). (ENG., Illus.). 62p. per. 15.00 (978-0-8447-7195-3(3), AEI Pr.) American Enterprise Institute for Public Policy Research.

Philion, Stephen & Philion, Stephen E. Workers' Democracy in China's Transition from State Socialism. 2008. (East Asia: History, Politics, Sociology & Culture Ser.). (ENG.). 178p. 125.00 (978-0-415-96206-3(4)) Routledge.

Pomp, Remco. Chinese Mines & Host Countries. 2009. 52p. pap. (978-3-639-10714-2(4)) VDM Verlag Dr. Mueller e.K.

Porter, Robin. From Mao to Market: China Reconfigured. 2011. (Columbia/Hurst Ser.). (ENG.). 288p. (gr. 17). 35.00 (978-0-231-70190-7(X)) Columbia Univ. Pr.

Powell, Barnaby & Mackinnon, Alex. China Calling: A Foot in the Global Door. 2008. (ENG., Illus.). 256p. 53.00 (978-0-230-21019-6(8)) Palgrave Macmillan.

Qixun Zhang, Lisa. Retail Internationalization in China: Expansion of Foreign Retailers. 2011. (ENG., Illus.). 192p. 90.00 (978-0-230-29337-3(9)) Palgrave Macmillan.

Redding, Gordon & Witt, Michael A. The Future of Chinese Capitalism. 2008. (ENG., Illus.). 275p. 75.00 *(978-0-19-921813-4(7))* Oxford Univ. Pr., Inc.

—The Future of Chinese Capitalism: Choices & Chances. 2010. (ENG., Illus.). 280p. pap. 34.95 *(978-0-19-957587-9(8))* Oxford Univ. Pr., Inc.

Reddy, B. Sudhakara, ed. Economic Reforms in India & China: Emerging Issues & Challenges. 2009. (Illus.). 440p. (C). 59.95 *(978-81-7829-838-2(4),* B98382C) SAGE Pubns., Inc.

Roett, Riordan. China's Expansion into the Western Hemisphere: Implications for Latin America & the United States. Paz, Guadalupe, ed. 2008. (ENG., Illus.). 276p. pap. 26.95 *(978-0-8157-7553-9(9))* Brookings Institution Pr.

Rosenthal, Jean-Laurent & Wong, Roy Bin. Before & Beyond Divergence: The Politics of Economic Change in China & Europe. 2011. (Illus.). 290p. 45.00 *(978-0-674-05791-3(0))* Harvard Univ. Pr.

Saee, John, ed. China & the Global Economy in the 21st Century. 2011. (Routledge Studies in the Growth Economies of Asia Ser.). (ENG., Illus.). 224p. (C). 130.00 *(978-0-415-67051-7(9))* Routledge.

Sanders, Richard & Yang, Chen, eds. China's Post-Reform Economy - Achieving Harmony, Sustaining Growth. 2012. (Routledge Studies on the Chinese Economy Ser.). (ENG., Illus.). 272p. (C). pap. 42.95 ***(978-0-415-54261-6(8))*** Routledge.

Sanders, Richard & Yang, Chen C., eds. China's Post-Reform Economy - Achieving Harmony, Sustaining Growth. 2008. (Routledge Studies on the Chinese Economy Ser.). (Illus.). XVI, 256p. 170.00 *(978-0-415-43432-4(7))* Routledge.

Sauter, John C., ed. U. S. Financial Crisis - Global Dimension & U. S. Policy Implications. 2010. (Financial Institutions & Services Ser.). (Illus.). ix, 188p. 115.00 *(978-1-60741-354-7(X))* Nova Science Pubs., Inc.

Saw, Swee-Hock & Wong, John. Regional Economic Development in China. 2009. (Illus.). xviii, 332p. *(978-981-230-941-9(1))* Institute of Southeast Asian Studies.

Schaeffer, Robert. Red Inc: Dictatorship & the Development of Capitalism in China, 1949-2009. 2011. (Illus.). 272p. 117.00 *(978-1-59451-711-2(8))* Paradigm Pubs.

Schaeffer, Robert K. Red: Dictatorship & the Development of Capitalism in China,1949-2009. 2012. (Illus.). 272p. pap. 29.95 *(978-1-59451-712-9(6))* Paradigm Pubs.

Schiere, Richard. China's Development Challenges: Economic Vulnerability & Public Sector Reform. 2012. (ENG., Illus.). 176p. (C). pap. 44.95 ***(978-0-415-62494-7(0))*** Routledge.

Schiere, Richard. China's Development Challenges: Public Sector Reform & Vulnerability to Poverty. 2008. (Routledge Studies on the Chinese Economy Ser.). (Illus.). 192p. 130.00 *(978-0-415-47865-6(0))* Routledge.

Shan, Wenhua & Gallagher, Norah. Chinese Investment Treaties: Policies & Practice. 2009. (Oxford International Arbitration Ser.). (ENG., Illus.). 330p. 387.50 *(978-0-19-923025-9(0))* Oxford Univ. Pr., Inc.

Sharma, Shalendra D. China & India in the Age of Globalization. 2009. (ENG., Illus.). 336p. (C). 99.00 *(978-0-521-51571-9(8))*; pap. 30.00 *(978-0-521-73136-2(4))* Cambridge Univ. Pr.

Shen, Raphael & Mantzopoulos, Victoria. Political Economy of China's Systemic Transformation: 1979 to the Present. 2011. (ENG., Illus.). 250p. 85.00 *(978-0-230-10303-0(0))* Palgrave Macmillan.

Sheng, Yuming. Economic Openness & Territorial Politics in China. 2010. (ENG., Illus.). 312p. 85.00 *(978-0-521-19538-6(1))* Cambridge Univ. Pr.

Shi, Li, et al, eds. Inequality & Public Policy in China. 2008. (ENG., Illus.). 384p. 98.00 *(978-0-521-87045-0(3))* Cambridge Univ. Pr.

Shi, Zhongquan & Yu, Jingsong. Ji Nian Gai Ge Kai Fang 30 Zhou Nian Lun Ji: Jinian Gaige Kaifang Sanshi Zhounian Lunji. 2010. (CHI.). *(978-7-5098-0444-5(2))* Chinese Communist Party History Pr.

Shih, Victor C. Factions & Finance in China: Elite Conflict & Inflation. 2007. (ENG., Illus.). 268p. 94.00 *(978-0-521-87257-7(X))* Cambridge Univ. Pr.

Shu, Fumin. Zhongguo Quan Mian Xiao Kang Fa Zhan Bao Gao: Zhongguo Quanmian Xiaokang Fazhan Baogao. 2nd ed. 2008. (CHI.). *(978-7-5097-0447-9(2))* China Social Science Documentation Publishing Hse.

Soares de Oliveira, Ricardo, et al. China Returns to Africa: A Rising Power & a Continent Embrace. 2008. (Columbia/Hurst Ser.). (ENG., Illus.). 400p. (gr. 17). 75.00 *(978-0-231-70098-6(9))* Columbia Univ. Pr.

Song, Guiwu. Peng Zhuang Zhongguo She Hui Jing Ji Wen Ti: Mian Zi, Xue Yuan, Quan Li = Pengzhuang Zhongguoshehui Jingjiwenti. 2010. (CHI., Illus.). *(978-7-5017-8787-6(5))* China Economics Publishing Hse.

Storz, Cornelia & Schäfer, Sebastian. Understanding Innovation - the Case of Japan & China. 2011. (Routledge Studies in Global Competition Ser.). (ENG., Illus.). 304p. (C). 140.00 *(978-0-415-55455-8(1))* Routledge.

Stou. Entrepreneurship & Economic Growth in China. 2011. 96.00 *(978-981-4273-36-7(8))* World Scientific Publishing Co., Inc.

Swamy & Swamy, Subramanian. Economic Development & Reforms in India & China: A Comparative Perspective. (Illus.). 336p. *(978-81-241-1535-0(4))* Har-Anand Pubns.

Swanson, Tim & Lin, Tun. Economic Growth & Environmental Regulation: China's Path to a Brighter Future. 2010. (Routledge Explorations in Environmental Economics Ser.). (Illus.). 370p. 135.00 *(978-0-415-55127-4(7))* Routledge.

Swanson, Timothy & Lin, Tun, eds. Economic Growth & Environmental Regulation: The People's Republic of China's Path to a Brighter Future. 2012. (ENG., Illus.). 370p. (C). pap. 43.56 ***(978-0-415-53984-5(6))*** Routledge.

Sweetman, Arthur & Zhang, Jun. Economic Transitions with Chinese Characteristics Vol. 1: Thirty Years of Reform & Opening Up. 2009. (ENG.). 232p. (C). *(978-1-55339-226-2(4))*; pap. *(978-1-55339-225-5(6))* McGill-Queen's Univ. Pr.

—Economic Transitions with Chinese Characteristics Vol. 2: Social Change During Thirty Years of Reform. 2009. (ENG.). 216p. (C). *(978-1-55339-235-4(3))*; pap. *(978-1-55339-234-7(5))* McGill-Queen's Univ. Pr.

A Tale of Two Economies: Development Dynamics of India & China. 2008. 138p. pap. 47.00 *(978-1-60692-317-7(X))* Nova Science Pubs., Inc.

Tang, Lei. The Chinese Consumer Market: Opportunities & Risks. 2009. (Chandos Asian Studies). (ENG., Illus.). 250p. 110.00 *(978-1-84334-332-5(0),* Chandos Publishing) Woodhead Publishing Ltd. GBR. Dist: Ingram Pub. Services.

Tsai, Kellee S. Capitalism Without Democracy: The Private Sector in Contemporary China. 2007. (Illus.). 268p. 63.95 *(978-0-8014-4513-2(2))*; per. 21.95 *(978-0-8014-7326-5(8))* Cornell Univ. Pr.

Tse, Edward. The China Strategy: Harnessing the Power of the World's Fastest-Growing Economy. 2012. (ENG.). 288p. (gr. 9). pap. 17.00 ***(978-0-465-02906-8(X))*** Basic Bks.

Tseng, Wanda S. India's & China's Recent Experience with Reform & Growth. Tseng, Wanda S. & Cowen, David G., eds. 2007. (ENG., Illus.). 336p. pap. 47.00 *(978-0-230-54281-5(6))* Palgrave Macmillan.

Tyler, Benjamin A. The Chinese Economy. 2010. (China in the 21st Century Ser.). 146p. 69.00 *(978-1-60876-937-7(2))* Nova Science Pubs., Inc.

Urio, Paolo. China, the West & the Myth of New Public Management. 2012. (Routledge Contemporary China Ser.). (ENG., Illus.). 336p. (C). 145.00 ***(978-0-415-69588-6(0))*** Routledge.

—Reconciling State Market & Civil Society in China: The Long March Towards Prosperity. 2010. (Routledge Contemporary China Ser.). (ENG., Illus.). 304p. (C). 135.00 *(978-0-415-56446-5(8))* Routledge.

Urio, Paolo. Reconciling State Market & Society in China. 2011. (ENG., Illus.). 300p. pap. 42.95 ***(978-0-415-69204-5(0))*** Routledge.

U.S. Interests in the Reform of China's Financial Services Sector: Hearing Before the Committee on Financial Services, U.S. House of Representatives, One Hundred Tenth Congress, First Session, June 6, 2007. 2007. iii, 131p. *(978-0-16-079524-4(9),* 552-070-36502-8) United States Government Printing Office.

Varum, Celeste Amorim & Huang, Can. China: Building an Innovative Economy. 2007. (Chandos Asian Studies). (ENG., Illus.). 152p. 110.00 *(978-1-84334-148-2(4),* Chandos Publishing) Woodhead Publishing Ltd. GBR. Dist: Ingram Pub. Services.

Walter, Carl & Howie, Fraser. Red Capitalism: The Fragile Financial Foundation of China's Extraordinary Rise. 2nd rev. ed. 2012. (ENG.). 260p. 29.95 ***(978-1-118-25510-0(0),*** Wiley) Wiley, John & Sons, Inc.

Wang, Enbao. The Origin, Process, & Outcome of China,s Reforms in the Past One Hundred Years: The Chinese Quest for National Rejuvenation. 2009. x, 383p. *(978-0-7734-3904-7(8))* Mellen, Edwin Pr., The.

Wang, Junmin. State-Market Interactions in China's Reform Era: Local State Competition & Global Market Building in the Tobacco Industry. 2012. (Routledge Contemporary China Ser.). (ENG., Illus.). 160p. (C). 125.00 ***(978-0-415-50694-6(8))*** Routledge.

Wang, Mengkui. Zhongguo Gai Ge 30 Nian: 1978-2008. 2009. (CHI., Illus.). *(978-7-80234-434-1(4))* China Development Pr.

Wang, Xiaolu, et al. Eliminating Poverty Through Development in China. 2008. (Illus.). xxiii, 250p. *(978-0-203-88772-1(7))* Routledge.

Wang, Yue. Thirty Years of China's Economic Reform: Institutions, Management Organizations & Foreign Investment. Ramburuth, Prem, ed. 2010. (China in the 21st Century Ser.). (Illus.). 241p. 89.00 *(978-1-60876-908-7(9))* Nova Science Pubs., Inc.

Wang, Zhikai. The Private Sector & China's Market Development. 2008. (Chandos Asian Studies). (ENG., Illus.). 138p. 110.00 *(978-1-84334-399-8(1),* Chandos Publishing) Woodhead Publishing Ltd. GBR. Dist: Ingram Pub. Services.

Wedeman, Andrew H. From Mao to Market: Rent Seeking, Local Protectionism, & Marketization in China. 2009. (Cambridge Modern China Ser.). (ENG., Illus.). 300p. pap. 38.99 *(978-0-521-10015-1(1))* Cambridge Univ. Pr.

Wei, Yi-Ming. Energy Economics: Modelling & Empirical Analysis in China. 2009. (Illus.). 320p. 133.95 *(978-1-4398-1121-4(0),* CRC Press) Taylor & Francis Group GBR. Dist: Taylor & Francis Group.

Whalley, John. China's Integration into the World Economy. 2010. (Illus.). 300p. 120.00 *(978-981-4304-78-8(6))* World Scientific Publishing Co., ll c.

Wilson, Scott Howard. Remade in China: Foreign Investors & Institutional Change in China. 2009. (ENG., Illus.). 304p. 65.00 *(978-0-19-538831-2(3))* Oxford Univ. Pr., Inc.

Witzel, Morgen, et al. Doing Business in China. 3rd rev. ed. 2008. (ENG., Illus.). 304p. (C). 170.00 *(978-0-415-43631-1(1))* Routledge.

Womack, Brantly. China's Rise in Historical Perspective. 2010. (ENG.). 272p. pap. 29.95 *(978-0-7425-6722-1(2))* Rowman & Littlefield Publishers, Inc.

Womack, Brantly, ed. China's Rise in Historical Perspective. 2010. (ENG.). 272p. 85.00 *(978-0-7425-6721-4(4))* Rowman & Littlefield Publishers, Inc.

Wong, John & Liu, Wei, eds. China's Surging Economy: Adjusting for More Balanced Development. 2007. (Ser. on Contemporary China Ser.). (Illus.). 380p. 99.00 *(978-981-270-627-0(5))* World Scientific Publishing Co., Inc.

Wong, Sam. Exploring 'Unseen' Social Capital in Community Participation: Everyday Lives of Poor Mainland Chinese Migrants in Hong Kong. 2008. (ICAS Publications Ser.). (Illus.). 220p. per. *(978-90-5356-034-1(3),* Leiden Univ. Pr.) Amsterdam Univ. Pr.

Wu, Jinglian. China's Long March Toward A. 2010. 316p. pap. 25.95 *(978-1-59265-063-7(5))* BetterLink Pr., Inc.

Wu, Xiaochen. Anti-Dumping Law & Practice of China. 2008. xxxvi, 430p. 185.00 *(978-90-411-2790-7(9))* Wolters Kluwer Law & Business.

Wu, Yanrui. Productivity, Efficiency & Economic Growth in China. 2008. (ENG., Illus.). 224p. 105.00 *(978-0-230-20212-2(8))* Palgrave Macmillan.

Wu, Zhongmin. China in the World Economy. Wu, Zhongmin, ed. 2009. (Routledge Studies on the Chinese Economy Ser.). (ENG., Illus.). 344p. (C). 190.00 *(978-0-415-47002-5(1))* Routledge.

—Financial Sector Reform & the International Integration of China. 2009. (ENG., Illus.). 300p. 190.00 *(978-0-415-47003-2(X))* Routledge.

Xiao, Li & Yibing, Ding. Regionalization of the Renminbi, Vol. 2. 2011. (Enrich Series on Chinese Currency Reform Ser.). 384p. 118.95 ***(978-981-4339-04-9(0))*** Enrich Professional Publishing (S)., Ltd. SGP. Dist: Independent Pubs. Group.

Xiaoxi, Li, et al. Emerging Markets Reform & Development in China. 2010. (Illus.). ix, 49p. pap. 49.00 *(978-1-61668-769-4(X))* Nova Science Pubs., Inc.

Xue, Muqiao. Chinese Economists on Economic Reform - Xue Muqiao. 2011. (Routledge Studies on the Chinese Economy Ser.). (Illus.). 224p. (C). 140.00 *(978-0-415-59821-7(4))* Routledge.

Yang, Dali L., ed. The Global Recession & China's Political Economy. 2012. (China in Transformation Ser.). (ENG., Illus.). 282p. 95.00 ***(978-0-230-34085-5(7))*** Palgrave Macmillan.

Yang, Keming. Entrepreneurship in China. 2007. 260p. 114.95 *(978-0-7546-4668-6(8))* Ashgate Publishing Co.

Yang, Qixian & Shi, Xiaomin. Reforming China: Theoretical Framework, vols. 5, Vol. 1. Li, Tiyeng, ed. 2010. (Enrich Series on China's Economic Reform Ser.). (ENG.). 272p. 88.00 ***(978-981-4298-00-1(X))*** Enrich Professional Publishing (S)., Ltd. SGP. Dist: Independent Pubs. Group.

Yang, Yao, et al, eds. Chinas Role in the World Economy. 2012. (PAFTAD (Pacific Trade & Development Conference Series) Ser.). (ENG.). 240p. (C). 125.00 ***(978-0-415-69116-1(8))*** Routledge.

Yao, Yang & Yueh, Linda, eds. Globalisation & Economic Growth in China. 2006. (Series on Economic Development & Growth). (Illus.). 289p. 96.00 *(978-981-256-855-7(7))* World Scientific Publishing Co., Inc.

Yao, Yang L., et al, eds. Reform & Development in China: What Can China Offer the Developing World. 2010. (Routledge Studies in Development Economics Ser.). (ENG., Illus.). 400p. (C). 155.00 *(978-0-415-55948-5(0),* Routledge) Taylor & Francis Group GBR. Dist: Taylor & Francis Group.

Yingming, Zhu. Analysis on Industrial Clusters in China. 2009. (ENG., Illus.). 248p. 133.95 *(978-1-4200-8919-6(6),* CRC Press) Taylor & Francis Group GBR. Dist: Taylor & Francis Group.

Yu, Guanghua. Comparative Corporate Governance in China: Political Economy & Legal Infrastructure. 2007. (ENG.). 208p. (C). 175.00 *(978-0-415-40306-1(5))*; per. 63.95 *(978-0-415-40307-8(3))* Routledge.

Yu, Hong. Economic Development & Inequality in China. 2010. (Routledge Studies in the Growth Economies of Asia Ser.). (ENG., Illus.). 272p. (C). 125.00 *(978-0-415-59658-9(0))* Routledge.

—Economic Development & Inequality in China: The Case of Guangdong. 2010. (Illus.). xviii, 252p. *(978-0-203-83950-8(1))* Routledge.

Yueh, Linda. The Economy of China. 2010. (Illus.). 264p. 112.00 *(978-1-84542-194-6(9))* Elgar, Edward Publishing, Inc.

Yueh, Linda Y. The Economy of China. 2012. (Illus.). 264p. pap. 39.95 ***(978-1-78100-398-5(X))*** Elgar, Edward Publishing, Inc.

Yusuf, Shahid & Nabeshima, Kaoru. Changing the Industrial Geography in Asia: The Impact of China & India. 2010. (ENG., Illus.). 280p. pap. 24.95 *(978-0-8213-8240-0(3),* 9780821382400) World Bank Pubns.

—Two Dragon Heads: Contrasting Development Paths for Beijing & Shanghai. 2010. (ENG., Illus.). 224p. pap. 19.95 *(978-0-8213-8048-2(6),* 9780821380482) World Bank Pubns.

Zeng, Benxiang. Tourism Development & Local Poverty - a Case Study of Qinling Mountain Region, Shaanxi Province, Chin. 2008. 196p. pap. *(978-3-639-00273-7(3))* VDM Verlag Dr. Mueller e.K.

Zeng, Douglas Zhihua, ed. Building Engines for Growth & Competitiveness in China: Experience with Special Economic Zones & Industrial Clusters. 2010. (Directions in Development Ser.). (ENG., Illus.). 256p. pap. 35.00 *(978-0-8213-8432-9(5),* 9780821384329) World Bank Pubns.

Zeng, Peiyan. Xi Bu Da Kai Fa Jue Ce Hui Gu. 2010. (Illus.). *(978-7-5098-0595-4(3))* Chinese Communist Party History Pr.

Zhang & Zhang, Lusong. Regulation Foreign Mergers & Acquisitions Involving Companies Listed in China. 2007. *(978-90-411-2594-1(9))* Kluwer Law International.

Zhang, Fengbo. A Chinese Economist's Journey. 2008. 100p. pap. 19.95 *(978-1-4357-5451-5(4))* Lulu Enterprises Inc.

Zhang, Jianjun. Marketization & Democracy in China. 2009. 278p. pap. 39.95 *(978-0-415-57428-0(5))* 2008. (Illus.). 304p. 170.00 *(978-0-415-45222-9(8))* Routledge.

Zhang, Si & Pearce, Robert. Multinationals in China: Business Strategy, Technology & Economic Development. 2012. (ENG.). 168p. 105.00 *(978-0-230-57741-1(5))* Palgrave Macmillan.

Zhang, Wei. Economic Reform in Modern China, 4 vols. 2011. (Critical Concepts in Economics Ser.). (ENG., Illus.). 1736p. 1250.00 *(978-0-415-56068-9(3))* Routledge.

—Economic Reform in Modern China V1, 4 vols. 2011. (Illus.). *(978-0-415-56945-3(1))* Routledge.

—Economic Reform in Modern China V2, 4 vols. 2011. (Illus.). *(978-0-415-56944-6(3))* Routledge.

—Economic Reform in Modern China V3, 4 vols. 2011. (Illus.). *(978-0-415-56942-2(7))* Routledge.

—Economic Reform in Modern China V4, 4 vols. 2011. (Illus.). *(978-0-415-56941-5(9))* Routledge.

Zhang, Xiaobo. Narratives of Chinese Economic Reforms: How Does China Cross the River? 2010. 200p. 88.00 *(978-981-4293-30-3(X))* World Scientific Publishing Co., Inc.

Zhang, Xinshi & Huang, Hongwen, eds. Science & Technology on Bio-hylic & Biomass Resources in China: A Roadmap To 2050: A Roadmap To 2050. 2010. (Illus.). 175p. pap. 99.00 *(978-3-642-05339-9(4),* 3642053394) Springer.

Zhang, Zhong. The Derivative Action & Good Corporate Governance in Chin. 2011. 268p. pap. ***(978-3-8443-2703-8(7))*** Lambert Academic Publishing.

Zhao, Suisheng, et al, eds. In Search of China's Development Model. 2011. (Routledge Contemporary China Ser.). (ENG., Illus.). 272p. (C). 140.00 *(978-0-415-58748-8(4))* Routledge.

Zheng, Yisheng. Poverty Reduction & Sustainable Development in Rural China. 2011. 365p. *(978-90-04-18817-4(7))* BRILL.

Zhimin, Chen, ed. China's Reforms & International Political Economy. 2007. (Routledge Studies on China in Transition Ser.). (ENG., Illus.). 256p. (C). 170.00 *(978-0-415-39613-4(1))* Routledge.

Zhong gong zhong yang wen xian yan jiu shi, Deng Xiaoping yan jiu zu Staff, contrib. by. Kai Chuang: Deng Xiaoping Jue Ce Gai Ge Kai Fang Shi Hua. 2008. (CHI., Illus.). 297p. *(978-7-5340-2557-0(5))* Zehjiang People's Fine Arts Publishing Hse.

Zhou, Dongtao. Reforming China: Experiences & Lessons, vols. 5, vol. 2. Tiyeng, Li, ed. 2010. (Enrich Series on China's Economic Reform Ser.). (ENG.). 464p. 138.00 *(978-981-4298-02-5(6))* Enrich Professional Publishing (S)., Ltd. SGP. Dist: Independent Pubs. Group.

Zhou, Xueguang. The State & Life Chances in Urban China: Redistribution & Stratification, 1949-1994. 2010. (ENG.). 400p. pap. 36.99 *(978-0-521-15384-3(0))* Cambridge Univ. Pr.

Zhu, Ying. The Everyday Impact of Economic Reform in China: Management Change, Enterprise Performance & Daily Life. 2010. (Routledge Studies in the Growth Economies of Asia Ser.). (ENG., Illus.). 224p. (C). 150.00 *(978-0-415-42841-5(6))* Routledge.

Zicheng, Ye. Inside China's Grand Strategy: The Perspective from the People's Republic. Liu, Guoli & Levine, Steven I., eds. 2010. (Asia in the New Millennium Ser.). (ENG., Illus.). 320p. 35.00 *(978-0-8131-2645-6(2))* Univ. Pr. of Kentucky.

Zweig, David & Chen, Zhimin, eds. China's Reforms & International Political Economy. 2009. (Illus.). 242p. pap. 39.95 *(978-0-415-54703-1(2))* Routledge.

CHINA—EMIGRATION AND IMMIGRATION

Auerbach, Sascha J., et al. Race, Law, & the Chinese Puzzle in Imperial Britain. 2009. (ENG., Illus.). 280p. 95.00 *(978-0-230-60949-5(X))* Palgrave Macmillan.

Chang, Felix & Rucker-Chang, Sunnie, eds. Chinese Migrants in Russia Central Asia & Eastern Europe. 2011. (Routledge Contemporary Russia & Eastern Europe Ser.). (ENG., Illus.). 256p. (C). 140.00 *(978-0-415-57874-5(4))* Routledge.

Chee-Beng, Tan, ed. Chinese Transnational Network. 2007. (Chinese Worlds Ser.). (Illus.). 214p. 160.00 *(978-0-415-39583-0(6))* Routledge.

Chee Ming Feng, Robin. Migrants Not Locals. 2011. 136p. pap. ***(978-3-8443-8350-8(6))*** Lambert Academic Publishing.

Chu, Julie Y. Cosmologies of Credit: Transnational Mobility & the Politics of Destination in China. 2010. (ENG., Illus.). 360p. 89.95 *(978-0-8223-4792-7(X))*; pap. 24.95 *(978-0-8223-4806-1(3))* Duke Univ. Pr.

Conwell, Russell Herman. Why & How: Why the Chinese Emigrate, & the Means they Adopt for the Purpose of Reaching America, with Sketches of Travel, Amusing incidents, Soci. 2006. 304p. per. 23.99 *(978-1-4255-2842-3(2))* MPublishing.

Dong Jie. Discourse, Identity, & China's Internal Migration: The Long March to the City. 2011. (Encounters Ser.). (Illus.). 176p. (ENG.). 119.95 *(978-1-84769-420-1(9))*; pap. 39.95 *(978-1-84769-419-5(5))* Multilingual Matters GBR. Dist: Univ. of Toronto Pr.

Fat, Paul B. Tjon Sie. Chinese New Migrants in Suriname: The Inevitability of Ethnic Performing. 2009. (UvA Proefschriften Ser.). 478p. pap. *(978-90-5629-598-1(5),* Vossiupers UvA) Amsterdam Univ. Pr.

Fong, Vanessa. Paradise Redefined: Transnational Chinese Students & the Quest for Flexible Citizenship in the Developed World. 2011. (ENG.). 280p. 60.00 ***(978-0-8047-7266-2(5))***; pap. 21.95 ***(978-0-8047-7267-9(3))*** Stanford Univ. Pr.

Gao, Yun, ed. Concealed Chains: Labour Exploitation & Chinese Migrants in Europe. 2010. (ENG., Illus.). 250p. pap. 36.00 *(978-92-2-121993-4(3))* International Labour Office.

Gransow, Bettina & Daming, Zhou. Migrants & Health in Urban China. 2011. (Illus.). 192p. pap. 49.95 ***(978-3-643-10912-5(1))*** Lit Verlag DEU. Dist: Transaction Pubs.

Groder, Joachim. Migration in 20th Century Macau. 2008. 440p. pap. *(978-3-639-00232-4(6))* VDM Verlag Dr. Mueller e.K.

Ho, Elaine Yee Lin & Kuehn, Julia. China Abroad: Travels, Subjects, Spaces. 2009. (ENG., Illus.). 304p. (gr. 17). 60.00 *(978-962-209-945-6(9))*; pap. 29.95 *(978-962-209-989-0(0))* Hong Kong Univ. Pr. HKG. Dist: Columbia Univ. Pr.

Hoyle, Caroline. Migration & Population China: Moving Peoples & Creating Change. 2007. (Routledge Research in Population & Migration Ser.). (ENG.). 256p. (C). 125.00 (978-0-415-18774-9(5)) Routledge.

Jonkers, Koen. Mobility, Migration & the Chinese Scientific Research System. 2010. (Routledge Contemporary China Ser.). (ENG., Illus.). 256p. (C). 130.00 (978-0-415-55689-7(9), Routledge) Taylor & Francis Group GBR. Dist: Taylor & Francis Group.

Kim, Hyejin. International Ethnic Networks & Intra-Ethnic Conflict: Koreans in China. 2010. (ENG., Illus.). 212p. 89.00 (978-0-230-10252-1(2)) Palgrave Macmillan.

Koo, Vi K. Status of Aliens in China. (Columbia University, Studies in the Social Sciences: No. 126). reprint ed. 35.00 (978-0-404-51126-5(0)) AMS Pr., Inc.

Kuhn, Philip A. Chinese among Others: Emigration in Modern Times. 2009. (State & Society East Asia Ser.). (ENG.). 452p. pap. 39.95 (978-0-7425-6749-8(4)) Rowman & Littlefield Publishers, Inc.

Lan, Shanshan. Diaspora & Class Consciousness: Chinese Immigrant Workers in Multiracial Chicago. 2011. (Studies in Asian Americans Ser.). (ENG., Illus.). 218p. (C). 125.00 (978-0-415-89036-6(5)) Routledge.

Lary, Diana. Chinese Migrations: The Movement of People, Goods, & Ideas over Four Millennia. 2012. (Critical Issues in World & International History Ser.). (ENG.). 248p. 75.00 (978-0-7425-6763-4(X)); pap. 29.95 (978-0-7425-6764-1(8)) Rowman & Littlefield Publishers, Inc.

Lau, Estelle T. Paper Families: Identity, Immigration Administration, & Chinese Exclusion. 2007. (Politics, History, & Culture Ser.). (ENG., Illus.). 232p. (C). 79.95 (978-0-8223-3735-5(5)) Duke Univ. Pr.

—Paper Families: Identity, Immigration Administration, & Chinese Exclusion. 2007. (Politics, History, & Culture Ser.). (ENG., Illus.). 232p. per. 22.95 (978-0-8223-3747-8(9)) Duke Univ. Pr.

Lee, Erika. At America's Gates. (978-0-8047-3948-1(X)) Stanford Univ. Pr.

Li, Yushi(Boni). Emigrating from China to the United States: A Comparison of Different Social Experiences. 2009. 250p. 52.95 (978-0-398-07899-7(8)); pap. 34.95 (978-0-398-07900-0(5)) Thomas, Charles C. Pub., Ltd.

Liu, Guofu. Chinese Immigration Law. 2010. (Law & Migration Ser.). 234p. 99.95 (978-1-4094-0940-3(6)) Ashgate Publishing Co.

Luk, Wai-Ki. Chinatown in Britain: Diffusions & Concentrations of the British New Wave Chinese Immigration. 2007. (C). 114.95 (978-1-934043-86-8(9)) Cambria Pr.

Mungello, D. E. Western Queers in China: Flight to the Land of Oz. 2012. (ENG.). 212p. (gr. 17). 60.00 (978-1-4422-1556-8(9)) Rowman & Littlefield Publishers, Inc.

Murata, Lynn. Transnationalism. 2009. 152p. pap. (978-3-639-15809-0(1)) VDM Verlag Dr. Mueller e.K.

Murphy, Rachel. Labour Migration & Social Development in Contemporary China. 2008. (Comparative Development & Policy in Asia Ser.). (Illus.). XIV, 210p. 160.00 (978-0-415-46801-5(9)) Routledge.

Nakao, Masayoshi, et al. Ecological Migration: Environmental Policy in China. 2011. (Illus.). 283p. pap. (978-3-0343-0343-9(2)) Lang, Peter Publishing, Inc.

Newendorp, Nicole Dejong. Uneasy Reunions: Immigration, Citizenship, & Family Life in Post-1997 Hong Kong. 2008. (ENG., Illus.). 312p. 24.95 (978-0-8047-5813-0(1)) Stanford Univ. Pr.

Nyiri, Pál & Nyiri, Pál. Chinese in Eastern Europe & Russia: A Middleman Minority in a Transnational ERA. 2008. (Chinese Worlds Ser.). (Illus.). 192p. 160.00 (978-0-415-44686-0(4)) Routledge.

Peilin, Li & Roulleau-Berger, Laurence, eds. China's Internal & International Migration. 2012. (China Policy Ser.). (ENG., Illus.). 320p. (C). 155.00 (978-0-415-53221-1(3)) Routledge.

Peterson, Glen. Overseas Chinese in the People's Republic of China. 2011. (Chinese Worlds Ser.). (ENG., Illus.). 248p. (C). 130.00 (978-0-415-61670-6(0)) Routledge.

Qin, Yucheng. The Diplomacy of Nationalism: The Six Companies & China's Policy Toward Exclusion. 2009. x, 213p. (C). 51.00 (978-0-8248-3274-2(4)) Univ. of Hawaii Pr.

Rajah Kumaran, Shangeetha. The Portrayal of Chinese Diaspora in Selected Novels by Amy Tan. 2010. 76p. pap. (978-3-8383-2088-5(3)) Lambert Academic Publishing.

Repnikova, Maria & Balzer, Harley D. Chinese Migration to Russia: Missed Opportunities. 2009. 56p. (978-1-933549-54-5(8)) Woodrow Wilson International Ctr. fo Scholars.

Russell, Bertrand. Migration & Social Protection in China. 2008. (Series on Contemporary China). 87.00 (978-981-279-049-1(7)) World Scientific Publishing Co., Inc.

Salaff, Janet W., et al. Hong Kong Movers & Stayers: Narratives of Family Migration. 2010. (Studies of World Migrations Ser.). (ENG.). 296p. pap. 30.00 (978-0-252-07704-3(0)); (Illus.). 80.00 (978-0-252-03518-0(6)) Univ. of Illinois Pr.

Siu, Lok C. D. Memories of a Future Home: Diasporic Citizenship of Chinese in Panama. 2007. (ENG., Illus.). 272p. per. 21.95 (978-0-8047-5846-8(8)) Stanford Univ. Pr.

Sun, Wanning. Media & the Chinese Diaspora: Community, Communications & Commerce. 2009. 226p. pap. 39.95 (978-0-415-54563-1(3)) Routledge.

Sussman, Nan M. Return Migration & Identity: A Global Phenomenon - A Hong Kong Case. 2010. (ENG & CHI., Illus.). 364p. (gr. 17). 50.00 (978-988-8028-83-2(9)); pap. 30.00 (978-988-8028-84-9(7)) Hong Kong Univ. Pr. HKG. Dist: Columbia Univ. Pr.

Tambar, Udai, ed. Movement of Global Talent: The Impact of High Skill Labor Flows from India & China. 2007. 225p. pap. 15.95 (978-0-9789595-1-7(5)) Policy Research Institute for the Region.

Tan, Chee-Beng. Chinese Transnational Networks. 2009. 214p. pap. 39.95 (978-0-415-56057-3(8)) Routledge.

Tan, Chee-Beng, ed. Routledge Handbook of the Chinese Diaspora. 2012. (ENG., Illus.). 560p. (C). 215.00 (978-0-415-60056-9(1)) Routledge.

Thuno, Mette, ed. Beyond Chinatown: New Chinese Migration & the Global Expansion of China. 2007. (Nias Studies in Asian Topics Ser.). (Illus.). 281p. pap. 27.00 (978-87-7694-000-3(4)) Nordic Institute of Asian Studies DNK. Dist: Univ. of Hawaii Pr.

Wanning, Sun. Media & the Chinese Diaspora: Community, Communications & Commerce. 2006. (Media, Culture, & Social Change in Asia Ser.: Vol. 5). (ENG., Illus.). 240p. (C). 170.00 (978-0-415-35204-8(5)) Routledge.

Zhang, Sheldon X. Chinese Human Smuggling Organizations: Families, Social Networks, & Cultural Imperatives. 2008. (ENG., Illus.). 304p. 45.00 (978-0-8047-5741-6(0)) Stanford Univ. Pr.

CHINA—ENVIRONMENTAL CONDITIONS

Abe, Ken-ichi & Nichum, James E., eds. Good Earths: Regional & Historical Insights into China's Environment. 2009. (Frontiers of Area Studies Ser.). 292p. 89.95 (978-1-920901-35-6(3)) Kyoto Univ. Pr. & Trans Pacific Pr. AUS. Dist: International Specialized Bk. Services.

Bennett, Jeff, et al, eds. Environmental Protection in China: Land-Use Management. 2008. (Illus.). 240p. (C). 119.00 (978-1-84720-589-6(5)) Elgar, Edward Publishing, Inc.

Bennett, Patricia M. Implications of Climate Change in China. 2011. (China in the 21st Century Ser.). 89.00 (978-1-61122-843-4(3)) Nova Science Pubs., Inc.

Bi, Liang-Liang. Transjurisdictional Water Pollution Management & Cooperation in Chin. 2011. 60p. pap. (978-3-8443-9194-7(0)) Lambert Academic Publishing.

Broadening the Bilateral: Seizing the Opportunity for Meaningful U.S.-China Collaboration on Climate Change: A Report to the Committee on Foreign Relations, United States Senate, One Hundred Eleventh Congress, First Session, July 21, 2009. 2009. v, 16p. (978-0-16-083887-3(8), 552-070-39576-8) United States Government Printing Office.

CER Publishing, ed. China's Environment 2008. 2007. 280p. pap. 44.50 (978-988-19149-1-0(4)) China Economic Review Publishing HKG. Dist: Trans-Atlantic Pubns., Inc.

Chang, Michael I. Pollution in China. 2011. (China in the 21st Century Ser.). (Illus.). x, 208p. 69.00 (978-1-61122-022-3(X)) Nova Science Pubs., Inc.

Chen, Zuyu. Shui Li Shui Dian Gong Cheng Feng Xian Fen Xi Ji Ke Kao du She Ji Ji Shu Jin Zhan. 2010. (CHI., Illus.). 366p. (978-7-5084-7143-3(1)) Zhongguo Shuili Shuidian Chubanshe.

Ci, Longjun & Yang, Xiaohui, eds. Desertification & its Control in China. 2010. (ENG., Illus.). 500p. 279.00 (978-3-642-01868-8(8), 3642018688) Springer.

Dahlman, Carl. The World under Pressure: How China & India Are Influencing the Global Economy & Environment. 2011. (ENG., Illus.). 326p. 65.00 (978-0-8047-7713-1(6), Stanford Economics & Finance) Stanford Univ. Pr.

Deng, Yingtao. A New Development Model & China's Future. 2012. (Routledge Studies on the Chinese Economy Ser.). (ENG.). 240p. (C). 140.00 (978-0-415-61092-6(3)) Routledge.

Ding Yihui. Monsoons over China. 2010. (Atmospheric & Oceanographic Sciences Library). (Illus.). 432p. pap. 329.00 (978-90-481-4161-6(3), 9048141613) Springer.

Economy, Elizabeth C. The River Runs Black: The Environmental Challenge to China's Future. 2nd rev. ed. 2010. (Council on Foreign Relations Book Ser.). (Illus.). 368p. 65.00 (978-0-8014-4924-6(3)); pap. 19.95 (978-0-8014-7613-6(5)) Cornell Univ. Pr.

Ehebruster, Marianne. Economic Boom - Blessing or Curse? Linking Economic Performance with Environmental Development by Analysing China's Water Resources. 2008. 116p. pap. (978-3-639-10339-7(4)) VDM Verlag Dr. Mueller e.K.

Elvin, Mark. The Retreat of the Elephants: An Environmental History of China. 2006. (ENG., Illus.). 592p. per. 24.00 (978-0-300-11993-0(3)) Yale Univ. Pr.

Elvin, Mark & Liu, Ts'ui-jung. Sediments of Time: Environment & Society in Chinese History, 2 vols. 2009. (Studies in Environment & History Ser.). (ENG., Illus.). 840p. pap. 100.00 (978-0-521-13569-6(9)) Cambridge Univ. Pr.

Fernández-Giménez, María Edith. Restoring Community Connections to the Land: Building Resilience Through Community-Based Rangeland Management in China & Mongolia. 2012. (Illus.). 272p. 125.00 (978-1-84593-894-9(1)); pap. 55.00 (978-1-84593-895-6(X)) CABI GBR. Dist: Stylus Publishing, LLC.

Fleming, Robert L., et al. Across the Tibetan Plateau: Ecosystems, Wildlife & Conservation. 2007. (ENG., Illus.). 120p. 49.95 (978-0-393-06117-8(5), 6117) Norton, W. W. & Co., Inc.

Fukao, Yoko & Yasutomi, Ayumu. Odo Kogen Midori o Tsumugidasu Hitobito: "Ryokusei" Shu Johitsu o Meguru Ugoki to Katari. 2010. (JPN., Illus.). 352p. (978-4-903235-14-1(9)) Seiun-sha.

Gao, Tao. Dust Storms in Northern China. 2011. (978-1-61209-778-7(2)) Nova Science Pubs., Inc.

Gil, Iker, ed. Shanghai Transforming. 2008. 272p. pap. (978-84-96954-66-3(8)) Actar Birkhauser Distribution.

Guo, Sujian. Environmental Protection Policy & Experience in the U. S. & China's Western Regions. 2010. (Challenges Facing Chinese Political Development Ser.). (ENG.) 214p. 62.99 (978-0-7391-4742-9(0)) Lexington Bks.

Han, Bo-Ping & Liu, Zhengwen, eds. Tropical & Sub-Tropical Reservoir Limnology in China: Theory & Practice. 2011. (Monographiae Biologicae Ser.). (ENG., Illus.). xiv, 369p. 209.00 (978-94-007-2006-0(8), 9400720068) Springer.

Hendrickson, Cary. Natural Resource Management & Local Development in Chin. 2011. 52p. pap. (978-3-8443-9363-7(3)) Lambert Academic Publishing.

Ho, Mun S. & Nielsen, Chris P., eds. Clearing the Air: The Health & Economic Damages of Air Pollution in China. 2007. (ENG., Illus.). 405p. (gr. 17). 53.00 (978-0-262-08358-4(2)) MIT Pr.

Huadong, Guo, ed. Atlas of Remote Sensing of the Wenchuan Earthquake. 2009. (ENG., Illus.). 259p. 159.95 (978-1-4398-1674-5(3), CRC Press) Taylor & Francis Group GBR. Dist: Taylor & Francis Group.

Jiang, Xiaoyi. Legal Issues for Implementing the Clean Development Mechanism in China. 2012. (ENG., Illus.). ix, 350p. 129.00 (978-3-642-24736-1(9), 3642247369) Springer.

Jiang, Zhenbai. Behind the Surface. 2010. 100p. pap. (978-3-8383-9134-2(9)) Lambert Academic Publishing.

Kong, Lingcheng & Xie, Jiaping. Xun Huan Jing Ji Tui Jin Zhan Lüe Yan Jiu: Xunhuanjingjituijinzhanlueyanjiu = Xunhuanjingji Tuijin Zhanlue Yanjiu. 2008. (CHI., Illus.). (978-7-80221-600-6(1)) China Modern Economic & Electronic Publishing Hse.

Lee, John Chi-Kin, et al. Schooling for Sustainable Development in Chinese Communities: Experience with Younger Children. Lee, John Chi-Kin & Williams, Michael, eds. 2009. (Schooling for Sustainable Development Ser.). (ENG., Illus.). 300p. 189.00 (978-1-4020-9685-3(2), 1402096852) Springer.

Lin, Aiming & Ren, Zhikun. The Great Wenchuan Earthquake of 2008: A Photographic Atlas of Surface Rupture & Related Disaster: A Photographic Atlas of Surface Rupture & Related Disaster. 2010. (ENG., Illus.). 120p. 139.00 (978-3-642-03758-0(5), 3642037585) Springer.

Madsen, D. B., et al, eds. Late Quaternary Climate Change & Human Adaptation in Arid China. 2007. (Developments in Quaternary Science Ser.: 9). (ENG., Illus.). 244p. 190.00 (978-0-444-52962-3(4), Elsevier Science) Elsevier Science & Technology Bks.

Marks, Robert. China: Its Environment & History. 2011. (978-1-4422-1277-0(2)); (ENG.). 464p. 42.95 (978-1-4422-1275-6(6)) Rowman & Littlefield Publishers, Inc.

Pang, Daomu. Sheng Tai Huan. 2010. (CHI., Illus.). (978-7-01-008561-6(7)) People's Publishing Hse., The.

Qin, B., et al. Eutrophication of Shallow Lakes with Special Reference to Lake Taihu, China. 2010. (Developments in Hydrobiology Ser.). viii, 328p. pap. 199.00 (978-90-481-7552-9(6), 9048175526) Springer.

Reiter, Florian C. Basic Conditions of Taoist Thunder Magic: Daojiao Lei Fa. 2007. (Abhandlungen Für Die Kunde des Morgenlandes Ser.). (GER & ENG.). 135p. (C). pap. 45.00 (978-3-447-05593-2(6)) Harrassowitz, Otto Verlag DEU. Dist: ISD.

Rooij, Benjamin Van. Regulating L & Pollution in China. 2006. (LUP Dissertaties Ser.). 472p. per. (978-90-8728-013-0(0), Leiden Univ. Pr.) Amsterdam Univ. Pr.

Schaller, George B. Tibet Wild: Journeys on the Roof of the World. 2012. (978-1-61091-172-6(5)) Island Pr.

Schröder, Miriam. Local Climate Governance in China: Hybrid Actors & Market Mechanisms. 2011. (International Political Economy Ser.). (ENG., Illus.). 248p. 85.00 (978-0-230-30161-0(4)) Palgrave Macmillan.

Shapiro, Judith. China's Environmental Challenges. 2012. (ENG.). 200p. 64.95 (978-0-7456-6090-5(8)); pap. 22.95 (978-0-7456-6091-2(6)) Polity Pr. GBR. Dist: Wiley, John & Sons, Inc.

Song, Liang & Woo, Wing Thye, eds. China's Dilemma: Economic Growth, the Environment & Climate Change. 2008. (Illus.). pap. (978-0-7315-3819-5(6)) Asia Pacific Pr.

Stafford, Brian. Environmental Aspects of China's Papermaking Fiber Supply. 2007. 28p. (978-1-932928-26-6(X)) Forest Trends.

Sukardjo, Sukristijono & Alongi, D. M. Mangroves of the South China Sea Ecology & Human Impacts on Indonesia's Forests. 2011. (Environmental Health - Physical, Chemical & Biological Factors Ser.). 230p. 75.00 (978-1-61470-358-1(5)) Nova Science Pubs., Inc.

Sun, Jichao & WANG, Guangqian. Riverbank Collapse Mechanism under Scouring. 2010. 104p. pap. (978-3-639-25360-3(4)) VDM Verlag Dr. Mueller e.K.

Sunderland, Terry C. H., et al, eds. Evidence-Based Conservation. 2012. (Earthscan Forest Library). (ENG., Illus.). 416p. (C). 125.00 (978-1-84971-394-8(4)) Routledge.

Talscott, Spencer B. Going Green in China: Policy & Potential. 2012. (978-1-62100-691-6(3)) Nova Science Pubs., Inc.

United Nations Environment Programme Staff, ed. Beijing 2008 Olympic Games an Environmental Review. 2007. (ENG.). 166p. 30.00 (978-92-807-2888-0(1)) United Nations Environment Programme KEN. Dist: National Bk. Network.

Wang, Weiguang, et al. China's Climate Change Policies. 2012. (ENG., Illus.). 292p. 155.00 (978-0-415-52085-0(1)); pap. 51.95 (978-1-84971-450-1(9)) Routledge.

Watts, Jonathan. When a Billion Chinese Jump: How China Will Save Mankind — Or Destroy It. 2010. (ENG., Illus.). 448p. pap. 17.00 (978-1-4165-8076-8(X), Scribner) Scribner.

Woo, Wing Thye & Song, Ligang. China's Dilemma: Economic Growth, the Environment & Climate Change. Song, Liang & Woo, Wing Thye, eds. 2008. (ENG., Illus.). 428p. pap. 32.95 (978-0-8157-3123-8(X)) Brookings Institution Pr.

Xie, Lei. Environmental Activism in China. (ENG., Illus.). 225p. 2011. pap. 42.95 (978-0-415-67339-6(9)) 2009. 150.00 (978-0-415-47869-4(3)) Routledge.

Xu, Xiangde, et al. Theory & Application for Warning & Prediction of Disastrous Weather Downstream from the Tibetan Plateau. 2012. pap. (978-1-62100-433-2(3)) Nova Science Pubs., Inc.

Yin, Runsheng, ed. An Integrated Assessment of China's Ecological Restoration Programs. 2009. (ENG., Illus.). xvi, 471p. 169.00 (978-90-481-2654-5(1), 9048126541) Springer.

Zeng, Ka & Eastin, Joshua. Greening China: The Benefits of Trade & Foreign Direct Investment. 2011. (Michigan Studies in International Political Economy Ser.). (ENG., Illus.). 250p. 65.00 (978-0-472-11768-0(8)) Univ. of Michigan Pr.

Zhou, Yong & Wu, Desheng Dash, eds. Modeling Risk Management for Resources & Environment in China. 2011. (Computational Risk Management Ser.). (ENG., Illus.). xiii, 576p. 189.00 (978-3-642-18386-7(7), 3642183867) Springer.

CHINA—ETHNIC RELATIONS

Abramson, Marc S. & Abramson, Marc Samuel. Ethnic Identity in Tang China. 2007. (Encounters with Asia Ser.). 288p. (C). 59.95 (978-0-8122-4052-8(9)) Univ. of Pennsylvania Pr.

Ashraf, Lubna & Syed, M. N. Wedding Cry ~ Death Dance: An Insight into Chinese Culture: an Ethnographic Study of Xuan'en, Hubei with Special Emphasis on Tujia Rites of Passage. 2008. (ENG.). 252p. pap. 39.50 (978-0-9801675-8-0(2)) Robertson Publishing.

Bai, Lian. Evolving On-Line Empowerment: The Manchu Identity Revival since the 1980s. 2008. 48p. (978-1-932330-25-0(9)) Maryland Series in Contemporary Studies.

Bellér-Hann, I. & Bellér-Hann, Ildikó. Community Matters in Xinjiang, 1880-1949: Towards a Historical Anthropology of the Uyghur. 2008. (China Studies). (Illus.). 500p. (978-90-04-16675-2(0)) BRILL.

Bovingdon, Gardner. The Uyghurs: Strangers in Their Own Land. 2010. (ENG., Illus.). 304p. (gr. 17). 45.00 (978-0-231-14758-3(9)) Columbia Univ. Pr.

Bulag, Uradyn E. Collaborative Nationalism: The Politics of Friendship on China's Mongolian Frontier. 2010. (Asia/Pacific/Perspectives Ser.). (ENG., Illus.). 302p. 85.00 (978-1-4422-0431-7(1)) Rowman & Littlefield Publishers, Inc.

Chan, Yeeshan. Abandoned Japanese in Postwar Manchuria. 2011. (Japan Anthropology Workshop Ser.). (ENG., Illus.). 208p. (C). 140.00 (978-0-415-59181-2(3)) Routledge.

Chen, Sanping. Multicultural China in the Early Middle Ages. 2012. (Encounters with Asia Ser.). 320p. (C). 79.95 (978-0-8122-4370-3(6)) Univ. of Pennsylvania Pr.

Cheng, Hsin-I. Culturing Interface: Identity, Communication, & Chinese Transnationalism. 2008. (Critical Intercultural Communication Studies: Vol. 11). 236p. (C). 69.95 (978-1-4331-0235-6(8)) Lang, Peter Publishing, Inc.

Deal, David. The Art of Ethnography: A Chinese Miao Album. Hostetler, Laura, tr. 2007. (Studies on Ethnic Groups in China). (ENG., Illus.). 208p. per. 22.50 (978-0-295-98616-6(6)) Univ. of Washington Pr.

Eber, Irene, tr. & intro. Voices from Shanghai: Jewish Exiles in Wartime China. 2008. (ENG., Illus.). 144p. 29.00 (978-0-226-18166-0(9)) Univ. of Chicago Pr.

Ehrlich, Avrum M. Jews & Judaism in Modern China. 2009. (ENG.). 292p. 135.00 (978-0-415-45716-3(5)) Routledge.

Ehrlich, M. Avrum. The Jewish-Chinese Nexus: A Meeting of Civilizations. Ehrlich, Avrum M., ed. 2008. (Routledge Jewish Studies Ser.). (Illus.). XXXIV, 294p. 140.00 (978-0-415-45715-6(7)) Routledge.

Ehrlich, M. Avrum, ed. The Jewish-Chinese Nexus. 2010. (Illus.). 328p. pap. 39.95 (978-0-415-59341-0(7)) Routledge.

Fong, Eric, et al, eds. Immigrant Adaptation in Multiethnic Societies. 2012. (Routledge Advances in Sociology Ser.: 78). (ENG., Illus.). 256p. (C). 125.00 (978-0-415-62854-9(7)) Routledge.

Guo, Xiaolin. State & Ethnicity in China's Southwest. 2008. (China Studies Ser.). (Illus.). 320p. (978-90-04-16775-9(7)) BRILL.

Gurung, Vikram. Gurung: A language in retreat in Hong Kong. 2009. 92p. pap. (978-3-639-13078-2(2)) VDM Verlag Dr. Mueller e.K.

Haibo, Yu. Identity & Schooling among the Naxi: Becoming Chinese with Naxi Identity. 2009. (Emerging Perspectives on Education in China Ser.). (ENG., Illus.). 252p. 73.50 (978-0-7391-3290-6(3)) Lexington Bks.

Hansen, Mette Halskov. Frontier People: Han Settlers in Minority Areas of China. 2007. (ENG., Illus.). 280p. pap. 29.95 (978-0-7748-1179-8(X)) UBC Pr. CAN. Dist: Univ. of Washington Pr.

Heberer, Thomas. Doing Business in Rural China: Liangshan's New Ethnic Entrepreneurs. 2007. (Studies on Ethnic Groups in China). (ENG., Illus.). 280p. 50.00 (978-0-295-98729-3(4)) Univ. of Washington Pr.

Jin, Wen. Pluralist Universalism: An Asian Americanist Critique of U.S. & Chinese Multiculturalisms. 2012. 280p. 52.95 (978-0-8142-1187-8(9)); cd-rom 14.95 (978-0-8142-9288-4(7)) Ohio State Univ. Pr.

Johnson, M. Dujon. Race & Racism in the Chinas: Chinese Racial attitudes toward Africans & African-Americans. 2007. 168p. per. 15.95 (978-1-4259-8175-4(5)) AuthorHouse.

Kaltman, Blaine. Under the Heel of the Dragon: Islam, Racism, Crime, & the Uighur in China. 2007. (Ohio RIS Global Ser.). (Illus.). 152p. per. 24.00 (978-0-89680-254-4(X)) Ohio Univ. Pr.

Khoo, Olivia. The Chinese Exotic: Modern Diasporic Femininity. 2007. (TransAsia: Screen Cultures Ser.). (ENG., Illus.). 228p. (gr. 17). 60.00 (978-962-209-879-4(7)) Hong Kong Univ. Pr. HKG. Dist: Columbia Univ. Pr.

Lee, Joseph Tse-Hei, et al. Marginalization in China: Recasting Minority Politics. Lee, Joseph Tse-Hei et al, eds. 2009. (ENG., Illus.). 276p. 105.00 (978-0-230-61423-9(X)) Palgrave Macmillan.

Lei, Daphne. Operatic China: Staging Chinese Identity Across the Pacific. 2006. (Palgrave Studies in Theatre & Performance History Ser.). (ENG., Illus.). 360p. 89.00 (978-1-4039-7327-6(X)) Palgrave Macmillan.

Leibold, James. Reconfiguring Chinese Nationalism: How the Qing Frontier & Its Indigenes Became Chinese. 2007. (ENG.). 288p. 95.00 *(978-1-4039-7479-2(9))* Palgrave Macmillan.

Lin, Gan. Zhongguo Gu Dai Bei Fang Min Zu Tong Lun. 2010. (CHI., Illus.). *(978-7-01-008621-7(4))* People's Publishing Hse., The.

Lin, Hsiao-Ting. Modern China's Ethnic Frontiers: A Journey to the West. 2010. (Routledge Studies in the Modern History of Asia Ser.). (ENG., Illus.). 224p. (C). 125.00 *(978-0-415-58264-3(4))* Routledge.

Liu, Xiaoyuan. Recast All under Heaven: Revolution, War, Diplomacy, & Frontier China in the 20th Century. 2010. (ENG., Illus.). 288p. 120.00 *(978-1-4411-6220-5(8))*; pap. 34.95 *(978-1-4411-3489-9(1))* Continuum International Publishing Group, Ltd. GBR. Dist: National Bk. Network.

Mackerras, Colin. Ethnic Minorities in Modern China: Critical Concepts in Asian Studies. 2011. *(978-0-415-57653-6(9))*; *(978-0-415-57654-3(7))*; *(978-0-415-57656-7(3))* Routledge.

—Ethnic Minorities in Modern China Vol. 2: Critical Concepts in Asian Studies. 2011. *(978-0-415-57655-0(5))* Routledge.

Mackerras, Colin, ed. Ethnic Minorities in Modern China, 4 vols. 2011. (Critical Concepts in Asian Studies). (ENG.). 1760p. 1295.00 *(978-0-415-57393-1(9))* Routledge.

Mallory, J. P. & Mair, Victor H. The Tarim Mummies: Ancient China & the Mystery of the Earliest Peoples from the West. 2008. (ENG., Illus.). 352p. pap. 29.95 *(978-0-500-28372-1(9))* Thames & Hudson.

Mathieu, Christine & Ho, Cindy, eds. Ancestral Realms of the Naxi: Quentin Roosevelt's China. 2011. (ENG., Illus.). 200p. 70.00 *(978-3-89790-343-2(1))* Arnoldsche Art Pubs. DEU. Dist: Antique Collectors' Club.

McCarthy, Susan K. Communist Multiculturalism: Ethnic Revival in Southwest China. 2009. (ENG., Illus.). 248p. 70.00 *(978-0-295-98908-2(4))*; pap. 25.00 *(978-0-295-98909-9(2))* Univ. of Washington Pr.

Michael Hsiao, Hsin-Huang, ed. Chinese Middle Classes: China, Taiwan, Macao & Hong Kong. 2013. (Routledge Contemporary China Ser.). (ENG.). 240p. (C). 125.00 *(978-0-415-67726-4(2))* Routledge.

Notar, Beth E. Displacing Desire: Travel & Popular Culture in China. 2007. (Illus.). 193p. per. 23.00 *(978-0-8248-3071-7(7))* Univ. of Hawaii Pr.

Ou, Chaoquan. Life in a Kam Village in Southwest China, 1930-49. 2007. (Illus.). 250p. *(978-90-04-16229-7(1))* BRILL.

Park, Yoon Jung. A Matter of Honour: Being Chinese in South Africa. 2009. (AsiaWorld Ser.). (ENG., Illus.). 248p. 70.00 *(978-0-7391-3553-2(8))* Lexington Bks.

Shin, Leo K. The Making of the Chinese State: Ethnicity & Expansion on the Ming Borderlands. 2011. (ENG.). 270p. pap. 50.00 *(978-0-521-18989-7(6))* Cambridge Univ. Pr.

Thuno, Mette, ed. Beyond Chinatown: New Chinese Migration & the Global Expansion of China. 2007. (Nias Studies in Asian Topics Ser.). (Illus.). 281p. pap. 27.00 *(978-87-7694-000-3(4))* Nordic Institute of Asian Studies DNK. Dist: Univ. of Hawaii Pr.

Toda, Ikuko. Chugoku Chosenzoku o Ikiru: Kyu Manshu No Kioku. (JPN., Illus.). xiii, 296p. *(978-4-00-023870-0(1)*, Nicholson) Iwanami Shoten.

Yu, Yeon Jung. China's Korean Minority. 2008. 72p. pap. *(978-3-639-05057-8(6))* VDM Verlag Dr. Mueller e.K.

Yunnan Sheng bian ji zu Staff & "Zhongguo shao shu min zu she hui li shi diao cha zi liao cong kan" xiu ding bian ji wei yuan hui Staff, contrib. by. Zhong Yang Fang Wen Tuan Di Er Fen Tuan Yunnan Min Zu Qing Kuang Hui Ji: Zhongyangfangwentuandierfentuanyunnanminzuqingkuanghuiji, 2 vols. 2009. (CHI.). *(978-7-105-08871-3(0))*; *(978-7-105-08872-0(9))* Nationalities Publishing Hse, The.

Zang, Xiaowei. Ethnicity & Urban Life in China: A Comparative Study of Hui Muslims & Han Chinese. (Illus.). 2011. (ENG.). 208p. pap. 42.95 ***(978-0-415-66643-5(0))*** 2007. 184p. 160.00 *(978-0-415-42120-1(9))* Routledge.

Zhou, Minglang & Hill, Ann Maxwell, eds. Affirmative Action in China & the U. S. A Dialogue on Inequality & Minority Education. 2010. (Comparative & Developmental Education Ser.). (ENG.). 284p. pap. 29.00 *(978-0-230-61334-8(9))* Palgrave Macmillan.

CHINA—FOREIGN ECONOMIC RELATIONS

Alden, Chris. China in Africa: Partner, Competitor or Hegemon? 2007. (African Arguments Ser.). (ENG., Illus.). 180p. 81.00 *(978-1-84277-863-0(3))*; 154p. per. 23.00 *(978-1-84277-864-7(1))* Zed Bks., Ltd. GBR. Dist: Macmillan.

Amitendu, Palit. China-India Economics. 2011. (Routledge Studies in the Growth Economies of Asia Ser.). (ENG., Illus.). 216p. (C). 136.00 *(978-0-415-59831-6(1))* Routledge.

Ampiah, Kweku & Naidu, Sanusha. Crouching Tiger, Hidden Dragon? Africa & China. Ampiah, Kweku & Naidu, Sanusha, eds. 2008. (Illus.). 357p. (C). pap. 44.95 *(978-1-86914-150-9(4))* University of Kwazulu-Natal Press ZAF. Dist: International Specialized Bk. Services.

Bangui, Thierry. China: A New Partner for Africa's Development - Are We Heading for the End of European Privileges on the Black Continent? 2012. (Asian Political, Economic & Security Issues Ser.). 210p. 95.00 ***(978-1-61324-923-9(3))*** Nova Science Pubs., Inc.

Barnett, S. A. & Sladkovskii, M. I. History of Economic Relations Between Russia & China: From Modernization to Maoism. 2007. (ENG.). 311p. (gr. 11). pap. 49.95 *(978-1-4128-0639-8(9))* Transaction Pubs.

Bergsten, C. Fred, et al. China's Rise: Challenges & Opportunities. (Illus.). 2009. 280p. pap. 13.95 *(978-0-88132-434-1(5))* 2008. 256p. 26.95 *(978-0-88132-417-4(5))* Peterson Institute for International Economics.

Berik, Günseli, et al, eds. Gender, China & the World Trade Organization: Essays from Feminist Economics. 2012. (ENG.). 344p. (C). pap. 42.95 ***(978-0-415-62335-3(9))*** Routledge.

Brand China: Global Perceptions & Representations. 2010. 304p. pap. 95.00 *(978-1-933782-22-5(6))* Berkshire Publishing Group.

Breslin, Shaun. China & the Global Political Economy. 2009. (ENG.). 246p. pap. 37.00 *(978-0-230-57793-0(8))* Palgrave Macmillan.

Broadman, Harry G. Africa's Silk Road: China & India's New Economic Frontier. 2006. (Stand Alones Ser.). (ENG., Illus.). 384p. per. 25.00 *(978-0-8213-6835-0(4)*, 9780821368350) World Bank Pubns.

Brown, Kerry. The Rise of the Dragon: Inward & Outward Investment in China in the Reform Period,1978-2007. 2008. (Chandos Asian Studies). (ENG., Illus.). 242p. per. 50.00 *(978-1-84334-481-0(5)*, Chandos Publishing) Woodhead Publishing Ltd. GBR. Dist: Ingram Pub. Services.

Brown, Seyom. Taiwan at a Turning Point. 2009. (Illus.). 98p. pap. *(978-1-932330-26-7(7))* Univ. of Maryland, Schl. of Law.

Cai, Tuo, ed. Chinese Perspectives on Globalization & Autonomy. 2012. (Issues in Contemporary Chinese Thought & Culture Ser.). (ENG.). xv, 376p. ***(978-90-04-21615-0(4))*** BRILL.

Cao, Tian Yu. The Chinese Model of Modern Development. 2009. 324p. 41.95 *(978-0-415-55525-8(6))* Routledge.

Casey, Michael J. The Unfair Trade: How Our Broken Global Financial System Destroys the Middle Class. 2012. (ENG.). 416p. 28.00 ***(978-0-307-88530-2(5)***, Crown Business) Crown Publishing Group.

Chen, Chunlai, ed. China's Integration with the Global Economy: WTO Accession, Foreign Direct Investment & International Trade. 2009. (Advances in Chinese Economic Studies). (Illus.). 240p. 119.00 *(978-1-84844-214-6(9))* Elgar, Edward Publishing, Inc.

Cheng, Shaoming. Preference Heterogeneity & Industrial Location: Location choices of Japanese FDI in China. 2007. 196p. per. *(978-3-8364-1650-4(6))* VDM Verlag Dr. Mueller e.K.

Cheung, Gordon C. K. & Cheung, Gordon. China Factors: Political Perspectives & Economic Interactions. 2007. (ENG.). 177p. (gr. 11). 49.95 *(978-0-7658-0342-9(9))* Transaction Pubs.

Cheung, Yin-Wong. China & Asia: Economic & Financial Interactions. Wong, Kar-yiu, ed. 2009. (Routledge Studies in the Modern World Economy Ser.). (Illus.). XVIII, 302p. 160.00 *(978-0-415-77609-7(0))* Routledge.

Cheung, Yin-Wong, et al. The Economic Integration of Greater China: Real & Financial Linkages & the Prospects for Currency Union. 2007. (ENG., Illus.). 172p. (gr. 17). 59.50 *(978-962-209-822-0(3))* Hong Kong Univ. Pr. HKG. Dist: Columbia Univ. Pr.

Chin, Gregory T. China's Automotive Modernization: The Party-State & Multinational Corporations. 2010. (International Political Economy Ser.). (ENG., Illus.). 304p. 100.00 *(978-0-230-22060-7(6))* Palgrave Macmillan.

Chow, Gregory C. China As a Leader of the World Economy. 2011. 54.00 ***(978-981-4368-79-7(2))***; pap. 28.00 ***(978-981-4368-80-3(6))*** World Scientific Publishing Co., Inc.

Chu. China's Accession to the Wto & Its Impact on Asian Economies. 2007. 304p. *(978-1-84542-842-6(0))* Elgar, Edward Publishing, Inc.

Chua, Christian. Chinese Big Business in Indonesia: The State of Capital. 2008. (Routledge Contemporary Southeast Asia Ser.). (Illus.). XVI, 176p. 150.00 *(978-0-415-45074-4(8))* Routledge.

Chung, Tan & Uberoi, Patricia. Rise of the Asian Giants: The Dragon-Elephant Tango. 2009. (Anthem Press India Ser.). (ENG.). 250p. 100.00 *(978-81-905835-9-6(X))* Anthem Pr. GBR. Dist: Books International, Inc.

Cooke, Jennifer. U. S. & Chinese Engagement in Africa: Prospects for Improving U. S. -China-Africa Cooperation. 2008. 68p. pap. 16.95 *(978-0-89206-538-7(9)*, CSIS Pr., The) Ctr. for Strategic & International Studies.

Council on Foreign Relations Staff. Beyond Humanitarianism: What You Need to Know about Africa & Why it Matters. 2007. 240p. pap. 17.95 *(978-0-87609-375-7(6))* Council on Foreign Relations.

Cram101 Textbook Reviews & Cram101 Textbook Reviews. Outlines & Highlights for Economic Openness & Territorial Politics in China by Yumin Sheng. 2011. 212p. pap. 30.95 ***(978-1-61830-592-3(1))*** Cram101 Inc.

Curtis, Emily Byrne. Glass Exchange Between Europe & China, 1550-1800: Diplomatic, Mercantile & Technological Interactions. 2009. (Transculturalisms 1400-1700 Ser.). (Illus.). 174p. 114.95 *(978-0-7546-6316-4(7))* Ashgate Publishing Co.

Dent, Christopher M., ed. China-Africa Development Relations. 2010. (Routledge Contemporary China Ser.). (ENG., Illus.). 208p. (C). 138.00 *(978-0-415-56933-0(8))* Routledge.

Dezan Shira & Associates, et al, eds. China's Neighbors: Who Is Influencing China & Who China Is Influencing in the New Emerging Asia. 3rd ed. 2012. (China Briefing Ser.). (ENG., Illus.). viii, 87p. pap. 49.95 ***(978-3-642-27614-9(8)***, 3642276148) Springer.

Dittmer, Lowell & Yu, George T., eds. China, the Developing World, & the New Global Dynamic. 2009. (Illus.). 255p. (C). 59.95 *(978-1-58826-700-9(8))*; pap. 22.50 *(978-1-58826-726-9(1))* Rienner, Lynne Pubs.

Dyke, Paul A. Van. Merchants of Hong Kong & Macau: Vol. 1: Politics & Strategies in Eighteenth Century Trade. 2011. (Illus.). 656p. ***(978-988-8053-77-3(9))*** Hong Kong Univ. Pr.

Faure, Michael & Zhang, Xinzhu, eds. Competition Policy & Regulation: Recent Developments in China, the US & Europe. 2011. (Illus.). 368p. 160.00 ***(978-1-84980-075-4(8))*** Elgar, Edward Publishing, Inc.

Feng, Lei. Hai Xia Liang an Jing Ji He Zuo Mo Shi Yan Jiu: Study on Cross-Straits Economic & Trade Cooperation Pattern. 2009. (CHI., Illus.). *(978-7-5097-0775-3(7))* China Social Science Documentation Publishing Hse.

Fung, K. C. & Garcia Herrero, Alicia, eds. Sino-Latin American Economic Relations. 2011. (Routledge Contemporary China Ser.). (ENG., Illus.). 320p. (C). 135.00 *(978-0-415-68172-8(3))* Routledge.

Gilboy, George J. & Heginbotham, Eric. Chinese & Indian Strategic Behavior: Growing Power & Alarm. 2012. (ENG.). 384p. pap. 34.99 ***(978-1-107-66169-1(2))***; (Illus.). 99.00 ***(978-1-107-02005-4(0))*** Cambridge Univ. Pr.

Gill, Bates & Murphy, Melissa. China-Europe Relations: Implication & Policy Responses for the United States. 2008. 60p. pap. 16.95 *(978-0-89206-533-2(8)*, CSIS Pr., The) Ctr. for Strategic & International Studies.

Gipouloux, François. The Asian Mediterranean: Port Cities & Trading Networks in China, Japan & South Asia, 13th-21st Century. 2011. (Illus.). 400p. 160.00 ***(978-0-85793-426-0(0))*** Elgar, Edward Publishing, Inc.

Gomez, Terence E. Chinese Business in Malaysia: Accumulation, Accommodation & Ascendance. 2012. (ENG.). 234p. pap. 44.95 ***(978-0-415-51737-9(0))*** Routledge.

Greenaway, David, et al, eds. China & the World Economy. 2010. (ENG., Illus.). 304p. 105.00 *(978-0-230-52152-0(5))* Palgrave Macmillan.

Gu, George Zhibin. China & the New World Order: How Entrepreneurship, Globalization, & Borderless Business Are Reshaping China & the World. 2006. 248p. 29.99 *(978-1-59682-108-8(6))*; pap. 22.99 *(978-1-59682-107-1(8))* Fultus Corp. (Fultus Publishing).

Guo, Sujian & Guo, Baogang. Greater China in an Era of Globalization. 2009. (Challenges Facing Chinese Political Development Ser.). (ENG.). 248p. 73.50 *(978-0-7391-3534-1(1))* Rowman & Littlefield Publishers, Inc.

Halper, Stefan. The Beijing Consensus: Legitimizing Authoritarianism in Our Time. 2012. (ENG.). 336p. (gr. 9). pap. 17.99 *(978-0-465-02523-7(4))* Basic Bks.

He, Kai. Institutional Balancing in the Asia Pacific: Economic Interdependence & China's Rise. 2008. (Illus.). 224p. 160.00 *(978-0-415-46952-4(X))* Routledge.

He, Kai. Institutional Balancing in the Asia Pacific: Economic Interdependence & China's Rise. 2012. (Routledge Contemporary China Ser.). (ENG., Illus.). 224p. (C). pap. 42.95 ***(978-0-415-54147-3(6))*** Routledge.

Hearn, Adrian H. & Manríquez, José Luis León, eds. China Engages Latin America: Tracing the Trajectory. 2011. (Illus.). 250p. 65.00 *(978-1-58826-767-2(9))* Rienner, Lynne Pubs.

Hickey, Dennis & Guo, Baogang. Dancing with the Dragon: China's Emergence in the Developing World. 2010. *(978-0-7391-4066-6(3))* Lexington Bks.

Hickey, Dennis & Guo, Baogang, eds. Dancing with the Dragon: China's Emergence in the Developing World. 2010. (Challenges Facing Chinese Political Development Ser.). (ENG.). 240p. 68.50 *(978-0-7391-4065-9(5))* Lexington Bks.

Ho, Lok Sang & Wong, John. Apec & the Rise of China. 2011. 248p. 85.00 *(978-981-4329-40-8(1))* World Scientific Publishing Co., Inc.

Hock, Saw, ed. Asean-China Economic Relations. 2006. (Illus.). 392p. *(978-981-230-422-3(3))* Institute of Southeast Asian Studies.

Investing in Tragedy: China's Money, Arms, & Politics in Sudan. 2008. pap. 10.00 *(978-0-9799975-1-8(8))* Human Rights First.

Isin, Engin F. Citizenship Between Past & Future. Nyers, Peter & Turner, Bryan S., eds. 2008. (ENG.). 176p. (C). 140.00 *(978-0-415-45441-4(7))* Routledge.

Jilberto, Alex E., et al, eds. Latin America Facing China: South-South Relations Beyond the Washington Concensus. 2010. (CEDLA Ser.). (Illus.). 216p. 75.00 *(978-1-84545-739-6(0))* Berghahn Bks., Inc.

Kang, Yuanfei. Performance & Network Governance in International Joint Ventures. 2010. 348p. pap. *(978-3-639-10623-7(7))* VDM Verlag Dr. Mueller e.K.

Kastner, Scott L. Political Conflict & Economic Interdependence Across the Taiwan Strait & Beyond. 2009. (Studies in Asian Security Ser.). (ENG., Illus.). 256p. 70.00 *(978-0-8047-6203-8(1))* Stanford Univ. Pr.

Kastner, Scott L. & Kastner, Scott. Political Conflict & Economic Interdependence Across the Taiwan Strait & Beyond. 2009. (Studies in Asian Security). (ENG., Illus.). 256p. pap. 24.95 *(978-0-8047-6204-5(X))* Stanford Univ. Pr.

Keller, William W. & Rawski, Thomas G., eds. China's Rise & the Balance of Influence in Asia. 2007. (Pitt Security Continuum Ser.). (Illus.). 328p. (C). per. 27.95 *(978-0-8229-5967-0(4))*; 284p. 65.00 *(978-0-8229-4312-9(3))* Univ. of Pittsburgh Pr.

Kessler, Martha B. Trade Barriers & China. 2008. 132p. pap. 50.00 *(978-1-60456-686-4(8))* Nova Science Pubs., Inc.

Khanna, Tarun. Billions of Entrepreneurs: How China & India Are Reshaping Their Futures — and Yours. 2011. (ENG.). 368p. pap. 16.95 *(978-1-4221-5728-2(8))* Harvard Business Review Pr.

—Billions of Entrepreneurs: How China & India Are Reshaping Their Futures & Yours. 2007. (ENG.). 353p. 29.95 *(978-1-4221-0383-8(8))* Harvard Business Review Pr.

Kraft, Christian. Joining the WTO: The Impact of Trade, Competition & Redistributive Conflicts on China's Accession to the World Trade Organization. 2007. (European University Studies 31 Ser.: Vol. 550). (Illus.). 174p. pap. *(978-3-631-56773-9(1))* Lang, Peter AG.

Kunzmann, Klaus, et al. China & Europe: The Implications of the Rise of China As a Global Economic Power for Europe. 2009. (Regions & Cities Ser.). (ENG., Illus.). 304p. (C). 130.00 *(978-0-415-55060-4(2))* Routledge.

Kynge, James. China Shakes the World: A Titan's Rise & Troubled Future — & the Challenge for America. 2006. (Edition 001 Ser.). (ENG.). 288p. 25.00 *(978-0-618-70564-1(3))* Houghton Mifflin Harcourt Trade & Reference Pubs.

—China Shakes the World: A Titan's Rise & Troubled Future - And the Challenge for America. 2007. (Edition 001 Ser.). (ENG.). 288p. per. 14.95 *(978-0-618-91906-2(6)*, Mariner Bks.) Houghton Mifflin Harcourt Trade & Reference Pubs.

Lam, Lai Sing. The International Environment & China's Twin Models of Development. 287p. pap. 69.95 *(978-3-03911-030-8(6))*; 2007. pap. 69.95 *(978-0-8204-9319-0(8))* Lang, Peter Publishing, Inc.

Lanteigne. China & International Institutions. 2007. pap. 39.95 *(978-0-415-45956-3(7))* Routledge.

Larcon. Chinese Multinationals. 2008. (Illus.). xxx, 269p. pap. 32.00 *(978-981-283-559-8(8))* World Scientific Publishing Co., Inc.

Li, Mingjiang & Kwa, Chong Guan. China-ASEAN Sub-Regional Cooperation: Progress, Problems & Prospect. 2011. xiii, 172p. ***(978-981-4340-42-7(1))*** World Scientific Publishing Co., Inc.

Lim, Hua Sing. Japan & China in East Asian Integration. 5th ed. 2008. (Illus.). xxxvii, 371p. pap. *(978-981-230-744-6(3))* Institute of Southeast Asian Studies.

Lim, Tai-Wei. Oil & Gas in China: The New Energy Superpower's Relations with Its Region. 2009. xviii, 161p. 111.00 *(978-981-4277-95-2(9))* World Scientific Publishing Co., Inc.

Liu. EUrope China Tax Treaties. 2010. xx, 298p. *(978-90-411-3216-1(3))* Kluwer Law International.

Liu, Guoguang, et al, eds. The China Economy Yearbook, Volume 1: Analysis & Forecast of China's Economy. 2008. (Chinese Academy of Social Sciences Yearbooks: Society Ser.). (Illus.). 451p. *(978-90-04-15638-8(0))* BRILL.

Liu, Yong. The Dutch East India Company's Tea Trade with China, 1757-1781. 2006. (Tanap Monographs on the History of the Asian-European Interaction Ser.: Vol. 6). (Illus.). 277p. lib. bdg. *(978-90-04-15599-2(6))* BRILL.

Lo, Chi. Phantom of the China Economic Threat: Shadow of the Next Asian Crisis DISTRIBUTION CANCELLED. 2008. (ENG.). 204p. pap. 42.50 *(978-0-230-51544-4(4))* Palgrave Macmillan.

Lyman, Princeton N. & Dorff, Patricia, eds. Beyond Humanitarianism: What You Need to Know about Africa & Why It Matters. 2007. (ENG.). 252p. per. 19.95 *(978-0-87609-371-9(3))* Council on Foreign Relations.

MacDonald, Greg, et al. Innovation in Chin: The Dawning of the Asian Century. 2008. 268p. per. *(978-1-905068-82-1(4))* Adonis & Abbey Publishers Ltd.

Marafa, Lawal Mohammed. African Business & Development Relationship with China: Seeking Moral & Capital Values of the Last Economic Frontier. 2009. (NAI Discussion Papers). 30p. pap. 12.95 *(978-91-7106-645-9(4))* Nordiska Afrikainstitutet SWE. Dist: Stylus Publishing, LLC.

Marcelo, Olarreaga, et al, eds. China's & India's Challenge to Latin America: Opportunity or Threat? 2008. (Latin American Development Forum Ser.). (ENG., Illus.). 360p. (C). pap. 35.00 *(978-0-8213-7308-8(0)*, 9780821373088) World Bank Pubns.

McGregor, James. One Billion Customers: Lessons from the Front Lines of Doing Business in China. 2007. (ENG.). 352p. pap. 15.99 *(978-0-7432-5841-8(X)*, Free Pr.) Free Pr.

Mengkui, Wang. China in the Wake of Asia's Financial Crisis. 2008. (Illus.). 320p. 180.00 *(978-0-415-46469-7(2))* Routledge.

Meredith, Robyn. The Elephant & the Dragon: The Rise of India & China & What It Means for All of Us. 2008. (ENG., Illus.). 256p. pap. 16.95 *(978-0-393-33193-6(8)*, 33193) Norton, W. W. & Co., Inc.

Michel, Serge & Beuret, Michel. China Safari: On the Trail of Beijing's Expansion in Africa. 2010. (ENG.). 336p. (gr. 9). pap. 17.50 *(978-1-56858-614-4(0)*, Nation Bks.) Basic Bks.

Monson, Jamie. Africa's Freedom Railway: How a Chinese Development Project Changed Lives & Livelihoods in Tanzania. 2011. (ENG., Illus.). 216p. pap. 24.95 *(978-0-253-22322-7(9)*, 0253223229) Indiana Univ. Pr.

Moran, Theodore. China's Strategy to Secure Natural Resources: Risks, Dangers, & Opportunities. 2010. 96p. pap. 19.95 *(978-0-88132-512-6(0))* Peterson Institute for International Economics.

Morrissey, Oliver & Zgovu, Evious. The Impact of China & India on Sub-Saharan Africa: Opportunities, Challenges & Policies. 2011. (ENG., Illus.). 90p. pap. 24.95 *(978-1-84929-055-5(5))* Commonwealth Secretariat GBR. Dist: Stylus Publishing, LLC.

Moyo, Dambisa. Winner Take All: China's Push for Resources & What It Means for the World. 2012. (ENG.). 240p. (gr. 9). 26.99 ***(978-0-465-02828-3(4))*** Basic Bks.

Nakano, Yoshiko. Where There Are Asians, There Are Rice Cookers: How 'national' Went Global Via Hong Kong. 2009. (Illus.). 228p. *(978-988-8028-07-8(3))* Hong Kong Univ. Pr.

Napoleoni, Loretta. Maonomics: Why Chinese Communists Make Better Capitalists Than We Do. Twilley, Stephen, tr. from ITA. 2011. (ENG., Illus.). 384p. 26.95 *(978-1-60980-341-4(8))* Seven Stories Pr.

Navarro, Peter. The Coming China Wars: Where They Will Be Fought & How They Can Be Won. 2nd exp. ed. 2008. (ENG.). 240p. pap. 15.99 *(978-0-13-235982-5(0))* FT Press.

—The Coming China Wars: Where They Will Be Fought & How They Can Be Won. 2006. (ENG., Illus.). 288p. 24.99 *(978-0-13-228128-7(7))* Prentice Hall PTR.

Nolan, Peter. Integrating China: Towards the Coordinated Market Economy. 2007. (Anthem Studies in Development & Globalization Ser.). (ENG., Illus.). 281p. 80.00 *(978-1-84331-237-6(9))* Anthem Pr. GBR. Dist: Books International, Inc.

Pant, Harsh. China's Rising Global Profile: The Great Power Tradition. 2012. (ENG.). 132p. pap. 24.95 **(978-1-84519-517-5(5))** Sussex Academic Pr. GBR. Dist: International Specialized Bk. Services.
Pant, Harsh V. China's Rising Global Profile: The Great Power Tradition. 2011. 132p. 45.00 (978-1-84519-457-4(8)) Sussex Academic Pr. GBR. Dist: International Specialized Bk. Services.
Patterson, Wayne. In the Service of His Korean Majesty: William Nelson Lovatt, the Pusan Customs, & Sino-Korea Relations, 1876-1888. 2011. **(978-1-55729-100-4(4))** Univ. of California, Institute of East Asian Studies.
Paus, Eva, et al. Global Giant: Is China Changing the Rules of the Game? 2009. (ENG.). 288p. 100.00 (978-0-230-61588-5(0)); pap. 44.00 (978-0-230-61589-2(9)) Palgrave Macmillan.
Powell, Barneby & Meckinnon, Alex. China Calling: A Foot in the Global Door. 2008. (ENG., Illus.). 256p. 53.00 (978-0-230-21019-6(8)) Palgrave Macmillan.
Quan, Rose. Outward Investment from Emerging Markets: Experiences of Chinese SME Managers. 2010. (Illus.). viii, 260p. pap. (978-3-8383-4014-2(0)) Lambert Academic Publishing.
Raine, Sarah. China's African Challenges. 2009. (Adelphi Ser.). (ENG., Illus.). 270p. pap. 19.95 (978-0-415-55693-4(7)) Routledge.
Rosen, Daniel & Whang, Zhi. The Implications of China-Taiwan Economic Liberalization. 2010. pap. 21.95 (978-0-88132-501-0(5)) Peterson Institute for International Economics.
Rotberg, Robert I., ed. China into Africa: Trade, Aid, & Influence. 2008. (ENG., Illus.). 339p. pap. 29.95 (978-0-8157-7561-4(X)) Brookings Institution Pr.
Saee, John, ed. China & the Global Economy in the 21st Century. 2011. (Routledge Studies in the Growth Economies of Asia Ser.). (ENG., Illus.). 224p. (C). 130.00 (978-0-415-67051-7(9)) Routledge.
Santiso, Javier, ed. The Visible Hand of China in Latin America. 2007. (ENG., Illus.). 200p. per. 45.00 (978-92-64-02796-1(3)) Organization for Economic Cooperation & Development.
Santos-Paulino, Amelia U. & Wan, Guanghua, eds. The Rise of China & India: Impacts, Prospects & Implications. 2010. (Studies in Development Economics & Policy Ser.). (ENG., Illus.). 336p. 110.00 (978-0-230-25273-8(7)) Palgrave Macmillan.
Scott, David. 'The Chinese Century'? The Challenge to Global Order. 2008. (Global Issues Ser.). (ENG., Illus.). 208p. 89.00 (978-0-230-53707-1(3)) Palgrave Macmillan.
Shinn, David H. & Eisenman, Joshua. China & Africa: A Century of Engagement. 2012. (Illus.). 520p. (C). 69.95 **(978-0-8122-4419-9(2))** Univ. of Pennsylvania Pr.
Sieren, Frank. The China Code: What's Left for Us. Rede, Thomas, tr. from GER. 2007. (ENG.). 320p. 59.00 (978-0-230-00135-0(1)) Palgrave Macmillan.
Simpfendorfer, Ben. The New Silk Road: How a Rising Arab World Is Turning Away from the West & Rediscovering China. 2009. (ENG.). 256p. 46.00 (978-0-230-58026-8(2)) Palgrave Macmillan.
—The New Silk Road - Revised & Updated: How a Rising Arab World Is Turning Away from the West & Rediscovering China. rev. ed. 2011. (ENG., Illus.). 224p. pap. 22.00 (978-0-230-28485-2(X)) Palgrave Macmillan.
Singla, S. K. India & China: Comparative Economic Performance. 2011. 274p. 45.25 **(978-81-7708-280-7(9))** New Century Publications IND. Dist: International Specialized Bk. Services.
Smith, S. A. Revolution & the People in Russia & China: A Comparative History. 2008. (Wiles Lectures). (ENG.). (C). 258p. 84.00 (978-0-521-88637-6(6)); 264p. pap. 30.99 (978-0-521-71396-2(X)) Cambridge Univ. Pr.
Solinger, Dorothy J. States' Gains, Labor's Losses: China, France, & Mexico Choose Global Liaisons, 1980-2000. 2009. (Illus.). 224p. 47.50 (978-0-8014-4777-8(1)) Cornell Univ. Pr.
Somarajah, Muthucumaraswamy & Wang, Jiangyu, eds. China, India & the International Economic Order. 2010. (ENG., Illus.). 660p. 125.00 (978-0-521-11057-0(2)) Cambridge Univ. Pr.
Sung, Yun-Wing. The China-Hong Kong Connection: The Key to China's Open Door Policy. 2009. (Trade & Development Ser.). (ENG.). 200p. (C). pap. 31.99 (978-0-521-10898-0(5)) Cambridge Univ. Pr.
Suryadinata, ed. Southeast Asia's Chinese Businesses in an Era of Globalization. 2006. 384p. (978-981-230-401-8(0)) Institute of Southeast Asian Studies.
Tan, Yinglan. Chinnovation: How Chinese Innovators Are Changing the World. 2011. (ENG., Illus.). 288p. 29.95 (978-0-470-82796-3(3), Wiley) Wiley, John & Sons, Inc.
Tanner, Murray Scot. Chinese Economic Coercion Against Taiwan: A Tricky Weapon to Use. 2007. 224p. pap. 25.00 (978-0-8330-3969-9(5), MG-507) RAND Corp., The.
Tóth, Viktor L. Commerce Between the EU & China: Background, Description & Analysis of the Present, Provisions for the Future. 2008. 52p. pap. (978-3-639-02161-5(4)) VDM Verlag Dr. Mueller e.K.
Tsai, Shin-Yuan. Globalization Effects on China's Influence on Taiwan Economy. 313p. pap. 62.95 (978-3-631-55737-2(X)); 2007. (Illus.). pap. 62.95 (978-0-8204-8728-1(7)) Lang, Peter Publishing, Inc.
Tselichtchev, Ivan. China Versus the West: The Global Power Shift of the 21st Century. 2012. (ENG.). 224p. 29.95 **(978-0-470-82972-1(9)**, Wiley) Wiley, John & Sons, Inc.
van Dijk, Meine Pieter, ed. The New Presence of China in Africa. 2010. (Eadi Ser.). (Illus.). 224p. pap. (978-90-8964-136-6(X)) Amsterdam Univ. Pr.
Virmani, Arvind. From Unipolar to Tripolar World: Multipolar Transition Paradox. 2011. (Illus.). 352p. 69.95 (978-81-7188-799-6(6)) Academic Foundation IND. Dist: Independent Pubs. Group.
Vuong, Monika. Intercultural Differences in Negotiation. 2010. 104p. pap. (978-3-639-22904-2(6)) VDM Verlag Dr. Mueller e.K.
Wang, Liming, ed. Rising China in the Changing World Economy. 2012. (Routledge Studies on the Chinese Economy Ser.). (ENG., Illus.). 448p. (C). 195.00 (978-0-415-61095-7(8)) Routledge.
Wende, Marc Alexander. China's Economic Expansion in Latin America: Motives, Drivers & the Status Quo of Relations in Light of the Global Economic Crisis. 2011. (Illus.). 112p. pap. **(978-3-639-32712-0(8))** VDM Verlag Dr. Mueller e.K.
Whalley, John. China's Integration into the World Economy. 2010. (Illus.). 300p. 120.00 (978-981-4304-78-6(6)) World Scientific Publishing Co., Inc.
Wilson, Scott Howard. Remade in China: Foreign Investors & Institutional Change in China. 2009. (ENG., Illus.). 304p. 65.00 (978-0-19-538831-2(3)) Oxford Univ. Pr., Inc.
World Bank Staff & Pigato, Miria. Strengthening China's & India's Trade & Investment Ties to the Middle East & North Africa. 2009. (ENG., Illus.). 216p. pap. 22.95 (978-0-8213-7776-5(0), 9780821377765) World Bank Pubns.
Wu, Guang. The Third Sino-Japanese War: Dream of Pacific Empire. 2011. (Series: Asian Political, Economic & Security Issues Ser.). vii, 115p. 47.00 (978-1-61324-489-0(4)) Nova Science Pubs., Inc.
Wu, Zhongmin. China in the World Economy. Wu, Zhongmin, ed. 2009. (Routledge Studies on the Chinese Economy Ser.). (ENG., Illus.). 344p. (C). 190.00 (978-0-415-47002-5(1)) Routledge.
Xiaoxi, Li, et al. Emerging Markets Reform & Development in China. 2010. (Illus.). ix, 49p. pap. 49.00 (978-1-61668-769-4(X)) Nova Science Pubs., Inc.
Xing, Li. The Rise of China & its Implication on World Order. 2010. (International Political Economy of New Regionalisms Ser.). (Illus.). 222p. 99.95 (978-0-7546-7913-4(6)) Ashgate Publishing Co.
Xu, L. China's Economy in the Post-WTO Environment: Stock Markets, FDI & Challenges of Sustainability. 2011. (Advances in Chinese Economic Studies Ser.). (Illus.). 288p. 135.00 **(978-1-84980-934-4(8))** Elgar, Edward Publishing, Inc.
Yang, Yao, et al, eds. Chinas Role in the World Economy. 2012. (PAFTAD (Pacific Trade & Development Conference Series) Ser.). (ENG.). 240p. (C). 125.00 **(978-0-415-69116-1(8))** Routledge.
Yu, Ying-shih. Trade & Expansion in Han Chin: A Study in the Structure of Sino-Barbarian Economic Relations. 2011. 266p. 40.00 **(978-1-59740-816-5(6))** ACLS Humanities E-Book.
Yusuf, Shahid & Nabeshima, Kaoru. Changing the Industrial Geography in Asia: The Impact of China & India. 2010. (ENG., Illus.). 280p. pap. 24.95 (978-0-8213-8240-0(3), 9780821382400) World Bank Pubns.
Zeng, Ka. China's Foreign Trade Policy: The New Constituencies. 2009. 186p. pap. 39.95 (978-0-415-54709-3(1)) Routledge.
Zhang, Yunling. China & Asia Regionalism. 2009. (Illus.). 240p. 96.00 (978-981-4282-22-2(7)) World Scientific Publishing Co., Inc.
Zhao, Jinghua, et al. Multinational Corporation Subsidiaries in China: An Empirical Study of Growth & Development Strategy. 2012. (Chandos Asian Studies). (ENG.). 264p. 120.00 **(978-0-85709-163-5(8)**, Chandos Publishing) Woodhead Publishing Ltd. GBR. Dist: Ingram Pub. Services.
Zhao, Suisheng, ed. China & East Asian Regionalism: Economic & Security Cooperation & Institution-Building. 2012. (ENG., Illus.). 232p. (C). 125.00 (978-0-415-61814-4(2)) Routledge.
Zheng, Biao. Zhongguo Guo Ji Zheng Zhi Jing Ji Xue: International Political Economics of Chinese Edition. 2008. (978-7-80211-284-1(2)) Cetial Compilation & Fanslation Pr.
Zheng, Yangwen. China on the Sea. 2011. (MUL., Illus.). 362p. **(978-90-04-19477-9(0))** BRILL.

CHINA—FOREIGN ECONOMIC RELATIONS—UNITED STATES

Allen, Wilfred J. & Young, Alex, eds. In China We Trust: The Impacts of Chinese Economic Policies. 2012. **(978-1-61942-828-7(8))** Nova Science Pubs., Inc.
Bell, Sandra. International Brand Management of Chinese Companies: Case Studies on the Chinese Household Appliances & Consumer Electronics Industry Entering US & Western European Markets. 2010. (Contributions to Economics Ser.). (ENG., Illus.). x, 370p. pap. 179.00 (978-3-7908-2549-7(2), 3790825492) Physica-Verlag DEU. Dist: Springer.
Beman Press Staff. Intellectual Property Law Guidebook - China. 2008. (ENG., Illus.). 186p. pap. 75.00 (978-1-59888-212-4(0)) Beman Assocs.
Brooks, Lucy M. & Watson, Julie E. China's Currency: Economic Issues & Background. 2011. (China in the 21st Century Ser.). 115.00 (978-1-61209-300-0(0)) Nova Science Pubs., Inc.
China's Exchange Rate Policy & Trade Imbalances: Hearing Before the Subcommittee on Economic Policy of the Committee on Banking, Housing, & Urban Affairs, United States Senate, One Hundred Eleventh Congress, Second Session, on Examining the Effect That China's Exchange Rate Policy Has on Trade Flow, U.S. Manufacturers, & Workers, April 22, 2010. 2010. (Illus.). iii, 91p. **(978-0-16-087774-2(1)**, 552-070-42285-4) United States Government Printing Office.
Cliff, Roger, et al. Ready for Takeoff: China's Advancing Aerospace Industry. 1 vol. 2011. (ENG.). 162p. (C). pap. 24.00 (978-0-8330-5180-6(6)) RAND Corp., The.
Cooke, Jennifer. U. S. & Chinese Engagement in Africa: Prospects for Improving U. S. -China-Africa Cooperation. 2008. 68p. pap. 16.95 (978-0-89206-538-7(9), CSIS Pr., The) Ctr. for Strategic & International Studies.
Currency Manipulation & Its Effect on U.S. Businesses & Workers: Hearing Before the Subcommittee on Trade of the Committee on Ways & Means, U.S. House of Representatives, Joint with the Subcommittee on Commerce, Trade, & Consumer Protection of the Committee on Energy & Commerce & the Subcommittee on Domestic & International Monetary Policy, Trade, & Technology of the Committee on Financial Services, U.S. House of Representatives, One Hundred Tenth C. 2009. (Illus.). v, 130p. (978-0-16-083286-4(1), 552-070-39114-2) United States Government Printing Office.
Devaland, Mary Jo. China's Economic Policy Impact on the United States. 2008. (Illus.). vii, 251p. 69.00 (978-1-60692-194-4(0)) Nova Science Pubs., Inc.
Ebeling, George. Fueling the Dragon: Chinese Energy Futures & Their Implications for the United States. 2011. (ENG., Illus.). 198p. 60.00 **(978-0-7391-6568-3(2))** Lexington Bks.
Elwell, Craig K., et al. Is China a Threat to the U. S. Economy? 2008. (Illus.). 88p. pap. 29.00 (978-1-60456-843-1(7)) Nova Science Pubs., Inc.
Enhancing the Safety of Our Toys: Lead Paint, the Consumer Product Safety Commission, & Toy Safety Standards: Hearings Before a Subcommittee of the Committee on Appropriations, United States Senate, One Hundred Tenth Congress, First Session, Special Hearings, June 18, 2007, Washington, DC [i.e. Chicago, IL], September 12, 2007, Washington, DC. 2008. (Illus.). iv, 162p. (978-0-16-080264-5(4), 552-070-36972-4) United States Government Printing Office.
Evenett, Simon J., ed. The US-Sino Currency Dispute: New Insights from Politics, Economics & Law. 2010. (Illus.). 232p. pap. (978-1-907142-16-1(9)) Ctr. for Economic Policy Research.
Finding Common Ground with a Rising China: Hearing Before the Committee on Foreign Relations, United States Senate, One Hundred Eleventh Congress, Second Session, June 23, 2010. 2010. iii, 56p. **(978-0-16-087689-9(3)**, 552-070-42241-2) United States Government Printing Office.
Finn, Jerald D., ed. China-US Economic & Geopolitical Relations. 2008. (C). 82.00 (978-1-60456-052-7(5)) Nova Science Pubs., Inc.
Grunor, Jerry A. Enough to Make You Sick- Tainted Counterfeit Imports! 2009. 362p. E-Book **(978-1-4401-4741-8(8))** iUniverse, Inc.
Guo, Sujian. 30 Years of China U. S. Relations: Analytical Approaches & Contemporary Issues. 2010. (Challenges Facing Chinese Political Development Ser.). (ENG., Illus.). 344p. 80.00 (978-0-7391-4696-5(3)) Lexington Bks.
Hao, Yufan. Macau & U. S. -China Relations. 2010. (ENG., Illus.). 330p. 80.00 (978-0-7391-4367-4(0)) Lexington Bks.
Hao, Yufan & Wang, Jianwei. Macao & Sino-U.S. Relations. 2010. (Illus.). vii, 360p. (978-0-7391-4369-8(7)) Lexington Bks.
International Piracy: The Challenges of Protecting Intellectual Property in the 21st Century: Hearing Before the Subcommittee on Courts, the Internet, & Intellectual Property of the Committee on the Judiciary, House of Representatives, One Hundred Tenth Congress, First Session, October 18, 2007. 2008. (Illus.). iii, 133p. (978-0-16-080799-2(9), 552-070-37388-8) United States Government Printing Office.
Johnson, Kendall, ed. Narratives of Free Trade & the Commercial Cultures of Early US-China Relations. 2011. (Illus.). 212p. **(978-988-8053-90-2(6))** Hong Kong Univ. Pr.
Kiernan, Peter D. Becoming China's Bitch: And Nine More Catastrophes We Must Avoid Right Now. 2012. (ENG.). 434p. 27.95 **(978-1-61858-005-4(1))** Turner Publishing Co.
Leeb, Stephen. Red Alert: How China's Growing Prosperity Threatens the American Way of Life. 2011. 272p. pap. 17.99 **(978-0-446-57624-6(7)**, Business Plus) Grand Central Publishing.
Mertha, Andrew C. The Politics of Piracy: Intellectual Property in Contemporary China. 2007. (Illus.). 241p. per. 21.95 (978-0-8014-7385-2(3)) Cornell Univ. Pr.
Moosa, Imad. The USndash;China Trade Dispute: Facts, Figures & Myths. 2012. 328p. 145.00 **(978-1-78100-154-7(5))** Elgar, Edward Publishing, Inc.
Navarro, Peter W. & Autry, Gregory W. Death by China: Confronting the Dragon - A Global Call to Action. 2011. (ENG.). 300p. 25.99 (978-0-13-218023-8(5)) Wharton Sch. Publishing.
Overton, Rachel H. China's Trade with the United States & the World. Overton, Rachel H., ed. 2008. (Illus.). viii, 71p. pap. 37.00 (978-1-60692-126-5(6)) Nova Science Pubs., Inc.
Prestowitz, Clyde. The Betrayal of American Prosperity: Free Market Delusions, America's Decline, & How We Must Compete in the Post-Dollar Era. 2010. (ENG., Illus.). 352p. 26.00 (978-1-4391-1979-2(1), Free Pr) Free Pr.
The Report to the Congress on International Economic & Exchange Rate Policies: Hearing Before the Committee on Banking, Housing, & Urban Affairs, United States Senate, One Hundred Ninth Congress, Second Session, on the Report to Congress on International Economic & Exchange Rate Policies, May 18, 2006. 2007. ii, 32p. (978-0-16-080286-7(5), 552-070-36981-3) United States Government Printing Office.
Risks & Reform: The Role of Currency in the U.S.-China Relationship: Hearing Before the Committee on Finance, United States Senate, One Hundred Tenth Congress, First Session, March 28, 2007. 2007. (Illus.). iii, 103p. (978-0-16-081517-1(7), 552-070-37873-1) United States Government Printing Office.
Roett, Riordan. China's Expansion into the Western Hemisphere: Implications for Latin America & the United States. Paz, Guadalupe, ed. 2008. (ENG., Illus.). 276p. pap. 26.95 (978-0-8157-7553-9(9)) Brookings Institution Pr.
Saxon, Mike. An American's Guide to Doing Business in China: Negotiating Contracts & Agreements; Understanding Culture & Customs; Marketing Products & Services. 2006. (ENG., Illus.). 256p. per. 14.95 (978-1-59337-730-4(4)) Adams Media Corp.
Schulze, Hannes & Peters, Emil, eds. Intellectual Property Infringement & Indigenous Innovation in China. 2011. (Intellectual Property in the 21st Century Ser.). 325.00 **(978-1-61470-745-5(6))** Nova Science Pubs., Inc.
Steinfeld, Edward S. Playing Our Game: Why China's Rise Doesn't Threaten the West. 2012. (ENG., Illus.). 280p. pap. 21.95 **(978-0-19-983708-3(2))** Oxford Univ. Pr., Inc.
Thompson, Helen. China & the Mortgaging of America: Economic Interdependence & Domestic Politics. 2010. (International Political Economy Ser.). (ENG., Illus.). 208p. 89.00 (978-0-230-24359-0(2)) Palgrave Macmillan.
Tian, Dexin. Grassroots Voices on the U S -China Copyright Disputes. 2009. 224p. pap. (978-3-639-14157-3(1)) VDM Verlag Dr. Mueller e.K.
The Treasury Department's Report on International Economic & Exchange Rate Policies: Hearing Before the Committee on Banking, Housing, & Urban Affairs, United States Senate, One Hundred Eleventh Congress, Second Session, on the Treasury Department's International Economic Exchange Rate Policy Report, & Examining the Impact of Economic & Trade Policies with China on the U.S. Economy, September 16, 2010. 2011. iii, 63p. **(978-0-16-088947-9(2)**, 552-070-42987-5) United States Government Printing Office.
Tsai, Shin-Yuan. Globalization Effects on China's Influence on Taiwan Economy. 2007. (Schriften zur Politischen Okonomik Ser.). (Illus.). 313p. pap. 62.95 (978-0-8204-8728-1(7)) Lang, Peter Publishing, Inc.
Tseng, Mitchell M. & Tabrizi, Behnam N. Transformation Through Global Value Chains: Taking Advantage of Business Synergies in the United States & China. 2007. (ENG., Illus.). 360p. 39.95 (978-0-8047-5482-8(9)) Stanford Univ. Pr.
U.S.-China Relations: Maximizing the Effectiveness of the Strategic & Economic Dialogue: Hearing Before the Subcommittee on Asia, the Pacific, & the Global Environment of the Committee on Foreign Affairs, House of Representatives, One Hundred Eleventh Congress, First Session, September 10, 2009. 2009. iii, 115p. (978-0-16-084729-5(X), 552-070-40206-3) United States Government Printing Office.
Waitley, Denis. The Dragon & the Eagle: China & America, Growing Together, Worlds Apart. 2008. (ENG., Illus.). 261p. 27.95 (978-0-9815058-0-0(5)) Morgan James Publishing.
Walsh, Jean. An American Cookie Seeks Her Fortune in China. 2009. 192p. pap. 66.95 (978-0-557-05502-9(4)) Lulu Enterprises Inc.
Yager, Loren. US - China Trade: Eliminating Nonmarket Economy Methodology Would Lower Antidumping Duties for Some Chinese Companies. 2006. (Illus.). 57p. (C). pap. 20.00 (978-1-4223-0593-5(7)) DIANE Publishing Co.

CHINA—FOREIGN POPULATION

see Aliens—China; Immigrants—China

CHINA—FOREIGN PUBLIC OPINION

Brand China: Global Perceptions & Representations. 2010. 304p. pap. 95.00 (978-1-933782-22-5(6)) Berkshire Publishing Group.
Buchanan, Tom. East Wind: China & the British Left, 1925-1976. 2012. (ENG., Illus.). 304p. 125.00 **(978-0-19-957033-1(7))** Oxford Univ. Pr., Inc.
Callahan, William A. China: The Pessoptimist Nation. (ENG., Illus.). 2012. 288p. pap. 29.95 **(978-0-19-960439-5(8))** 2010. 248p. 45.00 (978-0-19-954995-5(8)) Oxford Univ. Pr., Inc.
Clark, Anthony E. Beating Devils & Burning Their Books: Views of China, Japan & the West. 2010. (Illus.). 248p. pap. (978-0-924304-60-6(X)) Assn. for Asian Studies, Inc.
Herzstein, Robert Edwin. Henry R. Luce, Time, & the American Crusade in Asia. 2006. (ENG., Illus.). 364p. per. 31.99 (978-0-521-54368-2(1)) Cambridge Univ. Pr.
Hughes, Alex. France/China: Intercultural Imaginings. 2007. (Legenda Research Monographs in French Studies). 160p. (C). 74.00 (978-1-904350-93-4(3)) European Humanities Research Ctr. GBR. Dist: Brown, David Bk. Co., The.
Mölk, Ulrich & Detering, Heinrich, eds. Perspektiven der Modernisierung: Die Pariser Weltausstellung, die Arbeiterbewegung, das koloniale China in europäischen und amerikanischen Kulturzeitschriften um 1900. (Abhandlungen der Akademie der Wissenschaften zu Göttingen. Neue Folge Ser.). Tr. of Perspectives of Modernization. the Paris World Exhibition, the Labor Movement, Colonial China in European & American Cultural Journals Around 1900. (GER.). VI, 261p. 2011. 210.00 **(978-3-11-214953-9(X))** 2010. 140.00 (978-3-11-023425-1(4)) De Gruyter, Walter Inc.
Metrick-Chen, Lenore. Collecting Objects/Excluding People: Chinese Subjects & American Visual Culture, 1830-1900. 2012. (ENG.). 320p. 85.00 **(978-1-4384-4325-6(0))** State Univ. of New York Pr.
Novotny, Daniel. Torn Between America & China: Elite Perceptions & Indonesian Foreign Policy. 2010. (Illus.). xxiii, 400p. pap. **(978-981-4279-59-8(5))** Institute of Southeast Asian Studies.
Page, Benjamin I. & Xie, Tao. Living with the Dragon: How the American Public Views the Rise of China. 2010. (Contemporary Asia in the World Ser.). (ENG., Illus.). 232p. (gr. 17). 27.50 (978-0-231-15208-2(6)) Columbia Univ. Pr.
Takagi, Saiichiro, et al, eds. China Watching: Perspectives from Europe, Japan & the United States. 2006. (ENG.). 272p. (C). 190.00 (978-0-415-41396-1(6)) Routledge.
—China Watching: Perspectives from Europe, Japan & the United States. 2006. (Routledge Contemporary China Ser.). 261p. per. 43.95 (978-0-415-41397-8(4), Routledge) Taylor & Francis Group GBR. Dist: Taylor & Francis Group.
Tao, Zhijian. Drawing the Dragon: Western European Reinvention of China. 2009. (Illus.). 233p. pap. (978-3-03911-812-0(9)) Lang, Peter.

C

Wang, Sheng-Wei. China's Ascendancy: An Opportunity or a Threat?: What Every American Should Know about China. 2007. (978-0-9785095-3-8(6)) International Publishing Hse. for China's Culture.

Yang, Chi-Ming. Performing China: Virtue, Commerce, & Orientalism in Eighteenth-Century England, 1660-1760. 2011. (ENG., Illus.). 288p. (gr. 17). 70.00 (978-1-4214-0216-1(5)) Johns Hopkins Univ. Pr.

CHINA—FOREIGN RELATIONS

Abramowitz, Morton I. China-Japan-U.S. Relations: Meeting New Challenges. 104p. pap. 10.00 (978-4-88907-041-5(9)) Japan Ctr. for International Exchange JPN. Dist: Brookings Institution Pr.

Alden, Chris. China in Africa: Partner, Competitor or Hegemon? 2007. (African Arguments Ser.). (ENG., Illus.). 180p. 81.00 (978-1-84277-863-0(3)); 154p. per. 23.00 (978-1-84277-864-7(1)) Zed Bks., Ltd. GBR. Dist: Macmillan.

Alterman, Jon B. & Garver, John W. The Vital Triangle: China, the United States, & the Middle East. 2008. (Illus.). vii, 144p. pap. 16.95 (978-0-89206-529-5(X), CSIS Pr., The) Ctr. for Strategic & International Studies.

Ampiah, Kweku & Naidu, Sanusha. Crouching Tiger, Hidden Dragon? Africa & China. Ampiah, Kweku & Naidu, Sanusha, eds. 2008. (Illus.). 357p. (C). pap. 44.95 (978-1-86914-150-9(4)) University of Kwazulu-Natal Press ZAF. Dist: International Specialized Bk. Services.

Ampwera, Meshach K. China's un Peacekeeping Experience in Afric. 2011. 84p. pap. (978-3-8443-3012-0(7)) Lambert Academic Publishing.

Anderson, Eric C. China Restored: The Middle Kingdom Looks to 2020 & Beyond. 2010. xxiii, 323p. E-Book (978-0-313-38518-6(1)); 323p. 44.95 (978-0-313-38517-9(3), A2975C) Greenwood Publishing Group, Inc. (Praeger Pubs.).

Arthur Judson Brown. New Forces in Old China: An Inevitable Awakening. l.t. ed. 2006. (ENG.). 364p. pap. 18.99 (978-1-4264-0145-9(0)) BiblioBazaar.

Beal, Tim. Crisis in Korea: America, China, & the Risk of War, 1 vol. 2011. (ENG., Illus.). 288p. pap. 32.00 (978-0-7453-3162-1(9)); lib. bdg. 95.00 (978-0-7453-3161-4(0)) Pluto Pr. GBR. Dist: Macmillan.

Béja, Jean-Philippe. The Impact of China's 1989 Tiananmen Massacre. 2010. (China Policy Ser.). (ENG., Illus.). 272p. (C). 140.00 (978-0-415-57872-1(8)) Routledge.

Belopolsky, Helen. Russia & the Challengers: Russian Alignment with China, Iran & Iraq in the Unipolar Era. 2008. (ENG.). 272p. 95.00 (978-0-230-54549-6(1)) Palgrave Macmillan.

Bercovitch, Jacob. Conflict Management, Security & Intervention in East Asia: Third-party Mediation in Regional Conflict. 2009. 296p. pap. 39.95 (978-0-415-55878-5(6)) Routledge.

Berik, Gunseli, et al, eds. Gender, China & the World Trade Organization: Essays from Feminist Economics. 2009. (ENG., Illus.). 328p. 125.00 (978-0-415-49904-0(6)) Routledge.

Bickers, Robert. The Scramble for China: Foreign Devils in the Qing Empire, 1832-1914. 2011. (ENG., Illus.). 512p. 45.00 (978-0-7139-9749-1(4), Penguin Global) Penguin Group (USA) Inc.

Bijian, Zheng. China's Road to Peaceful Development. 2011. (Routledge Studies on the Chinese Economy Ser.). (ENG.). 352p. (C). 145.00 (978-0-415-55271-4(0)) Routledge.

Blanchard, Jean-Marc F. & Hickey, Dennis V., eds. New Thinking about the Taiwan Issue: Theoretical Insights into Its Origins, Dynamics, & Prospects. 2012. (Politics in Asia Ser.). (ENG., Illus.). 256p. (C). 125.00 (978-0-415-68453-8(6)) Routledge.

Boulger, Demetrius Charles. The Life of Sir Halliday Macartney, K. C. M. G. Commander of Li Hung Chang's Trained Force in the Taeping Rebellion, Founder of the First Chinese Arsenals, for Thirty Years Councillor & Secretary to the Chinese Legation in London. 2011. (Cambridge Library Collection - Travel & Exploration Ser.). (Illus.). 571p. pap. 39.99 (978-1-108-02626-0(5)) Cambridge Univ. Pr.

Brady, Anne-Marie. Looking North, Looking South: China, Taiwan, & the South Pacific. 2010. (Illus.). 316p. 94.00 (978-981-4304-38-2(7)) World Scientific Publishing Co., Inc.

Brady, Anne-Marie & Brown, Douglas, eds. Foreigners & Foreign Institutions in Republican China. 2012. (Chinese Worlds Ser.). (ENG., Illus.). 320p. (C). 135.00 (978-0-415-52865-8(8)) Routledge.

Breslin, Shaun & Shaun Breslin, eds. China's International Relations. 2010. (Routledge International Handbooks Ser.). (ENG., Illus.). 288p. instr.'s hndbk. ed. 300.00 (978-1-85743-508-5(7)) Routledge.

Breslin, Shaun & Shaw, Timothy M. China & the Global Political Economy. 2007. (International Political Economy Ser.). (ENG., Illus.). 256p. 106.00 (978-1-4039-8647-4(9)) Palgrave Macmillan.

Brown, Seyom. Taiwan at a Turning Point. 2009. (Illus.). 98p. pap. (978-1-932330-26-7(7)) Univ. of Maryland, Schl. of Law.

Bush, Richard. Untying the Knot: Making Peace in the Taiwan Strait. annot. ed. 2006. (ENG., Illus.). 416p. per. 24.95 (978-0-8157-1290-9(1)) Brookings Institution Pr.

Bush, Richard C. Taiwan de Wei Lai. 2010. (CHI., Illus.). 415p. (978-957-32-6639-6(3)) Yuan-liou Publishing Co., Ltd.

Cai, Kevin G. Cross-Taiwan Straits Relations since the 1980s: Attitude Change & Policy Adjustment Across the Straits. 2011. (Illus.). 400p. 107.00 (978-981-4282-60-4(X)) World Scientific Publishing Co., Inc.

Cai, Tuo, ed. Chinese Perspectives on Globalization & Autonomy. 2012. (Issues in Contemporary Chinese Thought & Culture Ser.). (ENG.). xv, 376p. (978-90-04-21615-0(4)) BRILL.

Callahan, William A. China: The Pessoptimist Nation. (ENG., Illus.). 2012. 288p. pap. 29.95 (978-0-19-960439-5(8)) 2010. 248p. 45.00 (978-0-19-954995-5(8)) Oxford Univ. Pr., Inc.

Callahan, William A. & Barabantseva, Elena, eds. China Orders the World: Normative Soft Power & Foreign Policy. 2012. (ENG.). 296p. (gr. 17). 55.00 (978-1-4214-0383-0(8)) Johns Hopkins Univ. Pr.

Cao, Huhua & Poy, Vivienne, eds. The China Challenge: Sino-Canadian Relations in the 21st Century. 2011. (ENG.). 310p. pap. (978-0-7766-0764-1(2)) Univ. of Ottawa Pr./Presses de l'Universite d'Ottawa.

Carlson, Allen & Ren, Xiao. New Frontiers in China's Foreign Relations: Zhongguo Waijiao de Xin Bianjiang. 2011. (978-0-7391-5027-6(8)) Lexington Bks.

Chan. China, the Us & the Power-Transition Theory. 2007. (ENG., Illus.). 208p. (C). 43.95 (978-0-415-44024-0(6)) Routledge.

Chan, Gerald. China's Compliance in Global Affairs: Trade, Arms Control, Environmental Protection, Human Rights. 2006. (Series on Contemporary China: Vol. 4). (Illus.). 249p. 87.00 (978-981-256-504-4(3)) World Scientific Publishing Co., Inc.

Chan, Gerald, et al. China Engages Global Governance. 2012. (China Policy Ser.). (ENG., Illus.). 296p. (C). 155.00 (978-0-415-55713-9(5)) Routledge.

Chan, Steve. China, the Us & the Power-Transition Theory. 2007. (Illus.). 208p. 180.00 (978-0-415-44023-3(8)) Routledge.

Chang, Chihyun. Government, Imperialism & Nationalism in China: The Maritime Customs Service & its Chinese Staff. 2012. (Routledge Studies in the Modern History of Asia Ser.). (ENG.). 256p. (C). 155.00 (978-0-415-53142-9(X)) Routledge.

Chau, Donovan C. Political Warfare in Sub-Saharan Africa: U. S. Capabilities & Chinese Operations in Ethiopia, Kenya, Nigeria, & South Africa. 2007. vii, 75p. pap. (978-1-58487-285-6(3)) Strategic Studies Institute, U.S. Army War College Commandant (AWCC-DSI/Pubns.).

Chen, Yi-Ru Regina. The Business of Corporate Government Affairs in China - Corporate Competitive Advantage in China's Marketization. 2008. 528p. per. (978-3-8364-3902-2(6)) VDM Verlag Dr. Mueller e.K.

Cheru, Fantu & Obi, Cyril, eds. The Rise of China & India in Africa: Challenges, Opportunities & Critical Interventions. 2010. (Africa Now Ser.). (ENG., Illus.). 272p. 125.95 (978-1-84813-436-2(3)); pap. 37.95 (978-1-84813-437-9(1)) Zed Bks., Ltd. GBR. Dist: Macmillan.

Chien-Nung, Li. The Political History of China, 1840-1928. Teng, Ssu-yu, ed. Ingalls, Jeremy, tr. 2011. 558p. 62.95 (978-1-258-10290-6(0)) Literary Licensing, LLC.

Chong, Chae-Ho. Charting China's Future: Political, Social, & International Dimensions. 2006. (ENG., Illus.). 232p. per. 39.95 (978-0-7425-5397-2(3)) Rowman & Littlefield Publishers, Inc.

Chung, Jae Ho. Charting Chinas Future: Political, Social, & International Dimensions. Chung, Jae Ho, ed. 2006. (ENG., Illus.). 232p. 92.00 (978-0-7425-5396-5(5)) Rowman & Littlefield Publishers, Inc.

Clegg. China & the Reshaping of the World Order. 2009. (ENG.). 288p. 100.00 (978-0-7453-2519-4(X)) Pluto Pr. GBR. Dist: Macmillan.

Cliff, Roger & Shlapak, David A. U. S. -China Relations after Resolution of Taiwan's Status. 2007. 39p. pap. 20.00 (978-0-8330-4036-7(7), mg567) RAND Corp., The.

Cliff, Roger, et al. New Opportunities & Challenges for Taiwan's Security. 2011. (ENG.). 172p. (C). pap. 23.50 (978-0-8330-5149-3(0)) RAND Corp., The.

Craig, Susan L. Chinese Perceptions of Traditional & Nontraditional Security Threats. 2007. pap. (978-1-58487-287-0(X)) Strategic Studies Institute, U.S. Army War College Commandant (AWCC-DSI/Pubns.).

Crossick, Stanley & Reuter, Etienne, eds. China-EU: A Common Future. 2008. (Illus.). 283p. 87.00 (978-981-270-776-5(X)) World Scientific Publishing Co., Inc.

Dent, Christopher M., ed. China & Africa Development Relations. 2011. (Illus.). 208p. pap. 42.95 (978-0-415-69007-2(2)) Routledge.

Doyle, Randall. America & China: Asia-Pacific Rim Hegemony in the Twenty-First Century. 2007. (ENG.). 222p. 73.50 (978-0-7391-1701-9(7)); per. 30.50 (978-0-7391-1702-6(5)) Lexington Bks.

Ellis, R. Evan. China in Latin America: The Whats & Wherefores. 2009. 300p. (C). 68.00 (978-1-58826-650-7(8)); pap. 26.50 (978-1-58826-675-0(3)) Rienner, Lynne Pubs.

Fei, Liu. The International Politics of EU-China Relations. Kerr, David, ed. 2008. (British Academy Occasional Papers). (ENG.). 260p. pap. 39.95 (978-0-19-726408-9(5)) Oxford Univ. Pr., Inc.

Fileva, Deya. Entry Mode Choices of Chinese Investors in Europe. 2011. 48p. pap. (978-3-8443-2048-0(2)) Lambert Academic Publishing.

Finn, Jerald D., ed. China-US Economic & Geopolitical Relations. 2008. (C). 82.00 (978-1-60456-052-7(5)) Nova Science Pubs., Inc.

Ford, Christopher A. The Mind of Empire: China's History & Modern Foreign Relations. 2010. (Asia in the New Millennium Ser.). (ENG., Illus.). 416p. 45.00 (978-0-8131-9263-5(3)) Univ. Pr. of Kentucky.

Gaens, Bart, et al. The Role of the European Union in Asia - China & India as Strategic Partners. 2009. (International Political Economy of New Regionalisms Ser.). (Illus.). 282p. 114.95 (978-0-7546-7790-1(7)) Ashgate Publishing Co.

Garver, John W. China & Iran: Ancient Partners in a Post-Imperial World. 2006. (ENG., Illus.). 392p. 50.00 (978-0-295-98630-2(1)); per. 24.95 (978-0-295-98631-9(X)) Univ. of Washington Pr.

Gilboy, George J. & Heginbotham, Eric. Chinese & Indian Strategic Behavior: Growing Power & Alarm. 2012. (ENG.). 384p. pap. 34.99 (978-1-107-66169-1(2)); (Illus.). 99.00 (978-1-107-02005-4(0)) Cambridge Univ. Pr.

Glaser, Bonnie & Glosserman, Brad. Promoting Confidence Building across the Taiwan Strait. 2008. 36p. pap. 12.95 net. (978-0-89206-550-9(8), CSIS Pr., The) Ctr. for Strategic & International Studies.

Gu, George Zhibin. China's Global Reach: (Revised & Updated Edition) rev. ed. 2006. 252p. (978-1-59682-094-4(2), Fultus Publishing) Fultus Corp.

Gungwu, Wang & Zheng, Yongnian, eds. China & the New International Order. 2009. (Illus.). 322p. pap. 39.95 (978-0-415-54645-4(1)) Routledge.

Guo, Sujian & Hua, Shiping, eds. New Dimensions of Chinese Foreign Policy. 2009. (Challenges Facing Chinese Political Development Ser.). (ENG.). 258p. pap. 31.50 (978-0-7391-1877-1(3)) Lexington Bks.

Guo/Teng. China's Quiet Rise: Peace Through Integration. 2011. (Challenges Facing Chinese Political Development Ser.). (ENG.). 192p. 60.00 (978-0-7391-4646-0(7)) Lexington Bks.

Halper, Stefan. The Beijing Consensus: Legitimizing Authoritarianism in Our Time. 2012. (ENG.). 336p. (gr. 9). pap. 17.99 (978-0-465-02523-7(4)) Basic Bks.

Hamelt-Sievers, Axel, et al. Chinese African Perspectives on China in Africa. 2010. (ENG., Illus.). 292p. pap. 27.95 (978-1-906387-33-4(8)) Pambazuka Pr. GBR. Dist: Independent Pubs. Group.

He, Kai. Institutional Balancing in the Asia Pacific: Economic Interdependence & China's Rise. 2008. (Illus.). 224p. 160.00 (978-0-415-46952-4(X)) Routledge.

He, Kai. Institutional Balancing in the Asia Pacific: Economic interdependence & China's Rise. 2012. (Routledge Contemporary China Ser.). (ENG., Illus.). 224p. (C). pap. 42.95 (978-0-415-54147-3(6)) Routledge.

Hearn, Adrian H. & Manriquez, José Luis León, eds. China Engages Latin America: Tracing the Trajectory. 2011. (Illus.). 250p. 65.00 (978-1-58826-767-2(9)) Rienner, Lynne Pubs.

Hofer, Markus B. & Ebel, Bernhard, eds. Business Success in China. 2006. (ENG., Illus.). viii, 275p. 74.95 (978-3-540-34614-2(7), 3540346147) Springer.

Hongyi, Lai. The Domestic Sources of China's Foreign Policy. 2011. (ENG., Illus.). 202p. (C). pap. 42.95 (978-0-415-69721-7(2)) Routledge.

Hongyi, Lai. The Domestic Sources of China's Foreign Policy: Regimes, Leadership, Priorities & Process. 2010. (China Policy Ser.). (ENG., Illus.). 216p. (C). 140.00 (978-0-415-56237-9(6), Routledge) Taylor & Francis Group GBR. Dist: Taylor & Francis Group.

Horner, Charles. Rising China & Its Postmodern Fate: Memories of Empire in a New Global Context. 2011. (Studies in Security & International Affairs Ser.). (ENG.). 240p. pap. 24.95 (978-0-8203-3878-1(8)) Univ. of Georgia Pr.

Hsiao, Hsin-Huang Michael & Lin, Cheng-yi, eds. Rise of China. 2011. (ENG., Illus.). 328p. pap. 42.95 (978-0-415-66713-5(5)) Routledge.

Hu, Angang. China In 2020: A New Type of Superpower. 2011. (Thornton Center Chinese Thinkers Ser.). (ENG., Illus.). 208p. 32.95 (978-0-8157-0478-2(X)) Brookings Institution Pr.

Hu, Angang & Hu, An'gang. Road Map of China's Rise. 2010. (Routledge Studies on the Chinese Economy Ser.). (ENG., Illus.). 512p. 150.00 (978-0-415-47992-9(4)) Routledge.

Hu, Weixing & Zha, Daojiong. Building a Neighbourly Community: Post-Cold War China, Japan, & Southeast Asia. 2007. (ENG., Illus.). 288p. 84.00 (978-0-7190-7064-8(3)) Manchester Univ. Pr. GBR. Dist: Macmillan.

Hulse, Janie. China's Expansion into & U. S. Withdrawal from Argentina's Telecommunications & Space Industries & the Implications for U. S. National Security. 2007. (978-1-58487-307-5(8)) Strategic Studies Institute, U.S. Army War College Commandant (AWCC-DSI/Pubns.).

Iiss. China. 2006. (Adelphi Papers Reissue Hardback Ser.). (ENG., Illus.). 590p. (C). 340.00 (978-0-415-39836-7(3)) Routledge.

Jiang, Xiyuan. Zhongguo de Shi Jie Hai Shi Shi Jie de Zhongguo: Zhongguo Wai Jiao Wen Hua Ben Yuan Yu Guo Ji Ti Xi Bian Hua Qu Shi = China of World or World of China: Cultural Principle of China's Diplomacy & Trends of Development of International System. 2009. (CHI.). (978-7-80232-209-7(X)) Current Affairs Publishing Hes.

Jiaxuan, Tang. Heavy Storm & Gentle Breeze: A Memoir of China's Diplomacy. 2011. (ENG., Illus.). 368p. 35.00 (978-0-06-206725-8(7)) HarperCollins Pubs.

Kaliff, Anders. Archaeology in the East & the West: Papers Presented at the Sino-Sweden Archaeology Forum, Beijing, in September 2005. Kaliff, Anders, ed. 2007. (ENG., Illus.). 302p. (C). pap. 36.00 (978-91-7209-469-7(9)) Riksantikvarieambetet och Statens historiska museer SWE. Dist: Brown, David Bk. Co., The.

Kavalski, Emilian. The Ashgate Research Companion to Chinese Foreign Policy. 2012. (Rethinking Asia & International Relations Ser.). 504p. 154.95 (978-1-4094-2270-9(4)) Ashgate Publishing Co.

Kavalski, Emilian. China & the Global Politics of Regionalization. 2009. (International Political Economy of New Regionalisms Ser.). 262p. 114.95 (978-0-7546-7599-0(8)) Ashgate Publishing Co.

Kent, Ann. Beyond Compliance: China, International Organizations, & Global Security. 2010. (Studies in Asian Security Ser.). (ENG.). 360p. pap. 29.95 (978-0-8047-7382-9(3)) Stanford Univ. Pr.

Kerr, Pauline, et al. China's "New" Diplomacy: Tactical or Fundamental Change? Kerr, Pauline et al, eds. 2008. (Palgrave Series in Asian Goverance Ser.). (ENG.). 320p. 100.00 (978-0-230-60772-9(1)) Palgrave Macmillan.

King, Winnie. Taiwan's Socio-Economic Relations with Mainland China: The Policy Impact of Non-State Actors. 2012. (Routledge Contemporary China Ser.). (ENG.). 256p. (C). 130.00 (978-0-415-67781-3(5)) Routledge.

Kinzelbach, Katrin. The EU's Human Rights Dialogue with China: Quiet Diplomacy & its Limits. 2013. (Routledge Research in Human Rights Ser.). (ENG.). 240p. (C). 135.00 (978-0-415-69846-7(4)) Routledge.

Kissinger, Henry. On China. (ENG.). (gr. 12). 2012. 624p. 18.00 (978-0-14-312131-2(6), Penguin (Non-Classics)) 2011. (Illus.). 608p. 36.00 (978-1-59420-271-1(0), Penguin Pr. HC, The) Penguin Group (USA) Inc.

Kitissou, Marcel, ed. Africa in China's Global Strategy. 2007. 208p. (978-1-905068-54-8(9)); (ENG.). per. (978-1-905068-88-3(3)) Adonis & Abbey Publishers Ltd.

Kopinski, Dominik, et al, eds. China's Rise in Africa. 2011. (ENG.). 120p. (C). 145.00 (978-0-415-68887-1(6)) Routledge.

Kuhrt, Natasha. Russian Policy Towards China & Japan. 2011. (ENG., Illus.). 240p. (C). pap. 44.95 (978-0-415-67488-1(3)) Routledge.

Lai, Hongyi & Lu, Yiyi, eds. China's Soft Power & International Relations. 2012. (China Policy Ser.). (ENG., Illus.). 232p. (C). 145.00 (978-0-415-60401-7(X)) Routledge.

Lampton, David M. The Three Faces of Chinese Power: Might, Money, & Minds. 2008. (Illus.). 361p. pap. 26.95 (978-0-520-25442-8(2)) Univ. of California Pr.

Lanqing, Li. Breaking Through: The Birth of China's Opening-Up Policy. 2010. (ENG., Illus.). 480p. 35.00 (978-0-19-801692-2(1)) Oxford Univ. Pr., Inc.

Lansdowne, Helen, ed. China Turns to Multilateralism: Foreign Policy & Regional Security. 2007. (Routledge Contemporary China Ser.). (Illus.). 303p. 170.00 (978-0-415-42571-1(9)) Routledge.

Lanteigne, Marc. Chinese Foreign Policy: An Introduction. 2009. (ENG., Illus.). 176p. (C). 150.00 (978-0-415-46523-6(0)); pap. 39.95 (978-0-415-46524-3(9)) Routledge.

Lanteigne, Marc & Hirono, Miwa, eds. Chinas Evolving Approach to Peacekeeping. 2012. (ENG.). 160p. (C). 125.00 (978-0-415-50852-0(5)) Routledge.

Lee, Keun. Power & Sustainability of the Chinese State. Kim, Joon-Han & Woo, Wing Thye, eds. 2009. (China Policy Ser.). (Illus.). 240p. 160.00 (978-0-415-46939-5(2)) Routledge.

Lee, Margaret C., et al. China in Africa. 2007. (NAI Current African Issues Ser.). (Illus.). 48p. pap. 14.95 (978-91-7106-589-6(X)) Nordiska Afrikainstitutet SWE. Dist: Stylus Publishing, LLC.

Leung, Pak-Wah. Managing China's Modernization: Perspectives on Diplomacy, Politics, Education & Ethnicity. 2011. (978-1-931907-74-3(9)) Homa & Sekey Bks.

Leung, Philip Y. & Colebrook, Claire. The Legitimation of New Orders: Case Studies in World History. 2007. (ENG., Illus.). 300p. (gr. 17). 42.00 (978-962-996-239-5(X)) Chinese Univ. of Hong Kong, The HKG. Dist: Columbia Univ. Pr.

Li, Mingjiang. Soft Power: China's Emerging Strategy in International Politics. 2009. (ENG.). 284p. 83.99 (978-0-7391-3377-4(2)) Lexington Bks.

Li, Mingjiang, ed. Soft Power: China's Emerging Strategy in International Politics. 2011. (ENG.). 284p. pap. 32.95 (978-0-7391-3378-1(0)) Lexington Bks.

Li, Xiaofei. China's Outward Foreign Investment: A Political Perspective. 2010. (ENG.). 260p. pap. 35.99 (978-0-7618-5263-6(8)) Univ. Pr. of America, Inc.

Li, Yu-Sheng. Equivocation in 'Reunification' for Taiwan & Mainland Chin. 2010. 360p. pap. (978-3-8383-7795-7(8)) Lambert Academic Publishing.

Lin, Hsiao-Ting. Tibet & Nationalist China's Frontier: Intrigues & Ethnopolitics, 1928-49. 2007. (Contemporary Chinese Studies). (ENG., Illus.). 304p. per. (978-0-7748-1302-0(4)) Univ. of British Columbia Pr.

Liu, Xiaoyuan. Recast All under Heaven: Revolution, War, Diplomacy, & Frontier China in the 20th Century. 2010. (ENG., Illus.). 288p. 120.00 (978-1-4411-6220-5(8)); pap. 34.95 (978-1-4411-3489-9(1)) Continuum International Publishing Group, Ltd. GBR. Dist: National Bk. Network.

Manji, Firoze & Manji, F., eds. African Perspectives on China in Africa. 2007. (ENG.). 188p. pap. 19.95 (978-0-9545637-3-8(5)) Pambazuka Pr. GBR. Dist: Independent Pubs. Group.

Maritime Disputes & Sovereignty Issues in East Asia: Hearing Before the Subcommittee on East Asian & Pacific Affairs of the Committee on Foreign Relations, United States Senate, One Hundred Eleventh Congress, First Session, July 15, 2009. 2009. iii, 50p. (978-0-16-084472-0(X), 552-070-39995-o) United States Government Printing Office.

McCormack, Jerusha Hull, ed. China & the Irish. 2009. (Illus.). 165p. 45.00 (978-1-84840-042-9(X)) New Island Books IRL. Dist: International Specialized Bk. Services.

Mederios, Evan S., et al. Pacific Currents: The Responses of U. S. Allies & Security Partners in East Asia to China's Rise. 2008. (Illus.). 308p. pap. 52.00 (978-0-8330-4464-8(8), mg-736) RAND Corp., The.

Men, Jing & Barton, Benjamin. China & the European Union in Africa: Partners or Competitors? 2011. (Illus.). 302p. 114.95 (978-1-4094-2047-7(7)) Ashgate Publishing Co.

Meng, S. M. The Tsungli Yamen: Its Organization & Functions. 2011. 154p. 41.95 (978-1-258-09541-3(6)) Literary Licensing, LLC.

Mochizuki, Mike, et al, eds. The Japan-U. S. Alliance & China-Taiwan Relations: Implications for Okinawa. 2007. per. 12.00 (978-0-9765283-1-9(2)) Sigur Ctr. for Asian Studies, The.

Monika, Pawar. Russia's Security Relations with China & India: Under Putin. 2011. 136p. pap. (978-3-639-33639-9(9)) VDM Verlag Dr. Mueller e.K.

Morse, Hosea B. The International Relations of the Chinese Empire, 3 vols. reprint ed. 375.00 (978-0-7222-2529-5(6)) Library Reprints, Inc.

Myers, Ramon Hawley & Zhang, Jialin. The Struggle Across the Taiwan Strait: The Divided China Problem. 2006. (Hoover Institution Press Publication Ser.: Vol. 542). 168p. per. 15.00 (978-0-8179-4692-0(6)) Hoover Institution Pr.

Narlikar, Amrita. New Powers: How to Become One & How to Manage Them. 2010. (Columbia/Hurst Ser.). (ENG.). 208p. (gr. 17). 45.00 (978-0-231-70202-7(7)) Columbia Univ. Pr.

Navarro, Peter. The Coming China Wars: Where They Will Be Fought & How They Can Be Won. 2nd exp. ed. 2008. (ENG.). 240p. pap. 15.99 *(978-0-13-235982-5(0))* FT Press.

—The Coming China Wars: Where They Will Be Fought & How They Can Be Won. 2006. (ENG., Illus.). 288p. 24.99 *(978-0-13-228128-7(7))* Prentice Hall PTR.

Nearing, Scott. Whither China? an Economic Interpretation of Recent Events in the Far East. 2011. 224p. 44.95 ***(978-1-258-06124-1(4))*** Literary Licensing, LLC.

Nolan, Peter. Is China Buying the World? 2012. (ENG.). 120p. 19.95 ***(978-0-7456-6078-3(9))*** Polity Pr. GBR. Dist: Wiley, John & Sons, Inc.

Odgaard, Liselotte. China & Coexistence: Beijing's National Security Strategy for the Twenty-First Century. 2012. (ENG., Illus.). 224p. (gr. 17). 45.00 ***(978-1-4214-0563-6(6))*** Woodrow Wilson Ctr. Pr.

Okamoto, Hiromichi. Ryukyu Okoku Kaijo Koshoshi Kenkyu. 2010. (JPN., Illus.). 255p. *(978-4-89805-142-9(1))* Yoju Shorin.

Ong, Russell. China's Security Interests in the 21st Century. annot. ed. 2007. (Routledgecurzon Security in Asia Ser.). (Illus.). 158p. 150.00 *(978-0-415-39215-0(2))* Routledge.

Pant, Harsh. China's Rising Global Profile: The Great Power Tradition. 2012. (ENG.). 132p. pap. 24.95 ***(978-1-84519-517-5(5))*** Sussex Academic Pr. GBR. Dist: International Specialized Bk. Services.

Pant, Harsh V. China's Rising Global Profile: The Great Power Tradition. 2011. 132p. 45.00 *(978-1-84519-457-4(8))* Sussex Academic Pr. GBR. Dist: International Specialized Bk. Services.

Pehrson, Christopher J. String of Pearls: Meeting the Challenge of China's Rising Power Across the Asian Littoral. 2006. (Carlisle Papers in Security Strategy). (Illus.). v, 30p. pap. *(978-1-58487-250-4(0))* Strategic Studies Institute, U.S. Army War College Commandant (AWCC-DSI/Pubns.).

Pollard, Robert T. China's Foreign Relations, 1917-1931. 2009. 436p. 65.00 *(978-1-59740-321-4(0))* 2008. 432p. pap. 43.00 *(978-1-59740-397-9(0))* ACLS Humanities E-Book.

Raine, Sarah. China's African Challenges. 2009. (Adelphi Ser.). (ENG., Illus.). 270p. pap. 19.95 *(978-0-415-55693-4(7))* Routledge.

Rebol, Max. Factor Endowments in a South- South Relation: Trade Preferences, Migration & Inequality for Chinain Africa. 2008. 52p. pap. *(978-3-639-11220-7(2))* VDM Verlag Dr. Mueller e.K.

Rebol, Max. Pragmatism & Non-Interference. 2011. 176p. pap. ***(978-3-8443-8205-1(4))*** Lambert Academic Publishing.

Reid, Anthony & Zheng, Yangwen. Negotiating Asymmetry: China's Place in Asia. 2009. (C). pap. 28.00 *(978-0-8248-3412-8(7))* Univ. of Hawaii Pr.

Rigger, Shelley. Why Taiwan Matters: Small Island, Global Powerhouse. 2011. (ENG., Illus.). 232p. 37.95 *(978-1-4422-0479-9(6))* Rowman & Littlefield Publishers, Inc.

Roraback, Amanda. China in a Nutshell. 2009. (Nutshell Notes Ser.). (ENG., Illus.). 108p. pap. 9.95 *(978-0-9763070-2-0(2))* Enisen Publishing.

Ross, Robert, et al, eds. Us-China-Eu Relations. 2011. (ENG.). (C). pap. 44.95 ***(978-0-415-68113-1(8))*** Routledge.

Russell, Bertrand. The Problem of China. 2008. 220p. 27.99 *(978-0-554-24817-2(4))* 2006. (ENG.). 196p. pap. 19.99 *(978-1-4264-7458-3(X))* 2007. 218p. pap. 22.99 *(978-1-4264-7535-1(7))* BiblioBazaar.

—The Problem of China. 2008. 188p. pap. *(978-1-4099-0103-7(3))* Dodo Pr.

—The Problem of China. 2007. (ENG.). 152p. per. *(978-1-4068-4109-1(9))* Echo Library.

—The Problem of China. 2009. (ENG.). 204p. pap. 13.95 *(978-1-4385-1290-7(2)*, Book Jungle) Standard Pubns., Inc.

Scott, David. China & the International System, 1840-1949: Power, Presence, & Perceptions in a Century of Humiliation. 2008. 384p. 85.00 *(978-0-7914-7627-7(8))* State Univ. of New York Pr.

—'The Chinese Century'? The Challenge to Global Order. 2008. (Global Issues Ser.). (ENG., Illus.). 208p. 89.00 *(978-0-230-53707-1(3))* Palgrave Macmillan.

Scott, David A. China & the International System, 1840-1949: Power, Presence, & Perceptions in a Century of Humiliation. 2009. 384p. pap. 29.95 *(978-0-7914-7628-4(6)*, Suny Pr.) State Univ. of New York Pr.

Sen, Tansen & Mair, Victor H. Traditional China in Asian & World History. 2011. pap. ***(978-0-924304-65-1(0))*** Assn. for Asian Studies, Inc.

Shambaugh. The China & Europe Engagement. 2007. (ENG., Illus.). 368p. (C). 180.00 *(978-0-415-43198-9(0))* Routledge.

Shambaugh, David, et al, eds. The China & Europe Engagement. 2007. (ENG., Illus.). 368p. (C). 44.95 *(978-0-415-43199-6(9))* Routledge.

Shen, Simon. Online Chinese Nationalism & China's Bilateral Relations. 2010. (Challenges Facing Chinese Political Development Ser.). (ENG., Illus.). 310p. 83.99 *(978-0-7391-3247-0(4))* Lexington Bks.

Shichor, Yitzhak. The Middle East in China's Foreign Policy, 1949-1977. 2008. (LSE Monographs in International Studies). (ENG.). 284p. pap. 38.99 *(978-0-521-10221-6(9))* Cambridge Univ. Pr.

Shinn, David H. & Eisenman, Joshua. China & Africa: A Century of Engagement. 2012. (Illus.). 520p. (C). 69.95 ***(978-0-8122-4419-9(2))*** Univ. of Pennsylvania Pr.

Smith, Shirley Ann. Imperial Designs: Italians in China, 1900-1947. 2012. (Fairleigh Dickinson University Press Series in Italian Studies). (ENG.). 208p. (gr. 17). 65.00 ***(978-1-61147-501-2(5))***; ***(978-1-61147-502-9(3))*** Fairleigh Dickinson Univ. Pr.

Soothill, William Edward. China & the West: A Short History of Their Contact from Ancient Times to the Fall of the Manchu Dynasty. 2009. (ENG., Illus.). 224p. pap. 14.95 *(978-1-59416-088-2(0))* Westholme Publishing.

Steinberg, David I. & Fan, Hongwei. Modern China-Myanmar Relations: Dilemmas of Mutual Dependence. 2012. (Illus.). 432p. ***(978-87-7694-095-9(0))***; pap. ***(978-87-7694-096-6(9))*** Nordic Institute of Asian Studies.

Steinmetz, George. The Devil's Handwriting: Precoloniality & the German Colonial State in Qingdao, Samoa, & Southwest Africa. 2007. (Chicago Studies in Practices of Meaning Ser.). (Illus.). 608p. 97.50 *(978-0-226-77241-7(1))*; per. 35.00 *(978-0-226-77243-1(8))* Univ. of Chicago Pr.

Strauss, Julia & Saavedra, Martha, eds. China & Africa: Volume 9: Emerging Patterns in Globalization & Development. 2009. (China Quarterly Special Issues Ser.). (ENG., Illus.). 196p. (C). pap. 41.00 *(978-0-521-12200-9(7))* Cambridge Univ. Pr.

Stumbaum, May-Britt U. The European Union & China: Decision-Making in EU Foreign & Security Policy Towards the People's Republic of China. 2009. (Illus.). 250p. pap. 43.00 *(978-3-8329-3744-7(7))* Nomos Verlagsgesellschaft DEU. Dist: International Specialized Bk. Services.

Su, Chi. Taiwan's Relations with Mainland China: A Tail Wagging Two Dogs. 2008. (Routledge Contemporary Asia Ser.). (Illus.). XX, 348p. 150.00 *(978-0-415-46454-3(4))* Routledge.

Sutter, Robert G. Chinese Foreign Relations: Power & Policy since the Cold War. 3rd ed. 2012. ***(978-1-4422-1136-0(9))***; (ENG.). 446p. (C). (gr. 13-17). 89.00 ***(978-1-4422-1134-6(2))***; (ENG.). 446p. (C). (gr. 13-17). pap. 39.95 ***(978-1-4422-1135-3(0))*** Rowman & Littlefield Publishers, Inc.

Suzuki, Shogo. Civilization & Empire. 2011. (ENG., Illus.). 256p. pap. 42.95 ***(978-0-415-66542-1(6))*** Routledge.

Szelezsan, Anett. Allowance Systems in Investment Laws in China & Hungary. 2008. 80p. pap. *(978-3-639-06226-7(4))* VDM Verlag Dr. Mueller e.K.

Takagi, Seiichiro, et al, eds. China Watching: Perspectives from Europe, Japan & the United States. 2006. (ENG.). 272p. (C). 190.00 *(978-0-415-41396-1(6))* Routledge.

—China Watching: Perspectives from Europe, Japan & the United States. 2006. (Routledge Contemporary China Ser.). 261p. per. 43.95 *(978-0-415-41397-8(4)*, Routledge) Taylor & Francis Group GBR. Dist: Taylor & Francis Group.

Tang, Shiping, et al. Living with China: Regional States & China Through Crises & Turning Points. Tang, Shiping et al, eds. 2009. (ENG.). 288p. 105.00 *(978-0-230-61670-7(4))* Palgrave Macmillan.

Tanner, Murray Scot. Chinese Economc Coercion Against Taiwan: A Tricky Weapon to Use. 2007. 224p. pap. 25.00 *(978-0-8330-3969-9(5)*, MG-507) RAND Corp., The.

Taylor, Ian. China & Africa: Engagement & Compromise. 2009. 234p. pap. 39.95 *(978-0-415-54552-5(8))* 2006. (Routledge Contemporary China Ser.: Vol. 14). 233p. 160.00 *(978-0-415-39740-7(5))* Routledge.

—China's New Role in Africa. 2008. (Illus.). 240p. 55.00 *(978-1-58826-636-1(2))* Rienner, Lynne Pubs.

Taylor, Paul D., ed. Latin American Security Challenges: A Collaborative Inquiry from North & South. 2006. (Newport Paper Ser.). (ENG.). 126p. pap. 11.00 *(978-0-16-076903-0(5)*, Dept. of the Navy) United States Government Printing Office.

Teremi, Kinga & Moorsel, Viktor. Taiwan Not Made in Chin. 2008. 60p. pap. *(978-3-639-07338-6(X))* VDM Verlag Dr. Mueller e.K.

Tian, Henian & Chen, Qiwen. Tai Hai Chun Qiu. 2009. (CHI.). *(978-7-80141-619-3(8))* Taihai Publishing House.

Tocci, Nathalie. Who Is a Normative Foreign Policy Actor? The European Union & Its Global Partners. 2008. (ENG., Illus.). 329p. pap. 30.00 *(978-92-9079-779-1(7))* Ctr. for European Policy Studies BEL. Dist: Brookings Institution Pr.

Torremans, Paul, et al. Intellectual Property & TRIPS Compliance in China: Chinese & European Perspectives. 2007. (New Horizons in Intellectual Property Ser.). (Illus.). 288p. (C). 124.00 *(978-1-84542-875-4(7))* Elgar, Edward Publishing, Inc.

Tung, Chen-yuan. Cross-Strait Economic Relations in the Era of Globalization. 2008. 508p. pap. *(978-3-639-09125-0(6))* VDM Verlag Dr. Mueller e.K.

Turnbull, Stephen. Pirate of the Far East: 811-1639. 2007. (Warrior Ser.). (ENG., Illus.). 64p. pap. 17.95 *(978-1-84603-174-8(5))* Osprey Publishing, Ltd. GBR. Dist: Random Hse., Inc.

Tyau, Min-Chien T. Z. China's New Constitution & International Problems. 2007. (ENG.). 312p. per. 28.95 *(978-0-548-31822-5(0))* Kessinger Publishing, LLC.

Upadhya, Sanjay. Nepal & the Geo-Strategic Rivalry Between China & India. 2012. (Routledge Studies in South Asian Politics Ser.). (ENG., Illus.). 240p. (C). 135.00 ***(978-0-415-69572-5(4))*** Routledge.

van der Putten, Frans-Paul & Shulong, Chu, eds. China, Europe & International Security: Interests, Roles, & Prospects. 2012. (ENG., Illus.). 218p. pap. 39.95 ***(978-0-415-53253-2(1))*** Routledge.

van Dijk, Meine Pieter, ed. The New Presence of China in Africa. 2010. (Eadi Ser.). (Illus.). 224p. pap. *(978-90-8964-136-6(X))* Amsterdam Univ. Pr.

Vogt, Roland. Europe & China: Strategic Partners or Rivals? 2012. (Global Connections Ser.). (ENG., Illus.). 276p. (gr. 17). 50.00 ***(978-988-8083-87-9(2))***; pap. 30.00 ***(978-988-8083-88-6(0))*** Hong Kong Univ. Pr. HKG. Dist: Columbia Univ. Pr.

Vukovich, Daniel, ed. China & Orientalism: Western Knowledge Production & the P. R. C. 2011. (Postcolonial Politics Ser.). (ENG.). 208p. (C). 130.00 *(978-0-415-59220-8(8))* Routledge.

Waldron, Arthur N., ed. China in Africa. 2009. (ENG.). 135p. pap. 24.95 *(978-0-9816905-0-6(5))* Jamestown Foundation, The.

Wang, Dong. China's Unequal Treaties: Narrating National History. 2008. (Asiaworld Ser.). (ENG.). 190p. pap. 26.50 *(978-0-7391-2806-0(X))* Lexington Bks.

Wang, Gabe T. China & the Taiwan Issue: Incoming War at Taiwan Strait. Wang, Gabe T., ed. 2006. (ENG., Illus.). 258p. 68.50 *(978-0-7618-3434-2(6))* Univ. Pr. of America, Inc.

Wang, Gungwu & Zheng, Yongnian. China & the New International Order. Gungwu, Wang & Yongnian, Zheng, eds. 2008. (Illus.). XIV, 322p. 170.00 *(978-0-415-44111-7(0))* Routledge.

Wang, Hui. Ya Zhou Shi Ye: Zhongguo Li Shi de Xu Shu. 2010. (CHI.). xxiii, 331p. *(978-0-19-801928-2(9))* Oxford Univ. Pr., Inc.

Wang, Wei. Di Yuan Zheng Zhi Yu Zhongguo Guo Jia an Quan. 2009. (CHI.). *(978-7-80150-778-5(9))* Military Bks. Publishing Hse. of Friendship and Culture.

Wang, Xiuyu. Chinas Last Imperial Frontier: Cb. 2011. (ENG., Illus.). 308p. (gr. 17). 80.00 ***(978-0-7391-6809-7(6))*** Lexington Bks.

Wang, Yi. Australia-China Relations Post 1949: Sixty Years of Trade & Politics. 2012. 266p. 114.95 ***(978-1-4094-3728-4(0))*** Ashgate Publishing Co.

Wei, C. X. George, et al, eds. Challenges to Chinese Foreign Policy: Diplomacy, Globalization, & the Next World Power. 2009. (Asia in the New Millennium Ser.). (ENG.). 416p. 75.00 *(978-0-8131-2529-9(4))*; pap. 29.95 *(978-0-8131-9202-4(1))* Univ. Pr. of Kentucky.

Wei, George, ed. Cross-Taiwan Strait Relations in a Global Context. 2012. (Routledge Contemporary China Ser.). (ENG., Illus.). 288p. (C). 130.00 *(978-0-415-60012-5(X))* Routledge.

Weitz, Richard. China-Russia Security Relations: Strategic Parallelism without Partnership or Passion? 2008. lib. bdg. *(978-1-58487-360-0(4))* Strategic Studies Institute, U.S. Army War College Commandant (AWCC-DSI/Pubns.).

Wesley-Smith, Terence. China in Oceania: New Forces in Pacific Politics. 2007. (Pacific Islands Policy Ser.: Vol. 2). 35p. pap. *(978-0-86638-210-6(0))* East-West Ctr.

Wiessala, Georg, et al, eds. The European Union & China: Interests & Dilemmas. 2009. (Illus.). 296p. 86.00 *(978-90-420-2741-1(X))* Rodopi.

Wilde, Tanguy De, et al. China, the European Union & the Restructuring of Global Governance. Wouters, Jan, ed. 2012. (Leuven Global Governance Ser.). 368p. 150.00 ***(978-1-78100-426-5(9))*** Elgar, Edward Publishing, Inc.

Womack, Brantly. China's Rise in Historical Perspective. 2010. (ENG.). 272p. pap. 29.95 *(978-0-7425-6722-1(2))* Rowman & Littlefield Publishers, Inc.

Womack, Brantly, ed. China's Rise in Historical Perspective. 2010. (ENG.). 272p. 85.00 *(978-0-7425-6721-4(4))* Rowman & Littlefield Publishers, Inc.

Wu, Guoguang, ed. China Turns to Multilateralism: Foreign Policy & Regional Security. 2011. (ENG., Illus.). 318p. pap. 42.95 ***(978-0-415-66646-6(5))*** Routledge.

—Chinas Challenges to Human Security. 2012. (China Policy Ser.). (ENG., Illus.). 336p. (C). 160.00 ***(978-0-415-52082-9(7))*** Routledge.

Xiao Yang, Suzanne. China in the un Security Council Decision-Making on Iraq. 2012. (New International Relations Ser.). (ENG., Illus.). 272p. (C). 130.00 *(978-0-415-61769-7(3))* Routledge.

Xu, Guoqi. China & the Great War: China's Pursuit of a New National Identity & Internationalization. 2011. (Studies in the Social & Cultural History of Modern Warfare Ser.). (ENG.). 342p. pap. 43.00 *(978-0-521-28323-6(X))* Cambridge Univ. Pr.

Xu, Zhuoyun. Rivers in Time: A Cultural History of China. 2012. 576p. ***(978-0-231-52818-4(3))*** Columbia Univ. Pr.

Xu, Zhuoyun & Hsu, Cho-yun. China: A New Cultural History. Baker, Timothy D. & Duke, Michael S., trs. from CHI. 2012. (Masters of Chinese Studies). (ENG., Illus.). 632p. (gr. 17). pap. 40.00 ***(978-0-231-15921-0(8))*** Columbia Univ. Pr.

Xu, Zhuoyun & Hsu, Cho-Yun. China: A New Cultural History. Baker, Timothy D. & Duke, Michael S., trs. from CHI. 2012. (Masters of Chinese Studies). (ENG., Illus.). 632p. (gr. 17). 120.00 ***(978-0-231-15920-3(X))*** Columbia Univ. Pr.

Yang, Jian. The Pacific Islands in China's Grand Strategy: Small States, Big Games. 2011. (ENG., Illus.). 288p. 85.00 *(978-0-230-11323-7(0))* Palgrave Macmillan.

Yongnian, Zheng, ed. China & International Relations: The Chinese View & the Contribution of Wang Gungwu. 2012. (ENG., Illus.). 384p. (C). pap. 44.95 ***(978-0-415-62546-3(7))*** Routledge.

—China & International Relations: The Chinese View & the Contribution of Wang Gungwu. 2010. (China Policy Ser.). (ENG., Illus.). 384p. (C). 155.00 *(978-0-415-57607-9(5)*, Routledge) Taylor & Francis Group GBR. Dist: Taylor & Francis Group.

Yu, Peter & Kao, Shawn. International Governance & Regimes: Case Studies from Beijing & Taipei. 2010. (ENG., Illus.). 224p. 73.50 *(978-0-7391-4319-3(0))* Lexington Bks.

Yu, Peter Kien-Hong. International Governance & Regimes: A Chinese Perspective. 2011. (Routledge Contemporary China Ser.). (ENG., Illus.). 232p. (C). 125.00 *(978-0-415-68199-5(5))* Routledge.

Zang, Yunhu. 20 Shi Ji de Zhongguo Yu Shi Jie: China & the World in the 20th Century. 2010. (CHI.). *(978-7-301-13688-1(9))* Beijing University Pr.

Zhang, Li. News Media & EU-China Relations. 2011. (Palgrave Macmillan Series in International Political Communication Ser.). (ENG., Illus.). 246p. 85.00 *(978-0-230-10502-7(5))* Palgrave Macmillan.

Zhang, Xin. Implementation of the WTO Agreements in China. 2006. (ENG.). 377p. *(978-1-898029-79-3(2))* Wildy, Simmonds & Hill.

Zheng, Biao. Zhongguo Guo Ji Zheng Zhi Jing Ji Xue: International Political Economics of Chinese Edition. 2008. *(978-7-80211-284-1(2))* Cetial Compilation & Fanslation Pr.

Zhimin, Chen, ed. China's Reforms & International Political Economy. 2007. (Routledge Studies on China in Transition Ser.). (ENG., Illus.). 256p. (C). 170.00 *(978-0-415-39613-4(1))* Routledge.

Zhu, Zhiqun. Global Studies: China. 13th ed. 2009. (Global Studies). (ENG.). 224p. (C). pap. 50.00 *(978-0-07-337987-6(5)*, 0073379875, McGraw-Hill/Dushkin) McGraw-Hill Higher Education.

CHINA—FOREIGN RELATIONS—1949-

Ahrari, Ehsan M. The Great Powers Versus the Hegemon. 2011. (ENG., Illus.). 256p. 85.00 *(978-0-230-27891-2(4))* Palgrave Macmillan.

Astarita, Claudia & Lim, Yves-Heng, eds. China & India in Asia: Paving the Way for a New Balance of Power. 2011. (Global Political Studies). 213p. 140.00 *(978-1-61324-850-8(4))* Nova Science Pubs., Inc.

Bates, Gillian & Gill, Bates. Rising Star: China's New Security Diplomacy. 2nd rev. ed. 2010. (ENG.). 267p. pap. 22.95 *(978-0-8157-0453-9(4))* Brookings Institution Pr.

Bo, Zhiyue & Wong, John. China's Reform in Global Perspective. 2010. (Illus.). 400p. 96.00 *(978-981-4289-24-5(8))* World Scientific Publishing Co., Inc.

Caffrey, Kevin, ed. The Beijing Olympics: Promoting China. 2010. (ENG., Illus.). 173p. (C). 125.00 *(978-0-415-59398-4(0))* Routledge.

Chan, Lai-Ha. China At 60: Global-Local Interactions. 2011. 352p. 98.00 *(978-981-4299-29-9(4))* World Scientific Publishing Co., Inc.

Chou. China's Policies on Its Borderlands & the International Implications. 2010. (Illus.). 296p. 95.00 *(978-981-4287-66-1(0))* World Scientific Publishing Co., Inc.

Deng, Yong. China's Struggle for Status: The Realignment of International Relations. 2008. (ENG., Illus.). 312p. 81.00 *(978-0-521-88666-6(X))*; pap. 31.99 *(978-0-521-71415-0(X))* Cambridge Univ. Pr.

Doyle, Randall & Boshu, Zhang. Modern China & the New World: The Reemergence of the Middle Kingdom in the 21st Century. 2011. (ENG.). 186p. (gr. 17). 60.00 ***(978-0-7391-7187-5(9))*** Lexington Bks.

Doyle, Randall Jordan & Zhang, Boshu. Modern China & the New World: The Reemergence of the Middle Kingdom in the 21st Century. 2011. E-Book ***(978-0-7391-7188-2(7))*** Lexington Bks.

Farndon, John. China Rises: How China's Astonishing Growth Will Change the World. 2008. (ENG., Illus.). 240p. pap. 14.95 *(978-0-7535-1349-1(8))* Virgin Bks. Ltd. GBR. Dist: Independent Pubs. Group.

Feng, Huiyun. Chinese Strategic Culture & Foreign Policy Decision-Making: Confucianism, Leadership & War. 2009. 188p. pap. 39.95 *(978-0-415-54520-4(X))* 2007. (Illus.). 185p. 160.00 *(978-0-415-41815-7(1))* Routledge.

Fravel, M. Taylor. Strong Borders, Secure Nation: Cooperation & Conflict in China's Territorial Disputes. 2008. (Princeton Studies in International History & Politics Ser.). (ENG., Illus.). 408p. (C). 72.50 *(978-0-691-13608-0(4))*; pap. 32.50 *(978-0-691-13609-7(2))* Princeton Univ. Pr.

Guo, Sujian & Hua, Shiping. New Dimensions of Chinese Foreign Policy. 2007. (New Dimensions in Chinese Foreign Policy Ser.). (ENG.). 258p. 68.50 *(978-0-7391-1876-4(5))* Lexington Bks.

Hagstrvm, Japan's China Policy. 2007. (Illus.). 256p. 39.95 *(978-0-415-43899-5(3))* Routledge.

Hauser, Gunther & Kernic, Franz, eds. China: The Rising Power. 2009. 216p. pap. 56.95 *(978-3-631-58269-5(2))* Lang, Peter GmbH, Europaischer Verlag der Wissenschaften DEU. Dist: Lang, Peter.

Hua, Shiping & Guo, Sujian, eds. China in the Twenty-First Century: Challenges & Opportunities. 2011. (ENG., Illus.). 296p. pap. 30.00 *(978-0-230-12072-3(5))* Palgrave Macmillan.

Huang, Jing & Li, Xiaoting. Inseparable Separation: The Making of China's Taiwan Policy. 2009. 330p. 96.00 *(978-981-4287-36-4(9))*, World Scientific Publishing Co., Inc.

Jacques, Martin. When China Rules the World: The End of the Western World & the Birth of a New Global Order. (ENG.). (gr. 12). 2009. 576p. 29.95 *(978-1-59420-185-1(4)*, Penguin Pr. HC, The) 2012. 848p. 20.00 *(978-0-14-311800-8(5)*, Penguin (Non-Classics)) Penguin Group (USA) Inc.

Kang, David C. China Rising: Peace, Power, & Order in East Asia. 2007. (ENG., Illus.). 296p. (gr. 17). 26.95 *(978-0-231-14188-8(2))* Columbia Univ. Pr.

Keith, Ronald C. China as a Rising World Power & Its Response To 'Globalization' 2008. 256p. pap. 39.95 *(978-0-415-46417-8(X))* Routledge.

Kennedy, Andrew. The International Ambitions of Mao & Nehru: National Efficacy Beliefs & the Making of Foreign Policy. 2011. (ENG., Illus.). 272p. 99.00 ***(978-0-521-19351-1(6))*** Cambridge Univ. Pr.

LaFleur, Robert André. China, 1 vol. 2009. (Asia in Focus Ser.). (Illus.). 504p. 85.00 *(978-1-59884-166-4(1)*, CHINAS1C) ABC-CLIO, LLC.

Lanteigne. China & International Institutions. 2007. pap. 39.95 *(978-0-415-45956-3(7))* Routledge.

Larus, Elizabeth Freund. Politics & Society in Contemporary China. 2012. (C). 275p. pap. 32.50 ***(978-1-58826-825-9(X))***; (Illus.). 75.00 ***(978-1-58826-800-6(4))*** Rienner, Lynne Pubs.

Lawrance, Alan. China Foreig Rel Sinc 1949 V13. 2007. 288p. 200.00 *(978-0-415-36157-6(5))* Routledge.

Leung, Beatrice. Sino-Vatican Relations: Problems in Conflicting Authority, 1976-1986. 2009. (LSE Monographs in International Studies). (ENG.). 440p. pap. 57.00 *(978-0-521-12256-6(2))* Cambridge Univ. Pr.

Levi, Werner. Modern China's Foreign Policy. 2009. (ENG.). 416p. pap. 60.00 *(978-0-8166-5817-6(X))* Univ. of Minnesota Pr.

C

Li, Mingjiang, ed. China's International Relations in Asia, 4 vols. 2010. (Critical Issues in Modern Politics Ser.). (ENG., Illus.). 1618p. 1075.00 *(978-0-415-47691-1(7))* Routledge.

Lumbers, Michael. Piercing the Bamboo Curtain: Tentative Bridge-Building to China During the Johnson Years. 2008. (ENG.). 272p. 84.00 *(978-0-7190-7778-4(8))* Manchester Univ. Pr. GBR. Dist: Macmillan.

Mark, Chi-kwan. China & the World Since 1945: An International History. 2011. (Making of the Contemporary World Ser.). (ENG., Illus.). 160p. 105.00 *(978-0-415-60650-9(0))* Routledge.

—China & the World since 1945: An International History. 2011. (Making of the Contemporary World Ser.). (ENG., Illus.). 160p. pap. 27.95 *(978-0-415-60651-6(9))* Routledge.

Monroe, Alice V., ed. China's Foreign Policy & Soft Power Influence. 2010. (China in the 21st Century Ser.). (Illus.). x, 184p. 115.00 *(978-1-60692-994-0(1))* Nova Science Pubs., Inc.

Mozingo, David. Chinese Policy Toward Indonesia, 1949-1967. 2010. (ENG.). 308p. per. 29.95 *(978-979-3780-54-2(1))* Equinox Publishing IDN. Dist: Univ. of Hawaii Pr.

Ong, Russell. China's Security Interests in the 21st Century. 2010. (ENG.). xii, 158p. pap. 39.95 *(978-0-415-59044-0(2))* Routledge.

Paltiel, Jeremy. The Empire's New Clothes: Cultural Particularism & Universal Value in China's Quest for Global Status. rev. ed. 2007. (ENG., Illus.). 332p. 95.00 *(978-1-4039-6198-3(0))* Palgrave Macmillan.

Pan, Junwu. Toward a New Framework for Peaceful Settlement of China's Territorial & Boundary Disputes. 2009. *(978-90-04-17428-3(1))* BRILL.

Rongji, Zhu. Zhu Rongji Meets the Press. 2011. (Illus.). 512p. 35.00 *(978-0-19-396641-3(7))* Oxford Univ. Pr., Inc.

Rose, Caroline. Sino-Japanese Relations: Facing the Past, Looking to the Future? 2009. 176p. pap. 39.95 *(978-0-415-54619-5(2))* Routledge.

Scott. China Stands up. 2007. (ENG.). 224p. (C). 43.95 *(978-0-415-40270-5(0))* Routledge.

Scott, David. China Stands Up: The PRC & the International System. 2007. 212p. 180.00 *(978-0-415-40269-9(7))* Routledge.

Shen, Simon & Blanchard, Jean-Marc F. Multidimensional Diplomacy of Contemporary China. 2010. (Challenges Facing Chinese Political Development Ser.). (Illus.). (ENG.). 336p. 83.99 *(978-0-7391-3994-3(0))*; vi, 322p. *(978-0-7391-3996-7(7))* Lexington Bks.

Snyder, Francis & Snyder, Francis G. The European Union & China, 1949-2006: Basic Documents & Commentary. 2009. (ENG.). 1128p. pap. 134.00 *(978-1-84113-724-7(3))* Hart Publishing Ltd. GBR. Dist: International Specialized Bk. Services.

Snyder, Scott. China¿s Rise & the Two Koreas: Politics, Economics, Security. 2009. (Illus.). 240p. (C). 57.00 *(978-1-58826-618-7(4))*; pap. *(978-1-58826-622-4(2))* Rienner, Lynne Pubs.

Strauss, Julia, ed. The History of the PRC (1949-1976) 2007. (China Quarterly Special Issues Ser.). (ENG., Illus.). 262p. per. 44.00 *(978-0-521-69696-8(8))* Cambridge Univ. Pr.

Sutter, Robert. Historical Dictionary of Chinese Foreign Policy. 2011. (Historical Dictionaries of Diplomacy & Foreign Relations Ser.). (ENG.). 352p. 95.00 *(978-0-8108-6860-1(1))* Scarecrow Pr., Inc.

van der Putten, Frans-Paul & Shulong, Chu, eds. China Europe & International Security. 2010. (Asian Security Studies). (ENG., Illus.). 232p. 130.00 *(978-0-415-58580-4(5)*, Routledge) Taylor & Francis Group GBR. Dist: Taylor & Francis Group.

Wang, Enbao. The Origin, Process, & Outcome of China,s Reforms in the Past One Hundred Years: The Chinese Quest for National Rejuvenation. 2009. x, 383p. *(978-0-7734-3904-7(8))* Mellen, Edwin Pr., The.

Xiao, Donglian. Liu Shi Nian Guo Shi Ji Yao. 2009. (CHI.). *(978-7-5438-6025-4(2))* Hunan Publishing Hse.

Xiao/Carlson, ed. New Frontiers in China's Foreign Relations: Zhongguo Waijiao de Xin Bianjiang. 2011. (Challenges Facing Chinese Political Development Ser.). (ENG.). 230p. 65.00 ***(978-0-7391-5025-2(1))*** Lexington Bks.

Zhang, Yunling. Rising China & World Order. 2010. 220p. 88.00 *(978-981-4304-21-4(2))* World Scientific Publishing Co., Inc.

CHINA—FOREIGN RELATIONS—ASIA

Balci, Bayram, et al, eds. China & India in Central Asia: A New Great Game? 2010. (Sciences Po Series in International Relations & Political Economy Ser.). (ENG., Illus.). 268p. 89.00 *(978-0-230-10356-6(1))* Palgrave Macmillan.

Bateman, Sam & Ho, Joshua. Southeast Asia & the Rise of Chinese & Indian Naval Power: Between Rising Naval Powers. 2010. (Routledge Security in Asia Pacific Ser.). (ENG., Illus.). 272p. (C). 130.00 *(978-0-415-55955-3(3)*, Routledge) Taylor & Francis Group GBR. Dist: Taylor & Francis Group.

Chan, Steve. Looking for Balance: China, the United States, & Power Balancing in East Asia. 2012. (Studies in Asian Security Ser.). (ENG.). 304p. 50.00 *(978-0-8047-7820-6(5))* Stanford Univ. Pr.

Chellaney, Brahma. Asian Juggernaut: The Rise of China, India, & Japan. 2010. 272p. pap. 15.99 *(978-0-06-136308-5(1)*, Harper Paperbacks) HarperCollins Pubs.

Chung, Chien-Peng. China's Multilateral Co-Operation in Asia & the Pacific: Institutionalizing Beijing's 'Good Neighbour Policy' 2010. (Politics in Asia Ser.). (ENG., Illus.). 192p. (C). 130.00 *(978-0-415-56914-9(1)*, Routledge) Taylor & Francis Group GBR. Dist: Taylor & Francis Group.

The Crisis in Tibet: Finding a Path to Peace: Hearing Before the Subcommittee on East Asian & Pacific Affairs of the Committee on Foreign Relations, United States Senate, One Hundred Tenth Congress, Second Session, April 23, 2008. 2009. iii, 81p. *(978-0-16-082860-7(0)*, 552-070-38835-4) United States Government Printing Office.

Cui, Shunji. Sino-Japanese Relations & a 'security Regime' in East Asi. 2010. 276p. pap. *(978-3-8383-9178-6(0))* Lambert Academic Publishing.

Dent, Christopher M., ed. China, Japan & Regional Leadership in East Asia. 328p. 2010. (Illus.). pap. 53.00 *(978-1-84980-082-2(0))* 2008. (C). 150.00 *(978-1-84720-749-4(9))* Elgar, Edward Publishing, Inc.

Devare, Sudhir T., et al, eds. Emerging China: Prospects of Partnership in Asia. 2012. (ENG.). (C). 95.00 ***(978-0-415-50236-8(5)***, Routledge India) Taylor & Francis Group GBR. Dist: Taylor & Francis Group.

Donze, Geralyn. One Country, Two Systems. 2010. 92p. pap. *(978-3-639-23040-6(X))* VDM Verlag Dr. Mueller e.K.

Faure, Guy. New Dynamics Between China & Japan in Asia: How to Build the Future from the Past? 2010. (Illus.). 368p. 108.00 *(978-981-4313-66-7(1))* World Scientific Publishing Co., Inc.

Friedberg, Aaron L. A Contest for Supremacy: China, America, & the Struggle for Mastery in Asia. 2011. (ENG., Illus.). 384p. 27.95 *(978-0-393-06828-3(5)*, 6828) Norton, W. W. & Co., Inc.

Garrison, Jean A. China & the Energy Equation in Asia: The Determinants of Policy Choice. 2009. (Illus.). 200p. 59.95 *(978-1-935049-05-0(4))* FirstForumPress.

Goh, Evelyn & Simon, Sheldon W., eds. China, the United States, & Southeast Asia: Contending Perspectives on Politics, Security, & Economics. 2007. (Asian Security Studies). (ENG., Illus.). 224p. (C). 160.00 *(978-0-415-42945-0(5))* Routledge.

Guo, Baogang & Teng, Chung-Chian, eds. Taiwan & the Rise of China: Cross-Strait Relations in the Twenty-first Century. 2012. (Challenges Facing Chinese Political Development Ser.). (ENG.). 188p. (gr. 17). 60.00 ***(978-0-7391-6692-5(1))*** Lexington Bks.

Hodder, R. N. W. Overseas Chinese & Trade Between the Philippines & China: The Intertwining of Family, Social, & Business Interests in Promoting Trade. 2006. (Illus.). 328p. 119.95 *(978-0-7734-5793-5(3))* Mellen, Edwin Pr., The.

Hongyi, Lai & Seng, Lim Tin, eds. Harmony & Development: ASEA - China Relations. 2007. 164p. 84.00 *(978-981-270-970-7(3))* World Scientific Publishing Co., Inc.

Huang. The Tibet Issue & China's Peaceful Development. 2011. 300p. 68.00 *(978-981-283-595-6(4))* World Scientific Publishing Co., Inc.

Huang, Michael L. Taiwan: Relations with China & the U. S. 2011. (Series: Asian Political, Economic & Security Issues Ser.). 89.00 *(978-1-61761-468-2(8))* Nova Science Pubs., Inc.

Kang, David C. China Rising: Peace, Power, & Order in East Asia. (ENG., Illus.). 296p. (gr. 17). 2009. pap. 19.50 *(978-0-231-14189-5(0))* 2007. 26.95 *(978-0-231-14188-8(2))* Columbia Univ. Pr.

Karrar, Hasan H. The New Silk Road Diplomacy: China's Central Asian Foreign Policy since the Cold War. 2010. (ENG., Illus.). 272p. (C). pap. 35.95 *(978-0-7748-1693-9(7))* UBC Pr. CAN. Dist: Univ. of Washington Pr.

—The New Silk Road Diplomacy: China's Central Asian Foreign Policy since the Cold War. 2009. (ENG.). 272p. ***(978-0-7748-1692-2(9))*** Univ. of British Columbia Pr.

Keyuan, Zou. China-Asean Relations & International Law. 2011. (Chandos Asian Studies). (ENG., Illus.). 250p. 110.00 *(978-1-84334-438-4(6)*, Chandos Publishing) Woodhead Publishing Ltd. GBR. Dist: Ingram Pub. Services.

Lee, Chun-Yi. Taiwanese Business or Chinese Security Asset: A Changing Pattern of Interaction Between Taiwanese Businesses & Chinese Governments. 2011. (Routledge/Leiden Series in Modern East Asian Politics & History Ser.). (ENG., Illus.). 184p. (C). 125.00 *(978-0-415-57593-5(1))* Routledge.

Lewis, John Wilson & Xue, Litai. Zhongguo Jun Shi Jue Ce Ji Zhi Ji Taiwan Chong Tu. 2007. ("Zhongguo Ju Shi " Xi Lie Ser.: Vol. 47). (CHI., Illus.). 7p. pap. *(978-1-932138-57-3(9))* Mirror Bks. USA.

Li, Mingjiang, ed. China & East Asian Strategic Dynamics: The Shaping of a New Regional Order. 2011. (ENG.). 312p. 75.00 *(978-0-7391-6794-6(4))* Lexington Bks.

—China's International Relations in Asia, 4 vols. 2010. (Critical Issues in Modern Politics Ser.). (ENG., Illus.). 1618p. 1075.00 *(978-0-415-47691-1(7))* Routledge.

—China's International Relations in Asia V1, 4 vols. 2010. (Illus.). 406p. *(978-0-415-48482-4(0))* Routledge.

—China's International Relations in Asia V2, 4 vols. 2010. (Illus.). 404p. *(978-0-415-48483-1(9))* Routledge.

—China's International Relations in Asia V3, 4 vols. 2010. (Illus.). 388p. *(978-0-415-48484-8(7))* Routledge.

—China's International Relations in Asia V4, 4 vols. 2010. (Illus.). 420p. *(978-0-415-48485-5(5))* Routledge.

Liu, Xiaoyuan. Reins of Liberation: An Entangled History of Mongolian Independence, Chinese Territoriality, & Great Power Hegemony, 1911-1950. 2006. (ENG., Illus.). 506p. 70.00 *(978-0-8047-5426-2(8))* Stanford Univ. Pr.

Lo, Bobo. Axis of Convenience: Moscow, Beijing, & the New Geopolitics. 2008. (ENG., Illus.). 277p. 32.95 *(978-0-8157-5340-7(3))* Brookings Institution Pr.

Lo, Shiu Hing. The Dynamics of Beijing-Hong Kong Relations: A Model for Taiwan? 2008. (ENG.). 344p. (gr. 17). 60.00 *(978-962-209-908-1(4))*; pap. 27.95 *(978-962-209-909-8(2))* Hong Kong Univ. Pr. HKG. Dist: Columbia Univ. Pr.

Marketos, Thrassy N. China's Energy Geopolitics. 2010. pap. 39.95 *(978-0-415-58617-7(8))* Routledge.

Percival, Bronson. The Dragon Looks South: China & Southeast Asia in the New Century, 1 vol. annot. ed. 2007. (Praeger Security International Ser.). 216p. 49.95 *(978-0-275-99426-6(0)*, C9426, Praeger Security International) Greenwood Publishing Group, Inc.

Reynolds, Julius David Alexander. The Construction of Regional Security in Eurasi. 2009. 80p. pap. *(978-3-639-17535-6(2))* VDM Verlag Dr. Mueller e.K.

Richardson, Sophie. China, Cambodia, & the Five Principles of Peaceful Coexistence. 2009. (ENG.). 344p. (gr. 17). 50.00 *(978-0-231-14386-8(9))* Columbia Univ. Pr.

Rozman, Gilbert. Chinese Strategic Thought Toward Asia. 2010. (Strategic Thought in Northeast Asia Ser.). (ENG.). 272p. 89.00 *(978-1-4039-7551-5(5))* Palgrave Macmillan.

Sato, Yoichiro & Cooney, Kevin J. The Rise of China & International Security: America & Asia Respond. Cooney, Kevin & Sato, Yoichiro, eds. 2008. (Asian Security Studies). (Illus.). 256p. 140.00 *(978-0-415-43396-9(7))* Routledge.

Scobell, Andrew & Wortzel, Larry M. Shaping China's Security Environment: The Role of the People's Liberation Army. 2006. vi, 314p. pap. *(978-1-58487-251-1(9))* Strategic Studies Institute, U.S. Army War College Commandant (AWCC-DSI/Pubns.).

Seng. Harmony & Development. 2007. pap. 1.00 *(978-981-270-971-4(1))* World Scientific Publishing Co., Inc.

Shichor, Yitzhak. Ethno-Diplomacy: The Uyghur Hitch in Sino-Turkish Relations. 2009. (Policy Studies: 53). 84p. pap. 10.00 *(978-1-932728-80-4(5))* East-West Ctr.

Simon, Sheldon W. China America & South-East Asia. 2009. 206p. pap. 39.95 *(978-0-415-56950-7(8))* Routledge.

Storey, Ian & Schofield, Clive. The South China Sea Dispute: Increasing Stakes & Rising Tensions. 2011. (ENG., Illus.). 42p. pap. 20.00 *(978-0-9816905-5-1(6))* Jamestown Foundation, The.

Tang, Shiping, et al. Living with China: Regional States & China Through Crises & Turning Points. Tang, Shiping et al, eds. 2009. (ENG.). 288p. 105.00 *(978-0-230-61670-7(4))* Palgrave Macmillan.

Wade. China & Southeast Asia V1, 6 vols. 2008. (Illus.). *(978-0-415-36753-0(0))* Routledge.

—China & Southeast Asia V2, 6 vols. 2008. (Illus.). *(978-0-415-36754-7(9))* Routledge.

—China & Southeast Asia V3, 6 vols. 2008. (Illus.). *(978-0-415-36755-4(7))* Routledge.

—China & Southeast Asia V4, 6 vols. 2008. (Illus.). *(978-0-415-36756-1(5))* Routledge.

—China & Southeast Asia V5, 6 vols. 2008. (Illus.). *(978-0-415-36757-8(3))* Routledge.

—China & Southeast Asia V6, 6 vols. 2008. (Illus.). *(978-0-415-36758-5(1))* Routledge.

Wade, Geof. Southeast Asia Fifteenth. (Illus.). 380p. pap. 32.00 *(978-9971-69-448-7(4))* National Univ. of Singapore Pr. SGP. Dist: Univ. of Hawaii Pr.

Wade, Geoff & Laichen, Sun, eds. Southeast Asia in the Fifteenth Century: The China Factor. 2010. (ENG., Illus.). 520p. (gr. 17). pap. 30.00 *(978-988-8028-48-1(0))* Hong Kong Univ. Pr. HKG. Dist: Columbia Univ. Pr.

Wade, Geoffrey & Chin, James K., eds. China & Southeast Asia. 2012. (Routledge Studies in the Modern History of Asia Ser.). (ENG.). 256p. (C). 125.00 *(978-0-415-58997-0(5))* Routledge.

Wishnick, Elizabeth. Russia, China, & the United States in Central Asia: Prospects for Great Power Competition & Cooperation in the Shadow of the Georgian Crisis. 2009. *(978-1-58487-379-2(5))* Strategic Studies Institute, U.S. Army War College Commandant (AWCC-DSI/Pubns.).

Womack, Brantly. China among Unequals: Asymmetric Foreign Relationships in Asia. 2010. (Illus.). 552p. 130.00 *(978-981-4295-27-7(2))* World Scientific Publishing Co., Inc.

Yoshida, Katutugu, et al. Taiwan's Long Road to Democracy: Bitter Taste of Freedom. 2009. (Illus.). 264p. 119.00 *(978-1-84844-078-4(2))* Elgar, Edward Publishing, Inc.

CHINA—FOREIGN RELATIONS—DEVELOPING COUNTRIES

Eisenman, Joshua, et al, eds. China & the Developing World: Beijing's Strategy for the Twenty-First Century. 2007. (ENG., Illus.). 256p. 103.95 *(978-0-7656-1712-5(9)*, East Gate Bk.) Sharpe, M.E. Inc.

Eisenman, Joshua, et al. China & the Developing World: Beijing's Strategy for the Twenty-First Century. Eisenman, Joshua et al, eds. 2007. (East Gate Bks.). (ENG., Illus.). 256p. per. 36.95 *(978-0-7656-1713-2(7)*, East Gate Bk.) Sharpe, M.E. Inc.

CHINA—FOREIGN RELATIONS—GREAT BRITAIN

Auerbach, Sascha J., et al. Race, Law, & the Chinese Puzzle in Imperial Britain. 2009. (ENG., Illus.). 280p. 95.00 *(978-0-230-60949-5(X))* Palgrave Macmillan.

Brunero, Donna. Britain's Imperial Cornerstone in China: The Chinese Maritime Customs Service, 1854-1949. 2009. 206p. pap. 39.95 *(978-0-415-54551-8(X))* Routledge.

Buchanan, Tom. East Wind: China & the British Left, 1925-1976. 2012. (ENG., Illus.). 304p. 125.00 ***(978-0-19-957033-1(7))*** Oxford Univ. Pr., Inc.

Hoe, Susanna & Roebuck, Derek. The Taking of Hong Kong: Charles & Clara Elliot in China Waters. 2009. (Echoes: Classics of Hong Kong Culture & History Ser.). (ENG., Illus.). 312p. (gr. 17). pap. 28.00 *(978-962-209-988-3(2))* Hong Kong Univ. Pr. HKG. Dist: Columbia Univ. Pr.

Knuesel, Araine. Framing China: Public Images & Diplomatic Debates in Britain the USA & Switzerland, 1900-1950. 2012. (Illus.). 298p. 124.95 ***(978-1-4094-2559-5(2))*** Ashgate Publishing Co.

Lin, Cheng-yi & Roy, Denny, eds. The Future of the United States, China, & Taiwan Relations. 2011. (ENG.). 266p. 85.00 *(978-0-230-11278-0(1))* Palgrave Macmillan.

Martin, Edwin W. Divided Counsel: The Anglo-American Response to Communist Victory in China. 2009. (ENG.). 288p. pap. 30.00 *(978-0-8131-9292-5(7))* Univ. Pr. of Kentucky.

Shai, Aron. Origins of the War in the East. 2010. (ENG.). 270p. 115.00 *(978-0-415-58540-8(6)*, Routledge) Taylor & Francis Group GBR. Dist: Taylor & Francis Group.

Wong, Pak Nung. Farewell to the Crown Colony: A Content Analysis of the British Press Coverage of the 1997 Sovereignty Reversion in Hong Kong. 2011. 88p. pap. ***(978-3-639-34000-6(0))*** VDM Verlag Dr. Mueller e.K.

Younghusband, Francis Edward. Peace in Tibet. Coates, Tim, ed. 2009. 296p. pap. *(978-1-84381-049-0(2))* Coates, Tim.

CHINA—FOREIGN RELATIONS—HONG KONG

Ma, Jiewei. Desiring Hong Kong, Consuming South China: Transborder Cultural Politics, 1970-2010. 2012. (Hong Kong Culture & Society Ser.). (ENG., Illus.). 220p. (gr. 17). 60.00 ***(978-988-8083-45-9(7))*** Hong Kong Univ. Pr. HKG. Dist: Columbia Univ. Pr.

CHINA—FOREIGN RELATIONS—INDIA

Astarita, Claudia & Lim, Yves-Heng, eds. China & India in Asia: Paving the Way for a New Balance of Power. 2011. (Global Political Studies). 213p. 140.00 *(978-1-61324-850-8(4))* Nova Science Pubs., Inc.

Athwal, Amardeep. China-India Relations: Contemporary Dynamics. 2009. 164p. pap. 39.95 *(978-0-415-54473-3(4))* 2007. (Illus.). 176p. 160.00 *(978-0-415-43735-6(0))* Routledge.

Ayres, Alyssa & Mohan, C. Raja, eds. Power Realignments in Asia: China, India & the United States. 2009. (Illus.). 356p. (C). 39.95 *(978-81-7829-948-8(8)*, B99488C) SAGE Pubns., Inc.

Bagchi, Prabodh Chandra. India & China: A Thousand Years of Cultural Relations. 3rd rev. ed. 2008. (Illus.). 232p. 52.50 *(978-81-215-1197-1(6))* Munshiram Manoharlal Pubs. Private, Ltd. IND. Dist: Coronet Bks.

Bahl, Raghav. Superpower? The Amazing Race Between China's Hare & India's Tortoise. 2010. (ENG., Illus.). 272p. (gr. 12). 26.95 *(978-1-59184-396-2(0)*, Portfolio (Hardcover)) Penguin Group (USA) Inc.

Bateman, Sam & Ho, Joshua, eds. Southeast Asia & the Rise of Chinese & Indian Naval Power: Between Rising Naval Powers. 2012. (ENG., Illus.). 272p. (C). pap. 44.95 ***(978-0-415-62552-4(1))*** Routledge.

Bhasin, Harsh. The Big Three. 2010. (Illus.). 168p. *(978-0-415-58430-2(2)*, Routledge) Taylor & Francis Group.

Bingman, Charles F. Changing Governments in India & Chin. 2011. 300p. pap. ***(978-1-84903-082-3(0))*** Schiel & Denver Publishing Ltd.

Holslag, Jonathan. China & India: Prospects for Peace. 2009. (Contemporary Asia in the World Ser.). (ENG., Illus.). 248p. (gr. 17). 37.50 *(978-0-231-15042-2(3))* Columbia Univ. Pr.

Huber, Toni. The Holy Land Reborn: Pilgrimage & the Tibetan Reinvention of Buddhist India. 2008. (Committee on Publications in Biology & Medicine Ser.). (Illus.). 464p. 45.00 *(978-0-226-35648-8(5))* Univ. of Chicago Pr.

Kapur, Ashok. The China-India-Pakistan Strategic Relationship. 2010. (Routledge Security in Asia Pacific Ser.). (ENG., Illus.). 224p. (C). 138.00 *(978-0-415-45466-7(2))* Routledge.

Kundu, Nivedita Das, ed. Russia India China: Evolution of Geo-Political Strategic Trends. 2011. 124p. 35.95 *(978-81-7188-782-8(1))* Academic Foundation IND. Dist: Independent Pubs. Group.

Malik, Mohan. China & India: Great Power Rivals. 2011. (Illus.). 385p. 79.95 *(978-1-935049-41-8(0))* FirstForumPress.

Mehra, Parshotam L. Essays in Frontier History: India, China, & the Disputed Border. 2006. (Illus.). 320p. 60.00 *(978-0-19-568375-2(7))* Oxford Univ. Pr., Inc.

Nadkarni, Vidya. Strategic Partnerships in Asia: Balancing Without Alliances. 2010. (ENG., Illus.). 272p. (C). 135.00 *(978-0-415-77774-2(7)*, Routledge) Taylor & Francis Group GBR. Dist: Taylor & Francis Group.

Noorani, A. G. India-China Boundary Problem, 1846-1947: History & Diplomacy, 1 vol. 2011. (ENG., Illus.). 360p. 65.00 *(978-0-19-807068-9(3))* Oxford Univ. Pr., Inc.

Pokharna, Bhawna. India-China Relations: Dimensions & Perspectives. 2009. 334p. 47.50 *(978-81-7708-192-3(6))* New Century Publications IND. Dist: International Specialized Bk. Services.

Sieff, Martin. Shifting Superpowers: The New & Emerging Relationships between the United States, China & India. 2010. (ENG.). 240p. 26.00 *(978-1-935308-21-8(1))* Cato Institute.

Thakur, Ravni. China & India: Comparative Perspectives-A Reader. 2007. (ENG.). 240p. pap. *(978-81-87943-77-8(7))* India Research Pr. IND. Dist: Independent Pubs. Group.

Verma, Bharat. Threat from China. 2011. 548p. 27.95 ***(978-1-935501-30-5(5))*** Lancer International, Lancer Pr. IND. Dist: Casemate Pubs. & Bk. Distributors, LLC.

Wang, Bangwei & Sen, Tansen, compiled by. India & China: Interactions through Buddhism & Diplomacy: A Collection of Essays by Professor Prabodh Chandra Bagchi. 2011. (Anthem Press India Ser.). 272p. 99.00 ***(978-93-80601-17-5(4))*** Anthem Pr. GBR. Dist: Books International, Inc.

Yousaf Khokhar, Amna. China-India Relations & Implications for Pakistan. 2011. 400p. pap. ***(978-3-8443-8786-5(2))*** Lambert Academic Publishing.

CHINA—FOREIGN RELATIONS—JAPAN

Bassett, R. Democracy & Foreign Policy. 2010. (ENG.). 630p. 165.00 *(978-0-415-59484-4(7))* Routledge.

Carnegie Endowment for International Peace Staff. The Sino-Japanese Negotiations of 1915: Japanese & Chinese Documents & Chinese Official Statement. reprint ed. 27.50 *(978-0-404-14473-9(X))* AMS Pr., Inc.

Cui, Shunji. Sino-Japanese Relations & a 'security Regime' in East Asi. 2010. 276p. pap. *(978-3-8383-9178-6(0))* Lambert Academic Publishing.

Curtis, Gerald L., et al. eds. Getting the Triangle Straight: Managing China-Japan-U. S. Relations. 2010. (ENG., Illus.). 280p. pap. 25.00 *(978-4-88907-080-4(X))* Japan Ctr. for International Exchange JPN. Dist: Brookings Institution Pr.

Esselstrom, Erik. Crossing Empire's Edge: Foreign Ministry Police & Japanese Expansionism in Northeast Asia. 2008. (World of East Asia Ser.). (Illus.). 264p. (C). 61.00 *(978-0-8248-3231-5(0))* Univ. of Hawaii Pr.

Fogel, Joshua A. Articulating the Sinosphere: Sino-Japanese Relations in Space & Time. 2009. (Edwin O. Reischauer Lectures: 2007). (Illus.). 216p. 37.00 *(978-0-674-03259-0(4))* Harvard Univ. Pr.

Fogel, Joshua A., ed. Crossing the Yellow Sea: Sino-Japanese Cultural Contacts, 1600-1950. 2007. 346p. pap. 29.95 *(978-1-891936-90-6(5))*, Signature Bks.) EastBridge.

Hagstrvm. Japan's China Policy. 2007. (Illus.). 256p. 39.95 *(978-0-415-43896-5(3))* Routledge.

Hsieh, Chiao-Min. Race the Rising Sun: A Chinese University's Exodus during the Second World War. 2009. (ENG.). 214p. pap. 31.99 *(978-0-7618-4148-7(2))* Univ. Pr. of America, Inc.

Hsiung, James C. China & Japan at Odds: Deciphering the Perpetual Conflict. 2007. (ENG.). 256p. 95.00 *(978-1-4039-7624-6(4))* Palgrave Macmillan.

Kawakami, K. K. Manchoukuo: Child of Conflict. reprint ed. 20.00 *(978-0-404-03639-3(2))* AMS Pr., Inc.

Keaveney, Christopher T. Beyond Brushtalk: Sino-Japanese Literary Exchange in the Interwar Period. 2008. (ENG., Illus.). 220p. (gr. 17). 50.00 *(978-962-209-928-9(9))* Hong Kong Univ. Pr. HKG. Dist: Columbia Univ. Pr.

King, Richard, et al. eds. Sino Japanese Transculturation: Late Nineteenth Century to the End of the Pacific War. 2011. (ENG.). 316p. (gr. 17). 75.00 ***(978-0-7391-7150-9(X))*** Lexington Bks.

King, Richard, et al. Sino-Japanese Transculturation: From the Late Nineteenth Century to the End of the Pacific War. 2011. ***(978-0-7391-7151-6(8))*** Lexington Bks.

Lai, Yew Meng. Nationalism & Power Politics in Japan's Relations with China: A Neoclassical Realist Interpretation. 2012. (Sheffield Centre for Japanese Studies/Routledge Ser.). (ENG.). 240p. (C). 135.00 ***(978-0-415-62911-9(X))*** Routledge.

Lam, Peng Er, ed. Japan's Relations with China: Facing a Rising Power. 2009. 250p. pap. 39.95 *(978-0-415-54682-9(6))* Routledge.

Liao, Xuanli, et al. Chinese Foreign Policy Think Tanks & China's Policy Towards Japan. 2006. (ENG.). 350p. (gr. 17). 49.00 *(978-962-996-266-1(7))* Chinese Univ. of Hong Kong, The HKG. Dist: Columbia Univ. Pr.

Rathus, Joel. Japan, China & Networked Regionalism in East Asia. 2011. (Critical Studies of the Asia-Pacific Ser.). (ENG., Illus.). 272p. 85.00 ***(978-0-230-30004-0(9))*** Palgrave Macmillan.

Reilly, James. Strong Society, Smart State: The Rise of Public Opinion in China's Japan Policy. 2011. (Contemporary Asia in the World Ser.). (ENG., Illus.). 352p. (gr. 17). 50.00 *(978-0-231-15806-0(8))* Columbia Univ. Pr.

Rose, Caroline. Sino-Japanese Relations: Facing the Past, Looking to the Future? 2009. 176p. pap. 39.95 *(978-0-415-54619-5(2))* Routledge.

Rose, Caroline, ed. Sino-Japanese Relations: History, Politics, Economy, 4 vols. 2011. (Critical Concepts in Asian Studies). (ENG.). 1552p. 1295.00 *(978-0-415-56614-8(2))* Routledge.

Schoenbaum, Thomas J. Peace in Northeast Asia: Resolving Japan's Territorial & Maritime Disputes with China, Korea & the Russian Federation. 2008. (Illus.). 144p. (C). 119.00 *(978-1-84720-665-7(4))* Elgar, Edward Publishing, Inc.

Self, Benjamin. The Dragon's Shadow: The Rise of China & Japan's New Nationalism. 2006. mass mkt. 20.00 *(978-0-9770023-3-7(0))* Stimson, Henry L. Ctr., The.

Sun, Jing. Japan & China as Charm Rivals: Soft Power in Regional Diplomacy. 2012. (ENG., Illus.). 272p. (C). 70.00 ***(978-0-472-11833-5(1))*** Univ. of Michigan Pr.

Taylor, Robert. The Sino-Japanese Axis. 132p. *(978-0-485-11263-4(9))* Continuum International Publishing Group, Ltd.

Vyas, Utpal. Soft Power in Japan-China Relations: State, Sub-State & Non-State Relations. 2011. (Routledge Contemporary Asia Ser.). (ENG., Illus.). 204p. (C). 125.00 *(978-0-415-55170-0(6))* Routledge.

Wan, Ming. Sino-Japanese Relations: Interaction, Logic, & Transformation. 2008. (ENG.). 498p. pap. 27.95 *(978-0-8047-6117-8(5))* Stanford Univ. Pr.

Wang, Ching-ch'un. Japan's Continental Adventure. 2010. (ENG.). 222p. 115.00 *(978-0-415-58783-9(2))* Routledge.

Wang, Zheng. Never Forget National Humiliation: Historical Memory in Chinese Politics & Foreign Relations. 2012. (Contemporary Asia in the World Ser.). (ENG., Illus.). 320p. (gr. 17). 32.50 ***(978-0-231-14890-0(9))*** Columbia Univ. Pr.

Williams, Frederick Vincent & Tanaka, Hideo. Chugoku No Senso Senden No Uchimaku: Nitchu Senso No Shinjitsu. 2009. (JPN., Illus.). 160p. *(978-4-8295-0467-3(6))* Fuyo Shobo Shuppan.

Willoughby, Westel W. Japan's Case Examined. 2007. (ENG.). 248p. per. *(978-1-4067-2293-2(6))* Read Bks.

Wood, David & Johnson, P. Louise, eds. Sporting Cultures: Hispanic Perspectives on Sport, Text & the Body. 2008. (Sport in the Global Society Ser.). (Illus.). XX, 188p. 140.00 *(978-0-415-45762-0(9))* Routledge.

Wu, Guang. The Third Sino-Japanese War: Dream of Pacific Empire. 2011. (Series: Asian Political, Economic & Security Issues Ser.). viii, 115p. 47.00 *(978-1-61324-489-0(4))* Nova Science Pubs., Inc.

Yang, Daqing, et al. Toward a History Beyond Borders: Contentious Issues in Sino-Japanese Relations. Liu, Jie et al, eds. Esselstrom, Erik et al, trs. 2012. (Harvard East Asian Monographs: 340). (ENG., Illus.). 488p. 49.95 *(978-0-674-06256-6(6))* Harvard Univ., Asia Ctr.

Yong, Jin & Ikeda, Daisaku. Compassionate Light in Asia: A Dialogue. 2012. (Echoes & Reflections Ser.). (ENG.). 256p. 50.00 *(978-1-84885-198-6(7))* I. B. Tauris & Co., Ltd. GBR. Dist: Macmillan.

Zachmann, Urs Matthias. China & Japan in the Late Meiji Period: China Policy & the Japanese Discourse on National Identity, 1895-1904. 2009. (Routledge/Leiden Series in Modern East Asian History & Politics Ser.). (ENG.). 256p. (C). 150.00 *(978-0-415-48191-5(0))* Routledge.

Zhou, Zhongfei. "Tai Du" de Guo Ji Bei Jing. 2009. *(978-7-80195-990-4(6))* Jiuzhou Publishing Hse.

CHINA—FOREIGN RELATIONS—KOREA

Chapman, John W. M. & Chiharu, Inaba, eds. Rethinking the Russo-Japanese War, 1904-05: The Nichinan Papers. 2006. (Illus.). 348p. *(978-1-905246-19-9(6))* BRILL.

Chung, Jae Ho. Between Ally & Partner: Korea-China Relations & the United States. (ENG., Illus.). 200p. (gr. 17). 2008. pap. 27.50 *(978-0-231-13907-6(1))* 2006. 80.00 *(978-0-231-13906-9(3))* Columbia Univ. Pr.

The Documentary History of the Truman Presidency Vol. 19: The Korean War - Response to Communist China's Intervention, October 1950-April 1951. Date not set. 185.00 *(978-1-55655-585-5(7))* ProQuest LLC.

Funabashi, Yoichi. The Peninsula Question: A Chronicle of the Second Korean Nuclear Crisis. 2007. (ENG.). 592p. 36.95 *(978-0-8157-3010-1(1))* Brookings Institution Pr.

Groves, Anita. North Korea's Regional Relations 2003 - 2006. 2010. 68p. pap. *(978-3-8383-1376-4(3))* Lambert Academic Publishing.

Larsen, Kirk W. Tradition, Treaties, & Trade - Qing Imperialism & Choson Korea, 1850-1910. 2011. (Harvard East Asian Monographs: 295). (ENG.). 328p. pap. 24.95 *(978-0-674-06073-9(3))* Harvard Univ., Asia Ctr.

North Korea: U.S. Policy Options: Hearing Before the Committee on Foreign Relations, United States Senate, One Hundred Ninth Congress, Second Session, July 20, 2006. 2007. iii, 58p. *(978-0-16-078960-1(5)*, 552-070-36078-6) United States Government Printing Office.

Snyder, Scott. China's Rise & the Two Koreas: Politics, Economics, Security. 2009. (Illus.). 240p. (C). 57.00 *(978-1-58826-618-7(4))*; pap. *(978-1-58826-622-4(2))* Rienner, Lynne Pubs.

CHINA—FOREIGN RELATIONS—PAKISTAN

Kapur, Ashok. The China-India-Pakistan Strategic Relationship. 2010. (Routledge Security in Asia Pacific Ser.). (ENG., Illus.). 224p. (C). 138.00 *(978-0-415-45466-7(2))* Routledge.

Yousaf Khokhar, Amna. China-India Relations & Implications for Pakistan. 2011. 400p. pap. ***(978-3-8443-8786-5(2))*** Lambert Academic Publishing.

CHINA—FOREIGN RELATIONS—SOVIET UNION

Bedeski, Robert & Swanström, Niklas, eds. Eurasia's Ascent in Energy & Geopolitics: China, Russia, & Central Asia. 2012. (Routledge Contemporary Asia Ser.). (ENG., Illus.). 256p. (C). 135.00 *(978-0-415-68150-6(2))* Routledge.

Bernstein, Thomas. China Learns from the Soviet Union 1949 Present. 2011. (Harvard Cold War Studies Book Ser.). (ENG.). 562p. pap. 48.95 ***(978-0-7391-4223-3(2))*** Lexington Bks.

Bernstein, Thomas P. China Learns from the Soviet Union, 1949-Present. 2010. (Harvard Cold War Studies Book Ser.). (ENG., Illus.). 562p. 115.50 *(978-0-7391-4222-6(4))* Lexington Bks.

Blank, Stephen. Russo-Chinese Energy Relations: Politics in Command. 2006. (Russian Foreign Energy Policy Reports). (ENG.). 40p. pap. 180.00 *(978-1-905050-43-7(7)*, GMB Publishing Ltd.) Blue Ibex Ltd. GBR. Dist: Ingram Pub. Services.

Day, Alan. China & the Soviet Union: Nineteen Forty-Nine to Nineteen Eighty-Four. 2nd ed. Date not set. (Illus.). 216p. pap. 4.95 *(978-0-582-90265-7(7))* Addison-Wesley Longman, Ltd. GBR. Dist: Trans-Atlantic Pubns., Inc.

Elleman, Bruce. Moscow & the Emergence of Communist Power in China, 1925-30: The Nanchang Rising & the Birth of the Red Army. 2009. (Routledge Studies in the Modern History of Asia Ser.). (ENG.). 234p. 160.00 *(978-0-415-77614-1(7))* Routledge.

Foo, Yee-Wah. Chiang Kaishek's Last Ambassador to Moscow: The Wartime Diaries of Fu Bingchang. 2011. (ENG., Illus.). 256p. 89.00 *(978-0-230-58477-8(2))* Palgrave Macmillan.

Gonzalez, Benjamin. Charting a New Silk Road? 2008. 112p. pap. *(978-3-8364-8780-1(2))* VDM Verlag Dr. Mueller e.K.

Khoo, Nicholas. Collateral Damage: Sino-Soviet Rivalry & the Termination of the Sino-Vietnamese Alliance. 2011. (ENG.). 280p. (gr. 17). 50.00 *(978-0-231-15078-1(4))*; 288p. E-Book 39.99 *(978-0-231-52163-5(4))* Columbia Univ. Pr.

Kuhrt, Natasha. Russian Policy Towards China & Japan. 2011. (ENG., Illus.). 240p. (C). pap. 44.95 ***(978-0-415-67488-1(3))*** Routledge.

Kundu, Nivedita Das, ed. Russia India China: Evolution of Geo-Political Strategic Trends. 2011. 124p. 35.95 *(978-81-7188-782-8(1))* Academic Foundation IND. Dist: Independent Pubs. Group.

Lam, Lai Sing. The Romance of the Three Kingdoms & Mao's Global Order of Tripolarity. 2011. 235p. pap. 55.95 ***(978-3-0343-0713-0(6))*** Lang, Peter AG GBR. Dist: Lang, Peter.

Li, Mingjiang. Mao's China & Sino-Soviet Split: Ideological Dilemma. 2012. (Routledge Contemporary China Ser.). (ENG.). 224p. (C). 125.00 ***(978-0-415-69836-8(7))*** Routledge.

Lo, Bobo. Axis of Convenience: Moscow, Beijing, & the New Geopolitics. 2008. (ENG., Illus.). 277p. 32.95 *(978-0-8157-5340-7(3))* Brookings Institution Pr.

Luthi, Lorenz M. The Sino-Soviet Split: Cold War in the Communist World. 2008. (Princeton Studies in International History & Politics). (Illus.). 400p. (C). 65.00 *(978-0-691-12934-1(7))*; (ENG., per. 32.95 *(978-0-691-13590-8(8))* Princeton Univ. Pr.

Marketos, Thrassy N. China's Energy Geopolitics: The Shanghai Cooperation Organization & Central Asia. 2009. (Routledge Contemporary China Ser.). (ENG., Illus.). 184p. (C). 160.00 *(978-0-415-45690-6(8))* Routledge.

Nadkarni, Vidya. Strategic Partnerships in Asia: Balancing Without Alliances. 2010. (ENG., Illus.). 272p. (C). 135.00 *(978-0-415-77774-2(7)*, Routledge) Taylor & Francis Group GBR. Dist: Taylor & Francis Group.

Pavolovsky, Michel N. Chinese Russian Relations. *(978-0-8022-1291-7(3))* Philosophical Library, Inc.

Radchenko, Sergey. Two Suns in the Heavens: The Sino-Soviet Struggle for Supremacy. 2009. (Cold War International History Project Ser.). (ENG.). 288p. 65.00 *(978-0-8047-5879-6(4))* Stanford Univ. Pr.

Reynolds, Julius David Alexander. The Construction of Regional Security in Eurasi. 2009. 80p. pap. *(978-3-639-17535-6(2))* VDM Verlag Dr. Mueller e.K.

Rogerson, David J., ed. China & Russia: Competition & Partnership. 2010. (Global Political Studies). xi, 163p. 130.00 *(978-1-61728-682-7(6))* Nova Science Pubs., Inc.

Shen, Zhihua & Li, Danhui. After Leaning to One Side: China & Its Allies in the Cold War. 2011. (Cold War International History Project Ser.). (ENG.). 360p. 60.00 ***(978-0-8047-7087-3(5))*** Stanford Univ. Pr.

Tan, Chester C. The Boxer Catastrophe: Columbia Studies in the Social Sciences, No. 583. 2011. 286p. 48.95 ***(978-1-258-07637-5(3))*** Literary Licensing, LLC.

Tang, Peter S. H. Russian & Soviet Policy in Manchuria & Outer Mongolia, 1911-1931. 2011. 522p. 60.95 ***(978-1-258-08450-9(3))*** Literary Licensing, LLC.

Utley, Freda. Last Chance in Chin. 2011. 408p. 54.95 ***(978-1-258-09616-8(1))*** Literary Licensing, LLC.

Zhihua, Shen. Mao, Stalin & the Korean War: Trilateral Communist Relations in The 1950s. 2012. (Cold War History Ser.). (ENG.). 264p. (C). 135.00 ***(978-0-415-51645-7(5))*** Routledge.

CHINA—FOREIGN RELATIONS—UNITED STATES

Ali, S. Mahmud. U. S.-China Relations in the "Asia-Pacific" Century. 2008. (ENG.). 288p. 95.00 *(978-0-230-60455-1(2))* Palgrave Macmillan.

Alterman, Jon B. & Garver, John W. The Vital Triangle: China, the United States, & the Middle East. 2008. (Illus.). vii, 144p. pap. 16.95 *(978-0-89206-529-5(X)*, CSIS Pr., The) Ctr. for Strategic & International Studies.

Asia Overview: Protecting American Interests in China & Asia: Hearing Before the Subcommittee on Asia & the Pacific of the Committee on Foreign Affairs, House of Representatives, One Hundred Twelfth Congress, First Session, March 31, 2011. 2011. (Illus.). iii, 106p. ***(978-0-16-088856-4(5)***, 552-070-42976-0) United States Government Printing Office.

Assessing China's Behavior & Its Impact on U.S. Interests: Briefing Before the Committee on Foreign Affairs, House of Representatives, One Hundred Twelfth Congress, First Session, January 19, 2011. 2011. (Illus.). iii, 66p. ***(978-0-16-088142-8(0)***, 552-070-42559-4) United States Government Printing Office.

Ayres, Alyssa & Mohan, C. Raja, eds. Power Realignments in Asia: China, India & the United States. 2009. (Illus.). 356p. (C). 39.95 *(978-81-7829-948-8(8)*, B99488C) SAGE Pubns., Inc.

Bader, Jeffrey A. Obama & China's Rise: An Insider's Account of America's Asia Strategy. 2012. (ENG.). 171p. 26.95 ***(978-0-8157-2242-7(7))*** Brookings Institution Pr.

Baldwin, Maria T. Amnesty International & U. S. Foreign Policy: Human Rights Campaigns in Guatemala, the United States, & China. 2008. (Law & Society Ser.). 314p. 75.00 *(978-1-59332-329-5(8))* LFB Scholarly Publishing LLC.

Bates, Gillian & Gill, Bates. Rising Star: China's New Security Diplomacy. 2nd rev. ed. 2010. (ENG.). 267p. pap. 22.95 *(978-0-8157-0453-9(4))* Brookings Institution Pr.

Bays, Daniel & Widmer, Ellen. China's Christian Colleges: Cross-Cultural Connections, 1900-1950. 2009. (ENG., Illus.). 432p. 65.00 *(978-0-8047-5948-9(0))*; pap. 24.95 *(978-0-8047-5949-6(9))* Stanford Univ. Pr.

Bhasin, Harsh. The Big Three. 2010. (Illus.). 168p. *(978-0-415-58430-2(2)*, Routledge) Taylor & Francis Group.

Braisted, William R. & Braisted, William Reynolds. Diplomats in Blue: U.S. Naval Officers in China, 1922-1933. 2009. (New Perspectives on Maritime History & Nautical Archaeology Ser.). (ENG., Illus.). 560p. 75.00 *(978-0-8130-3288-7(1))* Univ. Pr. of Florida.

Buderi, Robert & Huang, Gregory T. Guanxi (the Art of Relationships) Microsoft, China, & Bill Gates's Plan to Win the Road Ahead. 2007. (ENG., Illus.). 320p. pap. 19.99 *(978-0-7432-7323-7(0))* Simon & Schuster.

Bush, Richard C. & O'Hanlon, Michael E. A War Like No Other: The Truth about China's Challenge to America. 2007. (ENG., Illus.). 240p. 25.95 *(978-0-471-98677-5(1)*, Wiley) Wiley, John & Sons, Inc.

Campbell, Kurt M. & Steinberg, James B. Difficult Transitions: Foreign Policy Troubles at the Outset of Presidential Power. 2008. (ENG., Illus.). 204p. 26.95 *(978-0-8157-1340-1(1))* Brookings Institution Pr.

Caughey, John Hart & Jeans, Roger B. The Marshall Mission to China, 1945-1947: The Letters & Diary of Colonel John Hart Caughey. 2011. ***(978-1-4422-1296-1(9))*** Rowman & Littlefield Publishers, Inc.

Chan, Steve. Looking for Balance: China, the United States, & Power Balancing in East Asia. 2012. (Studies in Asian Security Ser.). (ENG.). 304p. 50.00 *(978-0-8047-7820-6(5))* Stanford Univ. Pr.

Cheng & Zheng, Mingxun. On Equal Terms: Redefining China's Relationship with America & the West. 2011. (ENG.). 216p. 29.95 *(978-0-470-82886-1(2)*, Wiley) Wiley, John & Sons, Inc.

China on the World Stage: Weighing the US Response, 2. 8th ed. 2006. (Illus.). 92p. (YA). pap. *(978-1-60123-004-1(4))* Choices Education Program, Watson Institute, Brown Univ.

Chow Economic Integration, Democratization & National Security in East Asia Shifting Paradigms in Us, China & Taiwan Relations. 2007. (Illus.). 336p. (C). 144.00 *(978-1-84542-978-2(8))* Elgar, Edward Publishing, Inc.

Chung, Jae Ho. Between Ally & Partner: Korea-China Relations & the United States. 2006. (ENG., Illus.). 200p. (gr. 17). 80.00 *(978-0-231-13906-9(3))* Columbia Univ. Pr.

Clark, Dick. U.S.-China Relations: Tenth Conference, March 24-30, 2008. 2008. 36p. pap. *(978-0-89843-489-7(0))* Aspen Institute, The.

Clegg. China's Global Strategy: Towards a Multipolar World. 2009. (ENG.). 288p. pap. 34.00 *(978-0-7453-2518-7(1))* Pluto Pr. GBR. Dist: Macmillan.

Cohen, Warren I. America's Response to China: A History of Sino-American Relations. 5th ed. 2010. (ENG., Illus.). 344p. (gr. 17). 84.50 *(978-0-231-15076-7(8))*; pap. 27.50 *(978-0-231-15077-4(6))* Columbia Univ. Pr.

Costa, Meredith A. & Silva, Jeremy P. China, Taiwan & the Evolution of One China Policy. 2011. (Series: China in the 21st Century Ser.). 181p. 185.00 *(978-1-61324-423-4(1))* Nova Science Pubs., Inc.

Curtis, Gerald L., et al. eds. Getting the Triangle Straight: Managing China-Japan-U. S. Relations. 2010. (ENG., Illus.). 280p. pap. 25.00 *(978-4-88907-080-4(X))* Japan Ctr. for International Exchange JPN. Dist: Brookings Institution Pr.

Davies, John Paton. China Hand: An Autobiography. 2012. (Haney Foundation Ser.). (Illus.). 376p. 34.95 ***(978-0-8122-4401-4(X))*** Univ. of Pennsylvania Pr.

Davis, Donald E. & Trani, Eugene P. Distorted Mirrors: Americans & Their Relations with Russia & China in the Twentieth Century. 2009. (ENG.). 496p. (C). 49.95 *(978-0-8262-1853-7(9))* Univ. of Missouri Pr.

De, Krassel Pete. Custom Maid Knowledge for New. 2008. 767p. pap. 25.95 *(978-988-97666-7-2(1))* Compendium GBR. Dist: Casemate Pubs. & Bk. Distributors, LLC.

Dillon, Dana R. The China Challenge: Standing Strong Against the Military, Economic, & Political Threats That Imperil America. 2007. (ENG., Illus.). 232p. 26.95 *(978-0-7425-5133-6(4))* Rowman & Littlefield Publishers, Inc.

Dinwiddie, Joseph. Aid to Nationalist Chin. 2011. 176p. 42.95 ***(978-1-258-06472-3(3))*** Literary Licensing, LLC.

Dobbs, Charles. Triangles, Symbols, & Constraints: The United States, the Soviet Union, & the People's Republic of China, 1963-1969. 2010. (ENG.). 328p. pap. 41.99 *(978-0-7618-4999-5(8))* Univ. Pr. of America, Inc.

Feng, Zhu. China's Ascent: Power, Security, & the Future of International Politics. Ross, Robert S., ed. 2008. (Cornell Studies in Security Affairs). (Illus.). 336p. 65.95 *(978-0-8014-4691-7(0))*; pap. 23.95 *(978-0-8014-7444-6(2))* Cornell Univ. Pr.

Finding Common Ground with a Rising China: Hearing Before the Committee on Foreign Relations, United States Senate, One Hundred Eleventh Congress, Second Session, June 23, 2010. 2010. iii, 56p. ***(978-0-16-087689-9(3)***, 552-070-42241-2) United States Government Printing Office.

Fingleton, Eamonn. In the Jaws of the Dragon: America's Fate in the Coming Era of Chinese Dominance. 2009. (ENG.). 368p. pap. 16.99 *(978-0-312-56162-8(8)*, St. Martin's Griffin) St. Martin's Pr.

Foot, Rosemary & Walter, Andrew. China, the United States, & Global Order. 2010. (ENG., Illus.). 352p. (C). 90.00 *(978-0-521-89800-3(5))*; pap. 32.99 *(978-0-521-72519-4(4))* Cambridge Univ. Pr.

Frank, Caroline. Objectifying China, Imagining America. 2012. (ENG., Illus.). 272p. 75.00 *(978-0-226-26027-3(5))* Univ. of Chicago Pr.

—Objectifying China, Imagining America: Chinese Commodities in Early America. 2012. (ENG., Illus.). 280p. pap. 25.00 *(978-0-226-26028-0(3))* Univ. of Chicago Pr.

Friedberg, Aaron L. A Contest for Supremacy: China, America, & the Struggle for Mastery in Asia. 2011. (ENG., Illus.). 384p. 27.95 *(978-0-393-06828-3(5)*, 6828) Norton, W. W. & Co., Inc.

The Future of Political, Economic, & Security Relations with China: Hearing Before the Committee on Foreign Affairs, House of Representatives, One Hundred Tenth Congress, First Session, May 1, 2007. 2007. iii, 41p. *(978-0-16-079098-0(0)*, 552-070-36194-4) United States Government Printing Office.

Gill, Bates. Meeting the Challenges & Opportunities of China's Rise: Expanding & Improving Interaction Between the American & Chinese Policy Communities: A Report of the CSIS Freeman Chair in China Studies. 2006. 41p. pap. 17.95 *(978-0-89206-493-9(5)*, CSIS Pr., The) Ctr. for Strategic & International Studies.

C

—Rising Star: China's New Security Diplomacy. 2007. (ENG.). 267p. 32.95 *(978-0-8157-3146-7(9))* Brookings Institution Pr.

Goh, Evelyn. Constructing the U. S. Rapprochement with China, 1961-1974: From 'Red Menace' to 'Tacit Ally' 2009. (ENG.). 316p. pap. 31.99 *(978-0-521-10862-1(4))* Cambridge Univ. Pr.

Goh, Evelyn & Simon, Sheldon W., eds. China, the United States, & Southeast Asia: Contending Perspectives on Politics, Security, & Economics. 2007. (Asian Security Studies). (ENG., Illus.). 224p. (C). 160.00 *(978-0-415-42945-0(5))* Routledge.

Grafstein, Robert & Wen, Fan. A Bridge Too Far? Commonalities & Differences Between China & the United States. 2009. (ENG., Illus.). 244p. 73.50 *(978-0-7391-2887-9(6))* Lexington Bks.

Griffiths, David. U.S.-China Maritime Confidence Building: Paradigms, Precedents, & Prospects. 2010. 28p. ***(978-1-884733-80-2(8))*** Naval War College Pr.

Guo, Sujian. 30 Years of China U. S. Relations: Analytical Approaches & Contemporary Issues. 2010. (Challenges Facing Chinese Political Development Ser.). (ENG., Illus.). 344p. 80.00 *(978-0-7391-4696-5(3))* Lexington Bks.

Guoliang, Gu & Rosecrance, Richard N. Power & Restraint: A Shared Vision for the U. S.-China Relationship. Rosecrance, Richard & Guoliang, Gu, eds. 2009. (ENG., Illus.). 272p. 25.95 *(978-1-58648-742-3(6))* PublicAffairs.

Haddad, John Rogers. The Romance of China: Excursions to China in U. S. Culture, 1776-1876. 2008. (Gutenberg-E Ser.). (ENG.). 348p. (gr. 17). 60.00 *(978-0-231-13094-3(5))* Columbia Univ. Pr.

Halper, Stefan. The Beijing Consensus: Legitimizing Authoritarianism in Our Time. 2012. (ENG.). 336p. (gr. 9). pap. 17.99 *(978-0-465-02523-7(4))* Basic Bks.

Hao, Yufan. Macau & U. S. -China Relations. 2010. (ENG., Illus.). 330p. 80.00 *(978-0-7391-4367-4(0))* Lexington Bks.

—Sino-American Relations: Challenges Ahead. 2010. (Illus.). 272p. 114.95 *(978-1-4094-0797-3(7))* Ashgate Publishing Co.

Herrmann/Zhang. Chinese Perceptions of the U. S. An Exploration of China's Foreign Policy Motivations. 2011. (ENG.). 282p. 70.00 ***(978-0-7391-7085-4(6))*** Lexington Bks.

Hills. U. S China Relations: an Affirmative: Independent Task Force Report No. 59. 2007. (ENG.). 144p. pap. 15.00 *(978-0-87609-403-7(5))* Council on Foreign Relations.

Hua, Shiping. Reflections on the Triangular Relations of Beijing-Taipei-Washington Since 1995: Status Quo at the Taiwan Straits? 2006. (ENG., Illus.). 320p. 89.00 *(978-1-4039-7061-9(0))* Palgrave Macmillan.

Humes, James C. & Ryals, Jarvis D. Only Nixon: His Trip to China Revisited & Restudied. 2009. (ENG., Illus.). 134p. pap. 24.50 *(978-0-7618-4738-0(3))* Univ. Pr. of America, Inc.

Jeans, Roger. The Marshall Mission to China, 1945D1947: The Letters & Diary of Colonel John Hart Caughey. 2011. (ENG.). 324p. 84.00 *(978-1-4422-1294-7(2))* Rowman & Littlefield Publishers, Inc.

Jensen, Lionel M. & Weston, Timothy B. China's Transformations: The Stories Beyond the Headlines. 2006. (ENG., Illus.). 378p. 97.00 *(978-0-7425-3862-7(1))*; per. 34.95 *(978-0-7425-3863-4(X))* Rowman & Littlefield Publishers, Inc.

Jingping, Wu. Select Telegrams Between Chiang Kai-Shek & T. V. Soong, 1940-1943. Kuo, Tai-chun, ed. 2008. (TV soong Ser.). (CHI & ENG., Illus.). 384p. pap. 15.00 *(978-7-309-05956-4(5))* Hoover Institution Pr.

Johnson, Kendall, ed. Narratives of Free Trade: The Commercial Cultures of Early US-China Relations. 2012. (Global Connections Ser.). (ENG., Illus.). 272p. (gr. 17). 50.00 *(978-988-8083-53-4(8))*; pap. 25.00 *(978-988-8083-54-1(6))* Hong Kong Univ. Pr. HKG. Dist: Columbia Univ. Pr.

Joiner, Lynne. Honorable Survivor: Mao's China, McCarthy's America, & the Persecution of John S. Service. 2009. (Illus.). 450p. 37.95 *(978-1-59114-423-6(X))* Naval Institute Pr.

Kaiser, Matthis. Engaging or Containing China? 2008. 148p. pap. *(978-3-639-08000-1(9))* VDM Verlag Dr. Mueller e.K.

Kalicki, J. H. The Pattern of Sino-American Crises: Political-Military Interactions in The 1950s. 2010. (LSE Monographs in International Studies). (ENG.). 296p. pap. 30.99 *(978-0-521-13686-0(5))* Cambridge Univ. Pr.

Karabell, Zachary. Superfusion: How China & America Became One Economy & Why the World's Prosperity Depends on It. 2010. (ENG.). 352p. pap. 16.00 *(978-1-4165-8371-4(8))* Simon & Schuster.

Kirby, William C., et al, eds. Normalization of U. S. -China Relations: An International History. 2007. (Harvard East Asian Monographs: 254). (Illus.). 425p. pap. 24.95 *(978-0-674-02594-3(6))* Harvard Univ., Asia Ctr.

Knuesel, Araine. Framing China: Public Images & Diplomatic Debates in Britain the USA & Switzerland, 1900-1950. 2012. (Illus.). 298p. 124.95 ***(978-1-4094-2559-5(2))*** Ashgate Publishing Co.

Krosby, Quincy. The Eagle & the Dragon: China's Economic Ascent. 2007. 256p. 27.95 *(978-0-470-04481-0(0)*, Wiley) Wiley, John & Sons, Inc.

Krysko, Michael A. American Radio in China: International Encounters with Technology & Communications, 1919-41. 2011. (ENG., Illus.). 304p. 85.00 *(978-0-230-25266-0(4))* Palgrave Macmillan.

Langellier, John. US Armed Forces in China 1856-1941. 2009. (Men-at-Arms Ser.). (ENG., Illus.). 48p. pap. 17.95 *(978-1-84603-493-0(0))* Osprey Publishing, Ltd. GBR. Dist: Random Hse., Inc.

Laughlin, Shepherd. U.S.-China Educational Exchange: Perspectives on a Growing Partnership. 2008. *(978-0-87206-307-5(0))*; (Illus.). xv, 116p. *(978-0-87206-308-2(9))* Institute of International Education.

Lee, Ann. What the U. S. Can Learn from China: An Open-Minded Guide to Treating Our Greatest Competitor as Our Greatest Teacher. 2012. (ENG.). 288p. 27.95 ***(978-1-60994-124-6(1))*** Berrett-Koehler Pubs., Inc.

Lewis, Jeffrey G. The Minimum Means of Reprisal: China's Search for Security in the Nuclear Age. 2007. (American Academy Studies in Global Security Ser.). (ENG., Illus.). 282p. (gr. 17). per. 24.00 *(978-0-262-62202-8(5))* MIT Pr.

Li, Yanhui. Zheng Zhi Jing Ji de Hu Dong Yu Zhong Mei Guan Xi: Yi Zhong Makesi Zhu Yi Guo Ji Zheng Zhi Jing Ji Xue de Fen Xi = Mutual-Drive of Politics & Economy on Sino-US Relations. 2009. (CHI.). *(978-7-80745-579-0(9))* Shanghai Academy of Social Sciences Pr.

Lin, Cheng-yi & Roy, Denny, eds. The Future of the United States, China, & Taiwan Relations. 2011. (ENG.). 266p. 85.00 *(978-0-230-11278-0(1))* Palgrave Macmillan.

Ling, Lily. Democratizing International Relations: Culture as Method. 2013. (New International Relations Ser.). (ENG.). 256p. (C). 135.00 *(978-0-415-60377-5(3))* Routledge.

Liu, Mingfu. Zhongguo Meng: Zhong Mei Shi Ji Dui Jue, Jun Ren Yao Fa Yan. 2010. (CHI.). x, 288p. *(978-962-231-062-9(1))* Chung Hwa Bk. Co., Ltd.

Lum, Thomas, et al. China & the U. S. Comparing Global Influence. 2010. (China in the 21st Century Ser.). 172p. 79.00 *(978-1-60692-995-7(X))* Nova Science Pubs., Inc.

Lum, Thomas G. Paying Our Way - Transforming Transportation Finance. Bartha, Simon D., ed. 2010. (Transportation Infrastructure - Roads, Highways, Bridges, Airports & Mass Transit Ser.). (Illus.). xxxi, 242p. 115.00 *(978-1-60741-995-2(5))* Nova Science Pubs., Inc.

Lumbers, Michael. Piercing the Bamboo Curtain: Tentative Bridge-Building to China During the Johnson Years. 2008. (ENG.). 272p. 84.00 *(978-0-7190-7778-4(8))* Manchester Univ. Pr. GBR. Dist: Macmillan.

MacMillan, Margaret. Nixon & Mao: The Week That Changed the World. 2008. (ENG., Illus.). 448p. pap. 17.00 *(978-0-8129-7057-9(6)*, Random Hse. Trade Paperbacks) Random House Publishing Group.

Mah, Ben. America & China. 2007. 300p. per. 22.95 *(978-0-595-40815-3(X))* iUniverse, Inc.

Marketos, Thrassy N. China's Energy Geopolitics: The Shanghai Cooperation Organization & Central Asia. 2009. (Routledge Contemporary China Ser.). (ENG., Illus.). 184p. (C). 160.00 *(978-0-415-45690-6(8))* Routledge.

Marshall, Samantha E. Taiwan - U. S. Relations. 2010. (Asian Economic & Political Issues Ser.). 152p. 89.00 *(978-1-60876-071-8(5))* Nova Science Pubs., Inc.

Martin, Edwin W. Divided Counsel: The Anglo-American Response to Communist Victory in China. 2009. (ENG.). 288p. pap. 30.00 *(978-0-8131-9292-5(7))* Univ. Pr. of Kentucky.

Mayer, Ruth. Trans-Pacific Interactions: The United States & China, 1880-1950. Künnemann, Vanessa & Mayer, Ruth, eds. 2009. (ENG., Illus.). 224p. 89.00 *(978-0-230-61905-0(3))* Palgrave Macmillan.

McGiffert, Carola. Chinese Soft Power & Its Implications for the United States: Competition & Cooperation in the Developing World, a Report of the CSIS Smart Power Initiative. 2009. (Illus.). 136p. pap. 25.00 *(978-0-89206-558-5(3)*, CSIS Pr., The) Ctr. for Strategic & International Studies.

McGiffert, Carola, ed. Smart Power in U. S. -China Relations: A Report of the CSIS Commission on China. 2009. 40p. pap. 15.95 net. *(978-0-89206-573-8(7)*, CSIS Pr., The) Ctr. for Strategic & International Studies.

Medeiros, Evan S. China's International Behavior: Activism, Opportunism, & Diversification. 2009. 278p. pap. 34.00 *(978-0-8330-4709-0(4)*, mg-850) RAND Corp., The.

Milligan-Whyte, John & Lui, Manhong. China & America's Emerging Partnership: A Realistic New Perspective. 2009. (ENG., Illus.). 506p. 32.95 *(978-1-56171-871-9(8))* SPI Bks.

National Security Implications of the Possible Merger of the China Off-Shore Oil Corporation (CNOOC) with UNOCAL Corporation: Hearing Before the Committee on Armed Services, House of Representatives, One Hundred Ninth Congress, First Session, Hearing Held, July 13, 2005. 2007. iii, 100p. *(978-0-16-079222-9(3)*, 552-070-36291-6) United States Government Printing Office.

Nickles, David P. & Keefer, Edward C., eds. China, 1973-1976, Vol. XVIII. 2008. (Foreign Relations of the United States, 1969-1976 Ser.). (ENG.). 1039p. (gr. 13). 68.00 *(978-0-16-077110-1(2)*, Bureau of Public Affairs, Office of the Historian) United States Government Printing Office.

Odgaard, Liselotte. The Balance of Power in Asia-Pacific Security. 2009. 278p. pap. 39.95 *(978-0-415-54702-4(4))* Routledge.

—The Balance of Power in Asia-Pacific Security: Us-China Policies on Regional Order. 2007. (Politics in Asia Ser.). (Illus.). 272p. 170.00 *(978-0-415-41591-0(8))* Routledge.

Ong, Russell. China's Strategic Competition with the United States. 2012. (Routledge Security in Asia Ser.). (ENG.). 184p. (C). 145.00 *(978-0-415-56107-5(8))* Routledge.

Owens, Kevin M. China's International Relations. 2011. (China in the 21st Century Ser.). (Illus.). 254p. 115.00 *(978-1-61761-506-1(4))* Nova Science Pubs., Inc.

Peck, James. Washington's China: The National Security World, the Cold War, & the Origins of Globalism. 2006. (Culture, Politics & the Cold War Ser.). 333p. 80.00 *(978-1-55849-536-4(3))*; per. 24.95 *(978-1-55849-537-1(1))* Univ. of Massachusetts Pr.

Perlmutter, David D. Picturing China in the American Press: The Visual Portrayal of Sino-American Relations in Time Magazine. 2007. (Lexington Studies in Political Communication Ser.). (ENG., Illus.). 294p. 94.50 *(978-0-7391-1819-1(6))* Lexington Bks.

—Picturing China in the American Press: The Visual Portrayal of Sino-American Relations in Time Magazine, 1949-1973. 2007. (Lexington Studies in Political Communication Ser.). (ENG., Illus.). 294p. per. 39.99 *(978-0-7391-1820-7(X))* Lexington Bks.

Platt, Nicholas. China Boys: How U. S. Relations with the PRC Began & Grew. A Personal Memoir. 2010. (Illus.). 386p. pap. 28.00 *(978-0-9844062-2-7(0)*, Vellum) New Academia Publishing, LLC.

Pollpeter, Kevin. Building for the Future: China's Progress in Space Technology during the Tenth 5-Year Plan & the U. S. Response. 2008. *(978-1-58487-347-1(7))* Strategic Studies Institute, U.S. Army War College Commandant (AWCC-DSI/Pubns.).

Qi, Shouhua. China Complex: U. S.-China Relations in the 21st Century: Crossroads or Collision Course. 2009. (ENG.). 224p. pap. 18.95 *(978-1-59265-079-8(1))* Long River Pr.

Qing, Simei. From Allies to Enemies: Visions of Modernity, Identity, & U. S. -China Diplomacy, 1945-1960. 2007. 410p. 60.50 *(978-0-674-02344-4(7))* Harvard Univ. Pr.

Rasmussen, Kathleen B., et al, eds. Foreign Relations of the United States, 1969-1976, Volume XXXI, Foreign Economic Policy, 1973-1976: Foreign Economic Policy, 1973-1976. 2010. (ENG.). 1131p. 75.00 *(978-0-16-084410-2(X)*, Bureau of Public Affairs, Office of the Historian) United States Government Printing Office.

Rhoads, Edward J. M. Stepping Forth into the World: The Chinese Educational Mission to the United States, 1872-81. 2011. (CHI., Illus.). 332p. ***(978-988-220-742-4(1))*** Hong Kong Univ. Pr.

Ross, Robert. Chinese Security Policy: Structure, Power & Politics. 2009. (ENG., Illus.). 342p. 170.00 *(978-0-415-77785-8(2))* Routledge.

Ross, Robert, et al, eds. Us-China-Eu Relations. 2011. (ENG.). (C). pap. 44.95 ***(978-0-415-68113-1(8))*** Routledge.

Sato, Yoichiro & Cooney, Kevin J. The Rise of China & International Security: America & Asia Respond. Cooney, Kevin & Sato, Yoichiro, eds. 2008. (Asian Security Studies). (Illus.). 256p. 140.00 *(978-0-415-43396-9(7))* Routledge.

Schnell, James. U S -China Relations. 2010. 300p. pap. *(978-3-639-22836-6(7))* VDM Verlag Dr. Mueller e.K.

Shaw, Samuel. The Journals of Major Samuel Shaw. 2009. (Revolutionary War Ser.). (ENG.). 380p. pap. 23.95 *(978-1-4290-1696-4(5))* Applewood Bks.

Shen, Simon. China & Antiterrorism. 2007. 233p. 89.00 *(978-1-60021-344-1(6))* Nova Science Pubs., Inc.

—Redefining Nationalism in Modern China: Sino-American Relations & the Emergence of Chinese Public Opinion in the 21st Century. 2007. (ENG., Illus.). 312p. 105.00 *(978-0-230-54939-5(X))* Palgrave Macmillan.

Sieff, Martin. Shifting Superpowers: The New & Emerging Relationships between the United States, China & India. 2010. (ENG.). 240p. 26.00 *(978-1-935308-21-8(1))* Cato Institute.

Song, Yuwu. Encyclopedia of Chinese-American Relations. Song, Yuwu, ed. alt. ed. 2009. (ENG., Illus.). 367p. pap. 50.00 *(978-0-7864-4593-6(9))* McFarland & Co., Inc. Pubs.

Steinfeld, Edward S. Playing Our Game: Why China's Rise Doesn't Threaten the West, 1 vol. 2010. (ENG., Illus.). 280p. 27.95 *(978-0-19-539065-0(2))* Oxford Univ. Pr., Inc.

Stuart, John Leighton & Chen, Lisong. Situ Leideng Ri Ji: Xiang Jian Shi Nan Bie Yi Nan. 2009. (CHI., Illus.). ***(978-7-5461-0241-2(3))*** Huangshan Publishing Hse.

Su, Chi. Taiwan's Relations with Mainland China. 2010. (ENG., Illus.). 368p. (C). pap. 39.95 *(978-0-415-58999-4(1))* Routledge.

Sutter, Robert. The A to Z of United States-China Relations. 2010. (A to Z Guide Ser.). (ENG.). 322p. pap. 34.45 *(978-0-8108-7552-4(7))* Scarecrow Pr., Inc.

—U. S. - Chinese Relations: Perilous Past, Pragmatic Present. 2010. (ENG.). 340p. pap. 33.00 *(978-0-7425-6842-6(3))* Rowman & Littlefield Publishers, Inc.

—U. S. -Chinese Relations: Perilous Past, Pragmatic Present. 2010. (ENG.). 340p. 49.95 *(978-0-7425-6841-9(5))* Rowman & Littlefield Publishers, Inc.

Sutter, Robert G. Positive Equilibrium in U.S.-China Relations: Durable or Not?: A Time of "Testing" in Sino-American Relations. 2009. 52p. ***(978-1-932330-29-8(1))*** Maryland Series in Contemporary Studies.

Swaine. Managing sino american Crises. 2006. 384p. (C). 62.95 *(978-0-87003-229-5(1))* Carnegie Endowment for International Peace.

Swaine, Michael D. America's Challenge: Engaging a Rising China in the Twenty-First Century. 2011. (ENG.). 673p. 49.95 *(978-0-87003-258-5(5))*; pap. 19.95 *(978-0-87003-257-8(7))* Carnegie Endowment for International Peace.

Swaine, Michael D. & Tuosheng, Zhang, eds. Managing Sino-American Crises: Case Studies & Analysis. 2007. (ENG., Illus.). 384p. per. 24.95 *(978-0-87003-228-8(3))* Carnegie Endowment for International Peace.

Tkacik, John. Reshaping the Taiwan Strait. 2007. 222p. *(978-0-89195-275-6(6))* Heritage Foundation.

Tucker, Nancy Bernkopf. The China Threat: Memories, Myths, & Realities in the 1950s. 2012. E-Book ***(978-0-231-52819-1(1))***; (ENG., Illus.). 312p. (gr. 17). 39.50 ***(978-0-231-15924-1(2))*** Columbia Univ. Pr.

Tucker, Nancy Bernkopf. Strait Talk: United States-Taiwan Relations & the Crisis with China. 2011. (ENG., Illus.). 404p. pap. 22.95 *(978-0-674-06052-4(0))* Harvard Univ. Pr.

Tucker, Nancy Bernkopf, ed. Dangerous Strait: The U. S. -Taiwan-China Crisis. 2008. (ENG., Illus.). 288p. (gr. 17). pap. 26.00 *(978-0-231-13565-8(3))* Columbia Univ. Pr.

Tudda, Chris. A Cold War Turning Point: Nixon & China, 1969-1972. 2012. (Illus.). 328p. pap. 27.50 ***(978-0-8071-4289-9(1))*** Louisiana State Univ. Pr.

Twomey, Christopher P. The Military Lens: Doctrinal Difference & Deterrence Failure in Sino-American Relations. 2010. (Cornell Studies in Security Affairs Ser.). (Illus.). 240p. 35.00 *(978-0-8014-4914-7(6))* Cornell Univ. Pr.

U.S. -China Relations: Hearing Before the Subcommittee on Asia, the Pacific, & the Global Environment of the Committee on Foreign Affairs, House of Representatives, One Hundred Tenth Congress, First Session, March 27, 2007. 2007. iii, 38p. *(978-0-16-078908-3(7)*, 552-070-36034-4) United States Government Printing Office.

Walton, Tracy M. U.S. & China Bilateral Relationship: Strains & Cooperation. 2011. (China in the 21st Century Ser.). 115.00 *(978-1-61122-766-6(6))* Nova Science Pubs., Inc.

Wang, Chi. George W. Bush & China: Policies, Problems, & Partnership. 2008. (ENG.). 156p. 47.50 *(978-0-7391-2917-3(1))* Lexington Bks.

Wang, Chi-Ni William. The Path to China's Modernisation. 2010. 344p. pap. *(978-3-8383-5283-1(1))* Lambert Academic Publishing.

Wang, Sheng-Wei. China's Ascendancy: An Opportunity or a Threat?: What Every American Should Know about China. 2007. *(978-0-9785095-3-8(6))* International Publishing Hse. for China's Culture.

Wang, Zheng. Never Forget National Humiliation: Historical Memory in Chinese Politics & Foreign Relations. 2012. (Contemporary Asia in the World Ser.). (ENG., Illus.). 320p. (gr. 17). 32.50 ***(978-0-231-14890-0(9))*** Columbia Univ. Pr.

Weston, Timothy B. China in & Beyond the Headlines. 3rd ed. 2012. (ENG.). 384p. pap. 35.00 ***(978-1-4422-0905-3(4))*** Rowman & Littlefield Publishers, Inc.

Weston, Timothy B. & Jensen, Lionel M. China in & Beyond the Headlines. 2011. ***(978-1-4422-0906-0(2))*** Rowman & Littlefield Publishers, Inc.

What Democracy Means in China after 30 Years of Reform: Roundtable Before the Congressional-Executive Commission on China, One Hundred Eleventh Congress, First Session, May 22, 2009. 2009. (Illus.). ii, 51p. *(978-0-16-084471-3(1)*, 552-070-39994-1) United States Government Printing Office.

Wheeler, Norton. The Role of American NGOs in China's Modernization: Invited Influence. 2012. (Asia's Transformations Ser.). (ENG., Illus.). 240p. (C). 135.00 ***(978-0-415-50657-1(3))*** Routledge.

Womack, Brantly. China among Unequals: Asymmetric Foreign Relationships in Asia. 2010. (Illus.). 552p. 130.00 *(978-981-4295-27-7(2))* World Scientific Publishing Co., Inc.

Wu, Xinbo. Managing Crisis & Sustaining Peace Between China & the United States. 2008. pap. *(978-1-60127-032-0(1))* U. S. Institute of Peace Pr. (USIP Pr.).

Xia, Yafeng. Negotiating with the Enemy: U. S. -China Talks during the Cold War, 1949-1972. 2006. (ENG., Illus.). 352p. 45.00 *(978-0-253-34758-9(0)*, 0253347580) Indiana Univ. Pr.

Xie, Tao. US-China Relations: China policy on Capitol Hill. 2010. (ENG., Illus.). xvi, 203p. pap. 39.95 *(978-0-415-59042-6(6))* Routledge.

Xie, Taofang & Xie, Tao. U.S.-China Relations: China Policy on Capitol Hill. 2008. (Routledge Contemporary China Ser.). (Illus.). 224p. 150.00 *(978-0-415-77688-2(0))* Routledge.

Xu, Guangqiu. Congress & the U. S. -China Relationship, 1949-1979. 2007. 410p. 59.95 *(978-1-931968-39-3(X))* Univ. of Akron Pr., The.

Yang, Jiemian. Guo Ji Wei Ji Fan Hua Yu Zhong Mei Gong Tong Ying Dui: Proliferation of International Crisis & Sino-US Joint Response. 2010. (CHI.). 10p. *(978-7-80232-305-6(3))* Current Affairs Publishing Hse.

Zhang, Biwu. Chinese Perceptions of the U.S: An Exploration of China's Foreign Policy Motivations. 2011. ***(978-0-7391-7086-1(4))*** Lexington Bks.

Zhao, Suisheng. China-US Relations Transformed: Perspectives & Strategic Interactions. 2009. 256p. pap. 39.95 *(978-0-415-49580-6(6))* Routledge.

Zhao, Suisheng, ed. China & the United States: Cooperation & Competition in Northeast Asia. 2008. (ENG.). 216p. 89.00 *(978-0-230-60848-1(5))* Palgrave Macmillan.

—China-US Relations Transformed: Perspectives & Strategic Interactions. 2008. (Routledge Contemporary China Ser.). (ENG., Illus.). 256p. (C). 160.00 *(978-0-415-43867-4(5))* Routledge.

Zhao, Xiuzhe (William). Fierce Urgency. 2009. 197p. pap. 15.95 *(978-0-557-09107-2(1))* Lulu Enterprises Inc.

Zhou, Zhongfei. "Tai Du" de Guo Ji Bei Jing. 2009. *(978-7-80195-990-4(6))* Jiuzhou Publishing Hse.

Zhu, Zhiqun. US-China Relations in the 21st Century: Power Transition & Peace. 2009. 228p. pap. 39.95 *(978-0-415-49734-3(5))* Routledge.

CHINA—FOREIGN RELATIONS—VIETNAM

Anderson, James. The Rebel Den of Nung Tri Cao: Loyalty & Identity along the Sino-Vietnamese Frontier. 2007. (ENG., Illus.). 296p. per. 32.95 *(978-0-295-98689-0(1))* Univ. of Washington Pr.

Cooke, Nola, et al, eds. The Tongking Gulf Through History. 2011. (Encounters with Asia Ser.). (Illus.). 240p. (C). 59.95 *(978-0-8122-4336-9(6))* Univ. of Pennsylvania Pr.

Hensengerth, Oliver. Regionalism in China-Vietnam Relations: Institution-Building in the Greater Mekong Subregion. 2009. (Routledge Contemporary Asia Ser.). (ENG., Illus.). 192p. 130.00 *(978-0-415-55143-4(9))* Routledge.

Khoo, Nicholas. Collateral Damage: Sino-Soviet Rivalry & the Termination of the Sino-Vietnamese Alliance. 2011. (ENG.). 280p. (gr. 17). 50.00 *(978-0-231-15078-1(4))*; 288p. E-Book 39.99 *(978-0-231-52163-5(4))* Columbia Univ. Pr.

Roberts, Priscilla Mary, ed. Behind the Bamboo Curtain: China, Vietnam, & the World Beyond Asia. 2006. (Cold War International History Project Ser.). (ENG.). 580p. 70.00 *(978-0-8047-5502-3(7))* Stanford Univ. Pr.
Tonnesson, Stein. Vietnam 1946: How the War Began. (From Indochina to Vietnam: Revolution & War in a Global Perspective Ser.). (ENG., Illus.). 2011. 388p. pap. 26.95 *(978-0-520-26993-4(4))* 2009. 346p. 45.00 *(978-0-520-25602-6(6))* Univ. of California Pr.

CHINA—GREAT WALL

see Great Wall of China (China)

CHINA—GUIDEBOOKS

Altenburger, Engelbert. China. 2nd ed. (Nelles Guides). (Illus.). 256p. pap. 14.95 *(978-3-88618-117-9(0))* Nelles Verlag DEU. Dist: 7 Hills Bk. Distributors.
Atkinson, Kim & Nadel, Gillian, eds. Mobil Travel Guide Beijing. 2008. (Mobil Travel Guide Ser.). (Illus.). 196p. 17.95 *(978-0-8416-0323-3(5))* Langenscheidt Publishing Group.
Barrett, Pam & Insight Guides Staff. Silk Road Insight Guide. 2011. (Insight Guides). (ENG., Illus.). 432p. pap. 23.99 *(978-981-258-840-1(X))* APA Publications Services SGP. Dist: Ingram Pub. Services.
Blue Sky Publishing Staff. Travel Around China: The Guide to Exploring the Sites, the Cities the Provinces, & More. 2008. (Illus.). 720p. pap. 24.95 *(978-0-06-147354-8(5))*, HarperCollins Pubs.
Bonavia, Judy. The Silk Road: From Xi'an to Kashgar. 8th rev. ed. 2007. (Odyssey Illustrated Guides). (Illus.). 367p. pap. 24.95 *(978-962-217-761-1(1))* Odyssey Pubns., Ltd. HKG. Dist: Norton, W. W. & Co., Inc.
Bond, Graham. Frommer's Shanghai Day by Day. 2nd ed. 2012. (Frommer's Day by Day - Pocket Ser.: 201). (ENG., Illus.). 192p. pap. 13.99 ***(978-1-119-97552-6(2)***, Frommers) Wiley, John & Sons, Inc.
Buckley, Michael. Tibet. 3rd rev. ed. 2012. (Bradt Travel Guide Ser.). (ENG., Illus.). 336p. pap. 26.99 ***(978-1-84162-382-5(2))*** Bradt Travel Guides GBR. Dist: Globe Pequot Pr., The.
Chan, Charis, et al. China: Renaissance of the Middle Kingdom, Ninth Edition. 9th ed. 2008. (Odyssey Illustrated Guides). (ENG., Illus.). 440p. pap. 19.95 *(978-962-217-794-9(8)*, 217794) Airphoto International/Odyssey HKG. Dist: Norton, W. W. & Co., Inc.
Christian Focus Publications, creator. A Christian's Pocket Guide to the Chinese. 2008. (ENG.). 64p. per. 4.99 *(978-1-84550-315-4(5))* Christian Focus Pubns. GBR. Dist: STL Distribution North America.
City Guides, LUXE. Shanghai. 10th ed. 2012. (ENG.). 20p. 9.99 ***(978-988-3000-94-4(2))*** Luxe Asia Ltd. HKG. Dist: SCB Distributors.
Clifford, Miriam, et al. China: Museums. 2009. (ENG., Illus.). 384p. pap. 29.95 *(978-962-217-804-5(9)*, 217804) Airphoto International/Odyssey HKG. Dist: Norton, W. W. & Co., Inc.
—China: Museums. 2009. (Illus.). 384p. pap. 29.95 ***(978-1-85759-593-2(9))*** Scala Pubs., Ltd. GBR. Dist: Antique Collectors' Club.
Dorling Kindersley Publishing Staff. Beijing & Shanghai. 2011. (Eyewitness Travel Guides). (ENG.). 240p. 23.00 *(978-0-7566-6976-8(6))* Dorling Kindersley Publishing, Inc.
—DK Eyewitness Travel Guide: China: China. 2012. (Eyewitness Travel Guide Ser.). (ENG.). 672p. pap. 30.00 ***(978-0-7566-8430-3(7))*** Dorling Kindersley Publishing, Inc.
Dorling Kindersley Publishing Staff. Eyewitness Travel Guide - China. 2010. (Eyewitness Travel Guides). (ENG.). 672p. pap. 30.00 *(978-0-7566-6098-7(X))* Dorling Kindersley Publishing, Inc.
Eagan, Angie. Cultureshock China, 1 vol. 2011. (ENG., Illus.). 240p. pap. 15.95 *(978-0-7614-6052-7(7))* Marshall Cavendish Corp.
Eaves, Megan. This Is China: A Guidebook for Teachers, Backpackers & Other Lunatics. 2009. 172p. pap. 14.98 *(978-0-557-08118-9(1))* Lulu Enterprises Inc.
Explorer Publishing. Berlin Residents' Guide. 2009. (ENG., Illus.). 510p. pap. 24.95 *(978-9948-8585-1-5(4))* Explorer Publishing UAE. Dist: Globe Pequot Pr., The.
Explorer Publishing, creator. Shanghai Explorer Residents' Guide. rev. ed. 2008. (Explorer (Explorer Publishing) Ser.). (ENG., Illus.). 465p. per. 24.95 *(978-9948-03-320-2(5))* Explorer Publishing UAE. Dist: Globe Pequot Pr., The.
Explorer Publishing & Distribution. Shanghai Mini Explorer. rev. ed. 2008. (ENG.). 200p. pap. 11.95 *(978-9948-03-321-9(3))* Explorer Publishing UAE. Dist: Globe Pequot Pr., The.
Explorer Publishing Staff. Beijing. 2008. (ENG., Illus.). 430p. pap. 24.95 *(978-9948-03-327-1(2))* Explorer Publishing UAE. Dist: Globe Pequot Pr., The.
Flower, Kathy. China: The Essential Guide to Customs & Culture. 2010. (Culture Smart! Ser.). (ENG., Illus.). 168p. pap. 9.95 *(978-1-85733-502-6(3))* Kuperard Pubs. GBR. Dist: Random Hse., Inc.
Fodor's Travel Publications, Inc. Staff. Fodor's Beijing, 3rd Edition. 3rd ed. 2011. (Full-Color Gold Guides). (ENG., Illus.). 272p. pap. 19.99 *(978-1-4000-0526-0(4)*, Fodor's) Fodor's Travel Pubns.
—Fodor's China, 7th Edition. 7th ed. 2011. (Full-Color Gold Guides). (ENG.). 800p. pap. 26.99 *(978-0-307-48053-8(4)*, Fodor's) Fodor's Travel Pubns.
—Fodor's Shanghai's 25 Best. 3rd Edition. 2010. (25 Best Ser.). (ENG.). 128p. pap. 11.99 *(978-1-4000-0396-9(2)*, Fodor's) Fodor's Travel Pubns.
—Shanghai. 2nd ed. 2009. (Fodor's Gold Guides). (ENG., Illus.). 272p. pap. 18.95 *(978-1-4000-0821-6(2)*, Fodor's) Fodor's Travel Pubns.
Forbes, Andrew. National Geographic Traveler - Shanghai. 2007. (National Geographic Traveler Ser.). (ENG., Illus.). 272p. pap. 22.95 *(978-1-4262-0148-6(6)*, National Geographic) National Geographic Society.
Foster, Simon. Adventure Guide China. 2008. (Adventure Guide to China Ser.). (Illus.). 631p. pap. 27.99 *(978-1-58843-641-2(1))* Hunter Publishing, Inc.
Foster, Simon, et al. Frommer's China. 5th ed. 2012. (Frommer's Complete Guides). (ENG.). 896p. pap. 29.99 ***(978-1-118-09419-8(0)***, Frommers) Wiley, John & Sons, Inc.
Freer. TRAVELMAG Das Reisemagazin Westfalen, Ruhrgebiet, Vol. 1. 30.00 *(978-0-934686-30-3(0))* Freer Gallery of Art, Smithsonian Institution.
Fuller, Sarah. Hong Kong: A City Guide for People with Disability. 2009. (Illus.). 252p. pap. 39.50 *(978-988-17832-1-9(6))* Wheel Away Disabled Travel HKG. Dist: Trans-Atlantic Pubns., Inc.
Hannon, Brent, et al. China Berlitz Handbook. 2011. (Illus.). 304p. pap. 17.99 ***(978-981-268-904-7(4))*** APA Publications Services SGP. Dist: Ingram Pub. Services.
Harper, Damian. China. 2011. (Full Color Country Guide Ser.). (ENG., Illus.). 448p. pap. 27.99 *(978-1-74220-289-1(6))*; 12th rev. ed. 1048p. pap. 31.99 *(978-1-74179-589-9(3))* Lonely Planet Pubns.
—China. 2nd ed. 2007. (National Geographic Traveler Ser.). (ENG., Illus.). 400p. pap. 27.95 *(978-1-4262-0035-9(8)*, National Geographic) National Geographic Society.
Harper, Damian. National Geographic Traveler: China, 3rd Ed. 3rd ed. 2012. (National Geographic Traveler Ser.). (ENG., Illus.). 400p. pap. 27.95 ***(978-1-4262-0858-4(8)***, National Geographic) National Geographic Society.
Healthy Chinese Cuisine: A Restaurant Ordering Guide. 2007. pap. 9.95 *(978-0-9773334-6-2(9))* True Run Advertising Co.
Herzberg, Larry & Herzberg, Qin. China Survival Guide: How to Avoid Travel Troubles & Mortifying Mishaps, Revised Edition. rev. ed. 2011. (ENG., Illus.). 232p. pap. 9.95 ***(978-1-933330-94-5(5))*** Stone Bridge Pr.
Hibbard, Peter. The Bund Shanghai: China Faces West. 2007. (Odyssey Illustrated Guides). (ENG., Illus.). 152p. pap. 24.95 *(978-962-217-772-7(7)*, 217772) Airphoto International/Odyssey HKG. Dist: Norton, W. W. & Co., Inc.
Hoenig, Alan. Eating Out in China: A Traveler's Resource. 2010. (ENG.). 300p. pap. 15.95 *(978-0-9822324-2-2(X))* EZChinesey.com.
Hu, Marybelle, et al. Shanghai, 1 vol. 2006. (Not Just A Good Food Guide Ser.). (ENG., Illus.). 248p. pap. 10.50 *(978-981-232-924-0(2))* Marshall Cavendish International (Asia) Private Ltd. SGP. Dist: Marshall Cavendish Corp.
Huai, Dong. An Essential Guide to China. 2010. 128p. pap. 9.95 *(978-1-60220-602-1(3))* BetterLink Pr., Inc.
Immersion Guides: Lhasa. 2007. pap. 15.95 *(978-0-9773334-3-1(4))* True Run Advertising Co.
Insight. Shanghai Insight City Guide. 3rd ed. 2011. (City Guide Ser.). (ENG., Illus.). 336p. pap. 19.99 *(978-981-282-363-2(8))* APA Publications Services SGP. Dist: Ingram Pub. Services.
Insight Guide, compiled by. China. 11th ed. 2011. (Insight Guides). (ENG., Illus.). 480p. pap. 24.99 *(978-981-282-063-1(9))* APA Publications Services SGP. Dist: Ingram Pub. Services.
Insight Guides, creator. Southern China & Hong Kong. 2008. (Insight Guides). (ENG., Illus.). 400p. pap. 23.95 *(978-981-258-484-7(6))* APA Publications Services SGP. Dist: Ingram Pub. Services.
Jones, Siân Pritchard & Gibbons, Bob. The Mount Kailash Trek: Tibet's Sacred Mountain & Western Tibet. 2010. (Illus.). 192p. vinyl bd. 22.95 *(978-1-85284-514-8(7))* Cicerone Pr. GBR. Dist: Midpoint Trade Bks., Inc.
Justman, Hope. Guide to Hiking China's Old Road to Shu. 2007. 448p. per. 27.95 *(978-0-595-42551-8(8))* iUniverse, Inc.
Knopf Guides Staff. Beijing. 2009. (Knopf Mapguides Ser.). (ENG., Illus.). 48p. pap. 10.95 *(978-0-375-71122-0(8)*, Knopf) Knopf Doubleday Publishing Group.
Lacey, Leo. Culture Wise China. 2011. (ENG., Illus.). 240p. pap. 17.95 *(978-1-907339-27-1(2))* Survival Bks., Ltd.
Law, Eugene. Intercontinental's Best of China, 1 vol. 2007. (ENG., Illus.). 544p. pap. *(978-0-7614-2602-8(7))* Marshall Cavendish Corp.
Lee, Khoon Choy. Passage Through China: This Land So Rich in Beauty. 2007. (Illus.). 566p. pap. *(978-981-4163-43-9(0))* China Knowledge Press Pte Ltd.
Leffman, David, et al. The Rough Guide to China. 6th ed. 2011. (ENG., Illus.). 1140p. 29.99 *(978-1-84836-660-2(4))* Rough Guides, Ltd. GBR. Dist: Dorling Kindersley Publishing, Inc.
Lewis, Simon & Rough Guides Staff. The Rough Guide to Shanghai. 2nd ed. 2011. (ENG., Illus.). 208p. 19.99 *(978-1-84836-625-1(6))* Rough Guides, Ltd. GBR. Dist: Dorling Kindersley Publishing, Inc.
Locken, E. Travel Journal China. 2009. 192p. pap. 19.99 *(978-0-557-08043-9(7))* Lulu Enterprises Inc.
—Travel Journal Fuzhou - China. 2010. 192p. pap. 19.99 *(978-0-557-42149-7(7))* Lulu Enterprises Inc.
—Travel Journal Guangzhou - China. 2010. 192p. pap. 19.99 *(978-0-557-42152-7(7))* Lulu Enterprises Inc.
—Travel Journal Guilin - China. 2010. 192p. pap. 19.99 *(978-0-557-42163-3(2))* Lulu Enterprises Inc.
Lonely Planet Staff & Pitts, Christopher. Shanghai. 2010. (Encounter Ser.). (ENG., Illus.). 2nd rev. ed. 160p. pap. 12.99 *(978-1-74179-411-3(0))* 5th rev. ed. 276p. pap. 21.99 *(978-1-74179-283-6(5))* Lonely Planet Pubns.
Mansfield, Stephen. China, Yunnan Province. 2nd ed. 2007. (Bradt Travel Guide Ser.). (ENG., Illus.). 288p. per. 23.95 *(978-1-84162-169-2(2))* Bradt Travel Guides GBR. Dist: Globe Pequot Pr., The.
McCue, Gary. Trekking Tibet: A Traveler's Guide. 3rd ed. 2010. (ENG., Illus.). 416p. pap. 29.95 *(978-1-59485-266-4(9))* Mountaineers Bks., The.
Michelin Must Sees. Michelin Must Sees Shanghai. 2010. (Must See Guides/Michelin Ser.). (Illus.). 160p. pap. 11.99 *(978-1-906261-99-3(7)*, Michelin Travel & Lifestyle.
Mo, Crystyl, ed. To Shanghai with Love: A Travel Guide for the Connoisseur. 2011. (To Asia with Love Ser.). (ENG.). 248p. pap. 21.93 *(978-1-934159-10-1(7))* ThingsAsian Pr.
Mooney, Paul. Beijing. 2008. (National Geographic Traveler Ser.). (ENG.). 272p pap. 22.95 *(978-1-4262-0231-5(8))* National Geographic Society.
Mooney, Paul & Hibbard, Peter. Beijing & Shanghai: China's Hottest Cities. 3rd ed. 2012. (Odyssey Illustrated Guides). (ENG., Illus.). 600p. pap. 27.95 *(978-962-217-797-0(2)*, 217797) Airphoto International/Odyssey HKG. Dist: Norton, W. W. & Co., Inc.
Mooney, Paul, et al. Xi'an, Shaanxi & the Terracotta Army. 2nd ed. 2009. (Odyssey Illustrated Guides). (ENG., Illus.). 336p. pap. 24.95 *(978-962-217-800-7(6)*, 217800) Airphoto International/Odyssey HKG. Dist: Norton, W. W. & Co., Inc.
Nanyan, Cao. China: World Heritage Sites. 2009. (Illus.). 400p. 25.00 *(978-1-905573-39-4(1))* Compendium GBR. Dist: Casemate Pubs. & Bk. Distributors, LLC.
Nicolson, Ken. The Happy Valley: A History & Tour of the Hong Kong Cemetery. 2010. (Illus.). 144p. ***(978-988-220-756-1(1))*** Hong Kong Univ. Pr.
—The Happy Valley: A History & Tour of the Hong Kong Cemetery. 2010. (ENG., Illus.). 144p. (gr. 17). pap. 22.00 *(978-988-8028-10-8(3))* Hong Kong Univ. Pr. HKG. Dist: Columbia Univ. Pr.
Owyang, Sharon. Frommer's Shanghai. 6th ed. 2010. (Frommer's Complete Guides: 857). (ENG., Illus.). 320p. pap. 19.99 *(978-0-470-64377-8(3)*, Frommers) Wiley, John & Sons, Inc.
Qinqin, Sun, et al. An Essential Guide China's. 2010. 166p. pap. 9.95 *(978-1-60220-601-4(5))* BetterLink Pr., Inc.
—Journey Through China: Exploring Major Sites & Cuisine in 10 Days. Reader's Digest Staff, ed. 2010. (ENG., Illus.). 200p. (gr. 12). pap. 14.95 *(978-1-60652-122-9(5))* Reader's Digest Assn., Inc., The.
Reynolds, Kev. Everest: A Trekker's Guide - Trekking Routes in Nepal & Tibet. 4th ed. 2012. (ENG., Illus.). 272p. pap. 24.95 ***(978-1-85284-680-0(1))*** Cicerone Pr. GBR. Dist: Midpoint Trade Bks., Inc.
Rough, Guides. Hong Kong & Macau - Pocket Rough Guide. 2012. (Rough Guide Pocket Guides). (ENG., Illus.). 160p. 12.99 *(978-1-4053-8534-3(0))* Rough Guides, Ltd. GBR. Dist: Dorling Kindersley Publishing, Inc.
Rough, Guides. The Rough Guide to Southwest China. 2012. (ENG., Illus.). 440p. 25.99 *(978-1-84836-482-0(2))* Rough Guides, Ltd. GBR. Dist: Dorling Kindersley Publishing, Inc.
Schütte, Hans-Wilm. China Baedeker Guide. 2012. (Baedeker Guides Ser.). (ENG., Illus.). 636p. pap. 25.00 ***(978-3-8297-6620-3(3))*** Marco Polo Travel Publishing GBR. Dist: Innovative Logistics.
Shanghai. 2012. (Select Ser.). (Illus.). 192p. pap. 15.00 ***(978-1-78005-283-0(3))*** APA Publications Services SGP. Dist: Ingram Pub. Services.
Shaw, Raynor & Bonavia, Judy. Three Gorges of the Yangzi River: Chongqing to Wuhan. 2nd ed. 2009. (Odyssey Illustrated Guides). (ENG.). 248p. pap. 22.95 *(978-962-217-801-4(4)*, 217801) Airphoto International/Odyssey HKG. Dist: Norton, W. W. & Co., Inc.
Shipman, Dan. Chinatized. 2009. pap. 14.99 *(978-1-60799-549-4(2))* Tate Publishing & Enterprises, LLC.
Singh, Sarina, et al. Pakistan & the Karakoram Highway. 7th rev. ed. 2008. (Lonely Planet Pakistan Ser.). (ENG., Illus.). 432p. pap. 26.99 *(978-1-74104-542-0(8))* Lonely Planet Pubns.
Strother, Barbara & Strother, Stuart. Moon Living Abroad in China: Including Hong Kong & Macau. 2009. (Living Abroad Ser.). (ENG., Illus.). 448p. pap. 19.95 *(978-1-59880-169-9(4))* Avalon Travel Publishing.
Thomas Cook Publishing Staff. Beijing & Northern China. 2nd ed. 2010. (Travellers - Thomas Cook Ser.). (ENG., Illus.). 192p. pap. 16.95 *(978-1-84848-227-2(2))* Cook, Thomas Publishing GBR. Dist: Globe Pequot Pr., The.
—China Travellers. 3rd ed. 2006. (Travellers - Thomas Cook Ser.). (ENG., Illus.). 192p. pap. 14.95 *(978-1-84157-599-5(2))* Cook, Thomas Publishing GBR. Dist: Globe Pequot Pr., The.
—Shanghai & Southern China. 2nd ed. 2010. (Travellers - Thomas Cook Ser.). (ENG., Illus.). 176p. pap. 16.95 *(978-1-84848-233-3(7))* Cook, Thomas Publishing GBR. Dist: Globe Pequot Pr., The.
Time Out Guides Staff. Time Out Shanghai. 3rd ed. 2008. (Time Out Guides). (ENG., Illus.). 310p. pap. 19.95 *(978-1-84670-067-5(1))* Time Out Guides Ltd. GBR. Dist: Perseus-PGW.
Tong, Tiger. China Business Guide, 4th Edition. 2008. 559p. pap. *(978-981-4163-47-7(3))* China Knowledge Press Pte Ltd.
TRAVELMAG Das Reisemagazin Westfalen, Ruhrgebiet. tchr. ed. 25.95 *(978-0-382-44543-9(0))* Cobblestone Publishing Co.
Wallpaper Magazine Editors, ed. Shanghai 2012 - Wallpaper City Guides. 4th ed. 2011. (ENG., Illus.). 128p. pap., pap. 9.95 *(978-0-7148-6204-0(5))* Phaidon Pr., Inc.
Weiner, Rebecca & EAGAN, ANGIE. Shanghai, 1 vol. 2008. (CultureShock! Ser.). (ENG.). 344p. pap. 15.95 *(978-0-7614-5493-9(4))* Marshall Cavendish Corp.
Wordie, Jason. Streets: Exploring Kowloon. 2007. (ENG., Illus.). 304p. (gr. 17) pap. 27.95 *(978-962-209-813-8(4))* Hong Kong Univ. Pr. HKG. Dist: Columbia Univ. Pr.
Yu, Peter Xiaoming & Doyle, G. Wright. China: Ancient Culture, Modern Society. 2009. 244p. 25.95 *(978-1-60860-635-1(X)*, Strategic Bk. Publishing) AEG Literary Publishing Services, Inc.
Zagat Survey Staff. Beijing. 2008. (ENG., Illus.). 128p. pap. 15.95 *(978-1-57006-959-8(X))* Zagat Survey.
—Hong Kong, Shanghai, Beijing: Restaurants & Hotels. Boland, Rory et al, eds. 2008. (ENG., Illus.). 160p. pap. 15.95 *(978-1-57006-962-8(X))* Zagat Survey.
—Shanghai Restaurants & Hotels. 2008. 80p. pap. 5.95 *(978-1-60478-067-3(3))* Zagat Survey.
Zhangshen, Lu. National Museum of China. 2011. (Illus.). 256p. 70.00 *(978-1-85759-654-0(4))* Scala, Editions FRA. Dist: National Bk. Network.

CHINA—HISTORIOGRAPHY

Bob Tadashi Wakabayashi Staff. The Nanking Atrocity 1937-38: Complicating the Picture. 2007. (Illus.). 456p. 39.95 *(978-1-84545-500-2(2))* Berghahn Bks., Inc.
Chuo Daigaku, Jinbun Kagaku Kenkyujo Staff, contrib. by. Toan No Sekai. 2009. (JPN., Illus.). xii, 250p. *(978-4-8057-4210-5(0))* Chuo Univ. Pr.
Farmer, J. Michael. The Talent of Shu: Qiao Zhou & the Intellectual World of Early Medieval Sichuan. 2008. (Illus.). xviii, 246p. pap. 29.95 *(978-0-7914-7164-7(0))* State Univ. of New York Pr.
Feuerwerker, Albert & Cheng, Sally. Chinese Communist Studies of Modern Chinese History. 2011. 316p. 50.95 ***(978-1-258-02515-1(9))*** Literary Licensing, LLC.
Flowerdew, John. Critical Discourse Analysis in Historiography: The Case of Hong Kong's Evolving Identity. 2011. (ENG., Illus.). 360p. 95.00 ***(978-0-230-30118-4(5))*** Palgrave Macmillan.
Harvard-Yenching Institute. Combined Indices to Shih Chi & the Notes of P'Ei Yin, Ssu-Ma Cheng, Chang Shou-Chieh, & Takigawa Kametaro. 2011. 754p. 71.95 ***(978-1-258-06737-3(4))*** Literary Licensing, LLC.
Hon, Tze-ki & Culp, Robert J., eds. The Politics of Historical Production in Late Qing & Republican China. 2007. (Leiden Ser. in Comparative Historiography Ser.). 350p. *(978-90-04-16023-1(X))* BRILL.
Ivanhoe, Philip. On Ethics & History: Essays & Letters of Zhang Xuecheng. 2009. (ENG.). 208p. 50.00 *(978-0-8047-6128-4(0))* Stanford Univ. Pr.
Johansson, Perry. Saluting the Yellow Emperor: A Case of Swedish Sinography. 2012. (ENG.). VIII, 244p. ***(978-90-04-22097-3(6))*** BRILL.
Lehner, Georg. China in European Encyclopedias, 1700-1850. 2011. 387p. *(978-90-04-20150-7(5))* BRILL.
Li, Wai-yee. The Readability of the Past in Early Chinese Historiography. 2008. (Harvard East Asian Monographs: 253). 425p. 49.50 *(978-0-674-01777-1(3))* Harvard Univ., Asia Ctr.
Lu, Suping. A Mission under Duress: The Nanjing Massacre & Post-Massacre Social Conditions Documented by American Diplomats. 2010. (ENG.). 394p. 84.50 *(978-0-7618-5149-3(6))* Univ. Pr. of America, Inc.
Miller, Peter N. & Louis, François. Antiquarianism & Intellectual Life in Europe & China, 1500-1800. 2012. (Bard Graduate Center Cultural Histories of the Material World Ser.). (ENG.). 448p. 65.00 ***(978-0-472-11818-2(3))*** Univ. of Michigan Pr.
Mote, Frederick W. China & the Vocation of History in the Twentieth Century: A Personal Memoir. 2010. (ENG., Illus.). 360p. (C). 29.95 *(978-0-691-14463-4(X))* Princeton Univ. Pr.
Wang Shiwei. Li Shi Wen Xian Yan Jiu. 2008. (CHI., Illus.). *(978-7-5013-3749-1(7))* Beijing Library Pr.
Zhongguo guo jia tu shu guan, Gu ji guan Staff, contrib. by. Di 2 Jie Di Fang Wen Xian Guo Ji Xue Shu Yan Tao Hui Lun Wen Ji. 2009. (CHI., Illus.). *(978-7-5013-4219-8(9))* Beijing Library Pr.

CHINA—HISTORY

Abramson, Marc S. & Abramson, Marc Samuel. Ethnic Identity in Tang China. 2007. (Encounters with Asia Ser.). 288p. (C). 59.95 *(978-0-8122-4052-8(9))* Univ. of Pennsylvania Pr.
Adamek, Wendi Leigh. The Teachings of Master Wuzhu: Zen & Religion of No-Religion. 2011. x, 208p. ***(978-0-231-10522-4(3))*** Columbia Univ. Pr.
Amann, Gustav. The Legacy of Sun Yatsen: A History of the Chinese Revolution. Glove, Frederick Philip, tr. 2007. (ENG.). 332p. 45.95 *(978-0-548-01873-6(1))* Kessinger Publishing, LLC.
Anderson, James. The Rebel Den of Nung Tri Cao: Loyalty & Identity along the Sino-Vietnamese Frontier. 2007. (ENG., Illus.). 296p. per. 32.95 *(978-0-295-98689-0(1))* Univ. of Washington Pr.
Assandri, Friederike & Martins, Dora, eds. From Early Tang Court Debates to China's Peaceful Rise. 2009. (ICAS Publications Ser.). (ENG.). 168p. pap. *(978-90-5356-795-1(X)*, Leiden Univ. Pr.) Amsterdam Univ. Pr.
Ba Lu Jun Shandong Zong Dui Shi, 2 vols. 2nd ed. 2007. (CHI., Illus.). *(978-7-209-01265-2(6))* Shandong People's Publishing Hse.
"Baoting Lizu Miaozu Zizhixian gai kuang" bian xie zu Staff, contrib. by. Baoting Lizu Miaozu Zizhixian Gai Kuang: BaotingLizuMiaozuZizhixiangaikuang. 2008. (CHI., Illus.). *(978-7-105-08617-7(3))* Nationalities Publishing Hse, The.
BarCharts, Inc. China: History. 2011. (ENG.). 6p. 5.95 *(978-1-4232-1538-4(5))* Barcharts, Inc.
Barrett, T. H. Taoism under the T'ang: Religion & Empire During a Golden Age of Chinese History. 2006. (History Ser.). (ENG.). 112p. pap. 25.00 *(978-1-891640-25-4(9))* Floating World Editions.
—The Woman Who Discovered Printing. 2008. (ENG., Illus.). 192p. 25.00 *(978-0-300-12728-7(6))* Yale Univ. Pr.
Bateman, Sam & Ho, Joshua. Southeast Asia & the Rise of Chinese & Indian Naval Power: Between Rising Naval Powers. 2010. (Routledge Security in Asia Pacific Ser.). (ENG., Illus.). 272p. (C). 130.00 *(978-0-415-55955-3(3)*, Routledge) Taylor & Francis Group GBR. Dist: Taylor & Francis Group.
Becker, Jasper. The City of Heavenly Tranquility: Beijing in the History of China. 2008. (Illus.). 384p. 27.95 *(978-0-19-530997-3(9))* Oxford Univ. Pr., Inc.

C

—Dragon Rising: An Inside Look at China Today. (ENG., Illus.). 264p. 2007. pap. 18.95 (978-1-4262-0116-5(8)) 2006. 35.00 (978-0-7922-6193-3(3)) National Geographic Society. (National Geographic).

Benelli, James. Ski Tales: The History of China Peak & Sierra Summit. 2009. (ENG.). 166p. pap. 10.95 (978-1-884995-66-8(7)) Linden Publishing Co., Inc.

Benjamin, C. The Yuezhi: Origin, Migration & the Conquest of Northern Bactria. 2007. (Silk Road Studies). (ENG.). 245p. (C). pap. 73.00 (978-2-503-52429-0(X)) Brepols Pubs. BEL. Dist: ISD.

Bianco, Lucien. Wretched Rebels: Rural Disturbances on the Eve of the Chinese Revolution. Liddell, Philip, tr. from FRE. 2010. (Harvard East Asian Monographs: 323). Orig. Title: Jacqueries et révolution dans la Chine du XXe Siècle. (Illus.). 300p. 39.95 (978-0-674-03542-3(9)) Harvard Univ., Asia Ctr.

Bishop, Carl. The Elephant & Its Ivory in Ancient China. 2010. pap. 18.04 (978-1-61143-019-6(4)) Gorgias Pr., LLC.

Blishen, Tony, tr. from CHI. The Art of Self Cultivation: Quotations from Chinese Wisdom. 2011. (ENG.). 108p. 12.95 (978-1-60220-133-0(1)) BetterLink Pr., Inc.

Blussé, Leonard. Visible Cities: Canton, Nagasaki, & Batavia & the Coming of the Americans. 2008. (Edwin O. Reischauer Lectures: 2006). (Illus.). 148p. 28.50 (978-0-674-02614-8(4)) Harvard Univ. Pr.

Boardman, John. The Relief Plaques of Eastern Eurasia & China: The 'Ordos Bronzes,' Peter the Great's Treasure, & their Kin. 2011. (Beazley archive: studies in gems & Jewellery Ser.). (ENG., Illus.). 93p. (C). 100.00 (978-1-903767-13-9(X)) Archaeopress GBR. Dist: Brown, David Bk. Co., The.

Bomino, Kathy. Armchair Travel to Heal the Planet. 2010. 264p. pap. 18.95 (978-1-59330-635-9(0)) Aventine Pr.

Bovingdon, Gardner. The Uyghurs: Strangers in Their Own Land. 2010. (ENG., Illus.). 304p. (gr. 17). 45.00 (978-0-231-14758-3(9)) Columbia Univ. Pr.

Boxer, C. R. South China in the Sixteenth Century. 2006. (ENG., Illus.). 36.00 (978-974-524-043-8(5)) Orchid Pr. THA. Dist: National Bk. Network.

Bredon, Juliet. Sir Robert Hart. 2008. 124p. 21.99 (978-0-554-38162-6(1)); 24.99 (978-0-554-28859-8(1)) BiblioBazaar.

Breuker. Pre-Modern States on China's North-Eastern Frontier: The Liao, 916-1125, & the Koryo, 918-1392. 2012. (Asian States & Empires Ser.). (ENG.). 240p. (C). 135.00 (978-0-415-77620-2(1)) Routledge.

Brodsgaard, Kjeld Erik & Brodsgaard, Kjeld Erik. Hainan: State, Society, & Business in a Chinese Province. 2008. (China Policy Ser.). (ENG., Illus.). 208p. (C). 168.00 (978-0-415-46033-0(6)) Routledge.

Brokaw, Cynthia J. Commerce in Culture: The Sibao Book Trade in the Qing & Republican Periods. 2007. (Harvard East Asian Monographs: 280). (Illus.). 673p. 44.95 (978-0-674-02449-6(4)) Harvard Univ., Asia Ctr.

Brooks, Bruce, et al. Warring States Papers. 2011. (978-1-936166-01-5(1)) Warring States Project.

Brooks, E. Bruce. Emergence of China. 2010. (Illus.). 256p. pap. 24.95 (978-1-936166-75-6(5)) Warring States Project.

Brown, Arthur Judson. New Forces in Old China. 2008. 368p. 31.99 (978-0-554-21418-4(0)) BiblioBazaar.

Brown, Shana Julia. Pastimes: From Art & Antiquarianism to Modern Chinese Historiography. 2011. 232p. 48.00 **(978-0-8248-3498-2(4))** Univ. of Hawaii Pr.

Burgess, Andrew Severance & Fu, Peng. Peng Fu from Junan: A Biography. 2011. 128p. 40.95 **(978-1-258-08618-3(2))** Literary Licensing, LLC.

Campany, Robert Ford. Making Transcendents: Ascetics & Social Memory in Early Medieval China. 2009. 336p. (C). 48.00 (978-0-8248-3333-6(3)) Univ. of Hawaii Pr.

Chan, Hanson. Chinese History Made Easy, Vol. 1. 2008.Tr. of Chinese History Made Easy, Vol 1. (CHI.). 238p. per. 10.00 (978-0-9777959-6-3(9)) Chan, Hanson.

Chan, Hong-Mo. The Birth of China Seen Through Poetry. 2011. 264p. pap. 22.00 (978-981-4335-33-1(9)) World Scientific Publishing Co., Inc.

Chaussende, Damien. Des Trois Royaumes Aux Jin: Légitimation du Pouvoir Impérial en Chine Au IIIe Siècle. 2010. (FRE., Illus.). 480p. (C). pap. 53.00 **(978-2-251-38104-6(X))** Societe d'edition Les Belles lettres FRA. Dist: ISD.

Chen, Rose, ed. Learning & Thinking about China: Introduction of Chinese Culture. 2nd ed. 2006. (CHI.). (YA). (978-0-9788074-0-5(5)) Rose Group for Cross-Cultural Understanding, The.

Chen, Stephen. Red Circle: China & Me 1949-2009. 2009. (ENG.). 552p. pap. 19.95 (978-1-4490-3365-1(2)) AuthorHouse.

Cheng & Lestz & Cram101 Textbook Reviews Staff. The Search for Modern Chin. 2007. 192p. per. 13.95 (978-1-4288-2234-4(8)) Cram101 Inc.

Cheng, huaweimin. VEO. 2008. (CHI.). pap. 20.00 (978-1-4276-3076-6(3)) Aardvark Global Publishing.

Chey, Ong Siew. China Condensed: 5000 Years of History & Culture, 1 vol. 2009. (ENG.). 176p. pap. 12.00 (978-981-261-619-7(5)) Marshall Cavendish International (Asia) Private Ltd. SGP. Dist: Marshall Cavendish Corp.

Chin-Chuan, Lee. Chinese Media, Global Contexts. 2009. 276p. pap. 39.95 (978-0-415-49736-7(1)) Routledge.

Chittick, Andrew. Patronage & Community in Medieval China: The Xiangyang Garrison, 400-600 Ce. 2010. (Illus.). 208p. pap. 23.95 (978-1-4384-2898-7(7), Suny Pr.) State Univ. of New York Pr.

Chong, Key Ray. Sun Yat-sen & the West: Western Influence on His Life & Thought. 2010. 484p. 129.95 (978-0-7734-1357-3(X)) Mellen, Edwin Pr., The.

Cody, Jeffrey W. & Terpak, Frances, eds. Brush & Shutter: Early Photography in China. 2011. (Illus.). 210p. (978-988-8083-16-9(3)) Hong Kong Univ. Pr.

Cohen, Paul A. Discovering History in China: American Historical Writing on the Recent Chinese Past. 2010. (Studies of the Weatherhead East Asian Institute, Columbia University Ser.). (ENG.). 296p. (gr. 17). 84.50 (978-0-231-15192-4(6)); pap. 27.50 (978-0-231-15193-1(4)) Columbia Univ. Pr.

Cole, Alan & Cole, A. Fathering Your Father: The Zen of Fabrication in Tang Buddhism. 2009. (ENG.). 368p. 65.00 (978-0-520-25484-8(8)); pap. 29.95 (978-0-520-25485-5(6)) Univ. of California Pr.

Collis, Maurice. Foreign Mud: Being an Account of the Opium Imbroglio at Canton 1947. 2007. (ENG.). 346p. 46.95 (978-0-548-05350-8(2)) Kessinger Publishing, LLC.

Cotterell, Arthur. The Imperial Capitals of China: A Dynastic History of the Celestial Empire. 2008. (ENG., Illus.). 336p. (gr. 12). 27.95 (978-1-59020-007-0(1)) Overlook Pr., The.

Craig, Albert M. The Heritage of Chinese Civilization. 3rd rev. ed. 2010. (ENG.). 208p. (C). pap. 56.20 (978-0-205-79054-8(2), Prentice Hall) Prentice Hall PTR.

Cram101 Textbook Reviews Staff. Outlines & Highlights for Cambridge Illustrated History of China by Patricia Buckley Ebrey, Isbn: 9780521669917. 2009. (Illus.). 90p. pap. 27.95 (978-1-4288-9602-4(3)) Cram101 Inc.

—Outlines & Highlights for Modern Chin: History by Moise, Edwin, ISBN. 2009. 64p. pap. 27.95 (978-1-4288-9445-7(4)) Cram101 Inc.

—Outlines & Highlights for Revolution & Its Past: Indentities & Change in Modern Chinese History by Schoppa, R. Keith, ISBN. 2009. 78p. pap. 27.95 (978-1-4288-9446-4(2)) Cram101 Inc.

Cui, Yuqing. Ipr & Environmental Sound Technology Transfer. 2010. 72p. pap. (978-3-8383-6100-0(8)) Lambert Academic Publishing.

Cunrui Xiong, Victor. Historical Dictionary of Medieval China. 2008. (Historical Dictionaries of Ancient Civilizations & Historical Eras Ser.). (ENG., Illus.). 856p. 158.00 (978-0-8108-6053-7(8)) Scarecrow Pr., Inc.

Cushing, Lincoln & Tompkins, Ann. Chinese Posters: Art from the Great Proletarian Cultural Revolution. 2007. (ENG., Illus.). 144p. pap. 19.95 (978-0-8118-5946-2(0)) Chronicle Bks. LLC.

Danielson, Eric N. Discover Shanghai. 2010. 176p. pap. 20.99 (978-981-261-782-8(5)) Marshall Cavendish International (Asia) Private Ltd. SGP. Dist: Marshall Cavendish Corp.

"Daozhen Gelaozu Miaozu Zizhixian gai kuang" bian xie zu Staff & "Daozhen Gelaozu Miaozu Zizhixian gai kuang" xiu ding ben bian xie zu Staff, contrib. by. Daozhen Gelaozu Miaozu Zizhixian Gai Kuang: DaozhenGelaozuMiaozuZizhixiangaikuang. 2007. (Zhongguo Shao Shu Min Zu Zi Zhi Di Fang Gai Kuang Cong Shu (Xiu Ding Ben) Ser.). (CHI., Illus.). (978-7-105-08537-8(1)) Nationalities Publishing Hse, The.

De Pee, Christian. The Writing of Weddings in Middle-Period China: Text & Ritual Practice in the Eighth Through Fourteenth Centuries. 2008. (SUNY Series in Chinese Philosophy & Culture). 365p. per. 29.95 (978-0-7914-7074-9(1)) State Univ. of New York Pr.

Delgado, James P. Khubilai Khan's Lost Fleet: In Search of a Legendary Armada. 2010. (ENG.). 240p. pap. 17.95 (978-0-520-26585-1(8)) Univ. of California Pr.

The Denial & Its Cost Reflections on the Nanking assacre70 years ago & Beyond. 2008. pap. 12.00 (978-1-59343-080-1(9), Cozy Publishing Hse.) Cozy Graphics Corp.

Dennerline, Jerry. Middle Kingdoms & Empires: Culture & Power in Chinese History. 2007. (ENG., Illus.). 320p. 40.00 (978-0-300-11512-3(1)) Yale Univ. Pr.

Dillon, Michael. China: A Modern History. 2010. (ENG., Illus.). 496p. 59.00 (978-1-85043-582-2(0)) I. B. Tauris & Co., Ltd. GBR. Dist: Macmillan.

—Xinjiang: China's Muslim Far Northwest. 2009. pap. 39.95 (978-0-415-54631-7(1)) Routledge.

Dingle, Edwin John. Across China on Foot. 2010. (Illus.). 192p. pap. 9.89 (978-1-77045-554-2(X)) General Bks. LLC.

Doll, Steffen. Im Osten des Meeres: Chinesische Emigrantenmönche und die frühen Institutionen des japanischen Zen-Buddhismus. 2010. (Munchener Ostasiatische Studien Ser.). (GER., Illus.). 201p. (C). pap. 57.00 (978-3-515-09794-9(5)) Steiner, Franz Verlag Wiesbaden GmbH DEU. Dist: Brown, David Bk. Co., The.

Du, Sen. Lenin & China- A Short Cut to Paris. 2012. pap. 13.95 **(978-0-7414-6854-3(9))** Infinity Publishing.

Du, Sen. Socialism in Two Time Frames. 2008. 117p. pap. 10.95 (978-0-7414-4567-4(0)) Infinity Publishing.

Duara, Prasenjit. The Global & Regional in China's Nation-Formation. 2009. (Asia's Transformations/Critical Asian Scholarship Ser.). 240p. (ENG.). (C). pap. 36.95 (978-0-415-48290-5(9)); 170.00 (978-0-415-48289-9(5)) Routledge.

Dunstan, Helen. State or Merchant? Political Economy & Political Process in 1740s China. 2006. (Harvard East Asian Monographs: 273). (Illus.). 523p. 54.95 (978-0-674-02262-1(9)) Harvard Univ., Asia Ctr.

E. China. 2009. 975.00 (978-0-415-44133-9(1)) Routledge.

Eber, Irene, tr. & intro. Voices from Shanghai: Jewish Exiles in Wartime China. 2008. (ENG., Illus.). 144p. 29.00 (978-0-226-18166-0(9)) Univ. of Chicago Pr.

Eberhard, Wolfram. A History of China. 2008. 504p. 35.99 (978-0-554-23663-6(X)) 2007. (ENG.). 446p. pap. 26.99 (978-1-4264-4853-9(8)) 2007. (ENG.). 502p. pap. 31.99 (978-1-4264-4896-6(1)) BiblioBazaar.

Ebrey, Patricia Buckley. The Cambridge Illustrated History of China. 2nd ed. 2010. (Cambridge Illustrated Histories Ser.). (ENG., Illus.). 384p. 115.00 (978-0-521-19620-8(5)); pap. 46.99 (978-0-521-12433-1(6)) Cambridge Univ. Pr.

Ebrey, Patricia Buckley & Bickford, Maggie, eds. Emperor Huizong & Late Northern Song China: The Politics of Culture & the Culture of Politics. 2006. (Harvard East Asian Monographs: 266). (Illus.). 625p. 59.95 (978-0-674-02127-3(4)) Harvard Univ., Asia Ctr.

Edelmann, Freder, ed. In the Chinese City/Positions. 2008. 516p. (978-84-96954-62-5(5)) Actar Birkhauser Distribution.

Edelmann, Frederic. In the Chinese City. 2008. 348p. (978-84-96954-49-6(8)) Actar Birkhauser Distribution.

Eisenberg, Andrew. Kingship in Early Medieval China. 2008. (Sinica Leidensia Ser.). (Illus.). 279p. (978-90-04-16381-2(6)) BRILL.

Elliott, Jeannette Shambaugh. The Odyssey of China's Imperial Art Treasures. 2007. (Samuel & Althea Stroum Bks.). (ENG., Illus.). 192p. per. 19.95 (978-0-295-98688-3(3)) Univ. of Washington Pr.

Elverskog, Johan. Our Great Qing: The Mongols, Buddhism, & the State in Late Imperial China. 2006. (Illus.). 272p. (C). 52.00 (978-0-8248-3021-2(0)) Univ. of Hawaii Pr.

Emerson, Edward Randolph. The History of Alcohol in the Far East - China, Japan, Philippines, Islands of the Pacific. 2011. 46p. pap. 6.95 **(978-1-4465-3488-5(X))** Harrison House Pubs.

Esherick, Joseph W. Ancestral Leaves: A Family Journey Through Chinese History. 2011. (ENG., Illus.). 371p. 60.00 (978-0-520-26699-5(4)); pap. 24.95 (978-0-520-26700-8(1)) Univ. of California Pr.

Eyferth, Jacob. Eating Rice from Bamboo Roots: The Social History of a Community of Handicraft Papermakers in Rural Sichuan, 1920-2000. 2009. (Harvard East Asian Monographs: 314). (Illus.). 335p. 45.00 (978-0-674-03288-0(8)) Harvard Univ., Asia Ctr.

Fang, Jian. Nan Song Nong Ye Shi. 2010. (CHI.). 40p. (978-7-01-008450-3(5)) People's Publishing Hse., The.

Fang, Xiangshu. The Rise of Ancient Chin. 2011. 328p. pap. **(978-3-8443-2282-8(5))** Lambert Academic Publishing.

Faure, David. Emperor & Ancestor: State & Lineage in South China. 2007. (ENG., Illus.). 480p. 50.00 (978-0-8047-5318-0(0)) Stanford Univ. Pr.

Fazzini, Gerolamo. The Red Book of Chinese Martyrs. 2008. 275p. pap. 16.95 (978-1-58617-244-2(1)) Ignatius Pr.

Feinglas, Mitchel. The History & Mystery of Chinese Drywall. 2010. 132p. pap. 19.99 (978-1-4520-4927-4(0)) AuthorHouse.

Fenby, Jonathan. Generalissimo: Chiang Kai-Shek & the China He Lost. 2006. (Illus.). 562p. reprint ed. 35.00 (978-1-4223-5775-0(9)) DIANE Publishing Co.

Feng, Li & Li, Feng. Bureaucracy & the State in Early China: Governing the Western Zhou. 2008. (ENG., Illus.). 400p. 125.00 (978-0-521-88447-1(0)) Cambridge Univ. Pr.

Fermin, Jose D. The Chinese Experience in U. S. World's Fairs. 2010. pap. 13.95 (978-0-7414-5958-9(2)) Infinity Publishing.

Ford, Daniel. Flying Tigers: Claire Chennault & His American Volunteers, 1941-1942. 2007. (ENG., Illus.). 400p. pap. 15.99 (978-0-06-124655-5(7), HarperPerennial) HarperCollins Pubs.

Fraser, Douglas. A Legacy of Opium: The True Story of How Three Brothers from Tenby Became Opium Traders in China, & of Their Legacy. 2010. (Illus.). 80p. pap. (978-0-9565396-0-1(2)) Tenby Heritage Pubns.

French, Paul. The Old Shanghai A-Z. 2010. (ENG., Illus.). 252p. (gr. 17). pap. 25.00 (978-988-8028-89-4(8)) Hong Kong Univ. Pr. HKG. Dist: Columbia Univ. Pr.

Friedman, Edward, et al. Revolution, Resistance, & Reform in Village China. 2007. (Yale Agrarian Studies). (ENG., Illus.). 368p. per. 22.00 (978-0-300-12595-5(X)) Yale Univ. Pr.

Fu, Xuancong & Zhang, Ru'an. Ningbo Tong Shi, 5 vols. 2009. (CHI., Illus.). (978-7-80743-403-0(1)) Ningbo Publishing Hse.

Gannes, Harry. When China Unites: An Interpretive History of the Chinese Revolution. 2011. 320p. 50.95 **(978-1-258-10106-0(8))** Literary Licensing, LLC.

Geis, John P., et al. Discord or Harmonious Society: China In 2030: China In 2030. Air War College (U.S.), Center for Strategy and Technology, ed. 2011. (ENG., Illus.). 144p. pap. 23.00 (978-1-58566-209-8(7), Dept. of the Air Force) United States Government Printing Office.

George Chung Wang And Jo Anne Lee Wang. Eye Witness History in the Making-1888-2009. 2009. 294p. pap. 29.99 (978-1-4415-0616-0(0)); pap. 19.99 (978-1-4415-0615-3(2)) Xlibris Corp.

Gerritsen, Anne. Ji'an Literati & the Local in Song-Yuan-Ming China. 2007. (China Studies). (Illus.). 258p. (978-90-04-15603-6(8)) BRILL.

Giles, Herbert Allen. China & the Manchus. 2007. (ENG.). 94p. per. 16.99 (978-1-4346-2926-5(0)); 104p. pap. 19.99 (978-1-4346-2927-2(9)) BiblioBazaar.

Goodman, David, ed. The New Rich in China: Future Rulers, Present Lives. 2008. (Illus.). XIV, 306p. 39.95 (978-0-415-45565-7(0)); 170.00 (978-0-415-45564-0(2)) Routledge.

Goodrich, L. Carrington. A Short History of the Chinese People. 2007. (ENG.). 332p. per. (978-1-4067-6976-0(2)) Read Bks.

Greenhalgh, Paul. Fair World: A History of World's Fairs & Expositions from London to Shanghai 1851-2010. 2011. (ENG., Illus.). 282p. 60.00 (978-1-906506-09-4(4)) Papadakis Dist A/C.

Guo, Jianlin & Guo, Hui. Han Lin Zong Tong Xu Shichang. 2010. (CHI., Illus.). 483p. (978-7-80214-904-5(5)) Unitp Publishing Hse.

Haar, Barend J. ter. Het Hemels Mandaat: De Geschiedenis van het Chinese Keizerrijk. 2009. (DUT., Illus.). (978-90-8964-120-5(3)) Amsterdam Univ. Pr.

Halperin, Mark. Out of the Cloister: Literati Perspectives on Buddhism in Sung China, 960-1279. 2006. (Harvard East Asian Monographs: 272). (Illus.). 400p. 49.95 (978-0-674-02265-2(3)) Harvard Univ., Asia Ctr.

Handa, Lin & Yuzhang, Cao. Tales from 5000 Years of Chinese History, Vol. 1. Ying, Wu & Kexi, Zhou, eds. 2010. (ENG.). 358p. 23.95 (978-1-60220-112-5(9)) BetterLink Pr., Inc.

—Tales from 5000 Years of Chinese History, Vol. 2. Lee, Yawtsong, tr. from CHI. 2010. (ENG.). 388p. 23.95 (978-1-60220-114-9(5)) BetterLink Pr., Inc.

Hart, Robert. These from the Land of Sinim: Essays on the Chinese Question. 2010. (ENG.). 268p. pap. 27.75 (978-1-176-37485-0(0)) 2010. 268p. pap. 27.75 (978-1-148-94923-9(2)) 2010. 260p. pap. 26.75 (978-1-142-97891-4(5)) 2009. 264p. 24.99 (978-1-103-92561-2(X)) 2009. 264p. pap. 18.99 (978-1-103-92553-7(9)) BiblioBazaar.

—These from the Land of Sinim: Essays on the Chinese Question. 2007. (ENG.). 264p. 42.95 (978-0-548-36645-5(4)); per. 27.95 (978-0-548-30942-1(6)) Kessinger Publishing, LLC.

Hartnett, Richard A. The Jixia Academy & the Birth of Higher Learning in China: A Cmparison of Fourth-Century B. C. Chinese Education with Ancient Greece. 2011. 320p. 129.95 **(978-0-7734-3912-2(9))** Mellen, Edwin Pr., The.

Haw, Stephen G. The Mongol Unification of China. 2009. (Illus.). 256p. 150.00 (978-0-415-41015-1(0)) Routledge.

Hayes, James. The Great Difference: Hong Kong's New Territories & Its People, 1898-2004. 2006. (ENG., Illus.). 332p. (gr. 17). 50.00 (978-962-209-794-0(4)) Hong Kong Univ. Pr. HKG. Dist: Columbia Univ. Pr.

Hayter-Menzies, Grant. The Empress & Mrs. Conger: The Uncommon Friendship of Two Women & Two Worlds. 2011. (Illus.). 364p. **(978-988-220-755-4(3)); (978-988-8053-70-4(1))** Hong Kong Univ. Pr.

—The Empress & Mrs. Conger: The Uncommon Friendship of Two Women & Two Worlds. 2011. (ENG., Illus.). 364p. (gr. 17). 35.00 (978-988-8083-00-8(7)) Hong Kong Univ. Pr. HKG. Dist: Columbia Univ. Pr.

He, Shu. Wei Mao Zhu Xi Er Zhan: Wen Ge Chongqing Da Wu Dou Shi Lu. 2010. (Illus.). 357p. (978-962-04-2995-8(8)) Joint Publishing Co.

Hedin, Sven. The Trail of War: On the Track of Big Horse in Central Asia. 2009. (ENG., Illus.). 272p. pap. 16.95 (978-1-84511-702-3(6), Tauris Parke Paperbacks) I. B. Tauris & Co., Ltd. GBR. Dist: Macmillan.

Herbert A. Giles, LL.D., MA. The Civilization of China. 2006. (ENG.). 148p. pap. 18.99 (978-1-4264-0094-0(2)); 138p. pap. 13.99 (978-1-4264-0223-4(6)) BiblioBazaar.

Herman, John E. Amid the Clouds & Mist: China's Colonization of Guizhou, 1200-1700. 2007. (Harvard East Asian Monographs: 293). (Illus.). 344p. 49.50 (978-0-674-02591-2(1)) Harvard Univ., Asia Ctr.

Hillemann, Ulrike. Asian Empire & British Knowledge: China & the Networks of British Imperial Expansion. 2009. (ENG.). 320p. 95.00 (978-0-230-20046-3(X)) Palgrave Macmillan.

Hirth, Friedrich. The Ancient History of China to the End of the Chou Dynasty. 2007. (ENG.). 402p. 49.95 (978-0-548-17494-4(6)); 404p. per. 34.95 (978-1-4304-7396-1(7)) Kessinger Publishing, LLC.

Hollmann, Thomas O. & Wang-Riese, Xiaobing, eds. Time & Ritual in Early China. 2010. (Asiatische Forschungen Ser.). (ENG.). 209p. (C). pap. 57.00 (978-3-447-06106-3(5)) Harrassowitz, Otto Verlag DEU. Dist: ISD.

House, Edward Howard. The Japanese Expedition to Formos. 2010. 184p. pap. 27.95 (978-1-4460-1047-1(3)) Audubon Pr. & Christian Bk. Service.

Huang, Chun-Chieh, et al. Notions of Time in Chinese Historical Thinking. Henderson, John B., ed. 2006. (ENG.). 300p. (gr. 17). 42.00 (978-962-996-222-7(5)) Chinese Univ. of Hong Kong, The HKG. Dist: Columbia Univ. Pr.

Huang, Pei. Reorienting the Manchus. 2011. (Illus.). 376p. 65.00 **(978-1-933947-22-8(5))** Cornell Univ. East Asia Program.

Huang, Yongwu. Xuanwu Hu Shi Hua. 2009. (CHI., Illus.). (978-7-80718-557-4(0)) Nanjing Pub. Hse.

Hunter, Alan. Peace Studies in the Chinese Century: International Perspectives. 2006. (Illus.). 236p. 120.00 (978-0-7546-4794-2(3)) Ashgate Publishing Co.

Idema, Wilt Lukas. Judge Bao & the Rule of Law: Eight Ballad-Stories, 1250-1450. 2009. (Illus.). 450p. 52.00 (978-981-4277-01-3(0)) World Scientific Publishing Co., Inc.

Isaacs, Harold & Isaacs, Harold Robert. The Tragedy of the Chinese Revolution. 2010. (ENG.). 550p. pap. 24.00 (978-1-931859-84-4(1)) Haymarket Bks.

Jacob, Ellis. The Shanghai I Knew: A Foreign Native in Pre-Revolutionary China. 2007. per. 18.95 (978-0-9793771-0-5(2)) ComteQ Publishing.

Jami, Catherine. The Emperor's New Mathematics: Western Learning & Imperial Authority During the Kangxi Reign (1662-1722) 2012. (ENG., Illus.). 464p. 135.00 **(978-0-19-960140-0(2))** Oxford Univ. Pr., Inc.

Jiang, Qisheng. My Life in Prison: Memoirs of a Chinese Political Dissident. 2012. **(978-1-4422-1224-4(1))** Rowman & Littlefield Publishers, Inc.

Jicai, Feng. Symbols of China. 2010. (Illus.). 256p. 25.00 (978-1-84912-018-0(8)) Compendium GBR. Dist: Casemate Pubs. & Bk. Distributors, LLC.

Jin, Jie. Chinese Music. 3rd ed. 2011. (Introductions to Chinese Culture Ser.). (ENG., Illus.). 156p. pap. 19.99 (978-0-521-18691-9(9)) Cambridge Univ. Pr.

Jin, Mei. Tang Dai Hun Yin Jia Ting Ji Cheng Fa Yan Jiu: Jian Yu Xi Fang Fa Bi Jiao. 2009. (CHI.). (978-7-5620-3511-4(3)) China Univ. of Political Science and Law Pr.

Jing, Zuo, contrib. by. Dong Wensheng: No Worldview for the Face. 2011. (ENG., Illus.). 130p. 35.00 (978-988-18906-4-1(0)) Timezone 8 Ltd. HKG. Dist: D.A.P./Distributed Art Pubs.

Johannsen, Anna Magdalena. Everlasting Pearl: One of China's Women. 2007. (Illus.). 96p. per. (978-1-4065-3476-4(5)) Dodo Pr.

Johnson, David. Spectacle & Sacrifice: The Ritual Foundations of Village Life in North China. 2010. (Harvard East Asian Monographs: 315). (Illus.). 450p. 49.95 *(978-0-674-03304-7(3))* Harvard Univ., Asia Ctr.

Johnson, Linda Cooke. Women of the Conquest Dynasties: Gender & Identity in Liao & Jin China. 2011. (Illus.). 280p. 52.00 *(978-0-8248-3404-3(6))* Univ. of Hawaii Pr.

Johnston, Reginald F. Lion & Dragon in Northern China. 2011. (Cambridge Library Collection - History Ser.). (ENG., Illus.). 560p. pap. 39.99 *(978-1-108-02964-3(7))* Cambridge Univ. Pr.

Johnston, Reginald Fleming. Lion & Dragon in Northern China. 2008. 332p. per. 24.95 *(978-0-9680459-6-1(0))* Soul Care Publishing CAN. Dist: Ingram Bk. Co.

—Twilight in the Forbidden City. 2007. 484p. per. *(978-1-84356-020-3(8))* Wallenberg, Simon Pr.

Kádár, Dániel Z. Historical Chinese Letter Writing. 2010. (ENG., Illus.). 288p. 140.00 *(978-0-8264-3088-5(0))* Continuum International Publishing Group, Ltd. GBR. Dist: National Bk. Network.

Kadeer, Rebiya & Cavelius, Alexandra. Dragon Fighter: One Woman's Epic Struggle for Peace with China. 2009. (ENG., Illus.). 426p. 28.95 *(978-0-9798456-1-1(0)*, 979841) Kales Pr.

Kadeer, Rebiya & Dalai Lama XIV. Dragon Fighter: One Woman's Epic Struggle for Peace with China. 2011. (ENG., Illus.). 426p. pap. 18.95 *(978-0-9798456-5-9(3)*, 979845) Kales Pr.

Kahn, Sonny. The Black Dragon the Tomb. 2008. (ENG.). 390p. pap. 29.95 *(978-0-9744683-4-1(7))* Kahn, Sonny Publishing & Movie Production Co.

Kayaoäÿlu, Turan. Legal Imperialism: Sovereignty & Extraterritoriality in Japan, the Ottoman Empire, & China. 2010. (ENG., Illus.). 248p. 90.00 *(978-0-521-76591-6(9))* Cambridge Univ. Pr.

Keay, John. China: A History. 2011. (ENG.). 608p. (gr. 9). pap. 19.99 *(978-0-465-02518-3(8))* 2009. (ENG., Illus.). 624p. (gr. 9). 35.00 *(978-0-465-01580-1(8))* 2009. (Illus.). 512p. *(978-0-00-722177-6(0))* Basic Bks.

Keenan, Barry C. Neo-Confucian Self-Cultivation. 2011. xxxii, 132p. 48.00 *(978-0-8248-3496-8(8))*; pap. 17.00 *(978-0-8248-3548-4(4))* Univ. of Hawaii Pr.

Keevak, Michael. The Story of a Stele: China's Nestorian Monument & Its Reception in the West, 1625-1916. 2008. (ENG., Illus.). 208p. (gr. 17). 45.00 *(978-962-209-895-4(9))* Hong Kong Univ. Pr. HKG. Dist: Columbia Univ. Pr.

Keith, Ronald C. China from the Inside Out: Fitting the People's Republic into the World. 2009. (ENG.). 176p. 88.00 *(978-0-7453-2855-3(5))*; pap. 26.00 *(978-0-7453-2854-6(7))* Pluto Pr. GBR. Dist: Macmillan.

Kempton, Nicole & Richardson, Nan, eds. Laogai: The Machinery of Repression in China. 2009. (ENG., Illus.). 160p. 45.00 *(978-1-884167-77-5(2))* Umbrage Editions.

Khoo, Salma Nasution. Sun Yat Sen in Penang. 2008. (Illus.). 130p. *(978-983-42834-8-3(2))* Starain Educational (M) Sdn Bhd.

King, Catherine & King, Dean. Unbound: A True Story of War, Love, & Survival. 2011. (ENG., Illus.). 448p. pap. 15.99 *(978-0-316-16709-3(6)*, Back Bay Bks.) Little Brown & Co.

King, Richard, et al. Sino-Japanese Transculturation: From the Late Nineteenth Century to the End of the Pacific War. 2011. ***(978-0-7391-7151-6(8))*** Lexington Bks.

Kirby, William C., et al. The People's Republic of China at 60: An International Assessment. 2011. (CHI & ENG., Illus.). 432p. pap. 29.95 *(978-0-674-06064-7(4))* Harvard Univ., Asia Ctr.

Kissinger, Henry. On China. (ENG.). (gr. 12). 2012. 624p. 18.00 ***(978-0-14-312131-2(6)***, Penguin (Non-Classics)) 2011. (Illus.). 608p. 36.00 *(978-1-59420-271-1(0)*, Penguin Pr. HC, The) Penguin Group (USA) Inc.

Konstam, Angus. Yangtze River Gunboats, 1900-49. 2011. (New Vanguard Ser.). (ENG., Illus.). 48p. pap. 17.95 *(978-1-84908-408-6(4))* Osprey Publishing, Ltd. GBR. Dist: Random Hse., Inc.

Kuhn, Dieter, et al. Chinese Silks. 2012. (Culture & Civilization of China Ser.). (ENG.). 624p. 85.00 ***(978-0-300-11103-3(7))*** Yale Univ. Pr.

Kurz. China's Southern Tang Dynasty, 937-975. 2011. (Asian States & Empires Ser.). (ENG., Illus.). 160p. (C). 138.00 *(978-0-415-45496-4(4))* Routledge.

Kwok, Ken. Middle Kingdom - Legendary Beginning of China & the Bible. 2008. 163p. pap. 19.95 *(978-0-557-00325-9(3))* Lulu Enterprises Inc.

Larsen, Jeanne. Manchu Palaces: A Novel. 2009. 368p. pap. 19.95 *(978-1-4401-3715-0(3))* iUniverse, Inc.

Lee, Khoon Choy. Passage Through China: This Land So Rich in Beauty. 2007. (Illus.). 566p. pap. *(978-981-4163-43-9(0))* China Knowledge Press Pte Ltd.

Leo, Jessieca. Sex in the Yellow Emperor's Basic Questions: Sex, Longevity, & Medicine in Early China. 2011. (Illus.). 237p. pap. 29.95 *(978-1-931483-18-6(3))* Three Pines Pr.

Leonard, Mark. What Does China Think? 2008. (ENG., Illus.). 176p. 22.95 *(978-1-58648-484-2(2))* PublicAffairs.

Lewis, Mark Edward. China Between Empires: The Northern & Southern Dynasties. 2009. (History of Imperial China Ser.: 2). (Illus.). 352p. 33.00 *(978-0-674-02605-6(5)*, Belknap Pr.) Harvard Univ. Pr.

—The Early Chinese Empires: Qin & Han. 2010. (History of Imperial China Ser.: 1). (ENG., Illus.). 336p. pap. 18.95 *(978-0-674-05734-0(1)*, Belknap Pr.) Harvard Univ. Pr.

Lewis, Mark Edward & Brook, Timothy. China Between Empires: The Northern & Southern Dynasties. 2011. (History of Imperial China Ser.: 2). (ENG., Illus.). 352p. pap. 18.95 *(978-0-674-06035-7(0)*, Belknap Pr.) Harvard Univ. Pr.

Li, Danke. Echoes of Chongqing: Women in Wartime China. 2009. (ENG., Illus.). 232p. 70.00 *(978-0-252-03489-3(9))*; pap. 25.00 *(978-0-252-07674-9(5))* Univ. of Illinois Pr.

Li, Mingjing. Nihon Bukkyo Setsuwashu No Genryu. 2007. (JPN.). vii, 334p. *(978-4-585-10433-9(X))* Bensei Shuppan.

Li, Qingdong. Duan Qirui Mu Fu Yu Mu Liao: DuanQirui Mufu Yu Muliao. 2010. (Illus.). *(978-7-5339-2819-3(9))* Zhejiang Pubn. Hse. of Literature and Art.

Li, Wei. China's Early Industrialization. 2008. 192p. pap. *(978-3-639-06824-5(6))* VDM Verlag Dr. Mueller e.K.

Li, Xiaoxiong. Poppies & Politics in China: Sichuan Province, 1840s To 1940s. 2009. (Illus.). 308p. 61.50 *(978-0-87413-054-6(9))* Univ. of Delaware Pr.

Li, Ying. Si Shi Jun Zai Chaoxian. 2010. (CHI., Illus.). *(978-7-205-06738-0(3))* Liaoning People's Publishing Hse.

Li, Zhengping. Chinese Wine. 3rd ed. 2011. (Introductions to Chinese Culture Ser.). (ENG., Illus.). 146p. pap. 19.99 *(978-0-521-18650-6(1))* Cambridge Univ. Pr.

Lighte, Peter. Pieces of China. 2009. 127p. pap. 18.00 *(978-0-557-15652-8(1))* Lulu Enterprises Inc.

Lin, Chun & Hendrischke, Hans. The Territories of the People's Republic of China. 2nd rev. ed. 2006. (Illus.). 272p. 265.00 *(978-1-85743-395-1(5))* Routledge.

Ling, Rich. Old Buddha. 2007. 190.00 *(978-0-7103-1111-5(7))* Taylor & Francis Group.

Link, Perry, ed. The Scholar's Mind: Essays in Honor of F. W. Mote. 2009. (ENG.). 316p. (gr. 17). 45.00 *(978-962-996-403-0(1))* Chinese Univ. of Hong Kong, The HKG. Dist: Columbia Univ. Pr.

Littlejohn, Ronnie L. Daoism. 2009. (I. B. Tauris Introductions to Religion Ser.). (ENG., Illus.). 240p. 89.00 *(978-1-84511-638-5(0))* I. B. Tauris & Co., Ltd. GBR. Dist: Macmillan.

—Daoism: An Introduction. 2009. (I. B. Tauris Introductions to Religion Ser.). (ENG., Illus.). 240p. pap. 26.00 *(978-1-84511-639-2(9))* I. B. Tauris & Co., Ltd. GBR. Dist: Macmillan.

Liu, Eleanor. The Red Thread. 2011. 354p. 29.99 ***(978-1-4568-7585-5(X))***; pap. 19.99 ***(978-1-4568-7584-8(1))*** Xlibris Corp.

Liu, Li. The Chinese Neolithic: Trajectories to Early States. 2007. (New Studies in Archaeology). (ENG.). 332p. pap. 72.00 *(978-0-521-01064-1(0))* Cambridge Univ. Pr.

Liu, Xun. Daoist Modern: Innovation, Lay Practice, & the Community of Inner Alchemy in Republican Shanghai. 2009. (Harvard East Asian Monographs: 313). (Illus.). 396p. 49.95 *(978-0-674-03309-2(4))* Harvard Univ., Asia Ctr.

Loewe, Michael. Dong Zhongshu, a 'Confucian' Heritage & the Chunqiu Fanlu. 2011. 380p. ***(978-90-04-19465-6(7))*** BRILL.

Lorge, Peter, ed. Five Dynasties & Ten Kingdoms. 2011. (ENG., Illus.). 288p. (gr. 17). 52.00 *(978-962-996-418-4(X))* Chinese Univ. of Hong Kong, The HKG. Dist: Columbia Univ. Pr.

Lovell, Julia. The Great Wall: China Against the World, 1000 BC - AD 2000. 2007. (ENG., Illus.). 432p. per. 15.00 *(978-0-8021-4297-9(4)*, Grove Pr.) Grove/Atlantic, Inc.

Lu, Duanfang. Remaking Chinese Urban Form: Modernity, Scarcity & Space, 1949-2005. 2006. (Planning, History, & the Environment Ser.). (ENG., Illus.). 216p. 165.00 *(978-0-415-35450-9(1))* Routledge.

Lu, Qiguo. Ji Xing de Fan Rong: Zu Jie Shi Qi de Shanghai. 2009. (CHI., Illus.). 229p. *(978-7-5473-0039-8(1))* Orient Publishing Ctr.

Lu, Tracey L. D. Prehistory of the Yangzi River Valley. Date not set. 288p. 75.00 *(978-0-7591-0377-1(1))* AltaMira Pr.

Luo, Shubao. A Concise Illustrated History of Chinese Printing. 2011. pap. ***(978-1-931907-67-5(6))*** Homa & Sekey Bks.

Luo, Xuewei & Xiao, Changchun. Jinggangshan Ge Ming Gen Ju Di Dang ce Jian She Shi. 2007. (CHI., Illus.). *(978-7-210-03692-0(X))* Jiangxi People's Publishing Hse.

Luo, Yuming. Quan Li Wan Jia: Zhongguo Li Shi Shang de Da Yin Mou. 2009. (CHI.). *(978-7-309-06483-4(6))* Fudan Univ. Pr.

Lutze, Thomas D. China's Inevitable Revolution: Rethinking America's Loss to the Communists. 2007. (ENG., Illus.). 272p. 100.00 *(978-1-4039-7977-3(4))* Palgrave Macmillan.

Mackinnon, Alex & Powell, Barnaby. China Counting: How the West Was Lost. 2009. (ENG., Illus.). 272p. 49.00 *(978-0-230-23403-1(8))* Palgrave Macmillan.

Man, John. The Great Wall: The Extraordinary Story of China's Wonder of the World. (ENG.). 2009. 384p. pap. 16.95 *(978-0-306-81839-4(6))* 2008. (Illus.). 352p. 26.00 *(978-0-306-81767-0(5))* Da Capo Pr., Inc.

Marsone, Pierre. La Steppe et L'empire: La Formation de la Dynastie Khitan (Liao) IVe-Xe Siècle. 2011. (FRE., Illus.). 336p. (C). pap. 41.00 ***(978-2-251-38109-1(0))*** Societe d'edition Les Belles lettres FRA. Dist: ISD.

Martin, Thomas R. & Martin, Christopher R. Herodotus & Sima Qian: the First Great Historians of Greece & China: A Brief History with Documents. 2009. (Bedford Series in History & Culture Ser.). (ENG., Illus.). 208p. (C). pap. 15.95 *(978-0-312-41649-2(0))* Bedford/Saint Martin's.

McGregor, Richard. The Party: The Secret World of China's Communist Rulers. 2010. (ENG.). 320p. 27.99 *(978-0-06-170877-0(1))* HarperCollins Pubs.

McMahon, Keith. Polygamy & Sublime Passion: Sexuality in China on the Verge of Modernity. 2010. vii, 215p. (C). 55.00 *(978-0-8248-3376-3(7))* Univ. of Hawaii Pr.

Meinert, Carmen, ed. Traces of Humanism in China: Tradition & Modernity. 2010. (ENG.). 210p. pap. 39.95 *(978-3-8376-1351-3(8))* Transcript Verlag DEU. Dist: Transaction Pubs.

Metraux, Daniel A., et al. The Problems Facing China Today: Politics, Economics Health, & Religion. 2007. 352p. 119.95 *(978-0-7734-5225-1(7))* Mellen, Edwin Pr., The.

Milburn, Olivia, et al. The Glory of Yue: An Annotated Translation of the Yuejue Shu. 2010. 430p. *(978-90-04-17969-1(0))* BRILL.

Millward, James. Eurasian Crossroads: A History of Xinjiang. 2009. (ENG.). 352p (gr. 17). pap. 24.50 *(978-0-231-13925-0(X))* Columbia Univ. Pr.

Millward, James A. & Millward, James. Eurasian Crossroads: A History of Xinjiang. 2007. (ENG., Illus.). 352p. (gr. 17). 45.00 *(978-0-231-13924-3(1))* Columbia Univ. Pr.

Min, Shen. Bamboo in China: Arts, Crafts & a Cultural History. Lee, Yawtsong, tr. 2011. (ENG., Illus.). 128p. 16.95 *(978-1-60220-132-3(3))* BetterLink Pr., Inc.

Ming, Ku Hung. Conduct of Life or the Universal Order O. 2006. pap. 16.95 *(978-1-4286-3820-4(2))* Kessinger Publishing, LLC.

Mitter, Rana. Modern China. 2008. (Very Short Introductions Ser.). (ENG., Illus.). 144p. pap. 11.95 *(978-0-19-922802-7(7))* Oxford Univ. Pr., Inc.

Mo, Tianci, et al. Tui Bei Tu Ji Zhu Ming Zhong Tai Gang Ao Yu Yan Da Quan. 2010. (CHI & ENG., Illus.). xiv, 299p. *(978-988-19053-1-4(1))* Mongol Study Publishing Hse.

Morrison, Elizabeth. The Power of Patriarchs: Qisong & Lineage in Chinese Buddhism. 2010. 306p. *(978-90-04-18301-8(9))* BRILL.

Morse, Edward S. Glimpses of China & Chinese Homes. 2007. (ENG.). 236p 41.95 *(978-0-548-36796-4(5))*; per. 26.95 *(978-0-548-31100-4(5))* Kessinger Publishing, LLC.

Morse, Hosea B. The International Relations of the Chinese Empire, 3 vols. reprint ed. 375.00 *(978-0-7222-2529-5(6))* Library Reprints, Inc.

Morse, Hosea Ballou. The Gilds of China with an Account of the Gild Merchant or Co Hong of Canton. 2007. (ENG.). 108p. 34.95 *(978-0-548-03054-7(5))* Kessinger Publishing, LLC.

Mostern, Ruth. 'Dividing the Realm in Order to Govern' The Spatial Organization of the Song State. 2011. (Harvard-Yenching Institute Monograph Ser.: 73). (Illus.). 396p. 49.95 *(978-0-674-05602-2(7))* Harvard Univ., Asia Ctr.

Mühlhahn, Klaus. Criminal Justice in China: A History. 2009. 376p. 31.50 *(978-0-674-03323-8(X))* Harvard Univ. Pr.

Mungello, D. E. Drowning Girls in China: Female Infanticide in China since 1650. 2008. (ENG., Illus.). 186p. 74.00 *(978-0-7425-5530-3(5))*; pap. 24.95 *(978-0-7425-5531-0(3))* Rowman & Littlefield Publishers, Inc.

Museum, Groninger. Famille Verte: Chinese Porcelain in Green Enamels, 1 vol. 2011. (ENG., Illus.). 208p. 50.00 ***(978-90-8586-589-6(1))*** Exhibitions International BEL. Dist: Innovative Logistics.

Nearing, Scott. Whither China? an Economic Interpretation of Recent Events in the Far East. 2011. 224p. 44.95 ***(978-1-258-06124-1(4))*** Literary Licensing, LLC.

Negotiated Power in Late Imperial China: The Zongli Yamen & the Politics of Reform. 2008. (Cornell East Asia Ser.). 246p. 42.00 *(978-1-933947-07-5(1))*; (ENG.). pap. 25.00 *(978-1-933947-37-2(3))* Cornell Univ. East Asia Program.

Nickel, Lukas. Gräber der Han-Zeit in Luoyang. 2010. (Munchener Ostasiatische Studien Ser.). (GER., Illus.). 325p. (C). pap. 90.00 *(978-3-515-09698-0(1)*, Steiner, Franz Verlag Wiesbaden GmbH DEU. Dist: Brown, David Bk. Co., The.

Nietupski, Paul Kocot. Labrang Monastery: A Tibetan Buddhist Community on the Inner Asian Borderlands, 1709-1958. (Illus.). 2011. xxxi, 273p. E-Book *(978-0-7391-6445-7(7))* 2010. (ENG., 306p. 80.00 *(978-0-7391-6443-3(0))* Lexington Bks.

O'Dowd, Edward C. Chinese Military Strategy in the Third Indo-China War: The Last Maoist War. 2007. (Asian Security Studies). (ENG., Illus.). 256p. (C). 170.00 *(978-0-415-41427-2(X))* Routledge.

—Chinese Military Strategy in the Third Indochina War: The Last Maoist War. 2007. pap. 39.95 *(978-0-415-54528-0(5))* Routledge.

Otie, Philippe. A Chinese Life. 2012. (Illus.). 720p. pap. 27.50 ***(978-1-906838-55-3(0)***, SelfMadeHero) Metro Media Ltd. GBR. Dist: Abrams.

Palucan, Ann. Chinese Emperors: The Reign-by-Reign Record of the Rulers of Imperial China. 2009. (ENG., Illus.). 224p. pap. 26.95 *(978-0-500-28764-4(3)*, 528764) Thames & Hudson.

Parker, Edward Harper. Ancient China Simplified. 2009. 298p. pap. *(978-0-217-17455-8(8))*; 304p. pap. *(978-0-217-68328-9(2))* Books LLC.

—Ancient China Simplified. 2006. (ENG.). pap. *(978-1-4068-3209-9(X))* Echo Library.

Perdue, Peter C. Shared Histories of Modernity: China, India & the Ottoman Empire. Islamoglu, Huricihan, ed. 2009. (Critical Asian Studies). 332p. 100.00 *(978-0-415-48166-3(X))* Taylor & Francis Group.

Pines, Yuri. Envisioning Eternal Empire: Chinese Political Thought of the Warring States Period. 2009. 320p. 57.00 *(978-0-8248-3275-9(2))* Univ. of Hawaii Pr.

Pletcher, Kenneth, ed. The Geography of China: Sacred & Historic Places. 2010. (Understanding China Ser.). (Illus.). 384p. (YA). 106.00 *(978-1-61530-185-0(2))*; lib. bdg. 53.00 *(978-1-61530-134-8(8))* Rosen Publishing Group, Inc., The.

—The History of China. 2010. (Understanding China Ser.). (Illus.). 330p. (YA). 106.00 *(978-1-61530-184-3(4))*; lib. bdg. 53.00 *(978-1-61530-109-6(7))* Rosen Publishing Group, Inc., The.

Pong, David. Encyclopedia of Modern China. 2009. *(978-0-684-31568-3(3))*; *(978-0-684-31567-6(X))*; *(978-0-684-31569-0(6))*; *(978-0-684-31570-6(X))*; 568.00 *(978-0-684-31566-9(1))* Cengage Gale. (Charles Scribner's Sons).

Qianshan Xian di fang zhi bian zuan wei yuan hui Staff, contrib. by. Qianshan Xian Zhi (1978-2002) 2007. (Anhui Sheng Di Fang Zhi Cong Shu Ser.). (Illus.). 8p. *(978-7-80707-880-7(4))* Huangshan Publishing Hse.

"Qinglong Manzu Zizhixian gai kuang" bian xie zu Staff & "Qinglong Manzu Zizhixian gai kuang" xiu ding ben bian xie zu Staff, contrib. by. Qinglong Manzu Zizhixian Gai Kuang: Qinglongmanzuzizhixiangaikuang. 2009. (CHI., Illus.). *(978-7-105-08672-6(6))* Nationalities Publishing Hse, The.

Qinqin, Sun, et al. Journey Through China: Exploring Major Sites & Cuisine in 10 Days. Reader's Digest Staff, ed. 2010. (ENG., Illus.). 200p. (gr. 12). pap. 14.95 *(978-1-60652-122-9(5))* Reader's Digest Assn., Inc., The.

Qisheng, Jiang. My Life in Prison: Memoirs of a Chinese Political Dissident. 2012. (ENG.). 240p. 45.00 ***(978-1-4422-1222-0(5))*** Rowman & Littlefield Publishers, Inc.

Roberts, John A. G. A History of China. 3rd rev. ed. 2011. (Palgrave Essential Histories Ser.). (ENG., Illus.). 400p. pap. 28.00 *(978-0-230-24984-4(1))* Palgrave Macmillan.

—A History of China: Third Edition. 3rd rev. ed. 2011. (Palgrave Essential Histories Ser.). (ENG., Illus.). 400p. 88.00 *(978-0-230-24983-7(3))* Palgrave Macmillan.

Robinson, David M., ed. Culture, Courtiers, & Competition: The Ming Court (1368-1644) 2008. (Harvard East Asian Monographs: 301). (Illus.). 475p. 49.50 *(978-0-674-02823-4(6))* Harvard Univ., Asia Ctr.

Robson, James. Power of Place: The Religious Landscape of the Southern Sacred Peak (Nanyue) in Medieval China. 2009. (Harvard East Asian Monographs: 316). (MUL., Illus.). 450p. 49.95 *(978-0-674-03332-0(9))*, Harvard Univ., Asia Ctr.

Rojas, Carlos. The Great Wall: A Cultural History. 2010. (ENG., Illus.). 232p. 24.95 *(978-0-674-04787-7(7))* Harvard Univ. Pr.

Rolls, Eric. Sojourners. (Illus.). 542p. pap. *(978-0-7022-2539-0(8))* Univ. of Queensland Pr.

Ropp, Paul. China in World History, 1 vol. 2010. (New Oxford World History Ser.). (ENG., Illus.). 208p. pap. 19.95 *(978-0-19-538195-5(5))* Oxford Univ. Pr., Inc.

Roraback, Amanda. China in a Nutshell. 2009. (Nutshell Notes Ser.). (ENG., Illus.). 108p. pap. 9.95 *(978-0-9763070-2-0(2))* Enisen Publishing.

Rosendorfer, Herbert. Der China-Schmitt: Neue Geschichten. (GER.). 517p. pap. *(978-3-462-02802-7(2))* Kiepenheuer & Witsch GmbH & Company KG DEU. Dist: International Bk. Import Service, Inc.

Rovere, Dennis. The Xingyi Quan of the Chinese Army: Huang Bo Nien's Xingyi Fist & Weapon Instruction. 2008. (ENG., Illus.). 176p. pap. 16.95 *(978-1-58394-257-4(2)*, Blue Snake Bks.) North Atlantic Bks.

Rowe, William T. China's Last Empire: The Great Qing. 2009. (History of Imperial China Ser.: 6). (Illus.). 368p. 37.00 *(978-0-674-03612-3(3)*, Belknap Pr.) Harvard Univ. Pr.

—Crimson Rain: Seven Centuries of Violence in a Chinese County. 2006. (ENG., Illus.). 456p. 65.00 *(978-0-8047-5496-5(9))* Stanford Univ. Pr.

Running Press Staff & Encyclopedia Britannica Staff. Modern China: A Comprehensive Introduction to the World's New Economic Giant. 2008. (Britannica Guide to Ser.). (ENG., Illus.). 288p. pap. 13.95 *(978-0-7624-3367-4(1))* Running Pr. Bk. Pubs.

Ruocheng, Ying, et al. Voices Carry: Behind Bars & Backstage During China's Revolution & Reform. 2008. (Asian Voices Ser.). (ENG., Illus.). 286p. 85.00 *(978-0-7425-5554-9(2))*; pap. 32.95 *(978-0-7425-5555-6(0))* Rowman & Littlefield Publishers, Inc.

"Sanjiang Dongzu Zizhixian gai kuang" bian xie zu Staff & "Sanjiang Dongzu Zizhixian gai kuang" xiu ding ben bian xie zu Staff, contrib. by. Sanjiang Dongzu Zizhixian Gai Kuang: SanjiangDongzuZizhixiangaikuang. 2008. (CHI., Illus.). *(978-7-105-08612-2(2))* Nationalities Publishing Hse, The.

Sausmikat, Nora. Kulturrevolution, Diskurs und Erinnerung: Eine Analyse lebensgeschichtlicher Erzahlungen von Chinesischen Frauen. (Europaische Hochschulschriften Ser.: Vol. 85). (GER., Illus.). 469p. 43.95 *(978-3-631-38424-4(6))* Lang, Peter Publishing, Inc.

Sawyer, Ralph D. Ancient Chinese Warfare. 2011. (ENG.). 576p. (gr. 9). 39.99 *(978-0-465-02145-1(X))* Basic Bks.

Schafer, Edward H. The Empire of Min: A South China Kingdom of the Tenth Century. 2006. (ENG.). 160p. pap. 40.00 *(978-1-891640-36-0(4))* Floating World Editions.

—The Vermilion Bird: T'Ang Images of the South. 2008. (ENG., Illus.). 392p. per. 50.00 *(978-1-891640-37-7(2))* Floating World Editions.

Schmalzer, Sigrid. The People's Peking Man: Popular Science & Human Identity in Twentieth-Century China. 2008. (Illus.). 368p. 85.00 *(978-0-226-73859-8(0))* Univ. of Chicago Pr.

Schmitt, Gary J. The Rise of China: Essays on the Future Competition. 2009. (ENG.). 160p. 21.95 *(978-1-59403-231-8(9))* Encounter Bks.

Shao, Xuehai. Xian Qin Yi Shu Shi. 2010. (Illus.). *(978-7-80713-881-5(5))* Shandong Pictorial Publishing Hse.

Shaughnessy, Edward L. & Shaughessy, Edward. China: El mundo chino, creencias y rituales, creacion y Descubrimientos. Portillo, Miguel, tr. 2009. (SPA.). 256p. pap. 15.95 *(978-84-8076-768-2(5))* Blume ESP. Dist: Independent Pubs. Group.

Shuyun, Sun. The Long March: The True History of Communist China's Founding Myth. 2008. (ENG., Illus.). 304p. pap. 16.00 *(978-0-307-27831-9(X)*, Anchor) Knopf Doubleday Publishing Group.

Skaff, Jonathan Karam. Sui-Tang China & Its Turko-Mongol Neighbors: Culture, Power, & Connections, 580-800, 1 vol. 2012. (Oxford Studies in Early Empires Ser.). (ENG., Illus.). 416p. 85.00 ***(978-0-19-973413-9(5))*** Oxford Univ. Pr., Inc.

Smith, Christopher J., et al. Chinas Geography: Globalization & the Dynamics of Political, Economic, & Social Change. 2nd ed. 2011. (Changing Regions in a Global Context: New Perspectives in Regional Geography Ser.). (ENG.). 400p. pap. 59.95 *(978-0-7425-6783-2(4))* Rowman & Littlefield Publishers, Inc.

Sommers, Amy L. & Phillips, Kara L. Real Estate Law in China: A Guide to Foreign Investment. 2012. (ENG.). 336p. pap. 134.95 ***(978-1-61438-001-6(5))*** American Bar Assn.

Soothill, William Edward. China & the West: A Short History of Their Contact from Ancient Times to the Fall of the Manchu Dynasty. 2009. (ENG., Illus.). 224p. pap. 14.95 *(978-1-59416-088-2(0))* Westholme Publishing.

Standen, Naomi. Unbounded Loyalty: Frontier Crossing in Liao China. 2007. (Illus.). 279p. 55.00 *(978-0-8248-2983-4(2))* Univ. of Hawaii Pr.

Steinmetz, George. The Devil's Handwriting: Precoloniality & the German Colonial State in Qingdao, Samoa, & Southwest Africa. 2007. (Chicago Studies in Practices of Meaning Ser.). (Illus.). 608p. per. 35.00 *(978-0-226-77243-1(8))* Univ. of Chicago Pr.

Sterckx, Roel. Food, Sacrifice, & Sagehood in Early China. 2011. (ENG., Illus.). 248p. 90.00 *(978-1-107-00171-8(4))* Cambridge Univ. Pr.

Strassberg, Richard E., tr. from CHI. Wandering Spirits: Chen Shiyuan's Encyclopedia of Dreams. 2008. (Illus.). 289p. 55.00 *(978-0-520-25294-3(2))* Univ. of California Pr.

Su, Shuyang. A Reader on China. 2010. 174p. pap. 9.95 *(978-1-60220-901-5(4))* BetterLink Pr., Inc.

Sun, Zhaohai & Sun, Yan. Minguo Shi Di Qi Kan Hui Bian, 6 vols. 2010. (CHI., Illus.). *(978-7-5013-3838-2(8))* Beijing Library Pr.

Sun, Zhouyong. Craft Production in the Western Zhou Dynasty (1046-771 BC) A Case Study of a Jue-Earrings Workshop at the Predynastic Capital Site, Zhouyuan, China. 2008. (Bar S Ser.). (Illus.). 127p. (C). 70.00 *(978-1-4073-0265-2(5))* British Archaeological Reports Ltd. GBR. Dist: Brown, David Bk. Co., The.

Swislocki, Mark. Culinary Nostalgia: Regional Food Culture & the Urban Experience in Shanghai. 2008. (ENG., Illus.). 320p. 30.00 *(978-0-8047-6012-6(8))* Stanford Univ. Pr.

Tan, Chester C. The Boxer Catastrophe: Columbia Studies in the Social Sciences, No. 583. 2011. 286p. 48.95 ***(978-1-258-07637-5(3))*** Literary Licensing, LLC.

Tan, Song. Changshou Lake: True Story of Former Rightists at Changshou Lake, Chongqing of China In 1957. 2011. 540p. 36.16 ***(978-1-4269-8939-1(3))***; pap. 26.16 ***(978-1-4269-8940-7(7))*** Trafford Publishing.

Tanham, George K. Communist Revolutionary Warfare: From the Vietminh to the Viet Cong, 1 vol. annot. ed. 2006. (PSI Classics of the Counterinsurgency Era Ser.). (Illus.). 152p. 74.95 *(978-0-275-99263-7(2)*, C9263, Praeger Security International) Greenwood Publishing Group, Inc.

Tanner, Harold M. China: A History of the One of the World's Oldest Civilizations. 2009. (Illus.). 520p. (C). 54.00 *(978-0-87220-916-9(4))* Hackett Publishing Co., Inc.

—China: From the Great Qing Empire to the People's Republic of China, 1644 - 2009, 2 vols. 2010. (Illus.). 312p. (C). pap. 18.95 *(978-1-60384-204-4(7))* Hackett Publishing Co., Inc.

—China, A History Vol. 1: From Neolithic Cultures through the Great Qing Empire, (10,000 BCE - 1799 CE), 2 vols. 2010. (Illus.). 424p. (C). 49.00 *(978-1-60384-203-7(9))*; pap. 19.95 *(978-1-60384-202-0(0))* Hackett Publishing Co., Inc.

—China, A History Vol. 2: From the Great Qing Empire through the People's Republic of China, (1644 - 2009), 2 vols. 2010. (Illus.). 312p. (C). 48.00 *(978-1-60384-205-1(5))* Hackett Publishing Co., Inc.

Tanner, Harold Miles. China: A History. 2009. (Illus.). 448p. (C). pap. 24.95 *(978-0-87220-915-2(6))* Hackett Publishing Co., Inc.

Tanzi, Vito. Peoples, Places & Policies: China, Japan & Southeast Asia. 2007. per. 19.95 *(978-0-9795576-5-1(8))* Pinto, Jorge Bks.

Taylor, Jay. The Generalissimo: Chiang Kai-Shek & the Struggle for Modern China. 2011. (ENG., Illus.). 752p. pap. 19.95 *(978-0-674-06049-4(0)*, Belknap Pr.) Harvard Univ. Pr.

the Curriculum Specialists at Primary Source. China in the World. 2008. (C). pap. 49.95 *(978-0-88727-621-7(0))* Cheng & Tsui Co.

This Is China: The First 5,000 Years. 2010. (ENG & CHI.). 172p. pap. 14.95 *(978-1-933782-20-1(X))* Berkshire Publishing Group.

Thomas, James. Real China: The Country & its People. 2009. 332p. pap. 22.38 *(978-1-4251-7880-2(4))* Trafford Publishing.

Thorp, Robert L. Visiting Historic Beijing: A Guide to Sites & Resources. 2007. (ENG., Illus.). 240p. pap. 24.95 *(978-1-891640-53-7(4))* Floating World Editions.

Tian, Min. Mei Lanfang & the Twentieth-Century International Stage: Chinese Theatre Placed & Displaced. 2011. (Palgrave Studies in Theatre & Performance History Ser.). (ENG., Illus.). 320p. 95.00 ***(978-0-230-11244-5(7))*** Palgrave Macmillan.

Tianjin Shi di fang zhi bian xiu wei yuan hui, Ban gong shi Staff & Tianjin (China), Si fa ju Staff, contrib. by. Tianjin Tong Zhi. 2008. (CHI., Illus.). 10p. *(978-7-80688-210-8(3))* Tianjin Social Sciences Academy Pr.

"Tianzhu Zangzu Zizhixian gai kuang" bian xie zu Staff & "Tianzhu Zangzu Zizhixian gai kuang" xiu ding ben bian xie zu Staff, contrib. by. Tianzhu Zangzu Zizhixian Gai Kuang: TianzhuZangzuZizhixiangaikuang. 2009. (CHI., Illus.). *(978-7-105-08624-5(6))* Nationalities Publishing Hse, The.

Tobing, Anne Lumban. Schriftkunst in Rot und Weiss: Kunstlersiegel der Ming- und Ch'ing-Zeit, unter besonderer Berucksichtigung der Siegel des Chao Chih-ch'ien (1829-1884) 2010. (Studien zur Ostasiatischen Schriftkunst Ser.). (GER., Illus.). 216p. (C). pap. 90.00 *(978-3-515-08376-8(6))* Steiner, Franz Verlag Wiesbaden GmbH DEU. Dist: Brown, David Bk. Co., The.

"Tongdao Dongzu Zizhixian gai kuang" bian xie zu Staff & "Tongdao Dongzu Zizhixian" xiu ding ben bian xie zu Staff, contrib. by. Tongdao Dongzu Zizhixian Gai Kuang: TongdaoDongzuZizhixiangaikuang. 2008. (CHI., Illus.). *(978-7-105-08608-5(4))* Nationalities Publishing Hse, The.

Tonia Eckfeld. Imperial Tombs in Tang China 618-907. 2011. (ENG., Illus.). 192p. pap. 42.95 ***(978-0-415-67492-8(1))*** Routledge.

Tregear, T. R. & Tregear, T. A Geography of China. 2007. (ENG., Illus.). 359p. (gr. 11). pap. 34.95 *(978-0-202-30999-6(1))* Aldine Transaction.

Tuan, Yi-Fu. A Historical Geography of China. 2008. (ENG., Illus.). 236p. pap. 29.95 *(978-0-202-36200-7(0))* Aldine Transaction.

Tung, Douglas S. & Tung, Teresa. 36 Stratagems Plus: Illustrated by International Cases. 2010. 388p. pap. 21.14 *(978-1-4269-2806-2(8))* Trafford Publishing.

Turnbull, Stephen & Turnbull, Stephen R. Chinese Walled Cities 221 BC-AD 1644. 2009. (Fortress Ser.). (ENG., Illus.). 64p. pap. 18.95 *(978-1-84603-381-0(0))* Osprey Publishing, Ltd. GBR. Dist: Random Hse., Inc.

Twitchett, Denis & Smith, Paul Jakov, eds. The Cambridge History of China Vol. 5, Pt. 1: The Sung Dynasty & Its Precursors, 907-1279. 2008. (Cambridge History of China Ser.). (ENG., Illus.). 1128p. 185.00 *(978-0-521-81248-1(8))* Cambridge Univ. Pr.

Veeck, Gregory, et al. Chinas Geography: Globalization & the Dynamics of Political, Economic, & Social Change. 2nd rev. ed. 2011. (Changing Regions in a Global Context: New Perspectives in Regional Geography Ser.). (ENG.). 400p. 125.00 *(978-0-7425-6782-5(6))* Rowman & Littlefield Publishers, Inc.

Wagner, Rudolf G. Joining the Global Public: Word, Image, & City in Early Chinese Newspapers, 1870-1910. 2008. (CHI & ENG., Illus.). ix, 249p. pap. 29.95 *(978-0-7914-7118-0(7))* State Univ. of New York Pr.

Wakeman, Frederic E., Jr. Telling Chinese History: A Selection of Essays. Wakeman, Lea H., ed. 2009. 432p. 60.00 *(978-0-520-25605-7(0))* Univ. of California Pr.

Wakeman, Frederic E., Jr. & Wakeman, F. E. Telling Chinese History: A Selection of Essays. Wakeman, Lea H., ed. 2009. (ENG.). 432p. pap. 26.95 *(978-0-520-25606-4(9))* Univ. of California Pr.

Wang, Aihe. Cosmology & Political Culture in Early China. 2006. (Cambridge Studies in Chinese History, Literature & Institutions Ser.). (ENG., Illus.). 256p. pap. 53.00 *(978-0-521-02749-6(7))* Cambridge Univ. Pr.

Wang, Bangwei & Sen, Tansen, compiled by. India & China: Interactions through Buddhism & Diplomacy: A Collection of Essays by Professor Prabodh Chandra Bagchi. 2011. (Anthem Press India Ser.). 272p. 99.00 ***(978-93-80601-17-5(4))*** Anthem Pr. GBR. Dist: Books International, Inc.

Wang, Chenghong. Wei le Hong Se Zhongguo: Zhongguo Gong Chan Dang Ying Lie Zhuan Lüe. 2009. (Illus.). *(978-7-207-08486-6(2))* Heilongjiang People's Publishing Hse.

Wang, Chong. Interpreting Zheng Chenggong: The Politics of Dramatizing a Historical Figure in Japan, China, & Taiwan (1700-1963) 2008. 76p. pap. *(978-3-639-09266-0(X))* VDM Verlag Dr. Mueller e.K.

Wang, Heming. Zhongguo Jia Pu Tong Lun. 2010. (CHI., Illus.). 8p. *(978-7-5325-5451-5(1))* Shanghai Classics Publishing Hse.

Wang, Hongjie. Power & Politics in Tenth-Century China: The Former Shu Regime. 2011. 404p. ***(978-1-60497-764-6(7))*** Cambria Pr.

Wang, Jianying. Hong Jun Shi Yi Nan Kao Bian. 2010. (CHI.). *(978-7-5098-0327-1(6))* Chinese Communist Party History Pr.

Wang, Lihua. Zhongguo Nong Ye Tong Shi. 2009. (CHI., Illus.). 11p. *(978-7-109-13995-4(6))* Agricultural Publishing Hse.

Wang, Richard G. The Ming Prince & Daoism: Institutional Patronage of an Elite. 2012. (ENG.). 288p. 74.00 ***(978-0-19-976768-7(8))*** Oxford Univ. Pr., Inc.

Wang, Xizhi. Jin Wang Xizhi Chuan Shi Mo Ji Xuan. 2010. (CHI.). 38p. *(978-7-5010-2933-4(4))* Cultural Relics Publishing Hse.

Wang, Yuguo & Hu, Zheng. Zhao Shang Ju Yu Taiwan: Zhao Shang Ju Yu Tai Wan. 2010. (CHI., Illus.). 201p. *(978-962-374-535-2(4))* Wen Wei Publishing Co., Ltd.

Wasserstrom, Jeff & Wasserstrom, Jeffrey N. Global Shanghai, 1850-2010: A History in Fragments. 2009. (Asia's Global Cities Ser.). (ENG., Illus.). 192p. (C). 39.95 *(978-0-415-21328-8(2)*, RU19884); 170.00 *(978-0-415-21327-1(4)*, RU19883) Routledge.

Westad, Odd Arne. Restless Empire: China & the World since 1750. 2012. (ENG.). 528p. (gr. 9). 32.00 ***(978-0-465-01933-5(1))*** Basic Bks.

Westwell, Ian. China. 2008. (Illus.). 256p. 12.99 *(978-0-7858-2374-2(3)*, Chartwell) Book Sales, Inc.

—Timeless China. 2007. (Timeless Ser.). (Illus.). 160p. 12.99 *(978-0-7858-2318-6(2)*, Chartwell) Book Sales, Inc.

Wetzel, Alexandra. China. 2009. (Dictionaries of Civilization Ser.). (ENG., Illus.). 384p. pap. 28.95 *(978-0-520-25907-2(6))* Univ. of California Pr.

White Star, et al. China. 2010. (Treasures Ancient Civilization Ser.). (ENG., Illus.). 208p. 35.00 *(978-88-544-0330-7(X))* White Star ITA. Dist: Random Hse., Inc.

Williams, Samuel Wells. The Middle Kingdom. 2009. 292p. pap. *(978-0-217-35670-1(2))*; 576p. pap. *(978-1-4588-8968-3(8))*; 600p. pap. *(978-0-217-09551-8(8))*; 562p. pap. *(978-1-4588-8971-3(8))*; 704p. pap. *(978-0-217-09547-1(X))* Books LLC.

—The Middle Kingdom. 2009. 370p. pap. 32.29 *(978-1-4588-8978-2(5))* General Bks. LLC.

Wilson, James Harrison. Under the Old Flag: Recollections of Military Operations in the War for the Union, the Spanish War, the Boxer Rebellion, etc., 2 vol., set. reprint ed. 250.00 *(978-0-7222-8303-5(2))*; 250.00 *(978-0-7222-7930-4(2))* Library Reprints, Inc.

WOLFRAM & Eberhard, Wolfram. History of China. 2nd ed. 2008. (ENG., Illus.). 400p. 200.00 *(978-0-415-36148-4(6))* Routledge.

Wong, Sin Kiong. Confucianism, Chinese History & Society. 2012. 300p. pap. 48.00 ***(978-981-4374-47-7(4))*** World Scientific Publishing Co., Inc.

Wright, David Curtis. The History of China. 2nd ed. 2011. E-Book *(978-0-313-37749-5(9)*, Greenwood Pr.); (Illus.). 329p. 49.95 *(978-0-313-37748-8(0)*, GR7748) Greenwood Publishing Group, Inc.

Wu, Guo. Zheng Guanying, Merchant Reformer of Late Qing China & His Influence on Economics, Politics, & Society. 2010. *(978-1-60497-705-9(1))* Cambria Pr.

Wu, Jiang. Enlightenment in Dispute: The Reinvention of Chan Buddhism in Seventeenth-Century China. 2008. (ENG., Illus.). 480p. 74.00 *(978-0-19-533357-2(8))* Oxford Univ. Pr., Inc.

Wu, Zhengqiang. Bei Song: Di Guo Shu Sheng Yi Qi. 2009. (CHI.). *(978-7-5339-2722-6(2))* Zhejiang Pubn. Hse. of Literature and Art.

Xia, Dongyuan. Yang Wu Yun Dong Shi. 2010. (CHI.). *(978-7-5617-6745-0(5))* East China Normal Univ. Pr.

Xiong, Victor Cunrui. The A to Z of Medieval China. 2010. (A to Z Guide Ser.). (ENG.). 854p. pap. 34.45 *(978-0-8108-7575-3(6))* Scarecrow Pr., Inc.

Xiu, Ouyang. Historical Records of the Five Dynasties. Davis, Richard L. & Davis, Richard Harding, trs. from CHI. 2007. (ENG., Illus.). 736p. (gr. 17). pap. 29.50 *(978-0-231-12827-8(4))* Columbia Univ. Pr.

Xu, Dong. Qian Nian Qiuci Gu Guo. 2010. (Illus.). *(978-7-80178-596-1(7))* Hua Ling Pr.

Xu, Goomoo. Modern China & the World in the Ancient Prophecies. 2010. (Illus.). 260p. pap. 15.99 *(978-1-4490-3813-7(1))* AuthorHouse.

Xu, Jijun. Nan Song Lin'an Gong Shang Ye. 2009. (CHI.). 40p. *(978-7-01-008449-7(1))* People's Publishing Hse., The.

Xu, Xianjiang. Bai Nian Zhongguo Shi Lu: 1911-2009. 2010. (CHI., Illus.). *(978-7-5098-0161-1(3))* Chinese Communist Party History Pr.

Xue, Bing. Qingliang Shan Shi Hua. 2009. (CHI., Illus.). *(978-7-80718-554-3(6))* Nanjing Pub. Hse.

"Yanbian Chaoxianzu Zizhizhou gai kuang" bian xie zu Staff & "Yanbian Chaoxianzu Zizhizhou gai kuang" xiu ding ben bian xie zu Staff, contrib. by. Yanbian Chaoxianzu Zizhizhou Gai Kuang: YanbianChaoxianzuZizhizhougaikuang. 2009. (CHI., Illus.). *(978-7-105-08642-9(4))* Nationalities Publishing Hse, The.

Yang, Bin. Between Winds & Clouds: The Making of Yunnan. 2008. (Gutenberg-E Ser.). (ENG.). 350p. (gr. 17). 60.00 *(978-0-231-14254-0(4))* Columbia Univ. Pr.

Yang, Liansheng, et al. Zhongguo Zhi du Shi Yan Jiu: Studies in Chinese Institutional History. 2nd ed. 2007. ("Hai Wai Zhongguo Yan Jiu" Cong Shu Ser.). 189p. *(978-7-214-02312-4(1))* Jiangsu People's Publishing Hse.

Yi, Dai. A Concise History of the Qing Dynasty, Vol. 4. 2012. (Concise History of the Qing Dynasty Ser.). (ENG.). 352p. 128.00 ***(978-981-4332-21-7(6)***, Silkroad Pr.) Enrich Professional Publishing (S)., Ltd. SGP. Dist: Independent Pubs. Group.

Young, Doug. The Party Line: How the Media Dictates Public Opinion in Modern China. 2013. (ENG.). 256p. pap. 22.95 ***(978-0-470-82853-3(6)***, Wiley) Wiley, John & Sons, Inc.

Yu, Peter Xiaoming & Doyle, G. Wright. Chin: Ancient Culture, Modern Society. 2009. 244p. 25.95 *(978-1-60860-635-1(X)*, Strategic Bk. Publishing) AEG Literary Publishing Services, Inc.

Zanasi, Margherita. Saving the Nation: Economic Modernity in Republican China. 2006. (ENG.). 336p. 60.00 *(978-0-226-97873-4(7))* Univ. of Chicago Pr.

Zapata, Janet, et al. Symphony of Jewels: The Art of Anna Hu. 2012. (ENG.). 168p. 75.00 ***(978-0-86565-290-3(2))*** Vendome Pr., The.

Zhang, Cong Ellen. Transformative Journeys. 2010. 328p. 49.00 *(978-0-8248-3399-2(6))* Univ. of Hawaii Pr.

Zhang, Kaiyuan. Distanciation & Return: Analysis on Traditional Culture & Modernization of China. 2011. (ENG.). 256p. 108.00 ***(978-981-4332-22-4(4))*** Enrich Professional Publishing (S)., Ltd. SGP. Dist: Independent Pubs. Group.

Zhang, Qizhi, ed. Sourcebook of Traditional Chinese Culture. 2012. (ENG.). 300p. pap. 22.95 ***(978-1-59265-125-2(9))*** Long River Pr.

Zhang, Xiantao. The Origins of the Modern Chinese Press: The Influence of the Protestant Missionary Press in Late Qing China. 2007. (Illus.). XII, 180p. 150.00 *(978-0-415-38066-9(9))* Routledge.

Zheng, Hongtai, et al. Grand Old Man of Hong Kong: Sir Shouson Chow. 2010. (Illus.). 332p. pap. ***(978-962-8269-52-5(6))*** Hong Kong Univ. Pr.

Zhongguo guo jia tu shu guan, Gu ji guan Staff, contrib. by. Di 2 Jie Di Fang Wen Xian Guo Ji Xue Shu Yan Tao Hui Lun Wen Ji. 2009. (CHI., Illus.). *(978-7-5013-4219-8(9))* Beijing Library Pr.

Zhu, Qiang & Gao, Dahai. Xi Nan Ke Ji Da Xue Xiao Shi. 2007. (Illus.). *(978-7-81114-662-2(2))* Univ. of Electronic Science & Technology of China, The.

Zhu, Zhiqun. China. 14th ed. 2011. (Global Studies). (ENG., Illus.). 208p. (C). pap. 50.00 *(978-0-07-802619-5(9)*, 0078026199, McGraw-Hill/Dushkin) McGraw-Hill Higher Education.

—Global Studies: China. 13th ed. 2009. (Global Studies). (ENG.). 224p. (C). pap. 50.00 *(978-0-07-337987-6(5)*, 0073379875, McGraw-Hill/Dushkin) McGraw-Hill Higher Education.

Zicheng, Ye. Inside China's Grand Strategy: The Perspective from the People's Republic. Liu, Guoli & Levine, Steven I., eds. 2010. (Asia in the New Millennium Ser.). (ENG., Illus.). 320p. 35.00 *(978-0-8131-2645-6(2))* Univ. Pr. of Kentucky.

CHINA—HISTORY—CHRONOLOGY

Cai, Degui. Ji Xianlin Nian Pu Chang Bian. 2010. (CHI., Illus.). *(978-7-5445-1156-8(1))* Changchun Publishing Pr.

Yong, Heming, et al. Chinese Lexicography: A History from 1046 BC to AD 1911. 2008. (ENG., Illus.). 448p. 175.00 *(978-0-19-953982-6(0))* Oxford Univ. Pr., Inc.

CHINA—HISTORY—PHILOSOPHY

Makeham, John. Lost Soul: Confucianism in Contemporary Chinese Academic Discourse. 2008. (Harvard-Yenching Institute Monograph Ser.: 64). (Illus.). 425p. 49.95 *(978-0-674-02811-1(2))* Harvard Univ., Asia Ctr.

CHINA—HISTORY—PICTORIAL WORKS

Griffioen, Pieter. China's Present Past/in Het Voorbijgaan: China/English/Dutch. pap. 29.95 *(978-90-72216-42-7(3))* Focus NLD. Dist: D.A.P./Distributed Art Pubs.

Liu, Heung Shing, ed. China: 25 Jahre TASCHEN. 2011. (25 Ser.). (ENG., Illus.). 424p. 29.99 ***(978-3-8365-3089-7(9))*** TASCHEN DEU. Dist: Ingram Pub. Services.

Lu, Hanchao. The Birth of a Republic: Francis Stafford's Photographs of China's 1911 Revolution & Beyond. 2010. (ENG., Illus.). 240p. 40.00 *(978-0-295-98940-2(8))* Univ. of Washington Pr.

Lui, Elizabeth Gill. Open Hearts Open Doors: Reflections on China's Past & Future. 2008. (Illus.). 250p. 50.00 *(978-0-9796165-0-1(6))*; 50.00 *(978-0-9796165-3-2(0))* Cornell Univ. Pr.

Makos, Christopher, photos by. Andy Warhol in China: the Photographs of Christopher Makos. 2008. (ENG., Illus.). 88p. 75.00 *(978-988-17144-8-0(6))* Timezone 8 Ltd. HKG. Dist: D.A.P./Distributed Art Pubs.

Philippi, Simone & Shing, Liu Heung, eds. China, Portrait of a Country. 2008. (FRE, GER & ENG., Illus.). 423p. 59.99 *(978-3-8365-0569-7(X))* TASCHEN DEU. Dist: Ingram Pub. Services.

Rubinfien, Leo, intro. Phantom Shanghai. 2007. (FRE & ENG., Illus.). 240p. 50.00 *(978-0-9739739-1-4(9))* Magenta Publishing for the Arts CAN. Dist: Consortium Bk. Sales & Distribution.

Ruigao, Peng. China's Great Wall: A Photographic Tour Through the Realm of Enchantmentas Viewed Through the Lens of Sun Chengyi. 2008. (ENG.). 224p. (gr. 12). 35.00 *(978-0-7621-0985-2(8))* Reader's Digest Assn., Inc., The.

Shing, Liu Heung & Smith, Karen. Shanghai: A History in Photographs 1842 - Today. 2011. (ENG., Illus.). 500p. (gr. 12). pap. 50.00 ***(978-0-670-08090-8(X)***, Penguin Global) Penguin Group (USA) Inc.

Song, Li. Everyday Dalian: Life in Modern Manchuria. 2008. 0.00 *(978-0-9763168-5-5(4))* DigitalKu.

Tong, Shaosu. Folk Culture in China's Zhejiang Province, Illustrated: The Flowing Mother River. 2009. pap. *(978-1-931907-62-0(5))* Homa & Sekey Bks.

Worswick, Clark & Santoyo, Maria, texts. Sheying. 2008. (ENG., Illus.). 172p. 50.00 *(978-84-7506-804-6(9))* Turner, Ediciones S.A. ESP. Dist: D.A.P./Distributed Art Pubs.

Yu, Wei & Qian, Sijie. Xin Wen Lao Zhao Pian de Bei Hou: Hong Qiang She Ying Jia Jing Tou Zhong de Gong He Guo Wang Shi. 2010. (CHI., Illus.). 8p. pap. *(978-7-5011-9085-0(2))* Xinhua Publishing Hse.

CHINA—HISTORY—SOURCES

Atwill, David, et al. Sources in Chinese History: Diverse Perspectives from 1644 to the Present. 2009. (ENG.). 432p. (C). pap. 56.40 *(978-0-13-233089-3(X)*, Prentice Hall) Prentice Hall PTR.

Hua dong shi fan da xue, Zhongguo dang dai shi yan jiu zhong xin Staff, contrib. by. Hebei Ji Xian Menzhuang Gong She Menzhuang Da Dui Dang An. 2009. (CHI.). *(978-7-80186-993-7(1))* Orient Publishing Ctr.

Jingping, Wu. Select Telegrams Between Chiang Kai-Shek & T. V. Soong, 1940-1943. Kuo, Tai-chun, ed. 2008. (TV soong Ser.). (CHI & ENG., Illus.). 384p. pap. 15.00 *(978-7-309-05956-4(5))* Hoover Institution Pr.

Ripa, Matteo. Memoirs of Father Ripa. 2009. 124p. pap. *(978-0-217-86405-3(8))* Books LLC.

—Memoirs of Father Ripa. 2009. 312p. pap. 21.42 *(978-0-217-96851-5(1))* General Bks. LLC.

Schaeffer, Kurtis R., et al. Sources of Tibetan Tradition. (Introduction to Asian Civilizations Ser.). 2013. (ENG., Illus.). 832p. (gr. 17). 120.00 *(978-0-231-13598-6(X))* 2013. (ENG., Illus.). 832p. (gr. 17). pap. 40.00 ***(978-0-231-13599-3(8))*** 2012. ***(978-0-231-50978-7(2))*** Columbia Univ. Pr.

Schoppa, R. Keith. Twentieth Century China: A History in Documents, 1 vol. 2nd ed. 2010. (Pages from History Ser.). (ENG., Illus.). 224p. (C). 44.95 *(978-0-19-973201-2(9))* Oxford Univ. Pr., Inc.

Wang, Shiwei. Li Shi Wen Xian Yan Jiu. 2008. (CHI., Illus.). *(978-7-5013-3749-1(7))* Beijing Library Pr.

Yonglin, Jiang. The Mandate of Heaven & the Great Ming Code. 2011. (Asian Law Ser.). (ENG.). 256p. (C). 65.00 *(978-0-295-99065-1(1))* Univ. of Washington Pr.

Zhou, Xun, ed. The Great Famine in China, 1958-1962: A Documentary History. 2012. (ENG., Illus.). 224p. 45.00 ***(978-0-300-17518-9(3))*** Yale Univ. Pr.

CHINA—HISTORY—TO 221 B.C.

Bielenstein, Hans. The Bureaucracy of Han Times. 2009. (Cambridge Studies in Chinese History, Literature & Institutions Ser.). (ENG.). 276p. pap. 36.99 *(978-0-521-10112-7(3))* Cambridge Univ. Pr.

Chang, Chun-Shu. The Rise of the Chinese Empire Vol. 1: Nation, State, & Imperialism in Early China, CA. 1600 B. C. -A. D. 8, 2 vols. 2007. (ENG., Illus.). 506p. 100.00 *(978-0-472-11533-4(2))* Univ. of Michigan Pr.

—The Rise of the Chinese Empire Vol. 2: Frontier, Immigration, & Empire in Han China, 130 B. C. -A. D. 157, 2 vols. 2007. (ENG., Illus.). 352p. 95.00 *(978-0-472-11534-1(0))* Univ. of Michigan Pr.

Ch'ien, Ssu-Ma. The Grand Scribe's Records Vol. VIII, Pt. 1: The Memoirs of Han China. Nienhauser, William H., Jr., ed. 2008. (ENG., Illus.). 512p. 49.95 *(978-0-253-34028-3(4)*, 0253340284) Indiana Univ. Pr.

Feng, Li. Landscape & Power in Early China: The Crisis & Fall of the Western Zhou, 1045-771 BC. 2009. (ENG., Illus.). 424p. (C). pap. 55.00 *(978-0-521-10811-9(X))* Cambridge Univ. Pr.

Johansson, Perry. Saluting the Yellow Emperor: A Case of Swedish Sinography. 2012. (ENG.). VIII, 244p. ***(978-90-04-22097-3(6))*** BRILL.

Kim, Hyun Jin. Ethnicity & Foreigners in Ancient Greece & China. 2009. 224p. 120.00 *(978-0-7156-3807-1(6))* Duckworth Publishers GBR. Dist: International Publishers Marketing.

Liu, Li & Chen, Xingcan. State Formation in Early China. 2010. (Duckworth Debates in Archaeology Ser.). (Illus.). 148p. pap. 24.95 *(978-0-7156-3224-6(8))* Duckworth Publishers GBR. Dist: International Publishers Marketing.

Loewe, Michael. Divination, Mythology & Monarchy in Han China. 2008. (University of Cambridge Oriental Publications). (ENG.). 376p. pap. 42.00 *(978-0-521-05220-7(3))* Cambridge Univ. Pr.

McKnight, Brian E. Law & Order in Sung China. 2007. (Cambridge Studies in Chinese History, Literature & Institutions Ser.). (ENG.). 576p. pap. 100.00 *(978-0-521-03371-8(3))* Cambridge Univ. Pr.

Olberding, Garret P. S. Dubious Facts: The Evidence of Early Chinese Historiography. 2012. (SUNY Series in Chinese Philosophy & Culture Ser.). (ENG.). 304p. 85.00 ***(978-1-4384-4389-8(7))*** State Univ. of New York Pr.

Rosendorfer, Herbert. Letters Back to Ancient China. Mitchell, Mike, tr. from GER. 2nd rev. ed. 2006. 274p. per. 12.99 *(978-1-903517-39-0(7))* Dedalus, Ltd.

Wood, Frances. China's First Emperor & His Terracotta Warriors. 2008. (ENG., Illus.). 224p. 24.95 *(978-0-312-38112-7(3))* St. Martin's Pr.

CHINA—HISTORY—221 B.C.-960 A.D.

Chen, Sanping. Multicultural China in the Early Middle Ages. 2012. (Encounters with Asia Ser.). 320p. (C). 79.95 ***(978-0-8122-4370-3(6))*** Univ. of Pennsylvania Pr.

Ch'ien, Ssu-Ma. The Grand Scribe's Records, Volume IX: The Memoirs of Han China, Part II. Nienhauser, William H., Jr., ed. 2010. (ENG., Illus.). 496p. 59.95 *(978-0-253-35590-4(7), 0253355907)* Indiana Univ. Pr.

Clements, Jonathan. The First Emperor of China: The Man Who Gave China Its Name. 2007. (ENG., Illus.). 256p. pap. 19.95 *(978-0-7509-3960-7(5))* History Pr. Ltd.,The GBR. Dist: Independent Pubs. Group.

—Wu: The Chinese Empress Who Schemed, Seduced, & Murdered Her Way to Become a Living God. 2007. (ENG., Illus.). 256p. 29.95 *(978-0-7509-3961-4(3))* History Pr. Ltd.,The GBR. Dist: Independent Pubs. Group.

De Luca, Araldo, photos by. The Eternal Army: The Terracotta Soldiers of the First Emperor. 2012. (ENG., Illus.). 288p. 24.95 ***(978-88-544-0627-8(9))*** White Star ITA. Dist: Sterling Publishing Co., Inc.

Lewis, Mark Edward. China's Cosmopolitan Empire: The Tang Dynasty. 2009. (History of Imperial China Ser.: 3). (Illus.). 368p. 37.00 *(978-0-674-03306-1(X)*, Belknap Pr.) Harvard Univ. Pr.

Lewis, Mark Edward & Brook, Timothy. China's Cosmopolitan Empire: The Tang Dynasty. 2012. (History of Imperial China Ser.: 3). (ENG., Illus.). 368p. pap. 19.95 ***(978-0-674-06401-0(1)***, Belknap Pr.) Harvard Univ. Pr.

Man, John. The Terra Cotta Army: China's First Emperor & the Birth of a Nation. 2009. (ENG.). 336p. pap. 16.95 *(978-0-306-81840-0(X))* Da Capo Pr., Inc.

Rothschild, N. Harry & Stearns, Peter N. Wu Zhao: China's Only Woman Emperor. 2007. (Library of World Biography Ser.). (ENG., Illus.). 256p. (C). per. 25.00 *(978-0-321-39426-2(7))* Longman Publishing Group.

Schafer, Edward H. Pacing the Void: T'ang Approaches to the Stars. 2006. (ENG.). 368p. pap. 50.00 *(978-1-891640-14-8(3))* Floating World Editions.

Turnbull, Stephen. The Great Wall of China 221 BC-AD 1644. 2007. (Fortress Ser.). (ENG., Illus.). 96p. pap. 18.95 *(978-1-84603-004-8(8))* Osprey Publishing, Ltd. GBR. Dist: Random Hse., Inc.

Wheatley, Paul. The Origins & Character of the Ancient Chinese City Vol. 1: The City in Ancient China, 2 vols. 2008. (ENG., Illus.). 364p. pap. 49.95 *(978-0-202-36202-1(7))* Aldine Transaction.

—The Origins & Character of the Ancient Chinese City Vol. 2: The Chinese City in Comparative Perspective. 2008. (ENG.). 378p. pap. 49.95 *(978-0-202-36203-8(5))* Aldine Transaction.

Wittfogel, Karl August & Chia-Sheng, Feng. Religion under the Liao Dynasty, 907-1125: Review of Religion, May 1948. 2011. 24p. 35.95 ***(978-1-258-08088-4(5))*** Literary Licensing, LLC.

Woo, X. L. Empress Wu the Great. 2008. 31.95 *(978-0-87586-661-1(1))*; pap. 21.95 *(978-0-87586-660-4(3))* Algora Publishing.

CHINA—HISTORY—HAN DYNASTY, 202 B.C.-220 A.D.

Brindley, Erica. Music, Cosmology, & the Politics of Harmony in Early China. 2012. (SUNY Series in Chinese Philosophy & Culture Ser.). (ENG.). 224p. 75.00 ***(978-1-4384-4313-3(7))*** State Univ. of New York Pr.

Chang, Chun-Shu. The Rise of the Chinese Empire Vol. 1: Nation, State, & Imperialism in Early China, CA. 1600 B. C. -A. D. 8, 2 vols. 2007. (ENG., Illus.). 506p. 100.00 *(978-0-472-11533-4(2))* Univ. of Michigan Pr.

—The Rise of the Chinese Empire Vol. 2: Frontier, Immigration, & Empire in Han China, 130 B. C. -A. D. 157, 2 vols. 2007. (ENG., Illus.). 352p. 95.00 *(978-0-472-11534-1(0))* Univ. of Michigan Pr.

Ch'ien, Ssu-Ma. The Grand Scribe's Records, Volume IX: The Memoirs of Han China, Part II. Nienhauser, William H., Jr., ed. 2010. (ENG., Illus.). 496p. 59.95 *(978-0-253-35590-4(7), 0253355907)* Indiana Univ. Pr.

Clark, Anthony E. Ban Gu's History of Early China. 2008. 109.95 *(978-1-60497-561-1(X))* Cambria Pr.

Dardess, John W. Governing China: 150-1850. 2010. (Illus.). 139p. 39.95 *(978-1-60384-312-6(4))*; pap. 12.95 *(978-1-60384-311-9(5))* Hackett Publishing Co., Inc.

de Crespigny, Rafe. A Biographical Dictionary of Later Han to the Three Kingdoms (23-220 AD) 2006. (Handbook of Oriental Studies. Section 4 China Ser.). (Illus.). 1306p. *(978-90-04-15605-0(4))* BRILL.

De Crespigny, Rafe. Imperial Warlord: A Biography of Cao Cao 155-220 AD. 2010. (Sinica Leidensia Ser.). (Illus.). 600p. *(978-90-04-18522-7(4))* BRILL.

Farmer, J. Michael. The Talent of Shu: Qiao Zhou & the Intellectual World of Early Medieval Sichuan. 2007. (Illus.). 246p. 85.00 *(978-0-7914-7163-0(2))* State Univ. of New York Pr.

Hinsch, Bret. Women in Early Imperial China. 2nd ed. 2010. (Asia/Pacific/Perspectives Ser.). (ENG.). 256p. 80.00 *(978-0-7425-6822-8(9))*; pap. 29.95 *(978-0-7425-6823-5(7))* Rowman & Littlefield Publishers, Inc.

Hung, Hing Ming. The Road to the Throne: How Liu Bang Founded China's Han Dynasty. 2011. pap. 22.95 *(978-0-87586-837-0(1))*; pap. 32.95 *(978-0-87586-838-7(X))* Algora Publishing.

Liu, Cary Y. & Richard, Naomi Noble, eds. Rethinking the Wu Family Shrines & Han China: Ideals, Practices, & Problems. 2008. (Illus.). 448p. pap. 35.00 *(978-0-943012-48-3(1))* Princeton Univ. Art Museum.

Liu, Cary Y., et al. Rethinking Recarving: Ideals, Practices, & Problems of the Wu Family Shrines & Han China. 2008. (ENG., Illus.). 384p. pap. 60.00 *(978-0-300-13704-0(4))* Yale Univ. Pr.

Loewe, Michael. The Government of the Qin & Han Empires, 221 BCE-220 CE. 2006. (Illus.). (C). 224p. 37.95 *(978-0-87220-819-3(2))*; 248p. pap. 12.95 *(978-0-87220-818-6(4))* Hackett Publishing Co., Inc.

Nylan, Michael & Loewe, Michael, eds. China's Early Empires: A Re-appraisal. 2010. (University of Cambridge Oriental Publications). (ENG., Illus.). 654p. 135.00 *(978-0-521-85297-5(8))* Cambridge Univ. Pr.

Scheidel, Walter. Rome & China: Comparative Perspectives on Ancient World Empires, 1 vol. 2010. (Oxford Studies in Early Empires Ser.). (ENG., Illus.). 256p. 29.95 *(978-0-19-975835-7(2))* Oxford Univ. Pr., Inc.

Yu, Ying-shih. Trade & Expansion in Han China: A Study in the Structure of Sino-Barbarian Economic Relations. 2011. 266p. 40.00 ***(978-1-59740-816-5(6))*** ACLS Humanities E-Book.

CHINA—HISTORY—960-1644

De Weerdt, Hilde. Competition over Content: Negotiating Standards for the Civil Service Examinations in Imperial China (1127-1279) 2007. (Harvard East Asian Monographs: 289). (Illus.). 508p. 49.50 *(978-0-674-02588-2(1))* Harvard Univ., Asia Ctr.

Delgado, James P. Khubilai Khan's Lost Fleet: In Search of a Legendary Armada. 2009. (ENG.). 240p. 40.00 *(978-0-520-25975-8(9))* Univ. of California Pr.

Fan, Chengda. Treatises of the Supervisor & Guardian of the Cinnamon Sea: The Natural World & Material Culture of Twelfth-Century China. Hargett, James M., tr. from CHI. 2011. (ENG., Illus.). 368p. (C). 80.00 *(978-0-295-99078-1(3))*; pap. 40.00 *(978-0-295-99079-8(1))* Univ. of Washington Pr.

Haw, Stephen G. Marco Polo's China: A Venetian in the Realm of Khubilai Khan. 2009. 216p. pap. 39.95 *(978-0-415-54600-3(1))* Routledge.

Hou, Naihui. Song Dai Yuan Lin Ji Qi Sheng Huo Wen Hua. 2010. (CHI., Illus.). *(978-957-14-5271-5(8))* San Min Bk. Co., Ltd.

Kuhn, Dieter. The Age of Confucian Rule: The Song Transformation of China. (History of Imperial China Ser.: 4). (Illus.). 368p. 2011. (ENG.). pap. 19.95 *(978-0-674-06202-3(7))* 2009. 38.50 *(978-0-674-03146-3(6))* Harvard Univ. Pr. (Belknap Pr.).

Turnbull, Stephen. The Great Wall of China 221 BC-AD 1644. 2007. (Fortress Ser.). (ENG., Illus.). 96p. pap. 18.95 *(978-1-84603-004-8(8))* Osprey Publishing, Ltd. GBR. Dist: Random Hse., Inc.

Wittfogel, Karl August & Chia-Sheng, Feng. Religion under the Liao Dynasty, 907-1125: Review of Religion, May 1948. 2011. 24p. 35.95 ***(978-1-258-08088-4(5))*** Literary Licensing, LLC.

CHINA—HISTORY—MING DYNASTY, 1368-1644

Brook, Timothy. The Troubled Empire: China in the Yuan & Ming Dynasties. 2010. (History of Imperial China Ser.: 5). (Illus.). 336p. 35.00 *(978-0-674-04602-3(1)*, Belknap Pr.) Harvard Univ. Pr.

Chan, Hok-lam. Ming Taizu (R. 1368-98)and the Foundation of the Ming Dynasty in China. 2011. (Variorum Collected Studies). (Illus.). 374p. 165.00 ***(978-1-4094-3128-2(2))*** Ashgate Publishing Co.

Clunas, Craig. Empire of Great Brightness: Visual & Material Cultures of Ming China, 1368-1644. 2012. (ENG., Illus.). 256p. pap. 55.00 ***(978-1-86189-360-4(4))*** Reaktion Bks., Ltd. GBR. Dist: Chicago Distribution Ctr.

Dardess, John. Ming China 1368-1644: A Concise History of a Resilient Empire. 2011. (Critical Issues in World & International History Ser.). (ENG.). 172p. 80.00 *(978-1-4422-0490-4(7))*; (C). (gr. 13-17). pap. 24.95 *(978-1-4422-0491-1(5))* Rowman & Littlefield Publishers, Inc.

Dardess, John W. Ming China, 1368-1644: A Concise History of a Resilient Empire. 2011. ***(978-1-4422-0492-8(3))*** Rowman & Littlefield Publishers, Inc.

De Bary, William Theodore. Self & Society in Ming Thought. 2008. 576p. pap. 57.00 *(978-1-59740-593-5(0))* ACLS Humanities E-Book.

Faure, David. Emperor & Ancestor: State & Lineage in South China. 2007. (ENG., Illus.). 480p. 50.00 *(978-0-8047-5318-0(0))* Stanford Univ. Pr.

Filipiak, Kai. Krieg, Staat und Militar in der Ming-Zeit (1368-1644) Auswirkungen militarischer und bewaffneter Konflikte auf Machtpolitik und Herrschaftsapparat der Ming-Dynastie. 2008. (Opera Sinologica Ser.). (GER., Illus.). 348p. (C). pap. 117.00 *(978-3-447-05852-0(8))* Harrassowitz, Otto Verlag DEU. Dist: ISD.

Fontana, Michela. Matteo Ricci: A Jesuit in the Ming Court. 2011. (ENG.). 336p. 44.95 *(978-1-4422-0586-4(5))* Rowman & Littlefield Publishers, Inc.

Gerritsen, Anne. Ji'an Literati & the Local in Song-Yuan-Ming China. 2007. (China Studies). (Illus.). 258p. *(978-90-04-15603-6(8))* BRILL.

Grant Guangren Shen. Elite Theatre in Ming China, 1368-1644. 2009. 188p. pap. 39.95 *(978-0-415-54589-1(7))* Routledge.

Hammond, Kenneth J. Pepper Mountain: The Life, Death & Posthumous Career of Yang Jisheng. 2007. (ENG., Illus.). 256p. 160.00 *(978-0-7103-1280-8(6))* Routledge.

Han, Xin. Zi Jin Cheng Jian Zheng, 2 vols. 2009. (CHI., Illus.). 434p. *(978-7-80168-490-5(7))* Study Publishing Hse.

Homer, Charles. Rising China & Its Postmodern Fate: Memories of Empire in a New Global Context. 2011. (Studies in Security & International Affairs Ser.). (ENG.). 240p. pap. 24.95 *(978-0-8203-3878-1(3))* Univ. of Georgia Pr.

Kafalas, Philip A. In Limpid Dream: Nostalgia & Zhang Dai's Reminiscences of the Ming. 2006. 288p. pap. 29.95 *(978-1-891936-63-0(8)*, Signature Bks.) EastBridge.

Li, Kangying. The Ming Maritime Policy in Transition 1367 To 1568. 2010. (East Asian Economic & Socio-Cultural Studies). (ENG., Illus.). 211p. (C). 72.00 *(978-3-447-06172-8(3))* Harrassowitz, Otto Verlag DEU. Dist: ISD.

Marks, Robert. Tigers, Rice, Silk, & Silt: Environment & Economy in Late Imperial South China. 2006. (Studies in Environment & History). (ENG., Illus.). 408p. pap. 58.00 *(978-0-521-02776-2(4))* Cambridge Univ. Pr.

Menzies, Gavin. 1421: The Year China Discovered America. 2008. (P. S. Ser.). (Illus.). 672p. pap. 15.99 *(978-0-06-156489-5(3)*, William Morrow Paperbacks) HarperCollins Pubs.

—1434: The Year a Magnificent Chinese Fleet Sailed to Italy & Ignited the Renaissance. (P. S. Ser.). 2009. (ENG.). 400p. pap. 15.99 *(978-0-06-149218-1(3)*, William Morrow Paperbacks) 2008. 384p. pap. 19.00 *(978-0-06-163264-8(3))* 2008. (ENG., Illus.). 384p. 26.95 *(978-0-06-149217-4(5)*, Morrow, William & Co.) HarperCollins Pubs.

Miller, Harry. State Versus Gentry in Late Ming Dynasty China, 1572-1644. 2008. (ENG.). 236p. 100.00 *(978-0-230-61134-4(6))* Palgrave Macmillan.

Mungello, David E. The Great Encounter of China & the West, 1500-1800. 3rd ed. 2009. (Critical Issues in World & International History Ser.). (ENG., Illus.). 184p. 79.00 *(978-0-7425-5797-0(9))*; pap. 24.95 *(978-0-7425-5798-7(7))* Rowman & Littlefield Publishers, Inc.

Schneewind, Sarah. A Tale of Two Melons: Emperor & Subject in Ming China. 2006. 141p. (C). pap. 32.95 *(978-0-87220-825-4(7))*; (Illus.). pap. 9.95 *(978-0-87220-824-7(9))* Hackett Publishing Co., Inc.

Schneewind, Sarah, et al. Long Live the Emperor! Uses of the Ming Founder across Six Centuries of East Asian History, No. 4. Schneewind, Sarah, ed. 2008. (Illus.). 508p. 80.00 *(978-0-9800639-0-5(6)*, Ctr. for Early Modern History.

Smith, Joanna Handlin. The Art of Doing Good: Charity in Late Ming China. 2009. (ENG., Illus.). 424p. 40.00 *(978-0-520-25363-6(9))* Univ. of California Pr.

Su, Tongbing. Ming Dai Shi Shi Yu Ren Wu. 2010. (CHI.). pap. *(978-7-80047-922-9(6))* Forbidden City Publishing Hse.

Swope, Kenneth M. A Dragon's Head & a Serpent's Tail: Ming China & the First Great East Asian War, 1592-1598. 2009. (Campaigns & Commanders Ser.). (ENG.). 432p. 34.95 *(978-0-8061-4056-8(9))* Univ. of Oklahoma Pr.

Wade, Geof. Southeast Asia Fifteenth. (Illus.). 380p. pap. 32.00 *(978-9971-69-448-7(4))* National Univ. of Singapore Pr. SGP. Dist: Univ. of Hawaii Pr.

Wade, Geoff & Laichen, Sun, eds. Southeast Asia in the Fifteenth Century: The China Factor. 2010. (ENG., Illus.). 520p. (gr. 17). pap. 30.00 *(978-988-8028-48-1(0))* Hong Kong Univ. Pr. HKG. Dist: Columbia Univ. Pr.

Wang, Yuan-kang. Harmony & War: Confucian Culture & Chinese Power Politics. 2010. (Contemporary Asia in the World Ser.). (Illus.). 352p. E-Book 39.99 *(978-0-231-52240-3(1))*; (ENG., 328p. (gr. 17). 50.00 *(978-0-231-15140-5(3))* Columbia Univ. Pr.

Wen, Gongyi. Ming Dai Huan Guan. 2010. (CHI.). 16p. *(978-7-80047-923-6(4))* Forbidden City Publishing Hse.

Wills, John E., Jr. China & Maritime Europe, 1500-1800: Trade, Settlement, Diplomacy, & Missions. 2010. (ENG., Illus.). 312p. (C). pap. 28.99 *(978-0-521-17945-4(9))* Cambridge Univ. Pr.

CHINA—HISTORY—1644-1795

Braam, André Everard van & de Saint-Méry, M. L. E. Moreau. An Authentic Account of the Embassy of the Dutch East-India Company, to the Court of the Emperor of China, in the Years 1794 & 1795 2 Volume Set. 2011. (Cambridge Library Collection - History Ser.). (ENG., Illus.). 682p. pap., pap. 57.00 *(978-1-108-02907-0(8))* Cambridge Univ. Pr.

Braam Houckgeest, André Everard van. An Authentic Account of the Embassy of the Dutch East-India Company, to the Court of the Emperor of China, in the Years 1794 and 1795. 2011. (Cambridge Library Collection - History Ser.). (ENG.). 332p. pap. 28.99 *(978-1-108-02906-3(X))*; (Illus.). 352p. pap. 29.99 *(978-1-108-02905-6(1))* Cambridge Univ. Pr.

Chang, Michael G. A Court on Horseback Vol. 287: Imperial Touring & the Construction of Qing Rule, 1680-1785. 2007. (Harvard East Asian Monographs: 287). (Illus.). 550p. 49.95 *(978-0-674-02454-0(0))* Harvard Univ., Asia Ctr.

Di Cosmo, Nicola. The Diary of a Manchu Soldier in Seventeenth-Century China: My Service in the Army, by Dzengseo. 2009. 142p. pap. 39.95 *(978-0-415-54447-4(5))* Routledge.

Di Cosmo, Nicola & Dzengseo. The Diary of a Manchu Soldier in Seventeenth-Century China. annot. ed. 2006. (Routledge Studies in the Early History of Asia: Vol. 4). (ENG., Illus.). 154p. (C). (gr. 13). 168.00 *(978-0-7007-1611-1(4)*, RU30686) Routledge.

D'Orleans, Pierre Joseph & Witsen, Nicholaas. History of the Two Tartar Conquerors of China: Including the Two Journeys into Tartary of Father Ferdinand Verhiest, in the Suite of the Emperor Kanh-Hi. Ellesemere, Earl of, tr. 2010. (Cambridge Library Collection - Travel & Exploration Ser.). (ENG.). 188p. pap. 19.99 *(978-1-108-00812-9(7))* Cambridge Univ. Pr.

Elliot, Mark & Stearns, Peter. Emperor Qianlong: Son of Heaven, Man of the World. 2009. (Library of World Biography Ser.). (ENG.). 208p. (C). pap. 25.00 *(978-0-321-08444-6(6))* Longman Publishing Group.

Isett, Christopher M. State, Peasant, & Merchant in Qing Manchuria, 1644-1862. 2006. (ENG., Illus.). 440p. 65.00 *(978-0-8047-5271-8(0))* Stanford Univ. Pr.

Perdue, Peter C. China Marches West: The Qing Conquest of Central Eurasia 2010. (ENG., Illus.). 752p. pap. 19.95 *(978-0-674-05743-2(0)*, Belknap Pr.) Harvard Univ. Pr.

Ray, Hem C. Dynastic History of Northern India (Early Medieval Period) 92.50 *(978-81-215-0330-3(2))* Munshiram Manoharlal Pubs. Private, Ltd. IND. Dist: Coronet Bks.

Ripa, Matteo. Memoirs of Father Ripa. 2009. 124p. pap. *(978-0-217-86405-3(6))* Books LLC.

—Memoirs of Father Ripa. 2009. 312p. pap. 21.42 *(978-0-217-96851-5(1))* General Bks. LLC.

Van Braam Houckgeest, André Everard Van. An Authentic Account of the Embassy of the Dutch East-India Company, to the Court of the Emperor of China, in the Years 1794 & 1795; Taken From. 2010. 336p. pap. 31.75 *(978-1-140-72808-5(3))*; 348p. pap. 32.75 *(978-1-140-72809-2(1))* BiblioBazaar. (Gale ECCO, Print Editions).

CHINA—HISTORY—CHING DYNASTY, 1644-1912

see China—History—Qing Dynasty, 1644-1912

CHINA—HISTORY—QING DYNASTY, 1644-1912

see also Manchus

Asian Civilisations Museum (Singapore) Staff, contrib. by. Reign of the Kangxi Emperor: Conference Proceedings, Asian Civilisations Museum, Singapore, 21 March 2009. 2010. (CHI & ENG., Illus.). 159p. *(978-981-08-5193-4(6))* Asian Civilisations Museum.

Bickers, Robert. The Scramble for China: Foreign Devils in the Qing Empire, 1332-1914. 2011. (ENG., Illus.). 512p. 45.00 *(978-0-7139-9749-1(4)*, Penguin Global) Penguin Group (USA) Inc.

Blakiston, Thomas Wright. Five Months on the Yang-Tsze: With a Narrative of the Exploration of its Upper Waters & Notices of the Present Rebellions in China. 2010. (Cambridge Library Collection - Travel & Exploration Ser.). (ENG., Illus.). 436p. pap. 34.99 *(978-1-108-01361-1(9))* Cambridge Univ. Pr.

Ch'ien, Ssu-Ma. The Grand Scribe's Records, Volume IX: The Memoirs of Han China, Part II. Nienhauser, William H., Jr., ed. 2010. (ENG., Illus.). 496p. 59.95 *(978-0-253-35590-4(7), 0253355907)* Indiana Univ. Pr.

Cochran, Sherman & Pickowicz, Paul G. China on the Margins. 2010. (ENG.). 336p. 50.00 *(978-1-933947-16-7(0))*; pap. 25.00 *(978-1-933947-46-4(2))* Cornell Univ. East Asia Program.

Cram101 Textbook Reviews Staff. Outlines & Highlights for the Search for Modern China by Jonathan D Spence, Antonina Krass, Isbn: 9780393973518. 2009. 72p. pap. 27.95 *(978-1-4288-9449-5(7))* Cram101 Inc.

Dai, Yi. A Concise History of the Qing Dynasty, 4 vols. (Concise History of the Qing Dynasty Ser.). (ENG.). Vol. 1. 2011. 296p. 128.00 *(978-981-4332-18-7(6))* Vol. 14. 2012. 1280p. 458.00 ***(978-981-4339-78-0(4))*** Enrich Professional Publishing (S)., Ltd. SGP. (Silkroad Pr.). Dist: Independent Pubs. Group.

Dai, Yingcong. The Sichuan Frontier & Tibet: Imperial Strategy in the Early Qing. 2009. (ENG., Illus.). 368p. 80.00 *(978-0-295-98951-8(3))*; pap. 30.00 *(978-0-295-98952-5(1))* Univ. of Washington Pr.

Deng. The Premodern Chinese Economy. 2007. (Illus.). 440p. 43.95 *(978-0-415-45864-1(1))* Routledge.

Deng, Zhanyun. Qing Dai de Yi Bai Ge Lao Bai Xing. 2009. (CHI.). *(978-7-5034-2259-1(9))* China Culture and History Pr.

Giles, Herbert A. China & the Manchus. 2012. (ENG.). 162p. pap. 19.99 ***(978-1-107-60602-9(0))*** Cambridge Univ. Pr.

—China & the Manchus. 2007. (ENG.). 84p. per. *(978-1-4065-4456-5(6))* Dodo Pr.

—China & the Manchus. 2010. 70p. 25.56 *(978-1-169-22101-7(7))*; pap. 13.56 *(978-1-162-65781-3(2))*; 31.95 *(978-1-161-42646-5(9))* Kessinger Publishing LLC.

Giles, Herbert Allen. China & the Manchus. 2010. (ENG.). 166p. pap. 21.75 *(978-1-177-62636-1(5))* BiblioBazaar.

—China & the Manchus. 2009. 72p. pap. *(978-1-151-69252-8(2))* Books LLC.

—China & the Manchus. 2010. (Illus.). 56p. pap. 20.00 *(978-1-4432-0303-6(3))* General Bks. LLC.

Guy, R. Kent. Qing Governors & Their Provinces: The Evolution of Territorial Administration in China, 1644-1796. 2010. (ENG & MUL., Illus.). 512p. (C). 80.00 *(978-0-295-99018-7(X))*; pap. 45.00 *(978-0-295-99019-4(6))* Univ. of Washington Pr.

Han, Xin. Zi Jin Cheng Jian Zheng, 2 vols. 2009. (CHI., Illus.). 434p. *(978-7-80168-490-5(7))* Study Publishing Hse.

Hayter-Menzies, Grant. Imperial Masquerade: The Legend of Princess der Ling. 2008. (ENG., Illus.). 444p. (gr. 17). 35.00 *(978-962-209-881-7(9))* Hong Kong Univ. Pr. HKG. Dist: Columbia Univ. Pr.

C

Horner, Charles. Rising China & Its Postmodern Fate: Memories of Empire in a New Global Context. 2011. (Studies in Security & International Affairs Ser.). (ENG.). 240p. pap. 24.95 (978-0-8203-3878-1(8)) Univ. of Georgia Pr.

Hung, Ho-Fung. Protest with Chinese Characteristics: Demonstration, Riots, & Petitions in the Mid-Qing Dynasty. 2011. (ENG., Illus.). 288p. (gr. 17). 50.00 (978-0-231-15202-0(7)) Columbia Univ. Pr.

Jin, Xingyao. Qing Dai Bi Huo L. 2010. (CHI.). pap. (978-7-80047-919-9(6)) Forbidden City Publishing Hse.

—Qing Dai Gong Ting Zheng Bian. 2010. (CHI.). (978-7-80047-926-7(9)) Forbidden City Publishing Hse.

Knoll, Arthur J. German Colonial Experience: Select Documents on German Rule in Africa, China, & the Pacific, 1884-1914. 2010. (ENG.). 564p. pap. 61.99 (978-0-7618-3900-2(3)) Univ. Pr. of America, Inc.

Mungello, David E. The Great Encounter of China & the West, 1500-1800. 3rd ed. 2009. (Critical Issues in World & International History Ser.). (ENG., Illus.). 184p. 79.00 (978-0-7425-5797-0(9)); pap. 24.95 (978-0-7425-5798-7(7)) Rowman & Littlefield Publishers, Inc.

Rhoads, Edward J. M. Stepping Forth into the World: The Chinese Educational Mission to the United States, 1872-81. 2011. (ENG., Illus.). 332p. (gr. 17). 45.00 (978-988-8028-86-3(3)); pap. 25.00 (978-988-8028-87-0(1)) Hong Kong Univ. Pr. HKG. Dist: Columbia Univ. Pr.

Su, Tongbing. Qing Dai Shi Shi Yu Ren Wu. 2010. (CHI.). (978-7-80047-921-2(8)) Forbidden City Publishing Hse.

Suzhou da xue, Tu shu guan Staff, contrib. by. Qi Xian Xie Zhen: Suzhou Da Xue Tu Shu Guan Cang Qing Dai Ren Wu Tu Xiang Xuan. 2008. (Illus.). (978-7-300-09168-6(7)) China Renmin Univ.Pr.

Xu, Guangyuan. Da Qing Huang Ling Mi Shi. 2010. (Illus.). 16p. (978-7-5077-3423-2(4)) Xueyuan Press.

Yi, Dai. A Concise History of the Qing Dynasty, 4 vols. 2011. (Concise History of the Qing Dynasty Ser.). (ENG.). Vol. 2. 224p. 128.00 **(978-981-4332-19-4(4))** Vol. 3. 336p. 128.00 **(978-981-4332-20-0(8))** Enrich Professional Publishing (S), Ltd. SGP. (Silkroad Pr.). Dist: Independent Pubs. Group.

Zhang, Jing. Wan Qing Xuan Guan Zhi du Bian Ge Yan Jiu. 2010. (CHI.). (978-7-5102-0236-0(1)) Zhongguo Jiancha Chubanshe.

Zhang, Wei-Bin. The Rise & Fall of China's Last Dynasty: The Deepening of the Chinese Servility. 2011. (Focus on Civilizations & Cultures Ser.). ix, 237p. 85.00 (978-1-61209-510-3(0)) Nova Science Pubs., Inc.

Zhang, Yu. Qing Dai Zhong Qi Chongqing de Shange Ye Gui Ze Yu Zhi Xu: Yi Ba Xian Dang an Wei Zhong Xin de Yan Jiu. 2010. (CHI.). 18p. (978-7-5620-3590-9(3)) China Univ. of Political Science and Law Pr.

Zheng, Yangwen. China on the Sea. 2011. (MUL., Illus.). 362p. **(978-90-04-19477-9(0))** BRILL.

CHINA—HISTORY—19TH CENTURY

see also China—History—Taiping Rebellion, 1850-1864; Sino-French War, 1884-1885

Bassin, Mark. Imperial Visions: Nationalist Imagination & Geographical Expansion in the Russian Far East, 1840-1865. 2006. (Cambridge Studies in Historical Geography Ser.). (ENG., Illus.). 348p. pap. 69.00 (978-0-521-02674-1(1)) Cambridge Univ. Pr.

Bellér-Hann, I. & Bellér-Hann, Ildikó. Community Matters in Xinjiang, 1880-1949: Towards a Historical Anthropology of the Uyghur. 2008. (China Studies). (Illus.). 500p. (978-90-04-16675-2(0)) BRILL.

Bergère, Marie-Claire. Shanghai: China's Gateway to Modernity. Lloyd, Janet, tr. from FRE. 2009. (ENG., Illus.). 520p. 80.00 (978-0-8047-4904-6(3)) Stanford Univ. Pr.

Bergere, Marie-Claire. Shanghai: China's Gateway to Modernity. Lloyd, Janet, tr. from FRE. 2009. (ENG., Illus.). 520p. pap. 29.95 (978-0-8047-4905-3(1)) Stanford Univ. Pr.

Bland, J. O. P. & Backhouse, Edmund. China under the Empress Dowager: The History of the Life & Times of Tzu Hsi. 2011. (ENG.). 552p. pap. 24.99 (978-988-18667-4-5(X)) Earnshaw Bks. HKG. Dist: Independent Pubs. Group.

Cram101 Textbook Reviews. Outlines & Highlights for Chinas Path to Modernization: A Historical Review from 1800 to the Present by Vohra. 2011. 62p. pap. 27.95 **(978-1-61906-228-3(3))** Cram101 Inc.

Crossley & Crossley, Pamela Kyle. The Wobbling Pivot, China since 1800: An Interpretive History. 2010. (Wiley Desktop Editions Ser.). (ENG., Illus.). 328p. pap. 35.95 (978-1-4051-6080-3(2), Wiley-Blackwell) Wiley, John & Sons, Inc.

Crossley, Pamela Kyle. The Wobbling Pivot, China since 1800: An Interpretive History. 2010. (ENG., Illus.). 328p. 99.95 (978-1-4051-6079-7(9), Wiley-Blackwell) Wiley, John & Sons, Inc.

Duan, Yunzhang & Ni, Junming. Chen Jiongming. 2009. (CHI., Illus.). (978-7-218-06590-8(2)) Guangdong Peoples Publishing Hse.

Duanmu, Cixiang. Na Yi Ci, Wo Men Ai Da Le: Zhong Ying Di Yi Ci Ya Pian Zhan Zheng Quan Jing Jie Du. 2007. (CHI., Illus.). (978-7-203-05973-8(1)) Shaanxi People's Publishing Hse.

Edgerton-Tarpley, Kathryn. Tears from Iron: Cultural Responses to Famine in Nineteenth-Century China. 2007. (Asia: Local Studies / Global Themes Ser.). (Illus.). 332p. 45.00 (978-0-520-25302-5(7)) Univ. of California Pr.

Elleman, Bruce & Paine, S. C. M. Modern China: Continuity & Change, 1644 to the Present. 2009. (ENG.). 528p. (C). pap. 64.80 (978-0-13-600060-0(6), Prentice Hall) Prentice Hall PTR.

Fagg, John Gerardus. Forty Years in South Chin. 2010. 326p. pap. 30.95 (978-1-4455-8325-9(9)) Research Pr.

Fenby, Jonathan. Modern China: The Fall & Rise of a Great Power, 1850 to the Present. 2009. 816p. pap. 19.99 (978-0-06-166117-4(1), HarperPerennial) HarperCollins Pubs.

—Modern China: The Fall & Rise of a Great Power, 1850 to the Present. 2008. 816p. 34.95 (978-0-06-166116-7(3), Ecco) HarperCollins Pubs.

Gao, James Z. The A to Z of Modern China (1800-1949) 2010. (A to Z Guide Ser.). (ENG.). 586p. pap. 34.45 (978-0-8108-7642-2(6)) Scarecrow Pr., Inc.

Gao, James Zheng. Modern China, 1800-1949. Gao/Woronoff, ed. 2009. (Historical Dictionaries of Ancient Civilizations & Historical Eras Ser.). (ENG., Illus.). 584p. 132.00 (978-0-8108-4930-3(5)) Scarecrow Pr., Inc.

Grasso, June, et al. Modernization & Revolution in China: From the Opium Wars to the Olympics. 4th rev. ed. 2009. (ENG., Illus.). 352p. (C). 94.95 (978-0-7656-2390-4(0)); pap. 37.95 (978-0-7656-2391-1(9)) Sharpe, M.E. Inc. (East Gate Bk.).

Hirth, Friedrich. The Mystery of Fu-lin. 2010. 83.84 (978-1-61143-449-1(1)); pap. 19.72 (978-1-61143-151-3(4)) Gorgias Pr., LLC.

Hoe, Susanna & Roebuck, Derek. The Taking of Hong Kong: Charles & Clara Elliot in China Waters. 2009. (Echoes: Classics of Hong Kong Culture & History Ser.). (ENG., Illus.). 312p. (gr. 17). pap. 28.00 (978-962-209-988-3(2)) Hong Kong Univ. Pr. HKG. Dist: Columbia Univ. Pr.

Isett, Christopher M. State, Peasant, & Merchant in Qing Manchuria, 1644-1862. 2006. (ENG., Illus.). 440p. 65.00 (978-0-8047-5271-8(0)) Stanford Univ. Pr.

Israeli, Raphael. Dabry de Thiersant. 2011. 344p. pap. **(978-3-8443-1563-9(2))** Lambert Academic Publishing.

Jarman, Robert L. Shanghai Political & Economic Reports, 1842-1943: British Government Records from the International City, 18 vols. 2008. (ENG., Illus.). 13500p. 9095.00 (978-1-84097-210-8(6)) Archive Editions, Ltd. GBR. Dist: Cambridge Univ. Pr.

King, Richard, et al, eds. Sino Japanese Transculturation: Late Nineteenth Century to the End of the Pacific War. 2011. (ENG.). 316p. (gr. 17). 75.00 **(978-0-7391-7150-9(X))** Lexington Bks.

Knight, Michael & Chan, Dany. Shanghai: Art of the City. 2010. (ENG., Illus.). 300p. 49.00 (978-0-939117-52-9(5)) Asian Art Museum of San Francisco.

Leibovitz, Liel & Miller, Matthew. Fortunate Sons: The 120 Chinese Boys Who Came to America, Went to School, & Revolutionized an Ancient Civilization. 2011. (ENG., Illus.). 320p. 26.95 (978-0-393-07004-0(2), 7004) Norton, W. W. & Co., Inc.

Leung, Pak-Wah. Managing China's Modernization: Perspectives on Diplomacy, Politics, Education & Ethnicity. 2011. (978-1-931907-74-3(9)) Homa & Sekey Bks.

Lu, Di. Bai Nian Chun Dong: Cong Lin Zexu Dao Sun Zhongshan. 2010. (CHI.). 473p. pap. (978-962-8744-49-7(6)) Mirror Bks. USA.

Mcpherson, D. War in China. 2009. (Illus.). 313p. 27.95 (978-1-935501-07-7(0)) Lancer International, Lancer Pr. IND. Dist: Casemate Pubs. & Bk. Distributors, LLC.

Miles, Steven B. The Sea of Learning: Mobility & Identity in Nineteenth-Century Guangzhou. 2006. (Harvard East Asian Monographs: 269). (Illus.). 450p. 49.95 (978-0-674-02134-1(7)) Harvard Univ., Asia Ctr.

Ouchterlony, Lie. Chinese War. 2009. (Illus.). 653p. 27.95 (978-1-935501-04-6(6)) Lancer International, Lancer Pr. IND. Dist: Casemate Pubs. & Bk. Distributors, LLC.

Qian, Nanxiu, et al. Different Worlds of Discourse: Transformations of Gender & Genre in Late Qing & Early Republican China. 2008. (China Studies: Vol. 16). (Illus.). 350p. (978-90-04-16776-6(5)) BRILL.

Schoppa, R. Keith. Revolution & Its Past: Identities & Change in Modern Chinese History. 3rd ed. 2010. (ENG.). 496p. (C). pap. 72.20 (978-0-205-72691-2(7), Prentice Hall) Prentice Hall PTR.

Wagner, Rudolf G., ed. Joining the Global Public: Word, Image, & City in Early Chinese Newspapers, 1870-1910. 2007. (SUNY Series in Chinese Philosophy & Culture). (CHI & ENG., Illus.). 249p. 80.00 (978-0-7914-7117-3(9)) State Univ. of New York Pr.

White, Trumbull. War in the East. 2010. 687p. 27.95 (978-1-935501-08-4(9)) Lancer International, Lancer Pr. IND. Dist: Casemate Pubs. & Bk. Distributors, LLC.

Williams, S. Wells. The Middle Kingdom: A Survey of the Geography, Government, Literature, Social Life, Arts & History of the Chinese Empire & Its in Habitants, 2 vols. 2006. (Kegan Paul China Library). (Illus.). 892p. 500.00 (978-0-7103-1167-2(2)) Taylor & Francis Group.

Yener, Emir. From the Sail to the Steam. 2010. 168p. pap. (978-3-8383-4899-5(0)) Lambert Academic Publishing.

Yi, Hong-Born. Asian Millenarianism: An Interdisciplinary Study of the Taiping & Tonghak Rebellions in a Global Context. 2007. (ENG.). 468p. (C). 114.95 (978-1-934043-42-4(7)) Cambria Pr.

CHINA—HISTORY—TAIPING REBELLION, 1850-1864

Boulger, Demetrius Charles. The Life of Sir Halliday Macartney, K. C. M. G. Commander of Li Hung Chang's Trained Force in the Taeping Rebellion, Founder of the First Chinese Arsenals, for Thirty Years Councillor & Secretary to the Chinese Legation in London. 2011. (Cambridge Library Collection - Travel & Exploration Ser.). (Illus.). 571p. pap. 39.99 **(978-1-108-02626-0(5))** Cambridge Univ. Pr.

Chesney, Charles Cornwallis. Essays in Military Biography, by Charles Cornwallis Chesney. 2006. 408p. per. 26.99 (978-1-4255-4344-0(8)) MPublishing.

Cornaby, W. Arthur. A String of Chinese Peach-Stones. 2010. (Cambridge Library Collection - Travel & Exploration Ser.). (Illus.). 500p. pap. 37.99 (978-1-108-01410-6(0)) Cambridge Univ. Pr.

Curwen, C. A. Taiping Rebel: The deposition of Li Hsiu-ch'eng. 2009. (Cambridge Studies in Chinese History, Literature & Institutions Ser.). (ENG.). 368p. pap. 38.99 (978-0-521-10486-9(6)) Cambridge Univ. Pr.

Mackie, J. Milton. Life of Tai-Ping-Wang, Chief of the Chinese Insurrection. 2007. (ENG.). 384p. per. 33.95 (978-1-4304-4443-5(6)) Kessinger Publishing, LLC.

Platt, Stephen R. Autumn in the Heavenly Kingdom: China, the West, & the Epic Story of the Taiping Civil War. 2012. (Vintage Ser.). (ENG., Illus.). 512p. pap. 16.95 **(978-0-307-47221-2(3)**, Vintage) Knopf Doubleday Publishing Group.

Wilson, Andrew. The 'Ever-Victorious Army' A History of the Chinese Campaign under Lt. Col. C. G. Gordon & of the Suppression of the Tai-Ping Rebellion. 2010. (Cambridge Library Collection - History Ser.). (Illus.). 472p. pap. 34.99 (978-1-108-02407-5(6)) Cambridge Univ. Pr.

Yi, Hong-Born. Asian Millenarianism: An Interdisciplinary Study of the Taiping & Tonghak Rebellions in a Global Context. 2007. (ENG.). 468p. (C). 114.95 (978-1-934043-42-4(7)) Cambria Pr.

Yu-Wen, Jen. The Taiping Revolutionary Movement. 2009. 650p. 97.00 (978-1-59740-743-4(7)); 648p. pap. 64.00 (978-1-59740-765-6(8)) ACLS Humanities E-Book.

CHINA—HISTORY—BOXER REBELLION, 1899-1901

Archibald, Alicia E. Neva. In the Land of the Blue Gown. 2010. (Cambridge Library Collection - Travel & Exploration Ser.). (ENG.). 396p. pap. 31.99 (978-1-108-01386-4(4)) Cambridge Univ. Pr.

Bickers, Robert, ed. The Boxers, China, & the World. 2007. (ENG., Illus.). 260p. 80.00 (978-0-7425-5394-1(9)) Rowman & Littlefield Publishers, Inc.

Bickers, Robert A. & Tiedemann, R. G., eds. The Boxers, China, & the World. 2007. (ENG., Illus.). 260p. pert. 31.95 (978-0-7425-5395-8(7)) Rowman & Littlefield Publishers, Inc.

Brown, Frederick. From Tientsin to Peking with the Allied Forces. 2009. 62p. pap. (978-1-151-31583-0(4)) Books LLC.

Edwards, E. H. Fire & Sword in Shansi: The Story of the Martyrdom of Foreigners & Chinese Christians. 2010. 430p. pap. 35.75 (978-1-142-22342-7(6)) BiblioBazaar.

Martin, William A. P. The Siege in Peking: Inside the Legations During the Boxer Uprising by One of the Besieged. 2010. 124p. (978-0-85706-076-1(7)); pap. (978-0-85706-075-4(9)) Leonaur Ltd.

Purcell, Victor. The Boxer Uprising: A Background Study. 2010. (ENG., Illus.). 364p. pap. 29.99 (978-0-521-14812-2(X)) Cambridge Univ. Pr.

Silbey, David J. The Boxer Rebellion & the Great Game in China, 1 vol. 2012. (ENG., Illus.). 304p. 26.95 **(978-0-8090-9477-6(0)**, Hill & Wang) Farrar, Straus & Giroux.

Spurny, Till. Die Plünderung Von Kulturgütern in Peking 1900-1901. 2008. (GER.). 113p. (978-3-86573-360-3(3), Spotlight Poets) Gaudig, Olaf, u. Klaus-Peter Veit, wvb Wissenschaftlicher Verlag Berlin.

Tan, Chester C. The Boxer Catastrophe: Columbia Studies in the Social Sciences, No. 583. 2011. 286p. 48.95 **(978-1-258-07637-5(3))** Literary Licensing, LLC.

Tuttle, A. H. Mary Porter Gamewell & the Siege of Peking: An American Lady's Experiences of the Boxer Uprising, China 1900. 2010. 208p. (978-0-85706-138-6(0)); pap. (978-0-85706-137-9(2)) Leonaur Ltd.

Wilson, James Harrison. Under the Old Flag: Recollections of Military Operations in the War for the Union, the Spanish War, the Boxer Rebellion, Etc., 2 vol., set. reprint ed. 250.00 (978-0-7222-9394-2(1)) Library Reprints, Inc.

CHINA—HISTORY—20TH CENTURY

Auerbach, Sascha J., et al. Race, Law, & the Chinese Puzzle in Imperial Britain. 2009. (ENG., Illus.). 280p. 95.00 (978-0-230-60949-5(X)) Palgrave Macmillan.

Backhouse, Edmund Trelawny. Decadence Mandchoue: The China Memoirs of Sir Edmund Trelawny Backhouse. Sandhaus, Derek, ed. 2011. (ENG.). 336p. 39.99 (978-988-19445-1-1(1)) Earnshaw Bks. HKG. Dist: Independent Pubs. Group.

Bailey, Paul John. Gender & Education in China: Gender Discourses & Women's Schooling in the Early Twentieth Century. 2007. (Routledge Contemporary China Ser.: Vol. 15). (Illus.). X, 246p. 170.00 (978-0-415-40283-5(2)) Routledge.

Belden, Jack. Still Time to Die. 2010. 332p. 36.76 (978-1-163-37700-0(7)) 2010. 332p. pap. 24.76 (978-1-162-79496-9(8)) 2007. (ENG.). 330p. 45.95 (978-0-548-06729-1(5)) Kessinger Publishing, LLC.

Benton, Gregor. Mao Zedong & the Chinese Revolution. 2007. XXIV, 416p. (978-0-415-44480-4(2)); X, 450p. (978-0-415-44483-5(7)); VIII, 442p. (978-0-415-44481-1(0)) Routledge.

Benton, Gregor, ed. Mao Zedong & the Chinese Revolution, 4 vols. 2007. (Critical Concepts in Asian Studies). 1936p. 1275.00 (978-0-415-40054-1(6)); 560p. (978-0-415-44484-2(5)) Routledge.

Benton, Gregor, intro. Reporting the Chinese Revolution: The Letters of Rayna Prohme. 2007. (ENG., Illus.). 216p. 37.00 (978-0-7453-2642-9(0)) Pluto Pr. GBR. Dist: Macmillan.

Bergère, Marie-Claire. Shanghai: China's Gateway to Modernity. Lloyd, Janet, tr. from FRE. 2009. (ENG., Illus.). 520p. 80.00 (978-0-8047-4904-6(3)) Stanford Univ. Pr.

Bergere, Marie-Claire. Shanghai: China's Gateway to Modernity. Lloyd, Janet, tr. from FRE. 2009. (ENG., Illus.). 520p. pap. 29.95 (978-0-8047-4905-3(1)) Stanford Univ. Pr.

Bing, Xu. Xu Bing, 1 vol. 2012. (ENG., Illus.). 280p. 85.00 **(978-0-9568670-0-1(6))** Albion Editions GBR. Dist: D.A.P./Distributed Art Pubs.

Bland, John Otway Percy & Backhouse, E. Recent Events & Present Policies in China. 596p. 2010. pap. 35.96 (978-1-167-02730-7(2)) 2010. 47.96 **(978-1-167-14393-9(0))** 2009. 59.95 (978-1-120-84840-6(7)) 2009. pap. 44.95 (978-1-120-68776-0(4)) Kessinger Publishing, LLC.

Bob Tadashi Wakabayashi Staff. The Nanking Atrocity 1937-38: Complicating the Picture. 2007. (Illus.). 456p. 39.95 (978-1-84545-500-2(2)) Berghahn Bks., Inc.

Brady, Anne-Marie & Brown, Douglas, eds. Foreigners & Foreign Institutions in Republican China. 2012. (Chinese Worlds Ser.). (ENG., Illus.). 320p. (C). 135.00 **(978-0-415-52865-8(8))** Routledge.

Brown, Jeremy. Dilemmas of Victory: The Early Years of the People's Republic of China. Pickowicz, Paul G., ed. & contrib. by. by. Wakeman, Frederic, Jr. et al, contrib. by. 2010. (Illus.). 480p. pap. 23.95 (978-0-674-04702-0(8)) Harvard Univ. Pr.

Chan, Leo Tak-hung. Twentieth Century Chinese Translation Theory: Modes, Issues & Debates. (Benjamins Translation Library: Vol. 51). xvi, 277p. 144.00 (978-1-58811-511-9(9)) Benjamins, John Publishing Co.

Cheek, Timothy. Living with Reform: China Since 1989. 2007. (Global History of the Present Ser.). (ENG., Illus.). 224p. 94.95 (978-1-84277-722-0(X)); per. 26.95 (978-1-84277-723-7(8)) Zed Bks., Ltd. GBR. Dist: Macmillan.

Chen. My Life's Journey: Reflections of an ... 2007. 82.00 (978-981-270-811-3(1)) World Scientific Publishing Co., Inc.

Chen, Dameng & Liu, Shi. Luo Jing Xia Shi: Zhong Cha Gaogang An. 2008. (CHI., Illus.). 429p. (978-1-932138-75-7(7)) Mirror Bks. USA.

Chen, Janet. Guilty of Indigence - the Urban Poor in China, 1900-1953. 2012. (ENG., Illus.). 320p. (C). 45.00 **(978-0-691-15210-3(1))** Princeton Univ. Pr.

Cheng & Lestz & Cram101 Textbook Reviews Staff. The Search for Modern Chin. 2007. 192p. per. 13.95 (978-1-4288-2234-4(8)) Cram101 Inc.

Cochran, Sherman & Pickowicz, Paul G. China on the Margins. 2010. (ENG.). 336p. 50.00 (978-1-933947-16-7(0)); pap. 25.00 (978-1-933947-46-4(2)) Cornell Univ. East Asia Program.

Cody, Jeffrey W., et al, eds. Chinese Architecture & the Beaux-Arts. 2010. (Illus.). 408p. (978-988-8028-71-9(5)) Hong Kong Univ. Pr.

Cohen, Paul A. Speaking to History: The Story of King Goujian in Twentieth-Century China. 2010. (Asia: Local Studies / Global Themes Ser.). (ENG., Illus.). 384p. pap. 25.95 (978-0-520-26583-7(1)) Univ. of California Pr.

Cram101 Textbook Reviews. Outlines & Highlights for Chinas Path to Modernization: A Historical Review from 1800 to the Present by Vohra. 2011. 62p. pap. 27.95 **(978-1-61906-228-3(3))** Cram101 Inc.

Cram101 Textbook Reviews Staff. Outlines & Highlights for the Search for Modern China by Jonathan D Spence, Antonina Krass, Isbn: 9780393973518. 2009. 72p. pap. 27.95 (978-1-4288-9449-5(7)) Cram101 Inc.

Crossley & Crossley, Pamela Kyle. The Wobbling Pivot, China since 1800: An Interpretive History. 2010. (Wiley Desktop Editions Ser.). (ENG., Illus.). 328p. pap. 35.95 (978-1-4051-6080-3(2), Wiley-Blackwell) Wiley, John & Sons, Inc.

Crossley, Pamela Kyle. The Wobbling Pivot, China since 1800: An Interpretive History. 2010. (ENG., Illus.). 328p. 99.95 (978-1-4051-6079-7(9), Wiley-Blackwell) Wiley, John & Sons, Inc.

Cunningham, Philip. Tiananmen Moon: Inside the Chinese Student Uprising Of 1989. 2010. (Asian Voices Ser.). (ENG.). 320p. pap. 19.95 (978-0-7425-6673-6(0)) Rowman & Littlefield Publishers, Inc.

Davies, John Paton. China Hand: An Autobiography. 2012. (Haney Foundation Ser.). (Illus.). 376p. 34.95 **(978-0-8122-4401-4(X))** Univ. of Pennsylvania Pr.

Dikötter, Frank. The Age of Openness: China before Mao. 2008. 140p. pap. (978-962-209-920-3(3)); pap. (978-0-520-25881-5(9)) Hong Kong Univ. Pr.

Dillon, Michael. Xinjiang & Expansion of Chinese Comm Power. 2011. (Routledge Studies in the Modern History of Asia Ser.). (ENG.). 256p. (C). 140.00 (978-0-415-58443-2(4)) Routledge.

Dillon, Nara & Oi, Jean C., eds. At the Crossroads of Empires: Middlemen, Social Networks, & State-Building in Republican Shanghai. 2007. (ENG.). 328p. 50.00 (978-0-8047-5619-8(8)) Stanford Univ. Pr.

Ding, Kaiwen. Bai Nian Lin Biao. 2007. (CHI., Illus.). 642p. (978-1-932138-54-2(4)) Mirror Bks. USA.

Dingle, Edwin. Across China on Foot. 2007. 300p. (ENG.). 98.99 (978-1-4280-7717-1(0)); per. 91.99 (978-1-4280-7715-7(4)) IndyPublish.com.

Driscoll, Mark. Absolute Erotic, Absolute Grotesque: The Living, Dead, & Undead in Japan's Imperialism, 1895-1945. 2010. (ENG., Illus.). 384p. 89.95 (978-0-8223-4740-8(7)); pap. 24.95 (978-0-8223-4761-3(X)) Duke Univ. Pr.

Edwards, E. H. Fire & Sword in Shansi: The Story of the Martyrdom of Foreigners & Chinese Christians. 2010. 430p. pap. 35.75 (978-1-142-22342-7(6)) BiblioBazaar.

Elleman, Bruce. Moscow & the Emergence of Communist Power in China, 1925-30: The Nanchang Uprising & the Birth of the Red Army. 2010. pap. 39.95 (978-0-415-59052-5(3)) Routledge.

Elleman, Bruce & Paine, S. C. M. Modern China: Continuity & Change, 1644 to the Present. 2009. (ENG.). 528p. (C). pap. 64.80 (978-0-13-600060-0(6), Prentice Hall) Prentice Hall PTR.

Fenby, Jonathan. Modern China: The Fall & Rise of a Great Power, 1850 to the Present. 2009. 816p. pap. 19.99 (978-0-06-166117-4(1), HarperPerennial) HarperCollins Pubs.

—Modern China: The Fall & Rise of a Great Power, 1850 to the Present. 2008. 816p. 34.95 (978-0-06-166116-7(3), Ecco) HarperCollins Pubs.

Feuchtwang, Stephan. After the Event: The Transmission of Grievous Loss in Germany, China & Taiwan. 2011. 246p. 95.00 (978-0-85745-086-9(7)) Berghahn Bks., Inc.

Fitzgerald, Stephen & Hewitt, Pamela. China in the Seventies: Australian Perspectives. (Illus.). iv, 187 p. (978-0-908160-92-1(5)) Bow Historical Bks.

French, Paul. Carl Crow - A Tough Old China Hand: The Life, Times, & Adventures of an American in Shanghai. 2006. (ENG., Illus.). 324p. (gr. 17).

35.00 *(978-962-209-802-2(9))* Hong Kong Univ. Pr. HKG. Dist: Columbia Univ. Pr.

Gao, James Z. The A to Z of Modern China (1800-1949) 2010. (A to Z Guide Ser.). (ENG.). 586p. pap. 34.45 *(978-0-8108-7642-2(6))* Scarecrow Pr., Inc.

Gao, James Zheng. Modern China, 1800-1949. Gao/Woronoff, ed. 2009. (Historical Dictionaries of Ancient Civilizations & Historical Eras Ser.). (ENG., Illus.). 584p. 132.00 *(978-0-8108-4930-3(5))* Scarecrow Pr., Inc.

Gao, Shuhua & Cheng, Tiejun. Nei Meng Wen Ge Feng Lei: Yi Wei Zao Fan Pai Ling Xiu de Kou Shu Shi. 2007. (Zhen Xiang Xi Lie Ser.: Vol. 41). (CHI., Illus.). 592p. pap. *(978-1-932138-56-6(0))* Mirror Bks. USA.

Goodman, Bryna & Goodman, David Sg, eds. Twentieth Century Colonialism & China: Localities, the Everyday, & the World. 2012. (ENG., Illus.). 272p. (C). 150.00 ***(978-0-415-68798-0(5))***; pap. 44.95 ***(978-0-415-68799-7(3))*** Routledge.

Grasso, June, et al. Modernization & Revolution in China: From the Opium Wars to the Olympics. 4th rev. ed. 2009. (ENG., Illus.). 352p. (C). 94.95 *(978-0-7656-2390-4(0))*; pap. 37.95 *(978-0-7656-2391-1(9))* Sharpe, M.E. Inc. (East Gate Bk.).

Hayter-Menzies, Grant. The Empress & Mrs. Conger: The Uncommon Friendship of Two Women & Two Worlds. 2011. (Illus.). 364p. ***(978-988-220-649-6(2))*** Hong Kong Univ. Pr.

Hewitt, Duncan. China: Getting Rich First: A Modern Social History. 2009. (ENG., Illus.). 480p. pap. 16.95 *(978-1-60598-061-4(7)*, 605061) Pegasus Bks.

Hinton, William. Through a Glass Darkly: American Views of the Chinese Revolution. 2006. (ENG.). 288p. per. 19.95 *(978-1-58367-141-2(2))* Monthly Review Pr.

Hua, Yu. China in Ten Words. 2012. (ENG.). 240p. pap. 15.00 ***(978-0-307-73979-7(1)***, Vintage) Knopf Doubleday Publishing Group.

Jarman, Robert L. Shanghai Political & Economic Reports, 1842-1943: British Government Records from the International City, 18 vols. 2008. (ENG., Illus.). 13500p. 9095.00 *(978-1-84097-210-8(6))* Archive Editions, Ltd. GBR. Dist: Cambridge Univ. Pr.

Johnson, Tina. Childbirth in Republican China: Delivering Modernity. 2011. (ENG., Illus.). 268p. 65.00 *(978-0-7391-6440-2(6))* Lexington Bks.

Johnson, Tina Phillips. Childbirth in Republican China: Delivering Modernity. 2011. (Illus.). xliv, 223p. E-Book ***(978-0-7391-6442-6(2))*** Lexington Bks.

Johnston, Reginald F. Twilight in the Forbidden City. 2011. (Cambridge Library Collection - History Ser.). (ENG., Illus.). 572p. pap. 43.00 *(978-1-108-02965-0(5))* Cambridge Univ. Pr.

Johnston, Reginald Fleming. Twilight in the Forbidden City. 2008. (Illus.). 488p. per. 28.95 *(978-0-9680459-5-4(2))* Soul Care Publishing CAN. Dist: Ingram Bk. Co.

Jowett, Philip. Chinese Warlord Armies, 1911-30. 2010. (Men-at-Arms Ser.). (ENG., Illus.). 48p. pap. 17.95 *(978-1-84908-402-4(5))* Osprey Publishing, Ltd. GBR. Dist: Random Hse., Inc.

Karl, Rebecca E. Mao Zedong & China in the Twentieth-Century World: A Concise History. 2010. (Asia-Pacific: Culture, Politics, & Society Ser.). (ENG.). 216p. 74.95 *(978-0-8223-4780-4(6))*; pap. 21.95 *(978-0-8223-4795-8(4))* Duke Univ. Pr.

King, Dean. Unbound: A True Story of War, Love, & Survival. 2010. (ENG., Illus.). 432p. 25.99 *(978-0-316-16708-6(8))* Little Brown & Co.

Knight, Michael & Chan, Dany. Shanghai: Art of the City. 2010. (ENG., Illus.). 300p. 49.00 *(978-0-939117-52-9(5))* Asian Art Museum of San Francisco.

Kuo, Ya-pei. Cultural Wars in Interwar China. 2013. (Routledge/Leiden Series in Modern East Asian History & Politics Ser.). (ENG.). 176p. (C). 130.00 *(978-0-415-55241-7(9))* Routledge.

Lam, Adam. Identity, Tradition & Globalism - Post-Cultural Revolution Chinese Feature Films 1977- 1996. 2008. 316p. pap. *(978-3-639-11106-4(0))* VDM Verlag Dr. Mueller e.K.

Lary, Diana. China's Republic. (New Approaches to Asian History Ser.). (ENG., Illus.). 242p. 2007. per. 34.99 *(978-0-521-60355-3(2))* 2006. 99.00 *(978-0-521-84256-3(5))* Cambridge Univ. Pr.

—Warlord Soldiers: Chinese Common Soldiers, 1911-1937. 2010. (Contemporary China Institute Publications). (ENG.). 188p. pap. 27.99 *(978-0-521-13629-7(6))* Cambridge Univ. Pr.

Lary, Diana, et al, eds. The Scars of War: The Impact of Warfare on Modern China. (ENG., Illus.). 224p. *(978-0-7748-0840-8(3))* Univ. of British Columbia Pr.

Lee, Ching Kwan & Yang, Guobin, eds. Re-Envisioning the Chinese Revolution: The Politics & Poetics of Collective Memories in Reform China. 2007. (ENG., Illus.). 320p. per. 24.95 *(978-0-8047-5853-6(0))* Stanford Univ. Pr.

—Re-Envisioning the Chinese Revolution: The Politics & Poetics of Collective Memory in Reform China. 2007. (ENG., Illus.). 320p. 60.00 *(978-0-8047-5852-9(2))* Stanford Univ. Pr.

Leese, Daniel. Mao Cult: Rhetoric & Ritual in the Cultural Revolution. 2011. (ENG., Illus.). 328p. 90.00 *(978-0-521-19367-2(2))* Cambridge Univ. Pr.

Leibold, James. Reconfiguring Chinese Nationalism: How the Qing Frontier & Its Indigenes Became Chinese. 2007. (ENG.). 288p. 95.00 *(978-1-4039-7479-2(9))* Palgrave Macmillan.

Leung, Edwin Pak-Wah. The A to Z of the Chinese Civil War. 2010. (A to Z Guide Ser.). (ENG.). 240p. pap. 34.45 *(978-0-8108-7627-9(2))* Scarecrow Pr., Inc.

Leung, Pak-Wah. Managing China's Modernization: Perspectives on Diplomacy, Politics, Education & Ethnicity. 2011. *(978-1-931907-74-3(9))* Homa & Sekey Bks.

Li, Gongqin. Bai Nian Da Ye: Zhonghua Minguo Fa Zhan Shi. 2010. (CHI., Illus.). 336p. *(978-957-574-769-5(0))* Youth Cultural Publishing Co.

Li, Ni. Li Shi Shang Kou: Er Shi Nian You Pai Xun Fang Ji. 2008. (Zhen Xiang Xi Lie Ser.: Vol. 50). (CHI., Illus.). 305p. *(978-1-932138-79-5(X))* Mirror Bks. USA.

Lin, Hsiao-Ting. Modern China's Ethnic Frontiers: A Journey to the West. 2010. (Routledge Studies in the Modern History of Asia Ser.). (ENG., Illus.). 224p. (C). 125.00 *(978-0-415-58264-3(4))* Routledge.

Linebarger, Aul. Sun Yat Sen & the Chinese Republic. 2008. 424p. *(978-1-4437-2433-8(6))* 2006. 420p. per. *(978-1-4067-2836-1(5))* Read Bks. (Hesperides Pr.).

Liu, Xiaoyuan. Recast All under Heaven: Revolution, War, Diplomacy, & Frontier China in the 20th Century. 2010. (ENG., Illus.). 288p. 120.00 *(978-1-4411-6220-5(8))*; pap. 34.95 *(978-1-4411-3489-9(1))* Continuum International Publishing Group, Ltd. GBR. Dist: National Bk. Network.

Loughman, Thomas J. Sterling Clark in China. 2012. (ENG., Illus.). 64p. pap. 19.95 ***(978-0-300-17968-2(5))*** Yale Univ. Pr.

Lu, Di. Guo Gong Wei Zao de Li Shi: Ling Xiu Men Liu Xia de Mi Tuan. 2010. (Illus.). 407p. pap. ***(978-962-8744-20-6(8))*** Mirror Bks. USA.

Luna, Adrian. Bringing the Inside Out. 2008. 212p. per. *(978-3-8364-3587-1(X))* VDM Verlag Dr. Mueller e.K.

Lynch, Catherine, et al. Radicalism, Revolution, & Reform in Modern China: Essays in Honor of Maurice Meisner. 2011. (AsiaWorld Ser.). (ENG.). 260p. 70.00 *(978-0-7391-6572-0(0))* Lexington Bks.

—Radicalism, Revolution, & Reform in Modern China: Essays in Honor of Maurice Meisner. 2011. *(978-0-7391-6574-4(7))* Rowman & Littlefield Publishers, Inc.

Lynch, Michael. China: From Empire to People's Republic, 1900-49. 2nd rev. ed. 2010. (Illus.). 170p. pap. 29.50 *(978-1-4441-1012-8(8))* Hodder Education GBR. Dist: Trans-Atlantic Pubns., Inc.

MacFarquhar, Roderick & Schoenhals, Michael. Mao's Last Revolution. 2008. (Illus.). 752p. per. 23.50 *(978-0-674-02748-0(5)*, Belknap Pr.) Harvard Univ. Pr.

Mackerras, Colin. China in Transformation: 1900-1949. 2nd ed. 2008. (Seminar Studies in History Ser.). (ENG., Illus.). 216p. (C). pap. 28.20 *(978-1-4058-4058-3(7))* Longman Publishing Group.

MacKinnon, Stephen R. Wuhan 1938: War, Refugees, & the Making of Modern China. 2008. (Illus.). 182p. 45.00 *(978-0-520-25445-9(7))* Univ. of California Pr.

Meyer, Mahlon. Remembering China from Taiwan: Divided Families & Bittersweet Reunions after the Chinese Civil War. 2012. (ENG., Illus.). 252p. (gr. 17). 30.00 ***(978-988-8083-86-2(4))*** Hong Kong Univ. Pr. HKG. Dist: Columbia Univ. Pr.

Moise, Edwin E. Modern China. 3rd ed. 2008. (ENG., Illus.). 296p. (C). pap. 54.40 *(978-0-582-77277-9(X))* Longman Publishing Group.

Mote, Frederick W. China & the Vocation of History in the Twentieth Century: A Personal Memoir. 2010. (ENG., Illus.). 360p. (C). 29.95 *(978-0-691-14463-4(X))* Princeton Univ. Pr.

Mungello, D. E. Western Queers in China: Flight to the Land of Oz. 2012. (ENG.). 212p. (gr. 17). 60.00 ***(978-1-4422-1556-6(9))*** Rowman & Littlefield Publishers, Inc.

Pakula, Hannah. The Last Empress: Madame Chiang Kai-shek & the Birth of Modern China. 2010. (ENG., Illus.). 816p. pap. 20.00 *(978-1-4391-4894-5(5))* Simon & Schuster.

Pomfret, John. Chinese Lessons: Five Classmates & the Story of the New China. 2007. (ENG., Illus.). 336p. pap. 16.99 *(978-0-8050-8664-5(1)*, Holt Paperback) Holt, Henry & Co.

Qian, Nanxiu, et al. Different Worlds of Discourse: Transformations of Gender & Genre in Late Qing & Early Republican China. 2008. (China Studies: Vol. 16). (Illus.). 350p. *(978-90-04-16776-6(5))* BRILL.

Rubinfien, Leo, intro. Phantom Shanghai. 2007. (FRE & ENG., Illus.). 240p. 50.00 *(978-0-9739739-1-4(9))* Magenta Publishing for the Arts CAN. Dist: Consortium Bk. Sales & Distribution.

Rummel, R. China's Bloody Century: Genocide & Mass Murder Since 1900. 2007. (ENG., Illus.). 348p. (gr. 11). pap. 29.95 *(978-1-4128-0670-1(4))* Transaction Pubs.

Schoppa, R. Keith. Revolution & Its Past: Identities & Change in Modern Chinese History. 3rd ed. 2010. (ENG.). 496p. (C). pap. 72.20 *(978-0-205-72691-2(7)*, Prentice Hall) Prentice Hall PTR.

—Twentieth Century China: A History in Documents, 1 vol. 2nd ed. 2010. (Pages from History Ser.). (ENG., Illus.). 224p. (C). pap. 29.95 *(978-0-19-973200-5(0))* Oxford Univ. Pr., Inc.

Schwartz, Barry. Northeast Asia's Difficult Past: Essays in Collective Memory. Kim, Mikyoung, ed. 2010. (Palgrave Macmillan Memory Studies). (ENG., Illus.). 320p. 95.00 *(978-0-230-23747-6(9))* Palgrave Macmillan.

Shao, Dan. Remote Homeland, Recovered Borderland: Manchus, Manchoukuo, & Manchuria, 1907-1985. 2011. 55.00 *(978-0-8248-3445-6(3))* Univ. of Hawaii Pr.

Sharman, Lyon. Sun Yat-Sen, His Life & Its Meaning: A Critical Biography. 436p. 2010. pap. 29.56 *(978-1-163-17005-2(4))* 2008. 51.95 *(978-1-4366-9152-9(4))* 2007. (ENG.). per. 36.95 *(978-1-4325-7176-4(1))* Kessinger Publishing, LLC.

Shen, Shuang. Cosmopolitan Publics: Anglophone Print Culture in Semi-Colonial Shanghai. 2009. (ENG., Illus.). 204p. 39.95 *(978-0-8135-4542-4(0))* Rutgers Univ. Pr.

Sherwood, Jack. Fond Memories of a Young Man in Old Chin. 2009. 288p. pap. 17.49 *(978-1-4490-0894-9(1))* AuthorHouse.

Smith, Shirley Ann. Imperial Designs: Italians in China, 1900-1947. 2012. (Fairleigh Dickinson University Press Series in Italian Studies). (ENG.). 208p. (gr. 17). 65.00 ***(978-1-61147-501-2(5))***; ***(978-1-61147-502-9(3))*** Fairleigh Dickinson Univ. Pr.

Soepa, Tenpa. 20 Years of My Life in China's Death Camp. 2008. 180p. pap. 19.99 *(978-1-4343-5910-0(7))* AuthorHouse.

Spurling, Hilary. Pearl Buck in China: Journey to the Good Earth. 2010. (ENG., Illus.). 320p. 27.00 *(978-1-4165-4042-7(3))* Simon & Schuster.

Thaxton, Ralph A., Jr. Catastrophe & Contention in Rural China: Mao's Great Leap Forward Famine & the Origins of Righteous Resistance in Da Fo Village. 2008. (Cambridge Studies in Contentious Politics Ser.). (ENG., Illus.). 408p. pap. 28.99 *(978-0-521-72230-8(6))* Cambridge Univ. Pr.

Tse-Tung, Mao. Selected Works of Mao Tse-Tung, 5 vols., Set. (Illus.). 343p. *(978-0-08-022262-2(5)*, Pergamon) Elsevier Science & Technology.

University of Pittsburgh Chinese Studies Faculty Staff & University of Pittsburgh Chinese Studies Faculty, eds. Contemporary Chinese Societies: Continuity & Change, CD for Windows and Macintosh. 2nd ed. 2007. (Edinburgh Edition of the Waverley Novels Ser.). (ENG.). (gr. 17). 51.50 *(978-0-231-13982-3(9))* Columbia Univ. Pr.

Wagner, Rudolf G., ed. Joining the Global Public: Word, Image, & City in Early Chinese Newspapers, 1870-1910. 2007. (SUNY Series in Chinese Philosophy & Culture). (CHI & ENG., Illus.). 249p. 80.00 *(978-0-7914-7117-3(9))* State Univ. of New York Pr.

Wakabayashi, Bob Tadashi. The Nanking Atrocity, 1937-38: Complicating the Picture. 2007. (Asia Pacific Studies). pap. *(978-1-84545-259-9(3))* Berghahn Bks., Inc.

Wakabayashi, Bob Tadashi, ed. The Nanking Atrocity 1937-1938: Complicating the Picture. 2007. (Asia Pacific Studies). (Illus.). 456p. (C). 90.00 *(978-1-84545-180-6(5))* Berghahn Bks., Inc.

Wang, David Der-wei. The Monster That Is History. *(978-0-8047-3969-6(2))* Stanford Univ. Pr.

Wang, Guangyuan. Jiang Jieshi Yu Xin Jun Fa Hun Zhan. 2010. (CHI., Illus.). *(978-7-5034-2560-8(1))* China Culture and History Pr.

Wang, Hui. Ya Zhou Shi Ye: Zhongguo Li Shi de Xu Shu. 2010. (CHI.). xxiii, 331p. *(978-0-19-801928-2(9))* Oxford Univ. Pr., Inc.

Wang, Xiangkun. Du Dong Liu Shaoqi: Dudong Liiu Shaoqi. 2010. *(978-7-220-07989-4(3))* Sichuan Renmin Chubanshe.

Weale, B. L. Putnam. The Fight for the Republic in China. 2008. 452p. 32.99 *(978-0-554-22076-5(8))* 2007. (ENG.). 414p. pap. 26.99 *(978-1-4264-1608-8(3))* 2007. (ENG.). 450p. pap. 28.99 *(978-1-4264-1696-5(2))* BiblioBazaar.

Wells, Michael. History for the IB Diploma: Causes, Practices & Effects of Wars. 2011. (Ib Ser.). (ENG.). 240p. pap. 32.00 *(978-0-521-18931-6(4))* Cambridge Univ. Pr.

Wen, Wen. Guo Min Dang Zhong Yang Xun Lian Tuan Yu Jun Shi Gan Bu Xun Lian Tuan. 2010. (CHI., Illus.). 8p. *(978-7-5034-2558-5(X))* China Culture and History Pr.

Wen, Xiang. Kai Guo Yuan Xun Xiang Jian Ji: Mao Zedong Yu Zhan You Men. 2008. (CHI., Illus.). 389p. *(978-1-932138-78-8(1))* Mirror Bks. USA.

Wiseman, Alexander W., 2nd & Huang, Tiedan, 1st, eds. The Impact & Transformation of Education Policy in China. 2011. (International Perspectives on Education & Society Ser.). 350p. ***(978-1-78052-186-2(3))*** Emerald Group Publishing Ltd.

Wu, Emily & Engelmann, Larry. Feather in the Storm: A Childhood Lost in Chaos. 2008. (ENG., Illus.). 352p. pap. 14.95 *(978-0-307-27662-9(7)*, Anchor) Knopf Doubleday Publishing Group.

Wu, Nanying & Cheng, Yuxia. Zhongguo Xin Quan Gui Zhi Guan Fu Ren. 2009. "Zhongguo Zhang Quan Zhe" Xi Lie Ser.: Vol. 24). (CHI., Illus.). 414p. *(978-1-932138-81-8(1))* Mirror Bks. USA.

Xinran, Xinran. China Witness. 2010. (ENG., Illus.). 464p. pap. 16.95 *(978-0-307-38853-7(0)*, Anchor) Knopf Doubleday Publishing Group.

Xu, Guangqiu. Congress & the U. S.-China Relationship, 1949-1979. 2007. 410p. 59.95 *(978-1-931968-39-3(X))* Univ. of Akron Pr., The.

Xue er. Guo Yun 1909: Qing Di Guo de Gai Ge Tu Wei. 2010. (CHI., Illus.). 317p. *(978-7-5613-4906-9(8))* Shaanxi Normal Univ. Pr.

—Jue Ban Jia Wu: Cong Hai Wai Shi Liao Jie Mi Zhong Ri Zhan Zheng. 2009. (CHI., Illus.). 216p. *(978-7-80741-604-3(1))* Wenhui Chubanshe.

Yang, Shengqun, et al. Deng Xiaoping Nian Pu: Yi Jiu Ling Si — Yi Jiu Qi Si, 3 vols. 2009. (CHI.). *(978-7-5073-2768-7(X))*; *(978-7-5073-2767-0(1))* Central Party Literature Audio & Video Publishing Hse.

Yeh Wen-hsin. Shanghai Splendor: A Cultrual History, 1843-1945. 2008. (Illus.). 320p. pap. 26.95 *(978-0-520-25817-4(7))* Univ. of California Pr.

Yoshida, Takashi. The Making of the Rape of Nanking: History & Memory in Japan, China, & the United States. 2009. (ENG.). 280p. pap. 21.95 *(978-0-19-538314-0(1))* Oxford Univ. Pr., Inc.

Young, Helen Praeger. Choosing Revolution: Chinese Women Soldiers on the Long March. 2007. (Illus.). 304p. per. 26.00 *(978-0-252-07456-1(4))* Univ. of Illinois Pr.

Zarrow, Peter Gue. After Empire: The Conceptual Transformation of the Chinese State, 1885-1924. 2012. (ENG.). 416p. 65.00 ***(978-0-8047-7868-8(X))***; pap. 27.95 ***(978-0-8047-7869-5(8))*** Stanford Univ. Pr.

Zhao, Zhongwei & Guo, Fei, eds. Transition & Challenge: China's Population at the Beginning of the 21st Century. 2007. (ENG., Illus.). 364p. 125.00 *(978-0-19-929929-4(3))* Oxford Univ. Pr., Inc.

Zhongguo di 2 li shi dang an guan Staff, contrib. by. Bei Yang Zheng Fu Dang An, 188 vols. 2010. (CHI., Illus.). 18p. *(978-7-5105-0173-9(3))* China Archives Publishing Hse.

Zhou, Xun, ed. The Great Famine in China, 1958-1962: A Documentary History. 2012. (ENG., Illus.). 224p. 45.00 ***(978-0-300-17518-9(3))*** Yale Univ. Pr.

CHINA—HISTORY—MAY FOURTH MOVEMENT, 1919

Chen, Xiaoming. From the May Fourth Movement to Communist Revolution: Guo Moruo & the Chinese Path to Communism. (Illus.). 2008. xi, 156p. pap. 24.95 *(978-0-7914-7138-8(1))* 2007. 156p. 60.00 *(978-0-7914-7137-1(3))* State Univ. of New York Pr.

Chow, Kai-wing. Beyond the May Fourth Paradigm: In Search of Chinese Modernity. Hon/Price/Chow/Ip, ed. 2008. (ENG., Illus.). 352p. 83.99 *(978-0-7391-1122-2(1))* Lexington Bks.

Hockx, Michel. Literary Societies of Republican China. 2008. (ENG., Illus.). 602p. 120.99 *(978-0-7391-1933-4(8))* Lexington Bks.

Hockx, Michel & Denton, Kirk A. Literary Societies of Republican China. 2008. (ENG., Illus.). 602p. pap. 49.50 *(978-0-7391-1934-1(6))* Lexington Bks.

Li, Yongcun. Ein Blick ins Frauenleben der ersten 30 Jahre des 20. Jahrhunderts: Das Werk Lu Yins. 2009. (Europäische Hochschulschriften. Reihe 27: Asiatische und Afrikanische Studien Ser.). (GER.). 328p. pap. 79.95 *(978-3-631-59252-6(3))* Lang, Peter GmbH, Europaischer Verlag der Wissenschaften DEU. Dist: Lang, Peter.

Ni, Tingting. "Wu Si" Wen Xue Lun Ji. 2007. (Ji Ming Cong Shu Ser.). (CHI.). 7p. *(978-7-02-006719-0(0))* People's Literature Publishing Hse.

Zheng, Wei. What Is Enlightenment: Can China Answer Kant's Question? 2011. 131p. pap. 23.95 ***(978-1-4384-3106-2(6)***, Suny Pr.) 2010. 112p. 50.00 *(978-1-4384-3105-5(8))* State Univ. of New York Pr.

CHINA—HISTORY—1937-1949

see also Sino-Japanese Conflict, 1937-1945

Chuan Hua, Lowe. Japan's Economic Offensive in China. 2010. (ENG., Illus.). 192p. 100.00 *(978-0-415-58530-9(9))* Routledge.

Dobsons, Richard P. China Cycle. 2006. 236p. per. *(978-1-4067-3378-5(4)*, Hesperides Pr.) Read Bks.

Hlavacek, John. Letters Home: An American Reporter in China, 1939-1944. 2009. 272p. pap. 19.95 *(978-0-9819034-5-3(2)*, Hlucky Bks.) Concierge Marketing, Inc.

Hsieh, Chiao-Min. Race the Rising Sun: A Chinese University's Exodus during the Second World War. 2009. (ENG.). 214p. pap. 31.99 *(978-0-7618-4148-7(2))* Univ. Pr. of America, Inc.

Iris Chang & the Forgotten Holocaust. 2007. pap. 10.00 *(978-1-59343-060-3(4)*, Cozy Publishing Hse.) Cozy Graphics Corp.

Jingping, Wu. Select Telegrams Between Chiang Kai-Shek & T. V. Soong, 1940-1943. Kuo, Tai-chun, ed. 2008. (TV soong Ser.). (CHI & ENG., Illus.). 384p. pap. 15.00 *(978-7-309-05956-4(5))* Hoover Institution Pr.

Lary, Diana. The Chinese People at War: Human Suffering & Social Transformation, 1937-1945. 2010. (New Approaches to Asian History Ser.). (ENG., Illus.). 248p. (C). 95.00 *(978-0-521-19506-5(3))*; pap. 29.99 *(978-0-521-14410-0(8))* Cambridge Univ. Pr.

Lin, Zhi P. Secrets of China's Anti Japanese War. (CHI.). pap. 12.95 *(978-7-200-02664-1(6))* China International Bk. Trading Corp. CHN. Dist: Distribooks, Inc.

MacManus, James. Ocean Devil: The Life & Legend of George Hogg. 2008. (ENG., Illus.). 288p. 12.95 *(978-0-00-727075-0(5))* HarperCollins Pubs. Ltd. GBR. Dist: Independent Pubs. Group.

Martin, Barry S. Forgotten Aviator: The Adventures of Royal Leonard. 2011. 256p. pap. 15.95 ***(978-1-60844-929-3(7))*** Dog Ear Publishing, LLC.

Moreira, Peter. Hemingway on the China Front: His WWII Spy Mission with Martha Gellhorn. 2007. (Illus.). 256p. per. 17.95 *(978-1-57488-882-9(X))* Potomac Bks., Inc.

Pan, Jian. Wang Wei Zheng Quan Cai Zheng Yan Jiu. 2009. (CHI.). *(978-7-5004-8241-3(8))* China Social Sciences Pr.

Snow, Edgar. Random Notes on Red China, 1936-1945: Harvard East Asian Monographs, No. 5. 2011. 164p. 41.95 ***(978-1-258-09189-7(5))*** Literary Licensing, LLC.

Tamanoi, Mariko. Memory Maps: The State & Manchuria in Postwar Japan. 2008. (World of East Asia Ser.). (Illus.). 224p. (C). 51.00 *(978-0-8248-3267-4(1))* Univ. of Hawaii Pr.

Tse-Tung, Mao. Strategic Problems of China's Revolutionary War. 2011. 90p. 38.95 ***(978-1-258-00443-9(7))*** Literary Licensing, LLC.

Ushan, Michael V. China since World War II. 2008. (World History Ser.). (ENG., Illus.). 104p. (YA). (gr. 7-10). lib. bdg. 33.45 *(978-1-4205-0097-4(X))*, Lucent Bks.) Cengage Gale.

Weng, Wenhao & Li, Xuetong. Weng Wenhao Ri Ji. 2010. (CHI.). *(978-7-101-05979-3(1))* Zhonghua Bk. Co.

Williams, Frederick Vincent & Tanaka, Hideo. Chugoku No Senso Senden No Uchimaku: Nitchu Senso No Shinjitsu. 2009. (JPN., Illus.). 160p. *(978-4-8295-0467-3(6))* Fuyo Shobo Shuppan.

CHINA—HISTORY—CIVIL WAR, 1945-1949

Vol. 6: The Chinese Civil War: Gen. George C. Marshall's Mission to China, 1945-1947. Date not set. lib. bdg. 185.00 *(978-1-55655-572-5(5))* ProQuest LLC.

Caughey, John Hart & Jeans, Roger B. The Marshall Mission to China, 1945-1947: The Letters & Diary of Colonel John Hart Caughey. 2011. ***(978-1-4422-1296-1(9))*** Rowman & Littlefield Publishers, Inc.

C

Feuchtwang, Stephan. After the Event: The Transmission of Grievous Loss in Germany, China & Taiwan. 2011. 246p. 95.00 *(978-0-85745-086-9(7))* Berghahn Bks., Inc.

Hinton, William & Magdoff, Fred. Fanshen: A Documentary of Revolution in a Chinese Village. 2008. (ENG., Illus.). 672p. pap. 28.95 *(978-1-58367-175-7(7))* Monthly Review Pr.

Jeans, Roger. The Marshall Mission to China, 1945D1947: The Letters & Diary of Colonel John Hart Caughey. 2011. (ENG.). 324p. 84.00 *(978-1-4422-1294-7(2))* Rowman & Littlefield Publishers, Inc.

Lew, Christopher & Lew, Christopher R. The Chinese Third Revolutionary Civil War, 1945-49: An Analysis of Communist Strategy & Leadership. 2009. (Asian States & Empires Ser.). (ENG., Illus.). 208p. 160.00 *(978-0-415-77730-8(5))* Routledge.

Lew, Christopher R. The Third Chinese Revolutionary Civil War 194549. 2011. (ENG., Illus.). 208p. pap. 42.95 ***(978-0-415-67386-0(0))*** Routledge.

Meyer, Mahlon. Remembering China from Taiwan: Divided Families & Bittersweet Reunions after the Chinese Civil War. 2012. (ENG., Illus.). 252p. (gr. 17). 30.00 ***(978-988-8083-86-2(4))*** Hong Kong Univ. Pr. HKG. Dist: Columbia Univ. Pr.

Stuart, John Leighton & Chen, Lisong. Situ Leideng Ri Ji: Xiang Jian Shi Nan Bie Yi Nan. 2009. (CHI., Illus.). ***(978-7-5461-0241-2(3))*** Huangshan Publishing Hse.

Tanner, Harold M. The Battle for Manchuria & the Fate of China: Siping 1946. 2012. (Twentieth-Century Battles Ser.). (ENG., Illus.). 272p. 35.00 ***(978-0-253-00723-0(2)***, 0253007232) Indiana Univ. Pr.

Wang, Shuzeng. Jie Fang Zhan Zheng, 2 vols. 2009. (CHI., Illus.). *(978-7-02-007373-3(5)); (978-7-02-007358-0(1))* People's Literature Publishing Hse.

CHINA—HISTORY—1949-

see also Sino-Indian Border Dispute, 1957-

Baum, Richard. China Watcher: Confessions of a Peking Tom. 2010. (Samuel & Althea Stroum Book Ser.). (ENG., Illus.). 336p. 29.95 *(978-0-295-98997-6(1))* Univ. of Washington Pr.

Benson, Linda. China Since 1949. 2nd rev. ed. 2011. (Seminar Studies in History Ser.). (ENG., Illus.). 244p. (C). pap. 27.33 *(978-1-4082-3769-4(5))* Longman Publishing Group.

Chen, Yu. Zhongguo Sheng Huo Ji Yi: Jian Guo 60 Nian Min Sheng Wang Shi. 2009. (CHI., Illus.). 347p. pap. *(978-7-5019-7054-4(8))* China Light Industry Pr.

Gittings, John. The Changing Face of China: From Mao to Market. 2006. (ENG., Illus.). 384p. per. 19.95 *(978-0-19-280734-2(X))* Oxford Univ. Pr., Inc.

Greenhalgh, Susan. Cultivating Global Citizens: Population in the Rise of China. 2010. (Edwin O. Reischauer Lectures: 2008). (ENG., Illus.). 156p. 29.95 *(978-0-674-05571-1(3))* Harvard Univ. Pr.

Hu, Xianzhong. Yin Mou Xia de Ren Sheng. 2008. (CHI.). 274p. pap. 25.00 *(978-1-931550-24-6(7))* Laogai Research Foundation, The.

Leutner, Mechthild, ed. Rethinking China in the 1950s. 2008. (Chinese History & Society Ser.). (GER & ENG.). 184p. pap. 36.95 *(978-3-8258-0291-2(4))* Lit Verlag DEU. Dist: Transaction Pubs.

Li, Charles N. The Bitter Sea: Coming of Age in a China Before Mao. 2009. 304p. pap. 14.99 *(978-0-06-170954-8(9)*, HarperPerennial) HarperCollins Pubs.

Liao, Gailong & Luo, Zhufeng, eds. Who's Who in China: Current Leaders. 2nd ed. 1037p. *(978-7-119-00725-0(4))* Bow Historical Bks.

Liu, Heung Shing, ed. China: 25 Jahre TASCHEN. 2011. (25 Ser.). (ENG., Illus.). 424p. 29.99 ***(978-3-8365-3089-7(9))*** TASCHEN DEU. Dist: Ingram Pub. Services.

Lynch, Michael & Lynch, Michael J. The People's Republic of China, 1949-76. 2nd ed. 2008. (ENG., Illus.). 192p. pap. 17.95 *(978-0-340-92927-8(8))* Hodder Education GBR. Dist: Oxford Univ. Pr., Inc.

Pan, Philip P. Out of Mao's Shadow: The Struggle for the Soul of a New China. 2009. (ENG., Illus.). 368p. pap. 16.00 *(978-1-4165-3706-9(6))* Simon & Schuster.

Steinberg, David I. & Fan, Hongwei. Modern China-Myanmar Relations: Dilemmas of Mutual Dependence. 2012. (Illus.). 432p. ***(978-87-7694-095-9(0))***; pap. ***(978-87-7694-096-6(9))*** Nordic Institute of Asian Studies.

Strauss, Julia, ed. The History of the PRC (1949-1976) 2007. (China Quarterly Special Issues Ser.). (ENG., Illus.). 262p. per. 44.00 *(978-0-521-69696-8(8))* Cambridge Univ. Pr.

Su, Weimin. Yang Shangkun Tan Xin Zhongguo Ruo Gan Li Shi Wen Ti. 2010. (CHI.). *(978-7-220-07987-0(7))* Sichuan Renmin Chubanshe.

Sullivan, Lawrence R. The A to Z of the People's Republic of China. 2010. (A to Z Guide Ser.). (ENG.). 718p. pap. 34.45 *(978-0-8108-7645-3(0))* Scarecrow Pr., Inc.

—Historical Dictionary of the People's Republic of China. 2nd ed. 2007. (Historical Dictionaries of Asia, Oceania, & the Middle East Ser.). (ENG.). 720p. 139.00 *(978-0-8108-5380-5(9))* Scarecrow Pr., Inc.

Szonyi, Michael. Cold War Island: Quemoy on the Front Line. 2008. (ENG., Illus.). 328p. 95.00 *(978-0-521-89813-3(7))*; pap. 31.00 *(978-0-521-72640-5(9))* Cambridge Univ. Pr.

Teiwes, Frederick C. & Sun, Warren. The End of the Maoist Era: Chinese Politics During the Twilight of the Cultural Revolution, 1972-1976. 2007. (Politics of Transition in China, 1972-1982 Ser.). (ENG.). 728p. 128.95 *(978-0-7656-1096-6(5)*, East Gate Bk.) Sharpe, M.E. Inc.

Uschan, Michael V. China since World War II. 2008. (World History Ser.). (ENG., Illus.). 104p. (YA). (gr. 7-10). lib. bdg. 33.45 *(978-1-4205-0097-4(X)*, Lucent Bks.) Cengage Gale.

Vernoff, Edward & Seybolt, Peter J. Through Chinese Eyes: Tradition, Revolution, & Transformation. 3rd ed. 2007. (Eyes Books Ser.). (ENG.). 381p. (C). (gr. 13-17). 44.95 *(978-0-938960-52-2(0))*; (Illus.). pap. 24.95 *(978-0-938960-51-5(2))* Rowman & Littlefield Publishers, Inc.

Wemheuer, Felix. Steinnudeln: Landliche Erinnerungen und staatliche Vergangenheitsbewaltigung der <GroBen Sprung>-Hungersnot in der chinesischen Provinz Henan. (GER., Illus.). 294p. pap. 62.95 *(978-3-631-56279-6(9))* Lang, Peter GmbH, Europaischer Verlag der Wissenschaften DEU. Dist: Lang, Peter Publishing, Inc.

Womack, Brantly. China's Rise in Historical Perspective. 2010. (ENG.). 272p. pap. 29.95 *(978-0-7425-6722-1(2))* Rowman & Littlefield Publishers, Inc.

Womack, Brantly, ed. China's Rise in Historical Perspective. 2010. (ENG.). 272p. 85.00 *(978-0-7425-6721-4(4))* Rowman & Littlefield Publishers, Inc.

Wright, Patrick. Passport to Peking: A Very British Mission to Mao's China. 2010. (ENG., Illus.). 352p. 34.95 *(978-0-19-954193-5(0))* Oxford Univ. Pr., Inc.

Xing, Sherry. My Story. 2007. 292p. 19.95 *(978-1-58982-450-8(4)*, Millennial Mind Publishing) American Bk. Publishing Group.

Zhao. China's Reforms at 30 (V14) 2009. (Illus.). xiii, 200p. 38.00 *(978-981-283-424-9(9))* World Scientific Publishing Co., Inc.

Zhao, Xu. Jia Bian Gou Can An: Fang Tan Lu. 2008. (CHI.). 437p. pap. 35.00 *(978-1-931550-21-5(2))* Laogai Research Foundation, The.

Zhu, Zhiqun & Lampton, David M. The People's Republic of China Today: Internal & External Challenges. 2010. 400p. 122.00 *(978-981-4313-50-6(5))* World Scientific Publishing Co., Inc.

CHINA—HISTORY—CULTURAL REVOLUTION, 1966-1969

Andreas, Joel. Rise of the Red Engineers: The Cultural Revolution & the Origins of China's New Class. 2009. (Contemporary Issues in Asia & Pacific Ser.). (ENG.). 368p. 75.00 *(978-0-8047-6077-5(2))*; pap. 27.95 *(978-0-8047-6078-2(0))* Stanford Univ. Pr.

Chen, Ming-May Jessie & Haque, Mazharul. Representation of the Cultural Revolution in Chinese Films by the Fifth Generation Filmmakers: Zhang Yimou, Chen Kaige, & Tian Zhuangzhuang. 2007. 216p. *(978-0-7734-5511-5(6))* Mellen, Edwin Pr., The.

Cheng, Chi & Maxwell, Alexander J. Grassland Journal: Nomads & the Red Sun. 2007. (Illus.). viii, 777p. *(978-0-9723807-3-7(6))* Cheng, Charlie.

Chiu, Melissa & Shengtian, Zheng. Art & China's Revolution. 2008. (Illus.). 280p. 65.00 *(978-0-300-14064-4(9))* Yale Univ. Pr.

Chiu, Melissa & Zheng, Shengtian. Art & China's Revolution. 2008. pap. *(978-0-87848-108-8(7))* Yale Univ. Pr.

Clark, Paul. The Chinese Cultural Revolution: A History. 2008. (ENG., Illus.). 368p. 85.00 *(978-0-521-87515-8(3))*; pap. 24.99 *(978-0-521-69786-6(7))* Cambridge Univ. Pr.

Gehrig, Sebastian & Mittler, Barbara, eds. Kulturrevolution als Vorbild? Maoismen im deutschsprachigen Raum. 2008. (GER., Illus.). 222p. pap. 56.95 *(978-3-631-57641-0(2))* Lang, Peter GmbH, Europaischer Verlag der Wissenschaften DEU. Dist: Lang, Peter.

Goldstein, Melvyn C., et al. On the Cultural Revolution in Tibet: The Nyemo Incident of 1969. (ENG., Illus.). 264p. 2010. pap. 17.95 *(978-0-520-26790-9(7))* 2009. 40.00 *(978-0-520-25682-8(4))* Univ. of California Pr.

Hannum, Emily. Education & Reform in China. 2009. 290p. pap. 39.95 *(978-0-415-54705-5(9))* Routledge.

Hay, Jeff, ed. The Chinese Cultural Revolution. 2012. (Perspectives on Modern World History Ser.). (ENG., Illus.). 224p. (gr. 10-12). lib. bdg. 41.70 ***(978-0-7377-5787-3(6)***, Greenhaven Pr., Inc.) Cengage Gale.

—The People's Republic of China. 2012. (Genocide & Persecution Ser.). (ENG.). 240p. (gr. 10-12). lib. bdg. 34.60 ***(978-0-7377-6253-2(5)***, Greenhaven Pr., Inc.) Cengage Gale.

He, Shu. Wei Mao Zhu Xi Er Zhan: Wen Ge Chongqing Da Wu Dou Shi Lu. 2010. (Illus.). 357p. *(978-962-04-2995-8(8))* Joint Publishing Co.

Jian, Guo. Historical Dictionary of the Cultural Revolution. 2006. (Historical Dictionaries of Ancient Civilizations & Historical Eras Ser.: Vol. 17). (ENG., Illus.). 504p. 108.90 *(978-0-8108-5461-1(9))* Scarecrow Pr., Inc.

Jian, Guo, et al. The A to Z of the Chinese Cultural Revolution. 83rd ed. 2009. (A to Z Guide Ser.: No. 83). (ENG.). 504p. pap. 34.45 *(978-0-8108-6870-0(9))* Scarecrow Pr., Inc.

Jiehong, Jiang H. Red: China's Cultural Revolution. 2011. (ENG., Illus.). 252p. 59.95 *(978-0-224-08781-0(9))* Random Hse. GBR. Dist: Independent Pubs. Group.

King, Richard, ed. Art in Turmoil: The Chinese Cultural Revolution, 1966-76. 2010. (ENG., Illus.). 318p. pap. 35.95 *(978-0-7748-1543-7(4))* UBC Pr. CAN. Dist: Univ. of Washington Pr.

Kraus, Richard Curt. The Cultural Revolution. 2012. (Very Short Introductions Ser.). (ENG., Illus.). 144p. pap. 11.95 ***(978-0-19-974055-0(0))*** Oxford Univ. Pr., Inc.

Lam, Adam. Identity, Tradition & Globalism - Post-Cultural Revolution Chinese Feature Films 1977- 1996. 2008. 316p. pap. *(978-3-639-11106-4(0))* VDM Verlag Dr. Mueller e.K.

Larson, Wendy. From Ah Q to Lei Feng: Freud & Revolutionary Spirit in 20th Century China. 2008. (ENG., Illus.). 336p. 55.00 *(978-0-8047-0075-7(3))* Stanford Univ. Pr.

Leese, Daniel. Mao Cult: Rhetoric & Ritual in the Cultural Revolution. 2011. (ENG., Illus.). 328p. 90.00 *(978-0-521-19367-2(2))* Cambridge Univ. Pr.

Lu, Shu Jiang. When Huai Flowers Bloom. 2011. 202p. pap. 23.95 ***(978-0-7914-7232-3(9)***, Suny Pr.) State Univ. of New York Pr.

Lu, Shu Jiang. When Huai Flowers Bloom: Stories of the Cultural Revolution. 2007. 224p. 50.00 *(978-0-7914-7231-6(0))* State Univ. of New York Pr.

Ma, Yue. The Catastrophe Remembered by the Non-Traumatic. 2009. 124p. pap. *(978-3-639-16527-2(6))* VDM Verlag Dr. Mueller e.K.

MacFarquhar, Roderick & Schoenhals, Michael. Mao's Last Revolution. 2008. (Illus.). 752p. per. 23.50 *(978-0-674-02748-0(5)*, Belknap Pr.) Harvard Univ. Pr.

Mei, Zhencai. Wen Ge Shi Ci Gou Chen. 2010. (CHI., Illus.). 534p. ***(978-962-8744-48-0(8))*** Mirror Bks. USA.

Mittler, Barbara. A Continuous Revolution: Making Sense of Cultural Revolution Culture. 2012. (Harvard East Asian Monographs: 343). (ENG., Illus.). 500p. 59.95 ***(978-0-674-06581-9(6))*** Harvard Univ., Asia Ctr.

Palmer, James. Heaven Cracks, Earth Shakes: The Tangshan Earthquake & the Death of Mao's China. 2012. (ENG., Illus.). 296p. (gr. 9). 26.99 *(978-0-465-01478-1(X))* Basic Bks.

Park, Albert, ed. Education & Reform in China. 2007. (Illus.). 282p. 170.00 *(978-0-415-77095-8(5))* Routledge.

Persson, Stefan & Heden, Anne. Röd Stjärna över Sverige: Folkrepubliken Kina Som Resurs I Den Svenska Vänsterradikaliseringen under 1960- Och 1970-Talen. 2008. (SWE., Illus.). 354p. *(978-91-85767-11-3(5))* Sekel Bokforlag.

Pomfret, John. Chinese Lessons: Five Classmates & the Story of the New China. 2007. (ENG., Illus.). 336p. pap. 16.99 *(978-0-8050-8664-5(1)*, Holt Paperback) Holt, Henry & Co.

Shen, Fuxiang. Zheng Rong Sui Yue: Shou Bu Gong Ren Zao Fan Pai Hui Yi Lu. 2010. (CHI.). *(978-988-19142-4-8(8))* Time International Publishing Ltd.

Su, Yang. Collective Killings in Rural China during the Cultural Revolution. 2011. (Cambridge Studies in Contentious Politics Ser.). (ENG., Illus.). 320p. 90.00 *(978-0-521-19808-0(9))*; 312p. pap. 27.99 *(978-0-521-17381-0(7))* Cambridge Univ. Pr.

Tan, Yuci. An American-Spy Father & His Daughter in Communist China: The Hopes of Two Generations. 2008. (ENG., Illus.). 272p. pap. 17.95 *(978-1-57733-207-7(5))* Blue Dolphin Publishing, Inc.

Teiwes, Frederick & Sun, Warren. The End of the Maoist Era: Chinese Politics During the Twilight of the Cultural Revolution, 1972-1976. 2007. (Politics of Transition in China, 1972-1982 Ser.). (ENG.). 728p. pap. 54.95 *(978-0-7656-1097-3(3)*, East Gate Bk.) Sharpe, M.E. Inc.

Walder, Andrew G. Fractured Rebellion: The Beijing Red Guard Movement. 2009. (Illus.). 416p. 42.00 *(978-0-674-03503-4(8))* Harvard Univ. Pr.

Wang, Helen. Chairman Mao Badges: Symbols & Slogans of the Cultural Revolution. 2008. (British Museum Research Publication Ser.). (Illus.). 184p. (C). pap. 70.00 *(978-0-86159-169-5(0))* British Museum Pr. GBR. Dist: Brown, David Bk. Co., The.

Wolin, Richard. Wind from the East: French Intellectuals, the Cultural Revolution, & the Legacy of the 1960s. 2010. (ENG., Illus.). 408p. 35.00 *(978-0-691-12998-3(3))* Princeton Univ. Pr.

Wolin, Richard. The Wind from the East: French Intellectuals, the Cultural Revolution, & the Legacy of the 1960s. 2012. (ENG., Illus.). 408p. (C). pap. 24.95 ***(978-0-691-15434-3(1))*** Princeton Univ. Pr.

Wu, Emily & Engelmann, Larry. Feather in the Storm: A Childhood Lost in Chaos. 2008. (ENG., Illus.). 352p. pap. 14.95 *(978-0-307-27662-9(7)*, Anchor) Knopf Doubleday Publishing Group.

Wu, Guang. China 1966-1976, Cultural Revolution Revisit: Can It Happen Again? 2011. (China in the 21st Century Ser.). 69.00 *(978-1-61209-337-6(X))* Nova Science Pubs., Inc.

Zhou, Shaochang. Xing Xing Chong Xing Xing: "Fan You Yun Dong" Ji. 2008. ("Wen Hua Qing Li" Xi Lie Ser.: Vol. 24). (CHI.). 322p. *(978-1-932138-69-6(2))* Mirror Bks. USA.

CHINA—HISTORY—TIANANMEN SQUARE INCIDENT, 1989

Béja, Jean-Philippe. The Impact of China's 1989 Tiananmen Massacre. 2010. (China Policy Ser.). (ENG., Illus.). 272p. (C). 140.00 *(978-0-415-57872-1(8))* Routledge.

Cai, Zheng. Yi Ge Jie Fang Jun de 1989. 2009. (Zhen Xiang Xi Lie Ser.: Vol. 54). (CHI., Illus.). 244p. *(978-1-932138-90-0(0))* Mirror Bks. USA.

Cheng, Eddie. Standoff at Tiananmen: How Chinese Students Shocked the World with a Magnificent Movement for Democracy & Liberty that Ended in the Tragic Tiananmen Massacre In 1989. 2009. 308p. pap. 18.95 *(978-0-9823203-0-3(2))* Sensys.

Chong, Denise. Egg on Mao: A Story of Love, Hope & Defiance. 2011. (ENG., Illus.). 256p. pap. 19.95 ***(978-0-307-35580-5(2)***, Vintage Canada) Random Hse. of Canada, Ltd. CAN. Dist: Random Hse., Inc.

Cunningham, Philip J. Tiananmen Moon: Inside the Chinese Student Uprising of 1989. 2009. (Asian Voices Ser.). (ENG.). 320p. 39.95 *(978-0-7425-6672-9(2))* Rowman & Littlefield Publishers, Inc.

Deng, Fang. Unintended Outcomes of Social Movements: The 1989 Chinese Student Movement. 2010. (International Library of Sociology Ser.). (ENG., Illus.). 168p. (C). 140.00 *(978-0-415-77933-3(2))* Routledge.

Fewsmith, Joseph. China since Tiananmen: From Deng Xiaoping to Hu Jintao. 2nd rev. ed. 2008. (Cambridge Modern China Ser.). (ENG., Illus.). 352p. (C). 75.00 *(978-0-521-86693-4(6))*; pap. 25.99 *(978-0-521-68605-1(9))* Cambridge Univ. Pr.

Gan, Cui. Yi Lin Chao. 2009. (CHI., Illus.). 259p. *(978-1-931550-31-4(X))* Laogai Research Foundation, The.

Jiang, Qisheng. Yi Sheng Shuo Zhen Hua. 2009. (CHI., Illus.). 466p. *(978-1-931550-32-1(8))* Laogai Research Foundation, The.

Kai Yee, Chan. Tiananmen's Tremendous Achievements: The Silent, Peaceful Coup D'état in China. 2011. 316p. 32.95 *(978-1-4502-8665-7(8))*; pap. 22.95 *(978-1-4502-8664-0(X))* iUniverse, Inc.

Kong, Belinda. Tiananmen Fictions outside the Square: The Chinese Literary Diaspora & the Politics of Global Culture. 2012. (Asian American History & Culture Ser.). (ENG., Illus.). 278p. pap. 26.95 ***(978-1-4399-0759-7(5))*** Temple Univ. Pr.

—Tiananmen Fictions Outside the Square: The Chinese Literary Diaspora & the Politics of Global Culture. 2012. E-Book ***(978-1-4399-0760-3(9))*** Temple Univ. Pr.

Liang, Diane Wei. Lake with No Name: A True Story of Love & Conflict in Modern China. 2009. (ENG., Illus.). 320p. pap. 14.00 *(978-1-4391-3686-7(6))* Simon & Schuster.

MacFarquhar, Roderick. Prisoner of the State: The Secret Journal of Premier Zhao Ziyang. 2009. (CHI., Illus.). 382p. pap. *(978-957-13-5052-3(4))* China Times Publishing Co.

CHINA—HISTORY—RETURN OF HONG KONG, 1997

see Hong Kong (China)—History—Transfer of Sovereignty from Great Britain, 1997

CHINA—HISTORY—21ST CENTURY

Brown, Kerry. Struggling Giant: China in the 21st Century. 2007. (China in the 21st Century Ser.). (ENG., Illus.). 169p. per. 22.95 *(978-1-84331-278-9(6))* Anthem Pr. GBR. Dist: Books International, Inc.

Cheek, Timothy. Living with Reform: China Since 1989. 2007. (Global History of the Present Ser.). (ENG., Illus.). 224p. 94.95 *(978-1-84277-722-0(X))*; per. 26.95 *(978-1-84277-723-7(8))* Zed Bks., Ltd. GBR. Dist: Macmillan.

China Photographers' Association Staff, et al. China's Thirty Years. 2011. (CHI & ENG., Illus.). 372p. 65.00 *(978-0-19-800897-2(X))* Oxford Univ. Pr., Inc.

Crossley & Crossley, Pamela Kyle. The Wobbling Pivot, China since 1800: An Interpretive History. 2010. (Wiley Desktop Editions Ser.). (ENG., Illus.). 328p. pap. 35.95 *(978-1-4051-6080-3(2)*, Wiley-Blackwell) Wiley, John & Sons, Inc.

Crossley, Pamela Kyle. The Wobbling Pivot, China since 1800: An Interpretive History. 2010. (ENG., Illus.). 328p. 99.95 *(978-1-4051-6079-7(9)*, Wiley-Blackwell) Wiley, John & Sons, Inc.

Dodson, Bill. China Inside Out: 10 Irreversible Trends Reshaping China & Its Relationship with the World. 2011. (ENG.). 200p. 29.95 *(978-0-470-82643-0(6)*, Wiley) Wiley, John & Sons, Inc.

Greenfeld, Karl Taro. China Syndrome: The True Story of the 21st Century's First Great Epidemic. 2007. 464p. pap. 14.99 *(978-0-06-058723-9(7)*, HarperPerennial) HarperCollins Pubs.

Guo, Sujian. China's 'Peaceful Rise'in the 21st Century: Domestic & International Conditions. 2006. 284p. 130.00 *(978-0-7546-4847-5(8))* Ashgate Publishing Co.

Hua, Yu. China in Ten Words. Barr, Allan H., tr. from CHI. 2011. (ENG.). 240p. 25.95 *(978-0-307-37935-1(3)*, Pantheon) Knopf Doubleday Publishing Group.

Hui, Wang. The End of the Revolution: China & the Limits of Modernity. 2011. (ENG.). 272p. pap. 22.95 *(978-1-84467-379-7(0)*, 844379) Verso Bks. GBR. Dist: Norton, W. W. & Co., Inc.

Kissinger, Henry, et al. Does the 21st Century Belong to China? The Munk Debate on China. 2011. (ENG.). 112p. pap. 14.95 ***(978-1-77089-062-6(9))*** House of Anansi Pr. CAN. Dist: Perseus-PGW.

Knight, Michael & Chan, Dany. Shanghai: Art of the City. 2010. (ENG., Illus.). 300p. 49.00 *(978-0-939117-52-9(5))* Asian Art Museum of San Francisco.

Merkel-Hess, Kate, et al. China in 2008: A Year of Great Significance. Merkel-Hess, ed. 2009. (ENG., Illus.). 344p. 55.00 *(978-0-7425-6659-0(5))*; pap. 29.95 *(978-0-7425-6660-6(9))* Rowman & Littlefield Publishers, Inc.

Wang, Mengkui. Zhongguo Gai Ge 30 Nian: 1978-2008. 2009. (CHI., Illus.). *(978-7-80234-434-1(4))* China Development Pr.

Wasserstrom, Jeffrey N. China in the 21st Century: What Everyone Needs to Know. 2010. (What Everyone Needs to Know Ser.). (ENG., Illus.). 224p. pap. 16.95 *(978-0-19-539412-2(7))* Oxford Univ. Pr., Inc.

Weiwei, Ai, et al. Art & Cultural Policy in China: A Conversation between Ai Weiwei, Uli Sigg & Yung Ho Chang, moderated by Peter Pakesch. 2009. (GER & ENG., Illus.). 132p. pap. 39.95 *(978-3-211-89240-4(0))* Springer Wien AUT. Dist: Actar Birkhauser Distribution.

Wiseman, Alexander W., 2nd & Huang, Tiedan, 1st, eds. The Impact & Transformation of Education Policy in China. 2011. (International Perspectives on Education & Society Ser.). 350p. ***(978-1-78052-186-2(3))*** Emerald Group Publishing Ltd.

Wu, Nanying & Cheng, Yuxia. Zhongguo Xin Quan Gui Zhi Guan Fu Ren. 2009. ("Zhongguo Zhang Quan Zhe" Xi Lie Ser.: Vol. 24). (CHI., Illus.). 414p. *(978-1-932138-81-8(1))* Mirror Bks. USA.

Xiaoxia, Li & Wolff, Martin, eds. China - Today's Thinking of Tomorrow's Leaders. 2011. (China in the 21st Century Ser.). 129.00 *(978-1-61209-677-3(8))* Nova Science Pubs., Inc.

Zhao, Quansheng. Managing the China Challenge: Global Perspectives. Liu, Guoli, ed. 2008. (Asian Security Studies). (Illus.). XVI, 264p. 160.00 *(978-0-415-46573-1(7))* Routledge.

CHINA—HISTORY, MILITARY

Allan, James. Under the Dragon Flag: My Experiences in Chino-Japanese War. 2006. 76p. pap. 16.99 *(978-1-4264-0275-3(9))* BiblioBazaar.

Barnes, A. A. S. The on Active Service with the Chinese Regiment: a Record Of. 2007. pap. 26.95 *(978-1-4304-9619-9(3))* Kessinger Publishing, LLC.

Boulay, N. W. H. Du. An Epitome of the Chino-Japanese War, 1894-95. 2010. 78p. pap. *(978-1-84574-823-4(9))* Naval & Military Pr., The.

Bussert, James. People's Liberation Army Navy. 2011. 256p. 36.95 *(978-1-59114-080-1(3))* Naval Institute Pr.

Cheung, Tai Ming, ed. China's Emergence as a Defense Technological Power. 2012. (ENG.). 208p. 140.00 ***(978-0-415-51984-7(5))*** Routledge.

De Crespigny, Rafe. Imperial Warlord: A Biography of Cao Cao 155-220 AD. 2010. (Sinica Leidensia Ser.). (Illus.). 600p. *(978-90-04-18522-7(4))* BRILL.

Di Cosmo, Nicola, ed. Military Culture in Imperial China. 2011. (ENG., Illus.). 456p. pap. 22.95 *(978-0-674-06072-2(5))* Harvard Univ. Pr.

Di Cosmo, Nicola & Dzengseo. The Diary of a Manchu Soldier in Seventeenth-Century China. annot. ed. 2006. (Routledge Studies in the Early History of Asia: Vol. 4). (ENG., Illus.). 154p. (C). (gr. 13). 168.00 *(978-0-7007-1611-1(4)*, RU30686) Routledge.

Filipiak, Kai. Krieg, Staat und Militar in der Ming-Zeit (1368-1644) Auswirkungen militarischer und bewaffneter Konflikte auf Machtpolitik und Herrschaftsapparat der Ming-Dynastie. 2008. (Opera Sinologica Ser.). (GER., Illus.). 348p. (C). pap. 117.00 *(978-3-447-05852-0(8))* Harrassowitz, Otto Verlag DEU. Dist: ISD.

Garrett, Richard J. The Defences of Macau: Forts, Ships, & Weapons over 450 Years. 2010. (ENG.). 288p. (gr. 17). 60.00 *(978-962-209-993-7(9))* Hong Kong Univ. Pr. HKG. Dist: Columbia Univ. Pr.

Garrett, Richard J. The Defences of Macau: Forts, Ships & Weapons over 450 Years. 2010. (Illus.). 288p. ***(978-988-8028-49-8(8))*** Hong Kong Univ. Pr.

—The Defences of Macau: Forts, Ships & Weapons over 450 Years. 2010. (ENG., Illus.). 288p. (gr. 17). pap. 30.00 *(978-988-8028-49-8(9))* Hong Kong Univ. Pr. HKG. Dist: Columbia Univ. Pr.

Graff. The Eurasian Way of War. 2011. (Asian States & Empires Ser.). (ENG.). 208p. (C). 150.00 *(978-0-415-46034-7(4))* Routledge.

Graff, David A. & Higham, Robin, eds. A Military History of China. 2nd ed. 2012. (ENG., Illus.). 344p. pap. 25.00 ***(978-0-8131-3584-7(2))*** Univ. Pr. of Kentucky.

Hase, P. H. The Six-Day War of 1899: Hong Kong in the Age of Imperialism. 2008. (Royal Asiatic Society Hong Kong Studies Ser.). (ENG., Illus.). 304p. (gr. 17). 45.00 *(978-962-209-899-2(1))* Hong Kong Univ. Pr. HKG. Dist: Columbia Univ. Pr.

Holmes, Linda Goetz. Guests of the Emperor: The Secret History of Japan's Mukden POW Camp. 2010. (Illus.). 192p. 29.95 *(978-1-59114-377-2(2))* Naval Institute Pr.

Jackson, Daniel. The Forgotten Squadron: The 449th Fighter Squadron in World War II Flying P-38s with the Flying Tigers, 14th AF. 2010. (Illus.). 256p. 69.99 *(978-0-7643-3537-2(5))* Schiffer Publishing, Ltd.

Jaw, Peter. Taiwan vs China 1958. 2009. 48p. pap. 19.49 *(978-1-4389-5729-6(7))* AuthorHouse.

Jiang, Kefu. Minguo Jun Shi Shi: A Military History of the Republic of China, 4 vols. 2009. (CHI.). *(978-7-229-00838-3(7))*; *(978-7-229-00840-6(9))*; *(978-7-229-00841-3(7))*; *(978-7-229-00839-0(5))* Chongqing Publishing Hse.

Jowett, Philip. Chinese Warlord Armies, 1911-30. 2010. (Men-at-Arms Ser.). (ENG., Illus.). 48p. pap. 17.95 *(978-1-84908-402-4(5))* Osprey Publishing, Ltd. GBR. Dist: Random Hse., Inc.

Jowett, Philip. Soldiers of the White Sun: The Chinese Army at War 1931-1949. 2011. (Illus.). 208p. 59.99 ***(978-0-7643-3956-1(7))*** Schiffer Publishing, Ltd.

Kamphausen, Roy, et al, eds. The People in the PLA: Recruitment, Training, & Education in China's Military. 2008. pap. *(978-1-58487-354-9(X))* Strategic Studies Institute, U.S. Army War College Commandant (AWCC-DSI/Pubns.).

Kane, Thomas. Ancient China on Post Modern War: Enduring Ideas from the Chinese Strategic Tradition. 2007. (Cass Military Studies). 193p. 160.00 *(978-0-415-38479-7(6))* Routledge.

Langellier, John. US Armed Forces in China 1856-1941. 2009. (Men-at-Arms Ser.). (ENG., Illus.). 48p. pap. 17.95 *(978-1-84603-493-0(0))* Osprey Publishing, Ltd. GBR. Dist: Random Hse., Inc.

Lary, Diana. Warlord Soldiers: Chinese Common Soldiers, 1911-1937. 2010. (Contemporary China Institute Publications). (ENG.). 188p. pap. 27.99 *(978-0-521-13629-7(6))* Cambridge Univ. Pr.

Li, Ling. Wei Yi de Gui Ze: "Sunzi" de Dou Zheng Zhe Xue. 2010. (CHI.). lxiii, 242p. *(978-962-996-442-9(2))* Chinese Univ. Pr. The.

Li, Xiaobing. China at War: An Encyclopedia. 2012. (Illus.). xxxiv, 605p. E-Book ***(978-1-59884-416-0(4))*** ABC-CLIO, LLC.

Li, Xiaobing. A History of the Modern Chinese Army. 2009. (ENG.). 432p. pap. 27.95 *(978-0-8131-9240-6(4))* Univ. Pr. of Kentucky.

Li, Xiaobing, ed. China at War: An Encyclopedia, 1 vol. 2012. (Illus.). 605p. 100.00 *(978-1-59884-415-3(6)*, A2846C) ABC-CLIO, LLC.

Li, Yu & Wen, Ming. Yi Ye Zhu Li Chuan Qi: Yiyezhuli Chuanqi. 2010. (CHI., Illus.). 360p. *(978-7-5460-0143-2(9))* Huang Publishing Hse.

Liu, Guoxiang. Zhongguo Gu Dai Zhan Lue Jia Ji Qi Zhu Zuo Jie du: Zhong Guo Gu Dai Zhan Lue Jia Ji Qi Zhu Zuo Jie Du. 2009. (CHI., Illus.). *(978-7-80752-471-7(5))* Bashu Publishing Hse.

Liu, Tong. Kua Hai Zhi Zhan: Jinmen, Hainan, Yijiangshan. 2010. (CHI., Illus.). pap. *(978-7-108-03199-0(X))* SDX Joint Publishing, Co.

Long, Jianyu. Mao Zedong, Jiang Jieshi de Ren Sheng Dao Lu. 2010. (CHI., Illus.). *(978-7-80257-117-4(0))* ET Pr.

Lorge, Peter & Roy, Kaushik, eds. Chinese & Indian Warfare â¿¿ from the Classical Age To 1870. 2012. (Asian States & Empires Ser.). (ENG.). 352p. (C). 160.00 ***(978-0-415-50244-3(6))*** Routledge.

Lu, Di. Mao Zhu Xi Yong Bing Zhen Ru Shen? 2011. (CHI.). 621p. ***(978-1-935981-25-1(0))*** Mirror Bks. USA.

Luard, Tim. Escape from Hong Kong: Admiral Chan Chak's Christmas-Day Dash 1941. 2012. (Royal Asiatic Society Hong Kong Studies Ser.). (ENG., Illus.). 384p. (gr. 17). 38.00 ***(978-988-8083-76-3(7))*** Hong Kong Univ. Pr. HKG. Dist: Columbia Univ. Pr.

McNeal, Robin. Conquer & Govern: Early Chinese Military Texts from the Yi Zhou shu. 2012. 240p. 48.00 ***(978-0-8248-3120-2(9))*** Univ. of Hawaii Pr.

Muscolino, Micah S. Fishing Wars & Environmental Change in Late Imperial & Modern China. 2009. (Harvard East Asian Monographs: 325). (Illus.). 300p. 39.95 *(978-0-674-03598-0(4))* Harvard Univ., Asia Ctr.

Olender, Piotr. Sino-French Naval War 1884-1885. 2012. (Maritime Ser.). (Illus.). 144p. pap. 39.00 ***(978-83-61421-53-5(X))*** Stratus, Wydawnictwo, Juszczak, Artur PCL. Dist: Casemate Pubs. & Bk. Distributors, LLC.

Peattie, Mark, et al, eds. The Battle for China: Essays on the Military History of the Sino-Japanese War Of 1937-1945. 2010. (ENG., Illus.). 664p. 65.00 *(978-0-8047-6206-9(6))* Stanford Univ. Pr.

Petroff, Serge P. Life Journey: A Family Memoir. 2008. 288p. 30.95 *(978-0-595-51165-5(1))*; pap. 20.95 *(978-0-595-51115-0(5))* iUniverse, Inc.

Pocock, Chris. The Black Bats: CIA Spy Flights over China from Taiwan, 1951-1969. 2010. (Illus.). 208p. 39.99 *(978-0-7643-3513-6(8))* Schiffer Publishing, Ltd.

Sawyer, Ralph D. Ancient Chinese Warfare. 2011. (ENG.). 576p. (gr. 9). 39.99 *(978-0-465-02145-1(X))* Basic Bks.

—The Tao of Deception: The History of Unorthodox Warfare in China. 2007. (ENG.). 512p. 29.95 *(978-0-465-07205-7(4))* Basic Bks.

Swope. The Military Collapse of China's Ming Dynasty, 1620-44. 2012. (ENG., Illus.). 256p. (C). 160.00 *(978-0-415-44927-4(8))* Routledge.

Swope, Kenneth M. A Dragon's Head & a Serpent's Tail: Ming China & the First Great East Asian War, 1592-1598. 2009. (Campaigns & Commanders Ser.). (ENG.). 432p. 34.95 *(978-0-8061-4056-8(9))* Univ. of Oklahoma Pr.

Torck, Mathieu. Avoiding the Dire Straits: An inquiry into Food Provisions & Scurvy in Maritime & Military History of China & wider East Asia. 2009. (East Asian Economic & Socio-Cultural Studies). (ENG.). 280p. (C). 72.00 *(978-3-447-05872-8(2))* Harrassowitz, Otto Verlag DEU. Dist: ISD.

Vautrin, Minnie, et al. The Undaunted Women of Nanking: The Wartime Diaries of Minnie Vautrin & Tsen Shui-Fang. Hu, Hualing, ed. 2010. (ENG., Illus.). 264p. 29.95 *(978-0-8093-2963-2(8))* Southern Illinois Univ. Pr.

Wang, Xiuyu. China's Last Imperial Frontier: Late Qing Expansion in Sichuan's Tibetan Borderlands. 2011. E-Book ***(978-0-7391-6810-3(X))*** Lexington Bks.

Wei, Bai. Si Ye Zhu Li Chuan Qi: Siyezhuli Chuanqi. 2010. (CHI., Illus.). *(978-7-5460-0140-1(4))* Huang Publishing Hse.

Wijer, Birgit van der. Tibetan Warriors: The Forgotten story of Tibet's Armed Resistance against China. 2010. (ENG., Illus.). 256p. 39.95 *(978-1-84868-985-5(3))* Amberley Publishing GBR. Dist: Casemate Pubs. & Bk. Distributors, LLC.

Worthing, Peter M. A Military History of Modern China: From the Manchu Conquest to Tian'anmen Square, 1 vol. 2007. (Praeger Security International Ser.). (Illus.). 240p. 49.95 *(978-0-275-98780-0(9)*, C8780, Praeger Security International) Greenwood Publishing Group, Inc.

Xu, Yan. Liu Shi Nian Guo Shi Ji Yao. 2009. *(978-7-5438-6028-5(7))* Hunan Publishing Hse.

Yefu. Fu Qin de Zhan Zheng. 2010. (CHI.). 512p. pap. *(978-988-219-181-5(9))* Cosmos Bks. Ltd.

Zhang, Jingshan. San Ye Zhu Li Chuan Qi: Sanyezhuli Chuanqi. 2010. (CHI., Illus.). 356p. *(978-7-5460-0141-8(2))* Huang Publishing Hse.

CHINA—INTELLECTUAL LIFE

Chan, Alan Kam-Leung & Lo, Yuet Keung. Interpretation & Literature in Early Medieval China. 2010. (SUNY series in Chinese Philosophy & Culture Ser.). (MUL.). 256p. 80.00 *(978-1-4384-3217-5(8))* State Univ. of New York Pr.

Chan/Lo. Philosophy & Religion in Early Medieva China. 2010. (SUNY series in Chinese Philosophy & Culture Ser.). (MUL.). 352p. 80.00 *(978-1-4384-3187-1(2))* State Univ. of New York Pr.

Chen, Pingao. Zhui Yi Yu Gan Huai: "Bo Lan Qun Shu" Za Zhi Jing Xuan Ji = Zhuiyi Yu Ganhuai. 2008. (CHI.). *(978-7-01-007213-5(2))* People's Publishing Hse., The.

Chen, Pingyuan. Dang Dai Zhongguo Ren Wen Guan Cha. 2010. (CHI.). *(978-7-301-16490-7(4))* Beijing University Pr.

Ching-Shing Chan, Alex. Intellectual Narratives: Theory, History, & Self-Characterization of Social Margins in Public Writings. 2011. (ENG.). 240p. pap. ***(978-3-0343-0695-9(4))*** Lang, Peter.

Fallman, Fredrik. Salvation & Modernity: Intellectuals & Faith in Contemporary China. 2008. (ENG.). 180p. pap. 34.99 *(978-0-7618-4090-9(7))* Univ. Pr. of America, Inc.

Farmer, J. Michael. The Talent of Shu: Qiao Zhou & the Intellectual World of Early Medieval Sichuan. 2008. (Illus.). xviii, 246p. pap. 29.95 *(978-0-7914-7164-7(0))* State Univ. of New York Pr.

Frankel, James D. Rectifying God's Name: Liu Zhi's Confucian Translation of Monotheism & Islamic Law. 2011. 48.00 *(978-0-8248-3474-6(7))* Univ. of Hawaii Pr.

Fung, Edmund S. K. The Intellectual Foundations of Chinese Modernity: Cultural & Political Thought in the Republican Era. 2010. (ENG.). 328p. 90.00 *(978-0-521-19511-9(X))* Cambridge Univ. Pr.

Goldman, Andrea. Opera & the City: The Politics of Culture in Beijing, 1770-1900. 2012. (ENG.). 386p. 55.00 ***(978-0-8047-7831-2(0))*** Stanford Univ. Pr.

Goldschmidt, Asaf. The Evolution of Chinese Medicine. 2011. (ENG., Illus.). 272p. pap. 42.95 ***(978-0-415-69202-1(4))*** Routledge.

Gu Chang-Sheng. Awaken: Memoirs of a Chinese Historian. 2009. 228p. 25.99 *(978-1-4490-0618-1(3))*; pap. 14.99 *(978-1-4490-0617-4(5))* AuthorHouse.

Hao, Zhidong. Whither Taiwan & Mainland China: National Identity, the State, & Intellectuals. 2010. (ENG.). 248p. (gr. 17). 40.00 *(978-962-209-100-9(8))* Hong Kong Univ. Pr. HKG. Dist: Columbia Univ. Pr.

Hao, Zhidong. Whither Taiwan & Mainland China: National Identity, the State & Intellectuals. 2010. (CHI.). 248p. ***(978-988-220-769-1(3))*** Hong Kong Univ. Pr.

Hart, Roger. The Chinese Roots of Linear Algebra. 2010. (ENG., Illus.). 304p. (gr. 17). 65.00 *(978-0-8018-9755-9(6))* Johns Hopkins Univ. Pr.

Hogg, James, et al. A Pragmatist & His Free Spirit: The Half-Century Romance of Hu Shi & Edith Clifford Williams. Francis, David et al, eds. 2009. (ENG.). 410p. (gr. 17). pap. 30.00 *(978-962-996-341-5(8))* Chinese Univ. of Hong Kong, The HKG. Dist: Columbia Univ. Pr.

Huang, Qijiang. Yi Wei Chan Yu Jiang Hu Shi: Nan Song Wen Xue Seng Yu Chan Wen Hua de Tui Bian. 2010. (CHI.). *(978-957-05-2487-1(1))* Commercial Pr. Ltd., The.

Hui, Wang. The End of the Revolution: China & the Limits of Modernity. 2011. (ENG.). 272p. pap. 22.95 *(978-1-84467-379-7(0)*, 844379) Verso Bks. GBR. Dist: Norton, W. W. & Co., Inc.

Kuhn, Dieter. The Age of Confucian Rule: The Song Transformation of China. (History of Imperial China Ser.: 4). (Illus.). 368p. 2011. (ENG.). pap. 19.95 *(978-0-674-06202-3(7))* 2009. 38.50 *(978-0-674-03146-3(6))* Harvard Univ. Pr. (Belknap Pr.).

Kuo, Ya-pei. Cultural Wars in Interwar China. 2013. (Routledge/Leiden Series in Modern East Asian History & Politics Ser.). (ENG.). 176p. (C). 130.00 *(978-0-415-55241-7(9))* Routledge.

Levenson, Joseph R. Confucian China & Its Modern Fate: A Trilogy. 2008. 644p. pap. 22.00 *(978-1-59740-592-8(2))* ACLS Humanities E-Book.

—Confucian China & its Modern Fate Vol. 14: The Problem of Intellectua Continuity, 3 vols. 2008. 248p. 190.00 *(978-0-415-36158-3(3))* Routledge.

Lo, Chan. Interpretation & Literature. Chan, Alan K. L., ed. 2011. 294p. pap. 24.95 ***(978-1-4384-3218-2(6)***, Suny Pr.) State Univ. of New York Pr.

—Philosophy & Religion in Early Medieval China. Chan, Alan K. L. & Lo, Yuet Keung, eds. 2011. 381p. pap. 26.95 ***(978-1-4384-3188-8(0)***, Suny Pr.) State Univ. of New York Pr.

Luo, Shen. Zhuan Zhi Wen Hua Xia de Zhongguo. 2009. ("Wen Hua Qing Li" Xi Lie Ser.: Vol. 26). (CHI.). 338p. *(978-1-932138-82-5(X))* Mirror Bks. USA.

Miller, Peter N. & Louis, François. Antiquarianism & Intellectual Life in Europe & China, 1500-1800. 2012. (Bard Graduate Center Cultural Histories of the Material World Ser.). (ENG.). 448p. 65.00 ***(978-0-472-11818-2(8))*** Univ. of Michigan Pr.

Murphy, Melissa. Decoding Chinese Politics: Intellectual Debates & Why They Matter. 2008. 28p. 12.95 net. *(978-0-89206-526-4(5)*, CSIS Pr., The) Ctr. for Strategic & International Studies.

Nyíri, Pál. Mobility & Cultural Authority in Contemporary China. 2010. (ENG., Illus.). 224p. 60.00 *(978-0-295-99015-6(5))*; pap. 25.00 *(978-0-295-99016-3(3))* Univ. of Washington Pr.

Obrist, Hans Ulrich, ed. & text. Battery City: A Post-Olympic Beijing Mini-Marathon. 2010. (ENG., Illus.). 138p. pap. 19.95 *(978-3-03764-096-8(0))* JRP Ringier Kunstverlag AG CHE. Dist: D.A.P./Distributed Art Pubs.

Platt, Stephen R. Provincial Patriots: The Hunanese & Modern China. 2007. (Illus.). 286p. 57.50 *(978-0-674-02665-0(9))* Harvard Univ. Pr.

Roberts, Claire. Friendship in Art: Fou Lei & Huang Binhong. 2010. (CHI., Illus.). 248p. ***(978-988-220-773-8(1))*** Hong Kong Univ. Pr.

—Friendship in Art: Fou Lei & Huang Binhong. 2010. (ENG & CHI., Illus.). 248p. (gr. 17). 40.00 *(978-988-8028-40-5(5))* Hong Kong Univ. Pr. HKG. Dist: Columbia Univ. Pr.

Schaeffer, Kurtis R., et al. Sources of Tibetan Tradition. (Introduction to Asian Civilizations Ser.). 2013. (ENG., Illus.). 832p. (gr. 17). 120.00 *(978-0-231-13598-6(X))* 2013. (ENG., Illus.). 832p. (gr. 17). pap. 40.00 ***(978-0-231-13599-3(8))*** 2012. ***(978-0-231-50978-7(2))*** Columbia Univ. Pr.

Smith, Richard J. Mapping China & Managing the World: Culture, Cartography & Cosmology in Late Imperial Times. 2012. (Asia's Transformations/Critical Asian Scholarship Ser.). (ENG., Illus.). 304p. (C). 150.00 *(978-0-415-68509-2(5))*; pap. 49.95 *(978-0-415-68510-8(9))* Routledge.

Su, Tongbing. Qing Dai Shi Shi Yu Ren Wu. 2010. (CHI.). *(978-7-80047-921-2(8))* Forbidden City Publishing Hse.

Suoqiao, Qian. Liberal Cosmopolitan: Lin Yutang & Middling Chinese Modernity. 2010. (Ideas, History, & Modern China Ser.). 271p. *(978-90-04-19213-3(1))* BRILL.

Sze, Arthur, ed. Chinese Writers on Writing. 2010. (Writer's World Ser.). (ENG.). 320p. 60.00 *(978-1-59534-062-7(9))*; pap. 18.95 *(978-1-59534-063-4(7))* Trinity Univ. Pr.

Tan, Tian Yuan. Songs of Contentment & Transgression: Discharged Officials & Literati Communities in Sixteenth-Century North China. 2010. (Harvard-Yenching Institute Monograph Ser.: 75). (ENG.). 314p. 39.95 *(978-0-674-05604-6(3))* Harvard Univ., Asia Ctr.

Tong, Q. S., et al. Critical Zone No. 2: A Forum of Chinese & Western Knowledge. 2007. (Critical Zone: a Forum of Chinese & Western Knowledge Ser.). (ENG., Illus.). 316p. (gr. 17). pap. 32.50 *(978-962-209-799-5(5))* Hong Kong Univ. Pr. HKG. Dist: Columbia Univ. Pr.

Wang, Fan-sen. Fu Ssu-nien: A Life in Chinese History & Politics. 2006. (Cambridge Studies in Chinese History, Literature & Institutions Ser.). (ENG.). 280p. pap. 58.00 *(978-0-521-03047-2(1))* Cambridge Univ. Pr.

Wang, Yugen. Ten Thousand Scrolls: Reading & Writing in the Poetics of Huang Tingjian & the Late Northern Song. 2011. (Harvard-Yenching Institute Monograph Ser.: 76). (ENG.). 300p. 39.95 *(978-0-674-06255-9(8))* Harvard Univ., Asia Ctr.

Wei, Betty Peh-T'i. Ruan Yuan, 1764-1849: The Life & Work of a Major Scholar-Official in Nineteenth-Century China Before the Opium War. 2006. (ENG., Illus.). 416p. (gr. 17). 60.00 *(978-962-209-785-8(5))* Hong Kong Univ. Pr. HKG. Dist: Columbia Univ. Pr.

Weisz, Tiberiu. The Covenant & the Mandate of Heaven: An In-Depth Comparative Cultural Study of Judaism & China. 2008. xviii, 243p. E-Book *(978-0-595-88777-4(5))* iUniverse, Inc.

Wilcox, Cynthia Waiying Wu. The Love of Lotus. 2006. xi, 217p. pap. 17.00 *(978-0-9786135-8-7(9))* Tyde House Bks.

Wong, Young-Tsu. Beyond Confucian China: The Rival Discourses of Kang Youwei & Zhang Binglin. 2010. (Academia Sinica on East Asia Ser.). (ENG.). 208p. (C). 125.00 *(978-0-415-58208-7(3))* Routledge.

Wu Hui. Once Iron Girls: Essays on Gender by Post-Mao Chinese Literary Women. (ENG.). 174p. 2011. pap. 27.95 *(978-0-7391-3422-1(1))* 2009. 57.99 *(978-0-7391-3421-4(3))* Lexington Bks.

Zhang, Chengjue. Dang Xiu Cai Yu Zhe Xiu Cai ... Ba Shi Nian Dai Zhongguo de Yi Chang Da Lun Zheng. 2009. (Illus.). 127p. pap. *(978-962-16-0236-7(X))* Forward Bk. Co.

Zhou, Qibo. Bai Ban Wei Qu Nan Qiu Quan. 2010. (CHI., Illus.). 262p. ***(978-1-183-43122-5(8))*** Cozy Graphics Corp.

CHINA—INTELLECTUAL LIFE—1949-

Guo, Zhenyi & Lamb, Stephen. International Comparisons of China's Technical & Vocational Education & Training System. 2010. (Technical & Vocational Education & Training: Issues, Concerns & Prospects Ser.). (Illus.). 175p. 159.00 *(978-90-481-8742-3(7)*, 9048187427) Springer.

Louie, Kam, ed. Hong Kong Culture: Word & Image. 2010. (ENG., Illus.). 324p. (gr. 17). pap. 30.00 *(978-988-8028-41-2(3))* Hong Kong Univ. Pr. HKG. Dist: Columbia Univ. Pr.

Mote, Frederick W. China & the Vocation of History in the Twentieth Century: A Personal Memoir. 2010. (ENG., Illus.). 360p. (C). 29.95 *(978-0-691-14463-4(X))* Princeton Univ. Pr.

CHINA—KINGS AND RULERS

Cawthorne, Nigel. Daughter of Heaven: The True Story of the Only Woman to Become Emperor of China. 2007. (ENG., Illus.). 350p. 24.95 *(978-1-85168-530-1(8))* Oneworld Pubns. GBR. Dist: National Bk. Network.

Clements, Jonathan. The First Emperor of China: The Man Who Gave China Its Name. 2007. (ENG., Illus.). 256p. pap. 19.95 *(978-0-7509-3960-7(5))* History Pr. Ltd., The GBR. Dist: Independent Pubs. Group.

De Luca, Araldo, photos by. The Eternal Army: The Terracotta Soldiers of the First Emperor. 2012. (ENG., Illus.). 288p. 24.95 ***(978-88-544-0627-8(9))*** White Star ITA. Dist: Sterling Publishing Co., Inc.

Dennerline, Jerry. Middle Kingdoms & Empires: Culture & Power in Chinese History. 2007. (ENG., Illus.). 320p. 40.00 *(978-0-300-11512-3(1))* Yale Univ. Pr.

Der Ling, Princess. Two Years in the Forbidden City. 2010. (ENG.). 436p. pap. 35.75 *(978-1-171-82430-5(0))* BiblioBazaar.

—Two Years in the Forbidden City. 2010. (Illus.). 140p. pap. 22.91 *(978-1-153-72975-8(X))* General Bks. LLC.

Der Ling, The Princess. Two Years in the Forbidden City. 2008. 244p. 24.99 *(978-1-60512-017-1(0))*; pap. 13.99 *(978-1-60512-117-8(7))* Akasha Publishing, LLC. (Akasha Classics).

—Two Years in the Forbidden City. 2008. 224p. pap. *(978-1-4099-2921-5(3))* Dodo Pr.

Elliott, Jeannette Shambaugh. The Odyssey of China's Imperial Art Treasures. 2007. (Samuel & Althea Stroum Bks.). (ENG., Illus.). 192p. per. 19.95 *(978-0-295-98688-3(3))* Univ. of Washington Pr.

Han, Xin. Zi Jin Cheng Jian Zheng, 2 vols. 2009. (CHI., Illus.). 434p. *(978-7-80168-490-5(7))* Study Publishing Hse.

Holdsworth, May & Courtauld, Caroline. Forbidden City: The Great Within. 2nd ed. 2008. (ENG.). 152p. pap. 24.95 *(978-962-217-792-5(1)*, 217792) Airphoto International/Odyssey HKG. Dist: Norton, W. W. & Co., Inc.

Hung, Hing Ming. The Road to the Throne: How Liu Bang Founded China's Han Dynasty. 2011. pap. 22.95 *(978-0-87586-837-0(1))*; pap. 32.95 *(978-0-87586-838-7(X))* Algora Publishing.

Johnston, Reginald F. Twilight in the Forbidden City. 2011. (Cambridge Library Collection - History Ser.). (ENG., Illus.). 572p. pap. 43.00 *(978-1-108-02965-0(5))* Cambridge Univ. Pr.

Johnston, Reginald Fleming. Twilight in the Forbidden City. 2008. (Illus.). 488p. per. 28.95 *(978-0-9680459-5-4(2))* Soul Care Publishing CAN. Dist: Ingram Bk. Co.

Lee, Hui-Shu. Empresses, Art, & Agency in Song Dynasty China. 2010. (ENG., Illus.). 336p. 65.00 *(978-0-295-98963-1(7))* Univ. of Washington Pr.

Ling, Der. Two Years in the Forbidden City. 2010. 442p. pap. 35.75 *(978-1-142-63531-2(7))*; 436p. pap. 35.75 *(978-1-142-11899-0(1))*; 444p. pap. 36.75 ***(978-1-143-21032-7(8))*** BiblioBazaar.

—Two Years in the Forbidden City. 2009. 164p. pap. *(978-1-150-52685-5(8))* Books LLC.

Ling, Princess Der. Two Years in the Forbidden City. 2007. (ENG.). 270p. pap. 19.99 *(978-988-17149-9-2(0))* Earnshaw Bks. HKG. Dist: Independent Pubs. Group.

—Two Years in the Forbidden City. 2010. 170p. pap. *(978-1-4076-5076-0(9))* HardPr.

Ling, Rich. Old Buddha. 2007. 190.00 *(978-0-7103-1111-5(7))* Taylor & Francis Group.

—Two Years in the Forbidden City. 2007. 190.00 *(978-0-7103-1112-2(5))* Taylor & Francis Group.

Ling, The Princess Der. Two Years in the Forbidden City. 2010. 180p. pap. 18.36 *(978-1-162-71509-4(X))*; 30.36 ***(978-1-169-27745-8(4))***; 37.95 *(978-1-161-48373-4(X))* Kessinger Publishing, LLC.

Luo, Yuming. Quan Li Wan Jia: Zhongguo Li Shi Shang de Da Yin Mou. 2009. (CHI.). *(978-7-309-06483-4(6))* Fudan Univ. Pr.

Paludan, Ann. Chinese Emperors: The Reign-by-Reign Record of the Rulers of Imperial China. 2009. (ENG., Illus.). 224p. pap. 26.95 *(978-0-500-28764-4(3)*, 528764) Thames & Hudson.

Pu Yi, Henry. The Last Manchu: The Autobiography of Henry Pu Yi, Last Emperor of China. Kramer, Paul, ed. 2010. (ENG.). 344p. pap. 14.95 *(978-1-60239-732-3(5)*, 239732) Skyhorse Publishing Co., Inc.

Rossabi, Morris & Rossabi, M. Khubilai Khan: His Life & Times. 20th anniv. ed. 2009. (ENG., Illus.). 348p. pap. 24.95 *(978-0-520-26132-7(1))* Univ. of California Pr.

Rothschild, N. Harry & Stearns, Peter N. Wu Zhao: China's Only Woman Emperor. 2007. (Library of World Biography Ser.). (ENG., Illus.). 256p. (C). per. 25.00 *(978-0-321-39426-2(7))* Longman Publishing Group.

Suski, P. M. The Year Names of China & Japan. 2010. (ENG.). 64p. 75.00 *(978-0-415-59417-2(0))* Routledge.

Tonia Eckfeld. Imperial Tombs in Tang China 618-907. 2011. (ENG., Illus.). 192p. pap. 42.95 ***(978-0-415-67492-8(1))*** Routledge.

Wilson, Ming & Wilson, Verity. Imperial Chinese Robes: From the Forbidden City. 2011. (ENG., Illus.). 128p. 50.00 *(978-1-85177-620-7(6))* V & A Pubns. GBR. Dist: Hachette Bk. Group.

Xu, Guangyuan. Da Qing Huang Ling Mi Shi. 2010. (Illus.). 16p. *(978-7-5077-3423-2(4))* Xueyuan Press.

CHINA—LANGUAGES

see also Hmong Language; Tungus-Manchu Languages; Ughur Language; Yi Language

Beckett, Gulbahar & Postiglione, Gerard, eds. China's Integrationist Language Policy. 2011. (Comparative Development & Policy in Asia Ser.). (ENG., Illus.). 256p. (C). 140.00 *(978-0-415-59605-3(X))* Routledge.

Bolton, Kingsley & Hutton, Christopher, eds. Western Linguists & the Languages of China Vols. 8-12: Chinese Dictionaries. 2nd ed. 2007. (Ganesha - Western Linguists & the Languages of China Ser.). (Illus.). 2476p. 695.00 *(978-1-86210-066-4(7))* Ganesha Publishing, Ltd. GBR. Dist: Chicago Distribution Ctr.

Brick, Jean. China: Language & Culture. 3rd ed. (Illus.). 372p. pap. *(978-0-85837-719-6(5))* Macquarie Univ.

Chen, Fukang. Zhongguo Yi Xue Shi. 2010. (CHI.). *(978-7-208-08715-6(6))* Shanghai People's Publishing Hse.

Gebremeskel, Tesfamaryam. Narrative Techniques in Chinua Achebe's Novels. 2009. 88p. pap. *(978-3-639-19590-3(6))* VDM Verlag Dr. Mueller e.K.

Li, yuming. Zhongguo Yu Yan Gui Hua Lun. 2010. *(978-7-100-06754-6(5))* Commercial Pr., The.

Lian, Yantang & Yang, Yi. Er Shi Shi Ji Zhongguo Fan Yi Wen Xue Shi: A History of 20th Century Literature Translated into Chinese. 2009. (CHI., Illus.). 30p. *(978-7-5306-5184-1(6))* Baihua Literature & Fine Arts Publishing Hse.

Liu, Jin. Chinese under Globalization: Emerging Trends in Language Use in China. 2011. 200p. 68.00 ***(978-981-4350-69-3(9))*** World Scientific Publishing Co., Inc.

Lu, Tian Qiao. A Grammar of Maonan. 2008. 428p. pap. *(978-1-59942-971-7(3))* Universal Pubs.

McDougall, Bonnie S. Translation Zones in Modern China: Authoritarian Command Versus Gift Exchange. 2011. *(978-1-60497-746-2(9))* Cambria Pr.

Pelkey, Jamin R. Dialectology as Dialectic: Interpreting Phula Variation. 2011. (Trends in Linguistics. Studies & Monographs [TiLSM] Ser.). (ENG., Illus.). XXXIV, 498p. 210.00 ***(978-3-11-187130-1(4))*** De Gruyter, Mouton DEU. Dist: de Gruyter, Walter GmbH & Co. KG.

Qi, Shouhua. Western Literature in China & the Translation of a Nation. 2012. (ENG., Illus.). 240p. 85.00 ***(978-0-230-12087-7(3))*** Palgrave Macmillan.

Setton, Robin. Interpreting Chinese, Interpreting China. 2011. (Illus.). viii, 188p. *(978-90-272-2259-6(2))*; *(978-90-272-8691-8(4))* Benjamins, John Publishing Co.

Sun & Liu. Languages of the Greater Himalayan Region, Volume 9 A Grammar of Anong: Language Death under Intense Contact. 2009. (Illus.). 276p. *(978-90-04-17686-7(1))* BRILL.

Tse, Shek Kam & Li, Hui. Early Child Cantonese: Facts & Implications. 2011. (Studies on Language Acquisition [SOLA] Ser.). (ENG., Illus.). XII, 202p. 210.00 ***(978-3-11-174516-9(3))*** De Gruyter, Mouton DEU. Dist: de Gruyter, Walter GmbH & Co. KG.

Wang. A Billion Voices: Languages & Peoples of China. 2011. 52.00 *(978-981-4287-72-2(5))* World Scientific Publishing Co., Inc.

Xu, Dan, ed. Space in Languages of China: Cross-linguistic, Synchronic & Diachronic Perspectives. (ENG., Illus.). viii, 276p. 2010. pap. 159.00 *(978-90-481-7841-4(X)*, 904817841X) 2008. 159.00 *(978-1-4020-8320-4(3)*, 1402083203) Springer.

Zhou, Faxiang. Er Shi Shi Ji Zhongguo Fan Yi Wen Xue Shi: A History of 20th Century Literature Translated into Chinese. 2009. (CHI., Illus.). *(978-7-5306-5182-7(X))* Baihua Literature & Fine Arts Publishing Hse.

Zhou, Minglang. Multilingualism in China: The Politics of Writing Reforms for Minority Languages 1949-2002. (Contributions to the Sociology of Language [CSL] Ser.). (ENG.). XXII, 458p. 225.00 ***(978-3-11-181249-6(9))*** De Gruyter, Mouton DEU. Dist: de Gruyter, Walter GmbH & Co. KG.

CHINA—MAPS

Benewick, Robert, et al. The State of China Atlas: Mapping the World's Fastest-Growing Economy. 2nd rev. ed. 2009. (ENG., Illus.). 128p. pap. 19.95 *(978-0-520-25610-1(7))* Univ. of California Pr.

China/Far East. (Illus.). pap. 11.95 *(978-3-8283-0094-1(4))* Hallwag Verlag GmbH DEU. Dist: Rand McNally.

Explorer Publishing Staff. Beijing. 2008. (ENG., Illus.). 230p. pap. 11.95 *(978-9948-03-328-8(0))* Explorer Publishing UAE. Dist: Globe Pequot Pr., The.

Gaubil, Antoine. A Description of the Plan of Peking, the Capital of China. 2010. pap. 19.96 *(978-1-61143-308-1(8))* Gorgias Pr., LLC.

Lyons, Thomas P. Townships in Fujian, Supplement 1: Mapping the Census. 2007. (Illus.). 170p. cd-rom 19.95 *(978-0-9729147-7-2(3))* Willow Creek of Trumansburg.

MapEasy Inc Staff. MapEasy's Guide to Beijing. 2006. 6.95 *(978-1-929038-03-9(8))* Mapeasy, Inc.

National Geographic Society Staff. Atlas of China: An Expansive Portrait of China Today with More Than 400 Maps & Illustrations. 2007. (ENG., Illus.). 128p. 26.00 *(978-1-4262-0136-3(2)*, National Geographic) National Geographic Society.

—China: An Expansive Portrait of China Today with More Than 400 Maps & Illustrations. 2009. (ENG., Illus.). 128p. pap. 21.95 *(978-1-4262-0327-5(6)*, National Geographic) National Geographic Society.

CHINA—MILITARY POLICY

Anderson, Eric C. China Restored: The Middle Kingdom Looks to 2020 & Beyond. 2010. xxiii, 323p. E-Book *(978-0-313-38518-6(1)*, Praeger Pubs.) Greenwood Publishing Group, Inc.

Blasko, Dennis J. The Chinese Army Today: Tradition & Transformation for the 21st Century. 2nd rev. ed. 2012. (Asian Security Studies). (ENG., Illus.). 312p. (C). 150.00 *(978-0-415-78321-7(6))*; pap. 39.95 *(978-0-415-78322-4(4))* Routledge.

Cheng, J. I. Economics & Foreign Investment in China. 2006. (Illus.). 229p. (C). 79.00 *(978-1-60021-238-3(7))* Nova Science Pubs., Inc.

China: Recent Security Developments. 2008. iii, 59p. *(978-0-16-082188-2(6)*, 552-070-38322-1) United States Government Printing Office.

Chinese Interrogation vs. Congressional Oversight: The Uighurs at Guantanamo: Hearing Before the Subcommittee on International Organizations, Human Rights, & Oversight of the Committee on Foreign Affairs, House of Representatives, One Hundred Eleventh Congress, First Session, July 16, 2009. 2009. iii, 81p. *(978-0-16-084987-9(X)*, 552-070-40366-3) United States Government Printing Office.

Cliff, Roger & Shlapak, David A. U. S. -China Relations after Resolution of Taiwan's Status. 2007. 39p. pap. 20.00 *(978-0-8330-4036-7(7)*, mg567) RAND Corp., The.

Cliff, Roger, et al. Entering the Dragon's Lair: The Implications of Chinese Anti-Access Strategies. 2007. (Illus.). 154p. pap. 27.50 *(978-0-8330-3995-8(4)*, mg524) RAND Corp., The.

—New Opportunities & Challenges for Taiwan's Security. 2011. (ENG.). 172p. (C). pap. 23.50 *(978-0-8330-5149-3(0))* RAND Corp., The.

Cole, Bernard. Great Wall at Sea-E02. 2nd ed. 2010. (Illus.). 416p. 36.95 *(978-1-59114-142-6(7))* Naval Institute Pr.

Cordesman, Anthony H. & Kleiber, Martin. Chinese Military Modernization: Force Development & Strategic Capabilities. 2007. (Significant Issues Ser.: No. 29). (Illus.). (C). pap. *(978-0-89206-496-0(X)*, CSIS Pr., The) Ctr. for Strategic & International Studies.

Craig, Susan L. Chinese Perceptions of Traditional & Nontraditional Security Threats. 2007. pap. *(978-1-58487-287-0(X))* Strategic Studies Institute, U.S. Army War College Commandant (AWCC-DSI/Pubns.).

Dobbins, James. Conflict with China: Prospects, Consequences, & Strategies for Deterrence. 2011. 25p. pap. 12.50 ***(978-0-8330-5831-7(2))*** RAND Corp., The.

Erickson, Andrew. Chinese Aerospace Power. Goldstein, Lyle, ed. 2011. 512p. 52.96 *(978-1-59114-241-6(5))* Naval Institute Pr.

Feng, Huiyun. Chinese Strategic Culture & Foreign Policy Decision-Making: Confucianism, Leadership & War. 2009. 188p. pap. 39.95 *(978-0-415-54520-4(X))* 2007. (Illus.). 185p. 160.00 *(978-0-415-41815-7(1))* Routledge.

Fisher, Richard D. China's Military Modernization: Building for Regional & Global Reach, 1 vol. 2008. (Praeger Security International Ser.). (Illus.). 344p. 75.00 *(978-0-275-99486-0(4)*, C9486, Praeger Security International) Greenwood Publishing Group, Inc.

—China's Military Modernization: Building for Regional & Global Reach. 2010. (Illus.). xxii, 309p. *(978-0-8047-7194-8(4))*; (ENG., 344p. pap. 25.95 *(978-0-8047-7195-5(2))* Stanford Univ. Pr.

The Future of Political, Economic, & Security Relations with China: Hearing Before the Committee on Foreign Affairs, House of Representatives, One Hundred Tenth Congress, First Session, May 1, 2007. 2007. iii, 41p. *(978-0-16-079098-0(0)*, 552-070-36194-4) United States Government Printing Office.

Gilboy, George J. & Heginbotham, Eric. Chinese & Indian Strategic Behavior: Growing Power & Alarm. 2012. (ENG.). 384p. pap. 34.99 ***(978-1-107-66169-1(2))***; (Illus.). 99.00 ***(978-1-107-02005-4(0))*** Cambridge Univ. Pr.

Goldstein, Lyle J., et al, eds. China's Future Nuclear Submarine Force. 2007. (Illus.). 412p. 46.95 *(978-1-59114-326-0(8))* Naval Institute Pr.

Goldstein, Lyle J. & Erickson, Andrew S., eds. China's Nuclear Force Modernization. 2006. (Newport Paper Ser.). 144p. pap. 11.00 *(978-0-16-076902-3(7)*, Defense Dept.) United States Government Printing Office.

Gordon, Yefim. Chinese Aircraft: China's Aviation Industry Since 1951. 2008. (Illus.). 264p. 56.95 *(978-1-902109-04-6(X))* Hikoki Pubns. GBR. Dist: Partners Pubs. Group, Inc.

Holslag, Jonathan. Trapped Giant. 2011. (Adelphi Ser.). (ENG., Illus.). 160p. (C). pap. 19.95 *(978-0-415-66989-4(8))* Routledge.

Howarth, Peter. China's Rising Sea Power: The PLA Navy's Submarine Challenge. 2008. 212p. pap. 37.95 *(978-0-415-49516-5(4))* Routledge.

Ju, Hailong. Zhongguo Hai Quan Zhan Lüe: The Stratage of Chinese Sea Power. 2010. (Illus.). *(978-7-80232-260-8(X))* Current Affairs Publishing Hse.

Kamphausen, Roy, et al, eds. Beyond the Strait: PLA Missions Other Than Taiwan. 2009. pap. *(978-1-58487-382-2(5))* Strategic Studies Institute, U.S. Army War College Commandant (AWCC-DSI/Pubns.).

—The People in the PLA: Recruitment, Training, & Education in China's Military. 2008. pap. *(978-1-58487-354-9(X))* Strategic Studies Institute, U.S. Army War College Commandant (AWCC-DSI/Pubns.).

—The PLA at Home & Abroad: Assessing the Operational Capabilities of China's Military. 2010. pap. *(978-1-58487-448-5(1))* Strategic Studies Institute, U.S. Army War College Commandant (AWCC-DSI/Pubns.).

Lampton, David M. The Three Faces of Chinese Power: Might, Money, & Minds. 2008. (Illus.). 384p. 55.00 *(978-0-520-24951-6(8))*; 361p. pap. 26.95 *(978-0-520-25442-8(2))* Univ. of California Pr.

Larus, Elizabeth Freund. Politics & Society in Contemporary China. 2012. (C). 275p. pap. 32.50 ***(978-1-58826-825-9(X))***; (Illus.). 75.00 ***(978-1-58826-800-6(4))*** Rienner, Lynne Pubs.

Leehy, Anthony G., et al. Military & Security Developments in China. 2012. ***(978-1-61942-009-0(0))*** Nova Science Pubs., Inc.

Lewis, Jeffrey G. The Minimum Means of Reprisal: China's Search for Security in the Nuclear Age. 2007. (American Academy Studies in Global Security Ser.). (ENG., Illus.). 282p. (gr. 17). per. 24.00 *(978-0-262-62202-8(5))* MIT Pr.

Lewis, John Wilson & Xue, Litai. Zhongguo Jun Shi Jue Ce Ji Zhi Ji Taiwan Chong Tu. 2007. ("Zhongguo Ju Shi " Xi Lie Ser.: Vol. 47). (CHI., Illus.). 7p. pap. *(978-1-932138-57-3(9))* Mirror Bks. USA.

Litai, Xue & Lewis, John Wilson. Imagined Enemies: China Prepares for Uncertain War. 2006. (ENG., Illus.). 384p. 65.00 *(978-0-8047-5391-3(1))* Stanford Univ. Pr.

Lynch, Jeremy F. China's Naval Modernization: Background, Implications & Issues. 2011. (China in the 21st Century Ser.). 89.00 *(978-1-61761-217-6(0))* Nova Science Pubs., Inc.

Macdonald, Bruce W. Chinese Military Space Capabilities & U. S. Security Policy. 2008. (ENG.). 48p. pap. 10.00 *(978-0-87609-406-8(X))* Council on Foreign Relations.

Marvel, Elisabette M., ed. China's Cyberwarfare Capability. 2010. pap. 43.00 *(978-1-61761-218-3(9))* Nova Science Pubs., Inc.

Mastro, Oriana Skylar, told to. Assessing the Threat: The Chinese Military & Taiwan's Security. 2007. (ENG., Illus.). 413p. per. 22.95 *(978-0-87003-238-7(0))* Carnegie Endowment for International Peace.

Military Power of the People's Republic of China: Hearing Before the Committee on Armed Services, House of Representatives, One Hundred Ninth Congress, Second Session, Hearing Held, June 22, 2006. 2007. iii, 69p. *(978-0-16-079305-9(X)*, 552-070-36383-1) United States Government Printing Office.

Pehrson, Christopher J. String of Pearls: Meeting the Challenge of China's Rising Power Across the Asian Littoral. 2006. (Carlisle Papers in Security Strategy). (Illus.). v, 30p. pap. *(978-1-58487-250-4(0))* Strategic Studies Institute, U.S. Army War College Commandant (AWCC-DSI/Pubns.).

Pivac, Nela, et al, eds. China Naval Modernization: Implications for U.S. Navy Capabilities. 2008. viii, 135p. (C). pap. 50.00 *(978-1-60456-709-0(0))* Nova Science Pubs., Inc.

Schneider, Mark. The Nuclear Doctrine & Forces of the People's Republic of China. 2007. 41p. *(978-0-9776221-5-3(0))* National Institute Pr.

Scobell, Andrew & Wortzel, Larry M. Shaping China's Security Environment: The Role of the People's Liberation Army. 2006. vi, 314p. pap. *(978-1-58487-251-1(9))* Strategic Studies Institute, U.S. Army War College Commandant (AWCC-DSI/Pubns.).

Shlapak, David A., et al. A Question of Balance: Political Context & Military Aspects of the China Taiwan Dispute (2009) 2009. (ENG.). 184p. pap. 30.00 *(978-0-8330-4746-5(9)*, mg-888) RAND Corp., The.

Twomey, Christopher P., ed. Perspectives on Sino-American Strategic Nuclear Issues. 2008. (Initiatives in Strategic Studies: Issues & Policies Ser.). (ENG., Illus.). 240p. 89.00 *(978-0-230-60660-9(1))* Palgrave Macmillan.

United States, Congress House Committee on Armed Services Staff, contrib. by. China's Military Power: Hearing Before the Committee on Armed Services, House of Representatives, One Hundred Ninth Congress, First Session, Hearing Held July 27, 2005. 2007. iii, 98p. *(978-0-16-077923-7(5)*, 552-070-35358-5) United States Government Printing Office.

Verma, Bharat. Threat from China. 2011. 548p. 27.95 ***(978-1-935501-30-5(5))*** Lancer International, Lancer Pr. IND. Dist: Casemate Pubs. & Bk. Distributors, LLC.

Wortzel, Larry M. China's Nuclear Forces: Operations, Training, Doctrine, Command, Control, & Campaign Planning. 2007. pap. *(978-1-58487-292-4(6))* Strategic Studies Institute, U.S. Army War College Commandant (AWCC-DSI/Pubns.).

Yoshihara, Toshi & Holmes, James R. Chinese Naval Strategy in the 21st Century: The Turn to Mahan. 2007. (Naval Policy & History Ser.). 167p. 160.00 *(978-0-415-77213-6(3))* Routledge.

CHINA—MILITARY RELATIONS

Bush, Richard C. The Perils of Proximity: China-Japan Security Relations. 2010. (ENG.). 421p. 32.95 *(978-0-8157-0474-4(7))* Brookings Institution Pr.

China: Recent Security Developments. 2009. iii, 44p. *(978-0-16-084149-1(6)*, 552-070-39750-7) United States Government Printing Office.

China: Recent Security Developments: Committee on Armed Services, House of Representatives, One Hundred Eleventh Congress, Second Session, Hearing Held January 13, 2010. 2010. (Illus.). iii, 90p. *(978-0-16-087106-1(9)*, 552-070-41962-4) United States Government Printing Office.

Erickson, Andrew, ed. China Us & 21st Century Sea Power. 2010. (Illus.). 496p. 47.95 *(978-1-59114-243-0(1))* Naval Institute Pr.

Fleischer, Samuel E., ed. Measuring China's Military Might. 2010. (China in the 21st Century Ser.). 69.00 *(978-1-60876-846-2(5))* Nova Science Pubs., Inc.

Kamphausen, Roy, et al, eds. The PLA at Home & Abroad: Assessing the Operational Capabilities of China's Military. 2010. pap. *(978-1-58487-448-5(1))* Strategic Studies Institute, U.S. Army War College Commandant (AWCC-DSI/Pubns.).

Li, Nan. Chinese Civil-Military Relations in the Post-Deng Era: Implications for Crisis Management & Naval Modernization: Implications for Crisis Management & Naval Modernization. Center for Naval Warfare Studies (U.S.) Staff & Naval War College Press (U.S.) Staff, eds. 2010. (ENG., Illus.). 55p. pap. 6.00 *(978-1-884733-73-4(5)*, Dept. of the Navy) United States Government Printing Office.

Pritchard, Charles L., et al. U. S. Policy Toward the Korean Peninsula: Independent Task Force Report. 2010. (ENG.). 88p. pap. 15.00 *(978-0-87609-475-4(2))* Council on Foreign Relations.

Swanson, Bruce, et al. A Plain Sailorman in China the Life & Times of Cdr. I.V. Gillis, USN, 1875-1948. 2012. ***(978-1-61251-105-4(8))*** Naval Institute Pr.

CHINA—NAVY

Erickson, Andrew & Goldstein, Lyle, eds. China Goes to Sea. 2009. (Illus.). 544p. 49.95 *(978-1-59114-242-3(3))* Naval Institute Pr.

Van Tilburg, Hans Konrad. Chinese Junks on the Pacific: Views from a Different Deck. 2007. (New Perspectives on Maritime History & Nautical Archaeology Ser.). (ENG., Illus.). 288p. 59.95 *(978-0-8130-3053-1(6))* Univ. Pr. of Florida.

CHINA—OFFICIALS AND EMPLOYEES

Bessard, Pierre, photos by. Pierre Bessard: Wuhan Boiler Company Workers. 2011. (ENG., Illus.). 170p. 60.00 *(978-988-17144-5-9(1))* Timezone 8 Ltd. HKG. Dist: D.A.P./Distributed Art Pubs.

Hill, Emily M. Smokeless Sugar: The Death of a Provincial Bureaucrat & the Construction of China's National Economy. 2011. (Contemporary Chinese Studies Ser.). (ENG., Illus.). 336p. pap. 35.95 *(978-0-7748-1654-0(6))* UBC Pr. CAN. Dist: Univ. of Washington Pr.

International Conference of Administrative Sciences, et al, contrib. by. De Nouveaux Defis Pour L'administration Du XXIeme Siecle: Fonction Publique Performante Et Administration Publique Decentralisee. 203p. *(978-4-274-90175-1(0))* Ohm-Sha.

Ouyang, Quan & Bai, Xiaoyun. Hu Wen Zhi Jian: Da Jia Sao Huang Shui Shi Zui Hou Ying Jia. 2007. ("Zhongguo Ju Shi " Xi Lie Ser.: Vol. 45). (CHI., Illus.). 421p. *(978-1-932138-58-0(7))* Mirror Bks. USA.

Wu, Ling. Zhu Hou Fu Bai. 2009. ("Zhongguo Zhang Quan Zhe" Xi Lie Ser.: Vol. 29). (CHI., Illus.). 420p. *(978-962-8744-02-2(X))* Mirror Bks. USA.

Yang, Qingxi & Xia, Fei. Shi Ba Da: Zhu Hou Jin Jing. 2010. (CHI., Illus.). 586p. pap. *(978-962-8744-42-8(9))* Mirror Bks. USA.

Yang, Suiping. Zhongguo Gu Dai Guan Yuan Xuan Ren Yu Guan Li Zhi du Yan Jiu. 2010. (CHI.). *(978-7-5087-1062-4(2))* China Society Pr.

Zhang, Cong Ellen. Transformative Journeys. 2010. 328p. 49.00 *(978-0-8248-3399-2(6))* Univ. of Hawaii Pr.

Zhang, Jing. Wan Qing Xuan Guan Zhi du Bian Ge Yan Jiu. 2010. (CHI.). *(978-7-5102-0236-0(1))* Zhongguo Jiancha Chubanshe.

CHINA—PICTORIAL WORKS

Barrett, J. May Lee, ed. Humanism in China: China Institute Edition. 2009. (ENG., Illus.). 34p. pap. *(978-0-9774054-4-2(3))* China Institute Gallery, China Institute in America.

Berner, R. Thomas. A smart eye in China. 2008. 66p. pap. 29.95 *(978-1-4357-4532-2(9))* Lulu Enterprises Inc.

Brahm, Laurence J. Elements of China: Water, Wood, Fire, Earth, Gold. 2008. (Illus.). 237p. *(978-7-5085-1392-8(4))* China Intercontinental Communication Ctr.

Brown, Nancy, photos by. Simply China. 2011. 289p. 50.00 ***(978-0-615-42824-6(X))*** brown, nancy photofraphy.

Campany, David & Higgie, Jennifer. China Between. 2010. (ENG., Illus.). 96p. 40.00 ***(978-1-904587-88-0(7))*** Lewis, Dewi Publishing GBR. Dist: Consortium Bk. Sales & Distribution.

Chang, Elizabeth Hope. Britain's Chinese Eye: Literature, Empire, & Aesthetics in Nineteenth-Century Britain. 2010. (ENG., Illus.). 256p. 55.00 *(978-0-8047-5945-8(6))* Stanford Univ. Pr.

Changfen, Chen, photos by. The Great Wall of China: Photographs by Chen Changfen. 2007. (ENG., Illus.). 168p. 45.00 *(978-0-300-12247-3(0))* Yale Univ. Pr.
Danysz, Magda, frwd. The Wrinkles of the City: Les Sillons de la Ville = Los Surcos de a Ciudad. 2011. (CHI, FRE, SPA & ENG., Illus.). 144p. 60.00 ***(978-88-88493-71-8(9))*** Drago Arts & Communication ITA. Dist: SCB Distributors.
Delano, James Whitlow, et al. Empire: Impressions from China. 2008. (ENG., Illus.). 128p. 35.00 *(978-88-7439-127-1(7))* 5 Continents ITA. Dist: Hachette Bk. Group.
Deluxe...Spirit of China. 2008. 256p. *(978-1-4075-3953-9(1))* Parragon, Inc.
Eijkelboom, Hans & Godfrey, Tony. Paris - New York - Shanghai: A Book about the Past, Present, & (Possibly) Future Capital of the World, 1 vol. 2007. (ENG., Illus.). 240p. 55.00 *(978-1-59711-044-0(2))* Aperture Foundation, Inc.
Freeman, Michael & Ahmed, Selena. The Tea Horse Road: China's Ancient Trade Road to Tibet. 2011. (ENG., Illus.). 340p. *(978-974-9863-93-0(3))*, River Bks. Pr. Dist A C) Antique Collectors' Club.
Friedman, Gary. The Road to China: Adventures of a Photographer turned English Teacher. 2007. 299p. per. 24.96 *(978-1-4116-9702-7(2))* Lulu Enterprises Inc.
Gao, Chunming. Exquisite Fabrics: Traditional Weaving & Embroidery Patterns in China. 2010. (ENG.). 652p. 250.00 *(978-1-60220-001-2(7))* BetterLink Pr., Inc.
Gauvrit, Jean-Philippe. Shanghai in .jpg: [Shanghai Ying Xiang. 2008. (CHI, FRE & ENG., Illus.). 87p. *(978-0-9814698-1-2(7))* International Publishing Hse. for China's Culture.
Guo, Guang, ed. China. 2009. (ENG., Illus.). 244p. 100.00 *(978-0-7892-1017-3(7))* Abbeville Pr., Inc.
—China: A Photographic Journey through the Middle Kingdom. 2010. (ENG.). 244p. 17.50 *(978-0-7892-1080-7(0))* Abbeville Pr., Inc.
Haedecke, Friederike. Luxury Trains. 2008. (ENG.). 24.95 *(978-3-8327-9251-0(1))* teNeues Publishing Co.
Hai'Er, Zhang. Fotografien Aus China: 1986-1989. (CHI & GER., Illus.). 128p. *(978-3-925835-93-3(8))* Braus, Edition, GmbH.
Hinton, Adam. Lovin' It. 2009. (ENG., Illus.). 96p. 35.00 *(978-1-904587-63-7(1))* Lewis, Dewi Publishing GBR. Dist: Consortium Bk. Sales & Distribution.
Hong, Deyuan, ed. Flora of China Illustrations, Vol. 11: Oxalidaceae through Aceraceae. 2009. (Illus.). 634p. 140.00 *(978-1-930723-78-8(4))* Missouri Botanical Garden Pr.
Jiagang, Chen, photos by. Chen Jiagang: the Great Third Front. 2009. (ENG., Illus.). 182p. 75.00 *(978-988-17522-2-2(1))* Timezone 8 Ltd. HKG. Dist: D.A.P./Distributed Art Pubs.
Jiangbo, Jin. Jin Jiangbo: Booming. 2009. (ENG., Illus.). 188p. 45.00 *(978-988-17522-8-4(0))* Timezone 8 Ltd. HKG. Dist: D.A.P./Distributed Art Pubs.
Kander, Nadav, photos by. Nadav Kander: Yangtze - The Long River. 2010. (ENG., Illus.). 188p. 95.00 *(978-3-7757-2683-2(7))* Hatje Cantz Verlag GmbH & Co KG DEU. Dist: D.A.P./Distributed Art Pubs.
Kenna, Michael. Huangshan. 2010. (JPN & ENG., Illus.). ***(978-1-59005-310-2(9))*** Nazraeli Pr.
Li, Dinu, photos by. The Mother of All Journeys. 2007. (ENG., Illus.). 96p. 45.00 *(978-1-904587-41-5(0))* Lewis, Dewi Publishing GBR. Dist: Consortium Bk. Sales & Distribution.
Lin, Aiming & Ren, Zhikun. The Great Wenchuan Earthquake of 2008: A Photographic Atlas of Surface Rupture & Related Disaster: A Photographic Atlas of Surface Rupture & Related Disaster. 2010. (ENG., Illus.). 120p. 139.00 *(978-3-642-03758-0(5)*, 3642037585) Springer.
Lindesay, William. The Great Wall Revisited: From the Jade Gate to Old Dragon's Head. 2008. (Illus.). 292p. 39.95 *(978-0-674-03149-4(0))* Harvard Univ. Pr.
Lloyd, Barbara. China: Travels Between the Yangtze & Yellow Rivers. 2007. (ENG., Illus.). 152p. 48.00 *(978-88-7624-938-9(9))* Skira Editore ITA. Dist: Random Hse., Inc.
Lunsford, Celina & Tannert, Christoph. China Naked. 2007. (GER & ENG., Illus.). 120p. 40.00 *(978-3-939583-11-0(1))* Kehrer Verlag Heidelberg, Klaus Kehrer DEU. Dist: Consortium Bk. Sales & Distribution.
Lyon, Danny, photos by. Deep Sea Diver: An American Photographer's Journey in Shanxi, China. 2011. (ENG., Illus.). 136p. 200.00 *(978-0-7148-6104-3(9))* Phaidon Pr., Inc.
Meniconzi, Alessandra. Hidden China. 2008. 320p. 69.95 *(978-0-8416-0353-0(7))* American Map Corp.
Michell, George, et al. Kashgar: Oasis City on China's Old Silk Road. 2008. (ENG., Illus.). 160p. 50.00 *(978-0-7112-2913-6(9))* Lincoln, Frances Ltd. GBR. Dist: Perseus-PGW.
National Geographic Society Staff. Inside China. 2007. (ENG., Illus.). 272p. 50.00 *(978-1-4262-0126-4(5)*, National Geographic) National Geographic Society.
Pao, Basil. China Revealed: An Extraordinary Journey of Rediscovery. 2007. (ENG., Illus.). 373p. 60.00 *(978-0-7892-0947-4(0))* Abbeville Pr., Inc.
Paoluzzo, Marco. China Memories. 2012. (ENG, FRE & GER., Illus.). 180p. 70.00 ***(978-3-7165-1694-2(5))*** Benteli Verlag CHE. Dist: National Bk. Network.
Pavan, Aldo. Yellow River. 2007. (ENG., Illus.). 272p. 45.00 *(978-0-500-51376-7(7))* Thames & Hudson.
Quintana, Josephine. Door, Windows, Temple & Gateways of Chin. 2008. 92p. pap. 36.95 *(978-1-60594-018-2(6))*, Llumina Pr.) Aeon Publishing Inc.
Rai, Raghu & Perkins, Jane. Tibet in Exile. 2010. (ENG., Illus.). 152p. 45.00 *(978-981-4217-72-9(7)*, Didier Millet,Csi) Continental Sales, Inc.
Rongyu, Su & Houmin, Li. China from Above. 2007. (ENG., Illus.). 400p. 50.00 *(978-88-544-0307-9(5)*, White Star) Rizzoli International Pubns., Inc.
Sans, Jerome, contrib. by. Peter Lindbergh: The Unknown. 2011. (ENG., Illus.). 200p. 68.00 ***(978-3-8296-0544-1(7))*** Schirmer/Mosel Verlag GmbH DEU. Dist: Prestel Publishing.
Schlotter, Kathrin, et al. Culinaria China: Country - Cuisine - Culture, 1 vol. 2010. (ENG., Illus.). 488p. 39.99 *(978-3-8331-4995-5(7))* h.f.ullmann DEU. Dist: Innovative Logistics.
Seibert, Andreas. From Somewhere to Nowhere: China's Internal Migrants. 2008. (Illus.). 316p. 54.95 *(978-3-03778-146-3(7)*, 3037781467) Springer.
Spirit of China. 2008. 240p. *(978-1-4075-2515-0(8))* Parragon, Inc.
Stahel. Kyungwoo Chun Thousands. 2008. (ENG., Illus.). 128p. 50.00 *(978-3-7757-2167-7(3))* Hatje Cantz Verlag GmbH & Co KG DEU. Dist: D.A.P./Distributed Art Pubs.
Stokes, Edward. Hong Kong Nature Landscapes. 2010. (ENG., Illus.). 176p. (gr. 17). 40.00 *(978-988-8028-18-4(9))* Hong Kong Univ. Pr. HKG. Dist: Columbia Univ. Pr.
Suzhou da xue, Tu shu guan Staff, contrib. by. Qi Xian Xie Zhen: Suzhou Da Xue Tu Shu Guan Cang Qing Dai Ren Wu Tu Xiang Xuan. 2008. (Illus.). *(978-7-300-09168-6(7))* China Renmin Univ.Pr.
Tan, Ju K. Greater Tibet: Where Earth Touches the Heavens, 1 vol. 2006. (ENG., Illus.). 136p. 30.00 *(978-981-232-747-5(9))* Marshall Cavendish International (Asia) Private Ltd. SGP. Dist: Marshall Cavendish Corp.
Tézenas, Ambroise, photos by. Beijing: Theatre of the People. 2007. (ENG., Illus.). 120p. 45.00 *(978-1-904587-36-1(4))* Lewis, Dewi Publishing GBR. Dist: Consortium Bk. Sales & Distribution.
Thomson, J. The Inmost Shrine: A Photographic Odyssey of China, 1873. 2009. *(978-1-929154-38-8(0))* Levenger Pr.
Thomson, John, et al. China: Through the Lens of John Thomson (1868-1872). 2nd ed. 2010. (ENG., Illus.). 168p. *(978-616-7339-00-9(7))*, River Bks. Pr. Dist A C) Antique Collectors' Club.
Tong, Kurt, photos by. In Case It Rains in Heaven. 2011. (ENG., Illus.). 96p. 40.00 ***(978-3-86828-188-0(6))*** Kehrer Verlag Heidelberg, Klaus Kehrer DEU. Dist: Consortium Bk. Sales & Distribution.
Wang, Fuchun. The North East Men. 2009. (CHI & ENG., Illus.). 101p. *(978-0-9814698-5-0(X))* International Publishing Hse. for China's Culture.
Wang, Xirong & Qiao, Lihua. Lu Xun's Shaoxing: A Photo. 2010. 300p. 29.95 *(978-1-60220-303-7(2))* BetterLink Pr., Inc.
Wardale, David & Haslbeck, Gunther. Steam on 4 Continents: China, Vol. 4. (GER & ENG., Illus.). 128p. 34.95 *(978-3-925314-03-2(2))* Arnoldsche Art Pubs. DEU. Dist: Antique Collectors' Club.
Wilson, Ming & Wilson, Verity. Imperial Chinese Robes: From the Forbidden City. 2011. (ENG., Illus.). 128p. 50.00 *(978-1-85177-620-7(6))* V & A Pubns. GBR. Dist: Hachette Bk. Group.
Yong, Xu. Backdrops & Backdrops, 1 vol. 2007. (ENG., Illus.). 236p. per. 30.00 *(978-988-99015-1-6(X))* Timezone 8 Ltd. HKG. Dist: D.A.P./Distributed Art Pubs.
Zeng, Han & Yang, ChangHong. Zeng Han & Yang Changhong: Soul Stealer. 2009. (ENG., Illus.). 104p. pap. 22.00 *(978-988-17521-0-9(8))* Timezone 8 Ltd. HKG. Dist: D.A.P./Distributed Art Pubs.
Zheng, Gu. Robert van der Hilst: Shanghai 1990-1993. 2009. (ENG., Illus.). 120p. 45.00 *(978-988-17521-5-4(9))* Timezone 8 Ltd. HKG. Dist: D.A.P./Distributed Art Pubs.
Zhonghua min zu wen hua cu jin hui Staff & Zhong gong Shanxi Sheng wei (Xi'an Shi, China), Xuan chuan bu Staff, contrib. by. Beautiful China. 2007. (CHI & ENG., Illus.). 183p. *(978-0-9785095-5-2(2))* International Publishing Hse. for China's Culture.
Zola, Alberto. China: A Land of Age-Old Culture. 2008. (Exploring Countries of the Wor Ser.). (ENG., Illus.). 128p. 9.95 *(978-88-544-0293-5(1))* White Star ITA. Dist: Random Hse., Inc.

CHINA—POETRY

Kam, Franklin "Frankie". Us: Chinese Immigrant Family, 3rd Generation. 2011. 132p. 29.99 ***(978-1-4653-4630-8(9))***; pap. 19.99 ***(978-1-4653-4629-2(5))*** Xlibris Corp.
Miller, Bradford. The Shattered Lute: A Collection of Poems from Tang Dynasty China. 2011. 312p. pap. 17.95 ***(978-1-4327-7334-2(8))*** Outskirts Pr., Inc.
Mott, Glenn. Analects on a Chinese Screen. 2007. 71p. pap. 16.00 *(978-0-925904-61-4(9))* Chax Pr.
Stone, C. P. China: Impressions in Verse. 2007. (Illus.). 68p. pap. 9.95 *(978-0-9796562-1-7(4))* IRIS Enterprises.
Ward, Jean Elizabeth, Poet Laureate. Chinese Memories. 2008. 196p. pap. 24.99 *(978-1-4357-1050-4(9))* Lulu Enterprises Inc.
Ward, Jean Elizabeth. Han yu: Remembered. 2009. 147p. pap. 23.49 *(978-1-4357-3281-0(2))* Lulu Enterprises Inc.
Woon, Koon. Water Chasing Water. 2012. (ENG., Illus.). 120p. pap. 14.95 *(978-1-885030-49-8(5))* Muae Publishing, Inc.

CHINA—POLITICS AND GOVERNMENT

Abhinandan, Netajee. China's Adaptation to Global Regimes: Dilemmas & Debates. 2011. 264p. pap. ***(978-3-8454-1598-7(3))*** Lambert Academic Publishing.
Ahern, Emily Martin. Chinese Ritual & Politics. 2007. (Cambridge Studies in Social & Cultural Anthropology Ser.). (ENG.). 160p. pap. 38.99 *(978-0-521-04090-7(6))* Cambridge Univ. Pr.
Ai, Jiabing. Guan Er Dai. 2011. (CHI., Illus.). 316p. ***(978-1-935981-23-7(4))*** Mirror Bks. USA.
Ai, Yanghua & Chen, Xiaoming. Gong Qing Tuan Shi Li. 2009. (CHI., Illus.). 431p. pap. *(978-962-8744-08-4(9))* Mirror Bks. USA.
—Tuan Hui Zhao Yao Zhongguo: Hu Jintao de Tuan Dui. 2nd ed. 2007. (CHI., Illus.). 378p. pap. *(978-1-932138-52-8(8))* Mirror Bks. USA.
Ali, Ayxem. Women in China's Muslim Northwest. 2011. (Illus.). 240p. (C). 145.00 *(978-0-415-55712-2(7))* Routledge.
Ali, S. Mahmud. U. S.-China Relations in the "Asia-Pacific" Century. 2008. (ENG.). 288p. 95.00 *(978-0-230-60455-1(2))* Palgrave Macmillan.
Alon, Ilan, et al, eds. China Rules: Globalization & Political Transformation. 2009. (ENG., Illus.). 291p. 105.00 *(978-0-230-57625-4(7))* Palgrave Macmillan.
Alpermann, Bjö, ed. Politics & Markets in Rural China. 2011. (Routledge Contemporary China Ser.). (ENG., Illus.). 264p. (C). 130.00 *(978-0-415-59657-2(2))* Routledge.
Anderson, Eric C. China Restored: The Middle Kingdom Looks to 2020 & Beyond, 1 vol. 2010. 323p. 44.95 *(978-0-313-38517-9(3)*, A2975C, Praeger Pubs.) Greenwood Publishing Group, Inc.
Arrighi, Giovanni. Adam Smith in Beijing: Lineages of the Twenty-First Century. 2007. (ENG., Illus.). 418p. 35.00 *(978-1-84467-104-5(6)*, 844104) Verso Bks. GBR. Dist: Norton, W. W. & Co., Inc.
Arthur Judson Brown. New Forces in Old China: An Inevitable Awakening. Lt. ed. 2006. (ENG.). 364p. pap. 18.99 *(978-1-4264-0145-9(0))* BiblioBazaar.
Bandelj, Nina & Solinger, Dorothy J., eds. Socialism Vanquished, Socialism Challenged: Eastern Europe & China, 1989-2009. 2012. (ENG.). 288p. 99.00 ***(978-0-19-989597-7(X))***; pap. 27.95 ***(978-0-19-989596-0(1))*** Oxford Univ. Pr., Inc.
Barnouin, Barbara, et al. Zhou Enlai: A Political Life. 2007. (ENG.). 404p. (gr. 17). pap. 25.00 *(978-962-996-280-7(2))* Chinese Univ. of Hong Kong, The HKG. Dist: Columbia Univ. Pr.
Bateman, Sam. Security & International Politics in the South China Sea: Towards a Cooperative Management Regime. Emmers, Ralf, ed. 2008. (Routledge Security in Asia Pacific Ser.). (Illus.). 272p. 160.00 *(978-0-415-46943-2(0))* Routledge.
Bedeski, Robert E. Human Security & the Chinese State: Historical Transformations & the Modern Quest for Sovereignty. 2007. (Routledge Contemporary China Ser.). (ENG., Illus.). 208p. (C). 160.00 *(978-0-415-41255-1(2))* Routledge.
Behrouzi, Majid. Democracy as the Political Empowerment of the Citizen: Direct-Deliberative E-Democracy. annot. ed. 2006. (ENG.). 252p. per. 28.50 *(978-0-7391-1809-2(9))* Lexington Bks.
Bell, Daniel A. China's New Confucianism: Politics & Everyday Life in a Changing Society. 2008. (ENG.). 258p. (C). 35.00 *(978-0-691-13690-5(4))* Princeton Univ. Pr.
Bennett, Jeff, et al, eds. Environmental Protection in China: Land-Use Management. 2008. (Illus.). 240p. (C). 119.00 *(978-1-84720-589-6(5))* Elgar, Edward Publishing, Inc.
Bergère, Marie-Claire. The Golden Age of the Chinese Bourgeoisie, 1911-1937. 2009. (Studies in Modern Capitalism Ser.). (ENG.). 372p. pap. 38.99 *(978-0-521-11071-6(8))* Cambridge Univ. Pr.
Bernstein, Thomas P. & Lü, Xiaobo. Taxation without Representation in Contemporary Rural China. 2008. (Cambridge Modern China Ser.). (ENG., Illus.). 308p. pap. 34.99 *(978-0-521-08289-1(7))* Cambridge Univ. Pr.
Besha, Patrick. Village Democracy & Social Unrest in China. 2008. 128p. per. *(978-3-8364-6091-0(2))* VDM Verlag Dr. Mueller e.K.
Bianco, Lucien. Wretched Rebels: Rural Disturbances on the Eve of the Chinese Revolution. Liddell, Philip, tr. from FRE. 2010. (Harvard East Asian Monographs: 323). Orig. Title: Jacqueries et révolution dans la Chine du XXe Siècle. (Illus.). 300p. 39.95 *(978-0-674-03542-3(9))* Harvard Univ., Asia Ctr.
Bingman, Charles F. Changing Governments in India & Chin. 2011. 300p. pap. ***(978-1-84903-082-3(0))*** Schiel & Denver Publishing Ltd.
Biographiq. Mao Zedong - the Great Helmsman. 2008. 76p. pap. 9.99 *(978-1-59986-036-7(8)*, Biographiq) Filiquarian Publishing, LLC.
Bland, J. O. P. & Backhouse, Edmund. China under the Empress Dowager: The History of the Life & Times of Tzu Hsi. 2011. (ENG.). 552p. pap. 24.99 *(978-988-18667-4-5(X))* Earnshaw Bks. HKG. Dist: Independent Pubs. Group.
Bowles, Paul & Harriss, John, eds. Globalization & Labour in China & India: Impacts & Responses. 2010. (International Political Economy Ser.). (ENG., Illus.). 288p. 89.00 *(978-0-230-23088-0(1))* Palgrave Macmillan.
Brady, Anne-Marie. Marketing Dictatorship: Propaganda & Thought Work in Contemporary China. 2007. (Asia/Pacific/Perspectives Ser.). (ENG., Illus.). 246p. 80.00 *(978-0-7425-4057-6(X))* Rowman & Littlefield Publishers, Inc.
Brady, Anne-Marie, ed. China's Thought Management. 2011. (Routledge Studies on China in Transition Ser.). (ENG., Illus.). 224p. (C). 125.00 *(978-0-415-61673-7(5))* Routledge.
BRAMALL. Chinese Economic Development. 2008. (Illus.). 640p. pap. 68.95 *(978-0-415-37348-7(4))* Routledge.
Breslin, Shaun & Shaw, Timothy M. China & the Global Political Economy. 2007. (International Political Economy Ser.). (ENG., Illus.). 256p. 106.00 *(978-1-4039-8647-4(9))* Palgrave Macmillan.
Breytenbach, Breyten. Notes from the Middle World. 2009. (ENG.). 220p. pap. 18.00 *(978-1-931859-91-2(4))* Haymarket Bks.
Brodsgaard, Kjeld Erik. Hainan - State, Society, & Business in a Chinese Province. 2012. (China Policy Ser.). (ENG., Illus.). 208p. (C). pap. 42.95 ***(978-0-415-54138-1(7))*** Routledge.
Brodsgaard, Kjeld Erik & Brodsgaard, Kjeld Erik. Hainan: State, Society, & Business in a Chinese Province. 2008. (China Policy Ser.). (ENG., Illus.). 208p. (C). 168.00 *(978-0-415-46033-0(6))* Routledge.
Browder, Greg, et al. Stepping Up: Improving the Performance of China's Urban Water Utilities. 2007. (ENG.). 150p. pap. 15.00 *(978-0-8213-7331-6(5)*, 9780821373316) World Bank Pubns.
Brown, Arthur Judson. New Forces in Old China. 2008. 368p. 31.99 *(978-0-554-21418-4(0))* BiblioBazaar.
Brown, Kerry. Ballot Box China. 2011. (Asian Arguments Ser.). (ENG.). 208p. pap. 29.95 *(978-1-84813-820-9(2))* Zed Bks., Ltd. GBR. Dist: Macmillan.
—Ballot Box China: Grassroots Democracy in the Final Major One Party State. 2011. (Asian Arguments Ser.). (ENG., Illus.). 208p. 125.95 *(978-1-84813-819-3(9))* Zed Bks., Ltd. GBR. Dist: Macmillan.
Brown, Miranda. The Politics of Mourning in Early China. (Illus.). 2008. xiv, 205p. pap. 29.95 *(978-0-7914-7158-6(6))* 2007. 205p. 75.00 *(978-0-7914-7157-9(8))* State Univ. of New York Pr.
Brownell, Susan. Beijing's Games: What the Olympics Mean to China. 2008. (Latin American Silhouettes Ser.). (ENG., Illus.). 230p. 77.00 *(978-0-7425-5640-9(9))*; per. 24.95 *(978-0-7425-5641-6(7))* Rowman & Littlefield Publishers, Inc.
Burman, Edward. China & Iran: Parallel History, Future Threat? 2009. (ENG., Illus.). 224p. pap. 24.95 *(978-0-7524-4854-1(4))* History Pr. Ltd., The GBR. Dist: Independent Pubs. Group.
Cai, Tuo, ed. Chinese Perspectives on Globalization & Autonomy. 2012. (Issues in Contemporary Chinese Thought & Culture Ser.). (ENG.). xv, 376p. ***(978-90-04-21615-0(4))*** BRILL.
Callahan, William A. China: The Pessoptimist Nation. (ENG., Illus.). 2012. 288p. pap. 29.95 ***(978-0-19-960439-5(8))*** 2010. 248p. 45.00 *(978-0-19-954995-5(8))* Oxford Univ. Pr., Inc.
Carlson, Allen, et al, eds. Contemporary Chinese Politics: New Sources, Methods, & Field Strategies. 2010. (ENG., Illus.). 336p. 99.00 *(978-0-521-19783-0(X))*; pap. 29.99 *(978-0-521-15576-2(2))* Cambridge Univ. Pr.
Chan, Chak Kwan, et al. Social Policy in China. 2008. (Illus.). (C). 234p. 90.00 *(978-1-86134-881-4(9))*; 248p. pap. 39.95 *(978-1-86134-880-7(0))* Policy Pr. GBR. Dist: International Specialized Bk. Services, Chicago Distribution Ctr.
Chan, Hok-lam. Ming Taizu (R. 1368-98)and the Foundation of the Ming Dynasty in China. 2011. (Variorum Collected Studies). (Illus.). 374p. 165.00 ***(978-1-4094-3128-2(2))*** Ashgate Publishing Co.
Chan, Thomas & Moser v. Filseck, Karin. Perceptions & Images of China. Assmann, Heinz-Dieter, ed. 2008. 298p. pap. 49.00 *(978-3-8329-3459-0(6))* Nomos Verlagsgesellschaft DEU. Dist: International Specialized Bk. Services.
Chang, Chihyun. Government, Imperialism & Nationalism in China: The Maritime Customs Service & its Chinese Staff. 2012. (Routledge Studies in the Modern History of Asia Ser.). (ENG.). 256p. (C). 155.00 ***(978-0-415-53142-9(X))*** Routledge.
Chang, Michael G. A Court on Horseback Vol. 287: Imperial Touring & the Construction of Qing Rule, 1680-1785. 2007. (Harvard East Asian Monographs: 287). (Illus.). 550p. 49.95 *(978-0-674-02454-0(0))* Harvard Univ., Asia Ctr.
Charlton, Sue Ellen M. Comparing Asian Politics: India, China, & Japan. 3rd ed. 2009. (ENG., Illus.). 400p. (C). pap. 40.00 *(978-0-8133-4414-0(X))* Westview Pr.
Cheek, Timothy. Living with Reform: China Since 1989. 2007. (Global History of the Present Ser.). (ENG., Illus.). 224p. 94.95 *(978-1-84277-722-0(X))*; per. 26.95 *(978-1-84277-723-7(8))* Zed Bks., Ltd. GBR. Dist: Macmillan.
Cheek, Timothy, ed. A Critical Introduction to Mao. 2010. (ENG., Illus.). 392p. (C). 90.00 *(978-0-521-88462-4(4))* Cambridge Univ. Pr.
Chen, Chunlai & Duncan, Ron, eds. Agriculture & Food Security in China: What Effect WTO Accession & Regional Trade Agreements? 2008. 512p. pap. *(978-0-7315-3817-1(X))* Asia Pacific Pr.
Chen, Gang. China's Climate Policy. 2012. ***(978-0-203-11745-3(X))***; (ENG., Illus.). 144p. (C). 136.00 ***(978-0-415-59313-7(1))*** Routledge.
Chen, Jie & Dickson, Bruce J. Allies of the State: China's Private Entrepreneurs & Democratic Change. 2010. (Illus.). 232p. 45.00 *(978-0-674-04896-6(2))* Harvard Univ. Pr.
Chen, Lanyan. Gender & Chinese Development: Towards an Equitable Society. 2008. (Routledge IAFFE Advances in Feminist Economics Ser.). (Illus.). X, 182p. 44.95 *(978-0-415-46723-0(3))*; 160.00 *(978-0-415-46722-3(5))* Routledge.
Chen, Nai-Ruenn, ed. Chinese Economic Statistics in the Maoist Era: 1949-1965. 2008. (ENG.). 570p. pap. 95.00 *(978-0-202-36281-6(7))* Aldine Transaction.
Chen, Shao-Kwan. System of Taxation in China in the Tsing. 2006. pap. 20.95 *(978-1-4286-5616-1(2))* Kessinger Publishing, LLC.
—The System of Taxation in China in the Tsing Dynasty, 1644-1911. 2008. 333p. pap. 19.75 *(978-0-554-68152-8(8))*; 274p. pap. 19.75 *(978-0-554-68155-9(2))* BiblioBazaar.
—The System of Taxation in China in the Tsing Dynasty, 1644-1911. 2007. (ENG.). 132p. 35.95 *(978-0-548-14366-7(8))* Kessinger Publishing, LLC.
Chen, Xi. Social Protest & Contentious Authoritarianism in China. 2011. (ENG., Illus.). 255p. 95.00 ***(978-1-107-01486-2(7))*** Cambridge Univ. Pr.
Chen, Y. P. Chinese Political Thought: Mao Tse-Tung & Liu Shao-Chi. 2010. 148p. pap. 137.00 *(978-90-481-8315-9(4)*, 9048183154) Springer.
Chen, Yi-Ru Regina. The Business of Corporate Government Affairs in China - Corporate Competitive Advantage in China's Marketization. 2008. 528p. per. *(978-3-8364-3902-2(6))* VDM Verlag Dr. Mueller e.K.
Chen, Zhongping. Modern China's Network Revolution: Chambers of Commerce & Sociopolitical Change in the Early Twentieth Century. 2011. (ENG.). 312p. 55.00 *(978-0-8047-7409-3(9))* Stanford Univ. Pr.

C

Cheng, J. I. Economics & Foreign Investment in China. 2006. (Illus.). 229p. (C). 79.00 (978-1-60021-238-3(7)) Nova Science Pubs., Inc.

Cheung, Gordon C. K. & Cheung, Gordon. China Factors: Political Perspectives & Economic Interactions. 2007. (ENG.). 177p. (gr. 11). 49.95 (978-0-7658-0342-9(9)) Transaction Pubs.

Chien-Nung, Li. The Political History of China, 1840-1928. Teng, Ssu-yu, ed. Ingalls, Jeremy, tr. 2011. 558p. 62.95 **(978-1-258-10290-6(0))** Literary Licensing, LLC.

Chikukutu, Josphat. Transformational Strategies for Companies in Transitional Economies. 2011. 116p. pap. **(978-3-8443-0483-1(5))** Lambert Academic Publishing.

China: Recent Security Developments. 2008. iii, 59p. (978-0-16-082188-2(6), 552-070-38322-1) United States Government Printing Office.

China Development Bank Staff & Renmin University Staff, contrib. by. Development Finance in China: Theory & Implementation, 3 vols., Vol. 1. 2011. (Enrich Series on Developmental Finance in China Ser.). (ENG.). 544p. 148.00 (978-981-4298-10-0(7)) Enrich Professional Publishing (S)., Ltd. SGP. Dist: Independent Pubs. Group.

China on the Eve of the Olympics: Hearing Before the Committee on Foreign Affairs, House of Representatives, One Hundred Tenth Congress, Second Session, July 23, 2008. 2008. ii, 63p. (978-0-16-081749-6(8), 552-070-37957-6) United States Government Printing Office.

China Photographers' Association Staff, et al. China's Thirty Years. 2011. (CHI & ENG., Illus.). 372p. 65.00 (978-0-19-800897-2(X)) Oxford Univ. Pr., Inc.

China's Citizen Complaint System: Prospects for Accountability: Roundtable Before the Congressional-Executive Commission on China, One Hundred Eleventh Congress, First Session, December 4, 2009. 2010. ii, 43p. (978-0-16-085828-4(3), 552-070-41040-6) United States Government Printing Office.

China's Far West: Conditions in Xinjiang One Year after Demonstrations & Riots: Roundtable Before the Congressional-Executive Commission on China, One Hundred Eleventh Congress, Second Session, July 19, 2010. 2010. ii, 34p. (978-0-16-087024-8(0), 552-070-41882-2) United States Government Printing Office.

Chittick, Andrew. Patronage & Community in Medieval China: The Xiangyang Garrison, 400-600 CE. 2009. (SUNY series in Chinese Philosophy & Culture Ser.). (Illus.). 208p. 75.00 (978-1-4384-2897-0(9)) State Univ. of New York Pr.

Cho, Young Nam. Local People's Congresses in China: Development & Transition. 2010. (ENG.). 206p. pap. 29.99 (978-0-521-18249-2(2)) Cambridge Univ. Pr.

Chong, Chae-Ho. Charting China's Future: Political, Social, & International Dimensions. 2006. (ENG., Illus.). 232p. per. 39.95 (978-0-7425-5397-2(3)) Rowman & Littlefield Publishers, Inc.

Chong, Denise. Egg on Mao: The Story of an Ordinary Man Who Defaced an Icon & Unmasked a Dictatorship. 2009. (ENG.). 256p. 26.00 (978-1-58243-547-3(2), Counterpoint Pr.) Basic Bks. GBR. Dist: Perseus-PGW.

Chong, Ja Ian. External Intervention & the Politics of State Formation: China, Indonesia, & Thailand, 1893#x2013;1952. 2012. (ENG., Illus.). 304p. 95.00 **(978-1-107-01375-9(5))** Cambridge Univ. Pr.

Chong, Key Ray. Sun Yat-sen & the West: Western Influence on His Life & Thought. 2010. 484p. 129.95 (978-0-7734-1357-3(X)) Mellen, Edwin Pr., The.

Chou, Bill K. P. Government & Policy-Making Reform in China: The Implications of Governing Capacity. 2009. (Comparative Development & Policy in Asia Ser.). (ENG., Illus.). 178p. 130.00 (978-0-415-43704-2(0)) Routledge.

Chu, Yin-Wah. Chinese Capitalisms: Historical Emergence & Political Implications. 2010. (International Political Economy Ser.). (ENG., Illus.). 272p. 89.00 (978-0-230-57649-0(4)) Palgrave Macmillan.

Chung, Jae Ho. Charting Chinas Future: Political, Social, & International Dimensions. Chung, Jae Ho, ed. 2006. (ENG., Illus.). 232p. 92.00 (978-0-7425-5396-5(5)) Rowman & Littlefield Publishers, Inc.

Chung, Jae Ho, ed. Chinas Crisis Management. 2011. (China Policy Ser.). (ENG., Illus.). 168p. (C). 140.00 (978-0-415-67780-6(7)) Routledge.

Chuo Daigaku, Jinbun Kagaku Kenkyujo Staff, contrib. by. Toan No Sekai. 2009. (JPN., Illus.). xiii, 250p. (978-4-8057-4210-5(0)) Chuo Univ. Pr.

Clarke, Michael E. Xinjiang & China's Rise in Central Asia - A History. 2011. (Routledge Contemporary China Ser.). (ENG.). 224p. (C). 140.00 (978-0-415-58456-2(6)) Routledge.

Clayton, Cathryn H. Sovereignty at the Edge: Macau & the Question of Chineseness. 2010. (Harvard East Asian Monographs: 324). (Illus.). 420p. 49.95 (978-0-674-03545-4(3)) Harvard Univ., Asia Ctr.

Creel, George. Russia's Race for Asi. 2011. 264p. 47.95 **(978-1-258-08211-6(X))** Literary Licensing, LLC.

Cui, Jing. Local Government Reform in Chin. 2010. 244p. pap. (978-3-8383-5111-7(8)) Lambert Academic Publishing.

Culp, Robert Joseph. Articulating Citizenship: Civic Education & Student Politics in Southeastern China, 1912-1940. 2007. (Harvard East Asian Monographs: 291). (Illus.). 400p. 49.50 (978-0-674-02587-5(3)) Harvard Univ., Asia Ctr.

Dahl-Madsen, Ingrid. Global Warming, the Us, & Chin. 2011. 124p. pap. **(978-3-8443-1017-7(7))** Lambert Academic Publishing.

Damm, Jens & Thomas, Simona, eds. Chinese Cyberspaces: Technological Changes & Political Effects. 2009. 184p. pap. 39.95 (978-0-415-54693-5(1)) Routledge.

de Blij, Harm. Why Geography Matters: More Than Ever. 2nd ed. 2012. (ENG., Illus.). 352p. pap. 16.95 **(978-0-19-991374-9(9))** Oxford Univ. Pr., Inc.

De Blij, Harm J. Why Geography Matters: Three Challenges Facing America: Climate Change, the Rise of China, & Global Terrorism. 2007. (ENG., Illus.). 320p. per. 16.95 (978-0-19-531582-0(0)) Oxford Univ. Pr., Inc.

Decker, Brett M. & Triplett, William C., II. Bowing to Beijing: How Barack Obama Is Hastening America's Decline & Ushering A Century of Chinese Domination. 2011. (ENG.). 256p. 27.95 (978-1-59698-289-5(6)) Regnery Publishing, Inc., An Eagle Publishing Co.

Deng, Kent G. China's Political Economy in Modern Times. 2011. (Routledge Studies in the Modern History of Asia Ser.). (ENG., Illus.). 320p. (C). 140.00 (978-0-415-67405-8(0)) Routledge.

Deng, Yong. China's Struggle for Status: The Realignment of International Relations. 2008. (ENG., Illus.). 312p. 81.00 (978-0-521-88666-6(X)); pap. 31.99 (978-0-521-71415-0(X)) Cambridge Univ. Pr.

Deng, Zhenglai. State & Civil Society: The Chinese Perspective. 2010. (Illus.). 452p. 125.00 (978-981-4313-57-5(2)) World Scientific Publishing Co., Inc.

Deng, Zhenglai & Guo, Sujian. Reviving Legitimacy: Lessons for & from China. 2011. **(978-0-7391-6888-2(6))** Lexington Bks.

Denoon, David B. H., ed. China: Contemporary Political, Economic, & International Affairs. 2007. (ENG., Illus.). 256p. 70.00 (978-0-8147-1999-2(6)); per. 21.00 (978-0-8147-2000-4(5)) New York Univ. Pr.

Dethier, Jean-Jacques, ed. Governance, Decentralization & Reform in China, India & Russia. 2010. (ENG.). 472p. pap. 269.00 (978-1-4419-4992-9(5), 1441949925) Springer.

Dewey, John. The Middle Works of John Dewey, 1899-1924 Vol. 11: 1918-1919, Essays on China, Japan, & the War. Boydston, Jo Ann, ed. 2008. (Collected Works of John Dewey Ser.). (ENG.). 478p. pap. 40.00 (978-0-8093-2806-2(2)) Southern Illinois Univ. Pr.

Dillon, Michael. Xinjiang & Expansion of Chinese Comm Power. 2011. (Routledge Studies in the Modern History of Asia Ser.). (ENG.). 256p. (C). 140.00 (978-0-415-58443-2(4)) Routledge.

Dillon, Nara & Oi, Jean C., eds. At the Crossroads of Empires: Middlemen, Social Networks, & State-Building in Republican Shanghai. 2007. (ENG.). 328p. 50.00 (978-0-8047-5619-8(8)) Stanford Univ. Pr.

Ding, Sheng. The Dragon's Hidden Wings: How China Rises with Its Soft Power. 2008. (Challenges Facing Chinese Political Development Ser.). (ENG., Illus.). 210p. 73.50 (978-0-7391-2392-8(0)) Lexington Bks.

Ding, Xiaojong. Policy Metamorphosis in China: A Case Study of Minban Education in Shanghai. 2011. **(978-0-7391-7186-8(0))** Lexington Bks.

Dreyer, June Teufel. China's Political System: Modernization & Tradition. 8th ed. 2011. (ENG., Illus.). 400p. (C). pap. 75.20 (978-0-205-00581-9(0), Prentice Hall) Prentice Hall PTR.

Dunstan, Helen. State or Merchant? Political Economy & Political Process in 1740s China. 2006. (Harvard East Asian Monographs: 273). (Illus.). 523p. 54.95 (978-0-674-02262-1(9)) Harvard Univ., Asia Ctr.

Dyke, Paul A. & Van Dyke, Paul A. Merchants of Canton & Macau: Politics & Strategies in Eighteenth-Century Trade. 2011. (ENG., Illus.). 672p. (gr. 17). 80.00 (978-988-8028-91-7(X)) Hong Kong Univ. Pr. HKG. Dist: Columbia Univ. Pr.

Eber, Irene. Wartime Shanghai & the Jewish Refugees from Central Europe: Survival, Co-Existence, & Identity in a Multi-Ethnic City. 2012. (New Perspectives on Modern Jewish History Ser.). (ENG., Illus.). XIV, 245p. (gr. 17). 140.00 **(978-3-11-026797-6(7))** De Gruyter, Walter Inc.

Ebrey, Patricia Buckley & Bickford, Maggie, eds. Emperor Huizong & Late Northern Song China: The Politics of Culture & the Culture of Politics. 2006. (Harvard East Asian Monographs: 266). (Illus.). 625p. 59.95 (978-0-674-02127-3(4)) Harvard Univ., Asia Ctr.

Economy, Elizabeth C. The River Runs Black: The Environmental Challenge to China's Future. 2nd rev. ed. 2010. (Council on Foreign Relations Book Ser.). (Illus.). 368p. 65.00 (978-0-8014-4924-6(3)); pap. 19.95 (978-0-8014-7613-6(5)) Cornell Univ. Pr.

Edwards, Louise. Gender, Politics, & Democracy: Women's Suffrage in China. 2007. (ENG., Illus.). 352p. 60.00 (978-0-8047-5688-4(0)) Stanford Univ. Pr.

Elsheshtawy. Dubai: An Emerging Urbanity? 2009. (Planning, History & Environment Ser.). (ENG., Illus.). 304p. (C). 115.00 (978-0-415-44461-3(6)) Routledge.

Emirates Center for Strategic Studies and Research Staff & Tauris, I. B. China, India & the United States: Competition for Energy Resources. 2009. (ENG., Illus.). 612p. pap. 51.00 (978-9948-00-929-0(0), Emirates Center for Strategic Studies) I. B. Tauris & Co., Ltd. GBR. Dist: Macmillan.

—China, India & the United States: Competition for Energy Resources. 2009. (ENG., Illus.). 612p. 102.00 (978-9948-00-930-6(4), Emirates Center for Strategic Studies) I. B. Tauris & Co., Ltd. GBR. Dist: Macmillan.

Eric, K. W. Desiring Hong Kong, Consuming South China: Transborder Cultural Politics, 1970-2010. 2011. (Hong Kong Culture & Society Ser.). (Illus.). 176p. **(978-988-8053-93-3(0))** Hong Kong Univ. Pr.

—Desiring Hong Kong, Consuming South China: Transborder Cultural Politics, 1970-2010. 2012. (Hong Kong Culture & Society Ser.). (ENG., Illus.). 220p. (gr. 17). pap. 25.00 **(978-988-8083-46-6(5))** Hong Kong Univ. Pr. HKG. Dist: Columbia Univ. Pr.

Espinosa De Godas, Eusebio. China 2008. 2008. (Illus.). 208p. pap. (978-0-7552-0410-6(7)) Authors OnLine, Ltd.

Fan, Lida. Social Policy & Migration in China. 2011. (Routledge Contemporary China Ser.). (ENG., Illus.). 168p. (C). 133.00 (978-0-415-60782-7(5)) Routledge.

Fang, Ning. Cao Gen Jing Ji Yu Min Zhu Zheng Zhi: She Hui Zhu Yi Shi Chang Jing Ji Yu She Hui Zhu Yi Min Zhu Zheng Zhi Xie Tong Fa Zhan de Taizhou Mo Shi Yan Jiu = Grassroots Economy & Democratic Politics. 2008. (CHI.). 9p. (978-7-5097-0434-9(0)) China Social Science Documentation Publishing Hse.

Feng, Li & Li, Feng. Bureaucracy & the State in Early China: Governing the Western Zhou. 2008. (ENG., Illus.). 400p. 125.00 (978-0-521-88447-1(0)) Cambridge Univ. Pr.

Field, Andrew. Shanghai's Dancing World: Cabaret Culture & Urban Politics, 1919 — 1954. 2011. (ENG.). 400p. (gr. 17). pap. 25.00 (978-962-996-448-1(1)) Chinese Univ. of Hong Kong, The HKG. Dist: Columbia Univ. Pr.

Florini, Ann, et al. China Experiments: From Local Innovations to National Reform. 2012. (ENG., Illus.). 216p. pap. 29.95 **(978-0-8157-2200-7(1))** Brookings Institution Pr.

Fokkema, Douwe. Perfect Worlds: Utopian Fiction in China & the West. 2012. (ENG., Illus.). 448p. pap. **(978-90-8964-350-6(8))** Amsterdam Univ. Pr.

Frazier, Mark W. Socialist Insecurity: Pensions & the Politics of Uneven Development in China. 2010. (Illus.). 224p. 35.00 (978-0-8014-4822-5(0)) Cornell Univ. Pr.

Friedman, Edward & Gilley, Bruce. Asia's Giants: Comparing China & India. Friedman, Edward & Gilley, Bruce, eds. 2008. (ENG.). 264p. pap. 34.00 (978-0-230-60616-6(4)) Palgrave Macmillan.

Fulda, Andreas. Social & Political Activism in China: How Citizen Activists are Silently Shaping China's Democracy. 2012. (China Policy Ser.). (ENG.). (C). 140.00 (978-0-415-61730-7(8)) Routledge.

Fulda, Andreas & Qinghua, Song. Participatory Democracy in China. 2012. (ENG.). 256p. (C). 145.00 (978-0-415-49452-6(4)) Routledge.

Gao, Mobo. The Battle for China's Past: Mao & the Cultural Revolution. 2008. (ENG.). 280p. 95.00 (978-0-7453-2781-5(8)); pap. 27.95 (978-0-7453-2780-8(X)) Pluto Pr. GBR. Dist: Macmillan.

Gao, Xiao. Ta Jiang Ling Dao Zhongguo: Xi Jinping Zhuan. 2010. ("Zhongguo Zhang Quan Zhe" Xi Lie Ser.). (Illus.). 570p. pap. **(978-962-8744-44-2(5))** Mirror Bks. USA.

Gao, Xuan. The Proliferation of Anti-Dumping & Poor Governance in Emerging Economies: Case Studies of China & South Africa. 2009. (NAI Discussion Papers). 30p. pap. 12.95 (978-91-7106-644-2(6)) Nordiska Afrikainstitutet SWE. Dist: Stylus Publishing, LLC.

Gao Yaojie: Physician, Grandmother, & Whistleblower in China's Fight Against HIV/AIDS: Roundtable Before the Congressional-Executive Commission on China, One Hundred Eleventh Congress, First Session, December 3, 2009. 2010. ii, 29p. (978-0-16-085802-4(X), 552-070-41019-8) United States Government Printing Office.

Geis, John P., et al. Discord or Harmonious Society: China In 2030: China In 2030. Air War College (U.S.), Center for Strategy and Technology, ed. 2011. (ENG., Illus.). 144p. pap. 23.00 (978-1-58566-209-8(7), Dept. of the Air Force) United States Government Printing Office.

Gibson, Richard Michael. The Secret Army: Chiang Kai-Shek & the Drug Warlords of the Golden Triangle. 2011. (ENG.). 384p. pap. 32.95 (978-0-470-83018-5(2), Wiley) Wiley, John & Sons, Inc.

Gill, Bates. Rising Star: China's New Security Diplomacy. 2007. (ENG.). 267p. 32.95 (978-0-8157-3146-7(9)) Brookings Institution Pr.

Gilley, Bruce & Diamond, Larry, eds. Political Change in China: Comparisons with Taiwan. 2008. (Illus.). 300p. (C). 65.00 (978-1-58826-568-5(4)); pap. 24.50 (978-1-58826-593-7(5)) Rienner, Lynne Pubs.

Global China. 2012. (C). 41.95 **(978-0-203-87739-5(X))** Routledge.

Gold, Thomas B., et al, eds. Laid-Off Workers in a Workers' State: Unemployment with Chinese Characteristics. 2009. (ENG., Illus.). 272p. 95.00 (978-0-230-61370-6(5)) Palgrave Macmillan.

Goldstein, Morris & Lardy, Nicholas R. The Future of China's Exchange Rate Policy, 87. 2009. (ENG., Illus.). 112p. pap. 20.95 (978-0-88132-416-7(7)) Peterson Institute for International Economics.

Gong, Ting & Ma, Stephen K., eds. Preventing Corruption in Asia. 2011. (Illus.). 272p. pap. 42.95 **(978-0-415-66599-5(X))** Routledge.

Gong, Yuzhi. Gong Yuzhi Dang Shi Lun Ji, 2 vols. 2009. (CHI.). (978-7-5438-6138-1(0)) Hunan Publishing Hse.

Gonzalez, Benjamin. Charting a New Silk Road? 2008. 112p. pap. (978-3-8364-8780-1(2)) VDM Verlag Dr. Mueller e.K.

Goodman, David S. G. Centre & Province in the People's Republic of China: Sichuan & Guizhou, 1955-1965. 2008. (Contemporary China Institute Publications). (ENG.). 272p. pap. 37.99 (978-0-521-10353-4(3)) Cambridge Univ. Pr.

Google & Internet Control in China: A Nexus Between Human Rights & Trade?: Hearing Before the Congressional-Executive Commission on China, One Hundred Eleventh Congress, Second Session, March 24, 2010. 2010. (Illus.). iii, 79p. (978-0-16-086206-9(X), 552-070-41304-9) United States Government Printing Office.

Gordon, David B. & Stearns, Peter N. Sun Yatsen: Seeking a Newer China (Library of World Biography Series) 2009. (Library of World Biography Ser.). (ENG.). 192p. (C). pap. 25.00 (978-0-321-33306-3(3), Prentice Hall) Prentice Hall PTR.

Gouysse, Vincent. Imperialisme et Anti-imperialisme. 2008. 408p. pap. 25.50 (978-1-4092-0321-6(2)) Lulu Enterprises Inc.

Grafstein, Robert & Wen, Fan. A Bridge Too Far? Commonalities & Differences Between China & the United States. 2009. (ENG., Illus.). 244p. 73.50 (978-0-7391-2887-9(6)) Lexington Bks.

Greenhalgh, Susan. Just One Child: Science & Policy in Deng's China. 2008. (Illus.). 440p. 55.00 (978-0-520-25338-4(8)); 403p. per. 26.95 (978-0-520-25339-1(6)) Univ. of California Pr.

Gu, Sharron. Law & Politics in Modern China: Under the Law, the Law, & above the Law. 2009. 124.99 (978-1-60497-604-5(7)) Cambria Pr.

Gu Zhenhong. Approaches to Energy Efficient Building Development: Studying under Chinese Contexts 2008. 100p. pap. (978-3-639-09361-2(5)) VDM Verlag Dr. Mueller e.K.

Guiheux, Gilles & Kuah-Pearce, Khun Eng, eds. Social Movements in China & Hong Kong: The Expansion of Protest Space. 2009. (ICAS Publications Ser.). (ENG.). 336p. pap. (978-90-8964-131-1(9)) Amsterdam Univ. Pr.

Gungwu, Wang. Divided China: Preparing for Reunification 883-947. 2007. 224p. (Illus.). pap. 54.00 (978-981-270-792-5(1)); 2nd ed. 87.00 (978-981-270-611-9(9)) World Scientific Publishing Co., Inc.

Gungwu, Wang & Zheng, Yongnian, eds. China & the New International Order. 2009. (Illus.). 322p. pap. 39.95 (978-0-415-54645-4(1)) Routledge.

Guo, ed. Challenges Facing Chinese Political Development. 2007. (Challenges Facing Chinese Political Development Ser.). (ENG.). 250p. pap. 34.99 (978-0-7391-2095-8(6)) Lexington Bks.

Guo, Baogang, ed. Challenges Facing Chinese Political Development. 2007. (Challenges Facing Chinese Political Development Ser.). (ENG., Illus.). 250p. 78.99 (978-0-7391-2094-1(8)) Lexington Bks.

Guo, Baogang & Li, He, eds. The Chinese Labyrinth: Exploring China's Model of Development. 2011. (Challenges Facing Chinese Political Development Ser.). (ENG.). 230p. (gr. 17). 65.00 **(978-0-7391-6575-1(5))** Lexington Bks.

Guo, Sujian. Chinese Politics & Government. 2012. (ENG., Illus.). 352p. (C). 160.00 **(978-0-415-55138-0(2))**; pap. 48.95 **(978-0-415-55139-7(0))** Routledge.

Guo, Sujian & Guo, Baogang. China in Search of a Harmonious Society. 2008. (Challenges Facing Chinese Political Development Ser.). (ENG., Illus.). 258p. 78.99 (978-0-7391-2623-3(7)); pap. 31.50 (978-0-7391-2624-0(5)) Lexington Bks.

Guo, Sujian & Zhenglai, Deng, eds. China's Search for Good Governance. 2011. (ENG., Illus.). 252p. 85.00 (978-0-230-11728-0(7)) Palgrave Macmillan.

Guo, Xiaolin. State & Ethnicity in China's Southwest. 2008. (China Studies Ser.). (Illus.). 320p. (978-90-04-16775-9(7)) BRILL.

Gustafsson, Bj_rn A., et al, eds. Inequality & Public Policy in China. 2010. (ENG.). 384p. pap. 36.99 (978-0-521-15905-0(9)) Cambridge Univ. Pr.

Guy, R. Kent. Qing Governors & Their Provinces: The Evolution of Territorial Administration in China, 1644-1796. 2010. (ENG & MUL., Illus.). 512p. (C). 80.00 (978-0-295-99018-7(X)); pap. 45.00 (978-0-295-99019-4(8)) Univ. of Washington Pr.

Halper, Stefan. The Beijing Consensus: Legitimizing Authoritarianism in Our Time. 2012. (ENG.). 336p. (gr. 9). pap. 17.99 (978-0-465-02523-7(4)) Basic Bks.

Hammond. Pepper Mountain. 2012. (ENG.). 256p. pap. 42.95 **(978-0-415-54189-3(1))** Routledge.

Hammond, Kenneth J. Pepper Mountain: The Life, Death & Posthumous Career of Yang Jisheng. 2007. (ENG., Illus.). 256p. 160.00 (978-0-7103-1280-8(6)) Routledge.

Hao, Zhidong. Macau History & Society. 2011. (ENG., Illus.). 328p. (gr. 17). pap. 38.00 (978-988-8028-54-2(5)) Hong Kong Univ. Pr. HKG. Dist: Columbia Univ. Pr.

Harris, Nigel. The Mandate of Heaven: Marx & Mao in Modern China. xi, 307p. 12.50 (978-0-7043-2191-5(2)) Quartet Bks., Ltd. GBR. Dist: Charles River Bks.

Hart, Robert. These from the Land of Sinim: Essays on the Chinese Question. 2010. (ENG.). 268p. pap. 27.75 (978-1-176-37485-0(0)) 2010. 268p. pap. 27.75 (978-1-148-94923-9(2)) 2010. 260p. pap. 26.75 (978-1-142-97891-4(5)) 2009. 264p. 24.99 (978-1-103-92561-2(X)) 2009. 264p. pap. 18.99 (978-1-103-92553-7(9)) BiblioBazaar.

—These from the Land of Sinim: Essays on the Chinese Question. 2007. (ENG.). 264p. 42.95 (978-0-548-36645-5(4)); per. 27.95 (978-0-548-30942-1(6)) Kessinger Publishing, LLC.

Hasmath, Reza & Hsu, Jennifer, eds. China in an Era of Transition: Understanding Contemporary State & Society Actors. 2009. (ENG., Illus.). 244p. 100.00 (978-0-230-61350-8(0)) Palgrave Macmillan.

He, Baogang. Rural Democracy in China: The Role of Village Elections. 2007. (ENG.). 292p. 95.00 (978-0-230-60016-4(6)) Palgrave Macmillan.

He, Peiran. Ways to Urbanisation: Post-War Road Development in Hong Kong. 2009. (CHI & ENG., Illus.). 364p. (978-962-209-051-4(6)) Hong Kong Univ. Pr.

He, Shu. Wei Mao Zhu Xi Er Zhan: Wen Ge Chongqing Da Wu Dou Shi Lu. 2010. (Illus.). 357p. (978-962-04-2995-8(8)) Joint Publishing Co.

He, Xiangzhou. Zheng Fu Jue Ce de Ji Hui Cheng Ben Wen Ti Yan Jiu. 2010. (CHI., Illus.). xiii, 235p. (978-7-03-026983-6(7)) Science Pr.

Heng, Derek. Sino-Malay Trade & Diplomacy from the Tenth through the Fourteenth Century. 2009. (Ohio RIS Southeast Asia Ser.). (ENG., Illus.). 304p. pap. 28.00 (978-0-89680-271-1(X)) Ohio Univ. Pr.

Herberer, Thomas, et al. Regime Legitimacy in Contemporary China: Institutional Change & Stability. Schubert, Gunter, ed. 2008. (Routledge Contemporary China Ser.). (ENG., Illus.). 320p. (C). 150.00 (978-0-415-46664-6(4)) Routledge.

Hill, Emily M. Smokeless Sugar: The Death of a Provincial Bureaucrat & the Construction of China's National Economy. 2011. (Contemporary Chinese Studies Ser.). (ENG., Illus.). 336p. pap. 35.95 (978-0-7748-1654-0(6)) UBC Pr. CAN. Dist: Univ. of Washington Pr.

Hinton, William. Through a Glass Darkly: American Views of the Chinese Revolution. 2006. (ENG.). 288p. per. 19.95 (978-1-58367-141-2(2)) Monthly Review Pr.

Hogg, James, et al. A Pragmatist & His Free Spirit: The Half-Century Romance of Hu Shi & Edith Clifford Williams. Francis, David et al, eds. 2009. (ENG.).

410p. (gr. 17). pap. 30.00 (978-962-996-341-5(8)) Chinese Univ. of Hong Kong, The HKG. Dist: Columbia Univ. Pr.

Holmes, James R. Chinese Naval Strategy in the 21st Century: The Turn to Mahan. 2009. 163p. pap. 39.95 (978-0-415-54534-1(X)) Routledge.

Hom, Sharon & Mosher, Stacy, eds. Challenging China: Struggle & Hope in an Era of Change. 2008. (ENG.). 313p. pap. 17.95 (978-1-59558-416-8(1)) New Pr., The.

Hong, Qing. Ta Jiang Shi Zhongguo Da Guan Jia: Li Keqiang Zhuan. 2010. ("Zhongguo Zhang Quan Zhe" Xi Lie Ser.: Vol. 42). (Illus.). 524p. (978-962-8744-47-3(X)) Mirror Bks. USA.

Hongyi, Lai. The Domestic Sources of China's Foreign Policy. 2011. (ENG., Illus.). 202p. (C). pap. 42.95 (978-0-415-69721-7(2)) Routledge.

Hongyi, Lai, ed. China into the Hu-Wen Era: Policy Initiatives & Challenges. 2006. (Series on Contemporary China: Vol. 5). (Illus.). 565p. 150.00 (978-981-256-732-1(1)) World Scientific Publishing Co., Inc.

Hu, Angang. China In 2020: A New Type of Superpower. 2011. (Thornton Center Chinese Thinkers Ser.). (ENG., Illus.). 208p. 32.95 (978-0-8157-0478-2(X)) Brookings Institution Pr.

Hu, Angang & Hu, An'gang. Road Map of China's Rise. 2010. (Routledge Studies on the Chinese Economy Ser.). (ENG., Illus.). 512p. 150.00 (978-0-415-47992-9(4)) Routledge.

Hu, Nien-Tsu Alfred & Mcdorman, Ted L., eds. Maritime Issues in the South China Sea. 2012. (ENG.). 176p. (C). 125.00 (978-0-415-50636-6(0)) Routledge.

Hua, Shiping & Guo, Sujian, eds. China in the Twenty-First Century: Challenges & Opportunities. 2007. (ENG.). 280p. 89.00 (978-1-4039-7975-9(8)) Palgrave Macmillan.

Huang, Jing & Li, Xiaoting. Inseparable Separation: The Making of China's Taiwan Policy. 2007. (ENG.). 330p. 59.95 (978-0-8157-3758-2(0)) Brookings Institution Pr.

Huang, Xiaoming. The Institutional Dynamics of China's Great Transformation. 2011. (China Policy Ser.). (ENG., Illus.). 272p. (C). 140.00 (978-0-415-58058-8(7)) Routledge.

Hucker, Charles O. The Traditional Chinese State in Ming Times, 1368-1644. 2011. 96p. 38.95 (978-1-258-05392-5(6)) Literary Licensing, LLC.

Human Rights & the Rule of Law in China: Hearing Before the Congressional-Executive Commission on China, One Hundred Eleventh Congress, First Session, October 7, 2009. 2010. iii, 59p. (978-0-16-085440-8(7), 552-070-40694-8) United States Government Printing Office.

Hutton, Will. The Writing on the Wall: Why We Must Embrace China as a Partner or Face It as an Enemy. 2006. (ENG., Illus.). 432p. 28.00 (978-0-7432-7528-6(4), Free Pr.) Free Pr.

Ip, Hung-Yok. Intellectuals in Revolutionary China,1921-1949. 2009. 334p. 39.95 (978-0-415-54656-0(7)) Routledge.

Jacques, Martin. When China Rules the World: The End of the Western World & the Birth of a New Global Order. 2009. (ENG.). 576p. (gr. 12). 29.95 (978-1-59420-185-1(4), Penguin Pr. HC, The) Penguin Group (USA) Inc.

Jamestown Foundation Staff & Lam, Willy. Changing of the Guard: Beijing Grooms Sixth-Generation Cadres for 2020s. 2011. (ENG.). 50p. pap. 25.00 (978-0-9816905-3-7(X)) Jamestown Foundation, The.

Jeffreys, Elaine. China's Governmentalities: Governing Change, Changing Government. 2009. (Routledge Studies on China in Transition Ser.). (ENG., Illus.). 184p. (C). 130.00 (978-0-415-54744-4(X)) Routledge.

Jeffries, Ian. China: A Guide to Economic & Political Developments. 2006. (Guides to Economic & Political Developments in Asia Ser.: Vol. 3). (Illus.). 673p. 210.00 (978-0-415-38223-6(8), RU238X) Routledge.

—China: A Guide to Economic & Political Developments. 2012. (Guides to Economic & Political Developments in Asia Ser.). (ENG., Illus.). 592p. pap. 44.95 (978-0-415-51422-4(3)) Routledge.

Jeffries, Ian. Economic Development in Contemporary China. 2010. (Guides to Economic & Political Developments in Asia Ser.). (ENG., Illus.). 736p. (C). 200.00 (978-0-415-47866-3(9), Routledge) Taylor & Francis Group GBR. Dist: Taylor & Francis Group.

Jha, Prem Shankar. Managed Chaos: The Fragility of the Chinese Miracle. 2009. 204p. (C). 34.95 (978-81-321-0076-8(X), B00768C) SAGE Pubns., Inc.

Jia, Xijin. Citizen Participation in Chin. 2011. 244p. pap. (978-3-8433-8239-7(5)) Lambert Academic Publishing.

Jiaxuan, Tang. Heavy Storm & Gentle Breeze: A Memoir of China's Diplomacy. 2011. (ENG., Illus.). 368p. 35.00 (978-0-06-206725-8(7)) HarperCollins Pubs.

Jin, Ruizi. Guangdong Ren Shi Zheng Duo Liu Shi Nian: Zhong Yang He Di Fang de an Zhan. 2011. (CHI., Illus.). 398p. (978-1-935981-17-6(X)) Mirror Bks. USA.

Jin, Xingyao. Qing Dai Gong Ting Zheng Bian. 2010. (CHI.). (978-7-80047-926-7(9)) Forbidden City Publishing Hse.

Joes, Anthony James. Victorious Insurgencies: Four Rebellions that Shaped Our World. 2010. (ENG., Illus.). 336p. 40.00 (978-0-8131-2614-2(2)) Univ. Pr. of Kentucky.

Johnson, Tim. Tragedy in Crimson: How the Dalai Lama Conquered the World but Lost the Battle with China. 2011. (ENG., Illus.). 352p. (gr. 9). 26.99 (978-1-56858-601-4(9)) Basic Bks.

Joseph, William, ed. Politics in China: An Introduction, 1 vol. 2010. (ENG., Illus.). 456p. pap. 39.95 (978-0-19-533531-6(7)) Oxford Univ. Pr., Inc.

Kaiser, Matthis. Engaging or Containing China? 2008. 148p. pap. (978-3-639-08000-1(9)) VDM Verlag Dr. Mueller e.K.

Kan, Shirley. China & Proliferation of Weapons of Mass Destruction & Missiles: Policy Issues. 2009. pap. 43.00 (978-1-60741-248-9(9)) Nova Science Pubs., Inc.

Karabell, Zachary. Superfusion: How China & America Became One Economy & Why the World's Prosperity Depends on It. 2009. (ENG.). 352p. 26.00 (978-1-4165-8370-7(X)) Simon & Schuster.

Kaske, Elisabeth. The Politics of Language in Chinese Education, 1895-1919. 2007. (Sinica Leidensia Ser.). (Illus.). 600p. (978-90-04-16367-6(0)) BRILL.

Kavalski, Emilian. China & the Global Politics of Regionalization. 2009. (International Political Economy of New Regionalisms Ser.). 262p. 114.95 (978-0-7546-7599-0(8)) Ashgate Publishing Co.

Keith, Ronald C. China from the Inside Out: Fitting the People's Republic into the World. 2009. (ENG.). 176p. 88.00 (978-0-7453-2855-3(5)); pap. 26.00 (978-0-7453-2854-6(7)) Pluto Pr. GBR. Dist: Macmillan.

Kempton, Nicole & Richardson, Nan, eds. Laogai: The Machinery of Repression in China. 2009. (ENG., Illus.). 160p. 45.00 (978-1-884167-77-5(2)) Umbrage Editions.

Killion, Ulric, ed. Modern Chinese Rules of Order: Paradox of Law & Economics. 2007. 79.00 (978-1-60021-837-8(7)) Nova Science Pubs., Inc.

Kim, Jaeyoon. Ethnicity, Local Conflicts & the Qing State. 2010. 212p. pap. (978-3-639-25419-8(8)) VDM Verlag Dr. Mueller e.K.

King Allen, Jana. Practicing Transparency - Foreign Lawyers in China's Transitional Economy. 2008. 220p. pap. (978-3-639-08367-5(9)) VDM Verlag Dr. Mueller e.K.

King, Richard, et al, eds. Sino Japanese Transculturation: Late Nineteenth Century to the End of the Pacific War. 2011. (ENG.). 316p. (gr. 17). 75.00 (978-0-7391-7150-9(X)) Lexington Bks.

King, Richard, et al. Sino-Japanese Transculturation: From the Late Nineteenth Century to the End of the Pacific War. 2011. (978-0-7391-7151-6(8)) Lexington Bks.

Kipnis, Andrew. Contemporary Chinese Society & Politics, 4 vols. Tomba, Luigi & Unger, Jonathan, eds. 2009. (Critical Concepts in Asian Studies). (ENG., Illus.). 1872p. 1430.00 (978-0-415-45748-4(3)) Routledge.

Kipnis, Andrew B., et al. Contemporary Chinese Society & Politics, 4 vols. 2009. (Illus.). Vol. 1. (978-0-415-45749-1(1)) Vol. 2. (978-0-415-45750-7(5)) Vol. 3. (978-0-415-45751-4(3)) Vol. 4. (978-0-415-45752-1(1)) Routledge.

Kirby, William C., et al. The People's Republic of China at 60: An International Assessment. 2011. (CHI & ENG., Illus.). 432p. pap. 29.95 (978-0-674-06064-7(4)) Harvard Univ., Asia Ctr.

Kiepinger, Lawrence. China House: An Inside Look at the "New" People's Republic of China & the Impending Downfall of the Current Communist Dynasty. 2007. 151p. 14.75 (978-1-4120-7066-9(X)) Trafford Publishing.

Kong, Bo. China's International Petroleum Policy, 1 vol. 2009. (Energy & Security Ser.). 229p. 44.95 (978-0-313-37791-4(X), C37791, Praeger Pubs.) Greenwood Publishing Group, Inc.

Koo, Telly. The Constitutional Development of the Western Han Dynasty. 2010. pap. 18.88 (978-1-61143-147-6(6)) Gorgias Pr., LLC.

Ku & Mok, Ka Ho. Social Cohesion in Greater China: Challenges for Social Policy & Governance. 2010. (Illus.). 400p. 118.00 (978-981-4291-92-7(7)) World Scientific Publishing Co., Inc.

Kuhn, Robert Lawrence. How China's Leaders Think: The Inside Story of China's Past, Current & Future Leaders. rev. ed. 2011. (ENG., Illus.). 576p. pap. 29.95 (978-1-118-08590-5(6), Wiley) Wiley, John & Sons, Inc.

Kuo, Ya-pei. Cultural Wars in Interwar China. 2013. (Routledge/Leiden Series in Modern East Asian History & Politics Ser.). (ENG.). 176p. (C). 130.00 (978-0-415-55241-7(9)) Routledge.

Kuo, Yen-Lien. The Evaluation of Residential Solid Waste Management Policies. 2009. 112p. pap. (978-3-639-09928-7(1)) VDM Verlag Dr. Mueller e.K.

Lai, Yew Meng. Nationalism & Power Politics in Japan's Relations with China: A Neoclassical Realist Interpretation. 2012. (Sheffield Centre for Japanese Studies/Routledge Ser.). (ENG.). 240p. (C). 135.00 (978-0-415-62911-9(X)) Routledge.

Laliberte, Andre & Lanteigne, Marc, eds. The Chinese Party-State in the 21st Century. 2011. (Illus.). 204p. pap. 42.95 (978-0-415-69218-2(0)) Routledge.

Lam, Tong. A Passion for Facts: Social Surveys & the Construction of the Chinese Nation-State, 1900-1949. 2011. (Asia Pacific Modern Ser.). (ENG., Illus.). 280p. 60.00 (978-0-520-26786-2(9)) Univ. of California Pr.

Lampton, David M. The Three Faces of Chinese Power: Might, Money, & Minds. 2008. (Illus.). 361p. pap. 26.95 (978-0-520-25442-8(2)) Univ. of California Pr.

Landry, Pierre. Decentralized Authoritarianism in China: The Communist Party's Control of Local Elites in the Post-Mao Era. 2008. (ENG., Illus.). 320p. 98.00 (978-0-521-88235-4(4)) Cambridge Univ. Pr.

Lansdowne, Helen, ed. China Turns to Multilateralism: Foreign Policy & Regional Security. 2007. (Routledge Contemporary China Ser.). (Illus.). 303p. 170.00 (978-0-415-42571-1(9)) Routledge.

Lary, Diana. Region & Nation: The Kwangsi Clique in Chinese Politics, 1925-1937. 2009. (Cambridge Studies in Chinese History, Literature & Institutions Ser.). (ENG.). 292p. pap. 38.99 (978-0-521-10488-3(2)) Cambridge Univ. Pr.

Lee, Keun, et al, eds. Power & Sustainability of the Chinese State. 2012. (China Policy Ser.). (ENG., Illus.). 240p. (C). pap. 42.95 (978-0-415-54198-5(0)) Routledge.

Lee, Seung-Joon. Gourmets in the Land of Famine: The Culture & Politics of Rice in Modern Canton. 2011. (ENG., Illus.). 320p. 55.00 (978-0-8047-7226-6(6), Stanford Univ. Pr.

Leese, Daniel. Mao Cult: Rhetoric & Ritual in the Cultural Revolution. 2011. (ENG., Illus.). 328p. 90.00 (978-0-521-19367-2(2)) Cambridge Univ. Pr.

Leib, Ethan J. Search for Deliberative Democracy in China. Leib, Ethan J. & He, Baogang, eds. 2010. (ENG.). 354p. pap. 31.00 (978-0-230-62034-6(5)) Palgrave Macmillan.

—The Search for Deliberative Democracy in China. He, Baogang, ed. annot. ed. 2006. (ENG.). 296p. 95.00 (978-1-4039-7416-7(0)) Palgrave Macmillan.

Leibovitz, Liel & Miller, Matthew. Fortunate Sons: The 120 Chinese Boys Who Came to America, Went to School, & Revolutionized an Ancient Civilization. 2011. (ENG., Illus.). 320p. 26.95 (978-0-393-07004-0(2), 7004) Norton, W. W. & Co., Inc.

Leonard, Mark. What Does China Think? 2008. (ENG., Illus.). 176p. 22.95 (978-1-58648-484-2(2)) PublicAffairs.

Leung, Philip Y. & Colebrook, Claire. The Legitimation of New Orders: Case Studies in World History. 2007. (ENG., Illus.). 300p. (gr. 17). 42.00 (978-962-996-239-5(X)) Chinese Univ. of Hong Kong, The HKG. Dist: Columbia Univ. Pr.

Levine, Ari Daniel. Divided by a Common Language: Factional Conflict in Late Northern Song China. 2008. (Illus.). 216p. (C). 57.00 (978-0-8248-3266-7(3)) Univ. of Hawaii Pr.

Lewis, Jeffrey G. The Minimum Means of Reprisal: China's Search for Security in the Nuclear Age. 2007. (American Academy Studies in Global Security Ser.). (ENG., Illus.). 282p. (gr. 17). 57.00 (978-0-262-12284-9(7)) MIT Pr.

Li, Cheng, ed. China's Changing Political Landscape: Prospects for Democracy. 2008. (ENG., Illus.). 342p. pap. 32.95 (978-0-8157-5209-7(1)) Brookings Institution Pr.

—China's Emerging Middle Class: Beyond Economic Transformation. 2010. (ENG., Illus.). 396p. pap. 34.95 (978-0-8157-0405-8(4)) Brookings Institution Pr.

Li-Chun, Hsu. Frontier China. (CHI., Illus.). 272p. (978-957-629-285-9(9)) Hilit Publishing Co., Ltd.

Li, Huaiyin. Village China under Socialism & Reform: A Micro History, 1948-2008. 2009. (ENG., Illus.). 424p. 65.00 (978-0-8047-5974-8(X)) Stanford Univ. Pr.

—Village China under Socialism & Reform: A Micro-History, 1948-2008. 2010. (ENG., Illus.). 424p. pap. 27.95 (978-0-8047-7657-8(1)) Stanford Univ. Pr.

Li, Kangying. The Ming Maritime Policy in Transition, 1367 To 1568. 2010. (East Asian Economic & Socio-Cultural Studies). (ENG., Illus.). 211p. (C). 72.00 (978-3-447-06172-8(3)) Harrassowitz, Otto Verlag DEU. Dist: ISD.

Li, Linda Chelan, ed. The Chinese State in Transition: Processes & Contests in Local China. 2008. (Routledge Studies on China in Transition Ser.). (ENG., Illus.). 208p. 158.00 (978-0-415-46667-7(9)) Routledge.

Li, Linda Chelan, ed. The Chinese State in Transition: Processes & contests in local China. 2012. (Routledge Studies on China in Transition Ser.). (ENG., Illus.). 208p. pap. 42.95 (978-0-415-54231-9(6)) Routledge.

Li, Mingjiang, ed. Soft Power: China's Emerging Strategy in International Politics. 2011. (ENG.). 284p. pap. 32.95 (978-0-7391-3378-1(0)) Lexington Bks.

Li, Minqi. The Rise of China & the Demise of the Capitalist World Economy, 1 vol. 2008. (Illus.). 240p. 29.95 (978-0-7453-2772-3(9)) Pluto Pr. GBR. Dist: Univ. of Michigan Pr.

Li, Qiang. Thirty Years of Reform & Social Changes in China. 2010. (Illus.). 514p. (978-90-04-18716-0(2)) BRILL.

Li, Qingdong. Duan Qirui Mu Fu Yu Mu Liao: DuanQirui Mufu Yu Muliao. 2010. (Illus.). (978-7-5339-2819-3(9)) Zhejiang Pubn. Hse. of Literature and Art.

Li, Zhou. Xian Dai Laozi: Zhu De. 2010. (CHI., Illus.). 376p. (978-962-8744-45-9(3)) Mirror Bks. USA.

Liang, Bin. The Changing Chinese Legal System, 1978 ndash; Present: Centralization of Power & Rationalization of the Legal System. 2012. (East Asia: History, Politics, Sociology & Culture Ser.). (ENG., Illus.). 266p. pap. 42.95 (978-0-415-54103-9(4)) Routledge.

Liang Chi-Chao. History of Chinese Political Thought. reprint ed. 34.50 (978-0-404-03985-1(5)) AMS Pr., Inc.

Lim, Tin Seng & Zhao, Litao. China's New Social Policy: Initiatives for a Harmonious Society. 2009. (Illus.). 244p. 99.00 (978-981-4277-73-0(8)) World Scientific Publishing Co., Inc.

Lin. China & Political Inquiry. 2011. 72.00 (978-981-256-895-3(6)) World Scientific Publishing Co., Inc.

Lin & Lin, George C. S. Developing China: Land, Politics & Social Conditions. 2009. (Routledge Contemporary China Ser.). (ENG., Illus.). 368p. (C). 145.00 (978-0-415-41322-0(2)) Routledge.

Lin, Hsiao-Ting. Tibet & Nationalist China's Frontier: Intrigues & Ethnopolitics, 1928-49. 2007. (Contemporary Chinese Studies). (ENG., Illus.). 304p. per. (978-0-7748-1302-0(4)) Univ. of British Columbia Pr.

Lin, Man-Houng. China Upside Down: Currency, Society, & Ideologies, 1808-1856. 2007. (Harvard East Asian Monographs: 270). (Illus.). 450p. 49.95 (978-0-674-02268-3(8)) Harvard Univ., Asia Ctr.

Ling, George Fusun. China Developing: Cultural Identity of Emerging Societies. 2008. 212p. 68.00 (978-981-277-863-5(2)) World Scientific Publishing Co., Inc.

Liu, Chang. Peasants & Revolution in Rural China: Rural Political Change in the North China Plain & the Yangzi Delta, 1850-1949. 2009. 262p. pap. 39.95 (978-0-415-54422-1(X)) 2007. (Illus.). 258p. 160.00 (978-0-415-42176-8(4)) Routledge.

Liu, Guoli. Politics & Government in China, 1 vol. 2011. (Understanding China Today Ser.). (Illus.). 160p. 35.00 (978-0-313-35730-5(7), GR5730) ABC-CLIO, LLC.

Liu, Jianlan & Tong, Yan. Zhongguo Dian Zi Dang Wu Jian She: Electronic Party Affairs in China. 2009. (CHI., Illus.). (978-7-5097-0882-8(6)) China Social Science Documentation Publishing Hse.

Liu, Mingfu. Zhongguo Meng: Zhong Mei Shi Ji Dui Jue, Jun Ren Yao Fa Yan. 2010. (CHI.). x, 288p. (978-962-231-062-9(1)) Chung Hwa Bk. Co., Ltd.

Liu, Runhe. Jing Ming Guo Zheng. 2010. (CHI.). 501p. (978-962-04-2993-4(1)) Joint Publishing Co.

Lo, Shiu-Hing. Political Change in Macao. 2008. (Illus.). 192p. 160.00 (978-0-415-39577-9(1)) Routledge.

Lo, Shiu Hing. Political Change in Macao. 2012. (Routledge Contemporary China Ser.). (ENG., Illus.). 192p. (C). pap. 42.95 (978-0-415-54191-6(3)) Routledge.

Lo, Shiu-Hung Sonny. Competing Chinese Political Visions: Hong Kong vs. Beijing on Democracy, 1 vol. 2010. (Praeger Security International Ser.). 294p. 59.95 (978-0-313-36505-8(9), C36505, Praeger Pubs.) Greenwood Publishing Group, Inc.

Loewe, Michael. The Government of the Qin & Han Empires, 221 BCE-220 CE. 2006. (Illus.). (C). 224p. 37.95 (978-0-87220-819-3(2)); 248p. pap. 12.95 (978-0-87220-818-6(4)) Hackett Publishing Co., Inc.

Long, Jianyu. Mao Zedong, Jiang Jieshi de Ren Sheng Dao Lu. 2010. (CHI., Illus.). (978-7-80257-117-4(0)) ET Pr.

Lorge, Peter, ed. Five Dynasties & Ten Kingdoms. 2011. (ENG., Illus.). 288p. (gr. 17). 52.00 (978-962-996-418-4(X)) Chinese Univ. of Hong Kong, The HKG. Dist: Columbia Univ. Pr.

Lu, Di. Bai Nian Chun Dong: Cong Lin Zexu Dao Sun Zhongshan. 2010. (CHI.). 473p. pap. (978-962-8744-49-7(6)) Mirror Bks. USA.

Lu, Jie & Wang, Ban. China & New Left Visions: Political & Cultural Interventions. 2012. (ENG.). 290p. (gr. 17). 75.00 (978-0-7391-6516-4(X)) Lexington Bks.

Lu, Rey-ching. Chinese Democracy & Elite Thinking. 2011. (ENG.). 192p. 89.00 (978-0-230-11083-0(5)) Palgrave Macmillan.

Lynch, Daniel C. Rising China & Asian Democratization: Socialization to Global Culture in the Political Transformations of Thailand, China, & Taiwan. 2006. (Issues in Asia & the Pacific Ser.). (ENG.). 320p. 65.00 (978-0-8047-5394-4(6)) Stanford Univ. Pr.

Ma, Qiusha. Non-Governmental Organizations in Contemporary China: Paving the Way to Civil Society? 2009. 244p. pap. 39.95 (978-0-415-54672-0(9)) Routledge.

Madl, Benedikt. Auslandsstudium, Brain-Drain und Regierungspolitik am Beispiel der VR China. (Europaische Hochschulschriften Ser.: 450). (GER., Illus.). 269p. 35.95 (978-3-631-39407-6(1)) Lang, Peter Publishing, Inc.

Manjikian, Mary. Threat Talk: The Comparative Politics of Internet Addiction. 2012. (Illus.). 200p. 99.95 (978-1-4094-3394-1(3)) Ashgate Publishing Co.

Mann, James. The China Fantasy: Why Capitalism Will Not Bring Democracy to China. 2008. (ENG.). 160p. (gr. 12-18). 13.00 (978-0-14-311292-1(9), Penguin (Non-Classics)) Penguin Group (USA) Inc.

McGregor, Richard. The Party: The Secret World of China's Communist Rulers. 2012. (ENG.). 336p. pap. 16.99 (978-0-06-170876-3(3), HarperPerennial) HarperCollins Pubs.

Medeiros, Evan S. Reluctant Restraint: The Evolution of China's Nonproliferation Policies & Practices, 1980-2004. 2007. (Studies in Asian Security Ser.). (ENG., Illus.). 376p. 65.00 (978-0-8047-5552-8(3)) Stanford Univ. Pr.

Meng, Xin, et al, eds. The Great Migration: Rural-Urban Migration in China & Indonesia. 2010. (Illus.). 288p. 125.00 (978-1-84844-644-1(6)) Elgar, Edward Publishing, Inc.

Minoru, Kitamura. Politics of Nanjing. 2006. (ENG.). 190p. pap. 34.99 (978-0-7618-3579-0(2)) Univ. Pr. of America, Inc.

Mohanty, Manoranjan. Grass-Roots Democracy in India & China: The Right to Participate. 2007. (Illus.). 498p. (978-81-7829-667-8(5)) SAGE Pubns., Inc.

Mohanty, Manoranjan, et al, eds. Grass-Roots Democracy in India & China: The Right to Participate. 2007. (Illus.). 500p. (C). 79.95 (978-0-7619-3515-5(0), B35150C) SAGE Pubns., Inc.

Moller Christensen, Peer. Politik Og Ideologi I Kina. 2010. (DAN.). 185p. pap. (978-87-7674-494-6(9)) Syddansk Universitetsforlag/Univ. Pr. of Southern Denmark.

Moore, Davon R. Russia, China & Eurasia: Social, Historical & Cultural Issues. 2010. (Russia, China & Eurasia: Social, Historical & Cultural Issues Ser.). 188p. 89.00 (978-1-61668-016-9(4)) Nova Science Pubs., Inc.

Morse, Hosea B. The International Relations of the Chinese Empire, 3 vols. reprint ed. 375.00 (978-0-7222-2529-5(6)) Library Reprints, Inc.

Mostern, Ruth. 'Dividing the Realm in Order to Govern' The Spatial Organization of the Song State. 2011. (Harvard-Yenching Institute Monograph Ser.: 73). (Illus.). 396p. 49.95 (978-0-674-05602-2(7)) Harvard Univ., Asia Ctr.

Muni, S. D. & Yong, Tan Tai, eds. A Resurgent China: South Asian Perspectives. 2012. (ENG.). (C). 95.00 (978-0-415-50191-0(1), Routledge India) Taylor & Francis Group GBR. Dist: Taylor & Francis Group.

Murphy, Melissa. Decoding Chinese Politics: Intellectual Debates & Why They Matter. 2008. 28p. 12.95 net. (978-0-89206-526-4(5), CSIS Pr., The) Ctr. for Strategic & International Studies.

Murphy, Rachel. Labour Migration & Social Development in Contemporary China. 2010. (ENG.). pap. 39.95 (978-0-415-59029-7(9)) Routledge.

Mustapha, Ahmed Badawi. The China Factor in Ghana's Textile & Construction Industries. 2011. 128p. pap. (978-3-8443-9725-3(6)) Lambert Academic Publishing.

Narlikar, Amrita. New Powers: How to Become One & How to Manage Them. 2010. (Columbia/Hurst Ser.). (ENG.). 208p. (gr. 17). 45.00 (978-0-231-70202-7(7)) Columbia Univ. Pr.

Nedostup, Rebecca. Superstitious Regimes: Religion & the Politics of Chinese Modernity. 2010. (Harvard East Asian Monographs: 322). (Illus.). 450p. 45.00 (978-0-674-03599-7(2)) Harvard Univ., Asia Ctr.

Nee, Victor & Opper, Sonja. Capitalism from Below: Markets & Institutional Change in China. 2012. (ENG., Illus.). 456p. 45.00 (978-0-674-05020-4(7)) Harvard Univ. Pr.

C

Negotiated Power in Late Imperial China: The Zongli Yamen & the Politics of Reform. 2008. (Cornell East Asia Ser.). 246p. 42.00 (978-1-933947-07-5(1)); (ENG.). pap. 25.00 (978-1-933947-37-2(3)) Cornell Univ. East Asia Program.

Newham, Mark. Limp Pigs: And the Five-Ring Circus. 2011. (Illus.). 338p. pap. (978-1-78003-049-4(5)) Pen Pr. Pubs., Ltd.

Nimick, Thomas G. Local Administration in Ming China: The Changing Roles of Magistrates, Prefects, & Provincials, No. 5. 2008. 205p. 65.00 (978-0-9800639-1-2(4)) Ctr. for Early Modern History.

Ning, Lutao. China's Rise in the World ICT Industry: Industrial Strategies & the Catch-up Development Model. (ENG., Illus.). 2012. 272p. (C). pap. 44.95 (978-0-415-62496-1(7)) 2009. 254p. 145.00 (978-0-415-48224-0(0)) Routledge.

Nolan, Ernest P. China in Focus: Economic, Political & Educational Issues. 2008. 150.00 (978-1-60021-543-8(2)) Nova Science Pubs., Inc.

O'Brien, Kevin J., ed. Popular Protest in China. 2008. (Harvard Contemporary China Ser.: 15). (Illus.). 288p. pap. 27.50 (978-0-674-03061-9(3)) Harvard Univ. Pr.

Oliveira, Jorge & Cardinal, Paulo. One Country, Two Systems, Three Legal Orders: Perspectives of Evolution: Essays on Macau's Legal Status after the Resumption of Sovereignty by China. 2008. xvii, 826p. 279.00 (978-3-540-68571-5(5)) Springer.

Ong, Aihwa. Neoliberalism as Exception: Mutations in Citizenship & Sovereignty. 2006. (ENG., Illus.). 304p. (C). 89.95 (978-0-8223-3736-2(3)); per. 24.95 (978-0-8223-3748-5(7)) Duke Univ. Pr.

Ownby, David. Falun Gong & the Future of China, 1 vol. (ENG., Illus.). 312p. 2010. pap. 19.95 (978-0-19-973853-3(X)) 2008. 29.95 (978-0-19-532905-6(8)) Oxford Univ. Pr., Inc.

Pan, Jian. Wang Wei Zheng Quan Cai Zheng Yan Jiu. 2009. (CHI.). (978-7-5004-8241-3(8)) China Social Sciences Pr.

Pant, Harsh. China's Rising Global Profile: The Great Power Tradition. 2012. (ENG.). 132p. pap. 24.95 (978-1-84519-517-5(5)) Sussex Academic Pr. GBR. Dist: International Specialized Bk. Services.

Pant, Harsh V. China's Rising Global Profile: The Great Power Tradition. 2011. 132p. 45.00 (978-1-84519-457-4(8)) Sussex Academic Pr. GBR. Dist: International Specialized Bk. Services.

Pantsov, Alexander & Levine, Steven I. Mao: The Real Story. 2012. (ENG., Illus.). 736p. 35.00 (978-1-4516-5447-9(2)) Simon & Schuster.

Peerenboom, Randall. China Modernizes: Threat to the West or Model for the Rest? 2007. (ENG., Illus.). 432p. 50.00 (978-0-19-920834-0(4)) Oxford Univ. Pr., Inc.

—China Modernizes: Threat to the West or Model for the Rest? 2008. (ENG., Illus.). 432p. pap. 21.95 (978-0-19-922612-2(1)) Oxford Univ. Pr., Inc.

Percival, Bronson. The Dragon Looks South: China & Southeast Asia in the New Century, 1 vol. annot. ed. 2007. (Praeger Security International Ser.). 216p. 49.95 (978-0-275-99426-6(0), C9426, Praeger Security International) Greenwood Publishing Group, Inc.

Perry, Elizabeth J. Anyuan: Mining China's Revolutionary Tradition. 2012. (Asia: Local Studies / Global Themes Ser.). (ENG.). 400p. 75.00 (978-0-520-27189-0(0)); pap. 34.95 (978-0-520-27190-6(4)) Univ. of California Pr.

Perry, Elizabeth J. & Goldman, Merle, eds. Grassroots Political Reform in Contemporary China. 2007. (Harvard Contemporary China Ser.: 14). 416p. per. 28.50 (978-0-674-02486-1(9)); (Illus.). 68.50 (978-0-674-02485-4(0)) Harvard Univ. Pr.

Peterson, Glen. Overseas Chinese in the People's Republic of China. 2011. (Chinese Worlds Ser.). (ENG., Illus.). 248p. (C). 130.00 (978-0-415-61670-6(0)) Routledge.

Phillips, Jack M. & Moore, Logan J., eds. China: Economics, Political & Social Issues. 2008. (Illus.). xi, 307p. 98.00 (978-1-60456-727-4(9)) Nova Science Pubs., Inc.

Pieke, Frank N. The Good Communist: Elite Training & State Building in Today's China. 2009. (ENG., Illus.). 240p. 93.00 (978-0-521-19990-2(5)) Cambridge Univ. Pr.

Pines, Yuri. Envisioning Eternal Empire: Chinese Political Thought of the Warring States Period. 2009. 320p. 57.00 (978-0-8248-3275-9(2)) Univ. of Hawaii Pr.

Poole, H. John. Global Warrior: Averting WWIII. 2011. (Illus.). 414p. pap. 15.95 net. (978-0-9818659-3-5(3)) Posterity Pr.

Pow, Choon-Piew. Gated Communities in China: Class, Privilege & the Moral Politics of the Good Life. 2009. (Routledge Pacific Rim Geographies Ser.). (ENG., Illus.). 224p. 130.00 (978-0-415-47810-6(3)) Routledge.

Qian, Yufang. Discursive Constructions Around Terrorism in the People's Daily (China) & The Sun (UK) Before & after 9/11. 2010. (Illus.). xvi, 166p. 65.95 (978-3-0343-0186-2(3)) Lang, Peter Publishing, Inc.

Qin, Yue. Weiji Jie Mi Dang An: Chong Xin Ren Shi Zhongguo Jue Ce Zhe. 2011. (CHI., Illus.). 518p. (978-1-935981-11-4(0)) Mirror Bks. USA.

Restarick, Henry Bond. Sun Yat Sen: Liberator of China. 2011. 206p. 44.95 (978-1-258-00718-8(5)) Literary Licensing, LLC.

Roland, Christian. Banking Sector Liberalization in India: Evaluation of Reforms & Comparative Perspectives on China. 2008. (Contributions to Economics Ser.). (Illus.). xvi, 299p. 139.00 (978-3-7908-1981-6(6)) Physica-Verlag DEU. Dist: Springer.

Rolandsen, Unn MÃ¥lfrid. Leisure & Power in Urban China. 2011. (Routledge Contemporary China Ser.). (ENG., Illus.). 240p. (C). 133.00 (978-0-415-60409-3(5)) Routledge.

Ross, Robert. Chinese Security Policy: Structure, Power & Politics. 2009. (ENG., Illus.). 342p. 41.95 (978-0-415-77786-5(0)) Routledge.

Ruocheng, Ying, et al. Voices Carry: Behind Bars & Backstage During China's Revolution & Reform. 2008. (Asian Voices Ser.). (ENG., Illus.). 286p. 85.00 (978-0-7425-5554-9(2)); pap. 32.95 (978-0-7425-5555-6(0)) Rowman & Littlefield Publishers, Inc.

Russell, Bertrand. The Problem of China. 2008. 220p. 27.99 (978-0-554-24817-2(4)) 2006. (ENG.). 196p. pap. 19.99 (978-1-4264-7458-3(X)) 2007. 218p. pap. 22.99 (978-1-4264-7535-1(7)) BiblioBazaar.

—The Problem of China. 2008. 188p. pap. (978-1-4099-0103-7(3)) Dodo Pr.

—The Problem of China. 2007. (ENG.). 152p. per. (978-1-4068-4109-1(9)) Echo Library.

—The Problem of China. 2009. (ENG.). 204p. pap. 13.95 (978-1-4385-1290-7(2), Book Jungle) Standard Pubns., Inc.

Saich, Anthony J. Providing Public Goods in Transitional China. 2008. (ENG.). 252p. 100.00 (978-0-230-60951-8(1)) Palgrave Macmillan.

Schmitt, Gary J. The Rise of China: Essays on the Future Competition. 2009. (ENG.). 160p. 21.95 (978-1-59403-231-8(9)) Encounter Bks.

Schneider, Mark. The Nuclear Doctrine & Forces of the People's Republic of China. 2007. 41p. (978-0-9776221-5-3(0)) National Institute Pr.

Schwartz, Jonathan. State & Society Responses to Social Welfare Needs in China: Serving the People. Schwartz, Jonathan & Shieh, Shawn, eds. 2009. (Routledge Contemporary China Ser.). (ENG., Illus.). 224p. 130.00 (978-0-415-45224-3(4)) Routledge.

Scott, Ian & Lam, Newman M. K., eds. Gaming, Governance & Public Policy in Macao. 2011. 320p. (978-988-8053-82-7(5)) Hong Kong Univ. Pr.

Scotton, James F. & Hachten, William A. New Media for a New China. 2010. (ENG., Illus.). 256p. 94.95 (978-1-4051-8797-8(2)); pap. 42.95 (978-1-4051-8796-1(4)) Wiley, John & Sons, Inc. (Wiley-Blackwell).

Shambaugh, David. China's Communist Party: Atrophy & Adaptation. 2009. (ENG.). 256p. pap. 24.95 (978-0-520-26007-8(4)) Univ. of California Pr.

Shambaugh, David, ed. Charting China's Future: Domestic & International Challenges. 2011. (ENG., Illus.). 208p. (C). pap. 51.95 (978-0-415-61955-4(6)) Routledge.

Shambaugh, David L. China's Communist Party: Atrophy & Adaptation. 2008. (Illus.). 234p. 50.00 (978-0-520-25492-3(9)) Univ. of California Pr.

Shi, Li, et al, eds. Inequality & Public Policy in China. 2008. (ENG., Illus.). 384p. 98.00 (978-0-521-87045-0(3)) Cambridge Univ. Pr.

Shi, Li, et al. Eliminating Poverty Through Development in China. 2008. (Illus.). 280p. 180.00 (978-0-415-46277-8(0)) Routledge.

Shichor, Yitzhak. Ethno-Diplomacy: The Uyghur Hitch in Sino-Turkish Relations. 2009. (Policy Studies: 53). 84p. pap. 10.00 (978-1-932728-80-4(5)) East-West Ctr.

Shih, Chih-Yu. Autonomy, Ethnicity, & Poverty in Southwestern China: The State Turned Upside Down. 2007. (ENG.). 272p. 100.00 (978-1-4039-8446-3(8)) Palgrave Macmillan.

Shih, Victor C. Factions & Finance in China: Elite Conflict & Inflation. (ENG., Illus.). 268p. 2009. pap. 31.99 (978-0-521-10647-4(8)) 2007. 94.00 (978-0-521-87257-7(X)) Cambridge Univ. Pr.

Shin, Leo K. The Making of the Chinese State: Ethnicity & Expansion on the Ming Borderlands. 2011. (ENG.). 270p. pap. 50.00 (978-0-521-18989-7(6)) Cambridge Univ. Pr.

Shirk, Susan L. China: Fragile Superpower. 2008. (ENG., Illus.). 336p. pap. 16.95 (978-0-19-537319-6(7)) Oxford Univ. Pr., Inc.

Shu, Yun. Lin Biao Hua Zhuan. 2007. (CHI., Illus.). 775p. pap. (978-1-932138-55-9(2)) Mirror Bks. USA.

Smith, Christopher H., ed. The Internet in China: A Tool for Freedom or Oppression?: Joint Congressional Hearing. 2006. 283p. (C). pap. 45.00 (978-1-4223-0781-6(6)) DIANE Publishing Co.

Snyder-Reinke, Jeffrey. Dry Spells: State Rainmaking & Local Governance in Late Imperial China. 2009. (Harvard East Asian Monographs: 311). (Illus.). 320p. 45.00 (978-0-674-03334-4(5)) Harvard Univ., Asia Ctr.

Song, Guiwu. Peng Zhuang Zhongguo She Hui Jing Ji Wen Ti: Mian Zi, Xue Yuan, Quan Li = Pengzhuang Zhongguoshehui Jingjiwenti. 2010. (CHI., Illus.). (978-7-5017-8787-6(5)) China Economics Publishing Hse.

Stover, Leon. Imperial China & the State Cult of Confucius. alt. ed. 2010. (ENG., Illus.). 224p. pap. 55.00 (978-0-7864-4936-1(5)) McFarland & Co., Inc. Pubs.

Strauss, Julia & Saavedra, Martha, eds. China & Africa: Volume 9: Emerging Patterns in Globalization & Development. 2009. (China Quarterly Special Issues Ser.). (ENG., Illus.). 196p. (C). pap. 41.00 (978-0-521-12200-9(7)) Cambridge Univ. Pr.

Stumbaum, May-Britt U. The European Union & China: Decision-Making in EU Foreign & Security Policy Towards the People's Republic of China. 2009. (Illus.). 250p. pap. 43.00 (978-3-8329-3744-7(7)) Nomos Verlagsgesellschaft DEU. Dist: International Specialized Bk. Services.

Sturgeon, Janet C. Border Landscapes: The Politics of Akha Land Use in China & Thailand. 2007. (Culture, Place, & Nature Ser.). (ENG., Illus.). 264p. per. 22.50 (978-0-295-98763-7(4)) Univ. of Washington Pr.

Su, Chi. Taiwan's Relations with Mainland China: A Tail Wagging Two Dogs. 2008. (Routledge Contemporary Asia Ser.). (Illus.). XX, 348p. 150.00 (978-0-415-46454-3(4)) Routledge.

Su, Xiaobo & Teo, Peggy. The Politics of Heritage Tourism in China: A View from Lijiang. 2009. (Routledge Contemporary China Ser.). (ENG., Illus.). 224p. 150.00 (978-0-415-47808-3(1)) Routledge.

Sung, Yun-Wing. The China-Hong Kong Connection: The Key to China's Open Door Policy. 2009. (Trade & Development Ser.). (ENG.). 200p. (C). pap. 31.99 (978-0-521-10898-0(5)) Cambridge Univ. Pr.

Svarverud, Rune. International Law as World Order in Late Imperial China: Translation, Reception & Discourse, 1847-1911. 2007. (Sinica Leidensia Ser.). (Illus.). 322p. (978-90-04-16019-4(1)) BRILL.

Sweetman, Arthur & Zhang, Jun. Economic Transitions with Chinese Characteristics Vol. 2: Social Change During Thirty Years of Reform. 2009. (ENG.). 216p. (C). (978-1-55339-235-4(3)) McGill-Queen's Univ. Pr.

Tai Zixue. Internet in China. 2006. (Routledge Studies in New Media & Cyberculture Ser.). (ENG., Illus.). 320p. 110.00 (978-0-415-97655-8(3)) Routledge.

Tai, Zixue. The Internet in China: Cyberspace & Civil Society. 2012. (ENG., Illus.). 320p. pap. 42.95 (978-0-415-53588-5(3)) Routledge.

Takagi, Seiichiro, et al, eds. China Watching: Perspectives from Europe, Japan & the United States. 2006. (ENG.). 272p. (C). 190.00 (978-0-415-41396-1(6)) Routledge.

—China Watching: Perspectives from Europe, Japan & the United States. 2006. (Routledge Contemporary China Ser.). 261p. per. 43.95 (978-0-415-41397-8(4), Routledge) Taylor & Francis Group GBR. Dist: Taylor & Francis Group.

Tan, Yan. Resettlement in the Three Gorges Project. 2008. (ENG., Illus.). 310p. (gr. 17). 60.00 (978-962-209-856-5(8)) Hong Kong Univ. Pr. HKG. Dist: Columbia Univ. Pr.

TANG. Gov & Urban Planning Pre-R China. 2008. 224p. 150.00 (978-0-415-36820-9(0)) Routledge.

Tang, Baiqiao & DiMarco, Damon. My Two Chinas: The Memoir of a Chinese Counter-Revolutionary. 2011. (ENG., Illus.). 350p. 26.00 (978-1-61614-445-6(9)) Prometheus Bks., Pubs.

Tanzi, Vito. Peoples, Places & Policies: China, Japan & Southeast Asia. 2007. per. 19.95 (978-0-9795576-5-1(8)) Pinto, Jorge Bks.

Thakur, Ravni. China & India: Comparative Perspectives-A Reader. 2007. (ENG.). 240p. pap. (978-81-87943-77-8(7)) India Research Pr. IND. Dist: Independent Pubs. Group.

Thornton, Patricia M. Disciplining the State: Virtue, Violence, & State-Making in Modern China. 2007. (Harvard East Asian Monographs: 283). (Illus.). 275p. 39.95 (978-0-674-02504-2(0)) Harvard Univ., Asia Ctr.

Tsai, Lily Lee. Accountability Without Democracy: Solidary Groups & Public Goods Provision in Rural China. 2007. (Cambridge Studies in Comparative Politics). (ENG., Illus.). 368p. (C). 88.99 (978-0-521-87197-6(2)); per. 32.99 (978-0-521-69280-9(6)) Cambridge Univ. Pr.

Tse-Tung, Mao. Selected Works of Mao Tse-Tung, 5 vols., Set. (Illus.). 348p. (978-0-08-022262-2(5), Pergamon) Elsevier Science & Technology.

Tubilewicz, Czeslaw. Critical Issues in Contemporary China. 2006. (ENG., Illus.). 288p. (C). 180.00 (978-0-415-39584-7(4)); per. 43.95 (978-0-415-39585-4(2)) Routledge.

Twomey, Christopher P., ed. Perspectives on Sino-American Strategic Nuclear Issues. 2008. (Initiatives in Strategic Studies: Issues & Policies Ser.). (ENG., Illus.). 240p. 89.00 (978-0-230-60660-9(1)) Palgrave Macmillan.

Tyau, Min-Chien T. Z. China's New Constitution & International Problems. 2007. (ENG.). 312p. per. 28.95 (978-0-548-31822-5(0)) Kessinger Publishing, LLC.

Umbsaar, Leelo. Good Governance in Government Agencies. 2010. 128p. pap. (978-3-8383-0147-1(1)) Lambert Academic Publishing.

Unger, Jonathan, ed. Associations & the Chinese State: Contested Spaces. 2008. (ENG.). 288p. pap. 43.95 (978-0-7656-1326-4(3), East Gate Bk.) Sharpe, M.E. Inc.

Urio, Paolo. Reconciling State Market & Society in China. 2011. (ENG., Illus.). 300p. pap. 42.95 (978-0-415-69204-5(0)) Routledge.

Utley, Freda. Last Chance in Chin. 2011. 408p. 54.95 (978-1-258-09616-8(1)) Literary Licensing, LLC.

Verma, Bharat. Threat from China. 2011. 548p. 27.95 (978-1-935501-30-5(5)) Lancer International, Lancer Pr. IND. Dist: Casemate Pubs. & Bk. Distributors, LLC.

Vukovich, Daniel, ed. China & Orientalism: Western Knowledge Production & the P. R. C. 2011. (Postcolonial Politics Ser.). (ENG.). 208p. (C). 130.00 (978-0-415-59220-8(8)) Routledge.

Wang, Aihe. Cosmology & Political Culture in Early China. 2006. (Cambridge Studies in Chinese History, Literature & Institutions Ser.). (ENG., Illus.). 256p. pap. 53.00 (978-0-521-02749-6(7)) Cambridge Univ. Pr.

Wang, Dong. China's Unequal Treaties: Narrating National History. 2008. (Asiaworld Ser.). (ENG.). 190p. pap. 26.50 (978-0-7391-2806-0(X)) Lexington Bks.

Wang, Enbao. The Origin, Process, & Outcome of China,s Reforms in the Past One Hundred Years: The Chinese Quest for National Rejuvenation. 2009. x, 383p. (978-0-7734-3904-7(8)) Mellen, Edwin Pr., The.

Wang, Gabe T. China & the Taiwan Issue: Incoming War at Taiwan Strait. Wang, Gabe T., ed. 2006. (ENG., Illus.). 258p. 68.50 (978-0-7618-3434-2(6)) Univ. Pr. of America, Inc.

Wang, Guiguo. Radiating Impact of WTO on Its Members' Legal System: The Chinese Perspective. 2011. (ENG., Illus.). 384p. pap. (978-90-04-21854-3(8)) BRILL.

Wang, Gungwu & Zheng, Yongnian. China & the New International Order. Gungwu, Wang & Yongnian, Zheng, eds. 2008. (Illus.). XIV, 322p. 170.00 (978-0-415-44111-7(0)) Routledge.

Wang, Hui. Ya Zhou Shi Ye: Zhongguo Li Shi de Xu Shu. 2010. (CHI.). xxiii, 331p. (978-0-19-801928-2(9)) Oxford Univ. Pr., Inc.

Wang, Laidi. Zhong Gong Chuang Shi Ren Fang Tan Lu. 2008. (Zhen Xiang Xi Lie Ser.: Vol. 43). (CHI., Illus.). 339p. (978-1-932138-63-4(3)) Mirror Bks. USA.

Wang, Mengkui. Zhongguo Gai Ge 30 Nian: 1978-2008. 2009. (CHI., Illus.). (978-7-80234-434-1(4)) China Development Pr.

Wang, Qisheng. Ge Ming Yu Fan Ge Ming: She Hui Wen Hua Shi Ye Xia de Minguo Zheng Zhi = Revolution Counter-Revolution. 2010. (978-7-5097-1237-5(8)) China Social Science Documentation Publishing Hse.

Wang, Sheng-Wei. China's Ascendancy: An Opportunity or a Threat?: What Every American Should Know about China. 2007. (978-0-9785095-3-8(6)) International Publishing Hse. for China's Culture.

Wang, Xiaoqi. China's Civil Service Reform. 2012. E-Book (978-0-203-12150-4(3)) Earthscan.

Wang, Zheng. Never Forget National Humiliation: Historical Memory in Chinese Politics & Foreign Relations. 2012. (Contemporary Asia in the World Ser.). (ENG., Illus.). 320p. (gr. 17). 32.50 (978-0-231-14890-0(9)) Columbia Univ. Pr.

Wayne, Martin I. China's War on Terrorism: Counter-Insurgency, Politics & Internal Security. 2009. 206p. pap. 39.95 (978-0-415-54518-1(8)) 2007. (Illus.). XII, 196p. 150.00 (978-0-415-45097-3(7)) Routledge.

Weale, B. L. Putnam. The Fight for the Republic in China. 2008. 452p. 32.99 (978-0-554-22076-5(8)) 2007. (ENG.). 414p. pap. 26.99 (978-1-4264-1608-8(3)) 2007. (ENG.). 450p. pap. 28.99 (978-1-4264-1696-5(2)) BiblioBazaar.

Wei, Betty Peh-T'i. Ruan Yuan, 1764-1849: The Life & Work of a Major Scholar-Official in Nineteenth-Century China Before the Opium War. 2006. (ENG., Illus.). 416p. (gr. 17). 60.00 (978-962-209-785-8(5)) Hong Kong Univ. Pr. HKG. Dist: Columbia Univ. Pr.

Wei, C. X. George, et al, eds. Challenges to Chinese Foreign Policy: Diplomacy, Globalization, & the Next World Power. 2009. (Asia in the New Millennium Ser.). (ENG.). 416p. 75.00 (978-0-8131-2529-9(4)); pap. 29.95 (978-0-8131-9202-4(1)) Univ. Pr. of Kentucky.

Wei, Cho-min. The Political Principles of Mencius. 2010. 62p. pap. (978-1-152-06022-7(8)) Books LLC.

Wen, Gongyi. Ming Dai Huan Guan. 2010. (CHI.). 16p. (978-7-80047-923-6(4)) Forbidden City Publishing Hse.

Wen, Siyong & Ren, Zhichu. Ta Ling Dao Zhongguo: Hu Jintao Xin Zhuan. 2010. (CHI., Illus.). 649p. pap. (978-962-8744-33-6(X)) Mirror Bks. USA.

Weston, Timothy B. & Jensen, Lionel M. China in & Beyond the Headlines. 2011. (978-1-4422-0906-0(2)) Rowman & Littlefield Publishers, Inc.

White, Tyrene. China's Longest Campaign: Birth Planning in the People's Republic, 1949-2005. 2009. (Illus.). 320p. pap. 24.95 (978-0-8014-7539-9(2)) Cornell Univ. Pr.

Wohl, Burton. China Syndrome. 20.95 (978-0-8488-1224-9(7)) Amereon LTD.

Wolff, Diane. Tibet Unconquered: An Epic Struggle for Freedom. 2010. (ENG., Illus.). 272p. 27.00 (978-0-230-62273-9(9)) Palgrave Macmillan.

Wong, Kam C. Police Reform in China. 2011. (Advances in Police Theory & Practice Ser.). (ENG., Illus.). 413p. 129.95 (978-1-4398-1969-2(6), CRC Press) Taylor & Francis Group GBR. Dist: Taylor & Francis Group.

World Bank, Africa Regional Office Staff. Public Finance in China: Reform & Growth for a Harmonious Society. Wang, Shuilin & Lou, Jiwei, eds. 2008. (Stand Alones Ser.). (ENG., Illus.). 400p. per. 35.00 (978-0-8213-6927-2(X), 9780821369272) World Bank Pubns.

Wu, Bin, et al, eds. China's Development & Harmonization: Towards a balance with nature, society & the international Community. 2012. (Routledge Studies on the Chinese Economy Ser.). (ENG.). 320p. (C). 155.00 (978-0-415-66567-4(1)) Routledge.

Wu, Guoguang, ed. China Turns to Multilateralism: Foreign Policy & Regional Security. 2011. (ENG., Illus.). 318p. pap. 42.95 (978-0-415-66646-6(5)) Routledge.

Wu, Guoguang & Lansdowne, Helen, eds. Zhao Ziyang & China's Political Future. (China Policy Ser.). (Illus.). 208p. 2012. (ENG.). (C). pap. 42.95 (978-0-415-54083-4(6)) 2008. 150.00 (978-0-415-46514-4(1)) Routledge.

Wu, Irene & Wu, Irene S. From Iron Fist to Invisible Hand: The Uneven Path of Telecommunications Reform in China. 2008. (ENG., Illus.). 208p. 45.00 (978-0-8047-5962-5(6)) Stanford Univ. Pr.

Wu, Ning. Mao Zhou en Chou Yu Gong Guo, 4 vols. 2010. (CHI.). 1313p. (978-1-59343-024-5(8)) Cozy Graphics Corp.

Wu, Zhiliang. Aomen Zheng Zhi Zhi du Shi. 2010. (CHI., Illus.). (978-7-218-06494-9(9)) Guangdong Peoples Publishing Hse.

Xia, Ming. The People's Congresses & Governance in China: Toward a Network Mode of Governance. 2007. (Illus.). 320p. 135.00 (978-0-415-34950-5(8), RU28074) Routledge.

Xiang, Debao. From Propaganda to Persuasion. 2010. 288p. pap. (978-3-639-24405-2(2)) VDM Verlag Dr. Mueller e.K.

Xiang, Jiangyu. Xi Jinping Ban Di. 2011. (CHI., Illus.). 389p. (978-1-935981-27-5(7)) Mirror Bks. USA.

Xiang, Jianhai, ed. Marine Science & Technology in China: A Roadmap To 2050: A Roadmap To 2050. 2010. (Illus.). 180p. pap. 99.00 (978-3-642-05345-0(9), 3642053459) Springer.

Xiao, Xinhuang & Lin, Zhengyi. Rise of China: Beijing's Strategies & Implications for the Asia-Pacific. Hsiao, Hsin-Huang Michael & Lin, Cheng-yi, eds. 2009. (Politics in Asia Ser.). (ENG., Illus.). 336p. (C). 170.00 (978-0-415-46882-4(5)) Routledge.

Xiaoqi, Wang. China's Civil Service Reform. 2012. (Comparative Development & Policy in Asia Ser.). (ENG., Illus.). 208p. (C). 140.00 (978-0-415-57748-9(9)) Routledge.

Xie, Zhibin. Religious Diversity & Public Religion in China. 2006. 168p. 99.95 (978-0-7546-5648-7(9)) Ashgate Publishing Co.

Xiong, Shihui, et al. Hai Sang Ji: Xiong Shihui Hui Yi Lu, 1907-1949. 2nd ed. 2008. (CHI., Illus.). 710p. pap. *(978-1-932138-70-2(6))* Mirror Bks. USA.

Xu, Feng. Looking for Work in Post-Socialist China. 2011. (Routledge Contemporary China Ser.). (ENG., Illus.). 192p. (C). 145.00 *(978-0-415-55968-3(5))* Routledge.

Xu, Xianjiang. Bai Nian Zhongguo Shi Lu: 1911-2009. 2010. (CHI., Illus.). *(978-7-5098-0161-1(3))* Chinese Communist Party History Pr.

Xue'er. Guo Yun 1909: Qing Di Guo de Gai Ge Tu Wei. 2010. (CHI., Illus.). 317p. *(978-7-5613-4906-9(8))* Shaanxi Normal Univ. Pr.

Xuetong, Yan. Ancient Chinese Thought, Modern Chinese Power. 2011. (Princeton-China Ser.). (ENG., Illus.). 312p. (C). 29.95 *(978-0-691-14826-7(0))* Princeton Univ. Pr.

Yahoo! Inc.'s Provision of False Information to Congress: Hearing Before the Committee on Foreign Affairs, House of Representatives, One Hundred Tenth Congress, First Session, November 6, 2007. 2008. iii, 62p. *(978-0-16-080164-8(8),* 552-070-36901-5) United States Government Printing Office.

Yang, Dali L., ed. Discontented Miracle: Growth, Conflict, & Institutional Adaptations in China. 2007. (Ser. on Contemporary China ndash; Vol. 10 Ser.). (Illus.). 311p. 113.00 *(978-981-270-354-5(3))* World Scientific Publishing Co., Inc.

Yang, Liansheng, et al. Zhongguo Zhi du Shi Yan Jiu: Studies in Chinese Institutional History. 2nd ed. 2007. ("Hai Wai Zhongguo Yan Jiu" Cong Shu Ser.). 189p. *(978-7-214-02312-4(1))* Jiangsu People's Publishing Hse.

Yang, Qingxi & Xia, Fei. Shi Ba Da: Zhu Hou Jin Jing. 2010. (CHI., Illus.). 586p. pap. *(978-962-8744-42-8(9))* Mirror Bks. USA.

Yao, Shujie, et al. Sustainable Reform & Development in Post-Olympic China. 2010. (Routledge Studies on the Chinese Economy Ser.). (ENG., Illus.). 240p. 140.00 *(978-0-415-55956-0(1),* Routledge) Taylor & Francis Group GBR. Dist: Taylor & Francis Group.

A Year after the March 2008 Protests: Is China Promoting Stability in Tibet?: Roundtable Before the Congressional-Executive Commission on China, One Hundredth Eleventh Congress, First Session, March 13, 2009. 2009. ii, 35p. *(978-0-16-083576-6(3),* 552-070-39294-7) United States Government Printing Office.

Yen, Hawkling L. Survey of Constitutional Development in China. (Columbia University, Studies in the Social Sciences: No. 104). reprint ed. 32.50 *(978-0-404-51104-3(X))* AMS Pr., Inc.

Yeung, Linda. China Voices. 2011. 92p. pap. 15.99 *(978-1-4628-6237-5(3))* Xlibris Corp.

Yonglin, Jiang. The Mandate of Heaven & the Great Ming Code. 2011. (Asian Law Ser.). (ENG.). 256p. (C). 65.00 *(978-0-295-99065-1(1))* Univ. of Washington Pr.

Yongnian. De Facto Federalism in China. 2007. (Ser. on Contemporary China Ser.). (Illus.). 350p. (C). 124.00 *(978-981-270-016-2(1))* World Scientific Publishing Co., Inc.

Yongnian, Zheng. China's Opening Society: The Non-State Sector & Governance. 2009. 252p. pap. 39.95 *(978-0-415-54639-3(7))* Routledge.

Yongnian, Zheng, ed. China & International Relations: The Chinese View & the Contribution of Wang Gungwu. 2012. (ENG., Illus.). 384p. (C). pap. 44.95 *(978-0-415-62546-3(7))* Routledge.

—China & International Relations: The Chinese View & the Contribution of Wang Gungwu. 2010. (China Policy Ser.). (ENG., Illus.). 384p. (C). 155.00 *(978-0-415-57607-9(5),* Routledge) Taylor & Francis Group GBR. Dist: Taylor & Francis Group.

Young, Doug. The Party Line: How the Media Dictates Public Opinion in Modern China. 2013. (ENG.). 256p. pap. 22.95 *(978-0-470-82853-3(6),* Wiley) Wiley, John & Sons, Inc.

Yousaf Khokhar, Amna. China-India Relations & Implications for Pakistan. 2011. 400p. pap. *(978-3-8443-8786-5(2))* Lambert Academic Publishing.

Yu, Jianxing, et al. A Path for Chinese Civil Society: A Case Study on Industrial Associations in Wenzhou, China. 2012. *(978-0-7391-7008-3(2))* Lexington Bks.

Yu, Keping. Democracy Is a Good Thing: Essays on Politics, Society, & Culture in Contemporary China. 2011. (Thornton Center Chinese Thinkers Ser.). (ENG.). 219p. pap. 26.95 *(978-0-8157-2218-2(4))* Brookings Institution Pr.

Yu, Peter Kien-Hong. International Governance & Regimes: A Chinese Perspective. 2011. (Routledge Contemporary China Ser.). (ENG., Illus.). 232p. (C). 125.00 *(978-0-415-68199-5(5))* Routledge.

Yu, Shiping. Xin Tai Z Shang. 2010. (CHI., Illus.). 517p. *(978-962-8744-32-9(1))* Mirror Bks. USA.

Yuan, Zaijun. Failure of Chinas Democratic Reforms. 2011. (Challenges Facing Chinese Political Development Ser.). (ENG.). 195p. 60.00 *(978-0-7391-6694-9(8))* Lexington Bks.

—The Failure of China's Democratic Reforms. 2011. *(978-0-7391-7089-2(9))* Lexington Bks.

Zarrow, Peter Gue. After Empire: The Conceptual Transformation of the Chinese State, 1885-1924. 2012. (ENG.). 416p. 85.00 *(978-0-8047-7868-8(X))*; pap. 27.95 *(978-0-8047-7869-5(8))* Stanford Univ. Pr.

Zhang, Shifei & Tang, Jun. Zhongguo She Hui Zheng Ce Yan Jiu Shi Nian: Zhuan Ti Bao Gao Ji, 1999-2008: Zhongguo She Hui Zhu Ti Xi de Shi Jian Yu Tan Suo = Chinese Social Policy Studies 1999-2008, Special Topic Reports: Practice & Exploration on Construction of Social Assistance System in China. 2010. (CHI., Illus.). *(978-7-5097-1213-9(0))* China Social Science Documentation Publishing Hse.

Zhang, Wei-Bin. New China's Long March from Servility to Freedom. 2007. 169.00 *(978-1-60021-791-3(5))* Nova Science Pubs., Inc.

Zhang, Xiaoling. The Transformation of Political Communication in China: From Propaganda to Hegemony. 2011. (Illus.). 300p. 110.00 *(978-981-4340-93-9(6))* World Scientific Publishing Co., Inc.

Zhang, Xiaoling & Zheng, Yongnian, eds. China's Information & Communications Technology Revolution: Social changes & state Responses. 2012. (ENG., Illus.). 176p. (C). pap. 44.95 *(978-0-415-62495-4(9))* Routledge.

Zhang, Xin. Social Transformation in Modern China: The State & Local Elites in Henan, 1900-1937. 2006. (Cambridge Modern China Ser.). (ENG., Illus.). 340p. pap. 48.00 *(978-0-521-02755-7(1))* Cambridge Univ. Pr.

Zhao, Yuezhi. Communication in China: Political Economy, Power & Conflict. 2008. (State & Society in East Asia Ser.). (ENG.). 384p. 90.00 *(978-0-7425-1965-7(1))* Rowman & Littlefield Publishers, Inc.

—Communication in China: Political Economy, Power, & Conflict. 2008. (State & Society in East Asia Ser.). (ENG.). 384p. pap. 34.95 *(978-0-7425-1966-4(X))* Rowman & Littlefield Publishers, Inc.

Zhao Ziyang. Prisoner of the State: The Secret Journal of Premier Zhao Ziyang. Ignatius, Adi et al, eds. Bao Pu et al, trs. 2010. (ENG., Illus.). 336p. pap. 16.00 *(978-1-4391-4939-3(9))* Simon & Schuster.

Zheng, Yongnian. Politics of Modern China, 4 vols. Zheng, Yongnian et al, eds. 2009. (ENG., Illus.). 1824p. 1075.00 *(978-0-415-44151-3(X))* Routledge.

—Politics of Modern China V4, 4 vols. Lu, Yiyi, ed. 2009. (Illus.). 400p. *(978-0-415-45622-7(3))* Routledge.

—Technological Empowerment: The Internet, State, & Society in China. 2007. (ENG., Illus.). 272p. 50.00 *(978-0-8047-5737-9(2))* Stanford Univ. Pr.

Zheng, Yongnian, et al, eds. Politics of Modern China V1, 4 vols. 2009. (Illus.). 400p. *(978-0-415-45619-7(3))* Routledge.

Zheng, Yongnian & Fewsmith, Joseph, eds. China's Opening Society: The Non-State Sector & Governance. 2008. (China Policy Ser.). (ENG., Illus.). 256p. (C). 150.00 *(978-0-415-45176-5(0))* Routledge.

Zheng, Yongnian & White, Lynn T., eds. Politics of Modern China V2, 4 vols. 2009. (Illus.). 400p. *(978-0-415-45620-3(7))* Routledge.

—Politics of Modern China V3, 4 vols. 2009. (Illus.). 400p. *(978-0-415-45621-0(5))* Routledge.

Zhenglai, Deng. Reviving Legitimacy: Lessons for & from China. 2011. (Challenges Facing Chinese Political Development Ser.). (ENG.). 226p. 65.00 *(978-0-7391-6522-5(4))* Lexington Bks.

Zhimin, Chen, ed. China's Reforms & International Political Economy. 2007. (Routledge Studies on China in Transition Ser.). (ENG., Illus.). 256p. (C). 170.00 *(978-0-415-39613-4(1))* Routledge.

Zhong, Lena. Communities, Crime & Social Capital in Contemporary China: Crime Prevention in Two Chinese Communities. 2008. (ENG., Illus.). 256p. 79.95 *(978-1-84392-405-0(6))* Willan Publishing GBR. Dist: Taylor & Francis Group.

Zhongguo di 2 li shi dang an guan Staff, contrib. by. Bei Yang Zheng Fu Dang An, 188 vols. 2010. (CHI., Illus.). 18p. *(978-7-5105-0173-9(3))* China Archives Publishing Hse.

Zhou, Jinghao. China's Peaceful Rise in a Global Context: A Domestic Aspect of China's Road Map to Democratization. (ENG.). 2012. 222p. pap. 29.99 *(978-0-7391-3338-5(1))* 2010. 232p. 68.50 *(978-0-7391-3337-8(3))* Lexington Bks.

Zhou, Kate. China's Long March to Freedom: Grassroots Modernization. 2009. (ENG., Illus.). 391p. 39.95 *(978-1-4128-1029-6(9))* Transaction Pubs.

Zhu, Zhiqun. Global Studies: China. 13th ed. 2009. (Global Studies). (ENG.). 224p. (C). pap. 50.30 *(978-0-07-337987-6(5),* 0073379875, McGraw-Hill/Dushkin) McGraw-Hill Higher Education.

CHINA—POLITICS AND GOVERNMENT—1949-

see also Chinese Reunification Question, 1949-

Bachman, David. Bureaucracy, Economy, & Leadership in China: The Institutional Origins of the Great Leap Forward. 2006. (ENG.). 288p. (C). pap. 42.00 *(978-0-521-03233-9(4))* Cambridge Univ. Pr.

Baum, Richard. China Watcher: Confessions of a Peking Tom. 2010. (Samuel & Althea Stroum Book Ser.). (ENG., Illus.). 336p. 29.95 *(978-0-295-98997-6(1))* Univ. of Washington Pr.

Blecher, Marc J. China Against the Tides: Restructuring Through Revolution, Radicalism & Reform. 3rd ed. 2009. (ENG., Illus.). 256p. 120.00 *(978-0-8264-2725-0(1))*; pap. 34.95 *(978-0-8264-2698-7(0))* Continuum International Publishing Group, Ltd. GBR. Dist: National Bk. Network.

Bo, Zhiyue. China's Elite Politics: Governance & Democratization. 2009. (Illus.). 550p. 111.00 *(978-981-283-672-4(1))* World Scientific Publishing Co., Inc.

Brown, Kerry. Friends & Enemies: The Past, Present & Future of the Communist Party of China. 2009. (China in the 21st Century Ser.). (ENG., Illus.). 224p. pap. 24.95 *(978-1-84331-781-4(8))* Anthem Pr. GBR. Dist: Books International, Inc.

Brugger, Bill & Brugger, William E. Democracy & Organisation in the Chinese Industrial Enterprise (1948-1953) 2010. (Contemporary China Institute Publications). (ENG.). 384p. pap. 31.99 *(978-0-521-13429-3(3))* Cambridge Univ. Pr.

Chan, Lai-Ha. China At 60: Global-Local Interactions. 2011. 352p. 98.00 *(978-981-4299-29-9(4))* World Scientific Publishing Co., Inc.

Chang, Jung & Halliday, Jon. Mao: The Unknown Story. 2006. (ENG., Illus.). 864p. pap. 20.00 *(978-0-679-74632-4(3),* Anchor) Knopf Doubleday Publishing Group.

Chen, Damang & Liu, Shi. Luo Jing Xia Shi: Zhong Cha Gaogang An. 2008. (CHI., Illus.). 429p. *(978-1-932138-75-7(7))* Mirror Bks. USA.

Designwallas, creator. Chairman Cool. 2009. (ICONoclastic Ser.). (ENG.). 128p. 12.95 *(978-81-7436-668-9(7))* Roli Bks. Private, Ltd. IND. Dist: Ingram Pub. Services.

Fravel, M. Taylor. Strong Borders, Secure Nation: Cooperation & Conflict in China's Territorial Disputes. 2008. (Princeton Studies in International History & Politics Ser.). (ENG., Illus.). 408p. (C). 72.50 *(978-0-691-13608-0(4))*; pap. 32.50 *(978-0-691-13609-7(2))* Princeton Univ. Pr.

Friedman, Edward, et al. Revolution, Resistance, & Reform in Village China. 2007. (Yale Agrarian Studies). (ENG., Illus.). 368p. per. 22.00 *(978-0-300-12595-5(X))* Yale Univ. Pr.

Gan, Cui. Yi Lin Chao. 2009. (CHI., Illus.). 259p. *(978-1-931550-31-4(X))* Laogai Research Foundation, The.

Gittings, John. The Changing Face of China: From Mao to Market. 2006. (ENG., Illus.). 334p. per. 19.95 *(978-0-19-280734-2(X))* Oxford Univ. Pr., Inc.

Heilmann, Sebastian & Perry, Elizabeth J., eds. Mao's Invisible Hand: The Political Foundations of Adaptive Governance in China. 2011. (Harvard Contemporary China Ser.). (ENG., Illus.). 336p. pap. 24.95 *(978-0-674-06063-0(6))* Harvard Univ., Asia Ctr.

Hu, Wanli. Mao's American Strategy & the Korean War. 2008. 284p. pap. *(978-3-8364-3770-7(3))* VDM Verlag Dr. Mueller e.K.

Hu, Weixing & Zha, Daojiong. Building a Neighbourly Community: Post-Cold War China, Japan, & Southeast Asia. 2007. (ENG., Illus.). 288p. 84.00 *(978-0-7190-7064-8(3))* Manchester Univ. Pr. GBR. Dist: Macmillan.

Hu, Xianzhong. Yin Mou Xia de Ren Sheng. 2008. (CHI.). 274p. pap. 25.00 *(978-1-931550-24-6(7))* Laogai Research Foundation, The.

Huang, Jing. Factionalism in Chinese Communist Politics. 2006. (Cambridge Modern China Ser.). (ENG.). 480p. (C). pap. 61.00 *(978-0-521-03258-2(X))* Cambridge Univ. Pr.

Laaksonen, Oiva. Management in China during & after Mao in Enterprises, Government, & Party. (De Gruyter Studies in Organization Ser.). (ENG.). X, 378p. 196.00 *(978-3-11-185183-9(4))* De Gruyter, Walter Inc.

Larus, Elizabeth Freund. Politics & Society in Contemporary China. 2012. (C). 275p. pap. 32.50 *(978-1-58826-825-9(X))*; (Illus.). 75.00 *(978-1-58826-800-6(4))* Rienner, Lynne Pubs.

Lee, Ann. What the U. S. Can Learn from China: An Open-Minded Guide to Treating Our Greatest Competitor as Our Greatest Teacher. 2012. (ENG.). 288p. 27.95 *(978-1-60994-124-6(1))* Berrett-Koehler Pubs., Inc.

Leutner, Mechthild, ed. Rethinking China in the 1950s. 2008. (Chinese History & Society Ser.). (GER & ENG.). 184p. pap. 36.95 *(978-3-8258-0291-2(4))* Lit Verlag DEU. Dist: Transaction Pubs.

Lewis, John W. Political Networks & the Chinese Policy Process. (Occasional Paper of the Northeast Asia-United States Forum on International Policy, Stanford University). 32p. (Orig.). pap. 6.00 *(978-0-935371-15-4(X))* Ctr. for International Security & Cooperation.

Li, Mingjiang. Mao's China & Sino-Soviet Split: Ideological Dilemma. 2012. (Routledge Contemporary China Ser.). (ENG.). 224p. (C). 125.00 *(978-0-415-69836-8(7))* Routledge.

Li, Ni. Li Shi Shang Kou: Er Shi Nian You Pai Xun Fang Ji. 2008. (Zhen Xiang Xi Lie Ser.: Vol. 50). (CHI., Illus.). 305p. *(978-1-932138-79-5(X))* Mirror Bks. USA.

Li, Xiaoting & Huang, Jing. Inseparable Separation: The Making of China's Taiwan Policy. 2007. (ENG.). 330p. pap. 24.95 *(978-0-8157-3759-9(9))* Brookings Institution Pr.

Lu, Di. Guo Gong Wei Zao de Li Shi: Ling Xiu Men Liu Xia de Mi Tuan. 2010. (Illus.). 407p. pap. *(978-962-8744-20-6(8))* Mirror Bks. USA.

Lynch, Catherine, et al. Radicalism, Revolution, & Reform in Modern China: Essays in Honor of Maurice Meisner. 2011. (AsiaWorld Ser.). (ENG.). 260p. 70.00 *(978-0-7391-6572-6(0))* Lexington Bks.

—Radicalism, Revolution, & Reform in Modern China: Essays in Honor of Maurice Meisner. 2011. *(978-0-7391-6574-4(7))* Rowman & Littlefield Publishers, Inc.

MacFarquhar, Roderick, ed. The Politics of China: Sixty Years of the People's Republic of China. 3rd rev. ed. 2011. (ENG., Illus.). 688p. (C). pap. 49.00 *(978-0-521-14531-2(7))*; 120.00 *(978-0-521-19693-2(0))* Cambridge Univ. Pr.

Ngo, Tak-Wing, ed. Contemporary China Studies, 8 vols., Vols. 1& 2, Set. 2011. (Illus.). 3328p. 1800.00 *(978-0-85702-820-4(0),* B28204C) SAGE Pubns., Ltd. GBR. Dist: SAGE Pubns., Inc.

—Contemporary China Studies Vol. 1: Politics. 2011. (Illus.). 1584p. 995.00 *(978-1-4129-4884-5(3),* B48845C) SAGE Pubns., Ltd. GBR. Dist: SAGE Pubns., Inc.

O'Brien, Kevin J. Reform without Liberalization: China's National People's Congress & the Politics of Institutional Change. 2008. (ENG.). 280p. pap. 34.99 *(978-0-521-04820-0(6))* Cambridge Univ. Pr.

Quigley, Harold S. China's Politics in Perspective. 2009. (ENG.). 290p. pap. 50.00 *(978-0-8166-6044-5(1))* Univ. of Minnesota Pr.

Shai, Aron. Zhang Xue-Liang: The General Who Never Fought. 2012. (ENG., Illus.). 184p. 80.00 *(978-0-230-27906-3(6))* Palgrave Macmillan.

Smith, Arthur H. China in Convulsion. 2009. (ENG.). 485p. 42.99 *(978-1-117-50255-7(4))*; pap. 28.99 *(978-1-117-50257-1(0),* BiblioLife); pap. 37.75 *(978-1-117-50256-4(2))* BiblioBazaar.

Snyder, Francis & Snyder, Francis G. The European Union & China, 1949-2006: Basic Documents & Commentary. 2009. (ENG.). 1128p. pap. 134.00 *(978-1-84113-724-7(3))* Hart Publishing Ltd. GBR. Dist: International Specialized Bk. Services.

State Secrets: China's Legal Labrynth. 2007. pap. *(978-0-9717356-3-7(8))* Human Rights In China.

Su, Weimin. Yang Shangkun Tan Xin Zhongguo Ruo Gan Li Shi Wen Ti. 2010. (CHI.). *(978-7-220-07987-0(7))* Sichuan Renmin Chubanshe.

Taylor, Ian. China & Africa: Engagement & Compromise. 2009. 234p. pap. 39.95 *(978-0-415-54552-5(8))* Routledge.

Teiwes, Frederick & Sun, Warren. The End of the Maoist Era: Chinese Politics During the Twilight of the Cultural Revolution, 1972-1976. 2007. (Politics of Transition in China, 1972-1982 Ser.). (ENG.). 728p. pap. 54.95 *(978-0-7656-1097-3(3),* East Gate Bk.) Sharpe, M.E. Inc.

Teiwes, Frederick C. & Sun, Warren. The End of the Maoist Era: Chinese Politics During the Twilight of the Cultural Revolution, 1972-1976. 2007. (Politics of Transition in China, 1972-1982 Ser.). (ENG.). 728p. 128.95 *(978-0-7656-1096-6(5),* East Gate Bk.) Sharpe, M.E. Inc.

Wang, Shengsong. Zhongguo Xiang Cun Zi Zhi Wen Ti Yan Jiu: Zhongguo Xiangcun Zizhi Wenti Yanjiu. 2009. (CHI.). *(978-7-01-007664-5(2))* People's Publishing Hse., The.

Wang, Xiangkun. Du Dong Liu Shaoqi: Dudong Liiu Shaoqi. 2010. *(978-7-220-07989-4(3))* Sichuan Renmin Chubanshe.

Womack, Brantly. China's Rise in Historical Perspective. 2010. (ENG.). 272p. pap. 29.95 *(978-0-7425-6722-1(2))* Rowman & Littlefield Publishers, Inc.

Womack, Brantly, ed. China's Rise in Historical Perspective. 2010. (ENG.). 272p. 85.00 *(978-0-7425-6721-4(4))* Rowman & Littlefield Publishers, Inc.

Zeng, Yongxian, et al. Cong Zuo Dao You Liu Shi Nian: Zeng Yongxian Xian Sheng Fang Tan Lu. 2009. (CHI., Illus.). *(978-986-02-1793-3(9))* Academia Sinica.

Zhao, Xu. Jia Bian Gou Can An: Fang Tan Lu. 2008. (CHI.). 437p. pap. 35.00 *(978-1-931550-21-5(2))* Laogai Research Foundation, The.

Zheng, Yongnian. Zhongguo Mo Shi: Jing Yan Yu Kun Ju. 2010. (CHI., Illus.). *(978-7-213-04190-7(8))* Zhejiang People's Publishing Hse.

Zhiyue, Bo. China's Elite Politics: Political Transition & Power Balancing. 2007. (Series on Contemporary China Ser.). (Illus.). 449p. 113.00 *(978-981-270-041-4(2))* World Scientific Publishing Co., Inc.

Zhou, Shaochang. Xing Xing Chong Xing Xing: "Fan You Yun Dong" Ji. 2008. ("Wen Hua Qing Li" Xi Lie Ser.: Vol. 24). (CHI.). 322p. *(978-1-932138-69-5(2))* Mirror Bks. USA.

Zhu, Zhiqun & Lampton, David M. The People's Republic of China Today: Internal & External Challenges. 2010. 400p. 122.00 *(978-981-4313-50-6(5))* World Scientific Publishing Co., Inc.

CHINA—POLITICS AND GOVERNMENT—1976-

Béja, Jean-Philippe. The Impact of China's 1989 Tiananmen Massacre. 2010. (China Policy Ser.). (ENG., Illus.). 272p. (C). 140.00 *(978-0-415-57872-1(3))* Routledge.

Bell, Daniel A. China's New Confucianism: Politics & Everyday Life in a Changing Society. 2010. (ENG.). 280p. (C). pap. 19.95 *(978-0-691-14585-3(7))* Princeton Univ. Pr.

Benewick, Robert, et al. The State of China Atlas: Mapping the World's Fastest-Growing Economy. 2nd rev. ed. 2009. (ENG., Illus.). 128p. pap. 19.95 *(978-0-520-25610-1(7))* Univ. of California Pr.

Bergsten, C. Fred, et al. China's Rise: Challenges & Opportunities. (Illus.). 2009. 280p. pap. 13.95 *(978-0-88132-434-1(5))* 2008. 256p. 26.95 *(978-0-88132-417-4(5))* Peterson Institute for International Economics.

Bijian, Zheng. China's Road to Peaceful Development. 2011. (Routledge Studies on the Chinese Economy Ser.). (ENG.). 352p. (C). 145.00 *(978-0-415-55271-4(0))* Routledge.

Bo, Zhiyue & Wong, John. China's Reform in Global Perspective. 2010. (Illus.). 400p. 96.00 *(978-981-4289-24-5(8))* World Scientific Publishing Co., Inc.

Breslin, Shaun. China & the Global Political Economy. 2009. (ENG.). 246p. pap. 37.00 *(978-0-230-57793-0(8))* Palgrave Macmillan.

Brodsgaard, Kjeld Erik. The Chinese Communist Party in Reform. 2009. 272p. pap. 39.95 *(978-0-415-54576-1(5))* Routledge.

Brown, Kerry. Hu Jintao: China's Silent Ruler. 2012. 256p. 45.00 *(978-981-4350-02-0(8))* World Scientific Publishing Co., Inc.

Brunnert, H. S. & Hagelstrom, V. V. Present Day Political Organization of China 2007. 572p. reprint ed. 160.00 *(978-0-7007-1018-8(3))* Routledge.

Cai, Yongshun. Collective Resistance in China: Why Popular Protests Succeed or Fail. 2010. (Studies of the Walter H. Shorenstein Asi Ser.). (ENG., Illus.). 304p. 65.00 *(978-0-8047-6339-4(9))*; pap. 22.95 *(978-0-8047-6340-0(2))* Stanford Univ. Pr.

China: Recent Security Developments. 2009. iii, 44p. *(978-0-16-084149-1(6),* 552-070-39750-7) United States Government Printing Office.

China's Human Rights Lawyers: Current Challenges & Prospects: Roundtable Before the Congressional-Executive Commission on China, One Hundred Eleventh Congress, First Session, July 10, 2009. 2009. iii, 48p. *(978-0-16-085553-5(5),* 552-070-40796-1) United States Government Printing Office.

Cho, Young Nam. Local People's Congresses in China: Development & Transition. 2008. (ENG., Illus.). 206p. 85.00 *(978-0-521-51562-7(9))* Cambridge Univ. Pr.

Chong, Denise. Egg on Mao: A Story of Love, Hope & Defiance. 2011. (ENG., Illus.). 256p. pap. 19.95 *(978-0-307-35580-5(2),* Vintage Canada) Random Hse. of Canada, Ltd. CAN. Dist: Random Hse., Inc.

Chu, Yun-han & Leng, Tse-Kang. Dynamics of Local Governance in China During the Reform Era. 2009. (Challenges Facing Chinese Political Development Ser.). (ENG., Illus.). 326p. 83.99 *(978-0-7391-2688-2(1))* Lexington Bks.

C

Doyle, Randall & Boshu, Zhang. Modern China & the New World: The Reemergence of the Middle Kingdom in the 21st Century. 2011. (ENG.). 186p. (gr. 17). 60.00 *(978-0-7391-7187-5(9))* Lexington Bks.

Doyle, Randall Jordan & Zhang, Boshu. Modern China & the New World: The Reemergence of the Middle Kingdom in the 21st Century. 2011. E-Book *(978-0-7391-7188-2(7))* Lexington Bks.

Dreyer, June Teufel. China's Political System: Modernization & Tradition. 7th ed. 2009. (ENG., Illus.). 400p. (C). pap. 78.00 *(978-0-205-70745-4(9))* Longman Publishing.

Duan, Qing. China's IT Leadership: The Political Struggle behind China's Information Revolution. 2007. 292p. per. *(978-3-8364-2762-3(1))* VDM Verlag Dr. Mueller e.K.

Duckett, Jane. The Chinese State's Retreat from Health: Policy & the Politics of Retrenchment. 2010. (Routledge Studies on China in Transition Ser.). (ENG., Illus.). 160p. (C). 130.00 *(978-0-415-57389-4(0)*, Routledge) Taylor & Francis Group GBR. Dist: Taylor & Francis Group.

Er. The Rise of China & India. 2009. viii, 169p. 90.00 *(978-981-4280-33-4(X))* World Scientific Publishing Co., Inc.

Farndon, John. China Rises: How China's Astonishing Growth Will Change the World. 2008. (ENG., Illus.). 240p. pap. 14.95 *(978-0-7535-1349-1(8))* Virgin Bks. Ltd. GBR. Dist: Independent Pubs. Group.

Fewsmith, Joseph. China since Tiananmen: From Deng Xiaoping to Hu Jintao. 2nd rev. ed. 2008. (Cambridge Modern China Ser.). (ENG., Illus.). 352p. (C). 75.00 *(978-0-521-86693-4(6))*; pap. 25.99 *(978-0-521-68605-1(9))* Cambridge Univ. Pr.

—China Today, China Tomorrow: Domestic Politics, Economy, & Society. 2010. (Illus.). (ENG.). 344p. 89.00 *(978-0-7425-6706-1(0))*; (ENG., 344p. pap. 34.95 *(978-0-7425-6707-8(9))*; ix, 334p. *(978-0-7425-6708-5(7))* Rowman & Littlefield Publishers, Inc.

The Future of Political, Economic, & Security Relations with China: Hearing Before the Committee on Foreign Affairs, House of Representatives, One Hundred Tenth Congress, First Session, May 1, 2007. 2007. iii, 41p. *(978-0-16-079098-0(0)*, 552-070-36194-4) United States Government Printing Office.

Gallagher, Mary Elizabeth. Contagious Capitalism: Globalization & the Politics of Labor in China. 2007. (ENG., Illus.). 256p. (C). per. 24.95 *(978-0-691-13036-1(1))* Princeton Univ. Pr.

Gao, Gao. Deng Xiaoping, Hu Yaobang, Zhao Ziyang San Tou Ma Che Shi Dai. 2009. (Zhen Xiang Xi Lie Ser.: Vol. 51). (CHI., Illus.). 345p. *(978-1-932138-80-1(3))* Mirror Bks. USA.

Goldman, Merle. From Comrade to Citizen: The Struggle for Political Rights in China. 2007. 304p. pap. 23.50 *(978-0-674-02544-8(X))* Harvard Univ. Pr.

—Political Rights in Post-Mao China. 2007. *(978-0-924304-51-4(0))* Assn. for Asian Studies, Inc.

Gries, Peter & Rosen, Stanley, eds. Chinese Politics: State, Society & the Market. 2010. (Asia's Transformations Ser.). (ENG., Illus.). 304p. (C). 44.95 *(978-0-415-56403-8(4))*; 153.00 *(978-0-415-56402-1(6))* Routledge.

Guo, Baogang. Chinas Quest for Political Legitimacy: The New Equity-Enhancing Politics. 2010. (Challenges Facing Chinese Political Development Ser.). (ENG., Illus.). 234p. 65.00 *(978-0-7391-2258-7(4))* Lexington Bks.

Guo, Baogang & Hickey, Dennis. Toward Better Governance in China: An Unconventional Pathway of Political Reform. 2009. (Challenges Facing Chinese Political Development Ser.). (ENG., Illus.). 226p. 73.50 *(978-0-7391-4027-7(2))* Lexington Bks.

Guo, Rongxing, ed. China's Political & Economic Transformation: Theory & Case Studies. 2010. (China in the 21st Century Ser.). pap. 43.00 *(978-1-60876-321-4(8))* Nova Science Pubs., Inc.

Guthrie, Doug. China & Globalization. 3rd rev. ed. 2012. (ENG., Illus.). 360p. 130.00 ***(978-0-415-50400-3(7))*** Routledge.

—China & Globalization: The Social, Economic & Political Transformation of Chinese Society. 3rd rev. ed. 2012. (ENG., Illus.). 360p. pap. 39.95 ***(978-0-415-50401-0(5))*** Routledge.

Heberer, Thomas & Schubert, Gunter, eds. Regime Legitimacy in Contemporary China. 2009. 306p. pap. 39.95 *(978-0-415-57430-3(7))* Routledge.

Hu, Ping & Song, Airu. Gai Ge Kai Fang Qin Li Ji: Hu Ping Fang Tan Lu. 2010. 20p. *(978-7-5073-2908-7(9))* Central Party Literature Audio & Video Publishing Hse.

Hua, Shiping & Guo, Sujian, eds. China in the Twenty-First Century: Challenges & Opportunities. 2011. (ENG., Illus.). 296p. pap. 30.00 *(978-0-230-12072-3(5))* Palgrave Macmillan.

Huang, Xiaoqin. Zhongguo Min Bian. 2009. (CHI., Illus.). 378p. pap. *(978-1-932138-94-8(3))* Mirror Bks. USA.

Huang, Yanzhong. Governing Health in Contemporary China. 2010. (China Policy Ser.). (ENG.). 240p. (C). 145.00 *(978-0-415-49845-6(7))* Routledge.

Hui, Wang. The End of the Revolution: China & the Limits of Modernity. 2011. (ENG.). 272p. pap. 22.95 *(978-1-84467-379-7(0)*, 844379) Verso Bks. GBR. Dist: Norton, W. W. & Co., Inc.

Hung, Chang-tai. Mao's New World: Political Culture in the Early People's Republic. 2010. (Illus.). 328p. 39.95 *(978-0-8014-4934-5(0))* Cornell Univ. Pr.

Jacques, Martin. When China Rules the World: The End of the Western World & the Birth of a New Global Order. rev. ed. 2012. (ENG.). 848p. (gr. 12). 20.00 *(978-0-14-311800-8(5)*, Penguin (Non-Classics)) Penguin Group (USA) Inc.

Jeffreys, Elaine, ed. China's Governmentalities. 2011. (ENG., Illus.). 184p. pap. 42.95 ***(978-0-415-66623-7(6))*** Routledge.

Jeffries, Ian. Political Developments in Contemporary China. 2010. (Guides to Economic & Political Developments in Asia Ser.). (ENG.). 1040p. (C). instr.'s gde. ed. 200.00 *(978-0-415-58085-4(4)*, Routledge) Taylor & Francis Group GBR. Dist: Taylor & Francis Group.

Jiang, Qisheng. My Life in Prison: Memoirs of a Chinese Political Dissident. 2012. ***(978-1-4422-1224-4(1))*** Rowman & Littlefield Publishers, Inc.

Keping, Yu. Democracy & Rule of Law in China. 2010. (Issues in Contemporary Chinese Thought & Culture Ser.). (ENG.). 300p. *(978-90-04-18212-7(8))* BRILL.

Keping, Yu, ed. The Reform of Governance. 2010. (Social Scientific Studies in Reform Era China Ser.). (ENG., Illus.). 492p. *(978-90-04-18631-6(X))* BRILL.

Kinzelbach, Katrin. The EU's Human Rights Dialogue with China: Quiet Diplomacy & its Limits. 2013. (Routledge Research in Human Rights Ser.). (ENG.). 240p. (C). 135.00 ***(978-0-415-69846-7(4))*** Routledge.

LaFleur, Robert André. China. 1 vol. 2009. (Asia in Focus Ser.). (Illus.). 504p. 85.00 *(978-1-59884-166-4(1)*, CHINAS1C) ABC-CLIO, LLC.

Lai, Qingxiu. Zhongnan Hai Shi Mian Mai Fu: Hu Wen Mian Lin de Kun Nan, Fen Qi He Qian Zai Chong Tu. 2nd ed. 2009. (CHI., Illus.). 445p. pap. *(978-1-932138-87-0(0))* Mirror Bks. USA.

Lam, Willy Wo-Lap. Chinese Politics in the Hu Jintao Era: New Leaders, New Challenges. 2006. (East Gate Bks.). (Illus.). 359p. 82.95 *(978-0-7656-1773-6(0))* Sharpe, M.E. Inc.

Lanteigne, Marc & Laliberte, Andre, eds. The Chinese Party-State in the 21st Century: Adaptation & the Reinvention of Legitimacy. 2008. (Routledge Contemporary China Ser.). (ENG., Illus.). 208p. (C). 160.00 *(978-0-415-45056-0(X))* Routledge.

Li, Mingjiang. Soft Power: China's Emerging Strategy in International Politics. 2009. (ENG.). 284p. 83.99 *(978-0-7391-3377-4(2))* Lexington Bks.

Liang, Bin. The Changing Chinese Legal System, 1978-Present: Centralization of Power & Rationalization of the Legal System. 2007. (East Asia: History, Politics, Sociology & Culture Ser.). (ENG., Illus.). 266p. 125.00 *(978-0-415-95859-2(8))* Routledge.

Litai, Xue & Lewis, John Wilson. Imagined Enemies: China Prepares for Uncertain War. 2006. (ENG., Illus.). 384p. 65.00 *(978-0-8047-5391-3(1))* Stanford Univ. Pr.

Liu, Tiansheng. Zhong Gong Zheng Zai Shu Diao de Zhan Zheng: Wang Luo Gai Bian Zhongguo. 2010. ("Zhongguo Ju Shi" Xi Lie Ser.: Vol. 62). (CHI., Illus.). 284p. pap. *(978-962-8744-29-9(1))* Mirror Bks. USA.

McNally, Christopher A. China's Emergent Political Economy: Capitalism in the Dragon's Lair. 2009. 262p. pap. 39.95 *(978-0-415-49718-3(3))* Routledge.

Mendes, Errol P. & Srighanthan, Sakunthala, eds. Confronting Discrimination & Inequality in China: Chinese & Canadian Perspectives. 2009. (ENG., Illus.). 438p. (gr. 10-12). pap. *(978-0-7766-0709-2(X))* Univ. of Ottawa Pr./Presses de l'Universite d'Ottawa.

Merriam, Beth. China's 'Tibetan' Frontiers: Sharing the Contested Ground, 1 vol. 2010. (ENG.). 256p. *(978-1-906876-30-2(4))* BRILL.

Mertha, Andrew C. China's Water Warriors: Citizen Action & Policy Change. (Illus.). 2011. 200p. pap. 21.00 *(978-0-8014-7668-6(2))* 2008. 168p. 52.50 *(978-0-8014-4636-8(8))* Cornell Univ. Pr.

Moody, Peter. Conservative Thought in Contemporary China. 2007. (ENG.). 232p. 73.50 *(978-0-7391-0935-9(9))*; 238p. pap. 30.50 *(978-0-7391-2046-0(8))* Rowman & Littlefield Publishers, Inc.

Naughton, Barry. Holding China Together: Diversity & National Integration in the Post-Deng ERA. Yang, Dali L., ed. 2010. (ENG.). 318p. pap. 39.99 *(978-0-521-16858-8(9))* Cambridge Univ. Pr.

O'Brien, Kevin J. & Zhao, Suisheng, eds. Grassroots Elections in China. 2010. (ENG., Illus.). 256p. (C). 133.00 *(978-0-415-57157-9(X))* Routledge.

Oi, Jean C., et al, eds. Growing Pains: Tensions & Opportunity in China's Transformation. 2010. (ENG., Illus.). 380p. pap. 28.95 *(978-1-931368-18-6(X))* Shorenstein, Walter H. Asia-Pacific Research Ctr.

Paltiel, Jeremy. The Empire's New Clothes: Cultural Particularism & Universal Value in China's Quest for Global Status. rev. ed. 2007. (ENG., Illus.). 332p. 95.00 *(978-1-4039-6198-3(0))* Palgrave Macmillan.

Pei, Minxin. China's Trapped Transition: The Limits of Developmental Autocracy. 2008. (Illus.). 308p. per. 22.50 *(978-0-674-02754-1(X))* Harvard Univ. Pr.

Perry, Elizabeth J. & Selden, Mark, eds. Chinese Society: Change, Conflict & Resistance. 3rd rev. ed. 2010. (Asia's Transformations Ser.). (ENG., Illus.). 344p. (C). 49.95 *(978-0-415-56074-0(8))* Routledge.

—Chinese Society: Change, Conflict & Resistance. 3rd ed. 2010. (Asia's Transformations Ser.). (ENG., Illus.). 344p. (C). *(978-0-415-56073-3(X)*, Routledge) Taylor & Francis Group.

Qisheng, Jiang. My Life in Prison: Memoirs of a Chinese Political Dissident. 2012. (ENG.). 240p. 45.00 ***(978-1-4422-1222-0(5))*** Rowman & Littlefield Publishers, Inc.

Ren, Hai. The Middle Class in Neoliberal China. 2012. (Routledge Contemporary China Ser.). (ENG.). 192p. (C). 125.00 ***(978-0-415-50135-4(0))*** Routledge.

Rongji, Zhu. Zhu Rongji Meets the Press. 2011. (Illus.). 512p. 35.00 *(978-0-19-396641-3(7))* Oxford Univ. Pr., Inc.

Saich, Tony. Governance & Politics of China. 3rd rev. ed. 2010. (Comparative Government & Politics Ser.). (ENG., Illus.). 400p. 115.00 *(978-0-230-27992-6(9))*; pap. 40.00 *(978-0-230-27993-3(7))* Palgrave Macmillan.

Salmenkari, Taru. Democracy, Participation, & Deliberation in Chin. 2008. 668p. pap. *(978-3-639-08901-1(4))* VDM Verlag Dr. Mueller e.K.

Sandby-Thomas, Peter. Legitimising the Chinese Communist Party's Rule since Tiananmen: A Critical Analysis of the Stability Discourse. 2010. (China Policy Ser.). (ENG.). 240p. (C). 130.00 *(978-0-415-55398-8(9)*, Routledge) Taylor & Francis Group GBR. Dist: Taylor & Francis Group.

Shambaugh, David, ed. Charting China's Future: Domestic & International Challenges. 2011. (ENG., Illus.). 208p. (C). 150.00 *(978-0-415-61954-7(8))* Routledge.

Sheng, Yuming. Economic Openness & Territorial Politics in China. 2010. (ENG., Illus.). 312p. 85.00 *(978-0-521-19538-6(1))* Cambridge Univ. Pr.

Sleeboom-Faulkner, Margaret. The Chinese Academy of Social Sciences (CASS) Shaping the Reforms, Academia & China (1977-2003) 2006. 300p. *(978-90-04-15323-3(3))* BRILL.

Sorman, Guy. The Empire of Lies: The Truth about China in the Twenty-First Century. Puri, Asha, tr. 2008. (ENG., Illus.). 325p. 25.95 *(978-1-59403-216-5(5))* Encounter Bks.

—Empire of Lies: The Truth about China in the Twenty-First Century. 2010. (ENG.). 280p. pap. 15.95 *(978-1-59403-263-9(7))* Encounter Bks.

Starr, John Bryan. Understanding China: A Guide to China's Economy, History, & Political Culture. 3rd rev. ed. 2010. (ENG., Illus.). 448p. pap. 17.95 *(978-0-8090-1651-8(6)*, Hill & Wang) Farrar, Straus & Giroux.

Sutter, Robert G. Chinese Foreign Relations: Power & Policy since the Cold War. 3rd ed. 2012. ***(978-1-4422-1136-0(9))***; (ENG.). 446p. (C). (gr. 13-17). 89.00 ***(978-1-4422-1134-6(2))***; (ENG.). 446p. (C). (gr. 13-17). pap. 39.95 ***(978-1-4422-1135-3(0))*** Rowman & Littlefield Publishers, Inc.

Sweetman, Arthur & Zhang, Jun. Economic Transitions with Chinese Characteristics Vol. 1: Thirty Years of Reform & Opening Up. 2009. (ENG.). 232p. (C). *(978-1-55339-226-2(4))*; pap. *(978-1-55339-225-5(6))* McGill-Queen's Univ. Pr.

Tan, Xiao. Bo Xilai Po Ju: Tai Zi Dang de "Chongqing Mo Shi" 2011. (CHI., Illus.). 483p. ***(978-1-935981-22-0(6))*** Mirror Bks. USA.

Tian, Henian & Chen, Qiwen. Tai Hai Chun Qiu. 2009. (CHI.). *(978-7-80141-619-3(8))* Taihai Publishing House.

University of Pittsburgh Chinese Studies Faculty Staff & University of Pittsburgh Chinese Studies Faculty, eds. Contemporary Chinese Societies: Continuity & Change, CD for Windows and Macintosh. 2nd ed. 2007. (Edinburgh Edition of the Waverley Novels Ser.). (ENG.). (gr. 17). 51.50 *(978-0-231-13982-3(9))* Columbia Univ. Pr.

Vogel, Ezra F. Deng Xiaoping & the Transformation of China. 2011. (ENG., Illus.). 928p. 39.95 *(978-0-674-05544-5(6)*, Belknap Pr.) Harvard Univ. Pr.

Wang, Juntao. Reverse Course: Political Neo-conservatism & Regime Stability in Post-Tiananmen China. 2008. 416p. pap. *(978-3-639-09032-1(2))* VDM Verlag Dr. Mueller e.K.

Weatherley, Robert. Mao's Forgotten Successor: The Political Career of Hua Guofeng. 2010. (ENG., Illus.). 224p. 89.00 *(978-0-230-54247-1(6))* Palgrave Macmillan.

Weston, Timothy B. China in & Beyond the Headlines. 3rd ed. 2012. (ENG.). 384p. pap. 35.00 ***(978-1-4422-0905-3(4))*** Rowman & Littlefield Publishers, Inc.

Weston, Timothy B. & Jensen, Lionel M., eds. China in & Beyond the Headlines. 3rd ed. 2012. (ENG.). 384p. 99.00 ***(978-1-4422-0904-6(6))*** Rowman & Littlefield Publishers, Inc.

Will, Pierre-Étienne. China, Democracy, & Law: A Historical & Contemporary Approach. Norberg, Naomi, tr. 2011. (Illus.). 900p. ***(978-90-04-17871-7(6))*** BRILL.

Wo-Lap Lam, Willy. Chinese Politics in the Hu Jintao Era: New Leaders, New Challenges. 2006. 359p. per. 29.95 *(978-0-7656-1774-3(9))* Sharpe, M.E. Inc.

Wright, Teresa. Accepting Authoritarianism: State-Society Relations in China's Reform Era. 2010. (ENG.). 264p. pap. 24.95 *(978-0-8047-6904-4(4))*; (Illus.). 70.00 *(978-0-8047-6903-7(6))* Stanford Univ. Pr.

Wu, Guang. China: Has the Last Opportunity Passed By?! 2009. (China in the 21st Century Ser.). xiii, 88p. pap. 43.00 *(978-1-60741-538-1(0))* Nova Science Pubs., Inc.

Yang, Yun & Fang, Yanhong. Nei Ge Xin San Jiao: Wen Jiabao, Li Keqiang, Wang Qishan Ying Zhan Wei Ji. 2nd ed. 2008. ("Zhongguo Zhang Quan Zhe" Xi Lie Ser.: Vol. 21). (CHI., Illus.). 539p. *(978-1-932138-67-2(6))* Mirror Bks. USA.

—Wen Jiabao Bian Ge. 2008. ("Zhongguo Ju Shi " Xi Lie Ser.: Vol. 50). (CHI., Illus.). 341p. *(978-1-932138-62-7(5))* Mirror Bks. USA.

Yongnian, Zheng. The Chinese Communist Party As Organizational Emperor: Culture, Reproduction, & Transformation. 2010. (China Policy Ser.). (ENG., Illus.). 272p. (C). 150.00 *(978-0-415-55963-8(4))*; pap. 44.95 *(978-0-415-55965-2(0))* Routledge.

Yu, Jie. Bu Yao Zuo Zhong Guo Ren de Hai Zi. 2008. (CHI.). 349p. pap. 18.00 *(978-1-931550-22-2(0))* Laogai Research Foundation, The.

Yu, Keping. Globalization & Changes in China's Governance. 2008. 225p. *(978-90-04-15682-1(8))* BRILL.

Zhao. China's Reforms at 30 (V14) 2009. (Illus.). xiii, 200p. 38.00 *(978-981-283-424-9(9))* World Scientific Publishing Co., Inc.

Zhao, Quansheng. Managing the China Challenge: Global Perspectives. Liu, Guoli, ed. 2008. (Asian Security Studies). (Illus.). XVI, 264p. 160.00 *(978-0-415-46573-1(7))* Routledge.

Zhou, Zhenghuan. Liberal Rights & Political Culture. 2010. 288p. pap. 39.95 *(978-0-415-88249-1(4))* Routledge.

Zweig, David & Chen, Zhimin, eds. China's Reforms & International Political Economy. 2009. (Illus.). 242p. pap. 39.95 *(978-0-415-54703-1(2))* Routledge.

CHINA—POPULAR CULTURE

see Popular Culture—China

CHINA—POPULATION

Borysevicz, Mathieu. Learning from Hangzhou. 2009. (ENG., Illus.). 330p. pap. 45.00 *(978-988-18033-6-8(5))* Timezone 8 Ltd. HKG. Dist: D.A.P./Distributed Art Pubs.

The China Population & Labor Yearbook, Volume 2: The Sustainability of Economic Growth from the Perspective of Human Resources. 2010. (Chinese Academy of Social Sciences Yearbooks: Society Ser.). *(978-90-04-17353-8(6))* BRILL.

Lee, James Z. & Campbell, Cameron D. Fate & Fortune in Rural China: Social Organization & Population Behavior in Liaoning 1774-1873. 2007. (Cambridge Studies in Population, Economy & Society in Past Time Ser.). (ENG., Illus.). 308p. pap. 61.00 *(978-0-521-03969-7(X))* Cambridge Univ. Pr.

Ma, Rong. Population & Society in Contemporary Tibet. 2011. (CHI., Illus.). 408p. ***(978-988-220-656-4(5))***; ***(978-988-220-728-8(6))***; ***(978-988-8053-76-6(0))*** Hong Kong Univ. Pr.

Mullaney, Thomas. Coming to Terms with the Nation: Ethnic Classification in Modern China. (Asia: Local Studies / Global Themes Ser.). (ENG., Illus.). 2011. 256p. pap. 29.95 ***(978-0-520-27274-3(9))*** 2010. 246p. 60.00 *(978-0-520-26278-2(6))* Univ. of California Pr.

Peng, Xizhe, et al. Ren Kou Yu Ren Kou Xue: Renkou Yu Renkouxue. 2009. (CHI., Illus.). *(978-7-208-09004-0(1))* Shanghai People's Publishing Hse.

Poston, Dudley L., ed. Fertility,Family Planning, & Population Policy in Chin. 2009. 212p. pap. 39.95 *(978-0-415-49738-1(8))* Routledge.

Rozman, Gilbert. Population & Marketing Settlements in Ch'ing China. 2009. (ENG.). 168p. pap. 26.99 *(978-0-521-10704-4(0))* Cambridge Univ. Pr.

Siu, Helen F. & Ku, Agnes S. Hong Kong Mobile: Making a Global Population. 2009. (ENG., Illus.). 508p. (gr. 17). 50.00 *(978-962-209-918-0(1))* Hong Kong Univ. Pr. HKG. Dist: Columbia Univ. Pr.

White, Tyrene. China's Longest Campaign: Birth Planning in the People's Republic, 1949-2005. 2009. (Illus.). 320p. pap. 24.95 *(978-0-8014-7539-9(2))* Cornell Univ. Pr.

Wolf, Charles, Jr., et al. China & India 2025: A Comparative Assessment. 2011. (ENG.). 170p. pap. 28.50 ***(978-0-8330-5042-7(7))*** RAND Corp., The.

Yang, Jisheng. Tombstone: The Great Chinese Famine, 1958-1962, 1 vol. Mosher, Stacy & Guo, Jian, trs. from CHI. 2012. (ENG., Illus.). 752p. 35.00 ***(978-0-374-27793-2(1))*** Farrar, Straus & Giroux.

Zhao, Zhongwei & Guo, Fei, eds. Transition & Challenge: China's Population at the Beginning of the 21st Century. 2007. (ENG., Illus.). 364p. 125.00 *(978-0-19-929929-4(3))* Oxford Univ. Pr., Inc.

Zhou, Xun, ed. The Great Famine in China, 1958-1962: A Documentary History. 2012. (ENG., Illus.). 224p. 45.00 ***(978-0-300-17518-9(3))*** Yale Univ. Pr.

CHINA—RELATIONS—FOREIGN COUNTRIES

Bagchi, Prabodh Chandra. India & China: A Thousand Years of Cultural Relations. 3rd rev. ed. 2008. (Illus.). 232p. 52.50 *(978-81-215-1197-1(6))* Munshiram Manoharlal Pubs. Private, Ltd. IND. Dist: Coronet Bks.

Bellacqua, James A., ed. The Future of China-Russia Relations. 2009. (Asia in the New Millennium Ser.). (ENG., Illus.). 372p. 50.00 *(978-0-8131-2563-3(4))* Univ. Pr. of Kentucky.

Benton, Gregor. Chinese Migrants & Internationalism: Forgotten Histories, 1917-1945. 2011. (ENG., Illus.). 192p. (C). pap. 44.95 ***(978-0-415-66645-9(7))*** Routledge.

Chansiri, Disaphol. The Chinese émigrés of Thailand in the Twentieth Century. 2007. (C). 99.95 *(978-1-934043-74-5(5))* Cambria Pr.

China: Recent Security Developments. 2008. iii, 59p. *(978-0-16-082188-2(6)*, 552-070-38322-1) United States Government Printing Office.

Clark, Anthony E. Beating Devils & Burning Their Books: Views of China, Japan & the West. 2010. (Illus.). 248p. pap. *(978-0-924304-60-6(X))* Assn. for Asian Studies, Inc.

Cooney, Kevin J. The Rise of China & International Security: America & Asia Respond. 2009. pap. 39.95 *(978-0-415-55876-1(X))* Routledge.

Currier, Carrie Liu & Dorraj, Manochehr. China's Energy Relations with the Developing World. 2011. (ENG., Illus.). 240p. 100.00 *(978-1-4411-7555-7(5))*; pap. 29.95 *(978-1-4411-4104-0(9))* Continuum International Publishing Group, Ltd. GBR. Dist: National Bk. Network.

Ding, Sheng. The Dragon's Hidden Wings: How China Rises with Its Soft Power. 2008. (Challenges Facing Chinese Political Development Ser.). (ENG., Illus.). 210p. 73.50 *(978-0-7391-2392-8(0))*; pap. 27.50 *(978-0-7391-2393-5(9))* Lexington Bks.

Fallows, James. Postcards from Tomorrow Square: Reports from China. 2008. (Vintage Ser.). (ENG., Illus.). 288p. pap. 15.00 *(978-0-307-45624-3(2)*, Vintage) Knopf Doubleday Publishing Group.

Gillissen, Christophe. Ireland — Looking East. 2010. 169p. pap. 45.95 *(978-90-5201-652-8(6))* PIE - Peter Lang BEL. Dist: Lang, Peter.

Goodman, Bryna & Goodman, David Sg, eds. Twentieth Century Colonialism & China: Localities, the Everyday, & the World. 2012. (ENG., Illus.). 272p. (C). 150.00 ***(978-0-415-68798-0(5))***; pap. 44.95 ***(978-0-415-68799-7(3))*** Routledge.

Guo, Sujian. Harmonious World & China's New Foreign Policy. Blanchard, Jean-Marc F., ed. 2010. (Challenges Facing Chinese Political Development Ser.). (ENG., Illus.). 264p. pap. 34.99 *(978-0-7391-2604-2(0))* Lexington Bks.

Guo, Sujian & Blanchard, Jean-Marc F. Harmonious World & China's New Foreign Policy. 2008. (Challenges Facing Chinese Political Development Ser.). (ENG.). 252p. 68.50 *(978-0-7391-2603-5(2))* Lexington Bks.

Heazle, Michael, et al, eds. China-Japan Relations in the Twenty-First Century: Creating a Future Past? 2007. (Illus.). 264p. (C). 119.00 *(978-1-84720-112-6(1))* Elgar, Edward Publishing, Inc.

Howard, David. A Tale of Three Cities: London, Shanghai & Hong Kong: Three Centuries of Sino-British Trade in the Decorative Arts. Date not set. (Illus.). 350p. 70.00 (978-0-9622588-3-1(0)) Sotheby's Pubns.

Hughes, Alex. France/China: Intercultural Imaginings. 2007. (Legenda Research Monographs in French Studies). 160p. (C). 74.00 (978-1-904350-93-4(3)) European Humanities Research Ctr. GBR. Dist: Brown, David Bk. Co., The.

Human Rights Watch (Organization) Staff, contrib. by. Appeasing China: Restricting the Rights of Tibetans in Nepal. 2008. (Illus.). 60p. pap. (978-1-56432-365-1(X)) Human Rights Watch.

Hutton, Will. The Writing on the Wall: Why We Must Embrace China as a Partner or Face It as an Enemy. 2013. (ENG.). 432p. pap. 27.99 (978-0-7432-7529-3(2), Free Pr.) Free Pr.

Jacques, Martin. When China Rules the World: The End of the Western World & the Birth of a New Global Order. rev. ed. 2012. (ENG.). 848p. (gr. 12). 20.00 (978-0-14-311800-8(5), Penguin (Non-Classics)) Penguin Group (USA) Inc.

Jilberto, Alex E., et al, eds. Latin America Facing China: South-South Relations Beyond the Washington Concensus. 2010. (CEDLA Ser.). (Illus.). 216p. 75.00 (978-1-84545-739-6(0)) Berghahn Bks., Inc.

Katzenstein, Peter J., ed. Sinicization & the Rise of China. 2012. (ENG., Illus.). 312p. (C). 135.00 **(978-0-415-80953-5(3))**; pap. 29.95 **(978-0-415-80952-8(5))** Routledge.

Kent, Ann. Beyond Compliance: China, International Organizations, & Global Security. 2007. (Studies in Asian Security Ser.). (ENG., Illus.). 360p. 65.00 (978-0-8047-5551-1(5)) Stanford Univ. Pr.

Kim, Hyejin. International Ethnic Networks & Intra-Ethnic Conflict: Koreans in China. 2010. (ENG., Illus.). 212p. 89.00 (978-0-230-10252-1(2)) Palgrave Macmillan.

Kurlantzick, Joshua. Charm Offensive: How China's Soft Power Is Transforming the World. (New Republic Book Ser.). 2008. (ENG.). 320p. pap. 17.00 (978-0-300-13628-9(5)) 2007. 432p. per. 35.00 (978-0-300-13154-3(2)) Yale Univ. Pr.

Lai, Him Mark & Hsu, Madeline Y. Chinese American Transnational Politics. 2010. (Asian American Experience Ser.). (ENG., Illus.). 296p. 75.00 (978-0-252-03525-8(9)); pap. 30.00 (978-0-252-07714-2(8)) Univ. of Illinois Pr.

Li, Hongshan. U. S. -China Educational Exchange: State, Society, & Intercultural Relations, 1905-1950. 2007. (ENG.). 296p. 49.95 (978-0-8135-4199-0(9)) Rutgers Univ. Pr.

Lustgarten, Abrahm. China's Great Train: Beijing's Drive West & the Campaign to Remake Tibet. 2009. (ENG., Illus.). 320p. pap. 18.00 (978-0-8050-9018-5(5), Holt Paperback) St. Martin's Pr.

Mackerras, Colin & Clarke, Michael, eds. China Xinjiang & Central Asia. 2011. (ENG., Illus.). 212p. pap. 42.95 **(978-0-415-67333-4(X))** Routledge.

McGiffert, Carola. Chinese Soft Power & Its Implications for the United States: Competition & Cooperation in the Developing World, a Report of the CSIS Smart Power Initative. 2009. (Illus.). 136p. pap. 25.00 (978-0-89206-558-5(3), CSIS Pr., The) Ctr. for Strategic & International Studies.

Medeiros, Evan S. Reluctant Restraint: The Evolution of China's Nonproliferation Policies & Practices, 1980-2004. 2007. (Studies in Asian Security Ser.). (ENG., Illus.). 376p. 65.00 (978-0-8047-5552-8(3)) Stanford Univ. Pr.

Men, Jing & Balducci, Giuseppe, eds. Prospects & Challenges for EU-China Relations in the 21st Century: The Partnership & Cooperation Agreement. 2010. (Cahiers du Collège d'Europe / College of Europe Studies). (Illus.). 262p. pap. 68.95 (978-90-5201-641-2(0)) PIE - Peter Lang BEL. Dist: Lang, Peter.

Ogunsanwo, Alaba. China's Policy in Africa, 1958-71. 2010. (LSE Monographs in International Studies). (ENG.). 328p. pap. 25.99 (978-0-521-13440-8(4)) Cambridge Univ. Pr.

Page, Benjamin I. & Xie, Tao. Living with the Dragon: How the American Public Views the Rise of China. 2010. (Contemporary Asia in the World Ser.). (ENG., Illus.). 232p. (gr. 17). 27.50 (978-0-231-15208-2(6)) Columbia Univ. Pr.

Porter, David. The Chinese Taste in Eighteenth-Century England. 2010. (ENG., Illus.). 240p. 90.00 (978-0-521-19299-6(4)) Cambridge Univ. Pr.

Reed, Marcia & Dematte, Paola, eds. China on Paper: European & Chinese Works from the Late Sixteenth to the Early Nineteenth Century. 2011. (ENG., Illus.). 248p. pap. 30.00 (978-1-60606-068-1(6)) Getty Pubns.

Shambaugh. The China & Europe Engagement. 2007. (ENG., Illus.). 368p. (C). 180.00 (978-0-415-43198-9(0)) Routledge.

Shambaugh, David, et al, eds. The China & Europe Engagement. 2007. (ENG., Illus.). 368p. (C). 44.95 (978-0-415-43199-6(9)) Routledge.

Soares de Oliveira, Ricardo, et al. China Returns to Africa: A Rising Power & a Continent Embrace. 2008. (Columbia/Hurst Ser.). (ENG., Illus.). 400p. (gr. 17). 75.00 (978-0-231-70098-6(9)) Columbia Univ. Pr.

Su, Chi. Taiwan's Relations with Mainland China. 2010. (ENG., Illus.). 368p. (C). pap. 39.95 (978-0-415-58999-4(1)) Routledge.

Svarverud, Rune. International Law as World Order in Late Imperial China: Translation, Reception & Discourse, 1847-1911. 2007. (Sinica Leidensia Ser.). (Illus.). 322p. (978-90-04-16019-4(1)) BRILL.

Taylor, Ian. China¿s New Role in Africa. 2010. 227p. (C). pap. 25.00 (978-1-58826-736-8(9)) Rienner, Lynne Pubs.

—The Forum on China- Africa Cooperation (FOCAC) (ENG., Illus.). (C). 2012. 126p. pap. 42.95 **(978-0-415-62851-8(2))** 2011. 144p. 118.00 (978-0-415-54860-1(8)) Routledge.

van der Putten, Frans-Paul & Shulong, Chu, eds. China Europe & International Security. 2010. (Asian Security Studies). (ENG., Illus.). 232p. 130.00 (978-0-415-58580-4(5), Routledge) Taylor & Francis Group GBR. Dist: Taylor & Francis Group.

Wachman, Alan. Why Taiwan? Geostrategic Rationales for China's Territorial Integrity. 2007. (Studies in Asian Security Ser.). (ENG., Illus.). 272p. 65.00 (978-0-8047-5553-5(1)); pap. 24.95 (978-0-8047-5554-2(X)) Stanford Univ. Pr.

Wang, Jian. Soft Power in China: Public Diplomacy through Communication. Wang, Jian, ed. 2010. (Global Public Diplomacy Ser.). (ENG., Illus.). 220p. 89.00 (978-0-230-10862-2(8)) Palgrave Macmillan.

Wang, Xiuyu. China's Last Imperial Frontier: Late Qing Expansion in Sichuan's Tibetan Borderlands. 2011. E-Book **(978-0-7391-6810-3(X))** Lexington Bks.

Wesley-Smith, Terence, et al, eds. China in Oceania: Reshaping the Pacific? 2010. (FAPS Ser.). (Illus.). 224p. 39.95 (978-1-84545-632-0(7)) Berghahn Bks., Inc.

Weston, Timothy B. & Jensen, Lionel M., eds. China in & Beyond the Headlines. 3rd ed. 2012. (ENG.). 384p. 99.00 **(978-1-4422-0904-6(6))** Rowman & Littlefield Publishers, Inc.

Wills, John E., Jr. China & Maritime Europe, 1500-1800: Trade, Settlement, Diplomacy, & Missions. 2010. (ENG., Illus.). 312p. (C). pap. 28.99 (978-0-521-17945-4(9)) Cambridge Univ. Pr.

A Year after the March 2008 Protests: Is China Promoting Stability in Tibet?: Roundtable Before the Congressional-Executive Commission on China, One Hundredth Eleventh Congress, First Session, March 13, 2009. 2009. ii, 35p. (978-0-16-083576-6(3), 552-070-39294-7) United States Government Printing Office.

Yee, Herbert S., ed. China's Rise - Threat or Opportunity? 2011. (Routledge Security in Asia Ser.). (ENG., Illus.). 320p. (C). 140.00 (978-0-415-57606-2(7)) Routledge.

CHINA—RELIGION

Adamek, Wendi Leigh. The Teachings of Master Wuzhu: Zen & Religion of No-Religion. 2011. (Translations from the Asian Classics Ser.). (ENG.). 224p. (gr. 17). 84.50 (978-0-231-15022-4(9)); pap. 27.50 (978-0-231-15023-1(7)) Columbia Univ. Pr.

Allan, Tony & Phillips, Charles. Ancient China's Myths & Beliefs. 2011. (World Mythologies Ser.). (ENG., Illus.). 144p. (YA). (gr. 9-12). lib. bdg. 39.95 **(978-1-4488-5991-7(3))** Rosen Publishing Group, Inc., The.

Ashiwa, Yoshiko & Wank, David L. Making Religion, Making the State: The Politics of Religion in Modern China. Ashiwa, Yoshiko & Wank, David, eds. 2009. (ENG.). 304p. 70.00 (978-0-8047-5841-3(7)); pap. 24.95 (978-0-8047-5842-0(5)) Stanford Univ. Pr.

Bai, Gengsheng. Bai Gengsheng Naxi Xue Lun Ji: BaiGengshengNaxixuelunji. 2008. (CHI.). (978-7-105-08466-1(9)) Nationalities Publishing Hse, The.

Baker, H. A. Visions Beyond the Veil: Visions of Heaven, Angels, Satan, Hell, & the End of the Age. 2006. 190p. per. 9.99 (978-0-88368-786-4(0)) Whitaker Hse.

Baptandier, Brigitte. The Lady of Linshui: A Chinese Female Cult. Fryklund, Kristin, tr. from FRE. 2008. (Asian Religions & Cultures Ser.). (ENG., Illus.). 392p. 65.00 (978-0-8047-4666-3(4)) Stanford Univ. Pr.

Beal, Samuel. A Catena of Buddhist Scriptures from the Chinese. 2010. (ENG.). 452p. pap. 36.75 (978-1-177-39825-1(7)); 498p. pap. 38.75 (978-1-176-23354-6(8)) BiblioBazaar.

—A Catena of Buddhist Scriptures from the Chinese. 2010. 326p. pap. (978-1-151-93706-3(1)) Books LLC.

—A Catena of Buddhist Scriptures from the Chinese. 2010. 452p. 42.36 (978-1-163-21917-1(7)); pap. 30.36 (978-1-162-73125-4(7)) Kessinger Publishing, LLC.

Boretz, Avron Albert. Gods, Ghosts, & Gangsters: Ritual Violence, Martial Arts, & Masculinity on the Margins of Chinese Society. 2010. (Illus.). 280p. 50.00 (978-0-8248-3377-0(5)); pap. 29.00 (978-0-8248-3491-3(7)) Univ. of Hawaii Pr.

Brashier, K. E. Ancestral Memory in Early China. 2011. (Harvard-Yenching Institute Monograph Ser.: 72). (ENG., Illus.). 484p. 39.95 (978-0-674-05607-7(8)) Harvard Univ., Asia Ctr.

Burnett, David. The Spirit of China: The Roots of Faith in 21st Century China, 1 vol. 2008. (Illus.). 384p. pap. 16.99 (978-0-8254-6146-0(4), Monarch Bks.) Lion Hudson PLC GBR. Dist: Kregel Pubns.

Cantonese Society in Hong Kong & Singapore: Gender, Religion, Medicine & Money. 2011. 626p. (978-9971-69-524-8(3)) Hong Kong Univ. Pr.

Chamberlain, Jonathan. Chinese Gods: An Introduction to Chinese folk Religion. 3rd ed. 2010. (ENG.). 240p. pap. 16.95 (978-988-17742-1-7(7)) Blacksmith Bks. HKG. Dist: National Bk. Network.

Chan/Lo. Philosophy & Religion in Early Medieval China. 2010. (SUNY series in Chinese Philosophy & Culture Ser.). (MUL.). 352p. 80.00 (978-1-4384-3187-1(2)) State Univ. of New York Pr.

Chao, Shin-Yi. Daoist Rituals, State Religion, & Popular Practices: Zhenwu Worship from Song to Ming (960-1644) 2011. (Routledge Studies in Taoism Ser.). (ENG., Illus.). 176p. (C). 130.00 (978-0-415-78056-7(7)) Routledge.

Chau, Adam. Miraculous Response: Doing Popular Religion in Contemporary China. 2008. (ENG.). 336p. pap. 24.95 (978-0-8047-6100-0(0)) Stanford Univ. Pr.

Chau, Adam Yuet. Religion in Contemporary China: Revitalization & Innovation. 2011. (Routledge Contemporary China Ser.). (ENG., Illus.). 264p. (C). 138.00 (978-0-415-45934-1(6)) Routledge.

Chavannes, Edouard. Le T'ai Chan: Essai de Monographie d'un Culte Chinoise. (Illus.). 591p. reprint ed. 42.00 (978-0-89644-171-2(7)) Coronet Bks.

Cook, Richard R. & Pao, David W., eds. After Imperialism: Christian Identity in China & the Global Evangelical Movement. 2011. (Studies in Chinese Christianity Ser.). 256p. pap. 28.00 **(978-1-60899-336-9(1)**, Pickwick Pubns.) Wipf & Stock Pubs.

Dean, Kenneth & Zheng, Zhenman. Ritual Alliances of the Putian Plain, 2 vols. 2009. (Illus.). 320p. (978-90-04-17602-7(0)); 840p. (978-90-04-17601-0(2)) BRILL.

DuBois, Thomas David. Religion & the Making of Modern East Asia. 2011. (New Approaches to Asian History Ser.). (ENG., Illus.). 272p. (C). 90.00 (978-1-107-00809-0(3)); pap. 27.99 (978-1-107-40040-5(6)) Cambridge Univ. Pr.

Edkins, Joseph. The Early Spread of Religious Ideas Especially in the Far East. 2007. (ENG.). 142p. 35.95 (978-0-548-05195-5(X)) Kessinger Publishing, LLC.

—Religion in China: Containing a Brief Account of the Three Religions. 2007. (ENG.). 284p. per. 27.95 (978-1-4304-4274-5(3)) Kessinger Publishing, LLC.

Falkenstine, Mike. The Chinese Puzzle: Putting the Pieces Together for a Deeper Understanding of China & Her Church. 2008. pap. 13.99 (978-1-60647-143-2(0)) Xulon Pr., Inc.

Fallman, Fredrik. Salvation & Modernity: Intellectuals & Faith in Contemporary China. 2008. (ENG.). 180p. pap. 34.99 (978-0-7618-4090-9(7)) Univ. Pr. of America, Inc.

Fan, Ruiping. Reconstructionist Confucianism: Rethinking Morality after the West. 2010. (Philosophical Studies in Contemporary Culture Ser.). (ENG.). xx, 296p. 139.00 (978-90-481-3155-6(3), 9048131553) Springer.

Fan, Ruiping, ed. The Renaissance of Confucianism in Contemporary China. 2011. (Philosophical Studies in Contemporary Culture Ser.). x, 265p. 139.00 (978-94-007-1541-7(2), 9400715412) Springer.

Feuchtwang, Stephan. The Anthropology of Religion, Charisma, & Ghosts: Chinese Lessons for Adequate Theory. 2010. (Religion & Society Ser.) (ENG.). VII, 213p. 112.00 **(978-3-11-022355-2(4))** De Gruyter, Walter Inc.

Feuchtwang, Stephen. The Anthropology of Religion, Charisma & Ghosts: Chinese Lessons for Adequate Theory. 2010. (Religion & Society Ser.). (ENG.). VII, 213p. 168.00 **(978-3-11-173951-9(1))** De Gruyter, Walter Inc.

Fowler, Merv & Fowler, Jeaneane. Chinese Religions: Beliefs & Practices. 2008. (ENG.). 320p. (C). pap. 32.50 (978-1-84519-172-6(2)) Sussex Academic Pr. GBR. Dist: International Specialized Bk. Services.

Giles, Herbert A. Religions of Ancient Chin. 2009. 72p. pap. 16.75 (978-1-110-40370-7(4)) BiblioBazaar.

—Religions of Ancient Chin. 2008. 52p. pap. 10.99 (978-1-59547-717-0(9)) NuVision Pubns., LLC.

—Religions of Ancient China. 2009. (ENG.). 71p. pap. 18.99 (978-1-110-40368-4(2)); pap. 16.99 (978-1-110-40366-0(6)) BiblioBazaar. (BiblioLife).

—Religions of Ancient China. 2007. (ENG.). 48p. per. (978-1-4065-4459-6(0)) Dodo Pr.

Goddard, Dwight & Borel, Henri. A Pocketful of Tao. 2009. 88p. pap. 8.95 (978-1-4357-4720-3(8)) Lulu Enterprises Inc.

Goossaert, Vincent & Palmer, David A. The Religious Question in Modern China. 2011. 480p. 40.00 (978-0-226-30416-8(7)) Univ. of Chicago Pr.

Gordon, George S. The Gateless Gate: Our Inward Journey Home, 1 vol. 2009. 185p. pap. 24.95 (978-1-60749-013-5(7)) PublishAmerica, Inc.

Goto, Akio. Kongoji-Bon "Sanbo Kanno Yoryakuroku" No Kenkyu/Osaka Daigaku Sanbo Kanno Roryakuroku Kenkyukai Hen; Goto Akio Kanshu. 2007. (CHI & JPN., Illus.). 262p. (978-4-585-03174-1(X)) Bensei Shuppan.

Grant, Beata & Idema, Wilt L., trs. from CHI. Escape from Blood Pond Hell: The Tales of Mulian & Woman Huang. 2011. (ENG.). 368p. (C). pap. 35.00 (978-0-295-99120-7(8)); 70.00 (978-0-295-99119-1(4)) Univ. of Washington Pr.

Halbertsma, T. H. F. Early Christian Remains of Inner Mongolia: Discovery, Reconstruction & Appropriation. 2008. (Sinica Leidensia Ser.). (Illus.). 400p. (978-90-04-16708-7(0)) BRILL.

Hamrin, Carol Lee. Salt & Light: Lives of Faith That Shaped Modern China. 2008. (Studies in Chinese Christianity Ser.). (Illus.). 252p. pap. 28.00 (978-1-55635-984-2(5), Pickwick Pubns.) Wipf & Stock Pubs.

Hatfield, D. J. W. Taiwanese Pilgrimage to China: Ritual, Complicity, Community. 2009. (ENG., Illus.). 288p. 95.00 (978-0-230-61603-5(8)) Palgrave Macmillan.

Hendrischke, Barbara. The Scripture on Great Peace: The Taiping Jing & the Beginnings of Daoism. 2007. (Daoist Classics Ser.). 410p. 70.00 (978-0-520-24788-8(4)) Univ. of California Pr.

Ho Dmin, Mdiv. The Dragon & the Cross. 2009. 260p. pap. 16.99 (978-1-60791-259-0(7)) Xulon Pr., Inc.

Hu, Xinsheng. Zhongguo Gu Dai Wu Shu. 2010. (CHI., Illus.). (978-7-01-008624-8(9)) People's Publishing Hse., The.

Huang, Hanli. Yi Jing Jiang Tang. 2010. (Lectures on I-Ching Ser.). (CHI., Illus.). 339p. (978-962-04-2921-7(4)) Joint Publishing Co.

Huang, Mingxin. Tufan Fo Jiao. 2010. (CHI.). (978-7-80253-229-8(9)) China Tibetology Publishing Hse.

Huang, Shih-shan Susan. Picturing the True Form: Daoist Visual Culture in Traditional China. 2012. (Harvard East Asian Monographs: 342). (ENG., Illus.). 500p. 69.95 **(978-0-674-06573-4(5))** Harvard Univ., Asia Ctr.

Hunter, Alan & Chan, Kim-kwong. Protestantism in Contemporary China. 2007. (Cambridge Studies in Ideology & Religion Ser.). (ENG., Illus.). 316p. pap. 61.00 (978-0-521-04691-6(2)) Cambridge Univ. Pr.

Jones, Stephen. Daoists of North China. 2010. (Illus.). 312p. 124.95 (978-1-4094-0615-0(6)) Ashgate Publishing Co.

Katz, Paul R. Divine Justice. 2009. 224p. pap. 39.95 (978-0-415-57433-4(1)) Routledge.

—Divine Justice: Religion & the Development of Chinese Legal Culture. 2009. (Academia Sinica on East Asia Ser.). (Illus.). 240p. 140.00 (978-0-415-44345-6(8)) Routledge.

Khechog, Nawang. Awakening Kindness: Finding Joy Through Compassion for Others. 2010. (ENG.). 208p. 23.00 (978-1-58270-252-0(7), Beyond Words/Atria Bks.) Atria Bks.

Khek Gee Lim, Francis, ed. Christianity in Contemporary China. 2012. (ENG., Illus.). 272p. (C). 145.00 **(978-0-415-52846-7(1))** Routledge.

KimFarrell. Simply I Ching. 2008. (Illus.). 160p. pap. (978-1-903065-57-0(7), Sterling/Zambezi) Sterling Publishing Co., Inc.

Kingsley, Peter. A Story Waiting to Pierce You: Mongolia, Tibet, & the Destiny of the Western World. 2010. (ENG.). 192p. 35.00 (978-1-890350-20-8(6)); pap. 14.95 (978-1-890350-21-5(4)) Golden Sufi Ctr., The.

Komjathy, Louis. Cultivating Perfection: Mysticism & Self-Transformation in Early Quanzheng Daoism. 2007. (Sinica Leidensia Ser.). (Illus.). 553p. (978-90-04-16038-5(8)) BRILL.

Kwok, Ken. Middle Kingdom - Legendary Beginning of China & the Bible. 2008. 163p. pap. 19.95 (978-0-557-00325-9(3)) Lulu Enterprises Inc.

Lagerwey, J. & Lü, P., eds. Early Chinese Religion, Part Two: The Period of Division (220-589 AD) 2009. 1200p. (978-90-04-17585-3(7)) BRILL.

Lagerwey, John. China: A Religious State. 2010. (Understanding China: New Viewpoints on History & Culture Ser.). (ENG., Illus.). 248p. (gr. 17). 40.00 (978-988-8028-03-0(0)); pap. 20.00 (978-988-8028-04-7(9)) Hong Kong Univ. Pr. HKG. Dist: Columbia Univ. Pr.

Lagerwey, John. Early Chinese Religion. 2011. 1256p. pap. **(978-90-04-20603-8(5))** BRILL.

Lagerwey, John & Kalinowski, Marc, eds. Part One: Shang through Han (1250 BC-220 AD) 2008. 1024p. (978-90-04-16835-0(4)) BRILL.

Lai, Pan-Chiu & Lam, Jason, eds. Sino-Christian Theology: A Theological Qua Cultural Movement in Contemporary China. 2010. (IC - Studien zur interkulturellen Geschichte des Christentums. Etudes d'histoire interculturelle de christianisme. Studies in the Intercultural History of Christianity Ser.). 248p. 69.95 (978-3-631-60435-9(1)) Lang, Peter GmbH, Europaischer Verlag der Wissenschaften DEU. Dist: Lang, Peter.

Laufer, Berthold. Jade: A Study in Chinese Archaeology & Religion. 2009. 466p. 52.95 (978-1-104-84195-9(9)) 2007. (ENG.). 464p. per. 37.95 (978-0-548-44548-8(6)) Kessinger Publishing, LLC.

—Jade: A Study in Chinese Archaeology & Religion. (Field Museum of Natural History Ser.: Vol. 10). (Illus.). 50.00 (978-0-527-01870-2(8)) Periodicals Service Co.

Lempert, Michael. Discipline & Debate: The Language of Violence in a Tibetan Buddhist Monastery. 2012. (ENG.). 238p. 65.00 **(978-0-520-26946-0(2))** Univ. of California Pr.

Li, Mingjing. Nihon Bukkyo Setsuwashu No Genryu. 2007. (JPN.). vii, 334p. (978-4-585-10433-9(X)) Bensei Shuppan.

Li, Xiangping. Xin Yang Dan Bu Ren Tong: Dang Dai Zhongguo Xin Yang de She Hui Xue Quan Shi = Believing Without Identifying: The Sociological Interpretation of Spiritual Beliefs in Contemporary China. 2010. (978-7-5097-1352-5(8)) China Social Science Documentation Publishing Hse.

Lin, Zichun. Duo Yuan Xing Han Yu Shen Xue Quan Shi: A Polyphonic View on Sino-Christian Theology. 2008. (978-7-80254-081-1(X)) China Religion and Culture Publishing Hse.

Lo, Chan. Philosophy & Religion in Early Medieval China. Chan, Alan K. L. & Lo, Yuet Keung, eds. 2011. 381p. pap. 26.95 **(978-1-4384-3188-8(0)**, Suny Pr.) State Univ. of New York Pr.

Loewe, Michael. Divination, Mythology & Monarchy in Han China. 2008. (University of Cambridge Oriental Publications). (ENG.). 376p. pap. 42.00 (978-0-521-05220-7(3)) Cambridge Univ. Pr.

lofting, chris. The Emotional I Ching. 2009. 510p. 50.40 (978-1-4092-7646-3(5)) Lulu Enterprises Inc.

Luo, Zhewen & Chai, Fushan. Zhonghua Ming Si Da Guan. 2008. (Illus.). xiii, 420p. (978-7-111-23793-8(5)) China Machine-Building Industry Pr.

Lyall, Alfred Comyn. Asiatic Studies Religious & Social. 2006. 352p. per. (978-1-4067-2403-5(3), Hesperides Pr.) Read Bks.

Ma, Xisha, et al. Popular Religion & Shamanism. 2011. (Religious Studies in Contemporary China Collection). (ENG.). VI, 502p. (978-90-04-17455-9(9)) BRILL.

Marsh, Christopher. Religion & the State in Russia & China: Suppression, Survival, & Revival. 2011. (ENG.). 288p. 120.00 (978-1-4411-0229-4(9)); pap. 29.95 (978-1-4411-1247-7(2)) Continuum International Publishing Group, Ltd. GBR. Dist: National Bk. Network.

McCurry, Steve, photos by. The Path to Buddha: A Tibetan Pilgrimage. 2012. (ENG.). 144p. pap. 29.95 **(978-0-7148-6314-6(9))** Phaidon Pr., Inc.

McDaniel, Richard Bryan. Zen Masters in China: The First Step East. 2012. (ENG., Illus.). 320p. 22.95 **(978-0-8048-4282-2(5))** Tuttle Publishing.

Miller, James. The Way of Highest Clarity: Nature, Vision & Revelation in Medieval China. 2008. 260p. pap. 30.00 (978-1-931483-09-4(4)) Univ. of Hawaii Pr.

Mollier, Christine. Buddhism & Taoism: Face to Face Scripture, Ritual, & Iconographic Exchange in Medieval China. 2008. (Illus.). 296p. (C). 55.00 (978-0-8248-3169-1(1)) Univ. of Hawaii Pr.

—Buddhism & Taoism Face to Face: Scripture, Ritual, & Iconographic Exchange in Medieval China. 2009. (Illus.). 241p. pap. 22.00 (978-0-8248-3411-1(9)) Univ. of Hawaii Pr.

Morris, T. M. & Glover, Richard. A Winter in North China. 2010. (Cambridge Library Collection - Travel & Exploration Ser.). (Illus.). 264p. pap. 23.99 *(978-1-108-01382-6(1))* Cambridge Univ. Pr.

Nadeau, Randall L., ed. The Wiley-Blackwell Companion to Chinese Religions. 2012. (Wiley-Blackwell Companions to Religion Ser.: 61). (ENG.). 512p. 199.95 ***(978-1-4051-9031-2(0)***, Wiley-Blackwell) Wiley, John & Sons, Inc.

Nedostup, Rebecca. Superstitious Regimes: Religion & the Politics of Chinese Modernity. 2010. (Harvard East Asian Monographs: 322). (Illus.). 450p. 45.00 *(978-0-674-03599-7(2))* Harvard Univ., Asia Ctr.

Nelson, Eugene "Eez". Consult I Ching with Ease. 2011. 84p. 24.99 ***(978-1-4628-4543-9(6))***; pap. 15.99 ***(978-1-4628-4542-2(8))*** Xlibris Corp.

Nukariya, Kaiten. Religion of the Samurai. 2008. 236p. 24.99 *(978-0-554-31190-6(9))*; 27.99 *(978-0-554-21887-8(9))* BiblioBazaar.

—Religion of the Samurai. 2006. pap. *(978-1-4068-3566-3(8))* Echo Library.

—Religion of the Samurai: A Study of Zen Philosophy & Discipline in China & Japan. 2006. (ENG.). 238p. pap. 20.99 *(978-1-4264-1191-5(X))*; 234p. pap. 22.99 *(978-1-4264-1167-0(7))* BiblioBazaar.

Oakes, Tim & Sutton, Donald S. Faiths on Display: Religion, Tourism, & the Chinese State. 2010. *(978-1-4422-0508-6(3))* Rowman & Littlefield Publishers, Inc.

Oakes/Sutton. Faiths on Display: Religion, Tourism, & the Chinese State. 2010. (ENG.). 292p. 85.00 *(978-1-4422-0506-2(7))* Rowman & Littlefield Publishers, Inc.

Overmyer, D. Local Religion in North China in the Twentieth Century: The Structure & Organization of Community Rituals & Beliefs. 2009. (Handbook of Oriental Studies. Section 4 China Ser.). 250p. *(978-90-04-17592-1(X))* BRILL.

Zertural, Zekine & Wilkens, Jens. Der östliche Manichäismus - Gattungs- und Werksgeschichte: Vorträge des Göttinger Symposiums vom 4./5. März 2010. 2011. (Abhandlungen der Akademie der Wissenschaften zu Göttingen. Neue Folge Ser.). (GER., Illus.). X, 237p. 140.00 ***(978-3-11-026137-0(5))*** De Gruyter, Walter Inc.

Palmer, David A., et al, eds. Chinese Religious Life, 1 vol. 2011. (ENG., Illus.). 296p. pap. 29.95 *(978-0-19-973138-1(1))* Oxford Univ. Pr., Inc.

Paterson, Ross & Farrell, Elisabeth. China: The Hidden Miracle. 184p. *(978-1-85240-130-6(3))* Sovereign World, Ltd.

Poceski, Mario. Introducing Chinese Religions. 2009. (ENG., Illus.). 304p. (C). 36.95 *(978-0-415-43406-5(8))*; 100.00 *(978-0-415-43405-8(X))* Routledge.

—Ordinary Mind as the Way: The Hongzhou School & the Growth of Chan Buddhism. 2007. (ENG., Illus.). 304p. 85.00 *(978-0-19-531996-5(6))* Oxford Univ. Pr., Inc.

Poon, Shuk-wah. Negotiating Religion in Modern China: State & Common People in Guangzhou, 1900 — 1937. 2011. (ENG., Illus.). 230p. (gr. 17). 45.00 *(978-962-996-421-4(X))* Chinese Univ. of Hong Kong, The HKG. Dist: Columbia Univ. Pr.

Porter, Bill & Pine, Red. Road to Heaven: Encounters with Chinese Hermits. 2009. (ENG.). 240p. pap. 15.95 *(978-1-58243-523-7(5)*, Counterpoint Pr.) Basic Bks. GBR. Dist: Perseus-PGW.

Ray, Reginald A. Touching Enlightenment: Finding Realization in the Body. 2008. 395p. 24.95 *(978-1-59179-618-3(0)*, BK01184) Sounds True, Inc.

Redmond, Geoffrey P. Science & Asian Spiritual Traditions, 1 vol. 2007. (Greenwood Guides to Science & Religion). 280p. 65.00 *(978-0-313-33462-7(5)*, GR3462, Greenwood Pr.) Greenwood Publishing Group, Inc.

Reiter, Florian C. Basic Conditions of Taoist Thunder Magic: Daojiao Lei Fa. 2007. (Abhandlungen Für Die Kunde des Morgenlandes Ser.). (GER & ENG.). 135p. (C). pap. 45.00 *(978-3-447-05593-2(6))* Harrassowitz, Otto Verlag DEU. Dist: ISD.

Rule, Paul, ed. The Church in China. 2010. (Interface Ser.). (ENG.). 123p. (C). pap. 20.00 ***(978-1-921511-96-7(6))*** ATF Theology AUS. Dist: Brown, David Bk. Co., The.

Sarkar, Benoy Kumar. Chinese Religion Though Hindu Eyes: A Study in the Tendencies of Asiatic Mentality 1916. 2007. (ENG.). 358p. 46.95 *(978-0-548-05425-3(8))* Kessinger Publishing, LLC.

Shaughnessy, Edward L. & Shaughnessy, Edward. China: El mundo chino, creencias y rituales, creacion y Descubrimientos. Portillo, Miguel, tr. 2009. (SPA.). 256p. pap. 15.95 *(978-84-8076-768-2(5))* Blume ESP. Dist: Independent Pubs. Group.

Standaert, Nicolas. The Interweaving of Rituals: Funerals in the Cultural Exchange Between China & Europe. 2008. (China Program Book Ser.). (ENG., Illus.). 336p. 65.00 *(978-0-295-98810-8(X))* Univ. of Washington Pr.

Starr, Chloe & Starr. Reading Christian Scriptures in China. 2008. (ENG.). 240p. 130.00 *(978-0-567-03292-8(2)*, T&T Clark Int'l) Continuum International Publishing Group, Ltd. GBR. Dist: National Bk. Network.

Szczepanski, Beth. Buddhist Instrumental Music of Wutaishan: Social & Ritual Contexts. 2012. (SOAS Musicology Ser.). (Illus.). 196p. 89.95 ***(978-1-4094-2743-8(9))*** Ashgate Publishing Co.

Tagliaferre, Lewis. Theofatalism: Personal Reformation for Troubled Souls. 2011. 356p. 32.95 ***(978-1-4620-2248-9(0))***; pap. 22.95 ***(978-1-4620-2247-2(2))*** iUniverse, Inc.

Thondup, Tulku. Incarnation: The History & Mysticism of the Tulku Tradition of Tibet. 2011. (ENG., Illus.). 128p. pap. 18.95 *(978-1-59030-839-4(5))* Shambhala Pubns., Inc.

Thong, Chan Kei. Faith of Our Fathers: God in Ancient China. 2007. (CHI., Illus.). 265p. pap. 20.00 *(978-0-9796269-0-6(0))* Leadership Development International.

Thong, Chan Kei, et al. Finding God in Ancient China: How the Ancient Chinese Worshiped the God of the Bible, 1 vol. 2009. (ENG.). 352p. pap. 24.99 *(978-0-310-29238-8(7))* Zondervan.

Tong, James. Revenge of the Forbidden City: The Suppression of the Falungong in China, 1999-2005. 2009. (ENG., Illus.). 288p. 49.95 *(978-0-19-537728-6(1))* Oxford Univ. Pr., Inc.

Wang, Aiming. Church in China: Faith, Ethics, Structure: The Heritage of the Reformation for the Future of the Church in China. 2009. 590p. pap. *(978-3-03911-814-4(5))* Lang, Peter.

Wang, Zhaoqian & Lü, Guangqun. Zhongguo Nuo Wen Hua: Zhongguonuowenhua. 2007. (CHI., Illus.). 352p. *(978-7-81120-077-5(5))* Shantou Daxue Chubanshe.

Waterbury, Florence. Bird Deities in China. 2007. *(978-1-57898-678-1(8))* Martino Publishing.

Weisz, Tiberiu. The Covenant & the Mandate of Heaven: An In-Depth Comparative Cultural Study of Judaism & China. 2008. xviii, 243p. E-Book *(978-0-595-88777-4(5))* iUniverse, Inc.

Wellens, Koen. Religious Revival in the Tibetan Borderlands: The Premi of Southwest China. 2010. (Studies on Ethnic Groups in China Ser.). (ENG., Illus.). 288p. (C). 70.00 *(978-0-295-99068-2(6))*; pap. 30.00 *(978-0-295-99069-9(4))* Univ. of Washington Pr.

Welter, Albert & Yanshou. Yongming Yanshou's Conception of Chan in the Zongjing Lu: A Special Transmission Within the Scriptures. 2011. (ENG.). 400p. 74.00 *(978-0-19-976031-2(4))* Oxford Univ. Pr., Inc.

Williams, Paul & Ladwig, Patrice, eds. Buddhist Funeral Cultures of Southeast Asia & China. 2012. (ENG., Illus.). 312p. 99.00 ***(978-1-107-00388-0(1))*** Cambridge Univ. Pr.

Wilson, Kevin. Hon-Sho: A Modern Manual for Digital Divination. 2012. (ENG., Illus.). 256p. pap. 18.95 ***(978-1-85906-340-8(3))*** Connections Bk. Publishing, Ltd. GBR. Dist: Red Wheel/Weiser.

Winkler, Dietmar & Tang, Li, eds. Hidden Treasures & Intercultural Encounters: Studies on East Syriac Christianity in China & Central Asia. 2011. (ENG.). 400p. pap. 39.95 *(978-3-643-50045-8(9))* Lit Verlag DEU. Dist: Transaction Pubs.

Wittfogel, Karl August & Chia-Sheng, Feng. Religion under the Liao Dynasty, 907-1125: Review of Religion, May 1948. 2011. 24p. 35.95 ***(978-1-258-08088-4(5))*** Literary Licensing, LLC.

Xiao, Ming. The Cultural Economy of Falun Gong in China: A Rhetorical Perspective. 2011. 152p. 44.95 *(978-1-57003-987-4(9))* Univ. of South Carolina Pr.

Xie, Zhibin. Religious Diversity & Public Religion in China. 2006. 168p. 99.95 *(978-0-7546-5648-7(9))* Ashgate Publishing Co.

Xinzhong Yao Staff & Gentz, Joachim. Understanding Chinese Religions. 2012. 160p. pap. 22.00 *(978-1-903765-77-7(3))* Dunedin Academic Pr. GBR. Dist: International Specialized Bk. Services.

Yang, Fenggang. Religion in China: Survival & Revival under Communist Rule, 1 vol. 2011. (ENG.). 264p. pap. 24.95 *(978-0-19-973564-8(6))* Oxford Univ. Pr., Inc.

Yang, Fenggang & Lang, Graeme. Social Scientific Studies of Religion in China: Methodology, Theories, & Findings. 2011. *(978-90-04-18246-2(2))* BRILL.

Yang, Fenggang & Tamney, Joseph, eds. Confucianism & Spiritual Traditions in Modern China & Beyond. 2011. (Religion in Chinese Societies Ser.). (Illus.). 355p. ***(978-90-04-21239-8(6))*** BRILL.

Yang, Jian. The Pacific Islands in China's Grand Strategy: Small States, Big Games. 2011. (ENG., Illus.). 288p. 85.00 *(978-0-230-11323-7(0))* Palgrave Macmillan.

Yang, Mayfair Mei-Hui. Chinese Religiosities: Afflictions of Modernity & State Formation. 2008. (Global, Area, & International Archive Ser.). (Illus.). 360p. pap. 39.95 *(978-0-520-09864-0(1))* Univ. of California Pr.

Yao, Xinzhong & Badham, Paul, eds. Religious Experience in Contemporary China. 2007. (University of Wales - Religion, Education, & Culture Ser.). (Illus.). 275p. 85.00 *(978-0-7083-2035-8(X))* Univ. of Wales Pr. GBR. Dist: Chicago Distribution Ctr.

Yao, Xinzhong & Zhao, Yanxia. Chinese Religion: A Contextual Approach. 2010. (ENG., Illus.). 256p. 39.95 *(978-1-84706-476-9(0))*; 130.00 *(978-1-84706-475-2(2))* Continuum International Publishing Group, Ltd. GBR. Dist: National Bk. Network.

Ye, Yi. Yi Jing de Qi Shi, 2 vols. 2010. (CHI., Illus.). 831p. *(978-988-219-147-1(9))*; *(978-988-219-148-8(7))* Cosmos Bks. Ltd.

Yen, Lu. Secret of the Golden Flower. 2007. (Illus.). 48p. per. 11.99 *(978-1-59547-919-8(8))* NuVision Pubns., LLC.

Yeo, Khiok-Khng. Musing with Confucius & Paul: Toward a Chinese Christian Theology. 2008. (ENG.). 508p. pap. 58.00 *(978-0-227-17283-4(3))* Clarke, James Co., Ltd. GBR. Dist: Brown, David Bk. Co., The.

Yu, Jimmy Yung Fung. Sanctity & Self-Inflicted Violence in Chinese Religions, 1500-1700. 2012. E-Book ***(978-0-19-984489-0(5))***; (ENG., Illus.). 288p. pap. 29.95 ***(978-0-19-984490-6(9))*** Oxford Univ. Pr., Inc.

Zhao, Weimin. Zhuangzi de Feng Shen: You Hu Die Zhi Bian Dao Qi Hua. 2010. (CHI., Illus.). 11p. *(978-957-08-3548-9(6))* Linking Publishing Co., Ltd.

Zhiming, Yuan. Lao Tzu & the Bible. Shangyu, Chen, tr. 2010. 404p. (ENG.). 29.99 *(978-1-4490-9110-1(5))*; pap. 19.99 *(978-1-4490-9108-8(3))* AuthorHouse.

CHINA—RURAL CONDITIONS

Beattie, Hilary J. Land & Lineage in China: A Study of T'ung-Ch'eng County, Anhwei, in the Ming & Ch'ing Dynasties. 2009. (Cambridge Studies in Chinese History, Literature & Institutions Ser.). (ENG., Illus.). 220p. pap. 31.99 *(978-0-521-10111-0(5))* Cambridge Univ. Pr.

Bislev, Ane & Thogersen, Stig, eds. Organizing Rural China - Rural China Organizing. 2012. (Challenges Facing Chinese Political Development Ser.). (ENG.). 248p. (gr. 17). 65.00 ***(978-0-7391-7009-0(0))*** Lexington Bks.

Chan, Anita, et al. Chen Village: Revolution to Globalization. 3rd ed. 2009. (Illus.). 400p. pap. 26.95 *(978-0-520-25931-7(9))* Univ. of California Pr.

Chen, Guidi & Wu, Chuntao. Will the Boat Sink the Water? 2007. *(978-0-7322-8305-6(1)*, Fourth Estate) HarperCollins Pubs. Australia.

Chu, Julie Y. Cosmologies of Credit: Transnational Mobility & the Politics of Destination in China. 2010. (ENG., Illus.). 360p. 89.95 *(978-0-8223-4792-7(X))*; pap. 24.95 *(978-0-8223-4806-1(3))* Duke Univ. Pr.

Cooper, Eugene. The Market & Temple Fairs of Rural China: Red Fire. 2012. (Asia's Transformations Ser.). (ENG., Illus.). 304p. (C). 135.00 ***(978-0-415-52079-9(7))*** Routledge.

Fei, Xiaotong, et al. Zhongguo Shi Shen: China's Gentry. 2009. pap. *(978-7-108-02694-1(5))* SDX Joint Publishing, Co.

Friedman, Edward, et al. Revolution, Resistance, & Reform in Village China. 2007. (Yale Agrarian Studies). (ENG., Illus.). 368p. per. 22.00 *(978-0-300-12595-5(X))* Yale Univ. Pr.

Gao, Mobo C. F. Gao Village. 288p. 39.00 *(978-0-8248-2205-7(6))* Univ. of Hawaii Pr.

—Gao Village: Rural Life in Modern China. 2007. (Illus.). 286p. per. 26.00 *(978-0-8248-3192-9(6))* Univ. of Hawaii Pr.

Giles, John, et al. The Elderly & Old Age Support in Rural China. 2012. (Directions in Development Ser.). (ENG.). 166p. pap. 25.00 *(978-0-8213-8685-9(9)*, 9780821386859) World Bank Pubns.

Guidi, Chen & Chuntao, Wu. Will the Boat Sink the Water? The Life of China's Peasants. Hong, Zhu, tr. 2007. (ENG.). 256p. per. 15.95 *(978-1-58648-441-5(9))* PublicAffairs.

Lee, James Z. & Campbell, Cameron D. Fate & Fortune in Rural China: Social Organization & Population Behavior in Liaoning 1774-1873. 2007. (Cambridge Studies in Population, Economy & Society in Past Time Ser.). (ENG., Illus.). 308p. pap. 61.00 *(978-0-521-03969-7(X))* Cambridge Univ. Pr.

Li, Huaiyin. Village China under Socialism & Reform: A Micro History, 1948-2008. 2009. (ENG., Illus.). 424p. 65.00 *(978-0-8047-5974-8(X))* Stanford Univ. Pr.

—Village China under Socialism & Reform: A Micro-History, 1948-2008. 2010. (ENG., Illus.). 424p. pap. 27.95 *(978-0-8047-7657-8(1))* Stanford Univ. Pr.

Li, Runliang. Wo Guo Nong Cun Nai Yong Xiao Fei Pin Xiao Fei Yan Jiu: Study on the Consumption of Durable Goods in Rural China. 2010. (CHI., Illus.). *(978-7-80247-555-7(4))* Intellectual Property Publishing Hse.

Long, Norman, et al, eds. Rural Transformations & Development in China: Policy Interventions for the 21st Century. 2010. (Illus.). 408p. 139.00 *(978-1-84980-093-8(6))* Elgar, Edward Publishing, Inc.

Lu, Caizhen. Poverty & Development in China: Alternative Approaches to Poverty Assessment. 2011. (Routledge Contemporary China Ser.). (ENG., Illus.). 304p. (C). 140.00 *(978-0-415-61822-9(3))* Routledge.

Organisation for Economic Co-operation and Development Staff. Oecd Rural Policy Reviews Oecd Rural Policy Reviews: China 2009. 2009. pap. 63.00 *(978-92-64-05956-6(3))* Organization for Economic Cooperation & Development.

Sargeson, Sally. Women, Gender & Development in Rural China. Jacka, Tamara, ed. 2011. (Illus.). 288p. 135.00 ***(978-1-84844-682-3(9))*** Elgar, Edward Publishing, Inc.

Siegal, Alan M. & Etzkorn, Irene. Simplicity. 2011. 256p. 25.00 *(978-1-58648-465-1(6))* PublicAffairs.

Song, Shunfeng & Chen, Aimin. China's Rural Economy after WTO: Problems & Strategies. 2006. (Chinese Economy Ser.). (Illus.). 384p. 130.00 *(978-0-7546-4695-2(5))* Ashgate Publishing Co.

Song, Shunfeng, et al. China's Agricultural Development: Challenges & Prospects. 2006. (Chinese Economy Ser.). (Illus.). 324p. 130.00 *(978-0-7546-4696-9(3))* Ashgate Publishing Co.

Su, Minzi. China's Rural Development Policy: Exploring the New Socialist Countryside. 2009. (Illus.). 280p. 69.95 *(978-1-935049-06-7(2))* FirstForumPress.

Su, Yang. Collective Killings in Rural China during the Cultural Revolution. 2011. (Cambridge Studies in Contentious Politics Ser.). (ENG., Illus.). 320p. 90.00 *(978-0-521-19808-0(9))*; 312p. pap. 27.99 *(978-0-521-17381-0(7))* Cambridge Univ. Pr.

Whiting, Susan H. Power & Wealth in Rural China: The Political Economy of Institutional Change. 2006. (Cambridge Modern China Ser.). (ENG.). 372p. pap. 50.00 *(978-0-521-02841-7(8))* Cambridge Univ. Pr.

Whyte, Martin King, ed. One Country, Two Societies: Rural-Urban Inequality in Contemporary China. 2010. (Harvard Contemporary China Ser.: 16). (Illus.). 460p. pap. 29.50 *(978-0-674-03632-1(8))* Harvard Univ. Pr.

Yang, C. K. A Chinese Village in Early Communist Transition. 2011. 296p. 48.95 ***(978-1-258-10308-8(7))*** Literary Licensing, LLC.

Zanasi, Margherita. Saving the Nation: Economic Modernity in Republican China. 2006. (ENG.). 336p. 60.00 *(978-0-226-97873-4(7))* Univ. of Chicago Pr.

Zhang, Qingzhong, et al. She Hui Zhu Yi Xin Nong Cun Jian She Yan Jiu. 2009. (CHI.). *(978-7-5097-0900-9(8))* China Social Science Documentation Publishing Hse.

Zhao, Yuepeng. China's Rural Financial System: Households' Demand for Credit & Recent Reforms. 2010. (Routledge Studies on the Chinese Economy Ser.). (ENG., Illus.). 192p. (C). 140.00 *(978-0-415-54793-2(8))* Routledge.

CHINA—SOCIAL CONDITIONS

"Aba Zangzu Qiangzu Zizhizhou gai kuang" bian xie zu Staff & "Aba Zangzu Qiangzu Zizhizhou gai kuang" xiu ding ben bian xie zu Staff, contrib. by. Aba Zangzu Qiangzu Zizhizhou Gai Kuang: AbaZangzuQiangzuZizhizhougaikuang. 2009. (CHI., Illus.). *(978-7-105-08670-2(X))* Nationalities Publishing Hse, The.

Acharya, Arabinda, et al. Ethnic Identity & National Conflict in China. 2010. (ENG.). 258p. 89.00 *(978-0-230-10305-4(7))* Palgrave Macmillan.

Ai, Jiabing. Guan Er Dai. 2011. (CHI., Illus.). 316p. ***(978-1-935981-23-7(4))*** Mirror Bks. USA.

Al-Dabbagh, Abdulla. Socialist Literature: Theory & Practice. 2012. (C). 77.95 ***(978-1-4331-1673-5(1))***; E-Book ***(978-1-4539-0221-9(X))*** Lang, Peter Publishing, Inc.

Alas, Ruth & Sun, Wei. Organizational Change in Chinese Organizations. 2009. (Chandos Asian Studies). (ENG., Illus.). 200p. 110.00 *(978-1-84334-352-3(5)*, Chandos Publishing) Woodhead Publishing Ltd. GBR. Dist: Ingram Pub. Services.

Alford, Lacey. The Great Firewall of Chin. 2010. 88p. pap. *(978-3-639-23537-1(1))* VDM Verlag Dr. Mueller e.K.

Alford, William P., et al, eds. The Professions in China. 2010. (Routledge Studies on Civil Society in Asia Ser.). (ENG., Illus.). 352p. (C). 130.00 *(978-0-415-55639-2(2))* Routledge.

Anonymous. China's Migrant Workers: Photographs 1990-2000. 2012. (ENG.). 225p. pap. 16.95 ***(978-1-59265-099-6(6))*** Long River Pr.

Auerbach, Sascha J., et al. Race, Law, & the Chinese Puzzle in Imperial Britain. 2009. (ENG., Illus.). 280p. 95.00 *(978-0-230-60949-5(X))* Palgrave Macmillan.

"Baoting Lizu Miaozu Zizhixian gai kuang" bian xie zu Staff, contrib. by. Baoting Lizu Miaozu Zizhixian Gai Kuang: BaotingLizuMiaozuZizhixiangaikuang. 2008. (CHI., Illus.). *(978-7-105-08617-7(3))* Nationalities Publishing Hse, The.

Basu, Parikshit K. & Bandara, Yapa, eds. WTO Accession & Socio-Economic Development in China. 2009. (Chandos Asian Studies). (ENG., Illus.). 234p. 110.00 *(978-1-84334-547-3(1)*, Chandos Publishing) Woodhead Publishing Ltd. GBR. Dist: Ingram Pub. Services.

Bell, Daniel A. China's New Confucianism: Politics & Everyday Life in a Changing Society. 2008. (ENG.). 258p. (C). 35.00 *(978-0-691-13690-5(4))* Princeton Univ. Pr.

Bergère, Marie-Claire. The Golden Age of the Chinese Bourgeoisie, 1911-1937. 2009. (Studies in Modern Capitalism Ser.). (ENG.). 372p. pap. 38.99 *(978-0-521-11071-6(8))* Cambridge Univ. Pr.

Besha, Patrick. Village Democracy & Social Unrest in Chin. 2008. 128p. per. *(978-3-8364-6091-0(2))* VDM Verlag Dr. Mueller e.K.

Bian, Yan-Jie, et al, eds. Sociology for Change: The Official Annual of the Hong Kong Sociological Association. 2007. (Social Transformations in Chinese Societies Ser.). 244p. pap. *(978-90-04-15706-4(9))* BRILL.

Bianco, Lucien. Wretched Rebels: Rural Disturbances on the Eve of the Chinese Revolution. Liddell, Philip, tr. from FRE. 2010. (Harvard East Asian Monographs: 323). Orig. Title: Jacqueries et révolution dans la Chine du XXe Siècle. (Illus.). 300p. 39.95 *(978-0-674-03542-3(9))* Harvard Univ., Asia Ctr.

Birge, Bettine. Women, Property, & Confucian Reaction in Sung & Y8an China (960-1368) 2010. (Cambridge Studies in Chinese History, Literature & Institutions Ser.). (ENG.). 368p. pap. 39.99 *(978-0-521-18072-6(4))* Cambridge Univ. Pr.

Blum, Susan. Lies That Bind: Chinese Truths, Other Truths. 2007. (ENG.). 242p. 77.00 *(978-0-7425-5404-7(X))* Rowman & Littlefield Publishers, Inc.

Blum, Susan Debra. Lies That Bind: Chinese Truths, Other Truths. 2007. (ENG.). 242p. per. 31.95 *(978-0-7425-5405-4(8))* Rowman & Littlefield Publishers, Inc.

Bodomo, Adams. Africans in China: A Sociocultural Study & Its Implications on Africa-China Relations. 2012. 14.99 ***(978-1-60497-790-5(6))*** Cambria Pr.

Borysevicz, Mathieu. Learning from Hangzhou. 2009. (ENG., Illus.). 330p. pap. 45.00 *(978-988-18033-6-8(5))* Timezone 8 Ltd. HKG. Dist: D.A.P./Distributed Art Pubs.

Brady, Anne-Marie & Brown, Douglas, eds. Foreigners & Foreign Institutions in Republican China. 2012. (Chinese Worlds Ser.). (ENG., Illus.). 320p. (C). 135.00 ***(978-0-415-52865-8(8))*** Routledge.

Brock, Darryl. China & Darwinian Evolution. 2010. 72p. pap. *(978-3-8383-5816-1(3))* Lambert Academic Publishing.

Brown, Jeremy. City Versus Countryside in Mao's China: Negotiating the Divide. 2012. (ENG., Illus.). 264p. 99.00 ***(978-1-107-02404-5(8))*** Cambridge Univ. Pr.

Cai, Peiling. Aomen Shen Xiang Ye. 2009. (Aomen Zhi Shi Cong Shu Ser.). (CHI., Illus.). 70p. *(978-962-04-2899-9(4))* Joint Publishing Co.

Callahan, William A. China: The Pessoptimist Nation. (ENG., Illus.). 2012. 288p. pap. 29.95 ***(978-0-19-960439-5(8))*** 2010. 248p. 45.00 *(978-0-19-954995-5(8))* Oxford Univ. Pr., Inc.

Campany, David & Higgie, Jennifer. China Between. 2010. (ENG., Illus.). 96p. 40.00 ***(978-1-904587-88-0(7))*** Lewis, Dewi Publishing GBR. Dist: Consortium Bk. Sales & Distribution.

Cao, Tianyu, et al. Culture & Social Transformations in Reform ERA China. 2010. 450p. *(978-90-04-17516-7(4))* BRILL.

CER Publishing, ed. China by Numbers 2008. 2007. 272p. 32.50 *(978-988-17149-2-3(3))* China Economic Review Publishing HKG. Dist: Trans-Atlantic Pubns., Inc.

Chan, Chak Kwan, et al. Social Policy in China. 2008. (Illus.). (C). 234p. 90.00 *(978-1-86134-881-4(9))*; 248p. pap. 39.95 *(978-1-86134-880-7(0))* Policy Pr. GBR. Dist: International Specialized Bk. Services, Chicago Distribution Ctr.

Chang, Chung-Li. The Chinese Gentry: Studies on Their Role in Nineteenth-Century Chinese Society. 2011. 270p. 47.95 ***(978-1-258-04437-4(4))*** Literary Licensing, LLC.

Chang, Kara & Cheng, Hong, eds. Advertising & Chinese Society: Impacts & Issues. 2009. (Illus.). 315p. pap. 63.00 *(978-87-630-0227-1(2))* Copenhagen Business Schl. Pr. DNK. Dist: International Specialized Bk. Services.

Chao, Emily. Lijiang Stories: Shamans, Taxi Drivers, & Runaway Brides in Reform-Era China. 2012. (ENG., Illus.). 256p. (C). 70.00 ***(978-0-295-99222-8(0))***; pap. 30.00 ***(978-0-295-99223-5(9))*** Univ. of Washington Pr.

Chee-Beng, Tan, ed. Chinese Transnational Network. 2007. (Chinese Worlds Ser.). (Illus.). 214p. 160.00 *(978-0-415-39583-0(6))* Routledge.

Chen, Bo. Comparisons of Urban Traffic & Traffic Management in the U. S. & China. 2007. pap. 15.00 *(978-0-8059-8899-4(8))* Dorrance Publishing Co., Inc.

Chen, Hesheng, ed. Large Research Infrastructures Development in China: A Roadmap To 2050: A Roadmap To 2050. 2011. (ENG., Illus.). 170p. pap. 99.00 *(978-3-642-19367-5(6)*, 3642193676) Springer.

Chen, Janet. Guilty of Indigence - the Urban Poor in China, 1900-1953. 2012. (ENG., Illus.). 320p. (C). 45.00 ***(978-0-691-15210-3(1))*** Princeton Univ. Pr.

Ch'en, Jerome & Tarling, Nicholas, eds. Studies in the Social History of China & South-East Asia: Essays in Memory of Victor Purcell. 2010. 434p. pap. 32.99 *(978-0-521-13374-6(2))* Cambridge Univ. Pr.

Chen, Sheying & Powell, Jason L., eds. Aging in China: Implications to Social Policy of a Changing Economic State. 2011. (Springer Series on International Aging Ser.). (ENG., Illus.). xii, 283p. 169.00 *(978-1-4419-8350-3(3)*, 1441983503) Springer.

Chen, Yawei. Shanghai Pudong. 2007. (Illus.). pap. 82.00 *(978-1-58603-747-5(1)*, Delft University Pr) IOS Pr., Inc.

Chen, Yong, ed. Energy Science & Technology in China: A Roadmap To 2050: A Roadmap To 2050. 2010. (Illus.). 103p. pap. 99.00 *(978-3-642-05319-1(X)*, 364205319X) Springer.

Cheung, Yuet Wah, ed. A Brighter Side: Protective & Risk Factors in the Rehabilitation of Chronic Drug Abusers in Hong Kong. 2009. 192p. 32.00 *(978-962-996-400-9(7))* Chinese Univ. of Hong Kong, The HKG. Dist: Columbia Univ. Pr.

Chiang, Howard, ed. Transgender China. 2012. (ENG.). 256p. 80.00 ***(978-0-230-34062-6(8))*** Palgrave Macmillan.

China's Far West: Conditions in Xinjiang One Year after Demonstrations & Riots: Roundtable Before the Congressional-Executive Commission on China, One Hundred Eleventh Congress, Second Session, July 19, 2010. 2010. ii, 34p. *(978-0-16-087024-8(0)*, 552-070-41882-2) United States Government Printing Office.

Chittick, Andrew. Patronage & Community in Medieval China: The Xiangyang Garrison, 400-600 CE. 2009. (SUNY series in Chinese Philosophy & Culture Ser.). (Illus.). 208p. 75.00 *(978-1-4384-2897-0(9))* State Univ. of New York Pr.

Chong, Chae-Ho. Charting China's Future: Political, Social, & International Dimensions. 2006. (ENG., Illus.). 232p. per. 39.95 *(978-0-7425-5397-2(3))* Rowman & Littlefield Publishers, Inc.

Chu, C. Y. Cyrus & Yu, Ruoh-Rong. Understanding Chinese Families: A Comparative Study of Taiwan & Southeast China. 2010. (ENG., Illus.). 224p. 90.00 *(978-0-19-957809-2(5))* Oxford Univ. Pr., Inc.

Chung, Jae Ho. Charting Chinas Future: Political, Social, & International Dimensions. Chung, Jae Ho, ed. 2006. (ENG., Illus.). 232p. 92.00 *(978-0-7425-5396-5(5))* Rowman & Littlefield Publishers, Inc.

Clayton, Cathryn H. Sovereignty at the Edge: Macau & the Question of Chineseness. 2010. (Harvard East Asian Monographs: 324). (Illus.). 420p. 49.95 *(978-0-674-03545-4(3))* Harvard Univ., Asia Ctr.

Cliff, Roger, et al. Shaking the Heavens & Splitting the Earth: Chinese Air Force Employment Concepts in the 21st Century. 2010. 300p. pap. 29.00 *(978-0-8330-4932-2(1)*, mg-915) RAND Corp., The.

Cockain, Alex. Young Chinese in Urban China. 2011. (Routledge Studies on China in Transition Ser.). (ENG., Illus.). 224p. (C). 125.00 *(978-0-415-67757-8(2))* Routledge.

Croll, Elisabeth. Feminism & Socialism in China. 2012. (Routledge Revivals Ser.). (ENG.). 378p. 140.00 ***(978-0-415-51915-1(2))*** Routledge.

Crow, Carl. 400 Million Customers: The Experiences -Some Happy, Some Sad of an American in China, & What They Taught Him. 2008. (Illus.). 276p. pap. *(978-0-9680459-0-9(1))* Soul Care Publishing.

Crow, Carl & Ayer, A. J. Four Hundred Million Customers. 2007. (ENG., Illus.). 256p. pap. 250.00 *(978-0-7103-1212-9(1))* Routledge.

Dahlman, Carl J., et al. Enhancing China's Competitiveness Through Lifelong Learning. 2007. (WBI Development Studies). (ENG., Illus.). 175p. per. 15.00 *(978-0-8213-6943-2(1)*, 9780821369432) World Bank Pubns.

Dajani, Adel & Man, Wong How. Islamic Frontiers of China: Peoples of the Silk Road. 2010. (ENG., Illus.). 160p. 50.00 *(978-1-84885-702-5(0))* I. B. Tauris & Co., Ltd. GBR. Dist: Macmillan.

"Daozhen Gelaozu Miaozu Zizhixian gai kuang" bian xie zu Staff & "Daozhen Gelaozu Miaozu Zizhixian gai kuang" xiu ding ben bian xie zu Staff, contrib. by. Daozhen Gelaozu Miaozu Zizhixian Gai Kuang: DaozhenGelaozuMiaozuZizhixiangaikuang. 2007. (Zhongguo Shao Shu Min Zu Zi Zhi Di Fang Gai Kuang Cong Shu (Xiu Ding Ben) Ser.). (CHI., Illus.). *(978-7-105-08537-8(1))* Nationalities Publishing Hse, The.

Dardess, John W. Governing China: 150-1850. 2010. (Illus.). 139p. 39.95 *(978-1-60384-312-6(4))*; pap. 12.95 *(978-1-60384-311-9(6))* Hackett Publishing Co., Inc.

Deng, Yingtao. A New Development Model & China's Future. 2012. (Routledge Studies on the Chinese Economy Ser.). (ENG.). 240p. (C). 140.00 *(978-0-415-61092-6(3))* Routledge.

Devare, Sudhir T., et al, eds. Emerging China: Prospects of Partnership in Asia. 2012. (ENG.). (C). 95.00 ***(978-0-415-50236-8(5)***, Routledge India) Taylor & Francis Group GBR. Dist: Taylor & Francis Group.

Devonshire-Ellis, Chris, et al, eds. Intellectual Property Rights in China. 2nd ed. 2011. (China Briefing Ser.). Orig. Title: Intellectual Property Rights in China. (ENG.). iv, 56p. pap. 49.95 *(978-3-642-15407-2(7)*, 3642154077) Springer.

Dikötter, Frank. Exotic Commodities: Modern Objects & Everyday Life in China. 2007. (ENG., Illus.). 384p. (gr. 17). 31.99 *(978-0-231-14116-1(5))* Columbia Univ. Pr.

Dodson, Bill. China Inside Out: 10 Irreversible Trends Reshaping China & Its Relationship with the World. 2011. (ENG.). 200p. 29.95 *(978-0-470-82643-0(6)*, Wiley) Wiley, John & Sons, Inc.

Dong, Erwei. Leisure Lifestyles in Urban China: Leisure Activities, Leisure Constraints, & Leisure Satisfaction. 2008. 176p. pap. *(978-3-639-10650-3(4))* VDM Verlag Dr. Mueller e.K.

Dong, Madeleine Yue & Goldstein, Joshua L., eds. Everyday Modernity in China. 2006. (Studies in Modernity & National Identity). (ENG., Illus.). 336p. per. 30.00 *(978-0-295-98602-9(6))* Univ. of Washington Pr.

Eric, K. W. Desiring Hong Kong, Consuming South China: Transborder Cultural Politics, 1970-2010. 2011. (Hong Kong Culture & Society Ser.). (Illus.). 176p. ***(978-988-8053-93-3(0))*** Hong Kong Univ. Pr.

—Desiring Hong Kong, Consuming South China: Transborder Cultural Politics, 1970-2010. 2012. (Hong Kong Culture & Society Ser.). (Illus.). 220p. (gr. 17). pap. 25.00 ***(978-988-8083-46-6(5))*** Hong Kong Univ. Pr. HKG. Dist: Columbia Univ. Pr.

Fa, Marietta Sze-Chie. Rape Myths in American & Chinese Laws & Legal Systems: Do Tradition & Culture Make the Difference? 2007. 109p. *(978-1-932330-21-2(6))* Maryland Series in Contemporary Studies.

Fan, C. Cindy. China on the Move: Migration, the State, & the Household. 2008. (Routledge Studies in Human Geography Ser.). (Illus.). 210p. 158.00 *(978-0-415-42852-1(1))* Routledge.

Fang, Chih-Hui. Lesbian Identity in British & Taiwanese Contemporary Novels. 2010. 208p. pap. *(978-3-8383-5382-1(X))* Lambert Academic Publishing.

Fang, Xiangxin, et al. He Xie She Hui Yu She Hui Jian She: Harmonious Society & Social Construction. 2008. (CHI., Illus.). 451p. *(978-7-5097-0282-6(8))* China Social Science Documentation Publishing Hse.

Fei, Si-yen. Negotiating Urban Space: Urbanization & Late Ming Nanjing. 2010. (Harvard East Asian Monographs: 320). (Illus.). 370p. 45.00 *(978-0-674-03561-4(5))* Harvard Univ., Asia Ctr.

Fei, Xiaotong, et al. Zhongguo Shi Shen: China's Gentry. 2009. pap. *(978-7-108-02694-1(5))* SDX Joint Publishing, Co.

Fei, Yan. Zhongguo Shi Da Fu Hao Jia Zu. 2011. (CHI., Illus.). 573p. ***(978-1-935981-13-5(7))*** Mirror Bks. USA.

Feng, Jinyuan. Yin Dao Zong Jiao Yu She Hui Zhu Yi She Hui Xiang Shi Ying de Li Lun Yu Shi Jian: The Theory & Practice of Guiding Religion to Adapt to the Socialist Society. 2009. (CHI., Illus.). *(978-7-5004-8028-0(8))* China Social Sciences Pr.

Feng, Wang. Boundaries & Categories: Rising Inequality in Post-Socialist Urban China. 2007. (Studies in Social Inequality Ser.). (ENG., Illus.). 264p. 55.00 *(978-0-8047-5794-2(1))* Stanford Univ. Pr.

Fernandez-Stembridge, Leila & Fisac, Taciana, eds. China Today. 2010. (Illus.). 286p. pap. 39.95 ***(978-0-415-60016-3(2))*** Routledge.

Finkelstein, David M. & Gunness, Kristen, eds. Civil-Military Relations in Today's China: Swimming in a New Sea. 2006. (ENG., Illus.). 344p. 100.95 *(978-0-7656-1659-3(9)*, East Gate Bk.); pap. 39.95 *(978-0-7656-1660-9(2))* Sharpe, M.E. Inc.

Florence, Eric & Defraigne Pierre, eds. Economy, Society & Politics in Twenty-First Century China: Striving for a New Development Paradigm. 2012. (Comparative Development & Policy in Asia Ser.). (ENG., Illus.). 224p. (C). 155.00 ***(978-0-415-53212-9(4))*** Routledge.

Florini, Ann, et al. China Experiments: From Local Innovations to National Reform. 2012. (ENG., Illus.). 216p. pap. 29.95 ***(978-0-8157-2200-7(1))*** Brookings Institution Pr.

Fong, Vanessa L. Chinese Citizenship: Views from the Margins. 2009. 198p. pap. 39.95 *(978-0-415-54586-0(2))* Routledge.

Friedman, Edward & Gilley, Bruce. Asia's Giants: Comparing China & India. Friedman, Edward & Gilley, Bruce, eds. 2008. (ENG.). 264p. pap. 34.00 *(978-0-230-60616-6(4))* Palgrave Macmillan.

Gamble Burgess Staff. Peking - a Social Survey. 2010. (Illus.). 562p. *(978-1-905246-83-0(8))* BRILL.

Gao, Fang. Becoming a Model Minority: Schooling Experiences of Ethnic Koreans in China. 2010. (Emerging Perspectives on Education in China Ser.). (ENG.). 144p. 57.99 *(978-0-7391-3683-6(6))* Lexington Bks.

Gao, Gao. Deng Xiaoping, Hu Yaobang, Zhao Ziyang San Tou Ma Che Shi Dai. 2009. (Zhen Xiang Xi Lie Ser.: Vol. 51). (CHI., Illus.). 345p. *(978-1-932138-80-1(3))* Mirror Bks. USA.

Gao, Mobo C. F. Gao Village. 288p. 39.00 *(978-0-8248-2205-7(6))* Univ. of Hawaii Pr.

—Gao Village: Rural Life in Modern China. 2007. (Illus.). 286p. per. 26.00 *(978-0-8248-3192-9(6))* Univ. of Hawaii Pr.

Garcia, Beatriz Carrillo. Small Town China: Rural Labour & Social Inclusion. 2011. (Routledge Studies on China in Transition Ser.). (ENG., Illus.). 232p. (C). 133.00 *(978-0-415-60023-1(5))* Routledge.

Gil, Iker, ed. Shanghai Transforming. 2008. 272p. pap. *(978-84-96954-66-3(8))* Actar Birkhauser Distribution.

Giles, Herbert A. China & the Chinese. 2007. (ENG.). 120p. per. *(978-1-4065-4455-8(8))* Dodo Pr.

Gordon, John, 4th, et al. How Domestic Trends in the U. S., China, & Iran Could Influence U. S. Navy Strategic Planning. 2009. 232p. pap. 41.00 *(978-0-8330-4562-1(8)*, mg-729) RAND Corp., The.

Griffiths, Michael. Consumption & Identity in the People's Republic of China. 2012. (Chinese Worlds Ser.). (ENG., Illus.). 272p. (C). 135.00 ***(978-0-415-53572-4(7))*** Routledge.

Grumbine, R. Edward. Where the Dragon Meets the Angry River: Nature & Power in the People's Republic of China. (Illus.). 256p. 2011. pap. 21.95 *(978-1-61091-160-3(1))* 2010. (ENG., 27.50 *(978-1-59726-551-5(9))* Island Pr.

Guidi, Chen & Chuntao, Wu. Will the Boat Sink the Water? The Life of China's Peasants. Hong, Zhu, tr. 2007. (ENG.). 256p. per. 15.95 *(978-1-58648-441-5(9))* PublicAffairs.

Guiheux, Gilles & Kuah-Pearce, Khun Eng, eds. Social Movements in China & Hong Kong: The Expansion of Protest Space. 2009. (ICAS Publications Ser.). (ENG.). 336p. pap. *(978-90-8964-131-1(9))* Amsterdam Univ. Pr.

Guo, Xiaolin. State & Ethnicity in China's Southwest. 2008. (China Studies Ser.). (Illus.). 320p. *(978-90-04-16775-9(7))* BRILL.

Hamrin, Carol Lee. Salt & Light: Lives of Faith That Shaped Modern China. 2008. (Studies in Chinese Christianity Ser.). (Illus.). 252p. pap. 28.00 *(978-1-55635-984-2(5)*, Pickwick Pubns.) Wipf & Stock Pubs.

Hamrin, Carol Lee & Bieler, Stacey, eds. Salt & Light, Three Volume Set: More Lives of Faith That Shaped Modern China. 2011. (Studies in Chinese Christianity: Ser.). 782p. pap. 80.00 ***(978-1-61097-690-9(8)***, Pickwick Pubns.) Wipf & Stock Pubs.

—Salt & Light, Volume 2: More Lives of Faith That Shaped Modern China. 2010. (Studies in Chinese Christianity Ser.). 252p. pap. 28.00 *(978-1-60608-553-2(2)*, Pickwick Pubns.) Wipf & Stock Pubs.

Hamrin, Carol Lee & Bieler, Stacey, eds. Salt & Light, Volume 3: More Lives of Faith That Shaped Modern China. 2011. (Studies in Chinese Christianity: Ser.). 278p. pap. 31.00 ***(978-1-61097-158-4(2)***, Pickwick Pubns.) Wipf & Stock Pubs.

Hao, Zhidong. Macau History & Society. 2011. (ENG., Illus.). 328p. (gr. 17). pap. 38.00 *(978-988-8028-54-2(5))* Hong Kong Univ. Pr. HKG. Dist: Columbia Univ. Pr.

Harney, Alexandra. The China Price: The True Cost of Chinese Competitive Advantage. 2009. (ENG., Illus.). 352p. (gr. 12-18). 16.00 *(978-0-14-311485-4(7)*, Penguin (Non-Classics)) Penguin Group (USA) Inc.

Hasmath, Raza & Hsu, Jennifer, eds. China in an Era of Transition: Understanding Contemporary State & Society Actors. 2009. (ENG., Illus.). 244p. 100.00 *(978-0-230-61350-8(0))* Palgrave Macmillan.

Hemmingsen, John & Hemmingsen, Cherie. 2000 Days in Chin: China 1998-2009. 2010. 250p. pap. 14.95 *(978-1-60264-538-7(8))* Virtualbookworm.com Publishing, Inc.

Hershatter, Gail. The Gender of Memory: Rural Women & China's Collective Past. 2011. (Asia Pacific Modern Ser.). (ENG., Illus.). 472p. 49.95 *(978-0-520-26770-1(2))* Univ. of California Pr.

Hewitt, Duncan. China: Getting Rich First: A Modern Social History. 2009. (ENG., Illus.). 480p. pap. 16.95 *(978-1-60598-061-4(7)*, 605061) Pegasus Bks.

—Getting Rich First: Life in a Changing China. 2008. (ENG., Illus.). 304p. pap. *(978-0-09-948879-8(5)*, Vintage) Knopf Doubleday Publishing Group.

Hillenbrand, Margaret & Starr, Chloe, eds. Documenting China: A Reader in Seminal Twentieth-Century Texts. 2011. (ENG & CHI.). 240p. (C). pap. 40.00 *(978-0-295-99127-6(5))* Univ. of Washington Pr.

Ho, Loretta Wing Wah. Gay & Lesbian Subculture in Urban China. (ENG., Illus.). 200p. 2011. pap. 42.95 ***(978-0-415-66619-0(8))*** 2009. (C). 130.00 *(978-0-415-55022-2(X))* Routledge.

Ho, Peter & Edmonds, Richard, eds. China's Embedded Activism: Opportunities & Constraints of a Social Movement. 2011. (ENG., Illus.). 288p. (C). pap. 44.95 ***(978-0-415-66650-3(3))*** Routledge.

Ho, Peter & Edmonds, Richard Louis, eds. China's Embedded Activism: Opportunities & Constraints of a Social Movement. 2007. (Illus.). 258p. 160.00 *(978-0-415-43374-7(6))* Routledge.

Holmes, Madelyn. Students & Teachers of the New China: Thirteen Interviews. 2007. (ENG., Illus.). 207p. per. 39.95 *(978-0-7864-3288-2(8))* McFarland & Co., Inc. Pubs.

Hom, Sharon & Mosher, Stacy, eds. Challenging China: Struggle & Hope in an Era of Change. (ENG.). 313p. 2008. pap. 17.95 *(978-1-59558-416-8(1))* 2007. 29.95 *(978-1-59558-132-7(4))* New Pr., The.

Hongyi, Lai, ed. China into the Hu-Wen Era: Policy Initiatives & Challenges. 2006. (Series on Contemporary China: Vol. 5). (Illus.). 565p. 150.00 *(978-981-256-732-1(1))* World Scientific Publishing Co., Inc.

Hsing, You-tien & Lee, Ching Kwan. Reclaiming Chinese Society: The New Social Activism. Hsing, You-tien & Lee, Ching Kwan, eds. 2009. (Asia's Transformations Ser.). (ENG., Illus.). 272p. 170.00 *(978-0-415-49137-2(1))* Routledge.

Hsing, You-tien & Lee, Ching Kwan, eds. Reclaiming Chinese Society: The New Social Activism. 2009. (Asia's Transformations Ser.). (ENG., Illus.). 272p. (C). pap. 42.95 *(978-0-415-49139-6(8))* Routledge.

Hsu, Carolyn L. Creating Market Socialism: How Ordinary People Are Shaping Class & Status in China. 2007. (Politics, History, & Culture Ser.). (ENG., Illus.). 240p. (C). 79.95 *(978-0-8223-4017-1(8))*; per. 22.95 *(978-0-8223-4036-2(4))* Duke Univ. Pr.

Hu, Angang. Economic & Social Transformation in China: Challenges & Opportunities. 2009. 282p. pap. 39.95 *(978-0-415-54557-0(9))* Routledge.

Hu, Angang, ed. Economic & Social Transformation in China: Challenges & Opportunities. 2006. (Routledge Studies on the Chinese Economy). (Illus.). 276p. 170.00 *(978-0-415-38067-6(7))* Routledge.

Huang, Xiaoming. The Institutional Dynamics of China's Great Transformation. 2011. (China Policy Ser.). (ENG., Illus.). 272p. (C). 140.00 *(978-0-415-58058-8(7))* Routledge.

Hung, Ho-Fung. Protest with Chinese Characteristics: Demonstration, Riots, & Petitions in the Mid-Qing Dynasty. 2011. (ENG., Illus.). 288p. (gr. 17). 50.00 *(978-0-231-15202-0(7))* Columbia Univ. Pr.

Hurst, William. The Chinese Worker after Socialism. 2009. (Illus.). 208p. 99.00 *(978-0-521-89887-4(0))* Cambridge Univ. Pr.

Hutton, Will. The Writing on the Wall: Why We Must Embrace China as a Partner or Face It as an Enemy. 2006. (ENG., Illus.). 432p. 28.00 *(978-0-7432-7528-6(4)*, Free Pr.) Free Pr.

Hwang, Kwang-Kuo. Foundations of Chinese Psychology: Confucian Social Relations. 2011. (International & Cultural Psychology Ser.). (ENG., Illus.). xxx, 378p. 129.00 ***(978-1-4614-1438-4(5)***, 1461414385) Springer.

Ine, et al. Supertrends of Future China: Billion Dollar Business Opportunities for China's Olympic Decade. 2008. xxii, 286p. 27.95 *(978-981-281-439-5(6))* World Scientific Publishing Co., Inc.

The Internet in China: Online Information & Social Connectivity. 2010. 325p. 95.00 *(978-1-933782-60-7(9))* Berkshire Publishing Group.

Islam, Nazrul, ed. Resurgent China: Issues for the Future. 2009. (ENG., Illus.). 264p. 131.00 *(978-0-230-53807-8(X))* Palgrave Macmillan.

Jacobs, Katrien. People's Pornography: Sex & Surveillance on the Chinese Internet. 2012. (Illus.). 203p. pap. 25.00 *(978-1-84150-493-3(9))* Intellect, Ltd. GBR. Dist: Chicago Distribution Ctr.

Jaffrelot, Christophe & Veer, Peter van der. Patterns of Middle Class Consumption in India & China. 2008. (Illus.). 308p. (C). 49.95 *(978-0-7619-3623-7(8)*, B36237C) SAGE Pubns., Inc.

Jankowiak, William R. Sex, Death, & Hierarchy in a Chinese City: An Anthropological Account. 2nd ed. 368p. pap. 27.50 *(978-0-231-13183-4(6))* Columbia Univ. Pr.

Jankowiak, William R., et al. Sex & World Peace. 2nd ed. 2012. (ENG.). 304p. (gr. 17). 26.50 *(978-0-231-13182-7(8))* Columbia Univ. Pr.

Jeffreys, Elaine. Sex & Sexuality in China. 2006. (Routledge Studies on China in Transition Ser.). (Illus.). 184p. 160.00 *(978-0-415-40143-2(7))* Routledge.

Jeffreys, Elaine, ed. Sex & Sexuality in China. 2009. 190p. pap. 39.95 *(978-0-415-54697-3(4))* Routledge.

Jiang, Zhenbai. Behind the Surface. 2010. 100p. pap. *(978-3-8383-9134-2(9))* Lambert Academic Publishing.

Johnson, M. Dujon. Race & Racism in the Chinas: Chinese Racial attitudes toward Africans & African-Americans. 2007. 168p. per. 15.95 *(978-1-4259-8175-4(5))* AuthorHouse.

Kim, Jaeyoon. Ethnicity, Local Conflicts & the Qing State. 2010. 212p. pap. *(978-3-639-25419-8(8))* VDM Verlag Dr. Mueller e.K.

Kipnis, Andrew. Contemporary Chinese Society & Politics, 4 vols. Tomba, Luigi & Unger, Jonathan, eds. 2009. (Critical Concepts in Asian Studies). (ENG., Illus.). 1872p. 1430.00 *(978-0-415-45748-4(3))* Routledge.

Kirby, William C., et al. The People's Republic of China at 60: An International Assessment. 2011. (CHI & ENG., Illus.). 432p. pap. 29.95 *(978-0-674-06064-7(4))* Harvard Univ., Asia Ctr.

Kolas, Ashild. Tourism & Tibetan Culture in Transition. 2011. (ENG., Illus.). 162p. (C). pap. 44.95 ***(978-0-415-67490-4(5))*** Routledge.

Kolatch, Jonathan. China Mosaic. 2008. (Illus.). 360p. 30.00 *(978-0-8246-0470-7(9))* David, Jonathan Pubs., Inc.

Kong, Travis S. K. Chinese Homosexualities: Memba, Tongzhi & Golden Boy. 2010. (Routledge Contemporary China Ser.). (ENG., Illus.). 320p. (C). 145.00 *(978-0-415-45189-5(2))* Routledge.

Ku & Mok, Ka Ho. Social Cohesion in Greater China: Challenges for Social Policy & Governance. 2010. (Illus.). 400p. 118.00 *(978-981-4291-92-7(7))* World Scientific Publishing Co., Inc.

Kubori, Hideaki & Kitao, Tetsuro. Chizai Sosho. 2010. (JPN., Illus.). 13p. *(978-4-417-01510-9(4))* Seirin Shoin.

Kwok-Bun, Chan, ed. Chinese Entertainment. 2011. (ENG.). 208p. (C). 125.00 ***(978-0-415-69556-5(2))*** Routledge.

Lai, Ming-Yan. Nativism & Modernity: Cultural Contestations in China & Taiwan under Global Capitalism. 2008. (SUNY Series, Explorations in Postcolonial Studies). 233p. 70.00 *(978-0-7914-7295-9(X))* State Univ. of New York Pr.

Lam, Tong. A Passion for Facts: Social Surveys & the Construction of the Chinese Nation-State, 1900-1949. 2011. (Asia Pacific Modern Ser.). (ENG., Illus.). 280p. 60.00 *(978-0-520-26786-2(9))* Univ. of California Pr.

Lan, Shan. Postmodern Aesthetics in Six-Generation Chinese Films. 2010. 72p. pap. *(978-3-8383-6129-1(6))* Lambert Academic Publishing.

Lary, Diana. The Chinese People at War: Human Suffering & Social Transformation, 1937-1945. 2010. (New Approaches to Asian History Ser.). (ENG., Illus.). 248p. (C). 95.00 *(978-0-521-19506-5(3))*; pap. 29.99 *(978-0-521-14410-0(8))* Cambridge Univ. Pr.

Law, Wing-Wah. Citizenship & Citizenship Education in a Global Age: Politics, Policies, & Practices in China. 2011. (C). pap. 35.95 *(978-1-4331-0801-3(1))* Lang, Peter Publishing, Inc.

—Citizenship & Citizenship Education in a Global Age: Politics, Policies, & Practices in China (CB) 2011. (C). 139.95 *(978-1-4331-0802-0(X))* Lang, Peter Publishing, Inc.

Le Pichon, Alain, ed. China Trade & Empire: Jardine, Matheson & Co. & the Origins of British Rule in Hong Kong, 1827-1843. 2006. (Records of Social & Economic History, New Ser.: Vol. 38). (ENG., Illus.). 592p. 150.00 (978-0-19-726337-2(2)) Oxford Univ. Pr., Inc.

Leeb, Stephen. Red Alert: How China's Growing Prosperity Threatens the American Way of Life. 2011. 272p. pap. 17.99 (978-0-446-57624-6(7), Business Plus) Grand Central Publishing.

Lei, Yifeng & Yi, Jiewei. Zhongguo Fan Kong Da Bu Bing. 2008. ("Zhongguo Ju Shi" Xi Lie Ser.: Vol. 52). (CHI., Illus.). 503p. (978-1-932138-68-9(4)) Mirror Bks. USA.

Leung, Helen Hok-Sze. Undercurrents: Queer Culture & Postcolonial Hong Kong. 2008. (Queer Asia Ser.). 166p. pap. (978-962-209-950-0(5)) Hong Kong Univ. Pr.

Li, Dinu, photos by. The Mother of All Journeys. 2007. (ENG., Illus.). 96p. 45.00 (978-1-904587-41-5(0)) Lewis, Dewi Publishing GBR. Dist: Consortium Bk. Sales & Distribution.

Li, Lillian M. Fighting Famine in North China: State, Market, & Environmental Decline, 1690s-1990s. 2007. (ENG., Illus.). 544p. 80.00 (978-0-8047-5304-3(0)) Stanford Univ. Pr.

Li, Xiaoxiong. Poppies & Politics in China: Sichuan Province, 1840s To 1940s. 2009. (Illus.). 308p. 61.50 (978-0-87413-054-6(9)) Univ. of Delaware Pr.

Li, Yushi(Boni). Emigrating from China to the United States: A Comparison of Different Social Experiences. 2009. 250p. 52.95 (978-0-398-07899-7(8)); pap. 34.95 (978-0-398-07900-0(5)) Thomas, Charles C. Pub., Ltd.

Liang, Bin. The Changing Chinese Legal System, 1978 ndash; Present: Centralization of Power & Rationalization of the Legal System. 2012. (East Asia: History, Politics, Sociology & Culture Ser.). (ENG., Illus.). 266p. pap. 42.95 (978-0-415-54103-9(4)) Routledge.

Liang, Xixiong. Aomen Yin Shi Ye Jin Xi. 2009. (CHI., Illus.). 87p. (978-962-04-2893-7(5)) Joint Publishing Co.

Liang, Zai. The Emergence of a New Urban China: Insiders' Perspectives. 2011. (978-0-7391-7012-0(0)) Lexington Bks.

Liang, Zai, et al, eds. The Emergence of a New Urban China: Insiders' Perspectives. 2012. (ENG., Illus.). 228p. (gr. 17). 60.00 (978-0-7391-7011-3(2)) Lexington Bks.

Lim, Tin Seng & Zhao, Litao. China's New Social Policy: Initiatives for a Harmonious Society. 2009. (Illus.). 244p. 99.00 (978-981-4277-73-0(8)) World Scientific Publishing Co., Inc.

Lin & Lin, George C. S. Developing China: Land, Politics & Social Conditions. 2009. (Routledge Contemporary China Ser.). (ENG., Illus.). 368p. (C). 145.00 (978-0-415-41322-0(2)) Routledge.

Lin, Budong. Huai He Zhong You: Fang Hong Kang Han Xin Fang Lüe. 2010. (CHI., Illus.). xi, 160p. (978-988-219-174-7(6)) Cosmos Bks. Ltd.

Lin, En-Ying. Luxury E-Branding in Greater Chin. 2010. 156p. pap. (978-3-8383-5287-9(4)) Lambert Academic Publishing.

Ling, George Fusun. China Developing: Cultural Identity of Emerging Societies. 2008. 212p. 68.00 (978-981-277-863-5(2)) World Scientific Publishing Co., Inc.

Liu, Petrus & Rofel, Lisa. Beyond the Strai(gh)ts: Transnationalism & Queer Chinese Politics. 2010. (ENG., Illus.). 289p. pap. 14.00 (978-0-8223-6737-6(8)) Duke Univ. Pr.

Liu, Shao-hua. Passage to Manhood: Youth Migration, Heroin, & AIDS in Southwest China. 2010. (Studies of the Weatherhead East Asian In Ser.). (ENG., Illus.). 248p. 60.00 (978-0-8047-7024-8(7)); pap. 22.95 (978-0-8047-7025-5(5)) Stanford Univ. Pr.

Lo, Shiu-Hung Sonny. Competing Chinese Political Visions: Hong Kong vs. Beijing on Democracy, 1 vol. 2010. (Praeger Security International Ser.). 294p. 59.95 (978-0-313-36505-8(9), C36505, Praeger Pubs.) Greenwood Publishing Group, Inc.

Logan, John R., ed. Urban China in Transition. 2008. (Studies in Urban & Social Change Ser.: 12). (ENG., Illus.). 384p. 94.95 (978-1-4051-6145-9(0)); pap. 39.95 (978-1-4051-6146-6(9)) Wiley, John & Sons, Inc. (Wiley-Blackwell).

Loyalka, Michelle Dammon. Eating Bitterness: Stories from the Front Lines of China's Great Urban Migration. 2012. (ENG., Illus.). 280p. 29.95 (978-0-520-26650-6(1)) Univ. of California Pr.

Lu. The Great Urbanization of China. 2011. 118.00 (978-981-4287-80-7(6)) World Scientific Publishing Co., Inc.

Lu, Yiyi. Non-Governmental Organisations in China. 2012. (China Policy Ser.). (ENG.). 172p. (C). pap. 42.95 (978-0-415-54183-1(2)) Routledge.

Ma, Jiewei. Desiring Hong Kong, Consuming South China: Transborder Cultural Politics, 1970-2010. 2012. (Hong Kong Culture & Society Ser.). (ENG., Illus.). 220p. (gr. 17). 60.00 (978-988-8083-45-9(7)) Hong Kong Univ. Pr. HKG. Dist: Columbia Univ. Pr.

Ma, Junya. Bei Xi Sheng de "Ju Bu" Huai Bei She Hui Sheng Tai Bian Qian Yan Jiu (1680-1949) 2010. (CHI., Illus.). 646p. (978-986-02-2875-5(2)) Academia Sinica.

Ma, Rong. Population & Society in Contemporary Tibet. 2011. (CHI., Illus.). 408p. (978-988-220-656-4(5)); (978-988-220-728-8(6)); (978-988-8053-76-6(0)) Hong Kong Univ. Pr.

Ma, Wei & Detels, Roger. Voluntary Hiv Counseling & Testing in Southwest Chin. 2010. 144p. pap. (978-3-639-25278-1(0)) VDM Verlag Dr. Mueller e.K.

Meng, Fanhua. The Phenomenon of Chinese Culture at the Turn of the 21st Century. 2011. 344p. 178.00 (978-981-4332-35-4(6), Silkroad Pr.) Enrich Professional Publishing (S)., Ltd. SGP. Dist: Independent Pubs. Group.

Michael Hsiao, Hsin-Huang, ed. Chinese Middle Classes: China, Taiwan, Macao & Hong Kong. 2013. (Routledge Contemporary China Ser.). (ENG.). 240p. (C). 125.00 (978-0-415-67726-4(2)) Routledge.

Miller, Harry. State Versus Gentry in Late Ming Dynasty China, 1572-1644. 2008. (ENG.). 236p. 100.00 (978-0-230-61134-4(6)) Palgrave Macmillan.

Min, Hosik. Son Preference & Fertility in Korea, China & the United States. 2009. 128p. pap. (978-3-639-17640-7(5)) VDM Verlag Dr. Mueller e.K.

Murphy, Rachel. Labour Migration & Social Development in Contemporary China. 2010. (ENG.). pap. 39.95 (978-0-415-59029-7(9)) Routledge.

Naisbitt, John & Naisbitt, Doris. Chinas Megatrends: Die 8 Säulen Einer Neuen Gesellschaft. 2010. 272p. 27.99 (978-0-06-185944-1(3), Collins) HarperCollins Pubs.

Nearing, Scott. Whither China? an Economic Interpretation of Recent Events in the Far East. 2011. 224p. 44.95 (978-1-258-06124-1(0)) Literary Licensing, LLC.

Newham, Mark. Limp Pigs: And the Five-Ring Circus. 2011. (Illus.). 338p. pap. (978-1-78003-049-4(5)) Pen Pr. Pubs., Ltd.

Ng, Maria Noelle. Pilgrimages: Memories of Colonial Macau & Hong Kong. 2009. (ENG., Illus.). 164p. (gr. 17). 25.00 (978-962-209-081-1(8)); pap. 18.00 (978-962-209-208-2(X)) Hong Kong Univ. Pr. HKG. Dist: Columbia Univ. Pr.

Oakes, Tim & Schein, Louisa, eds. Translocal China: Linkages, Identities & the Reimagining of Space. 2006. (Illus.). 240p. 39.95 (978-0-415-37938-0(5)) Routledge.

Ou, Antony. Just War & the Confucian Classics. 2010. 160p. pap. (978-3-639-15790-1(7)) VDM Verlag Dr. Mueller e.K.

Pai, Hsiao-Hung. Scattered Sand: The Story of China's Rural Migrants. 2012. (ENG.). 320p. 26.95 (978-1-84467-886-0(5), 844886) Verso Bks. GBR. Dist: Norton, W. W. & Co., Inc.

Peilin, Li, ed. Chinese Society - Change & Transformation. 2012. (China Policy Ser.). (ENG., Illus.). 320p. (C). 160.00 (978-0-415-50247-4(0)) Routledge.

Perkasa, Vidhyandika Djati. Poverty in a Chinese Community in West Java, Indonesi. 2010. 260p. pap. (978-3-8383-6099-7(0)) Lambert Academic Publishing.

Perry, Elizabeth J. Anyuan: Mining China's Revolutionary Tradition. 2012. (Asia: Local Studies / Global Themes Ser.). (ENG.). 400p. 75.00 (978-0-520-27189-0(0)); pap. 34.95 (978-0-520-27190-6(4)) Univ. of California Pr.

Peterson, E. W. Shanghai Policeman. 2012. (ENG.). 256p. pap. 19.99 (978-988-19983-8-5(7)) Earnshaw Bks. HKG. Dist: Independent Pubs. Group.

Phillips, Jack M. & Moore, Logan J., eds. China: Economics, Political & Social Issues. 2008. (Illus.). xi, 307p. 98.00 (978-1-60456-727-4(9)) Nova Science Pubs., Inc.

Powell, Jason L. China, Aging, & Theory. 2012. pap. (978-1-62100-915-3(7)) Nova Science Pubs., Inc.

Powers, Martin J. Pattern & Person: Ornament, Society, & Self in Classical China. 2006. (Harvard East Asian Monographs: 262). (Illus.). 424p. 49.95 (978-0-674-02139-6(8)) Harvard Univ., Asia Ctr.

Qi, Shouhua. China Complex: U. S.-China Relations in the 21st Century: Crossroads or Collision Course. 2009. (ENG.). 224p. pap. 18.95 (978-1-59265-079-8(1)) Long River Pr.

"Qinglong Manzu Zizhixian gai kuang" bian xie zu Staff & "Qinglong Manzu Zizhixian gai kuang" xiu ding ben bian xie zu Staff, contrib. by. Qinglong Manzu Zizhixian Gai Kuang: Qinglongmanzuzizhixiangaikuang. 2009. (CHI., Illus.). (978-7-105-08672-6(6)) Nationalities Publishing Hse, The.

Rofel, Lisa. Desiring China: Experiments in Neoliberalism, Sexuality, & Public Culture. 2007. (Perverse Modernities Ser.). (ENG.). 264p. 84.95 (978-0-8223-3935-9(8)); per. 23.95 (978-0-8223-3947-2(1)) Duke Univ. Pr.

Roulleau-Berger, Laurence & Li, Peilin. European & Chinese Sociology: A New Dialogue. 2011. (International Comparative Social Studies). (Illus.). 360p. (978-90-04-21174-2(8)) BRILL.

Rozeboom, Annelie. Waiting for the Dalai Lama: Stories from All Sides of the Tibetan Debate. 2011. (ENG.). 212p. pap. 15.95 (978-988-17742-0-0(9)) Blacksmith Bks. HKG. Dist: National Bk. Network.

Rozman, Gilbert. Population & Marketing Settlements in Ch'ing China. 2009. (ENG.). 168p. pap. 26.99 (978-0-521-10704-4(0)) Cambridge Univ. Pr.

Russell, Bertrand. Migration & Social Protection in China. 2008. (Series on Contemporary China). 87.00 (978-981-279-049-1(7)) World Scientific Publishing Co., Inc.

"Sanjiang Dongzu Zizhixian gai kuang" bian xie zu Staff & "Sanjiang Dongzu Zizhixian gai kuang" xiu ding ben bian xie zu Staff, contrib. by. Sanjiang Dongzu Zizhixian Gai Kuang: SanjiangDongzuZizhixiangaikuang. 2008. (CHI., Illus.). (978-7-105-08612-2(2)) Nationalities Publishing Hse, The.

Sargeson, Sally. Women, Gender & Development in Rural China. Jacka, Tamara, ed. 2011. (Illus.). 288p. 135.00 (978-1-84844-682-3(9)) Elgar, Edward Publishing, Inc.

Schaeffer, Kurtis R., et al. Sources of Tibetan Tradition. (Introduction to Asian Civilizations Ser.). 2013. (ENG., Illus.). 832p. (gr. 17). 120.00 (978-0-231-13598-6(X)) 2013. (ENG., Illus.). 832p. (gr. 17). pap. 40.00 (978-0-231-13599-3(8)) 2012. (978-0-231-50978-7(2)) Columbia Univ. Pr.

Schneewind, Sarah. A Tale of Two Melons: Emperor & Subject in Ming China. 2006. 141p. (C). pap. 32.95 (978-0-87220-825-4(7)); (Illus.). pap. 9.95 (978-0-87220-824-7(9)) Hackett Publishing Co., Inc.

Shambaugh, David, ed. Charting China's Future: Domestic & International Challenges. 2011. (ENG., Illus.). 208p. (C). pap. 51.95 (978-0-415-61955-4(6)) Routledge.

Shao, Daosheng. Zhongguo: Zu Ji Fu Bai = China: Anti-Corruption Campaign. 2009. (CHI.). (978-7-5097-1205-4(X)) China Social Science Documentation Publishing Hse.

Shek, Daniel T.L., ed. Quality of Life of Chinese People in a Changing World. 2010. (Social Indicators Research Ser.). (Illus.). vi, 198p. 79.95 (978-94-007-0223-3(X), 940070223X) Springer.

Shue, Vivienne & Wong, Christine, eds. Paying for Progress in China: Public Finance, Human Welfare & Changing Patterns of Inequality. 2008. 39.95 (978-0-415-48779-5(X)) 2007. (Illus.). 195p. 160.00 (978-0-415-42254-3(X)) Routledge.

Siu, Helen F. Merchants' Daughters: Women, Commerce, & Regional Culture in South China. 2010. 388p. (978-988-220-718-9(9)) Hong Kong Univ. Pr.

Siu, Helen F., ed. Merchants' Daughters: Women, Commerce, & Regional Culture in South China. 2010. (ENG.). 388p. (gr. 17). pap. 25.00 (978-988-8083-48-0(1)) Hong Kong Univ. Pr. HKG. Dist: Columbia Univ. Pr.

Sluglett, Peter & Huang, Xiyi. Power, Entitlement & Social Practice: Resource Distribution in North China Village. 2007. (ENG., Illus.). 220p. (gr. 17). 39.00 (978-962-996-315-6(9)) Chinese Univ. of Hong Kong, The HKG. Dist: Columbia Univ. Pr.

Smyer Ya, Dan. The Spread of Tibetan Buddhism in China: Charisma, Money, Enlightenment. 2011. (Routledge Critical Studies in Buddhism Ser.). (ENG.). 240p. (C). 130.00 (978-0-415-57532-4(X)) Routledge.

Song, Guiwu. Peng Zhuang Zhongguo She Hui Jing Ji Wen Ti: Mian Zi, Xue Yuan, Quan Li = Pengzhuang Zhongguoshehui Jingjiwenti. 2010. (CHI., Illus.). (978-7-5017-8787-6(5)) China Economics Publishing Hse.

Song, Yan & Ding, Chengri, eds. Smart Urban Growth for China. 2009. (ENG.). 296p. pap. 30.00 (978-1-55844-183-5(2)) Lincoln Institute of Land Policy.

Storey, Ian. Asean & the Rise of China. 2011. (Routledge Security in Asia Ser.). (ENG., Illus.). 384p. 145.00 (978-0-415-32621-6(4)) Routledge.

Sun, Jiaming. Chinese Globalization: Individual Connections & Social Consequence. 2012. (Routledge Contemporary China Ser.). (ENG.). 256p. (C). 125.00 (978-0-415-67303-7(8)) Routledge.

—Global Connectivity & Local Transformation: A Micro Approach to Studying the Effect of Globalization on Shanghai. 2008. (ENG., Illus.). 164p. per. 31.50 (978-0-7618-4008-4(7)) Univ. Pr. of America, Inc.

Suryadinata, Leo. Ethnic Chinese in Contemporary Indonesia. 2008. (Illus.). 224p. (978-981-230-835-1(0)) Institute of Southeast Asian Studies.

Sutherland, Dylan. Hiv/Aids in China. 2011. (Routledge Contemporary China Ser.). (ENG., Illus.). 184p. (C). 145.00 (978-0-415-41875-1(5)) Routledge.

Sweetman, Arthur & Zhang, Jun. Economic Transitions with Chinese Characteristics Vol. 1: Thirty Years of Reform & Opening Up. 2009. (ENG.). 232p. (C). (978-1-55339-226-2(4)); pap. (978-1-55339-225-5(6)) McGill-Queen's Univ. Pr.

—Economic Transitions with Chinese Characteristics Vol. 2: Social Change During Thirty Years of Reform. 2009. (ENG.). 216p. (C). (978-1-55339-235-4(3)); pap. (978-1-55339-234-7(5)) McGill-Queen's Univ. Pr.

Tan, Chee-Beng. Chinese Transnational Networks. 2009. 214p. pap. 39.95 (978-0-415-56057-3(8)) Routledge.

Tan, Yan. Resettlement in the Three Gorges Project. 2008. (ENG., Illus.). 310p. (gr. 17). 60.00 (978-962-209-856-5(8)) Hong Kong Univ. Pr. HKG. Dist: Columbia Univ. Pr.

Tang, Wenfang & Holzner, Burkart, eds. Social Change in Contemporary China: C. K. Yang & the Concept of Institutional Diffusion. 2006. (Illus.). 336p. 65.00 (978-0-8229-4297-9(6)); per. 26.95 (978-0-8229-5933-5(X)) Univ. of Pittsburgh Pr.

Templeman, David, ed. New views of Tibetan Culture. 2010. 196p. pap. 32.95 (978-1-876924-77-5(2), Monash Univ. Pr.) Monash Univ. Publishing AUS. Dist: International Specialized Bk. Services.

Tézenas, Ambroise, photos by. Beijing: Theatre of the People. 2007. (ENG., Illus.). 120p. 45.00 (978-1-904587-36-1(4)) Lewis, Dewi Publishing GBR. Dist: Consortium Bk. Sales & Distribution.

Thayer, Tobias. Cross-Cultural Management & Retention Management in Chin. 2010. 104p. pap. (978-3-639-27182-9(3)) VDM Verlag Dr. Mueller e.K.

"Tianzhu Zangzu Zizhixian gai kuang" bian xie zu Staff & "Tianzhu Zangzu Zizhixian gai kuang" xiu ding ben bian xie zu Staff, contrib. by. Tianzhu Zangzu Zizhixian Gai Kuang: TianzhuZangzuZizhixiangaikuang. 2009. (CHI., Illus.). (978-7-105-08624-5(6)) Nationalities Publishing Hse, The.

Toda, Ikuko. Chugoku Chosenzoku o Ikiru: Kyu Manshu No Kioku. (JPN., Illus.). xiii, 296p. (978-4-00-023870-0(1), Nicholson) Iwanami Shoten.

Tong, Yanqi & Lei, Shaohua. Social Protest in Contemporary China. 2012. (China Policy Ser.). (ENG.). 192p. (C). 130.00 (978-0-415-60569-4(5)) Routledge.

"Tongdao Dongzu Zizhixian gai kuang" bian xie zu Staff & "Tongdao Dongzu Zizhixian" xiu ding ben bian xie zu Staff, contrib. by. Tongdao Dongzu Zizhixian Gai Kuang: TongdaoDongzuZizhixiangaikuang. 2008. (CHI., Illus.). (978-7-105-08608-5(4)) Nationalities Publishing Hse, The.

Trouw, Jan. The Three Gorges Dam's Impact on Peasant Livelihood: China's Project on the Yangtze River. 2007. (Illus.). 130p. 16.90 (978-3-8334-8133-8(1)) Bks. on Demand.

Truong, Thuy-Huong & King, Brian, eds. Tourism Service Experiences in Vietnam. 2010. (Tourism & Hospitality Development & Management Ser.). 69p. pap. 43.00 (978-1-61728-034-4(8), Nova Novinka) Nova Science Pubs., Inc.

Tsai, Weipin. Reading Shenbao: Nationalism, Consumerism & Individuality in China 1919-37. 2010. (ENG., Illus.). 256p. 89.00 (978-0-230-01982-9(X)) Palgrave Macmillan.

Tsuen-hsuin, Tsien. Collected Writings on Chinese Culture. 2011. (ENG., Illus.). 430p. (gr. 17). 55.00 (978-962-996-422-1(8)) Chinese Univ. of Hong Kong, The HKG. Dist: Columbia Univ. Pr.

Tubilewicz, Czeslaw. Criticial Issues in Contemporary China. 2006. (ENG., Illus.). 288p. (C). 180.00 (978-0-415-39584-7(4)); per. 43.95 (978-0-415-39585-4(2)) Routledge.

Tuck, Robert J. Ethics of Chinese & Australian Business Managers: A Comparative Investigation about Corruption. 2011. (Ethical Issues in the 21st Century Ser.). (Illus.). 690p. 125.00 (978-1-61668-193-7(4)) Nova Science Pubs., Inc.

Unger, Jonathan, ed. Associations & the Chinese State: Contested Spaces. 2008. (ENG.). 288p. 93.95 (978-0-7656-1325-7(5), East Gate Bk.) Sharpe, M.E. Inc.

Urio, Paolo. Reconciling State Market & Civil Society in China: The Long March Towards Prosperity. 2010. (Routledge Contemporary China Ser.). (ENG., Illus.). 304p. (C). 135.00 (978-0-415-56446-5(8)) Routledge.

Van Luyn, Floris-Jan. A Floating City of Peasants: The Great Migration in Contemporary China. Ringold, Jeannette K., tr. from DUT. 2008. (ENG., Illus.). 219p. 35.00 (978-1-59558-138-9(3)) New Pr., The.

Van Ziegert, Sylvia. Global Spaces of Chinese Culture: Diasporic Chinese Communities in the United States & Germany. 2009. 232p. 39.95 (978-0-415-80578-0(3)) Routledge.

Vermeer, Eduard B. & Ho, Peter, eds. China's Limits to Growth: Greening State & Society. 2006. (Development & Change Special Issues Ser.). (ENG., Illus.). 288p. per. 39.95 (978-1-4051-5390-4(3), Wiley-Blackwell) Wiley, John & Sons, Inc.

Vernezze, Peter J. Socrates in Sichuan: Chinese Students Search for Truth, Justice, & the (Chinese) Way. 2011. 212p. 26.95 (978-1-59797-672-5(5)) Potomac Bks., Inc.

Vitiello, Giovanni. The Libertine's Friend: Homosexuality & Masculinity in Late Imperial China. 2011. (ENG., Illus.). 312p. 45.00 (978-0-226-85792-3(1)) Univ. of Chicago Pr.

Wang, Mei-Ling, et al. WTO, Globalization, & China's Health Care System. 2007. (ENG.). 384p. 137.00 (978-1-4039-4326-2(5)) Palgrave Macmillan.

Wang, Mingming. Empire & Local Worlds: A Chinese Model for Long-Term Historical Anthropology. 2009. (Critical Cultural Heritage Series, University College London Institute of Archaeology Publications). (ENG., Illus.). 344p. pap. 36.95 (978-1-59874-405-7(4)); lib. bdg. 89.00 (978-1-59874-404-0(6)) Left Coast Pr., Inc.

Wang, Yina. Understanding of Career & Attitudes Toward Career Counselling. 2010. 120p. pap. (978-3-639-23776-4(5)) VDM Verlag Dr. Mueller e.K.

Weng, Xiaoping & Caballero, Benjamin. Obesity & Its Related Diseases in China: Impact of the Nutrition Transition in Urban & Rural Adults. 2007. (ENG.). 144p. (C). 89.95 (978-1-934043-54-7(0)) Cambria Pr.

Weston, Timothy B. & Jensen, Lionel M. China in & Beyond the Headlines. 2011. (978-1-4422-0906-0(2)) Rowman & Littlefield Publishers, Inc.

Whyte, Martin King. Myth of the Social Volcano: Perceptions of Inequality & Distributive Injustice in Contemporary China. 2010. (ENG., Illus.). 264p. 80.00 (978-0-8047-6941-9(9)); pap. 27.95 (978-0-8047-6942-6(7)) Stanford Univ. Pr.

Wilson, Scott Howard. Remade in China: Foreign Investors & Institutional Change in China. 2009. (ENG., Illus.). 304p. 65.00 (978-0-19-538831-2(3)) Oxford Univ. Pr., Inc.

Winnington, Alan. The Slaves of the Cool Mountains: Travels among Head-Hunters & Slave-Owners. 2008. (Illus.). 212p. pap. 17.95 (978-1-897959-58-9(3)) Serif GBR. Dist: Interlink Publishing Group, Inc.

Wong, Sam. Exploring 'Unseen' Social Capital in Community Participation: Everyday Lives of Poor Mainland Chinese Migrants in Hong Kong. 2008. (ICAS Publications Ser.). (Illus.). 220p. per. (978-90-5356-034-1(3), Leiden Univ. Pr.) Amsterdam Univ. Pr.

Wong, Sin Kiong. Confucianism, Chinese History & Society. 2012. 300p. pap. 48.00 (978-981-4374-47-7(4)) World Scientific Publishing Co., Inc.

Wood, Frances. No Dogs & Not Many Chinese. (Illus.). xii, 368p. 50.00 (978-0-7195-5758-3(5)) Murray, John GBR. Dist: Trafalgar Square Publishing.

World Bank Staff, contrib. by. Reducing Inequality for Shared Growth in China: Strategy & Policy Options for Guangdong Province. 2010. (Directions in Development Ser.). (ENG.). 392p. pap. 35.00 (978-0-8213-8484-8(8), 9780821384848); (978-0-8213-8501-2(1)) World Bank Pubns.

Wu, Bin, et al, eds. China's Development & Harmonization: Towards a balance with nature, society & the international Community. 2012. (Routledge Studies on the Chinese Economy Ser.). (ENG.). 320p. (C). 155.00 (978-0-415-66567-4(1)) Routledge.

Wu, Fei. Suicide & Justice: A Chinese Perspective. 2009. (Routledge Contemporary China Ser.). (ENG., Illus.). 216p. 145.00 (978-0-415-55171-7(4)) Routledge.

Wu, Fulong. Marginalization in Urban China: Comparative Perspectives. Webster, C. J., ed. 2010. (International Political Economy Ser.). (ENG., Illus.). 336p. 95.00 (978-0-230-23772-8(X)) Palgrave Macmillan.

Wu, Guoguang. Socialist China, Capitalist China: Social Tension & Political Transition under Economic Globalisation. Wu, Guoguang & Lansdowne, Helen, eds. 2009. (China Policy Ser.). (ENG., Illus.). 240p. 160.00 (978-0-415-48226-4(7)) Routledge.

Wu, Xu. Farming, Cooking, & Eating Practices in the Central China Highland: How Hezha Foods Function to Establish Ethnic Identity. 2011. (ENG., Illus.). 400p. 129.95 (978-0-7734-1373-3(1)) Mellen, Edwin Pr., The.

Xi, Juan. Age Differentials in Anticipation of Involuntary Migration- the Psychological Stress & the Three Gorges Dam Project, China. 2007. 152p. per. (978-3-8364-1730-3(8)) VDM Verlag Dr. Mueller e.K.

Xin, Ru, et al, eds. The China Society Yearbook: China's Social Development; Analysis & Forecast. 2007. (Chinese Academy of Social Sciences Yearbooks: Society Ser.). (Illus.). 343p. (978-90-04-15637-1(2)) BRILL.

"Xinbin Manzu Zizhixian gai kuang" bian xie zu Staff & "Xinbin Manzu Zizhixian gai kuang" xiu ding ben bian xie zu Staff, contrib. by. Xinbin Manzu Zizhixian Gai Kuang: XinbinManzuZizhixiangaikuang. 2009. (CHI., Illus.). (978-7-105-08661-0(0)) Nationalities Publishing Hse, The.

Xu, Jiyuan. Chinesische Soziokultur als Grundlage der Personalfuhrung. (GER., Illus.). 371p. pap. 68.95 (978-3-631-56830-9(4)) Lang, Peter GmbH, Europaeischer Verlag der Wissenschaften DEU. Dist: Lang, Peter Publishing, Inc.

Yaghmaian, Behzad. The Accidental Capitalist: A People's Story of the New China, 1 vol. 2012. (ENG., Illus.). 256p. 29.00 **(978-0-7453-3230-7(7))**; lib. bdg. 99.00 **(978-0-7453-3231-4(5))** Pluto Pr. GBR. Dist: Macmillan.

Yan, Chunmei. Enhancing Prospects of Longer-Term Sustainability of Cross-Cultural INSET Initiatives in China. 2009. (Education in a Competitive & Globalizing World Ser.). 89.00 (978-1-60741-615-9(8)) Nova Science Pubs., Inc.

Yan, Hairong. New Masters, New Servants: Migration, Development, & Women Workers in China. 2008. (ENG., Illus.). 328p. pap. 24.95 (978-0-8223-4304-2(5)) Duke Univ. Pr.

—New Masters, New Servants: Migration, Development, & Women Workers in China. 2008. (ENG., Illus.). 328p. 89.95 (978-0-8223-4287-8(1)) Duke Univ. Pr.

Yan, Lijing L. Height, Health, & Hazards. 2010. 204p. pap. (978-3-8383-1483-9(2)) Lambert Academic Publishing.

Yan, Yunxiang. The Individualization of Chinese Society. 2009. (London School of Economics Monographs on Social Anthropology Ser.). (ENG., Illus.). 1p. 99.95 (978-1-84788-379-7(6)); 288p. pap. 34.95 (978-1-84788-378-0(8)) Berg Pubs. GBR. Dist: Macmillan.

"Yanbian Chaoxianzu Zizhizhou gai kuang" bian xie zu Staff & "Yanbian Chaoxianzu Zizhizhou gai kuang" xiu ding ben bian xie zu Staff, contrib. by. Yanbian Chaoxianzu Zizhizhou Gai Kuang: YanbianChaoxianzuZizhizhougaikuang. 2009. (CHI., Illus.). (978-7-105-08642-9(4)) Nationalities Publishing Hse, The.

Yang, C. K. The Chinese Family in the Communist Revolution. 2011. 256p. 47.95 **(978-1-258-10544-0(5))** Literary Licensing, LLC.

Yang, Dali L., ed. Discontented Miracle: Growth, Conflict, & Institutional Adaptations in China. 2007. (Ser. on Contemporary China ndash; Vol. 10 Ser.). (Illus.). 311p. 113.00 (978-981-270-354-5(3)) World Scientific Publishing Co., Inc.

Yang, Jisheng. Tombstone: The Great Chinese Famine, 1958-1962, 1 vol. Mosher, Stacy & Guo, Jian, trs. from CHI. 2012. (ENG., Illus.). 752p. 35.00 **(978-0-374-27793-2(1))** Farrar, Straus & Giroux.

Yao, Shujie, et al. Sustainable Reform & Development in Post-Olympic China. 2010. (Routledge Studies on the Chinese Economy Ser.). (ENG., Illus.). 240p. 140.00 (978-0-415-55956-0(1), Routledge) Taylor & Francis Group GBR. Dist: Taylor & Francis Group.

Yeung, Y. M. & Jianfa, Shen. The Pan-Pearl River Delta: An Emerging Regional Economy in a Globalizing China. 2008. (ENG.). 640p. (gr. 17). 59.00 (978-962-996-376-7(0)) Chinese Univ. of Hong Kong, The HKG. Dist: Columbia Univ. Pr.

Yip, Lin. Cultural Exclusion in China: State Education, Social Mobility & Cultural Difference. 2008. (Comparative Development & Policy in Asia Ser.). (ENG., Illus.). 192p. (C). 158.00 (978-0-415-45761-3(0)) Routledge.

Yiwu, Liao. The Corpse Walker: Real Life Stories: China from the Bottom Up. 2009. (ENG.). 352p. pap. 15.95 (978-0-307-38837-7(9), Anchor) Knopf Doubleday Publishing Group.

Yochim, Lorn. A Vocation of the Heart. 2008. 164p. pap. (978-3-639-05511-5(X)) VDM Verlag Dr. Mueller e.K.

Yu, Haiqing. Media & Cultural Transformation in China. (ENG., Illus.). 228p. 2011. pap. 42.95 **(978-0-415-67371-6(2))** 2009. 160.00 (978-0-415-44755-3(0)) Routledge.

Yu, Jianxing & Guo, Sujian, eds. Civil Society & Governance in China. 2012. (ENG., Illus.). 254p. 85.00 **(978-0-230-34096-1(2))** Palgrave Macmillan.

Yu, Jianxing, et al. A Path for Chinese Civil Society: A Case Study on Industrial Associations in Wenzhou, China. 2012. (Challenges Facing Chinese Political Development Ser.). (ENG., Illus.). 222p. (gr. 17). 65.00 **(978-0-7391-7007-6(4))** Lexington Bks.

Zamperini, Paola. Lost Bodies: Prostitution & Masculinity in Chinese Fiction. 2010. 250p. (978-90-04-17978-3(X)) BRILL.

Zang, Xiaowei. Ethnicity & Urban Life in China: A Comparative Study of Hui Muslims & Han Chinese. 2011. (ENG., Illus.). 208p. pap. 42.95 **(978-0-415-66643-5(0))** Routledge.

Zang, Xiaowei, ed. Understanding Chinese Society. 2011. (ENG., Illus.). 208p. (C). 140.00 (978-0-415-61988-2(2)); pap. 42.95 (978-0-415-61989-9(0)) Routledge.

Zeng, Yi, et al, eds. Healthy Longevity in China: Demographic, Socioeconomic, & Psychological Dimensions. 2009. (Springer Series on Demographic Methods & Population Analysis Ser.). xvi, 435p. pap. 79.95 (978-1-4020-9478-1(7), 1402094787) Springer.

Zha, Jianying. Tide Players: The Movers & Shakers of a Rising China. 2011. (ENG.). 224p. 24.95 (978-1-59558-620-9(2)) New Pr., The.

Zhang, Everett, et al, eds. Governance of Life in Chinese Moral Experience: The Quest for an Adequate Life. 2011. (ENG., Illus.). 296p. (C). 155.00 (978-0-415-59718-0(8)); pap. 54.95 (978-0-415-59719-7(6)) Routledge.

Zhang, Jianjun. Marketization & Democracy in China. 2008. (Routledge Studies on China in Transition Ser.). (Illus.). 304p. 170.00 (978-0-415-45222-9(8)) Routledge.

Zhang, Li & Ong, Aihwa, eds. Privatizing China: Socialism from Afar. 2008. (Illus.). 296p. 75.50 (978-0-8014-4596-5(5)); 282p. per. 22.95 (978-0-8014-7378-4(0)) Cornell Univ. Pr.

Zhao, Wen & Carolyn Pope Edwards, /. Chinese Teachers in Transformation. 2010. 320p. pap. (978-3-8383-0179-2(X)) Lambert Academic Publishing.

Zheng, Tiantian. Ethnographies of Prostitution in Contemporary China: Gender Relations, HIV/AIDS, & Nationalism. (ENG., 256p. 2012. Illus.). pap. 28.00 **(978-0-230-34099-2(7))** 2009. 89.00 (978-0-230-61741-4(7)) Palgrave Macmillan.

Zheng, Tiantian. Red Lights: The Lives of Sex Workers in Postsocialist China. 2009. (ENG.). 304p. pap. 22.50 (978-0-8166-5903-6(6)) Univ. of Minnesota Pr.

Zheng, Victor. Chinese Family Business & the Equal Inheritance System. 2010. (Routledge Contemporary China Ser.). (ENG., Illus.). 224p. (C). 135.00 (978-0-415-55638-5(4)) Routledge.

Zhou, Jinghao. China's Peaceful Rise in a Global Context: A Domestic Aspect of China's Road Map to Democratization. 2010. (ENG.). 232p. 68.50 (978-0-7391-3337-8(3)) Lexington Bks.

Zhou, Xueguang. The State & Life Chances in Urban China: Redistribution & Stratification, 1949-1994. 2010. (ENG.). 400p. pap. 36.99 (978-0-521-15384-3(0)) Cambridge Univ. Pr.

Zu, Liangrong. Corporate Social Responsibility, Corporate Restructuring & Firm's Performance: Empirical Evidence from Chinese Enterprises. 2010. (ENG., Illus.). xx, 308p. pap. 139.00 (978-3-642-08988-6(7), 3642089887) Springer.

CHINA—SOCIAL CONDITIONS—1949-

Bardhan, Pranab K. Awakening Giants, Feet of Clay: Assessing the Economic Rise of China & India. 2010. (ENG., Illus.). 192p. (C). 25.95 (978-0-691-12994-5(0)) Princeton Univ. Pr.

Bell, Daniel A. China's New Confucianism: Politics & Everyday Life in a Changing Society. 2010. (ENG.). 280p. (C). pap. 19.95 (978-0-691-14585-3(7)) Princeton Univ. Pr.

Benewick, Robert, et al. The State of China Atlas: Mapping the World's Fastest-Growing Economy. 2nd rev. ed. 2009. (ENG., Illus.). 128p. pap. 19.95 (978-0-520-25610-1(7)) Univ. of California Pr.

Bo, Zhiyue & Wong, John. China's Reform in Global Perspective. 2010. (Illus.). 400p. 96.00 (978-981-4289-24-5(8)) World Scientific Publishing Co., Inc.

Chan, Lai-Ha. China At 60: Global-Local Interactions. 2011. 352p. 98.00 (978-981-4299-29-9(4)) World Scientific Publishing Co., Inc.

Chen, Da. Colors of the Mountain. pap. (978-0-385-72864-5(6)) Knopf Doubleday Publishing Group.

Chen, Yu. Zhongguo Sheng Huo Ji Yi: Jian Guo 60 Nian Min Sheng Wang Shi. 2009. (CHI., Illus.). 347p. pap. (978-7-5019-7054-4(8)) China Light Industry Pr.

Clegg. China & the Reshaping of the World Order. 2009. (ENG.). 288p. 100.00 (978-0-7453-2519-4(X)) Pluto Pr. GBR. Dist: Macmillan.

Croll, Elisabeth. The Politics of Marriage in Contemporary China. 2010. (ENG.). 228p. pap. 32.99 (978-0-521-13068-4(9)) Cambridge Univ. Pr.

Diamant, Neil J. Embattled Glory: Veterans, Military Families, & the Politics of Patriotism in China, 1949-2007. (State & Society East Asia Ser.). (ENG.). 480p. 2010. pap. 37.50 (978-0-7425-5767-3(7)) 2009. 90.00 (978-0-7425-5766-6(9)) Rowman & Littlefield Publishers, Inc.

Fewsmith, Joseph. China Today, China Tomorrow: Domestic Politics, Economy, & Society. 2010. (Illus.). (ENG.). 344p. 89.00 (978-0-7425-6706-1(0)); (ENG., 344p. pap. 34.95 (978-0-7425-6707-8(9)); ix, 334p. (978-0-7425-6708-5(7)) Rowman & Littlefield Publishers, Inc.

Gommans, Jos & Zurndorfer, Harlet, eds. Roots & Routes of Development in China & India: Highlights of Fifty Years of the Journal of the Economic & Social History of the Orient (1957-2007) 2008. xl, 456p. (978-90-04-17060-5(X)) BRILL.

Greenhalgh, Susan. Cultivating Global Citizens: Population in the Rise of China. 2010. (Edwin O. Reischauer Lectures: 2008). (ENG., Illus.). 156p. 29.95 (978-0-674-05571-1(3)) Harvard Univ. Pr.

Gries, Peter & Rosen, Stanley, eds. Chinese Politics: State, Society & the Market. 2010. (Asia's Transformations Ser.). (ENG., Illus.). 304p. (C). 44.95 (978-0-415-56403-8(4)); 153.00 (978-0-415-56402-1(6)) Routledge.

Guthrie, Doug. China & Globalization. 3rd rev. ed. 2012. (ENG., Illus.). 360p. 130.00 **(978-0-415-50400-3(7))** Routledge.

—China & Globalization: The Social, Economic & Political Transformation of Chinese Society. 3rd rev. ed. 2012. (ENG., Illus.). 360p. pap. 39.95 **(978-0-415-50401-0(5))** Routledge.

Hanser, Amy. Service Encounters: Class, Gender, & the Market for Social Distinction in Urban China. 2008. (ENG., Illus.). 256p. 55.00 (978-0-8047-5836-9(0)); per. 21.95 (978-0-8047-5837-6(9)) Stanford Univ. Pr.

He, Xiongfei. Xin Yang Yu Wei Ji: Youtai Si Xiang He Zhongguo Wen Ti. 2010. (CHI., Illus.). (978-7-80178-694-4(7)) Hua Ling Pr.

Heberer, Thomas & Schubert, Gunter, eds. Regime Legitimacy in Contemporary China. 2009. 306p. pap. 39.95 (978-0-415-57430-3(7)) Routledge.

Herberer, Thomas, et al. Regime Legitimacy in Contemporary China: Institutional Change & Stability. Schubert, Gunter, ed. 2008. (Routledge Contemporary China Ser.). (ENG., Illus.). 320p. (C). 150.00 (978-0-415-46664-6(4)) Routledge.

Herold, David & Wolfgang Marolt, Peter, eds. Online Society in China: Creating, Celebrating, & Instrumentalising the Online Carnival. 2011. (Media, Culture & Social Change in Asia Ser.). (ENG.). 240p. (C). 145.00 (978-0-415-56539-4(1)) Routledge.

Hinton, William & Magdoff, Fred. Fanshen: A Documentary of Revolution in a Chinese Village. 2008. (ENG., Illus.). 672p. pap. 28.95 (978-1-58367-175-7(7)) Monthly Review Pr.

Ho, Wing-Chung. The Transition Study of Postsocialist China: An Ethnographic Study of a Model Community. 2010. (Illus.). 284p. 77.00 (978-981-4307-62-8(9)) World Scientific Publishing Co., Inc.

Hsing, You-tien. The Great Urban Transformation: Politics of Land & Property in China. 2010. (ENG., Illus.). 256p. 80.00 (978-0-19-956804-8(9)) Oxford Univ. Pr., Inc.

Hui, Wang. The End of the Revolution: China & the Limits of Modernity. 2011. (ENG.). 272p. pap. 22.95 (978-1-84467-379-7(0), 844379) Verso Bks. GBR. Dist: Norton, W. W. & Co., Inc.

Jensen, Lionel M. & Weston, Timothy B. China's Transformations: The Stories Beyond the Headlines. 2006. (ENG., Illus.). 378p. 97.00 (978-0-7425-3862-7(1)); per. 34.95 (978-0-7425-3863-4(X)) Rowman & Littlefield Publishers, Inc.

Johnson, Yanling L. Love Stories of Three Kinds: Finding Love, Faith, & Freedom in an Authoritarian Society, 1 vol. 2009. 404p. pap. 29.95 (978-1-60749-556-7(2)) PublishAmerica, Inc.

LaFleur, Robert André. China, 1 vol. 2009. (Asia in Focus Ser.). (Illus.). 504p. 85.00 (978-1-59884-166-4(1), CHINAS1C) ABC-CLIO, LLC.

Lai, Qingxiu. Zhongnan Hai Shi Mian Mai Fu: Hu Wen Mian Lin de Kun Nan, Fen Qi He Qian Zai Chong Tu. 2nd ed. 2009. (CHI., Illus.). 445p. pap. (978-1-932138-87-0(0)) Mirror Bks. USA.

Larus, Elizabeth Freund. Politics & Society in Contemporary China. 2012. (C). 275p. pap. 32.50 **(978-1-58826-825-9(X))**; (Illus.). 75.00 **(978-1-58826-800-6(4))** Rienner, Lynne Pubs.

Lee, Grace O. M. & Warner, Malcolm, eds. Unemployment in China: Economy, Human Resources & Labour Markets. 2012. (Routledge Contemporary China Ser.). (ENG., Illus.). 288p. (C). pap. 44.95 **(978-0-415-51159-9(3))** Routledge.

Lemos, Gerard. The End of the Chinese Dream: Why Chinese People Fear the Future. 2012. (ENG., Illus.). 352p. 38.00 (978-0-300-16924-9(6)) Yale Univ. Pr.

Li, Qiang. Thirty Years of Reform & Social Changes in China. 2010. (Illus.). 514p. (978-90-04-18716-0(2)) BRILL.

Liu, Heung Shing, ed. China: 25 Jahre TASCHEN. 2011. (25 Ser.). (ENG., Illus.). 424p. 29.99 **(978-3-8365-3089-7(9))** TASCHEN DEU. Dist: Ingram Pub. Services.

Liu, Tiansheng. Zhong Gong Zheng Zai Shu Diao de Zhan Zheng: Wang Luo Gai Bian Zhongguo. 2010. ("Zhongguo Ju Shi" Xi Lie Ser.: Vol. 62). (CHI., Illus.). 284p. pap. (978-962-8744-29-9(1)) Mirror Bks. USA.

Long, Norman, et al, eds. Rural Transformations & Development in China: Policy Interventions for the 21st Century. 2010. (Illus.). 408p. 139.00 (978-1-84980-093-8(6)) Elgar, Edward Publishing, Inc.

Lu, Tonglin. Confronting Modernity in the Cinemas of Taiwan & Mainland China. 2007. (ENG., Illus.). 260p. pap. 58.00 (978-0-521-03727-3(1)) Cambridge Univ. Pr.

Lu, Xueyi. Social Structure of Contemporary China. 2012. 330p. 114.00 **(978-981-4383-22-6(8))** World Scientific Publishing Co., Inc.

Mendes, Errol P. & Srighanthan, Sakunthala, eds. Confronting Discrimination & Inequality in China: Chinese & Canadian Perspectives. 2009. (ENG., Illus.). 438p. (gr. 10-12). pap. (978-0-7766-0709-2(X)) Univ. of Ottawa Pr./Presses de l'Universite d'Ottawa.

Mexico, Zachary. China Underground. 2009. (ENG.). 320p. pap. 16.95 (978-1-59376-223-0(2), Soft Skull Pr.) Counterpoint LLC.

Murphy, Rachel. Labour Migration & Social Development in Contemporary China. 2008. (Comparative Development & Policy in Asia Ser.). (Illus.). XIV, 210p. 160.00 (978-0-415-46801-5(9)) Routledge.

Naughton, Barry. Holding China Together: Diversity & National Integration in the Post-Deng ERA. Yang, Dali L., ed. 2010. (ENG.). 318p. pap. 39.99 (978-0-521-16858-8(9)) Cambridge Univ. Pr.

Ngo, Tak-Wing, ed. Contemporary China Studies 2: Economy & Society, 8 vols. 2011. (Illus.). 1624p. 995.00 **(978-1-4129-4883-8(5)**, B48838C) SAGE Pubns., Ltd. GBR. Dist: SAGE Pubns., Inc.

Ouyang, Quan & Bai, Xiaoyun. Hu Wen Zhi Jian: Da Jia Sao Huang Shui Shi Zui Hou Ying Jia. 2007. ("Zhongguo Ju Shi" Xi Lie Ser.: Vol. 45). (CHI., Illus.). 421p. (978-1-932138-58-0(7)) Mirror Bks. USA.

Pan, Philip P. Out of Mao's Shadow: The Struggle for the Soul of a New China. 2009. (ENG., Illus.). 368p. pap. 16.00 (978-1-4165-3706-9(6)) Simon & Schuster.

Perry, Elizabeth J. & Selden, Mark, eds. Chinese Society: Change, Conflict & Resistance. 3rd rev. ed. 2010. (Asia's Transformations Ser.). (ENG., Illus.). 344p. (C). 49.95 (978-0-415-56074-0(8)) Routledge.

—Chinese Society: Change, Conflict & Resistance. 3rd ed. 2010. (Asia's Transformations Ser.). (ENG., Illus.). 344p. (C). (978-0-415-56073-3(X), Routledge) Taylor & Francis Group.

Philippi, Simone & Shing, Liu Heung, eds. China, Portrait of a Country. 2008. (FRE, GER & ENG., Illus.). 423p. 59.99 (978-3-8365-0569-7(X)) TASCHEN DEU. Dist: Ingram Pub. Services.

Rein, Shaun. The End of Cheap China: Economic & Cultural Trends That Will Disrupt the World. 2012. (ENG.). 240p. 24.95 **(978-1-118-17206-3(X)**, Wiley) Wiley, John & Sons, Inc.

Ren, Hai. The Middle Class in Neoliberal China. 2012. (Routledge Contemporary China Ser.). (ENG.). 192p. (C). 125.00 **(978-0-415-50135-4(0))** Routledge.

Sanders, Richard & Yang, Chen, eds. China's Post-Reform Economy - Achieving Harmony, Sustaining Growth. 2012. (Routledge Studies on the Chinese Economy Ser.). (ENG., Illus.). 272p. (C). pap. 42.95 **(978-0-415-54261-6(8))** Routledge.

Schiere, Richard. China's Development Challenges: Economic Vulnerability & Public Sector Reform. 2012. (ENG., Illus.). 176p. (C). pap. 44.95 **(978-0-415-62494-7(0))** Routledge.

Seibert, Andreas. From Somewhere to Nowhere: China's Internal Migrants. 2008. (Illus.). 316p. 54.95 (978-3-03778-146-3(7), 3037781467) Springer.

Shambaugh, David, ed. Charting China's Future: Domestic & International Challenges. 2011. (ENG., Illus.). 208p. (C). 150.00 (978-0-415-61954-7(8)) Routledge.

Song, Yan & Ding, Chengri, eds. Urbanization in China: Critical Issues in an Era of Rapid Growth. 2007. (ENG.). 320p. pap. 30.00 (978-1-55844-175-0(1)) Lincoln Institute of Land Policy.

Sorman, Guy. The Empire of Lies: The Truth about China in the Twenty-First Century. Puri, Asha, tr. 2008. (ENG., Illus.). 325p. 25.95 (978-1-59403-216-5(5)) Encounter Bks.

—Empire of Lies: The Truth about China in the Twenty-First Century. 2010. (ENG.). 280p. pap. 15.95 (978-1-59403-263-9(7)) Encounter Bks.

Sun. Maid in China. 2008. (Routledge Studies in Asia's Transformations Ser.). (Illus.). 240p. 160.00 (978-0-415-39210-5(1)) Routledge.

Tao, Kang & Haiyan, Huang. What's Cool in China. 2007. 138p. pap. 14.95 (978-7-119-05163-5(6)) Beijing, Foreign Languages Press CHN. Dist: China Bks. & Periodicals, Inc.

Weston, Timothy B. China in & Beyond the Headlines. 3rd ed. 2012. (ENG.). 384p. pap. 35.00 **(978-1-4422-0905-3(4))** Rowman & Littlefield Publishers, Inc.

Weston, Timothy B. & Jensen, Lionel M., eds. China in & Beyond the Headlines. 3rd ed. 2012. (ENG.). 384p. 99.00 **(978-1-4422-0904-6(6))** Rowman & Littlefield Publishers, Inc.

Whyte, Martin King, ed. One Country, Two Societies: Rural-Urban Inequality in Contemporary China. 2010. (Harvard Contemporary China Ser.: 16). (Illus.). 460p. pap. 29.50 (978-0-674-03632-1(8)) Harvard Univ. Pr.

Wuwei, Li. How Creativity Is Changing China. 2011. (ENG., Illus.). 160p. 75.00 (978-1-84966-619-0(9)); pap. 25.95 (978-1-84966-616-9(4)) Bloomsbury Publishing.

Yu, Jie. Bu Yao Zuo Zhong Guo Ren de Hai Zi. 2008. (CHI.). 349p. pap. 18.00 (978-1-931550-22-2(0)) Laogai Research Foundation, The.

Zhang, Jianjun. Marketization & Democracy in China. 2009. 278p. pap. 39.95 (978-0-415-57428-0(5)) Routledge.

Zhang, Shifei & Tang, Jun. Zhongguo She Hui Zheng Ce Yan Jiu Shi Nian: Zhuan Ti Bao Gao Ji, 1999-2008: Zhongguo She Hui Jiu Zhu Ti Xi de Shi Jian Yu Tan Suo = Chinese Social Policy Studies 1999-2008, Special Topic Reports: Practice & Exploration on Construction of Social Assistance System in China. 2010. (CHI., Illus.). (978-7-5097-1213-9(0)) China Social Science Documentation Publishing Hse.

Zhang, Xin. Social Transformation in Modern China: The State & Local Elites in Henan, 1900-1937. 2006. (Cambridge Modern China Ser.). (ENG., Illus.). 340p. pap. 48.00 (978-0-521-02755-7(1)) Cambridge Univ. Pr.

Zheng, Yongnian. Zhongguo Mo Shi: Jing Yan Yu Kun Ju. 2010. (CHI., Illus.). (978-7-213-04190-7(8)) Zhejiang People's Publishing Hse.

CHINA—SOCIAL LIFE AND CUSTOMS

Abraham, Wendy. Chinese Phrasebook & Culture Guide. 2008. 336p. pap. 9.99 (978-0-470-22857-9(1)) Wiley, John & Sons, Inc.

Achten, Peter & Zhou, Tiehai. Brief aus Guo Mao: Kolumnen aus Asien. 2009. (GER., Illus.). 312p. (978-3-7245-1614-9(2)) Reinhardt, Friedrich AG.

Ai, Jiabing. Guan Er Dai. 2011. (CHI., Illus.). 316p. **(978-1-935981-23-7(4))** Mirror Bks. USA.

Archibald, Alicia E. Neva. In the Land of the Blue Gown. 2010. (Cambridge Library Collection - Travel & Exploration Ser.). (ENG.). 396p. pap. 31.99 (978-1-108-01386-4(4)) Cambridge Univ. Pr.

Arrington, Aminta, ed. Saving Grandmother's Face: And Other Tales from Christian Teachers in China. 2010. 128p. pap. 16.00 (978-1-60899-043-6(5), Resource Pubns.) Wipf & Stock Pubs.

Ashraf, Lubna & Syed, M. N. Wedding Cry ~ Death Dance: An Insight into Chinese Culture: an Ethnographic Study of Xuan'en, Hubei with Special Emphasis on Tujia Rites of Passage. 2008. (ENG.). 252p. pap. 39.50 (978-0-9801675-8-0(2)) Robertson Publishing.

Ayres, Gene. A Billion To: An American Insider in the New China. Strozier, M. Stefan & Torke, Kyle, eds. 2009. 264p. pap. 20.00 (978-1-935444-06-0(9)) World Audience Pubs.

—Inside the New China: An Ethnographic Memoir. 2010. (ENG.). 260p. pap. 29.95 (978-1-4128-1350-1(6)) Transaction Pubs.

Ayscough, Florence. The Autobiography of a Chinese Dog. 2011. 148p. 40.95 **(978-1-258-04430-5(7))** Literary Licensing, LLC.

Bai, Gengsheng. Bai Gengsheng Naxi Xue Lun Ji: BaiGengshengNaxixuelunji. 2008. (CHI.). (978-7-105-08466-1(9)) Nationalities Publishing Hse, The.

Baozhen, Luo. Shopping Cultures. 2007. 140p. per. (978-3-8364-3618-2(3)) VDM Verlag Dr. Mueller e.K.

Barbieri-Low, Anthony J. Artisans in Early Imperial China. 2007. (ENG., Illus.). 400p. 60.00 (978-0-295-98713-2(8)) Univ. of Washington Pr.

C

Barrett, J. May Lee, ed. Humanism in China: China Institute Edition. 2009. (ENG., Illus.). 34p. pap. *(978-0-9774054-4-2(3))* China Institute Gallery, China Institute in America.

Beredon, Juliet. Chinese New Year Festivals. (Illus.). 29p. reprint ed. pap. 19.50 *(978-0-89346-860-6(6))* Heian International Publishing, Inc.

Berg, Daria. The Quest for Gentility in China: Negotiations Beyond Gender & Class. 2009. 302p. pap. 39.95 *(978-0-415-54541-9(2))* Routledge.

Blake, C. Fred. Burning Money: The Material Spirit of the Chinese Lifeworld. 2011. (Illus.). 272p. 52.00 ***(978-0-8248-3532-3(8))*** Univ. of Hawaii Pr.

Blo Brtan Rdo Rje & Stuart, Charles Kevin. Life & Marriage in Skya Rgya, a Tibetan Village. 2008. 232p. pap. 33.50 *(978-0-9800508-4-4(7))* YBK Pubs., Inc.

Bond, Michael Harris. Handbook of Chinese Organizational Behavior: Integrating Theory, Research & Practice. Huang, Xu, ed. 2012. (Elgar Original Reference Ser.). 560p. 260.00 ***(978-0-85793-339-3(6))*** Elgar, Edward Publishing, Inc.

Brahm, Laurence J. Elements of China: Water, Wood, Fire, Earth, Gold. 2008. (Illus.). 237p. *(978-7-5085-1392-8(4))* China Intercontinental Communication Ctr.

Brandstadter, Susi, et al. Chinese Kinship: Contemporary Anthropological Perspectives. Santos, Gonçalo Duro dos, ed. 2008. (Routledge Contemporary China Ser.). (ENG., Illus.). 256p. (C). 150.00 *(978-0-415-45697-5(5))* Routledge.

Bredon, Juliet & Mitrophanow, Igor. The Moon Year - a Record of Chinese Customs & Festivals. 2009. 576p. pap. *(978-0-9812717-7-4(4))* Soul Care Publishing.

Brick, Jean. China: Language & Culture. 3rd ed. (Illus.). 372p. pap. *(978-0-85837-719-6(5))* Macquarie Univ.

Brines, Celia R. Dragon Tales. 2007. (ENG.). 124p. 35.95 *(978-0-548-09821-9(2))* Kessinger Publishing, LLC.

Brown, Miranda. The Politics of Mourning in Early China. 2007. (SUNY Series in Chinese Philosophy & Culture). (Illus.). 205p. 75.00 *(978-0-7914-7157-9(8))* State Univ. of New York Pr.

Burnett, David. The Spirit of China: The Roots of Faith in 21st Century China, 1 vol. 2008. (Illus.). 384p. pap. 16.99 *(978-0-8254-6146-0(4),* Monarch Bks.) Lion Hudson PLC GBR. Dist: Kregel Pubns.

Carter, Alden R. China: From the First Chinese to the Olympics. 2008. 216p. pap. 26.95 *(978-1-60145-455-3(4))* Booklocker.com, Inc.

Carter, Tom. China: Portrait of a People. 2010. (ENG.). 638p. pap. 24.95 *(978-988-99799-4-2(2))* Blacksmith Bks. HKG. Dist: National Bk. Network.

Chang, Jui-Shan. Making A Meal of It: Sex in Chinese & Western Cultural Settings. 2011. 387p. pap. 23.95 ***(978-1-4327-6821-8(2))*** Outskirts Pr., Inc.

Chao, Shin-Yi. Daoist Rituals, State Religion, & Popular Practices: Zhenwu Worship from Song to Ming (960-1644) 2011. (Routledge Studies in Taoism Ser.). (ENG., Illus.). 176p. (C). 130.00 *(978-0-415-78066-7(7))* Routledge.

Chee-beng, Tan. Southern Fujian: Reproduction of Traditions in Post-Mao China. Chee-Beng, Tan, ed. 2006. (ENG., Illus.). 300p. (gr. 17). 42.00 *(978-962-996-233-3(0))* Chinese Univ. of Hong Kong, The HKG. Dist: Columbia Univ. Pr.

Chen, Rose, ed. Learning & Thinking about China: Introduction of Chinese Culture. 2nd ed. 2006. (CHI.). (YA). *(978-0-9788074-0-5(5))* Rose Group for Cross-Cultural Understanding, The.

Chen, Sonia M. China Changing in My Eyes: People, Schools & Landscapes. 2010. 260p. pap. 14.99 *(978-1-4490-5060-3(3))* AuthorHouse.

Chen, Vin. The Practice of Guanxi by Business to the Government in Taiwan. 2008. 68p. pap. *(978-3-8364-8706-1(3))* VDM Verlag Dr. Mueller e.K.

Chen, Ya-chen. Women in Taiwan: Sociocultural Perspectives. 2009. 182p. pap. 29.95 *(978-1-880938-73-7(1))* Univ. of Indianapolis Pr.

Chen, Yu. Zhongguo Sheng Huo Ji Yi: Jian Guo 60 Nian Min Sheng Wang Shi. 2009. (CHI., Illus.). 347p. pap. *(978-7-5019-7054-4(8))* China Light Industry Pr.

Cheung, Shin-Yee & Bi, Qi. Food & Chinese Culture. 2009. (ENG.). 126p. pap. 23.60 *(978-0-9821816-3-8(9))* Commercial Pr., Inc., The.

Chiang, Cecilia & Weiss, Lisa. The Seventh Daughter: My Culinary Journey from Beijing to San Francisco. 2007. (ENG., Illus.). 256p. 35.00 *(978-1-58008-822-0(8))* Ten Speed Pr.

The China Society Yearbook, Volume 4. 2010. 356p. *(978-90-04-18221-9(7))* BRILL.

Christian Focus Publications, creator. A Christian's Pocket Guide to the Chinese. 2008. (ENG.). 64p. per. 4.99 *(978-1-84550-315-4(5))* Christian Focus Pubns. GBR. Dist: STL Distribution North America.

Clark, Hugh R. & Colebrook, Claire. Portrait of a Community: Society, Culture, & the Structures of Kinship in the Mulan River Valley (Fujian) from the Late Tang Through the Song. 2007. (ENG., Illus.). 270p. (gr. 17). 49.00 *(978-962-996-227-2(6))* Chinese Univ. of Hong Kong, The HKG. Dist: Columbia Univ. Pr.

Clissold, Lorraine. Why the Chinese Don't Count Calories: 16 Secrets from a 6,000-Year-Old Food Culture. 2008. 288p. pap. 12.95 *(978-1-60239-272-4(2))* Skyhorse Publishing Co., Inc.

Coltman, Robert. The Chinese, Their Present & Future. 212p. reprint ed. 98.00 *(978-0-7222-1845-7(1))* Library Reprints, Inc.

Conwell, Russell Herman. Why & How: Why the Chinese Emigrate, & the Means they Adopt for the Purpose of Reaching America, with Sketches of Travel, Amusing incidents, Soci. 2006. 304p. per. 23.99 *(978-1-4255-2842-3(2))* MPublishing.

Cooper, Eugene. The Market & Temple Fairs of Rural China: Red Fire. 2012. (Asia's Transformations Ser.). (ENG., Illus.). 304p. (C). 135.00 ***(978-0-415-52079-9(7))*** Routledge.

Cope, T. A. & Munro, Donald. Ethics in Action: Workable Guidelines for Private & Public Choices. 2008. (ENG.). 168p. (gr. 17). 33.00 *(978-962-996-380-4(9))* Chinese Univ. of Hong Kong, The HKG. Dist: Columbia Univ. Pr.

Cornaby, W. Arthur. A String of Chinese Peach-Stones. 2010. (Cambridge Library Collection - Travel & Exploration Ser.). (Illus.). 500p. pap. 37.99 *(978-1-108-01410-6(0))* Cambridge Univ. Pr.

Croll, Elisabeth. The Politics of Marriage in Contemporary China. 2010. (ENG.). 228p. pap. 32.99 *(978-0-521-13068-4(9))* Cambridge Univ. Pr.

Crouch, Christopher. Contemporary Chinese Visual Culture: Tradition, Modernity, & Globalization. 2010. *(978-1-60497-721-9(3))* Cambria Pr.

Crow, Carl. Foreign Devils in the Flowery Kingdom. 2007. (ENG.). 312p. pap. 19.99 *(978-988-99633-3-0(7))* Earnshaw Bks. HKG. Dist: Independent Pubs. Group.

—400 Million Customers: The Experiences -Some Happy, Some Sad of an American in China, & What They Taught Him. 2008. (Illus.). 276p. pap. *(978-0-9680459-0-9(1))* Soul Care Publishing.

Crow, Carl & Ayer, A. J. Four Hundred Million Customers. 2007. (ENG., Illus.). 256p. pap. 250.00 *(978-0-7103-1212-9(1))* Routledge.

Danielson, Eric N. Discover Shanghai. 2010. 176p. pap. 20.99 *(978-981-261-782-8(5))* Marshall Cavendish International (Asia) Private Ltd. SGP. Dist: Marshall Cavendish Corp.

Dautcher, Jay. Down a Narrow Road: Identity & Masculinity in a Uyghur Community in a Uyghur Community in Xinjiang China. 2009. (Harvard East Asian Monographs: 312). (Illus.). 350p. 39.95 *(978-0-674-03282-8(9))* Harvard Univ., Asia Ctr.

De Mente, Boye Lafayette. Etiquette Guide to China: Know the Rules That Make the Difference! 2008. (ENG.). 192p. pap. 14.95 *(978-0-8048-3943-3(3))* Tuttle Publishing.

Dean, Kenneth & Zheng, Zhenman. Ritual Alliances of the Putian Plain, 2 vols. 2009. (Illus.). 840p. *(978-90-04-17601-0(2))*; 320p. *(978-90-04-17602-7(0))* BRILL.

Devonshire-Ellis, Chris, et al, eds. Human Resources in China. 3rd ed. 2011. (China Briefing Ser.). (ENG., Illus.). ix, 125p. pap. 59.95 *(978-3-642-18208-2(9),* 3642182089) Springer.

Di, Xianghua. A Food-Lover's Journey Around China. 2007. (Illus.). 156p. 16.95 *(978-7-119-04175-9(4))* Beijing, Foreign Languages Press CHN. Dist: China Bks. & Periodicals, Inc.

Dickmann, Nancy. Chinese New Year, 1 vol. 2010. (Holidays & Festivals Ser.). (ENG., Illus.). 24p. (gr. -1-1). 21.99 *(978-1-4329-4050-8(3),* Acorn) Heinemann-Raintree.

Dodson, Bill. China Inside Out: 10 Irreversible Trends Reshaping China & Its Relationship with the World. 2011. (ENG.). 200p. 29.95 *(978-0-470-82643-0(6),* Wiley) Wiley, John & Sons, Inc.

Doolittle, Justus. Social Life of the Chinese V2 with Some. 2006. pap. 38.95 *(978-1-4286-3931-7(4))* Kessinger Publishing, LLC.

Dunlop, Fuchsia. Shark's Fin & Sichuan Pepper: A Sweet-Sour Memoir of Eating in China. 2009. (ENG.). 336p. pap. 17.95 *(978-0-393-33288-9(8),* 33288) Norton, W. W. & Co., Inc.

Eagan, Angie. Cultureshock China, 1 vol. 2011. (ENG., Illus.). 240p. pap. 15.95 *(978-0-7614-6052-7(7))* Marshall Cavendish Corp.

EAR Books, creator. Shanghai: City Between Cultures. 2007. (Ear Books Mini Ser.). (ENG., Illus.). 80p. 14.95 incl. lp *(978-3-937406-69-5(7))* Edel Classica Gmbh.

Edelmann, Frederic. In the Chinese City. 2008. 348p. *(978-84-96954-49-6(8))* Actar Birkhauser Distribution.

Fallman, Fredrik. Salvation & Modernity: Intellectuals & Faith in Contemporary China. 2008. (ENG.). 180p. pap. 34.99 *(978-0-7618-4090-9(7))* Univ. Pr. of America, Inc.

Fallows, Deborah. Dreaming in Chinese: Mandarin Lessons in Life, Love, & Language. (ENG.). 208p. 2011. pap. 13.00 *(978-0-8027-7914-4(X))* 2010. (Illus.). 22.00 *(978-0-8027-7913-7(1))* Walker & Co.

Fang Fang, et al, eds. Gao Yu: Specimen, 1 vol. Ambrozy, Lee, tr. 2008. (ENG., Illus.). 156p. 42.00 *(978-988-99617-4-9(1))* Timezone 8 Ltd. HKG. Dist: D.A.P./Distributed Art Pubs.

Field, Andrew. Shanghai's Dancing World: Cabaret Culture & Modernity in Old Shanghai, 1919-1954. 2010. (ENG., Illus.). 200p. (gr. 17). 45.00 *(978-962-996-373-6(6))* Chinese Univ. of Hong Kong, The HKG. Dist: Columbia Univ. Pr.

—Shanghai's Dancing World: Cabaret Culture & Urban Politics, 1919 — 1954. 2011. (ENG.). 400p. (gr. 17). pap. 25.00 *(978-962-996-448-1(1))* Chinese Univ. of Hong Kong, The HKG. Dist: Columbia Univ. Pr.

Finnane, Antonia. Changing Clothes in China: Fashion, History, Nation. 2008. (ENG., Illus.). 360p. (gr. 17). 40.00 *(978-0-231-14350-9(8))* Columbia Univ. Pr.

Flower, Kathy. China: The Essential Guide to Customs & Culture. 2010. (Culture Smart! Ser.). (ENG., Illus.). 168p. pap. 9.95 *(978-1-85733-502-6(3))* Kuperard Pubs. GBR. Dist: Random Hse., Inc.

Foster, Emily. The Banquet: My Grandma's Memories of China. 2008. 152p. pap. 14.95 *(978-0-595-52957-5(7))* iUniverse, Inc.

Frady, Shannon. The Long Kiss Goodbye: A Seven-Year Odyssey Through China's New Cultural Revolution. 2010. (ENG.). 239p. pap. 88.00 *(978-0-557-58273-0(3))* Lulu Enterprises Inc.

French, Paul. Carl Crow - A Tough Old China Hand: The Life, Times, & Adventures of an American in Shanghai. 2006. (ENG., Illus.). 324p. (gr. 17). 35.00 *(978-962-209-802-2(9))* Hong Kong Univ. Pr. HKG. Dist: Columbia Univ. Pr.

French, Paul & Crabbe, Matthew. Fat China: How Expanding Waistlines are Changing a Nation. 2010. (China in the 21st Century Ser.). (Illus.). 250p. pap. 29.95 *(978-0-85728-965-0(9))* Anthem Pr. GBR. Dist: Books International, Inc.

—Fat China: How Expanding Waistlines Are Changing a Nation. 2010. (China in the 21st Century Ser.). (ENG., Illus.). 250p. 99.00 *(978-0-85728-978-0(0))* Anthem Pr. GBR. Dist: Books International, Inc.

Gauvrit, Jean-Philippe. Shanghai in .jpg: [Shanghai Ying Xiang. 2008. (CHI, FRE & ENG., Illus.). 87p. *(978-0-9814698-1-2(7))* International Publishing Hse. for China's Culture.

Gichner, Lawrence E. Erotic Aspects of Chinese Culture. 2011. 132p. 40.95 ***(978-1-258-03037-7(3))*** Literary Licensing, LLC.

Gifford, Rob. China Road. 2008. (Playaway Adult Nonfiction Ser.). 74.99 *(978-1-60514-772-7(9))* Findaway World, LLC.

—China Road: A Journey into the Future of a Rising Power. (ENG., Illus.). 352p. 2008. pap. 17.00 *(978-0-8129-7524-6(3),* Random Hse. Trade Paperbacks) 2007. 26.95 *(978-1-4000-6467-0(8),* Random House) Random House Publishing Group.

Giles, Herbert A. China & the Chinese. 2007. (ENG.). 120p. per. *(978-1-4065-4455-8(8))* Dodo Pr.

—Chinese Sketches. 2007. 136p. per. *(978-1-4065-4458-9(2))* Dodo Pr.

—Chinese Sketches. 2007. 112p. per. *(978-1-4068-0927-5(6))* Echo Library.

Gilman, Susan Jane. Undress Me in the Temple of Heaven. 2010. (ENG.). 320p. pap. 13.99 *(978-0-446-69693-7(5))* Grand Central Publishing.

Grace, Stephen. Shanghai: Life, Love & Infrastructure in China's City of the Future. 2010. (ENG.). 300p. pap. 18.95 *(978-1-59181-083-4(3))* Sentient Pubns.

Gully, Patti. Sisters of Heaven: China's Barnstorming Aviatrixes: Modernity, Feminism, & Popular Imagination in Asia & the West. 2007. (ENG., Illus.). 448p. per. 24.95 *(978-1-59265-075-0(9))* Long River Pr.

Haedecke, Friederike. Luxury Trains. 2008. (ENG.). 24.95 *(978-3-8327-9251-0(1))* teNeues Publishing Co.

Hammond, Sally. Playing Chopsticks: Travels Through China. 2007. (ENG., Illus.). 224p. per. 14.95 *(978-1-74110-397-7(5))* New Holland Pubs. Pty, Ltd. AUS. Dist: Tuttle Publishing.

Headland, Isaac Taylor. Court Life in China. 2008. 224p. 27.99 *(978-0-554-29444-5(3))* BiblioBazaar.

—Court Life in China. 2007. (ENG.). 196p. per. *(978-1-4065-4425-1(6))* Dodo Pr.

—Court Life in China. 2007. (ENG.). 144p. per. *(978-1-4068-1605-1(1))* Echo Library.

Herbert A. Giles, LL.D., MA. Chinese Sketches. 2006. (ENG.). 188p. pap. 19.99 *(978-1-4264-0106-0(X))*; 186p. pap. 17.99 *(978-1-4264-0235-7(X))* BiblioBazaar.

Hessler, Peter. Country Driving: A Chinese Road Trip. 2011. (P. S. Ser.). (ENG.). 480p. pap. 15.99 *(978-0-06-180410-6(X),* HarperPerennial) HarperCollins Pubs.

—Country Driving: A Journey Through China from Farm to Factory. 2010. (ENG.). 416p. 27.99 *(978-0-06-180409-0(6))* HarperCollins Pubs.

Hinton, Adam. Lovin' It. 2009. (ENG., Illus.). 96p. 35.00 *(978-1-904587-63-7(1))* Lewis, Dewi Publishing GBR. Dist: Consortium Bk. Sales & Distribution.

Hlavacek, John. Letters Home: An American Reporter in China, 1939-1944. 2009. 272p. pap. 19.95 *(978-0-9819034-5-3(2),* Hlucky Bks.) Concierge Marketing, Inc.

Hobart, Alice Tisdale. By the City of the Long Sand: A Tale of New China. 2011. 372p. 53.95 ***(978-1-258-07052-6(9))*** Literary Licensing, LLC.

Hollmann, Thomas O. & Wang-Riese, Xiaobing, eds. Time & Ritual in Early China. 2010. (Asiatische Forschungen Ser.). (ENG.). 209p. (C). pap. 57.00 *(978-3-447-06106-3(5))* Harrassowitz, Otto Verlag DEU. Dist: ISD.

Hongwu, Peng, ed. +0086 Beijing Cool. 2009. (ENG & CHI., Illus.). 304p. pap. 19.95 *(978-988-18034-2-9(X))* Timezone 8 Ltd. HKG. Dist: D.A.P./Distributed Art Pubs.

Hou, Naihui. Song Dai Yuan Lin Ji Qi Sheng Huo Wen Hua. 2010. (CHI., Illus.). *(978-957-14-5271-5(8))* San Min Bk. Co., Ltd.

Hua, Yu. China in Ten Words. Barr, Allan H., tr. from CHI. 2011. (ENG.). 240p. 25.95 *(978-0-307-37935-1(3),* Pantheon) Knopf Doubleday Publishing Group.

Huang, Martin W. Male Friendship in Ming China. 2007. 188p. pap. *(978-90-04-16026-2(4))* BRILL.

Huang, Shih-shan Susan. Picturing the True Form: Daoist Visual Culture in Traditional China. 2012. (Harvard East Asian Monographs: 342). (ENG., Illus.). 500p. 69.95 ***(978-0-674-06573-4(5))*** Harvard Univ., Asia Ctr.

Huang Yuan Xiou. The Major Methods of Wudang Sword. Mei-hui, Lu, tr. from CHI. 2010. (ENG., Illus.). 136p. pap. 16.95 *(978-1-58394-239-0(4),* Blue Snake Bks.) North Atlantic Bks.

Hung, Chang-tai. Mao's New World: Political Culture in the Early People's Republic. 2010. (Illus.). 328p. 39.95 *(978-0-8014-4934-5(0))* Cornell Univ. Pr.

Jackson, Mark. An Intrepid Traveller: Breaking China with the Idiots Abroad. 2011. 320p. pap. 18.70 ***(978-1-4269-9487-6(7))*** Trafford Publishing.

Jankowiak, William. City Days, City Nights: China: 1981-2007. 288p. (gr. 17). pap. 27.50 ***(978-0-231-14867-2(4))***; 2011. 79.50 ***(978-0-231-14866-5(6))*** Columbia Univ. Pr.

Jaschok, Maria. Concubines & Bond Servants: The Social History of a Chinese Custom. 164p. 2009. 50.00 *(978-1-59740-367-2(9))* 2008. pap. 16.00 *(978-1-59740-685-7(6))* ACLS Humanities E-Book.

Jiao, Tianlong. Lost Maritime Cultures: China & the Pacific. 2007. *(978-1-58178-063-5(X))* Bishop Museum Pr.

Johnson, David. Spectacle & Sacrifice: The Ritual Foundations of Village Life in North China. 2010. (Harvard East Asian Monographs: 315). (Illus.). 450p. 49.95 *(978-0-674-03304-7(3))* Harvard Univ., Asia Ctr.

Johnston, Reginald F. Lion & Dragon in Northern China. 2011. (Cambridge Library Collection - History Ser.). (ENG., Illus.). 560p. pap. 39.99 *(978-1-108-02964-3(7))* Cambridge Univ. Pr.

Johnston, Reginald Fleming. From Peking to Mandalay: A Journey from North China to Burma through Tibetan Ssuch'uan & Yunnan. 2008. (Illus.). 428p. pap. 26.95 *(978-0-9680459-7-8(9))* Soul Care Publishing CAN. Dist: Ingram Bk. Co.

—Lion & Dragon in Northern China. 2008. 332p. per. 24.95 *(978-0-9680459-6-1(0))* Soul Care Publishing CAN. Dist: Ingram Bk. Co.

Junli, Feng. Grassroots Blogging Practice in America & China- Studies on 60 American & 60 Chinese Bloggers. 2007. 136p. per. *(978-3-8364-1773-0(1))* VDM Verlag Dr. Mueller e.K.

Kander, Nadav, photos by. Nadav Kander: Yangtze - The Long River. 2010. (ENG., Illus.). 188p. 95.00 *(978-3-7757-2683-2(7))* Hatje Cantz Verlag GmbH & Co KG DEU. Dist: D.A.P./Distributed Art Pubs.

Khoo, Olivia. The Chinese Exotic: Modern Diasporic Femininity. 2007. (TransAsia: Screen Cultures Ser.). (ENG., Illus.). 228p. (gr. 17). 60.00 *(978-962-209-879-4(7))* Hong Kong Univ. Pr. HKG. Dist: Columbia Univ. Pr.

Kidd, David. Peking Story. 2009. (ENG.). 164p. pap. 29.95 *(978-1-906011-00-0(1))* Eland Bks. GBR. Dist: Dufour Editions, Inc.

King, Marjorie. China's American Daughter: Ida Pruitt, 1888-1985. 2006. (ENG., Illus.). 296p. (gr. 17). 42.00 *(978-962-996-057-5(5))* Chinese Univ. of Hong Kong, The HKG. Dist: Columbia Univ. Pr.

—China's American Daughter: Ida Pruitt (1888-1985) 2007. (ENG., Illus.). 296p. (gr. 17). pap. 23.00 *(978-962-996-221-0(7))* Chinese Univ. of Hong Kong, The HKG. Dist: Columbia Univ. Pr.

Kipnis, Andrew B., et al. Contemporary Chinese Society & Politics, 4 vols. 2009. (Illus.). Vol. 1. *(978-0-415-45749-1(1))* Vol. 2. *(978-0-415-45750-7(5))* Vol. 3. *(978-0-415-45751-4(3))* Vol. 4. *(978-0-415-45752-1(1))* Routledge.

Kitto, Mark. Chasing China: How I Went to China in Search of a Fortune & Found a Life. 2009. (ENG.). 304p. 22.95 *(978-1-60239-657-9(4),* 239657) Skyhorse Publishing Co., Inc.

Knapp, Ronald G. Things Chinese: Antiques, Crafts, Collectibles. 2011. (ENG., Illus.). 144p. 24.95 *(978-0-8048-4187-0(X),* PeriplusEdition) Tuttle Publishing.

Ko, Dorothy. Cinderella's Sisters: A Revisionist History of Footbinding. 2007. (Illus.). 332p. per. 25.95 *(978-0-520-25390-2(6))* Univ. of California Pr.

Kolatch, Jonathan. China Mosaic. 2008. (Illus.). 360p. 30.00 *(978-0-8246-0470-7(9))* David, Jonathan Pubs., Inc.

Kong, Chu Yiu. Triads As Business. 2nd rev. ed. 2009. (Routledge Studies in the Modern History of Asia Ser.). 224p. 150.00 *(978-0-415-36001-2(3),* RU42644) Routledge.

Kong, Travis S. K. Chinese Male Homosexualities: Memba, Tongzhi & Golden Boy. 2012. (ENG., Illus.). 320p. (C). pap. 42.95 ***(978-0-415-51898-7(9))*** Routledge.

Kupfer, Peter. Wine in Chinese Culture: Historical, Literary, Social & Global Perspectives. 2011. (CHI & ENG.). 312p. pap. 49.95 ***(978-3-643-10854-8(0))*** Lit Verlag DEU. Dist: Transaction Pubs.

Kusamori, Shinichi. Moji No Tairiku, Owai No Miyako: Meijin Shinkoku Kenbunroku. 2010. (JPN.). 439p. *(978-4-469-23260-8(2))* Taishukan Publishing Co., Ltd.

Kutcher, Norman. Mourning in Late Imperial China: Filial Piety & the State. 2006. (Cambridge Studies in Chinese History, Literature & Institutions Ser.). (ENG.). 228p. pap. 48.00 *(978-0-521-03018-2(8))* Cambridge Univ. Pr.

Kwok, Ken. Middle Kingdom - Legendary Beginning of China & the Bible. 2008. 163p. pap. 19.95 *(978-0-557-00325-9(3))* Lulu Enterprises Inc.

L'abbate, Analia & Gao, Karina Qian. La estrategia del dragón/ the Strategy of Dragon. 2007. 93p. pap. 12.95 *(978-987-612-034-0(4))* V & R Editorial ARG. Dist: Baker & Taylor Bks.

Lacey, Leo. Culture Wise China. 2011. (ENG., Illus.). 240p. pap. 17.95 *(978-1-907339-27-1(2))* Survival Bks., Ltd.

Lagerwey, John. China: A Religious State. 2010. (Understanding China: New Viewpoints on History & Culture Ser.). (ENG., Illus.). 248p. (gr. 17). 40.00 *(978-988-8028-03-0(0))*; pap. 20.00 *(978-988-8028-04-7(9))* Hong Kong Univ. Pr. HKG. Dist: Columbia Univ. Pr.

Lai, Pan-Chiu & Lam, Jason, eds. Sino-Christian Theology: A Theological Qua Cultural Movement in Contemporary China. 2010. (IC - Studien zur interkulturellen Geschichte des Christentums. Etudes d'histoire interculturelle de christianisme. Studies in the Intercultural History of Christianity Ser.). 248p. 69.95 *(978-3-631-60435-9(1))* Lang, Peter GmbH, Europaischer Verlag der Wissenschaften DEU. Dist: Lang, Peter.

Lan Lin, Christi. Symbolism of Chinese Children's Bibs: A Mother's Affectionate Embrace. 2006. 143p. pap. 42.95 *(978-0-88093-866-2(8))* Univ. of Indianapolis Pr.

Langgner, Michael. Culpetence. 2009. 60p. pap. *(978-3-639-14753-7(7))* VDM Verlag Dr. Mueller e.K.

Lee, Stephen. Faraway Faces: The Vanishing World of Southwest China, 1 vol. 2007. (Discover Ser.). (ENG., Illus.). 144p. 32.00 *(978-981-261-212-0(2))* Marshall Cavendish International (Asia) Private Ltd. SGP. Dist: Marshall Cavendish Corp.

Lemos, Gerard. The End of the Chinese Dream: Why Chinese People Fear the Future. 2012. (ENG., Illus.). 352p. 38.00 *(978-0-300-16924-9(8))* Yale Univ. Pr.

Letts, Janis. A Glimpse of the Dragon - Beyond the Great Wall. 2008. 300p. pap. 24.95 *(978-1-4092-0273-8(9))* Lulu Enterprises Inc.

Levy, Michael. Kosher Chinese: Living, Teaching, & Eating with China's Other Billion. 2011. (ENG.). 256p. pap. 15.00 *(978-0-8050-9196-0(3),* Holt Paperback) Holt, Henry & Co.

Li, Xiangping. Xin Yang Dan Bu Ren Tong: Dang Dai Zhongguo Xin Yang de She Hui Xue Quan Shi = Believing Without Identifying: The Sociological Interpretation of Spiritual Beliefs in Contemporary China. 2010. *(978-7-5097-1352-5(8))* China Social Science Documentation Publishing Hse.

Li, Zhe. We Did Not Drink As Stupidly As Today's Young People. 2011. 188p. pap. ***(978-3-8443-1509-7(8))*** Lambert Academic Publishing.

Lin, David. Chinese Print Media in Nz Present Ideas of Chinese Cultural Identity. 2009. 100p. pap. *(978-3-639-14031-6(1))* VDM Verlag Dr. Mueller e.K.

Lin-Liu, Jen. Serve the People: A Stir-Fried Journey Through China. 2009. (ENG.). 352p. pap. 21.95 *(978-0-15-603374-9(7),* Mariner Bks.) Houghton Mifflin Harcourt Trade & Reference Pubs.

Ling, Rich. Two Years in the Forbidden City. 2007. 190.00 *(978-0-7103-1112-2(5))* Taylor & Francis Group.

Ling, Yun. Chinese Tea. 2010. 110p. 14.95 *(978-1-60220-124-8(2))* BetterLink Pr., Inc.

Lingyun, Huang. Tao of Chinese Tea. 2009. (ENG.). 144p. (gr. 12-18). 16.95 *(978-1-60652-050-5(4))* Reader's Digest Assn., Inc., The.

Lip, Evelyn. Your Face Is Your Fortune: An Introduction to Chinese Face Reading. 2009. (Illus.). 128p. pap. ***(978-981-261-635-7(7))*** Marshall Cavendish.

Little, Alicia E. Neva. My Diary in a Chinese Farm. 2010. (Cambridge Library Collection - Travel & Exploration Ser.). (ENG., Illus.). 100p. pap. 19.99 *(978-1-108-01383-3(X))* Cambridge Univ. Pr.

Liu, Heung Shing, ed. China: 25 Jahre TASCHEN. 2011. (25 Ser.). (ENG., Illus.). 424p. 29.99 ***(978-3-8365-3089-7(9))*** TASCHEN DEU. Dist: Ingram Pub. Services.

Liu, Tong. Chinese Tea. 3rd ed. 2012. (Introductions to Chinese Culture Ser.). (ENG.). 166p. pap. 19.99 ***(978-0-521-18680-3(3))*** Cambridge Univ. Pr.

Louie, Belinda Y. Learning Chinese: Through Stories & Activities. 2007. (Illus.). 48p. (J). (gr. -1-3). per. 14.95 *(978-1-887542-54-8(X))* Book Pubs. Network.

Lu, Hanchao. The Birth of a Republic: Francis Stafford's Photographs of China's 1911 Revolution & Beyond. 2010. (ENG., Illus.). 240p. 40.00 *(978-0-295-98940-2(8))* Univ. of Washington Pr.

Lu, Yiyi. Non-Governmental Organizations in China: The Rise of Dependent Autonomy. 2008. (China Policy Ser.). (ENG., Illus.). 172p. (C). 158.00 *(978-0-415-45858-0(7))* Routledge.

Lunsford, Celina & Tannert, Christoph. China Naked. 2007. (GER & ENG., Illus.). 120p. 40.00 *(978-3-939583-11-0(1))* Kehrer Verlag Heidelberg, Klaus Kehrer DEU. Dist: Consortium Bk. Sales & Distribution.

Lyon, Danny, photos by. Deep Sea Diver: An American Photographer's Journey in Shanxi, China. 2011. (ENG., Illus.). 136p. 200.00 *(978-0-7148-6104-3(9))* Phaidon Pr., Inc.

Ma, Shirley See Yan. Footbinding: A Jungian Engagement with Chinese Culture & Psychology. 2010. (ENG., Illus.). 208p. (C). 37.50 ***(978-0-415-48506-7(1))***; 105.00 *(978-0-415-48505-0(3))* Routledge.

McCormick, Elsie. The Unexpurgated Diary of a Shanghai Baby. 2007. 114p. pap. 27.50 *(978-988-99874-8-0(1))* China Economic Review Publishing HKG. Dist: Trans-Atlantic Pubns., Inc.

McCurry, Steve, photos by. The Path to Buddha: A Tibetan Pilgrimage. 2012. (ENG.). 144p. pap. 29.95 ***(978-0-7148-6314-6(9))*** Phaidon Pr., Inc.

McGetrick, Brendan, ed. Urban China Work in Progress. 2010. (ENG., Illus.). 208p. pap. 40.00 *(978-988-18033-9-9(X))* Timezone 8 Ltd. HKG. Dist: D.A.P./Distributed Art Pubs.

Medhurst, Walter Henry. The Foreigner in Far Cathay. 2010. (Cambridge Library Collection - Travel & Exploration Ser.). (ENG., Illus.). 208p. pap. 22.99 *(978-1-108-01468-7(2))* Cambridge Univ. Pr.

Merriam, Beth. China's 'Tibetan' Frontiers: Sharing the Contested Ground, 1 vol. 2010. (ENG.). 256p. *(978-1-906876-30-2(4))* BRILL.

Miles, Steven B. The Sea of Learning: Mobility & Identity in Nineteenth-Century Guangzhou. 2006. (Harvard East Asian Monographs: 269). (Illus.). 450p. 49.95 *(978-0-674-02134-1(7))* Harvard Univ., Asia Ctr.

Miller, Jeffrey. A One-Year Diary of an American Teacher in China. 2007. (ENG.). 216p. per. 24.95 *(978-1-4241-6250-5(5))* PublishAmerica, Inc.

Monfret, Anne-Laure. Saving Face in Chin: A First-Hand Guide for Any Traveller to China. 2011. 164p. 29.99 ***(978-1-4568-9064-3(6))***; pap. 19.99 ***(978-1-4568-9063-6(8))*** Xlibris Corp.

Morris-Suzuki, Tessa. To the Diamond Mountains: A Hundred-Year Journey Through China & Korea. 2010. (Illus.). xiii, 201p. ***(978-1-4422-0505-5(9))*** Rowman & Littlefield Publishers, Inc.

Morris-Suzuki, Tessa, ed. To the Diamond Mountains: A Hundred-Year Journey through China & Korea. 2010. (Asia/Pacific/Perspectives Ser.). (ENG., Illus.). 216p. 37.50 *(978-1-4422-0503-1(2))* Rowman & Littlefield Publishers, Inc.

Myler, Stephen F. The China Papers. 2011. 228p. pap. 9.99 ***(978-1-61667-317-8(6))*** Raider Publishing International.

National Centre for Language Training Staff & University of New South Wales Press Staff. Doing Business in China: A Guide for Australians. 2008. (ENG.). 128p. pap. 25.95 *(978-1-921410-34-5(5),* UNSW Press) NewSouth Publishing AUS. Dist: Independent Pubs. Group.

Nosirrah, N. 2013: How to Profit from the Prophets in the Coming End of the World. 2010. (ENG.). 109p. pap. 9.95 *(978-1-59181-095-7(7))* Sentient Pubns.

Nyíri, Pal. Scenic Spots: Chinese Tourism, the State, & Cultural Authority. 2007. (China Program Book Ser.). (ENG., Illus.). 152p. per. 22.50 *(978-0-295-98761-3(8))* Univ. of Washington Pr.

Oakes, Tim & Sutton, Donald S. Faiths on Display: Religion, Tourism, & the Chinese State. 2010. *(978-1-4422-0508-6(3))* Rowman & Littlefield Publishers, Inc.

Oakes/Sutton. Faiths on Display: Religion, Tourism, & the Chinese State. 2010. (ENG.). 292p. 85.00 *(978-1-4422-0506-2(7))* Rowman & Littlefield Publishers, Inc.

OCDF Publications & Dolphin Books, concepts. Chinese Traditional Holidays & Festivals - Chinese Culture Active Learning Series Book #1: Chinese Traditional Holidays & Festivals. 2007. (ENG & CHI., Illus.). 32p. (J). pap. 18.00 incl. cd-rom *(978-1-934487-00-6(7))* OCDF Pubns.

Otie, Philippe. A Chinese Life. 2012. (Illus.). 720p. pap. 27.50 ***(978-1-906838-55-3(0),*** SelfMadeHero) Metro Media Ltd. GBR. Dist: Abrams.

Ou, Chaoquan. Life in a Kam Village in Southwest China, 1930-49. 2007. (Illus.). 250p. *(978-90-04-16229-7(1))* BRILL.

Oxfeld, Ellen. Drink Water, but Remember the Source: Moral Discourse in a Chinese Village. 2010. (ENG., Illus.). 312p. 60.00 *(978-0-520-25094-8(5))*; pap. 24.95 *(978-0-520-26095-5(3))* Univ. of California Pr.

Palmer, David A., et al, eds. Chinese Religious Life, 1 vol. 2011. (ENG., Illus.). 296p. pap. 29.95 *(978-0-19-973138-1(1))* Oxford Univ. Pr., Inc.

Park, J. P. Art by the Book: Painting Manuals & the Leisure Life in Late Ming China, 1 vol. 2012. (ENG., Illus.). 336p. (C). 50.00 ***(978-0-295-99176-4(3))*** Univ. of Washington Pr.

Paul, Alan. Big in China: My Unlikely Adventures Raising a Family, Playing the Blues, & Becoming a Star in Beijing. 2011. (ENG.). 256p. 25.99 *(978-0-06-199315-2(8))* HarperCollins Pubs.

Peltier, Warren. The Ancient Art of Tea: Wisdom from the Ancient Chinese Tea Masters. 2011. (ENG., Illus.). 160p. 15.95 *(978-0-8048-4153-5(5,)* Tuttle Publishing.

Penny, Benjamin. The Religion of Falun Gong. 2012. (ENG.). 272p. 45.00 ***(978-0-226-65501-7(6))*** Univ. of Chicago Pr.

Philippi, Simone & Shing, Liu Heung, eds. China, Portrait of a Country. 2008. (FRE, GER & ENG., Illus.). 423p. 59.99 *(978-3-8365-0569-7(X))* TASCHEN DEU. Dist: Ingram Pub. Services.

Pierre, Ostrowski. It's All Chinese to Me: An Illustrated Overview of Culture & Etiquette in China. 2008. (Illus.). 208p. pap. 17.95 *(978-0-9764409-4-7(3))* All Out Pr. CAN. Dist: Independent Pubs. Group.

Poon, Shuk-wah. Negotiating Religion in Modern China: State & Common People in Guangzhou, 1900 — 1937. 2011. (ENG., Illus.). 230p. (gr. 17). 45.00 *(978-962-996-421-4(X))* Chinese Univ. of Hong Kong, The HKG. Dist: Columbia Univ. Pr.

Pruitt, Ida. A Daughter of Han: The Autobiography of a Chinese Working Woman. 2009. 270p. 39.00 *(978-1-59740-736-6(4))*; 268p. pap. 26.00 *(978-1-59740-758-8(5))* ACLS Humanities E-Book.

Pruitt, Ida & Tai Tai, Ning Lao. A Daughter of Han: The Autobiography of a Chinese Working Woman. 2011. 266p. pap. 10.50 ***(978-1-61427-094-2(5))*** Martino Publishing.

Qiu, Zhengbao, et al. Long Nan Baima Ren Min Su Wen Hua Yan Jiu: Longnan Baimaren Minzu Wenhua Yanjiu, 2 vols. 2009. (CHI., Illus.). *(978-7-226-03854-3(4))* Gansu People's Publishing Hse.

Quan, Li. Rewilded: Saving the South China Tiger. 2011. (ENG & CHI., Illus.). 248p. 49.00 ***(978-1-901268-54-6(3),*** 1901268543) Evans Mitchell Bks. GBR. Dist: MBI Distribution Services/Quayside Distribution.

Rebol, Max. Factor Endowments in a South- South Relation: Trade Preferences, Migration & Inequality for Chinain Africa. 2008. 52p. pap. *(978-3-639-11220-7(2))* VDM Verlag Dr. Mueller e.K.

Reid, Daniel P. The Art & Alchemy of Chinese Tea. 2011. (ENG.). 240p. ***(978-1-84819-086-3(7))*** Kingsley, Jessica Ltd.

Rennie, David Field. Peking & the Pekingese During the First Year of the British Embassy at Peking. 2009. 178p. pap. 19.99 *(978-1-150-00505-3(X))* General Bks. LLC.

Renouf, Alice & Ryan-Maher, Mary Beth. Yin-Yang: American Perspectives on Living in China. 2011. ***(978-1-4422-1271-8(3))*** Rowman & Littlefield Publishers, Inc.

Renouf/Ryan-Maher. China Survival Guide: American Perspectives on Living in China. 2011. (ENG.). 246p. 70.00 ***(978-1-4422-1269-5(1))*** Rowman & Littlefield Publishers, Inc.

—Yin-Yang: American Perspectives on Living in China. 2011. (ENG.). 246p. pap. 22.95 ***(978-1-4422-1270-1(5))*** Rowman & Littlefield Publishers, Inc.

Rhodes, Bill. Hillbilly in China. 2008. 80p. pap. 16.95 *(978-1-60672-344-9(8))* PublishAmerica, Inc.

Robson, James. Power of Place: The Religious Landscape of the Southern Sacred Peak (Nanyue) in Medieval China. 2009. (Harvard East Asian Monographs: 316). (MUL., Illus.). 450p. 49.95 *(978-0-674-03332-0(9))* Harvard Univ., Asia Ctr.

Rojas, Carlos. The Great Wall: A Cultural History. 2010. (ENG., Illus.). 232p. 24.95 *(978-0-674-04787-7(7))* Harvard Univ. Pr.

Ru, X. & Lu, X., eds. The China Society Yearbook, Volume 3: Analysis & Forecast of China's Social Development (2008) 2009. (Chinese Academy of Social Sciences Yearbooks: Society Ser.). *(978-90-04-17350-7(1))* BRILL.

Santangelo, Paolo & Middendorf, Ulrike. From Skin to Heart: Perceptions of Emotions & Bodily Sensations in Traditional Chinese Culture. 2006. (Lun Wen Ser.: Vol. 11). (ENG.). 332p. (C). pap. 87.00 *(978-3-447-05458-4(1))* Harrassowitz, Otto Verlag DEU. Dist: ISD.

Scott, Janet Lee. For Gods, Ghosts & Ancestors: The Chinese Tradition of Paper Offerings. 2007. 352p. pap. *(978-962-209-827-5(4))*; (ENG., Illus.). pap. *(978-0-295-98718-7(9))* Hong Kong Univ. Pr.

Scott, John Lee. Narrative of a Recent Imprisonment in China after the Wreck of the Kite. 2010. (Cambridge Library Collection - Travel & Exploration Ser.). (ENG., Illus.). 156p. pap. 19.99 *(978-1-108-01380-2(5))* Cambridge Univ. Pr.

Serejski, Eric. Chinese Kama Sutra. 2007. 186p. pap. 20.99 *(978-0-615-15310-0(0))* Innovations & Information, Inc.

—Kama Sutra Chinois. 2007. 176p. pap. 20.99 *(978-0-615-15337-7(2))* Innovations & Information, Inc.

Shanghai Daily. Snapshots Lifestyl. 2010. 132p. pap. 16.95 *(978-1-60220-402-7(0))* BetterLink Pr., Inc.

—Snapshots of New. 2010. 110p. pap. 15.95 *(978-1-60220-400-3(4))* BetterLink Pr., Inc.

Shaoming, Zhou. Funeral Rituals in Eastern Shandong, China: An Anthropological Study. 2009. (Illus.). 286p. 109.95 *(978-0-7734-3890-3(4))* Mellen, Edwin Pr., The.

Shaughnessy, Edward L. & Shaughessy, Edward. China: El mundo chino, creencias y rituales, creacion y Descubrimientos. Portillo, Miguel, tr. 2009. (SPA.). 256p. pap. 15.95 *(978-84-8076-768-2(5))* Blume ESP. Dist: Independent Pubs. Group.

Shek, Daniel T.L., et al. Positive Youth Development: Evaluation & Future Directions in a Chinese Context. 2011. pap. ***(978-1-62100-175-1(X))*** Nova Science Pubs., Inc.

Shepherd, Robert. Partners in Paradise: Tourism Practices, Heritage Policies, & Anthropological Sites. 2011. (Asian Thought & Culture Ser.). 152p. (C). pap. 68.95 ***(978-1-4331-1609-4(X))*** Lang, Peter Publishing, Inc.

Shih, Chuan-Kang. Quest for Harmony: The Moso Traditions of Sexual Union & Family Life. 2009. (ENG., Illus.). 352p. 65.00 *(978-0-8047-6199-4(X))* Stanford Univ. Pr.

Shirokogorov, Sergei M. Anthropology of Eastern China & Kwantung Province. (China Classic & Contemporary Works in Reprint Ser.). reprint ed. 42.50 *(978-0-404-56945-7(5))* AMS Pr., Inc.

Simons, Rowan. Bamboo Goalposts: One Man's Quest to Teach the People's Republic of China to Love Football. 2008. (ENG.). 386p. pap. 21.95 *(978-0-230-70702-3(5))* Macmillan Pubs., Ltd. GBR. Dist: Independent Pubs. Group.

—Bamboo Goalposts: One Man's Quest to Teach the People's Republic of China to Love Football. (ENG.). 2009. 400p. pap. 12.95 *(978-0-330-50672-4(2))* 2008. (Illus.). 386p. 29.95 *(978-0-230-70372-8(0))* Macmillan Pubs., Ltd. GBR. Dist: Independent Pubs. Group.

Sleith III, Eric A. That's How the Fortune Cookie Crumbles. 2009. 147p. pap. 14.98 *(978-0-557-10133-7(6))* Lulu Enterprises Inc.

Smith, Arthur Henderson. Chinese Characteristics. 2009. 236p. pap. *(978-1-4590-4134-9(8))* Books LLC.

—Chinese Characteristics. 2008. 378p. 48.95 *(978-1-4366-5728-0(8))*; 380p. pap. 33.95 *(978-0-548-89581-8(3))* Kessinger Publishing, LLC.

—Chinese Characteristics. 2008. 380p. pap. *(978-1-4097-9904-7(2))* Read Bks.

Smith, Robert, et al. Eastern & Western Daily Culture: Intercultural Communication in China. 2007. (ENG., Illus.). 252p. pe. 19.95 *(978-1-58736-790-8(4))* Wheatmark.

Standaert, Nicolas. The Interweaving of Rituals: Funerals in the Cultural Exchange Between China & Europe. 2008. (China Program Book Ser.). (ENG., Illus.). 336p. 65.00 *(978-0-295-98810-8(X))* Univ. of Washington Pr.

—Interweaving of Rituals: Funerals in the Cultural Exchange between China & Europe. 2008. (China Program Book Ser.). (ENG., Illus.). 336p. pap. 30.00 *(978-0-295-98823-8(1))* Univ. of Washington Pr.

Stein, Peter & Lowe, Felicia, prods. Chinatown. (Neighborhoods Ser.). *(978-0-912333-54-0(5),* SOMA Bks.) Bay Soma Publishing.

Stone, Laura. I Give Seven Chicken. 2007. 215p. pap. 16.95 *(978-1-4303-1001-3(4))* Lulu Enterprises Inc.

Strittmatter, Kai. China: An Introduction to the Culture & People. 2012. (Armchair Traveller Ser.). (ENG.). 171p. pap. 11.95 ***(978-1-907973-17-8(6))*** Haus Publishing GBR. Dist: Consortium Bk. Sales & Distribution.

Strittmatter, Kai. China A-Z. Tobler, Stefan, tr. from GER. 2006. (Armchair Traveller Ser.). (ENG., Illus.). 316p. 19.95 *(978-1-904950-80-6(9))* Haus Publishing GBR. Dist: Consortium Bk. Sales & Distribution.

Su-Ling, Wong & Cressy, Earl Herbert. Daughter of Confucius: A Personal History. 2011. 392p. 53.95 ***(978-1-258-06740-3(4))*** Literary Licensing, LLC.

Su, Shuyang. A Reader on China. 2010. 174p. pap. 9.95 *(978-1-60220-901-5(4))* BetterLink Pr., Inc.

Tadla, Ernie. How to Live & Do Business in China: Eight Lessons I Learned from the Communists. 2007. (Illus.). 148p. per. 19.13 *(978-1-4251-0120-6(8))* Trafford Publishing.

Tak-Kwong, Chan, et al, eds. Religion & Science in the Context of Chinese Culture. 2006. (Science & Theology Ser.). (ENG.). 206p. (C). per. 5.00 *(978-1-920691-19-6(7))* ATF Pr. AUS. Dist: Brown, David Bk. Co., The.

Tam, Kwok-kan & Siu-han Yip, Terry, eds. Gender, Discourse, & the Self in Literature: Issues in Mainland China, Taiwan, & Hong Kong. 2010. (ENG.). 250p. (gr. 17). 42.00 *(978-962-996-399-6(X))* Chinese Univ. of Hong Kong, The HKG. Dist: Columbia Univ. Pr.

Tarocco, Francesca. The Cultural Practices of Modern Chinese Buddhism: Attuning the Dharma. 2008. (Routledge Critical Studies in Buddhism Ser.). (ENG., Illus.). 208p. 160.00 *(978-0-415-37503-0(7))* Routledge.

Thargyal, Rinzin. Nomads of Eastern Tibet: Social Organization & Economy of a Pastoral Estate in the Kingdom of Dege. Huber, Toni, ed. 2007. (Brill's Tibetan Studies Library). (Illus.). 222p. *(978-90-04-15813-9(8))* BRILL.

Thomson, John, et al. China: Through the Lens of John Thomson (1868-1872) 2nd ed. 2010. (ENG., Illus.). 168p. *(978-616-7339-00-9(7),* River Bks. Pr. Dist A C) Antique Collectors' Club.

Thrasher, Alan R. Sizhu Instrumental Music of South China: Ethos, Theory & Practice. 2008. (Sinica Leidensia Ser.). (Illus.). 220p. *(978-90-04-16500-7(2))* BRILL.

Tong, Kurt, photos by. In Case It Rains in Heaven. 2011. (ENG., Illus.). 96p. 40.00 ***(978-3-86828-188-0(6))*** Kehrer Verlag Heidelberg, Klaus Kehrer DEU. Dist: Consortium Bk. Sales & Distribution.

Tong, Shaosu. Folk Culture in China's Zhejiang Province, Illustrated: The Flowing Mother River. 2009. pap. *(978-1-931907-62-0(5))* Homa & Sekey Bks.

Troost, J. Maarten. Lost on Planet China: One Man's Attempt to Understand the World's Most Mystifying Nation. 2009. (ENG.). 400p. pap. 14.95 *(978-0-7679-2201-2(8))* Broadway Bks.

Tsui, Christine. China Fashion: Conversations with Designers. 2010. (ENG., Illus.). 256p. 109.95 *(978-1-84520-514-0(6))* Berg Pubs. GBR. Dist: Macmillan.

—China Fashion: Conversations with Designers. 2010. (ENG., Illus.). 256p. pap. 39.95 *(978-1-84520-515-7(4))* Berg Pubs. GBR. Dist: Macmillan.

UC Publishing Staff & Newburn, Denny. Action Literacy: China. 2008. 32p. pap. 10.95 *(978-0-86431-695-0(X))* ACER Pr. AUS. Dist: International Specialized Bk. Services.

University of Pittsburgh Chinese Studies Faculty Staff & University of Pittsburgh Chinese Studies Faculty, eds. Contemporary Chinese Societies: Continuity & Change, CD for Windows and Macintosh. 2nd ed. 2007. (Edinburgh Edition of the Waverley Novels Ser.). (ENG.). (gr. 17). 51.50 *(978-0-231-13982-3(9))* Columbia Univ. Pr.

Van Ziegert, Sylvia. Global Spaces of Chinese Culture: Diasporic Chinese Communities in the United States & Germany. 2009. 232p. 39.95 *(978-0-415-80578-0(3))* Routledge.

Vernezze, Peter J. Socrates in Sichuan: Chinese Students Search for Truth, Justice, & the (Chinese) Way. 2011. 212p. 26.95 *(978-1-59797-672-5(5))* Potomac Bks., Inc.

Wang, Fuchun. The North East Men. 2009. (CHI & ENG., Illus.). 101p. *(978-0-9814698-5-0(X))* International Publishing Hse. for China's Culture.

Wang, Jinjie. Gay & Lesbian in Their Eyes: Chinese University Students' Perspectives TowardTheir Gay & Lesbian Peers. 2008. 124p. pap. *(978-3-639-10119-5(7))* VDM Verlag Dr. Mueller e.K.

Wang, Lin & Wei, Xiaohao. Living in China: How to Feel at Home, Make Friends & Enjoy Everyday Life. 2008. (Illus.). 84p. pap. 12.50 *(978-0-86647-267-8(3))* Hood, Alan C. & Co., Inc.

Wang, Robin R. Yinyang: The Way of Heaven & Earth in Chinese Thought & Culture. 2012. (New Approaches to Asian History Ser.). (ENG., Illus.). 196p. (C). pap. 26.99 ***(978-0-521-16513-6(X))*** Cambridge Univ. Pr.

Wang, Xueying, et al. Gateway to Chinese Language & Culture: A Complete Interactive Course, 6 vols. 2008. (C). stu. ed. 73.95 incl. cd-rom *(978-0-88727-432-9(3))* Cheng & Tsui Co.

Wang, Zhaoqian & Lü, Guangqun. Zhongguo Nuo Wen Hua: Zhongguonuowenhua. 2007. (CHI., Illus.). 352p. *(978-7-81120-077-5(5))* Shantou Daxue Chubanshe.

Wei, Liming. Chinese Festivals. 3rd ed. 2011. (Introductions to Chinese Culture Ser.). (ENG., Illus.). 146p. pap. 19.99 ***(978-0-521-18659-9(5))*** Cambridge Univ. Pr.

Wei, Xiang. Chinese Customs. Chang, Benjamin & Lingque, Hu, trs. 2010. (ENG., Illus.). 116p. pap. 15.95 *(978-1-60220-104-0(8))* BetterLink Pr., Inc.

Weiner, Rebecca. CultureShock! Shanghai. 2007. (Illus.). 344p. pap. 15.95 *(978-981-261-130-7(4))* Marshall Cavendish International (Asia) Private Ltd. SGP. Dist: Marshall Cavendish Corp.

Weiner, Rebecca & EAGAN, ANGIE. Shanghai, 1 vol. 2008. (CultureShock! Ser.). (ENG.). 344p. pap. 15.95 *(978-0-7614-5493-9(4))* Marshall Cavendish Corp.

Weiner, Rebecca, et al. China: CultureShock!, 1 vol. 2nd ed. 2007. (Cultureshock China: A Survival Guide to Customs & Etiquette Ser.). (ENG., Illus.). 32p. pap. 15.95 *(978-0-7614-5403-8(9))* Marshall Cavendish Corp.

Wellens, Koen. Religious Revival in the Tibetan Borderlands: The Premi of Southwest China. 2010. (Studies on Ethnic Groups in China Ser.). (ENG., Illus.). 288p. (C). 70.00 *(978-0-295-99068-2(6))*; pap. 30.00 *(978-0-295-99069-9(4))* Univ. of Washington Pr.

Wenzhong, Hu, et al. Encountering the Chinese: A Cultural Guide to the People's Republic. 3rd ed. 2010. (ENG., Illus.). 224p. pap. 24.95 *(978-1-931930-99-4(6))* Ebsco Publishing.

West, James. Beijing Blur: A Head-Spinning Journey into Modern China. 2008. 230p. pap. 14.95 *(978-0-9788259-6-6(9))* Chilmark Pr., The.

Wilcox, Cynthia Waiying Wu. The Love of Lotus. 2006. xi, 217p. pap. 17.00 *(978-0-9786135-8-7(9))* Tyde House Bks.

William Poy Lee. The Eighth Promise: An American Son's Tribute to His Toisanese Mother. 2007. pap. 12.50 *(978-1-60529-854-2(9))* Rodale Pr., Inc.

Williams, S. Wells. The Middle Kingdom: A Survey of the Geography, Government, Literature, Social Life, Arts & History of the Chinese Empire & Its in Habitants, 2 vols. 2006. (Kegan Paul China Library). (Illus.). 892p. 500.00 *(978-0-7103-1167-2(2))* Taylor & Francis Group.

Windridge, Charles. Tong Sing. 2011. (ENG., Illus.). 288p. pap. 19.95 ***(978-0-85783-010-4(4))*** Kyle Bks. GBR. Dist: National Bk. Network.

Wood, Frances. No Dogs & Not Many Chinese. (Illus.). xiii, 368p. 50.00 *(978-0-7195-5758-3(5))* Murray, John GBR. Dist: Trafalgar Square Publishing.

Wu, Baolin, et al. The Eight Immortals' Revolving Sword of Pure Yang. 2011. (Illus.). 210p. pap. 29.95 *(978-1-931483-19-3(1))* Three Pines Pr.

Wu, Cuncun & Stevenson, Mark, eds. Homoeroticism in Imperial China. 2012. (ENG.). 272p. (C). 130.00 ***(978-0-415-55144-1(7))*** Routledge.

C

Wu, Juanjuan. Chinese Fashion: From Mao to Now. 2009. (Dress, Body, Culture Ser.). (ENG., Illus.). 1p. 99.95 *(978-1-84520-778-6(5))*; pap. 34.95 *(978-1-84520-779-3(3))* Berg Pubs. GBR. Dist: Macmillan.

Wu, Yi-Li. Reproducing Women: Medicine, Metaphor, & Childbirth in Late Imperial China. 2010. (ENG., Illus.). 378p. 49.95 *(978-0-520-26068-9(6))* Univ. of California Pr.

Xiang, Debao. From Propaganda to Persuasion. 2010. 288p. pap. *(978-3-639-24405-2(2))* VDM Verlag Dr. Mueller e.K.

Xiang, Wei. Chinese Customs (Bilingual) 2010. 194p. pap. 11.95 *(978-1-60220-916-9(2))* BetterLink Pr., Inc.

Xinjiang Weiwu'er Zizhiqu cong kan bian ji zu Staff & "Zhongguo shao shu min zu she hui li shi diao cha zi liao cong kan" xiu ding bian ji wei yuan hui Staff, contrib. by. Ke'erkezi Zu She Hui Li Shi Diao Cha: Ke'erkezizushehuilishidiaocha. 2009. (CHI., Illus.). *(978-7-105-08780-8(3))* Nationalities Publishing Hse, The.

Xu, Zhuoyun. Rivers in Time: A Cultural History of China. 2012. 576p. ***(978-0-231-52818-4(3))*** Columbia Univ. Pr.

Xu, Zhuoyun & Hsu, Cho-Yun. China: A New Cultural History. Baker, Timothy D. & Duke, Michael S., trs. from CHI. 2012. (Masters of Chinese Studies). (ENG., Illus.). 632p. (gr. 17). 120.00 ***(978-0-231-15920-3(X))*** Columbia Univ. Pr.

Xu, Zhuoyun & Hsu, Cho-yun. China: A New Cultural History. Baker, Timothy D. & Duke, Michael S., trs. from CHI. 2012. (Masters of Chinese Studies). (ENG., Illus.). 632p. (gr. 17). pap. 40.00 ***(978-0-231-15921-0(8))*** Columbia Univ. Pr.

Yajun, Zhang. A Kaleidoscope of Chinese Culture. 2008. (CHI.). 256p. pap. 19.95 *(978-7-80200-400-9(4))* Sinolingua CHN. Dist: China Bks. & Periodicals, Inc.

Yang, Lu. Living in China. 2008. 344p. pap. 19.95 *(978-7-80228-501-9(1))* New World Pr. CHN. Dist: China Bks. & Periodicals, Inc.

Yang, Shifan. Ting Jian "Naluwan" (Na-Lu-Wan) Jin Wu Shi Nian Taibei Xian du Shi Yuan Zhu Min Min Yao de Xing Cheng Yu Liu Chuan Wen Hua Shi. 2009. (CHI., Illus.). 164p. *(978-986-6552-53-3(5))* Tonsan Pubn., Inc.

Yang, Shuhui & Yang, Yunqin. Essays from Women Writers. 2010. 130p. pap. 9.95 *(978-1-60220-900-8(6))* BetterLink Pr., Inc.

Yeh, Chiou-Ling. Making an American Festival: Chinese New Year in San Francisco's Chinatown. 2008. (Illus.). 336p. 60.00 *(978-0-520-25350-6(7))*; pap. 26.95 *(978-0-520-25351-3(5))* Univ. of California Pr.

Yeh, Wen-hsin. Shanghai Splendor: A Cultrual History, 1843-1945. 2008. (Illus.). 320p. pap. 26.95 *(978-0-520-25817-4(7))* Univ. of California Pr.

Yong, Wu. The Chinese You Need to Know: Get to Know the Chinese within Five Minutes. 2011. pap. 8.99 ***(978-1-61777-396-9(4))*** Tate Publishing & Enterprises, LLC.

Yu, Jimmy Yung Fung. Sanctity & Self-Inflicted Violence in Chinese Religions, 1500-1700. 2012. E-Book ***(978-0-19-984489-0(5))***; (ENG., Illus.). 288p. pap. 29.95 ***(978-0-19-984490-6(9))*** Oxford Univ. Pr., Inc.

Yu, Miao. Imagining & Inventing Shanghai. 2008. 88p. pap. *(978-3-639-05519-1(5))* VDM Verlag Dr. Mueller e.K.

Yu, Ning. The Chinese Heart in a Cognitive Perspective: Culture, Body, & Language. 2009. (Applications of Cognitive Linguistics [ACL] Ser.). (ENG., Illus.). IX, 444p. 137.00 *(978-3-11-020516-9(5))* De Gruyter, Mouton DEU. Dist: de Gruyter, Walter GmbH & Co. KG.

Yu, Ning. The Chinese HEART in a Cognitive Perspective: Culture, Body, & Language. 2009. (Applications of Cognitive Linguistics [ACL] Ser.). (ENG.). IX, 444p. 210.00 ***(978-3-11-173245-9(2))*** De Gruyter, Mouton DEU. Dist: de Gruyter, Walter GmbH & Co. KG.

Yu, Sinian. Wen Hua Yu Kuan Rong: Culture & Tolerance. 2009. (CHI.). *(978-7-5097-0960-3(1))* China Social Science Documentation Publishing Hse.

Yuan, Haiwang & Chunde, Zheng. Princess Peacock: Tales from the Other Peoples of China, 1 vol. 2008. (World Folklore Ser.). (Illus.). 332p. 35.00 *(978-1-59158-416-2(7)*, LU4167) Libraries Unlimited, Inc.

Yue, Guo & Farrow, Clare. Music, Food & Love: A Memoir with Recipes. 2009. (ENG., Illus.). 272p. pap. 19.95 *(978-0-7499-2934-3(0))* Piatkus Bks. GBR. Dist: Independent Pubs. Group.

Yun, Ling. Chinese Tea. 2010. (Discovering China Ser.). (ENG., Illus.). 112p. 14.95 *(978-1-60220-106-4(4))* BetterLink Pr., Inc.

Zhang, Kaiyuan. Distanciation & Return: Analysis on Traditional Culture & Modernization of China. 2011. (ENG.). 256p. 108.00 ***(978-981-4332-22-4(4))*** Enrich Professional Publishing (S)., Ltd. SGP. Dist: Independent Pubs. Group.

Zheng, Gu. Robert van der Hilst: Shanghai 1990-1993. 2009. (ENG., Illus.). 120p. 45.00 *(978-988-17521-5-4(9))* Timezone 8 Ltd. HKG. Dist: D.A.P./Distributed Art Pubs.

Zhou, Kate. China's Long March to Freedom: Grassroots Modernization. 2009. (ENG., Illus.). 391p. 39.95 *(978-1-4128-1029-6(9))* Transaction Pubs.

Zhou, Yiqun. Festivals, Feasts, & Gender Relations in Ancient China & Greece. 2010. (ENG.). 373p. 90.00 *(978-0-521-19762-5(7))* Cambridge Univ. Pr.

Zhu, Judy. Modern Chinese Cultural Encounters: Volume I Studying & traveling in China. 2009. 128p. pap. 13.95 *(978-1-4401-3323-7(9))* iUniverse, Inc.

Zuo, Wenjing. Uses of Discourse Markers in a Chinese English TV Show. 2010. 252p. pap. *(978-3-8383-7191-7(7))* Lambert Academic Publishing.

ZZ. China High: My Fast Times in the 010 - A Beijing Memoir. 2010. (ENG.). 368p. pap. 15.99 *(978-0-312-60556-8(0)*, St. Martin's Griffin) St. Martin's Pr.

CHINA—STUDY AND TEACHING

Chan, Adrian. Orientalism in Sinology. 2009. 264p. lib. bdg. *(978-1-933146-61-4(3))* Academica Pr., LLC.

Chandler, Marthe & Littlejohn, Ronnie, eds. Polishing the Chinese Mirror: Essays in Honor of Henry Rosemont, Jr. 2008. (ACPA Series of Chinese & Comparative Philosophy). 432p. pap. 35.00 *(978-1-59267-083-3(0))* Univ. of Hawaii Pr.

Chinese New Year. (Early Intervention Levels Ser.). 50.88 *(978-0-7362-2130-6(1))*; 8.48 *(978-0-7362-1907-5(2))* Hampton-Brown Bks.

Coughlan, Chia-Mei Jane. The Study of China in Universities: A Comparative Case Study of Australia & the United Kingdom. 2008. 104.95 *(978-1-60497-569-7(5))* Cambria Pr.

Dotson, Brandon. Contemporary Visions in Tibetan Studies: Proceedings of the First International Seminar of Young Tibetologists. 2009. *(978-1-932476-45-3(8))* Serindia Pubns., Inc.

Harvard-Yenching Institute Staff. Yenching Journal of Chinese Studies, 1927-1949, 20 vols. (CHI.). 700.00 *(978-0-89986-260-6(8))* Bluffton Bks.

Jin, Lixian & Cortazzi, Martin, eds. Researching Chinese Learners: Skills, Perceptions & Intercultural Adaptations. 2011. (ENG., Illus.). 336p. 85.00 *(978-0-230-24388-0(6))* Palgrave Macmillan.

Kan, Flora L. F. Hong Kong's Chinese History Curriculum from 1945: Politics & Identity. 2007. (ENG.). 190p. (gr. 17). 60.00 *(978-962-209-836-7(3))* Hong Kong Univ. Pr. HKG. Dist: Columbia Univ. Pr.

Kan, Flora Lai-Fong. Hong Kong's Chinese History Curriculum from 1945: Politics & Identity. 2007. (ENG.). 190p. (gr. 17). pap. 22.95 *(978-962-209-837-4(1))* Hong Kong Univ. Pr. HKG. Dist: Columbia Univ. Pr.

Lian, Qingji. Riben Jingdu Zhongguo Xue Yu Dong Ya Wen Hua. 2010. (CHI.). ii, 318p. *(978-957-15-1492-5(6))*; pap. *(978-957-15-1491-8(8))* Taiwan Student Book Co., Ltd.

Mackinnon, Alex & Powell, Barnaby. China Counting: How the West Was Lost. 2009. (ENG., Illus.). 272p. 49.00 *(978-0-230-23403-1(8))* Palgrave Macmillan.

Sun, Jin. Die Universität als Raum kultureller Differenzerfahrung: Chinesische Studenten an einer deutschen Hochschule. 2010. (Europäische Hochschulschriften. Reihe 11: Pädagogik Ser.). (GER.). 336p. pap. 81.95 *(978-3-631-58546-7(2))* Lang, Peter GmbH, Europaischer Verlag der Wissenschaften DEU. Dist: Lang, Peter.

Wilson, Ming. Europe Studies China: Papers from an International Symposium on the History of European Sinology. Cayley, John, ed. 2006. (History of European Sinology Ser.). (ENG., Illus.). 352p. 50.00 *(978-1-891640-27-8(5))* Floating World Editions.

CHINA (PORCELAIN)

see Porcelain

CHINA INLAND MISSION

Austin, Alvyn. China's Millions: The China Inland Mission & Late Qing Society 1832-1905. 2007. (Studies in the History of Christian Missions). (Illus.). 506p. per. 45.00 *(978-0-8028-2975-7(9))* Eerdmans, William B. Publishing Co.

Clements, Ronald. Point Me to the Skies: The Amazing Story of Joan Wales. 2007. 320p. per. 13.99 *(978-0-8254-6157-6(X))* Monarch Bks.

Hayman, Arnolis. A Foreign Missionary on the Long March: The Memoirs of Arnolis Hayman of the China Inland Mission. 2010. (Illus.). xxxviii, 160p. pap. *(978-1-878282-96-5(4))* St. Johann Pr.

Owen, John, et al. Douthwaite of the Double Dragon: Portrait of a Medical Missionary: A Life Spent for God & Man: The Story of Dr Arthur William Douthwaite .... 2007. (Illus.). 176p. per. *(978-1-898030-13-3(8))* Braiswick.

Taylor, and Howard, et al. Hudson Taylor's Spiritual Secret, 1 vol. 2009. (Moody Classics Ser.). (ENG., Illus.). 272p. pap. 7.99 *(978-0-8024-5658-8(8))* Moody Pubs.

Taylor, Howard & Taylor, Geraldine. Hudson Taylor's Spiritual Secret. 2008. 216p. 14.95 *(978-1-59856-253-8(3))* Hendrickson Pubs. Marketing, LLC.

Taylor, Howard and Geraldine. Hudson Taylor's Spritual Secret. 2007. 194p. pap. 9.99 *(978-1-929122-32-5(2))* OMF Bks.

CHINA PAINTING

Alexiev, Dony. Painting on Porcelain: Composition & Technique. (French Art & Craft Bks.). (Illus.). 80p. pap. 19.95 *(978-2-84415-001-1(2))* Ulisse Editions FRA. Dist: Penton Overseas, Inc.

Baskett, Mickey. Really Jazzy Pots: Glorious Gift Ideas. 2006. (ENG., Illus.). 128p. pap. 14.95 *(978-1-4027-4069-5(7))* Sterling Publishing Co., Inc.

Buckley, Cheryl, ed. Potters & Paintresses: Women Designers in the Pottery Industry, 1870-1955. (Illus.). 208p. pap. 39.95 *(978-0-7043-4211-8(1))* Women's Pr., Ltd., The GBR. Dist: Trafalgar Square Publishing.

Byass, Rachel. Ceramic Painter's Pattern Book. 2007. (ENG., Illus.). 96p. pap. 19.95 *(978-1-84448-201-6(4))* Search Pr., Ltd. GBR. Dist: Independent Pubs. Group.

Campana, D. M. Beginner in China Painting. Date not set. 4.00 *(978-0-939608-32-4(4))* Campana Art Co.

—Enamel & Raised Paste: For the China Painter. rev. ed. reprint ed. 4.50 *(978-0-939608-45-4(6))* Campana Art Co.

—Teacher of China Painting. (Illus.). 17.95 *(978-0-939608-00-3(6))* Campana Art Co.

Di Ozesanmuseum Bamberg, et al, eds. Fragiles: Porcelain, Glass & Ceramics. 2008. (Illus.). 279p. *(978-3-89955-208-9(3))* Die Gestalten Verlag.

Embry, Karen. Painting on Glass & Ceramic. 2008. (ENG., Illus.). 128p. 24.95 *(978-1-4027-5264-3(4))* Sterling Publishing Co., Inc.

Gillen, Arlene Swiatek. Gorgeous Glass: 20 Sparkling Ideas for Painting on Glass & China. 2008. (ENG., Illus.). 128p. pap. 24.99 *(978-1-60061-006-6(4)*, North Light Bks.) F&W Media, Inc.

Held, Peter, ed. Eden Revisited: The Ceramic Art of Kurt Weiser. 2007. (ENG.). 96p. ***(978-0-9777624-5-3(9))*** Arizona State Univ. Art Museum.

Imhof, Phyllis. Painting China. (Craft Library). (Illus.). 32p. pap. 4.95 *(978-0-85532-583-1(6)*, 583-6) Search Pr., Ltd. GBR. Dist: Independent Pubs. Group.

Newell-Dunkey, Patricia. Painting & Decorating Porcelain. 2010. (ENG., Illus.). 172p. 34.95 *(978-0-7090-8649-9(0))* Hale, Robert Ltd. GBR. Dist: Independent Pubs. Group.

Paul, Lewing. China Paint & Overglaze. 2007. 288p. 59.95 *(978-1-57498-269-5(9)*, CA52) American Ceramic Society, The.

Waller, Richard & Denker, Ellen Paul. Faces & Flowers: Painting on Lenox China. 2009. pap. *(978-0-9765047-5-7(8))* Univ. of Richmond Museums.

Wittig, Irene. The Clay Canvas: Revised Edition. 2011. 140p. pap. 49.00 ***(978-1-257-19825-2(4))*** Lulu Enterprises Inc.

CHINA SEA

Antony, Robert J. Elusive Pirates, Pervasive Smugglers: Violence & Clandestine Trade in the Greater China Seas. 2010. 220p. ***(978-988-220-691-5(3))*** Hong Kong Univ. Pr.

Antony, Robert J., ed. Elusive Pirates, Pervasive Smugglers: Violence & Clandestine Trade in the Greater China Seas. 2010. (ENG., Illus.). 220p. (gr. 17). 45.00 *(978-988-8028-11-5(1))* Hong Kong Univ. Pr. HKG. Dist: Columbia Univ. Pr.

Bateman, Sam & Emmers, Ralf, eds. Security & International Politics in the South China Sea: Towards a co-operative management Regime. 2012. (Routledge Security in Asia Pacific Ser.). (ENG., Illus.). 272p. (C). pap. 42.95 ***(978-0-415-54214-2(6))*** Routledge.

Nizam Basiron, Mohd. Dispute Resolution in the South China Sea. 2012. (Routledge Security in Asia Pacific Ser.). (ENG.). 224p. (C). 140.00 *(978-0-415-66564-3(7))* Routledge.

Song, Jinming. Biogeochemical Processes of Biogenic Elements in China Marginal Seas. 2009. (Advanced Topics in Science & Technology in China Ser.). (ENG., Illus.). 676p. 219.00 *(978-3-642-04059-7(4)*, 3642040594) Springer.

Storey, Ian & Schofield, Clive. The South China Sea Dispute: Increasing Stakes & Rising Tensions. 2011. (ENG., Illus.). 42p. pap. 20.00 *(978-0-9816905-5-1(6))* Jamestown Foundation, The.

Yüan, Yung-Lun. History of the Pirates Who Infested the China Sea from 1807 To 1810. 2011. (Cambridge Library Collection - History Ser.). (ENG., Illus.). 228p. pap. 22.99 *(978-1-108-02920-9(5))* Cambridge Univ. Pr.

Zou, Keyuan & Wu, Shicun. Maritime Security in the South China Sea: Regional Implications & International Cooperation. 2009. (Corbett Centre for Maritime Policy Studies). (Illus.). 284p. 114.95 *(978-0-7546-7727-7(3))* Ashgate Publishing Co.

CHINATOWN (NEW YORK, N.Y.)

Ostrow, Daniel. Manhattan's Chinatown. 2008. (Postcard History Ser.). (ENG., Illus.). 128p. per. 19.99 *(978-0-7385-5517-1(7))* Arcadia Publishing.

Tan, Wendy Wan-Yin. Chinatowns of New York City. 2008. (Then & Now Ser.). (ENG., Illus.). 128p. pap. 19.99 *(978-0-7385-5510-2(X))* Arcadia Publishing.

Tsui, Bonnie. American Chinatown: A People's History of Five Neighborhoods. 2010. (ENG., Illus.). 288p. pap. 15.00 *(978-1-4165-5724-1(5)*, Free Pr.) Free Pr.

Volkwein, Ann. Chinatown New York: Portraits, Recipes, & Memories. 2007. (Illus.). 224p. 34.95 *(978-0-06-118859-6(X)*, Collins Design) HarperCollins Pubs.

CHINATOWN (SAN FRANCISCO, CALIF.)

Bowen, Robert W. & Bowen, Brenda Young. San Francisco's Chinatown. 2008. (Illus.). 128p. pap. 19.99 *(978-0-7385-5925-4(3))* Arcadia Publishing.

Chinese Historical Society of America, et al. San Francisco's Chinatown. 2006. (Images of America Ser.). (ENG., Illus.). 128p. per. 21.99 *(978-0-7385-3130-4(8))* Arcadia Publishing.

Jan, Lyle. Old Chinatown- Revisited. 2010. pap. 13.95 *(978-0-7414-6031-8(9))* Infinity Publishing.

Jorae, Wendy Rouse. The Children of Chinatown: Growing up Chinese American in San Francisco, 1850-1920. 2009. (ENG., Illus.). 304p. 62.95 *(978-0-8078-3313-1(4))*; pap. 24.95 *(978-0-8078-5973-5(7))* Univ. of North Carolina Pr.

Mullen, Kevin. Chinatown Squad. 2008. 208p. pap. 18.95 *(978-0-926664-10-4(7))* CounterPULSE.

Robbins, Trina. Forbidden City: The Golden Age of Chinese Nightclubs. 2009. *(978-1-57273-947-5(9))* Hampton Pr., Inc.

Tom, Lawrence, et al. Sacramento's Chinatown. 2010. (Images of America Ser.). (Illus.). 128p. pap. 21.99 *(978-0-7385-8066-1(X))* Arcadia Publishing.

Tsui, Bonnie. American Chinatown: A People's History of Five Neighborhoods. 2010. (ENG., Illus.). 288p. pap. 15.00 *(978-1-4165-5724-1(5)*, Free Pr.) Free Pr.

Yep, Kathleen. Outside the Paint: When Basketball Ruled at the Chinese Playground. 2009. (Asian American History & Culture Ser.). (ENG., Illus.). 216p. 21.95 *(978-1-59213-942-2(6))* Temple Univ. Pr.

CHINAWARE

see Porcelain; Pottery

CHINCHILLAS

Alderton, David. Chinchillas, 1 vol. 2007. (ENG., Illus.). 112p. 11.95 *(978-0-7938-3790-8(1))* TFH Pubns., Inc.

Anastasi, Donna. Chinchillas. 2008. (Complete Care Made Easy: Ser.). (ENG., Illus.). 160p. pap. 9.95 *(978-1-933958-15-6(4))* BowTie Pr.

Bartl, Juliana. Chinchillas. 2009. (Complete Pet Owner's Manual Ser.). (ENG., Illus.). 64p. pap. 8.99 *(978-0-7641-4293-2(3))* Barron's Educational Series, Inc.

CHINCOTEAGUE ISLAND (VA.)

Kavanagh, James. Assateague/Chincoteague Seashore Life: An Introduction to Familiar Species. 2007. (Pocket Naturalist - Waterford Press Ser.). (ENG., Illus.). 1p. 5.95 *(978-1-58355-336-7(3))* Waterford Pr., Inc.

Pritchett, Virginia Aten. Beautiful Land Across the Waters. 2006. (Illus.). 149p. pap. 9.95 *(978-0-9788446-0-8(2)*, Lite Circle Bks) Lite Circle, Inc., The.

Tigner, James. Chincoteague Island. 2008. (Illus.). 128p. bds. 29.99 *(978-0-7643-2919-7(7))* Schiffer Publishing, Ltd.

CHINCOTEAGUE PONY

Hooks, R. Owen. Pine Ridge Horse Farm's Illustrated Guide to the Wild Pony Auction at Chincoteague (2006 Edition), 1. 2nd ed. 2006. (Illus.). 96p. ring bd. 19.95 *(978-0-9771317-1-6(8))* Pine Ridge Horse Farm, Inc.

CHINESE

Anon. California & the Oriental. 2009. 244p. pap. 28.45 *(978-1-4446-2159-4(9))* Research Pr.

Benedict, Gerald, ed. Chinese Wisdom: The Way of Perfect Harmony. 2010. (Sacred Wisdom Ser.). (ENG.). 192p. 8.95 *(978-1-906787-44-8(1)*, Watkins Publishing) Duncan Baird Pubs. GBR. Dist: Sterling Publishing Co., Inc.

Benton, Gregor. Chinese Migrants & Internationalism: Forgotten Histories, 1971-1945. 2007. (Chinese Worlds (Routledge) Ser.). (Illus.). 170p. 180.00 *(978-0-415-41868-3(2))* Routledge.

Chan, Joyce Chee Wun. Pernicious Anaemia in Chinese. 2011. 164p. pap. ***(978-3-8443-8484-0(7))*** Lambert Academic Publishing.

Chan, Kwok-Bun, ed. International Handbook of Chinese Families. 2012. (ENG., Illus.). xxvii, 725p. 179.00 *(978-1-4614-0265-7(4)*, 1461402654) Springer.

Chen, Charles P. & Lee, Wendy. Ethnicity & Careers of Chinese-Canadian Young Adults. 2012. pap. ***(978-1-61324-268-1(9))*** Nova Science Pubs., Inc.

Chiu, Hsin-hui. The Colonial 'civilizing Process' in Dutch Formosa, 1624-1662. 2008. (TANAP Monographs on the History of Asian-European Interaction). (Illus.). 300p. *(978-90-04-16507-6(X))* BRILL.

Dieleman, Marleen & Koning, Juliette, eds. Chinese Indonesians & Regime Change. 2010. (Chinese Overseas Ser.). 236p. *(978-90-04-19121-1(6))* BRILL.

Evans, Brian L. The Other Side of Gold Mountain: Glimpses of Early Chinese Pioneer Life on the Prairies from the Wallace B. Chung & Madeline H. Chung Collection. 2010. (CHI & ENG., Illus.). 63p. pap. 25.00 *(978-1-55195-189-8(4))* Univ. of Alberta Pr. CAN. Dist: Michigan State Univ. Pr., Chicago Distribution Ctr.

Gao, Yun, ed. Concealed Chains: Labour Exploitation & Chinese Migrants in Europe. 2010. (ENG., Illus.). 250p. pap. 36.00 *(978-92-2-121993-4(3))* International Labour Office.

Lei, Daphne. Operatic China: Staging Chinese Identity Across the Pacific. 2006. (Palgrave Studies in Theatre & Performance History Ser.). (ENG., Illus.). 360p. 89.00 *(978-1-4039-7327-6(X))* Palgrave Macmillan.

Lui, Mary Ting Yi. The Chinatown Trunk Mystery: Murder, Miscegenation, & Other Dangerous Encounters in Turn-of-the-Century New York City. 2007. (ENG., Illus.). 320p. (C). per. 26.95 *(978-0-691-13048-4(5))* Princeton Univ. Pr.

Myler, Stephen F. The China Papers. 2011. 228p. pap. 9.99 ***(978-1-61667-317-8(6))*** Raider Publishing International.

Park, Yoon Jung. A Matter of Honour: Being Chinese in South Africa. 2009. (ENG., Illus.). 220p. pap. 30.00 *(978-1-77009-568-7(3))* Jacana Media ZAF. Dist: Independent Pubs. Group.

Topley, Marjorie. Cantonese Society in Hong Kong & Singapore: Gender, Religion, Medicine & Money. DeBernardi, Jean, ed. 2011. (Royal Asiatic Society Hong Kong Studies). (CHI., Illus.). 624p. ***(978-988-220-657-1(3))*** Hong Kong Univ. Pr.

Watanabe, Yoshihiro. Ryo Kan ni Okeru Shi to Sanden. 2007. (JPN.). 463p. *(978-4-7629-2838-3(0))* Kyuko Shoin.

Willmott, Donald E. The National Status of the Chinese in Indonesia, 1900-1958. 2010. 186p. pap. 29.95 *(978-602-8397-28-5(8))* Equinox Publishing IDN. Dist: Univ. of Hawaii Pr.

Zhang, Xing. Preserving Cultural Identity Through Education: The Schools of the Chinese Community in Calcutta, India. 2010. 104p. pap. ***(978-981-4279-87-1(0))*** Institute of Southeast Asian Studies.

CHINESE—CANADA

Amos, Robert & Wong, Kileasa. Inside Chinatown: Ancient Culture in a New World, 1 vol. 2010. (ENG., Illus.). 160p. pap. *(978-1-894898-91-1(5))* TouchWood Editions.

Chan, Arlene. The Chinese in Toronto From 1878: From Outside to Inside the Circle. 2011. (ENG., Illus.). 241p. pap. 35.00 *(978-1-55488-979-2(0))* Dundurn CAN. Dist: Ingram Pub. Services.

Cho, Lily. Eating Chinese. 2010. (Cultural Spaces Ser.). (Illus.). 224p. ***(978-1-4426-4105-1(3))***; pap. ***(978-1-4426-1040-8(9))*** Univ. of Toronto Pr.

Ding, Yueya. Negotiating Individual Space. 2010. 252p. pap. *(978-3-639-27523-0(3))* VDM Verlag Dr. Mueller e.K.

Fernando, Shanti. Race & the City: Chinese Canadian & Chinese American Political Mobilization. 2007. (ENG.). 192p. pap. 29.95 *(978-0-7748-1346-4(6))* UBC Pr. CAN. Dist: Univ. of Washington Pr.

Lai, David Chuenyan. Chinese Community Leadership: Case Study of Victoria in Canada. 2010. (Illus.). 284p. 58.00 *(978-981-4295-17-8(5))* World Scientific Publishing Co., Inc.

Lin, Paul. In the Eye of the China Storm: A Life Between East & West. 2011. (Illus.). 256p. (C). *(978-0-7735-3857-3(7))* McGill-Queen's Univ. Pr.

Mar, Lisa Rose. Brokering Belonging: Chinese in Canada's Exclusion ERA, 1885-1945. 2010. (ENG., Illus.). 256p. 99.00 *(978-0-19-973313-2(9))*; pap. 24.95 *(978-0-19-973314-9(7))* Oxford Univ. Pr., Inc.

Price, Lily Hoy. I Am Full Moon: Stories of a Ninth Daughter, 1 vol. 2009. (ENG., Illus.). 192p. pap. *(978-1-897142-38-7(2))* Brindle & Glass Publishing.

Roth, Marilyn A. & Kobayashi, Karen M. Complementary & Alternative Medicine among Chinese Canadians. 2010. (Public Health in the 21st Century Ser.). (Illus.). vii, 62p. pap. 43.00 *(978-1-61728-014-6(3))*, Nova Biomedical Bks.) Nova Science Pubs., Inc.

Roy, Patricia E. Triumph of Citizenship (the) The Japanese & Chinese in Canada, 1941-67. 2007. (ENG., Illus.). 400p. *(978-0-7748-1380-8(6))* Univ. of British Columbia Pr.

Stanley, Timothy J. Contesting White Supremacy: School Segregation, Anti-Racism, & the Making of Chinese Canadians. 2011. (ENG., Illus.). 344p. pap. 37.95 ***(978-0-7748-1932-9(4))*** Univ. of British Columbia Pr. CAN. Dist: Univ. of Washington Pr.

Wolf, Jim & Owen, Patricia. Yi Fao: Speaking Through Memory - A History of New Westminster's Chinese Community,1858-1980, 1 vo . rev. ed. 2008. (ENG., Illus.). 144p. pap. *(978-1-894974-40-0(9))* Heritage Hse.

CHINESE—FOREIGN COUNTRIES

An, Wu Xiao. Chinese Business Mending Malay. 2010. (Illus.). 239p. pap. 28.00 *(978-9971-69-496-8(4))* National Univ. of Singapore Pr. SGP. Dist: Univ. of Hawaii Pr.

Archer, Louise & Francis, Becky. Understanding Minority Ethnic Achievement: Race, Gender, Class & Success. 2006. (Illus.). 205p. 160.00 *(978-0-415-37281-7(X))* Routledge.

—Understanding Minority Ethnic Achievement: Race, Gender, Class And 'Success' 2006. (Illus.). 205p. per. 46.95 *(978-0-415-37282-4(8))* Routledge.

Barabantseva, Elena. Overseas Chinese, Ethnic Minorities & Nationalism: De-Centering China. 2010. (Routledge Studies in Asia's Transformations Ser.). (ENG., Illus.). 224p. (C). 130.00 *(978-0-415-57950-6(3))* Routledge.

Barrett, Tracy C. The Chinese Diaspora in South-East Asia: The Overseas Chinese in Indo-China. 2012. (Library of China Studies). (ENG., Illus.). 256p. 95.00 ***(978-1-78076-134-3(1))*** I. B. Tauris & Co., Ltd. GBR. Dist: Macmillan.

Benton, Gregor. Chinatowns. 2015. (Cultural Spaces Ser.). (ENG.). 256p. 145.00 *(978-0-415-95217-0(4))*; pap. 31.95 *(978-0-415-95213-7(2))* Routledge.

—The Chinese in Cuba, 1847-Now. 2009. (AsiaWorld Ser.). (ENG., Illus.). 298p. 78.99 *(978-0-7391-3343-9(8))* Lexington Bks.

Benton, Gregor, et al. The Chinese in Britain, 1800-Present: Economy, Transnationalism & Identity. 2008. (Palgrave Macmillan Transnational History Ser.). (ENG., Illus.). 486p. 110.00 *(978-0-230-52229-9(7))* Palgrave Macmillan.

Cantonese Society in Hong Kong & Singapore: Gender, Religion, Medicine & Money. 2011. 626p. *(978-9971-69-524-8(3))* Hong Kong Univ. Pr.

Carter, Marina & Ng Foong Kwong, James. Abacus & Mah Jong: Sino-Mauritian Settlement & Economic Consolidation. 2009. (European Expansion & Indigenous Response Ser.). 200p. *(978-90-04-17572-3(5))* BRILL.

Chan, Kwok Bun. Chinese Identities, Ethnicity & Cosmopolitanism. 2009. 174p. pap. 39.95 *(978-0-415-54670-6(2))* Routledge.

Chee-Beng, Tan, ed. Chinese Transnational Network. 2007. (Chinese Worlds Ser.). (Illus.). 214p. 160.00 *(978-0-415-39583-0(6))* Routledge.

Ch'en, Jerome & Tarling, Nicholas, eds. Studies in the Social History of China & South-East Asia: Essays in Memory of Victor Purcell. 2010. 434p. pap. 32.99 *(978-0-521-13374-6(2))* Cambridge Univ. Pr.

Chu, Richard T. Chinese & Chinese Mestizos of Manila: Family, Identity, & Culture, 1860s-1930s. 2010. (Chinese Overseas Ser.). (Illus.). 451p. *(978-90-04-17339-2(0))* BRILL.

Dawis, Aimee. The Chinese of Indonesia & Their Search for Identity: The Relationship Between Collective Memory & the Media. 2009. 109.99 *(978-1-60497-606-9(3))* Cambria Pr.

Delgado, Grace. Making the Chinese Mexican: Global Migration, Localism, & Exclusion in the U. S.-Mexico Borderlands. 2012. (ENG.). 320p. 65.00 ***(978-0-8047-7814-5(0))*** Stanford Univ. Pr.

Dieleman, Mareen. The Rhythm of Strategy: A Corporate Biography of the Salim Group of Indonesia. 2008. (ICAS Publications Ser.). (Illus.). 205p. pap. *(978-90-5356-033-4(5))* Amsterdam Univ. Pr.

Fitzgerald, John. Big White Lie: Chinese Australians in White Australia. 2007. (ENG., Illus.). 312p. per. 40.95 *(978-0-86840-870-5(0)*, UNSW Press) NewSouth Publishing AUS. Dist: Independent Pubs. Group.

Fong, Eric & Luk, Chiu, eds. Chinese Ethnic Business: Global & Local Perspectives. 2009. 248p. pap. 39.95 *(978-0-415-54691-1(5))* 2006. (ENG., Illus.). 272p. (C). 180.00 *(978-0-415-39718-6(9))* Routledge.

Formoso, Bernard. De Jiao: A Religious Movement in Contemporary China & Overseas: Purple Qi from the East. 2010. (Illus.). 280p. pap. 28.00 *(978-9971-69-492-0(1))* National Univ. of Singapore Pr. SGP. Dist: Univ. of Hawaii Pr.

Gomez, Edmund Terence & Benton, Gregor. The Chinese in Britain, 1800 - Present: Economy, Transnationalism, Identity. 2011. (ENG., Illus.). 496p. pap. 28.95 *(978-0-230-29641-1(6))* Palgrave Macmillan.

Göransson, Kristina. The Binding Tie: Chinese Intergenerational Relations in Modern Singapore. 2009. (C). 57.00 *(978-0-8248-3259-9(0))*; (Illus.). x, 191p. pap. 26.00 *(978-0-8248-3352-7(X))* Univ. of Hawaii Pr.

Guan, Yeoh. Penang & Its Neighbors. 260p. pap. 28.00 *(978-9971-69-423-4(9))* National Univ. of Singapore Pr. SGP. Dist: Univ. of Hawaii Pr.

Haley, George T, et al. New Asian Emperors: The Business Strategies of the Overseas Chinese. rev. ed. 2009. (ENG., Illus.). 250p. pap. 24.95 *(978-0-470-82334-7(8)*, Wiley) Wiley, John & Sons, Inc.

Heald, Denise. The Journey Toward Employment for Chinese Student Teachers. 2008. 180p. pap. *(978-3-8364-9682-7(8))* VDM Verlag Dr. Mueller e.K.

Hoon, Chang-Yau. Chinese Identity in Post-Suharto Indonesia: Culture, Politics & Media. (Sussex Library of Asian Studies Ser.). 230p. 2011. pap. 34.95 *(978-1-84519-474-1(8))* 2008. (ENG.). (C). 69.95 *(978-1-84519-268-6(0))* Sussex Academic Pr. GBR. Dist: International Specialized Bk. Services.

Huang, Shu-Min. Reproducing Chinese Culture in Diaspora: Sustainable Agriculture & Petrified Culture in Northern Thailand. 2009. (ENG.). 146p. 62.99 *(978-0-7391-2599-1(0))* Lexington Bks.

Hui, Yew-Foong. Strangers at Home: History & Subjectivity among the Chinese Communities of West Kalimantan, Indonesia. 2011. (Chinese Overseas Ser.). (Illus.). XVI, 344p. ***(978-90-04-17340-8(4))*** BRILL.

Ip, Manying. Being Maori Chinese: Mixed Identities. 2008. (ENG., Illus.). 200p. pap. 34.95 *(978-1-86940-399-7(1))* Auckland Univ. Pr. NZL. Dist: Independent Pubs. Group.

Ip, Manying. Transmigration & the New Chinese: Theories & Practices from the New Zealand Experience. 2011. (CHI & ENG.). 300p. (gr. 17). pap. 19.50 ***(978-962-8269-58-7(5))*** Hong Kong Univ. Pr. HKG. Dist: Columbia Univ. Pr.

Ip, Manying, ed. The Dragon & the Taniwha: Maori & Chinese in New Zealand. 2009. (ENG., Illus.). 360p. pap. 34.95 *(978-1-86940-436-9(X))* Auckland Univ. Pr. NZL. Dist: Independent Pubs. Group.

Jin, Lixian & Cortazzi, Martin, eds. Researching Chinese Learners: Skills, Perceptions & Intercultural Adaptations. 2011. (ENG., Illus.). 336p. 85.00 *(978-0-230-24388-0(6))* Palgrave Macmillan.

Kawakami, K. K. Manchoukuo: Child of Conflict. reprint ed. 20.00 *(978-0-404-03639-3(2))* AMS Pr., Inc.

Khoo, Olivia. The Chinese Exotic: Modern Diasporic Femininity. 2007. (TransAsia: Screen Cultures Ser.). (ENG., Illus.). 228p. (gr. 17). 60.00 *(978-962-209-879-4(7))*; pap. 28.00 *(978-962-209-889-3(4))* Hong Kong Univ. Pr. HKG. Dist: Columbia Univ. Pr.

Kinloch-Cooke, Clement. Chinese Labour in the Transvaal. 39p. reprint ed. 88.00 *(978-0-7222-9811-4(0))* Library Reprints, Inc.

Koh, Ernest. Singapore Stories: Language, Class, & the Chinese of Singapore, 1945-2000. 2010. *(978-1-60497-677-9(2))* Cambria Pr.

Kuah-pearce, Khun Eng. At Home in the Chinese Diaspora: Memories, Identities & Belongings. Kuah-Pearce, Khun Eng & Davidson, Andrew P., eds. 2008. (ENG., Illus.). 288p. 100.00 *(978-0-230-50698-5(4))* Palgrave Macmillan.

Kuah-Pearce, Khun Eng. Rebuilding the Ancestral Village: Singaporeans in China. 2011. (ICAS Publications Ser.). (ENG.). 304p. pap. ***(978-90-8964-332-2(X))*** Amsterdam Univ. Pr.

—Rebuilding the Ancestral Village: Singaporeans in China. 2010. (CHI., Illus.). 308p. ***(978-988-8053-66-7(3))***; ***(978-988-220-733-2(2))*** Hong Kong Univ. Pr.

Kuhn, Philip A. Chinese among Others: Emigration in Modern Times. 2009. (State & Society East Asia Ser.). (ENG.). 452p. pap. 39.95 *(978-0-7425-6749-8(4))* Rowman & Littlefield Publishers, Inc.

L, Dinu, photos by. The Mother of All Journeys. 2007. (ENG., Illus.). 96p. 45.00 *(978-1-904587-41-5(0))* Lewis, Dewi Publishing GBR. Dist: Consortium Bk. Sales & Distribution.

Lin, David. Chinese Print Media in Nz Present Ideas of Chinese Cultural Identity. 2009. 100p. pap. *(978-3-639-14031-6(1))* VDM Verlag Dr. Mueller e.K.

Lo, Meihan. Quality of Life among Elderly Chinese Immigrants in Australi. 2010. 180p. pap. *(978-3-8383-1342-9(9))* Lambert Academic Publishing.

Luk, Wai-Ki. Chinatown in Britain: Diffusions & Concentrations of the British New Wave Chinese Immigration. 2007. (C). 114.95 *(978-1-934043-86-8(9))* Cambria Pr.

Moeller, Hans-Georg & Tan Editors. Chinese Overseas: Migration, Research & Documentation. Chee-Beng, Tan et al, eds. 2007. (ENG., Illus.). 420p. (gr. 17). 55.00 *(978-962-996-328-6(0))* Chinese Univ. of Hong Kong, The HKG. Dist: Columbia Univ. Pr.

Munro, Aeneas. The Transvaal Chinese Labour Problem. 164p. reprint ed. 88.00 *(978-0-7222-9813-8(7))* Library Reprints, Inc.

Ng, Maria & Holden, Philip. Reading Chinese Transnationalisms: Society, Literature, Film. 2006. (ENG., Illus.). 248p. (gr. 17). 60.00 *(978-962-209-796-4(0))*; pap. 24.95 *(978-962-209-797-1(9))* Hong Kong Univ. Pr. HKG. Dist: Columbia Univ. Pr.

Ngan, Lucille Lok-Sun & Kwok-bun, Chan. The Chinese Face in Australia: Multi-Generational Ethnicity among Australian-Born Chinese. 2012. (ENG., Illus.). xv, 140p. 129.00 ***(978-1-4614-2130-6(6)***, 1461421306) Springer.

Nyíri, Pal. Chinese in Eastern Europe & Russia: A Middleman Minority in a Transnational Era. 2012. (Chinese Worlds Ser.). (ENG., Illus.). 192p. (C). pap. 42.95 ***(978-0-415-54106-0(9))*** Routledge.

Nyíri, Pál & Nyíri, Pál. Chinese in Eastern Europe & Russia: A Middleman Minority in a Transnational ERA. 2008. (Chinese Worlds Ser.). (Illus.). 192p. 160.00 *(978-0-415-44686-0(4))* Routledge.

Ouyang, Yu. Chinese in Australian Fiction, 1888-1988. 2008. 556p. (C). 139.95 *(978-1-60497-516-1(4))* Cambria Pr.

Park, Yoon Jung. A Matter of Honour: Being Chinese in South Africa. 2009. (AsiaWorld Ser.). (ENG., Illus.). 248p. 70.00 *(978-0-7391-3553-2(8))* Lexington Bks.

Pearson, Stuart & Raben, Remco. Bittersweet: The Memoir of a Chinese Indonesian Family in the Twentieth Century. Shaffer, Wendie, tr. 2008. (Ohio RIS Southeast Asia Ser.). (ENG., Illus.). 352p. pap. 28.00 *(978-0-89680-264-3(7))* Ohio Univ. Pr.

Peterson, Glen. Overseas Chinese in the People's Republic of China. 2011. (Chinese Worlds Ser.). (ENG., Illus.). 248p. (C). 130.00 *(978-0-415-61670-6(0))* Routledge.

Rae, Ian & Witzel, Morgen. The Overseas Chinese of South East Asia: History, Culture, Business. 2008. (ENG.). 256p. 95.00 *(978-1-4039-9165-2(0))* Palgrave Macmillan.

Rastall, P. R. Internationalising the University: The Chinese Context. Coverdale-Jones, Tricia & Rastall, Paul, eds. 2009. (ENG., Illus.). 256p. 100.00 *(978-0-230-20351-8(5))* Palgrave Macmillan.

Reid, Anthony. The Chinese Diaspora in the Pacific. 2008. (Pacific World: Lands, Peoples & History of the Pacific, 1500-1900 Ser.). 444p. 190.00 *(978-0-7546-5749-1(3))* Ashgate Publishing Co.

Sai, Siew-Min & Hoon, Chang-Yau, eds. Chinese Indonesians Reassessed: History, Religion & Belonging. 2012. (Routledge Contemporary Southeast Asia Ser.). (ENG., Illus.). 256p. (C). 145.00 *(978-0-415-60801-5(5))* Routledge.

Siu, Lok C. D. Memories of a Future Home: Diasporic Citizenship of Chinese in Panama. 2007. (ENG., Illus.). 272p. per. 21.95 *(978-0-8047-5846-8(8))* Stanford Univ. Pr.

Skinner, G. William. Chinese Society in Thailand: An Analytical History. 2008. 492p. pap. 48.00 *(978-1-59740-606-2(6))* ACLS Humanities E-Book.

Somers, Mary F. Peranakan Chinese Politics in Indonesia. 2010. 84p. pap. 29.95 *(978-602-8397-35-3(0))* Equinox Publishing IDN. Dist: Univ. of Hawaii Pr.

Sun, Wanning. Media & the Chinese Diaspora: Community, Communications & Commerce. 2009. 226p. pap. 39.95 *(978-0-415-54563-1(3))* Routledge.

Suryadinata, ed. Southeast Asia's Chinese Businesses in an Era of Globalization. 2006. 384p. *(978-981-230-401-8(0))* Institute of Southeast Asian Studies.

Suryadinata, Leo. Ethnic Chinese in Contemporary Indonesia. 2008. (Illus.). 224p. *(978-981-230-835-1(0))* Institute of Southeast Asian Studies.

—Understanding the Ethnic Chinese in Southeast Asia. 2007. (Illus.). x, 310p. *(978-981-230-437-7(1))* Institute of Southeast Asian Studies.

Tan, Chee-Beng. Chinese Transnational Networks. 2009. 214p. pap. 39.95 *(978-0-415-56057-3(8))* Routledge.

Taylor Jeremy E. Rethinking Transnational Chinese Cinema. 2011. (Media, Culture & Social Change in Asia Ser.). (ENG., Illus.). 192p. (C). 140.00 *(978-0-415-49355-0(2))* Routledge.

Thunø, Mette, ed. Beyond Chinatown: New Chinese Migration & the Global Expansion of China. 2007. (Nias Studies in Asian Topics Ser.). (Illus.). 281p. pap. 27.00 *(978-87-7694-000-3(4))* Nordic Institute of Asian Studies DNK. Dist: Univ. of Hawaii Pr.

Tian, Xiaofei. Visionary Journeys: Travel Writings from Early Medieval & Nineteenth-Century China. 2012. (Harvard-Yenching Institute Monograph Ser.: 78). (ENG.). 398p. 39.95 *(978-0-674-06252-8(3))* Harvard Univ., Asia Ctr.

Tong, Chee Kiong. Identity & Ethnic Relations in Southeast Asia: Racializing Chineseness. 2010. (ENG.). viii, 274p. 189.00 *(978-90-481-8908-3(X)*, 904818908X) Springer.

Turner, Vernon. The Chinese in Indonesia - a Socio-Cultural History. 2008. 296p. pap. *(978-3-639-00350-5(0))* VDM Verlag Dr. Mueller e.K.

Van Ziegert, Sylvia. Global Spaces of Chinese Culture: Diasporic Chinese Communities in the United States & Germany. 2006. (Studies in Asian Americans Ser.). (Illus.). 229p. 130.00 *(978-0-415-97890-3(4))* Taylor & Francis Group.

Vasu, Norman. How Diasporic Peoples Maintain Their Identity in Multicultural Societies: Chinese, Africans, & Jews. 2009. (Illus.). iii, 273p. *(978-0-7734-4896-4(9))* Mellen, Edwin Pr., The.

Visscher, Sikko. The Business of Politics & Ethnicity: A History of the Singapore Chinese Chamber of Commerce & Industry. 2007. (Illus.). 372p. per. 32.00 *(978-9971-69-365-7(8))* Univ. of Hawaii Pr.

Wang, Hong. Skilled Migration & the Knowledge Society. 2008. 160p. pap. *(978-3-639-02348-0(X))* VDM Verlag Dr. Mueller e.K.

Wanning, Sun. Media & the Chinese Diaspora: Community, Communications & Commerce. 2006. (Media, Culture, & Social Change in Asia Ser.: Vol. 5). (ENG., Illus.). 240p. (C). 170.00 *(978-0-415-35204-8(5))* Routledge.

Wong, Pak Nung. Post-Colonial Statecraft in South East Asia: Sovereignty, State Building & the Chinese in the Philippines. 2012. (ENG., Illus.). 320p. 99.00 ***(978-1-84885-897-8(3))*** I. B. Tauris & Co., Ltd. GBR. Dist: Macmillan.

Wu, Bin. Whose Culture Has Capital: Class, Culture, Migration & Mothering. 2011. 205p. pap. *(978-3-0343-0605-8(9))* Lang, Peter.

Yen & Yan, Qinghuang. The Chinese in Southeast Asia & Beyond: Socioeconomic & Political Dimensions. 2008. 400p. (C). 104.00 *(978-981-279-047-7(0))* World Scientific Publishing Co., Inc.

Yoder, Lawrence M. The Muria Story: A History of the Chinese Mennonite Churches of Indonesia. (Illus.). 386p. 34.00 *(978-1-894710-60-2(6))* Pandora Pr. CAN. Dist: Herald Pr.

Yu, Shanjiang. Early Signs of Language Shifting. 2008. 212p. pap. *(978-3-639-07241-9(3))* VDM Verlag Dr. Mueller e.K.

Zhang, Wei. Academic Adaptation Experiences of Chinese Graduate Students in Japan. 2010. 132p. pap. *(978-3-8383-5516-0(4))* Lambert Academic Publishing.

Zimmer, Lisa. Germany through Chinese Eyes: Is Germany a Destination for Travelers from Chinaapart from a Stop at a Round Trip through Europe? 2008. 164p. pap. *(978-3-639-09445-9(X))* VDM Verlag Dr. Mueller e.K.

CHINESE—UNITED STATES

see also Chinese Americans

Ahmad, Diana L. The Opium Debate & Chinese Exclusion Laws in the Nineteenth-Century American West. 2011. 152p. pap. 21.95 *(978-0-87417-844-9(4))* 2007. (ENG.). 208p. 34.95 *(978-0-87417-698-8(0))* Univ. of Nevada Pr.

Bieler, Stacey. 'Patriots' Or 'Traitors'? A History of American-Educated Chinese Students. 2009. (ENG.). 544p. pap. 42.95 *(978-0-7656-1187-1(2)*, East Gate Bk.) Sharpe, M.E. Inc.

Bunnin, Nicholas, et al, eds. Lévinas Vol. 35: Chinese & Western Perspectives. 2009. (Journal of Chinese Philosophy Supplement Ser.: 1). (ENG.). 200p. pap. 39.95 *(978-1-4051-9545-4(2)*, Wiley-Blackwell) Wiley, John & Sons, Inc.

California. Legislature. Senate. Special. Chinese Immigration the Social, Moral, & Political Effect of Chinese Immigration Testimony Taken Before a Committee of the Senate of the State Of. 2006. 184p. per. 18.99 *(978-1-4255-1457-0(X))* MPublishing.

Chinese America: History & Perspectives, 1996. 185p. pap. *(978-0-9614198-9-9(X))* Chinese Historical Society of America.

Chinese America: History & Perspectives, 1997. 179p. pap. *(978-1-885864-05-5(1))* Chinese Historical Society of America.

Chinese America: History & Perspectives, 1998. 88p. pap. 15.00 *(978-1-885864-07-9(8))* Chinese Historical Society of America.

Conwell, Russell Herman. Why & How: Why the Chinese Emigrate, & the Means they Adopt for the Purpose of Reaching America, with Sketches of Travel, Amusing incidents, Soci. 2006. 304p. per. 23.99 *(978-1-4255-2842-3(2))* MPublishing.

Corbett, Christopher. The Poker Bride: The First Chinese in the Wild West. 2010. (ENG.). 240p. 24.00 *(978-0-8021-1909-4(3)*, Atlantic Monthly Pr.) Grove/Atlantic, Inc.

Evans, Karin. The Lost Daughters of China: Adopted Girls, Their Journey to America, & the Search for a Missing Past. 2008. (ENG.). 400p. (gr. 12-18). 14.95 *(978-1-58542-676-8(8)*, Tarcher) Penguin Group (USA) Inc.

Gibson, Otis. The Chinese in America. 2009. 176p. pap. *(978-0-217-07167-3(8))* Books LLC.

Kwong, Peter & Miscevic, Dusanka. Chinese America: The Untold Story of America's Oldest New Community. 2007. (ENG., Illus.). 518p. per. 21.95 *(978-1-59558-119-8(7))* New Pr., The.

Lee, Josephine Tsui Yueh. New York City's Chinese Community. 2007. (Images of America Ser.). (ENG., Illus.). 128p. per. 19.99 *(978-0-7385-5018-3(3))* Arcadia Publishing.

Lee, Su Kim. A Nyonya in Texas: Insights of a Straits Chinese Woman in the Lone Star State. 2007. (Illus.). xii, 186p. *(978-983-3346-10-3(3))* Marshall Cavendish Corp.

Leibovitz, Liel & Miller, Matthew. Fortunate Sons: The 120 Chinese Boys Who Came to America, Went to School, & Revolutionized an Ancient Civilization. 2011. (ENG., Illus.). 320p. 26.95 *(978-0-393-07004-0(2)*, 7004) Norton, W. W. & Co., Inc.

Lim, Kieng Sieu. Red Undertow. 2010. 622p. pap. 27.88 *(978-0-557-55476-8(4))* Lulu Enterprises Inc.

Ooligan Press. Dreams of the West: A History of the Chinese in Oregon, 1850-1950. 2007. (Illus.). 112p. 29.95 *(978-1-932010-21-3(1))* Ooligan Pr.

Schiavone Camacho, Julia María. Chinese Mexicans: Transpacific Migration & the Search for a Homeland, 1910-1960. 2012. (ENG., Illus.). 256p. 39.95 ***(978-0-8078-3540-1(4))*** Univ. of North Carolina Pr.

Soennichsen, John Robert. The Chinese Exclusion ACT of 1882. 2011. xvi, 179p. E-Book *(978-0-313-37947-5(5)*, Greenwood Pr.) Greenwood Publishing Group, Inc.

—The Chinese Exclusion Act of 1882. 2011. (Landmarks of the American Mosaic Ser.). 179p. 35.00 *(978-0-313-37946-8(7)*, GR7946) Greenwood Publishing Group, Inc.

Tingfang, Wu. America Through the Spectacles of an Oriental Diplomat. 2007. (Anthem Travel Classics Ser.). (ENG., Illus.). 174p. per. 18.99 *(978-1-84331-269-7(7))* Anthem Pr. GBR. Dist: Books International, Inc.

To, Wing-Kai & Chinese Historical Society of New England. Chinese in Boston: 1870-1965. 2008. (Images of America Ser.). (ENG., Illus.). 128p. per. 21.99 *(978-0-7385-5529-4(0))* Arcadia Publishing.

Tseng, Timothy & Chuck, James. The 2008 Report: Bay Area Chinese Churches Research Project, Phase II. 2009. 276p. pap. 20.00 *(978-0-578-01248-3(0))* ISAAC.

Tsuai, Yung Yung & Sorel, Marilyn Meeske. The Difference in Butterflies: A Chinese Dancer's Memoir of Her Flight from Inner & Outer Tyranny. 2007. 196p. per. 16.95 *(978-0-595-47325-0(3))* iUniverse, Inc.

Van Norden, Warner M. Who's Who of the Chinese in New York. 2008. 160p. 39.95 *(978-1-4181-7524-5(2))* MPublishing.

Woo, Helen. You Can Not Choose Your Parents. 2011. 92p. 19.95 ***(978-1-4620-3152-8(8))***; pap. 9.95 ***(978-1-4620-3153-5(6))*** iUniverse, Inc.

Yang, Belle. Forget Sorrow: An Ancestral Tale. 2011. (ENG., Illus.). 250p. pap. 15.95 *(978-0-393-33996-3(3)*, 33996) Norton, W. W. & Co., Inc.

Zhang, Gehui. New Immigrants, New Christians - Mainland Chinese Elders in American Churches. 2008. 64p. pap. *(978-3-8364-3911-4(5))* VDM Verlag Dr. Mueller e.K.

Zheng, Da. Chiang Yee: The Silent Traveller from the East — A Cultural Biography. 2010. (ENG., Illus.). 358p. (C). 49.95 *(978-0-8135-4693-3(1))* Rutgers Univ. Pr.

Zhou, Min. Contemporary Chinese America: Immigration, Ethnicity, & Community Transformation. 2009. (Asian American History & Culture Ser.). (ENG., Illus.).

C

328p. 91.50 (978-1-59213-857-9(8)); pap. 29.95 (978-1-59213-858-6(6)) Temple Univ. Pr.

CHINESE AMERICANS

Baozhen, Luo. Shopping Cultures. 2007. 140p. per. (978-3-8364-3618-2(3)) VDM Verlag Dr. Mueller e.K.

Bloom, Harold, ed. Amy Tan. 2nd rev. ed. 2008. (Bloom's Modern Critical Views Ser.). 216p. (C). (gr. 9). 45.00 (978-1-60413-179-6(9), Chelsea Hse.) Facts On File, Inc.

Brown, Rita Keeley. A Pawn of Fate: A true story of a search for Identity. 2008. 208p. pap. 14.95 (978-1-4327-2715-4(X)) Outskirts Pr., Inc.

Butcher, Beverly J. Chinese & Chinese American Ancestor Veneration in the Catholic Church, 635 A.D. to the Present. 2010. (CHI & ENG., Illus.). viii, 447p. 129.95 (978-0-7734-3624-4(3)) Mellen, Edwin Pr., The.

Chai, May-Lee. Hapa Girl: A Memoir. (Illus.). 232p. 2008. (ENG.). pap. 22.95 (978-1-59213-616-2(8)) 2007. 63.50 (978-1-59213-615-5(X)) Temple Univ. Pr.

Chan, Sucheng, et al, eds. Chinese Americans & the Politics of Race & Culture. 2008. (Asian American History & Culture Ser.). (ENG., Illus.). 288p. pap. 29.95 (978-1-59213-753-4(9)) Temple Univ. Pr.

Chan, Sucheng & Hsu, Madeline, eds. Chinese Americans & the Politics of Race & Culture. 2008. (Asian American History & Culture Ser.). (ENG., Illus.). 288p. (C). 83.50 (978-1-59213-752-7(0)) Temple Univ. Pr.

Chang, Derek. Citizens of a Christian Nation: Evangelical Missions & the Problem of Race in the Nineteenth Century. (Politics & Culture in Modern America Ser.). 248p. (C). 2012. pap. 24.95 **(978-0-8122-2206-7(7))** 2010. (Illus.). 39.95 (978-0-8122-4218-8(1)) Univ. of Pennsylvania Pr.

Chang, Ying-Ying. The Woman Who Could Not Forget: Iris Chang Before & Beyond the Rape of Nanking - A Memoir. 2011. (ENG., Illus.). 400p. 29.95 (978-1-60598-172-7(9), 605172) Pegasus Bks.

Chen, Stephen. Red Circle: China & Me 1949-2009. 2009. (ENG.). 552p. pap. 19.95 (978-1-4490-3365-1(2)) AuthorHouse.

Cheng, Hsin-I. Culturing Interface: Identity, Communication, & Chinese Transnationalism. 2008. (Critical Intercultural Communication Studies: Vol. 11). 236p. (C). 69.95 (978-1-4331-0235-6(8)) Lang, Peter Publishing, Inc.

Cheng, Shirley. The Revelation of a Star's Endless Shine: A Young Woman's Autobiography of 20-Year Victories over Victimization. 2008. 700p. pap. 36.97 (978-0-615-15044-4(6)) Dance With Your Heart! Publishing.

Chinese American Society. The Rocky Road to Liberty: A Documented History of Chinese Immigration & Exclusion. Dong, Jielin & Hu, Sen, eds. 2010. 252p. pap. 50.00 (978-1-60267-028-0(5), Business Pr.) Javvin Pr.

Chinese Historical and Cultural Project, et al. Chinese in San Jose & the Santa Clara Valley. 2007. (Images of America Ser.). (ENG., Illus.). 128p. per. 19.99 (978-0-7385-4777-0(8)) Arcadia Publishing.

Ching, Frank. Ancestors: The Story of China Told Through the Lives of an Extraordinary Family. 2010. (ENG., Illus.). 544p. pap. 14.95 (978-1-84604-177-8(5)) Random Hse. GBR. Dist: Independent Pubs. Group.

Chinn, Allen. A Kung-Fu Master's Journey. 2009. 128p. pap. 19.99 (978-0-557-11572-3(8)) Lulu Enterprises Inc.

Chinn, Allen. Rebirth from the Ashes. 2011. 104p. pap. 13.50 **(978-1-4583-7336-6(3))** Lulu Enterprises Inc.

Cho, Jenny & Chinese Historical Society of Southern California. Chinatown & China City in Los Angeles. 2011. (Postcard History Ser.). (Illus.). 128p. pap. 21.99 (978-0-7385-8165-1(8)) Arcadia Publishing.

—Chinatown in Los Angeles. 2009. (Images of America Ser.). (ENG., Illus.). 128p. pap. 21.99 (978-0-7385-6956-7(9)) Arcadia Publishing.

Chua, Amy. Battle Hymn of the Tiger Mother. 2011. (ENG.). 256p. (gr. 12). 16.00 **(978-0-14-312058-2(1)**, Penguin (Non-Classics)); (Illus.). 25.95 (978-1-59420-284-1(2), Penguin Pr. HC, The) Penguin Group (USA) Inc.

Chung, Arthur W. Bitter Roots. 2007. (Illus.). 157p. 18.00 (978-1-928753-25-4(6)) Pacific Heritage Bks.

Chung, Sue Fawn. In Pursuit of Gold: Chinese American Miners & Merchants in the American West. 2011. (Asian American Experience Ser.). (ENG., Illus.). 288p. 55.00 (978-0-252-03628-6(X)) Univ. of Illinois Pr.

Clayborn, Hannah. Historic Photos of the Chinese in California. 2009. (Historic Photos Ser.). (ENG.). 206p. 39.95 (978-1-59652-519-1(3)) Turner Publishing Co.

Corbett, Christopher. The Poker Bride: The First Chinese in the Wild West. (ENG.). 240p. 2011. pap. 14.95 (978-0-8021-4527-7(2), Grove Pr.) 2010. 24.00 (978-0-8021-1909-4(3), Atlantic Monthly Pr.) Grove/Atlantic, Inc.

Cup Choy, Robert K. Life's Road: The Legacy of David Ah Fong Cup Choy. Date not set. (Illus.). 74p. pap. (978-0-9670036-0-3(1)) Choy, Robert K. H. Cup.

Dong, Lan. Reading Amy Tan, 1 vol. 2009. (Pop Lit Book Club Ser.). 138p. 40.00 (978-0-313-35546-2(0), GR5546) Greenwood Publishing Group, Inc.

Du, Liang. Learning to Be Chinese American: Community, Education, & Ethnic Identity. 2010. (ENG.). 152p. 60.00 (978-0-7391-3848-9(0)) Lexington Bks.

Earth Passages: Journeys Through Childhood. 2008. 96p. 32.95 (978-0-615-18298-8(4)) Foo, Lora Jo.

Fat, Paul B. Tjon Sie. Chinese New Migrants in Suriname: The Inevitability of Ethnic Performing. 2009. (UvA Proefschriften Ser.). 478p. pap. (978-90-5629-598-1(5), Vossiupers UvA) Amsterdam Univ. Pr.

Fawn Chung, Sue. The Chinese in Nevada. 2011. (Images of America Ser.). (Illus.). 128p. pap. 21.99 (978-0-7385-7494-3(5)) Arcadia Publishing.

Feng, Pin-Chia. Diasporic Representations: Reading Chinese American Women's Fiction. 2011. 200p. pap. 49.95 **(978-3-643-10831-9(1))** Lit Verlag DEU. Dist: Transaction Pubs.

Fernando, Shanti. Race & the City: Chinese Canadian & Chinese American Political Mobilization. 2007. (ENG.). 192p. pap. 29.95 (978-0-7748-1346-4(6)) UBC Pr. CAN. Dist: Univ. of Washington Pr.

Fong, Gary. The Accidental Millionaire: How to Succeed in Life Without Really Trying. 2009. (ENG.). 272p. pap. 14.95 (978-1-933771-91-5(7)) BenBella Bks.

Fong-Torres, Ben. The Rice Room: Growing up Chinese-American from Number Two Son to Rock 'n' Roll. 2nd rev. ed. 2011. (ENG.). 296p. pap. 21.95 (978-0-520-26968-2(3)) Univ. of California Pr.

Fowler, Josephine. Japanese & Chinese Immigrant Activists: Organizing in American & International Communist Movements, 1919-1933. 2007. (ENG., Illus.). 296p. (C). 70.00 (978-0-8135-4040-5(2)); per. 27.95 (978-0-8135-4041-2(0)) Rutgers Univ. Pr.

Gong, Ginny. From Ironing Board to Corporate Board: My Chinese Laundry Experience in America. 2008. pap. (978-1-931907-50-7(1)) Homa & Sekey Bks.

Jih, Jiausen. An Ordinary Person. 2010. pap. 0.00 (978-1-4276-4594-4(9)) Aardvark Global Publishing.

Johnson, Yanling L. Love Stories of Three Kinds: Finding Love, Faith, & Freedom in an Authoritarian Society, 1 vol. 2009. 404p. pap. 29.95 (978-1-60749-556-7(2)) PublishAmerica, Inc.

Jorae, Wendy Rouse. The Children of Chinatown: Growing up Chinese American in San Francisco, 1850-1920. 2009. (ENG., Illus.). 304p. 62.95 (978-0-8078-3313-1(4)); pap. 24.95 (978-0-8078-5973-5(7)) Univ. of North Carolina Pr.

Jung, John. Chinese Laundries: Tickets to Survival on Gold Mountain. 2007. 258p. pap. 17.95 (978-1-4303-2979-4(3)) Lulu Enterprises Inc.

Jung, Moon-Ho. Coolies & Cane: Race, Labor, & Sugar in the Age of Emancipation. 2008. (ENG., Illus.). 288p. (gr. 17). pap. 27.00 (978-0-8018-9082-6(9)) Johns Hopkins Univ. Pr.

Kamen, Paula. Finding Iris: Friendship, Ambition, & an Extraordinary Mind. 2007. (ENG.). 304p. 26.00 (978-0-306-81466-2(8)) Da Capo Pr., Inc.

Kingston, Maxine Hong. I Love a Broad Margin to My Life. (Vintage International Ser.). (ENG.). 240p. 2012. pap. 15.00 **(978-0-307-45459-1(2)**, Vintage) 2011. 24.95 (978-0-307-27019-1(X), Knopf) Knopf Doubleday Publishing Group.

Kondo-Brown, Kimi & Brown, James Dean, eds. Teaching Chinese, Japanese, & Korean Heritage Language Students: Curriculum Needs, Materials, & Assessment. 2007. (ESL & Applied Linguistics Professional Ser.). 346p. per. 39.95 (978-0-8058-5878-5(4)); (Illus.). 130.00 (978-0-8058-5877-8(6)) Erlbaum, Lawrence Assocs., Inc.

Lai, Him Ma. Becoming Chinese American. 2008. (ENG.). 182p. pap. 29.95 (978-0-7591-0454-9(9)) AltaMira Pr.

Lai, Him Mark & Hsu, Madeline Y. Chinese American Transnational Politics. 2010. (Asian American Experience Ser.). (ENG., Illus.). 296p. 75.00 (978-0-252-03525-8(9)); pap. 30.00 (978-0-252-07714-2(8)) Univ. of Illinois Pr.

Lan, Shanshan. Diaspora & Class Consciousness: Chinese Immigrant Workers in Multiracial Chicago. 2011. E-Book **(978-0-203-12807-7(9))**; (ENG., Illus.). 218p. (C). 125.00 (978-0-415-89036-6(5)) Routledge.

Lau, Estelle T. Paper Families: Identity, Immigration Administration, & Chinese Exclusion. 2007. (Politics, History, & Culture Ser.). (ENG., Illus.). 232p. (C). 79.95 (978-0-8223-3735-5(5)) Duke Univ. Pr.

—Paper Families: Identity, Immigration Administration, & Chinese Exclusion. 2007. (Politics, History, & Culture Ser.). (ENG., Illus.). 232p. per. 22.95 (978-0-8223-3747-8(9)) Duke Univ. Pr.

Lee, Erika. At America's Gates. (978-0-8047-3948-1(X)) Stanford Univ. Pr.

Lee, Jennifer B. The Fortune Cookie Chronicles: Adventures in the World of Chinese Food. 2009. (ENG.). 320p. pap. 13.00 (978-0-446-69897-9(0), Twelve) Grand Central Publishing.

Lee, Murray K. In Search of Gold Mountain: A History of the Chinese in San Diego, California. 2010. (978-1-57864-644-9(8)) Donning Co. Pubs.

Lee, William Poy. The Eighth Promise: An American Son's Tribute to His Toisanese Mother. 2007. (ENG.). 336p. pap. 14.95 (978-1-59486-811-5(5)) Rodale Pr., Inc.

Leung, L. P. Portraits of Pride II - Chinese-American Legacies - First 160 Years in America. 2011. (Illus.). 288p. 40.00 (978-0-930377-01-4(X)) Chinese Historical Society of Southern California, Inc.

Li. Journey Across the Four Seas. 2006. 250p. pap. (978-1-931907-43-9(9)) Homa & Sekey Bks.

Li, Jinzhao. Race, Beauty, & Politics in Chinese American Festivals: A History of National & Transnational Identity Construction. 2012. (Studies in Asian Americans Ser.). (ENG.). 224p. 125.00 (978-0-415-87118-1(2)) Routledge.

Li, Wei. Ethnoburb: The New Ethnic Community in Urban America. 2009. (Illus.). 214p. (C). 56.00 (978-0-8248-3065-6(2)) Univ. of Hawaii Pr.

Lin, Jun. Parental Expectations of Chinese Immigrants for Children's School Achievement: Sociocultural Context, Psychological Adjustment, & Educational Consequences. 2009. 232p. 109.95 (978-0-7734-4837-7(3)) Mellen, Edwin Pr., The.

Ling, Huping. Chinese Chicago: Race, Transnational Migration, & Community Since 1870. 2012. (Asian America Ser.). (ENG., Illus.). 336p. 80.00 **(978-0-8047-7558-8(3))**; pap. 24.95 **(978-0-8047-7559-5(1))** Stanford Univ. Pr.

Ling, Huping. Chinese in St. Louis: 1857-2007. 2007. (Images of America Ser.). (ENG., Illus.). 128p. per. 19.99 (978-0-7385-5145-6(7)) Arcadia Publishing.

Liu, Wendy. Everything I Understand about America I Learned in Chinese Proverbs. 2009. 173p. pap. 16.95 (978-1-931907-52-1(8)) Homa & Sekey Bks.

Louie, Emma Woo. Chinese American Names: Tradition & Transition. alt. ed. 2008. (ENG., Illus.). 240p. pap. 29.95 (978-0-7864-3877-8(0)) McFarland & Co., Inc. Pubs.

Lydon, Sandy. Chinese Gold: The Chinese in the Monterey Bay Region. 2nd enl. ed. 2008. (Illus.). 592p. 29.95 (978-0-932319-10-4(6)); pap. 19.95 (978-0-932319-11-1(4)) Capitola Bk. Co.

Maisto, Michelle. The Gastronomy of Marriage: A Memoir of Food & Love. 2009. (ENG.). 256p. pap. 15.00 (978-0-8129-7919-0(2), Random Hse. Trade Paperbacks) Random House Publishing Group.

Mao, LuMing. Reading Chinese Fortune Cookie: The Making of Chinese American Rhetoric. 2006. 190p. per. 22.95 (978-0-87421-640-0(0), Utah State Univ. Pr.) Univ. Pr. of Colorado.

Murata, Lynn. Transnationalism. 2009. 152p. pap. (978-3-639-15809-0(1)) VDM Verlag Dr. Mueller e.K.

Ngai, Mae. The Lucky Ones: One Family & the Extraordinary Invention of Chinese America. 2010. (ENG., Illus.). 304p. 26.00 (978-0-618-65116-0(0)) Houghton Mifflin Harcourt Trade & Reference Pubs.

Nokes, R. Gregory. Massacred for Gold: The Chinese in Hells Canyon. 2009. (ENG.). 208p. pap. 18.95 (978-0-87071-570-9(4)) Oregon State Univ. Pr.

Paddison, Joshua. American Heathens: Religion, Race, & Reconstruction in California. 2012. (Western Histories Ser.). (ENG., Illus.). 278p. 44.95 **(978-0-87328-244-4(2))** Huntington Library Pr.

Pfaelzer, Jean. Driven Out: The Forgotten War against Chinese Americans. 2008. (Illus.). 432p. pap. 24.95 (978-0-520-25694-1(8)) Univ. of California Pr.

Qi, Shouhua. China Complex: U. S.-China Relations in the 21st Century: Crossroads or Collision Course. 2009. (ENG.). 224p. pap. 18.95 (978-1-59265-079-8(1)) Long River Pr.

Qin, Bibin. Earnings Attainment of Chinese Americans: A Multilevel Analysis. 2008. (New Americans). (Illus.). 222p. 62.00 (978-1-59332-259-5(3)) LFB Scholarly Publishing LLC.

Qin, Yucheng. The Diplomacy of Nationalism: The Six Companies & China's Policy Toward Exclusion. 2009. x, 213p. (C). 51.00 (978-0-8248-3274-2(4)) Univ. of Hawaii Pr.

Quan, Robert Seto. Lotus among the Magnolias: The Mississippi Chinese. 2007. (ENG.). 184p. per. 25.00 (978-1-934110-04-1(3)) Univ. Pr. of Mississippi.

Rekdal, Paisley. Intimate: An American Family Photo Album. 2012. (ENG.). 272p. 36.95 **(978-1-936797-08-0(9))**; 300p. pap. 19.95 **(978-1-932195-96-5(3))** Tupelo Pr., Inc.

Robbins, Trina. Forbidden City: The Golden Age of Chinese Nightclubs. 2009. (978-1-57273-947-5(9)) Hampton Pr., Inc.

Romero, Robert Chao. The Chinese in Mexico, 1882-1940. (ENG.). 272p. 2012. pap. 26.95 **(978-0-8165-1460-1(7))** 2010. (Illus.). 50.00 (978-0-8165-2772-4(5)) Univ. of Arizona Pr.

See, Lisa. Bai Nian Jin Shan: Wo de Mei Ji Hua Ren Jia Zu Fen Dou Shi = On Gold Mountain: The One-Hundred-Year Odyssey of My Chinese-American Family. 2010. (CHI., Illus.). (978-7-5633-9087-8(1)) Guangxi Teachers Univ. Pr.

See, Lisa. On Gold Mountain. 2012. (Vintage Ser.). (ENG., Illus.). 464p. pap. 15.95 **(978-0-307-95039-0(5)**, Vintage) Knopf Doubleday Publishing Group.

Silbergeld, Jerome, et al. Outside In: Chinese x American x Contemporary Art. 2009. (ENG., Illus.). 304p. 60.00 (978-0-300-12208-4(X)) Yale Univ. Pr.

Soennichsen, John Robert. The Chinese Exclusion ACT of 1882. 2011. xvi, 179p. E-Book (978-0-313-37947-5(5), Greenwood Pr.) Greenwood Publishing Group, Inc.

—The Chinese Exclusion Act of 1882. 2011. (Landmarks of the American Mosaic Ser.). 179p. 35.00 (978-0-313-37946-8(7), GR7946) Greenwood Publishing Group, Inc.

Song, Jingyi. Shaping & Reshaping Chinese American Identity: New York's Chinese During the Depression & World War II. 2010. 65.00 (978-0-7391-4309-4(3)); (ENG.). 210p. pap. 68.50 (978-0-7391-4307-0(7)) Lexington Bks.

Tom, Lawrence, et al. Sacramento's Chinatown. 2010. (Images of America Ser.). (Illus.). 128p. pap. 21.99 (978-0-7385-8066-1(X)) Arcadia Publishing.

Tong, Manny. Balancing Acts. 2008. pap. 22.95 (978-0-7414-4721-0(5)) Infinity Publishing.

Toyota, Tritia. Envisioning America: New Chinese Americans & the Politics of Belonging. 2009. (Asian America Ser.). (ENG.). 256p. 65.00 (978-0-8047-6241-0(4)); pap. 21.95 (978-0-8047-6242-7(2)) Stanford Univ. Pr.

Trieu, Monica M. Identity Construction among Chinese-Vietnamese Americans: Being, Becoming, & Belonging. 2009. (New Americans). 226p. 62.00 (978-1-59332-374-5(3)) LFB Scholarly Publishing LLC.

Tseng, Winston. Immigrant Community Services in Chinese & Vietnamese Enclaves. 2006. (New Americans). (Illus.). 316p. 75.00 (978-1-59332-131-4(7)) LFB Scholarly Publishing LLC.

Tsui, Bonnie. American Chinatown: A People's History of Five Neighborhoods. 2010. (ENG., Illus.). 288p. pap. 15.00 (978-1-4165-5724-1(5), Free Pr.) Free Pr.

Van Norden, Warner M. Who's Who of the Chinese in New York. 2008. 160p. 39.95 (978-1-4181-7524-5(2)) MPublishing.

Van Ziegert, Sylvia. Global Spaces of Chinese Culture: Diasporic Chinese Communities in the United States & Germany. 2009. 232p. 39.95 (978-0-415-80578-0(3)) Routledge.

—Global Spaces of Chinese Culture: Diasporic Chinese Communities in the United States & Germany. 2006. (Studies in Asian Americans Ser.). (Illus.). 229p. 130.00 (978-0-415-97890-3(4)) Taylor & Francis Group.

Wang, Chi. A Compelling Journey from Peking to Washington: Building a New Life in America. 2011. (ENG.). 210p. pap. 30.00 **(978-0-7618-5385-5(5))** Hamilton Bks.

Wang, Yupin. Manchurian American: A Memoir. 2009. (Illus.). vii, 156p. E-Book (978-1-4401-8677-6(4)) iUniverse, Inc.

Wei Li Fang. Dragons in the West: An Historical Profile of 20th Century Chinese American Pioneers. (Illus.). 224p. (978-0-9639266-0-9(8)); lib. bdg. (978-0-9639266-1-6(6)) Fang, Wei Li.

Welland, Sasha Su-Ling. A Thousand Miles of Dreams: The Journeys of Two Chinese Sisters. 2006. (Asian Voices Ser.). (ENG., Illus.). 392p. 26.95 (978-0-7425-5313-2(2)) Rowman & Littlefield Publishers, Inc.

Wilcox, Cynthia Waiying Wu. The Love of Lotus. 2006. xi, 217p. pap. 17.00 (978-0-9786135-8-7(9)) Tyde House Bks.

William Poy Lee. The Eighth Promise: An American Son's Tribute to His Toisanese Mother. 2007. pap. 12.50 (978-1-60529-854-2(9)) Rodale Pr., Inc.

Wong, Samuel. A Chinese from Singapore. 2009. 616p. 34.99 (978-1-4415-0198-1(3)); pap. 23.99 (978-1-4415-0197-4(5)) Xlibris Corp.

Wong, Scott. Americans First: Chinese Americans & the Second World War. 2008. (Asian American History & Culture Ser.). (ENG., Illus.). 272p. per. 21.95 (978-1-59213-840-1(3)) Temple Univ. Pr.

Wyman, Nona Mock. Bamboo Women: Stories from Ming Quong, a Chinese Orphanage in California. 2012. (ENG., Illus.). 225p. pap. 19.95 **(978-0-8351-0006-9(5))** Long River Pr.

Xing, Sherry. My Story. 2007. 292p. 19.95 (978-1-58982-450-8(4), Millennial Mind Publishing) American Bk. Publishing Group.

Yang, Belle. Forget Sorrow: An Ancestral Tale. (ENG., Illus.). 250p. 2011. pap. 15.95 (978-0-393-33996-3(3), 33996) 2010. 23.95 (978-0-393-06834-4(X), 6834) Norton, W. W. & Co., Inc.

Yang, Grace & Sames. It's a Long Way from China to Hollywood. 2011. 244p. 26.95 **(978-1-4502-9660-1(2))**; pap. 16.95 **(978-1-4502-9659-5(9))** iUniverse, Inc.

Yee, Ken & Yee, Nancy Wong. Chinese Pioneer Families of Maui, Molokai, & Lanai. 2009. 25.00 (978-0-8248-3449-4(6)) Univ. of Hawaii Pr.

Yeh, Chiou-Ling. Making an American Festival: Chinese New Year in San Francisco's Chinatown. 2008. (Illus.). 336p. 60.00 (978-0-520-25350-6(7)); pap. 26.95 (978-0-520-25351-3(5)) Univ. of California Pr.

Yep, Kathleen. Outside the Paint: When Basketball Ruled at the Chinese Playground. 2009. (Asian American History & Culture Ser.). (ENG., Illus.). 216p. 21.95 (978-1-59213-942-2(6)) Temple Univ. Pr.

Yung, Judy & Fung, Eddie. The Adventures of Eddie Fung: Chinatown Kid, Texas Cowboy, Prisoner of War. Yung, Judy, ed. 2007. (ENG., Illus.). 256p. per. 22.50 (978-0-295-98754-5(5)) Univ. of Washington Pr.

Yupin Wang. Manchurian American: A Memoir. 2009. 168p. 25.95 (978-1-4401-8678-3(2)); pap. 15.95 (978-1-4401-8676-9(6)) iUniverse, Inc.

Zesch, Scott. The Chinatown War: Chinese Los Angeles & the Massacre of 1871. 2012. (ENG.). 272p. 29.95 **(978-0-19-975876-0(X))** Oxford Univ. Pr., Inc.

Zhang, Donghui. Between Two Generations: Language Maintenance & Acculturation among Chinese Immigrant Families. 2008. (New Americans). 276p. 70.00 (978-1-59332-271-7(2)) LFB Scholarly Publishing LLC.

Zhao, Xiaojian. The New Chinese America: Class, Economy, & Social Hierarchy. 2010. (ENG.). 204p. 60.00 (978-0-8135-4691-9(5)); pap. 23.95 (978-0-8135-4692-6(3)) Rutgers Univ. Pr.

Zheng, Da. Chiang Yee: The Silent Traveller from the East — A Cultural Biography. 2010. (ENG., Illus.). 358p. (C). 49.95 (978-0-8135-4693-3(1)) Rutgers Univ. Pr.

Zheng, Su. Claiming Diaspora: Music, Transnationalism, & Cultural Politics in Asian/Chinese America, 1 vol. 2011. (American Musicspheres Ser.). (ENG.). 448p. pap. 29.95 **(978-0-19-987359-3(3))** Oxford Univ. Pr., Inc.

Zhou, Min. Contemporary Chinese America: Immigration, Ethnicity, & Community Transformation. 2009. (Asian American History & Culture Ser.). (ENG., Illus.). 328p. 91.50 (978-1-59213-857-9(8)); pap. 29.95 (978-1-59213-858-6(6)) Temple Univ. Pr.

Zhou, Xiaoyan. Qing Perceptions of Anti-Chinese Violence in the United States. 2009. 112p. pap. (978-3-639-14543-4(7)) VDM Verlag Dr. Mueller e.K.

ZZ. China High: My Fast Times in the 010 - A Beijing Memoir. 2010. (ENG.). 368p. pap. 15.99 (978-0-312-60556-8(0), St. Martin's Griffin) St. Martin's Pr.

CHINESE ARCHITECTURE

see Architecture—China

CHINESE ART

see Art, Chinese

CHINESE ASTROLOGY

see Astrology, Chinese

CHINESE ASTRONOMY

see Astronomy, Chinese

CHINESE BALLADS AND SONGS

see Folk Songs, Chinese; Songs, Chinese

CHINESE CALENDAR

see Calendar, Chinese

CHINESE CALLIGRAPHY

see Calligraphy, Chinese

CHINESE CHARACTERS

Ann & Peter Timonin. Chinese Characters. 2011. 388p. 29.99 **(978-1-4628-6063-0(X))**; pap. 19.99 **(978-1-4628-6062-3(1))** Xlibris Corp.

Choa, Nina Train. Chinese Characters. 2010. (Discovering China Ser.). (ENG., Illus.). 112p. 14.95 *(978-1-60220-107-1(2))* BetterLink Pr., Inc.

Doermann, David. Arabic & Chinese Handwriting Recognition. 2008. (Lecture Notes in Computer Science / Image Processing, Computer Vision, Pattern Recognition, & Graphics Ser.). pap. 79.95 *(978-3-540-78198-1(6), 3540781986)* Springer.

Grant, Glen Nolan, et al. Mastering Japanese Kanji: The Innovative Visual Method for Learning Japanese Characters. 2009. (ENG., Illus.). 256p. pap. 34.95 *(978-4-8053-0992-6(X))* Tuttle Publishing.

Han, Jiantang. Chinese Characters. 3rd ed. 2012. (Introductions to Chinese Culture Ser.). (ENG.). 168p. pap. 19.99 ***(978-0-521-18660-5(9))*** Cambridge Univ. Pr.

Heisig, James W., et al. Remembering Traditional Hanzi: How Not to Forget the Meaning & Writing of Chinese Characters, 2 vols. 2008. (Illus.). 440p. pap. 27.00 *(978-0-8248-3324-4(4))* Univ. of Hawaii Pr.

Jiang, Nai-Siang. Stories Told by Chinese Pictograms. 2009. 70p. pap. 15.99 *(978-1-4415-5468-0(8))* Xlibris Corp.

Kong, Wei-Ping & Kong, Si-Yuan. Introduction to Chinese Character Writing. 2nd rev. ed. 2010. (ENG.). 98p. pap. 30.45 *(978-0-7575-6137-5(3))* Kendall Hunt Publishing Co.

Kung, George. Read Chinese Without Knowing Chinese: A complete guide to Computer-aided Chinese Reading. 2008. (Illus.). 282p. pap. 44.95 *(978-0-9816933-0-9(X))* Kung, George.

Lee, Keekok. Warp & Weft, Chinese Language & Culture. 2008. 312p. 26.95 *(978-1-60693-247-6(0)*, Eloquent Bks.) AEG Literary Publishing Services, Inc.

Lee, Philip Yungkin. 250 Essential Chinese Characters, Vol. 2. 2nd rev. ed. 2010. (ENG., Illus.). 368p. pap. 34.95 *(978-0-8048-4036-1(9))* Tuttle Publishing.

Li, Wendan. Chinese Writing & Calligraphy. 2010. (C). pap. 25.00 *(978-0-8248-3364-0(3))* Univ. of Hawaii Pr.

Lo, Sukming. Picture Chinese: Art as Language. 2007. (Illus.). 325p. pap. 19.95 *(978-1-59265-069-9(4))* Long River Pr.

Matthews, Alison. The First 100 Chinese Characters: The Quick & Easy Method to Learn the 100 Most Basic Chinese Characters. 2007. (ENG & CHI., Illus.). 128p. pap. 14.95 *(978-0-8048-3832-0(1))* Tuttle Publishing.

Matthews, Alison & Matthews, Laurence. Learning Chinese Characters: A Revolutionary New Way to Learn & Remember the 800 Most Basic Chinese Characters, Vol. 1. 2007. (CHI & ENG., Illus.). 384p. per. 29.95 *(978-0-8048-3816-0(X))* Tuttle Publishing.

Matthews, Alison & Matthews, Lawrence. The Second 100 Chinese Characters, Simplified Character Edition: The Quick & Easy Method to Learn the Second 100 Basic Chinese Characters. 2007. (ENG.). 128p. pap. 15.95 *(978-0-8048-3831-3(3))* Tuttle Publishing.

Matthews, Lawrence, intro. The First 100 Chinese Characters: The Quick & Easy Method to Learn the 100 Most Basic Chinese Characters. 2007. (ENG & CHI., Illus.). 128p. pap. 14.95 *(978-0-8048-3830-6(5))* Tuttle Publishing.

—The Second 100 Chinese Characters: The Quick & Easy Method to Learn the 100 Basic Chinese Characters. 2007. (ENG.). 128p. pap. 15.95 *(978-0-8048-3833-7(X))* Tuttle Publishing.

Millen, John. Japanese Kanji Power: A Workbook for Mastering Japanese Characters. 2010. (JPN & ENG.). 320p. pap., wbk. ed. 26.95 *(978-4-8053-0859-2(1))* Tuttle Publishing.

Paton, Stewart. A Dictionary of Chinese Characters: Accessed by Phonetics. 2008. (CHI & ENG.). xiv, 258p. 145.00 *(978-0-415-46046-0(8))*; 44.95 *(978-0-415-46047-7(6))* Routledge.

Ren, Zhifang. A Handbook for Analyzing Chinese Characters. 2010. (ENG.). 1020p. pap. 100.00 *(978-0-89581-894-2(9))* Jain Publishing Company, Inc.

Ren, Zhifang, compiled by. A Handbook for Analyzing Chinese Characters. 2008. (ENG & CHI.). 1052p. 250.00 *(978-0-89581-895-9(7))* Jain Publishing Company, Inc.

Ross, Melanie H., et al. A Course in Modern Mandarin Chinese. 2010. (ENG.). 336p. pap., wbk. ed. 54.95 *(978-0-415-47248-7(2))* Routledge.

Shing, Jing Heng. Gateway to Chinese Character Writing. Kale, Tessa, ed. 2006. (CHI & ENG., Illus.). 200p. (gr. 17). pap. 23.00 *(978-962-996-292-0(6))* Chinese Univ. of Hong Kong, The HKG. Dist: Columbia Univ. Pr.

Tretiak, Daniel. The life & works of haku Maki. 2007. 132p. per. 39.95 *(978-1-4327-0575-6(X))* Outskirts Pr., Inc.

Tung, Tai. The Six Scripts or the Principles of Chinese Writing by Tai Tung: A Translation by L. C. Hopkins, with a Memoir of the Translator by W. Perceval Yetts. Hopkins, L. C., tr. from CHI. 2012. (ENG.). 114p. pap. 31.99 ***(978-1-107-60515-2(6))*** Cambridge Univ. Pr.

Wang, Guo'an. A Handbook for 1,000 Basic Chinese Characters. Guo'an, Wang, ed. 2007. (ENG.). 830p. (gr. 17). pap. 27.00 *(978-962-996-283-8(7))* Chinese Univ. of Hong Kong, The HKG. Dist: Columbia Univ. Pr.

Williams, Noriko Kurosawa. The Key to Kanji: A Visual History of 1100 Characters = Kanji Etoki. 2010. (JPN & ENG., Illus.). *(978-0-88727-736-8(5))* Cheng & Tsui Co.

Winalex Learning Company, et al. Chinese Character Practicing. 2007. per. 27.95 *(978-0-9790970-2-7(9))* Liu.

Wu, Jian-Hsin. The Way of Chinese Characters: The Origins of 400 Essential Words = [Han Zi Zhi Dao]. 2007. 30.95 *(978-0-88727-527-2(3))* Cheng & Tsui Co.

Yibin, Ni & Ni, Yibin. Symbols, Art, & Language from the Land of the Dragon: The Cultural History of 100 Chinese Characters. 2009. (ENG., Illus.). 192p. 50.00 *(978-1-84483-849-3(8))* Duncan Baird Pubs. GBR. Dist: Sterling Publishing Co., Inc.

CHINESE CHARACTERS—JAPAN

Bernabe, Marc. Japanese in MangaLand: Workbook 2. 2011. (Japanese in MangaLand Ser.). (Illus.). 96p. pap. 17.00 *(978-4-88996-270-3(0))* Japan Pubns. Trading Co. JPN. Dist: Oxford Univ. Pr., Inc.

Bernabe, Marc, et al. Kanji in Mangaland Vol. 1: Basic Kanji Course Through Manga, 1 vol. Cordukes, Olinda, tr. 2007. (Japanese in MangaLand Ser.). (ENG., Illus.). 240p. pap. 24.00 *(978-4-88996-221-5(2))* Japan Pubns. Trading Co. JPN. Dist: Oxford Univ. Pr., Inc.

—Kanji in MangaLand Vol. 2: Basic to Intermediate Kanji Course Through Manga. 2009. (Illus.). 368p. pap. 36.95 *(978-4-88996-261-1(1))* Japan Pubns. Trading Co. JPN. Dist: Oxford Univ. Pr., Inc.

Heisig, James W. Remembering the Kanji. 6th ed. 2011. (JPN & ENG.). pap. 34.00 *(978-0-8248-3592-7(1))* Univ. of Hawaii Pr.

—Remembering the Kanji Vol. 2: A Systematic Guide to Reading Japanese Characters. 3rd ed. 2008. (Remembering the Kanji Ser.). (JPN & ENG., Illus.). 404p. pap. 27.00 *(978-0-8248-3166-0(7))* Univ. of Hawaii Pr.

—Remembering the Kanji, Volume 1: A Complete Course on How Not to Forget the Meaning & Writing of Japanese Characters. 5th ed. 2007. (JPN & ENG.). 460p. per. 34.00 *(978-0-8248-3165-3(9))* Univ. of Hawaii Pr.

Heisig, James W & Sienko, Tanya. Remembering the Kanji 3: Writing & Reading Japanese Characters for Upper-Level Proficiency. 2nd ed. 2008. (Remembering the Kanji Ser.). (JPN & ENG., Illus.). 440p. pap. 32.00 *(978-0-8248-3167-7(5))* Univ. of Hawaii Pr.

Kanji, Text Rese. 250 Essential Japanese Kanji Characters, Vol. 1. 2nd rev. ed. 2008. (JPN & ENG., Illus.). 256p. pap. 26.95 *(978-4-8053-0946-9(6))* Tuttle Publishing.

Kanji Text Research Group Staff. 250 Essential Japanese Kanji Characters, Vol. 2. 2nd rev. ed. 2008. (JPN & ENG., Illus.). 224p. pap. 29.95 *(978-4-8053-0947-6(4))* Tuttle Publishing.

Kardy, Glenn. Kanji de Manga Volume 4: the Comic Book That Teaches You How to Read & Write Japanese! Vol. 4: The Comic Book That Teaches You How to Read & Write Japanese! 2006. (Kanji de Manga Ser.). (JPN & ENG., Illus.). 144p. (YA). pap. 9.99 *(978-4-921205-09-6(4))* Japanime Co., Ltd. JPN. Dist: Diamond Bk. Distributors.

—Kanji de Manga Volume 5: the Comic Book That Teaches You How to Read & Write Japanese! The Comic Book That Teaches You How to Read & Write Japanese! 2007. (Kanji de Manga Ser.). (JPN & ENG., Illus.). 144p. (YA). pap. 9.99 *(978-4-921205-10-2(8))* Japanime Co., Ltd. JPN. Dist: Diamond Bk. Distributors.

Kato, Toshihito. Acquisition of Japanese Vocabulary by Chinese Background Learners: The Roles of Transfer in the Productive & Receptive Acquisition of Cognates & Polysemy. 2008. 196p. pap. *(978-3-639-09219-6(6))* VDM Verlag Dr. Mueller e.K.

Kikuchi, Madoka & Bernal, Javier. Japanese Writing & Reading Practice Manual, 2 vols., Vol. 1. 2007. (ENG & JPN.). 212p. per. 25.00 *(978-0-9800682-1-4(5))* Bernal, Javier.

Kushner, Eve. Crazy for Kanji: A Student's Guide to the Wonderful World of Japanese Characters. 2008. (ENG., Illus.). 212p. pap. 19.95 *(978-1-933330-20-4(1))* Stone Bridge Pr.

Kusuya, Daiki. Kanji Starter 1. 2006. (ENG., Illus.). 207p. per. 9.95 *(978-1-933330-14-3(7))* Stone Bridge Pr.

—Kanji Starter 2. 2006. (ENG., Illus.). 197p. per. 9.95 *(978-1-933330-15-0(5))* Stone Bridge Pr.

Sato, Eriko & Tuttle Editors. he First 100 Japanese Kanji: The Quick & Easy Way to Learn the Basic Japanese Kanji. 2008. (JPN & ENG., Illus.). 128p. pap. 14.95 *(978-4-8053-1008-3(1))* Tuttle Publishing.

Stone Bridge Press, ed. The Stone Bridge Book of Everyday Kanji: Japanese Character Reference & Writing Guide. 2010. (ENG.). 800p. pap. 18.95 *(978-1-933330-49-5(X))* Stone Bridge Pr.

Takesaki, Kunii. An Introduction to Japanese Kanji Calligraphy. 2007. (Illus.). 128p. per. 24.95 *(978-4-88024-335-1(3))* Archipelago Pr IDN. Dist: Tuttle Publishing.

Takezaki, Kunii & Godin, Bob. An Introduction to Japanese Kanji Calligraphy. 2008. (ENG., Illus.). 128p. per. 24.95 *(978-4-8053-0925-4(3))* Tuttle Publishing.

Walsh, Len. Read Japanese Today: The Easy Way to Learn 400 Practical Kanji. 2008. (JPN & ENG.). 192p. pap. 19.95 *(978-4-8053-0981-0(4))* Tuttle Publishing.

Yamamoto, Hitomi. KANJI DRILL Elementary First Grade Level. 2009. 135p. pap. 19.99 *(978-0-557-07323-8(5))* Lulu Enterprises Inc.

CHINESE CHESS

Chinese Chess Players: Feng-Hsiung Hsu, Hou Yifan, Wang Yue, Bu Xiangzhi, Zhang Pengxiang, ni Hua, Wang Hao, Xie Jun, Ding Liren, Li Chao. 2010. 248p. pap. 19.99 *(978-1-155-73575-7(7))* General Bks. LLC.

CHINESE CULTS

see Cults—China

CHINESE DOCUMENT WRITING

see Document Writing, Chinese

CHINESE DRAMA

Wang, Chong. Interpreting Zheng Chenggong: The Politics of Dramatizing a Historical Figure in Japan, China, & Taiwan (1700-1963) 2008. 76p. pap. *(978-3-639-09266-0(X))* VDM Verlag Dr. Mueller e.K.

West, Stephen H. & Idema, Wilt L. Monks, Bandits, Lovers, & Immortals: Eleven Early Chinese Plays. 2010. 512p. (C). 48.00 *(978-1-60384-201-3(2))*; pap. 16.95 *(978-1-60384-200-6(4))* Hackett Publishing Co., Inc.

Ye, Tan. The A to Z of Chinese Theater. 2010. (A to Z Guide Ser.). (ENG., Illus.). 590p. pap. 34.45 *(978-0-8108-7610-1(8))* Scarecrow Pr., Inc.

—Chinese Theater. Woronoff, ed. 2008. (Historical Dictionaries of Literature & the Arts Ser.). (ENG., Illus.). 592p. 174.00 *(978-0-8108-5514-4(3))* Scarecrow Pr., Inc.

CHINESE DRAMA—HISTORY AND CRITICISM

Chang, Chung-Ho & Chang, Kang-i Sun. Qu Ren Hong Zhao. 2010. (CHI & ENG., Illus.). 284p. *(978-7-5633-9388-6(9))* Guangxi Teachers Univ. Pr.

Chen, Fan Pen Li. Chinese Shadow Theatre: History, Popular Religion, & Women Warriors. 2007. (ENG., Illus.). 368p. (C). *(978-0-7735-3197-0(1))* McGill-Queen's Univ. Pr.

Ferrari, Rossella. Pop Goes the Avant-Garde: Experimental Theater in Contemporary China. 2012. (Seagull Books - Enactments Ser.). (ENG., Illus.). 344p. pap. 25.00 ***(978-0-85742-045-9(3))*** Seagull Bks. GBR. Dist: Chicago Distribution Ctr.

Labedzka, I. Gao Xingjian's Idea of Theatre: From the Word to the Image. 2008. (Sinica Leidensia Ser.). 250p. *(978-90-04-16828-2(1))* BRILL.

Li, Zhi, et al. San Guo Yan Yi: Ming Jia Hui Ping Ben, 2 vols. 2007. (CHI.). *(978-7-5013-3494-0(3))* Beijing Library Pr.

Shen, Jing. Playwrights & Literary Games in Seventeenth-Century China: Plays by Tang Xianzu, Mei Dingzuo, Wu Bing, Li Yu, & Kong Shangren. 2010. (Challenges Facing Chinese Ser.). (Illus.). (ENG.). 334p. 80.00 *(978-0-7391-3857-1(X))*; xiii, 320p. *(978-0-7391-3859-5(6))* Lexington Bks.

Tan, Tian Yuan. Songs of Contentment & Transgression: Discharged Officials & Literati Communities in Sixteenth-Century North China. 2010. (Harvard-Yenching Institute Monograph Ser.: 75). (ENG.). 314p. 39.95 *(978-0-674-05604-6(3))* Harvard Univ., Asia Ctr.

Tian, Min. The Poetics of Difference & Displacement: Twentieth-Century Chinese-Western Intercultural Theatre. 2008. (ENG., Illus.). 292p. (gr. 17). 60.00 *(978-962-209-907-4(6))* Hong Kong Univ. Pr. HKG. Dist: Columbia Univ. Pr.

Volpp, Sophie. Worldly Stage - T: The Figure of the theatr in Seventeeth- Century China. 2011. (Harvard East Asian Monographs: 267). (Illus.). 350p. 44.95 *(978-0-674-02144-0(4))* Harvard Univ., Asia Ctr.

Xiao, Li-Ling. The Eternal Present of the Past: Illustration, Theatre, & Reading in the Wanli Period, 1573-1619. 2007. (China Studies). (Illus.). 320p. *(978-90-04-15643-2(7))* BRILL.

CHINESE ESSAYS

Ke, Qingming. Xian Dai Wen Xue Jing Xuan Ji. 2009. 275p. *(978-986-02-1004-0(7))* Hualien County Hacc.

Qian, Zhongshu. Humans, Beasts, & Ghosts: Stories & Essays. Rea, Christopher G., ed. 2010. (Weatherhead Books on Asia Ser.). (ENG.). 272p. (gr. 17). pap. 29.50 *(978-0-231-15275-4(2))* Columbia Univ. Pr.

Qian, Zhongshu & Hu, Dennis T. Humans, Beasts, & Ghosts: Stories & Essays. 2010. 272p. E-Book *(978-0-231-52654-8(7))* Columbia Univ. Pr.

Shanghai Writers Association. The City, the People. 2010. (Wen Hua Zhongguo = Cultural China Ser.). 340p. pap. 22.95 *(978-1-60220-200-9(1))* BetterLink Pr., Inc.

Wu, Xiaozhen. Chinese Landscapes (Essays) 2010. 156p. pap. 9.95 *(978-1-60220-903-9(0))* BetterLink Pr., Inc.

Yang, Shuhui & Yang, Yunqin. Essays from Women Writers. 2010. 130p. pap. 9.95 *(978-1-60220-900-8(6))* BetterLink Pr., Inc.

Zhongshu, Qian. Humans, Beasts, & Ghosts: Stories & Essays. Rea, Christopher G., ed. 2010. (Weatherhead Books on Asia Ser.). (ENG.). 272p. (gr. 17). 89.50 *(978-0-231-15274-7(4))* Columbia Univ. Pr.

CHINESE ETHICS

see Ethics—China

CHINESE FICTION

see also Short Stories, Chinese

Kim, Tong-Uk. Kyoyok T'aep'yong Kwanggi Onhae. 2009. (KOR.). *(978-89-8433-719-0(6))* Bogosa Publishing Co.

Xiao, et al. Tales & Traditions, 4, 4. 2010. (ENG & CHI.). 260p. pap. 19.95 *(978-0-88727-681-1(4))* Cheng & Tsui Co.

CHINESE FICTION—BIBLIOGRAPHY

Berry, Margaret. The Chinese Classic Novels: An Annotated Bibliography of Chiefly English-Language Studies. 2010. (Routledge Revivals Ser.). (ENG.). 324p. 115.00 *(978-0-415-59524-7(X))* Routledge.

CHINESE FICTION—HISTORY AND CRITICISM

Button, Peter. Configurations of the Real in Chinese Literary & Aesthetic Modernity. 2009. 316p. *(978-90-04-17095-7(2))* BRILL.

Chen, Jue. Record of an Ancient Mirror: An Interdisciplinary Reading. 2010. (Abhandlungen fur die Kunde des Morgenlandes Ser.). (ENG.). 212p. (C). 87.00 ***(978-3-447-06401-9(3))*** Harrassowitz, Otto Verlag DEU. Dist: ISD.

Choy, Howard Yuen Fung. Remapping the Past: Fictions of History in Deng's China, 1979-1997. 2008. (Leiden Ser. in Comparative Historiography Ser.). (Illus.). 300p. *(978-90-04-16704-9(8))* BRILL.

Dudbridge, Glen. The Hsi-Yu-Chi: A Study of Antecedents to the Sixteenth-Century Chinese Novel. 2009. (Cambridge Studies in Chinese History, Literature & Institutions Ser.). (ENG.). 240p. pap. 34.99 *(978-0-521-10281-0(2))* Cambridge Univ. Pr.

Durand-Dastes, V. La Conversion de L'Orient: Une peregrination didactique de Bodhidharma dans un roman chinois du XVIIe Siecle. 2008. (Melanges Chinois et Bouddhiques Ser.). (FRE.). 437p. (C). pap. 99.00 *(978-2-9600076-1-9(1))* Peeters Pubs. & Booksellers BEL. Dist: Brown, David Bk. Co., The.

Gu, Ming Dong. Chinese Theories of Fiction: A Non-Western Narrative System. 2007. (SUNY Series in Chinese Philosophy & Culture). 286p. per. 29.95 *(978-0-7914-6816-6(X))* State Univ. of New York Pr.

—A Chinese Theory of Fiction: A Non-Western Narrative System. 2006. (SUNY Series in Chinese Philosophy & Culture). xvi, 286p. (C). 80.00 *(978-0-7914-6815-9(1))* State Univ. of New York Pr.

Hanan, Patrick, tr. from CHI. Falling in Love: Stories from Ming China. 2006. 256p. per. 24.00 *(978-0-8248-2995-7(6))* Univ. of Hawaii Pr.

Hillenbrand, Margaret. Literature, Modernity, & the Practice of Resistance: Japanese & Taiwanese Fiction 1960-1990. 2007. (China Studies). 357p. *(978-90-04-15478-0(7))* BRILL.

Hu, Kemin. The Romance of Scholar's Stones: Adventures in Appreciation. 2011. (ENG.). 144p. 50.00 *(978-1-891640-61-2(5))* Floating World Editions.

Kinkley, Jeffrey C. Corruption & Realism in Late Socialist China: The Return of the Political Novel. 2006. (ENG.). 304p. 57.00 *(978-0-8047-5485-9(3))* Stanford Univ. Pr.

Knight, Sabina. The Heart of Time: Moral Agency in Twentieth-Century Chinese Fiction. 2006. (Harvard East Asian Monographs: 274). (Illus.). 306p. 44.95 *(978-0-674-02267-6(X))* Harvard Univ., Asia Ctr.

Komatsu, Takeo. Chugoku Kinsei Shosetsu No Densho to Keisei. 2010. (JPN.). 335p. *(978-4-87636-307-0(2))* Kenbun Shuppan.

Liu, Shuo. Hong Lou Meng Zhen Xiang. 2010. (CHI.). *(978-7-5333-2370-7(X))* Qilu Shushe.

Liu, Zaifu. Hong Lou Zhe Xue Bi Ji. 2010. (CHI.). 262p. pap. *(978-962-04-2859-3(5))* Joint Publishing Co.

Long, Tang. Tales of the Dragon: The Book of Lore. 2011. 164p. 29.99 ***(978-1-4628-9403-1(8))***; pap. 19.99 ***(978-1-4628-9402-4(X))*** Xlibris Corp.

Luo, Guanzhong & Fusek, Lois. The Three Sui Quash the Demons' Revolt. 2010. 352p. 49.00 *(978-0-8248-3406-7(2))* Univ. of Hawaii Pr.

Mei, Chun. The Novel & Theatrical Imagination in Early Modern China. 2011. (Illus.). xi, 277p. *(978-90-04-19166-2(6))* BRILL.

Nienhauser, William H., Jr. Tang Dynasty Tales. 2010. 340p. 58.00 *(978-981-4287-28-9(8))* World Scientific Publishing Co., Inc.

Sluglett, Peter & Hsieh, Daniel. Love & Women in Early Chinese Fiction. 2008. (ENG.). 300p. (gr. 17). 39.00 *(978-962-996-305-7(1))* Chinese Univ. of Hong Kong, The HKG. Dist: Columbia Univ. Pr.

Starr, Chloë F. Red-Light Novels of the Late Qing. 2007. (China Studies). 320p. *(978-90-04-15629-6(1))* BRILL.

Tambling, Jeremy. Madmen & Other Survivors: Reading Lu Xun's Fiction. 2007. (ENG.). 136p. (gr. 17). per. 18.00 *(978-962-209-825-1(8))* Hong Kong Univ. Pr. HKG. Dist: Columbia Univ. Pr.

Wan, Margaret B. Green Peony & the Rise of the Chinese Martial Arts Novel. (SUNY series in Chinese Philosophy & Culture Ser.). 2010. 248p. pap. 24.95 *(978-0-7914-7702-1(9)*, Suny Pr.) 2009. 240p. 70.00 *(978-0-7914-7701-4(0))* State Univ. of New York Pr.

Wang, Richard. Ming Erotic Novellas: Genre, Consumption, & Religiosity in Cultural Practice. 2011. (ENG., Illus.). 232p. (gr. 17). 50.00 *(978-962-996-458-0(9))* Chinese Univ. of Hong Kong, The HKG. Dist: Columbia Univ. Pr.

Wang, Weiling. Sui Yue Chuan Zhen: Wo He Dang Dai Zuo Jia. 2009. (CHI., Illus.). *(978-7-81119-534-7(8))* Capital Normal Univ. Pr.

Yang, Yang. Twin Sisters. 2010. 376p. 30.70 *(978-1-4269-0173-7(9))* Trafford Publishing.

Yang Yang. Twin Sisters. 2010. 376p. pap. 20.70 *(978-1-4269-0172-0(0))* Trafford Publishing.

Yip, Wai-lim. Zhongguo Xian Dai Xiao Shuo de Feng Mao. 2010. (CHI.). 245p. *(978-986-02-1274-7(0))* Academia Sinica.

Zeng, Liang. Ming Qing Tong Su Xiao Shuo Yu Hui Yan Jiu. 2009. (CHI.). *(978-7-5392-5064-9(X))* Jiangxi Education Publishing Hse.

CHINESE FICTION—TRANSLATIONS INTO ENGLISH

Denton, Kirk A., ed. China. 2008. (Traveler's Literary Companions Ser.). (ENG., Illus.). 256p. pap. 14.95 *(978-1-883513-23-8(5))* Whereabouts Pr.

Huan, Zhao. Foregrounding & English-Chinese Novel Translation. 2011. 68p. pap. ***(978-3-8443-0777-1(X))*** Lambert Academic Publishing.

Qi, Shouhua, ed. The Pearl Jacket & Other Stories: Flash Fiction from Contemporary China. 2008. (ENG.). 438p. pap. 16.95 *(978-1-933330-62-4(7))* Stone Bridge Pr.

Shanghai Writers Association. Under the Eaves: Selected I. 2010. 294p. pap. 22.95 *(978-1-60220-207-8(9))* BetterLink Pr., Inc.

—Under the Eaves: Selected II. 2010. 302p. pap. 22.95 *(978-1-60220-208-5(7))* BetterLink Pr., Inc.

CHINESE FIGHTING DOG

see Chinese Shar-Pei

CHINESE FLOWER ARRANGEMENT

see Flower Arrangement, Chinese

CHINESE FOLK SONGS

see Folk Songs, Chinese

CHINESE-FRENCH WAR, 1884-1885

see Sino-French War, 1884-1885

CHINESE IN THE UNITED STATES

see Chinese—United States

CHINESE-INDIAN BORDER DISPUTE, 1957-

see Sino-Indian Border Dispute, 1957-

CHINESE INSCRIPTIONS
see Inscriptions, Chinese

CHINESE-JAPANESE CONFLICT, 1937-1945
see Sino-Japanese Conflict, 1937-1945

CHINESE LANGUAGE

An, Kun, et al. Anything Goes: An Advanced Reader of Modern Chinese. 2006. (Princeton Language Program: Modern Chinese Ser.). (ENG.). 568p. (C). per. 50.00 *(978-0-691-12766-8(2))* Princeton Univ. Pr.

André, James St. & Hsiao-yen, Peng, eds. China & Its Others: Knowledge Transfer through Translation, 1829-2010. 2012. (Illus.). 316p. pap. 95.00 ***(978-90-420-3431-0(9))*** Rodopi.

Association of Northern California Chinese Schools, contrib. by. Chinese SAT II, Vol. 2. 2007. (YA). pap. 25.00 *(978-0-9791826-1-7(1))* Valley Graphics Printing Inc.

Baker, Hugh & Ho, Pui-Kei. Complete Cantonese: Everything You Need to Speak & Understand. 2nd ed. 2011. (Teach Yourself Language Ser.). (ENG.). 464p. pap. 26.00 *(978-0-07-175060-8(6)*, 0071750606) McGraw-Hill Cos., The.

Basic Cantonese. (Series of Language Courses). 69.95 *(978-1-57050-008-4(8))* Multilingua, Inc.

Bean, Cathy Bao & Chen, Dongdong. The Chopsticks-Fork Principle X 2: A Bilingual Reader. 2008. (CHI & ENG.). pap. *(978-1-931907-51-4(X))* Homa & Sekey Bks.

Beijing-2011. New Practical Chinese Reader 1: Annotated in English. 2nd ed. 2011. (CHI & ENG., Illus.). xii, 282p. pap. ***(978-7-5619-2623-9(5)***, Wiley-Blackwell) Beijing Language & Culture Univ. Pr., China.

Berlitz Publishing, ed. Berlitz Mandarin Chinese Vocabulary Study Cards. 2nd rev. ed. 2010. (Study Cards Ser.). (ENG & CHI.). 1000p. 14.99 *(978-981-268-915-3(X))* APA Publications Services SGP. Dist: Ingram Pub. Services.

Boden, Jeanne. Mindmapping China: Language, Discourse & Advertising in China. 2010. (ENG & CHI., Illus.). 228p. pap. 35.95 *(978-90-5487-690-8(5))* VUB Univ. Pr. BEL. Dist: Independent Pubs. Group.

Bourgerie, Dana Scott, et al. Colloquial Cantonese. 2nd rev. ed. 2010. (CHI & ENG., Illus.). 304p. pap. 29.95 *(978-0-415-47866-1(3))* Routledge.

—Colloquial Cantonese: The Complete Course for Beginners. 2nd ed. 2010. (CHI & ENG.). cd-rom *(978-0-415-56970-5(2))* Routledge.

Bruzzone, Catherine, et al. Chinese: An Interactive Picture Word Book. 2010. (Hide & Speak Ser.). 32p. (J). (gr. 2-6). pap. 7.99 *(978-0-7641-4518-6(5))* Barron's Educational Series, Inc.

Carroll, Sarah & Wang, Qiufu. Business Mandarin Chinese. 2009. (Teach Yourself Language Ser.). (ENG.). 128p. 39.95 *(978-0-07-154774-1(6)*, 0071547746) McGraw-Hill Cos., The.

Chan, Marjorie K. M. & Kang, Hana, eds. Proceedings of the 20th North American Conference on Chinese Linguistics (NACCL-20) 2008. (ENG & CHI.). Vol. 1. 526p. pap. *(978-0-9824715-0-0(5))* Vol. 2. 549p. pap. *(978-0-9824715-1-7(3))* Ohio State Univ., East Asian Studies Ctr.

Chen, Jianguo, et al. Teaching & Learning Chinese: Issues & Perspectives. 2010. *(978-1-61735-065-8(6))*; pap. *(978-1-61735-064-1(8))*; E-Book *(978-1-61735-066-5(4))* Information Age Publishing, Inc.

Chen, Matthew Y. Tone Sandhi: Patterns across Chinese Dialects. 2007. (Cambridge Studies in Linguistics Ser.). (ENG., Illus.). 576p. pap. 78.00 *(978-0-521-03340-4(3))* Cambridge Univ. Pr.

Chen, Qinghai, et al. Business Chinese. 2012. (ENG.). 256p. 200.00 *(978-0-415-66802-6(6))*; pap. 64.00 *(978-0-415-66803-3(4))* Routledge.

Ch'en, T. C., et al. Chinese Primer, 3 vols. rev. ed. 2007. (Princeton Language Program: Modern Chinese Ser.). (CHI & ENG., Illus.). 616p. (C). pap. 55.00 *(978-0-691-12991-4(6))* Princeton Univ. Pr.

Chen, Yea-fen, et al. Chaoyue: Advancing in Chinese - A Textbook for Intermediate & Pre-Advanced Students. 2010. (CHI & ENG., Illus.). 464p. (gr. 17). 105.00 *(978-0-231-14528-2(4))*; pap. 40.00 *(978-0-231-14529-9(2))* Columbia Univ. Pr.

Chiang, Joanne, et al. A New China - an Intermediate Reader of Modern Chinese 2e. 2011. (Princeton Language Program: Modern Chinese Ser.). (ENG.). 480p. (C). pap. 55.00 ***(978-0-691-14836-6(8))*** Princeton Univ. Pr.

Chinese Language Learning for Foreigners. Date not set. 141p. 18.95 *(978-7-80052-309-0(8))* Sinolingua CHN. Dist: China Bks. & Periodicals, Inc.

Chinese Speed Reading: Drills & Tests. Date not set. 380p. 15.95 *(978-7-80052-329-8(2))* Sinolingua CHN. Dist: China Bks. & Periodicals, Inc.

Ching, Eugene & Ching, Nora. 201 Mandarin Chinese Verbs: Compounds & Phrases for Everyday Usage. 2nd rev. ed. 2007. (201 Verb Ser.). (CHI & ENG.). 240p. per. 16.99 *(978-0-7641-3761-7(1))* Barron's Educational Series, Inc.

Chiu, Ka Man Aman. An Approach to Standardization. 2009. 180p. pap. *(978-3-639-16307-0(9))* VDM Verlag Dr. Mueller e.K.

Chou, Chih-P'ing, et al. Kaleidoscope of China: An Advanced Reader of Modern Chinese. 2010. (Princeton Language Program: Modern Chinese Ser.). (ENG.). 536p. (C). pap. 49.50 *(978-0-691-14691-1(8))* Princeton Univ. Pr.

Christensen, Matthew B. & Warnick, J. Paul. Performed Culture: An Approach to East Asian Language Pedagogy. 2006. (Pathways to Advanced Skills Ser.). *(978-0-87415-307-1(7))* Foreign Language Pubns.

Collins Publishers Staff. Cantonese Phrasebook: The Right Word In Your Pocket. 2008. (Collins Gem Ser.). (CHI & ENG.). 256p. pap. 6.95 *(978-0-00-724677-9(3))*; (Illus.). pap. 9.95 *(978-0-00-724697-7(8))* HarperCollins Pubs. Ltd. GBR. Dist: Independent Pubs. Group.

Committee on the U.S.-Chinese Glossary of Nuclear Security Terms & National Research Council. English-Chinese, Chinese-English Nuclear Security Glossary. 2008. (ENG.). 274p. pap. 57.25 *(978-0-309-11931-3(6))* National Academies Pr.

Counsilman, James Joseph, et al. The Easiest Way to Learn Mandarin: Image Maps, Word Images, & Other Mnemonics. 2nd ed. 2008. (Illus.). 211p. pap. *(978-0-9769259-5-8(8))* SinoAmerican Bks.

Dai, Chen & Chuanren, Ke. From Form-Focused to Task-Based CFL Instruction. 2010. *(978-0-87415-366-8(2))* Foreign Language Pubns.

De Mente, Boye Lafayette. The Chinese Mind: Understanding Traditional Chinese Beliefs & Their Influence on Contemporary Culture. 2009. (ENG.). 192p. pap. 16.95 *(978-0-8048-4011-8(3))* Tuttle Publishing.

Dong Jie. Discourse, Identity, & China's Internal Migration: The Long March to the City. 2011. (Encounters Ser.). (Illus.). 176p. (ENG.). 119.95 *(978-1-84769-420-1(9))*; pap. 39.95 *(978-1-84769-419-5(5))* Multilingual Matters GBR. Dist: Univ. of Toronto Pr.

Dorling Kindersley Publishing Staff. Chinese Visual Phrase Book: See It - Say It - Live It! 2009. (EW Travel Guide Phrase Bks.). (ENG.). 192p. 12.95 *(978-0-7566-4981-4(1))* Dorling Kindersley Publishing, Inc.

Duanmu, San. The Phonology of Standard Chinese. 2nd rev. ed. 2007. (Phonology of the World's Languages Ser.). (ENG.). 384p. per. 60.00 *(978-0-19-921579-9(0))* Oxford Univ. Pr., Inc.

Dummitt, Nathan. Chinese Through Tone & Color: A Unique Visual Method for Learning over 100 Basic Chinese Characters. 2008. (ENG., Illus.). 250p. pap. 24.95 *(978-0-7818-1204-7(6))* Hippocrene Bks., Inc.

Ehlert, Meilan Piao. Multilingualism & Language Practices of Minority Youths in Chin. 2011. 124p. pap. ***(978-3-8433-6291-7(2))*** Lambert Academic Publishing.

Ellis, D. L. & Stobbe, Gabriele. Just Enough Chinese: How to Get by & Be Easily Understood. 2nd rev. ed. 2009. (Just Enough Phrasebook Ser.). (CHI, ENG & SPA., Illus.). 176p. pap. 8.00 *(978-0-07-149223-2(2)*, 0071492232) McGraw-Hill Cos., The.

Everson, Michael Erwin & Shen, Helen H. Research among Learners of Chinese As a Foreign Language. 2010. (Illus.). 171p. pap. *(978-0-9800459-4-9(0))* National Foreign Language Resource Ctr.

Everson, Michael Erwin & Xiao, Yun. Teaching Chinese As a Foreign Language: Theories & Applications. 2008. (C). pap. 29.95 *(978-0-88727-668-2(7))* Cheng & Tsui Co.

Fallows, Deborah. Dreaming in Chinese: Mandarin Lessons in Life, Love, & Language. (ENG.). 208p. 2011. pap. 13.00 *(978-0-8027-7914-4(X))* 2010. (Illus.). 22.00 *(978-0-8027-7913-7(1))* Walker & Co.

Fang, Jiqing & Connelly, Michael, compiled by. Cheng & Tsui Chinese Measure Word Dictionary: A Chinese-English English-Chinese Usage Guide. 2008. pap. 29.95 *(978-0-88727-632-3(6))* Cheng & Tsui Co.

Fang, Leyan. Translation EZ. 2007. 108p. *(978-0-9785500-0-4(5))* Ford, Phyllis F. Liu.

Feng, Guangwu. A Theory of Conventional Implicature & Pragmatic Markers in Chinese. 2010. (Current Research in the Semantics/Pragmatics Interface Ser.). (Illus.). 241p. 124.95 *(978-1-84950-934-3(4))* Emerald Group Publishing Ltd. GBR. Dist: Turpin Distribution Services Ltd.

Fredlein, Shumang & Fredlein, Paul. Ni Hao Level 3 Textbook (Traditional Character Edition), 4 vols. 2nd rev. ed. 2007. pap. 35.95 *(978-0-88727-605-7(9))* Cheng & Tsui Co.

Fuxiang, Wang. Chinese Language Learning for Foreigners, Vol. 2. Date not set. 186p. 18.95 *(978-7-80052-310-6(1))* Sinolingua CHN. Dist: China Bks. & Periodicals, Inc.

Giles, Herbert Allen. China & the Chinese. 2009. (Illus.). 242p. 32.99 *(978-1-115-42098-3(4))* 2009. (Illus.). 242p. 28.99 *(978-1-115-42095-2(X))* 2009. (Illus.). 242p. pap. 26.75 *(978-1-115-42094-5(1))* 2009. (Illus.). 242p. pap. 25.75 *(978-1-115-42092-1(5))* 2009. 242p. 28.99 *(978-1-110-42400-9(0))* 2009. 242p. pap. 25.75 *(978-1-110-42398-9(5))* 2008. 136p. 21.99 *(978-0-554-33154-6(3))* 2008. 136p. 24.99 *(978-0-554-23851-7(9))* 2007. (ENG.). 124p. pap. 18.99 *(978-1-4264-5085-3(0))* 2006. 134p. pap. 19.99 *(978-1-4264-5386-1(8))* BiblioBazaar.

—China & the Chinese. 2008. 236p. pap. *(978-1-4097-9378-6(8))* Read Bks.

Goodman, Kenneth S., et al, eds. Reading in Asian Languages: The Process of Making Sense in Chinese, Japanese, & Korean. 2011. (ENG., Illus.). 296p. 135.00 *(978-0-415-89476-0(X))*; pap. 48.95 *(978-0-415-89477-7(8))* Routledge.

Gu, Sharron. A Cultural History of the Chinese Language. 2011. (ENG.). 270p. pap. 45.00 ***(978-0-7864-6649-8(9))*** McFarland & Co., Inc. Pubs.

Halliday, M. A. K. Studies in Chinese Language: Volume 8, 10 vols. Webster, Jonathan J., ed. 2009. (Collected Works M A Halliday Ser.). (ENG., Illus.). 386p. 49.95 *(978-1-84706-575-9(9))* Continuum International Publishing Group, Ltd. GBR. Dist: National Bk. Network.

He, Shisong. Ke Yan Di 200 Shou: Shou Lu Zui Xin Yi Bai Shou Ke Yan. 2009. (CHI., Illus.). 23p. *(978-957-11-5850-1(X))* Wu-Nan Bk., Inc.

He, Wayne. Chinese for Tomorrow: A New Five-Skilled Approach, 6 vols. 2008. (CHI & ENG., Illus.). (C). pap., tchr. ed. 79.95 *(978-0-88727-566-1(4))* Cheng & Tsui Co.

He, Wayne, et al. Chinese for Tomorrow, 6 vols. 2007. (C). pap., tchr. ed. 73.95 *(978-0-88727-570-8(2))*; pap., stu. ed. 62.95 *(978-0-88727-568-5(0))* Cheng & Tsui Co.

Heisig, James W. & Richardson, Timothy W. Remembering Simplified Hanzi: Book 1: How Not to Forget the Meaning & Writing of Chinese Characters. 2008. (Illus.). pap. 27.00 *(978-0-8248-3323-7(6))* Univ. of Hawaii Pr.

Heisig, James W., et al. Remembering Traditional Hanzi: How Not to Forget the Meaning & Writing of Chinese Characters, 2 vols. 2008. (Illus.). 440p. pap. 27.00 *(978-0-8248-3324-4(4))* Univ. of Hawaii Pr.

Hirth, Friedrich. The Mystery of Fu-lin. 2010. 83.84 *(978-1-61143-449-1(1))*; pap. 19.72 *(978-1-61143-151-3(4))* Gorgias Pr., LLC.

Ho, Yong. Beginner's Chinese. 2nd ed. 2010. (CHI & ENG.). 320p. *(978-0-7818-1257-3(7))* Hippocrene Bks., Inc.

Hong, Beverly. New Papers on Chinese Language Use. (Illus.). v, 189 p. *(978-0-86784-370-5(5))* Bow Historical Bks.

Hong, Huang. Everyday Chinese Handbook: Authentic Language for Real-Life Communication. 2007. (ENG.). 160p. (C). pap. 123.95 *(978-1-4282-2962-4(0))* Cengage Heinle.

Hong, Yinan. Hua Shuo Cheng Yu: Chinese Sayings Told in Pictures. (CHI & ENG., Illus.). 157p. *(978-957-9188-31-9(9))* Sinorama Magazine Co.

Howard & Howard, Jiaying. Huanying, 4 vols. 2009. pap., stu. ed. 59.95 *(978-0-88727-724-5(1))* Cheng & Tsui Co.

Howard & Xu, Lanting. Huanying, 4 vols. 2008. pap., stu. ed. 19.95 *(978-0-88727-616-3(4))*; pap., stu. ed. 22.95 *(978-0-88727-705-4(5))* Cheng & Tsui Co.

Howard, Jiaying & Xu, Lanting. Huanying: An Introduction to Chinese = [Huan Ying: Zhong Xue Han Yu Ke Ben], 4 vols. 2008. (CHI & ENG.). stu. ed. 79.95 *(978-0-88727-662-0(8))*; pap., stu. ed. 59.95 *(978-0-88727-615-6(6))* Cheng & Tsui Co.

Huang, Weijia & Ao, Qun. How Far Away Is the Sun? [Tai Yang de Yuan Jin. 2007. (CHI.). (C). pap. 19.95 *(978-0-88727-535-7(4))* Cheng & Tsui Co.

—The Moon Is Always Beautiful & Other Essays: [Yue Liang Zong Shi Mei Hao De]. 2008. (C). pap. 19.95 *(978-0-88727-637-8(7))* Cheng & Tsui Co.

Huang, Yan. The Syntax & Pragmatics of Anaphora. 2007. (Cambridge Studies in Linguistics Ser.). (ENG.). 352p. (C). per. 69.00 *(978-0-521-03960-4(6))* Cambridge Univ. Pr.

Integrated Chinese. 2008. (C). pap. 21.95 *(978-0-88727-641-5(5))* Cheng & Tsui Co.

Intermediate Cantonese. (Series of Language Courses). 125.00 *(978-1-57050-018-3(5))* Multilingua, Inc.

Jiang, Song. Chinese Buildercards: The Lightning Path to Mastering Vocabulary. 2008. (C). 52.95 *(978-0-88727-426-8(9))*; 52.95 *(978-0-88727-434-3(X))* Cheng & Tsui Co.

Jiang, Wenying. Acquisition of Word Order in Chinese as a Foreign Language. 2009. (Studies on Language Acquisition [SOLA] Ser.). (ENG., XIV, 320p. Illus.). 140.00 *(978-3-11-021618-9(3))*; 210.00 ***(978-3-11-173256-5(8))*** De Gruyter, Mouton DEU. Dist: de Gruyter, Walter GmbH & Co. KG.

Jiao, Dela, et al. Chinese for Tomorrow, 6 vols. 2007. (C). pap., stu. ed. 41.95 *(978-0-88727-569-2(9))* Cheng & Tsui Co.

Kadar, Daniel Z. & Pan, Yuling, eds. Chinese Discourse & Interaction: Theory & Practice. 2012. (ENG.). 320p. (C). 99.95 ***(978-1-84553-632-9(0))*** Equinox Publishing Ltd. GBR. Dist: ISD.

Kane, Daniel. Chinese Language: Its History & Current Usage. 2006. (ENG., Illus.). 192p. pap. 16.95 *(978-0-8048-3853-5(4))* Tuttle Publishing.

Kaske, Elisabeth. The Politics of Language in Chinese Education, 1895-1919. 2007. (Sinica Leidensia Ser.). (Illus.). 600p. *(978-90-04-16367-6(0))* BRILL.

Kirkpatrick, Andy & Xu, Zhichang. Chinese Rhetoric & Writing: An Introduction for Language Teachers. 2012. ***(978-1-60235-301-5(8))***; pap. ***(978-1-60235-300-8(X))*** Parlor Pr.

Kong, Wei-Ping & Kong, Si-Yuan. Introduction to Chinese. 2nd rev. ed. 2010. (ENG.). 252p. pap. 64.84 *(978-0-7575-5720-0(1))* Kendall Hunt Publishing Co.

Kubler, Cornelius C. Basic Spoken Chinese: An Introduction to Speaking & Listening for Beginners, Vol. 1. 2011. (ENG & CHI., Illus.). 384p. pap. 49.95 *(978-0-8048-4015-6(6))* Tuttle Publishing.

Kubler, Cornelius C. & Wang, Yang. Basic Spoken Chinese Practice Essentials: An Introduction to Speaking & Listening for Beginners, Vol. 1. 2011. (ENG & CHI., Illus.). 256p. pap. 24.95 *(978-0-8048-4014-9(8))* Tuttle Publishing.

Kung, George. Read Chinese Without Knowing Chinese: A complete guide to Computer-aided Chinese Reading. 2008. (Illus.). 282p. pap. 44.95 *(978-0-9816933-0-9(X))* Kung, George.

Kuo, Jane C. M. Open for Business. 2007. (CHI.). 121p. (C). pap. 41.95 incl. audio compact disk *(978-0-88727-500-5(1))* Cheng & Tsui Co.

—Open for Business 2 2nd Edition, 2 vols. 2nd rev. ed. 2007. (C). pap. 52.95 incl. audio compact disk *(978-0-88727-626-2(1))* Cheng & Tsui Co.

—Startup Business Chinese 2. 2008. pap. 73.95 *(978-0-88727-635-4(0))*; pap. 39.95 *(978-0-88727-636-1(9))* Cheng & Tsui Co.

Lee Chen, Joyce. How to Be a Certified Chinese Language Teacher. 2010. (CHI & ENG.). 167p. pap. 19.50 *(978-0-9788198-1-1(0))* Chang, Joyce.

Lee, Keekok. Warp & Weft, Chinese Language & Culture. 2008. 312p. 26.95 *(978-1-60693-247-6(0)*, Eloquent Bks.) AEG Literary Publishing Services, Inc.

Lee, Linda. Linda Lee Interactive Chinese. 2009. pap. *(978-1-61623-117-0(3))* Independent Pub.

Lee, Philip Yungkin. 250 Essential Chinese Characters, Vol. 2. 2nd rev. ed. 2010. (ENG., Illus.). 368p. pap. 34.95 *(978-0-8048-4036-1(9))* Tuttle Publishing.

Lee, Philip Yungkin, et al. 250 Essential Chinese Characters, Vol. 1. 2nd rev. ed. 2009. (CHI & ENG., Illus.). 368p. pap. 29.95 *(978-0-8048-4035-4(0))* Tuttle Publishing.

Leong, C. K. & Tamaoka, Katsuo, eds. Cognitive Processing of the Chinese & the Japanese Languages. 2010. (Neuropsychology & Cognition Ser.). 328p. pap. 218.00 *(978-90-481-5140-0(6)*, 9048151406) Springer.

Levine, Ari Daniel. Divided by a Common Language: Factional Conflict in Late Northern Song China. 2008. (Illus.). 216p. (C). 57.00 *(978-0-8248-3266-7(3))* Univ. of Hawaii Pr.

Li, Feng & Branner, David Prager, eds. Writing & Literacy in Early China: Studies from the Columbia Early China Seminar. 2011. (ENG., Illus.). 480p. (C). 50.00 *(978-0-295-99152-8(6))* Univ. of Washington Pr.

Li, Guo. Conversational Chinese for Business. Date not set. 115p. 7.95 *(978-7-301-02334-1(0))* Beijing University Pr. CHN. Dist: China Bks. & Periodicals, Inc.

Li, Kai & Dew, James E. Classical Chinese: A Functional Approach. (CHI & ENG.). (C). 2009. pap. 35.00 *(978-0-88727-737-5(3))* 2008. pap. 35.00 *(978-0-88727-630-9(X))* Cheng & Tsui Co.

Li, Rongzhen & Montanaro, John S. Encounters: Chinese Language & Culture Character Writing Workbook 2. 2012. 270p. pap. 29.99 *(978-0-300-16171-7(9))* Yale Univ. Pr.

Li, Suogui. Foreign-Inspired Chinese Terms: A Cognitive Semantic Approach. 2012. (ENG.). 344p. 129.95 ***(978-0-7734-2620-7(5))*** Mellen, Edwin Pr., The.

Li, Xiangyun. Li Hun Su Song Hua Yu Zhong Quan Li He Qin Mi Guan Xi de Xing Bie Jie du: Power & Solidarity in Divorce Litigation Discourse: A Gender Perspective. 2009. (CHI & ENG., Illus.). *(978-7-5607-3911-3(3))* Shandong University Pr.

Li, yuming. Zhongguo Yu Yan Gui Hua Lun. 2010. *(978-7-100-06754-6(5))* Commercial Pr., The.

Liao, Rongrong, et al. Mandarin Chinese: Speak & Understand Everyday Mandarin. 2008. (Streetwise... Ser.). (CHI & ENG., Illus.). 224p. 18.95 *(978-0-07-147489-4(7)*, 0071474897) McGraw-Hill Cos., The.

Lin, Wei. Zhong Xi Wen Hua Bi Jiao Ji Fan Yi Yan Jiu: Comparative Cultural & Translation Studies. 2009. (CHI & ENG., Illus.). *(978-7-5628-2633-0(1))* East China Univ. of Science and Technology Electronic &.

Liu, Jennifer Li-Chia & Li, Yan. Encounters I: A Cognitive Approach to Advanced Chinese. 2010. (ENG & CHI., Illus.). xii, 447p. pap. *(978-0-253-22111-7(0))* Indiana Univ. Pr.

—Encounters II: A Cognitive Approach to Advanced Chinese. 2010. (CHI & ENG., Illus.). xii, 504p. *(978-0-253-22113-1(7))*; *(978-0-253-22114-8(5))* Indiana Univ. Pr.

Liu, Jun. Introductory Chinese. 2012. (ENG.). 480p. (C). pap. 68.67 *(978-0-07-337188-7(2)*, 0073371882) McGraw-Hill Cos., The.

—Workbook/Lab Manual t/a Access Chinese. 2012. (ENG.). 224p. (C). pap. 62.00 *(978-0-07-728802-0(5)*, 0077288025) McGraw-Hill Cos., The.

Liu, Ruinian & Li, Duanduan. Reading into a New China: Integrated Skills for Advanced Chinese = [Bian Hua Zhong de Zhongguo], 2 vols. 2009. (CHI & ENG.). (C). pap. 39.99 *(978-0-88727-693-4(8))*; pap. 39.99 *(978-0-88727-627-9(X))* Cheng & Tsui Co.

Liu, Yuehua. Integrated Chinese, 4 vols. 3rd rev. ed. 2008. (C). pap. 21.95 *(978-0-88727-640-8(7))* Cheng & Tsui Co.

—Integrated Chinese: [Zhong Wen Ting Shuo du Xie], 4 vols. 3rd rev. ed. (CHI & ENG.). (C). 2009. 59.95 *(978-0-88727-680-4(6))* 2009. pap. 49.95 *(978-0-88727-679-8(2))* 2008. 49.95 *(978-0-88727-645-3(8))* 2008. 49.95 *(978-0-88727-644-6(X))* 2008. pap. 39.95 *(978-0-88727-638-5(5))* 2008. pap. 39.95 *(978-0-88727-639-2(3))* Cheng & Tsui Co.

Liu, Yuehua, et al. Integrated Chinese, 3 vols. 2nd rev. ed. 2007. (C). pap. 32.95 *(978-0-88727-581-4(8))*; pap. 39.95 *(978-0-88727-582-1(6))*; pap. 39.95 *(978-0-88727-532-6(X))*; pap. 32.95 *(978-0-88727-533-3(8))* Cheng & Tsui Co.

—Integrated Chinese 1/1, 4 vols. 3rd rev. ed. 2008. (C). pap. 21.95 *(978-0-88727-648-4(2))* Cheng & Tsui Co.

Lomba, Ana. Play & Learn Chinese with Audio CD. 2011. (ENG & CHI., Illus.). 64p. 20.00 incl. audio compact disk ***(978-0-07-175970-0(0)***, 0071759700) McGraw-Hill Cos., The.

Louie, Belinda Y. Learning Chinese: Through Stories & Activities. 2007. (Illus.). 48p. (J). (gr. -1-3). per. 14.95 *(978-1-887542-54-8(X))* Book Pubs. Network.

Lu, Xing. Rhetoric in Ancient China, Fifth to Third Century B. C. E: A Comparison with Classical Greek Rhetoric. 2011. (Studies in Rhetoric/Communication Ser.). (ENG.). 376p. pap. 24.95 ***(978-1-61117-053-5(2))*** Univ. of South Carolina Pr.

Mao, LuMing. Reading Chinese Fortune Cookie: The Making of Chinese American Rhetoric. 2006. 190p. per. 22.95 *(978-0-87421-640-0(0))*, Utah State Univ. Pr.) Univ. Pr. of Colorado.

Marton, Ference, et al, eds. On the Learning of Chinese. 2010. (Illus.). 196p. pap. *(978-94-6091-267-2(2))* Sense Pubs.

Mcdonald, Edward. Learning Chinese, Turning Chinese: Becoming Sinophone in a Globalised World. 2011. (Asia's Transformations Ser.). (ENG., Illus.). 264p. 44.95 *(978-0-415-55942-3(1))*; 155.00 *(978-0-415-55941-6(3))* Routledge.

Meng, Yeh, et al. Chaoyue: Advancing in Chinese - Practice for Intermediate & Pre-Advanced Students. 2010. (ENG & CHI., Illus.). 216p. (gr. 17). pap., wbk. ed. 24.50 *(978-0-231-15623-3(5))* Columbia Univ. Pr.

Meng, Yuanchao. Setting the Stage for Chinese, 2 vols. 2009. pap. 20.99 *(978-0-88727-530-2(3))* Cheng & Tsui Co.

—Setting the Stage for Chinese: Plays & Performances for Grades K-6, 2 vols. 2007. (CHI & ENG.). pap. 20.99 *(978-0-88727-529-6(X))* Cheng & Tsui Co.

Montanaro, John S., et al. Encounters: Chinese Language & Culture, Character Writing Workbook 1. 2011. (ENG.). 256p. pap. 29.99 *(978-0-300-16170-0(0))* Yale Univ. Pr.

Narrog, Heiko. Modality, Subjectivity, & Semantic Change: A Cross-Linguistic Perspective. 2012. (ENG., Illus.). 352p. 125.00 ***(978-0-19-969437-2(0))*** Oxford Univ. Pr., Inc.

Ning, Cynthia Y. & Montanaro, John S. Encounters: Chinese Language & Culture, Screenplay 1. 2011. 160p. pap. 29.99 ***(978-0-300-16605-7(2))*** Yale Univ. Pr.

—Encounters: Chinese Language & Culture, Student Book 1. 2011. (Illus.). 336p. pap. 94.99 *(978-0-300-16162-5(X))* Yale Univ. Pr.
—Encounters: Chinese Language & Culture, Student Book 2. 2012. (Illus.). 400p. pap. 94.99 *(978-0-300-16163-2(8))* Yale Univ. Pr.
Ning, Cynthia Y. & Montanaro, John S. Encounters - Chinese Language & Culture, Annotated Instructor#8242;s Edition 1. 2012. (ENG.). pap. ***(978-0-300-16166-3(2))*** Yale Univ. Pr.
Po-Ching, Yip. The Chinese Lexicon: A Comprehensive Survey. 2007. (CHI & ENG., Illus.). 400p. (C). per. 46.95 *(978-0-415-42954-2(4))* Routledge.
Qian, Yufang. Discursive Constructions Around Terrorism in the People's Daily (China) & The Sun (UK) Before & after 9/11. 2010. (Illus.). xvi, 166p. 65.95 *(978-3-0343-0186-2(3))* Lang, Peter Publishing, Inc.
Raatma, Lucia. Mandarin. 2011. (Languages of the World Ser.). (ENG.). 32p. (gr. k-2). 26.65 *(978-1-4329-5084-2(3))*; pap. 7.99 *(978-1-4329-5091-0(6))* Heinemann-Raintree. (Heinemann First Library).
Radtke, Oliver Lutz. More Chinglish: Speaking in Tongues, 1 vol. 2009. (ENG., Illus.). 112p. pap. 7.99 *(978-1-4236-0584-3(5))* Gibbs Smith, Publisher.
Rajeev, Dileep. Learning Chinese Characters: An Ideographic Approach, Vol. 1. 2010. 310p. pap. 21.41 *(978-0-557-55051-7(3))* Lulu Enterprises Inc.
Ross, Claudia, et al. The Rouledge Course in Modern Mandarin Simplified Level 1 Bundle, 2 vols. 2011. (ENG.). pap. 100.00 *(978-0-415-59682-4(3))* Routledge.
Ross, Claudia, et al. The Routledge Course in Modern Mandarin - Complete Simplified Bundle (Levels 1 And 2), 4 vols. 2012. pap. 180.00 ***(978-0-415-53541-0(7))*** Routledge.
Ross, Melanie H. A Course in Modern Mandarin Chinese. 2011. (CHI & ENG.). 392p. pap. 66.95 *(978-0-415-47253-1(9))* 2010. (ENG.). 328p. pap., wbk. ed. 54.95 *(978-0-415-47252-4(0))* Routledge.
—The Routledge Course in Modern Mandarin Chinese. 2010. (ENG & CHI., Illus.). 416p. pap. 64.95 *(978-0-415-47251-7(2))* Routledge.
Ross, Melanie H., et al. A Course in Modern Mandarin Chinese. 2011. (CHI & ENG.). 464p. pap. 72.95 *(978-0-415-47246-3(6))* 2010. (ENG.). 336p. pap., wbk. ed. 54.95 *(978-0-415-47248-7(2))* Routledge.
—The Routledge Course in Modern Mandarin Chinese. 2010. (ENG., Illus.). 416p. pap. 64.95 *(978-0-415-47249-4(0))* Routledge.
—Routledge Course in Modern Mandarin Chinese. 2011. (CHI & ENG., Illus.). 464p. pap. 70.00 *(978-0-415-47250-0(4))* Routledge.
The Routledge Course in Modern Mandarin Traditional Level 1 Bundle. 2010. (ENG.). pap. 95.00 *(978-0-415-59686-2(6))* Routledge.
The Routledge Course in Modern Mandarin Chinese Level 2 Simplified Bundle, 2 vols. 2012. (ENG.). pap. 105.00 ***(978-0-415-53307-2(4))*** Routledge.
Routledge Course in Modern Mandarin Level 2 Traditional Bundle, 2 vols. 2012. (ENG.). pap. 110.00 ***(978-0-415-53308-9(2))*** Routledge.
Rouzer, Paul. A New Practical Primer of Literary Chinese. 2007. (Harvard East Asian Monographs: 276). (Illus.). 540p. per. 29.95 *(978-0-674-02270-6(X))* Harvard Univ., Asia Ctr.
Sanders, Robert & Yao, Nora. Fundamental Spoken Chinese. 2009. (CHI & ENG., Illus.). 376p. pap. 39.00 *(978-0-8248-3156-1(X))* Univ. of Hawaii Pr.
Scarborough, William. A Collection of Chinese Proverbs. 2011. 522p. pap. 34.95 ***(978-1-4460-6291-3(0))*** Barclay Pr., Inc.
Scurfield, Elizabeth & Lianyi, Song. Read & Write Chinese Script: Learn The Script Step By Step. 2nd ed. 2011. (TY: Language Guides). (ENG.). 224p. pap. 13.00 *(978-0-07-175991-5(3))*, 0071759913, McGraw-Hill Cos., The.
Setton, Robin. Interpreting Chinese, Interpreting China. 2011. (Illus.). viii, 188p. *(978-90-272-2259-6(2))*; *(978-90-272-8691-8(4))* Benjamins, John Publishing Co.
Shen, Yan. AP Chinese Language & Culture. (CHI & ENG., Illus.). 2009. 576p. 29.99 *(978-0-7641-9400-9(3))* 2008. iv, 567p. (J). *(978-0-7641-3815-7(4))* Barron's Educational Series, Inc.
Shi, Guangchao. "Yongle Da Dian" Ji Yi Shu Gao. 2009. (CHI.). *(978-7-5348-3212-3(8))* Zhongzhou Ancient Bks. Publishing Hse.
Shum, Mark Shiu Kee & Zhang, De-lu, eds. Teaching Writing in Chinese Speaking Areas. 2010. (Studies in Writing Ser.). x, 276p. pap. 139.00 *(978-1-4419-3888-6(5))*, 1441938885) Springer.
Step by Step, Bk. 1. tchr. ed. 13.17 *(978-0-673-21568-0(7))* Addison-Wesley Educational Pubs., Inc.
Step by Step, Bk. 1. Incl. Bk. 1. tchr. ed. 13.17 *(978-0-673-21568-0(7))*; Set stu. ed. 18.93 *(978-0-673-21567-3(9))*; Set stu. ed. 20.74 *(978-0-673-21571-0(7))* Addison-Wesley Educational Pubs., Inc.
Summers, James. Learn Chinese for English Speakers. (CHI & ENG.). pap. 20.95 *(978-0-87557-009-9(7))* Saphrograph Corp.
Sun, Hao & Kádár, Dániel Z. It's the Dragon's Turn: Chinese Institutional Discourses. 2008. 262p. pap. *(978-3-03911-175-6(2))* Lang, Peter.
Swihart, De-An Wu. Success with Chinese: A Communicative Approach for Beginners: Reading & Writing, Level 1, 2 vols. 2nd rev. ed. 2007. (CHI & ENG., Illus.). 210p. (C). pap. 31.95 *(978-0-88727-601-9(5))* Cheng & Tsui Co.
—Success with Chinese, Level 2: A Communicative Approach for Intermediate Learners, 2 vols. 2006. (Illus.). (C). 342p. pap. 57.95 incl. audio compact disk *(978-0-88727-659-0(8))*; pap. 41.95 *(978-0-88727-660-6(1))* Cheng & Tsui Co.
Tate, Michelle, et al. Edexcel Chinese, Bk. 1. 2008. (CHI & ENG., Illus.). 144p. pap. 65.00 *(978-0-340-96784-3(6))* Hodder Education GBR. Dist: Trans-Atlantic Pubns., Inc.
Teng, Wen-Hua. Yufa! A Practical Guide to Mandarin Chinese Grammar. 2011. (CHI & ENG.). 352p. pap., instr.'s gde. ed. 22.95 *(978-1-4441-0913-9(8))* Hodder Education GBR. Dist: Oxford Univ. Pr., Inc.
Trimnell, Edward. Chinese Business Vocabulary in a Hurry: A Brief Study Guide. 2010. 110p. pap. 12.95 *(978-0-9828901-0-3(9))* Beechmont Crest Publishing.
Tsung, Linda. Teaching & Learning Chinese in Global Contexts: Multimodality & Literacy in the New Media Age. Cruickshank, Ken, ed. 2011. (ENG., Illus.). 256p. 140.00 *(978-1-4411-0039-9(3))* Continuum International Publishing Group, Ltd. GBR. Dist: National Bk. Network.
T'ung, P. C. & Pollard, D. E. Colloquial Chinese. 2012. (ENG & CHI.). 54.95 ***(978-0-415-52485-8(7))*** Routledge.
Valerie, Pellatt & Tin-Kun, Liu. Chinese: A Course in Translation Method - Chinese to English. 2010. (Thinking Translation Ser.). (CHI & ENG., Illus.). 240p. 150.00 *(978-0-415-47417-7(5))* Routledge.
—Thinking Chinese: A Course in Translation Method - Chinese to English. 2010. (Thinking Translation Ser.). (ENG & CHI., Illus.). 240p. pap. 45.95 *(978-0-415-47419-1(1))* Routledge.
van Crevel, Maghiel, et al, eds. Chinees in tien Verdiepingen 1: Mandarijn voor het voortgezet onderwijs, Werkboek. 2010. (DUT.). 64p. pap. *(978-90-8728-033-8(5))*, Leiden Univ. Pr.) Amsterdam Univ. Pr.
—Chinees in tien Verdiepingen 2: Mandarijn voor het voortgezet Onderwijs. 2009. (DUT., Illus.). 192p. pap. *(978-90-8728-042-0(4))*, Leiden Univ. Pr.) Amsterdam Univ. Pr.
—Chinees in tien Verdiepingen 2: Mandarijn voor het voortgezet onderwijs, Werkboek. 2010. (DUT.). 64p. pap. *(978-90-8728-037-5(8))*, Leiden Univ. Pr.) Amsterdam Univ. Pr.
Wang, Chun. Picture Chinese Characters: Finding Art, History, & Logic in Written Chinese. 2011. (ENG., Illus.). 220p. pap. 16.95 ***(978-1-59265-104-7(6))*** Long River Pr.
Wang, Guo'an. A Handbook for 1,000 Basic Chinese Characters. Guo'an, Wang, ed. 2007. (ENG.). 330p. (gr. 17). pap. 27.00 *(978-962-996-283-8(7))* Chinese Univ. of Hong Kong, The HKG. Dist: Columbia Univ. Pr.
Wang, Peihan Caroline. Actually & Qishi. 2009. 112p. pap. *(978-3-639-15356-9(1))* VDM Verlag Dr. Mueller e.K.
Wang, Wei, et al. Readings in Contemporary Chinese Cinema: A Textbook of Advanced Modern Chinese. 2008. (Princeton Language Program: Modern Chinese Ser.). (ENG.). 352p. (C). pap. 45.00 *(978-0-691-13109-2(0))* Princeton Univ. Pr.
Wang, Xueying. Chinese Odyssey. 6 vols. 2008. (Illus.). (C). stu. ed. 104.95 incl. cd-rom *(978-0-88727-516-6(8))*; pap., stu. ed. 49.99 *(978-0-88727-514-2(1))*; pap., stu. ed. 49.99 *(978-0-88727-515-9(X))* Cheng & Tsui Co.
—Chinese Odyssey Volume 1 Textbook (Simplified & Traditional) 2007. (C). pap., stu. ed. 31.95 *(978-0-88727-538-8(9))* Cheng & Tsui Co.
Wang, Xueying, et al. Chinese Odyssey, 6 vols. (C). 2007. pap., stu. ed. 43.95 *(978-0-88727-540-1(0))* 2007. pap., stu. ed. 27.95 *(978-0-88727-541-8(9))* 2006. pap. *(978-0-88727-542-5(7))* 2006. pap., stu. ed. 24.95 *(978-0-88727-539-5(7))* Cheng & Tsui Co.
—Gateway to Chinese Language & Culture: A Complete Interactive Course, 6 vols. 2008. (C). stu. ed. 73.95 incl. cd-rom *(978-0-88727-432-9(3))* Cheng & Tsui Co.
Wayne, He. Chinese for Tomorrow 2 Textbook Simplified Characters, 6 vols. 2008. (CHI & ENG., Illus.). (C). pap., stu. ed. 75.00 *(978-0-88727-608-8(3))* Cheng & Tsui Co.
—Chinese for Tomorrow 2 Textbook Traditional Characters, 6 vols. 2008. (CHI & ENG., Illus.). (C). pap., stu. ed. 75.00 *(978-0-88727-607-1(5))* Cheng & Tsui Co.
Wei, Jennifer M. Language Choice & Identity Politics in Taiwan. 2008. (ENG.). 152p. 52.50 *(978-0-7391-2352-2(1))* Lexington Bks.
Wei, William I., et al. A Handbook of Practical Medical Terms: (English Chinese) 4th rev. ed. 2008. (CHI & ENG.). 192p. (gr. 17). pap. 15.00 *(978-962-209-952-4(1))* Hong Kong Univ. Pr. HKG. Dist: Columbia Univ. Pr.
Wheatley, Julian K. Learning Chinese: A Foundation Course in Mandarin, Elementary Level. 2010. (ENG & CHI., Illus.). 656p. (C). pap. 65.00 *(978-0-300-14117-7(3))* Yale Univ. Pr.
Wightwick, Jane. Your First 100 Words in Chinese Mandarin. 2007. (Your First 100 Words In... Ser.). (ENG., Illus.). 80p. 16.95 *(978-0-07-149879-1(6))*, 0071498796) McGraw-Hill Cos., The.
Williams, Philip F. & Wu, Yenna. Mandarin Chinese the Easy Way. 2nd ed. 2008. (Illus.). xv, 361p. *(978-0-7641-3503-8(9))* Barron's Educational Series, Inc.
Wolfe, Albert. Chinese 24/7: Everyday Strategies for Speaking & Understanding Mandarin. 2009. (CHI & ENG., Illus.). 376p. pap. 24.95 *(978-1-933330-82-2(1))* Stone Bridge Pr.
Wu, Dorren D. Discourses of Cultural China in the Globalizing Age. 2008. (Studying Multicultural Discourses Ser.). (ENG.). 272p. (gr. 17). 60.00 *(978-962-209-912-8(2))*; pap. 30.00 *(978-962-209-913-5(0))* Hong Kong Univ. Pr. HKG. Dist: Columbia Univ. Pr.
Wu, Grace. Lang Lang: Chinese Biographies: Graded Readers = [Lang Lang: Gu Dian Yin Yue de Qi Cai: Ren Wu Zhuan Ji: Zhong Wen Pin Yin Fu Zhu du Ben]. 2010. (C). pap., stu. ed. 15.95 *(978-0-88727-758-0(6))* Cheng & Tsui Co.
—Yao Ming: Chinese Biographies: Graded Readers = [Yao Ming: Lan Qiu de Ju Xing: Ren Wu Zhuan Ji: Zhong Wen Pin Yin Fu Zhu du Ben]. 2010. (CHI & ENG.). (C). pap. 15.95 *(978-0-88727-759-7(4))* Cheng & Tsui Co.
Wu, Hsichen & Ling, R. Selected Contemporary Chinese Essays.Tr. of Dandai Zhongguo Sanwen Xuan. pap. 19.95 *(978-957-09-0649-3(9))* Cheng Chung Bk. Co., Ltd. TWN. Dist: Cheng & Tsui Co.
Wu, Justin. Advanced Level Chinese: A Complete Tutorial. 2007. 240p. per. 27.95 *(978-0-7156-3708-1(8))* Duckworth Publishers GBR. Dist: International Publishers Marketing.
Wu, Ping. Han Yu Te Shu Ju Shi de Shi Jian Yu Yi Fen Xi Yu Ji Suan: Hanyu Teshu Jushi de Shijian Yuyi Fenxi Yu Jisuan. 2009. (CHI., Illus.). *(978-7-5004-8454-7(2))* China Social Sciences Pr.
Wu, Ruiqing. Su Yu You Hua. 2010. (CHI., Illus.). xii, 148p. *(978-962-07-1899-1(2))* Commercial Pr., The.
Wu, Sue-Mei & Yu, Yueming. Chinese Link Pt. 2. 2nd rev. ed. 2011. (ENG & CHI.). 448p. (C). pap. 56.40 *(978-0-205-78279-6(5))*, Prentice Hall) Prentice Hall PTR.
Wu, Sue-Mei, et al. Beginning Chinese, Pts. 1. 2nd ed. 2010. (CHI & ENG.). (C). ring bd. 77.27 *(978-0-205-81956-0(7))*, Prentice Hall) Prentice Hall PTR.
—Character Book for Chinese Link Pt. 2: Beginning Chinese, Traditional & Simplified. 2nd ed. 2010. (ENG.). 132p. (C). pap. 33.33 *(978-0-205-78304-5(X))*, Prentice Hall) Prentice Hall PTR.
—Character Book for Chinese Link Intermediate, Level 2/Part 1. 2nd ed. 2011. (ENG.). 144p. (C). pap. 34.40 *(978-0-205-78376-2(7))*, Prentice Hall) Prentice Hall PTR.
—Character Book for Chinese Link Level Level 2/Part 2. 2nd ed. 2011. (ENG.). 144p. (C). pap. 33.33 *(978-0-205-78381-6(3))*, Prentice Hall) Prentice Hall PTR.
—Chinese Link. (C). 2nd ed. 2010. (ENG.). 312p. 122.67 *(978-0-205-78395-3(3))* 2nd rev. ed. 2011. (ENG.). 408p. 62.67 ***(978-0-205-75294-2(2))***Pt. 1. 2006. (ENG., Illus.). 144p. per. 40.00 *(978-0-13-156441-1(2))*Pt. 2. 2006. (ENG.). 168p. per., wbk. ed. 40.00 *(978-0-13-242979-5(9))*Pt. 2. 2nd ed. 2010. (ENG.). 311p. ring bd. 37.33 *(978-0-205-82550-9(8))*Pt. 2. 2nd ed. 2010. (CHI & ENG., Illus.). 336p. pap. 57.33 *(978-0-205-69199-9(4))* Prentice Hall PTR. (Prentice Hall).
—Chinese Link: Beginning Chinese. 2nd ed. 2010. (CHI & ENG.). (C). ring bd. 77.33 *(978-0-205-81954-6(0))*, Prentice Hall) Prentice Hall PTR.
—Chinese Link: Beginning Chinese, Simplified Character Version, Level 1/Part 1, Books a la Carte Edition. 2nd ed. 2010. (ENG.). 312p. (C). ring bd. 37.27 *(978-0-205-82349-9(1))*, Prentice Hall) Prentice Hall PTR.
—Chinese Link: Beginning Chinese, Simplified Character Version, Level 1/Part 1, Books a la Carte Plus MyChineseLab (6-month) 2nd ed. 2010. (ENG.). (C). ring bd. 61.33 *(978-0-205-00813-1(5))*, Prentice Hall) Prentice Hall PTR.
—Chinese Link: Beginning Chinese, Simplified Character Version, Level 1/Part 2, Books a la Carte Plus MyChineseLab (6-month) 2nd ed. 2010. (ENG.). (C). ring bd. 61.33 *(978-0-205-00814-8(3))*, Prentice Hall) Prentice Hall PTR.
—Chinese Link: Beginning Chinese, Simplified Character Version, Level 1/Parts 1 & 2, Books a la Carte Plus MyChineseLab (24-month) 2nd ed. 2010. (ENG.). (C). ring bd., ring bd. 118.67 *(978-0-205-02609-8(5))*, Prentice Hall) Prentice Hall PTR.
—Chinese Link: Beginning Chinese, Traditional. 2nd ed. 2010. (ENG.). 312p. (C). 122.67 *(978-0-205-79957-2(4))*, Prentice Hall) Prentice Hall PTR.
—Chinese Link: Beginning Chinese, Traditional Character Version. 2nd ed. 2010. (ENG.). 72p. (C). pap. 40.00 *(978-0-205-69639-0(2))*, Prentice Hall) Prentice Hall PTR.
—Chinese Link: Beginning Chinese, Traditional Character Version, Level 1/Part 1, Books a la Carte Edition. 2nd ed. 2010. (ENG.). 311p. (C). ring bd. 37.33 *(978-0-13-254701-7(5))*, Prentice Hall) Prentice Hall PTR.
—Chinese Link: Beginning Chinese, Traditional Character Version, Level 1/Part 1, Books a la Carte Plus MyChineseLab (6-month) 2nd ed. 2010. (ENG.). (C). ring bd. 61.33 *(978-0-205-00815-5(1))*, Prentice Hall) Prentice Hall PTR.
—Chinese Link: Beginning Chinese, Traditional Character Version, Level 1/Part 2, Books a la Carte Edition. 2nd ed. 2010. (ENG.). 336p. (C). ring bd. 37.33 *(978-0-205-82350-5(5))*, Prentice Hall) Prentice Hall PTR.
—Chinese Link: Beginning Chinese, Traditional Character Version, Level 1/Part 2, Books a la Carte Plus MyChineseLab (6-month) 2nd ed. 2010. (ENG.). (C). ring bd. 61.33 *(978-0-205-00816-2(X))*, Prentice Hall) Prentice Hall PTR.
—Chinese Link: Intermediate Chinese. 2007. (ENG., Illus.). 240p. (C). per. 40.00 *(978-0-13-613714-6(8))*, Prentice Hall) Prentice Hall PTR.
—Chinese Link: Intermediate Chinese, Level 2/Parts 1 & 2, Books a la Carte Plus MyChineseLab 24MO. 2nd ed. 2011. (ENG.). (C). ring bd., ring bd. 118.40 ***(978-0-205-21287-3(5))***, Prentice Hall) Prentice Hall PTR.
—Chinese Link Pt. 1: Beginning Chinese. 2nd ed. 2010. (ENG & CHI.). 312p. (C). pap. 57.33 *(978-0-205-63721-8(3))*, Prentice Hall) Prentice Hall PTR.
—Chinese Link Pt. 1: Beginning Chinese, Traditional & Simplified. 2nd ed. 2010. (ENG.). 104p. (C). pap. 33.33 *(978-0-205-78298-7(1))*, Prentice Hall) Prentice Hall PTR.
—Chinese Link Pt. 1, Level 1: Beginning Chinese, Traditional Character Version. 2nd ed. 2010. (CHI & ENG.). 312p. (C). pap. 57.33 *(978-0-205-69198-2(6))*, Prentice Hall) Prentice Hall PTR.
—Chinese Link Pt. 2: Beginning Chinese, Simplified Character Version. 2nd ed. 2010. (CHI & ENG., Illus.). 336p. (C). pap. 57.33 *(978-0-205-69196-8(X))*, Prentice Hall) Prentice Hall PTR.
—Chinese Link Pt. 2: Elementary Chinese Level 1. 2006. (CHI & ENG., Illus.). 384p. (C). per. 57.33 *(978-0-13-242977-1(2))*, Prentice Hall) Prentice Hall PTR.
—Chinese Link Pt. 2: Simplified Character Version. 2nd ed. 2010. (CHI & ENG.). 72p. (C). pap., stu. ed., wbk. ed. 40.00 *(978-0-205-74123-6(1))*, Prentice Hall) Prentice Hall PTR.
—Chinese Link Pt. 2: Zhongwen Tiandi, Intermediate Chinese. 2007. (ENG., Illus.). 432p. (C). per. 56.40 *(978-0-13-240931-5(3))*, Prentice Hall) Prentice Hall PTR.
—Chinese Link - Intermediate Chinese: Homework & Character Book. 2007. (ENG.). 288p. (C). pap., wbk. ed. 40.00 *(978-0-13-224977-5(4))*, Prentice Hall) Prentice Hall PTR.
—Chinese Link Elementary Chinese Traditional Character, Pt. 2. 2006. (ENG., Illus.). 384p. (C). per. 57.33 *(978-0-13-242978-8(0))* Prentice Hall) Prentice Hall PTR.
—Chinese Link Simplified Level 1, Pt. 1. 2006. (ENG.). 336p. (C). pap. 57.33 *(978-0-13-156442-8(0))*, Prentice Hall) Prentice Hall PTR.
—Chinese Link, Traditional Character, Pt. 2. 2006. (ENG., Illus.). 168p. (C). per., wbk. ed. 40.00 *(978-0-13-242980-1(2))*, Prentice Hall) Prentice Hall PTR.
—Chinese Link Traditional Character Version Elementary Chinese, Pt. 1. 2006. (ENG., Illus.). 336p. (C). per. 57.33 *(978-0-13-242974-0(8))*, Prentice Hall) Prentice Hall PTR.
—Student Activities Manual for Chinese Link Pt. 1: Beginning Chinese, Simplified Character Version. 2nd ed. 2010. (ENG.). 72p. (C). pap. 40.00 *(978-0-205-69638-3(4))*, Prentice Hall) Prentice Hall PTR.
—Student Activities Manual for Chinese Link Pt. 2: Beginning Chinese, Traditional Character Version. 2nd ed. 2010. (CHI & ENG.). 72p. (C). pap. 41.20 *(978-0-205-74138-0(X))*, Prentice Hall) Prentice Hall PTR.
—Student Activities Manual for Chinese Link Intermediate Level 2. 2nd ed. 2011. (ENG.). (C). Pt. 1. 150p. pap. 41.20 *(978-0-205-78377-9(5))*Pt. 2. 120p. pap. 40.00 *(978-0-205-78380-9(5))* Prentice Hall PTR. (Prentice Hall).
Xiang, Catherine Hua. Mastering Chinese with Two Audio CDs. 2011. (ENG.). 384p. (C). 40.00 *(978-0-07-176642-5(1))*, 0071766421) McGraw-Hill Cos., The.
Xiang, Wei. Chinese Customs (Bilingual) 2010. 194p. pap. 11.95 *(978-1-60220-916-9(2))* BetterLink Pr., Inc.
Xiao & Xiao, Yun. Tales & Traditions, 3 vols. 2009. (C). pap. 19.95 *(978-0-88727-682-8(2))* Cheng & Tsui Co.
Xiao, et al. Tales & Traditions, 4, 4. 2010. (ENG & CHI.). 260p. pap. 19.95 *(978-0-88727-681-1(4))* Cheng & Tsui Co.
Xiao, Yun. Tales & Traditions & Other Essays Vol. 2, 3 vols. 2008. (CHI & ENG.). (C). pap. 19.95 *(978-0-88727-646-0(6))* Cheng & Tsui Co.
Xiao, Yun, et al. Tales & Traditions & Other Essays: For Beginning Students, 3 vols. 2007. (C). pap. 19.95 *(978-0-88727-534-0(6))* Cheng & Tsui Co.
Xing, Janet Zhiqun. Studies of Chinese Linguistics: Functional Approaches. 2009. (ENG., Illus.). 248p. (gr. 17). 50.00 *(978-962-209-964-7(5))* Hong Kong Univ. Pr. HKG. Dist: Columbia Univ. Pr.
Xu, Changmo. Han Yu Yu Yan Jie Gou Yi Zheng: Li Lun Yu Jiao Xue Ying Yong. 2010. (CHI., Illus.). viii, 291p. *(978-986-6923-96-8(7))* Le Jin Bks., Ltd.
Xu, Goomoo. Dao de Jing: A Philosophy about Everything: Uncover the Essence of Laozi's Wisdom. 2010. 328p. pap. 19.99 *(978-1-4520-4861-1(4))* AuthorHouse.
Xu, Jiujiu. Xian Dai Han Yu Pian Zhang Yu Yan Xue: Text Linguistics in Contemporary Chinese. 2010. (CHI., Illus.). *(978-7-100-06691-4(3))* Commercial Pr., The.
Xu, Weiman. Cheng & Tsui Strive for a 5: AP Chinese Practice Tests. 2009. pap. 29.99 *(978-0-88727-764-1(0))* Cheng & Tsui Co.
Xuanmin Luo & Yuanjian He, eds. Translating China. 2009. (Topics in Translation Ser.). (ENG., Illus.). 232p. 139.95 *(978-1-84769-187-3(0))* Multilingual Matters GBR. Dist: Univ. of Toronto Pr.
Yang, Li-chin. Young Children's Refusal in Mandarin Chinese. 2008. 184p. pap. *(978-3-8364-8649-1(0))* VDM Verlag Dr. Mueller e.K.
Yao, Tao-chung. Integrated Chinese 1/2 Textbook Simplified Characters, 4 vols. 3rd rev. ed. 2008. (C). 59.95 *(978-0-88727-671-2(7))*; pap. 49.95 *(978-0-88727-670-5(9))* Cheng & Tsui Co.
—Integrated Chinese 1/2 Textbook Traditional Characters, 4 vols. 3rd rev. ed. 2008. (C). 59.95 *(978-0-88727-673-6(3))*; pap. 49.95 *(978-0-88727-672-9(5))* Cheng & Tsui Co.
Yao, Tao-chung, et al. Integrated Chinese: Level 2, 3 vols. 2nd ed. 2007. (C). pap., wbk. ed. 29.95 *(978-0-88727-482-4(X))* Cheng & Tsui Co.
Ye, Guoliang & Xu, Xingqing. Jianghu Shi Dai Riben Han Xue Yan Jiu Zhu Mian Xiang: Si Xiang Wen Hua Pian. 2009. (CHI., Illus.). xv, 493p. *(978-986-01-8374-0(0))* Academia Sinica.
Ye, Zinan & Shi, Lynette Xiaojing. Introduction to Chinese-English Translation: Key Concepts & Techniques. 2008. (ENG.). 256p. 19.95 *(978-0-7818-1216-0(X))* Hippocrene Bks., Inc.
Yin, Pinghua & Gu, Yilan. Easy Hanzi. 2008. 224p. per. 25.50 *(978-1-4357-0687-3(0))* Lulu Enterprises Inc.
Yip, Po-Ching & Rimmington, Don. Intermediate Chinese. 2nd rev. ed. 2009. (Grammar Workbooks Ser.). (ENG & CHI.). 392p. 39.95 *(978-0-415-48631-6(9))* Routledge.
—Intermediate Chinese: A Grammar & Workbook. 2nd ed. 2009. (Grammar Workbooks Ser.). (ENG & CHI.). 384p. 145.00 *(978-0-415-48630-9(0))* Routledge.
Yu, Ning. The Chinese Heart in a Cognitive Perspective: Culture, Body, & Language. 2009. (Applications of Cognitive Linguistics [ACL] Ser.). (ENG., Illus.). IX, 444p. 137.00 *(978-3-11-020516-9(5))* De Gruyter, Mouton DEU. Dist: de Gruyter, Walter GmbH & Co. KG.
—The Chinese HEART in a Cognitive Perspective: Culture, Body, & Language. 2009. (Applications of Cognitive Linguistics [ACL] Ser.). (ENG.). IX, 444p. 210.00 ***(978-3-11-173245-9(2))*** De Gruyter, Mouton DEU. Dist: de Gruyter, Walter GmbH & Co. KG.
Yu, Ning. From Body to Meaning in Culture: Papers on Cognitive Semantic Studies of Chinese. 2009. *(978-90-272-3262-5(8))*; pap. *(978-90-272-3263-2(6))* Benjamins, John Publishing Co.
Yu, Xiaorong, et al. Han Yu Shi Zhong de Yu Yan Jie Chu Wen Ti Yan Jiu. 2010. (CHI., Illus.). *(978-7-80241-106-7(6))* Language Publishing Hse.

C

Yu, Yueming & Wu, Sue-Mei. Chinese Link: Intermediate Chinese. 2nd rev. ed. 2010. (CHI & ENG.). 408p. (C). pap. 56.40 *(978-0-205-78280-2(9),* Prentice Hall) Prentice Hall PTR.

—Chinese Link Pt. 2: Intermediate Chinese. 2nd ed. 2011. (ENG.). 448p. (C). ring bd. 37.20 *(978-0-205-03701-8(1),* Prentice Hall) Prentice Hall PTR.

Yu, Yueming, et al. Chinese Link Pt. 1: Intermediate Chinese. 2nd ed. 2011. (ENG.). (C). ring bd. 81.20 *(978-0-205-03625-7(2),* Prentice Hall) Prentice Hall PTR.

—Chinese Link Pt. 2: Intermediate Chinese. 2nd ed. 2011. (ENG.). (C). ring bd. 60.67 *(978-0-205-03702-5(X));* ring bd. 81.20 *(978-0-205-03703-2(8))* Prentice Hall PTR. (Prentice Hall).

Yuan, Rong. Technology-Enhanced Chinese Learning. 2009. 112p. pap. *(978-3-639-13480-3(X))* VDM Verlag Dr. Mueller e.K.

Yuan, Xiaohui. Politeness & Audience Response in Chinese-English Subtitling. 2012. (New Trends in Translation Studies: 10). (ENG.). 236p. pap. 58.95 ***(978-3-0343-0732-1(2))*** Lang, Peter AG GBR. Dist: Lang, Peter.

Zhang, Ailing, et al. Written on Water. Huang, Nicole, ed. 2007. (Weatherhead Books on Asia Ser.). (ENG.). 240p. (gr. 17). pap. 24.50 *(978-0-231-13139-1(9))* Columbia Univ. Pr.

Zhang, Niina Ning. Coordination in Syntax. 2009. (Cambridge Studies in Linguistics Ser.). (ENG., Illus.). 294p. 105.00 *(978-0-521-76755-2(5))* Cambridge Univ. Pr.

Zhang, Yisheng. Xian Dai Han Yu Fu Ci Fen Xi: Xiandai Hanyu Fuci Fenxi. 2010. (CHI.). 8p. *(978-7-5426-3069-8(5))* SDX Joint Publishing, Co.

Zheng, Jixiong & Sato, Rentaro. Tai Ri Xue Zhe Lun Jing Dian Quan Shi Zhong de Yu Wen Fen Xi. 2010. (CHI.). x, 448p. *(978-957-15-1496-3(9))* Taiwan Student Book Co., Ltd.

Zhou, Xiaolin. Processing the Chinese Language: A Special Issue of Language & Cognitive Processes. 2009. (Special Issues of Language & Cognitive Processes Ser.). (ENG.). 384p. pap. 79.95 *(978-1-84872-722-9(4),* Psychology Press) Taylor & Francis Group GBR. Dist: Taylor & Francis Group.

Zhou, Yi. Working Mandarin for Beginners. 2007. (Working Languages Ser.). (Illus.). 325p. pap. incl. cd-rom *(978-1-58901-139-7(2))* Georgetown Univ. Pr.

Zhou, Yi & Gerber, M. Lynne. Working Mandarin for Beginners. 2nd rev. ed. 2007. (Working Languages Ser.). (CHI., Illus.). 352p. (C). pap. 64.95 *(978-1-58901-137-3(6))* Georgetown Univ. Pr.

CHINESE LANGUAGE—ALPHABET

see Chinese Characters

CHINESE LANGUAGE—COMPOSITION AND EXERCISES

Po-Ching, Yip. Chinese Vocabulary: A Graded Workbook & Reader. 2012. (CHI & ENG.). 500p. 140.00 *(978-0-415-43913-8(2))* Routledge.

Tate, Michelle, et al. Chinese, Bk. 2. 2009. (CHI & ENG., Illus.). 192p. (gr. 10-12). pap., stu. ed. 65.00 *(978-0-340-96785-0(4))* Hodder Education GBR. Dist: Trans-Atlantic Pubns., Inc.

Wang, Lisa & Zhu, Xiaoming. Chinese, Bk. 2. Tate, Michelle, ed. 2009. (Illus.). 160p. tchr. ed., spiral bd. 250.00 *(978-0-340-96783-6(8))* Hodder Education GBR. Dist: Trans-Atlantic Pubns., Inc.

Xu, Jialu, et al. Jia You! Chinese for the Global Community, Volume 1 (with Audio CDs) (Simplified & Traditional Character Edition) 2008. (ENG.). 350p. (C). 87.95 *(978-1-4282-6218-8(0))* Cengage Heinle.

Yan, Margaret M. & Liu, Jennifer Li-Chia. Interactions Audio: A Cognitive Approach to Beginning Chinese. 2009. (Chinese in Context Language Learning Ser.). (ENG.). cd-rom 39.95 *(978-0-253-35188-3(X),* 025335188X) Indiana Univ. Pr.

CHINESE LANGUAGE—CONVERSATION AND PHRASE BOOKS

Abraham, Wendy. Chinese Phrasebook & Culture Guide. 2008. 336p. pap. 9.99 *(978-0-470-22857-9(1))* Wiley, John & Sons, Inc.

—Chinese PhraseFinder & Dictionary. 2008. (Frommer's Phrase Bks.: 9). (ENG & CHI., Illus.). 256p. per. 8.99 *(978-0-470-17838-6(8),* Frommers) Wiley, John & Sons, Inc.

Abraham, Wendy. Frommer's Chinese PhraseFinder & Dictionary. 2nd ed. 2012. (Frommer's Phrase Bks.: 22). (ENG & CHI.). 256p. pap. 8.99 ***(978-1-118-14361-2(2),*** Frommers) Wiley, John & Sons, Inc.

Anderson, Qin-Hong, compiled by. Masterworks Chinese Companion. 2007. (Cheng & Tsui Asian Language Ser.). (ENG & CHI.). 208p. (C). pap. 25.95 *(978-0-88727-435-0(8))* Cheng & Tsui Co.

Assimil Staff. Chinois sans Peine (One) Chinese for French Speakers. (CHI & FRE.). 28.95 incl. audio *(978-0-8288-4379-9(1),* M12639) French & European Pubns., Inc.

—Chinois sans Peine (Two) Chinese for French Speakers. (CHI & FRE.). 28.95 incl. audio *(978-0-8288-4381-2(3),* M12650) French & European Pubns., Inc.

Barron's, creator. Now You're Talking Mandarin Chinese in No Time. 3rd ed. 2006. (Now You're Talking Ser.). (ENG & CHI., Illus.). 336p. stu. ed. 18.99 *(978-0-7641-7954-9(3))* Barron's Educational Series, Inc.

Berlitz Mandarin Chinese Phrase Book & CD. 4th ed. 2012. (Phrase Book & CD Ser.). (ENG & CHI., Illus.). 224p. pap. 14.99 ***(978-1-78004-277-0(9))*** APA Publications Services SGP. Dist: Ingram Pub. Services.

Berlitz Mandarin Chinese Phrase Book & Dictionary. 4th ed. 2012. (Phrase Book Ser.). (ENG & CHI.). 224p. pap. 8.99 ***(978-1-78004-265-7(5))*** APA Publications Services SGP. Dist: Ingram Pub. Services.

Berlitz Publishing, creator. Mandarin. 2007. (Phrase Book Ser.). (CHI & ENG., Illus.). 224p. pap. 8.95 *(978-981-268-035-8(7))* APA Publications Services SGP. Dist: Ingram Pub. Services.

Berlitz Publishing, ed. Cantonese Chinese. 2008. (Phrase Book & CD Ser.). (CHI & ENG., Illus.). 224p. 12.95 *(978-981-268-478-3(6))* APA Publications Services SGP. Dist: Ingram Pub. Services.

—Chinese Cantonese. 2nd rev. ed. 2008. (Phrase Book Ser.). (CHI & ENG., Illus.). 224p. pap. 8.95 *(978-981-268-475-2(1))* APA Publications Services SGP. Dist: Ingram Pub. Services.

Boyle, Elisabeth L. & Delbridge, Pauline N. Spoken Cantonese, Bk. 2. 410p. pap. 140.00 incl. audio *(978-0-87950-680-3(6))* Spoken Language Services, Inc.

Cannings, Michael & Lonely Planet Staff. China. 2009. (Phrasebook Ser.). (ENG., Illus.). 400p. pap. 10.99 *(978-1-74179-791-6(8))* Lonely Planet Pubns.

Chan, Peter, et al. Listen & Learn Mandarin Chinese. 2006. *(978-0-486-45755-0(9))* Dover Pubns., Inc.

Chan, Susan. Hide This Mandarin Chinese Phrase Book. 2011. (Hide This Phrase Book Ser.). (CHI & ENG., Illus.). 128p. pap. 7.99 *(978-981-268-582-7(0))* APA Publications Services SGP. Dist: Ingram Pub. Services.

Chapin, Alex & Zhang, Jin. Chinese Mandarin Phrasebook 2008. 2008. (ISpeak Audio Phrasebook Ser.). (ENG.). 64p. 14.95 *(978-0-07-159212-3(1),* 0071592121) McGraw-Hill Cos., The.

—ISpeak Chinese Phrasebook. 2007. (I Can Write Ser.). (ENG.). 64p. 12.95 *(978-0-07-149293-5(3),* 0071492933) McGraw-Hill Cos., The.

Collins Publishers Staff. Mandarin Phrasebook: The Right Word in Your Pocket. 2008. (Collins Gem Ser.). (CHI & ENG., Illus.). 256p. pap. 6.95 *(978-0-00-724681-6(1))* HarperCollins Pubs. Ltd. GBR. Dist: Independent Pubs. Group.

Collins Staff. Collins Mandarin Phrasebook & Dictionary. 2009. (Collins Gem Ser.). (CHI & ENG., Illus.). 192p. pap. 7.95 *(978-0-00-726461-2(5))* HarperCollins Pubs. Ltd. GBR. Dist: Independent Pubs. Group.

—Easy Learning Mandarin Phrasebook. 2nd ed. 2010. (Collins Gem Ser.). (ENG & CHI., Illus.). 256p. pap. 6.95 *(978-0-00-735851-9(2))* HarperCollins Pubs. Ltd. GBR. Dist: Independent Pubs. Group.

De Mente, Boye Lafayette. Chinese in Plain English. 2nd rev. ed. 2007. (ENG.). 352p. per. 14.95 *(978-0-07-148295-0(4),* 0071482954) McGraw-Hill Cos., The.

Dover Publications Inc. Staff, creator. Listen & Learn Mandarin Chinese. 2006. (Dover Language Guides Listen & Learn Ser.). (ENG.). 80p. pap. 14.95 *(978-0-486-99812-1(6))* Dover Pubns., Inc.

Ellis, Mike & Ellis, Michael. Chinese Slanguage: A Fun Visual Guide to Mandarin Terms & Phrases, 1 vol. 2010. (CHI & ENG., Illus.). 96p. pap. 7.99 *(978-1-4236-0750-2(3))* Gibbs Smith, Publisher.

EPLS. Chinese. 2nd ed. 2011. (Say It Right! Ser.). (ENG & CHI., Illus.). 192p. pap. 11.00 *(978-0-07-176773-6(8),* 0071766738) McGraw-Hill Cos., The.

Feng, Yu, compiled by. Pop Chinese: A Cheng & Tsui Bilingual Handbook of Contemporary Colloquial Expressions. 2nd rev. ed. 2006. (ENG & CHI.). (C). pap. 34.95 *(978-0-88727-563-0(X))* Cheng & Tsui Co.

Flanagan, Cheryn & Kolowich, Benjamin. Me No Speak China: China. 2nd ed. 2008. (ENG & CHI., Illus.). 96p. pap. 9.95 *(978-0-9787680-1-0(9))* Me No Speak.

Foreign Service Institute Staff. Basic Cantonese, Vol. I. unabr. ed. (CHI.). 392p. pap. 185.00 incl. audio *(978-0-88432-020-3(0),* AFC131) Norton, Jeffrey Pubs., Inc.

Gil, Sonia, reader. Fluenz Mandarin 1 2 3. 2010. (Fluenz Ser.). 519.00 *(978-0-9825410-1-2(5))* Fluenz.

Grobbelaar, Thea, ed. Mandarin in Your Pocket. 2008. (Globetrotter in Your Pocket Ser.). (CHI & ENG., Illus.). 192p. pap. 8.95 *(978-1-84537-556-0(4))* New Holland Pubs., Ltd. GBR. Dist: Globe Pequot Pr., The.

He, Wayne. Chinese for Tomorrow: A New Five-Skilled Approach: Textbook Volume One, 6 vols. 2007. (C). pap., stu. ed. 62.95 *(978-0-88727-565-4(6))* Cheng & Tsui Co.

Huihua, Jianyi H. Chinese Conversation, Simple. (CHI.). pap. 11.95 *(978-0-87557-010-5(0))* Saphrograph Corp.

Kendall, Amy. Simple Chinese for Adoptive Families. 2007. spiral bd. 30.00 incl. audio compact disk *(978-0-9796813-1-8(6))* Simple Language for Adoptive Families.

King, Brian. Conceptual Structure of Emotional Experience in Chinese. 2007. (MUL.). 240p. per. *(978-1-897367-09-4(0))* Global Language Press.

Kleeman, Julie & Larousse Editors, eds. Larousse Mandarin Chinese Phrasebook. 2006. (Larousse Phrasebook Ser.). (ENG.). 204p. (gr. 7). per. 5.95 *(978-2-03-542155-5(1))* Larousse, Editions FRA. Dist: Houghton Mifflin Harcourt Trade & Reference Pubs.

Larsen, Stein Ugelvik & Ma, Jing. Keys to Chinese Language: Workbook I, 4 vols. 2006. (ENG & CHI., Illus.). 80p. (gr. 17). pap. 6.00 *(978-962-996-211-1(X))* Chinese Univ. of Hong Kong, The HKG. Dist: Columbia Univ. Pr.

—Keys to Chinese Language: Workbook II, 4 vols. 2006. (ENG & CHI., Illus.). 104p. (gr. 17). pap. 7.00 *(978-962-996-213-5(6))* Chinese Univ. of Hong Kong, The HKG. Dist: Columbia Univ. Pr.

Leith, Elizabeth, et al. Harrap's Chinese Phrasebook. 2006. (Harrap's Phrasebook Ser.). (ENG., Illus.). 192p. pap. 7.95 *(978-0-07-148246-2(6),* 0071482466) McGraw-Hill Cos., The.

Liao, Rongrong, et al. Streetwise Mandarin Chinese: Speak & Understand Everyday Mandarin. 2009. (CHI & ENG., Illus.). ix, 372p. *(978-0-07-147490-0(0))* McGraw-Hill Cos., The.

Lingolook CHINA. 2007. (Illus.). 81p. 11.95 *(978-0-9790904-2-4(3))* Lingolook Publishing LLC.

Liu, Jennifer Li-Chia. Connections: A Cognitive Approach to Intermediate Chinese. 2009. (Chinese in Context Language Learning Ser.). (ENG.). cd-rom 39.95 *(978-0-253-35193-7(6),* 0253351936) Indiana Univ. Pr.

—Encounters I: A Cognitive Approach to Advanced Chinese. 2010. (Chinese in Context Language Learning Ser.). (ENG.). 464p. pap., wbk. ed. 39.95 *(978-0-253-22101-8(3),* 0253221013) Indiana Univ. Pr.

—Encounters II: A Cognitive Approach to Advanced Chinese. 2010. (Chinese in Context Language Learning Ser.). (ENG.). 520p. pap., wbk. ed. 39.95 *(978-0-253-22102-5(1),* 0253221021) Indiana Univ. Pr.

Lonely Planet Staff. Mandarin. (Phrasebook Ser.). (CHI & ENG., Illus.). 256p. 2009. 12.99 *(978-1-74179-931-6(7))* 7th ed. 2010. pap. 8.99 *(978-1-74220-088-0(5))* Lonely Planet Pubns.

Lonely Planet Staff, et al. Cantonese. 5th rev. ed. 2008. (Phrasebook Ser.). (CHI & ENG., Illus.). 260p. pap. 8.99 *(978-1-74059-934-4(9))* Lonely Planet Pubns.

Ma, Cheng & Wightwick, Jane. Chinese for Beginners: The Easiest Way to Learn to Communicate Right Away! 2nd ed. 2010. (ENG & CHI., Illus.). 112p. pap. 18.95 incl. audio compact disk *(978-0-07-173968-9(8),* 0071739688) McGraw-Hill Cos., The.

Oxford, ed. Oxford Beginner's Chinese Dictionary. 2006. (ENG & CHI.). 512p. pap. 15.95 *(978-0-19-929853-2(X))* Oxford Univ. Pr., Inc.

Pan, Jen. Travel Mandarin. 2007. (Illus.). 54p. per. 50.00 *(978-0-9797551-0-1(7))* Racewin Corp.

Pittman, Joann. Survival Chinese Lessons. 2008. 51p. pap. 20.00 *(978-0-9754236-3-9(0))* Lucerna Publishing.

Po-Ching, Yip. Chinese Vocabulary: A Graded Workbook & Reader. 2012. (CHI & ENG.). 500p. 36.95 *(978-0-415-43912-1(4))* Routledge.

Qian, Kan. Colloquial Chinese 2: The Next Step in Language Learning. 2006. (Colloquial 2 Ser.). (ENG & CHI., Illus.). 296p. per. 32.95 *(978-0-415-32818-0(7))* Routledge.

Qian, Kan & Kan, Qian. Colloquial Chinese: The Complete Course for Beginners. 2nd rev. ed. 2009. (Colloquial Ser.). (CHI & ENG., Illus.). 384p. 29.95 *(978-0-415-43415-7(7))* Routledge.

Rough, Guide. Mandarin Chinese - Rough Guide Phrasebook. 4th ed. 2011. (CHI & ENG., Illus.). 256p. 8.99 *(978-1-84836-733-3(3))* Rough Guides, Ltd. GBR. Dist: Dorling Kindersley Publishing, Inc.

Seligman, Scott D. & Chen, I-Chuan. Mandarin Chinese at a Glance. 3rd ed. 2006. (At a Glance Ser.). (ENG & CHI., Illus.). 336p. stu. ed., per. 8.99 *(978-0-7641-3556-9(2))* Barron's Educational Series, Inc.

Shanghai Animation Studio Staff. Chinese Buzzwords: With English Explanations. 2nd ed. 2010. (CHI & ENG., Illus.). 376p. pap. 5.95 *(978-1-60220-406-5(3))* BetterLink Pr., Inc.

Shi, Mingde & Cinanheim. Mandarin Conversation for English Speakers. 2010. 268p. pap. 19.95 *(978-1-4490-1393-6(7))* AuthorHouse.

Simmons, Richard VanNess. Shanghainese Dictionary & Phrasebook. 2011. (ENG.). 204p. pap. *(978-0-7818-1261-0(5))* Hippocrene Bks., Inc.

Smith, Elisabeth. Last-Minute Mandarin Chinese. 2nd ed. 2011. (TY: Language Guides). (ENG.). 16p. 14.95 *(978-0-07-175136-0(X),* 007175136X) McGraw-Hill Cos., The.

Spring, Madeline Kay. Making Connections: Enhance Your Listening Comprehension in Chinese. 2nd ed. 2010.Tr. of Gou Tong: Ti Sheng ni de Zhong Wen Ting Li. (ENG & CHI.). *(978-0-88727-767-2(5));* (CHI & ENG.). *(978-0-88727-665-1(2))* Cheng & Tsui Co.

Sun, Chaofen. Chinese: A Linguistic Introduction. 2006. (ENG., Illus.). 248p. per. 42.99 *(978-0-521-53082-8(2));* 99.00 *(978-0-521-82380-7(3))* Cambridge Univ. Pr.

Thomas, Jill & Thomas Cook Publishing Staff. Mandarin Chinese. 2009. (CHI & ENG., Illus.). 96p. pap. 7.95 *(978-1-84848-106-0(3))* Cook, Thomas Publishing GBR. Dist: Globe Pequot Pr., The.

Williams, Philip F. & Wu, Yenna. Mandarin Chinese the Easy Way. 2nd rev. ed. 2008. (Easy Way Ser.). (CHI & ENG., Illus.). 384p. 21.99 *(978-0-7641-9369-9(4))* Barron's Educational Series, Inc.

Winfield, Kim & Gillam, Paul. Very Simple Chinese: Chinese Proverbs & their English Equivalents. 2007. (ENG., Illus.). 86p. pap. 11.95 *(978-1-905299-47-8(8),* Stacey International) Stacey Publishing GBR. Dist: Midpoint Trade Bks., Inc.

Wu, Sue-Mei, et al. Chinese Link: Zhongwen Tiandi, Intermediate Chinese. 2007. (ENG.). 432p. (C). pap. 56.00 *(978-0-13-194766-5(4),* Prentice Hall) Prentice Hall PTR.

Wu, Yenna, et al. Me & China. 2006. (ENG., Illus.). 352p. (C). pap. 111.67 *(978-0-07-338578-5(6),* 0073385786) McGraw-Hill Cos., The.

Xu, Jialu, et al. Workbook for Xu/Chen/Wang/Zhu's JIA YOU! Chinese for the Global Community. 2008. (ENG.). (C). pap. 66.95 *(978-1-4282-6219-5(9))* Cengage Heinle.

Yao, Tao-chung, et al. Integrated Chinese: Level 1, 3 vols. 2nd ed. 2006. (C). pap., wbk. ed. 21.95 *(978-0-88727-461-9(7))* Cheng & Tsui Co.

Yuhua, Kang & Siping, Lai. Mandarin Chinese Learning Through Conversation: Volume 1: With Audio MP3. 2008. (ENG.). 258p. 29.99 *(978-0-7641-9517-4(4))* Barron's Educational Series, Inc.

CHINESE LANGUAGE—DATA PROCESSING

Huo, Qiang, et al, eds. Chinese Spoken Language Processing: 5th International Symposium, ISCSLP 2006 Singapore, December 13-16, 2006: Proceedings. 2007. (Lecture Notes in Computer Science Ser.). (Illus.). xxiv, 805p. pap. 139.00 *(978-3-540-49665-6(3),* 3540496653) Springer.

Lee, Chin-Hui, et al. Advances in Chinese Spoken Language Processing. 2006. (Illus.). 545p. 181.00 *(978-981-256-904-2(9))* World Scientific Publishing Co., Inc.

Lunde, Ken. CJKV Information Processing. 2nd rev. ed. 2009. (ENG., Illus.). 912p. pap. 59.99 *(978-0-596-51447-1(6))* O'Reilly Media, Inc.

Shen, Zhong Jun & Simon, Peter. Comparison of Learning Classical Singing Between European & Chinese Singers. 2011. 166p. pap. 16.00 ***(978-1-60976-424-1(2),*** Eloquent Bks.) AEG Literary Publishing Services, Inc.

Wong, Kam-Fai, et al. Introduction to Chinese Natural Language Processing. 2009. (Synthesis Lectures on Human Language Technologies Ser.). 148p. pap. 40.00 *(978-1-59829-932-8(8))* Morgan & Claypool Pubs.

Zhao, Shouhui & Baldauf, Richard B. Jr. Planning Chinese Characters: Reaction, Evolution or Revolution? 2010. (Language Policy Ser.). xx, 420p. pap. 189.00 *(978-1-4419-4306-4(4),* 1441943064) Springer.

Zhao, Shouhui, et al. Planning Chinese Characters: Reaction, Evolution or Revolution? 2007. (Language Policy Ser.). (Illus.). 418p. 189.00 *(978-0-387-48574-4(0))* Springer.

CHINESE LANGUAGE—DIALECTS

Chan, Peter, et al. Listen & Learn Mandarin Chinese. 2006. *(978-0-486-45755-0(9))* Dover Pubns., Inc.

Douglas, Carstairs. Chinese-English Dictionary of the Vernacular or Spoken Language of Amoy: With the Principal Variations of the Chang-chew & Chin-chew Dialects. 2007. (Ganesha - Western Linguists & the Languages of China Ser.). (Illus.). 914p. 275.00 *(978-1-86210-068-8(3))* Ganesha Publishing, Ltd. GBR. Dist: Chicago Distribution Ctr.

Ellis, Mike & Ellis, Michael. Chinese Slanguage: A Fun Visual Guide to Mandarin Terms & Phrases, 1 vol. 2010. (CHI & ENG., Illus.). 96p. pap. 7.99 *(978-1-4236-0750-2(3))* Gibbs Smith, Publisher.

Euro Talk. Talk Now! Cantonese. 2008. 29.99 *(978-1-84352-348-2(5))* TOPICS Entertainment.

—Talk Now! Chinese Mandarin. 2008. 29.99 *(978-1-84352-319-2(1))* TOPICS Entertainment.

—World Talk Cantonese. 2008. 29.99 *(978-1-84352-548-6(8))* TOPICS Entertainment.

Fee-yin, Lo Tam. Cantonese Colloquial Expressions. Haggith, Toby & Newman, Joanna, eds. 2007. (ENG.). 330p. (gr. 17). pap. 25.00 *(978-962-996-181-7(4))* Chinese Univ. of Hong Kong, The HKG. Dist: Columbia Univ. Pr.

Fielde, Adele Marion. A Pronouncing & Defining Dictionary of the Swatow Dialect: Arranged According to Syllables & Tones. 2007. (Ganesha - Western Linguists & the Languages of China Ser.). 638p. 195.00 *(978-1-86210-069-5(1))* Ganesha Publishing, Ltd. GBR. Dist: Chicago Distribution Ctr.

Gil, Sonia, reader. Fluenz Mandarin 1 2 3. 2010. (Fluenz Ser.). 519.00 *(978-0-9825410-1-2(5))* Fluenz.

Klöter, Henning. The Language of the Sangleys: A Chinese Vernacular in Missionary Sources of the Seventeenth Century. 2010. (Sinica Leidensia Ser.). (Illus.). 400p. *(978-90-04-18493-0(7))* BRILL.

Kurpaska, Maria. Chinese Language(S) A Look Through the Prism of the Great Dictionary of Modern Chinese Dialects. 2010. (Trends in Linguistics. Studies & Monographs [TiLSM] Ser.). (CHI & ENG., Illus.). XX, 276p. 140.00 *(978-3-11-021914-2(X))* De Gruyter, Mouton DEU. Dist: de Gruyter, Walter GmbH & Co. KG.

Kurpaska, Maria. Chinese Language(s) A Look through the Prism of the Great Dictionary of Modern Chinese Dialects. 2010. (Trends in Linguistics. Studies & Monographs [TiLSM] Ser.). (ENG.). XX, 276p. 210.00 ***(978-3-11-173332-6(7))*** De Gruyter, Mouton DEU. Dist: de Gruyter, Walter GmbH & Co. KG.

Lee, Peppina Po-lun. Cantonese Particles & Affixal Quantification. 2012. (Studies in Natural Language & Linguistic Theory Ser.: 87). (ENG & CHI., Illus.). xiv, 273p. 129.00 ***(978-94-007-4386-1(6),*** 9400743866) Springer.

Lee/ Sinonexus, Emma/ Fung-Ing. Learn Mandarin Chinese through Chinese Children's Songs. 2007. (CHI & ENG., Illus.). 192p. (J). 49.95 incl. audio compact disk *(978-0-9787664-1-2(5))* Sinonexus Publishing Co.

Li, Rulong & Li, Zhuqing. Minnan-English Dictionary. 2008. (CHI.). xxxiii, 184p. *(978-1-931546-48-5(7))* Dunwoody Pr.

Lonely Planet Staff, et al. Cantonese. 5th rev. ed. 2008. (Phrasebook Ser.). (CHI & ENG., Illus.). 260p. pap. 8.99 *(978-1-74059-934-4(9))* Lonely Planet Pubns.

Mandarin Phrasebook. 2006. pap. 7.99 *(978-0-9773334-2-4(6))* True Run Advertising Co.

Medhurst, Walter Henry. A Dictionary of the Hok-Keen Dialect of the Chinese Language: According to the Reading & Colloqueal Idioms: Containg about 12,000 Characters. 2007. (Ganesha - Western Linguists & the Languages of China Ser.). (Illus.). 924p. 275.00 *(978-1-86210-067-1(5))* Ganesha Publishing, Ltd. GBR. Dist: Chicago Distribution Ctr.

Ross, Melanie H., et al. The Routledge Course in Modern Mandarin Chinese Workbook Level 2 (Simplified) 2011. (CHI & ENG., Illus.). 392p. pap., wbk. ed. 60.00 *(978-0-415-47247-0(4))* Routledge.

Sher, Yung-ji. Develop of Lexicon Database from Speech Corpus for Taiwanese Pre-School Children. 2008. 204p. pap. *(978-3-639-00690-2(9))* VDM Verlag Dr. Mueller e.K.

Shi, Feng. Yu Yin Ge Ju: Yu Yin Xue Yu Yin Xi Xue de Jiao Hui Dian. (CHI., Illus.). *(978-7-100-05371-6(4))* Commercial Pr., The.

Simmons, Richard VanNess. Shanghainese Dictionary & Phrasebook. 2011. (ENG.). 204p. pap. *(978-0-7818-1261-0(5))* Hippocrene Bks., Inc.

Wang, Yalien. Explorations in the Development of Young Children's Speech Act of Threatening in Mandarin Chinese. 2008. 120p. pap. *(978-3-639-00302-4(0))* VDM Verlag Dr. Mueller e.K.

Williams, Philip F. & Wu, Yenna. Mandarin Chinese the Easy Way. 2nd ed. 2008. (Illus.). xv, 361p. *(978-0-7641-3711-2(5))* Barron's Educational Series, Inc.

Yong, Heming, et al. Chinese Lexicography: A History from 1046 BC to AD 1911. 2008. (ENG., Illus.). 448p. 175.00 *(978-0-19-953982-6(0))* Oxford Univ. Pr., Inc.

CHINESE LANGUAGE—DICTIONARIES

Abraham, Wendy. Chinese PhraseFinder & Dictionary. 2008. (Frommer's Phrase Bks.: 9). (ENG & CHI., Illus.). 256p. per. 8.99 *(978-0-470-17838-6(8),* Frommers) Wiley, John & Sons, Inc.

Abraham, Wendy. Frommer's Chinese PhraseFinder & Dictionary. 2nd ed. 2012. (Frommer's Phrase Bks.: 22). (ENG & CHI.). 256p. pap. 8.99 ***(978-1-118-14361-2(2),*** Frommers) Wiley, John & Sons, Inc.

APA Publications Staff. Mandarin Chinese Compact Dictionary: Chinese - English, English - Chinese. 2nd ed. 2011. (Berlitz Compact Dictionary Ser.). (ENG & CHI.). 672p. pap. 13.99 ***(978-981-268-649-7(5))*** APA Publications Services SGP. Dist: Ingram Pub. Services.

Assimil Staff. Ecriture Chinoise: Chinese Writing. (CHI & FRE.). 32.95 *(978-0-8288-4383-6(X),* M14581) French & European Pubns., Inc.

Barclay, Thomas & Douglas, Carstairs. Chinese-English Dictionary of the Vernacular or Spoken Language of Amoy. 276p. reprint ed. suppl. ed. *(978-957-9482-32-5(2),* RFE007) SMC Publishing, Inc.

Berlitz Publishing, creator. Mandarin Chinese Pocket Dictionary: Chinese-English/English-Chinese. 2007. (Berlitz Pocket Dictionary Ser.). (ENG & CHI.). 414p. pap. 7.99 *(978-981-246-941-0(9),* Berlitz Publishing.

Berlitz Publishing, ed. Chinese Cantonese. 2nd rev. ed. 2008. (Phrase Book Ser.). (CHI & ENG., Illus.). 224p. pap. 8.95 *(978-981-268-475-2(1))* APA Publications Services SGP. Dist: Ingram Pub. Services.

Burkhardt, Michael. TPS Frequency Dictionary of Mandarin Chinese. 2010. 612p. pap. 29.99 *(978-0-557-45344-3(5))* Lulu Enterprises Inc.

Chen, Young. Chinese-English/English-Chinese Pocket Legal Dictionary. 2008. (ENG & CHI.). 280p. pap. *(978-0-7818-1215-3(1))* Hippocrene Bks., Inc.

Chinese-English Dictionary. (CHI & ENG.). 28.95 *(978-0-87557-007-5(0))* Saphrograph Corp.

Chinese-English-Japanese Glossary of Natural Science Terms. (CHI, ENG & JPN.). 295.00 *(978-0-7859-9423-7(8))* French & European Pubns., Inc.

Choi, Kwan Kit, ed. Dictionary of Cantonese Colloquialisms in English. 378p. pap. 21.50 *(978-962-07-0131-3(3))* Commercial Pr., The CHN. Dist: Cheng & Tsui Co.

Collins Staff. Collins Mandarin Phrasebook & Dictionary. 2009. (Collins Gem Ser.). (CHI & ENG., Illus.). 192p. pap. 7.95 *(978-0-00-726461-2(5))* HarperCollins Pubs. Ltd. GBR. Dist: Independent Pubs. Group.

Commercial Press Staff. Chinese - English Medical Dictionary. (CHI & ENG.). 150.00 *(978-0-8288-2483-5(5),* F45700) French & European Pubns., Inc.

Concise English-Chinese Chinese English Dictionary. 755p. 16.95 *(978-7-100-02558-4(3),* COENC1) Commercial Pr., The CHN. Dist: China Bks. & Periodicals, Inc.

DeFrancis, John, et al. ABC English-Chinese Chinese-English Dictionary. 2010. (CHI & ENG.). 1272p. pap. 20.00 *(978-0-8248-3485-2(2))* Univ. of Hawaii Pr.

Dong, Li. Tuttle Compact Chinese Dictionary. 2010. (CHI & ENG., Illus.). 640p. pap. 24.95 *(978-0-8048-3993-8(X))* Tuttle Publishing.

—Tuttle Pocket Chinese Dictionary. 2011. (ENG & CHI., Illus.). 640p. pap. 12.95 *(978-0-8048-3775-0(9))* Tuttle Publishing.

Dorling Kindersley Publishing Staff. Mandarin Chinese. Wilkes, Angela & Heilman, Christine, eds. 2008. (DK Visual Dictionaries Ser.). (CHI & ENG., Illus.). 360p. (gr. 12). pap. 14.95 *(978-0-7566-3442-1(3))* Dorling Kindersley Publishing, Inc.

Douglas, Carstairs. Chinese-English Dictionary of the Vernacular or Spoken Language of Amoy: With the Principal Variations of the Chang-chew & Chin-chew Dialects. 2007. (Ganesha - Western Linguists & the Languages of China Ser.). (Illus.). 914p. 275.00 *(978-1-86210-068-8(3))* Ganesha Publishing, Ltd. GBR. Dist: Chicago Distribution Ctr.

Fielde, Adele Marion. A Pronouncing & Defining Dictionary of the Swatow Dialect: Arranged According to Syllables & Tones. 2007. (Ganesha - Western Linguists & the Languages of China Ser.). 638p. 195.00 *(978-1-86210-069-5(1))* Ganesha Publishing, Ltd. GBR. Dist: Chicago Distribution Ctr.

Foreign Languages Press. Pocket Chinese Dictionary. 2011. (ENG.). 580p. pap. 12.95 ***(978-1-59265-114-6(3))*** Long River Pr.

HarperCollins Publishers Ltd. Collins Beginner's Chinese Dictionary. 2012. (Collins Language Ser.). 680p. pap. 11.99 ***(978-0-06-212412-8(9))*** HarperCollins Pubs.

—Collins Chinese Concise Dictionary: Second Edition. 2012. 1296p. pap. 17.99 ***(978-0-06-218500-6(4))*** HarperCollins Pubs.

HarperCollins Publishers Ltd. Staff. Collins Chinese Dictionary. 2007. (Collins Gem Ser.). (Illus.). 640p. vinyl bd. 7.99 *(978-0-06-114190-4(9))* HarperCollins Pubs.

He, Guowei. Zhonghua Fan Yi Ci Ci Dian. 2008. iii, 522p. *(978-962-8930-65-4(6))* Chung Hwa Bk. Co., Ltd.

Hippocrene Editorial Staff. Cantonese-english/english-cantonese. 2011. (ENG & CHI.). 204p. pap. ***(978-0-7818-1279-5(6))*** Hippocrene Bks., Inc.

Ho, Yong. Chinese-English English-Chinese Practical Dictionary. 2009. (CHI & ENG.). 480p. *(978-0-7818-1236-8(4))* Hippocrene Bks., Inc.

Huang, Binhong. Han Yu Guan Yong Yu Ci Dian Hanyu Guanyongyu Cidian. 2009. (CHI.). ii, 13p. *(978-7-80103-632-2(8))* Commercial Pr. International Co., Ltd.

Huang, Quanyu. McGraw-Hill's Chinese Dictionary & Guide to 20,000 Essential Words: A New Method for Non-Native Speakers to Look up the 2,000 Most Commonly Used Characters in Chinese. 2010. (CHI & ENG.). 688p. 29.95 *(978-0-07-162924-9(6),* 0071629246) McGraw-Hill Cos., The.

International Monetary Fund Staff, ed. IMF Glossary; English-Chinese. 2007. 438p. pap. 49.00 *(978-1-58906-694-6(4))* International Monetary Fund.

Jiao, Liwei, et al. 500 Common Chinese Idioms. annot. ed. 2011. (ENG & CHI., Illus.). 328p. pap. 55.95 *(978-0-415-77682-0(1))* Routledge.

—500 Common Chinese Idioms: An Annotated Frequency Dictionary. 2011. (ENG & CHI., Illus.). 328p. 145.00 *(978-0-415-59893-4(1))* Routledge.

Kurpaska, Maria. Chinese Language(S) A Look Through the Prism of the Great Dictionary of Modern Chinese Dialects. 2010. (Trends in Linguistics. Studies & Monographs [TiLSM] Ser.). (CHI & ENG., Illus.). XX, 276p. 140.00 *(978-3-11-021914-2(X))* De Gruyter, Mouton DEU. Dist: de Gruyter, Walter GmbH & Co. KG.

Kurpaska, Maria. Chinese Language(s) A Look through the Prism of the Great Dictionary of Modern Chinese Dialects. 2010. (Trends in Linguistics. Studies & Monographs [TiLSM] Ser.). (ENG.). XX, 276p. 210.00 ***(978-3-11-173332-6(7))*** De Gruyter, Mouton DEU. Dist: de Gruyter, Walter GmbH & Co. KG.

Langenscheidt. Langenscheidt Pocket Dictionary Mandarin Chinese. 2011. (Langenscheidt Pocket Dictionaries Ser). (ENG.). 672p. pap. 14.99 *(978-3-468-98133-3(3))* Langenscheidt Publishing Group.

—Langenscheidt Universal Dictionary Chinese. 2nd ed. 2011. (Langenscheidt Universal Dictionaries Ser.). (ENG & CHI.). 560p. pap. 7.99 *(978-3-468-98184-5(8))* Langenscheidt Publishing Group.

Li, Rulong & Li, Zhuqing. Minnan-English Dictionary. 2008. (CHI.). xxxiii, 184p. *(978-1-931546-48-5(7))* Dunwoody Pr.

Lin, Marjorie & Leonard, Schalk. Dictionary of 1000 Chinese Idioms. 2011. (ENG & CHI.). 204p. pap. ***(978-0-7818-1278-8(7))*** Hippocrene Bks., Inc.

Liu, Eric S. Frequency Dictionary of Chinese Words. (Linguistic Structures, First Series: Chinese Ser.). (ENG.). XLIV, 236p. (C). 196.00 ***(978-3-11-174960-0(6))*** De Gruyter, Mouton DEU. Dist: de Gruyter, Walter GmbH & Co. KG.

Live ABC. McGraw-Hill's Chinese Dictionary with MP3 Disc (Book) 2009. (McGraw-Hill Dictionary Ser.). 176p. 21.95 *(978-0-07-161591-4(1),* 0071615911) McGraw-Hill Cos., The.

Live ABC Staff, et al. McGraw-Hill's Chinese Illustrated Dictionary: 1,500 Essential Words in Chinese Script & Pinyin Lay the Foundation of Your Language Learning. 2009. (ENG & CHI., Illus.). 176p. 21.95 incl. audio compact disk *(978-0-07-161590-7(3),* 0071615903) McGraw-Hill Cos., The.

Living Language Staff. Chinese (Mandarin) I.t. ed. 2008. (LL Complete Basic Courses Ser.). (ENG.). 384p. pap. 10.95 *(978-1-4000-2425-4(0),* Living Language) Random Hse. Information Group.

Lonely Planet Staff, et al. Cantonese. 5th rev. ed. 2008. (Phrasebook Ser.). (CHI & ENG., Illus.). 260p. pap. 8.99 *(978-1-74059-934-4(9))* Lonely Planet Pubns.

Longman Hong Kong Staff. Active Study Chinese Dictionary. Date not set. pap. *(978-962-359-367-0(8))* Addison-Wesley Longman, Inc.

Lutins Nomades, Lutins nomades. My first chinese Signs. 2010. 50p. pap. 13.95 *(978-0-557-25871-0(5))* Lulu Enterprises Inc.

Medhurst, Walter Henry. A Dictionary of the Hok-Keen Dialect of the Chinese Language: According to the Reading & Colloqueal Idioms: Containing about 12,000 Characters. 2007. (Ganesha - Western Linguists & the Languages of China Ser.). (Illus.). 924p. 275.00 *(978-1-86210-067-1(5))* Ganesha Publishing, Ltd. GBR. Dist: Chicago Distribution Ctr.

Merriam-Webster Inc. Merriam-Webster's Chinese-English Dictionary. 2010. (CHI & ENG.). 448p. (gr. 7). mass mkt. 6.50 *(978-0-87779-859-0(1))* Merriam-Webster, Inc.

Molinsky, Steven J. & Bliss, Bill. Word by Word Picture Dictionary English/Chinese. 2nd ed. 2008. (ENG.). (C). pap. 26.60 *(978-0-13-191631-9(9))* Prentice Hall, ESL Dept.

Oxford, ed. Oxford Beginner's Chinese Dictionary. 2006. (ENG & CHI.). 512p. pap. 15.95 *(978-0-19-929853-2(X))* Oxford Univ. Pr., Inc.

Oxford Dictionaries Staff. Oxford Chinese Dictionary. 2010. (CHI & ENG.). 2064p. 75.00 *(978-0-19-920761-9(5))* Oxford Univ. Pr., Inc.

Oxford Dictionaries Staff, ed. Pocket Oxford Chinese Dictionary. 4th ed. 2009. (ENG & CHI.). 1200p. pap. 19.95 *(978-0-19-800594-0(6))* Oxford Univ. Pr., Inc.

Peter Collin Publishing Staff. Dictionary of Chinese Law. (ENG & CHI.). 588p. *(978-1-901659-07-8(0),* T&AD Poyser) A & C Black.

Quo, James C. Concise Chinese-English Romanized Dictionary. 2006. (ENG., Illus.). 256p. per. 8.95 *(978-0-8048-3872-6(0))* Tuttle Publishing.

Schuessler, Axel. ABC Etymological Dictionary of Old Chinese. 2007. (Abc Chinese Dictionary Ser.). (CHI & ENG.). 656p. 64.00 *(978-0-8248-2975-9(1))* Univ. of Hawaii Pr.

Seligman, Scott D. & Chen, I-Chuan. Mandarin Chinese at a Glance. 3rd ed. 2006. (At a Glance Ser.). (ENG & CHI., Illus.). 336p. stu. ed., per. 8.99 *(978-0-7641-3556-9(2))* Barron's Educational Series, Inc.

Sher, Yung-ji. Develop of Lexicon Database from Speech Corpus for Taiwanese Pre-School Children. 2008. 204p. pap. *(978-3-639-00690-2(9))* VDM Verlag Dr. Mueller e.K.

Simmons, Richard VanNess. Shanghainese Dictionary & Phrasebook. 2011. (ENG.). 204p. pap. *(978-0-7818-1261-0(5))* Hippocrene Bks., Inc.

Tang, Gladys, ed. Dictionary of Hong Kong Sign Language. 2007. (ENG., Illus.). 900p. (gr. 17). 70.00 *(978-962-996-195-4(4))* Chinese Univ. of Hong Kong, The HKG. Dist: Columbia Univ. Pr.

Tessenow, Hermann & Unschuld, Paul U. A Dictionary of the Huang Di Nei Jing Su Wen. 2007. (CHI & ENG.). 812p. 95.00 incl. cd-rom *(978-0-520-25358-2(2))* Univ. of California Pr.

Winalex Learning Company. Common Chinese Vocabulary: Life. 2008. (ENG & CHI.). 200p. per. 27.95 *(978-0-9790970-5-8(3))* Liu.

Xiao, Richard, et al. A Frequency Dictionary of Mandarin Chinese: Core Vocabulary for Learners. 2011. 1p. cd-rom 155.00 *(978-0-415-60106-1(1))* 2009. (CHI & ENG., Illus.). 400p. pap. 35.95 *(978-0-415-45586-2(3))* Routledge.

Yoshimura, Zentaro. Glossary of Library Terms in Japanese-Chinese-English. Date not set. (JPN, CHI & ENG.). 345p. pap. 49.95 *(978-4-8419-0232-7(5))* Yushodo Shuppan JPN. Dist: Oak Knoll Pr.

Yuan, Boping & Church, Sally K. Oxford Chinese Mini Dictionary. Oxford Dictionaries Staff & Oxford Dictionaries, eds. 2nd ed. 2012. (CHI & ENG.). 656p. pap. 9.95 ***(978-0-19-969267-5(X))*** Oxford Univ. Pr., Inc.

Zhang, Wen-Hwa. Chinese-English & English-Chinese Dictionary of Foreign Trade Economy, Finance & Accounting. (CHI & ENG.). pap. 14.95 *(978-7-313-01523-5(2))* China International Bk. Trading Corp. CHN. Dist: Distribooks, Inc.

—English-Chinese & Chinese-English Dictionary of Traditional Chinese Medicine. (CHI & ENG.). 928p. pap. 19.95 *(978-7-5357-1656-9(3))* China International Bk. Trading Corp. CHN. Dist: Distribooks, Inc.

—Selected Chinese-English & English-Chinese Dictionary. (CHI & ENG., Illus.). 1100p. pap. 12.95 *(978-7-100-00589-0(2))* China International Bk. Trading Corp. CHN. Dist: Distribooks, Inc.

CHINESE LANGUAGE—ETYMOLOGY

Huang, Chungliang Al. Quantum Soup: Fortune Cookies in Crisis New & enlarged Edition. 2011. (ENG., Illus.). 160p. (Orig.). pap. ***(978-1-84819-054-2(9))*** Singing Dragon.

Pialat, François. Wonderful Winding Words: Touring in Four Languages (Chinese, English, French, German) 2011. (Illus.). xiv, 189p. pap. 31.35 ***(978-1-4567-8924-4(4))*** AuthorHouse.

Schuessler, Axel. ABC Etymological Dictionary of Old Chinese. 2007. (Abc Chinese Dictionary Ser.). (CHI & ENG.). 656p. 64.00 *(978-0-8248-2975-9(1))* Univ. of Hawaii Pr.

Ye, Yuying. Gu Wen Zi Gou Xing Yu Shang Gu Yin Yan Jiu. 2009. (CHI.). *(978-7-5615-3323-9(3))* Xiamen Univ. Pr.

CHINESE LANGUAGE—GRAMMAR

Åfarli, Tor A. Chinese Matters: From Grammar to First & Second Language Acquisition. Wilder, Chris, ed. 2010. 212p. pap. 56.00 *(978-82-519-2536-5(3))* Tapir Forlag NOR. Dist: International Specialized Bk. Services.

Bai, Jianhua. Chinese Grammar Made Easy: A Practical & Effective Guide for Teachers. 2008. (CHI & ENG.). 336p. pap. 51.00 *(978-0-300-12279-4(9))* Yale Univ. Pr.

bousquet, jean guy. Chinese grammar putonghua pinyin Tutor. 2008. 203p. pap. 22.50 *(978-0-557-00249-8(4))* Lulu Enterprises Inc.

Chou, Chih-p#8242;ing, et al. A Trip to China - Intermediate Reader of Modern Chinese 2e. 2011. (Princeton Language Program: Modern Chinese Ser.). (ENG.). 336p. (C). pap. 55.00 ***(978-0-691-15309-4(4))*** Princeton Univ. Pr.

Colloquial Chinese Mp3. 2009. cd-rom 34.95 ***(978-0-415-55159-5(5))*** Routledge.

Ding, Picus Sizhi. Studies on Ba Resultative Construction: A Comprehensive Approach to Mandarin Ba Sentences. 2007. (Illus.). vi, 108p. pap. *(978-3-89586-491-9(9))* Lincom GmbH.

Fang, Ji. The Verb Copy Construction & the Post-Verbal Constraint in Chinese. 2009. 180p. pap. *(978-3-639-13021-8(9))* VDM Verlag Dr. Mueller e.K.

Farmer, Rachel, et al. Speak Mandarin Chinese with Confidence. 2nd ed. 2010. (Teach Yourself Language Ser.). (ENG.). 48p. (C). 19.95 *(978-0-07-173606-0(9),* 0071736069) McGraw-Hill Cos., The.

Hammel, A. W. Eminent Chinese of the Ch'ing Period, 1644-1942, 2 vols., Set. 1103p. reprint ed. *(978-957-638-065-5(0),* HSE018) SMC Publishing, Inc.

Harrap. Harrap's Pocket Chinese Grammar & Script. 2009. (Harrap's Language Guides). (ENG.). 176p. pap. 10.95 *(978-0-07-163624-7(2),* 0071636242) McGraw-Hill Cos., The.

Hashimoto, Mantaro J. The Hakka Dialect: A Linguistic Study of its Phonology, Syntax & Lexicon. 2010. (Princeton/Cambridge Studies in Chinese Linguistics Ser.). (ENG.). 612p. pap. 39.99 *(978-0-521-13367-8(X))* Cambridge Univ. Pr.

Herzberg, Qin Xue & Herzberg, Larry. Basic Patterns of Chinese Grammar: A Student's Guide to Correct Structures & Common Errors. 2010. (ENG.). 128p. pap. 12.95 ***(978-1-933330-89-1(9))*** Stone Bridge Pr.

Hodge, Stephen. Reading Buddhism Through Chinese: An Introductory Grammar & Reader. 2008. 272p. 170.00 *(978-0-7007-1225-0(9));* pap. 45.95 *(978-0-7007-1258-8(5))* Taylor & Francis Group. (RoutledgeCurzon).

Howie, John Marshall. Acoustical Studies of Mandarin Vowels & Tones. 2010. (Princeton/Cambridge Studies in Chinese Linguistics Ser.). (ENG.). 308p. pap. 25.99 *(978-0-521-13425-5(0))* Cambridge Univ. Pr.

Hsueh, F. S. Phonology of Old Mandarin. (Janua Linguarum. Series Practica Ser.). (ENG.). 142p. 210.00 ***(978-3-11-179684-0(1))*** De Gruyter, Mouton DEU. Dist: de Gruyter, Walter GmbH & Co. KG.

Li, Eden Sum-Hung & Li. A Systemic Functional Grammar of Chinese. 2007. (ENG., Illus.). 292p. 180.00 *(978-0-8264-9104-6(9))* Continuum International Publishing Group, Ltd. GBR. Dist: National Bk. Network.

Liu, Feng-hsi & Farrell, C. Frederick. Side by Side Chinese & English Grammar. 2012. (ENG.). 144p. (C). pap. 14.00 ***(978-0-07-179706-1(8),*** 0071797068) McGraw-Hill Cos., The.

Living Language. Living Language Chinese. unabr. ed. 2011. (Platinum Ser.). (ENG.). 368p. 179.00 *(978-0-307-47913-6(7),* Living Language) Random Hse. Information Group.

Loar, Jian Kang. Chinese Syntactic Grammar: Functional & Conceptual Principles. 2010. ***(978-1-4331-1252-2(3))*** Lang, Peter Publishing, Inc.

Matthews. Cantonese: A Comprehensive Grammar. 2nd ed. 2011. (Comprehensive Grammars Ser.). (CHI & ENG.). 448p. 200.00 *(978-0-415-47130-5(3))* Routledge.

Matthews, Stephen & Yip, Virginia. Cantonese. 2nd rev. ed. 2011. (Comprehensive Grammars Ser.). (ENG & CHI.). 544p. pap. 67.95 *(978-0-415-47131-2(1))* Routledge.

Mcenery. Corpus-Based Contrastive Studies of English & Chinese. 2010. (Routledge Advances in Corpus Linguistics Ser.). (ENG., Illus.). 216p. (C). 133.00 *(978-0-415-99245-9(1))* Routledge.

Po-Ching, Yip & Rimmington, Don. Basic Chinese. 2nd rev. ed. 2009. (Grammar Workbooks Ser.). (CHI & ENG.). 384p. wbk. ed. 135.00 *(978-0-415-47216-6(4))* Routledge.

Po-Ching, Yip, et al. Basic Chinese. 2nd rev. ed. 2009. (Grammar Workbooks Ser.). (CHI & ENG.). 384p. pap. 38.95 *(978-0-415-47215-9(6))* Routledge.

Qian, Kan & Kan, Qian. Colloquial Chinese: The Complete Course for Beginners. 2nd rev. ed. 2009. (Colloquial Ser.). (CHI & ENG., Illus.). 384p. 29.95 *(978-0-415-43415-7(7))* Routledge.

Quirk, Erin & Dong, Tanying. Advanced Chinese. 2011. (CHI & ENG.). ***(978-0-307-97167-8(8),*** Living Language) Random Hse. Information Group.

—Essential Chinese. 2011. (CHI & ENG.). ***(978-0-307-97165-4(1),*** Living Language) Random Hse. Information Group.

—Intermediate Chinese. 2011. (CHI & ENG.). ***(978-0-307-97166-1(X),*** Living Language) Random Hse. Information Group.

Ratliff, Martha. Meaningful Tone. 2010. (ENG., Illus.). 288p. (C). pap. 29.00 *(978-0-87580-636-5(8))* Northern Illinois Univ. Pr.

Robson, Shin Yong. Speed up your Chinese. 2012. (ENG & CHI.). 256p. 135.00 ***(978-0-415-50151-4(2));*** pap. 43.95 ***(978-0-415-50152-1(0))*** Routledge.

Ross, Claudia. Schaum's Outline of Chinese Grammar. 2009. (Schaum's Outline Ser.). (ENG & CHI., Illus.). 288p. (C). pap. 18.95 *(978-0-07-163526-4(2),* 0071635262) McGraw-Hill Cos., The.

Ross, Claudia & Sheng Ma, Jing-Heng. Modern Mandarin Chinese Grammar: A Practical Guide. 2006. (Modern Grammars Ser.). (ENG & CHI., Illus.). 432p. 140.00 *(978-0-415-70009-2(4),* RU00094); per. 44.95 *(978-0-415-70010-8(8),* RU00108) Routledge.

Ross, Claudia, et al. Modern Mandarin Chinese Grammar Workbook. 2006. (Modern Grammars Ser.). (ENG & CHI., Illus.). 184p. per., wbk. ed. 39.95 *(978-0-415-70011-5(6),* RU00116) Routledge.

Scurfield, Elizabeth. Complete Mandarin Chinese. 3rd ed. 2010. (ENG., Illus.). 432p. pap. 35.00 incl. audio compact disk, audio compact disk *(978-0-07-173727-2(8),* 0071737278) McGraw-Hill Cos., The.

—Complete Mandarin Chinese: Everything You Need to Speak Read & Write. 3rd ed. 2010. (ENG., Illus.). 432p. pap. 17.95 *(978-0-07-173728-9(6),* 0071737286) McGraw-Hill Cos., The.

Sybesma, Rint. The Mandarin VP. 2010. (Studies in Natural Language & Linguistic Theory Ser.). 242p. pap. 179.00 *(978-90-481-5132-5(5),* 9048151325) Springer.

Teng, Wen-Hua. Yufa! A Practical Guide to Mandarin Chinese Grammar. 2011. (CHI & ENG.). 352p. pap., instr.'s gde. ed. 22.95 *(978-1-4441-0913-9(8))* Hodder Education GBR. Dist: Oxford Univ. Pr., Inc.

Xu, Dan. Typological Change in Chinese Syntax. 2006. (ENG.). 272p. 140.00 *(978-0-19-929756-6(8))* Oxford Univ. Pr., Inc.

Xu, Dan, ed. Space in Languages of China: Cross-linguistic, Synchronic & Diachronic Perspectives. 2010. (ENG., Illus.). viii, 276p. pap. 159.00 *(978-90-481-7841-4(X),* 904817841X) Springer.

Xu, Jialu, et al. Jia You! Chinese for the Global Community, Volume 1 (with Audio CDs) (Simplified & Traditional Character Edition) 2008. (ENG.). 350p. (C). 87.95 *(978-1-4282-6218-6(0))* Cengage Heinle.

Yang, Guowen. The Semantics of Chinese Aspects: Theoretical Descriptions & a Computational Implementation. 2007. 425p. pap. 82.95 *(978-3-631-56811-8(8))* Lang, Peter GmbH, Europaischer Verlag der Wissenschaften DEU. Dist: Lang, Peter Publishing, Inc.

Yuan, Nai-Ying, et al. Classical Chinese Supplement 1: Introduction to Grammar. 2013. (Princeton Language Program: Modern Chinese Ser.). (ENG.). 224p. (C). pap. 19.95 *(978-0-691-11835-2(3))* Princeton Univ. Pr.

Zadrapa, Lukas. World-Class Flexibility in Classical Chinese: Verbal & Adverbial Uses of Nouns. 2011. (CHI & ENG.). 320p. *(978-90-04-20631-1(0))* BRILL.

Zhang, Grace Qiao. Using Chinese Synonyms. 2010. (ENG & CHI.). 446p. (C). pap. 39.99 *(978-0-521-61787-1(1))* Cambridge Univ. Pr.

Zhang, Phyllis. Developing Chinese Fluency. 2010. (ENG.). 1p. (C). pap. 62.95 *(978-1-111-34222-7(9))* Cengage Heinle.

—Developing Chinese Fluency Workbook (with access key to Online Workbook) 2010. (ENG.). (C). pap. 39.95 *(978-1-111-34223-4(7))* Cengage Heinle.

Zhu, Yongping. Linguistic Analysis of Meaning & Syntactic Change in the Grammaticalization of Chinese Prepositions: Charting the Constraints of Locality on Language Development Through Three Millennia of Chinese Documents. 2010. 264p. 109.95 *(978-0-7734-1470-9(3))* Mellen, Edwin Pr., The.

CHINESE LANGUAGE—JUVENILE LITERATURE

Kudela, Katy R. My First Book of Mandarin Chinese Words. 2009. (Bilingual Picture Dictionaries Ser.). (MUL.). 32p. (gr. 1-2). pap. 47.70 *(978-1-4296-4372-6(2),* Aplus Bks.) Capstone Pr., Inc.

CHINESE LANGUAGE—ORTHOGRAPHY AND SPELLING

Lai, Yu Da. Auditory Lexical Access of Chinese Monomorphemic Compounds. 2008. 96p. pap. *(978-3-639-03000-6(1))* VDM Verlag Dr. Mueller e.K.

CHINESE LANGUAGE—PHONETICS

Hashimoto, Oi-kan Yue. Studies in Yue Dialects 1: Phonology of Cantonese. 2011. (Princeton/Cambridge Studies in Chinese Linguistics Ser.). (ENG & CHI.). 780p. pap. 75.00 *(978-0-521-18982-8(9))* Cambridge Univ. Pr.

Howie, John Marshall. Acoustical Studies of Mandarin Vowels & Tones. 2010. (Princeton/Cambridge Studies in Chinese Linguistics Ser.). (ENG.). 308p. pap. 25.99 *(978-0-521-13425-5(0))* Cambridge Univ. Pr.

Jialing, Wang & Smith, Norval, eds. Studies in Chinese Phonology. (Linguistic Models Ser.). (ENG.). 289p. 255.00 ***(978-3-11-187086-1(3))*** De Gruyter, Mouton DEU. Dist: de Gruyter, Walter GmbH & Co. KG.

Liao, Rongrong, et al. Streetwise Mandarin Chinese: Speak & Understand Everyday Mandarin. 2009. (CHI & ENG., Illus.). ix, 372p. *(978-0-07-147490-0(0))* McGraw-Hill Cos., The.

Liu, Lezhong. Chinese Word Segmentation & Language Processing. 2008. 264p. pap. *(978-3-639-02465-4(6))* VDM Verlag Dr. Mueller e.K.

Pan. Contrastive Linguistics: History, Philosophy & Methodology. 2007. (ENG., Illus.). 304p. 180.00 *(978-0-8264-8634-9(7))* Continuum International Publishing Group, Ltd. GBR. Dist: National Bk. Network.

Ratliff, Martha. Meaningful Tone. 2010. (ENG., Illus.). 288p. (C). pap. 29.00 *(978-0-87580-636-5(8))* Northern Illinois Univ. Pr.

Ross, Claudia. Chinese Demystified: A Self-Teaching Guide. 2010. (Demystified Ser.). (CHI & ENG., Illus.). 448p. pap., tchr. ed. 22.00 *(978-0-07-147725-3(X)*, 007147725X) McGraw-Hill Cos., The.

Schuessler, Axel & Karlgren, Bernhard. Minimal Old Chinese & Later Han Chinese: A Companion to Grammata Serica Recensa. 2008. (CHI & ENG.). 456p. (C). 58.00 *(978-0-8248-3264-3(7))* Univ. of Hawaii Pr.

Shi, Feng. Yu Yin Ge Ju: Yu Yin Xue Yu Yin Xi Xue de Jiao Hui Dian. (CHI., Illus.). *(978-7-100-05371-6(4))* Commercial Pr., The.

CHINESE LANGUAGE—PRONUNCIATION

Beyond Measure. 2008. spiral bd., per. 15.00 *(978-0-9669997-0-9(3))* 66 Communication, Inc.

China, Yu yan wen zi ying yong guan li si Staff, et al, contrib. by. Han Yu Pin Yin 50 Nian. 2010. (CHI., Illus.). *(978-7-80241-115-9(7))* Language Publishing Hse.

EPLS. Chinese. 2nd ed. 2011. (Say It Right! Ser.). (ENG & CHI., Illus.). 192p. pap. 11.00 *(978-0-07-176773-6(8)*, 0071767738) McGraw-Hill Cos., The.

—Say It Right in Chinese: The Fastest Way to Correct Pronunciation. 2009. (Say It Right! Ser.). (ENG & CHI.). 64p. 16.95 incl. audio compact disk *(978-0-07-162877-8(0)*, 0071628770) McGraw-Hill Cos., The.

Hockett, Charles F. Progressive Exercises in Chinese Pronunciation: Mirror Series A, No. 2. 2011. 82p. 37.95 ***(978-1-258-08172-0(5))*** Literary Licensing, LLC.

Hsueh, F. S. Phonology of Old Mandarin. (Janua Linguarum. Series Practica Ser.). (ENG.). 142p. 210.00 ***(978-3-11-179684-0(1))*** De Gruyter, Mouton DEU. Dist: de Gruyter, Walter GmbH & Co. KG.

Lin, Yen-Hwei. The Sounds of Chinese. 2007. (CHI & ENG., Illus.). 336p. pap. 50.00 *(978-0-521-60398-0(6))* Cambridge Univ. Pr.

Live ABC Staff. Chinese Pronunciation: Your Comprehensive,Interactive Guide to Mastering Sounds & Tones in Chinese. 2009. (CHI & ENG., Illus.). 144p. pap. 19.95 incl. cd-rom *(978-0-07-162736-8(7)*, 0071627367) McGraw-Hill Cos., The.

Rouzer, Paul. A New Practical Primer of Literary Chinese. 2007. (Harvard East Asian Monographs Ser.: Vol. 276). (Illus.). 540p. 59.95 *(978-0-674-02269-0(6))* Harvard Univ., Asia Ctr.

Sher, Yung-ji. Develop of Lexicon Database from Speech Corpus for Taiwanese Pre-School Children. 2008. 204p. pap. *(978-3-639-00690-2(9))* VDM Verlag Dr. Mueller e.K.

Xu, Jialu, et al. Workbook for Xu/Chen/Wang/Zhu's JIA YOU! Chinese for the Global Community. 2008. (ENG.). (C). pap. 66.95 *(978-1-4282-6219-5(9))* Cengage Heinle.

CHINESE LANGUAGE—READERS

Beijing Language Institute Staff. Practical Chinese Reader Bk. 1: Simplified Character Text: Hong Kong Edition. (CHI.). 564p. pap. 19.95 *(978-962-07-4051-0(3))* Commercial Pr., The CHN. Dist: Cheng & Tsui Co.

—Practical Chinese Reader Bk. 2: Simplified Character Text: Character Exercise Book. (CHI., Illus.). 114p. pap. 5.95 *(978-7-100-00093-2(9))* Commercial Pr., The CHN. Dist: Cheng & Tsui Co.

—Practical Chinese Reader Bk. 2: Simplified Character Text: Hong Kong Edition. (CHI.). 506p. pap. 19.95 *(978-962-07-4052-7(1))* Commercial Pr., The CHN. Dist: Cheng & Tsui Co.

—Practical Chinese Reader Bk. 4: Simplified Character Text. (CHI.). pap. 16.95 *(978-7-100-00091-8(2))* Commercial Pr., The CHN. Dist: Cheng & Tsui Co.

Cao, Wenxuan, et al. Straw Houses. 2010. 160p. pap. 9.95 *(978-1-60220-908-4(1))* BetterLink Pr., Inc.

Chang, Richard I. Read Chinese: A Beginning Text in the Chinese Character, Book 2. Wang, Fang-Yu, ed. 2011. 234p. 46.95 ***(978-1-258-08174-4(1))*** Literary Licensing, LLC.

Chen, Zu-yan. Li Bai & du Fu: An Advanced Reader of Chinese Language & Literature = [Li Bai Yu du Fu]. 2008. (C). pap. 39.95 *(978-0-88727-537-1(0))* Cheng & Tsui Co.

Chen, Zu-yan & Zhang, Hong. Cultural Chinese: Readings in Art, Literature, & History. 2012. (CHI & ENG.). 272p. pap. 49.95 ***(978-1-58901-882-2(6))*** Georgetown Univ. Pr.

Chen, Zu-yan & Zhang, Hong. Li Bai & du Fu. 2008. (C). pap. 39.95 *(978-0-88727-602-6(4))* Cheng & Tsui Co.

Cheung, Shin-Yee & Bi, Qi. Food & Chinese Culture. 2009. (ENG.). 126p. pap. 23.60 *(978-0-9821816-3-8(9))* Commercial Pr., Inc., The.

Chou, Chih-P'ing, et al. Oh, China! - Elementary Reader of Modern Chinese for Advanced Beginners 2e. 2011. (Princeton Language Program: Modern Chinese Ser.). (ENG & CHI.). 432p. (C). pap. 55.00 ***(978-0-691-15308-7(6))*** Princeton Univ. Pr.

Commercial Press Staff. Practical Chinese Readers. 65.00 *(978-0-8351-1545-2(3))*; Vol. 2. 65.00 *(978-0-8351-1546-9(1))* China Bks. & Periodicals, Inc.

Confucius & Chen, Zu-yan. Confucius's Analects: An Advanced Reader of Chinese Language & Culture. 2010. (CHI & ENG., Illus.). 312p. (C). pap. 39.95 *(978-1-58901-635-4(1))* Georgetown Univ. Pr.

Gray, Phebe X. The Three Character Classic: A Bilingual Reader of China's ABC's. 2010. (CHI & ENG.). pap. *(978-1-931907-71-2(4))* Homa & Sekey Bks.

Gray, Phebe X. The Three Character Classic: A Bilingual Reader of China's ABCs. 2nd ed. 2012. pap. ***(978-1-931907-78-1(1))*** Homa & Sekey Bks.

Hsun, Lu. Capturing Chinese Stories: Including Lu Xun, Hu Shi, Zhu Ziqing, Zhou Zuoren, & Lin Yutang: Prose & Poems by Revolutionary Chinese Authors. Nadolny, Kevin John & Niu, Ivan, eds. 2011. (Illus.). 200p. pap. 21.88 ***(978-0-9842762-3-3(8))*** Capturing Chinese Pubns. LLC.

Hullot-Kentor, Robert, et al. Keys to Chinese Language: Textbook I, 4 vols., Bk. 1. 2006. (ENG & CHI., Illus.). 352p. (gr. 17). pap. 22.00 *(978-962-996-210-4(1))* Chinese Univ. of Hong Kong, The HKG. Dist: Columbia Univ. Pr.

Kadar, Daniel Z. Historical Chinese Letter Writing. 2011. (ENG.). 284p. pap. 49.95 ***(978-1-4411-8036-0(2))*** Continuum International Publishing Group, Ltd. GBR. Dist: National Bk. Network.

Larsen, Stein Ugelvik & Ma, Jing. Keys to Chinese Language: Textbook II, 4 vols., Bk. 2. 2006. (ENG & CHI., Illus.). 418p. (gr. 17). pap. 25.00 *(978-962-996-212-8(8))* Chinese Univ. of Hong Kong, The HKG. Dist: Columbia Univ. Pr.

Lee, Kunshan Carolyn. Advanced Chinese. 2009. (ENG., Illus.). 384p. 140.00 *(978-0-415-55204-2(4))* Routledge.

—The Routledge Advanced Chinese Multimedia Course: Crossing Cultural Boundaries. 2009. (Illus.). xiv, 368p. *(978-0-203-88071-5(4))* Routledge.

Madl, Benedikt. Auslandsstudium, Brain-Drain und Regierungspolitik am Beispiel der VR China. (Europaische Hochschulschriften Ser.: 450). (GER., Illus.). 269p. 35.95 *(978-3-631-39407-6(1))* Lang, Peter Publishing, Inc.

Ross, Claudia & Fang-Yu Wang, Fred. The Lady in the Painting: A Basic Chinese Reader; Traditional Characters. exp. ed. 2008. (ENG & CHI., Illus.). 139p. pap. 30.00 incl. cd-rom *(978-0-300-11549-9(0))* Yale Univ. Pr.

Ross, Claudia & Wang, Fred Fang-Yu. The Lady in the Painting: A Basic Chinese Reader. 2008. (Illus.). 139p. pap. 30.00 incl. cd-rom *(978-0-300-12516-0(X))* Yale Univ. Pr.

Soseki, Natsume, et al. Classical Chinese Primer (Reader + Workbook) Bourdaghs, Michael et al, eds. 2009. (ENG.). 610p. (gr. 17). pap. 42.00 *(978-962-996-286-9(1))* Chinese Univ. of Hong Kong, The HKG. Dist: Columbia Univ. Pr.

Wang, John C. Y., et al. Classical Chinese Primer (Reader) Ueda, Atsuko, ed. 2007. (ENG., Illus.). 456p. (gr. 17). pap. 35.00 *(978-962-996-339-2(6))* Chinese Univ. of Hong Kong, The HKG. Dist: Columbia Univ. Pr.

Wang, Susan. The Fat Woman: Six Original Short Stories in Simplified Chinese & Fanti with Pinyin Annotation Pang Nü Ren. 2008. (CHI., Illus.). xviii, 181p. *(978-0-9822137-0-4(0))* Shidai Zhuanji Chinese Literary Collections, Inc.

Wei, Hua-hei, et al. Anything Goes - an Advanced Reader of Modern Chinese 2e. 2nd ed. 2011. (Princeton Language Program: Modern Chinese Ser.). (ENG & CHI.). 456p. (C). pap. 55.00 ***(978-0-691-15311-7(6))*** Princeton Univ. Pr.

Wen, Yu He. Modern Thousand Character Primer with Chinese & English Notes. 2008. (CHI & ENG.). 55p. (J). pap. *(978-0-9580004-3-7(3))* Asia-pacific Multiculture Publishing Development Pty Ltd.

Wu, Sue-Mei, et al. Classical Chinese Primer. Ueda, Atsuko, ed. 2007. (ENG., Illus.). 160p. (gr. 17). pap., wbk. ed. 12.00 *(978-962-996-340-8(X))* Chinese Univ. of Hong Kong, The HKG. Dist: Columbia Univ. Pr.

Xia, Yan, et al. All Things Considered - an Advanced Reader of Modern Chinese 2e. 2nd ed. 2011. (Princeton Language Program: Modern Chinese Ser.). (ENG & CHI.). 488p. (C). pap. 50.00 ***(978-0-691-15310-0(8))*** Princeton Univ. Pr.

Yang, Lien-sheng, ed. Selected Chinese Texts in the Classical & Colloquial Styles. 2011. 214p. 44.95 ***(978-1-258-09789-9(3))*** Literary Licensing, LLC.

CHINESE LANGUAGE—SELF-INSTRUCTION

Assimil Staff. Chinois sans Peine (One) Chinese for French Speakers. (CHI & FRE.). 28.95 incl. audio *(978-0-8288-4379-9(1)*, M12639) French & European Pubns., Inc.

—Chinois sans Peine (Two) Chinese for French Speakers. (CHI & FRE.). 28.95 incl. audio *(978-0-8288-4381-2(3)*, M12650) French & European Pubns., Inc.

Baker, Hugh & Ho, Pui-Kei. Complete Cantonese with Two Audio CDs: A Teach Yourself Guide. 2nd ed. 2011. (TY: Language Guides). (ENG.). 464p. pap. 40.00 incl. audio compact disk *(978-0-07-175059-2(2)*, 0071750592) McGraw-Hill Cos., The.

Berlitz Publishing, creator. Berlitz Mandarin Chinese Guaranteed. 2008. (Playaway Adult Nonfiction Ser.). 59.99 *(978-1-60640-739-4(2))* Findaway World, LLC.

Berlitz Publishing, ed. Cantonese Chinese. 2008. (Phrase Book & CD Ser.). (CHI & ENG., Illus.). 224p. 12.95 *(978-981-268-478-3(6))* APA Publications Services SGP. Dist: Ingram Pub. Services.

Beyond Measure. 2008. spiral bd., per. 15.00 *(978-0-9669997-0-9(3))* 66 Communication, Inc.

Carroll, Sarah & Wang, Qiufu. Business Mandarin Chinese. 2009. (Teach Yourself Language Ser.). (ENG.). 128p. 39.95 *(978-0-07-154774-1(6)*, 0071547746) McGraw-Hill Cos., The.

Editor, John. Learning to Emulate the Wise: The Genesis of Chinese Philosophy as an Academic Discipline in Twentieth-Century China. 2011. (ENG., Illus.). 296p. (gr. 17). 49.00 ***(978-962-996-478-8(3))*** Chinese Univ. of Hong Kong, The HKG. Dist: Columbia Univ. Pr.

EPLS. Chinese. 2nd ed. 2011. (Say It Right! Ser.). (ENG & CHI., Illus.). 192p. pap. 11.00 *(978-0-07-176773-6(8)*, 0071767738) McGraw-Hill Cos., The.

—Say It Right in Chinese: The Fastest Way to Correct Pronunciation. 2009. (Say It Right! Ser.). (ENG & CHI.). 64p. 16.95 incl. audio compact disk *(978-0-07-162877-8(0)*, 0071628770) McGraw-Hill Cos., The.

Euro Talk. Talk Business Mandarin Chinese. 2008. 29.99 *(978-1-84606-219-3(5))* TOPICS Entertainment.

—Talk More Cantonese. 2008. 29.99 *(978-1-60077-217-7(X))* TOPICS Entertainment.

—Talk More Chinese Mandarin. 2008. 29.99 *(978-1-60077-233-7(1))* TOPICS Entertainment.

—Talk Now! Cantonese. 2008. 29.99 *(978-1-84352-348-2(5))* TOPICS Entertainment.

—Talk Now! Chinese Mandarin. 2008. 29.99 *(978-1-84352-319-2(1))* TOPICS Entertainment.

—Talk the Talk Mandarin Chinese. 2008. 29.99 *(978-1-84606-419-7(8))* TOPICS Entertainment.

—Vocabulary Builder Cantonese. 2008. 24.99 *(978-1-84352-748-0(0))* TOPICS Entertainment.

—Vocabulary Builder Chinese Mandarin. 2008. 24.99 *(978-1-84352-719-0(7))* TOPICS Entertainment.

—World Talk Cantonese. 2008. 29.99 *(978-1-84352-548-6(8))* TOPICS Entertainment.

—World Talk Chinese Mandarin. 2008. 29.99 *(978-1-84352-519-6(4))* TOPICS Entertainment.

Farmer, Rachel, et al. Speak Mandarin Chinese with Confidence. 2nd ed. 2010. (Teach Yourself Language Ser.). (ENG.). 48p. (C). 19.95 *(978-0-07-173606-0(9)*, 0071736069) McGraw-Hill Cos., The.

Gil, Sonia, reader. Fluenz Mandarin 1 2 3. 2010. (Fluenz Ser.). 519.00 *(978-0-9825410-1-2(5))* Fluenz.

Instant Immersi. Instant Immersion Chinese V3. 0. 2008. 29.99 *(978-1-60077-329-7(X))* TOPICS Entertainment.

Kershul, Kristine K. Chinese. 7th ed. 2008. (10 Minutes a Day Ser.). (ENG., Illus.). 132p. 24.95 *(978-1-931873-01-7(1))* Bilingual Bks., Inc.

Language, Living. Ll COMPL Basics Chinese Bk. 2008. pap. 1.11 *(978-1-4000-1864-2(1)*, Living Language) Random Hse. Information Group.

Lee / Sinonexus, Emma / Fung-Ing. Learn Mandarin Chinese through Children's Songs from Around the World. 2007. (CHI & ENG., Illus.). 192p. (J). 49.95 incl. audio compact disk *(978-0-9787664-2-9(3))* Sinonexus Publishing Co.

Lee, Carolyn. An Advanced Chinese Multimedia Course: Crossing Cultural Boundaries. 2009. (ENG., Illus.). 384p. 62.95 *(978-0-415-77407-9(1))* Routledge.

Lin, Helen T. & Rong, Du. Speaking Chinese about China. (CHI.). Vol. 1. pap. *(978-7-80052-098-3(6))* Vol. 2. pap. *(978-7-80052-154-6(0))* Sinolingua.

Liu, Jennifer Li-Chia. Connections: A Cognitive Approach to Intermediate Chinese. 2009. (Chinese in Context Language Learning Ser.). (ENG.). cd-rom 39.95 *(978-0-253-35193-7(6)*, 0253351936) Indiana Univ. Pr.

Liu, Jun. Access Chinese, Book 2. 2012. (ENG.). 480p. (C). pap. 68.67 ***(978-0-07-757217-4(3)***, 0077572173) McGraw-Hill Cos., The.

Live ABC. Chinese on the Go. 2011. (ENG., Illus.). 160p. pap. 18.00 incl. audio compact disk *(978-0-07-176891-7(2)*, 0071768912) McGraw-Hill Cos., The.

Live ABC Staff. Beginning Chinese. 2008. (CHI & ENG., Illus.). 160p. pap. 24.95 *(978-0-07-160412-3(X)*, 007160412X) McGraw-Hill Cos., The.

Living Language Staff. Chinese (Mandarin) l.t. ed. 2008. (LL Complete Basic Courses Ser.). (ENG.). 384p. pap. 10.95 *(978-1-4000-2425-4(0)*, Living Language) Random Hse. Information Group.

—Ultimate Chinese Beginner-Intermediate (BK) l.t. ed. 2009. (Ultimate Basic-Intermed Ser.). (ENG.). 416p. pap. 19.99 *(978-1-4000-0973-2(1)*, Living Language) Random Hse. Information Group.

—Ultimate Chinese Beginner-Intermediate (PKG) unabr. l.t. ed. 2009. (Ultimate Basic-Intermed Ser.). (ENG.). 79.99 *(978-1-4000-0972-5(3)*, Living Language) Random Hse. Information Group.

Mey, Monika. Modern Mandarin Chinese: With 2 Audio CDs. 2008. 160p. 24.99 *(978-0-7641-3925-3(8))* Barron's Educational Series, Inc.

—Modern Mandarin Chinese for Beginners, 3 vols. 2008. (CHI & ENG., Illus.). 160p. 24.99 *(978-0-7641-9456-6(9))* Barron's Educational Series, Inc.

Newton, John. Complete Conduct Principles for the 21st Century: The English - Simplified Chinese Page to Page Correspondence Display Edition, Useful for Learning Chinese. 2008. (ENG & CHI.). 360p. 54.44 *(978-0-9673705-3-8(1))*; pap. 34.44 *(978-0-9673705-2-1(3))* Nicer Century World Publishing.

Ning, Cynthia. Exploring in Chinese, Volume 1: A DVD-Based Course in Intermediate Chinese, 2 vols. 2007. (CHI & ENG., Illus.). 336p. 44.00 *(978-0-300-11569-7(5))* Yale Univ. Pr.

—Exploring in Chinese, Volume 2: A DVD-Based Course in Intermediate Chinese, 2 vols. 2007. (CHI & ENG., Illus.). 288p. 44.00 *(978-0-300-11583-3(0))* Yale Univ. Pr.

Robson, Shin Yong. Speed up your Chinese. 2012. (ENG & CHI.). 256p. 135.00 ***(978-0-415-50151-4(2))***; pap. 43.95 ***(978-0-415-50152-1(0))*** Routledge.

Scurfield, Elizabeth. Complete Mandarin Chinese. 3rd ed. 2010. (ENG., Illus.). 432p. pap. 35.00 incl. audio compact disk, audio compact disk *(978-0-07-173727-2(8)*, 0071737278) McGraw-Hill Cos., The.

—Complete Mandarin Chinese: Everything You Need to Speak Read & Write. 3rd ed. 2010. (ENG., Illus.). 432p. pap. 17.95 *(978-0-07-173728-9(6)*, 0071737286) McGraw-Hill Cos., The.

Scurfield, Elizabeth & Lianyi, Song. Get Started in Mandarin Chinese: Specially Created for Absolute Beginners. 5th ed. 2011. (TY: Language Guides). (ENG.). 384p. pap. 15.00 *(978-0-07-174994-7(2)*, 0071749942) McGraw-Hill Cos., The.

—Get Started in Mandarin Chinese with Two Audio CDs: A Teach Yourself Guide. 5th ed. 2011. (TY: Language Guides). (ENG.). 384p. pap. 28.00 incl. audio compact disk *(978-0-07-174993-0(4)*, 0071749934) McGraw-Hill Cos., The.

Smith, Elisabeth. Last-Minute Mandarin Chinese. 2nd ed. 2011. (TY: Language Guides). (ENG.). 16p. 14.95 *(978-0-07-175136-0(X)*, 007175136X) McGraw-Hill Cos., The.

Summers, James. Learn Chinese for English Speakers. (CHI & ENG.). pap. 20.95 *(978-0-87557-009-9(7))* Saphrograph Corp.

Tang, Bridget-Tao. Spoken Chinese — Advanced (I) ed. 2007. (ENG & CHI.). 88p. spiral bd. *(978-1-929457-09-0(X))* China Bridge.

Topics Entertainment Staff. Instant Immersion Chinese Levels 1, 2 & 3, Vol. 2. 2011. cd-rom 49.99 *(978-1-60077-919-0(0))* TOPICS Entertainment.

Wightwick, Jane & Cheng, Ma. Read & Speak Chinese for Beginners: The Easiest Way to Learn to Communicate Right Away! 2nd ed. 2010. (CHI & ENG., Illus.). 96p. *(978-0-07-173969-6(6))*; pap. *(978-0-07-173967-2(X))* McGraw-Hill Cos., The.

Yan, Margaret M. & Liu, Jennifer Li-Chia. Interactions Audio: A Cognitive Approach to Beginning Chinese. 2009. (Chinese in Context Language Learning Ser.). (ENG.). cd-rom 39.95 *(978-0-253-35188-3(X)*, 025335188X) Indiana Univ. Pr.

Yuhua, Kang & Siping, Lai. Mandarin Chinese Learning Through Conversation: Volume 1: With Audio MP3. 2008. (ENG.). 258p. 29.99 *(978-0-7641-9517-4(4))* Barron's Educational Series, Inc.

CHINESE LANGUAGE—VOCABULARY

Chou, Chih-p#8242;ing, et al. A Trip to China - Intermediate Reader of Modern Chinese 2e. 2011. (Princeton Language Program: Modern Chinese Ser.). (ENG.). 336p. (C). pap. 55.00 ***(978-0-691-15309-4(4))*** Princeton Univ. Pr.

Euro Talk. Vocabulary Builder Cantonese. 2008. 24.99 *(978-1-84352-748-0(0))* TOPICS Entertainment.

—Vocabulary Builder Chinese Mandarin. 2008. 24.99 *(978-1-84352-719-0(7))* TOPICS Entertainment.

Harrap. Harrap's Pocket Chinese Vocabulary. 2009. (Harrap's Language Guides). (ENG.). 320p. pap. 12.95 *(978-0-07-163616-2(1)*, 0071636161) McGraw-Hill Cos., The.

Kennedy, George Alexander, ed. Minimum Vocabularies of Written Chinese. 2011. 44p. 35.95 ***(978-1-258-08178-2(4))*** Literary Licensing, LLC.

Living Language Staff. Chinese Vocabulary. unabr. l.t. ed. 2009. (Flash Forward Ser.). (ENG.). 19.99 *(978-1-4000-0614-4(7)*, Living Language) Random Hse. Information Group.

Lixin, Dai Guifu Liu & Haiyan, Li. Elementary Spoken Chinese: Text & Exercise w/2CDs Voc. /Text Tran. /Key. 2nd ed. 2006. 217;99p. 27.95 *(978-7-301-06628-7(7)*, ELSPC1); 184p. 16.95 *(978-7-301-06629-4(5)*, ELSPC2) Beijing University Pr. CHN. Dist: China Bks. & Periodicals, Inc.

Pang, Elizabeth. Cross-Linguistic Transfer of Reading Skills in Bilingual Children. 2009. 108p. pap. *(978-3-639-16859-4(3))* VDM Verlag Dr. Mueller e.K.

Pittman, Joann. Survival Chinese Lessons. 2008. 51p. pap. 20.00 *(978-0-9754236-3-9(0))* Lucerna Publishing.

Po-Ching, Yip. Chinese Vocabulary: A Graded Workbook & Reader. 2012. (CHI & ENG.). 500p. 36.95 *(978-0-415-43912-1(4))* Routledge.

Wightwick, Jane & Cheng, Ma. Read & Speak Chinese for Beginners: The Easiest Way to Learn to Communicate Right Away! 2nd ed. 2010. (CHI & ENG., Illus.). 96p. *(978-0-07-173969-6(6))*; pap. *(978-0-07-173967-2(X))* McGraw-Hill Cos., The.

Winalex Learning Company. Common Chinese Vocabulary: Life. 2008. (ENG & CHI.). 200p. per. 27.95 *(978-0-9790970-5-8(3))* Liu.

Xie, Yanping & Li, Duan-Duan. Schaum's Outline of Chinese Vocabulary. 2009. (Schaum's Outline Ser.). (ENG & CHI.). 288p. (C). pap. 18.95 *(978-0-07-161160-2(6)*, 0071611606) McGraw-Hill Cos., The.

Yan, Tong & Fu, Ying. Chinese Crosswords. 2007. (CHI & ENG., Illus.). 186p. pap. 12.95 *(978-1-59265-073-6(2))* Long River Pr.

Zeng, Liang. Ming Qing Tong Su Xiao Shuo Yu Hui Yan Jiu. 2009. (CHI.). *(978-7-5392-5064-9(X))* Jiangxi Education Publishing Hse.

CHINESE LANGUAGE—WRITING

see also Chinese Characters; Document Writing, Chinese

Blakney, Raymond. A Course in the Analysis of Chinese Characters. 2007. (CHI.). 148p. per. *(978-1-897367-11-7(2))* Global Language Press.

Bush, Christopher. Ideographic Modernism: China, Writing, Media, 1 vol. 2010. (ENG.). 224p. 49.95 *(978-0-19-539382-8(1))* Oxford Univ. Pr., Inc.

Chn, Clara Yan Ho. The Europeanization of Modern Written Chinese: A Case Study of the Changing Third Person Pronouns in the Twentieth Century & Beyond. 2011. (Europäische Hochschulschriften. Reihe 21: Linguistik Ser.). 345p. pap. *(978-3-03911-657-7(6))* Lang, Peter.

Doermann, David. Arabic & Chinese Handwriting Recognition. 2008. (Lecture Notes in Computer Science / Image Processing, Computer Vision, Pattern Recognition, & Graphics Ser.). pap. 79.95 *(978-3-540-78198-1(6)*, 3540781986) Springer.

Dye, Daniel S. A Grammar of Chinese Lattice. (Illus.). 469p. reprint ed. 35.00 *(978-957-9482-40-0(3), ATE008)* SMC Publishing, Inc. TWN. Dist: Antique Collectors' Club.

Fenollosa, Ernest. The Chinese Written Character As a Medium for Poetry. Pound, Ezra, ed. 2011. 48p. 35.95 ***(978-1-258-02340-9(7))*** Literary Licensing, LLC.

Fenollosa, Ernest. The Chinese Written Character as a Medium for Poetry: A Critical Edition. Klein, Lucas & Saussy, Haun, eds. 2010. (ENG., Illus.). 256p. pap. 19.00 *(978-0-8232-2869-0(X))* Fordham Univ. Pr.

Fenollosa, Ernest, et al. The Chinese Written Character As a Medium for Poetry. Saussy, Haun & Stalling, Joseph, eds. 3rd ed. 2008. (CHI & ENG., Illus.). 256p. 28.00 *(978-0-8232-2868-3(1))* Fordham Univ. Pr.

Han, Jiantang. Chinese Characters. 3rd ed. 2012. (Introductions to Chinese Culture Ser.). (ENG.). 168p. pap. 19.99 ***(978-0-521-18660-5(9))*** Cambridge Univ. Pr.

Harrap. Harrap's Pocket Chinese Grammar & Script. 2009. (Harrap's Language Guides). (ENG.). 176p. pap. 10.95 *(979-0-07-163624-7(2), 0071636242)* McGraw-Hill Cos., The.

Hayot, Eric. Sinographies: Writing China. Saussy, Haun & Yao, Steven G., eds. 2008. (Illus.). 408p. 82.50 *(978-0-8166-4724-8(0))* Univ. of Minnesota Pr.

Hayot, Eric, et al, eds. Sinographies: Writing China. 2007. (Illus.). 408p. per. 27.50 *(978-0-8166-4725-5(9))* Univ. of Minnesota Pr.

Jiang, Nai-Siang. Stories Told by Chinese Pictograms. 2009. 70p. pap. 15.99 *(978-1-4415-5468-0(8))* Xlibris Corp.

Kennedy, George Alexander ed. Minimum Vocabularies of Written Chinese. 2011. 44p. 35.95 ***(978-1-258-08178-2(4))*** Literary Licensing, LLC.

Kubler, Jerling Guo & Kubler, Cornelius C. Basic Written Chinese: An Introduction to Reading & Writing for Beginners. 2012. (CHI & ENG., Illus.). 384p. pap. 49.95 *(978-0-8048-4016-3(4))* Tuttle Publishing.

—Basic Written Chinese Practice Essentials: An Introduction to Reading & Writing for Beginners. 2012. (CHI & ENG., Illus.). 224p. pap. 24.95 *(978-0-8048-4017-0(2))* Tuttle Publishing.

Liu, Jennifer Li-Chia. Encounters I: A Cognitive Approach to Advanced Chinese. 2010. (Chinese in Context Language Learning Ser.). (ENG.). 464p. pap., wbk. ed. 39.95 *(978-0-253-22101-8(3), 0253221013)* Indiana Univ. Pr.

—Encounters II: A Cognitive Approach to Advanced Chinese. 2010. (Chinese in Context Language Learning Ser.). (ENG.). 520p. pap., wbk. ed. 39.95 *(978-0-253-22102-5(1), 0253221021)* Indiana Univ. Pr.

Matthews, Alison. The First 100 Chinese Characters: The Quick & Easy Method to Learn the 100 Most Basic Chinese Characters. 2007. (ENG & CHI., Illus.). 128p. pap. 14.95 *(978-0-8048-3832-0(*))* Tuttle Publishing.

Matthews, Lawrence, intro. The First 100 Chinese Characters: The Quick & Easy Method to Learn the 100 Most Basic Chinese Characters. 2007. (ENG & CHI., Illus.). 128p. pap. 14.95 *(978-0-8048-3830-6(5))* Tuttle Publishing.

Quong, Rose. Chinese Characters: Their Art & Wisdom. 2007. (Dover Language Guides). (ENG., Illus.). 80p. per. 9.95 *(978-0-486-45434-4(7))* Dover Pubns., Inc.

Quong, Rose. Chinese Wit, Wisdom & Written Characters. 2011. 70p. 36.95 ***(978-1-258-01539-8(0))*** Literary Licensing, LLC.

Ricci, Roslyn Joy. Romancing the Chinese Characters in Classical Chinese Poetry. 2010. 92p. pap. *(978-3-639-23949-2(0))* VDM Verlag Dr. Mueller e.K.

Shing, Jing Heng. Gateway to Chinese Character Writing. Kale, Tessa, ed. 2006. (CHI & ENG., Illus.). 200p. (gr. 17). pap. 23.00 *(978-962-996-292-0(6))* Chinese Univ. of Hong Kong, The HKG. Dist: Columbia Univ. Pr.

Tung, Tai. The Six Scripts or the Principles of Chinese Writing by Tai Tung: A Translation by L. C. Hopkins, with a Memoir of the Translator by W. Perceval Yetts. Hopkins, L. C., tr. from CHI. 2012. (ENG.). 114p. pap. 31.99 ***(978-1-107-60515-2(6))*** Cambridge Univ. Pr.

Wong, Chung Kin & Mui, King Chau. Shu Fa Chu Yu: Four Specimens of Chinese Calligraphy. 2011. 76p. 36.95 ***(978-1-258-03779-6(3))*** Literary Licensing, LLC.

Wu, Jian-Hsin. The Way of Chinese Characters: The Origins of 400 Essential Words = [Han Zi Zhi Dao]. 2007. 30.95 *(978-0-88727-527-2(3))* Cheng & Tsui Co.

Yao, Nora, et al. Fundamental Written Chinese: Simplified Character Version. 2009. (CHI & ENG., Illus.). 312p. (C). pap. 39.00 *(978-0-8248-3157-8(8))* Univ. of Hawaii Pr.

CHINESE LITERATURE

see also Chinese Drama; Chinese Essays; Chinese Fiction; Chinese Poetry; Chinese Wit and Humor

Dong, Lan. Mulan's Legend & Legacy in China & the United States. 2010. (ENG., Illus.). 280p. 70.50 *(978-1-59213-970-5(1))*; pap. 27.95 *(978-1-59213-971-2(X))* Temple Univ. Pr.

Geiss, James, et al. Classical Chinese: Supplementary Selections from Philosophical Texts. 2006. (Princeton Language Program: Modern Chinese Ser.). (CHI & ENG.). 328p. (C). per. 39.95 *(978-0-691-11833-8(7))* Princeton Univ. Pr.

Giles, Herbert Allen. China & the Chinese. 2009. (Illus.). 242p. 28.99 *(978-1-115-42095-2(X))* 2009. (Illus.). 242p. 32.99 *(978-1-115-42098-3(4))* 2009. (Illus.) 242p. pap. 25.75 *(978-1-115-42094-5(1))* 2009. (Illus.). 242p. pap. 25.75 *(978-1-115-42092-1(5))* 2009. 242p. 28.99 *(978-1-110-42400-9(0))* 2009. 242p. pap. 25.75 *(978-1-110-42398-9(5))* 2008. 136p. 21.99 *(978-0-554-33154-6(3))* 2008. 136p. 24.99 *(978-0-554-23851-7(9))* 2007. (ENG.). 124p. pap. 18.99 *(978-1-4264-5085-3(0))* 2006. 134p. pap. 19.99 *(978-1-4264-5386-1(8))* BiblioBazaar.

—China & the Chinese. 2008. 236p. pap. *(978-1-4097-9378-6(8))* Read Bks.

Hillenbrand, Margaret & Starr, Chloe, eds. Documenting China: A Reader in Seminal Twentieth-Century Texts. 2011. (ENG & CHI.). 240p. (C). pap. 40.00 *(978-0-295-99127-6(5))* Univ. of Washington Pr.

Holloway, Kenneth & Holloway, Kenneth W. Guodian: The Newly Discovered Seeds of Chinese Religious & Political Philosophy. 2009. (ENG.). 224p. 55.00 *(978-0-19-537145-1(3))* Oxford Univ. Pr., Inc.

Hsun, Lu. Capturing Chinese Stories: Including Lu Xun, Hu Shi, Zhu Ziqing, Zhou Zuoren, & Lin Yutang: Prose & Poems by Revolutionary Chinese Authors. Nadolny, Kevin John & Niu, Ivan, eds. 2011. (Illus.). 200p. pap. 21.88 ***(978-0-9842762-3-3(8))*** Capturing Chinese Pubns. LLC.

Huang, Shang. Shower of Flowers: Vol I. 2010. 194p. pap. 11.95 *(978-1-60220-912-1(X))* BetterLink Pr., Inc.

—Shower of Flowers: Vol II. 2010. 190p. pap. 11.95 *(978-1-60220-913-8(8))* BetterLink Pr., Inc.

Li, Tien-Yi & Liu Wu-Chi, eds. Readings in Modern Chinese Literature, 2 vols. Incl. Vol. 1. Readings in Modern Chinese Literature: Plays & Poems. 3rd ed. 8.95 incl. audio *(978-0-88710-071-0(6))*; Vol. 11. Readings in Modern Chinese Literature: Stories. rev. ed. (C). pap. 8.95 incl. audio *(978-0-88710-072-7(4))*; 1953. o.p. *(978-0-88710-073-4(2))* Yale Univ., Far Eastern Pubns.

Lin, Yutang. Family Letters of a Chinese Poet.Tr. of Bangiao Jia Hua. pap. 11.95 *(978-957-09-0952-4(8))* Cheng Chung Bk. Co., Ltd. TWN. Dist: Cheng & Tsui Co.

Liu, Wu-Chi & Li, Tien-yi, eds. Readings in Contemporary Chinese Literature, V1-2: Plays & Poems, Stories. 2011. 420p. 54.95 ***(978-1-258-08446-2(5))*** Literary Licensing, LLC.

Lu, Jianchu. "Shang Shu" Shi Shi Kao. 2010. (Illus.). *(978-7-80730-977-2(6))* Xuelin Publishing Hse.

Lu, Jie, ed. China's Literary & Cultural Scenes at the Turn of the 21st Century. 2008. (ENG., Illus.). 304p. 140.00 *(978-0-415-42078-5(4))* Routledge.

Mair, Victor. Painting & Performance: Picture Recitation & Its Indian Genesis. 2009. (ENG.). 304p. pap. 50.00 *(978-1-891640-55-1(0))* Floating World Editions.

McGrath, Jason. Postsocialist Modernity: Chinese Cinema, Literature, & Criticism in the Market Age. 2010. (ENG., Illus.). 320p. pap. 24.95 *(978-0-8047-7363-8(7))* Stanford Univ. Pr.

Meyer, Andrew Seth, tr. from CHI. The Dao of the Military: Liu An's Art of War. 2012. (Translations from the Asian Classics Ser.). (ENG.). 176p. (gr. 17). pap. 19.50 ***(978-0-231-15333-1(3))*** Columbia Univ. Pr.

—The Dao of the Military - Liu An's Art of War. 2012. (Translations from the Asian Classics Ser.). (ENG.). 176p. (gr. 17). 60.00 ***(978-0-231-15332-4(5))*** Columbia Univ. Pr.

A Pictorial Series of Ten Classics of Chinese Literature. (Illus.). 216p. *(978-957-629-040-4(6))* Hilit Publishing Co., Ltd.

Schafer, Edward H. Shore of Pearls: Hainan Island in Early Times. 2010. (ENG.). 174p. pap. 40.00 *(978-1-891640-52-0(6))* Floating World Editions.

TeWuMa, Tom. Tutor. 2007. (ENG., Illus.). 160p. per. 9.95 *(978-0-9792328-2-4(1))* Helm Publishing.

Watson, Burton. The Analects of Confucius. 2009. (Translations from the Asian Classics Ser.). (ENG.). 176p. (gr. 17). pap. 15.95 *(978-0-231-14165-9(3))* Columbia Univ. Pr.

Xi, Xu. Fifty-Fifty 2010. 304p. pap. 15.00 *(978-988-98819-7-9(7))* National Bk. Network.

Ye, Guoliang & Xu, Xingqing. Jianghu Shi Dai Riben Han Xue Yan Jiu Zhu Mian Xiang: Si Xiang Wen Hua Pian. 2009. (CHI., Illus.). xv, 493p. *(978-986-01-8374-0(0))* Academia Sinica.

Zhang, Jie. She Knocked at the Door. 2010. 194p. pap. 11.95 *(978-1-60220-909-1(X))* BetterLink Pr., Inc.

CHINESE LITERATURE—BIBLIOGRAPHY

Knechtges, David R. & Chang, Taiping, eds. Ancient & Early Medieval Chinese Literature: A Reference Guide. 2010. (Handbook of Oriental Studies. Section 4 China Ser.). 792p. *(978-90-04-19127-3(5))* BRILL.

Timofeevich, Andrew. Unknown China. Issue 1. 2008. 256p. pap. 27.95 *(978-1-4092-0139-7(2))* Lulu Enterprises Inc.

Ying, Li-Hua. The A to Z of Modern Chinese Literature. 2010. (A to Z Guide Ser.). (ENG.). 500p. pap. 34.45 *(978-0-8108-7614-9(0))* Scarecrow Pr., Inc.

Ying, Li-Hua & Woronoff, Jon. Historical Dictionary of Modern Chinese Literature. 2009. (Historical Dictionaries of Literature & the Arts Ser.). (ENG.). 494p. 105.00 *(978-0-8108-5516-8(X))* Scarecrow Pr., Inc.

CHINESE LITERATURE—HISTORY AND CRITICISM

Achard, Jean-Luc. Enlightened Rainbows: The Life & Works of Shardza Tashi Gyeltsen. 2008. (Brill's Tibetan Studies Library Ser.). 500p. *(978-90-04-16823-7(0))* BRILL.

Al-Dabbagh, Abdulla. Socialist Literature: Theory & Practice. 2012. (C). 77.95 ***(978-1-4331-1673-5(1))***; E-Book ***(978-1-4539-0221-9(X))*** Lang, Peter Publishing, Inc.

Altenburger, Roland. The Sword or the Needle: The Female Knight-Errant (Xia) in Traditional Chinese Narrative. 2009. 425p. *(978-3-0343-0036-0(0))* Lang, Peter.

Asselin, Mark Laurent. A Significant Season: Cai Yong (Ca. 133-192) & His Contemporaries. 2010. *(978-0-940490-27-7(7))* American Oriental Society.

Barnett, Robert & Schwartz, Ronald, eds. Proceedings of the Tenth Seminar of the IATS, 2003, Volume 11 Tibetan Modernities: Notes from the Field on Cultural & Social Change. 2008. (Illus.). 480p. *(978-90-04-15522-0(8))* BRILL.

Beecroft, Alexander. Authorship & Cultural Identity in Early Greece & China: Patterns of Literary Circulation. 2010. (ENG.). 338p. 89.00 *(978-0-521-19431-0(8))* Cambridge Univ. Pr.

Berg, Daria. Women Writers & the Literary World in Early Modern China. 2012. (Routledge Studies in the Early History of Asia Ser.). (ENG.). 256p. (C). 155.00 ***(978-0-415-53341-6(4))*** Routledge.

Besio, Kimberly & Tung, Constantine, eds. Three Kingdoms & Chinese Culture. 2007. (SUNY Series in Chinese Philosophy & Culture). (Illus.). 193p. 65.00 *(978-0-7914-7011-4(3))* State Univ. of New York Pr.

Bi, Lijun. Chinese Children's Literature in the 20th Century. 2010. 260p. pap. *(978-3-8383-7082-8(1))* Lambert Academic Publishing.

Bieg, Lutz. Bibliographie zur chinesischen Literatur in deutscher Sprache Vol. 8. rev. ed. 2006. (GER.). 400p. *(978-3-598-24548-0(3))* Saur, K. G. Verlag GmbH & Co.

Burkus-Chasson, Anne. Through a Forest of Chancellors: Fugitive Histories in Liu Yuan's Lingyan Ge, an Illustrated Book from Seventeenth-Century Suzhou. 2010. (Harvard-Yenching Institute Monograph Ser.: 66). (Illus.). 450p. 60.00 *(978-0-674-03280-4(2))* Harvard Univ., Asia Ctr.

Buswell, Robert E., Jr., tr. from KOR. Cultivating Original Enlightenment: Wonhyo's Exposition of the Vajrasamadhi-Sutra (Kumgang Sammaegyong Non) 2007. (International Association of Wonhyo Studies Collected Works of Wonhyo). 424p. 49.00 *(978-0-8248-3076-2(8))* Univ. of Hawaii Pr.

Chan, Alan Kam-Leung & Lo, Yuet Keung. Interpretation & Literature in Early Medieval China. 2010. (SUNY series in Chinese Philosophy & Culture Ser.). (MUL.). 256p. 80.00 *(978-1-4384-3217-5(8))* State Univ. of New York Pr.

Chan, Shelley W. A Subversive Voice in China: The Fictional World of Mo Yan. 2010. *(978-1-60497-719-6(1))* Cambria Pr.

Chang, Kang-i Sun & Owen, Stephen, eds. The Cambridge History of Chinese Literature, 2 vols. 2010. (Illus.). *(978-0-521-85559-4(4))*;Set. 1704p. 325.00 *(978-0-521-11677-0(5))* Cambridge Univ. Pr.

Chen, Jianguo. The Aesthetics of the Beyond: Phantasm, Nostalgia, & the Literary Practice in Contemporary China. 2009. 51.50 *(978-0-87413-017-1(4))* Univ. of Delaware Pr.

Chen, Jo-Shui. Liu Tsung-Yüan & Intellectual Change in T'ang China, 773-819. 2006. (Cambridge Studies in Chinese History, Literature & Institutions Ser.). (ENG.). 236p. pap. 48.00 *(978-0-521-03010-6(2))* Cambridge Univ. Pr.

China: Classic & Contemporary Works in Reprint, 41 bks. in 57 vols. (Reprint Ser.). reprint ed. 2066.50 *(978-0-404-56900-6(5))* AMS Pr., Inc.

Chou, Chih-P'ing. Yüan Hung-tao & the Kung-an School. 2006. (Cambridge Studies in Chinese History, Literature & Institutions Ser.). (ENG.). 184p. pap. 39.99 *(978-0-521-02765-6(9))* Cambridge Univ. Pr.

Davis, Jessica Milner & Chey, Jocelyn. Humour in Chinese Life & Letters: Classical & Traditional Approaches. 2011. 320p. ***(978-988-8053-94-0(9))*** Hong Kong Univ. Pr.

—Humour in Chinese Life & Letters: Classical & Traditional Approaches. 2011. (ENG., Illus.). 312p. (gr. 17). 60.00 ***(978-988-8083-51-0(1))***; pap. 25.00 ***(978-988-8083-52-7(X))*** Hong Kong Univ. Pr. HKG. Dist: Columbia Univ. Pr.

De Pee, Christian. The Writing of Weddings in Middle-Period China: Text & Ritual Practice in the Eighth Through Fourteenth Centuries. 2007. (SUNY Series in Chinese Philosophy & Culture). (Illus.). 365p. 75.00 *(978-0-7914-7073-2(3))* State Univ. of New York Pr.

Denecke, Wiebke. The Dynamics of Masters Literature: Early Chinese Thought from Confucius to Han Feizi. 2011. (Harvard-Yenching Institute Monograph Ser.: 74). (ENG.). 386p. 39.95 *(978-0-674-05609-1(4))* Harvard Univ., Asia Ctr.

Du, Qi. Dunhuang Wen Xue Lun Ji: Dunhuang Wenxue Lunji. 2009. *(978-7-80588-767-8(5))* Gansu People's Fine Arts Publishing Hse.

Dudbridge, Glen & Berg, Daria. Reading China: Fiction, History & the Dynamics of Discourse. Essays in Honour of Professor Glen Dudbridge. 2006. (China Studies). (Illus.). 322p. *(978-90-04-15483-4(3))* BRILL.

Duo, Duo. Snow Plain. Crespi, John A., tr. 2010. (ENG.). 200p. pap. 17.00 *(978-0-9815521-8-7(8),* Zephyr Pr.) Chicago Review Pr., Inc.

Egan, Ronald C. The Literary Works of Ou-Yang Hsiu (1007-72) 2009. (Cambridge Studies in Chinese History, Literature & Institutions Ser.). (ENG.). 276p. pap. 36.99 *(978-0-521-10154-7(9))* Cambridge Univ. Pr.

Eoyang, Eugene. Two-Way Mirrors: Cross-Cultural Perspectives in Chinese-Western Comparative Literature. 2007. (ENG.). 240p. 78.99 *(978-0-7391-0500-9(0))* Lexington Bks.

Fong, Grace S. Herself an Author: Gender, Agency, & Writing in Late Imperial China. 2008. (Illus.). 256p. (C). 57.00 *(978-0-8248-3186-8(1))* Univ. of Hawaii Pr.

Fong, Grace S. & Widmer, Ellen. The Inner Quarters & Beyond: Women Writers from Ming Through Qing. 2010. 400p. *(978-90-04-18521-0(6))* BRILL.

Gao, Yuanbao. Yi Zhu Ou Shi: Zhongguo Xian Dai Wen Xue Shi Zha Ji. 2010. (CHI.). *(978-7-301-16219-4(7))* Beijing University Pr.

Giles, Herbert A. A History of Chinese Literature. 2008. 456p. 37.95 *(978-1-4344-6525-2(X))*; pap. 29.95 *(978-1-4344-6524-5(1))* Wildside Pr., LLC.

Gong, Haomin. Uneven Modernity: Literature, Film & Intellectual Discourse in Postsocialist China. 2012. (Illus.). 224p. 47.00 ***(978-0-8248-3531-6(X))*** Univ. of Hawaii Pr.

Greenbaum, Jamie. Chen Jiru (1558-1639) The Development & Subsequent Uses of Literary Personae. 2007. (Sinica Leidensia Ser.). 350p. *(978-90-04-16358-4(1))* BRILL.

Ha, Jingjun. Remapping Chinese Literature. 2008. 84p. pap. *(978-3-639-08329-3(6))* VDM Verlag Dr. Mueller e.K.

Hakkenberg, Christopher. Re-Articulating Literary Dissent - an Analysis of Wang Shuo's Playing for Thrills. 2008. 104p. pap. *(978-3-639-02143-1(6))* VDM Verlag Dr. Mueller e.K.

Hayot, Eric R. J. Chinese Dreams: Pound, Brecht, Tel Quel. 2011. (ENG.). 242p. pap. 26.95 ***(978-0-472-03486-4(3))*** Univ. of Michigan Pr.

Heller, Amy & Orofino, Giacomella, eds. Discoveries in Western Tibet & the Western Himalayas: Essays on History, Literature, Archeology & Art. 2007. (Brill's Tibetan Studies Library). (Illus.). 240p. *(978-90-04-15520-6(1))* BRILL.

Hockx, Michel. Literary Societies of Republican China. 2008. (ENG., Illus.). 602p. 120.99 *(978-0-7391-1933-4(8))* Lexington Bks.

Hockx, Michel & Denton, Kirk A. Literary Societies of Republican China. 2008. (ENG., Illus.). 602p. pap. 49.50 *(978-0-7391-1934-1(6))* Lexington Bks.

Honey, David B. The Southern Garden Poetry Society: Literary Culture & Social Memory in Guangdong. 2011. (ENG.). 200p. (gr. 17). 45.00 *(978-962-996-467-2(8))* Chinese Univ. of Hong Kong, The HKG. Dist: Columbia Univ. Pr.

Hong, Zicheng & Day, Michael M. A History of Contemporary Chinese Literature. 2009. xix, 636p. pap. *(978-90-04-17366-8(8))* BRILL.

Hsieh, Liu. The Literary Mind & the Carving of Dragons: A Study of Thought & Pattern in Chinese Literature. Shih, Vincent Yu-chung, tr. 2011. 344p. 51.95 ***(978-1-258-05048-1(X))*** Literary Licensing, LLC.

Huang, Alexander C. Y. Chinese Shakespeares: Two Centuries of Cultural Exchange. 2009. (Global Chinese Culture Ser.). (ENG., Illus.). 368p. (gr. 17). 84.50 *(978-0-231-14848-1(8))*; pap. 26.50 *(978-0-231-14849-8(6))* Columbia Univ. Pr.

Huang, Yibing. Contemporary Chinese Literature: From the Cultural Revolution to the Future. 2007. (ENG.). 240p. 95.00 *(978-1-4039-7982-7(0))* Palgrave Macmillan.

Huss, Ann & Liu, Jianmei. The Jin Yong Phenomenon: Chinese Martial Arts Fiction & Modern Chinese Literary History. 2007. (ENG.). 356p. (C). 114.95 *(978-1-934043-08-0(7))* Cambria Pr.

Idema, W. L., et al. Text, Performance, & Gender in Chinese Literature & Music: Essays in Honor of Wilt Idema. 2009. 468p. *(978-90-04-17906-6(2))* BRILL.

Inglis, Alister D. & Inglis, Alister David. Hong Mai's Record of the Listener & Its Song Dynasty Context. annot. ed. 2007. (SUNY Series in Chinese Philosophy & Culture). (Illus.). 237p. per. 29.95 *(978-0-7914-6822-7(4))* State Univ. of New York Pr.

Inglis, Alister David. Hong Mai's Record of the Listener & Its Song Dynasty Context. 2006. (SUNY Series in Chinese Philosophy & Culture). (Illus.). 237p. 65.00 *(978-0-7914-6821-0(6))* State Univ. of New York Pr.

Jones, Andrew F. Developmental Fairy Tales: Evolutionary Thinking & Modern Chinese Culture. 2011. (ENG., Illus.). 272p. 49.95 *(978-0-674-04795-2(8))* Harvard Univ. Pr.

Kádár, Dániel Z. Historical Chinese Letter Writing. 2010. (ENG., Illus.). 288p. 140.00 *(978-0-8264-3088-5(0))* Continuum International Publishing Group, Ltd. GBR. Dist: National Bk. Network.

Keaveney, Christopher T. Beyond Brushtalk: Sino-Japanese Literary Exchange in the Interwar Period. 2008. (ENG., Illus.). 220p. (gr. 17). 50.00 *(978-962-209-928-9(9))* Hong Kong Univ. Pr. HKG. Dist: Columbia Univ. Pr.

Kern, Martin, ed. Text & Ritual in Early China. 2008. (ENG., Illus.). 362p. pap. 27.95 *(978-0-295-98787-3(1))* Univ. of Washington Pr.

Knechtges, David R. The Han Rhapsody: A Study of the Fu of Yang Hsiung (53 B. C. -A. D. 18) 2008. (Cambridge Studies in Chinese History, Literature & Institutions Ser.). (ENG.). 176p. pap. 31.99 *(978-0-521-10346-6(0))* Cambridge Univ. Pr.

Knechtges, David R. & Chang, Taiping. Ancient & Early Medieval Chinese Literature: A Reference Guide, 2 vols. 2010. 2000p. *(978-90-04-18016-1(8))* BRILL.

Knight, Sabina. Chinese Literature: A Very Short Introduction, 1 vol. 2012. (Very Short Introductions Ser.). (ENG., Illus.). 144p. pap. 11.95 ***(978-0-19-539206-7(X))*** Oxford Univ. Pr., Inc.

Kong, Belinda. Tiananmen Fictions outside the Square: The Chinese Literary Diaspora & the Politics of Global Culture. (Asian American History & Culture Ser.). (ENG., Illus.). 278p. 2012. pap. 26.95 ***(978-1-4399-0759-7(5))*** 2011. 86.50 ***(978-1-4399-0758-0(7))*** Temple Univ. Pr.

—Tiananmen Fictions Outside the Square: The Chinese Literary Diaspora & the Politics of Global Culture. 2012. E-Book ***(978-1-4399-0760-3(9))*** Temple Univ. Pr.

Kong, Chaopeng. Guan Xing de Fan Si: Fan Xian Dai Yi Shi Yu 20 Shi Ji Zhongguo Wen Xue. 2009. (CHI.). *(978-7-5601-5047-5(0))* Jilin Univ. Pr.

Kozen, Hiroshi. Chugoku Bungaku Riron No Tenkai. 2008. (JPN.). 682p. *(978-4-7924-0629-5(3))* Seibundo Shuppan.

—Shinpan Chugoku No Bungaku Riron. 2008. 514p. *(978-4-7924-0630-1(7))* Seibundo Shuppan.

Lai, Xianzong & Zhang, Weiyi. Wen Ben Yu Quan Shi: Ren Wen Chuan Tong Ji Qi Dang Dai Quan Shi. 2010. (CHI., Illus.). xix, 333p. *(978-957-748-374-4(7))* Li Wen Pubs. Co., Ltd.

Larson, Wendy. From Ah Q to Lei Feng: Freud & Revolutionary Spirit in 20th Century China. 2008. (ENG., Illus.). 336p. 55.00 *(978-0-8047-0075-7(3))* Stanford Univ. Pr.

Laughlin, Charles A. The Literature of Leisure & Chinese Modernity. 2008. 242p. 57.00 *(978-0-8248-3125-7(X))* Univ. of Hawaii Pr.

Lee, Haiyan. Revolution of the Heart: A Genealogy of Love in China, 1900-1950. (ENG.). 384p. 2010. pap. 27.95 *(978-0-8047-7327-0(0))* 2006. (Illus.). 65.00 *(978-0-8047-5417-0(9))* Stanford Univ. Pr.

Lee, Yu-Lin. Writing Taiwan. 2008. 240p. pap. *(978-3-639-07510-6(2))* VDM Verlag Dr. Mueller e.K.

C

Lei, Da. Jin San Shi Nian Zhongguo Wen Xue Si Chao: Jinsanshinian Zhongguowenxuesichao. 2009. (CHI.). 314p. *(978-7-311-03244-9(X))* Lanzhou Daxue Chubanshe.

Li, Kai & Dew, James E. Classical Chinese: A Functional Approach. 2009. (CHI & ENG.). (C). pap. 35.00 *(978-0-88727-737-5(3))* Cheng & Tsui Co.

Li, Ningyi. Mythic & Folk Elements in Modern Chinese Literature: A Study of Six Writers. 2008. 284p. 109.95 *(978-0-7734-5008-0(4))* Mellen, Edwin Pr., The.

Li, Xiaorong. Women's Poetry of Late Imperial China: Transforming the Inner Chambers. 2012. (ENG., Illus.). 264p. (C). 70.00 ***(978-0-295-99205-1(0))***; pap. 30.00 ***(978-0-295-99229-7(8))*** Univ. of Washington Pr.

Li, Yongcun. Ein Blick ins Frauenleben der ersten 30 Jahre des 20. Jahrhunderts: Das Werk Lu Yins. 2009. (Europäische Hochschulschriften. Reihe 27: Asiatische und Afrikanische Studien Ser.). (GER.). 328p. pap. 79.95 *(978-3-631-59252-6(3))* Lang, Peter GmbH, Europaischer Verlag der Wissenschaften DEU. Dist: Lang, Peter.

Liang, Hongying. Shou Wang Wen Xue de Tian Kong. 2009. *(978-7-5063-4781-5(4))* Writers' Publishing Hse.

Littlejohn, Ronnie & Dippmann, Jeffrey W., eds. Riding the Wind with Liezi: New Perspectives on the Daoist Classic. 2011. (SUNY series in Chinese Philosophy & Culture Ser.). 240p. 75.00 *(978-1-4384-3455-1(3))* State Univ. of New York Pr.

Liu, Yuanru. You Guan: Zuo Wei Shen Ti Ji Yi de Zhong Gu Wen Xue Yu Zong Jiao = Inner Landscape Visualized: Techniques of the Body in Medieval Chinese Literature & Religion. 2009. (CHI., Illus.). vi, 19p. *(978-986-02-0747-7(X))* Academia Sinica.

Lo, Chan. Interpretation & Literature. Chan, Alan K. L., ed. 2011. 294p. pap. 24.95 ***(978-1-4384-3218-2(6)***, Suny Pr.) State Univ. of New York Pr.

Louie, Kam. Eileen Chang: Romancing Languages, Cultures & Genres. 2012. (ENG., Illus.). 288p. (gr. 17). 60.00 ***(978-988-8083-79-4(1))***; pap. 25.00 ***(978-988-8083-72-5(4))*** Hong Kong Univ. Pr. HKG. Dist: Columbia Univ. Pr.

Lu, Hsin-Hung. Text Analysis of Different Translated Versions: Using Virginia Woolf's Short Story as an Example. 2008. 144p. pap. *(978-3-8364-9117-4(6))* VDM Verlag Dr. Mueller e.K.

Lu, Tina. Accidental Incest, Filial Cannibalism, & Other Peculiar Encounters in Late Imperial Chinese Literature. 2009. (Harvard East Asian Monographs: 304). (Illus.). 306p. 39.95 *(978-0-674-03156-2(3))* Harvard Univ., Asia Ctr.

Luo, Yuming & Ye, Yang. A Concise History of Chinese Literature, 2 vols. 2011. 394p. *(978-90-04-20366-2(4))*; xxvii, 987p. *(978-90-04-20368-6(0))*; xxvii, 987p. *(978-90-04-20369-3(9))* BRILL.

Mé, et al. Cultural Hybridity. 2011. 124p. pap. ***(978-3-8454-1189-7(9))*** Lambert Academic Publishing.

Ma, Yue. The Catastrophe Remembered by the Non-Traumatic. 2009. 124p. pap. *(978-3-639-16527-2(6))* VDM Verlag Dr. Mueller e.K.

Mair, Victor H., ed. The Columbia History of Chinese Literature. 2010. (ENG., Illus.). 1342p. (gr. 17). pap. 40.00 *(978-0-231-10985-7(7))* Columbia Univ. Pr.

Mann, Susan. The Talented Women of the Zhang Family. 2007. (Illus.). 352p. 60.00 *(978-0-520-25089-5(3))*; 322p. per. 26.95 *(978-0-520-25090-1(7))* Univ. of California Pr.

Meynard, Thierry. The Religious Philosophy of Liang Shuming: The Hidden Buddhist. 2010. (Modern Chinese Philosophy Ser.). 226p. *(978-90-04-17151-0(7))* BRILL.

Ng, Maria & Holden, Philip. Reading Chinese Transnationalisms: Society, Literature, Film. 2006. (ENG., Illus.). 248p. (gr. 17). 60.00 *(978-962-209-796-4(0))*; pap. 24.95 *(978-962-209-797-1(9))* Hong Kong Univ. Pr. HKG. Dist: Columbia Univ. Pr.

Ni, Tingting. "Wu Si" Wen Xue Lun Ji. 2007. (Ji Ming Cong Shu Ser.). (CHI.). 7p. *(978-7-02-006719-0(0))* People's Literature Publishing Hse.

Nienhauser, William H., Jr. & Lévy, André. Chinese Literature, Ancient & Classical. Nienhauser, William H., Jr., tr. from FRE. 2007. (ENG.). 184p. pap. 19.95 *(978-0-253-21365-5(7)*, 0253213657) Indiana Univ. Pr.

Osho. The Empty Boat: Encounters with Nothingness. Osho International Foundation, ed. 2011. (ENG.). 224p. pap. 16.95 *(978-0-9818341-9-1(1))* Osho International.

Patterson, Anna. The Lost Art of I Ching. 2007. (Illus.). 96p. 7.95 *(978-1-59359-858-7(0))* Peter Pauper Pr. Inc.

Ptak, Roderich. Birds & Beasts in Chinese Texts & Trade: Lectures Related to South China & the Overseas World. 2011. (Maritime Asia Ser.). (ENG., Illus.). 140p. (C). 57.00 ***(978-3-447-06449-1(8))*** Harrassowitz, Otto Verlag DEU. Dist: ISD.

Qian, Nanxiu, et al. Different Worlds of Discourse: Transformations of Gender & Genre in Late Qing & Early Republican China. 2008. (China Studies: Vol. 16). (Illus.). 350p. *(978-90-04-16776-6(5))* BRILL.

Rojas, Carlos. The Naked Gaze: Reflections on Chinese Modernity. 2009. (Harvard East Asian Monographs: 308). (Illus.). 350p. 45.00 *(978-0-674-03174-6(1))* Harvard Univ., Asia Ctr.

Rojas, Carlos & Chow, Eileen, eds. Rethinking Chinese Popular Culture. 2011. (ENG.). 304p. pap. 42.95 ***(978-0-415-66711-1(9))*** Routledge.

Rojas, Carlos & Wang, David Der-Wei, eds. Writing Taiwan: A New Literary History. 2007. (Asia-Pacific Ser.). (ENG.). 424p. (C). 94.95 *(978-0-8223-3851-2(3))* Duke Univ. Pr.

Rojas, Carlos & Wang, David Der-wei, eds. Writing Taiwan: A New Literary History. 2007. (Asia-Pacific Ser.). (ENG.). 424p. per. 26.95 *(978-0-8223-3867-3(X))* Duke Univ. Pr.

Schafer, Edward & Schafer, Edward H. Divine Woman: Dragon Ladies & Rain Maidens in T'ang Literature. 2012. (ENG.). 264p. pap. 50.00 *(978-1-891640-48-3(8))* Floating World Editions.

Schaffer, Kay & Song, Xianlin. Women's Writing in Post-Socialist China. 2011. (ASAA Women in Asia Ser.). 240p. (C). 140.00 *(978-0-415-68274-9(6))* Routledge.

Shu, Jingnan. Zhu Xi Yan Jiu. (CHI.). 40p. *(978-7-01-007171-8(3))* People's Publishing Hse., The.

Shui, Laiyou. Mi Fu Shu Fa Shi Liao Ji. 2009. (CHI., Illus.). *(978-7-80725-192-7(1))* Shanghai Calligraphy and Painting Publishing Hse.

Smith, Norman. Resisting Manchukuo: Chinese Women Writers & the Japanese Occupation. 2007. (ENG., Illus.). 216p. 85.00 *(978-0-7748-1335-8(0))* UBC Pr. CAN. Dist: Univ. of Washington Pr.

Stuckey, G. Andrew. Old Stories Retold: Narrative & Vanishing Pasts in Modern China. 2010. (ENG.). 210p. 62.99 *(978-0-7391-2362-1(9))* Lexington Bks.

Suoqiao, Qian. The Bilingual Essays of Lin Yutang. 2010. (ENG.). 352p. (gr. 17). pap. 20.00 *(978-962-996-435-1(X))* Chinese Univ. of Hong Kong, The HKG. Dist: Columbia Univ. Pr.

—Liberal Cosmopolitan: Lin Yutang & Middling Chinese Modernity. 2010. (Ideas, History, & Modern China Ser.). 271p. *(978-90-04-19213-3(1))* BRILL.

Sze, Arthur, ed. Chinese Writers on Writing. 2010. (Writer's World Ser.). (ENG.). 320p. 60.00 *(978-1-59534-062-7(9))*; pap. 18.95 *(978-1-59534-063-4(7))* Trinity Univ. Pr.

Tambling, Jeremy. Madmen & Other Survivors: Reading Lu Xun's Fiction. 2007. (ENG.). 136p. (gr. 17). 50.00 *(978-962-209-824-4(X))* Hong Kong Univ. Pr. HKG. Dist: Columbia Univ. Pr.

Tan, Tian Yuan. Songs of Contentment & Transgression: Discharged Officials & Literati Communities in Sixteenth-Century North China. 2010. (Harvard-Yenching Institute Monograph Ser.: 75). (ENG.). 314p. 39.95 *(978-0-674-05604-6(3))* Harvard Univ., Asia Ctr.

Tian, Xiaofei. Beacon Fire & Shooting Star: The Literary Culture of the Liang (502-557) 2007. (Harvard-Yenching Institute Monograph Ser.: 63). (Illus.). 450p. 49.50 *(978-0-674-02602-5(0))* Harvard Univ., Asia Ctr.

Tsu, Jing. Sound & Script in Chinese Diaspora. 2011. (ENG., Illus.). 320p. 45.00 *(978-0-674-05540-7(3))* Harvard Univ. Pr.

Tsu, Jing & Wang, David Der-wei, eds. Global Chinese Literature: Critical Essays. 2010. x, 231p. *(978-90-04-18765-8(0))* BRILL.

Tsu, Jing & Wang, Dewei, eds. Global Chinese Literature. 2010. (Chinese Overseas Ser.). x, 231p. pap., stu. ed. *(978-90-04-16905-0(9))* BRILL.

Wang, Dewei, et al. Yi Jiu Si Jiu Yi Hou. 2010. (CHI.). x, 531p. *(978-0-19-396127-2(X))* Oxford Univ. Pr., Inc.

Wang, Meng. Jin Gu de Ling Hun Yu Zheng Zha de Hui Xin: Wan Ming Zhi Minguo Nü Xing Chuang Zuo Zhu Ti Yi Shi Yan Jiu. 2009. (CHI.). 9p. *(978-7-81091-712-4(9))* Henan Univ. Pr.

Wang, Xirong & Qiao, Lihua. Lu Xun's Shaoxing: A Photo. 2010. 300p. 29.95 *(978-1-60220-303-7(2))* BetterLink Pr., Inc.

Watson, Burton. Early Chinese Literature. 2011. 314p. 50.95 ***(978-1-258-07487-6(7))*** Literary Licensing, LLC.

Wonhyo & Kim, Ho-Gwi. Kumgang Sammaegyong Non. 2010. (KOR.). 537p. *(978-89-26-81439-0(4))* Korean Studies Information Co., Ltd.

Wu, Hui. Once Iron Girls: Essays on Gender by Post-Mao Chinese Literary Women. (ENG.). 174p. 2011. pap. 27.95 *(978-0-7391-3422-1(1))* 2009. 57.99 *(978-0-7391-3421-4(3))* Lexington Bks.

Xu, Goomoo. Modern China & the World in the Ancient Prophecies. 2010. (Illus.). 260p. pap. 15.99 *(978-1-4490-3813-7(1))* AuthorHouse.

Yan, Haiping. Chinese Women Writers & the Feminist Imagination, 1905-1948. 2008. (Illus.). 320p. pap. 39.95 *(978-0-415-47458-0(2))* Routledge.

Yang, Jianhong. Xin Sheng, Xin Li, Xin Chao: Guan Yu Han Yu Wang Luo Wen Xue de Shen Shi Yu Si Kao. 2009. *(978-7-5649-0002-1(4))* Henan Univ. Pr.

Yang, Zhao. Wu Yu Hua: Zhan Hou Taiwan Wen Xue Shi San Lun. 2010. 597p. *(978-957-708-935-9(6))* Business Weekly Pubns., A Division of Cit'e Publishing, Ltd.

Yao, Dan, et al. Chinese Literature. 3rd ed. 2012. (Introductions to Chinese Culture Ser.). (ENG.). 260p. pap. 19.99 ***(978-0-521-18678-0(1))*** Cambridge Univ. Pr.

Yeung, Jessica. Ink Dances in Limbo: Gao Xingjian's Writing As Cultural Transition. 2008. (ENG.). 200p. (gr. 17). 50.00 *(978-962-209-921-0(1))* Hong Kong Univ. Pr. HKG. Dist: Columbia Univ. Pr.

Yip, Wai-lim. Zhongguo Xian Dai Xiao Shuo de Feng Mao. 2010. (CHI.). 245p. *(978-986-02-1274-7(0))* Academia Sinica.

Yoshida, Tomio. Yoshida Tomio Sensei Taikyu Kinen Chugokugaku Ronshu. 2008. (JPN., Illus.). xxviii, 521p. *(978-4-7629-2832-1(1))* Kyuko Shoin.

Yu, Anthony C. Comparative Journeys: Essays on Literature & Religion East & West. 2008. (Masters of Chinese Studies). (ENG.). 432p. (gr. 17). 55.00 *(978-0-231-14326-4(5))* Columbia Univ. Pr.

Yuan, Liangjun. Zhang Ailing Lun. 2010. (CHI.). 9p. *(978-7-80178-705-7(6))* Hua Ling Pr.

Zeitlin, Judith T. The Phantom Heroine: Ghosts & Gender in Seventeenth-Century Chinese Literature. 2007. (Illus.). 296p. 61.00 *(978-0-8248-3091-5(1))* Univ. of Hawaii Pr.

Zhang, Fa. Shi Jie Yu Jing Zhong de Zhongguo Wen Xue Li Lun. 2010. (CHI.). *(978-7-5336-5422-1(6))* Anhui Educational Publishing Hse.

Zhang, Fugui. "Huo Zhe" de Lu Xun: Lu Xun Wen Hua Xuan Ze de Dang Dai Yi Yi. 2010. (CHI.). 8p. *(978-7-5097-1326-6(9))* China Social Science Documentation Publishing Hse.

Zhang, Lianggao. Cao Xueqin Yi Shi Bian. 2009. (CHI & ENG.). 12p. *(978-7-112-11299-9(0))*; *(978-7-112-18428-6(2))* China Architecture & Building Pr.

Zhang, Lijun. Xiang Tu Zhongguo Xian Dai Xing de Wen Xue Xiang Xiang: Xian Dai Zuo Jia de Nong Min Guan Yu Nong Min Xing Xiang Shan Bian Yan Jiu. 2009. *(978-7-5426-3119-0(5))* SDX Joint Publishing, Co.

Zhang, Quanzhi. Xian Dai Shi Ye Zhong de Wen Xue Chao Xi: Xiandai Shiye Zhong de Wenxue Chaoxi. 2009. ix, 281p. *(978-7-80225-735-1(2))* New Star Publishing Hse.

Zhong, Xueping. Mainstream Culture Refocused: Television Drama, Society, & the Production of Meaning in Reform-Era China. 2010. 256p. 57.00 *(978-0-8248-3417-3(8))*; pap. 27.00 *(978-0-8248-3469-2(0))* Univ. of Hawaii Pr.

Zhou, Gang. Placing the Modern Chinese Vernacular in Transnational Literature. 2011. (ENG.). 190p. 84.00 *(978-0-230-10939-1(X))* Palgrave Macmillan.

Zhou, Hao. Representations of Cities in Republican-Era Chinese Literature. 2011. 116p. pap. ***(978-3-8443-1549-3(7))*** Lambert Academic Publishing.

Zhou, Jianming. Erzählstrategie in der Turmdarstellung der Deutschen Romantik und der Chinesischen Ming- und Qing-Dynastie: Eine Literarisch-Kulturelle Untersuchung. 2006. (GER.). 400p. (C). 68.00 *(978-3-89971-264-3(1))* Vandenhoeck & Ruprecht GmbH & Co. KG DEU. Dist: ISD.

Zhu, Aijun. Feminism & Global Chineseness: The Cultural Production of Controversial Women Authors. 2007. (ENG.). 356p. (C). 114.95 *(978-1-934043-12-7(5))* Cambria Pr.

Zhuang, Wanshou. Shi Tong Tong Lun. 2009. (CHI., Illus.). 16p. *(978-957-739-646-4(1))* Wan Juan Liou Books Co., Ltd.

Zicheng, Hong. A History of Contemporary Chinese Literature. Day, Michael M., tr. from CHI. 2007. (Brill's Humanities in China Library). 636p. *(978-90-04-15754-5(9))* BRILL.

CHINESE LITERATURE—POLITICAL ASPECTS

Zhang, Xudong. Postsocialism & Cultural Politics: China in the Last Decade of the Twentieth Century. 2008. (Post-Contemporary Interventions Ser.). (ENG., Illus.). 352p. (C). 94.95 *(978-0-8223-4212-0(X))*; pap. 26.95 *(978-0-8223-4230-4(8))* Duke Univ. Pr.

CHINESE LITERATURE—TRANSLATIONS

Findeisen, Raoul David, et al, eds. At Home in Many Worlds: Reading, Writing & Translating from Chinese & Jewish Cultures. 2010. (Veröffentlichungen des Ostasien-Instituts der Ruhr-Universität Bochum Ser.). (ENG.). 332p. (C). pap. 102.00 *(978-3-447-06135-3(9))* Harrassowitz, Otto Verlag DEU. Dist: ISD.

Ng, Elaine Yin Ling. Translating Style. 2010. 388p. pap. *(978-3-8383-6413-1(9))* Lambert Academic Publishing.

Pederzoli, Roberta. Écrire et Traduire Pour les Enfants: Voix, Images et Mots: Writing & Translating for Children: Voices, Images & Texts. Elefante, Chiara & Di Giovanni, Elena, eds. 2010. (FRE, ITA & ENG.). 343p. pap. 55.95 *(978-90-5201-660-3(7))* PIE - Peter Lang BEL. Dist: Lang, Peter.

Wanlong Gao. Recasting Lin Shu. 2009. 264p. pap. 20.21 *(978-1-4251-9221-1(1))* Trafford Publishing.

Wimsatt, Genevieve, et al, trs. The Lady of the Long Wall: A Ku Shih or Drum Song of China. 2011. 92p. 38.95 ***(978-1-258-05241-6(5))*** Literary Licensing, LLC.

CHINESE LITERATURE—TRANSLATIONS INTO ENGLISH

Anonymous. Chinese Literature: Comprising the Analects of Confucius, the Sayings of Mencius, the Shi-King, the Travels of Fa-Hien, & the Sorrows of Han. 2007. (ENG.). 366p. pap. 26.99 *(978-1-4264-3972-8(5))*; 328p. pap. 23.99 *(978-1-4264-3914-8(8))* BiblioBazaar.

Arnander, Christopher, et al. Pavillions in the Air: Chinese Proverbs & Their English Equivalents. 2008. (ENG., Illus.). 96p. 15.00 *(978-1-905299-67-6(2)*, Stacey International) Stacey Publishing GBR. Dist: Midpoint Trade Bks., Inc.

Beal, Samuel. A Catena of Buddhist Scriptures from the Chinese. 2010. (ENG.). 452p. pap. 36.75 *(978-1-177-39825-1(7))*; 498p. pap. 38.75 *(978-1-176-23354-6(8))* BiblioBazaar.

—A Catena of Buddhist Scriptures from the Chinese. 2010. 326p. pap. *(978-1-151-93706-3(1))* Books LLC.

—A Catena of Buddhist Scriptures from the Chinese. 2010. 452p. 42.36 *(978-1-163-21917-1(7))*; pap. 30.36 *(978-1-162-73125-4(7))* Kessinger Publishing, LLC.

Hogg, James, et al. A Chronology of Translation in China & the West: From the Legendary Period To 2004. Francis, David et al, eds. 2009. (ENG.). 600p. (gr. 17). 55.00 *(978-962-996-355-2(8))* Chinese Univ. of Hong Kong, The HKG. Dist: Columbia Univ. Pr.

Hong, Xiao. The Field of Life & Death & Tales of Hulun River. Goldblatt, Howard, tr. from CHI. rev. ed. 2006. 384p. pap. 29.95 *(978-0-88727-392-6(0))* Cheng & Tsui Co.

Jia, Zongpei & Xiu, Xiaolin. Selected Short Stories China. 2010. 322p. pap. 20.00 *(978-7-5321-2773-3(7))* BetterLink Pr., Inc.

Lau, Joseph S. M. & Goldblatt, Howard, eds. The Columbia Anthology of Modern Chinese Literature. 2nd ed. 2007. (Modern Asian Literature Ser.). (ENG.). 784p. (gr. 17). pap. 37.50 *(978-0-231-13841-3(5))*; (Illus.). 105.00 *(978-0-231-13840-6(7))* Columbia Univ. Pr.

Legge, James. The Chinese Classics: With a Translation, Critical & Exegetical Notes, Prolegomena, & Copious Indexes. 2010. 538p. pap. 40.75 *(978-1-145-83911-3(8))* BiblioBazaar.

—The Chinese Classics, Tr into English, with Preliminary Essays & Explanatory Notes by James Legge. 2006. 344p. per. 23.99 *(978-1-4255-3502-5(X))* MPublishing.

Lu, Xun, et al. The Power of Weakness: Four Stories of the Chinese Revolution. 2007. (Two by Two Ser.). (ENG.). 96p. pap. 12.95 *(978-1-55861-548-9(2))* Feminist Pr. at The City Univ. of New York.

Mair, Victor H. & Bender, Mark, eds. The Columbia Anthology of Chinese Folk & Popular Literature. 2011. (Translations from the Asian Classics Ser.). (ENG., Illus.). 800p. (gr. 17). 105.00 *(978-0-231-15312-6(0))*; pap. 37.50 *(978-0-231-15313-3(9))* Columbia Univ. Pr.

Mencius. Mencius. Bloom, Irene, tr. from CHI. 2009. (Translations from the Asian Classics Ser.). (ENG.). 208p. (gr. 17). 29.50 *(978-0-231-12204-7(7))* Columbia Univ. Pr.

Menglong, Feng. Stories to Caution the World, Vol. 2. Yang, Shuhui & Yang, Yunqin, trs. from CHI. 2007. (ENG.). 792p. per. 50.00 *(978-0-295-98568-8(2))* Univ. of Washington Pr.

Pan, Xiangli. Chinese Women. 2010. 196p. pap. 15.00 *(978-7-5321-2772-6(9))* BetterLink Pr., Inc.

Shanghai Writers Association. The City, the People. 2010. (Wen Hua Zhongguo = Cultural China Ser.). 340p. pap. 22.95 *(978-1-60220-200-9(1))* BetterLink Pr., Inc.

Sze, Arthur, ed. Chinese Writers on Writing. 2010. (Writer's World Ser.). (ENG.). 320p. 60.00 *(978-1-59534-062-7(9))*; pap. 18.95 *(978-1-59534-063-4(7))* Trinity Univ. Pr.

To Wang Chen, Chihling. Traditional Chinese Tales. 2006. 240p. per. *(978-1-4067-3718-9(6)*, Hesperides Pr.) Read Bks.

Wang, Hui. Translating Chinese Classics in a Colonial Context: James Legge & His Two Versions of the Zhongyong. 2008. (Welten Ostasiens / Worlds of East Asia / Mondes de l'Extrême-Orient Ser.). 224p. *(978-3-03911-631-7(2))* Lang, Peter.

Xiaobin, Xu. Dunhuang Dream. 2011. (ENG.). 208p. pap. 15.00 *(978-1-4165-8390-5(4)*, Beyond Words/Atria Bks.) Atria Bks.

Xiaobo, Wang. Wang in Love & Bondage: Three Novellas by Wang Xiaobo. Sommer, Jason & Zhang, Hongling, trs. from CHI. 2007. 155p. 26.00 *(978-0-7914-7065-7(2))* State Univ. of New York Pr.

Xu, Yigua. The Sprinkler. 2010. 142p. pap. 12.95 *(978-1-60220-922-0(7))* BetterLink Pr., Inc.

Yang, Shuhui & Yang, Yunqin, trs. from CHI. Stories to Awaken the World, Vol. 3. 2009. (ENG.). 992p. 100.00 *(978-0-295-98903-7(3))* Univ. of Washington Pr.

CHINESE LITERATURE—TRANSLATIONS INTO GERMAN

Bieg, Lutz. Bibliographie zur chinesischen Literatur in deutscher Sprache Vol. 8. rev. ed. 2006. (GER.). 400p. *(978-3-598-24548-0(3))* Saur, K. G. Verlag GmbH & Co.

CHINESE LOGOGRAPHS

see Chinese Characters

CHINESE MATHEMATICS

see Mathematics, Chinese

CHINESE MEDICINE

see Medicine, Chinese

CHINESE MUSIC

see Music, Chinese

CHINESE MYTHOLOGY

see Mythology, Chinese

CHINESE NEWSPAPERS

Contemporary China Institute. A Bibliography of Chinese Newspapers & Periodicals in European Libraries. 2011. (Contemporary China Institute Publications). (ENG.). 1114p. pap. 78.00 *(978-0-521-18886-9(5))* Cambridge Univ. Pr.

Su, Yingkui. Yun Ling Xie Ying: Yunnan Xin Wen Chu Ban Ye Gai Ge Kai Fang 30 Nian Hui Gu. 2008. (CHI.). *(978-7-81112-595-5(1))* Yunnan Univ. Pr.

Taaks, Christian. Federführung für die Nation ohne Vorbehalt: Deutsche Medien in China während der Zeit des Nationalsozialismus. 2009. (Beitrage zur Kommunikationsgeschichte (BKG) Ser.). (GER.). 664p. (C). 124.00 *(978-3-515-08739-1(7))* Steiner, Franz Verlag Wiesbaden GmbH DEU. Dist: Brown, David Bk. Co., The.

Wagner, Rudolf G. Joining the Global Public: Word, Image, & City in Early Chinese Newspapers, 1870-1910. 2008. (CHI & ENG., Illus.). ix, 249p. pap. 29.95 *(978-0-7914-7118-0(7))* State Univ. of New York Pr.

Wagner, Rudolf G., ed. Joining the Global Public: Word, Image, & City in Early Chinese Newspapers, 1870-1910. 2007. (SUNY Series in Chinese Philosophy & Culture). (CHI & ENG., Illus.). 249p. 80.00 *(978-0-7914-7117-3(9))* State Univ. of New York Pr.

CHINESE PAINTING

see Painting, Chinese

CHINESE PERIODICALS

Contemporary China Institute. A Bibliography of Chinese Newspapers & Periodicals in European Libraries. 2011. (Contemporary China Institute Publications). (ENG.). 1114p. pap. 78.00 *(978-0-521-18886-9(5))* Cambridge Univ. Pr.

Taaks, Christian. Federführung für die Nation ohne Vorbehalt: Deutsche Medien in China während der Zeit des Nationalsozialismus. 2009. (Beitrage zur Kommunikationsgeschichte (BKG) Ser.). (GER.). 664p. (C). 124.00 *(978-3-515-08739-1(7))* Steiner, Franz Verlag Wiesbaden GmbH DEU. Dist: Brown, David Bk. Co., The.

CHINESE PHILOSOPHY

see Philosophy, Chinese

CHINESE POETRY

Lin, Julia C., ed. & tr. Twentieth-Century Chinese Women's Poetry: An Anthology. 2009. (ENG.). 272p. 74.95 *(978-0-7656-2368-3(4))*, East Gate Bk.) Sharpe, M.E. Inc.

Sun, Seunghye. The Lure of Painted Poetry: Japanese & Korean Art. 2011. (Illus.). 109p. ***(978-1-935294-04-7(0))*** Cleveland Museum of Art.

Wadell, Helen. Lyrics from the Chinese. pap. 6.00 *(978-0-87957-003-3(2))* Brookville Bks.

YeShell. How to Write Classical Chinese Poems (Chinese Version, CQ Size) 2009. (CHI.). 86p. pap. 9.98 *(978-0-557-05247-9(5))* Lulu Enterprises Inc.

Zhongguo min jian wen xue ji cheng quan guo bian ji wei yuan hui Staff & Zhongguo ge yao ji cheng Anhui juan bian ji wei yuan hui Staff, contrib. by. Zhongguo Ge Yao Ji Cheng. 2008. (CHI., Illus.). 10p. *(978-7-5076-0307-1(5))* China ISBN Agency.

Zhongguo min jian wen xue ji cheng quan guo bian ji wei yuan hui Staff & Zhongguo ge yao ji cheng Heilongjiang juan bian ji wei yuan hui Staff, contrib. by. Zhongguo Ge Yao Ji Cheng. 2007. (CHI., Illus.). 10p. *(978-7-5076-0305-7(9))* China ISBN Agency.

Zhongguo min jian wen xue ji cheng quan guo bian ji wei yuan hui Staff & Zhongguo ge yao ji cheng Hubei juan bian ji wei yuan hui Staff, contrib. by. Zhongguo Ge Yao Ji Cheng. 2009. (CHI., Illus.). 10p. *(978-7-5076-0230-2(3))* China ISBN Agency.

Zhongguo min jian wen xue ji cheng quan guo bian ji wei yuan hui Staff & Zhongguo ge yao ji cheng Liaoning juan bian ji wei yuan hui Staff, contrib. by. Zhongguo Ge Yao Ji Cheng. 2008. (CHI., Illus.). 10p. *(978-7-5076-0303-3(2))* China ISBN Agency.

Zhongguo min jian wen xue ji cheng quan guo bian ji wei yuan hui Staff & Zhongguo ge yao ji cheng Neimenggu juan bian ji wei yuan hui Staff, contrib. by. Zhongguo Ge Yao Ji Cheng. 2007. (CHI., Illus.). 10p. *(978-7-5076-0302-6(4))* China ISBN Agency.

Zhongguo min jian wen xue ji cheng quan guo bian ji wei yuan hui Staff & Zhongguo ge yao ji cheng Qinghai juan bian ji wei yuan hui Staff, contrib. by. Zhongguo Ge Yao Ji Cheng. 2008. (CHI., Illus.). 10p. *(978-7-5076-0313-2(X))* China ISBN Agency.

Zhongguo min jian wen xue ji cheng quan guo bian ji wei yuan hui Staff & Zhongguo ge yao ji cheng Shanxi juan bian ji wei yuan hui (Shaanxi Sheng, China) Staff, contrib. by. Zhongguo Ge Yao Ji Cheng. 2009. (CHI., Illus.). 10p. *(978-7-5076-0311-8(3))* China ISBN Agency.

Zhongguo min jian wen xue ji cheng quan guo bian ji wei yuan hui Staff & Zhongguo ge yao ji cheng Shanxi juan bian ji wei yuan hui Staff, contrib. by. Zhongguo Ge Yao Ji Cheng. 2009. (CHI., Illus.). 10p. *(978-7-5076-0301-9(6))* China ISBN Agency.

Zhongguo min jian wen xue ji cheng quan guo bian ji wei yuan hui Staff & Zhongguo ge yao ji cheng Tianjin juan bian ji wei yuan hui Staff, contrib. by. Zhongguo Ge Yao Ji Cheng. 2008. (CHI., Illus.). 808p. *(978-7-5076-0300-2(8))* China ISBN Agency.

Zhongguo min jian wen xue ji cheng quan guo bian ji wei yuan hui Staff & Zhongguo ge yao ji cheng Xinjiang juan bian ji wei yuan hui Staff, contrib. by. Zhongguo Ge Yao Ji Cheng, 2 vols. 2009. (CHI., Illus.). 10p. *(978-7-5076-0312-5(1))* China ISBN Agency.

CHINESE POETRY—HISTORY AND CRITICISM

Ashmore, Robert. The Transport of Reading: Text & Understanding in the World of Tao Qian (365 - 427) 2010. (Harvard East Asian Monographs: 327). (ENG.). 275p. 39.95 *(978-0-674-05321-2(4))* Harvard Univ., Asia Ctr.

Au, Chung-to. Modernist Aesthetics in Taiwanese Poetry since The 1950s. 2008. (Sinica Leidensia Ser.). (Illus.). 225p. *(978-90-04-16707-0(2))* BRILL.

Bryant, D. The Great Recreation: Ho Ching-ming (1483-1521) & His World. 2008. (Sinica Leidensia Ser.). 800p. *(978-90-04-16817-6(6))* BRILL.

Cai, Zong-Qi & Cui, Jie. How to Read Chinese Poetry Workbook. 2012. (ENG & CHI.). 232p. (gr. 17). pap. 25.00 ***(978-0-231-15658-5(8))*** Columbia Univ. Pr.

Chan, Timothy Wai Keung. Considering the End: Mortality in Early Medieval Chinese Poetic Representation. 2012. ***(978-90-04-22209-0(X))*** BRILL.

Chen, Jack W. The Poetics of Sovereignty: On Emperor Taizong of the Tang Dynasty. 2011. (Harvard-Yenching Institute Monograph Ser.: 71). (ENG.). 468p. 49.95 *(978-0-674-05608-4(6))* Harvard Univ., Asia Ctr.

Chen, Zhiping. Chen Xianzhang Shu Ji Yan Jiu. 2009. (CHI., Illus.). 10p. *(978-7-5010-2887-0(7))* Cultural Relics Publishing Hse.

Crespi, John A. Voices in Revolution: Poetry & the Auditory Imagination in Modern China. 2009. 240p. (C). 47.00 *(978-0-8248-3365-7(1))* Univ. of Hawaii Pr.

Crevel, M. van, ed. Chinese Poetry in Times of Mind, Mayhem & Money. 2008. (Sinica Leidensia Ser.). 500p. (C). *(978-90-04-16382-9(4))* BRILL.

Davis, A. R. T'ao Yüan-Ming: Additional Commentary, Notes & Biography - His Works & their Meaning. 2009. (Cambridge Studies in Chinese History, Literature & Institutions Ser.). (ENG.). 232p. pap. 34.99 *(978-0-521-10453-1(X))* Cambridge Univ. Pr.

—Translation & Commentary: His Works & Their Meaning. 2009. (Cambridge Studies in Chinese History, Literature & Institutions Ser.). (ENG.). 280p. pap. 38.99 *(978-0-521-10452-4(1))* Cambridge Univ. Pr.

Ding, Xuhui. Taiwan Xian Dai Shi Zhong de Lao Zhuang Shen Ying Yu Dao Jia Mei Xue Shi Jian. 2010. (CHI.). 9p. *(978-986-6327-08-7(6))* Chun Hui Pr.

Fang, Rixi. Song Ci Bi Jiao Yan Jiu. 2010. (CHI.). *(978-7-81110-706-7(6))* Anhui Univ. Pr.

Fenollosa, Ernest. The Chinese Written Character As a Medium for Poetry. Pound, Ezra, ed. 2011. 48p. 35.95 ***(978-1-258-02340-9(7))*** Literary Licensing, LLC.

Fenollosa, Ernest. The Chinese Written Character As a Medium for Poetry: A Critical Edition. Klein, Lucas & Saussy, Haun, eds. 2010. (ENG., Illus.). 256p. pap. 19.00 *(978-0-8232-2869-0(X))* Fordham Univ. Pr.

Fenollosa, Ernest, et al. The Chinese Written Character As a Medium for Poetry. Saussy, Haun & Stalling, Joseph, eds. 3rd ed. 2008. (CHI & ENG., Illus.). 256p. 28.00 *(978-0-8232-2868-3(1))* Fordham Univ. Pr.

Goh, Meow. Sound & Sight: Poetry & Courtier Culture in the Yongming Era (483-493) 2010. (ENG.). 208p. 50.00 *(978-0-8047-6859-7(5))* Stanford Univ. Pr.

Hart, Henry H. The Hundred Names: A Short Introduction to the Study of Chinese Poetry. 2011. 240p. 46.95 ***(978-1-258-05000-9(5))*** Literary Licensing, LLC.

Holzman, Donald. Poetry & Politics: The Life & Works of Juan Chi, A. D. 210-263. 2009. (Cambridge Studies in Chinese History, Literature & Institutions Ser.). (ENG.). 332p. pap. 36.99 *(978-0-521-10256-8(1))* Cambridge Univ. Pr.

Huang, Qijiang. Yi Wei Chan Yu Jiang Hu Shi: Nan Song Wen Xue Seng Yu Chan Wen Hua de Tui Bian. 2010. (CHI.). *(978-957-05-2487-1(1))* Commercial Pr. Ltd., The.

Hughes, E. R. Two Chinese Poets: Vignettes of Han Life & Thought. 2011. 282p. 47.95 ***(978-1-258-10344-6(3))*** Literary Licensing, LLC.

Kelen, Christopher. Spring Wind Brings the Fireworks. Vong, Agnes, tr. 2007. (ENG & CHI.). 176p. per. 15.00 *(978-0-9772974-9-8(7))* Virtual Artists Collective.

Kroll, Paul W. Essays in medieval chinese literature & cultural History. 2009. (Variorum Collected Studies). (Illus.). 362p. 170.00 *(978-0-7546-5990-7(9))* Ashgate Publishing Co.

—Studies in medieval taoism & the poetry of li Po. 2009. (Variorum Collected Studies). (Illus.). 374p. 170.00 *(978-0-7546-5989-1(5))* Ashgate Publishing Co.

Lin, Julia C., ed. & tr. Twentieth-Century Chinese Women's Poetry: An Anthology. 2009. (ENG.). 272p. pap. 26.95 *(978-0-7656-2369-0(2))*, East Gate Bk.) Sharpe, M.E. Inc.

Lupke, Christopher. New Perspectives on Contemporary Chinese Poetry. 2007. (ENG., Illus.) 256p. 95.00 *(978-1-4039-7607-9(4))* Palgrave Macmillan.

Mei, Zhencai. Wen Ge Shi Ci Gou Chen. 2010. (CHI., Illus.). 534p. ***(978-962-8744-48-0(8))*** Mirror Bks. USA.

Meng, Liuxi. Poetry as Power: Yuan Mei's Female Disciple Qu Bingyun (1767-1810) 2007. (ENG., Illus.). 246p. 68.50 *(978-0-7391-1257-1(0))* Lexington Bks.

Nugent, Christopher M. B. Manifest in Words, Written on Paper: Producing & Circulating Poetry in Tang Dynasty China. 2011. (Harvard-Yenching Institute Monograph Ser.: 70). (ENG., Illus.). 360p. 39.95 *(978-0-674-05603-9(5))* Harvard Univ., Asia Ctr.

Owen, Stephen. The Making of Early Chinese Classical Poetry. 2006. (Harvard East Asian Monographs: 261). (Illus.). 370p. 49.95 *(978-0-674-02136-5(3))* Harvard Univ., Asia Ctr.

Pan, Daan. The Lyrical Resonance of Chinese Poets & Painters: The Tradition & Poetics of Tihuashi. 2011. *(978-1-60497-741-7(8))* Cambria Pr.

Parry, Amie Elizabeth. Interventions into Modernist Cultures: Poetry from Beyond the Empty Screen. 2007. (Perverse Modernities Ser.). (ENG., 200p. Illus.). 79.95 *(978-0-8223-3803-1(3))*; per. 22.95 *(978-0-8223-3818-5(1))* Duke Univ. Pr.

Qian, Zhaoming, ed. Ezra Pound's Chinese Friends: Stories in Letters. 2008. (ENG., Illus.). 272p. 39.95 *(978-0-19-923860-6(X))* Oxford Univ. Pr., Inc.

Ricci, Roslyn Joy. Romancing the Chinese Characters in Classical Chinese Poetry. 2010. 92p. pap. *(978-3-639-23949-2(0))* VDM Verlag Dr. Mueller e.K.

Sargent, Stuart H. The Poetry of He Zhu (1052-1152) Genres, Contexts, & Creativity. 2007. (Sinica Leidensia Ser.: Vol. 74). (CHI & ENG., Illus.). 502p. *(978-90-04-15711-8(5))* BRILL.

Schmidt, J. D. Within the Human Realm: The Poetry of Huang Zunxian, 1848-1905. 2007. (Cambridge Studies in Chinese History, Literature & Institutions Ser.). (CHI & ENG.). 368p. pap. 47.00 *(978-0-521-03666-5(6))* Cambridge Univ. Pr.

Stearns, Peter & Hwa, Lily. Ban Zhao. 2006. 192p. (C). pap. 20.00 *(978-0-321-24807-7(4))* Longman Publishing.

Sun, Cecile Chu-Chin. The Poetics of Repetition in English & Chinese Lyric Poetry. 2011. (ENG., Illus.). 304p. 45.00 *(978-0-226-78020-7(1))* Univ. of Chicago Pr.

Sun, Yushi. Zhongguo Xian Dai Shi Xue Cong Lun. 2010. (CHI.). *(978-7-301-15930-9(7))* Beijing University Pr.

Swartz, Wendy. Reading Tao Yuanming: Shifting Paradigms of Historical Reception (427 - 1900) 2008. (Harvard East Asian Monographs: 306). (Illus.). 350p. 49.95 *(978-0-674-03184-5(9))* Harvard Univ., Asia Ctr.

van Crevel, Maghiel. Chinese Poetry in Times of Mind, Mayhem & Money. 2011. 518p. pap. ***(978-90-04-20563-5(2))*** BRILL.

Wang, Yugen. Ten Thousand Scrolls: Reading & Writing in the Poetics of Huang Tingjian & the Late Northern Song. 2011. (Harvard-Yenching Institute Monograph Ser.: 76). (ENG.). 300p. 39.95 *(978-0-674-06255-9(8))* Harvard Univ., Asia Ctr.

Wong, Lisa Lai-Ming. Rays of the Searching Sun: The Transcultural Poetics of Yang Mu. 2009. (Nouvelle poétique comparatiste - New Comparative Poetics Ser.). 300p. pap. 50.95 *(978-90-5201-545-3(7))* PIE - Peter Lang BEL. Dist: Lang, Peter.

Wu, Fusheng. Written at Imperial Command: Panegyric Poetry in Early Medieval China. 2008. (SUNY Series in Chinese Philosophy & Culture). 289p. 80.00 *(978-0-7914-7369-6(4))* State Univ. of New York Pr.

Wu, Fusheng & WJ, F. Written at Imperial Comm: Panegyric Poetry in Early Medieval China. 2009. (SUNY Series in Chinese Philosophy & Culture). 299p. pap. 29.95 *(978-0-7914-7370-2(8))* State Univ. of New York Pr.

Xiaolong, Qiu. 100 Poems from Tang & Song Dynasties. 2009. 232p. pap. 22.95 *(978-1-60652-029-1(6))* Reader's Digest Assn., Inc., The.

Yan, Zhixiong & Yim, Lawrence C. H. The Poet-historian Qian Qianyi. 2009. (Academia Sinica on East Asia Ser.). (ENG., Illus.). 240p. (C). 130.00 *(978-0-415-49460-1(5))* Routledge.

Yang, Jingqing, et al. The Chan Interpretations of Wang Wei's Poetry: A Critical Review. 2007. (ENG., Illus.). 380p. (gr. 17). 45.00 *(978-962-996-232-6(2))* Chinese Univ. of Hong Kong, The HKG. Dist: Columbia Univ. Pr.

Zheng, Yi. From Burke & Wordsworth to the Modern Sublime in Chinese Literature. 2011. (Comparative Cultural Studies). 148p. pap. 39.95 *(978-1-55753-576-4(0))* Purdue Univ. Pr.

Zhongguo qu yi zhi quan guo bian ji wei yuan hui Staff & "Zhongguo qu yi zhi, Guangdong juan" bian ji wei yuan hui Staff, contrib. by. Zhongguo Qu Yi Zhi. 2008. (CHI., Illus.). *(978-7-5076-0268-5(0))* China ISBN Agency.

Zhongguo qu yi zhi quan guo bian ji wei yuan hui Staff & "Zhongguo qu yi zhi, Jiangxi juan" bian ji wei yuan hui Staff, contrib. by. Zhongguo Qu Yi Zhi. 2008. (CHI., Illus.). *(978-7-5076-0270-8(2))* China ISBN Agency.

Zhongguo qu yi zhi quan guo bian ji wei yuan hui Staff & "Zhongguo qu yi zhi, Ningxia juan" bian ji wei yuan hui Staff, contrib. by. Zhongguo Qu Yi Zhi. 2008. (CHI., Illus.). *(978-7-5076-0260-9(5))* China ISBN Agency.

Zhongguo qu yi zhi quan guo bian ji wei yuan hui Staff & "Zhongguo qu yi zhi, Zhejiang juan" bian ji wei yuan hui Staff, contrib. by. Zhongguo Qu Yi Zhi. 2009. (CHI., Illus.). *(978-7-5076-0226-5(5))* China ISBN Agency.

CHINESE POETRY—TRANSLATIONS INTO ENGLISH

Barnstone, Tony & Ping, Chou, eds. Chinese Erotic Poems. Barnstone, Tony & Ping, Chou, trs. from CHI. 2007. (Everyman's Library Pocket Poets Ser.). (ENG.). 256p. 12.50 *(978-0-307-26567-8(6)*, Everyman's Library) Knopf Doubleday Publishing Group.

Bullett, Gerald. The Golden Year of Fan Cheng-Ta: A Chinese Rural Sequence Rendered into English Verse. 2011. (ENG.). 46p. pap. 21.99 *(978-1-107-67923-8(0))* Cambridge Univ. Pr.

Cai, Zong-Qi & Cui, Jie. How to Read Chinese Poetry Workbook. 2012. (ENG & CHI.). 232p. (gr. 17). pap. 25.00 ***(978-0-231-15658-5(8))*** Columbia Univ. Pr.

Carson, Anne. Songs of Love, Moon, & Wind: Poems from the Chinese. Weinberger, Eliot, ed. Rexroth, Kenneth, tr. from CHI. 2009. (CHI & ENG.). 96p. pap. 12.95 *(978-0-8112-1836-8(8)*, 21836) New Directions Publishing Corp.

Chan, Hong-Mo. The Birth of China Seen Through Poetry. 2011. 264p. pap. 22.00 *(978-981-4335-33-1(9))* World Scientific Publishing Co., Inc.

Chu, Charles. Clouds Thick, Whereabouts Unknown. Egan, Charles, tr. 2010. (Translations from the Asian Classics Ser.). (ENG & CHI., Illus.). 328p. (gr. 17). 99.50 *(978-0-231-15038-5(5))* Columbia Univ. Pr.

—Clouds Thick, Whereabouts Unknown: Poems by Zen Monks of China. Egan, Charles, tr. 2010. (Translations from the Asian Classics Ser.). (ENG & CHI., Illus.). 328p. (gr. 17). pap. 29.50 *(978-0-231-15039-2(3))* Columbia Univ. Pr.

Davis, A. R. T'ao Yüan-Ming: Additional Commentary, Notes & Biography - His Works & their Meaning. 2009. (Cambridge Studies in Chinese History, Literature & Institutions Ser.). (ENG.). 232p. pap. 34.99 *(978-0-521-10453-1(X))* Cambridge Univ. Pr.

—Translation & Commentary: His Works & Their Meaning. 2009. (Cambridge Studies in Chinese History, Literature & Institutions Ser.). (ENG.). 280p. pap. 38.99 *(978-0-521-10452-4(1))* Cambridge Univ. Pr.

Du, Fu. Du Fu: A Life in Poetry. Young, David, tr. from CHI. 2008. (ENG., Illus.). 256p. pap. 17.95 *(978-0-375-71160-2(0))*, Knopf) Knopf Doubleday Publishing Group.

Er, Zhang & Dongdong, Chen, eds. Another Kind of Nation: An Anthology of Contemporary Chinese Poetry. 2007. 451p. pap. 25.95 *(978-1-58498-057-5(5))* Talisman Hse., Pubs.

Graham, A. C., tr. from CHI. Poems of the Late T'ang. 2008. (New York Review Books Classics). (ENG.). 184p. pap. 14.95 *(978-1-59017-257-5(4))* New York Review of Bks., Inc., The.

Han Shan. Cold Mountain Poems: Zen Poems of Han Shan, Shih-Te, & Wang Fan-Chih. Seaton, J. P., tr. from CHI. 2009. (Shambhala Library). (ENG.). 192p. 18.95 *(978-1-59030-646-8(5))* Shambhala Pubns., Inc.

Hargett, James M. & Huang, Xiyi. Riding the River Home: A Complete & Annotated Translation of Fan Chengda's (1126 — 1193) Travel Diary Record of a Boat Trip to Wu (Wuchuan Lu) 2008. (ENG., Illus.). 400p. (gr. 17). 55.00 *(978-962-996-302-6(7))* Chinese Univ. of Hong Kong, The HKG. Dist: Columbia Univ. Pr.

Hart, Henry H. The Hundred Names: A Short Introduction to the Study of Chinese Poetry. 2011. 240p. 46.95 ***(978-1-258-05000-9(5))*** Literary Licensing, LLC.

Hinton, David. Classical Chinese Poetry: An Anthology. 2010. (ENG., Illus.) 512p. pap. 25.00 *(978-0-374-53190-4(0))* Farrar, Straus & Giroux.

Idema, Wilt L., tr. from CHI. Heroines of Jiangyong: Chinese Narrative Ballads in Women's Script. 2009. (ENG., Illus.). 192p. 60.00 *(978-0-295-98841-2(X))*; pap. 25.00 *(978-0-295-98842-9(8))* Univ. of Washington Pr.

Kelen, Christopher. Spring Wind Brings the Fireworks. Vong, Agnes, tr. 2007. (ENG & CHI.). 176p. per. 15.00 *(978-0-9772974-9-8(7))* Virtual Artists Collective.

Lian, Yang & Herbert, W. N. Jade Ladder? 2012. (ENG.). 320p. 26.95 ***(978-1-85224-895-5(5))*** Bloodaxe Bks. GBR. Dist: Dufour Editions, Inc.

Monro, Alex. China. 2011. (Poetry of Place Ser.). (ENG.). 80p. pap. 16.95 *(978-1-906011-30-7(3))* Eland Bks. GBR. Dist: Dufour Editions, Inc.

Qian, Zhaoming, ed. Ezra Pound's Chinese Friends: Stories in Letters. 2008. (ENG., Illus.). 272p. 39.95 *(978-0-19-923860-6(X))* Oxford Univ. Pr., Inc.

Shanghai Writers Association. Voices from the Sea: An. 2010. 152p. 21.95 *(978-1-60220-205-4(2))* BetterLink Pr., Inc.

Stoehr, Taylor. I Hear My Gate Slam: Chinese Poets Meeting & Parting. 2007. 138p. pap. 12.00 *(978-0-9785156-2-1(5))* Pressed Wafer Pr.

Waley, Arthur. More Translations from the Chinese. 2009. 82p. pap. *(978-0-217-26264-4(3))* Books LLC.

—More Translations from the Chinese. 2008. 80p. pap. *(978-1-4068-7520-1(1))* Echo Library.

Wang, Qingping, ed. Push Open the Window: Contemporary Poetry from China. 2011. (ENG.). 450p. pap. 23.00 ***(978-1-55659-330-7(9))*** Copper Canyon Pr.

Ward, Jean Elizabeth. Wang wei: Remembered. 2008. 150p. pap. 23.50 *(978-1-4357-3272-8(3))* Lulu Enterprises Inc.

Xiaolong, Qiu. Evoking Tang. 2007. (ENG.). 176p. pap. 16.95 *(978-0-9760675-1-1(X))* PenUltimate Press, Inc.

—100 Poems from Tang & Song Dynasties. 2009. 232p. pap. 22.95 *(978-1-60652-029-1(6))* Reader's Digest Assn., Inc., The.

Zi, Hai. Over Autumn Rooftops. Murphy, Dan, tr. 2010. (ENG & CHI.). 271p. 35.00 *(978-0-924047-75-6(5))*; pap. 15.00 *(978-0-924047-76-3(3))* Host Pubns., Inc.

CHINESE PORCELAIN

see Porcelain, Chinese

CHINESE POTTERY

see Pottery, Chinese

CHINESE PROPAGANDA

see Propaganda, Chinese

CHINESE QUESTION

see China—History; Eastern Question (Far East)

CHINESE REUNIFICATION QUESTION, 1949-

Leehy, Anthony G., et al. Military & Security Developments in China. 2012. ***(978-1-61942-009-0(0))*** Nova Science Pubs., Inc.

Li, Xiaohui. Kun Ju Yu Tu Po: Xianggang Nan Dian Wen Ti Zhuan Ti Yan Jiu. 2010. 440p. *(978-988-219-140-2(1))* Cosmos Bks. Ltd.

Li, Yu-Sheng. Equivocation in 'Reunification' for Taiwan & Mainland Chin. 2010. 360p. pap. *(978-3-8383-7795-7(8))* Lambert Academic Publishing.

Mastro, Oriana Skylar, told to. Assessing the Threat: The Chinese Military & Taiwan's Security. 2007. (ENG., Illus.). 413p. per. 22.95 *(978-0-87003-238-7(0))* Carnegie Endowment for International Peace.

Myers, Ramon Hawley & Zhang, Jialin. The Struggle Across the Taiwan Strait: The Divided China Problem. 2006. (Hoover Institution Press Publication Ser.: Vol. 542). 168p. per. 15.00 *(978-0-8179-4692-0(6))* Hoover Institution Pr.

Su, Chi. Taiwan's Relations with Mainland China. 2010. (ENG., Illus.). 368p. (C). pap. 39.95 *(978-0-415-58999-4(1))* Routledge.

—Taiwan's Relations with Mainland China: A Tail Wagging Two Dogs. 2008. (Routledge Contemporary Asia Ser.). (Illus.). XX, 348p. 150.00 *(978-0-415-46454-3(4))* Routledge.

Tian, Henlan & Chen, Qiwen. Tai Hai Chun Qiu. 2009. (CHI.). *(978-7-80141-619-3(8))* Taihai Publishing House.

Tkacik, John. Reshaping the Taiwan Strait. 2007. 222p. *(978-0-89195-275-6(6))* Heritage Foundation.

Tung, Chen-yuan. Cross-Strait Economic Relations in the Era of Globalization. 2008. 508p. pap. *(978-3-639-09125-0(6))* VDM Verlag Dr. Mueller e.K.

Zhou, Zhongfei. "Tai Du" de Guo Ji Bei Jing. 2009. *(978-7-80195-990-4(6))* Jiuzhou Publishing Hse.

CHINESE RITES

Here are entered works dealing with the controversy concerning the participation of Christian converts in Chinese rites and ceremonies.

Dunne, George H. Generation of Giants: The Story of the Jesuits in China in the Last Decades of the Ming Dynasty. 2007. (ENG., Illus.). 416p. 49.95 *(978-0-548-07792-4(4))* Kessinger Publishing, LLC.

CHINESE SHADOWS

see Shadow Shows

CHINESE SHAR-PEI

Linzy, Jan & Pata, Sharae. Chinese Shar Pei Champions, 2001-2005. 2006. (Illus.). 165p. spiral bd. 46.95 *(978-1-55893-202-9(X))* Camino E.E. & Bk. Co.

CHINESE SONGS

see Songs, Chinese

CHINESE STUDIES

see China—Study and Teaching

CHINESE WIT AND HUMOR

Davis, Jessica Milner & Chey, Jocelyn. Humour in Chinese Life & Letters: Classical & Traditional Approaches. 2011. 320p. ***(978-988-8053-94-0(9))*** Hong Kong Univ. Pr.

—Humour in Chinese Life & Letters: Classical & Traditional Approaches. 2011. (ENG., Illus.). 312p. (gr. 17). 60.00 ***(978-988-8083-51-0(1))***; pap. 25.00 ***(978-988-8083-52-7(X))*** Hong Kong Univ. Pr. HKG. Dist: Columbia Univ. Pr.

Ristaino, Marcia R. China's Intrepid Muse. 2009. (ENG.). 176p. pap. 40.00 *(978-1-891640-57-5(7))* Floating World Editions.

CH'ING HSUAN-TUNG, EMPEROR OF CHINA, 1906-1967

see Puyi, 1906-1975

C

CH'ING SHENG-TSU, EMPEROR OF CHINA, 1654-1722
see Kangxi, Emperor of China, 1654-1722

CHINGPAWS
see Kachin (Asian People)

CHINNERY, GEORGE, 1774-1852
Conner, Patrick. The Flamboyant Mr Chinnery: An English Artist in India & China. 2012. (ENG., Illus.). 88p. pap. 25.00 ***(978-616-7339-12-2(0))*** River Bks. THA. Dist: National Bk. Network.

CHINOOK INDIANS
see Indians of North America—Northwest, Pacific

CHINOOK JARGON
Gibbs, George. Dictionary of the Chinook Jargon. 2007. 68p. per. *(978-1-4068-0924-4(1))* Echo Library.

—Dictionary of the Chinook Jargon, or, Trade Language of Oregon. 2007. 100p. per. *(978-1-4065-2834-3(X))* Dodo Pr.

—Dictionary of the Chinook Jargon, or Trade Languages of Oregon. (Library of American Linguistics: No. 12). (CHN.). reprint ed. 42.75 *(978-0-404-50992-7(4))* AMS Pr., Inc.

Lang, George. Making Wawa: The Genesis of Chinook Jargon. 2009. (ENG., Illus.). 216p. pap. 29.95 *(978-0-7748-1527-7(2))* UBC Pr. CAN. Dist: Univ. of Washington Pr.

Palmer, Joel & Spalding, Henry. Ocean to Ocean on Horseback: Being the Story of a Tour in the Saddle from the Atlantic to the Pacific. 2007. (Travel in America Ser.). (ENG.). 304p. 49.95 *(978-1-4290-0256-1(5))*; per. 24.95 *(978-1-4290-0257-8(3))* Applewood Bks.

Ross, Alexander. Ross's Adventures of the First Settlers on the Oregon or Columbia River, 1810-13. 2007. (Travel in America Ser.). (ENG.). 328p. 49.95 *(978-1-4290-0270-7(0))*; per. 24.95 *(978-1-4290-0271-4(9))* Applewood Bks.

Shaw, George C. The Chinook Jargon: And How to Use It. 81p. (C). reprint ed. pap. 9.38 *(978-1-55567-614-8(6))* Coyote Pr.

Thwaites, Reuben Gold. Early Western Travels, 1748-1846: Palmer's Journal of Travels over the Rocky Mountains, 1845-1846, Vol. XXX. 2007. cd-rom 15.95 *(978-0-7884-4408-1(5))* Heritage Bks.

—Early Western Travels, 1748-1846: Ross's Adventures of the First Settlers on the Oregon or Columbia River, 1810-1813, Vol. VII. 2007. cd-rom 15.95 *(978-0-7884-4444-9(1))* Heritage Bks.

Winthrop, Theodore. The Canoe & the Saddle. 2009. 162p. pap. *(978-0-217-62376-6(X))*; 238p. pap. *(978-0-217-62374-2(3))* Books LLC.

—The Canoe & the Saddle. Lindholdt, Paul J., ed. 2006. (ENG., Illus.). 240p. pap. 13.95 *(978-0-8032-9863-7(3)*, Bison Bks.) Univ. of Nebraska Pr.

—The Canoe & the Saddle: Adventures among the Northwestern Rivers & Forests & Isthmiana. (Illus.). 332p. reprint ed. lib. bdg. 98.00 *(978-0-7222-4715-0(X))* Library Reprints, Inc.

CHINOOK SALMON
Gee, Nina Foran. Springer's Quest: Life of a Pacific Chinook Salmon. 2009. *(978-0-87961-277-1(0))* Naturegraph Pubs., Inc.

Keating, Dan. Keating on Kings: Great Lakes Chinook Tactics Way Beyond the Basics. Pudaite Keating, Mary, ed. 2006. (ENG., Illus.). 256p. per. 24.95 *(978-0-9774273-0-7(7))* Two Fish Publishing.

CHINOOKAN LANGUAGES
Icon Group International, Inc. Staff, compiled by. Webster's Chinook - English Thesaurus Dictionary. 2008. 72p. ring bd. 28.95 incl. audio compact disk *(978-0-497-83470-8(7))* Icon Group International, Inc.

The Chinuk Wawa Dictionary Project. Chinuk Wawa / kakwa nsayka ulman-tilixam laska munk-kemteks nsayka / As Our Elders Teach Us to Speak It, 1 vol. 2012. (ENG., Illus.). 400p. pap. 29.95 ***(978-0-295-99186-3(0)***, Confederated Tribes of the Grand Ronde Community of Oregon) Univ. of Washington Pr.

CHINTZ
Crill, Rosemary. Chintz: Indian Textiles for the West. 2008. (ENG., Illus.). 144p. 55.00 *(978-1-85177-532-3(3))* V & A Pubns. GBR. Dist: Hachette Bk. Group.

CHINYANJA LANGUAGE
see Nyanja Language

CHIPYONG-NI, BATTLE OF, CHIPYONG-NI, KOREA, 1951
Graney, Douglas. Cottonseed Easy Six. 2010. 190p. pap. 13.95 *(978-1-4327-5745-8(8))* Outskirts Pr., Inc.

CHIPBOARD
see Particle Board

CHIPPEWA INDIANS
see Indians of North America—Northwest, Old

CHIPPEWA LANGUAGE
see Ojibwa Language

CHIPS (ELECTRONICS)
see Integrated Circuits

CHIRALITY
Ahuja, Satinder (Sut), ed. Chiral Separation Methods for Pharmaceutical & Biotechnological Products. 2010. (ENG., Illus.). 495p. 142.00 *(978-0-470-40691-5(7)*, Wiley) Wiley, John & Sons, Inc.

Amabilino, David B., ed. Chirality at the Nanoscale: Nanoparticles, Surfaces, Materials & More. 2009. (ENG., Illus.). 440p. 220.00 *(978-3-527-32013-4(X)*, Wiley-VCH) Wiley, John & Sons, Inc.

Amouri, Hanie, et al. Chirality in Transition Metal Chemistry: Molecules, Supramolecular Assemblies & Materials. (Inorganic Chemistry: a Textbook Ser.). (ENG., Illus.). 260p. 2009. pap. 80.00 *(978-0-470-06054-4(9))* 2008. 215.00 *(978-0-470-06053-7(0))* Wiley, John & Sons, Inc. (Wiley).

Ayissi, Serge. Simulation of Chiral Ordering Process by Monte Carlo Methods. 2010. 196p. pap. *(978-3-639-23629-3(7))* VDM Verlag Dr. Mueller e.K.

Berova, Nina. Comprehensive Chiroptical Spectroscopy Vol. 2: Applications in Stereochemical Analysis of Synthetic Compounds, Natural Products, & Biomolecules. 2012. (ENG.). 872p. 225.00 ***(978-1-118-01292-5(5)***, Wiley) Wiley, John & Sons, Inc.

Berova, Nina, et al. Advances in Chiroptical Methods. 2012. (ENG.). 808p. 225.00 ***(978-1-118-01293-2(3)***, Wiley) Wiley, John & Sons, Inc.

Berova, Nina, et al. Comprehensive Chiroptical Spectroscopy, 2 vols., Set. 2012. (ENG.). 1840p. 395.00 *(978-0-470-64135-4(5)*, Wiley) Wiley, John & Sons, Inc.

Berthod, Alain, ed. Chiral Recognition in Separation Methods: Mechanisms & Applications. 2010. (ENG., Illus.). xv, 337p. 189.00 *(978-3-642-12444-0(5)*, 3642124445) Springer.

Buch, A., et al. Clues for the Space Analysis of Chirality. 2011. (Space Science, Exploration & Policies Ser.). 132p. 69.00 *(978-1-61761-331-9(2))* Nova Science Pubs., Inc.

Busch, Marianna A. & Busch, Kenneth W., eds. Chiral Analysis. 2006. (ENG., Illus.). 720p. 355.00 *(978-0-444-51669-5(7)*, Elsevier Science) Elsevier Science & Technology Bks.

Crego-Calama, Mercedes & Reinhoudt, David N. Supramolecular Chirality. 2010. (Topics in Current Chemistry Ser.). (Illus.). xii, 312p. pap. 379.00 *(978-3-642-06878-2(2)*, 3642068782) Springer.

Dai, Li-Xin & Hou, Xue-Long, eds. Chiral Ferrocenes in Asymmetric Catalysis: Synthesis & Applications. 2010. (ENG., Illus.). 431p. 215.00 *(978-3-527-32280-0(9)*, Wiley-VCH) Wiley, John & Sons, Inc.

Flügel, Rolf M. Chirality & Life: A Short Introduction to the Early Phases of Chemical Evolution. 2011. (ENG., Illus.). ix, 90p. pap. 139.00 *(978-3-642-16976-2(7)*, 3642169767) Springer.

Garrison, A. Wayne, et al. Chiral Pesticides: Stereoselectivity & Its Consequences. 2012. (ACS Symposium Ser.: 1085). (ENG.). 240p. 150.00 ***(978-0-8412-2679-1(2))*** American Chemical Society.

Gübitz, Gerald & Schmid, Martin G., eds. Chiral Separations: Methods & Protocols. 2010. (Methods in Molecular Biology Ser.). (Illus.). 448p. pap. 149.00 *(978-1-61737-390-9(7)*, 1617373907) Humana Pr.

Guijarro, Albert & Yusty, Miguel. The Origin of Chirality in the Molecules of Life: A Revision from Awareness to the Current Theories & Perspectives of this Unsolved Problem. 2008. (ENG., Illus.). 164p. (C). 160.00 ***(978-0-85404-156-5(7))*** Royal Society of Chemistry, The GBR. Dist: Ingram Pub. Services.

Hasanovic, Moamer. Inhomogeneous Chirality in Scattering Problems: Solution Algorithms Based on Method of Moments. 2008. 160p. pap. *(978-3-8364-8258-5(4))* VDM Verlag Dr. Mueller e.K.

Hayashi, Tamio & Shintani, Ryo, eds. Privileged Chiral Ligands in Asymmetric Catalysis. 2010. 450p. 215.00 *(978-3-527-32405-7(4)*, Wiley-VCH) Wiley, John & Sons, Inc.

Itsuno, Shinichi, ed. Polymeric Chiral Catalyst Design & Chiral Polymer Synthesis. 2011. (ENG., Illus.). 528p. 149.95 *(978-0-470-56820-0(8)*, Wiley) Wiley, John & Sons, Inc.

Kallenborn, R. & Hühnerfuss, H. Chiral Environmental Pollutants: Trace Analysis & Ecotoxicology. 2010. (ENG., Illus.). xviii, 209p. pap. 209.00 *(978-3-642-08569-7(5)*, 3642085695) Springer.

Konno, Ryuichi, et al. D-Amino Acids: Practical Methods & Protocols, Volume 1: Analytical Methods for D-Amino Acids. 2009. (D-Amino Acids: Practical Methods & Protocols Ser.). 145.00 *(978-1-60741-376-9(0))* Nova Science Pubs., Inc.

—D-Amino Acids: Practical Methods & Protocols, Volume 2: Free D-Amino Acids. 2009. (D-Amino Acids: Practical Methods & Protocols Ser.). 145.00 *(978-1-60741-377-6(9))* Nova Science Pubs., Inc.

—D-Amino Acids: Practical Methods & Protocols, Volume 3: D-Amino Acids in Peptides & Proteins. 2009. (D-Amino Acids: Practical Methods & Protocols Ser.). 145.00 *(978-1-60741-378-3(7))* Nova Science Pubs., Inc.

—D-Amino Acids: Practical Methods & Protocols, Volume 4: Enzymes Involved in the Metabolism of D-Amino Acids. 2009. (D-Amino Acids: Practical Methods & Protocols Ser.). 145.00 *(978-1-60741-379-0(5))* Nova Science Pubs., Inc.

Lemaire, Marc & Mangeney, Pierre. Chiral Diazaligands for Asymmetric Synthesis. 2010. (Topics in Organometallic Chemistry Ser.). (Illus.). x, 301p. pap. 349.00 *(978-3-642-06538-5(4)*, 3642065384) Springer.

Mason, S. F., ed. Optical Activity & Chiral Discrimination. 2010. (NATO Science Series C: (closed) Ser.). 388p. pap. 239.00 *(978-90-481-8355-5(3)*, 9048183553) Springer.

Naaman, Ron, et al, eds. Electronic & Magnetic Properties of Chiral Molecules & Supramolecular Architectures. 2011. (Topics in Current Chemistry Ser.). (ENG., Illus.). xi, 311p. 349.00 *(978-3-642-18103-0(1)*, 3642181031) Springer.

Nandi, Nilashis. Chirality in Biological Nanospaces: Reactions in Active Sites. 2011. (ENG., Illus.). 209p. 119.95 *(978-1-4398-4002-3(4)*, CRC Press) Taylor & Francis Group GBR. Dist: Taylor & Francis Group.

Nugent, Thomas C., ed. Chiral Amine Synthesis: Methods, Developments & Applications. 2010. (ENG., Illus.). 520p. 230.00 *(978-3-527-32509-2(3)*, Wiley-VCH) Wiley, John & Sons, Inc.

Paci, Irina, ed. Chirality & the Solid Surface. 2011. (Illus.). 496p. 169.95 *(978-1-4200-8656-0(1))* CRC Pr. LLC.

Pellissier, Hélène. Chirality from Dynamic Kinetic Resolution. 2011. (ENG., Illus.). 318p. (C). 160.00 ***(978-1-84973-197-3(7))*** Royal Society of Chemistry, The GBR. Dist: Ingram Pub. Services.

Pellissier, Hélène. Chiral Sulfur-Containing Ligands: Asymmetric Catalysis. 2009. (RSC Catalysis Ser.). (ENG., Illus.). 402p. (C). 224.00 *(978-1-84755-924-1(7))* Royal Society of Chemistry, The GBR. Dist: Ingram Pub. Services.

Pu, Lin. 1, 1'-Binaphthyl-Based Chiral Materials: Our Journey. 2009. (Illus.). 368p. 111.00 *(978-1-84816-411-6(4))* Imperial College Pr. GBR. Dist: World Scientific Publishing Co., Inc.

Sheldon, Roger A. Chirotechnology. 2nd ed. 2009. 500p. 169.95 *(978-1-57444-741-5(6))* CRC Pr. LLC.

Soai, Kenso. Amplification of Chirality. 2010. (Topics in Current Chemistry Ser.). (Illus.). xii, 206p. pap. 289.00 *(978-3-642-09668-6(9)*, 3642096689) Springer.

Soai, Kenso, ed. Amplification of Chirality. 2008. (Topics in Current Chemistry Ser.). (Illus.). 205p. 289.00 *(978-3-540-77868-4(3))* Springer.

Subramanian, Ganapathy. Chiral Separation Techniques: A Practical Approach. Subramanian, Ganapathy, ed. 3rd ed. 2007. (ENG., Illus.). 641p. 275.00 *(978-3-527-31509-3(8)*, Wiley-VCH) Wiley, John & Sons, Inc.

Toda, Fumio, ed. Enantiomer Separation: Fundamentals & Practical Methods. 2010. viii, 336p. pap. 179.00 *(978-90-481-6640-4(3)*, 9048166403) Springer.

Van Eeckhaut, Ann & Michotte, Yvette, eds. Chiral Separations by Capillary Electrophoresis. 2009. (Chromatographic Science Ser.). (ENG., Illus.). 543p. 174.95 *(978-1-4200-6933-4(0)*, CRC Press) Taylor & Francis Group GBR. Dist: Taylor & Francis Group.

Wagnière, Georges H. On Chirality & the Universal Asymmetry: Reflections on Image & Mirror Image. 2007. (ENG., Illus.). 256p. pap. 139.00 *(978-3-906390-38-3(1)*, Wiley-VCH) Wiley, John & Sons, Inc.

Wenzel, Thomas J. Discrimination of Chiral Compounds Using NMR Spectroscopy. 2007. (ENG., Illus.). 576p. 150.00 *(978-0-471-76352-9(7)*, Wiley-Interscience) Wiley, John & Sons, Inc.

Wolf, Christian & Royal Society of Chemistry Staff. Dynamic Stereochemistry of Chiral Compounds: Principles & Applications. 2007. (ENG., Illus.). 532p. (C). 80.00 *(978-0-85404-246-3(6))* Royal Society of Chemistry, The GBR. Dist: Ingram Pub. Services.

Yamamoto, Hisashi & Carreira, Erick M. Comprehensive Chirality. 2012. (ENG.). 3995.00 ***(978-0-08-095167-6(8)***, Elsevier Science) Elsevier Science & Technology Bks.

Zehnacker, Anne, ed. Chiral Recognition in the Gas Phase. 2010. (ENG., Illus.). 247p. 99.95 *(978-1-4200-8227-2(2)*, CRC Press) Taylor & Francis Group GBR. Dist: Taylor & Francis Group.

Zhang, Weicheng. Development of Effective Chiral Ligands for Asymmetric Hydrogenation. 2009. 160p. pap. *(978-3-639-19545-3(0))* VDM Verlag Dr. Mueller e.K.

CHIRALITY (NUCLEAR PHYSICS)
see Particles (Nuclear Physics)—Chirality

CHIRICO, GIORGIO DE, 1888-1978
see De Chirico, Giorgio, 1888-1978

CHIROGRAPHY
see Penmanship; Writing

CHIROMANCY
see Palmistry

CHIROPODY
see Podiatry

CHIROPRACTIC
see also Naturopathy

Abblett, David E. & Abblett, Terry Ann. The New Chiropractic Cash Practice Survival Guide: How to Successfully Start-up or Convert Your Practice. 2nd rev. ed. 2006. (Illus.). 168p. per. 68.95 *(978-0-7637-4449-6(2))* Jones & Bartlett Learning, LLC.

Acampora, Christina L. Selling Chiropractic to Medical Practices. 2008. 329p. (C). pap. 63.95 *(978-0-7637-5194-4(4))* Jones & Bartlett Learning, LLC.

Arbeitman, Larry & Gertner, George. The Gift of Hope. 2007. 92p. pap. 14.95 *(978-1-933889-33-7(0))* Ctr. Path Publishing.

Bergmann, Thomas F. & Peterson, David H. Chiropractic Technique: Principles & Procedures. 3rd ed. 2010. (ENG., Illus.). 496p. 155.00 *(978-0-323-04969-6(9)*, Mosby) Elsevier - Health Sciences Div.

Byfield, David. Technique Skills in Chiropractic. 2011. (ENG., Illus.). 412p. (C). pap. 155.00 *(978-0-7020-3424-4(X)*, Churchill Livingstone) Elsevier - Health Sciences Div.

Carlson, Geri L. I Stand Amazed. 2007. (ENG.). 164p. per. 13.99 *(978-1-60034-874-7(2))* Xulon Pr., Inc.

ChiroCode Institute, abr. 2008 ChiroCode DeskBook. 2007. spiral bd. 99.00 *(978-0-9677104-0-2(5))* Chirocode Institute.

Coding Guide for Chiropractic Services. 2007. per. 114.95 *(978-1-56337-862-1(0))* OptumInsight, Inc.

Cram101 Textbook Reviews & Cram101 Textbook Reviews. Outlines & Highlights for Differential Diagnosis & Management for the Chiropractor: Protocols & Algorithms by Thomas A. Souza, ISBN. 2011. 290p. pap. 32.95 ***(978-1-61461-571-2(3))*** Cram101 Inc.

Davies, Neil J. & Fallon, Joan. Chiropractic Pediatrics: A Clinical Handbook. 2nd ed. 2010. (ENG., Illus.). 448p. 143.00 *(978-0-7020-3129-8(1)*, Churchill Livingstone) Elsevier - Health Sciences Div.

Davis, James, ed. 2008 Coding Guide Chiropractic Services. 2007. per. 129.95 *(978-1-57066-467-0(6))* Practice Management Information Corp.

Dible, Donald, ed. The Well-Adjusted Soul: Feel-Good Stories from the Heart of Chiropractic, vol. 1. 2010. (Illus.). 300p. 14.95 *(978-0-615-38960-8(0))* Parker Seminars.

Fuhr, Arlan W. The Activator Method. 2nd ed. 2008. (ENG., Illus.). 592p. (C). 139.00 *(978-0-323-04852-1(8)*, Mosby) Elsevier - Health Sciences Div.

Greene-Orndorff, Laura & Reizer, John L. Chiropractic Mavericks: the Story of Helen & Dr. Gordon Brown. 2010. 114p. pap. 25.00 *(978-0-557-44717-6(8))* Lulu Enterprises Inc.

Haneline, Michael T. Evidence-Based Chiropractic Practice. 2006. (Illus.). 453p. per. 96.95 *(978-0-7637-3571-5(X))* Jones & Bartlett Learning, LLC.

Hyde, Thomas E. & Gengenbach, Marianne S., eds. Conservative Management of Sports Injuries. 2nd rev. ed. 2007. (Illus.). 1173p. 174.95 *(978-0-7637-3252-3(4)*, 0763732524) Jones & Bartlett Learning, LLC.

Ingenix, creator. Chiropractic Services: A Comprehensive Illustrated Guide to Coding & Reimbursement. 2007. 399p. spiral bd. 119.95 *(978-1-60151-070-9(5))* OptumInsight, Inc.

Kjersem, Jens Anders. Learn to Heal: How to Activate Normal Physiologic Reactions in order for Tissues to Heal Naturally. 2009. 204p. 25.50 *(978-1-60693-692-4(1)*, Eloquent Bks.) AEG Literary Publishing Services, Inc.

Kooyers, Jo, photos by. Hello Chiropractic, Goodbye Colic: Gentle adjustments give happy Babies. 2010. 140p. pap. 9.95 *(978-0-9827031-0-6(4))* Kooyers, Steve.

Leavitt, D. Henry, ed. 2009 ChiroCode DeskBook. 2008. 600p. spiral bd. 99.00 *(978-0-9677104-1-9(3))* Chirocode Institute.

Long, Preston H. The Naked Chiropractor. 21.95 *(978-0-9722816-0-7(6))* Evidence-Based Health Services, Inc.

Mawhiney, R. B. D. C. D. I. S. R. C. Rise & Demise of the Chiropractic Profession. 2010. 96p. 24.99 *(978-1-4535-1269-2(1))*; pap. 15.99 *(978-1-4535-1268-5(3))* Xlibris Corp.

Maynard, Joseph Edward. Healing Hands: The Story of the Palmer Family, Discoverers & Developers of Chiropractic. 2011. 386p. 53.95 ***(978-1-258-00416-3(X))*** Literary Licensing, LLC.

McDonald, William P. Chiropractic Peace. 2009. 192p. pap. 28.95 *(978-1-4269-0722-7(2))* Trafford Publishing.

Modern Chiropractic: The Way to A Pain-Free Lifestyle. 2006. pap. 24.95 *(978-0-9788556-0-4(4))* Katenial Publishing.

Myers, Thomas W. Anatomy Trains: Myofascial Meridians for Manual & Movement Therapists. 2nd ed. 2008. (ENG., Illus.). 440p. pap. 66.95 *(978-0-443-10283-7(X)*, Churchill Livingstone) Elsevier - Health Sciences Div.

Nambudripad, Devi S. The NAET Guide Book: The Companion to Say Good-Bye to Illness. 2009. (ENG.). 96p. pap. 12.00 *(978-1-934523-09-4(7))* Delta Publishing Co.

Oliver, Charles. Complete Manual Therapy: Chiropractic & Physical Therapy in One Approach. 2010. 413p. pap. 79.00 *(978-0-692-00786-0(5))* Integrative Pr. LLC.

Palmer, D. d. & Palmer, D. D. The Chiropractor. 2010. 124p. 35.95 *(978-1-161-35560-4(X))* Kessinger Publishing, LLC.

Paton, Scott. Health Beyond Medicine: A Chiropractic Miracle. 2009. (ENG.). 332p. pap. 19.95 *(978-0-9818083-0-7(1))* Healthcare Unity Pr.

Reizer, John. Chiropractic marketing tools that will absolutely grow your Practice. 2008. 136p. pap. 19.95 *(978-1-4357-4319-9(9))* Lulu Enterprises Inc.

—Depression - Proofing Your Chiropractic Career. 2009. 148p. pap. 30.00 *(978-0-557-06042-9(7))* Lulu Enterprises Inc.

—Teaching Your Patients Chiropractic. 2006. 120p. per. 19.95 *(978-1-58961-487-1(9))* PageFree Publishing, Inc.

Robert T. Story, D. C. Alternatives. 2009. 160p. pap. 11.99 *(978-1-4389-8174-1(0))* AuthorHouse.

Rochester, Roderic P. & Eriksen, Kirk. Orthospinology Procedures: An Evidence-Based Approach to Spinal Care. 2007. (Illus.). 320p. 125.99 *(978-0-7817-8436-8(0))* Lippincott Williams & Wilkins.

School of, Cats Careers & Technology, Chiropractic. Cross-Training the Chiropractic Assistant Textbook. 2010. 175p. pap. 125.00 *(978-0-557-31142-2(X))* Lulu Enterprises Inc.

—Cross-Training the Chiropractic Assistant Workbook. 2010. 90p. pap. 75.00 *(978-0-557-31152-1(7))* Lulu Enterprises Inc.

Schwabegger, Anton & Schwabegger, Anton H., eds. Congenital Thoracic Wall Deformities: Diagnosis, Therapy & Current Developments. 2011. (ENG., Illus.). xi, 347p. 219.00 *(978-3-211-99137-4(9)*, 3211991379) Springer.

Senzon, Simon A. Chiropractic Foundations: D. D. Palmer's Traveling Library, Volume 3. 2007. per. *(978-1-59872-980-1(2))* Instant Pub.

Sheldon, Roger A. Chirotechnology. 2nd ed. 2009. 500p. 169.95 *(978-1-57444-741-5(6))* CRC Pr. LLC.

Silverman, Gerald M. Your Miraculous Back: A Step-by-Step Guide to Relieving Neck & Back Pain. 2006. (New Harbinger Self-Help Workbook Ser.). (ENG., Illus.). 184p. per. 18.95 *(978-1-57224-452-8(6))* New Harbinger Pubns.

Souza, Thomas A. Differential Diagnosis & Management for the Chiropractor: Protocols & Algorithms. 4th rev. ed. 2008. (Illus.). 1138p. 139.95 *(978-0-7637-5282-8(7))* Jones & Bartlett Learning, LLC.

Spages, Jonathan B. The Wellness Approach: The Secrets of Health your Doctor is Afraid to Tell You. 2011. (ENG.). 134p. pap. 14.00 *(978-1-60037-830-0(7))* Morgan James Publishing.

Tanaka, Paul K. ICD-9 CM Easy Coder Chiropractic. 2008. (Easy Coder Ser.). 152p. spiral bd. 69.00 *(978-1-56781-565-8(0))* Unicor Medical, Inc.

Wiles, Michael. Strategic Planning for the Chiropractic Practice. 2007. 154p. (C). pap. 56.95 *(978-0-7637-5085-5(9))* Jones & Bartlett Learning, LLC.

Wiles, Michael R., et al. Essentials of Dermatology for Chiropractors. rev. ed. 2010. 280p. pap. 86.95 *(978-0-7637-6157-8(5))* Jones & Bartlett Learning, LLC.

You Can Be Well. 2008. 208p. pap. 19.95 *(978-1-933889-37-5(3))* Ctr. Path Publishing.

CHIROPRACTORS

Behncke, F. H. Pioneer Teachers in Dietetics. 2006. pap. 12.95 *(978-1-4286-7068-6(8))* Kessinger Publishing, LLC.

—Pioneer Teachers in Natural Therapeutics in the United States. 2006. pap. 12.95 *(978-1-4286-7067-9(X))* Kessinger Publishing, LLC.

Frye, Barbara. Body Mechanics for Manual Therapists: A Functional Approach to Self-Care. 3rd rev. ed. 2008. (LWW Massage Therapy & Bodywork Educational Ser.). Orig. Title: Body Mechanics for Manual Therapist: A Functional approch to Self-Care & Injury Prevention. (ENG., Illus.). 304p. pap. 47.99 *(978-0-7817-7463-3(7))* Lippincott Williams & Wilkins.

Haneline, Michael T. & Meeker, William C. Introduction to Public Health for Chiropractors. rev. ed. 2009. 424p. pap. 84.95 *(978-0-7637-5822-6(1))* Jones & Bartlett Learning, LLC.

Jamison, Jennifer R. Patient Education & Wellness: A handbook for manual Therapists. 2010. (ENG., Illus.). 375p. pap. 57.95 *(978-0-7020-4041-2(X),* Churchill Livingstone) Elsevier - Health Sciences Div.

Maynard, Joseph Edward. Healing Hands: The Story of the Palmer Family, Discoverers & Developers of Chiropractic. 2011. 386p. 53.95 ***(978-1-258-00416-3(X))*** Literary Licensing, LLC.

Morgan, Corrine. Dr. Corrine Morgan Presents the Light Within You. 2011. 75p. pap. 14.95 ***(978-0-9826841-6-0(9))*** September Summer.

Taber, Douglas J., DC & Van Vorst, Douglas, DC. Spinal Stabilization: A Functional Rehab Program. 2010. 56p. pap. 15.49 *(978-0-557-15847-8(8))* Lulu Enterprises Inc.

Wilk, Chester A. Living a Prophesy: A Chiropractor. 2009. 88p. pap. 10.99 *(978-1-60791-753-3(X))* Xulon Pr., Inc.

CHIROPTERA

see Bats

CHITTAHS

see Cheetah

CHIVALRY

see also Bushido; Civilization, Medieval; Courtly Love; Crusades; Feudalism; Heraldry; Honor; Knights and Knighthood; Tournaments

Barthélemy, Dominique. The Serf, the Knight, & the Historian. Edwards, Graham Robert, tr. from FRE. 2009. 368p. pap. 29.95 *(978-0-8014-7560-3(0))* Cornell Univ. Pr.

Barthelemy, Dominique. The Serf, the Knight, & the Historian. Edwards, Graham Robert, tr. from FRE. 2009. 368p. 99.95 *(978-0-8014-3690-2(X))* Cornell Univ. Pr.

Black, William H. Illustrations of Ancient State & Chivalry. reprint ed. 38.50 *(978-0-404-17136-0(2))* AMS Pr., Inc.

Bulfinch, Thomas. The Age of Chivalry. 2010. (ENG.). 432p. pap. 35.75 *(978-1-177-47637-9(1))* 2010. 340p. pap. 31.75 *(978-1-142-56531-2(9))* 2010. 438p. pap. 35.75 *(978-1-141-98006-2(1))* 2009. 424p. 41.99 *(978-1-117-50458-2(1))* 2009. (ENG.). 423p. pap. 34.75 *(978-1-117-50459-9(X))* 2009. 392p. 29.99 *(978-0-559-10466-4(9))* 2009. 392p. 31.99 *(978-0-559-10452-7(9))* 2009. 392p. pap. 33.75 *(978-0-559-10455-8(3))* 2009. 392p. pap. 32.75 *(978-0-559-10461-9(8))* BiblioBazaar.

—The Age of Chivalry. 2009. 232p. pap. ***(978-0-217-29299-3(2))*** Books LLC.

—The Age of Chivalry. 2008. 344p. pap. *(978-1-4099-2391-6(6))* Dodo Pr.

—The Age of Chivalry. 2010. (Illus.). 218p. pap. 30.06 *(978-1-153-69141-3(8))* General Bks. LLC.

—The Age of Chivalry. 2010. 320p. pap. *(978-1-4076-2918-6(2))* HardPr.

—The Age of Chivalry. 2008. 262p. pap. 16.95 *(978-1-4357-3323-7(1))* Lulu Enterprises Inc.

—The Age of Chivalry. 2008. 424p. pap. *(978-1-4086-9953-9(2))* Read Bks.

—Legends of Charlemagne; 2006. 408p. per. 26.99 *(978-1-4255-4410-2(X))* MPublishing.

Christine, et al. Le Livre des Faits et Bonnes Murs du Roi Charles V le Sage. (FRE.). 370p. *(978-2-234-02377-2(7))* Stock, Editions.

Cram101 Textbook Reviews. Outlines & Highlights for Strong of Body, Brave & Noble: Chivalry & Society in Medieval France by Constance Brittain Bouchard, ISBN. 2011. 68p. pap. 27.95 ***(978-1-61812-382-4(3))*** Cram101 Inc.

Delpech, Henri M. La Tactique aux XIII Siecle, 2 vols., Set. reprint ed. 110.00 *(978-0-404-17140-7(0))* AMS Pr., Inc.

Duarte, Dom. The Royal Book of Horsemanship, Jousting & Knightly Combat. Muhlberger, Steven, ed. Preto, Antonio & Preto, Luis, trs. from POR. 2010. 180p. 32.95 *(978-1-891448-34-8(X))* Chivalry Bookshelf, The.

Ferguson, Arthur B. The Indian Summer of English Chivalry: Studies in the Decline & Transformation of Chivalric Idealism. 2011. 260p. 47.95 ***(978-1-258-08589-6(5))*** Literary Licensing, LLC.

Fraser, John. America & the Patterns of Chivalry. 2009. (ENG.). 312p. pap. 42.00 *(978-0-521-11009-9(2))* Cambridge Univ. Pr.

Geitzenauer, Dan. Get over Yourself! A True Life Story of Overcoming Insecurities & Learning the Lost Art of Chivalry. 2009. 124p. pap. 13.95 *(978-1-4389-8221-2(6))* AuthorHouse.

Hipshon, David. Richard III & the Death of Chivalry. 2009. (ENG., Illus.). 224p. 39.95 *(978-0-7509-5074-9(9))* History Pr. Ltd.,The GBR. Dist: Independent Pubs. Group.

Hoche, Dominique T. & Matheson, Lister M. The Reception of Christine De Pizan's Fais D'Armes in Fifteenth-Century England: Chivalric Self-Fashioning. 2008. 220p. 109.95 *(978-0-7734-5158-2(7))* Mellen, Edwin Pr., The.

Hull, Jeffrey. Knightly Dueling: The Fighting Arts of German Chivalry. Maziarz, Monika & Zabinski, Grzegorz, trs. from GEH. 2008. (Illus.). 254p. pap. 30.00 *(978-1-58160-674-4(5))* Paladin Pr.

Hurd, Richard. Hurd's Letters on Chivalry & Romance, with the Third Elizabethan Dialogue. 2009. 90p. pap. *(978-1-151-59306-1(0))* Books LLC.

Hystad, Wallace. An Ambiguity Named Freedom: A Tea Partier's View of America's Recent History & Politics. 2011. pap. 16.99 ***(978-1-61777-559-8(2))*** Tate Publishing & Enterprises, LLC.

James, George Payne Rainsford. History of Chivalry. 2006. pap. 31.95 *(978-1-4286-3403-9(7))* Kessinger Publishing, LLC.

Jones, Robert. The Knight: The Warrior & World of Chivalry. 2011. (ENG., Illus.). 240p. 29.95 *(978-1-84908-312-6(6))* Osprey Publishing, Ltd. GBR. Dist: Random Hse., Inc.

Jordan, Brent / Kenton. The Chivalry Code: Discussions on Becoming a Man in a Modern World. 2007. pap. 14.50 *(978-0-9703441-3-7(9))* Satsu Multimedia Pr.

Kaeuper, Richard W. Holy Warriors: The Religious Ideology of Chivalry. 2009. (Middle Ages Ser.). (Illus.). 344p. (C). 59.95 *(978-0-8122-4167-9(3))* Univ. of Pennsylvania Pr.

Kottenkamp, F. The History of Chivalry & Armour: With 60 Full-Color Plates. 2007. (Dover Books on History, Political & Social Science Ser.). (Illus.). 128p. per. 22.95 *(978-0-486-45742-0(7))* Dover Pubns., Inc.

Lombatti, Antonio. Geoffroy de Charny. Il cavaliere della Sindone. 2010. 57p. pap. 13.50 *(978-1-4452-9226-7(2))* Lulu Enterprises Inc.

Lull, Ramon, pseud. The Order of Chivalry. Ellis, F. S., ed. Caxton, William, tr. from FRE. reprint ed. 45.00 *(978-0-404-18352-3(2))* AMS Pr., Inc.

Meller, Walter Clifford. A Knight's Life in the Days of Chivalry. 2007. (ENG.). 328p. 45.95 *(978-0-548-03818-5(X))* Kessinger Publishing, LLC.

Mills, Charles. The History of Chivalry. reprint ed. 32.00 *(978-0-404-17156-8(7))* AMS Pr., Inc.

—The History of Chivalry. 2009. 170p. pap. *(978-1-4588-8363-6(9))* Books LLC.

—History of Chivalry or Knighthood & It. 2006. pap. 27.95 *(978-1-4286-4215-7(3))* Kessinger Publishing, LLC.

Phillips, Charles. The Glorious Age of Chivalry: An Exploration of the Golden Age of Knighthood & How It Was Expressed in Art, Literature & Song. 2011. (ENG., Illus.). 128p. pap. 17.99 *(978-1-84476-974-2(7))* Anness Publishing GBR. Dist: National Bk. Network.

—The Illustrated History of Knights & the Golden Age of Chivalry: The History, Myth And Romance of the Medieval Knight & the Chivalric Code Explored, with over 500 Stunning Images of Castles, Quests, Battles, Tournaments, Courts, Honours & Triumphs. 2008. (ENG., Illus.). 256p. 35.00 *(978-0-7548-1855-7(1))* Anness Publishing GBR. Dist: National Bk. Network.

Prestage, Edgar. Chivalry. 2010. pap. 45.00 *(978-0-415-56905-7(2))* Routledge.

Rodriguez-Velasco, Jesús D. Order & Chivalry: Knighthood & Citizenship in Late Medieval Castile. Ferguson, Eunice Rodriguez, tr. from SPA. 2010. (Middle Ages Ser.). 304p. (C). 65.00 *(978-0-8122-4212-6(2))* Univ. of Pennsylvania Pr.

Sainte-Pelaye, Jean-Baptiste. Memoires sur l'Ancienne Chevalerie, 2 vols., Set. reprint ed. 59.50 *(978-0-404-18306-6(9))* AMS Pr., Inc.

Saporiti, Adrien. Chivalry Is Not Dead: Boston. Dabrowski, Laura, ed. 2011. 82p. pap. 9.95 ***(978-0-9840572-8-3(5))*** Thumbs Up Publishing.

Saul, Nigel. Chivalry in Medieval England. 2011. (Illus.). 440p. 35.00 *(978-0-674-06368-6(6))* Harvard Univ. Pr.

Spingarn, J. E. Chivalric Ideals & Renaissance Books of Love. reprint ed. 150.00 *(978-0-7222-1761-0(7))* Library Reprints, Inc.

Wacyf, Boutros G. La Tradition Chevaleresque des Arabes. reprint ed. 41.50 *(978-0-404-18356-1(5))* AMS Pr., Inc.

Whetham, D. & Whetham, David. Just Wars & Moral Victories: Surprise, Deception & the Normative Framework of European War in the Later Middle Ages. 2009. (History of Warfare Ser.). 282p. *(978-90-04-17153-4(3))* BRILL.

Wolabaugh, Josh. The Gentleman's Guide to Chivalry. 2010. 32p. pap. 5.50 *(978-0-557-55678-3(8))* Lulu Enterprises Inc.

Wollock, Jennifer G. Rethinking Chivalry & Courtly Love. 2011. viii, 341p. E-Book *(978-0-313-03850-1(3))* ABC-CLIO, LLC.

—Rethinking Chivalry & Courtly Love, 1 vol. 2011. (Praeger Series on the Middle Ages Ser.). 341p. 54.95 *(978-0-275-98488-5(5),* C8488, Praeger Pubs.) Greenwood Publishing Group, Inc.

CHIVALRY—ROMANCES

see Romances

CHIVINGTON, JOHN MILTON, 1821-1894

Craig, Reginald S. The Fighting Parson: Biography of Colonel John M. Chivington. 2011. 296p. 48.95 ***(978-1-258-04749-8(7))*** Literary Licensing, LLC.

CHLAMYDOPHORIDAE

see Armadillos

CHLEUH LANGUAGE

see Shilha Language

CHLORIDES

see also specific chlorides

Baldys, S. Bromide, Chloride, & Sulfate Concentrations & Loads at U.S. Geological Survey Streamflow-Gaging Stations 07331600 Red River at Denison Dam, 07335500 Red River at Arthur City, & 07336820 Red River near DeKalb, Texas, 2007-09. 2010. (Illus.). vi, 30p. ***(978-1-4113-2869-3(8))*** United States Geological Survey.

Bittar, E. Edward, ed. Chloride Movements Across Cellular Membranes. 2007. (Advances in Molecular & Cell Biology Ser.: 38). (ENG., Illus.). 392p. 169.95 *(978-0-444-52872-8(5),* Elsevier Science) Elsevier Science & Technology Bks.

Hussain, Raja Rizwan, et al. Corrosion of Rc Structures under Severe Environmental Actions. 2010. 120p. pap. *(978-3-639-24113-6(4))* VDM Verlag Dr. Mueller e.K.

Sircus, Mark. Transdermal Magnesium Therapy: A New Modality for the Maintenance of Health. 2011. 356p. 33.95 ***(978-1-4502-8355-7(1))***; pap. 23.95 ***(978-1-4502-8354-0(3))*** iUniverse, Inc.

Suryavanshi, Arvind Krishnajirao. Chloride-Induced Corrosion of Steel in Concrete. 2010. 344p. pap. *(978-3-8383-9364-3(3))* Lambert Academic Publishing.

Yang, Cui. Pge2 Receptors, Chloride Channels. 2011. 196p. pap. ***(978-3-8443-8404-8(9))*** Lambert Academic Publishing.

CHLORINE

see also Organochlorine Compounds

Mangione, Roger & Carlyle, Dana, eds. Chlorine: Properties, Applications & Health Effects. 2011. (Chemical Engineering Methods & Technology Ser.). (Illus.). 361p. 140.00 ***(978-1-61470-954-1(8))*** Nova Science Pubs., Inc.

Tarabanko, Nikolay & Tarabanko, Valery. Vanadium Catalysts of the Deacon Process. 2011. 104p. pap. ***(978-3-8454-1852-0(4))*** Lambert Academic Publishing.

Timmer, Matthias. Ab Initio Theory of Electronic Excitations at Surfaces. 2011. 172p. pap. ***(978-3-8381-2269-4(0))*** Südwestdeutscher Verlag für Hochschulschriften AG & Co. KG.

CHLORINE COMPOUNDS

see also Organochlorine Compounds

Stringer, Ruth & Johnston, Paul. Chlorine & the Environment: An Overview of the Chlorine Industry. 2010. 448p. pap. 219.00 *(978-90-481-5645-0(9),* 9048156459) Springer.

CHLORINE ORGANIC COMPOUNDS

see Organochlorine Compounds

CHLOROFLUOROCARBONS

Cox, Stan. Losing Our Cool: Uncomfortable Truths about Our Air Conditioned World (And Finding New Ways to Get Through the Summer) 2010. (ENG.). 272p. 24.95 *(978-1-59558-489-2(7))* New Pr., The.

Cox, Stan. Losing Our Cool: Uncomfortable Truths about Our Air-Conditioned World (and Finding New Ways to Get Through the Summer) 2012. (ENG., Illus.). 272p. pap. 17.95 ***(978-1-59558-775-6(6))*** New Pr., The.

CHLOROFORM

Guthrie, O. Memoirs of Dr Samuel Guthrie & the His. 2006. pap. 16.95 *(978-1-4286-5633-8(2))* Kessinger Publishing, LLC.

Stratman, Linda. Chloroform: The Quest for Oblivion. 2006. (Illus.). 258p. reprint ed. 30.00 *(978-1-4223-5355-4(9))* DIANE Publishing Co.

CHLOROPHYLL

Grimm, Bernhard, et al, eds. Chlorophylls & Bacteriochlorophylls: Biochemistry, Biophysics, Functions & Applications. (Advances in Photosynthesis & Respiration Ser.). (Illus.). 2010. xxix, 603p. pap. 449.00 *(978-90-481-7140-8(7),* 9048171407) 2006. 603p. 449.00 *(978-1-4020-4515-8(8),* 1402045158) Springer.

Le, Hua & Salcedo, Elsa. Chlorophyll: Structure, Production & Medicinal Uses. 2012. (Botanical Research & Practices Ser.). (Illus.). 218p. 95.00 ***(978-1-61470-974-9(2))*** Nova Science Pubs., Inc.

Papageorgiou, George C. & Govindjee, eds. Chlorophyll a Fluorescence: A Signature of Photosynthesis. 2009. (Advances in Photosynthesis & Respiration Ser.). (ENG., Illus.). xxxii, 820p. pap. 139.00 *(978-90-481-3882-1(5),* 9048138825) Springer.

Smith, Alison & Witty, Michael, eds. Heme, Chlorophyll, & Bilins: Methods & Protocols. 2010. (Illus.). 352p. pap. 169.00 *(978-1-61737-365-7(6),* 1617373656) Humana Pr.

Suggett, David J., et al, eds. Chlorophyll a Fluorescence in Aquatic Sciences: Methods & Applications. 2010. (Developments in Applied Phycology Ser.). xviii, 323p. 199.00 *(978-90-481-9267-0(6),* 9048192676) Springer.

Warren, Martin & Smith, Alison, eds. Tetrapyrroles: Birth, Life & Death. 2010. (Molecular Biology Intelligence Unit Ser.). (ENG., Illus.). xx, 406p. pap. 209.00 *(978-1-4419-2691-3(7),* 1441926917) Springer.

Warren, Martin J. & Smith, Alison G. Tetrapyrroles: Birth, Life, & Death. 2008. (Molecular Biology Intelligence Unit Ser.). (Illus.). 415p. 209.00 *(978-0-387-78517-2(5))* Springer.

CHLOROPLASTIDS

see Chromatophores

CHLOROPLASTS

see also Chromatophores

Biswal, U. C. & Rava, M. K. Chloroplast Biogenesis: From Proplastid to Gerontoplast. 2010. 380p. pap. 279.00 *(978-90-481-6415-8(X),* 904816415X) Springer.

BOCK, Ralph & Knoop, Volker, eds. Genomics of Chloroplasts & Mitochondria. 2012. (Advances in Photosynthesis & Respiration Ser.). (ENG., Illus.). xxxiii, 458p. 279.00 ***(978-94-007-2919-3(7),*** 9400729197) Springer.

Daniell, Henry & Chase, Christine D., eds. Molecular Biology & Biotechnology of Plant Organelles: Chloroplasts & Mitochondria. 2010. (Illus.). xxvi, 659p. pap. 289.00 *(978-90-481-6711-1(6),* 9048167116) Springer.

Kebeish, Rashad Mohamed Ahmed. A Novel Approach for Bypassing Photorespiration in C3 Plants. 2008. 180p. pap. *(978-3-639-05079-0(7))* VDM Verlag Dr. Mueller e.K.

Rebeiz, Constantin, et al, eds. The Chloroplast: Basics & Applications. 2010. (Advances in Photosynthesis & Respiration Ser.). (Illus.). 500p. 279.00 *(978-90-481-8530-6(0),* 9048185300) Springer.

Sandelius, Anna Stina. The Chloroplast. 2008. (Plant Cell Monographs). (Illus.). xiv, 300p. 199.00 *(978-3-540-68692-7(4))* Springer.

Smith, William K., et al, eds. Photosynthetic Adaptation: Chloroplast to Landscape. 2010. (Ecological Studies). (Illus.). xii, 316p. pap. 159.00 *(978-1-4419-1965-6(1),* 1441919651) Springer.

CHOATE, RUFUS, 1799-1859

Choate, Rufus & Brown, Samuel Gilman. The Works of Rufus Choate V1: with a Memoir of His Life. 2007. pap. 43.95 *(978-1-4304-4898-3(9))* Kessinger Publishing, LLC.

Parker, Edward G. Reminiscences of Rufus Choate, the Great American Advocate. 2010. (Illus.). 288p. pap. 23.46 *(978-1-151-06295-6(2))*; 262p. pap. 29.89 *(978-1-154-98672-3(1))* General Bks. LLC.

CHOCOLATE

see also Cocoa; Cooking (Chocolate)

Aaron, Shara & Bearden, Monica. Chocolate: A Healthy Passion. 2008. (ENG., Illus.). 336p. bds. 19.98 *(978-1-59102-653-2(9))* Prometheus Bks., Pubs.

Afoakwa, Emmanuel Ohene. Chocolate Science & Technology. 2010. (ENG., Illus.). 296p. 220.95 *(978-1-4051-9906-3(7),* Wiley-Blackwell) Wiley, John & Sons, Inc.

Almond, Steve. Candyfreak: A Journey Through the Chocolate Underbelly of America. 2009. 256p. pap. 13.00 *(978-1-4379-6870-5(8))* 2003. 266p. 22.00 *(978-1-4379-5077-9(9))* DIANE Publishing Co.

—Candyfreak: A Journey Through the Chocolate Underbelly of America. 2008. (Playaway Adult Nonfiction Ser.). 44.99 *(978-1-60640-931-2(X))* Findaway World, LLC.

—Candyfreak: A Journey Through the Chocolate Underbelly of America. 2009. 13.09 *(978-0-7848-2124-4(0),* Everbind) Marco Bk. Co.

Ashton, John. A Chocolate a Day Keeps the Doctor Away. Date not set. pap. *(978-0-312-30758-6(6),* St. Martin's Griffin); mass mkt. *(978-0-312-98592-9(4),* St. Martin's Paperbacks) St. Martin's Pr.

Beckett, Stephen T. & Beckett, S. T. The Science of Chocolate. 2nd rev. ed. 2008. (ENG., Illus.). 250p. 40.00 *(978-0-85404-970-7(3))* Royal Society of Chemistry, The GBR. Dist: Ingram Pub. Services.

Beckett, Steve T., ed. Industrial Chocolate Manufacture & Use. 4th rev. ed. 2009. (ENG., Illus.). 720p. 305.00 *(978-1-4051-3949-6(8),* Wiley-Blackwell) Wiley, John & Sons, Inc.

Cadbury, Deborah. Chocolate Wars: The 150-Year Rivalry Between the World's Greatest Chocolate Makers. (ENG., Illus.). 384p. 2011. pap. 15.99 *(978-1-61039-051-4(2))* 2010. 27.95 *(978-1-58648-820-8(1))* PublicAffairs.

Carruthers, Karen. Candy Quilts: Design & Create Custom Candy Molds at Home. 2008. 96p. pap. 19.95 *(978-1-4327-2521-1(1))* Outskirts Pr., Inc.

Chiaro, Alfredo. Premium Chocolate. 2011. 76p. pap. ***(978-3-8443-9072-8(3),*** Lambert Academic Publishing.

Chocolate. Date not set. 256p. 7.98 *(978-0-7525-9947-2(X))*; 96p. *(978-1-4075-0795-8(3))*; 240p. *(978-1-4075-2622-5(7))*; 240p. *(978-1-4075-1384-3(2))*; 240p. *(978-1-4075-0982-2(9))*; 256p. *(978-1-4075-0420-9(7))*; 256p. *(978-1-4054-2554-4(7))* Parragon, Inc.

Chocolate. 2008. (ENG., Illus.). 128p. *(978-1-84510-280-7(0))* Top That! Publishing PLC.

Chrystal, Paul & Dickinson, Joe. Chocolate: The British Chocolate Industry. 2011. (Shire Library). (ENG., Illus.). 96p. pap. 15.95 *(978-0-7478-0841-1(4))* Shire Pubns., Ltd. GBR. Dist: Random Hse., Inc.

Coady, Chantal. The Chocolate Companion: A Connoisseur's Guide. 2nd ed. 2006. (ENG., Illus.). 160p. pap. 18.95 *(978-0-7624-2897-7(X))* Running Pr. Bk. Pubs.

Coe, Sophie D. & Coe, Michael D. The True History of Chocolate. 2nd rev. ed. 2007. (ENG., Illus.). 288p. pap. 21.95 *(978-0-500-28696-8(5),* 528696) Thames & Hudson.

Coleman, Mary, ed. Chocolate. (Illus.). 64p. pap. 5.95 *(978-1-86396-173-8(9))* ACP Publishing Pty. Ltd. AUS. Dist: Graphic Arts Ctr. Publishing Co.

Cuvelier, Paule. Chocolate. 2011. (ENG., Illus.). 192p. 17.98 *(978-2-08-020092-1(5))* Flammarion et Cie FRA. Dist: Random Hse., Inc.

Deseine, Trish. Chocolate. 2010. (ENG., Illus.). 160p. pap. 24.95 *(978-1-55285-833-2(2))* Whitecap Bks., Ltd. CAN. Dist: Midpoint Trade Bks., Inc.

Dreiss, Meredith L. & Greenhill, Sharon Edgar. Chocolate: Pathway to the Gods. 2008. (ENG., Illus.). 208p. 30.00 *(978-0-8165-2464-8(5))* Univ. of Arizona Pr.

Engoron, Ed. Choclatique: 150 Simply Elegant Desserts. 2011. (ENG., Illus.). 272p. 27.00 *(978-0-7624-3964-5(5))* Running Pr. Bk. Pubs.

Evans, Sarah Jane. Chocolate Unwrapped: Taste & Enjoy the World's Finest Chocolate. 2010. (ENG., Illus.). 240p. 24.95 *(978-1-86205-859-0(8))* Chrysalis Children's Bks. GBR. Dist: Independent Pubs. Group.

Fine Cooking Magazine Editors, ed. Absolutely Chocolate: Irresistible Excuses to Indulge. 2009. (ENG., Illus.). 304p. 29.95 *(978-1-60085-133-9(9))* Taunton Pr., Inc.

Fitzgerald, Robert. Rowntree & the Marketing Revolution, 1862-1969. 2007. (ENG., Illus.). 768p. pap. 126.00 *(978-0-521-02378-8(5))* Cambridge Univ. Pr.

Goodbody, Mary. Best of Chocolate. Date not set. pap. 14.95 *(978-0-06-757020-3(8))* HarperCollins Pubs.

Green & Black's Staff. Green & Black's Organic Ultimate Chocolate Recipes: The New Collection. 2010. 176p. 24.95 *(978-1-906868-32-1(8))* Cathie Kyle Ltd. GBR. Dist: National Bk. Network.

C

Greweling, Peter P. Chocolates & Confections: Formula, Theory, & Technique for the Artisan Confectioner. 2nd ed. 2012. (ENG., Illus.). 528p. 65.00 *(978-0-470-42441-4(9)*, Wiley) Wiley, John & Sons, Inc.

—Chocolates & Confections at Home with the Culinary Institute of America. 2009. (At Home with the Culinary Institute of America Ser.: 2). (ENG., Illus.). 304p. 34.95 *(978-0-470-18957-3(6)*, Wiley) Wiley, John & Sons, Inc.

Greweling, Peter P. & Culinary Institute of America Staff. Chocolates & Confections: Formula, Theory, & Technique for the Artisan Confectioner. 2007. (ENG., Illus.). 400p. 65.00 *(978-0-7645-8844-0(3)*, Wiley) Wiley, John & Sons, Inc.

Grivetti, Louis E. & Shapiro, Howard-Yana. Chocolate: History, Culture, & Heritage. 2009. (ENG., Illus.). 1064p. 99.95 *(978-0-470-12165-8(3)*, Wiley) Wiley, John & Sons, Inc.

Hardy-Gould, Janet. Chocolate. 3rd ed. 2011. (ENG., Illus.). 64p. pap. 9.38 ***(978-0-19-478730-7(3))*** Oxford Univ. Pr., Inc.

Hawkins, Kathryn. Chocolate! Rich & Luscious Recipes for Cakes, Cookies, Desserts, & Treats, 1 vol. 2008. (ENG.). 176p. spiral bd. 19.95 *(978-1-56148-620-5(5))* Good Bks.

Jayne-Stanes, Sara. Chocolate: The Definitive Guide. 2008. (Illus.). 240p. pap. *(978-1-904943-12-9(8))* Grub Street.

Kenney, Matthew & Baird, Meredith. Raw Chocolate, 1 vol. 2012. (ENG., Illus.). 144p. 24.99 ***(978-1-4236-2105-8(0))*** Gibbs Smith, Publisher.

Kimmerle, Beth. Chocolate: The Sweet History. 2009. (ENG.). 179p. 40.00 *(978-1-4379-6948-1(8))* DIANE Publishing Co.

Knapp, Arthur W. Cocoa & Chocolate: Their History from Plantation to Consumer. 2007. (Illus.). 216p. per. *(978-1-4065-2921-0(4))* Dodo Pr.

—Cocoa & Chocolate: Their History from Plantation to Consumer. 2007. 220p. 39.95 *(978-0-548-53048-1(3))*; (ENG.). per. 24.95 *(978-0-548-47901-8(1))* Kessinger Publishing, LLC.

Knapp, Arthur William. Cocoa & Chocolate: Their History from Plantation to Consumer. 2007. (ENG.). 194p. pap. 19.99 *(978-1-4264-9563-2(3))*; 218p. pap. 22.99 *(978-1-4264-9944-9(2))* BiblioBazaar.

Ledesma, Antonio Colmenero de. Chocolate: Or, an Indian Drinke. Wadsworth, James, tr. 2007. 48p. per. *(978-1-4065-3565-5(6))* Dodo Pr.

Lorenz, Patricia, et al. Chicken Soup for the Chocolate Lover's Soul: Indulging in Our Sweetest Moments. 2007. (Chicken Soup for the Soul Ser.). (ENG., Illus.). 220p. pap. 14.95 *(978-0-7573-0630-3(6))* Health Communications, Inc.

Maron, Linda, illus. Forget Love, I'd Rather Fall in Chocolate. 2009. 64p. 9.99 *(978-0-7369-2606-5(2))* Harvest Hse. Pubs.

McNeil, Cameron L., ed. Chocolate in Mesoamerica: A Cultural History of Cacao. 2009. (Maya Studies). (ENG., Illus.). 544p. pap. 34.95 *(978-0-8130-3382-2(9))* Univ. Pr. of Florida.

Mohos, Ferenc Á. Confectionery & Chocolate Engineering: Principles & Applications. 2010. (ENG., Illus.). 712p. 269.95 *(978-1-4051-9470-9(7)*, Wiley-Blackwell) Wiley, John & Sons, Inc.

Moss, Sarah & Badenoch, Alexander. Chocolate: A Global History. 2009. (Reaktion Books - Edible Ser.). (ENG., Illus.). 128p. 15.95 *(978-1-86189-524-0(0))* Reaktion Bks., Ltd. GBR. Dist: Chicago Distribution Ctr.

Norton, Marcy. Sacred Gifts, Profane Pleasures: A History of Tobacco & Chocolate in the Atlantic World. 2010. (Illus.). 352p. pap. 24.95 *(978-0-8014-7632-7(1))* Cornell Univ. Pr.

Notter, Ewald. The Art of the Chocolatier: From Classic Confections to Sensational Showpieces. 2011. (ENG., Illus.). 416p. 65.00 *(978-0-470-39884-5(1)*, Wiley) Wiley, John & Sons, Inc.

Odesser-Torpey, Marilyn. The Hershey, Pennsylvania Cookbook: Fun Treats & Trivia from the Chocolate Capital of the World. 2007. (ENG., Illus.). 160p. per. 16.95 *(978-0-7627-4155-7(4))* Globe Pequot Pr., The.

Orey, Cal. The Healing Powers of Chocolate. 2010. (ENG.). 304p. 14.00 *(978-0-7582-3820-7(7))* Kensington Publishing Corp.

Paoletti, Rodolfo, et al, eds. Chocolate & Health. 2011. (ENG., Illus.). xii, 188p. 189.00 *(978-88-470-2037-5(9)*, 8847020379) Springer.

Park, Frances & Park, Ginger. Chocolate Chocolate: The True Story of Two Sisters, Tons of Treats, & the Little Shop That Could. 2011. (ENG.). 288p. 23.99 *(978-0-312-65293-7(3)*, Dunne, Thomas Bks.) St. Martin's Pr.

Parloa, Miss & McKenzie Hill, Janet. Chocolate & Cocoa Recipes by Miss Parloa & Home Made Candy Recipes by Mrs. Janet Mckenzie Hill. 2008. 100p. pap. 11.95 *(978-1-4357-3312-1(6))* Lulu Enterprises Inc.

Parragon Publishing Staff. Chocolate: The Ultimate Ingredient for Tempting Treats Including 100 Delicious Recipes. 2010. (100 Best Recipes Ser.). pap. *(978-1-4054-0383-2(7))* Parragon Bk. Service Ltd.

Paul, Michael. Sweet Paris: A Love Affair with Parisian Chocolate, Pastries & Desserts. 2012. (ENG., Illus.). 263p. 29.95 ***(978-1-74270-186-8(8))*** Rizzoli International Pubns., Inc.

Presilla, Maricel & Presilla, Maricel E. The New Taste of Chocolate: A Cultural & Natural History of Cacao with Recipes. 2nd rev. ed. 2009. (ENG., Illus.). 256p. 35.00 *(978-1-58008-950-0(X))* Ten Speed Pr.

Robertson, Emma. Chocolate, Women & Empire. 2010. (Studies in Imperialism Ser.). (ENG., Illus.). 272p. 89.95 *(978-0-7190-7777-7(X))* Manchester Univ. Pr. GBR. Dist: Macmillan.

Rosenblum, Mort. Chocolate: A Bittersweet Saga of Dark & Light. 2006. (ENG., Illus.). 304p. per. 14.00 *(978-0-86547-730-8(2)*, North Point Pr.) Farrar, Straus & Giroux.

—Chocolate: A Bittersweet Saga of Dark & Light. l.t. ed. 29.95 *(978-0-7862-7834-3(X)*, Large Print Pr.) Thorndike Pr.

Ryan, Orla. Chocolate Nations: Living & Dying for Cocoa in West Africa. 2011. (African Arguments Ser.). (ENG.). 176p. 107.95 *(978-1-84813-004-3(X))*; 192p. pap. 14.95 *(978-1-84813-005-0(8))* Zed Bks., Ltd. GBR. Dist: Macmillan.

Shotts, Andrew Garrison. Making Artisan Chocolates: Flavor-Infused Chocolates, Truffles, & Confections. 2007. (ENG., Illus.). 176p. pap. 24.99 *(978-1-59253-310-7(8)*, 1592533108, Quarry Books) Quayside.

Southern Living Magazine Editors. Simply Chocolate: 60 Chunky, Nutty, Creamy Creations. 2009. (ENG., Illus.). 112p. 19.95 *(978-0-8487-3301-8(0))* Oxmoor Hse., Inc.

Talbot, G., ed. Science & Technology of Enrobed & Filled Chocolate, Confectionery & Bakery Products. 2009. (Illus.). 468p. *(978-1-84569-390-9(6))* Woodhead Publishing Ltd.

Van Der Gaag, Nikki. The Bittersweet World of Chocolate. Wells, Troth, ed. 2007. (Chunky Cook Book: Supporting Fair Trade Ser.). (ENG., Illus.). 176p. pap. 24.95 *(978-1-904456-25-4(1))* New Internationalist Pubns., Ltd. GBR. Dist: Consortium Bk. Sales & Distribution.

Wells, Troth & Gaag, Nikki Van Der. The Bittersweet World of Chocolate: Sumptuous Recipes Using Fair Trade Chocolate. 2008. (ENG., Illus.). 176p. pap. 19.95 *(978-1-904456-86-5(3))* New Internationalist Pubns., Ltd. GBR. Dist: Consortium Bk. Sales & Distribution.

Wexler, Barbara. Chocolate: Treat Yourself to a Healthy Heart. 2007. (Woodland Health Ser.). (Illus.). 30p. pap. 4.95 *(978-1-58054-112-1(7))* Woodland Publishing, Inc.

A World of Chocolate. 2011. 90.00 ***(978-0-9567667-3-1(0)***, Buckingham Bk. Publishing LTD) Midpoint Trade Bks., Inc.

Wybauw, Jean-Pierre. Fine Chocolates: Great Experience. 2007. (ENG., Illus.). 230p. 105.00 *(978-90-209-5914-7(X))* Lannoo Pubs./Racine.

—Fine Chocolates 2: Great Ganache Experience. 2008. (ENG., Illus.). 208p. 105.00 *(978-90-209-7588-8(9))* Lannoo Pubs./Racine.

CHOCOLATE-TREE

see Cacao

CHOCTAW INDIANS

see Five Civilized Tribes; Indians of North America—Southern States

CHODERLOS DE LACLOS, PIERRE-AMBROISE-FRANCOIS, 1741-1803

see Laclos, Choderlos de, 1741-1803

CHOICE, SOCIAL

see Social Choice

CHOICE (PSYCHOLOGY)

see also Commitment (Psychology); Decision Making; Dissonance (Psychology)

Ainslie, George. Picoeconomics: The Strategic Interaction of Successive Motivational States within the Person. 2010. (Studies in Rationality & Social Change Ser.). (ENG.). 458p. pap. 40.00 *(978-0-521-15870-1(2))* Cambridge Univ. Pr.

Andrews, Andy. The Butterfly Effect: How Your Life Matters. 2010. 112p. 14.95 *(978-1-4041-8780-1(4))* Nelson, Thomas Inc.

Archer, Margaret. The Reflexive Imperative in Late Modernity. 2012. (ENG., Illus.). 352p. 95.00 ***(978-1-107-02095-5(6))***; pap. 36.99 ***(978-1-107-60527-5(X))*** Cambridge Univ. Pr.

Asher, Winona. Life & Making Choices. 2009. 104p. pap. 13.99 *(978-1-4490-1748-4(7))* AuthorHouse.

Barnes, Mark. An Ordinary, Happy Man: Living Rich When You're Not Wealthy. 2007. (Nuts & Bolts Ser.). (ENG.). 118p. per. *(978-1-933255-29-3(3))* DNA Pr.

Bechta, Barry Thomas. I Am Creating My Own Experience: 369 Conscious Days. 2010. ***(978-0-9686835-9-0(2))*** Unconditional Love Bks.

Bennett, Cliff. Challenging Choices: Welcome Life's Invitations to Increase Your Vision. 2011. (ENG.). 194p. pap. 9.99 ***(978-1-4536-4724-0(4))*** CreateSpace.

Bines, Deric & Griggs, Sherry. Don't Let This Be Your Story: How to Make Better Choices. 2009. 148p. pap. 23.95 *(978-1-4327-4605-6(7))* Outskirts Pr., Inc.

Boston, Mike W. Now or Later. 2008. 140p. pap. 14.95 *(978-0-9779690-9-8(6))* Dare2Dream Books.

Carson, Rick. A Master Class in Gremlin-Taming: The Absolutely Indispensable Next Step for Freeing Yourself from the Monster of the Mind. 2008. (ENG., Illus.). 208p. pap. 14.95 *(978-0-06-114840-8(7)*, Harper Paperbacks) HarperCollins Pubs.

Chan, David K. Moral Psychology Today: Essays on Values, Rational Choice, & the Will. Chan, David K., ed. 2008. (Philosophical Studies Ser.). (Illus.). X, 250p. (C). 239.00 *(978-1-4020-6871-3(9)*, 1402068719) Springer.

Chan, David K., ed. Moral Psychology Today: Essays on Values, Rational Choice, & the Will. 2010. (Philosophical Studies Ser.). x, 250p. pap. 239.00 *(978-90-481-7746-2(4)*, 9048177464) Springer.

Ch'Ng, Kean Siang. The Evolutionary & Adaptive Economic Behavior. 2009. 192p. pap. *(978-3-639-17088-7(1))* VDM Verlag Dr. Mueller e.K.

Corey. I Never Knew I Had a Choice. Date not set. (Counseling Ser.). pap., tchr. ed. *(978-0-534-02088-0(7))* Brooks/Cole.

Corey, Gerald & Corey, Marianne Schneider. I Never Knew I Had A Choice: Explorations in Personal Growth. 9th ed. 2008. (PSY 103 Towards Self-Understanding Ser.). (ENG.). 464p. (C). pap. 144.95 *(978-0-495-60229-3(9))* Brooks/Cole.

Cottrell, David. Monday Morning Choices: 12 Powerful Ways to Go from Everyday to Extraordinary. 2008. (ENG.). 208p. 21.99 *(978-0-06-145191-1(6)*, Collins) HarperCollins Pubs.

Cram101 Textbook Reviews Staff. Outlines & Highlights for I Never Knew I Had a Choice: Explorations in Personal Growth by Gerald Corey, ISBN. 2009. 74p. pap. 27.95 *(978-1-4288-7967-6(6))* Cram101 Inc.

—Outlines & Highlights for Marriages & Families: Making Choices in a Diverse Society by Lamanna, ISBN. 2008. 168p. pap. 12.95 *(978-1-4288-6164-0(5))* Cram101 Inc.

Dagmar (Kapala) Kellogg, Irene. Words of Wisdom. 2011. 100p. pap. 12.99 ***(978-1-4583-3334-6(5))*** Lulu Enterprises Inc.

Dolan, Raymond J. & Sharot, Tali, eds. Neuroscience of Preference & Choice: Cognitive & Neural Mechanisms. 2011. (ENG.). 356p. 79.95 ***(978-0-12-381431-9(6)***, Academic Pr.) Elsevier Science & Technology Bks.

Dorris, David W. Life Is to Short: Choices in Life (2nd Edition) 2008. ,132p. pap. 9.95 *(978-1-60594-045-8(3)*, Llumina Pr.) Aeon Publishing Inc.

—Life Is Too Short: Choices in Life (2nd Edition) 2008. 132p. 23.95 *(978-1-60594-117-2(4)*, Llumina Pr.) Aeon Publishing Inc.

Elster, Jon, et al, eds. Understanding Choice, Explaining Behaviour. 2006. 282p. 59.00 *(978-82-7477-237-3(7)*, Oslo Academic Pr.) Unipub forlag NOR. Dist: International Specialized Bk. Services.

Elster, Jon & Skog, Ole-Jorgen, eds. Getting Hooked: Rationality & Addiction. 2007. (ENG., Illus.). 300p. pap. 60.00 *(978-0-521-03879-9(0))* Cambridge Univ. Pr.

Fasina, Omisona. Inner View - Choosing Authenticity. 2011. 192p. pap. ***(978-1-907722-29-5(7))*** Ecademy Pr. Ltd.

Frid, Marcia C. I Like You, I Like Me, Too! A Teacher/Parent Guide to Help Children Aged 6-10 Develop Self-Esteem Based on Choice Theory. 2008. (Illus.). 184p. pap. *(978-1-894431-25-5(1))* Your Nickel's Worth Publishing.

Gambetta, Diego. Were They Pushed or Did They Jump? Individual Decision Mechanisms in Education. 2009. (Studies in Rationality & Social Change Ser.). (ENG., Illus.). 248p. pap. 36.99 *(978-0-521-10770-9(9))* Cambridge Univ. Pr.

Gault, Carolyn Rabon. Choices: The Secret to Making Wise Choices. 2010. 136p. 28.95 *(978-1-4497-0353-0(4))*; pap. 11.95 *(978-1-4497-0352-3(6))* Author Solutions, Inc. (WestBow Pr.).

George, Elizabeth. A Young Woman's Guide to Making Right Choices: Your Life God's Way. 2009. 208p. pap. 10.99 *(978-0-7369-2107-7(9))* Harvest Hse. Pubs.

Glimcher, Paul W. Foundations of Neuroeconomic Analysis, 1 vol. 2010. (ENG., Illus.). 496p. 69.95 *(978-0-19-974425-1(4))* Oxford Univ. Pr., Inc.

Greene, William H. & Hensher, David A. Modeling Ordered Choices: A Primer. 2010. (ENG., Illus.). 382p. 110.00 *(978-0-521-19420-4(2))*; pap. 48.99 *(978-0-521-14237-3(7))* Cambridge Univ. Pr.

Greenfield, Kent. The Myth of Choice: Personal Responsibility in a World of Limits. 2011. (Illus.). 256p. 27.00 *(978-0-300-16950-8(7))* Yale Univ. Pr.

Grüne-Yanoff, Till & Hansson, Sven Ove, eds. Preference Change: Approaches from philosophy, economics & Psychology. 2009. (Theory & Decision Library A: Ser.). (ENG., Illus.). xii, 268p. 139.00 *(978-90-481-2592-0(8))* Springer.

Hartmann, Tilo, ed. Media Choice: A Theoretical & Empirical Overview. 2009. (ENG., Illus.). 320p. 131.00 *(978-0-415-96456-2(3))* Routledge.

Herndon Sr., Robert. Shadow Forces: 2007. pap. 17.99 *(978-1-60034-970-6(6))* Xulon Pr., Inc.

Hollett, Russell. The Happy Heretic: Look Within-Life's Difficulties Can Be Golden Opportunites. 2010. 156p. pap. 12.95 *(978-1-4269-2851-2(3))* Trafford Publishing.

House, Ernest R. Evaluating with Validity (PB) *(978-1-61735-131-0(8))* Information Age Publishing, Inc.

Howarth, Gerald E. Five Principles of Life, 1 vol. 2010. 50p. pap. 16.95 *(978-1-4489-5961-7(6))* PublishAmerica, Inc.

Iyengar, Sheena. The Art of Choosing: The Decisions We Make Everyday - What They Say about Us & How We Can Improve Them. (ENG., 2011. Illus.). 368p. pap. 14.99 *(978-0-446-50411-9(4))* 2010. 352p. 25.99 *(978-0-446-50410-2(6))* Grand Central Publishing. (Twelve).

Jasper, James M. Getting Your Way: Strategic Dilemmas in the Real World. 2006. 224p. 28.00 *(978-0-226-39475-6(1))* Univ. of Chicago Pr.

—Getting Your Way: Using Strategy in Everyday Life. 2006. pap. 27.00 *(978-0-226-39477-0(8))* Univ. of Chicago Pr.

Johnson, Barbie. Common Choices for Uncommon People: Going from Ordinary to Extraordinary with a Single Choice. 2010. 145p. pap. 15.95 *(978-1-4327-5051-0(8))* Outskirts Pr., Inc.

Kendall, Graham, et al. The Iterated Prisoners' Dilemma: 20 Years On. 2007. (Advances in Natural Computation Ser.). (Illus.). 262p. 121.00 *(978-981-270-697-3(6))* World Scientific Publishing Co., Inc.

Khader, Serene J. Adaptive Preferences & Women's Empowerment, 1 vol. 2011. (Studies in Feminist Philosophy Ser.). (ENG.). 264p. 99.00 *(978-0-19-977788-4(8))*; pap. 24.95 *(978-0-19-977787-7(X))* Oxford Univ. Pr., Inc.

Knight, Robert Marsden. Balanced Living: Don't Let Your Strength Become Your Weakness. 2008. 212p. pap. 23.00 *(978-1-55635-838-8(5)*, Resource Pubns.) Wipf & Stock Pubs.

Kristjánsson, Kristján. Social Freedom: The Responsibility View. 2007. (ENG.). 236p. pap. 51.00 *(978-0-521-04413-4(8))* Cambridge Univ. Pr.

Lamanna, Mary Ann & Riedmann, Agnes. Marriages & Families: Making Choices in a Diverse Society. 11th ed. 2011. (ENG.). 240p. (C). pap. 78.95 *(978-1-111-35252-3(6))* Wadsworth.

—Marriages, Families, & Relationships: Making Choices in a Diverse Society. 11th ed. 2011. (ENG.). 656p. (C). 178.95 *(978-1-111-30154-5(9))* Wadsworth.

Lawson, David, et al. How to Make Choices You Won't Regret. 2009. (40-Minute Bible Studies). (ENG.). 80p. pap. 7.99 *(978-0-307-45764-6(8)*, WaterBrook Pr.) Doubleday Religious Publishing Group, The.

Lazar, Silas. Rejoice by Choice. 2009. *(978-1-55452-424-2(5))* Essence Publishing.

Lerner, Sharon. The War on Moms: On Life in a Family-Unfriendly Nation. 2010. (ENG.). 224p. 25.95 *(978-0-470-17709-9(8)*, Wiley) Wiley, John & Sons, Inc.

Li, Ping. Awakening: Fulfilling your soul's purpose on Earth. 2009. 300p. pap. 27.00 *(978-1-4251-8055-3(8))* Trafford Publishing.

Loewenstein, George. Exotic Preferences: Behavioral Economics & Human Motivation. 2007. (ENG., Illus.). 688p. 135.00 *(978-0-19-925707-2(8))* Oxford Univ. Pr., Inc.

—Intertemporal Choice. 2006. 320p. (ENG.). 39.95 *(978-0-19-925706-5(X))*; 99.00 *(978-0-19-925705-8(1))* Oxford Univ. Pr., Inc.

Lowe, E. J. Personal Agency: The Metaphysics of Mind & Action. (ENG.). 2010. 240p. pap. 35.00 *(978-0-19-959250-0(0))* 2008. (Illus.). 224p. 75.00 *(978-0-19-921714-4(9))* Oxford Univ. Pr., Inc.

Macartney, James W. Crisis to Creation: Our Power of Choice. 2010. 210p. pap. *(978-1-935359-32-6(0))* Book Pubs. Network.

Makridakis, Spyros, et al. Dance with Chance: Making Luck Work for You. 2010. (ENG., Illus.). 336p. pap. 14.95 *(978-1-85168-720-6(3))* Oneworld Pubns. GBR. Dist: National Bk. Network.

Margolis, Char. Discover Your Inner Wisdom: Using Intuition, Logic, & Common Sense to Make Your Best Choices. 2008. (ENG.). 240p. pap. 15.99 *(978-0-7432-9790-5(3)*, Touchstone) Touchstone.

Margolis, Howar. Cognition & Extended Rational Choice. 2007. (Illus.). 241p. 190.00 *(978-0-415-70197-6(X))* Routledge.

McGibbon, Amalia, et al. The Choice Effect: Love & Commitment in an Age of Too Many Options. 2010. (ENG.). 224p. pap. 16.95 *(978-1-58005-293-1(2))* Seal Pr.

Meisner, Lucina M. Nine Years of Making the Wrong Choices: How Not to Be a Prey of a Man's Abuse, 1 vol. 2009. 73p. pap. 16.95 *(978-1-61546-672-6(X))* PublishAmerica, Inc.

Miller, Daniel A. Losing Control, Finding Serenity: How the Need to Control Hurts Us & How to Let It Go. 2011. 211p. pap. 14.95 *(978-0-9828930-0-5(0))* Ebb and Flow Pr.

Mittelberg, Mark. Eligiendo Tu Fe: En un Mundo de Opciones Espirituales. 2008.Tr. of Choosing Your Faith: In a World of Spiritual Options. (SPA.). 320p. pap. 12.99 *(978-1-4143-2063-2(9)*, Tyndale Espanol) Tyndale Hse. Pubs.

Mittelberg, Mark, et al. Choosing Your Faith: In a World of Spiritual Options. 2009. 180p. pap. 14.99 *(978-1-4143-1580-5(5))* Tyndale Hse. Pubs.

—Choosing Your Faith Study Guide. 2009. 180p. pap. 7.99 *(978-1-4143-2387-9(5))* Tyndale Hse. Pubs.

Mollicone-Long, Gina. Think or Sink: The One Choice That Changes Everything. 2010. (ENG.). 256p. pap. 14.95 *(978-0-9821392-1-9(7))* Sterling & Ross Pubs.

Moore, James W. Jesus' Parables about Making Choices. 2007. 112p. pap. 11.50 *(978-0-687-49133-9(9)*, Dimensions For Living) Abingdon Pr.

Muñoz Fonnegra, Sergio. Das gelingende Gutsein: Über Liebe und Anerkennung bei Kierkegaard. 2010. (Kierkegaard Studies. Monograph Ser.). (GER.). 197p. 119.00 *(978-3-11-022686-7(3))* De Gruyter, Walter Inc.

Pegues, Deborah Smith & Temple, Ricky. Why Smart People Make Dumb Choices. 2010. 192p. pap. 11.99 *(978-0-7369-2852-6(9))* Harvest Hse. Pubs.

Price-Palmer, Cherry. Lessons for the Lost: And the Losers Who Love Them. 2010. 60p. pap. 27.00 *(978-1-4269-3231-1(6))* Trafford Publishing.

Reader's Digest Editors. Your Health: What Works, What Doesn't. 2010. (ENG.). 416p. (gr. 12). 17.95 *(978-1-60652-150-2(0))* Reader's Digest Assn., Inc., The.

Rls. Life, It's All about Choices. 2011. 80p. 24.99 ***(978-1-4568-7730-9(5))***; pap. 15.99 ***(978-1-4568-7729-3(1))*** Xlibris Corp.

Rolando, Gripaldo. Circumstantialism: An Essay on Situational Determinism. 2011. 100p. pap. ***(978-3-639-32886-8(8))*** VDM Verlag Dr. Mueller e.K.

Ross, Don, et al. Midbrain Mutiny Vol. 2: The Picoeconomics & Neuroeconomics of Disordered Gambling - Economic Theory & Cognitive Science. 2012. (ENG., Illus.). 312p. (gr. 17). pap. 20.00 ***(978-0-262-51758-4(2))*** MIT Pr.

Ross, Don, et al. Midbrain Mutiny - The Picoeconomics & Neuroeconomics of Disordered Gambling: Economic Theory & Cognitive Science. 2008. (ENG., Illus.). 312p. (gr. 17). 40.00 *(978-0-262-18265-2(3))* MIT Pr.

Ryce, Michael. Why Is This Happening to Me... Again?! And What You Can Do about It. 2006. pap. 15.00 *(978-1-886562-29-5(6))* HeartLand Aramaic Mission.

Saleci, Renata. The Tyranny of Choice. 2011. (ENG.). 224p. pap. 15.95 ***(978-1-84668-186-8(3))*** Profile Bks. Ltd. GBR. Dist: Consortium Bk. Sales & Distribution.

Sanders, Ryan L. Early Choices, 1 vol. 2009. 133p. pap. 19.95 *(978-1-61582-791-6(9))* PublishAmerica, Inc.

Schelling, Thomas C. Strategies of Commitment & Other Essays. 2007. (Illus.). 360p. per. 23.50 *(978-0-674-02567-7(9))* Harvard Univ. Pr.

Schelling, Thomas C. & Schelling, Thomas. Micromotives & Macrobehavior. 2006. (ENG., Illus.). 272p. pap. 17.95 *(978-0-393-32946-9(1)*, 32946) Norton, W. W. & Co., Inc.

Sherman, Karen. Mindfulness & the Art of Choice: Transform Your Life. 2008. (Illus.). 124p. per. *(978-1-932690-51-4(4))* Loving Healing Pr., Inc.

Sherman, Karen H. Mindfulness & the Art of Choice: Transform Your Life, 2nd Edition. 2010. 140p. pap. 16.95 *(978-1-61599-032-0(1))* Loving Healing Pr., Inc.

Silf, Margaret. Wise Choices: A Spiritual Guide to Making Life's Decisions. 2007. (ENG.). 128p. per. 14.00 *(978-1-933346-04-5(3))* BlueBridge.

Silvious, Jan. Smart Girls Think Twice: Making Wise Choices When It Counts, 0 vols. 2008. 224p. pap. 14.99 *(978-0-7852-2815-8(2))* Nelson, Thomas Inc.

Skrlloff, Ronald. Living Through Self-Purpose. 2010. pap. 19.95 (978-0-9729445-9-5(1)) River's Bend Pr.

Skyrms, Brian. Choice & Chance. Date not set. (Philosophy Ser.). pap. 4.00 net. (978-0-8221-6775-4(1)) Wadsworth.

Smallwood, Beverly. This Wasn't Supposed to Happen to Me, 0 vols. 2009. 336p. pap. 16.99 (978-0-7852-9731-4(6)) Nelson, Thomas Inc.

Stone, Pamela. Opting Out? Why Women Really Quit Careers & Head Home. (Illus.). 2008. 310p. pap. 21.95 (978-0-520-25657-6(3)) 2007. 295p. 45.00 (978-0-520-24435-1(4)) Univ. of California Pr.

—Opting Out? Why Women Really Quit Careers & Head Home. 2007. (Illus.). 496p. pap. 24.95 (978-0-520-90207-7(6)) Univ. of California Pr.

Stubnson, Gene. Pants Hanging Down. 2007. per. 18.50 (978-0-9798776-5-0(2)) Great American Pr., The.

Tasler, Nick. The Impulse Factor: An Innovative Approach to Better Decision Making. 2009. (ENG.). 272p. pap. 15.00 (978-1-4391-5727-5(8), Touchstone) Touchstone.

Taylor, Eldon. Choices & Illusions: How Did I Get Where I Am, & How Do I Get Where I Want to Be? 2007. (ENG., Illus.). 160p. per. 14 95 (978-1-4019-1853-8(0)) Hay Hse., Inc.

Thaler, Richard H. Nudge: Improving Decisions about Health, Wealth, & Happiness. 2008. 532p. pap. 45.00 (978-0-300-14470-3(9)) Yale Univ. Pr.

Thaler, Richard H. & Sunstein, Cass R. Nudge: Improving Decisions about Health, Wealth, & Happiness. 2009. (ENG.). 320p. (gr. 12-18). 16.00 (978-0-14-311526-7(X), Penguin (Non-Classics)) Penguin Group (USA) Inc.

—Nudge: Improving Decisions about Health, Wealth, & Happiness. 2008. (ENG., Illus.). 304p. 27.95 (978-0-300-12223-7(3)) Yale Univ. Pr.

Ubel, Peter A. The Other End of the Stethoscope. 2012. (ENG.). 304p. 26.99 **(978-0-06-210382-6(2)**, HarperOne) HarperCollins Pubs.

Veldkamp, Laura. Information Choice in Macroeconomics & Finance. 2011. (ENG., Illus.). 180p. (C). 45.00 (978-0-691-14220-3(3)) Princeton Univ. Pr.

Weisbrode, Kenneth. On Ambivalence: The Problems & Pleasures of Having It Both Ways. 2012. (ENG., Illus.). 88p. (gr. 17). 10.95 **(978-0-262-01731-2(8))** MIT Pr.

White, Jerry E. The Joseph Road: Choices That Determine Your Destiny. 2010. (Living the Letters Ser.). (ENG., Illus.). 208p. pap. 14.99 (978-1-60006-269-8(5)) NavPress Publishing Group.

Witte, W. F (Bud). Choices Choices Choices That s Life. 2011. 114p. pap. 11.99 (978-1-61215-565-4(0)) Xulon Pr., Inc.

Zeff, Joel. Make the Right Choice: Creating a Positive, Innovative, & Productive Work Life. 2007. (ENG.). 176p. 21.95 (978-0-470-09929-2(1), Wiley) Wiley, John & Sons, Inc.

Zsolnai, Laszlo. Responsible Decision Making. 2008. (ENG.). 214p. 59.95 (978-1-4128-0818-7(9)) Transaction Pubs.

CHOICE OF BOOKS

see Book Selection; Books and Reading

CHOICE OF COLLEGE

see College Choice

CHOICE OF PROFESSION

see Vocational Guidance

CHOICE OF SCHOOL

see School Choice

CHOIR BOOKS

see Service Books (Music)

CHOIR STALLS

Tammen, Bjoern R. Musik & Bild: Im Chorraum Mittelalterlicher Kirchen 1100-1500. (GER., Illus.). 552p. (978-3-496-01218-4(8)) Reimer, Dietrich.

CHOIRBOY TRAINING

see Choirboys—Training

CHOIRBOYS—TRAINING

Mould, Alan. The English Chorister: A History. 2008. (ENG., Illus.). 384p. per. 34.95 (978-1-84725-058-2(0), Hambledon Continuum) Continuum International Publishing Group, Ltd. GBR. Dist: National Bk. Network.

CHOIRS (MUSIC)

see also Chapels (Music); Children's Choirs; Choral Conducting; Choral Singing

Abingdon Press, creator. Choir Director's Organzier. 2007. (Illus.). 99p. spiral bd. 15.00 (978-0-687-64251-9(5)) Abingdon Pr.

Acker, Mark. The Passion-Driven Youth Choir. annot. ed. 2007. 138p. per. 12.00 (978-0-687-49224-4(6)) Abingdon Pr.

Alfred Publishing Staff. Banuwa — Three African Songs. 2007. (Faber Edition: Choral Programme Ser.). (ENG.). pap. 6.95 (978-0-571-52655-0(1)) Faber & Faber, Ltd. GBR. Dist: Alfred Publishing Co., Inc.

—You'll Never Walk Alone: And Other Sporting Anthems. 2007. (Faber Edition: Choral Basics Ser.). (ENG.). pap. 5.50 (978-0-571-52620-8(9)) Faber & Faber, Ltd. GBR. Dist: Alfred Publishing Co., Inc.

Anderson, Toni P. Tell Them We Are Singing for Jesus: The Original Fisk Jubilee Singers & Christian Reconstruction, 1871- 2009. (Illus.). 352p. 45.00 (978-0-88146-112-1(1)) Mercer Univ. Pr.

Andrew Lloyd Webber. 2008. (Sing with the Choir Ser.). (ENG.). 40p. pap. 14.95 incl. audio compact disk (978-1-4234-5341-3(7), 1423453417) Leonard, Hal Corp.

Boublil, Schonberg, et al. Les Miserables: Sing with the Choir Volume 9. 2009. (ENG.). 56p. pap. 14.99 incl. audio compact disk (978-1-4234-4037-6(4), 1423440374) Leonard, Hal Corp.

Bullard, Alan, ed. The Oxford Book of Flexible Anthems: A Complete Resource for Every Church Choir. 2007. 296p. pap. 19.95 (978-0-19-335895-9(6)) Oxford Univ. Pr., Inc.

Chesnokov, Pavel. The Choir & How to Direct It. Rommereim, John, tr. from RUS. 2009.Tr. of Khor i upravlenie Im. pap. (978-0-9701767-3-8(2)) Musica Russica.

Chilcott, Bob. Bob Chilcott Anthems 2. 2009. (ENG.). 64p. pap. 12.95 (978-0-19-336493-6(X)) Oxford Univ. Pr., Inc.

Corp, Ronald. Choral Singers Companion. (Illus.). 222p. pap. 29.95 (978-1-84609-334-0(1), TH980012, Bosworth) Music Sales Corp.

Cottrell, Travis, contrib. by & creator. Glorious Day: A Modern Worship Choir Collection; SATB. 2008. 190p. pap. 7.95 (978-5-557-42397-7(4), Brentwood-Benson Music Publishing, Inc.) Brentwood Music, Inc.

Davis, B. J., et al, contrib. by. Still Amazed Live at Southeast Christian Church: Satb. 2007. 134p. pap. 7.95 (978-5-557-61410-8(9), Brentwood-Benson Music Publishing, Inc.) Brentwood Music, Inc.

Devender, Jeff Van. Elementary Choir Handbook & Guide. 2011. 50p. pap. 9.99 **(978-0-557-87000-4(3))** Lulu Enterprises Inc.

Elmer, István. Madrigáltörténet: A Budapesti Madrigálkórus ötven éve (1957-2007) 2008. (HUN., Illus.). 148p. (978-963-346-834-0(5)) Holnap Konyvkiado Kft.

Hal Leonard Corporation Staff, creator. Broadway. 2008. (Sing with the Choir Ser.). (ENG.). 48p. pap. 14.95 incl. audio compact disk (978-1-4234-5509-7(6), 1423455096) Leonard, Hal Corp.

—Christmas Carols: Sing with the Choir Volume 13. 2009. (ENG.). 40p. pap. 14.99 incl. audio compact disk (978-1-4234-8480-6(0), 1423484800) Leonard, Hal Corp.

—Christmas Favorites: Sing with the Choir Volume 10. 2008. (ENG.). 46p. pap. 14.95 incl. audio compact disk (978-1-4234-5814-2(1), 1423458141) Leonard, Hal Corp.

—Christmas Time Is Here: Sing with the Choir Volume 11. 2008. (ENG.). 48p. pap. 14.95 incl. audio compact disk (978-1-4234-5815-9(X), 142345815X) Leonard, Hal Corp.

—Disney Favorites: Sing with the Choir Volume 7. 2008. (ENG.). 56p. pap. 14.95 incl. audio compact disk (978-1-4234-3986-8(4), 1423439864) Leonard, Hal Corp.

—Disney Hits: Sing with the Choir Volume 8. 2008. (ENG.). 40p. pap. 14.95 incl. audio compact disk (978-1-4234-3987-5(2), 1423439872) Leonard, Hal Corp.

—Glee: Sing with the Choir. 2010. (ENG.). 72p. pap. 16.99 incl. audio compact disk (978-1-4234-9293-1(5), 1423492935) Leonard, Hal Corp.

—3. Standards: Sing with the Choir Volume 3. 2008. 40p. pap. 14.95 incl. audio compact disk (978-1-4234-5510-3(X), 142345510X) Leonard, Hal Corp.

—The 1950s Vol. 4: Sing with the Choir. 2008. (ENG.). 40p. pap. 14.95 incl. audio compact disk (978-1-4234-3740-6(3), 1423437403) Leonard, Hal Corp.

—The 1960s: Sing with the Choir Volume 5. 2008. (ENG.). 48p. pap. 14.95 incl. audio compact disk (978-1-4234-3741-3(1), 1423437411) Leonard, Hal Corp.

—The 1970s: Sing with the Choir Volume 6. 2008. (ENG.). 48p. pap. 14.95 incl. audio compact disk (978-1-4234-3742-0(X), 142343742X) Leonard, Hal Corp.

Hall, Stephanie, ed. America's Newest Worship Favorites: 10 Top Songs of the Church. 2009. 131p. pap. 7.99 (978-1-4234-8907-8(1)) Leonard, Hal Corp.

Haugen, Marty. Ritual Song: Choir Edition. Cymbala, Michael A. et al, eds. 23.50 (978-0-941050-86-9(6), G-4500C) G I A Pubns., Inc.

Janz, DeEtta. You Can Improvise: A Church Pianist's Guide to the Art of Reading Between the Notes. 2009. (ENG.). spiral bd. 19.99 (978-0-615-29526-8(6)) DeJanz Production.

Keen, Basil. The Bach Choir 1878-1928. 2008. (Illus.). 334p. 124.95 (978-0-7546-5477-3(X)) Ashgate Publishing Co.

Kirkland, Camp, creator. 30-Minute Choir Book: 20 Time-Saving Arrangments Easily Learned in One Short, Half-Hour Rehearsal! 2008. 205p. pap. 8.95 (978-5-557-38245-8(3), Brentwood-Benson Music Publishing, Inc.) Brentwood Music, Inc.

Kohler, Christine. Music Performance: Vocals & Band. 2012. (Glee Club Ser.). (ENG.). 64p. (YA). (gr. 7-12). pap. 12.95 **(978-1-4488-6885-8(8))**; lib. bdg. 31.95 **(978-1-4488-6875-9(0))** Rosen Publishing Group, Inc., The.

Lauridsen, Morten. Contre Qui, Rose: String Quartet. 2011. (ENG.). 12p. pap. 19.95 **(978-1-4584-1679-7(8)**, 1458416798) Peermusic Classical.

Lippoldt Mack, Valerie. Putting the SHOW in CHOIR: The Ultimate Handbook for Your Rehearsal & Performance. 2011. (ENG.). 140p. pap. 12.99 (978-1-61774-323-8(2), 1617743232) Shawnee Pr., Inc.

Lord, thou hast been our Refuge. 2008. 8p. pap. 3.95 (978-0-19-336327-4(5)); 20p. pap. 2.75 (978-0-19-336274-1(0)) Oxford Univ. Pr., Inc.

Maile, Roger. Choir for All Seasons. (Illus.). 96p. pap. (978-1-873319-00-0(2)) Creative Monochrome GBR. Dist: Vine Hse. Distribution.

Mauldin, Russell & Fettke, Tom, contrib. by. This We Believe: An Easter Musical for Every Choir. 2010. (ENG.). 108p. pap. 7.99 (978-0-8341-7846-5(X), 9780834178465) Lillenas Publishing Co.

Mees, Arthur. Choirs & Choral Music. 2010. 290p. pap. 28.75 (978-1-177-67416-4(5)); 294p. pap. 28.75 (978-1-145-00387-3(7)) BiblioBazaar.

—Choirs & Choral Music. 2009. 172p. pap. (978-0-217-33866-0(6)) Books LLC.

—Choirs & Choral Music. 2009. 174p. pap. 19.99 (978-0-217-81099-9(3)) General Bks. LLC.

—Choirs & Choral Music. 2008. 280p. 42.95 (978-1-4369-5003-9(1)); pap. 27.95 (978-1-4368-0463-9(9)) Kessinger Publishing, LLC.

Onovwerosuoke, Fred. Tribute to Great African Composers No. 1: Tribute to Dr. Ephraim Amu. 2007. (ENG & TWI.). spiral bd. 75.00 (978-1-934621-06-6(4)) African Music Pubs.

—Tribute to Great African Composers No. 2: Rhapsody on Nketia's Republic Suite. 2007. spiral bd. 75.00 (978-1-934621-10-3(2)) African Music Pubs.

Pethel, Stan. Gospel Voices, Vol. 2. 2011. (ENG.). 56p. pap. 5.95 (978-1-61774-266-8(X), 161774266X, Glory Sound) Shawnee Pr., Inc.

Phillips, Christopher, et al, contrib. by. He Still Leads: Satb. 2008. audio compact disk 10.00 (978-5-557-48398-8(5), Brentwood-Benson Music Publishing, Inc.) Brentwood Music, Inc.

—He Still Leads: Satb. 2008. (ENG.). 215p. pap. 8.99 (978-5-557-48401-5(9)) Brentwood-Benson Music Publishing.

Pulkingham, Betty. This Is My Story This Is My Song: A Life Journey. 2011. 240p. pap. 17.95 **(978-1-4497-2339-2(X)**, WestBow Pr.) Author Solutions, Inc.

Puresound Student Worship Ministries, contrib. by. Let It Be Said of Us: A Student Worship Choir Collection. 2010. (ENG.). 120p. pap. 8.99 (978-0-8341-7676-2(1), 9780834178762) Lillenas Publishing Co.

Rattray, Brenda. The Joy of Singing: 20 Inspirational Songs for Schools & Communities. 2008. (Faber Edition Ser.). (ENG.). pap. 60.25 (978-0-571-52439-6(7)) Faber & Faber, Ltd. GBR. Dist: Alfred Publishing Co. Inc.

Reneau, April. Criteria for Choral Voice Classification: Determining Basic Voice Classification of High SchoolChoir Students. 2008. 68p. pap. (978-3-639-09791-7(2)) VDM Verlag Dr. Mueller e.K.

Ritchie, Ian, et al, eds. A Choir Book for the Queen: A collection of contemporary sacred music in celebration of the Diamond Jubilee. 2011. 480p. pap. 47.99 **(978-1-84825-115-1(7)**, Canterbury Pr. Norwich) Hymns Ancient & Modern Ltd GBR. Dist: Westminster John Knox Pr.

Rodgers, Richard & Hammerstein II, Oscar. The Sound of Music: Sing with the Choir Volume 12. 2010. (ENG.). 48p. pap. 14.99 incl. audio compact disk (978-1-4234-8316-8(2), 1423483162) Leonard, Hal Corp.

Schram, Ruth Elaine & Hayden, Tim. Gather 'Round & Sing: 6 Rounds for 2-Part & 3-Part Children's Choirs. 2008. (ENG.). 48p. pap. 19.95 (978-0-7390-5034-7(6)) Alfred Publishing Co., Inc.

—Gather 'Round & Sing: 6 Rounds for 2-Part & 3-Part Children's Choirs, Book & CD. 2008. (ENG.). 48p. pap. 44.95 (978-0-7390-5035-4(4)) Alfred Publishing Co., Inc.

Seelig, Timothy. The Perfect Rehearsal: Everything You Wanted to Know about Rehearsals! 2006. (ENG., Illus.). 138p. per. 24.99 (978-1-59235-152-7(2), 1592351522) Shawnee Pr., Inc.

Sherr, Richard, tr. Masses for the Sistine Chapel: Vatican City, Biblioteca Apostolica Vaticana, Cappella Sistina, MS 14. 2010. (Monuments of Renaissance Music Ser.). (ENG., Illus.). 616p. 295.00 (978-0-226-75259-4(3)) Univ. of Chicago Pr.

Trapp, Lynn & Leitschuh, Carol, eds. In Harmony with God: Choir Member Edition. 2008. 32p. 6.95 (978-0-8146-3087-7(1), Liturgical Pr. Bks.) Liturgical Pr.

Weaver, Mike & Hart, Colleen. Sweat, Tears & Jazz Hands: The Official History of Show Choir from Vaudeville to Glee. 2011. (ENG., Illus.). 208p. pap. 22.99 (978-1-55783-772-1(4), 1557837724) Leonard, Hal Corp.

Wilberg. Come, come ye saints for SATB & orgran or Orhestra. 2009. 16p. spiral bd. 90.00 (978-0-19-380488-3(3)) Oxford Univ. Pr., Inc.

Wilberg, Mack. Come, Come, Ye Saints for Satb & Organ or Orchestra. 2008. 12p. 1.95 (978-0-19-380489-0(1)) Oxford Univ. Pr., Inc.

Williams, Malcolm. The Cotswold Male Voice Choir. 2009. (ENG., Illus.). 128p. pap. 24.95 (978-0-7524-5006-3(9)) History Pr. Ltd.,The GBR. Dist: Independent Pubs. Group.

Williamson, Scott. Ampe'd. 2007. (ENG.). 114p. pap. 19.99 (978-1-59802-092-2(7), 1598020927) Brentwood Music, Inc.

Wyrick, Ginger G. Singing Between the Lines: Fifteen-Minute Music Theory Lessons for Your Church Choir. 2006. (Illus.). 88p. per. 18.00 (978-0-687-49748-5(5)) Abingdon Pr.

York, Terry W. New Choir Membership Kit. 2007. 14.99 (978-0-687-65051-4(8)) Abingdon Pr.

CHOIRS, CHILDREN'S

see Children's Choirs

CHOLAS

Karuppiah, K. A Socio-Cultural History of the Later Colas: As Gleaned Through Epigraphy. 2010. (Illus.). xxx, 202p. (978-81-88934-68-3(2), Library of Congress — New Delhi Overseas Office) Sharada Publishing Hse.

Lynton, Norbert. Krishen Khanna: Chola Migrations. 2007. (Contemporary Indian Artists Ser.). (ENG., Illus.). 120p. 60.00 (978-0-944142-54-7(0)) Mapin Publishing Pvt. Ltd IND. Dist: National Bk. Network.

CHOLELITHIASIS

see Gallstones

CHOLERA

Bailey, Diane. Cholera. 2010. (Epidemics & Society Ser.). (ENG.). 80p. (YA). lib. bdg. 30.60 (978-1-4358-9437-2(5)) Rosen Publishing Group, Inc., The.

Byun, Roy. The Evolution of Cholera - Molecular Evolution of the Pathogenic Clones of Vibrio Cholerae. 2008. 300p. pap. (978-3-639-05303-6(6)) VDM Verlag Dr. Mueller e.K.

Chaudhuri, Keya & Chatterjee, S. N. Cholera Toxins. 2009. (ENG., Illus.). xiv, 322p. 209.00 (978-3-540-88451-4(3), 3540884513) Springer.

Echenberg, Myron J. Africa in the Time of Cholera: A History of Pandemics from 1817 to the Present. 2011. (African Studies). (ENG., Illus.). 114p. 85.00 (978-1-107-00149-7(8)); 232p. pap. 27.99 (978-0-521-18820-3(2)) Cambridge Univ. Pr.

Faruque, Shah M. & Nair, G. Balakrish, eds. Vibrio Cholerae: Genomics & Molecular Biology. 2008. (Illus.). 218p. 319.00 (978-1-904455-33-2(6)) Caister Academic Pr. GBR. Dist: International Specialized Bk. Services.

Gilbert, Pamela K. Cholera & Nation: Doctoring the Social Body in Victorian England. (SUNY Series, Studies in the Long Nineteenth Century). 2009. 241p. pap. 24.95 (978-0-7914-7344-3(9)) 2008. 231p. 75.00 (978-0-7914-7343-6(0)) State Univ. of New York Pr.

Halliday, Stephen. The Great Filth: Disease, Death & the Victorian City. 2011. (ENG., Illus.). 256p. pap. 22.95 **(978-0-7524-6175-5(3))** History Pr. Ltd.,The GBR. Dist: Independent Pubs. Group.

Hamlin, Christopher. Cholera: the Biography. 2009. (Biographies of Diseases Ser.). (ENG., Illus.). 256p. 24.95 (978-0-19-954624-4(X)) Oxford Univ. Pr., Inc.

Hempel, Sandra. The Strange Case of the Broad Street Pump: John Snow & the Mystery of Cholera. 2007. (Illus.). 321p. 35.00 (978-0-520-25049-9(4)) Univ. of California Pr.

Johnson, Steven. The Ghost Map: The Story of London's Most Terrifying Epidemic — and How It Changed Science, Cities, & the Modern World. 2007. (ENG., Illus.). 320p. (gr. 12-18). 15.00 (978-1-59448-269-4(1), Riverhead Trade (Paperbacks)) Penguin Group (USA) Inc.

Joslin, B. F. (Benjamin Franklin). Homoeopathic Treatment of Epidemic Choera by B F Joslin. 2006. 256p. per. 23.99 (978-1-4255-2248-3(3)) MPublishing

Koch, Tom. Disease Maps: Epidemics on the Ground. 2011. (ENG., Illus.). 344p. 45.00 (978-0-226-44935-7(1)) Univ. of Chicago Pr.

Leuchars, Chris. No Court for King Cholera. 2007. 321p. pap. 18.50 (978-1-4303-1612-1(8)) Lulu Enterprises Inc.

Madoroba, E., ed. Cholera: Current African Perspectives. 2009. (Public Health in the 21st Century Ser.). pap. 43.00 (978-1-61728-294-2(4), Nova Novinka) Nova Science Pubs., Inc.

Mahiya, Innocent. Meanings That Residents in Budiriro Attach to the Cholera Illness. 2011. 56p. pap. **(978-3-8443-1906-4(9))** Lambert Academic Publishing.

Melbourne, Evelyn L. Cholera: Symptoms, Diagnosis & Treatment. 2011. (Tropical Diseases - Etiology, Pathogenesis & Treatments Ser.). 129.00 (978-1-61761-789-8(X), Nova Biomedical Bks.) Nova Science Pubs., Inc.

O'Connor, Erin. Raw Material. (978-0-8047-3839-2(4)) Stanford Univ. Pr.

Ramamurthy, Thandavarayan, ed. Cholera: Molecular & Epidemiological Aspects. 2009. (Infectious Disease Ser.). (Illus.). 320p. 189.00 (978-1-60327-264-3(X)) Humana Pr.

Simons, J. Hume. The Planter's Guide & Family Book of Medicine for the Instruction & Use of Planters, Families, Country People, & All Others Who May Be Out of the Reach of Physicians, or Unable to Employ Them. 2010. (AccessAble Bks.). (ENG.). 210p. pap. 18.95 (978-1-57003-930-0(5)) Univ. of South Carolina Pr.

Thomas, Amanda J. The Lambeth Cholera Outbreak Of 1848-1849: The Setting, Causes, Course & Aftermath of an Epidemic in London. 2009. (ENG., Illus.). 274p. pap. 45.00 (978-0-7864-3989-8(0)) McFarland & Co., Inc. Pubs.

Watson, William E., et al. The Ghosts of Duffy's Cut: The Irish Who Died Building America's Most Dangerous Stretch of Railroad, 1 vol. 2006. (Illus.). 240p. 49.95 (978-0-275-98727-5(2), C8727, Praeger Pubs.) Greenwood Publishing Group, Inc.

CHOLERA, ASIATIC

see Cholera

CHOLESTEROL

see also Food—Cholesterol Content

Anand, Vijaya & KALAVATHY, S. Clinical Utility of High Sensitivity C-Reactive Protein. 2011. 224p. pap. **(978-3-8443-9715-4(9))** Lambert Academic Publishing.

Bentley, Ryan E. Sex, Lies & Cholesterol. 2010. 128p. 22.49 (978-1-4520-7220-3(5)); pap. 15.95 (978-1-4520-7221-0(3)) AuthorHouse.

Bittner, Vera. 100 Q&A about Controlling Your Cholesterol. rev. ed. 2011. 122p. pap. 22.95 (978-0-7637-5679-6(2)) Jones & Bartlett Learning, LLC.

Brewer, Sarah. Cut Your Cholesterol: An Easy-to-Follow Guide to Lower & Manage Your Cholesterol. 2011. (ENG., Illus.). 64p. 7.95 (978-1-84724-728-5(8)) Quercus GBR. Dist: Independent Pubs. Group.

Conkling, Winifred & DeVries, Stephen R. Cholesterol: The Latest Natural Treatments & Scientific Advances in One Breakthrough Program. 2007. (ENG., Illus.). 224p. per. 14.99 (978-0-446-69773-6(7)) Grand Central Publishing.

Cook, Wade B. Crimes Against the Heart, 1. 2010. 128p. per. 16.95 (978-0-9786778-0-0(3)) Liberty Network, Inc.

Cooper - Naturopath, Frank. Cholesterol & the French Paradox. 2009. 218p. pap. 20.00 (978-1-4452-2130-4(6)) Lulu Enterprises Inc.

Cram101 Textbook Reviews & Cram101 Textbook Reviews. Outlines & Highlights for the Hdl Handbook: Biological Functions & Clinical Implications by Tsugikazu Komoda, ISBN. 2011. 118p. pap. 28.95 **(978-1-61461-240-7(4))** Cram101 Inc.

Gajbhiye, Sagarika. Pharmacological Research of an Indigenous Polyherbal Formulation. 2011. 148p. pap. **(978-3-8443-1817-3(8))** Lambert Academic Publishing.

Graveline, Duane. Statin Drugs Side Effects. 2008. 196p. pap. 20.00 (978-0-9700817-9-7(0)) Graveline, Duane E.

Harris, J. Robin, ed. Cholesterol Binding & Cholesterol Transport Proteins: Structure & Function in Health & Disease. 2010. (Subcellular Biochemistry Ser.). (Illus.). 400p. 269.00 (978-90-481-8621-1(8), 9048186218) Springer.

Holmqvist, Gunnar N., ed. Statins. 2009. 89.00 (978-1-60692-103-6(7)) Nova Science Pubs., Inc.

Icon Health Publications Staff. Official Patients Sourcebook on High Blo. 2006. 188p. per. 28.95 (978-0-497-11188-5(8)) Icon Group International, Inc.

Levitan, Irena, et al. Cholesterol Regulation of Ion Channels & Receptors. 2012. (ENG.). 304p. 125.00 **(978-0-470-87432-5(5)**, Wiley) Wiley, John & Sons, Inc.

Mihaly, Mary. The Complete Guide to Lowering Your Cholesterol. 2011. (ENG.). 288p. mass mkt. 7.99 (978-0-312-53419-6(1), St. Martin's Paperbacks) St. Martin's Pr.

Miyazaki, Akira. New Frontiers in Lifestyle-Related Diseases. 2008. (ENG., Illus.). xxii, 160p. 79.95 (978-4-431-76427-4(5), 4431764275) Springer.

Miyazaki, Akira & Imawari, Michio, eds. New Frontiers in Lifestyle-Related Diseases. 2010. (ENG., Illus.). xxii, 160p. pap. 79.95 **(978-4-431-99839-6(X)**, 443199839X) Springer.

Nicolade, Carlos. Colesterol. (SPA.). pap. 16.95 (978-950-768-406-7(9)) Grupo Imaginador de Ediciones S.A. ARG. Dist: Distribooks, Inc.

Pagano, Irwin S. & Strait, Nathan B. HDL & LDL Cholesterol: Physiology & Clinical Significance. 2009. (Biochemistry Research Trends Ser.). 129.00 (978-1-60741-767-5(7), Nova Biomedical Bks.) Nova Science Pubs., Inc.

Rinzler, Carol Ann. Controlling Cholesterol for Dummies. 2nd ed. 2008. (ENG., Illus.). 360p. pap. 21.99 (978-0-470-22759-6(1), For Dummies) Wiley, John & Sons, Inc.

Rubin, Jordan. The Great Physician's Rx for High Cholesterol, 0 vols. 2010. (Great Physician's Rx Ser.). 128p. pap. 10.99 (978-0-7852-9787-1(1)) Nelson, Thomas Inc.

Rubin, Jordan S. The Great Physician's RX for High Cholesterol, 0 vols. 2007. (Great Physican's RX Ser.). 128p. 9.99 (978-0-7852-1948-4(X)) Nelson, Thomas Inc.

Semple, Jane. Cholesterol & Inflammation: A Naturopathic Approach. 2007. (Woodland Health Ser.). 32p. pap. 4.95 (978-1-58054-108-4(9)) Woodland Publishing, Inc.

Steinberg, Daniel, ed. The Cholesterol Wars: The Skeptics vs. the Preponderance of Evidence. 2007. (ENG., Illus.). 248p. 80.95 (978-0-12-373979-7(9), Academic Pr.) Elsevier Science & Technology Bks.

Tate, Suresh. Cholesterol & Complex Lipids in Medicine: Membrane Building Blocks. 2012. (Colloquium Series on the Cell Biology of Medicine Ser.). 100p. pap. 35.00 (978-1-61504-273-9(3)) Morgan & Claypool Life Science Publishers.

Truswell, A. Stewart. Cholesterol & Beyond: The Research on Diet & Coronary Heart Disease 1900-2000. 2010. (ENG.). xiv, 240p. 39.95 (978-90-481-8874-1(1), 9048188741) Springer.

Udall, Kate Gilbert. Flaxseed & Flaxseed Oil. 3rd ed. 2011. (Woodland Health Ser.). 32p. pap. 4.95 **(978-1-58054-203-6(4))** Woodland Publishing, Inc.

Vikstedt, Riikka. Phospholipid Transfer Protein & Cholesteryl Ester Transfer Protein. 2010. 112p. pap. (978-3-8383-1854-7(4)) Lambert Academic Publishing.

CHOLESTEROL, DIETARY
see Low-Cholesterol Diet

CHOLESTEROL CONTENT OF FOOD
see Food—Cholesterol Content

CHOLINESTERASE

Satoh, Tetsuo & Gupta, Ramesh C., eds. Anticholinesterase Pesticides: Metabolism, Neurotoxicity, & Epidemiology. 2011. (ENG., Illus.). 625p. 158.00 (978-0-470-41030-1(2), Wiley) Wiley, John & Sons, Inc.

White, Cecelia J. & Tait, Janice E. Cholinesterase: Production, Uses, & Health Effects. 2012. **(978-1-62100-673-2(5))** Nova Science Pubs., Inc.

CHOMSKY, NOAM, 1928-

Barrie, Michael. Dynamic Antisymmetry & the Syntax of Noun Incorporation. 2011. (Studies in Natural Language & Linguistic Theory Ser.). (Illus.). x, 250p. 139.00 (978-94-007-1569-1(2), 9400715692) Springer.

Barsky, Robert F. The Chomsky Effect: A Radical Works Beyond the Ivory Tower. (ENG., Illus.). 400p. (gr. 17). 2009. pap. 15.95 (978-0-262-51316-6(1)) 2007. 29.95 (978-0-262-02624-6(4)) MIT Pr.

Boeckx, Cedric. Linguistic Minimalism: Origins, Concepts, Methods, & Aims. 2006. (ENG., Illus.). 256p. per. 44.99 (978-0-19-929758-0(4)) Oxford Univ. Pr., Inc.

Chomsky, Noam. New World of Indigenous Resistance. Meyer, Lois & Maldonado, Benjamin, eds. 2010. (City Lights Open Media Ser.). (ENG.). 300p. pap. 18.95 (978-0-87286-533-4(9)) City Lights Bks.

—Power & Terror: Conflict, Hegemony, & the Rule of Force. 2011. 192p. 98.00 (978-1-59451-970-3(6)); pap. 25.95 (978-1-59451-971-0(4)) Paradigm Pubs.

Chomsky, Noam & Baillargeon, Normand. L'université Selon Chomsky. 2011. (FRE.). 159p. (978-2-7605-2452-1(3)) Presses de l'Universite du Quebec.

Chomsky, Noam & Foucault, Michel. The Chomsky-Foucault Debate: On Human Nature. 2006. (ENG.). 213p. pap. 15.95 (978-1-59558-134-1(0)) New Pr., The.

Chomsky, Noam & McGilvray, James. The Science of Language: Interviews with James McGilvray. 2012. (ENG., Illus.). 328p. 75.00 **(978-1-107-01637-8(1))**; pap. 24.99 **(978-1-107-60240-3(8))** Cambridge Univ. Pr.

Chomsky, Noam, et al. Understanding Power: The Indispensable Chomsky. 432p. pap. 35.00 (978-0-908011-72-8(5)) Scribe Pubns. AUS. Dist: Independent Pubs. Group.

Cogswell, David. Chomsky for Beginners. 2007. (For Beginners Ser.). (ENG., Illus.). 160p. pap. 14.95 (978-1-934389-17-1(X), For Beginners) Steerforth Pr.

Collins Publishers Staff. Chomsky. 2008. (Guides for the Perplexed Ser.). (ENG., Illus.). 242p. 22.95 (978-0-8264-8663-9(0)); 90.00 (978-0-8264-8662-2(2)) Continuum International Publishing Group, Ltd. GBR. Dist: National Bk. Network.

Franck, Julie & Bricmont, Jean, eds. Chomsky Notebook. 2010. (Columbia Themes in Philosophy Ser.). (ENG., Illus.). 360p. (gr. 17). 89.50 (978-0-231-14474-2(1)); pap. 29.50 (978-0-231-14475-9(X)) Columbia Univ. Pr.

Galasso, Joseph. Minimum of English Grammar: An Introduction to Feature Theory with a special note on the nature of early child grammars of English. 2009. (Illus.). 600p. (C). pap. 133.95 (978-1-934269-41-1(7)) Univ. Readers.

Hacken, Plus ten. Chomskyan Linguistics & Its Competitors. (ENG.). 320p. (C). 2009. pap. 35.00 (978-1-84553-554-4(5)) 2007. (Illus.). 85.00 (978-1-84553-054-9(3)) Equinox Publishing Ltd. GBR. Dist: ISD.

Kfoury, Assaf, ed. Inside Lebanon: Journey to a Shattered Land with Noam & Carol Chomsky. 2007. (ENG., Illus.). 176p. 65.00 (978-1-58367-154-2(4)); per. 14.95 (978-1-58367-153-5(6)) Monthly Review Pr.

Maher, John. Introducing Chomsky. 2011. (Introducing Ser.). (ENG., Illus.). 176p. pap. 9.95 **(978-1-84831-206-7(7))** Totem Bks. GBR. Dist: Consortium Bk. Sales & Distribution.

Mikhail, John. Elements of Moral Cognition: Rawls' Linguistic Analogy & the Cognitive Science of Moral & Legal Judgment. 2011. (ENG., Illus.). 430p. 90.00 (978-0-521-85578-5(0)) Cambridge Univ. Pr.

Newson, Mark & Cook, Vivian J. Chomsky's Universal Grammar: An Introduction. 3rd rev. ed. 2007. (ENG., Illus.). 336p. 129.95 (978-1-4051-1186-7(0)); pap. 52.95 (978-1-4051-1187-4(9)) Wiley, John & Sons, Inc. (Wiley-Blackwell).

CHONDRIOSOMES
see Mitochondria

CHOOSE-YOUR-OWN STORY PLOTS
see Plot-Your-Own Stories

CHOPIN, FREDERIC, 1810-1849

Bellman, Jonathan. Polish Ballade: Op. 38 As Narrative of National Martyrdom. 2009. (ENG., Illus.). 216p. 40.00 (978-0-19-533886-7(3)) Oxford Univ. Pr., Inc.

Biographiq. Frtdtric Chopin - Polish Romantic Composer. 2008. 56p. pap. 9.99 (978-1-59986-366-5(9), Biographiq) Filiquarian Publishing, LLC.

Finck, Henry T. Chopin & Other Musical Essays. 2007. 284p. 43.95 (978-0-548-11045-4(X)) Kessinger Publishing, LLC.

Finck, Henry Theophilus. Chopin, & Other Musical Essays. 2009. 104p. pap. (978-1-151-39078-3(X)) Books LLC.

—Chopin & Other Musical Essays. 2009. 284p. 30.99 (978-1-115-48849-5(X)) 2008. 180p. 22.99 (978-0-554-36621-0(5)) 2008. 180p. 25.99 (978-0-554-27318-1(7)) 2007. (ENG.). 158p. per. 19.99 (978-1-4346-2969-2(4)) 2007. (ENG.). 180p. per. 21.99 (978-1-4346-2987-6(2)) BiblioBazaar.

—Chopin & Other Musical Essays. 2009. 104p. pap. (978-1-151-31254-9(1)) Books LLC.

—Chopin & Other Musical Essays. 2007. 148p. per. (978-1-4065-2406-2(9)) Dodo Pr.

Franke, Nils, ed. Romantic Piano Anthology. 2008. (ENG.). 48p. pap. 12.95 incl. audio compact disk (978-1-902455-92-1(4), 1902455924) Schott Music Corp.

Gide, André. Notes on Chopin. (978-0-8022-0587-2(9)) Philosophical Library, Inc.

Goldberg, Halina. Music in Chopin's Warsaw. 2008. (ENG., Illus.). 320p. 45.00 (978-0-19-513073-7(1)) Oxford Univ. Pr., Inc.

Grabowski, Christophe & Rink, John, eds. An Annotated Catalogue of Chopin's First Editions. 2008. (ENG., Illus.). 994p. 225.00 (978-0-521-81917-6(2)) Cambridge Univ. Pr.

Hadden, J. Cuthbert 1861-1914. Chopin. 2011. 284p. pap. 28.75 **(978-1-175-27512-7(3))** BiblioBazaar.

Hadden, James Cuthbert. Chopin. 2012. 286p. pap. 28.75 **(978-1-278-89889-6(1))** 2011. 276p. pap. 27.75 **(978-1-175-27774-9(6))** BiblioBazaar.

Hadden, J.Cuthbert. Chopin. 2010. 278p. 34.36 (978-1-163-32227-7(X)) 2010. 278p. pap. 22.36 (978-1-162-80130-8(1)) 2007. (ENG.). 276p. 42.95 (978-0-548-01004-4(8)) Kessinger Publishing, LLC.

Hall-Swadley, Janita. The Collected Writings of Franz Liszt, Vol. 1. 2011. (Illus.). 288p. 75.00 (978-0-8108-8101-3(2)) Scarecrow Pr., Inc.

Holcman, Jan. The Legacy of Chopin. 2011. 124p. 40.95 **(978-1-258-07703-7(5))** Literary Licensing, LLC.

Hueffer, Francis. Musical Studies: A Series of Contributions. 2009. (Cambridge Library Collection - Music Ser.). (ENG.). 276p. pap. 23.99 (978-1-108-00473-2(3)) Cambridge Univ. Pr.

Hughes. Liszts Chopin. 2011. (ENG., Illus.). 192p. 90.00 (978-0-7190-8568-0(3)) Manchester Univ. Pr. GBR. Dist: Macmillan.

Hughes, Meirion, ed. Liszt's 'Chopin' 2011. (ENG., Illus.). 192p. pap. 24.95 (978-0-7190-8351-8(6)) Manchester Univ. Pr. GBR. Dist: Macmillan.

Huneker, James. Chopin. 2009. 220p. pap. (978-1-4588-1888-1(8)) Books LLC.

—Chopin. 2007. 160p. per. (978-1-4068-1372-2(9)) Echo Library.

—Chopin: The Man & His Music. 2008. 428p. 30.99 (978-0-559-50983-4(9)) 2008. 424p. 30.99 (978-0-559-48720-0(7)) 2008. 424p. pap. 34.75 (978-0-559-48717-0(7)) 2008. 428p. pap. 34.75 (978-0-559-50980-3(4)) 2006. 222p. pap. 20.99 (978-1-4264-1911-9(2)) 2007. (ENG.). 210p. pap. 22.99 (978-1-4264-2022-1(6)) BiblioBazaar.

—Chopin: The Man & His Music. 2009. 200p. pap. (978-1-4099-7074-3(4)) Dodo Pr.

Karasowski, Moritz. Frederic Chopin His Life & Letters V2. 2006. pap. 24.95 (978-1-4286-5025-1(3)) Kessinger Publishing, LLC.

Kobbé, Gustav. The Loves of Great Composers. 2008. (ENG.). 92p. pap. 18.75 (978-1-4375-0764-5(6)); 102p. pap. 18.75 (978-1-4375-0765-2(4)) BiblioBazaar.

—The Loves of Great Composers. 2007. (Illus.). 100p. per. (978-1-4065-2938-8(9)) Dodo Pr.

—The Loves of Great Composers. 2009. 238p. 41.95 (978-1-104-94773-6(0)); pap. 26.95 (978-1-104-91804-0(8)) Kessinger Publishing, LLC.

Laporte, Gilles. The Story of Chopin's Life. 2011. 300p. pap. 24.95 (978-2-7472-1549-7(0)) Eska, Editions FRA. Dist: International Publishers Marketing.

Lederer, Victor. Chopin: A Listener's Guide to the Master of the Piano. 2006. (Unlocking the Masters Ser.: No. 11). (ENG.). 146p. pap. 22.99 incl. audio compact disk (978-1-57467-148-3(0), 1574671480, Amadeus Press) Leonard, Hal Corp.

Lenz, Wilhelm von. The Great Piano Virtuosos of Our Time. 2009. 78p. pap. (978-0-217-38705-7(5)) Books LLC.

Liszt, Franz. Life of Chopin. 2008. 156p. 22.99 (978-0-554-39233-2(X)); 25.99 (978-0-554-29930-3(5)) BiblioBazaar.

—Life of Chopin. Cook, Martha Walker, tr. 2007. (ENG.). 138p. pap. 18.99 (978-1-4346-8758-6(9)); 154p. pap. 21.99 (978-1-4346-8759-3(7)) BiblioBazaar.

—Life of Chopin. 2006. (ENG.). pap. (978-1-4068-1434-7(2)) Echo Library.

—Life of Chopin. 2008. 208p. pap. (978-1-4437-1245-3(0)) Read Bks.

—Life of Chopin. 2007. (ENG.). 128p. per. 8.95 (978-1-60424-176-1(4), Book Jungle) Standard Pubns., Inc.

Mason, Daniel G. Romantic Composers. reprint ed. 29.50 (978-0-404-04223-3(6)) AMS Pr., Inc.

Mayer-Skumanz, Lene. F. Chopin. 2007. (Illus.). 29p. (J). incl. audio compact disk (978-84-96646-07-0(6)) Loguez Ediciones.

Niecks, Frederick. Frederick Chopin As a Man & Musician. 2008. 436p. 30.99 (978-0-554-31546-1(7)); 352p. 29.99 (978-0-554-22093-2(8)); 436p. 32.99 (978-0-554-22243-1(4)); 352p. 28.99 (978-0-554-31396-2(0)) BiblioBazaar.

—Frederick Chopin As a Man & Musician. 2007. 704p. per. (978-1-4065-4043-7(9)) Dodo Pr.

—Frederick Chopin As a Man & Musician. 2009. 576p. pap. (978-1-4068-5229-5(5)) Echo Library.

—Frederick Chopin, As a Man & Musician. 2008. 328p. pap. (978-1-4099-0569-1(1)); 368p. pap. (978-1-4099-0570-7(5)) Dodo Pr.

—Frederick Chopin, as a Man & Musician, Vol. 1. 2006. 366p. pap. 25.99 (978-1-4264-1625-5(3)) BiblioBazaar.

—Frederick Chopin, As a Man & Musician, Vol. 1. l.t. ed. 2007. (ENG.). 348p. pap. 24.99 (978-1-4264-1713-9(6)) BiblioBazaar.

—Frederick Chopin, as a Man & Musician, Vol. 2. 2007. (ENG.). 396p. pap. 25.99 (978-1-4264-1924-9(4)) BiblioBazaar.

—Frederick Chopin, As a Man & Musician, Vol. 2. l.t. ed. 2007. (ENG.). 434p. pap. 28.99 (978-1-4264-2035-1(8)) BiblioBazaar.

Niecks, Friedrich. Frederick Chopin As A Man & A Musician. 2006. (ENG.). pap. 33.95 (978-1-4286-4962-0(X)); pap. 33.95 (978-1-4286-4961-3(1)) Kessinger Publishing, LLC.

Paetsch, Annabelle. Performance Practices in Chopin's Piano Sonatas, Op 35 And 58. 2009. 256p. pap. (978-3-639-21367-6(X)) VDM Verlag Dr. Mueller e.K.

Rink, John & Samson, Jim, eds. Chopin Studies 2. 2006. (Cambridge Composer Studies). (ENG.). 264p. pap. 53.00 (978-0-521-03433-3(7)) Cambridge Univ. Pr.

Smialek, William. Fredric Chopin: A Research & Information Guide. 2nd rev. ed. 2011. (Routledge Music Bibliographies Ser.). (ENG.). 336p. 150.00 (978-0-415-99884-0(0)) Routledge.

Szczurko, Elzbieta & Guz, Tadeusz, eds. Fryderyk Chopin: Sein und Werk Being & Work. 2011. (Ars Musica. Interdisziplinäre Studien Ser.). 586p. 115.95 (978-3-631-60622-3(2)) Lang, Peter GmbH, Europaischer Verlag der Wissenschaften DEU. Dist: Lang, Peter.

CHOPIN, KATE, 1851-1904

Beer, Janet, ed. The Cambridge Companion to Kate Chopin. 2008. (Cambridge Companions to Literature Ser.). (ENG.). 208p. (C). 81.00 (978-0-521-88344-3(X)); pap. 29.99 (978-0-521-70982-8(2)) Cambridge Univ. Pr.

Bloom, Harold. The Awakening - Kate Chopin. 2011. (Bloom's Modern Critical Interpretations Ser.). 194p. (C). (gr. 9). 45.00 (978-1-60413-363-9(5), Chelsea Hse.) Facts On File, Inc.

Bloom, Harold, ed. Kate Chopin. 2nd rev. ed. 2007. (Bloom's Modern Critical Views Ser.). 240p. (C). (gr. 9). 45.00 (978-0-7910-9369-6(7), Chelsea Hse.) Facts On File, Inc.

Bryfonski, Dedria, ed. Women's Issues in Kate Chopin's the Awakening. 2011. (Social Issues in Literature Ser.). (Illus.). 224p. (ENG.). pap. 26.50 (978-0-7377-5820-7(1), Greenhaven Pr., Inc.); (YA). (gr. 9-12). 38.45 (978-0-7377-5819-1(8)) Cengage Gale.

Chopin, Kate. The Awakening. 2011. 102p. pap. 4.50 **(978-1-61427-160-4(7))** Martino Publishing.

Chopin, Kate. The Collected Works of Kate Chopin, 4 vols., Set. Incl. At Fault. reprint ed. 65.00 (978-0-403-04558-7(4)); Bayou Folk. reprint ed. 65.00 (978-0-403-04559-4(2)); Night in Acadie. 65.00 (978-0-403-04560-0(6)); 225.00 (978-0-403-03454-3(X)) Somerset Pubs., Inc.

Evans, Robert C., ed. Close Readings. 2nd rev. ed. 2006. 328p. pap. 21.95 (978-0-9785311-1-9(6)) MBF Pr.

Gale, Robert L. Characters & Plots in the Fiction of Kate Chopin. 2009. (ENG.). 199p. 75.00 (978-0-7864-4005-4(8)) McFarland & Co., Inc. Pubs.

Koloski, Bernard, ed. Awakenings: The Story of the Kate Chopin Revival. (Southern Literary Studies). 2012. 240p. pap. 18.95 **(978-0-8071-4366-7(9))** 2009. 232p. 35.00 (978-0-8071-3495-5(3)) Louisiana State Univ. Pr.

Sasa, Ghada. The Femme Fatale in American Naturalism. 2008. 99.95 (978-1-60497-535-2(0)) Cambria Pr.

Svrljuga, Zeljka. Hysteria & Melancholy as Literary Style in the Works of Charlotte Perkins Gilman, Kate Chopin, Zelda Fitzgerald, & Djuna Barnes. 2011. (Illus.). 260p. 129.95 (978-0-7734-1517-1(3)) Mellen, Edwin Pr., The.

CHORAL CONDUCTING
see also Choirs (Music); Choral Singing; Conductors (Music)

Abingdon Press, creator. Choir Director's Organzier. 2007. (Illus.). 99p. spiral bd. 15.00 (978-0-687-64251-9(5)) Abingdon Pr.

Acker, Mark. The Passion-Driven Youth Choir. annot. ed. 2007. 138p. per. 12.00 (978-0-687-49224-4(6)) Abingdon Pr.

Chesnokov, Pavel. The Choir & How to Direct It. Rommereim, John, tr. from RUS. 2009.Tr. of Khor i upravlenie Im. pap. (978-0-9701767-3-8(2)) Musica Russica.

Flummerfelt, Joseph & Nally, Donald. Conversations with Joseph Flummerfelt: Thoughts on Conducting, Music, & Musicians. 2010. (ENG.). 230p. (gr. 17). pap. 42.00 (978-0-8108-6976-9(4)) Scarecrow Pr., Inc.

Garnett, Liz. Choral Conducting & the Construction of Meaning: Gesture, Voice, Identity. 2009. (Illus.). 242p. 99.95 (978-0-7546-6379-9(5)) Ashgate Publishing Co.

Green, Jonathan D. A Conductor's Guide to Nineteenth-Century Choral-Orchestral Works. 2007. (ENG.). 350p. 78.00 (978-0-8108-6046-9(5)) Scarecrow Pr., Inc.

Jordan, James. The Choral Rehearsal: Techniques & Procedures. 2007. 482p. 39.95 (978-1-57999-673-4(6), G-7128) G I A Pubns., Inc.

Mbuh, Mbuh. The Life of Mzee Ondego. 2008. 50p. pap. (978-9966-7182-0-4(6)) Kwani Trust KEN. Dist: Michigan State Univ. Pr.

Rundus, Katharin. Cantabile: A Manual about Beautiful Singing for Singers, Teachers of Singing & Choral Conductors. 2009. (ENG.). 192p. pap. 59.95 (978-1-934596-03-6(5), 1934596035) Leonard, Hal Corp.

Seelig, Timothy. The Perfect Rehearsal: Everything You Wanted to Know about Rehearsals! 2006. (ENG., Illus.). 138p. per. 24.99 (978-1-59235-152-7(2), 1592351522) Shawnee Pr., Inc.

Simpson, Eugene Thamon. Hall Johnson: His Life, His Spirit, & His Music. 2008. (ENG., Illus.). 404p. 87.00 (978-0-8108-6038-4(4)) Scarecrow Pr., Inc.

Trapp, Lynn & Leitschuh, Carol, eds. In Harmony with God: Choir Member Edition. 2008. 32p. 6.95 (978-0-8146-3087-7(1), Liturgical Pr. Bks.) Liturgical Pr.

CHORAL MUSIC
Here are entered works on choral music. Musical compositions for or with chorus are entered under the headings Choruses or Choruses, Sacred.
see also Choirs (Music); Choral Conducting; Choral Singing; Part Songs

Acker, Mark. The Passion-Driven Youth Choir. annot. ed. 2007. 138p. per. 12.00 (978-0-687-49224-4(6)) Abingdon Pr.

Albrecht, Sally K. & Althouse, Jay. Movin' in the Right Direction! (A Program or Songbook to Build Character & Integrity in Young People for Unison & 2-Part Voices) A Program or Songbook to Build Character & Integrity in Young People for Unison & 2-Part Voices. 2008. (ENG.). 56p. pap. 59.99 (978-0-7390-5243-3(8)) Alfred Publishing Co., Inc.

—Movin' in the Right Direction! (A Program or Songbook to Build Character & Integrity in Young People for Unison & 2-Part Voices) Teacher's Handbook (100% Reproducible) 2008. (ENG.). 56p. pap. 29.95 (978-0-7390-5241-9(1)) Alfred Publishing Co., Inc.

Albrecht, Sally K. & Beck, Andy. Showbiz! A Choral Movement DVD, DVD. 2011. (Choral Movement Ser.). 39.99 **(978-0-7390-8049-8(0))** Alfred Publishing Co., Inc.

Alfred Publishing Staff. Ave Maria: Choral Octavo. 2010. (Faber Edition: Choral Signature Ser.). (ENG.). pap. 3.50 (978-0-571-53540-8(2)) Faber & Faber, Ltd. GBR. Dist: Alfred Publishing Co., Inc.

—The Carol Singer's Carol: Choral Octavo. 2011. (Faber Edition: Choral Signature Ser.). (ENG.). pap. 3.95 **(978-0-571-53671-9(9))** Faber & Faber, Ltd. GBR. Dist: Alfred Publishing Co., Inc.

—Christ Is Born of Maiden Fair: Choral Octavo. 2011. (Faber Edition: Choral Signature Ser.). (ENG.). pap. 3.95 **(978-0-571-52467-9(2))** Faber & Faber, Ltd. GBR. Dist: Alfred Publishing Co., Inc.

—Far from Home: Choral Octavo. 2011. (Faber Edition: Choral Signature Ser.). (ENG.). pap. 3.95 **(978-0-571-52985-8(2))** Faber & Faber, Ltd. GBR. Dist: Alfred Publishing Co., Inc.

—Hail, Gladdening Light: Choral Octavo. 2010. (Faber Edition: Choral Signature Ser.). (ENG.). pap. 3.50 (978-0-571-53551-4(8)) Faber & Faber, Ltd. GBR. Dist: Alfred Publishing Co., Inc.

—Haven't Met You Yet: Choral Octavo. 2010. (Faber Edition: Choir Rocks Ser.). (ENG.). pap. 2.50 (978-0-571-53490-6(2)) Faber & Faber, Ltd. GBR. Dist: Alfred Publishing Co., Inc.

—If Ye Love Me: Choral Octavo. 2010. (Faber Edition: Choral Signature Ser.). (ENG.). pap. 3.50 (978-0-571-53553-8(4)) Faber & Faber, Ltd. GBR. Dist: Alfred Publishing Co., Inc.

—Let All the World in Every Corner Sing: Choral Octavo. 2011. (Faber Edition: Choral Signature Ser.). (ENG.). pap. 3.95 **(978-0-571-53648-1(4))** Faber & Faber, Ltd. GBR. Dist: Alfred Publishing Co., Inc.

—Love Comes Quietly: Choral Octavo. 2011. (Faber Edition: Choral Signature Ser.). pap. 3.50 **(978-0-571-53620-7(4))** Faber & Faber, Ltd. GBR. Dist: Alfred Publishing Co., Inc.

—Lullaby: Choral Octavo. 2011. (Faber Edition: Choral Signature Ser.). (ENG.). pap. 5.50 **(978-0-571-53136-3(9))** Faber & Faber, Ltd. GBR. Dist: Alfred Publishing Co., Inc.
—Mirabile Dictu: From Manchester Carols, Choral Octavo. 2010. (Faber Edition: Choral Signature Ser.). (ENG.). pap. 3.95 **(978-0-571-53567-5(4))** Faber & Faber, Ltd. GBR. Dist: Alfred Publishing Co., Inc.
—Moments of Vision: Choral Octavo. 2011. (Faber Edition: Choral Signature Ser.). (ENG.). pap. 6.95 **(978-0-571-53639-9(5))** Faber & Faber, Ltd. GBR. Dist: Alfred Publishing Co., Inc.
—My Beloved Spake: Choral Octavo. 2011. (Faber Edition Choral Signature Ser.). (ENG.). pap. 3.95 **(978-0-571-52464-8(8))** Faber & Faber, Ltd. GBR. Dist: Alfred Publishing Co., Inc.
—My Song Is Love Unknown: Choral Octavo. 2011. (Faber Edition: Choral Signature Ser.). (ENG.). pap. 3.95 **(978-0-571-53649-8(2))** Faber & Faber, Ltd. GBR. Dist: Alfred Publishing Co., Inc.
—O Magnum Mysterium: Choral Octavo. 2011. (Faber Edition: Choral Signature Ser.). (ENG.). pap. 3.95 **(978-0-571-53670-2(0))** Faber & Faber, Ltd. GBR. Dist: Alfred Publishing Co., Inc.
—O Sapientia: Choral Octavo. 2011. (Faber Edition: Choral Signature Ser.). (ENG.). pap. 3.50 *(978-0-571-53542-2(9))* Faber & Faber, Ltd. GBR. Dist: Alfred Publishing Co., Inc.
—Psalm 23: Choral Octavo. 2011. (Faber Edition: Choral Signature Ser.). (ENG.). pap. 3.95 **(978-0-571-52466-2(4))** Faber & Faber, Ltd. GBR. Dist: Alfred Publishing Co., Inc.
—Sing at First Sight Reproducible Companion, Bk 2: Foundations in Choral Sight-Singing, Book & CD. 2009. (ENG.). 80p. pap. 39.95 *(978-0-7390-6145-9(3))* Alfred Publishing Co., Inc.
—Song of June: Choral Octavo. 2011. (Faber Edition: Choral Signature Ser.). (ENG.). pap. 3.95 **(978-0-571-52639-0(X))** Faber & Faber, Ltd. GBR. Dist: Alfred Publishing Co., Inc.
—A Song of the New Jerusalem: Choral Octavo. 2011. (Faber Edition: Choral Signature Ser.). (ENG.). pap. 3.95 **(978-0-571-53675-7(1))** Faber & Faber, Ltd. GBR. Dist: Alfred Publishing Co., Inc.
—The Souls of the Righteous: Choral Octavo. 2011. (Faber Edition: Choral Signature Ser.). (ENG.). pap. 3.50 *(978-0-571-53552-1(5))* Faber & Faber, Ltd. GBR. Dist: Alfred Publishing Co., Inc.
—Veni Jesu: Choral Octavo. 2010. (Faber Edition: Choral Signature Ser.). (ENG.). pap. 3.50 *(978-0-571-53543-9(7))* Faber & Faber, Ltd. GBR. Dist: Alfred Publishing Co., Inc.
—You Raise Me Up: A Treasury of Inspirational Favorites (Preview Pack), Book & CD. 2009. (ENG.). pap. 16.95 *(978-0-7390-6129-9(1))* Alfred Publishing Co., Inc.
Ames, Jeffery. A Pioneering Twentieth Century African-American Musician. 2009. 196p. pap. *(978-3-639-15351-4(0))* VDM Verlag Dr. Mueller e.K.
Argento, Dominick. Cenotaph: Chorus & Orchestra SATB Chorus & Piano Reduction Vocal Score. 2009. (ENG.). 56p. pap. 10.99 *(978-1-4234-6810-3(4),* 1423468104) Boosey & Hawkes, Inc.
Berry, Cindy. The Best of Cindy Berry: 10 Solo Piano Arrangements of Her Original Choral Works. 2009. (Sacred Performer Collections). (ENG.). 44p. pap. 12.95 *(978-0-7390-6086-5(4))* Alfred Publishing Co., Inc.
Boersma, Susan Bentall. The Yearning: Satb. 2011. 10p. pap. 1.95 **(978-1-4291-2590-1(X))** Lorenz Corp., The.
Boersma, Susan Bentall & Martin, Joseph M. Give Me a Grateful Heart: SATB or Two-Part Mixed. 2011. 12p. pap. 1.95 **(978-1-4291-2539-0(X))** Lorenz Corp., The.
Boesiger, R. Kevin. Shout to God with Thanksgiving: SATB with Opt. Brass & Percussion. 2011. 16p. pap. 1.95 **(978-1-4291-2561-1(6))** Lorenz Corp., The.
—A Silent Night Brings New Light: SATB with Opt. Solos. 2011. 11p. pap. 1.95 **(978-1-4291-2527-7(6))** Lorenz Corp., The.
Brown, Timothy, ed. Choral Works with Orchestra. 2009. (William Walton Edition Ser.). 328p. pap. 195.00 *(978-0-19-368307-5(5))* Oxford Univ. Pr., Inc.
Burton, Sean M. The Unaccompanied Choral Music of Pierre Villette: A Conductor's Analysis. 2008. (LAD., Illus.). 132p. 99.95 *(978-0-7734-4967-1(1))* Mellen, Edwin Pr., The.
Carmina Burana: Choral Score. 2007. 72p. pap. 17.95 *(978-3-7957-9500-9(1),* 3795795001) Schott Music Corp.
Carver, Anthony F. Cori Spezzati: Volume 1, the Development of Sacred Polychoral Music to the Time of Schutz, 2 vols. 2009. (ENG., Illus.). 300p. pap. 38.99 *(978-0-521-10632-0(X))* Cambridge Univ. Pr.
Carver, Anthony F., ed. Cori Spezzati: Volume 2: An Anthology of Sacred Polychoral Music, 2 vols. 2009. (ENG., Illus.). 172p. pap. 26.99 *(978-0-521-10635-1(4))* Cambridge Univ. Pr.
Chilcott, Bob. Salisbury Vespers. 2009. (ENG.). 96p. pap. 13.95 *(978-0-19-336395-3(X))* Oxford Univ. Pr., Inc.
Choplin, Pepper. Come, Emmanuel! SATB with Opt. Orchestra. 2011. 11p. pap. 1.95 **(978-1-4291-2592-5(6))** Lorenz Corp., The.
—How Long? SATB a Capella. 2011. 8p. pap. 1.85 **(978-1-4291-2591-8(8))** Lorenz Corp., The.
—I Bring a Heart of Thanks: Satb. 2011. 16p. pap. 1.95 **(978-1-4291-2575-8(6))** Lorenz Corp., The.
—Open Prayer: Satb. 2011. 8p. pap. 1.85 **(978-1-4291-2493-5(8))** Lorenz Corp., The.
Choral Club. 12.00 incl. audio *(978-0-687-09124-9(1))*; 12.00 incl. audio *(978-0-687-09128-7(4))*; 12.00 incl. audio *(978-0-687-09129-4(2))*; 12.00 incl. audio *(978-0-687-08934-5(4))*; 12.00 incl. audio *(978-0-687-08947-5(6))*; incl. audio compact disk *(978-0-687-08612-2(4))*; incl. audio compact disk *(978-0-687-08552-1(7))*; 12.00 incl. audio *(978-0-687-08828-7(3))* Abingdon Pr.
Curry, Sheldon. Now & Then: SATB Choral Score, Choral Score. 2011. (ENG.). 64p. pap. 8.99 **(978-0-7390-8496-0(8))** Alfred Publishing Co., Inc.
de Quadros, Andre, ed. The Cambridge Companion to Choral Music. 2012. (Cambridge Companions to Music Ser.). (ENG., Illus.). 384p. 99.00 **(978-0-521-11173-7(0))**; pap. 29.99 **(978-0-521-12895-7(1))** Cambridge Univ. Pr.
Di Grazia, Donna. Nineteenth Century Choral Music. 2012. (ENG., Illus.). 496p. 150.00 *(978-0-415-98852-0(7))*; pap. 53.95 *(978-0-415-98853-7(5))* Routledge.
Eladio, Valenzuela. Choral Music in Mexico: A Survey of Music Between 1575-1775. 2011. 164p. pap. **(978-3-639-32628-4(8))** VDM Verlag Dr. Mueller e.K.
Fettke, Tom, et al. An Evening in December: Orchestration. 2008. (ENG.). 624p. pap. 350.00 *(978-0-7390-5472-7(4))* Alfred Publishing Co., Inc.
—An Evening in December: SATB Choral Score, Choral Score. 2008. (ENG.). 104p. pap. 8.95 *(978-0-7390-5468-0(6))* Alfred Publishing Co., Inc.
Fettke, Tom, contrib. by. God Is with Us: SATB Choral Score, Choral Score. 2011. 104p. pap. 8.99 **(978-0-7390-8251-5(5))** Alfred Publishing Co., Inc.
Fleming, Gail H. Alice Parker: American Choral Composer, Arranger, & Educator. 2008. 232p. pap. *(978-3-8364-3840-7(2))* VDM Verlag Dr. Mueller e.K.
Forsyth, Cecil. Choral Orchestration. 2008. 116p. pap. 19.95 *(978-1-4368-0471-4(X))* Kessinger Publishing, LLC.
Fry, Steve. Let It Be Said of Us: SATB with Opt. Percussion & Digital Strings. 2011. 12p. pap. 2.10 **(978-1-4291-2422-5(9))** Lorenz Corp., The.
—Let It Be Said of Us: TTBB with Opt. Percussion & Digital Strings. 2011. 12p. pap. 2.10 **(978-1-4291-2423-2(7))** Lorenz Corp., The.
Gallina, Michael & Gallina, Jill. Puttin' on the Kidz: Building Foundations for Standing Ovations! 2010. (ENG.). 64p. pap. 12.99 *(978-1-4234-9077-7(0),* 1423490770) Shawnee Pr., Inc.
Gilpin, Greg. How to Be a Pirate in Seven Easy Songs: A Mini-Musical for the Pirate in Us All. 2008. (ENG., Illus.). 92p. pap. 49.95 incl. audio compact disk *(978-1-59235-242-5(1),* 1592352421) Shawnee Pr., Inc.
Gilpin, Greg, creator. Let the Men Sing! 10 Reproducible Chorals for Tenor & Baritone Vocals. 2009. 76p. pap. 49.95 incl. audio compact disk *(978-1-59235-252-4(9))* Shawnee Pr., Inc.
Green, Jonathan D. A Conductor's Guide to Nineteenth-Century Choral-Orchestral Works. 2007. (ENG.). 350p. 78.00 *(978-0-8108-6046-9(5))* Scarecrow Pr., Inc.
Hal Leonard Corporation Staff, creator. Christmas Favorites - Bass: Big Band Play-along Volume 5. 2008. (ENG.). 24p. pap. 14.95 incl. audio compact disk *(978-1-4234-5855-5(9),* 1423458559) Leonard, Hal Corp.
—Christmas Favorites - Drums: Big Band Play-along Volume 5. 2008. (ENG.). 24p. pap. 14.95 incl. audio compact disk *(978-1-4234-5856-2(7),* 1423458567) Leonard, Hal Corp.
—Christmas Favorites - Guitar: Big Band Play-along Volume 5. 2008. (ENG.). 24p. pap. 14.95 incl. audio compact disk *(978-1-4234-5853-1(2),* 1423458532) Leonard, Hal Corp.
—Mighty to Save: 30 of Today's Most Powerful Modern Worship Songs. 2008. (ENG.). 216p. pap. 16.95 *(978-1-4234-5873-9(7),* 1423458737) Leonard, Hal Corp.
Hamlin, Carolyn. Was I Faithful? SAB with Opt. Orchestra. 2011. 11p. pap. 1.95 **(978-1-4291-2488-1(1))** Lorenz Corp., The.
—Was I Faithful? SATB with Opt. Orchestra. 2011. 11p. pap. 1.95 **(978-1-4291-2487-4(3))** Lorenz Corp., The.
Hayes, Mark, contrib. by. What a Friend: SATB & Soloist with Opt. Instrumental Ensemble. 2011. 15p. pap. 1.95 **(978-1-4291-2484-3(9))** Lorenz Corp., The.
—Zion's Walls: SAB with 4-Hand Piano or Opt. 2-Hand Piano. 2011. 15p. pap. 1.95 **(978-1-4291-2547-5(0))** Lorenz Corp., The.
—Zion's Walls: SATB with 4-Hand Piano or Opt. 2-Hand Piano. 2011. 15p. pap. 1.95 **(978-1-4291-2546-8(2))** Lorenz Corp., The.
The Holy Child Online Choral Response. 0.50 *(978-0-687-03664-6(X))* Abingdon Pr.
Hopson, Hal H., ed. The Psalter, Choral Edition: Psalms & Canticles for Singing. 2011. (ENG.). 136p. pap. 20.00 *(978-0-664-23704-2(5))* Westminster John Knox Pr.
Hoskisson, Darin. Something to Say. 2008. 196p. pap. *(978-3-639-07112-2(3))* VDM Verlag Dr. Mueller e.K.
Johnson, Victor C. Be Still & Know: SATB Divisi. 2011. 7p. pap. 1.85 **(978-1-4291-2536-9(5))** Lorenz Corp., The.
Kern, Philip. Star of Wonder, Star of Night: Seasonal Piano Arrangements. 2011. (ENG.). 44p. pap. 16.95 **(978-1-4584-0673-6(3),** 1458406733) Shawnee Pr., Inc.
La Violette, Wesley. The Song of the Angels. 2011. 38p. 35.95 **(978-1-258-05333-8(0))** Literary Licensing, LLC.
Laird, Paul R. & Budds, Michael J. The Chichester Psalms of Leonard Bernstein. 2009. (Illus.). 255p. *(978-1-57647-152-4(7))* Pendragon Pr.
Larson, Lloyd. Light a Candle in the Night: Unison or Two-Part Any Combination with Opt. Congregation & Narration. 2011. 12p. pap. 1.95 **(978-1-4291-2554-3(3))** Lorenz Corp., The.
—You Are My God! SATB Divisi with Opt. Brass & Percussion. 2011. 12p. pap. 1.95 **(978-1-4291-2588-8(8))** Lorenz Corp., The.
Larson, Lloyd, contrib. by. Joy of Every Longing Heart: SATB with Opt. C-Instrument & Cello. 2011. 11p. pap. 1.95 **(978-1-4291-2584-0(5))** Lorenz Corp., The.
Leeson, Jane Eliza. Savior, Teach Me: SATB or SAB with Opt. Solo & Rhythm. 2011. 11p. pap. 1.95 **(978-1-4291-2557-4(8))** Lorenz Corp., The.
L'Estrange, Alexander. A Christmas Special. 2010. (Faber Edition: Choral Basics Ser.). (ENG.). pap. 5.50 *(978-0-571-52370-2(6))* Faber & Faber, Ltd. GBR. Dist: Alfred Publishing Co., Inc.
Limbaugh, Matt. Who's the Little Baby? SATB or Two-Part Mixed with Opt. Percussion. 2011. 12p. pap. 1.95 **(978-1-4291-2535-2(7))** Lorenz Corp., The.
Lister, Michael. Singer Placement & the Male Chorus. 2011. 200p. pap. **(978-3-8443-1498-4(9))** Lambert Academic Publishing.
Lorenz Publishing, creator. The Organist's Library, Volume 50. 2011. 98p. pap. 19.95 **(978-1-4291-2172-9(6))** Lorenz Corp., The.
Macgimsey, Robert. Sweet Little Jesus Boy: SATB with Opt. Orchestra. 2011. 11p. pap. 2.10 **(978-1-4291-2473-7(3))** Lorenz Corp., The.
Madura Ward-Steinman, Patrice. Becoming a Choral Music Teacher: A Field Experience. 2009. (ENG., Illus.). 248p. wbk. ed. 44.95 *(978-0-415-99841-3(7))* Routledge.
Martin, Pamela. Echo Christmas Joy: SAB with Opt. Orchestra or Instrumental Ensemble. 2011. 11p. pap. 1.95 **(978-1-4291-2480-5(6))** Lorenz Corp., The.
—Echo Christmas Joy: SATB with Opt. Orchestra or Instrumental Ensemble. 2011. 11p. pap. 1.95 **(978-1-4291-2479-9(2))** Lorenz Corp., The.
—The Time for Turning: Sab. 2011. 8p. pap. 1.85 **(978-1-4291-2538-3(1))** Lorenz Corp., The.
—The Time for Turning: Ssa. 2011. 8p. pap. 1.85 **(978-1-4291-2537-6(3))** Lorenz Corp., The.
McDonald, Mary. Give Him Glory: SATB with Opt. Instrumental Ensemble. 2011. 12p. pap. 1.95 **(978-1-4291-2558-1(6))** Lorenz Corp., The.
McDonald, Mary, contrib. by. America: SATB with Opt. Orchestra or Solo Trumpet. 2011. 12p. pap. 1.95 **(978-1-4291-2518-5(7))** Lorenz Corp., The.
—America: TTBB with Opt. Orchestra of Solo Trumpet. 2011. 12p. pap. 1.95 **(978-1-4291-2520-8(9))** Lorenz Corp., The.
—O Come to Set Us Free: SATB with Opt. Acoustic Bass & Drumset or Bongos. 2011. 8p. pap. 1.85 **(978-1-4291-2567-3(5))** Lorenz Corp., The.
McGuire, Jan. The Voice of God: SATB with Opt. Cello. 2011. 11p. pap. 1.95 **(978-1-4291-2586-4(1))** Lorenz Corp., The.
Mees, Arthur. Choirs & Choral Music. 2010. 290p. pap. 28.75 *(978-1-177-67416-4(5))*; 294p. pap. 28.75 *(978-1-145-00387-3(7))* BiblioBazaar.
—Choirs & Choral Music. 2009. 172p. pap. *(978-0-217-33866-0(6))* Books LLC.
—Choirs & Choral Music. 2009. 174p. pap. 19.99 *(978-0-217-81099-9(3))* General Bks. LLC.
—Choirs & Choral Music. 2008. 280p. 42.95 *(978-1-4369-5003-9(1))*; pap. 27.95 *(978-1-4368-0463-9(9))* Kessinger Publishing, LLC.
Meredith Music Publications, creator. The Choral Director's Cookbook: Insights & Inspired Recipes for Beginners & Experts. 2006. (ENG., Illus.). 126p. per. 24.95 *(978-1-57463-078-7(4),* 1574630784) Meredith Music Pubns.
Perry, Dave & Perry, Jean. The Hundred-Year Snooze: The Story of Sleeping Beauty. 2008. (ENG.). 80p. pap. 29.95 *(978-1-59235-240-1(5),* 1592352405); 48p. pap. 34.95 *(978-1-59235-241-8(3),* 1592352413) Shawnee Pr., Inc.
Pitman, Walter. Elmer Iseler: Choral Visionary. 2008. (ENG., Illus.). 352p. 40.00 *(978-1-55002-815-7(4),* Dundurn Pr.) Dundurn CAN. Dist: Ingram Pub. Services.
Rastall, Richard, ed. The Secular Latin Motet in the Renaissance. 2010. (Illus.). viii, 253p. *(978-0-7734-1404-4(5))* Mellen, Edwin Pr., The.
Schram, Ruth Elaine. When You Call: Satb. 2011. 8p. pap. 1.85 **(978-1-4291-2491-1(1))** Lorenz Corp., The.
Seelig, Timothy. The Music Within: Discovering the Joy - Again! One Man's Story, Everyone's Journey. 2010. (ENG.). 15p. pap. 34.99 *(978-1-4234-7611-5(5),* 1423476115) Shawnee Pr., Inc.
Shackley, Larry, contrib. by. Climbin' up the Mountain, Children: Satb. 2011. 12p. pap. 1.95 **(978-1-4291-2555-0(1))** Lorenz Corp., The.
—How Firm a Foundation: Satb. 2011. 8p. pap. 1.85 **(978-1-4291-2587-1(X))** Lorenz Corp., The.
—The Moon & Stars Were Shining: SATB with Opt. Instrumental Ensemble. 2011. 11p. pap. 1.95 **(978-1-4291-2578-9(0))** Lorenz Corp., The.
Shafferman, Jean Anne, contrib. by. Make Us Instruments of Your Peace: SATB or SAB. 2011. 8p. pap. 1.85 **(978-1-4291-2589-5(6))** Lorenz Corp., The.
Sharp, Tim & Prucha, Christina. American Choral Directors Association. 2009. (Images of America Ser.). (ENG., Illus.). 128p. pap. 21.99 *(978-0-7385-6072-4(3))* Arcadia Publishing.
Sheak, James. Rural Students, Aspiration, Motivation, & Music Education. 2009. 212p. pap. *(978-3-639-11299-3(7))* VDM Verlag Dr. Mueller e.K.
Steinberg, Micheal. Choral Masterworks: A Listener's Guide. 2008. (ENG., Illus.). 336p. per. 16.95 *(978-0-19-534066-2(3))* Oxford Univ. Pr., Inc.
Summer, Robert J. & Moe, Daniel. Choral Masterworks from Bach to Britten: Reflections of a Conductor. 2007. (ENG., Illus.). 224p. per. 52.00 *(978-0-8108-5903-6(3))* Scarecrow Pr., Inc.
Tomlin, Chris, et al. How Great Is Our God: SATB or SAB with Opt. Rhythm. 2011. 12p. pap. 2.10 **(978-1-4291-2392-1(3))** Lorenz Corp., The.
Town, Stephen. Essays on British Choral Music. 2012. (Illus.). 324p. 119.95 **(978-0-7546-0536-2(1))** Ashgate Publishing Co.
Unger, Melvin P. Historical Dictionary of Choral Music. 2010. (Historical Dictionaries of Literature & the Arts Ser.). (ENG.). 584p. 137.00 *(978-0-8108-5751-3(0))* Scarecrow Pr., Inc.
Wagner, Douglas E. Bless the Lord, O My Soul: SATB or Two-Part Mixed with Opt. Handbells or Handchimes (2 Oct.) 2011. 12p. pap. 1.95 **(978-1-4291-2522-2(5))** Lorenz Corp., The.
—The Rose of Bethlehem: SATB with Opt. Instrumental Ensemble. 2011. 12p. pap. 1.95 **(978-1-4291-2476-8(8))** Lorenz Corp., The.
133 Choral Club Rehearsal Accompaniment. 10.00 incl. audio compact disk *(978-0-687-04379-8(4))* Abingdon Pr.

CHORAL MUSIC—BIBLIOGRAPHY

Childs, David N., et al. Composers on Composing for Choir. Wine, Tom, ed. 2007. 251p. 24.95 *(978-1-57999-664-2(7),* G-7110) G I A Pubns., Inc.
Sharp, Avery T. & Floyd, James Michael. Choral Music. 2nd rev. ed. 2011. (Routledge Music Bibliographies Ser.). (ENG.). 388p. 150.00 *(978-0-415-99419-4(5))* Routledge.

CHORAL MUSIC—DISCOGRAPHY

Blyth, Alan, ed. Choral Music on Record. 2007. (ENG.). 320p. pap. 47.00 *(978-0-521-03583-5(X))* Cambridge Univ. Pr.

CHORAL MUSIC—HISTORY AND CRITICISM

see Choral Music

CHORAL READING

see Choral Speaking

CHORAL RECITATIONS

Brauninger, Dallas A. In the Beginning Was the Word: Scriptures for the Lectionary Speaking Choir. 2008. *(978-0-7880-2571-6(6))* CSS Publishing Co.
—In the Beginning Was the Word: Scriptures for the Lectionary Speaking Choir: Cycle C, Revised. 2009. *(978-0-7880-2623-2(2))* CSS Publishing Co.
Wang, Tao. Teaching Mathematics Through Choral Responses: A Study of Two Sixth Grade Classrooms in China. 2010. (ENG.). 148p. 99.95 *(978-0-7734-3628-2(6))* Mellen, Edwin Pr., The.

CHORAL SINGING

see also Choirboys—Training; Choirs (Music); Choral Conducting

Ahlquist, Karen, ed. Chorus & Community. 2006. (Illus.). 336p. pap. 31.00 *(978-0-252-07284-0(7))*; 65.00 *(978-0-252-03037-6(0))* Univ. of Illinois Pr.
Beck, Andy, et al. Sing at First Sight - Level 2: Foundations in Choral Sight-Singing. 2007. (ENG.). 88p. pap. 7.99 *(978-0-7390-4924-2(0))* Alfred Publishing Co., Inc.
Corp, Ronald. Choral Singers Companion. (Illus.). 222p. pap. 29.95 *(978-1-84609-334-0(1),* TH980012, Bosworth) Music Sales Corp.
Coward, Henry. Choral Technique & Interpretation. 2010. 144p. pap. *(978-1-151-96753-4(X))* Books LLC.
—Choral Technique & Interpretation. 2007. (ENG.). 348p. per. *(978-1-4067-8939-3(9),* Home Farm Bks.) Read Bks.
Cram101 Textbook Reviews. Outlines & Highlights for Teaching Choral Music by Collins, Isbn: 0130813567. 2011. 178p. pap. 29.95 **(978-1-61830-025-6(3))** Cram101 Inc.
Ferris, William. The Care & Feeding of Singers: A Handbook of Choral Vocalises. Date not set. 37p. tchr. ed. 6.95 *(978-0-937690-25-3(2))* World Library Pubns.
—The Care & Feeding of Singers: A Handbook of Choral Vocalises-Chorister Edition. Date not set. wbk. ed. 2.95 *(978-2-937690-26-4(2))* World Library Pubns.
Freer, Patrick K. Getting Started with Middle School Chorus. 2nd ed. 2009. (ENG.). 124p. pap. 22.95 *(978-1-60709-163-9(1))* Rowman & Littlefield Education.
—TIPS: The First Weeks of Middle School Chorus. 2009. (TIPS Ser.). (ENG.). 48p. pap. 16.95 *(978-1-60709-165-3(8))* Rowman & Littlefield Education.
Hal Leonard Corp., creator. Choir for Dummies - Book/cd Pack. 2012. (ENG.). 112p. pap. 19.99 incl. audio compact disk *(978-1-4234-7390-9(6),* 1423473906) Leonard, Hal Corp.
Jackson, George Pullen. The Story of the Sacred Harp, 1844-1944. 2010. (ENG., Illus.). 56p. lib. bdg. 22.50 *(978-0-8265-1018-1(3))* Vanderbilt Univ. Pr.
Jordan, James. The Choral Rehearsal: Techniques & Procedures. 2007. 482p. 39.95 *(978-1-57999-673-4(6),* G-7128) G I A Pubns., Inc.
Kleinig, John W. Lord's Song: The Basis, Function & Significance of Choral Music in Chronicles. 2009. (Library of Hebrew Bible/Old Testament Studies, the Ser.). (ENG.). 236p. 39.95 *(978-0-567-02417-6(2),* T&T Clark) Continuum International Publishing Group, Ltd. GBR. Dist: National Bk. Network.
McGill, Stan & Volk, Elizabeth. Beyond Singing: Blueprint for the Exceptional Choral Program. 2007. (ENG.). 252p. pap. 24.99 incl. audio compact disk *(978-1-4234-2043-9(8),* 1423420438) Leonard, Hal Corp.
Miller, Kiri. Traveling Home: Sacred Harp Singing & American Pluralism. 2010. (Music in American Life Ser.). (ENG., Illus.). 272p. pap. 25.00 *(978-0-252-07757-9(1))* Univ. of Illinois Pr.
Mould, Alan. The English Chorister: A History. 2008. (ENG., Illus.). 384p. per. 34.95 *(978-1-84725-058-2(0),* Hambledon Continuum) Continuum International Publishing Group, Ltd. GBR. Dist: National Bk. Network.
Olson, Margaret. The Solo Singer in the Choral Setting: A Handbook for Achieving Vocal Health. 2010. (ENG.). 220p. (gr. 17). 80.00 *(978-0-8108-7735-1(X))*; (ENG.). 220p. (gr. 17). pap. 39.95 *(978-0-8108-6913-4(6))*; E-Book *(978-0-8108-6914-1(4))* Scarecrow Pr., Inc.
Peloquin, C. Alexander. Choral Precision. 2011. 56p. 36.95 **(978-1-258-01525-1(0))** Literary Licensing, LLC.
Reneau, April. Criteria for Choral Voice Classification: Determining Basic Voice Classification of High SchoolChoir Students. 2008. 68p. pap. *(978-3-639-09791-7(2))* VDM Verlag Dr. Mueller e.K.

C

Smith, Brenda & Sataloff, Robert. Choral Pedagogy & the Older Singer. 2012. (ENG.). pap. 55.00 *(978-1-59756-438-0(9))* Plural Publishing, Inc.
Vesilind, Priit, et al. The Singing Revolution: How Culture Saved a Nation. (Illus.). 178p. *(978-9985-3-1623-8(1))* Varrak AS.
Walton, William. Belshazzar's Feast: Vocal Score. 2008. 136p. pap. 16.95 *(978-0-19-335954-3(5))* Oxford Univ. Pr., Inc.
WEST-E Exam Secrets Test Prep Staff, ed. WEST-E Music Choral (035) Secrets Study Guide: WEST-E Test Review for the Washington Educator Skills Tests-Endorsements. 2011. (C). 62.99 *(978-1-61403-773-6(6))* Mometrix Media LLC.
Wilson Jr., Eli. Equipping the Church Choir for Ministry: A Resource for Church Music Leaders & Choir Members. 2008. 124p. pap. 10.99 *(978-1-4389-0351-4(0))* AuthorHouse.
Zabriskie, et al. Foundations of Choral Tone: A Proactive & Healthy Approach to Vocal Technique & Choral Tone. 2009. (Illus.). iv, 75p. *(978-0-9814817-1-5(X))* USingersPubs.

CHORAL SOCIETIES

see also Choirs (Music); Community Music

Alexander, Heywood. The Handel Society of Dartmouth College 1807-2007. 2006. per. 20.00 *(978-0-9790147-0-3(0))* Handel Society of Dartmouth College.
Rapkin, Mickey. Pitch Perfect: The Quest for Collegiate a Cappella Glory. 2009. (ENG.). 288p. (gr. 12-18). 15.00 *(978-1-59240-463-6(4)*, Gotham) Penguin Group (USA) Inc.

CHORAL SPEAKING

see also Choral Recitations

Wang, Tao. Teaching Mathematics Through Choral Responses: A Study of Two Sixth Grade Classrooms in China. 2010. (ENG.). 148p. 99.95 *(978-0-7734-3628-2(6))* Mellen, Edwin Pr., The.

CHORALE

Here are entered works about the chorale. Musical compositions in this form are entered under the heading Chorales.

Travis &. Emery, &. Emery & Terry, Charles Sanford. Bach's Chorals Part 1 - the Hymns & Hymn Melodies of the Passions & Oratorios [Facsimile of 1915 Edition]. 2010. 102p. pap. *(978-1-906857-26-4(1))* Travis & Emery Music Bookshop.
—Bach's Chorals Part 2 - the Hymns & Hymn Melodies of the Cantatas & Motetts [Facsimile of 1917 Edition, Part II]. 2010. 638p. pap. *(978-1-906857-28-8(8))* Travis & Emery Music Bookshop.
—Bach's Chorals Part 3 - the Hymns & Hymn Melodies of the Organ Works [Facsimile of 1921 Edition, Part III]. 2010. 388p. pap. *(978-1-906857-30-1(X))* Travis & Emery Music Bookshop.

CHORALE—HISTORY AND CRITICISM

see Chorale

CHORALE PRELUDES

Leahy, Anne. J. S. Bach's Leipzig Chorale Preludes: Music, Text, Theology. 2011. (Contextual Bach Studies). (ENG., Illus.). 326p. (gr. 17). 80.00 *(978-0-8108-8181-5(0))* Scarecrow Pr., Inc.
Leahy, Anne & Leaver, Robin A. J. S. Bach's "Leipzig" Chorale Preludes: Music, Text, Theology. 2011. (Illus.). xxviii, 295p. E-Book *(978-0-8108-8182-2(9))* Scarecrow Pr., Inc.

CHORALES

Here are entered musical compositions. Works about the chorale are entered under the heading Chorale.
see also Chorale Preludes; Choruses, Sacred

Te Velde, Rebecca Groom. Hymn Miniatures: 28 practical settings for the church's Year. 2009. (ENG.). 40p. pap. 19.95 *(978-0-19-537712-5(5))* Oxford Univ. Pr., Inc.
Terry, Charles Sanford, ed. Four-Part Chorals of J S Bach with German Text & English Translations. 2009. 592p. pap. *(978-1-906857-24-0(5))* Travis & Emery Music Bookshop.

CHORALES—ANALYSIS, APPRECIATION

Alexander, Peter Lawrence. Street Smart Guide to the Bach Chorales. 2009. 296p. pap. 29.95 *(978-0-939067-92-3(7))* Alexander Publishing.

CHORALES—HISTORY AND CRITICISM

see Chorale

CHOREA

see also Huntington's Chorea

Walker, Ruth H. The Differential Diagnosis of Chorea. 2010. (ENG., Illus.). 464p. 79.95 *(978-0-19-539351-4(1))* Oxford Univ. Pr., Inc.
Walker, Ruth H., et al, eds. Neuroacanthocytosis Syndromes II. 2010. (ENG., Illus.). xxvi, 295p. pap. 189.00 *(978-3-642-09082-0(6)*, 3642090826) Springer.

CHOREA, EPIDEMIC

Hecker, Justus Fried. The Dancing Mania & the Black Death. 2006. pap. *(978-1-4068-1239-8(0))* Echo Library.
Hecker, Justus Friedrich Carl. The Black Death: The Dancing Mania. I.t. ed. 2007. (ENG.). 140p. pap. 19.99 *(978-1-4346-1798-9(X))*; 128p. pap. 18.99 *(978-1-4346-1629-6(0))* BiblioBazaar.
Waller, John. The Dancing Plague: The Strange, True Story of an Extraordinary Illness. 2009. (ENG.). 288p. pap. 14.99 *(978-1-4022-1943-6(1))* Sourcebooks, Inc.

CHOREOGRAPHERS

Abdul, Paula. All the Right Moves: My Autobiography. 2006. (ENG., Illus.). 256p. *(978-1-85227-365-1(8))* Virgin Bks. Ltd. GBR. Dist: Independent Pubs. Group.
Baird, Bruce. Hijikata Tatsumi & Butoh: Dancing in a Pool of Gray Grits. 2012. (Palgrave Studies in Theatre & Performance History Ser.). (ENG., Illus.). 310p. 95.00 ***(978-0-230-12040-2(7))*** Palgrave Macmillan.
Bradley, Karen K. Rudolph Laban. 2008. (Routledge Performance Practitioners Ser.). (ENG., Illus.). 160p. 110.00 *(978-0-415-37524-5(X))*; pap. 30.95 *(978-0-415-37525-2(8))* Routledge.
Bramley, Ian. Fifty Contemporary Choreographers. Bremser, Martha, ed. 2nd rev. ed. 2011. (Routledge Key Guides). (ENG.). 400p. pap. 29.95 *(978-0-415-38082-9(0))* Routledge.
Burke, Cheryl. Dancing Lessons: How I Found Passion & Potential on the Dance Floor & in Life. (ENG.). 2012. 256p. pap. 14.95 ***(978-1-118-15806-7(7))*** 2011. (Illus.). 272p. 24.95 *(978-0-470-64000-5(6))* Wiley, John & Sons, Inc. (Wiley).
Celichowska, Renata. Seven Statements of Survival. 2009. (Seven Statements of Survival Ser.). 192p. 25.90 *(978-1-60853-105-9(8))*; (gr. 9-9). 49.90 *(978-1-60853-104-2(X))* Rosen Publishing Group, Inc., The. (Dance & Movement Pr.).
—Seven Statements of Survival: Conversations with Dance Professionals. 2008. (Illus.). 192p. 24.95 *(978-1-4042-9716-6(2))* Rosen Publishing Group, Inc., The.
Chazin-Bennahum, Judith. René Blum & the Ballets Russes: In Search of a Lost Life. 2011. (ENG., Illus.). 304p. 29.95 *(978-0-19-539933-2(1))* Oxford Univ. Pr., Inc.
Climenhaga, Royd. Pina Bausch. 2009. (Routledge Performance Practitioners Ser.). (ENG., Illus.). 160p. pap. 32.95 *(978-0-415-37522-1(3))* Routledge.
Climenhaga, Royd, ed. The Bausch Sourcebook. 2012. (ENG., Illus.). 288p. 115.00 *(978-0-415-61801-4(0))*; pap. 39.95 *(978-0-415-61802-1(9))* Routledge.

Coleman, Bud & Sebesta, Judith A., eds. Women in American Musical Theatre: Essays on Composers, Lyricists, Librettists, Arrangers, Choreographers, Designers, Directors, Producers & Performance Artists. 2008. (ENG., Illus.). 292p. pap. 45.00 *(978-0-7864-3382-7(5))* McFarland & Co., Inc. Pubs.
Cutcher, Jenai. Bob Fosse. (Library of American Choreographers Ser.). (ENG.). 48p. (gr. 5-8). 2009. 53.00 *(978-1-60853-456-2(1)*, Rosen Central) 2006. (Illus.). pap. 11.75 *(978-1-4042-0640-3(X))* Rosen Publishing Group, Inc., The.
Dalbotten, Ted. To Bear Witness. 2007. 324p. per. 22.99 *(978-1-4257-5552-2(6))* Xlibris Corp.
Doerr, Evelyn. Rudolf Laban: The Dancer of the Crystal. 2007. (ENG., Illus.). 312p. per. 60.00 *(978-0-8108-6007-0(4))* Scarecrow Pr., Inc.
Eden, Lesley Ann. Fire in My Hands: Through the Land of Colour. 2010. 194p. pap. 12.99 *(978-1-60911-259-2(8)*, Eloquent Bks.) AEG Literary Publishing Services, Inc.
Eichenbaum, Rose. Masters of Movement: Portraits of America's Great Choreographers. 2007. (ENG., Illus.). 288p. pap. 27.95 *(978-1-58834-248-5(4))* Smithsonian Institution Pr.
Ewing, Alex C. Bravura! Lucia Chase & the American Ballet Theatre. 2009. (ENG., Illus.). 400p. 36.00 *(978-0-8130-3376-1(4))* Univ. Pr. of Florida.
Franceschina, John Charles. Hermes Pan: The Man Who Danced with Fred Astaire, 1 vol. 2012. (ENG., Illus.). 320p. 35.00 ***(978-0-19-975428-8(2))*** Oxford Univ. Pr., Inc.
Franchi, Cristina, ed. Kenneth MacMillan at the Royal Opera House. 2006. (Illus.). 136p. pap. 40.00 *(978-1-84002-623-8(5))* Oberon Bks., Ltd. GBR. Dist: Consortium Bk. Sales & Distribution.
Franko, Mark. Martha Graham in Love & War: The Life in the Work. 2012. (ENG., Illus.). 240p. 29.95 ***(978-0-19-977766-2(7))*** Oxford Univ. Pr., Inc.
Gitelman, Claudia & Martin, Randy, eds. The Returns of Alwin Nikolais: Bodies, Boundaries & the Dance Canon. 2007. (ENG., Illus.). 312p. pap. 27.95 *(978-0-8195-6576-1(8))*; lib. bdg. 75.00 *(978-0-8195-6575-4(X))* Wesleyan Univ. Pr.
Goldner, Nancy. Balanchine Variations. 2008. (ENG., Illus.). 160p. pap. 24.95 *(978-0-8130-3226-9(1))* Univ. Pr. of Florida.
—More Balanchine Variations. 2011. (ENG., Illus.). 160p. pap. 24.95 *(978-0-8130-3753-0(0))* Univ. Pr. of Florida.
Gottlieb, Robert. George Balanchine: The Ballet Maker. 2010. (Eminent Lives Ser.). (ENG., Illus.). 224p. pap. 13.99 *(978-0-06-075071-8(5)*, HarperPerennial) HarperCollins Pubs.
Henderson, Heidi, ed. Growing Place: Interviews with Arists. 2nd ed. 2007. (Illus.). per. 15.00 *(978-0-937645-08-6(7))* Contact Editions.
Hogan, Anne, ed. Balanchine Then & Now. 2009. (ENG., Illus.). 128p. pap. 45.00 *(978-0-9552963-9-0(0))* Sylph Editions GBR. Dist: D.A.P./Distributed Art Pubs.
Ian, Bramley. Fifty Contemporary Choreographers. Bremser, Martha, ed. 2nd rev. ed. 2011. (Routledge Key Guides). (ENG.). 400p. 110.00 *(978-0-415-38081-2(2))* Routledge.
Jordan, Stephanie. Michael Clark. Cotter, Suzanne & Violette, Robert, eds. 2011. (ENG., Illus.). 348p. 85.00 *(978-1-900828-33-8(2))* Violette Editions GBR. Dist: D.A.P./Distributed Art Pubs.
Kloetzel, Melanie & Pavlik, Carolyn. Site Dance: Choreographers & the Lure of Alternative Spaces. 2009. (ENG., Illus.). 360p. 34.95 *(978-0-8130-3400-3(0))* Univ. Pr. of Florida.
Kloetzel, Melanie & Pavlik, Carolyn, eds. Site Dance: Choreographers & the Lure of Alternative Spaces. 2011. (ENG., Illus.). 344p. pap. 27.50 *(978-0-8130-3693-9(3))* Univ. Pr. of Florida.
Lambert-Beatty, Carrie. Being Watched: Yvonne Rainer & the 1960s. 2008. (October Bks.). (ENG., Illus.). 384p. (gr. 17). 36.95 *(978-0-262-12301-3(0))* MIT Pr.
—Being Watched: Yvonne Rainer & The 1960s. 2011. (October Bks.). (ENG., Illus.). 384p. (gr. 17). pap. 19.95 *(978-0-262-51607-5(1))* MIT Pr.
Lerman, Liz. Hiking the Horizontal: Field Notes from a Choreographer. 2011. (ENG., Illus.). 332p. 29.95 *(978-0-8195-6951-6(8))* Wesleyan Univ. Pr.
Lewin, Yael Tamar & Collins, Janet. Night's Dancer: The Life of Janet Collins. 2011. (ENG., Illus.). 404p. 37.00 *(978-0-8195-7114-4(8))* Wesleyan Univ. Pr.
Long, Robert Emmet. Broadway, the Golden Years: Jerome Robbins & the Great Choreographer-Directors, 1940 to the Present. 2006. (ENG., Illus.). 312p. pap. 16.95 *(978-0-8264-1883-8(X))* Continuum International Publishing Group, Ltd. GBR. Dist: National Bk. Network.
Manning, Frankie & Millman, Cynthia R. Frankie Manning: Ambassador of Lindy Hop. (Illus.). 312p. 2008. (ENG.). pap. 21.95 *(978-1-59213-564-6(1))* 2007. 63.50 *(978-1-59213-563-9(3))* Temple Univ. Pr.
Moore, Carol-Lynne. The Harmonic Structure of Movement, Music, & Dance According to Rudolf Laban: An Examination of His Unpublished Writings & Drawings. 2009. (Illus.). 360p. 119.95 *(978-0-7734-4777-6(6))* Mellen, Edwin Pr., The.
Nelson, Miriam. My Life Dancing with the Stars. 2009. 328p. pap. 24.95 *(978-1-59393-333-3(9))* BearManor Media.
Poll, Heinz. A Time to Dance: The Life of Heinz Poll. Poll, Heinz & Schubert, Barbara, eds. 2008. (Ohio History & Culture Ser.). (ENG., Illus.). 212p. pap. 19.95 *(978-1-931968-52-2(7))* Univ. of Akron Pr., The.
Poll, Heinz & Schubert, Barbara, eds. A Time to Dance: The Life of Heinz Poll. 2008. (Ohio History & Culture Ser.). (Illus.). 212p. 29.95 *(978-1-931968-51-5(9))* Univ. of Akron Pr., The.
Reis, Sérgio Rodrigo. Rodrigo Pederneiras e o Grupo Corpo: Dança Universal. 2008. (POR., Illus.). 193p. *(978-85-7060-618-1(4))* Imprensa Oficial do Estado S/A Imesp.
Rothfuss, Joan, ed. Eiko & Koma: Time Is Not Even, Space Is Not Empty. 2011. (ENG., Illus.). 288p. pap. 35.00 *(978-0-935640-97-7(5))* Walker Art Ctr.
Schmidt, Jochen. Pina Bausch. (GER.). *(978-3-612-26513-5(X))* Econ-Verlag GmbH DEU. Dist: International Bk. Import Service, Inc.
Schwartz, Peggy & Schwartz, Murray. The Dance Claimed Me: A Biography of Pearl Primus. 2011. (ENG., Illus.). 352p. 35.00 *(978-0-300-15534-1(4))* Yale Univ. Pr.
Signer, Roman. Roman Signer: Projektionen, 1975-2008, 1 vol. 2009. (ENG., Illus.). 176p. 85.00 *(978-3-86521-747-9(8))* Steidl, Gerhard Druckerei und Verlag DEU. Dist: Innovative Logistics.
Spier. William Forsythe. 2011. (ENG., Illus.). 200p. 100.00 *(978-0-415-97822-4(X))*; pap. 30.95 *(978-0-415-97823-1(8))* Routledge.
Teachout, Terry. All in the Dances: A Brief Life of George Balanchine. 2007. (Illus.). 185p. *(978-1-4223-6715-5(0))* DIANE Publishing Co.
Tsuai, Yung Yung & Sorel, Marilyn Meeske. The Difference in Butterflies: A Chinese Dancer's Memoir of Her Flight from Inner & Outer Tyranny. 2007. 196p. per. 16.95 *(978-0-595-47325-0(3))* iUniverse, Inc.
Tune, Tommy. Footnotes: A Memoir. 2008. (ENG.). 233p. 24.00 *(978-1-4379-5235-3(6))* DIANE Publishing Co.
Vaill, Amanda. Somewhere: The Life of Jerome Robbins. 2008. (ENG., Illus.). 720p. pap. 22.95 *(978-0-7679-0421-6(4))* Broadway Bks.
Van Dantzig, Rudi. Life Behind the Metaphor: Rudolf Nureyev & the Dutch National Ballet. 2007. 144p. 100.00 *(978-0-9761233-1-6(2))* Urban, Roger.
Wood, Catherine. Yvonne Rainer: The Mind Is a Muscle. 2007. (One Work Ser.). (ENG., Illus.). 128p. (gr. 17). 35.00 *(978-1-84638-038-9(3))*; pap. 16.00 *(978-1-84638-037-2(5))* Afterall Publishing GBR. Dist: MIT Pr.

CHOREOGRAPHY

see also Ballet; Dance Notation

Barbour, Karen N. Dancing Across the Page: Narrative & Embodied Ways of Knowing. 2011. (ENG., Illus.). 187p. pap. 40.00 *(978-1-84150-421-6(1))* Intellect, Ltd. GBR. Dist: Chicago Distribution Ctr.
Boiocchi, Pamela. Dolci Evasioni. 2010. (ITA.). 76p. pap. 14.50 *(978-1-4457-7559-3(X))* Lulu Enterprises Inc.
Bournonville, August & Jurgensen, Knud Ame. Letters on Dance & Choreography. (Illus.). 77p. 19.95 *(978-1-85273-073-4(0))* Princeton Bk. Co. Pubs.
Brannigan, Erin. Dancefilm: Choreography & the Moving Image, 1 vol. 2011. (ENG., Illus.). 256p. pap. 27.95 *(978-0-19-536724-9(3))* Oxford Univ. Pr., Inc.
Burrows, Jonathan. Choreographer's Handbook. 2010. (ENG., Illus.). 240p. 95.00 *(978-0-415-55529-6(9))*; pap. 25.95 *(978-0-415-55530-2(2))* Routledge.
Butterworth, Jo. Dance Studies: The Basics. 2012. (Basics Ser.). (ENG., Illus.). 224p. (C). 90.00 ***(978-0-415-58254-4(7))***; pap. 19.95 ***(978-0-415-58255-1(5))*** Routledge.
Butterworth, Jo & Wildschut, Liesbeth. Contemporary Choreography. 2009. (ENG., Illus.). 480p. pap. 36.95 *(978-0-415-49087-0(1))* Routledge.
—Contemporary Choreography: A Critical Reader. 2009. (ENG., Illus.). 480p. 130.00 *(978-0-415-49086-3(3))* Routledge.
Charles, Joseph & Joseph, Charles M. Stravinsky & Balanchine: A Journey of Invention. 2011. (ENG., Illus.). 464p. pap. 45.00 ***(978-0-300-17697-1(X))*** Yale Univ. Pr.
Climenhaga, Royd. Pina Bausch. 2009. (Routledge Performance Practitioners Ser.). (ENG., Illus.). 160p. pap. 32.95 *(978-0-415-37522-1(3))* Routledge.
De Leon, Jennifer. Dance & Stillness; a Danced Inquiry to the Experience of Stillness. 2009. 136p. pap. *(978-3-639-14027-9(3))* VDM Verlag Dr. Mueller e.K.
Elkins, Leslie. Body-Presence. 2010. 288p. pap. *(978-3-8383-5344-9(7))* Lambert Academic Publishing.
Emoruwa, Felix. Choreographic Quest in Asawogidigba & Biripo Dances in Nigeri. 2011. 140p. pap. ***(978-3-8433-8876-4(8))*** Lambert Academic Publishing.
FOSTER, Susan. Choreographing Empathy. 2010. (ENG., Illus.). 296p. 115.00 *(978-0-415-59655-8(6))* Routledge.
—Choreographing Empathy: Kinesthesia in Performance. 2010. (ENG., Illus.). 296p. pap. 48.95 *(978-0-415-59656-5(4))* Routledge.
Franchi, Cristina, ed. Kenneth MacMillan at the Royal Opera House. 2006. (Illus.). 136p. pap. 40.00 *(978-1-84002-623-8(5))* Oberon Bks., Ltd. GBR. Dist: Consortium Bk. Sales & Distribution.
Goldner, Nancy. More Balanchine Variations. 2011. (ENG., Illus.). 160p. pap. 24.95 *(978-0-8130-3753-0(0))* Univ. Pr. of Florida.
Gordon, Eric & Bogen, David. Attention Please! 2012. (ENG.). 240p. 150.00 *(978-0-415-88023-7(8))*; pap. 34.95 *(978-0-415-88024-4(6))* Routledge.
Hodson, Millicent & Archer, Kenneth. Nijinsky's Bloomsbury Ballet: Reconstruction of Dance & Design for Jeux. 2007. (Wendy Hilton Dance & Music Ser.). (C). *(978-1-57647-042-8(3))* Pendragon Pr.
Ibargüen, VanNia. Through the Distance: Creating virtual extensions in Dance. 2010. (Illus.). 64p. pap. *(978-3-8383-6723-1(5))* Lambert Academic Publishing.
Kloetzel, Melanie & Pavlik, Carolyn. Site Dance: Choreographers & the Lure of Alternative Spaces. 2009. (ENG., Illus.). 360p. 34.95 *(978-0-8130-3400-3(0))* Univ. Pr. of Florida.
Kloetzel, Melanie & Pavlik, Carolyn, eds. Site Dance: Choreographers & the Lure of Alternative Spaces. 2011. (ENG., Illus.). 344p. pap. 27.50 *(978-0-8130-3693-9(3))* Univ. Pr. of Florida.
Kolb, Alexandra. Performing Femininity: Dance & Literature in German Modernism. 2009. (Illus.). 330p. pap. 61.95 *(978-3-03911-351-4(8))* Lang, Peter AG GBR. Dist: Lang, Peter.
Kreng, John. Fight Choreography: The Art of Non-Verbal Dialogue. 2007. (ENG., Illus.). 544p. per. 34.99 *(978-1-59200-679-3(5))* Course Technology.
Kurnaedy, Karen. A Choreographer's Process. 2010. 148p. pap. *(978-3-639-27662-6(0))* VDM Verlag Dr. Mueller e.K.
Lansdale, Janet, ed. Decentring Dancing Texts: The Challenge of Interpreting Dances. 2008. (ENG., Illus.). 232p. 89.00 *(978-0-230-54259-4(X))* Palgrave Macmillan.
Lerman, Liz. Hiking the Horizontal: Field Notes from a Choreographer. 2011. (ENG., Illus.). 332p. 29.95 *(978-0-8195-6951-6(8))* Wesleyan Univ. Pr.
Mayer, Ruth Ann. The Theme of My Praise: Choreography Skills for God's Dancers. 2007. 55p. 20.00 *(978-0-9702329-3-9(4))* One Accord Ministries.
McAsh, F. Braun. Fight Choreography: A Practical Guide for Stage, Film & Television, 1 vol. 2011. (ENG., Illus.). 192p. 27.95 *(978-1-84797-223-1(3))* Crowood Pr., Ltd. GBR. Dist: Independent Pubs. Group.
Midgelow, Vida L. Reworking the Ballet: Counter Narratives & Alternative Bodies. 2007. (ENG., Illus.). 240p. (C). 33.95 *(978-0-415-97603-9(0))* Routledge.
—Reworking the Ballet: Counter-Narratives & Alternative Bodies. 2007. (Illus.). 240p. 125.00 *(978-0-415-97602-2(2))* Routledge.
Minton, Sandra Cerny. Choreography: A Basic Approach Using Improvisation. 3rd rev. ed. 2007. (ENG., Illus.). 176p. (gr. 9-16). per. 26.95 *(978-0-7360-6476-7(1))* Human Kinetics Pubs.
Moore, Carol-Lynne & Yamamoto, Kaoru. Beyond Words. 2nd rev. ed. 2011. (ENG., Illus.). 256p. 110.00 *(978-0-415-61001-8(X))*; pap. 31.95 *(978-0-415-61002-5(8))* Routledge.
Mroz, Daniel. The Dancing Word: An Embodied Approach to the Preparation of Performers & the Composition of Performances. 2011. (ENG., Illus.). 219p. pap. 64.00 *(978-90-420-3330-6(4))* Rodopi.
Mullally, Robert. The Carole: A Study of A Medieval Dance. 2011. (Illus.). 172p. 99.95 *(978-1-4094-1248-9(2))* Ashgate Publishing Co.
Pomer, Janice. Dance Composition: An Interrelated Arts Approach. 2009. (ENG., Illus.). 208p. (gr. 9-16). 42.00 *(978-0-7360-6790-4(6))* Human Kinetics Pubs.
Popat, Sita. Invisible Connections. 2010. (Illus.). 178p. pap. 39.95 *(978-0-415-57632-1(6))* Routledge.
Pulinkala, Ivan. Piper of the Soul. 2010. 76p. pap. *(978-3-8383-1149-4(3))* Lambert Academic Publishing.
Schweizer, Jean A. The New Choreography of Consciousness: New Evolutionary Movements Creating A Quantum Leap, Attaining Our Highest Human Potential. 2011. 112p. pap. 37.33 *(978-1-4389-8573-2(8))* AuthorHouse.
Seed, Patricia, ed. José Limón & la Malinche: The Dancer & the Dance. 2008. (Joe R. & Teresa Lozano Long Series in Latin American & Latino Art & Culture). (ENG., Illus.). 208p. 34.95 *(978-0-292-71735-0(0))* Univ. of Texas Pr.
Shacklock, Karla. Dance Consciousness. 2010. 292p. pap. *(978-3-8383-8352-1(4))* Lambert Academic Publishing.
Smith-Autard, Jacqueline M. Dance Composition: Creative Success in Dance Making. 6th ed. 2010. (ENG., Illus.). 320p. pap. 29.95 *(978-1-4081-1564-0(6)*, Methuen Drama) A & C Black GBR. Dist: Macmillan.
Steele, Amber. High Technology Dance. 2010. (Illus.). 100p. pap. *(978-3-8383-1844-8(7))* Lambert Academic Publishing.
Sunderland, Margot & Pickering, Kenneth. Choreographing the Stage Musical. 2nd ed. 2009. 157p. *(978-0-88734-977-5(3))* Players Pr., Inc.
Sutton. Customized Version of Dance Appreciation. 2007. 168p. 42.82 *(978-0-7575-4594-8(7))* Kendall Hunt Publishing Co.
Trenton, Trisha. Trisha Trenton: A Journey through the Art & Craft of Making Dances: the Choreographer. 2007. mass mkt. 88.00 *(978-0-9727410-3-3(8))* TEG Publishing.

Webb, Brian, ed. Ode au Corps: Une Histoire de Danse. (FRE & ENG., Illus.). 128p. pap. 14.95 *(978-0-920159-98-9(2))* Banff Centre Pr. CAN. Dist: Literary Pr. Group of Canada.
Weisbeck, Markus, ed. William Forsythe: Suspense. 2008. (ENG & GER., Illus.). 148p. pap. 55.00 *(978-3-905829-75-4(4))* JRP Ringier Kunstverlag AG CHE. Dist: D.A.P./Distributed Art Pubs.
Wilson, Adrienne. Synchronicity. 2010. 136p. pap. *(978-3-8383-5855-0(4))* Lambert Academic Publishing.
Wong, Yutian. Choreographing Asian America. 2010. (ENG.). 280p. (C). 75.00 *(978-0-8195-6702-4(7))*; pap. 27.95 *(978-0-8195-6703-1(5))* Wesleyan Univ. Pr.

CHORIOCARCINOMA
Johnson, Tara & Schwartz, Meredith Celene. Gestational Trophoblastic Neophasia: A Guide for Women Dealing with Tumors of the Placenta, Such As Choriocarcinoma, Molar Pregnancy & Other Forms of GTN. 2007. (Illus.). 240p. per. 29.95 *(978-1-4251-0695-9(1))* Trafford Publishing.

CHORIONITIS
see Scleroderma (Disease)

CHOROID—DISEASES
Penn, J. S., ed. Retinal & Choroidal Angiogenesis. 2008. (Illus.). 557p. 179.00 *(978-1-4020-6779-2(8))* Springer.
Penn, John, ed. Retinal & Choroidal Angiogenesis. 2010. xxiv, 568p. pap. 179.00 *(978-90-481-7724-0(3), 9048177243)* Springer.
Wolff, Johannes. Choroid Plexus Tumor Protocol CPT-SIOP-2000 2nd Edt. 2010. 108p. pap. 19.40 *(978-0-557-31432-4(1))* Lulu Enterprises Inc.

CHORUSES
Here are entered collections of sacred and secular choral compositions for various groups of voices (men's, mixed, women's, etc.) both accompanied and unaccompanied. Works about choruses are entered under the heading Choral Music. Works about choruses as performance groups are entered under headings such as Choirs (Music) or Choral Societies.
see also Cantatas; Choruses, Sacred; Motets
Albrecht, Sally K., et al. Of Thee I Sing! A Celebration of America's Music for 2-Part Choirs. 2007. (ENG.). 112p. pap. 34.99 *(978-0-7390-4657-9(8))* Alfred Publishing Co., Inc.
Anders, Roger D. Thirty-Seven Songs & Choruses: For Sunday School, Vacation Bible School, or Special Children Services. 2010. pap. 8.99 *(978-1-60799-589-0(1))* Tate Publishing & Enterprises, LLC.
Argento, Dominick. A Nation of Cowslips: Seven Bagatelles for Unaccompanied SATB Chorus. 2009. (ENG.). 88p. pap. 8.99 *(978-1-4234-6945-2(3), 1423469453)* Boosey & Hawkes, Inc.
—Walden Pond: Set of Instrumental Parts (Three Violoncellos & Harp) 2010. (ENG.). 52p. pap. 19.99 *(978-1-4234-9217-7(X), 142349217X)* Boosey & Hawkes, Inc.
Bryant, William Cullen. To A Waterfowl. 2006. (Illus.). pap. 15.95 *(978-1-4286-4395-5(8))* Kessinger Publishing, LLC.
Burrows, Donald, ed. Ode for Saint Cecilia's Day. 2009. (ENG.). 78p. pap. 16.00 *(978-1-84772-906-4(1), 1847729061)* Novello & Co.
Chilcott, Bob. Salisbury Vespers. 2009. 12p. pap. 3.50 *(978-0-19-336464-6(6))* Oxford Univ. Pr., Inc.
Copland, Aaron. Old American Songs Complete: SATB & Piano. 2011. (ENG.). 100p. pap. 8.95 *(978-1-61780-392-5(8), 1617803928)* Boosey & Hawkes, Inc.
Cowper, William. John Gilpin. 2006. pap. 9.95 *(978-1-4286-8114-9(0))* Kessinger Publishing, LLC.
Drake, Jeremy. Let's Have Some Music. 2009. (ENG.). 12p. pap. 7.95 *(978-1-4234-7825-6(8), 1423478258)* Leonard, Hal Corp.
—Let's Have Some Music: (Collection) 2009. (ENG.). 34p. pap. 16.95 *(978-1-4234-7824-9(X), 142347824X)* Leonard, Hal Corp.
Gambill, Luke, et al, contrib. by. Sing the Hits: Choral Collection, SATB. 2008. 167p. per. 7.95 *(978-5-557-48299-8(7))*, Brentwood-Benson Music Publishing, Inc.) Brentwood Music, Inc.
Herbeck, Johann. Johann Herbeck: For Unaccompanied Men's Chorus: Selected German Works. Hettrick, William E., ed. 2008. pap. 175.00 net. *(978-0-89579-628-8(7))* A-R Editions, Inc.
Jenkins, Karl. The Karl Jenkins Piano Album. 2007. 42p. pap. 16.95 *(978-0-85162-540-9(1), 0851625401)* Leonard, Hal Corp.
—A Parliament of Owls: Mixed Chorus, Saxophone, Percussion, & Piano Duet Vocal Score. 2010. (ENG.). 56p. pap. 17.95 *(978-0-85162-608-6(4), 0851626084)* Boosey & Hawkes, Inc.
—This Land of Ours: Männerchor (TTBB) und Klavier (Orge) 2009. (ENG.). 64p. pap. 22.95 *(978-0-85162-575-1(4), 0851625754)* Boosey & Hawkes, Inc.
Monk, Meredith. Three Heavens & Hells. 2011. (ENG.). 80p. pap. 9.95 *(978-1-4554-0320-9(3), 1458403203)* Boosey & Hawkes, Inc.
Schram, Scott. The Last Noel: A Christmas Musical for Children. 2007. (ENG.). pap. 22.50 *(978-0-7390-4483-4(4))*; pap. 16.95 *(978-0-7390-4486-5(9))* Alfred Publishing Co., Inc.
Slobin, Mark, et al, eds. Emily's Songbook: Music in 1850s Albany. 2011. pap. 125.00 net *(978-0-89579-706-3(2))* A-R Editions, Inc.
Terry, Charles S., ed. The Four-Part Chorals of J. S. Bach. reprint ed. 49.50 *(978-0-404-12857-9(2))* AMS Pr., Inc.
Tredici, David Del. David Del Tredici - Paul Revere's Ride: Amplified Soprano Solo, SATB Chorus, & Orchestra Piano/Vocal Score. 2011. (ENG.). 114p. pap. 22.95 *(978-1-61780-410-6(X), 161780410X)* Boosey & Hawkes, Inc.
Whitacre, Eric. Eric Whitacre Collection: For SATB Chorus Unaccompanied. 2010. (ENG.). 56p. pap. 14.95 *(978-1-84772-688-9(7), 1847726887)* Chester Music GBR. Dist: Leonard, Hal Corp.
—Light & Gold: (Choral Collection) 2011. (ENG.). 80p. pap. 15.95 *(978-1-84938-856-6(3), 1849388563)* Chester Music GBR. Dist: Leonard, Hal Corp.
Williams, Ralph. Serenade to Music. 2008. (ENG.). 24p. 11.95 *(978-0-19-336002-0(0))* Oxford Univ. Pr., Inc.

CHORUSES—BIBLIOGRAPHY
Green, Jonathan D. A Conductor's Guide to Nineteenth-Century Choral-Orchestral Works. 2007. (ENG.). 350p. 78.00 *(978-0-8108-6046-9(5))* Scarecrow Pr., Inc.
Rosewall, Michael. Directory of Choral-Orchestral Music. 2006. (ENG.). 352p. 130.00 *(978-0-415-98004-3(6))* Routledge.
Shrock, Dennis. Choral Repertoire. 2009. (ENG.). 784p. 74.00 *(978-0-19-532778-6(0))* Oxford Univ. Pr., Inc.

CHORUSES—HISTORY AND CRITICISM
see Choral Music

CHORUSES, SACRED
see also Anthems; Chorales; Sacred Vocal Music; Service Books (Music)
Adore Him: A Christmas Worship Experience. 2007. (ENG., Illus.). 168p. pap. 8.99 *(978-0-8341-7562-4(2), 0834175622)* Lillenas Publishing Co.
Alfred Publishing Staff. Mary Slept: Choral Octavo. 2010. (Faber Edition: Choral Signature Ser.). (ENG.). pap. 3.50 *(978-0-571-53541-5(0))* Faber & Faber, Ltd. GBR. Dist: Alfred Publishing Co., Inc.
—O Praise God in His Holiness (Psalm 150) Choral Octavo. 2010. (Faber Edition: Choral Signature Ser.). (ENG.). pap. 3.50 *(978-0-571-53550-7(X))* Faber & Faber, Ltd. GBR. Dist: Alfred Publishing Co., Inc.
—Sittin' in with the Big Band, Vol 2: Trombone, Book & CD. 2008. (Sittin' in with the Big Band Ser.). (ENG.). 32p. pap. 14.95 *(978-0-7390-5702-5(2))* Alfred Publishing Co., Inc.
—You Raise Me Up: A Treasury of Inspirational Favorites (Preview Pack), Book & CD. 2009. (ENG.). pap. 16.95 *(978-0-7390-6129-9(1))* Alfred Publishing Co., Inc.
Ball, Karen. Fount of Every Blessing: Artistic Piano Solos. 2008. (ENG.). 72p. pap. 16.99 *(978-0-8341-7690-4(4), 9780834176904)* Lillenas Publishing Co.
Blanton, Gail, et al. Scripts of Hope & Restoration. 2006. (ENG.). 56p. pap. 19.99 *(978-0-8341-7537-2(1), 0834175371)* Lillenas Publishing Co.
Blended Worship 2: 12 Praise & Worship Songs with 12 Praise & Worship Hymns Arranged in 12 Medleys. 2007. (ENG.). 128p. pap. 6.99 *(978-0-8341-7592-1(4), 0834175924)* Lillenas Publishing Co.
Brentwood-Benson Music Publishing Staff, creator. Jars of Clay Christmas Songs. 2007. 95p. per. 14.95 *(978-5-557-52191-8(7))*, Brentwood-Benson Music Publishing, Inc.) Brentwood Music, Inc.
Brown, Timothy, ed. Choral Works with Orchestra. 2009. (William Walton Edition Ser.). 328p. pap. 195.00 *(978-0-19-368307-5(5))* Oxford Univ. Pr., Inc.
Burleigh, Harry T. The Spirituals of Harry T. Burleigh: High Voice. 2007. (ENG.). pap. 44.95 *(978-0-7390-4526-8(1))* Alfred Publishing Co., Inc.
—The Spirituals of Harry T. Burleigh: Low Voice. 2007. (ENG.). pap. 44.95 *(978-0-7390-4528-2(8))* Alfred Publishing Co., Inc.
Carver, Anthony F. Cori Spezzati: Volume 1, the Development of Sacred Polychoral Music to the Time of Schutz, 2 vols. 2009. (ENG., Illus.). 300p. pap. 38.99 *(978-0-521-10632-0(X))* Cambridge Univ. Pr.
Carver, Anthony F., ed. Cori Spezzati: Volume 2: An Anthology of Sacred Polychoral Music, 2 vols. 2009. (ENG., Illus.). 172p. pap. 26.99 *(978-0-521-10635-1(4))* Cambridge Univ. Pr.
Chapman, Steven Curtis. Steven Curtis Chapman - This Moment. 2007. (ENG.). 82p. pap. 16.95 *(978-1-4234-5283-6(6), 1423452836)* Leonard, Hal Corp.
Chilcott, Bob. Bob Chilcott Carols 2: 10 carol arrangements for mixed Voices. 2009. 72p. pap. 12.95 *(978-0-19-336507-0(3))* Oxford Univ. Pr., Inc.
Choplin, Pepper. Fall on Your Knees: SAB with Opt. Orchestra. 2011. 11p. pap. 1.95 ***(978-1-4291-2560-4(8))*** Lorenz Corp., The.
—Fall on Your Knees: SATB with Opt. Orchestra. 2011. 11p. pap. 1.95 ***(978-1-4291-2559-8(4))*** Lorenz Corp., The.
Christ Is Risen! Alleluia! An Easter Presentation of 5 Songs in Unison/2-Part. 2009. (ENG.). 40p. pap. 5.99 *(978-0-8341-7752-9(8), 9780834177529)* Lillenas Publishing Co.
Clark, Dave & Thompson, Jayme, creators. Angels We Have Heard: Unison. 2008. (Simple Plus Series for Kids Ser.). 69p. pap. 6.95 *(978-5-557-40950-6(5))*, Brentwood-Benson Music Publishing, Inc.) Brentwood Music, Inc.
Come & See: An Easter Celebration for Any Choir. 2009. (ENG.). 88p. pap. 6.99 *(978-0-8341-7737-6(4), 9780834177376)* Lillenas Publishing Co.
Curry, Craig, et al. Snow Falling on Ivory: Seasonal Piano Solos with Optional Instruments. 2008. (ENG.). 88p. pap. 24.95 *(978-1-59235-262-3(6), 1592352626)*, Glory Sound) Shawnee Pr., Inc.
Curry, Craig, contrib. by. The Power of His Blood. 2011. 15p. pap. 1.95 *(978-1-4291-2130-9(0))* Lorenz Corp., The.
Davis, B. J., et al, contrib. by. Made Me Glad: A Choral Collection of Songs from Hillsong Church. 2008. 127p. pap. 8.95 *(978-5-557-38649-4(1))* Point of Grace Entertainment Group.
Davy, Richard. Richard Davy: Reconstructed from the Eton Choirbook with Lyrics in Latin & English. Duffin, Ross W., ed. 2011. pap. 100.00 net. ***(978-0-89579-705-6(4))*** A-R Editions, Inc.
Dennis, Allen, contrib. by. Contemporary Praise for Ladies' Voices 2: 14 Arrangements for Ensemble or Choir. 2007. (ENG.). 128p. pap. 8.99 *(978-0-8341-7589-1(4), 0834175894)* Lillenas Publishing Co.
Dick, Viktor. Piano, Christian Hymns & Chorals, Volume 1: 21 Famous Christian Hymns & Chorals for Piano, 2 vols., Vol.1. 2007. 32p. (YA). pap. 19.95 *(978-0-9799248-0-4(4))* New Fields World Wide Ministries Inc.
—Piano, Christian Hymns & Chorals, Volume 2: 17 Famous Christian Hymns & Chorals for Piano, 2 vols., Vol.2. 2007. 32p. (YA). pap. 19.95 *(978-0-9799248-1-1(2))* New Fields World Wide Ministries Inc.
Ellis, Graham J. The Morland Responses. 2008. 4p. pap. 2.25 *(978-0-19-395016-0(2))* Oxford Univ. Pr., Inc.
Endicott, Stan & Barron, Chris. The Risen One: Resurrection Songs for Choir-Led Worship. 2006. (ENG.). 136p. pap. 8.99 *(978-0-8341-7544-0(4), 0834175444)* Lillenas Publishing Co.
Farlow, Wenceslaus, compiled by. The Church & Israel. unabr. ed. pap. *(978-0-914936-28-2(X))* City Christian Publishing.
Ferrin, Paul. And Can It Be? Hymn Enhancements for Piano & Organ. 2007. (ENG., Illus.). 104p. pap. 18.99 *(978-0-8341-7580-8(0), 0834175800)* Lillenas Publishing Co.
Fettke, Tom, contrib. by. Messiah Christmas Suite: SAB & Solo with Opt. Orchestra or Instrumental Ensemble. 2011. 15p. pap. 1.95 ***(978-1-4291-2486-7(5))*** Lorenz Corp., The.
—Messiah Christmas Suite -SATB. 2011. 15p. pap. 1.95 ***(978-1-4291-2485-0(7))*** Lorenz Corp., The.
Fettke, Tom, et al. Southern Gospel Favorites: 15 Outstanding Arrangements for Choir. 2006. (ENG.). 96p. pap. 6.99 *(978-0-8341-7541-9(X), 083417541X)* Lillenas Publishing Co.
Gambill, Luke, creator. Glory to God in the Highest: Unison. 2008. audio compact disk 10.00 *(978-5-557-40892-9(4))*, Brentwood-Benson Music Publishing, Inc.) Brentwood Music, Inc.
Glorysound, creator. One Rehearsal Wonders, Volume 2. 2007. audio compact disk 16.95 *(978-5-557-49843-2(5))*, Glory Sound) Shawnee Pr., Inc.
Goss, Lari & Stone, Regi, contrib. by. Make a Joyful Noise: A Worship Choir Collection. 2007. audio compact disk 10.00 *(978-5-557-49690-2(4))*, Word Music) Word Entertainment.
—Make a Joyful Noise: A Worship Choir Collection: SATB. 2007. 119p. pap. 8.95 *(978-5-557-49727-5(7))*, Word Music) Word Entertainment.
Hal Leonard Corporation Staff, creator. The Complete Wedding Music Planner. 2009. (ENG.). 288p. pap. 29.99 incl. audio compact disk *(978-0-8256-3731-5(7), 0825637317)* Music Sales Corp.
—Holy Is the Lord. 2008. (Worship Band Play-along Ser.: Vol. 1). (ENG.). 56p. pap. 12.95 incl. audio compact disk *(978-1-4234-1711-8(9), 1423417119)*; 64p. pap. 12.95 incl. audio compact disk *(978-1-4234-1713-2(5), 1423417135)*; 72p. pap. 12.95 incl. audio compact disk *(978-1-4234-1712-5(7), 1423417127)*; 40p. pap. 12.95 incl. audio compact disk *(978-1-4234-1715-6(1), 1423417151)*; 64p. pap. 12.95 incl. audio compact disk *(978-1-4234-1714-9(3), 1423417143)* Leonard, Hal Corp.
—One Rehearsal Wonders Vol. 2: Almost Instant Anthems for Any Occasion. 2007. (ENG.). 80p. pap. 7.99 *(978-1-59235-183-1(2), 1592351832*, Glory Sound) Shawnee Pr., Inc.
—Sister Act: E-Z Play Today Volume 300. 2009. (ENG.). 32p. pap. 8.99 *(978-1-4234-8654-1(4), 1423486544)* Leonard, Hal Corp.
—12 Wedding Solos: High Voice. 2008. (ENG.). 48p. pap. 19.95 incl. audio compact disk *(978-1-4234-3689-8(X), 142343689X)* Leonard, Hal Corp.
—12 Wedding Solos: Low Voice. 2008. (ENG.). 48p. pap. 19.95 incl. audio compact disk *(978-1-4234-3691-1(1), 1423436911)* Leonard, Hal Corp.
Hammerschmidt, Andreas. Andreas Hammerschmidt: Including a Setting of Martin Opitz's Salomons des Hebreischen Königes Hohes Liedt: Geistlicher Dialogen Ander Theil. Tilley, Janette, ed. 2008. 108p. pap. 85.00 net. *(978-0-89579-625-7(2))* A-R Editions, Inc.
Have No Fear: A Christmas Worship Experience. 2008. (ENG.). pap. 9.99 *(978-0-8341-7657-7(2), 9780834176577)* Lillenas Publishing Co.
Henson, John M., ed. Celestial Voices: A Superior Collection of Sacred Songs, Suitable for All Religious Work & Worship. 2011. 166p. 41.95 ***(978-1-258-02008-8(4))*** Literary Licensing, LLC.
Immanuel: An Advent Collection. 2007. (ENG., Illus.). 72p. pap. 4.99 *(978-0-8341-7554-9(1), 0834175541)* Lillenas Publishing Co.
Jenkins, Karl. Gloria: SATB & keyboard Reduction. 2010. 80p. pap. 14.95 *(978-0-85162-598-0(3), 0851625983)* Leonard, Hal Corp.
—Te Deum: For SATB Chorus & Orchestra. 2009. (ENG.). 56p. pap. 17.95 *(978-0-85162-597-3(5), 0851625975)* Boosey & Hawkes, Inc.
Johnson, Victor C. Listen, Children, Hear the Angels Sing! SATB Divisi, a Capella, with Opt. Solo. 2011. 8p. pap. 1.85 ***(978-1-4291-2583-3(7))*** Lorenz Corp., The.
Joseph M. Martin, et al. The Weeping Tree: A Service for Holy Week. 2007. (ENG.). 72p. pap. 7.95 *(978-1-59235-182-4(4), 1592351824*, Flammer, Harold Music) Shawnee Pr., Inc.
Joseph M. Martin, ed. Just Voices: A Capella Anthems for Any Occasion. 2007. (ENG.). 88p. pap. 7.95 *(978-1-59235-173-2(5), 1592351735*, Glory Sound) Shawnee Pr., Inc.
Labenske, Victor. My Jesus, I Love Thee: Devotional Hymns for the Journey of Faith. 2007. (ENG., Illus.). 56p. pap. 15.99 *(978-0-8341-7583-9(5), 0834175835)* Lillenas Publishing Co.
Lehman, Clayton. Sacred Music for Christmas. 2010. 93p. pap. 25.00 *(978-0-578-04320-3(3))* Harmonies for Life.
Liebergen, Patrick M. Singer's Library of Arias: Low Voice. 2008. (ENG.). 120p. pap. 15.95 *(978-0-7390-5140-5(7))* Alfred Publishing Co., Inc.
Lomer, Beverly. Hildegard of Bingen. 2009. 290p. pap. *(978-3-639-17921-7(8))* VDM Verlag Dr. Mueller e.K.
Luther, Martin. Hymns of Martin Luther. 2008. 156p. 25.99 *(978-0-554-21549-5(7))*; 22.99 *(978-0-554-30852-4(5))* BiblioBazaar.
—Hymns of Martin Luther. Bacon, Leonard Woolsey, ed. 2006. (ENG.). 146p. pap. 18.99 *(978-1-4264-0340-8(2))*; 152p. pap. 21.99 *(978-1-4264-0391-0(7))* BiblioBazaar.
Martin, Joseph. The Song Everlasting: A Sacred Cantata based on Early American Songs. 2011. (ENG.). 100p. pap. 8.95 ***(978-1-4584-1550-9(3)***, 1458415503, Flammer, Harold Music) Shawnee Pr., Inc.
Mauldin, Russell, contrib. by. We Will Stand: 10 Timeless Songs of Faith & Inspiration. 2007. audio compact disk 10.00 *(978-5-557-49258-3(2))*, Word Music) Word Entertainment.
—We Will Stand: 10 Timeless Songs of Faith & Inspiration: SATB. 2007. 143p. pap. 8.95 *(978-5-557-49273-7(9))*, Word Music) Word Entertainment.
McDonald, Mary. His Grace Will Lead Us Through: SATB with Opt. Orchestra. 2011. 11p. pap. 1.95 ***(978-1-4291-2404-1(0))*** Lorenz Corp., The.
—His Grace Will Lead Us Through: TTBB with Opt. Orchestra. 2011. 11p. pap. 1.95 ***(978-1-4291-2405-8(9))*** Lorenz Corp., The.
McDonough, Daniel. '... for the Waters Are Come in unto My Soul...' - Fragments of Psalm 69 - Music for Mixed Chorus. 2008. 52p. pap. *(978-3-8364-8014-7(X))* VDM Verlag Dr. Mueller e.K.
McDowall, Cecilia. Ave Maris Stella. 2008. (New Horizons Ser.). (ENG.). 24p. pap. 10.95 *(978-0-19-335949-9(9))* Oxford Univ. Pr., Inc.
Men Sing Praise: Dynamic Praise & Worship, Hymns & Gospel Arrangements for Men. 2009. (ENG.). 136p. pap. 8.99 *(978-0-8341-7741-3(2), 9780834177413)* Lillenas Publishing Co.
Meyer, Sandra, contrib. by. Religious Classics for Soprano. 2006. (ENG., Illus.). 48p. pap. 19.98 incl. audio compact disk *(978-1-59615-524-4(8), 1596155248)* Music Minus One.
Morosan, Vladimir, ed. Roman Hurko: Vespers. 2008. (Illus.). 71p. 14.95 *(978-0-9701767-1-4(6))* Musica Russica.
The Name... Jesus: A Christmas Musical Celebrating Emmanuel the King of Kings. 2008. (ENG.). 136p. pap. 8.99 *(978-0-8341-7644-7(0), 0834176440)* Lillenas Publishing Co.
The New Oxford Easy Anthem Book. 2006. 256p. spiral bd. 26.95 *(978-0-19-335578-1(7))* Oxford Univ. Pr., Inc.
O Holy Child of Bethlehem: Christmas Carols Arranged for Solo Piano. 2008. (ENG.). 48p. pap. 15.99 *(978-0-8341-7647-8(5), 9780834176478)* Lillenas Publishing Co.
Owens, Jimmy, et al. The Country Favorites: How to Write & Select Songs for Worship. 2009. (ENG.). 174p. pap. 19.99 *(978-1-4234-3536-5(2), 1423435362)* Leonard, Hal Corp.
Parks, Marty. O for a Dozen Tongues to Sing - Gospel Hymns: Six Ready-to-Sing Anthems for Two-part Mixed Voices. 2009. spiral bd. 29.95 *(978-1-4267-0016-3(4))* Abingdon Pr.
—Once upon a Miracle: A Christmas Musical for Senior Adult Choir. 2007. (ENG., Illus.). 80p. pap. 7.99 *(978-0-8341-7556-3(8), 0834175568)* Lillenas Publishing Co.
—Songs of Hope & Restoration: Arranged for Any Choir. 2006. (ENG.). 120p. pap. 8.99 *(978-0-8341-7540-2(1), 083-417-5401)* Lillenas Publishing Co.
Pearsall, Robert. Let Your Light So Shine. 2009. pap., pap. 2.00 *(978-0-19-395388-8(9))* Oxford Univ. Pr., Inc.
Perti, Giacomo Antonio. Giacomo Antonio Perti: Five-Voice Motets for the Assumption of the Virgin Mary. Zitellini, Rodolfo, ed. 2007. pap. 115.00 net. *(978-0-89579-613-4(9))* A-R Editions, Inc.
Pethel, Stan. He Is Born, the Divine Christ Child: Christmas Portraits Arranged for Solo Piano. 2007. (ENG., Illus.). 48p. pap. 15.99 *(978-0-8341-7582-2(7), 0834175827)* Lillenas Publishing Co.
Psallite: Sacred Song for Liturgy & Life Year C. 2006. 350p. 24.95 *(978-0-8146-3065-5(0))* Liturgical Pr.
Purcell, Henry, et al. Harmonia Sacra or Divine Hymns & Dialogues: With a Through-Bass for the Theobro-Lute, Bass-Viol, Harpsichord or Organ. Composed by the Best Masters O. 2008. 124p. pap. *(978-1-904331-62-9(9))* Travis & Emery Music Bookshop.
Reverence: Music for Choir-Led Worship. 2007. (ENG., Illus.). 152p. pap. 8.99 *(978-0-8341-7579-2(7), 0834175797)* Lillenas Publishing Co.
Ritual Dances for Orchestra: Study Score. 2007. (ENG.). 140p. pap. 50.00 *(978-3-7957-6418-0(1), 3795764181)* Schott Musik International GmbH & Co. KG DEU. Dist: Leonard, Hal Corp.
Robertson, Barny & Robertson, Carter, contrib. by. Ready for Worship: 12 Complete Worship Sets with No Transposition or Transitions Required. 2007. (ENG.). 176p. pap. 9.99 *(978-0-8341-7596-9(7), 0834175967)* Lillenas Publishing Co.
Robertson, Carter & Robertson, Barney, contrib. by. Ready for Worship: 12 Complete Worship Sets with No Transpositions or Transitions Required. 2007. (ENG.). 158p. pap. 19.99 *(978-0-8341-7601-0(7), 0834176017)* Lillenas Publishing Co.
Rovetta, Giovanni. Giovanni Rovetta: Masses. Drennan, Jonathan R. J., ed. 2006. (Recent Researches in the Music of the Baroque Era Ser.: B146). 220p. pap. 123.00 net. *(978-0-89579-600-4(7))* A-R Editions, Inc.
Saveiio. Your Own Song to Sing: Volume 2. 2011. 398p. pap. 19.99 ***(978-1-4568-8772-8(6))*** Xlibris Corp.
Schalit, Heinrich. Sabbath Eve Liturgy for Cantor, Baritone or Tenor, ed Voices, Satb, & Organ: Liturgiyah Shel Lel Shabat. 2011. 92p. 38.95 ***(978-1-258-10373-6(7))*** Literary Licensing, LLC.

Schram, Ruth Elaine, contrib. by. Follow the Christmas Star: Two-Part Any Combination with Opt. Percussion. 2011. 15p. pap. 1.95 *(978-0-7877-0652-4(3))* Lorenz Corp., The.

Shafferman, Jean Anne. Simple Sacred Songs for Children: 6 Delightfully Easy Songs for Unison or 2-Part with Reproducible Song Sheets. 2007. (ENG.). 36p. pap. 14.95 *(978-0-7390-4798-9(1))*; pap. 37.95 *(978-0-7390-4799-6(X))* Alfred Publishing Co., Inc.

Shawnee Press Staff. Celtic Sunday Morning. 2009. 88p. pap. 24.95 *(978-1-59235-232-6(4)*, SB1048) Shawnee Pr., Inc.

—Guitar Praise & Worship Level 1. 2008. (ENG.). 48p. pap. 29.95 *(978-1-59235-195-4(6)*, 1592351956) Shawnee Pr., Inc.

—One Rehearsal Wonders. 2006. (ENG.). 72p. pap. 6.95 *(978-1-59235-156-5(5)*, 1592351565, Glory Sound) Shawnee Pr., Inc.

—Smoky Mountain Sunday: 40 Favorite Hymns & Gospel Songs. 2008. (ENG.). 90p. pap. 24.95 incl. audio compact disk *(978-1-59235-236-4(7)*, 1592352367) Shawnee Pr., Inc.

Skempton, Howard. The Virgin's Name Was Mary. 2009. 4p. pap. 1.85 *(978-0-19-336570-4(7))* Oxford Univ. Pr., Inc.

Smith, J. Daniel, contrib. by. Creation: Satb. 2008. 119p. pap. 7.95 *(978-5-557-48309-4(8)*, Brentwood-Benson Music Publishing, Inc.) Brentwood Music, Inc.

Sorenson, Heather. We Have Met to Worship: Hymns & Songs of Adoration. 2007. (ENG., Illus.). 64p. pap. 16.99 *(978-0-8341-7585-3(1)*, 0834175851) Lillenas Publishing Co.

Southern Gospel Favorites: 15 Outstanding Arrangements for Choir. 2006. (ENG.). 132p. pap. 19.99 *(978-0-8341-7548-8(7)*, 0834175487) Nazarene Publishing Hse.

Speck, Mike & Whitmire, Stan. Everlasting Praise 2: A Timeless Resource for Congregation & Choir. 2008. (ENG.). 180p. spiral bd. 9.99 *(978-0-8341-7666-9(1)*, 9780834176669) Lillenas Publishing Co.

Speck, Mike & Whitmire, Stan. Everlasting Praise 3: A Timeless Resource for Congregation & Choir. 2012. (ENG.). 192p. pap. 9.99 ***(978-0-8341-8119-9(3)***, 0834181193) Lillenas Publishing Co.

Speck, Mike, et al. Redeemed: Songs for the Soul-Winning Church. 2006. (ENG.). 168p. pap. 8.99 *(978-0-8341-7547-1(9)*, 0834175479) Lillenas Publishing Co.

Sprunger, Ron & Sprunger, Linda. Glory, Honor & Praise! Inspirational Organ & Piano Duets. 2008. (ENG.). 104p. pap. 18.99 *(978-0-8341-7691-1(2)*, 9780834176911) Lillenas Publishing Co.

Sterling, Robert, et al, contrib. by. Simply... the Best Easter, Volume 3: Satb. 2007. 39p. pap. 3.50 *(978-5-557-53116-0(5)*, Word Music) Word Entertainment.

Sterling, Robert, contrib. by & creator. I've Seen Jesus: Encountering the Risen Christ. 2007. 59.95 *(978-5-557-53125-2(4)*, Word Music) Word Entertainment.

Tavener, John. John Tavener - Requiem: Our Glory Lies Where We Cease to Exist Vocal Score (Piano Reduction) 2010. (ENG.). 70p. pap. 19.95 *(978-1-84938-439-1(8)*, 1849384398) Chester Music GBR. Dist: Leonard, Hal Corp.

Tomlin, Chris, et al. How Can I Keep from Singing? SATB with Opt. Rhythm. 2011. 12p. pap. 2.10 ***(978-1-4291-2562-8(4))*** Lorenz Corp., The.

Tornquist, Carol. Medleys for Blended Worship, Bk 2: 10 Contemporary Arrangements of Praise Songs with Hymns. 2011. (Sacred Performer Collections). (ENG.). 40p. pap. 12.99 *(978-0-7390-6995-0(0))* Alfred Publishing Co., Inc.

—Medleys for Blended Worship, Bk 3: 10 Contemporary Arrangements of Praise Songs with Hymns. 2011. (Sacred Performer Collections). (ENG.). 44p. pap. 12.99 *(978-0-7390-6996-7(9))* Alfred Publishing Co., Inc.

Tranchell, Peter. If Ye Would Hear the Angels Sing. 2009. 4p. pap. 2.50 *(978-0-19-395018-4(9))* Oxford Univ. Pr., Inc.

Trapp, Lynn & Leitschuh, Carol, eds. In Harmony with God: Director Edition. 2008. 52p. 9.95 *(978-0-8146-3091-4(X)*, Liturgical Pr. Bks.) Liturgical Pr.

Turner, William. Magnificat & Nunc Dimittis in A. 2009. 20p. pap. 4.95 *(978-0-19-395017-7(0))* Oxford Univ. Pr., Inc.

Walton, William. Belshazzar's Feast: Vocal Score. 2008. 136p. pap. 16.95 *(978-0-19-335954-3(5))* Oxford Univ. Pr., Inc.

Wesley, Charles. Testament of Praise. 2006. (ENG.). 76p. pap. 6.95 *(978-1-59235-157-2(3)*, 1592351573, Flammer, Harold Music) Shawnee Pr., Inc.

White, Robert & Dunkley, Sally. Lamentations. 2009. 48p. 10.95 *(978-0-19-380491-3(3))* Oxford Univ. Pr., Inc.

WILBERG, Mack. Rest in Me(Suo-Gân) 2009. 8p. pap. 1.85 *(978-0-19-386989-9(6))* Oxford Univ. Pr., Inc.

Williams, J. Paul, et al. One Rehearsal Wonders Vol. 3: Almost Instant Anthems for Any Occasion. 2009. (ENG.). 88p. pap. 7.95 *(978-1-4234-8817-0(2)*, 1423488172) Shawnee Pr., Inc.

Williamson, Dave, et al, contrib. by. Amazing Grace-My Chains are Gone: An Easter Celebration of Worship for Congregation & Choir. 2007. (ENG.). 104p. pap. 8.99 *(978-0-8341-7590-7(8)*, 0834175908) Lillenas Publishing Co.

Wonder of Wonders: 10 Dynamic Arrangements for Senior Adult Choir. 2008. (ENG.). pap. 7.99 *(978-0-8341-7663-8(7)*, 9780834176638) Lillenas Publishing Co.

Zarlino, Gioseffo. Gioseffo Zarlino: Part 2: Eleven Motets from Musici quinque vocum moduli (Venice, 1549): Motets From 1549. Judd, Cristle Collins, ed. 2007. (Recent Researches in the Music of the Renaissance Ser.: R149). 112p. pap. 67.00 net. *(978-0-89579-608-0(2))* A-R Editions, Inc.

CHORUSES, SACRED—HISTORY AND CRITICISM
see Choral Music

CHOSEN PEOPLE (JEWS)
see Jews—Election, Doctrine Of

CHOSES
see Personal Property

CHOSES IN ACTION
see also Assignments; Negotiable Instruments

López Hernández, Cristina Victoria & Hernández, Cristina Victoria López. La Protección Frente a Los Gravámenes Ocultos. 2008. (SPA.). 373p. *(978-84-9876-188-7(3))* Tirant lo Blanch.

CHOTA NAGPUR (INDIA)

Bhengra, Dilbar. Archaeology of the Chotanagpur Division (Jharkhand) 2007. (Illus.). xvi, 186p. *(978-81-7320-063-2(7))* Agam Kala Prakashan.

Rajgarhia, Sushil. The Tribal Soldiers of Mahatma Gandhi, 1920-1947. 2010. (Illus.). 289p. *(978-93-80190-17-4(4)*, Library of Congress — New Delhi Overseas Office) Satyam Publishing House.

CHOU, EN-LAI, 1898-1976
see Zhou, Enlai, 1898-1976

CHOUANS

Hutt, Maurice. Chouannerie & Counter-Revolution: Puisaye, the Princes & the British Government in The 1790s. 2008. (ENG.). 380p. pap. 53.00 *(978-0-521-08914-2(X))* Cambridge Univ. Pr.

—Chouannerie & Counter-Revolution, Part 1: Puisaye, the Princes & the British Government in The 1790s. 2008. (ENG.). 292p. pap. 38.99 *(978-0-521-08913-5(1))* Cambridge Univ. Pr.

CHOW CHOW (DOG BREED)

Dunbar, Lady. Chow Chow. 2007. 140p. per. *(978-1-4067-8956-0(9))* Read Bks.

Elwins, Dannie. Chow Chow Dogs Revealed: How to Take Care of Your Chow Chow. 2009. 44p. pap. 16.99 *(978-0-557-15570-5(3))* Lulu Enterprises Inc.

CHOW CHOWS (DOGS)
see Chow Chow (Dog Breed)

CHOWAN COUNTY (N.C.)

Boyce, W. Scott. Economic & Social History of Chowan County, N.C. 1880-1915. (Columbia University, Studies in the Social Sciences: No. 179). reprint ed. 20.00 *(978-0-404-51179-1(1))* AMS Pr., Inc.

Boyce, Warren Scott. Economic & Social History of Chowan County, North Carolina, 1880-1915. 2009. 298p. 30.99 *(978-1-115-51441-5(5))*; 34.99 *(978-1-115-51440-8(7))*; pap. 27.75 *(978-1-115-51443-9(1))* BiblioBazaar.

—Economic & Social History of Chowan County, North Carolina, 1880-1915. 2009. 194p. pap. *(978-0-217-20407-1(4))* Books LLC.

—Economic & Social History of Chowan County, North Carolina, 1880-1915. 2009. 300p. 43.95 *(978-1-104-16355-6(1))*; pap. 28.95 *(978-1-104-12070-2(4))* Kessinger Publishing, LLC.

—Economic & Social History of Chowan County, North Carolina, 1880-1915. 293p. reprint ed. 98.00 *(978-0-7222-7440-8(8))* Library Reprints, Inc.

CHOZARS
see Khazars

CHRESTOMATHIES
see Anthologies; Readers

CHRETIEN, DE TROYES, 12TH CENT.

Bergeron, Guillaume. Les combats chevaleresques dans l'oeuvre de Chrétien de Troyes. 2008. 256p. pap. 64.95 *(978-3-03911-012-4(8))* Lang, Peter AG GBR. Dist: Lang, Peter.

Bruckner, Matilda Tomaryn. Chrétien Continued: A Study of the Conte du Graal & Its Verse Continuations. 2009. (ENG., Illus.). 296p. 125.00 *(978-0-19-955721-9(7))* Oxford Univ. Pr., Inc.

Farina, William. Chretien de Troyes & the Dawn of Arthurian Romance. 2010. (ENG., Illus.). 255p. pap. 35.00 *(978-0-7864-4866-1(0))* McFarland & Co., Inc. Pubs.

Georgescu, Georgeta. Les Visages Du Heros Dans les Romans de Chretien de Troyes. 2008. (FRE.). 160p. 99.95 *(978-0-7734-5049-3(1))* Mellen, Edwin Pr., The.

Lacy, Norris J. & Grimbert, Joan Tasker, eds. A Companion to Chrétien de Troyes. 2008. (Arthurian Studies: Volume 63). 260p. pap. 34.95 *(978-1-84384-161-6(4)*, D. S. Brewer) Boydell & Brewer, Ltd. GBR. Dist: Boydell & Brewer, Inc.

Maddox, Donald. The Arthurian Romances of Chrètien de Troyes: Once & Future Fictions. 2008. (Cambridge Studies in Medieval Literature Ser.). (ENG.). 196p. pap. 42.00 *(978-0-521-07057-7(0))* Cambridge Univ. Pr.

Murray, K. Sarah-Jane. From Plato to Lancelot: A Preface to Chrétien de Troyes. 2008. (C). 26.95 *(978-0-8156-3160-6(X))* Syracuse Univ. Pr.

Reason, Joseph H. Inquiry into the Structural Style & Originality of Chrestien's Yvain. (Catholic University of America, Studies in Romance Languages & Literatures: No. 57). reprint ed. 37.50 *(978-0-404-50357-4(8))* AMS Pr., Inc.

Simpson, James R. Troubling Arthurian Histories: Court Culture, Performance & Scandal in Chretien de Troyes's Erec et Enide. 2007. (Medieval & Early Modern French Studies: Vol. 5). 520p. pap. 99.95 *(978-3-03911-385-9(2))* Lang, Peter Publishing, Inc.

Stahuljak, Zrinka, et al. Thinking Through Chretien de Troyes. 2011. (Gallica Ser.: Volume 19). 212p. 90.00 *(978-1-84384-254-5(8)*, D. S. Brewer) Boydell & Brewer, Ltd. GBR. Dist: Boydell & Brewer, Inc.

Tether, Leah. The Continuations of Chrétien's Perceval: Content & Construction, Extension & Ending. 2012. (Arthurian Studies: Volume 79). 256p. 95.00 ***(978-1-84384-316-0(1)***, D. S. Brewer) Boydell & Brewer, Ltd. GBR. Dist: Boydell & Brewer, Inc.

Topsfield, L. T. Chrètien de Troyes: A Study of the Arthurian Romances. 2010. (ENG.). 376p. pap. 31.99 *(978-0-521-15529-8(0))* Cambridge Univ. Pr.

CHRIST
see Jesus Christ

CHRIST APOSTOLIC CHURCH

Olusheye, E. H. L., frwd. Great Revivals, Great Revivalist - Joseph Ayo Babalola. 2007. 350p. per. 39.99 *(978-0-9795299-0-0(5))* Omega Pubs.

CHRIST CHURCH (UNIVERSITY OF OXFORD)

Carroll, Lewis, pseud. The New Belfry of Christ Church, Oxford. reprint ed. lib. bdg. 98.00 *(978-0-7426-2275-3(4))* Classic Bks.

Holdsworth, Fiona, ed. Christ Church, Oxford: A Portrait of the House. 2007. (ENG., Illus.). 212p. 70.00 *(978-1-903942-46-8(2))* Third Millenium Publishing GBR. Dist: National Bk. Network.

CHRISTCHURCH (N.Z.)

Hood, Lynley. A City Possessed: The Christchurch Civic Creche Case. 672p. *(978-1-877135-62-0(3)*, Longacre Pr.) Random Hse. New Zealand.

Locken, E. Travel Journal Christ Church - Barbados. 2010. 192p. pap. 19.99 *(978-0-557-42198-5(5))* Lulu Enterprises Inc.

Mersch, Marc. Accessibility & Attractiveness: - Key Features towards Central City Revitalisation: A Case Study of Christchurch, New Zealand. 2008. 252p. pap. *(978-3-639-00303-1(9))* VDM Verlag Dr. Mueller e.K.

Teal, Jane. Shaping a Colonial Church: Bishop Harper & the Anglican Diocese of Christchurch, 1856-1890. Brown, Colin & Peters, Marie, eds. 2006. (ENG., Illus.). 316p. pap. 27.99 *(978-1-877257-44-5(3))* Canterbury Univ. Pr. NZL. Dist: Independent Pubs. Group.

CHRISTENING
see Baptism

CHRISTIAN, FLETCHER, 1764-1793

Barrow, John. Eventful History of the Mutiny & Pirat. 2006. pap. *(978-1-4065-1084-3(X))* Dodo Pr.

Kirk, Robert W. Pitcairn Island, the Bounty Mutineers & Their Descendants: A History. 2008. (ENG., Illus.). 263p. 55.00 *(978-0-7864-3471-8(6))* McFarland & Co., Inc. Pubs.

Souhami, Diana. Coconut Chaos: Pitcaim, Mutiny & A Seduction at Sea ... 2007. (ENG., Illus.). 272p. 32.95 *(978-0-297-84787-8(2))* Orion Publishing Group, Ltd. GBR. Dist: Independent Pubs. Group.

—Coconut Chaos: Pitcaim, Mutiny & a Seduction at Sea ... 2008. (ENG., Illus.). 272p. pap. 16.95 *(978-0-7538-2367-5(5)*, Phoenix) Orion Publishing Group, Ltd. GBR. Dist: Independent Pubs. Group.

CHRISTIAN ALEXANDRIAN SCHOOL
see Alexandrian School, Christian

CHRISTIAN AND MISSIONARY ALLIANCE

Barlow, Lauren. Inspired by Tozer: 50 Artists, Writers & Leaders Share the Insights & Passion They've Gained from A.W. Tozer. 2011. ***(978-0-8307-6253-8(1)***, Regal Bks.) Gospel Light Pubns.

Nienkirchen, Charles W. A. B. Simpson & the Pentecostal Movement: A Study in Continuity, Crisis, & Change. 2010. 178p. pap. 20.00 *(978-1-60899-618-6(2))* Wipf & Stock Pubs.

Samuel, V. & Sugden, Chris. Mission as Transformation. 540p. 22.99 *(978-1-870345-13-2(4))* Regnum Bks.

Snyder, James & Snyder, James L. The Life of A.W. Tozer: In Pursuit of God. 2009. (ENG., Illus.). 256p. pap. 14.99 *(978-0-8307-4694-1(3))* Gospel Light Pubns.

Tozer, A. W. And He Dwelt among Us: Teachings from the Gospel of John. 2009. (ENG.). 224p. pap. 12.99 *(978-0-8307-4691-0(9))* Gospel Light Pubns.

Tozer, A. w. The Best of A. W. Tozer, Book One, Vol. 1. 2007. 251p. pap. 14.99 *(978-1-60066-043-6(6))* WingSpread Publishers.

Tozer, A. W. How to Be Filled with the Holy Spirit/Filled with the Holy Spirit. 2008. iii, 165p. pap. 6.99 *(978-1-60066-122-8(X))* WingSpread Publishers.

Tozer, A. w. Renewed Day by Day: Volume 1: Daily Devotional Readings, Vol. 1. 2010. 386p. pap. 16.99 *(978-1-60066-009-2(6))* WingSpread Publishers.

Van De Walle, Bernie A. The Heart of the Gospel: A. B. Simpson, the Fourfold Gospel, & Late Nineteenth-Century Evangelical Theology. 2008. (Princeton Theological Monographs). 228p. pap. 25.00 *(978-1-55635-940-8(3)*, Pickwick Pubns.) Wipf & Stock Pubs.

CHRISTIAN ANTIQUITIES
see also Architecture, Gothic; Catacombs; Christian Art and Symbolism; Church Architecture; Church Furniture; Church Vestments; Crosses; Fasts and Feasts; Fonts; Heraldry, Sacred; Sepulchral Monuments

Adams, William Y. The Churches of Nobadia, 2 vols. 2009. (Bar S Ser.). (ENG., Illus.). 292p. (C). pap. 177.50 *(978-1-4073-0536-3(0))* British Archaeological Reports Ltd. GBR. Dist: Brown, David Bk. Co., The.

Aldsworth, F. & Shaw, Ian. Qasr Ibrim: The Cathedral Church. 2010. (Excavation Memoirs Ser.). (ENG., Illus.). 169p. (C). pap. 130.00 *(978-0-85698-187-6(7))* Egypt Exploration Society GBR. Dist: Brown, David Bk. Co., The.

Andrews, William. Curious Church Gleanings. 2009. 290p. 30.99 *(978-1-113-67489-0(X))*; 290p. pap. 27.75 *(978-1-113-67485-2(7))*; 290p. pap. 28.75 *(978-1-113-67486-9(5))*; 292p. 24.99 *(978-1-103-19224-3(8))*; 292p. pap. 18.99 *(978-1-103-19223-6(X))* BiblioBazaar.

—Curious Church Gleanings. 2010. 108p. pap. *(978-1-152-01600-2(8))* Books LLC.

—Curious Church Gleanings. 2008. 296p. pap. *(978-1-4097-1180-3(3))* Read Bks.

—Old Church Lore. 2007. (ENG.). 268p. 42.95 *(978-0-548-10533-7(2))* Kessinger Publishing, LLC.

Andrews, William, ed. Curious Church Gleanings. 2007. (ENG.). 300p. 43.95 *(978-0-548-08700-8(8))* Kessinger Publishing, LLC.

Bell, Gertrude Lowthian. Churches & Monasteries of the Tūr 'Abdīn & Neighbouring Districts. 2010. 94.88 *(978-1-61719-509-9(X))* Gorgias Pr., LLC.

Bingham, Joseph. Works of the Reverend Joseph Bingham V3. 2006. pap. 45.95 *(978-1-4286-5108-1(X))* Kessinger Publishing, LLC.

—Works of the Reverend Joseph Bingham V7. 2006. pap. 37.95 *(978-1-4286-5107-4(1))* Kessinger Publishing, LLC.

Brand, John. Observations on Popular Antiquities: Chiefly Illustrating the Origin of our Vulgar Customs, Ceremonies & Superstitions. Ellis, Henry, ed. 2011. (Cambridge Library Collection - History Ser.). (ENG.). 516p. pap. 37.99 ***(978-1-108-03646-7(5))***; 746p. pap. 48.00 ***(978-1-108-03647-4(3))*** Cambridge Univ. Pr.

Buhagiar, Mario. The Christianisation of Malta: Catacombs, Cult Centres, & Churches in Malta to 1530. 2007. (Bar S Ser.). (Illus.). xiv, 321p. (C). 112.50 *(978-1-4073-0109-9(8))* British Archaeological Reports Ltd. GBR. Dist: Brown, David Bk. Co., The.

Bull, Raoul, et al. Holywell Priory & the development of Shoreditch to C 1600: Archaeology from the London Overground East London Line. 2011. (MoLAS Monograph Ser.). (ENG., Illus.). 192p. (C). 44.00 ***(978-1-901992-99-1(3))*** Museum of London Archaeology Service GBR. Dist: Brown, David Bk. Co., The.

Butler, Alfred J. The Ancient Coptic Churches of Egypt [vol. 2]. 2009. 424p. pap. 24.95 *(978-0-557-03554-0(6))* Lulu Enterprises Inc.

Eaton-Krauss, M., et al, eds. Egypt 1350 BC to Ad 1800: Art Historical & Archaeological Studies for Gawdat Gabra. 2011. (Sprachen und Kulturen des Christlichen Orients Ser.). (ENG., Illus.). 176p. (C). 100.00 ***(978-3-89500-820-7(6))*** Reichert, Ludwig Dr. DEU. Dist: Brown, David Bk. Co., The.

Edwards, Nancy. A Corpus of Medieval Inscribed Stones & Stone Sculpture in Wales Vol. 2: South-West Wales, 2 vols. 2008. (Illus.). 480p. 110.95 *(978-0-7083-1963-5(7))* Univ. of Wales Pr. GBR. Dist: Chicago Distribution Ctr.

Evans, Donald F & Evans, Donald F. A Pictorial Guide to the 7 (Seven) Churches of the Apocalypse (The Revelation to St. John) & the Island of Patmos, or, A Pilgrim's Tour Guide to the 7 (Seven) Churches of the Bible in Anatolia, Turkey. 2009. (Illus.). 162p. *(978-0-9822409-0-8(2))* Constantine Pr., LLC.

Friesen, Steven, et al, eds. Corinth in Context: Comparative Studies on Religion & Society. 2010. XXVI, 518p. pap. *(978-90-04-18211-0(X))* BRILL.

Friesen, Steven J., et al. Corinth in Context: Comparative Studies on Religion & Society. 2010. (Illus.). 500p. *(978-90-04-18197-7(0))* BRILL.

Frommel, Christoph Luitpold. L'antica Basilica Di San Lorenzo in Damaso: Indagini Archeologiche Nel Palazzo Della Cancelleria, 1988-1993. 2009. (ITA & ENG., Illus.). *(978-88-8016-911-6(4))*; *(978-88-8016-846-1(0))* De Luca Editori d'Arte.

Gabra, Gawdat & Van Loon, Gertrud J. M. The Churches of Egypt: From the Journey of the Holy Family to the Present Day. Ludwig, Carolyn, ed. 2007. (ENG., Illus.). 368p. 59.95 *(978-977-416-106-3(8))* American Univ. in Cairo Pr. EGY. Dist: Oxford Univ. Pr., Inc.

Goldhill, Simon. The End of Dialogue in Antiquity. Goldhill, Simon, ed. 2009. (ENG.). 274p. 99.00 *(978-0-521-88774-8(7))* Cambridge Univ. Pr.

Hamlin, Ann Elizabeth. The Archaeology of Early Christianity in the North of Ireland. Kerr, Thomas R., ed. 2008. (Bar Ser.). (Illus.). 424p. (C). 137.50 *(978-1-4073-0285-0(X))* British Archaeological Reports Ltd. GBR. Dist: Brown, David Bk. Co., The.

Hasek, Vladimir & Unger, Josef. Religious Architecture in the Czech Republic in the Light of Geophysical Prospection & Archaeological Excavation. 2010. (Bar S Ser.). (ENG., Illus.). 90p. (C). pap. 125.00 *(978-1-4073-0669-8(3))* British Archaeological Reports Ltd. GBR. Dist: Brown, David Bk. Co., The.

Henig, Martin & Ramsay, Nigel, eds. Intersections: The Archaeology & History of Christianity in England, 400-1200. 2010. (Bar Ser.). (ENG., Illus.). 266p. (C). pap. 122.50 *(978-1-4073-0540-0(9))* British Archaeological Reports Ltd. GBR. Dist: Brown, David Bk. Co., The.

Johnson, Walter. Byways in British Archaeology. 2011. (ENG.). 542p. pap. 39.99 ***(978-0-521-22877-0(8))*** Cambridge Univ. Pr.

Keevak, Michael. The Story of a Stele: China's Nestorian Monument & Its Reception in the West, 1625-1916. 2008. (ENG., Illus.). 208p. (gr. 17). 45.00 *(978-962-209-895-4(9))* Hong Kong Univ. Pr. HKG. Dist: Columbia Univ. Pr.

Kerr, Thomas R. Early Christian Settlement in North-West Ulster. 2007. (Bar S Ser.). (ENG., Illus.). 143p. (C). pap. 80.00 *(978-1-4073-0015-3(6))* British Archaeological Reports Ltd. GBR. Dist: Brown, David Bk. Co., The.

Khroushkova, Liudmila. Les Monuments Chretiens de la Cote Orientale de la Mer Noire: Abkhazie: IVe-XIVe Siecles. 2007. (Bibliothèque de l'Antiquité Tardive Ser.). (Illus.). 340p. pap. 139.00 *(978-2-503-52387-3(0))* Brepols Pubs. BEL. Dist: Brown, David Bk. Co., The.

King, C. W. Early Christian Numismatics & Other an. 2006. pap. 31.95 *(978-1-4286-4739-8(2))* Kessinger Publishing, LLC.

Kühne, Hartmut & Lambacher, Lothar, eds. Das Zeichen am Hut im Mittelalter: Europäische Reisemarkierungen. 2008. (Europäische Wallfahrtsstudien Ser.). (GER & ENG., Illus.). 404p. pap. 86.95 *(978-3-631-57408-9(8))* Lang, Peter GmbH, Europaischer Verlag der Wissenschaften DEU. Dist: Lang, Peter.

Lilley, Keith D. City & Cosmos: The Medieval World in Urban Form. 2009. (ENG., Illus.). 256p. 49.00 *(978-1-86189-441-0(4))* Reaktion Bks., Ltd. GBR. Dist: Chicago Distribution Ctr.

Lowrie, Walter. Christian Art & Archaeology Being A Ha. 2006. pap. 37.95 *(978-1-4286-3923-2(3))* Kessinger Publishing, LLC.

McLeroy, Leigh. Treasured: Knowing God by the Things He Keeps. 2009. (ENG.). 224p. 14.99 *(978-1-4000-7481-5(9),* WaterBrook Pr.) Doubleday Religious Publishing Group, The.

Meredith-Lobay, Megan. A Contextual Landscape Study of the Early Christian Churches of Argyll. 2009. (ENG., Illus.). 170p. (C). pap. 90.00 *(978-1-4073-0443-4(7))* British Archaeological Reports Ltd. GBR. Dist: Brown, David Bk. Co., The.

Pagoulatos, Gerasimos P. Tracing the Bridegroom in Dura: The Bridal Initiation Service of the Dura-Europos Christian Baptistery as Early Evidence of the Use of Images in Christian & Byzantine Worship. 2007. per. 47.00 *(978-1-59333-738-4(8))* Gorgias Pr., LLC.

Pixner, Bargil. Paths of the Messiah. 2010. 500p. pap. 29.95 *(978-0-89870-865-3(6))* Ignatius Pr.

Potter, John F. Patterns in Stonework: The Early Church in Britain & Ireland. 2009. (Illus.). 191p. (C). pap. 132.50 *(978-1-4073-0600-1(6))* British Archaeological Reports Ltd. GBR. Dist: Brown, David Bk. Co., The.

Ramsay, William Mitchell & Bell, Gertrude Lowthian. The Thousand & One Churches. Jackson, Mark P. C. & Ousterhout, Robert G., eds. 2008. (Illus.). 618p. (C). 49.95 *(978-1-934536-05-6(9),* Univ. of Pennsylvania Museum of Archaeology & Anthropology) Univ. Museum Pubns.

Reed, Jonathan L. The HarperCollins Visual Guide to the New Testament: What Archaeology Reveals about the First Christians. 2007. (ENG., Illus.). 176p. pap. 24.95 *(978-0-06-084249-9(0),* HarperOne) HarperCollins Pubs.

Roffey, Simon. Chantry Chapels: And Medieval Strategies for the Afterlife. 2008. (ENG., Illus.). 208p. pap. 42.95 *(978-0-7524-4571-7(5))* History Pr. Ltd.,The GBR. Dist: Independent Pubs. Group.

Seeliger, Hans Reinhard & Krumeich, Kirsten. Archäologie der Antiken Bischofssitze. 2007. (Sprachen und Kulturen des Christlichen Orients Ser.). (GER., Illus.). 176p. (C). 84.00 *(978-3-89500-501-5(0))* Reichert, Ludwig Dr. DEU. Dist: Brown, David Bk. Co., The.

Sloane, Barney. The Augustinian nunnery of St Mary Clerkenwell, London: Excavations 1974-96. 2012. (MoLAS Monograph Ser.). (ENG., Illus.). 300p. (C). 54.00 ***(978-1-907586-11-8(3))*** Museum of London Archaeology Service GBR. Dist: Brown, David Bk. Co., The.

Sorries, Reiner. Christliche Archäologie Compact. 2011. (GER., Illus.). 502p. (C). 168.00 ***(978-3-89500-792-7(7))*** Reichert, Ludwig Dr. DEU. Dist: Brown, David Bk. Co., The.

Stalley, Roger, ed. Limerick & South-West Ireland: Medieval Art & Architecture. 2011. (Baa conference transactions Ser.). (ENG., Illus.). 271p. (C). 130.00 *(978-1-907625-07-7(0));* pap. 62.00 *(978-1-907625-08-4(9))* Maney Publishing GBR. Dist: Brown, David Bk. Co., The.

Steele, Alison, et al. The Cluniac Priory & Abbey of St Saviour, Bermondsey, Surrey: Excavations, 1984-95. 2011. (MoLAS Monograph Ser.). (ENG., Illus.). 297p. (C). 54.00 *(978-1-901992-96-0(9),* Museum of London Archaeology) Museum of London Archaeology Service GBR. Dist: Brown, David Bk. Co., The.

Stillman, Christi. Jesus Boat. 2009. (ENG.). 205p. 24.99 *(978-0-615-25252-0(4))* Jesus Boat Co., LLC, The.

Sukenik, Eleazar Lipa. The Earliest Records of Christianity: With a New Introduction by George Kiraz. 2007. (Analecta Gorgiana Ser.: 1). per. 24.00 *(978-1-59333-500-7(8))* Gorgias Pr., LLC.

Xanthopoulou, M. Les lampes en bronze a l'epoque Paleochretienne. 2010. (Bibliotheque de l'antiquite Tardive Ser.). (FRE., Illus.). 352p. (C). pap. 102.00 *(978-2-503-53369-8(8))* Brepols Pubs. BEL. Dist: Brown, David Bk. Co., The.

CHRISTIAN ARCHAEOLOGY
see Christian Antiquities

CHRISTIAN ART AND SYMBOLISM
see also Altarpieces; Art and Religion; Bible—Illustrations; Catacombs; Cathedrals; Christian Antiquities; Church Architecture; Church Decoration and Ornament; Church Furniture; Church Vestments; Cistercian Art; Crosses; Emblems; Fishes—Folklore; Fonts; Heraldry, Sacred; Icons; Illumination of Books and Manuscripts; Jewish Art and Symbolism; Judgment Day in Art; Mosaics; Symbolism in the Bible; Symbolism of Numbers
also subdivision Art under various subjects, e.g. Jesus Christ—Art

Alchermes, et al, eds. Anachmata Eoptika. 2010. (ENG., Illus.). 346p. (C). 135.00 ***(978-3-8053-4101-1(6))*** Zabern, Philipp von Verlag, GmbH DEU. Dist: Brown, David Bk. Co., The.

Anderson, M. D. Animal Carvings in British Churches. 2011. (ENG.). 110p. pap. 19.99 *(978-0-521-18205-8(0))* Cambridge Univ. Pr.

Appleton, LeRoy H. & Bridges, Stephen. Symbolism in Liturgical Art. 2011. 130p. 40.95 ***(978-1-258-04270-7(3))*** Literary Licensing, LLC.

Aquilina, Mike. Signs & Mysteries: Revealing ancient christian Symbols. 2008. per. 15.95 *(978-1-59276-450-1(9))* Our Sunday Visitor, Publishing Div.

Arellano, Ignacio & Martinez Pereira, Ana. Emblemática y Religión en la Península Ibérica. 2010. (Illus.). 327p. pap. 44.00 *(978-84-8489-474-2(6))* Iberoamericana Vervuert Publishing Corp.

Arya, Rina. Francis Bacon: Painting in a Godless World. 2012. (Illus.). 176p. 80.00 ***(978-1-84822-044-7(8),*** Lund Humphries Pubs.) Ashgate Publishing, Ltd. GBR. Dist: Ashgate Publishing Co.

Ashe, Steven. Qabalah - the Complete Golden Dawn Initiate. 2008. 596p. pap. 35.95 *(978-1-4092-3050-2(3))* Lulu Enterprises Inc.

Aston, Nigel. Art & Religion in Eighteenth-Century Europe. 2009. (ENG., Illus.). 320p. 45.00 *(978-1-86189-377-2(9))* Reaktion Bks., Ltd. GBR. Dist: Chicago Distribution Ctr.

Athnos, Gregory S. The, Art of the Roman Catacombs: Themes of Deliverance in the Age of Persecution. 2011. (ENG.). 161p. pap. 39.95 ***(978-1-4327-7449-3(2));*** pap. 43.95 ***(978-1-4327-7651-0(7))*** Outskirts Pr., Inc.

Baeck, Philippe De. Angels, 1 vol. Diman, Paz, ed. 2009. (DUT, FRE, GER & ENG., Illus.). 480p. pap. 14.95 *(978-94-6065-001-7(5))* booQs Publishers bvba BEL. Dist: Innovative Logistics.

Baert, B. Interspaces between Word, Gaze & Touch: The Bible & the Visual Medium in the Middle Ages. Collected Essays on Noli me tangere, the Woman with the Haemorrhage, the Head of John the Baptist. 2011. (Annua Nuntia Lovaniensia Ser.). (ENG.). 155p. (C). pap. 70.00 ***(978-90-429-2399-7(7))*** Peeters Pubs. & Booksellers BEL. Dist: Brown, David Bk. Co., The.

Baert, Barbara, ed. Fluid Flesh: The Body, Religion, & the Visual Arts. 2009. (Lieven Gevaert Ser. Volume 8 Ser.). (Illus.). 160p. pap. 39.50 *(978-90-5867-716-7(8))* Leuven Univ. Pr. BEL. Dist: Cornell Univ. Pr.

Bagnoli, Martina. Treasures of Heaven: Saints, Relics, & Devotion in Medieval Europe. 2010. (Illus.). xviii, 259p. pap. *(978-0-911886-74-0(5))* Cleveland Museum of Art.

Bailey, Gauvin A. Between Renaissance & Baroque: Jesuit Art in Rome, 1565-1610. 2009. (ENG., Illus.). 552p. pap. *(978-1-4426-1030-9(1))* Univ. of Toronto Pr.

Baker, Audrey, et al. English Panel Paintings, 1400-1508: A Survey of Figure Paintings on East Anglian Rood Screens. 2011. (ENG., Illus.). 249p. pap. 125.00 ***(978-1-904982-69-2(7))*** Archetype Pubns. GBR. Dist: National Bk. Network.

Ballian, Anna. Relics of the Past: Treasures of the Greek Orthodox Church & the Population Exchange. 2011. (ENG & FRE., Illus.). 232p. pap. 42.50 *(978-88-7439-575-0(2))* 5 Continents ITA. Dist: Hachette Bk. Group.

Barcham, William, et al. Passion in Venice: Crivelli to Tintoretto & Veronese - The Man of Sorrows in Venetian Art. 2011. (ENG., Illus.). 176p. 45.00 *(978-1-904832-82-9(2))* Giles, D. Ltd. GBR. Dist: Antique Collectors' Club.

Barker, Margaret. The Gate of Heaven: The History & Symbolism of the Temple in Jerusalem. 2008. 212p. pap. *(978-1-906055-42-4(4))* Sheffield Phoenix Pr.

Barlow, H. C. Essays on Symbolism. 2007. (ENG.). 164p. 36.95 *(978-0-548-10669-3(X))* Kessinger Publishing, LLC.

Barton, Paulette E. Mercy & the Misericord in Late Medieval England: Cathedra Theology & Architecture. 2009. (Illus.). 272p. 109.95 *(978-0-7734-4841-4(1))* Mellen, Edwin Pr., The.

Batalov, A. L. & Smirnova, E. S. Drevnerusskoe Iskusstvo: Ideia I Obraz, Opyty Izucheniia Vizantiiskogo I Drevnerusskogo Iskusstva. 2009. (Illus.). 478p. *(978-5-94431-303-4(X))* Severnyj palomnik.

Becker, Erich. Malta Sotterranea: Studies of its Early Christian & Jewish Sepulchural Art. Fenech, Katrin, ed. & tr. by. from GER. 2009. (Maltese social studies Ser.). (ENG., Illus.). 268p. (C). 40.00 *(978-99932-7-247-2(7))* Midsea Bks. Ltd. MLT. Dist: Brown, David Bk. Co., The.

Beckett, Sr. Wendy. Real Presence: Sr. Wendy on the Earliest Icons. 2010. (Illus.). 128p. 25.00 *(978-1-57075-898-0(0))* Orbis Bks.

Bedouelle, Guy. An Illustrated History of the Church: The Great Challenges. 2007. (Illus.). 271p. 90.00 *(978-1-56854-516-5(9))* Liturgy Training Pubns.

Bellinato, Claudio. Giotto, the Scrovegni Chapel. 2006. 143p. 90.00 *(978-88-7200-241-4(9))* Vianello Libri ITA. Dist: Antique Collectors' Club.

Benner, Juliet. Contemplative Vision: A Guide to Christian Art & Prayer. 2010. (ENG.). 191p. pap. 17.00 *(978-0-8308-3544-7(X),* IVP Bks.) InterVarsity Pr.

Bernat Vistarini, Antonio, et al. Book of Honors for Empress Maria of Austria: Composed by the College of the Society of Jesus of Madrid on the Occasion of Her Death (1603) = Libro de Las Honras a la Emperatriz Maria de Austria: Compuesto Por el Colegio de la Compañía de Jesús de Madrid con Ocasión de Su Muerte (1603) 2011. ***(978-0-916101-73-2(8))*** St. Joseph's Univ. Pr.

Biancolini Fea, Daniela, et al. Il Tesoro Della Sindone: Mirabilia Del Sacro e Incisioni Sindoniche Di Umberto II Di Savoia. 2010. (ITA., Illus.). 124p. *(978-88-7889-242-2(4))* Piazza D.

Bisceglia, Anna & Cianti, Lia Brunori, eds. Palazzo dei Vicari a Scarperia e Raccolta darte sacra 'Don Corrado Paoli' a Sant'Agata: Guida alla visita del museo e alla scoperta del Territorio. 2008. (Piccoli, grandi Musei Ser.). (ENG & ITA., Illus.). 328p. (C). pap. 24.00 *(978-88-596-0369-6(2))* Polistampa ITA Dist: Brown, David Bk. Co., The.

Bishop, William. Roman Church Mosaics of the First Nine Centuries with Especial Regard to Their Position In. 2009. pap. 19.72 *(978-1-60724-512-4(4))* Gorgias Pr., LLC.

Blick, Sarah & Gelfand, Laura Deborah. Push Me, Pull You: Imaginative, Emotional, Physical, & Spatial Interaction in Late Medieval & Renaissance Art, 2 vols. 2011. (Studies in Medieval & Reformation Traditions: History, Culture, Religion, Ideas). (Illus.). 1408p. ***(978-90-04-20573-4(X))*** BRILL.

Boehme, Jacob. The Signature of All Things; of the Supersensual Life; of Heaven & Hell; Discourse Between Two Souls. 2010. 308p. 43.95 *(978-1-161-35067-8(5))* Kessinger Publishing, LLC.

—True Resignation. 2010. 70p. 31.95 *(978-1-161-35081-4(0))* Kessinger Publishing, LLC.

Boele, Vincent. Splendour & Glory: Art of the Russian Orthodox Church. 2011. (ENG., Illus.). 336p. pap. 66.00 ***(978-90-78653-25-7(6))*** Exhibitions International BEL. Dist: Innovative Logistics.

Boerner, Maria-Christina, et al. Ars Sacra: Christian Art in the Western World. Toman, Rolf, ed. 2010. (ENG., Illus.). 800p. 199.00 *(978-3-8331-5140-8(4))* h.f.ullmann DEU. Dist: Innovative Logistics.

Borromeo, Federico. Sacred Painting. Museum. 2010. (I Tatti Renaissance Library: 44). (LAT & ENG., Illus.). 336p. 29.95 *(978-0-674-04758-7(3))* Harvard Univ. Pr.

Boscani Leoni, Simona. Essor et fonctions des images religieuses dans les Alpes: L'exemple de l'ancien diocèse de Coire (1200-1530 Env.) 2008. 703p. pap. *(978-3-03911-167-1(1))* Lang, Peter.

Bosch Ballbona, Joan. Agustí Pujol: La culminació de l'escultura renaixentista a Catalunya. 2009. 388p. pap. *(978-84-475-3330-5(1))* Univ. de Barcelona Pubns.

Bosco, Louis. Images of the Unseen: The Mysteries of Life Revealed in Sacred Art. 2011. ***(978-0-8189-1336-5(3))*** St Pauls.

Boylan, Alexis L., ed. Thomas Kinkade: The Artist in the Mall. 2011. (ENG., Illus.). 320p. 94.95 *(978-0-8223-4839-9(X));* pap. 25.95 *(978-0-8223-4852-8(7))* Duke Univ. Pr.

Bray, Xavier, et al. The Sacred Made Real: Spanish Painting & Sculpture, 1600-1700. 2009. (ENG., Illus.). 224p. 65.00 *(978-1-85709-422-0(0))* Yale Univ. Pr.

Brewer, Christopher. Art That Tells the Story. Brewer, Christopher, ed. 2011. (ENG.). pap. 24.99 *(978-0-615-42601-3(8))* Gospel through Shared Experience.

Brind, Jan & Wilkinson, Tessa. Crafts for Creative Worship. 2nd ed. 2010. (ENG., Illus.). 224p. pap. 34.99 *(978-1-84825-004-8(5),* Canterbury Pr. Norwich) Hymns Ancient & Modern Ltd GBR. Dist: Westminster John Knox Pr.

Brown, Anne. Brother Mel Lifetime of Making Art. 2009. (Illus.). 236p. 65.00 *(978-0-578-03493-5(X))* Arts Co. Pr., The.

Brown, Jonathan. Murillo: Virtuoso Draftsman. 2012. (ENG., Illus.). 316p. 75.00 *(978-0-300-17570-7(1))* Yale Univ. Pr.

Brown, Michelle P. & Brown, Michelle. The Lion Companion to Christian Art. 2008. (ENG., Illus.). 448p. 49.95 *(978-0-7459-5177-5(5))* Lion Hudson PLC GBR. Dist: Independent Pubs. Group.

Brusic, Robert M. & Evenrud, Jerry. And Grace Will Lead Me Home: The Jerry Evenrud Collection of Images of the Parable of the Prodigal Son. 2007. (ENG., Illus.). 200p. 40.00 *(978-1-932688-18-4(8),* Lutheran Univ. Pr.) Kirk Hse. Pubs.

Bucker, Andreas, et al, eds. Resonances: Historical Essays on Continuity & Change. 2011. (Ritus et Artes Ser.). (ENG., Illus.). 266p. (C). 116.00 *(978-2-503-53493-0(7))* Brepols Pubs. BEL. Dist: ISD.

Burgwinkle, Howie, et al. Sanctity & Pornography in Medieval Culture. 2011. (Manchester Medieval Literature Ser.). (ENG., Illus.). 224p. 90.00 *(978-0-7190-8029-6(0))* Manchester Univ. Pr. GBR. Dist: Macmillan.

Bush, Darrell, illus. Beside Still Waters: Refreshing Moments to Restore Your Soul. 2010. 48p. 12.99 *(978-0-7369-2632-4(1))* Harvest Hse. Pubs.

Byron, Robert. The Birth of Western Painting (Routledge Revivals) A history of colour, form & iconography. 2012. (Routledge Revivals Ser.). (ENG.). 120.00 ***(978-0-415-80918-4(5))*** Routledge.

Caneva, Caterina. Museo D'arte Sacra Dell'Abbazia Di Vallombrosa: Guida Alla Visita Del Museo e Alla Scoperta Del Territorio. 2007. (Piccoli, grandi Musei Ser.). (Illus.). 257p. (C). 24.00 *(978-88-596-0212-5(2))* Polistampa ITA. Dist: Brown, David Bk. Co., The.

—Tre Piccoli, Grandi Musei e Altre Testimonianze, Scritti 2002-2008. Paolini, Claudio, ed. 2009. (Interventi e Testimonianze Ser.). (ITA., Illus.). 144p. (C). pap. 28.00 *(978-88-596-0692-5(6))* Polistampa ITA. Dist: Brown, David Bk. Co., The.

Capretti, Elena. Dagli Eredi Di Giotto Al Primo Cinquecento. 2007. (ITA & ENG., Illus.). 192p. (C). 66.00 *(978-88-596-0277-4(7))* Polistampa ITA. Dist: Brown, David Bk. Co., The.

Caterina Proto Pisani, Rosanna. La Valle Dei Tesori: Capolavori Allo Specchio. 2006. (Piccoli, grandi Musei Ser.). (ITA & ENG., Illus.). 185p. (C). 29.50 *(978-88-596-0068-8(5))* Edizioni Polistampa ITA. Dist: Brown, David Bk. Co., The.

Chazelle, Celia. The Crucified God in the Carolingian Era: Theology & Art of Christ's Passion. 2007. (ENG., Illus.). 356p. per. 74.00 *(978-0-521-03945-1(2))* Cambridge Univ. Pr.

Cherry, John. Holy Thorn Reliquary. 2010. (Objects in Focus Ser.). (ENG., Illus.). 56p. (C). pap. 10.00 *(978-0-7141-2820-7(1))* British Museum Pr. GBR. Dist: Brown, David Bk. Co., The.

Chivot, Dominique. Vatican. 2009. (ENG., Illus.). 224p. 65.00 *(978-2-7594-0393-6(9))* Assouline FRA. Dist: Perseus Distribution.

Church Banner Designs: 72 Unique Ideas Using Calico, Batik & Other Cotton Prints. 2007. (ENG., Illus.). 96p. per. 10.99 *(978-0-7586-1333-2(4))* Concordia Publishing Hse.

City Museum Freiburg. Augustiner Museum: Masterpieces from the Middle Ages to the Baroque. 2010. (ENG.). 200p. pap. 28.00 *(978-3-422-06949-7(6),* Art Stock Bks. Ltd/Csi) Continental Sales, Inc.

Cornwell, Hilarie, et al. Saints, Signs, & Symbols: The Symbolic Language of Christian Art. 3rd rev. ed. 2009. (Illus.). 168p. pap. 20.00 *(978-0-8192-2345-6(X),* Morehouse Publishing) Church Publishing, Inc.

Cuadriello, Jaime. The Glories of the Republic of Tlaxcala: Art & Life in Viceregal Mexico. Follett, Christopher J., tr. from SPA. 2011. (ENG., Illus.). 400p. 55.00 *(978-0-292-72360-3(1))* Univ. of Texas Pr.

Cutler, Anthony & Papaconstantinou, Arietta, eds. The Material & the Ideal: Essays in Medieval Art & Archaeology in Honour of Jean-Michel Spieser. 2007. (Medieval Mediterranean Ser.). (FRE, GER & ENG., Illus.). 240p. *(978-90-04-16286-0(0))* BRILL.

Daley, Michael J. Our Catholic Symbols: A Rich Spiritual Heritage. 2009. 120p. pap. 12.95 *(978-1-58595-753-8(4))* Twenty-Third Pubns./Bayard.

De Giorgio, Cynthia. The Conventual Church of the Knights of Malta. Splendour, history & art of St John's Co-Cathedral, Valletta. 2010. (ENG., Illus.). 144p. (C). 110.00 *(978-99932-7-291-5(4))* Midsea Bks. Ltd. MLT. Dist: Brown, David Bk. Co., The.

de Gruchy, John. Icons as a Means of Grace. 2011. 85p. pap. 17.95 *(978-0-7963-0578-7(1))* NB Pubs. Ltd. ZAF. Dist: International Publishers Marketing.

Decker, John. The Technology of Salvation & the Art of Geertgen Tot Sint Jans. 2009. (Visual Culture in Early Modernity Ser.). (Illus.). 182p. 114.95 *(978-0-7546-6453-6(8))* Ashgate Publishing Co.

Degl'Innocenti, Martina & Marinone, Stella. Bible Stories. 2010. (ENG., Illus.). 612p. 19.95 *(978-0-8109-8996-2(4))* Abrams.

Dickerson, C. D., et al. A Nativity from Naples: Presepe Sculpture of the Eighteenth Century. 2008. (Illus.). ix, 115p. *(978-0-912804-49-1(1))* Kimbell Art Museum.

Didron, M. Christian Iconography or the History of. 2006. pap. 40.95 *(978-1-4286-3862-4(8))* Kessinger Publishing, LLC.

DiPasqua, Sandra & Calamari, Barbara. Holy Cards. 2012. (ENG., Illus.). 144p. pap. 19.95 ***(978-1-4197-0227-3(0))*** Abrams.

Dober, Hans Martin. Die Zeit ins Gebet nehmen: Medien und Symbole im Gottesdienst als Ritual. 2009. (Arbeiten zur Pastoraltheologie, Liturgik und Hymnologie Ser.). (GER., Illus.). 303p. (C). pap. 68.00 *(978-3-525-62408-1(5))* Vandenhoeck & Ruprecht GmbH & Co. KG DEU. Dist: ISD.

Doel, Fran & Doel, Geoff. The Green Man in Britain. (ENG., Illus.). 160p. pap. 24.99 *(978-0-7524-1916-9(1))* History Pr. Ltd.,The GBR. Dist: Trafalgar Square Publishing.

Domes & Spires. 2008. 128p. 29.99 *(978-0-9796044-2-3(7))* Tribune-Democrat, The.

Domínguez García, Javier. Memorias Del Futuro: Ideología y Ficción en el Símbolo de Santiago Apóstol. 2008. (SPA.). 144p. pap. 24.80 *(978-84-8489-373-8(1))* Iberoamericana Vervuert Publishing Corp.

Donghi, Antonio. Words & Gestures in the Liturgy. 2009. pap. 18.95 *(978-0-8146-6222-9(6))* Liturgical Pr.

Durant, Massimo. Piety & Pragmatism: Spiritualism in Futurist Art. Adams, Christopher et al, eds. 2010. (ENG & ITA., Illus.). 128p. pap. 41.95 *(978-88-492-1310-2(7))* Gangemi ITA. Dist: International Publishers Marketing.

Dyrness, William A. Senses of the Soul: Art & the Visual in Christian Worship. 2008. (Art for Faith's Sake: Ser.). 198p. pap. 23.00 *(978-1-55635-864-7(4),* Cascade Bks.) Wipf & Stock Pubs.

Dzon, Mary & Kenney, Theresa M. The Christ Child in Medieval Culture: Alpha es et O! 2012. (ENG., Illus.). 360p. ***(978-0-8020-9894-8(0))*** Univ. of Toronto Pr.

Eaton-Krauss, M., et al, eds. Egypt 1350 BC to Ad 1800: Art Historical & Archaeological Studies for Gawdat Gabra. 2011. (Sprachen und Kulturen des Christlichen Orients Ser.). (ENG., Illus.). 176p. (C). 100.00 ***(978-3-89500-820-7(6))*** Reichert, Ludwig Dr. DEU. Dist: Brown, David Bk. Co., The.

Ecker, Diana. Das Mainzer Dom-Museum: Geschichte und Geschichten. 2008. (GER., Illus.). 238p. *(978-3-935647-42-7(5))* Schmidt, Hermann, Verlag, Mainz GmbH & Co. KG.

Eisler, Robert. The Fisher God As a Culture Hero & Teacher of Humanity - 2006. pap. 12.95 *(978-1-4286-8586-4(3))* Kessinger Publishing, LLC.

—The Orpheus & Good Shepherd Pictures in Early Christian Art - 2006. pap. 12.95 *(978-1-4286-8584-0(7))* Kessinger Publishing, LLC.

Elmer M. Haygood, M. Haygood & Elmer M. Haygood. The Cross Trap: A Layman's Theory. 2009. 124p. pap. 13.95 *(978-1-4401-7625-8(6))* iUniverse, Inc.

Emmerling, Mary. Art of the Cross, 1 vol. 2006. (ENG., Illus.). 128p. 21.99 *(978-1-4236-0115-9(7))* Gibbs Smith, Publisher.

Evans, E. p. & Evans, E. P. Animal Symbolism in Ecclesiastical Architecture. 2010. 390p. 48.95 *(978-1-161-38110-8(4))* Kessinger Publishing, LLC.

Evans, Joan. The Romanesque Architecture of the Order of Cluny. 2011. (ENG., Illus.). 438p. pap. 32.99 *(978-1-107-60138-3(X))* Cambridge Univ. Pr.

Exum, J. Cheryl & Nutu, Ela. Between the Text & the Canvas: The Bible & Art in Dialogue. Exum, J. Cheryl & Nutu, Ela, eds. 2007. (Illus.). 264p. *(978-1-906055-19-6(X))* Sheffield Phoenix Pr.

Fang, Natalia S. Y. Dali's 'Le Christ' Religious or Sacrilegious? 2008. 76p. pap. *(978-3-639-10752-4(7))* VDM Verlag Dr. Mueller e.K.

Feigenbaum, Gail, et al. Sacred Possessions: Collecting Italian Religious Art, 1500-1900. 2011. (Issues & Debates Ser.). (ENG., Illus.). 256p. pap. 30.00 *(978-1-60606-042-1(2))* Getty Pubns.

Fernández Castiñeiras, Enrique & Monterroso Montero, Juan M. Piedra Sobre Agua: El Monacato en Torno a la Ribeira Sacra: Opus Monasticorum IV. 2010. (SPA.). 306p. *(978-84-95892-83-6(9))* Fundación Pedro Barrie de la Maza.

Fleck, Cathleen A. The Clement Bible at the Medieval Courts of Naples & Avignon: A Story of Papal Power Royal Prestige & Patronage. 2010. (Illus.). 370p. 124.95 *(978-0-7546-6980-7(7))* Ashgate Publishing Co.

Fliegel, Stephen J. Sacred Meaning in the Christian Art of the Middle Ages. 2009. (The Sacred Landmarks Ser.). (Illus.). 19.95 *(978-0-9638675-5-1(5))* Levin College of Urban Affairs, Cleveland State Univ.

C

Fliegel, Stephen N. A Higher Contemplation: Sacred Meaning in the Christian Art of the Middle Ages. 2011. (Sacred Landmarks Ser.). 136p. 42.00 (978-1-60635-093-5(5)) Kent State Univ. Pr.

Folda, Jaroslav. Crusader Art: The Art of the Crusaders in the Holy Land, 1099-1291. 2008. (Illus.). 176p. 100.00 (978-0-85331-995-5(2), Lund Humphries Pubs.) Ashgate Publishing, Ltd. GBR. Dist: Ashgate Publishing Co.

Folga-Januszewska, Dorota & Majewski, Lech. The Mystic Middle Ages. 2008. 160p. 50.00 (978-83-87730-59-8(9)) Bosz, Szymanik i wspolnicy POL. Dist: Independent Pubs. Group.

Fontana, Bernard L. A Gift of Angels: The Art of Mission San Xavier del Bac. 2010. (Southwest Center Ser.). (ENG., Illus.). 376p. 75.00 (978-0-8165-2840-0(3)) Univ. of Arizona Pr.

Frankhä, et al. Götter, Helden, Heilige: Italienische Malerei des Barock aus dem Landesmuseum Mainz. 2009. (GER., Illus.). 128p. (978-3-422-02157-0(4)) Deutscher Kunstverlag GmbH.

Frugoni, Chiara & Armandi Barbolini, Marina. The Cathedral of Modena, 3 vols. 2009. (ITA & ENG., Illus.). 1340p. 1160.00 (978-88-7686-982-2(4)) Panini Franco Cosimo ITA. Dist: Antique Collectors' Club.

Galavaris, George. Colours, Symbols, Worship: The Mission of the Byzantine Artist. 2012. (ENG.). 440p. (C). 300.00 (978-1-899828-68-5(0)) Pindar Pr. GBR. Dist: Brown, David Bk. Co., The.

Geertgen & Reinhard-Felice, Mariantonia. Venite, Adoremus: Geertgen Tot Sint Jans & the Adoration of the Kings. 2007. (Illus.). 96p. pap. 39.00 (978-3-7774-4025-5(6)) Hirmer Verlag GmbH DEU. Dist: Chicago Distribution Ctr.

Gerdes, Louise. Should Religious Symbols Be Allowed on Public Land? 2011. (At Issue Ser.). 128p. pap. 22.50 (978-0-7377-5168-0(1)); lib. bdg. 31.80 (978-0-7377-5167-3(3)) Cengage Gale. (Greenhaven Pr., Inc.).

Geronimus, Dennis. Piero Di Cosimo: Visions Beautiful & Strange. 2007. (ENG., Illus.). 366p. 80.00 (978-0-300-10911-5(3)) Yale Univ. Pr.

Gerov, Georgi. Christian Art Icons from Melnik & the Melnik Region, Bulgaria. 2007. (Series Christian Art Ser.). 180p. 110.00 (978-954-642-285-9(1)) Pensoft Pubs. BGR. Dist: Coronet Bks.

Gerstel, Sharon E. J. Beholding the Sacred Mysteries: Programs of the Byzantine Sanctuary. 2009. 226p. 34.00 (978-1-59740-724-3(0)); pap. 22.00 (978-1-59740-746-5(1)) ACLS Humanities E-Book.

Giebelhausen, Michaela. Painting the Bible: Representation & Belief in Mid-Victorian Britain. 2006. (British Art & Visual Culture since 1750 New Readings Ser.). (Illus.). 270p. 130.00 (978-0-7546-3074-6(9)) Ashgate Publishing Co.

Giorgi, Rosa. History of the Church in Art. 2009. (Guide to Imagery Ser.). (Illus.). 384p. pap. 24.95 (978-0-89236-936-2(1)) Oxford Univ. Pr., Inc.

Giorgi, Rosa. Saints & Their Symbols. 2012. (ENG., Illus.). 420p. 19.95 **(978-1-4197-0224-2(6))** Abrams.

Gisolfi, Diana. The Rule, the Bible, & the Council: The Library of the Benedictine Abbey at Praglia. 2009. 218p. 32.00 (978-1-59740-725-0(9)); pap. 22.00 (978-1-59740-747-2(X)) ACLS Humanities E-Book.

Givens, Terryl C. People of Paradox: A History of Mormon Culture. 2007. (ENG., Illus.). 432p. 29.99 (978-0-19-516711-5(2)) Oxford Univ. Pr., Inc.

Givens, Terryl L. People of Paradox: A History of Mormon Culture. 2012. (ENG., Illus.). 464p. pap. 24.95 **(978-0-19-991598-9(9))** Oxford Univ. Pr., Inc.

Gossman, Lionel. The Making of a Romantic Icon: The Religious Context of Friedrich Overbeck's Italia und Germania. 2007. (978-0-87169-975-6(3)) American Philosophical Society.

Gray, Douglas. Christian Symbology: A Collection of Symbol Definitions, Liturgical Terms, Images, & Illustrations. 2007. lib. bdg. 29.99 (978-1-59872-806-4(7)) Instant Pub.

Grove, Daisy E. The Apocalypse & Initiation. 2007. (ENG.). 156p. 36.95 (978-0-548-00658-0(X)) Kessinger Publishing, LLC.

Guiderdoni, A. & Dekoninck, R., eds. Emblemata Sacra: The Rhetoric & Hermeneutics of Sacred Discourse in Images. 2007. (Imago Figurata Studies). (ENG & FRE.). 652p. (C). 138.00 (978-2-503-52469-6(9)) Brepols Pubs. BEL. Dist: ISD.

Guillen-Nuñez, Cesar. Macao's Church of Saint Paul: A Glimmer of the Baroque in China. 2008. (ENG., Illus.). 196p. (gr. 17). 45.00 (978-962-209-922-7(X)) Hong Kong Univ. Pr. HKG. Dist: Columbia Univ. Pr.

Guilloux, Fabien. Saint François D'Assise et L'ange Musicien: Thème et Varations Iconographiques Dans les Collections du Museo Francescano de Rome. 2010. (FRE., Illus.). 165p. (978-88-88001-73-9(5)) Ist. Storico dei Cappuccini.

Gurrieri, Francesco & Manetti, Renzo. Dieci Secoli per la Basilica Di San Miniato Al Monte. 2007. (ITA., Illus.). 173p. (C). 46.00 (978-88-596-0236-1(X)) Edizioni Polistampa ITA. Dist: Brown, David Bk. Co., The.

Gusti, A. M., et al. The Baptistery of San Giovanni in Florence, 2 vols. 2009. (ENG., Illus.). 1152p. 980.00 (978-88-7686-274-8(9)) Panini Franco Cosimo ITA. Dist: Antique Collectors' Club.

Hachlili, Rachel. Ancient Mosaic Pavements: Themes, Issues, & Trends. 2008. (Illus.). 362p. (978-90-04-16754-4(4)) BRILL.

Hahn, Cynthia J. Strange Beauty: Issues in the Making & Meaning of Reliquaries, 400-Circa 1204. 2012. (ENG.). 336p. **(978-0-271-05078-2(0))** Pennsylvania State Univ. Pr.

Hahn, Sylvia, et al. Paradies: Neue Blicke auf einen alten Traum. 2009. (GER., Illus.). 135p. (978-3-422-06898-8(8)) Deutscher Kunstverlag GmbH.

Hall, Marcia B. The Sacred Image in the Age of Art: Titian, Tintoretto, Barocci, el Greco, Caravaggio. 2011. (ENG., Illus.). 352p. 75.00 (978-0-300-16967-6(1)) Yale Univ. Pr.

Hamburger, Jeffrey F. & Marti, Susan, eds. Crown & Veil: Female Monasticism from the Fifth to the Fifteenth Centuries. Hamburger, Dietlinde, tr. from GER. 2008. (ENG., Illus.). 344p. (gr. 17). 45.00 (978-0-231-13980-9(2)) Columbia Univ. Pr.

Hansen, Gerald E. & Brinkerhoff, Val. Sacred Walls: Learning from Temple Symbols. 2009. (Illus.). ix, 86p. (978-1-59811-772-1(6), North Winds Pr) Covenant Communications, Inc.

Haustein-Bartsch, Eva & Wolf, Norbert, eds. Icons. 2008. (ENG., Illus.). 96p. pap. 9.99 (978-3-8228-5478-5(6)) TASCHEN DEU. Dist: Ingram Pub. Services.

Haynes, Gregory R. Tree of Life, Mythical Archetype: Revelations from the Symbols of Ancient Troy. 2009. (Illus.). 347p. pap. (978-0-9824034-5-7(3)) Symbolon Pr.

Hellemans, Babette. La Bible Moralisée: Une Uvre à Part Entière: Création, Sémiotique et Temporalité Au XIIIe Siècle. 2010. (FRE., Illus.). 272p. (C). pap. 102.00 **(978-2-503-53204-2(7))** Brepols Pubs. BEL. Dist: ISD.

Henderson, George. Vision & Image in Early Christian England. 2011. (ENG.). 310p. pap. 39.99 (978-0-521-18073-3(2)) Cambridge Univ. Pr.

Heuclin, Jean. Parole et Lumière: Autour de L'an Mil. 2011. (FRE., Illus.). 336p. pap. (978-2-7574-0178-1(5)) Presses Universitaires du Septentrion.

Hickson, Sally Anne. Women Art & Architectural Patronage in Renaissance Mantua: Matrons Mystics & Monasteries. 2012. (Women & Gender in the Early Modern World Ser.). (Illus.). 204p. 104.95 **(978-1-4094-2752-0(8))** Ashgate Publishing Co.

Hofmann, Friedhelm. 'Kometenstreifen des Himmels' Über das Geistliche in der Kunst. 2nd ed. 2009. (GER., Illus.). 107p. (978-3-429-03070-4(6)) Echter Wuerzburg.

Hourihane, Colum, ed. Interactions: Artistic Interchange Between the Eastern & Western Worlds in the Medieval Period. 2007. (Penn State Press Ser.). (Illus.). 300p. 85.00 (978-0-9768202-4-6(2)); per. 35.00 (978-0-9768202-5-3(0)) Index of Christian Art, Princeton Univ., The.

—Time in the Medieval World: Occupations of the Months & Signs of the Zodiac in the Index of Christian Art. 2007. (Index of Christian Art Resources Ser.: Vol. 3). (ENG., Illus.). 328p. pap. 35.00 (978-0-9768202-3-9(4)); 85.00 (978-0-9768202-2-2(6)) Index of Christian Art, Princeton Univ., The.

Howard, Erica. Law & the Wearing of Religious Symbols: European Bans on the Wearing of Religious Symbols in Education. 2011. (ENG.). 240p. 125.00 (978-0-415-60264-8(5)) Routledge.

Howard, Rachel. Can't Breathe Without You. 2008. (ENG., Illus.). 48p. 30.00 (978-0-9545949-0-9(8)) Other Criteria GBR. Dist: Hachette Bk. Group.

Howes, Graham. The Art of the Sacred: An Introduction to the Aesthetics of Art & Belief. 2007. (ENG., Illus.). 200p. 85.00 (978-1-84511-005-5(6)); pap. 28.00 (978-1-84511-006-2(4)) I. B. Tauris & Co., Ltd. GBR. Dist: Macmillan.

Huerta, Pedro Luis. Maestros Del Románico en el Camino de Santiago. 2010. (SPA., Illus.). 239p. (978-84-89483-71-2(X)) Fundacion Santa Maria La Real, Centro de Estudios del Romanico.

Hurll, Estelle M. The Life of Our Lord in Art: With Some Account of the Artistic Treatment of the Life of St. John the Baptist. 2007. (ENG.). 386p. 48.95 (978-0-548-15063-4(X)); 388p. per. 33.95 (978-1-4304-4402-2(9)) Kessinger Publishing, LLC.

Hyde, Virginia. The Risen Adam. 2008. pap. 24.95 (978-0-271-02845-3(9)) Pennsylvania State Univ. Pr.

Imhof, Verlag Michael & Sander, Jochen. Kult Bild: Das Altar- und Andachtsbild von Duccio bis Perugino. Begleitbuch zur Ausstellung im Städel in Frankfurt vom 7. Juli bis 22. Oktober 2006. 2007. 312p. 49.95 (978-3-86568-128-7(X)) Imhof, Michael Verlag GmbH & Co. KG DEU. Dist: Independent Pubs. Group.

Immerzeel, M. Identity Puzzles: Medieval Christian Art in Syria & Lebanon. 2009. (Orientalia Lovaniensia Analecta Ser.). (ENG.). 334p. (C). 116.00 (978-90-429-2149-8(8)) Peeters Pubs. & Booksellers BEL. Dist: Brown, David Bk. Co., The.

Inman, Thomas. Ancient Pagan & Modern Christian Symbolism. 2009. 212p. 28.99 (978-1-110-75428-1(0)); pap. 23.75 (978-1-110-75426-7(4)) BiblioBazaar.

—Ancient Pagan & Modern Christian Symbolism. 2007. (ENG.). 208p. per. 10.99 (978-1-4209-2987-4(9)) Digireads.com.

—Ancient Pagan & Modern Christian Symbolism. 2007. (ENG.). 208p. per. (978-1-4067-5183-3(9)) Read Bks.

It Was Good: Making Art to the Glory of God. 2nd exp. ed. 2007. (Illus.). 355p. per. 24.99 (978-0-9785097-1-2(4), 7500) Square Halo Bks.

Jackson, Deirdre. Marvellous to Behold: Miracles in Illuminated Manuscripts. 2007. (ENG., Illus.). 160p. 35.00 (978-0-7123-4946-8(4)) British Library, The GBR. Dist: Chicago Distribution Ctr.

Jacob, Mar Ignatius, 3rd. History of the Monastery of Saint Matthew in Mosul. Moosa, Matti, tr. from ARA. 2008. 150p. 74.00 (978-1-59333-788-9(4)) Gorgias Pr., LLC.

Jaggi, Carola & Staecker, Jorn, eds. Archäologie der Reformation: Studien zu den Auswirkungen des Konfessionswechsels auf die materielle Kultur. 2007. (Arbeiten Zur Kirchengeschichte Ser.). (GER., Illus.). X, 487p. 231.00 (978-3-11-019513-2(5)) De Gruyter, Walter Inc.

Jameson, Anna Brownell. Legends of the Monastic Orders As Represented in the Fine Arts. 2007. (ENG.). 532p. 55.95 (978-0-548-01618-3(6)) Kessinger Publishing, LLC.

—Sacred & Legendary Art. 2010. 474p. pap. 37.75 (978-1-149-52905-8(9)) 2009. 440p. 41.99 (978-1-117-59963-2(9)) 2009. (ENG.). 439p. pap. 26.99 (978-1-117-59965-6(5), BiblioLife) 2009. (ENG.). 439p. pap. 34.75 (978-1-117-59964-9(7)) 2009. 464p. 42.99 (978-1-117-13778-0(3)) 2009. 464p. pap. 36.75 (978-1-117-13779-7(1)) 2009. (ENG.). 463p. pap. 28.99 (978-1-117-13780-3(5), BiblioLife) 2009. 444p. 34.99 (978-1-113-21559-8(3)) 2009. 444p. pap. 35.75 (978-1-113-21557-4(7)) BiblioBazaar.

—Sacred & Legendary Art. 2010. 280p. pap. (978-1-153-14587-9(1)) Books LLC.

—Sacred & Legendary Art. 2010. (Illus.). 290p. pap. 23.84 (978-1-154-33441-8(4)) General Bks. LLC.

Janes, Dominic. God & Gold in Late Antiquity. 2010. (ENG., Illus.). 225p. pap. 30.99 (978-0-521-15874-9(5)) Cambridge Univ. Pr.

Jaritz, Gerhard. Angels, Devils: The Supernatural & Its Visual Representation. 2011. pap. (978-615-5053-22-1(7)) Central European Univ. Pr.

Jaritz, Gerhard, ed. Angels, Devils: The Supernatural & Its Visual Representation. 2011. (ENG.). 205p. (978-615-5053-21-4(9)) Central European Univ. Pr.

Jenner, Henry. Christian Symbolism. 2007. (ENG.). 292p. 43.95 (978-0-548-07407-7(0)) Kessinger Publishing, LLC.

Joby, Christopher Richard & Joby, C. R. Calvinism in the Arts: A Re-Assessment. 2007. (Studies in Philosophical Theology Ser.). (ENG., Illus.). 240p. (C). pap. 63.00 (978-90-429-1923-5(X)) Peeters Pubs. & Booksellers BEL. Dist: Brown, David Bk. Co., The.

Johnson, Frederick Ernest. Religious Symbolism. Johnson, Frederick Ernest, ed. 2011. 274p. 47.95 **(978-1-258-03838-0(2))** Literary Licensing, LLC.

Karahan, A. Byzantine Holy Images - Transcendence & Immanence. the Theological Background of the Iconography & Aesthetics of the Chora Church. 2010. (Orientalia Lovaniensia Analecta Ser.). (ENG.). 365p. (C). 109.00 (978-90-429-2080-4(7)) Peeters Pubs. & Booksellers BEL. Dist: Brown, David Bk. Co., The.

Kenaan-Kedar, Nurith. Ha-Madonah Shel Siah Ha-Tsabar: Masoret Ve-Hidush Ba-Tsiyur Ha-Notsri Ba-Arets Ba-Meot Ha-19 Veha-20: Kenesiyat Ha-Bikur Be-En-Kerem U-Khenesiyat Ba-Besorah Be-Natsrat. 2009. (HEB., Illus.). 158p. (978-965-217-300-3(2)) Yad Izhak Ben-Zvi.

Kessler, Herbert L. & Nirenberg, David, eds. Judaism & Christian Art: Aesthetic Anxieties from the Catacombs to Colonialism. 2011. (Illus.). 456p. (C). 69.95 (978-0-8122-4285-0(8)) Univ. of Pennsylvania Pr.

King, C. W. Early Christian Numismatics & Other an. 2006. pap. 31.95 (978-1-4286-4739-8(2)) Kessinger Publishing, LLC.

Klein, Patricia S. Worship Without Words: The Signs & Symbols of Our Faith. exp. ed. 2007. (Illus.). 255p. per. 19.95 (978-1-55725-504-4(0)) Paraclete Pr., Inc.

Klinkenberg, Emanuel S. Compressed Meanings: The Donor's Model in Medieval Art to Around 1300 Origin - Spread & Significance of an Architectural Image in the Realm of Tension Between Tradition & Likeness. 2009. (Architectura Medii Aevi Ser.). (ENG., Illus.). 310p. (C). pap. 152.00 (978-2-503-52835-9(X)) Brepols Pubs. BEL. Dist: ISD.

Koch, Guntram. Early Christian Art & Architecture: An Introduction. Bowden, John, tr. from GER. 2012. (Illus.). 160p. **(978-0-334-02632-7(6)**, SCM Pr.) Hymns Ancient & Modern Ltd.

Kogman-Appel, Katrin & Meyer, Mati, eds. Between Judaism & Christianity: Art Historical Essays in Honor of Elisheva (Elisabeth) Revel-Neher. 2008. (Medieval Mediterranean Ser.). 394p. (C). (978-90-04-17106-0(1)) BRILL.

Kotzur, Hans-Jürgen. Dommuseum Mainz: Führer Durch Die Sammlung. 2008. (GER., Illus.). 148p. (C). 20.00 (978-3-8053-3871-4(6)) Zabern, Philipp von Verlag, GmbH DEU. Dist: Brown, David Bk. Co., The.

Krause, Hans-Joachim & Ranft, Andreas. Studien Zur Mittelalterlichen und Frühneuzeitlichen Kunstgeschichte und Geschichte. 2009. (GER & ENG., Illus.). 176p. (978-3-7776-1666-7(4)) Hirzel, S. Verlag GmbH & Co.

Krazl, Carol. Banners for Visual Worship: 70 Banner Designs from Lutheran Service. 2008. 19.99 (978-0-7586-1504-6(3)) Concordia Publishing Hse.

Kroesen, J. E. A. Staging the Liturgy: The Medieval Altarpiece in the Iberian Peninsula. 2009. (Liturgia Condenda Ser.). (ENG.). 607p. (C). pap. 95.00 (978-90-429-2116-0(1)) Peeters Pubs. & Booksellers BEL. Dist: Brown, David Bk. Co., The.

Kumler, Aden. Translating Truth: Ambitious Images & Religious Knowledge in Late Medieval France & England. 2011. (ENG., Illus.). 290p. 65.00 (978-0-300-16493-0(9)) Yale Univ. Pr.

Küster, Volker. Visual Arts & Religion. Alma, Hans & Barnard, Marcel, eds. 2011. (ENG.). 208p. pap. 44.95 (978-3-8258-0708-5(8)) Lit Verlag DEU. Dist: Transaction Pubs.

Lawless, Cather. Life Virgin Tuscan Icon 1300-1528. 2006. (Routledge Studies in Medieval Religion & Culture Ser.). (ENG.). 125.00 (978-0-415-36101-9(X)) Routledge.

Lees, Orton Wood, et al. Fragments of History: Rethinking the Ruthwell & Bewcastle Monuments. 2008. (ENG., Illus.). 320p. 89.00 (978-0-7190-7256-7(5)) Manchester Univ. Pr. GBR. Dist: Macmillan.

L'Estrange, Elizabeth. Holy Motherhood: Gender, Dynasty & Visual Culture in the Later Middle Ages. (Manchester Medieval Studies). (ENG., Illus.). 320p. 2012. pap. 39.95 **(978-0-7190-8726-4(0))** 2008. 88.00 (978-0-7190-7543-8(2)) Manchester Univ. Pr. GBR. Dist: Macmillan.

Lewis-Anthony, Justin. Circles of Thorns: Hieronymus Bosch & Being Human. 2009. (ENG., Illus.). 192p. (978-1-84706-509-4(0)) Continuum International Publishing Group, Ltd.

—Circles of Thorns: Hieronymus Bosch & Being Human. 2009. (ENG., Illus.). 200p. 27.95 (978-1-906286-21-7(3)) Mowbray, A. R. & Co., Ltd. GBR. Dist: National Bk. Network.

Loverance, Rowena. Christian Art. 2007. (Illus.). 248p. 35.00 (978-0-674-02479-3(6)) Harvard Univ. Pr.

Lowrie, Walter. Art in the Early Church. 2007. (ENG.). 436p. per. (978-1-4067-5291-5(6)) Read Bks.

—Christian Art & Archaeology Being A Ha. 2006. pap. 37.95 (978-1-4286-3923-2(3)) Kessinger Publishing, LLC.

Lubbock, Jules. Storytelling in Christian Art from Giotto to Donatello. 2006. (Illus.). 353p. 50.00 (978-0-300-11727-1(2)) Yale Univ. Pr.

Lucie-Smith, Edward & Scala Group Staff. The Face of Jesus. 2011. (ENG., Illus.). 320p. 19.95 (978-1-4197-0080-4(4)) Abrams.

Mailleux, P. A. & Stanton, E. S. The Vladimir Mother of God. 2011. 26p. 35.95 **(978-1-258-08192-8(X))** Literary Licensing, LLC.

Manetti, Renzo. La lingua degli Angeli: Simboli e segreti della basilica di San Miniato a Firenze. 2009. (storia Raccontata Ser.). (ITA., Illus.). 88p. (C). pap. 20.00 (978-88-596-0550-8(4)) Edizioni Polistampa ITA. Dist: Brown, David Bk. Co., The.

Mann, Janice. Romanesque Architecture & Its Sculptural Decoration in Christian Spain, 1000-1120: Exploring Frontiers & Defining Identities. 2009. (ENG., Illus.). 300p. (978-0-8020-9324-0(8)) Univ. of Toronto Pr.

Mann, Vivian, et al. Uneasy Communion: Jews, Christians, & the Altarpieces of Medieval Spain. 2010. (ENG., Illus.). 176p. 60.00 (978-1-904832-70-6(9)) Giles, D. Ltd. GBR. Dist: Antique Collectors' Club.

Mann, Vivian B., ed. & contrib. by. Uneasy Communion: Jews, Christians, & the Altarpieces of Medieval Spain. 2010. 49.95 (978-0-9777839-6-0(0)) Museum of Biblical Art.

Marchese, Ronald & Breu, Marlene. Splendor & Pageantry: Textile Treasures from the Armenian Orthodox Churches of Istanbul. 2011. 397p. pap. 155.00 (978-9944-424-78-3(1)) Citlembik/Nettleberry Pubns. TUR. Dist: National Bk. Network.

Martellini, Patrizia Angiolini, ed. The Basilica of San Vitale in Ravenna, 2 vols. 2008. (ITA & ENG., Illus.). 670p. 825.00 (978-88-7686-806-1(2)) Panini Franco Cosimo ITA. Dist: Antique Collectors' Club.

Martin, Kathleen J. Indigenous Symbols & Practices in the Catholic Church: Visual Culture Missionization & Appropriation. 2010. (Vitality of Indigenous Religions Ser.). (Illus.). 300p. 99.95 (978-0-7546-6631-8(X)) Ashgate Publishing Co.

Marx, Annegret, et al. Arise & Go Toward the South: 2000 Years of Christianity in Ethiopia. 2009. (GER & ENG., Illus.). 368p. 59.00 (978-3-932942-28-0(0)) Legat-Verlag GmbH & Company KG DEU. Dist: Independent Pubs. Group.

Mazza, Antonino & Zuffetti, Zaira. Il Miracolo Dell'Incoronata: Un Capolavoro Visto Da Vicino. 2010. (ITA., Illus.). 207p. (978-88-7827-191-3(8)) Bolis.

McClinton, Katharine Morrison & Poland, Reginald. Christian Church Art Through the Ages. 2011. 240p. 46.95 **(978-1-258-08398-4(1))** Literary Licensing, LLC.

McCollough, Charles. The Art of Parables: Reinterpreting the Teaching Stories of Jesus in Word & Sculpture. 2008. (ENG., Illus.). 256p. pap. 34.95 (978-1-55145-563-1(3), Copperhouse) Wood Lake Publishing, Inc. CAN. Dist: Westminster John Knox Pr.

McGrath, Michael O'Neill & Fragomeni, Richard. At the Name of Jesus: The Way, the Truth, the Life. 2007. (Illus.). pap. 24.95 (978-1-58459-352-2(0)) World Library Pubns.

McGrath, Michael O'Neill & Fragomeni, Richard N. At the Name of Jesus: The Way, the Truth, the Life. 2006. (Illus.). 90p. 39.95 (978-1-58459-314-0(8)) World Library Pubns.

—Blessed Art Thou: Mother, Lady, Mystic, Queen. 2007. (Illus.). pap. 24.95 (978-1-58459-351-5(2)) World Library Pubns.

Mcnally, Dennis. Art for Church Cloth of Gold: Cloth of Gold, Cloak of Lead. 2011. (ENG.). 208p. pap. 29.95 **(978-0-7618-5602-3(1))** Hamilton Bks.

Meinberg, Cloud Herman. An Outline History of Sacred Art. 2011. 318p. 50.95 **(978-1-258-10270-8(6))** Literary Licensing, LLC.

Mell, Ulrich. Christliche Hauskirche und Neues Testament: Die Ikonologie des Baptisteriums von Dura Europos und das Diatessaron Tatians. 2010. (Novum Testamentum et Orbis Antiquus/Studien zur Umwelt des Neuen Testaments (NTOA/StUNT) Ser.). (GER., Illus.). 340p. (C). 98.00 (978-3-525-53394-9(2)) Vandenhoeck & Ruprecht GmbH & Co. KG DEU. Dist: ISD.

Merback, Mitchell B., ed. Beyond the Yellow Badge: New Approaches to Anti-Judaism & Antisemitism in Medieval & Early Modern Visual Culture. 2007. (Brill's Ser. in Jewish Studies Ser.). (Illus.). 432p. (978-90-04-15165-9(6)) BRILL.

Merriam, Susan. Seventeenth-Century Flemish Garland Paintings: Still Life & the Devotional Image. 2012. (Visual Culture in Early Modernity Ser.). (Illus.). 200p. 104.95 **(978-1-4094-0305-0(X))** Ashgate Publishing Co.

Mâle, Emile. The Gothic Image: Religious Art in France in the Thirteenth-Century. 2008. 456p. pap. 41.00 (978-1-59740-502-7(7)) ACLS Humanities E-Book.

Miles, Margaret R. Image as Insight: Visual Understanding in Western Christianity & Secular Culture. 2006. (Illus.). 232p. pap. 25.00 (978-1-59752-902-0(8), Wipf and Stock) Wipf & Stock Pubs.

Milhouse, Paul William. Christian Worship in Symbol & Ritual. 2011. 142p. 40.95 **(978-1-258-00268-8(X))** Literary Licensing, LLC.

Millos, Elias Ioannes, intro. John of Mosul's Book of Beautiful Guidance. 2010. (SYR.). 116.00 (978-1-60724-878-1(6)) Gorgias Pr., LLC.

Mochizuki, Mia M. The Netherlandish Image after Iconoclasm, 1566-1672: Material Religion in the Dutch Golden Age. 2008. (Illus.). 424p. 144.95 (978-0-7546-6104-7(0)) Ashgate Publishing Co.

Moffitt, John F. Our Lady of Guadalupe: The Painting, the Legend & the Reality. 2006. (ENG., Illus.). 271p. per. 39.95 (978-0-7864-2667-6(5)) McFarland & Co., Inc. Pubs.

—Painterly Perspective & Piety: Religious Uses of the Vanishing Point, from the 15th to the 18th Century. 2008. (ENG., Illus.). 320p. pap. 45.00 (978-0-7864-3505-0(4)) McFarland & Co., Inc. Pubs.

Monheim, Florian. Echoes of Heaven: The Fine Art of Cathedrals & Their Hymns. 2006. (ENG.). 14.95 incl. lp (978-3-937406-52-7(2)) Edel Classica Gmbh.

Montgomery, Scott B. St. Ursula & the Eleven Thousand Virgins of Cologne: Relics, Reliquaries & the Visual Culture of Group Sanctity in Late Medieval Europe. 2009. (Illus.). 207p. pap. 60.95 *(978-3-03911-852-6(8))* Lang, Peter AG GBR. Dist: Lang, Peter.

Moraldi, Luigi. The Secret Gospels: An Illustrated Journey Through the Four Gnostic Gospels of Thomas, Mary, Truth, & Philip. 2007. (ENG., Illus.). 256p. 24.95 *(978-88-544-0228-7(1),* White Star) Rizzoli International Pubns., Inc.

More Abingdon Christian Clip Art CD ROM Software. 39.95 incl. cd-rom *(978-0-687-01177-3(9))* Abingdon Pr.

Morey, Charles Rufus. East Christian Paintings in the Freer Collection. 2010. pap. 27.88 *(978-1-61719-336-1(4));* pap. 27.88 *(978-1-61719-353-8(4))* Gorgias Pr., LLC.

Morton, Chris. The Notre Dame de Grâce de Cambrai & Netherlandish Painting. 2009. 92p. pap. *(978-3-639-20750-7(5))* VDM Verlag Dr. Mueller e.K.

Najafi, Sina & Turner, Christopher, eds. Cabinet Issue 29: Sloth. 2008. (ENG., Illus.). 112p. pap. 12.00 *(978-1-932698-27-5(2))* Cabinet.

Nancy, Jean-Luc. Noli Me Tangere: On the Raising of the Body. Clift, Sarah et al, trs. from FRE. 3rd ed. 2008. (Perspectives in Continental Philosophy Ser.). (ENG., Illus.). 128p. 70.00 *(978-0-8232-2889-8(4));* pap. 22.00 *(978-0-8232-2890-4(8))* Fordham Univ. Pr.

Nicolai, Vincenzo F., et al. The Christian Catacombs of Rome. 2009. (ENG.). 208p. pap. 39.95 *(978-3-7954-2212-7(4),* Art Stock Bks. Ltd/Csi) Continental Sales, Inc.

Noga-Banai, Galit. The Trophies of the Martyrs: An Art Historical Study of Early Christian Silver Reliquaries. 2008. (Oxford Studies in Byzantium Ser.). (ENG., Illus.). 300p. 170.00 *(978-0-19-921774-8(2))* Oxford Univ. Pr., Inc.

Nolan, Charles E. Splendors of Faith: New Orleans Catholic Churches, 1727-1930. 2010. (Illus.). 144p. 39.95 *(978-0-8071-3682-9(4))* Louisiana State Univ. Pr.

O'Hagan, Thomas. The Genesis of Christian Art. 2011. 170p. 41.95 ***(978-1-258-08314-4(0))*** Literary Licensing, LLC.

O'Kane, Martin, ed. Bible, Art, Gallery. 2011. 220p. ***(978-1-906055-63-9(7))*** Sheffield Phoenix Pr.

ONeill, P. R. What Do I Have to Do… . Paint You A Picture? 2009. 83p. pap. 38.90 *(978-0-557-15373-2(5))* Lulu Enterprises Inc.

Pagoulatos, Gerasimos P. Tracing the Bridegroom in Dura: The Bridal Initiation Service of the Dura-Europos Christian Baptistery as Early Evidence of the Use of Images in Christian & Byzantine Worship. 2007. per. 47.00 *(978-1-59333-738-4(8))* Gorgias Pr., LLC.

Paleotti, Gabriele & McCuaig, William. Discourse on Sacred & Profane Images. 2012. pap. ***(978-1-60606-116-9(X))*** Getty Pubns.

Palmer, Michael. Paul Tillich's Philosophy of Art. (Theologische Bibliothek Töpelmann Ser.). (ENG.). XXII, 217p. 195.00 ***(978-3-11-177692-7(1))*** De Gruyter, Walter Inc.

Palmer, William. Introduction to Early Christian Symbols. 2006. pap. 19.95 *(978-1-4286-4805-0(4))* Kessinger Publishing, LLC.

Parton, Anthony. Goncharova: The Art & Design of Natalia Goncharova. 2010. (ENG., Illus.). 520p. *(978-1-85149-605-1(X,* Antique Collectors Club Dist) Antique Collectors' Club.

Parys, Johan Van & Van Parys, Johan. Symbols That Surround Us: Faithful Reflections. 2011. ***(978-0-7648-2070-0(2))*** Liguori Pubns.

Pastoureau, Michel. The Bear: History of a Fallen King. Holoch, George, tr. from FRE. 2011. Orig. Title: L' ours: Histoire d'un roi Déchu. (ENG., Illus.). 384p. 29.95 *(978-0-674-04782-2(6),* Belknap Pr.) Harvard Univ. Pr.

Paterson, James. Jim's Grandiose Big Bible Picture Book. 2007. (ENG., Illus.). 96p. 35.00 *(978-0-9782221-4-7(8))* ECW Pr. CAN. Dist: Independent Pubs. Group.

Paul, Benjamin. Nuns & Reform Art in Early Modern Venice: The Architecure of Santi Cosma E Damiano & Its Decoration from Tintoretto to Tiepolo. 2012. (Illus.). 344p. 124.95 ***(978-1-4094-1186-4(9))*** Ashgate Publishing Co.

Petermann, Kerstin. Bernt Notke: Arbeitsweise & Werkstattorganisation im spaeten Mittelalter. (GER., Illus.). 275p. *(978-3-496-01217-7(X))* Reimer, Dietrich.

Pfordresher, John & Pfordresher, John. Jesus & the Emergence of a Catholic Imagination: An Illustrated Journey. 2008. (Illus.). 333p. per. 27.95 *(978-0-8091-4453-2(0),* 4453-2) Paulist Pr.

Phaidon Press Editors. Descent. 2006. (SPA.). 12.95 *(978-0-7148-9823-0(6))* Phaidon Pr., Inc.

Pheysey, Dawn C. The Master's Hand: The Art of Carl Heinrich Bloch. 2010. 168p. 32.99 *(978-1-60641-926-7(9))* Deseret Bk. Co.

Piper, Raymond Frank. The Hungry Eye: An Introduction to Cosmic Art. 2011. 142p. 40.95 ***(978-1-258-04573-9(7))*** Literary Licensing, LLC.

Pongracz, Patricia. Biblical Art & the Asian Imagination. 2007. *(978-0-9777839-2-2(8))* Museum of Biblical Art.

Pongracz, Patricia C., et al. The Christian Story: Five Asian Artists Today. 2007. (ENG., Illus.). 168p. pap. 39.95 *(978-1-904832-20-1(2))* Giles, D. Ltd. GBR. Dist: Antique Collectors' Club.

Porter, Arthur Kingsley. Pilgrimage Sculpture. 2009. pap. 22.36 *(978-1-60724-451-6(9))* Gorgias Pr., LLC.

Post, W. Ellwood. Saints, Signs & Symbols. 2011. 82p. 37.95 ***(978-1-258-00438-5(0))*** Literary Licensing, LLC.

Powell, Amy Knight. Depositions: Scenes from the Late Medieval Church & the Modern Museum. 2012. (ENG., Illus.). 384p. (gr. 17). 34.95 ***(978-1-935408-20-8(8))*** Zone Bks.

Prentice, Sartell. The Voices of the Cathedral: Tales in Stone & Legends in Glass. 2007. (ENG.). 390p. 48.95 *(978-0-548-03678-5(0))* Kessinger Publishing, LLC.

Proto Pisani, Rosanna Caterina. La Gerusalemme Di San Vivaldo: Guida Alla Visita Del Museo e Alla Scoperta Del Territorio. 2006. (Piccoli, grandi Musei Ser.). (Illus.). 244p. (C). pap. 24.00 *(978-88-596-0125-8(8))* Polistampa ITA. Dist: Brown, David Bk. Co., The.

—Museo D'arte Sacra Di Certaldo: Guida Alla Visita Del Museo e Alla Scoperta Del Territorio. 2006. (Piccoli, grandi Musei Ser.). (Illus.). 271p. (C). 24.00 *(978-88-596-0078-7(2))* Polistampa ITA. Dist: Brown, David Bk. Co., The.

—Museo D'arte Sacra Di Montespertoli: Guida Alla Visita Del Museo e Alla Scoperta Del Territorio. 2006. (Piccoli, grandi Musei Ser.). (Illus.). 259p. (C). 24.00 *(978-88-596-0069-5(3))* Polistampa ITA. Dist: Brown, David Bk. Co., The.

Raguin, Virginia Chieffo. Art, Piety & Destruction in the Christian West, 1500-1700. 2010. (Visual Culture in Early Modernity Ser.). (Illus.). 238p. 109.95 *(978-0-7546-6946-3(7))* Ashgate Publishing Co.

Ramshaw, Gail. Christian Worship: 100,000 Sundays of Symbols & Rituals. 2009. 224p. 30.00 *(978-0-8006-6233-2(4),* Fortress Pr.) Augsburg Fortress, Pubs.

Raw, Barbara Catherine. Anglo-Saxon Crucifixion Iconography & the Art of the Monastic Revival. 2009. (Cambridge Studies in Anglo-Saxon England Ser.). (ENG., Illus.). 328p. (C). pap. 42.00 *(978-0-521-09308-8(2))* Cambridge Univ. Pr.

Rebecca, E. & Zorach. Idols in the Age of Art: Objects Devotions & Early Modern World. Cole, Michael W., ed. 2009. (Objects, Devotions & the Early Modern World Ser.). (Illus.). 384p. 124.95 *(978-0-7546-5290-8(4))* Ashgate Publishing Co.

Recht, Roland. Believing & Seeing: The Art of Gothic Cathedrals. Whittall, Mary, tr. from FRE. (ENG., Illus.). 392p. 2010. pap. 27.50 *(978-0-226-70607-8(9))* 2008. 45.00 *(978-0-226-70606-1(0))* Univ. of Chicago Pr.

Refice, Paola. Museo D'arte Sacra Della Collegiata Di San Lorenzo a Montevarchi: Guida Alla Visita Del Museo e Alla Scoperta Del Territorio. 2007. (Piccoli, grandi Musei Ser.). (ITA & ENG., Illus.). 203p. (C). 24.00 *(978-88-596-0208-8(4))* Polistampa ITA. Dist: Brown, David Bk. Co., The.

Reinhart-Felice, M. Venite Adoremus, the Adoration of the Kings. 2008. (Illus.). 96p. pap. *(978-3-7774-3815-3(4))* Hirmer Verlag GmbH.

Rice, Edwin W. Stories of Great Painters or Religion in Art. 2007. (ENG.). 243p. 41.95 *(978-0-548-02863-6(X))* Kessinger Publishing, LLC.

Rimmer, Alfred. Ancient Stone Crosses of England. 2010. 178p. pap. 22.75 *(978-1-177-91896-1(X))* 2010. 182p. pap. 22.75 *(978-1-149-27954-0(0),* 2010. 176p. pap. 22.75 *(978-1-141-61502-5(9))* 2009. 176p. pap. 26.99 *(978-1-110-12452-7(X))* 2009. 176p. pap. 21.75 *(978-1-110-12449-7(X))* 2009. (ENG.). 174p. pap. 19.99 *(978-1-110-12446-6(5),* BiblioLife) 2009 (ENG.). 174p. pap. 21.99 *(978-1-110-12447-3(3),* BiblioLife) BiblioBazaar.

—Ancient Stone Crosses of England. 2010. 60p. pap. 14.31 *(978-1-153-27425-8(6))* General Bks. LLC.

—Ancient Stone Crosses of England. 2010. 170p. 37.95 *(978-1-161-35538-3(3))* Kessinger Publishing, LLC.

Robert, Christian-Nils. La Justice Dans Ses Décors (XVe-XVIe Siècles) 2006 (Chr Ser.). (FRE., Illus.). 112p. (C). pap. 30.00 ***(978-2-600-01053-5(X))*** Droz, Librairie CHE. Dist: Brown, David Bk. Co., The.

Rorem, Paul. The Medieval Development of Liturgical Symbolism. 2009. 88.00 *(978-1-60724-355-7(5))* Gorgias Pr., LLC.

Rosewell, Roger. Medieval Wall Paintings in English & Welsh Churches. 2011. (Illus.). 380p. pap. 34.95 *(978-1-84383-484-7(7),* Boydell Press) Boydell & Brewer, Ltd. GBR. Dist: Boydell & Brewer, Inc.

Ruck, Carl A. P. & Hoffman, Mark Alwin. The Effluents of Deity: Alchemy & Psychoactive Sacraments in Medieval & Renaissance Art. 2012. 372p. 50.00 ***(978-1-61163-041-1(X))*** Carolina Academic Pr.

Rudy, Kathryn & Baert, Barbara, eds. Weaving, Veiling & Dressing: Textiles & Their Metaphors in the Late Middle Ages. 2007. (Medieval Church Studies). (ENG., Illus.). 364p. (C). 152.00 *(978-2-503-51527-4(4))* Brepols Pubs. BEL. Dist: ISD.

Rush, John. The Mushroom in Christian Art: The Identity of Jesus in the Development of Christianity. 2011. (ENG., Illus.). 400p. pap. 29.95 *(978-1-55643-960-5(1))* North Atlantic Bks.

Ruskin, John. Mornings in Florence. 2009. 72p. pap. *(978-1-151-35833-2(9))* Books LLC.

—Mornings in Florence. 2007. (ENG.). 116p. per. *(978-1-4065-6372-6(2,)* Dodo Pr.

—Mornings in Florence. 2007. (ENG.). 88p. per. *(978-1-4068-4087-2(4))* Echo Library.

—Mornings in Florence. 2009. 176p. pap. 7.95 *(978-1-151-25399-6(5))* General Bks. LLC.

—Mornings in Florence. 2007. (ENG.). 192p. per. *(978-1-4067-8848-8(1),* Pomona Pr.) Read Bks.

—Mornings in Florence. 2009. (ENG.). 116p. pap. *(978-1-4385-1462-8(X),* Book Jungle) Standard Pubns., Inc.

Sachs, Hannelore. Erklarendes Woerterbuch der Christlichen Kunst. (GER.). 384p. 29.95 *(978-0-7859-8459-7(3),* 3768493059) French & European Pubns., Inc.

Scheicher, Harald & Biller, Barbara. Macht des Bildes - Visionen des Göttliche: Kunst und Transzendent in Österreich im 20. Jahrhundert. Katalogbuch zur Ausstellung in Bleiburg, 26.04.2009-08.11.2009, Werner Berg Museum Bleiburg. 2009. (Illus.). 383p. *(978-3-7774-8055-8(X))* Hirmer Verlag GmbH.

Schneider Adams, Laurie. The Iconography of Piero Della Francesca's Arezzo Frescoes. 2011. 104p. pap. ***(978-3-8443-0129-8(1))*** Lambert Academic Publishing.

Seaman, Natasha T. The Religious Paintings of Hendrick Ter Brugghen: Reinventing Christian Painting after the Reformation in Utrecht. 2012. (Visual Culture in Early Modernity Ser.). (Illus.). 200p. 104.95 ***(978-1-4094-3495-5(8))*** Ashgate Publishing Co.

Senior, John. The Restoration of Christian Culture. 2008. (ENG., Illus.). 192p. (Orig.). per. 24.95 *(978-1-932528-16-9(4))* IHS Pr.

Serrano, Andres. Andres Serrano: Holy Works. 2012. (ENG., Illus.). 96p. 50.00 ***(978-88-6208-209-9(6))*** Damiani ITA. Dist: D.A.P./Distributed Art Pubs.

Sherlock, Peter. Monuments & Memory in Early Modern England. 2008. (Illus.). 296p. 124.95 *(978-0-7546-6093-4(1))* Ashgate Publishing Co.

Shields, Mark A. Gospel Symbols: Finding the Creator in His Creations. 2010. pap. 12.99 *(978-1-59955-269-9(8))* Cedar Fort, Inc./CFI Distribution.

Simari, Maria Matilde, ed. Il Museo di Arte Sacra di San Donnino: Guida alla visita del museo e alla scoperta del Territorio. 2010. (Piccoli, grandi Musei Ser.). (ENG & ITA., Illus.). 264p. (C). pap. 25.00 *(978-88-596-0836-3(8))* Polistampa ITA. Dist: Brown, David Bk. Co., The.

Simari, Maria Matilde & Bisceglia, Anna. Museo D'arte Sacra e Religiosità Popolare "Beato Angelico" a Vicchio: Guida Alla Visita Del Museo e Alla Scoperta Del Territorio. 2008. (Piccoli, grandi Musei Ser.). (Illus.). 404p. (C). 24.00 *(978-88-596-0381-8(1))* Polistampa ITA. Dist: Brown, David Bk. Co., The.

Sinkevic, Ida. Knights in Shining Armor: Myth & Reality 1450-1650. 2006. (ENG., Illus.). 84p. 35.00 *(978-1-59373-055-0(1))* Bunker Hill Publishing, Inc.

Siracusano, Gabriela. Pigments & Power in the Andes: From the Material to the Symbolic in Andean Cultural Practices, 1500-1800. 2011. (ENG., Illus.). 256p. pap. 70.00 *(978-1-904982-56-2(5))* Archetype Pubns. GBR. Dist: National Bk. Network.

Snelders, B. Identity in Christian-Muslim Interaction: Medieval Art of the Syrian Orthodox from the Mosul Area. 2010. (Orientalia Lovaniensia Analecta Ser.). (ENG.). 591p. (C). 124.00 *(978-90-429-2386-7(5))* Peeters Pubs. & Booksellers BEL. Dist: Brown, David Bk. Co., The.

Sorries, Reiner. Christliche Archaologie Compact. 2011. (GER., Illus.). 502p. (C). 168.00 ***(978-3-89500-792-7(7))*** Reichert, Ludwig Dr. DEU. Dist: Brown, David Bk. Co., The.

Spier, Jeffrey. Late Antique & Early Christian Gems. 2007. (Spatantike, Fruhes Christentum, Byzanz Ser.). (ENG.). 374p. (C). 337.00 *(978-3-89500-434-6(C))* Reichert, Ludwig Dr. DEU. Dist: Brown, David Bk. Co., The.

—Picturing the Bible: The Earliest Christian Art. (Illus.). 2009. (ENG.). 328p. pap. 50.00 *(978-0-300-14934-0(4))* 2007. xv, 309p. pap. *(978-0-912804-47-7(5))* Yale Univ. Pr.

Stokes, Margaret. Early Christian Art in Ireland. 2010. 248p. pap. 26.75 *(978-1-141-30430-1(9))* BiblioBazaar.

Stratton-Pruitt, Suzanne L., et al, eds. The Virgin, Saints, & Angels: South American Paintings 1600-1825 from the Thoma Collection. 2006. (ENG., Illus.). 288p. 55.00 *(978-88-7624-613-5(4))* Skira Editore ITA. Dist: Random Hse., Inc.

Stratton, Suzanne L. & Cummins, Thomas B. F. The Virgin, Saints, & Angels: South American Paintings 1600-1825, from the Thoma Collection. 2006. (Illus.). 231p. pap. *(978-88-7624-698-2(3))* Oxford Univ. Pr., Inc.

Suzawa, Yukako. The Genesis of Early Christian Art. 2009. (Bar S Ser.). (ENG., Illus.). 163p. (C). pap. 82.50 *(978-1-4073-0372-7(4))* British Archaeological Reports Ltd. GBR. Dist: Brown, David Bk. Co., The.

Synder, Janet E. Early Gothic Column-Figure Sculpture in France: Appearance Materials & Significance. 2011. (Illus.). 306p. 119.95 *(978-1-4094-0065-3(4))* Ashgate Publishing Co.

Tammen, Bjoern R. Musik & Bild: Im Chorraum Mittelalterlicher Kirchen 1100-1500. (GER., Illus.). 552p. *(978-3-496-01218-4(8))* Reimer, Dietrich.

Tartuferi, Angelo, ed. Arte a Figline Valdarno: Dal Maestro della Maddalena a Masaccio. 2010. (citta degli Uffizi Ser.). (ITA., Illus.). 200p. (C). 60.00 *(978-88-596-0832-5(5))* Polistampa ITA. Dist: Brown, David Bk. Co., The.

Taylor, Stephen. Fylfot File. 2006. *(978-1-905399-22-2(7))* Perfect Pubs.

Thibodeau, Timothy M., ed. The Rationale Divinorum Officiorum of William Durand of Mende Bk. 1: A New Translation of the Prologue. (Records of Western Civilization Ser.). (ENG.). 168p. (gr. 17). 2010. pap. 18.50 *(978-0-231-14181-9(5))* 2007. (Illus.). 40.00 *(978-0-231-14180-2(7))* Columbia Univ. Pr.

Thistlethwaite, David. The Art of God & the Religions of Art. 2008. (Illus.). 198p. pap. 23.00 *(978-1-55635-721-3(4))* Wipf & Stock Pubs.

Tolan, John V. Saint Francis & the Sultan: The Curious History of a Christian-Muslim Encounter. 2009. (ENG., Illus.). 416p. 60.00 *(978-0-19-923972-6(X))* Oxford Univ. Pr., Inc.

Toman, Rolf, ed. Ars Sacra. 2010. 800p. 199.00 *(978-0-8416-7223-9(7))* Langenscheidt Publishing Group.

Torriti, Paolo & Scarpellini, Margherita Gilda. Sacra Mirabilia: Tesori Da Castiglion Fiorentino. 2010. (ITA., Illus.). 127p. *(978-88-7970-393-2(5))* Edifir.

Tradigo, Alfredo. Icons & Saints of the Eastern Orthodox Church. Sartarelli, Stephen, tr. from ITA. 2006. (Guide to Imagery Ser.). (Illus.). 384p. pap. 24.95 *(978-0-89236-845-7(4))* Oxford Univ. Pr., Inc.

Trent D.D., Kenneth E. Types of Christ in the Old Testament: A Conservative Approach to Old Testament Typology. 2010. 160p. 30.95 *(978-1-61507-148-7(2));* pap. 13.99 *(978-1-61507-147-0(4))* Cross Bks. Publishing.

Twining, Louisa. Symbols & Emblems of Early & Medieval Christian Art. 2010. 426p. pap. 35.75 *(978-1-143-52107-2(2))* BiblioBazaar.

Van Belle, G., et al, eds. Miracles & Imagery in Luke & John: Festschrift Ulrich Busse. 2008. (Bibliotheca Ephemeridum Theologicarum Lovaniensium Ser.). (ENG., Illus.). 287p. (C). pap. 114.00 *(978-90-429-2115-3(3))* Peeters Pubs. & Booksellers BEL. Dist: Brown, David Bk. Co., The.

Van Buhren, Ralf. Die Werke der Barmherzigkeit in der Kunst des 12.-18. Jahrhunderts. Date not set. (Studien zur Kunstgeschichte Ser.: Bd. 115). (GER., Illus.). 424p. *(978-3-487-10319-8(2))* Olms, Georg Verlag AG.

Verlag, Hirmer & Hirmer Verlag. Meisterwerke mittelalterlicher Kunst au dem Nationalmuseum Warschau. 2006. (GER., Illus.). 192p. (C). pap. 42.00 *(978-3-7774-3275-5(X))* Hirmer Verlag GmbH DEU. Dist: Brown, David Bk. Co., The.

Viladesau, Richard. The Triumph of the Cross: The Passion of Christ in Theology & the Arts from the Renaissance to the Counter-Reformation. 2008. (ENG., Illus.). 368p. 49.95 *(978-0-19-533566-8(X))* Oxford Univ. Pr., Inc.

Viladesau, Richard, et al. The Beauty of the Cross: The Passion of Christ in Theology & the Art - From the Catacombs to the Eve of the Renaissance. 2008. (ENG., Illus.). 240p. pap. 21.95 *(978-0-19-536711-9(1))* Oxford Univ. Pr., Inc.

Virtue, Doreen. Archangel Michael Oracle Cards: A 44-Card Deck & Guidebook. 2009. (ENG.). 44p. instr.'s gde. ed. 15.95 *(978-1-4019-2273-3(2),* 876) Hay Hse., Inc.

Wagner, Wolfgang Eric. Die Liturgische Gegenwart des Abwesenden Königs: Gebetsverbrüderung und Herrscherbild Im Frühen Mittelalter. 2010. (GER & ENG.). 392p. ***(978-90-04-18923-2(8))*** BRILL.

Wake, Eleanor. Framing the Sacred: The Indian Churches of Early Colonial Mexico. 2010. (ENG.). 368p. (C). 65.00 *(978-0-8061-4033-9(X))* Univ. of Oklahoma Pr.

Walker, Alicia & Luyster, Amanda. Negotiating Secular & Sacred in Medieval Art: Christian, Islamic, & Buddhist. 2009. (Illus.). 242p. 119.95 *(978-0-7546-6327-0(2))* Ashgate Publishing Co.

Warr, Cordelia. Dressing for Heaven: Religious Clothing in Italy, 1215-1545. 2010. (ENG., Illus.). 288p. 95.00 *(978-0-7190-7983-2(7))* Manchester Univ. Pr. GBR. Dist: Macmillan.

Waters, Clara Erskine Clement. A Handbook of Legendary & Mythological Art. 2009. 212p. pap. *(978-0-217-15873-2(0));* 310p. pap. *(978-0-217-67037-1(7));* 216p. pap. *(978-1-4432-8366-0(3));* 338p. pap. *(978-1-4432-8365-6(7))* Books LLC.

Weller, Alan. Christian Art & Imagery. 2009. (Dover Pictura Electronic Clip Art Ser.). (ENG., Illus.). 128p. pap. 39.95 *(978-0-486-99027-9(3))* Dover Pubns., Inc.

—Christian Motifs & Symbols CD-ROM & Book. 2009. (Dover Electronic Clip Art Ser.). (ENG.). 48p. pap. 16.95 *(978-0-486-99055-2(9))* Dover Pubns., Inc.

Westheider, Ortrud. Zwischen Himmel und Hölle: Kunst des Mittelalters von der Gotik bis Baldung Grien. Katalogbuch zur Ausstellung Hamburg 19.09.2009-10.01.2010 Bucerius Kunst Forum. Westheider, Ortrud & Philipp, Michael, eds. 2009. (GER., Illus.). 256p. (C). 64.00 *(978-3-7774-2201-5(0))* Hirmer Verlag GmbH DEU. Dist: Brown, David Bk. Co., The.

White, Gary & Aviva, Elyn. Powerful Places on the Caminos de Santiago. 2010. (Illus.). 122p. pap. 8.95 *(978-0-9790909-9-8(7))* Pilgrims Process, Inc.

Whitelaw, Susan L. The Art of Romeo Celleghin: Preserving Our Religious Art Heritage: A Cleveland Case Study. 2009. (The Sacred Landmarks Ser.). (Illus.). 30p. per. 19.95 *(978-0-9638675-6-8(3))* Levin College of Urban Affairs, Cleveland State Univ.

Whittemore, Carroll E. Symbols of the Church: Together with Saints & Their Emblems. 2011. 20p. 35.95 ***(978-1-258-00581-8(6))*** Literary Licensing, LLC.

Williams, Herb. Christian Arts: Winning Souls Through the Gifts of God. 2007. 172p. per. 24.95 *(978-1-4241-8667-9(6))* PublishAmerica, Inc.

Williamson, Paul. Object of Devotion: Medieval English Alabaster Sculpture from the Victoria & Albert Museum. 2011. (Illus.). 224p. pap. 49.95 *(978-0-88397-156-7(9))* Art Services International.

Wollesen, Jens. The Frescoes in the Royal Chapel at Pyrga on Cyprus: New Evidence & Datings. 2010. (Studies & Texts). (ENG., Illus.). 194p. 95.00 *(978-0-88844-169-0(X))* Pontifical Institute of Mediaeval Studies, Dept. of Pubns. CAN. Dist: Univ. of Toronto Pr.

Wright, Rosemary Muir & Wright, Rosemary. Sacred Distance: Representing the Virgin Mary in Italian Alterpieces, 1300-1630. 2006. (ENG., Illus.). 176p. 84.00 *(978-0-7190-5545-4(8))* Manchester Univ. Pr. GBR. Dist: Macmillan.

Yeo, K. K. The Spirit Hovers: Journeying through Chaos with Prayers. 2011. 124p. pap. 15.00 ***(978-1-61097-506-3(5),*** Cascade Bks.) Wipf & Stock Pubs.

Yeo, K. K. The Spirit Intercedes. 2009. 132p. pap. 16.00 *(978-1-60608-794-7(0),* Cascade Bks.) Wipf & Stock Pubs.

Zacchedду, Maria Pia, ed. Il museo di Arte Sacra di San Martino a Gangalandi: Guida alla visita del museo e alla scoperta del Territorio. 2010. (Piccoli, grandi Musei Ser.). (ENG & ITA., Illus.). 240p. (C). pap. 25.00 *(978-88-596-0835-6(X))* Polistampa ITA. Dist: Brown, David Bk. Co., The.

Zastrow, Oleg. Crosses & Crucifixes: Treasures from the 8th to 19th Centuries. 2009. (ENG & ITA., Illus.). 352p. 95.00 *(978-88-7439-523-1(X))* 5 Continents ITA. Dist: Hachette Bk. Group.

Zegeye, Abebe. Zerihun Yetmgeta: The Magical Universe of Art. 2008. (Illus.). 76p. pap. 22.50 *(978-1-86888-500-8(3))* Unisa Press / Uitgewers GBR. Dist: International Specialized Bk. Services.

Zieg, Tom. 300 Christian & Inspirational Patterns for Scroll Saw Woodworking. 2nd rev. expurg. ed. 2009. (ENG.). 192p. pap. 19.95 *(978-1-56523-430-7(8))* Fox Chapel Publishing Co., Inc.

CHRISTIAN ATHEISM

see Death of God Theology

C

CHRISTIAN BIOGRAPHY

see also Apostles; Apostolic Fathers; Bishops; Cardinals; Clergy; Fathers of the Church; Hermits; Martyrs; Missionaries; Monks; Nuns; Popes; Puritans; Saints; Theologians

Abed, Zaher. America in the Memory of an Arab. 2008. 696p. pap. 37.95 *(978-1-4401-1095-5(6))* iUniverse, Inc.

Accom, Sylvana C. Under the Ocean over My Soul. 2011. 112p. pap. 19.99 ***(978-1-4568-9931-8(7))*** Xlibris Corp.

Adam, David. Fire of the North. (Illus.). 144p. 17.95 *(978-0-281-04698-0(0))* International Publishers Marketing.

Adamkiewicz, Catherine L. Broken & Blessed: A Life Story. 2007. 180p. per. 12.99 *(978-0-9794976-6-7(3))* Bezalel Bks.

Adams, Apryll. The Minister's Mistress: From Devastation to Destiny. 2010. 14.99 *(978-0-578-06323-2(9))* Adams, Apryll D.

Adams, Carl L. Wanted: Lost Souls. 2011. 360p. 22.99 ***(978-1-4568-8221-1(X))***; pap. 15.99 ***(978-1-4568-8220-4(1))*** Xlibris Corp.

Adams, Eve N. A Shattered Soul: My Life with Dissociative Identity Disorder. 2009. 300p. pap. 18.99 *(978-1-60791-894-3(3))* Xulon Pr., Inc.

Adams, LaNell. Broken but Not Shattered: My Life's Journey, God's Plan & Purpose for His Earthen Vessel. 2006. 124p. pap. 13.99 *(978-1-4141-0655-7(6))* Pleasant Word.

Adams, Nehemiah. Catharine. 2009. 194p. 37.95 *(978-1-104-68117-3(X))*; pap. 22.95 *(978-1-104-63083-6(4))* Kessinger Publishing, LLC.

Adams, Ronald. No Mountain Too High to Climb, 1 vol. 2010. 342p. pap. 29.95 *(978-1-4489-4359-3(0))* PublishAmerica, Inc.

Ahn, Ché. Say Goodbye to Powerless Christianity: Walking in Supernatural Surrender & Significance. 2009. 172p. pap. 16.99 *(978-0-7684-3113-1(1))* Destiny Image Pubs.

Aikman, David. Billy Graham: His Life & Influence, 0 vols. 2007. 356p. 24.99 *(978-0-8499-1702-8(6))* Nelson, Thomas Inc.

Aird, Polly. Mormon Convert, Mormon Defector: A Scottish Immigrant in the American West, 1848-1861. 2009. (ENG.). 320p. (C). 39.95 *(978-0-87062-369-1(9)*, Clark, Arthur H. Co., The) Univ. of Oklahoma Pr.

Aist, Rodney, et al, eds. Adomnan of Iona: Theologian, Lawmaker, Peacemaker. 2010. 335p. 70.00 *(978-1-84682-102-8(9))* Four Courts Pr. IRL. Dist: International Specialized Bk. Services.

Ajibola, Babatunde Ezekiel. A call to honour, a biography of apostle joseph ayo Babalola. 2008. 212p. 55.95 *(978-1-4092-1304-8(8))* Lulu Enterprises Inc.

Akers, Michelle & Nelson, Judy. Face to Face with Michelle Akers. Date not set. (Illus.). 87p. pap. 4.99 *(978-1-57902-049-1(6))* Integrated Resources.

Aki, Andre C. Treasured Writings. 2010. 64p. pap. 11.00 *(978-1-4269-2581-8(6))* Trafford Publishing.

Aldous, David. O Love That Will Not Let Me Go. 2007. (ENG.). 100p. 17.99 *(978-1-86024-610-4(9))* Authentic Media.

Alexander, Archibald. Biographical Sketches of the Founder & Principal Alumni of the Log College. 2009. 284p. 30.99 *(978-1-116-11413-3(5))*; 34.99 *(978-1-116-11412-6(7))*; pap. 28.75 *(978-1-116-11414-0(3))*; pap. 27.75 *(978-1-116-11415-7(1))* BiblioBazaar.

—Biographical Sketches of the Founder & Principal Alumni of the Log College. 2006. 284p. per. 23.99 *(978-1-4255-2577-4(6))* MPublishing.

Alexander, Archibald, ed. Biographical Sketches of the Founder & Principal Alumni of the Log College. 2007. (ENG.). 278p. 42.95 *(978-0-548-21212-7(0))*; 280p. per. 27.95 *(978-1-4325-3122-5(0))* Kessinger Publishing, LLC.

Alexander, Dwight. Through These Doors: A True Inspirational Story of a Family in Crisis. 2006. 21.95 *(978-1-59571-125-0(2))*; per. 14.95 *(978-1-59571-123-6(6))* Word Association Pubs.

Alexander, Robert E. Half Heaven Half Heartache. 2008. 264p. 26.99 *(978-1-60791-140-1(X))*; pap. 16.99 *(978-1-60791-094-7(2))* Xulon Pr., Inc.

Alexander, Ron. Don't Tell Me What to Do a Spiritual Memoir. 2009. 142p. pap. 14.99 *(978-1-60860-789-1(5)*, Eloquent Bks.) AEG Literary Publishing Services, Inc.

Alexander, Sharisse M. In His Presence. 2008. 72p. pap. 10.99 *(978-1-60647-820-2(6))* Xulon Pr., Inc.

Alexandrenko, Nikolai. Grace then Freedom. 2007. pap. 12.95 *(978-0-9794379-0-8(3))* Nikolai Foundation.

Allen, Cindy L. I Thought I Heard the Lions Roar. 2009. 164p. 12.99 *(978-1-60696-306-7(6))* Tate Publishing & Enterprises, LLC.

Allen, Julie. When Your Partner Doesn't Know Jesus. 2006. 93p. pap. *(978-1-903725-78-8(X))* New Wine Pr.

Allred, Frank. Why I Love Jesus: A Personal Testimony. 2008. 88p. pap. *(978-0-946462-73-5(9))* Grace Pubns. Trust.

Alzamora, Julia. Un Pacto con Dios y Su Poder en Mi Vida. 2007. (SPA.). *(978-1-59835-050-0(1))* Cambridge BrickHouse, Inc.

Alzamora, Rudy. Jesús Anunció Su Retorno: ¿Estás Preparado para Encontrarte con Él? 2008. (SPA.). *(978-1-59835-074-6(9))* Cambridge BrickHouse, Inc.

—Jesus Told Me: He's Coming Back: Are You Ready to Meet Him? 2007. *(978-1-59835-059-3(5))* Cambridge BrickHouse, Inc.

Andersen, Oyvind Gaarder. The Tiger Pastor. 2008. 164p. pap. 13.99 *(978-1-60477-905-9(5))* Xulon Pr., Inc.

Anderson, Douglas S. Her Name Is Happiness: The Inspirational Account of the Life of Happiness Emejuru. 2009. 292p. pap. 16.99 *(978-1-61579-241-2(4))* Xulon Pr., Inc.

Anderson, Elliott. Answers in Abundance: A Miraculous Adoption Journey as Told from a Father's Heart. 2007. (ENG.). per. 16.95 *(978-1-60037-232-2(5))* Morgan James Publishing.

Anderson, Elliott J. Answers in Abundance: A Miraculous Adoption Journey as Told from a Father's Heart. 2007. (ENG., Illus.). 248p. 24.95 *(978-1-60037-233-9(3))* Morgan James Publishing.

Anderson, John D., ed. William of St. Thierry: Exposition on the Epistle to the Romans. Hasbrouk, John Baptist, tr. 2006. (Cistercian Fathers Ser.). 301p. per. 16.95 *(978-0-87907-527-9(9))* Cistercian Pubns., Inc.

Anderson, Robert L. The Life, Beliefs & Divine Detours of a Tennessee Mountain Man. 2009. 296p. pap. 16.99 *(978-1-61579-062-3(4))* Xulon Pr., Inc.

Anderson, Vivi. And He Walks with Me. 2011. 244p. pap. 15.99 ***(978-1-61379-301-5(4))*** Xulon Pr., Inc.

—And he Walks with Me. 2011. 246p. ***(978-1-61379-073-1(2))*** Xulon Pr., Inc.

Anding, Rose Maria McCarthy. High Heels, Honey Lips, & White Powder: The Tales & Salvation of a Proverbs 5 Woman. 2010. pap. 14.99 *(978-1-61663-360-8(3))* Tate Publishing & Enterprises, LLC.

Andreoli, Angela. A Rainbow in December. 2010. 88p. pap. 27.49 *(978-1-4520-9542-4(6))* AuthorHouse.

Andrews, Reg. Timber: A Call to Personal & Corporate Renewal. 2007. 176p. per. *(978-1-55452-224-8(2))* Essence Publishing.

Andrus, Ira R., Jr. Dead Man Living. 2009. pap. 14.99 *(978-1-60799-950-8(1))* Tate Publishing & Enterprises, LLC.

Angelo, Virji. The News from the Master. 2008. 112p. pap. 11.99 *(978-1-60647-627-7(0))* Xulon Pr., Inc.

Anne, Mary. Living with the Light. 2010. 285p. pap. 21.50 *(978-1-4457-3032-5(4))* Lulu Enterprises Inc.

Antillon, Ramona. Ashleigh: God's Miracle Baby: For with God Nothing Shall Be Impossible. 2011. 108p. 22.50 ***(978-1-4634-1775-8(6))***; pap. 14.99 ***(978-1-4634-1776-5(4))*** AuthorHouse.

Antonation, Kelly. 12 Stones & Borrowed Stones. Dewey, Sadie, ed. 2011. 88p. pap. ***(978-1-77067-273-4(7))*** FriesenPress.

Arend, Mark J. One. 2011. 170p. 29.99 ***(978-1-4568-9852-6(3))***; pap. 19.99 ***(978-1-4568-9851-9(5))*** Xlibris Corp.

Armaugh, Mitch. Whistle for the Flies, Jesus - Whistle for the Bees on Terry Shafer. 2011. 252p. pap. 19.95 *(978-1-4502-9602-1(5))* iUniverse, Inc.

Armour, Margaret. Through the Siege: One Woman's Struggle Back from the Brink of Despair. 2006. (Illus.). 137p. per. 11.99 *(978-1-59886-627-8(3))* Tate Publishing & Enterprises, LLC.

Armstrong, Chris R. Patron Saints for Postmoderns: Ten from the Past Who Speak to Our Future. 2009. (ENG., Illus.). 249p. pap. 16.00 *(978-0-8308-3719-9(1)*, IVP Bks.) InterVarsity Pr.

Arvizu, Edmundo. Sitting on the Moon: (A Life of Supernatural Favor) 2008. 135p. pap. 24.95 *(978-1-60474-888-8(5))* PublishAmerica, Inc.

Asare, James Adu. Preaching God's Word. 2007. (ENG.). 76p. per. 16.95 *(978-1-4241-6848-4(1))* PublishAmerica, Inc.

Atchinson, Glenn A. A Sliver of Light Out of Darkness: Gathering Truth Through Life Stories. 2008. 80p. pap. 8.95 *(978-0-595-53253-7(5))* iUniverse, Inc.

Atherstone, Andrew. Oxford's Protestant Spy: The Controversial Career of Charles Golightly. 2007. (Studies in Evangelical History & Thought Ser.). (ENG.). 333p. per. 36.99 *(978-1-84227-364-7(7)*, Paternoster) Authentic Media.

Atkins, Gaius Glenn. Pilgrims of the Lonely Road. 2007. (ENG.). 344p. 46.95 *(978-0-548-08783-1(0))* Kessinger Publishing, LLC.

Aughtmon, Susanna Foth. All I Need Is Jesus & a Good Pair of Jeans: The Tired Supergirl's Search for Grace. 2009. 192p. pap. 13.99 *(978-0-8007-3172-4(7))* Revell.

Austin, William E. Gone but Not Forgotten: The Life & Times of William Oscar Austin Jr. 2009. 128p. 29.99 *(978-1-4415-9977-3(0))* Xlibris Corp.

Authentic Sources, compiled by. The Life of Little Nellie of Holy God, 1903-1908: The Little Violet of the Blessed Sacrament. 2007. (Illus.). 99p. pap. 9.00 *(978-0-89555-852-7(1)*, TAN Bks.) St. Benedict Pr., LLC.

Autrey, C. E. You Can Win Souls: A Practical Guide for the Christian in Meeting His Major Responsibility. 2011. 168p. 41.95 ***(978-1-258-06513-3(4))*** Literary Licensing, LLC.

Autry, James A. Looking Around for God: The Oddly Reverent Observations of an Unconventional Christian. 2007. 140p. per. 16.00 *(978-1-57312-484-3(2))* Smyth & Helwys Publishing, Inc.

Avery, Kevin & Long, John. Where Strangers Cross. 2010. 300p. pap. 18.99 *(978-1-60957-845-9(7))* Xulon Pr., Inc.

Avila, Luis. El Llamado del Crimen: Called from Crime. (SPA.). 104p. *(978-84-7228-299-5(6)*, 220539) Clie, Editorial.

Baepler, Richard, ed. Witness to His Generation: Selected Writings of John Streitelmeier. 2006. (Illus.). 212p. pap. 16.00 *(978-1-932688-16-0(1)*, Lutheran Univ. Pr.) Kirk Hse. Pubs.

Bailey, Becky. God Is Bigger Than Dr Phil. 2011. 176p. pap. 16.95 ***(978-1-257-80299-9(2))*** Lulu Enterprises Inc.

Bailey, Faith Coxe. Tales for Teens: Heroes of the Christian Faith. 2011. 128p. 40.95 ***(978-1-258-08232-1(2))*** Literary Licensing, LLC.

Bailey, Gene. Beyond the Ordinary: Health, Wealth, & Wisdom Strategies for Dynamic Living. 2008. 14.95 *(978-0-615-22226-4(9))* Bailey, Gene.

Bailey, Kathy. The Full Circle of Coming Out. 2008. 148p. pap. 13.99 *(978-1-60477-874-8(1))* Xulon Pr., Inc.

Bailey, Pat. But This I Know. 2009. 288p. pap. 15.99 *(978-0-9821835-6-4(9))* This Joy Bks.

Baillie, John. A Memoir of Adelaide Leaper Newton. 2009. 368p. 38.99 *(978-1-117-21724-6(8))*; 372p. 26.99 *(978-1-103-89787-2(X))*; 372p. pap. 20.99 *(978-1-103-89778-0(0))* BiblioBazaar.

—A Memoir of Adelaide Leaper Newton. 2007. (ENG.). 368p. 48.95 *(978-0-548-35564-0(9))*; per. 33.95 *(978-0-548-29824-4(6))* Kessinger Publishing, LLC.

—A Memoir of Adelaide Leaper Newton. 2006. (ENG.). 380p. per. 26.99 *(978-1-4255-4039-5(2))* MPublishing.

Bainton, Roland H. The Travail of Religious Liberty: Nine Biographical Studies. 2008. (Roland Bainton Reprint Ser.). (Illus.). 272p. pap. 30.00 *(978-1-55635-876-0(8))* Wipf & Stock Pubs.

Baker, Janie. Divine Madness: A Memoir of Religious Psychosis. 2006. 196p. pap. 24.95 *(978-1-4241-2831-0(5))* PublishAmerica, Inc.

Baker, Phil J. Lessons in the Rearview Mirror: Finding Wisdom along the Journey. 2008. 192p. pap. 14.99 *(978-1-60791-101-2(9))* Xulon Pr., Inc.

Balderston, Thomas W. Wake up! Wake up! the Testimony of a Layman. 2009. pap. 13.99 *(978-1-60799-492-3(5))* Tate Publishing & Enterprises, LLC.

Ball, David A. The Crucifixion & Death of a Man Called Jesus: From the Eyes of a Physician. 2010. 172p. pap. 14.99 *(978-1-61507-128-9(8))* Cross Bks. Publishing.

Ballard, Kelly. My Dog Is a Morning Person. 2010. 111p. pap. 14.99 *(978-0-578-03099-9(3))* BeyondWorship.

Bandiola, Benjamin. Nothing to Fear: A poignant story of my life as a self-supporting student in the Philippines & how I later became a full professor & department Ch. 2011. 108p. 24.99 ***(978-1-4628-5926-9(7))***; pap. 15.99 ***(978-1-4628-5925-2(9))*** Xlibris Corp.

Baptist History Celebration Steering Committee Staff, contrib. by. Baptist History Celebration - 2007: A Symposium on Our History, Theology, & Hymnody: Convened As a Tercentenary Anniversary Tribute to the Founding of the Philadelphia Baptist Association in 1707, Held at the First Baptist Church of Charleston, South Carolina on August 1-3, 2007. 2008. (Illus.). xviii, 590p. *(978-1-888514-30-8(2))* Particular Baptist Pr.

Baranowski BSN, Brenda S. Just Like Your Father, 1 vol. 2010. 56p. pap. 16.95 *(978-1-4489-4569-6(0))* PublishAmerica, Inc.

Barba, Effie Darlene. A Broken & Contrite Heart. 2011. 120p. pap. 10.99 ***(978-1-4567-5590-4(0))*** AuthorHouse.

Barlatier, Jeffrey. Street Dreams for God's Child. 2008. 111p. pap. 17.67 *(978-0-615-16458-8(7))* Kingdom Bk & Gift.

Barlow, Kate. Abode of Love: Growing up in a Messianic Cult. 2006. (ENG., Illus.). 240p. pap. 14.95 *(978-0-86492-457-5(7))* Goose Lane Editions CAN. Dist: Univ. of Toronto Pr.

Barnes, Adilah. On My Own Terms. 2008. 304p. 29.99 *(978-1-4257-9033-2(X))*; pap. 19.99 *(978-1-4257-9008-0(9))* Xlibris Corp.

Barnett, Beverly James. For God & Country: Memoirs of a military Chaplain. 2008. 380p. pap. 19.99 *(978-1-60477-891-5(1))* Xulon Pr., Inc.

Barnette, Henke. Clarence Jordan Turning Dreams into Deeds. 10.00 *(978-0-687-82173-0(8))* Abingdon Pr.

Barrely, Christine & Chronicle Books Staff. The Little Book of Saints. 2011. (ENG.). 192p. 19.95 *(978-0-8118-7747-3(7))* Chronicle Bks. LLC.

Barron, Lisa. Precious in His Sight: A Mother's Journey of Faith with Her Special Needs Child. 2008. 184p. pap. 15.95 *(978-0-595-48487-4(5))* iUniverse, Inc.

Barton, Cheryl. River of Delights: International Testimonies of God's Abundant Blessings. 2009. (Illus.). 96p. pap. *(978-1-59317-372-2(5))* Warner Pr. Pubs.

Basil. Against Eunomius. DelCogliano, Mark & Radde-Gallwitz, Andrew, trs. from GEC. 2011. 224p. 34.95 *(978-0-8132-0122-1(5))* Catholic Univ. of America Pr.

Batty, Otto. An Easy Dig Thru 39 Ancient Sites. 2007. 356p. per. 22.99 *(978-1-60266-597-2(4))* Xulon Pr., Inc.

Bauer, Carlene. Not That Kind of Girl: A Memoir. 2010. 288p. pap. 13.99 *(978-0-06-084055-6(2)*, HarperPerennial) HarperCollins Pubs.

Bauer, Ilona. God & I & Elvis. 2012. 384p. pap. 19.95 ***(978-0-533-16451-6(6))*** Vantage Pr., Inc.

Bausch, William J. An Anthology of Saints: Official, Unofficial, & Should-Be Saints. 2011. (ENG.). 226p. pap. 19.95 ***(978-1-58595-845-0(X))*** Twenty-Third Pubns./Bayard.

Bbib. His Purpose. 2008. 34p. pap. 9.00 *(978-0-8059-7372-3(9))* Dorrance Publishing Co., Inc.

Beam, T. A. Trevor's Song: The Miraculous True Story of God's Healing Power after a Tragic Farm Accident. 2009. 148p. pap. 14.99 *(978-0-924748-99-8(0))* Milestones International Publishers.

Beatty, J. Changing Step. Date not set. 160p. pap. 6.99 *(978-1-871676-68-6(1))* Christian Focus Pubns. GBR. Dist: Spring Arbor Distributors, Inc.

Beckwith, Francis J. Return to Rome: Confessions of an Evangelical Catholic. 2009. 144p. pap. 14.99 *(978-1-58743-247-7(1))* Brazos Pr.

Bedell-Kwiatkowski, Linda. The Kid from Saint Mary's Orphanage. 2008. 80p. pap. 15.99 *(978-1-4363-8413-1(3))* Xlibris Corp.

Beeston, Blanche W. Now My Servant: A Brief Biography of A Firstborn Son of Aaron. 2011. 216p. 44.95 ***(978-1-258-03444-3(1))*** Literary Licensing, LLC.

Beevers, John. St Teresa of Avil. 2011. 190p. 42.95 ***(978-1-258-02083-5(1))*** Literary Licensing, LLC.

Beldon, Kees. Wrestling with Adulthood: Unitarian Universalist Men Talk about Growing Up. 2008. xii, 166p. pap. 15.00 *(978-1-55896-534-8(3)*, Skinner Hse. Bks.) Unitarian Universalist Assn.

Bell, Steve & Bell, Valerie. Real Survivors. 182p. pap. 10.99 *(978-0-8307-3481-8(3)*, Regal Bks.) Gospel Light Pubns.

Bellinger, Martha E. From Robe to Robe: A Lesbian's Spiritual Journey. 2010. 148p. (ENG.). 23.95 *(978-1-4269-3349-3(5))*; pap. 13.95 *(978-1-4269-3348-6(7))* Trafford Publishing.

Belmonte, Kevin. D. L. Moody, 0 vols. 2010. (Christian Encounters Ser.). 208p. pap. 12.00 *(978-1-59555-047-7(X))* Nelson, Thomas Inc.

Beltran, Helen Marie. Always a Sister. 2011. 136p. 29.99 ***(978-1-4628-7357-9(X))***; pap. 19.99 ***(978-1-4628-7356-2(1))*** Xlibris Corp.

Bemis, Alma. Engraved. 2009. 80p. pap. 10.99 *(978-1-60791-106-7(X))* Xulon Pr., Inc.

Bengtson, Jonathan & Earnshaw, Gabrielle, eds. Turning the Wheel: Henri Nouwen & Our Search for God. 2007. (Illus.). 256p. pap. 20.00 *(978-1-57075-727-3(5))* Orbis Bks.

Bennett, John Scott. Milton J. Stewart: A Man of the Spirit. 2009. 324p. pap. 18.99 *(978-1-60791-192-0(2))* Xulon Pr., Inc.

Bennett, Winston. Fight for Your Life: From tragedy to Triumph. 2011. pap. 28.99 *(978-1-61739-666-3(4))* Tate Publishing & Enterprises, LLC.

Benoit, Cathleen. Simply Calling: A Memoir of My Life in Christ. 2007. 120p. per. 12.95 *(978-0-595-45219-4(1))* iUniverse, Inc.

Benson, Kristina. God, Prayer, & Sarah Palin. 2008. 148p. pap. 16.95 *(978-1-60332-062-7(8))* Equity Pr.

Benton, Josephine Moffett. Saints & Mystics. 2011. 76p. 36.95 ***(978-1-258-02038-5(6))*** Literary Licensing, LLC.

Berg, Glenn. If I Quit... Satan Wins. 2009. 143p. pap. 12.97 *(978-0-557-07631-4(5))* Lulu Enterprises Inc.

Berhane, Asfaw D. Heaven Is Empty, Hell Is Full: A Revelation of Heaven & Hell. 2008. (ENG.). 144p. pap. 10.99 *(978-1-59979-399-3(7)*, Creation Hse.) Charisma Media.

Berlanga, Richard Sotelo. Our Final Hour: A Vision of the Future. 2008. 76p. pap. 15.00 *(978-1-4327-3111-3(4))* Outskirts Pr., Inc.

Berrigan, Daniel. To Dwell in Peace: An Autobiography. 2007. (Daniel Berrigan Reprint Ser.). 364p. pap. 40.00 *(978-1-55635-473-1(8))* Wipf & Stock Pubs.

Berry, Gary Lee. A Handicapped Cowboy's Story. 2010. 112p. pap. 10.99 *(978-1-4490-9555-0(0))* AuthorHouse.

Berry, Glenn. Darn It! Maybe I Missed Something! Musings of a Spiritually Challenged Redneck. 2011. pap. 12.99 *(978-1-61663-920-4(2))* Tate Publishing & Enterprises, LLC.

Berthelson, Sarah. Only by His Grace. 2007. 116p. per. 10.99 *(978-1-60266-769-3(1))* Xulon Pr., Inc.

Beuerlein, Drew. Catching Grace: Understanding God's Grace in Everyday Life. l.t. ed. 2012. (ENG.). 110p. (YA). 15.95 ***(978-0-9744617-7-9(6)***, RICHER Pubns.) Richer Life, LLC.

Beukes, Wynand. The Kings Handbook. 2009. 227p. pap. 24.58 *(978-1-4092-9450-4(1))* Lulu Enterprises Inc.

Bevier, Bob. Our Journey Through Cancer with God: No Subtitle. 2008. 96p. pap. 9.99 *(978-1-60647-597-3(5))* Xulon Pr., Inc.

Bewes, Cecil. Letters with Love. 2011. (ENG.). 384p. 19.99 ***(978-1-84550-739-8(8))*** Christian Focus Pubns. GBR. Dist: STL Distribution North America.

Beyer, Susan Meredith. Above Reality: Where Miracles Happen & Healing Begins. 2007. 230p. pap. 14.95 *(978-0-9764822-8-4(2))* Beyer Printing, Inc.

Binion, William Lavon. Diary of a Dead Beat Dad. 2009. 248p. 25.99 *(978-1-60791-472-3(7))*; pap. 15.99 *(978-1-60791-471-6(9))* Xulon Pr., Inc.

Birai, A. B. S. A. L. O. M. Except for the Lord. 2008. 184p. pap. 14.95 *(978-0-9795851-9-7(8))* Sahel Bks. Inc.

Biros, Zushka. God Knocked Me off My Bike: My personal journey through marriage, divorce, struggle, addiction, & Suicide, 1 vol. 2010. 150p. pap. 24.95 *(978-1-4489-4911-3(4))* PublishAmerica, Inc.

Black, Barry C. From the Hood to the Hill: A Story of Overcoming, 0 vols. 2006. 240p. 22.99 *(978-0-7852-1881-4(5))* Nelson, Thomas Inc.

Blackman, Lora. Suffering in Silence: How I Overcame Guilt & Condemnation after Abortion. 2010. 48p. pap. 9.95 *(978-1-61507-188-3(1))* Cross Bks. Publishing.

Blackmer, Robert B. Miracles from God, 1 vol. 2009. 143p. pap. 24.95 *(978-1-4489-9136-5(6))* PublishAmerica, Inc.

Blackmore, Cindy. The Journal of Our Journey: Five Years with Doc & Cindy Blackmore. 2011. 774p. 47.99 ***(978-1-61379-034-2(1))***; pap. 31.99 ***(978-1-61379-009-0(0))*** Xulon Pr., Inc.

Blight, Wendy & Moody Publishing Staff. Hidden Joy in a Dark Corner: The Transforming Power of God's Story, 1 vol. 2009. (ENG.). 208p. pap. 13.99 *(978-0-8024-1496-0(6))* Moody Pubs.

Blocker, Teresa. How Can I Live. 2008. 88p. pap. 9.99 *(978-1-60477-977-6(2))* Xulon Pr., Inc.

Blue, L. My Affair with Christianity. 164p. *(978-0-340-66906-8(3)*, Hodder & Stoughton) Hodder General Publishing Div.

Bock, Lewis L. To Know This Mystery: A Doctor's Life-Changing Prescription Written in Poetic Verse. 2010. pap. 13.99 *(978-1-60799-940-9(4))* Tate Publishing & Enterprises, LLC.

Bockmann, Melanie. UnRapped: The Myers Brothers Flip from Fame to Glory. 2007. *(978-0-8280-2073-2(6))* Review & Herald Publishing Assn.

Boerop, Joy K. Joy in Living: A Memoir of an MK, an MW & an MM. 2010. 340p. 37.99 *(978-1-4141-1644-0(6))*; pap. 19.99 *(978-1-4141-1569-6(5))* Pleasant Word.

Boersma, David. Prophets of the Bible. 2008. 388p. 29.99 *(978-1-4257-3849-5(4))*; pap. 19.99 *(978-1-4257-3848-8(6))* Xlibris Corp.

Bolshakoff, Sergius. Russian Mystics. 2009. Orig. Title: I Mistici Russi. 334p. 16.00 *(978-1-60724-144-7(7))* Gorgias Pr., LLC.

Bomgaars, Sharon. In His Feathers: The Letters & Journals of Sharon Bomgaars 1956-2002. Schaap, James, ed. 2006. (Illus.). 280p. per. 18.00 *(978-0-932914-68-2(3))* Dordt College Pr.

Bonds, Charles L. Ain't That Something? The Musings, Adventures, & Experiences of a Southern Country Boy Reflecting over Forty-Nine Years of

Pastoral Ministry. 2009. 136p. 23.95 *(978-1-4401-4331-1(5))*; pap. 13.95 *(978-1-4401-4333-5(1))* Universe, Inc.

Bonilla, German Y. Gloria. Esperanza Despues Del Dolor: Porque Todas Las Cosas Ayudan para Bien. 2010. 116p. pap. 12.95 *(978-1-4502-2351-5(6))* iUniverse, Inc.

Bornstein, Kate. A Queer & Pleasant Danger: The True Story of a Nice Jewish Boy Who Joins the Church of Scientology & Leaves Twelve Years Later to Become the Lovely Lady She Is Today. 2012. (ENG.). 280p. pap. 24.95 ***(978-0-8070-0165-3(1))*** Beacon Pr.

Bost, John R. Repo: The Church in Foreclosure. 2009. 156p. pap. 14.99 *(978-1-61579-081-4(0))* Xulon Pr., Inc.

Bowen, Wendy. Confessions of a Recovering Type A. 2010. 282p. 19.95 *(978-0-615-34642-7(1))* New Street, Inc.

Bowie, Terry F. Experiences & Prejudices: A memoir dealing with both; endeavoring to Understand. 2009. 220p. pap. 19.99 *(978-1-4500-1335-2(X))* Xlibris Corp.

Bowman, Bj. From Desolation to Restoration. 2011. 76p. pap. 19.95 ***(978-1-4626-2232-0(1))*** PublishAmerica, Inc.

Bowman, K. R. Testify: How I got to here from There. 2009. 184p. pap. 16.95 *(978-1-4401-2854-7(5))* iUniverse, Inc.

Boylan, Bill. Him N Me. 2011. 294p. pap. 16.99 ***(978-1-61379-635-1(8))*** Xulon Pr., Inc.

Braboy, Cynthia. God's Masterpiece: Suffering in Silence. 2007. 252p. per. 19.95 *(978-0-615-17736-6(0))* Braboy, Cynthia Enterprise.

Bracken M.S.W. C.P.C., Robert A. God Doesn't Want This Boy to Die: A Mother's Appeal that Was Heard & Granted by God! 2010. 244p. pap. 15.45 *(978-1-4490-7099-1(X))* AuthorHouse.

Brady, Larry. Undiagnosed: Losing the Son I Didn't Know. 2011. pap. 18.99 *(978-1-61739-446-1(7))* Tate Publishing & Enterprises, LLC.

Brake, Jacqueline. The Victim of Abuse. 2008. 132p. per. 12.95 *(978-1-4327-1507-6(0))* Outskirts Pr., Inc.

Braschler, Todd & Laffoon, Jill. Common Bond. 2007. (Illus.). 128p. 13.99 incl. audio compact disk *(978-0-89221-679-6(4))* New Leaf Pr., Inc.

Breaking Through Poverty with a Spiritual Heart: A Biblical Understanding of Ourselves. 2007. 204p. per. 16.99 *(978-1-59886-922-4(1))* Tate Publishing & Enterprises, LLC.

Bredi, Richardette. A Nu You. 2011. 272p. 25.99 ***(978-1-61379-613-9(7))*** Xulon Pr., Inc.

Brendel, Doug. Why I Quit the Church. 2011. 248p. pap. 19.95 ***(978-0-557-36810-0(6))*** Lulu Enterprises Inc.

Brewer, James D. Broken Soldiers: The Making of Heroes. 2011. 194p. pap. 24.95 ***(978-1-4626-4123-9(7))*** PublishAmerica, Inc.

Brewer, Melvin. My Beloved Winkie. 2006. 160p. per. 12.95 *(978-0-9777558-4-4(3))* Rogers Publishing & Consulting, Inc.

Brewin, Patricia Jane. The Diary of A Christian: The Evangelism of A Soul, & Other Life Lessons. 2011. (ENG.). 210p. pap. 22.95 ***(978-1-4327-6355-8(5))*** Outskirts Pr., Inc.

Brewster, Joy. Diminishment: A Memoir. 2011. 19.95 ***(978-1-894667-88-3(3))*** Clements Publishing.

Brice, Genea Sheles. Weaned in the Desert: Souvenirs from Sacred Seasons with My Savior. 2010. 134p. pap. 14.99 *(978-1-61579-727-1(0))* Xulon Pr., Inc.

Brief Memoir of the Late Rezeau Brown, A. M. 2010. pap., pap. 19.96 *(978-1-61143-165-0(4))* Gorgias Pr., LLC.

Briggs, Carolyn S. Higher Ground: A Memoir of Salvation Found & Lost. 2011. (ENG.). 320p. pap. 16.95 ***(978-1-4422-1438-5(4))*** Rowman & Littlefield Publishers, Inc.

Briscoe, Stuart. Flowing Streams. 1 vol. 2008. (ENG.). 208p. pap. 16.99 *(978-0-310-27719-4(1))* Zondervan.

Broadbooks, Bob. How to Bless Your Pastor: Stories of Uncommon Graces. 2010. (ENG.). 128p. pap. 8.99 *(978-0-8341-2551-3(X))*, 9780834125513) Beacon Hill Pr. of Kansas City.

Broadman and Holman Publishers Staff. Tough-Minded Christianity: Legacy of John Warwick Montgomery. 1 vol. Dembski, William & Schirrmacher, Thomas, eds. 2009. (ENG.). 800p. pap. 31.99 *(978-0-8054-4783-5(0)*, B&H Academic) B&H Publishing Group.

Broadway, Anna. Sexless in the City: A Memoir of Reluctant Chastity. 2008. (ENG.). 320p. pap. 12.95 *(978-0-385-51839-0(0)*, Galilee Trade) Doubleday Religious Publishing Group, The.

Brodhagen, Diana. My Pastor My Husband: Smiles & Tears from the Other Side of the Pulpit. 2009. (ENG.). 144p. 12.95 *(978-0-9824145-0-7(1))* Lifebridge Bks.

Brooks, Nevia. He Wouldn't Let It Be So. 2008. 53p. pap. 16.95 *(978-1-60563-628-3(2))* PublishAmerica, Inc.

Brooks, Susie A. He Really Is My Father. 2006. 192p. pap. 16.99 *(978-1-4141-0491-1(X))* Pleasant Word.

Broussard, Ronsard P. A Touch of Heaven on Earth: At the Crossroads of Life. 2011. 64p. pap. 15.49 ***(978-1-4567-6317-6(2))*** AuthorHouse.

Brown, Betty C. The Journey, Book: A Story of the Exodus. 2008. 156p. pap. 14.95 *(978-0-9724586-5-8(4))* PearlStone Publishing, Inc.

Brown-Burns, Shirley. Walking with My Father: An Incredible Journey of Faith. 2009. 236p. pap. 15.99 *(978-1-60791-787-8(4))* Xulon Pr., Inc.

Brown, L. Duane & Nelsen, T. Mark. Forgotten Lay Leaders. 2011. 136p. pap. 11.99 ***(978-0-9832039-8-8(9))*** Faithful Life Pubs.

Brown, Mamie Dell. Born to Be a Blessing. 2009. 32p. pap. 12.99 *(978-1-4490-3575-4(2))* AuthorHouse.

Brown, Nadine. 1000 Flowers for You. 2011. 48p. pap. 21.99 ***(978-1-4535-9106-2(0))*** Xlibris Corp.

Brown, Phyllis Kennedy. His "Time of Refreshing, Behind the Seen! Reflections from the Life of an Ordinary Woman Whom God Loves! 2008. 284p. pap. 15.99 *(978-1-60647-366-5(2))* Xulon Pr., Inc.

Brown, Stephanie. Grace Growing Up. 2007. 96p. per. *(978-1-55452-242-2(0)*, Guardian Bks.) Essence Publishing.

Brown, Terwana J. Living My Life in Reverse. 2009. 96p. pap. 14.99 *(978-0-557-13412-0(9))* Lulu Enterprises Inc.

Brown, Tricia Gates. Jesus Loves Women: A Memoir of Body & Spirit. 2011. 266p. pap. 15.95 ***(978-1-931038-91-1(0)***, DreamSeeker Bks.) Cascadia Publishing Hse., LLC.

Bruce, James. Prophecy, Miracles, Angels, & Heavenly Light? The Eschatology, Pneumatology, & Missiology of Adomnan's Life of Columbus. 2007. (Studies in Christian History & Thought Ser.). 312p. pap. 31.00 *(978-1-59752-731-6(9)*, Wipf and Stock) Wipf & Stock Pubs.

Brunsvik, Ruth Bohling. A Life Lived in Faith. 2011. 176p. pap. 13.95 ***(978-1-4497-1896-1(5)***, WestBow Pr.) Author Solutions, Inc.

Bruschi, Giovanni. I Need You. 2008. 180p. 22.99 *(978-1-60647-571-3(1))*; pap. 14.99 *(978-1-60647-570-6(3))* Xulon Pr., Inc.

Bryan, Matthew. Desperation. 2010. 96p. pap. 9.99 *(978-0-578-01948-2(5))* Bryan, Matthew.

Bryant, Tommy. A Thug Cop's Redemption. 2011. 102p. pap. 10.99 ***(978-1-61379-130-1(5))*** Xulon Pr., Inc.

Buck, Bryant. The Prayer Warrior. 2007. 184p. per. 13.99 *(978-1-60266-535-4(4))* Xulon Pr., Inc.

Buckingham, Jaime. El Fin del Indomito Johnson: The End of Youngblood Johnson. (SPA.). 240p. *(978-84-7228-423-4(9)*, 360200) Clie, Editorial.

Buds on the Vine. 2007. 148p. per. 11.99 *(978-1-59886-541-7(2))* Tate Publishing & Enterprises, LLC.

Bullock, John & Crabb, David. Hms Life. 2007. 260p. per. 15.99 *(978-1-60477-205-0(0))* Xulon Pr., Inc.

Bunyan, John. Grace Abounding: With Other Spiritual Autobiographies. Stachniewski, John & Pacheco, Anita, eds. 2008. (Oxford World's Classics Ser.). (ENG.). 336p. pap. 11.95 *(978-0-19-955498-0(6))* Oxford Univ. Pr., Inc.

—Grace Abounding to the Chief of Sinners. 2008. 148p. 21.99 *(978-0-559-79474-2(6))*; 148p. pap. 20.75 *(978-0-559-79472-8(X))*; 152p. 21.99 *(978-0-554-37023-1(9))*; 152p. 24.99 *(978-0-554-27720-2(4))* BiblioBazaar.

—Grace Abounding to the Chief of Sinners. 2007. (Authentic Original Classic Ser.). 173p. per. 13.99 *(978-0-7684-2457-7(7))* Destiny Image Pubs.

—Grace Abounding to the Chief of Sinners. 2007. (ENG.). 88p. per. *(978-1-4068-2294-6(9))* Echo Library.

—Grace Abounding to the Chief of Sinners. 2007. (Hendrickson Christian Classics Ser.). 165p. 9.95 *(978-1-59856-142-5(1))*; 6.97 *(978-1-59856-206-4(1))* Hendrickson Pubs. Marketing, LLC.

—Grace Abounding to the Chief of Sinners. 2007. per. 9.99 *(978-1-4245-0793-1(6))* Treasures Media Inc.

—Grace Abounding to the Chief of Sinners: In a Faithful Account of the Life & Death of John Bunyan. 2007. 244p. (ENG.). 24.95 *(978-1-60206-458-4(X))*; per. 10.95 *(978-1-60206-457-7(1))* Cosimo, Inc.

—La Peregrina: Christiana's Journey.Tr. of Pilgrim's Progress. (SPA.). 200p. *(978-84-7228-561-3(8)*, 220683) Clie, Editorial.

—The Riches of Bunyan. 2007. (ENG.). pap. *(978-1-4065-1429-2(2))* Dodo Pr.

Burke, Leanne. The Fight of My Life the Purpose of My Pain. 2009. 156p. 23.50 *(978-1-60860-030-4(0)*, Strategic Bk. Publishing) AEG Literary Publishing Services, Inc.

Burns, Zorina A. Tattoo Love. 2009. 96p. pap. 10.99 *(978-1-60791-781-6(5))* Xulon Pr., Inc.

Burnside, Houston M. A Pew-Sitter's Search for God. 2010. 156p. 22.49 *(978-1-4520-4606-8(9))*; pap. 14.99 *(978-1-4520-4607-5(7))* AuthorHouse.

Burrows, Elizabeth MacDonald. Mystic Voyage: Gateway to Immortality. 2007. 320p. pap. 19.95 *(978-1-59663-527-2(4)*, Seaboard Pr.) Rock, James A. & Co. Pubs.

Burrows, William & Gornick, Mark, eds. Understanding World Christianity. 2011. 240p. pap. *(978-1-57075-949-9(9))* Orbis Bks.

Burton Mains. Dialogando Con Dios: Karen Karen. (SPA.). 224p. *(978-84-7228-571-2(5)*, 220279) Clie, Editorial.

Burwell, Clint F. A Wretch Like Me. 2006. 102p. per. 9.99 *(978-1-59886-545-5(5))* Tate Publishing & Enterprises, LLC.

Bus, Anthony. A Mother's Plea: Lifting the Veil in Sanctuary. 2008. (ENG., Illus.). 317p. per. 16.95 *(978-1-59614-184-1(0))* Marian Pr.

Butler, Alban, et al, contrib. by. Butler's Lives of the Saints. rev. ed. (Illus.). 1p. *(978-0-86012-250-0(6)*, Burns & Oates) Continuum International Publishing Group, Ltd.

Butts, Courtney E. Inside My Head. 2008. pap. *(978-1-934363-13-3(8))* Zoe Life Publishing.

Byford, Jovan. Denial & Repression of Anti-Semitism: Post-Communist Rehabilitation of the Serbian Bishop Nikolaj Velimirovic. 2008. (ENG.). 200p. 35.00 *(978-963-9776-15-9(7))* Central European Univ. Pr.

Bythewood, Lisa. Waiting on the Promise. 2011. pap. 7.99 ***(978-1-61739-618-2(4))*** Tate Publishing & Enterprises, LLC.

C. M. Lantz. Drawing Closer to the Father's Heart: A Journey through the Lord's Prayer. 2009. 124p. pap. 13.95 *(978-1-4389-1872-3(0))* AuthorHouse.

Cabaniss, Allen, tr. from LAT. Benedict of Aniane: the Emperor's Monk: Ardo's Life. 2008. (Cistercian Studies). (Illus.). 112p. pap. 13.95 *(978-0-87907-320-6(9))* Cistercian Pubns., Inc.

Cady, G. Scott & Webber, Christopher L. A Year with American Saints. 2006. 650p. per. 30.00 *(978-0-89869-530-4(9))* Church Publishing, Inc.

Cain, Hamilton. This Boy's Faith: Notes from a Southern Baptist Upbringing. 2011. 272p. 25.00 *(978-0-307-46394-4(X)*, Crown) Crown Publishing Group.

Cairns, John. Principal Cairns. 2008. 136p. 24.99 *(978-0-554-27102-6(8))* 2008. 136p. 21.99 *(978-0-554-36405-6(0))* 2007. (ENG.). 122p. pap. 18.99 *(978-1-4346-2528-1(1))* 2007. (ENG.). 132p. pap. 19.99 *(978-1-4346-2544-1(3))* BiblioBazaar.

—Principal Cairns. 2009. 124p. pap. *(978-1-4099-2196-7(4))* Dodo Pr.

—Principal Cairns. 2007. (ENG.). 88p. per. *(978-1-4068-4157-2(9))* Echo Library.

Came, David. Pope Benedict's Divine Mercy Mandate. 2009. (ENG.). 88p. pap. 6.95 *(978-1-59614-203-9(0))* Marian Pr.

Cameron, Kirk. Still Growing: An Autobiography. 2008. (ENG., Illus.). 256p. 22.99 *(978-0-8307-4451-0(7))* Gospel Light Pubns.

Campbell, Iain D. & Campbell, Iain D. Fixing the Indemnity: The Life & Work of Sir George Adam Smith (1856-1942) 2007. (Paternoster Theological Monographs: Ser.). 292p. pap. 31.00 *(978-1-59752-741-5(6)*, Wipf and Stock) Wipf & Stock Pubs.

Campbell, Mary. Carried in His Arms. 2006. 224p. per. 12.99 *(978-0-9759049-7-8(3))* Master Pr.

Campbell, Susan. Dating Jesus: A Story of Fundamentalism, Feminism, & the American Girl. 2010. (ENG.). 224p. pap. 16.00 *(978-0-8070-1072-3(3))* Beacon Pr.

Cannings, Mable L. The Heart & Soul of Business: One Woman's Journey. 2008. 248p. pap. 14.99 *(978-1-60647-345-0(X))* Xulon Pr., Inc.

Cannon, Janice. A Soul in Peril. 2006. 232p. pap. 24.95 *(978-1-4241-5127-1(9))* PublishAmerica, Inc.

Canon, Patrick K. The Light of the World. 2010. 56p. pap. 10.49 *(978-1-4520-2636-7(X))* AuthorHouse.

Cantrell, Doyne. Living with Consequences - BOOK ONE - 2009. 144p. pap. 16.95 *(978-0-557-08230-8(7))* Lulu Enterprises Inc.

Cantu, Anita C. My Life Under His Wing. 2007. per. *(978-1-60458-190-4(5))* Instant Pub.

Carelli, Paulette E. A Basket Full of Miracles. 2010. ***(978-1-77069-134-6(0))*** Word Alive Pr.

Carey-Miller, Di'Anne. Jail Bait. 2009. 88p. pap. 15.99 *(978-1-4415-2144-6(5))* Xlibris Corp.

Cariello, Andrew. Going Through Life with the Angels. 2011. 52p. pap. 12.99 *(978-1-4567-2773-4(7))* AuthorHouse.

Carole, Barbara. Twelve Stones: Notes on a Miraculous Journey - A Memoir. 2009. (ENG.). 320p. 22.99 *(978-0-8307-4606-4(4))* Gospel Light Pubns.

Carolyn Rathbun-Sutton with Delmar Mock & Carolyn Rathbun-Sutton with Delmar Mock. Fool's Gold: Chronicles of a Country Doctor. 2009. 124p. pap. 13.95 *(978-1-4401-8526-7(3))* iUniverse, Inc.

Caron Gagnon, Phyllis May & Hubele, Michelle, eds. Walking with the Living God: Real people. A real God. 2009. 224p. 18.99 *(978-0-9819662-0-5(9))* Bugle Bks. LLC.

Carpenter, Kim & Carpenter, Krickett. The Vow: The True Events that Inspired the Movie. I.t. ed. 2012. (ENG.). 208p. pap. 17.99 ***(978-1-59415-420-1(1))*** Cengage Gale.

Carpenter, Kim, et al. The Vow: The True Events that Inspired the Movie. 2012. (ENG., Illus.). 208p. pap. 14.99 ***(978-1-4336-7579-9(X)***, B&H Bks.) B&H Publishing Group.

Carroll, James. Practicing Catholic. 2009. (ENG.). 400p. 28.00 *(978-0-618-67018-5(1))* Houghton Mifflin Harcourt Trade & Reference Pubs.

Carroll, L. Patrick. The Right Place for Love: Memories in Interesting Times. 2011. 210p. pap. 19.99 ***(978-1-4653-5569-0(3))*** Xlibris Corp.

Carslaw, William H. The Life & Letters of James Renwick: The Last Scottish Martyr. 2009. 280p. pap. 20.00 *(978-1-59925-204-9(X))* Solid Ground Christian Bks.

Carson, Teresea. Act Yesterday: A Journey of Personal Growth. 2011. 154p. pap. 24.95 ***(978-1-4560-9100-2(X))*** PublishAmerica, Inc.

Carswell, D. J. Live Wires: Powerful Stories of Changed Lives. 2008. (ENG.). 208p. 16.99 *(978-1-85078-737-2(9))* Authentic Media.

Carter, Anthony J., ed. Glory Road: The Journeys of 10 African-Americans into Reformed Christianity. 2009. (Illus.). 192p. pap. 15.99 *(978-1-4335-0584-3(3))* Crossway.

Carter, Gloria J. A Heart to Live in Troubled Times: Psalms of Exhortation & Comfort. 2010. pap. 12.99 *(978-1-61663-149-9(X))* Tate Publishing & Enterprises, LLC.

Carter, Pat Harold. God Gave Me a Rhyme: Adventuring with God. 2009. 324p. 29.95 *(978-1-4401-2455-6(8))*; pap. 19.95 *(978-1-4401-2453-2(1))* iUniverse, Inc.

Carter, Sydney. Rock of Doubt. 2006. (ENG., Illus.). 104p. 21.95 *(978-0-8264-9355-2(6))* Continuum International Publishing Group, Ltd. GBR. Dist: National Bk. Network.

Carty, Austin. High Points & Lows: Life, Faith, & Figuring It All Out. 2010. (ENG.). 208p. (gr. 12-18). 14.00 *(978-0-452-29580-3(7)*, Plume) Penguin Group (USA) Inc.

Cash Tate, Kimberly. More Christian Than African-American: And Other Ways Jesus Turned My Life Upside Down. 2008. (ENG.). 176p. pap. 13.99 *(978-1-933204-84-0(2))* Deep River Bks.

Casten, Robbie L. Hope for the Heart. 2011. 124p. 19.99 ***(978-1-61379-553-8(X))***; pap. 11.99 ***(978-1-61379-552-1(1))*** Xulon Pr., Inc.

Cayce, Richard. Finding God: Secret Messages of the Bib. 2006. 503p. pap. 34.95 *(978-1-4241-0168-9(9))* PublishAmerica, Inc.

Chadwick, Henry. Augustine of Hippo: A Life. 2009. (ENG.). 160p. 19.95 *(978-0-19-956830-7(8))* Oxford Univ. Pr., Inc.

Chandler, Bukeka. A Prophetic Love Letter: Invitation to A Love Promised to Be Fulfilled. 2011. pap. 11.99 ***(978-1-61346-109-9(7))*** Tate Publishing & Enterprises, LLC.

Chapman, Geraldine. Dressed Like Your Father: A Battered Wife's Story of Survival. 2007. 192p. per. *(978-1-55452-220-0(X)*, Guardian Bks.) Essence Publishing.

Chapman, Jimmie L. The Road to Kingston Springs. 2010. 129p. pap. 18.16 *(978-0-557-27656-1(X))* Lulu Enterprises Inc.

Chapman, Mary Beth & Vaughn, Ellen. Choosing to SEE: A Journey of Struggle & Hope. 2011. pap. 16.99 *(978-0-8007-2085-8(7))* 2010. (Illus.). 288p. 21.99 *(978-0-8007-1991-3(3))* 2010. (Illus.). 288p. pap. 13.99 *(978-0-8007-1992-0(1))* Revell.

Charles, Apostle Wislet. Hell Is Real. 2011. 56p. pap. 15.00 ***(978-1-4634-0263-1(5))*** AuthorHouse.

Charlick, Richard. Mission Possible. 2010. 446p. pap. 22.99 *(978-1-60957-084-2(7))* Xulon Pr., Inc.

Chase, Gloria. Courage under Fire. 2007. 60p. pap. 10.95 *(978-0-9796180-4-8(5))* Williams, Benjamin Publishing.

Chastain, Dolorette. The Not Rich & Famous down South. 2008. 80p. pap. 15.99 *(978-1-4363-1655-2(3))* Xlibris Corp.

Chastang, Sirena. The Miracle Child. 2010. 88p. pap. *(978-1-55452-590-4(X)*, Guardian Bks.) Essence Publishing.

Chenoweth, Kristin. A Little Bit Wicked: Life, Love, & Faith in Stages. 2010. (ENG., Illus.). 256p. pap. 15.00 *(978-1-4165-8056-0(5)*, Touchstone) Touchstone.

Chesnut, M. Kathleen. Dancing into Joy: A spiraling Easter Dance. 2006. pap. 14.95 *(978-0-9785090-0-2(5))* DewSpirit Publishing.

Chestnut, Bobbie Jean. Whew How Did I Ever Do It? 2008. 152p. 22.99 *(978-1-60647-858-5(3))* Xulon Pr., Inc.

Chestnut, Bobby Jean. Whew How Did I Ever Do It? 2008. 152p. pap. 14.99 *(978-1-60647-857-8(5))* Xulon Pr., Inc.

Chichester, George. Recipe for A Happy Life: The Main Ingredient Is God... . Then Add A Lot of Love. 2010. pap. 14.99 *(978-1-61579-782-0(3))* Xulon Pr., Inc.

Chikane, Frank. No Life of My Own: An Autobiography. 2010. 158p. pap. 18.00 *(978-1-60899-287-4(X)*, Wipf and Stock) Wipf & Stock Pubs.

Chilson, A. J. A J Chilson: A Poet in Transition. 2011. 30p. pap. 16.95 ***(978-1-4626-0950-5(3))*** PublishAmerica, Inc.

Chin, Peter. Reflections on Revelations. Mourey, Edie, ed. 2011. 276p. pap. 16.99 ***(978-0-9837561-1-8(2))*** Furrow Pr.

Chisholm, Robert B., Jr. & Chisholm, Robert B. A Workbook for Intermediate Hebrew: Grammar, Exegesis, & Commentary on Jonah & Ruth. 1 vol. 2006. (ENG & HEB.). 304p. pap. 21.99 *(978-0-8254-2390-1(2))* Kregel Pubns.

Choate, Stanley. Battle for the Mind: Psychological Warfare. 2007. (Illus.). 88p. *(978-1-55452-186-9(6))* Essence Publishing.

Christian, Carolyn T. I Could Not See God, but God Could See Me: It All Happened for a Reason. 2010. 324p. pap. 19.95 *(978-1-4502-2883-1(6))*; (ENG.). 29.95 *(978-1-4502-2884-8(4))* iUniverse, Inc.

Christie, Vance. John & Betty Stam: Missionary Martyr. 2008. (History Makers Ser.). (ENG.). 208p. pap. 13.99 *(978-1-84550-376-5(7))* Christian Focus Pubns. GBR. Dist: STL Distribution North America.

Chute, Anthony. Father Mercer: The Story of a Baptist Statesman. 2011. 160p. pap. 20.00 *(978-0-88146-262-3(4))* Mercer Univ. Pr.

Clapper, Colleen. The Raindrops on the Windshield Sound Like Popcorn. 2009. 112p. pap. 16.95 *(978-1-57921-971-0(3))* WinePress Publishing.

Clark, Barbara. Blessings Served on a Silver Platter. 2007. 100p. per. 16.95 *(978-1-4241-7968-8(8))* PublishAmerica, Inc.

Clark, Glenn. The Man Who Tapped the Secrets of the Universe. pap. 4.95 *(978-0-910924-10-8(4))* Macalester Park Publishing Co., Inc.

Clark, R. J. Teachings for the Heart: A Primer. 2008. 288p. pap. 15.99 *(978-1-60477-922-6(5))* Xulon Pr., Inc.

Clark, Tim. With God All Things Are Possible. 2011. 192p. pap. 14.95 ***(978-1-4575-0222-4(4))*** Dog Ear Publishing, LLC.

Clarke, Loris. Fresh Oil. 2008. 48p. pap. 15.99 *(978-1-4257-9946-5(9))* Xlibris Corp.

Claus, Mary T. Mary's Little Star. 2011. 111p. pap. 12.95 *(978-1-4327-7293-2(7))* Outskirts Pr., Inc.

Clay, Evelyn Sue. Wrapped up in Clovers: A Memoir of Love. 2011. pap. 12.99 ***(978-1-61346-508-0(4))*** Tate Publishing & Enterprises, LLC.

Cline, Cecil. Sunrise over Appalachi. 2006. 232p. per. 15.95 *(978-1-59858-205-5(4))* Dog Ear Publishing, LLC.

Clissold, Henry. The Last Hours of Eminent Christians: from the Commencement Of. 2007. (ENG.). 576p. per. 43.95 *(978-1-4304-4611-8(0))* Kessinger Publishing, LLC.

Clitheroe, Eleanor, ed. Women Rising: How Canadian Women Are Breaking Free from Criminal Pasts & Building a Better Future. 2007. (ENG.). 160p. pap. 17.95 *(978-0-9782221-2-3(1))* ECW Pr. CAN. Dist: Independent Pubs. Group.

Cloutier, Annette. Praey to God. 2011. 728p. 34.99 ***(978-1-4500-4238-3(4))***; pap. 23.99 ***(978-1-4363-1555-5(7))*** Xlibris Corp.

Cluff, Anthony T. In Search of the Great White God: From Big Bang to Coba & Beyond. 2010. 306p. 31.95 *(978-1-4327-4977-4(3))*; (ENG.). pap. 17.95 *(978-1-4327-4941-5(2))* Outskirts Pr., Inc.

Clutterbuck, Ivan. The Pelican in the Wilderness. 2008. (Illus.). 176p. pap. *(978-0-85244-621-8(7))* Gracewing, Ltd.

C

Coats Sr., Connie Ray. Society's Nobody Is God's Somebody. 2011. 190p. pap. 24.95 (978-1-4512-7855-2(1)) PublishAmerica, Inc.

Cobb, Nancy. Suitcase Carrier for God. 2007. 185p. pap. 24.95 (978-1-4241-9398-1(2)) PublishAmerica, Inc.

Cobble, Tara Leigh. Here's to Hindsight: Letters to My Former Self. 2006. 195p. per. 12.99 (978-0-9768175-9-8(4)) Relevant Media Group, Inc.

Cody, Lauren. Glass House: Confessions of a Pastor's Wife. 2006. 125p. pap. 19.95 (978-1-4241-5175-2(9)) PublishAmerica, Inc.

Coffey, Cara Ann. Uncovered No More: Clothed by God. 2011. pap. 16.99 (978-1-61739-555-0(2)) Tate Publishing & Enterprises, LLC.

Coffman, Harry E. Good Enough: Discovering the Secret of Your True Identity. 2011. 188p. 26.95 (978-1-4502-7593-4(1)); pap. 16.95 (978-1-4502-7592-7(3)) iUniverse, Inc.

Cofield, Ben. Threads of Miracles, 1 vol. 2010. 162p. pap. 24.95 (978-1-4489-4587-0(9)) PublishAmerica, Inc.

Cohen, Benyamin. My Jesus Year: A Rabbi's Son Wanders the Bible Belt in Search of His Own Faith. 2009. (ENG.). 240p. pap. 14.99 (978-0-06-124518-3(6), HarperOne) HarperCollins Pubs.

Coiner, Lewis. String. 2009. 108p. 10.99 (978-1-60696-063-9(6)) Tate Publishing & Enterprises, LLC.

Cole, Pastor Carolyn. My Life. 2010. 80p. pap. (978-1-4490-7524-8(X)) AuthorHouse.

Coleman, Alfred L. I Have a Dream Too: My Resume, 1 vol. 2009. (ENG.). 206p. pap. 24.95 (978-1-60703-773-6(4)) PublishAmerica, Inc.

Collier, Betty. Living Inside the Testimony: A Testimony of GOD's Amazing Love & Abundant Blessings. 2010. 112p. 27.99 (978-1-61507-117-3(2)); pap. 12.99 (978-1-61507-079-4(6)) Cross Bks. Publishing.

Collier, Phillip. Along the River. 2009. 220p. pap. 14.49 (978-1-4389-4684-9(8)) AuthorHouse.

Collins, Ace. I Saw Him in Your Eyes: Everyday People Making Extraordinary Impact in the Lives of Karen Kingsbury, Terri Blackstock, Bobby Bowden, Charlie Daniels, S. Truett Cathy, & More. l.t. ed. 2006. (Thorndike Inspirational Ser.). 245p. 27.95 (978-0-7862-8857-1(4)) Thorndike Pr.

Collins, Gary Tim. The Light That Illuminates the Flame: Make God Your Focus in Good Times & Bad. 2011. pap. 22.99 (978-1-61739-741-7(5)) Tate Publishing & Enterprises, LLC.

Collins, Z. D. A Will to Live: Can I Tell Your Story. 2011. 172p. 27.95 (978-1-4520-9151-8(X)); pap. 15.95 (978-1-4520-9152-5(8)) AuthorHouse.

Collyer, Robert. Father Taylor. 2009. 68p. pap. 13.99 (978-1-103-06891-3(1)) BiblioBazaar.

—Father Taylor. 2008. 68p. pap. 16.95 (978-1-4368-4525-0(4)) Kessinger Publishing, LLC.

Colter IV, Herman. From Tears to Laughter: Surviving Hard Times on Broken Pieces: Part Two, 1 vol. 2009. 79p. pap. 16.95 (978-1-61546-000-7(4)) PublishAmerica, Inc.

Corner, John. Life Through the Seasons: A Story Collection. 2009. 288p. pap. 20.95 (978-1-4401-2198-2(2)) iUniverse, Inc.

Comfort, Ray, compiled by. Wesley Gold: Pure. Refined. 2007. (Gold Ser.). (Illus.). 176p. 13.99 (978-0-88270-408-1(7)) Bridge-Logos Foundation.

Con Amor de Padre Pensamientos. (SPA.). 504p. 10.95 (978-958-607-407-0(2)) Sociedad de San Pablo ESP. Dist: St Pauls/Alba Hse. Pubs.

Conklin, Caroline. The Deacon Letters. 2007. 280p. per. 15.99 (978-1-60266-447-0(1)) Xulon Pr., Inc.

Contreras, Eli. And Then I Heard His Voice. 2010. pap. 15.99 (978-1-61579-555-0(3)) Xulon Pr., Inc.

Cook, David C., 3rd. Memoirs: David C. Cook, the Friend of the Sunday School. 2011. 164p. 41.95 (978-1-258-09323-5(5)) Literary Licensing, LLC.

Cook, Faith. Fearless Pilgrim: The Life & Times of John Bunyan. 2008. (Illus.). 528p. (978-0-85234-680-8(8)) Evangelical Pr.

—Overcoming the World. 2007. (Et Perspectives Ser.). (Illus.). 79p. per. (978-0-9500129-4-0(7)) Evangelical Times.

—Stars in God's Sky. 2009. (Illus.). 160p. pap. (978-0-85234-696-9(4)) Evangelical Pr.

Cook, William R. Lives of Great Christians. 2007. per. 34.95 (978-1-59803-331-1(X)) Teaching Co., LLC, The.

Cooper, Karen. Growing up Brown. 2007. 152p. per. 13.99 (978-1-60266-994-9(5)) Xulon Pr., Inc.

Cooper, Ken. Held Hostage: A Serial Bank Robber's Road to Redemption. 2009. 320p. pap. 14.99 (978-0-8007-9456-9(7)) Chosen Bks.

Copling-Holliday, Linda. Woman of God: A Dedicated Vessel: A Memoir. 2006. 109p. per. 12.95 (978-0-9786032-8-1(1)) Milligan Bks.

Corbliss, Matt. The Godyssey with Christ. 2010. 172p. pap. 15.95 (978-1-4401-9018-6(6)) iUniverse, Inc.

Corbly, Don. Pastor John Corbly. 2008. 336p. pap. 19.95 (978-1-4357-4755-5(0)) Lulu Enterprises Inc.

Corelli, Marie. The Master-Christian. 2008. 660p. 39.99 (978-0-554-28612-9(2)) 2008. 660p. 35.99 (978-0-554-37915-9(5)) 2007. 586p. pap. 30.99 (978-1-4346-5875-3(9)) 2007. (ENG.). 656p. pap. 34.99 (978-1-4346-5876-0(7)) BiblioBazaar.

—The Master-Christian. 2009. 480p. pap. (978-0-217-12449-2(6)) Books LLC.

—The Master-Christian. 2007. (ENG.). 592p. per. (978-1-4065-1543-5(4)) Dodo Pr.

Cornelius, Diane L. Diane's Story: From Darkness into the Light. 2008. 76p. pap. 10.95 (978-0-595-48455-3(7)) iUniverse, Inc.

Cornell, John J. Autobiography of John J Cornell Containi. 2006. pap. 40.95 (978-1-4286-5627-7(8)) Kessinger Publishing, LLC.

Cosby, Brian H. John Bunyan: The Journey of a Pilgrim. 2009. (ENG.). 160p. mass mkt. 8.99 (978-1-84550-458-8(5)) Christian Focus Pubns. GBR. Dist: STL Distribution North America.

Cosio, Deborah A. Adam's Rib Disorder: A Misconception of Submission. 2009. 188p. 24.99 (978-1-4490-0338-8(9)); pap. 14.99 (978-1-4490-0337-1(0)) AuthorHouse.

Cotton, Yolanda Atkins. Behind the Desert: The Making of a Christian Soldier. 2007. (ENG.). 96p. per. 11.95 (978-1-58736-838-7(2)) Wheatmark.

Cottrell, Dana George. Visions & Dreams: Prophetic Gifts of the Holy Spirit. 2011. 188p. 30.95 (978-1-4497-2149-7(4)); pap. 13.95 (978-1-4497-2148-0(6)) Author Solutions, Inc. (WestBow Pr.).

Coursen, Randy. Brighter Side of Darkness. 2006. pap. 9.99 (978-1-60034-849-5(1)) Xulon Pr., Inc.

Cowart, James D. Yes, God! The Adventures of First Time Missionaries. 2008. 125p. pap. 19.95 (978-1-60474-006-6(X)) PublishAmerica, Inc.

Cox, Bo Don. God Is Not in the Thesaurus: Stories from an Oklahoma Prison. (Illus.). 160p. pap. 3.95 (978-0-88028-214-7(2), 1552) Forward Movement Pubns.

Cox, Ruth Ann. No Scrip for my Journey, 48 vols. Pratt, William, ed. 2011. (Illus.). 456p. pap. 29.95 (978-1-884820-10-6(7)) SAFE GOODS/ATN Publishing.

Cozzutto, Velma. When Your Father Says Come with Me. 2006. 96p. per. (978-1-894928-81-6(4)) Word Alive Pr.

Craig, Rochelle Doan. The Twelve Years of Christmas: 1984-1995: the Hotly Contested Memoirs of A Slightly Sub-Normal, Rural Family Through the Use & Abuse of Those Dreaded Form Letters. 2011. 304p. 31.95 (978-1-4502-7456-2(0)); pap. 21.95 (978-1-4502-7455-5(2)) iUniverse, Inc.

Crandall, Chauncey W., IV. Raising the Dead: A Doctor Encounters the Miraculous. 2010. (ENG.). 224p. 19.99 (978-0-446-55720-7(X), 1319515) FaithWords.

Crane, Charlie. Image of a Black Father. 2007. 132p. (ENG.). 21.99 (978-1-60266-713-6(6)); per. 13.99 (978-1-60266-657-3(1)) Xulon Pr., Inc.

Crane, Demetrius M. A Love Affair with the Lord. 2012. (978-1-55452-769-4(4)) Essence Publishing.

Creation Speaks. 2007. per. 10.95 (978-1-59352-289-6(4)) Christian Services Publishing.

Croasmun, Becky. Legacy of Faith. 2011. 228p. pap. 15.95 (978-1-4620-3587-8(6)) iUniverse, Inc.

Crosby, Jean. I Too Touched the Hem of His Garment, 1 vol. 2009. 271p. pap. 27.95 (978-1-4241-8221-3(2)) PublishAmerica, Inc.

Croskell, Merle. My Life His Glory. 2011. 130p. pap. 19.99 (978-1-4568-8305-8(4)) Xlibris Corp.

Cross, Carlene. Fleeing Fundamentalism: A Minister's Wife Examines Faith. 2006. (ENG.). 288p. 23.95 (978-1-56512-498-1(7), 1565124987) Algonquin Bks. of Chapel Hill.

Cryer, Dan. Being Alive & Having to Die: The Spiritual Odyssey of Forrest Church. 2011. (ENG., Illus.). 368p. 27.99 (978-0-312-59943-0(9)) St. Martin's Pr.

Culwell, Glennon. My Life in the Potter's Hands. 2010. 223p. pap. 11.95 (978-1-4327-5818-9(7)) Outskirts Pr., Inc.

Cumming, James Elder. Holy Men of God: Dating Back to St. Augustine. 2011. 254p. 46.95 (978-1-258-02446-8(2)) Literary Licensing, LLC.

Cummins, D. Duane. Kenneth L. Teegarden: The Man, the Church, the Time. 2007. (Illus.). 240p. 20.00 (978-0-87565-339-6(1)) Texas Christian Univ. Pr.

Cundiff, Margaret. Called to Be Me. 5.00 (978-0-687-85112-6(2)) Abingdon Pr.

Cunningham, Joseph P. & Fleischmann, Ruth. Aloys Fleischmann (1880-1964) Immigrant Musician in Ireland. 2010. (Illus.). 420p. 69.00 (978-1-85918-462-2(6)) Cork Univ. Pr. IRL. Dist: Stylus Publishing, LLC.

Cunningham, Sarah. Picking Dandelions: A Search for Eden among Life's Weeds, 1 vol. 2010. (ENG.). 224p. pap. 14.99 (978-0-310-29247-0(6)) Zondervan.

Current, Richard C. Walking Through the Valley. 2010. 236p. 25.99 (978-1-60957-340-9(4)); pap. 25.99 (978-1-60957-339-3(0)) Xulon Pr., Inc.

Curtiss, Bev. From Coffee Shop to Coffee Shop. 2009. (ENG.). 304p. pap. 24.95 (978-1-58982-477-5(6), Millennial Mind Publishing) American Bk. Publishing Group.

Cushing, D. J. The Gift of Schizophrenia: A Testimony. 2010. 94p. pap. 20.95 (978-1-4327-6356-5(3)) Outskirts Pr., Inc.

Cymbala, Carol. He's Been Faithful: Trusting God to Do What Only He Can Do, 1 vol. 2010. (ENG.). 176p. pap. 14.99 (978-0-310-29339-2(1)) Zondervan.

Cynthia Kay Elias. From Knowledge to Revelation: My Testimony of God's Mercy & Grace. 2009. 176p. pap. 15.95 (978-1-4401-6219-0(0)) iUniverse, Inc.

Dabbs, Reggie. Reggie: You Can't Change Your Past, but You Can Change Your Future. 2011. 240p. pap. 15.99 (978-0-8499-4626-4(3)) Nelson, Thomas Inc.

Dahlberg, Rosemary Coplin. Gravel & Grit: Childhood Memories of Life on a Kansas Farm. 2010. 128p. pap. 12.99 (978-1-61507-111-1(3)) Cross Bks. Publishing.

Dailey, Howard & Pannell, Barbara. A Gentle Tug. 2011. 156p. 30.95 (978-1-4497-1337-9(8)); pap. 13.95 (978-1-4497-1335-5(1)) Author Solutions, Inc. (WestBow Pr.).

Dalbey, Gordon. No Small Snakes: A Journey into Spiritual Warfare, 0 vols. 2008. 368p. pap. 14.99 (978-0-8499-1984-8(3)) Nelson, Thomas Inc.

Dale, Thomas Pelham. A Life's Motto Illustrated by Biographical Examples by the Rev Thomas Pelham Dale with a Frontispiece by J D Watson. 2006. (Illus.). 356p. per. 26.99 (978-1-4255-3643-5(3)) MPublishing.

Dallin, Joseph. Perfect. 2009. 260p. pap. 15.95 (978-0-557-09130-0(6)) Lulu Enterprises Inc.

Dalton, Robert E. Learning to Receive from God. 2008. 116p. pap. 12.96 (978-1-4357-2523-2(9)) Lulu Enterprises Inc.

Daly, Jim. Finding Home: An Imperfect Path to Faith & Family. 2007. 224p. pap. 14.99 (978-0-7814-4866-6(2)) Cook, David C.

—Finding Home - Focus on the Family Edition: An Imperfect Path to Faith & Family. 2007. 232p. 22.99 (978-1-4347-9994-4(8)) Cook, David C.

Daly, Patricia. Chosen with the Circle of Angels: Here & Beyond, 1 vol. 2010. 54p. pap. 16.95 (978-1-60836-618-7(9)) PublishAmerica, Inc.

Daniels, Danny D. Danny D. Daniels - an Autobiography: Bridge to the Bible. 2007. per. 15.00 (978-0-9792016-1-5(6)) Milligan Bks.

Danzig, Daxx. From Acid to the Body of Christ: A Memoir. 2009. 256p. pap. 16.95 (978-1-60844-128-0(8)) Dog Ear Publishing, LLC.

Darden, Kelvin. Life Without Christ. 2011. 24p. 11.32 (978-1-4520-2794-4(3)) AuthorHouse.

Darlington, Gurmay. My Journey to Spiritual Restoration. 2010. 100p. pap. 12.95 (978-1-4327-5460-0(2)) Outskirts Pr., Inc.

Darroch, David & Alice. Feeding on His Faithfulness. 2006. pap. 17.99 (978-1-60034-478-7(X)) Xulon Pr., Inc.

Darrow, Estelle. Journey of the Pink Bracelet. 2007. 76p. per. 16.95 (978-1-60441-176-8(7)) PublishAmerica, Inc.

David C. Cook Publishing Company Staff. What We Want to Say to Grads, 1 vol. 2009. (ENG.). 112p. pap. 9.99 (978-1-4347-6791-2(4)) Cook, David C.

Davidson, Roy. God Is Real: Undeniable Proof That Will Change Your Life. 2008. (ENG.). 224p. 17.99 (978-1-59979-396-2(2), Creation Hse.) Charisma Media.

Davies, Gaius. Genius, Grief & Grace: A Doctor Looks at Suffering & Success. rev. ed. 2008. (ENG.). 384p. pap. 22.99 (978-1-84550-359-8(7)) Christian Focus Pubns. GBR. Dist: STL Distribution North America.

Davies, Haydn. A Night Out with the Boys. 2007. (ENG.). 208p. per. 14.99 (978-1-85078-735-8(2)) Authentic Media.

Davis, Elaine. Looking Inside Out. 2009. 388p. 32.99 (978-1-60791-330-6(5)); pap. 20.99 (978-1-60791-329-0(1)) Xulon Pr., Inc.

Davis, Evelyn Rose. Equipped to Serve: How God Used a Sinner's Journey Through the Fire to Grow the Kingdom. 2007. 96p. per. 9.99 (978-1-60247-338-6(2)) Tate Publishing & Enterprises, LLC.

Davis, Jean & Robertson, Ed. Keep on Keeping On. 2008. 312p. 27.99 (978-1-60647-061-9(2)) Xulon Pr., Inc.

—Keep on Keeping On: Two Parents & Their Son's Journey Through Addiction & Parents Journey to Justice. 2008. 312p. pap. 17.99 (978-1-60647-060-2(4)) Xulon Pr., Inc.

Davis, Linda. Flying Free: Answering God's Call to Freedom. 2007. 139p. per. 11.99 (978-1-59886-648-3(6)) Tate Publishing & Enterprises, LLC.

Davis, Robin E. Broken. 2009. 64p. pap. 11.99 (978-1-4389-8982-2(2)) AuthorHouse.

Davis, Stacie H. The House that Taft Built. 2010. 64p. pap. 10.99 (978-1-60957-363-8(3)) Xulon Pr., Inc.

Dawson, David C. The World Loves It's Own: Being a Christian Warrior During Troubled Times. 2009. 188p. 26.95 (978-0-595-51496-0(0)); pap. 16.95 (978-0-595-48981-7(8)) iUniverse, Inc.

Day, Dorothy & Ellsberg, Robert. The Duty of Delight: The Diaries of Dorothy Day. 2008. 669p. (978-0-87462-023-8(6)) Marquette Univ. Pr.

De Halleux, Andre. Philoxene de Mabbog: Sa Vie, Ses Ecrits, Sa Theologie. (Orthodoxies & Heresies in the Early Church Ser.). reprint ed. 64.50 (978-0-404-62387-6(5)) AMS Pr., Inc.

De Jong, James A. Henry J. Kuiper: Shaping the Christian Reformed Church, 1907-1962, Vol. 55. 2007. (Historical Series of the Reformed Church in America: No. 55). (Illus.). 270p. per. 28.00 (978-0-8028-2585-8(0)) Eerdmans, William B. Publishing Co.

de La Motte, Jeanne-Marie Bouvier. Autobiography of Madame Guyon. 2007. (Authentic Original Classic Ser.). 447p. per. 15.99 (978-0-7684-2529-1(8)) Destiny Image Pubs.

Deakin, Michelle Bates. Social Action Heroes: Unitarian Universalists Who Are Changing the World. 2011. xi, 136p. pap. 12.00 (978-1-55896-646-8(3)); E-Book 9.60 (978-1-55896-647-5(1)) Unitarian Universalist Assn. (Skinner Hse. Bks.).

Dean, Stephen D. Sr. Backpacking with Jesus. 2011. 306p. 29.99 (978-1-4568-6743-0(1)); pap. 19.99 (978-1-4568-6742-3(3)) Xlibris Corp.

Deane, David J. Robert Moffat: The Missionary Hero of Kuruman. 2007. (ENG.). 126p. pap. 18.99 (978-1-4264-8581-7(6)); 138p. pap. 19.99 (978-1-4264-8638-8(3)) BiblioBazaar.

—Robert Moffat: The Missionary Hero of Kuruman. 2008. (Illus.). 140p. pap. (978-1-4099-0442-7(3)) Dodo Pr.

Debbrecht, Sherri. Learning to Walk Again Was the 'Easy' Part. 2007. 156p. per. 13.99 (978-1-60266-014-4(X)) Xulon Pr., Inc.

Debrino, Preacher Frank. The Way Maker (A Street Called Straight) The Premier Guide to Deliverance from Addictions. 2008. 96p. pap. 9.99 (978-1-60647-536-2(3)) Xulon Pr., Inc.

Dehart, Paige. Unmasked: One Soul's Journey from Anonymity to Identity. 2007. 295p. per. 22.99 (978-1-59886-736-7(9)) Tate Publishing & Enterprises, LLC.

DeLano, Jan. Prayers from the Playa. 2009. 111p. pap. 14.99 (978-0-557-03387-4(X)) Lulu Enterprises Inc.

Demetrios, Athena. The Seasoning of a Soul: When Comprehension Comes through Trial & Experience. 2010. (Illus.). 491p. pap. 19.95 (978-1-4327-5239-2(1)) Outskirts Pr., Inc.

DeMuth, Mary E. Thin Places: A Memoir, 1 vol. 2010. (ENG.). 224p. pap. 14.99 (978-0-310-28418-5(X)) Zondervan.

Denae. God Granted Me. 2009. 120p. pap. 11.99 (978-1-60791-633-8(9)) Xulon Pr., Inc.

Dennen, Nicholas P. 23: Time to Choose. 2006. (Illus.). 233p. per. 19.95 (978-1-59298-145-8(3)) Beaver's Pond Pr., Inc.

Derr, Jane Ann. Trailblazing with God. 2008. 232p. pap. 14.99 (978-1-60477-866-3(0)) Xulon Pr., Inc.

DeYoung, Donald B. Pioneer Explorers of Intelligent Design: Scientists Who Made a Difference. 2006. (Illus.). 101p. per. 12.99 (978-0-88469-073-3(3)) BMH Bks.

Diamond, Susan Ward. The Daily Grind: God with Your Coffee. 2011. 172p. 24.99 (978-1-4567-5213-2(8)); pap. 17.99 (978-1-4567-5214-9(6)) AuthorHouse.

Dianovich, Elizabeth Benlian. God Saved Me in the Orient Express & I Came to Americ. 2008. 148p. per. 14.99 (978-1-60477-016-2(3)) Xulon Pr., Inc.

Dickerson, Anthony & Dickerson, Larisha. The Christian Life at Its Best. 2008. 333p. pap. 19.95 (978-1-4357-1135-8(1)) Lulu Enterprises Inc.

Diedrich, Mark. Little Paul: Christian Leader of the Dakota Peace party. 2010. 232p. pap. 29.95 (978-1-892415-04-2(6)) Coyote Bks.

Dilmore, Don. God Was There All the Time: The Meanest Man in San Saba County, until He Met God. 2006. 181p. pap. 24.95 (978-1-4241-3437-3(4)) PublishAmerica, Inc.

Dippon, Rhonda. I Met a Witch: Battling Evil with Holy Spirit Power. 2006. (ENG.). 200p. per. 24.95 (978-1-4241-1135-0(8)) PublishAmerica, Inc.

Ditto, Laurie. Go Tell Others about Me. 2007. 152p. per. 13.99 (978-1-60266-455-5(2)) Xulon Pr., Inc.

Divine, Dionysius The. The Life & Times of Dionysius the Divine: And his Forty Year Journey in the Desert of Life. 2011. 224p. pap. 19.99 (978-1-4568-7573-2(6)) Xlibris Corp.

Dixon, Kristi. God's Faithful Servant. 2007. 216p. pap. 25.00 (978-0-615-14197-8(8)) Dixon, Kristi.

Dixon Wilford, Jennifer Cheniere. Blessed: Therapy. 2009. 148p. 24.95 (978-1-4490-2322-5(3)); pap. 15.95 (978-1-4490-2323-2(1)) AuthorHouse.

Dobbs, K. A. There's a Light at the End of the Tunnel: And It's Not a Train! 2009. 132p. pap. 14.99 (978-1-61579-086-9(1)) Xulon Pr., Inc.

Dobson, Edward G. The Year of Living Like Jesus: My Journey of Discovering What Jesus Would Really Do, 1 vol. 2009. (ENG.). 304p. 19.99 (978-0-310-24777-7(2)) Zondervan.

Dobson, Leonard. Ten Cents for the World. 2010. (Illus.). 156p. pap. 43.49 (978-1-4520-1591-0(0)) AuthorHouse.

Dobson, Leonard D. Ten Cents for the World: An exposé of extraterrestrial influence in the world Today. 2010. 168p. pap. 46.49 (978-1-4520-1625-2(9)) AuthorHouse.

Doddridge, Philip. The Life of Col. James Gardiner: Who Was Slain at the Battle of Prestonpans Septem. 2007. (ENG.). 132p. pap. 18.99 (978-1-4346-2202-0(9)); 148p. pap. 19.99 (978-1-4346-2262-4(2)) BiblioBazaar.

Dolan, Robert. My Wonderful Life with My Beautiful Wife. 2009. 200p. 24.99 (978-1-4389-7935-9(5)); pap. 16.95 (978-1-4389-7934-2(7)) AuthorHouse.

Donald Miller. Blue Like Jazz: Nonreligious Thoughts on Christian Spirituality. l.t. ed. 2007. (ENG.). 370p. (J). pap. 16.95 (978-1-59415-154-5(7), Walker Large Print) Cengage Gale.

Donovan, Joyce. Grasping the Nettle. 2006. 260p. per. 15.99 (978-1-60034-870-9(X)) Xulon Pr., Inc.

Dorius, Guy L., et al, eds. Regional Studies in Latter-day Saint Church History: Ohio & Upper Canada. 2006. (Studies in Latter-Day Saint History: 6). (Illus.). 218p. pap. 14.95 (978-0-8425-2653-1(6), Brigham Young Univ. Religious Studies Ctr.) Brigham Young Univ.

Dorothy, Steve: My Special Needs Son. 2010. 64p. pap. 14.95 (978-1-4327-5355-9(X)) Outskirts Pr., Inc.

Doss, Jenny. More Precious Than Gold: A True Story of Triumph over Tragedy. 2008. 304p. 28.99 (978-1-60791-158-6(2)); 300p. pap. 18.99 (978-1-60791-107-4(8)) Xulon Pr., Inc.

Douglas, Lois Smith & Armstrong, A. Joseph. Through Heavens Back Door: A Biography of A. Joseph Armstrong. 2011. 300p. 48.95 (978-1-258-08653-4(0)) Literary Licensing, LLC.

Douglas, Tom. The Longest Mile... Does God Care If We're Abused? 2010. 140p. pap. 11.99 (978-1-4490-7823-2(0)) AuthorHouse.

Dowdell, Bette. On We March: A memoir of growing up in the Salvation Army. 2009. 320p. pap. 19.95 (978-0-9717728-5-4(1)) Confident Faith Institute.

Downing, Jim. Living Legacy. 2008. (Discipleship Journal Bible Study Ser.). (ENG.). 144p. pap. 9.99 (978-0-9729023-8-0(4)) NavPress Publishing Group.

Doyle, Richard. Winston Churchill Was a Catholic Priest: Memoirs from Thirty-Seven Years as a Public High School Teacher. 2008. 164p. pap. 19.95 (978-1-4389-1294-3(3)) AuthorHouse.

Doyle, Tom. Breakthrough: The Return of Hope to the Middle East. 2009. (ENG.). 217p. pap. 17.99 (978-1-934068-63-2(2)) Authentic Media.

Draguet, Rene, ed. Julien d'Halicarnasse et Sa Controverse avec Severe d'Antioch sur l'Incorruptibilite du Corps du Christ. (Orthodoxies & Heresies in the Early Church Ser.). reprint ed. 45.00 (978-0-404-62382-1(4)) AMS Pr., Inc.

Dredla, Larry Michael. Praying for Strength: Memoir of an Ex Suicidal, Alcoholic, Drug Addict. 2011. 124p. pap. 11.68 (978-1-4567-4749-7(5)) AuthorHouse.

Droppo, Richard. Forever! They'll All Be There — - Won't They??? 2011. 544p. pap. 23.28 (978-1-4670-3515-6(7)) AuthorHouse.

Duckworth, Marion. Naked on God's Doorstep: A Memoir. 2007. (ENG.). 240p. per. 17.99 (978-1-59052-956-0(1), Multnomah) Doubleday Religious Publishing Group, The.

Dudley, Geoffrey V. Prayer Answers Guaranteed! Learn How to Ask God ... & Receive It! 2009. 106p. pap. 13.95 (978-1-4327-3207-3(2)) Outskirts Pr., Inc.

Duke, Wendy. The Grace by Which We Stand. 2008. 132p. pap. 19.99 (978-1-4363-7178-0(3)) Xlibris Corp.

Dunn, Dorsey Jerome. When the Power of Christ Compels You. 2010. 122p. pap. 11.99 *(978-1-60957-483-3(4))* Xulon Pr., Inc.
Duriez, Colin. Francis Schaeffer: An Authentic Life. 2008. (Illus.). 240p. 24.99 *(978-1-58134-857-6(6))* Crossway.
Dust, Harmony. Scars & Stilettos: The Transformation of an Exotic Dancer, 1 vol. 2009. (ENG.). 252p. pap. 12.99 *(978-0-8254-6309-9(2),* Monarch Bks.) Lion Hudson PLC GBR. Dist: Kregel Pubns.
Dwyer, Dennis E. God, Country & Tattoos. 2011. 268p. pap. 16.99 *(978-1-61215-798-6(X))* Xulon Pr., Inc.
Eadie, John. Life of John Kitto. 2007. (ENG.). 428p. 51.95 *(978-0-548-09355-9(5))* Kessinger Publishing, LLC.
Eason, Randy. To Be Still & Know: Back Roads & Bridges. 2011. 116p. 28.95 ***(978-1-4497-1755-1(1))***; pap. 11.95 ***(978-1-4497-1754-4(3))*** Author Solutions, Inc. (WestBow Pr.).
Easter, Sheri. Hear My Heart. 2011. 254p. 36.99 ***(978-1-61379-821-8(0))*** Xulon Pr., Inc.
Eckerman, Carol O. Lessons in Simply Being: Finding the Peace within Tumult. 2012. (ENG.). 224p. pap. 16.95 ***(978-1-84694-723-0(5))*** Hunt, John Publishing Ltd. GBR. Dist: National Bk. Network.
Ed, Brother. To Heaven, Hell & Home Again: My Encounters with GOD. 2009. 248p. pap. 24.95 *(978-1-61546-470-8(0))* PublishAmerica, Inc.
Edwards, Leland & Williams, Ron. Chasing the Vision. 2006. (ENG., Illus.). 176p. pap. 11.99 *(978-1-59979-019-0(X),* Creation Hse.) Charisma Media.
Edwards, Marva J. Bound to Be Free: Breaking Free from Domestic Violence. 2010. 124p. (ENG.). 23.50 *(978-1-4490-8517-9(2))*; pap. 13.99 *(978-1-4490-8513-1(X))* AuthorHouse.
Eichhorn, J. Martin. Escape from the Cocoon: The true story of how a near-death experience in the wilderness of Alaska propelled the transformation of one man who Despise. 2008. 104p. pap. 12.95 *(978-1-4327-3072-7(X))* Outskirts Pr., Inc.
Eldar, Dorthy Murray. Whispers from God. 2011. 348p. pap. 18.99 *(978-1-61215-459-6(X))* Xulon Pr., Inc.
Elizabeth Clare Prophet. Preparation for My Mission. 2009. 428p. pap. 26.95 *(978-1-4401-7394-3(X))* Universe, Inc.
Elliott, Cheryl. What Were You Thinking? Interviewing Bible-Time Women in a Modern-Day Classroom. 2009. 228p. pap. 15.99 *(978-1-60791-823-3(4))* Xulon Pr., Inc.
Elliott, Dale L. What Does God Want Me to Give. 2011. 128p. pap. 13.95 *(978-1-4502-7920-8(1))* iUniverse, Inc.
Elliott, John and Della. Wendy Update:) in HIS HANDS. 2006. pap. 14.99 *(978-1-60034-552-4(2))* Xulon Pr., Inc.
Ellis, Caroline. I Married a Preacher with Deep Dark Secrets. 2007. 172p. per. 13.99 *(978-1-60477-211-1(5))* Xulon Pr., Inc.
Ellis, Johnny L. & Rose, Abraham. Johnny & His Rose: A True Story of Eternal Love. 2007. (ENG., Illus.). 93p. per. 15.00 *(978-0-9789461-2-8(X))* His Rose, Inc.
Ellis, Raff. Kisses from a Distance: An Immigrant Family Experience. 2007. (Illus.). 311p. 29.95 *(978-1-885942-45-6(1))*; per. 17.95 *(978-1-885942-46-3(X))* Cune Pr., LLC.
Elrod, Eileen Razzari. Piety & Dissent: Race, Gender, & Biblical Rhetoric in Early American Autobiography. 2008. (Illus.). 240p. lib. bdg. 80.00 net. *(978-1-55849-628-6(9))*; 230p. per. 24.95 net. *(978-1-55849-629-3(7))* Univ. of Massachusetts Pr.
Elsadai, John. In the Land of Sojourners. 2008. 204p. pap. 14.99 *(978-1-60647-008-4(6))* Xulon Pr., Inc.
Elwood, Lynne Marie. Rollingaround. 2008. 184p. pap. 14.99 *(978-1-60647-758-8(7))* Xulon Pr., Inc.
Empey, Linda J. I Really Died & Survived. 2008. 85p. pap. 16.95 *(978-1-60563-293-3(7))* PublishAmerica, Inc.
Englar, Jill Buchanan. Dear Tommy. 2011. 62p. pap. 19.95 ***(978-1-4626-1778-4(6))*** PublishAmerica, Inc.
Escobar, Mark. Counting My Blessings: A Voice of Seasons. 2011. (ENG.). 465p. pap. 18.95 ***(978-1-4327-8213-9(4))*** Outskirts Pr., Inc.
Espinoza, Aaron. Sonia, Esta es la Vida (This Is Life) (SPA.). 64p. *(978-84-7228-175-2(2),* 220851) Clie, Editorial.
Eszterhas, Joe. Crossbearer: A Memoir of Faith. 2009. (ENG.). 256p. pap. 16.99 *(978-0-312-58758-1(9),* St. Martin's Griffin) St. Martin's Pr.
Etheridge, Brenda F. Jesus, Bucky, & Me. 2007. (Illus.). (ENG.). 368p. per. 14.99 *(978-1-59979-221-7(4))*; v. 350p. *(978-1-59979-252-1(4))* Charisma Media. (Creation Hse.).
Evans, A. Joyce Engdahl. Pressing Toward the Prize: My Odyssey of Faith. 2006. (Illus.). 242p. per. 18.95 *(978-1-57736-372-9(8))* Providence Hse Pubs.
Evans, Christopher H. The Kingdom Is Always but Coming: A Life of Walter Rauschenbusch. 2010. (ENG.). 376p. (Orig.). pap. 34.95 *(978-1-60258-209-5(2))* Baylor Univ. Pr.
Evans, Cynthia. Voices of Cyn... Traces of A Backslider. 2012. (ENG.). pap. 15.00 ***(978-0-9833461-4-2(3))*** NCM Publishing.
Evans, Gerald. In the Shadow of the Cross: Volume One. 2007. 48p. per. 16.95 *(978-1-4241-7665-6(4))* PublishAmerica, Inc.
Evans, Vircy. My Awakening. 2008. 44p. pap. 14.96 *(978-1-4357-2163-0(2))* Lulu Enterprises Inc.
Everett, James. Memoirs of the Life Character & Ministry of William Dawson. 2009. 548p. 43.99 *(978-1-115-95399-3(0))*; 36.99 *(978-1-115-95400-6(8))*; pap. 41.75 *(978-1-115-95401-3(6))*; pap. 40.75 *(978-1-115-95402-0(4))* BiblioBazaar.
—Memoirs of the Life Character & Ministry of William Dawson. 2007. (ENG.). 412p. 49.95 *(978-0-548-02923-7(7))* Kessinger Publishing, LLC.
Everhart, Fred F. Death's Door Denied: The Man That Should Have Died, Would Have Died, but Could Not Die. 2011. 80p. pap. 9.99 *(978-1-4567-3664-4(7))* AuthorHouse.
Ewing, Dick. Milagros de Fe en el Desierto: The Adventure of the Iron Camels. (SPA.). 176p. *(978-84-7228-587-3(1),* 220589) Clie, Editorial.
Ezell, Lee. Finding Hope When Life's Not Fair. 2009. 240p. 5.99 *(978-0-8007-8776-3(1),* Revell.
Fagan, Charlie. Winning Freedom from Religion: (the Birthing of the New World out of the Womb of the Present World) 2010. 136p. pap. 14.99 *(978-1-4490-7024-3(8))* AuthorHouse.
Farrar, F. W. Men I Have Known. 2007. (ENG.). 408p. 49.95 *(978-0-548-02322-8(0))* Kessinger Publishing, LLC.
Fatica, Justin. Hard as Nails: A Mission to Awaken Youth to the Power of God's Love. 2009. (ENG.). 208p. pap. 14.00 *(978-0-385-52717-0(9),* Image) Doubleday Religious Publishing Group, The.
Faulk, Randy. Led by the Spirit. 2011. 176p. pap. 19.99 ***(978-1-4415-1793-7(6))*** Xlibris Corp.
Fausel, Donald F. From Blind Obedience to A Responsible Faith: The Memoir of A Cradle Catholic. 2010. 428p. 36.95 *(978-1-4502-4459-6(9))*; pap. 26.95 *(978-1-4502-4457-2(2))* iUniverse, Inc.
Feaver, John A. Into the Light: The Academic & Spiritual Legacy of Dr. Howard Malmstadt. 2007. (ENG.). 144p. pap. 11.99 *(978-1-57658-411-8(9))* YWAM Publishing.
Federico, Breanna & Erdman, Jacob. Confessions from the Smoking Bench. 2011. 140p. pap. 11.95 ***(978-1-4497-2330-9(6),*** WestBow Pr.) Author Solutions, Inc.
Fedewa, Marilyn H. Maria of Agreda: Mystical Lady in Blue. 2010. (ENG., Illus.). 355p. pap. 29.95 *(978-0-8263-4644-5(8))* Univ. of New Mexico Pr.
Feinberg, Margaret. The Sacred Echo: Hearing God's Voice in Every Area of Your Life, 1 vol. 2008. (ENG.). 224p. 16.99 *(978-0-310-27417-9(6))* Zondervan.
Fendrich, Jr. Where Life Began: A Native's Perspective of the Nation's Capital in the 30's And 40's. 2011. 202p. pap. 24.95 ***(978-1-4560-6893-6(8))*** PublishAmerica, Inc.
Ferguson, Richard. A Real-Life Christian Spiritual Journey. 2011. 312p. 31.95 ***(978-1-4620-1674-7(X))***; pap. 21.95 ***(978-1-4620-1672-3(3))*** iUniverse, Inc.
Ferguson, Richard. A Real Life Christian Spiritual Journey: A Story of Real Life Spiritual Experiences on the Way Back to God. 2010. 312p. pap. 23.50 *(978-1-4389-9190-0(8))* AuthorHouse.
Fiesel, Chris. The Christmas Cactus, 1 vol. 2009. 144p. pap. 24.95 *(978-1-61546-571-2(5))* PublishAmerica, Inc.
Finch, Henrietta Roberts. God's Amazing Grace. 2008. 152p. pap. 13.99 *(978-1-60647-285-9(2))* Xulon Pr., Inc.
Find Happiness! By Looking, Feeling, & Living Better. 2007. per. 16.95 net. *(978-0-9772868-0-5(0))* Knight For Christ Publishing.
Findlay, Alison & Findlay. Women in Shakespeare: A Dictionary. 2010. (Continuum Shakespeare Dictionaries Ser.). (ENG.). 564p. 275.00 *(978-0-8264-5889-6(0))* Continuum International Publishing Group, Ltd. GBR. Dist: National Bk. Network.
Finlayson, Linda. Strength & Devotion: Volume 2. 2009. (ENG., Illus.). 128p. 8.99 *(978-1-84550-492-2(5))* Christian Focus Pubns. GBR. Dist: STL Distribution North America.
Finney, Jack. With God's Help: An Autobiography & Fond Memories of Jack Finney. 2010. 336p. pap. 20.95 *(978-1-4327-5998-8(1))* Outskirts Pr., Inc.
Fitch, Pamela. Set Free Indeed. 2011. 80p. pap. 11.99 ***(978-1-60844-960-6(2))*** Dog Ear Publishing, LLC.
Flagg. From Ploughshare to Crook. (Illus.). 144p. 10.95 *(978-0-281-05213-4(1))* International Publishers Marketing.
Flaum, Lenny. Dyed: A Painfully Beautiful Journey to Truth. 2011. pap. 13.99 *(978-1-61739-695-3(8))* Tate Publishing & Enterprises, LLC.
Fleck, Rick. Life Without Parole: Drugs, Murder, Prison, New Life in God. 2008. 248p. pap. *(978-0-8163-2228-2(7))* Pacific Pr. Pubns.
Fleming, Amy. The City of Our God. 2007. 200p. per. 14.99 *(978-1-60266-595-8(8))* Xulon Pr., Inc.
Fleming, Kimberly Smith. When the Thunder Roars Will You Choose Victory or Defeat? Will You Choose Victory or Defeat? 2011. 54p. pap. 15.99 ***(978-1-4653-3725-2(3))*** Xlibris Corp.
Flemming, Herb & King, Timothy. From Hitler Youth to American Soldier. 2009. (Illus.). 396p. *(978-1-889283-18-0(5))* Golden Morning Publishing
Fornicola, Gary. Unshackled: Breaking the Bonds of Sin & Addiction. 2011. pap. 12.99 ***(978-1-61346-680-3(3))*** Tate Publishing & Enterprises, LLC.
Foster, Penny. Cast the First Stone. 2009. (Illus.). 244p. pap. 14.49 *(978-1-4389-6471-3(4))* AuthorHouse.
Foster, Thelma Louise Elisher. Born to Be a Leader According to God's Plan by Teaching Others to Heal Inside No More Shame: Destined for Leadership When All Seems Hopeless. 2010. 118p. pap. 11.99 *(978-1-61579-708-0(4))* Xulon Pr., Inc.
Fountain, David. Lord Radstock & the Russian Awakening. (Illus.). 82p. pap. 8.99 *(978-0-907821-04-5(9))* Revival Literature.
Fowler, Gary. Walk Through Time. 2006. (Illus.). 210p. 30.07 *(978-1-4122-0213-8(2))* Trafford Publishing.
Fowler, Gary H. Walk Through Time. 2006. (Illus.). 210p. pap. 16.85 *(978-1-4120-9577-8(8))* Trafford Publishing.
Fox, Alfred. A Soul Redeemed. 2009. vii, 67p. pap. *(978-1-934363-22-5(7))* Zoe Life Publishing.
Foxe, John. Foxe's Book of Martyrs. Berry, W., ed. 2007. (ENG.). 428p. per. 18.95 *(978-1-933993-57-7(X))* Apocryphile Pr.
—Foxe's Book of Martyrs. Berry, William Grinton, ed. 2009. 444p. 51.95 *(978-1-120-38638-0(1))*; pap. 36.95 *(978-1-120-28290-3(X))* Kessinger Publishing, LLC.
—Foxe's Book of Martyrs: A History of the Lives, Sufferings, & Triumphant Deaths of the Early Christian & the Protestant Martyrs. 2010. (Illus.). 288p. pap. 14.95 *(978-0-9824881-8-8(1))* Lighthouse Trails Publishing Co.
Foxe, Richard. Expression of a Nightmare, the Richard L Foxe Story: How I Became a Servant of Allah-God. 2009. 152p. pap. 17.99 *(978-1-4389-8722-4(6))* AuthorHouse.
Foxworth Holman, Debra. Thanks to Jesus, I Am Still Here: My not so Private Journey. 2009. 108p. 24.99 *(978-1-4490-0936-6(0))*; pap. 15.99 *(978-1-4490-0938-0(7))* AuthorHouse.
Frame, Mickey. Weed,Speed & Other Stuff: The Life of A Teenage Boy in the Late 60's. 2010. 60p. pap. 14.95 *(978-1-4269-4483-3(7))* Trafford Publishing.
Franklin, Theresa. Journey to Fulfillment: From Stumbling Blocks to Stepping Stones. 2011. pap. 12.99 *(978-1-61739-773-8(3))* Tate Publishing & Enterprises, LLC.
Franklin, Yusef. From the Penitentiary to the Pulpit, 1 vol. 2009. 75p. pap. 14.95 *(978-1-61546-572-9(3))* PublishAmerica, Inc.
Franks, Wade. Never Forgotten. 2006. pap. 9.99 *(978-1-60034-577-7(8))* Xulon Pr., Inc.
Frassetto, Michael. The Great Medieval Heretics: Five Centuries of Religious Dissent. (ENG.). 256p. 2010. pap. 15.95 *(978-1-933346-23-6(X))* 2008. 24.95 *(978-1-933346-12-0(4))* BlueBridge.
Frecka, Andy. Winter Road. 2009. 280p. pap. 16.99 *(978-1-60791-387-0(9))* Xulon Pr., Inc.
Fried, Brenda. Bridging the Gap of Faith: A Nice Jewish Girl's Journey to Find the Messiah. 2010. 156p. 25.95 *(978-1-4520-2318-2(2))*; (ENG.). pap. 14.95 *(978-1-4520-2319-9(0))* AuthorHouse.
Frimoth, Bud. Bring in the Clowns - a Metaphor for Ministry. 2006. (ENG.). 276p. per. 16.99 *(978-1-4141-0772-1(2))* Pleasant Word.
Frist, Tom. The Thoughts of a Good Man: Sermons & Talks of Dr. John Chester Frist Sr. 2009. 120p. pap. 10.95 *(978-1-4401-3197-4(X))* iUniverse, Inc.
Frone, Barbara. My Journey with God. 2010. 108p. (ENG.). 28.95 *(978-1-4497-0137-6(X))*; pap. 11.95 *(978-1-4497-0135-2(3))* Author Solutions, Inc. (WestBow Pr.).
Frost, Andy. Losing Faith: Those Who Have Walked Away. 2010. (ENG.). 160p. 12.99 *(978-1-85078-879-9(0))* Authentic Media.
Furseth, Inger. From Quest for Truth to Being Oneself: Religious Change in Life Stories. 2006. (Illus.). 325p. pap. *(978-0-8204-9944-4(7))* Lang, Peter AG.
G., Michael. Hope in the Morning: One Man's Struggle with Addiction And What It Means for You. 2009. 212p. 25.99 *(978-1-60791-171-5(X))* Xulon Pr., Inc.
Gadol, Kohen Ben. Epilogue & Testimony of Kohen Ben Gadol. 2008. 68p. pap. 9.95 *(978-0-7414-4435-6(6))* Infinity Publishing.
Galbraith, James C. There Is Something about an Aqua Velva Man: Read this book & find out what it is! 2009. 112p. 23.99 *(978-1-4343-4712-1(5))* AuthorHouse.
Gall, Pete. My Beautiful Idol, 1 vol. 2008. (ENG.). 304p. pap. 12.99 *(978-0-310-28310-2(8))* Zondervan.
Gallo, Mario R. It's My Life. 2006. (Illus.). 184p. spiral bd. 12.50 *(978-1-60002-033-9(X),* 3756) Mountain Valley Publishing, LLC.
Gary Eugene Tucker. Face to Face: The Experience. 2009. 240p. pap. 18.49 *(978-1-4343-9016-5(0))* AuthorHouse.
Gateley, Edwina. Christ in the Margins. 2009. (ENG., Illus.). 155p. pap. 20.00 *(978-1-57075-814-0(X))* Orbis Bks.
Gaudion, Eric. Braving the Storm: Survival Tactics. 2007. (ENG.). 240p. per. 16.99 *(978-1-85078-739-6(5))* Authentic Media.
Geeting, Jim. Shots Fired Shots Forgiven - the Steve Watt Story. 2010. 212p. pap. 19.99 *(978-0-557-40193-2(3))* Lulu Enterprises Inc.
Geil, Harold Alfredo. The Heart of Man; God's Target. 2009. 420p. pap. 22.99 *(978-1-61579-092-0(6))* Xulon Pr., Inc.
Gelpi, Donald L. Closer Walk: Confessions of A U. S. Jesuit Yat. 2006. (ENG., Illus.). 430p. per. 57.99 *(978-0-7618-3404-5(4))* Hamilton Bks.
Gent, Heather. Embracing the Journey of Walking in Faith: For the New Believer Part I, 1 vol. 2009. 60p. pap. 16.95 *(978-1-4489-2442-4(1))* PublishAmerica Inc.
George, Christian Timothy. Jonathan Edwards: An American Genius. 2008. (Trail Blazers Ser.). (ENG.). 160p. pap. 8.99 *(978-1-84550-329-1(5))* Christian Focus Pubns. GBR. Dist: STL Distribution North America.
Gibbons, Alice. Where the Earth Ends. 2009. 284p. pap. 16.99 *(978-1-60791-571-3(5))* Xulon Pr., Inc.
Gibson, Janet & Arrington, Billy Wayne. And God Was Watching: A Biography of Billy Wayne. 2011. 188p. 30.95 ***(978-1-61507-745-8(6))***; pap. 13.95 ***(978-1-61507-744-1(8))*** Cross Bks. Publishing.
Gibson, Jean. Joyful in Hope: Finding God in the Extremes. 2010. (ENG.). 160p. 12.99 *(978-1-86024-808-5(X))* Authentic Media.
Gibson, Kathleen. West Nile Diary: One Couple's Triumph over a Deadly Disease. 2009. *(978-1-926645-01-8(4))* BPS Bks.
Gifford, Elisabeth. The House of Hope: A Story of God's Love & Provision for the Abandoned Orphans of China, 1 vol. 2011. (Illus.). 224p. pap. 13.99 ***(978-0-85721-059-3(9),*** Monarch Bks.) Lion Hudson PLC GBR. Dist: Kregel Pubns.
Gilbert, Two Rivers Church, compiled by. Not by Chance. 2007. pap. 14.95 *(978-0-9792475-7-6(8))* Good Catch Publishing.
Gilchrist, Francine. From Darkness to Light: From the Street to Ministry. 2010. ***(978-1-77069-131-5(6))*** Word Alive Pr.
Gilchrist, Jeffrey L. Assault of Innocence: A Christian's Struggle & Victory over Child Pornography. 2006. (ENG.). 76p. per. 16.95 *(978-1-4241-4653-6(4))* PublishAmerica, Inc.
Gilden, Laura. God's Handprints: True Stories of God's Presence in the Every Day Lives of His People. 2007. (ENG.). 156p. per. 15.99 *(978-1-4141-0926-8(1))* Pleasant Word.
Gillard, Linda. The Broken Boy. 2008. 132p. pap. 11.95 *(978-1-4327-2678-2(1))*, Outskirts Pr., Inc.
Gipson, Ralph E. Coming Full Circle: A Memoir. 2011. pap. 21.99 *(978-1-61739-744-8(X))* Tate Publishing & Enterprises, LLC.
Glading, Dale M. Unconditional Surrender: A Living History of the First 20 Years of the Saints Prison Ministry. 2007. pap. 14.95 *(978-1-59571-190-8(2))* Word Association Pubs.
Glover, Jerry. Play to Win: Keys to Victory in the Game of Life. 2008. 180p. pap. 16.95 *(978-0-595-52260-6(2))* iUniverse, Inc.
God Still Loves the French. 2006. pap. 13.99 *(978-1-60034-284-4(1))* Xulon Pr., Inc.
Goggins, Shanile Sharay & Taylor, Benita. The Summer That Changed My Life: A True, Inspiring Testament of a Young College Student, who one Summer Took a Journey that Carried her to the Ends of the Earth, to the Presence of God. 2010. 45p. pap. 12.95 *(978-1-4327-4209-6(4))* Outskirts Pr., Inc.
Goldbach, Robert. Faith in an Imperfect World: A Letter to My Grandchildren, 1 vol. 2009. (ENG.). 51p. pap. 16.95 *(978-1-4489-7678-2(2))* PublishAmerica, Inc.
Goldstein, David. Autobiography of a Campaigner for Christ. 432p. 2008. 51.95 *(978-1-4366-9374-5(8))* 2007. (ENG.). per. 36.95 *(978-1-4304-9477-5(8))* Kessinger Publishing, LLC.
Gomez, Cheree Carter. Glitz, Glamour & God: Radiate with the Glitter of Your Spirit & the Sparkle of Your Soul by Discovering Jesus. 2009. 216p. pap. 15.99 *(978-1-60791-905-6(2))* Xulon Pr., Inc.
Gonce, Bruce & Gonce, Aimie. Stand by to First Class. 2010. 68p. pap. 10.99 *(978-1-4490-6230-9(X))* AuthorHouse.
Gong, Amelia. God Never Forsakes Me. 2009. 240p. 28.95 *(978-1-4401-7247-2(1))*; pap. 18.95 *(978-1-4401-7246-5(3))* iUniverse, Inc.
Gonleh, John & Bessie. Refuge. 2009. 288p. pap. 14.95 *(978-1-57921-930-7(6))* WinePress Publishing.
Gonzalez, Jose M. Dark Lonely Road. 2011. 56p. pap. 9.95 ***(978-1-4620-1581-8(6))*** iUniverse, Inc.
Good, James I. Famous Missionaries of the Reformed Church. 2009. 440p. pap. 28.00 *(978-1-59925-225-4(2))* Solid Ground Christian Bks.
Gooden, Darla L. The Restorer of the Breach: Finding Hope & Healing on the Edge of Despair. 2010. 120p. (ENG.). 21.49 *(978-1-4490-7512-5(6))*; pap. 17.95 *(978-1-4490-7511-8(8))* AuthorHouse.
Goodhew, Kathy. A Vision Beyond Abuse. 2011. pap. 10.99 *(978-1-61739-599-4(4))* Tate Publishing & Enterprises, LLC.
Goodrich, Donna Clark. Healing in God's Time: Trusting in God's Faithfulness on the Journey to a Miracle. 2009. (ENG.). 129p. pap. 14.99 *(978-0-9817061-1-5(8))* Believe Bks., LLC.
Goodson, Narda. Will the Real Me, Please Stand Up! 2007. 224p. per. 18.95 *(978-0-9791566-5-6(3))* To His Glory Publishing Co., Inc.
Goodwin, Craig L. Year of Plenty. 2011. 224p. pap. 12.95 ***(978-1-4514-0074-8(6),*** Sparkhouse Pr.) Spark Hse.
Goodwin, Jacqueline L. Healing in the Vesse. 2009. 136p. pap. 14.99 *(978-0-557-09230-7(2))* Lulu Enterprises Inc.
Gordon, A. How Christ Came to Church: The Pastors Drea a Spiritual Autobiography, 1 vol. Gibson, Scott, ed. 2010. 136p. pap. 12.99 *(978-0-8254-2687-2(1))* Kregel Pubns.
Gordon, Ernesto B. A. J. Gordon: Su Vida y Su Obra.Tr. of A. J. Gordon: His Life & His Work. (SPA.). *(978-84-7645-282-0(9),* 223336) Clie, Editorial.
Gore, Ralph. Grace Tried in the Fire. 2007. 84p. per. 9.99 *(978-1-60266-055-7(7))* Xulon Pr., Inc.
Gore, Susan. A Blessing of Sunshine & Wrath. 2010. 136p. pap. 12.95 *(978-1-60844-385-7(X))* Dog Ear Publishing, LLC.
Gorham, Jewel. The Burning Bush 2007. 2007. 108p. (ENG.). 18.99 *(978-1-60266-688-7(1))*; per. 10.99 *(978-1-60266-687-0(3))* Xulon Pr., Inc.
Gorman, Thomas. To Believe or Not Believe, That Is the Question. 2007. 296p. per. 15.99 *(978-1-60034-988-1(9))* Xulon Pr., Inc.
Gospel Light Publications Staff. Preschool Smart Pages. 2010. (ENG.). 240p. (J). (gr. -1-k). 49.99 *(978-0-8307-5156-3(4))* Gospel Light Pubns.
Gosselin, Kate. Eight Little Faces, 1 vol. 2009. (ENG.). 48p. 14.99 *(978-0-310-31846-0(7))* Zondervan.
Graber, Jerome. What My Two-Year-Old Taught Me about Grace: A Father's Heart. 2008. 48p. pap. 16.95 *(978-1-60563-042-7(X))* PublishAmerica, Inc.
Grafton, Anthony & Weinberg, Joanna. I Have Always Loved the Holy Tongue: Isaac Casaubon, the Jews, & a Forgotten Chapter in Renaissance Scholarship. 2011. (Carl Newell Jackson Lectures). (Illus.). 392p. 35.00 *(978-0-674-04840-9(7),* Belknap Pr.) Harvard Univ. Pr.
Graham, David. They Ride White Horses: The End of the Search for Significance. 2011. (ENG.). 192p. pap. 14.95 ***(978-1-936417-26-1(X))*** Pilot Communications Group, Inc.
Graham, Isabella. The Power of Faith. 2008. 400p. 29.99 *(978-0-554-35193-3(5))*; 31.99 *(978-0-554-25890-4(0))* BiblioBazaar.
—The Power of Faith: Exemplified in the Life & Writings of the Late Mrs. Isabella Graham. 2007. (ENG.). 346p. pap. 23.99 *(978-1-4346-0002-8(5))*; 396p. pap. 26.99 *(978-1-4346-0087-5(4))* BiblioBazaar.

C

Graham, James H. Reflective Sympathy: True Love Story. 2011. 292p. 28.55 (978-1-4567-4032-0(6)); pap. 17.98 (978-1-4567-4033-7(4)) AuthorHouse.
Graham, R.C. I Healed You with My Word. 2007. 464p. (ENG.). 35.99 (978-1-60034-721-4(5)); per. 23.99 (978-1-60034-720-7(7)) Xulon Pr., Inc.
Grandison, Frank Anthony. The Journey of This Invisible Soul Through the Mysteries of Life. 2009. 372p. pap. 18.99 (978-1-4389-2200-3(0)) AuthorHouse.
Graves, Ressurrection. Identity Crisis, Identity Christ Is: A Journey to Love. 2011. 240p. 29.99 (978-1-4415-5271-6(5)); pap. 19.99 (978-1-4415-5270-9(7)) Xlibris Corp.
Gray, Billy. From Prosecutor to Prison to Preacher. 2008. 104p. pap. 10.99 (978-1-60791-113-5(2)) Xulon Pr., Inc.
Greathouse, Cindy. Terrors of the Night, 1 vol. 2009. 173p. pap. 24.95 (978-1-4489-9260-7(5)) PublishAmerica, Inc.
Green, Janelle. This Earthly Tent: Me, God & MS. 2008. 124p. 19.99 (978-1-60791-154-8(X)); pap. 11.99 (978-1-60647-612-3(2)) Xulon Pr., Inc.
Green, Umekki. The Proverbs 31 Imposter: Walking Worthy in Our Vocation of Holiness. 2009. (Illus.). pap. 14.99 (978-0-615-27394-5(7)) Renaissance Vineyard Ministries.
Grey, Mary. Meister Eckhart: Mystic Theologian. 274p. 24.95 (978-0-281-04520-4(8)) International Publishers Marketing.
Grey-Smith, Sandra E. A Piece of Me. 2011. 198p. pap. 14.99 (978-1-61379-134-9(8)) Xulon Pr., Inc.
Griffin, Jack. My New Life. 2006. pap. 14.99 (978-1-60034-480-0(1)) Xulon Pr., Inc.
Griffin, William, Jr. C. S. Lewis: Spirituality for Mere Christians. 2007. (C. S. Lewis Secondary Studies Ser.). 220p. pap. 24.00 (978-1-59752-649-4(5)) Wipf & Stock Pubs.
Griffith, Jimmy David. Liberating the Eagle Within: Locked in the Liberty of Christ. 2009. 116p. 19.99 (978-1-61579-599-4(5)); pap. 11.99 (978-1-61579-598-7(7)) Xulon Pr., Inc.
Griffith, Stephen, compiled by. Ruth Bell Graham: Celebrating the Extraordinary Life, 0 vols. 2007. (Illus.). 208p. per. 12.99 (978-0-8499-1986-2(X)) Nelson, Thomas Inc.
Grimaldi, Marc J. Ocd: Finding Hope on the Edge of Insanity. 2010. 108p. pap. 11.95 (978-1-4327-5614-7(1)) Outskirts Pr., Inc.
Grimes, Anne. Dumplings 'n More: Our Story: Recollections & Recipes. 2007. (Illus.). 176p. 25.00 (978-0-9796418-0-0(2)) Southwestern Publishing Group, Inc.
Grimes, Kimberly. The Raging Storm. 2010. 104p. pap. 10.49 (978-1-4520-3258-0(0)) AuthorHouse.
Groom, Joe. The Journey of a Simple Man. 2007. 176p. per. (978-1-55452-223-1(4), Epic Pr.) Essence Publishing.
Grossman, Marc. The Jim Knuppe Story. 2009. 296p. pap. 15.49 (978-1-4389-4781-5(X)) AuthorHouse.
Grover, Mark L. A Land of Promise & Prophecy: Elder A Theodore Tuttle in South America, 1960-1965. 2008. (Illus.). 368p. 25.95 (978-0-8425-2713-2(3), Brigham Young Univ. Pr.) Brigham Young Univ.
Grumbling, Amy. Only for a Season: The Baby in Bed No1. 2009. 252p. pap. 15.99 (978-1-60696-681-5(2)) Tate Publishing & Enterprises, LLC.
Guenther, Margaret. Just Passing Through: Notes from a Sojourner. 2007. 192p. per. 16.00 (978-1-59627-050-3(0)) Church Publishing, Inc.
Guidry, Rhonda. Relationship with My Savior. 2010. 73p. pap. 9.95 (978-0-557-29331-5(5)) Lulu Enterprises Inc.
Guillebaud, Simon. For What It's Worth: A Call to No Holds Barred Discipleship, 1 vol. 2007. 224p. pap. 12.99 (978-0-8254-6123-1(5), Monarch Bks.) Lion Hudson PLC GBR. Dist: Kregel Pubns.
Guinness, Michele. Chosen: An Autobiography, 1 vol. 2008. (Illus.). 384p. pap. 14.99 (978-0-8254-6283-2(5), Monarch Bks.) Lion Hudson PLC GBR. Dist: Kregel Pubns.
Gunder, Claude A. Life of Claude A Gunder Saved by the Blo. 2006. pap. 16.95 (978-1-4286-5442-6(9)) Kessinger Publishing, LLC.
Guy, John. Thomas Becket: Warrior, Priest, Rebel. 2012. (ENG., Illus.). 448p. 35.00 (978-1-4000-6907-1(6), Random House) Random House Publishing Group.
Guzder, Deena. Divine Rebels: American Christian Activists for Social Justice. 2011. (ENG.). 320p. pap. 16.95 (978-1-56976-264-6(3), Hill, Lawrence Bks.) Chicago Review Pr., Inc.
Haberman, Hardy. Soul of a Second Skin: The Journey of a Gay Christian Leatherman. 2007. 126p. per. 16.95 (978-1-934625-38-5(8)) Nazca Plains Corp., The.
Hagemann, Gerard. Show Us Your Face: A Story of Leo Papin Dupont. 2011. 94p. 38.95 (978-1-258-09576-5(9)) Literary Licensing, LLC.
Hahn, Ellen. Hush, Hush, Little Baby. 2007. 138p. pap. 24.95 (978-1-4241-8023-3(6)) PublishAmerica, Inc.
Hale, Marjorie. Another Side of God. 2011. 74p. 24.99 (978-1-4568-7878-8(6)); pap. 15.99 (978-1-4568-7877-1(8)) Xlibris Corp.
Haley, J. Bronson. The Depth of Grace: Finding Hope at Rock Bottom. 2011. 296p. 37.95 (978-1-4497-1047-7(6)); pap. 22.95 (978-1-4497-1046-0(8)) Author Solutions, Inc. (WestBow Pr.).
Hall, Dustin M. Letter from the Grave. 2009. 139p. pap. 13.96 (978-0-557-08705-1(8)) Lulu Enterprises Inc.
Hall, James. My Close Encounter with Jesus Christ: An Award-Winning Newspaper & Magazine Journalist's Amazing, Supernatural, True Story. 2008. 132p. pap. 13.95 (978-1-60145-558-1(5)) Booklocker.com, Inc.
Hall, John. In Christ There Is Life after Death. 2007. (ENG.). 56p. per. 16.95 (978-1-4241-0084-2(4)) PublishAmerica, Inc.
Hall, Tammie. Journey of Courage: A healing workbook for those who've experienced or are experiencing Abuse. 2010. pap. 14.99 (978-1-61566-956-1(6)) Tate Publishing & Enterprises, LLC.
Hallman, Tom. A Stranger's Gift: True Stories of Faith in Unexpected Places. 2012. (ENG.). 240p. 19.99 (978-1-4516-1750-4(X), Howard Bks.) Howard Books.
Hallock, E. F. Preacher Hallock: All the Promises - The Remarkably Inspiring Autobiography of One Who Believed in Life Direction Through Bible Promises. 2006. 118p. pap. 16.00 (978-1-59752-694-4(0), Wipf and Stock) Wipf & Stock Pubs.
Hallock, William A. Memoir of Harlan Page or the Power of Pr. 2006. pap. 26.95 (978-1-4286-6234-6(0)) Kessinger Publishing, LLC.
Hambrick, Deborah. Who Called You? 2010. 76p. pap. 16.00 (978-1-4520-6756-8(2)) AuthorHouse.
Hamilton, Charles, Sr. A Step of Faith. 2006. (ENG.). 292p. per. 15.95 (978-1-59800-888-3(9)) Outskirts Pr., Inc.
Hamilton, Denise. Tabernacle Stories of Faith: Snapshots of God's Faithfulness to his People at Tabernacle Baptist Church. Cartersville, Georgia. 2007. pap. 15.99 (978-1-60477-326-2(X)) Xulon Pr., Inc.
Hamilton, Patricia. I'll Have Nuggets with My Prayers, Please. 2007. 48p. per. 16.95 (978-1-4241-7589-5(5)) PublishAmerica, Inc.
Hamlett, Robert L. Surviving Depression. 2008. (ENG.). 147p. pap. 11.95 (978-0-533-15904-8(0)) Vantage Pr., Inc.
Hamm, Regie. Angels & Idols: The Rise, Fall, & Redemption of a Would-Be Pop Star. 2010. pap. 14.99 (978-1-61663-440-7(5)) Tate Publishing & Enterprises, LLC.
Hammock, Lo-Dee. It's Not Odd - It's GOD!! God' Miracles & other Stories of His Grace & Mercy in the Lifetime of an Old Lady. 2007. 208p. per. 16.95 (978-0-9800625-0-2(0), Sun King Pr.) Sun King Media.
Hampl, Patricia. Sacramental Self: Catholic Roots of Contemporary Memoir. 2008. 32p. (978-0-9795709-1-9(3)) St. Mary's College.
Hamrin, Carol Lee. Salt & Light: Lives of Faith That Shaped Modern China. 2008. (Studies in Chinese Christianity Ser.). (Illus.). 252p. pap. 28.00 (978-1-55635-984-2(5), Pickwick Pubns.) Wipf & Stock Pubs.
Hamrin, Carol Lee & Bieler, Stacey, eds. Salt & Light, Three Volume Set: More Lives of Faith That Shaped Modern China. 2011. (Studies in Chinese Christianity: Ser.). 782p. pap. 80.00 (978-1-61097-690-9(8), Pickwick Pubns.) Wipf & Stock Pubs.
—Salt & Light, Volume 2: More Lives of Faith That Shaped Modern China. 2010. (Studies in Chinese Christianity Ser.). 252p. pap. 28.00 (978-1-60608-955-2(2), Pickwick Pubns.) Wipf & Stock Pubs.
Hamrin, Carol Lee & Bieler, Stacey, eds. Salt & Light, Volume 3: More Lives of Faith That Shaped Modern China. 2011. (Studies in Chinese Christianity: Ser.). 278p. pap. 31.00 (978-1-61097-158-4(2), Pickwick Pubns.) Wipf & Stock Pubs.
Hancock, Fumi Stephanie Ogunleye. Beyond Idol Worship! 2007. 316p. per. 17.99 (978-1-60266-476-0(5)) Xulon Pr., Inc.
Haney, J. Curt. Grace for the Prodigal: The Story of One Man's Journey Back to the Cross, 1 vol. 2009. 183p. pap. 24.95 (978-1-61546-876-8(5)) PublishAmerica, Inc.
Hannah, Deborah. Unlit Path. 2006. 25.99 (978-1-60034-485-5(2)); pap. 15.99 (978-1-60034-484-8(4)) Xulon Pr., Inc.
Harbinson, Adam. Savage Shepherds: One Man's Story of Overcoming Spiritual Abuse. 2007. (ENG.). 142p. per. 12.99 (978-1-86024-574-9(9)) Authentic Media.
Harder, Gary. Dancing Through Thistles in Bare Feet: A Pastoral Journey. 2008. 15.99 (978-0-8361-9386-2(5)) Herald Pr.
Hardy, Richard K. The Truth of a Gentleman. 2011. 199p. pap. 19.99 (978-1-58909-831-2(5)) Bookstand Publishing.
Harkcom, Romayne & Harkcom, Bob. God Still Works Miracles: A Journal of One Couple's Struggle with Guillain-Barre' Syndrome. 2009. 104p. pap. 10.99 (978-1-61579-536-9(7)) Xulon Pr., Inc.
Harper, Don R. Methodism's Founder John Wesley Believed in Angels. 2008. 228p. pap. 15.99 (978-1-60477-301-9(4)) Xulon Pr., Inc.
Harper Ms, Carolyn. Why Didnt Anybody Ever Tell Me about Thi. 2006. (ENG.). 24.99 (978-1-60034-905-8(6)); pap. 14.99 (978-1-60034-904-1(8)) Xulon Pr., Inc.
Harrell, Jerry P. It Took a Cross to Raise Me. 2009. 92p. pap. 16.95 (978-1-60749-574-1(0)) PublishAmerica, Inc.
Harrell, Sheena. How God Delivered Me from a Spirit of Fear. 2008. 72p. pap. 10.99 (978-1-60791-121-0(3)) Xulon Pr., Inc.
Harris, Sonny. The Good Samaritan. 2011. 156p. 30.95 (978-1-4497-2306-4(3)); pap. 13.95 (978-1-4497-2304-0(7)) Author Solutions, Inc. (WestBow Pr.).
Harrison House Publishers, compiled by. Legacy of Faith COLL Box Set: T. L. Osborn, Marilyn Hickey, Norvel Hayes. 2010. 68.97 (978-1-60683-030-7(9)) Harrison House Pubs.
Harrison, Megan Bernadette. Favorite Memories of Days Gone By: Book 1. 2011. 44p. pap. 16.95 (978-1-4626-2578-9(9)) PublishAmerica, Inc.
Hart, Inez. For a Hope & a Future. 2008. 228p. per. 14.99 (978-1-60477-780-2(X)) Xulon Pr., Inc.
Hartman, Patricia Coury. A Funny Thing Happened on My Way to Heaven. 2009. 324p. pap. 18.99 (978-1-60791-344-3(5)) Xulon Pr., Inc.
Hartmann, Joseph James. Sentenced to Death, Destined for Life: The Janiece Turner-Hartmann Story. 2011. (Illus.). 344p. pap. 19.95 (978-0-9842422-4-5(4)) VaryMedia.
Harvey, Christopher Howell. Until My Blindfold Comes Off. 2008. 196p. pap. 14.99 (978-1-60647-909-4(1)) Xulon Pr., Inc.
Hattaway, Paul. China's Christian Martyrs, 1 vol. 2007. (Illus.). 496p. pap. 16.99 (978-0-8254-6127-9(8), Monarch Bks.) Lion Hudson PLC GBR. Dist: Kregel Pubns.
Hattaway, Paul & Yun, Brother. Yun: The Illustrated Story of the Heavenly Man. 2006. (Illus.). 128p. pap. 11.99 (978-0-8254-6128-6(6), Monarch Bks.) Lion Hudson PLC GBR. Dist: Kregel Pubns.
Hauerwas, Stanley M. Hannah's Child: A Theologian's Memoir. 2010. 308p. 24.99 (978-0-8028-6487-1(2)) Eerdmans, William B. Publishing Co.
Hausmann, Cynthia. Priest & Patriot: The Life & Letters of Father Carl Hausmann, SJ. 2008. 388p. 34.95 (978-0-595-51586-8(X)); pap. 24.95 (978-0-595-52687-1(X)) iUniverse, Inc.
Havergal, Maria Vernon G. Memorials of Frances Ridley Havergal. 2006. pap. 34.95 (978-1-4286-5283-5(3)) Kessinger Publishing, LLC.
Havlicek, Brenda. It Started at the Church: Trapped in Love & Trouble. 2011. 140p. pap. 16.99 (978-1-4634-2631-6(3)) AuthorHouse.
Hawes, Joel. Memoir of Normand Smith or the Christian. 2006. pap. 17.95 (978-1-4286-5339-9(2)) Kessinger Publishing, LLC.
Haworth, Martin. Beyond Coral Shores: Life & Work with a Remote Tribe. 2006. (Missionary Life Stories Ser.). (ENG., Illus.). 256p. per. 16.99 (978-1-85078-665-8(8)) Authentic Media.
Hawthorne, Steven. Preaching: A Hustle or a Heavenly Call? 2008. 54p. pap. 16.95 (978-1-60610-561-0(2)) PublishAmerica, Inc.
Hayden, Jim. The Year of God's Promise. 2009. 340p. 29.99 (978-1-4490-2436-9(X)); pap. 18.99 (978-1-4490-2435-2(1)) AuthorHouse.
Hayes, Lacresha. The Rape of Innocence: Taking Captivity Captive. 2007. 164p. per. 19.95 (978-0-9798154-0-9(1)) Living Waters Publishing Co.
Hayes, Norvel. Legacy of Faith Collection: Norvel Hayes. 2010. 368p. 22.99 (978-1-60683-016-1(3)) Harrison House Pubs.
Hayward, John. The Book of Religions; Comprising the Views, Creeds, Sentiments, or Opinions of All the Principal Religious Sects in the World Particularly of All Chr. 2006. 436p. per. 26.99 (978-1-4255-4815-5(6)) MPublishing.
Heard, Gerald. The Gospel According to Gamaliel. 2009. (Gerald Heard Reprint Ser.). 182p. pap. 21.00 (978-1-60608-982-8(X), Wipf and Stock) Wipf & Stock Pubs.
Heath, Darrel L. Love Tells the Truth. 2008. 100p. per. 9.99 (978-1-60266-898-0(1)) Xulon Pr., Inc.
Heckel, Jim. Hit from Behind. 2008. 92p. pap. 10.99 (978-1-60791-034-3(9)) Xulon Pr., Inc.
Hedges, Andrew H. & Holzapfel, Richard Neitzel, eds. Within These Prison Walls: Lorenzo Snow's Record Book 1886 - 1897. 2010. (Illus.). 216p. 21.99 (978-0-8425-2762-0(1), Brigham Young Univ. Religious Studies Ctr.) Brigham Young Univ.
Hedrick, Charles W., et al. When Faith Meets Reason: Religion Scholars Reflect on Their Spiritual Journeys. Hedrick, Charles W., ed. 2008. 160p. pap. 20.00 (978-1-59815-010-0(3)) Polebridge Pr.
Heidish, Marcy. Defiant Daughters: Christian Women of Conscience. 2010. 256p. pap. 16.99 (978-0-7648-1950-6(X)) Liguori Pubns.
Heinrich, Ira. The Tenderness of Stone. 2008. 139p. pap. 18.96 (978-0-615-18695-5(5)) Girl Marga Pr.
Heisler, Jay & Heisler, Paulette. A Lesson for the Teacher: A Plan from Above. 2009. 92p. pap. 10.99 (978-1-60791-893-6(5)) Xulon Pr., Inc.
Henderson-Davis, Beth Lee. Death's Doorbell Rang for Me. 2008. 124p. pap. 19.95 (978-1-60563-759-4(9)) PublishAmerica, Inc.
Hendrickson, Sara. The King of Kings: A Biography. 143p. pap. 14.95 (978-1-892861-18-4(6)) Vision Publishing Group.
Henson Jr., William Plato. Stupid Things I Have Done, 1 vol. 2010. 100p. pap. 16.95 (978-1-4489-7451-1(8)) PublishAmerica, Inc.
Hernández, Charlie. Dare to Be Transparent. 2009. 208p. pap. 15.99 (978-1-60791-876-9(5)) Xulon Pr., Inc.
Herndon, Larry. In the Cool of the Day. 2009. 306p. pap. 29.95 (978-1-4241-9275-5(7)) PublishAmerica, Inc.
Herrera, Michael. Rendezvous with Divine Destiny: The Spiritual Journey of a Vietnam Veteran. 2007. 136p. per. 24.95 (978-1-4241-6732-6(9)) PublishAmerica, Inc.
Herrington, Loretta M. Piece of Soul Through the Heart: A Soul's Journey. 2011. 80p. pap. 9.99 (978-1-4634-5254-4(3)) AuthorHouse.
Hester, Thomas H. There by the Grace of God Go I. 2006. 134p. pap. 14.00 (978-1-932657-65-4(7)) Third Millennium Pubns.
Hibbert, John. Upon This Rock: A Life Story of Simon Peter. 2010. 248p. pap. 25.85 (978-1-4520-4638-9(7)) AuthorHouse.
Hickey, Marilyn. Legacy of Faith Collection: Marilyn Hickey. 2010. 368p. 22.99 (978-1-60683-028-4(7)) Harrison House Pubs.
Hicks, Philip T. & Grage, Kim. The Cross & the ,357 Magnum. 2007. (Illus.). xi, 243p. pap. (978-0-88270-320-6(X)) Bridge-Logos Foundation.
Hicks, Tim. Walking with My Savior. 2008. 172p. pap. 14.96 (978-1-4357-6051-6(4)) Lulu Enterprises Inc.
Higgins, Brent, et al. I Would Die for You: One Student's Story of Passion, Service & Faith. 2008. (Illus.). 224p. (YA). pap. 13.99 (978-0-8007-3244-8(8)) Revell.
Higgins, Gregory C. Profiles in Discipleship: Stories of Faith & Courage. 2012. (978-1-61643-053-5(2)); 272p. pap. 19.95 (978-0-8091-4745-8(9)) Paulist Pr.
Hill, Anthony. Parsifal's Journal: Being the Life & Concerns of Christ. 2009. (Illus.). 184p. pap. (978-1-84748-565-6(0)) Athena Pr.
Hill, Dana Maria. Blazing Guns, Wild Horses, & the Grace of God: The James Kilpatrick Story. 2011. 112p. 21.99 (978-1-4567-4397-0(X)) AuthorHouse.
Hill, Jamie C. Inspiration on a Poetic Level. 2008. 100p. per. 9.99 (978-1-60477-739-0(7)) Xulon Pr., Inc.
Hillard, Judith. Other Woman at the Well. 2006. pap. 14.99 (978-1-60034-877-8(7)) Xulon Pr., Inc.
Hiltz, William. Deliverance to the Captives. 2009. 188p. pap. 14.99 (978-1-60791-418-1(2)) Xulon Pr., Inc.
Hippen, Karyn Gall. Make Me New: One woman's fight to mend a broken Past. 2009. pap. 14.99 (978-1-60799-782-5(7)) Tate Publishing & Enterprises, LLC.
Hitchens, Peter. The Rage Against God: How Atheism Led Me to Faith, 1 vol. 2010. (ENG.). 240p. 22.99 (978-0-310-32031-9(3)) Zondervan.
Hjelde, Sigurd. Sigmund Mowinckel und seine Zeit: Leben und Werk eines norwegischen Alttestamentlers. 2006. (Forschungen zum Alten Testament Ser.: Vol. 50). (GER., Illus.). 365p. 119.00 (978-3-16-148734-7(6)) Mohr Siebeck GmbH & Co. KG DEU. Dist: Eisenbrauns, Inc.
Hoch, Wesley A. Dai Uy Hoch: A Legend in Remote Seas - U. S. N. Military Advisor to the Junk Force - The Strangest War Armada in Naval History. 2009. 444p. pap. 22.99 (978-1-61579-394-5(1)) Xulon Pr., Inc.
Hodges, George. Henry Codman Potter, Seventh Bishop of New York. 2009. 416p. pap. 33.75 (978-1-115-57634-5(8)) BiblioBazaar.
—Henry Codman Potter, Seventh Bishop of New York. 2009. 276p. pap. (978-0-217-48215-8(5)) Books LLC.
—Saints & Heroes since the Middle Ages. 2009. 356p. 33.99 (978-1-116-88855-3(6)); 356p. 38.99 (978-1-116-88854-6(8)); (ENG.). 355p. pap. 26.99 (978-1-116-88858-4(0), BiblioLife); 356p. pap. 32.75 (978-1-116-88856-0(4)); (ENG.). 355p. pap. 25.99 (978-1-116-88859-1(9), BiblioLife); 356p. pap. 31.75 (978-1-116-88857-7(2)) BiblioBazaar.
—Saints & Heroes since the Middle Ages. 2010. 86p. pap. 20.00 (978-1-152-03676-5(9)) General Bks. LLC.
—Saints & Heroes since the Middle Ages. 2010. 352p. 46.95 (978-1-161-39066-7(9)) Kessinger Publishing, LLC.
—Saints & Heroes since the Middle Ages. 2007. (ENG.). 352p. per. (978-1-4067-6831-2(6)) Read Bks.
—Saints & Heroes since the Middle Ages (Yesterday's Classics) 2006. (J). per. 9.95 (978-1-59915-094-9(8)) Yesterday's Classics.
Hodgson, John. The Nature of the Scarecrow Kid. 2007. 75p. pap. 15.95 (978-1-4357-0178-6(X)) Lulu Enterprises Inc.
Hoffman, Lee. My Personal Walk & Talk with Jesus. 2011. 208p. 33.95 (978-1-4497-1134-4(0)); pap. 17.95 (978-1-4497-1135-1(9)) Author Solutions, Inc. (WestBow Pr.).
Holland, John. The Spirit Whisperer: Chronicles of a Medium. 2010. (ENG.). 264p. pap. 15.95 (978-1-4019-2287-0(2)) Hay Hse., Inc.
Hollis, Heidi. Jesus Is No Joke: A True Story of an Unlikely Witness Who Saw Jesus. 2008. 188p. pap. 16.95 (978-0-615-19005-1(7)) Level Head Publishing.
Holzapfel, Lawrence J. The Ignorance of God, 1 vol. 2010. 166p. pap. 24.95 (978-1-4489-7933-2(1)) PublishAmerica, Inc.
Honer, Mary Andersen. The Downing Legacy: Six Decades at Rift Valley Academy. 2010. 196p. 26.95 (978-1-4502-1368-4(5)) iUniverse, Inc.
—The Downing Legacy: Six Decades at Rift Valley Academy. 2010. 196p. pap. 16.95 (978-1-4502-1366-0(9)) iUniverse, Inc.
Hooper, Andrew. Sons of God, Come Forth!!! 2007. 112p. per. (978-1-55452-182-1(3)) Essence Publishing.
Horton, Edward Allen. Philosophy of an Angel: An Autobiography of One Man's Trials & Redemption. 2007. 148p. per. 11.99 (978-1-60247-293-8(9)) Tate Publishing & Enterprises, LLC.
Hough, John B. Solitude. 2007. (ENG.). 228p. per. 39.99 (978-0-7618-3720-6(5)) Hamilton Bks.
Houser, Leon. Only the Strong Shall Survive. 2009. 56p. pap. 10.49 (978-1-4343-7915-3(9)) AuthorHouse.
Hovey, Alvah. Barnas Sears, a Christian Educator. 2009. 80p. pap. (978-1-4590-9543-4(X)) Books LLC.
—Barnas Sears, a Christian Educator. 2009. 78p. pap. 14.14 (978-0-217-77592-2(6)) General Bks. LLC.
Howard, Sara M. Tuesday s Grace. 2011. 222p. pap. 15.99 (978-1-61215-589-0(8)) Xulon Pr., Inc.
Howat, Irene. Patricia St. John: The Story Behind the Stories. 2008. (Trail Blazers Ser.). (ENG.). 160p. pap. 8.99 (978-1-84550-328-4(7)) Christian Focus Pubns. GBR. Dist: STL Distribution North America.
Howat, Irene & Orme, Georgie. In Strength Not Our Own: A Maasai Medical Miracle. 2008. (ENG., Illus.). 256p. pap. 11.99 (978-1-84550-334-5(1)) Christian Focus Pubns. GBR. Dist: STL Distribution North America.
Howeth, Paul. The Way It Was, Paul's Story. 2011. 24p. pap. 16.95 (978-1-4560-9111-8(5)) PublishAmerica, Inc.
Hsu, Lily M. The Unforgettable Memoirs. 2011. 394p. pap. 20.99 (978-1-61215-787-0(4)); pap. 20.99 (978-1-61215-786-3(6)) Xulon Pr., Inc.
Huckabee, Mike. A Simple Christmas: Twelve Stories That Celebrate the True Holiday Spirit. (ENG.). (gr. 12). 2012. 240p. pap. 15.00 (978-1-59523-098-0(X)) 2009. 160p. 22.95 (978-1-59523-062-1(9)) Penguin Group (USA) Inc. (Sentinel).
Hudson, Henry & Hudson, Shirley. Recollections & Reflections. 2010. 248p. pap. 19.95 (978-1-4502-4281-3(2)) iUniverse, Inc.
Hughes, Bruce D. The Snare Is Broken. 2011. 364p. pap. 20.99 (978-1-61215-474-9(3)) Xulon Pr., Inc.

Hughes, Nancy. Healing for the Heart a Guide for Survival in the World of the Widow. 2007. 60p. per. 9.99 *(978-1-60266-974-1(0))* Xulon Pr., Inc.
Huhs, Christine. Furnace of Affliction. 2007. (ENG.). 164p. per. 13.95 *(978-0-7414-3962-8(X))* Infinity Publishing.
Hull, Henry. Memoir of the Life & Religious Labours of Henry Hull. 2007. (ENG.). 340p. 46.95 *(978-0-548-14002-4(2))* 2006. pap. 31.95 *(978-1-4286-5195-1(0))* Kessinger Publishing, LLC.
Humphrey, Stinson E. All That I Am. 2011. 280p. 27.48 *(978-1-4269-5548-8(0))*; pap. 17.48 *(978-1-4269-5547-1(2))* Trafford Publishing.
Humphreys, Brian. The Accidental Christian. 2008. 180p. pap. 53.99 *(978-1-4389-1351-3(6))* AuthorHouse.
Hundley, Mandisa. Idoleyes: My New Perspective on Faith, Fat & Fame. 2008. (ENG., Illus.). 288p. pap. 15.99 *(978-1-4143-1603-1(8))* Tyndale Hse. Pubs.
Hunt, C. Robert B Thieme, Jr - His Ancestry, His Life. 2007. 124p. per. 11.95 *(978-1-59858-234-5(8))* Dog Ear Publishing, LLC.
Hunt, Ruth. East Wind: A Survivor's True Story of Faith Inside the Gulag of World War II. 2007. (ENG., Illus.). 240p. per. 12.99 *(978-1-928660-37-8(1))* Berean Call, The.
Huyard, David. God Who Are You? 2009. 224p. pap. 15.99 *(978-1-61579-152-1(3))* Xulon Pr., Inc.
Hylton-Lindsay, Althea. Marrying a LIE: Mistaking a MONSTER for a MIRACLE. 2006. (ENG.). 192p. per. 24.95 *(978-1-4241-2311-7(9))* PublishAmerica, Inc.
Ibekwe, Jada M. Defeating the Double Mind. 2009. 80p. pap. 15.49 *(978-1-4343-8435-5(7))* AuthorHouse.
I'D Rather Be Better, Than Bitter. 2007. 460p. per. 23.99 *(978-1-60266-450-0(1))* Xulon Pr., Inc.
Igho, Aforen S. O. G. Discover the Real you & Change Your World. 2010. 178p. pap. 14.99 *(978-1-60957-677-6(2))* Xulon Pr., Inc.
Ilibagiza, Immaculée & Erwin, Steve. The Boy Who Met Jesus: Segatashya of Kibeho. 2011. (ENG., Illus.). 256p. 19.95 *(978-1-4019-3581-8(8))* Hay Hse., Inc.
Ingwerson, Lucille. The Dove & the Sparrow. 2009. 260p. pap. 19.95 *(978-1-4401-5456-0(2))* iUniverse, Inc.
Inman, Cecil. A Celebration of Life. 2006. pap. 17.99 *(978-1-59781-499-7(7))* Xulon Pr., Inc.
Irish, Patrick. The Day God Asked Me a Question. 2007. 243p. per. 18.99 *(978-1-59886-943-9(4))* Tate Publishing & Enterprises, LLC.
Irivuzumugabe, Eric & Lawrence, Tracey D. My Father, Maker of the Trees: How I Survived the Rwandan Genocide. 2009. 208p. 17.99 *(978-0-8010-1320-1(8))* Baker Bks.
Irwin, Mary. Luna No Es Suficiente: Moon Is Not Enough. (SPA.). 256p. *(978-84-7228-467-8(0)*, 220560) Clie, Editorial.
Irwin, Russ. The Peanut Butter Man. 2010. pap. 14.99 *(978-1-61566-726-0(1))* Tate Publishing & Enterprises, LLC.
Isaacs, Susan E. Angry Conversations with God. 2011. (ENG.). 256p. pap. 13.99 *(978-0-446-55544-9(4))* FaithWords.
Isley, Brouycie. The Deacon's Story. 2008. 132p. pap. 19.99 *(978-1-4363-7173-5(2))* Xlibris Corp.
Ivison, Pam. In the Palm of His Hand. 2008. 224p. pap. *(978-1-55452-271-2(4))* Essence Publishing.
Jackson, Ardelia. Singled Out: Chosen by God. 2009. 104p. pap. 10.99 *(978-1-60791-725-0(4))* Xulon Pr., Inc.
Jackson, Arlene. My Walking Miracle. 2009. pap. 11.99 *(978-1-60799-428-2(3))* Tate Publishing & Enterprises, LLC.
Jackson Coleman, Sheila. The Dark Side of a Miracle. 2009. 92p. pap. 12.99 *(978-1-4389-9142-9(8))* AuthorHouse.
Jackson, Denise J. It's All about Him: Finding the Love of My Life, 0 vols. 2007. (Illus.). 256p. 24.99 *(978-0-7852-2776-2(8))* Nelson, Thomas Inc.
Jackson, Gene. The Pew Warmers. 2008. 192p. pap. 13.99 *(978-1-60477-607-2(2))* Xulon Pr., Inc.
Jackson, J. Not by Chance but for the Glory of God. 2010. 85p. pap. 14.95 *(978-1-4327-5688-8(5))* Outskirts Pr., Inc.
Jackson, Rachel. Pete's Story: A Remarkable Account of Tragedy & Hope. 2006. (ENG.). 256p. per. 14.99 *(978-1-86024-545-9(5))* Authentic Media.
Jackson SFO, Vickie L. Holy Ground in L. A. 2006. 77p. pap. 16.95 *(978-1-4241-4945-2(2))* PublishAmerica, Inc.
Jacob, Richard Alfred. When He Has Tried Me. 2008. 252p. pap. 15.99 *(978-1-60647-437-2(5))* Xulon Pr., Inc.
Jacobs, Alan. Looking Before & After: Testimony & the Christian Life. 2008. (Stob Lectures 2006 Ser.). 120p. pap. 14.00 *(978-0-8028-4981-6(4))* Eerdmans, William B. Publishing Co.
—The Narnian: The Life & Imagination of C. S. Lewis. 2008. (Plus Ser.). (ENG., Illus.). 384p. pap. 14.95 *(978-0-06-144872-0(9)*, HarperOne) HarperCollins Pubs.
Jacobs, K. Ellen. Designed by the Master: Women of Permeating Influence. 2010. pap. 16.99 *(978-1-60791-689-5(4))* Xulon Pr., Inc.
Jagwe, Kim. God's Perfect Size: Gain Victory, Lose Food Addiction for Life. 2010. pap. 12.99 *(978-1-61663-040-9(X))* Tate Publishing & Enterprises, LLC.
Jamerson, Ann. God's Grace Is Sufficient, Ann. 2006. 80p. per. 9.95 *(978-1-58275-176-4(5))* Black Forest Pr.
Jane & Rebecca. Why Me, Oh Lord, Why Me? 2009. 208p. pap. 13.95 *(978-1-4327-4146-4(2))* Outskirts Pr., Inc.
Janis, Larry W. Greasy Creek. 2010. 108p. 28.95 *(978-1-4497-0452-0(2))*; pap. 11.95 *(978-1-4497-0451-3(4))* Author Solutions, Inc. (WestBow Pr.).
Jeffers, R. A Harvest of Memories: Farming Reflections on Times Gone by: A Story. 2006. (Illus.). 244p. per. 18.25 *(978-1-4251-0522-8(X))* Trafford Publishing.
Jeffries, Josephine. Lost Soul. 2007. 280p. per. 15.99 *(978-1-60477-174-9(7))* Xulon Pr., Inc.
Jeffs, Brent W. & Szalavitz, Maia. Lost Boy: The True Story of One Man's Exile from a Polygamist Cult & His Brave Journey to Reclaim His Life. 2010. (ENG.). 256p. pap. 14.99 *(978-0-7679-3178-6(5))* Broadway Bks.
Jenkins, Brenda. How My Mother Became My Guardian Angel. 2011. 280p. 29.99 ***(978-1-4568-3371-8(5))***; pap. 19.99 ***(978-1-4568-3370-1(7))*** Xlibris Corp.
Jenkins, Christal M. N. Discovering the True Love Within: Uncovering a Secret Never Meant to Be Kept Unknown. 2009. 120p. pap. 11.99 *(978-1-61579-026-5(8))* Xulon Pr., Inc.
Jenkins, Susan Elaine. Scandalon: Running from Shame & Finding God's Scandalous Love. 2009. 288p. pap. 13.99 *(978-0-9818929-0-0(6))* CLADACH Publishing.
Jenkins, Tonie. God Is Great: The Undeniable Truth - 52 Inspirations of Hope & Faith. 2010. (Little Book. Big Idea Ser.). (ENG.). 176p. pap. 15.00 *(978-1-57826-292-2(5))* Hatherleigh Co., Ltd., The.
Jenkins, Willie Mae. My Calling: A True Life Story, 1 vol. 2010. 58p. pap. 16.95 *(978-1-61582-664-3(5))* PublishAmerica, Inc.
Jernigan, A. Jack. The Harvest: Finding the Best. 2009. 683p. pap. 27.50 *(978-1-4343-7283-3(9))* AuthorHouse.
Jerubaal, Donovan & Jerubaal, Claire. The Day the Holy Spirit Blew In Vol. 1: Man Eater. 2009. 248p. pap. 15.99 *(978-1-60791-878-3(1))* Xulon Pr., Inc.
Jessee, Dean C., et al, eds. The Joseph Smith Papers Vol. 1: Journals, 1832-1839. 2008. 512p. 49.95 *(978-1-57008-849-0(7))* Deseret Bk. Co.
Jimason, James A. Chapter Two: The Winds of Change. 2007. pap. 15.95 *(978-0-7414-3967-3(0))* Infinity Publishing.
Jiosa, Susan Taber. Never Let Go of God, He Is Real! 2007. 121p. pap. 19.95 *(978-1-4241-2670-5(3))* PublishAmerica, Inc.
John Bunyan. Grace Abounding to the Chief of Sinners. 2007. (ENG.). 136p. pap. 18.99 *(978-1-4346-3844-1(8))* BiblioBazaar.
—Grace Abounding to the Chief of Sinners. 2010. 132p. pap. 4.49 *(978-1-60386-289-9(7)*, Merchant Bks.) Rough Draft Printing.
—Grace Abounding to the Chief of Sinners. l.t. ed. 2007. (ENG.). 150p. pap. 19.99 *(978-1-4346-3845-8(6))* BiblioBazaar.
John, Merica Saint. Let the Seed Fall: Growing from a Seed to a Tree by God's Power. 2011. 220p. 25.45 *(978-1-4269-5607-2(X))*; pap. 15.45 *(978-1-4269-5605-8(3))* Trafford Publishing.
Johnny. This Is My Life, My Journey: A Look into the Past. 2011. 80p. pap. 10.95 *(978-1-4502-9210-8(0))* iUniverse, Inc.
Johnson, Aaron & Rev. Aaron Johnson With Deb Cleveland. Man from Macedonia: My life of service, struggle, faith, & Hope. 2010. 272p. pap. 19.95 *(978-1-4497-0029-4(2)*, WestBow Pr.) Author Solutions, Inc.
Johnson, Carolyn. In the Stink of Life Smell the Rose of Sharon. 2007. 184p. per. 13.99 *(978-1-60477-282-1(4))* Xulon Pr., Inc.
Johnson, Clifton H., ed. God Struck Me Dead: Voices of Ex-Slaves. 2011. 202p. pap. 22.00 *(978-1-61097-047-1(0)*, Wipf and Stock) Wipf & Stock Pubs.
Johnson, Dale A. Your Life Is None of Your Business. 2009. 116p. pap. 14.94 *(978-0-557-00375-4(X))* Lulu Enterprises Inc.
Johnson, Maria Poggi. Strangers & Neighbors: What I Have Learned about Christianity by Living among Orthodox Jews, 0 vols. 2006. 160p. pap. 13.99 *(978-0-8499-1151-4(6))* Nelson, Thomas Inc.
Johnson, Vernard. 1000 Consecutive Days of Fasting. 2010. 320p. 29.99 *(978-1-4490-7012-0(4))*; pap. 19.99 *(978-1-4490-7011-3(6))* AuthorHouse.
Jon'E. I Pray the Lord My Soul to Take, 1 vol. 2009. 130p. pap. 24.95 *(978-1-60813-038-2(X))* PublishAmerica, Inc.
Jones, Anne. By His Hand. 2007. 124p. per. 10.99 *(978-1-60034-872-3(6))* Xulon Pr., Inc.
Jones, Barbara. Little Is Much When God Is in It. 2011. 108p. pap. 11.92 ***(978-1-4269-9121-9(5))*** Trafford Publishing.
Jones, Barbara S. Through the Valleys. 2006. 153p. pap. 13.95 *(978-0-7414-3291-9(9))* Infinity Publishing.
Jones, Carlos. 25 Years to Freedom: My Journey to GOD. 2006. 65p. pap. 16.95 *(978-1-4241-5094-6(9))* PublishAmerica, Inc.
Jones, Debby Fields. A Rose among the Ashes: Discovering Hope When There Doesn't Seem to Be Any. 2007. (ENG.). 144p. per. 14.99 *(978-1-4141-0588-8(6))* Pleasant Word.
Jones, Denise. Who Said It Couldn't Be Done? 2010. 312p. 27.99 *(978-1-4520-0353-5(X))*; (ENG.). pap. 21.95 *(978-1-4520-0354-2(8))* AuthorHouse.
Jones, Dennis. Pressing On... (Perseverance until Deliverance) 2010. 124p. 22.49 *(978-1-4520-2039-6(6))*; pap. 11.99 *(978-1-4520-2038-9(8))* AuthorHouse.
Jones, Dennis R. Climbing Out of Adversity: A Story of Life's Lessons to Encourage the Heart, Awaken the Church, & Challenge the Nation. 2011. xi, 257p. E-Book ***(978-1-61638-465-4(4))*** Excel Bks.
Jones Hudson, Emily. Water-Walking Faith. 2009. 80p. pap. 11.49 *(978-1-4389-3363-4(0))* AuthorHouse.
Jones, Janice. Still Standing. 2007. (ENG.). 80p. per. 14.95 *(978-0-9779445-8-3(1))* Zoe Life Publishing.
Jones, Ken. A Prodigal Return: Reflections from a Grateful Heart. 2009. pap. 29.99 *(978-1-60799-965-2(X))* Tate Publishing & Enterprises, LLC.
Jones, Lot. Memoir of Mrs. Sarah Louisa Taylor or an. 2006. pap. 30.95 *(978-1-4286-5997-1(8))* Kessinger Publishing, LLC.
Jones, Marlene Stewart. Sacred Memories. 2011. 496p. 34.99 ***(978-1-4568-4583-4(7))***; pap. 23.99 ***(978-1-4568-4582-7(9))*** Xlibris Corp.
Jones, Nick. The Joshua Davidson, Christian: the Story of the Life of One Who, In. Loud, Halah H., ed. 2007. (ENG.). 332p. per. 30.95 *(978-1-4304-4561-6(0))* Kessinger Publishing, LLC.
Jones, Vanessa L. Cracked, Broken, Shattered... Vessel of Honor: Book 3: Bills to God's Power. 2007. 15.00 *(978-0-8059-8411-8(9))* Dorrance Publishing Co., Inc.
—Cracked, Broken, Shattered... Vessel of Honor: Book 4: Where Is He? 2007. 14.00 *(978-0-8059-8407-1(0))* Dorrance Publishing Co., Inc.
Jordan, Bridgett. Our Journey to Faith. 2010. 52p. pap. 9.95 *(978-1-61507-172-2(5))* Cross Bks. Publishing.
Jordan, Joe. Hangin' Out with God: A Personal Journey into the World of Joy. 2008. 92p. pap. 10.99 *(978-1-60791-206-4(6))* Xulon Pr., Inc.
Jordan, Robert Smith. A Newsman Remembered: Ralph Burdette Jordan & His Times 1896-1953. 2011. 216p. 27.95 *(978-1-4502-8956-6(8))* iUniverse, Inc.
Journey of Faith. 2009. 292p. pap. 16.99 *(978-1-60791-260-6(0))* Xulon Pr., Inc.
Judkins, Joe. I Don't Blaspheme the Lord Do I? 2011. 120p. pap. 9.95 ***(978-1-935105-94-7(9))*** Avid Readers Publishing Group.
Juma, Florence Akumu. All Things Work Together for Good. 2010. *(978-1-926676-97-5(1))* Word Alive Pr.
Kafer, Bruce. Santa in & Around Town, 1 vol. 2009. 59p. pap. 16.95 *(978-1-60749-920-6(7))* PublishAmerica, Inc.
Karefa-Smart, John Albert Musselman. Rainbow Happenings. 2010. (ENG.). 188p. 29.99 *(978-1-4415-0168-4(1))* Xlibris Corp.
Karns, Mark F. The Serpent Messiah: His History, His Views & His Future Plans. 2010. 148p. (ENG.). 34.95 *(978-1-4490-0513-9(6))*; pap. 19.95 *(978-1-4490-0512-2(8))* AuthorHouse.
Kasich, John. Every Other Monday: Twenty Years of Life, Lunch, Faith, & Friendship. (ENG.). 240p. 2011. pap. 15.00 *(978-1-4391-4828-0(7))* 2010. 25.00 *(978-1-4391-4827-3(9))* Atria Bks. (Beyond Words/Atria Bks.).
Kate. Hearts of Stone. 2008. 108p. pap. 10.99 *(978-1-4389-2911-8(0))* AuthorHouse.
Kavanagh, Julia. Women of Christianity, Exemplary for Acts of Piety & Charity. 2007. (ENG.). 486p. 53.95 *(978-0-548-15553-0(4))*; pap. 38.95 *(978-1-4304-4992-8(6))* Kessinger Publishing, LLC.
Kazel, Dorothy Chapon & Flannery, Sr. Mary Ann. The Voice: A missionary's call to give her Life. 2008. 156p. pap. 13.99 *(978-1-60647-321-4(2))* Xulon Pr., Inc.
Keilstrup, Duane Victor. The Christian Professor in the Secular University. 2010. 280p. pap. 16.99 *(978-1-60957-791-9(4))* Xulon Pr., Inc.
Kell, Tricia. Chain of Miracles. 2008. 432p. pap. *(978-1-897373-23-1(6))* Word Alive Pr.
Keller, Ursula E. Reflections of My Life. 2007. 100p. per. 9.99 *(978-1-60477-343-9(X))* Xulon Pr., Inc.
Kelly, J. N. D. & Walsh, Michael. A Dictionary of Popes. 2nd ed. 2010. (ENG., Illus.). 384p. pap. 19.95 *(978-0-19-929581-4(6))* Oxford Univ. Pr., Inc.
Kelly, Jill. Without a Word: How a Boy's Unspoken Love Changed Everything. 2010. (ENG., Illus.). 272p. 23.99 *(978-0-446-56337-6(4))* FaithWords.
Kemp, Elkan V. The Disciple Whom Jesus Loved. 2008. 248p. pap. 15.99 *(978-1-4343-7205-5(7))* AuthorHouse.
Kemp, Tracy A. Abused, Confused, Misused: A Women saved by the grace of God becomes a Conqueror. 2007. 68p. per. 9.95 *(978-0-595-43961-4(6))* iUniverse, Inc.
Kennedy, Kimberley. Left at the Altar: My Story of Hope & Healing for Every Woman Who Has Felt the Heartbreak of Rejection, 0 vols. 2009. 192p. pap. 14.99 *(978-0-7852-2878-3(0))* Nelson, Thomas Inc.
Kenworthy-Browne CJ, Christina, ed. Mary Ward (1585-1645) 'A Briefe Relation', with Autobiographical Fragments & a Selection of Letters. 2008. (Catholic Record Society Ser.). (Illus.). 90.00 *(978-91-0-011194-6(5))* Catholic Record Society GBR. Dist: Boydell & Brewer, Inc.
Ker, John. The Psalms in History & Biography. 2007. (ENG.). 244p. 41.95 *(978-0-548-12671-4(2))* Kessinger Publishing, LLC.
—Psalms in History & Biography. 2006. pap. 26.95 *(978-1-4286-3663-7(3))* Kessinger Publishing, LLC.
Kerr, Lady Cecil. Teresa Helena Higginson Servant of God the Spouse of the Crucified. 2008. 404p. pap. *(978-0-85244-181-7(9))* Gracewing, Ltd.
Key, James D. Touch-and-Go: From the Streets of South Central Los Angeles to the War in Iraq. 2010. 172p. pap. 12.50 *(978-1-60911-342-1(X)*, Eloquent Bks.) AEG Literary Publishing Services, Inc.
Kidd, Virginia Bates. Stones of Grace. 2010. 72p. pap. 11.99 *(978-1-61507-113-5(X))* Cross Bks. Publishing.
Kidder, Virelle. The Best Life Ain't Easy: But It's Worth It. 2008. (ENG.). 176p. pap. 13.99 *(978-0-8024-4862-0(3))* Moody Pubs.
Kiefert, Dwight. On Our Way Home: A True Story of a Family's Triumph over Tragedy. 2007. 77p. per. 8.99 *(978-1-59886-717-6(2))* Tate Publishing & Enterprises, LLC.
Kincaid, Rebekah. A Rainbow in the Darkness. 2007. 56p. per. 16.95 *(978-1-4241-6972-6(0))* PublishAmerica, Inc.
Kincheloe, Donna. I Never Walk the Halls Alone. 2007. (ENG.). 160p. pap. 18.95 *(978-1-932124-90-3(X))* ACW Pr.
King, Heather. Redeemed: Stumbling Toward God, Sanity, & the Peace That Passes All Understanding. 2009. (ENG.). 256p. (gr. 12-18). 16.00 *(978-0-14-311506-9(5)*, Penguin (Non-Classics)) Penguin Group (USA) Inc.
King, Mike. The God Delusion Revisited. 2007. 336p. 52.50 *(978-1-4303-2008-1(7))*; pap. 31.50 *(978-1-4303-1268-0(8))* Lulu Enterprises Inc.
King, Minister VerNell. A Legal Question. 2006. (ENG.). 56p. per. 16.95 *(978-1-4241-4485-3(X))* PublishAmerica, Inc.
Kingsmore, Barbara. I Remember Grandma. 2008. 164p. pap. 24.95 *(978-1-60441-091-4(4))* PublishAmerica, Inc.
Kinley, Kenneth Cowboy. Spending Time with God. 2010. pap. 14.99 *(978-1-61579-805-6(6))* Xulon Pr., Inc.
Klenk, Phyllis K. Wounded Trapped & Voiceless... All Things Are Possible. 2010. pap. 14.99 *(978-1-61579-707-3(6))* Xulon Pr., Inc.
Kline, Angela. Take Your Place. 2009. 268p. pap. 16.99 *(978-1-60791-261-3(9))* Xulon Pr., Inc.
Knotek, Pastor Jim. Angels & Miracles, Grief & Hope. 2011. 180p. 23.95 ***(978-1-4620-2468-1(8))***; pap. 13.95 ***(978-1-4620-2467-4(X))*** iUniverse, Inc.
Kobayashi, Aiko Sano. In God's Embrace. 2009. pap. 12.99 *(978-1-60696-708-9(8))* Tate Publishing & Enterprises, LLC.
Koehler, Mark. Jc & Me: A Relationship, A Journey. 2009. 148p. pap. 12.95 *(978-1-4389-4472-2(1))* AuthorHouse.
Kolb, Patricia. He Restoreth My Soul. 2011. 94p. pap. 10.99 ***(978-1-61379-319-0(7))*** Xulon Pr., Inc.
Kopaska, Kc & Liston, Carole. Afterburn: the Kc Kopaska Story: A Story of Tragedy, Redemption, & Transformation. 2011. 172p. pap. 13.95 ***(978-1-4497-1890-9(6)***, WestBow Pr.) Author Solutions, Inc.
Kosak, Hellen Battle. If I Forget You, O Jerusalem. 2008. 380p. 32.99 *(978-1-60647-034-3(5))*; pap. 20.99 *(978-1-60647-033-6(7))* Xulon Pr., Inc.
Kotzabassi, Sofia. Das hagiographische Dossier der heiligen Theodosia von Konstantinopel: Einleitung, Edition und Kommentar. 2009. (Byzantinisches Archiv Ser.).Tr. of Hagiographic Dossier of Saint Theodosia of Constantinople. (GER.). XV, 196p. 140.00 *(978-3-11-021985-2(9))*; 210.00 ***(978-3-11-173622-8(9))*** De Gruyter, Walter Inc.
Kowalska, Maria Faustina. Saint Maria Faustina Kowalska Diary: Divine Mercy in My Soul. 3rd ed. 2008. (ENG., Illus.). 772p. lthr. 29.95 *(978-1-59614-190-2(5))* Marian Pr.
Kramer, Richard. From a Simple Man. 2007. 66p. per. 8.99 *(978-1-59886-795-4(4))* Tate Publishing & Enterprises, LLC.
Krazeise, Andrea. He Came Back for Me: A Journey to Restoration. 2009. 232p. pap. 15.99 *(978-1-60791-835-6(8))* Xulon Pr., Inc.
Krehbiel, Allie. Allie's Story: ... of the Miracles of God. 2009. 124p. pap. 11.99 *(978-1-61579-186-6(8))* Xulon Pr., Inc.
Kristi Bowman. Journey To: A Woman's Story of Emotional Healing & Spiritual Awakening. 2009. 284p. 30.95 *(978-1-4401-7913-6(1))*; pap. 20.95 *(978-1-4401-7911-2(5))* iUniverse, Inc.
Krusen, Cristobal. Let Me Have My Son. 2007. 192p. per. 13.95 *(978-0-9787554-2-3(1))* Hollywood Jesus Bks.
Kuhn, Craig. From Cult to Christ. 2007. 264p. per. 15.99 *(978-1-60266-620-7(2))* Xulon Pr., Inc.
Kuncaitis, Amy. Joy in the Morning. 2007. 96p. per. 9.99 *(978-1-60266-800-3(0))* Xulon Pr., Inc.
Küng, Hans. Disputed Truth Vol. 2: Memoirs, Volume 2. 2008. (ENG., Illus.). 576p. 34.95 *(978-0-8264-9910-3(4))* Continuum International Publishing Group, Ltd. GBR. Dist: National Bk. Network.
Kuntz, M. L. Guillaume Postel: Prophet of the Restitution of All ThingsHis Life & Thought. 2010. (International Archives of the History of Ideas / archives internationales d'histoire des Idées Ser.). 304p. pap. 279.00 *(978-90-481-8268-8(9)*, 9048182689) Springer.
Kurtz, Elam S. & Kurtz, Michael D. Crossings: Memoirs of a Mountain Medical Doctor. 2010. 108p. pap. 11.95 *(978-1-4502-6246-0(5))* iUniverse, Inc.
Kushnir, Vera. Only One Life: Story of Missionary Resilience. Date not set. (RUS.). 350p. (Orig.). pap. 9.95 *(978-1-885024-05-3(3))* Slavic Christian Publishing.
Kwitchen, Mary Augustine. James Alphonsus Mcmaster A Study in Amer. 2006. pap. 26.95 *(978-1-4286-6130-1(1))* Kessinger Publishing, LLC.
Kyeyune, Pastor Stephen. When God Calls a Man. 2010. 624p. pap. 23.49 *(978-1-4520-0230-9(4))* AuthorHouse.
Kyle, I. Of Intense Brightness: The Spirituality of Uncommon Christian James Brainerd Taylor. 2008. (ENG.). 186p. pap. 33.99 *(978-0-7618-3970-5(4))* Univ. Pr. of America, Inc.
Lacey, Sandra, et al. People Like Us: Life with Rob Lacey, 1 vol. 2011. (ENG.). 272p. pap. 14.99 *(978-0-310-31904-7(8))* Zondervan.
Laine, E. E. Praise God for Tattered Dreams. 2009. 208p. pap. 19.57 *(978-0-578-03375-4(5))* Laine, E.E.
Lake, Jimmy. Footlights, Fistfights, & Femmes: The Jimmy Lake Story. Giblo, Helen, ed. 2011. 258p. 47.95 ***(978-1-258-07402-9(8))*** Literary Licensing, LLC.
Laker, Michael A. The Tourguide. 2011. 266p. pap. 16.99 ***(978-1-61379-199-8(2))*** Xulon Pr., Inc.
—The Tourguide: How God Guided Me from Psychosis to Life in Christ. 2011. 266p. 26.99 ***(978-1-61379-050-2(3))*** Xulon Pr., Inc.
LaMann, J. B. Dark Valley & Beyond. 2007. 244p. 24.99 *(978-1-60034-962-1(5))*; per. 14.99 *(978-1-60034-957-7(9))* Xulon Pr., Inc.
Lamott, Anne. Grace (Eventually) Thoughts on Faith. 2008. (ENG.). 272p. (gr. 12-18). 14.00 *(978-1-59448-287-8(X)*, Riverhead Trade (Paperbacks)) Penguin Group (USA) Inc.
—Grace (Eventually) Thoughts on Faith. l.t. ed. 2007. (Thorndike Core Ser.). 287p. 32.95 *(978-0-7862-9622-4(4))* Thorndike Pr.
—Plan B: Further Thoughts on Faith. l.t. ed. 32.95 *(978-0-7862-7814-5(5)*, Large Print Pr.) Thorndike Pr.
—Traveling Mercies: Some Thoughts on Faith. pap. *(978-0-385-49963-7(9))* Knopf Doubleday Publishing Group.
Lancaster, James Wayne. Preacher Dad to Preacher Son: Prison Letters. 2011. 168p. pap. 13.95 ***(978-1-4497-2657-7(7)***, WestBow Pr.) Author Solutions Inc.
Landis, Jonnie. His Desire Is Toward Me. 2007. 168p. per. 13.99 *(978-1-60266-241-4(X))* Xulon Pr., Inc.

C

Langa, Beki P. Living & Working with Cancer. 2010. (Illus.). 54p. pap. (978-1-84748-713-1(0)) Athena Pr.

Lanny Saumer. My Guardian Angel. 2009. 160p. 24.95 (978-1-4401-6924-3(1)); pap. 14.95 (978-1-4401-6923-6(3)) iUniverse, Inc.

Lapole, H. W. Chip. Rise of the Fallen Man: Deliverance from Bondage & Staying Free. 2008. 68p. pap. 17.95 (978-1-4327-3191-5(2)) Outskirts Pr., Inc.

Laurie, Greg & Vaughn, Ellen Santilli. Lost Boy: My Story. 2011. (ENG.). 256p. pap. 14.99 (978-0-8307-5955-2(7)) Gospel Light Pubns.

Lavender, Debbie. Overcoming Being Overcome. 2009. 180p. pap. 14.99 (978-1-61579-390-7(9)) Xulon Pr., Inc.

Lawrence, Alexander. 2nd Victory in Jesus: Book 3 of the Goins Bricolage: A Saga of Tecumseh & Stonewall Counties in the State of Indiana: 1980-1981. 2010. 488p. 35.95 (978-1-4502-2982-1(4)); pap. 25.95 (978-1-4502-2981-4(6)) iUniverse, Inc.

Lawrence, Jon. See You. 2009. 212p. pap. 14.49 (978-1-4389-7755-3(7)) AuthorHouse.

Lawson, James G. When God's Spirit Falls: How Renowned Christians Received the Holy Spirit. 2007. 366p. per. 12.99 (978-0-88368-604-1(X)) Whitaker Hse.

Lawson, James Gilchrist. Deeper Experiences of Famous Christians. 2009. 206p. pap. (978-0-217-70264-5(3)) Books LLC.

—Deeper Experiences of Famous Christians. 2008. 20.00 (978-1-60416-317-9(8)); pap. 13.00 (978-1-60416-316-2(X)) Reformation Pubs.

—Deeper Experiences of Famous Christians. 3rd l.t. abr. ed. 2007. 184p. per. 9.95 (978-1-59317-180-3(3)) Warner Pr. Pubs.

Lax, Eric. Faith, Interrupted: A Spiritual Journey. 2011. (Vintage Ser.). (ENG.). 288p. pap. 15.95 (978-0-307-45554-3(8), Vintage) Knopf Doubleday Publishing Group.

Leahy, Sr. Kathryn. God's Brat. 2007. 280p. 24.95 (978-1-4327-0502-2(4)); per. 24.95 (978-1-4327-0409-4(5)) Outskirts Pr., Inc.

LeBlanc, Katie & Kushindana, Adimu O. From Caterpillar to Butterfly: New Life in Christ. 2010. xx, 135p. (978-1-4490-5811-1(6)) AuthorHouse.

Ledwith, Stuart. John the Baptist; As His Soul Remembers. 2007. 164p. per. 14.95 (978-0-9627250-1-2(3)) Soul Works International.

Lee, Dallas. The Cotton Patch Evidence: The Story of Clarence Jordan & the Koinonia Farm Experiment (1942Ð1970) 2011. 254p. pap. 28.00 **(978-1-61097-642-8(8)**, Wipf and Stock) Wipf & Stock Pubs.

Lee, Jewel. From Destruction 2 Deliverance: My Damascus Experience. 2011. 48p. pap. 9.99 **(978-1-4634-0282-2(1))** AuthorHouse.

Lee, Joseph. Growing up a Witness, 1 vol. 2009. 73p. pap. 16.95 (978-1-60749-755-4(7)) PublishAmerica, Inc.

Lee, R. L. How I Became Born Again: And other miracles & Testimonials. 2009. pap. 10.99 (978-1-60799-664-4(2)) Tate Publishing & Enterprises, LLC.

Lee, Victoria. Unforgettable Grady. Date not set. pap. (978-1-888225-05-1(X)) A Touch of Heart.

Lehmann, Stephen. Under His Wings: Mission Vietnam. 2011. (ENG., Illus.). 256p. 26.95 **(978-1-937190-07-1(2))** Serenity Bk. Publishers.

LeMaster, Donald. The Lord Is My Shepherd. 2011. pap. 9.99 **(978-1-61777-881-0(8))** Tate Publishing & Enterprises, LLC.

Leonard, Lynn Cochrane. Not by Chance: God's Coincidental Guidance of My Life. 2010. 160p. pap. 13.95 (978-1-4497-0679-1(7), WestBow Pr.) Author Solutions, Inc.

LeRoy, Matthew & Summers, Jeremy. The Way Forward: Discovering the Classic Message of Holiness. 2007. (978-0-89827-356-4(0)) Wesleyan Publishing Hse.

Levine, Roger S. A Living Man from Africa: Jan Tzatzoe, Xhosa Chief & Missionary, & the Making of Nineteenth-Century South Africa. 2010. (New Directions in Narrative History Ser.). (ENG., Illus.). 328p. 30.00 (978-0-300-12521-4(6)) Yale Univ. Pr.

Lewis, C. S. Surprised by Joy: The Shape of My Early Life. 22.95 (978-0-8488-1078-8(3)) Amereon LTD.

—Surprised by Joy / the Four Loves. 2011. (ENG.). 336p. 22.00 (978-0-547-59939-7(0)) Houghton Mifflin Harcourt Trade & Reference Pubs.

Lewis, James. Evidence Not Destroyed. 2011. 144p. pap. 17.50 **(978-1-257-91620-7(3))** Lulu Enterprises Inc.

Lewis, Joseph. From Glory to Glory: The Joe Lewis Story. 2009. 116p. 19.99 (978-1-60791-911-7(7)); pap. 11.99 (978-1-60791-910-0(9)) Xulon Pr., Inc.

Lewis, Randy. The Kingdom Found Within, 1 vol. 2010. 240p. pap. 24.95 (978-1-4489-4274-9(8)) PublishAmerica, Inc.

Lewis, Roy. Broken Things: How to move beyond the pain of Brokenness. 2010. 140p. pap. 13.95 (978-1-4401-9813-7(6)) iUniverse, Inc.

Liardon, Roberts. God's Generals: The Revivalists. (ENG., Illus.). 2009. 496p. pap. 14.99 (978-1-60374-095-1(3), 770951) 2008. 22.99 (978-1-60374-025-8(2)) Whitaker Hse.

Liebeschuetz, J. H. W. G. Ambrose & John Chrysostom: Clerics between Desert & Empire. 2011. (ENG.). 320p. 110.00 (978-0-19-959664-5(6)) Oxford Univ. Pr., Inc.

Liggins Jr., David. I Found Me When I Found the Lord! 2007. 73p. pap. 16.95 (978-1-4241-8111-7(9)) PublishAmerica, Inc.

Lightsey, Dan. Grace Overcomers Addiction Ministry: Founded on the Finished Work of Jesus Christ. 2010. pap. 11.99 (978-1-61663-225-0(9)) Tate Publishing & Enterprises, LLC.

Lipscomb, T. R. Dearest Children. 2008. 304p. pap. 19.00 (978-1-59755-128-1(7), Advantage Inspirational) Advantage Bks.

LiVecchi, Amalia. Two Stories in One Book: I'm a Consumer Like You Screwed Our of Millions; & Las Vegas: the Sins of Man Is Greed. 2007. 14.00 (978-0-8059-9190-1(5)) Dorrance Publishing Co., Inc.

Livingston, Kevin. The Highway to Heaven, 1 vol. 2009. (ENG.). 225p. pap. 24.95 (978-1-60749-768-4(9)) PublishAmerica, Inc.

Ljutic, Sanja. Homeless in St. Louis & Sleeping in Churches. 2009. 77p. pap. 36.10 (978-0-557-08433-3(4)) Lulu Enterprises Inc.

Lloyd, David. And God Was Watching. 2010. 150p. pap. 12.99 (978-0-557-33793-4(3)) Lulu Enterprises Inc.

Lloyd, James. Reflections of a Dinosaur Priest. 2006. 348p. per. 18.95 (978-1-59858-176-8(7)) Dog Ear Publishing, LLC.

Loane, Marcus L. Let God Arise: Landmarks in Church History. 2008. (ENG., Illus.). 128p. 10.99 (978-1-84550-380-2(5)) Christian Focus Pubns. GBR. Dist: STL Distribution North America.

Lobdell, William. Losing My Religion: How I Lost My Faith Reporting on Religion in America - And Found Unexpected Peace. 2009. (ENG.). 304p. 25.99 (978-0-06-162681-4(3)) HarperCollins Pubs.

LoBrutto III, Joseph. Is There More to Life Than What We Know? A Spiritual Journey & Awakening to finding God. 2008. 212p. per. 15.95 (978-0-595-43449-7(5)) iUniverse, Inc.

Logan, Annette E. & Johnson, Heather Hope. My Life as A Pastor's Wife: The Biography of Annette E. Logan. 2011. 60p. pap. 15.00 **(978-1-4634-3998-9(9))** AuthorHouse.

Loggins, Robert F., Sr. The Journey to Wholeness & Holiness: Fasting & Praying. 2nd rev. ed. 2007. 271p. pap. 19.99 (978-0-9797899-8-4(2)) Robert F Loggins Ministries Llc.

Long, Al & Long, Tad Allen. They Called Him Joe: An Extraordinary Story of an Ordinary Man. 2007. 166p. 19.95 (978-1-929478-61-3(5)) Power Publishing.

Long, Al, et al. They Called Him Joe: An Extraordinary Story of an Ordinary Man. 2008. 166p. pap. 14.95 (978-0-9790174-3-8(2)) Power Publishing.

Long, Alfred T., Sr. Grasping at the Wind: How to Go from Ashes to Beauty Using God's Word-Practical Biblical Solutions for Complex Life Problems. 2008. 152p. pap. 13.99 (978-1-60477-983-7(7)) Xulon Pr., Inc.

Long, Bonita. De Terebinthus: A Modern Gospel. 2006. pap. 11.95 (978-1-58736-630-7(4)) Wheatmark.

Long, Jennifer D. On the Road 2 Recover. 2011. 120p. 21.99 **(978-1-4567-6205-6(2))** AuthorHouse.

Lonzo, Paul. Move to the Light. 2009. 84p. pap. 18.95 (978-1-4389-7567-2(8)) AuthorHouse.

Lopeshinskaya, Elena. Martyr Bishop Confessors under Communism. (RUS.). pap. 5.00 (978-0-89981-055-3(1)) Eastern Orthodox Bks.

Loranger, Patricia L. Child of Woe, Child of Sorrow. 2011. **(978-1-77069-258-9(4))** Word Alive Pr.

Lorett, Pat. To-1944: Oklahoma Farm Life. 2007. (Illus.). 457p. per. 29.99 (978-1-60247-022-4(7)) Tate Publishing & Enterprises, LLC.

Lori May Dill. Whose Little Girl Are You. 2009. 116p. pap. 13.99 (978-1-4389-1450-3(4)) AuthorHouse.

Loth, Peter & Rath, Sandra Kellogg. Peace by Piece. 2008. 216p. pap. 14.99 (978-1-60647-121-0(X)) Xulon Pr., Inc.

Lott, Tim. Growing up Catholic: The Pursuit of Truth from Tradition to Satisfaction. 2007. (Illus.). 191p. per. 21.99 (978-0-9791188-3-8(2)) Abundant Publishing Co.

Louise, Claire. Mask Off! Mettle One. 2010. 244p. pap. 14.49 (978-1-4520-8003-1(8)) AuthorHouse.

Lovasik, Lorenzo G. Vida Ilustrada de Jesus. 2008. (Illus.). 64p. (J). (gr. -1-3). 6.95 (978-0-89942-987-8(4)) Catholic Bk. Publishing Corp.

Love, Patricia. All's Well That End's Well: Only the Strong Will Survive. 2009. 88p. pap. 9.95 (978-1-4327-1170-2(9)) Outskirts Pr., Inc.

Lovett, Richard. Tamate. (SPA.). 192p. (978-84-7228-320-6(8), 220864) Clie, Editorial.

Lovingsworth, Ra Kelly. Broken into Wholeness: The Beauty of Truth. 2008. pap. 14.99 (978-1-60647-007-7(8), Crown Oak Pr.) Xulon Pr., Inc.

Lowerre, Sandra. The Cross-Dressing Female Saints in Wynkyn de Worde's 1495 Edition of the Vitas Patrum: A Study & Edition of the Lives of Saints Pelage, Maryne, Eufrosyne, Eugene, & Mary of Egypt. 2006. (ENM & ENG.). 89.95 (978-0-8204-9886-7(6)) Lang, Peter Publishing, Inc.

Lowry, Kenneth and Deany. Not Many Wise Are Called. 2008. 116p. pap. 11.99 (978-1-60647-693-2(9)) Xulon Pr., Inc.

Lucas, Pro. Kemba Jarena. The Traveling Suitcase: A Journey Lesson for Men. 2009. 66p. pap. 18.99 (978-0-557-12930-0(3)) Lulu Enterprises Inc.

—The Traveling Suitcase: A Journey Lesson for Women. 2009. 66p. pap. 18.99 (978-0-557-10667-7(2)) Lulu Enterprises Inc.

Luce, Annie. Time Together. 2011. 238p. pap. 15.99 (978-1-61215-630-9(4)) Xulon Pr., Inc.

Lukenbill, David H. The Criminal, the Cross & the Christ: The Interior Journey. 2008. 100p. pap. 14.95 (978-0-9791670-6-5(X)) LampStand Foundation, The.

—The Criminal's Search for God: Criminal Transformation, Catholic Social Teaching, Deep Knowledge Leadership, & Communal Reentry. 2006. per. 20.00 (978-0-9791670-0-3(0)) LampStand Foundation, The.

Lunsford, Fred B. God's Messengers from the Mountains. 2010. 312p. 37.95 (978-1-4497-0821-4(8)); pap. 22.95 (978-1-4497-0819-1(6)) Author Solutions, Inc. (WestBow Pr.).

Lyles, Charles Abraham. Miracles of My Life. 2009. 54p. pap. 12.95 (978-1-4489-8980-5(9)) PublishAmerica, Inc.

Ma B. The Apostle's Wife. 2008. 48p. pap. 16.95 (978-1-60703-331-8(3)) PublishAmerica, Inc.

MacDonald, Donnie, told to. Obeying the Voice of God: Jack MacDonald's Journey. 2008. 350p. pap. 19.99 (978-0-9778545-1-6(5)) Borrego Publishing.

MacDonald, Jill Nickerson. Sow Bountifully. 2011. 60p. pap. 12.95 **(978-0-9830007-4-7(3))** Fiction Publishing, Inc.

Mack. A Walk Through the Garden. 2011. 116p. 21.23 **(978-1-4490-1657-9(X))**; pap. 10.68 **(978-1-4490-1656-2(1))** AuthorHouse.

Mackenzie. Billy Graham Just Get up Out of Your Sea. 2007. (Trailblazers Ser.). (ENG.). 144p. pap. 8.99 (978-1-84550-095-5(4)) Christian Focus Pubns. GBR. Dist: STL Distribution North America.

MacKenzie, Catherine. Christian Heroines: Just Like You? 2009. (ENG.). 176p. pap. 6.99 (978-1-84550-460-1(7)) Christian Focus Pubns. GBR. Dist: STL Distribution North America.

Mackenzie, Catherine. David Livingstone: Who Is the Bravest? 2008. (Little Lights Ser.). (ENG.). 24p. 7.99 (978-1-84550-384-0(8)) Christian Focus Pubns. GBR. Dist: STL Distribution North America.

MacKey, Terrance G. Through the Eyes of God: A Supernatural Experience. 2011. 124p. pap. 11.99 **(978-1-61379-156-1(9))** Xulon Pr., Inc.

Maddex, Mike. Musings of a Story Teller Wannabe. 2010. 211p. pap. 13.94 (978-0-557-19742-2(2)) Lulu Enterprises Inc.

Magli, Ida. Taboo & Transgression: Jesus of Nazareth. Ellis, Andrew, tr. 2009. 144p. pap. (978-88-95145-41-9(0)) Italian Paths of Culture.

Maguire, John Francis. Father Mathew: A Biography, by John Francis Maguire ... 2006. 576p. per. 32.99 (978-1-4255-6271-7(X)) MPublishing.

Mahler, Ron. My Fanatical, Regrettable Tour of Ministry. 2011. 296p. pap. **(978-1-77069-305-0(X))** Word Alive Pr.

Malo, Remme. House of Treasures. 2007. 152p. per. 13.99 (978-1-60477-179-4(8)) Xulon Pr., Inc.

Malone, David. The Seeds of Mercy: One Cop's Struggle with Stress. 2010. 176p. pap. 16.99 (978-1-4520-0482-2(X)) AuthorHouse.

Maloney, James. The Wounded Cry: A Testimony of Acceptance in Jesus Christ. 2011. 52p. pap. 9.95 **(978-1-4497-2392-7(6)**, WestBow Pr.) Author Solutions, Inc.

Malony, H. Newton. The Amazing John Wesley: An Unusual Look at an Uncommon Life. 2010. (ENG.). 174p. pap. 14.99 (978-1-60657-092-0(7), Authentic Bibles) Authentic Media.

Manning, Charlene Reams. Memories of My Earth Home: 40 Meditations on Our Natural World. 2006. 178p. pap. 24.95 (978-1-4241-2092-5(6)) PublishAmerica, Inc.

Manning, Gwennette. Killings in the Hous (Church) 2008. pap. 13.00 (978-0-8059-8090-5(3)) Dorrance Publishing Co., Inc.

Manning, John E. Blessings Unlimited. 2011. 84p. pap. 11.49 **(978-1-4634-0771-1(8))** AuthorHouse.

Mansfield, Denise. Warm Hugs for Dark Nights. 2010. 270p. pap. 23.80 (978-0-557-21674-1(5)) Lulu Enterprises Inc.

Mansfield, Stephen. WHERE HAS OPRAH TAKEN US? International Edition: The Religious Influence of the World's Most Famous Woman. 2011. 272p. pap. 15.99 **(978-0-7852-3710-5(0))** Nelson, Thomas Inc.

Marjanen, Antti & Luomanen, Petri. A Companion to Second-Century Christian "Heretics" 2008. pap. (978-90-04-17038-4(3)) BRILL.

Martin, Becky Allen. A Promise Kept: The Life & Ministry of Rev. Sam Allen. 2010. 216p. pap. 18.49 (978-1-4490-6557-7(0)) AuthorHouse.

Martin, Daniel. Who Lied & Said We Left the Garden of Eden? Memoirs of a Homeless Man. 2008. 129p. pap. 12.95 (978-1-4327-2939-4(X)) Outskirts Pr., Inc.

Martin, James. My Life with the Saints. 2007. (ENG.). 432p. per. 15.95 (978-0-8294-2644-1(2)) Loyola Pr.

Martin, Kelly A. Clueless to Commissioned: A Female Officer's Journey with God through Fifteen Years with the Fort Worth Police Department. 2009. 232p. pap. 15.99 (978-1-4389-2956-9(0)) AuthorHouse.

Martin, Maria Eugenia. Eternal Life. 2007. 160p. per. 17.00 (978-1-4120-9671-3(5)) Trafford Publishing.

Martin, R. Merial. Welford Street Miracles: A Stranger's Touch, A Life Restored. 2009. pap. 13.99 (978-1-60696-049-3(0)) Tate Publishing & Enterprises, LLC.

Martin, Raymond D. By God's Amazing Grace. 2008. 396p. (ENG.). 31.99 (978-1-60477-458-0(4)); per. 19.99 (978-1-60477-187-9(9)) Xulon Pr., Inc.

Martin, Sheila. When They Were Mine: Memoirs of a Branch Davidian Wife & Mother. Wessinger, Catherine, ed. 2009. (ENG., Illus.). 235p. pap. 29.95 (978-1-60258-000-8(6)) Baylor Univ. Pr.

Martinez, Janice. How Do I Know There Is a Heaven? 2008. 189p. pap. 24.95 (978-1-60610-136-0(6)) PublishAmerica, Inc.

Martinez, José M. Abba, Padre: Abba, Father. (SPA.). (978-84-7645-383-4(3), 223533) Clie, Editorial.

Martins, Olu. A Journey Interrupted. 2007. 68p. per. 9.99 (978-1-60266-718-1(7)) Xulon Pr., Inc.

Martoia, Ron. The Bible As Improv: Seeing & Living the Script in New Ways, 1 vol. 2010. (ENG.). 224p. pap. 14.99 (978-0-310-28770-4(7)) Zondervan.

Marx, Victor, et al. With God, All things are Possible: The Victor Marx Story. 2008. (ENG., Illus.). 230p. (YA). pap. (978-0-9791303-0-4(1)) ATP Publishing.

Mary Alston Brooks Aka ~ Mary B. Truthful Ignition. 2011. 80p. pap. 19.95 **(978-1-4560-2127-6(3))** PublishAmerica, Inc.

Massey, Marilyn Chapin. Christ Unmasked: The Meaning of the Life of Jesus in German Politics. 2011. (ENG.). 193p. pap. 30.00 **(978-0-8078-9723-2(X))** Univ. of North Carolina Pr.

Massingale, Leola. A Country Girl Meets Jesus. 2007. 19.00 (978-0-8059-8369-2(4)) Dorrance Publishing Co., Inc.

Master's Pen Staff. My Spirit Speaks. 2008. 140p. pap. 13.99 (978-1-60477-696-6(X)) Xulon Pr., Inc.

Master's Pen Staff, ed. My Spirit Speaks. 2008. 140p. 21.99 (978-1-60647-009-1(4)) Xulon Pr., Inc.

Mathai, Ipe. A Handful of Clay in the Potter's Hand. 2008. 172p. 22.99 (978-1-60647-620-8(3)); pap. 14.99 (978-1-60647-619-2(X)) Xulon Pr., Inc.

Matthew, Gladstone. Eternal: Autobiography of Gladstone Matthew. 2011. 120p. pap. 12.33 **(978-1-4269-6753-5(5))** Trafford Publishing.

Maupin, Timothy. Touches of Grace. 2010. pap. 10.99 (978-1-61663-012-6(4)) Tate Publishing & Enterprises, LLC.

Mauriello, Matthew R. Mercies Remembered. 2011. 376p. 32.99 (978-1-61215-005-5(5)) Xulon Pr., Inc.

Maxwell, Madeline. The Red Grip. 2007. 160p. per. 13.99 (978-1-60266-259-9(2)) Xulon Pr., Inc.

Maxwell, Stanley M. Him Big God Day & Other Remarkable Sabbath Stories. 2011. pap. **(978-0-8163-2617-4(7))** Pacific Pr. Publishing Assn.

Mayatt, Jack. A Better Man: An Inspirational book Written in Layman Terms to Motivate the Common Man. 2010. 140p. (ENG.). 24.99 (978-1-4490-8718-0(3)); pap. 13.99 (978-1-4490-8717-3(5)) AuthorHouse.

McAfee, Donald R. Called but it should be Called? 2010. (ENG.). pap. 19.95 (978-1-58982-605-2(1), Millennial Mind Publishing) American Bk. Publishing Group.

McAnally, Thomas S. Bishop with a Pastor's Heart: Kenneth W. Copeland. 2006. (Illus.). 240p. 24.95 (978-1-57736-378-1(7)) Providence Hse Pubs.

Mcatee, Christina. Carmen Potito's Sweet Promise: Which Can Only Be Told by His Soul Mate, Maria Potito. 2009. 108p. 23.95 (978-1-4327-5181-4(6)) Outskirts Pr., Inc.

Mcbane, Michael. The Narrow Road of A Grand & Curious Opportunity. 2011. 98p. pap. 11.95 **(978-1-4620-3271-6(0))** iUniverse, Inc.

McBride, Jeff. Living in -2- Worlds. 2011. 110p. 19.99 **(978-1-61379-629-0(3))**; pap. 11.99 **(978-1-61379-628-3(5))** Xulon Pr., Inc.

McCallie, David, ed. THM - A Memoir. 2011. 164p. 30.95 **(978-1-4497-1084-2(0))**; pap. 13.95 **(978-1-4497-1082-8(4))** Author Solutions, Inc. (WestBow Pr.).

McCandless, Evie. A Time to Mourn, a Time to Dance: Life with Our Children. 2006. 34p. pap. (978-0-914733-33-1(8)) Desert Ministries, Inc.

McCann, Lloyd. Seven Brothers. 2008. 312p. 31.00 (978-1-4251-5153-9(1)) Trafford Publishing.

McCaskill, Jane. God Makes No Mistakes. 2008. 272p. pap. 15.99 (978-1-60477-863-2(6)) Xulon Pr., Inc.

Mccaughey, Bobbi & Mccaughey, Kenny. Seven from Heaven, 0 vols. 2009. 306p. pap. 13.99 (978-0-7852-9745-1(6)) Nelson, Thomas Inc.

McClain, Grace. To Give You a Future & a Hope: More Than a Biography. 2010. 152p. pap. 11.99 (978-1-4490-7938-3(5)) AuthorHouse.

McClellan, Niashanta. The Five Men of My Life. 2008. 200p. pap. 14.99 (978-1-60647-275-0(5)) Xulon Pr., Inc.

McClure, Ronald. Reverend John Thompson Price, 1866-1951: Presbyterian Preacher from the War-Ravaged Hills of East Tennessee. 2009. 228p. 25.99 (978-1-60791-845-5(5)); pap. 15.99 (978-1-60791-844-8(7)) Xulon Pr., Inc.

McConkie, Bruce R. The Mortal Messiah: From Bethlehem to Calvary. 2008. (Illus.). (978-1-59811-702-8(5), Debolsillo) Covenant Communications, Inc.

McCord, Matthew. Good Hope. 2008. 142p. pap. 14.95 (978-0-615-26323-6(2)) McCord, Matthew M.

McCracken, David. From Greed to Grace: Or How God Taught Me about the Stock Market. 2011. 236p. 26.95 **(978-1-60976-338-1(6)**, Eloquent Bks.) AEG Literary Publishing Services, Inc.

McCraney, William Edgar. Find a Way or Make a Way. 2011. 458p. 34.99 **(978-1-4628-9639-4(1))**; pap. 23.99 **(978-1-4628-9638-7(3))** Xlibris Corp.

McCulloch, John. Refined in the Furnace of Affliction. 2008. 148p. pap. 14.95 (978-1-4327-3785-6(6)) Outskirts Pr., Inc.

McCullough, James E. Understanding the Power of GOD: Is your marriage pleasing to GOD, or just your Self? 2011. 80p. pap. 10.95 (978-1-4502-9069-2(8)) iUniverse, Inc.

McCullough, Loyce Agnew M. A. An Extraordinary Journey with Jesus: A Forty-Day Guide to Experiencing the Lenten Season (or Any Season) 2011. 128p. pap. 19.99 **(978-1-4628-8901-3(8))** Xlibris Corp.

McCullough, Nancy. Adoption Is for A Lifetime: God's Plan for A Family Through All the Phases of Adoption. 2008. 132p. pap. 13.99 (978-1-60647-655-0(6)) Xulon Pr., Inc.

McCully, Beth A. Starting Over... AGAIN: A Journal of Life's Transitions. 2011. 192p. 30.95 **(978-1-4497-1480-2(3))**; pap. 13.95 **(978-1-4497-1479-6(X))** Author Solutions, Inc. (WestBow Pr.).

McCutchen, Sr. One of the Whosoevers: The Life Story & A Collection of Sermons. 2007. 244p. (ENG.). 29.95 (978-0-595-70224-4(4)); per. 19.95 (978-0-595-46452-4(1)) iUniverse, Inc.

Mcdaniel, Crystal. Predestined to Reign: For Such A Time as This. 2010. pap. 21.99 (978-1-61566-544-0(7)) Tate Publishing & Enterprises, LLC.

McDonagh, Enda. Remembering to Forgive: A Tribute to una O'Higgins O'Malley. McDonagh, Enda, ed. 2nd rev. ed. 2010. (ENG.). 171p. pap. 25.95 (978-1-84730-156-7(8)) Veritas Pubns. IRL. Dist: Dufour Editions, Inc.

McDonagh, Enda, ed. Remembering to Forgive: A Tribute to una O'Higgins O'Malley. 2009. pap. 25.95 (978-1-84730-050-8(2)) Veritas Pubns. IRL. Dist: Dufour Editions, Inc.

McFarlane, Doreen. God Speaks, Are You Listening? 2009. 98p. pap. (978-1-55452-414-3(8)) Essence Publishing.

McGaw, Francis A., et al. Praying Hyde. pap. 4.99 (978-1-56632-009-2(7)) Revival Literature.

McGinn, Bernard. The Doctors of the Church: Thirty-Three Men & Women Who Shaped Christianity. 2nd ed. 2009. (ENG.). 280p. pap. 29.95 *(978-0-8245-2549-1(3))* Crossroad Publishing Co., The.

McGinnis M. D., Melissa J. Miracles & Mercies, 1 vol. 2009. 89p. pap. 16.95 *(978-1-4489-2537-7(1))* PublishAmerica, Inc.

McGowan, Pearlie. From the Sticks to the Bricks: Unlocking theá Secrets of My Life. 2007. 116p. per. 19.95 *(978-1-4241-7217-7(9))* PublishAmerica, Inc.

McGraw, Robin. Inside My Heart Guided Journal: Choosing to Live with Passion & Purpose, 0 vols. 2007. 224p. per. 17.99 *(978-1-4185-1436-5(5))* Nelson, Thomas Inc.

Mcintosh, D. Scott. Life Lessons Learned in the Backseat of a Ford. 2009. 120p. pap. 11.99 *(978-1-60791-413-6(1))* Xulon Pr., Inc.

McKee, John. The Long Road Home. 2007. 200p. per. 15.99 *(978-1-58930-203-7(6))* Selah Publishing Group, LLC.

McKinnon, John. Visitations. 2010. 24p. pap. 15.99 *(978-1-4500-5699-1(7))* Xlibris Corp.

McKneely, Roslyn. The Chain of Forgiveness. 2007. 116p. per. 10.99 *(978-1-60266-380-0(7))* Xulon Pr., Inc.

McKoy, Sandra H. God's Diamond among Rocks: Rewards & Challenges of Single Parent Adoption While Facing a Physical Challenge. 2009. 256p. pap. 16.99 *(978-1-4389-7909-0(6))* AuthorHouse.

McLeod, Cecelia. And God Said to Me Do the Part of It You Love to Do: Enjoy the Journey. 2009. 292p. pap. 15.49 *(978-1-4389-0296-8(4))* AuthorHouse.

McNeill, Katherine. Art by Faith. 2009. 68p. pap. 15.00 *(978-1-4490-2180-1(8))* AuthorHouse.

McNutt, Ramon. The World of Prison. 2006. 13.00 *(978-0-8059-9125-3(5))* Dorrance Publishing Co., Inc.

McPherson, Anna Talbott. Forgotten Saints: The Stories of Those Behind the Scenes in the Lives of the Great. 2011. 114p. 39.95 ***(978-1-258-02353-9(9))*** Literary Licensing, LLC.

McPhie, Leslie Harston. illus. My First Story of the Latter-Day Prophets. 2010. *(978-1-60641-155-1(1))* Deseret Bk. Co.

McRae, William. Faith that Kept Me: How You Stay Committed to Your Purpose. 2010. 116p. pap. 15.00 *(978-1-4520-4485-9(6))* AuthorHouse.

McReynolds, Kathy. The Pilgrim Psalms: A Sacred Journey to Revitalize Your Life. 2006. (ENG.). 128p. 12.99 *(978-1-85792-927-0(6))* Christian Focus Pubns. GBR. Dist: STL Distribution North America.

McSwain, Larry. Loving Beyond Your Theology: The Life & Ministry of Jimmy Raymond Allen. 2010. (Baptists Ser.). (Illus.). 288p. 35.00 *(978-0-88146-205-0(5))* Mercer Univ. Pr.

Mcwilliamson, Michael. Wisdom from A Turtle: Thirty-Something Years of Seemingly Unimportant Decisions. 2011. 176p. pap. 22.95 ***(978-1-4620-0257-3(9))*** iUniverse, Inc.

Meagher, George T. & Kasper, Mary. With Attentive Ear & Courageous Heart: A Biography of Mother Mary Kasper, Foundress of the Poor Handmaids of Jesus Christ. 2011. 282p. 47.95 ***(978-1-258-09026-5(0))*** Literary Licensing, LLC.

Mehling, Robert. Mea Saurus: An Artist's Confessions. 2008. pap. 18.00 *(978-0-8059-7949-7(2))* Dorrance Publishing Co., Inc.

Mejia, Jose Medardo. Victory! 2010. 134p. pap. 14.99 *(978-1-60957-175-7(4))* Xulon Pr., Inc.

Mell, P. H. Life of Patrick Hues Mell. 2009. 262p. 30.99 *(978-1-110-49959-5(0))*; pap. 26.75 *(978-1-110-49956-4(6))* BiblioBazaar.

Melton, Overseer Donna. My Faith Journey. 2010. 48p. pap. 15.99 *(978-1-4500-5082-1(4))* Xlibris Corp.

Mendez, Junior. My Little Garden of Eden: I'm god, we're all Gods. 2010. 512p. (ENG.). 30.99 *(978-1-4490-7304-6(2))*; pap. 20.49 *(978-1-4490-7303-9(4))* AuthorHouse.

Mendoza, Jesus E. My God Giving Dreams: My Story about the Dreams & Goals Acheived with My Lord's Help. 2010. 68p. pap. 9.95 *(978-1-61507-259-0(4))* Cross Bks. Publishing.

Mensch, Christine. Give God the Ashes. 2009. 272p. pap. *(978-1-55452-406-8(7))* Essence Publishing.

Mercer, Jeff. Small Victories. 2007. 268p. per. 17.99 *(978-1-60477-263-0(8))* Xulon Pr., Inc.

Merritt, Hannah T. Storms... in Our Lives: How God Brought Us Through. 2010. 172p. 25.95 *(978-1-4502-2175-7(0))*; pap. 15.95 *(978-1-4502-2173-3(4))* iUniverse, Inc.

Merriweather, Eric T. Knowing Your Identity Through Christ: Light in the Dark Times. 2011. pap. 14.99 *(978-1-61739-408-9(4))* Tate Publishing & Enterprises, LLC.

Merton, T. Diarios (1939-1960) (SPA.). 216p. *(978-84-95456-39-7(7)*, 86933); (Illus.). 284p. *(978-84-95456-53-3(2)*, 86936) Ediciones Oniro S.A.

Mesanko, Kerin Lee. Broken Beads on My Moccasins. 2009. 162p. pap. 14.99 *(978-1-60791-912-4(5))* Xulon Pr., Inc.

Messerschmitt, Jim. Beyond Expectations. 2010. 372p. pap. 17.99 *(978-1-4520-3882-7(1))* AuthorHouse.

Metcalfe, Lou Ann. Delivered from the Torment: A Christian Perspective on Schizophrenia, 1 vol. 2010. 128p. pap. 19.95 *(978-1-4489-3391-4(9))* PublishAmerica, Inc.

Metzger, John Mackay. The Hand & the Road: The Life & Times of John A. Mackay. 2010. (ENG.). 560p. pap. 40.00 *(978-0-664-23524-6(7))* Westminster John Knox Pr.

Meyer, F. B. Vide y Luz de los Hombres (Light & Life of Men) (SPA.). 320p. *(978-84-7228-802-7(1)*, 222911) Clie, Editorial.

Meyers, Marilyn. Through Fire & Sea: Adventures on the Mercy Ship: A Family's Journey to the World's Forgotten Poor. 2007. *(978-1-897213-33-9(6))* BayRidge Bks.

Mihoan, Kirk A. Thoughts from the Cradle. 2008. 228p. 25.99 *(978-1-60647-983-4(0))*; pap. 15.99 *(978-1-60647-981-0(4))* Xulon Pr., Inc.

Mikita, Steve. I Sit All Amazed: The Extraordinary Power of a Mother's Love. 2011. (Illus.). 128p. pap. 15.99 *(978-1-60641-938-0(2))* Deseret Bk. Co.

Miliner, Derrick K. From the Projects to the Pulpit: God's Grace Is Sufficient. 2009. 68p. pap. 16.95 *(978-1-4389-7711-9(5))* AuthorHouse.

Milkon, Phyllis A. Earthly Angels [Special Reprint for David's 100th Birthday]: David Chen's Survival of Famine & Persecution. 2007. (Illus.). 160p. pap. 14.00 *(978-0-9630025-3-2(8))* Burgess Creative Ventures.

Miller, Calvin. Life Is Mostly Edges: A Memoir, 0 vols. 2010. 208p. pap. 18.99 *(978-0-7852-9798-7(7))* Nelson, Thomas Inc.

Miller, Donald. Blue Like Jazz: Nonreligious Thoughts on Christian Spirituality. 2006. (Thorndike Inspirational Ser.). (Illus.). 338p. 28.95 *(978-0-7862-8843-4(4))* Thorndike Pr.

—Blue Like Jazz: Nonreligious Thoughts on Christian Spirituality. movie tie-in ed. 2012. 256p. pap. 16.99 ***(978-1-4002-0458-8(5))*** Nelson, Thomas Inc.

—Searching for God Knows What. Lt. ed. 2010. (ENG.). 352p. pap. 17.99 *(978-1-59415-324-2(6))* Cengage Gale.

—Searching for God Knows What. 2010. (Playaway Adult Nonfiction Ser.). (ENG.). 59.99 ***(978-1-61587-627-3(8))*** Findaway World, LLC.

—Searching for God Knows What, 0 vols. 2010. 272p. pap. 15.99 *(978-1-4002-0275-1(2))* Nelson, Thomas Inc.

Miller, Gary. Sing to the Lord a New Song: Transforming Life through Scripture. 2010. pap. 12.99 *(978-1-61663-335-6(2))* Tate Publishing & Enterprises, LLC.

Miller, Mary R. Earnestly Contend for the Faith: [a Biography of Eli D. Kramer (1899-1966)]. 2007. 128p. 7.20 *(978-0-7399-2383-2(8))* Rod & Staff Pubs., Inc.

Miller, Samuel. Night of Tears, Years of Joy. 2008. 176p. 21.99 *(978-1-60647-055-8(8))*; pap. 13.99 *(978-1-60647-054-1(X))* Xulon Pr., Inc.

MILLS, Phyllis. The Call to Africa: Bob & Phyllis Mills Answered the Call & in Faith Went to Work for the Lord in Africa. 2008. pap. 13.99 *(978-1-60647-569-0(X))* Xulon Pr., Inc.

Mills, Saundra. Angel in a Tent: Heeding to the Call. 2010. 400p. pap. 22.49 *(978-1-4520-3281-8(5))* AuthorHouse.

Mills, Sheri D. Called Out of Darkness. 2009. 304p. pap. 18.99 *(978-1-61579-185-9(X))* Xulon Pr., Inc.

Milton, Michael A. What God Starts, God Completes: Gospel Hope for Hurting People. 2007. (ENG.). 160p. per. 12.99 *(978-1-84550-276-8(0))* Christian Focus Pubns. GBR. Dist: STL Distribution North America.

Milton, Simonia E. She's Vocal/He's Instrumental: A True Story of Faith, Love, & Music. 2011. 116p. pap. 14.99 ***(978-1-56229-221-8(8)***, Christian Living Bks., Inc.) Pneuma Life Publishing, Inc.

Minor, Zazell & Elkins, Christy. For the Love of Zazell. 2010. (ENG.). 83p. pap. 30.00 *(978-0-557-27295-2(5))* Lulu Enterprises Inc.

Mirandette, Erik. The Only Road North: 9,000 Miles of Dirt & Dreams, 1 vol. 2007. (ENG., Illus.). 304p. (gr. 13). pap. 12.99 *(978-0-310-27435-3(4))* Zondervan.

Mirelez, Lupe. Of Moments & Miracles: A Collection of Ordinary People's Extraordinary Stories. 2010. 240p. pap. 12.95 *(978-1-59858-993-1(8))* Dog Ear Publishing, LLC.

Miss Martha'S Man. Miss Marth: The Love Story of a Most Precious Sweetheart & Wife. 2008. 285p. pap. 27.95 *(978-1-4241-9819-1(4))* PublishAmerica, Inc.

Mitchell, Patricia Marie. Michael Mitchell - Criminal or Rescuer? 2008. 112p. 29.99 *(978-1-4363-1430-5(5))*; pap. 19.99 *(978-1-4363-1429-9(1))* Xlibris Corp.

Mobyed, John. In the Wind. 2011. 68p. 24.99 ***(978-1-4628-4751-8(X))***; pap. 15.99 ***(978-1-4628-4750-1(1))*** Xlibris Corp.

Mock, Betty Jean. Persimmon Days: A Real Adoption Story. 2008. 252p. pap. 15.99 *(978-1-60477-937-0(3))* Xulon Pr., Inc.

Monroe Kullberg, Kelly, ed. Finding God at Harvard: Spiritual Journeys of Thinking Christians. 2007. (Veritas Bks.). (ENG., Illus.). 375p. per. 18.00 *(978-0-8308-3433-4(8))*, IVP Bks.) InterVarsity Pr.

Montecristo, J. The Girl That Wouldn't Die, 1 vol. 2010. 53p. pap. 16.95 *(978-1-4489-5992-1(6))* PublishAmerica, Inc.

Monterio, Alice. Saved by Grace. 2007. 244p. per. 14.99 *(978-1-60266-336-7(X))* Xulon Pr., Inc.

Moon, Sarah Little. To Be Set Free. 2010. 216p. (ENG.). 28.99 *(978-1-4490-6483-9(3))*; pap. 15.99 *(978-1-4490-6482-2(5))* AuthorHouse.

Moore, Beth. To Live Is Christ: Joining Paul's Journey of Faith. 2008. (ENG.). 336p. 19.99 *(978-0-8054-4561-9(7))* B&H Publishing Group.

Moore, Carolyn A. Supernatural Intervention in My Life. 2010. 104p. pap. 10.99 *(978-1-4490-8982-5(8))* AuthorHouse.

Moore, James. My First 30 Years: My Autobiography 1977-2007. 2007. 240p. per. 11.95 *(978-1-4327-0902-0(X))* Outskirts Pr., Inc.

Moore, Rebecca. To Dance with Jesus. 2008. 52p. pap. 16.95 *(978-1-60474-756-0(0))* PublishAmerica, Inc.

Moore, Rosemary. The History of the Life of Thomas Ellwood: Written by Himself. 2010. (Sacred Literature Trust Ser.). (ENG.). 240p. pap. 27.95 *(978-0-300-16514-2(5))* Yale Univ. Pr.

Moore, Teran. Saved by the Flame: How the Values of Being a Firefighter Have Saved My Life. 2011. pap. 8.99 ***(978-1-61346-116-7(X))*** Tate Publishing & Enterprises, LLC.

Moore, Willis Trueman. Face Like Flint. 2010. 416p. pap. 22.99 *(978-1-61507-049-7(4))* Cross Bks. Publishing.

Moran, Gabriel. Fashioning a People Today: The Educational Insights of Maria Harris. 2007. 185p. per. 16.95 *(978-1-58595-605-0(8))* Twenty-Third Pubns./Bayard.

Moran, Michael & Overton, Ann K., eds. As We Knew Him: Reflections on M. Basil Pennington. 2008. (ENG., Illus.). 207p. (gr. 13). 29.95 *(978-1-55725-539-6(3))* Paraclete Pr., Inc.

Morgan, Elisa & Alonzo, Rebecca Nichols. The Devil in Pew Number Seven. 2010. (ENG.). 288p. pap. 14.99 *(978-1-4143-2659-7(9))* Tyndale Hse. Pubs.

Morgan, Frank. Both Sides of the Altar. 2011. (ENG.). 208p. pap. 19.00 *(978-1-58731-080-5(5))* St. Augustine's Pr., Inc.

Morgan, Giles. St George: Knight, Martyr, Patron Saint & Dragonslayer. 2009. (ENG.). 160p. 8.99 *(978-0-7858-2232-5(1)*, 0785822321, Chartwell) Book Sales, Inc.

Morgan, Robert & Stanton, Graham, eds. Christ Alive & at Large: The Unpublished Writings of C. F. D. Moule. 2010. (Canterbury Studies in Spiritual Theology Ser.). (ENG.). 192p. pap. 29.99 *(978-1-84825-018-5(5)*, Canterbury Pr. Norwich) Hymns Ancient & Modern Ltd GBR. Dist: Westminster John Knox Pr.

Morris, Laurie. Shattered, & Then a Journey to Sexual Healing & Integration. 2008. 152p. per. 13.99 *(978-1-60477-622-5(6))* Xulon Pr., Inc.

Morris, Lorelei. Held by Angels. 2006. pap. 9.99 *(978-1-60034-435-0(6))* Xulon Pr., Inc.

Morse, Stan. But for the Grace of God: One Man's Spiritual Walk from Self Destruction to Salvation. 2010. 332p. pap. 17.99 *(978-1-4490-6509-6(0))*; (ENG.). 28.49 *(978-1-4490-6510-2(4))* AuthorHouse.

Morton, Ralph. God, Kate, & I. 2009. 336p. 28.99 *(978-1-61579-345-7(3))*; pap. 18.99 *(978-1-61579-153-8(1))* Xulon Pr., Inc.

Motley, James B. Spiritual Warfare. 2008. 224p. 24.99 *(978-1-60477-619-5(6))* Xulon Pr., Inc.

Mott, Jim. My Walk with the Lord Through the Valley Called Cancer. 2007. 54p. pap. 16.95 *(978-1-60441-803-3(6))* PublishAmerica, Inc.

Mount, Elaine C. Beyond the Mountain: One Woman's Journey to Discovering Absolute Truth. 2008. 124p. 18.99 *(978-1-60647-529-4(0))*; pap. 10.99 *(978-1-60647-528-7(2))* Xulon Pr., Inc.

Ms. Bobbie Dorsey Young. God Is Able: Are you confused & searching for the right direction? the path to Righteousness. 2009. 112p. pap. 13.99 *(978-1-4343-9632-7(0))* AuthorHouse.

Mull, Melissa. My Own Worst Enemy. 2006. 48p. pap. 16.95 *(978-1-4241-4718-2(2))* PublishAmerica, Inc.

Mullan, David George. Narratives of the Religious Self in Early-Modern Scotland. 2010. (St Andrews Studies in Reformation History Ser.). (Illus.). 464p. 134.95 *(978-0-7546-6832-9(0))* Ashgate Publishing Co.

Mullins, Larry. Bodyguard to the Prophets. 2010. pap. 10.99 *(978-1-59955-336-8(8))* Cedar Fort, Inc./CFI Distribution.

Mumford, Nigel W. D. & Temple, Caroline. Hand to Hand: From Combat to Healing. 2006. (Illus.). 176p. per. 18.00 *(978-0-89869-535-9(X))* Church Publishing, Inc.

Munro, Harry C. Noble Lives: Old Testament Biography. Stevenson, Marion, ed. 2011. 90p. 38.95 ***(978-1-258-09013-5(9))*** Literary Licensing, LLC.

Munro, William Fraser. Men Like Mountains: Studies in Dynamic Discipleship. 2011. 74p. 36.95 ***(978-1-258-02881-7(6))*** Literary Licensing, LLC.

Murphy, Cindy A. Grace Heaped upon Grace: An authorized biography of Dr. Bob W. Smith. 2006. lib. bdg. 20.00 *(978-1-59971-809-5(X))* Aardvark Global Publishing.

Murphy, Gannon. Voices of Reason in Christian History: Their Lives & Legacies. 2009. 240p. pap. 20.00 *(978-1-60608-489-2(5)*, Wipf and Stock) Wipf & Stock Pubs.

Murphy, Tim. From Crack to the Cross: A Journey of Hope. 2007. 328p. 25.95 *(978-1-4327-0773-6(6))*; per. 16.95 *(978-1-4327-0694-4(2))* Outskirts Pr., Inc.

Murray, Jeffrey. Alive Based on A True Story. 2006. 100p. pap. 23.00 *(978-1-4120-9155-8(1))* Trafford Publishing.

Myers, Andrea. God Loves Africa the Most. 2009. 78p. pap. 15.99 *(978-1-4415-1206-2(3))* Xlibris Corp.

Myers, Herman. The Unlikely Making of a Mennonite Minister. 2010. 368p. pap. 19.99 *(978-1-4520-8088-8(7))* AuthorHouse.

Napoleon, Marion. Lady Silverstone's Darkest Hour. 2007. (Lady Silverstone Ser.). 223p. 24.99 *(978-0-9709263-1-9(6))* Robinson Omnimedia Publishing & Studios.

Narby, Crystal L. Daddy's Little Princess. 2010. 25.99 *(978-1-61579-954-1(0))*; 220p. pap. 15.99 *(978-1-61579-756-1(4))* Xulon Pr., Inc.

Narramore, Clyde M. Every Person Is Worth Understanding. 2011. 272p. 35.95 ***(978-1-61507-694-9(8))***; pap. 19.95 ***(978-1-61507-693-2(X))*** Cross Bks. Publishing.

Natale, Steve. My Sexuality My Canoe Trip. 2010. 74p. pap. 15.99 *(978-1-4535-3550-9(0))* Xlibris Corp.

Nathan, P. Durrell. City Streets to Destiny. 2006. 59p. per. 8.95 *(978-1-59824-282-9(2))* E-BookTime LLC.

Naylor, Carma. A Mormon's Unexpected Journey, Volume 2: Finding the Grace I Never Knew. 2010. pap. 20.95 *(978-1-57921-904-8(7))* WinePress Publishing.

Nelson, Alan. The Only Alternative: Christian Nonviolent Peacemakers in America. 2008. 190p. pap. 22.00 *(978-1-55635-262-1(X)*, Wipf and Stock) Wipf & Stock Pubs.

Nelson, Jason M. Miserable Joy: Chronic Pain in the Christian Life. 2007. per. *(978-0-8100-1749-8(0))* Northwestern Publishing Hse.

Nelson, Toni. A Beggars Purse. 2010. pap. 10.99 *(978-1-61663-117-8(1))* Tate Publishing & Enterprises, LLC.

Newell, Marvin J. A Martyr's Grace: Stories of Those Who Gave All for Christ & His Cause. 2006. (ENG., Illus.). 224p. per. 13.99 *(978-0-8024-7829-0(8))* Moody Pubs.

Newhard, Howard. Lifeletter. 2008. 332p. pap. 18.99 *(978-1-60647-980-3(6))* Xulon Pr., Inc.

Newhouse, Deborah. My New Normal. 2010. 172p. pap. 14.99 *(978-1-60957-610-3(1))* Xulon Pr., Inc.

Ng, Chi. Adventures of a World Traveler: How God filled my every need richly in 19 Countries. 2008. 212p. pap. 13.00 *(978-1-4357-3415-9(7))* Lulu Enterprises Inc.

Nichols, Stephen J. Pages from Church History: A Guided Tour of Christian Classics. 2006. (Illus.). 329p. per. 15.99 *(978-0-87552-636-2(5))* P & R Publishing.

Nicholson, May. More Miracles from Mayhem. 2009. (ENG.). 192p. mass mkt. 8.99 *(978-1-84550-449-6(6))* Christian Focus Pubns. GBR. Dist: STL Distribution North America.

Niles, Bruce Alan. Running Wild: (or God Ain't Late), 1 vol. 2009. 76p. pap. 16.95 *(978-1-4489-8992-8(2))* PublishAmerica, Inc.

Nimmo, Beth & Scott, Darrell. Rachel's Tears: The Spiritual Journey of Columbine Martyr Rachel Scott, 0 vols. 10th anniv. ed. 2009. (Illus.). 224p. pap. 14.99 *(978-1-4003-1347-1(3))* Nelson, Thomas Inc.

No one sees my Pain: Life without God. 2007. per. 12.99 *(978-0-9786208-0-6(1))* Naylor, Angela.

Noble, James. The Truth Encounters the Catholic Church. 2008. 125p. pap. 19.95 *(978-1-4241-7342-6(6))* PublishAmerica, Inc.

Nobles, Juanita. A Heritage of Faith. 2010. (ENG.). 280p. 25.99 *(978-1-4490-7684-9(X))*; pap. 16.99 *(978-1-4490-7683-2(1))* AuthorHouse.

Nolan, Dawn. A Mother's Search for Sant. 2009. 56p. pap. 9.95 *(978-1-4401-3531-6(2))* iUniverse, Inc.

Noll, Mark A. & Nystrom, Carolyn. Clouds of Witnesses: Christian Voices from Africa & Asia. 2011. (ENG.). 286p. 25.00 *(978-0-8308-3834-9(1))*, IVP Bks.) InterVarsity Pr.

Norris, Gloria. Just a Closer Walk with Thee. 2009. 140p. pap. 11.99 *(978-1-4389-2078-8(4))* AuthorHouse.

Nunn, Charles, Jr. The Life & Times of a Baptist Nunn, 1 vols., bk. 1. 2010. (Illus.). 350p. 14.95 *(978-0-615-39028-4(5))* Nunn,, Charles B. Jr.

Nyabero, Wilson Achoki. From Meteerere to the City: Green & yet Determined to Succeed: My Story, 1 vol. 2010. 82p. pap. 19.95 *(978-1-4489-4069-1(9))* PublishAmerica, Inc.

Oake, Robin. Father Forgive. 2012. (ENG.). 160p. pap. 12.99 ***(978-1-85078-765-5(4))*** Authentic Media.

Oakland, Roger. Let There Be Light: From Evolutionist to Creationist How One Man Left His Canadian Farm to Spread the Gospel Throughout the World. 2011. pap. ***(978-0-9846366-9-3(2))*** Lighthouse Trails Publishing Co.

Oaks, Marcus. Diary of a Preacher's Life: A Journey from Grace to Disgrace to Grace. 2006. mass mkt. 16.95 *(978-0-9772730-1-0(6))*; 264p. per. 22.00 *(978-0-9772730-2-7(4))* Hill & Oaks Pubs.

Oblinger, Joseph. Fisher of Men. 2006. (Illus.). 145p. per. 19.95 *(978-1-59879-166-2(4))* Lifevest Publishing, Inc.

Obras de Wesley, 14 vols., Set. Incl. Cartas, Tomo I. González, Justo L., ed. 1998. 34.95 *(978-1-57736-068-1(0))*; Cartos, Tomo II. González, Justo L., ed. 1998. 34.95 *(978-1-57736-069-8(9))*; Defensa del Metodismo. González, Justo L., ed. 472p. 1997. 34.95 *(978-1-57736-035-3(4))*; Diarios, Tomo I. González, Justo L., ed. 1998. 34.95 *(978-1-57736-066-7(4))*; Diarios, Tomo II. González, Justo L., ed. 1998. 34.95 *(978-1-57736-067-4(2))*; Notas al Nuevo Testamento: Primera Parte. González, Justo L., ed. 1998. 34.95 *(978-1-57736-064-3(8))*; Notas al Nuevo Testamento: Secunda Parte. González, Justo L. 1998. 34.95 *(978-1-57736-065-0(6))*; Primeras Sociedades Metodistas. González, Justo L., ed. 395p. 1997. 34.95 *(978-1-57736-034-6(6))*; Sermones I. González, Justo L., ed. 422p. 1996. 34.95 *(978-1-57736-001-8(X))*; Sermones II. González, Justo L., ed. 408p. 1996. 34.95 *(978-1-57736-002-5(8))*; Sermones III. González, Justo L., ed. 344p. 1996. 34.95 *(978-1-57736-003-2(6))*; Sermones IV. González, Justo L., ed. 408p. 1996. 34.95 *(978-1-57736-004-9(4))*; Tratados Teologicos. González, Justo L., ed. 1998. 34.95 *(978-1-57736-063-6(X))*; Vida Christiana. González, Justo L., ed. 1998. 34.95 *(978-1-57736-062-9(1))*; (SPA.). 349.95 *(978-1-57736-000-1(1))* Wesley Heritage Foundation, Inc.

O'Callaghan, Denis. Putting Hand to the Plough: A Memoir. 2008. (ENG.). 200p. pap. 23.95 *(978-1-84730-026-3(X))* Veritas Pubns. IRL. Dist: Dufour Editions, Inc.

Ofor, Ogonnaya Vincent. The Wife of Woes a Romantic Nightmare. 2008. 68p. pap. 15.99 *(978-1-4363-0498-6(9))* Xlibris Corp.

O'Laughlin, Michael. Henri Nouwen: His Life & Vision. 2009. (ENG., Illus.). 140p. pap. 16.00 *(978-1-57075-822-5(0))* Orbis Bks.

O'Leary, Jeffrey. Footprints in Time: Fulfilling God's Destiny for Your Life, 0 vols. 2006. 288p. per. 13.99 *(978-0-7852-6197-1(4))* Nelson, Thomas Inc.

Olley, Linda. Holy Hunches. 2010. 208p. pap. *(978-1-55452-538-6(1)*, Guardian Bks.) Essence Publishing.

Ologe, Kingsley O. Help from Above: The Travails & Triumph of A Child of God. 2011. 412p. pap. 23.03 ***(978-1-4567-7868-2(4))*** AuthorHouse.

Oloimooja, Rev. Joseph. Angels Walk among Us: From Every Tribe, Kindred & Nation. 2011. 224p. pap. 19.00 ***(978-0-578-07850-2(3))*** Kindness Mission Inc.

O'Malley, Cardinal Seán, frwd. All along the Way: Gifts, Blessings & Graces from Our Loving God. 2010. (Illus.). 190p. pap. 15.00 *(978-1-883551-39-1(0)*, Jubilee Studio) Attic Studio Publishing Hse.

O'Malley, William. Dare to Dream: Stories of 16 People Who Became Somebody. 2009. 192p. pap. 12.95 *(978-1-59471-201-2(8))* Ave Maria Pr.

O'Reilly, Bernard. Good News for Catholics: What We Were Never Told. 2006. 147p. pap. 24.95 *(978-1-4241-4887-5(7))* PublishAmerica, Inc.

O'Roark, Bobby. They Call Me Bubbins: Reflections in Time. 2011. 212p. 27.95 ***(978-1-4620-3408-6(X))***; pap. 17.95 ***(978-1-4620-3407-9(1))*** iUniverse, Inc.

Ortiz, Sandra K. Last Dance: A Story of Great Faith & Courage. 2008. 104p. pap. 10.99 *(978-1-60791-162-3(0))* Xulon Pr., Inc.

O'Ryan, Mercedes. The Wind Demon Within Me: The True Story of One Woman's Lifelong Battle with Demonic Possession after Becoming a Jehovah's Witness. 2008. 260p. pap. 15.60 *(978-1-4389-2999-6(4))* AuthorHouse.

Osborn, T. L. Legacy of Faith Collection: T. L. Osborn. 2010. 368p. 22.99 *(978-1-60683-029-1(5))* Harrison House Pubs.

Osburn, Charlie & Osburn, Jeanne. Love Walks by Faith: You Got to Give It All to Jesus. 2007. pap. 14.00 *(978-0-929375-29-8(7))* Whitney, Harvey Bks. Co.

Osland, Nalley T. My God Makes House Calls. 2009. 128p. 23.95 *(978-1-4401-2173-9(7))*; pap. 13.95 *(978-1-4401-2172-2(9))* iUniverse, Inc.

Ouellette, E. J. The Majesties of His Kingdom. 2008. 67p. pap. 16.95 *(978-1-60563-863-8(3))* PublishAmerica, Inc.

Overhulser, Josephine. Called According to His Purpose. Ummel, Richard, ed. 2007. 244p. per. 14.99 *(978-1-60266-448-7(X))* Xulon Pr., Inc.

Owens, Charles. Living on the Edge. 2007. 108p. 24.40 *(978-1-4251-5447-9(6))* Trafford Publishing.

Owojori, F. O. I Was in Heaven. 2011. 60p. pap. 12.10 ***(978-1-4567-8375-4(0))*** AuthorHouse.

Palmer, Jim. Divine Nobodies: Shedding Religion to Find God (And the Unlikely People Who Help You), 0 vols. 2006. 224p. per. 13.99 *(978-0-8499-1398-3(5))* Nelson, Thomas Inc.

—Wide Open Spaces: Beyond Paint-by-Number Christianity, 0 vols. 2007. 224p. per. 13.99 *(978-0-8499-1399-0(3))* Nelson, Thomas Inc.

Palmer, Ralph. Vignettes of A Wonderful Life! The Amalgamated Autobiographies of Mary Maxine & Ralph Thomas Palmer. 2011. 420p. 42.95 ***(978-1-4497-2896-0(0))***; pap. 27.95 ***(978-1-4497-2895-3(2))*** Author Solutions, Inc. (WestBow Pr.).

Paponetti, Giovanna, illus. Kateri, Native American Saint: The Life & Miracles of Kateri Tekakwitha. 2010. *(978-1-57416-098-7(2))* Clear Light Pubs.

Parham Jr. An Affirmation of Faith. 2011. 338p. 28.99 ***(978-1-60957-861-9(9))*** Xulon Pr., Inc.

Park, Mirae. Signs & Wonders: Super Natural Power in Daily Life. 2009. 248p. pap. 15.99 *(978-1-61579-171-2(X))* Xulon Pr., Inc.

Parker, Donald James. Homeless Like Me. 2009. 212p. pap. 12.95 *(978-0-578-03282-5(1))* Sword of the Spirit Publishing.

Parker, L. J. My Son, My Search. 2006. pap. 13.99 *(978-1-59781-821-6(6))* Xulon Pr., Inc.

Parkins, Daniel. Daydreams: An End to My Nightmares. 2006. 175p. per. 12.99 *(978-1-59886-458-8(0))* Tate Publishing & Enterprises, LLC.

Parsons, Yvette. From Fear to Love. 2007. 128p. per. 13.99 *(978-1-60266-175-2(8))* Xulon Pr., Inc.

Pastore, Frank. Shattered: Struck down, but Not Destroyed. 2010. (ENG.). 240p. pap. 13.99 *(978-1-58997-611-5(8))* Tyndale Hse. Pubs.

Patel, Haresh. Thoughts from the Cosmic Field in the Life of a Thinking Insect [A Latter-Day Saint]. 2009. 396p. 31.50 *(978-1-60693-846-1(0)*, Eloquent Bks.) AEG Literary Publishing Services, Inc.

Patterson, Steve. Thirteen Months with an Angel: Learning to See God's Plan During the Trials. 2009. 152p. 24.95 *(978-0-595-51536-3(3))*; pap. 14.95 *(978-0-595-52772-4(8))* iUniverse, Inc.

Paul, Tessa. An Illustrated Dictionary of Saints: A guide to the lives & works of over 300 of the world's most notable saints, with expert commentary & more than 350 beautiful illustrations. 2012. (ENG., Illus.). 160p. pap. 19.99 *(978-1-84476-847-9(3))* Anness Publishing GBR. Dist: National Bk. Network.

Paulk, Norma. Stand By Your Man: A Story of a Preachers Wife. pap. 7.99 *(978-0-917595-57-8(2))* Cathedral of the Holy Spirit.

Paulson, J. Barrie. Hripsime. 2007. (ENG.). 124p. per. 19.95 *(978-1-4241-6602-2(0))* PublishAmerica, Inc.

Payne, Leanne. Heaven's Calling: A Memoir of One Soul's Steep Ascent. 2008. (Illus.). 352p. 19.99 *(978-0-8010-1312-6(7))* Baker Bks.

Pearce, Brenda. Deliverance from Darkness into the Light, 1 vol. 2009. 84p. pap. 16.95 *(978-1-60749-644-1(5))* PublishAmerica, Inc.

Pearson, Tania Sue. Delicate Flowers: The Life of a Child Seperated from Her Heavenly Father. 2008. 140p. 26.95 *(978-1-4389-2155-6(1))*; pap. 19.95 *(978-1-4389-2156-3(X))* AuthorHouse.

Pecora, Valerie. The Seasons of My Soul. 2007. 216p. (ENG.). 24.99 *(978-1-60477-303-3(0))*; per. 14.99 *(978-1-60477-302-6(2))* Xulon Pr., Inc.

Pelton, Robert W. George Washington: God's Chosen Leader? 2008. 317p. pap. 16.95 *(978-0-7414-3728-0(7))* Infinity Publishing.

Pence, Wanda Jo. Housekeeping for God. 2009. 132p. pap. 12.49 *(978-1-4389-9895-4(3))* AuthorHouse.

Penksa, Gnsh. The Scoop on Ruth: All in the Family, Sense & Nun-sense, along the Way, the P Source. 2009. 180p. pap. 14.49 *(978-1-4389-5360-1(7))* AuthorHouse.

Pequena Fe: Little Girl Names Faith. (SPA.). 104p. *(978-84-7228-324-4(0)*, 220682) Clie, Editorial.

Perez, Joey. I Lived to Tell about It. 2008. 248p. (J). pap. 17.00 *(978-0-9801064-0-4(0))* Worldwide Evangelistic Ministries, Inc.

Perry, Lloyd. A Diamond in the Rough: Cowboying Around. 2011. pap. 21.99 ***(978-1-61346-092-4(9))*** Tate Publishing & Enterprises, LLC.

Peters, Tina. The Barbed Wire Fence. 2008. 172p. pap. 13.99 *(978-1-60647-324-5(7))* Xulon Pr., Inc.

Petersen, Trina. Good Morning Great Day. 2007. 204p. per. 16.95 *(978-0-9791566-0-1(2))* To His Glory Publishing Co., Inc.

Peterson, Polly & Forsyth-Vail, Gail. Stirring the Nation's Heart: Eighteen Stories of Prophetic Unitarians & Universalists of the Nineteenth Century. 2010. pap. 15.00 *(978-1-55896-570-6(X)*, Skinner Hse. Bks.) Unitarian Universalist Assn.

Pettaway, Curtis & Pettaway, Janice, compiled by. After God's Own Heart. 2011. 148p. pap. 14.99 ***(978-1-61379-187-5(9))*** Xulon Pr., Inc.

Pettijohn, Steve. A Whole Mess Load of Grace. 2009. 136p. pap. 14.99 *(978-1-61579-307-5(0))* Xulon Pr., Inc.

Pfatteicher, Philip H. New Book of Festivals & Commemorations: A Proposed Common Calendar of Saints. 2008. 718p. (C). 50.00 *(978-0-8006-2128-5(X)*, Fortress Pr.) Augsburg Fortress, Pubs.

Phemister, Mary Anne. Lessons from a Broken Chopstick. 2009. 160p. pap. 14.95 *(978-1-934749-62-3(1))* Hannibal Bks.

Phillips, Beverly Jane. From Heaven to My Heart: God's Journey with Me. 2011. 396p. 35.95 *(978-1-4502-5995-8(2))*; pap. 25.95 *(978-1-4502-5993-4(6))* iUniverse, Inc.

Phillips, Robin. Saints & Scoundrels from King Herod to Jim Elliot. 2011. ***(978-1-59128-104-7(0))*** Canon Pr.

Philson, Ernest J. Delivered: My Journey to an Addiction-Free Life. 2011. pap. 9.99 *(978-1-61739-696-0(6))* Tate Publishing & Enterprises, LLC.

Phyllis, Thompson. Sadhu Sundar Singh. 2007. (ENG.). 1p. pap. 12.99 *(978-1-85078-656-6(9))* Authentic Media.

Pickens, Correna Wilson & Bazzrea, Farah. Sheltered in His Arms: A Mother's Faith in God Sustained Chuck, Wieland, & Aaron Norris. Bazzrea, Farah, ed. l.t. ed. 2008. (Illus.). 304p. pap. 19.99 *(978-0-9818611-1-1(3))* Granny's Bks. Publishing Hse.

Pierce, Chonda. Roadkill on the Highway to Heaven, 1 vol. 2006. (ENG.). 208p. pap. 14.99 *(978-0-310-23527-9(8))* Zondervan.

Pierce, David W. To Kill a Zombie: The Year I Came Back to Life — and Why. 2012. (ENG.). 240p. pap. 14.99 *(978-0-89112-267-8(2)*, Leafwood Pubs.) Abilene Christian Univ. Pr.

Pierce, Lenard. Testimonial Poetry, 1 vol. 2010. 62p. pap. 19.95 *(978-1-4512-9004-2(7))* PublishAmerica, Inc.

Pierson, Arthur T. George Muller of Bristol. 2009. 264p. pap. *(978-1-4068-9375-5(7))* Echo Library.

—George Muller of Bristol. 2007. (ENG.). 462p. 52.95 *(978-0-548-21237-0(6))*; 464p. per. 37.95 *(978-1-4325-3150-8(6))* Kessinger Publishing, LLC.

—George Müller of Bristol (1805-1898) A Hendrickson Classic Biography. 2008. 466p. 17.95 *(978-1-59856-252-1(5))* Hendrickson Pubs. Marketing, LLC.

Pigno, Sam J. Autobiography of Sam J Pigno: A School System's Fall into Disgrace. 2011. 90p. 24.99 ***(978-1-4653-5211-8(2))***; pap. 15.99 ***(978-1-4653-5210-1(4))*** Xlibris Corp.

Pignot, Hélène. Christians under the Ottoman Turks. 2009. 105.00 *(978-1-59333-922-7(4))* Gorgias Pr., LLC.

Pinkston, Beulah W. In Spite of Ourselves... The Ministry of Otis & Beulah Pinkston. 2009. 128p. pap. 14.99 *(978-1-61579-518-5(9))* Xulon Pr., Inc.

Piper, Don & Murphey, Cecil. 90 Minutes in Heaven: A True Story of Death & Life. (Illus.). 2007. 208p. 17.99 *(978-0-8007-1905-0(0))* 2006. 304p. pap. 16.99 *(978-0-8007-3166-3(2))* Revell.

—90 Minutes in Heaven: An Inspiring Story of Life Beyond Death. 2009. E-Book 12.99 ***(978-1-58558-949-4(7))*** 2008. 128p. 12.99 *(978-0-8007-1909-8(3))* Revell.

Piper, Don & Murphey, Cecil. 90 Minutes in Heaven Member Workbook: Seeing Life's Troubles in a Whole New Light, 1 vol. 2010. 160p. pap. 12.99 *(978-1-936034-01-7(8))* Revell.

Piper, John. The Hidden Smile of God: The Fruit of Affliction in the Lives of John Bunyan, William Cowper, & David Brainerd. 2008. (Swans Are Not Silent Ser.). 176p. pap. 15.99 *(978-1-4335-0189-0(9))* Crossway.

Pirinelli, John. Consider It Done. 2006. pap. 13.99 *(978-1-60034-448-0(8))* Xulon Pr., Inc.

Pittman, Keeshler La'Chaunt. Refined & Defined by God: An Autobiography. 2011. 54p. pap. 16.95 ***(978-1-4560-0403-3(4))*** PublishAmerica, Inc.

Pitts, Daniele. In God I Do Not Have a Past. 2010. 56p. pap. 12.00 *(978-1-4520-4032-5(X))* AuthorHouse.

Platt, Rita J. I Am His: Experiencing the Comfort of Abba's Love. 2009. (Sword of Lyric Ser.). (ENG.). 128p. pap. 9.99 *(978-1-60006-387-9(X))* NavPress Publishing Group.

Plekon, Michael. Saints As They Really Are: Voices of Holiness in Our Time. 2012. (ENG., Illus.). 288p. pap. 30.00 ***(978-0-268-03838-0(4))*** Univ. of Notre Dame Pr.

Plourde, Joseph C. Rising from the Dark Side of Life: One Man's Spiritual Journey from Fear to Enlightenment. 2011. 168p. 25.95 ***(978-1-4502-1037-9(6))***; pap. 15.95 ***(978-1-4502-1039-3(2))*** iUniverse, Inc.

Policastro, Merry. Talk Yourself into a Miracle. 2007. 60p. per. 9.99 *(978-1-60266-124-0(3))* Xulon Pr., Inc.

Pollard, T. Dale. I Knew There Was More. 2008. 256p. pap. 16.99 *(978-1-60647-907-0(5))* Xulon Pr., Inc.

Pollock, John. A Fistful of Heroes: Christians at the Forefront of Change. 2008. (History Makers (Christian Focus) Ser.). (ENG.). 250p. pap. 10.99 *(978-1-84550-346-8(5))* Christian Focus Pubns. GBR. Dist: STL Distribution North America.

Ponce Jr., Ernest F. In Too Deep. 2011. 24p. pap. 8.99 ***(978-1-61215-624-8(X))*** Xulon Pr., Inc.

Popcorn Miracles: Little Reminders of God's Nearness. 2008. (Illus.). per. 12.99 *(978-0-9799903-0-4(0))* Majesty Hse.

Prainito, Bill T. A Prophet's Ministry: Testimony Teaching Guide. 2008. 172p. pap. 13.99 *(978-1-60647-506-5(1))* Xulon Pr., Inc.

Pressley, Karen Schless. Escaping Scientology: An Insider's True Story. 2007. 288p. 24.99 *(978-1-59669-066-0(6))* New Hope Pubs.

Prince, Alphonso X. Imagine Me. 2008. 224p. (ENG.). 21.95 *(978-1-4327-2278-4(6))*; per. 13.95 *(978-1-4327-2252-4(2))* Outskirts Pr., Inc.

Prophet, Elizabeth Clare. Preparation for My Mission. 2009. 428p. 36.95 *(978-1-4401-7396-7(6))* iUniverse, Inc.

Publishing, Jaycen Moody. From the Crack-House to the House of God. 2009. pap. 14.99 *(978-1-60791-489-1(1))* Xulon Pr., Inc.

Purves, Rodrick. Crosswalk: One Nation under God. 2008. 316p. per. 15.95 *(978-1-4327-1473-4(2))* Outskirts Pr., Inc.

Quewea, Zon G. 23 Days of Intensive Care: A Story of Miracles: Overcoming Medical Disorders & Tragedies. 2010. 204p. (ENG.). 27.95 *(978-1-4502-2325-6(7))*; pap. 17.95 *(978-1-4502-2327-0(3))* iUniverse, Inc.

Quewea, Zon G. 23 Jours D'Hospitalisation Dans le Service des Soins Intensifs: RéCits Miraculeux: Victoire Sur la Maladie et les TragéDies MéDicales. 2011. 268p. pap. 20.95 ***(978-1-4620-3054-5(8))*** iUniverse, Inc.

Rabbitt, Karen. Trading Fathers: Forgiving Dad, Embracing God. 2009. 336p. pap. 15.95 *(978-1-57921-995-6(0))* WinePress Publishing.

Raburn, Sally Knight. Mama's Amazing Love: Biography about an exceptional Christian woman: Ruby Lee Mullis Knight. 2009. pap. 14.99 *(978-1-60799-479-4(8))* Tate Publishing & Enterprises, LLC.

Radford, D. Evans. Dry Eyes of Innocence. 2008. 128p. 23.00 *(978-1-934925-27-0(6))*; pap. 14.99 *(978-1-934925-19-5(5))* AEG Literary Publishing Services, Inc. (Strategic Bk. Publishing).

Railey, Robert R. Half Drunk, Half Sober. 2006. 49p. pap. 16.95 *(978-1-4241-1546-4(9))* PublishAmerica, Inc.

Rainsford, William Stephen. The Story of a Varied Life: An Autobiography. 2010. 510p. pap. 39.75 *(978-1-143-43686-4(5))* 2010. 512p. pap. 39.75 *(978-1-141-88120-8(9))* 2009. 502p. pap. 37.75 *(978-1-116-22156-5(X))* 2009. (ENG.). 500p. pap. 30.99 *(978-1-116-22157-2(8)*, BiblioLife) BiblioBazaar.

—The Story of a Varied Life: An Autobiography. 2009. 382p. pap. 26.34 *(978-1-4589-3835-0(2))* General Bks. LLC.

—The Story of a Varied Life: An Autobiography. 500p. 2010. pap. 31.16 *(978-1-164-10706-4(2))* 2010. 43.16 ***(978-1-164-44167-0(1))*** 2008. 53.95 *(978-1-4365-9647-3(5))* 2007. (ENG.). reprint ed. per. 38.95 *(978-0-548-80412-4(5))* Kessinger Publishing, LLC.

Ram-Mar. Del Rio Rojo. 2007. *(978-1-59835-057-9(9))* Cambridge BrickHouse, Inc.

Ramandt, Dianne. Death's Doorstep Prayer & a Miracle. 2011. ***(978-1-77069-232-9(0))*** Word Alive Pr.

Rambaldo, Chuck. A Man of His Word: My Walk, My Witness. 2009. 240p. pap. 15.99 *(978-1-4389-8800-9(1))* AuthorHouse.

Rambissoon, P. "Moses". The Scrolls of Heaven. 2011. 112p. pap. 11.99 ***(978-1-61215-577-7(4))*** Xulon Pr., Inc.

Ramdhan, Kevin J. The Revelation of Faith. 2011. 104p. pap. 10.99 ***(978-1-61379-712-9(5))*** Xulon Pr., Inc.

Ramón, Connie. In a Space of Time: Lessons to Last a Lifetime. 2009. 108p. pap. 11.99 *(978-1-60791-446-4(8))* Xulon Pr., Inc.

Ramos, Sandi. He Carries Me: A Message of Hope & Understanding for the Caregivers of Terminally Ill Loved Ones. 2010. pap. 10.99 *(978-1-61663-091-1(4))* Tate Publishing & Enterprises, LLC.

Rand, Stephen. Guinea Pig for Lunch. (Illus.). 208p. pap. *(978-0-340-72158-2(8)*, Hodder & Stoughton) Hodder General Publishing Div.

Randolph, Richard. Faith under Fire. 2007. 200p. per. 14.95 *(978-1-933912-48-6(0))* Westview Publishing Co., Inc.

Rasanen, Dick. From One Heart to Another. 2006. pap. 13.99 *(978-1-60034-507-4(7))* Xulon Pr., Inc.

Ratcliff-Rondeau, Nancy. Peace, Power, Perseverance, & Prophecy. 2010. 79p. pap. 14.00 *(978-0-557-30363-2(X))* Lulu Enterprises Inc.

Rath, Sandra Kellogg. Peace by Piece. 2008. 216p. 24.99 *(978-1-60647-122-7(8))* Xulon Pr., Inc.

Ray, Charles. Mrs. C. H. Spurgeon: A Biography of Susannah Spurgeon. 2006. per. 5.00 *(978-1-60208-018-8(6))* FBC Pubns. & Printing.

Ray, Crystol T. My Sistahs, You're Chasing the Wrong Man. 2008. 52p. pap. 16.95 *(978-1-60474-938-0(5))* PublishAmerica, Inc.

Read, Maureen Hay. Like a Watered Garden. 2007. (ENG., Illus.). 156p. pap. 8.99 *(978-0-60126-077-2(6))* Masthof Pr.

Ream, Jack. When God Acts. 2011. 134p. pap. 24.95 ***(978-1-4560-3405-4(7))*** PublishAmerica, Inc.

Reaville, Lauren. The Timeless Present. 2011. 384p. pap. ***(978-1-77067-315-1(6))*** FriesenPress.

Reed, Veronica L. & Harrill, Vanessa. From Welfare to Wealth: A True Testimony of Faith & the Power of Positive Thinking. 2010. 212p. 24.99 *(978-1-4490-3127-5(7))*; pap. 14.95 *(978-1-4490-3126-8(9))* AuthorHouse.

Reese, Ed. Reese Chronological Encyclopedia of Christian Biographies. 2007. (ENG., Illus.). 1500p. (gr. 11). 34.99 *(978-0-89957-397-7(5))* AMG Pubs.

Reese, Rose. Desert Rose. 2007. 120p. per. 10.99 *(978-1-60266-295-7(9))* Xulon Pr., Inc.

Reeve, W. Paul & Parshall, Ardis E. Mormonism: A Historical Encyclopedia. 2010. (Illus.). xxviii, 449p. E-Book *(978-1-59884-108-4(4))* ABC-CLIO, LLC.

Reeve, W. Paul & Parshall, Ardis E., eds. Mormonism: A Historical Encyclopedia, 1 vol. 2010. (Illus.). 449p. 85.00 *(978-1-59884-107-7(6)*, MORMON1C) ABC-CLIO, LLC.

Reeves, Donald. The Memoirs of a 'Very Dangerous Man' 2009. (ENG., Illus.). 232p. 34.95 *(978-1-84706-313-7(6))* Continuum International Publishing Group, Ltd. GBR. Dist: National Bk. Network.

Reeves, Kevin. The Other Side of the River: When Mystical Experiences & Strange Doctrines Overtake His Church One Man Risks All to Find the Truth a True Story. 2007. (ENG., Illus.). 248p. per. 12.95 *(978-0-9791315-0-9(2))* Lighthouse Trails Publishing Co.

Register, Margaret A. No Place for Plastic Saints: Earthquakes, Chicken Feet, & Candid Confessions of a Missionary Wife. 2009. 440p. pap. 22.99 *(978-1-60647-976-6(8))* Xulon Pr., Inc.

Reid, Russell. The Voyage of a Veteran. 2006. 240p. per. 16.99 *(978-1-58169-230-3(7))* Genesis Communications, Inc.

Reinecke, Thomas C. Is Your Religion Robbing You? 2008. 312p. pap. 18.99 *(978-1-60647-738-0(2))* Xulon Pr., Inc.

Reiterman, Tim. Raven: The Untold Story of the Rev. Jim Jones & His People. 2008. (ENG., Illus.). 688p. (gr. 12-18). 18.95 *(978-1-58542-678-2(4)*, Tarcher) Penguin Group (USA) Inc.

REM007. New Beginnings: How God Delivered Me from Alcohol & Drugs! 2011. 100p. pap. 15.00 *(978-1-4269-5298-2(8))* Trafford Publishing.

Resko, John Allen. The Gates of Saint Charles: Testing the Waters of a Religious Vocation - A Memoir. 2010. 232p. pap. 18.95 *(978-1-4401-9299-9(5))* iUniverse, Inc.

Reynolds, Ruth Morgan. My Wounds Have Made Me Well. 2010. 84p. pap. 9.95 *(978-1-61507-261-3(6))* Cross Bks. Publishing.

Reynolds, Suzanne & Delgado, Alvaro. Born with A Veil: Tragedy to Triumph. 2010. pap. 15.99 *(978-1-61579-776-9(9))* Xulon Pr., Inc.

Rhodes, Cecil. Jack's Journey. 2011. 96p. pap. 9.95 *(978-1-4497-1141-2(3)*, WestBow Pr.) Author Solutions, Inc.

Rhody, Donald. Surprised by a Garden: Discovering God in Unexpected Places. 2010. pap. 23.99 *(978-1-61663-602-9(5))* Tate Publishing & Enterprises, LLC.

Rice, Jim. A View of God from My Rearview Mirror: Seeing God's Presence in Everyday Life. 2010. pap. 16.99 *(978-1-61579-902-2(8))* Xulon Pr., Inc.

Richards, Claude & Kimball, J. Golden. J Golden Kimball: The Story of A Unique Personality. 2011. 424p. 56.95 ***(978-1-258-03092-6(6))*** Literary Licensing, LLC.

Richards, Michelle. Trauma to Treasure. 2008. 156p. pap. 13.99 *(978-1-60647-474-7(X))* Xulon Pr., Inc.

Richardson, B. Louis. Late Dream: Finding Purpose. 2011. 108p. 20.95 ***(978-1-4620-0092-0(4))***; pap. 10.95 ***(978-1-4620-0091-3(6))*** iUniverse, Inc.

Richardson, Lucille. Embracing destiny's Crossroads. 2006. pap. 13.99 *(978-1-60034-386-5(4))* Xulon Pr., Inc.

Richmond, Helen. Living Past the Pain: Reflections of the Past. 2008. 119p. pap. 21.95 *(978-1-4357-4226-0(5))* Lulu Enterprises Inc.

Richmond, Rhonda. The Waterfall Chronicles. 2008. 145p. pap. 13.95 *(978-0-557-03447-5(7))* Lulu Enterprises Inc.

Rieser, Bill. They Called Me White Jesus: I was a Legend... Now I'm Something More, 1 vol. 2009. (ENG.). 192p. pap. 14.99 *(978-0-8024-2298-9(5))* Moody Pubs.

Riess, Jerry Brian. The Chorba Trail. 2009. 244p. 25.99 *(978-1-61579-622-9(3))*; pap. 15.99 *(978-1-61579-512-3(X))* Xulon Pr., Inc.

Rini, Patricia Ann. The Power of Choice: The Journey from Addiction - Trial by Fire & Blind Faith. 2008. 300p. pap. 17.99 *(978-1-60477-984-4(5))* Xulon Pr., Inc.

Rinker, Roger R. On the Road To: An Amazing True Story. 2009. 212p. pap. 15.99 *(978-1-60791-773-1(4))* Xulon Pr., Inc.

Rish, Terrye Ann. Born to Darkness: Wife, Mother, Escort, Lesbian, a Child of God. 2008. pap. 11.99 *(978-1-60477-723-9(0))* Xulon Pr., Inc.

Ritch, Jeremy. My Beautiful Mess. 2009. 163p. pap. 9.95 *(978-0-557-03937-1(1))* Lulu Enterprises Inc.

Rix, Jallen. Ex-Gay No Way: Survival & Recovery from Religious Abuse. 2010. (ENG.). 256p. pap. 19.95 *(978-1-84409-187-4(2))* Findhorn Pr. GBR. Dist: Independent Pubs. Group.

Robbins, Janet B. & Robbins, Earl. Our Story: To God Be the Glory. 2007. 108p. per. 12.33 *(978-0-9790446-9-4(3))* Pen & Publish Inc.

Roberg, Jerry O. The Parable of the Fig Tree. 324p. 2015. 35.99 ***(978-1-61379-822-5(9))*** 2011. pap. 21.99 ***(978-1-61379-819-5(9))*** Xulon Pr., Inc.

Roberts, Augustine. Finding the Treasure: Letters from a Global Monk. 2011. E-Book ***(978-0-87907-206-3(7))*** Cistercian Pubns., Inc.

Roberts, Karen Lynn. The Day God Pulled My Truck Out of the Mud: And Other True Stories. 2007. 80p. per. 9.95 *(978-0-595-47182-9(X))* iUniverse, Inc.

Robertson, Annette. Love & Acceptance. 2009. pap. 13.99 *(978-1-60799-760-3(6))* Tate Publishing & Enterprises, LLC.

Robertson, C. K. A Dangerous Dozen: Twelve Christians Who Threatened the Status Quo but Taught Us to Live Like Jesus. 2011. 160p. pap. 16.99 *(978-1-59473-298-0(1))* SkyLight Paths Publishing.

Robertson, Jean. A Place of My Own: A Memoir. 2010. 202p. pap. 15.99 *(978-1-61579-757-8(2))* Xulon Pr., Inc.

Robertson, Judy. Out of Mormonism: A Woman's True Story. rev. ed. 2011. pap. 14.99 *(978-0-7642-0901-7(9))* Bethany Hse. Pubs.

Robinette, Marty. Delicious on My Ears: The Story of Missionary John Newman. 2009. 208p. pap. 15.99 *(978-1-61579-144-6(2))* Xulon Pr., Inc.

Robinson, Bob. God Don't Make Junk: From Ramblings of an Old Man. 2008. 286p. pap. 27.95 *(978-1-60610-353-1(9))* PublishAmerica, Inc.

Robinson, John. Get off Your Knees: A Story of Faith, Courage, & Determination. 2011. (Illus.). 141p. pap. 19.95 ***(978-0-8156-0961-2(2))*** Syracuse Univ. Pr.

Robinson, John. Somebody's Child: The Story of a Man Who Found Hope — and Took It Back to the Streets, 1 vol. 2007. (Illus.). 176p. pap. 11.99

(978-0-8254-6149-1(9), Monarch Bks.) Lion Hudson PLC GBR. Dist: Kregel Pubns.

Robinson, John & Allen, Dave. Get off Your Knees. 2009. 176p. 24.95 (978-0-8156-0922-3(1)) Syracuse Univ. Pr.

Robson, Abigail. Secret Scars: One Woman's Story of Overcoming Self-Harm. 2007. (ENG.). 176p. per. 14.99 (978-1-85078-721-1(2)) Authentic Media.

Roche, Alyosius. Christians Courageous. 2009. (J). pap. 14.95 (978-1-933184-54-8(X)) Sophia Institute Pr.

Rodgers, June Scobee. Silver Linings: My Life Before & after Challenger 7. 2010. (Illus.). 334p. 28.00 (978-1-57312-570-3(9)) Smyth & Helwys Publishing, Inc.

Rodriguez, Hector. Pardon: The Autobiography of a Gangster. 2010. 252p. 24.99 (978-1-4520-1711-2(5)); (ENG.). pap. 14.49 (978-1-4520-1712-9(3)) AuthorHouse.

Roethe, Jami. Teaching Tales: Lessons & Laughter from a Christian School. 2008. 97p. pap. 16.95 (978-1-60610-137-7(4)) PublishAmerica, Inc.

Rogalewski, Tadeusz. Founder of the Marians: Fr. Stanislaus Papczynski. (978-0-944203-28-6(0)) Marian Pr.

Rogers, Jonathan. St. Patrick: Christian Encounters Series, 0 vols. 2010. (Christian Encounters Ser.). 160p. pap. 12.00 (978-1-59555-305-8(3)) Nelson, Thomas Inc.

Rogers, Jordan. Angels Watching over Me. 2008. 144p. pap. 17.99 (978-0-9816212-0-3(1)) Word Revolution.

Rogers, Judy & Trena. We Will Carry On. 2009. 124p. 19.99 (978-1-60791-666-6(5)); pap. 11.99 (978-1-60791-665-9(7)) Xulon Pr., Inc.

Rogers, Ronii. Oh! Jesus, Help Me over the Hump of My Rainbow. 2008. 188p. 29.99 (978-1-4363-4514-9(6)); pap. 19.99 (978-1-4363-4513-2(8)) Xlibris Corp.

Rokholm, Esben. When Jesus Came into My Room. 2010. 222p. pap. 15.99 (978-1-60957-256-3(4)) Xulon Pr., Inc.

Roland, Lin S. From My Weakness, I Am Strong: One Woman's Relentless Pursuit of Pressing On. 2009. pap. 9.99 (978-1-60696-625-9(1)) Tate Publishing & Enterprises, LLC.

Rolle, Richard. The Fellowship of Angels. Hick, Henrietta, tr. from ENM. 2008. (Illus.). 84p. pap. (978-0-85244-123-7(1)) Gracewing, Ltd.

Rooke, Chris. Living by God's Plan, 1 vol. 2009. 100p. pap. 16.95 (978-1-60703-975-4(3)) PublishAmerica, Inc.

Rooyen, Pieter Van. Business Unusual. 2010. 490p. 34.99 (978-1-4500-5783-7(7)); pap. 23.99 (978-1-4500-5782-0(9)) Xlibris Corp.

Rorheim, Art. Art Rorheim, Mr. Awana: Over 60 Years of Impacting the World for Christ. 2011. (978-1-60265-028-2(4)) Grace Acres Pr.

—Mr. Awana: Sixty-plus Years of Changing the World for Christ. 2011. (ENG., Illus.). 288p. pap. 19.95 (978-1-60265-027-5(6)) Grace Acres Pr.

Rosales, Raymond S. Casiodoro De Reina, Patriarca Del Protestantismo Hispano. 2009. 249p. 16.99 (978-0-911770-74-2(7)) Concordia Seminary.

Rose-Deane, Vilma M. Tried but Not Tired! A True Story. 2011. 64p. pap. 9.95 (978-1-4502-8202-4(4)) iUniverse, Inc.

Rose, Dorothy. Bus from Bangkok: An Astonishing True Story. 2006. (ENG.). 239p. per. 12.99 (978-1-84291-263-8(1)) Kingsway Pubns. GBR. Dist: STL Distribution North America.

Rose, Prophetess Gail. My Past Was Just a Set up for My Future. 2007. 208p. per. 16.95 (978-1-4327-1479-6(1)) Outskirts Pr., Inc.

Rosen, Sandy. Off the Map: The Compelling Story of Believers Who Learned the Power & Love of God During a Spirit-Led Five Year Journey. 2007. 185p. per. 13.99 (978-88-89127-34-6(1)) Destiny Image Europe ITA. Dist: Destiny Image Pubs.

Ross, Delmer G. Iner S. Ritchie, Medical Evangelist. 2007. pap. 20.00 net. (978-0-9789294-0-4(3)) Stahl Ctr. Pubns.

Ross, Nina P. God Will Provide: M.A. Thomas, a Biography. 19.95 (978-0-9668796-0-5(0)); pap. 9.95 (978-0-9668796-1-2(9)) Stone Word Bks.

Rothschild, Jennifer. Fingerprints of God: Recognizing God's Touch on Your Life. 2006. (ENG.). 160p. pap. 14.99 (978-1-60142-037-4(4), Multnomah) Doubleday Religious Publishing Group, The.

Rotter, Arlene. Travels with Jesus: Memoirs of a Jewish Woman, 1 vol. 2010. 211p. pap. 24.95 (978-1-4489-8866-2(7)) PublishAmerica, Inc.

Rowe, Eleanor. The Desperate Search. 2007. 212p. per. 14.99 (978-1-60266-612-2(1)) Xulon Pr., Inc.

Rubio, John Agustin. Wounded Dogs & Werewolves: Out of a Life of Wreckage. 2011. 264p. 35.95 **(978-1-4497-1851-0(5))**; pap. 19.95 **(978-1-4497-1852-7(3))** Author Solutions, Inc. (WestBow Pr.).

Ruiz, David G. If God Made Heaven & Earth, Then Who Created the World I Live In. 2009. 80p. pap. 12.00 (978-1-4389-4554-5(X)) AuthorHouse.

Runkles, Alyene. Life: A Daily Adventure. 2007. pap. 19.99 (978-1-60477-459-7(2)) Xulon Pr., Inc.

Ruth, Peggy Joyce. Psalm 91. 2007. xiv, 237p. (978-1-59979-095-4(5), Creation Hse.) Charisma Media.

Ruth, Peggy Joyce & Schum, Angelia. Psalm 91 Workbook: God's Shield of Protection. 2007. (Illus.). 137p. pap. 8.00 (978-0-9708257-6-6(5)) Impact Christian Bks., Inc.

Rutherford, Tony. Please Touch: Shaped by the Master. 2009. pap. 16.99 (978-1-61579-010-4(1)) Xulon Pr., Inc.

Ryan, Trish. A Maze of Grace: A Memoir of Second Chances. 2010. (ENG.). 256p. 19.99 (978-0-446-54581-5(3)) FaithWords.

Sacher, Laurie & Meeder, Kim. Blind Hope: An Unwanted Dog & the Woman She Rescued. 2010. (ENG.). 208p. pap. 13.99 (978-1-60142-280-4(6), Multnomah) Doubleday Religious Publishing Group, The.

Sahai, Kaysha. The Biblical Path to Wellness: A Simple Guide to Achieving Balance in Your Life. 2011. (ENG.). 80p. pap. 10.98 (978-1-4609-1027-6(3)) CreateSpace.

Sailors, Obie. My Walk with Christ Jesus. 2010. 340p. pap. 19.52 (978-1-4269-3748-4(2)) Trafford Publishing.

Salacuri, Antonio. Saint Johnny Walker's 'How to... Become a SaintApos. 2009. pap. 41.95 (978-0-9558556-0-3(8)) Salacuri, Antonio GBR. Dist: Lulu Enterprises Inc.

Saldana, Stephanie. The Bread of Angels: A Journey to Love & Faith. 2011. 320p. pap. 15.00 (978-0-307-28046-6(2), Anchor) Knopf Doubleday Publishing Group.

Salemink, T., ed. 'You Will Be Called Repairer of the Breach' The Diary of J. G. M. Willebrands, 1958-1961. 2009. (Instrumenta Theologica Ser.). (DUT & ENG.). 450p. (C). pap. 64.00 (978-90-429-2257-0(5)) Peeters Pubs. & Booksellers BEL. Dist: Brown, David Bk. Co., The.

Salisbury, Bill. Uncle Bill. 2011. 272p. pap. 15.95 (978-1-4567-2001-8(5)) AuthorHouse.

Sallquist, Gary. A Seminary Journey-Reflections of a Second-Career Student. 2008. 130p. pap. 14.95 (978-1-929733-51-4(8)) MicroPress, Inc.

Salty Cove Press. The Sunshine Revolution: An Invitation to Transcend the Ordinary. 2007. (Illus.). 218p. pap. 17.95 (978-0-9799611-1-3(4), Green Parrot) Salty Cove Pr.

Samson, Lisa & Samson, Ty. Love Mercy: A Mother & Daughter's Journey from the American Dream to the Kingdom of God, 1 vol. 2010. (ENG.). 176p. pap. 14.99 (978-0-310-28477-2(5)) Zondervan.

Sanders, Elizabeth. My Life Story: A Living Testimony God Did It. 2007. 118p. pap. 13.00 (978-0-8059-7358-7(3)) Dorrance Publishing Co., Inc.

Sanidad, Benjamin R., Jr. & Murphey, Cecil. Choosing to Live: Dr. Ben's Miracle. (978-0-9720982-0-5(8)) Sanidad, Benjamin.

Sanok, Catherine. Her Life Historical: Exemplarity & Female Saints' Lives in Late Medieval England. 2007. (Middle Ages Ser.). (Illus.). 280p. (C). 65.00 (978-0-8122-3986-7(5)) Univ. of Pennsylvania Pr.

Sarro, Nicholas. Old Friends. 2008. 180p. 24.95 (978-1-58909-509-0(X)) Bookstand Publishing.

Saunders, Cotia. Mama Please Love Me. 2011. 142p. pap. 13.99 **(978-1-58930-269-3(9))** Selah Publishing Group, LLC.

Savage, H. H. And Peter: Meditations Concerning the Apostle Peter's Experiences with His Lord. 2011. 62p. 36.95 **(978-1-258-01161-1(1))** Literary Licensing, LLC.

Scarnati, Rick. Soul Explosion. 2011. pap. 24.99 **(978-1-61777-588-8(6))** Tate Publishing & Enterprises, LLC.

Schaeffer, Frank. Sex, Mom, & God: How the Bible's Strange Take on Sex Led to Crazy Politics — and How I Learned to Love Women (and Jesus) Anyway. (ENG.). 320p. 2012. pap. 16.00 **(978-0-306-82073-1(0))** 2011. (Illus.). 26.00 (978-0-306-81928-5(7)) Da Capo Pr., Inc.

Schaufel, Laura. Life, It's A Beautiful Thing. 2011. 108p. 21.23 **(978-1-4670-3880-5(6))**; pap. 10.68 **(978-1-4634-4041-1(3))** AuthorHouse.

Schlink, M. Basilea. Mi Todo para El: My All for Him. (SPA.). 168p. (978-84-7228-387-9(9), 220606) Clie, Editorial.

Schneider, Don C. & Wade, Kenneth R. Really Living 2: More Stories of Lives Changed by Jesus. 2011. pap. 14.99 (978-0-8163-2449-1(2)) Pacific Pr. Publishing Assn.

Schoeman, Roy H., compiled by. Honey from the Rock: Sixteen Jews Find the Sweetness of Christ. 2007. (Illus.). 289p. pap. 16.95 (978-1-58617-115-5(1)) Ignatius Pr.

Schroer, Cornelia R. Tetsuzo, the Son of a Samurai. 2011. 82p. 37.95 **(978-1-258-09195-8(X))** Literary Licensing, LLC.

Schuler, Charles. The Schuler Sag. 2011. 326p. 39.95 **(978-0-557-56579-5(0))** Lulu Enterprises Inc.

Scott, Christina M. Glorifying the King: Encouraging You & Glorifying Him. 2008. 120p. pap. 13.99 (978-1-4389-1883-9(6)) AuthorHouse.

Scott, Janet. Sin Is a Dead End Street. 2007. (Illus.). 131p. per. 12.95 (978-1-933290-84-3(6)) Tate Publishing & Enterprises, LLC.

Scott, Sophie. Crying Scarlet Tears: My Journey Through Self-Harm, 1 vol. 2008. 160p. pap. 12.99 (978-0-8254-6169-9(3), Monarch Bks.) Lion Hudson PLC GBR. Dist: Kregel Pubns.

Searles, H. Louise. Mama's Monkey Puzzle! A Life Interrupted! The Life Story of Carridene Narron by Sparkle, Vol. 1. 80p. (978-0-9706187-1-9(9)) As Sparkle Speaks & Informs/ASSI.

Secord, Rev. Thomas A. From Rebel to Reverend: The Journey of a Lifetime. 2011. 188p. pap. 24.95 **(978-1-4512-7900-9(0))** PublishAmerica, Inc.

Segotta, Robert. Seeking God in a Twisting Americ. 2009. 228p. 25.99 (978-1-4490-3668-3(6)); pap. 15.49 (978-1-4490-3669-0(4)) AuthorHouse.

Seibert, Virginia Ozue. Nurturing Journey's from Both Sides of the Veil. 2009. 252p. 29.95 (978-1-60844-364-2(7)); pap. 15.95 (978-1-60844-329-1(9)) Dog Ear Publishing, LLC.

Seligman, Arnold D. Mad at God, Are You? Let Me Tell You My Story. 2010. 76p. pap. 9.95 (978-1-61507-237-8(3)) Cross Bks. Publishing.

Sempangi, F. Kefa. From the Dust. Melvin, J. & Melvin, Jennifer, eds. 2008. (ENG.). 124p. pap. 33.00 (978-0-7188-9197-8(X)) Lutherworth Pr., The GBR. Dist: Brown, David Bk. Co., The.

Senack, John Andrew. God Comes Softly. 2008. pap. 11.00 (978-0-8059-8579-5(4)) Dorrance Publishing Co., Inc.

Seraphima. Saint Seraphim of Sofia: His Life, Teachings, Miracles, & Glorification. 2008. (Illus.). 230p. pap. (978-0-911165-67-8(3)) Ctr. for Traditionalist Orthodox Studies.

Setan, et al. Miracles in the Forgotten Land & Beyond. 2010. 232p. pap. 15.99 (978-1-60957-774-2(4)) Xulon Pr., Inc.

Severino, Sally. Becoming Fire. 2009. 160p. 24.95 (978-0-9824530-0-1(0), Epigraph Bks.) Monkfish Bk. Publishing Co.

Shackelford, Rose. Partying to Praying: My Story, God's Glory. 2008. 80p. pap. 10.95 (978-0-595-50188-5(5), iUniverse, Inc.) iUniverse, Inc.

Sharp, Christopher J. Stones from the River: The Autobiography of a Christian. 2007. 252p. per. (978-1-84748-048-4(9)) Athena Pr.

Sharp, Myrtle Jean. When the Angel Came. 2011. 214p. 29.99 **(978-1-4568-0498-5(7))**; pap. 19.99 **(978-1-4568-0497-8(9))** Xlibris Corp.

Shaw, Mark E. Relapse: Biblical Prevention Strategies. 2011. (ENG.). 112p. pap. 12.95 **(978-1-885904-91-1(6))** Focus Publishing.

Shenton, Tim. Two 'Heretics' Burned: The stories of John Lambert & John Philpot, martyred for Christ during the English Reformation. 2008. (History Today Ser.). 13.00 (978-1-84625-085-9(4)) DayOne Pubns. GBR. Dist: STL Distribution North America.

Shephard, Timothy. Can We Help Us? Growing up Bi-Racial in America. 2011. 220p. 24.59 **(978-1-4567-5462-4(9))**; pap. 14.03 **(978-1-4567-5888-2(8))** AuthorHouse.

Shepherd, Marjorie. Out of the Chrysalis. 2007. 292p. pap. 25.50 (978-1-84799-223-9(4)) Lulu Enterprises Inc.

Sheppard, Arlene Joy. A Princess Meets Her Prince Charming. 2007. 132p. (ENG.). 21.99 (978-1-60477-056-8(2)); per. 13.99 (978-1-60477-055-1(4)) Xulon Pr., Inc.

Sherman, Cecil. By My Own Reckoning. 2008. (Illus.). 288p. 24.00 (978-1-57312-506-2(7)) Smyth & Helwys Publishing, Inc.

Shey, Tim. High Plains Drifter: A Hitchhiking Journey Across America. 2008. 129p. pap. 19.95 (978-1-60703-390-5(9)) PublishAmerica, Inc.

Shorter, Calvin B. A Product of the System: Who Am I?, 1 vol. 2009. 63p. pap. 16.95 (978-1-4489-1925-3(8)) PublishAmerica, Inc.

Shusherin, Ioann. From Peasant to Patriarch: Account of the Birth, Upbringing, & Life of His Holiness Nikon, Patriarch of Moscow & All Russia. Kain, Kevin & Levintova, Katia, trs. 2007. (ENG.). 214p. per. 27.50 (978-0-7391-1580-0(4)) Lexington Bks.

Simmons, Roy. Divine Guidance: The Master's Hand. 2008. 160p. pap. 13.95 (978-1-4327-2754-3(0)) Outskirts Pr., Inc.

Sinclair, Amy. Dirt Roads & High Topped Shoes. 2009. 60p. pap. 10.99 (978-1-60791-613-0(4)) Xulon Pr., Inc.

Sinetar, Marsha. Ordinary People as Monks & Mystics: Lifestyles for Spiritual Wholeness. rev. ed. 2007. 183p. per. 14.95 (978-0-8091-4284-2(8), 4284-2) Paulist Pr.

Singh, Christina. From Krishna to Christ. 2011. 100p. pap. 14.98 **(978-1-4567-6702-0(X))** AuthorHouse.

Singleton, Angie. Diamond's Fate. 2011. 220p. 29.99 **(978-1-4568-8878-7(1))**; pap. 19.99 **(978-1-4568-8877-0(3))** Xlibris Corp.

Sister Marytherese, O. C. D. S. Heroes & Heroines Canonized in the Twentieth Century: Book II (1951 - 1999) 2009. 260p. pap. 18.99 (978-1-4343-4335-2(9)) AuthorHouse.

—Heroes & Heroines Canonized in the Twentieth Centurybook II. 2009. 260p. 27.99 (978-1-4343-4336-9(7)) AuthorHouse.

Six, Anne T. Muses along the Way: Book II. 2010. 200p. pap. 15.04 (978-1-4269-1533-8(0)) Trafford Publishing.

Skakle, Sybil Austin. Valley of the Shadow: A journey through Grief. 2009. 160p. 23.95 (978-1-4401-3415-9(4)); pap. 13.95 (978-1-4401-3413-5(8)) iUniverse, Inc.

Skelton, Dane. Jungle Flight: Spiritual Adventures at the Ends of the Earth. 2009. 104p. pap. 10.99 (978-1-60791-922-3(2)) Xulon Pr., Inc.

Skinner, Howard & Skinner, Betty. Secrets to Our Supernatural Walk with God. 2011. 224p. 33.95 **(978-1-4497-1732-2(2))**; pap. 17.95 **(978-1-4497-1733-9(0))** Author Solutions, Inc. (WestBow Pr.).

Skinny. Skinny. 2007. pap. 19.99 (978-1-4257-8067-8(9)) Xlibris Corp.

Slattery, Kathryn. Lost & Found: One Daughter's Story of Amazing Grace. 2008. 223p. 17.99 (978-0-8249-4734-7(7), GuidepostsBooks) Ideals Pubns.

Small, Frank J., Jr. President of His Class. 2006. (ENG.). 260p. per. 42.00 (978-0-7618-3518-9(0)) Hamilton Bks.

Smalley, David. Baptized Atheist. 2010. 200p. pap. 18.00 (978-1-57884-008-3(2)) American Atheist Pr.

Smallwood Jr., Ernest C. 32 Years of Non-Disclosure on Adoption: A Shocking Revelation!, 1 vol. 2010. 76p. pap. 19.95 (978-1-4489-5499-5(1)) PublishAmerica, Inc.

Smarto, Don. Mended by God. 2011. 154p. pap. 14.99 **(978-1-60957-042-2(1))** Xulon Pr., Inc.

Smith, Albert J. One Preacher's Life Story. 2007. 208p. per. 24.95 (978-1-4241-8674-7(9)) PublishAmerica, Inc.

Smith, Annette. The Whispers of Angels: Stories to Touch Your Heart. 2010. 208p. pap. 11.99 (978-0-7369-2865-6(0)) Harvest Hse. Pubs.

Smith, Betty T. Nothing Wasted: When Evil Befalls You, Know That God Keeps You Standing. 2009. (ENG.). 176p. pap. 12.99 (978-1-59979-772-4(0), Creation Hse.) Charisma Media.

Smith, Clariss Brubaker. The Song of Unsung Heroes: Chronicles from God's Messengers Who Helped Bring down Those Iron Curtain Walls. 2011. 184p. 30.95 **(978-1-4497-1965-4(1))**; pap. 13.95 **(978-1-4497-1963-0(5))** Author Solutions, Inc. (WestBow Pr.).

Smith, Gwen. Broken into Beautiful: Let God Restore Your Wounded Heart. 2008. 250p. pap. 12.99 (978-0-7369-2317-0(9)) Harvest Hse. Pubs.

Smith, Leonard. The Unitarians: A Short History. 2nd ed. 2008. (Illus.). 208p. pap. 25.00 (978-0-9816402-0-4(6)) Blackstone Editions.

Smith, Madlyn. Mischief Maker. 2009. 48p. pap. 10.49 (978-1-4490-4158-8(2)) AuthorHouse.

Smith, Margaret M. A Spiritual Journey: An Autobiography. 2009. 172p. pap. 17.50 (978-1-4389-6603-8(2)) AuthorHouse.

—A Spiritual Journey: Book II. 2009. 140p. pap. 16.50 (978-1-4490-0817-8(8)) AuthorHouse.

Smith, Michelle. From Lesbianism to Grace: The Power of Change. 2009. pap. 10.99 (978-1-60799-842-6(4)) Tate Publishing & Enterprises, LLC.

Smith, Sarah Margaret. In the Shadow of His Hand. 2006. 148p. 24.95 (978-1-59824-395-6(0)); per. 10.95 (978-1-59824-394-9(2)) E-BookTime LLC.

Smith, Shirley Jean. The Love of a Father. 2007. 168p. 21.99 (978-1-60266-843-0(4)); per. 13.99 (978-1-60266-842-3(6)) Xulon Pr., Inc.

Smith, W. D. Women & Womb: A Journey Through the Transfer of a Destiny, 1 vol. 2010. 168p. pap. 24.95 (978-1-4489-4334-0(5)) PublishAmerica, Inc.

Snoke, Howard. There Is an Angel on My Shoulder. 2009. 312p. pap. 15.95 (978-1-4389-7112-4(5)) AuthorHouse.

Snow, Rhonda. The Prison Gates Are Broken. 2007. 184p. per. 13.99 (978-1-60266-318-3(1)) Xulon Pr., Inc.

Snyder, Mary E. Aunt Lillian. 2008. pap. 13.99 (978-1-60647-311-5(5)) Xulon Pr., Inc.

Soles, Cynthia Yates. A Piece of Heaven on Earth. 2009. 120p. 21.99 (978-1-4490-3693-5(7)); pap. 12.99 (978-1-4490-3692-8(9)) AuthorHouse.

Solomon, Rev. James A. Deliverance from Demonic Covenants & Curses. 2010. 288p. pap. 16.99 (978-1-60957-338-6(2)) Xulon Pr., Inc.

Somers, Julie Ann. Chiseled: Discover Your True Belonging. 2011. 136p. 23.95 (978-1-4502-5674-2(0)); pap. 13.95 (978-1-4502-5673-5(2)) iUniverse, Inc.

Sonnenberg, Joel. Joel, 1 vol. 2006. (SPA.). 224p. per. 9.99 (978-0-8297-4595-5(5)) Vida Pubs.

Soske, Becky. I Am Not Ashamed. 2008. 80p. pap. 16.95 (978-1-60610-091-2(2)) PublishAmerica, Inc.

Southers, Terry M. Grace I Never Knew. 2008. 192p. 21.99 (978-1-60647-038-1(8)); pap. 13.99 (978-1-60477-999-8(3)) Xulon Pr., Inc.

Southwell, Rex. Price of Pride. 2009. 172p. pap. 11.95 (978-1-60594-216-2(2), Llumina Pr.) Aeon Publishing Inc.

Spain, William S. God Never Wastes an Experience. 2008. 92p. pap. 12.95 (978-0-9816883-6-7(5)) PearlStone Publishing, Inc.

Sparks, Matthew. The Fragments of Me: Inspired by True Events. 2009. 234p. pap. 19.95 (978-1-4489-2400-4(6)) PublishAmerica, Inc.

Spellman, Lynne. Unbolting the Dark, A Memoir. 2011. (ENG.). 104p. pap. 22.95 **(978-0-7618-5584-2(X))** Hamilton Bks.

Spencer, Evangelist Crystal R. The Root of Fear & the Anchor of Faith. 2011. 52p. pap. 9.99 **(978-1-4567-4581-3(6))** AuthorHouse.

Spencer, John H. Life of Thomas Jefferson Fisher the Cele. 2006. pap. 24.95 (978-1-4286-5321-4(X)) Kessinger Publishing, LLC.

Spillari, Maria. Aunque un Ejercito Acampe Contra Mi... El Secuestro de Mi Hijo de 6 Anos y Su Padre. 2009. 244p. pap. 15.99 (978-1-60791-234-7(1)) Xulon Pr., Inc.

Spink, Kathryn. The Miracle the Message the Story: Jean Vanier & L'Arche. 2006. (Illus.). 305p. per. 16.95 (978-1-58768-038-0(6), 038-6, HiddenSpring) Paulist Pr.

Spirit of Error Spirit of Truth: Preparing People for the Manifestation of God's Power in Their Lives. 2007. (Illus.). 344p. per. 16.95 (978-1-57921-832-4(6)) WinePress Publishing.

Spoto, Donald. Joan: The Mysterious Life of the Heretic Who Became a Saint. 2009. (Playaway Adult Nonfiction Ser.). (ENG.). 64.99 (978-1-61545-735-9(6)) Findaway World, LLC.

—Joan: The Mysterious Life of the Heretic Who Became a Saint. 2008. (ENG.). 240p. pap. 14.95 (978-0-06-118918-0(9), HarperOne) HarperCollins Pubs.

Spurgeon, Charles H. The Complete John Ploughman: John Ploughman's Talk/John Ploughman's Pictures. 2007. (ENG., Illus.). 320p. per. 12.99 (978-1-84550-278-2(7), Christian Heritage) Christian Focus Pubns. GBR. Dist: STL Distribution North America.

Spurgeon, Charles H. & Spurgeon, C. H. Sermons on Men of the Bible. 2008. 350p. (978-1-59856-302-3(5)) Hendrickson Pubs. Marketing, LLC.

St Francis of Assisi. 2008. (ENG.). pap. 19.95 (978-1-58002-491-4(2)) Journeys of Faith.

St. George, William. The Saint's Way: My Personal Journey to Discovery. 2009. 160p. 24.95 (978-0-595-51865-4(6)); pap. 14.95 (978-0-595-46828-7(4)) iUniverse, Inc.

Stafford, B. E. When the Scales Fall Off: Discovering the Truth of God's Word. 2011. pap. 12.99 **(978-1-61777-410-2(3))** Tate Publishing & Enterprises, LLC.

Stafford, Bill. The Adventure of Spirit Filled Giving. 2007. pap. 10.99 (978-1-60477-117-6(8)) Xulon Pr., Inc.

Stahl, John Dewey. Metamorphosis: Johnny Meets John. 2010. 224p. (ENG.). 33.95 (978-1-4497-0111-6(6)); pap. 17.95 (978-1-4497-0109-3(4)) Author Solutions, Inc. (WestBow Pr.).

Standish, Colin D. Uncle Russell & Daddy Stories. 2007. (ENG., Illus.). (YA). per. 14.95 (978-0-923309-24-4(1)) Hartland Pubns.

Stanek, Stephen. Out of Darkness into Daylight. 2007. 49p. per. 8.95 (978-1-59824-482-3(5)) E-BookTime LLC.

Stanley, Lee. Faith in the Land of Make Believe: What God Can Do... Even in Hollywood, 1 vol. 2011. (ENG.). 272p. 19.99 (978-0-310-32545-1(5)) Zondervan.

Starbuck, Margot. The Girl in the Orange Dress: Searching for a Father Who Does Not Fail, 1 vol. 2009. (ENG., Illus.). 201p. pap. 16.00 *(978-0-8308-3627-7(6)*, IVP Bks.) InterVarsity Pr.

Starwitness. Welcome Home as Is. 2008. 112p. pap. 10.99 *(978-1-60477-938-7(1))* Xulon Pr., Inc.

Statesel, Frank. Jewels: Some of the Unheralded Heroes & Heroines from the Bible, 1 vol. 2009. 56p. pap. 16.95 *(978-1-61582-754-1(4))* PublishAmerica, Inc.

Steckel, Les & Suggs, Robb. One Yard Short: Turning Your Defeats into Victories, 0 vols. 2008. (Illus.). 224p. pap. 14.99 *(978-0-8499-2907-6(5))* Nelson, Thomas Inc.

Steel, Robert. Doing Good or, the Christian in Walks of Usefulness. 2007. (ENG.). 442p. 51.95 *(978-0-548-15222-5(5))*; 444p. per. 36.95 *(978-1-4304-4586-9(6))* Kessinger Publishing, LLC.

Steinfield, David. Gods Glorious Green Mountain (subtitle) the demons Within. 2009. 134p. pap. 9.95 *(978-0-578-04327-2(0))* Morris Publishing.

Stephen, James. Essays in Ecclesiastical Biography V1. 2007. (ENG.). 352p. 46.95 *(978-0-548-10621-1(5))* Kessinger Publishing, LLC.

—Essays in Ecclesiastical Biography V2. 2007. (ENG.). 336p. 45.95 *(978-0-548-10622-8(3))* Kessinger Publishing, LLC.

Stephens, Clara. I Am Not Forgotten God Knows My Name. 2009. 124p. pap. 11.99 *(978-1-60791-776-2(9))* Xulon Pr., Inc.

Stevens, Alec. E. J. Pace: Christian Cartoonist. 2007. (Illus.). 250p. pap. 19.95 *(978-0-9778214-1-9(2))* Calvary Comics.

Stevens, Minister Howard. Seven Mysteries of the Book of Revelation Revealed: The End of the Church Age. 2009. 136p. pap. 14.99 *(978-1-61579-506-2(5))* Xulon Pr., Inc.

Stevens, William Bertrand. Editor's Quest: A Memoir of Frederic Cook Morehouse. 2011. 256p. 47.95 ***(978-1-258-07380-0(3))*** Literary Licensing, LLC.

Stewart, Charles & Stewart, Saundra. A Supernatural Encounter with God. 2007. 124p. per. 10.99 *(978-1-60266-759-4(4))* Xulon Pr., Inc.

Stockhausen Bazliel, Yvonne & Bazliel, Yvonne Stockhausen. Miracle or Coincidence. 2007. 52p. per. *(978-1-84748-192-4(2))* Athena Pr.

Story, Mike. One Man's Journey: A Pastor's Progress in Discipleship. 2007. 160p. per. 14.95 *(978-0-9788201-9-0(3))* IMD Pr.

The Story of Nannie Helen Burroughs. 2006. pap. 10.99 *(978-1-56309-848-2(2))* Woman's Missionary Union.

Streidl, Max. Brought down to Be Raised Up. 2011. 84p. 24.99 ***(978-1-4653-0075-1(9))***; pap. 15.99 ***(978-1-4653-0074-4(0))*** Xlibris Corp.

Stringer, Margaret. From Cannibalism to Christianity. 2007. per. 14.00 *(978-0-9778936-9-0(3))* Hyles Pubns.

Stringfield, Michael. Cancer & Me. 2011. 52p. 24.99 ***(978-1-4628-9014-9(8))***; pap. 15.99 ***(978-1-4628-9015-6(6))*** Xlibris Corp.

Strong, Minister Jimmie. A Practical Way: For Kingdom Living, Spiritual Repentance, Serenity, Peace, & Sanctification. 2010. 196p. 24.99 *(978-1-4490-5412-0(9))* AuthorHouse.

Studt, Kimberley. Let the Glory Come Down. 2007. (ENG.). 244p. per. *(978-1-55452-146-3(7))* Essence Publishing.

Stulberg, Miriam. God Calls Me Miriam: The Spiritual Journey of a Jewish-Christian: The Struggle with a Crippling Disease: A Life Changing Bonding with Gulag Survivors in Post-Soviet Russia. 299p. *(978-1-897145-07-4(1))* Madonna Hse. Pubns.

Sullivan, K. Catherine Mcauley & the Tradition of Mercy. 400p. 45.00 *(978-1-85182-199-0(6))* Four Courts Pr. IRL. Dist: International Specialized Bk. Services.

Sullivan, Karla. Imagine That. 2007. 76p. per. 16.95 *(978-1-4241-1154-1(4))* PublishAmerica, Inc.

Sumner, Rainy. A Message from God: A True Story. 2009. 136p. pap. 12.49 *(978-1-4490-4953-9(2))* AuthorHouse.

Sunami, Christopher. Hero for Christ: 30 Ways to Be More Like Mother Teresa, Martin Luther King, Jr. , & Twenty Other World-Changing Christians. 2008. (Illus.). 256p. pap. 16.95 *(978-0-9702438-2-9(0)*, Kitoba Bks.) Nimbus, Inc.

Supernatural Soldier. Another-Way: Living to Live Again. 2011. 280p. 37.48 *(978-1-4269-5980-6(X))*; pap. 27.48 *(978-1-4269-5981-3(8))* Trafford Publishing.

Susag, S. O. Personal Experiences of S. O. Susag. l.t. ed. 2007. (ENG.). 170p. pap. 21.99 *(978-1-4264-3463-1(4))* BiblioBazaar.

Swanson, Jennifer J. Life in the Faith Lane: Living the Supernatural Life in a Natural World. 2009. 428p. pap. 22.99 *(978-1-61579-167-5(1))* Xulon Pr., Inc.

Swindell, Taneen M. Shattered Silence: "Breaking Free" 2011. 274p. 29.99 ***(978-1-4653-3802-0(0))***; pap. 19.99 ***(978-1-4653-3801-3(2))*** Xlibris Corp.

Swing, David. The Message of David Swing to His Generation: Addresses & Papers. 2007. (ENG.). 300p. 43.95 *(978-0-548-11945-7(7))* Kessinger Publishing, LLC.

Swinney, Joanna & Swinney, Jo. Through the Dark Woods: A Young Woman's Journey Out of Depression. 2007. 160p. pap. 11.99 *(978-0-8254-6133-0(2)*, Monarch Bks.) Lion Hudson PLC GBR. Dist: Kregel Pubns.

Sykes, Lowell Beach. Twenty years with alzheimer's Disease. 2007. 292p. pap. 22.96 *(978-1-4357-0382-7(0))* Lulu Enterprises Inc.

Sykes, Wanda. I Was a Hypocrite, Now I Am Delivered & Set Free. 2008. 129p. pap. 19.95 *(978-1-60441-068-6(X))* PublishAmerica, Inc.

Szulc, Tad. Pope John Paul II. 2007. (ENG.). 624p. pap. 38.95 *(978-1-4165-8886-3(8))* Pocket Books.

Tada, Joni Eareckson. A Lifetime of Wisdom: Filled with God's Priceless Rubies, 1 vol. 2009. (ENG.). 240p. 21.99 *(978-0-310-27342-4(0))* Zondervan.

Tadda, Jami. Then the Rain Came. 2011. 188p. pap. 14.99 ***(978-1-61379-064-9(3))*** Xulon Pr., Inc.

Tadema, Pearl. An Ordinary Farm Girl Meets an Extra-Ordinary God. 2007. 220p. per. 14.99 *(978-1-60266-576-7(1))* Xulon Pr., Inc.

Talib & Johnson 8th, Benjamin. When the Spirit Moves. 2008. 100p. pap. 12.49 *(978-1-4343-9880-2(3))* AuthorHouse.

Tallman, Matthew William. Demos Shakarian¿ the Life, Legacy, & Vision of a Full Gospel Business Man. 2010. 265p. pap. 18.00 net. *(978-1-60947-002-9(8))* Emeth Pr.

Tater. November December: A Holiday Carol, 1 vol. 2009. 197p. pap. 19.95 *(978-1-61546-774-7(2))* PublishAmerica, Inc.

Tawny "Mae" Harris. Jeans/Genes. 2010. 140p. pap. 13.95 *(978-1-4401-8872-5(6))* iUniverse, Inc.

Taylor, Apostle Jenette. Prisoner of Warfare: P. O. W. 2008. 50p. pap. 9.00 *(978-0-8059-7683-0(3))* Dorrance Publishing Co., Inc.

Taylor, C. I. For God I Live: Quiet Deception of the Eastern Star, 1 vol. 2007. (ENG.). 73p. per. 19.95 *(978-1-60441-273-4(9))* PublishAmerica, Inc.

Taylor, Faye Hooley Byers. His Treasure in Earthen Vessels: Fifty Years of Sharing His Treasure in Mexico. 2009. 256p. pap. 16.99 *(978-1-61579-040-1(3))* Xulon Pr., Inc.

Taylor, Jacqueline. Waiting for the Call: From Preacher's Daughter to Lesbian Mom. 2007. (ENG.). 232p. 64.50 *(978-0-472-11594-5(4))*; per. 19.95 *(978-0-472-03238-9(0))* Univ. of Michigan Pr.

Taylor, Kimberley Raunikar. The Intentional Family: Celebrating Adoption. annot. ed. 2007. (ENG.). 192p. per. 14.99 *(978-0-8341-2313-7(4)*, 083-412-3134) Beacon Hill Pr. of Kansas City.

Taylor, P. J. Called to Serve: A Review of the Work of a Permanent Deacon over a Period of Thirty Years. 2007. (Illus.). 156p. per. *(978-1-84401-904-5(7))* Athena Pr.

Tchividjian, Anthony, et al. Invitation: Billy Graham & the Lives God Touched. 2008. (ENG., Illus.). 144p. 19.99 *(978-1-60142-149-4(4)*, Multnomah) Doubleday Religious Publishing Group, The.

Teachers & Preachers of Recent Times. 2007. 228p. per. *(978-1-4067-8930-0(5)*, Pierides Pr.) Read Bks.

Tebow, Tim & Whitaker, Nathan. Through My Eyes. 2011. (ENG.). 256p. 26.99 *(978-0-06-200728-5(9))*; pap. 26.99 *(978-0-06-208154-4(3)*, HarperLuxe) HarperCollins Pubs.

Tegeler, Linda. A Traumatic Brain Injury. 2007. 132p. per. 13.99 *(978-1-60266-955-0(4))* Xulon Pr., Inc.

Tekakwitha: Holy Native, Mohawk Virgin, 1656-1680. 2007. per. *(978-0-9796390-0-5(X))* Sherman, Edward.

ten Boom, Corrie. In My Father's House. 2011. pap. *(978-0-9846366-2-4(5))* Lighthouse Trails Publishing Co.

—Not Good If Detached. 2009. (ENG.). 165p. pap. 9.99 *(978-0-87508-947-8(X))* CLC Pubns.

Terrillion, Dale. Journey to the Backwoods. 2007. (ENG.). 536p. per. 27.99 *(978-1-4141-0864-3(8))* Pleasant Word.

Thek, Joseph C. The Second Greatest Story Ever Told - Volume 1. 2008. 342p. pap. 29.95 *(978-1-60610-903-8(0))* PublishAmerica, Inc.

Therrien, Stéphane. The Refining Journey of a Warrior. 2011. (Illus.). viii, 118p. pap. ***(978-1-77069-304-3(1))*** Word Alive Pr.

Thomas, Asher. Destination Sinai: From Missionary Christianity to Orthodox Judaism, 1 vol. 2009. 222p. pap. 24.95 *(978-1-60672-707-2(9))* PublishAmerica, Inc.

Thomas, Carmen M. As a Man Thinketh in His Heart So Is He. 2006. (ENG.). 84p. per. 9.95 *(978-0-7414-3590-3(X))* Infinity Publishing.

Thomas, Eva. Warrior Women for Christ. 2009. (J). pap. 12.99 *(978-1-60799-486-2(0))* Tate Publishing & Enterprises, LLC.

Thomas, Harvey. Pastors Are People Too: Pastoral Life Experiences. 2010. 188p. pap. 16.95 *(978-1-4502-1245-8(X))* iUniverse, Inc.

Thomas Nelson Publishing Staff. From Power to Purpose, 0 vols. 2009. 242p. pap. 13.99 *(978-1-59555-277-8(4))* Nelson, Thomas Inc.

Thomas, Patricia. What Ever Happened to Ratsy Patsy. 2011. 158p. pap. 14.99 *(978-1-61215-445-9(X))* Xulon Pr., Inc.

Thompson, Doreen Debra. The Silent Years. 2011. 44p. pap. 16.95 ***(978-1-4626-2664-9(5))*** PublishAmerica, Inc.

Thompson, George E. From Christianity to Sin & Back Again. 2008. 208p. 29.99 *(978-1-4363-2902-6(7))*; pap. 19.99 *(978-1-4363-2901-9(9))* Xlibris Corp.

Thompson, Grant. The Southern! Witness in the Natural & Spiritual, 1 vol. 2010. 82p. pap. 19.95 *(978-1-4489-4028-8(1))* PublishAmerica, Inc.

Thompson, Jill. Soul Battle: It's Not Against Flesh & Blood. 2006. (ENG., Illus.). 132p. per. 10.99 *(978-1-928915-94-2(9))* Evangel Publishing Hse.

Thomsen, Richard. Is God on Our Side? My Side? Your Side? Their Side? 2010. 253p. 29.95 *(978-1-4327-6053-3(X))*; (Illus.). pap. 15.95 *(978-1-4327-6038-0(6))* Outskirts Pr., Inc.

Thornton, AndrZcaron; & Janssen, Al. Triumph Born of Tragedy: The Story of Romance & Courage in the Life of AndrZcaron; Thornton: As Told to Al Janssen. 2011. 156p. pap. 18.00 *(978-1-60899-408-3(2)*, Resource Pubns.) Wipf & Stock Pubs.

Thornton, Claude Edward. Ambition in the Eyes of a Child. 2008. 128p. pap. 12.00 *(978-1-4343-8544-4(2))* AuthorHouse.

Tikalsky, Susan C. A Prayer Journal Through Mental Illness. 2008. 122p. pap. 19.95 *(978-1-60474-790-4(0))* PublishAmerica, Inc.

Tilley, Janice. Barb Letters. 2007. 112p. per. *(978-1-55452-125-8(4)*, Guardian Bks.) Essence Publishing.

Tim, LaHaye, frwd. Giving an Account: The Life & Ministry of Richard H. Vigneulle. 2009. (Illus.). 334p. 24.95 *(978-1-59421-053-2(5))* Seacoast Publishing, Inc.

Timothy, Brother. A Child by Mercy: Out of Darkness & into God's Grace. 2010. 252p. 29.95 *(978-1-4502-2463-5(6))*; (ENG.). pap. 19.95 *(978-1-4502-2461-1(X))* iUniverse, Inc.

Tobin, Greg. The Good Pope - The Making of a Saint & the Remaking of the Church: A Biography of Saint John XXIII & Vactican II. 2012. (ENG.). 288p. 26.99 ***(978-0-06-208943-4(9)***, HarperOne) HarperCollins Pubs.

—The Good Pope & His Great Council LP: The Making of a Saint & the Re-Making of the Church - The Story of John XXIII & Vatican II. l.t. ed. 2012. (ENG.). 288p. pap. 26.99 ***(978-0-06-220157-7(3)***, HarperLuxe) HarperCollins Pubs.

Tofanelli, Dave. Cancer, a Marriage & a Miracle. 2008. 224p. pap. 15.99 *(978-1-60647-724-3(2))* Xulon Pr., Inc.

Tonya K. Brown. Just How Much You Can Bear. 2007. 84p. per. 12.95 *(978-1-4327-0798-9(1))* Outskirts Pr., Inc.

Tosti, John. The Walls of Salvation: The Dualitas. 2011. 182p. pap. 12.99 ***(978-0-557-84906-2(3))*** Lulu Enterprises Inc.

Towle, Eleanor A. John Mason Neale: A Memoir. 2009. 364p. 26.99 *(978-1-103-88038-6(1))*; pap. 20.99 *(978-1-103-88035-5(7))* BiblioBazaar.

Trading Faces. (Bratz Photostories Ser.). 96p. pap. *(978-1-4054-8743-6(7))* Parragon, Inc.

Trammell, Rebecca Starr. The Life & Legacy of William R. Starr. 2009. pap. *(978-1-61584-702-0(2))* Independent Pub.

Trigilio, John & Brighenti, Kenneth. Saints for Dummies. 2010. (ENG., Illus.). 384p. pap. 19.99 *(978-0-470-53358-1(7*, For Dummies) Wiley, John & Sons, Inc.

Troost, Catherine M. Catskill Mountain Memories. 2008. 172p. pap. 14.99 *(978-1-60791-071-8(3))* Xulon Pr., Inc.

Troute, Grady W. Glimpses of Communion: Presiding over Communion for the Lord's Church. 2009. 124p. 19.99 *(978-1-61579-113-2(2))*; pap. 11.99 *(978-1-60791-963-6(X))* Xulon Pr., Inc.

Tubbs, Tammie T. I Still Have Joy. 2006. 11.00 *(978-0-8059-9194-9(8))* Dorrance Publishing Co., Inc.

Tuminaro, Joel A. The Work of Faith Made Perfect. 2011. pap. 10.95 ***(978-0-7414-6551-1(5))*** Infinity Publishing.

Tuohy, Leigh Anne, et al. In a Heartbeat: Sharing the Power of Cheerful Giving. 2010. (ENG., Illus.). 288p. 24.00 *(978-0-8050-9338-4(9))* Holt, Henry & Co.

—In a Heartbeat: Sharing the Power of Cheerful Giving. 2011. (ENG., Illus.). 288p. pap. 14.99 *(978-0-312-57718-6(4)*, St. Martin's Griffin) St. Martin's Pr.

—In a Heartbeat: Sharing the Power of Cheerful Giving. l.t. ed. 2010. 32.99 *(978-1-4104-2922-3(9))* Thorndike Pr.

Turner, Carole Nana. God Delivers Again: And Again & Again. 2008. (Illus.). 193p. pap. 14.95 *(978-0-9794861-9-7(X))* Truth Pubs.

Turner, Frank. Raised from the Dead: The Personal Testimony of America's First Evangelical Anchorman. 2008. (Illus.). 300p. 24.95 *(978-1-934363-27-0(8))* Zoe Life Publishing.

Turner, Jerome. Thank God for Cancer! 2008. 136p. per. 13.99 *(978-1-60477-665-2(X))* Xulon Pr., Inc.

Turner, Matthew Paul. Churched: One Kid's Journey Toward God Despite a Holy Mess. (ENG.). 2010. 256p. pap. 14.99 *(978-0-307-45801-8(6))* 2008. 240p. 18.99 *(978-1-4000-7471-6(1))* Doubleday Religious Publishing Group, The. (WaterBrook Pr.).

Turpin, Joanne. Women in Church History: 21 Stories for 21 Centuries. 2007. 232p. per. 14.95 *(978-0-86716-776-4(9))* Franciscan Media.

Tweedie, Donald. Reminiscence: The Progress of a Christian Pilgrim. 2009. 332p. pap. 18.99 *(978-1-61579-417-1(4))* Xulon Pr., Inc.

Tyndall, Carolyn Corbett. The Journey. 2009. 152p. pap. 14.99 *(978-1-60791-856-1(0))* Xulon Pr., Inc.

Tyson, Joan. A Missionary Journey Remembering His Marvelous Works. 2009. pap. *(978-1-61623-895-7(X))* Independent Pub.

Tyson, John R. Faith, Doubt, & Courage in 15 Great People of Faith: And What We Can Learn from Them. 2008. 140p. pap. 12.00 *(978-0-687-64726-2(6))* Abingdon Pr.

Uhuangho, Blessing. A New Name. 2009. *(978-1-55452-382-5(6))* Essence Publishing.

Umphery-Anderson, Angela Marie. Chasing Love. 2011. 118p. pap. 19.95 ***(978-1-4626-3223-7(8))*** PublishAmerica, Inc.

Unger, Peter/B. Elmer's Ethics: A Pennsylvania Dutch Biography. 2010. (Illus.). 178p. pap. 18.95 *(978-1-59630-064-4(7))* Science & Humanities Pr.

Ussher, Elizabeth. Extracts from the Letters of Elizabeth L. 2006. pap. 21.95 *(978-1-4286-5295-8(7))* Kessinger Publishing, LLC.

Valentine, Jack. Motley Rock Stories. 2006. pap. 17.99 *(978-1-60034-774-0(6))* Xulon Pr., Inc.

Valentine, Leigh. Successfully You! 2008. pap. 15.99 *(978-0-7684-2613-7(8))* Destiny Image Pubs.

Vallés, Carlos G. Ligero de Equipaje. 240p. 8.95 *(978-958-607-818-4(3))* Sociedad de San Pablo COL. Dist: St Pauls/Alba Hse. Pubs.

Valusek, Jay E. The Secret Sorrow: A Memoir of Mourning the Death of God. 2010. 152p. pap. 14.95 *(978-1-4502-5829-6(8))* iUniverse, Inc.

Van Dellen, Idzerd. In God's Crucible: An Autobiography. 2011. 134p. 40.95 ***(978-1-258-08959-7(9))*** Literary Licensing, LLC.

van Leenen, Dirk. Resistance on a Bicycle. 2007. 340p. (ENG.). 27.99 *(978-1-60266-905-5(8))*; per. 17.99 *(978-1-60266-751-8(9))* Xulon Pr., Inc.

Van Norman, Kasey. Named by God: Overcoming Your Past, Transforming Your Present, Embracing Your Future. 2012. (ENG.). 256p. pap. 15.99 ***(978-1-4143-6474-2(1))*** Tyndale Hse. Pubs.

van Oort, J. & Wyrwa, D., eds. Autobiographie und Hagiographie in der christlichen Antike. 2009. (Patristic Studies). (GER.). 129p. (C). pap. 53.00 *(978-90-429-2212-9(5))* Peeters Pubs. & Booksellers BEL. Dist: Brown, David Bk. Co., The.

Van Winkle Jr., Ed. Against All Odds: Life's Experiences Told as Stories. 2008. 128p. pap. 12.49 *(978-1-4343-9164-3(7))* AuthorHouse.

Vande Kappelle, Robert P. Into Thin Places: One ManÕs Search for the Center. 2011. 432p. pap. 48.00 *(978-1-61097-093-8(4)*, Resource Pubns.) Wipf & Stock Pubs.

Varnado, Curtis. From under the Porch to the Pulpit. 2011. 64p. pap. 15.99 ***(978-1-4628-9088-0(1))*** Xlibris Corp.

Vaughn, Mary K. The Wait: How God Sustains & Explains When His Answer Is Wait. 2007. (Illus.). 79p. per. 12.95 *(978-1-58597-415-3(3))* Leathers Publishing.

Vaus, Will. My Father Was a Gangster: The Jim Vaus Story. 2007. (ENG., Illus.). 240p. 14.99 *(978-0-9787428-2-9(6))* Believe Bks., LLC.

Vedella, Joe. That's No Story, That's My Life. 2008. 304p. pap. 18.99 *(978-1-60647-492-1(8))* Xulon Pr., Inc.

Velthouse, Lisa. Craving Grace: A Story of Faith, Failure, & My Search for Sweetness. 2011. (ENG.). 272p. 16.99 *(978-1-4143-3577-3(6)*, SaltRiver) Tyndale Hse. Pubs.

Verlato, Zeno. Le Vite di Santi del codice Magliabechiano XXXVIII. 110 della Biblioteca Nazionale Centrale di Firenze: Un leggendario volgare trecentesco italiano Settentrionale. 2009. (Beihefte Zur Zeitschrift Für Romanische Philologie Ser.). (ITA.). XII, 782p. *(978-3-484-52348-7(4))* Verlag Max Niemeyer.

Vial, Theodore. Schleiermacher: A Guide for the Perplexed. 2012. (Guides for the Perplexed Ser.). (ENG.). 176p. 80.00 *(978-0-567-52009-8(9))*; pap. 24.95 *(978-0-567-41598-1(8))* Continuum International Publishing Group, Ltd. GBR. (T&T Clark Int'l). Dist: National Bk. Network.

Viale, Minister Gene D. I Remember Gospel: And I Keep on Singing. 2010. 272p. 26.95 *(978-1-4490-7681-8(5))* AuthorHouse.

Vick, Dale. The I Am Book. 2008. 84p. pap. 12.95 *(978-0-615-26325-0(9))* Rock Ministries, Inc., The.

Victor, Bradford & Bradford, Victor. The Book Life: Life's Pathway to Peace through the True & Living God. 2010. 176p. (ENG.). 27.99 *(978-1-4269-3115-4(8))*; pap. 17.99 *(978-1-4269-3114-7(X))* Trafford Publishing.

Victor, P. J. 3,000,452 Ways I Survived My Life. 2011. 144p. pap. 24.95 ***(978-1-4560-0692-1(4))*** PublishAmerica, Inc.

Vincent Havelund, Havelund & Vincent Havelund. The Jewel Within. 2009. 296p. pap. 21.95 *(978-1-4401-6340-1(5))* iUniverse, Inc.

Vining, Bruce. Survival. 2007. 100p. pap. 16.95 *(978-1-4241-7603-8(4))* PublishAmerica, Inc.

Virgo, Terry & Newfrontiers-USA. No Well-Worn Paths. 2008. 276p. pap. 14.50 *(978-0-9814803-2-9(2))* Newfrontiers USA.

Visser, Tom, told to. Brother Tom: The People's Preacher. 2007. pap. 11.99 *(978-0-9799919-0-5(0))* Morningside Pr.

Voges, Aletha. My Will, God's Response: God's Will, My Response: A Memoir of Losing A Loved One. 2010. pap. 13.99 *(978-1-61566-269-2(3))* Tate Publishing & Enterprises, LLC.

Vollmer, Philip. John Calvin: Man of the Millennium. Strackbein, Wesley, ed. 2008. (Illus.). 341p. 20.00 *(978-1-934554-35-7(9))* Vision Forum, Inc., The.

Von Hagel, Thomas A. One Lord, One Faith, One Baptism: Christians Through the Centuries. 2006. (Illus.). 256p. per. 17.49 *(978-0-7586-0760-7(1))* Concordia Publishing Hse.

Vrtik, Michal. God in You: The Book of Thoughts, 1 vol. 2009. 105p. pap. 14.95 *(978-1-61546-960-4(5))* PublishAmerica, Inc.

W., Joye. Walking Through the 'C' Word: A Victorious Journey Through Cancer, Divorce & Despair. 2008. 132p. pap. 11.95 *(978-1-4327-2561-7(0))* Outskirts Pr., Inc.

Wace, Henry & Piercy, William C., eds. A Dictionary of Christian Biography & Literature to the End of the Sixth Century A. D. 2011. pap. 286.70 *(978-1-61143-930-4(2))* Gorgias Pr., LLC.

Wacks, Steve. Steve's Story: (A Life Unraveled & Reconstructed) 2008. 370p. pap. 29.95 *(978-1-60672-273-2(5))* PublishAmerica, Inc.

Waddell, Brian R. Letters Unsent Words Unspoken. 2008. 244p. 25.99 *(978-1-60791-073-2(X))*; pap. 15.99 *(978-1-60791-072-5(1))* Xulon Pr., Inc.

Wagler, Ira. Growing up Amish: A Memoir. l.t. ed. 2011. lib. bdg. 34.95 ***(978-1-61173-196-5(8))*** Ctr. Point Large Print.

—Growing up Amish: A Memoir. 2011. (ENG.). 288p. pap. 14.99 *(978-1-4143-3936-8(4))* Tyndale Hse. Pubs.

Wahl, Bob. Contending with Horses. 2009. 326p. pap. 19.95 *(978-1-4327-3538-8(1))* Outskirts Pr., Inc.

Waite, Don, et al. Traveling Home: A Young Man's Story of Courage & Faith, 1 vol. 2008. 144p. pap. 11.99 *(978-0-8254-2899-9(8))* Kregel Pubns.

Wakefield, Dan. How Do We Know When It's God? A Spiritual Memoir. 2010. 270p. pap. 21.95 *(978-0-9825214-5-8(6))* Beech River Bks.

Wakefield, Margery. To Be Christian & Gay. 2010. 186p. pap. 19.99 *(978-0-557-15986-4(5))* Lulu Enterprises Inc.

Wakeley, J. B. Anecdotes of the Wesleys. 2009. 396p. 38.99 *(978-1-117-15553-1(6))*; (ENG.). 394p. pap. 25.99 *(978-1-117-15555-5(2)*, BiblioLife); 396p. pap. 32.75 *(978-1-117-15554-8(4))* BiblioBazaar.

Walker, Brenda & Ring, Karen. How to Be a Compassionate Human Being. 2008. 196p. pap. 13.99 *(978-1-60647-593-5(2))* Xulon Pr., Inc.

Walker, David & Walker, Kathy. The Journey: Walking with the Walkers. 2009. 326p. 28.99 *(978-1-61579-033-3(0))*; pap. 18.99 *(978-1-61579-032-6(2))* Xulon Pr., Inc.
Walker Jr., Robert A. C. Where's the Brothas? 2008. 138p. pap. 24.95 *(978-1-60610-927-4(8))* PublishAmerica, Inc.
Walker, Williston. Great Men of the Christian Church. 2009. 388p. 38.99 *(978-1-115-52529-9(8))*; 33.99 *(978-1-115-52530-5(1))*; pap. 33.75 *(978-1-115-52531-2(X))* BiblioBazaar.
—Great Men of the Christian Church. 2009. 144p. pap. *(978-1-151-11606-2(8))* Books LLC.
Wallace, Archer. The Religious Faith of Great Men. 2007. (ENG.). 226p. 41.95 *(978-0-548-07104-5(7))* Kessinger Publishing, LLC.
Walls, Ralph C. The Button Club, the Mourning of a Repentive Man. 2009. 176p. pap. 12.95 *(978-1-936051-26-7(5))* Peppertree Pr., The.
Walsh, Beau. U. S. Special Operations: The Forerunner Spirit & the End Time Church. 2006. 140p. per. 11.99 *(978-1-59886-425-0(4))* Tate Publishing & Enterprises, LLC.
Ward, Alan Robert. My Walk with Christ. 2008. 324p. pap. 31.95 *(978-1-4092-2699-4(9))* Lulu Enterprises Inc.
—Pink Hopscotch. 2008. 327p. pap. 31.50 *(978-1-4092-4711-1(2))* Lulu Enterprises Inc.
Ward, Benjamin. Quick Fix: For Bible Junkies. 2010. 332p. pap. 22.95 *(978-1-61507-161-6(X))* Cross Bks. Publishing.
Ward, Elizabeth Hamler. Through a Glass Darkly: the Silhoutte: Memoir of a Woman's Life. 2008. pap. 24.99 *(978-1-60034-560-9(3))* Xulon Pr., Inc.
Ward-Ling, Shelah. Your Glory Reflected: Twenty Outstanding Christians of the 20th Century. 288p. pap. 19.95 *(978-0-8189-9457-9(6))* St Pauls/Alba Hse. Pubs.
Warholak, George. The Reprobate. 2011. pap. 18.99 ***(978-1-61777-782-0(X))*** Tate Publishing & Enterprises, LLC.
Warner, Sandy. Parables & Signs: God's Hidden Love Stories. 2008. 191p. pap. 14.50 *(978-1-4357-2498-3(4))* Lulu Enterprises Inc.
Warrington, Janatte. The Humpty Dumpty Syndrome. 2006. (ENG., Illus.). 208p. pap. 13.99 *(978-1-59185-998-7(0)*, Creation Hse.) Charisma Media.
Watkins, Donna L. Bought Free. 2007. 96p. per. 9.99 *(978-1-50477-266-1(2))* Xulon Pr., Inc.
Watson, Bebee. Can a Sister Talk to You. 2008. 172p. pap. 14.99 *(978-1-60647-711-3(0))* Xulon Pr., Inc.
Watson, Tommy. When God Opens a Door Run Through It. 2009. 232p. pap. 18.95 *(978-1-4269-1607-6(8))* Trafford Publishing.
Watson, William M. Organ Lessons. 2009. 130p. pap. 19.99 *(978-1-4415-2176-7(3))* Xlibris Corp.
Weatherly, Lori Clark. Facets of Life. 2011. 142p. 22.99 ***(978-1-61379-147-9(X))***; pap. 14.99 ***(978-1-61379-146-2(1))*** Xulon Pr., Inc.
Webb-Mitchell, Brett. Follow Me: Christian Growth on the Pilgrim's Way. 2006. 175p. per. 16.00 *(978-1-59627-025-1(X))* Church Publishing, Inc.
Webb, Scott Wright. A Curse, My Blessing. 2007. 324p. pap. 18.95 *(978-1-4303-1840-8(6))* Lulu Enterprises Inc.
Weber, Martin. God Was There: True Stories of a Police Chaplain. 2009. 127p. pap. 12.99 *(978-0-8163-2348-7(8))* Pacific Pr. Publishing Assn.
Webling, A. F. Something Beyond. 2012. (ENG.). 338p. pap. 27.00 ***(978-1-107-53224-0(2))*** Cambridge Univ. Pr.
Weiss, Janice. God Was Thinking? 2011. 220p. pap. 15.99 ***(978-1-61379-304-6(9))*** Xulon Pr., Inc.
Welch, Brian. Washed by Blood: Lessons from My Time with Korn & My Journey to Christ. 2008. (ENG.). 224p. pap. 13.95 *(978-0-06-155580-0(0)*, HarperOne) HarperCollins Pubs.
Wellman, Stacey. Brokenhearted: Adultery Through a Daughter's Eyes. 2008. 136p. 10.99 *(978-1-60462-822-7(7))* Tate Publishing & Enterprises, LLC.
Wells, Edna C. Listen & Obey. 2008. 52p. pap. 15.99 *(978-1-4363-3000-8(9))* Xlibris Corp.
Wells, Janet. Safe in God's Love. 2006. (ENG.). 104p. per. 9.95 *(978-1-59526-447-3(7))* Aeon Publishing Inc.
West, Glen. Blessed are the Poor: Developing an Innovative Approach for Overcoming Poverty. 2011. pap. 12.99 ***(978-1-61777-830-8(3))*** Tate Publishing & Enterprises, LLC.
West, Marion Bond. Praying for My Life. 2006. 288p. 17.95 *(978-0-8249-4705-7(3)*, Guideposts Books) Ideals Pubns.
West, Matthew. Experiencing the Story of Your Life. 2012. 144p. pap. 9.99 *(978-0-7369-4659-9(4))* Harvest Hse. Pubs.
West, Patty Old. Good & Faithful Servant: Remembering Ken Old, Missionary to Pakistan. 2010. pap. 21.99 *(978-1-61663-089-8(2))* Tate Publishing & Enterprises, LLC.
—Once Met, Never Forgotten: Remembering Ken Old, a Man of Integrity. 2010. pap. 20.99 *(978-1-61663-100-0(7))* Tate Publishing & Enterprises, LLC.
Westover, Duke. Wow! What a Ride: My Life & Journey with Jerry Falwell. 2010. (ENG.). 192p. 19.99 *(978-0-9824428-9-0(0))* 21st Century Pr.
When I Am Weak, Then I Am Strong: Keeping Faith through Adversities. 2011. 148p. 30.95 *(978-1-4497-2204-3(0))*; pap. 13.95 ***(978-1-4497-2203-6(2))*** Author Solutions, Inc. (WestBow Pr.).
Whitaker, Terri. Yespadam: The Foot of Jesus, Reaching India's Untouched. 2007. (ENG., Illus.). 222p. 14.99 *(978-0-9787428-3-6(4))* Believe Bks., LLC.
White, Alma. Looking Back from Beulah. 2009. 142p. pap. 19.99 *(978-1-150-27073-4(X))* General Bks. LLC.
White, James. Life Incidents, in Connection with the Great Advent Movement, As Illustrated by the Three Angels of Revelation Xiv by Elder James White. 2006. (Illus.). 376p. per. 26.99 *(978-1-4255-3930-6(0))* MPublishing.
White, John V., Jr. They Thought She Was Dead: The Modern Day Job. 2010. 15.99 *(978-1-935354-31-4(0))* Amethyst Moon Publishing and Services.
White, Michael L. A Time for Everything: The Kevin Zimmerman Story. 2008. 112p. pap. 12.75 *(978-0-9786557-4-4(1))* Parson Place Pr., LLC.
White, Nora. Armed with God's Power. 2008. 224p. 14.99 *(978-1-60462-622-3(4))* Tate Publishing & Enterprises, LLC.
White, Ollie M. I Live to Tell the Story: God Favors Me. 2010. 128p. 23.99 *(978-1-4520-5146-8(1))*; pap. 16.99 *(978-1-4520-5145-1(3))* AuthorHouse.
White, Rebecca J. From the Barstool to the Pulpit. 2008. 188p. pap. 19.99 *(978-0-9818753-3-0(5))* Leading Lady Pubns.
Whitner, Richard G. Links of Time: Life's Memories Chained Together. 2009. 112p. 23.95 *(978-1-4269-0810-1(5))* Trafford Publishing.
Who Was LS Chang? Character-the Key to China. 2006. (Illus.). 140p. per. 11.99 *(978-1-59886-558-5(7))* Tate Publishing & Enterprises, LLC.
Whong, Matthew. Power of Dream, Love, Mission: My Memoir of 54 Years in the U. S. 2009. 204p. pap. 15.99 *(978-1-60791-277-4(5))* Xulon Pr., Inc.
Wiersbe, Warren W. 50 People Every Christian Should Know: Learning from Spiritual Giants of the Faith, 1 vol. 2009. 400p. pap. 17.99 *(978-0-8010-7194-2(1))* Baker Bks.
Wiggins, Janie. My Life with Jesus on My Side. 2011. 48p. pap. *(978-1-55452-591-1(8)*, Guardian Bks.) Essence Publishing.
Wiggins Jr, Minister Willie Aka Reveren. Og Willie J: The Jack of All Trades. 2011. 166p. pap. 24.95 ***(978-1-4560-6835-6(0))*** PublishAmerica, Inc.
Wigton Jr, Donald Meade. Spirit Warrior: Journals of a Christian Outdoorsman. 2007. 144p. (ENG.). 24.95 *(978-0-595-69530-0(2))*; per. 14.95 *(978-0-595-44269-0(2)*, iUniverse, Inc.
Wilcox, Donna K. Falling into Faith. 2007. 184p. per. 12.99 *(978-1-59886-762-6(8))* Tate Publishing & Enterprises, LLC.
Wiley, James H. The Dawn Will Come. 2008. 212p. pap. 24.95 *(978-1-60563-250-6(3))* PublishAmerica, Inc.
Wilfred, Elise. Pain & Perseverance-A Testimony of Life's Lessons. 2009. 128p. 22.99 *(978-1-4490-3106-0(4))*; pap. 16.99 *(978-1-4490-3105-3(6))* AuthorHouse.
Wilhite, Jud & Taaffe, Bill. Uncensored Grace: Stories of Hope from the Streets of Vegas. 2008. (ENG.). 240p. 13.99 *(978-1-60142-146-3(X)*, Multnomah) Doubleday Religious Publishing Group, The.
Willard, F. Burleigh. The Legacy of Frances. 2007. 96p. per. *(978-1-55452-185-2(8))* Essence Publishing.
Willard, Francis Burleigh, Sr. The Legacy of Frances. 2007. (Illus.). 96p. per. *(978-1-55452-183-8(1)*, Guardian Bks.) Essence Publishing.
Willbanks, Shane. I Need a Vacation, 1 vol. 2009. 88p. pap. 16.95 *(978-1-60749-059-3(5))* PublishAmerica, Inc.
Williams, Andrew, et al. Out of the Box: Building Robots, Transforming Lives, 1 vol. 2009. (ENG., Illus.). 176p. pap. 14.99 *(978-0-8024-6760-7(1)*, Lift Every Voice) Moody Pubs.
Williams, Chris. Life after Suffering: A Memoir of Subversive Hope. 2011. 166p. pap. 19.00 *(978-1-60608-701-5(0)*, Wipf and Stock) Wipf & Stock Pubs.
Williams, Cornelius. Transition: From Homosexual to Preacher. 2009. 192p. 26.93 *(978-1-4389-9038-5(3))*; pap. 21.93 *(978-1-4389-8359-2(X))* AuthorHouse.
Williams, Darryl K. Surviving the Hell: The Key for Making it Through Difficult Times. 2011. 60p. pap. 14.98 ***(978-1-4634-4327-6(7))*** AuthorHouse.
Williams, Eno Udo. From Trials to Triumphs. 2009. 188p. 22.99 *(978-1-60791-925-4(7))* Xulon Pr., Inc.
—From Trials to Triumphs (The Coscharis Story) The Biography of Dr. Cosmas & Mrs. Charity Maduka. 2009. 188p. pap. 14.99 *(978-1-60791-924-7(9))* Xulon Pr., Inc.
Williams, Michael. Authorised Lives in Early Christian Biography: Between Eusebius & Augustine. (Cambridge Classical Studies). (ENG.). 2011. 276p. pap. 50.00 *(978-0-521-34952-9(4))* 2008. 274p. 99.00 *(978-0-521-89490-6(5))* Cambridge Univ. Pr.
Williams, Paul J. I Witness. 2011. 148p. 29.99 ***(978-1-4653-5664-2(9))***; pap. 19.99 ***(978-1-4653-5663-5(0))*** Xlibris Corp.
Williamson, Vet. Purposes A Real Love Story. 2007. 73p. pap. 16.95 *(978-1-4241-5312-1(3))* PublishAmerica, Inc.
Wills, Larry G. Please Don't Worry: A True Story of Faith, Hope & Love. 2010. 198p. 27.95 *(978-1-59594-345-3(5))*; pap. 13.95 *(978-1-59594-362-0(5))* WingSpan Publishing. (Wingspan Pr.).
Willy, Eugene Linor. Standing Through Faith with Matters of the Heart. 2008. 64p. pap. 9.99 *(978-1-60477-834-2(2))* Xulon Pr., Inc.
Wilson, David C. Conversation with God: A Christian Experience of Depression. 2006. (Illus.). 196p. pap. *(978-1-84401-803-1(2))* Athena Pr.
Wilson, Rob. Be Always Converting Be Always Converted: An American Poetics. 2009. (Illus.). 336p. 47.50 *(978-0-674-03343-6(4))* Harvard Univ. Pr.
Wilton, Kay Bradberry. My Journey Through Life: The Story of My Life. 2009. 178p. pap. 16.24 *(978-1-4269-1920-6(4))* Trafford Publishing.
Winner, Lauren F. Still: Notes on a Mid-Faith Crisis. 2012. (ENG.). 256p. 24.99 ***(978-0-06-176811-8(1)***, HarperOne) HarperCollins Pubs.
Winslow, Octavius. Life in Jesus: A Memoir of Mrs. Mary Winslow, Arranged from Her Correspondence, Diary, & Thoughts. by Her Son Octavius Winslow, D. D.... 2006. 436p. per. 26.99 *(978-1-4255-4786-8(9))* MPublishing.
Winston, Arlita Morken. Heart-Cry. 2007. 276p. 30.50 *(978-1-4251-6313-6(0))*; pap. 19.69 *(978-1-4251-2172-3(1))* Trafford Publishing.
Winter, James F. Baptism by Toilet Water. 2010. pap. 19.99 *(978-1-61663-980-8(6))* Tate Publishing & Enterprises, LLC.
Wise, Joe. I Want to Go to Heaven but Not Yet. 2011. 184p. 29.99 ***(978-1-4568-0131-7(7))***; pap. 19.99 ***(978-1-4568-0130-4(9))*** Xlibris Corp.
Wise, Lorraine. God Is Real. 2011. (ENG.). pap. 20.00 net. *(978-1-57579-437-2(3))* Pine Hill Pr., Inc.
Wohlfelder, Peter. My Missionary Adventure: A True Story. 2009. 100p. pap. 14.00 *(978-1-4490-3646-1(5))* AuthorHouse.
Wonser, Mark. My Eye: A Vision of Christ: The Gnostic Christian Autobiography of Mark Wonser. 2011. 244p. 24.95 ***(978-1-4634-1922-6(8))***; pap. 14.95 ***(978-1-4634-1923-3(6))*** AuthorHouse.
Wood, Vivienne. Tony. (Illus.). xii, 96p. pap. 7.99 *(978-0-907821-05-2(7))* Revival Literature.
Wooten, Calvin. The Book of Love: Through the Eyes of a Child. 2008. 148p. pap. 15.99 *(978-1-4343-5710-6(4))* AuthorHouse.
Worden, Larry D. You Have Me. 2008. 204p. pap. 15.99 *(978-1-60647-634-5(3))* Xulon Pr., Inc.
World Bible Translation Center, creator. The Life of Jesus. 2008. 190p. pap. 1.75 *(978-1-932438-33-8(5))* World Bible Translation Ctr., Inc.
Worrill, Jack. Parables for Plain People. 2010. 286p. pap. 16.99 *(978-1-60957-521-2(0))* Xulon Pr., Inc.
Worsham, L'Trece Ann. Unsheltered: I've Been Through the Fire & Come Out Pure Gold. 2010. 156p. pap. 14.95 *(978-1-4502-4663-7(X))* iUniverse, Inc.
Worth, Kenneth F. Hard Times & Great Blessings: The Story of My Life. 2008. 124p. pap. 12.95 *(978-1-4327-2308-8(1))* Outskirts Pr., Inc.
Worth, Roland H., Jr. Shapers of Early Christianity: 52 Biographies, A. D. 100-400. 2007. (ENG., Illus.). 201p. 75.00 *(978-0-7864-2923-3(2))* McFarland & Co., Inc. Pubs.
Worth, Roland H. Shapers of Early Christianity: 52 Biographies, A. D. 100-400. alt. ed. 2012. (ENG.). 201p. pap. 25.00 ***(978-0-7864-6942-0(0))*** McFarland & Co., Inc. Pubs.
Wright, J. H., ed. John Stott: A Portrait by His Friends. 2011. (Illus.). 217p. 16.25 ***(978-1-84474-516-6(3))*** InterVarsity Pr.
Wright, Roberta. Blessings in the Storm: Samuel Wesley Gathing: A Closer Look. 2011. 100p. pap. 11.65 ***(978-1-4269-3770-5(9))*** Trafford Publishing.
Yanich, Voyeslav. Lives of the Serbian Saints. 2009. 136p. 21.99 *(978-1-113-80694-9(X))* BiblioBazaar.
Yanich, Voyeslav & Hankey, Cyril Patrick. Lives of the Serbian Saints. 2009. 148p. 35.95 *(978-1-104-27109-1(5))*; pap. 20.95 *(978-1-104-24606-8(6))* Kessinger Publishing, LLC.
Young, Bonnie. The Nehemiah Principle, 1 vol. 2009. 157p. pap. 24.95 *(978-1-4489-9503-5(5))* PublishAmerica, Inc.
Young, Carol Ann. Mother, Please Don't Throw My Life Away: The cry of the unborn & the voices of those longing to be Heard. 2008. 96p. pap. 12.95 *(978-1-4327-3149-6(1))* Outskirts Pr., Inc.
Young, Donna L. Apologies from a Repentant Christian. 2011. 238p. pap. 15.99 ***(978-1-61379-193-6(3))*** Xulon Pr., Inc.
Young, Richard. Joyce Meyer: A Life of Redemption & Destiny. 2009. 192p. pap. 13.99 *(978-1-60374-112-5(7)*, 771125) Whitaker Hse.
Young, Richard & Young, Brenda. Messengers of Healing: The Miraculous Life & Ministry of Charles & Frances Hunter. 2009. 208p. pap. 12.99 *(978-1-60374-106-4(2)*, 771065) Whitaker Hse.
Youngs, Bettie B. The House That Love Built: The Story of Millard & Linda Fuller, Founders of Habitat for Humanity & the Fuller Center for Housing. 2007. (ENG., Illus.). 424p. 26.95 *(978-1-57174-546-0(7))* Hampton Roads Publishing Co., Inc.
Yun, Brother & Hattaway, Paul. The Heavenly Man: The Remarkable True Story of Chinese Christian Brother Yun. 2009. (Illus.). 351p. 19.95 *(978-1-59856-392-4(0))* Hendrickson Pubs. Marketing, LLC.
Zagrans, Maura. Miracles Every Day: The Story of One Physician's Inspiring Faith & the Healing Power of Prayer. 2010. (ENG.). 256p. 19.99 *(978-0-385-53181-8(8)*, Doubleday Religion) Doubleday Religious Publishing Group, The.
Zann, And Then We Danced. 2007. 172p. per. 13.99 *(978-1-60477-081-0(3))* Xulon Pr., Inc.
Zapata, Angel Ariel. Dark & Divine Faces. 2011. pap. 20.95 ***(978-0-7414-6506-1(X))*** Infinity Publishing.
Zapata, Clemencia. Life Through My Eyes: God's gift to see His face of success, gain wisdom & obtains happiness in Him. 2011. 124p. pap. 61.99 ***(978-1-4568-5711-0(8))*** Xlibris Corp.
Zemba, William. David & the Old Man. 2010. 152p. 30.95 *(978-1-4497-0572-5(3))*; pap. 13.95 *(978-1-4497-0571-8(5))* Author Solutions, Inc. (WestBow Pr.).
Zenzelle, Kalifa Obioma. God Is, That Is Why I Am! 2011. 230p. pap. 24.95 ***(978-1-4512-7535-3(8))*** PublishAmerica, Inc.
Zimmerman, Frank. A Painful Journey. 2007. 90p. per. 9.99 *(978-1-59886-918-7(3))* Tate Publishing & Enterprises, LLC.
Zobeck, Holly. A Journey of Grace & Faith. 2006. 60p. per. 7.99 *(978-1-59886-577-6(3))* Tate Publishing & Enterprises, LLC.
Zulu, Princess Kasune. Warrior Princess: Fighting for Life with Courage & Hope. 2009. (ENG.). 272p. 22.00 *(978-0-8308-3725-0(6)*, IVP Bks.) InterVarsity Pr.

CHRISTIAN CHURCH IN TEXAS

Mallory, Pat. Into Each Life Some Rain Must Fall... but, God! 2010. 110p. pap. 11.99 *(978-1-60957-522-9(9))* Xulon Pr., Inc.
Woods, Lonnie. It's in the System. 2010. 130p. 22.99 *(978-1-60957-574-8(1))*; pap. 14.99 *(978-1-60957-573-1(3))* Xulon Pr., Inc.

CHRISTIAN CIVILIZATION

see also Christianity and Culture; Church and Social Problems

Amirav, Hagit, et al, eds. From Rome to Constantinople: Studies in Honour of Averil Cameron. 2007. (Late Antique History & Religion Ser.). (ENG., Illus.). 425p. (C). 102.00 *(978-90-429-1971-6(X))* Peeters Pubs. & Booksellers BEL. Dist: Brown, David Bk. Co., The.
Brunner, Emil. Christianity & Civilisation: Foundations & Specific Problems. 2009. (ENG.). 326p. pap. 53.00 *(978-0-227-17289-6(2))* Clarke, James Co., Ltd. GBR. Dist: Brown, David Bk. Co., The.
Dawson, Christopher. The Formation of Christendom. 2008. 320p. (C). pap. 17.95 *(978-1-58617-239-8(5))* Ignatius Pr.
Dimitrov, Bozhidar. Bulgarian Christian Civilization. 2007. 164p. pap. 110.00 *(978-954-8745-03-1(8))* KOM Foundation BGR. Dist: Coronet Bks.
Eckfeldt, Edgar L. The Christian Legacy: Taming Brutish Human Nature in Western Civilization. 2011. (ENG.). 560p. pap. 35.95 ***(978-0-89226-106-2(4))*** Paragon Hse. Pubs.
Ferrero, Guglielmo. Peace & War. 2007. (ENG.). 260p. per. *(978-1-4067-4401-9(8))* Read Bks.
Gilk, Paul. Polemics & Provocations. 2010. (Illus.). 192p. pap. 22.00 *(978-1-60899-371-0(X)*, Wipf and Stock) Wipf & Stock Pubs.
Jenkins, John Philip. Jesus Wars: How Four Patriarchs, Three Queens, & Two Emperors Decided What Christians Would Believe for the Next 1,500 Years. 2010. (ENG.). 352p. 26.99 *(978-0-06-176894-1(4)*, HarperOne) HarperCollins Pubs.
—The Lost History of Christianity: The Thousand-Year Golden Age of the Church in the Middle East, Africa, & Asia — And How It Died. 2009. (ENG.). 304p. pap. 15.99 *(978-0-06-147281-7(6)*, HarperOne) HarperCollins Pubs.
McGuckin, John Anthony. The Ascent of Christian Law: Patristic & Byzantine Formulations of a New Civilization. 2012. ***(978-0-88141-403-5(4))*** St. Vladimir's Seminary Pr.
Niebuhr, Reinhold. Does Civilization Need Religion? A Study in the Social Resources & Limitations of Religion in Modern Life. 2010. 242p. pap. 21.00 *(978-1-60899-800-5(2)*, Wipf and Stock) Wipf & Stock Pubs.
Rogers, Glenn. Understanding American Culture: The Theological & Philosophical Shaping of the American Worldview. 2007. pap. 21.95 *(978-0-9774396-9-0(0))* Mission & Ministry Resources.
Royal, Robert. The God That Did Not Fail: How Religion Built & Sustains the West. 2010. (ENG.). 336p. pap. 16.95 *(978-1-59403-517-3(2))* Encounter Bks.
Seidler, Victor J. Jewish Philosophy & Western Culture: A Modern Introduction. 2007. (ENG.). 256p. 84.00 *(978-1-84511-280-6(6))*; pap. 28.00 *(978-1-84511-281-3(4))* I. B. Tauris & Co., Ltd. GBR. Dist: Macmillan.
Siedell, Daniel A. God in the Gallery: A Christian Embrace of Modern Art. 2008. (Cultural Exegesis Ser.). (Illus.). 192p. (C). pap. 25.00 *(978-0-8010-3184-7(2))* Baker Academic.
Stark, Rodney. The Victory of Reason: How Christianity Led to Freedom, Capitalism, & Western Success. annot. ed. 2006. (ENG., Illus.). 304p. per. 15.95 *(978-0-8129-7233-7(3)*, Random Hse. Trade Paperbacks) Random House Publishing Group.
Tilson, Everett. The Conscience of Culture. 2011. 128p. 40.95 ***(978-1-258-04832-7(9))*** Literary Licensing, LLC.
Wolf, Beat. Jerusalem und Rom: Mitte, Nabel - Zentrum, Haupt: Die Metaphern Umbilicus mundi und Caput mundi in den Weltbildern der Antike und des Abendlands bis in die Zeit der Ebstorfer Weltkarte. 2006. (GER.). 414p. pap. *(978-3-03911-161-9(2))* Lang, Peter.
Young, Frances M. Biblical Exegesis & the Formation of Christian Culture. 2007. (ENG.). 340p. pap. 69.00 *(978-0-521-04513-1(4))* Cambridge Univ. Pr.

CHRISTIAN COALITION

Rozell, Mark J. & Wilcox, Clyde, eds. The Values Campaign: The Christian Right & the 2004 Elections. 2006. (Religion & Politics Ser.). (ENG., Illus.). 282p. per. 19.95 *(978-1-58901-108-3(2))* Georgetown Univ. Pr.

CHRISTIAN COMMUNES

see Christian Communities

CHRISTIAN COMMUNITIES

Here are entered works on groups of Christians who live and-or work together to achieve common spiritual and social objectives. Works on groups of Christians who live together without vows are entered under Societies Living in Common Without Vows. Works on groups of Christians who live together under religious vows are entered under Monasticism and Religious Orders.

see also Monasticism and Religious Orders; Societies Living in Common without Vows

also names of particular communities

Ballou, Adin & Heywood, William S. History of the Hopedale Community. 2010. (Illus.). xxvii, 339p. pap. ***(978-0-9816402-3-5(0))*** Blackstone Editions.
Bechtel, Carol M. Disciples. 2008. (Illus.). 157p. *(978-1-59255-435-5(0))* Faith Alive Christian Resources.
Bosco, Antoinette. Mother Benedict: Foundress of the Abbey of Regina Laudis. 2007. (Illus.). 423p. 19.95 *(978-1-58617-186-5(0))* Ignatius Pr.
Chalke, Steve. Change Agents: 25 Hard-Learned Lessons in the Art of Getting Things Done, 1 vol. 2007. (ENG., Illus.). 160p. pap. 10.99 *(978-0-310-27549-7(0))* Zondervan.
Crabb, Larry. Becoming a True Spiritual Community: A Profound Vision of What the Church Can Be, 0 vols. 2007. (Illus.). 256p. per. 14.99 *(978-0-8499-1884-1(7))* Nelson, Thomas Inc.
Drogus, Carol Ann & Stewart-Gambino, Hannah. Activist Faith: Grassroots Women in Democratic Brazil & Chile. 2008. (ENG.). 272p. pap. 30.00 *(978-0-271-02550-6(6))* Pennsylvania State Univ. Pr.

C

Durland, William. God or Nations: Radical Theology for the Religious Peace Movement. 2010. (Catholic Worker Reprint Ser.). 332p. (Orig.). pap. 36.00 (978-1-60899-055-9(9), Wipf and Stock) Wipf & Stock Pubs.

Farnham, Suzanne G. Listening Hearts: Discerning Call in Community. 2011. E-Book **(978-0-8192-2449-1(9)**, Morehouse Publishing) Church Publishing, Inc.

Forman, Mary, ed. One Heart, One Soul: Many Communities. 2009. 220p. pap. 24.95 (978-0-8146-9925-6(1), St. John's Bible Bks.) Liturgical Pr.

Geniesse, Jane. American Priestess: The Extraordinary Story of Anna Spafford & the American Colony in Jerusalem. 2009. (ENG., Illus.). 416p. pap. 17.95 (978-0-307-27772-5(0), Anchor) Knopf Doubleday Publishing Group.

Gibbs, Eddie & Cohick, Lynn. ChurchMorph: How Megatrends Are Reshaping Christian Communities, 1 vol. 2009. (Allelon Missional Ser.). (Illus.). 224p. (C). pap. 20.00 (978-0-8010-3762-7(X)) Baker Academic.

Gonzalez, Adele J. The Spirituality of Community. 2009. 128p. pap. 14.00 (978-1-57075-718-1(6)) Orbis Bks.

Grenz, Stanley J. The Social God & the Relational Self: A Trinitarian Theology of the Imago Dei. 2007. (ENG.). 360p. per. 50.00 (978-0-664-23238-2(8)) Westminster John Knox Pr.

Haar Romeny, R. B. ter. Religious Origins of Nations? The Christian Communities of the Middle East. 2009. 384p. (978-90-04-17375-0(7)) BRILL.

Haggard, Ted. Dog Training, Fly Fishing, & Sharing Christ in the 21st Century: Empowering Your Church to Build Community Through Shared Interests, 0 vols. 2008. (Illus.). 224p. pap. 14.99 (978-0-8499-2897-0(4)) Nelson, Thomas Inc.

The Harder I Laugh, the Deeper I Hurt: Lessons for Faith Communities. 2008. (ENG.). pap. 24.99 (978-0-8341-2379-3(7), 9780834123793) Beacon Hill Pr. of Kansas City.

Hayes, Kate. More Than Bricks & Ritual: Am I a Team Player for God? 2006. (Re: Action: Small Group Resources Ser.). 41p. pap. 8.00 (978-1-85999-769-7(4)) Scripture Union GBR. Dist: STL Distribution North America.

Hembd, Adam Jon. The Forbidden Family Dream. 2010. 170p. pap. 19.99 (978-1-4535-2837-2(7)) Xlibris Corp.

Hennecke, Christian. Kleine christliche Gemeinschaften verstehen: Ein Weg, Kirche mit Menschen zu sein. 2009. (GER.). 286p. pap. (978-3-429-03144-2(3)) Echter Wuerzburg.

Jones, Toby. The Way of Jesus: Re-Forming Spiritual Communities in a Post-Church Age. 2010. 154p. pap. 18.00 (978-1-60899-152-5(0), Resource Pubns.) Wipf & Stock Pubs.

Kling, Fritz. The Meeting of the Waters: 7 Global Currents That Will Propel the Future Church, 1 vol. 2010. (ENG.). 240p. pap. 16.99 (978-1-4347-6484-3(2)) Cook, David C.

Latini, Theresa F. The Church & the Crisis of Community: A Practical Theology of Small Group Ministry. 2011. 248p. pap. 29.00 (978-0-8028-6586-1(0)) Eerdmans, William B. Publishing Co.

Leahy, Brendan & Leahy, Breandan. Ecclesial Movements & Communities: Origins, Significance, & Issues. 2011. pap. 14.95 **(978-1-56548-396-5(0))** New City Pr.

Lett, Gabe. Let's Get Together: Building Community in the Church. 2008. (Illus.). 160p. per. 12.99 (978-1-60247-893-0(7)) Tate Publishing & Enterprises, LLC.

Ludlow, Morwenna. The Early Church: The I. B. Tauris History of the Christian Church. 2009. (I. B. Tauris History of the Christian Church Ser.). (ENG., Illus.). 256p. 42.00 (978-1-84511-366-7(7)) I. B. Tauris & Co., Ltd. GBR. Dist: Macmillan.

Lwhorn, Shannon. Reaching the City for the King: God's Blueprint for Effective Outreach Ministry in the Inner City. 2009. pap. 12.99 (978-1-61584-915-4(7)) Independent Pub.

McKanan, Dan. Touching the World: Christian Communities Transforming Society. 2007. 162p. per. 14.95 (978-0-8146-3175-1(4)) Liturgical Pr.

Merrill, Timothy. Community: Our Community Now & in God's Future. 2007. (Great Themes of the Bible Ser.). (Illus.). 85p. per. 8.50 (978-0-687-64342-4(2)) Abingdon Pr.

Moffitt, Bob. If Jesus Were Mayor: How Your Local Church Can Transform Your Community, 1 vol. 2006. (Illus.). 392p. pap. 15.99 (978-0-8254-6129-3(4), Monarch Bks.) Lion Hudson PLC GBR. Dist: Kregel Pubns.

Muther, Urs-Ullrich. Paulinische Ökonomie: Der Effizienzbegriff in 1. Korinther 12 und seine Bedeutung für die Gemeindekonzeption. 2010. (Religion in der Öffentlichkeit Ser.). (GER.). 386p. 90.95 (978-3-631-60941-5(8)) Lang, Peter GmbH, Europaischer Verlag der Wissenschaften DEU. Dist: Lang, Peter.

Muthiah, Robert A. The Priesthood of All Believers in the Twenty-First Century: Living Faithfully as the Whole People of God in a Postmodern Context. 2009. 194p. pap. 22.00 (978-1-60608-094-8(6), Pickwick Pubns.) Wipf & Stock Pubs.

O'Halloran, James. Living Cells: Vision & Practicalities of Small Christian Communities & Groups. 2010. (ENG., Illus.). 312p. pap. 29.95 (978-1-85607-699-9(7)) Columba Pr. IRL. Dist: Dufour Editions, Inc.

—Three Dancers One Dance: Vision & Practicalities of Small Christian Communities. 2010. (ENG.). 69p. pap. 14.95 (978-1-85607-653-1(9)) Columba Pr. IRL. Dist: Dufour Editions, Inc.

Ortberg, John, et al. 1 & 2 Samuel: Growing a Heart for God, 1 vol. 2008. (New Community Bible Study Ser.). (ENG.). 96p. pap. 7.99 (978-0-310-28049-1(4)) Zondervan.

Owens, L. Roger. The Shape of Participation: A Theology of Church Practices. 2010. 204p. pap. 22.00 (978-1-60608-519-6(0), Cascade Bks.) Wipf & Stock Pubs.

Pompey, Ayeshia Nicole. Moving Mountains. 2010. 182p. pap. 14.99 (978-1-60957-158-0(4)) Xulon Pr., Inc.

Rhodes, Robert. Nightwatch: An Inquiry into Solitude: Alone on the Prairie with the Hutterites, 1 vol. 2009. (ENG.). 160p. pap. 9.95 (978-1-56148-666-3(3)) Good Bks.

Riccardi, Andrea & Community of Sant'Egidio Staff. Sant Egidio Bk of Prayer. 2009. 224p. pap. 14.95 (978-1-59471-206-7(9)) Ave Maria Pr.

Saint Meinrad, The Monks of, ed. The Tradition of Catholic Prayer: The Monks of Saint Meinrad Archabbey. 2007. (Illus.). 304p. per. 24.95 (978-0-8146-3184-3(3), Liturgical Pr. Bks.) Liturgical Pr.

Samra, James G. Being Conformed to Christ in Community: A Study of Maturity, Maturation & the Local Church in the Undisputed Pauline Epistles. 2008. (Library of New Testament Studies, the Ser.). (ENG.). 280p. 44.95 (978-0-567-56398-9(7), T&T Clark Int'l) Continuum International Publishing Group, Ltd. GBR. Dist: National Bk. Network.

Sherlin, Keith A. How Can God Be All-Powerful & Totally Loving When He Planned a World with Sin & Suffering? A Reformed Evangelical Dispensational Theodicy, 1 vol. 2009. 127p. pap. 19.95 (978-1-60610-680-8(5)) PublishAmerica, Inc.

Smith, Luther E. Jr., et al. Intimacy & Mission: Intentional Community as Crucible for Radical Discipleship. 2007. 188p. pap. 22.00 (978-1-55635-537-0(8), Wipf and Stock) Wipf & Stock Pubs.

Stenhouse, John & Knowles, Brett, eds. Christianity in the Post Secular West. 2007. (Illus.). 290p. per. 20.00 (978-1-920691-75-2(8)) ATF Pr. AUS. Dist: International Publishers Marketing.

Tate, Kenneth J. The Importance of Mobilizing the Christian Church As a Family Preparation Center for Daily Christian Living. 2009. 156p. pap. 11.99 (978-1-4490-0563-4(2)) AuthorHouse.

Tatlock, Mike. Faith in Real Life: Creating Community in the Park, Coffee Shop, & Living Room, 1 vol. 2010. (ENG.). 352p. pap. 14.99 (978-0-310-29190-9(9)) Zondervan.

Thompson, Beverly & Thompson, George B. Grace for the Journey: Practices & Possibilities for In-Between Times. 2011. **(978-1-56699-420-0(9))** Alban Institute, Inc.

Toler, Stan. The Community-Minded Church: Resources for Connecting with the World Outside Your Walls. 2009. (ENG.). 192p. ring bd. 49.99 (978-0-8341-2277-2(4), 9780834122772) Beacon Hill Pr. of Kansas City.

Van Engen, John & Van Engen, John H. Sisters & Brothers of the Common Life: The Devotio Moderna & the World of the Later Middle Ages. 2008. (Middle Ages Ser.). (Illus.). 448p. (C). 65.00 (978-0-8122-4119-8(3)) Univ. of Pennsylvania Pr.

Watts, Edward Jay. Riot in Alexandria: Tradition & Group Dynamics in Late Antique Pagan & Christian Communities. 2010. (Transformation of the Classical Heritage Ser.). (Illus.). 312p. 55.00 (978-0-520-26207-2(7)) Univ. of California Pr.

Wilhoit, James C. Spiritual Formation As If the Church Mattered: Growing in Christ Through Community. 2008. (Illus.). 240p. (C). pap. 22.99 (978-0-8010-2776-5(4)) Baker Academic.

Wilk, Karen. Don't Invite Them to Church: Moving from a Come & See to a Go & Be Church. 2010. 128p. (978-1-59255-531-4(4)) Faith Alive Christian Resources.

CHRISTIAN CONTEMPORARY MUSIC

see Contemporary Christian Music

CHRISTIAN CONVERTS

see Converts

CHRISTIAN CONVERTS FROM ISLAM

Alam, Christopher. Out of Islam: One Muslim's Journey to Faith in Christ. 2006. (ENG.). 208p. pap. 13.99 (978-1-59185-890-4(9), Charisma Hse.) Charisma Media.

Bradley, Mark. Iran: Open Hearts in a Closed Land. 2007. (ENG.). 116p. per. 9.99 (978-1-85078-770-9(0)) Authentic Media.

Caner, Emir Fethi & Pruitt, H. Edward. The Costly Call: The Untold Story. 2006. 176p. pap. 11.99 (978-0-8254-3564-5(1)) Kregel Pubns.

Corwin, Gary. The Desert Is Alive: Streams of Living Water from Muscat to Marrakech. 2007. (ENG., Illus.). 168p. per. 14.99 (978-1-85078-697-9(6)) Authentic Media.

Crane, Demetrius M. A Love Affair with the Lord. 2012. **(978-1-55452-769-4(4))** Essence Publishing.

Fluckiger, Jay D. Radical Religion: The Incredible, True Story of a Muslim's Conversion to Mormonism. 2011. 192p. pap. 13.99 **(978-1-59955-964-3(1))** Bonneville B.V. NLD. Dist: Cedar Fort, Inc./CFI Distribution.

Haile, Ahmed Ali & Shenk, David W., told to. Teatime in Mogadishu: My Journey As a Peace Ambassador in the World of Islam. 2011. pap. (978-0-8361-9557-6(4)) Herald Pr.

Kuhn, Mike. Fresh Vision for the Muslim World. 2009. (ENG.). 287p. pap. 14.99 (978-1-60657-019-7(6)) Authentic Media.

Michael, S. & McAlister, L. Dare to Explore2. 2011. 184p. pap. 16.99 **(978-1-61379-748-8(6))** Xulon Pr., Inc.

Nasser, David. Jumping Through Fires: The Gripping Story of One Man's Escape from Revolution to Redemption. 2009. (Illus.). 224p. 17.99 (978-0-8010-1335-5(6)); (ENG.). 176p. pap. 13.99 **(978-0-8010-7259-8(X))** Baker Bks.

Nealson, Jay. Baghdad Believer. 2007. 112p. per. 14.45 (978-0-9792352-0-7(0)) Hillcrest Publishing Group, Inc.

Saleem, Kamal. The Blood of Lambs: A Former Terrorist's Memoir of Death & Redemption. 2009. (ENG.). 352p. 24.99 (978-1-4165-7780-5(7), Howard Bks.) Howard Books.

Williams, Benny. What It Means to Put on the Full Armor of God. 2007. 67p. per. 12.95 (978-0-9796180-0-0(2)) Williams, Benjamin Publishing.

Yousef, Mosab Hassan. Son of Hamas: A Gripping Account of Terror, Betrayal, Political Intrigue, & Unthinkable Choices. (ENG.). 2011. 304p. pap. 14.99 (978-1-4143-3308-3(0)) 2010. (Illus.). 288p. 26.99 (978-1-4143-3307-6(2)) Tyndale Hse. Pubs. (SaltRiver).

Yousef, Mosab Hassan & Brackin, Ron. Son of Hamas: A Gripping Account of Terror, Betrayal, Political Intrigue, & Unthinkable Choices. 2010. (Illus.). xv, 265p. (978-1-4143-3668-8(3), SaltRiver) Tyndale Hse. Pubs.

CHRISTIAN CONVERTS FROM JUDAISM

see also Jews—Conversion To Christianity

Bernstein, A. James. Surprised by Christ: My Journey from Judaism to Orthodox Christianity. 2008. 337p. pap. 18.95 (978-1-888212-95-2(0)) Conciliar Pr.

Brown, Michael L. Answering Jewish Objections to Jesus: New Testament Objections, 4 vols. 2006. (Answering Jewish Objections to Jesus Ser.). 384p. pap. 27.00 (978-0-8010-6426-5(0)) Baker Bks.

Costigan, Lúcia Helena. Through Cracks in the Wall: Modern Inquisitions & New Christian Letrados in the Iberian Atlantic World. 2010. (Atlantic World Ser.). 256p. (978-90-04-17920-2(8)) BRILL.

Dorsett, Lyle W. And God Came In: The Extraordinary Story of Joy Davidman. 2009. (Illus.). xviii, 189p. 17.95 (978-1-59856-356-6(4)) Hendrickson Pubs. Marketing, LLC.

Edersheim, Alfred. The Abridged Edersheim. 2009. 498p. pap. 23.99 (978-1-4415-5467-3(X)) Xlibris Corp.

Guinness, Michele. Chosen: An Autobiography, 1 vol. 2008. (Illus.). 384p. pap. 14.99 (978-0-8254-6283-2(5), Monarch Bks.) Lion Hudson PLC GBR. Dist: Kregel Pubns.

Mills, Gerrie Hyman. Oy Vey! Such a Deal! Jazzed by Faith & Chocolate Pudding. 2007. (ENG., Illus.). 256p. per. 13.99 (978-1-59979-264-4(8), Creation Hse.) Charisma Media.

Mishkin, David. The Wisdom of Alfred Edersheim. 2008. 210p. pap. 23.00 (978-1-55635-939-2(X), Wipf and Stock) Wipf & Stock Pubs.

Mitchell, Matthew. Abortion & the Apostolate. 2009. 111.08 (978-1-60724-057-0(2)) Gorgias Pr., LLC.

Oesterreicher, John M. Walls Are Crumbling. (Illus.). 10.00 (978-0-8159-7201-3(6)) Devin-Adair Pubs., Inc.

Roth, Sid. They Thought for Themselves. 2009. pap. 16.99 (978-0-7684-2842-1(4)) Destiny Image Pubs.

Schoeman, Roy H., compiled by. Honey from the Rock: Sixteen Jews Find the Sweetness of Christ. 2007. (Illus.). 289p. pap. 16.95 (978-1-58617-115-5(1)) Ignatius Pr.

Tartakoff, Paola. Between Christian & Jew: Conversion & Inquisition in the Crown of Aragon, 1250-1391. 2012. (Middle Ages Ser.). (Illus.). 264p. (C). 55.00 **(978-0-8122-4421-2(4))** Univ. of Pennsylvania Pr.

Venturi, Pietro Tacchi & Maryks, Robert Aleksander. "Pouring Jewish Water into Fascist Wine" Untold Stories of (Catholic) Jews from the Archive of Mussolini's Jesuit Pietro Tacchi Venturi. 2011. (ENG & ITA., Illus.). XVI, 392p. **(978-90-04-21670-9(7))** BRILL.

Walton, Michael Thomson. Anthonius Margaritha & the Jewish Faith: Jewish Life & Conversion in Sixteenth-Century Germany. 2012. **(978-0-8143-3800-1(3))** Wayne State Univ. Pr.

Weinreich, Gabriel. Confessions of a Jewish Priest: From Secular Jewish War Refugee to Physicist & Episcopal Clergyman. 2010. 192p. pap. 22.00 (978-1-60899-209-6(8), Resource Pubns.) Wipf & Stock Pubs.

Weisbord, Robert G. & Sillanpoa, Wallace P. Chief Rabbi, the Pope, & the Holocaust: An Era in Vatican-Jewish Relations. 2008. (ENG., Illus.). 240p. pap. 29.95 (978-1-4128-0791-3(3)) Transaction Pubs.

Winner, Lauren F. Mudhouse Sabbath: An Invitation to a Life of Spiritual Discipline. 2007. (ENG.). 162p. (gr. 12). per. 14.99 (978-1-55725-532-7(6)) Paraclete Pr., Inc.

Winner, Lauren F. Still: Notes on a Mid-Faith Crisis. 2012. (ENG.). 256p. 24.99 **(978-0-06-176811-8(1)**, HarperOne) HarperCollins Pubs.

CHRISTIAN COUNTY (KY.)

Gilkey, Chris & Turner, William T. Christian County. 2008. (IOA Ser.). (ENG., Illus.). 128p. pap. 21.99 (978-0-7385-6701-3(9)) Arcadia Publishing.

Turner, William T. & Gilkey, Chris. Edgar Cayce's Hometown: Hopkinsville, Kentucky. 2010. (Illus.). 128p. pap. 21.95 (978-1-934898-08-6(2)) McClanahan Publishing Hse., Inc.

CHRISTIAN DEMOCRACY

see also Catholic Action; Center Parties; Church and Labor

Cripps, Stafford. Towards Christian Democracy. (978-0-8022-0315-1(9)) Philosophical Library, Inc.

Irving, R. E. M. Christian Democracy in France (Routledge Revivals) 2010. (ENG.). 216p. pap. 39.95 (978-0-415-58276-6(8)) Routledge.

—Christian Democracy in France (Routledge Revivals) 2010. (Routledge Revivals Ser.). 312p. 115.00 (978-0-415-58268-1(7), Routledge) Taylor & Francis Group GBR. Dist: Taylor & Francis Group.

Moreno, Antonio F. Church, State, & Civil Society in Postauthoritarian Philippines: Narratives of Engaged Citizenship. 2008. 372p. (C). pap. 39.00 (978-971-550-494-2(9)) Univ. of Hawaii Pr.

Seeleib-Kaiser, Martin, et al. Party Politics & Social Welfare: Comparing Christian & Social Democracy in Austria, Germany & the Netherlands. (Globalization & Welfare Ser.). 232p. 2010. pap. 45.00 (978-1-84980-028-0(6)) 2008. (Illus.). 119.00 (978-1-84542-542-5(1)) Elgar, Edward Publishing, Inc.

Van Kemseke, Peter. Towards an Era of Development: The Globalization of Socialism & Christian Democracy. 2006. (KADOC Studies on Religion, Culture & Society: 5). 328p. (Orig.). per. 40.50 (978-90-5867-560-6(2)) Leuven Univ. Pr. BEL. Dist: Cornell Univ. Pr.

CHRISTIAN DENOMINATIONS

see Christian Sects

CHRISTIAN DEVOTIONAL CALENDARS

see Devotional Calendars

CHRISTIAN DEVOTIONAL LITERATURE

see Devotional Literature

CHRISTIAN DOCTRINE

see Theology, Doctrinal

CHRISTIAN DOCTRINE (CATHOLIC CHURCH)

see Catechetics—Catholic Church

CHRISTIAN EDUCATION

Here are entered works dealing with instruction in the Christian religion in schools and private life. Works on the relation of the church to education in general, and works on the history of the part that the church has taken in secular education are entered under Church and Education.

see also Catechetical Sermons; Catechetics; Catechisms; Catechumens; Christian Leadership; Church and College; Church and Education; Church Schools; Jesus Christ—Teaching Methods; Puppet Theater in Christian Education; Sunday Schools; Theology—Study and Teaching

Abingdon. Walk It Out Director's Manual. 2008. 14.00 (978-0-687-65222-8(7)) Abingdon Pr.

Abingdon Press. Rock-a-Bye Babies & Woddlers Ministry Guide: Teaching Faith in the Nursery. 2009. (Rock-a-Bye Ser.). 64p. 14.00 (978-0-687-65891-6(8)) Abingdon Pr.

Abingdon Press, creator. Serving from the Heart for Youth: Finding Your Gifts & Talents for Service. 2007. (Abingdon Press & Church of the Resurrection Ministry Guides). 55p. per. 10.00 (978-0-687-49728-7(0)) Abingdon Pr.

—Word Up! Speaking & Living for Jesus. 2007. (Fifth in Abingdon's Afro-Centric Intergenerational Program Ser.). 62.00 (978-0-687-64300-4(7)) Abingdon Pr.

Abingdon Press, ed. One Room Sunday School. 2010. pap. 12.50 (978-1-4267-0136-8(5)); pap. 57.00 (978-1-4267-0147-4(0)) Abingdon Pr.

Achtemeier, Paul J. Romans. 2010. (Interpretation: A Bible Commentary Ser.). (ENG., Illus.). 256p. pap. 25.00 (978-0-664-23438-6(0)) Westminster John Knox Pr.

Adam, Gottfried, ed. Die Inhalte von Kinderbibeln. Kriterien ihrer Auswahl. 2008. (Arbeiten zur Religionspadagogik Ser.). (GER., Illus.). 365p. (C). 68.00 (978-3-89971-489-0(X)) Vandenhoeck & Ruprecht GmbH & Co. KG DEU. Dist: ISD.

Adam, Gottfried & Lachmann, Rainer. Neues Gemeindepädagogisches Kompendium. 2008. (Arbeiten zur Religionspadagogik Ser.). (GER., Illus.). 482p. (C). 84.00 **(978-3-89971-524-8(1)**, V&R unipress) Vandenhoeck & Ruprecht GmbH & Co. KG DEU. Dist: ISD.

Albl, Martin C. Reason, Faith, & Tradition: Explorations in Catholic Theology. 2009. pap. 41.00 (978-0-88489-982-2(9)) St. Mary's Pr.

Aldredge-Clanton, Jann. God, A Word for Girls & Boys. 2007. 160p. pap. 18.00 (978-1-55635-280-5(8), Wipf and Stock) Wipf & Stock Pubs.

Allen, Holly Catterton, ed. Nurturing Children's Spirituality: Christian Perspectives & Best Practices. 2008. (Illus.). 416p. pap. 46.00 (978-1-55635-558-5(0)) Wipf & Stock Pubs.

Almquist, Beth, et al. Growing in God's Love: Weekly Meeting Plans for Voyager Leaders. 2007. (J). 19.95 (978-0-9743503-4-9(6)) Pioneer Clubs.

—Growing in God's Way: Weekly Meeting Plans for Voyager Leaders. 2007. (J). 19.95 (978-0-9743503-3-2(8)) Pioneer Clubs.

Alsleben-Baumann, Claudia. Synagoga - Typologien eines christlich-kultivierten Antijudaismus: Einsichten und Auswege im Fokus anamnetischer Religionspädagogik. 2009. (Übergänge. Studien zur Evangelischen und Katholischen Theologie/Religionspädagogik Ser.). (GER.). 200p. pap. 56.95 (978-3-631-58576-4(4)) Lang, Peter GmbH, Europaischer Verlag der Wissenschaften DEU. Dist: Lang, Peter.

Amazing Bible Race: Gospels & the Early Church. 2010. 128p. 10.00 (978-1-4267-0898-5(X)) Abingdon Pr.

Amodei, Michael. Catholic Essentials: An Overview of the Faith. 2009. (Illus.). 379p. (YA). pap. 19.95 (978-1-59471-145-9(3)) Ave Maria Pr.

—Send Out Your Spirit: A Confirmation Candidate's Handbook for Faith. rev. ed. 2010. 256p. pap. 11.95 (978-1-59471-225-8(5)) Ave Maria Pr.

—Send Out Your Spirit: Preparing Teens for Confirmation (Leader's Manual) rev. ed. 2010. 192p. pap. 22.95 (978-1-59471-246-3(8)) Ave Maria Pr.

—Send Out Your Spirit: Sponsor's Handbook. rev. ed. 2010. 48p. pap. 3.95 (978-1-59471-247-0(6)) Ave Maria Pr.

Anthony, Michael, ed. Perspectives on Children's Spiritual Formation. 2007. (Perspectives Ser.). (ENG.). 352p. pap. 24.99 (978-0-8054-4186-4(7), B&H Academic) B&H Publishing Group.

Armenio, Peter V. & Socias, James. The History of the Church. 2010. (978-1-936045-15-0(X)) Midwest Theological Forum.

—The Mystery of Redemption & Christian Discipleship. 2010. (978-1-936045-06-8(0)) Midwest Theological Forum.

Arthur, Ginny. Best of Blessings: Lent, Holy Week, & Easter. 150p. pap. 19.95 (978-1-55126-212-3(6), 1469) Forward Movement Pubns.

Atwood, Dennis. Words that Shape & Form: A 40-Day Journey in Spiritual Formation. 2008. 140p. spiral bd. 7.95 *(978-0-9795847-2-5(8))* Cooperative Baptist Fellowship.
Aukerman, John H. Discipleship That Transforms: An Introduction to Christian Education from a Wesleyan Holiness Perspective. 2011. (ENG.). 389p. (C). pap. 39.95 *(978-1-59317-541-2(8))* Warner Pr. Pubs.
Babler, Susan E. Look It up — in the Bible, Book 1. 2007. 159p. spiral bd. 17.95 *(978-0-7880-2447-4(7))* CSS Publishing Co.
Ball, Ann. Crafty Catholic Kids: Great Activities for Family Fun & Faith. 2008. (Illus.). 118p. pap. 19.95 *(978-1-59276-280-4(8))* Our Sunday Visitor, Publishing Div.
Ball, Wanda L., 1st. Kids Ask the Darndest Things about God & the Beginning: Answers from the First Five Books of the Bible. 2007. 132p. per. 15.00 *(978-0-9800069-0-2(2))* Ball Pubns.
Baptist Adults. 1.49 *(978-0-7673-5698-5(5))* LifeWay Christian Resources.
Barnes, Michael. Interreligious Learning: Dialogue, Spirituality & the Christian Imagination. 2011. (ENG.). 306p. 95.00 ***(978-1-107-01234-4(8))*** Cambridge Univ. Pr.
Barone, John. A Place for All: Ministry for Youth with Special Needs. 2008. (Illus.). 131p. pap. 26.25 *(978-0-88489-972-3(1))* St. Mary's Pr.
Barry, John F. Una Sola Fe, un Solo Señor: Creencias Catolicas Basicas = One Faith, One Lord. 2009. (Illus.). 224p. *(978-0-8215-5565-1(0))* Sadlier, William H. Inc.
Basile, Alex. The Gentle Road to Jesus: Teaching Christ in Every Parish, School, & Home. 2010. *(978-0-8189-1301-3(0))* St Pauls/Alba Hse. Pubs.
Batty, Otto. Student Workbook for an Easy Dig Thru 39 Ancient Sites. 2007. 252p. per. 16.99 *(978-1-60266-875-1(2))* Xulon Pr., Inc.
Baumann, Eddie Karl. Worldview as Worship: The Dynamics of a Transformative Christian Education. 2011. 352p. pap. 39.00 ***(978-1-61097-108-9(6)***, Wipf and Stock) Wipf & Stock Pubs.
becker, ellen c. & barnes, mary t. Advent in the Home: Activities for Families. 2008. (Illus.). 120p. pap. 14.95 *(978-1-59276-430-3(4))* Our Sunday Visitor, Publishing Div.
Beecher, Catharine E. (Catharine Esther). Religious Training of Children in the School, the Family, & the Church by Catharine E Beecher. 2006. 424p. per. 26.99 *(978-1-4255-4594-9(7))* MPublishing.
Beeke, Joel R. Bringing the Gospel to Covenant Children. 2nd ed. 2010. 96p. pap. *(978-1-60178-117-8(2))* Reformation Heritage Bks.
Beers, Stephen Thomas. The Soul of a Christian University: A Field Guide for Educators. 2008. (Illus.). 208p. pap. 18.95 *(978-0-89112-520-4(5)*, ACU Pr.) Abilene Christian Univ. Pr.
Belzman, Michael. Handbook for Christ-Centered Substance Abuse & Addiction Counselors. 2010. 556p. pap. 27.99 *(978-1-60957-809-1(0))* Xulon Pr., Inc.
Bennion, M. Lynn & Washburn, J. A. Principles of the Restored Church at Work: Course Thirteen for the Sunday Schools of the Church of Jesus Christ of Latter-Day Saints. 2011. 206p. 44.95 ***(978-1-258-07740-2(X))*** Literary Licensing, LLC.
Berger, Alison, contrib. by. Into the Fields: Teaching Specific Catholic Topics, Year 3: Catechist & Teacher Formation for the Whole Community. 2007. (Into the Fields Ser.). (Illus.). 121p. pap. 24.95 incl. audio compact disk *(978-1-58595-592-3(2))* Twenty-Third Pubns./Bayard.
Bergt, Carolyn S., et al. Concordia Curriculum Guide, 8 vols. 2007. 29.99 *(978-0-7586-1427-8(6))*; 30.99 *(978-0-7586-1433-9(0))*; 29.99 *(978-0-7586-1429-2(2))*; 30.99 *(978-0-7586-1435-3(7))*; 30.99 *(978-0-7586-1437-7(3))*; 31.99 *(978-0-7586-1439-1(X))*; 31.99 *(978-0-7586-1441-4(1))*; 29.99 *(978-0-7586-1431-5(4))* Concordia Publishing Hse.
Berryman, Jerome W. The Complete Guide to Godly Play, Volume 6: 15 Enrichment Presentations for Fall: Key Figures among the People of God. 2006. (Complete Guide to Godly Play Ser.). (Illus.). 132p. per. 24.95 *(978-1-931960-42-7(9)*, Living the Good News) Church Publishing, Inc.
—Teaching Godly Play: How to Mentor the Spiritual Development of Children. 2nd rev. ed. 2009. 160p. pap. 25.00 *(978-1-60674-048-4(2))* Morehouse Education Resources.
Betts, George Herbert. Leading Children to Faith: A Manual of Effective Christian Education for Contemporary Church & Home School Teachers. 2009. 156p. pap. 13.95 *(978-1-4357-4331-1(8))* Lulu Enterprises Inc.
Bibbs, Alvin C. Crazy Enough to Care: Changing Your World Through Compassion, Justice & Racial Reconciliation, 1 vol. 2009. (Willow Creek Resources Ser.). (ENG.). 150p. pap. 16.00 *(978-0-8308-2115-0(5)*, IVP Conn.) InterVarsity Pr.
Bickel, Paul V. Discipling Discipline in the Christian School. 2009. 112p. pap. 11.99 *(978-1-61579-088-3(8))* Xulon Pr., Inc.
Binz, Stephen J. Jesus, the Suffering Servant. 2012. ***(978-1-58595-864-1(6))*** Twenty-Third Pubns./Bayard.
Bitter, Gottfried, et al. Christliche Spiritualität Lehren, Lernen und Leben: Unserem Freund, Lehrer und Kollegen Gottfried Bitter Zu Seinem 70. Geburtstag Am 24. Oktober 2006. 2006. (GER., Illus.). 278p. (C). 35.00 *(978-3-89971-342-8(7))* Vandenhoeck & Ruprecht GmbH & Co. KG DEU. Dist: ISD.
Blackaby, Henry T., et al. Experiencing God Member Book: Knowing & Doing the Will of God. 2007. (Illus.). 272p. per. 14.95 *(978-1-4158-5838-7(1))* LifeWay Christian Resources.
Blair, Anthony L. Church & Academy in Harmony: Models of Collaboration for the Twenty-First Century. 2010. 142p. pap. 18.00 *(978-1-60899-507-3(0)*, Pickwick Pubns.) Wipf & Stock Pubs.
Blevins, Dean Gray & Maddix, Mark A. Discovering Discipleship: Dynamics of Christian Education. 2010. (ENG.). 384p. 44.99 *(978-0-8341-2496-7(3)*, 9780834124967) Beacon Hill Pr. of Kansas City.
Blomberg, Doug. Wisdom & Curriculum: Christian Schooling after Postmodernity. 2007. pap. *(978-0-932914-73-6(X))* Dordt College Pr.
Boice, Trina. Great Ideas for Primary Activity Days. 2007. (Illus.). 121p. per. 12.95 *(978-1-932898-69-9(7))* Spring Creek Bk. Co.
Booth, Edwin P. Letters to Live By: A Course for Young People. 2011. 158p. 41.95 ***(978-1-258-09144-6(5))*** Literary Licensing, LLC.
Bousquet, Tom. The Rapture, How Will You Prepare for It? A Practical Book. 2009. 172p. pap. 14.99 *(978-1-60791-790-8(4))* Xulon Pr., Inc.
Boye, Vicki, et al. Concordia Curriculum Guide, 8 vols. 2007. 23.99 *(978-0-7586-1434-6(9))*; 24.99 *(978-0-7586-1442-1(X))*; 24.99 *(978-0-7586-1440-7(3))*; 23.99 *(978-0-7586-1438-4(1))*; 23.99 *(978-0-7586-1436-0(5))*; 22.99 *(978-0-7586-1432-2(2))*; 22.99 *(978-0-7586-1430-8(6))*; 22.99 *(978-0-7586-1428-5(4))* Concordia Publishing Hse.
Bridgeman, Les. A Teacher's Notebook. 2010. 344p. pap. 31.95 *(978-1-4497-0114-7(0)*, WestBow Pr.) Author Solutions, Inc.
Broadman and Holman. Perspectives on Your Child's Education: Four Views, 1 vol. Jones, Timothy Paul, ed. 2009. (ENG.). 144p. pap. 19.99 *(978-0-8054-4844-3(6)*, B&H Academic) B&H Publishing Group.
Brogsdale-Davis, Latrice. Their Future Is in Your Hands. 2009. (ENG.). 64p. pap. *(978-1-55452-378-8(8)*, Guardian Bks.) Essence Publishing.
Brown, Michael B. Five Facets of a Diamond: A Look at Five Indispensable Elements of Christian Discipleship. 2007. 180p. per. 24.95 *(978-1-4241-7720-2(0))* PublishAmerica, Inc.
Bryant, Helen C. Emotional Intelligence: The Biblical Connection. 2011. 108p. pap. 14.95 ***(978-0-9834307-4-2(8))*** G Publishing LLC.
Bubmann, Peter, et al, eds. Gemeindepädagogik. 2012. (De Gruyter Studium Ser.).Tr. of Education in the Parish. (GER.). XVI, 357p. (C). (gr. 13-16). pap. 35.00 ***(978-3-11-022108-4(X))*** De Gruyter, Walter Inc.
Buchholz, Pamela. A United Methodist Is. 2010. 64p. pap. 16.00 *(978-0-687-64761-3(4))* Abingdon Pr.
Buela, Carlos Miguel. Catechism for Youth. 2008. 331p. (YA). pap. 16.95 *(978-1-933871-48-6(2))* IVE Pr.
Bullock, Monica. 50 Ideas for Kids Church. 2009. 71p. pap. 15.84 *(978-0-557-17263-4(2))* Lulu Enterprises Inc.
Burningham, Janet. Monday Nights in Jerusalem. 2009. 144p. pap. 14.99 *(978-1-59955-377-1(5))* Cedar Fort, Inc./CFI Distribution.
Burns, Jim. Dramas, Skits & Sketches. 2009. (Uncommon Ser.). (ENG.). 224p. (J). (gr. 6-12). 34.99 *(978-0-8307-4791-7(5))* Gospel Light Pubns.
—The Life of Jesus. 2009. (Uncommon Ser.). (ENG.). 208p. (J). (gr. 9-12). pap. 14.99 *(978-0-8307-4726-9(5))* Gospel Light Pubns.
—Parents & Family. 2010. (Uncommon Ser.). (ENG.). 208p. (gr. 9-12). pap. 14.99 *(978-0-8307-5097-9(5))* Gospel Light Pubns.
Bushnell, Horace. Christian Nurture. 2010. (ENG.). 412p. pap. 34.75 *(978-1-176-48205-0(X))*; 418p. pap. 34.75 *(978-1-175-07243-6(5))*; 412p. 41.99 *(978-1-140-54073-1(4))*; 402p. pap. 34.75 *(978-1-144-76322-8(3))*; 412p. pap. 34.75 *(978-1-141-98679-8(5))* BiblioBazaar.
—Christian Nurture. 2009. 252p. pap. *(978-0-217-45721-7(5))*; 202p. pap. *(978-1-4590-4184-4(4))* Books LLC.
—Christian Nurture. 2009. 182p. pap. 19.99 *(978-0-217-81218-4(X))* General Bks. LLC.
—Christian Nurture. 2010. 412p. pap. 27.96 *(978-1-162-97582-5(2))* 2007. (ENG.). 412p. 49.95 *(978-0-548-13099-5(X))* 2006. (ENG.). pap. 34.95 *(978-1-4286-4146-4(7))* Kessinger Publishing, LLC.
—Christian Nurture. 2006. (ENG.). 420p. per. 26.99 *(978-1-4255-4496-6(7))* MPublishing.
Bushnell, Horace, abr. Views of Christian Nurture. 2009. (Amer Philosophy, Religion Ser.). (ENG.). 256p. pap. 17.95 *(978-1-4290-1936-1(0))* Applewood Bks.
Bushnell, Horace & Weigle, Luther Allan. Christian Nurture. 2010. 404p. pap. 34.75 *(978-1-175-07242-9(7))* BiblioBazaar.
Bytheway, John. What I Wish I'd Known in High School. 2008. 144p. pap. 15.95 *(978-1-59038-864-8(X)*, Shadow Mountain) Deseret Bk. Co.
Caldwell, Chris. James: Gaining True Wisdom. 2011. ***(978-0-9823842-4-4(6))*** Smyth & Helwys Publishing, Inc.
Caldwell, Elizabeth F. Making a Home for Faith: Nurturing the Spiritual Life of Your Children. 2007. 139p. per. *(978-0-8298-1769-0(7))* Pilgrim Pr., The/United Church Pr.
Calhoun, Shayla L. I Read It, Like I Eat It!, 1 vol. 2010. 62p. pap. 19.95 *(978-1-4489-3322-8(6))* PublishAmerica, Inc.
Callaghan, Tonya. That's So Gay!- Homophobia in Canadian Catholic Schools. 2007. 260p. per. *(978-3-8364-2497-4(5))* VDM Verlag Dr. Mueller e.K.
Camp Gramma: Putting down Spiritual Stakes for Your Grandchildren. 2008. (ENG.). 192p. pap. 14.99 *(978-0-8341-2373-1(8)*, 9780834123731) Beacon Hill Pr. of Kansas City.
Campbell, Andrew. The Latin-Centered Curriculum: A Homeschooler's Guide to a Classical Education. 2008. pap. 17.95 *(978-1-930953-73-4(9))* ISI Bks.
Campbell, Jim. 52 Simple Ways to Talk with Your Kids about Faith: Opportunities for Catholic Families to Share God's Love. 2007. (ENG.). 208p. per. 12.95 *(978-0-8294-2474-4(1))* Loyola Pr.
Carlson, Gregory C. Rock Solid Teacher: Discover the Joy of Teaching Like Jesus. 2006. (ENG.). 256p. pap. 14.99 *(978-0-8307-4353-7(7))* Gospel Light Pubns.
Carpenter, Tracy. Kids' Choice Camp. 2006. (Camp Ser.). (ENG.). (J). cd-rom 59.99 *(978-0-7847-1893-3(8))* Standard Publishing.
Carr, Beverly Oliver. Tales from Behind the Teacher S Desk. 2011. 226p. pap. 15.99 *(978-1-61215-456-5(5))* Xulon Pr., Inc.
Carter, James E. The Gospel of Mark: Jesus' Works & Words. 2007. 154p. pap. *(978-1-931060-98-1(3))* Baptistway.
Carter, William James. Down the Via Doloros: The Road to Victory. 2010. 28p. pap. 7.99 *(978-0-88144-528-2(2)*, Thorncrown Publishing) Yorkshire Publishing Group.
Cartledge, Tony W. Old Testament Promises to God. 2009. pap. *(978-0-9821806-8-6(3))* NextSunday Resources.
Cartmill, Carol, et al. Serving from the Heart for Youth: Finding Your Gifts & Talents for Service. 2007. 80p. per. 17.00 *(978-0-687-49718-8(3))* Abingdon Pr.
Cassell, Bo. Water, Fire, Wind: The Elements of Following Christ. 2007. (ENG.). 126p. pap. 9.99 *(978-0-8341-5017-1(4)*, 083-415-0174) Beacon Hill Pr. of Kansas City.
Cataldo, Jodi L. Hugging the World: Children's Mission Study & Teacher's Guide: Faith, Hope, Love in Action. 2010. (Illus.). 48p. (J). pap. 8.00 *(978-1-933663-42-5(1)*, WD/GBGM Bks.) General Board of Global Ministries, The United Methodist Church.
Catholic Church, United States Conference of Catholic Bishops Committee on Evangelization and Catechesis Staff, contrib. by. Catechetical Formation in Chaste Living: Guidelines for Curriculum Design & Publication. 2008. 27p. pap. *(978-1-60137-043-3(1))* United States Conference of Catholic Bishops.
—Doctrinal Elements of a Curriculum Framework for the Development of Catechetical Materials for Young People of High School Age. 2008. iv, 53p. pap. *(978-1-60137-042-6(3))* United States Conference of Catholic Bishops.
Chadwick, Owen. Christian School Curriculum. 15.99 *(978-0-88469-228-7(0))* BMH Bks.
Champions Challenge Holiday Club Programme. 2007. 80p. pap. *(978-1-84427-270-9(2))* Scripture Union.
Chandler, Phyllis, et al. Sharing the Faith with Your Child: From Birth to Age Four. 2006. 112p. per. 5.95 *(978-0-7648-1523-2(7))* Liguori Pubns.
Cheesman, Graham. The Bible College Movement in the Uk. 2009. 284p. pap. *(978-3-639-13272-4(6))* VDM Verlag Dr. Mueller e.K.
China Educational Commission. Christian Education in China: A Study. reprint ed. 34.50 *(978-0-404-14474-6(8))* AMS Pr., Inc.
Chlachula, Roxane Kadrlik & Shrader, Mary. Exploring Liturgical Seasons with Young Adolescents. 2008. (Illus.). 103p. pap. 29.50 *(978-0-88489-729-3(X))* St. Mary's Pr.
Cloud, Henry, et al. ReGroup: Training Groups to Be Groups, 1 vol. 2007. (ENG.). 160p. pap., instr.'s gde. ed. 9.99 *(978-0-310-27785-9(X))* Zondervan.
Cobb, Robert William. Called. 2011. 152p. pap. 14.99 ***(978-1-61215-833-4(1))*** Xulon Pr., Inc.
Cohen, M. A. We're Dancin' to His Righteous Rhythm Keepin' It Real. 2007. 200p. per. 23.95 *(978-0-595-44993-4(X))* iUniverse, Inc.
Concordia Publishing House, creator. Rotation Basics: A Practical Guide for Sunday School & VBS. 2009. 79p. pap. 16.99 *(978-0-7586-1630-2(9))* Concordia Publishing Hse.
Cook, Gene R. Teaching by the Spirit. 2011. 232p. pap. 17.99 *(978-1-60641-958-8(7))* Deseret Bk. Co.
Costello, Gwen. Praying with Children. 2007. (Jump Starts for Catechists Ser.). 41p. (J). (gr. 2). pap. 4.95 *(978-1-58595-635-7(X))* Twenty-Third Pubns./Bayard.
Cottrell, Stephen & Croft, Steven. How to Live: A Guide to the Journey of Faith. 2011. 144p. pap. 14.99 ***(978-0-7151-4240-0(2))*** Church Hse. Publishing GBR. Dist: Westminster John Knox Pr.
Cowan, Richard O., ed. Teaching the Word: Religious Education at Brigham Young University. 2008. (Illus.). 96p. 11.95 *(978-0-8425-2708-8(7)*, Brigham Young Univ. Pr.) Brigham Young Univ.
Cox, Michael H. Creative Devotions with Dad. 2010. 110p. pap. 13.99 *(978-1-60957-526-7(1))* Xulon Pr., Inc.
Cram, Barry & Daniel, Brian. Soul Cafe: A Guide to Spiritual Conversations. 2008. (Illus.). 62p. 5.99 *(978-1-57494-421-1(5)*, Serendipity Hse.) LifeWay Christian Resources.
Crenshaw, Curtis I. Keeping Covenant & Educating Our Children. 125p. pap. 3.00 *(978-1-877818-09-7(7))* Footstool Pubns.
Culbertson, Diana. The Body of Christ. 2007. x, 52p. pap. *(978-1-56077-835-6(0))* Center for Learning, The.
Cunningham, J. Michael. Your Walk, Their Walk - Workbook. 2010. 164p. pap. 12.99 *(978-0-88144-113-0(9)*, Thorncrown Publishing) Yorkshire Publishing Group.
Curry, Lorraine. Easy Homeschooling Techniques General Edition: The Real How-to Guide. 2006. (ENG., Illus.). 264p. per. 18.99 *(978-0-9709965-4-1(3))* God's Gardener.
Daley, Sheela. Leave 'em Wanting More: Children's Ministry That Thrills as It Teaches. 2007. (Illus.). 271p. per. 20.99 *(978-1-60247-236-5(X))* Tate Publishing & Enterprises, LLC.
Daly, Laurie. Let's Have Fun: An Interactive Approach to Children's Church. 2006. 196p. per. 12.95 *(978-1-59886-087-0(9))* Tate Publishing & Enterprises, LLC.
Danesco, Lee. The Confident Catechist: Strategies for the New & Not-So-New Volunteer. 2007. 72p. per. 12.50 *(978-0-88489-961-7(6))* St. Mary's Pr.
Dant, James & Dant, James C. How Does the Church Decide? 2009. pap. *(978-0-9821806-6-2(7))* NextSunday Resources.
David C. Cook Publishing Company Staff. Cosmic City Director's Guide. 2007. (Vacation Bible School Ser.). 144p. (J). pap. 14.99 *(978-1-4347-9964-7(6))* Cook, David C.
—Cosmic City Outler LimitsUpper Elementary Guide. 2007. (Vacation Bible School Ser.). 112p. (YA). (gr. 9-12). pap. 9.99 *(978-1-4347-9953-1(0))* Cook, David C.
—Deeper Space Music & Bible Memory Guide. 2007. (Vacation Bible School Ser.). 48p. (J). (gr. 3-12). pap. 6.99 *(978-1-4347-9959-3(X))* Cook, David C.
—SuperNova SuperMart Craft Guide. 2007. (Vacation Bible School Ser.). 48p. (J). (gr. 3-12). pap. 6.99 *(978-1-4347-9962-3(X))* Cook, David C.
—Theater of the Galaxies Bible Drama Guide. 2007. (Vacation Bible School Ser.). 48p. (J). (gr. 3-12). pap. 6.99 *(978-1-4347-9961-6(1))* Cook, David C.
—Wonder U Lab Guide. 2007. (Vacation Bible School Ser.). 48p. (J). (gr. 3-12). pap. 9.99 *(978-1-4347-9957-9(3))* Cook, David C.
David C. Cook Publishing Company Staff, creator. Bible Games That Teach. 2008. (Bible Fun Stuff for Preschool Ser.). (Illus.). 112p. (J). (gr. -1-k). pap. 19.99 *(978-1-4347-6863-6(5))* Cook, David C.
Davis, Kim. Cocoon. 2009. 320p. pap. *(978-1-55452-365-8(6)*, Guardian Bks.) Essence Publishing.
Dawson, Christopher. The Crisis of Western Education. 2010. (ENG.). 192p. pap. 24.95 *(978-0-8132-1683-6(4))* Catholic Univ. of America Pr.
Day, Daniel. Stoked. 2010. pap. 9.95 *(978-0-7414-5904-6(3))* Infinity Publishing.
De Francisco, Carrie. Building a Homeschool: One Prayer at A Time. 2009. 93p. pap. 16.95 *(978-1-4327-4323-9(6))* Outskirts Pr., Inc.
—Building a Homeschool One Room at A Time: Teaching with Mary¿s Philosophy & Using Martha¿s Methodologies. 2007. 124p. pap. 15.95 *(978-1-4327-0126-0(6))* Outskirts Pr., Inc.
de Jesus Alzate, Maria. Grupos Juveniles & Vocacionales. (SPA.). 240p. 10.95 *(978-958-607-696-8(2))* Sociedad de San Pablo ESP. Dist: St Pauls/Alba Hse. Pubs.
Deborah, Rowley. Before They Turn Twelve. 2007. 128p. pap. 9.95 *(978-1-59038-847-1(X))* Deseret Bk. Co.
DeKoven, Stan. Administrative Manual. 2006. 52p. per. 5.00 *(978-1-931178-31-0(3))* Vision Publishing.
—Transferring the Vision. 2007. 84p. per. 8.95 *(978-1-931178-44-0(5))* Vision Publishing.
Delnay, Robert G. Teach As He Taught. 2008. 140p. pap. 14.99 *(978-0-9749836-7-7(5))* Faithful Life Pubs.
Demaray, Donald. Things Unshakeable: Spiritual Formation Reflections from the Pen of Paul S. Rees. 2011. 106p. pap. 33.00 *(978-1-60947-015-9(X))* Emeth Pr.
Denman, William F. A Look at Christian Home School Co-Op Groups. 2008. 136p. pap. 24.95 *(978-1-60813-108-2(4))* PublishAmerica, Inc.
Derr, Colleen. Explore. 2009. (Illus.). ***(978-0-89827-418-9(4))*** Wesleyan Publishing Hse.
Desafíos en la Escuela. (Bible Studies for Teens Vivencias de la Vida Real (Real Deal) Ser.).Tr. of School Challenges. (SPA.). 88p. 14.99 *(978-0-7586-0608-2(7))* Concordia Publishing Hse.
Desafíos en la Familia. (Bible Studies for Teens Vivencias de la Vida Real (Real Deal) Ser.).Tr. of Family Challenges. (SPA.). 14.99 *(978-0-7586-0656-3(7))* Concordia Publishing Hse.
Desafíos Personales. (Bible Studies for Teens Vivencias de la Vida Real (Real Deal) Ser.).Tr. of Personal Challenges. (SPA.). 80p. 14.99 *(978-0-7586-0607-5(9))* Concordia Publishing Hse.
Devries, Lynn. Building a Foundation: A Primer for Cross-Cultural Teachers. 2009. 133p. pap. 11.95 *(978-1-4327-4906-4(4))* Outskirts Pr., Inc.
Dieterich, Veit-Jakobus. Religionslehrplan in Deutschland (1870-2000) Gegenstand und Konstruktion des Evangelischen Religionsunterrichts Im Religionspädagogischen Diskurs und in Den Amtlichen Vorgaben. 2006. (Arbeiten zur Religionspadagogik Ser.). (GER.). 735p. (C). 104.00 *(978-3-89971-324-4(9))* Vandenhoeck & Ruprecht GmbH & Co. KG DEU. Dist: ISD.
Dilmore, Pamela & Neinast, Helen R. Attentiveness: Being Present: Leader Guide. ldr.'s ed. 2006. (Living the Good Life Together Ser.). 62p. pap. 12.00 *(978-0-687-46550-7(8))* Abingdon Pr.
Dingwall, Cindy. More Bible Times with Kids: 200+ Bible-Based Activities to Use with Children. 2006. (Illus.). 154p. per. 24.00 *(978-0-687-49230-5(0))* Abingdon Pr.
Dockery, David S. Renewing Minds: Serving Church & Society Through Christian Higher Education, Revised & Updated. 2008. (ENG.). 240p. pap. 19.99 *(978-0-8054-4788-0(1)*, B&H Academic) B&H Publishing Group.
Dorrell, Jimmy & Dorrell, Janet. Plunge2Poverty: An Intensive Poverty Simulation Experience. 2007. (ENG.). 160p. pap. 14.99 *(978-1-59669-087-5(9))* New Hope Pubs.
Downey, Deane E. D. & Porter, Stanley E., eds. Christian Worldview & the Academic Disciplines: Crossing the Academy. 2009. (McMaster Divinity College Press General Ser.). 542p. pap. 53.00 *(978-1-60608-529-5(8)*, Pickwick Pubns.) Wipf & Stock Pubs.
Drache, Hiram M. A Century in the Park: Oak Grove Luthern School. 2006. 320p. 40.00 *(978-0-913163-40-5(6)*, DRA3406) Hobar Pubns.
Dunagan, Ann. The Mission Minded Child: Raising a New Generation to Fulfill God's Purpose. 2007. (ENG., Illus.). 255p. per. 14.99 *(978-1-932805-88-8(5))* Authentic Media.
Dunbar, David Michael. Dosing Froggy: Who Died & Made You God? 2010. (Illus.). 352p. pap. 18.95 *(978-1-4327-5924-7(8))* Outskirts Pr., Inc.
Durbin, Kara G. Parenting with Scripture: A Topical Guide for Teachable Moments. 2012. (ENG.). 256p. pap. 14.99 ***(978-0-8024-0849-5(4))*** Moody Pubs.

C

East, Thomas. Leadership for Catholic Youth Ministry: A Comprehensive Resource. 2009. 352p. pap. 27.95 (978-1-58595-732-3(1)) Twenty-Third Pubns./Bayard.

Easton, Laurine M. Crafting Faith: 101 Crafts to Help Kids Grow in Their Faith. 2008. pap. 15.95 (978-0-8294-2704-2(X)) Loyola Pr.

Eaton, Robert I. & Beecher, Mark. Becoming a Great Gospel Teacher: Bringing the Gospel Classroom to Life. 2007. xi, 185p. (978-1-59811-255-9(4)) Covenant Communications.

Eberle, Melda. Holidays: Holy or Hollow?, 1 vol. 2010. 334p. pap. 29.95 (978-1-4489-4415-6(5)) PublishAmerica, Inc.

EBS Adult Bible Study Guide. 3.15 (978-0-7673-4123-3(6)) LifeWay Christian Resources.

EBS Adult Commentary. 4.60 (978-0-7673-4958-1(X)) LifeWay Christian Resources.

EBS Adult Leader Guide. 4.00 (978-0-7673-4944-4(X)) LifeWay Christian Resources.

EBS Adult Leader Pack. 16.50 (978-0-7673-5086-0(3)) LifeWay Christian Resources.

EBS Adult Learner Guide. 1.50 (978-0-7673-4887-4(7)); 1.50 (978-0-7673-4930-7(X)) LifeWay Christian Resources.

Edwards, Grant. Passing the Baton: Guide Your Child to Follow Jesus. 2009. (ENG.). 143p. pap. 14.99 (978-0-7644-3875-2(1)) Group Publishing, Inc.

Ellis, Carl, Jr. Go Global: Beyond the Boundaries. 2010. 98p. stu. ed. 9.95 (978-0-940955-95-0(4)) UMI (Urban Ministries, Inc.).

Ellis, Lynne & Fields, Doug. Mission Trips from Start to Finish: How to Organize & Lead Impactful Mission Trips. 2008. 148p. pap. 49.00 incl. cd-rom (978-0-7644-6064-7(1)) Group Publishing, Inc.

Engle, Joel. The Exchange: Tired of Living the Christian Life on Your Own? 2007. (Illus.). 128p. pap. 7.95 (978-1-4158-5270-5(7)) LifeWay Christian Resources.

Ennis, Ralph. Relationships: Bringing Jesus into My World. 2008. (Illus.). 191p. pap. (978-1-60006-261-2(X)) NavPress Publishing Group.

Enns, Peter. Telling God's Story: A Parents' Guide to Teaching the Bible. 2011. (Telling God's Story Ser.). (ENG., Illus.). 140p. pap. 11.95 (978-1-933339-46-7(2), 333946) Peace Hill Pr.

Erler, H. Raphael. Winds of Change: Saint Mary's Press from 1957-1974. 2010. pap. (978-1-59982-023-1(4)) St. Mary's Pr.

Erves, Tonia. It Is Written Luke 19:46: Skits, Plays, & a Vacation Bible School Guide from the Old & New Testament. 2011. 64p. pap. 48.78 (978-1-4269-5251-7(1)) Trafford Publishing.

Esqueda, Octavio. Cuban Christian Theological Higher Education. 2010. 200p. pap. (978-3-8383-1925-4(7)) Lambert Academic Publishing.

Estep, James R. & Kim, Jonathan H., eds. Christian Formation: Integrating Theology & Human Development, 1 vol. 2010. (ENG.). 288p. 29.99 (978-0-8054-4838-2(1), B&H Academic) B&H Publishing Group.

Estep, James R., et al. A Theology for Christian Education. 2008. (ENG.). 320p. (C). 34.99 (978-0-8054-4457-5(2), B&H Academic) B&H Publishing Group.

Evans, Roderick L. The Teaching Ministry: Exploring the Teaching Office & Gift. 2009. 42p. pap. 9.95 (978-1-60141-051-1(4), 433649) Kingdom Builders Publishing.

Everett, Randel. The Letters of James & John: Real Faith. 2010. 136p. pap. (978-1-934731-55-0(2)) Baptistway.

FBS Youth Teacher. 3.35 (978-0-7673-4988-8(1)) LifeWay Christian Resources.

Ferguson, Nancy. Christian Educators' Guide to Evaluating & Developing Curriculum. 2008. 104p. per. 17.00 (978-0-8170-1523-7(X)) Judson Pr.

Fidellow, Edward. Getting Your Money's Worth Workbook. 2007. 8.00 (978-0-9772965-2-1(0)) Cross Mountain Pr.

Fider, Carol. Integration of Faith & Learning. 2009. 116p. pap. (978-3-639-06235-9(3)) VDM Verlag Dr. Mueller e.K.

First Place 4 Health Staff. Leader's Guide. ldr.'s ed. 2008. (First Place Ser.). (ENG.). 128p. pap. 19.99 (978-0-8307-4525-8(4)) Gospel Light Pubns.

Fischer, Roland E. Bildung im Gottesdienst: Die Bibelschule der Adventgemeinde. 2008. (Friedensauer Schriftenreihe. Reihe A: Theologie Ser.). 272p. pap. 65.95 (978-3-631-57478-2(9)) Lang, Peter GmbH, Europäischer Verlag der Wissenschaften DEU. Dist: Lang, Peter.

Five Practices for Children. 2011. 130p. pap. 16.00 (978-1-4267-1642-3(7)) Abingdon Pr.

Floy, James. Bible Morality; or, Elements of Moral Science for Sunday-Schools. 2006. 292p. per. 23.99 (978-1-4255-2715-0(9)) MPublishing.

Francis, Leslie J. & Astley, Jeff. Children, Churches & Christian Learning: A Practical Resource. 304p. 33.00 (978-0-281-05532-6(7)) SPCK Publishing GBR. Dist: Pilgrim Pr., The/United Church Pr.

Frank, Jona, photos by. Right: Portraits from the Evangelical Ivy League. 2008. (ENG.). 144p. 35.00 (978-0-8118-8962-9(9)) Chronicle Bks. LLC.

Frater, George. Our Humanist Heritage. 2010. 450p. pap. 24.99 (978-1-60957-364-5(1)) Xulon Pr., Inc.

Friedrich, Laura Dean. Equipped to Lead: Children's Sunday School Guide. 2008. 96p. pap. 16.00 (978-0-88177-542-6(8)) Upper Room Bks.

Funk, Camille. Learning to Read Using the Book of Morman Volume One: 1 Nephi Through 2 Nephi 26. 2007. (Learning to Read Using the Book of Mormon Ser.). (Illus.). 220p. pap. 19.99 (978-1-59955-002-2(4)) Cedar Fort, Inc./CFI Distribution.

G-Man. Where Are the Teachers? 2009. 96p. pap. 10.99 (978-1-60791-462-4(X)) Xulon Pr., Inc.

Galindo, Israel. How to Be the Best Christian Study Group Leader Ever in the Whole History of the Universe. 2006. (Illus.). 160p. pap. 16.00 (978-0-8170-1500-8(0)) Judson Pr.

Galindo, Israel & Canaday, Marty. Planning for Christian Education Formation: A Community of Faith Approach. 2010. 144p. pap. 16.99 (978-0-8272-3011-8(7)) Chalice Pr.

Gee, Joy. Ants Work Best Together: 31 Object Lessons from Nature. 2007. (Illus.). 79p. per. (978-0-7880-2411-5(6)) CSS Publishing Co.

Gee, Martha Bettis. Piece Work / Peace Work: Working Together for Peace & Sudan: 2009-2010 Mission Study for Children (Teacher's Guide) 2009. (ENG.). 100p. (J). pap. 7.00 (978-1-933663-34-0(0), WD/GBGM Bks.) General Board of Global Ministries, The United Methodist Church.

Gerdes, Dan. Coaching for Character. 160p. pap. 10.99 (978-1-58169-126-9(2), Evergreen Pr.) Genesis Communications, Inc.

Glavich, Mary Kathleen. Prayer First: A New Agenda for Catholic Schools. 2008. 144p. pap. (978-1-58595-703-3(8)) Twenty-Third Pubns./Bayard.

God's Hidden Treasures. Date not set. pap. 5.95 (978-0-87162-642-4(X)) Warner Pr. Pubs.

Gospel Light Publications Staff. Baby Beginnings Nursery Smart Pages. 2008. (ENG.). 272p. 39.99 (978-0-8307-4498-5(3)) Gospel Light Pubns.

Gothard, Bill. Commands of Christ, Series 7. 2007. 84p. 10.00 (978-0-916888-33-6(9)) Institute in Basic Life Principles.

Goulooze, William. A Young People's Study of the Confession of Faith. 2011. 156p. 41.95 (978-1-258-01461-2(0)) Literary Licensing, LLC.

Green, Phil. SUBstance. 2010. 80p. pap. (978-1-84427-525-0(6)) Scripture Union.

Greenwood, Rebecca. Let Our Children Go. 2011. E-Book (978-1-61638-568-2(5), Charisma Hse.) Charisma Media.

Gregory, A. J. Silent Savior: Daring to Believe He's Still There. 2009. 192p. pap. 12.99 (978-0-8007-3285-1(5)) Revell.

Gregory, Frank. Never Alone. 2010. 72p. pap. 9.99 (978-0-88144-507-7(X)) Yorkshire Publishing Group.

Griffiths, Paul J. Intellectual Appetite: A Theological Grammar. 2009. 248p. pap. 24.95 (978-0-8132-1686-7(9)) Catholic Univ. of America Pr.

Group Publishing. Children's Ministry Pocket Guide to Special Needs: Quick Tips to Reach Every Child. 2008. 16p. pap. 12.99 (978-0-7644-3701-4(1)) Group Publishing, Inc.

Group Publishing, creator. Coloring Creations 2. 2007. (Illus.). 110p. per. 19.99 (978-0-7644-3506-5(X)) Group Publishing, Inc.

—Crafts: 110 Totally Awesome Crafts for All Ages. 2006. (Illus.). 127p. per. 17.99 (978-0-7644-3439-6(X), Group) Group Publishing, Inc.

—Mailable Follow-up Foto Frame. 2008. (Power Lab Ser.). (Illus.). 9.99 (978-5-557-52124-6(0)) Group Publishing, Inc.

—Paul & the Underground Church Leader Manual. 2009. (Rome: Paul & the Underground Church Ser.). (Illus.). 39p. pap. 9.99 (978-0-7644-3779-3(8)) Group Publishing, Inc.

—Shopkeeper Leader Manual. 2009. (Rome: Paul & the Underground Church Ser.). (Illus.). 70p. pap. 9.99 (978-0-7644-3778-6(X)) Group Publishing, Inc.

—Squeaky Beaker's Preschool Director Manual. 2008. (Power Lab Ser.). (Illus.). 35p. pap. 12.99 (978-0-7644-3577-5(9)) Group Publishing, Inc.

—Ultimate Director Go-to Guide. 2009. (Rome: Paul & the Underground Church Ser.). 14.99 (978-0-7644-3775-5(5)) Group Publishing, Inc.

Group Publishing Staff, contrib. by. Group's The Humongous Book of Preschool Ideas 2. 2008. pap. (978-0-7644-3813-4(1)) Group Publishing, Inc.

Group Publishing Staff & MOPS International, Inc Staff, contrib. by. Lively Bible Lessons for MOPPETS. 2007. pap. (978-0-7644-3573-7(6)) Group Publishing, Inc.

Guidelines for Leading Your Congregation 2009-2012 - Christian Education: Planning for Lifelong Faith Formation. 2008. 2.95 (978-0-687-64941-9(2)) Abingdon Pr.

Guidelines for Leading Your Congregation 2009-2012 - Lay Leader/Lay Member: Connecting Your Congregation & Your Annual Conference. 2008. 2.95 (978-0-687-64811-5(4)) Abingdon Pr.

Hadley, Suzanne. Faithgirlz! Handbook: How to Let Your Faith Shine Through, 1 vol. enl. rev. exp. ed. 2012. (Faithgirlz! Ser.). (ENG.). 160p. (J). pap. 7.99 (978-0-310-72697-5(2)) Zonderkidz.

Hahn, Kimberly & Barber, Michael. Genesis to Jesus: Studying Scripture from the Heart of the Church. 2007. (Journey Through Scripture Ser.). (Illus.). 133p. per. 9.99 (978-0-86716-837-2(4), Servant Bks.) Franciscan Media.

Hahn, Scott & Socias, James. Comprender Las Escrituras: Curso Completo para el Estudio de la Biblia. 2010. (SPA.). (978-1-936045-33-4(8)) Midwest Theological Forum.

—Faith & Revelation: Knowing God Through Sacred Scripture. 2009. (978-1-936045-01-3(X)) Midwest Theological Forum.

—Understanding the Scriptures. 2010. (978-1-936045-12-9(5)) Midwest Theological Forum.

Haidle, David, et al. God Made the World & Me: Thirteen Comprehensive 6-In-1 Curriculum Lessons: Includes Special Centers for Older Students & Younger Students. 2009. (Illus.). 160p. (J). pap. (978-0-89051-563-1(8)) Master Bks.

Hailer, Gretchen. Echoing the Word: An Introductory Catechist Formation Process. 2008. 96p. pap. 19.95 (978-0-8091-4563-8(4)) Paulist Pr.

Hailer, Gretchen & Pacatte, Rose. Our Media World: Teaching Kids K-8 about Faith & Media. 2010. (978-0-8198-5441-4(7)) Pauline Bks. & Media.

Halverson, Delia. Ready, Set, Teach! Training & Supporting Volunteers in Christian Education. 2010. (Illus.). 96p. pap. 15.00 (978-1-4267-0937-1(4)) Abingdon Pr.

Hamilton, Eleanor. Hide His Word in Their Hearts: Ways You Can Encourage Your Students to Learn God's Word. 2007. cd-rom (978-0-9755173-6-9(8)) Autumn Light Pubns.

Hamilton, Eleanor P. The Narrow Gate: Where Jesus Walked. 2011. ring bd. 25.00 (978-0-9755173-4-5(1)) Autumn Light Pubns.

—Passing the Standard: A History of the Restoration Movement for 4th & 5th Graders. 2006. cd-rom 8.00 (978-0-9755173-5-2(X)) Autumn Light Pubns.

Hammer, Randy, et al. What's So Amazing about Polar Bears? Teaching Kids to Care for Creation. 2011. (978-0-8298-1877-2(4)) Pilgrim Pr., The/United Church Pr.

Hampsch, John H. Miracle Power at Your Fingertips. 24p. pap. 1.25 (978-1-57918-085-0(X), 7170) Queenship Publishing Co.

—Prayer with Rolled-Up Sleeves: Rescuing Your Wayward Loved Ones. 24p. pap. 1.25 (978-1-57918-103-1(1), 7185) Queenship Publishing Co.

—Seven Misunderstandings about Repentance. 24p. pap. 1.25 (978-1-57918-098-0(1), 7183) Queenship Publishing Co.

—Three Ways to Carry a Cross. 24p. pap. 1.25 (978-1-57918-079-9(5), 7164) Queenship Publishing Co.

Hancock, Jim & International Justice Mission. The Justice Mission: A Video-Enhanced Curriculum Reflecting the Heart of God for the Oppressed of the World, 1 vol. 2006. (ENG.). (gr. 13). pap. 37.99 incl. DVD (978-0-310-27707-1(8)) Zondervan.

Hanson, Buddy. How to de-Program Yourself from All of the Blasphemous Ideas You Learned in Public School. 2009. 440p. pap. 25.00 (978-0-9771773-5-6(1)) Hanson Group.

Hargestam, Karl. The Assignment Workbook. 2010. 82p. pap. 9.99 (978-0-88144-519-0(3)) Yorkshire Publishing Group.

Hauerwas, Stanley M. The State of the University: Academic Knowledges & the Knowledge of God. 2007. (Illuminations: Theory & Religion Ser.). (ENG.). 232p. 110.95 (978-1-4051-6247-0(3)); pap. 44.95 (978-1-4051-6248-7(1)) Wiley, John & Sons, Inc. (Wiley-Blackwell).

Hayden, Wesley. Weekly Nuggets of Wisdom. 2007. 208p. pap. 19.95 (978-0-9764945-9-1(0)) Williams, Benjamin Publishing.

Haynes, Brian. Shift: What It Takes to Finally Reach Families Today. 2009. pap. (978-0-7644-3898-1(0)) Group Publishing, Inc.

Hays, Rita B. The Children's Minister. 2008. 127p. per. 13.00 (978-0-88177-527-3(4)) Discipleship Resources.

Head, Heno. Simple Science Object Talks: Over 100 Science Object Talks You Can Do. 2007. (Object Talks Ser.). (Illus.). 224p. (J). pap. 19.99 (978-0-7847-1982-4(9)) Standard Publishing.

Heard, James. Inside Alpha: Explorations in Evangelism. 2010. (Studies in Evangelical History & Thought Ser.). 288p. pap. 33.00 (978-1-60899-450-2(3), Wipf and Stock) Wipf & Stock Pubs.

Heath, Robert C. How Are You Doing That? 2008. 148p. pap. 14.99 (978-0-88144-325-7(5)) Yorkshire Publishing Group.

Hedges, Andrew A. Creative Bible Lessons on the Trinity: 12 Sessions to Help Students Understand Their Place in God's Story: Perfect for Sunday School, Youth Meetings, Small Groups, & More!, 1 vol. 2012. (Creative Bible Lessons Ser.). (ENG.). 160p. pap. 16.99 (978-0-310-67119-0(1)) Zondervan.

Heer, Ken. Ephesians: Lectio Divina for Youth. 2009. (Ancient Faith Ser.). (ENG.). 80p. pap. 7.99 (978-0-8341-5028-7(X), 9780834150287) Beacon Hill Pr. of Kansas City.

Heft, S.M., James L & Hallinan, Kevin, eds. Engineering Education & Practice: Embracing a Catholic Vision. 2011. (ND Studies in Ethics & Culture Ser.). (ENG., Illus.). 240p. pap. 34.00 (978-0-268-03110-7(X)) Univ. of Notre Dame Pr.

Hegeman, Johan, et al. Practice & Profile: Christian Formation for Vocation. 2011. 338p. pap. 37.00 (978-1-61097-091-4(8), Wipf and Stock) Wipf & Stock Pubs.

Henderson, Dorothy. Learning God's Stories Together: Intergenerational Program for Church & Home. 2007. (ENG., Illus.). 160p. per. 24.95 (978-1-55145-559-4(5)) Wood Lake Publishing, Inc. CAN. Dist: Westminster John Knox Pr.

Henry, Barbara. Making Disciples in Your Community: Coming Together to Grow in Christ. 2009. (Following God Discipleship Ser.). (ENG.). 176p. (gr. 11). pap. 14.99 (978-0-89957-346-5(0)) AMG Pubs.

Herbst, Michael & Rosenstock Roland, eds. Zeitumstände: Bildung und Mission: Festschrift für Jörg Ohlemacher zum 65. Geburtstag. 2009. (Greifswalder theologische Forschungen Ser.). (GER., Illus.). 304p. 79.95 (978-3-631-59119-2(5)) Lang, Peter GmbH, Europäischer Verlag der Wissenschaften DEU. Dist: Lang, Peter.

Hesperides. Education for Christian Service. 2007. 364p. per. (978-1-4067-6477-2(9), Hesperides Pr.) Read Bks.

Hess, Lisa M. Artisanal Theology: Intentional Formation in Radically Covenantal Companionship. 2009. 150p. pap. 19.00 (978-1-55635-875-3(X), Cascade Bks.) Wipf & Stock Pubs.

Hoch, Ronald E. & Smith, David P. Old School, New Clothes: The Cultural Blindness of Christian Education. 2011. 166p. pap. 19.00 (978-1-61097-161-4(2), Wipf and Stock) Wipf & Stock Pubs.

Hockett, Richard S. Foundations of Wisdom. 2009. 136p. pap. 14.99 (978-1-60791-713-7(0)) Xulon Pr., Inc.

Hoeck, Andreas & Manhardt, Laurie. Come & See: Ezekiel, Hebrews, Revelation. 2010. 224p. pap. 19.95 (978-1-931018-65-4(0)) Emmaus Road Publishing.

Hoffhines, Emily. Bible Lessons with Babies. 2007. 80p. pap. 12.95 (978-0-615-17178-4(8)) Hoffhines, Emily.

Hoffmann, Mary Byrne. Catechesis in a Multi-Media World: Connecting to Today's Students. 2011. pap. (978-0-8091-4708-3(4)) Paulist Pr.

Holford, Karen. 100 Creative Ways to Learn Memory Verses. 2009. (978-0-8127-0505-8(X)) Autumn Hse. Publishing Co.

Holladay, Tom, et al. The Bible: 11 Core Truths to Build Your Life On, 1 vol. 2008. (Foundations Ser.). (ENG., Illus.). 80p. (gr. 13). pap. 6.99 (978-0-310-27670-8(5)) Zondervan.

—Holy Spirit: Small Group Study, 1 vol. 2008. (Foundations Ser.). (ENG., Illus.). 80p. pap. 6.99 (978-0-310-27676-0(4)) Zondervan.

Holmen, Mark & Teixeira, David. Take It Home: Inspiration & Events to Help Parents Spiritually Transform Their Children. 2007. (ENG.). 160p. 49.99 (978-0-8307-4491-6(6)) Gospel Light Pubns.

Holzapfel, Richard Neitzel & Jackson, Kent P., eds. Teach One Another Words of Wisdom: Selections from the Religious Educator. 2008. (Illus.). pap. (978-0-8425-2717-0(6), Brigham Young Univ. Religious Studies Ctr.) Brigham Young Univ.

Hooper, A. Duane. Christian School Teacher: Ministry of Caring for Kids. 2008. 284p. pap. 16.99 (978-1-60791-138-8(8)) Xulon Pr., Inc.

Horn, Christine Van. God in Schools. 2010. 226p. 25.99 (978-1-60957-342-3(0)) Xulon Pr., Inc.

Hough, Lee. Common Sense for Christians. 2008. 176p. 24.50 (978-1-60693-345-9(0), Strategic Bk. Publishing) AEG Literary Publishing Services, Inc.

House, H. Wayne & Habermas, Ronald T. Introduction to Christian Education & Formation, 1 vol. 2008. (ENG.). 256p. 29.99 (978-0-310-27426-1(5)) Zondervan.

Howard, Rosetta. Learning to Play Is Playing to Learn. 2006. 124p. per. 10.99 (978-1-60034-608-8(1)) Xulon Pr., Inc.

Hudson, Anneke O. Bevilacqua. 2007. 212p. per. 14.99 (978-1-60477-332-3(4)) Xulon Pr., Inc.

Huebsch, Bill & Anslinger, Leisa. Great Expectations: A Pastoral Guide for Partnering with Parents: For Catechists & Teachers, Pastors, Principals, & Parish Catechetical Leaders. 2010. (Illus.). 58p. pap. (978-1-58595-752-1(6)) Twenty-Third Pubns./Bayard.

Huntington, John T. Our Schools & Colleges by Rev John T Huntington. 2011. 36p. pap. 11.99 (978-1-4181-9505-2(7)) MPublishing.

Husmann, Bä, et al. Das Eigene finden: Eine qualitative Studie zur Religiosität Jugendlicher. Arbeiten zur Religionspädagogik 36. 2008. (Arbeiten zur Religionspadagogik Ser.). (GER.). 240p. (C). 62.00 (978-3-89971-471-5(7)) Vandenhoeck & Ruprecht GmbH & Co. KG DEU. Dist: ISD.

Indiana. (Rand Mcnally Wall Maps Ser.). 229.00 (978-0-528-86137-6(9)) Rand McNally.

Iowa. (Proseries Wall Map Ser.). 229.00 (978-0-528-85858-1(0)) Rand McNally.

Iwas, Alya. Adult Identity Formation Model in the Syriac Orthodox Church. 2011. 116p. pap. (978-3-8433-6389-1(7)) Lambert Academic Publishing.

Jackson, Brenda S. & Hicks, Patricia. Crossroads. 2010. 160p. pap. 11.99 (978-1-933972-20-6(3)) PriorityONE Pubns.

Jackson, Kent P. & Skinner, Andrew C., eds. A Witness for the Restoration: Essays in Honor of Robert J. Matthews. 2007. (Illus.). 24.95 (978-0-8425-2676-0(5), Brigham Young Univ. Religious Studies Ctr.) Brigham Young Univ.

Jackson, Thais/ Sherell. Where Is God? Jackson, Thais/ Sherell, ed. 2011. (Illus.). 24p. (J). pap. 15.00 (978-0-9814774-3-5(7)) N-Spired Productions.

Jacobs, Rivkah L. Pieces of the Puzzle. 201p. 17.95 (978-1-56871-246-8(4)) Targum Pr., Inc.

James, Michael, et al. Education's Highest Aim: Teaching & Learning through a Spirituality of Communion. 2010. 152p. pap. 14.95 (978-1-56548-336-1(7)) New City Pr.

Jerusalemkidz Outreach Ministry & Sheffield, Victoria. The Alpha Curriculum: (Christian Based Learning) 2011. (Illus.). (J). pap. 25.00 (978-0-578-08515-9(1)) Aardvark Global Publishing.

Jingling, Kathy & McGhee, Quentin, eds. Children's Ministry- Student Manual. 2nd ed. 2011. (Illus.). spiral bd. 25.00 (978-1-931984-64-5(6)) Faith & Action Team.

Johnson, Alvin W. & Yost, Frank H. Separation of Church & State in the United States. 2009. (ENG.). 287p. pap. 50.00 (978-0-8166-5965-4(6)) Univ. of Minnesota Pr.

Johnson, Heather. The Precious Teacup. 2011. 32p. pap. 12.99 (978-1-4567-3144-1(0)) AuthorHouse.

Johnson, Kevin. Follow: Walk in the Rhythm of Jesus, 1 vol. 2009. (Higher Ser.). (ENG.). 112p. pap. 8.99 (978-0-310-28264-8(0)) Zondervan.

—Soar, 1 vol. 2009. (Higher Ser.). (ENG.). 112p. pap. 8.99 (978-0-310-28267-9(5)) Zondervan.

—Thrive, 1 vol. 2009. (Higher Ser.). (ENG.). 112p. pap. 8.99 (978-0-310-28265-5(9)) Zondervan.

Joiner, Reggie. Orange Leader Handbook: A Think Orange Companion. 2010. (Illus.). 183p. E-Book (978-1-4347-0186-2(7)) Kingsway Pubns.

—The Think Orange: Imagine the Impact When Church & Family Collide... 2009. (ENG.). 272p. 21.99 (978-1-4347-6483-6(4)) Cook, David C.

Jones, Charles Colcock. The Religious Instruction of Negroes. 38p. reprint ed. lib. bdg. 88.00 (978-0-7222-0859-5(6)) Library Reprints, Inc.

—The Religious Instruction of the Negroes. 2008. (Civil War Ser.). (ENG.). 56p. pap. 9.95 (978-1-4290-1179-2(3)) Applewood Bks.

Jones, Timothy Paul & Jones, Timothy P. Family Ministry Field Guide: How the Church Can Equip Parents to Make Disciples. 2011. (Illus.). 224p. (978-0-89827-457-8(5)) Wesleyan Publishing Hse.

Jongeneel, J. A. B. Christian Mission & Education in Modern China, Japan, & Korea: Historical Studies. 2009. xii, 177p. pap. 53.95 (978-3-631-58862-8(3)) Lang, Peter GmbH, Europäischer Verlag der Wissenschaften DEU. Dist: Lang, Peter.

Jossey-Bass Publishers Staff. Inspiration from Parker Palmer: Pd ToolKit. 2008. 1072p. 74.03 *(978-0-470-42053-9(7),* Jossey-Bass) Wiley, John & Sons, Inc.
Joyner, Alex. Where Do I Go Now, God? 2007. 95p. pap. 13.00 *(978-0-687-33556-5(6))* Abingdon Pr.
Kansas. (Proseries Wall Map Ser.). 229.00 *(978-0-528-85859-8(9))* Rand McNally.
Kawasaki, Shauna. My Eternal Family: 2009 Activities for Children. 2008. 64p. 14.95 *(978-1-60641-002-8(4))* Deseret Bk. Co.
Kee, Florence R. How to Reach the Children for Jesus. 2011. 60p. 36.95 ***(978-1-258-08586-5(0))*** Literary Licensing, LLC.
Keeley, Robert J. Helping Our Children Grow in Faith: How the Church Can Nurture the Spiritual Development of Kids. 2008. 160p. pap. 15.00 *(978-0-8010-6829-4(0))* Baker Bks.
Kelly, Maureen A. Call to Celebrate: Confirmation. 2008. (Illus.). iv, 140p. (J). pap. *(978-0-15-901662-6(2))* Harcourt Religion Pubs.
Kenlaw, Will. Fathers Guide to Raising Daughters for W. 2006. (ENG.). 21.99 *(978-1-60034-725-2(8));* pap. 13.99 *(978-1-60034-724-5(X))* Xulon Pr., Inc.
Kentucky. (Proseries Wall Map Ser.). 229.00 *(978-0-528-85860-4(2))* Rand McNally.
Kern, Betty J. Personal Wellness for the Christian College Student. 2008. (Personal Wellness Ser.). (ENG., Illus.). 101p. spiral bd. 34.95 *(978-1-932802-30-6(4),* Holy Macro! Bks.) Tickling Keys, Inc.
Key, Donald. A Blueprint for Christian Education: Knowing & Understanding Those You Teach. 2006. (ENG.). 204p. per. 24.95 *(978-1-4241-5860-7(5))* PublishAmerica, Inc.
King, Paul L. Finding Your Niche: 12 Keys to Opening God's Doors for Your Life. 2008. 184p. pap. 12.95 *(978-0-9785352-8-5(6))* Word & Spirit Pr.
Kirkpatrick, Diane. 52 Weeks of Family Night 2: Scripture Study Edition. 2009. *(978-1-60641-198-8(5))* Deseret Bk. Co.
Kowalczuk, Ruth. I Came Only for English. 2007. 180p. per. 13.99 *(978-1-60266-704-4(7))* Xulon Pr., Inc.
Kumalo, Raymond Simangaliso. From Sheep to Sheperds. 2011. 304p. pap. ***(978-3-8443-1244-7(7))*** Lambert Academic Publishing.
Kunzman, Robert. Write These Laws on Your Children: Inside the World of Conservative Christian Homeschooling, 1 vol. (ENG.). 2010. 240p. pap. 20.00 *(978-0-8070-3292-3(1))* 2009. 256p. 27.95 *(978-0-8070-3291-6(3))* Beacon Pr.
Kurth, Erwin W. Catechetical Helps. (CHI.). 187p. pap. 5.00 *(978-0-570-09979-6(X),* 16-6038) Concordia Publishing Hse.
Kyere, David S. Yes I Can. 2011. 108p. pap. 11.99 *(978-1-61215-489-3(1))* Xulon Pr., Inc.
Kyle, Margaret. Bible Stories for All Ages - Year A: With Activities for the Very Young. 2007. (ENG., Illus.). 256p. per. 34.00 *(978-1-55145-546-4(3))* Wood Lake Publishing, Inc. CAN. Dist: Westminster John Knox Pr.
Lachmann, Rainer, et al. Theologische Schlüsselbegriffe: Biblisch - systematisch - didaktisch. 2010. (Theologie fur lehrerinnen und Lehrer Ser.). (GER.). 408p. (C). pap. 36.00 *(978-3-525-61420-4(9))* Vandenhoeck & Ruprecht GmbH & Co. KG DEU. Dist: ISD.
Laing, Sam & Laing, Geri. Raising Awesome Kids — Reloaded: Becoming the Most Important Influence in Your Child's Life. 2009. 270p. pap. 15.00 *(978-1-57782-234-9(X))* Discipleship Pubns. International.
Lamb, Pat. Let the Children Come. 2009. 175p. pap. 12.99 *(978-1-60696-397-5(X))* Tate Publishing & Enterprises, LLC.
Lamoreaux, Antoinette Abernethy. The Unfolding Life: A Study of Development with Reference to Religious Training. 2007. 88p. per. *(978-1-4065-2579-3(0))* Dodo Pr.
Lantinga, Nick. Christian Higher Education in the Global Context: Implications for Curriculum, Pedagogy, & Administration: Proceedings of the International Conference, International Association for the Promotion of Christian Higher Education, 15-19 November 2006, Granada, Nicaragua. 2008. 385p. pap. *(978-0-932914-78-1(0))* Dordt College Pr.
Lassiter, Perry. The Gospel of Luke: Good News of Great Joy. 2009. 188p. pap. *(978-1-934731-39-0(0))* Baptistway.
Latkovich, Sallie. Excavando en el Significado de la Biblia: Más Allá de Las Palabras. 2011.Tr. of Mining the Meaning of the Bible: Beyond the Literal Word. (SPA.). 64p. *(978-0-7648-2050-2(8))* Liguori Pubns.
Laurie, Watson Manhardt. Come & See Wisdom. 2009. 228p. 19.95 *(978-1-931018-55-5(3))* Emmaus Road Publishing.
Le Fevre, Brian J. Cracked Foundation. 2011. 88p. pap. 10.99 ***(978-1-61379-031-1(7))*** Xulon Pr., Inc.
Lebar, Lois. Educacion Que Es Cristiana: Una Introduccion a la Filosofia de la Educacion Cristiana. Anderas-Lundquist, Kerstin & Anderas-Solgevik, Agneta, trs. 2009. (SPA., Illus.). 269p. pap. 12.95 *(978-1-58802-421-3(0))* Editorial Patmos.
Leckey, Dolores R. The Laity & Christian Education: Apostolicam Actuositatem, Gravissimum Educationis. 2007. (Rediscovering Vatican II Ser.). 113p. per. 14.95 *(978-0-8091-4220-0(1),* 4220-1) Paulist Pr.
Lee, Constance King Nebuchadnezzar: The First Biblical Werewolf. 2011. 336p. pap. 22.01 ***(978-1-4567-3281-3(1))*** AuthorHouse.
Lee, HeeKap. Faith-Based Education That Constructs. 2010. 324p. pap. 36.00 *(978-1-60608-674-2(X),* Wipf and Stock) Wipf & Stock Pubs.
Lefgren, Beth. Object Lessons Made Easy: Memorable Ideas for Gospel Teaching. 2010. 128p. pap. 12.99 *(978-1-60641-899-4(8))* Deseret Bk. Co.
LifeWay Press Staff, contrib. by. Colossians: Navigating Successfully Through Cultural Chaos: Connect with God, Connect with Others, Connect with Life. 2008. 175p. pap. 13.95 *(978-1-4158-6712-9(7))* LifeWay Christian Resources.
Light, Joel. Field Guide to Christian Environmental Education: A Complete Guide to Creation Care. 2008. 114p. pap. 19.95 *(978-1-58518-664-8(3),* Healthy Learning) Coaches Choice.
Lingo, Susan. Scripture Memory Makers. 2007. 108p. pap. 13.99 *(978-0-9760696-5-2(2))* Lingo, Susan Bks.
Lingo, Susan L. Disciple Makers. 2008. 132p. pap. 19.99 *(978-0-9760696-6-9(0))* Lingo, Susan Bks.
—Faith Finders. 2008. 132p. pap. 19.99 *(978-0-9760696-7-6(9))* Lingo, Susan Bks.
—Hope Finders. 2008. 132p. pap. 19.99 *(978-0-9760696-8-3(7))* Lingo, Susan Bks.
—Joy Builders. 2008. 132p. pap. 19.99 *(978-1-935147-00-8(5))* Lingo, Susan Bks.
—Kids-Tell-'Em Bible Stories. 2008. 116p. pap. 14.99 *(978-1-935147-05-3(6))* Lingo, Susan Bks.
—Make & Serve. 2007. 116p. pap. 10.99 *(978-0-9760696-0-7(1))* Lingo, Susan Bks.
—Making Scripture Memorable. 2007. 132p. (gr. -1 — 1). pap. 12.99 *(978-0-9760696-1-4(X))* Lingo, Susan Bks.
—Peace Makers. 2008. 132p. pap. 19.99 *(978-1-935147-01-5(3))* Lingo, Susan Bks.
—Power Boosters. 2008. 132p. pap. 19.99 *(978-1-935147-02-2(1))* Lingo, Susan Bks.
—Servant Leaders. 2008. 132p. pap. 19.99 *(978-1-935147-03-9(X))* Lingo, Susan Bks.
—Worship Wow! 2008. 128p. pap. 14.99 *(978-1-935147-04-6(8))* Lingo, Susan Bks.
—20/20 Crafts & Object Talks That Teach about God's Power. 2007. 96p. pap. 12.99 *(978-0-9760696-3-8(6))* Lingo, Susan Bks.
Lockman, Diane B. Trivium Mastery: How to Give Your Child an Authentic Classical Home Education. 2009. 312p. pap. 21.95 *(978-1-4327-3328-5(1))* Outskirts Pr., Inc.
Loop, Katherine A. Beyond Numbers: A Practical Guide to Teaching Math Biblically. 2nd ed. 2011. (Illus.). 116p. pap. 8.99 ***(978-0-9773611-3-7(6))*** Christian Perspective.
Louisiana. (Rand Mcnally Wall Maps Ser.). 229.00 *(978-0-528-86150-5(6))* Rand McNally.
Lucia, Tercilio Díaz. Vision Juvenil Cristian: Despertando al Caimán Dormido. 2010. 52p. pap. 10.64 *(978-1-4251-8666-1(1))* Trafford Publishing.
LW Bible Discoverers. 1.55 *(978-0-7673-5376-2(5))* LifeWay Christian Resources.
LW Bible Discoverers Teacher. 3.75 *(978-0-7673-5418-9(4))* LifeWay Christian Resources.
LW Bible Learners Teacher. 3.75 *(978-0-7673-5474-5(5))* LifeWay Christian Resources.
LW Bible Searchers Teacher. 3.75 *(978-0-7673-5362-5(5))* LifeWay Christian Resources.
LW Directions Bible Studies for Adults 18-24. 1.55 *(978-0-7673-4562-C(2))* LifeWay Christian Resources.
Lyerly-Wiener, Michelle. The Brimstone Legacy: the Misadventures of Brimstone Biblical Academy. 2009. 206p. pap. 17.95 *(978-0-557-08461-6(X))* Lulu Enterprises Inc.
Lyle, JaNell. Men of Valor: Overcoming Fear, Doubt & Unbelief. 2007. per. 8.95 *(978-0-9778261-4-8(7))* Truth Pubs.
Lyons, Gabe & Herbst, Norton. The Whole Gospel Vol. 3: Revisiting Our Message to the World, 1 vol. 2010. (Q Society Room Ser.). (ENG.). 112p. pap., instr.'s gde. ed. 9.99 *(978-0-310-32519-2(6))* Zondervan.
Macelintal, Diana. The Eucharist. 2009. (Illus.). 136p. spiral bd., instr.'s gde. ed. 26.25 *(978-0-88489-765-1(6))* St. Mary's Pr.
MacPherson, Ryan C., et al, eds. Telling the Next Generation: The Evangelical Lutheran Synod's Vision for Christian Education, 1918-2011 & Beyond. 2011. (Illus.). 480p. pap. 23.95 *(978-0-931057-01-4(9))* Lutheran Synod Bk. Co.
Mark, R. Joshua. Returning to Joy: A Self-Care Guide to Overcoming Depression. 234p. pap. 14.99 *(978-1-56871-236-9(7))* Targum Pr., Inc.
Marshall, Andrea. Remember Remember: Teaching Memory Verses to Children. 2010. (Click Ser.). 64p. pap. *(978-1-905564-75-0(9))* Good Bk. Co.
Martineau, Mariette, et al. Intergenerational Faith Formation: All Ages Learning Together. 2008. (Illus.). 160p. pap. 19.95 *(978-1-58595-653-1(8))* Twenty-Third Pubns./Bayard.
Martins Miller, Susan. You-Can-Do-It Family Ministry Events: Building Faith & Community in the Families of Your Church. 2007. 128p. (J). per. 15.99 *(978-0-7847-1976-3(4))* Standard Publishing.
Maselli, Christopher P. N., et al. 180 Faith-Charged Games for Children's Ministry. 2008. (ENG.). 192p. (gr. k-6). pap. 15.99 *(978-1-60418-113-5(3),* Carson-Dellosa Christian) Carson-Dellosa Publishing, LLC.
Mathson, Patricia L. Plant the Seed: Sharing the Gospels with Children. 2011. *(978-0-7648-2009-0(5))* Liguori Pubns.
Matlock, Mark. Raising Wise Children. 2012. (ENG.). 176p. pap. 12.99 ***(978-0-310-66937-1(5))*** Zondervan.
Matthiesen, Michael. Sidewalk Sundaes on Saturday. 2008. 28p. pap. 10.99 *(978-0-88144-307-3(7))* Yorkshire Publishing Group.
Maxwell, Chris & Standard Publishing Staff. Season One: Episodes 27-39. Cain, Kristi & Derico, Laura, eds. 2008. (Faith Cafe Ser.). (ENG., Illus.). 64p. pap., instr.'s gde. ed. 14.99 *(978-0-7847-2205-3(6))* Standard Publishing.
—Season One: Episodes 27-39 - Participant's Guide. Cain, Kristi & Derico, Laura, eds. 2008. (Faith Cafe Ser.). (ENG., Illus.). 32p. pap. 3.99 *(978-0-7847-2206-0(4))* Standard Publishing.
May, David M. Easter Confessions. 2009. pap. *(978-0-9821806-5-5(9))* NextSunday Resources.
May, Scottie & Kenney, Cindy. Children's Curriculum for Grades 1-6. Date not set. (Nineteen Ninety-Eight Fifty-Day Spiritual Adventure Ser.). (Illus.). 128p. wbk. ed. 25.00 *(978-1-57849-057-8(X))* Mainstay Church Resources.
May, Scottie, et al. Children's Curriculum for Grades 1-6. Date not set. (50-Day Spiritual Adventure Ser.). (Illus.). 128p. pap., wbk. ed. 25.00 *(978-1-57849-016-5(2))* Chapel of the Air.
Mazariegos, Emilio. Seducido Por El Crucificado. 224p. 8.95 *(978-958-607-763-7(2))* Sociedad de San Pablo COL. Dist: St Pauls/Alba Hse. Pubs.
McClendon, Bernice M. I'm in His Hands: The Lord & I. 2011. 40p. pap. 16.95 ***(978-1-4626-2491-1(X))*** PublishAmerica, Inc.
McCoy, Terrell. Why They Must Go: A Biblical Mandate for Seventh-day Adventist Christian Education. 2011. 100p. pap. 11.95 *(978-1-4502-7300-8(9))* iUniverse, Inc.
McCullar, Michael D. Stewardship: A Way of Living. 2009. pap. *(978-0-9821806-9-3(1))* NextSunday Resources.
McCulley, Murriell. Beyond the Classroom: Teach for Life. 2007. (Illus.). 154p. pap. ***(978-7-7745-7192-9(2))*** Somers, William F.
McDonald, Glenn. Living Beyond the Sanctuary. 2008. pap. 14.99 *(978-1-932902-78-5(3))* FaithWalk Publishing.
McDowell, Josh. Christ up Close & Personal: Youth Group 8 Session Leader Guide. 2006. 128p. (YA). 17.99 *(978-1-932587-89-0(6))* Green Key Bks.
—Christ up Close & Personal / Youth Group Course Kit. 2006. 128p. (YA). DVD 129.99 *(978-1-932587-88-3(8))* Green Key Bks.
McKenzie, Janet. Communion with the Saints: A Family Preparation Program for First Communion & Beyond in the Spirit of St. Therese. 2007. 152p. (J). per. 27.95 *(978-1-934185-18-6(3))* Biblio Resource Pubns., Inc.
McLeod, Frank E. Whatcha' See? Are You Getting Used to the Dark? 2010. 134p. 22.50 *(978-1-60911-141-0(9),* Eloquent Bks.) AEG Literary Publishing Services, Inc.
McNeill, Leon A., et al. The Way of Life: The Colportage Library V1, No. 7, June 15 1895. 2011. 130p. 40.95 ***(978-1-258-05957-6(6))*** Literary Licensing, LLC.
Mejia, Martin. 'Conquista' 2008. (SPA.). 136p. pap. 19.95 *(978-1-58909-515-1(4))* Bookstand Publishing.
Melick, Jr., Richard R., Richard R & Melick, Shera. Teaching that Transforms: Facilitating Life Change through Adult Bible Teaching, 1 vol. 2010. (ENG.). 352p. 29.99 *(978-0-8054-4856-6(X),* B&H Academic) B&H Publishing Group.
Mercadante, Fred T. Senior High Ministry That Works: A Parish-Based Initiation Model. 2008. 160p. pap. *(978-1-58595-704-0(6))* Twenty-Third Pubns./Bayard.
Merken, Howard & Merken M.S., Casandra. Beyond Classical: The Next Step in Christian Education. 2011. 140p. pap. 11.95 ***(978-1-61507-721-2(5))*** Cross Bks. Publishing.
Michael, Sheehan. Apologetics & Catholic Doctrine: Catholic Classics. 2009. (Illus.). 686p. pap. *(978-1-905574-45-2(2))* Baronius Pr. Ltd.
Miller, Janet I., et al. Forming Ministers for Whole Community Faith Formation. 2006. 100p. *(978-0-89390-647-4(6))* Resource Pubns., Inc.
Miller, R. J. Christian Educator John Knox Montgomery. 2006. pap. 28.95 *(978-1-4286-6042-7(9))* Kessinger Publishing, LLC.
Mills, Joni. Christian School Heartbreak, 1 vol. 2010. 167p. pap. 24.95 *(978-1-4489-8826-6(8))* PublishAmerica, Inc.
Mississippi. (Rand Mcnally Wall Maps Ser.). 229.00 *(978-0-528-86151-2(4))* Rand McNally.
Missouri. (Proseries Wall Map Ser.). 229.00 *(978-0-528-85862-8(9))* Rand McNally.
Mitchell, Alison. Check It Out: Bible Discovery for Families. 2010. (Table Talk Ser.). 48p. (J). pap. *(978-1-904889-13-7(1))* Good Bk. Co.
—Comings & Goings: Bible Discovery for Children. 2010. (XTB Ser.). 96p. (J). pap. *(978-1-873166-25-3(7))* Good Bk. Co.
—Comings & Goings: Bible Discovery for Families. 2010. (Illus.). 48p. (J). pap. *(978-1-873166-97-0(4))* Good Bk. Co.
—Travels Unravelled: Bible Discovery for Children. 2010. 80p. (J). pap. *(978-1-873166-10-9(9))* Good Bk. Co.
Mitchell, Michael R. Leading, Teaching, & Making Disciples: World-Class Christian Education in the Church, School, & Home. 2010. 452p. pap. 34.95 *(978-1-61507-040-4(0))* Cross Bks. Publishing.
Moineau, Rachel Jovan. The and Little Seedling. 2011. 28p. pap. 15.99 ***(978-1-61379-739-6(7))*** Xulon Pr., Inc.
Moore, Dwayne. Pure Praise for Youth: A Heart-Focused Study on Worship. 2011. pap. ***(978-0-7644-6657-1(7,*** Group) Group Publishing, Inc.
Moore, James W. On the Road Again: A Faith Journey: A Lenten Study for Adults. 2006. 60p. pap. 6.00 *(978-0-687-33246-5(X))* Abingdon Pr.
Moore, Mark. Acts: Lectio Divina for Youth. 2009. (Ancient Faith Ser.). (ENG.). 80p. pap. 7.99 *(978-0-8341-5027-0(1),* 9780834150270) Beacon Hill Pr. of Kansas City.
Moran, Gabriel. Fashioning a People Today: The Educational Insights of Maria Harris. 2007. 185p. per. 16.95 *(978-1-58595-605-0(8))* Twenty-Third Pubns./Bayard.
Moulds, Russ, ed. A Teacher of the Church: Theology, Formation, & Practice for the Ministry of Teaching. 2007. 172p. pap. 17.00 *(978-1-55635-089-4(9),* Wipf and Stock) Wipf & Stock Pubs.
Mukamuri, Ephiel. Pillars to Becoming A Strong Christian: A Handbook for Every Christian Disciple. 2007. pap. 9.99 *(978-1-60266-279-7(7))* Xulon Pr., Inc.
Mulderink, Kathryn. The Way of the Cross for Children. 2008. 40p. pap. 8.95 *(978-0-9800483-7-7(0))* Bezalel Bks.
My Very Own Bulletin. Vol. 1. 22.25 *(978-0-87162-673-8(X))* Vol. 2. 22.25 *(978-0-87162-699-8(3))* Warner Pr. Pubs.
Nebraska. (Proseries Wall Map Ser.). 229.00 *(978-0-528-85864-2(5))* Rand McNally.
Nelson, Carl Ellis. Growing up Christian: A Congregational Strategy for Nurturing Disciples. 2008. pap. 16.00 *(978-1-57312-523-9(7))* Smyth & Helwys Publishing, Inc.
Neuberger, Anne E. A Circle of Saints: Stories & Activities for Children. 2009. pap. 16.95 *(978-1-58595-750-7(X))* Twenty-Third Pubns./Bayard.
Neverson, Joyce M. The Grand Becoming. 2011. 412p. 34.99 ***(978-1-61379-083-0(X))*** Xulon Pr., Inc.
Newell, Edward J. Education Has Nothing to Do with Theology: James Michael Lee's Social Science Religious Instruction. 2006. (Princeton Theological Monographs). 130p. pap. 17.00 *(978-1-59752-527-5(8),* Pickwick Pubns.) Wipf & Stock Pubs.
Newland, Mary Reed. How to Raise Good Catholic Children. 2006. Orig. Title: We & Our Children (Garden City, New York: Image Books, 1961). 336p. per. 15.95 *(978-1-928832-86-7(5))* Sophia Institute Pr.
Ngur, Dan O. May This be the Year. 2011. 280p. pap. 16.99 ***(978-1-61379-048-9(1))*** Xulon Pr., Inc.
Nielson, Kathleen Buswell. Proverbs: The Ways of Wisdom. 2007. (Living Word Bible Studies). 182p. spiral bd. 12.99 *(978-1-59638-081-3(0))* P & R Publishing.
North Dakota. (Rand Mcnally Wall Maps Ser.). 229.00 *(978-0-528-86154-3(9))* Rand McNally.
Northcote, Vivien. The Use of Italian Renaissance Art in Victorian Religious Education: How the National Society Shaped Our Modern Idea of Christ. 2011. (Illus.). 312p. 129.95 *(978-0-7734-3641-1(3))* Mellen, Edwin Pr., The.
Novelli, Michael. Enter the Story: Seven Experiences to Unlock the Bible for Your Students, 1 vol. 2010. (ENG.). 176p. pap. 18.99 *(978-0-310-66927-2(8))* Zondervan.
Oesch, Jackie. God s Plan, Our Choice. 2010. 96p. pap. 12.99 *(978-1-60957-878-7(3))* Xulon Pr., Inc.
O'Harae, Ian. Leadership in Christian Schools. 2010. 344p. pap. *(978-3-8383-8655-3(8))* Lambert Academic Publishing.
Oklahoma. (Rand Mcnally Wall Maps Ser.). 229.00 *(978-0-528-86155-0(7))* Rand McNally.
Olshine, David. The Philippians, Colossians, First & Second Thessalonians, 1 vol. 2009. (Studies on the Go Ser.). (ENG.). 176p. pap. 8.99 *(978-0-310-28549-6(6))* Zondervan.
—Proverbs, 1 vol. 2009. (Studies on the Go Ser.). (ENG.). 176p. pap. 8.99 *(978-0-310-28548-9(8))* Zondervan.
Omeje, Glad Ifeyinwa. Elementary Teachings about Christ. 2010. 61p. pap. 15.99 *(978-1-4500-9646-1(8))* Xlibris Corp.
Ortlund, Dane. A New Inner Relish: Christian Motivation in the Thought of Jonathan Edwards. 2008. (ENG.). 272p. pap. 14.99 *(978-1-84550-349-9(X))* Christian Focus Pubns. GBR. Dist: STL Distribution North America.
Ortlund, Jani. His Loving Law, Our Lasting Legacy: Living the Ten Commandments & Giving Them to Our Children. 2007. 176p. pap. 11.99 *(978-1-58134-868-2(1))* Crossway.
Orton, Elizabeth. Fun Activities for LDS Families. 2007. 96p. pap. 14.95 *(978-1-59992-077-1(8))* Leatherwood Pr.
Osborn, Ronald E. La Fe Que Afirmamos: Creencias Basicas de la Iglesia Cristiana (Discipulos de Cristo) Jimenez, Glorimar Camareno, tr. from ENG. 2007. (SPA.). 99p. per. 12.99 *(978-0-8272-1040-0(X))* Chalice Pr.
Our Life in Christ Bk. 5: Adult Bible Study. rev. ed. 6.50 *(978-0-570-07920-0(9))* Concordia Publishing Hse.
Our Life in Christ Bk. 8: Adult Bible Study. rev. ed. 6.50 *(978-0-570-07923-1(3),* 20-3242) Concordia Publishing Hse.
Palmer, Alison. Sharing Through Primary Songs, Volume Three: I'll Follow Him in Faith, Vol. 3. 2006. (Illus.). 136p. per. 12.99 *(978-0-88290-813-7(8),* Horizon Pubs.) Cedar Fort, Inc./CFI Distribution.
—Sharing Through Song: My Eternal Family. 2008. 128p. (J). pap. 14.99 *(978-0-88290-953-0(3))* Cedar Fort, Inc./CFI Distribution.
Paprocki, Joe. The Catechist's Toolbox: How to Thrive as a Religious Education Teacher. 2007. (ENG., Illus.). 152p. per. 9.95 *(978-0-8294-2451-5(2))* Loyola Pr.
Parent, Neil A. A Concise Guide to Adult Faith Formation. 2009. 192p. pap. 16.95 *(978-1-59471-208-1(5))* Ave Maria Pr.
Parrett, Gary A. & Kang, S. Steve. Teaching the Faith, Forming the Faithful: A Biblical Vision for Education in the Church. 2009. (ENG.). 461p. pap. 30.00 *(978-0-8308-2587-5(8),* IVP Acad.) InterVarsity Pr.
Paul, VI. Dec Christian Education. 21p. pap. *(978-0-8198-1827-0(5),* 332-054) Pauline Bks. & Media.
Pazmiño, Robert W. Foundational Issues in Christian Education: An Introduction in Evangelical Perspective. 3rd ed. 2008. (Illus.). 304p. (C). pap. 29.99 *(978-0-8010-3593-7(7))* Baker Academic.
—So What Makes Our Teaching Christian? Teaching in the Name, Spirit, & Power of Jesus. 2008. 136p. pap. 17.00 *(978-1-55635-943-9(8))* Wipf & Stock Pubs.
Pearson, Sharon Ely. The Prayer Book Guide to Christian Education. Szoke, Robyn, ed. 3rd rev. ed. 2009. 336p. pap. 24.00 *(978-0-8192-2337-1(9),* Morehouse Publishing) Church Publishing, Inc.
Pendleton Jones, Susan & Jones, L. Gregory. Attentiveness: Being Present: Study & Reflection Guide. 2006. (Living the Good Life Together Ser.). (Illus.). 62p. pap. 9.00 *(978-0-687-46540-8(0))* Abingdon Pr.

C

Pennock, Michael. Encountering Jesus in the New Testament. 2009. (Illus.). 332p. (YA). pap., stu. ed. 24.95 *(978-1-59471-165-7(8))* Ave Maria Pr.

Peterfy, Ida. Catechist Companion: Ready-To-Use Lesson Plans: Creed, Sacraments, Commandments, & Saints. 2009. (Illus.). vii, 226p. pap. *(978-1-56854-797-8(8))* Liturgy Training Pubns.

Peucker, Paul & Lempa, Heikki, eds. Self, Community, World. 2010. (Illus.). 300p. 55.00 *(978-0-9801496-5-4(7))* Lehigh Univ. Pr.

Phillips, Anne. The Faith of Girls: Childrens'spirituality & Transition to Adulthood. 2011. (Explorations in Practical, Pastoral & Empirical Theology Ser.). 218p. 89.95 ***(978-1-4094-2198-6(8))*** Ashgate Publishing Co.

Plant, Marian R. Faith Formation in Vital Congregations. 2009. *(978-0-8298-1813-0(8))* Pilgrim Pr., The/United Church Pr.

Polich, Laurie. Romans. 1 vol. 2009. (Studies on the Go Ser.). (ENG.). 128p. pap. 8.99 *(978-0-310-66874-9(3))* Zondervan.

Ponessa, Joseph & Manhardt, Laurie Watson. Moses & the Torah: Exodus, Leviticus, Numbers, Deuteronomy. 2007. (Come & See Catholic Bible Study Ser.). (Illus.). 220p. per. 19.95 *(978-1-931018-45-6(6))* Emmaus Road Publishing.

Powell, Kara. Friends & Peer Pressure. 2009. (Uncommon Ser.). (ENG.). 192p. (J). (gr. 6-8). 14.99 *(978-0-8307-4790-0(7))* Gospel Light Pubns.

Powell, Kara, ed. The Life of Jesus. 2009. (Uncommon Ser.). (ENG.). 192p. (J). pap. 14.99 *(978-0-8307-4643-9(9))* Gospel Light Pubns.

—Listening to God: Junior High Group Study. 2012. (Uncommon Ser.). (ENG.). 192p. pap. 14.99 ***(978-0-8307-6136-4(5))*** Gospel Light Pubns.

Powell, Kara, ed. Parents & Family. 2010. (Uncommon Ser.). (ENG.). 192p. (J). (gr. 7-9). pap. 14.99 *(978-0-8307-5099-3(1))* Gospel Light Pubns.

Powell, Kara Eckmann. The Armor of God. 2011. pap. ***(978-0-8307-5899-9(2))*** Gospel Light Pubns.

Priolo, Louis Paul & Payne, Brenda. Teach Them Diligently: How to Use the Scriptures in Child Training. 2008. 100p. pap. 11.50 *(978-1-889032-60-3(3))* Timeless Texts, Inc.

Pritchard, David, et al. Going Public: Your Child Can Thrive in Public School. 2008. (ENG., Illus.). 224p. per. 12.99 *(978-0-8307-4577-7(7))* Gospel Light Pubns.

Proctor, Frank. What Matters to Children & Families: Engaging Six Vital Themes of Our Faith. 2009. 82p. pap. 13.00 *(978-0-8298-1864-2(2))* Pilgrim Pr., The/United Church Pr.

Prosser, Bo. Is God Calling? 2011. ***(978-1-936347-04-9(0))*** Smyth & Helwys Publishing, Inc.

Radanovich, George. The and New World Order Is the Old World Order. 2011. 22.99 ***(978-1-61379-263-6(8))***; 162p. pap. 14.99 ***(978-1-61379-262-9(X))*** Xulon Pr., Inc.

Rahn, Dave & Linhart, Terry. Evangelism Remixed: Empowering Students for Courageous & Contagious Faith, 1 vol. 2009. (ENG.). 176p. pap. 16.99 *(978-0-310-29293-7(X))* Zondervan.

Reagan, Wesley C., ed. The Higley Lesson Commentary: 1933-2008. 2007. (Higley Lesson Commentary Ser.). (Illus.). 530p. per. 15.95 *(978-1-886763-32-6(1))* Higley Publishing Corp.

—The Higley Lesson Commentary: Based on the International Sunday School Lessons. 2007. (Illus.). 530p. 19.95 *(978-1-886763-33-3(X))* Higley Publishing Corp.

—The Higley Lesson Commentary: Based on the International Sunday School Lessons, King James Version, 77th Annual Volume. 2009. (Higley Lesson Commentary Ser.). (Illus.). 520p. pap. 15.95 *(978-1-886763-36-4(4))* Higley Publishing Corp.

Ream, Todd C., et al, eds. Beyond Integration? Inter/Disciplinary Possibilities for the Future of Christian Higher Education. 2012. 224p. pap. ***(978-0-89112-317-0(2),*** ACU Pr.) Abilene Christian Univ. Pr.

Reasons, Allen. The Gospel of Luke: Good News of Great Joy. 2009. 212p. pap. *(978-1-934731-41-3(2))* Baptistway.

Regular Baptist Press. Nuestro Gran Dios - Maestro: La Palabra de Dios para Principiantes. Meyer, Richard E., ed. 2009.Tr. of Our Great God. (SPA., Illus.). 88p. 8.00 *(978-1-932607-26-0(9))* Editorial Bautista Independiente.

Reid, Kathryn Goering & Hawkley, Ken. Children Together: Teaching Girls & Boys to Value Themselves & Each Other. 2010. 128p. pap. 16.00 *(978-1-60899-183-9(0),* Resource Pubns.) Wipf & Stock Pubs.

Reynolds, Aaron. The Fabulous Reinvention of Sunday School: Transformational Techniques for Reaching & Teaching Kids, 1 vol. 2007. (ENG., Illus.). 320p. pap. 14.99 *(978-0-310-27433-9(8))* Zondervan.

Rice, Wayne. Generation to Generation: Practical & Creative Ideas for Raising Kids to Know & Love God. 2010. (ENG.). 208p. pap. 14.99 *(978-0-7847-2125-4(4))* Standard Publishing.

Richards, Michelle. Tending the Flame: The Art of Unitarian Universalist Parenting. 2010. pap. 14.00 *(978-1-55896-563-8(7),* Skinner Hse. Bks.) Unitarian Universalist Assn.

Richardson, Susan. Child by Child: Supporting Children with Learning Differences & Their Families. 2011. E-Book ***(978-0-8192-2752-2(8),*** Morehouse Publishing) Church Publishing, Inc.

Ridlon, Robert W., et al. Christian Kids Explore Chemistry. 2007. (Christian Kids Explore Ser.). (Illus.). 384p. pap. 29.95 *(978-1-892427-18-2(4))* Bright Ideas! Educational Resources.

Rigsby, Sandy & Mason, Steve. Exploring the Sunday Lectionary: A Teenager's Guide to the Readings - Cycle A. 2007. 208p. pap. 19.95 *(978-0-8091-9583-1(6),* 9583-1) Paulist Pr.

Roberto, John. Living Well: Christian Practices for Everyday Life. 2009. (Illus.). *(978-0-9823031-0-8(6))* Lifelongfaith Assocs.

Roberts, Carlos C. Christian Education Teaching Methods - from Modern to Postmodern: Teaching the faith to Post-moderns. 2009. 256p. 29.99 *(978-1-4490-5310-9(6))*; pap. 21.99 *(978-1-4490-5311-6(4))* AuthorHouse.

Roberts, Dave. The Twilight Gospel: The Spiritual Roots of the Stephenie Meyer Vampire Saga, 1 vol. 2009. (ENG., Illus.). 160p. pap. 12.99 *(978-1-85424-976-0(2),* Monarch Bks.) Lion Hudson PLC GBR. Dist: Kregel Pubns.

Roberts, Edwinna. Has God Forgotten? A Practical Guide for Christians Effected by Learning Disabilities. 2008. 128p. pap. 15.95 *(978-1-4327-3246-2(3))* Outskirts Pr., Inc.

Robinson, Connie. How Big Is Your God? 2011. 216p. pap. ***(978-1-77069-374-6(2))*** Word Alive Pr.

Robinson, Evelina M. Let's Act It Out: Character Building Skits & Plays for the Christian Community. 2007. 140p. per. 10.95 *(978-1-4327-0498-8(2))* Outskirts Pr., Inc.

Robinson, Zoe. And God Created You. 2011. 28p. pap. 15.99 ***(978-1-4634-2772-6(7))*** AuthorHouse.

Rock Solid Tween FaithZine Fall 2011. 2011. (Efs Ser.). 24 Pages (Selfp. 5.65 ***(978-1-4267-0566-3(2),*** Cokesbury) Abingdon Pr.

Roehlkepartain, Jolene L. 101 More Great Games for Kids: Active, Bible-Based Fun for Christian Education. 2007. (Illus.). per. 18.99 *(978-0-687-33407-0(1))* Abingdon Pr.

Romanowski, Michael H. & McCarthy, Teri. Teaching in a Distant Classroom: Crossing Borders for Global Transformation. 2009. (ENG.). 224p. pap. 17.00 *(978-0-8308-3743-4(4),* IVP Bks.) InterVarsity Pr.

Rosin, Frank & Frank, Jona. Right: Portraits from the Evangelical Ivy League. 2008. (ENG., Illus.). 128p. 35.00 *(978-0-8118-6533-3(9))* Chronicle Bks. LLC.

Rosin, Hanna. God's Harvard: A Christian College on a Mission to Save America. (ENG.). 2008. 312p. pap. 14.00 *(978-0-15-603499-9(9),* Mariner Bks.) 2007. 304p. 25.00 *(978-0-15-101262-6(8))* Houghton Mifflin Harcourt Trade & Reference Pubs.

Ross, Mary H. Short & Sweet with a Treat: 52 Already Done, Ready-For Fun Family Home Evenings. 2008. (Illus.). 104p. pap. *(978-1-59811-505-5(7))* Covenant Communications.

Ross, Melanie H. & Guymon-King. Primary Partners: Ages 8 to 11 (New Testament) pap., tchr. ed. 9.95 *(978-1-57734-344-8(1),* 01113658) Covenant Communications, Inc.

Ross, Steve. Blinded: The Story of Paul the Apostle. 2008. 224p. pap. 20.00 *(978-1-59627-091-6(8),* Seabury Bks.) Church Publishing, Inc.

Rozema, Bob. Hc & Me Year 2: The Heidelberg Catechism for Christian Living. 2007. (Illus.). 144p. per. 12.95 *(978-1-59255-254-2(4))*; 173p. per. 19.95 *(978-1-59255-255-9(2))* Faith Alive Christian Resources.

Runk, Wesley T. Jesus, the Servant King. 4.75 *(978-1-55673-559-2(6))* CSS Publishing Co.

Ryan, Jay. Signs & Seasons: Understanding the Elements of Classical Astronomy. 2007. (Illus.). 280p. (YA). 39.99 *(978-0-9792211-0-1(2))* Fourth Day Pr.

Sacraments: Celebrating, Living & Believing. 2008. *(978-0-15-901884-2(6))* Harcourt Trade Pubs.

Saggio, Joseph J. & Dempsey, Jim. American Indian College: A Witness to the Tribes: A Compilation of Works & Essays in Honor of the First Fifty Years of American Indian College of the Assemblies of God in Phoenix, Arizona, 1957-2007. 2008. (Illus.). xiv, 433p. pap. *(978-1-60585-167-9(1))* Gospel Publishing Hse.

Salmon, Haskel T. The Man God Made. 2009. 148p. pap. 12.95 *(978-1-4327-2349-1(9))* Outskirts Pr., Inc.

Sampson, Robin. The Heart of Wisdom Teaching Approach: Bible Based Homeschooling. 2007. 508p. pap. 34.95 *(978-0-9701816-7-1(1))* Heart of Wisdom Publishing, Inc.

—Wisdom: An Internet-Linked Unit Study. 2007. 120p. pap. 21.95 *(978-0-9701816-6-4(3))* Heart of Wisdom Publishing, Inc.

Saunders, Martin. The Ideas Factory: 100 Adaptable Discussion Starters to Get Teens Talking, 1 vol. 2008. 320p. pap. 14.99 *(978-0-8254-6173-6(1),* Monarch Bks.) Lion Hudson PLC GBR. Dist: Kregel Pubns.

—The Think Tank: 100 Adaptable Discussion Starters to Get Teens Talking, 1 vol. 2010. 320p. pap. 15.99 *(978-1-85424-964-7(9),* Monarch Bks.) Lion Hudson PLC GBR. Dist: Kregel Pubns.

Scheeres, Julia. Jesus Land: A Memoir. 2006. (ENG.). 384p. per. 15.95 *(978-1-58243-354-7(2))* Counterpoint LLC.

Scheid, Edward G. Catholic Teaching on Church. 2010. viii, 75p. pap. ***(978-1-56077-902-5(0))*** Center for Learning, The.

Schlachter, Gail A. & Weber, R. David. Money for Christian College Students, 2007-2009. 2nd ed. 2007. 280p. *(978-1-58841-149-5(4))* Reference Service Pr.

Schmidt, Ken M. Not Afraid to Tell the Truth: Exposing Apostacy & the Conspiracy of Silence in the last Days! 2011. 804p. pap. 23.99 ***(978-1-4653-3448-0(3))*** Xlibris Corp.

Schnase, Robert. Intentional Faith Development. 2008. 32p. pap. 7.00 *(978-1-4267-0003-3(2))* Abingdon Pr.

Schorr, Vernie & Haystead, Wes. Staffing Your ChildrenÕs Ministry. 2009. 112p. pap. 13.00 *(978-1-60608-492-2(5),* Wipf and Stock) Wipf & Stock Pubs.

Schulenburg, Brian. When I: 500 Sentence-Finishers to Get Your Students Talking, 1 vol. 2008. (Quick Questions Ser.). (ENG.). 144p. pap. 10.99 *(978-0-310-28327-0(2))* Zondervan.

Schweikert, Gigi. Church Nanny SOS: Teaching Discipline Essentials for Preschool Ministry Volunteers. 2007. (ENG.). 208p. per. 12.99 *(978-1-59669-043-1(7))* New Hope Pubs.

Scripture Union. SUbstance. 2011. 82p. pap. *(978-1-84427-527-4(2))* Scripture Union.

Scripture Union Staff, contrib. by. Matchday Programme: Holiday Club Resource Material for 5 to 11 Year-Olds. 2007. 64p. pap. ***(978-1-84427-333-1(4))*** Scripture Union.

Seymour, Susan. Apostasy: The Deceived Generation - Rescuing Our Youth from Satan's Influence. 2008. (ENG.). 368p. pap. 14.99 *(978-1-59979-456-3(X),* Creation Hse.) Charisma Media.

Shelburne, Gene, et al. The Higley Lesson Commentary: KJV Based on the International Sunday School Lessons. Reagan, Wesley, ed. 77th ed. 2009. (Illus.). 520p. (J). 19.95 *(978-1-886763-37-1(2))* Higley Publishing Corp.

Shoemaker, Tim. Smashed Tomatoes, Bottle Rockets: And Other Outdoor Devotionals You Can Do with Your Kids. 2007. (Illus.). 150p. pap. 12.99 *(978-1-60066-150-1(5))* WingSpread Publishers.

Shurden, Walter B. & Weaver, C. Douglas. Baptist Freedom: Celebrating Our Baptist Heritage. 2011. pap. ***(978-1-936347-03-2(2))*** NextSunday Resources.

Simpson, Tim. No Object Object Talks. 2007. (Big Books (Gospel Light) Ser.). (ENG., Illus.). 224p. (J). 29.99 *(978-0-8307-4358-2(8))* Gospel Light Pubns.

Singer-Towns, Brian. The Catholic Faith Handbook for Youth. 2nd ed. 2008. (Illus.). 474p. per. 19.95 *(978-0-88489-987-7(X))* St. Mary's Pr.

Singer-Towns, Brian, et al. The Catholic Faith Handbook for Youth. 2nd ed. 2008. (Illus.). 474p. 28.25 *(978-0-88489-988-4(8))* St. Mary's Pr.

Sleeth, Matthew. The Gospel According to the Earth: Why the Good Book Is a Green Book. 2010. (ENG.). 208p. 22.99 *(978-0-06-173053-5(X),* HarperOne) HarperCollins Pubs.

Small, Joseph D., et al. Alive to God in Jesus Christ: 40 Daily Readings for the Purposeful Presbyterian. 2009. (ENG.). v, 106p. pap. 12.95 *(978-1-57153-146-9(7),* Witherspoon Pr.) Curriculum Publishing, Presbyterian Church (U. S. A.).

Smith, David & Smith, James K. A. Teaching & Christian Practices: Reshaping Faith & Learning. 2011. 240p. pap. 22.00 ***(978-0-8028-6685-1(9))*** Eerdmans, William B. Publishing Co.

Smith, Gregory & McNeill, Charles J. The Divine Love Story, Part: The Sacraments. 2011. 58p. 36.95 ***(978-1-258-04707-8(1))*** Literary Licensing, LLC.

Smith, Mandy. Making a Mess & Meeting God: Unruly Ideas & Everyday Experiments for Worship. 2010. (ENG.). 144p. pap. 17.99 *(978-0-7847-2392-0(3))* Standard Publishing.

Smith, Wallace P. & Smith, Wallace R. Baptism Ahead: A Road Map for Young Disciples. 2009. 128p. (J). pap. 15.00 *(978-0-8170-1551-0(5))* Judson Pr.

Smith, Wallace R. Baptism Ahead. 2009. *(978-0-8170-1570-1(1))* Judson Pr.

Smith, Yolanda Y. Reclaiming the Spirituals: New Possibilities for African American Christian Education. 2010. 192p. pap. 22.00 *(978-1-60899-591-2(7),* Wipf and Stock) Wipf & Stock Pubs.

Snow, Patrick. Leading Preteens. 2008. (Growing Ministry Guide Ser.). (ENG.). (J). pap. 12.99 *(978-0-7847-2180-3(7))* Standard Publishing.

Socias, James. Introduction to Catholicism: A Complete Course. 2nd ed. 2011. ***(978-1-936045-61-7(3))*** Midwest Theological Forum.

South Dakota. (Rand Mcnally Wall Maps Ser.). 229.00 *(978-0-528-86157-4(3))* Rand McNally.

Spear, Samuel T. (Samuel Thayer). Religion & the State, or, the Bible & the Public Schools, by Samuel T Spear. 2006. 392p. per. 26.99 *(978-1-4255-4128-6(3))* MPublishing.

Spears, Paul D. & Loomis, Steven R. Education for Human Flourishing: A Christian Perspective. 2009. (Christian Worldview Integration Ser.). (ENG.). 251p. pap. 22.00 *(978-0-8308-2812-8(5),* IVP Acad.) InterVarsity Pr.

Speidell, Todd H., ed. Edification-Journal of the Society of Christian Psychology: Volume 1, Issue 2 2007. 2010. (Ray S. Anderson Collection Ser.). 82p. pap. 11.00 *(978-1-60899-396-3(5),* Wipf and Stock) Wipf & Stock Pubs.

Stafford, Wess & Merrill, Dean. Just a Minute: In the Heart of a Child, One Moment... Can Last Forever. 2012. (ENG.). 224p. 19.99 ***(978-0-8024-0472-5(3))*** Moody Pubs.

Stainback, Lily. Teaching Christ-Like Virtues in the Home. 2008. pap. 12.99 *(978-0-88290-844-1(8))* Cedar Fort, Inc./CFI Distribution.

Standard Publishing Staff. Challenge at the Ancient Ruins. 2008. (Superstart!: A Preteen Curriculum Ser.). (ENG., Illus.). 96p. (J). pap., tchr. ed. 19.99 *(978-0-7847-2224-4(2))* Standard Publishing.

—Dictionary & Bible Skills Activities. 2006. (HeartShaper Resources-Elementary Ser.). (ENG.). (J). (gr. 1-5). cd-rom 14.99 *(978-0-7847-1874-2(1))* Standard Publishing.

—Overwhelming Evidence. 2006. cd-rom 24.99 *(978-0-7847-1878-0(4))* Standard Publishing.

Standke, Linda, et al. Bible Story Puzzle 'n' Learn! 2008. (ENG.). 176p. pap. 12.99 *(978-1-60418-111-7(7))*; (gr. 1-2). pap. 12.99 *(978-1-60418-273-6(3))*; (gr. 3-4). pap. 12.99 *(978-1-60418-274-3(1))* Carson-Dellosa Publishing, LLC.

Stanley, Andy & Hall, Stuart. The Seven Checkpoints for Student Leaders: Seven Principles Every Teenager Needs to Know. rev. ed. 2011. (ENG.). 272p. (J). pap. 14.99 *(978-1-4391-8933-7(1),* Howard Bks.) Howard Books.

Stephen, Skelton. Gilligan's Island Bible Study Study Guide. 2007. (ENG.). 42p. pap. 7.99 *(978-0-9791259-5-9(2))* Entertainment Ministry, The.

Stern, Julian & Stern. Schools & Religions: Imagining the Real. 2007. (Continuum Studies in Research in Education Ser.). (ENG.). 224p. 150.00 *(978-0-8264-8504-5(9))* Continuum International Publishing Group, Ltd. GBR. Dist: National Bk. Network.

Stoner, Marcia. Drama Queens (and Kings) Positive Ways for Tweens to Act Out. 2006. (Illus.). 64p. (J). (gr. 4-7). pap. 10.00 *(978-0-687-49699-0(3))* Abingdon Pr.

Storm, Jeff. Stripped Clean: Down to Nothing but the Cross. 2009. 128p. pap. 9.99 *(978-0-7644-3862-2(X))* Group Publishing, Inc.

Streng, William D. The Faith We Teach. 2011. 162p. 41.95 ***(978-1-258-04673-6(3))*** Literary Licensing, LLC.

Strukova, Jana. Kitchen Table Youth Ministry: Inviting God to Dinner. 2010. pap. *(978-0-8298-1840-6(5))* Pilgrim Pr., The/United Church Pr.

SUbstance. 2010. 80p. pap. *(978-1-84427-386-7(5))* Scripture Union.

SUbstance 5: Telling Others. 2009. 80p. pap. *(978-1-84427-385-0(7))* Scripture Union.

Suchocki, Marjor, GBuilding A Heart of Faith. 2009. 96p. pap. 10.00 *(978-0-687-46496-8(X))* Abingdon Pr.

Summers, Sue L. Terrible Tenderness: The Bride, a Burnt Offering. pap. 10.00 *(978-0-9676616-3-6(3))* Media Alert!

Talbot, Dee Dee. The Word Made Flesh: Study Guide 4. 2007. 240p. pap. 21.50 *(978-1-4303-1554-4(7))* Lulu Enterprises Inc.

Tassi, Peter & Tassi, Filomena. Greatness in Our Teenagers: A 10 Step Guide for Parents & Educators. 2009. (Illus.). 104p. pap. 9.95 *(978-0-8091-4604-8(5))* Paulist Pr.

Tavares, Victor & Weiss, Rebekah, illus. The Survivors: For Kids in Tough Places. 2009. (Crocodile Dock Ser.). 45p. pap. 0.79 *(978-0-7644-3872-1(7))* Group Publishing, Inc.

Taylor, Allan. Sunday School in HD: Sharpening the Focus on What Makes Your Church Healthy. 2009. (ENG.). 208p. pap. 14.99 *(978-0-8054-4973-0(6),* B&H Bks.) B&H Publishing Group.

Thompson, David W. A Stranger's Journey. 2007. 124p. per. 10.99 *(978-1-60477-471-9(1))* Xulon Pr., Inc.

Thompson, Steven G. He That Hath an Ear: A down-to-Earth Commentary & Outline of the Book of Revelation. 2011. 148p. pap. 20.95 ***(978-1-4620-1175-9(6))*** iUniverse, Inc.

Thrasher, Charles. A Paradigm Looking At: Book Two. 2009. 332p. pap. 19.99 *(978-1-4389-7377-7(2))* AuthorHouse.

Toddlers & Twos Leader's Guide. 2007. 19.99 *(978-0-687-05787-0(6))* Abingdon Pr.

Toddlers & Twos Leader's Guide (2008-2009) 2008. (TODDLERS & TWOS Ser.). 21.00 *(978-0-687-49039-4(1))* Abingdon Pr.

Tomberg, Markus. Religionsunterricht Als Praxis der Freiheit: Überlegungen Zu Einer Religionsdidaktisch Orientierten Theorie Gläubigen Handelns. 2010. (Praktische Theologie im Wissenschaftsdiskurs Ser.).Tr. of Religious Instruction as Exercise of Freedom. Considerations on a religious didactically oriented theory of action based on Faith. (GER.). XIII, 402p. 140.00 *(978-3-11-022197-8(7))* De Gruyter, Walter Inc.

Torres, Aramis. Foundational Studies: Establishing Foundations. 2010. 156p. pap. 11.99 *(978-1-4490-8345-8(5))* AuthorHouse.

Trent, John & Vogel, Jane. FaithLaunch. 2008. (ENG.). 192p. pap. 14.99 *(978-1-58997-531-6(6))* Tyndale Hse. Pubs.

Trent, Mary Alice, et al, eds. Religion, Culture, Curriculum, & Diversity in 21st Century America. 2006. (ENG.). 184p. per. 34.99 *(978-0-7618-3558-5(X))* Univ. Pr. of America, Inc.

Trujillo, Kelli B. Faith-Filled Moments: Helping Kids See God in Everyday Life. 2009. *(978-0-89827-406-6(0))* Wesleyan Publishing Hse.

Turner, Paul. Show Who You Know: The Essentials of Student Leadership: Leader Guide. 2008. (Illus.). 64p. (YA). pap. 9.95 *(978-1-4158-6538-5(8))* LifeWay Christian Resources.

Tye, Karen. Christian Education in the Small Membership Church. 2008. (Ministry in the Small Membership Church Ser.). 110p. pap. 15.00 *(978-0-687-65099-6(2))* Abingdon Pr.

Tyler, Clark. Singin' in the Reign: A Collection of Original Musical Plays Created for the Purpose of Teaching Biblical Lessons to Children & also to Serve as an Outreach Ministry to Nursing & Retirement Homes & to the Community. 2011. 432p. pap. 25.46 *(978-1-4567-3917-1(4))* AuthorHouse.

Tyrrell, Mabel. A Missionary in the Making. 2007. 168p. per. 13.99 *(978-1-60266-915-4(5))* Xulon Pr., Inc.

Vacation Bible School 2010 Galactic Blast Assembly Leader VBS: A Cosmic Adventure Praising God. 2009. 4.99 *(978-1-4267-0382-9(1))* Abingdon Pr.

Vacation Bible School 2010 Galactic Blast Bible Story Activity Stickers VBS: A Cosmic Adventure Praising God. 2009. 1p. 0.99 *(978-1-4267-0538-0(7))* Abingdon Pr.

Vacation Bible School 2010 Galactic Blast Bible Storyteller VBS: A Cosmic Adventure Praising God. 2009. 6.99 *(978-1-4267-0464-2(X))* Abingdon Pr.

Vacation Bible School 2010 Galactic Blast Craft Leader VBS: A Cosmic Adventure Praising God. 2009. 6.99 *(978-1-4267-0465-9(8))* Abingdon Pr.

Vacation Bible School 2010 Galactic Blast Craft Theme Stickers (package of 12 sheets) VBS: A Cosmic Adventure Praising God. 2009. 1p. 8.99 *(978-1-4267-0554-0(9))* Abingdon Pr.

Vacation Bible School 2010 Galactic Blast Decorating Guide VBS: A Cosmic Adventure Praising God. 2009. 4.99 *(978-1-4267-0467-3(4))* Abingdon Pr.

Vacation Bible School 2010 Galactic Blast Director VBS: A Cosmic Adventure Praising God. 2009. 19.99 *(978-1-4267-0463-5(1))* Abingdon Pr.

Van Der Veer, Andrew. Bible Lessons for Juniors: (four volume Set) 2007. (J). *(978-1-60178-016-4(8))* Reformation Heritage Bks.

van der Velden, Frank. Die Heiligen Schriften des anderen im Unterricht: Bibel und Koran im christlichen und islamischen Religionsunterricht einsetzen. van der Velden, Frank, ed. 2011. (GER.). 244p. (C). pap. 44.00

(978-3-89971-630-6(2)) Vandenhoeck & Ruprecht GmbH & Co. KG DEU. Dist: ISD.

Van Dyk, John. Fostering a Reflective Culture in the Christian School: The Maplewood Story. 2007. pap. *(978-0-932914-72-9(1))* Dordt College Pr.

Van Heemst, David B. College: What's the Point? Embracing the Mystery of the Kingdom in a Postmodern World. 2011. 240p. pap. 17.95 ***(978-1-4497-2412-2(4)***, WestBow Pr.) Author Solutions, Inc.

van Rooyen, Leon. Well Done! ... good & faithful Servant. 2011. 142p. pap. 15.00 ***(978-1-935298-77-9(1))*** Truth Pubs.

van Wiele, J. Faith & Culture: The Construction of a Christian Identity in Interaction with the Other World Religions in Education. 2008. (Annua Nuntia Lovaniensia Ser.). (ENG.). 234p. (C). pap. 76.00 *(978-90-429-1931-0(0))* Peeters Pubs. & Booksellers BEL. Dist: Brown, David Bk. Co., The.

VanDervennen, Robert E. A University for the People: A History of the Institute for Christian Studies. 2008. 292p. pap. 18.00 *(978-0-932914-75-0(6))* Dordt College Pr.

VBS 08 Bulletin Inserts. 2007. (Vacation Bible School Ser.). (J). (gr. 3-12). pap. 9.99 *(978-1-4347-9952-4(2))* Cook, David C.

Vermont. 2009. 382p. pap. 34.98 *(978-1-4589-9247-5(0))* General Bks. LLC.

Vos Wezeman, Phyllis. 100 Ways to Tell God's Great Story. 2006. (Illus.). 96p. per. 15.00 *(978-0-687-33443-8(8))* Abingdon Pr.

Walker, James Barr. The Bible in School. 2011. 26p. pap. 11.99 ***(978-1-4181-9236-5(8))*** MPublishing.

Walley-Daniels, Pauline. School of Prophetic Deliverance. 2008. (ENG.). 272p. pap. 13.99 *(978-1-59979-548-5(5)*, Creation Hse.) Charisma Media.

Walsh, Catherine. Shut up & Get in Line! 2009. 202p. pap. 14.96 *(978-0-578-01163-9(8))* Mystical Rose Pr.

Wang, Dong. Managing God's Higher Learning: U. S.-China Cultural Encounter & Canton Christian College (Lingnan University), 1888-1952. Wang, Dong, ed. 2007. (ENG., Illus.). 226p. pap. 36.99 *(978-0-7391-1936-5(2))* Lexington Bks.

—Managing Gods Higher Learning: U. S.-China Cultural Encounter & Canton Christian College (Lingnan University), 1888-1952. Wang, Dong, ed. 2007. (ENG., Illus.). 226p. 89.50 *(978-0-7391-1935-8(4))* Lexington Bks.

Ware, Bruce A. Big Truths for Young Hearts: Teaching & Learning the Greatness of God. 2009. *(978-1-4335-0602-4(5))*; 240p. pap. 15.99 *(978-1-4335-0601-7(7))* Crossway.

Waring, Diana, ed. Ancient Civilizations & the Bible: A Biblical World History Curriculum from Creation to Jesus Christ. 2008. (History Revealed Ser.). (Illus.). (J). 39.99 *(978-1-60092-168-1(X))* Answers in Genesis Ministries.

—Ancient Civilizations & the Bible: Creation to Jesus Christ: Elementary Activity Book. 2008. (History Revealed Ser.). (Illus.). 80p. (J). pap. 12.99 *(978-1-60092-172-8(8))* Answers in Genesis Ministries.

—Ancient Civilizations & the Bible: From Creation to Jesus Christ. 2008. (History Revealed Ser.). (J). pap. 8.99 *(978-1-60092-176-6(0))*; (Illus.). 312p. pap. 29.99 *(978-1-60092-170-4(1))* Answers in Genesis Ministries.

—Romans, Reformers, Revolutionaries: A Biblical World History Curriculum Resurrection to Revolution AD 30-AD 1799. 2008. (Illus.). 351p. (J). pap. 29.99 *(978-1-60092-171-1(X))* Answers in Genesis Ministries.

—Romans, Reformers, Revolutionaries: Resurrection to Revolution AD 30-AD 1799. 2008. (History Revealed Ser.). (J). pap. 8.99 *(978-1-60092-177-3(9))*; (Illus.). 39.99 *(978-1-60092-169-8(8))* Answers in Genesis Ministries.

Warren, Kay & Holladay, Tom. Good & Evil: 11 Core Truths to Build Your Life On, 1 vol. 2008. (Foundations Ser.). (ENG.). 80p. pap. 7.99 *(978-0-310-27687-6(X))* Zondervan.

—Sanctification. 1 vol. 2008. (Foundations Ser.). (ENG.). 80p. pap. 7.99 *(978-0-310-27684-5(5))* Zondervan.

—11 Core Truths to Build Your Life On: The Second Coming, 1 vol. 2008. (Foundations Ser.). (ENG.). 80p. pap. 7.99 *(978-0-310-27695-1(0))* Zondervan.

Warwick, Stacie Brown. Around the World Brothers. 2008. (ENG.). 24p. pap. 11.95 *(978-1-4343-7514-8(5))* AuthorHouse.

Wayment, Thomas A. To Teach As Jesus Taught: 11 Attributes of a Master Teacher. 2009. pap. 12.99 *(978-1-59955-285-9(X))* Cedar Fort, Inc./CFI Distribution.

Weaver, K. D. Chasing Chariots: Eleven Biblical Lessons for Christian Growth. 2008. *(978-0-7880-2610-2(0))* CSS Publishing Co.

West Virginia. (Proseries Wall Map Ser.). 229.00 *(978-0-528-35868-0(8))* Rand McNally.

Wezeman, Phyllis. BIBLE BASICS Lessons for Life: New Testament Epistles of Paul: Romans - Philemon. 2007. 19.95 *(978-0-9774304-2-0(1))* Active Learning Associates, Inc.

—BIBLE BASICS Lessons for Life: New Testament Generea Epistles/Prophecy: Hebrews - Revelation. 2007. 15.95 *(978-0-9774304-3-7(X))* Active Learning Associates, Inc.

Wezeman, Phyllis Vos. 50 Interactive Bible Stories for Children Ages 5-8. 2009. 80p. (J). pap. 16.95 *(978-1-58595-701-9(1))* Twenty-Third Pubns./Bayard.

White, Joseph D. Multisensory Methods in Catechesis. 2007. (Catechist's Companion Ser.). (Illus.). 7p. pap. 2.95 *(978-1-59276-289-7(1))* Our Sunday Visitor, Publishing Div.

White, Marjorie. Memoirs of an American Teacher. 2007. 480p. 35.99 *(978-1-60266-792-1(6))*; per. 23.99 *(978-1-60266-791-4(5))* Xulon Pr., Inc.

White, Marjorie A. The Five Books of Moses. 2011. 280p. 26.99 ***(978-1-60957-993-7(3))*** Xulon Pr., Inc.

Whitesel, Bob. Waypoint: Navigating Your Spiritual Journey. 2010. *(978-0-89827-432-5(X))* Wesleyan Publishing Hse.

Who Is Jesus? A Six-Week Study for Tweens. 2010. 64p. pap. 15.95 *(978-0-687-65800-8(4))* Abingdon Pr.

Widder, Richard A. & Widder, Wendy. The Forest & the Trees: Helping Teachers Integrate a Biblical Worldview Across the Curriculum. 2008. 152p. pap. 17.00 *(978-1-55635-054-2(6))* Wipf & Stock Pubs.

Wilcox, Douglas J., et al. Do What Is Right: 52 Fun Motivators for LDS Families. 2009. (Illus.). xiii, 205p. *(978-1-59811-677-9(0))* Covenant Communications.

Williams, Michael E. Ephesians, Philippians, Colossians: Living with Faithfulness & Joy. 2008. 158p. pap. *(978-1-934731-16-1(1))* Baptistway.

Wilson, William J. The Christian School in Secular Society: Rationale & Pattern for Christian Schooling. 2009. 348p. pap. 18.99 *(978-1-60791-767-0(X))* Xulon Pr., Inc.

Wimberly, Anne E. Streaty. Nurturing Faith & Hope: Black Worship as a Model for Christian Education. 2010. 236p. pap. 26.00 *(978-1-60899-234-8(9)*, Wipf and Stock) Wipf & Stock Pubs.

Windley-Daoust, Jerry. Touching the Hearts of Teens: Saint Mary's Press 1943-2001. 2009. *(978-1-59982-057-6(9))* St. Mary's Pr.

—Touching the Hearts of Teens: Saint Mary's Press from 1943-2001. 2009. pap. *(978-0-88489-825-2(3))* St. Mary's Pr.

Windley-Daoust, Jerry & Kilmartin, Lorraine. Living Justice & Peace 2008: Catholic Social Teaching in Practice. 2nd ed. 2008. (Illus.). 336p. pap. 26.25 *(978-0-88489-985-3(3))* St. Mary's Pr.

Wisconsin. (Rand Mcnally Wall Maps Ser.). 229.00 *(978-0-528-86146-8(8))* Rand McNally.

Wolf, Carol S. Biblical Storytelling in Youth Ministry: Twelve-Year-Olds, Chosen & Blessed: Hoglah, Deborah, Samuel, Jesus, & Jairus' Daughter. 2009. (Illus.). 62p. pap. *(978-0-7880-2217-3(2)*, Fairway Pr.) CSS Publishing Co.

Wright, Michael & Arthur, James. Leadership in Christian Higher Education. 2010. (ENG.). 250p. pap. 34.90 *(978-1-84540-189-4(1))* Imprint Academic GBR. Dist: Ingram Pub. Services.

Wyoming. (Rand Mcnally Wall Maps Ser.). 229.00 *(978-0-528-86158-1(1))* Rand McNally.

Yancey, Philip & Yancey. The Jesus I Never Knew: Six Sessions on the Life of Christ, 1 vol. 2008. (ENG.). 96p. pap., pupil's gde. ed. 9.99 *(978-0-310-27530-5(X))* Zondervan.

York, Dick. God's Eternal Purpose: The Making of Man in God's Image. York, Dick, ed. 2007. (Illus.). 128p. pap. 7.95 *(978-1-889575-01-8(1))* SOF Pubs.

Yount, William. Created to Learn: A Christian Teacher's Introduction to Educational Psychology, Second Edition, 1 vol. 2010. (ENG.). 432p. pap. 49.99 *(978-0-8054-4727-9(X)*, B&H Academic) B&H Publishing Group.

—The Teaching Ministry of the Church: Second Edition. 2nd ed. 2008. (ENG.). 400p. 39.99 *(978-0-8054-4737-8(7)*, B&H Academic) B&H Publishing Group.

Yust, Karen-Marie & Anderson, E. Byron. Taught by God: Teaching & Spiritual Formation. annot. ed. 2006. 186p. per. 21.99 *(978-0-8272-3649-3(2))* Chalice Pr.

Zondervan. Manual de referencia para el ministro de education Cristiano, 1 vol. 2011. (SPA.). 146p. spiral bd. 14.95 ***(978-0-88243-900-6(6))*** Vida Pubs.

CHRISTIAN ETHICS

see also Casuistry; Guilt; Human Acts; Jesus Christ—Ethics; Social Ethics; Ten Commandments

Abbott, Lorraine. Ethics Through Christianity for OCR B GCSE Religious Studies. 2nd ed. 2009. (Illus.). 140p. pap. 35.00 *(978-0-340-98412-3(0))* Hodder Education GBR. Dist: Trans-Atlantic Pubns., Inc.

Abraham, Susan & Procario-Foley, Elena. Frontiers in Catholic Feminist Theology: Shoulder to Shoulder. Abraham, Susan, ed. 2009. 272p. (C). pap. 29.00 *(978-0-8006-6439-8(6)*, Fortress Pr.) Augsburg Fortress, Pubs.

Adams, William. The Elements of Christian Science; a Treatise upon Moral Philosophy & Practice by William Adams. 2006. 384p. per. 26.99 *(978-1-4255-4006-7(6))* MPublishing.

Aers, David. Salvation & Sin: Augustine, Langland, & Fourteenth-Century Theology. 2009. (ENG.). 304p. pap. 38.00 *(978-0-268-02033-0(7))* Univ. of Notre Dame Pr.

Alden, Joseph. Christian Ethics; or, the Science of Duty. 2006. 176p. per. 18.99 *(978-1-4255-1391-7(3))* MPublishing.

Alexander, Archibald. Outlines of Moral Science. 2009. (Amer Philosophy, Religion Ser.). (ENG.). 276p. pap. 18.95 *(978-1-4290-1656-8(6))* Applewood Bks.

—Outlines of Moral Science. 2009. 274p. 30.99 *(978-1-110-69566-9(7))*; pap. 26.75 *(978-1-110-69564-5(0))* BiblioBazaar.

—Outlines of Moral Science. 2009. 110p. pap. *(978-1-4588-9453-3(3))* Books LLC.

—Outlines of Moral Science. 2008. 272p. 42.95 *(978-1-4365-2057-7(6))* 2007. (ENG.). 276p. per. 27.95 *(978-0-548-72083-7(5))* Kessinger Publishing, LLC.

—Outlines of Moral Science by Archibald Alexander. 2006. 280p. per. 23.99 *(978-1-4255-2497-5(4))* MPublishing.

Allen, Bernice. Touchstones for Women: Creating a Lasting Memorial for the Little Girls in Your Life. 2010. pap. 12.99 *(978-1-61663-594-7(0))* Tate Publishing & Enterprises, LLC.

Allsopp, Michael E. Models of Christian Ethics. 2006. 93p. pap. 19.95 *(978-1-58966-054-0(4))* Univ. of Scranton Pr.

Alston, Leonard. The Stoic & Christian in the Second Century: a Comparison Of. 2007. (ENG.). 156p. per. 21.95 *(978-1-4304-4578-4(5))* Kessinger Publishing, LLC.

Anscombe, G. E. M. Faith in a Hard Ground: Essays on Religion, Philosophy & Ethics. Geach, Mary & Gormally, Luke, eds. 2008. (St Andrews Studies in Philosophy & Public Affairs Ser.). (ENG.). 250p. 80.00 *(978-1-84540-143-6(3))* Imprint Academic GBR. Dist: Ingram Pub. Services.

Arndt, Emily K. Demanding Our Attention: The Hebrew Bible As a Source for Christian Ethics. 2011. 240p. pap. 30.00 *(978-0-8028-6569-4(0))* Eerdmans, William B. Publishing Co.

Aschenbrenner, George. The Examination of Conscience. 2007. 1.95 *(978-0-8294-2482-9(2))* Loyola Pr.

Atze, Stefan. Ethik als Steigerungsform Von Theologie? Systematische Rekonstruktion und Kritik Eines Strukturprozesses Im Neuzeitlichen Protestantismus. 2008. (Theologische Bibliothek Topelmann Ser.). (GER.). XIII, 669p. 175.00 *(978-3-11-020390-5(1))* De Gruyter, Walter Inc.

Banner Michael. Doctrine of God & Theological Ethics. Banner, Michael & Torrance, Alan, eds. 2006. (ENG.). 240p. 60.00 *(978-0-567-08461-3(2)*, T&T Clark Int'l) Continuum International Publishing Group, Ltd. GBR. Dist: National Bk. Network.

Banner, Michael C. & Banner, Michael. Christian Ethics: A Brief History. 2009. (Blackwell Brief Histories of Religion Ser.: 19). (ENG.). 160p. 93.95 *(978-1-4051-1517-9(3)*, Wiley-Blackwell) Wiley, John & Sons, Inc.

Banner, Michael C., et al. Christian Ethics: A Brief History. 2009. (Blackwell Brief Histories of Religion Ser.: 18). (ENG.). 160p. pap. 26.95 *(978-1-4051-1518-6(1)*, Wiley-Blackwell) Wiley, John & Sons, Inc.

Baron, Ross. Social Ethics of the Church of Jesus Christ of Latter-Day Saints. 2008. 248p. pap. *(978-3-639-04825-4(3))* VDM Verlag Dr. Mueller e.K.

Barrera, Albino. Market Complicity & Christian Ethics. 2011. (New Studies in Christian Ethics Ser.). (ENG.). 324p. 88.00 *(978-1-107-00315-6(6))*, Cambridge Univ. Pr.

Barreto, Raimundo. Facing the Poor. 2009. 314p. pap. *(978-3-639-17703-9(7))* VDM Verlag Dr. Mueller e.K.

Barry, F. R. Christianity & the New World an Approa. 2006. pap. 30.95 *(978-1-4286-6000-7(3))* Kessinger Publishing, LLC.

Bash, Anthony. Forgiveness & Christian Ethics. (New Studies in Christian Ethics Ser.). (ENG.). 2010. 222p. pap. 31.99 *(978-0-521-14777-4(8))* 2007. 220p. 94.00 *(978-0-521-87880-7(2))* Cambridge Univ. Pr.

Batour, Charbel. How Can Lacan & Vasse Inform a Christian Understanding of Desire? 2008. 424p. pap. *(978-3-8364-9326-0(8))* VDM Verlag Dr. Mueller e.K.

Bayer, Oswald. Freedom in Response: Lutheran Ethics: Sources & Controversies. Cayzer, Jeff, tr. from GER. 2007. (Oxford Studies in Theological Ethics Ser.). (ENG.). 224p. 110.00 *(978-0-19-924909-1(1))* Oxford Univ. Pr., Inc.

Beach, Waldo. Conscience on Campus: An Interpretation of Christian Ethics for College Life. 2011. 126p. 40.95 ***(978-1-258-06681-9(5))*** Literary Licensing, LLC.

Beck, Richard. Unclean: Meditations on Purity, Hospitality, & Mortality. 2012. (ENG.). 212p. pap. 39.00 ***(978-0-7188-9256-2(9))*** Lutherworth Pr., The GBR. Dist: Brown, David Bk. Co., The.

—Unclean: Meditations on Purity, Hospitality, & Mortality. 2011. 212p. pap. 23.00 *(978-1-60899-242-3(X)*, Cascade Bks.) Wipf & Stock Pubs.

Belleville, Linda L. Sex, Lies, & the Truth: Developing A Christian Ethic in A Post-Christian Society. 2010. 136p. pap. 17.00 *(978-1-60899-519-6(4)*, Wipf and Stock) Wipf & Stock Pubs.

Bellinger, Charles. The Trinitarian Self: The Key to the Puzzle of Violence. 2008. (Princeton Theological Monographs). 190p. pap. 22.00 *(978-1-55635-232-4(8)*, Pickwick Pubns.) Wipf & Stock Pubs.

Bellinger, Charles K. The Trinitarian Self: The Key to the Puzzle of Violence. 2010. (ENG.). 190p. (C). pap. 38.00 *(978-0-227-17333-6(3))* Clarke, James Co., Ltd. GBR. Dist: Brown, David Bk. Co., The.

Berdiaev, Nikolai. The Destiny of Man. 3rd ed. 2009. pap. *(978-1-59731-256-1(8))* Perennis, Sophia.

Biggar. Good Life. 176p. 19.00 *(978-0-281-05023-9(6))* SPCK Publishing GBR. Dist: Pilgrim Pr., The/United Church Pr.

Blodgett, Barbara J. Lives Entrusted: An Ethic of Trust for Ministry. 2008. (Prisms Ser.). 176p. (C). pap. 21.00 *(978-0-8006-6321-6(7)*, Fortress Pr.) Augsburg Fortress, Pubs.

Boardman, Henry A. (Henry Augustus). The Bible in the Counting-House: A Course of Lectures to Merchants. by H. A. Boardman, D. D. 2006. 420p. per. 26.99 *(978-1-4255-4524-6(6))* MPublishing.

Boer, Theo A. & Gustafson, James M., eds. Moral Discernment in the Christian Life: Essays in Theological Ethics. 2007. (Library of Theological Ethics Ser.). (ENG.). 261p. per. 30.00 *(978-0-664-23070-8(9))* Westminster John Knox Pr.

Boesel, Chris. Risking Proclamation, Respecting Difference: Christian Faith, Imperialistic Discourse & Abraham. 2010. (ENG.). 305p. (C). pap. 43.00 *(978-0-227-17314-5(7))* Clarke, James Co., Ltd. GBR. Dist: Brown, David Bk. Co., The.

Bonzo, J. Matthew. Indwelling the Forsaken Other: The Trinitarian Ethics of Jurgen Moltmann. 2009. (Distinguished Dissertations in Christian Theology Ser.). 152p. pap. 14.00 *(978-1-55635-141-9(0)*, Pickwick Pubns.) Wipf & Stock Pubs.

Bowie, Robert A. Christianity Ethics. Bartlett, Cynthia, ed. 2009. (ENG., Illus.). pap., stu. ed. 37.50 *(978-1-4085-0456-7(1))* Nelson Thornes Ltd. GBR. Dist: Trans-Atlantic Pubns., Inc.

Brennecke, H. C., ed. Ethik im antiken Christentum. 2011. (Patristic Studies). (GER.). 113p. (C). pap. 50.00 *(978-90-429-2442-0(X))* Peeters Pubs. & Booksellers BEL. Dist: Brown, David Bk. Co., The.

BRETHERTON, Luke. Hospitality as Holiness: Christian Witness amid Moral Diversity. 2010. 226p. pap. 29.95 *(978-1-4094-0349-4(1))* Ashgate Publishing Co.

Brewer, Mark. What Is Your Spiritual Quotient? 2008. pap. 15.99 *(978-0-7684-2675-5(8))* Destiny Image Pubs.

Brock, Brian. Christian Ethics in a Technological Age. 2010. x, 408p. pap. 34.00 *(978-0-8028-6517-5(8))* Eerdmans, William B. Publishing Co.

—Singing the Ethos of God: On the Place of Christian Ethics in Scripture. 2007. 386p. per. 34.00 *(978-0-8028-0379-5(2))* Eerdmans, William B. Publishing Co.

Brown, Kate & Brown, Malcolm. Studying Christian Ethics Today. 2010. 288p. pap. ***(978-0-281-05827-3(X))*** SPCK Publishing.

Browne, Thomas. Religio Medici. 2009. 276p. pap. *(978-0-217-74912-1(7))*; 108p. pap. *(978-1-4589-6148-8(6))*; 154p. pap. *(978-0-217-74909-1(7))* Books LLC.

—Religio Medici. Winny, James, ed. 2008. (ENG.). 192p. pap. 37.99 *(978-0-521-09055-1(5))* Cambridge Univ. Pr.

—Religio Medici. 2008. 316p. *(978-1-4437-3387-8(3)*, Pomona Pr.) Read Bks.

—Religio Medici, Hydriotaphia, & the Letter to a Friend. 2009. 110p. pap. *(978-1-4589-6151-8(6))* Books LLC.

—Religio Medici, Hydriotaphia, & the Letter to a Friend. 2007. (ENG.). 116p. per. *(978-1-4068-2454-4(2))* Echo Library.

Browne, Thomas & Denonain, Jean-Jacques. Religio Medici. 2009. (ENG.). 128p. pap. 31.99 *(978-0-521-10076-2(3))* Cambridge Univ. Pr.

Browning, Don S. God & Globalization: Volume 2: The Spirit & the Modern Authorities, 4 vols. Stackhouse, Max L., ed. 2009. (Theology for the 21st Century Ser.). (ENG.). 260p. pap. 34.95 *(978-0-567-00705-6(7)*, T&T Clark Int'l) Continuum International Publishing Group, Ltd. GBR. Dist: National Bk. Network.

BRUCE L. MOODY, James D. White. Once free of it All. 2009. (ENG.). 122p. pap. 13.95 *(978-0-557-13985-9(6))* Lulu Enterprises Inc.

Brunn, Frank Martin. Selbstbestimmung in der Perspektive theologischer Ethik: [Self-determination from the Perspective of Theological Ethics]. Alexander Dietz & Frank Martin Brunn, eds. 2011. (Marburger Theologische Studien Ser.). (GER.). 168p. (C). pap. 39.00 ***(978-3-374-02888-7(8))*** Evangelische Verlagsanstalt GmbH DEU. Dist: Brown, David Bk. Co., The.

Buchanan, George Wesley Litt. D. D. Jesus the Statesman. 2008. 268p. 29.99 *(978-1-4257-8836-0(X))*; pap. 19.99 *(978-1-4257-8835-3(1))* Xlibris Corp.

Buddies: Bulletin. 14.95 *(978-0-687-06973-6(4))* Abingdon Pr.

Budziszewski, J. What We Can?t Not Know: A Guide. 2011. 291p. pap. 17.95 *(978-1-58617-481-1(9))* Ignatius Pr.

Bunn, Bob. Path of Purity: A Family Guide. 2010. 143p. pap. *(978-1-4158-6876-8(X))* LifeWay Christian Resources.

Butler, Sheila. AQA (B) GCSE Religious Studies: Religion & Life Issues & Religion & Morality. 2009. (Illus.). 64p. pap. 20.00 *(978-0-340-98718-6(9))* Hodder Education GBR. Dist: Trans-Atlantic Pubns., Inc.

—Christianity: Ethics. 2009. (Illus.). 80p. pap. 20.00 *(978-1-4441-0079-2(3))*; 2nd ed. 168p. pap. 44.50 *(978-0-340-98656-1(5))* Hodder Education GBR. Dist: Trans-Atlantic Pubns., Inc.

Callan, Charles & McHugh, John A. Moral Theology V1: A Complete Course Based on St. Thomas Aquinas & the Best Modern Authorities. 2011. 704p. 70.95 ***(978-1-258-02081-1(5))*** Literary Licensing, LLC.

—Moral Theology V2: A Complete Course Based on St. Thomas Aquinas & the Best Modern Authorities. 2011. 812p. 74.95 ***(978-1-258-02085-9(8))*** Literary Licensing, LLC.

Cameron, Scott W., et al, eds. Life in the Law: Service & Integrity. 2009. (Illus.). 275p. *(978-0-8425-2738-5(9))*; pap. *(978-0-8425-2741-5(9))* Brigham Young Univ. (Brigham Young Univ. Pr.).

Camosy, Charles C. Peter Singer & Christian Ethics: Beyond Polarization. 2012. (ENG.). (C). 284p. 95.00 ***(978-0-521-19915-5(8))***; 288p. pap. 29.99 ***(978-0-521-14933-4(9))*** Cambridge Univ. Pr.

Campbell, John W. OOPS, We Lost Our Values: A Discussion of the Erosion of Morality & Ethics in the United States. 2007. 148p. per. 11.99 *(978-1-59886-700-8(8))* Tate Publishing & Enterprises, LLC.

Campolo, Tony. Is Jesus a Democrat or a Republican?, 0 vols. 2009. 208p. pap. 11.99 *(978-0-8499-2927-4(X))* Nelson, Thomas Inc.

Cannon, Katie Geneva, et al, eds. Womanist Theological Ethics: A Reader. 2011. (Library of Theological Ethics Ser.). (ENG.). 224p. pap. 30.00 *(978-0-664-23537-6(9))* Westminster John Knox Pr.

Caramuel Lobkowitz, Juan & Sabaino, Daniele. Il Tractatus Expendens Propositiones Damnatas Ab Alexandro VII Di Juan Caramuel Lobkowitz: Studio Introduttivo Ed Edizione Critica. 2010. (LAT, ITA & ENG.). 139.95 *(978-0-7734-3608-4(1))* Mellen, Edwin Pr., The.

Carrette, Paul. Raising Godly Children: A Manual for Faith-Based Parenting. 2008. pap. 14.99 *(978-1-60647-149-4(X))* Xulon Pr., Inc.

Cathy, S. Truett. Wealth: Is It Worth It? 2011. 200p. 20.00 *(978-1-929619-40-5(5))* Looking Glass Bks.

Chalke, Steve & Mann, Alan. Different Eyes: The Art of Living Beautifully, 1 vol. 2010. (ENG.). 144p. pap. 14.99 *(978-0-310-32680-9(X))* Zondervan.

Cherry, Mark J., ed. The Death of Metaphysics; the Death of Culture: Epistemology, Metaphysics, & Morality. 2010. (Philosophical Studies in Contemporary Culture Ser.). xxi, 279p. pap. 169.00 *(978-90-481-7155-2(5)*, 9048171555) Springer.

Childs, James M., Jr. Ethics in the Community of Promise: Faith, Formation, & Decision. 2nd rev. ed. 2006. (Illus.). 224p. per. 19.00 *(978-0-8006-3797-2(6)*, Fortress Pr.) Augsburg Fortress, Pubs.

Chouinard, Larry, et al, eds. Christian Ethics: The Issues of Life & Death. 2010. 476p. pap. 52.00 *(978-1-60899-499-1(6)*, Wipf and Stock) Wipf & Stock Pubs.

Christian Ethics [Microsoft Reader]. 10.00 *(978-0-687-00063-0(7))* Abingdon Pr.

Ciancio, Jack. Where Christ Presides: A Quaker Perspective on Moral Discernment. 2009. 176p. pap. 15.99 *(978-1-4141-1376-0(5))* Pleasant Word.

Cirillo, Joseph. Life Lessons. 2007. 176p. per. 14.49 *(978-1-4343-0708-8(5))* AuthorHouse.

Clawson, Julie. Everyday Justice: The Global Impact of Our Daily Choices, 1 vol. 2009. (ENG.). 208p. pap. 16.00 *(978-0-8308-3628-4(4)*, IVP Bks.) InterVarsity Pr.

Clements, Keith. The Moot Papers: Faith, Freedom & Society, 1938-1944. 2010. (ENG., Illus.). 752p. 295.00 *(978-0-567-03257-7(4)*, T&T Clark Int'l) Continuum International Publishing Group, Ltd. GBR. Dist: National Bk. Network.

Clifton-Soderstrom, Michelle A. Angels, Worms, & Bogeys: The Christian Ethic of Pietism. 2010. (Cascade Companions Ser.). 126p. pap. 16.00 *(978-1-60608-041-2(5)*, Cascade Bks.) Wipf & Stock Pubs.

Cloutier, David, ed. Leaving & Coming Home. 2010. (Illus.). 282p. pap. 31.00 *(978-1-60899-091-7(5)*, Cascade Bks.) Wipf & Stock Pubs.

Cobbe, Frances Power. Studies New & Old of Ethical & Social Subjects by Frances Power Cobbe. 2006. 452p. per. 26.99 *(978-1-4255-4972-5(1))* MPublishing.

Cochran, Elizabeth Agnew. Receptive Human Virtues: A New Reading of Jonathan Edwards's Ethics. 2010. 216p. 59.95 *(978-0-271-03752-3(0))* Pennsylvania State Univ. Pr.

Codrut M. Magheru. Quantum Christian Virtues: A Catalogue of Enlightenment. 2010. 136p. 23.95 *(978-1-4502-2763-6(5))* iUniverse, Inc.

Coleman, John & Coleman, John Aloysius. Christian Political Ethics. 2007. (Ethikon Series in Comparative Ethics). 289p. 66.00 *(978-0-691-13140-5(6))* Princeton Univ. Pr.

Coleman, John Aloysius. Christian Political Ethics. Coleman, John A., ed. 2007. (Ethikon Series in Comparative Ethics). (ENG.). 308p. (C). per. 26.95 *(978-0-691-13481-9(2))* Princeton Univ. Pr.

Comiskey, Joel. Planting Churches that Reproduce: Starting a Network of Simple Churches. 2008. (ENG.). 205p. pap. 15.95 *(978-0-9790679-6-9(0)*, CCS Publishing) CCS Pubs.

Connolly, R. Hugh, ed. Didascalia Apostolorum: The Syriac Version Translated & Accompanied by the Verona Latin Fragments. 2010. (Ancient Texts & Translations Ser.). 386p. pap. 45.00 *(978-1-55635-669-8(2)*, Wipf and Stock) Wipf & Stock Pubs.

Cook, Christopher C. H. Alcohol, Addiction & Christian Ethics. 2008. (New Studies in Christian Ethics Ser.). (ENG.). 236p. pap. 34.99 *(978-0-521-09134-3(9))* Cambridge Univ. Pr.

Cook, Tony. Moral Maze. (Illus.). 192p. 15.00 *(978-0-281-04038-4(9))* SPCK Publishing GBR. Dist: Pilgrim Pr., The/United Church Pr.

Costanza, Christina. Einübung in die Ewigkeit: Julius Kaftans eschatologische Theologie und Ethik. 2009. (Forschungen Zur Systematischen und Okumenischen Theologie Ser.). (GER.). 375p. (C). 96.00 *(978-3-525-56351-9(5))* Vandenhoeck & Ruprecht GmbH & Co. KG DEU. Dist: ISD.

Cram101 Textbook Reviews & Cram101 Textbook Reviews. Outlines & Highlights for Social Ethics in the Making: Interpreting an American Tradition by Gary J. Dorrien, ISBN. 2011. 262p. pap. 31.95 ***(978-1-61461-600-9(0))*** Cram101 Inc.

Cronin, Kieran. Rights & Christian Ethics. 2009. (New Studies in Christian Ethics Ser.). (ENG.). 348p. (C). pap. 46.00 *(978-0-521-09294-4(9))* Cambridge Univ. Pr.

Crowe, Brent. Chasing Elephants: Wrestling with the Gray Areas of Life. 2010. (NavPress Devotional Readers Ser.). 192p. pap. 14.99 *(978-1-61521-121-0(7))* NavPress Publishing Group.

Cunningham, David. Christian Ethics: The End of the Law. 2008. XIV, 402p. 120.00 *(978-0-415-37599-3(1))* Routledge.

Cunningham, David S. The End of the Law. 2008. (ENG.). 416p. (C). pap. 39.95 *(978-0-415-37600-6(9))* Routledge.

Curran, Charles. Moral Theology of John Paul II. 2007. (ENG.). 280p. *(978-0-567-03093-1(8)*, T&T Clark) Continuum International Publishing Group, Ltd.

Daly, Cahal B. Law & Morals. 72p. pap. 9.95 *(978-1-85182-119-8(8))* Four Courts Pr. IRL. Dist: International Specialized Bk. Services.

Daniel, Dr., Carrel. Is Biblical Morality Outdated? 2007. (ENG.). 272p. pap. 14.99 *(978-1-932124-87-3(X))* ACW Pr.

Dann, G. Elijah. God & the Public Square. 2010. xxviii, 147p. *(978-0-7391-4711-5(0))* Lexington Bks.

Davis, James Calvin. In Defense of Civility: How Religion Can Unite America on Seven Moral Issues that Divide Us. 2010. (ENG.). 240p. pap. 20.00 *(978-0-664-23544-4(1))* Westminster John Knox Pr.

De La Torre, Miguel A. Latina/o Social Ethics: Moving Beyond Eurocentric Moral Thinking. 2010. (New Perspectives in Latina/o Religion Ser.). (ENG., Illus.). 160p. (C). pap. 24.95 *(978-1-60258-294-1(7))* Baylor Univ. Pr.

De La Torre, Miguel A. & Floyd-Thomas, Stacey M., eds. Beyond the Pale: Reading Ethics from the Margins. 2011. (ENG.). 304p. pap. 40.00 *(978-0-664-23680-9(4))* Westminster John Knox Pr.

De Tavernier, J., et al, eds. Responsibility, God & Society. Theological Ethics in Dialogue: Festschrift Roger Burggraeve. 2008. (Bibliotheca Ephemeridum Theologicarum Lovaniensium Ser.). (ENG., Illus.). 413p. (C). pap. 109.00 *(978-90-429-2119-1(6))* Peeters Pubs. & Booksellers BEL. Dist: Brown, David Bk. Co., The.

De Waal Dryden, J. Theology & Ethics in 1 Peter: Paraenetic Strategies for Christian Character Formation. 2006. (Wissenschaftliche Untersuchungen Zum Neuen Testament 2 Ser.: Vol. 209). 237p. (C). pap. 89.50 *(978-3-16-148910-5(1))* Mohr Siebeck GmbH & Co. KG DEU. Dist: Coronet Bks.

Deburgh, W. G. From Morality to Religion. 2007. (ENG.). 372p. 48.95 *(978-0-548-06107-7(6))* Kessinger Publishing, LLC.

Decisions. pupil's gde. ed. 6.75 *(978-1-56212-648-3(2)*, 138600) Faith Alive Christian Resources.

Diaz, Gwendolyn Mitchell. Sticking up for What Is Right: Answers to the Moral Dilemmas Teenagers Face. 2008. 140p. pap. 14.99 *(978-1-60791-103-6(5))* Xulon Pr., Inc.

Disbrey, Claire. Wrestling with Life's Tough Issues: What Should a Christian Do? 2008. 185p. pap. 16.95 *(978-1-59856-314-6(9))* Hendrickson Pubs. Marketing, LLC.

Dorner, I. A. System of Christian Ethics. Mead, C. M., tr. 2007. (ENG.). 624p. 60.95 *(978-0-548-15181-5(4))* Kessinger Publishing, LLC.

—System of Christian Ethics. Mead, C. M. & Cunningham, R. T., trs. 2007. (ENG.). 628p. per. 45.95 *(978-1-4304-4539-5(4))* Kessinger Publishing, LLC.

Dorrien, Gary. Social Ethics in the Making: Interpreting an American Tradition. 2010. (ENG.). 752p. pap. 46.95 *(978-1-4443-3730-3(0)*, Wiley-Blackwell) Wiley, John & Sons, Inc.

Dorrien, Gary J. Social Ethics in the Making: Interpreting an American Tradition. 2008. (ENG., Illus.). 752p. 164.95 *(978-1-4051-8687-2(9)*, Wiley-Blackwell) Wiley, John & Sons, Inc.

Douglas, Lynette, compiled by. Promises from God for Purposeful Living. 2006. (Promises from God for... Ser.). 155p. *(978-1-86920-536-2(7))* Christian Art Pubs.

Duffy, Eugene & Hannon, Patrick, eds. Beauty, Truth & Love: Essays in Honour of Enda Mcdonagh. 2010. (ENG.). 236p. pap. 28.95 *(978-1-85607-662-3(8))* Columba Pr. IRL. Dist: Dufour Editions, Inc.

Durbin, Kara G. Parenting with Scripture: A Topical Guide for Teachable Moments. 2012. (ENG.). 256p. pap. 14.99 ***(978-0-8024-0849-5(4))*** Moody Pubs.

Dussel, Enrique. Ethics & Community. 2008. 272p. pap. 31.00 *(978-1-55635-995-8(0)*, Wipf and Stock) Wipf & Stock Pubs.

Dyer, Keith & Neville, David, eds. Resurrection & Responsibility: Essays on Theology, Scripture, & Ethics in Honor of Thorwald Lorenzen. 2009. 290p. pap. 32.00 *(978-1-60608-461-8(5)*, Pickwick Pubns.) Wipf & Stock Pubs.

Eckfeldt, Edgar L. The Christian Legacy: Taming Brutish Human Nature in Western Civilization. 2011. (ENG.). 560p. pap. 35.95 ***(978-0-89226-106-2(4))*** Paragon Hse. Pubs.

Edwards, Jonathan. Freedom of the Will, Vol. 1. Ramsey, Paul, ed. 2009. (Works of Jonathan Edwards Ser.). (ENG.). 512p. pap. 20.00 *(978-0-300-15840-3(8))* Yale Univ. Pr.

—Religious Affections, Vol. 2. Smith, John E., ed. 2009. (Works of Jonathan Edwards Ser.). (ENG.). 536p. pap. 20.00 *(978-0-300-15841-0(6))* Yale Univ. Pr.

—A Treastise Concerning Religious Affections. 2007. 308p. per. 29.99 *(978-1-59547-947-1(3))* NuVision Pubns., LLC.

Ekeke, Emeka C. Issues in Biomedical Ethics: A christian Perspective. 2011. 184p. pap. ***(978-3-8433-6203-0(3))*** Lambert Academic Publishing.

Ellis, Tom. Judah Inherits Christianity. 2008. (ENG.). pap. 13.95 *(978-0-533-15790-7(0))* Vantage Pr., Inc.

Evans, G. R. The Good, the Bad & the Moral Dilemma. 2008. (ENG.). 224p. pap. 12.95 *(978-0-7459-5268-0(2))* Lion Hudson PLC GBR. Dist: Independent Pubs. Group.

Feil, Michael. Die Grundlegung der Ethik bei Friedrich Schleiermacher und Thomas von Aquin. (Theologische Bibliothek Töpelmann Ser.). (GER.). X, 290p. 225.00 ***(978-3-11-181983-9(3))*** De Gruyter, Walter Inc.

Feinberg, John S. & Feinberg, Paul D. Ethics for a Brave New World. 2nd rev. ed. 2010. 848p. pap. 35.00 *(978-1-58134-712-8(X))* Crossway.

Fernández, Aurelio. Teología Moral: Curso Fundamental de la Moral Católica. 4th ed. 2010. (SPA.). 716p. *(978-84-9840-394-7(4))* Palabra, Ediciones S.A.

Fiala, Andrew G. What Would Jesus Really Do? The Power & Limits of Jesus' Moral Teachings. 2007. (ENG.). 216p. 21.95 *(978-0-7425-5260-9(8))* Rowman & Littlefield Publishers, Inc.

Finlan, Stephen. The Family Metaphor in Jesus' Teaching: Gospel & Ethics. 2009. 154p. pap. 18.00 *(978-1-55635-938-5(1)*, Cascade Bks.) Wipf & Stock Pubs.

Fisher (The Prophet Ok-ta-ha), C. B. Chaos Revolution & Redemption. 2008. 172p. 24.99 *(978-1-4343-8733-2(X))*; pap. 17.70 *(978-1-4343-8732-5(1))* AuthorHouse.

Fleming, Amelia, ed. Contemporary Irish Moral Discourse: Essays in Honour of Patrick Hannon. 2007. (ENG.). 180p. pap. 33.95 *(978-1-85607-558-9(3))* Columba Pr. IRL. Dist: Dufour Editions, Inc.

Fleming, Julia A. Defending Probabilism: The Moral Theology of Juan Caramuel. 2006. (Moral Traditions Ser.). (ENG.). 224p. 44.95 *(978-1-58901-113-7(9))* Georgetown Univ. Pr.

Foreman, Mark W. Christianity & Bioethics: Confronting Clinical Issues. 2011. 300p. pap. 33.00 ***(978-1-61097-370-0(4)***, Wipf and Stock) Wipf & Stock Pubs.

Forrester, Duncan B. Forrester on Christian Ethics: Collected Writings on Christianity India & the Social Order. 2010. (Ashgate Contemporary Thinkers on Religion: Collected Works Ser.). 536p. 144.95 *(978-0-7546-6438-3(4))* Ashgate Publishing Co.

Forsyth, P. T. The Christian Ethic of War. 2008. 204p. 39.95 *(978-1-4365-1174-2(7))* 2007. (ENG.). 208p. per. 24.95 *(978-0-548-73099-7(7))* Kessinger Publishing, LLC.

Fosdick, Harry Emerson. Jesus' Ethical Message Confronts the World. 2011. 16p. pap. 35.95 ***(978-1-258-02540-3(X))*** Literary Licensing, LLC.

Fountain, David. Let Conscience Speak. 32p. pap. 0.99 *(978-0-85479-810-0(2))* Revival Literature.

Fowler, Hank. The Whole Armor of God-Volume I -Foundations of Christianity: Separating Truth from Custom, Tradition & Counterfeit. 2008. 254p. pap. 20.00 *(978-0-8059-7801-8(1))* Dorrance Publishing Co., Inc.

Fraley, Paul. Witan Primer Series: Four Lectures in One. 2007. 110p. pap. 12.95 *(978-0-7414-4363-2(5))* Infinity Publishing.

Frame, John M. The Doctrine of the Christian Life. 2008. xxxi, 1069p. *(978-0-87552-796-3(5))* P & R Publishing.

France, Mary. For We Wrestle Not Against Flesh & Blood. 2008. 248p. pap. 12.99 *(978-1-935105-11-4(6))* Avid Readers Publishing Group.

Fuller, Thomas. The Holy & Profane States by Thomas Fuller with Some Account of the Author & His Writings. 2006. 336p. per. 23.99 *(978-1-4255-3357-1(4))* MPublishing.

Gap Lee, Seung. The Hope of the Earth. 2008. 240p. pap. *(978-3-639-04030-2(9))* VDM Verlag Dr. Mueller e.K.

Garcia, Joaquin F. The Natural Law: Foundation of Morality. 2011. 26p. 35.95 ***(978-1-258-04068-0(9))*** Literary Licensing, LLC.

Garden of Virtues: Assortment. 35.00 *(978-0-687-02000-3(X))* Abingdon Pr.

Gardner, E. Clinton. Justice & Christian Ethics. 2009. (New Studies in Christian Ethics Ser.). (ENG.). 196p. pap. 30.00 *(978-0-521-05055-5(3))* Cambridge Univ. Pr.

Garrod, Heathcote William. The Religion of All Good Men & Other Studies in Christian Ethics. 2007. (ENG.). 270p. 42.95 *(978-0-548-15001-6(X))*; 272p. per. 27.95 *(978-1-4304-4327-8(8))* Kessinger Publishing, LLC.

Geisler, Norman L. Christian Ethics: Contemporary Issues & Options, 1 vol. 2nd ed. 2010. (ENG.). 448p. (C). pap. 26.99 *(978-0-8010-3879-2(0))* Baker Academic.

Geisler, Norman L. & Snuffer, Ryan P. Love Your Neighbor: Thinking Wisely about Right & Wrong. 2007. (Illus.). 192p. pap. 14.99 *(978-1-58134-945-0(9))* Crossway.

Gemser Publications Staff, et al. Virtues & Values: 52 Weeks of Family Night Fun. 2011. 128p. pap. 19.99 ***(978-1-59955-861-5(0)***, Bonneville Bks.) Cedar Fort, Inc./CFI Distribution.

Gibson, Margaret Dunlop, ed. The Didascalia Apostolorum in Syriac: Edited from a Mesopotamian Manuscript with Various Readings & Collations of Other MSS. 2011. (Cambridge Library Collection - Religion Ser.). (SYR.). 254p. pap. 23.99 *(978-1-108-01896-8(3))* Cambridge Univ. Pr.

Gibson, Margaret Dunlop, tr. The Didascalia Apostolorum in English. 2011. (Cambridge Library Collection - Religion Ser.). (ENG.). 138p. pap. 19.99 *(978-1-108-01897-5(1))* Cambridge Univ. Pr.

Gill, Robin. Health Care & Christian Ethics. 2008. (New Studies in Christian Ethics Ser.). (ENG.). 244p. pap. 28.99 *(978-0-521-05574-1(1))* Cambridge Univ. Pr.

—A Textbook of Christian Ethics. 3rd rev. ed. 2006. (ENG.). 480p. 44.95 *(978-0-567-03112-9(8)*, T&T Clark Int'l) Continuum International Publishing Group, Ltd. GBR. Dist: National Bk. Network.

Gill, Robin, ed. The Cambridge Companion to Christian Ethics. 2nd rev. ed. 2011. (Cambridge Companions to Religion Ser.). (ENG.). 342p. (C). 90.00 ***(978-1-107-00007-0(6))***; pap. 29.99 ***(978-0-521-16483-2(4))*** Cambridge Univ. Pr.

Gillis, James M. The Moral Law: In the Heart of Man & on the Tablets of Stone. 2011. 88p. 38.95 ***(978-1-258-05164-8(8))*** Literary Licensing, LLC.

Gilson, Etienne. Moral Values & the Moral Life the Ethi. 2006. pap. 31.95 *(978-1-4286-4701-5(5))* Kessinger Publishing, LLC.

Goheen, Michael W. & Glanville, Erin. The Gospel & Globalization: Exploring the Religious Roots of a Globalized World. 2009. 384p. pap. *(978-1-57383-440-7(8))* Regent College Publishing.

Gore, Charles. Christian Moral Principles: Seven Sermons Preached in Grosvenor Chapel as a Lenten Course In 1921. 2008. 131p. pap. 11.00 *(978-1-60608-265-2(5)*, Wipf and Stock) Wipf & Stock Pubs.

Grabill, Stephen J. Rediscovering the Natural Law in Reformed Theological Ethics. 2006. (Emory University Studies in Law & Religion). 310p. per. 38.00 *(978-0-8028-6313-3(2))* Eerdmans, William B. Publishing Co.

Graham, Mark E. Sustainable Agriculture: A Christian Ethic of Gratitude. 2009. 256p. pap. 28.00 *(978-1-60608-806-7(8)*, Wipf and Stock) Wipf & Stock Pubs.

Grant, Colin. Altruism & Christian Ethics. 2009. (New Studies in Christian Ethics Ser.). (ENG.). 288p. pap. 41.00 *(978-0-521-09361-3(9))* Cambridge Univ. Pr.

Greene, J. P. Virtudes Fundamentales - Manual: Christian Morals of Our . . . (SPA.). *(978-84-7645-259-2(4)*, 223320) Clie, Editorial.

Greening, John. A Man & His Ethics. 2007. 96p. pap. *(978-1-59402-332-3(8))* Regular Baptist Pr.

Grey, Mary. Questioning Belief. 224p. 15.00 *(978-0-281-04885-4(1))* SPCK Publishing GBR. Dist: Pilgrim Pr., The/United Church Pr.

Grimsrud, Ted. Embodying the Way of Jesus: Anabaptist Convictions for the Twenty-First Century. 2007. 262p. pap. 27.00 *(978-1-59752-987-7(7)*, Wipf and Stock) Wipf & Stock Pubs.

Groenhout, Ruth E. Bioethics: A Reformed Look at Life & Death Choices. 2009. *(978-1-59255-263-4(3))* Faith Alive Christian Resources.

Gudorf, Christine E. Journal of the Society of Christian Ethics: Spring/Summer 2006, Vol. 26 No. 1. Lauritzen, Paul, ed. 2006. (ENG.). 232p. pap. 60.00 *(978-1-58901-098-7(1))* Georgetown Univ. Pr.

Gudorf, Christine E. & Lauritzen, Paul, eds. Journal of the Society of Christian Ethics No. 2: 2006. 2nd rev. ed. 2006. 240p. pap. 50.00 *(978-1-58901-099-4(X))* Georgetown Univ. Pr.

Gustafson, James M. Christ & the Moral Life. 2008. (Library of Theological Ethics Ser.). (ENG.). 300p. pap. 30.00 *(978-0-664-23295-5(7))* Westminster John Knox Pr.

Haddorff, David. Christian Ethics as Witness. 2011. (ENG.). 494p. pap. 58.00 *(978-0-227-17374-9(0))* Clarke, James Co., Ltd. GBR. Dist: Brown, David Bk. Co., The.

—Christian Ethics as Witness: Barth's Ethics for A World at Risk. 2010. 494p. pap. 54.00 *(978-1-60899-282-9(9)*, Cascade Bks.) Wipf & Stock Pubs.

Hallett, Garth L. Priorities & Christian Ethics. 2008. (New Studies in Christian Ethics Ser.). (ENG.). 220p. pap. 34.00 *(978-0-521-09085-8(7))* Cambridge Univ. Pr.

Hanna, Ralph, ed. Speculum Vitae: A Reading Text, Volumes 1 And 2. 2009. (Early English Text Society Original Ser.). (Illus.). 390p. 175.00 *(978-0-19-956401-9(9))* Oxford Univ. Pr., Inc.

Hannon, Patrick. Right or Wrong? Essays in Moral Theology. 2009. (ENG.). 150p. pap. 22.95 *(978-1-84730-129-1(0))* Veritas Pubns. IRL. Dist: Dufour Editions, Inc.

Härle, Wilfried. Ethik. 2011. (De Gruyter Studium Ser.). (GER.). (C). 56.00 ***(978-3-11-017812-8(5))*** De Gruyter, Walter Inc.

Harlow, S. Ralph. Thoughts for Times Like These. 2011. 190p. 42.95 ***(978-1-258-07436-4(2))*** Literary Licensing, LLC.

Harries, Richard. Questions on Life & Death: Christian Faith & Medical Intervention. 2010. 160p. pap. ***(978-0-281-06241-6(2))*** SPCK Publishing.

Harris, Nigel, ed. The Light of the Soul: The lumen Anime C & Ulrich Putsch's Das Liecht der Sel Critical Edition with Introduction. 2007. (LAT, GER & ENG.). 487p. pap. 99.95 *(978-3-03910-737-7(2))* Lang, Peter Publishing, Inc.

Harrod, John A. Weaving the Tapestry of Moral Judgement: Christian Ethics in a Plural World. 2007. 360p. per. *(978-0-7162-0618-7(8))* Epworth Pr., The.

Harvey, A., ed. Las Ensenanzas de los Misticos Cristianos. (SPA.). 252p. 11.00 *(978-84-89920-53-8(2)*, 86914) Ediciones Oniro S.A. ESP. Dist: Lectorum Pubns., Inc.

Harvey, John F. Moral Theology of the Confessions of Saint Augustine. 2009. 194p. pap. 22.00 *(978-1-60608-423-6(2)*, Wipf and Stock) Wipf & Stock Pubs.

Harvey, John F. Moral Theology of the Confessions of St Augustine. 2011. 194p. 42.95 ***(978-1-258-02235-8(4))*** Literary Licensing, LLC.

Harvey, Sharon R. Open Theism & Environmental Responsibilities- a Promotion of Environmental Ethics. 2007. 156p. per. *(978-3-8364-1740-2(5))* VDM Verlag Dr. Mueller e.K.

Harvie, Timothy. Jürgen Moltmann's Ethics of Hope: Eschatological Possibilities for Moral Action. 2009. (New Critical Thinking in Religion, Theology & Biblical Studies). 238p. 99.95 *(978-0-7546-6481-9(3))* Ashgate Publishing Co.

Hauerwas, Stanley. Christian Existence Today: Essays on Church, World, & Living in Between. 2010. 282p. pap. 31.00 *(978-1-60899-710-7(3)*, Wipf and Stock) Wipf & Stock Pubs.

Hauerwas, Stanley & Wells, Samuel, eds. The Blackwell Companion to Christian Ethics. 2nd ed. 2011. (Wiley-Blackwell Companions to Religion Ser.: 60). (ENG.). 592p. 194.95 *(978-1-4443-3134-9(5)*, Wiley-Blackwell) Wiley, John & Sons, Inc.

Hayes, Teresa. Recovering from Church Hurt: Has the Church become a Revolving Door? 2010. 62p. pap. 15.95 *(978-1-4327-6024-3(6))* Outskirts Pr., Inc.

Hayward, Douglas James & Baker, Dwight P. Serving Jesus with Integrity: Ethics & Accountability in Mission. 2010. *(978-0-87808-023-6(6))* Carey, William Library Pubs.

Hegeman, Johan, et al. Practice & Profile: Christian Formation for Vocation. 2011. 338p. pap. 37.00 *(978-1-61097-091-4(8)*, Wipf and Stock) Wipf & Stock Pubs.

Henson, Herbert H. Christian Morality, Natural, Developing, Final. (Gifford Lectures: 1935-36). reprint ed. 37.50 *(978-0-404-60494-3(3))* AMS Pr., Inc.

Herdt, Jennifer A. Putting on Virtue: The Legacy of the Splendid Vices. (ENG.). 472p. 2012. pap. 35.00 ***(978-0-226-32719-8(1))*** 2008. 55.00 *(978-0-226-32724-2(8))* Univ. of Chicago Pr.

Hester, Joseph P. An Ethic of Hope. 2008. 163p. pap. 12.95 *(978-0-7414-4485-1(2))* Infinity Publishing.

Hill Sr, Steven Lawrence. I Have Rights Too! Christians among Chains. 2007. 110p. 23.95 *(978-0-615-14056-8(4))* ASA Publishing Co.

Hobson, Tom. WhatÕs on GodÕs Sin List for Today? 2011. 114p. pap. 14.00 *(978-1-61097-279-6(1)*, Wipf and Stock) Wipf & Stock Pubs.

Holmes, Arthur Frank. Ethics: Approaching Moral Decisions. 2nd rev. ed. 2007. (Contours of Christian Philosophy Ser.). (ENG.). 150p. per. 15.00 *(978-0-8308-2803-6(6)*, IVP Acad.) InterVarsity Pr.

Holmes, Christopher R. J. Ethics in the Presence of Jesus. 2012. (ENG.). 176p. 120.00 *(978-0-567-14428-7(3))*; pap. 34.95 *(978-0-567-49173-2(0))* Continuum International Publishing Group, Ltd. GBR. (T&T Clark Int'l). Dist: National Bk. Network.

Hoose, Bernard. Moral Theology for the Twenty-First Century: Essays in Celebration of Kevin Kelly. Clague, Julie & Mannion, Gerard, eds. 2008. (ENG., Illus.). 320p. 140.00 *(978-0-567-03285-0(X)*, T&T Clark Int'l) Continuum International Publishing Group, Ltd. GBR. Dist: National Bk. Network.

Hoose, Bernard, et al, eds. Moral Theology for the 21st Century: Essays in Celebration of Kevin T. Kelly. 2011. (ENG.). 320p. pap. 44.95 *(978-0-567-62143-6(X)*, T&T Clark Int'l) Continuum International Publishing Group, Ltd. GBR. Dist: National Bk. Network.

Hopkins, Mark. The Law of Love & Love as a Law. 2009. (Amer Philosophy, Religion Ser.). (ENG.). 364p. pap. 22.95 *(978-1-4290-1782-4(1))* Applewood Bks.

—The Law of Love & Love As a Law: Or, Christian Ethics. 3rd ed. reprint ed. 42.50 *(978-0-404-59197-7(3))* AMS Pr., Inc.

Houston, Tom. Public & Private Morality: Reflections on King David for Today's Leaders. 2006. (ENG.). 224p. 11.99 *(978-1-85792-967-6(5)*, Christian Focus) Christian Focus Pubns. GBR. Dist: STL Distribution North America.

Hovey, Craig. Speak Thus: Christian Language in Church & World. 2008. (ENG.). 172p. pap. 42.50 *(978-0-227-17271-1(X))* Clarke, James Co., Ltd. GBR. Dist: Brown, David Bk. Co., The.

Hovey, Craig R. Speak Thus: Christian Language in Church & World. 2008. 170p. pap. 20.00 *(978-1-55635-504-2(1)*, Cascade Bks.) Wipf & Stock Pubs.

Huckabee, Mike. Character Makes a Difference: Where I'm from, Where I've Been, & What I Believe. 2007. (ENG.). 227p. per. 11.99 *(978-0-8054-4677-7(X)*, B&H Bks.) B&H Publishing Group.

Huebner, Harry J. An Introduction to Christian Ethics: History, Movements, People. 2012. (ENG.). 656p. (C). pap. 59.95 ***(978-1-60258-063-3(4))*** Baylor Univ. Pr.

Hughes, Hugh. Ethical Christianity. 2007. (ENG.). 190p. 37.95 *(978-0-548-05208-2(5))* Kessinger Publishing, LLC.

Human, Dirk J., ed. Psalmody & Poetry in Old Testament Ethics. 2012. (Library Hebrew Bible/Old Testament Studies). (ENG.). 192p. 130.00 ***(978-0-567-28267-5(8)**,* T&T Clark Int'l) Continuum International Publishing Group, Ltd. GBR. Dist: National Bk. Network.

Hunneysett, Edna. Pastoral Care Mental Health. 2009. 256p. pap. *(978-1-84747-883-2(2))* Chipmunkapublishing.

Hunt, John & Penwell, Dan, eds. AMG's Handi-Reference World Religions & Cults. 2008. (AMG Handi-Reference Ser.). (ENG.). 800p. pap. 9.99 *(978-0-89957-113-3(1))* AMG Pubs.

Hurlin, Stephen J. Courage to Doubt. 2009. 162p. pap. 8.99 *(978-1-61667-002-3(9))* Raider Publishing International.

Hybels, Bill, et al. Excellent Living: Giving God Your Best, 1 vol. 2009. (Interactions Ser.). (ENG.). 96p. pap. 7.99 *(978-0-310-28064-4(8))* Zondervan.

Hyde, Daniel R. The Good Confession: An Exploration of the Christian Faith. 2007. 192p. pap. 22.00 *(978-1-59752-869-6(2)*, Wipf and Stock) Wipf & Stock Pubs.

Illingworth, J. R. Christian Character: Being Some Lectures on the Elements of Christian Ethics. 2007. (ENG.). 220p. 39.95 *(978-0-548-12615-8(1))* 2006. pap. 24.95 *(978-1-4286-3595-1(5))* Kessinger Publishing, LLC.

Ilo, Stan Chu. The Church & Development in Africa: Aid & Development from the Perspective of Catholic Social Ethics. 2011. (African Christian Studies). 342p. pap. 38.00 ***(978-1-60899-779-4(0)**,* Pickwick Pubns.) Wipf & Stock Pubs.

Iozzio, Mary Jo. Journal of the Society of Christian Ethics No. 1: Spring/Summer 2008, 2 vols. Jung, Patricia Beattie, ed. 2nd rev. ed. 2008. (ENG.). 284p. pap. 60.00 *(978-1-58901-198-4(8))* Georgetown Univ. Pr.

Iozzio, Mary Jo & Jung, Patricia Beattie, eds. Journal of the Society of Christian Ethics: Fall/Winter 2009. 2009. (ENG.). 264p. pap. 60.00 *(978-1-58901-271-4(2))* Georgetown Univ. Pr.

—Journal of the Society of Christian Ethics: Fall/Winter 2010. 2010. (ENG.). 272p. pap. 60.00 *(978-1-58901-643-9(2))* Georgetown Univ. Pr.

—Journal of the Society of Christian Ethics: Fall/Winter 2011. 2011. (ENG.). 232p. pap. 60.00 *(978-1-58901-745-0(5))* Georgetown Univ. Pr.

—Journal of the Society of Christian Ethics: Spring - Summer 2010. 2010. (ENG.). 272p. pap. 60.00 *(978-1-58901-641-5(6))* Georgetown Univ. Pr.

—Journal of the Society of Christian Ethics: Spring/Summer 2009. 2009. (ENG.). 288p. pap. 60.00 *(978-1-58901-270-7(4))* Georgetown Univ. Pr.

—Journal of the Society of Christian Ethics: Spring/Summer 2011. 2011. (ENG.). 264p. pap. 60.00 *(978-1-58901-744-3(7))* Georgetown Univ. Pr.

—Journal of the Society of Christian Ethics Vol. 27, No. 1: Spring - Summer 2007. 2nd rev. ed. 2007. (ENG.). 352p. per. 60.00 *(978-1-58901-167-0(8))* Georgetown Univ. Pr.

Iserte, Salvador. Formacion Etica de la Personalidad: Building up Ethics in Your Person. (SPA.). 176p. *(978-84-7228-606-1(1)*, 220415) Clie, Editorial.

Isherwood, Lisa. The Fat Jesus: Christianity & Body Image. 2008. 176p. per. 20.00 *(978-1-59627-094-7(2)*, Seabury Bks.) Church Publishing, Inc.

Jeffery, Sandra. Salvation for the Twenty-First Century & Beyond: A reference guide on Christian Ethics. 2010. pap. 18.95 *(978-1-60494-407-5(2))* Wheatmark.

Jennings, Brian K. Leading Virtue: A Model for the Contextualisation of Christian Ethics. 2009. (IC - Studien zur interkulturellen Geschichte des Christentums. Etudes d'histoire interculturelle de christianisme. Studies in the Intercultural History of Christianity Ser.). 154p. 47.95 *(978-3-631-59300-4(7))* Lang, Peter GmbH, Europaischer Verlag der Wissenschaften DEU. Dist: Lang, Peter.

Johnson, Kelly S. The Fear of Beggars: Stewardship & Poverty in Christian Ethics. 2007. (Eerdmans Ekklesia Ser.). 236p. per. 20.00 *(978-0-8028-0378-8(4))* Eerdmans, William B. Publishing Co.

Johnson, Lance T. Don't Die a Caterpillar: The Power of Transformation. 2007. 125p. per. 10.99 *(978-1-60247-072-9(3))* Tate Publishing & Enterprises, LLC.

Johnson, Samuel. Sir Thomas Brownes Christian Morals Wit. 2007. 240p. per. *(978-1-4067-8892-1(9)*, Pomona Pr.) Read Bks.

Jones, E. Marcel. The Naked Truth: The Gospel According to Singles. 2008. 216p. 25.99 *(978-1-60791-205-7(8))*; pap. 15.99 *(978-1-60791-135-7(3))* Xulon Pr., Inc.

Jones, Tony. The Teaching of the Twelve: Believing & Practicing the Primitive Christianity of the Ancient Didache Community. 2009. (ENG.). 128p. (gr. 13). pap. 14.99 *(978-1-55725-590-7(3))* Paraclete Pr., Inc.

Joyner, Rick. Breaking the Power of Evil. 2008. 334p. pap. 15.99 *(978-0-7684-2618-2(9))* Destiny Image Pubs.

Judy, J. M. Questionable Amusements & Worthy Substitutes. 2007. 92p. per. *(978-1-4065-4678-1(X))* Dodo Pr.

—Questionable Amusements & Worthy Substitutes. 2009. 76p. pap. *(978-1-4068-5378-0(X))* Echo Library.

—Questionable Amusements & Worthy Substitutes. 2010. (Illus.). 60p. pap. 20.00 *(978-1-153-68237-4(0))* General Bks. LLC.

Jung, Patricia Beattie & Vigen, Aana Marie. God, Science, Sex, Gender: An Interdisciplinary Approach to Christian Ethics. 2010. (ENG., Illus.). 296p. 75.00 *(978-0-252-03537-1(2))*; pap. 30.00 *(978-0-252-07724-1(5))* Univ. of Illinois Pr.

Kö, et al. Ethik im Krankenhaus: Diakonie - Seelsorge - Medizin. 2007. (GER.). 238p. (C). pap. 35.00 *(978-3-525-62399-2(2))* Vandenhoeck & Ruprecht GmbH & Co. KG DEU. Dist: ISD.

Kania, Walter. A Credible Christianity. 2010. 204p. 26.99 *(978-1-4520-2831-6(1))* AuthorHouse.

Kerr, Ralph. The Sin of Apathy. 2009. 168p. pap. 14.99 *(978-1-60791-132-6(9))* Xulon Pr., Inc.

Kilzer, John Turner. Responsibility as Emmanuel Levinas's Mission to the Gentiles. 2011. (ENG.). 221p. pap. 40.00 ***(978-1-60947-024-1(9))*** Emeth Pr.

King, Barbara L. Who's Angry? 2008. 184p. per. 13.99 *(978-1-60477-585-3(8))* Xulon Pr., Inc.

King, Peter, et al. Christian Ethics. 2012. (Guides for the Perplexed Ser.). (ENG.). 192p. 19.95 *(978-0-567-03220-1(5)*, T&T Clark Int'l) Continuum International Publishing Group, Ltd. GBR. Dist: National Bk. Network.

King, Rolfe, et al. Christian Ethics. 2012. (Guides for the Perplexed Ser.). (ENG.). 192p. 90.00 *(978-0-567-03219-5(1)*, T&T Clark Int'l) Continuum International Publishing Group, Ltd. GBR. Dist: National Bk. Network.

Knickerbocker, Thomas J. God's Design for Clothing. 2009. 108p. pap. 8.99 *(978-0-9821408-4-0(3))* Faithful Life Pubs.

Knight, William Angus. The Christian Ethic. 2009. 196p. 22.99 *(978-1-103-36265-3(8))*; pap. 16.99 *(978-1-103-36262-2(3))* BiblioBazaar.

—The Christian Ethic. 2009. 132p. pap. *(978-0-217-57706-9(7))* Books LLC.

—The Christian Ethic. 2007. (ENG.). 192p. 37.95 *(978-0-548-15185-3(7))*; 196p. per. 22.95 *(978-1-4304-4543-2(2))* Kessinger Publishing, LLC.

Kretzmann, O. p. God & Caesar: A Christian Approach to Social Ethics. Quanbeck, Warren A., ed. 2011. 214p. 44.95 ***(978-1-258-02568-7(X))*** Literary Licensing, LLC.

KüNg. On Being a Christian. 2008. (ENG.). 720p. 32.95 *(978-1-84706-406-6(X))* Continuum International Publishing Group, Ltd. GBR. Dist: National Bk. Network.

Kunhiyop, Samuel W. African Christian Ethics, 1 vol. 2008. (Hippo Ser.). (ENG.). 416p. pap. 24.99 *(978-9966-805-36-2(2))* Zondervan.

Kurtén, Tage, et al. Mot Bättre Vetande: Festskrift till Tage Kurtén På 60-Arsdagen. 2010. (NOR, SWE & ENG., Illus.). xx, 343p. *(978-951-765-526-2(6))* Abo Akademis forlag.

Lacueva, Francisco. Etica Cristiana: Christian Ethics, 1 vol. 2008. (SPA.). 232p. pap. 10.99 *(978-84-7228-176-9(0)*, 220237) Clie, Editorial ESP. Dist: Zondervan.

Leahy, D. G. Beyond Sovereignty: A New Global Ethics & Morality. 2010. (Illus.). xxxi, 353p. *(978-1-934542-19-4(9))* Davies Group Pubs., The.

Lee, Hak Joon. The Great World House: Martin Luther King, Jr. & Global Ethics. 2011. ***(978-0-8298-1821-5(9))*** Pilgrim Pr., The/United Church Pr.

Lee, Witness. Caracter. 2008.Tr. of Character. (SPA.). pap. 5.75 *(978-0-7363-3754-0(7))* Living Stream Ministry.

Lehmann, Paul L. Ethics in a Christian Context. 2006. (Library of Theological Ethics Ser.). (ENG.). 390p. per. 40.00 *(978-0-664-23005-0(9))* Westminster John Knox Pr.

Logan, James Samuel. Good Punishment? Christian Moral Practice & U. S. Imprisonment. 2008. 261p. per. 20.00 *(978-0-8028-6324-9(8))* Eerdmans, William B. Publishing Co.

Long, D. Stephen. Christian Ethics: A Very Short Introduction. 2010. (Very Short Introductions Ser.). (ENG., Illus.). 144p. pap. 11.95 *(978-0-19-956886-4(3))* Oxford Univ. Pr., Inc.

—The Goodness of God: Theology, the Church, & Social Order. 2008. 336p. pap. 37.00 *(978-1-55635-675-9(7))* Wipf & Stock Pubs.

—Tragedy, Tradition, Transformism: The Ethics of Paul Ramsey. 2007. 232p. pap. 26.00 *(978-1-55635-547-9(5)*, Wipf and Stock) Wipf & Stock Pubs.

Long, Jason. The Religious Condition: Answering & Explaining Christian Reasoning. 2008. 284p. pap. 20.95 *(978-1-4401-0648-4(7))* iUniverse, Inc.

Lovett, Joseph. The Good News: The World's One True Religion. 2007. pap. 10.00 *(978-0-8059-7902-2(6))* Dorrance Publishing Co., Inc.

Lowery, Kevin Twain. Salvaging Wesley's Agenda: A New Paradigm for Wesleyan Virtue Ethics. 2008. (Princeton Theological Monographs). 348p. pap. 38.00 *(978-1-55635-377-2(4)*, Pickwick Pubns.) Wipf & Stock Pubs.

Ludwick, James R. Fundamentals of Christian Life: (in a Fallen World) 2007. 88p. per. 16.95 *(978-1-4241-4707-6(7))* PublishAmerica, Inc.

Luthardt, Christoph Ernst. Apologetic Lectures on the Moral Truths of Christianity. 2009. 268p. pap. *(978-0-217-43854-4(7))*; 266p. pap. *(978-0-217-43856-8(3))*; 276p. pap. *(978-0-217-68677-8(X))* Books LLC.

—Apologetic Lectures on the Moral Truths of Christianity. Taylor, Sophia, tr. 2007. (ENG.). 428p. 51.95 *(978-0-548-15552-3(6))*; pap. 36.95 *(978-1-4304-4991-1(8))* Kessinger Publishing, LLC.

MacNamara, Vincent. The Call to be Human: Making Sense of Morality. 2010. (ENG.). 240p. pap. 21.95 *(978-1-84730-213-7(0))* Veritas Pubns. IRL. Dist: Dufour Editions, Inc.

Maguire, Daniel C. Ethics: A Complete Method for Moral Choice. 2009. (Illus.). 320p. pap. 35.00 *(978-0-8006-6443-5(4)*, Fortress Pr.) Augsburg Fortress, Pubs.

Markham, Ian S. Do Morals Matter? A Guide to Contemporary Religious Ethics. 2006. (ENG.). 224p. 108.95 *(978-1-4051-5377-5(6))*; pap. 36.95 *(978-1-4051-5378-2(4))* Wiley, John & Sons, Inc. (Wiley-Blackwell).

Marshall, Ellen Ott. Christians in the Public Square: Faith That Transforms Politics. 2008. 133p. pap. 18.00 *(978-0-687-64698-2(7))* Abingdon Pr.

Maston, Jason. Divine & Human Agency in Second Temple Judaism & Paul: A Comparative Study. 2010. (Illus.). 226p. pap. 110.00 *(978-3-16-150570-6(0))* Mohr Siebeck GmbH & Co. KG DEU. Dist: Coronet Bks.

Mathewes, Charles. Understanding Religious Ethics. 2010. (ENG., Illus.). 280p. 110.95 *(978-1-4051-3351-7(1)*, Wiley-Blackwell) Wiley, John & Sons, Inc.

—Understanding Religious Ethics. 2010. (Wiley Desktop Editions Ser.). (ENG., Illus.). 280p. pap. 42.95 *(978-1-4051-3352-4(X)*, Wiley-Blackwell) Wiley, John & Sons, Inc.

Mattison, William C., III. Introducing Moral Theology: True Happiness & the Virtues. 2008. 432p. (C). pap. 29.99 *(978-1-58743-223-1(4))* Brazos Pr.

May, William E. Standing with Peter: Reflections of a Lay Moral Theologian on God's Loving Providence. 2006. 96p. per. 9.95 *(978-0-9788687-0-3(6)*, Requiem Pr.

McCabe, Joseph. The Sources of Christian Morality: Little Blue Book No. 1095. Haldeman-Julius, E., ed. 2011. 66p. 36.95 ***(978-1-258-05044-3(7))*** Literary Licensing, LLC.

McDowell, Sean. Ethix: Being Bold in a Whatever World. 2006. (ENG., Illus.). 159p. (gr. 8-13). per. 9.99 *(978-0-8054-4519-0(6)*, B&H Bks.) B&H Publishing Group.

McKenny, Gerald. The Analogy of Grace: Karl Barth's Moral Theology. 2010. (ENG.). 320p. 120.00 *(978-0-19-958267-9(X))* Oxford Univ. Pr., Inc.

McMaster, Johnston. A Passion for Justice: Social Ethics in the Celtic Tradition. 2008. (Illus.). 242p. pap. 26.50 *(978-1-906716-04-2(8))* Dunedin Academic Pr. GBR. Dist: International Specialized Bk. Services.

McNamara, William. The Human Experience: A Divine Madness. 2010. 328p. pap. 15.95 *(978-0-9841991-2-9(8))* Beckham Pubns. Group, Inc.

McSwain, Larry L., ed. Twentieth-Century Shapers of Baptist Social Ethics. 2008. 354p. 45.00 *(978-0-88146-100-8(8))* Mercer Univ. Pr.

Mealey, Ann Marie. The Identity of Christian Morality. 2009. (New Critical Thinking in Religion, Theology & Biblical Studies). 196p. 99.95 *(978-0-7546-6073-6(7))* Ashgate Publishing Co.

Messenger, Ruth E. Ethical Teachings in the Latin Hymns of Medieval England. (Columbia University, Studies in the Social Sciences: No. 321). reprint ed. 20.00 *(978-0-404-51321-4(2))* AMS Pr., Inc.

Messer, Neil. Selfish Genes & Christian Ethics: Theological & Ethical Reflections of Evolutionary Biology. 2007. 280p. per. *(978-0-334-02996-0(1))* Hymns Ancient & Modern Ltd.

Migliore, Daniel L. Commanding Grace: Studies in Karl Barth's Ethics. 2010. pap. 30.00 *(978-0-8028-6570-0(4))* Eerdmans, William B. Publishing Co.

Miller, Daniel. Animal Ethics & Theology: The Lens of the Good Samaritan. 2011. (Routledge Studies in Religion Ser.). (ENG., Illus.). 250p. (C). 125.00 ***(978-0-415-80875-0(8))*** Routledge.

Miller, Stephen M., ed. Los Cristianos en un Mundo Perverso. 2008. 124p. pap. 8.98 *(978-1-56344-594-1(8))* Casa Nazarena de Publicaciones.

Mitchell, Jolyon. Media Violence & Christian Ethics. 2007. (New Studies in Christian Ethics Ser.). (ENG., Illus.). 348p. 109.00 *(978-0-521-81256-6(9))* Cambridge Univ. Pr.

Moltmann, Jurgen. Ethics of Hope. 2012. 288p. (C). pap. 29.00 ***(978-0-8006-9858-4(4)**,* Fortress Pr.) Augsburg Fortress, Pubs.

Montgomery, Dan & Kate. CHRISTIAN PERSONALITY THEORY: A Self Compass for Humanity. 2009. 226p. pap. 24.95 *(978-0-557-19667-8(1))* Lulu Enterprises Inc.

Moore, Frank. Dismantling the Myths: The Connection Between Faith & Morality. 2008. (ENG., Illus.). 224p. pap. 16.99 *(978-0-8341-2376-2(2)*, 9780834123762) Beacon Hill Pr. of Kansas City.

Moral Maze. 16.00 *(978-0-687-85770-8(8))* Abingdon Pr.

Morey, Robert A. A Bible Handbook on Slander & Gossip. 2009. (Illus.). 240p. pap. 15.99 *(978-1-61579-356-3(9))* Xulon Pr., Inc.

Moseley, Lyndsay, ed. Holy Ground: A Gathering of Voices on Caring for Creation. 2008. (ENG.). 224p. 22.00 *(978-1-57805-160-1(6))* Sierra Club Bks.

Moser, Antonio & Leers, Bernardino. Moral Theology: Dead Ends & Alternatives. Burns, Paul, tr. 2006.Tr. of Teologia Moral: Impasses e Alternativas. 256p. pap. 26.00 *(978-1-59752-911-2(7)*, Wipf and Stock) Wipf & Stock Pubs.

Mott, Stephen Charles. Biblical Ethics & Social Change, 1 vol. 2nd ed. 2011. (ENG.). 264p. pap. 29.95 *(978-0-19-973937-0(4))* Oxford Univ. Pr., Inc.

Muers, Rachel. Living for the Future: Theological Ethics for Coming Generations. (ENG.). 240p. 2011. pap. 44.95 ***(978-0-567-15575-7(7))*** 2008. 130.00 *(978-0-567-03225-6(6))* Continuum International Publishing Group, Ltd. GBR. (T&T Clark Int'l). Dist: National Bk. Network.

Murphy, Mark C. God & Moral Law: On the Theistic Explanation of Morality. 2012. (ENG.). 216p. 65.00 ***(978-0-19-969366-5(8))*** Oxford Univ. Pr., Inc.

Murray, John Clark. A Handbook of Christian Ethics. 2009. 344p. 25.99 *(978-1-103-64076-8(3))*; pap. 19.99 *(978-1-103-64072-0(0))* BiblioBazaar.

—A Handbook of Christian Ethics. 2009. 246p. pap. *(978-0-217-15854-1(4))* Books LLC.

—A Handbook of Christian Ethics. 2007. (ENG.). 352p. 46.95 *(978-0-548-10081-3(0))* Kessinger Publishing, LLC.

Neil Messer Staff & Dowler, Edward. Theological Ethics. 2011. (Illus.). 256p. pap. 45.00 ***(978-0-334-04199-3(6)**,* SCM Pr.) Hymns Ancient & Modern Ltd GBR. Dist: Westminster John Knox Pr.

Nelson, Emmitt J. The Fruit of the Spirit. 2nd Lt. ed. 87p. (Orig.). pap. 9.00 *(978-0-9664896-2-0(4))* Nelson Consulting, Inc.

Nethö & fel, Wolfgang. Verantwortungsethik als Theologie des Wirklichen. Dabrock, Peter et al, eds. 2009. (GER., Illus.). 300p. (C). pap. 68.00 *(978-3-525-56810-1(X))* Vandenhoeck & Ruprecht GmbH & Co. KG DEU. Dist: ISD.

Neusner, Jacob & Chilton, Bruce D., eds. Golden Rule: The Ethics of Reciprocity in World Religions. 2009. (ENG.). 192p. 130.00 *(978-1-84706-295-6(4))* Continuum International Publishing Group, Ltd. GBR. Dist: National Bk. Network.

Newlands, George M. Making Christian Decisions. 2008. (Traces of Liberality: the George Newlands Reprint Ser.). 138p. pap. 17.00 *(978-1-55635-916-3(0))* Wipf & Stock Pubs.

Newman, Elizabeth. Untamed Hospitality: Welcoming God & Other Strangers. annot. ed. 2007. (Christian Practice of Everyday Life Ser.). 236p. (C). pap. 25.00 *(978-1-58743-176-0(9))* Brazos Pr.

Ng, Wai Hang. Die Leidenschaft der Liebe: Schelers Liebesbegriff als eine Antwort auf Nietzsches Kritik an der christlichen Moral und seine soteriologische Bedeutung. 2009. (Internationale Theologie / International Theology Ser.). (GER.). 192p. 61.95 *(978-3-631-59102-4(0))* Lang, Peter GmbH, Europaischer Verlag der Wissenschaften DEU. Dist: Lang, Peter.

Ng'etich, Elias. Ethics in a Christian Perspective. 2011. 84p. pap. ***(978-3-8443-0517-3(3))*** Lambert Academic Publishing.

Niebuhr, Reinhold. An Interpretation of Christian Ethics. 2010. 156p. pap. 21.00 *(978-1-60899-799-2(5)*, Wipf and Stock) Wipf & Stock Pubs.

Nimmo, Paul T. Being in Action: The Theological Shape of Barth's Ethical Vision. 2011. (ENG.). 214p. pap. 39.95 *(978-0-567-09919-8(9)*, T&T Clark Int'l) Continuum International Publishing Group, Ltd. GBR. Dist: National Bk. Network.

Nimmo, Paul T. & Nimmo. Being in Action: The Theological Shape of Barth's Ethical Vision. 2007. (ENG.). 224p. 156.00 *(978-0-567-03149-5(7)*, T&T Clark Int'l) Continuum International Publishing Group, Ltd. GBR. Dist: National Bk. Network.

Northcott, Michael S. A Moral Climate: The Ethics of Global Warming. 2007. 336p. per. 24.00 *(978-1-57075-711-2(9))* Orbis Bks.

Obodoechina, Uchechukwu. The Imperative of Self-Reliance for the Churches in Africa: A Study in Christian Social Ethics, Vol. 873. 2006. (European University Studies Ser.: Vol. 23). xx,354p. pap. 62.95 *(978-0-8204-8730-4(9))* Lang, Peter Publishing, Inc.

Odhner, Hugo. The Moral Life: Some Reflections on Morality & Its Virtues. 2011. 152p. 41.95 ***(978-1-258-05310-9(1))*** Literary Licensing, LLC.

Okereke, Okoro Chima. Called to Marketplace Discipleship. 2011. 200p. pap. ***(978-1-84903-075-5(8))*** Schiel & Denver Publishing Ltd.

Oladejo-Lawrence, Femi. 40 Entrepreneurial Principles of Jesus Christ. 2007. 94p. pap. 16.95 *(978-1-84799-988-7(3))* Lulu Enterprises Inc.

Osborn, Eric. Ethical Patterns in Early Christian Thought. 2009. (ENG.). 268p. pap. 36.99 *(978-0-521-09291-3(4))* Cambridge Univ. Pr.

Osso, Maria Brusco & Jones, Deanna Blackmon. Superficial Society. 2011. 182p. pap. 14.99 *(978-1-61215-927-0(3))* Xulon Pr., Inc.

Paddison, Angus. Scripture: A Very Theological Proposal. 2009. (ENG.). 184p. 39.95 *(978-0-567-03424-3(0))*; 130.00 *(978-0-567-03423-6(2))* Continuum International Publishing Group, Ltd. GBR. (T&T Clark Int'l). Dist: National Bk. Network.

Patrick, Anne E. Conscience in Context: Vocation, Virtue & History. 2013. (ENG.). 160p. 24.95 *(978-1-4411-4452-1(8))* Continuum International Publishing Group, Ltd. GBR. Dist: National Bk. Network.

Pearson, Michael. Millennial Dreams & Moral Dilemmas: Seventh-Day Adventism & Contemporary Ethics. 2008. (ENG.). 340p. (C). pap. 46.00 *(978-0-521-09148-0(9))* Cambridge Univ. Pr.

Peiter, Hermann. Christliche Ethik bei Schleiermacher - Christian Ethics according to Schleiermacher: Gesammelte AufsScaron;tze und Besprechungen - Collected Essays & Reviews. Tice, Terrence N., ed. Lawler, Edwina, tr. 2010. (Princeton Theological Monographs). (GER.). 800p. pap. 80.00 *(978-1-55635-440-3(1)*, Pickwick Pubns.) Wipf & Stock Pubs.

Pembroke, Neil. Moving Toward Spiritual Maturity: Psychological, Contemplative, & Moral Challenges in Christian Living. 2007. (ENG.). 202p. 116.00 *(978-0-7890-3365-9(8))*; per. 50.50 *(978-0-7890-3366-6(6))* Routledge.

Penn, William. No Cross, No Crown; a Discourse Shewing the Nature & Discipline of the Holy Cross of Christ, & That the Denial of Self & Daily Bearing of Christ. 2006. 436p. per. 26.99 *(978-1-4255-4777-6(X))* MPublishing.

Penrose, John. Of Christian Sincerity. 2007. (ENG.). 186p. 37.95 *(978-0-548-15205-8(5))*; 188p. per. 22.95 *(978-1-4304-4563-0(7))* Kessinger Publishing, LLC.

Perkins, Robert L., ed. Without Authority. 2007. (International Kierkegaard Commentary Ser.: 18). 353p. 50.00 *(978-0-88146-048-3(6))* Mercer Univ. Pr.

Phiri, Stephen. Zimbabwean Political Crisis. 2011. 80p. pap. ***(978-3-8443-8703-2(X))*** Lambert Academic Publishing.

Piironen, Henry M. The Holy Life of Christianity: The Workbook on Demystifying the Christian Ethics of the Holy Life in the New Testament. 2008. 480p. pap. 40.95 *(978-1-4401-0427-5(1))* iUniverse, Inc.

Pinckaers & Pinckaers, OP, Servais. Sources of Christian Ethics. 3rd ed. (ENG., Illus.). 1p. 80.00 *(978-0-567-29287-2(8)*, T&T Clark) Continuum International Publishing Group, Ltd. GBR. Dist: National Bk. Network.

Plant, Stephen & Wüstenberg, Ralf K., eds. Religion, Religionlessness & Contemporary Western Culture: Explorations in Dietrich Bonhoeffer's Theology. 2008. 134p. 39.95 *(978-3-631-57754-7(0))* Lang, Peter GmbH, Europaischer Verlag der Wissenschaften DEU. Dist: Lang, Peter.

Plekon, Michael. Hidden Holiness. 2009. (ENG.). 240p. pap. 25.00 *(978-0-268-03893-9(7))* Univ. of Notre Dame Pr.

C

Pope, Stephen J. Human Evolution & Christian Ethics. (New Studies in Christian Ethics Ser.). (ENG.). 374p. 2011. pap. 45.00 *(978-0-521-17530-2(5))* 2008. 102.00 *(978-0-521-86340-7(6))* Cambridge Univ. Pr.

Portaro, Sam. Transforming Vocation. 2008. (Transformations Ser.). 160p. pap. 16.00 *(978-0-89869-586-1(4))* Church Publishing, Inc.

Pregeant, Russell. Knowing Truth, Doing Good: Engaging New Testament Ethics. 2008. 400p. per. 35.00 *(978-0-8006-3846-7(8),* Fortress Pr.) Augsburg Fortress, Pubs.

Preston, Ronald H. Confusions in Christian Social Ethics: Problems for Geneva & Rome. 2011. 224p. ***(978-0-334-02573-3(7),*** SCM Pr.) Hymns Ancient & Modern Ltd.

Priestley, Joseph & Ware, Jr. The Views of Christian Truth, Piety, & Morality: Selected From. 2007. (ENG.). 292p. per. 28.95 *(978-1-4304-4579-1(3))* Kessinger Publishing, LLC.

Puckett, James E. When the Boss Is Not Looking. 2008. 58p. pap. 9.95 *(978-0-7414-4512-4(3))* Infinity Publishing.

Pugh, Jeffrey. Devil's Ink: Blog from the Basement Office. 2011. 192p. pap. 11.95 *(978-0-8006-9814-0(2),* Fortress Pr.) Augsburg Fortress, Pubs.

Quash. Christian Ethics: An Introductory Reader. Wells, Samuel, ed. 2010. (ENG.). 360p. 99.95 *(978-1-4051-6886-1(2),* Wiley-Blackwell) Wiley, John & Sons, Inc.

Ramos, Jason. Jesus. 2008. 88p. pap. *(978-3-639-00170-9(2))* VDM Verlag Dr. Mueller e.K.

Ramsey, Ian T., ed. Christian Ethics & Contemporary Philosophy. 2011. (Ian T. Ramsey Reprint Ser.). 400p. pap. 47.00 ***(978-1-61097-209-3(0),*** Wipf and Stock) Wipf & Stock Pubs.

Ramsey, Paul. Nine Modern Moralists. 2011. 284p. 48.95 ***(978-1-258-03190-9(6))*** Literary Licensing, LLC.

Rashdall, Hastings. Conscience & Christ: Six Lectures on Christian Ethics. 2010. 338p. pap. 31.75 *(978-1-146-22589-2(X))* BiblioBazaar.

—Conscience & Christ: Six Lectures on Christian Ethics. 2010. 336p. 45.95 *(978-1-161-40053-3(2))* Kessinger Publishing, LLC.

Rasmussen, Larry L. Earth-honoring Faith: Religious Ethics in a New Key. 2012. 432p. 45.00 ***(978-0-19-991700-6(0))*** Oxford Univ. Pr., Inc.

Rauschenbusch, Walter. The Social Principles of Jesus. 2012. 214p. pap. 24.75 ***(978-1-276-67184-2(9))*** 2011. 214p. pap. 24.75 ***(978-1-179-88367-0(5))*** 2010. (ENG.). 212p. pap. 24.75 *(978-1-177-62141-0(X))* 2010. 214p. pap. 24.75 *(978-1-141-44497-7(6))* BiblioBazaar.

—The Social Principles of Jesus. 2009. 134p. pap. *(978-1-4589-3621-9(X))* Books LLC.

—The Social Principles of Jesus. 2010. (Illus.). 116p. pap. 20.68 *(978-1-153-82262-6(8))* General Bks. LLC.

—The Social Principles of Jesus. 2010. 214p. 31.96 ***(978-1-163-49145-4(4))*** 2010. 214p. pap. 19.96 ***(978-1-163-08871-5(4))*** 2007. (ENG.). 212p. 39.95 *(978-0-548-18806-4(8))* 2007. (ENG.). 216p. per. 24.95 *(978-1-4304-9203-0(1))* Kessinger Publishing, LLC.

—The Social Principles of Jesus. 2010. 262p. pap. 19.95 *(978-1-935758-04-4(7))* WordStream Publishing, LLC.

Reed, Esther D. Good Work: Christian Ethics in the Workplace. 2010. (ENG., Illus.). 132p. pap. 24.95 *(978-1-60258-295-8(5))* Baylor Univ. Pr.

Reinders, Hans S. Receiving the Gift of Friendship: Profound Disability, Theological Anthropology, & Ethics. 2008. 404p. pap. 36.00 *(978-0-8028-6232-7(2))* Eerdmans, William B. Publishing Co.

Reuschling, Wyndy Corbin & Corbin Reuschling, Wyndy. Reviving Evangelical Ethics: The Promises & Pitfalls of Classic Models of Morality. 2008. 192p. (C). pap. 24.00 *(978-1-58743-189-0(0))* Brazos Pr.

Rich, Antony D. Discernment in the Desert Fathers: Diakrisis in the Life & Thought of Early Egyptian Monasticism. 2007. (Studies in Christian History & Thought Ser.). 366p. pap. 43.00 *(978-1-55635-339-0(1),* Wipf and Stock) Wipf & Stock Pubs.

Rich, Arthur & Enderle, Georges. Business & Economic Ethics: The Ethics of Economic Systems. Rich, A., ed. 4th ed. 2006. (ENG., Illus.). 672p. (C). pap. 66.00 *(978-90-429-1439-1(4))* Peeters Pubs. & Booksellers BEL. Dist: Brown, David Bk. Co., The.

Riggs, Marcia C. & Logan, James Samuel, eds. Ethics That Matters: African, Caribbean, & African American Sources. 2011. 288p. (C). pap. 29.00 *(978-0-8006-1976-3(5),* Fortress Pr.) Augsburg Fortress, Pubs.

Ritari, Katja. Saints & Sinners in Early Christian Ireland: Moral Theology in the Lives of Saints Brigit & Columba. 2010. (Studia Traditionis Theologiae Ser.). (ENG.). 202p. (C). pap. 102.00 *(978-2-503-53315-5(9))* Brepols Pubs. BEL. Dist: ISD.

Rivas, Solomon. Discerning the Unknown. 2010. 488p. pap. *(978-3-639-24900-2(3))* VDM Verlag Dr. Mueller e.K.

Robbins, Anna M., ed. Ecumenical & Eclectic: The Unity of the Church in the Contemporary World: Essays in Honour of Alan P. F. Sell. 2007. (Studies in Christian History & Thought: Ser.). (Illus.). 338p. pap. 40.00 *(978-1-55635-478-6(9),* Wipf and Stock) Wipf & Stock Pubs.

Roberts, Samuel K. African American Christian Ethics. 2008. 318p. pap. 35.00 *(978-1-60608-143-3(8))* Wipf & Stock Pubs.

Robinson, Michael. There Are Moral Absolutes How to Be Abs. 2006. 160p. pap. 10.95 *(978-1-59800-766-4(1))* Outskirts Pr., Inc.

Rollins, Peter. The Fidelity of Betrayal: Towards a Church Beyond Belief. 2008. 196p. pap. 19.95 *(978-1-55725-560-0(1));* (ENG.). 164p. pap. 19.95 *(978-1-55275-560-0(6))* Paraclete Pr., Inc.

Rose, Matthew. Ethics with Barth: God, Metaphysics & Morals. 2010. (Barth Studies). 234p. 89.95 *(978-1-4094-0623-5(7))* Ashgate Publishing Co.

Rudman, Stanley. Concepts of Person & Christian Ethics. 2008. (New Studies in Christian Ethics Ser.). (ENG.). 424p. pap. 55.00 *(978-0-521-09024-7(5))* Cambridge Univ. Pr.

Russell, Letty M. Just Hospitality: God's Welcome in a World of Difference. 2009. (ENG.). 168p. pap. 20.00 *(978-0-664-23315-0(5))* Westminster John Knox Pr.

Saint Paul the Apostle. Letters of Saint Paul. 2008. 304p. pap. 7.95 *(978-0-8198-4524-5(8))* Pauline Bks. & Media.

Salierno, Lori. When Roosters Crow: A Fresh Approach to Accountability & Integrity. 2007. (ENG., Illus.). 212p. per. 14.95 *(978-1-59317-181-0(1))* Warner Pr. Pubs.

Sanders, Cheryl J. Ministry at the Margins: The Prophetic Mission of Women, Youth & the Poor. 2009. 144p. (Orig.). pap. 18.00 *(978-1-60608-760-2(6),* Wipf and Stock) Wipf & Stock Pubs.

Sandin, Steve. Make the Right Choice. 2011. 114p. pap. 11.99 ***(978-1-61379-164-6(X))*** Xulon Pr., Inc.

Sansom, Dennis L. Christian Ethics: How Distinctive Features of Christianity Shape Ethics. rev. ed. 2012. (ENG.). 180p. pap. 34.50 *(978-0-7575-8777-1(1))* Kendall Hunt Publishing Co.

Schlabach, Theron F. War, Peace, & Social Conscience: Guy F. Hershberger & Mennonite Ethics. 2009. 39.99 *(978-0-8361-9426-5(8))* Herald Pr.

Schlachtenhaufen, Harold D. Faith Ethics. 2008. 304p. pap. 19.99 *(978-1-4343-7115-7(8))* AuthorHouse.

Schlafer, David J. & Sedgwick, Timothy. Preaching What We Practice: Proclamation & Moral Discernment. 2007. 176p. per. 20.00 *(978-0-8192-2218-3(6))* Church Publishing, Inc.

Schleiermacher, Friedrich. Selections from Friedrich Schleiermacher's Christian Ethics. Brandt, James M., ed. & tr. by. from GER. 2010. (Library of Theological Ethics Ser.). (ENG.). 192p. pap. 40.00 *(978-0-664-22611-4(6))* Westminster John Knox Pr.

Schliesser, Christine. Everyone Who Acts Responsibly Becomes Guilty: Bonhoeffer's Concept of Accepting Guilt. 2008. (ENG., Illus.). 224p. pap. 35.00 *(978-0-664-23216-0(7))* Westminster John Knox Pr.

Schubeck, Thomas Louis. Love That Does Justice. 2007. 211p. per. 22.00 *(978-1-57075-746-4(1))* Orbis Bks.

Scott, Lindy, ed. Christians, the Care of Creation, & Global Climate Change. 2008. 158p. pap. 17.00 *(978-1-55635-844-9(X),* Pickwick Pubns.) Wipf & Stock Pubs.

Scott, Peter M. Anti-Human Theology: Nature, Technology & the Post-Natural. Deane-Drummond, Celia, ed. 2010. (SCM Revisioning Ethics Ser.). (ENG.). 256p. pap. 90.00 *(978-0-334-04354-6(9),* SCM Pr.) Hymns Ancient & Modern Ltd GBR. Dist: Westminster John Knox Pr.

Scullard, H. Early Christian Ethics in the West: From Clement to Ambrose. 2007. (ENG.). 306p. 43.95 *(978-0-548-05246-4(8))* Kessinger Publishing, LLC.

Scullard, H. H. The Ethics of the Gospel & the Ethics of Nature. 2007. 280p. per. *(978-1-4067-8858-7(9),* Pomona Pr.) Read Bks.

Seed, Hal. The God Questions Gift Edition. 2008. (ENG.). 125p. pap. 4.99 *(978-0-9787153-2-8(2))* Outreach, Inc.

Seed, Hal & Grider, Dan. The God Questions: Fourth Edition. 2007. 196p. pap. 12.95 *(978-0-9787153-0-4(6))* Outreach, Inc.

Sehat, David. The Myth of American Religious Freedom, 1 vol. 2011. (ENG.). 384p. 29.95 *(978-0-19-538876-3(3))* Oxford Univ. Pr., Inc.

Shahan, Michael, ed. A Report from the Front Lines: Conversations on Public Theology: A Festschrift in Honor of Robert Benne. 2008. 184p. pap. 30.00 *(978-0-8028-4863-5(X))* Eerdmans, William B. Publishing Co.

Shults, F. LeRon & Waters, Brent. Christology & Ethics. 2010. pap. 28.00 *(978-0-8028-4509-2(6))* Eerdmans, William B. Publishing Co.

Siegler, Philip G. & Bartel, Michelle J. Explorations in Christian Theology & Ethics: Essays in Conversation with Paul L Lehmann. 2009. 206p. 99.95 *(978-0-7546-6358-4(2))* Ashgate Publishing Co.

Simmons, Paul D. Faith & Health: Religion, Science, & Public Policy. 2008. (Illus.). 293p. per. 30.00 *(978-0-88146-085-8(0))* Mercer Univ. Pr.

Sloane, Andrew. At Home in a Strange Land: Using the Old Testament in Christian Ethics. 2009. (C). pap. 21.99 *(978-0-8010-4840-1(0))* Baker Academic.

—At Home in a Strange Land: Using the Old Testament in Christian Ethics. 2008. 280p. pap. *(978-1-59856-084-8(0))* Hendrickson Pubs. Marketing, LLC.

Smith, E. A. The End of Seven Days. 2007. 139p. pap. 24.95 *(978-1-60441-829-3(X))* PublishAmerica, Inc.

Smith, J. Warren. Christian Grace & Pagan Virtue: The Theological Foundation of Ambrose's Ethics. 2010. (Oxford Studies in Historical Theology Ser.). (ENG.). 368p. 74.00 *(978-0-19-536993-9(9))* Oxford Univ. Pr., Inc.

Smyth, Newman. Christian Ethics. 2007. (ENG.). 524p. 55.95 *(978-0-548-11728-6(4))* Kessinger Publishing, LLC.

Snarr, C. Melissa & Snarr. Social Selves & Political Reforms: Five Visions in Contemporary Christian Ethics. 2007. (ENG.). 160p. 150.00 *(978-0-567-02603-3(5),* T&T Clark Int'l) Continuum International Publishing Group, Ltd. GBR. Dist: National Bk. Network.

Sölle, Dorothee & Denef, Lawrence W. Creative Disobedience. 2007. 96p. pap. 13.00 *(978-1-55635-640-7(4))* Wipf & Stock Pubs.

Sproul, R. C. How Should I Live in This World? 2009. *(978-1-56769-180-1(3))* Ligonier Ministries.

Stackhouse. God & Globalization Vol. 3: Christ & the Dominions of Civilization, 4 vols. Stackhouse, Max L. & Obenchain, Diane B., eds. 2009. (Theology for the 21st Century Ser.). (ENG.). 360p. 32.95 *(978-0-567-43931-4(3),* T&T Clark Int'l) Continuum International Publishing Group, Ltd. GBR. Dist: National Bk. Network.

Stackhouse, Max L., ed. God & Globalization: Volume 1: Religion & the Powers of the Common Life, 4 vols. 2009. (Theology for the 21st Century Ser.). (ENG.). 304p. pap. 34.95 *(978-0-567-46246-6(3),* T&T Clark Int'l) Continuum International Publishing Group, Ltd. GBR. Dist: National Bk. Network.

Stackhouse, Max L. & Stackhouse. Globalization & Grace, Vol. 4. 2007. (God & Globalization Ser.). (ENG.). 288p. 110.00 *(978-0-8264-2885-1(1),* T&T Clark Int'l) Continuum International Publishing Group, Ltd. GBR. Dist: National Bk. Network.

—God & Globalization Vol. 4: Globalization & Grace, 4 vols. 2009. (Theology for the 21st Century Ser.). (ENG.). 288p. 32.95 *(978-0-567-11482-2(1),* T&T Clark Int'l) Continuum International Publishing Group, Ltd. GBR. Dist: National Bk. Network.

Stapleford, John E. Bulls, Bears & Golden Calves: Applying Christian Ethics in Economics, 1 vol. 2nd rev. ed. 2009. (ENG.). 282p. pap. 22.00 *(978-0-8308-2724-4(2),* IVP Acad.) InterVarsity Pr.

Staton, Knofel. Check Your Morality. 2009. 144p. (Orig.). pap. 17.00 *(978-1-60608-211-9(6),* Wipf and Stock) Wipf & Stock Pubs.

Stivers, Laura A., et al. Christian Ethics-4th Edition: A Case Method Approach. 4th ed. 2012. 352p. pap. 28.00 ***(978-1-57075-966-6(9))*** Orbis Bks.

Stock, Konrad. Einleitung in Die Systematische Theologie. 2011. (De Gruyter Studium Ser.). (GER.). (C). 56.00 ***(978-3-11-021800-8(3))*** De Gruyter, Walter Inc.

Stone, Rachel. Morality & Masculinity in the Carolingian Empire. 2011. (Cambridge Studies in Medieval Life & Thought: Fourth Ser.). (ENG., Illus.). 420p. 99.00 ***(978-1-107-00674-4(0))*** Cambridge Univ. Pr.

Strong, Thomas B. Christian Ethics Eight Lectures Preached. 2006. pap. 34.95 *(978-1-4286-3518-0(1))* Kessinger Publishing, LLC.

Sttiphan, Em. Christian Ethics, Issues & Insights. 2007. 157p. *(978-81-8069-363-2(5))* Concept Publishing Co.

Stygles, John M. Scammed by Society. 2009. 94p. pap. 16.76 *(978-0-557-17861-2(4))* Lulu Enterprises Inc.

Sutton, Agneta. Christian Bioethics. 2008. (Guides for the Perplexed Ser.). (ENG.). 192p. 24.95 *(978-0-567-03197-6(7),* T&T Clark Int'l) Continuum International Publishing Group, Ltd. GBR. Dist: National Bk. Network.

Swinton, John & Swinton. Theology, Disability & the New Genetics: Why Science Needs the Church. Brock, Brian, ed. 2007. (ENG., Illus.). 264p. 155.00 *(978-0-567-04543-0(9),* T&T Clark Int'l) Continuum International Publishing Group, Ltd. GBR. Dist: National Bk. Network.

—Theology, Disability & the New Genetics: Why Science Needs the Church. Brock, Brian, ed. 2007. (ENG., Illus.). 264p. 41.95 *(978-0-567-04558-4(7),* T&T Clark Int'l) Continuum International Publishing Group, Ltd. GBR. Dist: National Bk. Network.

Taylor, Nathaniel. Lectures on the Moral Government of God. 2009. (Amer Philosophy, Religion Ser.). (ENG.). 436p. pap. 26.95 *(978-1-4290-1798-5(8));* Vol. 1. pap. 26.95 *(978-1-4290-1882-1(8))* Applewood Bks.

Taylor, Nathaniel W. Lectures on the Moral Government of God. 2006. 436p. per. 26.99 *(978-1-4255-4771-4(0));* per. 26.99 *(978-1-4255-4808-7(3))* MPublishing.

Thielicke, Helmut. Theological Ethics, 2 vols. Incl. Vol. III. Sex. pap. 8.95 *(978-0-8028-1794-5(7));* Set pap. 31.50 o.p. *(978-0-8028-1795-2(5))* Eerdmans, William B. Publishing Co.

Thomas à Kempis. Vera Sapientia or True Wisdom. 2006. pap. 18.95 *(978-1-60206-016-6(9),* Cosimo Classics) Cosimo, Inc.

Thompson, R. Motson. Nietzsche & Christian Ethics. 2011. 104p. 39.95 ***(978-1-258-07975-8(5))*** Literary Licensing, LLC.

Thompson, Ross. Wounded Wisdom: A Buddhist & Christian Response to Evil, Hurt & Harm. 2011. (ENG.). 348p. pap. 26.95 *(978-1-84694-597-7(6))* Hunt, John Publishing Ltd. GBR. Dist: National Bk. Network.

Tite, Philip L. Valentinian Ethics & Paraenetic Discourse: Determining the Social Function of Moral Exhortation in Valentinian Christianity. 2009. 380p. *(978-90-04-17507-5(5))* BRILL.

Titus, Craig Steven. The Person & the Polis: Faith & Values Within the Secular State. 2007. (John Henry Cardinal Newman Lectures: Vol. 1). 187p. per. 29.95 *(978-0-9773103-0-2(2))* Institute for the Psychological Science Pr., The.

Tong, Joy Kooi-Chin. Overseas Chinese Christian Entrepreneurs in Modern China: A Case Study of the Influence of Christian Ethics on Business Life. 2012. (Key Issues in Modern Sociology Ser.). (Illus.). 180p. 99.00 ***(978-0-85728-353-5(7))*** Anthem Pr. GBR. Dist: Books International, Inc.

Torrance, Alan J. & Banner, Michael, eds. Doctrine of God & Theological Ethics. 2006. (Theology & Philosophy Ser.). (ENG.). 240p. 190.00 *(978-0-567-08451-4(5),* T&T Clark Int'l) Continuum International Publishing Group, Ltd. GBR. Dist: National Bk. Network.

Townes, Emilie M. Womanist Ethics & the Cultural Production of Evil. 2006. (Black Religion, Womanist Thought, Social Justice Ser.). (ENG.). 224p. 95.00 *(978-1-4039-7272-9(9));* pap. 30.00 *(978-1-4039-7273-6(7))* Palgrave Macmillan.

Trainor, Brian. Christ, Society & the State. 2012. (ENG.). 614p. (C). pap. 40.50 *(978-1-921511-58-5(3))* ATF Pr. AUS. Dist: Brown, David Bk. Co., The.

Trull, Joe E. Walking in the Way: An Introduction to Christian Ethics. pap. 24.99 *(978-0-8054-2082-1(7))* B&H Publishing Group.

Twomey, Vincent. Moral Theology after Humanae Vitae - Fundamental Issues in Moral Theology & Sexual Ethics. 2010. 226p. 45.00 *(978-1-84682-201-8(7))* Four Courts Pr. IRL. Dist: International Specialized Bk. Services.

Unfried, Michael B. God & the Universe Are Waiting for the Children of God to Be Revealed, 1 vol. 2009. 60p. pap. 16.95 *(978-1-60836-082-6(2))* PublishAmerica, Inc.

VanDemark, Gail. A Warrior's Journey. 2007. 121p. pap. 19.95 *(978-1-60441-392-2(1))* PublishAmerica, Inc.

VanDrunen, David. Bioethics & the Christian Life: A Guide to Making Difficult Decisions. 2009. 256p. pap. 19.99 *(978-1-4335-0144-9(9))* Crossway.

Von Haering, Theodor. Ethics of the Christian Life. 2006. pap. 38.95 *(978-1-4286-3957-7(8))* Kessinger Publishing, LLC.

Wace, Henry. Christianity & Morality or the Correspondence of the Gospel with the Moral Nature of Man. 2007. (ENG.). 328p. 45.95 *(978-0-548-04824-5(X))* Kessinger Publishing, LLC.

Wadell, Paul J. Happiness & the Christian Moral Life: An Introduction to Christian Ethics. 2nd ed. 2012. ***(978-1-4422-0974-9(7));*** (ENG.). 308p. 80.00 ***(978-1-4422-0972-5(0));*** (ENG.). 308p. pap. 29.95 ***(978-1-4422-0973-2(9))*** Rowman & Littlefield Publishers, Inc.

Waitz, J. P. Bible Bombshell! Explosive Vital-to-Understand Truths for End-Time People of God! 2010. 300p. 25.99 *(978-1-4520-1705-1(0));* pap. 15.49 *(978-1-4520-1706-8(9))* AuthorHouse.

Walsh, Chad & Montizambert, Eric. Faith & Behavior: Christian Answers to Moral Problems. 2011. 190p. 42.95 ***(978-1-258-02911-1(1))*** Literary Licensing, LLC.

Wannenwetsch, Bernd. Political Worship. 2009. (Oxford Studies in Theological Ethics Ser.). (ENG.). 416p. pap. 55.00 *(978-0-19-956812-3(X))* Oxford Univ. Pr., Inc.

Wariboko, Nimi. Ethics & Time: Ethos of Temporal Orientation in Politics & Religion of the Niger Delta. 2010. xiv, 178p. *(978-0-7391-5030-6(8))* Lexington Bks.

Waters, Brent. This Mortal Flesh: Incarnation & Bioethics, 1 vol. 2009. 208p. (C). pap. 22.00 *(978-1-58743-251-4(X))* Brazos Pr.

Watts, Fraser, ed. Christians & Bioethics. 96p. 12.00 *(978-0-281-05194-6(1))* SPCK Publishing GBR. Dist: Pilgrim Pr., The/United Church Pr.

Wayland, Francis. The Elements of Moral Science. 2009. (Amer Philosophy, Religion Ser.). (ENG.). 404p. pap. 24.95 *(978-1-4290-1877-7(1))* Applewood Bks.

—The Elements of Moral Science. 2010. 412p. pap. 34.75 *(978-1-143-66804-3(9))* 2010. 418p. pap. 34.75 *(978-1-143-33626-3(7))* 2010. 414p. pap. 34.75 *(978-1-142-00561-0(5))* 2010. 416p. pap. 34.75 *(978-1-142-24913-7(1))* 2010. 416p. pap. 34.75 *(978-1-142-97310-0(7))* 2010. 418p. pap. 34.75 *(978-1-141-96095-8(8))* 2010. 388p. pap. 33.75 *(978-1-142-29654-4(7))* 2010. 408p. pap. 34.75 *(978-1-143-10272-1(X))* 2010. 416p. pap. 34.75 *(978-1-143-08691-5(0))* 2010. 418p. pap. 34.75 *(978-1-142-01197-0(6))* 2010. 416p. pap. 34.75 *(978-1-142-25350-9(3))* 2010. 418p. pap. 34.75 *(978-1-142-34689-8(7))* 2010. 224p. pap. 25.75 *(978-1-141-62769-1(8))* 2010. 416p. pap. 34.75 *(978-1-142-98795-4(7))* 2009. 464p. 42.99 *(978-1-115-51015-8(0))* 2009. 464p. pap. 35.99 *(978-1-115-51016-5(9))* 2009. 464p. pap. 36.75 *(978-1-115-51018-9(5))* 2009. 464p. pap. 37.75 *(978-1-115-51017-2(7))* 2009. 256p. 24.99 *(978-1-103-32964-9(2))* 2009. 256p. pap. 18.99 *(978-1-103-32963-2(4))* 2008. 404p. 32.99 *(978-0-559-01609-7(3))* 2008. 404p. 30.99 *(978-0-559-01613-4(1))* 2008. 404p. pap. 33.75 *(978-0-559-01612-7(3))* 2008. 404p. pap. 34.75 *(978-0-559-01610-3(7))* BiblioBazaar.

—The Elements of Moral Science. 2009. 270p. pap. *(978-1-151-14522-2(X));* 220p. pap. *(978-0-217-94843-2(X));* 306p. pap. *(978-0-217-94842-5(1));* 286p. pap. *(978-0-217-29210-8(0))* Books LLC.

—The Elements of Moral Science. 2009. 298p. pap. 21.51 *(978-1-4588-7911-0(9))* General Bks. LLC.

—The Elements of Moral Science by Francis Wayland. 2006. 408p. per. 26.99 *(978-1-4255-4359-4(6))* MPublishing.

Weber, Max. The Protestant Ethic & the Spirit of Capitalism. 2006. pap. 8.95 *(978-1-4288-1499-8(X))* Cram101 Inc.

—The Protestant Ethic & the Spirit of Capitalism. Swedberg, Richard, ed. 2009. (Norton Critical Editions Ser.). (ENG.). 312p. (C). pap. 14.00 net. *(978-0-393-93068-9(8),* 93068) Norton, W. W. & Co., Inc.

—The Protestant Ethic & the Spirit of Capitalism with Other Writings on the Rise of the West. Kalberg, Stephen, ed. 4th ed. 2008. (ENG.). 608p. (C). pap. 44.95 *(978-0-19-533253-7(9))* Oxford Univ. Pr., Inc.

Webster, John. God Without Measure: Essays in Christian Doctrine. 2013. (ENG.). 240p. 120.00 ***(978-0-567-13942-9(5),*** T&T Clark Int'l) Continuum International Publishing Group, Ltd. GBR. Dist: National Bk. Network.

Webster, John Bainbridge. Barth's Ethics of Reconciliation. 2007. (ENG.). 252p. pap. 51.00 *(978-0-521-04411-0(1))* Cambridge Univ. Pr.

Welch, D. Don. Conflicting Agendas: Personal Morality in Institutional Settings. 2009. 206p. pap. 23.00 *(978-1-60608-217-1(5),* Wipf and Stock) Wipf & Stock Pubs.

Wells, Samuel. Christian Ethics Course Set. 2010. (ENG.). 760p. pap. 82.95 *(978-1-4443-2369-6(5),* Wiley-Blackwell) Wiley, John & Sons, Inc.

Wells, Samuel, ed. Christian Ethics: An Introductory Reader. 2010. (ENG.). 360p. pap. 49.95 *(978-1-4051-6887-8(0),* Wiley-Blackwell) Wiley, John & Sons, Inc.

Wells, Samuel & Quash, Ben. Introducing Christian Ethics. 2010. (ENG.). 400p. 99.95 *(978-1-4051-5277-8(X));* pap. 46.95 *(978-1-4051-5276-1(1))* Wiley, John & Sons, Inc. (Wiley-Blackwell).

Whately, Richard. Introductory Lessons on Morals & Christian Evidences. 2007. (ENG.). 348p. 46.95 *(978-0-548-15219-5(5));* 352p. per. 31.95 *(978-1-4304-4580-7(7))* Kessinger Publishing, LLC.

—Introductory Lessons on Morals, & Christian Evidences. 2009. 352p. 25.99 *(978-1-103-63095-0(4));* pap. 19.99 *(978-1-103-63091-2(1))* BiblioBazaar.

—Introductory Lessons on Morals, & Christian Evidences. 2009. 244p. pap. *(978-0-217-93537-1(0))* Books LLC.

—Introductory Lessons on Morals, & Christian Evidences. 2006. 352p. per. 26.99 *(978-1-4255-3595-7(X))* MPublishing.

—Introductory Lessons on Morals, & Christian Evidences. 2007. (ENG.). 348p. per. (978-1-4086-2546-0(6)) Read Bks.
Wheless, Joseph. Forgery in Christianity: A Documented Record of the Foundations of the Christian Religion. 2007. pap. 19.99 (978-1-59986-910-0(1)) Filiquarian Publishing, LLC.
White, Jerry. Honesty, Morality, & Conscience: Making Wise Choices in the Gray Areas of Life. 2007. (Modern Girl's Bible Study Ser.). (ENG.). 272p. pap. 14.99 (978-1-60006-218-6(0)) NavPress Publishing Group.
Wildman, et al. Found in the Middle! Theology & Ethics for Christians Who Are Both Liberal & Evangelical. 2009. (978-1-56699-381-4(4)) Alban Institute, Inc.
Wilkens, Steve. Beyond Bumper Sticker Ethics: An Introduction to Theories of Right & Wrong. 2nd rev. ed. 2011. (ENG.). 230p. pap. 20.00 (978-0-8308-3936-0(4), IVP Acad.) InterVarsity Pr.
Wilson, Bryan & Ikeda, Daisaku. Human Values in a Changing World: A Dialogue on the Social Role of Religion. Gage, Richard L., ed. & tr. by. 2008. (Echoes & Reflections Ser.). (ENG.). 384p. 52.00 (978-1-84511-597-5(X)) I. B. Tauris & Co., Ltd. GBR. Dist: Macmillan.
Wilson, Jonathan R. Living Faithfully in a Fragmented World, Second Edition. 2nd rev. ed. 2011. (ENG.). 102p. pap. 31.25 (978-0-7188-9241-8(0)) Lutherworth Pr., The GBR. Dist: Printondemand-worldwide.com.
—Living Faithfully in a Fragmented World, Second Edition. 2nd ed. 2009. (New Monastic Library: Resources for Radical Discipleship Ser.). 102p. pap. 14.00 (978-1-55635-898-2(9), Cascade Bks.) Wipf & Stock Pubs.
Wilson, William. God Vision. 2008. 68p. pap. 9.95 (978-1-4401-0494-7(8)) iUniverse, Inc.
Wogaman, J. Philip. Christian Ethics, Second Edition: A Historical Introduction. 2nd ed. 2010. (ENG.). 400p. pap. 35.00 (978-0-664-23409-6(7)) Westminster John Knox Pr.
—Moral Dilemmas: An Introduction to Christian Ethics. 2009. (ENG.). 176p. pap. 20.00 (978-0-664-23316-7(3)) Westminster John Knox Pr.
Wogaman, J. Philip, ed. Communitarian Ethics: Later Writings of Walter G. Muelder. 2007. 102p. 26.95 (978-0-9711146-4-7(1)); pap. 11.95 (978-0-9711146-3-0(3)) Boston Wesleyan Pr. (BW Pr.).
Woods, G. F. A Defence of Theological Ethics: Hulsean Lectures 1964. 2009. (ENG.). 148p. pap. 28.99 (978-0-521-11353-3(9)) Cambridge Univ. Pr.
Woods, Walter J. Walking with Faith: New Perspectives on the Sources & Shaping of Catholic Moral Life. 2010. 544p. (Orig.). pap. 67.00 (978-1-60899-285-0(3), Wipf and Stock) Wipf & Stock Pubs.
Wright, Frank. Exploration into Goodness. 2012. 128p. pap. (978-0-334-00423-3(3), SCM Pr.) Hymns Ancient & Modern Ltd.
Wuttke, Adolf. Christian Ethics. 2009. 358p. 33.99 (978-1-115-19441-9(0)); 358p. 38.99 (978-1-115-19443-3(7)); 358p. pap. 32.75 (978-1-115-19440-2(2)); 368p. 26.99 (978-1-103-98719-1(4)); 368p. pap. 20.99 (978-1-103-98710-8(0)); 368p. 26.99 (978-1-103-43109-0(9)); 368p. pap. 20.99 (978-1-103-43108-3(0)) BiblioBazaar.
—Christian Ethics. 2009. 294p. pap. (978-1-4588-1930-7(2)); 284p. pap. (978-0-217-46106-1(9)); 272p. pap. (978-0-217-45705-7(3)) Books LLC.
—Christian Ethics. 2006. 368p. per. 26.99 (978-1-4255-3855-2(X)) MPublishing.
—Christian Ethics. 2008. 396p. pap. (978-1-4097-9942-9(5)) Read Bks.
—Christian Ethics: History of Ethics V1. 2007. (ENG.). 396p. 49.95 (978-0-548-09828-8(X)) Kessinger Publishing, LLC.
—Christian Ethics: Pure Ethics V2. 2007. (ENG.). 372p. 48.95 (978-0-548-09827-1(1)) Kessinger Publishing, LLC.
Yang, Chan-Ho. Begründung der Ethik bei Barth und Elert. 2008. (Europäische Hochschulschriften. Reihe 23: Theologie Ser.). 286p. pap. 74.95 (978-3-631-58215-2(3)) Lang, Peter GmbH, Europaischer Verlag der Wissenschaften DEU. Dist: Lang, Peter.
Zimmerman, Earl. Practicing the Politics of Jesus: The Origin & Significance of John Howard Yoder's Social Ethics. 2007. (C. Henry Smith Ser.: Vol. 8). 276p. pap. 22.95 (978-1-931038-43-0(0)) Cascadia Publishing Hse., LLC.

CHRISTIAN ETHICS—ANGLICAN AUTHORS

Bayer, Oswald & Suggate, Alan, eds. Worship & Ethics: Lutherans & Anglicans in Dialogue. (Theologische Bibliothek Töpelmann Ser.). (ENG.). XV, 293p. 255.00 (978-3-11-179433-4(4)) De Gruyter, Walter Inc.
Biggar, Nigel. Behaving in Public: How to Do Christian Ethics. 2010. 136p. pap. 16.00 (978-0-8028-6400-0(7)) Eerdmans, William B. Publishing Co.
Joyce, A. J. Richard Hooker & Anglican Moral Theology. 2012. (ENG.). 320p. 125.00 (978-0-19-921616-1(9)) Oxford Univ. Pr., Inc.
Lewis, C. S. Mere Christianity; The Screwtape Letters; The Great Divorce, Set. 2009. 59.99 (978-0-06-166489-6(7), HarperOne) HarperCollins Pubs.
Sedgwick, Peter H. The Market Economy & Christian Ethics. 2007. (New Studies in Christian Ethics Ser.). (ENG.). 340p. pap. 69.00 (978-0-521-04484-4(7)) Cambridge Univ. Pr.
Sedgwick, Timothy F. The Christian Moral Life: Practices of Piety. 2008. 176p. pap. 20.00 (978-1-59627-100-5(0), Seabury Bks.) Church Publishing, Inc.

CHRISTIAN ETHICS—CATHOLIC AUTHORS

Abraham, Michael. Repent the Secondary Sin & Receive Your True Power to Get Wealth from God: (subtitle is the provisions column, too Long) 2007. 176p. per. 24.95 (978-1-4241-7705-9(7)) PublishAmerica, Inc.
Armenio, Peter V. & Socias, James. Our Moral Life in Christ: College Edition. 2nd ed. 2009. (978-1-890177-87-4(3)) Midwest Theological Forum.
Armenio, Peter V. & Socias, James. Our Moral Life in Christ: Semester Edition. 2009. (J). pap. (978-1-890177-69-0(5)) Midwest Theological Forum.
Barrera, Albino. Economic Compulsion & Christian Ethics. 2007. (New Studies in Christian Ethics Ser.). (ENG.). 268p. pap. 55.00 (978-0-521-04357-1(3)) Cambridge Univ. Pr.
Barrett, Melanie Susan. Love's Beauty at the Heart of the Christian Moral Life: The Ethics of Catholic Theologian Hans Urs von Balthasar. 2009. 332p. (978-0-7734-4649-6(4)) Mellen, Edwin Pr., The.
Benedict XVI, pseud. On Conscience. 2007. (Bioethics & Culture Ser.). 82p. 14.95 (978-1-58617-160-5(7)) Ignatius Pr.
Bernardin, Joseph. The Seamless Garment: Writings on the Consistent Ethic of Life. Nairn, Thomas A., ed. 2008. 305p. pap. 30.00 (978-1-57075-764-8(X)) Orbis Bks.
Billy, Dennis Joseph. Contemplative Ethics: An Introduction. 2011. (Illus.). 168p. pap. 15.95 (978-0-8091-4680-2(0)) Paulist Pr.
Boff, Leonardo. Virtues: For Another Possible World. Guilherme, Alex, tr. from POR. 2010. 282p. pap. 31.00 (978-1-60899-075-7(3), Cascade Bks.) Wipf & Stock Pubs.
Bowie, Robert A. Roman Catholicism: Ethics. Bartlett, Cynthia, ed. 2009. (ENG., Illus.). 144p. pap., stu. ed. 37.50 (978-1-4085-0510-6(X)) Nelson Thornes Ltd. GBR. Dist: Trans-Atlantic Pubns., Inc.
Brakman, Sarah-Vaughan & Fozard Weaver, Darlene, eds. The Ethics of Embryo Adoption & the Catholic Tradition: Moral Arguments, Economic Reality & Social Analysis. 2010. (Philosophy & Medicine / Catholic Studies in Bioethics Ser.). x, 326p. pap. 189.00 (978-90-481-7568-0(2), 9048175682) Springer.
Brett, Stephen F. The Law of Love: From Autonomy to Communion. 2010. (ENG.). 195p. pap. 18.00 (978-1-58966-207-0(5)) Univ. of Scranton Pr.
Brunk, Timothy M. A Critical Assessment of Sacrament & Ethics in the Thought of Louis-Marie Chauvet. 2007. (American University Studies: Vol. 254). xiv, 262p. (C). 74.95 (978-0-8204-8689-5(2)) Lang, Peter Publishing, Inc.
Cates, Diana Fritz. Aquinas on the Emotions: A Religious-Ethical Inquiry. 2009. (Moral Traditions Ser.). (ENG.). 304p. pap. 29.95 (978-1-58901-505-0(3)) Georgetown Univ. Pr.
Cessario, O.P., Romanus. The Moral Virtues & Theological Ethics, Second Edition. 2nd ed. 2008. (ENG.). 240p. pap. 25.00 (978-0-268-02297-6(6)) Univ. of Notre Dame Pr.
Clairmont, David A. Moral Struggle & Religious Ethics: On the Person as Classic in Comparative Theological Contexts. 2011. (ENG., Illus.). 256p. 109.95 (978-1-4443-3682-5(7), Wiley-Blackwell) Wiley, John & Sons, Inc.
Connell, Francis J. Father Connell Answers Moral Questions. Weitzel, Eugene J., ed. 2011. 224p. 44.95 (978-1-258-02213-6(3)) Literary Licensing, LLC.
—Outlines of Moral Theology. 2011. 258p. 47.95 (978-1-258-03635-5(5)) Literary Licensing, LLC.
Connors, Russell B., Jr. & Connors, Russell B. La Moral Cristiana: En el Aliento Divino. Walters, Thomas P., ed. 2009. (Fundamentos de la Fe Catolica Ser.) (SPA., Illus.). 128p. per. 7.95 (978-0-8294-2373-0(7)) Loyola Pr.
Conway, John Donald. Modern Moral Problems: Catholic Viewpoint on Controversial Questions. 2011. 128p. 40.95 (978-1-258-03626-3(6)) Literary Licensing, LLC.
Curran, Charles E. Catholic Moral Theology in the United States: A History. 2nd rev. ed. 2008. (Moral Traditions Ser.). (ENG.). 368p. 59.95 (978-1-58901-195-3(3)); pap. 29.95 (978-1-58901-196-0(1)) Georgetown Univ. Pr.
Curran, Charles E. & Rubio, Julie Hanlon, eds. Marriage: Readings in Moral Theology No. 15. 2009. (Readings in Moral Theology Ser.). 480p. pap. 34.95 (978-0-8091-4575-1(8)) Paulist Pr.
Cushing, Richard. The Christian & the Community: Pastoral Letter. 2011. 34p. 35.95 (978-1-258-03192-3(2)) Literary Licensing, LLC.
Demmer, Klaus. Living the Truth: A Theory of Action. McNeil, Brian, tr. from GER 2010. (Moral Traditions Ser.). (ENG.). 176p. pap. 34.95 (978-1-58901-697-2(1)) Georgetown Univ. Pr.
Durkin, Mary Greeley, et al. Virtues & Vices: Stories of the Moral Life. 2007. (ENG.). 148p. per. 20.00 (978-0-664-23235-1(3)) Westminster John Knox Pr.
Dussel, Enrique D. Ethics of Liberation: In the Age of Globalization & Exclusion. Vallega, Alejandro A., ed. Bustillo, Camilo Pérez et al, trs. from SPA. 2012. (Latin America Otherwise Ser.). (ENG., Illus.). 800p. 124.95 (978-0-8223-5201-3(X)) Duke Univ. Pr.
—Ethics of Liberation: In the Age of Globalization & Exclusion. Vallega, Alejandro A., ed. Angulo, Yolanda et al, trs. from SPA. 2012. (Latin America Otherwise Ser.). (ENG., Illus.). 800p. pap. 34.95 (978-0-8223-5212-9(5)) Duke Univ. Pr.
Finn, Daniel K. The Moral Dynamics of Economic Life: An Extension & Critique of Caritas in Veritate. 2012. E-Book (978-0-19-985834-7(9)) Oxford Univ. Pr., Inc.
Finn, Daniel K., ed. The Moral Dynamics of Economic Life: An Extension & Critique of Caritas in Veritate, 1 vol. 2012. (ENG.). 192p. pap. 29.95 (978-0-19-985835-4(7)) Oxford Univ. Pr., Inc.
Flynn, Eileen. Ten Commandments: Case Studies in Catholic Morality. 2010. 160p. pap. 9.95 (978-1-59471-223-4(9)) Ave Maria Pr.
Furton, Edward J. & Cataldo, Peter J., eds. Catholic Health Care Ethics: A Manual for Ethics Committees. 2009. (ENG.). pap. 59.95 (978-0-935372-54-0(7)) National Catholic Bioethics Ctr., The.
Furton, Edward James. Urged on by Christ: Catholic Health Care in Tension with Contemporary Culture. 2009. (SPA & ENG.). pap. 19.95 (978-0-935372-52-6(0)) National Catholic Bioethics Ctr., The.
Gascoigne, Robert. The Public Forum & Christian Ethics. 2008. (New Studies in Christian Ethics Ser.). (ENG.). 264p. pap. 40.00 (978-0-521-08605-9(1)) Cambridge Univ. Pr.
Genilo, Eric Marcelo O. John Cuthbert Ford, SJ: Moral Theologian at the End of the Manualist ERA. 2007. (Moral Traditions Ser.). (ENG.). 240p. 49.95 (978-1-58901-181-6(3)) Georgetown Univ. Pr.
Gilleman, Gérard. The Primacy of Charity in Moral Theology. Carpentier, René, ed. 2011. 458p. 57.95 (978-1-258-05188-4(5)) Literary Licensing, LLC.
Harrington, Daniel J. & Keenan, James F., eds. Paul & Virtue Ethics: Building Bridges Between New Testament Studies & Moral Theology. 2010. (ENG.). 220p. 40.00 (978-0-7425-9959-8(0)) Rowman & Littlefield Publishers, Inc.
Hogan, Linda, ed. Applied Ethics in a World Church: The Padua Conference. 2008. 287p. pap. 28.00 (978-1-57075-759-4(3)) Orbis Bks.
Iozzio, Mary Jo, et al. Calling for Justice Throughout the World: Catholic Women Theologians on the HIV/AIDS Pandemic. Roche, Mary M. Doyle, ed. 2009. (ENG.). 288p. 90.00 (978-0-8264-2863-9(0)); pap. 34.95 (978-0-8264-2864-6(9)) Continuum International Publishing Group, Ltd. GBR. Dist: National Bk. Network.
Jone, Heribert & Adelman, Urban. Moral Theology. 2011. 654p. 68.95 (978-1-258-02847-3(6)) Literary Licensing, LLC.
Keenan, James F. Catholic Theological Ethics in the World Church: The Plenary Papers from the First Cross-cultural Conference on Catholic Theological Ethics. 2007. (ENG.). 336p. 105.00 (978-0-8264-2765-6(0)) Continuum International Publishing Group, Ltd. GBR. Dist: National Bk. Network.
—Ethics of the Word: Voices in the Catholic Church Today. 2010. (ENG.). 198p. 55.00 (978-0-7425-9956-7(6)); pap. 19.95 (978-0-7425-9957-4(4)) Rowman & Littlefield Publishers, Inc.
—Moral Wisdom: Lessons & Texts from the Catholic Tradition. 2nd ed. 2010. (ENG.). 200p. 79.00 (978-1-4422-0296-2(3)); pap. 27.50 (978-1-4422-0297-9(1)) Rowman & Littlefield Publishers, Inc.
—The Works of Mercy: The Heart of Catholicism. 2nd ed. 2007. (ENG.). 136p. per. 19.95 (978-0-7425-6021-5(X)) Rowman & Littlefield Publishers, Inc.
Keenan, James F., ed. Catholic Theological Ethics, Past, Present, & Future: The Trento Conference. 2012. 304p. pap. 40.00 (978-1-57075-941-3(3)) Orbis Bks.
Keenan, James F. & Keenan. Catholic Theological Ethics in the World Church: The Plenary Papers from the First Cross-Cultural Conference on Catholic Theological Ethics. 2007. (ENG.). 336p. pap. 35.95 (978-0-8264-2766-3(9)) Continuum International Publishing Group, Ltd. GBR. Dist: National Bk. Network.
—A History of Catholic Moral Theology in the Twentieth Century: From Confessing Sins to Liberating Consciences. 2010. (ENG.). 256p. 85.00 (978-0-8264-2928-5(9)); pap. 29.95 (978-0-8264-2929-2(7)) Continuum International Publishing Group, Ltd. GBR. Dist: National Bk. Network.
Kennedy, Eugene. Blogging Towards Bethlehem: Discovering the Eternal in the Seasons of Ordinary Time. 2007. (Illus.). 320p. 25.00 (978-1-58768-042-7(4), 042-7, HiddenSpring) Paulist Pr.
Kenny, John P. Principles of Medical Ethics. 2011. 224p. 44.95 (978-1-258-09853-7(9)) Literary Licensing, LLC.
Kessler, Mathew, compiled by. Living the Ten Commandments as a Catholic Today. 2009. 96p. pap. 10.95 (978-0-7648-1849-3(X), Liguori) Liguori Pubns.
Kloft, Christopher P. Living the Love Story: Catholic Morality in the Modern World. 2008. (978-0-8189-1263-4(4), St. Pauls) St Pauls/Alba Hse. Pubs.
Lamoureux, Patricia & Wadell, Paul J. The Christian Moral Life: Faithful Discipleship for a Global Society. 2010. 328p. pap. 30.00 (978-1-57075-881-2(6)) Orbis Bks.
Lanza, Antonio & Palazzini, Pietro. General Moral Theology V1: Principles of Moral Theology. Collins, W. J., tr. 2011. 250p. 46.95 (978-1-258-03262-3(7)) Literary Licensing, LLC.
Lucie-Smith, Alexander. Narrative Theology & Moral Theology: The Infinite Horizon. 2007. (Ashgate New Critical Thinking in Religion, Theology, & Biblical Studies). 242p. 99.95 (978-0-7546-5680-7(2)) Ashgate Publishing Co.
MacDonald, Sebastian Killoran. The Sacramental Roots of Human Freedom: A Catholic Basis for Morality. 2008. 212p. 109.95 (978-0-7734-4986-2(8)) Mellen, Edwin Pr., The.
Manning, Robert. The Moral Entertainments on the Most Important Practical Truths Of. 2006. (ENG.). 236p. per. 26.95 (978-1-4286-5694-9(4)) Kessinger Publishing, LLC.
May, William E. Catholic Bioethics & the Gift of Human Life. 2nd ed. 2007. 368p. per. 19.95 (978-1-59276-330-6(8)) Our Sunday Visitor, Publishing Div.
McCarthy, David Matzko & Lysaught, M. Therese, eds. Gathered for the Journey: Moral Theology in Catholic Perspective. 2007. 356p. per. 28.00 (978-0-8028-2595-7(8)) Eerdmans, William B. Publishing Co.
McDonagh, Enda. Theology in Winter Light. 2010. (ENG.). 169p. pap. 26.95 (978-1-85607-683-8(0)) Columba Pr. IRL. Dist: Dufour Editions, Inc.
McDonagh, Enda & MacNamara, Vincent, eds. An Irish Reader in Moral Theology the Legacy of the Last Fifty Years Vol. 2: Sex, Marriage & the Family. 2011. (ENG.). 472p. pap. 49.95 (978-1-85607-739-2(X)) Columba Pr. IRL. Dist: Dufour Editions, Inc.
Medina, Jose Antonio. Temas Calientes para Los Jovenes Cristianos/Controversial Topics for Young Christians: El Aborto, la Eutanasia, la Pena de Muerte, en Defensa de la Vida/ Abortion, Euthanasia, Death Penalty, in Defense of Life. 2007. (Illus.). 63p. pap. 3.95 (978-0-7648-1527-0(X), Libros Liguori) Liguori Pubns.
Morneau, Robert F. Pathways to Community: Four Weeks on Prudence, Justice, Fortitude, & Temperance. 2008. (7 x 4 A Meditation a Day for a Span of Four Weeks Ser.). 72p. pap. 8.95 (978-1-56548-303-3(0)) New City Pr.
Morris, John F. Medicine, Health Care, & Ethics: Catholic Voices. 2007. 371p. per. 39.95 (978-0-8132-1483-2(1)) Catholic Univ. of America Pr.
Nairn, Thomas A., ed. The Consistent Ethic of Life: Assessing Its Reception & Relevance. 2008. 224p. pap. 25.00 (978-1-57075-792-1(5)) Orbis Bks.
Nau, Louis J. Readings on Fundamental Moral Theology. 2011. 110p. 39.95 (978-1-258-04336-0(X)) Literary Licensing, LLC.
O'Brien, Patrick. Emotions & Morals: Their Place & Purpose in Harmonious Living. 2011. 254p. 47.95 (978-1-258-02210-5(9)) Literary Licensing, LLC.
Oderberg, David S. Human Values: New Essays on Ethics & Natural Law. Oderberg, David S. & Chappell, Timothy, eds. 2008. (ENG.). 256p. pap. 33.00 (978-0-230-57375-8(4)) Palgrave Macmillan.
Ong, Andre. John Paul II's Philosophy of the Acting Person: A Personalistic Approach to Life. 2009. (Illus.). 356p. 119.95 (978-0-7734-4893-3(4)) Mellen, Edwin Pr., The.
O'Rourke, Kevin D. & Boyle, Philip J. Medical Ethics: Sources of Catholic Teachings. 4th rev. ed. 2011. (ENG.). 352p. (C). pap. 39.95 (978-1-58901-742-9(0)) Georgetown Univ. Pr.
Osbourn, James C. The Morality of Imperfections. 2011. 260p. 47.95 (978-1-258-05167-9(2)) Literary Licensing, LLC.
Patrick, Anne E. Women, Conscience, & the Creative Process. 2011. (Madeleva Lecture in Spirituality Ser.). 96p. pap. 9.95 (978-0-8091-4706-9(8)) Paulist Pr.
Payne, Craig. Why a Fetus Is a Human Person from the Moment of Conception: A Revisionist Interpretation of Thomas Aquinas's Treatise on Human Nature. 2010. 480p. 129.95 (978-0-7734-1321-4(9)) Mellen, Edwin Pr., The.
Pieper, Josef. Christian Idea of Man. Farrelly, Dan, tr. from GER. 2011. 64p. pap. 8.00 (978-1-58731-112-3(7)) St. Augustine's Pr., Inc.
—The Christian Idea of Man. Farrelly, Dan, tr. from GER. 2011. 64p. 16.00 (978-1-58731-111-6(9)) St. Augustine's Pr., Inc.
Rubio, Julie Hanlon. Family Ethics: Practices for Christians. 2010. (Moral Traditions Ser.). (ENG.). 272p. pap. 29.95 (978-1-58901-639-2(4)) Georgetown Univ. Pr.
Ruland, Ludwig & Rattler, T. A. Foundations of Morality: God, Man, Lower Creatures. Thompson, Newton, ed. 2011. 398p. 54.95 (978-1-258-02401-7(2)) Literary Licensing, LLC.
Rziha, John. Perfecting Human Actions. 2009. 320p. pap. 39.95 (978-0-8132-1672-0(9)) Catholic Univ. of America Pr.
Schade, Joseph I. Catholic Morality. 2007. (ENG.). 264p. 42.95 (978-0-548-05917-3(9)) Kessinger Publishing, LLC.
Sherwin, Michael S. By Knowledge & by Love: Charity & Knowledge in the Moral Theology of St. Thomas Aquinas. 2011. (Illus.). 269p. pap. 35.00 (978-0-8132-1871-7(3)) Catholic Univ. of America Pr.
Smith, Janet E. & Kaczor, Christopher. Life Issues, Medical Choices: Questions & Answers for Catholics. 2007. 188p. per. 14.99 (978-0-86716-808-2(0), Servant Bks.) Franciscan Media.
Sniegocki, John. Catholic Social Teaching & Economic Globalization: The Quest for Alternatives. 2009. pap. 37.00 (978-0-87462-744-2(3)) Marquette Univ. Pr.
Spinello, Richard A. The Genius of Pope John Paul II: The Great Pope's Moral Wisdom. 2006. (ENG.). 224p. 22.95 (978-1-58051-206-0(2), Sheed & Ward) Rowman & Littlefield Publishers, Inc.
Talley, Alan J. Christian Morality & Justice. 2009. (Illus.). 122p. spiral bd., instr.'s gde. ed. 26.25 (978-0-88489-766-8(4)) St. Mary's Pr.
Titus, Craig Steven, ed. The Psychology of Character & Virtue. 2009. (John Henry Cardinal Newman Lecture Ser.). 152p. pap. 24.95 (978-0-9773103-4-0(5)) Institute for the Psychological Science Pr., The.
Tollefsen, Christopher, ed. John Paul II's Contribution to Catholic Bioethics. 2010. (Philosophy & Medicine / Catholic Studies in Bioethics Ser.). v, 191p. pap. 149.00 (978-90-481-6801-9(5), 9048168015) Springer.
Vaghi, Peter J. The Commandments We Keep: A Catholic Guide to Living a Moral Life. 2011. 160p. pap. 12.95 (978-1-59471-261-6(1)) Ave Maria Pr.
Verstraeten, Johan, ed. Scrutinizing the Signs of the Times in the Light of the Gospel. 2007. (Bibliotheca Ephemeridum Theologicarum Lovaniensium Ser.). (ENG.). 334p. (C). pap. 108.00 (978-90-429-1978-5(7)) Peeters Pubs. & Booksellers BEL. Dist: Brown, David Bk. Co., The.
Weaver, Darlene Fozard. The Acting Person & Christian Moral Life. 2011. (Moral Traditions Ser.). 226p. pap. 32.95 (978-1-58901-772-6(2)) Georgetown Univ. Pr.
Winright, Tobias L., ed. Green Discipleship: Catholic Theological Ethics & the Environment. 2011. (ENG.). 500p. pap. 39.95 (978-1-59982-024-8(2)) St. Mary's Pr.
Wojtyla, Karol. Man in the Field of Responsibility. Kemp, Kenneth W. & Kieron, Zuzanna Maslanka, trs. from POL. 2011. 112p. 17.00 (978-1-58731-491-9(6)) St. Augustine's Pr., Inc.
Zaborowski, Holger, ed. Natural Moral Law in Contemporary Society. 2010. (ENG.). 360p. 59.95 (978-0-8132-1786-4(5)) Catholic Univ. of America Pr.
Zagar, Janko Op. Acting on Principles: A Thomistic Perspective in Making Moral Decisions. Thompson, Augustine Op, ed. 2010. 246p. pap. 27.00 (978-1-60899-804-3(5), Wipf and Stock) Wipf & Stock Pubs.
Zalot, Jozef D. & Guevin, Benedict. Catholic Ethics in Todays World. 2008. pap. (978-0-88489-959-4(4)) St. Mary's Pr.
Zalot, Jozef D. & Guevin, OSB, Benedict, Benedict. Catholic Ethics in Today's World, Revised Edition. 2nd rev. ed. 2011. (ENG.). 312p. (C). pap. 30.95 (978-1-59982-102-3(8)) St. Mary's Pr.

CHRISTIAN ETHICS—DICTIONARIES

Chung, Paul S. Christian Spirituality & Ethical Life. 2010. (Illus.). 178p. pap. 20.00 (978-1-55635-790-9(7), Pickwick Pubns.) Wipf & Stock Pubs.
Plass, Adrian. Bacon Sandwiches & Salvation: A Humorous Antidote for the Pharisee in All of Us. 2008. (ENG.). 257p. pap. 14.99 (978-1-934068-76-2(4)) Authentic Media.

C

Williams, Donald T. The Devil's Dictionary of the Christian Faith. 2008. 128p. pap. 16.99 *(978-0-8272-0638-0(0))* Chalice Pr.

CHRISTIAN ETHICS—STUDY AND TEACHING

Climbing Higher. ldr.'s ed. (Discover Life Ser.). 7.35 *(978-1-56212-864-7(7),* 153315) Faith Alive Christian Resources.

Davila, Marcos. Walking in the Spirit. 2010. (ENG.). 174p. pap. 14.99 *(978-0-557-35609-6(1))* Lulu Enterprises Inc.

Kaiser, Walter C. Jr. & Kaiser, Walter C. What Does the Lord Require? A Guide for Preaching & Teaching Biblical Ethics. 2009. (C). pap. 22.00 *(978-0-8010-3636-1(4))* Baker Academic.

Ryan, Mark. The Politics of Practical Reason: Why Theological Ethics Must Change Your Life. 2011. (Theopolitical Visions Ser.). 240p. pap. 26.00 ***(978-1-60899-466-3(X),*** Cascade Bks.) Wipf & Stock Pubs.

Talley, Alan J. Christian Morality & Justice. 2009. (Illus.). 122p. spiral bd., instr.'s gde. ed. 26.25 *(978-0-88489-766-8(4))* St. Mary's Pr.

CHRISTIAN ETIQUETTE

see Church Etiquette

CHRISTIAN EVIDENCES

see Apologetics

CHRISTIAN GIVING

Here are entered works on the duty of the individual Christian to contribute financially to the church. Works on the duty of the individual Christian to contribute time, talents, and material possessions in the service of God are entered under Christian Stewardship. Works on the solicitation and administration of church funds are entered under Church Finance.

Amaradio, Tony & Amaradio, Carin. Faithful with Much: Breaking down the Barriers to Generous Giving. 2009. (Illus.). 157p. *(978-0-7814-0484-6(3))* Kingsway Pubns.

Byfield, Richard & Shaw, James P. Your Money & Your Church. 2011. 236p. 46.95 ***(978-1-258-10211-1(0))*** Literary Licensing, LLC.

Carter, Doug. Raising More Than Money: Redefining Generosity, Reflecting God's Heart, 0 vols. 2007. 224p. 24.99 *(978-1-4185-1957-5(X))* Nelson, Thomas Inc.

Clements, C. Justin. Time, Talent, & Treasure: Reflections on the U. S. Bishops' Model for Parish Stewardship. 2006. 112p. per. 14.95 *(978-0-7648-1500-3(8))* Liguori Pubns.

Crosson, Russ. Your Life... Well Spent: The Eternal Rewards of Investing Yourself & Your Money in Your Family. 2012. 208p. pap. 12.99 ***(978-0-7369-4624-7(1))*** Harvest Hse. Pubs.

Dodson, Valerie. Don't Delay Your Increase. 2009. (ENG.). 288p. mass mkt. 6.99 *(978-1-60162-942-5(7))* Urban Bks.

Edwards-Wright, Tracy. Living to Give: The Gift of Giving. 2011. 60p. pap. 19.95 ***(978-1-4626-1172-0(9))*** PublishAmerica, Inc.

Green, Patricia. Will A Man Rob God? A Challenge for Change. 2011. 102p. pap. 10.95 ***(978-1-4327-7101-0(9))*** Outskirts Pr., Inc.

Green, William C. 52 Ways to Ignite Your Congregation — Generous Giving. 2010. *(978-0-8298-1852-9(9))* Pilgrim Pr., The/United Church Pr.

Jones, Clifford A., Sr. Star Book for Stewardship. 2012. (ENG.). 224p. 15.99 ***(978-0-8170-1665-4(1))*** Judson Pr.

Leaman, Jack. Faith Brings an Empty Basket. 2006. pap. 13.99 *(978-1-56722-692-8(2))* Word Aflame Pr.

Leblanc, Douglas. Tithing: Test Me in This. 2010. 192p. pap. 12.99 *(978-0-8499-4608-0(5));* 176p. 17.99 *(978-0-8499-0095-2(6))* Nelson, Thomas Inc.

McSwain, Stephen B. The Giving Myths: Giving Then Getting the Life You've Always Wanted. 2007. 248p. per. *(978-1-57312-495-9(8))* Smyth & Helwys Publishing, Inc.

Miller, Lynn A. Viviendo Las Primicias: Dando a Dios lo Mejor de Nosotros. 2nd ed. 2007. (ENG & SPA.). 99p. per. 7.99 *(978-0-8361-9371-8(7))* Herald Pr.

Mosser, David N. Stewardship Services. 2007. (Just in Time! (Abingdon Press) Ser.). 102p. per. 12.00 *(978-0-687-33516-9(7))* Abingdon Pr.

Perrotta, Kevin. Prayer, Fasting, & Almsgiving: Spiritual Practices That Draw Us Closer to God. 2012. ***(978-1-59325-197-0(1))*** Word Among Us Pr.

Pink, Arthur W. Tithing. 2011. 46p. pap. 8.99 ***(978-1-61203-315-0(6))*** Bottom of the Hill Publishing.

Pringle, Phil. Keys to Financial Excellence. 2008. 239p. pap. 12.99 *(978-1-60374-053-1(8))* Whitaker Hse.

Quiggle, James D. Why Christians Should Not Tithe. 2009. 174p. pap. 20.00 *(978-1-60608-926-2(9),* Wipf and Stock) Wipf & Stock Pubs.

Robinson, Anthony B. Stewardship for Vital Congregations. 2011. *(978-0-8298-1869-7(3))* Pilgrim Pr., The/United Church Pr.

Ronsvalle, John L. & Ronsvalle, Sylvia. The State of Church Giving Through 2009: Jesus Christ, the Church in the U. S., & the 16 No-Progress-in-Child Deaths Nations, 10 Being 84% Christian. 21st ed. 2011. (Illus.). 207p. pap. 36.00 ***(978-0-9843665-1-4(2))*** Empty Tomb, Inc.

Satterlee, Craig Alan. Preaching & Stewardship: Proclaiming God's Invitation to Grow. 2011. ***(978-1-56699-417-0(9))*** Alban Institute, Inc.

Schnase, Robert C. Practicing Extravagant Generosity: Daily Readings on the Grace of Giving. 2011. 72p. pap. 10.00 *(978-1-4267-2855-6(7))* Abingdon Pr.

Sharpe, Sally D. & Reeves, Michael. Extravagant Generosity: The Heart of Giving. ldr.'s ed. 2011. 48p. pap. 15.00 *(978-1-4267-2911-9(1))* Abingdon Pr.

Smith, Christian, et al. Passing the Plate: Why American Christians Don't Give Away More Money. 2008. (ENG., Illus.). 240p. 24.95 *(978-0-19-533711-2(5))* Oxford Univ. Pr., Inc.

Sweetser, Terry & Milnor, Susan. The Abundance of Our Faith: Award-Winning Sermons on Giving, Plus Suggestions for Group Discussion. 2006. x, 212p. pap. 16.00 *(978-1-55896-516-4(5),* Skinner Hse. Bks.) Unitarian Universalist Assn.

Wells, A. Bruce. Tithing: Nailed to the Cross. 2011. 144p. pap. 18.95 ***(978-1-4567-5807-3(1))*** AuthorHouse.

Willmer, Wesley K. A Revolution in Generosity: Transforming Stewards to Be Rich Toward God. 2008. (ENG., Illus.). 432p. 24.99 *(978-0-8024-6753-9(9))* Moody Pubs.

Wright, Lauren Tyler. Giving - The Sacred Art: Creating a Lifestyle of Generosity. 2007. 176p. pap. 16.99 *(978-1-59473-224-9(8))* SkyLight Paths Publishing.

CHRISTIAN HYMNS

see Hymns

CHRISTIAN LEADERSHIP

Here are entered works on leadership within Christian institutions and organizations. Works on religious views of leadership are entered under Leadership—Religious Aspects.

see also Church Officers

Addington, T. J. High-Impact Church Boards: How to Develop Healthy, Intentional, & Empowered Church Leaders. 2010. (LifeChange Ser.). 224p. pap. 14.99 *(978-1-60006-674-0(7))* NavPress Publishing Group.

—Leading from the Sandbox: How to Develop, Empower, & Release High-Impact Ministry Teams. 2010. (Becoming a Woman Of ... Ser.). 208p. pap. 14.99 *(978-1-60006-675-7(5))* NavPress Publishing Group.

Alderman, Richard C. A Little Church in a Big World. 2008. 124p. pap. 19.95 *(978-1-4241-9827-6(5))* PublishAmerica, Inc.

Alexander, Estrelda & Yong, Amos, eds. Philip's Daughters: Women in Pentecostal-Charismatic Leadership. 2008. (Princeton Theological Monographs). 260p. pap. 27.00 *(978-1-55635-832-6(6),* Pickwick Pubns.) Wipf & Stock Pubs.

Alexander Paul, Isiko. The Succession Crisis to the Diocesan See of Muhabura, Church of Ugand. 2011. 200p. pap. ***(978-3-8443-9616-4(0))*** Lambert Academic Publishing.

Allender, Dan & Beach, Nancy. Gifted to Lead: The Art of Leading As a Woman in the Church. 2008. (ENG.). 176p. 14.99 *(978-0-310-28596-0(8))* Zondervan.

Ammons, Edsel A., et al. The Confessions of Three Ebony Bishops. 2008. 140p. pap. 16.00 *(978-0-687-64847-4(5))* Abingdon Pr.

Anderson, Neil T. Freedom in Christ Bible. ldr.'s ed. 2008. (ENG.). 144p. pap. 19.99 *(978-0-8307-4652-1(8))* Gospel Light Pubns.

Anderson, Ray S. Minding GodÕs Business. 2008. (Ray S. Anderson Collection Ser.). 164p. pap. 19.00 *(978-1-60608-219-5(1),* Wipf and Stock) Wipf & Stock Pubs.

Anene, Dr Chibundo & Anene, Chibundo. The and Christian & the Word. 2011. 172p. pap. 14.99 ***(978-1-61215-825-9(0))*** Xulon Pr., Inc.

Archangel, Priscilla. The Call to Faith Centered Leadership. 2010. 304p. pap. *(978-1-55452-500-3(4),* Essence Publishing) Essence Publishing.

Arendell, Randy. Modern Church: Where Tradition Trumps Truth. 2008. 220p. (ENG.). 24.99 *(978-1-60477-669-0(2));* per. 14.99 *(978-1-60477-668-3(4))* Xulon Pr., Inc.

Armerding, Hudson T. El Lider Cristiano: Leadership. (SPA.). 122p. *(978-84-7228-482-1(4),* 220538) Clie, Editorial.

Armstrong, Richard Stoll. A Sense of Being Called. 2011. 210p. pap. 23.00 *(978-1-60899-404-5(X),* Cascade Bks.) Wipf & Stock Pubs.

Ashley, Evelyn. Paul's Defense of His Ministerial Style: A Study of His Second Letter to the Corinthians. 2011. 352p. 129.95 *(978-0-7734-1557-7(2))* Mellen, Edwin Pr., The.

Associated Mennonite Biblical Seminary, Church Leadership Center Staff & Institute of Mennonite Studies (Elkhart, Ind.) Staff, contrib. by. Engaging Pastors Papers & Reflections from the Summative Conference. 2010. *(978-0-936273-45-7(3))* Institute of Mennonite Studies.

Atkinson, David. Leadership - by the Book. 2007. 280p. per. 15.99 *(978-1-60266-251-3(7))* Xulon Pr., Inc.

Atkinson, David M. Leadership - by the Book. 2008. 280p. 25.99 *(978-1-60791-058-9(6))* Xulon Pr., Inc.

Avery, William O. & Gaede, Beth Ann. If This Is the Way the World Works: Science, Congregations, & Leadership. 2007. *(978-1-56699-355-5(5))* Alban Institute, Inc.

Baars, Conrad W., et al. I Will Give Them a New Heart: Reflections on the Priesthood & the Renewal of the Church. 2007. *(978-0-8189-1245-0(6),* St. Pauls) St Pauls/Alba Hse. Pubs.

Baker, Dori Grinenko. Greenhouses of Hope: Congregations That Grow Young Leaders Who Will Change the World. 2010. *(978-1-56699-409-5(8))* Alban Institute, Inc.

Bandy, Thomas G. Spirited Leadership: Empowering People to Do What Matters. 2008. (Illus.). 170p. per. 19.99 *(978-0-8272-3468-0(6))* Chalice Pr.

—Why Should I Believe You? Rediscovering Clergy Credibility. 2007. 152p. per. 15.00 *(978-0-687-33529-9(9))* Abingdon Pr.

Barentsen, Jack. Emerging Leadership in the Pauline Mission: A Social Identity Perspective on Local Leadership Development in Corinth & Ephesus. 2011. (Princeton Theological Monographs). 396p. pap. 44.00 ***(978-1-61097-244-4(9),*** Pickwick Pubns.) Wipf & Stock Pubs.

Barna, George. The Power of Vision: Discover & Apply God's Vision for Your Life & Ministry. 2009. (ENG.). 208p. pap. 14.99 *(978-0-8307-4728-3(1))* Gospel Light Pubns.

Barnard, Tom. E-Couragement: Meditations for Leaders. 2008. (ENG.). 192p. pap. 14.99 *(978-0-8341-2358-8(4),* 083-412-3584) Beacon Hill Pr. of Kansas City.

Barr, Robert. In the World but Not of It-Serving Christ in the Modern World: God's Principles for Living. 2008. (Illus.). 192p. pap. 18.95 *(978-1-4327-3312-4(5))* Outskirts Pr., Inc.

Barton, Ruth Haley. Strengthening the Soul of Your Leadership: Seeking God in the Crucible of Ministry. 2008. (Transforming Center Set Ser.). (ENG.). 231p. 18.00 *(978-0-8308-3513-3(X),* IVP Bks.) InterVarsity Pr.

Basic Friendship Curriculum: Adult (Year 1) tchr. ed. 13.25 *(978-1-56212-727-5(6),* 300115); stu. ed. 13.25 *(978-1-56212-726-8(8),* 300110) Faith Alive Christian Resources.

Basic Friendship Curriculum: Adult (Year 2) tchr. ed. 13.25 *(978-0-933140-81-3(9),* 300215) Faith Alive Christian Resources.

Basic Friendship Curriculum: Adult (Year 3) tchr. ed. 13.25 *(978-0-933140-97-4(5),* 300315) Faith Alive Christian Resources.

Basic Friendship Curriculum: Group Leader's Kit, Year 1. 189.95 *(978-1-56212-725-1(X),* 300105) Faith Alive Christian Resources.

Basic Friendship Curriculum: Group Leader's Kit, Year 2. 189.95 *(978-1-56212-731-2(4),* 300205) Faith Alive Christian Resources.

Basic Friendship Curriculum: Group Leader's Kit, Year 3. 189.95 *(978-1-56212-735-0(7),* 300305) Faith Alive Christian Resources.

Basic Friendship Curriculum: Year 1. instr.'s gde. ed. 22.25 *(978-0-933140-40-0(1),* 300100) Faith Alive Christian Resources.

Basic Friendship Curriculum: Year 3. stu. ed. 13.25 *(978-1-56212-736-7(5),* 300310) Faith Alive Christian Resources.

Bass, Richard. Leadership in Congregations. 2006. xv, 199p. *(978-1-56699-334-0(2))* Alban Institute, Inc.

Batterson, Mark. Soulprint: Discovering Your Divine Destiny. 2011. (ENG.). 192p. pap. 14.99 *(978-1-60142-039-8(0),* Multnomah) Doubleday Religious Publishing Group, The.

Baylor, David. Developing Leaders in the Two-Thirds World Church: Evaluation, Trends, & Challenges. 2008. 124p. pap. *(978-3-8364-8256-1(8))* VDM Verlag Dr. Mueller e.K.

Beausay, William, II. The Leadership Genius of Jesus: Ancient Wisdom for Modern Business, 0 vols. 2009. 132p. pap. 10.99 *(978-1-59555-325-6(8))* Nelson, Thomas Inc.

Beck, James P., Jr. & Silverberg, Neil. Not Many Fathers. 2007. (ENG.). per. 12.99 *(978-1-60037-222-3(8))* Morgan James Publishing.

Beck, Pete, Jr. Heart of an Apostle. 2007. (ENG.). per. 9.95 *(978-1-60037-103-5(5))* Morgan James Publishing.

Beck, Pete, Jr. & Silverberg, Neil. No Muchos Padres. 2007. (SPA.). per. 12.99 *(978-1-60037-106-6(X))* Morgan James Publishing.

Beeley, Christopher A. Leading God's People: Wisdom from the Early Church for Today. 2012. pap. ***(978-0-8028-6700-1(6))*** Eerdmans, William B. Publishing Co.

Bell, Christopher. The Black Clergy's Misguided Worship Leadership: No More Idol Gods for Black People. 2010. 136p. pap. 19.00 *(978-1-4251-7806-2(5))* Trafford Publishing.

Berenberg, Sanford. Learn & Grow Daily! 2009. 232p. pap. 15.99 *(978-1-60791-458-7(1))* Xulon Pr., Inc.

Berkley, James D., ed. Leadership Handbook of Management & Administration. rev. ed. 2008. 560p. pap. 24.99 *(978-0-8010-6814-0(2))* Baker Bks.

Berntsen, John A. Cross-Shaped Leadership: On the Rough & Tumble of Parish Practice. 2008. *(978-1-56699-375-3(X))* Alban Institute, Inc.

Blanchard, Ken & Hodges, Phil. Lead Like Jesus: Lessons from the Greatest Leadership Role Model of All Time. 2007. (Illus.). 174p. per. 12.99 *(978-0-9793855-0-6(4))* Lead Like Jesus.

—Lead Like Jesus: Lessons from the Greatest Leadership Role Model of All Time, 0 vols. 2008. 272p. pap. 15.99 *(978-1-4003-1420-1(8))* Nelson, Thomas Inc.

Bliss, William G. Leadership Lessons from the BOOK. 2009. pap. 19.95 *(978-1-61623-028-9(2))* Independent Pub.

Blue, Michael A. Building Credibility in Leadership: Principles for Secondary Leaders. 2011. (ENG.). 256p. pap. 13.99 ***(978-1-61638-586-6(3),*** Creation Hse.) Charisma Media.

Boardman, Henry Augustus. 2 Discourses on the Common Objections to the Doctrin of Election. 2009. 89p. pap. 9.99 *(978-1-879737-64-8(7))* Calvary Pr.

Bohannon, Richard R. The Organization & Leadership of the First Century Church: A Study. 2011. 152p. 30.95 *(978-1-4497-1343-0(2));* pap. 13.95 *(978-1-4497-1342-3(4))* Author Solutions, Inc. (WestBow Pr.).

Boles, Olin D. Second-Mile Leadership Principles. 2011. 196p. 33.95 ***(978-1-61507-717-5(0));*** pap. 17.95 ***(978-1-61507-716-8(2))*** Cross Bks. Publishing.

Bonem, Mike. In Pursuit of Great & Godly Leadership: Tapping the Wisdom of the World for the Kingdom of God. 2012. (Jossey-Bass Leadership Network Ser.: 58). (ENG.). 288p. 24.95 ***(978-0-470-94742-5(X),*** Jossey-Bass) Wiley, John & Sons, Inc.

Borg, Richard A. The Chief Steward. 2008. 408p. pap. 21.99 *(978-1-60477-507-5(6))* Xulon Pr., Inc.

Bowling, John C. Grace-Full Leadership: Understanding the Heart of a Christian Leader. 2nd ed. 2011. (ENG.). 192p. 17.99 *(978-0-8341-2602-2(8),* 9780834126022) Beacon Hill Pr. of Kansas City.

Bredfeldt, Gary. Gran Líder, Gran Maestro (Great Leader, Great Teacher) 2011. (SPA.). 216p. pap. 13.95 ***(978-1-58802-443-5(1))*** Editorial Patmos.

Bridges, Vestinia M. & Johnson, Madonna P. The Spirit of Wisdom & Revelation II: Daily Bread Renewing, Reviving, & Restoring the Remnant. 2009. 80p. pap. 10.99 *(978-1-60647-371-9(9))* Xulon Pr., Inc.

Britt, Billy M. Self-Supported Ministers: Lest We Forget. 2007. (Illus.). 178p. pap. 27.50 *(978-0-942727-32-6(0))* North Carolina Yearly Meeting Pubns. Board.

Brouwer, Barbara. Leading with Love. (Core Values Ser.). tchr. ed. 3.50 *(978-1-56212-201-0(0),* 152052) Faith Alive Christian Resources.

Brown, L. Duane & Nelsen, T. Mark. Forgotten Lay Leaders. 2011. 136p. pap. 11.99 ***(978-0-9832039-8-8(9))*** Faithful Life Pubs.

Brown, Pattiejean. What on Earth Am I Doing? 2009. 80p. pap. *(978-1-55452-437-2(7),* Guardian Bks.) Essence Publishing.

Bugg, Charles B. Transformational Leadership: Leading with Integrity. 2010. pap. *(978-1-57312-558-1(X))* Smyth & Helwys Publishing, Inc.

Burdette, Dallas R. Old Texts Through New Eyes. 2009. 504p. 36.99 *(978-1-60791-379-5(8));* pap. 24.99 *(978-1-60791-377-1(1))* Xulon Pr., Inc.

Byrne, Herbert. The Pastor As Church Leader & Educator. 2006. pap. 16.99 *(978-1-60034-546-3(8))* Xulon Pr., Inc.

Cairney, Paul D. On Target: Bible-Based Leadership for Military Professionals. 2010. 196p. pap. 21.49 *(978-1-4520-7230-2(2))* AuthorHouse.

Calhoun, Mike & Garland, Ric. Where Was God When? 2010. 120p. (YA). lib. bdg. 14.95 *(978-1-935475-10-1(X))* Word of Life Fellowship, Inc.

Campbell, Regi, et al. Mentor Like Jesus, 1 vol. 2009. (ENG.). 176p. 16.99 *(978-0-8054-4811-5(X),* B&H Bks.) B&H Publishing Group.

Carder, Kenneth & Warner, Laceye. Grace to Lead: Practicing Leadership in the Wesleyan Tradition. 2010. 100p. pap. 12.95 *(978-0-938162-76-6(4))* United Methodist Board of Higher Education & Ministry.

Carl Townsend. Beyond Illusion: Leading from Reality. 2009. 276p. 30.95 *(978-1-4401-9111-4(5));* pap. 20.95 *(978-1-4401-9110-7(7))* iUniverse, Inc.

Carpenter, Venetia. Following the Heart of the Great Shepherd: Relevant Shepherding for These Last Days. 2009. 52p. pap. 10.99 *(978-1-61579-470-6(0))* Xulon Pr., Inc.

Cartmill, Carol & Gentile, Yvonne. Leadership Essentials: Practical Tools for Leading in the Church. 2006. 141p. per. 16.00 *(978-0-687-33595-4(7))* Abingdon Pr.

Catt, Steven R. When Do I Cry Wolf? 2009. 120p. pap. 11.99 *(978-1-60791-194-4(9))* Xulon Pr., Inc.

Chand, Samuel R. Cracking Your Church's Culture Code: Seven Keys to Unleashing Vision & Inspiration. 2010. (Jossey-Bass Leadership Network Ser.: 54). (ENG., Illus.). 224p. 24.95 *(978-0-470-62781-5(6),* Jossey-Bass) Wiley, John & Sons, Inc.

Chandler, John P. Courageous Church Leadership: Conversations with Effective Practitioners. 2007. (Columbia Partnership Leadership Ser.). (Illus.). 127p. per. 19.99 *(978-0-8272-0506-2(6))* Chalice Pr.

Chase, Gloria. Shush My Baby & Don't You Cry. 2007. 81p. pap. 9.95 *(978-0-9796180-8-6(8))* Williams, Benjamin Publishing.

Chez, Thom. Firm Foundation. 2008. 151p. pap. 24.95 *(978-1-60474-668-6(8))* PublishAmerica, Inc.

Choong, Gary K. G. Counter-Cultural Paradigmatic Leadership: Ethical Use of Power in Confucian Societies. 2011. 152p. pap. 17.00 ***(978-1-61097-136-2(1),*** Wipf and Stock) Wipf & Stock Pubs.

Clarke, Andrew D. Called to Serve: A Pauline Theology of Leadership. 2008. (Library of New Testament Studies, the Ser.). (ENG.). 220p. 130.00 *(978-0-567-04560-7(9),* T&T Clark Int'l) Continuum International Publishing Group, Ltd. GBR. Dist: National Bk. Network.

Clarke, P.J. Lives That Made a Difference: An RSME Book for Schools. 2011. 270p. pap. 16.95 ***(978-1-60976-870-6(1),*** Eloquent Bks.) AEG Literary Publishing Services, Inc.

Cole, Neil. Journeys to Significance: Charting a Leadership Course from the Life of Paul. 2011. (Jossey-Bass Leadership Network Ser.: 48). (ENG., Illus.). 208p. 24.95 *(978-0-470-52944-7(X),* Jossey-Bass) Wiley, John & Sons, Inc.

—Organic Leadership: Leading Naturally Right Where You Are, 1 vol. 2010. (Shapevine Ser.). (ENG.). 320p. pap. 16.99 *(978-0-8010-7238-3(7))* Baker Bks.

Collins, Travis. Tough Calls: Game-Winning Principles for Leaders under Pressure. 2008. (ENG.). 208p. pap. 14.99 *(978-1-59669-229-9(4))* New Hope Pubs.

Comiskey, Joel. Coach: Empower Others to Effectively Lead a Small Group. 2007. (ENG.). 95p. per. 9.95 *(978-0-9790679-1-4(X),* CCS Publishing) CCS Pubs.

—How to Lead a Great Small Group Meeting: ... So People Want to Come Back. 2010. (Illus.). 137p. pap. 16.99 *(978-0-9825352-2-6(8))* Touch Pubns.

Cook, Jerry & Baldwin, Stanley C. Love, Acceptance & Forgiveness: Being Christian in a Non-Christian World. 2009. (ENG.). 192p. pap. 12.99 *(978-0-8307-4753-5(2))* Gospel Light Pubns.

Cormode, Scott. Making Spiritual Sense: Christian Leaders as Spiritual Interpreters. 2006. 139p. per. 15.00 *(978-0-687-49223-7(8))* Abingdon Pr.

Cotton, Dorothy. If Your Back's Not Bent: The Role of the Citizenship Education Program in the Civil Rights Movement. 2012. pap. ***(978-0-7432-9684-7(2));*** (ENG., Illus.). 352p. 25.00 ***(978-0-7432-9683-0(4))*** Atria Bks. (Beyond Words/Atria Bks.).

Cousins, Don. Experiencing LeaderShift. 2008. 256p. pap. *(978-1-4347-6833-9(3))* Cook, David C.

Cousins, Don & Bugbee, Bruce. Experiencing LeaderShift Together: A Step-by-Step Strategy for Small Groups & Ministry Teams. ldr.'s ed. 2008. (LeaderShift Ser.). (ENG.). 160p. 24.99 *(978-1-4347-6812-4(0))* Cook, David C.

—Experiencing Leadership Together - Participant's Guide: A Step-by-Step Strategy for Small Groups & Ministry Teams. 2008. (LeaderShift Ser.). (ENG.). 144p. pap. 10.99 *(978-1-4347-6810-0(4))* Cook, David C.

Cousins, Don, et al. Experiencing LeaderShift: Letting Go of Leadership Heresies. 2008. (LeaderShift Ser.). (ENG.). 272p. 22.99 *(978-1-4347-6854-4(6))* Cook, David C.

Creps, Earl. Off-Road Disciplines: Spiritual Adventures of Missional Leaders. 2006. (Jossey-Bass Leadership Network Ser.: 20). (ENG., Illus.). 240p. 23.95 *(978-0-7879-8520-2(1))*, Jossey-Bass) Wiley, John & Sons, Inc.

Creps, Earl & Creps, Earl G. Reverse Mentoring: How Young Leaders Can Transform the Church & Why We Should Let Them. 2008. (Jossey-Bass Leadership Network Ser.: 26). (ENG., Illus.). 240p. 24.95 *(978-0-470-18898-9(7))*, Jossey-Bass) Wiley, John & Sons, Inc.

Croft, Steven. Ministry in Three Dimensions: Ordination & Leadership in the Local Church. 226p. pap. *(978-0-232-52313-3(4))*, 441411) Darton, Longman & Todd, Ltd.

Crossley, Gareth. Growing Leaders in the Church: A Leadership Development Resource. 2007. (Illus.). 302p. per. *(978-0-85234-553-5(4))* Evangelical Pr.

Crumpler, Anne. Entering the New Testament. 2008. 112p. pap. 15.00 *(978-0-8358-9968-0(3))* Upper Room Bks.

Cuartas, Victor H. Capacitando L'deres Hispanos: Un Modelo en L'nea. 2010. 176p. pap. 20.00 *(978-1-60899-657-5(3))*, Resource Pubns.) Wipf & Stock Pubs.

Dadswell, David. Consultancy Skills for Mission & Ministry. 2011. 224p. pap. 35.00 ***(978-0-334-04373-7(5))***, SCM Pr.) Hymns Ancient & Modern Ltd GBR. Dist: Westminster John Knox Pr.

Dale, Robert D. & Dale, Robert. Leading Edge: Leadership Strategies from the New Testament. 2006. (Illus.). 142p. pap. 18.00 *(978-1-59752-895-5(1))*, Wipf and Stock) Wipf & Stock Pubs.

Damazio, Frank. A City Vision All Leaders Must Have: Cultivating a Passion to Impact Your City. 2006. (Life Impact Ser.). 151p. 9.99 *(978-1-59383-034-2(3))* City Christian Publishing.

—Preaching with Purpose & Passion: The Greatest Call on Earth. 2006. (Life Impact Ser.). 145p. 9.99 *(978-1-59383-036-6(X))* City Christian Publishing.

Davies, Mervyn & Dodds, Graham. Leadership in the Church for a People of Hope. 2011. (ENG., Illus.). 200p. 110.00 *(978-0-567-38621-2(X))*; pap. 32.95 *(978-0-567-01407-8(X))* Continuum International Publishing Group, Ltd. GBR. (T&T Clark Int'l). Dist: National Bk. Network.

Decker, John & Decker, Sonja. Doing What Jesus Did: Ministering in the Power of the Holy Spirit. 2007. (ENG.). 344p. pap. 14.99 *(978-1-59979-086-2(6))*, Creation Hse.) Charisma Media.

Dejean, Edgar K. A Belief System from Beyond the Box. 2009. 208p. 25.75 *(978-1-4389-6787-5(X))*; pap. 15.70 *(978-1-4389-6788-2(8))* AuthorHouse.

DeKoven, Stan. Prelude to a Requiem. 2008. (Illus.). 64p. pap. 10.00 *(978-1-931178-54-9(2))* Vision Publishing.

Dekoven, Stan. Seven Reasons. 2009. 70p. pap. 10.00 *(978-1-61529-003-1(6))* Vision Publishing.

—Visionary Leadership. 2008. 208p. per. 20.00 *(978-1-931178-14-3(3))* Vision Publishing.

Delaney, H. G. Stop the Church, I Want to Get Off: Friendly Fire in the Army of God. 2008. 200p. pap. 24.95 *(978-1-60474-051-6(5))* PublishAmerica, Inc.

Dezeeuw, Glen W. Clu. Becoming a Salt & Light Leader. 2011. 130p. 38.99 ***(978-1-59781-690-8(6))*** Xulon Pr., Inc.

Dick, Dan R. Bursting the Bubble: Rethinking Conventional Wisdom about Church Leadership. 2008. (Illus.). 130p. pap. 17.00 *(978-0-687-45513-2(3))* Abingdon Pr.

Dilmore, Pamela & Neinast, Helen R. Attentiveness: Being Present: Leader Guide. ldr.'s ed. 2006. (Living the Good Life Together Ser.). 62p. pap. 12.00 *(978-0-687-46550-7(8))* Abingdon Pr.

Discovery Group Leader's Guide. Date not set. (Discipleship Ser.: No. 1). 39p. pap. 4.99 *(978-0-86605-135-4(X))* Integrated Resources.

Ditewig, William T. The Emerging Diaconate: Servant Leaders in a Servant Church. 2007. (Illus.). 272p. pap. 21.95 *(978-0-8091-4449-5(2))*, 4449-5) Paulist Pr.

Dorr, Donal. Faith at Work: A Spirituality of Leadership. 2007. 171p. per. 14.95 *(978-0-8146-3182-9(7))* Liturgical Pr.

Dorsett, Terry W. Developing Leadership Teams in the Bivocational Church. 2010. 160p. pap. 19.95 *(978-1-61507-252-1(7))* Cross Bks. Publishing.

Downes, Martin, compiled by. Risking the Truth: Handling error in the Church. 2009. (ENG.). 192p. 14.99 *(978-1-84550-284-3(1))* Christian Focus Pubns. GBR. Dist: STL Distribution North America.

Dragt, Gordon R. One Foot Planted in the Center, the Other Dangling off the Edge: How Intentional Leadership Can Transform Your Church. 2009. (ENG.). 192p. pap. 19.95 *(978-1-58982-494-2(6))*, Millennial Mind Publishing) American Bk. Publishing Group.

Dresselhaus, Richard L. Deacon Ministry: Empowering Volunteers. 2009. 122p. pap. 5.95 *(978-0-88243-851-1(4))* Gospel Publishing Hse.

Driscoll, Mark. On Church Leadership. 2008. (Book You'll Actually Read Ser.). 96p. pap. 9.99 *(978-1-4335-0137-1(6))* Crossway.

Driscoll, Mark & Breshears, Gerry. Vintage Church Team Stucy Pack. 2009. 384p. 109.99 *(978-1-4335-1366-4(8))* Crossway.

Driver, Thomas L. 7 Keys to Effective Lay Ministry. 2012. 96p. pap. ***(978-1-55452-834-9(8))*** Essence Publishing.

Drummond, Sarah B. Holy Clarity: The Practice of Planning & Evaluation. 2009. *(978-1-56699-387-6(3))* Alban Institute, Inc.

D'Souza, Anthony. Como Ser un Lider: How to Be a Leader. (SPA.). *(978-84-7645-198-4(9))*, 223234) Clie, Editorial.

Duncan, Graham. Partnership in Mission: A Critical Historical Evaluation of the Relationship between 'older' & younger' Churches with Special Reference to the Church of Scotland. 2008. 284p. pap. *(978-3-639-08865-6(4))* VDM Verlag Dr. Mueller e.K.

Eagles Aka King David Tha Vessel, David. What It Takes & What It Doesn't: A 21st Century Guide to Leadership in the Church. 2011. 60p. pap. 19.95 ***(978-1-4560-4274-5(2))*** PublishAmerica, Inc.

Easum, Bill. Sacred Cows Make Gourmet Burgers: Ministry Anytime, Anywhere, by Anyone. Kim, Hyo Shick, tr. 2007. pap. 15.00 *(978-0-687-49031-8(6))* Abingdon Pr.

Ebener, Dan R. Servant Leadership Models for Your Parish. 2010. (Illus.). 288p. pap. 24.95 *(978-0-8091-4653-6(3))* Paulist Pr.

Eberle, Harold R. & Trench, Martin. Victorious Eschatology: A Partial Preterist View. 2nd ed. 2007. (Illus.). 337p. per. 16.95 *(978-1-882523-33-7(4))* Worldcast Publishing.

Eims, LeRoy. Como Ser el Lider Que Debieras Ser: Be the Leader You Were Meant to Be. (SPA.). *(978-84-7645-240-0(3))*, 223313) Clie, Editorial.

Ekeke, Chima. Leadership Wisdom. 2007. 204p. per. 14.99 *(978-1-60266-685-6(7))* Xulon Pr., Inc.

Ellis, Delton. Preparing to Bear Arms Workbook: An Armorbearer's Guide to Making Your Pastor Look Good. 2007. pap. 11.99 *(978-1-60477-234-0(4))* Xulon Pr., Inc.

English, Margaret. Removing the Veil: Revealing God's Truth for Women. 2008. 224p. pap. 13.99 *(978-0-88270-465-4(6))* Bridge-Logos Foundation.

Epperly, Bruce Gordon. Starting with Spirit: Nurturing Your Call to Pastoral Leadership. 2010. *(978-1-56699-408-8(X))* Alban Institute, Inc.

Esposito, Cheryl. In the Spirit of Leadership: Reflections along the Journey. 2008. 108p. spiral bd. 16.95 *(978-0-9799252-2-1(3))* Plumb Road Publishing.

Evans, Daniel & Godwin, Joseph. Elder Governance: Insights into Making the Transition. 2011. 140p. pap. 17.00 *(978-1-60899-796-1(0))*, Resource Pubns.) Wipf & Stock Pubs.

Everist, Norma Cook & Nessan, Craig L. Transforming Leadership: New Vision for a Church in Mission. 2007. (Prisms Ser.). 250p. (C). pap. 22.00 *(978-0-8006-2048-6(8))*, Fortress Pr.) Augsburg Fortress, Pubs.

Fairbanks, E. LeBron & Toler, Stan. Learning to Be Last: Leadership for Congregational Transformation. 2008. (ENG., Illus.). 160p. pap. 14.99 *(978-0-8341-2353-3(3))*, 083-412-3533) Beacon Hill Pr. of Kansas City.

Falwell, Jonathan. Innovatechurch: Innovative Leadership for the Next Generation Church. 2008. (ENG.). 288p. pap. 14.99 *(978-0-8054-4826-9(8))*, B&H Bks.) B&H Publishing Group.

Farley, Rick. God's Standard-Bearer: The True Measure of a Leader. 2009. pap. 15.99 *(978-0-7684-3110-0(7))* Destiny Image Pubs.

Ferguson, Nancy & Witt, Kevin. The Retreat Leader's Manual: A Complete Guide to Organizing Meaningful Christian Retreats. 2006. 126p. per. 15.00 *(978-0-88177-428-3(6))* Discipleship Resources.

Fernando, Ajith. Un Llamado, Gozo y Sufrimiento: Lo Que Todo Lider Debe Saber Sobre Servicio y Dedicación. 2009. Orig. Title: The Call to Joy & Pain. (SPA.). 208p. pap. 9.99 *(978-1-4143-2399-2(9))*, Tyndale Espanol) Tyndale Hse. Pubs.

Fitz, Raymond, frwd. Black Belt Leader, Peaceful Leader: An Introduction to Catholic Servant Leadership. 2008. 140p. per. 19.95 *(978-0-9768627-5-8(1))* Asogomi Publishing International.

Fluckiger, Wilford Lynn. Dynamic Leadership. 2011. 122p. 40.95 ***(978-1-258-07087-8(1))*** Literary Licensing, LLC.

Forman, Rowland, et al. The Leadership Baton: An Intentional Strategy for Developing Leaders in Your Church, 1 vol. 2007. (ENG.). 224p. pap. 14.99 *(978-0-310-28480-2(5))* Zondervan.

Forster, Walter O. Zion on the Mississippi. 606p. 25.99 *(978-0-570-04539-7(8))* Concordia Publishing Hse.

Foss, Michael W. From Members to Disciples: Leadership Lessons from the Book of Acts. 2007. 100p. per. 16.00 *(978-0-687-46730-3(6))* Abingdon Pr.

Fowler, Mark. Mentoring into Vocation: Touchstones for the Journey. rev. ed. 2010. pap. 0.00 *(978-0-938162-73-5(X))* United Methodist Board of Higher Education & Ministry.

Friend, Howard E. Gifts of an Uncommon Life: The Practice of Contemplative Activism. 2008. *(978-1-56699-374-6(1))* Alban Institute, Inc.

Friendship Program Guide. (Welcome to Friendship Ser.). 5.95 *(978-1-56212-916-3(3))*, 301000) Faith Alive Christian Resources.

Fryling, Robert A. The Leadership Ellipse: Shaping How We Lead by Who We Are. 2009. (ENG.). 220p. pap. 17.00 *(978-0-8308-3538-6(5))*, IVP Bks.) InterVarsity Pr.

Fukuda, Mitsuo. Mentoring Like Barnabas. Cozens, Simon, tr. 2011.Tr. of バルナバのように人を育てる. 90p. pap. ***(978-0-9565943-9-6(5))*** Wide Margin Bks. GBR. Dist: Gardners Bks. Ltd.

Gaga, John. The Role of Church Leaders in Hiv & Aids Prevention. 2011. 140p. pap. ***(978-3-8443-8252-5(6))*** Lambert Academic Publishing.

Galbreath, Paul. Leading from the Table. 2008. *(978-1-56699-362-3(8))* Alban Institute, Inc.

Gangel, Kenneth O. Coaching Ministry Teams: Leadership & Management in Christian Organizations. 2006. 232p. pap. 26.00 *(978-1-59752-657-9(6))*, Wipf and Stock) Wipf & Stock Pubs.

—Surviving Toxic Leaders: How to Work for Flawed People in Churches, Schools, & Christian Organizations. 2007. 106p. pap. 13.00 *(978-1-55635-090-0(2))* Wipf & Stock Pubs.

Gathogo, Julius. Responsible Church Leaders in Afric. 2011. 132p. pap. ***(978-3-8443-9155-8(X))*** Lambert Academic Publishing.

Gedeon, Jean-Paul. Building Vision. 2010. (Illus.). 204p. pap. 22.00 *(978-1-60608-848-7(3))*, Wipf and Stock) Wipf & Stock Pubs.

Gentry, Dave T. Crisis in the Camp. 2010. 152p. pap. 14.99 *(978-1-60957-519-9(9))* Xulon Pr., Inc.

Geoffrey, Kevin. Being a Disciple of Messiah: Leader's Guide (the Messianic Life Discipleship Series / Bible Study) 2007. 96p. pap. 9.95 *(978-0-9785504-3-1(9))* Perfect Word Ministries.

George, Carl. Nine Keys to Effective Small Group Leadership: How Lay Leaders Can Establish Dynamic & Healthy Cells, Classes, or Teams. 2007. 216p. per. 14.95 *(978-0-9795350-0-0(X))* CDLM.

George, Denise. What Pastors Wish Church Members Knew, 1 vol. 2009. (ENG.). 176p. 16.99 *(978-0-310-28395-9(7))* Zondervan.

Gill. Strategic Church Leadership. 104p. 15.00 *(978-0-281-04901-1(7))* SPCK Publishing GBR. Dist: Pilgrim Pr., The/United Church Pr.

Gillies, Susan E. & Dvirnak, M. Ingrid. Empowering Laity, Engaging Leaders: Tapping the Root for Ministry. 2012. pap. ***(978-0-8170-1710-1(0))*** Judson Pr.

Goldsmith, Elizabeth. Against All Odds: God at Work in an Impossible Situation. 2007. (Missionary Life Stories Ser.). (ENG.). 244p. per. 16.99 *(978-1-85078-759-4(X))* Authentic Media.

Golemon, Larry A. Finding Our Story: Narrative Leadership & Congregational Change. 2009. *(978-1-56699-376-0(8))* Alban Institute, Inc.

—Living Our Story: Narrative Leadership & Congregational Culture. 2009. *(978-1-56699-378-4(4))* Alban Institute, Inc.

—Teaching Our Story: Narrative Leadership & Pastoral Formation. 2009. *(978-1-56699-377-7(6))* Alban Institute, Inc.

Gongwer, Todd. Lead ... for God's Sake! A Parable for Finding the Heart of Leadership. 2011. (ENG.). 256p. 22.99 ***(978-1-4143-7055-2(5))*** Tyndale Hse. Pubs.

Gortner, Bob. Christian Tigers: Lessons Learned & Timeless Tips from One Who Tried to be One. 2009. 136p. 23.99 *(978-1-4389-7949-6(5))*; pap. 13.99 *(978-1-4389-7948-9(7))* AuthorHouse.

Graves, Joel. Leadership Paradigms in Chaplaincy. 2007. 232p. per. 25.95 *(978-1-58112-372-2(8))*, Dissertation.com) Universal Pubs.

Gray, Joan S. Spiritual Leadership for Church Officers: A Handbook. 2009. (ENG.). 128p. pap. 18.00 *(978-0-664-50305-5(5))* Geneva Pr.

GreeneBarr, Cecelia. Guide My Feet: Ministry Transformed Through Mentoring. 2007. per. 18.00 *(978-0-9796366-0-8(4))* GreeneHouse, LLC.

Greggo, Stephen P. Trekking Toward Wholeness: A Resource for Care Group Leaders. 2008. (ENG.). 293p. pap. 23.00 *(978-0-8308-2824-1(9))*, IVP Acad.) InterVarsity Pr.

Griffin, Mark L. Pastor, CEO. 2010. 100p. pap. 10.99 *(978-1-60957-783-4(3))* Xulon Pr., Inc.

Griggs Developing Leadership in Church. *(978-0-687-10509-0(9))* Abingdon Pr.

Grundy, Malcolm. Leadership & Oversight: New Models for Episcopal Ministry. 2011. (ENG.). 256p. pap. 27.95 *(978-1-4411-4401-0(3))* Mowbray, A. R. & Co., Ltd. GBR. Dist: National Bk. Network.

Guidelines 2001-2004 Booklets. 49.00 *(978-0-687-01587-0(1))* Abingdon Pr.

Guidelines 2001-2004 Booklets with Slipcase. 55.00 *(978-0-687-01567-2(7))* Abingdon Pr.

Guidelines 2001-2004 Mens Ministries. 2.50 *(978-0-687-03526-7(0))* Abingdon Pr.

Guidelines for Leading Your Congregation 2009-2012 - Adult Ministries: Ministries that Help Adults Love God & Neighbor. 2008. 2.95 *(978-0-687-64682-1(0))* Abingdon Pr.

Guidelines for Leading Your Congregation 2009-2012 - Children's Ministries: Ministries that Help Children Grow in Faith. 2008. 2.95 *(978-0-687-64951-8(X))* Abingdon Pr.

Guidelines for Leading Your Congregation 2009-2012 - Christian Education: Planning for Lifelong Faith Formation. 2008. 2.95 *(978-0-687-64941-9(2))* Abingdon Pr.

Guidelines for Leading Your Congregation 2009-2012 - Church Council: Connecting Vision & Ministry in Your Church. 2008. 2.95 *(978-0-687-64791-0(6))* Abingdon Pr.

Guidelines for Leading Your Congregation 2009-2012 - Church Historians: Remembering the Past & Inspiring the Future. 2008. 2.95 *(978-0-687-64851-1(3))* Abingdon Pr.

Guidelines for Leading Your Congregation 2009-2012 - Committee on Lay Leadership: Identifying, Equipping, & Deploying Spiritual Leaders for the Mission of the Church. 2008. 2.95 *(978-0-687-64771-2(1))* Abingdon Pr.

Guidelines for Leading Your Congregation 2009-2012 - Communications: Telling Your Church's Story. 2008. 2.95 *(978-0-687-64861-0(0))* Abingdon Pr.

Guidelines for Leading Your Congregation 2009-2012 - Evangelism: Sharing the Good News. 2008. 2.95 *(978-0-687-64921-1(8))* Abingdon Pr.

Guidelines for Leading Your Congregation 2009-2012 - Family Ministries: Helping Families Become Centers of Faith Formation. 2008. 2.95 *(978-0-687-64702-6(9))* Abingdon Pr.

Guidelines for Leading Your Congregation 2009-2012 - Finance: Funding Ministries that Nurture Persons in Their Faith. 2008. 2.95 *(978-0-687-64891-7(2))* Abingdon Pr.

Guidelines for Leading Your Congregation 2009-2012 - Lay Leader/Lay Member: Connecting Your Congregation & Your Annual Conference. 2008. 2.95 *(978-0-687-64811-5(4))* Abingdon Pr.

Guidelines for Leading Your Congregation 2009-2012 - Men's Ministries: Ministry to & through Men. 2008. 2.95 *(978-0-687-64732-3(0))* Abingdon Pr.

Guidelines for Leading Your Congregation 2009-2012 - Mission: Reaching the World. 2008. 2.95 *(978-0-687-64931-0(5))* Abingdon Pr.

Guidelines for Leading Your Congregation 2009-2012 - Pastor: Providing Spiritual Leadership for the Church in Mission. 2008. 2.95 *(978-0-687-64801-6(7))* Abingdon Pr.

Guidelines for Leading Your Congregation 2009-2012 - Pastor-Parish Relations: Connecting the Pastor, Staff, & Congregation. 2008. 2.95 *(978-0-687-64781-1(9))* Abingdon Pr.

Guidelines for Leading Your Congregation 2009-2012 - Small Group Ministries: Where Two or Three Are Gathered ... 2008. 2.95 *(978-0-687-64841-2(6))* Abingdon Pr.

Guidelines for Leading Your Congregation 2009-2012 - Small Membership Church: Serving with Significance in Your Context. 2008. 2.95 *(978-0-687-64952-5(8))* Abingdon Pr.

Guidelines for Leading Your Congregation 2009-2012 - Stewardship: Yes, It's about Money, but a whole Lot More — Using God's Resources Responsibly. 2008. 2.95 *(978-0-687-64911-2(0))* Abingdon Pr.

Guidelines for Leading Your Congregation 2009-2012 - Trustees: Managing the Property, Equipment, & Investments God Has Entrusted to our Ministry. 2008. 2.95 *(978-0-687-64881-8(5))* Abingdon Pr.

Guidelines for Leading Your Congregation 2009-2012 - Women's Ministries: I now remind you to stir into flame the gift of God which is within you... -2 Timothy 1:6. 2008. 2.95 *(978-0-687-64712-5(6))* Abingdon Pr.

Guidelines for Leading Your Congregation 2009-2012 - Worship: The Gifts of God from the People of God. 2008. 2.95 *(978-0-687-64901-3(3))* Abingdon Pr.

Guidelines for Leading Your Congregation 2009-2012 - Youth Ministries: Ministries for, by, & with Youth. 2008. 2.95 *(978-0-687-64692-0(8))* Abingdon Pr.

Guidry, Dustin. Turning the Ship. 2009. 164p. 22.99 *(978-1-60791-263-7(5))*; pap. 14.99 *(978-1-60791-262-0(7))* Xulon Pr., Inc.

Guise, Marty. Seeing from the Summit: The Journey to an Effective Church. 2010. 158p. pap. 18.00 *(978-1-60899-932-3(7))*, Resource Pubns.) Wipf & Stock Pubs.

Gunderson, Denny. The Leadership Paradox: A Challenge to Servant Leadership in a Power-Hungry World. 2006. (Discipleship Essentials Ser.). (ENG.). 206p. 11.99 *(978-1-57658-379-1(1))* YWAM Publishing.

Hamblin, Paul. Angels above Us, 1 vol. 2009. 144p. pap. 24.95 *(978-1-4489-9971-2(5))* PublishAmerica, Inc.

Hamilton, Adam. Selling Swimsuits in the Arctic: Seven Simple Keys to Growing Churches. ldr.'s ed. 2006. (Illus.). 99.00 incl. cd-rom *(978-0-687-33393-6(8))* Abingdon Pr.

Hamm, Richard L. Recreating the Church: Leadership for the Postmodern Age. 2007. (Columbia Partnership Leadership Ser.). (Illus.). 130p. per. 19.99 *(978-0-8272-3253-2(5))* Chalice Pr.

Harcum, E. Rae. Saving Our Church: Five Systemic Diseases Pose a Vital Mission for the Organized Church. 2009. xiv, 129p. E-Book *(978-0-7618-4699-4(9))* Hamilton Bks.

Harder, Duane. Releasing God's Government in the Earth. 2011. 178p. pap. 14.99 *(978-1-61215-545-6(6))* Xulon Pr., Inc.

Hardin, Molly. A Joshua Generation. 2011. 88p. pap. 9.95 ***(978-1-61507-655-0(7))*** Cross Bks. Publishing.

—A Joshua Generation: A Study Guide. 2011. 144p. pap. 16.95 ***(978-1-61507-751-9(0))*** Cross Bks. Publishing.

Harney, Kevin. Leadership from the Inside Out: Examining the Inner Life of a Healthy Church Leader, 1 vol. 2007. (Leadership Network Innovation Ser.). (ENG., Illus.). 208p. (gr. 13). pap. 18.99 *(978-0-310-25943-5(6))* Zondervan.

Harper, Kenneth C. Stepping Up: Inspiration for Leaders. 2010. 204p. pap. 14.49 *(978-1-4490-4900-3(1))* AuthorHouse.

Harris, Harold L., Jr. The 4 Faces of the Apostolic & the Prophetic. 2007. 64p. pap. 7.95 *(978-0-9788590-7-7(3))* Armour of Light Publishing.

Harvey, James E. Cops, Crooks, & Clergy: A Long Journey to Inside the Catholic Church. 2007. 244p. per. 11.95 *(978-1-4327-1264-8(0))* Outskirts Pr., Inc.

Hayes, Victor. Eliminating Church Fights with by-Laws: Quick Wisdom for Church Leadership. 2008. 94p. pap. 9.96 *(978-0-557-02464-3(1))* Lulu Enterprises Inc.

Hemphill, Ken. Eternal Impact: The Passion of Kingdom-Centered Communities. 2008. (ENG.). 93p. pap. 6.95 *(978-1-4276-2735-3(5))* Auxano Pr.

—Eternal Impact: The Passion of Kingdom-Centered Communities. 2008. (ENG.). 240p. per. 14.99 *(978-0-8054-4660-9(5))*, B&H Bks.) B&H Publishing Group.

Henderson, Daniel. Defying Gravity: How to Survive the Storms of Pastoral Ministry, 1 vol. 2010. (ENG.). 192p. pap. 14.99 *(978-0-8024-0952-2(0))* Moody Pubs.

Hester, Richard L. & Walker-Jones, Kelli. Know Your Story & Lead with It: The Power of Narrative in Clergy Leadership. 2009. *(978-1-56699-388-3(1))* Alban Institute, Inc.

Heward-Mills, Dag. The Art of Leadership. 2008. (ENG.). 411p. 19.99 *(978-0-7963-0971-6(X))* Lux Verbi - BM ZAF. Dist: STL Distribution North America.

—The Art of Leadership. 2007. (ENG.). 464p. pap. 14.99 *(978-9988-596-40-8(5))* Parchment Hse. GHA. Dist: STL Distribution North America.

—Leaders & Loyalty: The Laws of Loyalty. annot. ed. 2007. (ENG.). 234p. per. 10.99 *(978-9988-596-51-4(0))* Parchment Hse. GHA. Dist: STL Distribution North America.

—Loyalty & Disloyalty. 2007. (ENG.). 176p. pap. 13.99 *(978-9988-7798-4-9(4))* Parchment Hse. GHA. Dist: STL Distribution North America.

Hillman, George M. Ministry Greenhouse: Cultivating Environments for Practical Learning. 2008. *(978-1-56699-360-9(1))* Alban Institute, Inc.

Hoge, Dean & Jewell, Marti. The Next Generation of Pastoral Leaders: What the Church Needs to Know. 2010. (ENG.). 208p. pap. 11.95 *(978-0-8294-2650-2(7))* Loyola Pr.

C

Holeman, Virginia Todd & Martyn, Stephen L. Inside the Leader's Head: Unraveling Personal Obstacles to Ministry. 2008. (Illus.). 160p. pap. 17.00 (978-0-687-64728-6(2)) Abingdon Pr.

Honeygosky, Paulette, Sr. A Race to Be Won: All You Need to Know about Personal Integrity, Good Works, & Christian Leadership. 2008. 49p. pap. 16.95 (978-1-60703-099-7(3)) PublishAmerica, Inc.

Hooper, William L. Worship Leadership for Worship Leaders: Vol. 1 Developing Effective Leadership Skills. 2007. 128p. pap. 16.95 (978-0-939067-78-7(1)) Alexander Publishing.

Hotchkiss, Dan. Governance & Ministry: Rethinking Board Leadership. 2009. (978-1-56699-370-8(9)) Alban Institute, Inc.

Houston, Kirk. The Church's Return Policy: Equipping the Church to Minister to Ex-Offenders. 2008. 96p. pap. 12.95 (978-1-4389-2965-1(X)) AuthorHouse.

How to Reach Baby Boomers. 13.00 incl. audio (978-0-687-76222-4(7)) Abingdon Pr.

Hull, Bill & Mascarella, Paul. Etl: Lead as Jesus Led. 2007. 172p. pap. 11.99 (978-0-7375-0138-4(3)) Biblical Studies Pr.

Hull, William E. Strategic Preaching: The Role of the Pulpit in Pastoral Leadership. 2007. (Illus.). 277p. per. 32.99 (978-0-8272-3467-3(8)) Chalice Pr.

Humphreys, Kent. Shepherding Horses: Understanding God's Plan for Transforming Leaders. 2008. 64p. pap. 5.99 (978-0-9800877-1-0(6)) Diakonia Publishing.

Hunt, Johnny M. Building Your Leadership Resume: Developing the Legacy that Will Outlast You. 2009. (ENG.). 240p. pap. 14.99 (978-0-8054-4964-8(7), B&H Bks.) B&H Publishing Group.

Hurt, Pat Harper. A and Ransom for Righteousness. 2011. 204p. pap. 15.99 **(978-1-61379-517-0(3))** Xulon Pr., Inc.

Hybels, Bill. Courageous Leadership, 1 vol. 2008. (ENG.). 256p. pap. 16.99 (978-0-310-29157-2(7)) Zondervan.

Iorg, Jeff. Is God Calling Me? Answering the Question Every Leader Asks. 2008. (ENG.). 128p. pap. 9.99 (978-0-8054-4722-4(9), B&H Bks.) B&H Publishing Group.

—The Painful Side of Leadership: Moving Forward Even When It Hurts. 2009. (ENG.). 288p. pap. 14.99 (978-0-8054-4870-2(5), B&H Bks.) B&H Publishing Group.

Isbell, Jennifer & Isbell, Jennifer L. Leading Quakers: Disciple Leadership, a Friends Model. 2008. 144p. pap. (978-1-879117-20-4(7)) Earlham Pr.

Iwanski, Sandra, et al. The Practical Guide to High School Campus Ministry. 2007. 102p. per. 26.25 (978-0-88489-963-1(2)) St. Mary's Pr.

J-12: Be Like Jesus, Get Your 12. 2007. per. (978-0-9768299-3-5(2)) Faith Christian Ctr.

Jackson, Charles E. The Burden. 2010. 172p. pap. (978-1-77069-083-7(2)) Word Alive Pr.

Jackson, John. God-Size Your Church: Beyond Growth for Growth's Sake. 2008. 184p. pap. 20.00 (978-0-687-64909-9(9)) Abingdon Pr.

—Pastorpreneur. 2009. 176p. pap. 17.00 (978-0-687-65842-8(X)) Abingdon Pr.

Jackson, Thomas. Church of God in Christ: Leadership Guidebook for Ministers. 2010. 180p. 29.99 (978-1-4415-9568-3(6)); pap. 19.99 (978-1-4415-9567-6(8)) Xlibris Corp.

Jacobsen, Eric O., ed. The Three Tasks of Leadership: Worldly Wisdom for Pastoral Leaders. 2009. (Illus.). 224p. pap. 22.00 (978-0-8028-6398-0(1)) Eerdmans, William B. Publishing Co.

Jibben, Ken. Emerge: Leaders to Continue a Life of Vision & Purpose. 2009. 198p. pap. 13.95 (978-1-4327-3951-5(4)) Outskirts Pr., Inc.

Jinadu, Philip & Lawrence, David. Winning Ways: How to Create a Culture of Outreach in Your Church. 2007. (ENG., Illus.). 192p. per. 14.99 (978-1-85078-738-9(7)) Authentic Media.

Job, Rueben. Becoming a Praying Congregatio: Churchwide Leadership Tools. 2009. 192p. pap. 39.00 (978-1-4267-0282-2(5)) Abingdon Pr.

Johnson, Abigail. Shaping Spiritual Leaders: Supervision & Formation in Congregations. 2007. (978-1-56699-350-0(4)) Alban Institute, Inc.

Johnson, Bill, et al. Reformer's Pledge. 2010. (ENG.). pap. 16.99 (978-0-7684-3269-5(3)) Destiny Image Pubs.

Johnson, Craig. Lead Vertically: Inspire People to Volunteer & Build Great Teams that Last. 2010. (ENG.). 224p. 17.99 (978-0-8307-5215-7(3)) Gospel Light Pubns.

Johnson, Derric. Life Lessons for Leaders. 2009. 12.99 (978-0-89827-426-4(5)) Wesleyan Publishing Hse.

Johnson, Gary, et al. Reflect His Character. 2010. (Illus.). 120p. pap. 9.99 (978-0-89900-978-0(6)) College Pr. Publishing Co., Inc.

Johnson-Medland, N. Thomas. Feed My Sheep; Lead My Sheep: A Handbook of Leadership Formation for Individuals & Groups. 2011. 198p. pap. 23.00 **(978-1-61097-140-9(X)**, Resource Pubns.) Wipf & Stock Pubs.

Johnson, Reginald & Demaray, Donald. Spiritual Formation for Christian Leaders. 2007. 122p. per. 13.00 (978-0-687-49504-7(0)) Abingdon Pr.

Jones, Jeffrey D. Heart, Mind, & Strength: Theory & Practice for Congregational Leadership. 2008. (978-1-56699-380-7(6)) Alban Institute, Inc.

Kageler, Len. The Volunteer's Field Guide to Youth Ministry: Practical Ways to Make a Permanent Difference in Teenagers. 2011. pap. (978-0-7644-4682-5(7)) Group Publishing, Inc.

Keel, Tim. Intuitive Leadership: Embracing a Paradigm of Narrative, Metaphor, & Chaos. 2007. (Emersion Ser.). 272p. pap. 16.99 (978-0-8010-6813-3(4)) Baker Bks.

Keels, Shonn. Maximize Your Leadership. 2009. 94p. pap. 11.95 (978-1-4401-5683-0(2)) iUniverse, Inc.

Kemp, Bill. Ezekiel's Bones: Rekindling Your Congregation's Spiritual Passion. 2007. 112p. per. (978-0-88177-498-6(7)) Discipleship Resources.

—Jonah's Whale: Reconnecting the Congregation with Mission. 2007. (Illus.). 108p. per. 6.00 (978-0-88177-516-7(9)) Discipleship Resources.

Kendrick, Stephen, et al. The Resolution for Men. 2011. (ENG.). 272p. pap. 14.99 (978-1-4336-7122-7(0), B&H Bks.) B&H Publishing Group.

—The Resolution for Men. l.t. ed. 2011. pap. 17.99 (978-1-59415-385-3(X)) Cengage Gale.

Kenerson, Ed. The Cheshire Teens Story. 2008. 124p. 19.99 (978-1-60647-513-3(4)); pap. 11.99 (978-1-60647-512-6(6)) Xulon Pr., Inc.

Keucher, Gerald W. Humble & Strong: Mutually Accountable Leadership in the Church. 2010. 160p. pap. 18.00 (978-0-8192-2408-8(1), Morehouse Publishing) Church Publishing, Inc.

Kibbey, Sue Nilson. Ultimately Responsible: When You're in Charge of Igniting a Ministry. 2006. (Illus.). 173p. 19.00 (978-0-687-33492-6(6)) Abingdon Pr.

Killinger, John. Bread for the Wilderness, Wine for the Journey: Leader's Guide. 96p. (C). reprint ed. tchr. ed. 6.00 (978-1-887730-07-5(9)) Intermundia Pr., LLC., The.

—Bread for the Wilderness, Wine for the Journey: Response Manual. 80p. (C). reprint ed. wbk. ed. 6.00 (978-1-887730-08-2(7)) Intermundia Pr., LLC., The.

King, Braxton. The Brother up Next. 2011. 152p. pap. 13.95 **(978-1-4497-1649-3(0)**, WestBow Pr.) Author Solutions, Inc.

King, Mother Jessie. Mother May I? Yes, You May! No, You May Not! 2008. 100p. pap. 11.99 (978-0-88144-297-7(6)) Yorkshire Publishing Group.

Kirkland, James. Elders & Deacons & Saints, Oh My! Defining Biblical Roles, Structure & Organization for a Team Ministry that Achieves the Fivefold Purpose of T. 2011. 200p. 33.95 **(978-1-61507-824-0(X))**; pap. 17.95 **(978-1-61507-823-3(1))** Cross Bks. Publishing.

Kizinna, Doris E. Go Deep: Spiritual Practices for Youth Ministry. 2009. (ENG.). 256p. pap. 29.95 (978-1-55145-575-4(7), Copperhouse) Wood Lake Publishing, Inc. CAN. Dist: Westminster John Knox Pr.

Kong, Paul. Servant Leadership & Job Satisfaction. 2009. 120p. pap. (978-3-639-17270-6(1)) VDM Verlag Dr. Mueller e.K.

Land, Darin H. The Diffusion of Ecclesiastical Authority: Sociological Dimensions of Leadership in the Book of Acts. 2008. (Princeton Theological Monographs). 256p. pap. 28.00 (978-1-55635-575-2(0), Pickwick Pubns.) Wipf & Stock Pubs.

Laniak, Timothy. While Shepherds Watch Their Flock. 2009. 266p. 29.95 (978-1-929097-23-4(9)) HigherLife Development Services, Inc.

Largent, Phil. Maximum Service Bk. 1: Practical Truths for Followers of Jesus: from A-Z Book 1. 2008. 64p. 5.95 (978-0-9769622-7-4(6)) IMD Pr.

—Maximum Service Bk. 2: Practical Truths for Followers of Jesus: from A-Z Book 2. 2008. 64p. 5.95 (978-0-9769622-8-1(4)) IMD Pr.

—Maximum Service Bk. 3: Practical Truths for Followers of Jesus: from A-Z Book 3. 2008. 64p. 5.95 (978-0-9769622-9-8(2)) IMD Pr.

Laster, John E. Gaining Traction: Filed Guide for Leadership Teams. 2007. (Illus.). 166p. per. 16.99 (978-0-8272-1253-4(4)) Chalice Pr.

Laubach, David C. 12 Steps to Congregational Transformation: A Practical Guide for Leaders. 2006. (Illus.). 143p. per. 12.00 (978-0-8170-1502-2(7)) Judson Pr.

Lawrence, James. Growing Leaders: Cultivating Discipleship for Yourself & Others. 2006. (Illus.). 274p. per. 16.95 (978-1-56563-997-3(9)) Hendrickson Pubs. Marketing, LLC.

Lawrenz, Mel & Lawrenz. Whole Church: Leading from Fragmentation to Engagement. 2009. (Jossey-Bass Leadership Network Ser.: 31). (ENG., Illus.). 208p. 24.95 (978-0-470-25934-4(5), Jossey-Bass) Wiley, John & Sons, Inc.

Lawson, Russ. Everybody Needs a Tonto Help for Hurting Christians. 2007. 76p. per. 9.50 (978-1-4303-1287-1(4)) Lulu Enterprises Inc.

The Leadership & Fellowship Manual for Christians. 2009. pap. 14.95 (978-1-61584-254-4(3)) Independent Pub.

Leadership Network Innovation Series Bundle, ZCS. 2008. (Leadership Network Innovation Ser.). pap., pap., pap. 84.95 (978-0-310-68050-5(6)) Zondervan.

LeaderTreks, creator. Avalanche Vol 1 Facilitator's Guide: Unstoppable Leadership. 2007. 32p. (YA). 19.95 (978-1-934577-55-4(3)) LeaderTreks NFP.

—Avalanche Vol 1 Student Guide: Unstoppable Leadership. 2007. (ENG.). 40p. (YA). 9.95 (978-1-934577-54-7(5)) LeaderTreks NFP.

—Avalanche Vol 2 Facilitator's Guide: Unstoppable Leadership. 2007. (ENG.). 32p. (YA). 19.95 (978-1-934577-57-8(X)) LeaderTreks NFP.

—Avalanche Vol 2 Student Guide: Unstoppable Leadership. 2007. (ENG.). 40p. (YA). 9.95 (978-1-934577-56-1(1)) LeaderTreks NFP.

Leading by Example: Peter's Way for the Church Today. 2008. (ENG.). 198p. pap. 22.99 (978-1-84227-604-4(2), Paternoster) Authentic Media.

Learning & Leading in Ministry. 2008. pap. 10.99 (978-1-56722-725-3(2)) Word Aflame Pr.

Lee, Harris W. The Leadership Factor: A Sourcebook for Effective Church Leadership. 2011. **(978-1-933794-42-6(9))** Kirk Hse. Pubs.

Lesniewski, Linda. Connecting Women: A Relational Guide for Leaders in Women's Ministry. 2007. 256p. pap. 16.99 (978-0-8010-6811-9(8)) Baker Bks.

Lewis, Jacquie J. The Power of Stories a Guide for Leading Multiracial & Multicultural Congregations. 2008. 154p. pap. 16.00 (978-0-687-65069-9(0)) Abingdon Pr.

Lewis, Rick. Mentoring Matters: Building Strong Christian Leaders, Avoiding Burnout, Reaching the Finishing Line, 1 vol. 2009. 256p. pap. 15.99 (978-0-8254-6301-3(7), Monarch Bks.) Lion Hudson PLC GBR. Dist: Kregel Pubns.

Lifestyle Tis a Gift Leader. 5.00 (978-0-687-37326-0(3)) Abingdon Pr.

Lingenfelter, Sherwood G. Leading Cross-Culturally: Covenant Relationships for Effective Christian Leadership. 2008. 176p. (C). pap. 16.99 (978-0-8010-3605-7(4)) Baker Academic.

Little, Steve. Leading God's Way. 2010. 100p. pap. 11.99 (978-1-61507-083-1(4)) Cross Bks. Publishing.

Living Your Strengths - Catholic Edition. 2006. (978-1-59562-012-5(5)) Gallup Pr.

Long, Jimmy. The Leadership Jump: Building Partnerships Between Existing & Emerging Christian Leaders, 1 vol. 2008. (ENG.). 205p. pap. 16.00 (978-0-8308-3364-1(1), IVP Bks.) InterVarsity Pr.

Long, Zeb Bradford, et al. Growing the Church in the Power of the Holy Spirit: Seven Principles of Dynamic Cooperation, 1 vol. 2009. (ENG.). 240p. pap. 16.99 (978-0-310-29209-8(3)) Zondervan.

Louden, G H. Is There a Leadership Crisis in the Church? 2006. (Illus.). 107p. per. 15.95 (978-1-60002-232-6(4), 4213) Mountain Valley Publishing, LLC.

Lynch, Don. The Spirit & Power of Elijah: Prophetic Parallels of the Ancient Prophets & Leaders of Today. 2007. 188p. per. 15.99 (978-0-7684-2590-1(5)) Destiny Image Pubs.

Lynne, Deborah. The Anchored Soul. 2011. 108p. pap. 10.68 **(978-1-4567-5825-7(X))** AuthorHouse.

Lytle, Richard S. Abandon the Ordinary: Building a Distinctive Leadership Brand in Business, Family, & Church. 2010. 240p. 19.99 (978-0-89112-541-9(8), Leafwood Pubs.) Abilene Christian Univ. Pr.

MacArthur, John. The Book on Leadership, 0 vols. 2006. 240p. per. 13.99 (978-0-7852-8838-1(4)) Nelson, Thomas Inc.

MacDonald, G. Jeffrey. Thieves in the Temple: The Christian Church & the Selling of the American Soul. 2010. (ENG.). 256p. (gr. 9). 25.95 (978-0-465-00932-9(8)) Basic Bks.

Mack, Michael. I'm a Leader ... Now What? How to Guide an Effective Small Group. 2007. (Small Group Help Guides). (Illus.). 96p. per. 8.99 (978-0-7847-2076-9(2)) Standard Publishing.

Mack, Michael C. Launch into Community Life: Building a Master Plan of Action with Your Small Group. 2008. (Community Life Ser.). 64p. pap. 9.95 (978-0-9788779-5-8(0), Cell Group Resources) Touch Pubns.

Mackenzie, Geoffrey Shisumu, et al. Church Splits. 2011. 76p. pap. **(978-3-8443-3337-4(1))** Lambert Academic Publishing.

Mancini. Church Unique: How Missional Leaders Cast Vision, Capture Culture, & Create Movement. 2008. (Jossey-Bass Leadership Network Ser.). (ENG.). 304p. pap. 23.95 (978-0-470-58039-4(9), Jossey-Bass) Wiley, John & Sons, Inc.

Mancini, Will. Church Unique: How Missional Leaders Cast Vision, Capture Culture, & Create Movement. 2008. (Jossey-Bass Leadership Network Ser.: 23). (ENG., Illus.). 304p. 24.95 (978-0-7879-9683-3(1), Jossey-Bass) Wiley, John & Sons, Inc.

Maranatha Publications. How to Become a Dynamic Speaker. 2011. (ENG.). 102p. (Orig.). pap. 14.97 (978-0-938558-19-4(6)) Maranatha Pubns.

Marcus, Cesar Leo. Jesus A Successful Leader. 2009. 110p. pap. 19.95 (978-1-4357-3863-8(2)) Lulu Enterprises Inc.

—Jesus un Lider Exitoso. 2007. 110p. pap. 19.50 (978-1-4303-1210-9(6)) Lulu Enterprises Inc.

Marcuson, Margaret J. Leaders Who Last: Sustaining Yourself & Your Ministry. 2009. 160p. pap. 20.00 (978-1-59627-095-4(0), Seabury Bks.) Church Publishing, Inc.

Markle, David. Next Steps to Ministry: Entering a Life in Christian Ministry. 2007. xiii, 253p. pap. (978-1-59317-175-9(7)) Warner Pr. Pubs.

Martinez, Juan. Caminando Entre el Pueblo. 2008. 144p. pap. 18.00 (978-0-687-49276-3(9)) Abingdon Pr.

Mathew, Thomson K. What Will Your Tombstone Say? 2008. 272p. per. 15.99 (978-1-60477-758-1(3)) Xulon Pr., Inc.

Maxwell, John C. Be a People Person: Effective Leadership Through Effective Relationships. 2007. (ENG.). 192p. 16.99 (978-0-7814-4843-7(3)) Cook, David C.

—Think on These Things: Meditations for Leaders: 30th Anniversary Edition. 30th ed. 2010. (ENG.). 192p. 15.99 (978-0-8341-2500-1(5), 9780834125001) Beacon Hill Pr. of Kansas City.

Maxwell, John C. & EQUIP. Courageous Leadership, 0 vols. 2008. (EQUIP Leadership Ser.). (Illus.). 192p. per., wbk. ed. 17.99 (978-1-4185-1786-1(0)) Nelson, Thomas Inc.

May, David. Prostitutes, Tax Collectors, & You: Church Leadership for Non-Leaders. 2009. 116p. pap. 9.95 (978-1-4327-5247-7(2)) Outskirts Pr., Inc.

Mccall, Kenneth E. On the Move for Christ: Armed & Ready. 2010. 48p. pap. 15.99 (978-1-4500-5190-3(1)) Xlibris Corp.

McCormick, Deb. Making the Connection: A Reference Guide for Small Group Ministry Leaders. 2006. 24p. 8.95 (978-0-9801644-1-1(9)) Teamed UP, LLC.

McDowell, Josh. Sigue la Verdad y Triunfa: Ninos Mayores. Date not set. (Right from Wrong Ser.).Tr. of Truth Works. (SPA.). 40p. pap. 5.95 (978-0-311-11087-2(8)) Casa Bautista de Publicaciones.

McFayden, Kenneth J. Strategic Leadership for a Change: Facing Our Losses, Finding Our Future. 2009. (978-1-56699-392-0(X)) Alban Institute, Inc.

McIntosh, Gary L. & Rima, Samuel D. Overcoming the Dark Side of Leadership: How to Become an Effective Leader by Confronting Potential Failures. rev. ed. 2007. 256p. pap. 16.99 (978-0-8010-6835-5(5)) Baker Bks.

McKenna, David L. The Leader's Legacy: Preparing for Greater Things. 2006. 172p. pap. 15.00 (978-1-59498-007-7(1)) Barclay Pr., Inc.

McKenna, Robert. Dying to Lead. 2008. 208p. 25.99 (978-1-60647-685-7(8)); pap. 15.99 (978-1-60647-684-0(X)) Xulon Pr., Inc.

McLean, Terry D. The Truth about Pastors & Christian Leadership. 2011. 88p. 24.99 **(978-1-4628-8386-8(9))**; pap. 15.99 **(978-1-4628-8385-1(0))** Xlibris Corp.

McMahan, Oliver. Becoming a Shepherd: Contemporary Pastoral Ministry. 2009. 235p. pap. 11.99 (978-87-14-81162-4(6)) Pathway Pr.

McNeal, Reggie. A Work of Heart: Understanding How God Shapes Spiritual Leaders. 2nd ed. 2011. (Jossey-Bass Leadership Network Ser.: 60). (ENG.). 240p. 24.95 (978-1-118-10318-0(1), Jossey-Bass) Wiley, John & Sons, Inc.

McNeal, Reggie & McNeal. The Present Future: Six Tough Questions for the Church. 2009. (Jossey-Bass Leadership Network Ser.: 42). (ENG.). 176p. pap. 16.95 (978-0-470-45315-5(X), Jossey-Bass) Wiley, John & Sons, Inc.

Mech, Timothy J. Pastors & Elders: Caring for the Church & One Another. 2012. 104p. pap. 12.99 **(978-0-7586-2747-6(5))** Concordia Publishing Hse.

Melander, Rochelle. A Generous Presence: Spiritual Leadership & the Art of Coaching. 2006. xii, 370p. (978-1-56699-325-8(3)) Alban Institute, Inc.

Menéndez Antuña, Luis. Mujer y poder en el Cristianismo Antiguo. 2008. 245p. pap. 27.95 (978-1-84799-065-5(7)) Lulu Enterprises Inc.

Michael, Larry J. Spurgeon on Leadership: Key Insights for Christian Leaders from the Prince of Preachers, 1 vol. 2nd ed. 2010. 240p. pap. 16.99 (978-0-8254-3536-2(6)) Kregel Pubns.

Miles, Brenda J. To the Best of My Ability: Growing up in Jesus. 2010. 74p. pap. 12.95 (978-1-4327-5240-8(5)) Outskirts Pr., Inc.

Miller, Bruce B. Your Church in Rhythm: The Forgotten Dimensions of Seasons & Cycles. 2011. (Jossey-Bass Leadership Network Ser.: 52). (ENG., Illus.). 224p. 24.95 (978-0-470-59887-0(5), Jossey-Bass) Wiley, John & Sons, Inc.

Miller, Chuck. The Spiritual Formation of Leaders. 2007. 348p. (ENG.). 27.99 (978-1-60477-314-9(6)); per. 17.99 (978-1-60477-313-2(8)) Xulon Pr., Inc.

Miller D.D: Founder and Presiding Prelate, Arch-Bishop D. A. The Ministry of an Armourbearer: A Spiritual Approach, 1 vol. 2010. 52p. pap. 16.95 (978-1-4489-9134-1(X)) PublishAmerica, Inc.

Miller, James F. Go Grow Your Church! Spiritual Leadership for African American Congregations. 2008. (Illus.). 176p. (978-0-8298-1801-7(4)) Pilgrim Pr., The/United Church Pr.

Miller, Linda J. & Hall, Chad W. Coaching for Christian Leaders: A Practical Guide. 2007. (Columbia Partnership Leadership Ser.). (Illus.). 148p. per. 19.99 (978-0-8272-0507-9(4)) Chalice Pr.

Miller, Tim E. 30x60x100: A Manual for Making Disciples & Developing Discipleship Curriculum. 2008. 150p. per. (978-0-9788201-6-9(9)) IMD Pr.

Mills, Bill. Keys to Effective Leadership: Developing Your Followership Skills. 2007. 41p. pap. 5.00 (978-0-9709482-4-3(7)) Leadership Resources International.

Moore, Bill. Show Us the Father. 2008. 140p. pap. 13.99 (978-1-60477-498-6(3)) Xulon Pr., Inc.

Moore, Sue. Rendezvous Leader's Guide. 2007. 3.99 (978-0-8341-2315-1(0)) Nazarene Publishing Hse.

Morrison, A. J. I Change Not: A Message for the Family of God. 2011. 48p. pap. 8.95 **(978-1-4620-3194-8(3))** iUniverse, Inc.

Moser, Ken. Changing the World 2: Creative Christian Ideas for Youth Groups. 2010. 130p. pap. (978-1-906334-25-3(0)) Good Bk. Co.

Moss, Claudette. Washed White & the Seven Spirits of God. 2009. 244p. 25.99 (978-1-60791-484-6(0)); pap. 15.99 (978-1-60791-483-9(2)) Xulon Pr., Inc.

Myers, Gregory A. Maximize the Leader in You. 2011. 178p. pap. 14.99 (978-1-61215-511-1(1)) Xulon Pr., Inc.

Nance, Terry. God's Armorbearer: Running with Your Pastor's Vision. 2008. (God's Armorbearer Ser.). 166p. per. 14.99 (978-0-7684-2611-3(1)) Destiny Image Pubs.

Neal, Norma D. The Code of Silence in Ministry. 2011. 128p. pap. 19.95 **(978-1-4626-0414-2(5))** PublishAmerica, Inc.

Nees, Tom. Best Practices of Growing Churches: Profiles & Conversations with Ministry Leaders. 2006. (Voices Ser.). (ENG.). 160p. per. 14.99 (978-0-8341-2304-5(5), 083-412-3045) Beacon Hill Pr. of Kansas City.

Nembhard-Colquhoun, Deborah. Evangelism God's Way Manual: Discipleship, Educating, & Leadership. 2011. 240p. 33.95 **(978-1-4497-1870-1(1))**; pap. 17.95 **(978-1-4497-1812-1(4))** Author Solutions, Inc. (WestBow Pr.).

Noland, Rory. The Worshiping Artist: Equipping You & Your Ministry Team to Lead Others in Worship, 1 vol. 2007. (ENG., Illus.). 224p. pap. 18.99 (978-0-310-27334-9(X)) Zondervan.

Norris, Richard. The Business of All Believers: Reflections on Leadership. Sedgwick, Timothy F., ed. 2009. 144p. pap. 16.00 (978-1-59627-119-7(1), Seabury Bks.) Church Publishing, Inc.

O. Riordain, John J. Before the Night Grows Late. 2009. (ENG.). 188p. pap. 26.95 (978-1-85607-646-3(6)) Columba Pr. IRL. Dist: Dufour Editions, Inc.

Oak, John H. Called to Awaken the Laity. 2007. (ENG.). 352p. per. 15.99 (978-1-84550-224-9(8)) Christian Focus Pubns. GBR. Dist: STL Distribution North America.

Ogenaarekhua, Mary J. Keys to Successful Mentoring Relationships. 2008. 204p. pap. 18.95 (978-0-9791566-6-3(1)) To His Glory Publishing Co., Inc.

Ogne, Steve & Roehl, Tim. TransforMissional Coaching: Empowering Leaders in a Changing Ministry World. 2008. (ENG.). 304p. 19.99 (978-0-8054-4781-1(4), B&H Bks.) B&H Publishing Group.

Olds, J. Howard, et al. Led to Follow: Leadership Lessons from an Improbable Pastor & a Reluctant CEO. 2008. 115p. pap. 16.00 (978-0-687-65079-8(8)) Abingdon Pr.

Olford, David & Broadman and Holman Publishers Staff. Find Us Faithful: Leadership That Leaves a Legacy, 1 vol. 2009. (ENG.). 208p. pap. 12.99 *(978-0-8054-4548-0(X),* B&H Bks.) B&H Publishing Group.

O'Neal, Sean. Bridges to People. 2007. 288p. per. 15.99 *(978-1-60266-268-1(1))* Xulon Pr., Inc.

Orr, Robert A. Authentic Managerial Leadership. 2011. 160p. pap. 57.99 ***(978-1-61379-609-2(9))*** Xulon Pr., Inc.

Osborne, Larry. Sticky Teams: Keeping Your Leadership Team & Staff on the Same Page, 1 vol. 2010. (ENG.). 192p. pap. 16.99 *(978-0-310-32464-5(5))* Zondervan.

Page, Frank. The Nehemiah Factor: 16 Characteristics of a Missional Leader. 2008. (ENG.). 208p. pap. 14.99 *(978-1-59669-223-7(5))* New Hope Pubs.

Page, Frank & Perry, John. The Incredible Shrinking Church. 2008. (ENG.). 160p. per. 14.99 *(978-0-8054-4661-6(3),* B&H Bks.) B&H Publishing Group.

Papesh, Michael L. Good News Parish Leadership: Trust-Building Guidelines, Tools & Ideas. 2008. 280p. pap. *(978-1-58595-705-7(4))* Twenty-Third Pubns./Bayard.

Parrott, Roger. The Longview: Lasting Strategies for Rising Leaders. 2009. (ENG.). 256p. 16.99 *(978-1-4347-6749-3(3))* Cook, David C.

Pastor King: Martin Luther King, Jr. , as Spiritual Leader. 2011. pap. 19.00 *(978-0-687-64496-4(8))* Abingdon Pr.

Pattillo, Beth. Faith Leader. 2008. 42.99 *(978-0-8272-1043-1(4));* 17.99 *(978-0-8272-1042-4(6))* Chalice Pr.

Paulsen, Jan. Where Are You Going? We Have Nothing to Fear for the Future, Except We Shall Forget the Way the Lord Has Led Us, & His Teaching in Our Past History. 2011. pap. 13.99 ***(978-0-8163-2509-2(X))*** Pacific Pr. Publishing Assn.

Payne, Patricia Ann. The Deceit of the Church. 2008. 80p. per. 9.99 *(978-1-60477-500-6(9))* Xulon Pr., Inc.

Peck, Kirk. Ignatian Spirituality in Higher Education. 2009. 280p. pap. *(978-3-639-17580-6(8))* VDM Verlag Dr. Mueller e.K.

Perry, Christopher W. The Church Mouse: Leadership Lessons from the Magic Kingdom. 2011. *(978-0-8298-1874-1(X))* Pilgrim Pr., The/United Church Pr.

Phelps, Owen. The Catholic Vision for Leading Like Jesus: Introducing S3 Leadership: Servant, Steward, Shepherd. 2009. (Illus.). 144p. 14.95 *(978-1-59276-605-5(6))* Our Sunday Visitor, Publishing Div.

—The Catholic Vision for Leading Like Jesus Leader's Guide: Introducing Leadership S3 Leadership Servant, Steward, Shepherd. 2009. 8p. pap. 2.95 *(978-1-59276-675-8(7))* Our Sunday Visitor, Publishing Div.

Philip, Mathew. You Can Lead Effectively! 2008. 272p. pap. 15.99 *(978-1-60647-250-7(X))* Xulon Pr., Inc.

Pickard, Stephen. Theological Foundations for Collaborative Ministry: One of Another. 2009. (Explorations in Practical, Pastoral & Empirical Theology Ser.). 266p. pap. 34.95 *(978-0-7546-6835-0(5))* Ashgate Publishing Co.

—Theological Foundations for Collarborative Ministry: One of Another. 2009. (Explorations in Practical, Pastoral & Empirical Theology Ser.). 266p. 114.95 *(978-0-7546-6829-9(0))* Ashgate Publishing Co.

Pier, Mac. Spiritual Leadership in the Global City. 2008. (ENG., Illus.). 256p. pap. 19.99 *(978-1-59669-241-1(3))* New Hope Pubs.

Pitchford. Abc for the Pcc 5th Ed (p) 5th rev. ed. 2008. (ENG.). 228p. pap. 24.95 *(978-1-906286-07-1(8))* Mowbray, A. R. & Co., Ltd. GBR. Dist: National Bk. Network.

Plass, Adrian. Looking Good Being Bad: The Subtle Art of Churchmanship. 2011. (ENG., Illus.). 160p. 12.99 *(978-1-85078-898-0(7),* Authentic Lifestyle) Authentic Media.

Plueddemann, James E. Leading Across Cultures: Effective Ministry & Mission in the Global Church. 2009. (ENG.). 230p. pap. 20.00 *(978-0-8308-2578-3(9),* IVP Acad.) InterVarsity Pr.

Powell, Kara. Essential Leadership: Ministry Team Meetings That Work, 1 vol. 2009. (ENG., Illus.) 128p. pap., instr.'s gde. ed. 9.99 *(978-0-310-66934-0(0))* Zondervan.

—Ministry Team Meetings That Work, 1 vol. ldr.'s ed. 2009. (ENG.). 144p. pap. 14.99 *(978-0-310-66933-3(2))* Zondervan.

Pratt, Wallace R. The Turning Point That Changed Everything: Choosing to Accept the Unpredictable. 2009. 240p. 25.99 *(978-1-61579-631-1(2));* pap. 15.99 *(978-1-61579-521-5(9))* Xulon Pr., Inc.

Pringle, Phil. Top 10 Qualities of a Great Leader. 225p. 2008. pap. 14.99 *(978-1-57794-939-3(0))* 2007. 19.99 *(978-1-57794-913-8(7))* Harrison House Pubs.

Prophet, Erin L. Prophet's Daughter: My Life with Elizabeth Clare Prophet Inside the Church Universal & Triumphant. 2008. (ENG., Illus.). 304p. 24.95 *(978-1-59921-425-2(3),* Lyons Pr.) Globe Pequot Pr., The.

Provencher, Maureen F. Never Too Young to Lead: Developing Leadership in Young Adolescents. 2006. 96p. per. 24.25 *(978-0-88489-873-3(3))* St. Mary's Pr.

Quinn, Kay. How Much Does God CoST? 2009. 120p. 21.49 *(978-1-4490-3998-1(7));* pap. 14.95 *(978-1-4490-3997-4(9))* AuthorHouse.

Rainer, Thom S. Breakout Churches: Discover How to Make the Leap, 1 vol. 2009. (ENG.). 272p. pap. 16.99 *(978-0-310-29347-7(2))* Zondervan.

Ramey, David & Jewell, Marti. The Changing Face of the Church: Emerging Models of Parish Leadership. 2010. (ENG.). 176p. pap. 11.95 *(978-0-8294-2647-2(7))* Loyola Pr.

Ramirez, Antonio. Manual para Líderes Laicos de Hoy. 2011. (SPA.). ***(978-0-7648-2048-9(6))*** Liguori Pubns.

Redmon, Terry. Biblical Keys to Spiritual Leadership. 2007. 128p. (ENG.). 21.99 *(978-1-60266-446-3(3));* per. 13.99 *(978-1-60266-445-6(5))* Xulon Pr., Inc.

Rees, Christina & Percy, Martyn, eds. Apostolic Women, Apostolic Authority: Transfiguring Leadership in Today's Church. 2011. (Canterbury Studies in Agnlicanism Ser.). 160p. pap. 18.00 *(978-0-8192-2450-7(2),* Morehouse Publishing) Church Publishing, Inc.

Rees, Erik & Jernigan, Jeff. Tilt: Small Shifts in Leadership That Make a Big Difference. 2010. 209p. pap. 19.00 *(978-1-4267-0579-3(4))* Abingdon Pr.

Reid, Rich. Legacy of Ministry: Hitting the Bull's Eye for Eternal Impact. 2009. 184p. pap. 14.99 *(978-1-60791-686-4(X))* Xulon Pr., Inc.

Reiland, Dan. Amplified Leadership: 5 Practices to Establish Influence, Build People, & Impact Others for a Lifetime. 2012. (Illus.). xxvii, 209p. E-Book ***(978-1-61638-635-1(5));*** (ENG., 240p. pap. 14.99 ***(978-1-61638-472-2(7))*** Charisma Media. (Charisma Hse.).

Rendle, Gilbert R. & Beaumont, Susan K. When Moses Meets Aaron: Staffing & Supervision in Large Congregations. 2007. *(978-1-56699-351-7(2))* Alban Institute, Inc.

Reynolds, Jim. Why We Don't Shoot the Wounded. 2010. 254p. pap. 16.99 *(978-1-61579-278-8(3))* Xulon Pr., Inc.

Rhea, Ronald D. How to Finish First by Being. 2008. 192p. (ENG.). 21.99 *(978-1-60266-996-3(1));* per. 13.99 *(978-1-60266-995-6(3))* Xulon Pr., Inc.

Riccards, Michael P. Faith & Leadership: The Papacy & the Roman Catholic Church. 2012. (ENG.). 650p. (gr. 17). 110.00 ***(978-0-7391-7132-5(1))*** Lexington Bks.

Richey, Russel E. Extension Ministers: Mr. Wesley's True Heirs. 2008. 168p. pap. 12.95 *(978-0-938162-88-9(8))* United Methodist Board of Higher Education & Ministry.

Ritchey, Blair A. Collaborate: Working with God on What Matters Most. 2011. ***(978-0-89827-470-7(2))*** Wesleyan Publishing Hse.

Robertson, C. K. A Dangerous Dozen: Twelve Christians Who Threatened the Status Quo but Taught Us to Live Like Jesus. 2011. 160p. pap. 16.99 *(978-1-59473-298-0(1))* SkyLight Paths Publishing.

Robinson, Anthony B. Leadership for Vital Congregations. 2006. (Congregational Vitality Ser.). 127p. per. *(978-0-8298-1712-6(3))* Pilgrim Pr., The/United Church Pr.

Robinson, Bill. Incarnate Leadership, 1 vol. 2009. (ENG.). 128p. 14.99 *(978-0-310-29113-8(5))* Zondervan.

Robinson, Dick. More Than We Can Imagine. 2008. 144p. pap. 13.99 *(978-1-60477-848-9(2))* Xulon Pr., Inc.

Rogers. Building a House for All God's Children: Diversity Leadership in the Church. 2008. 162p. pap. 14.00 *(978-0-687-64999-0(4))* Abingdon Pr.

Rojas, Ronald R. A Relational Identity for Deacon Spirituality. 2009. 256p. pap. 15.50 *(978-1-59330-616-8(4))* Aventine Pr.

Ross, Pam. Serving, Leading & Loving. 2011. 180p. pap. 14.99 *(978-1-61215-617-0(7))* Xulon Pr., Inc.

Rumble, Alexander R., ed. Leaders of the Anglo-Saxon Church: From Bede to Stigand. 2012. (Pubns Manchester Centre for Anglo-Saxon Studies: Volume 12). (Illus.). 216p. 95.00 ***(978-1-84383-700-8(5),*** Boydell Press) Boydell & Brewer, Ltd. GBR. Dist: Boydell & Brewer, Inc.

Rutledge-Gordon, Lawanda. Don't Follow Me. 2010. 52p. pap. 15.49 *(978-1-4520-6427-7(X))* AuthorHouse.

Saccone, Steve. Relational Intelligence: Discussion Guide. 2010. 38p. pap. 16.98 *(978-0-557-12150-2(7))* Lulu Enterprises Inc.

Salierno, Lori. When Roosters Crow: A Fresh Approach to Accountability & Integrity. 2007. (ENG., Illus.). 212p. per. 14.95 *(978-1-59317-181-0(1))* Warner Pr. Pubs.

Samuel, Kenneth L. Solomon's Success: Four Essential Keys to Leadership. 2006. 109p. per. *(978-0-8298-1572-6(4))* Pilgrim Pr., The/United Church Pr.

Sanders, J. Oswald. Spiritual Leadership: Principles of Excellence for Every Believer. rev. ed. 2007. (ENG.). 208p. per. 14.99 *(978-0-8024-8227-3(9))* Moody Pubs.

Sandidge,; Dmin. A Book to Change Your Life. 2009. 192p. pap. 14.99 *(978-1-60791-400-6(X))* Xulon Pr., Inc.

Scharen, Christian. Faith as a Way of Life: A Vision for Pastoral Leadership. 2008. 128p. pap. 15.00 *(978-0-8028-6231-0(4))* Eerdmans, William B. Publishing Co.

Schmitz, Eileen. Staying in Bounds: Straight Talk on Boundaries for Effective Ministry. 2010. 208p. pap. 25.99 *(978-0-8272-3481-9(3))* Chalice Pr.

Schofield-Bodt, Brian R. Educating for the Transition from a Pastoral to a Program Church: A Leadership Development Model. pap. 13.75 *(978-1-56699-152-0(8),* OD113) Alban Institute, Inc.

Scott, Katherine Tyler. Transforming Leadership. 2010. (Transformations Ser.). 144p. pap. 16.00 *(978-0-89869-599-1(6))* Church Publishing, Inc.

Search, Bill. Simple Small Groups: A User-Friendly Guide for Small Group Leaders. 2008. 192p. pap. 13.99 *(978-0-8010-7153-9(4))* Baker Bks.

Servanthood. 2006. 15.00 *(978-0-9768564-0-5(9))* Payne, Janice Denise.

Shaw, Christopher. Lift up Your Eyes: Daily Encounters with God for Leaders. 2008. (ENG.). 379p. pap. 14.99 *(978-0-87508-989-8(5))* CLC Pubns.

Shawchuck, Norman & Heuser, Roger. Leading the Congregation: Caring for Yourself While Serving the People. rev. ed. 2010. 320p. pap. 30.00 *(978-1-4267-1139-8(5))* Abingdon Pr.

Sherlin, Keith A. Satan's Strategy to Curse Christ's Congregation: An Analysis of How Anarchy & Apostasy Develop in Christian Congregations & Elderships. 2010. 240p. 25.00 *(978-1-4520-7382-8(1));* pap. 17.00 *(978-1-4520-7383-5(X))* AuthorHouse.

Shields, Brian. The Scarlet Siren & the Southbound Sage, 1 vol. 2009. 52p. pap. 12.95 *(978-1-4489-8511-1(0))* PublishAmerica, Inc.

Shiflett, M. S. Exceptional Man. 2006. pap. 13.99 *(978-1-60034-740-5(1))* Xulon Pr., Inc.

Shockley, Gary A. The Meandering Way: Leading by Following the Spirit. 2007. *(978-1-56699-342-5(3))* Alban Institute, Inc.

Sipe, James W. & Frick, Don M. Seven Pillars of Servant Leadership: Practicing the Wisdom of Leading by Serving. 2009. (Illus.). 256p. pap. 21.95 *(978-0-8091-4560-7(X))* Paulist Pr.

Slattery, Margaret. The Highway to Leadership. 2007. (ENG.). 150p. 36.95 *(978-0-548-06937-0(9))* Kessinger Publishing, LLC.

Slaughter, Michael. Momentum for Life: Biblical Practices for Sustaining Physical Health Personal Integrity. 2008. 135p. pap. 18.00 *(978-0-687-65009-5(7))* Abingdon Pr.

Slaughter, Michael B. Change the World: Study for Leadership Teams. 2010. 16p. 39.00 *(978-1-4267-1012-4(7))* Abingdon Pr.

—Momentum for Life Participant DVD Journal. 2008. 10.00 *(978-0-687-65273-0(1))* Abingdon Pr.

Slaughter, Micheal. Momentum for Life. ldr.'s ed. 2008. 48p. pap. 15.00 *(978-0-687-65263-1(4))* Abingdon Pr.

—Momentum for Life Workbook. 2008. 112p. pap. 10.00 *(978-0-687-65303-4(7))* Abingdon Pr.

—Unlearning Church. 2008. 129p. pap. 18.00 *(978-0-687-64708-8(8))* Abingdon Pr.

Smith, Craig H. Every Monday: Finding God on Tough Days. 2009. 176p. 25.49 *(978-1-4389-3923-0(X));* pap. 15.99 *(978-1-4389-3922-3(1))* AuthorHouse.

Smith, Jack. Climbing the Ladder for Christ. 2008. 168p. (ENG.). 21.99 *(978-1-60477-151-0(8));* per. 13.99 *(978-1-60477-150-3(X))* Xulon Pr., Inc.

Smith, Joseph Nathan. He Gave Some to Be Pastors. 2010. 176p. pap. 18.99 *(978-0-557-49274-9(2))* Lulu Enterprises Inc.

Snyder, John. These Sheep Bite. 2006. per. 18.95 *(978-0-9764256-1-8(0))* Appleseed Pr.

Sofield, Loughlan & Juliano, Carroll. Principled Ministry: A Guidebook for Catholic Church Leaders. 2011. (Illus.). 192p. pap. 16.95 *(978-1-59471-263-0(8))* Ave Maria Pr.

Sorenson, David. Moral Failure. 2007. pap. *(978-0-9711384-2-1(7))* Northstar Baptist Church, Inc.

Standish, N. Graham. Humble Leadership: Being Radically Open to God's Guidance & Grace. 2007. *(978-1-56699-336-4(9))* Alban Institute, Inc.

Stanley, Andy. Making Vision Stick. 2007. (Leadership Library). (ENG.). 80p. 9.99 *(978-0-310-28305-8(1))* Zondervan.

Stearns, Robert, et al. Return to Authentic Christianity: An in-depth look at 12 Vital Issues Facing Today's Church. 2010. (ENG.). pap. 14.99 *(978-0-7684-3134-6(4))* Destiny Image Pubs.

Steinke, Peter L. Congregational Leadership in Anxious Times: Being Calm & Courageous No Matter What. 2006. (Illus.). xvi, 183p. *(978-1-56699-328-9(8))* Alban Institute, Inc.

Stevens, Tim. Pop Goes the Church: Should the Church Engage Pop Culture? 2008. (Illus.). 256p. pap. 16.95 *(978-0-9790174-9-0(1))* Power Publishing.

Stevenson, Phil. 5 Things Anyone Can Do to Help Start a Church. 2008. 96p. pap. 7.99 *(978-0-89827-382-3(X))* Wesleyan Publishing Hse.

—5 Things Anyone Can Do to Lead Effectively. 2007. (You Can! Ser.). 96p. per. 7.99 *(978-0-89827-365-6(X))* Wesleyan Publishing Hse.

Stewart, Rodney D. Church Vipers. 2006. 132p. per. 15.00 *(978-1-4251-0286-9(7))* Trafford Publishing.

Stott, John. Christian Leadership, 1 vol. 2009. (LifeGuide Bible Studies). (ENG.). 64p. pap. 8.00 *(978-0-8308-3126-5(6),* IVP Conn.) InterVarsity Pr.

Stout, Larry. Time for Change. 2006. (Ideal Leadership Ser.). (Illus.). 222p. per. 14.99 *(978-0-7684-2384-6(8))* Destiny Image Pubs.

Strauch, Alexander. Love or Die: Christ's Wake-up Call to the Church. 2008. 112p. pap. 9.99 *(978-0-936083-28-5(X))* Lewis & Roth Pubs.

Strom, Andrew. The Out-of-Church Christians. 2008. 116p. pap. 9.88 *(978-0-9799073-5-7(7))* RevivalSchl.

Styles, George. Ethical Pursuits. 2008. 60p. pap. 12.95 *(978-1-886057-10-4(9))* Warren Publishing, Inc.

Suggs, George G. Washing the Disciples' Feet: Vignettes of White Oak Original Free Will Baptist Church of Bladenboro, North Carolina. 2011. 116p. pap. 12.95 ***(978-1-4620-4124-4(8))*** iUniverse, Inc.

Surratt, Geoff, et al. A Multi-Site Church Roadtrip: , 1 vol. 2009. (Leadership Network Innovation Ser.). (ENG.). 256p. (C). pap. 18.99 *(978-0-310-29394-1(4))* Zondervan.

Swanson, Eric & Rusaw, Rick. The Externally Focused Quest: Becoming the Best Church for the Community. 2010. (Jossey-Bass Leadership Network Ser.: 44). (ENG., Illus.). 272p. 24.95 *(978-0-470-50078-1(6),* Jossey-Bass) Wiley, John & Sons, Inc.

Sweet, Leonard. Aquachurch 2.0: Piloting Your Church in Today's Fluid Culture. 2008. (ENG.). 384p. pap. 14.99 *(978-1-4347-6757-8(4))* Cook, David C.

Swindoll, Charles R. Hand Me Another Brick Bible Companion: Timeless Lessons on Leadership, 0 vols. 2007. (Illus.). 224p. per. 9.99 *(978-1-4185-2751-8(3))* Nelson, Thomas Inc.

—Hand Me Another Brick: Timeless Lessons on Leadership: How Effective Leaders Motivate Themselves & Others, 0 vols. 2007. (Illus.). 256p. per. 14.99 *(978-0-8499-1460-7(4))* Nelson, Thomas Inc.

Symes, Kenneth G. Jews, Gentiles & the Church Age. 2008. 88p. per. 9.99 *(978-1-60477-540-2(8))* Xulon Pr., Inc.

Taylor, Ill. Equipping Laity for Servant Leadership: Modeling A Servant's Heart, in the Rural Black Church. 2009. 176p. 14.95 *(978-1-4490-4728-3(9));* pap. 14.95 *(978-1-4490-4727-6(0))* AuthorHouse.

Taylor, Jim & Clark, Kristine Setting. The Fire Within. 2010. (ENG.). 224p. 24.95 *(978-1-60078-344-9(9))* Triumph Bks.

TenElshof, Phyllis, ed. The Church Leader's Answer Book: A Reference Guide for Effective Ministry. 2006. (ENG.). 704p. 29.97 *(978-1-4143-0354-3(8))* Tyndale Hse. Pubs.

Tener. Bryan Patrick. Squeezed: Youth Ministry During Tough Economic Times. 2009. mass mkt. 5.00 *(978-1-4267-0261-7(2))* Abingdon Pr.

Tetz, Myrna. Leadership Lessons from the Life of Neal Wilson. 2011. pap. 10.99 *(978-0-8163-2484-2(0))* Pacific Pr. Publishing Assn.

They Smell Like Sheep, Volume 2: Leading with the Heart of a Shepherd. 2011. (ENG.). 272p. pap. 17.99 *(978-1-4516-3631-4(8),* Howard Bks.) Howard Books.

Thompson, Frederick M. Identifying & Developing Leaders: A Biblical, Historical & Theological Perspective. 2007. 184p. per. 13.99 *(978-1-60266-505-7(2))* Xulon Pr., Inc.

Thompson, Martin. Searching for the Perfect Youth Ministry. 2008. 104p. per. 9.99 *(978-1-60477-692-8(7))* Xulon Pr., Inc.

Tidball, Derek. Ministry by the Book: New Testament Patterns for Pastoral Leadership, 1 vol. 2009. (ENG.). 277p. pap. 25.00 *(978-0-8308-3859-2(7),* IVP Acad.) InterVarsity Pr.

Tkacik, Michael J. & McGonigle, Thomas C. Pneumatic Correctives: What Is the Spirit Saying to the Church of the 21st Century? 2006. (ENG.). 228p. per. 39.99 *(978-0-7618-3569-1(5))* Univ. Pr. of America, Inc.

Towns, Elmer & Stetzer, Ed. 11 Innovations in the Local Church: How Today's Leaders Can Learn, Discern & Move into the Future. 2007. 256p. 14.99 *(978-0-8307-3786-4(3),* Regal Bks.) Gospel Light Pubns.

Tozer, A. w. Tozer on Christian Leadership: A 366-Daily Devotional. 2007. (Tozer for Today Ser.). 386p. pap. 16.99 *(978-1-60066-120-4(3))* WingSpread Publishers.

Tunis, Rick. Do You Love Me — Feed My Sheep: When Faith Meets Action. 2010. 190p. ***(978-0-7684-3506-1(4)); (978-0-7684-3505-4(6))*** Destiny Image Pubs.

Turner, J. J. Deacons, Wake Up! A First-Century Call for Servants in the Twenty-First Century to Imitate Jesus. 2006. *(978-0-929540-61-0(1))* Publishing Designs, Inc.

Underwood, Richard & Boley, Brian. Leadership in Practice 1. 2010. (Learn2Lead Ser.). 64p. pap. *(978-1-905564-73-6(2))* Good Bk. Co.

—Leadership in Practice 2. 2010. (Learn2Lead Ser.). 64p. pap. *(978-1-905564-74-3(0))* Good Bk. Co.

—Understanding Leadership. 2010. (Learn2Lead Ser.). 64p. pap. *(978-1-905564-72-9(4))* Good Bk. Co.

Upper Room Staff. Entering the New Testament. 2008. 96p. pap., wbk. ed. 10.00 *(978-0-8358-9967-3(5))* Upper Room Bks.

Vainio, Ed. Insights of Pastoral Significance. 2010. 141p. pap. 18.96 *(978-0-557-33981-5(2))* Lulu Enterprises Inc.

Valentine, Gilbert M. The Prophet & the Presidents: Ellen G. White & Adventist Church Leadership, 1887-1913. 2010. *(978-0-8280-2558-4(4))* Review & Herald Publishing Assn.

Valley, Clinton A. Help! I'm Being Followed: What to Do When You've Been Asked to Lead. 2007. (Illus.). 128p. pap. 12.99 *(978-0-8127-0461-7(4))* Autumn Hse. Publishing Co.

Van Gelder, Craig, ed. The Missional Church & Leadership Formation: Helping Congregations Develop Leadership Capacity. 2009. (ENG.). 248p. pap. 20.00 *(978-0-8028-6493-2(7))* Eerdmans, William B. Publishing Co.

Vandegrift, Sharon L. Keeping Your Balance: Seven Strategies for Remaining Steady in the Midst of Hectic Church Life. 2011. 68p. pap. 10.95 ***(978-1-4620-5836-5(1))*** iUniverse, Inc.

Voyles, David W. A Shepherd's Trial: Feeding or Fleecing the Flock of God? A Look at the Relationship that Today's Pastor has with the Congregation. 2010. 148p. 22.95 *(978-1-60911-031-4(5),* Eloquent Bks.) AEG Literary Publishing Services, Inc.

Wager, Dave. Beyond the Resistance: Learning to Face Adversity. 2007. (Intimate Warrior Ser.). 104p. per. 11.95 *(978-1-60265-001-5(2),* BTR) Grace Acres Pr.

Wagner, C. Peter. Apostles Today: Biblical Government for Biblical Power. 2007. (ENG.). 160p. pap. 11.99 *(978-0-8307-4362-9(6))* Gospel Light Pubns.

Waking to God's Dream. 15.00 *(978-0-687-00564-2(7))* Abingdon Pr.

Walley, Pauline. School of Mentoring & Leadership I/ the Act of Mentoring: 2008. pap. 10.99 *(978-1-60034-845-7(9))* Xulon Pr., Inc.

Ward, Paul. The Power of Honor. 2010. pap. 14.99 *(978-1-61579-657-1(6))* Xulon Pr., Inc.

Webb, Thomas. Beyond the Pulpit, Beyond the Church. 2006. pap. 14.99 *(978-1-60034-742-9(8))* Xulon Pr., Inc.

Webster, Douglas. Under the Radar A Conversation on Spirit. 2007. 96p. per. *(978-1-57383-385-1(1),* Regent College Publishing) Regent College Publishing.

Weems, Lovett H. Church Leadership: Vision, Team, Culture, & Integrity. 2010. 146p. pap. 18.00 *(978-1-4267-0302-7(3))* Abingdon Pr.

West, Hal. The Pickled Priest & the Perishing Parish: Boomer Pastors Bouncing Back. 2011. 140p. 28.95 ***(978-1-61507-928-5(9));*** pap. 11.95 ***(978-1-61507-915-5(7))*** Cross Bks. Publishing.

Where Is Your Church Going? Essentials of a Quality Church: 1 Timothy. 2008. (Illus.). 125p. ***(978-1-59402-669-0(6)); (978-1-59402-666-9(1))*** Regular Baptist Pr.

Who Is Jesus? A Six-Week Study for Tweens. 2010. 64p. pap. 15.95 *(978-0-687-65800-8(4))* Abingdon Pr.

C

Wiersbe, Warren W. Be Confident: Live by Faith, Not by Sight. 2009. (Be Series Commentary Ser.). (ENG.). 192p. pap. 12.99 (978-1-4347-6735-6(3)) Cook, David C.

—Be Joyful: Even When Things Go Wrong, You Can Have Joy. 2008. (Be Ser.). (ENG.). 160p. pap. 12.99 (978-1-4347-6846-9(5)) Cook, David C.

—Be Right: How to Be Right with God, Yourself, & Others. 2008. (Be Ser.). (ENG.). 192p. pap. 12.99 (978-1-4347-6847-6(3)) Cook, David C.

—Mature: Growing up in Christ. 2008. (Be Ser.). (ENG.). 192p. pap. 12.99 (978-1-4347-6845-2(7)) Cook, David C.

Wikstrom, Erik Walker. Serving with Grace: Lay Leadership As a Spiritual Practice. 2010. pap. 12.00 (978-1-55896-562-1(9), Skinner Hse. Bks.) Unitarian Universalist Assn.

Wilcox M.P.H., Howard D. Divine Providence: Fifty Life Lessons from the Book of Esther. 2011. 336p. 37.95 **(978-1-61507-731-1(6))** Cross Bks. Publishing.

Williams, David R. Emerging Leaders. 2011. (Illus.). 172p. pap. 12.95 (978-0-938020-79-0(X)) Decapolis Publishing.

Williams, Ritva H. Stewards, Prophets, Keepers of the Word: Leadership in the Early Church. 2006. 228p. per. 24.95 (978-1-56563-949-2(9)) Hendrickson Pubs. Marketing, LLC.

Willis, Deborah. New Century First Lady & First Gentleman Handbook, Vol. 1. 2007. 66p. pap. 10.95 (978-0-7414-3944-4(1)) Infinity Publishing.

Willis, Kerry W. Relational Leadership: What I Learned from a Fisherman about Leading a Church. 2009. (ENG.). 128p. pap. 11.99 (978-0-8341-2472-1(6), 9780834124721) Beacon Hill Pr. of Kansas City.

Willis, Mike, ed. A Crisis in Leadership. 2010. 298p. pap. 21.95 (978-1-58427-299-1(6)) Guardian of Truth Foundation.

Wilson-Bridges, Cheryl. Levite Praise: God's Biblical Design for Praise & Worship. 2009. (ENG.). 192p. 19.99 (978-1-59979-722-9(4), Creation Hse.) Charisma Media.

Winford, Rick & Stephenson, Andy. Taking the Plunge: Leaders Guide. 2011. (Ultimate Adventure Ser.). (ENG., Illus.). 113p. pap. 16.00 (978-1-59317-527-6(2)) Warner Pr. Pubs.

Winseman, Albert L. Growing an Engaged Church: How to Stop Doing Church & Start Being the Church Again. 2007. (ENG., Illus.). 192p. 22.95 (978-1-59562-014-9(1)) Gallup Pr.

Winseman, Albert L., et al. Living Your Strengths: Discover Your God-Given Talents, & Inspire Your Community. 2nd ed. 2008. xviii, 249p. (978-1-59562-023-1(0)); (978-1-59562-022-4(2)) Gallup Pr.

Withers, Robert. Charting the Course - the Pastoral Search Process. 2007. 199p. pap. 19.95 (978-1-4303-2178-1(4)) Lulu Enterprises Inc.

Witmer, Timothy Z. The Shepherd Leader: Achieving Effective Shepherding in Your Church. 2010. pap. (978-1-59638-131-5(0)) P & R Publishing.

Wolpert, Daniel. Leading a Life with God: The Practice of Spiritual Leadership. 2006. 187p. per. 17.00 (978-0-8358-1003-6(8)) Upper Room Bks.

Woods, C. Jeff & Woods, Charles Jeffrey. On the Move: Adding Strength, Speed, & Balance to Your Congregation. 2009. 19.99 (978-0-8272-2728-6(0)) Chalice Pr.

Woolever, Cynthia, et al. Places of Promise: Finding Strength in Your Congregation's Location. 2008. (ENG., Illus.). 130p. pap. 20.00 (978-0-664-23023-4(7)) Westminster John Knox Pr.

Wragg, Jerry. Exemplary Spiritual Leadership: Facing the Challenges, Escaping the Dangers. 2010. (Ministry & Mission Ser.). 153p. pap. (978-1-84625-200-6(8)) DayOne Pubns.

Yaconelli, Mike & Christie, Les. When Church Kids Go Bad: How to Love & Work with Rude, Obnoxious, & Apathetic Students, 1 vol. 2008. (ENG.). 192p. pap. 16.99 (978-0-310-27665-4(9)) Zondervan.

Young, Robert A. How to Lead a Church to Reach People & Grow. 2009. 218p. pap. 17.99 (978-1-60791-857-8(9)) Xulon Pr., Inc.

Youseef, Michael. Liderazgo Al Estilo de Jesus: Leadership Style of Jesus. (SPA.). (978-84-7645-189-2(X), 223232) Clie, Editorial.

Zigarelli, Michael. Management by Proverbs. 2008. 376p. 32.99 (978-1-60791-018-3(7)); pap. 20.99 (978-1-60791-017-6(9)) Xulon Pr., Inc.

Zondervan Publishing Staff. Purpose Driven Leadership: Lesson on Leadership from Nehemiah. 2006. 272p. 12.99 (978-0-8297-4894-9(6)) Vida Pubs.

Zuck, Roy, ed. Vital Church Issues: Examining Principles & Practices in Church Leadership. 2006. (Vital Issues Ser.). 248p. pap. 26.00 (978-1-59752-682-1(7), Wipf and Stock) Wipf & Stock Pubs.

2009-2012 United Methodist Membership Records Manual. 2009. 12.00 (978-0-687-65563-2(3)) Abingdon Pr.

CHRISTIAN LEGENDS

Gabriele, Matthew. An Empire of Memory: The Legend of Charlemagne, the Franks, & Jerusalem before the First Crusade. 2011. (ENG., Illus.). 256p. 99.00 (978-0-19-959144-2(X)) Oxford Univ. Pr., Inc.

Gonzalez, Fernando M. Marcial Maciel: Los Legionarios de Cristo. 2006. (SPA.). 480p. pap. 24.95 (978-970-699-150-8(6)) Tusquets Editores ESP. Dist: Ediciones Urano S. A.

Lieu, Samuel N. C. & Montserrat, Dominic, eds. Constantine: History, Historiography & Legend. 2012. (ENG.). 264p. pap. 42.95 **(978-0-415-51890-1(3))** Routledge.

Moore, John K. Libro de Los Huéspedes (Escorial MS H.I.13) A Critical Edition. 2008. (ENG & SPA.). (C). (978-0-86698-397-6(X)) Arizona State Univ., Arizona Ctr. for Medieval & Renaissance Studies.

St. John, Bayle. Legends of the Christian East. 2009. 218p. 39.95 (978-1-120-79824-4(8)); pap. 24.95 (978-1-120-63543-3(8)) Kessinger Publishing, LLC.

CHRISTIAN LIFE

see also Asceticism; Christian Ethics; Christian Stewardship; Devotional Exercises; Discipling (Christianity); Piety

A D E K A N M I, Y. I. N. K. A. The Glorious Manifestation of the Sons of God. 2011. 220p. pap. 15.99 **(978-1-61379-004-5(X))** Xulon Pr., Inc.

A, Jessica. Unveiled. 2011. 282p. pap. 16.99 **(978-1-61379-491-3(6))** Xulon Pr., Inc.

A Monk of St. Tikhon's Monastery Staff, compiled by. These Truths We Hold: The Holy Orthodox Church, Her Life & Teachings. 2nd rev. ed. 2010. (Illus.). 393p. pap. (978-1-878997-32-6(7)) St. Tikhon's Seminary Pr.

Aalders, Cynthia Y. To Express the Ineffable: The Hymns & Spirituality of Anne Steele. 2009. (Studies in Baptist History & Thought Ser.). 234p. pap. 26.00 (978-1-60608-600-1(6), Wipf and Stock) Wipf & Stock Pubs.

Abayilo, Lami. Beyond Limits: Discover Life's Winning Strategies. 2009. pap. 14.99 (978-88-89127-66-7(X)) Destiny Image Europe ITA. Dist: Destiny Image Pubs.

Abbate, Michael. Gardening Eden: How Creation Care Will Change Your Faith, Your Life, & Our World 2009. (ENG.). 272p. 13.99 (978-0-307-44499-8(6), WaterBrook Pr.) Doubleday Religious Publishing Group, The.

Abbott, Jacob. The Corner Stone. 2007. (ENG.). 378p. 48.95 (978-0-548-04060-7(5)) Kessinger Publishing, LLC.

Abbott, Jacob. The Corner Stone; or, a Familiar Illustration of the Principles of Christian Truth. 2011. 374p. pap. 31.95 **(978-1-4460-5777-3(1)**, Kent Pr.) Kent Communications, Ltd.

Abbott, Matt. Behind the Scenes. 2007. 176p. per. 13.99 (978-1-60477-235-7(2)) Xulon Pr., Inc.

Abdulsalam, Bishop Kenny. A Call to Follow: Discover the Journey from followership to Leadership. 2009. 140p. pap. 14.95 (978-1-4327-4538-7(7)) Outskirts Pr., Inc.

Abel, Robert. Heavenly Treasure. 2009. (Illus.). 72p. pap. 5.99 (978-0-9796331-3-3(3)) Valentine Publishing Hse. LLC.

Abell, Dave. Common Sense Apologetics: One God, One Book, One Way. 2010. 224p. 33.95 (978-1-4497-0422-3(0)); pap. 17.95 (978-1-4497-0424-7(7)) Author Solutions, Inc. (WestBow Pr.).

Abeyasingha, Nihal. The Order of the Mass. 2011. 84p. pap. 16.48 **(978-1-257-62840-7(2))** Lulu Enterprises Inc.

Abingdon. Faces on Faith - Joan Chittister, Marcus Borg, James Lawson: Classic Interviews with 20th-Century Leaders. 2008. cd-rom 25.00 (978-0-687-65353-9(3)) Abingdon Pr.

—Faces on Faith: Desmond Tutu, Parker Palmer, Adele Gonzales: Classic Interviews with 20th-Century Leaders. 2008. cd-rom 25.00 (978-0-687-65402-4(5)) Abingdon Pr.

—Faces on Faith: Huston Smith, Rita Nakashima Brock, Chaim Potok: Classic Interviews with 20th-Century Leaders. 2008. cd-rom 25.00 (978-0-687-65343-0(6)) Abingdon Pr.

—Real World Christians: Being Yourself, Belonging to God. 12.00 (978-0-687-02038-6(7)); 5.00 (978-0-687-02018-8(2)) Abingdon Pr.

—Under the Baobab Tree Starter Kit, Vol. 2. 45.00 (978-0-687-00746-2(1)) Abingdon Pr.

Abingdon Press, creator. Living the Faith. 2006. (Faith Matters for Young Adults Ser.). 112p. per. 11.00 (978-0-687-49380-7(3)) Abingdon Pr.

—Word Up! Speaking & Living for Jesus. 2007. (Fifth in Abingdon's Afro-Centric Intergenerational Program Ser.). 62.00 (978-0-687-64300-4(7)) Abingdon Pr.

Abingdon Press, ed. What's in the Bible about Church? 2009. (Why Is That in the Bible & Why Should I Care? Ser.). 68p. pap. 8.00 (978-0-687-65294-5(4)) Abingdon Pr.

—Whats in the Bible & Where D. 2009. (Why Is That in the Bible & Why Should I Care? Ser.). 112p. pap. 10.00 (978-0-687-65324-9(X)) Abingdon Pr.

Abingdon Press Upper Room & Discipleship Resources. (978-0-687-97103-9(9)) Abingdon Pr.

Abraham, Adelaide Mary. Divine Intimacy with My Saviour: Dedicated to the Most Precious Blood of Our Lord & Saviour Jesus Christ. 2009. 112p. pap. 35.49 (978-1-4343-7628-2(1)) AuthorHouse.

Abramowicz, Danny, et al. Crossing the Goal Playbook on Our Father. 2010. (Crossing the Goal Ser.). (Illus.). 142p. spiral bd. 12.95 (978-1-931018-66-1(9)) Emmaus Road Publishing.

Abrams, Jeff. Sticks & Stones: A Study of Hurtful Words & Helpful Remedies. 2011. 136p. 28.95 (978-1-4497-1198-6(7)); pap. 11.95 (978-1-4497-1197-9(9)) Author Solutions, Inc. (WestBow Pr.).

Abrams, Prophet Rodney. The Broken Vessel Made Whole. 2010. 116p. 21.49 (978-1-4520-4291-6(8)); pap. 15.99 (978-1-4520-4290-9(X)) AuthorHouse.

Abresch, Michael G. In the Light of Day. 2010. 204p. pap. 15.95 (978-1-4520-2154-6(6)) AuthorHouse.

Le Absolutes de Dieu: Les Principes pour Construire une Fondation Solide dans notre Vie Chretienne. 2007.Tr. of Principles for Building a Solid Foundation in our Christian Life. (FRE.). per. 14.99 (978-0-9795244-0-0(7)) Absolutes Pr., The.

Accattoli, Luis. Karol Wojtyla: El Hombre Mas Famoso del Mundo (The Most Outstanding Man of the World) (SPA.). 352p. pap. 9.95 (978-958-607-303-5(3)) Sociedad de San Pablo COL. Dist: St Pauls/Alba Hse. Pubs.

Achampong, Nana S. Empowernomics. 2008. 172p. pap. 20.51 (978-0-615-18068-7(X)) Achampong & Sons.

Acharjee, Sandy. The Light, the Truth & the Way. 2011. 120p. 21.50 (978-1-4567-2453-5(3)); pap. 14.50 (978-1-4567-2454-2(1)) AuthorHouse.

Acheampong, Kwame. Fashion & Faith: Where Contemporary Meets Morality. 2007. 116p. per. 8.95 (978-1-4327-1431-4(7)) Outskirts Pr., Inc.

Acker, Katina S. The Turning Point: When the Pleaser of Man Becomes a Servant of the Lord. 2009. 160p. 22.95 (978-1-4389-9678-3(0)); pap. 17.95 (978-1-4389-9677-6(2)) AuthorHouse.

Actis, Ronald George. Spiritual Dn: What Jesus Said about God, Peace of Mind, Happiness, Mankind. 2008. 368p. pap. 29.95 (978-1-4327-2062-9(7)) Outskirts Pr., Inc.

Adam of Bremen. Mirror Images. 2007. xiii, 130p. pap. (978-0-281-05774-0(5)) SPCK Publishing.

Adamkiewicz, Catherine L. Broken & Blessed: A Life Story. 2007. 180p. per. 12.99 (978-0-9794976-6-7(3)) Bezalel Bks.

Adams, Aisha Z. The Walk of Faith. 2011. 56p. pap. 15.99 **(978-1-4628-2929-3(5))** Xlibris Corp.

Adams, Andy. Don't Scare the Lost Sheep: Equipping You to Assist Others on Their Journey to Christ. 2009. 256p. 26.99 (978-1-61579-388-4(7)); pap. 16.99 (978-1-61579-387-7(9)) Xulon Pr., Inc.

Adams, Anthony. Scriptural Advice Concerning Your Finances: Running on 90% High Efficiency. 2007. 264p. per. 27.95 (978-1-4241-8003-5(1)) PublishAmerica, Inc.

Adams, Beresford. Principles of Belief & Practices of Faith: A Guide to Successful Living. 2009. 283p. 41.82 (978-0-557-08318-3(4)); (ENG.). pap. 20.82 (978-0-557-08409-8(1)) Lulu Enterprises Inc.

Adams, Carl L. God's Dream Catcher. 2008. 260p. 26.99 (978-1-60647-716-8(1)); pap. 16.99 (978-1-60647-715-1(3)) Xulon Pr., Inc.

Adams, Carol. Ten Steps to Proper Christian Dating: The Divine Order of God. 2009. 88p. pap. 15.99 (978-1-4363-3892-9(1)) Xlibris Corp.

Adams, David V. Lifestyle Worship: The Worship God Intended Then & Now. 2010. 154p. pap. 18.00 (978-1-60899-583-7(6), Resource Pubns.) Wipf & Stock Pubs.

Adams, Jay E. Day by Day along the Way. 2011. pap. 14.99 (978-1-889032-66-5(2)) Timeless Texts, Inc.

—Greg Dawson & the Psychology Class. 2008. 149p. pap. 11.99 (978-1-889032-63-4(8)) Timeless Texts, Inc.

Adams, Jay Edward. Aprenda a Volar Conmigo.Tr. of Come Fly with Me. (SPA.). 120p. (978-84-7228-205-6(8), 220042) Clie, Editorial.

—Capacitados Para Restaurar. 2008.Tr. of Ready to Restore. (SPA.). 168p. pap. 9.99 (978-84-7645-083-3(4), 223132) Clie, Editorial ESP. Dist: Zondervan.

—Compassionate Counseling. 2007. 94p. per. 12.00 (978-1-889032-59-7(X)) Timeless Texts, Inc.

—Encouragement Isn't Enough. 2007. 98p. per. 12.00 (978-1-889032-57-3(3)) Timeless Texts, Inc.

—Por Que Me Cuesta Tanto.Tr. of How Come It's Taking Me So Long To. (SPA.). 160p. (978-84-7228-582-8(0), 220703) Clie, Editorial.

—Vida Cristiana en el Hogar.Tr. of Christian Living in the Home. (SPA.). 107p. pap. 5.95 (978-1-55883-027-1(8), 6701-0580C) Libros Desafio.

Adams, Jessie. A Guide to the Spiritual Development of Children: Seventeen Subjects Every Christian Parent Needs to Focus Upon. 2010. 112p. pap. 11.95 (978-1-61507-175-3(X)) Cross Bks. Publishing.

Adams, Kenny & Peachey, Marlaine. Grace Through the Storm. 2007. 96p. per. 9.99 (978-1-60266-371-8(8)) Xulon Pr., Inc.

Adams, Latitia R. I Didn't Know What I Thought I Knew. 2008. 80p. per. 9.99 (978-1-60477-595-2(5)) Xulon Pr., Inc.

Adams, Marilyn McCord. Some Later Medieval Theories of the Eucharist: Thomas Aquinas, Gilles of Rome, Duns Scotus, & William Ockham. 2010. (ENG.). 288p. 55.00 (978-0-19-959105-3(9)) Oxford Univ. Pr., Inc.

Adams, Markus E. A Biography of the Holy Trinity & Man. 2009. 388p. pap. 20.99 (978-1-60791-661-1(4)) Xulon Pr., Inc.

Adams, Mary E. On the Way There: Making the Most Out of Life's Journey. 2010. 22.99 (978-1-61579-879-7(X)); pap. 14.99 (978-1-61579-878-0(1)) Xulon Pr., Inc.

Adams, Michael S. Manhood. 2010. 120p. pap. 11.99 (978-1-60957-248-8(3)) Xulon Pr., Inc.

Adams, Patricia E. Detouring Away from My Original Position of Oneness: On the Intimacy with God Journey, Vol. 3. rev. ed. 2012. (One Heart Ser.: Vol. 3). (ENG., Illus.). 392p. pap. 24.95 (978-0-9700976-2-0(X), Shekinah Publishing Hse.) Shekinah Publishing Hse.

Adams, Robert L. The Blessed Pastor: A Lyrical Interpretation of the Sermon on the Mount Especially for Pastors. 2010. 116p. pap. 14.00 (978-1-4520-0257-6(6)) AuthorHouse.

Adams, Yolanda. Points of Power: Discover a Spirit-Filled Life of Joy & Purpose. 2010. (ENG.). 256p. 19.99 (978-0-446-54578-5(3)) FaithWords.

Adamson, Tonilee & Brooks, Bobbye. Building Divine Intimacy: How to Become a Daily Disciple of the Living God. 2007. 202p. per. 14.99 (978-0-9788726-4-9(9)) HonorNet.

Addison, Bonnita. How to Stay up in a down World. 2007. 144p. per. 11.99 (978-1-58169-252-5(8)) Genesis Communications, Inc.

Addison, Cynthia. Mamma Said. 2009. 52p. pap. 15.49 (978-1-4389-4060-1(2)) AuthorHouse.

Adeboye, E. A. Divine Intimacy. 2009. pap. (978-1-61623-900-8(X)) Independent Pub.

Adegbesan, Oladipo A. I Shall Not Want. 2011. 68p. 24.99 **(978-1-4653-5295-8(3))**; pap. 15.99 **(978-1-4653-5294-1(5))** Xlibris Corp.

Adelaja, Sunday. Church Shift. 2008. (ENG.). 224p. pap. 14.99 (978-1-59979-097-8(1), Charisma Hse.) Charisma Media.

Ademuwagun, Yomi. The Case for Holiness. 2010. 108p. (ENG.). 21.49 (978-1-4520-4403-3(1)); pap. 12.99 (978-1-4520-4402-6(3)) AuthorHouse.

Adeola, Dayo. Winning Habits. 2008. 148p. pap. 14.99 (978-1-60647-692-5(0)) Xulon Pr., Inc.

Adeosun, Sam-Sunday. Unveiling the Potency of Time: 170 Wisdom Quotetables for Success. 2008. 80p. pap. 9.99 (978-1-60477-934-9(9)) Xulon Pr., Inc.

Adesina, Kehinde. Become All That God Has Created & Ordained You to Be. 2008. pap. (978-0-9556892-6-0(0)) Purpose2Destiny TK Ltd.

Adesina, Kehinde & Adesina, Taiwo. Become All That God Has Created & Ordained You to Be. 2008. 192p. pap. 25.50 (978-0-9556892-1-5(X)) Purpose2Destiny TK Ltd. GBR. Dist: Lulu Enterprises Inc.

Adesogan, E. Faith, Politics & Challenges a Christian's First-Hand Account. 2007. 244p. pap. (978-978-129-830-1(8)) Heinemann Educational Bks. (Nigeria), Ltd. NGA. Dist: Michigan State Univ. Pr.

Adetona, Sam. Overcoming the Angry World. 2011. 134p. pap. 24.95 **(978-1-4560-3809-0(5))** PublishAmerica, Inc.

Adkins, Glenn. Never a Dull Moment: Taking Light into the Darkness. 2009. 276p. pap. 16.99 (978-1-60791-822-6(6)) Xulon Pr., Inc.

Adler, Marlys. My Spirit Wears Shoes: Written for those other spirits that wear Shoes. 2009. 136p. 21.49 (978-1-4389-5490-5(5)); pap. 10.99 (978-1-4389-5491-2(3)) AuthorHouse.

Adsit, Chris/B. Personal Disciplemaking Seminar: DVD Training Series. 2007. 73p. ring bd. 99.95 (978-0-9671227-7-9(5)) Disciplemakers International.

Aduloju, Funsho Bishop & Aduloju, Bola. Don t Buy the Picture. 2010. 258p. pap. 16.99 (978-1-60957-551-9(2)) Xulon Pr., Inc.

Aeschliman, Gordon & Campolo, Tony. Everybody Wants to Change the World: Practical Ideas for Social Justice. 2006. (ENG.). 220p. per. 14.99 (978-0-8307-4283-7(2)) Gospel Light Pubns.

Afectividad y Vida Religiosa. (SPA.). 256p. 8.95 (978-958-607-638-8(5)) Sociedad de San Pablo COL. Dist: St Pauls/Alba Hse. Pubs.

Afolabi, Modupe. Postcode: Exploring the Secret Place of God. 2011. 84p. pap. 12.10 **(978-1-4567-7923-8(0))** AuthorHouse.

Afrodytess. Love, Love, Love, It's All about Love! 2009. (Illus.). 30p. (J). pap. 18.95 (978-1-4327-4798-5(3)) Outskirts Pr., Inc.

Agagbor, Ifeanyi. The Disciples' Prayer. 2007. 88p. per. 9.99 (978-1-60477-312-5(X)) Xulon Pr., Inc.

Agbonson, George. Journey of Faith. 2011. 188p. pap. 14.99 **(978-1-61215-930-0(3))** Xulon Pr., Inc.

Aghostspen. My Testimoknee; the Fire Behind the Flame. 2009. 68p. pap. 8.95 (978-1-4401-0236-3(8)) iUniverse, Inc.

Agnew, April Dawn. Daddy's Girl Uncovered: Validating Your Relationship with God. 2011. pap. 10.99 **(978-1-61739-729-5(6))** Tate Publishing & Enterprises, LLC.

Agnew, Gary. Watch What He Does with This: 12 Steps Revisited. 2011. 148p. pap. 34.95 (978-1-4327-6560-6(4)) Outskirts Pr., Inc.

Agradecimientos Y Bendiciones. 24p. 2.95 (978-958-607-912-9(0)) Sociedad de San Pablo COL. Dist: St Pauls/Alba Hse. Pubs.

Aguiar, Ron. Keeping Your Church Safe: No Subtitle. 2008. 148p. pap. 13.99 (978-1-60647-332-0(8)) Xulon Pr., Inc.

Aguilar, Geronimo. Soulwinning Is Not a Gift. 2009. pap. 14.95 (978-1-61584-476-0(7)) Independent Pub.

Aguilar, Mario. Contemplating God Changing the World. 2009. 192p. pap. 18.00 (978-1-59627-108-1(6), Seabury Bks.) Church Publishing, Inc.

Ahems, Richard. 10 Things Your Pastor Should Tell You. 2008. 76p. 8.99 (978-1-60604-555-8(5)) Tate Publishing & Enterprises, LLC.

Ahlgren, David. A Primer on the Christian Life. 2009. 201p. pap. 15.96 (978-0-557-08575-0(6)) Lulu Enterprises Inc.

Ahn, Ché. Say Goodbye to Powerless Christianity: Walking in Supernatural Surrender & Significance. 2009. 172p. pap. 16.99 (978-0-7684-3113-1(1)) Destiny Image Pubs.

Ahn, Ché, et al. Catching God's Heart: The Wisdom & Power of Intimacy. 2010. (ENG.). pap. 16.99 (978-0-7684-3250-3(2)) Destiny Image Pubs.

Aikenhead, Mary. The Everyday Wisdom of Mary Aikenhead. 2008. (ENG., Illus.). 208p. pap. 16.95 (978-1-84730-035-5(9)) Veritas Pubns. IRL. Dist: Dufour Editions, Inc.

Aikman, David. The Mirage of Peace: Understanding the Never-Ending Conflict in the Middle East. 2009. (ENG.). 256p. 22.99 (978-0-8307-4605-7(6)) Gospel Light Pubns.

Ajibola, Babatunde Ezekiel. Introduction to christian living:a baptismal & membership class Tutorial. 2008. 111p. pap. 20.95 (978-1-4092-4955-9(7)) Lulu Enterprises Inc.

Akey, Mary. 7 Steps to A Transformational Heart: A Christians Journey to the Life God Intended. 2007. (ENG.). 100p. per. 11.95 (978-1-4327-1328-7(0)) Outskirts Pr., Inc.

Akindebe, Bunmi. When God's Word Does Not Make Sense to Your Natural Senses... Obey. 2009. 92p. pap. 9.95 (978-1-4327-4968-2(4)) Outskirts Pr., Inc.

Akonawe, Elo Hannah. Achieving Excellence. 2008. 116p. pap. 10.99 (978-1-4389-1385-8(0)) AuthorHouse.

Akporeha, Thompson. Angels' Protection. 2010. 54p. pap. 15.99 (978-1-4500-7917-4(2)) Xlibris Corp.

Al Luke. Living Mahalo: (Life in the Presence of the Spirit) 2008. pap. 11.99 (978-1-60647-656-7(4)) Xulon Pr., Inc.

Alao, Abimbola Gbemi. The Goshen Principle: A Shelter in the Time of Storm. 2010. 72p. pap. 10.49 (978-1-4520-0313-9(0)) AuthorHouse.

Alario, Janet. Live Well, Love Much, Laugh Often. 2006. 104p. pap. 14.99 (978-1-4141-0665-6(3)) Pleasant Word.

Alario, Janet Teresa. Live Well, Love Much, Laugh Often: Journal. 2006. 216p. pap. 16.99 (978-1-4141-0567-3(3)) Pleasant Word.

Albertin, David M. It's a Matter of Faith & Life, 3 vols., Set. 54.50 (978-0-7880-1196-2(0)) CSS Publishing Co.

Albright, Kendall Richard. Living Truth for Believers by Atlanta G Wilkerson. 2011. 126p. pap. 19.99 **(978-1-4653-5726-7(2))** Xlibris Corp.

Alcorn, Randy C. El Cielo: Guía de Estudio. 2006. (SPA.). 96p. per. 7.99 (978-1-4143-1276-7(8), Tyndale Espanol) Tyndale Hse. Pubs.

—El Cielo: Respuestas Bíblicas a Sus Preguntas. 2007.Tr. of Heaven. (SPA.). 64p. pap. 0.99 (978-1-4143-1492-1(2), Tyndale Espanol) Tyndale Hse. Pubs.

—The Goodness of God: Assurance of Purpose in the Midst of Suffering. 2010. (ENG.). 128p. 12.99 (978-1-60142-343-6(8), Multnomah) Doubleday Religious Publishing Group, The.

—If God Is Good: Faith in the Midst of Suffering & Evil. 2009. (ENG.). 528p. 24.99 (978-1-60142-132-6(X), Multnomah) Doubleday Religious Publishing Group, The.

—El Principio del Tesoro: Descubra el Secreto del Dador Alegre. 2007.Tr. of Treasure Principle. 112p. per. 2.99 (978-0-7899-1593-1(6)) Editorial Unilit.

Aldridge, Mark. Calling All Catholics: A Message from the Word of God. 2009. pap. 14.99 (978-1-60799-942-3(0)) Tate Publishing & Enterprises, LLC.

Alexander, Angela. Miracles in Action: Turning Pain into Power & Grief into Peace. 2008. (Illus.). 211p. pap. 15.95 (978-0-9778472-0-4(9)) Running Springs Pr.

Alexander, Charles. Angels Don't Wear Shoes. 2007. (ENG.). 228p. per. (978-1-55452-124-1(6)) Essence Publishing.

Alexander, Dallal. My Little Friend. 2009. pap. 10.99 (978-1-60799-851-8(3)) Tate Publishing & Enterprises, LLC.

Alexander, Donald L. Walk in Light & Love: The Message of First John. 2011. 84p. pap. 9.95 **(978-1-4497-2795-6(6)**, WestBow Pr.) Author Solutions, Inc.

Alexander, Eric. The Summit. 2010. pap. 14.99 (978-0-89221-701-4(4), New Leaf Pr.) New Leaf Pr., Inc.

Alexander, Frank S. & Witte, John, Jr., eds. Christianity & Human Rights: An Introduction. 2010. (ENG.). 400p. 90.00 (978-0-521-19441-9(5)) Cambridge Univ. Pr.

Alexander, Gladys L. The Covenant Leadership of God: A Leadership Manual. 2011. 136p. pap. 19.99 **(978-1-4653-4954-5(5))** Xlibris Corp.

Alexander, Inez. Walking the Walk in a Real World: Anecdotes to Inspire & Encourage. 2008. (ENG.). 144p. per. 10.99 (978-1-59979-256-9(7), Creation Hse.) Charisma Media.

Alexander, Jr. Fred H. & Alexander, Jr. Ridiculous Thoughts from a Preacher & a Few Friends. 2009. 176p. 25.49 (978-1-4490-2084-2(4)); pap. 13.49 (978-1-4490-2085-9(2)) AuthorHouse.

Alexander, Karyn. Familiar Spirits. 2008. 156p. per. 13.99 (978-1-60477-368-2(5)) Xulon Pr., Inc.

Alexander, Kerry. Heaven's Choice: True stories of love beyond Life. 2011. 92p. 24.99 **(978-1-4568-8289-1(9))**; pap. 15.99 **(978-1-4568-8288-4(0))** Xlibris Corp.

Alexander, Mae W., et al. Under the Palm of Deborah: Counsel from Wise Women of God. 2008. 188p. pap. 14.99 (978-1-933972-14-5(9)) PriorityONE Pubns.

Alexander, Shaun. The Walk: Clear Direction & Spiritual Power for Your Life. (ENG.). 240p. 2011. pap. 13.99 (978-0-307-73025-1(5)) 2010. 17.99 (978-0-307-45951-0(9)) Doubleday Religious Publishing Group, The. (WaterBrook Pr.).

Alflatt, Hilary. Forgiveness: Revelation of the Kingdom of God. 2009. (Illus.). 212p. pap. (978-1-84748-541-0(3)) Athena Pr.

Alibrando, Samuel J. Christians in the Arena: Stepping into the Arenas of Leadership, Influence & Political Controversy. 2nd exp. rev. ed. 2006. (ENG., Illus.). 180p. per. 14.99 (978-1-933853-46-8(8)) Tsaba Hse.

Alien, Kalix. God's Own. 2011. 132p. pap. 13.95 **(978-1-4620-2108-6(5))** iUniverse, Inc.

Alikin, Valeriy A. The Earliest History of the Christian Gathering: Origin, Development, & Content of the Christian Gathering in the First to Third Centuries. 2010. (Illus.). 342p. (978-90-04-18309-4(4)) BRILL.

All Ages. 6.50 (978-0-687-03153-5(2)) Abingdon Pr.

All God's Children Sing: Musical Resource. 152p. pap. (978-0-919599-97-0(4)) Wood Lake Publishing, Inc.

All the Good You Can: The Case for the Common Good. 2011. pap. 15.00 (978-1-4267-1241-8(3)) Abingdon Pr.

Allberry, Sam. Lifted: Experiencing the Resurrection Life. 2012. pap. **(978-1-59638-431-6(X))** P & R Publishing.

Allee, Susan. From Darkness to Light: A Memoir about Finding Healing in Heartbreak. 2011. pap. 11.99 **(978-1-61777-126-2(0))** Tate Publishing & Enterprises, LLC.

Alleine, Richard & Alleine, Joseph. Heaven Opened. 2007. (ENG.). 146p. 35.95 (978-0-548-00574-3(5), Kessinger Publishing, LLC.

Allen, Beth. Ground & Spring: Foundations of Quaker Discipleship. 2007. 132p. per. (978-0-901689-67-2(X)) Quaker Books.

Allen, Beverly D. Good Women in Bad Situations: And the Grace That Awaits Them. 2009. 116p. pap. 11.99 (978-1-61579-222-1(8)) Xulon Pr., Inc.

Allen, Dale. Discover & Recover. 2008. 172p. pap. 16.99 (978-1-60791-033-6(0)) Xulon Pr., Inc.

Allen, Daryl. The Present & Coming Move of God. 2007. 108p. pap. 14.78 (978-1-4303-2931-2(9)) Lulu Enterprises Inc.

Allen, David. The Remaining Factors: Seeking Eternal Treasures. 2009. 76p. pap. 11.99 (978-1-4389-4392-3(X)) AuthorHouse.

Allen, Dennis. When You're Fifty or So. 1.05 (978-0-7673-0099-5(8)) LifeWay Christian Resources.

Allen, Diogenes. Traces of God. 25th rev. ed. 2006. 114p. per. 14.00 (978-1-59627-031-2(4)) Church Publishing, Inc.

Allen, Gary, ed. 365 Devotions. 2007. (365 Devotions Ser.). 384p. per. 7.99 (978-0-7847-2114-8(9)); per. 13.99 (978-0-7847-2115-5(7)) Standard Publishing.

Allen, Greg. Builder of the Spirit. 192p. pap. 11.99 (978-1-58169-108-5(4), Evergreen Pr.) Genesis Communications, Inc.

Allen, Horace & Russell, Joseph. On Common Ground: The Story of the Revised Common Lectionary. 112p. 12.50 (978-1-85311-219-5(4)) Norwich Bks. & Music GBR. Dist: Morehouse Publishing.

Allen, I. Fountaine. Purposefully Made. 2008. 104p. per. 14.95 (978-1-4327-1930-2(0)) Outskirts Pr., Inc.

Allen, James. The Gate & the Way. 2006. pap. 12.95 (978-1-4286-6578-1(1)) Kessinger Publishing, LLC.

—Through the Gates of Good, or Christ & Conduct. 2009. 48p. pap. 5.99 (978-1-60459-608-3(2)) Wilder Pubns., Ltd.

Allen, John L., Jr. 10 Things Pope Benedict XVI Wants You to Know. 2007. 45p. per. 2.95 (978-0-7648-1672-7(1)) Liguori Pubns.

Allen-Johnson, Angela. My View of God's Tapestry: The Road Less Traveled. 2009. 174p. pap. 14.95 (978-1-4327-4689-6(8)) Outskirts Pr., Inc.

Allen, Julie. When Your Partner Doesn't Know Jesus. 2006. 93p. pap. (978-1-903725-78-8(X)) New Wine Pr.

Allen, Lanny. Lord of My Life. 12.00 (978-0-7673-0761-1(5), LifeWay Christian Resources.

Allen, Matthew. Devotional Lectures on the Graces, Purity, Strength & Happiness Of. 2007. (ENG.). 468p. per. 37.95 (978-1-4304-4601-9(3)) Kessinger Publishing, LLC.

Allen, Michael. It Is Not about Us: A Book for the Maturing Christian. 2011. 96p. pap. 9.95 **(978-1-4497-2566-2(X)**, WestBow Pr.) Author Solutions, Inc.

Allen, Stowe H. God's Little Baptist Boy: A Memoir. 2011. pap. 14.99 (978-1-61739-582-6(X)) Tate Publishing & Enterprises, LLC.

Allen, Valerie. I Am Inspired: The Beginning. 2009. 50p. pap. 12.95 (978-1-4327-2904-2(7)) Outskirts Pr., Inc.

Allen, William J. Fractured Fellowships: Or, How the Church Lost its First Love. 2010. 236p. pap. 17.95 (978-1-4497-0223-6(6), WestBow Pr.) Author Solutions, Inc.

Allender, Dan B. To Be Told: Know Your Story, Shape Your Future. 2006. (ENG.). 240p. pap. 14.99 (978-1-57856-951-9(6), WaterBrook Pr.) Doubleday Religious Publishing Group, The.

Allender, Dan B. & Longman, Tremper, III. Breaking the Idols of Your Heart: How to Navigate the Temptations of Life. 2007. (ENG.). 191p. per. 15.00 (978-0-8308-3441-9(9), IVP Bks.) InterVarsity Pr.

Allman, Mark J. & Winright, Tobias L. After the Smoke Clears: The Just War Tradition & Post War Justice. 2010. 232p. pap. 20.00 (978-1-57075-859-1(X)) Orbis Bks.

Allman, Summer. On the Night He Was Betrayed. 2010. 16p. 12.99 (978-1-4490-8694-7(2)) AuthorHouse.

Alman, Ann Marie. Confronting the Spirit of Religion. 2008. 164p. pap. 13.99 (978-1-60647-078-7(7)) Xulon Pr., Inc.

Almighty, God. Simple. 2010. 76p. pap. 12.99 (978-1-4490-4097-0(7)) AuthorHouse.

Almquist, Beth, et al. Growing in God's Way: Weekly Meeting Plans for Voyager Leaders. 2007. (J). 19.95 (978-0-9743503-3-2(8)) Pioneer Clubs.

Alonso, Heriberto. Blessed, Balanced & Complete. 2008. 208p. 25.99 (978-1-60647-677-2(7)); pap. 15.99 (978-1-60647-676-5(9)) Xulon Pr., Inc.

Alsdorf, Debbie. A Different Kind of Wild: Is Your Faith Too Tame? 2009. 207p. pap. 12.99 (978-0-8007-3366-7(5)) Revell.

—He Is My Freedom: Living the Promise of a Changed Life. 2008. (Design4Living Ser.). (ENG.). 208p. pap. 14.99 (978-1-4347-6787-5(6)) Cook, David C.

—He Is My Life: Living to Love Others as Jesus Did. 2008. (Design4Living Ser.). (ENG.). 192p. pap. 12.99 (978-1-4347-6788-2(4)) Cook, David C.

Alsdorf, Debbie & Alsdorf, Ray. Beyond the Brady Bunch: Hope & Help for Blended Families, 1 vol. 2010. (ENG.). 240p. pap. 14.99 (978-1-4347-6645-8(4)) Cook, David C.

Alsobrook, David. You Can Be Free from Your SELF: The Grace of Soul Transformation. 2010. 248p. pap. 16.95 (978-1-4327-5987-2(6)) Outskirts Pr., Inc.

Alsobrook, W. Aubrey. A Religious Columnist Speaks. 2007. 52p. per. 9.95 (978-1-57736-383-5(3)) Providence Hse Pubs.

Alspach, J. A. The Veil: Inspirational Life Story of Esther Turner. 2009. 80p. pap. 10.99 (978-1-60791-186-9(8)) Xulon Pr., Inc.

Altrogge, Stephen. Game Day for the Glory of God: A Guide for Athletes, Fans, & Wannabes. 2008. (Illus.). 128p. pap. 9.99 (978-1-4335-0139-5(2)) Crossway.

Alvarez, Manuel Díaz. Antonio de Padua, San.Tr. of St. Anthony of Padua. (SPA.). 136p. pap. 5.95 (978-980-350-253-9(0)) Sociedad de San Pablo VEN. Dist: St Pauls/Alba Hse. Pubs.

Amankwah, Yaw. Wise Thoughts for Understanding & Joy: The Serenity in Practical Biblical Self-Counselling & Direction. 2009. 152p. pap. 11.99 (978-1-4389-2817-3(3)) AuthorHouse.

Amariah, Esther. Mercy & Grace: Victory Through Hardships. 2011. 188p. 30.95 **(978-1-4497-1539-7(7))**; pap. 13.95 **(978-1-4497-1538-0(9))** Author Solutions, Inc. (WestBow Pr.).

Amata, Jean & Burnett, Teresa. Apocalypse of the Soul: Facing the End of Your Days & Maybe, the End of the World. 2010. 172p. 22.95 (978-1-4490-6445-7(0)) AuthorHouse.

Ambrose, Ubong Afiaowo. Mortal Gods: The Stars & the Laboratory. 2011. 426p. pap. 29.95 **(978-1-4626-1239-0(3))** PublishAmerica, Inc.

American Bible Society Staff. The Essential Study Bible: Everything You Need for a Deeper Understanding of the Bible. 2011. (ENG.). 1888p. (gr. 12-18). 19.95 (978-1-58542-736-9(5), Tarcher) Penguin Group (USA) Inc.

Amerman, Pastor Pete. Fired Up! The Church in the Book of Acts. 2008. 305p. pap. 29.95 (978-1-4241-7576-5(3)) PublishAmerica, Inc.

Amerson, Melvin & Amerson, James. Celebrating the Offering. 2008. 108p. per. 12.00 (978-0-88177-526-6(6)) Discipleship Resources.

Amesbury, Richard & Newlands, George M. Faith & Human Rights: Christianity & the Global Struggle for Human Dignity. 2008. (Facets Ser.). 166p. per. 9.99 (978-0-8006-2132-2(8), Fortress Pr.) Augsburg Fortress, Pubs.

Amplaw, Alex. You've Got to Hear from God & It's Not Cheap. 2007. 216p. per. 14.99 (978-1-59781-613-7(2)) Xulon Pr., Inc.

Amritzer, Johannes. How Jesus Healed the Sick: And How You Can Too! 2008. pap. 14.99 (978-88-89127-62-9(7)) Destiny Image Europe ITA. Dist: Destiny Image Pubs.

Anastasi, Gasper. Stop Hurting, Start Healing. 2010. (ENG.). pap. 14.99 (978-0-7684-3251-0(0)) Destiny Image Pubs.

Anaya-Aragon, Donna Marie. My Second Chance... At Living My Life the Way That God Wanted Me to the First Time Around. 2009. 60p. pap. 10.99 (978-1-60791-338-2(0)) Xulon Pr., Inc.

Andersen, Roger D. The Executive Calling: Corporate Success Without Selling Your Soul. 2008. (ENG.). 240p. 19.99 (978-1-59979-346-7(6), Creation Hse.) Charisma Media.

Anderson, Brian & Whitwer, Glynnis. The Character of God: Understanding His heart for Us. 2007. 96p. per. 7.99 (978-0-9786394-3-3(X)) Ampelon Publishing, LLC.

—Six Habits of Highly Effective Christians. 2007. 96p. per. 7.99 (978-0-9786394-2-6(1)) Ampelon Publishing, LLC.

—Small Group in a Box Volume #1: Worship: Nearing the Heart of God. 2007. 75.00 (978-0-9798104-6-6(9)) Ampelon Publishing, LLC.

—Small Group in a Box Volume #2: Six Habits of Highly Effective Christians. 2007. 75.00 (978-0-9798104-7-3(7)) Ampelon Publishing, LLC.

—Small Group in a Box Volume #3: The Character of God. 2007. 75.00 (978-0-9798104-8-0(5)) Ampelon Publishing, LLC.

—Small Group in a Box Volume #4: Welcome to Community. 2007. 75.00 (978-0-9798104-9-7(3)) Ampelon Publishing, LLC.

—Welcome to Community: Experiencing life the way God Intended. 2007. 96p. per. 7.99 (978-0-9786394-4-0(8), 5,000) Ampelon Publishing, LLC.

Anderson, C. Thomas. Too Much Money God's Way: How Much Is Too Much? 2009. pap. 20.00 (978-1-58588-159-8(7)) Winword Publishing.

Anderson, Dave. How to Run Your Business by the Book: A Biblical Blueprint to Bless Your Business. 2nd rev. expurg. ed. 2011. (ENG.). 252p. pap. 18.95 (978-1-118-02237-5(8), Wiley) Wiley, John & Sons, Inc.

Anderson, Dean. A Sacred Trust: Sermons on the Distinctive Beliefs of Baptists. 2010. 172p. 29.99 (978-1-61507-132-6(6)); pap. 14.99 (978-1-61507-068-8(0)) Cross Bks. Publishing.

Anderson, Elder Richard C. After the Call: The Life of the Minister. 2011. 98p. pap. 15.99 **(978-1-4628-6033-3(8))** Xlibris Corp.

Anderson, Larry. Raptured Alive: Return of A Prodigcal Son. 2007. 152p. per. 14.95 (978-1-4327-1363-8(9)) Outskirts Pr., Inc.

Anderson, Leith. How to Act Like a Christian. 2006. (Illus.). 153p. per. 12.00 (978-0-687-33555-8(8)) Abingdon Pr.

Anderson, Leith & Collison, Dan. How to Act Like a Christian: Leader's Guide. 2006. (Illus.). 134p. pap., ldr.'s planning gde. ed. 30.00 (978-0-687-33565-7(5)) Abingdon Pr.

Anderson, Mark. Humility: The Hidden Key to Walking in Signs & Wonders. 2010. (ENG.). pap. 14.99 (978-0-7684-3252-7(9)) Destiny Image Pubs.

Anderson, N. Asesoramiento Que Discipula.Tr. of Discipleship Counselling. (SPA.). wbk. ed. 1.99 (978-0-7899-0575-8(2), 497649) Editorial Unilit.

—El Dios Imponente.Tr. of Awesome God. 8.99 (978-0-7899-0319-8(9), 497647) Editorial Unilit.

Anderson, N. & Mylander, Charles. Los Pasos para Libertar a Su Iglesia.Tr. of Steps to Setting Your Church Free. (SPA.). 1.99 (978-0-7899-0423-2(3), 493784) Editorial Unilit.

Anderson, Neil T. Breaking Through to Spiritual Maturity. (Aglow Bible Study Ser.). 150p. pap. 17.00 (978-0-8307-2655-4(1), Gospel Light) Gospel Light Pubns.

—The Core of Christianity: Rediscovering Authentic Unity & Personal Wholeness in Christ. l.t. ed. 2010. (ENG.). pap. 17.99 (978-1-59415-310-5(8)) Cengage Gale.

—The Core of Christianity: Rediscovering Authentic Unity & Personal Wholeness in Christ. 2010. 240p. pap. 14.99 (978-0-7369-2506-8(6)) Harvest Hse. Pubs.

—Freedom from Bondage. Date not set. (Bondage Breaker Ser.). 100p. pap. 7.99 (978-0-7369-1183-2(9)) Harvest Hse. Pubs.

Anderson, Neil T., et al. Walking in Freedom: 21 Day Devotional to Help Establish Your Freedom in Christ. 2009. (ENG.). 224p. pap. 14.99 (978-0-8307-4718-4(4)) Gospel Light Pubns.

Anderson, Niki. Whiskers, Wit & Wisdom: True Cat Tales & the Lessons They Teach. 2009. (ENG., Illus.). 192p. 15.99 (978-1-4165-9068-2(4), Howard Bks.) Howard Books.

Anderson, Phil. The Lord of the Ring: In Search of Count von Zinzendorf. 2007. (ENG.). 192p. per. 14.99 (978-0-8307-4327-8(8)) Gospel Light Pubns.

Anderson, Ray S. The Seasons of Hope: Empowering Faith Through the Practice of Hope. 2008. (Ray S. Anderson Collection Ser.). (Illus.). 164p. pap. 19.00 (978-1-55635-814-2(8)) Wipf & Stock Pubs.

Anderson, Ray S. Soulprints. 2011. (Ray S. Anderson Collection Ser.). 196p. pap. 23.00 **(978-1-61097-133-1(7)**, Wipf and Stock) Wipf & Stock Pubs.

Anderson, Russell F. Lectionary Preaching Workbook: Series V, Cycle B. 2008. (Lectionary Preaching Workbook Ser.). 420p. pap. 49.95 (978-0-7880-2574-7(0)) CSS Publishing Co.

Anderson, Shawn D. Living Dangerously: Seven Keys to Intentional Discipleship. 2010. 166p. pap. 19.00 (978-1-60608-547-9(6), Wipf and Stock) Wipf & Stock Pubs.

Anderson, Sonya T. The Pride of Life. 2007. 96p. pap. 11.99 (978-0-615-15235-6(X)) Claymaker Publishing House.

Anderson, Tom & Anderson, Maureen. A Marriage Beyond the Dream. 2010. (ENG.). 242p. pap. 16.99 (978-1-58588-987-7(3)) Winword Publishing.

Anderson, Vivi. And He Walks with Me. 2011. 244p. pap. 15.99 **(978-1-61379-301-5(4))** Xulon Pr., Inc.

—And he Walks with Me. 2011. 246p. **(978-1-61379-073-1(2))** Xulon Pr., Inc.

Anderson, Winston. Holy Water: You can Lead a Horse to Water but you can't make him Drink. 2008. 312p. per. 14.95 (978-1-59800-911-8(7)) Outskirts Pr., Inc.

Andrew, Kevin. One Answer. 2007. 72p. per. 12.09 (978-1-4251-0533-4(5)) Trafford Publishing.

Andrew Murray. The Master's Indwelling. 2009. 108p. pap. 4.95 (978-1-60386-216-5(1), Merchant Bks.) Rough Draft Printing.

Andrewes, Lancelot. Works, 11 vols. reprint ed. 1375.00 (978-0-7222-2169-3(X)) Library Reprints, Inc.

Andrews, Jim. Polishing God's Monuments: Pillars of Hope for Punishing Times. 2007. 296p. per. 14.95 (978-0-9767582-7-3(X)) Shepherd Pr. Inc.

Andrews McMeel Publishing Staff, creator. The Little Book of Church Signs. 2008. (ENG., Illus.). 144p. pap. 5.99 (978-0-7407-7237-5(6)) Andrews McMeel Publishing.

Andrews Sr., James R. Your Sons & Daughters Shall Prophesy. 1 vol. 2009. 48p. pap. 16.95 (978-1-60749-277-1(6)) PublishAmerica, Inc.

Andria R. Smith. Guidance from the Heart: A Christian Resource Guide for Young People. 2010. 200p. pap. 16.95 (978-0-595-48267-2(8)) iUniverse, Inc.

Andringa, Susan. The Esteemed Journey: Leader Kit: Discovering Your Full Worth in Christ. 2007. 29.99 (978-5-557-54487-0(9)) Group Publishing, Inc.

Andringa, Susan L. The Esteemed Journey: Guidebook: Discovering Your Full Worth in Christ. 2007. (Illus.). 62p. pap. 9.99 (978-0-7644-3559-1(0)) Group Publishing, Inc.

Andry, Duane. Blogosphere Madness 2010: More Ravings of a Religious Fanatic 2009: Dogmasphere. 2010. 296p. spiral bd. (978-0-9798444-0-9(1)) Andry, Duane & Assocs.

—The Great Consolidation: Reconciling the Family of God. 2007. 390p. spiral bd. (978-0-9798444-2-3(8)) Andry, Duane & Assocs.

—Reconciliation: The Children of Abraham. 2007. 531p. 48.95 (978-0-9798444-1-6(X)) Andry, Duane & Assocs.

Andry, Kimberly. A Time to Live: Surviving Suicidal Thoughts. 2007. 240p. per. 15.95 (978-1-4327-0430-8(3)) Outskirts Pr., Inc.

Angel, Sue. Here Comes the Bride. 2010. 248p. pap. 15.99 (978-1-60957-308-9(0)) Xulon Pr., Inc.

Angelo, Virji. The News from the Master. 2008. 112p. pap. 11.99 (978-1-60647-627-7(0)) Xulon Pr., Inc.

Angier, Ida M. Life - Frustration or Fulfillment: Enjoying the Beauty of God. 2009. 108p. pap. 11.99 (978-1-60791-657-4(6)) Xulon Pr., Inc.

Angier, Peter. Foundations for Life-Long Significance. 2007. 96p. per. 9.99 (978-1-60477-307-1(3)) Xulon Pr., Inc.

Angier, Peter B. Rough Waters, Polished Stones: Victorious Living Based on Biblical Truths. 2008. pap. 10.99 (978-1-60647-076-3(0)) Xulon Pr., Inc.

Angove, Nancy. The Chocolate Cake Principle. 2007. 128p. per. 13.99 (978-1-60266-132-5(4)) Xulon Pr., Inc.

Ann, Froelichm Mary & Chambers, Oswald. Hope: A Holy Promise. 2009. (ENG.). 176p. 12.99 (978-1-57293-308-8(9)) Discovery Hse. Pubs.

Anónimo & Lardon. El Puente de la Vida: The Bridge of Life. (SPA.). 64p. (978-84-7228-703-7(3), 220732) Clie, Editorial.

Anonymous. Cosmic Pandect. 2010. 104p. pap. 13.95 (978-1-4461-9506-2(6)) Lulu Enterprises Inc.

—In Search of an Earthly Sanctuary with Fodder. 2009. 84p. pap. 10.99 (978-1-60791-535-5(9)) Xulon Pr., Inc.

Ansdell, Allan & Ansdell, Yvonne. 1001 Things You Should Know Before You Die. 2008. 201p. per. 13.99 (978-0-88270-470-8(2), Bridge-Logos) Bridge-Logos Foundation.

Ansell, Dave. R. U. N. for Life. 2008. (ENG.). 160p. pap. 12.95 (978-0-9817608-2-7(1)) Lifebridge Bks.

Ansinger, Leisa & Shepp, Victoria. Forming Generous Hearts: Stewardship Planning for Lifelong Faith Formation. 2007. 146p. per. 14.95 (978-1-58595-542-5(2)) Twenty-Third Pubns./Bayard.

Anthony, Gavin. The Refiner's Fire: In All Things, God Works for Good. 2007. (978-0-8280-2007-7(8)) Review & Herald Publishing Assn.

Anthony, Wayne. I've Given My Life to God, Now What? 2011. 60p. pap. 12.10 **(978-1-4567-7025-9(X))** AuthorHouse.

Antoinette, Christy. Children of the Water: Venture into Another World & Become Who You Were Born to Be. 2009. 157p. pap. 12.99 (978-1-60696-647-1(2)) Tate Publishing & Enterprises, LLC.

Antonakos, John. Life's Objective. 2009. 328p. pap. 22.99 (978-1-4490-1439-1(9)) AuthorHouse.

Antonation, Kelly. 12 Stones & Borrowed Stones. Dewey, Sadie ed. 2011. 88p. **(978-1-77067-272-7(9))**; pap. **(978-1-77067-273-4(7))** FriesenPress.

Antonucci, Vince. Guerrilla Lovers: Changing the World with Revolutionary Compassion, 1 vol. 2010. (ENG.). 256p. pap. 14.99 *(978-0-8010-6816-4(9))* Baker Bks.

Antrim, Patrick. White Collar. 2009. 48p. pap. 12.99 *(978-1-61579-072-2(1))* Xulon Pr., Inc.

Antwi, Paul. Why Is Satan Against Christians? Proverbs 4:16 ? 1Peter 5:8. 2011. 172p. pap. 12.99 ***(978-1-4634-4237-8(8))*** AuthorHouse.

Anyabwile, Thabiti M. Holy, Holy, Holy: Proclaiming the Perfections of God. 2010. *(978-1-56769-205-1(2))* Reformation Pubs.

Apostle Rudolph S. Johnson, Sr. The Power of Forgiveness: The Glory of Christianity Is to Conquer by Forgiveness. 2009. 64p. pap. 10.49 *(978-1-4389-5986-3(9))* AuthorHouse.

Appel, Dan M. The Choice: Brenda's Husband Had Been Dead Almost a Year. Then He Came Back. 2008. 215p. pap. 14.99 *(978-0-8127-0463-1(0))* Review & Herald Publishing Assn.

Applegate, Scott. Noblesse Oblige: Spending Your Life on What Matters Most. 2009. pap. 10.99 *(978-1-60696-634-1(0))* Tate Publishing & Enterprises, LLC.

Apprehended by God. Date not set. 32p. per. 3.00 *(978-1-890820-00-8(8))* Battlecry Pr.

Arceneaux, Kitty. Yo' God! Can Ya' Hear Me? 2006. pap. 9.99 *(978-1-60034-402-2(X))* Xulon Pr., Inc.

Archer, Antoinette. And I Saw Heaven. 2006. pap. 13.99 *(978-1-60034-709-2(6))* Xulon Pr., Inc.

—The Art of War, Experiencing Victory Aganist Your Spiritual Adversary. 2007. 120p. per. 10.99 *(978-1-60266-007-6(7))* Xulon Pr., Inc.

Archie, Stan. Beyond Purpose: A Greater Understanding of Your Identity in Christ. 2010. 188p. pap. 49.95 *(978-1-4327-5326-9(6))* Outskirts Pr., Inc.

Are You Practicing What You Preach? If Not, Here's Something to Live By. 2006. per. 18.00 *(978-0-615-13344-7(4))* Ahsrat Publishing, LLC.

Arekion, Glenn. The Blood of Favor. 2006. 176p. pap. 14.99 *(978-88-89127-29-2(5))* Destiny Image Europe ITA. Dist: Destiny Image Pubs.

Argudo, Juan M. Yo y la Gran Comision: Great Comission & Me. (SPA.). 112p. *(978-84-7228-938-3(9),* 223015) Clie, Editorial.

Arillotta, Richard. Possessing All in Christ. 2007. 456p. (ENG.). 35.99 *(978-1-60266-130-1(8))*; per. 23.99 *(978-1-60266-129-5(4))* Xulon Pr., Inc.

Arinze, Cardinal Francis. Meeting Jesus & Following Him. 2010. 120p. pap. 12.95 *(978-1-58617-423-1(1))* Ignatius Pr.

Aristizabal, Otty Ossa. Apariciones de la V. M. En Betania. 112p. 3.95 *(978-980-350-111-2(9))* Sociedad de San Pablo VEN. Dist: St Pauls/Alba Hse. Pubs.

Arite, Michael D. God Isn't Finished Yet: The Journey He Has Taken Me On. 2011. 140p. 28.95 ***(978-1-61507-713-7(8))***; pap. 11.95 ***(978-1-61507-712-0(X))*** Cross Bks. Publishing.

Armbrecht, Doug, compiled by. Quiet Time Prepack for Families (Quiet Time Devotionals). 21. 2007. (Illus.). (YA). per. 347.79 *(978-1-931235-63-1(5),* gbookpack) Word of Life Fellowship, Inc.

Armistead, Kathy. How God Takes Our Little & Makes it Much Leaders Guide. 2010. 70p. pap. 11.00 *(978-1-4267-0879-4(3))* Abingdon Pr.

Armstrong, Beverly. Delivered by Grace. 2007. 268p. per. 14.95 *(978-0-9779445-5-2(7))* Zoe Life Publishing.

Armstrong, Bill. Musings from the Mountaintop. 2008. 176p. pap. 13.95 *(978-1-59330-543-7(5))* Aventine Pr.

Armstrong, Dave. Development of Catholic Doctrine: Evolution, Revolution, or an Organic Process? 2007. 204p. per. 16.95 *(978-1-4303-2106-4(7))* Lulu Enterprises Inc.

Armstrong, Holly. More of His Presence: Understanding the More That God Has for Your Everyday Life. 2007. 152p. (ENG.). 24.95 *(978-0-595-70736-2(X))*; per. 14.95 *(978-0-595-46171-4(9))* iUniverse, Inc.

Armstrong, Jerry. It's All Yours, Lord: A Family's Journey of Purpose & Hope. 2010. 26.99 *(978-1-61579-781-3(5))*; 288p. pap. 16.99 *(978-1-61579-780-6(7))* Xulon Pr., Inc.

Armstrong, Karen. The Case for God: What Religion Really Means. (ENG.). 432p. 2010. pap. 16.95 *(978-0-307-38980-0(4),* Anchor) 2009. 27.95 *(978-0-307-26918-8(3),* Knopf) Knopf Doubleday Publishing Group.

Armstrong, Kristin. Work in Progress: An Unfinished Woman's Guide to Grace. 2009. (ENG.). 240p. 18.99 *(978-0-446-19800-4(5))* FaithWords.

Arnaudova, Elena. Growing in the Fruit of the Holy Spirit: No Subtitle. 2008. 96p. pap. 9.99 *(978-1-60647-639-0(4))* Xulon Pr., Inc.

Arnold, David. Manual de Discipulado. 2008. (SPA.). 112p. pap. 9.95 *(978-1-58802-411-4(3))* Editorial Patmos.

—Why Do Bad Things Happen to Good People? Answers to One of Life's Greatest Moral Questions. 2008. (ENG.). 88p. pap. 7.99 *(978-1-59979-485-3(3),* Creation Hse.) Charisma Media.

Arnold, Heini. Discipleship: Living for Christ in the Daily Grind. 2011. ***(978-0-87486-876-0(9))***; ***(978-978-087-486-5(0))*** Plough Publishing Hse.

Arnold, Johann Christoff. Why Forgive? 2010. (Illus.). 232p. pap. 18.00 *(978-1-57075-876-8(X))* Orbis Bks.

Arnold, Rochelle. Sojourners. 2007. 156p. per. 13.99 *(978-1-60266-567-5(2))* Xulon Pr., Inc.

Arnold, Thomas. The Christian Life: Its Course, Its Hindrances, & Its Helps. 2006. (ENG.). 326p. pap. 23.99 *(978-1-4264-6780-6(X))* 2007. 366p. pap. 26.99 *(978-1-4264-6843-8(1))* BiblioBazaar.

Arpin-Ricci, C.J., Jamie, Jamie. The Cost of Community: Jesus, St. Francis & Life in the Kingdom. 2011. (ENG.). 237p. pap. 16.00 ***(978-0-8308-3635-2(7),*** IVP Bks.) InterVarsity Pr.

Arquidiocesis de Cali Staff. Sacramento de la Confirmacion (The Sacrament of Confirmation) (SPA.). 112p. pap. 3.95 *(978-958-607-759-0(4))* Sociedad de San Pablo COL. Dist: St Pauls/Alba Hse. Pubs.

Arterburn, Stephen & Cherry, Debra. Feeding Your Appetites: Take Control of What's Controlling You!, 0 vols. 2007. (Illus.). 224p. per. 14.99 *(978-0-7852-8924-1(0))* Nelson, Thomas Inc.

Arterburn, Stephen & Shore, John. Being Christian: Exploring Where You, God, & Life Connect. 2009. 240p. pap. 13.99 *(978-0-7642-0640-5(0))* Bethany Hse. Pubs.

—Regret-Free Living: Hope for Past Mistakes & Freedom from Unhealthy Patterns. 2009. 240p. 17.99 *(978-0-7642-0424-1(6))* Bethany Hse. Pubs.

Arterburn, Stephen & Stoop, David. The Life Recovery Journal: Becoming a New You - One Step at a Time. 2009. (ENG.). 128p. pap. 9.99 *(978-1-4143-2823-2(0))* Tyndale Hse. Pubs.

Arterburn, Stephen, et al. Being Christian: Exploring Where You, God, & Life Connect. 2009. 160p. pap., wbk. ed. 9.99 *(978-0-7642-0677-1(X))* Bethany Hse. Pubs.

Arthur, James P. God Deserves Our Worship: The Prelude Book 1. 2010. pap. 23.99 *(978-1-61566-756-7(3))* Tate Publishing & Enterprises, LLC.

Arthur, Kay. Comfort Me O God. 2011. 288p. pap. 13.99 *(978-0-7369-3920-1(2))* Harvest Hse. Pubs.

—Discovering What the Future Holds. 2009. (40-Minute Bible Studies). (ENG., Illus.). 112p. pap. 7.99 *(978-0-307-45758-5(3),* WaterBrook Pr.) Doubleday Religious Publishing Group, The.

—Having a Real Relationship with God. 2009. (40-Minute Bible Studies). (ENG., Illus.). 64p. pap. 7.99 *(978-0-307-45760-8(5),* WaterBrook Pr.) Doubleday Religious Publishing Group, The.

—How Do You Walk the Walk You Talk? 2009. (40-Minute Bible Studies). (ENG.). 64p. pap. 7.99 *(978-0-307-45763-9(X),* WaterBrook Pr.) Doubleday Religious Publishing Group, The.

—What Happens When We Die? Date not set. 96p. 9.99 *(978-0-7369-1072-9(7))* Harvest Hse. Pubs.

—When the Hurt Runs Deep: Healing & Hope for Life's Desperate Moments. 2010. (ENG.). 256p. 22.99 *(978-0-307-45711-0(7),* WaterBrook Pr.) Doubleday Religious Publishing Group, The.

Arthur, Kay, et al, contrib. by. Faithful Abundant True Weekend Retreat & Study Guide: Three Lives Going Deeper Still. 2010. (Faithful, Abundant, True Ser.). (Illus.). 155p. pap. *(978-1-4158-6898-0(0))* LifeWay Christian Resources.

Arthur, Kay, et al. Living Like You Belong to God. 2009. (40-Minute Bible Studies). (ENG.). 96p. pap. 7.99 *(978-0-307-45866-7(0),* WaterBrook Pr.) Doubleday Religious Publishing Group, The.

—Loving God & Others: the Heart of True Faith. 2009. (40-Minute Bible Studies). (ENG.). 96p. pap. 7.99 *(978-0-307-45868-1(7),* WaterBrook Pr.) Doubleday Religious Publishing Group, The.

Arthur, T. S. Steps Towards Heaven or, Religion in Common Life: a Series of Lay. 2007. (ENG.). 408p. per. 34.95 *(978-1-4304-4358-2(8))* Kessinger Publishing, LLC.

Arthur, T. S. (Timothy Shay). Steps Towards Heaven; or, Religion in Common Life a Series of Lay Sermons for Converts in the Great Awakening by T S Arthur. 2006. 408p. per. 26.99 *(978-1-4255-4360-0(X))* MPublishing.

Arzave, Jose J. Rabbit the Baker. 2011. 18p. pap. 15.99 *(978-1-61215-448-0(4))* Xulon Pr., Inc.

... as a tale that Is Told. 2006. pap. 13.99 *(978-1-60034-188-5(8))* Xulon Pr., Inc.

Ash, Christopher. Listen Up! A Practical Guide to Listening to Sermons. 2010. 32p. pap. *(978-1-906334-67-3(6))* Good Bk. Co.

Ashburn Jr., Thomas. God's Greater Glory. 2008. 132p. pap. 14.99 *(978-1-60647-849-3(4))* Xulon Pr., Inc.

Ashley, Kenny. Waterholes in the Wilderness. 2007. 304p. per. 17.99 *(978-1-60266-716-7(0))* Xulon Pr., Inc.

Ashton, Linda D. Faith Through Dark Days. 2009. 68p. pap. *(978-1-55452-341-2(9))* Essence Publishing.

Ashuah, Dror B. Conversation with Angels. 2008. 380p. pap. 21.00 *(978-0-9798828-8-3(5),* Epigraph Bks.) Monkfish Bk. Publishing Co.

Ashurst, April Ashley. The Art of Perception: Why Settle When You Can Have It All? 2010. pap. 14.99 *(978-1-61579-875-9(7))* Xulon Pr., Inc.

Ashwin, Angela. Woven into Prayer: A Flexible Pattern of Daily Prayer Through the Christian Year. (Illus.). 224p. 22.95 *(978-1-85311-247-8(X))* Norwich Bks. & Music GBR. Dist: Morehouse Publishing.

Asomugha, Lilian I. The Advent of a New Hope. 2010. 184p. pap. 14.99 *(978-1-60957-536-6(9))* Xulon Pr., Inc.

Assoc for Hispanic Theological Education. Introduccion a la Unidad Cristiana: Introduction to Christian Unity Spanish. 2011. 112p. pap. 20.00 *(978-0-687-66063-6(7))* Abingdon Pr.

—Introduccion a las Disciplinas Espirituales AETH: Introduction to the Spiritual Disciplines Spanish. 2008. 128p. pap. 20.00 *(978-0-687-65580-9(3))* Abingdon Pr.

Astley. Learning Christ in the Ordinary Way. 2007. pap. *(978-0-281-05880-8(6))* SPCK Publishing.

Astley, Jeff. Choosing Life? Christianity & Moral Problems. (Exploring Faith Ser.). 160p. *(978-0-232-52368-3(1))* Darton, Longman & Todd, Ltd.

Aston, John. Set Free. 4.95 *(978-962-7329-02-2(9))* Living Bks. For All HKG. Dist: CLC Pubns.

Asumang, Annang. Immigrants of the Kingdom of God: Reflections on Immigration as a Metaphor of Christian Discipleship. 2008. 122p. pap. 15.00 *(978-1-55635-829-6(6),* Wipf and Stock) Wipf & Stock Pubs.

Atamian, Robyn Louise. The Cosmic Unfoldment. 2010. 88p. pap. 9.95 *(978-1-4497-0212-0(0),* WestBow Pr.) Author Solutions, Inc.

Atchinson, Glenn A. A Sliver of Light Out of Darkness: Gathering Truth Through Life Stories. 2008. 80p. pap. 8.95 *(978-0-595-53253-7(5))* iUniverse, Inc.

Atherstone, Andrew. Heart of Faith: Following Christ in the Church of England. 2008. (ENG.). 180p. pap. 33.00 *(978-0-7188-3072-4(5))* Lutherworth Pr., The GBR. Dist: Brown, David Bk. Co., The.

Atherton, John. Christianity & the Market. 304p. 22.00 *(978-0-281-04603-4(4))* SPCK Publishing GBR. Dist: Pilgrim Pr., The/United Church Pr.

Atkinson, Marie. Ugly Mask: Beautiful You! 2011. 114p. pap. 19.95 ***(978-1-4626-0936-9(8))*** PublishAmerica, Inc.

Atteberry, Mark. Let It Go: Come Home from Your Guilt Trip. 2010. (ENG.). 160p. pap. 12.99 *(978-0-7847-2364-7(8))* Standard Publishing.

—The 10 Dumbest Things Christians Do, 0 vols. 2006. 224p. per. 13.99 *(978-0-7852-1148-8(9))* Nelson, Thomas Inc.

Aturu, Ola. The Prayer Complement. 2008. 104p. pap. 10.99 *(978-1-60647-551-5(7))* Xulon Pr., Inc.

Atwood, Dennis. Words that Shape & Form: A 40-Day Journey in Spiritual Formation. 2008. 140p. spiral bd. 7.95 *(978-0-9795847-2-5(8))* Cooperative Baptist Fellowship.

Aubrecht, Michael. The Southern Cross: A Civil War Devotional. 2008. 192p. pap. 19.99 *(978-0-9796000-1-2(4))* Patriot Pr.

Aubrey, Roger. The Circle of Life. 2007. 128p. per. 13.99 *(978-1-60266-185-1(5))* Xulon Pr., Inc.

Aubrey, Roger. Stars & Sand - a View of Life. 2011. 190p. pap. ***(978-1-908105-77-6(1))*** Grosvenor Hse. Publishing Ltd.

Auch, Ron & Niforatos, Dean. The Jesus Sensitive Church: Where Would Jesus Worship? 2006. 166p. per. 12.99 *(978-0-89221-657-4(3))* New Leaf Pr., Inc.

Auditor, Chantel. Butterfly Kisses. 2008. 58p. pap. 22.78 *(978-0-557-01263-3(5))* Lulu Enterprises Inc.

—Ribbons in the Sky. 2008. 49p. pap. 20.08 *(978-0-557-00367-9(9))* Lulu Enterprises Inc.

Augustin, J. Kendall. God's Blueprint for Life. 2007. 144p. per. *(978-1-55452-152-4(1),* Guardian Bks.) Essence Publishing.

Augustine & Ramsey, Boniface. Trilogy on Faith & Happiness. 2010. pap. *(978-1-56548-359-0(6))* New City Community Pr.

Augustine, Peg & LOPEZ, Pedro. Promice of Easter. 2009. 16p. pap. 3.00 *(978-1-4267-0036-1(9))* Abingdon Pr.

Augustine, Saint. The St. Augustine Lifeguide: Words to Live by from the Great Christian Saint. 2006. (LAT & ENG.). 70p. per. 5.00 *(978-1-58731-756-9(7))* St. Augustine's Pr., Inc.

Augustine, Sue. Sanity Secrets for Stressed-Out Women: Energize & Renew Your Life. 2009. (Illus.). 288p. pap. 12.99 *(978-0-7369-2417-7(5))* Harvest Hse. Pubs.

Aurich, Pastor L. H. What's in a Name? 2008. 217p. pap. 24.95 *(978-1-60610-379-1(2))* PublishAmerica, Inc.

Austin, Greta. Law, Theology & 'Forgery' Around the Year 1000: The Decretum of Burchard of Worms. Bolton, Brenda, ed. 2009. (Church, Faith & Culture in the Medieval West Ser.). 358p. 134.95 *(978-0-7546-5091-1(X))* Ashgate Publishing Co.

Austin, Jill. Flying Lessons. 2009. 224p. pap. 14.99 *(978-1-59979-078-7(5),* Charisma Hse.) Charisma Media.

Austin, Miles J. How Was I Supposed to Know That God Has Created a Perfect World/Universe? 2009. 240p. 19.95 *(978-1-56492-366-0(5))* Laredo Publishing Co., Inc.

Austin, Phyllis. From Parent to Power. 2008. (Illus.). 232p. per. 15.00 *(978-0-9759917-1-8(X))* Austin Reprographics.

Avant, John. The Passion Promise: Living a Life Only God Can Imagine. 2006. 176p. pap. 11.99 *(978-1-60142-044-2(7),* Multnomah) Doubleday Religious Publishing Group, The.

Avison, Margaret. A Kind of Perseverance. 2010. (ENG., Illus.). 56p. pap. 12.95 *(978-0-88984-326-4(0))* Porcupine's Quill, Inc. CAN. Dist: Univ. of Toronto Pr.

Avraham, Yisrael Ben. Kingdom Armor. 2008. 172p. pap. 14.99 *(978-1-60647-691-8(2))* Xulon Pr., Inc.

Awakening Youth Discipleship in a Commodity Culture. 16.00 *(978-0-687-05227-1(0))* Abingdon Pr.

Awasu, Wilson. The Conflict. 2008. 180p. pap. 13.99 *(978-1-60647-036-7(1))* Xulon Pr., Inc.

—Kathy's Good News. 2011. 118p. 25.95 *(978-1-4327-6935-2(9))*; pap. 10.95 *(978-1-4327-6934-5(0))* Outskirts Pr., Inc.

—Kathy's Good News: No Subtitle. 2008. 140p. pap. 13.99 *(978-1-60477-913-4(6))* Xulon Pr., Inc.

Awmi, creator. Grace: The Power of the Gospel Study Guide: the Power of the Gospel. 2007. spiral bd. 35.00 *(978-1-59548-066-8(8))* Wommack, Andrew Ministries, Inc.

AWMI, creator. Knowledge & Truth. 2006. per. 35.00 *(978-1-59548-086-6(2))* Wommack, Andrew Ministries, Inc.

Aydin, H. Numan. Events & Persecutions of Tur Abdin. 2010. (SYR.). 90.08 *(978-1-61143-198-8(0))* Gorgias Pr., LLC.

Ayers, David. Preacher's Kids on the Trail Of: Faithfulness. 2011. 28p. pap. 13.95 ***(978-1-4497-2504-4(X),*** WestBow Pr.) Author Solutions, Inc.

Ayers, Philip. A Proverb a Day Keeps the Devil Away. 2008. 380p. pap. 23.99 *(978-1-60647-844-8(3))* Xulon Pr., Inc.

AyiL. Yeshua's Choice the Ignored Gospel of JESUS the Christ: A Document of Being for Youth of the World. 2011. 136p. pap. 13.99 *(978-1-4520-5374-5(X))* AuthorHouse.

Babb, Marlene. Declarations & Decrees of a Warrior. 2008. 164p. 22.99 *(978-1-60791-080-0(2))*; pap. 14.99 *(978-1-60647-750-2(1))* Xulon Pr., Inc.

Babinsky (Editor), Joseph & Padgett (Recorder), James E. Little Book of Truths. 2009. 148p. pap. 15.95 *(978-0-557-07512-6(2))* Lulu Enterprises Inc.

Baca, Janice F. God's Healing Plan: Hope for the Emotionally & Spiritually Wounded. 2011. pap. 13.99 *(978-1-61739-681-6(8))* Tate Publishing & Enterprises, LLC.

Bach, Randy. God's Realm of Faith. 2008. 256p. per. 15.99 *(978-1-60477-431-3(2))* Xulon Pr., Inc.

Bachota Jr., Joseph. Holiness: Can the Church Do This or Not? 2009. 108p. 22.95 *(978-0-595-63615-0(2))*; pap. 12.95 *(978-0-595-52946-9(1))* iUniverse, Inc.

Backlund, Steve. Cracks in the Foundation. 2007. per. *(978-1-59872-734-0(6))* Instant Pub.

Backstrom, Joel. What it's All About! 2011. 62p. pap. 10.99 ***(978-1-61379-511-8(4))*** Xulon Pr., Inc.

Bacon, Leonard. Christian Self-Culture; or, Counsels for the Beginning & Progress of a Christian Life. 2006. 248p. per. 23.99 *(978-1-4255-2289-6(0))* MPublishing.

Bacote, Vincent, ed. Precepts for Living Annual Commentary 2008-2009. 11th rev. ed. 2008. (Precepts for Living Ser.). 512p. pap. 16.95 *(978-1-60352-329-5(4))* UMI (Urban Ministries, Inc.).

Badaki, Eunice. Thanksgiving: More than Just Turkey. 2009. 56p. pap. 9.95 *(978-1-4401-2092-3(7))* iUniverse, Inc.

Bader-Saye, Scott. Following Jesus in a Culture of Fear. 2007. (Christian Practice of Everyday Life Ser.). 172p. pap. 18.00 *(978-1-58743-192-0(0))* Brazos Pr.

Baehr, Ted. How to Succeed in Hollywood: A Field Guide for Christian Screenwriters, Actors, Producers, Directors, & More. 2011. pap. 15.95 *(978-1-936488-27-8(2))* WND Bks, Inc.

Baer, Jackson. What the Hell: How Did We Get it so Wrong? Eternity, Grace, & the Message of Love. 2011. (ENG.). 139p. pap. 14.95 ***(978-1-4327-8137-8(5))*** Outskirts Pr., Inc.

Bagby, Daniel G. Healing Our Hurts: Coping with Difficult Emotions. 2012. ***(978-1-57312-613-7(6))***; ***(978-81-573-1261-0(2))*** Smyth & Helwys Publishing, Inc.

Bagby, Josephine E. Blessings & Testings: A Twentieth Century Christian Life. 2009. 200p. pap. 14.49 *(978-1-4490-4984-3(2))* AuthorHouse.

Baggaley, Phil & Mitton, Michael. Still Small Voice. pap. *(978-1-898938-29-3(6),* Alpha) Authentic Media.

Bagster, Samuel. Daily Light. 2010. (Abridged Christian Classics Ser.). (ENG.). 192p. pap. 2.99 *(978-1-60260-858-0(X),* Barbour Bks.) Barbour Publishing, Inc.

Bah, Chalkou. The Only Way to Eternal Life. 2006. pap. 23.99 *(978-1-60034-272-1(8))* Xulon Pr., Inc.

Bahr, Patricia. Captured by Heaven. 2009. 84p. pap. 10.99 *(978-1-60791-975-9(3))* Xulon Pr., Inc.

Balden, Stephen E. In Evil Days: The Biblical Path & Power of the Righteous. 2011. 80p. 18.95 ***(978-1-4620-5352-0(1))***; pap. 8.95 ***(978-1-4620-5350-6(5))*** iUniverse, Inc.

Bailey, Dimon. The Well Within: Parables for Living & Dying. 120p. pap. *(978-0-232-52172-6(7))* South Asia Bks.

Bailey, Gene. Beyond the Ordinary: Health, Wealth, & Wisdom Strategies for Dynamic Living. 2008. 14.95 *(978-0-615-22226-4(9))* Bailey, Gene.

Bailey, H. J. Reminiscences of a Christian Life. 2007. (ENG.). 430p. 51.95 *(978-0-548-04086-7(9))* Kessinger Publishing, LLC.

Bailey, Jarvis E. Three Minutes with God: A Weekly Devotional for Inspiration & Encouragement. 2008. 236p. 25.00 *(978-1-4389-2497-7(6))*; pap. 20.00 *(978-1-4389-2496-0(8))* AuthorHouse.

Bailey, Keith M. Servants in Charge: A Training Manual for Elders & Deacons. 2007. 186p. pap. 11.99 *(978-1-60066-104-4(1))* WingSpread Publishers.

Bailey, Pat. But This I Know. 2009. 288p. pap. 15.99 *(978-0-9821835-6-4(9))* This Joy Bks.

Bailey, Roger. The Greatest Family Game: 2007. (ENG.). 184p. 21.99 *(978-1-60266-002-1(6))* Xulon Pr., Inc.

—Parking Lot Meditations. 2007. 168p. per. 13.99 *(978-1-60266-477-7(3))* Xulon Pr., Inc.

Bailey, Rosalind "Nisey". Don't Change Your Faith. 2nd ed. 2007. per. 18.95 *(978-0-9787674-5-7(4))* Aztec Bk. Publishing.

Bailey, Sandra. Called to Worship: A Lifestyle of Praise. 2007. 100p. per. 10.95 *(978-1-4327-0292-2(0))* Outskirts Pr., Inc.

Baird, James O. And I Say unto You... pap. 8.99 *(978-0-89098-120-7(5))* Twentieth Century Christian Bks.

Baker, Amy. Getting to the Heart of Friendships. 2010. 204p. pap. 13.95 *(978-1-885904-87-4(8))* Focus Publishing.

Baker, Bacer J. Smile, Laugh & Be Happy. 2011. 134p. pap. 14.99 ***(978-1-61379-239-1(5))*** Xulon Pr., Inc.

Baker, Brenda and Linda. Intimate Conversations with God Almighty. 2007. pap. 19.99 *(978-1-60034-986-7(2))* Xulon Pr., Inc.

Baker, Bruce. Spiritual Maturity: The Road to Wonderland. 2009. (ENG.). pap. 19.95 *(978-1-60265-024-4(1))* Grace Acres Pr.

Baker, C. D. 101 Cups of Water: Relief & Refreshment for the Tired, Thirsty Soul. 2008. (ENG., Illus.). 224p. 13.99 *(978-1-4000-7399-3(5))* Doubleday Religious Publishing Group, The.

Baker, Carol. Walking with Jesus. 2009. 116p. pap. 19.99 *(978-1-4415-4782-8(7))* Xlibris Corp.

Baker, Dilly. A Place at the Table: Liturgies & Resources for Christ-Centred Hospitality. 2008. (Illus.). 130p. pap. 24.99 (978-1-85311-772-5(2)) Canterbury Pr.
Baker, Ed. The Elephant in the Room. 2008. 96p. pap., wbk. ed. 9.99 (978-0-9793654-1-6(4)) First Command Inc.
—The Elephant in the Room: Sharing the Secrets for Pursuing Real Financial Success. 2007. (Illus.). 142p. 14.95 (978-0-9793654-0-9(6)) First Command Inc.
Baker, Judith Anne. Spiritual Care in Nursing: Christ Has No Hands but Ours. 2006. 112p. per. 10.95 (978-0-9727260-2-3(0)) Calvin College.
Baker, Linda Katherine. Faith Lessons in a Changing World. 2010. pap. 10.99 (978-1-61739-126-2(3)) Tate Publishing & Enterprises, LLC.
Baker, Phil J. Lessons in the Rearview Mirror: Finding Wisdom along the Journey. 2008. 192p. pap. 14.99 (978-1-60791-101-2(9)) Xulon Pr., Inc.
Baker Publishing Group Staff. All Things New: Transforming Promises from the Word of God, 1 vol. 2010. (ENG.). 144p. 9.99 (978-0-8007-1930-2(1)); im. lthr. 12.99 (978-0-8007-7178-2(8)) Revell.
—Ignite Your Faith: 365 Devotions to Set Your Faith on Fire, 1 vol. 2009. 384p. (YA). pap. 14.99 (978-0-8007-3388-9(6)) Revell.
—Moments of Peace for a Woman's Heart. 2008. 384p. 14.99 (978-0-7642-0550-7(1)) Bethany Hse. Pubs.
Baker Publishing Group Staff & Harrison, Nonna Verna. God's Many-Splendored Image: Theological Anthropology for Christian Formation, 1 vol. 2010. (ENG.). 208p. (C). pap. 24.00 (978-0-8010-3471-8(X)) Baker Academic.
Baker, Rick. I Never Knew You: Are you saved? Are you Sure? 2011. pap. 12.99 (978-1-61739-829-2(2)) Tate Publishing & Enterprises, LLC.
Baker, Rolland & Baker, Heidi. There's Always Enough. 192p. (978-1-85240-287-7(3)) Sovereign World, Ltd.
Baker, Shirley. What a Difference a Day Makes. 2010. 102p. pap. 10.99 (978-1-60957-821-3(X)) Xulon Pr., Inc.
Baker, Stephen. Relationship & Fellowship. 2008. 92p. pap. 9.95 (978-1-4116-9896-3(7)) Lulu Enterprises Inc.
Baker, Tim. Acts of God. 2007. 144p. pap. 10.99 (978-0-8007-5884-4(6)); pap. 10.99 (978-0-8007-5885-1(4)) Revell.
—Leave a Footprint Change the Whole World, 1 vol. 2008. (ENG.). 160p. (YA). pap. 9.99 (978-0-310-27885-6(6)) Zondervan.
Baker, Tina M. Understanding the Pain. 156p. 12.99 (978-1-59160-239-2(4)) Xulon Pr., Inc.
Bakken, Kenneth L. The Call to Wholeness: Health as a Spiritual Journey. 2009. 128p. pap. 16.00 (978-1-60608-911-8(0), Wipf and Stock) Wipf & Stock Pubs.
Bakker, Jay. Fall to Grace: A Revolution of God, Self & Society. (ENG.). 2012. pap. 14.99 (978-0-446-53949-4(X), Jericho Bks.) 2011. 224p. 19.99 (978-0-446-53950-0(3)) FaithWords.
Bakley, Kurt B. The Balanced Life. 2011. 112p. pap. 14.99 (978-1-4634-0591-5(X)) AuthorHouse.
Balabat, Janina. Conversations with an Atheist: The Good News of God's Plan of Salvation for Mankind. 2007. (ENG.). 400p. per. 16.99 (978-1-59979-266-8(4), Creation Hse.) Charisma Media.
Balcells, Janet. The Message of the Lord's Prayer. 2007. 284p. per. 15.99 (978-1-60266-360-2(2)) Xulon Pr., Inc.
Baldock, Gene. The Neutralized Church. 2011. 460p. pap. 24.95 (978-1-4269-5921-9(4)) Trafford Publishing.
Baldwin, Cpa. Spiritual Seeds to Be Planted. 2009. 144p. pap. 14.99 (978-1-60791-804-2(8)) Xulon Pr., Inc.
Baldwin, David J. Choices. 2011. 110p. pap. 11.99 (978-1-61379-802-7(4)) Xulon Pr., Inc.
Baldwin, Nathaniel. Whispers of Love. 2009. 228p. pap. 15.99 (978-1-61579-235-1(X)) Xulon Pr., Inc.
Baldwin, Robert H. & Blom, Galen E. The Missing Church: The Power of Being the Body of Christ in the Family, Neighborhood & Workplace. 2010. pap. 27.99 (978-1-60696-145-2(4)) Tate Publishing & Enterprises, LLC.
Baldwin, Stephen. Livin It: What It Is. 2006. (Livin It Ser.). (Illus.). 148p. (J). (gr. 6-11). pap. 16.99 (978-0-8054-4350-9(9)) B&H Publishing Group.
—Livin It Testimonies. 2006. (Livin It Ser.). (ENG., Illus.). 137p. (gr. 7-11). per. 14.99 (978-0-8054-4346-2(0), B&H Bks.) B&H Publishing Group.
Baldwin, Tracy L. God Is Bigger Than Your FBI. 2008. 220p. pap. 19.95 (978-0-615-18766-2(8)) Baldwin, Tracy L.
Bales, David O. Scenes of Glory: Subplots of God's Long Story. 2008. (978-0-7880-2554-9(6)) CSS Publishing Co.
Balko, Eldon. Letters to My Choir: Reflections on Excellence in Ministry. 20p. pap. 2.95 (978-0-570-01343-3(7), 99-1320) Concordia Publishing Hse.
Ball, Cissandra G. Moments in Eternity. 2010. pap. 14.99 (978-1-61579-883-4(8)) Xulon Pr., Inc.
Ballagh, Debbie. Encouragement for Soldiers. 2007. 120p. per. 10.99 (978-1-60266-159-2(6)) Xulon Pr., Inc.
Ballan, David. Unresolved Stress: Thirsting for Peace. 2007. per. 10.99 (978-1-59886-871-5(3)) Tate Publishing & Enterprises, LLC.
Ballestrero, Anastasio. Martha & Mary: Meeting Christ as Friend. pap. 11.50 (978-0-8189-9483-8(5)) St Pauls/Alba Hse. Pubs.
Ballew, George. The Man Christ Jesus. 2007. pap. (978-0-9778728-5-5(8)) Bush Publishing Inc.
Ballinger, Jean Mills. In the Presence of Angels. 2008. 168p. pap. 17.99 (978-1-4389-0350-7(2)) AuthorHouse.
Ballou, Hugh, ed. Transforming Power. 2008. 160p. pap. 17.00 (978-0-88177-531-0(2)) Discipleship Resources.
Balloy, Magdalene Patricia. Beyond the Darkness: My Transforming Journey with Jesus. 2010. 172p. 25.95 (978-1-4502-5690-2(2)); pap. 15.95 (978-1-4502-5689-6(9)) iUniverse, Inc.
Balsiger, David W. The Case for Christ's Resurrection. 2007. 310p. (978-0-88270-410-4(9)) Bridge-Logos Foundation.
Balthrop, Chad & Cunningham, Jim. Everday People. 2011. 152p. pap. 12.99 (978-0-88144-202-1(X)) Yorkshire Publishing Group.
—Everyday People: Workbook. 2011. 56p. pap. 9.99 (978-0-88144-203-8(8)) Yorkshire Publishing Group.
Bamford, Nicholas. Deified Person: A Study of Deification in Relation to Person & Christian Becoming. 2011. (ENG.). 176p. (gr. 17). 60.00 (978-0-7618-5727-3(3)) Univ. Pr. of America, Inc.
Bandy, Rodney E. Complete you. Complete Life. Complete Seven: (Seven Life Changing Messages) 2009. 164p. pap. 14.99 (978-1-60791-325-2(9)) Xulon Pr., Inc.
—Complete You. Complete Life. Complete Seven: (Seven Life Changing Messages) 2009. 164p. 22.99 (978-1-60791-326-9(7)) Xulon Pr., Inc.
Bankens, Pastor Rodney. A New Beginning. 2010. 140p. pap. 14.99 (978-1-60957-605-9(5)) Xulon Pr., Inc.
Banks, Bertina. God Give Me More of You: Devotional readings for the woman seeking more of God's Presence. 2009. 70p. pap. 15.99 (978-1-4415-6168-8(4)) Xlibris Corp.
Banks, Deborrah M. Loving Life, I Live. 2011. 124p. pap. 51.99 (978-1-4568-1577-6(6)) Xlibris Corp.
Banks, M. The Multi-Faceted Woman. 96p. pap. 7.99 (978-1-58169-117-7(3), Evergreen Pr.) Genesis Communications, Inc.
Banks, Mary. Be Ye Perfect: Destroying Any Mindsets That Exalts Itself above the Knowledge of God. 2009. 144p. pap. 14.99 (978-1-61579-466-9(2)) Xulon Pr., Inc.
—Be Ye Perfect: Destroying Any Mindst That Exalts Itsel above the Knowledge of God. Wendel, Pamela J., ed. 2006. 144p. pap. 19.95 (978-0-9672864-1-9(7)) Fishers of Men Pubn.
BANTA, L. E. E. E. TEMPTATIONS of A PLAYA; Overcoming the Call of the World Through God's Word. 2009. 98p. pap. 17.37 (978-0-557-18094-3(5)) Lulu Enterprises Inc.
Banta, Lee. Eternally Yours... 2010. 100p. pap. 17.00 (978-0-557-27822-0(8)) Lulu Enterprises Inc.
—The Toughest Gang in the World & How to Join. 2010. (ENG.). 59p. pap. 10.00 (978-0-557-32761-4(X)) Lulu Enterprises Inc.
Banta, Lee E. There are No Steps in God's House. 2009. 50p. pap. 15.50 (978-0-557-18502-3(5)) Lulu Enterprises Inc.
Bar Hebraeus, Gregory. Book of Directions. 2010. (SYR.). pap. 52.84 (978-1-61719-919-6(2)) Gorgias Pr., LLC.
—Book of Hints & Predictions. 2010. (SYR.). pap. 67.84 (978-1-61719-917-2(5)) Gorgias Pr., LLC.
Barba, Effie Darlene. A Broken & Contrite Heart. 2011. 120p. pap. 10.99 (978-1-4567-5590-4(0)) AuthorHouse.
Barbara A. Holt Holloway. From Cottonfields to Mission Fields. 2009. 92p. pap. 10.49 (978-1-4389-8332-5(8)) AuthorHouse.
Barber, John J. My Almost for His Highest. 2010. 148p. pap. 18.00 (978-1-60899-632-2(8), Wipf and Stock) Wipf & Stock Pubs.
Barbour Publishing. NLV Gift & Award 2. 2009. (New life Bible Ser.). (ENG.). 960p. pap. 7.97 (978-1-59789-806-5(6), Barbour Bks.) Barbour Publishing, Inc.
Barbour Publishing, Inc. Blissfully Blended. 2010. (ENG.). 384p. pap. 9.99 (978-1-60260-521-3(1), DayMaker) Barbour Publishing, Inc.
—¿Qué Dice la Biblia Sobre el Dinero? 2010. (What the Bible Says About... Ser.). (ENG & SPA.). 192p. pap. 3.99 (978-1-60260-872-6(5), Casa Promesa) Barbour Publishing, Inc.
Barbour Publishing Staff. Bible Answers for the New Year. 2009. (Value Bks.). (ENG.). 160p. pap. 1.99 (978-1-60260-384-4(7), Barbour Bks.) Barbour Publishing, Inc.
—NLV Gift & Award Bible. 2009. (New life Bible Ser.). (ENG.). 960p. pap. 7.97 (978-1-59789-804-1(X), Barbour Bks.) Barbour Publishing, Inc.
BarCharts, Inc. History of Christianity. 2010. (ENG.). 6p. 5.95 (978-1-4232-1422-9(6)) Barcharts, Inc.
Barclay, Jim. Lessons for Parents from a Perfect Parent. 2006. 212p. pap. 17.99 (978-1-4141-0669-4(6)) Pleasant Word.
Barclay, Mike. The Passionate Pursuit: 21 Days of Revival & Christian Maturity 2008. 75p. pap. 16.95 (978-1-60610-995-3(2)) PublishAmerica, Inc.
Barclay, Oliver R. Developing a Christian Mind. Stonier, Geoffrey, ed. 2006. (ENG.). 160p. per. 10.99 (978-1-84550-149-5(7)) Christian Focus Pubns. GBR. Dist: STL Distribution North America.
Barclay, William. Epilogues & Prayers. 12th ed. 2012. 223p. (978-0-334-00378-6(4), SCM Pr.) Hymns Ancient & Modern Ltd.
—Insights - Joy: What the Bible Tells Us about Joy. 2011. (Insights Ser.). 80p. pap. 12.50 (978-0-7152-0886-1(1)) Saint Andrew Pr., Ltd. GBR. Dist: Westminster John Knox Pr.
Barcroft, Susan. Guide to the Lord's Library. 2007. 104p. per. 11.95 (978-0-9778311-5-9(9)) Joshua Tree Publishing.
Barfield, Ray. Wayfarin' Stranger. 248p. 13.99 (978-1-59160-513-3(X)) Xulon Pr., Inc.
Barfoot, Peter E. Faith God's Gift Gift to the Human Heart: How to put it to good Use. 2010. (ENG.). 236p. pap. (978-1-84748-784-1(X)) Athena Pr.
Barker, Ken. Young Men Rise Up. 2010. (ENG.). 176p. pap. 12.95 (978-1-58979-578-5(4)) Taylor Trade Publishing.
Barker, Kim, et al. Birthed in Prayer: Pregnancy as a Spiritual Journey. 2003. 256p. pap. 18.00 (978-0-8358-9941-3(1)) Upper Room Bks.
Barksdale, J. T. Someone to Devour: Winning the Spiritual Battle within Human Conflict. 2011. 134p. pap. 24.95 (978-1-4626-3372-2(2)) PublishAmerica, Inc.
Barlow, Grant. We are Risen 1. 2008. 440p. pap. 37.00 (978-1-4092-0970-6(9)) Lulu Enterprises Inc.
—We are Risen 3. 2008. 500p. pap. 33.50 (978-1-4092-1123-5(1)) Lulu Enterprises Inc.
Barlow, Norman. How to Really Change Your Life. 2007. 172p. per. 13.99 (978-1-60477-059-9(7)) Xulon Pr., Inc.
Barnes, Allen & Barnes, Patti. Christian Apparel: An Index of the Heart. 2nd ed. 2009. 52p. per. 9.95 (978-1-57258-029-9(1), 945-5880) TEACH Services, Inc.
Barnes, Apostle H. R. Did My Faith Fail Me? Or Did I Fail My Faith ? 2011. 164p. pap. 14.99 (978-1-61379-514-9(9)) Xulon Pr., Inc.
Barnes, Apostle H. R. & Barnes, Hural. Did My Faith Fail Me? Or Did I Fail My Faith ? 2015. 164p. 22.99 (978-1-61379-515-6(7)) Xulon Pr., Inc.
Barnes, Tom. Atonement Matters: A Call to Declare the Biblical View of the Atonement. 2008. (Emmaus Ser.). 342p. pap. (978-0-85234-660-0(3)) Evangelical Pr.
Barnett, Barry W. The Cure for the Dysfunctional Church: Becoming What We Were Created to Be. 2009. pap. 14.99 (978-1-60799-333-9(3)) Tate Publishing & Enterprises, LLC.
Barnett, Bonnie. Bobo's Daughter: One Woman's Journey to Find Hope, Healing, & the Father behind the Face Paint. 2010. 232p. 23.95 (978-0-9842358-7-2(6)) Synergy Bks.
Barnett, Brenton M. Times of Refreshing: 100 Devotions to Enrich Your Walk with God. 2009. 322p. pap. 18.50 (978-1-59330-614-4(8)) Aventine Pr.
Barnett, Joe. He Will Never Give up on You! Never? Never! 192p. pap. 12.99 (978-1-892435-13-2(6)) Covenant Publishing, Inc.
Barnett, Paul. 1 Corinthians: Holiness & Hope of a Rescued People. 2011. (Focus on the Bible Ser.). (ENG.). 320p. 15.99 (978-1-84550-721-3(5)) Christian Focus Pubns. GBR. Dist: STL Distribution North America.
Barnhouse, Meg. Did I Say That Out Loud? Musings from a Questioning Soul. 2006. (ENG.). 1p. pap. 12.00 (978-1-55896-509-6(2), Skinner Hse. Bks.) Unitarian Universalist Assn.
Baron, Mary Lee. Natural Family Planning: A Catholic Approach. 2009. 48p. pap. 4.95 (978-0-7648-1833-2(3)) Liguori Pubns.
BARR, BURTON, JR. Amazing Grace. 2009. 148p. pap. 15.00 (978-0-9769117-5-3(2)) Kobalt Bks.
Barr, Alan. The Right Yoke? 2010. 92p. pap. 18.50 (978-1-4461-1836-8(3)) Lulu Enterprises Inc.
Barr, Robert. In the World but Not of It-Serving Christ in the Modern World: God's Principles for Living. 2008. (Illus.). 192p. pap. 18.95 (978-1-4327-3312-4(5)) Outskirts Pr., Inc.
Barrera, Ambrosio. Abide in Me. 2008. 51p. pap. 16.95 (978-1-60672-797-3(4)) PublishAmerica, Inc.
Barrett, Ethel. Se Prohibe Mirar: Don't Look Now. (SPA.). (978-84-7228-235-3(X), 220811) Clie, Editorial.
—Signo Secreto: Secret Sign. (SPA.). 160p. (978-84-7228-234-6(1), 220843) Clie, Editorial.
Barrett, Mike. The Danger Habit: How to Grow Your Love of Risk Into Life-Changing Faith. 2007. (ENG.). 192p. per. 17.99 (978-1-59052-740-5(2), Multnomah) Doubleday Religious Publishing Group, The.
Barrett, Telford. Our Journey into Eternity. 2008. 68p. pap. 10.99 (978-1-60791-188-3(4)) Xulon Pr., Inc.
Barricks, Jeri. I used to be Afraid. 2007. (Illus.). 36p. (J). 11.00 (978-0-9743512-1-6(0)) Barricks, Jeri Ministry.
Barrientos, Marco. Cree Todo Es Posible. 2008. (ENG & SPA.). 160p. 11.99 (978-1-59979-141-8(2), Casa Creacion) Charisma Media.
Barrier, Julie Tacker & Engeler, Brianna Barrier. Bored in Big Church. 2011. 232p. 25.99 (978-1-61379-473-9(8)); pap. 15.99 (978-1-61379-472-2(X)) Xulon Pr., Inc.
Barrier, Roger & Engeler, Brianna Barrier. Got Guts Get Godly! 2011. (Illus.). 394p. 32.99 (978-1-61379-550-7(5)); pap. 20.99 (978-1-61379-549-1(1)) Xulon Pr., Inc.
Barrineau Curtis, Cindy. Touching the Heart of God. 2007. 68p. pap. 14.95 (978-0-615-17466-2(3)) Curtis, Cindy.
Barrow, Julie. A Walk with Christ. 2006. (ENG.). 88p. per. 16.95 (978-1-4241-6223-9(8)) PublishAmerica, Inc.
Barrow, Julie A. Entering the Narrow Gate. 2008. 110p. pap. 19.95 (978-1-60610-969-4(3)) PublishAmerica, Inc.
Barry, Alfred. Religion for Every Day: Lectures to Men. 2007. (ENG.). 136p. 35.95 (978-0-548-09803-5(4)) Kessinger Publishing, LLC.
Barry, Dana. The Power of Prayer a Science Educator's Experience. 2009. 70p. pap. 9.99 (978-1-60860-748-8(8), Strategic Bk. Publishing) AEG Literary Publishing Services, Inc.
Bartel, Blaine. Reality Check: Finding God's Truth in TV's Reality. 2006. (Illus.). 242p. per. 13.99 (978-1-57794-801-8(7)) Harrison House Pubs.
—Start Poor Finish Rich. 2008. 224p. pap. 13.99 (978-1-57794-839-1(4)) Harrison House Pubs.
Bartkowski, Renee. Regaining Joy: Overcoming Stress & Sadness. 2007. 74p. per. 7.95 (978-0-7648-1580-5(6)) Liguori Pubns.
Bartlett, R. Charles. Visions, Dreams & Healing. 2006. (ENG.). 25.99 (978-1-60034-791-7(6)); pap. 15.99 (978-1-60034-790-0(8)) Xulon Pr., Inc.
Bartley, Lester M. 150 A. T. (after the Tribulation) 2006. 11.00 (978-0-8059-8352-4(X)) Dorrance Publishing Co., Inc.
Barton. Resurrection. (Illus.). 248p. 31.95 (978-0-281-04775-8(8)) International Publishers Marketing.
Barton, David & Thomason, Nita. Foundations of Character, Kit. 2006. (Drive Thru History America Ser.). (ENG.). 144p. (gr. 7-12). 49.99 (978-1-4143-1183-8(4)) Tyndale Hse. Pubs.
Barton, Hilda Marie. There's Life in the Word. 2011. 336p. pap. 19.75 (978-1-4269-6220-2(7)) Trafford Publishing.
Barton, Hilda Marie. There's No Room for Doubt: The just shall live by Faith. 2011. 200p. pap. 15.25 (978-1-4269-5346-0(1)) Trafford Publishing.
—There's No Room for Doubt: The just shall live by Faith. 2011. 200p. pap. (978-1-4269-6401-5(3)) Trafford Publishing (UK) Ltd.
Barton, Kathy. The Shrink Wrapped Armor of God. 2010. 108p. pap. 10.99 (978-1-4490-8735-7(3)) AuthorHouse.
Barton, Stephen. Resurrection. 2013. (New Century Theology Ser.). (ENG.). 224p. 24.95 (978-0-8264-7648-7(1)) Continuum International Publishing Group, Ltd. GBR. Dist: National Bk. Network.
Basic Friendship Curriculum: Youth (Year 1) tchr. ed. 13.25 (978-0-933140-41-7(X), 300125) Faith Alive Christian Resources.
Basic Friendship Curriculum: Youth (Year 2) tchr. ed. 13.25 (978-0-933140-80-6(0), 300225) Faith Alive Christian Resources.
Basil, Duncan. Eyes on the Lord: View of a Contemplative. pap. 10.95 (978-0-8189-9476-0(2)) St Pauls/Alba Hse. Pubs.
Basnight, Charletta. Would Jesus Be Pleased? 2011. 94p. 24.99 (978-1-4568-6389-0(4)); pap. 15.99 (978-1-4568-6388-3(6)) Xlibris Corp.
Bass, Christopher David. That You May Know: Assurance of Salvation in 1 John. 2008. (New American Commentary Studies in Bible & Theology Ser.). (ENG.). 256p. 24.99 (978-0-8054-4761-3(X), B&H Academic) B&H Publishing Group.
Bass, Dorothy C. & Briehl, Susan. On Our Way: Christian Practices for Living a Whole Life. 2010. 239p. 17.00 (978-0-8358-1017-3(8)) Upper Room Bks.
Bass, Howard L. Your Best Is yet to Come! Discover the Keys to Unlocking Your Destiny & Achieve Your God-Given Dreams. 2008. 232p. pap. 14.99 (978-1-60647-563-8(0)) Xulon Pr., Inc.
Bassham, Hugh H. Better Health & a Plan to Achieve It: The Dawning of a New Day & a New You. 2010. 76p. pap. 9.95 (978-1-61507-231-6(4)) Cross Bks. Publishing.
Bastian, Howard. The Ancient Path. 2009. 52p. pap. 9.95 (978-1-60693-837-9(1), Strategic Bk. Publishing) AEG Literary Publishing Services, Inc.
Bastos, Carla. The Walk. 2009. 104p. pap. 11.95 (978-1-60264-417-5(9)) Virtualbookworm.com Publishing, Inc.
Batchelor, Carla Hutton. Dear Son. 2008. 120p. per. 10.99 (978-1-60477-366-8(9)) Xulon Pr., Inc.
Bates, Joshua. Lectures on Christian Character. 2009. 320p. pap. 24.95 (978-1-4588-3014-2(4)) General Bks. LLC.
—Lectures on Christian Character. 2007. (ENG.). 606p. 59.95 (978-0-548-15204-1(7)); 608p. per. 44.95 (978-1-4304-4562-3(9)) Kessinger Publishing, LLC.
Bates, Paul R. Virtuous Vision: Sustaining God's Call for Your Life in Times of Discouragement & Drought. 2010. pap. 14.99 (978-1-61663-367-7(0)) Tate Publishing & Enterprises, LLC.
Bates, Walter Leigh. Internal Achievement. 2007. (ENG.). 160p. per. 12.95 (978-0-9770398-5-2(4)) Lifebridge Bks.
—Two-Sided People: Which Side Are You? 2006. (ENG.). 144p. 12.95 (978-0-9786581-2-0(4)) Lifebridge Bks.
Batterson, Mark. Primal: A Quest for the Lost Soul of Christianity. 2009. (ENG.). 192p. 17.99 (978-1-60142-131-9(1), Multnomah) Doubleday Religious Publishing Group, The.
—Wild Goose Chase: Rediscover the Adventure of Pursuing God. 2008. (ENG.). 192p. pap. 13.99 (978-1-59052-719-1(4), Multnomah) Doubleday Religious Publishing Group, The.
Battistelli, Kate. Growing Great Kids: Partner with God to Cultivate His Purpose in Your Child's Life. 2012. E-Book (978-1-61638-655-9(X)); (ENG.). 240p. pap. 14.99 (978-1-61638-654-2(1)) Charisma Media. (Charisma Hse.).
Bauer, Ilona. God & I & Elvis. 2012. 384p. pap. 19.95 (978-0-533-16451-6(6)) Vantage Pr., Inc.
Baugh, Clifford. Finances God's Way. 2007. 108p. per. 10.99 (978-1-60477-116-9(X)) Xulon Pr., Inc.
Bauman, Cheryl. Faith Is Possible. 2008. 153p. pap. 24.95 (978-1-60672-457-6(6)) PublishAmerica, Inc.
Bauman, Lynn C. The Gospel of Thomas: Wisdom of the Twin. 2nd ed. 2012. (ENG.). 176p. pap. 16.95 (978-1-935952-02-2(1)) White Cloud Pr.
Baumbich, Charlene Ann. Don't Miss Your Life! An Uncommon Guide to Living with Freedom, Laughter, & Grace. 2009. (ENG.). 272p. pap. 14.99 (978-1-4165-6299-3(0), Howard Bks.) Howard Books.
Baumgardner, Frances Garrett. Surviving Illness & Death. 2007. 72p. per. 9.99 (978-1-60266-143-1(X)) Xulon Pr., Inc.
Bauserman, Kelly. Sin: Satan's Playground. 2010. 108p. 22.95 (978-1-4269-4543-4(4)); pap. 12.95 (978-1-4269-4542-7(6)) Trafford Publishing.
Bautista, Benjamin F. Why You Need Jesus. 2009. 420p. 34.99 (978-1-60791-302-3(X)); pap. 22.99 (978-1-60791-459-4(X)) Xulon Pr., Inc.
Baxter, Batsell Barrett, et al. Timeless Sermons. pap. 24.99 incl. audio (978-0-89098-132-0(9)) Twentieth Century Christian Bks.
Baxter, Malcolm W. Auacious Faith: Leaving Your Comfort Zone to Grasp Hold of Jesus. 2008. 125p. pap. (978-1-905991-05-1(3)) New Wine Pr.
Baxter, Richard. A Call to the Unconverted. 2008. 211p. 24.99 (978-0-554-89098-2(4)); 211p. 27.99 (978-0-554-89087-6(9)); 217p. pap.

C

25.75 (978-0-554-89096-8(8)); 197p. pap. 26.75 (978-0-554-89090-6(9)) BiblioBazaar.
—Esperanza Cristiana para Otra Vida.Tr. of Christian's Hope for the Life. (SPA.). 112p. (978-84-7228-912-3(5), 222320) Clie, Editorial.
—The Godly Home. Pederson, Randall J., ed. 2010. 224p. pap. 17.99 (978-1-4335-1344-2(7)) Crossway.
Bayley. One New Humanity. 344p. 19.95 (978-0-281-04923-3(8)) International Publishers Marketing.
Be Faithful unto the End. 63p. pap. 10.00 (978-0-9706641-0-5(9)) Roberts, Elizabeth Elliot.
Beach, Nancy & Groeschel, Craig. It: How Churches & Leaders Can Get It & Keep It: How Churches & Leaders Can Get It & Keep It, 1 vol. 2008. (ENG.). 160p. 18.99 (978-0-310-28682-0(4)) Zondervan.
Beall, James L. Colocando los Fundamentos: Laying the Foundation. (SPA.). 384p. (978-84-7228-436-4(0), 360100) Clie, Editorial.
Beam, Joe & Wilson, Lee. The True Heaven: Not What You Thought, Better Than You Expected. 2010. 224p. 14.99 (978-0-89112-643-0(0), Leafwood Pubs.) Abilene Christian Univ. Pr.
Bean, James. To Have & to Hold: A Christian Minister's Advice to a Married Couple. 2010. 94p. pap. 12.00 (978-1-59925-148-6(5)) Solid Ground Christian Bks.
Bear This in Mind. 4.00 (978-0-687-06526-4(7)) Abingdon Pr.
Beason, Kelly. Amazing Moments with the Savior. 2009. 140p. 22.99 (978-1-61579-229-0(5)); pap. 14.99 (978-1-61579-228-3(7)) Xulon Pr., Inc.
Beauchene, Valerie A. In the Shadow of the Almighty. 2007. (Wonders of Practical Christianity: A Teaching Ser.). 81p. per. 11.99 (978-1-59879-282-9(2)) Lifevest Publishing, Inc.
—Rise & Shine: A Trilogy on Revival for the Christian. 2007. 231p. per. 19.99 (978-1-59879-281-2(4)) Lifevest Publishing, Inc.
—To Whom Has the Arm of the Lord Been Revealed. 2007. (Wonders of Practical Christianity: A Teaching Ser.). 81p. per. 11.99 (978-1-59879-430-4(2)) Lifevest Publishing, Inc.
Beaumont, John. Roads to Rome: A Guide to Notable Converts from Britain & Ireland from the Reformation to The. 2010. (ENG.). 480p. 55.00 (978-1-58731-720-0(6)) St. Augustine's Pr., Inc.
Beauplan, Smith. The Friend of God: Who Is He That Is A Friend of God? 2010. pap. 10.99 (978-1-61579-785-1(8)) Xulon Pr., Inc.
Beaverson, Alex A. This Walk with Christ: A book about Christianity & how to start at a young age. Foreword by Kelly Carnahan. 2011. 102p. pap. 19.95 (978-1-4626-2926-8(1)) PublishAmerica, Inc.
Bebslin. Tithing & Winning Souls: Sharing the Good News to Others. 2008. 100p. pap. 10.99 (978-1-60647-896-7(6)) Xulon Pr., Inc.
Beck, James. Pragmatism vs. Accountability. 2008. 60p. pap. 10.99 (978-1-60647-927-8(X)) Xulon Pr., Inc.
Beckett, Lucy. In the Light of Christ: Writings in the Western Tradition. 2006. 648p. pap. 21.95 (978-1-58617-107-0(0)) Ignatius Pr.
Beckley, Timothy G. & Tessman, Diane. Your Passport to Heaven. (Illus.). 150p. pap. 14.95 (978-0-938294-88-7(1)) Inner Light - Global Communications.
Beckwith, Roger. Daily & Weekly Worship: From Jewish to Christian. 2009. 88.00 (978-1-60724-346-5(6)) Gorgias Pr., LLC.
Becton, Austin & Binion, Nathaniel. Village Life. 2010. 84p. pap. 12.99 (978-0-557-50193-9(8)) Lulu Enterprises Inc.
Bediako, Kwame. Theology & Identity: The Impact of Culture upon Christian Thought in the Second Century & in Modern Africa. 2011. (Regnum Studies in Mission Ser.). 526p. pap. 63.00 (978-1-61097-440-0(9), Wipf and Stock) Wipf & Stock Pubs.
Beebe, Linda. Hearing the Still Small Voice. 2007. (ENG.). 132p. per. (978-1-55452-165-4(3)) Essence Publishing.
Beebe, Ruth. Are You Being Told What to Believe? How Important Is What We Believe? 2010. 152p. pap. 10.95 (978-1-4269-3983-9(3)) Trafford Publishing.
Beeke, Joel R., ed. The Soul of Life: The Piety of John Calvin. 2009. (Illus.). pap. 10.00 (978-1-60178-057-7(5)) Reformation Heritage Bks.
Beeke, Joel R. & La Belle, James A. Living by God's Promises. 2010. 192p. pap. (978-1-60178-104-8(0)) Reformation Heritage Bks.
Beeke, Mary. The Law of Kindness: Serving with Heart & Hands. 2007. per. (978-1-60178-029-4(X)) Reformation Heritage Bks.
Beemer, Scott. The Third Man Rising. 2006. 136p. per. 12.95 (978-1-58275-178-8(1)) Black Forest Pr.
Beemer, Scott E. The Sent Pool. 2008. 160p. per. 12.95 (978-1-58275-202-0(8)) Black Forest Pr.
Beers, Ronald A. & Beers, V. Gilbert. The Complete Book of Life's Questions: With Answers from the Bible. 2007. (ENG.). 784p. per. 14.97 (978-1-4143-0730-5(6)) Tyndale Hse. Pubs.
Beers, Ronald A. & Mason, Amy E. Divine Moments: Everyday Inspiration from God's Word. 2008. (ENG.). 384p. pap. 3.97 (978-1-4143-1225-5(3)) Tyndale Hse. Pubs.
—Divine Moments for Leaders: Everyday Inspiration from God's Word. 2008. (ENG.). 336p. pap. 3.97 (978-1-4143-1229-3(6)) Tyndale Hse. Pubs.
—God's Daily Promises: Daily Wisdom from God's Word. Needham, Michal, ed. 2007. (ENG.). 416p. pap. 3.97 (978-1-4143-1230-9(X)) Tyndale Hse. Pubs.
—TouchPoints for Men: God's Answers for Your Daily Needs. rev. ed. 2010. (ENG.). 288p. pap. 4.99 (978-1-4143-2018-2(3)) Tyndale Hse. Pubs.
—TouchPoints for New Believers. 2009. (ENG.). 288p. pap. 4.99 (978-1-4143-2022-9(1)) Tyndale Hse. Pubs.
—TouchPoints for Recovery. 2009. (ENG.). 288p. pap. 4.99 (978-1-4143-2023-6(X)) Tyndale Hse. Pubs.
—TouchPoints for Students. 2009. (ENG.). 288p. pap. 4.99 (978-1-4143-2021-2(3)) Tyndale Hse. Pubs.
Beeson, Ray. The Real Battle. 2007. 232p. pap. 16.95 (978-0-9748269-3-6(6)) Overcomers Ministries.
Beginnings Study VHS + 1 DVD - for Getting Started Kit. 325.00 (978-0-687-05836-5(8)) Abingdon Pr.
Beginnings Study VHS + 1 DVD - for Planning Kit. 125.00 (978-0-687-07319-1(7)) Abingdon Pr.
Behrend, Genevieve. The Wisdom of Genevieve Behrend. 2008. 128p. 19.99 (978-1-60459-289-4(3)); pap. 14.99 (978-1-60459-287-0(7)) Wilder Pubns., Ltd.
Being There. 6.00 (978-0-687-85063-1(0)) Abingdon Pr.
Beit, Einer Nuh K. The Nemesis Apple. 2011. 298p. pap. 16.99 (978-1-61215-906-5(0)) Xulon Pr., Inc.
Bekgaard, Wm. F. The Parables of Jesus Revisited: An Innovative Approach to Understanding & Interpreting the Parables. 2011. 172p. 25.95 (978-1-4620-3803-9(4)); pap. 15.95 (978-1-4620-3804-6(2)) iUniverse, Inc.
Belchen, Richard P. Ministry Helps in Acts. 72p. (C). reprint ed. pap. 6.95 (978-0-925703-62-0(1)) Crown Pubns., Inc.
Belcher, Joseph. Sketches from Life; or, Illustrations of the Influence of Christianity. 2006. 548p. per. 29.99 (978-1-4255-6043-0(1)) MPublishing.
Beldin, Don. Yours for a Meeting in the Air: Sixty Years with God as My Co-Pilot. 2007. (Illus.). 120p. per. 10.99 (978-1-60247-002-6(2)) Tate Publishing & Enterprises, LLC.
Believer Implementation Resource. 5.00 (978-0-687-07583-6(1)) Abingdon Pr.
Believer Video #1. 40.00 (978-0-687-98205-9(7)) Abingdon Pr.
Believer Video #2. 40.00 (978-0-687-98215-8(4)) Abingdon Pr.
Believer Video #3. 40.00 (978-0-687-98225-7(1)) Abingdon Pr.
Believer Video #4. 40.00 (978-0-687-98235-6(9)) Abingdon Pr.
Believing & Belonging. 5.00 (978-0-687-85075-4(4)) Abingdon Pr.
Bell, Alexander. 12-Day Journey of Obedience & Love. 2009. 152p. pap. 14.99 (978-1-60791-655-0(X)) Xulon Pr., Inc.
Bell, Gordon W. A Cowboy Goes to India. 2010. 320p. pap. 18.99 (978-1-60957-201-3(7)) Xulon Pr., Inc.
Bell, Herbert G., Jr. Speaking in Tongues: A Biblical Brief. 2009. 54p. pap. 9.95 (978-1-4401-4864-4(3)) iUniverse, Inc.
Bell, James & Sumner, Tracy. God to Go: Delivering a Portable Celebration of Faith, Inspiration, & Grace. 2006. (ENG.). 192p. per. 9.95 (978-1-59337-604-8(9)) Adams Media Corp.
Bell, James R. Practicing the Presence of God. 2010. 178p. pap. 14.99 (978-1-60957-824-4(4)) Xulon Pr., Inc.
Bell, James Stuart & Littleton, Jeanette Gardner. His Forever: Stories of Real People Finding Jesus. 2006. (ENG.). 256p. per. 14.95 (978-1-59869-050-7(7)) Adams Media Corp.
Bell, Matt. Money, Purpose, Joy Discussion Guide: The Proven Path to Uncommon Financial Success. 2008. (Acts 29 Ser.). 96p. pap. 8.99 (978-1-60006-322-0(5)) NavPress Publishing Group.
Bell, Regina. On the Potter's Wheel. 2011. 52p. pap. 15.99 (978-1-4568-7682-1(1)) Xlibris Corp.
Bell, Rob. Love Wins: A Book about Heaven, Hell, & the Fate of Every Person Who Ever Lived. (ENG.). 224p. 2012. pap. 14.99 (978-0-06-204965-0(8)) 2011. 24.99 (978-0-06-204964-3(X)) HarperCollins Pubs. (HarperOne).
—Velvet Elvis. 2012. (ENG.). 208p. pap. 14.99 (978-0-06-219721-4(5), HarperOne) HarperCollins Pubs.
Bell, Rob & Zondervan Publishing Staff. Collection 001, 1 vol. 2009. (Nooma Ser.). (ENG.). 96p. pap. 9.99 (978-0-310-32540-6(4)) Zondervan.
Bell Sr., Pastor Thornton. The Money Tree - Good & Evil Roots. 2007. 104p. pap. 15.01 (978-0-615-15183-0(3)) Impact Now Ministries.
Bell, Stephen. No Other Gods. 5th rev. ed. Date not set. 26p. pap. 3.95 (978-1-891050-02-2(8)) Key Ministries Pubns., International.
Bell, Thornton, Sr. The Kingdom of God Passport. 2007. 103p. pap. 14.95 (978-0-615-16358-1(0)) Impact Now Ministries.
Bell, W. F. Ruin, Redemption, Regeneration. pap. 0.06 (978-0-87377-122-1(2)) GAM Pubns.
Bellamy, Gerald E. The and Agreement. 2011. 96p. pap. 10.99 (978-1-61379-338-1(3)) Xulon Pr., Inc.
Bellanton-BienAime, Marthe. Deceive No More! 2008. pap. 13.99 (978-1-60647-267-5(4)) Xulon Pr., Inc.
Bellavia, William D. Roman Baptist: A Comparison of Two Denominations. 2009. 196p. pap. 22.50 (978-1-4303-2920-6(3)) Lulu Enterprises Inc.
Belle, Belinda. Help!!! My kid Is on Drugs! A Mother's heart speaks out Loud!!! 2009. 88p. pap. 14.95 (978-1-4327-2179-4(8)) Outskirts Pr., Inc.
Bellett, J. G. The Moral Glory of the Lord Jesus Christ. pap. 2.95 (978-0-88172-176-8(X)) Believers Bookshelf, Inc.
Bellini, Peter J. Truth Therapy. 2009. 156p. 24.99 (978-1-60791-315-3(1)); pap. 14.99 (978-1-60791-652-9(5)) Xulon Pr., Inc.
Bellot, Joan. Trust, Delight, Commit, Rest: Why has God not answered our prayers? Why does God forsake us in our times of need? These are some of the questions that we sometimes ask as we face a world full of Chaos. 2009. 57p. pap. 11.95 (978-1-4327-4047-4(4)) Outskirts Pr., Inc.
ben David, Eliyahu. Holy Order Restored: Or Bible Study of Angels, Eden, Tree of Life, Adam & Eve, Marriage, Family, Government, Lucifer as Satan, Sin, Cain, Abel, Nephilim, the First Patriarchs, Seth, Enoch, Methuselah, Last Days of the Pre-Flood World & Noah's Ark Informs the End Times Sons of God to Take Dominion. 2007. 140p. per. 15.80 (978-0-9679471-1-2(1), Zarach) Bfree Publishing.
Benavides, Alia. Inspirational Journal. 2011. 150p. 18.99 (978-1-935268-93-2(7)) Halo Publishing International.
Bender, Albert C. You Are Forever in Time: A Theological Alternative to Ones Own Religious Belief. 2009. 107p. pap. 15.95 (978-1-4327-3578-4(0)) Outskirts Pr., Inc.
Bender, Betty. What's a Woman to Do? Committing Yourself to God. pap. 6.99 (978-0-89098-137-5(X)) Twentieth Century Christian Bks.
Bendicional (The Book of Blessings) (SPA.). 592p. 69.95 (978-970-693-063-7(9)) Obra Nacional de la Buena Prensa, A.C. MEX. Dist: St Pauls/Alba Hse. Pubs.
Benedict. Charity in Truth. 2008. 150p. 14.95 (978-1-58617-280-0(8)) Ignatius Pr.
Benedict, Gerald S., ed. Celtic Wisdom: The Poetry & Prose of a Mystic Tradition. 2008. (Sacred Wisdom Ser.). (ENG.). 192p. 8.95 (978-1-905857-87-6(X), Watkins Publishing) Duncan Baird Pubs. GBR. Dist: Sterling Publishing Co., Inc.
Benedict XVI, Pope. Values in a Time of Upheaval. McNeil, Brian, tr. from GER. 2006. (ENG.). 176p. 19.95 (978-0-8245-2373-2(3)) Crossroad Publishing Co., The.
Benedict XVI, pseud. The Apostles: The Origin of the Church & Their Co-Workers. 2007. (Illus.). 174p. 14.95 (978-1-59276-405-1(3)) Our Sunday Visitor, Publishing Div.
—Heart of the Christian Life. 2010. 150p. 14.95 (978-1-58617-432-3(0)) Ignatius Pr.
—Sacrament of Charity. 2007. 114p. per. 6.95 (978-0-8198-7103-9(6)) Pauline Bks. & Media.
—Saved in Hope: Spe Salve. 2008. 107p. 14.95 (978-1-58617-251-0(4)) Ignatius Pr.
—The Word of God: In Conversation with God. 2009. (Spiritual Thoughts Ser.). 90p. pap. 6.95 (978-1-60137-065-5(2)) United States Conference of Catholic Bishops.
Benefield, Alma. The Love of God: A Devotional Book of LOVE, Faith & Miracles, & the COMING of the Lord. 2009. 64p. pap. 18.95 (978-1-4389-9880-0(5)) AuthorHouse.
Benefield, Cheryl Smith. Nathan's Story. 2009. 64p. pap. 10.99 (978-1-60791-386-3(0)) Xulon Pr., Inc.
Benevides, Kerrie. The Christmas Heart. 2007. 64p. per. 11.99 (978-1-60477-185-5(2)) Xulon Pr., Inc.
Benjamin I., Phinnah. Yoked with Unbelief. 2008. 128p. pap. 14.99 (978-1-60647-999-5(7)) Xulon Pr., Inc.
Bennett, Christopher Joseph. Here a Little, There a Little: Isaiah 28:9-10. 2008. 160p. pap. 12.95 (978-1-4327-2495-5(9)) Outskirts Pr., Inc.
Bennett, D. L. Alzheimer's, Depression & Dementi. 2008. 180p. 22.99 (978-1-60647-744-1(7)); pap. 14.99 (978-1-60647-743-4(9)) Xulon Pr., Inc.
Bennett, Jana Marguerite & Nussbaum, Melissa Musick. Free to Leave, Free to Stay: Fruits of the Spirit & Church Choice. 2009. 114p. pap. 15.00 (978-1-55635-899-9(7)) Cascade Bks.
Bennett, John Scott. Milton J. Stewart: A Man of the Spirit. 2009. 324p. pap. 18.99 (978-1-60791-192-0(2)) Xulon Pr., Inc.
Bennett, Phyllis. Our Wise Counselor: Trusting God's Guidance. 2007. (Walking with God (Navpress) Ser.). (ENG.). 64p. 8.99 (978-1-60006-220-9(2)) NavPress Publishing Group.
Bennett, Terry. The Man Who Once Was & Now Is. pap. (978-0-9667720-1-2(6)) Emmanuel Foundation, The.
Bennett, Vincent. The Possible You. 2007. (ENG.). 108p. 33.95 (978-0-548-07081-9(4)) Kessinger Publishing, LLC.
Bens, Charles K. Blessed by Disease: How Illness Can Help You Become Stronger & Live Longer. 2007. per. (978-0-9692286-8-4(6)) Healthy at Work.
Benson, Dan. Que Occurre Con los Que No Son Sanados (What about Us Who Are Not) (SPA.). (978-84-7228-431-9(X), 360600) Clie, Editorial.
Benson, Katrina. The Last Stand. 2008. 408p. pap. 19.99 (978-1-4389-0417-7(7)) AuthorHouse.
Benson, Robert. Digging In: Tending to Life in Your Own Backyard. 2007. (ENG.). 176p. per. 12.99 (978-1-4000-7173-9(9), WaterBrook Pr.) Doubleday Religious Publishing Group, The.
—A Good Neighbor: Benedict's Guide to Community. 2009. (ENG.). 96p. (gr. 13). pap. 14.99 (978-1-55725-582-2(2)) Paraclete Pr., Inc.
Benton, John. Why Join a Small Church. 2008. (ENG.). 7.99 (978-1-84550-407-6(0)) Christian Focus Pubns. GBR. Dist: STL Distribution North America.
Benzel, Fred. The Force of Joy: Thriving in Turbulent Times. 2011. pap. 13.99 (978-1-61777-305-1(0)) Tate Publishing & Enterprises, LLC.
Berenberg, Sanford. Learn & Grow Daily! 2009. 232p. pap. 15.99 (978-1-60791-458-7(1)) Xulon Pr., Inc.
Beresford, Jennifer. Creating Confidence in Women: A Handbook for Women in Churches. (Illus.). 112p. 13.00 (978-0-281-05146-5(1)) SPCK Publishing GBR. Dist: Pilgrim Pr., The/United Church Pr.
Berg, Daniel. Hard Faith. 2006. (ENG.). 18.99 (978-1-60034-597-5(2)); pap. 10.99 (978-1-60034-389-6(9)) Xulon Pr., Inc.
Berg, Jim. God Is More Than Enough: Foundations for a Quiet Soul. 2010. (978-1-60682-057-5(5)); (978-1-60682-056-8(7)) BJU Pr.
Berger, Betty. Heaven to Earth. 2009. 486p. pap. 20.49 (978-1-4389-9514-4(8)) AuthorHouse.
Berger, Steve & Berger, Sarah. Have Heart: Bridging the Gulf Between Heaven & Earth. 2010. 147p. 15.99 (978-1-936355-03-7(5)) Grace Chapel.
Berghuis, Kent. Christian Fasting - a Theological Approach. 2007. 308p. pap. 19.95 (978-0-7375-0146-9(4)) Biblical Studies Pr.
Berglund, Pierrette Nicole Gagnon. Cries of Despair! 2009. 268p. pap. 16.99 (978-1-60791-785-4(8)) Xulon Pr., Inc.
Bergman, Ingmar. Sonntagskinder. Reichel, Verena, tr. (GER.). 479p. pap. (978-3-462-02685-6(2)) Kiepenheuer & Witsch GmbH & Company KG DEU. Dist: International Bk. Import Service, Inc.
Berhane, Asfaw D. Heaven Is Empty, Hell Is Full: A Revelation of Heaven & Hell. 2008. (ENG.). 144p. pap. 10.99 (978-1-59979-399-3(7), Creation Hse.) Charisma Media.
Berinti, Benjamin. Firestarters: For the Seasons of Our Life. 2011. 300p. pap. 18.95 (978-1-4327-6944-4(8)) Outskirts Pr., Inc.
Bernard, A. R. Happiness Is... Simple Steps to a Life of Joy. 2011. (ENG.). 224p. pap. 15.99 (978-1-4516-2922-4(2), Touchstone) Touchstone.
Bernard, Daniel. The Church at Its Best. 2007. 176p. pap. 12.99 (978-1-58169-254-9(4)) Genesis Communications, Inc.
Bernard, David K. & Bernard, Loretta A. In Search of Holiness. 2011. (978-1-56722-949-3(2)) Word Aflame Pr.
Bernier, Ronald. Christian Foundations. 2011. 246p. pap. 16.99 (978-1-61529-017-8(6)) Vision Publishing.
Berquist, Nita G. Somewhere with God: Studies on Being Led by His Spirit. 2010. 276p. pap. 13.95 (978-1-4327-3427-5(X)) Outskirts Pr., Inc.
Berrigan, Daniel. Ten Commandments for the Long Haul. 2009. (Daniel Berrigan Reprint Ser.). 160p. pap. 18.00 (978-1-60608-518-9(2), Wipf and Stock) Wipf & Stock Pubs.
Berriman, Dan H. Too Much Baggage for the Promised Land. 2009. 120p. pap. 10.50 (978-1-60860-054-0(8), Eloquent Bks.) AEG Literary Publishing Services, Inc.
Berry, Dan. Addicted... to Hope. 2010. 106p. pap. 11.99 (978-1-60957-384-3(6)) Xulon Pr., Inc.
Berry, John F. Do It His Way: Experiencing a Glorious Spirit-Filled Life. 2010. 224p. 33.95 (978-1-61507-101-2(6)); pap. 17.95 (978-1-61507-100-5(8)) Cross Bks. Publishing.
Berry, Shareta. A Release from Within. 2007. 76p. per. 10.95 (978-1-4327-0455-1(9)) Outskirts Pr., Inc.
—Translations. 2009. 68p. pap. 14.95 (978-1-4327-3491-6(1)) Outskirts Pr., Inc.
Bettinger, Jim & Bettinger, Julie S. The Book of Bowden: Words of Wisdom, Faith, & Motivation by & about Bobby Bowden, College Football's Most Inspirational Coach. 2007. (ENG., Illus.). 126p. per. 9.95 (978-1-58979-339-2(0)) Taylor Trade Publishing.
Betts, Barbara. Heavenly Sandpaper: A Caregiver's Journey Through a Stem Cell Transplant. 2010. 196p. pap. 14.99 (978-1-61507-141-8(5)) Cross Bks. Publishing.
Betts, Chris. Architects of Babylon - the Evil Behind the Intended New World Order. 2011. 246p. pap. (978-1-908105-79-0(8)) Grosvenor Hse. Publishing Ltd.
Beukes, Wynand. The Kings of the Kingdom. 2009. 131p. pap. 18.26 (978-1-4092-9237-1(1)) Lulu Enterprises Inc.
Bevan, Ray. Journey to the Center Of. 2007. (ENG.). 127p. pap. 9.99 (978-1-86024-608-1(7)) Authentic Media.
Bevan, Tom. Un Heroe Vestido Con Piel de Lobo: Hero in Wolf's Clothing. (SPA.). 328p. (978-84-7228-267-4(8), 220451) Clie, Editorial.
Bevere, John. Extraordinary: The Life You're Meant to Live. 2010. (ENG.). 240p. pap. 14.99 (978-0-307-45773-8(7), WaterBrook Pr.) Doubleday Religious Publishing Group, The.
—Extraordinary Pack: Keys to a Breakthrough Life, 10. 2010. (ENG.). 64p. pap. 19.90 (978-0-307-72945-3(1), WaterBrook Pr.) Doubleday Religious Publishing Group, The.
—Relentless: The Power You Need to Never Give Up. 2011. (ENG.). 256p. 19.99 (978-0-307-45775-2(3), WaterBrook Pr.) Doubleday Religious Publishing Group, The.
Beyene, Nike. Fifteen Mysteries Blind the Church. 2011. 54p. pap. 15.99 (978-1-4653-6127-1(8)) Xlibris Corp.
Beyond the Cross: The Final Chapter of Man's Destiny. 2007. 142p. per. 11.99 (978-1-59886-591-2(9)) Tate Publishing & Enterprises, LLC.
Bialik, Stan. I Never Promised You a Pink Cadillac. 2009. 80p. pap. 10.99 (978-1-60791-465-5(4)) Xulon Pr., Inc.
Bianchi, J.M. God Chose to Save: Why Men Cannot & Will Not Be Saved Apart from Election. 2007. (ENG.). 91p. pap. 9.99 (978-0-85234-497-2(X)) Calvary Pr.
Bianchi, Joseph M. My Friend Grace: A Child Learns about the Mercy & Sovereignty of God. 2007. 24p. (J). pap. 9.99 (978-1-879737-52-5(3)) Calvary Pr.
Biblical Living: The Promise of a Holy Life. 2008. (ENG.). 128p. pap. 11.99 (978-0-8341-2385-4(1), 9780834123854) Beacon Hill Pr. of Kansas City.
Bice, Frank. Your Cross Is Your Gift. 2011. 84p. pap. 11.95 (978-1-60910-744-4(6)) Booklocker.com, Inc.
Bickel, Bruce & Jantz, Stan. Bible Answers 101: A User-Friendly Guide to Life's Biggest Questions. 2009. (Christianity 101 Ser.). 272p. pap. 13.99 (978-0-7369-2525-9(2)) Harvest Hse. Pubs.
—Goodbye High School, Hello World: A Real-Life Guide for Graduates. 2008. (ENG.). 208p. (YA). pap. 6.99 (978-0-8307-3733-8(2)) Gospel Light Pubns.
—Now That You're a Christian: A Guide to Your Faith in Plain Language. 2008. (Christianity 101 Ser.). 43p. per. 5.99 (978-0-7369-2316-3(0)) Harvest Hse. Pubs.
Bickel, Carol & Bickel, Kurt. Lasting Friendship Skills. 134p. pap. 19.99 (978-0-570-05231-9(9), 20-2638) Concordia Publishing Hse.

Bickerstaff, Marcella. Dog Is God Spelled Backwards. 2011. 192p. pap. 14.99 (978-1-61379-157-8(7)) Xulon Pr., Inc.

Bicket, Tammy L., et al. Hugs for Cat Lovers: Stories, Sayings, & Scriptures to Encourage & Inspire. 2008. (Hugs Ser.). (ENG., Illus.). 128p. 11.99 (978-1-4165-5705-0(9), Howard Bks.) Howard Books.

Bickle, Mike. After God's Own Heart: The Key to Knowing & Living God's Passionate Love for You. 2009. (ENG.). 256p. pap. 14.99 (978-1-59979-530-0(2), Charisma Hse.) Charisma Media.

—Passion for Jesus: Cultivating Extravagant Love for God. rev. ed. 2007. (ENG.). 224p. pap. 14.99 (978-1-59979-060-2(2), Charisma Hse.) Charisma Media.

Biddington, Terry. Risk-Shaped Discipleship: On Going Deeper into the Life of God. 2010. pap. (978-0-89390-693-1(X)) Resource Pubns., Inc.

Biebel, David B. Finding Your Way after the Suicide of Someone You Love. 2008. (ENG.). 191p. 25.00 (978-1-4223-9436-6(0)) DIANE Publishing Co.

Bieker, Judy. Revival Begins with Me. Marconette, Gennifer, ed. 2008. 140p. per. (978-0-9794167-1-2(X)) Simple Ink, LLC.

Bieniosek, Jan. Earthen Vessels. 2010. 146p. pap. 14.99 (978-1-61579-564-2(2)) Xulon Pr., Inc.

Bierle, Don. Surprised by Faith Study & Discussion Guide. 2007. 112p. per. 13.00 (978-0-9745524-0-8(2)) FaithSearch International.

Bierman, Dominiquae. Yes 2008. 212p. 25.99 (978-1-60647-988-9(1)); pap. 15.99 (978-1-60647-987-2(3)) Xulon Pr., Inc.

Bigelow, Kevin Jay. A Biblical Quest for Truth: A Personal or Small Group Study Guide. 2009. pap. 12.99 (978-1-60799-447-3(X)) Tate Publishing & Enterprises, LLC.

Bigler, Scott. Seven Keys to Living by Faith. 2009. pap. 11.99 (978-1-60799-064-2(4)) Tate Publishing & Enterprises, LLC.

Bilbrough, Dave. Worship & the Presence of God. 2007. (Worship And... Ser.). 62p. pap. (978-1-903725-77-1(1)) New Wine Pr.

Billheimer, Paul E. Destined to Overcome: Exercising Your Spiritual Authority. 2006. 126p. reprint ed. pap. 14.00 (978-0-7642-0304-6(5)) Bethany Hse. Pubs.

Billy Graham Evangelistic Association, creator. The Billy Graham Christian Worker's Handbook: A Topical Guide with Biblical Answers to the Urgent Concerns of Our Day. 2007. (Illus.). 320p. spiral bd. (978-1-59328-036-9(X)) Graham, Billy Evangelistic Assn.

—Thirty Discipleship Exercises: The Pathway to Christian Maturity. 2007. 78p. pap. (978-1-59328-029-1(7)) Graham, Billy Evangelistic Assn.

Billy Graham Evangelistic Association, prod. Preparing Your Church for New Christians. 2008. (Christian Growth Ser.). 31p. pap. 1.95 (978-0-89066-305-9(X), 6305X) World Wide Pubns.

Bing, Charles C. Lordship Salvation. 2010. 244p. pap. 15.99 (978-1-60957-580-9(6)) Xulon Pr., Inc.

Bing, Elder George. Alms Sunday School Lessons. 2008. 220p. pap. 17.00 (978-1-4389-3817-2(9)) AuthorHouse.

Bing, Shirley Watts. Whispers in the Wind. 2009. 268p. pap. 16.99 (978-1-61579-480-5(8)) Xulon Pr., Inc.

Binns, Berkli. A Minute for Mommy: Reflecting on the Blessings of Motherhood. 2010. pap. 14.99 (978-1-61663-965-5(2)) Tate Publishing & Enterprises, LLC.

Binz, Stephen J. Being Disciples of Jesus. 2006. (Six Weeks with the Bible Ser.). (ENG.). 96p. per. 7.95 (978-0-8294-2355-6(9)) Loyola Pr.

Bird, Matt & Borlace, Craig. Manifesto for Life. 169p. pap. 13.99 (978-0-340-75673-7(X), Hodder & Stoughton) Hodder General Publishing Div. GBR. Dist: Trafalgar Square Publishing.

Birnbaum, Ben. Take Heart: Catholic Writers on Hope in Our Time. Birnbaum, Ben, ed. 2007. (Boston College Church in the 21st Century Ser.). (ENG.). 240p. pap. 14.95 (978-0-8245-2461-6(6), Crossroad) Crossroad Publishing Co., The.

Biscardi, Jim. Getting Around in Christian Circles. 2007. pap. 9.95 (978-0-9753786-3-2(5)) Mantle Ministries.

Bishop, Darlene, frwd. Success by Design: Becoming the Person You Were Destined to Be. 2007. 89p. per. 12.00 (978-1-60403-000-6(3)) Durik Publishing.

Bishop, Gary. Seis Ruedas Al Norte: Six Wheels Northward. (SPA.). (978-84-7228-266-7(X), 220808) Clie, Editorial.

Bishop-Joe, Leslie. Essentials for Frontline Living. 2008. 96p. per. 9.99 (978-1-60477-424-5(X)) Xulon Pr., Inc.

Bishop-Leonard, Sherri. Joy after the Storm. 2009. 159p. pap. 15.95 (978-1-4327-3787-0(2)) Outskirts Pr., Inc.

Bishop, Mark. Seeing Is Believing: A Christmas Gift. 24.95 (978-1-883755-10-2(7)) Lost River Pr.

Bishop, Mark Paul. God's Perfect Plan: A Family Physician's Search for the Absolute Truth. 2011. pap. 18.99 **(978-1-61739-842-1(X))** Tate Publishing & Enterprises, LLC.

Bishops Comm on Liturgy Staff. Rite of Penance Leaflet. 6p. pap. (978-0-8198-6445-1(5), 332-302) Pauline Bks. & Media.

Bittleston, Adam. Our Spiritual Companions: From Angels & Archangels to Cherubim & Seraphim. 128p. pap. 19.95 (978-0-86315-433-1(6)) Floris Bks. GBR. Dist: SteinerBooks, Inc.

Bixby, Douglas J. The Honest to God Church: A Pathway to God's Grace. 2007. (978-1-56699-344-9(X)) Alban Institute, Inc.

Black, Doris & Mize, Charlotte. But How Can I? pap. 7.99 (978-0-89098-204-4(X)) Twentieth Century Christian Bks.

Black, George. In the Midst of the Congregation: Psalms for Worship, RCL Feasts & Holy Days:Cantor. 16.95 (978-1-55126-295-6(9), 1668) Anglican Bk. Ctr. CAN. Dist: Forward Movement Pubns.

Black, Gregory L. The and Measure of a Minister. 2011. 272p. pap. 16.99 **(978-1-61379-318-3(9))** Xulon Pr., Inc.

Black, Jerome Lamont. Priest Hood of the Believers. 2011. 56p. pap. 15.99 **(978-1-4568-8978-4(8))** Xlibris Corp.

Black, John. A Special Parish Mission: Including All Talks & Instructions. 2008. 220p. pap. 15.95 (978-0-595-45957-5(9)) iUniverse, Inc.

Blackaby, Henry & Blackaby, Melvin. Experiencing the Resurrection: The Everyday Encounter That Changes Your Life. 2008. (ENG.). 224p. 16.99 (978-1-59052-757-3(7), Multnomah) Doubleday Religious Publishing Group, The.

—Experiencing the Resurrection Study Guide: The Everyday Encounter That Changes Your Life. 2008. (ENG.). 112p. per. 9.99 (978-1-59052-758-0(5), Multnomah) Doubleday Religious Publishing Group, The.

Blackaby, Henry & Blackaby, Norman C. El Llamado de Dios: El Proposito de Dios Para Todo Creyente. 2010. (ENG.). 192p. pap. 11.99 (978-1-59669-248-0(0)) New Hope Pubs.

Blackaby, Henry & Blackaby, Tom. The Man God Uses: Devotional Journal. 14.99 (978-0-8054-3526-9(3)) B&H Publishing Group.

Blackaby, Henry, et al. Experiencia Con Dios: Knowing & Doing the Will of God, 1 vol. rev. exp. ed. 2009. (ENG.). 368p. pap. 12.99 (978-0-8054-4938-9(8), B&H Espanol) B&H Publishing Group.

—Revelation, 0 vols. 2008. (Encounters with God Ser.). 96p. pap. 9.99 (978-1-4185-2656-6(8)) Nelson, Thomas Inc.

Blackaby, Henry T. & Blackaby, Melvin D. A God Centered Church: Experiencing God Together. 2007. 301p. per. 14.99 (978-0-8054-4551-0(X), B&H Bks.) B&H Publishing Group.

Blackaby, Henry T. & Blackaby, Norman. Called & Accountable: Discovering Your Place in God's Eternal Purpose. 2007. (ENG.). 224p. 19.99 (978-1-59669-047-9(X)) New Hope Pubs.

Blackaby, Henry T. & Blackaby, Richard. Experiencing God Day-by-Day: Devotional. 2006. (ENG.). 404p. 14.99 (978-0-8054-4478-0(5), B&H Bks.) B&H Publishing Group.

Blackaby, Henry T. & Blackaby, Tom. Anointed to Be God's Servants: How God Blesses Those Who Serve Together, 0 vols. 2006. 208p. per. 13.99 (978-0-7852-8807-7(4)) Nelson, Thomas Inc.

Blackaby, Henry T., et al. Experiencing God Member Book: Knowing & Doing the Will of God. 2007. (Illus.). 272p. per. 14.95 (978-1-4158-5838-7(1)) LifeWay Christian Resources.

Blackaby, Henry T., et al. Fresh Encounter: Experiencing God's Power for Spiritual Awakening. 2009. (Illus.). 173p. pap. **(978-1-4158-6687-0(2))** B&H Publishing Group.

Blackaby, Tom & Blackaby, Kim. The Family God Uses: Becoming a Home of Influence. 2009. (ENG.). 192p. 18.99 (978-1-59669-251-0(0)) New Hope Pubs.

Blackburn, Lawton. Fear of God Agreement, 1 vol. 2009. 48p. pap. 16.95 (978-1-4489-9966-8(9)) PublishAmerica, Inc.

Blacker, Michael. The Second Coming of Christ Jesus. 2007. 112p. per. 12.95 (978-1-4327-0361-5(7)) Outskirts Pr., Inc.

Blackmon, Bill. Sacred Balance. 2007. 132p. per. (978-1-897373-05-7(8)) Word Alive Pr.

Blackmon, Sharon D. A Woman with Sight & No Vision. 2009. 96p. pap. 10.49 (978-1-4389-7087-5(0)) AuthorHouse.

Blackmon, Valerie. The Making of a Woman: Discovering the Life-Giver Within You. 2010 pap. 15.99 (978-1-61579-882-7(X)) Xulon Pr., Inc.

Blackwell, John. A Whole New World: The Gospel of Matthew. 2011. (ENG.). 156p. pap. 13.95 **(978-1-60037-561-3(8))** Morgan James Publishing.

Blaike, Joseph J. The Essential Guide to Jesus, 1 vol. 2009. 139p. pap. 24.95 (978-1-61546-215-5(5)) PublishAmerica, Inc.

Blair, Eugene. What Kind of Man Is Joseph, & What Kind of Man Are You? 2009. 87p. pap. 10.00 (978-0-88177-561-7(4)) Discipleship Resources.

Blair, John J., Jr. Foundation Principles for the New Christian. 2006. per. 14.95 (978-1-59094-125-6(X)) Jawbone Publishing Corp.

Blair, Tony. The Bartender's Assistant: A Guide for the Journey. 2010. 50p. pap. 7.00 (978-1-60899-555-4(0), Resource Pubns.) Wipf & Stock Pubs.

Blake, Barry. Hearts to the Front! Greasing the Financial Gears of the Church. 2009. 52p. pap. 10.99 (978-1-61579-371-6(2)) Xulon Pr., Inc.

Blake, Jr. Valiant Living. 2009. 228p. pap. 15.99 (978-1-60791-637-6(1)) Xulon Pr., Inc.

Blakeney, Shaun & Brotherton, Marcus. Chiseled: A Young Man's Guide to Shaping Character, True Toughness, & a Life That Matters. 2008. (ENG.). 192p. pap. 12.99 (978-0-8307-4668-2(4)) Gospel Light Pubns.

Blamires, David The Book of the Perfect Life: Theologia Deutsch-Theologia Germanica. 2010. (Sacred Literature Trust Ser.). (ENG.). 112p. pap. 24.95 (978-0-300-16511-1(0)) Yale Univ. Pr.

Blamires, Harry. The Offering of Man. 2006. 158p. pap. 19.00 (978-1-55635-130-3(5), Wipf and Stock) Wipf & Stock Pubs.

—The Post-Christian Mind. 209p. pap. 10.99 (978-0-8307-3470-2(8), Regal Bks.) Gospel Light Pubns.

—Where Do We Stand? a Christian Response. 2006. 172p. per. (978-1-57383-316-5(9), Regent College Publishing) Regent College Publishing.

Blanchard, John. Ultimate Questions-NKJV. 2007. (Illus.). 32p. pap. (978-0-85234-534-4(8)) Evangelical Pr.

Blanchard, Ken & Cathy, S. Truett. The Generosity Factor: Discover the Joy of Giving Your Time, Talent, & Treasure, 1 vol. 2009. (ENG.). 128p. pap. 9.99 (978-0-310-32499-7(8)) Zondervan.

Blanchon, Margaret F. The Evangelist's Book of Helps. 2011. 244p. pap. 16 26 (978-1-4269-4711-7(9)) Trafford Publishing.

Blank, Renold J. Aprender a Amar en Pareja. (SPA.). 80p. 4.95 (978-958-607-498-8(6)) Sociedad de San Pablo COL. Dist: St Pauls/Alba Hse. Pubs.

Blankenship, Richard. Young Men's L. I. F. E. Guide, XXX Church. com. Laaser, Mark, ed. 2007. (YA). per. 19.95 (978-0-9771662-3-7(6)) Freedom Every Day LLC.

Blankenship, Sherry. Draw Near: One Pilgrim's Journey Through Grief to the Lap of Jesus. 2007. 197p. 19.99 (978-1-60247-069-9(3)) Tate Publishing & Enterprises, LLC.

Blanton, Christopher. Today I Choose-an 18 Day Prayer Guide for Believers. 2008. 56p. pap. 9.95 (978-1-60693-414-2(7), Eloquent Bks.) AEG Literary Publishing Services, Inc.

Blaylock, Janet. Giving up or Pressing Onward. 2007. 132p. 26.00 (978-0-615-16986-6(4)); 122p. pap. 14.50 (978-0-615-14826-7(3)) Blaylock, Janet.

Blea-Torres, Antonia. On the Wings of Hope: Devotions on Life Transformation. 2011. pap. 10 99 (978-1-61739-718-9(0)) Tate Publishing & Enterprises, LLC.

Bleichner, Howard P. In the Circle of Mysteries: The Coherence of Catholic Belief. 2008. (ENG.). 344p. pap. 34.95 (978-0-8245-2447-0(0)) Crossroad Publishing Co , The.

The Blessing of a Father's Love. 2008. (ENG., Illus.). 54p. 8.95 (978-0-8249-5878-7(0)) Ideals Pubns.

Blevins, Dean Gray & Maddix, Mark A. Discovering Discipleship: Dynamics of Christian Education. 2010. (ENG.). 384p. 44.99 (978-0-8341-2496-7(3), 9780834124967) Beacon Hill Pr. of Kansas City.

Blewett, James. Can I Get Baptized in Fruit Punch? 2010. pap. 10.99 (978-1-61739-014-2(3)) Tate Publishing & Enterprises, LLC.

Blight, Wendy & Moody Publishing Staff. Hidden Joy in a Dark Corner: The Transforming Power of God's Story, 1 vol. 2009. (ENG.). 208p. pap. 13.99 (978-0-8024-1496-0(6)) Moody Pubs.

Bliss, Joan. God Signs. 2010. 196p. pap. 14.99 (978-1-60957-510-6(5)) Xulon Pr., Inc.

Bliss, William G. Leadership Lessons from the BOOK. 2009. pap. 19.95 (978-1-61623-028-9(2)) Independent Pub.

Blocker, Simon. The Secret of Radiant Christian Living. 2011. 110p. 39.95 **(978-1-258-05329-1(2))** Literary Licensing, LLC.

Bloomer, George. More of Him. 2006. 224p. 12.99 (978-0-88368-790-1(9)) Whitaker Hse.

Bowers David. Rise up, o men of God! 2006. pap. 12.99 (978-1-60034-047-5(4)) Xulon Pr., Inc.

Blue, Ken. Having the Right Bait: A Fishermen's Guide to Soul Wining. pap. 3.25 (978-1-930452-08-4(X)) Local Church Publishing.

Blue, Kevin. Practical Justice: Living off-Center in a Self-Centered World. 2006. (ENG.). 143p. per. 15.00 (978-0-8308-3368-9(4), IVP Bks.) InterVarsity Pr.

Blue, Paul. Am I? 2008. 140p. pap. 14.99 (978-1-60647-807-3(9)) Xulon Pr., Inc.

Blue, Ron & White, Jeremy L. Surviving Financial Meltdown: Confident Decisions in an Uncertain World. 2009. (ENG.). 144p. pap. 12.99 (978-1-4143-2995-6(4)) Tyndale Hse. Pubs.

The Blue Scapular. (978-0-944203-25-5(6)) Marian Pr.

Blythe, Ronald. The Circling Year: Perspectives from a Country Parish. (Illus.). 224p. 29.95 (978-1-85311-365-9(4)) Norwich Bks. & Music GBR. Dist: Morehouse Publishing.

Boafo, Evangelist Francis. Re-Created for Greatness: The Quest for the Promised Glory. 2011. 192p. 30.95 **(978-1-4497-2422-1(1))**; pap. 13.95 **(978-1-4497-2421-4(3))** Author Solutions, Inc. (WestBow Pr.).

Boafo, Francis. Awaken to Your New Creation. 2006. pap. 13 99 (978-1-60034-083-3(0)) Xulon Pr., Inc.

Boahene, Joyce A. The Count It All Joy Devotional / Prayer Journal. 2007. 87p. per. 8.95 (978-1-59824-380-2(2)) E-BookTime LLC.

—The Count It All Joy Quiet Time Companion. 2007. 200p. per. 12.95 (978-1-59824-383-3(7)) E-BookTime LLC.

—Don't You Quit 2007. 103p. per. 8.95 (978-1-59824-381-9(0)) E-BookTime LLC.

Boal, Tim. Building Authentic Community: Enjoying Christ's Church in a Postmodern Age. 2006. 236p. per. 13.99 (978-0-88469-307-9(4)) BMH Bks.

Boardman, W. E. The Higher Christian Life. 2009. 336p. 29.99 (978-1-116-56942-1(6)); pap. 31.75 (978-1-116-56944-5(2)); pap. 30.75 (978-1-116-56945-2(0)) BiblioBazaar.

—The Higher Christian Life. Fessenden, David E., ed. 2007. (ENG.). 164p. pap. 12.99 (978-0-87508-894-5(5)) CLC Pubns.

Boardman, William Edwin. The Higher Christian Life. 2008. 336p. 28.99 (978-0-559-69881-1(X)); pap. 30.75 (978-0-559-69878-1(X)) BiblioBazaar.

—The Higher Christian Life. 2009. 164p. pap. (978-1-4589-1946-5(3)) Books LLC.

—The Higher Christian Life. 2007. (ENG.). 334p. 45.95 (978-0-548-15187-7(3)); 336p. per. 30 95 (978-1-4304-4545-6(9)) Kessinger Publishing, LLC.

—The Higher Christian Life. 2006. (ENG.). 336p. per. 23.99 (978-1-4255-3406-6(6)) MPublishing.

Bob Violino. Children of the Light: Inspiring Stories of Christians Living the Faith-and Changing the World. 2009. 152p. 24.95 (978-1-4401-7366-0(4)); pap. 14.95 (978-1-4401-7364-6(8)) iUniverse, Inc.

Bobo, Nell Tant. It Rained on My Parade. 2010. 160p. 30.95 (978-1-61507-235-4(7)); pap. 13.95 (978-1-61507-234-7(9)) Cross Bks. Publishing.

Bock, Lewis L. To Know This Mystery: A Doctor's Life-Changing Prescription Written in Poetic Verse. 2010. pap. 13.99 (978-1-60799-940-9(4)) Tate Publishing & Enterprises, LLC.

Boctor, Nadia G. The Teaching of the Master. 2010. 190p. 22.99 (978-1-61579-892-6(7)) Xulon Pr., Inc.

Bodeutsch, Calvin. Prayer: Touching Heaven. 2008. (Illus.). mass mkt. 18.99 (978-0-89814-067-5(6)) Grace Pubns., Inc.

Body & Soul. Date not set. 3.95 (978-0-687-00311-2(3)) Abingdon Pr.

Boeneim, John. An Essay of Reflection Yes, Virginia There Is a God: A Patriotic Christian View. 2009. 76p. pap. 10.49 (978-1-4389-9282-2(3)) AuthorHouse.

Boehme, Jacob. A Description of the Process & Surpassing Virtue of Sophia's Pearl. 2006. pap. 12.95 (978-1-4286-7450-9(0)) Kessinger Publishing, LLC.

—The Epistles. unabr. ed. 2007. (ENG.). 236p. per. (978-1-897352-28-1(X)) Providence University.

—In What Manner God Forgives Stan & How You Become a Child Of. 2006. pap. 9.95 (978-1-4286-7384-7(9)) Kessinger Publishing, LLC.

—The Knowledge of God & All Things Including a Short Declaration. 2006. pap. 12.95 (978-1-4286-7431-8(4)) Kessinger Publishing, LLC.

—The Manifestation of the Deity by the Creation of Angels & Men. 2006. pap. 12.95 (978-1-4286-7408-0(X)) Kessinger Publishing, LLC.

—Of Our Death. 2006. pap. 12.95 (978-1-4286-7457-8(8)) Kessinger Publishing, LLC.

—Of the Origin of Faith & Why Faith & Doubt Dwell Together. 2006. pap. 9.95 (978-1-4286-7362-5(8)) Kessinger Publishing, LLC.

—The of the Property of Faith & How It Goes Out from the Will Into. 2006. pap. 9.95 (978-1-4286-7381-6(4)) Kessinger Publishing, LLC.

—The Open Fountain in the Heart of Jesus Christ Be Our Refreshment. 2006. pap. 9.95 (978-1-4286-7299-4(0)) Kessinger Publishing, LLC.

—The Open Fountain of God in the Heart of Jesus Christ Be Our 2006. pap. 9.95 (978-1-4286-7347-2(4)) Kessinger Publishing, LLC.

—The Salvation & Light of God in the Life of Jesus Christ Enlighten. 2006. pap. 9.95 (978-1-4286-7369-4(5)) Kessinger Publishing, LLC.

—Signature of All Things. 2007. (ENG.). 300p. per. 14.95 (978-1-60206-397-6(4)) Cosimo, Inc.

—That the Person of Christ As Well As His Incarnation Cannot Be. 2006. pap. 12.95 (978-1-4286-7426-4(8)) Kessinger Publishing, LLC.

—The True & Highly Precious Gate of the Holy Trinity. 2006. pap. 9.95 (978-1-4286-7338-0(5)) Kessinger Publishing, LLC.

—Why the Statute of One Deceased Wept or Shed Tears. 2006. pap. 9.95 (978-1-4286-7320-5(2)) Kessinger Publishing, LLC.

Boelter, Vance Luther. Original Ability: Can Man Obey God? 2008 pap. (978-1-60034-197-7(7)) Xulon Pr., Inc.

Boggler, L. Sue. Four Legs of the Stool: Using the Four Aspects of Our Humanity to Balance A Christian Life. 2011. 152p. 30.95 **(978-1-4582-0064-8(7))**; pap. 13.95 **(978-1-4582-0063-1(9))** Author Solutions, Inc. (Abbott Pr.).

Boggs Brenda. Holy Spirit, Teach Me. 2008. 172p. per. 13.99 (978-1-60477-425-2(8)) Xulon Pr., Inc.

Bohner, Olivine Nadeau. Into the Blizzard: The Adventures of Jack Zachary, Heretic of the Northland. 2009. (ENG., Illus.). 176p. pap. 12.95 (978-1-57258-158-6(1), 945-6025) TEACH Services, Inc.

Bolden Karen. Karen's Anointed Expressions Presents Blessed. 2009. 48p. pap 19 49 (978-1-4389-1794-8(5)) AuthorHouse.

Bolduc Kathleen Deyer. Autism & Alleluias. 2010. 144p. pap. 14.00 (978-0-8170-1568-8(X)) Judson Pr.

Bolin, Jim. The Rope of Hope. 2008. pap. 9.66 (978-0-9665831-9-9(1)) Kairos Publishing.

Bolt, Zach. Letters from the Father's Heart. 2009. 247p. pap. 19.99 (978-0-88144-306-6(9), Thorncrown Publishing) Yorkshire Publishing Group.

Bolton, B. J. Ayudando a los Pequenos: ICL Ways to Help Them. (SPA.). 168p. (978-84-7228-951-2(6), 223036) Clie, Editorial.

Bolton, Martha. When You Walk Through Green Pastures Stick to the Path. 190p. pap. 10.99 (978-0-8307-3521-1(6), Regal Bks.) Gospel Light Pubns.

Bolz-Weber, Nadia. Salvation on the Small Screen? 24 Hours of Christian Television. 2008. 176p. pap. 17.00 (978-1-59627-086-2(1), Seabury Bks.) Church Publishing, Inc.

Bonar, Horatius. Absolutely Basic. 2009. (Great Christian Classics Ser.). 95p. pap. (978-0-946462-79-7(8)) Evangelical Pr.

—Como Acercarse a Dios: How Shall I Go to God. (SPA.). (978-84-7228-851-5(X), 220215) Clie, Editorial.

—God's Way of Peace. 2009. 82p. pap. (978-1-4590-9630-1(4)) Books LLC.

—Night of Weeping & Morning of Joy. 2008. per. (978-1-60178-032-4(X)) Reformation Heritage Bks.

Bond, Douglas. Fathers & Sons, Volume 1: Stand Fast in the Way of Truth. 2008. 331p. per. (978-1-59638-076-9(4)) P & R Publishing.

—Fathers & Sons, Volume 2: Hold Fast in a Broken World. 2008. (Fathers & Sons Ser.). 285p. pap. 14.99 (978-1-59638-077-6(2)) P & R Publishing.

Bond, Johnathan & Ginger. God's Still God. 2008. 112p. (ENG.). 18.99 (978-1-60477-621-8(8)); per. 10.99 (978-1-60477-620-1(X)) Xulon Pr., Inc.

Bond, Jonnnie D, Sr. 24 Minute Ministry Family Devotional: A Revolutionary New Concept in Ministry. 2008. 322p. pap. 39.95 (978-0-9786088-1-1(X)) True Vine Publishing Co.

Bond, P. Pebbles. 2007. 152p. 21.99 (978-1-60266-839-3(6)) Xulon Pr., Inc.

Bonds, Charles L. Ain't That Something? The Musings, Adventures, & Experiences of a Southern Country Boy Reflecting over Forty-Nine Years of Pastoral Ministry. 2009. 136p. 23.95 (978-1-4401-4331-1(5)); pap. 13.95 (978-1-4401-4333-5(1)) iUniverse, Inc.

Bonds, Jeanette. Love Lifted Me. 2008. 76p. pap. 12.98 (978-1-4389-2351-2(1)) AuthorHouse.

C

Bonenberger, Steve. Hovering Presence. 2007. (Through Gates of Fire Ser.). 304p. per. 22.99 (978-1-60247-083-5(9)) Tate Publishing & Enterprises, LLC.
Bonner, Millard. There Is a God. 2007. (ENG.). 88p. per. 16.95 (978-1-4241-4034-3(X)) PublishAmerica, Inc.
Bonnet, David J. Coming Out of Hell: A Journey from Chaos to Redemption. 2007. 205p. per. 14.99 (978-0-924748-77-6(X)) Milestones International Publishers.
Bonzo, J. Matthew & Stevens, Michael R. Wendell Berry & the Cultivation of Life: A Reader's Guide. 2008. 208p. pap. 22.00 (978-1-58743-195-1(5)) Brazos Pr.
Book of Discipline 2008 Korean. 2009. 18.00 (978-0-687-65165-8(4)) Abingdon Pr.
Book of the Holy Rites. 2010. (SYR.). 116.48 (978-1-61143-348-7(7)) Gorgias Pr., LLC.
Booker, Robert. Maxim: Practical Advice for the 21st-Century Christian. 2007. 76p. per. 16.95 (978-1-4241-9494-0(6)) PublishAmerica, Inc.
Booker, Shawn E. Fastforward to the Beginning: The way it began Is the way it will End. 2009. 74p. pap. 13.95 (978-1-4327-3797-9(X)) Outskirts Pr., Inc.
Boonstra, Juan S. Hogar y Familia en el Siglo XX: Home & Family in the XX Century. (SPA.). (978-84-7645-271-4(3), 223360) Clie, Editorial.
Booram, Beth. Picturing the Face of Jesus: Encountering Christ Through Art. 2009. 112p. pap. 15.00 (978-0-687-65743-8(1)) Abingdon Pr.
Booth, Imogen. In Darkness & in Light. 2011. 562p. 47.99 (978-1-61379-376-3(6)); pap. 32.99 (978-1-61379-375-6(8)) Xulon Pr., Inc.
Booth, Leo. The Wisdom of Letting Go: The Path of the Wounded Soul. 2009. (ENG.). 375p. pap. 12.95 (978-0-7573-0791-1(4)) Health Communications, Inc.
Booth, Michael. Ride in the Boat ? or Walk on Water. 2011. 158p. 29.99 (978-1-4653-0027-0(9)); pap. 19.99 (978-1-4653-0026-3(0)) Xlibris Corp.
Borden, Lisa Repko. Approaching God, 1 vol. 2010. (Illus.). 128p. 14.99 (978-1-85424-948-7(7), Monarch Bks.) Lion Hudson PLC GBR. Dist: Kregel Pubns.
Borden, Troy. Christians Gotta Have a Dream! Pursue the Dream That Will Enable You to Achieve Your God-Given Destiny. 2007. 128p. per. 13.95 (978-0-595-44593-6(4)) iUniverse, Inc.
Borden, Troy. Leave A Mark: A Complete Guide to Pursuing the Dream That Will Enable You to Achieve Your God-Given Destiny. 2011. 180p. pap. 16.95 (978-1-4620-6083-2(8)) iUniverse, Inc.
Bordon, David & Winters, Tom. Everything Christmas. 2010. (ENG., Illus.). 320p. 14.99 (978-0-307-72929-3(X), WaterBrook Pr.) Doubleday Religious Publishing Group, The.
Borg, Marcus. Embracing an Adult Faith: Marcus Borg on What it Means to Be Christian: A 5-Session Study. 2010. 96p. pap. 12.95 (978-1-60674-057-6(1)) Morehouse Education Resources.
Borg, Marcus J. Jesus: Uncovering the Life, Teachings, & Relevance of a Religious Revolutionary. l.t. ed. 2007. (ENG.). 608p. pap. 24.95 (978-0-06-114592-6(0), HarperLuxe) HarperCollins Pubs.
Borik, Anne D. O. Prayer Prescribed: A path to restoring & preserving your health & Well-being. 2011. 114p. 29.99 (978-1-4653-6338-1(6)); pap. 19.99 (978-1-4653-6337-4(8)) Xlibris Corp.
Borlace, Craig. The Naked Christian. 193p. pap. (978-0-340-78529-4(2), Hodder & Stoughton) Hodder General Publishing Div.
Borreson, Glenn L. Water for Your Soul. 2008. 110p. pap. 10.95 (978-0-7414-4437-0(2)) Infinity Publishing.
Borthwick, Paul. How to Be a World-Class Christian: Becoming Part of Gods Global Kingdom. rev. ed. 2009. (ENG.). 237p. pap. 14.99 (978-1-934068-34-2(9)) Authentic Media.
Bosch, Henry, et al. Christmas: Quiet Moments for the Season. 2007. (Strength for the Soul from Our Daily Bread Ser.). (ENG.). 128p. per. 5.99 (978-1-57293-259-3(7)) Discovery Hse. Pubs.
Bosco, Antoinette. Radical Forgiveness. 2009. xiii, 161p. pap. 16.00 (978-1-57075-815-7(8)) Orbis Bks.
Boston, Jane. Reigning in His Power: A Study on how to Rein in the Power of the Holy Spirit in Your Daily Walk. 2011. 136p. pap. 16.95 (978-1-4497-1124-5(3), WestBow Pr.) Author Solutions, Inc.
Bostrom, Kathleen. Making Space for the Spirit: 100 Simple Ways to Nurture Your Soul. 2010. (ENG.). 96p. pap. 13.00 (978-0-664-23462-1(3)) Westminster John Knox Pr.
Boteler, Lori. A Common Sens Approach toJob. 2007. 105p. per. 20.00 (978-0-9798207-1-7(5)) LoJo Publishing.
—A Common Sense Approach to Esther. 2007. per. 20.00 (978-0-9798207-0-0(7)) LoJo Publishing.
—A Common Sense Approach to Exodus. 2008. per. 20.00 (978-0-9798207-4-8(X)) LoJo Publishing.
—A Common Sense Approach to Genesis. 2007. per. 20.00 (978-0-9789555-8-8(7)) LoJo Publishing.
Botero, Silvio. Dinamicas Grupales de Reflexion. 160p. 6.95 (978-958-607-011-9(5)) Sociedad de San Pablo COL. Dist: St Pauls/Alba Hse. Pubs.
—Hacia una Nueva Etica Conyugal. (SPA.). 176p. 7.95 (978-958-607-740-8(3)) Sociedad de San Pablo COL. Dist: St Pauls/Alba Hse. Pubs.
Botsford, Nancy. A Day in Hell: Death to Life to Hope. 2010. pap. 12.99 (978-1-61663-251-9(8)) Tate Publishing & Enterprises, LLC.
Bottorff, Marjorie Ward. A String of Pearls: Finding Humor in Life's Daily Challenges. 2009. pap. 10.99 (978-1-60696-980-9(3)) Tate Publishing & Enterprises, LLC.
Bouchard, L. J. A Lesson from the Ruby, 1 vol. 2009. 64p. pap. 16.95 (978-1-60813-228-7(5)) PublishAmerica, Inc.
Boulding, Marked for Life. 3rd ed. 128p. 14.95 (978-0-281-04926-4(2)) International Publishers Marketing.
Bouman, Stephen Paul. Grace All Around Us: Embracing God's Promise in Tragedy & Loss. 2007. 128p. per. 13.99 (978-0-8066-5325-9(6), Augsburg Bks.) Augsburg Fortress, Pubs.
Bounds, E. M. The Necessity of Prayer. 2008. 84p. pap. 6.99 (978-1-60459-378-5(4)) Wilder Pubns., Ltd.
Bounds, E. M. Power Through Prayer. 2010. 80p. pap. 6.99 (978-1-61203-003-6(3)) Bottom of the Hill Publishing.
Bounds, Edward M. The Necessity of Prayer. 2007. (ENG.). 144p. per. 9.99 (978-1-84550-208-9(6)) Christian Focus Pubns. GBR. Dist: STL Distribution North America.
—Power Through Prayer. 2007. (ENG.). 132p. per. 8.50 (978-1-60206-541-3(1)) Cosimo, Inc.
—Power Through Prayer. 2007. (Authentic Original Classic Ser.). 160p. per. 13.99 (978-0-7684-2516-1(6)) Destiny Image Pubs.
—Power Through Prayer. 2007. per. 6.99 (978-1-4245-0809-9(6)) Treasures Media Inc.
Bourgond, Greg. A Rattling of Sabers: Preparing Your Heart for Life's Battles. 2010. 324p. 32.95 (978-1-4502-3881-6(5)); (ENG.). pap. 22.95 (978-1-4502-3880-9(7)) iUniverse, Inc.
Bourn-Heard, Carmilla. Overwhelming, Overpowering, Triumphant Victory! 2008. 77p. pap. 12.00 (978-1-4357-5460-7(3)) Lulu Enterprises Inc.
Bousa, Jess. The Discipleship Dare: Living Dangerously for God. 2010. 171p. pap. (978-1-933715-96-4(0), Tremendous Life Bks.) Executive Bks.
Bouteneff, Peter C. Beginnings: Ancient Christian Readings of the Biblical Creation Narratives. 2008. 256p. (C). pap. 25.00 (978-0-8010-3233-2(4)) Baker Academic.
bouter, chris. Everybody His Own God. 2007. 149p. pap. 13.95 (978-1-84799-741-8(4)) Lulu Enterprises Inc.
Bouwense, Francine L. Through His Eyes: A Heavenly View of Earthly Matters. 2009. 28p. pap. 16.99 (978-1-61579-046-3(2)) Xulon Pr., Inc.
Bouwer, J., ed. Successful Ageing, Spirituality & Meaning: Multidisciplinary Perspectives. 2010. (Studies in Spirituality Supplements Ser.). (ENG.). 284p. (C). pap. 70.00 (978-90-429-2268-6(0)) Peeters Pubs. & Booksellers BEL. Dist: Brown, David Bk. Co., The.
Bovines, Julie. Got God? 2010. 200p. pap. 15.99 (978-1-60957-489-5(3)) Xulon Pr., Inc.
Bowell, Gary. Stones with Fair Colors. pap. 7.99 (978-0-88019-111-1(2)) Schmul Publishing Co., Inc.
Bowen, Dorothy. Keep Your Fingers in the Dirt. 2009. 256p. pap. 16.99 (978-1-60791-340-5(2)) Xulon Pr., Inc.
Bowen, John P. Growing up Christian: Why Young People Stay in Church, Leave Church, & (Sometimes) Come Back to Church. 2010. (978-1-57383-431-5(9)) Regent College Publishing.
Bowen, Shyll. Longing for Home: Our Citizenship Is in Heaven. pap. 9.99 (978-0-89098-183-2(3)) Twentieth Century Christian Bks.
Bowen, Wendy. Confessions of a Recovering Type A. 2010. 282p. 19.95 (978-0-615-34642-7(1)) New Street, Inc.
Bower, Christy. Best Friends with God: Falling in Love with the God Who Loves You. 2010. (ENG.). 128p. pap. 10.99 (978-1-57293-372-9(0)) Discovery Hse. Pubs.
Bower, Matt. Standing by the Pillar. 2008. (ENG.). 248p. pap. 24.99 (978-1-60477-511-2(4)) Xulon Pr., Inc.
Bowers, Gary. Out of the Abyss: Can the number of the beast be Solved? 666. 2011. 304p. 37.95 (978-1-4497-1039-2(5)); pap. 22.95 (978-1-4497-1038-5(7)) WestBow Pr. A Div. of Thomas Nelson.
Bowers, Katherine. You Don't Dig for Water under the Outhouse. 2006. (ENG.). 244p. per. 24.95 (978-1-4241-4440-2(0)) PublishAmerica, Inc.
Bowie Guillory, Joyce A. The Door. 2009. 180p. pap. 14.99 (978-1-60791-426-6(3)) Xulon Pr., Inc.
The Bowl Judgments. pap. 0.95 (978-0-937408-11-7(5)) GMI Pubns.
Bowlin. Vitally Alive! 2009. 304p. pap. 18.99 (978-1-60791-640-6(1)) Xulon Pr., Inc.
Bowling, Sarah. Upside Down. 2008. pap. 15.99 (978-0-7684-2663-2(4)) Destiny Image Pubs.
Bowman, Aaron. Heir of God: What the Devil Doesn't Want You to Know. 2009. (J). pap. 10.99 (978-1-60799-838-9(6)) Tate Publishing & Enterprises, LLC.
Bowman, Bob. A Chosen Life Study: Conversations, Scriptures & Poems. 2009. 200p. pap. 19.99 (978-1-4490-0123-0(8)) AuthorHouse.
Bowman, Khalani. A Rose Is Still a Rose. 2006. pap. 13.99 (978-1-60034-781-8(9)) Xulon Pr., Inc.
Boyack, Merrilee. 52 Weeks of Fun Family Service. 2007. 224p. pap. 14.95 (978-1-59038-848-8(8)) Deseret Bk. Co.
Boyd, Aaron & Borlase, Craig. God of This City: Greater Things Have yet to Come. 2010. (ENG.). 144p. pap. 12.99 (978-0-8307-5223-2(4)) Gospel Light Pubns.
Boyd, Austin. The Proof. 2006. (Mars Hill Classified Ser.). (ENG., Illus.). 480p. per. 12.99 (978-1-57683-945-4(1)) NavPress Publishing Group.
Boyd, Gregory A. The Myth of a Christian Religion: Losing Your Religion for the Beauty of a Revolution, 1 vol. 2009. (ENG.). 224p. 19.99 (978-0-310-28383-6(3)) Zondervan.
Boyd, Tommy. Write the Vision. 2011. 56p. pap. 26.99 (978-1-4567-6907-9(3)) AuthorHouse.
Boyer, Dorothy Lundahl. F a I T H. 2009. 156p. pap. 14.99 (978-1-60791-477-8(8)) Xulon Pr., Inc.
Boyett, Jason & Boyett. Sainthood: A Field Manual for the Super Virtuous Life. 2009. (ENG., Illus.). 240p. pap. 12.95 (978-0-470-37310-1(5), Jossey-Bass) Wiley, John & Sons, Inc.
Boykin, Cynthia. Elephant Faith. annot. ed. 2006. (ENG.). 64p. pap. 6.99 (978-1-59979-053-4(X), Creation Hse.) Charisma Media.
Boynes, Janet. Called Out: A Former Lesbian's Discovery of Freedom. 2008. (ENG.). 224p. pap. 13.99 (978-1-59979-385-6(7), Creation Hse.) Charisma Media.
Boysen, Patricia. Joyful Perspective. 2007. 340p. (ENG.). 29.99 (978-1-4257-9862-8(4)); per. 19.99 (978-1-4257-9852-9(7)) Xlibris Corp.
Brackeen, Tamara Alise. The Siren's Beckoning Call. 2007. 116p. per. 10.99 (978-1-60477-468-9(1)) Xulon Pr., Inc.
Bradbury, Richard. Losing My Religion: The Radical Message of the Kingdom. 2011. 154p. pap. 13.99 (978-1-907728-17-4(1)) Pneuma Springs Publishing GBR. Dist: Lightning Source, Inc.
Braddy, Judi. It All Comes Out in the Wash: Sorting Through Priorities When Your Load Is Out of Balance. 2006. (ENG.). 192p. per. 14.99 (978-0-8341-2259-8(6), 083-412-2596) Beacon Hill Pr. of Kansas City.
—True North: Staying on Course Through Life's Changing Circumstances. 2007. (ENG.). 192p. pap. 14.99 (978-0-8341-2341-0(X), 083-412-341X) Beacon Hill Pr. of Kansas City.
Bradfield, B. Wayne. No One Has Hired Us: Bible Truths for the Unemployed. 2011. 116p. pap. 11.95 (978-1-4497-0943-3(5), WestBow Pr.) Author Solutions, Inc.
Bradley, Edward L. As the Son Rose: Jesus Is the Light. 2011. 228p. 24.59 (978-1-4520-4925-0(4)); pap. 14.03 (978-1-4520-4924-3(6)) AuthorHouse.
Bradley, Gene. Ten Turning Points in My Life. 2007. pap. 9.99 (978-1-60034-135-9(7)) Xulon Pr., Inc.
Bradley, Ian. God Save the Queen: The Spiritual Heart of the Monarchy. 2012. (ENG.). 336p. pap. 19.95 (978-1-4411-9367-4(7)) Continuum International Publishing Group, Ltd. GBR. Dist: National Bk. Network.
Bradley, J. 'You Shall surely not Die' The Concepts of Sin & Death as Expressed in the Manuscript Art of Northwestern Europe, C. 800-1200, 2 vols. 2008. (Illus.). 448p. (978-90-04-16910-4(5)) BRILL.
Bradley, Rebecca. I Am Redeemed: A Three-Step Program on the Road to Redemption. 2006. (Illus.). 60p. per. 12.95 (978-1-58597-405-4(6)) Leathers Publishing.
Bradley, Robert L. Necessity of Adversity. 2008. 188p. per. 13.99 (978-1-60477-548-8(3)) Xulon Pr., Inc.
Bradley, Roger L. Brass Tacks Christianity & Beyond! 2011. 240p. 27.95 (978-1-4269-5172-5(8)); pap. 17.95 (978-1-4269-5171-8(X)) Trafford Publishing.
Bradley/Toussaint. God's Roadmap to Peace: A Study of the Book of Revelation. 2011. (ENG.). 298p. pap. 32.95 (978-0-7618-5520-0(3)) Hamilton Bks.
Brady, Amy. When All Else Fails... Stand. 2011. 98p. pap. 12.99 (978-1-60957-678-3(0)) Xulon Pr., Inc.
Brady, Mary. The Truth. 2007. 112p. per. 10.99 (978-1-60034-686-6(3)) Xulon Pr., Inc.
Brady, Phyllis & Grogan, Brian. Meetings Matter: Representing the Spirit at Meetings. 2010. (ENG.). 136p. pap. 16.95 (978-1-84730-196-3(7)) Veritas Pubns. IRL. Dist: Dufour Editions, Inc.
Brady-Powell, Janet. The Energy of Encouragement: How Affirmation Can Lift You & Everyone Around You. 2008. (ENG.). 144p. pap. 13.99 (978-1-933204-52-9(4)) Deep River Bks.
Brady, Veronica. The God-Shaped Hole. 2008. 124p. pap. 10.00 (978-1-920691-87-5(1)) ATF Pr. AUS. Dist: International Publishers Marketing.
Bragwell, Edward. The Course of This World. 2007. 88p. per. 10.95 (978-1-58427-214-4(7)) Guardian of Truth Foundation.
Bramsen, P. D. One God One Message: Discover the Mystery, Take the Journey. 3rd ed. 2009. (ENG.). 432p. pap. 14.95 (978-0-9798706-6-7(7)) ROCK International.
Brancheau, Ted. Your Ministry Matters: From the Parking Lot to the Pulpit. 2010. pap. 12.99 (978-1-61566-644-7(3)) Tate Publishing & Enterprises, LLC.
Brannan, William J. Spiritual DNA. 2008. 272p. pap. 16.99 (978-1-60791-191-3(4)) Xulon Pr., Inc.
Branon, Dave. Beyond the Valley: Finding Hope in Life's Losses. 2010. (ENG.). 176p. pap. 10.99 (978-1-57293-373-6(9)) Discovery Hse. Pubs.
Branon, Dave & Discovery House Publishers Staff. When You Don't Know What to Say: Words of Caring for All Occasions 2nd Edition. 2nd rev. ed. 2010. (ENG.). 176p. pap. 10.99 (978-1-57293-379-8(8)) Discovery Hse. Pubs.
Brantley, Carolyn. Reminders from Russia. 2007. 109p. per. 10.99 (978-1-60247-256-3(4)) Tate Publishing & Enterprises, LLC.
Brantley, T. Charles. You Can't Have the Head Without the Body: Diligo Corpus Sarcalogos (Love the Body of Christ) 2008. 108p. pap. 13.95 (978-1-4327-3405-3(9)) Outskirts Pr., Inc.
Brantschen, Niklaus. Fasting: What * Why * How. 2010. (ENG.). 112p. pap. 14.95 (978-0-8245-2540-8(X)) Crossroad Publishing Co., The.
Branzell, Kathy. Prayer Warrior. 2006. pap. 12.99 (978-1-60034-463-3(1)) Xulon Pr., Inc.
Braschler, Todd & Laffoon, Jill. Common Bond. 2007. (Illus.). 128p. 13.99 incl. audio compact disk (978-0-89221-679-6(4)) New Leaf Pr., Inc.
Brash, Pauline. Perils to Pearls. 2011. 120p. pap. 11.99 (978-1-61379-143-1(7)) Xulon Pr., Inc.
Braswell, Pat K. Through the Fires - God. 2008. 108p. 21.99 (978-1-60477-813-7(X)); pap. 10.99 (978-1-60477-812-0(1)) Xulon Pr., Inc.
Brathwaite, Chris. Titus: A Biblical Study of the Book of Titus. 2010. 76p. pap. 14.95 (978-1-934449-51-6(2)) Legacy Publishing Services, Inc.
Brauns, Chris. Unpacking Forgiveness: Biblical Answers for Complex Questions & Deep Wounds. 2008. 240p. pap. 17.99 (978-1-58134-980-1(7)) Crossway.
Brawner, William. Before WE Become Extinct. 2008. 112p. pap. 17.48 (978-1-4357-4423-3(3)) Lulu Enterprises Inc.
Braxton, Coraeen F. Living in the Amazing Grace of God. 2007. 84p. per. 10.99 (978-0-9798084-1-8(3)) Leading Lady Pubns.
Braxton, Virgie. Random Parables. 2008. 92p. pap. 10.99 (978-1-60647-668-0(8)) Xulon Pr., Inc.
Brazelton, Katie, et al. Character Makeover: 40 Days with a Life Coach to Create the Best You, 1 vol. 2007. (ENG., Illus.). 336p. (gr. 13). pap. 14.99 (978-0-310-25653-3(4)) Zondervan.
Brech, Ronald. Christianity for the Twenty-first Century? A Personal Exposition of the Drama of Christ. 2008. 184p. pap. (978-1-84748-399-7(2)) Athena Pr.
Bree, Kevin & Bree, Amy. Powerflow. 2008. 96p. pap. 11.99 (978-0-88144-316-5(6)) Yorkshire Publishing Group.
Breedlove, Steve, et al. The Shame Exchange: Trading Shame for God's Mercy & Freedom. 2009. (Becoming a Woman Of ... Ser.). (ENG.). 192p. pap. 12.99 (978-1-60006-625-2(9)) NavPress Publishing Group.
Breisch, Francis, Jr. El Ministerio de Cristo en Palestina, Libro 1. (SPA.). 192p. pap. 6.00 (978-1-55883-019-6(7), 6700-0510C) Libros Desafio.
—El Ministerio de Cristo Hasta lo Ultimo de la Tierra, Libro 3. (SPA.). 168p. pap. 6.00 (978-1-55883-021-9(9), 6700-0530C) Libros Desafio.
Brennan, Patrick McKinely. The Vocation of the Child. 2008. 432p. (C). pap. 36.00 (978-0-8028-6240-2(3)) Eerdmans, William B. Publishing Co.
Brenneman, Robert. Homies & Hermanos: God & the Gangs in Central America, 1 vol. 2011. (ENG., Illus.). 312p. 99.00 (978-0-19-975384-0(9)); pap. 24.95 (978-0-19-975390-1(3)) Oxford Univ. Pr., Inc.
Brennt, Brian & Riches, Mike. Big 10 Discipleship. 2007. per. 19.99 (978-1-934290-61-3(0)) Revelasio Ministries Publishing.
—Freedom 2: Yearning for the Heart of Christ. 3rd ed. 2007. per. 19.99 (978-1-934290-31-6(9)) Revelasio Ministries Publishing.
—Freedom Class Manual. 2007. per. 19.99 (978-1-934290-00-2(9)) Revelasio Ministries Publishing.
—Freedom Resource Manual. 2007. per. 19.99 (978-1-934290-15-6(7)) Revelasio Ministries Publishing.
Brewer, Charlotte. God Deliver Me from Me. 2007. 212p. per. 14.99 (978-1-60266-808-9(6)) Xulon Pr., Inc.
Brewer, Jeff M. The Parable of the Four Stones. 2008. 160p. 21.99 (978-1-60647-618-5(1)); pap. 13.99 (978-1-60647-617-8(3)) Xulon Pr., Inc.
Brewer, Saundra Strong. Released into God's Hands. 2008. 196p. pap. 24.95 (978-1-60474-879-6(6)) PublishAmerica, Inc.
Brewin, Patricia Jane. The Diary of A Christian: The Evangelism of A Soul, & Other Life Lessons. 2011. (ENG.). 210p. pap. 22.95 (978-1-4327-6355-8(5)) Outskirts Pr., Inc.
Brewster, Joy. Diminishment: A Memoir. 2011. 19.95 (978-1-894667-88-3(3)) Clements Publishing.
Brewster, Joy. The Rugged Road to Freedom: A Prayer Process for Change. 2006. (ENG.). 200p. per. (978-1-894667-72-2(7)) Clements Publishing.
Brice, Joseph. The Shadow of Cliff College. pap. 5.99 (978-0-88019-172-2(4)) Schmul Publishing Co., Inc.
Brickey, Beth. Remember: Says the Lord. 2010. 160p. pap. (978-1-55452-466-2(0), Guardian Bks.) Essence Publishing.
Bridgeforth, E. Richard. The Art of Asking & Receiving. 2009. pap. 10.99 (978-1-60791-820-2(X)) Xulon Pr., Inc.
Bridgeman, Valerie & Fosua, Safiyah, eds. Companion to the Africana Worship Book. 2008. 159p. 22.00 (978-0-88177-533-4(9)) Discipleship Resources.
Bridger House Publishers. Manuel Pour le Nouveau Paradigme. 2008. 168p. pap. 6.95 (978-0-9799176-0-8(3)) Bridger Hse. Pubns., Inc.
Bridges, Jerry & Bridges, Gerald. The Fruitful Life: The Overflow of God's Love Through You. 2006. (Living the Questions Ser.). (ENG., Illus.). 192p. per. 12.99 (978-1-60006-027-4(7)) NavPress Publishing Group.
—Respectable Sins: Confronting the Sins We Tolerate. 2007. (TH1NK Reference Collection). (ENG.). 192p. 19.99 (978-1-60006-140-0(0)) NavPress Publishing Group.
—Transforming Grace: Living Confidently in God's Unfailing Love. 2008. (Hollywood Nobody Ser.). (ENG.). 272p. pap. 14.99 (978-1-60006-303-9(9)) NavPress Publishing Group.
—Transforming Grace Discussion Guide Living Confidently in God's Unfailing Love. 2008. (Hollywood Nobody Ser.). 112p. pap. 9.99 (978-1-60006-304-6(7)) NavPress Publishing Group.
—Trusting God: Even When Life Hurts. 2008. (Hollywood Nobody Ser.). (ENG.). 240p. pap. 14.99 (978-1-60006-305-3(5)) NavPress Publishing Group.
—Trusting God Discussion Guide: Even When Life Hurts. 2008. (Hollywood Nobody Ser.). 144p. pap. 9.99 (978-1-60006-306-0(3)) NavPress Publishing Group.
Bridgwater, Mary Ann. Prayers for the Faithful: Fervent Daily Prayer & Meditations for Christians Serving Around the World. 2008. (ENG., Illus.). 448p. 18.99 (978-0-8054-4752-1(0)) B&H Publishing Group.
Bridwell, Lance Lee. Voices. 2009. 88p. pap. 11.49 (978-1-4389-6483-6(9)) AuthorHouse.
Briggs, Melody & Briggs, Richard. Living for God: Studies for Disciples in the 21st Century. 2008. (Illus.). 232p. pap. (978-1-903689-48-6(1)) Piquant Editions Ltd.

Bright, Arthur. Fatherlessness. 2007. 140p. pap. 14.95 *(978-0-9797062-0-2(3))* Bright Publishing Co., A.
Bright, Bill. Your New Life: Steps to Strengthening Your New Relationship with Christ. rev. ed. 36p. 1.95 *(978-1-57229-054-9(4))* FamilyLife.
Brighton, Mark. Mark: An Introductory Course. (Journeys Through God's Word Ser.). pap., stu. ed. 8.99 *(978-0-570-06871-6(1),* 20-2814); pap. 8.99 *(978-0-570-06872-3(X),* 20-2815) Concordia Publishing Hse.
Briney, Larry. More Grace for the Daily Grind: Daily Devotional Readings. 2009. 374p. pap. 20.99 *(978-1-61579-080-7(2))* Xulon Pr., Inc.
Brinkley, Timothy L. Stupid Questions Asked of Jesus. 2011. 116p. 29.99 ***(978-1-4568-5786-8(X))***; pap. 19.99 ***(978-1-4568-5785-1(1))*** Xlibris Corp.
Briscoe, Jill. Faith Dancing: Conversations in Good Company, 1 vol. 2009. (Illus.). 144p. 13.99 *(978-0-8254-6288-7(6),* Monarch Bks.) Lion Hudson PLC GBR. Dist: Kregel Pubns.
—Heart Cry: Searching for Answers in a World Without Meaning. 2007. (By Design Ser.). (ENG.). 208p. per. 14.99 *(978-1-57683-981-2(8))* NavPress Publishing Group.
Brittingham, Les. Christianity Is a White Collar Job. 2011. 316p. pap. 18.99 ***(978-1-61379-120-2(8))*** Xulon Pr., Inc.
Brittingham, Les. Kingdom Combat. 2008. 416p. per. 21.99 *(978-1-60477-574-7(2))* Xulon Pr., Inc.
Britton, James. The Overcomers. 2008. 120p. pap. 10.99 *(978-1-60647-400-6(6))* Xulon Pr., Inc.
Brixey, Maggie. It Is I, 1 vol. 2010. 48p. pap. 16.95 *(978-1-4489-4182-7(2))* PublishAmerica, Inc.
Broadbooks, Bob. How to Bless Your Pastor: Stories of Uncommon Graces. 2010. (ENG.). 128p. pap. 8.99 *(978-0-8341-2551-3(X),* 9780834125513) Beacon Hill Pr. of Kansas City.
Broadman and Holman Publishers Staff, prod. Bible Promises for Men. 2008. (ENG., Illus.). 128p. pap. 3.99 *(978-0-8054-4767-5(9),* B&H Bks.) B&H Publishing Group.
—Bible Promises for Women. 2008. (ENG.). 128p. pap. 3.99 *(978-0-8054-4769-9(5),* B&H Bks.) B&H Publishing Group.
Broadman Comments. 6.20 *(978-0-7673-4845-4(1))* LifeWay Christian Resources.
Broadwater, Donald A. God's Fire Starters. 2008. 244p. 25.99 *(978-1-60647-870-7(2))*; pap. 15.99 *(978-1-60647-869-1(9))* Xulon Pr., Inc.
Brock, Brian. Singing the Ethos of God: On the Place of Christian Ethics in Scripture. 2007. 386p. per. 34.00 *(978-0-8028-0379-5(2))* Eerdmans, William B. Publishing Co.
Brock, Brian & Harasta, Eva. Evoking Lament: A Theological Discussion. 2009. (ENG.). 240p. 49.95 *(978-0-567-03390-1(2))*; 140.00 *(978-0-567-03389-5(9))* Continuum International Publishing Group, Ltd. GBR. (T&T Clark Int'l). Dist: National Bk. Network.
Brock, R. G. Chronological Framework. 2010. 152p. pap. 11.99 *(978-0-88144-499-5(5))* Yorkshire Publishing Group.
Brockway, Margaret. A Man of God. 2011. 12p. 8.32 *(978-1-4567-3455-8(5))* AuthorHouse.
Brodhagen, Randy C. Excellence! God's Quality in You. 2007. (ENG.). 160p. per. 12.95 *(978-0-9786581-3-7(2))* Lifebridge Bks.
—The Helpers Handbook: How to Offer Christian Care & Guidance. 2007. (ENG.). 160p. pap. 12.95 *(978-0-9786581-9-9(1))* Lifebridge Bks.
—A Word from the Lord. 2006. (ENG.). 143p. per. 12.95 *(978-0-9770398-6-9(2))* Lifebridge Bks.
Brohl, Donald. Called by My Name. 2008. 168p. pap. 14.99 *(978-1-60791-109-8(4))* Xulon Pr., Inc.
Bromley, Nicole Braddock. Breathe: Finding Freedom to Thrive in Relationships after Childhood Sexual Abuse, 1 vol. 2009. (ENG.). 192p. pap. 12.99 *(978-0-8024-4865-1(8))* Moody Pubs.
Bronson, Will. How to Get to Heaven. 2009. 151p. pap. 14.00 *(978-0-615-24785-4(7))* Bronson Enterprises LLC.
Brook, Linda Rios. Jesus for Adults: The Search for Meaning & Purpose. 2006. 219p. per. 14.99 *(978-0-7684-2389-1(9))* Destiny Image Pubs.
Brookins, Rev. Larry A. It's All about the Kingdom: 10 Sermons with Kingdom Themes. 2010. 108p. 23.99 *(978-1-4490-6153-1(2))*; pap. 19.99 *(978-1-4490-6152-4(4))* AuthorHouse.
Brooks, Bryan. Creating a Tech Sabbath Habit: Unplug Your Mind, Restore Your Spirit, & Transform Your Technology Lifestyle. 2011. pap. 15.99 ***(978-1-61777-404-1(9))*** Tate Publishing & Enterprises, LLC.
Brooks, Christoph. Kingdom Dreaming. 2009. 192p. 14.95 *(978-1-934363-38-6(3))* Zoe Life Publishing.
Brooks, Francine. Ministry vs Family. 2007. 56p. per. 9.99 *(978-1-60266-963-5(5))* Xulon Pr., Inc.
Brooks, Jennifer. Embracing an Aching Heart: Addressing the Horrors of Human Trafficking. 2009. 76p. pap. 10.99 *(978-1-61579-370-9(4))* Xulon Pr., Inc.
Brooks, Keith. Superhero. 2007. 196p. per. 13.99 *(978-1-60266-700-6(4))* Xulon Pr., Inc.
Brooks, Lisa C. In the Process. 2009. 104p. pap. 12.99 *(978-1-4490-0224-4(2))* AuthorHouse.
Brother Bob, Bob, et al. A Dancing Heart. 2009. 156p. pap. 16.95 *(978-1-4327-3928-7(X))* Outskirts Pr., Inc.
Brother Lawrence. The Practice of the Presence of God. 2010. 48p. pap. 4.50 *(978-1-57898-899-0(3))* Martino Publishing.
Brott, Rich. Biblical Principles for Achieving Personal Success: 8 Critical Insights You Must Discover! 2008. 252p. per. 19.99 *(978-1-60185-013-3(1))* ABC Book Publishing.
—Biblical Principles That Create Success Through Productivity: How God Blesses Our Work Ethic. 2008. 224p. per. 19.99 *(978-1-60185-007-2(7))* ABC Book Publishing.
—How to Receive Prosperity & Provision: 17 Biblical Principles You Must Know. 2008. 296p. per. 19.99 *(978-1-60185-005-8(0))* ABC Book Publishing.
—Prosperity Has A Purpose: 27 Biblical Principles to Understand. 2008. 288p. per. 19.99 *(978-1-60185-006-5(9))* ABC Book Publishing.
Brower, Patricia W. Daily Mercies Revealed, Part II. 2008. 240p. pap. 14.95 *(978-0-9724586-4-1(6))* PearlStone Publishing, Inc.
Brower, Susan, ed. Reflections on the Lord's Prayer, 1 vol. 2009. (ENG.). 128p. 14.99 *(978-0-310-28106-1(7))* Zondervan.
Brown, Adolphus. Diary of the Little People: The Art of Survival. 2009. 52p. pap. 12.95 *(978-1-4327-0709-5(4))* Outskirts Pr., Inc.
Brown, Anthony. Wind... Be Faithful to Me. 2006. pap. 9.99 *(978-1-60034-572-2(7))* Xulon Pr., Inc.
Brown, Bea L. Sparkles of God: Stories of Spiritual Encounters with God's Special Servants. 2010. pap. 11.99 *(978-1-61566-838-0(1))* Tate Publishing & Enterprises, LLC.
Brown, Bishop Ronnie. Don't Turn Back! 2011. 108p. 23.89 *(978-1-4520-8259-2(6))*; pap. 13.73 *(978-1-4520-8257-8(X))* AuthorHouse.
Brown, Bobette. Jesus Said, Come! Trust Him As You Walk by Faith. 2010. pap. 14.99 *(978-1-61579-731-8(9))* Xulon Pr., Inc.
Brown Campbell, Joan. Living into Hope: A Call to Spiritual Action for Such a Time As This. 2010. 192p. 21.99 *(978-1-59473-283-6(3))* SkyLight Paths Publishing.
Brown, Carol A. The Mystery of Spiritual Sensitivity: Your Practical Guide to Responding to Burdens You Feel from God's Heart. 2008. 349p. per. 16.99 *(978-0-7684-2592-5(1))* Destiny Image Pubs.
Brown, Cedrick D. The Racial & Cultural Divide: Are We Still Prejudiced? 2009. 171p. pap. 12.99 *(978-1-60604-610-4(1))* Tate Publishing & Enterprises, LLC.
Brown, David. A Is for Adam, E Is for Eve: A Biblical Guide for Naming Your Child. 2009. pap. 9.99 *(978-1-60799-089-5(X))* Tate Publishing & Enterprises, LLC.
Brown, Didi. A Spoon of God. 2008. 328p. (ENG.). 27.99 *(978-1-60477-365-1(0))*; per. 17.99 *(978-1-60477-364-4(2))* Xulon Pr., Inc.
Brown, Donovan O. Jesus Is My Help. 2009. 116p. pap. 12.95 *(978-1-4401-2911-7(8))* iUniverse, Inc.
Brown, Elizabeth B. Living Successfully with Screwed-up People. 256p. reprint ed. 2010. pap. 12.99 *(978-0-8007-3288-2(X))* 2007. (gr. 13-18). pap. 12.99 *(978-0-8007-5708-3(4))* Revell.
Brown, F. Scott. Out of the Valley: One Man's Stand Against Darkness. 2008. (ENG.). 192p. 19.99 *(978-1-59979-532-4(9),* Creation Hse.) Charisma Media.
Brown, James. You Shall See His Glory in the Morning. 2006. pap. 17.99 *(978-1-60034-782-5(7))* Xulon Pr., Inc.
Brown, James Baldwin. The Soul's Exodus & Pilgrimage. 2008. 440p. 30.99 *(978-0-559-49956-2(6))*; pap. 34.75 *(978-0-559-49952-4(3))* BiblioBazaar
—The Soul's Exodus & Pilgrimage. 2008. 452p. 52.95 *(978-1-4374-1631-2(4))* 2008. 452p. pap. 37.95 *(978-1-4373-2988-9(3))* 2007. (ENG.). 460p. 52.95 *(978-0-548-09300-9(8))* Kessinger Publishing, LLC.
Brown, John. Christ: The Way, the Truth, & the Life. 2008. 372p. 29.99 *(978-0-554-39735-1(8))*; (ENG.). 336p. pap. 30.75 *(978-1-4375-0252-7(0))*; 372p. 31.99 *(978-0-554-30432-8(5))*; 370p. pap. 32.75 *(978-1-4375-0253-4(9))* BiblioBazaar.
—Rhythm of a Captured Heart. 2011. 99p. pap. 10.00 *(978-0-9826018-3-9(2))* Oasis Hse.
Brown, Kate. Christ the Sacramental Word. 224p. 31.95 *(978-0-281-04929-5(7))* International Publishers Marketing.
Brown, La-Tavia. Living God's Word: A Revelation of the Spirit, 1 vol. 2009. 54p. pap. 16.95 *(978-1-60813-535-6(7))* PublishAmerica, Inc.
Brown, Marlene. His Second Coming: Prophetic Visions of Christ & His Return 2010. (ENG.). 224p. 20.99 *(978-1-61638-132-5(9),* Creation Hse.) Charisma Media.
Brown, Michael B. Five Facets of a Diamond: A Look at Five Indispensable Elements of Christian Discipleship. 2007. 180p. per. 24.95 *(978-1-4241-7720-2(0))* PublishAmerica, Inc.
Brown, Nancy. Suddenly-Your World Falls Apart. 2007. pap. 10.99 *(978-1-60034-908-9(0))* Xulon Pr., Inc.
Brown, Nathan. Seven Reasons Life Is Better with God. 2007. 159p. per. 12.99 *(978-0-8127-0436-5(3))* Autumn Hse. Publishing Co.
Brown, Nicole. Now What? A Beginner's Guide to Living Saved. 2009. 92p. pap. 11.95 *(978-1-4401-6528-3(9))* iUniverse, Inc.
Brown, Patricia D. Pilgrimage: Meditations on a Journey of Faith. 2007. 155p. per. 12.00 *(978-0-687-64464-3(X))* Abingdon Pr.
Brown, Priestess D. God in Me: This That & Thee Other. 2007. pap. 13.99 *(978-1-60266-226-1(6))* Xulon Pr., Inc.
Brown, Rebecca. Unperfectly Saved. 2010. 72p. pap. 10.50 *(978-1-4490-5883-8(3))* AuthorHouse.
Brown, Reeree Mckinstry. God's Beacon. 2011. 100p. pap. 15.99 ***(978-1-4568-6356-2(8))*** Xlibris Corp.
Brown, Steve. What Was I Thinking? Things I've Learned since I Knew It All. annot. ed. 2006. (ENG.). 224p. 17.99 *(978-1-58229-570-1(0),* Howard Bks.) Howard Books.
Brown, Sue. Spirit Unbroken: A Journey of Hope, Survival, & Beating the Odds. 2008. 200p. pap. 24.95 *(978-1-60563-408-1(5))* PublishAmerica, Inc.
Brown, Tracey. I Found My Father in a Women's Prison: The Journey Begins. 2007. (ENG.). 264p. 15.95 *(978-0-9793075-3-6(8))*; (Illus.). 292p. 21.95 *(978-0-9793075-4-6(6))* Casa de Snapdragon LLC.
Brown, W. Granville. Choices. 2009. 252p. pap. 15.95 *(978-1-59858-906-1(7))* Dog Ear Publishing, LLC.
Brown, William H. Unleashing the Power of God: Words of Empowerment. 2008. 103p. pap. 16.95 *(978-1-60563-203-2(1))* PublishAmerica, Inc.
Browne, Thomas. Religio Medici. 2009. 276p. pap. *(978-0-217-74912-1(7))*; 154p. pap. *(978-0-217-74909-1(7))*; 108p. pap. *(978-1-4589-6148-8(6))* Books LLC.
—Religio Medici. Winny, James, ed. 2008. (ENG.). 192p. pap. 37.99 *(978-0-521-09055-1(5))* Cambridge Univ. Pr.
—Religio Medici. 2008. 316p. *(978-1-4437-3387-8(3),* Pomona Pr.) Read Bks.
—Religio Medici & Urne-Burial. Greenblatt, Stephen & Targoff, Ramie, eds. 2012. (ENG.). 288p. pap. 16.95 *(978-1-59017-488-3(7),* NYRB Classics) New York Review of Bks., Inc., The.
—Religio Medici, Hydriotaphia, & the Letter to a Friend. 2009. 110p. pap. *(978-1-4589-6151-8(6))* Books LLC.
—Religio Medici, Hydriotaphia, & the Letter to a Friend. 2007. (ENG.). 116p. per. *(978-1-4068-2454-4(2))* Echo Library.
Browne, Thomas & Denonain, Jean-Jacques. Religio Medici. 2009. (ENG.). 128p. pap. 31.99 *(978-0-521-10076-2(3))* Cambridge Univ. Pr.
Brownlee, John. The Hole in Your Heart. 2008. 156p. per. 13.99 *(978-1-60477-522-8(X))* Xulon Pr., Inc.
Broyles, Danny. Creation to Revelation: The Continuing Story of Truth. 2009. 384p. pap. 20.99 *(978-1-61579-377-8(1))* Xulon Pr., Inc.
Bruce, Bob and Gloria. Does God Really Care? 2008. pap. 9.99 *(978-1-60477-912-7(8))* Xulon Pr., Inc.
Bruce, Cindy. Fulfill Your Destiny: Spiritual Gifts As Tools for Believers. 2009. 216p. pap. 15.99 *(978-1-60791-190-6(6))* Xulon Pr., Inc.
Bruce, Joel. Our Generous God: Discover God's Generosity to You in Christ. 2011. 192p. 30.95 ***(978-1-4497-1749-0(7))***; pap. 13.95 ***(978-1-4497-1747-6(0))*** Author Solutions, Inc. (WestBow Pr.).
Bruce, Lisa. Redeemed to Return. 2009. 176p. pap. 19.99 *(978-1-4415-4996-9(X))* Xlibris Corp.
Bruce, W. Robert. Orando los Unos por los Otros. (Serie Discipulo - Discipleship Ser.).Tr. of Praying for One Another. (SPA.). 1.79 *(978-1-56063-896-4(6),* 498250) Editorial Unilit.
Bruins, Cor. God & Relationships. 2006. 108p. per. *(978-0-901860-36-1(0))* Scripture Truth Pubns.
Brummette, M. A. Seeking My Father's Love: Dear Dad, More than anything I need your Love... 2011. 40p. pap. 13.95 *(978-1-4497-1116-0(2),* WestBow Pr.) Author Solutions, Inc.
Bruner, Kurt D. Oprah's Jesus. 2010. (ENG.). pap. 14.99 *(978-0-7684-3139-1(5))* Destiny Image Pubs.
Bruner, Patrick A. Road Trip to Freedom: The Practical Art of Christian Growth 2008. 300p. pap. 19.95 *(978-1-58982-471-3(7),* Millennial Mind Publishing) American Bk. Publishing Group.
Brunner, J. Michael. Memoirs from the Middle: How I Survived Being a Middle Child. 2009. 64p. pap. 10.95 *(978-1-4327-4265-2(5))* Outskirts Pr., Inc.
Bruno, J. Gardy. The Grumblings of the Soul: How Is Depression A Natural Response of the Body. 2010. pap. 10.99 *(978-1-61579-720-2(3))* Xulon Pr., Inc.
Bruschi, Giovanni. I Need You. 2008. 180p. 22.99 *(978-1-60647-571-3(1))*; pap. 14.99 *(978-1-60647-570-6(3))* Xulon Pr., Inc.
Brusherd A.K.A. Yosef, Joe. Hebraic Insights: Messages Exploring the Hebrew Roots of Christian Faith. 2011. 264p. 29.95 ***(978-1-4620-3865-7(4))***; pap. 19.95 ***(978-1-4620-3866-4(2))*** iUniverse, Inc.
Bryan, Matthew. Desesperación. 2011. 106p. pap. 9.99 ***(978-1-4583-1562-5(2))*** Lulu Enterprises Inc.
Bryant, L. Laque. Strength for the Fight. 2008. 72p. per. 9.99 *(978-1-60477-616-4(1))* Xulon Pr., Inc.
Bryant, Phillip C. Living Beyond the Maze. 2008. 80p. pap. 12.95 *(978-1-59858-787-6(0))* Dog Ear Publishing, LLC.
Bryant, Vicki. For Such a Time As This. 2007. 460p. (ENG.). 35.99 *(978-1-60266-782-2(9))*; per. 23.99 *(978-1-60266-707-5(1))* Xulon Pr., Inc.
Bryant, Vicki Renee. A Transforming Journey: From Common Ground to Holy Ground. 2009. 484p. pap. 24.99 *(978-1-61579-376-1(3))* Xulon Pr., Inc.
Bs, Mark D. Hamilton M. Ed Thb. The Plan. 2009. 60p. pap. 15.99 *(978-1-4415-4851-1(3))* Xlibris Corp.
Bucer, Martin. Instruction in Christian Love [1523]. Fuhrmann, Paul Traugott, tr. 2008. 68p. pap. 6.00 *(978-1-60608-100-6(4))* Wipf & Stock Pubs.
Buchan, Angus. A Farmer's Year: Daily Truth to Change Your Life, 1 vol. Waldeck, Val, ed. 2007. (Illus.). 384p. 14.99 *(978-0-8254-6183-5(9),* Monarch Bks.) Lion Hudson PLC GBR. Dist: Kregel Pubns.
Buchanan, Alex. Anger, Mercy, & the Heart of God. 96p. pap. *(978-1-85240-271-6(7))* Sovereign World, Ltd.
Buchanan, Michael. Standing on Significance. 2007. pap. 13.99 *(978-1-60034-433-6(X))* Xulon Pr., Inc.
Buchholz, Pamela. Choosing to Be A Christian. 2009. 64p. pap. 15.00 *(978-0-687-64741-5(X))* Abingdon Pr.
Buchli, Barbara. Messages from God. 2011. 191p. pap. 14.95 ***(978-1-4327-7558-2(8))*** Outskirts Pr., Inc.
Buckeridge, John. 100 Instant Discussion Starters. 2006. (ENG.). 253p. per. 12.99 *(978-0-85476-807-3(6))* Kingsway Pubns. GBR. Dist: STL Distribution North America.
Buckhalter, Vanessa. Isaiah 26: 3-4 Perfect Peace. 2010. 112p. pap. 8.99 *(978-1-4520-4932-8(7))* AuthorHouse.
Buckland, Donna. When the Waiting Is the Doing. 2009. 112p. pap. *(978-1-55452-356-6(7))* Essence Publishing.
Buckley, James F. Blogs on God: A Unique Collection of Brief, High-Impact, This & Thats on God, the Bible, & the Human Race. 2007. (ENG.). 144p. per. 7.99 *(978-1-59979-255-2(9),* Creation Hse.) Charisma Media.
Buckner, Kay. Glorious Gleanings from the Fields of Life: For a Lifetime of Joy & Contentment. 2008. pap. 9.99 *(978-1-60477-811-3(3))* Xulon Pr., Inc.
Buckner, Ollie and Daisy. Loaded with Benefits. 2009. 111p. pap. 15.00 *(978-0-557-04460-3(X))* Lulu Enterprises Inc.
Budd, Joel & Budd, Linda. Fill Me or Kill Me. 2007. 128p. pap. 10.99 *(978-0-9743876-2-8(2))* CrossStaff Publishing.
Buddies: Bulletin. 14.95 *(978-0-687-06973-6(4))* Abingdon Pr.
Budzban, Annettee. Spend a Moment with God. 2007. 136p. pap. 13.95 *(978-0-7414-4093-8(8))* Infinity Publishing.
Buehrens, John A. & Parker, Rebecca Ann. A House for Hope: The Promise of Progressive Religion for the Twenty-First Century. 2010. (ENG.). 208p. 25.95 *(978-0-8070-7738-2(0))* Beacon Pr.
Buford, Bob. Beyond Halftime: Practical Wisdom for Your Second Half, 1 vol. 2008. (ENG.). 176p. 12.99 *(978-0-310-28423-9(6))* Zondervan.
Buford, Martha. Miracles. 2010. 104p. pap. 10.99 *(978-1-4520-3652-6(7))* AuthorHouse.
Buford, Martha Jean. The True Vine. 2008. pap. 10.00 *(978-0-8059-7994-7(8))* Dorrance Publishing Co., Inc.
Building a Healthly Minister's Family: Harding Preachers' Forum 1996. pap. 8.99 *(978-0-89225-462-0(9))* Gospel Advocate Co., Inc.
Bull, Samson. Escape the Flood of Wrath. 2009. (J). pap. 14.99 *(978-1-60799-031-4(8))* Tate Publishing & Enterprises, LLC.
Bullon, Alejandro. Knowing Jesus Is Everything. 2009. 88p. *(978-0-8127-0488-4(6))* Autumn Hse. Publishing Co.
Bunch, David. Prayer & Prophecy: The Essential Kenneth Leech. Bunch, David & Ritchie, Angus, eds. 2009. 256p. pap. 30.00 *(978-1-59627-115-9(9),* Seabury Bks.) Church Publishing, Inc.
Bundschuh, Rick. Deep Like Me: Extremely Profound Thoughts on Faith from a Disciple in over His Head. 2011. (ENG.). 192p. pap. 12.99 *(978-0-8307-4688-0(9))* Gospel Light Pubns.
Bunn, Bob. Path of Purity: A Family Guide. 2010. 143p. pap. *(978-1-4158-6876-8(X))* LifeWay Christian Resources.
Bunyan, John. The Celestial City. 2006. pap. 9.95 *(978-1-4286-7592-6(2),* Kessinger Publishing, LLC.
—Order & Cause of Salvation & Damnation Chart. pap. 3.99 *(978-0-87377-028-6(5))* GAM Pubns.
Burden, Larry. Kingdom Life: Finding Life Beyond Church. 2009. 140p. pap. 11.99 *(978-1-932503-83-8(8))* Insight Publishing Group.
Burdette, Dallas R. From Legalism to Freedom: A Spiritual Narrative of Liberation. 2008. 496p. 35.99 *(978-1-60647-737-3(4))*; pap. 23.99 *(978-1-60647-736-6(6))* Xulon Pr., Inc.
—Old Texts Through New Eyes. 2009. 504p. 36.99 *(978-1-60791-379-5(8))*; pap. 24.99 *(978-1-60791-377-1(1))* Xulon Pr., Inc.
Burger, Nancy. Daniel's 70th Week. 2007. 76p. per. 9.99 *(978-1-60266-766-2(7),* Xulon Pr., Inc.
Burgess, George. Sermons on the Christian Life. 2009. 314p. pap. 30.75 *(978-1-116-03550-6(2))*; 314p. pap. 29.75 *(978-1-116-03551-3(0))*; 312p. 25.99 *(978-1-103-37719-0(1))*; 312p. pap. 19.99 *(978-1-103-37716-9(7))* BiblioBazaar.
—Sermons on the Christian Life. 2009. 104p. pap. 19.99 *(978-0-217-55415-2(6))* General Bks. LLC.
—Sermons on the Christian Life. 2008. 310p. 45.95 *(978-1-4372-3963-6(8))*; pap. 30.95 *(978-1-4371-1187-3(4))* Kessinger Publishing, LLC.
—Sermons on the Christian Life. 2006. 316p. per. 23.99 *(978-1-4255-3086-0(9))* MPublishing.
Burgess, Gina. Refreshment in Refuge. 2011. 236p. pap. 17.95 *(978-1-4497-1212-9(6),* WestBow Pr.) Author Solutions, Inc.
Burkart, Gina. Finding Meaning in Narni: A Voyage on the Dawn Treader. 2011. 176p. pap. 16.52 ***(978-1-60888-098-0(2))*** Nimble Bks. LLC.
Burke, Shelly. What Should I Say? 2007. 228p. per. 14.99 *(978-1-60266-682-5(2),* Xulon Pr., Inc.
Burkes, Norris. No Small Miracles: Heartwarming, Humorous, & Hopefilled Stories from a Pediatric Chaplain, 0 vols. 2009. 192p. pap. 12.99 *(978-0-8499-2975-5(X))* Nelson, Thomas Inc.
Burkett, Larry. La Familia y sus Finanzas, 1 vol. 2009. Orig. Title: Your Finances in Changing Times. (SPA.). 160p. pap. 8.99 *(978-0-8254-1213-4(7),* Editorial Portavoz) Kregel Pubns.
Burkhart, Roy Abram. The Person You Can Be. 2011. 280p. 47.95 ***(978-1-258-09629-8(3))*** Literary Licensing, LLC.
Burklo, Jim. Open Christianity: Home by Another Road. 2008. (ENG.). 288p. pap. 17.00 *(978-1-878282-06-4(9))* St. Johann Pr.
Burley, Eddie. This Is Why We Pray. 2010. 63p. pap. 15.98 *(978-0-557-36664-4(X))* Lulu Enterprises Inc.
Burne, Martin J. Remember Lot's Wife: Scriptural Reflections on How to Lose Your Life & Save It. 2007. 170p. per. *(978-0-8189-1241-2(3))* St Pauls/Alba Hse. Pubs.
Burnett, Lorena. Just Tools Used by God. 2011. 44p. pap. 16.59 ***(978-1-4634-1338-5(6))*** AuthorHouse.
Burnette, Billy. Why Are So Many Relationships Failing? Spiritual Bruises. 2010. 240p. 33.95 *(978-1-4497-0901-3(X))*; pap. 17.95 *(978-1-4497-0900-6(1))* Author Solutions, Inc. (WestBow Pr.).

C

Burnette, Cecil. Beyond Higher Power: Responding to the Call of the Kingdom of God. 2007. pap. 13.95 (978-1-934130-06-3(0)) Flood Crest Pr.

Burnham, Jon. In the Big Inning. 2008. 220p. pap. 14.99 (978-1-60477-771-0(0)) Xulon Pr., Inc.

Burns, Alan J. The Potter & His Clay: How to Know God's Present Purpose for Your Life. 2008. 260p. pap. 15.99 (978-1-60477-964-6(0)) Xulon Pr., Inc.

Burns, Irene. A Light Shines in God's Country: Hilarious & Heartwarming Stories from Our Home to Yours. 2007. (ENG.). 224p. per. 13.99 (978-1-59979-242-2(7), Creation Hse.) Charisma Media.

Burns, Jim. Accept Nothing Less: God's Best for Your Body, Mind, & Heart. 2008. (Pure Foundations Ser.). 224p. (YA). pap. 12.99 (978-0-7642-0212-4(X)) Bethany Hse. Pubs.

—The Christian Life. 2008. (Uncommon Ser.). (ENG.). 208p. (gr. 9-12). pap. 14.99 (978-0-8307-4644-6(7)) Gospel Light Pubns.

—10 Building Blocks for a Solid Family: The Homeword Guide to Parenting. 2010. (ENG.). 224p. pap. 14.99 (978-0-8307-4783-2(4)) Gospel Light Pubns.

Burnside-Edwards, Edie Jean. Below the Line. 2008. 56p. pap. 9.99 (978-1-60647-207-1(0)) Xulon Pr., Inc.

Burpo, Todd. Heaven Is for Real: A Little Boy's Astounding Story of His Trip to Heaven & Back. 2011. 192p. 21.99 (978-0-8499-4836-7(3)) Nelson, Thomas Inc.

Burpo, Todd & Burpo, Colton. Heaven Is for Real: Participant's Guide. 2011. 128p. pap. 7.99 (978-1-4185-5068-4(X)) Nelson, Thomas Inc.

Burpo, Todd, et al. Heaven Is for Real: A Little Boy's Astounding Story of His Trip to Heaven & Back. 2011. (Playaway Adult Nonfiction Ser.). 59.99 (978-1-61707-021-1(1)) Findaway World, LLC.

—Heaven Is for Real: A Little Boy's Astounding Story of His Trip to Heaven & Back. 2010. (Illus.). 192p. pap. 16.99 (978-0-8499-4615-8(8)) Nelson, Thomas Inc.

—Heaven Is for Real: A Little Boy's Astounding Story of His Trip to Heaven & Back. Lt. ed. 2011. (ENG.). 320p. pap. 17.99 (978-1-59415-355-6(8), Large Print Pr.) Thorndike Pr.

Burr, Richard A. Praying Your Prodigal Home: Unleashing God's Power to Set Your Loved Ones Free. 2008. (Illus.). 106p. pap. 11.99 (978-1-60066-128-0(9)) WingSpread Publishers.

Burrell, Cindy. Divorce God's Way. 2010. 234p. pap. 14.98 (978-0-557-38801-1(5)) Lulu Enterprises Inc.

Burress, Virginia. My Journal, Online Dating: Finding Love with God's Help. 2008. 424p. pap. 29.95 (978-1-4241-9455-1(5)) PublishAmerica, Inc.

Burrier, Doug. Here to There. 2008. 164p. 21.99 (978-1-60477-751-2(6)); pap. 13.99 (978-1-60477-750-5(8)) Xulon Pr., Inc.

Burroughs, Dillon. Undefending Christianity: Embracing Truth Without Having All the Answers. 2011. 160p. pap. 11.99 (978-0-7369-3702-3(1)) Harvest Hse. Pubs.

Burroughs, Jeremiah. Moses' Self-Denial. 2010. 160p. (978-1-60178-094-2(X), Soli Deo Gloria Pubns.) Reformation Heritage Bks.

Burroughs, Jeremiah & Kistler, Don. Moses' Choice: With His Eye Fixed upon Heaven: Discovering the Happy Condition of a Self-Denying Heart with His Eye Fixed upon Heaven: Delivered in a Treatise upon Hebrews 11:25-26. 2012. (978-0-9826155-9-1(0)) Northampton Pr., The.

Burroughs, Yolanda. Never Beaten in the Battle: the Right Attire Matters: An in-Depth Look at the Armor of God. 2011. pap. 12.99 (978-1-61346-076-4(7)) Tate Publishing & Enterprises, LLC.

Burrows, Ruth. Before the Living God. 2008. 128p. pap. 15.00 (978-1-58768-050-2(5), HiddenSpring) Paulist Pr.

—Love Unknown: The Archbishop of Canterbury's Lent Book 2012. 2012. (ENG.). 184p. pap. 14.95 (978-1-4411-0372-7(4)) Continuum International Publishing Group, Ltd. GBR. Dist: National Bk. Network.

Burse, Cassandra Regina Johnson. Getting Through Life s Struggles, Coming Out with the Victory! 2010. 216p. pap. 15.99 (978-1-60957-928-9(3)) Xulon Pr., Inc.

Burton, Debbie. There's a Flea in My Boxers. 2006. 92p. per. 12.99 (978-1-59879-183-9(4)) Lifevest Publishing, Inc.

Burton, Jerry. Getting It Right: Establishing a God-Centered Life. 2010. pap. 10.99 (978-1-61663-546-6(0)) Tate Publishing & Enterprises, LLC.

Burton, Kenneth. God's Warriors. 2008. 56p. pap. 9.95 (978-0-595-52477-8(X)) iUniverse, Inc.

Burton, Leonard. Are There Thorns in Your Life. 2011. 192p. pap. 14.99 (978-1-61379-353-4(7)) Xulon Pr., Inc.

Burton, Robert J. Reflections: The Challenge & Excitement of the Committed Christian Life Volume 1. 2009. 188p. pap. 14.49 (978-1-4389-8692-0(0)) AuthorHouse.

Burton, Valorie. Why Not You? 28 Days to Authentic Confidence. 2007. (ENG.). 240p. per. 13.99 (978-1-4000-7336-8(7), WaterBrook Pr.) Doubleday Religious Publishing Group, The.

Burwell, Clint F. A Wretch Like Me. 2006. 102p. per. 9.99 (978-1-59886-545-5(5)) Tate Publishing & Enterprises, LLC.

Bush, Angelique L. Warring for the Lord: Preparing for Spiritual Combat in the Earth. 2009. 320p. pap. 18.99 (978-1-61579-064-7(0)) Xulon Pr., Inc.

Bush, Belinda. A Lifestyle of Excellence. 2008. pap. 9.99 (978-1-60647-115-9(5)) Xulon Pr., Inc.

Bush, L. C. Brown. Faith to Find a Job. 2010. 214p. pap. 15.99 (978-1-60957-844-2(9)) Xulon Pr., Inc.

Bush, Robert. Shortcut to Heaven. 2011. 180p. 27.99 (978-1-61379-051-9(1)); pap. 14.99 (978-1-61215-914-0(1)) Xulon Pr., Inc.

Bussey, Loyce J. Never Enough: The Martha Syndrome. 2008. 128p. 9.95 (978-0-942407-86-0(5)) Father & Son Publishing.

Butcher, Catherine. Special to God, 1 vol. 2009. (ENG.). 112p. pap. (978-1-85345-508-7(3)) Crusade for World Revival.

—What You Always Wanted to Know about Heaven. 2007. 112p. (978-1-85345-444-8(3)) Crusade for World Revival.

Butler, Andre. God's Plan for the Church. 2006. per. (978-0-9768299-2-8(4)) Faith Christian Ctr.

—Living Life to the Full. 2007. (ENG.). 208p. pap. 12.99 (978-1-59979-194-4(3), Creation Hse.) Charisma Media.

Butler, Carolyn. Under African Skies: Reflections for Advent & Christmas. 2011. 96p. pap. 9.95 (978-0-7963-0850-4(0)) NB Pubs. Ltd. ZAF. Dist: International Publishers Marketing.

Butler, Eli. Man Church vs Christ Church: Deception in man Church. 2009. 96p. pap. 11.95 (978-1-4401-2372-6(1)) iUniverse, Inc.

Butler, Fay Ellis. Rejection, the Ruling Spirit. 2008. 116p. pap. 11.99 (978-1-60647-224-8(0)) Xulon Pr., Inc.

Butler, Jeff. Is the Church Armed but Not Dangerous? How His Beloved Bride Becomes a Battle-Ready Warrior Through Six Prayer Principles. 2006. 147p. per. 12.00 (978-1-886296-41-1(3)) Arrow Pubns., Inc.

Butler, Jon. Temptation & Testing. 2007. pap. (978-0-281-05840-2(7)) SPCK Publishing.

Butler, Sheila. Roman Catholicism: Ethics. 2nd ed. 2009. 152p. pap. 36.50 (978-0-340-98657-8(3)) Hodder Education GBR. Dist: Trans-Atlantic Pubns., Inc.

—Roman Catholicism - Ethics. 2009. (Illus.). 64p. pap. 20.00 (978-0-340-98717-9(0)) Hodder Education GBR. Dist: Trans-Atlantic Pubns., Inc.

Butler Tom & Butler, Tom. Religion & Public Life: Tom Butler's Thoughts for the Day. 2012. (ENG.). 216p. pap. 22.95 (978-1-4411-0177-8(2)) Continuum International Publishing Group, Ltd. GBR. Dist: National Bk. Network.

Butt, Sheila. Seeking Spiritual Beauty. pap. 7.95 (978-0-929540-26-9(3)) Publishing Designs, Inc.

Butterworth, Bill. The Short List: In a Life Full of Choices, There Are Only Four That Matter. 2009. (ENG.). 160p. pap. 13.99 (978-1-4143-1566-9(X)) Tyndale Hse. Pubs.

Butterworth, Eric. Unity: Una Busqueda de la Verdad. Date not set. (SPA.). 162p. pap. 11.95 (978-0-87159-249-1(5), 280, Unity Hse.) Unity Schl. of Christianity.

Buttram, Larry. The Greatest Gift. 2007. 179p. per. 13.95 (978-0-9755030-5-8(7)) New Virginia Pubns.

Buttrick, John A. Fighting Temptation. 2008. 100p. pap. 15.99 (978-1-4363-9343-0(4)) Xlibris Corp.

Butts, Courtney E. Inside My Head. 2008. pap. (978-1-934363-13-3(8)) Zoe Life Publishing.

Butts, Jr. Are You Sanctified?, 1 vol. 2009. 144p. pap. 24.95 (978-1-60703-438-4(7)) PublishAmerica, Inc.

Butz, Jr. Theology & Human Action; 2009. 200p. pap. 15.99 (978-1-60791-463-1(8)) Xulon Pr., Inc.

Buxton, Graham. Celebrating Life: Beyond the Sacred-Secular Divide. 2007. (ENG., Illus.). 220p. pap. 19.99 (978-1-84227-507-8(0), Paternoster) Authentic Media.

Buzzard, Justin. Hebrews: Consider Jesus: 8 Studies for Individuals or Groups. 2010. (Good Book Guides). (Illus.). 94p. pap. (978-1-906334-42-0(0)) Good Bk. Co.

Byerly, Dwayne. Today's Democrats & Christianity: No Subtitle. 2008. 88p. pap. 9.99 (978-1-60647-752-6(8)) Xulon Pr., Inc.

Byers, Samuel Hawkins Marshall. With Fire & Sword. 203p. reprint ed. 98.00 (978-0-7222-8230-4(3)) Library Reprints, Inc.

Bynum, Juanita. Walking in Your Destiny: How to Receive Your Spiritual Inheritance Now. 2006. 284p. per. 14.99 (978-1-59979-000-8(9), Charisma Hse.) Charisma Media.

Bynum, Larry R. Thank You Holy Spirit. 2010. 122p. pap. 26.95 (978-1-4327-4497-7(6)) Outskirts Pr., Inc.

Byrd, Andy & Feucht, Sean. Fire & Fragrance. 2010. (ENG.). pap. 14.99 (978-0-7684-3290-9(1)) Destiny Image Pubs.

Byrne, Lavinia. Hidden Tradition. 26.00 (978-0-687-85471-4(7)) Abingdon Pr.

Bytheway, John. Seeing As God Sees. 2009. audio compact disk 14.95 (978-1-60641-133-9(0)) Deseret Bk. Co.

—What I Wish I'd Known in High School. 2008. 144p. pap. 15.95 (978-1-59038-864-8(X), Shadow Mountain) Deseret Bk. Co.

—You're Gonna Make It Through Junior High. 2006. (Illus.). 128p. (YA). pap. 10.95 (978-1-59038-733-7(3)) Desert Bks.

Cadiente, Terri. Live Courageously: Revelations from the Life of a Stuntwoman: Choose to be the Real You. 2009. pap. 16.99 (978-0-7684-2820-9(3)) Destiny Image Pubs.

Cadwallader, Alan. Beyond the Word of a Woman: Recovering the Bodies of the Syrophoenician Woman. 2011. (ATF Biblical Ser.). (ENG.). 400p. (C). pap. 26.00 (978-1-920691-85-1(5)) ATF Pr. AUS. Dist: Brown, David Bk. Co., The.

Caffery, Larry E. Years of Grace, Life of Mercy: The Story of an Angry Man who Finds Happiness. 2010. pap. 11.99 (978-1-61566-671-3(0)) Tate Publishing & Enterprises, LLC.

Cage, Ernestine. Let Us Pray. 2010. pap. 9.99 (978-1-61566-313-2(4)) Tate Publishing & Enterprises, LLC.

Cage, Mary. A Gift from the Heart. 2006. pap. 9.99 (978-1-60034-442-8(9)) Xulon Pr., Inc.

Cairns, Scott. The End of Suffering: Finding Purpose in Pain. 2009. (ENG.). 144p. (gr. 13). pap. 15.99 (978-1-55725-563-1(6)) Paraclete Pr., Inc.

Calderon, Eduardo Caballero. El Cristo de Espaldas.Tr. of Christ Backwards. (SPA.). pap. (978-958-02-0505-0(1), 619) Distribuidora Norma, Inc.

Caldwell, D. W. License to Drive. 2010. 234p. 25.99 (978-1-60957-612-7(8)); pap. 15.99 (978-1-60957-611-0(X)) Xulon Pr., Inc.

Caldwell, Happy. How to Thrive in Perilous Times: Living Beyond the World System. 2009. 96p. pap. 4.99 (978-1-57794-981-7(1)) Harrison House Pubs.

Caldwell, Jacquie. Back from the Edge: Recovering from Broken Trust. 2009. 152p. pap. 14.99 (978-1-60791-821-9(8)) Xulon Pr., Inc.

Caldwell, Suzette T. Praying to Change Your Life: A Guide to Productive Prayer. 2009. pap. 16.99 (978-0-7684-2751-6(7)) Destiny Image Pubs.

Calheiros, Izes. Dressed for Ministry: No Subtitle. 2008. 180p. pap. 13.99 (978-1-60647-553-9(3)) Xulon Pr., Inc.

Callahan, Danny L. Triumphant Warriors in a Turbulent World. 2008. 156p. pap. 14.99 (978-1-60647-490-7(1)) Xulon Pr., Inc.

Callahan, David. Day by Day: A Walk Through the Scriptures. 2007. (Illus.). 44p. pap. (978-0-915143-09-2(7)) Francis Asbury Society.

Callahan, Kevin. Soul Space: Ancient Realities in Post-Modern Worship Spaces. 2008. 160p. pap. 15.95 (978-0-595-48466-9(2)) iUniverse, Inc.

Callahan, Sidney. Created for Joy: A Christian View of Suffering. 2007. (ENG.). 256p. pap. 19.95 (978-0-8245-2566-8(3), Crossroad) Crossroad Publishing Co., The.

Callaway, Phil. Tales of Amusing Grace: Stories of What It's Really Like at My House. Date not set. 200p. 9.99 (978-0-7369-0234-2(1)) Harvest Hse. Pubs.

Calver, Clive. Dying to Live: The Paradox of the Crucified Life. 2009. (ENG.). 174p. pap. 14.99 (978-1-934068-80-9(2)) Authentic Media.

Calver, Clive, et al. On the Front Line: A Father & Son, 30 Years Apart, Debate What It Means to Live All Out for Jesus, 1 vol. 2007. 176p. pap. 12.99 (978-0-8254-6148-4(0), Monarch Bks.) Lion Hudson PLC GBR. Dist: Kregel Pubns.

Calvert, Aulbrey W. Got Fruit? 2007. 96p. per. 15.99 (978-1-4257-6263-6(8)) Xlibris Corp.

Calvert, Shannan. The King Has Dethroned a Queen: Allowing God to Remove the Crown of Worry. 2011. pap. 9.99 (978-1-61346-502-8(5)) Tate Publishing & Enterprises, LLC.

Calvin, John. The Christian Life. Leith, John H., ed. 2009. 128p. pap. 16.00 (978-1-60608-743-5(6), Wipf and Stock) Wipf & Stock Pubs.

—Golden Booklet of the True Christian Life. 2012. (ENG.). 96p. pap. 7.95 (978-1-61010-060-1(3), Great Christian Books) Rotolo Media.

—On the Christian Life - the Institutes Abridged with Biblical & French Phrase Indexes. 2011. 58p. (978-1-84902-426-6(X)) Benediction Classics.

Calvin, Lynn. I Have Two Daddies: An Earthly Daddy & A Heavenly Daddy. 2008. 40p. pap. 20.99 (978-1-4343-6943-7(9)) AuthorHouse.

Calvinistic Action Committee. God-Centered Living or Calvinism in Action: A Symposium. 2011. 270p. 47.95 (978-1-258-09832-2(6)) Literary Licensing, LLC.

Cameneti, Joe. God's Opinion on Today's Hottest Sex Topics. 2007. 289p. 14.99 (978-0-9788726-5-6(7)) HonorNet.

Camerer, Lori Kallander. His Still Small Voice. 2008. 168p. 34.95 (978-1-4327-0710-1(8)) Outskirts Pr., Inc.

Cameron, Oac. 12 Deep Breaths: The Faith as It Was Meant to Be, 1 vol. 2009. 124p. pap. 19.95 (978-1-4489-2428-8(6)) PublishAmerica, Inc.

Cameron, Peter. Why Preach: The Heart of Preaching: Encountering Christ in God's Word. 2009. 250p. pap. 16.95 (978-1-58617-272-5(7)) Ignatius Pr.

Camon, Angela R. Have You Been Fishing Lately? Winning Souls for Christ. 2010. 76p. pap. 12.00 (978-1-4269-3434-6(3)) Trafford Publishing.

Campbell, Alvin. A Colorful Attitude. 2007. 80p. per. 10.95 (978-1-4327-0149-9(5)) Outskirts Pr., Inc.

Campbell, Arden J. Walking Forward. 2010. 136p. pap. 14.99 (978-1-60957-595-3(4)) Xulon Pr., Inc.

Campbell, Barrie. Exposing the Enemy. 2006. 81p. pap. 16.95 (978-1-4241-4444-0(2)) PublishAmerica, Inc.

Campbell, Bessie B. Living a True Christian Life: A Spirit-filled Life Following the Example of Jesus Christ. 2011. 68p. pap. 19.95 (978-1-4626-3197-1(5)) PublishAmerica, Inc.

Campbell, Bill. The Magnificent Life. 2009. 168p. pap. 14.99 (978-1-61579-465-2(4)) Xulon Pr., Inc.

Campbell, Cherish. How Is Your Walk: If God Came Today Would You Be Ready? 2009. 208p. pap. 15.99 (978-1-61579-061-6(6)) Xulon Pr., Inc.

Campbell, Kenneth. God Called My Name. 2009. 104p. pap. 10.99 (978-1-61579-373-0(9)) Xulon Pr., Inc.

Campbell, Norman. How I Defeated Schizophrenia. 2009. 180p. pap. (978-1-84748-584-7(7)) Athena Pr.

Campbell, R. K. Divine Principles of Gathering. 40p. pap. 0.45 (978-0-88172-015-0(1)) Believers Bookshelf, Inc.

—Essentials of the Christian Life. 46p. pap. 0.95 (978-0-88172-008-2(9)) Believers Bookshelf, Inc.

—Outside the Camp. 16p. pap. 0.30 (978-0-88172-157-7(3)) Believers Bookshelf, Inc.

Campbell, Regi. About My Father's Business: Taking Your Faith to Work. 2009. (ENG.). 240p. pap. 14.99 (978-1-60142-226-2(1), Multnomah) Doubleday Religious Publishing Group, The.

Campbell, Regi, et al. Mentor Like Jesus, 1 vol. 2009. (ENG.). 176p. 16.99 (978-0-8054-4811-5(X), B&H Bks.) B&H Publishing Group.

Campbell, Roger. Staying Positive in a Negative World: Attitudes That Enhance the Joy of Living, 1 vol. 2009. 128p. pap. 10.99 (978-0-8254-2427-4(5)) Kregel Pubns.

Campbell, Scott. The Ten Testaments: Lessons from the Greatest Teacher of All Time. 2009. 96p. pap. 9.95 (978-1-57921-954-3(3)) WinePress Publishing.

Campbell, Tommy, Jr. God Can Change You. 2008. 352p. pap. 19.99 (978-1-60477-902-8(0)) Xulon Pr., Inc.

Campillo, Luis. A un Amigo con Sincero Afecto.Tr. of Letter to an Unsaved Friend. (SPA.). 48p. (978-84-7228-846-1(3), 220007) Clie, Editorial.

Campolo, Rose. Weathering the Storms of Life: Stories of Miracles & the Power of Prayer. 2009. pap. 10.99 (978-1-61566-012-4(7)) Tate Publishing & Enterprises, LLC.

Campolo, Tony. Carpe Diem: Seize the Day, 0 vols. 2008. 240p. pap. 12.99 (978-0-8499-2089-9(2)) Nelson, Thomas Inc.

—It's Friday but Sunday's Comin', 0 vols. 2008. (Illus.). 160p. pap. 12.99 (978-0-8499-2090-5(6)) Nelson, Thomas Inc.

—Who Switched the Price Tags?, 0 vols. 2008. 208p. pap. 12.99 (978-0-8499-2087-5(6)) Nelson, Thomas Inc.

Campus Crusade for Christ Staff. Action Group Leader's Guide. Date not set. (Discipleship Ser.: No. 3). 47p. pap., tchr. ed. 4.99 (978-0-86605-133-0(3)) Integrated Resources.

—Discipleship Leader's Guide. Date not set. (Discipleship Ser.: No. 2). 39p. pap. 4.99 (978-0-86605-137-8(6)) Integrated Resources.

Canclini, Arnoldo. Cuando Hay Que Decidirse: When You Have to Make a Decision. (SPA.). 104p. (978-84-7228-242-1(2), 220228) Clie, Editorial.

Candler, Dana. Entirety: Love Gives All. 2008. 111p. per. 11.00 (978-1-60530-066-5(7)) Forerunner Books.

—Mourning for the Bridegroom: His Return. Our Hope. 2010. 130p. pap. 10.00 (978-0-9823262-4-4(6)) Forerunner Books.

Candler, Peter M., Jr. The Grandeur of Reason: Religion, Tradition & Universalism. Cunningham, Conor, ed. 2010. (Veritas Ser.). (ENG.). 512p. pap. 110.00 (978-0-334-04346-1(8), SCM Pr.) Hymns Ancient & Modern Ltd GBR. Dist: Westminster John Knox Pr.

Caneva, Cipriano. Aura de Tu Caricia. 128p. 6.50 (978-958-607-445-2(5)) Sociedad de San Pablo ESP. Dist: St Pauls/Alba Hse. Pubs.

Canfield, Jack L., et al. Chicken Soup for the Soul: Christian Teen Talk: Christian Teens Share Their Stories of Support, Inspiration & Growing Up. 2008. (Chicken Soup for the Soul Ser.). (ENG.). 380p. pap. 14.95 (978-1-935096-12-2(5)) Chicken Soup for the Soul Publishing, LLC.

Canner, Rod. Jesus Is Coming. 2009. 108p. pap. 11.99 (978-1-60791-993-3(1)) Xulon Pr., Inc.

Cannon, C. P. Chosen to Suffer. 2010. 120p. 21.49 (978-1-4520-0222-4(3)); (ENG.). pap. 10.99 (978-1-4520-0223-1(1)) AuthorHouse.

Cannon, Carol. Hooked on Unhappiness: Breaking the Cycle of Discontent. 2008. pap. (978-0-8163-2260-2(0)) Pacific Pr. Pubns.

Cannon, Steven & Gaizat, Eric. Sharing Your Faith. 2008. 109p. pap. 9.95 (978-0-557-00795-0(X)) Lulu Enterprises Inc.

Cano, Ronnie M. Through the Eyes of Love. 112p. pap. 5.95 (978-1-56236-979-8(2)) Aspen Bks.

Canora, Rocco Frank. Roc & Roll. 2009. 132p. pap. 10.99 (978-1-60791-811-0(0)) Xulon Pr., Inc.

Canovas Sanchez, Francisco. Autocontrol. (SPA.). 80p. 3.95 (978-958-607-433-9(1)) Sociedad de San Pablo COL. Dist: St Pauls/Alba Hse. Pubs.

Cantalamessa, Raniero. Beatitudes: Eight Steps to Happiness. 2009. (ENG.). 146p. pap. 13.99 (978-0-86716-922-5(2)) Franciscan Media.

Cantelon, Lee. The Words: Jesus of Nazareth. 2007. (ENG.). 176p. per. 14.99 (978-0-9787620-4-9(5)) Credo Hse. Pubs.

Canty, Helen. Eclipse of the Heart. 2008. 159p. 19.95 (978-1-934363-21-8(9)) Zoe Life Publishing.

Canyon View Assembly of God, compiled by. Bridge to Triumph. 2007. pap. 14.95 (978-0-9792475-6-9(X)) Good Catch Publishing.

Capaccio, Salvatore. Crying Wisdom. 2010. 328p. pap. 18.99 (978-1-60957-525-0(3)) Xulon Pr., Inc.

Capdevila, L. A. Bread in Gods Hands. 2006. 21.99 (978-1-60034-576-0(X)) Xulon Pr., Inc.

Capers Jr., William T. Dunamis: The Missing Link in the Black Church. 2011. 182p. pap. 24.95 (978-1-4626-1010-5(2)) PublishAmerica, Inc.

Capone, Patti. A Walking Testimony, 1 vol. 2009. 100p. pap. 16.95 (978-1-60610-313-5(X)) PublishAmerica, Inc.

Capozzoli, Krista. Stained Glass Windows. 2011. 254p. pap. 16.99 (978-1-61379-217-9(4)) Xulon Pr., Inc.

Capps, Beverly. God's Creative Power for Kids. 2008. (ENG.). 54p. (J). pap. 10.00 (978-0-9747513-6-8(7)) Capps Publishing.

Carder, Jaime. Quien, Yo? (Who, Me?) (SPA.). (978-84-7645-199-1(7), 223233) Clie, Editorial.

Cardinale, Deena Anderson. A Plan for You. 2008. 224p. pap. 15.99 (978-1-60791-079-4(9)) Xulon Pr., Inc.

Carelock, Joyce L. Church Hurts Can Make You Bitter or Better. 2009. 100p. pap. 10.99 (978-1-61579-069-2(1)) Xulon Pr., Inc.

—On My Way down I Looked up And. 2010. 72p. pap. 10.99 (978-1-60957-203-7(3)) Xulon Pr., Inc.

Carelock, Joyce L. Youth Halted Between: Bad Choices & God's Purpose. 2011. 190p. pap. 14.99 (978-1-61379-377-0(4)) Xulon Pr., Inc.

Carey, Denise M. But, God I'm Not an Intercessor!! 2008. 144p. pap. 13.99 (978-1-60647-420-4(0)) Xulon Pr., Inc.

Carey, William H. The Basics of New Testament Teaching: an Apostolic Guide to Doctrine. 2009. 99p. pap. 12.19 *(978-0-557-03659-2(3))* Lulu Enterprises Inc.

Carl, Kimberley. 505 Reasons to Live & Laugh! And Poetry Selections. 2007. 76p. per. 16.95 *(978-1-4241-9233-5(1))* PublishAmerica, Inc.

Carlin, Joyce. Daughters of the Most High. 2006. 128p. pap. 17.00 *(978-1-59752-863-4(3),* Resource Pubns.) Wipf & Stock Pubs.

—A Time to Be Deborah. 2009. 134p. pap. 17.00 *(978-1-60608-288-1(4),* Resource Pubns.) Wipf & Stock Pubs.

Carline, Brian. Were Only Married in the Bed. 2009. pap. 14.99 *(978-1-60791-646-8(0))* Xulon Pr., Inc.

Carlson, Amelia. From Victim to Victor: Setting the Captives Free from Bondage. 2009. 264p. pap. 19.95 *(978-1-4327-4861-6(0))* Outskirts Pr., Inc.

Carlson, Melody. Dear Mom: Everything Your Teenage Daughter Wants You to Know but Will Never Tell You. 2009. (ENG.). 224p. 13.99 *(978-1-4000-7491-4(6),* WaterBrook Pr.) Doubleday Religious Publishing Group, The.

—Life: A Teen Devotional, 1 vol. 2009. (Words from the Rock Ser.). 192p. (YA). pap. 11.99 *(978-0-8007-3255-4(3))* Revell.

Carlson, R. Harold T. 'Dawg Gone... Movin' on!!Apos. 2008. 212p. per. 14.99 *(978-1-60477-306-4(5))* Xulon Pr., Inc.

Carlson, Rev. Glenda. Fear Not. 2011. 292p. 31.99 ***(978-1-61379-056-4(2))***; pap. 16.99 ***(978-1-61215-550-0(2))*** Xulon Pr., Inc.

Carmelites of Indianapolis Staff. God in Ordinary Time: Carmelite Reflections on Everyday Life. rev. exp. ed. 76p. 10.95 *(978-1-886873-16-2(X))* Carmelites of Indianapolis.

Carmichael, Amy. Candles in the Dark: Letters of Hope & Encouragement. 2009. (ENG.). 115p. mass mkt. 6.99 *(978-0-87508-085-7(5))* CLC Pubns.

Carmichael, Nancie. Surviving One Bad Year: 7 Spiritual Strategies to Lead You to a New Beginning. 2009. (ENG.). 208p. pap. 14.99 *(978-1-4391-0324-1(0),* Howard Bks.) Howard Books.

Carnell, C. Mitchell. Christian Civility in an Uncivil World. 2009. pap. *(978-1-57312-537-6(7))* Smyth & Helwys Publishing, Inc.

Carothers, Merlin R. Alabanza Da Resultado: Praise Works. (SPA.). 224p. *(978-84-7228-501-9(4),* 360020) Clie, Editorial.

Carr, Josie. Inspire for Teachers: Prayers Promises, & Proverbs for Those Who Change Lives & Tough Hearts. 2008. (Illus.). 92p. pap. 4.99 *(978-1-57794-884-1(X))* Harrison House Pubs.

Carrington, Patty LaVerne. Seasoned Psongs for the Soul. 2010. pap. 15.95 *(978-0-7414-6017-2(3))* Infinity Publishing.

Carroll. Excuse Me, Lord, Did You Say China? 2007. 180p. per. 15.95 *(978-0-595-44963-7(8))* iUniverse, Inc.

Carroll, Jackson W. As One with Authority, Second Edition: Reflective Leadership in Ministry. 2011. 234p. pap. 26.00 ***(978-1-60899-737-4(5),*** Cascade Bks.) Wipf & Stock Pubs.

Carroll, Lesley & Smyth, Geraldine. Glimpses of God: Reflections for Days & Seasons. 2010. (ENG.). 128p. pap. 15.95 *(978-1-84730-094-2(4))* Veritas Pubns. IRL. Dist: Dufour Editions, Inc.

Carroll, Michael. Meehall. 2010. 221p. pap. 21.99 *(978-0-557-22073-1(4))* Lulu Enterprises Inc.

Carson, D. A. The Intolerance of Tolerance. 2009. 256p. 24.00 *(978-0-8028-3170-5(2))* Eerdmans, William B. Publishing Co.

Carson, Dana. Let's Get Real! 2006. (ENG.). 143p. per. 12.95 *(978-0-9770398-4-5(6))* Lifebridge Bks.

Carson, Megan. A Year of Blind Dates: A Single Girl's Search for the One. 2009. (ENG.). 192p. pap. 12.99 *(978-0-8307-4810-5(5))* Gospel Light Pubns.

Carson, Timothy L. Your Calling as a Christian. 2007. (Your Calling As... Ser.). 88p. per. 9.99 *(978-0-8272-4413-9(4))* Chalice Pr.

Carstens, Larry. God Rules: the Commandments, the Beatitudes & the Virtues for Teens & Young Adults. 2009. 139p. pap. 13.81 *(978-0-557-09089-1(X))* Lulu Enterprises Inc.

Carswell, D. J. Live Wires: Powerful Stories of Changed Lives. 2008. (ENG.). 208p. 16.99 *(978-1-85078-737-2(9))* Authentic Media.

Carswell, Roger. Things God Wants Us to Know: Find Purpose in Your Life. 2007. (ENG.). 64p. 7.99 *(978-1-84550-242-3(6))* Christian Focus Pubns. GBR. Dist: STL Distribution North America.

—The Thinker: Thoughts from the Heart of an Evangelist. 2006. (ENG.). 224p. per. 14.99 *(978-1-85078-713-6(1))* Authentic Media.

Carter, Archie. The Sunday Morning Experience. 2007. 360p. (ENG.). 31.99 *(978-1-60266-194-3(4))*; per. 19.99 *(978-1-60266-193-6(6))* Xulon Pr., Inc.

Carter, Ken. Living Our Beliefs. 2009. 144p. pap. 13.00 *(978-0-88177-571-6(1))* Discipleship Resources.

Carter, Les. When Pleasing You Is Killing Me: A Workbook. 2007. (ENG.). 240p. pap. 14.99 *(978-0-8054-4489-6(0),* B&H Bks.) B&H Publishing Group.

Carter, Lilli. When Panic Attacks. 2008. 132p. pap. 14.99 *(978-1-60647-959-9(8))* Xulon Pr., Inc.

Carter, Lois. Boundless Grace: Devotions from a Caregiver's Heart. 2010. pap. 8.99 *(978-1-61663-500-8(2))* Tate Publishing & Enterprises, LLC.

Carter, Paul. Mile 1: Beyond the First Step & into the Heart of Following Jesus. 2010. *(978-1-77069-018-9(2))* Word Alive Pr.

Carter, Paul. The Narrow Way. 2012. 216p. pap. ***(978-1-77069-530-6(3))*** Word Alive Pr.

Carter, Thad. Download Faith, Not Fear. 2007. 48p. per. 16.95 *(978-1-4241-9880-1(1))* PublishAmerica, Inc.

Carter, Yvonne. My Gifts to the King. 2009. 136p. pap. 11.99 *(978-1-60791-619-2(3))* Xulon Pr., Inc.

Cartmell, Todd. Respectful Kids: The Complete Guide to Bringing Out the Best in Your Child. 2006. (Growing in Christ Ser.). (ENG.). 208p. per. 17.99 *(978-1-57683-984-3(2))* NavPress Publishing Group.

Cartrett, Shannon. One Extraordinary Life to Come an in-Depth Study of the Book of Revelation. 2009. spiral bd. 17.99 *(978-1-61623-241-2(2))* Independent Pub.

Caruana, Vicki. Before the Bell Rings. 2006. (ENG., Illus.). 362p. 12.99 *(978-1-58229-571-8(9),* Howard Bks.) Howard Books.

Caruthers, Devin E. Somewhere in Between: A Spiritual Guide to Mentoring Young Men. 2011. 112p. pap. 15.99 ***(978-1-4567-5531-7(5))*** AuthorHouse.

Carvajal, Nelson. Una Revelacion de Dios. 2006. pap. 13.99 *(978-1-60034-021-5(0))* Xulon Pr., Inc.

Casad, Betty. Visitors to My Heart. 2008. 76p. pap. 10.99 *(978-1-60647-051-0(5))* Xulon Pr., Inc.

Case, Steven L. Crash, 1 vol. 2008. (ENG.). 144p. pap. 14.99 *(978-0-310-28774-2(X))* Zondervan.

—Crash: Prayers from the Collision of Heaven & Earth, 1 vol. 2008. (ENG.). 160p. (YA). pap. 9.99 *(978-0-310-28775-9(8))* Zondervan.

Casey, Matthew J. The Return: An EndTime Epistle to the Church in America. 2010. (ENG.). 128p. pap. 11.99 *(978-0-9718428-5-4(X))* Elijah Bks.

Cash, Lillian. Judged Faithful: Praying God's Word over Teenagers. 2009. 104p. pap. 10.99 *(978-1-61579-269-6(4))* Xulon Pr., Inc.

Cash, Teresa. Memories Washed Clean. 2008. 84p. pap. 9.99 *(978-1-932503-77-7(3))* Insight Publishing Group.

Casiday. The Orthodox Christian World. 2012. (Routledge Worlds Ser.). (ENG., Illus.). 608p. (C). 220.00 *(978-0-415-45516-9(2))* Routledge.

Caster, Carol Anne. Walking in the Light. 2009. 148p. pap. 14.99 *(978-1-60791-328-3(3))* Xulon Pr., Inc.

Caster, Craig. Parenting Is a Ministry. 2007. 296p. per. 15.99 *(978-1-60266-198-1(7))* Xulon Pr., Inc.

Castillo, Salvador. Temas y Programas Para Actividades Cristianas. (SPA.). 50p. *(978-0-9644410-3-3(9))* Castillo, Salvador.

Castleberry, Carolyn. It's about Time! 10 Smart Strategies to Avoid Time Traps & Invest Yourself Where It Matters. 2009. (ENG., Illus.). 256p. pap. 16.99 *(978-1-4165-6845-2(X),* Howard Bks.) Howard Books.

Castleberry, Joseph Lee. Your Deepest Dream: Discovering God's True Vision for Your Life. 2012. (Experience the Life Ser.). 144p. pap. 12.99 ***(978-1-61521-826-4(2))*** NavPress Publishing Group.

Catemor, Ebenezer N. Are Demons the Cause of Your Sickness? (Revised Edition) 2010. pap. 14.99 *(978-1-61579-881-0(1))* Xulon Pr., Inc.

Cates, A. Nicole. For Those Moments, 1 vol. 2009. 156p. pap. 24.95 *(978-1-60813-418-2(0))* PublishAmerica, Inc.

Cates, Tim, contrib. by. Glory in the Highest: A New Hallelujah. 2010. (ENG.). 128p. pap. 8.99 *(978-0-8341-7778-9(1),* 9780834177789) Allegis Pubns.

Catholic Book Publishing Co, creator. Angels Surround Us. 2008. (St. Joseph Rattle Board Bks.). (Illus.). 14p. (gr. -1-k). bds. 4.95 *(978-0-89942-724-9(3))* Catholic Bk. Publishing Corp.

Cati, W. L. Married to Muhammed: One Woman's Marriage to a Muslim & His Religion. 10.99 *(978-0-88419-794-2(8),* Creation Hse.) Charisma Media.

Catt, Michael. Fireproof Your Life: Building a Faith That Survives the Flames. 2008. 176p. pap. 12.99 *(978-0-87508-984-3(4))* CLC Pubns.

Catt, Michael, et al. Honor Begins at Home: The Courageous Bible Study. 2011. (ENG., Illus.). 163p. pap. 11.25 ***(978-1-4158-6983-3(9))*** LifeWay Christian Resources.

Catt, Michael, et al. The Power of Desperation: Breakthroughs in Our Brokenness, 1 vol. 2009. (ENG.). 320p. pap. 14.99 *(978-0-8054-4867-2(5))* B&H Publishing Group.

Cavaliere, Pat. Who's Real, What Matters: Living Your Life from a Spiritual Perspective. 2009. 144p. pap. 11.99 *(978-1-60799-036-9(9))* Tate Publishing & Enterprises, LLC.

Cavallaro, MaryJane. Divine Intervention. 2009. 92p. pap. 15.99 *(978-1-4415-8949-1(X))* Xlibris Corp.

Cavazos-GonzDagger;lez, Gilberto. Beyond Piety: The Christian Spiritual Life, Justice, & Liberation. 2010. 138p. pap. 18.00 *(978-1-60899-509-7(7),* Wipf and Stock) Wipf & Stock Pubs.

Cave, Sydney. The Christian Way. *(978-0-8022-0225-3(X))* Philosophical Library, Inc.

Cavins, Jeff, et al, eds. Amazing Grace for Families: 101 Stories of Faith, Hope, Inspiration, & Humor. 2008. (Amazing Grace Ser.). (Illus.). 329p. per. 13.99 *(978-1-934217-35-1(2))* Ascension Pr.

—Amazing Grace for Fathers: 75 Stories of Faith, Hope, Inspiration, & Humor. 2006. 295p. per. *(978-1-932645-99-6(3))* Ascension Pr.

Cawhorne, Joshua. Moses: Perfect in Imperfection. 2010. 48p. pap. 20.35 *(978-0-557-33790-3(9))* Lulu Enterprises Inc.

Caza, Rene. An Outdated Gospel: The Setting of the Cross in the West. 2011. 184p. 30.95 *(978-1-4497-0960-0(5))*; pap. 13.95 *(978-1-4497-0961-7(3))* Author Solutions, Inc. (WestBow Pr.).

Ceballos, Tony. I Will If You Will: Embracing God's Will for Your Life. 2007. 296p. pap. 16.99 *(978-0-924748-84-4(2))* Milestones International Publishers.

Celebrating My First Communion: Mother of Pearl Boys Set. 21.95 *(978-0-89942-751-5(0),* C806/82B, Resurrection Pr.) Catholic Bk. Publishing Corp.

Celebrating My First Communion: Mother of Pearl Girls Set. 21.95 *(978-0-89942-750-8(2),* C806/82W, Resurrection Pr.) Catholic Bk. Publishing Corp.

Celebrating My First Communion: Padded Boys Set. 12.95 *(978-0-89942-749-2(9),* C806/42B, Resurrection Pr.) Catholic Bk. Publishing Corp.

Celebrating My First Communion: Padded Girls Set. 12.95 *(978-0-89942-748-5(0),* C806/42W, Resurrection Pr.) Catholic Bk. Publishing Corp.

Celia, Dan. All for the Master: Reflections on the Stewardship of Our Gifts, 0 vols. 2008. 128p. pap. 12.98 *(978-0-7852-8969-2(0))* Nelson, Thomas Inc.

—Bigger Kingdom or Bigger Barns: Estate Planning from a Biblical Perspective. 2009. 112p. pap. 10.99 *(978-1-60799-500-5(X))* Tate Publishing & Enterprises, LLC.

Cellier, Patsy. In Times Like These: Moments of Meditation. 2010. pap. 10.99 *(978-1-61663-035-5(3))* Tate Publishing & Enterprises, LLC.

Cenkus, Lee. This Much I Know. 2007. 140p. per. 13.99 *(978-1-60266-551-4(6))* Xulon Pr., Inc.

Center for Learning Staff. Christian Service. 2007. (Religion Ser.). 124p. (YA). spiral bd. 18.95 *(978-1-56077-841-7(5))* Center for Learning, The.

Cervone, John & Fleagle, Arnold R. Foundations 1: Basic Building Block for Building a Life of Faith. 2008. 79p. *(978-1-60066-093-1(2))* WingSpread Publishers.

Cfp, compiled by. Christian Focus Imprint Catalogue 2010: Good books with the real message of Hope. 2010. (ENG.). 24p. *(978-1-84550-541-7(7))* Christian Focus Pubns. GBR. Dist: STL Distribution North America.

, CFP Staff,, C. F. P. Staff. CF4K Children's Resources Catalogue 2009/10: Because you're never too young to know Jesus! 2009. (ENG.). 32p. *(978-1-84550-515-8(8))* Christian Focus Pubns. GBR. Dist: STL Distribution North America.

Chabo, Ysaac J. Catholic: My Simple Spiritual Journey. 2010. 112p. 21.49 *(978-1-4520-8700-9(8))*; pap. 13.99 *(978-1-4520-8701-6(6))* AuthorHouse.

Chace, Sharon R. Protestant Pulse: Heart Hopes for God. 2009. 134p. pap. 17.00 *(978-1-60608-705-3(3),* Resource Pubns.) Wipf & Stock Pubs.

Chadwick, Samuel. Unico Camino a la Victoria: Only Way to Victory. (SPA.). 160p. *(978-84-7228-987-1(7),* 223047) Clie, Editorial.

Chaffey, Tim. God & Cancer. 2009. 220p. pap. 15.99 *(978-1-60791-373-3(9))* Xulon Pr., Inc.

Chaffin, Eric. Everything I Know about God I Learned from Football. 2008. 220p. pap. 14.99 *(978-1-60604-621-0(7))* Tate Publishing & Enterprises, LLC.

Chalke, Steve. Apprentice: Walking in the Way of Christ, 1 vol. 2009. (ENG.). 208p. pap. 14.99 *(978-0-310-29154-1(2))* Zondervan.

—Apprentice: Walking the Way of Christ, 1 vol. 2009. (ENG.). 80p. pap. 9.99 *(978-0-310-32234-4(0))* Zondervan.

Chalke, Steve & Mann, Alan. Different Eyes: The Art of Living Beautifully, 1 vol. 2010. (ENG.). 144p. pap. 14.99 *(978-0-310-32680-9(X))* Zondervan.

Challies, Tim. The Discipline of Spiritual Discernment. 2007. 208p. pap. 17.99 *(978-1-58134-909-2(2))* Crossway.

Chamberlain, Doug. Other-Wise. 2010. 94p. pap. 10.99 *(978-1-60957-881-7(3))* Xulon Pr., Inc.

Chambers, Arron. Eats with Sinners: Reaching Hungry People Like Jesus Did. 2009. (ENG.). 224p. pap. 12.99 *(978-0-7847-2318-0(4))* Standard Publishing.

—Go! From Studio Audience to Center Stage. 2009. (ENG.). 144p. pap. 9.99 *(978-0-7847-2282-4(X))* Standard Publishing.

—Remember Who You Are: Unleashing the Power of an Identity-Driven Life. 2007. (ENG.). 224p. per. 12.99 *(978-0-7847-2065-3(7))* Standard Publishing.

Chambers, Arron & Karpenske, Nancy. Go! Group Member Discussion Guide: From Studio Audience to Center Stage. 2009. (ENG.). 64p. pap. 6.99 *(978-0-7847-2283-1(8))* Standard Publishing.

Chambers, Linda Giles. What on Earth Does God Want with Me? 8 Steps to Finding Your Place in God. 2009. 132p. pap. 14.99 *(978-1-60791-469-3(7))* Xulon Pr., Inc.

Chambers, Oswald. Run Today's Race. 6.99 *(978-1-898009-04-7(X))* Chambers, Oswald Pubns. Assoc., Ltd. GBR. Dist: CLC Pubns.

Chambers, Oswald & Discovery House Publishers Staff. Power Up! - Diamond: Devotional Thoughts for Baseball Fans. Branon, Dave, ed. 2009. (ENG.). 224p. 11.99 *(978-1-57293-318-7(6))* Discovery Hse. Pubs.

Chan, Francis. Crazy Love: Overwhelmed by a Relentless God. 2010. (ENG.). 256p. pap. 17.99 *(978-1-59415-347-1(7))* Cengage Gale.

—Crazy Love: Overwhelmed by a Relentless God. 2008. (ENG., Illus.). 192p. pap. 14.99 *(978-1-4347-6851-3(1))* Cook, David C.

—Forgotten God: Reversing Our Tragic Neglect of the Holy Spirit. lt. ed. 2010. 256p. pap. 17.99 *(978-1-59415-345-7(0))* Cengage Gale.

—Forgotten God: Reversing Our Tragic Neglect of the Holy Spirit. 2009. (ENG.). 208p. pap. 14.99 *(978-1-4347-6795-0(7))* Cook, David C.

Chan, Francis & Sprinkle, Preston. Eliminamos el Infierno? 2011. (SPA.). 208p. pap. 10.99 ***(978-1-61638-081-6(0),*** Casa Creacion) Charisma Media.

—Erasing Hell: What God Said about Eternity, & the Things We've Made Up. 2011. (ENG.). 208p. pap. 14.99 ***(978-0-7814-0725-0(7))*** Cook, David C.

Chan, Loi. To Bank or Not to Bank: From Pauper to Millionaire, from Hopeless to Hopeful. 2010. pap. 22.99 *(978-1-61566-815-1(2))* Tate Publishing & Enterprises, LLC.

Chancey, Jennie & McDonald, Stacy. Passionate Housewives Desperate for God: Fresh Vision for the Hopeful Homemaker. 2007. 206p. per. 16.00 *(978-1-934554-15-9(4))* Vision Forum, Inc., The.

Channer, Carol J. Strength for Today While My Soldier Is Away. 2008. 130p. per. 10.99 *(978-1-60247-813-8(9))* Tate Publishing & Enterprises, LLC.

Chanski, Mark. Manly Dominion: (in a Passive-Purple-Four-Ball World) 2007. (ENG.). 247p. pap. 19.99 *(978-1-879737-55-6(8))* Calvary Pr.

Chant, Ken. Discovery. 2009. 284p. pap. 21.00 *(978-1-931178-67-9(4))* Vision Publishing.

Chantry, Walter. Fatherhood of God. pap. 0.06 *(978-0-87377-123-3(0))* GAM Pubns.

—I Heard What You Said. pap. 0.06 *(978-0-87377-124-5(9))* GAM Pubns.

Chaos, Steven Clark. This Present Chaos. pap. 9.99 *(978-0-89098-239-6(2))* Twentieth Century Christian Bks.

Chaplain, Roger Turner. Love & Forgiveness. 2011. 176p. 22.99 ***(978-1-61379-557-6(2))***; pap. 14.99 ***(978-1-61379-556-9(4),*** Xulon Pr., Inc.

Chapman, Bishop Laverne. Intimate Love. 2010. 132p. 21.49 *(978-1-4520-5220-5(4))*; pap. 10.99 *(978-1-4520-5219-9(0),* AuthorHouse.

Chapman, Gary. El Matrimonio Que Siempre Ha Deseado, 1 vol.Tr. of Marriage You've Always Wanted. (SPA.). 160p. 2009. pap. 5.99 *(978-0-8254-0504-4(1))* 2006. pap. 9.99 *(978-0-8254-1111-3(4))* Kregel Pubns. (Editorial Portavoz).

Chapman, Gary & Thomas, Jennifer. Los Cinco Lenguajes de la Disculpa. (SPA.). 304p. 2009. pap. 13.99 *(978-1-4143-2568-2(1))* 2006. 18.97 *(978-1-4143-1289-7(X))* Tyndale Hse. Pubs. (Tyndale Espanol).

Chapman, Gary D. Anger: Handling a Powerful Emotion in a Healthy Way. rev. ed. 2007. (ENG., Illus.). 240p. per. 14.99 *(978-1-881273-88-2(1))* Northfield Publishing.

—The Marriage You've Always Wanted. 2009. (ENG.). 160p. pap. 14.99 *(978-0-8024-7297-7(4))* Moody Pubs.

Chapman, James F. Supernatural Knowledge: Seven Lessons Gained from Supernatural Knowledge. 2009. 48p. pap. 10.99 *(978-1-60791-104-3(3))* Xulon Pr., Inc.

Chapman, Jimmie L. Entering the Great Tribulation. 2009. 122p. pap. 16.99 *(978-0-557-10807-7(1))* Lulu Enterprises Inc.

—Mountain Moving Faith. 2009. 106p. pap. 16.99 *(978-0-557-11230-2(3))* Lulu Enterprises Inc.

—666 the Mark of the Beast. 2010. 114p. pap. 17.95 *(978-0-557-38770-0(1))* Lulu Enterprises Inc.

Chapman, John & Thornborough, Tim. Me? A Christian?, 10 vols. 2010. 16p. pap. *(978-1-904889-74-8(3))* Good Bk. Co.

Chapman, Mary Beth & Vaughn, Ellen. Choosing to SEE: A Journey of Struggle & Hope. 2011. pap. 16.99 *(978-0-8007-2085-8(7))* 2010. (Illus.). 288p. 21.99 *(978-0-8007-1991-3(3))* 2010. (Illus.). 288p. pap. 13.99 *(978-0-8007-1992-0(1))* Revell.

Chapman, Michael D. The Charter of Christian Liberty: Examining Paul's Letter to the Galatians. 2006. 240p. pap. 24.95 *(978-1-4241-4395-5(0))* PublishAmerica, Inc.

Chapman, Shirley. A Display of Miracles: Light & Darkness Dwelling in One. 2011. 34p. pap. 19.99 ***(978-1-4415-1117-1(2))*** Xlibris Corp.

Chapman, Steve. 365 Things Every Hunter Should Know. 2008. 192p. mass mkt. 6.99 *(978-0-7369-2248-7(2))* Harvest Hse. Pubs.

Chapman, Steven Curtis & Smith, Scotty. Restoring Broken Things: What Happens When We Catch a Vision of the New World Jesus Is Creating, 0 vols. 2007. 272p. per. 14.99 *(978-0-8499-1896-4(0))* Nelson, Thomas Inc.

Chappell Iii, John R. Free from the Past. 2009. 184p. pap. 15.99 *(978-1-934769-17-1(7))* McDougal & Assocs.

Chappell, Iii John R. Living in His Glorious Presence. 2008. pap. 13.99 *(978-1-934769-08-9(8))* McDougal & Assocs.

Charbonnet Sr., Allen. Is Financial Prosperity for Us Today or. 2006. (ENG.). 21.99 *(978-1-60034-495-4(X))*; pap. 13.99 *(978-1-60034-494-7(1))* Xulon Pr., Inc.

Chardey, Kokou Barth. Pastor Release the Church. 2011. 202p. pap. 19.99 ***(978-1-4568-8955-5(9))*** Xlibris Corp.

Chargois, Paige Lanier. The Work of the Greeter. 2009. (Those Preachin' Women Ser.: 14). 132p. pap. 12.00 *(978-0-8170-1540-4(X))* Judson Pr.

Charisma House Staff, contrib. by. One Minute Insights: How to Make Great Choices, Live with Passion, & Get It Right. 2010. (ENG.). 123p. pap. 9.99 *(978-1-61638-150-9(7),* Charisma Hse.) Charisma Media.

Charnock, Stephen. Not I, but Christ. 192p. *(978-1-85792-181-6(X))* Christian Focus Pubns. GBR. Dist: Riverside.

Chase, Emily Parke. Help! My Family's Messed Up. 2008. 128p. (J). pap. 9.99 *(978-0-8254-2438-0(0))* Kregel Pubns.

Chase, Gloria. God Is Large & in Charge. 2007. 50p. pap. 8.95 *(978-0-9796180-6-2(1))* Williams, Benjamin Publishing.

—Shush My Baby & Don't You Cry. 2007. 81p. pap. 9.95 *(978-0-9796180-8-6(8))* Williams, Benjamin Publishing.

—Stop Speaking, Carrying & Delivering Those Devilish Lies. 2007. 68p. pap. 9.95 *(978-0-9796180-7-9(X))* Williams, Benjamin Publishing.

Cheatley, Ann M. Teach Me How to B A Lady. 2009. pap. 10.99 *(978-1-61579-066-1(7))* Xulon Pr., Inc.

Cheatham, Melvin L. New Every Morning: A Devotional Journal. 2008. (ENG.). 192p. 12.99 *(978-1-934770-60-3(4))* Ellie Claire & Summerside Pr.

Chegeh, Armstrong. Developing Relationships with Integrity: Impact Others by Seeking God First. 2010. (ENG.). 208p. pap. 12.99 *(978-1-61638-175-2(2),* Creation Hse.) Charisma Media.

Chellew-Hodge, Candace. Bulletproof Faith: A Spiritual Survival Guide for Gay & Lesbian Christians. 2008. (ENG.). 192p. pap. 18.95 *(978-0-470-27928-1(1),* Jossey-Bass) Wiley, John & Sons, Inc.

Cherot, Andrea. Salvation Puppet Skits for Missions & Outreaches! 2007. 57p. pap. 14.95 *(978-0-615-17835-6(9))* Lion & Lamb Pubns.

Cherbonneau, Jan & Cherbonneau, Allen. Two Eggs Three Yolks - Learning to Hear & Follow God. 2007. 248p. per. 15.95 *(978-1-59858-410-3(3))* Dog Ear Publishing, LLC.

Cherie, Lizzie. Accountability: Here & Now or There & Later. 2008. 480p. 42.95 *(978-1-4357-0906-5(3))* Lulu Enterprises Inc.

C

Chernov, Ghelly V., et al, eds. Redundancy, Inference & Prediction in SI: A probability-prediction model of simultaneous interpretation based on the Russian school of Activity Theory. (Benjamins Translation Library: Vol. 57). (Illus.). 298p. 138.00 *(978-1-58811-583-6(6))* Benjamins, John Publishing Co.

Cherry, Rozanna M. It Gets Better. 2008. 96p. per. 9.99 *(978-1-60477-606-5(4))* Xulon Pr., Inc.

Cherry, Stephen. Healing Agony: Re-Imagining Forgiveness. 2012. (ENG.). 248p. pap. 22.95 *(978-1-4411-1938-4(8))* Continuum International Publishing Group, Ltd. GBR. Dist: National Bk. Network.

Chesher, Rick. Learning to Walk: Taking Baby Steps to Christian Maturity. 2011. pap. 11.99 *(978-1-61739-286-3(3))* Tate Publishing & Enterprises, LLC.

Chester, Tim. You Can Change: God's Transforming Power for Our Sinful Behavior & Negative Emotions. 2010. 192p. pap. 15.99 *(978-1-4335-1231-5(9))* Crossway.

—Zechariah: God's Big Plan for Struggling Christians: Six Studies for Individuals or Groups. 2010. (Good Book Guides). 64p. pap. *(978-1-904889-26-7(3))* Good Bk. Co.

Chesterton, G. K. Heretics & Orthodoxy. 2009. 276p. pap. 7.95 *(978-1-60386-207-3(2)*, Merchant Bks.) Rough Draft Printing.

Chestnut, Oscar. Less Religion More Spirituality. 2010. 250p. 14.95 net. *(978-0-9821114-4-4(4))* Pecan Tree Publishing.

Chevalier, Elena A. In Chemo: Candid Conversations with God. 2010. pap. 14.99 *(978-1-61579-561-1(8))* Xulon Pr., Inc.

Chevreau, Guy. Vital Signs of a Healthy Church: A Diagnostic. 2007. 127p. pap. *(978-1-905991-01-3(0))* New Wine Pr.

—We Dance Because We Cannot Fly. 240p. pap. *(978-1-85240-320-1(9))* Sovereign World, Ltd.

Chevres, Rafael A. En Busqueda de el Gran Todo. 2008. 164p. 21.99 *(978-1-60477-732-1(X))* Xulon Pr., Inc.

—En Busqueda de el Gran Todo: El Preconocimiento de Dios. 2008. 164p. pap. 13.99 *(978-1-60477-731-4(1))* Xulon Pr., Inc.

Chia, Roland. Radical Discipleship: Reflections on the Sermon on the Mount. 2006. 122p. pap. 16.00 *(978-1-59752-525-1(1)*, Wipf and Stock) Wipf & Stock Pubs.

Chiaro, Karl. The Secret Is!There Is No Secret. 2008. 56p. pap. 16.95 *(978-1-60610-190-2(0))* PublishAmerica, Inc.

Chiedu, Vincent. The Wisdom of the Serpent - Understanding Your Role in the Kingdom of God. 2007. 312p. (ENG.). 27.99 *(978-1-60266-581-1(8))*; per. 17.99 *(978-1-60266-436-4(6))* Xulon Pr., Inc.

Chiestder, Yolanda. Holding On. 2006. (ENG.). 97p. 14.99 *(978-0-9713416-5-4(6))* Sonflower Publishing.

Childers, Genevah. The Bride's Manifesto. 2008. 196p. pap. 14.99 *(978-1-934769-14-0(2))* McDougal & Assocs.

A Childs Beattitudes Anthem. 1.25 *(978-0-687-05195-3(9))* Abingdon Pr.

Childs, Ernest. The Gates of Jerusalem. 2007. 116p. per. 10.99 *(978-1-60266-774-7(8))* Xulon Pr., Inc.

Chinapen, Joel. My Faith Looks up to Thee. 2007. 52p. per. 9.99 *(978-1-60477-421-4(5))* Xulon Pr., Inc.

Chineme, Christiana I. God Didn't Do It; He Only Signed off on It: Living a Purposeful Life Through the Storm. 2010. 428p. pap. 20.49 *(978-1-4490-5809-8(4))* AuthorHouse.

Chinn, Jack. Holy Wind Through Time & Eternity. 2008. 211p. pap. 24.95 *(978-1-60610-254-1(0))* PublishAmerica, Inc.

Chipman-Sullivan, Lois. What Happened to the Gifts. 2010. 32p. pap. 19.99 *(978-1-60957-830-5(9))* Xulon Pr., Inc.

Chironna, Mark J. Live Your Dream: Planning for Success. 2009. 271p. pap. 16.99 *(978-0-7684-3102-5(6))* Destiny Image Pubs.

Chisholm, Bob. Step by Step: A 90-Day Walk with Jesus Through the Gospel of Mark. pap. 12.50 *(978-0-89098-170-2(1))* Twentieth Century Christian Bks.

Chisley, Darlene Laverne. Wisdom Is the Key: Wisdom quips while listening to Him. 2011. 52p. pap. 15.99 ***(978-1-4628-6705-9(7))*** Xlibris Corp.

Chittister, Joan. Illuminated Life: Monastic Wisdom for Seekers of Light. 2010. 144p. pap. 16.00 *(978-1-57075-878-2(6))* Orbis Bks.

Chladek, David. How to Receive from the Kingdom of God. 2008. 120p. pap. 9.95 *(978-1-4327-2489-4(4))* Outskirts Pr., Inc.

Cho, David Yonggi. Dr. David Yonggi Cho: Ministering Hope for 50 Years. 2008. (Illus.). 158p. pap. 11.99 *(978-0-88270-480-7(X)*, Bridge-Logos) Bridge-Logos Foundation.

—4th Dimensional Living in a 3 Dimensional World. 2007. 150p. per. 9.99 *(978-0-88270-312-1(9))* Bridge-Logos Foundation.

Choate, Stanley. Battle for the Mind: Psychological Warfare. 2007. 144p. per. *(978-1-55452-184-5(X)*, Guardian Bks.) Essence Publishing.

Chole, Alicia Britt. Anonymous: Jesus' hidden years... & Yours. 2011. 194p. pap. 15.99 ***(978-0-7852-9839-7(8))*** Nelson, Thomas Inc.

Cholley, Beverly A. The Lord Says. 2008. 136p. pap. 13.99 *(978-1-60477-836-6(9))* Xulon Pr., Inc.

Chopra, Elma. Born Again Catholic. 2010. 460p. pap. 24.99 *(978-1-60957-367-6(6))* Xulon Pr., Inc.

Chorey, Michael. Cross-Eyed. 2006. 184p. per. 14.95 *(978-1-59919-014-3(1))* Elim Publishing.

Choung, James. Based on a True Story. 2008. (IVP Booklets Ser.). (ENG.). 32p. 1.50 *(978-0-87784-037-4(7)*, IVP Bks.) InterVarsity Pr.

Christ & Barabbas. 1.95 *(978-0-687-06774-9(X))* Abingdon Pr.

Christ In Youth (CIY). Experience. 2007. (Mission Trip Devotions & Journals). 160p. (YA). 9.99 *(978-0-7847-2190-2(4))* Standard Publishing.

Christ up Close & Personal: Youth DVD 5-Part Leader Guide. 2006. 65p. (YA). 9.99 *(978-1-932587-91-3(8))* Green Key Bks.

Christensen, Gary. Beyond the Second Curtain. 2008. 144p. pap. 14.99 *(978-1-60647-468-6(5))* Xulon Pr., Inc.

Christensen, Marvin. Genesis. 2010. 92p. pap. 10.99 *(978-1-60957-343-0(9))* Xulon Pr., Inc.

Christensen, Skip. From Abstinence to Deliverance. 2008. 54p. pap. 8.00 *(978-0-8059-7121-7(1))* Dorrance Publishing Co., Inc.

Christenson, Derek. The Path Back to Eden. 2007. 124p. 27.50 *(978-1-4303-1362-5(5))* Lulu Enterprises Inc.

Christenson, Evelyn. Lord, Change Me. 2008. (ENG.). 160p. pap. 10.99 net. *(978-0-9817467-0-8(5))* Christenson, Evelyn Ministry.

Christian Art Gifts, creator. Baxter Supreme Quality Notebook. 2007. 192p. *(978-5-557-42342-7(7))*; *(978-5-557-42343-4(5))* Christian Art Pubs.

Christian, David. Finding Jesus: To Learn Abba's Worldview. 2011. 168p. 23.00 ***(978-1-4634-0521-2(9))***; pap. 12.00 ***(978-1-4634-0522-9(7))*** AuthorHouse.

The Christian Home. 0.75 *(978-0-89265-511-3(9))* Randall Hse. Pubns.

Christian, Karla J. Perspectives from a Smart Christian. 2007. 119p. pap. 11.99 *(978-1-56722-708-6(2))* Word Aflame Pr.

Christian, Michael Darren Procella. A Prodigal Son. 2011. 316p. pap. 18.99 *(978-1-61215-536-4(7))* Xulon Pr., Inc.

Christian, Shirley. Keys to a Sound MInd. 2008. 48p. pap. 9.95 *(978-0-615-18974-1(1))* Christian, Shirley Ministries.

Christian, Terry Allan. What Did Jesus Say... 2011. 176p. 22.99 ***(978-1-61379-500-2(9))***; pap. 14.99 ***(978-1-61379-499-9(1))*** Xulon Pr., Inc.

Christianity & the Market. 20.00 *(978-0-687-85119-5(X))* Abingdon Pr.

Christianity Today International Staff. Cti Sg Series: Faith & Pop Culture, 0 vols. 2009. (Christianity Today Study Ser.). 128p. pap. 9.99 *(978-1-4185-3409-7(9))* Nelson, Thomas Inc.

Christianity Today International Staff, creator. Engaging the Culture, 0 vols. 2008. (Christianity Today Study Ser.). 176p. pap. 9.99 *(978-1-4185-3423-3(4))* Nelson, Thomas Inc.

—Faith & Work, 0 vols. 2008. (Christianity Today Study Ser.). 160p. pap. 9.99 *(978-1-4185-3425-7(0))* Nelson, Thomas Inc.

—Politics, 0 vols. 2008. (Christianity Today Study Ser.). 128p. pap. 9.99 *(978-1-4185-3426-4(9))* Nelson, Thomas Inc.

Christians & Emotions. 0.75 *(978-0-89265-517-5(8))* Randall Hse. Pubns.

Christie, Don. Soaring Through Spirit Space. 2010. 188p. pap. 14.99 *(978-1-60957-184-9(3))* Xulon Pr., Inc.

Christodonte, Marcos, Sr. Confessions Made in His Blood. 2008. 88p. pap. 16.52 *(978-0-615-16962-0(7))* Lords of His Majesty.

Christopher, Karen D. Wait on God. 2007. 56p. per. 16.95 *(978-1-4241-8652-5(8))* PublishAmerica, Inc.

Christopherson, Arden. Speak Plainly God. 2009. 396p. 32.99 *(978-1-60791-332-0(1))*; pap. 20.99 *(978-1-60791-331-3(3))* Xulon Pr., Inc.

Chuck, Milian. We're Just Friends & Other Dating Lies: Practical Wisdom for Healthy Relationships. 2010. 208p. pap. 15.99 *(978-1-935273-83-7(3))* New Growth Pr.

Chudy, Marla K. Somewhere under the Rainbow: My Walk with God Through Depression, Bipolar Disorder, VNS Therapy. 2008. 160p. 12.99 *(978-1-60462-903-3(7))* Tate Publishing & Enterprises, LLC.

Chudyk, Amanda. The King Is Glorified Through Our Valleys. 2007. 108p. per. 10.99 *(978-1-60266-809-6(4))* Xulon Pr., Inc.

Chukwuocha, A. C. & Chukwuocha, A. The War Within: Christians & Inner Conflicts, 1 vol. 2009. (ENG.). 144p. pap. 16.99 *(978-9966-805-39-3(7))* Zondervan.

Chung, Peter. Figments of a Purposeful Imagination. 2008. 200p. pap. 14.00 *(978-0-8059-7689-2(2))* Dorrance Publishing Co., Inc.

Church, Forrest. Love & Death: My Journey Through the Valley of the Shadow. (ENG.). 160p. 2009. pap. 16.00 *(978-0-8070-7297-4(4))* 2008. 22.00 *(978-0-8070-7293-6(1))* Beacon Pr.

Church Missionary Society Staff. 365 Days of Yes: Daily Prayers & Readings for A Missional Church. 2011. 400p. 34.99 *(978-1-84825-060-4(6)*, Canterbury Pr. Norwich) Hymns Ancient & Modern Ltd GBR. Dist: Westminster John Knox Pr.

Church of England, Commission on Urban Priority Areas Staff, contrib. by. Faith in the City: A Call for Action by Church & Nation. 2012. (Illus.). xvi, 398p. pap. ***(978-0-7151-3709-3(3))*** Church Hse. Publishing.

Church of God in Christ. No Substitute: There Is no substitute for knowing Jesus for Yourself. 2007. (Illus.). 50p. per. 10.00 *(978-0-9760730-5-5(6)*, Ne'Rak Pubns.) His Spirit Creations.

Churcher, John. Setting Jesus Free. 2009. (ENG., Illus.). 240p. pap. 24.95 *(978-1-84694-249-5(7))* Hunt, John Publishing Ltd. GBR. Dist: National Bk. Network.

Churton, Tobias. The Missing Family of Jesus: A Historical Account of Jesus' Family, Their Heritage, & Their Destiny. 2010. (ENG., Illus.). 256p. 24.95 *(978-1-907486-02-9(X)*, Watkins Publishing) Duncan Baird Pubs. GBR. Dist: Sterling Publishing Co., Inc.

Chuta, Edith N. Get More out of Your Prayers. 2007. (ENG.). 84p. per. 16.95 *(978-1-4241-7374-7(4))* PublishAmerica, Inc.

Chute, Zach. Out of My Prison: A Poetic Journey to Peace. 2011. 56p. pap. 9.95 ***(978-1-4497-2920-2(7)***, WestBow Pr.) Author Solutions, Inc.

Ciarlo, Simona. Miles Across This Tightrope. 2006. (Illus.). 277p. per. 21.95 *(978-1-59886-363-5(0))* Tate Publishing & Enterprises, LLC.

Çiçek, Julius Yeshu, ed. Voices of Tur Abdin. 2010. (SYR.). 99.68 *(978-1-61143-205-3(7))* Gorgias Pr., LLC.

Cirillo, Joseph. Life Lessons. 2007. 176p. per. 14.49 *(978-1-4343-0708-8(5))* AuthorHouse.

City of Refuge: Triumph over Life's Greatest Obstacles. 2007. pap. 14.95 *(978-0-9785152-8-7(5))* Good Catch Publishing.

Claiborne, Jeff. The Young Person's Guide to Wisdom: A Biblical Guide to the Wisdom of God Revealed in Scripture. 2010. 250p. pap. 16.99 *(978-1-61579-877-3(3))* Xulon Pr., Inc.

Clairmont, Patsy. All Cracked Up, 0 vols. 2009. 208p. pap. 12.99 *(978-1-4002-7805-3(8))* Nelson, Thomas Inc.

—All Cracked Up: Experiencing God in the Broken Places. l.t. ed. 2008. (Walker Large Print Ser.). (ENG.). 256p. pap. 17.95 *(978-1-59415-226-9(8)*, Walker Large Print) Cengage Gale.

—Wof: Finding God in the Broken Places, 0 vols. 2008. (Women of Faith Study Guide Ser.). 128p. pap. 9.99 *(978-1-4185-3220-8(7))* Nelson, Thomas Inc.

Clark, Chap, et al. Deep Justice in a Broken World: Helping Your Kids Serve Others & Right the Wrongs Around Them, 1 vol. 2007. (ENG., Illus.). 256p. pap. 18.99 *(978-0-310-27377-6(3))* Zondervan.

Clark, Freddy James. Hospitality: An Ecclesiological Practice of Ministry. 2007. (ENG.). 82p. per. 25.50 *(978-0-7618-2982-9(2))* Hamilton Bks.

Clark, Glenn. The Way, the Truth & the Life. 2007. (ENG.). 188p. 37.95 *(978-0-548-08438-0(6))* Kessinger Publishing, LLC.

Clark, James. A Layman's THEOLOGY. 2008. 248p. pap. 20.95 *(978-1-4357-1212-6(9))* Lulu Enterprises Inc.

Clark, Jerusha. The Life You Crave: The Promise of Discernment. 2008. (Modern Girl's Bible Study Ser.). (ENG.). 256p. (YA). per. 14.99 *(978-1-60006-055-7(2)*, Th1nk Bks.) NavPress Publishing Group.

Clark, Jim. The Narrow Way. 2011. 136p. pap. 14.99 ***(978-1-61379-029-8(5))*** Xulon Pr., Inc.

Clark, Jonas. The Weapons of Your Warfare. 2009. 22p. pap. 3.00 *(978-1-886885-39-4(7))* Spirit of Life.

Clark, Jonas A. Come Out! Handbook for the Serious Deliverance Minister. 110p. pap. 9.99 *(978-1-886885-10-3(9))* Spirit of Life.

—Prophecy Without Permission. 2008. 26p. pap. 3.00 *(978-1-886885-31-8(1))* Spirit of Life.

—Sanidad para el Rechazo y el Abuso Emocional. 2011. (SPA.). 22p. pap. 3.50 ***(978-1-886885-55-4(9))*** Spirit of Life.

Clark, Jonas A. Unlocking Prophetic Imaginations. 2008. 24p. pap. 3.00 *(978-1-886885-34-9(6))* Spirit of Life.

Clark, Jonas B. Casting down Imaginations. (Illus.). 100p. (Orig.). pap. 8.00 *(978-1-886885-03-5(6))* Spirit of Life.

Clark, Kent Ward, ed. The and Christ of God. 2011. 218p. pap. 15.99 ***(978-1-61379-049-6(X))*** Xulon Pr., Inc.

Clark, Laura. Sindone, the Divine Remedy. 2009. 142p. pap. 19.50 *(978-0-9789499-4-5(3))* Cradle Pr.

Clark, Marc. A Father's Word to His Children. 2011. pap. 29.99 ***(978-1-61346-230-0(1))*** Tate Publishing & Enterprises, LLC.

Clark, Mindy Starns. The House That Cleans Itself: Creative Solutions for a Clean & Orderly House in Less Time Than You Can Imagine. 2007. 240p. pap. 12.99 *(978-0-7369-1880-0(9))* Harvest Hse. Pubs.

Clark, Paul. Southern Cross: Lost & Found on the Streets & in the Jungles of Peru. 2008. 180p. per. *(978-0-9809231-0-0(7))* BPS Bks.

Clark, Ruby McCormick. God & Depression: Living with Depression. 2009. 156p. pap. 14.99 *(978-1-60791-110-4(8))* Xulon Pr., Inc.

Clarke, David E. The Grace of God: No Subtitle. 2008. 184p. pap. 15.99 *(978-1-60647-473-0(1))* Xulon Pr., Inc.

Clarke Iii, Charles Linwood. Love Is Our Final Destination. 2008. 212p. 24.99 *(978-1-60477-628-7(5))* Xulon Pr., Inc.

Clarke-Milton, Christopher. Dawn of the Messiah Book1. 2008. 204p. per. 16.99 *(978-1-60477-792-5(3))* Xulon Pr., Inc.

Clarke, Robert B. The Royal Line of Christ the Logos: A Jungian View of the Roots & Meaning of the Orthodox/Gnostic Christian Mystery. 2010. (ENG.). 200p. pap. 15.95 *(978-0-9842612-0-8(6))* Hologram Bks., LLC.

Clarke, Shaneen. Dare to Be Great: Forget Your Past! Live Your Dream! 2009. (ENG.). 144p. pap. 12.95 *(978-0-9793192-9-7(3))* Lifebridge Bks.

Clarke, Timothy J. Paying the Price to Win. 2008. 132p. pap. 14.99 *(978-1-60647-629-1(7))* Xulon Pr., Inc.

Clarkson, Sally. Dancing with My Father: How God Leads Us into a Life of Grace & Joy. 2010. (ENG.). 224p. pap. 13.99 *(978-0-307-45706-6(0)*, WaterBrook Pr.) Doubleday Religious Publishing Group, The.

Clawson, Anne. Dancing on the Rim. 2011. 380p. pap. 19.00 ***(978-0-557-48717-2(X))*** Lulu Enterprises Inc.

Claxton, W. O. "Bill". Inspections Commercial Construction, 1 vol. 2007. 366p. 89.00 *(978-0-9728590-1-1(2))* Word Prodns.

Clay, Evangelist Jessie. Rescued & Redirected: Cast down but Not Destroyed!! 2009. 84p. pap. 10.95 *(978-1-4401-1138-9(3))* iUniverse, Inc.

Clayton, Jeffrey. Backslider Like Me. 2007. 152p. per. 13.99 *(978-1-60266-705-1(5))* Xulon Pr., Inc.

Clayton, Jimmy. New Ark of the Covenant Found! 2007. 188p. (ENG.). 21.99 *(978-1-60266-619-1(9))*; per. 13.99 *(978-1-60266-618-4(0))* Xulon Pr., Inc.

Clayton, Jimmy C. Name It & Claim It Prosperity Preachers: The Thief Cometh but to Steal. 2009. 184p. pap. 14.99 *(978-1-61579-384-6(4))* Xulon Pr., Inc.

Clayton, Joan. Life Is Delicious. 2006. (ENG.). 144p. per. 24.95 *(978-1-4137-5267-0(5))* PublishAmerica, Inc.

—A Time for Praise. 2008. 124p. pap. 19.95 *(978-1-60672-639-6(0))* PublishAmerica, Inc.

Cleek, Corey, ed. Devotional Ventures: 60 Inspiring Devotions for Business Professionals by Business Professionals. 2007. (ENG.). 224p. 14.99 *(978-0-8307-4314-8(6))* Gospel Light Pubns.

Clegg, Tom & Bird, Warren. Missing in America: Making an Eternal Difference in the World Next Door. 2007. 195p. per. 14.99 *(978-0-7644-3563-8(9))* Group Publishing, Inc.

Clemens, Philip K. Beyond the Law: Living the Sermon on the Mount. 2007. (Illus.). 224p. per. 13.99 *(978-0-8361-9361-9(X))* Herald Pr.

Clement, Arthur J. Los pentecostales y Carismaticos.Tr. of Pentecostals & Charismatics. (SPA.). 231p. 8.99 *(978-0-7586-0606-8(0))* Concordia Publishing Hse.

Clement, Kim. Call Me Crazy, but I'm Hearing God. 2007. 203p. per. 15.99 *(978-0-7684-2494-2(1))* Destiny Image Pubs.

Clements, Keith. A Patriotism for Today: Love of Country in Dialogue with the Witness of Dietrich Bonhoeffer. 2011. 192p. pap. 22.00 ***(978-1-61097-127-0(2)***, Wipf and Stock) Wipf & Stock Pubs.

Clements, Kirby. The Spirit Friendly Church: Reuniting a Divided Church. 98p. pap. *(978-0-917595-61-5(0))* Cathedral of the Holy Spirit.

Clements, Kirby & Clements, Sandra. The Struggle & Triumph of the Believer. 147p. pap. *(978-0-917595-60-8(2))* Cathedral of the Holy Spirit.

Clements, Melinda. Hands: Finding Inspiration in the Daily Gifts You're Given. 2008. (Illus.). 36p. 7.95 *(978-1-929774-53-1(2)*, Olive Tree) Greenleaf Book Group.

Clemons, Nashia. I Went Through a Lot but by the Grace of God He Never Left My Side. 2010. 56p. pap. 10.49 *(978-1-4520-1202-5(4))* AuthorHouse.

Clermont, Betty. The Neo-Catholics: Implementing Christian Nationalism in America. 2009. 252p. pap. 19.95 *(978-0-932863-63-8(9))* Clarity Pr., Inc.

Cleveland, Rich. Discovering the God We Call Father: A Catholic Bible Study on the Lord's Prayer. 2008. 112p. pap. 9.95 *(978-1-59325-136-9(X))* Word Among Us Pr.

Clevenger, Jerry. Paths to Prosperity: Steps from Credit Chaos to Financial Freedom. 2006. (ENG., Illus.). 224p. per. 14.99 *(978-0-9766243-8-7(9))* 21st Century Pr.

Clever, Charles Huntley. The Wise Shall Understand. 2009. 204p. 25.99 *(978-1-60791-307-8(0))*; pap. 15.99 *(978-1-60791-575-1(8))* Xulon Pr., Inc.

Clifford, Catherine E. One Teacher: Doctrinal Authority in the Church. 2010. 186p. pap. 26.00 *(978-0-8028-2598-8(2))* Eerdmans, William B. Publishing Co.

Clifford, Don. Grace Enough for Three: Losing Three Children but Finding God's All-Sufficient Grace. 2008. 252p. pap. 15.99 *(978-1-60477-764-2(8))* Xulon Pr., Inc.

Clifford, Don and Karen. Heavenly Grief: A Christian Guide to Spiritual & Emotional Healing. 2008. 84p. pap. 9.99 *(978-1-60477-681-2(1))* Xulon Pr., Inc.

Clifton, Kenneth. The Christian Superhero Training Guide. 2010. 152p. pap. 11.00 *(978-0-557-12593-7(6))* Lulu Enterprises Inc.

Clifton, Sandra. From New Age to New Life: A Passage from Darkness to the Light of Christ. 2007. (ENG.). 160p. per. 10.99 *(978-1-59979-171-5(4)*, Creation Hse.) Charisma Media.

Clinebell-Joy of Wholeness. *(978-0-687-20596-7(4))* Abingdon Pr.

Clinton, John. Are You Thinking Like A Pharesee? 2008. pap. 12.95 *(978-0-9801357-4-9(5))* Tree of Life Publishing Hse.

Clinton, John L. Come to Me. 2007. pap. 12.00 *(978-0-9801357-0-1(2))* Tree of Life Publishing Hse.

Clinton Jr., John L. Am I Righteous Enough to Serve God? Living in the Shadows of His Grace, 1 vol. 2010. 132p. pap. 24.95 *(978-1-4489-6273-0(0))* PublishAmerica, Inc.

Clinton, Julie & Byers, Mary M. Extraordinary Women: Discovering the Dream God Created for You. 2009. 256p. pap. 13.99 *(978-0-7369-2375-0(6))* Harvest Hse. Pubs.

Clinton, Megan & Clinton, Tim. Totally God's: Every Girl's Guide to Faith, Friends, & Family (BTW, Guys 2!) 2008. 150p. (YA). pap. 9.99 *(978-0-7369-2128-2(1))* Harvest Hse. Pubs.

Clopton, Beverly. Heaven or Bust: Journey to Glory. 2009. 252p. pap. 14.99 *(978-1-4389-0733-8(8))* AuthorHouse.

Closs, Howard. Christian Life Accountability Program. 2011. 184p. pap. 13.95 ***(978-1-4627-0651-8(7))*** Cross Bks. Publishing.

Cloud, David W. Promise Keepers Beware!, Vol. II. Date not set. (Illus.). 53p. pap. 4.00 *(978-1-58318-046-4(X)*, WOL490B) Way of Life Literature.

Cloud, Henry. The One-Life Solution: Reclaim Your Personal Life While Achieving Greater Professional Success. 2008. (ENG.). 304p. 24.95 *(978-0-06-146642-7(5)*, Collins); 432p. pap. 24.95 *(978-0-06-156281-5(5)*, HarperLuxe) HarperCollins Pubs.

—The One-Life Solution Workbook, 1 vol. 2009. (ENG.). 176p. pap. 9.99 *(978-0-310-29367-5(7))* Zondervan.

—The Secret Things of God: Unlocking the Treasures Reserved for You. 2009. (ENG., Illus.). 224p. pap. 13.99 *(978-1-4391-1781-1(0)*, Howard Bks.) Howard Books.

—Los Secretos de Dios: Descubra los Tesoros Reservados para Usted. 2008. (SPA., Illus.). 256p. pap. 14.99 *(978-1-4165-7891-8(9)*, Howard Bks.) Howard Books.

Cloud, Henry & Townsend, John. It's Not My Fault: The No Excuse Plan for Overcoming Life's Obstacles to Enjoy God's Best, 0 vols. 2007. 272p. 22.99 *(978-1-59145-473-1(5))* Nelson, Thomas Inc.

—What to Do When You Don't Know What to Do: 8 Principles for Finding God's Way, 0 vols. 2009. 128p. 12.99 *(978-1-4041-8773-3(1))* Nelson, Thomas Inc.

—What to Do When You Don't Know What to Do: Discouragement & Depression. 0 vols. 2009. (What to Do When You Don't Know Ser.). 102p. pap. 9.99 (978-0-8499-2965-6(2)) Nelson, Thomas Inc.

Cloud, Henry, et al. Boundaries: When to Say Yes, How to Say No to Take Control of Your Life. 1 vol. rev. ed. 2007. (ENG.). 128p. (gr. 13). pap. 9.99 (978-0-310-27808-5(2)) Zondervan.

Cloud, Thomas & Ragsdale, Trey. Circle of Fellowship: A Men's Small Group Discussion Guide Designed to Make Disciples of Jesus. 2009. 152p. pap. 14.99 (978-1-60791-159-9(X)) Xulon Pr., Inc.

Clouston, Craig. Snapshots: A Spiritual Look at Daily Life. 2010. pap. 27.99 (978-1-61566-651-5(6)) Tate Publishing & Enterprises, LLC.

Cluck, Harold T. Are You Really a Christian? 2007. 125p. per. 10.99 (978-1-59886-942-2(6)) Tate Publishing & Enterprises, LLC.

Clymer, R. Swinburne. The Soul's Descent. 2006. pap. 12.95 (978-1-4286-7941-2(3)) Kessinger Publishing, LLC.

Coate. Sin Guilt & Forgiveness. 240p. 16.00 (978-0-281-04781-9(2)) SPCK Publishing GBR. Dist: Pilgrim Pr., The/United Church Pr.

Coats, Vivian. His Perfect Way: The Hermit Crab Story. 2011. 36p. pap. 15.14 (978-1-4567-3482-4(2)) AuthorHouse.

Cobb, Chuck. To Know a Warrior. 2008. 172p. pap. 14.00 (978-1-59755-156-4(2), Advantage Inspirational) Advantage Bks.

Cobb Jr., John B., ed. Resistance: The New Role of Progressive Christians. 2008. (ENG.). 328p. pap. 20.00 (978-0-664-23287-0(6)) Westminster John Knox Pr.

Cobb, Tyrone W. Day of the Lord. 2008. 196p. pap. 14.99 (978-1-60791-015-2(2)) Xulon Pr., Inc.

—The Secret Made Manifest. 2009. 284p. pap. 16.99 (978-1-60791-607-9(X)) Xulon Pr., Inc.

Cobbey, Nan. Final Acts. 48p. pap. 1.95 (978-0-88028-226-0(6), 1603) Forward Movement Pubns.

Coby, Malcolm W. Until Morning Comes: A Word of Hope & Peace Through the Night. 2010. pap. 11.99 (978-1-61566-411-5(4)) Tate Publishing & Enterprises, LLC.

Codrut M. Magheru. Quantum Christian Virtues: A Catalogue of Enlightenment. 2010. 136p. 23.95 (978-1-4502-2763-6(5)); pap. 13.95 (978-1-4502-2761-2(9)) iUniverse, Inc.

Coe, George Albert. The Religion of a Mature Mind. 2009. 174p. pap. 19.99 (978-1-4589-3626-4(0)) General Bks. LLC.

—The Religion of a Mature Mind. 2007. (ENG.). 444p. 51.95 (978-0-548-09141-8(2)) Kessinger Publishing, LLC.

Coffer, Anna. You Can't Take Your Credit Card with You When You Go: The Moment of Truth - Oneness - 2008. 160p. pap. 14.95 (978-1-4343-9900-7(1)) AuthorHouse.

Coggins, Chuck. 101 Facts Every Person Should Know about God. 2011. 112p. pap. 6.99 (978-1-936314-39-3(8)) Word & Spirit Resources, LLC.

Coghlan, Patrick. A Glass of Homemade Lemonade: A Guide to Spirituality for the Over-Fifties. 2008. (ENG.). 102p. pap. 16.95 (978-1-84730-081-2(2)) Veritas Pubns. IRL. Dist: Dufour Editions, Inc.

Cohen, M. A. We're Dancin' to His Righteous Rhythm Keepin' It Real. 2007. 200p. per. 23.95 (978-0-595-44993-4(X)) iUniverse, Inc.

Cohen, Rabbi Herbert J. Texas Torah: The Interface of the Weekly Torah Portion with Everyday Life. 2010. 256p. (ENG.). 29.95 (978-1-4502-3931-8(5)); pap. 19.95 (978-1-4502-3930-1(7)) iUniverse, Inc.

Coiley, Trudy. Crossing the Pilgrim Journey: Challenges & Solutions. 2007. 148p. (ENG.). 19.95 (978-1-4327-0802-3(3)); per. 13.95 (978-1-4327-0740-8(X)) Outskirts Pr., Inc.

Coker, Elizabeth. F a I T H Faithful Actions Initiated Through Him: A Twelve Week Discipleship Course for Women. 2010. 220p. 33.95 (978-1-61507-267-5(5)); pap. 17.95 (978-1-61507-266-8(7)) Cross Bks. Publishing.

Colbert, Deborah Susan. Dwelling in God with Toddlers at Your Feet. 2008. 112p. per. 10.99 (978-1-60477-240-1(9)) Xulon Pr., Inc.

Colbert, Don. Depression & Anxiety. 2009. (ENG.). 128p. pap. 8.99 (978-1-59979-760-1(7), Siloam Pr.) Charisma Media.

—The New Bible Cure for Diabetes: Expanded Editions Include Twice As Much Information! 2009. (ENG.). 128p. pap. 8.99 (978-1-59979-759-5(3), Siloam Pr.) Charisma Media.

—Stress Less: Break the Power of Worry, Fear, & Other Unhealthy Habits Uncover the Truth about Cortisol & Stress Hormones Communicate Feelings Without Increasing Anxiety. 2008. (ENG.). 304p. pap. 14.99 (978-1-59979-313-9(X), Siloam Pr.) Charisma Media.

Colbert, Don & Colbert, Kyle. Get Fit & Live! The Simple Fitness Program That Can Help You Lose Weight, Build Muscle, & Live Longer. 2010. (ENG.). 208p. pap. 17.99 (978-1-61638-026-7(8), Siloam Pr.) Charisma Media.

Coldiron, Jim. Expository Messages in the Epistle of 1 John. 2010. 112p. pap. 11.95 (978-1-61507-169-2(5)) Cross Bks. Publishing.

Cole, D. What Jesus Says to You. 2011. 78p. pap. 9.95 (978-1-4327-6657-3(0)) Outskirts Pr., Inc.

Cole, Lorraine M. How Great Is Our God! A Study of the Trinity-the Father, Jesus Christ, & the Holy Spirit. 2009. pap. 12.99 (978-1-60696-967-0(6)) Tate Publishing & Enterprises, LLC.

Cole, Lynne Junkins. God's Question. 2010. 438p. pap. 22.99 (978-1-60957-932-6(1)) Xulon Pr., Inc.

Cole, Paul Louis. Daring: A Call to Courageous Manhood. 2011. (Illus.). 201p. pap. 14.99 (978-1-931682-40-4(2)) Word & Spirit Resources, LLC.

Cole, Tom & Cole, Donna. Pure Heart: Restoration of the Heart Through the Beatitudes. 2008. 148p. pap. 13.99 (978-1-60477-993-6(4)) Xulon Pr., Inc.

Cole, Trafford R. Achieving Success the Lord's Way. 2008. pap. 12.99 (978-1-59955-091-6(1)) Cedar Fort, Inc./CFI Distribution.

Cole, Virginia A. Overcoming Adversities. 2010. pap. 15.99 (978-1-61663-046-1(9)) Tate Publishing & Enterprises, LLC.

Coleman, George. To Hell with Hell: Starvation & the Church. 2008. 220p. pap. 16.95 (978-1-4327-2649-2(8)) Outskirts Pr., Inc.

Coleman, Karon. Don't Count Me Out: When something little becomes Big. 2011. 124p. 28.95 (978-1-61507-822-6(3)); pap. 11.95 (978-1-61507-821-9(5)) Cross Bks. Publishing.

Coleman, Nykia. Keeping Family & Friends in God's Hands. 2008. 76p. per. 9.99 (978-1-60477-645-4(5)) Xulon Pr., Inc.

Coles, Rhianne. Faith: For an Abundant Life. 2008. 96p. pap. 31.99 (978-1-4389-0059-9(7)) AuthorHouse.

Coleson, Joseph, ed. The Church Jesus Builds: A Dialogue on the Church in the 21st Century. 2006. (Wesleyan Theological Perspectives Ser.). 205p. per. 14.99 (978-0-89827-349-6(8)) Wesleyan Publishing Hse.

Coley, Ella Jane. The Father's Heartbeat. 2009. 456p. pap. 20.49 (978-1-4389-9838-1(4)) AuthorHouse.

—The Father's Heartbeat: How Great the Father's Love for Us How Rich & Beyond Measure! Divine Revelations from His Heart to Ours. 2009. 456p. 30.99 (978-1-4389-9841-1(4)) AuthorHouse.

Colledge, Sandy. Visions of Jesus & Glimpses of Heaven. 2007. 108p. per. 10.99 (978-1-60266-531-6(1)) Xulon Pr., Inc.

Collett, Tom. Further into Our Presence. 2010. 90p. pap. 10.00 (978-1-4500-9023-0(0)) Xlibris Corp.

Collie, Kelafo Z. You Are My Father, I Am Your Son- Understanding Kingdom Sonship. 2009. 236p. pap. 15.99 (978-1-61579-458-4(1)) Xulon Pr., Inc.

Collier, Bryan D. Gentle Interventions: God's Graceful Work in Our Lives. 2008. pap. 9.99 (978-1-60647-435-8(9)) Xulon Pr., Inc.

Collier, John D. Real Christian Living, Vol. 1. 2008. 216p. per. 14.99 (978-1-60477-569-3(6)) Xulon Pr., Inc.

Collier, John Richard. Inside Out. 2007. 224p. per. 14.99 (978-1-60477-340-8(5)) Xulon Pr., Inc.

Collier, Joseph Avery. The Christian Home, or, Religion in the Family. 2006. 204p. per. 20.99 (978-1-4255-1686-4(6)) MPublishing.

Collins, Ace. Gratitude: Practicing Contagious Optimism for Positive Change. 1 vol. 2010. (ENG.). 192p. pap. 14.99 (978-0-310-32477-5(7)) Zondervan.

Collins, Anita. Jezebel's Apprentice. 2008. 124p. pap. 10.99 (978-1-60477-864-9(4)) Xulon Pr., Inc.

Collins, Clint. The Climb: Overcoming the Obstacles that Cloud Your View of the Top. 2010. pap. 15.99 (978-1-61663-179-6(1)) Tate Publishing & Enterprises, LLC.

Collins, Florence O. Inside-Out Christianity. pap. 6.50 (978-0-89098-135-1(3)) Twentieth Century Christian Bks.

Collins Ii, Glen. Sin, the Silent Killer. 2008. 100p. pap. 10.99 (978-1-60647-903-2(2)) Xulon Pr., Inc.

Collins, John. God Is Trying to Talk to You: Twelve Miracles that Will Expand Your Faith in God. 2006. 108p. pap. 19.95 (978-1-4241-4432-7(9)) PublishAmerica, Inc.

Collins, John T. Passionate Spirituality: Living & Loving God's Message. 2008. (978-0-7880-2606-5(2)) CSS Publishing Co.

Collins, Joshua. The Knowledge of Good & Evil. 2008. 412p. pap. 19.95 (978-0-9801674-9-8(3)) Global Education Advance.

Collins, Peggy & Olivet, Linda. Fitting It All Together. pap. 7.99 (978-0-89098-058-3(6)) Twentieth Century Christian Bks.

Collins, Rev. C. Randall Sr. Ministry & Divorce: Can God Use You after Divorce? 2011. 54p. 24.99 (978-1-4628-4634-4(3)); pap. 15.99 (978-1-4628-4633-7(5)) Xlibris Corp.

Collins, Stanley. Coraje y Sumision: Courage & Submission. (SPA.). 128p. (978-84-7228-421-0(2), 220191) Clie, Editorial.

Collins, Susan Elaine. Quiet Whispers. 2006. 156p. pap. 24.95 (978-1-4241-4314-6(4)) PublishAmerica, Inc.

Collins, Terry. Affliction & the Lord's Grace. 2010. pap. 14.99 (978-1-61579-968-8(0)) Xulon Pr., Inc.

Collinson, Sylvia Wilkey. Making Disciples: The Significance of Jesus' Educational Methods for Today's Church. 2007. (Paternoster Theological Monographs: Ser.). 308p. pap. 31.00 (978-1-59752-796-5(3), Wipf and Stock) Wipf & Stock Pubs.

Colman, M. E. Sometimes a Star. 2008. 374p. per. 22.00 (978-0-9787113-2-0(7), Ithaca Pr.) Authors & Artists Publishers of New York, Inc.

Cologna, Ann. Parresia. 2007. pap. 15.99 (978-1-60034-443-5(7)) Xulon Pr., Inc.

Colombero, Giuseppe. De las Palabras al Dialogo. (SPA.). 304p. 9.95 (978-958-607-764-4(0)) Sociedad de San Pablo ESP. Dist: St Pauls/Alba Hse. Pubs.

Colquhoun. My God & King. (Illus.). 114p. 6.00 (978-0-281-04706-2(5)) SPCK Publishing GBR. Dist: Pilgrim Pr., The/United Church Pr.

Colquhoun, Lady. Worlds Religion As Contrasted with Genui. 2006. pap. 24.95 (978-1-4286-3497-8(5)) Kessinger Publishing, LLC.

Colson, Charles. The Good Life Small-Group. 2006. (ENG.). 464p. pap. 14.99 (978-1-4143-1149-4(4)) Tyndale Hse. Pubs.

Colson, Charles W. The Faith. 2008. (ENG.). 96p. pap., instr.'s gde. ed. 8.99 (978-0-310-27607-4(1)) Zondervan.

—The Faith Curriculum Kit. 2008. (ENG.). pap. 52.99 (978-0-310-29373-6(1)) Zondervan.

Colson, Charles W. & Fickett, Harold. The Good Life: Lessons. 2006. pap. (978-1-4143-1362-7(4)) Tyndale Hse. Pubs.

Colter IV, Herman. From Tears to Laughter: Surviving Hard Times on Broken Pieces: Part Two. 1 vol. 2009. 79p. pap. 16.95 (978-1-61546-000-7(4)) PublishAmerica, Inc.

Colton, Ann Ree & Murro, Jonathan. The Anointed: Sacred Keys to Healing, Exorcism & the Divine Marriage. (Illus.). 442p. (978-0-917189-06-7(X)) Ann Ree Colton Foundation of Niscience, Inc.

Colvin, Karen Washington. Sessions in Pain. 2011. 252p. pap. 16.99 (978-1-61379-306-0(5)) Xulon Pr., Inc.

Come, Follow Me: Discipleship Booklet with Baptism Certificate. 16p. 3.49 (978-0-7847-0781-4(2), 01170) Standard Publishing.

Comer, Marian. My God, My Lord, My All. 2007. 112p. per. 10.99 (978-1-60266-522-4(2)) Xulon Pr., Inc.

Comfort, Ray. God Has a Wonderful Plan for Your Life: The Myth of the Modern Message. 2010. (ENG.). 128p. pap. 8.99 (978-1-878859-49-5(8)) Living Waters Pubns.

—How to Live Forever Without Being Religious. 2007. (Illus.). 110p. per. 9.99 (978-0-88270-425-8(7)) Bridge-Logos Foundation.

—World Religions in a Nutshell. 2008. (Illus.). 176p. 14.99 (978-0-88270-669-6(1)) Bridge-Logos Foundation.

—You Can Lead an Atheist to Evidence, but You Can't Make Him Think: Answers to Questions from Angry Skeptics. 2009. 160p. 22.95 (978-1-935071-06-8(8)) WND Bks, Inc.

Comfort, William M. Dr. William M. Comfort: A Fighter & Champion. 2011. 126p. pap. 13.99 (978-0-9826841-5-3(0)) September Summer.

Comision de Catequesis de Caldas Staff. Creciendo Con Jesus Alumno. 104p. 3.95 (978-958-607-949-5(X)) Sociedad de San Pablo COL. Dist: St Pauls/Alba Hse. Pubs.

—Creciendo Con Jesus Catequista. 112p. 4.95 (978-958-607-948-8(1)) Sociedad de San Pablo COL. Dist: St Pauls/Alba Hse. Pubs.

Comiskey, Joel. Elim. 2011. 136p. pap. 12.95 (978-1-935789-12-3(0), CCS Publishing) CCS Pubs.

Como Vivir la Vida Victoriosa: How to Live a Victorious Life. (SPA.). 180p. (978-84-7228-630-6(4), 220208) Clie, Editorial.

Concordia Lutheran Church. God the Builder Student Builder Booklet. 2007. (Illus.). 20p. (J). (978-0-9786707-7-1(9)) Concordia Impact Ministries.

Concordia Publishing Staff. Communicating God's Way. (Scriptural Foundation for Parenting Ser.: Course 1). pap., stu. ed. 4.75 (978-0-570-09640-5(5), 20-2806); pap. 5.75 (978-0-570-09641-2(3)) Concordia Publishing Hse.

Conde, Bertha. The Human Element in the Making of a Christian. 2007. (ENG.). 172p. 37.95 (978-0-548-03062-2(6)) Kessinger Publishing, LLC.

Conger, Walt. Heart Refined: My Journey Toward Intimacy with God. 2011. 132p. 28.95 (978-1-61507-905-6(X)); pap. 11.95 (978-1-61507-904-9(1)) Cross Bks. Publishing.

Congr for Divineworship Staff. Use Vernacular Languages. 80p. pap. 3.95 (978-0-8198-5438-4(7), 332-266) Pauline Bks. & Media.

Congr Inst Consecrated lfe Staff. Instr Contemplative Life. 56p. pap. 3.95 (978-0-8198-3679-3(6), 332-134) Pauline Bks. & Media.

Conley, Jeff. A Charge to Keep. 2008. 92p. pap. 9.95 (978-1-60693-499-9(6), Strategic Bk. Publishing) AEG Literary Publishing Services, Inc.

Connell, John C. Catholics Mean Business: 30 Days to Managing Your Work Week, God's Way. 2009. 81p. pap. 9.95 (978-1-4327-2974-5(8)) Outskirts Pr., Inc.

Connelly, Francis J. Jesus Says. 2008. 448p. pap. 21.99 (978-1-60647-538-6(X)) Xulon Pr., Inc.

Connelly, Lee. In Your Hand: Living, Moving & Having Our Being in God. 2007. 136p. per. 12.95 (978-1-4327-1722-3(7)) Outskirts Pr., Inc.

Conner, Ann. Enter the Open Door. 2008. 396p. pap. 23.99 (978-1-60647-803-5(6)) Xulon Pr., Inc.

Conner, Ben. A Simple Guide to Finding God & Happiness for the Working Man of America. 2008. 84p. pap. 9.99 (978-1-60647-015-2(9)) Xulon Pr., Inc.

Conner, Michael D. I Sing a New Way. 2011. 186p. pap. 24.95 (978-1-4560-3887-8(7)) PublishAmerica, Inc.

Conolly, Jazmin. The Way God Blessed Old Man Hammer. 2009. 76p. pap. 10.99 (978-1-61579-234-4(1)) Xulon Pr., Inc.

Conrad (Gailey), Judy. Protected by Angels: Blessed by God. 1 vol. 2010. 110p. pap. 19.95 (978-1-60836-717-7(7)) PublishAmerica, Inc.

Conrad, Michael Francis. A Contemplative Mind in a Computer Age: The Nexus Between Spirituality & Technology. 2008. 160p. per. 15.95 (978-1-930301-11-5(1)) Learning Doctor, The.

—You Are My Heritage: Thoughts on How Much You Mean to Me. 2008. 112p. per. 12.95 (978-1-930301-95-5(2)) Learning Doctor, The.

Conrad, Myrna. Discarded Lives. 2007. 196p. per. 13.99 (978-1-60266-488-3(9)) Xulon Pr., Inc.

Constant, Florence L. M. God Answers Prayer: A Season of Prayer for all People. 2008. 68p. pap. 7.95 (978-1-4327-2204-3(2)) Outskirts Pr., Inc.

Conti, Angelina. Spirit Rising: Young Quaker Voices. 2010. (978-1-888305-86-9(X)) Quaker Pr. of Friends General Conference.

Cook, Dean. Chaplaincy: Being God's Presence in Closed Communities: A Free Methodist History 1935-2010. 2010. 200p. pap. 15.49 (978-1-4490-8301-4(3)) AuthorHouse.

Cook, E. Dean. Chaplaincy: Being God's Presence in Closed Communities. 2010. 200p. 24.99 (978-1-4520-2610-7(6)) AuthorHouse.

Cook, Faith. Overcoming the World. 2007. (Et Perspectives Ser.). (Illus.). 79p. per. (978-0-9500129-4-0(7)) Evangelical Times.

Cook, Jerry. The Monday Morning Church: Out of the Sanctuary & into the Streets. 2011. (ENG.). 224p. pap. 15.99 (978-1-4516-3618-5(0), Howard Bks.) Howard Books.

Cook, John G. A Compassionate Journey: Coming Alongside People with Disabilities or Chronic Illnesses. 2008. (978-1-59255-399-0(0)) Faith Alive Christian Resources.

Cook, Marshall. Growing Old Isn't for Sissies. 2010. 300p. (ENG.). 28.30 (978-1-4269-2488-0(7)); pap. 18.30 (978-1-4269-2487-3(9)) Trafford Publishing.

Cook, Ryan. Reform Your World: Understanding the Past to Change the Future. 2008. 169p. pap. 15.99 (978-0-7684-2647-2(2)) Destiny Image Pubs.

Cook, Sharon. God Can & God Will! 2011. 108p. pap. 11.99 (978-1-61379-346-6(4)) Xulon Pr., Inc.

Cook, Tony. Moral Maze. (Illus.). 192p. 15.00 (978-0-281-04038-4(9)) SPCK Publishing GBR. Dist: Pilgrim Pr., The/United Church Pr.

Cook, Walter. Meeting the Test. (978-0-687-24656-4(3)) Abingdon Pr.

Cooke, Sarah A. Wayside Sketches. pap. 7.99 (978-0-88019-196-8(1)) Schmul Publishing Co., Inc.

Cooke, Shae. Single Parent's Guide to Love, Dating, & Relationships: Finding Love in All the Right Places. 2011. (ENG.). pap. 14.99 (978-0-7684-3663-1(X)) Destiny Image Pubs.

—The Single Parent's Guide to Love, Dating, & Relationships: Finding Love in All the Right Places. 2011. 220p. (978-0-7684-3664-8(8)) Destiny Image Pubs.

Cooke, Shae. Single Parent's Guide to Raising Godly Children. 2010. (ENG.). pap. 14.99 (978-0-7684-3198-8(0)) Destiny Image Pubs.

Coon, Christian, et al. 365 Meditations for Men by Men. Sharpe, Sally D., ed. 2008. 280p. pap. 16.00 (978-0-687-65198-6(0)) Abingdon Pr.

Cooper, Daniel. Passing the Peace. 2008. 119p. pap. 10.00 (978-1-4357-1829-6(1)) Lulu Enterprises Inc.

Cooper, Ladonna S. Spoken For: Embracing God's Will for Life. 2009. 62p. pap. 16.95 (978-1-61546-939-0(7)) PublishAmerica, Inc.

Cooper, Lester. Where Are Today's Daniels? Looking for Daniels... but Finding Lions! 2009. 126p. pap. 11.99 (978-1-60791-967-4(2)) Xulon Pr., Inc.

Cooper, Tim. Awestruck: Life-Changing Encounters with Jesus. 2011. 100p. pap. 14.00 (978-1-61097-090-7(X), Resource Pubns.) Wipf & Stock Pubs.

—Miles Past Normal. 2010. (Illus.). 126p. pap. 16.00 (978-1-60899-673-5(5), Resource Pubns.) Wipf & Stock Pubs.

Cope, Landa. An Introduction to the Old Testament Template: Rediscovering God's Principles for Discipling Nations. 2nd ed. 2011. (ENG.). 240p. pap. 15.99 (978-1-57658-560-3(3)) YWAM Publishing.

Cope, Mike. Meagan's Secret: How My Mentally Disabled Daughter Taught Me to Live. 2011. pap. 14.99 (978-0-89112-286-9(9), Leafwood Pubs.) Abilene Christian Univ. Pr.

Cope, Mike & Shelly, Rubel. What Would Jesus Do Today. 2008. (ENG.). 206p. pap. 15.95 (978-1-4165-9796-4(4), Howard Bks.) Howard Books.

Copeland, Gloria. Blessed Beyond Measure: Experience the Extraordinary Goodness of God. 2008. (ENG.). 208p. pap. 11.99 (978-0-446-51127-8(7)) FaithWords.

—God's Master Plan for Your Life: Ten Keys to Fulfilling Your Destiny. Lt. ed. 2009. (ENG.). 454p. pap. 17.95 (978-1-59415-284-9(5)) Cengage Gale.

—God's Master Plan for Your Life: Ten Keys to Fulfilling Your Destiny. 2009. (ENG.). 304p. (gr. 12-18). 16.00 (978-0-425-22859-3(2), Berkley Trade) Penguin Group (USA) Inc.

—Live Long, Finish Strong: The Divine Secret to Living Healthy, Happy, & Healed. (ENG.). 272p. 2011. pap., pap. 13.99 (978-0-446-55927-0(X)) 2010. 21.99 (978-0-446-55928-7(8)) FaithWords.

—To Know Him: Beyond Religion Waits a Relationship That Will Change Your Life. 2008. (ENG.). 224p. pap. 11.99 (978-0-446-51124-7(2)) FaithWords.

Copeland, Kris. Living Life to Its Fullest: Implementing God's Blessing into Our Everyday Lives. 2011. pap. 10.99 (978-1-61777-019-7(1)) Tate Publishing & Enterprises, LLC.

Copping, Thomas L. The Big Lie, Exposed! 2011. 408p. 32.95 (978-1-4620-0044-9(4)); pap. 22.95 (978-1-4620-0045-6(2)) iUniverse, Inc.

Corban, D. Shake the World. 2008. 108p. 19.99 (978-1-60647-574-4(6)); pap. 11.99 (978-1-60647-561-4(4)) Xulon Pr., Inc.

Corben, Russell & Smith, Brian. Your Money or Your Life. 2007. 184p. per. (978-1-897373-15-6(5)) Word Alive Pr.

Corbett, Steve & Fikkert, Brian. When Helping Hurts: How to Alleviate Poverty Without Hurting the Poor ... & Yourself. (ENG.). 2012. 288p. pap. 14.99 (978-0-8024-5706-6(1)) 2009. 232p. pap. 14.99 (978-0-8024-5705-9(3)) Moody Pubs.

Cornelius, Bill. I Dare You to Change: Discover the Difference Between Dreaming a Better Life & Living It. 2010. 212p. pap. 19.99 (978-0-8249-4818-4(1), GuidepostsBooks) Ideals Pubns.

Cornelius, Jon N. The Commandments of Men. 2008. pap. 17.99 (978-1-60647-142-5(2)) Xulon Pr., Inc.

Cornelius Peter Theophilus, Peter Theoph & Cornelius Peter Theophilus. Blessed Is the King of Kings: Are We in the End of Civilizations? 2010. 224p. pap. 18.95 (978-1-4502-1091-1(0)) iUniverse, Inc.

Cornell, David M. God Moments: Lingering Long in the Cool of God's Shadow. 2011. pap. 12.99 (978-1-61777-020-3(5)) Tate Publishing & Enterprises, LLC.

Corprew-Boyd, Angela L. Church Hurt: The Wounded Trying to Heal. 2008. (ENG.). 128p. 14.99 (978-1-59979-371-9(7), Creation Hse.) Charisma Media.

Correa, Guillem. La Familia Segun Dios: God's Plan for the Christian Family (SPA.). (978-84-7645-461-9(9), 223542) Clie, Editorial.

Corsello, Lily. The Judas Personality: Dealing with Antisocial Personality Disorder & Its Victims from the Christian Perspective. 2007. 140p. per. 15.99 (978-1-60477-085-8(6)) Xulon Pr., Inc.

C

Cortes, Joseph. Faith Pleases God. 2006. pap. 9.99 *(978-1-60034-855-6(6))* Xulon Pr., Inc.

Cosby, Brian H. John Bunyan: The Journey of a Pilgrim. 2009. (ENG.). 160p. mass mkt. 8.99 *(978-1-84550-458-8(5))* Christian Focus Pubns. GBR. Dist: STL Distribution North America.

Cosgrove, Charles H. & Edgerton, W. Dow. In Other Words: Incarnational Translation for Preaching. 2007. (Illus.). 232p. per. 16.00 *(978-0-8028-4037-0(X))* Eerdmans, William B. Publishing Co.

Cosgrove, Eugene Milne. The High Walk of Discipleship 1945. 2007. (ENG.). 422p. 51.95 *(978-0-548-05488-8(6))* Kessinger Publishing, LLC.

Coss, Erin. A Tidbit Romance: Falling in Love with God's Word One Devotion at a Time. 2010.Tr. of 186. (ENG.). pap. *(978-0-9817847-3-1(9))* k2e Bks., Inc.

Costello, Nick. Kiss What. 2010. 102p. pap. 10.99 *(978-1-60957-876-3(7))* Xulon Pr., Inc.

Costello, Stephen J. Hermeneutics & the Psychoanalysis of Religion. 2010. (Illus.). 257p. pap. 55.95 *(978-3-0343-0124-4(3))* Lang, Peter AG GBR. Dist: Lang, Peter.

Coston, J. L. Escape to Pray! 2009. 124p. pap. 11.99 *(978-1-60791-795-3(5))* Xulon Pr., Inc.

Cote, Carolyn. Two Trees Revealed: How Our Knowledge of Good & Evil Keeps Us from Life Through Christ. 2009. 160p. 22.95 *(978-1-4389-3230-9(8))*; pap. 12.95 *(978-1-4389-3229-3(4))* AuthorHouse.

Cottingham, Kristen. Life Beyond Laundry. 2008. 84p. pap. 12.95 *(978-0-9792739-7-1(8))* Ajoyin Publishing, Inc.

Cottrell, Stephen & Croft, Steven. How to Live: A Guide to the Journey of Faith. 2011. 144p. pap. 14.99 ***(978-0-7151-4240-0(2))*** Church Hse. Publishing GBR. Dist: Westminster John Knox Pr.

Coty, Debora M. Everyday Hope. 2009. (Spiritual Refreshment Ser.). (ENG.). 224p. pap. 9.99 *(978-1-60260-453-7(3)*, Barbour Bks.) Barbour Publishing, Inc.

Coughlin, Paul. Five Secrets Great Dads Know, 1 vol. 2010. (ENG.). 64p. 3.99 *(978-0-7642-0768-6(7))* Bethany Hse. Pubs.

Coulombe, Charles A. Everyman Today Call Rome. 2011. 154p. (Orig.). pap. 9.95 ***(978-0-9842365-6-5(2))*** Tumblar Hse.

Countryman, J. God's Promises for Your Every Need. pap. 3.95 *(978-0-937347-45-4(0))* C&D International.

Countryman, Jack. God's Wisdom for Business Success, 0 vols. 2008. 308p. pap. 14.99 *(978-1-4041-7557-0(1))* Nelson, Thomas Inc.

—God's Wisdom for Fathers, 0 vols. 2010. 216p. pap. 4.99 *(978-1-4041-8761-0(8))*; 196p. 9.99 *(978-1-4041-8777-1(4))* Nelson, Thomas Inc.

Cousins, Don. Unexplainable: Pursuing a Life Only God Can Make Possible, 1 vol. 2009. (ENG.). 272p. pap. 16.99 *(978-1-4347-6808-7(2))* Cook, David C.

Coutts, Frederich. Siempre en Pie de Guerra: No Discharge in This War. (SPA.). *(978-84-399-6908-2(2)*, 220826) Clie, Editorial.

Covington, Debbie Sutton. If I I Will. 2010. 104p. pap. 10.99 *(978-1-60957-561-8(X))* Xulon Pr., Inc.

Covington, John. Who Is God & What Am I Doing Here? A Quick Guide to Paradise. 2011. pap. 10.99 ***(978-1-61777-421-8(9))*** Tate Publishing & Enterprises, LLC.

Cowell, Cheri. Direction: Discernment for the Decisions of Your Life. 2007. (ENG.). 192p. per. 14.99 *(978-0-8341-2335-9(5)*, 083-412-3355) Beacon Hill Pr. of Kansas City.

Cowles, Debbie. Slaying Dragons. 2006. pap. 14.99 *(978-1-60034-568-5(9))* Xulon Pr., Inc.

Cox, Betty E. The Blessing of the Dead Rat. 2008. 132p. pap. 13.95 *(978-1-59858-664-0(5))* Dog Ear Publishing, LLC.

Cox, Bo Don. God Is Not in the Thesaurus: Stories from an Oklahoma Prison. (Illus.). 160p. pap. 3.95 *(978-0-88028-214-7(2)*, 1552) Forward Movement Pubns.

Cox, Christy. Death of an Angel. 2009. 68p. pap. 10.99 *(978-1-60791-195-1(7))* Xulon Pr., Inc.

Cox, Danny. High on a Lie. 2007. 268p. per. 18.99 *(978-0-88144-267-0(4))* Yorkshire Publishing Group.

Cox, Eddie. The Matrix of the Mind: Learning to Recognize Truth from Illusion & Correcting Abnormal Thinking. 2006. 107p. per. 11.00 *(978-1-59824-313-0(6))* E-BookTime LLC.

Cox, Esta Freeland. One Day at a Time. 2008. 372p. pap. 24.95 *(978-1-4401-0926-3(5))* iUniverse, Inc.

Cox, Kelly. The Only Book You Need. 2007. 152p. per. 24.95 *(978-1-4241-5816-4(8))* PublishAmerica, Inc.

Cox, Louise Barnett. Heart's Bouquet. pap. 7.99 *(978-0-89098-207-5(4))* Twentieth Century Christian Bks.

Cox, Michael H. Creative Devotions with Dad. 2010. 110p. pap. 13.99 *(978-1-60957-526-7(1))* Xulon Pr., Inc.

Cox, Phil. The Gift of Silence. 2011. 60p. pap. 9.95 ***(978-1-4626-4066-9(4))*** PublishAmerica, Inc.

Cox, Richard A. I, We, Us: A Journey of Personal Growth & Development. 2010. pap. 9.99 *(978-1-61566-156-5(5))* Tate Publishing & Enterprises, LLC.

Cox, Shel Eugene. God's Navy. 2008. 244p. per. 11.95 *(978-1-4327-1340-9(X))* Outskirts Pr., Inc.

Coxe, Arthur Cleveland. Apollos or the Way of God: A Plea for the Religion of Scripture. 2007. (ENG.). 278p. 42.95 *(978-0-548-04200-7(4))* Kessinger Publishing, LLC.

Crabb, Larry. Inside Out. 2007. (Katie Parker Production Ser.). (ENG., Illus.). 352p. per. 15.99 *(978-1-60006-099-1(4))* NavPress Publishing Group.

Crabtree, Sue. Let's Be Great Teachers. (Illus.). pap. 15.99 *(978-0-89098-219-8(8))* Twentieth Century Christian Bks.

Crack Cocaine Let My People Go Appropriate Prayeer Results in Deliverance. 2007. per. *(978-1-59916-196-6(5))* Printing Systems.

Craddock, Fred. Reflections on My Call to Prea. 2009. 128p. pap. 14.99 *(978-0-8272-3257-0(8))* Chalice Pr.

Crafton, Barbara C. Jesus Wept: When Faith & Depression Meet. 2009. (ENG.). 192p. 19.95 *(978-0-470-37195-4(1)*, Jossey-Bass) Wiley, John & Sons, Inc.

Craig, Chad M. Building with Balance. 2011. 226p. pap. 15.99 ***(978-1-61215-836-5(6))*** Xulon Pr., Inc.

Craig, Chad M. Divine Design for Discipleship: Following God's Blueprint for Spiritual Development. 2008. 348p. pap. 17.99 *(978-1-60647-643-7(2))* Xulon Pr., Inc.

Craig, Drew. Heart Warming Truths. 2011. 152p. pap. ***(978-1-926765-36-5(2))*** Gospel Folio Pr.

Craik, Judith. Freud's Contribution to the Church: A Theological Response to Psychoanalytic Thought. 2009. 192p. pap. 23.95 *(978-1-4327-4363-5(5))* Outskirts Pr., Inc.

Cramer, Steven A. Putting on the Armor of God: How to Win Your Battles with Satan. 2011. xvii, 302p. 18.95 *(978-1-55517-091-2(9))* Cedar Fort, Inc./CFI Distribution.

Crandall, Patricia. Faith of Truth. 2010. 116p. 21.49 *(978-1-4490-7661-0(0))*; pap. 10.99 *(978-1-4490-7662-7(9))* AuthorHouse.

Crane-Freeman, Leigh. The Desperate Christian: Disappointed with Church, It's Time for the Serious Christian to Come Straight to God. 2011. 164p. pap. 12.95 *(978-1-4327-4158-7(6))* Outskirts Pr., Inc.

Crane, Sonia Gwen. Rise up My Beloved. 2008. 220p. pap. 15.99 *(978-1-60647-002-2(7))* Xulon Pr., Inc.

Craun, Janie. Heirlooms. pap. 8.95 *(978-0-929540-33-7(6))* Publishing Designs, Inc.

Cravens, Mark. The Ten Commandments of Investing: Discover 10 Keys to Find High-Return Investments Without Losing Your Hard-Earned Money. 2008. (ENG.). pap. 13.95 *(978-1-60037-428-9(X))* Morgan James Publishing.

Crawford, Clark. Thank God for My Enemies. 2009. 88p. pap. 9.95 *(978-1-934749-55-5(9)*, 800-747-0738, CrossHouse Publishing) Hannibal Bks.

—Thank God I Got Caught: From Prisoner to Worshiper. 2009. pap. 9.95 *(978-1-934749-51-7(6)*, CrossHouse Publishing) Hannibal Bks.

Crawford, Dan. God's Formula for Genuine Happiness. 2007. 96p. per. 12.95 *(978-0-929292-28-1(6)*, 800-747-0738) Hannibal Bks.

Crawford, Jeff. Image of God. 2008. 252p. pap. 16.99 *(978-1-60647-921-6(0))* Xulon Pr., Inc.

Crawford, Robert. The Battle for the Soul. 2011. (ENG.). 266p. 85.00 *(978-0-230-60944-0(9))* Palgrave Macmillan.

Craycraft, Ron. It's Comeback Time. 2008. 148p. 22.99 *(978-1-60647-972-8(5))*; pap. 14.99 *(978-1-60647-971-1(7))* Xulon Pr., Inc.

Credo. Viginti: A Young Man. 2009. pap. 10.99 *(978-1-60791-715-1(7))* Xulon Pr., Inc.

Creech, R. P. SavoryTimelessTruths (paperback-binding) 2009. 225p. pap. 16.96 *(978-0-578-00232-3(9))* SavoryTruth ScriptWriters.

Creekmore, Brandy. Born Again, Now What? 2007. 164p. per. 24.95 *(978-1-4241-8554-2(8))* PublishAmerica, Inc.

Creel, Richard E. Love of Jesus: The Heart of Christianity. 2010. 146p. pap. 18.00 *(978-1-60899-322-2(1)*, Resource Pubns.) Wipf & Stock Pubs.

Cremer, Judith. Which Way the Wind Blows. 2007. 196p. per. 13.99 *(978-1-60266-227-8(4))* Xulon Pr., Inc.

Crenshaw, Dolly Nance. Faith, Healing & Prayer: These Must Be Balanced. 2008. 52p. pap. 10.95 *(978-1-59800-735-0(1))* Outskirts Pr., Inc.

Crews, Jim. The Journey from Milk to Meat: A Guide to Growth in the Christian Life. 2009. 152p. pap. 14.99 *(978-1-61579-213-9(9))* Xulon Pr., Inc.

—The Journey from Milk to Meat: Growth in the Christian Life. 2009. 152p. instr.'s gde. ed. 22.99 *(978-1-61579-230-6(9))* Xulon Pr., Inc.

Crews, Kelly. The Designer's Original. 2011. (Illus.). 100p. 15.00 ***(978-0-9774890-4-6(3))*** L.T.A. Productions.

Cribb, C. C. Flying High Against the Sky: If God Has It I Want It! pap. 2.95 *(978-0-932046-16-1(9))* Manhattan, Ltd., Publishers.

Crim, Mort. Good News for Tough Times. 176p. pap. 10.99 *(978-0-8307-3431-3(7)*, Regal Bks.) Gospel Light Pubns.

Crimp, Susan, et al. The Last Wish of Pope John Paul II: The Life & Messages of Saint Faustina Kowalska. 2009. 200p. 24.99 *(978-1-4389-7746-1(8))*; pap. 16.99 *(978-1-4389-7745-4(X))* AuthorHouse.

Cripe, William E. The Proper Pursuit of Prosperity: Balancing the Promises of Heaven with the Experiences of Earth. 2011. pap. 14.99 ***(978-1-61346-101-3(1))*** Tate Publishing & Enterprises, LLC.

Crisler-Draper, Leatrice Renee. The Last Days: And the angels of God that are assigned to your Life. 2010. 144p. pap. 15.95 *(978-1-4490-5472-4(2))* AuthorHouse.

Crismier, Charles. Out of Egypt! Preparing the Way of the Lord in Your Life for History's Final Hour. annot. ed. 2006. (ENG.). 293p. per. 16.99 *(978-0-9718428-3-0(3))* Elijah Bks.

—Seduction of the Saints: Staying Pure in a World of Deception. 2009. (ENG.). 384p. 17.99 *(978-0-9718428-4-7(1))* Elijah Bks.

Crist, James E. The Testimony of Brother Crist: The Poor Brother on 31. 2009. 252p. pap. 16.99 *(978-1-61579-089-0(6))* Xulon Pr., Inc.

Critchlow. Preaching on Common Worship Lectures. 176p. 15.00 *(978-0-281-05256-1(5))* SPCK Publishing GBR. Dist: Pilgrim Pr., The/United Church Pr.

Critchlow, Stephen. Finding the Yes in the Mess. 2007. 216p. per. 14.99 *(978-1-60266-110-3(3))* Xulon Pr., Inc.

Crocker, David W. The Samaritan Way: A Call to Lifestyle Compassion Ministry. 2008. (Columbia Partnership Leadership Ser.). 19.99 *(978-0-8272-3469-7(4))* Chalice Pr.

Croft, Brian. Visit the Sick: Ministering God's Grace in Times of Illness. 2008. (Ministering the Master's Way Ser.). (Illus.). 92p. pap. *(978-1-84625-143-6(5))* DayOne Pubns.

Croft, Steven. Exploring God's Mercy: Five Images of Salvation. 2010. (ENG.). iv, 84p. pap. 8.99 *(978-0-7151-4224-0(0))* Church Hse. Publishing GBR. Dist: Westminster John Knox Pr.

Cromarty, Jim. Pacific Adventures. 2009. (ENG., Illus.). 96p. pap. 8.99 *(978-1-84550-475-5(5))* Christian Focus Pubns. GBR. Dist: STL Distribution North America.

Crone, David. Power of Your Life Message. 2010. (ENG.). 236p. pap. 14.99 *(978-0-7684-3274-9(X))* Destiny Image Pubs.

Cronk, Sandra Lee & Grundy, Martha Paxson. A Lasting Gift: The Journal & Selected Writings of Sandra L. Cronk. 2009. *(978-1-888305-84-5(3))* Quaker Pr. of Friends General Conference.

Crosby, Howard. The Healthy Christian: An Appeal to the Church. 2007. 168p. 36.95 *(978-0-548-52433-6(5))*; (ENG.). per. 21.95 *(978-0-548-47359-7(5))* Kessinger Publishing, LLC.

—The Healthy Christian: An Appeal to the Church. 2006. 168p. per. 18.99 *(978-1-4255-1297-2(6))* MPublishing.

Crosby, Linda Ann. Laughing in the Midst of Mothering: Finding Joy in Being a Mom. 2008. 105p. pap. 10.99 *(978-0-89265-557-1(7))* Randall Hse. Pubns.

Crosby, Stephen. Authority, Accountability, & the Apostolic Movement. 2006. 232p. pap. 17.99 *(978-1-4141-0640-3(8))* Pleasant Word.

Crosse, Renee & Crosse, Clay. Reclaiming Stolen Intimacy: When Your Marriage Is Invaded by Pornography. 2008. (Illus.). 128p. pap. *(978-1-57494-423-5(1)*, Serendipity Hse.) LifeWay Christian Resources.

Crossman, Meg, ed. Pathlight: Toward Global Awareness. 2008. (ENG., Illus.). 133p. per. 16.99 *(978-1-57658-414-9(3))* YWAM Publishing.

Crosthwaite, Woody. Tetras. 2006. pap. 10.99 *(978-1-60034-634-7(0))* Xulon Pr., Inc.

Crouch, Marlene C. Whose Voice Are You Listening To? A Comparison of the Catholic Catechism to the Bible. 2010. pap. 22.99 *(978-1-61566-261-6(8))* Tate Publishing & Enterprises, LLC.

Crow, Mark. Extraordinary Living: Eight Steps to Improving Your Life. 2007. 183p. 24.99 *(978-1-933188-51-5(0))* Victory Christian Ctr.

Crowder, Bill. Windows on Easter. 2010. (ENG.). 128p. pap. 8.99 *(978-1-57293-367-5(4))* Discovery Hse. Pubs.

Crowder, David & Hogan, Mike. Everybody Wants to Go to Heaven, but Nobody Wants to Die. 2006. 208p. pap. 14.99 *(978-0-9777480-0-6(6))* Relevant Media Group, Inc.

—Everybody Wants to Go to Heaven, but Nobody Wants to Die, 1 vol. rev. ed. 2009. (ENG.). 256p. pap. 16.99 *(978-0-310-29191-6(7))* Zondervan.

Crowe, Bob. Not Determined to Be Happy. 2007. 268p. per. 15.99 *(978-1-60266-550-7(8))* Xulon Pr., Inc.

Crowe, Brent. Chasing Elephants: Wrestling with the Gray Areas of Life. 2010. (NavPress Devotional Readers Ser.). 192p. pap. 14.99 *(978-1-61521-121-0(7))* NavPress Publishing Group.

Crowl, Carl T. God Lives. 2007. 148p. 29.95 *(978-1-4251-4547-7(7))* Trafford Publishing.

Cruchley-Jones, Peter, ed. God at Ground Level: Reappraising Church Decline in the UK Through the Experience of Grass Roots Communities & Situations. 2007. 132p. pap. 32.95 *(978-3-631-57494-2(0))* Lang, Peter Publishing, Inc.

Cruikshank, Robert. Words from the Mountain. 2011. 80p. pap. ***(978-1-4269-6072-7(7))*** Trafford Publishing (UK) Ltd.

Crum, Carlene. Something of Value: A Mother's Spiritual Journey with a Special-Needs Child. 2008. 160p. pap. 13.99 *(978-1-60647-192-0(9))* Xulon Pr., Inc.

Crum, David J. Through Divorce by Man's Ways or with Ways of God. 2007. 140p. pap. 14.95 *(978-0-9797979-0-3(X))* Ministering Pr.

Crump, Dennis G. Approaching the Holy: A Season in God's House. 2007. 168p. per. 10.95 *(978-1-4327-0365-3(X))* Outskirts Pr., Inc.

Crump, Olivia. Conversations with God: A direct line to Deliverance. 2008. 48p. pap. 12.95 *(978-1-4327-3100-7(9))* Outskirts Pr., Inc.

Crumpler, Anne. Entering the New Testament. 2008. 112p. pap. 15.00 *(978-0-8358-9968-0(3))* Upper Room Bks.

Crutcher, Mark. The Flaming Sword. 2007. 84p. per. 9.99 *(978-1-60266-067-0(0))* Xulon Pr., Inc.

Crutcher, Mark E. Operating in the Fulfillment of Divine Purpose. 2011. 176p. 22.99 ***(978-1-61379-465-4(7))*** Xulon Pr., Inc.

Cruz, Nicky. Solitario Pero No Solo: Lonely but Not Alone. (SPA.). 160p. *(978-84-7228-985-7(0)*, 223037) Clie, Editorial.

Cuesta, Rogelio. Escaping from the Prisons Within: Ethics as a Process of Liberation. 2008. pap. 17.99 *(978-1-60647-037-4(X))* Xulon Pr., Inc.

Cullen, Joseph A. My God, My Companion. 2010. ***(978-1-77069-080-6(8))*** Word Alive Pr.

Culwell, Glennon. Princes Dressed Like Paupers: The Ministry of the Thorn?Ç£13 Chapter Study/Discussion Guides?Ç¥. 2011. 214p. pap. 12.95 *(978-1-4327-6919-2(7))* Outskirts Pr., Inc.

Cummings, Mary. The Restlessness of the Call: Remaining Faithful through the Process of Being Appointed, Anointed, & Prepared. 2006. pap. 15.95 *(978-0-9777053-1-3(5))* McDougal & Assocs.

Cundiff, Margaret. I'd Like You to Meet. 5.00 *(978-0-687-85533-9(0))* Abingdon Pr.

—Living by the Book. 2.00 *(978-0-687-85689-3(2))* Abingdon Pr.

Cunneen, James. Seven Principles of Ministry for the Average, Radical Christian. 2011. 290p. pap. 32.00 *(978-1-61097-137-9(X)*, Resource Pubns.) Wipf & Stock Pubs.

Cunningham, J. Michael. Your Walk, Their Walk. 2010. 218p. pap. 14.99 *(978-0-88144-111-6(2)*, Thorncrown Publishing) Yorkshire Publishing Group.

Cunningham, Karen Mayer. Defying Austism: A Miraculous Story of Hope. 2009. (ENG.). 128p. 14.99 *(978-1-59979-628-4(7)*, Creation Hse.) Charisma Media.

Cunningham, Loren. Tu fe y tu Dinero: Principios para una vida bajo el control de Dios. (ENG & SPA.). 200p. pap. 7.99 *(978-1-886930-03-2(1))* Editorial Libertad.

Curley, Marie Paul. See Yourself Through God's Eyes: 52 Meditations to Grow in Self-Esteem. 2009. pap. 9.95 *(978-0-8198-7127-5(3))* Pauline Bks. & Media.

Currall, Arnold & Tubbs, Anne. Church Times Book of the Garden. (Illus.). 192p. 12.50 *(978-1-85311-183-9(X))* Norwich Bks. & Music GBR. Dist: Morehouse Publishing.

Curran, Samuel. I-Witness Devotions. 2007. 408p. per. 21.99 *(978-1-60266-756-3(X))* Xulon Pr., Inc.

Currington, Rebecca & Webb, Joan. Bendiciones para Cada Día: Refeigerio Espirtual para Mujeres. 2010. (Spiritual Refreshment Ser.).Tr. of Everyday Blessings. (ENG & SPA.). 224p. pap. 4.99 *(978-1-60260-870-2(9)*, Casa Promesa) Barbour Publishing, Inc.

Curry, Joanne. God's Inner Voice; Have You Heard Him Yet? Jeremiah 7. 2009. 48p. pap. 15.49 *(978-1-4490-1342-4(2))* AuthorHouse.

Curry, Kelvin. I'm Telling the Truth. 2008. (ENG.). 130p. pap. 12.99 *(978-1-59979-484-6(5)*, Creation Hse.) Charisma Media.

Curry, Lorraine. Fields with God. 2006. (Illus.). 144p. per. 12.99 *(978-0-9709965-5-8(1))* God's Gardener.

Curtis, Barbara. Reaching the Left from the Right: Talking about Social Issues with People Who Don't Think Like You. 2006. (ENG.). 192p. per. 14.99 *(978-0-8341-2202-4(2)*, 083-412-2022) Beacon Hill Pr. of Kansas City.

Curtis, Cassandra. When you are Hurt by the Church. 2010. 48p. pap. 17.95 *(978-1-4327-6430-2(6))* Outskirts Pr., Inc.

Curtis, Edward M. & Brugaletta, John. Transformed Thinking: Loving God with All Your Mind. 2011. 208p. pap. 23.00 *(978-1-60899-589-9(5)*, Wipf and Stock) Wipf & Stock Pubs.

Cutler, Mary Davis. Till the Full Light of Day. 2008. 356p. pap. 19.99 *(978-1-60477-806-9(7))* Xulon Pr., Inc.

Cutshall, Bryan. Get up, Get Out, Get Blessed: Delivered from Bondage, through the Wilderness, & into Your Promised Land. 2008. 272p. pap. 12.99 *(978-1-60374-054-8(6)*, 770548) Whitaker Hse.

Cymbala, Jim. When God's People Pray. 2007. (ENG.). 24.99 *(978-0-310-26735-5(8))* Zondervan.

Cymbala, Jim & Cymbala. When God's People Pray: Six Sessions on the Transforming Power of Prayer, 1 vol. 2007. (ENG., Illus.). 144p. pap. 9.99 *(978-0-310-26734-8(X))* Zondervan.

Cymbala, Jim & Merrill, Dean. You Were Made for More: The Life You Have, the Life God Wants You to Have. 2008. (ENG.). 224p. pap. 12.99 *(978-0-310-27419-3(2))* Zondervan.

Cymbala, Jim, et al. You Were Made for More: The Life You Have, the Life God Wants You to Have, 1 vol. 2008. (ENG.). 224p. 19.99 *(978-0-310-24127-0(8))* Zondervan.

Cynthia Kay Elias. From Knowledge to Revelation: My Testimony of God's Mercy & Grace. 2009. 176p. pap. 15.95 *(978-1-4401-6219-0(0))* iUniverse, Inc.

Dabbs, Reggie. Reggie: You Can't Change Your Past, but You Can Change Your Future. 2011. 240p. pap. 15.99 *(978-0-8499-4626-4(3))* Nelson, Thomas Inc.

Dabel, Gregory. The Kingdom Message. 2006. pap. 13.99 *(978-1-60034-111-3(X))* Xulon Pr., Inc.

Dagba, Alain Yaovi M. Secrets to Divine Manifestations: Finding Your Life Purpose Through the Rebirth of Your Soul. 2010. pap. 18.99 *(978-1-61566-782-6(2))* Tate Publishing & Enterprises, LLC.

Dagle, Bruce A. The Perfect Law of Liberty. 2007. 556p. pap. 24.95 *(978-0-7414-3608-5(6))* Infinity Publishing.

Dahler, Craig. Heaven Help Me, I'm Human. 2007. 248p. per. 14.99 *(978-1-60266-112-7(X))* Xulon Pr., Inc.

Dahlstrom, Kathryn. Street Games. Date not set. (Good News Club Ser.). pap. 4.99 *(978-1-55976-830-6(4))* CEF Pr.

Dahne, Laura K. The Master Gardener. 2007. 112p. per. 10.99 *(978-1-60477-508-2(4))* Xulon Pr., Inc.

Dailey, Tim. Raising a Healthy Disciple. 2007. 100p. per. 11.95 *(978-1-931178-22-8(4))* Vision Publishing.

Dale, Jonathan. Faith in Action: Quaker Social Testimony Writings in Britain Yearly Meeting. Cave, Elizabeth & Morley, Ros, eds. 2007. 296p. per. *(978-0-85245-320-9(5))* Quaker Books.

Dales, Douglas. Light to the Isles. 2010. (ENG.). 188p. pap. 42.50 *(978-0-227-17341-1(4))* Clarke, James Co., Ltd. GBR. Dist: Brown, David Bk. Co., The.

Dalgliesh, Ryan. Love Notes. 2008. 236p. per. 14.99 *(978-1-60477-687-4(0))* Xulon Pr., Inc.

D'Aloisio, Michael G. 5 C Hero: The Joel Stephens Story. 2009. 220p. 24.99 *(978-1-4490-5419-9(6))*; pap. 14.95 *(978-1-4490-5418-2(8))* AuthorHouse.

Dalton, Ryan. Moved. 2010. (Illus.). 164p. pap. 11.99 *(978-1-4490-8069-3(3))* AuthorHouse.
Daly, Jim. Finding Home: An Imperfect Path to Faith & Family. 2007. 224p. pap. 14.99 *(978-0-7814-4866-6(2))* Cook, David C.
—Finding Home - Focus on the Family Edition: An Imperfect Path to Faith & Family. 2007. 232p. 22.99 *(978-1-4347-9994-4(8))* Cook, David C.
Daly, Richard. God's Little Book of Love: Words of Joy & Delight for Caring Souls. 2007. (ENG., Illus.). 160p. per. 7.95 *(978-0-00-724623-6(4))* HarperCollins Pubs. Ltd. GBR. Dist: Independent Pubs. Group.
—God's Little Book of Peace: Words of Comfort & Reassurance for Weary Souls. 2007. (ENG., Illus.). 160p. per. 7.95 *(978-0-00-724624-3(2))* HarperCollins Pubs. Ltd. GBR. Dist: Independent Pubs. Group.
—Joy: Words of Encouragement & Inspiration to Lift the Soul. 2008. (God's Little Book Of Ser.). (ENG., Illus.). 160p. pap. 8.95 *(978-0-00-727837-4(3))* HarperCollins Pubs. Ltd. GBR. Dist: Independent Pubs. Group.
—Words of Peace & Refreshment for Weary Souls. 2008. (God's Little Book Of Ser.). (ENG., Illus.). 160p. pap. 8.95 *(978-0-00-727838-1(1))* HarperCollins Pubs. Ltd. GBR. Dist: Independent Pubs. Group.
Daly, Robert J. & Daly. Sacrifice Unveiled: The True Meaning of Christian Sacrifice. 2009. (ENG.). 280p. 44.95 *(978-0-567-03421-2(6))*; 140.00 *(978-0-567-03420-5(8))* Continuum International Publishing Group, Ltd. GBR. (T&T Clark Int'l). Dist: National Bk. Network.
Damazio, Frank. The Attitude of Faith: Saying Yes to God's Power in Your Life. 2009. 224p. pap. 13.99 *(978-1-60374-114-9(3),* 771149) Whitaker Hse.
—Discovering Church Life: 24 Keys to Building Community. 2007. 136p. pap., tchr. ed. 19.99 *(978-1-59383-041-0(6))*; 108p. pap., stu. ed. 15.99 *(978-1-59383-040-3(8))* City Christian Publishing.
Damian, Cheryl. Whispers of a Soul: Inspirational Thoughts & Prayers. 2011. 140p. 28.95 ***(978-1-4627-0514-6(6))***; pap. 11.95 ***(978-1-4627-0513-9(8))*** Cross Bks. Publishing.
Dammer, Tammy. And Their Fall Will Be Great. 2011. 78p. pap. 19.95 ***(978-1-4526-1864-4(2))*** PublishAmerica, Inc.
Daniel, Dr., Carrel. Is Biblical Morality Outdated? 2007. (ENG.). 272p. pap. 14.99 *(978-1-932124-87-3(X))* ACW Pr.
Daniel, Darla. The Polluted Pump: Help for Cleaning Out the Filth in Our Lives. 2011. pap. 9.99 *(978-1-61739-623-6(0))* Tate Publishing & Enterprises, LLC.
Daniel, Desmon R. Giant Slayers. 2010. 76p. pap. 10.99 *(978-1-61579-696-0(7))* Xulon Pr., Inc.
Daniel, Grady. A Love That Changes Lives. 2011. 166p. pap. 14.99 *(978-1-61215-598-2(7))* Xulon Pr., Inc.
Daniel Lee Staneart. Drawing a Line in the Sand. 2009. 256p. 24.99 *(978-1-4389-6046-3(8))*; pap. 14.49 *(978-1-4389-6045-6(X))* AuthorHouse.
Daniel, Nathan. Freedom Through Forgiveness. 2007. 104p. per. 10.99 *(978-1-931178-18-1(6))* Vision Publishing.
Daniel, Samuel. Why Worry God Is in Control. 2006. pap. 15.99 *(978-1-60034-501-2(8))* Xulon Pr., Inc.
Daniels, D. Gail. A Hunger from Within. 2008. 96p. pap. 9.99 *(978-1-60477-495-5(9))* Xulon Pr., Inc.
Daniels, Dianne. Mothering Like the Father: Following God's Example in Parenting Young Children. 2008. 156p. pap. 11.95 *(978-1-4327-3237-0(4))* Outskirts Pr., Inc.
Daniels, Keith J. As for Me & My House, We Will Serve the Lord: No Subtitle. 2008. 344p. pap. 17.99 *(978-1-60647-514-0(2))* Xulon Pr., Inc.
Daniels, Kimberly. Inside Out: Dump the Baggage & Discover Hope Through Inner Healing. 2008. (ENG.). 240p. pap. 14.99 *(978-1-59979-279-8(6),* Charisma Hse.) Charisma Media.
Dannah Gresh Endcap. *(978-0-8024-5232-0(9))* Moody Pubs.
Danowski, Edwin K. A Dog, a Cat, & a Crow! The very real & heart-catching story about a boy & his truly amazing, real-life, feathered & furry Friends. 2008. 399p. pap. 29.95 *(978-1-60563-352-7(6))* PublishAmerica, Inc.
Dara, Sr. The Principles of Faith. 2008. 72p. pap. 15.00 *(978-1-4389-2896-8(3))* AuthorHouse.
D'Arcy, Paula. Waking up to This Day: Seeing the Beauty Right Before Us. 2009. 144p. pap. 17.00 *(978-1-57075-849-2(2))* Orbis Bks.
Dargan, Isaac B. Intricacies of the Tabernacle of Moses: The Brazen Altar. 2009. 204p. pap. 15.99 *(978-1-61579-334-1(8))* Xulon Pr., Inc.
Dargan, Samuel J. Good Decisions Now, Not Poor Choices Later. 2008. 112p. per. 10.99 *(978-1-60477-627-0(7))* Xulon Pr., Inc.
Darland, Kevin D. It Is Written. 2007. 120p. per. 10.99 *(978-1-60477-477-1(0))* Xulon Pr., Inc.
Darling, Dan. Jesus Core Values. 2007. pap. 13.99 *(978-1-60266-050-2(6))* Xulon Pr., Inc.
Darlison, Bill. The Gospel & the Zodiac. 2009. (ENG.). 304p. (gr. 12). pap. 14.95 *(978-1-59020-160-2(4))* Overlook Pr., The.
Darnell, Betty J. The Preacher Woman. 2011. 106p. pap. 11.99 ***(978-1-61379-003-8(1))*** Xulon Pr., Inc.
Daugherty, Billy Joe. 101 Days to Absolute Victory: Powerful Devotions & Declarations of Faith to Energize Your Life. 2006. 214p. per. 13.99 *(978-1-57794-820-9(3))* Harrison House Pubs.
—360° Life: Ten Ways You Can Live More Richly, Deeply, Fully. 2010. (ENG.). 224p. 19.99 *(978-0-307-45932-9(2),* WaterBrook Pr.) Doubleday Religious Publishing Group, The.
Daugherty, Clifford E. Quest for Excellence: Living the Supernatural Life Naturally. 2006. 247p. per. 14.99 *(978-1-59886-431-1(9))* Tate Publishing & Enterprises, LLC.
Daugherty, Matt. Run for Your Life. 2008. 132p. pap. 24.95 *(978-1-60610-068-4(8))* PublishAmerica, Inc.
Davenport, Donald. 7 Healthy Stages in Male & Female Relationships. 2008. 208p. per. 15.99 *(978-1-60477-362-0(6))* Xulon Pr., Inc.
Davenport, Minister Paul G. To My Teenager from God & Me. 2009. 80p. pap. 10.99 *(978-1-60791-628-4(2))* Xulon Pr., Inc.
Davey, Jim & Winford, Rick. Feeling the Wind: Student's Journal. 2011. (ENG., Illus.). 184p. (YA). pap. 15.00 ***(978-1-59317-533-7(7))*** Warner Pr. Pubs.
Davey, John. Partners in God's Love. 2007. 404p. per. 24.99 *(978-1-60266-217-9(7))* Xulon Pr., Inc.
David, Samson. How to Get God to Return Your Calls. 2008. (ENG.). 144p. pap. 10.95 *(978-1-56171-825-2(4))* SPI Bks.
Davidson, Ivor J. & Rae, Murray A. God of Salvation: Essays in Systematic Theology. 2010. 208p. 99.95 *(978-0-7546-6619-6(0))* Ashgate Publishing Co.
—God of Salvation: Soteriology in Theological Perspective. 2010. 208p. pap. 39.95 *(978-1-4094-2167-2(8))* Ashgate Publishing Co.
Davidson, Kimberly. Breaking the Cover Girl Mask: Toss Out Toxic Thoughts. 2009. pap. 19.99 *(978-1-60799-847-1(5))* Tate Publishing & Enterprises, LLC.
Davidson, Roy. God Is Real: Undeniable Proof That Will Change Your Life. 2008. (ENG.). 224p. 17.99 *(978-1-59979-396-2(2),* Creation Hse.) Charisma Media.
Davies, Brian. Thinking about God. 2010. 362p. pap. 40.00 *(978-1-60899-627-8(1),* Wipf and Stock) Wipf & Stock Pubs.
Davies, Douglas & Davies. The Theology of Death. 2008. (ENG.). 208p. 34.95 *(978-0-567-03049-8(0))*; 120.00 *(978-0-567-03048-1(2))* Continuum International Publishing Group, Ltd. GBR. (T&T Clark Int'l). Dist: National Bk. Network.
Davies, John. Be Born in Us Today: The Message of the Incarnation for Today. (Illus.). 160p. 13.95 *(978-1-85311-320-8(4))* Norwich Bks. & Music GBR. Dist: Morehouse Publishing.
Davies, Pennar. Diary of a Soul. Hughes, Howard, tr. from WEL. 2012. (ENG.). 256p. pap. 17.95 ***(978-1-84771-376-6(9))*** Y Lolfa GBR. Dist: Dufour Editions, Inc.
Davis, Anna L. The College Precipice. 2008. 128p. 21.99 *(978-1-60647-318-4(2))*; pap. 13.99 *(978-1-60477-846-5(6))* Xulon Pr., Inc.
Davis, Donald G. The Demise of Compassion: A Casualty of a Changing Culture. 2011. pap. 14.99 ***(978-1-61777-759-2(5))*** Tate Publishing & Enterprises, LLC.
Davis, Elaine. Looking Inside Out. 2009. 388p. 32.99 *(978-1-60791-330-6(5))*; pap. 20.99 *(978-1-60791-329-0(1))* Xulon Pr., Inc.
Davis, Eric N. House of Faith House of Cards: One Man's Journey through the World of Mormonism, Magic, & Murderers. 2010. 388p. (ENG.). 28.49 *(978-1-4490-8522-3(9))*; pap. 18.99 *(978-1-4490-8521-6(0))* AuthorHouse.
Davis, Evon, et al. Black Light: Stories of Illumination & Inspiration. 2007. 80p. pap. 12.99 *(978-0-9792132-1-2(5))* Reflections Publishing, Inc.
Davis, Francis L. The Christian's Warfare: It's a Family Affair. 2008. 224p. pap. 14.99 *(978-1-60647-278-1(X))* Xulon Pr., Inc.
—The Christian's Warfare: It's A Family Affair. 2008. 224p. 24.99 *(978-1-60647-279-8(8))* Xulon Pr., Inc.
Davis, Frank R. God's Mysterious Ways Revealed: Experiencing Abundant Life in Jesus Christ. 2011. 204p. pap. 15.04 ***(978-1-4269-8224-8(0))*** Trafford Publishing.
Davis, Garrison R. So, Why Did God Let This Happen? The Answer Has Been with Us the Whole Time... 2010. pap. 10.99 *(978-1-61579-854-4(4))* Xulon Pr., Inc.
Davis, Gerard W. The Image of God. 2007. 92p. pap. 11.00 *(978-0-8059-7426-3(1))* Dorrance Publishing Co., Inc.
Davis, Helen Jordan. The Covenant Principles. 2010. 162p. pap. 15.00 *(978-1-59755-131-1(7),* Advantage Inspirational) Advantage Bks.
Davis, J. E. El Camino de la Vida: The Way to Life. (SPA.). *(978-84-7645-041-3(9),* 223099) Clie, Editorial.
Davis, James & Roe, Sheila. Beginnings: Daily Christian Studies to Begin Your Grief Recovery. 2009. spiral bd. 6.95 *(978-1-61623-822-3(4))* Independent Pub.
Davis, Jimmie L. Virtual You! 189p. pap. 10.99 *(978-0-8307-3512-9(7),* Regal Bks.) Gospel Light Pubns.
Davis-Jones, Audre'L Chantel. Battle Scars of Emotions. 2008. 240p. 24.99 *(978-1-60477-997-4(7))*; pap. 14.99 *(978-1-60477-996-7(9))* Xulon Pr., Inc.
Davis, Juanita E. A Message for the Disciples... You Too, Peter. 2009. 188p. pap. 14.99 *(978-1-61579-604-5(5))* Xulon Pr., Inc.
Davis, Kim. Cocoon. 2009. 320p. pap. *(978-1-55452-365-8(6),* Guardian Bks.) Essence Publishing.
Davis, L. Edward, Jr. The Effective Will of God: Right-Brain Thinking for Left-Brain People & Vice-Versa in Ephesians One. 2009. 156p. pap. 14.99 *(978-1-61579-338-9(0))* Xulon Pr., Inc.
Davis, Les. The Power of the Lord Is My Strength: The Man Who Is Stronger Than Chains. 2011. 54p. pap. 15.99 ***(978-1-4628-9996-8(X))*** Xlibris Corp.
Davis, Linda. Aids in the Church. 2009. 132p. pap. 16.49 *(978-1-4343-7077-8(1))* AuthorHouse.
Davis, Mike. The Christian Entrepreneur. 160p. pap. 10.99 *(978-1-58169-128-3(9),* Evergreen Pr.) Genesis Communications, Inc.
Davis, Paris. Hearing God in Battle. 2007. 284p. (ENG.). 25.99 *(978-1-60266-815-7(9))*; per. 15.99 *(978-1-60266-814-0(0))* Xulon Pr., Inc.
Davis, Paul. Supernatural Fire. 2007. 308p. per. 17.99 *(978-1-60034-917-1(X))* Xulon Pr., Inc.
DAVIS, R. O. S. I. E. The Closing of Time. 2007. 48p. per. 10.00 *(978-0-9776348-6-0(7))* Affordable Pub.
Davis, Robert Clarence. Alive unto God. 2011. 104p. 39.95 ***(978-1-258-06039-8(6))*** Literary Licensing, LLC.
Davis, Sandra. You Have Problems? Listen to God's Guidance. 2008. 68p. pap. 16.95 *(978-1-60672-832-1(6))* PublishAmerica, Inc.
Davis, Sherry. 25 Lessons Learned from My Dog Morgan. 2008. 72p. pap. 9.99 *(978-1-60647-403-7(0))* Xulon Pr., Inc.
Davis, Sr. Roderic B. 'Barry'. From My Heart. 2008. 312p. pap. 17.99 *(978-1-60477-837-3(7))* Xulon Pr., Inc.
Davis, Steve. Take a Knee: Humorous & Inspiring Devotionals from the World of Sports. 2008. 124p. pap. 12.99 *(978-0-9712204-4-7(1))* Vabella Publishing.
Davis, Tom. Fields of the Fatherless: Discover the Joy of Compassionate Living. 2008. (ENG.). 192p. pap. 14.99 *(978-0-7814-4847-5(6))* Cook, David C.
—Red Letters: Living a Faith That Bleeds. 2007. (ENG.). 192p. per. 14.99 *(978-0-7814-4535-1(3))* Cook, David C.
Davis-Vaughn, Cheryl. Hope's Storyboard Surfing on the Promises of God the Love Story. 2010. 183p. pap. 15.99 *(978-0-557-23460-8(3))* Lulu Enterprises Inc.
Dawn, Marva J. Being Well When We're Ill: Wholeness & Hope in Spite of Infirmity. 2008. 284p. pap. 14.99 *(978-0-8066-8038-5(5),* Augsburg Bks.) Augsburg Fortress, Pubs.
Dawson, David C. The World Loves It's Own: Being a Christian Warrior During Troubled Times. 2009. 188p. 26.95 *(978-0-595-51496-0(0))*; pap. 16.95 *(978-0-595-48981-7(8))* iUniverse, Inc.
The Day Is Yours: Slow Spirituality in a FastMoving World. 2008. (ENG.). 160p. 19.99 *(978-1-84227-600-6(X),* Paternoster) Authentic Media.
The Day That Changed America. 2008. (Illus.). 120p. pap. 6.95 *(978-0-9612999-6-5(7))* Christian Life Services.
Daye, Patricia E. Successful Living God's Way. 2011. 94p. pap. 15.99 ***(978-1-4535-9729-3(8))*** Xlibris Corp.
Dayton, Edward. Estrategia Para el Exito: Strategy for Living. (SPA.). 224p. *(978-84-7228-427-2(1),* 220383) Clie, Editorial.
De Angelis, Rae Lynn. Nothing but Your Truth Will Help Me, God! 2007. 224p. per. 14.99 *(978-1-60266-273-5(8))* Xulon Pr., Inc.
de Blas, Alonso. Climb the Hill with Jesus. 2007. per. 4.95 *(978-0-9719921-7-7(7))* Tau Publishing.
De Graaf, S. G. El Pueblo de la Promesa: El Ministerio y la Muerte de Cristo. (SPA.). Vol. III. 413p. pap. 16.00 *(978-1-55883-067-7(7),* 6700-2530C) Vol. IV. 248p. pap. 12.00 *(978-1-55883-068-4(5),* 6700-2540C) Libros Desafio.
De Heredia, Juan F. Cronica de Morea. Date not set. (Dialect Ser.). *(978-0-942260-49-6(X))* Hispanic Seminary of Medieval Studies.
De Jesus-Coniglio, Pura M. The Bronx: Exposing Its True DNA & Breaking the Stigma - Discover One of Urban America's Greatest Hidden Truths. 2009. 352p. 32.99 *(978-1-61579-606-9(1))*; pap. 20.99 *(978-1-61579-330-3(5))* Xulon Pr., Inc.
De Jong, Norman. Lies, Lies, & More Lies! 2009. 236p. pap. 15.99 *(978-1-60791-327-6(5))* Xulon Pr., Inc.
De Klerk, Cornel & Munger, Kylie, compiled by. Promises from God for Parents - Blue. 2008. (Promises from God for... Ser.). 128p. pap. *(978-1-86920-971-1(0))* Christian Art Pubs.
—Promises from God for Parents - Pink. 2008. (Promises from God for... Ser.). 128p. pap. *(978-1-86920-970-4(2))* Christian Art Pubs.
de Kock, Dan. It's Time to Walk on Water, 1 vol. 2009. 94p. pap. 14.95 *(978-1-4489-9742-8(9))* PublishAmerica, Inc.
De Kock, Dan. Standing Firm in a Time of Shaking. 2007. 96p. per. 9.99 *(978-1-60477-054-4(6))* Xulon Pr., Inc.
de la Rosa, Cassandra. The Power of Submission: Revealing the Truth about One of Life's Greatest Challenges. 2008. (ENG.). 57p. pap. *(978-1-85756-628-4(9))* Janus Publishing Co.
De Seguirant, Laurie. Wise up, O Man of God. 2008. 55p. pap. 16.95 *(978-1-60610-941-0(3))* PublishAmerica, Inc.
de-Vaux Balbirnie, Jason K. Short accounts of the imperfect Christian. 2010. (ENG.). 146p. pap. 16.95 *(978-1-4461-6789-2(5))* Lulu Enterprises Inc.
De Vries, Attie. A Miracle. 2008. (ENG., Illus.). 144p. 14.99 *(978-1-59979-311-5(3),* Creation Hse.) Charisma Media.
de Waal, Esther. God under My Roof: Celtic Songs & Blessings. 2006. (Illus.). 72p. 14.95 *(978-1-55725-516-7(4))* Paraclete Pr., Inc.
Deace, Steven. Without a Vision the People Perish. 2007. 276p. per. 15.99 *(978-1-60266-642-9(3))* Xulon Pr., Inc.
Deadmond, Rick. The Betrothed Bride of Messiah. 2007. 408p. per. 21.99 *(978-1-60266-151-6(0))* Xulon Pr., Inc.
Dean, Chuck. Nam Vet Vol. 11: Making Peace with Your Past. pap. 10.99 *(978-0-9679371-0-6(8))* Selah Publishing Group, LLC.
Dean, Daren J. Choosing Truth, Finding Freedom: God Speaks. 2006. 185p. pap. 24.95 *(978-1-4241-4042-8(0))* PublishAmerica, Inc.
Dean, David. Planting A Dream: Tree of Life. 2006. (ENG.). 164p. per. 24.95 *(978-1-4241-3427-4(7))* PublishAmerica, Inc.
Dean, Jennifer Kennedy. Life Unhindered! Five Keys to Walking in Freedom. 2010. (ENG.). 208p. pap. 14.99 *(978-1-59669-286-2(3))* New Hope Pubs.
Dean, Randy. Radiance: If We Are the Light of the World, Why Is Everything So Dark? 2011. 268p. ***(978-0-7684-3617-4(6))***; ***(978-0-7684-3618-1(4))*** Destiny Image Pubs.
Deane, Dona. Honor Your Gifts. 2007. 232p. (ENG.). 24.99 *(978-1-60477-153-4(4))*; per. 14.99 *(978-1-60477-152-7(6))* Xulon Pr., Inc.
Dear, John. Transfiguration: A Meditation on Transforming Ourselves & Our World. 2007. (ENG.). 256p. pap. 11.95 *(978-0-385-51008-0(X),* Image) Doubleday Religious Publishing Group, The.
Dear Parents: Letters & Speeches from a Christian Coach to Families. 2011. 236p. 33.95 ***(978-1-4497-2067-4(6))***; pap. 17.95 ***(978-1-4497-2066-7(8))*** Author Solutions, Inc. (WestBow Pr.).
Debardelaben, E. C. At Their Feet. 2009. 74p. pap. 15.99 *(978-1-4415-0211-7(4))* Xlibris Corp.
Deblase, Jeffrey. Born to Raze Hell. 2008. 132p. pap. 13.99 *(978-1-60647-350-4(6))* Xulon Pr., Inc.
DeBlock-Hayford, Debra. Cold Paws, Warm Heart: The Christian Parent's Guide to Teaching Children How God Feels about Animals, How He Wants Us to Treat Them, & What the Bible Says about Animals & Heaven. 2008. 356p. pap. 19.99 *(978-1-60647-263-7(1))* Xulon Pr., Inc.
Dechane, Robert. Continuing Journey: A Catastrophic Event Doesn't End It. 2011. pap. 7.99 ***(978-1-61346-186-0(0))*** Tate Publishing & Enterprises, LLC.
Decker, Ed. My Kingdom Come. 2007. 440p. per. 21.99 *(978-1-60477-378-1(2))* Xulon Pr., Inc.
Decker, John. The Technology of Salvation & the Art of Geertgen Tot Sint Jans. 2009. (Visual Culture in Early Modernity Ser.). (Illus.). 182p. 114.95 *(978-0-7546-6453-6(8))* Ashgate Publishing Co.
Deeb, Michael. The Journey That Makes a Difference. 2007. 172p. per. 13.99 *(978-1-60266-662-7(8))* Xulon Pr., Inc.
Dees, James W. Reconciliation. 2008. 272p. pap. 23.95 *(978-1-4357-1162-4(9))* Lulu Enterprises Inc.
Deghelder, Susie. The Gate Called Beautiful. 2008. 108p. pap. 10.95 *(978-1-4327-2546-4(7))* Outskirts Pr., Inc.
Deighton, Rick. Ready to Give an Answer. 2007. 176p. per. 13.99 *(978-1-60266-188-2(X))* Xulon Pr., Inc.
Deir, Costa & Zeller, Stephanie. It's Time to Grow Up. 2006. 192p. per. 13.95 *(978-1-59919-015-0(X))* Elim Publishing.
Deising, Richard. Some Prayerful Thoughts. 2008. 148p. 11.99 *(978-1-60604-650-0(0))* Tate Publishing & Enterprises, LLC.
Deiss, Raymond F. God, the Same Yesterday, Today, & Tomorrow. 2011. 108p. 24.99 ***(978-1-4568-8027-9(6))***; pap. 15.99 ***(978-1-4568-8026-2(8))*** Xlibris Corp.
Dekoven, Stan. Grace & Truth. 2011. 56p. pap. 8.00 ***(978-1-61529-021-5(4))*** Vision Publishing.
Dekoven, Stan. On Belay! an Introduction to Christian Counseling. 2009. 206p. pap. 21.00 *(978-1-61529-010-9(9))* Vision Publishing.
DeKoven, Stan. Prelude to a Requiem. 2008. (Illus.). 64p. pap. 10.00 *(978-1-931178-54-9(2))* Vision Publishing.
Delaney, H. G. Stop the Church, I Want to Get Off: Friendly Fire in the Army of God. 2008. 200p. pap. 24.95 *(978-1-60474-051-6(5))* PublishAmerica, Inc.
DeLashmutt, Gary. Loving God's Way: A Fresh Look at the One Another Passages. 2007. (ENG.). 144p. pap. 14.99 *(978-1-59067-007-1(8))* Xenos Christian Fellowship.
DelBene, Ron. Alone with God. 13.35 *(978-0-687-60016-8(2))* Abingdon Pr.
DeLee, Andrew. The and Shepherd's Challenge. 2011. 128p. 22.99 ***(978-1-61379-291-9(3))***; pap. 14.99 ***(978-1-61379-290-2(5))*** Xulon Pr., Inc.
Dell, Katharine. Seeking a Life That Matters: Wisdom for Today from the Book of Proverbs. 128p. pap. 13.00 *(978-0-232-52402-4(5))* Abingdon Pr.
Dellerba, Andre. Hear God's Voice. 2011. 174p. pap. 14.99 ***(978-1-61379-395-4(2))*** Xulon Pr., Inc.
Delmon, Marty. Destined for Healing. 2011. (ENG., Illus.). 102p. pap. 12.99 ***(978-0-9828277-1-0(7))*** RPJ & Co., Inc.
DeLoatch, Patricia. Kingdom Living: Walking in the Power of God's Word. 2010. pap. 9.99 *(978-1-61663-146-8(5))* Tate Publishing & Enterprises, LLC.
Delong, Elder Lloyd. The Soul of Man. 2009. 152p. pap. 14.99 *(978-1-60647-374-0(3))* Xulon Pr., Inc.
Delong, Lloyd. The Fruits of the Spirit: Your Path to Victory. 2007. 80p. per. 9.99 *(978-1-60477-250-0(6))* Xulon Pr., Inc.
Deloriea, Wayne. Coach Without a Whistle. 2009. 132p. pap. 14.99 *(978-1-60791-202-6(3))* Xulon Pr., Inc.
DeLoriea, Wayne. Coach Without A Whistle. 2009. *(978-1-60791-301-6(1))* Xulon Pr., Inc.
Delph, Ed. Finding an Ancient God in the 21st Century: Redefining God for Friends, Family, & Community. 2008. pap. 15.99 *(978-0-7684-2705-9(3))* Destiny Image Pubs.
—The Five Minute Miracle: Starting Each Day with Radiant Inspiration. 2008. pap. 15.99 *(978-0-7684-2765-3(7))* Destiny Image Pubs.
Demaray, Donald E. Mile Markers: 40 Intimate Journeys with Jesus. 2007. (Illus.). 169p. 9.99 *(978-1-928915-96-6(5))* Evangel Publishing Hse.
Demarest, Bruce. Seasons of the Soul: Stages of Spiritual Development, 1 vol. 2009. (ENG.). 191p. pap. 16.00 *(978-0-8308-3535-5(0),* IVP Bks.) InterVarsity Pr.
DeMartino, Danielle. From the Natural to the Supernatural: True life Stories... 2011. 156p. 30.95 ***(978-1-4497-1533-5(8))***; pap. 13.95 ***(978-1-4497-1532-8(X))*** Author Solutions, Inc. (WestBow Pr.).
Demkovich, Michael. Introducing Meister Eckhart. 2006. (Illus.). 178p. per. 18.95 *(978-0-7648-1507-2(5))* Liguori Pubns.
Demong, Carol H. The Bleating of the Sheep & Other Essays. 2008. 144p. pap. 14.99 *(978-1-60647-775-5(7))* Xulon Pr., Inc.
DeMoss, Nancy Leigh. Brokenness, Surrender, Holiness: A Revive Our Hearts Trilogy. 2008. (Revive Our Hearts Ser.). (ENG.). 416p. 19.99 *(978-0-8024-1282-9(3))* Moody Pubs.
—Choosing Gratitude: Your Journey to Joy. (ENG.). 240p. 2011. pap. 14.99 *(978-0-8024-3255-1(7))* 2009. 17.99 *(978-0-8024-3252-0(2))* Moody Pubs.
—Sea Agradecido, 1 vol. 2010. Orig. Title: Choosing Gratitude. (SPA.). 224p. pap. 10.99 *(978-0-8254-1214-1(5),* Editorial Portavoz) Kregel Pubns.

C

DeMoss, Nancy Leigh & Grissom, Tim. Seeking Him: Experiencing the Joy of Personal Revival. 2009. (ENG.). 288p. pap. 19.99 (978-0-8024-1362-8(5)) Moody Pubs.

DeMoss, Nancy Leigh, et al. Lies Young Women Believe: And the Truth That Sets Them Free. 2008. (ENG.). 160p. pap. 13.99 (978-0-8024-7291-5(5)) Moody Pubs.

Demritte, Dlen. Getting Through the Night. 2008. pap. 11.99 (978-1-60647-205-7(4)) Xulon Pr., Inc.

Den Besten, Kris. Shine: Five Principles for a Rewarding Life. 2008. 191p. per. 15.99 (978-0-7684-2608-3(1)) Destiny Image Pubs.

DeNeff, Steve. 7 Saving Graces: Living above the Deadly Sins. 2010. (978-0-89827-420-2(6)) Wesleyan Publishing Hse.

Deneff, Steve, et al. SoulShift: The Measure of a Life Transformed. 2011. (Illus.). 189p. **(978-0-89827-476-9(1))** Wesleyan Publishing Hse.

Denn, George. Hey by George! 2007. 164p. (ENG.). 21.99 (978-1-60266-298-8(3)); per. 13.99 (978-1-60266-297-1(5)) Xulon Pr., Inc.

Denn, George W. Hey by George! Ii: On the Northwest Side of Wita Lake. 2009. 140p. 22.99 (978-1-61579-052-4(7)); pap. 14.99 (978-1-61579-051-7(9)) Xulon Pr., Inc.

Denney, Loleen. Ruach Hakodesh. 2008. pap. 9.99 (978-1-60477-821-2(0)) Xulon Pr., Inc.

Dennis, A. J. Imagining God. 128p. 12.00 (978-0-281-05040-6(6)) SPCK Publishing GBR. Dist: Pilgrim Pr., The/United Church Pr.

Dennis, Chris/D. In This Communion. 2008. 72p. pap. 10.00 (978-0-615-21642-3(0)) In This Communion Ministries LLC.

Dennis, Trevor. Keeping God Company. 96p. 10.00 (978-0-281-05464-0(9)) SPCK Publishing GBR. Dist: Pilgrim Pr., The/United Church Pr.

Depew, Catherine. Blue Star in My Window. 2007. 256p. per. 15.99 (978-1-60477-281-4(6)) Xulon Pr., Inc.

Deratany, Edward. Refugio en el Lugar Secreto: Refuge in the Secret Place. (SPA.). (978-84-7228-154-7(X), 220753) Clie, Editorial.

Derbyshire, A. Raising Kids with a Passion for God. 2008. 112p. pap. 12.99 (978-0-9800033-1-4(8)) 90 Minute Bks.

Derosa, Pamela & Stefanowski, Lois. It's Time! To Turn Brokenness into Blessing! 2008. 124p. 19.99 (978-1-60791-156-2(6)); pap. 11.99 (978-1-60647-995-7(4)) Xulon Pr., Inc.

Derrick, Deborah. 'Can-Do!' Christianity. 2007. 148p. per. 13.99 (978-1-60266-537-8(0)) Xulon Pr., Inc.

Desai, D. J. Dory's. 2009. 244p. pap. 15.99 (978-1-60791-830-1(7)) Xulon Pr., Inc.

deSales, Francis. Introduction to the Devout Life. 2.00 (978-0-8358-0161-4(6)) Upper Room Bks.

deSouza, Junior. Be Yourself! 2007. 148p. per. 13.99 (978-1-60266-846-1(9)) Xulon Pr., Inc.

Dettmann, Heidi. The God of No Importance? A Call for America to Return to Biblical Lifestyle & Behavior. 2008. 68p. pap. 10.99 (978-1-60647-688-8(2)) Xulon Pr., Inc.

Devaul, Gary & Thallander, Mark. Champions Plus. 2007. 232p. per. 14.95 (978-1-59330-501-7(X)) Aventine Pr.

Deverell, Garry J. The Bonds of Freedom: Vows, Sacraments, & the Formation of the Christian Self. 2009. (Paternoster Theological Mongraphs Ser.). (ENG.). 214p. 39.99 (978-1-84227-527-6(5), Paternoster) Authentic Media.

—The Bonds of Freedom: Vows, Sacraments & the Formation of the Christian Self. 2008. (Paternoster Theological Monographs). 230p. pap. 26.00 (978-1-60608-312-3(0), Wipf and Stock) Wipf & Stock Pubs.

Devlin, Jennifer. Verses We Know by Heart: Discovering the Details of Familiar Old Testament Passages. 2008. 124p. per. 10.99 (978-0-89265-565-6(8)) Randall Hse. Pubns.

Devotion to the Precious Blood. 2008. 3.00 (978-0-89555-880-0(7), TAN Bks.) St. Benedict Pr., LLC.

Devotional Life. 0.75 (978-0-89265-523-6(2)) Randall Hse. Pubns.

DeVries, John, contrib. by. The Kids Hymnal: Piano Accompaniment. 2007. (Illus.). 153p. (J). (gr. k-5). pap. 19.95 (978-1-59856-216-3(9)) Hendrickson Pubs. Marketing, LLC.

Dew, Frank & Murden, Jane. Improving Our Acoustics for Hearing the Gospel. 2011. 178p. pap. 14.99 **(978-1-61379-623-8(4))** Xulon Pr., Inc.

Dewar. Invitations - P. (Illus.). 176p. 16.00 (978-0-281-04948-6(3)) SPCK Publishing GBR. Dist: Pilgrim Pr., The/United Church Pr.

Dewberry, William Edward. God's Redeeming Plan: From the Creation to the Revelation. 2011. 492p. 44.95 **(978-1-4497-1986-9(4))**; pap. 34.95 **(978-1-4497-1985-2(6))** Author Solutions, Inc. (WestBow Pr.).

DeWitt, E. E. Days of Whine & Rousing: (A 20th Century Theologian Looks at 21st Century Life as a Christian) 2006. 185p. pap. 24.95 (978-1-4241-4601-7(1)) PublishAmerica, Inc.

Dewitt, Russell Christy. The Red Letters of Matthew. 2007. 308p. per. 17.99 (978-1-60266-086-1(7)) Xulon Pr., Inc.

Di Pardo De Has. Introduccion a la Educacion Cristiana: Introduction to Christian. (SPA.). (978-84-7645-180-9(6), 223215) Clie, Editorial.

Dianovich, Elizabeth Benlian. God Saved Me in the Orient Express & I Came to Americ. 2008. 148p. per. 14.99 (978-1-60477-016-2(3)) Xulon Pr., Inc.

Diaz, Danny. A Life Designed by God: Discovering Who You Were Meant to Be. 2007. (Illus.). 155p. per. 12.99 (978-0-88368-621-8(X)) Whitaker Hse.

Diaz de Almeida, Carmen Cecelia. Refrantes De La Villa Del Garrote. 286p. 4.50 (978-958-607-645-6(8)) Sociedad de San Pablo COL. Dist: St Pauls/Alba Hse. Pubs.

Diaz, Gwendolyn Mitchell. Sticking up for What I Believe. 2008. 260p. pap. 14.99 (978-1-60647-792-2(7)) Xulon Pr., Inc.

—Sticking up for Who I Am! 2009. 136p. pap. 14.99 (978-1-60791-342-9(9)) Xulon Pr., Inc.

DiCello, Carmen. Truth in Balance: Doing Apologetics in a Postmodern Culture. 2009. 168p. pap. 19.00 (978-1-60608-778-7(9), Wipf and Stock) Wipf & Stock Pubs.

Dickason, Ken. A Layman's Christianity. 2010. 176p. 30.95 (978-1-4497-0547-3(2)); pap. 13.95 (978-1-4497-0545-9(6)) Author Solutions, Inc. (WestBow Pr.).

Dickerson, Anthony. Living Out Your Identity in Christ. 2011. 226p. pap. 19.95 **(978-1-257-00337-2(2))** Lulu Enterprises Inc.

Dickerson, Anthony & Dickerson, Larisha. The Christian Life at Its Best. 2008. 333p. pap. 19.95 (978-1-4357-1135-8(1)) Lulu Enterprises Inc.

Dickie, Robert L. Authentic Christianity 101. 2007. 47p. pap. (978-0-85234-672-3(7)) Evangelical Pr.

Dickson, Jane. Tell Me Where It Hurts. 2007. 196p. per. 12.99 (978-1-60247-065-1(0)) Tate Publishing & Enterprises, LLC.

Did You Miss the Rapture? pap. 6.95 (978-0-929540-15-3(8)) Publishing Designs, Inc.

Diederich, Brian. CHRIST: the DARK YEARS New Edition. 2009. 121p. pap. 10.99 (978-0-615-22119-9(X)) Diederich, Brian D.

Diener, Carl. Revelation from Creation - True Tales from the North Woods. 2009. 92p. pap. 10.99 (978-1-58930-230-3(3)) Selah Publishing Group, LLC.

Diggs, Gwendolyn Wilson, ed. A Place of My Own to Give God Glory: Forty Days of Inspirational Devotions for Reflection & Meditation. 2011. 120p. 20.95 **(978-1-4502-9655-7(6))**; pap. 10.95 **(978-1-4502-9653-3(X))** iUniverse, Inc.

Diggs, Steve. Life's Too Short to Miss the Big Picture: Making the Most of What's Most Important. 2010. 224p. 14.99 (978-0-89112-640-9(6), Leafwood Pubs.) Abilene Christian Univ. Pr.

DiGirolamo, Vincent. Grace Divine. 2008. 100p. pap. 10.99 (978-0-9786815-6-2(8)); (ENG., Illus.). 296p. (978-0-9786815-7-9(6)) Celestine Publishing, LLC.

Dilday, Russell H. Higher Ground: A Call for Christian Civility. 2007. 148p. per. 17.00 (978-1-57312-469-0(9)) Smyth & Helwys Publishing, Inc.

Dill, Robin. Walking with Grace: Tools for Implementing & Launching a Congregational Respite Program. 2009. 168p. pap. 24.95 (978-1-4401-3063-2(9)) iUniverse, Inc.

Dillard, F. Douglas, Jr., Jr. Journeying with God: A Book of 40 Sermons to Comfort, Guide & Strengthen you for the Journey of Faith. 2007. (ENG.). 184p. pap. 19.95 (978-1-932124-92-7(6)) ACW Pr.

Dillard, Patricia. Inspirational Reflections for Life Challenges. 2007. 132p. per. 13.99 (978-1-60266-177-6(4)) Xulon Pr., Inc.

Dillard, Judy L. The Beauty of Pain: My experience & practical advice for Christians with chronic illness. 2008. 92p. pap. 10.95 (978-1-4327-2669-0(2)) Outskirts Pr., Inc.

Dillon, Christine. 1-2-1 Discipleship. 2009. (Omf Ser.). (ENG.). 160p. 9.99 (978-1-84550-425-0(9)) Christian Focus Pubns. GBR. Dist: STL Distribution North America.

Dillon, Patrick. Steadfast Christian: A higher call to faith, family, & Hope. 2010. 249p. (ENG.). 24.95 (978-1-4327-5066-4(6)); (Illus.). pap. 15.95 (978-1-4327-4879-1(3)) Outskirts Pr., Inc.

Dillow, Linda. Calm My Anxious Heart: A Woman's Guide to Finding Contentment. 2007. (TH1NK Reference Collection). (ENG.). 256p. pap. 15.99 (978-1-60006-141-7(9)) NavPress Publishing Group.

—A Deeper Kind of Calm: Steadfast Faith in the Midst of Adversity. 2006. (Hollywood Nobody Ser.). (ENG.). 144p. per. 12.99 (978-1-60006-075-5(7)) NavPress Publishing Group.

—My Journey to Contentment: A Companion Journal for Calm My Anxious Heart. 2007. (Storm Warriors Ser.). (ENG.). 144p. 9.99 (978-1-60006-186-8(9)) NavPress Publishing Group.

DiMarco, Hayley & DiMarco, Michael. Unstuff: Making Room in Your Life for What Really Matters. 2010. (ENG.). 192p. pap. 14.99 (978-1-4143-3478-3(8)) Tyndale Hse. Pubs.

Dimensions for Living, creator. My Daily Walk Calendar & Journal: Living a Life of Forgiveness. 2007. (Illus.). 264p. pap. 15.00 (978-0-687-49233-6(5), Dimensions For Living) Abingdon Pr.

DiMickele, Susan. Chasing Superwoman: A Working Mom's Adventures in Life & Faith, 1 vol. 2010. (ENG.). 224p. pap. 14.99 (978-1-4347-6462-1(1)) Cook, David C.

Dinkins, B. J. The Sabbath Breaker. 2008. 260p. 25.99 (978-1-60647-019-0(1)) Xulon Pr., Inc.

—The Sabbath Breaker: The Church Jesus Christ Will Not Rapture. 2008. pap. 15.99 (978-1-60477-664-5(1)) Xulon Pr., Inc.

Dinnanauth, Robin. Every Day with Jesus. 2007. 124p. 18.99 (978-1-60477-177-0(1)); per. 10.99 (978-1-60477-176-3(3)) Xulon Pr., Inc.

Dinnen, Stewart. How Are You Doing? Give Your Life a Spiritual Health Check. 208p. 7.99 (978-1-85792-669-9(2), Christian Focus) Christian Focus Pubns. GBR. Dist: Riverside.

Dinsmore, Julia K. My Name Is Child of God... Not "Those People" A First-Person Look at Poverty. 2007. 176p. per. 14.99 (978-0-8066-5624-3(7), Augsburg Bks.) Augsburg Fortress, Pubs.

Dioso, Marconi M. Wind & Fire: A Life of St. Luke. 2011. 136p. 29.99 **(978-1-4628-6932-9(7))**; pap. 19.99 **(978-1-4628-6931-2(9))** Xlibris Corp.

Discafani, Tom. One Tube, One Boy, One Awesome God, 1 vol. 2010. 54p. pap. 16.95 (978-1-4489-8122-9(0)) PublishAmerica, Inc.

The Disciple. 2009. 378p. pap. (978-0-217-27975-8(9)); 130p. pap. (978-1-4588-7093-3(6)) Books LLC.

Disciple 4 Handbook Korean. (978-0-687-07379-5(0)) Abingdon Pr.

Disciple I Revised Adult Study Manual. rev. ed. stu. ed. 30.00 (978-0-687-76349-6(6)) Abingdon Pr.

Disciple Youth. 2nd ed. incl. VHS (978-0-687-71688-3(8)) Abingdon Pr.

Discipulado Cristiano. 2.25 (978-0-7673-5684-8(5)) LifeWay Christian Resources.

Discovery House Publishers Staff. Power Up! - Outdoor: Devotional Thoughts for Sportsmen. Branon, Dave, ed. 2009. (ENG.). 224p. 11.99 (978-1-57293-319-4(4)) Discovery Hse. Pubs.

Discovery House Publishers Staff & Branon, Dave. Better Than Life: Today's Stories of Faith at Any Cost. 2007. (ENG.). 160p. per. 9.99 (978-1-57293-265-4(1)) Discovery Hse. Pubs.

Disman, Jason. Realizations of a Wayward Christian, 1 vol. 2009. 64p. pap. 16.95 (978-1-60813-929-3(8)) PublishAmerica, Inc.

Distasi, Richard. The Fleeing Youth. 2009. 351p. pap. 16.56 (978-0-557-08609-2(4)) Lulu Enterprises Inc.

Ditchfield, Christin. A Family Guide to the Bible. 2009. 304p. pap. 15.99 (978-1-58134-891-0(6)) Crossway.

Ditommaso, Stephanie. The Truth about the Secret. 2008. 164p. pap. 13.99 (978-1-60647-404-4(9)) Xulon Pr., Inc.

Ditrick, Eleanor & Chap. Flutter By. 2008. 292p. pap. 16.00 (978-1-59858-792-0(7)) Dog Ear Publishing, LLC.

Dixon, Ameka K. Fed up with Church Mess. 2008. 64p. pap. 16.95 (978-1-60474-927-4(X)) PublishAmerica, Inc.

Dixon, Carl. False Prophets, 1 vol. 2009. 158p. pap. 24.95 (978-1-60672-596-2(3)) PublishAmerica, Inc.

Dixon, Dr Joyce Marie & Dixon, Joyce Marie. A Word in Due Season. 2010. 208p. pap. 15.99 (978-1-60957-426-0(5)) Xulon Pr., Inc.

Dixon, James & Dixon, James, II. If God Is So Good, Why Are Blacks Doing So Bad? 2007. (ENG.). 160p. per. 12.95 (978-0-9786581-7-5(5)) Lifebridge Bks.

Dixon, James, II. Unleash Your Faith — Unlock God's Power: How to Experience the Extraordinary. 2008. (ENG.). 160p. 12.95 (978-0-9793192-7-3(7)) Lifebridge Bks.

Doall, Treber. Revolutionary Faith. 2007. 176p. per. 13.99 (978-1-60266-465-4(X)) Xulon Pr., Inc.

Dobson, Edward G. The Year of Living Like Jesus: My Journey of Discovering What Jesus Would Really Do, 1 vol. 2009. (ENG.). 304p. 19.99 (978-0-310-24777-7(2)) Zondervan.

Dobson, James C. Todo Sobre la Voluntad de Dios.Tr. of Dr. Dobson Talks About the Will of God. (SPA.). 56p. (978-84-7228-250-6(3), 220893) Clie, Editorial.

Dobson, Ryan & Smith, Brian. To Die For: The Dangerous Truth about Following Christ. 2007. (ENG.). 144p. (YA). (gr. 8-16). per. 10.99 (978-1-4143-1753-3(0)) Tyndale Hse. Pubs.

Dockery, Amie & Alessi, Mary. When Women Worship: Creating an Atmosphere of Intimacy with God. 2007. (ENG., Illus.). 144p. per. 12.99 (978-0-8307-4279-0(4)) Gospel Light Pubns.

Doctor, Jonathan. Prophetic Grace: God's Set Time. 2009. (J). pap. 23.99 (978-1-60799-660-6(X)) Tate Publishing & Enterprises, LLC.

Dodd, Christine. Making Scripture Work. (Illus.). 167p. pap. (978-0-225-66524-6(7), Burns & Oates) Continuum International Publishing Group, Ltd.

Dodd, Robert V. Advent: A Calendar of Devotions 2010. 2010. 0.75 (978-1-4267-1081-0(X)) Abingdon Pr.

Doddridge, Philip. The Rise & Progress of Religion in the Soul. 2009. 166p. pap. 19.99 (978-1-4589-3703-2(8)) General Bks. LLC.

Dods, Marcus. How to Become Like Christ. 2009. 48p. pap. (978-1-4099-7661-5(0)) Dodo Pr.

—How to Become Like Christ. 2007. (ENG.). 48p. per. (978-1-4068-2560-2(3)) Echo Library.

Dodson, Jeffrey Tad. Promises to Our Father: Gods Account of Mankind. 2009. 210p. pap. 18.95 (978-1-4327-1201-3(2)) Outskirts Pr., Inc.

Doerksen, Brian. Make Love, Make War: NOW Is the Time to Worship. 2009. (ENG.). 224p. pap. 14.99 (978-1-4347-6682-3(9)) Cook, David C.

Does God Really Exist? 2.50 (978-0-570-09986-4(2), 16-6044) Concordia Publishing Hse.

Does Scientific Evidence Support Evolution or Creation by God? 2.50 (978-0-570-09985-7(4), 16-6043) Concordia Publishing Hse.

Doherty, Catherine de Hueck. Light in the Darkness: A Christian Vision for Unstable Times. 96p. (978-1-897145-06-7(3)) Madonna Hse. Pubns.

Doherty, Eddie. Tumbleweed: A Biography of Catherine Doherty. 2nd ed. (Illus.). 203p. pap. (978-0-921440-12-3(X)) Madonna Hse. Pubns.

Dohoney, Steven. Hope. 2009. 156p. pap. 14.99 (978-1-60791-588-1(X)) Xulon Pr., Inc.

Dolabani, Philoxenos. Book of the Bee. 2010. (SYR.). 94.40 (978-1-61143-347-0(9)) Gorgias Pr., LLC.

Dolan, Kathy. One Way Walk. 2010. pap. 12.99 (978-1-61566-461-0(0)) Tate Publishing & Enterprises, LLC.

Dolan, Timothy M. Doers of the Word: Putting Your Faith into Practice. 2009. 128p. pap. 9.95 (978-1-59276-639-0(0)) Our Sunday Visitor, Publishing Div.

Dole, George F. Sorting Things Out. 273p. pap. (978-0-9626795-3-7(4)) Appleseed, J. & Co.

Doles, Jeff. Miracles & Manifestations of the Holy Spirit in the History of the Church. 2007. 280p. pap. 24.95 (978-0-9744748-9-2(4)) Walking Barefoot Ministries.

Doles, Warner. In Defense of the Gospel. 2011. 140p. pap. 14.99 **(978-1-61215-824-2(2))** Xulon Pr., Inc.

—The Kingdom of God Is Near: A Pastor's Look at the Gospel of Mark. 2009. 176p. pap. 14.99 (978-1-61579-244-3(9)) Xulon Pr., Inc.

—Letters of Encouragement. 2010. 134p. pap. 14.99 (978-1-60957-775-9(2)) Xulon Pr., Inc.

Dollar, Creflo A. Claim Your Victory Today: 10 Steps That Will Revolutionize Your Life. rev. ed. 2007. (ENG.). 208p. per. 12.99 (978-0-446-17817-4(9)) FaithWords.

—Winning in Troubled Times: God's Solutions for Victory over Life's Toughest Challenges. 2010. (ENG.). 256p. 21.99 (978-0-446-55337-7(9)) FaithWords.

Dollar, Gregory. Understanding the Destructive Power of Assumption & How to Control It. 2009. 144p. pap. 14.99 (978-1-61579-323-5(2)) Xulon Pr., Inc.

Dollar, Jason & Pinkerton, Bradley. Contend: A Survey of Christian Apologetics on a High School Level. 2009. 300p. pap. 16.95 (978-1-59330-583-3(4)) Aventine Pr.

Dollar, Taffi L. Kidz Faith Confessions. 2nd ed. 2007. 50p. pap. 5.00 (978-1-59944-089-7(X)) Creflo Dollar Ministries Pubns.

—Your Spiritual Makeover: Experience the Beauty of a Balanced Life: Spirit, Soul & Body. 224p. 2010. pap. 13.99 (978-1-57794-974-9(9)) 2007. 19.99 (978-1-57794-914-5(5)) Harrison House Pubs.

—21 Days to Your Spiritual Makeover. 2007. 93p. per. 4.99 (978-1-57794-911-4(0)) Harrison House Pubs.

Dollard, Renee. Are You One of These Eight Reasons: Reasons for Not Accepting Christ from Everyday People. 2006. pap. 9.00 (978-0-8059-7174-3(2)) Dorrance Publishing Co., Inc.

Domencic, Peter. Watching Children Follow the Spirit. 2008. 172p. 22.99 (978-1-60647-923-0(7)) Xulon Pr., Inc.

Dompreh, Dominic. Dare to Believe in Him. 2006. 113p. per. 10.99 (978-1-59886-483-0(1)) Tate Publishing & Enterprises, LLC.

Donald, Be' Trice Ronique Jenkins. God's Appointed Destiny: Life - A Preplanned Destiny. 2010. pap. 16.99 (978-1-61566-138-1(7)) Tate Publishing & Enterprises, LLC.

Donald, Bruce. Modifying Creation? 2006. (ENG.). 182p. pap. 24.99 (978-1-84227-100-1(8), Paternoster) Authentic Media.

Donaldson, Hal & Horn, Ken, eds. Jesus & You: 25 ways to grow your life in Christ. 2006. pap. 14.95 (978-1-880689-15-8(4)) Onward Bks., Inc.

Donaldson, Stacey. Psalm 23: Wonders of God's Love. 2008. 64p. pap. 9.99 (978-1-60647-531-7(2)) Xulon Pr., Inc.

Donatelli, Rose. God Is the Messiah. 2011. 74p. pap. 12.99 **(978-1-61379-933-8(0))** Xulon Pr., Inc.

Donelan, Thomas. Filling the Empty Life. 2009. 40p. pap. 10.00 (978-0-557-21424-2(6)) Lulu Enterprises Inc.

Donnelly, Edward. Life in Christ: Walking in Newness of Life. 2007. 112p. per. (978-1-85049-224-5(7)) Bryntirion Pr.

Donoho, Tim. Arguing with God. 2008. (ENG.). 224p. 20.99 (978-1-59979-501-0(9), Creation Hse.) Charisma Media.

Doohan, Leonard. Enjoying Retirement: Living Life to the Fullest. 2010. 192p. pap. 14.95 (978-0-8091-4635-2(5)) Paulist Pr.

Doran, Adron. Restoring New Testament Christianity. pap. 9.99 (978-0-89098-161-0(2)) Twentieth Century Christian Bks.

Dorey, Daniel R. The Olive Principle: Finding Your Way Back to God. 2011. 108p. 22.95 (978-1-4502-7775-4(6)); pap. 12.95 (978-1-4502-7774-7(8)) iUniverse, Inc.

Dornacher, Karla. Give Thanks, 0 vols. 2009. 80p. 14.99 (978-1-4041-8753-5(7)) Nelson, Thomas Inc.

Dornhecker, Ken. The Soul of a Generation. 2007. 232p. per. 14.99 (978-1-60266-729-7(2)) Xulon Pr., Inc.

Doroclak, Rick. Reclaiming God: 10 Commitments to Living a Full Life, 1 vol. 2009. 104p. pap. 16.95 (978-1-60813-283-6(8)) PublishAmerica, Inc.

Dorpat, David. God Is Faithful: The Reformation of a Lutheran Pharisee. 2008. (ENG.). 272p. per. 14.99 (978-1-59979-248-4(6), Creation Hse.) Charisma Media.

Dorr, Donal. Spirituality: Our Deepest Heart's Desire. 2009. (ENG.). 160p. pap. 25.95 (978-1-85607-629-6(6)) Columba Pr. IRL. Dist: Dufour Editions, Inc.

Doss, Jenny. More Precious Than Gold: A True Story of Triumph over Tragedy. 2008. 304p. 28.99 (978-1-60791-158-6(2)); 300p. pap. 18.99 (978-1-60791-107-4(8)) Xulon Pr., Inc.

Dotson, Earlene L. The Healthy Anointed Life. 2010. 170p. 22.99 (978-1-60957-782-7(5)); pap. 14.99 (978-1-60957-781-0(7)) Xulon Pr., Inc.

Dotson, LaToya C. A Living Epistle: Read by All Men. 2010. 184p. (ENG.). 30.95 (978-1-4497-0106-2(X)); pap. 13.95 (978-1-4497-0104-8(3)) Author Solutions, Inc. (WestBow Pr.).

Dougherty, Rose Mary. Discernment: A Path to Spiritual Awakening. 2009. 96p. pap. 9.95 (978-0-8091-4554-6(5)) Paulist Pr.

Douglas, Herman, Sr. Prayer Power in the Eyes of Faith: A Historical Examination of Prayer over Time & How Prayer Moved Mountains Out of God's Children's Way. 2007. 14.00 (978-0-8059-8904-5(8)) Dorrance Publishing Co., Inc.

Douglas, Stauffer D. Freedom's Ring: Life, Liberty & the Pursuit of Salvation. 2008. (Illus.). 400p. 29.95 (978-0-9677016-9-1(4)) McCowen Mills Pubs.

Doumit, Peter G. What I Know about Baseball Is What I Know about Life. 2007. (Illus.). 179p. per. 12.99 (978-1-60247-164-1(9)) Tate Publishing & Enterprises, LLC.

Douno, Beinca. Sacred Words of the Master: A Call to the Disciple 1940. 2007. (ENG.). 124p. 35.95 (978-0-548-05511-3(4)) Kessinger Publishing, LLC.

Dowdell, Bette. How to Be a Christian Without Being Annoying. l.t. ed. 2009. 196p. pap. 19.95 (978-0-9717728-3-0(5)) Confident Faith Institute.

—On We March: A memoir of growing up in the Salvation Army. 2009. 320p. pap. 19.95 (978-0-9717728-5-4(1)) Confident Faith Institute.
Dowdle, John R. Ignore the Detours. 2012. (978-1-55452-802-8(X)) Essence Publishing.
Dowdy, Naomi. Moving on & Moving Up. 2006. (SPA.). 8.00 (978-1-934201-01-5(4)); 8.00 (978-1-934201-00-8(6)); (IND.). 8.00 (978-1-934201-02-2(2)) Dowdy, Naomi Pubns.
Downing, Donald R. Born in His Image, Birthed in His Likeness. 2009. 184p. pap. 14.99 (978-1-60791-095-4(0)) Xulon Pr., Inc.
—Heart Almanac Expository & Curriculum: A Complete Expository & Curriculum of the Heart. 2008. 156p. pap. 16.99 (978-1-60647-639-5(0)) Xulon Pr., Inc.
Downing, Jim. Living Legacy. 2008. (Discipleship Journal Bible Study Ser.). (ENG.). 144p. pap. 9.99 (978-0-9729023-8-0(4)) NavPress Publishing Group
Downing, Pamela J. Honoring Your Pastor's Wife: The Keys to Her & Your Success. 2009. 152p. pap. 14.99 (978-1-60791-645-1(2)) Xulon Pr., Inc.
Downs, Christina. Learning to Live a Simply Balanced Life Workbook. 2007. spiral bd. (978-0-9794248-2-3(8)) Cross Your Heart Pubns.
—Simply Balanced: Bible 'Contradictions' Teach Balanced Living. 2007. (Illus.). 144p. per. 12.95 (978-0-9794248-1-6(X)) Cross Your Heart Pubns.
Doyle, Adelaide. Thoughts on a Sunday Afternoon. 2008. (978-1-55452-214-9(5)) Essence Publishing.
Doyle, G. Wright. Jesus: The Complete Man. 2008. 176p. pap. 11.99 (978-1-4389-2793-0(2)) AuthorHouse.
Doyle, John H. 100 Quotes for Yokes. 2011. 228p. pap. 15.99 (978-1-60957-319-5(6)) Xulon Pr., Inc.
Doyle, Mary K. Seven Principles of Sainthood: Following St. Mother Theodore Guerin. 2008. 156p. pap. 12.95 (978-0-87946-355-7(4)) ACTA Pubns.
Dozier, Rosita. A Message to the Overcomer. 2008. 128p. pap. 14.99 (978-1-60791-036-7(5)) Xulon Pr., Inc.
Drake, Donald. Simon Says. 2007. 252p. (ENG.). 25.99 (978-1-60266-364-0(5)); per. 15.99 (978-1-60266-363-3(7)) Xulon Pr., Inc.
Drakes, Najeh. Divine Java: A Personal Affirmations Journal to Extract Your Bold Flavor from God's Divine Cup. 2009. 254p. 26.95 (978-1-4327-4877-7(7)) Outskirts Pr., Inc.
Drane, John. After Mcdonaldization: Mission, Ministry, & Christian Discipleship in an Age of Uncertainty. 2008. (Illus.). 192p. (C). pap. 23.00 (978-0-8010-3611-8(9)) Baker Academic.
Drane, John William. Cultural Change & Biblical Faith. 192p. pap. 14.99 (978-0-85364-979-3(0), Paternoster) Authentic Media.
Draper, Brian. Searching 4 Faith. 2007. (Questions of Faith Ser.). (Illus.). 126p. pap. 9.97 (978-1-59856-304-7(1)); 156p. pap. 14.95 (978-1-59856-137-1(5)) Hendrickson Pubs. Marketing, LLC.
Drayton, Evelyn. Sweet Success after Bitter Defeat. 2007. 132p. per. 13.99 (978-1-60266-763-1(2)) Xulon Pr., Inc.
Drescher, John M. Doing What Comes Spiritually. 2008. (ENG.). 326p. pap. (978-1-60126-106-9(3)) Masthof Pr.
—Doing What Comes Spiritually. 2007. 326p. pap. 36.00 (978-1-55635-644-5(7)) Wipf & Stock Pubs.
Dresser, Horatio W. Living by the Spirit. 2007. (ENG.). 110p. 34.95 (978-0-548-08715-0(8)) Kessinger Publishing, LLC.
Drew, Betty. Grandmama's Recipes for Triumphant Living. 2010. 234p. pap. 16.99 (978-1-58169-350-8(8), Axiom Pr.) Genesis Communications, Inc.
Drew, Cherie J. The Widow's Might. 2008. 104p. pap. 9.99 (978-1-60647-397-9(2)) Xulon Pr., Inc.
Driscoll, Jeffrey. How We Are Healed. 2007. 184p. per. 13.99 (978-1-60266-659-7(8)) Xulon Pr., Inc.
Driscoll, Jeremy. A Monk's Alphabet: Moments of Stillness in a Turning World. 2007. (ENG.). 224p. per. 14.00 (978-1-59030-462-4(4), New Seeds Bks.) Shambhala Pubns., Inc.
Driver, Cynthia. Turning Hearts Back to God. 2010. 108p. 21.50 (978-1-4490-9722-6(7)); pap. 15.00 (978-1-4490-9723-3(5)) AuthorHouse.
Dropping in to Say. 3.50 (978-0-687-06114-3(8)) Abingdon Pr.
Druary, Dick. Why We Are Here: Sketches of grace from the Star of Hope. 2011. 66p. pap. 15.99 (978-1-4628-6024-1(9)) Xlibris Corp.
Drummond, Henry. Addresses. 2011. 340p. pap. 31.75 (978-1-175-38886-5(6)) 2011. 298p. pap. 28.75 (978-1-176-04055-7(3)) 2010. 282p. pap. 28.75 (978-1-172-27501-4(7)) 2010. (ENG.). 410p. pap. 34.75 (978-1-176-16561-8(5)) 2010. (ENG.). 370p. pap. 32.75 (978-1-176-16570-0(4)) 2010. 394p. pap. 33.75 (978-1-149-12522-9(5)) 2010. 412p. pap. 34.75 (978-1-144-36645-0(3)) 2010. 344p. pap. 32.75 (978-1-144-61842-9(8)) 2010. 356p. pap. 32.75 (978-1-145-10020-6(1)) 2009. (ENG.). 289p. pap. 21.99 (978-1-115-21222-9(2), BiblioLife) 2009. (ENG.). 289p. pap. 23.99 (978-1-115-21224-3(9), BiblioLife) BiblioBazaar.
—Addresses. 2010. (Illus.). 60p. pap. 20.00 (978-1-153-58225-4(2)) General Bks. LLC.
—Addresses. 2010. 384p. 39.16 (978-1-163-31521-7(4)); pap. 27.16 (978-1-162-57451-6(8)) Kessinger Publishing, LLC.
—Addresses (Includes Love. 2008. 112p. pap. 7.99 (978-1-60450-172-8(3)) Arc Manor.
—The Changed Life. 2011. 40p. pap. 7.99 (978-1-61203-221-4(4)) Bottom of the Hill Publishing.
—The Changed Life. 2008. 64p. pap. (978-1-4097-9559-9(4)) Read Bks.
—The Changed Life. 2008. 48p. per. 7.99 (978-1-60459-177-4(3)) Wilder Pubns., Ltd.
—The City Without a Church. 2008. 48p. per. 7.99 (978-1-60459-176-7(5)) Wilder Pubns., Ltd.
—Henry Drummond Collection. 2011. 148p. (gr. -1-2). pap. 14.99 (978-1-61203-227-6(3)) Bottom of the Hill Publishing.
—The Henry Drummond Reader. 2008. 508p. 29.99 (978-1-60459-185-9(4)); per. 19.99 (978-1-60459-186-6(2)) Wilder Pubns., Ltd.
—A Life for A Life & Other Addresses. 2008. 48p. per. 7.99 (978-1-60459-178-1(1)) Wilder Pubns., Ltd.
—A Life for a Life & Other Addresses. 2011. 40p. pap. 7.99 (978-1-61203-223-8(0)) Bottom of the Hill Publishing.
—Pax Vobiscum. 2008. 63p. pap. 9.95 (978-0-557-02272-4(X)) Lulu Enterprises Inc.
Drummond, Henry. Stones Rolled Away & Other Addresses. 2011. 102p. pap. 9.99 (978-1-61203-311-2(3)) Bottom of the Hill Publishing.
—Stones Rolled Away & Other Addresses. 2008. 52p. per. 8.99 (978-1-60459-134-2(6)) Wilder Pubns., Ltd.
Drummond, Henry & Dawson, W. J. Addresses. 2011. 152p. pap. 21.75 (978-1-175-55535-3(9)) BiblioBazaar.
Drysdale, Dainty A. 31 Days of Devotionals. 2009. 36p. pap. 16.99 (978-1-4389-5443-1(3)) AuthorHouse.
du Toit, Johan. Secrets of Financial Blessing: 52 Week Devotional on the Blessing of Giving. 2010. (ENG.). 112p. 12.99 (978-1-61638-163-9(9), Creation Hse.) Charisma Media.
Dudley, Crystal. The Divine Flow of Revelation. 2007. 76p. per. 16.95 (978-1-4241-8801-7(6)) PublishAmerica, Inc.
Dudley, Tasha. Lord Open Our Eyes: Daily Devotional. 2008. pap. (978-1-59781-539-5(6)) Xulon Pr., Inc.
Dudu, Emmanuel. An Enemy Worst Than the Devil. 2011. 86p. pap. 15.99 (978-1-4628-6259-7(4)) Xlibris Corp.
Duggan, Ken. Lessons Learned in Obscurity. 2008. 84p. pap. 10.99 (978-1-60477-717-8(6)) Xulon Pr., Inc.
Duggan, Theresa. Inspiration for Your Soul. 2006. pap. 7.00 (978-1-888081-70-1(8)) Good News Fellowship Ministries.
Duggar, Jim Bob & Duggar, Michelle. The Duggars: 20 & Counting! - Raising One of America's Largest Families - How They Do It. 2008. (ENG., Illus.). 240p. pap. 17.99 (978-1-4165-8563-3(X), Howard Bks.) Howard Books.
Duggar, Michelle & Duggar, Jim Bob. A Love That Multiplies: An Up-Close View of How They Make It Work. 2011. (ENG., Illus.). 288p. 19.99 (978-1-4391-8381-6(3), Howard Bks.) Howard Books.
Duggins, Dana. Marriage, God's Way. 2007. 112p. per. 19.95 (978-1-4241-8743-0(5)) PublishAmerica, Inc.
Duhart, Carol. Acceptable to God. 2007. 228p. per. 14.99 (978-1-60477-203-6(4)) Xulon Pr., Inc.
Duke, Jerry R. The Generation of Crisis. 2009. 308p. 28.99 (978-1-60791-480-8(8)); pap. 18.99 (978-1-60791-479-2(4)) Xulon Pr., Inc.
Duke, Wendy. The Grace by Which We Stand. 2008. 132p. pap. 19.99 (978-1-4363-7178-0(3)) Xlibris Corp.
Dukhia, Monita. Out of the Miry Clay. 2007. 488p. 35.99 (978-1-60477-248-7(4)) Xulon Pr., Inc.
Duncan, Emanuel Vivian. When Destiny Calls. 2007. 200p. per. 14.99 (978-1-60477-181-7(X)) Xulon Pr., Inc.
Duncan, Ligon. Fear Not! Death & the Afterlife from a Christian Perspective. 2008. (ENG.). pap. 10.99 (978-1-84550-358-1(9)) Christian Focus Pubns. GBR. Dist: STL Distribution North America.
Duncan, Malcolm. Kingdom Come: The Local Church as a Catalyst for Social Change, 1 vol. 2008. 352p. pap. 14.99 (978-0-8254-6151-4(0), Monarch Bks.) Lion Hudson PLC GBR. Dist: Kregel Pubns.
Duncan, Malcolm & Duncan. Building a Better World: Faith at Work for Change in Society. 2006. (ENG.). 184p. 19.95 (978-0-8264-9152-7(9)) Continuum International Publishing Group, Ltd. GBR. Dist: National Bk. Network.
Duncan Raynor Staff. Who Is Right about God? 2008. (ENG.). 144p. pap. 24.95 (978-1-84694-103-0(2)) Hunt, John Publishing Ltd. GBR. Dist: National Bk. Network.
Duncan, William Garrel. Around the Master's Table: Seed Thoughts for Today's Christian Designed to Help You in Your Study & Walk with the Lord. 2008. 90p. pap. 16.95 (978-1-60474-542-9(8)) PublishAmerica, Inc.
Duncan-Williams. Destined to Make an Impact. 2008. pap. (978-1-60034-410-7(0)) Xulon Pr., Inc.
Dungy, Tony. Dare to Be Uncommon Leader Pack, 3 vols. 2009. 24.99 (978-0-7644-3918-6(9)) Group Publishing, Inc.
—Dare to Be Uncommon Men's Bible Study: Discovering How to Impact Your World. 2009. 96p. pap. 9.99 (978-0-7644-3920-9(0)) Group Publishing, Inc.
—Quiet Strength: The Principles, Practices, & Priorities of a Winning Life. (ENG., Illus.). 2008. 352p. pap. 14.99 (978-1-4143-1802-8(2)) 2007. 336p. 26.99 (978-1-4143-1801-1(4)) Tyndale Hse. Pubs.
—Quiet Strength: Men's Bible Study: Discovering God's Game Plan for a Winning Life. 2007. (Illus.). 80p. per. 9.99 (978-0-7644-3662-8(7)) Group Publishing, Inc.
Dunk, Krista. Step Out & Take Your Place: How to Discover & Live Your Everyday Calling. 2011. 220p. 33.95 (978-1-4497-1565-6(6)); pap. 17.95 (978-1-4497-0639-5(8)) Author Solutions, Inc. (WestBow Pr.).
Dunlap, John. Out of the Mouth of the Lion. 2006. pap. 16.99 (978-1-60034-591-3(3)) Xulon Pr., Inc.
Dunlap, Ozell Strong. A Journey Worth Taking. 2006. 96p. per. 8.99 (978-1-59886-682-7(6)) Tate Publishing & Enterprises, LLC.
Dunlap-Slaughter, Kimley. Enter into His Presence with Exceeding Joy: Move Past Your Trials with Immeasurable Peace. 2008. (ENG.). 400p. pap. 16.99 (978-1-59979-480-8(2), Creation Hse.) Charisma Media.
Dunlop, L. C. Cornbread Christianity. 2008. 302p. pap. 16.95 (978-0-7414-4492-9(5)) Infinity Publishing.
Dunn, Jim. Starting a Relationship with God. 2007. (D Ser.). (Illus.). 64p. per. 7.99 (978-0-89827-359-5(5)) Wesleyan Publishing Hse.
Dunn, Ronald. When Heaven Is Silent: Trusting God When Life Hurts. 2008. (ENG.). 237p. pap. 12.99 (978-0-87508-982-9(8)) CLC Pubns.
Dunn, Todd. Lost? 2007. 208p. per. 14.99 (978-1-60477-014-8(7)) Xulon Pr., Inc.
Dunnam. Irresistible Invitation Program Kit: Cultivating Joyful Giving in Your Church. 2008. 78.00 (978-0-687-64779-8(7)) Abingdon Pr.
Dunnam, Maxie. Irresistible Invitation Participant's Workbook: Responding to the Extravagant Heart of God. 2008. 56p. pap. 4.50 (978-0-687-64869-6(6)) Abingdon Pr.
Dunnam, Maxie D. Irresistible Invitation: Responding to the Extravagant Heart of God. 2008. 310p. pap. 18.00 (978-0-687-64879-5(3)) Abingdon Pr.
Duplantis, Jesse. The Everyday Visionary: Focus Your Thoughts, Change Your Life. 2008. (ENG.). 240p. 24.00 (978-1-4165-4976-5(5), Touchstone) Touchstone.
DuPraw, E. J. Joy, Joy: Jesus Christ! - His Life Before & after Death. 2009. 312p. pap. 22.99 (978-1-60462-954-5(1)) Tate Publishing & Enterprises, LLC.
Dupree, Debra La Chelle. God's Fragrance: The Fragrance of Life. 2009. 156p. 22.99 (978-1-60791-974-2(5)); pap. 14.99 (978-1-60791-973-5(7)) Xulon Pr., Inc.
Duque, Hernando. Desarrollo Integral del Nino: 0-3 Anos. (SPA.). 64p. 3.95 (978-958-607-417-9(X)) Sociedad de San Pablo COL. Dist: St Pauls/Alba Hse. Pubs.
—Desarrollo Integral del Nino 3-6 Anos. (SPA.). 104p. 4.95 (978-958-607-496-4(X)) Sociedad de San Pablo COL. Dist: St Pauls/Alba Hse. Pubs.
Duque, Hernando & Bedoya, William. Cicatrices de la Vida Familiar, 2 vols. (SPA.). Set. 112p. 5.95 (978-958-607-755-2(1)) Vol. 2. 128p. 6.95 (978-958-607-810-8(8)) Sociedad de San Pablo COL. Dist: St Pauls/Alba Hse. Pubs.
Duquin, Lorene Hanley. Catholic Parent Know How: Why Do We Have to Go to Mass. 2007. (Illus.). 8p. per. 11.95 (978-1-59276-401-3(0)) Our Sunday Visitor, Publishing Div.
—Why Do We Have to Go to Mass? 2007. (Catholic Parent Know-How Ser.). (Illus.). 7p. pap. 1.95 (978-1-59276-324-5(3)) Our Sunday Visitor, Publishing Div.
Duren, Marty & Wright, Todd. Journeys: Transitioning Churches to Relevance. 2008. 192p. per. 14.99 (978-0-9798053-1-8(7)) Missional Pr.
Durham, Stella. Lord Help MeIÂ I Still Love Him. 2008. 81p. pap. 16.95 (978-1-60672-108-7(9)) PublishAmerica, Inc.
Duriez, Colin. Ad 33: The Year That Changed the World. 2007. (ENG., Illus.). 256p. 22.00 (978-0-8308-3396-2(X), IVP Bks.) InterVarsity Pr.
Durr, James A. Process & Development. 2008. 256p. 25.99 (978-1-60647-233-0(X)); pap. 15.99 (978-1-60647-232-3(1)) Xulon Pr., Inc.
Dusek, Robert. Facing the Music. 2008. 220p. 24.99 (978-1-60647-270-5(4)); pap. 14.99 (978-1-60647-269-9(0)) Xulon Pr., Inc.
Dutcher, Greg & Discovery House Publishers Staff. Power Up! - Links: Devotional Thoughts for Golfers. Branon, Dave, ed. 2009. (ENG.). 224p. 11.99 (978-1-57293-320-0(8)) Discovery Hse. Pubs.
Dutko, Robert. Truth. 2011. 120p. 29.99 (978-1-4568-4061-7(4)); pap. 19.99 (978-1-4568-4060-0(6)) Xlibris Corp.
Dutton, Anne. A Heart Renewed. 2008. 80p. pap. 11.99 (978-1-60647-303-0(4)) Xulon Pr., Inc.
Dwayne & Thelma. If You Cannot Believe God's Word, Then Believe His Works. 2011. 54p. pap. 16.95 (978-1-4560-4218-9(1)) PublishAmerica, Inc.
Dwyer, Dennis E. God, Country & Tattoos. 2011. 268p. pap. 16.99 (978-1-61215-798-6(X)) Xulon Pr., Inc.
Dyal, Darell B. For Such A Time as This ... We Must Walk in the Power of the Holy Spirit. 2011. 144p. 24.95 (978-1-4620-5142-7(1)); pap. 14.95 (978-1-4620-5141-0(3)) iUniverse, Inc.
Dyer, Dena. Let the Crow's Feet & Laugh Lines Come. 2010. (Turning Points Ser.). (ENG.). 224p. pap. 7.99 (978-1-60260-451-3(7), Barbour Bks.) Barbour Publishing, Inc.
Dyer, Rose. Words from Heaven. 2008. (Illus.). 211p. per. 17.99 (978-0-9779445-9-0(X)) Zoe Life Publishing.
The Dying Love Anthem. 1.50 (978-0-687-07793-9(1)) Abingdon Pr.
Dymally, Billye. Don't Be Afraid of the Holy Spirit. 2006. 158p. pap. 12.95 (978-0-7414-3385-5(0)) Infinity Publishing.
—Fourfold Prayer. 2006. 184p. pap. 13.95 (978-0-7414-3383-1(4)) Infinity Publishing.
E-Bennie. God Is Love! I Don't Think So! 2008. 32p. pap. 8.00 (978-0-8059-7376-1(1)) Dorrance Publishing Co., Inc.
E. Dale Davis. Does God Care about You & Me? 2009. 192p. 24.99 (978-1-4389-6922-0(8)); pap. 14.49 (978-1-4389-6920-6(1)) AuthorHouse.
Eagle, White. White Eagle On... the Great Spirit. 128p. pap. 13.50 (978-0-85487-150-6(0)) White Eagle Publishing Trust GBR. Dist: DeVorss & Co.
Eames, S. Morris. Essays in the Religious Life. 2006. 128p. per. 13.95 (978-0-595-40502-2(9)) iUniverse, Inc.
Earley, Dave. 21 Reasons Bad Things Happen to Good People. 2007. (Barbour Value Fiction Ser.). (ENG.). 176p. per. 9.97 (978-1-59789-661-0(6), Barbour Bks.) Barbour Publishing, Inc.
—21 Reasons Bad Things Happen to Good People. 2008. (21 Most Ser.). (ENG.). 176p. pap. 4.99 (978-1-60260-219-9(0), Barbour Bks.) Barbour Publishing, Inc.
Easley, Kendell H. 52 Words Every Christian Should Know. 2006. (ENG., Illus.). 124p. per. 4.99 (978-0-8054-4058-4(5), Holman Reference) B&H Publishing Group.
Easley, Terri. Seasons of Destiny: A Series of Personal Collected Works to Reflect on, While Seizing Your Destiny. 2008. (Illus.). 136p. pap. 13.99 (978-1-60647-152-4(X)) Xulon Pr., Inc.
East, Sun Hui. First Love. 2006. 200p. per. 16.99 (978-1-934388-08-2(4)) First Love Pr., Inc.
—Savory Food. 2006. 200p. per. 16.99 (978-1-934388-09-9(2)) First Love Pr., Inc.
—When I Hold His Hand. 2011. pap. 16.99 (978-1-61663-591-6(6)) Tate Publishing & Enterprises, LLC.
Easter, Esther. Inside the Core. 2009. 151p. pap. 14.99 (978-0-557-16154-6(1)) Lulu Enterprises Inc.
Eastman, Glenn. God's Most Wanted. 2009. 192p. pap. 12.98 (978-0-557-10849-7(7)) Lulu Enterprises Inc.
Eastman, Hubbard. Noyesism Unveiled. 2009. 212p. pap. (978-0-217-52007-2(3)) Books LLC.
Easton, Danielle. Infidelity - A Journey to Forgiveness. 2009. 112p. 19.99 (978-1-60791-516-4(2)); pap. 11.99 (978-1-60791-515-7(4)) Xulon Pr., Inc.
Easton, Shawn. Divine Connections: The Key to Unlocking Your Purpose in the Kingdom. 2008. 312p. 28.99 (978-1-60647-183-8(X)); pap. 18.99 (978-1-60647-182-1(1)) Xulon Pr., Inc.
Eccleston, Theodore. A Treatise Concerning the Life of God in the Soul of Man. 2007. (ENG.). 164p. 36.95 (978-0-548-15696-4(4)); pap. 21.95 (978-1-4304-5174-7(2)) Kessinger Publishing, LLC.
Echevarria, Michelle. Only Believe: Increasing Faith by the Word of God. 2008. 112p. 22.95 (978-0-595-50167-0(2)); pap. 12.95 (978-0-595-50371-1(3)) iUniverse, Inc.
Echols, Ronald. They Still Reject Jesus. 2009. 188p. 22.99 (978-1-60791-182-1(5)); pap. 14.99 (978-1-60791-112-8(4)) Xulon Pr., Inc.
Eckhardt, John J. The Prophetic Flow. 57p. (Orig.). reprint ed. 5.00 (978-0-9630567-5-7(1)) Crusaders Ministries.
Ecuyer, Michael. Enlarge the Place of Your Tent. 2006. pap. 13.99 (978-1-60034-508-1(5)) Xulon Pr., Inc.
Ed. Pub. Concepts Staff, prod. What Did Jesus Say? Bible Verses on Issues You Deal With. 2010. (ENG.). 192p. (J). pap. 9.99 (978-1-4143-3180-5(0)) Tyndale Hse. Pubs.
Eddy, Damon. Walks with Mr Smith. 2011. 98p. pap. 12.95 (978-0-557-53881-2(5)) Lulu Enterprises Inc.
Ederer, Dorothy K. The Golfer's Prayer Book: Walking the Fairway with the Master. 2010. 96p. 12.00 (978-1-58768-059-5(9), HiddenSpring) Paulist Pr.
Edior, Martin. His Spoken Words. 2011. 50p. pap. 15.99 (978-1-4653-4432-8(2)) Xlibris Corp.
Edmondson, Jeff. Gutsy Faith: Hard Conversations with God. 2006. 189p. per. 14.99 (978-0-8341-2262-8(6), 083-412-2626) Nazarene Publishing Hse.
Edmondson, Jeff & Ross, Michael. The Grind: Living a 'God-Life' in the Real World. 2008. (ENG., Illus.). 128p. pap. 11.99 (978-0-8341-5023-2(9), 9780834150232) Beacon Hill Pr. of Kansas City.
Edson, Aline. Our Whirling World: To Be in It but Not of It:A Pilgrim Writes of Passage. 2008. 192p. pap. 24.95 (978-1-60610-381-4(4)) PublishAmerica, Inc.
Edwards. Jesus Viene Otra Vez.Tr. of Jesus Is Coming. (SPA.). pap. 0.45 (978-0-7899-0077-7(7), 492301) Editorial Unilit.
Edwards, Carolyn. Answered Prayers in Alask. 2008. 60p. pap. 9.99 (978-1-60477-981-3(0)) Xulon Pr., Inc.
Edwards, Dwight. Kindling for the Fire: Meditations to Warm the Heart & Ignite the Spirit. 2012. (ENG.). 160p. 19.95 (978-1-936474-08-0(5)) Bright Sky Pr.
Edwards, Gene. How Paul Trained Men. 2007. per. 7.95 (978-0-9778033-6-1(8)) Seedsowers, The.
Edwards, Gilbert H. The Tabernacle, the Priesthood & Their Functions. 2010. 128p. 23.49 (978-1-4520-7071-1(7)); pap. 16.49 (978-1-4520-7072-8(5)) AuthorHouse.
Edwards, Jimmy. The Father's Call: God's Invitation to Spiritual Intimacy. 2010. 140p. pap. 22.95 (978-1-4490-8427-1(3)); (ENG.). 64p. pap. 15.95 (978-1-4520-0836-3(1)) AuthorHouse.
Edwards, John. Discerning of Spirits. (What Christians Should Know about Ser.). 56p. pap. (978-1-85240-277-8(6)) Sovereign World, Ltd.
Edwards, Kyle. From Pieces to Peace. 2007. 64p. per. 9.99 (978-1-60477-219-7(0)) Xulon Pr., Inc.
Edwards, Maria. Como Prepararte para Tu Propia Muerte. 2007. (SPA.). 144p. per. 16.99 (978-1-4251-0744-4(3)) Trafford Publishing.
Edwards, Marty & Edwards, Debbie. The Saddlebag Gospels. 2011. 128p. pap. 11.99 (978-1-4567-5235-4(9)) AuthorHouse.
Edwards, Marty, et al. The Saddlebag Gospels. 2011. 128p. 23.99 (978-1-4567-5234-7(0)) AuthorHouse.
Edwards, Matt. Behold the Faithfulness of God. 2008. 192p. pap. (978-1-55452-324-5(9)); pap. (978-1-55452-323-8(0), Guardian Bks.) Essence Publishing.
Edwards, Melva Hammon. Covenant Love. 2010. 300p. 25.99 (978-1-4520-5080-5(5)); pap. 15.99 (978-1-4520-5079-9(1)) AuthorHouse.
Edwards, Randy. Discerning the Voice of God. 2010. 17.95 (978-1-935529-64-4(1)) Intermedia Publishing Group.
Edwards, Sandra D. Even Christians Make Mistakes: A Mask. 2007. 60p. per. 16.95 (978-1-4241-7255-9(1)) PublishAmerica, Inc.

C

Edwards, Shirley. Don't Praise Me, Praise God. 2008. 90p. pap. 16.95 *(978-1-60563-181-3(7))* PublishAmerica, Inc.
Edwards, Syl. In Your Face Devil Takin' Back My Stuff. 2008. 220p. pap. 15.99 *(978-1-60647-686-4(6))* Xulon Pr., Inc.
Eggleston, Terry. The Corinthian Syndrome. 2007. 84p. per. 9.99 *(978-1-60266-580-4(X))* Xulon Pr., Inc.
Egli, Jim. Upward, Inward, Outward, Forward: Improving the 4 Dynamics of Your Small Group. 3rd ed. 2007. 71p. pap. 11.25 *(978-0-9788779-4-1(2))* Touch Pubns.
Egziabher, Haile Gebre. Dream for World Unity. 2009. 610p. pap. 34.95 *(978-1-4327-3554-8(3))* Outskirts Pr., Inc.
—Witnessing. 2009. 466p. pap. 29.95 *(978-1-4327-2425-2(8))* Outskirts Pr., Inc.
Eichhorn, J. Martin. Escape from the Cocoon: The true story of how a near-death experience in the wilderness of Alaska propelled the transformation of one man who Despise. 2008. 104p. pap. 12.95 *(978-1-4327-3072-7(X))* Outskirts Pr., Inc.
Eichman, Phillip. The God of All Comfort: Hope for Christians in a World of Suffering. 2010. 73p. pap. 12.95 *(978-1-4327-6549-1(3))* Outskirts Pr., Inc.
Eiximenis, Francesc. Francesc Eiximenis: An Anthology. Hughes, Robert D., tr. from SPA. 2008. (Textos B Ser.: Volume 50). 168p. pap. 29.95 *(978-1-85566-162-2(4),* Tamesis Bks.) Boydell & Brewer, Ltd. GBR. Dist: Boydell & Brewer, Inc.
Eke, Jane. Costly Discipleship. 2011. 124p. pap. ***(978-1-908596-04-8(X))*** Grosvenor Hse. Publishing Ltd.
Ekpenyong, Sandra. Biblical Dysfunctional Families That Made It & Now So Can You, No More Excuses! 2008. 268p. 26.99 *(978-1-60791-085-5(3));* pap. 16.99 *(978-1-60791-084-8(5))* Xulon Pr., Inc.
Eks, Christian. Whose God Is Their Belly: The Worship of Our Appetites, 1 vol. 2009. 96p. pap. 16.95 *(978-1-60703-257-1(0))* PublishAmerica, Inc.
Ekstrand, Becky. God's Truth for His Little Lamb Why Was Jesus Born. 2008. 28p. 13.50 *(978-1-4357-1174-7(2))* Lulu Enterprises Inc.
Ekundayo, John M. O. His Helping Hands. 2008. 160p. pap. 13.99 *(978-1-60647-264-4(X))* Xulon Pr., Inc.
Ekunwe, Ebun. Choose Victory. 2008. 144p. pap. 24.95 *(978-1-60474-138-4(4))* PublishAmerica, Inc.
Eldeiry, Subhi. Queen Esther of Ancient Persi. Eldeiry, Leslie, ed. 2009. 80p. pap. 17.00 *(978-0-9664057-5-0(7))* Eldeiry, Subhi.
Eldredge, John. Desire. l.t. rev. ed. 2008. (Walker Large Print Ser.). (ENG.). 325p. pap. 17.95 *(978-1-59415-222-1(5),* Walker Large Print) Cengage Gale.
—Desire: The Journey We Must Take to Find the Life God Offers, 0 vols. 2007. 240p. per. 15.99 *(978-0-7852-8842-8(2))* Nelson, Thomas Inc.
—Epic: The Story God Is Telling, 0 vols. 2007. 112p. 9.99 *(978-0-7852-8878-7(3));* per. 2.99 *(978-0-7852-8879-4(1))* Nelson, Thomas Inc.
—Knowing the Heart of God: 365 Daily Readings, 0 vols. 2009. 384p. 14.99 *(978-1-4002-0252-2(3))* Nelson, Thomas Inc.
—A Personal Guide to Walking with God, 0 vols. 2008. 208p. pap. 17.99 *(978-1-4185-2821-8(8))* Nelson, Thomas Inc.
—Waking the Dead: The Glory of a Heart Fully Alive, 0 vols. 2006. 256p. pap. 15.99 *(978-0-7852-8829-9(5))* Nelson, Thomas Inc.
—Walking with God: Talk to Him. Hear from Him. Really. l.t. ed. 2010. (ENG.). 320p. pap. 17.99 *(978-1-59415-333-4(7))* Cengage Gale.
—Walking with God: Talk to Him. Hear from Him. Really, 0 vols. 2010. 240p. pap. 15.99 *(978-1-4002-0290-4(6))* Nelson, Thomas Inc.
—The Way of the Wild Heart. l.t. ed. 2007. (Walker Large Print Ser.). (ENG.). 479p. per. 17.95 *(978-1-59415-189-7(X),* Walker Large Print) Cengage Gale.
—The Way of the Wild Heart. 2006. 320p. pap. 13.99 ***(978-0-7852-8868-8(6))*** Nelson, Thomas Inc.
—The Way of the Wild Heart. l.t. ed. 2007. (Thorndike Inspirational Ser.). 495p. 30.95 *(978-0-7862-9612-5(7))* Thorndike Pr.
—The Way of the Wild Heart: A Map for the Masculine Journey, 0 vols. 2006. 256p. 22.99 *(978-0-7852-0677-4(9))* Nelson, Thomas Inc.
Eldredge, John & Eldgredge, John. Fathered by God: Learning What Your Dad Could Never Teach You. l.t. ed. 2009. (ENG.). 584p. pap. 17.95 *(978-1-59415-287-0(X))* Cengage Gale.
Eldredge, John & McConnell, Craig. The Way of the Wild Heart Manual: A Personal Map for Your Masculine Journey, 0 vols. 2006. 288p. per. 17.99 *(978-1-4185-1413-6(6))* Nelson, Thomas Inc.
Elenchin, William J. Hidden Courage: Reconnecting Faith & Character with Mental Wellness. 2008. 140p. pap. 17.00 *(978-1-60608-111-2(X),* Wipf and Stock) Wipf & Stock Pubs.
Elfstrand, Mark. 10 Passions of a Man's Soul. 2006. (ENG.). 208p. per. 14.99 *(978-0-8024-0866-2(4))* Moody Pubs.
Eli, R. George. Chasing the Wind. 2007. pap. 17.99 *(978-1-60266-404-3(8))* Xulon Pr., Inc.
Ellies, Russell G. Faith That Moves Mountains & Smashes Strongholds: Understanding Mountain-Moving Faith. Krames, Jim, ed. 2007. (Neuma Nation Dissertation Ser.). 182p. pap. 21.00 *(978-1-55635-467-0(3))* Wipf & Stock Pubs.
Ellingsen, Mark. Sin Bravely: A Joyful Alternative to a Purpose-Driven Life. 2009. (ENG.). 160p. pap. 17.95 *(978-0-8264-2964-3(5))* Continuum International Publishing Group, Ltd. GBR. Dist: National Bk. Network.
Elliot, Elisabeth. God's Guidance: Finding His Will for Your Life. 2nd ed. 2006. 160p. (gr. 10). reprint ed. pap. 15.00 *(978-0-8007-3133-5(6))* Revell.
—The Mark of a Man: Following Christ's Example of Masculinity. 2007. (E Ser.). 192p. reprint ed. pap. 13.99 *(978-0-8007-3132-8(8))* Revell.
—The Path of Loneliness: Finding Your Way Through the Wilderness to God. 2007. 200p. reprint ed. pap. 13.99 *(978-0-8007-3206-6(5))* Revell.
Elliott, Iva Lee. Thanks Lord! How God Speaks. 2011. 172p. 30.95 ***(978-1-61507-786-1(3));*** pap. 13.95 ***(978-1-61507-785-4(5))*** Cross Bks. Publishing.
Elliott, Matthew. Feel: The Power of Listening to Your Heart. 2008. (ENG.). 288p. pap. 13.99 *(978-1-4143-1664-2(X))* Tyndale Hse. Pubs.
Ellis, Alex. Restoring the Male Image. 2007. 132p. (ENG.). 21.99 *(978-1-60266-374-9(2));* per. 13.99 *(978-1-60266-373-2(4))* Xulon Pr., Inc.
Ellis, Charles (Jay). The Prophet & the Maniac: The Inspired Writings of Jay Ellis. 2009. 292p. pap. 21.95 *(978-1-4327-2411-5(8))* Outskirts Pr., Inc.
Ellis, Connie C. Don't Eat the Chicken Livers. 2008. 61p. pap. 16.95 *(978-1-60672-463-7(0))* PublishAmerica, Inc.
Ellis, Jimmie A. Taking Territory - Keys to Possessing Your Promised Land. 2009. 120p. pap. 11.99 *(978-1-58930-220-4(6))* Selah Publishing Group, LLC.
Ellis, Pamela S. Honor Your Father & Mother. 2008. 244p. pap. 15.99 *(978-1-60647-760-1(9))* Xulon Pr., Inc.
Ellis, Patrice. A Woman's Guide to Excellence & Elegance. 2007. pap. 10.99 *(978-1-60034-951-5(X))* Xulon Pr., Inc.
Ellis, Sharon. Communions with Christ. 2008. 212p. pap. 15.99 *(978-1-60647-889-9(3))* Xulon Pr., Inc.
Ellison, Edna. Deeper Still: A Woman's Study to a Closer Walk with God. 2006. (ENG.). 240p. per. 14.99 *(978-1-59669-013-4(5))* New Hope Pubs.
Ellison, Edna & Gilden, Linda. Mommy Pick-Me-Ups: Refreshing Stories to Lighten Your Load. 2008. (ENG.). 176p. per. 10.99 *(978-1-59669-218-3(9))* New Hope Pubs.
Elmer & Klassen, Leonore Friesen. Kingdoms Are Destroyed When Believers Confess Jesus Christ Is Lord. 2010. 122p. pap. 11.99 *(978-1-61579-865-0(X))* Xulon Pr., Inc.
Elmer, Robert. Beetle Bunker, 1 vol., Vol. 2. 2006. (Wall Ser.). (ENG.). 160p. (J). pap. 6.99 *(978-0-310-70944-2(X))* Zonderkidz.
—Smuggler's Treasure, 1 vol., Vol. 3. 2006. (Wall Ser.). (ENG.). 160p. (J). pap. 6.99 *(978-0-310-70945-9(8))* Zonderkidz.
Elmore, Ernest. The Spirit of the Christ: If Anyone's Name Was Not Found Written in the Book of Life, He Was Thrown into the Lake of Fire. Revelation 20:15. 2009. 108p. pap. 11.99 *(978-1-61579-337-2(2))* Xulon Pr., Inc.
Elwood, Doug. Peacemaking in an Age of Terrorism. 2006. (ENG.). 264p. per. 18.99 *(978-1-4141-0743-1(9))* Pleasant Word.
Elwood, Lynne Marie. Rollingaround. 2008. 184p. pap. 14.99 *(978-1-60647-758-8(7))* Xulon Pr., Inc.
Ely, Marian. Glimpses of Wisdom from an Ordinary Christian. 2010. 214p. pap. 14.95 *(978-1-4327-5410-5(6))* Outskirts Pr., Inc.
Elzinga, John. Sailing the Seven Seas of Life. 2007. 224p. 24.99 *(978-1-59858-482-0(0));* per. 14.99 *(978-1-59858-444-8(8))* Dog Ear Publishing, LLC.
Emerzian, Matthew & Bozza, Kelly. Every Monday Matters: 52 Ways to Make a Difference, 0 vols. 2008. (Illus.). 144p. pap. 15.99 *(978-1-4041-0512-6(3))* Nelson, Thomas Inc.
Emlet, Michael R. Angry Children: Understanding & Helping Your Child Regain Control. 2008. (ENG.). 24p. 3.99 *(978-1-934885-26-0(6))* New Growth Pr.
—Chronic Pain: Living by Faith When Your Body Hurts. 2010. 24p. 3.99 *(978-1-935273-64-6(7))* New Growth Pr.
—Help for the Caregiver: Facing the Challenges with Understanding & Strength. 2008. (ENG.). 24p. 3.99 *(978-1-934885-50-5(9))* New Growth Pr.
Emlet, Michael/Ray. CrossTalk: Where Life & Scripture Meet. 2009. 212p. pap. 15.99 *(978-1-935273-12-7(4))* New Growth Pr.
Empson, Lila. 100 Answers to 100 Questions about God's Promises for You. 2008. (100 Answers to 100 Questions Ser.). (ENG.). 224p. pap. 10.99 *(978-1-59979-273-6(7))* Charisma Media.
—100 Answers to 100 Questions Every Graduate Should Know. 2009. (ENG.). 224p. pap. 10.99 *(978-1-59979-479-2(9))* Charisma Media.
Encouraged: Everyone Needs Christ over Unbelief, Remember All God Endured to Discover. 2006. per. 11.95 *(978-0-9787915-0-6(9))* Catch The Revelation Publishing Group.
Enderby, P. Everyday Light. 2008. 200p. pap. 12.99 *(978-0-9800033-0-7(X))* 90 Minute Bks.
Enderle, Ron C. Time under the Cross: Surrendering to the Will of God, 1 vol. 2010. 134p. pap. 24.95 *(978-1-4489-4848-2(7))* PublishAmerica, Inc.
Enejoh, Jerry. Invoking God's Intervention in Challenging Moments. 2007. 176p. per. 13.99 *(978-1-60266-271-1(1))* Xulon Pr., Inc.
Enevoldsen, Don. Simple Prayer. 2008. 136p. pap. 13.99 *(978-1-60647-502-7(9))* Xulon Pr., Inc.
Engelberth, Otto. Is There a Creator? Why It Matters What You Believe! 2011. 78p. pap. 12.95 ***(978-1-60910-759-8(4))*** Booklocker.com, Inc.
Engelken, Ruth. Matagatos: Catkiller. (SPA.). 208p. *(978-84-7228-155-4(8),* 220578) Clie, Editorial.
England, Don. God, Are You Really There? pap., tchr. ed. 7.99 *(978-0-89098-106-1(X))* Twentieth Century Christian Bks.
England, Eric. The Best Investment Money Can't Buy: This Book Will Change Your Life. 2010. 128p. pap. 14.99 *(978-1-61579-695-3(9))* Xulon Pr., Inc.
England, Shari. Lessons from the Sticker Patch: Recognizing God's Immeasurable Love in Everyday Life. 2010. pap. 14.99 *(978-1-61566-727-7(X))* Tate Publishing & Enterprises, LLC.
Engle, Joel. The Exchange: Tired of Living the Christian Life on Your Own? 2007. (Illus.). 128p. pap. 7.95 *(978-1-4158-5270-5(7))* LifeWay Christian Resources.
Englehart, Charles E. God Good & Evil. 2010. 218p. pap. 15.99 *(978-1-60957-523-6(7))* Xulon Pr., Inc.
Ennis, Patricia A. & Tatlock, Lisa. Practicing Hospitality: The Joy of Serving Others. 2008. 256p. pap. 15.99 *(978-1-58134-942-9(4))* Crossway.
Ennis, Ralph. Life: Thriving in a Complex World. 2008. (Illus.). 191p. pap. *(978-1-60006-260-5(1))* NavPress Publishing Group.
Enochs, Tim. Every Day Is Game Day! 2007. 256p. per. 15.99 *(978-1-60266-677-1(6))* Xulon Pr., Inc.
Enoma, Belinda. The Bilhah Moment: How to Wait on God in Desperate Times. 2009. (ENG.). 192p. 14.99 *(978-0-9822855-0-3(7))* Dunamis Pr.
Enongene, Prosper. The Christian Investor. 2011. 94p. pap. 10.99 ***(978-1-61379-256-8(5))*** Xulon Pr., Inc.
Enzler, Clarence J. Let Us Be What We Are: The Joys & Challenges of Living the Little Way. 2012. 192p. pap. 12.95 ***(978-0-87061-256-5(5),*** Christian Classic) Ave Maria Pr.
Epperly, Bruce Gordon. Holy Adventure: 41 Days of Audacious Living. 2008. 208p. pap. 17.00 *(978-0-8358-9970-3(5))* Upper Room Bks.
Epps, Virdie. Seeing by Faith: Moved by Compassion. 2007. pap. 9.99 *(978-1-60266-585-9(0))* Xulon Pr., Inc.
Erasmus, Desiderius. Handbook of the Militant Christian. Dolan, John P., tr. 2011. 158p. 41.95 ***(978-1-258-07800-3(7))*** Literary Licensing, LLC.
Erasmus, Desiderius. The Pilgrimage of Pure Devotion. 2007. 48p. per. *(978-1-4065-3352-1(1))* Dodo Pr.
Erickson, Dan. Finding Your Greater Yes: Living a Life That Echoes in Eternity, 0 vols. 2009. 240p. pap. 13.99 *(978-0-7852-9778-9(2))* Nelson, Thomas Inc.
—Finding Your Greater Yes! Study Guide. 2006. pap. 9.99 net. *(978-0-9787620-2-5(9))* Credo Hse. Pubs.
Eristhee, Thomas. Now You Are Saved. 2007. 48p. per. *(978-1-55452-158-6(0))* Essence Publishing.
Erlandson, Brad. Walking This Walk. 2007. 204p. per. 14.99 *(978-1-60266-065-6(4))* Xulon Pr., Inc.
Erlandson, Brad W. Faith for Modern Times. 2009. 212p. pap. 14.99 *(978-1-4389-4916-1(2))* AuthorHouse.
Ernest, Carolyn. Revelation Unlocked: Part I. 2009. 138p. pap. 11.99 *(978-1-60696-505-4(0))* Tate Publishing & Enterprises, LLC.
Erre, Mike. The Jesus of Suburbia: Have We Tamed the Son of God to Fit Our Lifestyle?, 0 vols. annot. ed. 2006. 224p. per. 13.99 *(978-0-8499-0059-4(X))* Nelson, Thomas Inc.
Erwin, Gayle D. Not Many Mighty. 2007. (ENG.). 208p. per. 12.95 *(978-1-56599-256-6(3))* Yahshua Publishing.
Esan, Ade. A New Birth: The Key to All of God's Provisions. 2011. 120p. 21.23 ***(978-1-4567-6103-5(X));*** pap. 11.99 ***(978-1-4567-6104-2(8))*** AuthorHouse.
Esau, Terry. Be the Surprise: Experiments in Spontaneous Faith. 2007. (ENG., Illus.). 176p. per. 12.99 *(978-1-60006-196-7(6))* NavPress Publishing Group.
Escobar, Mark A. Thoms & Thistles: Pathways to Discipleship. 2010. 298p. pap. 19.95 *(978-1-4327-5329-0(0))* Outskirts Pr., Inc.
Escobar, Mark Alba. On Bits & Pieces: Along with Crooked Lines. 2007. 284p. per. 16.95 *(978-1-4327-0487-2(7))* Outskirts Pr., Inc.
Espindola, Silvano & Espindola, Patricia. Stop: Solo para Atrevidos: Sentimientos, Noviazgo y Sexo, 1 vol. 2007. (SPA.). 192p. (gr. 13). per. 9.99 *(978-0-8297-5447-6(4))* Zondervan.
Espinosa, Emmanuel. Ensename a Vivir, 0 vols. 2007. (SPA.). 160p. 9.99 *(978-1-60255-000-1(X))* Grupo Nelson.
Espinoza, Erica. Arise & Shine. 2010. 260p. pap. 16.99 *(978-1-60957-832-9(5))* Xulon Pr., Inc.
Essany, Michael. The Devil Can't Cook Spaghetti: Using Faith to Overcome Fear. 2009. 112p. pap. 14.00 *(978-1-58768-049-6(1),* HiddenSpring) Paulist Pr.
Essence Publishing & Gilden, Linda, compiled by. When God Steps In. 2006. pap. *(978-1-55452-005-3(3))* Essence Publishing.
Essex, Lorene. Thine Will Be Done. 64p. pap. 8.95 *(978-1-892861-25-2(9))* Vision Publishing Group.
Essien, Bassey B. How to Let Christ Be Formed In You. 2011. 202p. 29.99 ***(978-1-4628-5707-4(8));*** pap. 19.99 ***(978-1-4628-5706-7(X))*** Xlibris Corp.
Esterline, Dan, Sr. A Weekly Discipleship Journal: 52 Commands of Christ. 2009. 144p. pap. 13.99 *(978-1-57921-555-2(6))* Pleasant Word.
Esterman, Vince. Miracle Conversions. 128p. pap. *(978-1-85240-323-2(3))* Sovereign World, Ltd.
Estes, Marc. What Now: Making Sense of Who You Are & Where You're Going. 2006. (Illus.). 219p. 19.99 *(978-0-9776167-5-6(4))* Relevant Media Group, Inc.
—What Now - Discovery Guide. 2006. 104p. 9.99 *(978-1-59383-026-7(2))* City Christian Publishing.
—What Now? Life by Design: Your roadmap to an authentic, meaningful & visionary Life. 2008. 240p. 21.99 *(978-1-59979-381-8(4))* Charisma Media.
Etbs: Youth Student. 1.55 *(978-0-7673-5184-3(3))* LifeWay Christian Resources.
ETE, King Solomon David Jesse. I love you - I love you Too. 2008. 271p. pap. 38.95 *(978-0-9559801-3-8(5))* King Solomon Spiritual Library GBR. Dist: Lulu Enterprises Inc.
The Eternal Word of God. 0.75 *(978-0-89265-524-3(0))* Randall Hse. Pubns.
Ethridge, Shannon. Completely Forgiven: Responding to God's Transforming Grace. 2007. (Loving Jesus Without Limits Ser.). (ENG.). 144p. per. 9.99 *(978-1-4000-7112-8(7),* WaterBrook Pr.) Doubleday Religious Publishing Group, The.
—Completely His: Loving Jesus Without Limits. 2007. (Loving Jesus Without Limits Ser.). (ENG.). 208p. 15.99 *(978-1-4000-7110-4(0),* WaterBrook Pr.) Doubleday Religious Publishing Group, The.
—Completely Loved: Recognizing God's Passionate Pursuit of Us. 2007. (Loving Jesus Without Limits Ser.). (ENG.). 144p. per. 9.99 *(978-1-4000-7111-1(9),* WaterBrook Pr.) Doubleday Religious Publishing Group, The.
Etterling II, Paul. Genuine Faith & the Test of Love. 2006. pap. 9.99 *(978-1-60034-883-9(1))* Xulon Pr., Inc.
Etzkorn, Girard J. Reflections of a Christian Pilgrim. 2007. 192p. per. 11.99 *(978-1-4259-8497-7(5))* AuthorHouse.
Evans, Charlotte E. In the Arms of God: The Life of Charlotte Evans. 2010. pap. 9.99 *(978-1-61566-251-7(0))* Tate Publishing & Enterprises, LLC.
Evans, David. Dare to Be a Man: The Truth Every Man Must Know... & Every Woman Needs to Know about Him. 2010. (ENG.). 336p. (gr. 12). 15.00 *(978-0-425-23645-1(5),* Berkley Trade) Penguin Group (USA) Inc.
Evans, David & Fearon, Mike. From Strangers to Neighbours: How You Can Make the Difference in Your Community. (Illus.). 230p. pap. *(978-0-340-69455-8(6),* Hodder & Stoughton) Hodder General Publishing Div.
Evans, James. Compassionate Confrontation. 2007. 184p. per. 13.99 *(978-1-60266-701-3(2))* Xulon Pr., Inc.
Evans, Jennifer. What the Locusts Had Eaten. 2007. 284p. per. 15.99 *(978-1-60266-530-9(3))* Xulon Pr., Inc.
Evans, Jerry & Evans, Becky. Quiet Time: A Guide to an Effective Time Alone with God. 2010. 96p. pap. 9.95 *(978-1-4497-0389-9(5),* WestBow Pr.) Author Solutions, Inc.
Evans, Jimmy & Billington, Ann. Freedom from Your Past. 2009. (Illus.). 288p. pap. 14.95 *(978-1-931585-05-7(9))* Majestic Media.
Evans, Jr. Live the Perfect Life. 2007. 112p. per. 9.99 *(978-1-58169-237-2(4))* Genesis Communications, Inc.
Evans, Karl. Tales & Prayers for New Life in Christ: Multiple-Use Life-Enriching Stories. 2008. 167p. per. *(978-0-7880-2557-0(0))* CSS Publishing Co.
Evans, Lois. Stones of Remembrance: A Rock-Hard Faith from Rock-Hard Places. 2006. (ENG.). 176p. per. 12.99 *(978-0-8024-8398-0(4))* Moody Pubs.
Evans, Phillip. Eternal Security Proved! 2008. 305p. pap. 17.08 *(978-1-4357-1615-5(9))* Lulu Enterprises Inc.
Evans, Roderick L. Kingdom Basics 101: Foundational Studies for Kingdom Living & Service. 2009. 94p. pap. 14.95 *(978-1-60141-019-1(0),* 216579) Kingdom Builders Publishing.
Evans, Tony. God's Unlikely Path to Success: How He Uses Less-Than-Perfect People. 2012. 192p. pap. 12.99 ***(978-0-7369-3998-0(9))*** Harvest Hse. Pubs.
Evans, Tony. Victory in Spiritual Warfare: Outfitting Yourself for the Battle. 2011. (Illus.). 288p. pap. 13.99 *(978-0-7369-3999-7(7))* Harvest Hse. Pubs.
Evans, Tony & Evans, Jonathan. Get in the Game: An Athlete's Guide for the Spiritual Journey. 2006. (ENG.). 160p. per. 10.99 *(978-0-8024-4406-6(7))* Moody Pubs.
Evans, Wanda S. Ripe or Rotten? Let's Talk about Fruit. 2011. pap. 14.99 ***(978-1-61777-662-5(9))*** Tate Publishing & Enterprises, LLC.
Everett-Green, Evelyn. For the Faith. 2008. 228p. 24.99 *(978-0-554-34412-6(2))* 2008. 228p. 27.99 *(978-0-554-25109-7(4))* 2007. (ENG.). 200p. pap. 19.99 *(978-1-4264-8162-8(4))* BiblioBazaar.
—For the Faith. 2007. 204p. per. *(978-1-4065-3386-6(6))* Dodo Pr.
Everhart, Gary E. The Right Perception of Bible Holiness. 2011. 119p. pap. 9.95 *(978-1-4327-6945-1(6))* Outskirts Pr., Inc.
Evers, O. Naomi. Nobody but God! 2010. 108p. pap. 11.99 *(978-1-60957-200-6(9))* Xulon Pr., Inc.
Evert, Jason & Evert, Crystalina. How to Find Your Soulmate Without Losing Your Soul: 21 Secrets for Women. 2011. (C). 24.95 *(978-0-9830923-0-8(3))* Totus Tuus Pr.
Everts, Don. Getting Your Feet Dirty: A down-to-Earth Look at Following Jesus. 2007. (ENG.). 132p. per. 8.00 *(978-0-8308-3604-8(7),* IVP Bks.) InterVarsity Pr.
Exley, Richard. The Gift of Gratitude. 2008. 128p. pap. 6.99 *(978-1-59379-098-1(8))* White Stone Bks.
Exploring 1 for Leaders. 2.04 *(978-0-7673-5803-3(1))* LifeWay Christian Resources.
Exploring 2. 1.45 *(978-0-7673-5755-5(8))* LifeWay Christian Resources.
Exploring 2 for Leaders. 2.04 *(978-0-7673-5773-9(6))* LifeWay Christian Resources.
Exploring for Younger Children. 1.45 *(978-0-7673-5785-2(X))* LifeWay Christian Resources.
Exploring God's Word: Kindergarten, Parent Communication Pack. (Voyages Ser.). 6.95 *(978-0-570-00251-2(6),* 57-0011) Concordia Publishing Hse.
Eyrich, Howard. Grief: Learning to Live with Loss. 2010. pap. *(978-1-59638-203-9(1))* P & R Publishing.
Ezeji-Okoye, Fredrick K. Can I Take a Little Wine? 2009. 104p. pap. 10.99 *(978-1-60791-203-3(1))* Xulon Pr., Inc.
Fabing, Robert. To Live in Christ-Discipleship: Growing in Daily Spirituality. 2007. 64p. pap. 2.95 *(978-0-8091-9675-3(1),* 9675-3) Paulist Pr.
Fabyan, Sandy M. Where Eagles Dare, 1 vol. 2009. 130p. pap. 19.95 *(978-1-61546-570-5(7))* PublishAmerica, Inc.
Fafowora, Olaniran. The Voice of Jehovah. 2007. 104p. per. 16.95 *(978-1-4241-7534-5(8))* PublishAmerica, Inc.
Fairchild, Sabrina. Faith & the S. T. O. P. Principle: Learning to Surrender, Trust, Obey, & Patiently Wait upon the Lord. 2010. pap. 15.99 *(978-1-61663-543-5(6))* Tate Publishing & Enterprises, LLC.
Fairman, Ray. Are You Destined to Lead? A Biblical Analysis of Leadership Skills & Principles. 2009. 136p. 23.95 *(978-1-4401-2982-7(7));* pap. 13.95 *(978-1-4401-2981-0(9))* iUniverse, Inc.
"Faith"CFD. God's Grace. 2011. 88p. pap. 9.95 *(978-1-4620-0544-4(6))* iUniverse, Inc.

Faithwriters. Faithwriters - Abundance of Life. 2007. 256p. pap. 18.99 (978-1-4141-0950-3(4)) Pleasant Word.
Faithwriters.com. FaithWriters - Inspiration at Your Fingertips. 2006. 204p. pap. 17.99 (978-1-4141-0830-8(3)) Pleasant Word.
Fajfr, Ruth S. From the Land of Moab to the Line of the Messiah. pap. 2.49 (978-1-56632-030-6(5)) Revival Literature.
Falaq, Taliba. White Light: The Eye View of God. 2nd ed. 2006. (Illus.). 328p. per. 16.95 (978-1-60002-075-9(5), 3751) Mountain Valley Publishing, LLC.
Fall Like Rain. 7.50 (978-0-8054-5970-8(7)) B&H Publishing Group.
Falsani, Cathleen. Sin Boldly: A Field Guide for Grace, 1 vol. 2008. (ENG.). 224p. 19.99 (978-0-310-27947-1(X)) Zondervan.
Falwell, Jerry. Building Dynamic Faith, 0 vols. 2007. 240p. per. 14.99 (978-0-8499-1983-1(5)) Nelson, Thomas Inc.
Familetti, Shirley. The 12 Months to Christmas Meeting with the King. 2007. 52p. per. 16.95 (978-1-4241-4312-2(8)) PublishAmerica, Inc.
Fann, Joey. The Way Back to Mayberry: Lessons from a Simpler Time. 2010. (ENG.). 208p. pap. 12.99 (978-1-4336-7046-6(1), B&H Bks.) B&H Publishing Group.
Farabaugh, David. A Pew Sitters Devotions in Revelation: Guide to Devotions in Revelation. 2009. pap. 13.99 (978-1-60696-952-6(8)) Tate Publishing & Enterprises, LLC.
Farhart, Scott & King, Elizabeth. The Christian Woman's Complete Guide to Health: Everything you Need to Know about You - Adolescence to Menopause & Beyond. 2008. (ENG., Illus.). 320p. pap. 15.99 (978-1-59979-207-1(9), Siloam Pr.) Charisma Media.
Farikanayi, Sarai-Sarah-Hall of Faith, 1 vol. 2010. 188p. pap. 24.95 (978-1-4489-8580-7(3)) PublishAmerica, Inc.
Farley, Andrew. Naked Gospel: The Truth You May Never Hear in Church. 2009. (ENG.). 224p. pap. 14.99 (978-0-310-29306-4(5)) Zondervan.
Farnham, Suzanne G. & Grayson, Timothy H. Keeping in Tune with God: Listening Hearts Discernment for Clergy. 2011. E-Book (978-0-8192-2446-0(4), Morehouse Publishing) Church Publishing, Inc.
Farquharson, Arnold. Strategic Planning from God's Perspective the Vision. 2008. 272p. 25.99 (978-1-60477-730-7(3)) Xulon Pr., Inc.
—Strategic Planning from God's Perspective the Vision: A Divine Revelation of God's Eternal Purpose for Man. 2008. 272p. pap. 15.99 (978-1-60477-729-1(X)) Xulon Pr., Inc.
Farr, Jason. Jesus Is a Black Man. 2011. 92p. pap. 15.99 (978-1-4568-8135-1(3)) Xlibris Corp.
Farrar, F. W. Everyday Christian Life or Sermons by the Way. 2007. (ENG.). 306p. 43.95 (978-0-548-02107-1(4)) Kessinger Publishing, LLC.
Farrar, Steve. Gettin' There - A Passage Through the Psalms: How a Man Finds His Way on the Trail of Life. 2007. (ENG.). 252p. pap. 16.99 (978-1-59052-987-4(1), Multnomah) Doubleday Religious Publishing Group, The.
Farrelly, John. The Art of Balance: Creating Calm in a Chaotic World. 2008. (ENG.). 104p. pap. 16.95 (978-1-84730-065-2(0)) Veritas Pubns. IRL. Dist: Dufour Editions, Inc.
Farrer, Austin. Science of God. 2009. (Illus.). 127p. pap. 19.95 (978-0-281-06150-1(5)) SPCK Publishing GBR. Dist: Westminster John Knox Pr.
Farris, Michael. What a Daughter Needs from Her Dad: How a Man Prepares His Daughter for Life. 2012. 176p. pap. 9.99 (978-0-7642-1005-1(X)) Bethany Hse. Pubs.
Fasol, Al & Fasol, Malinda S. What Do a Christian Be? From Belief to Behavior. 2008. 512p. 30.99 (978-1-4389-1528-9(4)); pap. 20.49 (978-1-4389-1527-2(6)) AuthorHouse.
Fathering: Not Just a Stroll in the Park. 5.95 (978-1-57494-004-6(X), Serendipity Hse.) LifeWay Christian Resources.
Faurot, Randal. The Pilgrim's Progress from the City of Destruction to the Celestial City of Refuge, from a Gospel Stand-Point, Containing Interviews with Sectarians. 2006. 224p. per. 20.99 (978-1-4255-1878-3(8)) MPublishing.
Favre, Deanna & Stanford, Shane. The Cure for the Chronic Life: Overcoming the Hopelessness That Holds You Back. 2010. 144p. 18.00 (978-1-4267-1001-8(1)) Abingdon Pr.
Fbs: The Herschel Hobbs Commentary. 4.75 (978-0-7673-4901-7(6)) LifeWay Christian Resources.
FBS Adult. 1.45 (978-0-7673-4790-7(0)) LifeWay Christian Resources.
FBS Adults. 1.45 (978-0-7673-4804-1(4)) LifeWay Christian Resources.
FBS Bible & Me Learner Guide. 1.60 (978-0-7673-5583-4(0)) LifeWay Christian Resources.
FBS Youth. 1.45 (978-0-7673-4063-2(9)) LifeWay Christian Resources.
Fea, John, et al. eds. Confessing History: Explorations in Christian Faith & the Historian's Vocation. 2010. (ENG.). 384p. pap. 35.00 (978-0-268-02903-6(2)) Univ. of Notre Dame Pr.
Fearrington, Kimberly. Holy Hookups: Developing Godly Relationships. 2009. pap. 11.99 (978-1-60799-438-1(0)) Tate Publishing & Enterprises, LLC.
Feaver, Douglas & Morales, Hada Maria. El Mundo En Que Vivio Jesus, 0 vols. Cuadra, Samuel, tr. 2007. (SPA.). 128p. pap. 11.99 (978-0-89922-023-9(1)) Grupo Nelson.
Fedor, Evangeline Mae. Embracing His Phrases. 2008. 500p. pap. 24.99 (978-1-60647-818-9(4)) Xulon Pr., Inc.
Feigh, Craig T. The Sure Way to Him. 2008. 216p. per. 14.99 (978-1-60477-781-9(8)) Xulon Pr., Inc.
Feinberg, Margaret. The Organic God, 1 vol. 2007. (ENG.). 224p. (gr. 13). 16.99 (978-0-310-27244-1(0)) Zondervan.
Feist-Heilmeier, Christina. Nurses Are from Heaven. 2008. 184p. 22.99 (978-1-60647-911-7(3)); pap. 14.99 (978-1-60647-910-0(5)) Xulon Pr., Inc.
Feldmeier, Peter. The Developing Christian: Spiritual Growth Through the Life Cycle. 2007. 294p. per. 24.95 (978-0-8091-4438-9(7), 4438-9) Paulist Pr.
Feliz, Guido. Que Es lo Mejor?Tr. of Which Is the Best? (SPA.). 80p. (978-84-7228-291-9(0), 220738) Clie, Editorial.
—Ruta Luminosa: Shining Pathway. (SPA.). 84p. (978-84-7228-161-5(2), 220780) Clie, Editorial.
Fellowship of Christian Athletes Staff. Excellence: The Heart & Soul in Sports. Britton, Dan, ed. 2009. (ENG.). 160p. pap. 12.99 (978-0-8307-4629-3(3)) Gospel Light Pubns.
Femrite, Tommie. Invading the Seven Mountains with Intercession: How to Reclaim Society Through Prayer. 2011. (ENG.). 256p. pap. 13.99 (978-1-61638-666-5(5), Creation Hse.) Charisma Media.
Fenderson, Darnell. Double Edged Sword Vol. 1 2nd Edition. 2010. 103p. pap. 10.00 (978-0-557-01651-8(7)) Lulu Enterprises Inc.
Fenimore, Brian. The Voice of the Lord Thunders. 2010. 202p. pap. 13.99 (978-0-557-12359-9(3)) Lulu Enterprises Inc.
Fenn, McKenzi. God's Olympics: A 5-Session Study for Children on Running the Christian Race. 2008. (Illus.). 48p. (YA). pap. 9.99 (978-1-59317-204-6(4)) Warner Pr. Pubs.
Fenner, Richard. Men of Valor! Women of Virtue! 2007. 116p. (ENG.). 18.99 (978-1-60266-712-9(8)); per. 10.99 (978-1-60266-566-8(4)) Xulon Pr., Inc.
Ferguson, Doreen. Life Through to a Shout of Joy. 2007. 208p. per. 14.99 (978-1-60477-045-2(7)) Xulon Pr., Inc.
Ferguson, HollyKay. Encouragements from the Heart. 2007. (Illus.). per. 14.95 (978-0-9783267-2-4(2)) Now U No Publishing.
Ferguson, Jerry. A Home for Ida. 2008. 68p. pap. 10.99 (978-1-60647-805-9(2)) Xulon Pr., Inc.
Ferguson, Lashawn D. Echoes of God in the Refreshing Springs. 2009. 252p. pap. 16.99 (978-1-61579-071-5(3)) Xulon Pr., Inc.
Ferguson, Shirley Roland. Birth Cry: A Personal Story of the Life of Hannah D. Mitchell, Nurse Midwife. 2011. 308p. 37.95 (978-1-4497-2742-0(5)); pap. 22.95 (978-1-4497-2741-3(7)) Author Solutions, Inc. (WestBow Pr.).
Fergusson, Rob. Life Bridges. 256p. pap. (978-1-85240-341-6(1)) Sovereign World, Ltd.
Fern, Fanny. Fern Leaves from Fanny's Port-Folio 2d Series with Original Designs by Fred M Coffin. 2006. 420p. per. 26.99 (978-1-4255-4538-3(6)) MPublishing.
Fernald, Daniel Horace. Atheism Answered. 2008. 108p. pap. 11.99 (978-1-60647-694-9(7)) Xulon Pr., Inc.
Fernander, Delton D. The Kingdom Focused Life. 2008. 120p. pap. 10.99 (978-1-60647-340-5(9)) Xulon Pr., Inc.
Fernandes. The Atheist Delusion. 2009. 228p. pap. 15.99 (978-1-60791-582-9(0)) Xulon Pr., Inc.
Fernandes, Phil. Contend Earnestly for the Faith: A Survey of Christian Apologetics. 2008. 457p. pap. 29.95 (978-1-60474-024-0(8)) PublishAmerica, Inc.
Fernandez, Nancy. Amor en Peligro: Love in Danger. (SPA.). 112p. (978-84-7228-335-0(6), 220023) Clie, Editorial.
Fernandez, S. La Presencia de Dios y la Oracion.Tr. of Presence of God & Prayer. (SPA.). 3.99 (978-1-56063-948-0(2), 493034) Editorial Unilit.
Ferrar, Nicholas. The Story Books of Little Gidding. 2009. 222p. pap. (978-0-217-13406-4(8)) Books LLC.
—The Story Books of Little Gidding: Being the Religious Dialogues Recited in the Great Room, 1631-2. 2009. 364p. 26.99 (978-1-103-26983-9(6)); pap. 20.99 (978-1-103-26979-2(8)) BiblioBazaar.
—The Story Books of Little Gidding: Being the Religious Dialogues Recited in the Great Room, 1631-32 (1899) 2008. 356p. 46.95 (978-0-548-93352-7(9)) 2007. 360p. per. 31.95 (978-0-548-59880-1(0)) Kessinger Publishing, LLC.
Ferraro, Rudy. Choose Your Way There. 2008. 124p. pap. 10.99 (978-1-60647-477-8(4)) Xulon Pr., Inc.
Ferree, Mamie. Women's L. I. F. E. Guide, Rev. Laaser, Mark, ed. 2007. per. 19.95 (978-0-9771662-7-5(9)) Freedom Every Day LLC.
—Women's L. I. F. E. Guide, XXX, Church. com. laaser, Mark, ed. 2007. per. 19.95 (978-0-9771662-4-4(4)) Freedom Every Day LLC.
Ferrell, Emerson. Immersed in Him. 2010. (ENG.). 204p. pap. 14.99 (978-0-7684-3265-7(0)) Destiny Image Pubs.
Ferres, Michael. Civil War. 2007. 436p. per. 21.99 (978-1-60477-204-3(2)) Xulon Pr., Inc.
Ferrie, Alastair. Evangelism in a Post Christian Culture. 2008. 232p. pap. 18.95 (978-0-595-53005-2(2)) iUniverse, Inc.
Ferrini, Cindi. Balancing the Active Life: An Interactive Bible Study. 2011. pap. 16.99 (978-1-61777-416-4(2)) Tate Publishing & Enterprises, LLC.
Fiala, David, illus. God Is Bigger Than Your Cancer: Christian Insights for Cancer Patients. 2008. 128p. 16.99 (978-0-9801591-0-3(5)) Fresh Water Pr.
Fiand, Barbara. From Religion Back to Faith: A Journey of the Heart. 2007. (ENG.). 200p. pap. 16.95 (978-0-8245-2417-3(9)) Crossroad Publishing Co., The.
Ficalora, Mary T. Choosing Honor: An American Woman's Search for God, Family, & Country in an Age of Corruption. (Illus.). 179p. 2009. pap. (978-0-9799359-1-6(1)) 2008. 22.95 (978-0-9799359-0-9(3)) Avail Pr.
Field, Anne. Blessed by Our Brokenness: Finding Peace in the Challenges of Aging & Illness. 2007. 9.95p. pap. 9.95 (978-1-59325-111-6(4)) Word Among Us Pr.
Fields, Doug. Jesus Loves Me This I Know... but what about everything Else: Grinding Through Life's Tough Questions. 2009. 240p. pap. 14.99 (978-0-7644-6299-3(7)) Group Publishing, Inc.
—Living on Purpose. 2006. pap. 59.00 incl. cd-rom (978-0-7644-6003-6(X)) Group Publishing, Inc.
Fields, Doug. Refuel: An Uncomplicated Guide to Connecting with God. 2011. 144p. pap. 12.99 (978-0-7852-9840-3(1)) Nelson, Thomas Inc.
Fields, Michael. Firstfruits: Revelation for Increase & Excellence. 2008. 120p. 18.99 (978-1-60477-719-2(2)); pap. 10.99 (978-1-60477-718-5(4)) Xulon Pr., Inc.
Fields, Norman E. Overcoming Pain. 2010. 156p. pap. 14.99 (978-1-61579-855-1(2)) Xulon Pr., Inc.
Fillinger, A. D. The Meaning of Life. 2007. 124p. per. 12.95 (978-0-595-45854-7(8)) iUniverse, Inc.
Financial Success Workbook: A Spending Program for Managing Your Resources. 2007. per. 12.95 (978-0-9776765-1-4(X)) G & G Publishing, Inc.
Fincher, Dale & Fincher, Jonalyn. Coffee Shop Conversations: Making the Most of Spiritual Small Talk, 1 vol. 2010. (ENG.). 224p. pap. 14.99 (978-0-310-31887-3(4)) Zondervan.
Fincher, Kathy, illus. Remembrance of My First Holy Communion-Girl. 2008. 28p. 14.95 (978-0-88271-781-4(2)) Regina Pr., Malhame & Co.
Findlater, John. Perfect Love. pap. 8.99 (978-0-88019-168-5(6)) Schmul Publishing Co., Inc.
Fink, Diane M. True Identity. 2008. 136p. pap. 15.00 (978-0-9792739-8-8(6)) Ajoyin Publishing, Inc.
Finley, Deborah. What Your Future Holds & What You Can Do to Change It. 2007. 260p. (ENG.). 25.99 (978-1-60266-579-8(6)); per. 15.99 (978-1-60266-578-1(8)) Xulon Pr., Inc.
Finley, Jeanne Torrence & Job, Reuben P. Three Simple Rules for Christian Living. 2008. (ENG.). 71p. pap. 8.00 (978-1-4267-0025-5(3), Abingdon Press) Abingdon Pr.
Finley, Robert. The Time Is at Hand. 2008. 308p. pap. 18.99 (978-1-60791-026-8(8)) Xulon Pr., Inc.
Finnegan, Sean & Paver, A. S. Ad Completorium: How to Sing Compline According to the Breviarium Romanum of 1960. (LAT & ENG.). 64p. (978-1-901157-11-6(3)) St. Austin Pr.
Finney, Charles. Living Your Faith. 2008. 320p. per. 13.99 (978-1-60374-037-1(6)) Whitaker Hse.
Finney, Charles G. Verdadera Sumision (True Submission) (SPA.). 128p. (978-84-7228-750-1(5), 220936) Clie, Editorial.
Finney, Jerald. Seperation of Church & State: God's Churches - Spiritual or Legal Entities? 2009. 108p. pap. 11.99 (978-1-60791-341-2(0)) Xulon Pr., Inc.
Finnigan, William J. The Demon of Depression. 2008. 148p. pap. 13.99 (978-1-60477-886-1(5)) Xulon Pr., Inc.
Fiorenza, Sally & Peckham, Gerald. Beyond Envy. 2008. 134p. 27.50 (978-0-557-00910-7(3)) Lulu Enterprises Inc.
Fiorini, Donna. The Answer. 2007. 120p. per. 20.00 (978-1-59919-020-4(6)) Elm Publishing.
Firmin, Connie S. Sparkle: Reflecting Purity in Today's World. 2011. pap. 10.99 (978-1-61777-565-9(7)) Tate Publishing & Enterprises, LLC.
First Place 4 Health. Giving Christ Control. 2009. (First Place Ser.). (ENG.). 256p. 19.99 (978-0-8307-5112-9(2)) Gospel Light Pubns.
—Simple Ideas for Healthy Living. 2008. (First Place 4 Health Ser.). (ENG., Illus.). 240p. pap. 14.99 (978-0-8307-4581-4(5)) Gospel Light Pubns.
First Wesleyan Church, First Wesleyan Church. Walking the Walk: Step by Step. 2007. 218p. pap. 16.50 (978-1-4357-0319-3(7)) Lulu Enterprises Inc.
Fischer, Marilyn Rhodes. Dear God, Love, M: Letters to God about ordinary everyday Experiences. 2009. 112p. pap. 13.95 (978-1-4327-1163-4(6)) Outskirts Pr., Inc.
Fish, Henry Clay. Primitive Piety Revived, or, the Aggressive Power of the Christian Church a Premium Essay. 2006. 268p. per. 23.99 (978-1-4255-2404-3(4)) MPublishing.
Fishburne, George, Jr. A Higher Calling: Serving God, His Leaders, & His People with Excellence. 2007. (ENG.). 155p. per. (978-0-9792511-0-8(9)) Tribute Publishing, LLC.
Fishcer, Mary Jane. Praying with Peter, Volume 2: Exciting Insights into the Words of First Peter. 2007. 132p. pap. 10.99 (978-1-58169-239-6(0), Gazelle Pr.) Genesis Communications, Inc.
Fisher, Douglas R. Surveying Truths in the Word of God: A New Inspirational Way to Study Your Bible. 2010. pap. 14.99 (978-1-61566-583-9(8)) Tate Publishing & Enterprises, LLC.
Fisher, Lynda Reynolds. E-Mails from the Church Dog: Lessons from A Therapy Dog for the Ministry. 2011. 280p. pap. 19.95 (978-1-4497-3094-9(9), WestBow Pr.) Author Solutions, Inc.
Fisher, Timothy W. Contagious but Not Quarantined: An Adventure in Telling Others about Jesus. 2010. 113p. pap. 13.95 (978-1-4327-4927-9(7)) Outskirts Pr., Inc.
Fischella, Anthony J. One Solitary Life: Book III - the Christ Epoch. 2008. 276p. pap. 15.95 (978-1-4343-5413-6(X)) AuthorHouse.
Fitch, Lauren B. The (Im)Perfect Christian Life. 2011. 218p. pap. 12.95 (978-1-4327-6740-2(2)) Outskirts Pr., Inc.
Fitzgerald, Brenna. Answers. 2008. 74p. pap. 16.95 (978-1-60563-383-1(6)) PublishAmerica, Inc.
FitzGerald, Paula & Fitzgerald, Edward. The Son of Man Trilogy, 3 pts., Set. 461p. (Orig.). pap. 18.00 (978-0-935915-03-7(6)) Corinthian Pubns.
Fitzgerald, Troy. Live Like You Mean It: Wisdom for the Journey Home. 2010. 15.99 (978-0-8163-2380-7(1)) Pacific Pr. Publishing Assn.
Fitzgerald, William John. A Contemporary North American Prayer Book. 2008. 157p. per. 12.95 (978-0-87946-335-9(X)) ACTA Pubns.
Fitzpatrick, Patricia J. There Once Was a Crooked Lady. 2008. 196p. pap. 14.99 (978-1-60647-729-8(3)) Xulon Pr., Inc.
Fitzwater, Darryl. Exposing the Darkness: Lighting the Way to Life in Christ. 2011. pap. 12.99 (978-1-61739-107-1(7)) Tate Publishing & Enterprises, LLC.
Flaaten, Rosemary. A Woman & Her Relationships: Transforming the Way We Connect. 2007. (ENG.). 192p. per. 14.99 (978-0-8341-2338-0(X), 083-412-338X) Beacon Hill Pr. of Kansas City.
Flaherty, Regis J. God's on the Phone: Stories of Grace in Action. 2011. (978-0-86716-978-2(8), Servant Bks.) Franciscan Media.
Flakes, Fredrika J. How to Separate & Divorce As a Christian. 2010. 424p. 34.99 (978-1-61579-860-5(9)) Xulon Pr., Inc.
Flamming, Peter James. Healing the Heartbreak of Grief. 2010. 113p. pap. 12.00 (978-1-4267-0221-1(3)) Abingdon Pr.
Fletcher, George P. Predictive Prophecy. pap. 0.15 (978-0-87377-091-0(9), GAM Pubns.
Fletcher, Jean C. Light upon the Sand. 2007. 140p. (ENG.). 29.99 (978-1-4257-9304-3(5)); per. 19.99 (978-1-4257-9284-8(7)) Xlibris Corp.
Fletcher, Jim & Fletcher, Jim F. It's the End of the World as We Know It (And I Feel Fine) How to Stop Worrying & Learn to Love These End Times. 2009. (ENG., Illus.). 224p. pap. 14.99 (978-1-59979-472-3(1)) Charisma Media.
Flores, Ernest R. Tempted to Leave the Cross: Renewing the Call to Discipleship. 2007. 130p. per. 14.00 (978-0-8170-1524-4(8)) Judson Pr.
—Tentado a Dejar la Cruz: Renovando el Llamado al Discipulado. 2008.Tr. of Tempted to Leave the Cross: Renewing the Call to Discipleship. (SPA.). 160p. pap. 14.00 (978-0-8170-1535-0(3)) Judson Pr.
Flores, Francisco. Moralejas para el Alm. 2011. 224p. pap. 19.99 (978-1-4653-6073-1(5)) Xlibris Corp.
Flowers, Pastor Jacqueline. Where the Spirit of the Lord Is. 2011. 60p. pap. 7.95 (978-0-9634196-6-8(8), Llumina Christian Bks.) Aeon Publishing Inc.
Floyd, Jefferson. Confident Obedience: Studies in the Lifestyle of Faith. 2007. (ENG.). 208p. per. 14.99 (978-1-60266-081-6(6)) Xulon Pr., Inc.
Fluga, Jack. God Throws down the Gauntlet. 2011. 54p. pap. 11.95 (978-1-4327-6889-8(1)) Outskirts Pr., Inc.
Flynn, Cynthia. God, the Financial Genius. 2011. pap. 8.99 (978-1-61777-142-2(2)) Tate Publishing & Enterprises, LLC.
Flynn, Leslie B. Yo Ser Como Jesus? Me Be Like Jesus? (SPA.). 160p. (978-84-7228-391-6(7), 220985) Clie, Editorial.
Flynn, Paul. Waking up from Syncretism: The Power of Pure Worship. 2008. 240p. pap. 14.99 (978-1-60647-013-8(2)) Xulon Pr., Inc.
Flynt, Mike. The Power-Based Life: 12 Proven Strategies to Develop Strength in Your Body, Mind, & Spirit. 2010. 224p. pap. 14.99 (978-1-4016-0434-9(X)) Nelson, Thomas Inc.
Fobbs, Ollie. The Spirit of Direct Obedience. 2011. 92p. pap. 9.95 (978-1-4626-3880-2(5)) PublishAmerica, Inc.
Foglio, Frank. Face to Face with the Heart of Grace. 2011. 276p. pap. 17.99 (978-1-4343-1099-6(X)) AuthorHouse.
Foley, Barbara. The Bride Wears Army Boots! Spiritual Weapons & Tools for Healing & Development. 2010. 320p. 37.95 (978-1-4497-0206-9(6)); pap. 22.95 (978-1-4497-0205-2(8)) Author Solutions, Inc. (WestBow Pr.).
Foley, Marc. Peace of Heart: Reflections on Choices in Daily Life. 2008. 69p. pap. 8.95 (978-1-56548-293-7(X)) New City Pr.
Following Jesus Christ. 7.95 (978-0-89942-338-8(8)) Catholic Bk. Publishing Corp.
Fondong, Pastor Columbu. 10 Keys to Turn Your Dreams & Desires. 2006. x, 147p. pap. (978-0-7552-0252-2(X)) Authors OnLine, Ltd.
Fontenot, Sidney. Mini-Messages for Maximum Living: A Collection of Inspirational Messages for Living a Life of Success & Significance. 2008. per. 19.99 (978-0-9801644-3-5(5)) Teamed UP, LLC.
Foote, Carol. A Reel Meaning for Christmas: Finding Yourself in the Classic Christmas Films. 2007. 68p. per. 14.99 (978-1-4141-0552-9(3)) Pleasant Word.
Footit, Anthony. A Gospel of Wild Flowers. 2006. (ENG., Illus.). 128p. 19.99 (978-0-7153-2572-8(8)) F&W Media, Inc.
Foppe, John P. What's Your Excuse? Making the Most of What You Have, 0 vols. 2008. 236p. pap. 14.99 (978-1-59555-238-9(3)) Nelson, Thomas Inc.
Force for Christ. 6.99 (978-1-871676-07-5(X)) Christian Focus Pubns. GBR. Dist: Spring Arbor Distributors, Inc.
Ford, Aundria H. Hawkins. From the Pastor's Daughter: A testimony of life in the ministry through the eyes of the Pastor's Child. 2010. pap. 12.99 (978-1-60799-803-7(3)) Tate Publishing & Enterprises, LLC.
Ford, Billie Ford. The Road to Inner Peace. 2007. pap. 15.00 (978-0-8059-7112-5(2)) Dorrance Publishing Co., Inc.
Ford, David F. Christian Wisdom: Desiring God & Learning in Love. 2007. (Cambridge Studies in Christian Doctrine Ser.). (ENG.). 426p. 99.00 (978-0-521-87545-5(5)); 428p. per. 41.00 (978-0-521-69838-2(3)) Cambridge Univ. Pr.
Ford, Errick A. Iron Sharpens Iron: Wisdom of the Ages. 2010. pap. 11.99 (978-1-61566-793-2(8)) Tate Publishing & Enterprises, LLC.
Ford, James Stuart. Israel: God's Time Clock! 2008. 88p. pap. 9.99 (978-1-60477-867-0(9)) Xulon Pr., Inc.
Ford, Melvin. Pass It On. pap. 6.95 (978-1-56794-201-9(6)) Star Bible & Tract Corp.
Ford, Virginia "Kitty". One on One with the Master. 2011. 392p. pap. 24.99 (978-1-4520-8495-4(5)) AuthorHouse.
Forde, Gerhard O. The Preached God: Proclamation in Word & Sacrament. Mattes, Mark C. & Paulson, Steven D., eds. 2007. (Luthern Quarterly Books).

329p. per. 32.00 (978-0-8028-2821-7(3)) Eerdmans, William B. Publishing Co.

Fordyce, Michelle. Morgan Where Are You Running To? 2008. 92p. pap. 9.95 (978-1-4327-2217-3(4)) Outskirts Pr., Inc.

Forehand, Chrissie. Do I Have to Be a Cereal Bowl? Questioning the Potter. 2007. (Illus.). 65p. per. 12.99 (978-1-59879-331-4(4)) Lifevest Publishing, Inc.

Foreman, Jay W. Still Learning. 2011. 120p. 28.95 (978-1-61507-760-1(X)); pap. 11.95 (978-1-61507-759-5(6)) Cross Bks. Publishing.

ForenHorst, Christine. Afterwards I Knew: Stories from the First & Second World Wars. 2010. (Time to Eternity Ser.). (ENG.). 208p. 8.99 (978-1-84550-563-9(8)) Christian Focus Pubns. GBR. Dist: STL Distribution North America.

Forge, Anvil. Living Each Day Led by the Spirit. 2008. 128p. (ENG.). 21.99 (978-1-60477-776-5(1)); per. 13.99 (978-1-60477-775-8(3)) Xulon Pr., Inc.

Forgiveness: Where Real Life & Faith Come Together. 2006. 10.95 (978-0-9776892-4-8(7)) Signature Editions.

Forman, Edward. Angel at My Side. 2008. pap. 9.00 (978-0-8059-8637-2(5)) Dorrance Publishing Co., Inc.

Fornof, Theodore W. Living with Angels. 2010. 110p. 19.99 (978-1-60957-358-4(7)); pap. 11.99 (978-1-60957-357-7(9)) Xulon Pr., Inc.

Forshee, Kenneth. The Love Puzzle. 2006. (ENG.). 100p. per. 16.95 (978-1-4241-6283-3(1)) PublishAmerica, Inc.

Forster, Carl. From the Valley to the Mountaintop. 2008. 204p. pap. 14.99 (978-1-60477-788-8(5)) Xulon Pr., Inc.

Forsyth, James. Saints Alive! The Christian Life in Christian Lives. 2010. (ENG.). 244p. pap. 18.49 (978-1-4389-4393-0(8)) AuthorHouse.

Forsyth, Jerrilyn. Sandra. 2008. 48p. pap. 16.95 (978-1-60474-120-9(1)) PublishAmerica, Inc.

Forte, Marshell. Broken to Forgive When Other's Don't! It Is our Christian Duty to Forgive one another as Christ Has Forgiven Us!! 2009. 60p. pap. 14.95 (978-1-4389-2475-5(5)) AuthorHouse.

Fortener, Dorathea. God Speaks: Do We Listen? 2010. pap. 17.99 (978-1-61663-498-8(7)) Tate Publishing & Enterprises, LLC.

—A Life of Promise: Surviving Adversity through Faith. 2009. pap. 23.99 (978-1-60799-417-6(8)) Tate Publishing & Enterprises, LLC.

Fortosis, Stephen. Embracing the Untouchables: The Story of Tommy Tillman. 2008. 140p. pap. 13.99 (978-1-60477-678-2(1)) Xulon Pr., Inc.

Fortson, John Edward. A Relationship, Not Just a Religion: A Book of Biblical Insight with Scriptural References & 21st Century Psalms, 1 vol. 2009. 110p. pap. 19.95 (978-1-60836-417-6(8)) PublishAmerica, Inc.

Fosdick, Harry Emerson. The Second Mile. 2009. 58p. pap. 16.75 (978-1-110-59480-1(1)) BiblioBazaar.

Foster, Charles. The Sacred Journey: The Ancient Practices. 2010. 252p. pap. 12.99 (978-0-8499-4609-7(3)) Nelson, Thomas Inc.

—Steward: Living as Disciples in Everyday Life Kit. 125.00 (978-0-687-09944-3(7)) Abingdon Pr.

Foster, David. Convierta Sus Adversidades en Oportunidades, 1 vol. 2006. (SPA.). 238p. per. 9.99 (978-987-557-101-3(6)) Vida Pubs.

Foster, Eric. Destiny of Discipleship. 2006. 176p. per. 12.50 (978-1-59919-013-6(3)) Elim Publishing.

Foster, Mark R. Stem Cells & Cloning: Who should Decide? 2008. 284p. pap. 16.99 (978-0-9821408-0-2(0)) Faithful Life Pubs.

Foster, Richard J. A Year with God: Living Out the Spiritual Disciplines. 2009. (ENG.). 432p. 22.99 (978-0-06-176820-0(0), HarperOne) HarperCollins Pubs.

Foster, Robert. World Stage. 2009. 48p. pap. 16.95 (978-1-60749-891-9(X)) PublishAmerica, Inc.

Foster, Russell J. How Many Lightbulbs Does It Take to Change a Christian? A Pocket Guide to Shrinking Your Ecological Footprint. 2008. (Illus.). 64p. pap. (978-0-7151-4127-4(9), Seabury Bks.) Church Publishing, Inc.

Foster, Sr. A God Worth Waiting For. 2008. 180p. pap. 14.99 (978-1-60647-829-5(X)) Xulon Pr., Inc.

Fountain, David. Let Conscience Speak. 32p. pap. 0.99 (978-0-85479-810-0(2)) Revival Literature.

Fournier, Robert R. The Trials & Triumphs. 2009. 84p. pap. 10.99 (978-1-60791-475-4(1)) Xulon Pr., Inc.

Foutz, Brian, et al. From Misery to Ministry: A Walk of Faith through the Loss of a Loved One. 2011. pap. 12.99 (978-1-61777-177-4(5)) Tate Publishing & Enterprises, LLC.

Fowler-Hillstock, Jacqueline. Prayer Works Volume 1: And It Shall Come to Pass, That Before They Call, I Will Answer, & While They Are yet Speaking, I Will Hear. Isaiah 65:24. 2010. pap. 14.99 (978-1-61579-833-9(1)) Xulon Pr., Inc.

Fowler, Joshua. Id Required. 2007. 112p. per. 10.99 (978-1-58930-201-3(X)) Selah Publishing Group, LLC.

Fowler, Samuel Whittemore. Meditations on the Glory of God. 2010. 326p. pap. 18.99 (978-1-60957-178-8(9)) Xulon Pr., Inc.

Fox, Emmet. Getting Results by Prayer/The Great Adventure/You Must Be Born Again. pap. 3.00 (978-0-87516-747-3(0)) DeVorss & Co.

—The Golden Key, Vol. 1. 3.00 (978-0-87516-737-4(3), Devorss Pubns.) DeVorss & Co.

—The Golden Key. 2011. 12p. pap. 35.95 (978-1-258-00520-7(4)) Literary Licensing, LLC.

—Life Is Consciousness. 2011. 44p. pap. 5.95 (978-1-61427-142-0(9)) Martino Publishing.

Fox, Emmet. The Yoga of Love. 3.00 (978-0-87516-741-1(1)) DeVorss & Co.

Fox, George & Wallace, T. H. S. Have Salt in Yourselves: A Book of QuakerPsalms. 2010. 120p. pap. 10.00 (978-0-9701375-4-8(0)) Foundation Pubns.

Fox, Michael. Complete in Christ. 2007. 300p. per. 20.99 (978-1-60266-348-0(3)) Xulon Pr., Inc.

Fox, Sandra. Lord Renew My Hope. 2008. 128p. pap. 14.99 (978-1-60647-687-1(4)) Xulon Pr., Inc.

Foxcroft, Rosemary, ed. Bullet-Point Belief: The Best of Colin Morris. 2008. 196p. pap. 16.99 (978-1-85311-838-8(9)) Canterbury Pr.

Foxe, John. Foxe's Christian Martyrs. 2010. (Abridged Christian Classics Ser.). (ENG.). 192p. pap. 2.99 (978-1-60260-857-3(1), Barbour Bks.) Barbour Publishing, Inc.

Foyil, Karen. The Mirror of a Warrior. 2008. 116p. pap. 10.99 (978-1-60266-855-3(8)) Xulon Pr., Inc.

Fracasso, Anselmo. Arte De Vivir Feliz. 144p. 2.95 (978-958-607-639-5(3)) Sociedad de San Pablo COL. Dist: St Pauls/Alba Hse. Pubs.

Fragoso de Weyand, Edith. Zona Libre de Ofensa: Comience Hoy una Vida Nueva Sin Ofensa. 2008. pap. 22.99 (978-1-60647-077-0(9)) Xulon Pr., Inc.

Frailey, A. K. The Road Goes Ever On: A Christian Journey Through the Lord of the Rings. 2011. 176p. pap. 15.95 (978-1-4502-8810-1(3)) iUniverse, Inc.

France, Mary. For We Wrestle Not Against Flesh & Blood. 2008. 248p. pap. 12.99 (978-1-935105-11-4(6)) Avid Readers Publishing Group.

Francis K.F. Iselowo (Rev.). Prayers from the Heart. 2011. 196p. 29.99 (978-1-4568-0552-4(5)); pap. 19.99 (978-1-4568-0551-7(7)) Xlibris Corp.

Francis, Leslie J. & Astley, Jeff. Children, Churches & Christian Learning: A Practical Resource. 304p. 33.00 (978-0-281-05532-6(7)) SPCK Publishing GBR. Dist: Pilgrim Pr., The/United Church Pr.

Francis, Mary. Chastity, Poverty, & Obedience: Recovering the Vision for the Renewal of Religious Life. 2007. 118p. per. 10.95 (978-1-58617-119-3(4)) Ignatius Pr.

Francisco, Garcia. Semblanzas: Similarities. (SPA., Illus.). 192p. (978-84-7228-670-2(3), 220810) Clie, Editorial.

Francois, Jean Daniel. The No-Nonsense Approach to a Successful Life. 2008. 284p. 25.99 (978-1-60477-505-1(X)); pap. 15.99 (978-1-60477-504-4(1)) Xulon Pr., Inc.

Frangipane, F. Los Tres Campos de la Lucha.Tr. of Three Battlegrounds. (SPA.). 7.99 (978-958-9354-12-4(2), 550075) Editorial Unilit.

Frangipane, Francis. The Shelter of the Most High: Accessing the Divine Protection of God in Times of Trouble. 2008. (ENG.). 208p. pap. 12.99 (978-1-59979-281-1(8), Charisma Hse.) Charisma Media.

Frank, Penny. Deja Ir a Mi Pueblo (Let My People Go!) (SPA.). 1.50 (978-0-8423-6305-1(X), 490310) Editorial Unilit.

Franklin, Apostle Frederick E. The Door Is Closing on the Last Oppurtunity for Immortality. 2011. 160p. pap. 11.70 (978-1-4634-1089-6(1)) AuthorHouse.

Franklin, Barbara Washington. When You're down to Nothing, God Is Upto Something: No Subtitle. 2008. 256p. 25.99 (978-1-60647-120-3(1)); 252p. pap. 15.99 (978-1-60647-119-7(8)) Xulon Pr., Inc.

Franklin, Jentezen. Believe That You Can: It's Time to Make It Happen! 2008. (ENG.). 240p. 21.99 (978-1-59979-348-1(2), Charisma Hse.) Charisma Media.

—Fasting Study Guide: 5-Week Interactive Study Resource. 2009. (ENG.). 112p. pap. 9.99 (978-1-59979-768-7(2), Charisma Hse.) Charisma Media.

—Fear Fighters: How to Live by Faith in a World Driven by Fear. 2009. (ENG.). 224p. 21.99 (978-1-59979-762-5(3), Charisma Hse.) Charisma Media.

—Right People, Right Place, Right Plan: Discerning the Voice of God. 2007. 205p. 19.99 (978-0-88368-276-0(1)) Whitaker Hse.

—Right People, Right Place, Right Plan Devotional: 30 Days of Discerning the Voice of God. 2008. 142p. 9.99 (978-1-60374-059-3(7)) Whitaker Hse.

Frantz, Nadine Pence & Stimming, Mary T., eds. Hope Deferred: Heart-Healing Reflections on Reproductive Loss. 2010. 144p. pap. 18.00 (978-1-60899-214-0(4), Resource Pubns.) Wipf & Stock Pubs.

Franzen, Robert E. Creation under Fire from Within the Church. 2009. 364p. pap. 20.99 (978-1-60791-643-7(6)) Xulon Pr., Inc.

Frary, Reg. You Can't Keep a Good Tune Down: ... No Matter How Hard the Choir Tries. 2011. 144p. pap. 12.99 (978-1-84825-084-0(3), Canterbury Pr. Norwich) Hymns Ancient & Modern Ltd GBR. Dist: Westminster John Knox Pr.

Fraser, Andrew. Love Cares. 2011. 164p. pap. 14.99 (978-1-61379-265-0(4)); 96p. pap. 10.99 (978-1-61379-267-4(0)) Xulon Pr., Inc.

Frasure, Jack V. Is This Really You? 2008. 172p. pap. 14.99 (978-1-60791-086-2(1)) Xulon Pr., Inc.

Frasure, Kim. Korners for Inspiration. 2007. per. 13.00 (978-1-60416-000-0(4), Williams Printing Co.) Reformation Pubs.

Frazer, Dennesha K. The Wiles of the Devil: Using the Whole Armour of God. 2011. 120p. 28.95 (978-1-4497-2865-6(0)); pap. 11.95 (978-1-4497-2864-9(2)) Author Solutions, Inc. (WestBow Pr.).

Frazier, Rochelle. He Gave Me Pearls: A Journey to the Relationship for Which Your Heart Was Designed. 2011. 140p. 28.95 (978-1-4497-2326-2(8)); pap. 11.95 (978-1-4497-2325-5(X)) Author Solutions, Inc. (WestBow Pr.).

Frecka, Andy. Winter Road. 2009. 280p. pap. 16.99 (978-1-60791-387-0(9)) Xulon Pr., Inc.

Fred Ithurbum. God's Gift to You: A Sequel. 2009. 216p. 21.98 (978-1-4269-1667-0(1)); pap. 11.98 (978-1-4269-1666-3(3)) Trafford Publishing.

Fredericks, Geoff & Martens, Kathleen. Adventures in Christianity: The Trip. 2007. 308p. (ENG.). 27.99 (978-1-60266-541-5(9)); per. 17.99 (978-1-60266-538-5(9)) Xulon Pr., Inc.

Fredrickson, David. When the Church Leaves the Building: A Story of A People who followed their passion where they least expected it to take Them. 2006. per. 12.95 (978-1-59594-079-7(0), Wingspan Pr.) WingSpan Publishing.

Freed, Frank. 8 Steps to Positive Living: How to Think Differently, Know You Are Loved, & Change Your Life. 2007. (ENG.). 144p. per. 9.99 (978-0-8249-4727-9(4), Guideposts) Ideals Pubns.

Freed, Sandie. Strategies from Heaven's Throne: Claiming the Life God Wants for You. 2007. 224p. pap. 14.00 (978-0-8007-9430-9(3)) Chosen Bks.

Freeman, Bill. The Christian Life Is a Supplied Life: A Study in the Book of Philippians. Date not set. 300p. (Orig.). pap. 7.50 (978-0-914271-67-3(9)) Ministry Pubns.

Freeman, Kirk & Freeman, Jared. Sweatin' the Small Stuff. 2010. 152p. 25.49 (978-1-4520-0939-1(2)); pap. 15.49 (978-1-4520-0938-4(4)) AuthorHouse.

Freeman, Pat. From Despair to Delight: A True Story of God's Faithfulness to Change a Life Forever & Always. 2009. (ENG.). pap. 14.95 (978-1-60037-486-9(7)) Morgan James Publishing.

Freeman, Terrence/Lyle. Elements of Faith: Hope Love Peace. 2008. (Illus.). 127p. spiral bd. 11.95 (978-0-9770035-0-1(7)) TransEd.

Freidzon, Claudio. Rendido Totalmente: Un Llamado a la Consagracion y la Santidad de la Vida Diaria A Traves de las Siete Zambullidas de Naaman, 1 vol. 2006. (SPA.). 176p. per. 9.99 (978-0-8297-4873-4(3)) Vida Pubs.

Frenn, Jason. Power to Reinvent Yourself: How to Break the Destructive Patterns in Your Life. 2010. (ENG.). 288p. 19.99 (978-0-446-54622-5(4)) FaithWords.

—Rompiendo las Barreras: Venciendo la Adversidad y Alcanzando Tu Máximo Potencial. 2009. (SPA.). 304p. pap. 12.99 (978-0-446-55178-6(3)) FaithWords.

Frey, Harold. Prisoners of the Paradigm. 2008. 368p. pap. 19.99 (978-1-60647-251-4(8)) Xulon Pr., Inc.

Friedman, Bob. Sobrevivir: Survival. (SPA.). 110p. (978-84-7228-286-5(4), 220846) Clie, Editorial.

Friesen, Nadine. Thirsting for More: A Group Study in Getting to Know God. 76p. pap. 3.95 (978-0-921788-53-9(3)) Kindred Productions.

Frishcosy, Unofficial Pastor Douglas E. Back Way into Heaven: Living for Life. 2008. 60p. pap. 16.95 (978-1-60474-978-6(4)) PublishAmerica, Inc.

Frisina, Michael E. Metamorphosis: Why Christians Don't Change. 2008. 184p. pap. 14.99 (978-1-60791-187-6(6)) Xulon Pr., Inc.

Fritts, Garner. A Journey Through Time & Eternity. 2006. pap. 13.99 (978-1-60034-387-2(2)) Xulon Pr., Inc.

From Life-Closets to Life-Journeys. 2006. pap. 9.99 (978-1-60034-152-6(7)) Xulon Pr., Inc.

Frost, Jack. Spiritual Slavery to Spiritual Sonship. 2006. (Illus.). 220p. per. 15.99 (978-0-7684-2385-3(6)) Destiny Image Pubs.

Fry, Minister Scheharyl S. A Widow at Forty-Five: Until Death Do Us Part. 2009. 108p. 21.49 (978-1-4490-5440-3(4)); pap. 12.49 (978-1-4490-5439-7(0)) AuthorHouse.

Frye, Carol. Wounded Wings. 2007. pap. 14.99 (978-1-60034-603-3(0)) Xulon Pr., Inc.

Fudge, Edward. The Sound of His Voice: Discovering the Secrets of God's Guidance. 160p. pap. 10.95 (978-0-9714289-4-2(8), Leafwood Pubs.) Abilene Christian Univ. Pr.

Fueston, Loyd L., Jr. The Peace of Christ: Surpassing All Understanding. 2007. 62p. pap. 9.00 (978-1-55635-550-9(5), Wipf and Stock) Wipf & Stock Pubs.

Fugate, J. Richard & Fugate, Virginia Ruth. What the Bible Says about Being a Man. 2nd ed. 2009. (Illus.). 190p. pap. 11.95 (978-1-889700-31-1(2)) Foundation for Biblical Research (TM).

Fukuda, Mitsuo. Upward, Outward, Inward: Passing on the baton of Discipleship. Cozens, Simon, tr. 2010.Tr. of Keiten-aijin. (Illus.). 134p. pap. (978-0-9565943-1-0(X)) Wide Margin Bks.

Fuller, Apostle Vernice. You Can t SHUSH My Praise. 2011. 92p. pap. 10.99 (978-1-61215-816-7(1)) Xulon Pr., Inc.

Fuller, Cheri. Connect with Your Grandkids: Fun Ways to Bridge the Miles. 2009. (ENG.). 240p. pap. 13.99 (978-1-58997-536-1(7)) Tyndale Hse. Pubs.

Fuller, Millard. Building Materials for Life: Volume 3. 2007. pap. 15.00 (978-1-57312-486-7(9)) Smyth & Helwys Publishing, Inc.

Fuller, Pastor Brett Everett. Relate Well: Properly Relating to Your World & the People Most Important to You. 2010. 612p. 44.95 (978-1-4497-0158-1(2)); pap. 38.95 (978-1-4497-0157-4(4)) Author Solutions, Inc. (WestBow Pr.).

Furey., Robert. The Art of Affirmation. 2007. (Illumination Bks.). 128p. pap. 9.95 (978-0-8091-4432-7(8), 4432-8) Paulist Pr.

Furman Hall, Barb. Lessons from Doctor Lowell. 2011. pap. 11.99 (978-1-61739-409-6(2)) Tate Publishing & Enterprises, LLC.

Furr, Chip. Thin Places: Suprising Collisions Between Teh Human Spirit & the Presence of God. 2010. (ENG.). 192p. pap. 14.99 (978-1-935245-25-4(2)) HigherLife Development Services, Inc.

Furtick, Steven. Sun Stand Still: What Happens When You Dare to Ask God for the Impossible. 2010. (ENG.). 224p. pap. 14.99 (978-1-60142-322-1(5), Multnomah) Doubleday Religious Publishing Group, The.

Fuson, Steven D. Kingdom & Dominion: A Bold Proclamation of Kingdom Citizenship. 2011. pap. 12.99 (978-1-61739-195-8(6)) Tate Publishing & Enterprises, LLC.

G., Michael. Hope in the Morning: One Man's Struggle with Addiction And What It Means for You. 2009. 212p. 25.99 (978-1-60791-171-5(X)); pap. 15.99 (978-1-60791-170-8(1)) Xulon Pr., Inc.

Gaba, Latif Haki. The Book of Psalms in English & Latin. 2009. 194p. pap. 23.91 (978-0-557-10863-3(2)) Lulu Enterprises Inc.

Gabriel-Dane, Lori. Beyond the Holy. 2009. 192p. pap. 24.95 (978-1-4489-2164-5(3)) PublishAmerica, Inc.

Gabriel, Ruben. A Divine Word from a Revelation: God Is Longing for the World to Listen to His Message. 2010. pap. 16.99 (978-1-61663-490-2(1)) Tate Publishing & Enterprises, LLC.

Gacutan, Dawn A. Living Life Loved: Keys to Understanding, Accepting & Living in the Love of God. 2011. pap. 12.99 (978-1-61739-451-5(3)) Tate Publishing & Enterprises, LLC.

Gaddie, L. Edward. The Commander's Anointing. 2007. 200p. per. 15.99 (978-0-9777053-4-4(X)) McDougal & Assocs.

Gaddis, Todd. The Spiritual It Factor. 2010. 160p. pap. (978-1-55452-546-1(2), Guardian Bks.) Essence Publishing.

Gagne, Henry. Revealing Eschatologyii: Expanded Edition from Genesis to Revelation. 2009. 724p. pap. 29.95 (978-1-4327-2984-4(5)) Outskirts Pr., Inc.

Gahan, Patrick. Foundations of Discipleship. 2010. 153p. pap. 14.95 (978-0-557-41454-3(7)) Lulu Enterprises Inc.

Gaillardetz, Richard R. Transforming Our Days: Finding God amid the Noise of Modern Life. rev. ed. 2007. (Illus.). 128p. per. 15.95 (978-0-7648-1622-2(5)) Liguori Pubns.

Gaines, Charles. Perspective. 2006. pap. 21.99 (978-1-60034-727-6(4)) Xulon Pr., Inc.

Gaines Jr, Pastor Jake & Gaines Jr., Pastor Jake. Staring down the Barrel of My Faith. 2010. 132p. pap. 12.95 (978-0-9826490-0-8(2)) ASA Publishing Co.

Galan, Vicente. Respuestas Para Grandes Dudas: Answers to Crucial Questions. (SPA.). (978-84-7645-021-5(4), 223085) Clie, Editorial.

Galbraith, James C. There Is Something about an Aqua Velva Man: Read this book & find out what it is! 2009. 112p. 23.99 (978-1-4343-4712-1(5)) AuthorHouse.

Galilea, Segundo. Secuimiento de Cristo. (SPA.). 112p. 4.95 (978-958-607-431-5(5)) Sociedad de San Pablo COL. Dist: St Pauls/Alba Hse. Pubs.

Gallagher, Michael Paul. Faith Maps: Ten Religious Explorers from Newman to Joseph Ratzinger. 2010. 208p. pap. (978-0-8091-4698-7(3)) Paulist Pr.

Gallagher, Patrick. Being a Godparent. 2006. (Illus.). 11p. pap. 3.95 (978-0-8146-3159-1(2), Liturgical Pr. Bks.) Liturgical Pr.

Gallagher, Sharon, ed. Where Faith Meets Culture. 2009. 240p. pap. 24.00 (978-1-60899-144-0(X), Cascade Bks.) Wipf & Stock Pubs.

Gallagher, Steve. Intoxicated with Babylon: The Seduction of God's People in the Last Days. annot. ed. 2007. (ENG.). 240p. per. 13.99 (978-0-9758832-4-2(0)) Pure Life Ministries.

Gallagher, Steve & Gallagher, Kathy. Create in Me a Pure Heart: Answers for Struggling Women. 2007. (ENG.). 272p. per. 13.99 (978-0-9758832-7-3(5)) Pure Life Ministries.

—Create in Me a Pure Heart Workbook: Answers for Struggling Women. 2007. (ENG.). 126p. per. 8.99 (978-0-9758832-8-0(3)) Pure Life Ministries.

Gallaher, Brian K. Radical Christianity for the End Times. 2011. 172p. pap. 14.99 (978-1-61379-340-4(5)) Xulon Pr., Inc.

Gallardo, Rudy. Noah's Time. 2008. 48p. pap. 16.95 (978-1-60563-103-5(5)) PublishAmerica, Inc.

Gallaty, Robby. Creating an Atmosphere to Hear God Speak. 2009. 132p. pap. 11.99 (978-1-60791-696-3(7)) Xulon Pr., Inc.

Galli, Mark. A Companion Guide to Beyond Smells & Bells. 2008. (ENG.). 63p. (gr. 13). pap. 6.95 (978-1-55725-594-5(6)) Paraclete Pr., Inc.

Gallivan, Helen. Dawn Without Darkness: Biblical Companions for a Modern Journey. 2008. (ENG.). 160p. pap. 23.95 (978-1-84730-053-9(7)) Veritas Pubns. IRL. Dist: Dufour Editions, Inc.

Gálvez Velasco, José Antonio. El Sabor de la Vida. 2010. (SPA.). 145p. (978-84-9948-137-1(X)) Club Universitario, Editorial.

Gandy, Nicholas. Seeking an Heir: Getting to the Marriage Altar God's Way: A Study of the Love Story of Isaac & Rebekah. 2010. pap. 10.99 (978-1-61663-171-0(6)) Tate Publishing & Enterprises, LLC.

Gangel, Kenneth O. The Family First. pap. 5.99 (978-0-88469-106-8(3)) BMH Bks.

Gann, Johnny. The Center of His Work, 1 vol. 2009. 58p. pap. 12.95 (978-1-4489-8332-2(0)) PublishAmerica, Inc.

Gano, Ryan. Change Your Life / Change Your World. 2008. 114p. (YA). per. (978-0-9794471-1-2(9)) World Changers Youth Ministry.

Ganuza, Juan. Salve, Aurora Jubilosa. (SPA.). 128p. pap. 3.95 (978-980-207-304-7(0)) Paulinas VEN. Dist: St Pauls/Alba Hse. Pubs.

Garande, Jaimie Oliver. In Pursuit of Destiny: 10 keys to fulfilling your purpose & transforming your Life. 2010. 160p. pap. 13.49 (978-1-4490-9614-4(X)) AuthorHouse.

Garber, Susan Carter. For the Rough Spots in Life: Prayers & Meditations. 2008. pap. 9.99 (978-1-60647-059-6(0)) Xulon Pr., Inc.

Garcia, Benjamin. La Perdida de un Ser Querido.Tr. of Loss of a Loved One. (SPA.). 304p. pap. 4.95 (978-980-350-391-8(X)) Sociedad de San Pablo VEN. Dist: St Pauls/Alba Hse. Pubs.

Garcia, Clara E. Peace of Mind II. 2006. pap. 8.00 (978-0-8059-6764-7(8)) Dorrance Publishing Co., Inc.

Garcia, Gaspar. Building Blocks for Relationships: Qualities for Christian Living. 2008. 160p. 24.95 (978-0-595-61924-5(X)); pap. 14.95 (978-0-595-49156-8(1)) iUniverse, Inc.

Gardiner, Dianne. Breaking the Curse of Condemnation. 2007. pap. 10.99 (978-1-60266-013-7(1)) Xulon Pr., Inc.

Gardner, Ethel M. The Makings of You. 2007. 164p. per. 20.99 (978-1-4257-2290-6(3)) Xlibris Corp.

Gardner, John E. The Three Rs: The View of a Common Man. 2008. 168p. pap. 14.95 (978-1-59858-596-4(7)) Dog Ear Publishing, LLC.

Gardner, Kendrx J. Maximizing Your New Life in Christ. 2008. 140p. pap. 14.99 *(978-1-60647-674-1(2))* Xulon Pr., Inc.

Gardner, Thom. Turn Toward Mercy: Experience the Passion, the Presence & the Glory of God. 2007. 206p. per. 11.99 *(978-0-88270-344-2(7))* Bridge-Logos Foundation.

Garland, Valerie. A Life Worth Living. 2011. 52p. 24.99 ***(978-1-4568-9009-4(3))***; pap. 15.99 ***(978-1-4568-9008-7(5))*** Xlibris Corp.

Garrett, Emlen. The Mark of a Christian. 2007. 192p. 21.99 *(978-1-60266-120-2(0))*; per. 13.99 *(978-1-60266-119-6(7))* Xulon Pr., Inc.

Garrett, Greg. Stories from the Edge: A Theology of Grief. 2008. (ENG., Illus.). 176p. pap. 15.00 *(978-0-664-23204-7(3))* Westminster John Knox Pr.

Garrett, Michael J. 66 Reasons to Run On. 2011. 84p. pap. 19.95 ***(978-1-4560-6845-5(8))*** PublishAmerica, Inc.

Garrick, Gene. Stones of Rememberance. 2007. 144p. per. 13.99 *(978-1-60034-768-9(1))* Xulon Pr., Inc.

Gartrell, Joe. Life Is Simple. 2008. 160p. pap. 13.99 *(978-1-60477-794-9(X))* Xulon Pr., Inc.

Gary, Angela Y. Life in Christ Jesus from A to Z. 2007. 69p. per. 8.95 *(978-1-59624-464-9(7))* E-BookTime LLC.

Gary, Bert. Heaven for Skeptics: A Conversation for Thinking People. 2007. pap. *(978-1-932902-72-3(4))* FaithWalk Publishing.

Gary Eugene Tucker. Face to Face: The Experience. 2009. 240p. pap. 18.49 *(978-1-4343-9016-5(0))* AuthorHouse.

Garza, Crystal. The Modest Heart. 2007. 108p. per. 10.99 *(978-1-60477-276-0(X))* Xulon Pr., Inc.

Garza, Ray. ProVerbs for Teens. 2010. (ENG.). 64p. (YA). 12.95 *(978-0-9795680-5-3(6))* Believers Publishing.

Gast, David. Musing & Muttering Through Cancer. 2008. 108p. per. *(978-1-897373-18-7(X))* Word Alive Pr.

Gateau, Michelle. Mike's Story. 112p. 7.00 *(978-0-281-05036-9(8))* SPCK Publishing GBR. Dist: Pilgrim Pr., The/United Church Pr.

Gateley, Edwina. I Hear a Seed Growing. 2010. (ENG.). 320p. pap. 22.00 *(978-1-57075-900-0(6))* Orbis Bks.

Gates, Elaine. All That I Am, I Owe to God. 2009. 108p. pap. 20.00 *(978-1-4389-2832-6(7))* AuthorHouse.

Gates, Everett. Helping You Is Killing Me: The Armorbearers Call to Serve. 2008. pap. 13.99 *(978-1-60647-295-8(X))* Xulon Pr., Inc.

Gatewood, Otis. You're Not Old at 65. pap. *(978-1-56794-215-6(6)*, C-2156) Star Bible & Tract Corp.

Gatty, Eugene. If You Do, God Will: Secrets to Receiving God's Infinite Blessings. 2011. pap. 10.99 *(978-1-61663-947-1(4))* Tate Publishing & Enterprises, LLC.

Gatumu, Kabiro wa. The Pauline Concept of Supernatural Powers: A Reading from the African Worldview. 2009. (Paternoster Biblical Monographs). 326p. pap. 38.00 *(978-1-60608-472-4(0)*, Wipf and Stock) Wipf & Stock Pubs.

Gaughan, Nancy C. Building Trust: God as Our Role Model in Parenting. 2008. 192p. pap. 24.95 *(978-1-60703-915-0(X))* PublishAmerica, Inc.

Gaukroger, Stephen. It Makes Sense. 3rd ed. (Illus.). 128p. pap. *(978-1-85999-743-7(0))* Scripture Union.

Gaul, Teresa. My Sunshine Daughter of Sacrifice. 2010. pap. 19.95 *(978-0-578-04853-6(1))* Revelation News Pubs.

Gautier, Theophile. The Wife of King Candaules. 2007. (ENG.). 122p. 35.95 *(978-0-548-07209-7(4))* Kessinger Publishing, LLC.

Gaw, Margaret. One Holy Moment. 2010. 48p. pap. 9.95 *(978-1-4497-0504-6(9)*, WestBow Pr.) Author Solutions, Inc.

Gay, Jodi. Bride of Christ. 2011. 46p. pap. 9.99 ***(978-1-61379-212-4(3))*** Xulon Pr., Inc.

Gebel, Dante. Pasion de Multitudes/Passion for the Multitudes, 1 vol. 2008. (SPA.). 208p. pap. 8.99 *(978-0-8297-5503-9(9))* Vida Pubs.

Gebhardt, Daniel. I Am This One Walking Beside Me: Meditations of an HIV Positive Gay Man. 2010. 128p. pap. 16.00 *(978-1-60899-193-8(8)*, Resource Pubns.) Wipf & Stock Pubs.

Gee, Bea. Very Interesting: The World Today. 2008. 80p. pap. 12.99 *(978-1-4343-8397-6(0))* AuthorHouse.

Geertson, Donna. Ready & Waiting: Preparing for Jesus in Every Area of Your Life. 2011. pap. 14.99 *(978-1-61739-944-2(2))* Tate Publishing & Enterprises, LLC.

Geiger, Eric. Identity: Who You Are in Christ. 2008. (ENG.). 208p. 16.99 *(978-0-8054-4689-0(3))* B&H Publishing Group.

Geisel, Ray, compiled by. Walking the 12 Steps with Jesus Christ. 16th ed. 2008. 160p. stu. ed., per. 12.75 *(978-0-9798761-0-3(9))* Christian 12 Step Ministry, Inc.

Geisler, Norman L. & Brooks, Ron. Cuando los Escepticos Pregunten.Tr. of When the Skeptics Ask. (SPA.). 367p. pap. *(978-0-7899-0028-9(9))* Editorial Unilit.

Geiss, Robert. Nearing Midnight: Exploring End-time Prophecy. 2011. pap. 25.99 *(978-1-61739-325-9(8))* Tate Publishing & Enterprises, LLC.

Geoffrey, Kevin. Being a Disciple of Messiah: Building Character for an Effective Walk in Yeshua (the Messianic Life Discipleship Series / Bible Study) 2007. 196p. pap. 13.95 *(978-0-9785504-2-4(0))* Perfect Word Ministries.

—Being a Disciple of Messiah: Building Character for an Effective Walk in Yeshua (the Messianic Life Series / Bookshelf Edition) 2009. 148p. pap. 11.95 *(978-0-9785504-6-2(3))* Perfect Word Ministries.

—Being a Disciple of Messiah: Leader's Guide (the Messianic Life Discipleship Series / Bible Study) 2007. 96p. pap. 9.95 *(978-0-9785504-3-1(9))* Perfect Word Ministries.

George, Carl. Thank You for the Book of Mormon. 2007. 132p. per. 13.99 *(978-1-60266-230-8(4))* Xulon Pr., Inc.

George, Denise. God's Gentle Whisper. 2007. (ENG.). 144p. per. 12.99 *(978-1-84550-236-2(1))* Christian Focus Pubns. GBR. Dist: STL Distribution North America.

George E. Abbas Sr. Jump Starters: Reason & Rhyme. 2009. 380p. pap. 24.95 *(978-1-4401-8250-1(7))* iUniverse, Inc.

George, Elizabeth. Finding God's Path Through Your Trials: His Help for Every Difficulty You Face. 2007. 252p. per. 13.99 *(978-0-7369-1374-4(2))* Harvest Hse. Pubs.

—Jueces/Rut Cultiva una Vida de Integridad, 1 vol. 2010. (mujer conforme al coraz#xF3;n de Dios Ser.). Orig. Title: Judges/Ruth, Cultivating a Life of Character. (SPA.). 160p. pap. 8.99 *(978-0-8254-1256-1(0)*, Editorial Portavoz) Kregel Pubns.

George, Evelyn. Bible Numerics Relating to Countdown to Redemption. 2007. 352p. per. 19.99 *(978-1-60477-509-9(2))* Xulon Pr., Inc.

George Guiver Cr Staff. Vision upon Vision: Processes of Change & Renewal in Christian Worship. 2009. (ENG., Illus.). 256p. pap. 29.99 *(978-1-85311-992-7(X)*, Canterbury Pr. Norwich) Hymns Ancient & Modern Ltd GBR. Dist: Westminster John Knox Pr.

George, Jim. A Man after God's Own Heart: Devoting Your Life to What Really Matters. 2008. 288p. pap. 13.99 *(978-0-7369-2296-8(2))* Harvest Hse. Pubs.

Georges, Robyn Power. What Christ Did for Women. 2011. 338p. 29.99 ***(978-1-4535-9045-4(5))***; pap. 19.99 ***(978-1-4535-9044-7(7))*** Xlibris Corp.

Georgia Yates Blount & Olivia Sebastian. From God the Promise: Memoir of a Holy Women. 2009. 312p. 29.95 *(978-1-4389-7033-2(1))*; pap. 23.95 *(978-1-4389-7034-9(X))* AuthorHouse.

Gerald, Kevin. Mind Monsters: Conquering Fear, Worry, Guilt & Other Negative Thoughts That Work Against You. 2012. (ENG.). 128p. pap. 9.99 ***(978-1-61638-738-9(6)**, Charisma Hse.)* Charisma Media.

Gerberding, Keith A. Las Meditacion Transcendental. (Serie Respuesta).Tr. of Transcendental Meditation. (SPA.). 40p. pap. 2.95 *(978-0-570-04942-5(3)*, 09-2538) Concordia Publishing Hse.

Gerhardt, Darlene. Heavenbound?, 1 vol. 2009. 73p. pap. 16.95 *(978-1-61546-734-1(3))* PublishAmerica, Inc.

Gerner, Terri J. The One Deadly Mistake... We All Make: No Subtitle. 2008. 212p. pap. 14.99 *(978-1-60647-242-2(9))* Xulon Pr., Inc.

Gerth, Holly. Rain on Me: Devotions of Hope & Encouragement for Difficult Times. 2009. (ENG.). 192p. 12.99 *(978-1-934770-49-8(3))* Ellie Claire & Summerside Pr.

Getting A New Identity. 2006. pap. 12.99 *(978-1-60034-347-6(3))* Xulon Pr., Inc.

Getz, Gene & Getz, Elaine. Famine to Fairytale: Ruth & Naomi's Path to Redemption. 2006. pap. 7.99 *(978-1-57494-230-9(1)*, Serendipity Hse.) LifeWay Christian Resources.

Ghazarian, Jacob G. Turkey - the Heritage of the Land. 2009. (Illus.). 222p. pap. *(978-0-7552-1172-2(3))* Authors OnLine, Ltd.

Gibbs, Daunte. Soul Food: Soul Nourishing Devotionals & Recipes. 2010. 108p. pap. 18.95 *(978-1-934363-88-1(X))* Zoe Life Publishing.

Gibbs De Peza, Hazel Ann. My Faith - Spiritual Baptist Christian. 2007. 96p. per. 9.99 *(978-1-60266-509-5(5))* Xulon Pr., Inc.

Gibbs, Doug. A Few Minutes with God. 2009. 140p. pap. 14.99 *(978-1-61579-303-7(8))* Xulon Pr., Inc.

Gibbs, Joe. Game Plan for Life: Your Personal Playbook for Success. 2011. (ENG.). 336p. pap. 14.99 *(978-1-4143-3319-9(6))* Tyndale Hse. Pubs.

Gibbs, Joe & Grey, Derwin L. Game Plan for Life Small Group Leader Kit, Volume 1, Group Edition. 2010. pap. incl. cd-rom *(978-1-4158-7038-9(1))* LifeWay Christian Resources.

Gibbs, Joe, et al. Game Plan for Life, Vol. 1: Joe Gibbs. 2010. (Game Plan for Life Ser.). (Illus.). 126p. pap. *(978-1-4158-6837-9(9))* LifeWay Christian Resources.

Gibbs, Terri, compiled by. Glimmers of Grace: Sparkling Reminders to Encourage You, 0 vols. 2008. (Women of Faith Ser.). (Illus.). 128p. 12.99 *(978-1-4041-0478-5(X))* Nelson, Thomas Inc.

Gibbs, Terri, ed. Deeper Than Tears: Promises of Comfort & Hope, 0 vols. 2007. 128p. 13.99 *(978-1-4041-0466-2(6))* Nelson, Thomas Inc.

Gibson, Andrenna C. Girls Set the Ground Rule: I'm not an Ordinary Chick! I'm an Extraordinary Woman! 2009. 99p. pap. 14.95 *(978-1-4327-3468-8(7))* Outskirts Pr. Inc.

Gibson, David & Watson, Francis. Reading the Decree: Exegesis, Election & Christology in Calvin & Barth. 2009. (T&T Clark Studies in Systematic Theology Ser.). (ENG.). 240p. 130.00 *(978-0-567-46874-1(7)*, T&T Clark Int'l) Continuum International Publishing Group, Ltd. GBR. Dist: National Bk. Network.

Gibson, J. Mark. Blind Faith? 2011. pap. 8.95 ***(978-0-533-16262-8(9))*** Vantage Pr., Inc.

Gibson, Janet & Arrington, Billy Wayne. And God Was Watching: A Biography of Billy Wayne. 2011. 188p. 30.95 ***(978-1-61507-745-8(6))***; pap. 13.95 ***(978-1-61507-744-1(8))*** Cross Bks. Publishing.

Gibson, Lisa. Life in Death: A Journey from Terrorism to Triumph. 2008. pap. 14.99 *(978-1-60647-564-5(9))* Xulon Pr., Inc.

Gibson, Noel & Gibson, Phyl. Excuse Me Your Rejection Is Showing. 255p. *(978-1-85240-110-8(9))* Sovereign World, Ltd.

Gibson, Randy. Biblical Seeds for Success. 2007. 84p. per. 9.99 *(978-1-60266-616-0(4))* Xulon Pr., Inc.

Gibson, Robert. Sacred Compass: The Participant's Guide. 2009. (ENG.). 48p. pap., instr.'s gde. ed. 5.99 *(978-1-55725-673-7(X))* Paraclete Pr., Inc.

Gieselmann, Rob. The Episcopal Call to Love. 2008. 88p. pap. 9.95 *(978-1-933993-60-7(X))* Apocryphile Pr.

Giffard Smith, Sheila. Talking & Walking with God. 2008. 336p. per. *(978-1-84749-264-8(3))* Athena Pr.

Giglio, Louie, contrib. by. Hope: When Life Hurts Most. 2008. audio compact disk 14.99 *(978-5-557-44620-4(6))* Point of Grace Entertainment Group.

—How Great Is Our God. 2008. audio compact disk 14.99 *(978-5-557-44624-2(9))* Point of Grace Entertainment Group.

—Indescribable. 2008. audio compact disk 14.99 *(978-5-557-44623-5(0))* Point of Grace Entertainment Group.

Gilbert, Greg. If Your Baby Could Talk Would You Listen? 2008. 88p. per. 9.99 *(978-1-60477-579-2(3))* Xulon Pr., Inc.

Gilbert, Jennifer. Churchin' Ain't Easy: What All Christians Need to Know but Few Take the Time to Share! 2011. 112p. 22.95 *(978-1-4502-9091-3(4))*; pap. 12.95 *(978-1-4502-9089-0(2))* iUniverse, Inc.

Gilding, David. Spiritual Baptist: Is it a Christian Religion? 2010. pap. 9.95 *(978-0-7414-5866-7(7))* Infinity Publishing.

Giles, Henry. Christian Thought on Life in a Series of Discourses. 2006. 300p. per. 23.99 *(978-1-4255-2882-9(1))* MPublishing.

Giles, Richard. At Heaven's Gate: Reflections on Leading Worship. 2010. (ENG.). xiii, 152p. pap. 14.99 *(978-1-84825-046-8(0)*, Canterbury Pr. Norwich) Hymns Ancient & Modern Ltd GBR. Dist: Westminster John Knox Pr.

Gillon, Heather & Snell, Holly. Dancing on My Ashes: Learning to Love the One Who Gives & Takes Away. 2010. pap. 16.99 *(978-1-60799-871-6(8))* Tate Publishing & Enterprises, LLC.

Gill, A. L., compiled by. Promesas de Dios para Cada una de Sus Necesidades, 0 vols. 2007.Tr. of God's Promises for Your Every Need. (SPA.). 320p. im. lthr. 12.99 *(978-0-89922-584-5(5))* Grupo Nelson.

Gill, Richard L. God's Abundance: It's for You. 2009. 180p. 26.95 *(978-0-595-51081-8(7))*; pap. 16.95 *(978-0-595-52312-2(9))* iUniverse, Inc.

Gilley, Gary E. Is That You Lord? Hearing the Voice of the Lord, a Biblical Perspective. 2007. 96p. per. *(978-0-85234-652-5(2))* Evangelical Pr.

Gilliam, L. A. The Heart Garden: Keys to the Kingdom Series Book One Breaking down Sowing & Reaping. 2007. pap. 10.99 *(978-1-60477-229-6(8))* Xulon Pr., Inc.

Gilliard, Francis E. Walking in Affluence. 2009. 248p. pap. 15.99 *(978-1-60791-257-6(0))* Xulon Pr., Inc.

Gilligan, Neil. Transformed by the Power of God. 2010. (ENG.). pap. 15.99 *(978-0-7684-3258-9(8))* Destiny Image Pubs.

Gilliland, Brian. His Gentle Hand. 2008. 252p. pap. 16.99 *(978-1-60791-116-6(7))* Xulon Pr., Inc.

Gillmore, Lottie. Supernatural Flying Monkeys & Dancing Chickens. 2009. 176p pap. 14.99 *(978-1-4389-6836-0(1))* AuthorHouse.

Gillquist, Peter E. Amor Ahora: Love Is Now. (SPA.). 148p. *(978-84-7228-144-8(2)*, 220021) Clie, Editorial.

Gills, James P. Believe & Rejoice: Changed by Faith, Filled with Joy. rev. ed. 2007. (ENG.). 144p. pap. 10.99 *(978-1-59979-169-2(2)*, Creation Hse.) Charisma Media.

—Rx for Worry: A Thankful Heart. 2007. (ENG., Illus.). 176p. pap. 12.99 *(978-1-59979-090-9(4)*, Creation Hse.) Charisma Media.

Gilman, Dan. Learn to Love: Becoming the People God Intended. 2010. 215p. pap. 14.95 *(978-1-4327-0785-9(X))* Outskirts Pr., Inc.

Gilmer, Charles. A Cry of Hope a Call to Action: Unleashing the Next Generation of Black Christian Leaders. 2009. (ENG.). 176p. pap. 12.99 *(978-1-59979-605-5(8)*, Creation Hse.) Charisma Media.

Gilmore, Pam & Lynn, David. Daily Directions. 2008. pap. 13.99 *(978-1-60647-000-8(0))* Xulon Pr., Inc.

Gilyard, Tara. Three Important Promises Given to Those in Relationship with God: Faith - Hope - Love, 1 vol. 2010. 66p. pap. 19.95 *(978-1-4489-3939-8(9))* PublishAmerica, Inc.

Giorgio, Eric. The Body of Christ Unleashed. 2008. 168p. pap. 13.99 *(978-1-60477-915-8(2))* Xulon Pr., Inc.

Giovannetti, Bill. How to Keep Your Inner Mess from Trashing Your Outer World: Creating Peace from Your Inner Chaos, 1 vol. 2008. 256p. pap. 13.99 *(978-0-8254-6285-6(1)*, Monarch Bks.) Lion Hudson PLC GBR. Dist: Kregel Pubns.

Giovannetti, Richard. Crossing Your Jordan. 2007. 88p. per. 9.99 *(978-1-60477-284-5(0))* Xulon Pr., Inc.

Gipson, Norman. The Blessed Man. 96p. pap. 6.95 *(978-1-56794-146-3(X)*, C-2483) Star Bible & Tract Corp.

Girard, Robert C. The Book of Hebrews, 0 vols. Richards, Larry, ed. 2008. (Smart Guide to the Bible Ser.). 384p. pap. 14.99 *(978-1-4185-1008-4(4))* Nelson, Thomas Inc.

Gish, Duane T. Teorias Sobre el Origen de la Vida: The Beginning of Life. (SPA.). 112p. *(978-84-7228-548-4(0)*, 220643) Clie, Editorial.

Githaite, Sabina. God Remembers, He Forgets Not. 2007. 284p. per. 15.99 *(978-1-60266-511-8(7))* Xulon Pr., Inc.

Gladden, Marie C. Inspiration Connection: Empowering Your Faith. 2011. pap. 19.99 *(978-1-61777-181-1(3))* Tate Publishing & Enterprises, LLC.

Gladden, Washington. Ruling Ideas of the Present Age. 2010. (ENG.). 314p. pap. 30.75 *(978-1-177-96886-7(X))* 2009. 310p. pap. 28.75 *(978-1-113-88569-2(6))* 2009. 312p. 25.99 *(978-1-103-43663-7(5))* 2009. 312p. pap. 19.99 *(978-1-103-43661-3(9))* BiblioBazaar.

—Ruling Ideas of the Present Age. 2009. 98p. pap. 14.14 *(978-1-151-36526-2(2))* General Bks. LLC.

—Ruling Ideas of the Present Age. 2008. 312p. 45.95 *(978-1-4365-2580-0(2))* 2007. (ENG.). 316p. per. 30.95 *(978-0-548-69754-2(X))* Kessinger Publishing, LLC.

Glass, Alberta. The Golden Steps to a Brand New You. 2011. 140p. pap. 24.95 ***(978-1-4560-3780-2(3))*** PublishAmerica, Inc.

Glass, John. Released from the Snare. pap. 5.99 *(978-1-898938-84-2(9)*, Alpha) Authentic Media.

Gleason, Edward S. Dying We Live. 188p. pap. 2.95 *(978-1-56101-014-1(6)*, 1747) Forward Movement Pubns.

Gleaves, G. Seeking a Life That Counts. 2006. 132p. per. 8.99 *(978-0-89225-555-9(2))* Gospel Advocate Co., Inc.

Glennon, Jim. Your Healing Is Within You. 189p. pap. *(978-0-340-24009-0(1)*, Hodder & Stoughton) Hodder General Publishing Div.

Glidewell, Roger. Growing Up: Youth Ministry Coming of Age. 2008. 148p. (C). pap. 14.99 *(978-0-615-19753-1(1))* Global Youth Ministry.

Glory to God. 5.00 *(978-0-687-02477-3(3))* Abingdon Pr.

Glover, Bernadette. Whispers Overheard. 2010. 70p. pap. 10.99 *(978-1-61579-857-5(9))* Xulon Pr., Inc.

Glover, Betty Joyce. Woe unto the Pastors: Warning! Warning! Warning! 2009. 172p. pap. 14.99 *(978-1-61579-581-9(2))* Xulon Pr., Inc.

Glover, Sterling E. Obsession. 2011. (Illus.). 160p. pap. 12.95 ***(978-1-4327-6585-9(X))*** Outskirts Pr., Inc.

Gnanaharan, R. The Lamb of God & the Seven-Sealed Scroll. 2007. 248p. per. 14.99 *(978-1-60477-061-2(9))* Xulon Pr., Inc.

Gockel, Herman W. Cristo, mi Salvador (What Jesus Means to Me) 2011. 96p. pap. 2.99 ***(978-0-7586-2684-4(3))*** Concordia Publishing Hse

—La Cruz y el Hombre Comun (The Cross & the Common Man) (SPA.). 144p. pap. 3.95 *(978-0-570-05115-2(0))* Concordia Publishing Hse.

—Que Valor Tiene Cristo en Tu Vida? (What Does Jesus Mean to Me?) (SPA.). 92p. pap. 3.95 *(978-0-570-09907-9(2)*, 16-1008) Concordia Publishing Hse.

God at Work. 2007. per. *(978-0-9740109-1-5(X))* It's About Lives Ministries.

God Is in Control: Gift Book. 9.90 *(978-0-87162-683-7(7))* Warner Pr. Pubs.

God Made the World to See Graded Press. 1.95 *(978-0-687-70151-3(1))* Abingdon Pr.

God Sightings: the One Year Companion Guide. 2009. 112p. pap. 9.99 *(978-0-7644-3925-4(1))* Group Publishing, Inc.

God Sightings: the One Year Small Group Leader Guide. 2009. 120p. pap. 9.99 *(978-0-7644-3926-1(X))* Group Publishing, Inc.

Goddard, Arthur C. Walk with Me on Life's Highway. 2009. 188p. pap. 14.99 *(978-1-61579-007-4(1))* 2008. 112p. 19.99 *(978-1-60647-888-2(5))* 2008. 112p. 11.99 *(978-1-60647-887-5(7))* Vol. 2. 2009. 188p. 22.99 *(978-1-61579-490-4(5))* Xulon Pr., Inc.

Godfree, Margaret. Praying for Mission. (What Christians Should Know about Ser.). 48p. pap. *(978-1-85240-295-2(4))* Sovereign World, Ltd.

Godfrey, Erika R. Single Ladies, C L a P Your Hands - Celebrating Life Always Praising. 2008. 80p. pap. 10.99 *(978-1-60647-759-5(5))* Xulon Pr., Inc.

Godley, Pamela. Gods Pearl. 2006. pap. 10.99 *(978-1-60034-482-4(8))* Xulon Pr., Inc.

Godley-Ramos, J. A Bastard's Refuge II Rejected by Man but Adopted by God. 2007. 432p. pap. 21.00 *(978-0-615-15836-5(6))* Gutter to Grace to Glory Ministries Int Inc.

God's Creative Power for Babies & Toddlers. 2007. 33p. (J). pap. 0.00 *(978-0-9747513-8-2(3))* Capps Publishing.

God's Creative Power for Grandparents. 2007. 54p. pap. 8.00 *(978-0-9747513-9-9(1))* Capps Publishing.

God's Creative Power for PreSchoolers. 2007. 34p. (J). pap. 8.00 *(978-0-9747513-7-5(5))* Capps Publishing.

God's Financial Partner: A Bible Course on God, Money & You. *(978-0-9607644-0-2(2))* Financial Partners Publishing.

God's Grace in the Sixties. (Yearbook Bible Studies). 6.99 *(978-0-570-06947-8(5)*, 20-3052) Concordia Publishing Hse.

God's Plan for Growing Up. ldr.'s ed. 11.95 *(978-1-57153-300-5(1))* Curriculum Publishing, Presbyterian Church (U. S. A.).

God's Plan for Growing Up: Parent's Guide. 6.99 *(978-1-57153-303-6(6))* Curriculum Publishing, Presbyterian Church (U. S. A.).

Godsil, Richard. Building a Strong & Loving Family: Six Interactive Lessons to Becoming A More Fulfilled Family. 2009. 151p. pap. 11.95 *(978-1-4327-2502-0(5))* Outskirts Pr., Inc.

Godwin, Sue Eudy. Living Temple or Rundown Shack: The Christian's Biblical Responsibility for Body Care. 2007. 84p. per. 11.95 *(978-1-4251-0633-1(1))* Trafford Publishing.

Goebel, Sarah. Satisfied Woman. 2006. pap. 17.99 *(978-1-60034-803-7(3))* Xulon Pr., Inc.

Goering, Gloria (Vermaas). God's Appointments. 2011. 474p. pap. 24.99 ***(978-1-61379-059-5(7))*** Xulon Pr., Inc.

Goertzmiller, Ashley K. Behavior Boosters. 2011. 86p. pap. 10.99 *(978-1-61379-016-8(3))* Xulon Pr., Inc.

Goetz, Dave L. Death by Suburb: How to Keep the Suburbs from Killing Your Soul. annot. ed. 2007. (ENG.). 240p. per. 13.99 *(978-0-06-085968-8(7)*, HarperOne) HarperCollins Pubs.

Goetz, Stewart. Freedom, Teleology, & Evil. 2011. (ENG.). 226p. pap. 44.95 ***(978-1-4411-8769-7(3))*** Continuum International Publishing Group, Ltd. GBR. Dist: National Bk. Network.

Goff, Bryant. Justification, Imputed Righteousness, Assurance, Unity & Diversity. 205p. pap. 9.95 *(978-1-56794-182-1(6)*, C-2526) Star Bible & Tract Corp.

C

Goings, Louise. When Your Dreams Don't Come True: Awaken to God's Perfect Plans for Your Life. 2008. (ENG.). 80p. pap. 9.99 (978-1-59979-450-1(0), Creation Hse.) Charisma Media.
Goldberg, Bruce. Soul Healing. 2008. (ENG., Illus.). 304p. pap. 16.95 (978-1-57968-021-3(6)) Goldberg, Bruce Inc.
Golden, Tim. Faith of Starlit Hours. 2011. 112p. 28.95 **(978-1-4627-0635-8(5))**; pap. 11.95 **(978-1-4627-0634-1(7))** Cross Bks. Publishing.
Goldman, Jonathan. The Divine Name: The Sound That Can Change the World. 2010. (ENG.). 240p. pap. 17.95 (978-1-4019-2699-1(1)) Hay Hse., Inc.
Goldwell, Bruce, et al. Mastery of Abundant Living - Christian Keys to the Law of Attraction. 2007. 216p. per. (978-1-897512-01-2(5)) Saga Bks.
—Mastery of Abundant Living - New Life Resolutions. 2007. 236p. per. (978-1-894936-96-5(5)) Saga Bks.
Golemon, Larry A. Living Our Story: Narrative Leadership & Congregational Culture. 2009. (978-1-56699-378-4(4)) Alban Institute, Inc.
Goll, James W. Hearing God: How Does God Speak to Me? Practical Helps for Listening to Him, Avoiding Confusion. 2008. (Beginner's Guide To Ser.). (ENG.). 160p. per. 12.99 (978-0-8307-4611-8(0)) Gospel Light Pubns.
Goll, James W. & Engle, Lou. The Call of the Elijah Revolution: The Passion for Radical Change. 2008. 262p. per. 15.99 (978-0-7684-2544-4(1)) Destiny Image Pubs.
Goll, James W. & Goll, Michal Ann. Compassion. 2006. (Women on the Front Lines Ser.). 206p. per. 14.99 (978-0-7684-2386-0(4)) Destiny Image Pubs.
Golson Jr, William T. On the matter of Relationships. 2007. pap. 15.99 (978-1-60266-023-6(9)) Xulon Pr., Inc.
Gomez-Kelley, Sally. Your Family & the Sacraments. 2007. (978-0-8294-2492-8(X)) Loyola Pr.
Gomez, Michele J. Teach Us to Pray a Perspective on the Our Father: A Guide to Activating A Vital & Powerful Personal Prayer Life! 2009. 112p. pap. 11.99 (978-1-61579-141-5(8)) Xulon Pr., Inc.
Gomez, S. F. Stitch by Stitch: The Threads of Truth, Reason, Hope & Faith. 2009. 116p. pap. 11.99 (978-1-61579-332-7(1)) Xulon Pr., Inc.
Gondeck, John. Building Blocks to Great Faith. 2010. 112p. 21.49 (978-1-4520-6831-2(3)); pap. 12.49 (978-1-4520-6828-2(3)) AuthorHouse.
Gonzales, Rafaelita. Secrets in the Beacon Light. 2011. 148p. 29.99 **(978-1-4628-6200-9(4))**; pap. 19.99 **(978-1-4628-6199-6(7))** Xlibris Corp.
Gonzales, Sharon. Justice Wrapped in Mercy. 2007. per. (978-1-59872-543-8(2)) Instant Pub.
Gonzalez, Miguel. Introduction to the Essential Doctrines. 2006. 160p. pap. 13.95 (978-1-4327-0116-1(9)) Outskirts Pr., Inc.
Good, Jim. Selected to Suffer. 2010. pap. 10.99 (978-1-61663-097-3(3)) Tate Publishing & Enterprises, LLC.
Good, Kenneth. The Answer Is Yes: Both/and Theology in an Either/or World. 2008. 280p. pap. 27.95 (978-1-60474-886-4(9)) PublishAmerica, Inc.
Goodall, Wayde & Goodall, Wayde I. Success Kills: Sidestep the Snares That Will Steal Your Dreams. 2009. 159p. pap. (978-0-89221-692-5(1)) New Leaf Pr., Inc.
Goode, Christee T. Thirty Something. 2007. 104p. per. 9.99 (978-1-59886-620-9(6)) Tate Publishing & Enterprises, LLC.
Gooden, Charles L. Piercing the Darkness of the Heart. 2009. 72p. pap. 15.99 (978-1-4415-4390-5(2)) Xlibris Corp.
Goodenough, John B. Witness to Grace. 2008. 85p. pap. 16.95 (978-1-60474-767-6(6)) PublishAmerica, Inc.
Goodine, Wayne. Dp I'm Free. 1.05 (978-0-7673-1102-1(7)) LifeWay Christian Resources.
Goodman Emory. Our New Life in Christ: Ministry Training School: Level One. 2007. (Ministry Training School Ser.). (ENG.). 167p. per. 19.95 (978-1-932433-38-8(4)) Gatekeeper Publishing.
Goodmiller, Roy. The Secret Place. pap. 6.99 (978-0-89098-124-5(8)) Twentieth Century Christian Bks.
Goodrich, George M. Adventures with Apples & Snakes: From the Garden of Eden. 2010. 208p. 24.99 (978-1-4520-2842-2(7)); (ENG.). pap. 14.49 (978-1-4520-2843-9(5)) AuthorHouse.
Goodroe, Scot A. America's Sustainability: How Do We Keep in Existence the Christian Values Our Country Set up to Preserve & Pass on to Future Generations? 2008. 64p. pap. 9.99 (978-1-60647-090-9(6)) Xulon Pr., Inc.
Goodwin, Craig L. Year of Plenty. 2011. 224p. pap. 12.95 (978-1-4514-0074-8(8), Sparkhouse Pr.) Spark Hse.
Goodwin, Samuel. Just How Dumb Do You Think I Am? 2008. 192p. pap. 13.99 (978-1-60477-673-7(0)) Xulon Pr., Inc.
Gool, Marilyn. Come up Higher, Pt. 1. Date not set. 90p. (Orig.). pap. 5.95 (978-0-9648460-2-9(0)) Conquerors Publishing.
Goolsby, Monica. If It Had Not Been for the Lord. 2011. 140p. 22.99 **(978-1-61379-231-5(X))**; pap. 14.99 **(978-1-61379-230-8(1))** Xulon Pr., Inc.
Goonewardene, Angela. Light of the Harvest: Jesus Is the Light. 2011. 100p. pap. 12.05 **(978-1-4567-8816-2(7))** AuthorHouse.
Goosen, Gideon. Spacetime & Theology in Dialogue. 2008. pap. (978-0-87462-734-3(6)) Marquette Univ. Pr.
Goossen, Gayle. Rock the World: An Interactive Study of Our Faith Heritage. 48p. pap. 12.95 (978-0-921788-28-7(2)) Kindred Productions.
—Rocking the World: An Interactive Study of Our Faith Heritage. pap. 20.95 incl. VHS (978-0-921788-36-2(3)) Kindred Productions.
Goral, Ricki. Sins of the Fathers. 2011. 348p. pap. 18.99 **(978-1-61215-783-2(1))** Xulon Pr., Inc.
Gordon, Bob. Learning to Minister Like Jesus. (Illus.). 208p. pap. (978-1-85240-198-6(2)) Sovereign World, Ltd.
Gordon, Bob & Fardouly, David. The Foundations of Christian Living. 2007. (Illus.). 276p. pap. **(978-1-85240-479-6(5))** Sovereign World, Ltd.
Gordon, Dana & McNutt, Antione. Straight Talk to the Soul. 2010. 65p. pap. 12.95 (978-1-4327-5069-5(0)) Outskirts Pr., Inc.
Gordon, Elizabeth. Creator of My Heart: A New Heart Is What I Need. 2011. 144p. 28.95 (978-1-4497-0971-6(0)); pap. 11.95 (978-1-4497-0969-3(9)) Author Solutions, Inc. (WestBow Pr.).
Gordon, Glenn. Healthy Living. 2007. 140p. per. 14.95 (978-0-9791566-4-9(5)) To His Glory Publishing Co., Inc.
Gordon, Melissa. Broken but Healed. 2011. 66p. pap. 19.95 **(978-1-4560-5660-5(3))** PublishAmerica, Inc.
Gordon, Raymond M. Rivers of Righteousness: Quiet, Quicken, Quench. 2007. 254p. pap. 15.95 (978-0-7414-4397-7(X)) Infinity Publishing.
Gordon, S. D. Consejos Practicos Como Seguir a Cristo: Quiet Talks on Following Christ. (SPA.). 176p. (978-84-7228-765-5(3), 222240) Clie, Editorial.
—Quiet Talks on Power. 2009. (ENG.). 221p. 32.99 (978-1-117-71250-5(8)); pap. 20.99 (978-1-117-71252-9(4), BiblioLife); pap. 24.75 (978-1-117-71251-2(6)) BiblioBazaar.
—Quiet Talks on Power. 218p. 2011. 39.95 **(978-1-169-84700-2(5))** 2010. 31.96 (978-1-163-21979-9(7)) 2010. pap. 19.96 (978-1-162-72440-9(4)) Kessinger Publishing, LLC.
Gordon, S. D. Quiet Talks on Service. 2009. 214p. 28.99 (978-1-110-58450-5(4)) 2009. 214p. pap. 23.75 (978-1-110-58449-9(0)) 2009. (ENG.). 212p. pap. 20.99 (978-1-110-58447-5(4), BiblioLife) 2009. (ENG.). 212p. pap. 22.99 (978-1-110-58448-2(2), BiblioLife) 2008. 156p. 22.99 (978-0-554-33602-2(2)) 2008. 156p. 25.99 (978-0-554-24299-6(0)) 2006. (ENG.). 140p. pap. 18.99 (978-1-4264-6164-4(X)) 2006. (ENG.). 152p. pap. 21.99 (978-1-4264-6219-1(0)) BiblioBazaar.
—Quiet Talks on Service. 2007. (ENG.). 88p. per. (978-1-4068-6238-6(X)) Echo Library.
Gordon, S. d. & Gordon, S. D. Quiet Talks on Power. 2010. 222p. 32.99 (978-1-140-29165-7(3)); pap. 24.75 (978-1-140-29166-4(1)) BiblioBazaar.
—Quiet Talks on Power. 2010. (Illus.). 88p. pap. 20.00 (978-1-153-75629-7(3)) General Bks. LLC.
—Quiet Talks on Service. 2010. (Illus.). 76p. pap. 20.00 (978-1-153-68241-1(9)) General Bks. LLC.
Gordon, S. D. (Samuel Dickey). Quiet Talks on Power. 2012. 128p. pap. **(978-3-8472-3361-9(0))** Tredition GmbH.
Gordon, S. d. 1859-1936. Quiet Talks on Power. 2011. 226p. pap. 25.75 **(978-1-245-20923-6(X))** 2010. (ENG.). 290p. pap. 28.75 (978-1-171-60022-0(4)) BiblioBazaar.
—Quiet Talks on Service. 2011. 222p. pap. 24.75 **(978-1-245-20716-4(4))** BiblioBazaar.
Gordon, Samuel Dickey. Quiet Talks on Power. 2010. 222p. pap. 24.75 (978-1-141-71858-0(8)) 2008. 148p. pap. 24.99 (978-0-554-29209-0(2)) 2008. 224p. 24.99 (978-0-554-52367-5(1)) 2008. 224p. 27.99 (978-0-554-52360-6(4)) 2008. 148p. 21.99 (978-0-554-38512-9(0)) 2008. 224p. pap. 23.75 (978-0-554-52363-7(9)) 2008. 224p. pap. 24.75 (978-0-554-52361-3(2)) 2007. (ENG.). 130p. per. 18.99 (978-1-4346-7144-8(5)) 2007. (ENG.). 146p. per. 19.99 (978-1-4346-7145-5(3)) BiblioBazaar.
—Quiet Talks on Power. 2009. 96p. pap. 18.38 (978-1-151-55485-7(5)) General Bks. LLC.
—Quiet Talks on Service. 2010. 220p. pap. 24.75 (978-1-149-12020-0(7)) 2010. 218p. pap. 24.75 (978-1-146-41963-5(5)) 2009. 214p. 28.99 (978-1-115-42641-1(9)) 2009. 214p. 32.99 (978-1-115-42643-5(5)) 2009. 214p. pap. 23.75 (978-1-115-42637-4(0)) 2009. 214p. pap. 24.75 (978-1-115-42639-8(7)) 2009. (ENG.). 212p. pap. 20.99 (978-1-115-42634-3(6), BiblioLife) 2009. (ENG.). 212p. pap. 22.99 (978-1-115-42636-7(2), BiblioLife) BiblioBazaar.
—Quiet Talks on Service. 2009. 80p. pap. (978-1-151-67175-2(4)) Books LLC.
—Quiet Talks on Service. 2010. 212p. pap. 19.96 (978-1-163-26556-7(X)) 2010. 212p. 31.96 **(978-1-163-54506-5(6))** 2007. (ENG.). 210p. 39.95 (978-0-548-24377-0(8)) 2007. (ENG.). 212p. per. 24.95 (978-1-4326-4561-8(7)) Kessinger Publishing, LLC.
Gordon, Sandra Kay & McKanders, Carolyn M. Nakia's Gift: A Mother's Journey from Misery to Ministry. 2009. 128p. 15.99 (978-1-933972-16-9(5)) PriorityONE Pubns.
Gore, Nancy N. Out of Darkness, into His Marvelous Light: Receive God's Grace & Love. 2008. (ENG.). 96p. pap. 7.99 (978-1-59979-457-0(8), Creation Hse.) Charisma Media.
Gorini, Frederick D. Truth about Lies. 2009. 80p. pap. 10.99 (978-1-60791-873-8(0)) Xulon Pr., Inc.
—Truth Be Told: A Sequel to the Unkonwn God. 2008. 248p. pap. 15.99 (978-1-60791-139-5(6)) Xulon Pr., Inc.
Gorman, Mary Jane. Watching the Disciples - Learning from Their Mistakes: A Lenten Study for Adults. 2008. 64p. pap. 7.00 (978-0-687-64788-0(6)) Abingdon Pr.
Gorslin, Sherry. Prepared in the Wilderness: A Devotional Journal. 2009. 244p. pap. 15.99 (978-1-60791-353-5(4)) Xulon Pr., Inc.
Gort, Steven. Annointed Words of Faith. 2006. pap. 19.00 (978-0-8059-7126-2(2)) Dorrance Publishing Co., Inc.
Gosling, Glenys Evelyn & Gosling, Les Aron. Messiah's Mum: A Controversial & Radical Reconsideration of the Life of the Holy Family. 2009. 160p. pap. 23.99 (978-1-4389-3954-4(X)) AuthorHouse.
The Gospel According to Jesus: What Is Authentic Faith?, 1 vol. 2010. (ENG.). 304p. pap. 4.49 (978-0-310-32675-5(3)) Zondervan.
Gospel Light Publications Staff. Rock-Solid Followers: Helping Kids Discover Jesus' Love for Them & the World. 2008. (ENG.). 256p. (J). (gr. -1-7). 49.99 (978-0-8307-5114-3(9)) Gospel Light Pubns.
Gospel Light Publications Staff, creator. Discipleship Basics. 2007. (Big Books (Gospel Light) Ser.). (ENG., Illus.). 224p. (J). 29.99 (978-0-8307-4401-5(0)) Gospel Light Pubns.
—Start Living. 2006. (First Place Bible Study Ser.). (Illus.). 253p. pap. 19.99 incl. audio compact disk (978-0-8307-3925-7(4), Regal Bks.) Gospel Light Pubns.
Gossett, Mary Wood. A Bargain in a Shed. 2008. 92p. pap. 16.95 (978-1-60474-660-0(2)) PublishAmerica, Inc.
Gossiaux, Pamela. Why Is There a Lemon in My Fruit Salad? 2008. (Illus.). 110p. per. 12.95 (978-1-934363-06-5(5)) Zoe Life Publishing.
Gothard, Bill. The Power of the House of God. 2007. (Illus.). 160p. (978-0-916888-39-8(8)) Institute in Basic Life Principles.
Goulburn, Edward Meyrick. The Pursuit of Holiness: A Sequel to Thoughts on Personal Religion. intended to Carry the Reader Somewhat Further Onward in the Spiritual Life. by E. 2006. 296p. per. 23.99 (978-1-4255-2829-4(5)) MPublishing.
—The Pursuit of Holiness: a Sequel to Thoughts on Personal Religion. 2007. (ENG.). 292p. per. 28.95 (978-1-4304-4355-1(3)) Kessinger Publishing, LLC.
Gould, El. Don t Give up the Palace for a Night. 2010. 292p. 26.99 (978-1-61579-609-0(6)); pap. 16.99 (978-1-61579-608-3(8)) Xulon Pr., Inc.
Gould, Mamie McCormick. My Destiny Is Not the Wilderness. 2008. 128p. 21.99 (978-1-60647-174-6(0)); pap. 13.99 (978-1-60647-173-9(2)) Xulon Pr., Inc.
Goure, Jim. Jesus: Mission & Message. 2008. 164p. pap. 18.95 (978-1-4327-3835-8(6)) Outskirts Pr., Inc.
Gouveia-Whitehead, Maureen M. Morvet's Memoirs - God's Divine Intervention & Protection. 2008. 52p. per. 9.99 (978-1-60477-793-2(1)) Xulon Pr., Inc.
Goyer, Tricia. Blue Like Play Dough: The Shape of Motherhood in the Grip of God. 2009. (ENG.). 208p. pap. 13.99 (978-1-60142-152-4(4), Multnomah) Doubleday Religious Publishing Group, The.
Gozar, Ave Siao. Ignite Your Fire! 2011. 400p. 26.99 **(978-1-931232-99-9(7))** Xulon Pr., Inc.
Grabner, C. S. C. Gazing into God's Open Heart: 101 Pathways to Joy. 2009. 220p. pap. 14.95 (978-1-4389-1339-1(7)) AuthorHouse.
Grace, Clifford A. Let There Be Light. 2011. 378p. pap. 15.99 **(978-1-61379-727-3(3))** Xulon Pr., Inc.
Grace, Forest. God Is an Illusion: To Live Is to Experience. 2011. 120p. pap. 21.99 (978-1-926780-15-3(9)) Key Publishing Hse., Inc., The CAN. Dist: AtlasBooks Distribution.
Grace, Marie. Thoughts Aplenty: The Collected Works of Marie Grace (in alphabetical Order) 2009. (J). pap. 14.99 (978-1-60799-797-9(5)) Tate Publishing & Enterprises, LLC.
Grace, Marion. The Hidden Treasures in the Darkness & Secret Places. 2011. 278p. 31.99 **(978-1-61379-069-4(4))** Xulon Pr., Inc.
Grace, Tammy. Eyes Wide Open. 2007. 68p. per. 11.99 (978-1-60266-942-0(2)) Xulon Pr., Inc.
Gracious Imperatives. 13.00 incl. audio (978-0-687-76223-1(5)) Abingdon Pr.
Graff, Jim. A Significant Life: Fulfilling Your Eternal Potential Every Day. 2006. (ENG.). 240p. 19.99 (978-1-4000-7262-0(X)); pap. 13.99 (978-1-4000-7349-8(9)) Doubleday Religious Publishing Group, The. (WaterBrook Pr.).
—Una Vida con Significado: Realice su Potencial Eterno Cada Día. Magnet, Alberto, tr. from ENG. 2007. (Vintage Espanol Ser.). (SPA & ENG.). 288p. pap. 16.00 (978-0-307-38597-0(3), Vintage) Knopf Doubleday Publishing Group.
Graham, Billy. Beginning Your Christian Life. 2007. pap. 4.95 (978-1-59328-138-0(2)) Graham, Billy Evangelistic Assn.
—Christian Life & Witness Course. (Christian Growth Ser.). 66p. wbk. ed. 2.95 (978-0-89066-299-1(1), 62991) World Wide Pubns.
—Hagamos Discipulos.Tr. of Disciple Making. (SPA.). 10.99 (978-0-7899-0340-2(7), 491055) Editorial Unilit.
—The Journey: How to Live by Faith in an Uncertain World. l.t. ed. 2008. (ENG.). 462p. (J). pap. 17.95 (978-1-59415-164-4(4), Walker Large Print) Cengage Gale.
—The Journey: How to Live by Faith in an Uncertain World, 0 vols. 2007. 320p. per. 15.99 (978-0-8499-1887-2(1)) Nelson, Thomas Inc.
—Led to Believe: Inspiring Words from Billy Graham & a Personal Stories from Those Whose Lives He Touched. l.t. ed. 2009. (ENG.). 320p. pap. 16.95 (978-1-59415-278-8(0)) Cengage Gale.
—Led to Believe by Billy Graham: Inspiring Words from Billy Graham & Others on Living by Faith. 2007. (ENG.). 176p. 14.99 (978-0-8249-4726-2(6), Guideposts) Ideals Pubns.
—Nearing Home: Life, Faith, & Finishing Well. 2011. 192p. 19.99 (978-0-8499-4832-9(0)) Nelson, Thomas Inc.
—Nearing Home: Life, Faith, & Finishing Well. l.t. ed. 2012. (ENG.). 240p. 30.99 **(978-1-4104-4287-1(X))** Thorndike Pr.
—Peace with God. 2011. 304p. pap. 14.99 (978-0-8499-1013-5(7)) Nelson, Thomas Inc.
—Secrets of Happiness. 2011. 224p. pap. 14.99 (978-0-8499-0999-3(6)) Nelson, Thomas Inc.
—Wisdom for Each Day, 0 vols. 2008. 384p. 15.99 (978-1-4041-8693-4(X)) Nelson, Thomas Inc.
Graham, Charles. Another Year of Encouragement. 2006. (ENG.). 25.99 (978-1-60034-820-4(3)); pap. 15.99 (978-1-60034-819-8(X)) Xulon Pr., Inc.
Graham, Eduardo. Sangre y Agua. (SPA.). 272p. 9.95 (978-950-861-133-8(2)) Sociedad de San Pablo ARG. Dist: St Pauls/Alba Hse. Pubs.
Graham, Franklin. All for Jesus. 2008. pap. (978-1-59328-217-2(6)) Graham, Billy Evangelistic Assn.
Graham, Isabella. The Power of Faith: Exemplified in the Life & Writings of the Late Mrs. Isabella Graham. 2007. (ENG.). 346p. pap. 23.99 (978-1-4346-0002-8(5)); 396p. pap. 26.99 (978-1-4346-0087-5(4)) BiblioBazaar.
Graham, Jack. A Man of God: Essential Priorities for Every Man's Life. 2007. 256p. pap., pupil's gde. ed. 16.99 (978-1-58134-874-3(6)) Crossway.
—Powering Up: The Fulfillment & Fruit of a God-Fueled Life. 2009. 224p. pap. 14.99 (978-1-4335-0658-1(0)) Crossway.
Graham, Jack, et al. Are You Fit for Life? 2008. 176p. 17.99 (978-1-58134-912-2(2)) Crossway.
Graham, L. C. The Holy Bible: A History of Failure. 2008. 104p. pap. 13.00 (978-0-8059-7799-8(6)) Dorrance Publishing Co., Inc.
Graham, Ruth. Fear Not Tomorrow, God Is Already There: Trusting Him in Uncertain Times. 2009. (ENG.). 288p. 22.99 (978-1-4165-5843-9(8), Howard Bks.) Howard Books.
—In Every Pew Sits a Broken Heart: Hope for the Hurting. 2008. (ENG.). 224p. pap. 14.99 (978-0-310-29079-7(1)) Zondervan.
Graham, Ruth Bell. Prodigals & Those Who Love Them. 2007. per. (978-1-59328-166-3(8)) Graham, Billy Evangelistic Assn.
—Prodigals & Those Who Love Them: Words of Encouragement for Those Who Wait. 2008. 160p. (gr. 13). reprint ed. pap. 14.99 (978-0-8010-7155-3(0)) Baker Bks.
—Sitting by My Laughing Fire. 2007. (Illus.). 175p. per. (978-1-59328-119-9(6)); (978-1-59328-118-2(8)) Graham, Billy Evangelistic Assn.
Graham, W. N. "Billy". Breaking the Shackles. 2009. 120p. pap. 11.99 (978-1-60791-412-9(3)) Xulon Pr., Inc.
Grahame, Kenneth. Pagan Papers. 2008. (ENG.). 56p. per. (978-1-4065-8834-7(2)) Dodo Pr.
—Pagan Papers. 2006. (ENG.). pap. (978-1-4068-3345-4(2)) Echo Library.
Grainger, Roger. Faith, Hope, & Therapy: Counseling with St. Paul. 2011. 140p. 22.87 **(978-1-4269-9582-8(2))**; pap. 12.87 **(978-1-4269-9583-5(0))** Trafford Publishing.
Grambow, LuAnn. HopeFound in Paradise Lost. 2006. pap. 13.99 (978-1-60034-831-0(9)) Xulon Pr., Inc.
Grams, Judy. Marks of Christ: Lessons from the Fruit of the Spirit. 2007. 196p. per. 24.95 (978-1-4241-9534-3(9)) PublishAmerica, Inc.
Granberry, Elder Allen. The Sayings Are Your Lifeline. 2011. 110p. 29.99 **(978-1-4568-5061-6(X))**; pap. 19.99 **(978-1-4568-5060-9(1))** Xlibris Corp.
Grandma Jo Staff. The Sunbeam Job. 2008. 168p. pap. 24.95 (978-1-60563-093-9(4)) PublishAmerica, Inc.
Grant, Edward F. Wisdom for the Good Life. 2011. 404p. pap. 25.95 **(978-1-4502-9309-9(3))** iUniverse, Inc.
Grant, Eveleaner. Pass the Blessings! 2010. 332p. pap. 21.99 (978-1-60957-656-1(X)) Xulon Pr., Inc.
Grant, Julie. Conversations. 2008. 84p. pap. 9.00 (978-1-931178-55-6(0)) Vision Publishing.
Grant, L. M. First & Second Corinthians. 194p. 6.95 (978-0-88172-154-6(9)) Believers Bookshelf, Inc.
—God's Order: Is It Possible Today? pap. 0.95 (978-0-88172-153-9(0)) Believers Bookshelf, Inc.
Grant, Patricia. In Due Season (Revelations from God) 2010. 87p. pap. 15.03 (978-0-557-11867-0(0)) Lulu Enterprises Inc.
Grant, Pennie. God's Heart. 2008. 252p. pap. 16.99 (978-1-60647-407-5(3)) Xulon Pr., Inc.
Grant, Raymond. Time Honored. 2009. 112p. pap. 13.99 (978-1-4389-9277-8(7)) AuthorHouse.
Grant, Robin J. So You Think God Called You to Minister in Convalescent Homes???? 2010. pap. 12.99 (978-1-61579-607-6(X)) Xulon Pr., Inc.
Grassi, Joseph A. God Makes Me Laugh. 2009. 152p. pap. 17.00 (978-1-60608-565-3(4), Wipf and Stock) Wipf & Stock Pubs.
Grasso Jr., Peter. In God We Betrayed. 2006. (ENG.). 21.99 (978-1-60034-565-4(4)); pap. 13.99 (978-1-60034-564-7(6)) Xulon Pr., Inc.
Grasso, Kevin. Living Eternally. 2010. 172p. pap. 12.77 (978-0-557-58504-5(X)) Lulu Enterprises Inc.
Graves, Carol. Fully in Focus. 2010. 216p. pap. 15.99 (978-1-60957-598-4(9)) Xulon Pr., Inc.
Graves, Christopher. Encourage My Soul & Let Me Journey On. 2006. (ENG.). 18.99 (978-1-60034-278-3(7)); pap. 10.99 (978-1-60034-277-6(9)) Xulon Pr., Inc.
Graves, Joshua. The Feast: How to Serve Jesus in a Famished World. 2009. 208p. pap. 14.99 (978-0-89112-639-3(2), Leafwood Pubs.) Abilene Christian Univ. Pr.
Graves, Maya. Cartas de tu Padre Dios. 2006. (SPA.). pap. 15.99 (978-1-60034-846-4(7)) Xulon Pr., Inc.
Gray, Ronald K. Enter to Worship - Exit to Serve. 2008. 88p. pap. 10.99 (978-1-60647-799-1(4)) Xulon Pr., Inc.
Gray Sr., Bob. Suffering? 2010. 168p. pap. 14.99 (978-1-60957-505-2(9)) Xulon Pr., Inc.
Graybeal, Lynda L., et al. Prayer & Worship: A Spiritual Formation Guide. 2007. (ENG.). 144p. pap. 14.99 (978-0-06-084125-6(7), HarperOne) HarperCollins Pubs.
Great Texts Discipleship. 19.00 (978-0-687-09047-1(4)) Abingdon Pr.

Green. How to Make a Graceful Exit: Letting Go of the Past. 2009. 124p. pap. 12.95 *(978-1-4389-9439-0(7))* AuthorHouse.

Green, Geneva. My Spiritual Journey. 2009. 24p. pap. 11.49 *(978-1-4389-7149-0(4))* AuthorHouse.

Green, Hollis. Discipleship. 2007. 128p. per. 14.95 *(978-0-9796019-5-8(9))* Global Education Advance.

—Fighting the Amalekites. 2007. 112p. per. 14.95 *(978-0-9796019-2-7(4))* Global Education Advance.

Green, Hollis L. Dynamics of Christian Discipleship: An Adventure in Christian Living. 2011. 114p. 39.95 ***(978-1-258-07308-4(0))*** Literary Licensing, LLC.

Green, Janelle. This Earthly Tent: Me, God & MS. 2008. 124p. 19.99 *(978-1-60791-154-8(X))* Xulon Pr., Inc.

Green, Ken. To Corinth with Love. 175p. pap. *(978-0-340-28226-7(6)*, Hodder & Stoughton) Hodder General Publishing Div.

Green, M. Demons & You. 2008. 156p. pap. 11.95 *(978-0-615-20892-3(4))* Kepler Enterprises, LLC.

—Life with God. 2007. 168p. pap. 11.95 *(978-0-615-16801-2(9))* Kepler Enterprises, LLC.

Green, Martha E. Pioneers in Pith Helmets: No Subtitle. 2008. 448p. pap. 21.99 *(978-1-60477-814-4(8))* Xulon Pr., Inc.

Green, Mike. Kingdom Living. 2008. 324p. pap. 19.95 *(978-0-615-21600-3(5))* Kepler Enterprises, LLC.

Green, Weldon. What do i do Now? 2007. (ENG.). 124p. per. 10.99 *(978-1-60266-004-5(2))* Xulon Pr., Inc.

Green, Win. All You Ever Wanted. 2008. 236p. 14.99 *(978-1-60604-531-2(8))* Tate Publishing & Enterprises, LLC.

Greene, H. Leon. A Guide to Short Term Missions: A Comprehensive Manual for Planning an Effective Mission Trip. 2006. (ENG.). 275p. pap. 14.99 *(978-1-884543-73-9(1))* Authentic Media.

Greene, Mark. The Best Idea in the World: How Putting Relationships First Transforms Everything. 1 vol. 2009. (ENG.). 160p. pap. 9.99 *(978-0-310-29075-9(9))* Zondervan.

Greenfield, Susan. Would the Real Church PLEASE Stand Up! 2007. pap. 13.99 *(978-1-60266-025-0(5))* Xulon Pr., Inc.

Greenhill, William. The Sound-Hearted Christian. 2010. 25.00 *(978-1-60178-099-7(0))* Reformation Heritage Bks.

Greenlaw, Ronald Wellesley. Star Witness. 2008. 348p. per. 20.99 *(978-1-60477-562-4(9))* Xulon Pr., Inc.

Greenlee, Anna. Goin' on a Road Trip without Any Wheels: Having the Adventure of a Lifetime for My Soul. 2010. 116p. 22.95 *(978-1-4502-2272-3(2))* iUniverse, Inc.

—Goin' on a Road Trip without Any Wheels: Having the Advanture of a Lifetime for My Soul. 2010. 116p. pap. 12.95 *(978-1-4502-2270-9(6))* iUniverse, Inc.

Greenman, Marta E. Bound to be Free. 2010. 233p. 18.00 *(978-0-615-37767-4(X))* RUTH Ministries International.

Greenslade, Philip. Voice from the Hills. 2008. (Illus.). 168p. *(978-1-85345-469-1(9))* Crusade for World Revival.

Greenway, Roger. Apostoles a la Ciudad. (SPA.). 101p. pap. 5.95 *(978-1-55883-088-2(X)*, 6707-2510C) Libros Desafio.

Greenwood, R. E. Fire in the House. 2006. 143p. per. 10.99 *(978-1-58169-227-3(7)*, Gazelle Pr.) Genesis Communications, Inc.

Greenwood, Rebecca. Destined to Rule: Spiritual Strategies for Advancing the Kingdom of God. 2007. 176p. pap. 13.00 *(978-0-8007-9433-0(8))* Chosen Bks.

Greer, Ronald J. If You Know Who You Are You'll Know What to Do: Living with Integrity. 2009. 126p. pap. 15.00 *(978-0-687-65773-5(3))* Abingdon Pr.

Greer, Rowan A. The Fear of Freedom. 2008. 228p. per. 24.95 *(978-0-271-02799-9(1))* Pennsylvania State Univ. Pr.

Gregg, Webster. From a Prince to a Slave: Two Families-Black & White-Brought Together by Slavery, United by Christian Love. 2009. (ENG.). 160p. pap. 12.99 *(978-1-59979-629-1(5)*, Creation Hse.) Charisma Media.

Gregory, A. J. Messy Faith: Daring to Live by Grace. 2008. 208p. pap. 12.99 *(978-0-8007-3284-4(7))* Revell.

Gregory, Chaplain Bunny & Gregory, Chaplain Blonnie. Trucking for Jesus: Beating the Highway Blues. 2010. pap. 23.99 *(978-1-61663-535-0(5))* Tate Publishing & Enterprises, LLC.

Gregory, David. The Next Level: A Parable of Finding Your Place in Life. 2008. (ENG.). 128p. 12.99 *(978-1-4000-7243-9(3)*, WaterBrook Pr.) Doubleday Religious Publishing Group, The.

Gregory, Frank. Never Alone. 2010. 72p. pap. 9.99 *(978-0-83144-507-7(X))* Yorkshire Publishing Group.

Gregory, Susan. The Daniel Fast: Feed Your Soul, Strengthen Your Spirit, & Renew Your Body. 2010. (ENG.). 288p. pap. 14.99 *(978-1-4143-3413-4(3))* Tyndale Hse. Pubs.

Greig, Pete. God on Mute: Engaging the Silence of Unanswered Prayer. 2012. (ENG.). 304p. pap. 16.99 ***(978-0-8307-6436-5(4))*** Gospel Light Pubns.

Greiner, John. Rise up & Reap: Letting God's Ideas Multiply Your Money. 2006. 116p. pap. 12.99 *(978-1-59755-027-7(2))* Advantage Bks.

Greiner, Laura & Kohring, Sharon. Rendezvous Joy Ride Philippians: Bible Study Leader Guide. 2007. (Illus.). 96p. pap. 24.99 incl. cd-rom *(978-0-7644-3512-6(4))* Group Publishing, Inc.

—Rendezvous Joy Ride Phillipians: Personal Guidebook for Bible Study. 2007. (Illus.). 80p. per. 7.99 *(978-0-7644-3511-9(6))* Group Publishing, Inc.

Grenier, Brian. Family Life in Christ. 111p. pap. 4.95 *(978-0-8189-7037-5(5))* St Pauls/Alba Hse. Pubs.

—Jesus the Teacher. 148p. pap. 11.50 *(978-0-8189-7032-0(4))* St Pauls/Alba Hse. Pubs.

Grenier, Lynn. His Gentle Words of Love: Prophetic Encouragement from God's Heart to Yours. 2009. 252p. pap. 15.99 *(978-1-4389-4159-2(5))* AuthorHouse.

Greta, Gordon. The 600 Pound Gorilla in the Sanctuary. 1 vol. 2010. 64p. pap. 16.95 *(978-1-4489-5800-9(8))* PublishAmerica, Inc.

Grey, Mary. The Big Question. 144p. 12.95 *(978-0-281-04797-0(9))* International Publishers Marketing.

—Celtic Heart. 144p. pap. 6.99 *(978-0-281-05028-4(7))* International Publishers Marketing.

—Consuming Passion. 128p. 11.95 *(978-0-281-04844-1(4))* International Publishers Marketing.

—Different Gospels. 240p. 13.00 *(978-0-281-04690-4(5))* SPCK Publishing GBR. Dist: Pilgrim Pr., The/United Church Pr.

—Free to Fail. 160p. 9.00 *(978-0-281-04527-3(5))* SPCK Publishing GBR. Dist: Pilgrim Pr., The/United Church Pr.

—New Day for Preaching. rev. ed. 128p. 15.00 *(978-0-281-04967-7(X))* SPCK Publishing GBR. Dist: Pilgrim Pr., The/United Church Pr.

—To Be a Pilgrim. 240p. 10.00 *(978-0-281-04372-9(8))* SPCK Publishing GBR. Dist: Pilgrim Pr., The/United Church Pr.

Grey, Stephanie. Preparing Our Communities: God's Way! 2011. 28p. pap. 15.99 ***(978-1-4628-7963-2(2))*** Xlibris Corp.

Greystone, Peter. Detox Your Spiritual Life in 40 Days. 2007. 172p. per. 16.95 *(978-1-59856-085-5(9))* Hendrickson Pubs. Marketing, LLC.

Gribble, Richard. Living as an American Catholic in the 21st Century: A Short, Self-Guided Retreat. 2011. 104p. pap. ***(978-0-8091-4731-1(9))*** Paulist Pr.

Grieg, Phil & Brush, Sarah. Moving Images, Changing Lives: Exploring the Christian Life & Confirmation with Young People Through Film. 2011. (Illus.). 128p. pap. 39.99 *(978-0-7151-4207-3(0))* Church Hse. Publishing GBR. Dist: Westminster John Knox Pr.

Grieve, Rick. On the Way. 2009. 176p. 24.99 *(978-1-60791-308-5(9))*; pap. 14.99 *(978-1-60791-490-7(5))* Xulon Pr., Inc.

Griffin, Anthony L., et al. Christian Living Study Guide. 2009. 80p. pap. 21.99 *(978-1-4259-0017-5(8))* AuthorHouse.

Griffin, Deborah. Single for a Season, Married for a Reason. 2007. (ENG.). 64p. per. 6.99 *(978-1-59979-092-3(0)*, Creation Hse.) Charisma Media.

Griffin, Emilie. The Reflective Executive: A Spirituality of Business & Enterprise. 2008. 180p. pap. 21.00 *(978-1-55635-626-1(9))* Wipf & Stock Pubs.

Griffin, Everett D. The Devil Don't Want You to Know: It Is Time for You to Know. 2009. 52p. pap. 10.99 *(978-1-60791-840-0(4))* Xulon Pr., Inc.

Griffin, Jack. My New Life. 2006. pap. 14.99 *(978-1-60034-480-0(1))* Xulon Pr., Inc.

Griffith, Allen. Parenting: One Chance to Do It Right. 2007. 160p. pap. 12.95 *(978-0-9749836-3-9(2))* Faithful Life Pubs.

Griffith, Kay. Don't Let Your Tongue Lick You. 1 vol. 2010. 48p. pap. 16.95 *(978-1-4489-4910-6(6))* PublishAmerica, Inc.

Griffiths, Ken. Oh God, Change This Scene! Changing the Situation. 2008. 300p pap. 21.95 *(978-1-4327-2896-0(2))* Outskirts Pr., Inc.

Griggs, Doug. March Gladness. 2008. 164p. 22.99 *(978-1-60647-852-3(4))*; pap. 14.99 *(978-1-60647-851-6(6))* Xulon Pr., Inc.

Grigsby, Vickie. The Fear Factor. 2010. 176p. pap. 14.99 *(978-1-60957-375-1(7))* Xulon Pr., Inc.

Grim, Francis. Palabra Que Ayuda: Word That Helps. (SPA.). *(978-84-7228-087-8(X)*, 220664) Clie, Editorial.

Grimm, Roger. God + Some Golf + Religion. 2011. 72p. pap. 19.95 ***(978-1-4626-2057-9(4))*** PublishAmerica, Inc.

Grinstead, Peggy. A Remnant Shall Return: Isaiah Deliverance & Comfort for the Faithful. 2008. 356p. pap. 22.99 *(978-1-60647-301-6(8))* Xulon Pr., Inc.

Griscom, Chris. The Evolution of God. 2007. (Illus.). 336p. 28.00 *(978-0-9772249-1-3(0))* Light Institute Pr.

Grisham, Mary-Ellen Singer. Eternally Yours. 2008. pap. 14.99 *(978-1-60477-747-5(8))* Xulon Pr., Inc.

Groeschel, Benedict J. After This Life: What Catholics Believe about What Happens Next. 2009. 128p. pap. 12.95 *(978-1-59276-442-6(8))* Our Sunday Visitor, Publishing Div.

Groeschel, Craig. Chazown: Define Your Vision. Pursue Your Passion. Live Your Life on Purpose. 2010. (ENG.). 256p. pap. 14.99 *(978-1-60142-313-9(6)*, Multnomah) Doubleday Religious Publishing Group, The.

—Daring to Drop the Pose: Ten Things Christians Think but Are Afraid to Say. 2010. (ENG.). 224p. pap. 14.99 *(978-1-60142-314-6(4)*, Multnomah) Doubleday Religious Publishing Group, The.

—Soul Detox: Pure Living in a Polluted World. 2012. pap. ***(978-0-310-33382-1(2))***; (ENG.). 240p. 19.99 ***(978-0-310-33368-5(7))*** Zondervan.

Groeschel, Craig. Weird: Because Normal Isn't Working. 1 vol. 2011. (ENG.). 256p. 19.99 *(978-0-310-32790-5(3))* Zondervan.

Groody, Daniel G., ed. Gustavo Gutierrez: Spiritual Writings. 2011. 176p. pap. 20.00 *(978-1-57075-947-5(2))* Orbis Bks.

Grooms, D. K. Christianity Broken. 2011. 160p. 24.95 ***(978-1-4620-4024-7(1))***; pap. 14.95 ***(978-1-4620-4023-0(3))*** iUniverse, Inc.

Groseclose, Win. No Nice Christians! 2010. (ENG.). 150p. pap. 12.49 *(978-0-557-39378-7(7))* Lulu Enterprises Inc.

Gross, Estelle E. The Prayer of Agreement. 2008. 124p. pap. 10.99 *(978-1-60647-478-5(2))* Xulon Pr., Inc.

Gross, Thomas Pelham. Israel's Holocaust & Resurrection. 2009. 236p. pap. 15.99 *(978-1-60791-727-4(0))* Xulon Pr., Inc.

Grossett, Vanessa. Don't Look Back! The Harmful Consequences of Backsliding. 2010. pap. 11.99 *(978-1-61566-128-2(X))* Tate Publishing & Enterprises, LLC.

Grosz, Edward. Walking with Jesus. 40p. pap. 2.50 *(978-0-8198-8299-8(2)*, 332-408) Pauline Bks. & Media.

Group Publishing, compiled by. Simply Relevant Chocolate Boutique: Relational Bible Series for Women. 2007. (Illus.). 80p. per. 9.99 *(978-0-7644-3445-7(4))* Group Publishing, Inc.

—Simply Relevant Heart Spa: Relational Bible Series for Women. 2007. (Illus.). 80p. per. 9.99 *(978-0-7644-3444-0(6))* Group Publishing, Inc.

Group Publishing, creator. Reeled In: 3 Big Whoppers from God's Word. 2007. (Simply Junior High Ser.). DVD, audio compact disk 30.00 *(978-5-557-54489-4(5))* Group Publishing, Inc.

—Rome @ Home 10 Faith-Building, Family-Friendly Devotions. 2009. pap. 16.99 *(978-0-7644-3823-3(9))* Group Publishing, Inc.

Groves, Anthony Norris. Christian Devotedness. 2010. (Illus.). 58p. pap. *(978-1-897117-97-2(3))* Gospel Folio Pr.

Groves, J. & Newfrontiers-USA. Foundations: Seven group studies to introduce the essentials of Christian Living. 2008. 100p. pap. 6.50 *(978-0-9814803-0-5(6))* Newfrontiers USA.

Growing by Choice. Date not set. pap. *(978-0-87162-567-0(9))* Warner Pr. Pubs.

Grubb, Norman. Touching the Invisible. 2007. (ENG.). 95p. mass mkt. 5.99 *(978-0-87508-975-1(5))* CLC Pubns.

Grubb, S. God Bless the Ravens. 2008. 204p. 25.99 *(978-1-60647-825-7(7))*; pap. 15.99 *(978-1-60647-824-0(9))* Xulon Pr., Inc.

Grubbs, Esther. God Also Said. 2008. 320p. 35.87 *(978-1-4303-0823-2(0))* Lulu Enterprises Inc.

Grube, Edward C. It's About the Students! 2011. 128p. 5.99 ***(978-0-7586-2722-3(X))*** Concordia Publishing Hse.

Gruen, George & Gruen, Jean. Let's Witness to Jews: A Practical Guide for Sharing Your Faith- an Individual or Small Group Study. 2009. pap. 14.99 *(978-1-60799-260-8(4))* Tate Publishing & Enterprises, LLC.

Grumett, David & Muers, Rachel. Theology on the Menu: Asceticism, Meat Eating & the Christian Diet. 2010. (ENG.). 224p. (C). 39.95 *(978-0-415-49683-4(7))*; 125.00 *(978-0-415-49682-7(9))* Routledge.

Grunlan, Stephen. Climbing with Jesus. 2009. 100p. pap. 14.00 *(978-1-60899-037-5(0)*, Resource Pubns.) Wipf & Stock Pubs.

Grupo Nelson, creator. Respuestas de Dios: Para su Vida. 0 vols. 2007. (SPA.). 320p. im. lthr. 12.99 *(978-0-88113-582-4(8))* Grupo Nelson.

Gryder, Rog. Memoirs of a Sojourner: Life Beyond Time & Space. 2011. 168p. pap. 11.70 *(978-1-4567-4029-0(6))* AuthorHouse.

Gryn, Hugo. Three Minutes of Hope: Hugo Gryn on the God Slot. Gryn, Naomi, ed. 2010. (ENG., Illus.). 288p. 19.95 *(978-1-4411-4035-7(2))* Continuum International Publishing Group, Ltd. GBR. Dist: National Bk. Network.

Gtrrez, Marin. Tres Columnas: Three Pillars of the Christian. (SPA.). *(978-84-7645-318-6(3)*, 223445) Clie, Editorial.

Guice, Dewitt. A Youth's Heart Spoken Thoughts. 2010. 120p. (ENG.). 22.49 *(978-1-4389-7399-9(3))*; pap. 16.99 *(978-1-4389-7398-2(5))* AuthorHouse.

Guidelines for Leading Your Congregation 2009-2012 - Worship: The Gifts of God from the People of God. 2008. 2.95 *(978-0-687-64901-3(3))* Abingdon Pr.

Guidry, Dustin. Turning the Ship. 2009. 164p. 22.99 *(978-1-60791-263-7(5))*; pap. 14.99 *(978-1-60791-262-0(7))* Xulon Pr., Inc.

Guidry, Rhonda. Relationship with My Savior. 2010. 73p. pap. 9.95 *(978-0-557-29331-5(6))* Lulu Enterprises Inc.

Guimaraes, Atila Sinke. Will He Find Faith? Inveniet Fidem?, 11 Vols., Vol. 6. 2007. (ENG.). pap. 20.00 *(978-0-9726516-6-0(7))* Tradition in Action, Inc.

Guinness. Child of the Covenant. pap. *(978-0-340-72226-8(6))*; 160p. pap. *(978-0-340-36479-6(3))* Hodder General Publishing Div. (Hodder & Stoughton).

Guinness, Abby & Guinness, Michele. Word of the Wives: Monologues from the Unheard Women of the Bible. 2010. (ENG.). 174p. 12.99 *(978-1-85078-670-3(3))* Authentic Media.

Guinness, Os & Seel, John, eds. No God but God: Breaking with the Idols of Our Age. 18.99 *(978-0-8024-6336-4(3)*, 230) Moody Pubs.

Gulver. Pursuing the Mystery. (Illus.). 240p. 19.95 *(978-0-281-04991-2(2))* International Publishers Marketing.

Gulledge, Gregg. Breaking the Cycle of Shame. 2008. 164p. pap. 14.99 *(978-1-60647-525-6(8))* Xulon Pr., Inc.

Gullestad, Gullestad, Marianne. Picturing Pity: Pitfalls & Pleasures in Cross-Cultural Communication - Image & Word in a North Cameroon Mission. 2007. (Illus.). 368p. 90.00 *(978-1-84545-343-5(3))* Berghahn Bks., Inc.

Gulley, Philip. The Evolution of Faith: How God Is Creating a Better Christianity. (ENG.). 2012. 224p. pap. 14.99 ***(978-0-06-168993-2(9))***, HarperOne) 2011. 256p. 24.99 *(978-0-06-073660-6(7)*, HarperOne) 2011. 256p. pap. 24.99 *(978-0-06-206527-8(0)*, HarperLuxe) HarperCollins Pubs.

Gulley, Philip & Mulholland, James. If Grace Is True: Why God Will Save Every Person. 2010. (Plus Ser.). (ENG.). 256p. pap. 14.99 *(978-0-06-192608-2(6)*, HarperOne) HarperCollins Pubs.

Gungor, Ed. One Small Barking Dog: How to Live a Life That's Hard to Ignore. 2010. (ENG.). 240p. 19.99 *(978-1-4165-9256-3(3)*, Howard Bks.) Howard Books.

—The Vow: How a Forgotten Ancient Practice Can Transform Your Life. 0 vols. 2008. 240p. per. 14.99 *(978-0-8499-1911-4(8))* Nelson, Thomas Inc.

—What Bothers Me Most about Christianity: Honest Reflections from an Open-Minded Christ Follower. 2009. (ENG.). 256p. pap. 15.99 *(978-1-4165-9255-6(5)*, Howard Bks.) Howard Books.

Gunn, Robin Jones & Hannan, Cindy. Take Flight! 2006. (Sisterchicks Ser.). (ENG., Illus.). 120p. 14.99 *(978-1-59052-537-1(X)*, Multnomah Fiction) Doubleday Religious Publishing Group, The.

Gunton, Colin E. & Gunton. Revelation & Reason: Prolegomena to Systematic Theology. Brazier, Paul, ed. 2009. (ENG., Illus.). 248p. 34.95 *(978-0-567-03356-7(2))*; 120.00 *(978-0-567-03355-0(4))* Continuum International Publishing Group, Ltd. GBR. (T&T Clark Int'l). Dist: National Bk. Network.

Gurath, Ann M. Turning Inside Out. 2007. 184p. per. 13.99 *(978-1-60477-391-0(X))* Xulon Pr., Inc.

Gurnall, William. The Christian in Complete Armour. 2009. 446p. pap. 35.75 *(978-1-115-66667-1(3))* BiblioBazaar.

—The Christian in Complete Armour. 2009. 374p. pap. *(978-0-217-07320-2(4))*; 334p. pap. *(978-0-217-57301-6(0))* Books LLC.

—The Christian in Complete Armour. 2010. (Illus.). 656p. 29.97 *(978-1-59856-885-1(X))* Hendrickson Pubs. Marketing, LLC.

—The Christian in Complete Armour, or, a Treatise of the Saints' War Against the Devil, Wherein a Discovery Is Made of That Grand Enemy of God. 2010. 372p. pap. *(978-1-151-96900-2(1))*; 400p. pap. *(978-1-151-95903-3(6))* Books LLC.

—The Christian in Complete Armour, or, a Treatise on the Saints War with the Devil; Wherein a Discovery Is Made of the Policy, Power. 2010. 214p. pap. *(978-1-151-96897-5(8))* Books LLC.

—Extracts from the Writings of William Gurnall. 2008. 100p. pap. *(978-0-901860-82-8(4))* Scripture Truth Pubns.

Guru, Gospel. Gospel Guru's Fruitful Handbook for Believers on Holy Days: A Guide for Helping You Through Life's Valley Experiences. 2007. 48p. per. 13.95 *(978-1-4241-8766-9(4))* PublishAmerica, Inc.

Gushee, David P. Only Human: Christian Reflections on the Journey Toward Wholeness. 2010. (Enduring Questions in Christian Life Ser.: 6). (ENG., Illus.). 256p. pap. 24.95 *(978-0-470-88961-9(6)*, Jossey-Bass) Wiley, John & Sons, Inc.

Gustafson, Eleanor. Stones Study Guide. 2009. 52p. pap. 6.99 *(978-1-60374-103-3(8))* Whitaker Hse.

Guthrie, Nancy. Hearing Jesus Speak into Your Sorrow. 2009. (ENG.). 192p. 14.99 *(978-1-4143-2548-4(7))* Tyndale Hse. Pubs.

Gutierrez, Bob. Almost Home. 2010. 108p. 24.99 *(978-1-4535-4007-7(5))*; pap. 15.99 *(978-1-4535-4006-0(7))* Xlibris Corp.

Gutierrez, Jaime Luis. Cavilaciones.Tr. of Thoughts. (SPA.). 152p. 6.95 *(978-958-607-921-1(X))* Sociedad de San Pablo COL. Dist: St Pauls/Alba Hse. Pubs.

Guy, Geoffrey Cruzen. Practical Truth: For Encouragement, Guidance & Hope in This Life & to Prepare You for the Next. 2010. 188p. 30.95 *(978-1-4497-0398-1(4))*; pap. 13.95 *(978-1-4497-0399-8(2))* Author Solutions, Inc. (WestBow Pr.).

Guyon, Jeanne. A Short & Easy Method of Prayer. Brook, Thomas, tr. 2007. 92p. per. 12.50 *(978-1-60206-372-3(9))* Cosimo, Inc.

Guyton, Dorothy. The Politics of Prayer. 2010. pap. 17.95 *(978-0-7414-6171-1(4))* Infinity Publishing.

Guzman, Juan A. Si Tu Puede. 2011. 160p. pap. 14.99 ***(978-1-61379-396-1(0))*** Xulon Pr., Inc.

Guzman, Ramsey B. Lock up with Faith. 2011. 74p. 24.99 ***(978-1-4568-2694-9(8))***; pap. 15.99 ***(978-1-4568-2693-2(X))*** Xlibris Corp.

H. Ray Dunning. Becoming Christlike Disciples. 2010. 128p. pap. 11.95 *(978-1-4497-0014-0(4)*, WestBow Pr.) Author Solutions, Inc.

H. Ray, Dunning & H. Ray Dunning. Becoming Christlike Disciples. 2010. 128p. 28.95 *(978-1-4497-0015-7(2)*, WestBow Pr.) Author Solutions, Inc.

Haas, Jerry P. & Kirk, Cynthia Langston. Rhythm & Fire: Experiencing the Holy in Community & Solitude. 2008. 128p. pap. 15.00 *(978-0-8358-9964-2(0))* Upper Room Bks.

Haas, Melissa. Spouses' L. I. F. E. Guide, XXX Church. com. Laeser, Mark, ed. 2007. per. 19.95 *(978-0-9771662-5-1(2))* Freedom Every Day LLC.

Haas, Peter. The God Who Is Here: A contemplative guide to transforming your relationship with God & the Church. 2010. 19.50 *(978-0-615-37336-2(4))* Lantern Light Publishing.

Haase, Albert. Coming Home to Your True Self: Leaving the Emptiness of False Attractions. 2008. (ENG., Illus.). 180p. pap. 15.00 *(978-0-8308-3517-1(2)*, IVP Bks.) InterVarsity Pr.

—Living the Lord's Prayer: The Way of the Disciple. 1 vol. 2009. (ENG.). 252p. pap. 18.00 *(978-0-8308-3529-4(6)*, IVP Bks.) InterVarsity Pr.

Haase, Bridget. Generous Faith: Stories to Inspire Abundant Living. 2009. (ENG.). 36p. pap., instr.'s gde. ed. 6.99 *(978-1-55725-672-0(1))* Paraclete Pr., Inc.

Haase, Bridget, abr. Generous Faith: Stories to Inspire Abundant Living. 2009. (ENG.). 152p. (gr. 13). pap. 16.99 *(978-1-55725-615-7(2))* Paraclete Pr., Inc.

Hack, Keith. Colossians 3 Principle. 2006. pap. 9.99 *(978-1-60034-776-4(2))* Xulon Pr., Inc.

Hackett, Sonya Lang. A Personal Perspective: From My Heart to Yours. 2010. pap. 10.99 *(978-1-61663-528-2(2))* Tate Publishing & Enterprises, LLC.

Hafley, George A. Your Way Is Not God's Way: No Subtitle. 2008. 288p. pap. 15.99 *(978-1-60647-180-7(5))* Xulon Pr., Inc.

Hagberg, Amy Hammond. How Do You Know He's Real? God Unplugged. 2006. (Illus.). 447p. per. 14.99 *(978-0-7684-2388-4(0))* Destiny Image Pubs.

Hagee, John. God's Two-Minute Warning. 0 vols. 2009. 140p. pap. 9.99 *(978-1-4041-7559-4(8))* Nelson, Thomas Inc.

—Life Challenges — Your Opportunities: God Has Given You a Promise You've Come into a Problem... How You Respond Will Determine How Quickly the Provision Comes... 2008. (ENG.). 256p. 21.99 *(978-1-59979-269-9(9)*, Charisma Hse.) Charisma Media.

C

Hagee, Matthew. Response-Able. 2011. E-Book (978-1-61638-419-7(0), Charisma Hse.) Charisma Media.
—Response-Able: Lessons from My Father Taught Me about Life & Making a Difference. 2011. (ENG., Illus.). 240p. pap. 15.99 (978-1-61638-136-3(1), Charisma Hse.) Charisma Media.
—Shaken, Not Shattered: Finding the Purpose, Passion & Power to Stand Firm When Your World Falls Apart. 2009. (ENG.). 224p. pap. 14.99 (978-1-59979-464-8(0), Charisma Hse.) Charisma Media.
Haggai, John Edmund. How to Win over Worry: Positive Steps to Anxiety-Free Living. 2009. 224p. pap. 12.99 (978-0-7369-2627-0(5)) Harvest Hse. Pubs.
Haggard, T. Primera Prioridad.Tr. of Primary Purpose. (SPA.). pap. 6.99 (978-958-9354-17-9(3), 550054) Editorial Unilit.
Haggart, G. P. Mechanics of Demonology. 2010. 368p. 37.95 (978-0-557-41139-9(4)) Lulu Enterprises Inc.
Hagin, Kenneth E. Como Puede ser Dirigido por el Espiritu de Dios.Tr. of How You Can Be Led by the Spirit of God. (SPA.). 188p. 6.95 (978-0-89276-137-1(7), 137) Faith Library Pubns., Inc.
—Marriage, Divorce, & Remarriage. 174p. 16.95 (978-0-89276-531-7(3), 531) Faith Library Pubns., Inc.
Hagin, Kenneth W., Jr. Como Vivir Libre de la Preocupacion.Tr. of How to Live Worry-Free. (SPA.). 71p. 3.95 (978-0-89276-127-2(X)) Faith Library Pubns., Inc.
—How to Fulfill Your Divine Destiny. 150p. 7.00 (978-0-89276-738-0(3)) Faith Library Pubns., Inc.
—Overflow: Living above Life's Limits. 2006. 156p. per. 9.95 (978-0-89276-745-8(6)) Faith Library Pubns., Inc.
—Staying Positive in a Negative World. 176p. 9.95 (978-0-89276-743-4(X), 743) Faith Library Pubns., Inc.
Hagin, Kenneth W. Where Is God in My Storm? Finding an Anchor in Life's Rough Waters. 2009. 146p. pap. 10.95 (978-0-89276-751-9(0)) Faith Library Pubns., Inc.
—You Can Make It! Winning in Troubled Times. 2009. 73p. pap. 5.95 (978-0-89276-750-2(2)) Faith Library Pubns., Inc.
Hagstrom, Richard. Guia a la Eficiencia Personal: Getting along with Yourself. (SPA.). 320p. (978-84-7228-782-2(3), 222337) Clie, Editorial.
Hague, Daryl R., ed. A Love of Learning. 2011. pap. (978-0-8425-2791-0(5), Brigham Young Univ. Studies) Brigham Young Univ.
Hahn, Scott. Many Are Called: Rediscovering the Glory of the Priesthood. 2010. (ENG.). 160p. 14.99 (978-0-307-59077-0(1), Doubleday Religion) Doubleday Religious Publishing Group, The.
Haigh, Christopher. The Plain Man's Pathways to Heaven: Kinds of Christianity in Post-Reformation England, 1570-1640. 2007. (ENG., Illus.). 266p. 60.00 (978-0-19-921650-5(9)) Oxford Univ. Pr., Inc.
Haines, Stephanie Boughton. The Bible & Decision Making. 2010. (Insights: Bible Studies for Growing Faith Ser.). 48p. pap. 7.00 (978-1-60899-224-9(1), Wipf and Stock) Wipf & Stock Pubs.
Haldane. Reasonable Faith. 2010. (ENG.). 224p. (C). pap. 43.95 (978-0-415-43025-8(9)) Routledge.
Haldane, Katie-Anne. God Hears. 2007. 88p. per. 10.99 (978-1-60266-961-1(9)) Xulon Pr., Inc.
Hale, Elnader. The Ultimatum Game. 2009. 71p. pap. 15.94 (978-0-557-06233-1(0)) Lulu Enterprises Inc.
Hale, Tom & Thorson, Steve. The Applied Old Testament Commentary: Applying God's Word to Your Life. 2007. (ENG., Illus.). 1344p. 39.99 (978-0-7814-4864-2(6)) Cook, David C.
Hall. I Will Arise! Inspiring Hope, Worth, & Possibilities... 2008. 140p. pap. 13.99 (978-1-4343-9814-7(5)) AuthorHouse.
Hall, Brian P. Spiritual Connections: The Journey of Discipleship & Christian Values. 2006. (Illus.). 178p. (Orig.). pap. 21.00 (978-1-59752-701-9(7), Wipf and Stock) Wipf & Stock Pubs.
Hall, Donna M. Love. 2009. 428p. pap. 25.99 (978-1-60791-492-1(1)) Xulon Pr., Inc.
Hall, Howard W. Understanding God's First Earth. Bazzrea, Farah, ed. 2011. 122p. (YA). pap. 9.99 (978-0-9818611-9-7(9)) Granny's Bks. Publishing Hse.
Hall, Ieisha K. M. B. Sprinkles. 2010. 16p. 12.99 (978-1-4490-6569-0(4)) AuthorHouse.
Hall, Jack. Gods Literal Plan of Creation - vs. - the Great Satan Generation of Viper. 2010. 108p. 22.95 (978-1-4502-4837-2(3)); pap. 12.95 (978-1-4502-4835-8(7)) iUniverse, Inc.
Hall, John. What's Wrong with the Name It & Claim it Gospel? 2011. (ENG.). 50p. pap. 6.99 (978-1-4664-1576-8(2)) CreateSpace.
Hall, L. E. No Longer I: A Life Transformed. 2011. 188p. 30.95 (978-1-4497-1942-5(2)); pap. 13.95 (978-1-4497-1940-1(6)) Author Solutions, Inc. (WestBow Pr.).
Hall, Olivia. When All Hell Breaks Loose. 2006. 62p. per. 7.99 (978-1-59886-394-9(0)) Tate Publishing & Enterprises, LLC.
Hall, Robert. Help to Zion's Travellers: Being an Attempt to Remove Various Stumbling Blocks Out of the Way, Relating to Doctrinal, Experimental, & Practical Reli. 2006. 256p. per. 23.99 (978-1-4255-2264-3(5)) MPublishing.
Hall, Shirley. Jesus: The Same Yesterday, Today & Forever. 2010. 100p. pap. 11.99 (978-1-4520-1153-0(2)) AuthorHouse.
—The Voice of God: A Church with Hearing Ears. 2010. 108p. pap. 12.99 (978-1-4520-3040-1(5)) AuthorHouse.
Hall, Wendy C. His Messages in My Dreams. 2009. 64p. pap. 12.99 (978-1-60791-568-3(5)) Xulon Pr., Inc.
Halley, Charles. The Heart of the Matter: Changing the World God's Way. 2006. 179p. per. 19.99 (978-0-8272-1452-1(9)) Chalice Pr.
Halsch, Kelly Leigh. The Way of Love. 2008. 176p. pap. 13.99 (978-1-60647-075-6(2)) Xulon Pr., Inc.
Halsey, Jeanne. What's That You Have in Your Hands? 2010. 128p. pap. 14.99 (978-0-557-42704-8(5)) Lulu Enterprises Inc.
Halverson, Richard. Cristianismo Autentico: Be Yourself & God's. (SPA.). (978-84-7228-218-6(X), 220202) Clie, Editorial.
Hamer, James E. God Is Still Talking. 2009. 220p. pap. 14.99 (978-1-60799-497-8(6)) Tate Publishing & Enterprises, LLC.
Hamer, Sadie E. Standing on Planted Seeds. 2011. 218p. pap. 24.95 (978-1-4560-7043-4(6)) PublishAmerica, Inc.
Hamid, Minister Michael. The Power in Giving: (Practical Guidelines for Tithing & Giving of Offerings) 2008. 48p. pap. 9.99 (978-1-60647-660-4(2)) Xulon Pr., Inc.
Hamilton, Adam. Christianity's Family Tree Leader's Guide: What Other Christians Believe & Why. ldr.'s ed. 2007. (Illus.). 133p. 12.00 (978-0-687-49116-2(9)) Abingdon Pr.
—When Christians Get It Wrong. 2010. 144p. pap. 14.00 (978-1-4267-0914-2(5)) Abingdon Pr.
—24 Hours That Changed the World Leader's Guide. 2010. 80p. 11.99 (978-1-4267-1207-4(3)) Abingdon Pr.
Hamilton, Brittney N. All the Mortal Idols Abandoned. 2010. 108p. 28.95 (978-1-4497-0396-7(8)); pap. 11.95 (978-1-4497-0397-4(6)) Author Solutions, Inc. (WestBow Pr.).
Hamilton, Charles, Sr. From Darkness to Light. 2009. 377p. 24.95 (978-1-4327-2112-1(7)); pap. 16.95 (978-1-4327-1115-3(6)) Outskirts Pr., Inc.
Hamilton, Denise. Trials to Treasure. 2008. 264p. pap. 15.99 (978-1-60647-623-9(8)) Xulon Pr., Inc.
Hamilton, Denise & Barker, Barbara. Faith Pointes. 2007. 320p. per. 17.99 (978-1-60266-238-4(X)) Xulon Pr., Inc.
Hamilton, James. Life in Earnest Six Lectures, on Christian Activity & Ardor by the Rev James Hamilton. 2006. 172p. per. 18.99 (978-1-4255-1396-2(4)) MPublishing.
Hamilton, Katie F. Spells & Incantations of Yesteryear. 8.00 (978-1-889023-10-6(8)) Metheglin Pr.
Hamilton, Lisa B. Wisdom from the Middle Ages for Middle-Aged Women. 2007. 240p. per. 20.00 (978-0-8192-2237-4(2), Morehouse Publishing) Church Publishing, Inc.
Hamilton, Patricia. I'll Have Nuggets with My Prayers, Please. 2007. 48p. per. 16.95 (978-1-4241-7589-5(5)) PublishAmerica, Inc.
Hamm, Regie. Angels & Idols: The Rise, Fall, & Redemption of a Would-Be Pop Star. 2010. pap. 14.99 (978-1-61663-440-7(5)) Tate Publishing & Enterprises, LLC.
Hammari, Kimiko. I Know the Scriptures Are True. 2010. 160p. pap. 14.99 (978-1-59955-428-0(3)) Cedar Fort, Inc./CFI Distribution.
Hammer, Olav. Alternative Christs. Hammer, Olav, ed. 2009. (ENG., Illus.). 316p. 98.00 (978-0-521-88902-5(2)) Cambridge Univ. Pr.
Hammer, Randy. 52 Ways to Ignite Your Congregation — Practical Hospitality. 2009. (978-0-8298-1825-3(1)) Pilgrim Pr., The/United Church Pr.
Hammock, Lo-Dee. It's Not Odd - It's GOD!! God' Miracles & other Stories of His Grace & Mercy in the Lifetime of an Old Lady. 2007. 208p. per. 16.95 (978-0-9800625-0-2(0), Sun King Pr.) Sun King Media.
Hammond, Bryan. I Put to Death Fornication & so Can You. 2011. 72p. pap. 10.99 (978-1-61379-551-4(3)) Xulon Pr., Inc.
Hammond, Lynne. When Healing Doesn't Come Easily. 2006. pap. 8.99 (978-1-57399-321-0(2)) Mac Hammond Ministries.
Hammonds, Gregory. Come Now, My Brother! From the Womb to God's Glory. 2007. 64p. per. 12.95 (978-0-9774513-9-5(9)) Changing Lives Publishing.
Hamp, Bob. Think Differently, Live Differently Keys to A Life of Freedom. 2010. (Illus.). 252p. pap. (978-1-4507-0920-0(6)) Independent Pub.
Hampsch, Carl. Opposites Attract: Understanding God's Design for Lasting Relationships. 2007. pap. 15.99 (978-0-7684-2504-8(2)) Destiny Image Pubs.
Hampsch, John H. Amazing Grace: Your Expendable Quota of Divine Life. 24p. pap. 1.25 (978-1-57918-095-9(7), 7180) Queenship Publishing Co.
—The Art of Suffering: Way to Grow. 24p. pap. 1.25 (978-1-57918-093-5(0), 7178) Queenship Publishing Co.
—Boosting Your Love Potential. 24p. pap. 1.25 (978-1-57918-092-8(2), 7177) Queenship Publishing Co.
—Coping with Life's Darkest Moments. 24p. pap. 1.25 (978-1-57918-091-1(4), 7176) Queenship Publishing Co.
—Four Types of Counterfeit Faith. 24p. pap. 1.25 (978-1-57918-090-4(6), 7175) Queenship Publishing Co.
—Getting to Know Your Guardian Angel. 24p. pap. 1.25 (978-1-57918-089-8(2), 7174) Queenship Publishing Co.
—Joy, the Sparkle of Life. 24p. pap. 1.25 (978-1-57918-088-1(4), 7173) Queenship Publishing Co.
—Meekness Is Not Weakness. 24p. pap. 1.25 (978-1-57918-086-7(8), 7171) Queenship Publishing Co.
—Nesting in the Hand of God. 24p. pap. 1.25 (978-1-57918-084-3(1), 7169) Queenship Publishing Co.
—The Poison of Bad Example. 24p. pap. 1.25 (978-1-57918-082-9(5), 7167) Queenship Publishing Co.
—Sharing the Lifeboat: The Meaning of Christian Fellowship. 24p. pap. 1.25 (978-1-57918-081-2(7), 7166) Queenship Publishing Co.
—Speak up Lord, I Can't Hear You. 24p. pap. 1.25 (978-1-57918-080-5(9), 7165) Queenship Publishing Co.
—Thought Control: Architect of Character. 24p. pap. 1.25 (978-1-57918-075-1(2), 7160) Queenship Publishing Co.
—Treatment for Anemic Christians. 24p. pap. 1.25 (978-1-57918-078-2(7), 7163) Queenship Publishing Co.
—When You Mess up, 'Fess Up. (SPA.). 24p. pap. 1.25 (978-1-57918-101-7(5), 7186) Queenship Publishing Co.
—The World's Greatest Secret. 24p. pap. 1.25 (978-1-57918-076-8(0), 7161) Queenship Publishing Co.
Hampton, Lee M. What the Bible Says Concerning Sin & the Christian. 2007. 20.00 (978-1-60416-090-1(X)); pap. 13.00 (978-1-60416-089-5(6)) Reformation Pubs.
Hamrick, Frank & Thornton, champ. Dynamic Christian Living. 2nd ed. 2008. (ENG., Illus.). 252p. pap. 14.95 (978-1-59557-050-5(0)) Positive Action For Christ.
Hanabusa, George. Second Chances Gospel. 2007. 104p. per. 9.99 (978-1-60266-237-7(1)) Xulon Pr., Inc.
Hanaoka, Nobuaki. On the Back of a Buffalo- Eastern Stories for Western Journey. 2007. 183p. pap. 12.95 (978-0-7414-4391-5(0)) Infinity Publishing.
Hanby-Robie, Sharon. The Simple Home: A Faith-Filled Guide to Simplicity, Peace, & Joy in Your Home. 2006. (Spirit of Simple Living Ser.). (Illus.). 180p. pap. 14.95 (978-0-8249-4702-6(9)) Ideals Pubns.
Hancock, Kathryn. Music to His Ears. 2009. 140p. pap. 14.99 (978-1-60791-357-3(7)) Xulon Pr., Inc.
Hancock, Sandy. Letting Go: Pathway to an Amazing Life. 2008. 164p. pap. 15.95 (978-0-595-48624-3(X)) iUniverse, Inc.
Hancock, Wayne. It Matters What You Believe. 2010. 80p. pap. 10.99 (978-1-61579-835-3(8)) Xulon Pr., Inc.
Hancok, Maxine. Ama, Respeta y Se Libre: Love, Honor & Be Free. (SPA.). 232p. (978-84-7228-382-4(8), 220017) Clie, Editorial.
Hands, H. a. Hope Write Here Right Now: Reflections upon fragile faith strengthened by our loving father God. 2009. 52p. pap. 10.49 (978-1-4389-6007-4(7)) AuthorHouse.
Hanegraaff, Hank. The Bible Answer Book: Volume 2, 0 vols., Vol. 2. 2007. 256p. 14.99 (978-1-4041-0303-0(1)) Nelson, Thomas Inc.
—The Complete Bible Answer Book, 0 vols. collector's ed. 2009. 560p. 21.99 (978-1-4041-1381-7(9)) Nelson, Thomas Inc.
Hanes, Mary. Mas Alla del Sufrimiento: Beyond Heartache. (SPA.). (978-84-7645-052-9(4), 223112) Clie, Editorial.
—El Nino Que Esta en Camino.Tr. of Child Within. (SPA.). 120p. (978-84-7228-766-2(1), 222340) Clie, Editorial.
Haniah, Laneen. A Spiritual Famine: The Testing of Your Faith. 2008. 169p. pap. 22.50 (978-0-9794210-2-0(0)) Victoriously Free! Publishing.
Hanks, Scott. Take Heed to Thyself. 2007. spiral bd. 7.00 (978-0-9799518-5-5(2)) Hanks, Scott.
—Take Heed to Thyself for Kids. 2007. (J). spiral bd. 7.00 (978-0-9799518-7-9(9)) Hanks, Scott.
Hanna, Janice & Y'Barbo, Kathleen. The House Is Quiet, Now What? 2009. (Turning Points Ser.). (ENG.). 224p. pap. 7.99 (978-1-60260-452-0(5), Barbour Bks.) Barbour Publishing, Inc.
Hanna, L. J. The Rocky Road: Extraordinary Testimonies from an Ordinary Person. 2011. 124p. pap. 13.95 (978-1-4620-5708-5(X)) iUniverse, Inc.
Hannan, Peter. Follow Your Dream: Restoring Lost Intimacy. 2nd rev. ed. 2008. (ENG.). 201p. (Orig.). pap. 23.95 (978-1-85607-615-9(6)) Columba Pr. IRL. Dist: Dufour Editions, Inc.
Hannon, Patrick. The Geography of God's Mercy: Stories of Compassion & Forgiveness. 2007. 159p. 17.95 (978-0-87946-332-8(5)); per. 12.95 (978-0-87946-333-5(3)) ACTA Pubns.
—The Long Yearning's End: Stories of Sacrament & Incarnation. 2009. 128p. 17.95 (978-0-87946-402-8(X)); pap. 12.95 (978-0-87946-403-5(8)) ACTA Pubns.
—Right or Wrong? Essays in Moral Theology. 2009. (ENG.). 150p. pap. 22.95 (978-1-84730-129-1(0)) Veritas Pubns. IRL. Dist: Dufour Editions, Inc.
Hannon, Ruth & Hoagland, Victor, eds. Catholic Baby's First Bible-Nab. 2008. (Illus.). 93p. 10.95 (978-0-88271-147-8(4)) Regina Pr., Malhame & Co.
Hansen, Andy. How to Become One with Jesus. 12p. pap. 0.99 (978-0-89900-320-7(6)); 30p. pap., tchr. ed. 1.99 (978-0-89900-444-0(X)) College Pr. Publishing Co., Inc.
Hansen, Marsha & Huchthausen, Peter A. Finding God in the Shadows: Stories from the Battlefield of Life. 2007. 188p. per. 16.99 (978-0-8066-5326-6(4), Augsburg Bks.) Augsburg Fortress, Pubs.
Hanson, Buddy. Making Your Daily Reads. 2008. 180p. pap. 20.00 (978-0-9771773-8-7(6)) Hanson Group.
Hanson, Evangelist Bernadette. 30 Days with Jesus: A Prophetic Word from Our Lord & Savior. 2009. 80p. pap. 12.99 (978-1-4389-4339-8(3)) AuthorHouse.
Hanson, Marty & Kriva, William A. Life Pearls. 2010. 116p. 28.95 (978-1-4497-0281-6(3)); pap. 11.95 (978-1-4497-0280-9(5)) Author Solutions, Inc. (WestBow Pr.).
Hanson, Robert. Conquering with God. 2006. pap. 9.99 (978-1-60034-582-1(4)) Xulon Pr., Inc.
—Continuing with God. 2006. pap. 9.99 (978-1-60034-581-4(6)) Xulon Pr., Inc.
—In Search of God - Growing in Him Book1. 2007. 76p. per. 9.99 (978-1-60266-321-3(1)) Xulon Pr., Inc.
—Walking in Christ. 2007. 88p. per. 9.99 (978-1-60266-872-0(8)) Xulon Pr., Inc.
—What Am I to Do? 2007. 96p. per. 9.99 (978-1-60266-873-7(6)) Xulon Pr., Inc.
Hanson, Robert A. Dealing with the Dampers of the Soul. 2008. 152p. per. 13.99 (978-1-60477-636-2(6)) Xulon Pr., Inc.
—What Am I to Be? 2008. 116p. per. 10.99 (978-1-60477-600-3(5)) Xulon Pr., Inc.
Hanson, Sandy. A Camel's Story. 2011. 54p. 24.99 (978-1-61215-821-1(8)); pap. 26.99 (978-1-61215-820-4(X)) Xulon Pr., Inc.
Hanson, Sharon. The Fall of Babylon , the Fall of Man's Self Rule. 2007. 188p. pap. 15.50 (978-0-615-15333-9(X)) Hanson, Sharon.
Happy about My Christian Faith: 10 Stories That Will Touch Your Soul. 2007. 175p. per. 16.95 (978-1-60005-007-7(7)) Partnerships For Community, Inc.
Harber, Jane E. Walking Toward the Light: A Study for New Believers & Veteran Christians. 2011. pap. 15.99 (978-1-61739-297-9(9)) Tate Publishing & Enterprises, LLC.
Harbinson, Adam, ed. The Jesus I Know. 2010. (ENG.). 142p. pap. 18.95 (978-1-85607-654-8(7)) Columba Pr. IRL. Dist: Dufour Editions, Inc.
Harcum, E. Incidental Psychotherapy within Christian Relationships: Mental Health Benefits from Therapeutic Alliances Built on the Caring Love of Christians. 2010. (ENG.). 102p. pap. 18.99 (978-0-7618-5397-8(9)) Hamilton Bks.
Hardaway, Cheri. Worth Every Tear. 2010. 408p. pap. 22.99 (978-1-60957-653-0(5)) Xulon Pr., Inc.
The Harder I Laugh, the Deeper I Hurt: Lessons for Faith Communities. 2008. (ENG.). pap. 24.99 (978-0-8341-2379-3(7), 9780834123793) Beacon Hill Pr. of Kansas City.
Harder Tangvald, Christine. Thank You, God, for My Two Feet. Date not set. 5.99 (978-1-55513-931-5(0)) Cook, David C.
Hardin, Leslie. The Spirituality of Jesus: Nine Disciplines Christ Modeled for Us, 1 vol. 2009. 208p. pap. 12.99 (978-0-8254-2905-7(6)) Kregel Pubns.
Hardin, Philip K. Lions Were Born to Roar. 2011. 142p. pap. 14.99 (978-1-61379-242-1(5)) Xulon Pr., Inc.
Harding, April. Single Dose: Finding Peace, Fulfillment, & Contentment Being Single. 2007. 168p. (ENG.). 25.95 (978-0-595-69617-8(1)); per. 15.95 (978-0-595-44635-3(3)) iUniverse, Inc.
Harding, Leander S. Reverence for the Heart of the Child. 2011. 178p. pap. 20.00 (978-1-61097-398-4(4), Wipf and Stock) Wipf & Stock Pubs.
Hardman, Norman E. Kingdom Gps. 2008. 228p. pap. 14.99 (978-1-60647-319-1(0)) Xulon Pr., Inc.
Hardnett, Leon. Are You Getting Prepared for Your Exit Exam? 2008. 64p. pap. 12.99 (978-1-60791-039-8(X)) Xulon Pr., Inc.
Hare, Julius. The Victory of Faith. 2007. (ENG.). 366p. 48.95 (978-0-548-05203-7(4)) Kessinger Publishing, LLC.
Harewood, David. I Will Bless Thee. 2011. 242p. pap. 17.99 (978-1-934769-15-7(0)) McDougal & Assocs.
Harger, Tracy. Bible Topics. 2011. 182p. pap. 14.99 (978-1-61379-165-3(8)) Xulon Pr., Inc.
Hargrave, Terry. Boomers on the Edge: Three Realities That Will Change Your Life Forever, 1 vol. 2008. (ENG.). 272p. pap. 14.99 (978-0-310-27659-3(4)) Zondervan.
Hargrove, A. Shepherd's Heart John. A Shepherd's Heart. 2009. 193p. pap. 16.95 (978-0-557-19817-7(8)) Lulu Enterprises Inc.
Hargrove, Verna. Scaling New Heights. 2007. 192p. per. 24.95 (978-1-4241-7405-8(8)) PublishAmerica, Inc.
Harkness, Georgia. The Fellowship of the Holy Spirit. (978-0-687-12886-0(2)) Abingdon Pr.
Harlow, Duane. Breaking Out of Religious Christianity. 2006. pap. 14.99 (978-0-7684-2383-9(X)) Destiny Image Pubs.
Harmon, Catherine. I Do... until Death Do Us Part? Gaining A New Perspective on Traditional Wedding Vows. 2008. 108p. pap. 10.99 (978-1-60647-583-6(5)) Xulon Pr., Inc.
Harmon, Hugh. The GraceFUL Life. 2010. 124p. pap. 15.99 (978-0-557-26310-3(7)) Lulu Enterprises Inc.
—Worthy Art Thou. 2007. 105p. pap. 17.50 (978-0-615-15281-3(3)) Kingdom Bk & Gift.
Harmon, Richard. Desires of the Heart. 2008. 156p. pap. 13.99 (978-1-60647-537-9(1)) Xulon Pr., Inc.
—The Victories of God's People. 2009. 156p. pap. 14.99 (978-1-60791-902-5(8)) Xulon Pr., Inc.
Harmon, Tom. For Me & My House. 2011. 96p. pap. 10.95 (978-1-60920-030-5(6)) Ajoyin Publishing, Inc.
Harmon, Tom. You Must Be Born Again. 2008. 84p. pap. 14.99 (978-1-4389-3703-8(2)) AuthorHouse.
Harms, Silke. Glauben üben: Grundlinien einer evangelischen Theologie der geistlichen Übung und ihre praktische Entfaltung am Beispiel der ¿Exerzitien im Alltag¿. 2011. (Arbeiten zur Pastoraltheologie, Liturgik und Hymnologie Ser.). (GER., Illus.). 288p. (C). pap. 68.00 (978-3-525-57016-6(3)) Vandenhoeck & Ruprecht GmbH & Co. KG DEU. Dist: ISD.
Harney, Jan. Freewheeling. 2007. (ENG.). 160p. 17.99 (978-1-85078-752-5(2)) Authentic Media.
Harney, Kevin & Harney, Kevin G. Organic Outreach: Communicating God's Love in Ordinary Ways, 1 vol. 2009. (ENG.). 256p. pap. 14.99 (978-0-310-27395-0(1)) Zondervan.
Harney, Kevin G. Seismic Shifts, 1 vol. 2008. (ENG.). 288p. pap. 12.99 (978-0-310-29158-9(5)) Zondervan.
Harnish, James A. Simple Rules for Money: John Wesley on Earning, Saving, & Giving. 2010. 79p. pap. 10.00 (978-0-687-46616-0(4)) Abingdon Pr.
—Strength for the Broken Places. 2009. 163p. pap. 15.00 (978-0-687-65763-6(6)) Abingdon Pr.

Harper, Chandi J. From Where I Am, with What I've Got: Real Life Lessons from Walking with A Real God. 2008. 96p. pap. 13.95 *(978-1-4327-3173-1(4))* Outskirts Pr., Inc.
Harper, Don R. Methodism's Founder John Wesley Believed in Angels. 2008. 228p. pap. 15.99 *(978-1-60477-301-9(4))* Xulon Pr., Inc.
Harper, Lisa. What Every Girl Wants: A Portrait of Perfect Love & Intimacy in the Song of Solomon. 2009. (ENG.). 128p. pap. 9.99 *(978-1-4143-3003-7(0))* Tyndale Hse. Pubs.
Harper, Tom R. Career Crossover: Leaving the Marketplace for Ministry. 2007. 208p. pap. 12.99 *(978-0-8054-4441-4(6)*, B&H Bks.) B&H Publishing Group.
Harpman, Tim. Visions. 2010. 192p. pap. 14.99 *(978-1-60957-570-0(9))* Xulon Pr., Inc.
Harrell, LaTonia. One Night Changed My Life. 2010. 76p. pap. 8.95 *(978-1-4502-7500-2(1))* iUniverse, Inc.
Harrelson, Bob. The Privilege of Pain: Help for Those Who Are Hurting. 2010. 164p. 30.95 *(978-1-61507-292-7(6))*; pap. 13.95 *(978-1-61507-291-0(8))* Cross Bks. Publishing.
Harrelson, Walter. Ten Commandments for Today. 2006. 128p. pap. 14.95 *(978-0-664-00931-1(X))* Westminster John Knox Pr.
Harrington, Chrsanna. Held Close by an Angel: A Guide for Survivors of Childhood Trauma Who Find Themselves Single Again. 2011. pap. 10.99 *(978-1-61739-662-5(1))* Tate Publishing & Enterprises, LLC.
Harrington, Peter. Las Diez Preguntas Mas Frecuentes Entre los Nuevos Cristianos. (SPA.). 48p. 19.95 *(978-0-88177-330-9(1))* Discipleship Resources.
—10 FAQ's of New Christians. 48p. 19.95 *(978-0-88177-304-0(2))* Discipleship Resources.
Harrington, Wilfrid J. From the Presence of the Lord: A God Too Gracious. 2006. (ENG.). 66p. per. 15.95 *(978-1-85607-516-9(8))* Columba Pr. IRL. Dist: Dufour Editions, Inc.
Harris, April Marshaun. Give Love. 2011. 74p. pap. 15.99 **(978-1-4568-7311-0(3))** Xlibris Corp.
Harris, Cheryl. Living Beyond the Frame. 2006. (ENG., Illus.). 176p. pap. 12.99 *(978-1-59979-010-7(6)*, Creation Hse.) Charisma Media.
Harris, Diane L. Stepping into the Light: You're a Christian, what Now? 2008. 257p. pap. 20.00 *(978-1-4357-1894-4(1))* Lulu Enterprises Inc.
Harris, Harold L., Jr. The 4 Faces of the Apostolic & the Prophetic. 2007. 64p. pap. 7.95 *(978-0-9788590-7-7(3))* Armour of Light Publishing.
Harris, Jerry. Micropolitan Church: Doing Mega-Ministry in America's Small Towns. 2011. 212p. pap. 17.95 **(978-1-61507-722-9(7))** Cross Bks. Publishing.
Harris, Joseph. God's Relationship with Man. 2008. 128p. 10.99 *(978-1-60604-520-6(2))* Tate Publishing & Enterprises, LLC.
Harris, Joy. Authentic Joy. 2010. 190p. pap. 14.99 *(978-1-60957-430-7(3))* Xulon Pr., Inc.
Harris, Laura Leigh. Wanted: God's Women for America - Adventure Group (Booklet 10), 12 vols., Vol. 10. 2007. 32p. stu. ed. 6.99 *(978-0-9797389-0-6(3))* Jeremiah's Tree Adventures LLC.
—Wanted: God's Women for America - Adventure Group (Booklet 11), 12 vols., Vol. 11. 2007. 32p. stu. ed. 6.99 *(978-0-9797389-1-3(1))* Jeremiah's Tree Adventures LLC.
—Wanted: God's Women for America - Adventure Group (Booklet 12), 12 vols., Vol. 12. 2007. 34p. 6.99 *(978-0-9797389-2-0(X))* Jeremiah's Tree Adventures LLC.
—Wanted: God's Women for America - Adventure Group (Leader's Guide) 2007. 32p. ldr.'s hndbk. ed. 6.99 *(978-0-9797389-3-7(8))* Jeremiah's Tree Adventures LLC.
Harris, Mark R. Find Your Wings. 2006. (ENG., Illus.). 64p. 13.99 *(978-1-4155-3759-5(7)*, Howard Bks.) Howard Books.
Harris, Paula. A Woman of All Seasons: Daily Divine Deliverance. 2009. 128p. pap. 12.95 *(978-1-4401-2294-1(6))* iUniverse, Inc.
Harris, Ralph. God's Astounding Opinion of You: Understanding Your Identity Will Change Your Life. 2011. pap. 12.99 *(978-0-7369-3783-2(8))* Harvest Hse. Pubs.
Harris, Reverend James R. Jesus in Columbus. 2010. 140p. 22.49 *(978-1-4490-5876-0(0))* AuthorHouse.
Harris, Trudy. Glimpses of Heaven: True Stories of Hope & Peace at the End of Life's Journey. 2008. 192p. pap. 13.99 *(978-0-8007-3251-6(0))* Revell.
Harrison, Bob. Power Points for Increase. 2010. 240p. 19.99 *(978-1-60683-018-5(X))* Harrison House Pubs.
Harrison, Graham. Beginning at the Beginning. 144p. pap. *(978-1-85049-154-5(2))* Whitaker Pr., The.
Harrison, Harry H., Jr. 1001 Things Every College Student Needs to Know: Like Buying Your Books Before Exams Start, 0 vols. 2008. (1001 Things Ser.). 304p. pap. 9.99 *(978-1-4041-0434-1(8))* Nelson, Thomas Inc.
Harrison House, creator. Scripture Confessions for Finances: Life-Changing Words of Faith for Every Day. 2007. (Scripture Confessions Ser.). 27p. pap. 1.99 *(978-1-57794-874-2(2))* Harrison House Pubs.
—Scripture Confessions Gift Collection: Life-Changing Words of Faith for Every Day. 2007. (SCRIPTURE CONFESSIONS Ser.). 192p. pap. 13.99 *(978-1-57794-916-9(1))* Harrison House Pubs.
Harrison House, Inc. Staff. Scripture Confessions for New Believers. 2009. 32p. pap. 1.99 *(978-1-57794-949-7(8))* Harrison House Pubs.
Harrison, Jim. What Makes God Cry the Most. 2008. 72p. pap. 10.99 *(978-1-60647-924-7(5))* Xulon Pr., Inc.
Harrison, Rick E. The Estrogen Conspiracy. 2011. 80p. pap. 10.99 **(978-1-61379-201-8(8))** Xulon Pr., Inc.
Harrison, Warren. Reflections on Christian Living in Americ. 2007. 200p. per. 13.95 *(978-1-4327-0805-4(8))* Outskirts Pr., Inc.
Harrod, Allen F. Deception by Design: The Mormon Story. 2011. 484p. 44.95 **(978-1-4497-2795-7(0))**; pap. 34.95 **(978-1-4497-2796-3(4))** Author Solutions, Inc. (WestBow Pr.).
Harry, Josiah. Embracing Your Destiny. 2010. 122p. 19.99 *(978-1-61579-995-4(8))* Xulon Pr., Inc.
Hart, Inez. For a Hope & a Future. 2008. 228p. per. 14.99 *(978-1-60477-780-2(X))* Xulon Pr., Inc.
Hart, Joan. How to Have Victory Through Prayer. 2010. pap. 7.99 *(978-1-61663-130-7(9))* Tate Publishing & Enterprises, LLC.
Hart, Thomas. Bajando de la Montana: Cómo hacer que tu retiro sea una vivencia de todos os Días. 2007. (SPA.). 128p. pap. 10.95 *(978-0-8091-4456-3(5)*, 4456-3) Paulist Pr.
Hart, Tom, et al. Being a Disciple. 2009. (40-Minute Bible Studies). (ENG.). 80p. pap. 7.99 *(978-0-307-45756-1(7)*, WaterBrook Pr.) Doubleday Religious Publishing Group, The.
Hart, Tony. Winning Is Everything. 2008. 148p. pap. 13.99 *(978-1-60477-674-4(9))* Xulon Pr., Inc.
Hartley, Andrew M. Christian & Humanist Foundations for Statistical Inference: Religious Control of Statistical Paradigms. 2007. 138p. pap. 18.00 *(978-1-55635-549-3(1))* Wipf & Stock Pubs.
Hartley, Robert. Call to the Wall. 2006. pap. 5.00 *(978-0-9753905-2-8(X)*, 10000) New Grid Bks.
Hartman, Anne. Though He Slay Me. 2010. 324p. pap. 18.99 *(978-1-60957-646-2(2))* Xulon Pr., Inc.
Hartman, Laura M. The Christian Consumer: Living Faithfully in a Fragile World, 1 vol. 2011. (ENG., Illus.). 272p. 29.95 *(978-0-19-974642-2(7))* Oxford Univ. Pr., Inc.
Hartmann, Alexander T. The Task. 2008. 52p. pap. *(978-3-00-023397-5(0))* Hartmann, Thomas Alexander.
Hartmann, Joseph James. Sentenced to Death, Destined for Life: The Janiece Turner-Hartmann Story. 2011. (Illus.). 344p. pap. 19.95 **(978-0-9842422-4-5(4))** VaryMedia.
Hartvigsen, Kirsten Marie. Prepare the Way of the Lord: Towards a Cognitive Poetic Analysis of Audience Involvement with Characters & Events in the Markan World. 2011. (Beihefte zur Zeitschrift für die neutestamentliche Wissenschaft und die Kunde der älteren Kirche Ser.). (ENG.). 560p. 182.00 **(978-3-11-025347-4(X))**; (Illus.). 280.00 **(978-3-11-219097-5(1))** De Gruyter, Walter Inc.
Hartzell, Tamara. In the Name of Purpose: Sacrificing Truth on the Altar of Unity. 2007. (ENG.). 400p. 32.99 *(978-1-4257-3627-9(0))*; per. 22.99 *(978-1-4257-3626-2(2))* Xlibris Corp.
The Harvest. 2008. 173p. per. 9.99 *(978-0-7684-2642-7(1))* Destiny Image Pubs.
Harvey, Dorothy. God Did It. 2009. 184p. pap. 15.95 *(978-1-4389-7776-8(X))* AuthorHouse.
Harvey, Jim & Harvey, Val. What a Difference a Name Makes: A Practical Guide for a Study of the Name Yahweh. 2011. 180p. 30.95 **(978-1-4627-0532-0(4))**; pap. 13.95 **(978-1-4627-0531-3(6))** Cross Bks. Publishing.
Harvey K. McKelvey. God's Answer to 21st Century Terrorists: A How-to Manual. 2009. 84p. pap. 7.84 *(978-1-4269-1772-1(4))* Trafford Publishing.
Harvey, P. T. Scout, a Journey in Faith. 2008. 309p. pap. 29.95 *(978-1-4241-9281-6(1))* PublishAmerica, Inc.
Harvey, Verna. The Blessedness of Waiting on God: How to Deal with the Stress of Holding Patterns. 2007. (ENG.). 188p. per. 16.99 *(978-1-4141-0794-3(3))* Pleasant Word.
Harvin, Martha J. For Gods Glory & My Good. 2009. pap. 10.99 *(978-1-60791-420-4(4))* Xulon Pr., Inc.
Harwell, Dan. Gathering the Priests. 2007. 188p. per. 13.99 *(978-1-60266-675-7(X))* Xulon Pr., Inc.
Hasbún, Cristina de. Dile Adiós Al Pasado. 2006. (SPA & ENG.). 192p. 9.99 *(978-1-59185-846-1(1)*, Casa Creacion) Charisma Media.
Hash, Chris. God Is Not Angry with You. 2011. 102p. pap. 10.99 **(978-1-61379-836-2(9))** Xulon Pr., Inc.
Haskell, Stephen N. The Story of the Seer of Patmos. 448p. (Orig.). 2010. 41.56 *(978-1-163-39249-2(9))* 2010. pap. 29.56 *(978-1-162-92014-6(9))* 2007. (ENG.). 51.95 *(978-0-548-08417-5(3))* Kessinger Publishing, LLC.
Haskin, Leslie. God Has Not Forgotten about You: And He Cares More Than You Can Imagine. 2009. 208p. pap. 13.99 *(978-0-7642-0604-7(4))* Bethany Hse. Pubs.
Hastings, Horace. Last Judgment. pap. 1.49 *(978-0-87377-041-5(2))* GAM Pubns.
Hatchell, Sandra H. Spiritual Warfare: A How to Guide for Defeating Satan: Putting on the Armor of God. 2007. 281p. per. 15.99 *(978-1-59886-643-8(5))* Tate Publishing & Enterprises, LLC.
Hatchett, Cat. Walk Right Through It. 2009. 96p. pap. 10.99 *(978-1-60791-424-2(7))* Xulon Pr., Inc.
Hater, Robert J. Journeys of Discovery: Transitions, Rites of Passage, & the Sacramental Life of Faith. 2009. 208p. pap. 19.95 *(978-1-58595-708-8(9))* Twenty-Third Pubns./Bayard.
Hatfield, Tyrel & Hatfield, Justin. In our Father's Hands: A daily devotional guide for the Family. Garber, Nancy, ed. 2007. (Illus.). 388p. (YA). per. 15.99 *(978-0-9766703-4-6(8))* Little Acorn LLC.
Hatmaker, Jennifer. Girl Talk: Getting Past the Chitchat. 2007. (Modern Girl's Bible Study Ser.) (ENG.). 208p. per. 12.99 *(978-1-57683-895-2(1))* NavPress Publishing Group.
—Make Over: Revitalizing the Many Roles You Fill. 2007. (Modern Girl's Bible Study Ser.) (ENG.). 208p. pap. 12.99 *(978-1-57683-894-5(3))* NavPress Publishing Group.
—Ms. Understood: Rebuilding the Feminine Equation. 2008. (Real Life Stuff for Couples Ser.). (ENG.). 224p. pap. 12.99 *(978-1-60006-216-2(4))* NavPress Publishing Group.
—Road Trip: Five Adventures You're Meant to Live. 2006. (Modern Girl's Bible Study Ser.). (ENG., Illus.). 192p. per. 12.99 *(978-1-57683-892-1(7))* NavPress Publishing Group.
Hattingh, Charl. Bridal Garment. 2007. 128p. per. 13.99 *(978-1-60266-985-7(6))* Xulon Pr., Inc.
Haugan, Harald K. Dying Church, Rising Body. 2010. 188p. pap. 14.49 *(978-1-4520-5083-6(X))* AuthorHouse.
Haugen, Gary A. Just Courage: God's Great Expedition for the Restless Christian. 2008. (ENG.). 150p. 18.00 *(978-0-8308-3494-5(X)*, IVP Bks.) InterVarsity Pr.
Haughey, John C., ed. In Search of the Whole: Twelve Essays on Faith & Academic Life. 2011. (Illus.). 232p. pap. 29.95 *(978-1-58901-781-8(1))* Georgetown Univ. Pr.
Havard, Dalton. Core Beliefs of the Christian Faith. 2009. 124p. pap. 11.99 *(978-1-60791-886-8(2))* Xulon Pr., Inc.
Havergal, Frances R. Guardados Para el Uso Del Senor: Kept for the Master's Use.Tr. of Kept for the Master's Use. (SPA.). 128p. *(978-84-7228-871-3(4)*, 220436) Clie, Editorial.
—My King. pap. 3.99 *(978-0-87377-042-2(0))* GAM Pubns.
Havergal, Frances Ridley. Kept for the Master's Use. 2011. 106p. pap. 7.99 **(978-1-61203-074-6(2))** Bottom of the Hill Publishing.
Havergal, Frances Ridley. Morning Bells; or, Waking Thoughts for Little Ones. 2007. 72p. per. *(978-1-4065-4365-0(9))* Dodo Pr.
Hawk, Nina. Romancing in the Light. 2008. 148p. 20.00 *(978-0-8059-7742-4(2))* Dorrance Publishing Co., Inc.
Hawkins, Andrew. Whispers That Delight. 2008. 176p. per. *(978-1-897373-16-3(3))* Word Alive Pr.
Hawkins, Cheryl K. Louder Than Thunder. 2008. pap. 9.99 *(978-1-60647-441-9(3))* Xulon Pr., Inc.
Hawkins, David. When Pleasing Others Is Hurting You: Finding God's Patterns for Healthy Relationships. 2010. 240p. pap. 12.99 *(978-0-7369-2778-9(6))* Harvest Hse. Pubs.
Hawkins, Ray L. & Gale, A. B. Becoming A Mighty Man of God: No Subtitle. 2008. 152p. pap. 13.99 *(978-1-60647-628-4(9))* Xulon Pr., Inc.
Hawkins, Tim. The Cry of My Heart: How to Be a Genuine Disciple. 2010. 156p. (YA). pap. *(978-1-905564-78-1(3))* Good Bk. Co.
Hawley, Dannie. Dealing with Our Fears When Letting Go Seems Impossible. 2011. 244p. 35.95 **(978-1-4497-1911-1(2))**; pap. 19.95 **(978-1-4497-1910-4(4))** Author Solutions, Inc. (WestBow Pr.).
Hawley, Michael L. Searching for Truth with a Broken Flashlight. 2010. 202p. pap. 13.95 *(978-1-59330-685-4(7))* Aventine Pr.
Hawthorne, Andy. Hope Unleashed: Serving God Through Words & Actions. 2009. (ENG.). 176p. pap. 12.99 *(978-1-4347-6448-5(6))* Cook, David C.
Hayden, Kathryn. Forgiveness. 2009. 32p. pap. 12.49 *(978-1-4389-8534-3(7))* AuthorHouse.
Hayes, Charles F. Bring University Students to Christ. 292p. 2015. 26.99 **(978-1-61379-510-1(6))** 2011. pap. 16.99 **(978-1-61379-509-5(2))** Xulon Pr., Inc.
Hayes, H. Randy. Don't Shoot the Horse. 2007. 276p. 25.99 *(978-1-60266-909-3(0))*; per. 15.99 *(978-1-60266-907-9(4))* Xulon Pr., Inc.
Hayes, John B. Sub-Merge: Living Deep in a Shallow World: Service, Justice & Contemplation among the World's Poor. 2007. (ENG., Illus.). 302p. per. 16.99 *(978-0-8307-4306-3(5))* Gospel Light Pubns.
Hayes, Kate. Chosen for Change: Am I Part of God's Big Plan? 2006. (Re: Action: Small Group Resources Ser.). (Illus.). 47p. pap. 8.00 *(978-1-85999-623-2(X))* Scripture Union GBR. Dist: STL Distribution North America.
—For the Tough Times: Does God Care When I Am Hurting? 2006. (Re: Action: Small Group Resources Ser.). (Illus.). 48p. pap. 8.00 *(978-1-85999-622-5(1))* Scripture Union GBR. Dist: STL Distribution North America.
—A Journey of Discovery: On the Road with Jesus' Followers. 2006. 64p. pap. 8.00 *(978-1-84427-180-1(3))* Scripture Union GBR. Dist: STL Distribution North America.
—A Journey of Love: Reaching Out as Jesus Did. 2006. 64p. pap. 8.00 *(978-1-84427-232-7(X))* Scripture Union GBR. Dist: STL Distribution North America.
—More Than Bricks & Ritual: Am I a Team Player for God? 2006. (Re: Action: Small Group Resources Ser.). 41p. pap. 8.00 *(978-1-85999-769-7(4))* Scripture Union GBR. Dist: STL Distribution North America.
—More Than Fine Words: Does My Faith Impact 24/7? 2006. (Re: Action: Small Group Resources Ser.). 46p. pap. 8.00 *(978-1-85999-770-3(5))* Scripture Union GBR. Dist: STL Distribution North America.
Hayes, Norvel. Faith Has No Feelings. 2011. 1.99 *(978-1-57794-089-0(X))* Harrison House Pubs.
—Financial Dominion. 2011. 96p. (Orig.). pap. 6.99 *(978-0-89274-703-0(X)*, HH703) Harrison House Pubs.
—Getting to Know God. pap. 1.00 *(978-1-57794-081-4(4))* Harrison House Pubs.
—God's Fire. pap. 1.00 *(978-1-57794-077-7(6))* Harrison House Pubs.
—God's Light. pap. 1.00 *(978-1-57794-079-1(2))* Harrison House Pubs.
—How to Get God's Attention. pap. 1.00 *(978-1-57794-076-0(8))* Harrison House Pubs.
—How to Pass God's Test. pap. 1.00 *(978-1-57794-090-6(3))* Harrison House Pubs.
—How to Receive God's Benefits. pap. 1.00 *(978-1-57794-096-8(2))* Harrison House Pubs.
—Jesus, Your Deliverer. pap. 1.00 *(978-1-57794-095-1(4))* Harrison House Pubs.
—Let Not Your Heart Be Troubled. (Mini-Bks.). 48p. pap. 1.00 *(978-0-89274-640-8(8)*, HH-640) Harrison House Pubs.
—The Master Teacher. pap. 1.00 *(978-1-57794-093-7(8))* Harrison House Pubs.
—Putting Your Angels to Work. 2011. 64p. (Orig.). pap. 6.99 *(978-0-89274-571-5(1)*, HH571) Harrison House Pubs.
—The True Riches. pap. 1.00 *(978-89-27-40920-5(5))* Harrison House Pubs.
—Worship: Your Foundation. pap. 1.00 *(978-0-89274-087-1(6))* Harrison House Pubs.
—You Have Authority. pap. 1.00 *(978-0-89274-097-0(3))* Harrison House Pubs.
—You Must Know Your Authority. pap. 1.00 *(978-0-89274-083-3(3))* Harrison House Pubs.
Hayes, Teresa. Recovering from Church Hurt: Has the Church become a Revolving Door? 2010. 62p. pap. 15.95 *(978-1-4327-6024-3(6))* Outskirts Pr., Inc.
Hayford, Jack W. The Divine Visitor: What Really Happened When God Came Down, 0 vols. 2007. 304p. per. 14.99 *(978-0-8499-1895-7(2))* Nelson, Thomas Inc.
—Genesis: Promises & Beginnings, 0 vols. 2009. (Spirit-Filled Life Study Guide Ser.). 128p. pap. 9.99 *(978-1-4185-4119-4(2))* Nelson, Thomas Inc.
—God's Way to Wholeness, 0 vols. 2008. (Spirit-Filled Life Study Guide Ser.). 128p. pap. 9.99 *(978-1-4185-3331-1(9))* Nelson, Thomas Inc.
—Our Daily Walk. 96p. *(978-1-85240-192-4(3))* Sovereign World, Ltd.
—Perfect Will, Perfect Way: How to find God's will for your life choices & Goals. 2010. 240p. pap. 14.99 *(978-1-59979-855-4(7)*, Charisma Hse.) Charisma Media.
—Rebuilding the Real You: The Definitive Guide to the Holy Spirit's Work in Your Life. 2009. (ENG.). 240p. pap. 14.99 *(978-1-59979-471-6(3)*, Charisma Hse.) Charisma Media.
Hayles, Mary Nordia. Definitive Guide to Love God. 2007. 48p. 16.95 *(978-1-4241-1763-5(1))* PublishAmerica, Inc.
Haymes, Brian. On Being the Church: Revisionist Baptist Identity. 2009. (Studies in Baptist History & Thought Ser.). 236p. pap. 27.00 *(978-1-60608-598-1(0)*, Wipf and Stock) Wipf & Stock Pubs.
Haynes, De'Angela La'shawnde. Encourage Yourself in the Lord. 2010. pap. 10.99 *(978-1-61579-837-7(4))* Xulon Pr., Inc.
Haynes, Frederick D., 3rd. Soul Fitness with Frederick D. Haynes III. 2007. 128p. pap. 12.00 *(978-0-8170-1519-0(1))* Judson Pr.
Haynes, Joy. How to Live When the Doctors Say You Are Going to Die. 2007. 84p. per. 9.99 *(978-1-60266-276-6(2))* Xulon Pr., Inc.
Haynes, Michael L. It Just Doesn't Make Sense. 2009. 108p. pap. 11.99 *(978-1-60791-829-5(3))* Xulon Pr., Inc.
Haynes, Sharon. Winds of Change. 2008. 72p. pap. 9.99 *(978-1-60477-928-8(4))* Xulon Pr., Inc.
Hays, Edward M. Chasing Joy: Musings on Life in a Bittersweet World. 2007. 188p. per. 13.95 *(978-0-939516-78-0(0)*, Forest of Peace Publishing) Ave Maria Pr.
Hays, Rita B. Most Important Space in the Ch. 2009. 128p. pap 14.00 *(978-0-88177-568-6(1))* Discipleship Resources.
Hays, Tommy. Morning by Morning: A Prayer Journey with Tommy Hays. 2008. 440p. pap. 16.95 *(978-1-59858-692-3(0))* Dog Ear Publishing, LLC.
Haystead, Wesley. No Se Puede Empezar Demasiado Pronto: ICL You Can't Begin Too Soon. (SPA.). 144p. *(978-84-7228-342-8(9)*, 220631) Clie, Editorial.
Hayward, Chris. The End of Rejection: Your Past Is Not Your Future. 2007. (ENG., Illus.). 160p. per. 12.99 *(978-0-8307-4317-9(0))* Gospel Light Pubns.
Haywood, Frank. In Search of the Father. 2010. 92p. pap. 10.49 *(978-1-4520-2402-8(2))* AuthorHouse.
Headley, Anthony J. Reframing Your Ministry: Balancing Professional Responsibilities & Personal Needs. 2007. 205p. per. 16.99 *(978-1-928915-97-3(3))* Evangel Publishing Hse.
Headlund, Peggy. The Spirit Moves. 2007. 216p. (ENG.). 24.99 *(978-1-60477-158-9(5))*; per. 14.99 *(978-1-60477-157-2(7))* Xulon Pr., Inc.
Headlund, Peggy L. The Spirit Praises. 2008. 128p. 22.99 *(978-1-60647-794-6(3))*; pap. 14.99 *(978-1-60647-793-9(5))* Xulon Pr., Inc.
Headrick, Vanessa. The H Word: Bringing the Truth of Homosexuality out of the Closet. 2011. pap. 12.99 *(978-1-61739-739-4(3))* Tate Publishing & Enterprises, LLC.
Heald, Cynthia. Becoming a Woman of Grace: Therefore the Lord longs to be gracious to you, & therefore He waits on high to have compassion on you. Isaiah 30:18. 2009. (Becoming a Woman Of ... Ser.). (ENG.). 112p. pap. 9.99 *(978-1-61521-022-0(9))* NavPress Publishing Group.
—Uncommon Beauty: 7 Qualities of a Beautiful Woman. 2007. (ENG.). 208p. per. 12.99 *(978-1-4143-0085-6(9))* Tyndale Hse. Pubs.
Healy, Marti. The God-Dog Connection Pet Ministry. 2008. 28p. pap. 9.95 *(978-0-9791277-2-4(6))* Design Group Pr., The.
—The God-Dog Connection Study Guide. 2008. 56p. pap. 9.95 *(978-0-9791277-1-7(8))* Design Group Pr., The.
Heard, A. B. Your Best Life Later. 2007. 196p. per. 13.99 *(978-1-60266-674-0(1))* Xulon Pr., Inc.
Heath, Elaine A. The Gospel according to Twilight: Women, Sex, & God. 2011. (Gospel according To... Ser.). (ENG.). 176p. pap. 17.00 *(978-0-664-23678-6(2))* Westminster John Knox Pr.

C

Heath, Elaine A. & Kisker, Scott T. Longing for Spring. 2011. (ENG.). 116p. pap. 31.25 (978-0-7188-9242-5(9)) Lutherworth Pr., The GBR. Dist: Printondemand-worldwide.com.

—Longing for Spring. 2009. (New Monastic Library: Resources for Radical Discipleship Ser.). 118p. pap. 17.00 (978-1-55635-519-6(X), Cascade Bks.) Wipf & Stock Pubs.

Heath, Mel. False Doctrines in the Christian Church. 2008. 208p. per. 14.99 (978-1-60477-643-0(9)) Xulon Pr., Inc.

Heaven Awaits. 2008. 159p. per. 6.99 (978-1-60374-036-4(8)) Whitaker Hse.

A Heavenly View of Displaced Children. 2006. pap. 12.99 (978-1-60034-285-1(X)) Xulon Pr., Inc.

Hebblethwaite, Brian. The Christian Hope. 2nd rev. ed. 2010. (ENG.). 224p. 99.00 (978-0-19-958947-0(X)); 240p. pap. 35.00 (978-0-19-958946-3(1)) Oxford Univ. Pr., Inc.

Heckel, Jim. Hit from Behind. 2008. 92p. pap. 10.99 (978-1-60791-034-3(9)) Xulon Pr., Inc.

Heddendorf, Russell. From Faith to Fun: The Secularisation of Humor. 2009. (ENG.). 218p. pap. 38.00 (978-0-7188-9186-2(4)) Lutherworth Pr., The GBR. Dist: Brown, David Bk. Co., The.

Hedges, Eddie. The Heart of Financial Matters: Seeking A Servant's Heart. 2011. 156p. 24.95 **(978-1-4620-5107-6(3))**; pap. 14.95 **(978-1-4620-5106-9(5))** iUniverse, Inc.

Hefley, Jim. Ser un Hombre: Be a Man. (SPA.). 64p. (978-84-7228-375-6(5), 220817) Clie, Editorial.

Hege, Brent A. R. Faith at the Intersection of History & Experience: The Theology of Georg Wobbermin. 2008. 222p. pap. 24.00 (978-1-55635-941-5(1), Wipf and Stock) Wipf & Stock Pubs.

Heichberger, Robert L. Five Years on the Cutting Edge. 2008. pap. 19.99 (978-1-60477-714-7(1)) Xulon Pr., Inc.

Heidelberg, Clinton William, Jr. Is Jesus Fake: What You Need to Know. 2008. 216p. per. 14.45 (978-0-9791105-1-1(3)) CJ & Assocs.

Heijkoop, H. L. The Glories of Christ: As Seen in the Offerings. 358p. 7.95 (978-0-88172-178-2(6)) Believers Bookshelf, Inc.

Heim, Joanne. Living Simply: Choosing Less in a World of More. annot. ed. 2006. (ENG.). 224p. pap. 13.99 (978-1-59052-728-3(3), Multnomah) Doubleday Religious Publishing Group, The.

Hein, David & Henery, Charles R. Spiritual Counsel in the Anglican Tradition. 2010. (ENG.). 195p. pap. 53.00 (978-0-227-17270-4(1)) Clarke, James Co., Ltd. GBR. Dist: Brown, David Bk. Co., The.

Hein, Marvin. On the Shoulders of Giants: A Group Study in Our Faith Heritage. 73p. pap. 8.95 incl. VHS (978-0-921788-34-8(7)); pap. 3.95 (978-0-921788-27-0(4)) Kindred Productions.

Heinicke, Arlan D. Living Within the Love of God. 2009. 210p. 29.99 (978-1-4415-4249-6(3)); pap. 19.99 (978-1-4415-4248-9(5)) Xlibris Corp.

Heinsohn, Laura Lee. Cracking the Parenting Code: 6 Clues to Solving the Mystery of Meeting Your Child's Needs. 2008. (ENG.). 192p. pap. 12.99 (978-1-59669-207-7(3)) New Hope Pubs.

Heitzig, Lenya. Holy Moments: Recognizing God's Fingerprints on Your Life. 2006. (ENG., Illus.). 138p. 12.99 (978-0-8307-4287-5(5)) Gospel Light Pubns.

Heitzig, Lenya & Rose, Penny Pierce. Live Intimately: Lessons from the Upper Room. 2008. (Fresh Life Ser.). (ENG.). 280p. pap. 17.99 (978-1-4347-6790-5(6)) Cook, David C.

Heltzman, Mary Fran & Knudson, Sharon M. Starting from Scratch When You're Single Again: 23 Women Share Stories, Encouragement, Recipes, & Lessons Learned When Starting over Was All They Could Do. 2008. (ENG., Illus.). 240p. pap. 14.99 (978-1-59979-254-5(0)) Charisma Media.

Heline, Corinne. America's Invisible Guidance. 176p. 2010. pap. 18.36 (978-1-163-14245-5(X)) 2008. 37.95 (978-1-4367-1473-0(7)) 2007. (ENG.). per. 22.95 (978-1-4304-9803-2(X)) Kessinger Publishing, LLC.

Heller, Alan, et al. Learning How to Trust... Again. 2007. (Illus.). 198p. per. 15.99 (978-0-7684-2419-5(4)) Destiny Image Pubs.

Hellmann, Maxie L. From Our Wicked Ways. 2011. pap. 12.99 (978-1-61739-663-2(X)) Tate Publishing & Enterprises, LLC.

Helm, Katie. Trust Me! Fantastic Adventures in Trusting Him! 2009. 292p. 25.99 (978-1-4389-8147-5(3)); pap. 15.99 (978-1-4389-8148-2(1)) AuthorHouse.

Helmintoller, Philip. Becoming Christ. 2010. 123p. pap. 12.95 (978-1-4327-5494-5(7)) Outskirts Pr., Inc.

Helmling, Dirk. The Cost of the Disconnect. 2011. 238p. pap. 15.99 **(978-1-61379-234-6(4))** Xulon Pr., Inc.

Help Lord! I'm in Trouble. 2008. 194p. pap. 17.99 (978-0-615-19229-1(7)) By His Spirit Publishing.

Help Me, I've Fallen & I Can't Get Up! 2008. 165p. per. 9.99 (978-0-7684-2644-1(8)) Destiny Image Pubs.

Help 4 Families, Denise Shick And. When Hope Seems Lost. 2011. 332p. pap. 18.99 **(978-1-60957-045-3(6))** Xulon Pr., Inc.

Hemby, Sr. Crites in the Church. 2008. 148p. pap. 13.99 (978-1-60647-302-3(6)) Xulon Pr., Inc.

Hemphill, Ken. God Will: Devotions Empowered by Biblical Statements of Faith. 2008. (Kingdom Promises Ser.). (ENG.). 128p. pap. 3.99 (978-0-8054-4768-2(7), B&H Bks.) B&H Publishing Group.

Hemphill, Ken. Live It Up. 2011. (ENG.). 148p. pap. 8.99 **(978-0-578-08001-7(X))** Auxano Pr.

Hemphill, Ken, et al. You Are Gifted: Your Spiritual Gifts & the Kingdom of God, 1 vol. 2009. (ENG.). 240p. 17.99 (978-0-8054-4862-7(4), B&H Bks.) B&H Publishing Group.

Hemphill, Steve. My Search for the Real Heaven. 2009. pap. 15.99 (978-1-60799-023-9(7)) Tate Publishing & Enterprises, LLC.

Hemsley, Phil. The Leap. 2009. 68p. pap. 10.49 (978-1-4389-2935-4(8)) AuthorHouse.

Hendershot, John C. The Eastside Devotional. 2008. 369p. pap. 19.95 (978-0-615-26245-1(7)) Pirate Parrot Pr.

Henderson, D. Michael. The Ladder of Faithfulness. 2009. 88p. pap. 10.99 (978-1-61579-101-9(9)) Xulon Pr., Inc.

Henderson Davis, Claire. After the Church: Divine Encounter in a Sexual Age. 2007. 79p. per. 15.99 (978-1-85311-736-7(6)) Canterbury Pr.

Henderson, Dorothy. Learning God's Stories Together: Intergenerational Program for Church & Home. 2007. (ENG., Illus.). 160p. per. 24.95 (978-1-55145-559-4(5)) Wood Lake Publishing, Inc. CAN. Dist: Westminster John Knox Pr.

Henderson, Jason. Not I but Christ. 2007. 98p. 12.00 (978-0-9796285-2-8(0)) International Fellowship of Covenant Ministries, The.

Henderson, Michael L. Those Who Are Wise Will Shine! Understanding the Work of God in Your Redemption. 2011. 280p. 35.95 (978-1-4497-0958-7(3)); pap. 19.95 (978-1-4497-0957-0(5)) Author Solutions, Inc. (WestBow Pr.).

Henderson, Suzanne Watts. Christology & Discipleship in the Gospel of Mark. 2008. (Society for New Testament Studies Monograph Ser.). (ENG.). 304p. pap. 44.00 (978-0-521-09139-8(X)) Cambridge Univ. Pr.

Henderson, Warren. Glories Seen & Unseen: A Study of the Head Covering. 2007. 160p. per. 11.95 (978-0-9795387-2-8(6)) Henderson, Warren.

—The Olive Plants. 2007. 252p. per. (978-1-897117-51-4(5)) Gospel Folio Pr.

Hendricks, James. A Good Day to Die. 2007. (ENG., Illus.). 303p. per. 14.95 (978-0-9759453-2-2(7)) Augustus Publishing.

Hendrickson, Antoinette. Receive the Kingdom of God As a Child. 2009. 68p. pap. 13.99 (978-1-4389-3560-7(9)) AuthorHouse.

Hendrickson Publishers, creator. God's Priorities for Your Life for Men. 2006. (Illus.). 318p. (J). per. 14.95 (978-1-59856-133-3(2)) Hendrickson Pubs. Marketing, LLC.

—God's Priorities for Your Life for Teens. 2006. (Illus.). 318p. (YA). (gr. 8-12). per. 14.95 (978-1-59856-134-0(0)) Hendrickson Pubs. Marketing, LLC.

—God's Priorities for Your Life for Women. 2006. (Illus.). 318p. (J). per. 14.95 (978-1-59856-124-1(3)) Hendrickson Pubs. Marketing, LLC.

Hendrix, Shelley. On Purpose for a Purpose. 2007. 180p. per. 13.99 (978-1-60266-649-8(0)) Xulon Pr., Inc.

Henegan, Ramona E. Miracles Visions & Dreams. 2009. 92p. pap. 15.99 (978-1-4415-3219-0(6)) Xlibris Corp.

Henegar, Bill & Rushford, Jerry. Forever Young: The Life & Times of M. Norvel Young & Helen M. Young. 25.00 (978-0-89098-167-2(1)) Twentieth Century Christian Bks.

Henein, Karen. Bent Out of Shape. 2008. 408p. pap. (978-1-897373-44-6(9)) Word Alive Pr.

—Counsel of the Most High. 2006. 296p. per. (978-1-894928-99-1(7)) Word Alive Pr.

Hennessy, Brian J. Valley of the Steeples. 2008. 201p. pap. 14.95 (978-0-9801420-7-5(5)) Ketch Publishing.

Hennings, Chad. Rules of Engagement: Finding Faith & Purpose in a Disconnected World. 2011. (ENG.). 208p. pap. 13.99 (978-0-446-54538-9(4)) FaithWords.

Henrichsen, Walter. El Discipulo Se Hace, No Nace: Disciples Are Made, Not Born. (SPA.). 160p. (978-84-7228-046-5(2), 220313) Clie, Editorial.

Henry, Casalnnie. Neutralizing the Power of Fear: How to Subdue Your Fears & Make Them Harmless. 2008. 312p. 31.95 (978-1-4401-0440-4(9)) iUniverse, Inc.

Henry, Dale. Ten Cans: Are You an Opener? 2007. (Illus.). 127p. pap. 17.99 (978-0-8127-0473-0(8)) Review & Herald Publishing Assn.

Henry, Denlin. Who Is jesus Christ?-and What Was His Pursose on Earth? 2007. per. 9.95 (978-0-9771082-6-8(0)) Milligan Bks.

Henry Drummond. The Greatest Thing in the World & Other Addresses. 2009. 80p. pap. 3.95 (978-1-60386-221-9(8), Merchant Bks.) Rough Draft Printing.

Henry, Gary. Obeying the Gospel: Daily Motivation to Act on Our Faith. 2014. (ENG.). 388p. pap. 18.95 (978-0-9713710-4-0(0)) WordPoints.

Henry, Jerome A. The and Well Eternal. 2011. 452p. pap. 24.99 **(978-1-61379-619-1(6))** Xulon Pr., Inc.

Henry M. Piironen. Divinity: A Portrait of Human Spirituality. 2010. 464p. 38.95 (978-1-4502-1408-7(8)) iUniverse, Inc.

Henry, Matthew. Como Incrementar Nuestra Com. Con: How to Improve Our Fellowship. (SPA.). (978-84-7228-896-6(X), 222012) Clie, Editorial.

Henry, Veleria I. The Value of Time: How Are You Spending Your Time? 2009. 76p. pap. 10.99 (978-1-61579-395-2(X)) Xulon Pr., Inc.

Henson, Belinda C. The Veil of Flesh. 2008. 128p. pap. 11.95 (978-1-4327-2313-2(8)) Outskirts Pr., Inc.

Heras, Ruth. My Pastures of Many Colors: A Diverse Journey to Godly Healing. 2010. 208p. 25.99 (978-1-61579-538-3(3)); pap. 15.99 (978-1-61579-537-6(5)) Xulon Pr., Inc.

Herbert, Igho. Poverty from the Pulpit. 2010. 308p. 27.99 (978-1-4490-7194-3(5)); pap. 18.69 (978-1-4490-7193-6(7)) AuthorHouse.

Herd, Jared Howard. More Lost Than Found: Finding a Way Back to Faith. 2011. 208p. pap. 15.99 (978-1-4002-0303-1(1)) Nelson, Thomas Inc.

Heriford, James. Perfection Perfection,What Is Perfection. 2008. 78p. pap. 16.50 (978-0-615-23687-2(1)) Heriford, James R.

Hering, Donna. Trials Must Come What Will You Do? 2011. 100p. pap. 10.99 **(978-1-61215-776-4(9))** Xulon Pr., Inc.

Herman, Harvey A. Discipleship by Design. 2008. 204p. pap. 14.99 (978-1-60647-644-4(0)) Xulon Pr., Inc.

Hernandez, Alice. A Lamp unto My Feet & a Light unto My Path: The Word. 2010. 222p. pap. 14.95 (978-1-4327-6310-7(5)) Outskirts Pr., Inc.

Herndon, Annette. Hope for Today. 2008. 116p. pap. 10.99 (978-1-60647-433-4(2)) Xulon Pr., Inc.

Herndon Sr., Robert. Shadow Forces: 2007. pap. 17.99 (978-1-60034-970-6(6)) Xulon Pr., Inc.

Herr, Ojoma E. Ojoma's Song: Becoming a Woman Nigerian Style. 2008. (ENG.). 96p. pap. 15.95 (978-1-934668-01-6(X)) ACW Pr.

Hersey, Sandra. Help! I'm Alone with My Mind! A Guide to Having Victory over Your Thoughts. 2011. 116p. pap. 12.99 **(978-0-9840409-0-2(0))** Hersey, Sandra Ministries.

Hershey, Terry. The Power of Pause: Becoming More by Doing Less. 2011. (ENG.). 256p. pap. 12.95 (978-0-8294-3546-7(8)) Loyola Pr.

Herzog, David. Mysteries of the Glory Unveiled: A New Wave of Signs & Wonders. 2008. 173p. per. 13.99 (978-0-7684-2639-7(1)); 215p. per. 15.99 (978-0-7684-2607-6(3)) Destiny Image Pubs.

Heslop, W. G. The Preacher's Friend. pap. 5.99 (978-0-88019-161-6(9)) Schmul Publishing Co., Inc.

Hession, Patrick J. Preparing the Army of God - a Basic Training Manual for Spiritual Warfare. 2008. 96p. pap. 9.95 (978-0-615-20264-8(0)) Noisseh Publishing.

Hession, Revel. The Calvary Road. 2010. (Illus.). 38p. pap. 14.14 (978-1-153-76829-0(1)) General Bks. LLC.

Hession, Roy. The Calvary Road. 2008. 60p. pap. 8.95 (978-1-4385-1060-6(8)); pap. 8.95 (978-1-60597-221-3(5)) Standard Pubns., Inc. (Book Jungle).

Hester, Joseph P. An Ethic of Hope. 2008. 163p. pap. 12.95 (978-0-7414-4485-1(2)) Infinity Publishing.

Hester, Judith M. God Lives in Miracles. 2011. 82p. pap. 10.99 **(978-1-61215-017-8(9))** Xulon Pr., Inc.

Heuertz, Christopher L. Simple Spirituality: Learning to See God in a Broken World. 2008. (ENG.). 160p. pap. 15.00 (978-0-8308-3621-5(7), IVP Bks.) InterVarsity Pr.

Heward-Mills, Dag. 100% Answered Prayer. 2008. (ENG.). 38p. 5.99 (978-0-7963-0814-6(4)) Lux Verbi - BM ZAF. Dist: STL Distribution North America.

—100% Answered Prayer. 2007. (ENG.). 48p. pap. 3.99 (978-9988-596-06-4(5)) Parchment Hse. GHA. Dist: STL Distribution North America.

Heyer, Walt. Perfected with Love: A Powerful & Inspiring True Story. 2009. 116p. pap. 11.99 (978-1-60791-838-7(2)) Xulon Pr., Inc.

Hibdon, Stephen. What's Extraordinary about Being Ordinary? 2008. 56p. pap. 10.99 (978-1-60647-899-8(0)) Xulon Pr., Inc.

Hickey, Marilyn. Be Healed. 235p. (Orig.). pap. 9.95 (978-1-56441-021-4(8)) Hickey, Marilyn Ministries.

—Blessing Journal. pap. 4.95 (978-1-56441-003-0(X)) Hickey, Marilyn Ministries.

—Bold Men Win. 48p. (Orig.). pap. 1.00 (978-1-56441-121-1(4)) Hickey, Marilyn Ministries.

—A Cry for Miracles. pap. 7.95 (978-1-56441-001-6(3)) Hickey, Marilyn Ministries.

—Dear Marilyn. pap. 7.95 (978-1-56441-006-1(4)) Hickey, Marilyn Ministries.

—Freedom from Bondages. pap. 7.95 (978-0-914307-29-7(0)) Hickey, Marilyn Ministries.

—Gift Wrapped Fruit. pap. 2.95 (978-1-56441-019-1(6)) Hickey, Marilyn Ministries.

—God's Covenant for Your Family. (Orig.). pap. 7.95 (978-1-56441-009-2(9)) Hickey, Marilyn Ministries.

—God's Rx for a Hurting Heart. pap. 4.95 (978-1-56441-010-8(2)) Hickey, Marilyn Ministries.

—How to Be a Mature Christian. pap. 7.95 (978-1-56441-011-5(0)) Hickey, Marilyn Ministries.

—Maximize Your Day ... God's Way. pap. 7.95 (978-1-56441-013-9(7)) Hickey, Marilyn Ministries.

—The Power of the Blood. 40p. (Orig.). pap. 1.00 (978-1-56441-161-7(3)) Hickey, Marilyn Ministries.

—Satan-Proof Your Home. pap. 7.95 (978-1-56441-015-3(3)) Hickey, Marilyn Ministries.

—Signs in the Heavens. pap. 7.95 (978-1-56441-016-0(1)) Hickey, Marilyn Ministries.

—Speak the Word. 19p. (Orig.). pap. 1.00 (978-1-56441-166-2(4)) Hickey, Marilyn Ministries.

—Standing in the Gap. 37p. (Orig.). pap. 1.00 (978-1-56441-167-9(2)) Hickey, Marilyn Ministries.

—You Can Bounce Back from Your Setback. 19.95 (978-1-56441-040-5(4)) Hickey, Marilyn Ministries.

Hickman, Claude. Live Life on Purpose. 2011. 200p. per. 16.99 (978-1-57921-826-3(1)) WinePress Publishing.

Hickman, Frank S. Christian Vocation: A Study in Religious Experience. 2007. (ENG.). 238p. 41.95 (978-0-548-05931-9(4)) Kessinger Publishing, LLC.

Hicks, Charity. Saved by Grace Memoirs of Mary Magdalene. 2007. 95p. pap. 16.95 (978-1-4241-6450-9(8)) PublishAmerica, Inc.

Hicks, Jimmie. The and Spiritual Vital Signs of a Christian Life. 2011. 144p. pap. 14.99 **(978-1-61379-558-3(0))** Xulon Pr., Inc.

Hicks, John Mark, et al, contrib. by. Grace, Faith, Works: How Do They Relate? pap. 7.95 (978-0-929540-14-6(X)) Publishing Designs, Inc.

Hicks, Lon Edwin. Daily Wisdom Vitamins. 2008. 380p. pap. 19.99 (978-1-60477-722-2(2)) Xulon Pr., Inc.

Hiers, Eva M. A Spiritual Awakening. 2008. 120p. pap. 10.99 (978-1-60647-535-5(5)) Xulon Pr., Inc.

Higgins, B. M. Scattered Shepherds: A True Story. 2009. 434p. pap. 20.49 (978-1-4389-8540-4(1)) AuthorHouse.

Higgins, Evelyn. The Mystery of Happiness. 2007. 136p. (ENG.). 21.99 (978-1-60266-556-9(7)); per. 13.99 (978-1-60266-510-1(9)) Xulon Pr., Inc.

Higgins, Franklin. Sine Quo Non: The Essential Elements of Life. 2007. 204p. per. 24.95 (978-1-4241-9059-1(2)) PublishAmerica, Inc.

Higgs, Liz Curtis. A Wreath of Snow. 2012. (ENG.). 224p. 14.99 (978-1-4000-7217-0(4), WaterBrook Pr.) Doubleday Religious Publishing Group, The.

Higham, Vernon. Unsearchable Riches: Invest in a Relationship That Lasts an Eternity. 176p. 7.99 (978-1-85792-768-9(0), Christian Focus) Christian Focus Pubns. GBR. Dist: Riverside.

A Higher Calling: Serving God, His Leaders, & His People with Excellence Guide & Workbook. 2007. per. (978-0-9792511-1-5(7)) Tribute Publishing, LLC.

Hilbun, John C. The Disciple s Life in Christ Jesus. 2010. 184p. pap. 16.99 (978-1-60957-517-5(2)) Xulon Pr., Inc.

Hildebrand, Lloyd, ed. All of Grace. 2007. (Pure Gold Classics). (ENG., Illus.). 142p. pap. 11.99 incl. audio compact disk (978-0-88270-335-0(8)) Bridge-Logos Foundation.

Hilgeman, Matthew J. 1:1 with Jesus: A Month-Long Daily Devotional from the Gospel of Matthew, 1 vol. 2010. 110p. pap. 19.95 (978-1-4489-4622-8(0)) PublishAmerica, Inc.

Hill, David L. Chronicles of a Poetic Warrior. 2008. 80p. per. 11.00 (978-0-9779886-1-7(9)) RGC Pr., LLC.

Hill, Don. Israel & the Body of Christ. 2011. 228p. 28.95 **(978-1-4620-3569-4(8))**; pap. 18.95 **(978-1-4620-3567-0(1))** iUniverse, Inc.

Hill, Grace Livingston. Time of the Singing of Birds. 20.95 (978-0-89190-072-6(1)) Amereon LTD.

Hill, Herschel. Fighting over Faith. 2009. 156p. pap. 13.95 (978-1-60264-495-3(0)) Virtualbookworm.com Publishing, Inc.

Hill, Jamie C. Inspiration on a Poetic Level. 2008. 100p. per. 9.99 (978-1-60477-739-0(7)) Xulon Pr., Inc.

Hill, Jeffrey. Just a Thought. 2007. 196p. per. 16.99 (978-0-88144-284-7(4)) Yorkshire Publishing Group.

Hill, Louis. Faith Is... The assurance of things hoped for, the evidence of things not Seen. 2009. pap. 12.99 (978-1-60696-972-4(2)) Tate Publishing & Enterprises, LLC.

Hill, Richard J. ", et al. A Glimpse of the Chosen: Glimpses of God's Elective Grace. 2010. 140p. pap. 11.95 (978-1-61507-209-5(8)) Cross Bks. Publishing.

Hill, Robert E. Deception in the Body of Christ: Unveiled Mysteries & Neurolinguistic Dialectics. 2010. 130p. pap. 16.00 (978-1-60899-102-0(4), Resource Pubns.) Wipf & Stock Pubs.

Hill, Sharon Patterson. When I Can't Live Without You. 2008. 336p. 27.99 (978-1-60477-660-7(9)); pap. 17.99 (978-1-60477-659-1(5)) Xulon Pr., Inc.

Hill Sr, Steven Lawrence. I Have Rights Too! Christians among Chains. 2007. 110p. 23.95 (978-0-615-14056-8(4)) ASA Publishing Co.

Hilliard, Donald, Jr. Faith in the Face of Fear. 144p. pap. 9.99 (978-1-58169-105-4(X), Evergreen Pr.) Genesis Communications, Inc.

—Handling Life's Pressure Situations. 16p. 1.99 (978-1-58169-077-4(0), Evergreen Pr.) Genesis Communications, Inc.

Hilliard, Donald & Hilliard, Donald, Jr. After the Fall: Resurrecting Your Life from Shame, Disgrace, & Guilt. 2007. 187p. per. 15.99 (978-0-7684-2496-6(8)) Destiny Image Pubs.

Hilliard, I. V. Men@Work: How Men Can Renew Their Commitments to God, Their Families, & Themselves. 224p. 2009. pap. 13.99 (978-1-57794-973-2(0)) 2008. 19.99 (978-1-57794-879-7(3)) Harrison House Pubs.

Hilliard, Jack. Pain & Suffering: Friend or Foe? 2007. (ENG.). 336p. pap. 14.00 (978-0-9800285-0-8(7)) O'More Publishing.

Hillig, Chuck. Looking for God: Seeing the Whole in One. 2007. (ENG., Illus.). 150p. per. 15.95 (978-1-59181-059-9(0)) Sentient Pubns.

Hillis, Newell Dwight. Faith & Character. 2007. (ENG.). 132p. 35.95 (978-0-548-12194-8(X)) Kessinger Publishing, LLC.

Hillman, Kirk E. Kingdom Language Vol. 2: Forgiveness. 2009. 112p. 22.99 (978-1-61579-143-9(4)); pap. 11.99 (978-1-61579-142-2(6)) Xulon Pr., Inc.

Hillman, Os. Today God Is First (Spanish) 2007. pap. 13.99 (978-0-7684-2446-1(1)) Destiny Image Pubs.

Hilt, Carolyn. More Than I Imagined! 2007. 300p. per. 17.99 (978-1-60477-096-4(1)) Xulon Pr., Inc.

Hiltz, William. Deliverance to the Captives. 2009. 188p. pap. 14.99 (978-1-60791-418-1(2)) Xulon Pr., Inc.

Hinderer, Crystal. Under the Shadow of His Wings. 2006. pap. 9.99 (978-1-60034-783-2(5)) Xulon Pr., Inc.

Hines, Latasha G. I Love Him Lord, but He's Not a Christian: The Christian Woman's Guide to Deliverance from Toxic Relationships - Revised Edition. 2nd rev. ed. 2007. 136p. per. 12.00 (978-0-9778322-1-7(X)) Jewel Pubs., LLC.

Hines, Samuel George & DeYoung, Curtiss Paul. Beyond Rhetoric: Reconciliation as a Way of Life. 2011. 192p. pap. 22.00 **(978-1-61097-214-7(7)**, Wipf and Stock) Wipf & Stock Pubs.

Hinkle, Carl C. Building a Life. 2007. (ENG.). 118p. 34.95 (978-0-548-05884-8(9)) Kessinger Publishing, LLC.

Hinn, Benny. Blood in the Sand: A Journey Through the Middle East Conflict — The Stakes, the Solutions, & Why There Is Hope. 2009. (ENG.). 256p. pap. 15.99 (978-1-59979-770-0(4), Frontline) Charisma Media.

—Prayer, the Key That Opens Heaven: Experience the Life-Changing Adventure of a Deeper Connection with God. 2009. 224p. 21.99 *(978-1-59979-347-4(4),* Charisma Hse.) Charisma Media.

Hinnant, Greg. Word Portraits: Five Illustrations of the Mature Christian. annot. ed. 2009. (ENG.). 192p. pap. 12.99 *(978-1-59979-087-9(4),* Creation Hse.) Charisma Media.

Hinnant, Kevin, Sr. & Hinnant, Laura. Help Me with The 90% 2007. 68p. per. 9.99 *(978-0-9770936-9-4(7),* Dreams Bks.) Dreams Publishing Co.

Hinthorn, A. The Gift. 2008. 104p. pap. 12.99 *(978-0-9800032-2-1(6))* 90 Minute Bks.

Hinton, Scott. Stop Sleeping So Much: Wake Up! 2009. 72p. pap. 11.95 *(978-1-4327-3621-7(3))* Outskirts Pr., Inc.

Hinton, Sharon. Spiritual Reflections: Journal for Nurses & Health Advocates. 2010. 32p. rng bd. *(978-1-55452-502-7(0))* Essence Publishing.

Hinton, Sharon T. Spiritual Reflections: Journal for Nurses & Health Advocates. 2010. *(978-1-55452-503-4(9))* Essence Publishing.

Hirko, Andy. The Inspirational Internet. 2007. 140p. per. 13.99 *(978-1-60266-080-9(8))* Xulon Pr., Inc.

Hirmer, Oswald & Guerrero, Alfonso. Como Compartir la Biblia en Grupos. 80p. 5.95 *(978-980-350-103-7(8))* Sociedad de San Pablo CCL. Dist: St Pauls/Alba Hse. Pubs.

Hirsch, Alan & Hirsch, Debra. Untamed: Reactivating a Missional Form of Discipleship, 1 vol. 2010. (Shapevine Ser.). (ENG.). 208p. pap. 14.99 *(978-0-8010-1343-0(7))* Baker Bks.

Hirsch, Ryan. A Dark Pathway to Light. 2009. 62p. pap. 16.95 *(978-1-60749-939-8(8))* PublishAmerica, Inc.

Hirsch, William Rodriguez. God Wants You to Know: Pathways to Healing. 2009. 128p. 22.99 *(978-1-60791-750-2(5));* pap. 14.99 *(978-1-60791-749-6(1))* Xulon Pr., Inc.

Historia Sagrada Texto. 224p. 6.95 *(978-958-607-012-6(3))* Sociedad de San Pablo COL. Dist: St Pauls/Alba Hse. Pubs.

Historias Biblicas Preesc Maestros. 3.25 *(978-0-7673-4646-7(7))* LifeWay Christian Resources.

Hitchcock, Tim. My King, My God, My Worship: A Study in Practical Church Worship. 2009. 188p. pap. 14.99 *(978-1-60791-716-8(5))* Xulon Pr., Inc.

Hitchens, Peter. The Rage Against God: How Atheism Led Me to Faith, 1 vol. 2010. (ENG.). 240p. 22.99 *(978-0-310-32031-9(3))* Zondervan.

Hite, Robert L. Let It Be Written, Let It Be Done. 2009. 60p. pap. 14.99 *(978-1-4389-5357-1(7))* AuthorHouse.

Hitt, Michael Olin. The Word of God upon My Lips: A Messenger Speaks. 2007. (Religion Ser.). 224p. 21.95 *(978-1-879290-33-4(2),* PageMill Pr.) Council Oak Bks.

Hladio, Bohdan. Northopraxis: Or from Pastoral Life. 2009. 143p. pap. *(978-0-9643478-6-1(5))* HDM Pr., Inc.

Ho, Betty Yulin. Healing with Your Blood. 2008. pap. 15.00 *(978-0-8059-7961-9(1))* Dorrance Publishing Co., Inc.

Hoagland, Victor, ed. The Book of Catholic Prayers. 2008. (Illus.). 220p. vinyl bd. 9.95 *(978-0-88271-124-9(5))* Regina Pr., Malhame & Co.

—A Catholic Child's First Prayer Book. 2008. (Illus.). 37p. (J). (gr. -1-2). 9.95 *(978-0-88271-146-5(2))* Regina Pr., Malhame & Co.

—The Illustrated Lives of the Saints: Abridged Easy to Read Edition. 2008. (Illus.). 159p. pap. 8.95 *(978-0-88271-048-8(6))* Regina Pr., Malhame & Co.

Hoban, Stephanie E. Positioning Yourself for Increase. 2008. 72p. pap. 11.99 *(978-1-60477-816-8(4))* Xulon Pr., Inc.

Hobba, Cheryl. The Kingdom Hillbillies. 2008. 160p. per. 13.99 *(978-1-60477-658-4(7))* Xulon Pr., Inc.

Hobbs, Vel. Seasons of the Heart. 2008. 316p. 27.99 *(978-1-60647-210-1(0));* pap. 17.99 *(978-1-60647-209-5(7))* Xulon Pr., Inc.

Hobgood-Oster, Laura. The Friends We Keep: Unleashing Christianity's Compassion for Animals. 2010. (ENG., Illus.). 230p. pap. 19.95 *(978-1-60258-264-4(5))* Baylor Univ. Pr.

Hockett, Richard S. Foundations of Wisdom. 2009. 136p. pap. 14.99 *(978-1-60791-713-7(0))* Xulon Pr., Inc.

Hodge, Balyine. After All of the Tears. 2009. 156p. pap. 14.99 *(978-1-4389-8816-0(8))* AuthorHouse.

Hodge, Charles B. Amazing Grace! pap. 8.99 *(978-0-89096-032-3(2))* Twentieth Century Christian Bks.

Hodge, Kent. Christ in You: An Introduction to the New Covenant & the Christian Life. 2009. 672p. 36.49 *(978-1-4389-5290-1(2));* pap. 25.99 *(978-1-4389-5224-6(4))* AuthorHouse.

Hodges, Bobbi. Experience God... His Love ... His Blessings ... His Power ... 2011. 116p. pap. 12.19 *(978-1-4669-0146-9(2))* Trafford Publishing.

Hodges, M. Priscilla. Amplius. 2008. 88p. per. 9.99 *(978-1-60477-376-7(6))* Xulon Pr., Inc.

Hodgson, Geraldine E. Early English Instructions & Devotions. 2007. (ENG.). 150p. 36.95 *(978-0-548-07409-1(7))* Kessinger Publishing, LLC.

Hoekema, Antonny. El Cristiano Visto Por Si Mismo: The Christian Looks at Himself. (SPA.). 160p. *(978-84-7228-508-8(1),* 220203) Clie, Editorial.

Hoffman, James B. Verses That Say in the Kingdom of God: A book of short bible Studies. 2011. 300p. pap. 19.95 *(978-1-4575-0108-1(2))* Dog Ear Publishing, LLC.

Hoffman, Scott. Acts 29: Writing the Next Chapter, 1 vol. 2009. 164p. pap. 24.95 *(978-1-60836-164-9(0))* PublishAmerica, Inc.

Hofmann, Bob. Live Prepared! A layman's view of living a Christian Life. 2011. 132p. 22.95 *(978-1-4567-3861-7(5));* pap. 13.95 *(978-1-4567-3862-4(3))* AuthorHouse.

Hogan, Martin. Jesus Our Teacher: Reflections on the Sunday Readings for Matthew's Year. 2007. (ENG.). 144p. pap. 18.95 *(978-1-85607-586-2(9))* Columba Pr. IRL. Dist: Dufour Editions, Inc.

Hohnberger, Jim. Escapando Hacia Dios. (SPA.). pap. *(978-1-883012-98-4(8))* Remnant Pubns.

—Facing Frienemy Fire: When Friends Attack — Thrive, Don't Just Survive. 2008. 159p. 16.99 *(978-0-8163-2241-1(4))* Pacific Pr. Publishing Assn.

Hohnberger, Sally. Parenting Your Infant/Toddler by the Spirit: Yes, You Can Lay the Foundation for a Godly Character. 2008. 15.99 *(978-0-8163-2283-1(X))* Pacific Pr. Publishing Assn.

Holbrook, Ernest E. Looking to Christ's Millennium. 2010. pap. 14.99 *(978-1-61579-832-2(3))* Xulon Pr., Inc.

Holbrook, Fred. Daddy Your Shoes Didnt Fit My Feet. 2007. (ENG.). 21.99 *(978-1-60034-886-0(6));* pap. 13.99 *(978-1-60034-885-3(8))* Xulon Pr., Inc.

Holcomb, Tiffany. Return to Me: What If God Hates Religion? 2011. 76p. pap. 9.95 *(978-1-4497-1394-2(7),* WestBow Pr.) Author Solutions, Inc.

Holcombe, Ken. The Coming of Mashiach. 2011. 74p. 24.99 *(978-1-4653-3731-3(8));* pap. 15.99 *(978-1-4653-3730-6(X))* Xlibris Corp.

Holden, Nick. Magnify the Lord. 2007. 296p. per. 15.99 *(978-1-60266-931-4(7))* Xulon Pr., Inc.

Holder, Andrea. The Armor of Righteousness. 2011. 118p. pap. 11.99 *(978-1-61379-709-9(5))* Xulon Pr., Inc.

Holderby, Olen. Do I Understand My Child? 2011. 54p. pap. 9.95 *(978-1-58427-327-1(5))* Guardian of Truth Foundation.

Holding, James Patrick. Blowing the Doors Off! A Defense Manual for Christian Students. 2008. pap. 22.99 *(978-1-60647-991-9(1))* Xulon Pr., Inc.

Holl, Adolf. Falls ich Papst werden Sollte. (GER.). *(978-3-612-65065-8(3))* Econ-Verlag GmbH DEU. Dist: International Bk. Import Service, Inc.

Holladay, Tom, et al. The Bible: 11 Core Truths to Build Your Life On, 1 vol. 2008. (Foundations Ser.). (ENG., Illus.). 80p. (gr. 13). pap. 6.99 *(978-0-310-27670-8(5))* Zondervan.

—Creation: 11 Core Truths to Build Your Life On, 1 vol. 2008. (Foundations Ser.). (ENG., Illus.). 80p. (gr. 13). pap. 6.99 *(978-0-310-27678-4(0))* Zondervan.

Holland, Monica C. No Ironing on Sundays: Restoring Reverence for God. 2008. (ENG.). 172p. per. 15.99 *(978-1-57921-610-8(2))* Pleasant Word.

Holley, David M. Meaning & Mystery: What It Means to Believe in God. 2010. (ENG.). 256p. pap. 33.95 *(978-1-4051-9344-3(1),* Wiley-Blackwell) Wiley, John & Sons, Inc.

Hollies, Linda H. Beloved, You Can Win! Strategies for Walking Your Talk. 2008. 144p. 16.00 *(978-0-8298-1792-8(1))* Pilgrim Pr., The/United Church Pr.

Hollingsworth, Mary & Boultinghouse, Philis. Big Hugs for Women. 2009. (ENG., Illus.). 256p. 15.99 *(978-1-4165-4187-5(X),* Howard Bks.) Howard Books.

Hollingsworth, R. C. Why Did You Do That? 2011. 46p. 24.99 *(978-1-4568-7066-9(1));* pap. 15.99 *(978-1-4568-7065-2(3))* Xlibris Corp.

Hollis, Mitchell. Run for God: The 5K Challenge A practical guide to running & a 12-week training plan with a Christian Focus. 2010. 156p. pap. 19.99 *(978-1-61507-253-8(5))* Cross Bks. Publishing.

—Run for God: The 5K Challenge A practical guide to running & a 12-week training plan with a Christian focus - Instructor's Edition. 2010. 140p. pap. 16.95 *(978-1-61507-256-9(X))* Cross Bks. Publishing.

—Run for God - The 5k Challenge: A Practical Guide to Running & a 12-Week Training Plan with a Christian Focus. 2010. 156p. 30.95 *(978-1-61507-255-2(1))* Cross Bks. Publishing.

Holloway, Beverly. Until We Meet, My Love: A journey of healing & discovery through letters & Prayers. 2011. pap. 12.99 *(978-1-61739-512-3(9))* Tate Publishing & Enterprises, LLC.

Holloway, Richard. Dancing on the Edge. xv, 204p. pap. 15.95 *(978-0-00-628041-5(2))* HarperCollins Pubs. Ltd. GBR. Dist: Trafalgar Square Publishing.

Holloway, S. Christian Family. pap. 8.00 *(978-0-927936-85-9(2))* Vincom Pubng. Co.

Holman. Towards Equality. 176p. 17.95 *(978-0-281-05046-8(5))* International Publishers Marketing.

Holmberg, Edward Wallace. Been Looking for God Lately. 2007. 64p. per. 16.95 *(978-1-60441-271-0(2))* PublishAmerica, Inc.

Holmes, C. Raymond. The Road I Travel: My Journey along the Narrow Way. 2011. *(978-0-8280-2581-2(9))* Review & Herald Publishing Assn.

Holmes, Greg. Chronicles of a Two Year Old. 2006. 88p. per. *(978-1-897373-00-2(7))* Word Alive Pr.

Holmes, Karen L. He Provides the Shoes. 2008. 236p. pap. 15.99 *(978-1-60647-796-0(X))* Xulon Pr., Inc.

Holmes, Pauline. The Perfectionism Trap: Its Hidden Origin & Certain Cure. 2010. pap. 14.99 *(978-1-61579-794-3(7))* Xulon Pr., Inc.

Holmes, Peter R. The Fasting Journey: Sacrifice. Clarity. Purpose. Joy. 2009. (ENG.). 222p. pap. 15.99 *(978-1-60657-018-0(8))* Authentic Media.

Holmes, Stephen & Rook, Russell, eds. Walk This Way: 40 Days on the Road with Jesus. 2009. (ENG.). 176p. 14.99 *(978-1-84227-640-2(9))* Authentic Media.

Holsopple, Jerry L. Turning Toward Jesus: A Video & Study Resource for New Believers. 120p. 149.95 *(978-1-877736-16-2(3))* Mennonite Mission Network.

Holt, Vickie Hodge. The Weavers. 2010. 148p. pap. 13.99 *(978-1-61507-118-0(3))* Cross Bks. Publishing.

Holtz, Albert. From Holidays to Holy Days: A Benedictine Walk Through Advent 2008. 136p. pap. 16.00 *(978-0-8192-2316-6(6),* Morehouse Publishing) Church Publishing, Inc.

Holy Happenings. 39.00 *(978-0-687-06657-5(3))* Abingdon Pr.

The Holy Spirit: Matrix of Destiny & Redemption. Date not set. 192p. pap. 29.95 *(978-1-898595-38-0(0),* Alpha Pr.) Sussex Academic Pr. GBR. Dist: International Specialized Bk. Services.

Holzapfel, Richard Neitzel. When It Feels Like Saints Aren't Saints. 2007. 18.95 *(978-1-59038-787-0(2))* Deseret Bk. Co.

Honeygosky, Paulette, Sr. A Race to Be Won: All You Need to Know about Personal Integrity, Good Works, & Christian Leadership. 2008. 49p. pap. 16.95 *(978-1-60703-099-7(3))* PublishAmerica, Inc.

Hontz, Marilyn. Shame Lifter: Replacing Your Fears & Tears with Forgiveness, Truth, & Hope. 2009. (ENG.). 240p. pap. 14.99 *(978-1-4143-1896-7(0))* Tyndale Hse. Pubs.

Hood Dana. I Will Change Your Name: Messages from the Father to a Heart Broken by Divorce. 2007. 122p. 10.99 *(978-0-89112-509-9(4),* Leafwood Pubs.) Abilene Christian Univ. Pr.

Hood, Dannie. The Desperation Zone. 160p. pap. 10.99 *(978-1-58169-139-9(4),* Evergreen Pr.) Genesis Communications, Inc.

Hood, Keith. God Consciousness: The Stages of Spiritual Life or Spiritual Death. 2010. pap. 7.99 *(978-1-61566-441-2(6))* Tate Publishing & Enterprises, LLC.

Hood, Vanessa. Overcoming Grief/Lonliness/Fear/Worry. 2007. per. *(978-1-59581-352-7(7),* Brentwood Christian Pr.) Brentwood Communications Group.

—Prosperity in All Areas of Life. 2007. per. *(978-1-59581-366-4(7),* Brentwood Christian Pr.) Brentwood Communications Group.

Hooey, Zachary F. The Nazarite Vow. 2008. 204p. 13.99 *(978-1-60462-987-3(8))* Tate Publishing & Enterprises, LLC.

Hooker. Love the Stranger. 2nd ed. 160p. 16.95 *(978-0-281-04686-7(7))* International Publishers Marketing.

Hooker, Adele. Close Encounters of the God Kind: Exploring the Infinite Riches of God. 2007. 256p. per. 27.95 *(978-1-4241-6333-5(1))* PublishAmerica, Inc.

—Close Encounters of the God Kind - Exploring the infinite riches of God. 2009. 255p. pap. 23.20 *(978-0-557-14958-2(4))* Lulu Enterprises Inc.

Hooker, Merry Jo. Behold I Stand at the Door & KnockApos. 2008. pap. 19.99 *(978-1-60477-876-2(8))* Xulon Pr., Inc.

Hooker, Morna D. & Vincent, John J. The Drama of Mark. 2010. (ENG.). 80p. pap. 10.00 *(978-0-7162-0664-4(1))* Epworth Pr., The GBR. Dist: Westminster John Knox Pr.

Hooks, James H. Should Christians Prosper. 2008. 124p. per. 13.95 *(978-1-4327-1438-3(4))* Outskirts Pr., Inc.

Hooper, Dan. Destiny Decisions: Get Your Life Going Again. 2007. (ENG.). 160p. per. 12.95 *(978-0-9793192-0-4(X))* Lifebridge Bks.

Hoover, David W. Lo Oculto (The Occult) (Serie Respuesta). (SPA.). 40p. pap. 2.95 *(978-0-570-04939-5(3),* 09-2512) Concordia Publishing Hse.

Hoover, Ray. Through the Rent Veil. 2011. 72p. pap. 8.99 *(978-1-936750-22-1(8))* Yorkshire Publishing Group.

Hope, Pamela J. Life Just Moves Right Along. 2010. 80p. pap. 15.99 *(978-1-4535-3696-4(5))* Xlibris Corp.

The Hope You Need: From the Lord's Prayer, 1 vol. 2010. 224p. pap. 3.99 *(978-0-310-32894-0(2))* Zondervan.

Hopf, Sharon I. His Glory Gang: Inside Out & Upside down - Workbook. 2009 pap. 21.99 *(978-1-60696-421-7(6))* Tate Publishing & Enterprises, LLC.

—His Glory Gang: Teacher's Guide. 2009. pap. 24.99 *(978-1-60799-371-1(6))* Tate Publishing & Enterprises, LLC.

Hopkins, Frank D. A Faithful Servant: Live a Life That Pleases Christ, 1 vol. 2009. 226p. pap. 24.95 *(978-1-61582-714-5(5))* PublishAmerica, Inc.

Hopkins, Marjorie E. Dying to Meet Him: Wit & Wisdom from a Funeral Director's Wife. 2011. pap. 11.99 *(978-1-61346-489-2(4))* Tate Publishing & Enterprises, LLC.

Hoppe, Maurice. High Priest & Coming King. 2009. 140p. 29.99 *(978-1-4415-2544-4(0));* pap. 19.99 *(978-1-4415-2543-7(2))* Xlibris Corp.

Hopper, Bobby. Win Build & Send. 2008. pap. 13.99 *(978-1-60034-536-4(0))* Xulon Pr., Inc.

Hopper, Bobby E. I Will Speak Using Stories: A Thirty-one Day Devotional. 2009. 140p. 27.49 *(978-1-4389-7859-8(6));* pap. 13.99 *(978-1-4389-7858-1(8))* AuthorHouse.

Horace, Richard D. When Potential Pushes You into Purpose: Discovering Purpose & Residing in Destiny. 2008. pap. 9.99 *(978-1-60647-508-9(8))* Xulon Pr., Inc.

Horlacher, Millie. Seasons of Salt: Meditations. 2009. 260p. 29.95 *(978-1-4401-6167-4(4));* pap. 19.95 *(978-1-4401-6166-7(6))* iUniverse, Inc.

Horn, Donna & Horn, John. Looking from the Inside Out. 2007. 20.00 *(978-1-60416-058-1(6));* per. 13.00 *(978-1-60416-057-4(8))* Reformation Pubs. (Williams Printing Co.).

Horrocks, Don. Laws of the Spiritual Order: Innovation & Reconstruction in the Soteriology of Thomas Erskine of Linlathen. 2007. (Studies in Evangelical History & Thought Ser.). 389p. pap. 39.00 *(978-1-59752-754-5(8),* Wipf and Stock) Wipf & Stock Pubs.

Horta, Armand J. God's Intentions for Mankind. 2009. 212p. pap. 18.00 *(978-1-4269-1415-7(6))* Trafford Publishing.

Horton, Michael. The Gospel-Driven Life: Being Good News People in a Bad News World. 272p. 2012. pap. 16.99 *(978-0-8010-1463-5(8))* 2009. 19.99 *(978-0-8010-1319-5(4))* Baker Bks.

Horton, Ronald Arthur. Mood Tides: Divine Purpose in the Rhythms of Life. 2008. 194p. per. *(978-1-59166-780-3(1))* BJU Pr.

Horvath, Rosangela. O Outro Lado Da Moed. 2008. (POR.). 104p. per. 9.99 *(978-1-60477-474-0(6))* Xulon Pr., Inc.

Hosey, LaToya M. Forever Sisters. 2010. 528p. pap. 26.99 *(978-1-60957-665-3(9))* Xulon Pr., Inc.

Hoskins, Catina L. From Pain to Power: Forgiveness Is the Key. 2008. pap. 9.99 *(978-1-60477-647-8(1))* Xulon Pr., Inc.

Hostetler, Bob. Quit Going to Church. 2012. (ENG.). 224p. pap. 14.99 *(978-0-915547-70-8(8),* Leafwood Pubs.) Abilene Christian Univ. Pr.

Hostetler, Ron. Becoming Champions for Life. 2010. 204p. pap. 15.99 *(978-1-60957-511-3(3))* Xulon Pr., Inc.

Hotchkin, Beriah B. (Beriah Bishop). Upward from Sin, Through Grace, to Glory by Rev B B Hotchkin. 2006. 296p. per. 23.99 *(978-1-4255-2806-5(6))* MPublishing.

Houdmann, S. Michael. Got Questions? Bible Questions Answered - Answers to the Questions People Are Really Asking. 2009. 720p. 47.99 *(978-1-4141-1202-2(5));* pap. 31.99 *(978-1-4141-1208-4(4))* Pleasant Word.

Hougan, Judith. Transformed into Fire: Discovering Your True Identity as God's Beloved, 1 vol. 2009. 240p. pap. 13.99 *(978-0-8254-2754-1(1))* Kregel Pubns.

Hough, Lee. Common Sense for Christians. 2008. 176p. 24.50 *(978-1-60693-345-9(0),* Strategic Bk. Publishing) AEG Literary Publishing Services, Inc.

House, H. Wayne, et al. Apologetics & Christian Evidences, 1 vol. 2006. (ZondervanCharts Ser.). (ENG., Illus.). 144p. pap. 18.99 *(978-0-310-21937-8(X))* Zondervan.

House, Patricia. Wow! Look at God! 2011. 30p. pap. 9.99 *(978-1-933972-24-4(6))* PriorityONE Pubns.

Houston, Bishop E. H. Bad Words or Bad People? 2011. 108p. 21.25 *(978-1-4567-3736-8(8));* pap. 12.00 *(978-1-4567-3737-5(6))* AuthorHouse.

Houston, Bobbie. I'll Have What She's Having: The Ultimate Compliment to Any Woman Daring to Change Her World, 0 vols. 2008. (Illus.). 192p. pap. 14.99 *(978-0-8499-1977-0(0))* Nelson, Thomas Inc.

Houston, Brian. For This I Was Born: Aligning Your Vision to God's Cause, 0 vols. 2008. 192p. per. 14.99 *(978-0-8499-1913-8(4))* Nelson, Thomas Inc.

Houston, Walter. Justice: The Biblical Challenge. 2010. (Biblical Challenges in the Contemporary World Ser.). (ENG.). 165p. (C). 95.00 *(978-1-34553-887-3(0))* Equinox Publishing Ltd. GBR. Dist: ISD.

Hovca, Penny Meyer. And He Said, Praise Me! An Inspirational Reflection of One Woman's Journey Through Breast Cancer. 2010. pap. 8.99 *(978-1-61566-776-5(8))* Tate Publishing & Enterprises, LLC.

Hovestol, Tom. Extreme Righteousness. 2008. (ENG.). 256p. 16.99 *(978-1-85078-761-7(1))* Authentic Media.

How the Church Grew: Teacher Guide. 124p. tchr. ed. 17.95 *(978-0-7586-0471-2(8))* Concordia Publishing Hse.

How to Grow in Grace. 2006. 129p. per. 12.99 *(978-0-9741657-4-5(3))* Galaxia Publishing Group, LLC.

How to Hear God to Prosper. 2009. (ENG.). 112p. 29.95 *(978-0-9744366-3-0(1))* Found Treasure Publishing.

Howard Books. Love Is... Discovering the Beauty of God's Love Through the H. 2011. (ENG.). 80p. pap. 9.99 *(978-1-4516-4149-3(4),* Howard Bks.) Howard Books.

Howard Books Staff. Kisses from a Friend's Heart: Heartwarming Messages that Encourage & Inspire. 2008. (ENG., Illus.). 128p. 11.99 *(978-1-4165-5857-6(8),* Howard Bks.) Howard Books.

Howard Books Staff, contrib. by. Hello Future! Insights for the Graduate: A Guide to Fulfilling Your Dreams. 2007. (Illus.). 219p. *(978-1-58229-669-2(3),* Howard Bks.) Howard Books.

Howard Books Staff, creator. Thanks! 2006. (Hugs Expression Ser.). (ENG., Illus.). 96p. 11.99 *(978-1-4165-3538-6(1),* Howard Bks.) Howard Books.

Howard Books Staff & Howard Books. Hugs for the Heart: A Story Collection That Touches the Heart as Only a Hug Can Do. 2007. (Hugs for the Heart Ser.). (ENG.). 256p. pap. 16.99 *(978-1-4165-3562-9(9),* Howard Bks.) Howard Books.

—I'm a Graduate Now What? Step into Your Future-Live Out Your Dreams. 2009. (ENG., Illus.). 256p. 14.99 *(978-1-4165-8916-7(3),* Howard Bks.) Howard Books.

—Kisses of Love: Heartwarming Messages to Say I Love You. 2008. (ENG., Illus.). 128p. 11.99 *(978-1-4165-5866-8(7),* Howard Bks.) Howard Books.

Howard, Chris E. Running God's Spiritual Railroad. 2007. 156p. per. 13.99 *(978-1-60266-844-7(2))* Xulon Pr., Inc.

Howard, J. N. Fire in the Mountains. 2008. 320p. pap. 18.99 *(978-1-60647-735-9(8))* Xulon Pr., Inc.

Howard, Karol. Who's Praying for Me. 2007. per. *(978-0-9794861-0-4(6))* Truth Pubs.

Howard, Kathy. God's Truth Revealed: Biblical Foundations for the Christian Faith. 2010. (ENG.). 192p. pap. 14.99 *(978-1-59669-268-8(5))* New Hope Pubs.

Howard, Loretta Y. Walking on Broken Pieces: Discovering God in Times of Hardship. 2010. pap. 10.99 *(978-1-61663-929-7(6))* Tate Publishing & Enterprises, LLC.

Howard, Ron. Breaking the Cycle of Sin. 2008. 148p. pap. 15.99 *(978-1-60477-875-5(X))* Xulon Pr., Inc.

Howat, Irene. Inspired by a Blank Screen: Re-Boot Your Spiritual Life. 2007. (ENG.). 176p. per. 10.99 *(978-1-84550-263-8(9))* Christian Focus Pubns. GBR. Dist: STL Distribution North America.

Howell-Grant, Saundra. Ten Reasons to Live & Thrive. 2009. 52p. pap. 10.99 *(978-1-60791-917-9(6))* Xulon Pr., Inc.

Howell, Greg. If: Simple Word, Profound Biblical Implications. 2008. 104p. 9.99 *(978-1-60462-871-5(5))* Tate Publishing & Enterprises, LLC.

C

Howell Jr., Gerald. Outline of a Christian Life. 2007. 100p. per. 16.95 *(978-1-4241-8921-2(7))* PublishAmerica, Inc.

Howie, Margaret-Ann. Single Supplement: Paying the Price & Enjoying the Journey. 2011. 128p. pap. 11.95 ***(978-1-61507-695-6(6))*** Cross Bks. Publishing.

Howsare, Rodney & Howsare. Balthasar. 2009. (Guides for the Perplexed Ser.). (ENG.). 200p. 110.00 *(978-0-567-03198-3(5)*, T&T Clark Int'l) Continuum International Publishing Group, Ltd. GBR. Dist: National Bk. Network.

Howze, Rita. He's Able. 2009. 64p. pap. 10.99 *(978-1-60791-417-4(4))* Xulon Pr., Inc.

Hoyer, Kevin V. In the Absence of Orders: For we walk by faith, not by sight. -2 Corinthians 5. 2007. 156p. per. 14.95 *(978-0-595-45313-9(9))* iUniverse, Inc.

Hryniewicz, Wacaw. The Challenge of Our Hope: Christian Faith in Dialogue. 2006. (Polish Philosophical Studies). pap. *(978-1-56518-237-0(5))* Council for Research in Values & Philosophy.

Hubbard, Norm. Coming to Terms with Your Faith. 2010. (Ancient Expectations Ser.). (ENG.). 144p. pap. 12.99 *(978-1-4347-6689-2(6))* Cook, David C.

Huch, Larry. Libre al Fin: Removiendo el pasado de su Futuro. 2009. Orig. Title: Free at Last: Removing Your Past from Your Future. (SPA & ENG.). 272p. pap. 10.99 *(978-1-60374-113-2(5)*, 771132) Whitaker Hse.

—10 Curses That Block the Blessing. 2006. 224p. per. 12.99 *(978-0-88368-207-4(9)*, 772079) Whitaker Hse.

—10 Maldiciones Que Bloquean la Bendicion. 2007. (SPA.). 252p. per. 10.99 *(978-0-88368-585-3(X))* Whitaker Hse.

Hudson, Anthony. Sprinkled with Angel's DUST: Evidence of angelic Visitations. 2009. 146p. pap. 19.99 *(978-1-4415-9097-8(8))* Xlibris Corp.

Hudson, Conni. Journeying with Jesus Through the Basics. 2007. 452p. per. 25.00 *(978-0-9794858-0-0(0))* Journeying with Jesus Ministries.

Hudson, Jackie. Compassionate Living: A Road to Emotional Growth & Healing. 2010. 80p. pap. 11.00 *(978-1-60899-502-8(X)*, Wipf and Stock) Wipf & Stock Pubs.

Hudson, Lloyd. Will All Christians Go to Heaven? 2007. 116p. pap. 13.99 *(978-0-88144-251-9(8))* Yorkshire Publishing Group.

Hudson, Shirley L. Meditations of My Heart. 2009. 224p. pap. 18.95 *(978-1-4401-3995-6(4))* iUniverse, Inc.

Hudson, Wayne T. Metamorphosis: Unapologetically Finding Hope in Changing Political Parties. 2010. (ENG.). 126p. 11.99 *(978-1-61638-144-8(2)*, Creation Hse.) Charisma Media.

Huebsch, William. The New Scripture Way of the Cross. 32p. pap. 0.99 *(978-0-89622-551-0(8)*, C-95) Twenty-Third Pubns./Bayard.

Huey, Margaret. Messianic Winter Holiday Helper. 2011. (ENG.). 210p. pap. 16.99 ***(978-1-4679-5202-6(8))*** CreateSpace.

Huff, Ivan. Cause or Effect: Are tragedies God-caused or an effect of the World? 2009. pap. 14.99 *(978-1-60799-552-4(2))* Tate Publishing & Enterprises, LLC.

Huff, Rick. The Witness: 40 Days of Outreach. 2008. 164p. pap. 11.95 *(978-1-4327-2288-3(3))* Outskirts Pr., Inc.

Huffman, Carol. Widow s Club. 2011. 60p. 37.99 *(978-1-61215-541-8(3))*; pap. 27.99 *(978-1-61215-619-4(3))* Xulon Pr., Inc.

Hügel, Friedrich. Eternal Life: A Study of Its Implications & Applications. 2007. pap. *(978-1-59731-404-6(8))* Perennis, Sophia.

Huggett. Open to God. (Illus.). 144p. pap. *(978-0-340-51488-7(4)*, Hodder & Stoughton) Hodder General Publishing Div.

Huggins, Beresford. Your Reaction Defines God's Action. 2008. 208p. 25.99 *(978-1-60647-946-9(6))*; pap. 15.99 *(978-1-60647-440-2(5))* Xulon Pr., Inc.

Hughes, Barbara & Hughes, R. Kent. Disciplines of a Godly Family. annot. ed. 2007. 256p. pap. 15.99 *(978-1-58134-941-2(6))* Crossway.

Hughes, Chris B. The Porpoise-Given Life: Inspiration from the Cetacean Nation. 2008. 160p. pap. 14.95 *(978-1-57736-413-9(9))* Providence Hse Pubs.

Hughes, Dewi & Hughes, Dewi Arwel. Power & Poverty: Divine & Human Rule in a World of Need, 1 vol. 2009. (ENG.). 253p. pap. 25.00 *(978-0-8308-2809-8(5)*, IVP Acad.) InterVarsity Pr.

Hughes, I. G. Instructions Are Included: The Bible, God's Instruction Manual. 2009. pap. 14.99 *(978-1-60799-442-8(9))* Tate Publishing & Enterprises, LLC.

Hughes, James. 2 Corinthians 1-7: True Discipleship: Good Book Guide. 2010. (Good Book Guides). 96p. pap. *(978-1-906334-75-8(7))* Good Bk. Co.

Hughes, Pat. Know When to Dust Your Feet 1. 2006. 21.99 *(978-1-60034-696-5(0))*; pap. 13.99 *(978-1-60034-695-8(2))* Xulon Pr., Inc.

Hughes, Patricia A. Our Redeemer-Husband: Our Head. 2010. 148p. pap. 12.99 *(978-1-58930-249-5(4))* Selah Publishing Group, LLC.

Hughes, Robert. Beloved Dust: Tides of the Spirit in the Christian Life. 2008. (ENG.). 432p. pap. 39.95 *(978-0-8264-2843-1(6))* Continuum International Publishing Group, Ltd. GBR. Dist: National Bk. Network.

Hughes, Robert Don. Satan's Whispers: Breaking the Lies That Bind. 2006. 174p. pap. 21.00 *(978-1-59752-969-3(9)*, Wipf and Stock) Wipf & Stock Pubs.

Hughes, Sandra. Arise, Shine. 2007. 32p. pap. *(978-0-9723370-7-6(5))* Royal Pr. Publishing.

Hughes, Selwyn. Life's Most Important Questions. 2007. (Illus.). 64p. *(978-1-85345-425-7(7))* Crusade for World Revival.

—What to Say When People Need Help: A Short Guide, 1 vol. 2009. 98p. pap. *(978-1-85345-514-8(8))* Crusade for World Revival.

—7 Laws of Spiritual Success. 2008. 280p. *(978-1-85345-468-4(0))* Crusade for World Revival.

Hula, Steven D. God Money & You. 2009. 88p. pap. 10.99 *(978-1-60791-837-0(4))* Xulon Pr., Inc.

Hull, Bill. Christlike: The Pursuit of Uncomplicated Obedience. 2010. (Becoming a Woman Of ... Ser.). (ENG.). 224p. pap. 14.99 *(978-1-60006-694-8(1))* NavPress Publishing Group.

—The Complete Book of Discipleship: On Being & Making Followers of Christ. annot. ed. 2006. (Navigators Reference Library). (ENG.). 352p. pap. 16.99 *(978-1-57683-897-6(8))* NavPress Publishing Group.

Hull, Bill & Mascarella, Paul. Etl: Believe as Jesus Believed. 2007. 160p. pap. 11.99 *(978-0-7375-0130-8(8))* Biblical Studies Pr.

Hulse, David. Take Another Look: A Scriptural Review of Traditional Christian Doctrine. 2010. 168p. 27.99 *(978-1-4520-0703-8(9))*; (ENG.). pap. 18.00 *(978-1-4520-0704-5(7))* AuthorHouse.

Hultin, Jeremy F. The Ethics of Obscene Speech in Early Christianity & Its Environment. 2008. (Novum Testamentum Supplements Ser.). (Illus.). 304p. *(978-90-04-16803-9(6))* BRILL.

Hultquist, Lee. Siguieron Al Flautista: They Followed the Piper. (SPA.). 208p. *(978-84-7228-450-0(6)*, 360145) Clie, Editorial.

Humble, Myron. The Scribe & the Sword. 2009. 198p. pap. 20.92 *(978-0-557-08380-0(X))* Lulu Enterprises Inc.

Hume, Karen C. The Babies. 2009. 124p. pap. 11.99 *(978-1-60791-714-4(9))* Xulon Pr., Inc.

Hummel, Ruth. Where Do Babies Come From? 2008. pap. 12.99 *(978-0-7586-1416-2(0))*; pap. 12.99 *(978-0-7586-1410-0(1))* Concordia Publishing Hse.

Humphreys, Fisher, et al. For Faith & Friendship. 2010. *(978-0-914520-52-8(0))* Insight Pr.

Humphreys, Kent. Encouragement for Your Journey Alone: Meditations of Hope for Widows. 2009. pap. 12.99 *(978-1-60799-318-6(X))* Tate Publishing & Enterprises, LLC.

Hundley, Ray Johnthon. Smell the Steel - Avoid the Trap. 2008. 112p. 19.99 *(978-1-60647-568-3(1))*; pap. 11.99 *(978-1-60647-567-6(3))* Xulon Pr., Inc.

Hungry Planet Media Staff & Tyndale House Publishers Staff, prods. No Room at the Inn: Real Stories of How Faith Can Change Homelessness Includes the Christmas Story as Read by Families Touched by Homelessness. 2009. (Hungry Planet Bible Project Ser.). (ENG.). 2p. 14.99 *(978-1-4143-3572-8(5))* Tyndale Hse. Pubs.

Hunnings, Dixie Lea. Ask Your Heart. 2011. 436p. 34.99 ***(978-1-4568-9276-0(2))***; pap. 23.99 ***(978-1-4568-9275-3(4))*** Xlibris Corp.

Hunt, Dave. Cosmos, Creator & Human Destiny: Answering Darwin, Dawkins, & the New Atheists. 2010. (ENG.). 606p. 30.00 *(978-1-928660-64-4(9))* Berean Call, The.

—Seeking & Finding God. 2007. (ENG.). 123p. pap. 7.99 *(978-1-928660-23-1(1))* Berean Call, The.

—An Urgent Call to a Serious Faith: A Prophetic Alarm for the Bride of Christ. 2007. (ENG.). 254p. 21.99 *(978-1-928660-33-0(9))* Berean Call, The.

Hunt, E. Marlene. Hard Heads, Hard Hearts. pap. 3.00 *(978-1-893555-29-7(1))* Grace Publishing.

—Why Folks Don't Get Healed. pap. 3.00 *(978-1-893555-22-8(4))* Grace Publishing.

Hunt, Franklin. The Book of Faith. 2007. per. *(978-1-59581-360-2(8)*, Brentwood Christian Pr.) Brentwood Communications Group.

—The Book of Faith. 2007. 92p. per. 9.99 *(978-1-60266-745-7(4))* Xulon Pr., Inc.

Hunt, John, compiled by. Essential Writings of Amer. 2007. (ENG.). 800p. (gr. 11). 24.99 *(978-0-89957-648-0(6))* AMG Pubs.

Hunt, June. The Complete Biblical Counseling Concordance: Every Scripture Verse You'll Need to Apply the Bible to Life's Problems. 2013. 352p. mass mkt. 11.99 *(978-0-7369-2330-9(6))* Harvest Hse. Pubs.

Hunt, Mary. The Financially Confident Woman: The Least Every Woman Needs to Know to Manage Her Finances & Prepare for the Future. 2nd ed. 2008. 227p. pap. 14.95 *(978-1-934508-01-5(2))* DPL Pr.

Hunt, Ruth. Viento del Este: Eastwind. (SPA.). *(978-84-7228-350-3(X)*, 220943) Clie, Editorial.

Hunt Th.D., Jason. Reasons for the Seasons: Origins of the Christian Holidays, 1 vol. 2010. 142p. pap. 24.95 *(978-1-4489-5186-4(0))* PublishAmerica, Inc.

Hunt, Tony, et al. "Cher Alme" Texts of Anglo-Norman Piety. 2010. (ROA & ENG.). *(978-0-86698-433-1(X))* Arizona State Univ., Arizona Ctr. for Medieval & Renaissance Studies.

Hunter, A. M. The Fifth Evangelist. 2012. 136p. pap. ***(978-0-334-00477-6(2)***, SCM Pr.) Hymns Ancient & Modern Ltd.

Hunter, Jonathan. Breaking Free from the Spirit of Death. 2008. 52p. pap. 9.99 *(978-1-60477-727-7(3))* Xulon Pr., Inc.

Hunter, Todd D. Christianity Beyond Belief: Following Jesus for the Sake of Others. (ENG.). 199p. 2010. pap. 16.00 *(978-0-8308-3256-9(4))* 2009. 22.00 *(978-0-8308-3315-3(3))* InterVarsity Pr. (IVP Bks.).

Hupp, Sarah M. The Roller Coaster of Unemployment: Trusting God for the Ride. 2010. (ENG.). 160p. pap. 9.99 *(978-1-57293-376-7(3))* Discovery Hse. Pubs.

Hurlburt, Bev. Your 40 Day Journey: Getting Closer to God Each Day. 2010. 92p. pap. 9.95 *(978-1-4497-0949-5(4)*, WestBow Pr.) Author Solutions, Inc.

Humard, Hanna. Andando Entre lo Invisible: Walking among the Unseen. (SPA.). 168p. *(978-84-7228-575-0(8)*, 220019) Clie, Editorial.

—Pies de Ciervas en los Lugares Altos: Hinds Feet on High Places. (SPA.). 200p. *(978-84-7228-315-2(1)*, 220688) Clie, Editorial.

Humard, Hannah. Hinds' Feet on High Places. 2009. (ENG.). 317p. pap. 7.99 *(978-0-8423-1429-9(6)*, Living Bks.) Tyndale Hse. Pubs.

Humard, Hannah. Hinds Feet on High Places. 2011. 136p. pap. 8.99 ***(978-1-61203-097-5(1))*** Bottom of the Hill Publishing.

Hurst, Tracy. Tuesdays with Tracy. 2008. 164p. pap. 13.99 *(978-1-60647-469-3(3))* Xulon Pr., Inc.

Hurt, Wade M. Unveiled Faith: A Last Day Revelation of Faith. 2009. pap. 16.99 *(978-1-60799-349-0(X))* Tate Publishing & Enterprises, LLC.

Hurth, Donna-Lynette. Ocean's Triumph. 2010. 115p. pap. 15.96 *(978-0-557-44667-4(8))* Lulu Enterprises Inc.

Hurts, Arthur. The Holy Hoax, Illuminations of the Light-Bearer: A Collection of Seculosophy. 2011. 162p. pap. 24.95 ***(978-1-4626-4209-0(8))*** PublishAmerica, Inc.

Huston, Paula. By Way of Grace: Moving from Faithfulness to Holiness. 2007. (ENG.). 224p. 19.95 *(978-0-8294-2331-0(1))* Loyola Pr.

Hutchcraft, Ron. A Life That Matters: Making the Greatest Possible Difference with the Rest of Your Life. rev. ed. 2007. (ENG.). 192p. per. 14.99 *(978-0-8024-3649-8(8))* Moody Pubs.

Hutchinson, Dave. The Riches of Grace! The Good News to the Believer! God's exciting answer to Why am I Here? 2009. 124p. 24.99 *(978-1-4490-2364-5(9))*; pap. 14.99 *(978-1-4490-2363-8(0))* AuthorHouse.

Hutchison, Joyce & Rupp, Joyce. May I Walk You Home-Rev. 10th ed. 2009. 192p. pap. 12.95 *(978-1-59471-214-2(X))* Ave Maria Pr.

Hutchison, Taryn R. We Wait You: Waiting on God in Eastern Europe. 2008. 244p. pap. 17.99 *(978-1-4141-1174-2(6))* Pleasant Word.

Hutton, Larry Jon. Long Life: An Assignment from God. 2010. per. 9.99 *(978-0-9747558-2-3(6))* Force of Faith Pubns.

Huynh, Andre. In Harmony with God. 2007. 165p. per. 12.99 *(978-1-59886-961-3(2))* Tate Publishing & Enterprises, LLC.

Hybels, Bill. Axiom: Powerful Leadership Proverbs. 2008. (ENG.). 128p. pap. 12.99 *(978-0-310-28259-4(4))* Zondervan.

—Divina Insatisfacción: Avivando la llama que enciende tú Visión, 1 vol. 2007. (SPA.). 176p. (gr. 13). per. 6.99 *(978-0-8297-5177-2(7))* Zondervan.

—Holy Discontent. 2007. (ENG.). 128p. pap. 12.99 *(978-0-310-27613-5(6))* Zondervan.

—Holy Discontent: Fueling the Fire That Ignites Personal Vision, 1 vol. (ENG.). 2008. 160p. pap. 3.49 *(978-0-310-28583-0(6))* 2007. 128p. (gr. 13). 14.99 *(978-0-310-27228-1(9))* Zondervan.

—Just Walk Across the Room: Simple Steps Pointing People to Faith. 2006. (ENG.). 224p. pap. 14.99 *(978-0-310-27218-2(1))* Zondervan.

—The Power of a Whisper: Hearing God, Having the Guts to Respond. 2010. pap. *(978-0-310-52022-1(3))*; (ENG.). 24.99 *(978-0-310-32947-3(7))*; (ENG.). 96p. pap. 9.99 *(978-0-310-32948-0(5))*; (ENG.). 288p. 22.99 *(978-0-310-32074-6(7))*; (ENG.). 272p. pap. ***(978-0-310-52019-1(3))*** Zondervan.

—Who You Are When No One's Looking: Choosing Consistency, Resisting Compromise. enl. ed. 2010. (Willow Creek Resources Ser.). (ENG.). 159p. pap. 15.00 *(978-0-8308-3749-6(3)*, IVP Bks.) InterVarsity Pr.

Hybels, Bill, et al. Excellent Living: Giving God Your Best, 1 vol. 2009. (Interactions Ser.). (ENG.). 96p. pap. 7.99 *(978-0-310-28064-4(8))* Zondervan.

—Influence: Maximizing Your Impact for God, 1 vol. 2009. (Interactions Ser.). (ENG.). 96p. pap. 7.99 *(978-0-310-28066-8(4))* Zondervan.

—Nehemiah, 1 vol. 2008. (New Community Bible Study Ser.). (ENG.). 96p. pap. 7.99 *(978-0-310-28055-2(9))* Zondervan.

Hylton, Jim. The Supernatural Skyline: Where Heaven Touches Earth. 2010. 302p. ***(978-0-7684-3449-1(1))***; ***(978-0-7684-3450-7(5))*** Destiny Image Pubs.

Hynes, Julianna. Living on Purpose: Keys to Discovering Your God-given Destiny. 2007. 23.95 *(978-0-9661832-5-2(8))* Liberation Pr.

Iannucci, Anthony. Surviving the Desert: Overcoming Life's Extremes. 2010. 260p. pap. 16.99 *(978-1-61579-795-0(5))* Xulon Pr., Inc.

Ibanez, Debbie. Beloved Believer: Return to the Arms of Jesus. 2009. (J). pap. 14.99 *(978-1-60799-792-4(4))* Tate Publishing & Enterprises, LLC.

Ibe, abr. Perfect Storm - Russian. 2008. (RUS.). *(978-0-9785848-3-2(X))* IBE, Inc.

I'D Rather Be Better, Than Bitter. 2007. 460p. per. 23.99 *(978-1-60266-450-0(1))* Xulon Pr., Inc.

La Iglesia de Dios en Mision. *(978-0-633-00597-9(5))* LifeWay Christian Resources.

Ijeh, Ike. Mystery of Godliness. 2006. pap. 13.99 *(978-1-60034-538-8(7))* Xulon Pr., Inc.

Ikomi, Tai. 77 Names of God. 2007. 232p. per. 14.99 *(978-1-890430-47-4(1))* Triumph Publishing.

Illingworth, J. R. Christian Character: Being Some Lectures on the Elements of Christian Ethics. 2007. (ENG.). 220p. 39.95 *(978-0-548-12615-8(1))* 2006. pap. 24.95 *(978-1-4286-3595-1(5))* Kessinger Publishing, LLC.

Ilo, Norbert P. Coat of Many Colours. 2007. 96p. per. 9.95 *(978-1-4327-0995-2(X))* Outskirts Pr., Inc.

Impersonal Life. 2007. per. 9.99 *(978-1-4209-2862-4(7))* Digireads.com.

Imprinting Finishing or Packing. *(978-0-687-26525-1(8))* Abingdon Pr.

In God's Likeness. 4.50 *(978-0-687-06683-4(2))* Abingdon Pr.

Inch, Morris A. In Christ & on Track: The Essential Paul. 2007. (ENG.). 102p. pap. 26.50 *(978-0-7618-3965-1(8))* Univ. Pr. of America, Inc.

—Thumbs up for the Family. 2010. 160p. pap. 12.00 *(978-1-60860-813-3(1)*, Eloquent Bks.) AEG Literary Publishing Services, Inc.

Ineson, Emma & Ineson. Busy Living: Blessing Not Burden. 2007. (ENG.). 216p. 21.95 *(978-0-8264-9117-6(0))* Continuum International Publishing Group, Ltd. GBR. Dist: National Bk. Network.

Infant Joe. 128p. pap. 4.95 *(978-0-937408-24-7(7))* GMI Pubns.

Inge, William Ralph. Personal Religion & the Life of Devotion. 2007. 96p. per. *(978-1-4067-8889-1(9)*, Pomona Pr.) Read Bks.

Ingleby, Jonathan. Christians & Catastrophe. 2010. 44p. pap. *(978-0-9565943-0-3(1))* Wide Margin Bks. GBR. Dist: Gardners Bks. Ltd.

Ingram, Arthur Foley Winnington. A Mission of the Spirit. 2007. (ENG.). 228p. 41.95 *(978-0-548-05720-9(6))* Kessinger Publishing, LLC.

Ingram, Berta. My Lord, My Shepherd. 90p. pap. 12.95 *(978-1-892861-12-2(7))* Vision Publishing Group.

Ingram, Chip. Good to Great in God's Eyes: 10 Practices Great Christians Have in Common. rev. ed. 2012. 256p. pap. 15.99 ***(978-0-8010-1427-7(1))*** Baker Bks.

Ingram, Chip. Living on the Edge: Dare to Experience True Spirituality. 2011. (ENG.). 304p. pap. 14.99 *(978-1-4391-9052-4(6)*, Howard Bks.) Howard Books.

Ingwerson, Lucille. The Dove & the Sparrow. 2009. 260p. pap. 19.95 *(978-1-4401-5456-0(2))* iUniverse, Inc.

Insights to Help You Survive the Peaks & Valleys: Can You Stand to Be Blessed? 2008. 207p. per. 14.99 *(978-0-7684-2621-2(9))* Destiny Image Pubs.

Inspirio Staff. Peace for a Woman's Soul: Finding Rest for Your Spirit, 1 vol. deluxe ed. 2007. (ENG., Illus.). 208p. lthr. 14.99 *(978-0-310-81913-4(X))* Inspirio.

Iona. Fall down & Worship Him! 2006. pap. 9.99 *(978-1-60034-460-2(7))* Xulon Pr., Inc.

Iorg, Jeff. Is God Calling Me? Answering the Question Every Leader Asks. 2008. (ENG.). 128p. pap. 9.99 *(978-0-8054-4722-4(9)*, B&H Bks.) B&H Publishing Group.

Irby, Tara. Delivered: A Personal Testimony of Barrenness, Loss & Deliverance. 2008. 96p. pap. 9.99 *(978-1-60647-179-1(1))* Xulon Pr., Inc.

Ireland, Kathy & Lund, James L. Real Solutions for Busy Moms: Your Guide to Success & Sanity. 2009. (ENG.). 240p. 23.99 *(978-1-4165-6318-1(0)*, Howard Bks.) Howard Books.

Ireri, Rev Dr Stephen N. & Ireri, Rev. Stephen N. The Word of God - Our Medicine. 2010. 128p. pap. 10.95 *(978-1-936051-97-7(4))* Peppertree Pr., The.

Irizarry, Myra. Pearls from Heaven. 2007. (ENG.). 21.99 *(978-1-60034-738-2(X))*; pap. 13.99 *(978-1-60034-737-5(1))* Xulon Pr., Inc.

Ironside, Henry A. Seguridad Absoluta: Full Assurance. (SPA.). *(978-84-7645-142-7(3)*, 223183) Clie, Editorial.

Irving, Eldon. Personalities in the Pews. 2010. pap. 16.95 *(978-0-7414-6169-8(2))* Infinity Publishing.

Irwin, Brian. The Life Exchanger. 2010. 232p. pap. 15.99 *(978-1-60957-768-1(X))* Xulon Pr., Inc.

Irwin, Michael Q. A Nation in Shadows: A Prophetic Survey of the United States. 2009. 396p. pap. 18.95 *(978-1-4327-4770-1(3))* Outskirts Pr., Inc.

Isaac, Edna L. Aprendiendo A Volar Sobre la Tormenta. 2010. 166p. pap. 14.99 *(978-1-60957-267-9(X))* Xulon Pr., Inc.

Isaac, Edna L. Learning to Fly over the Storm. 2011. 178p. pap. 14.99 ***(978-1-61379-507-1(6))*** Xulon Pr., Inc.

Isbell, Raymond E. Paul, God's Evangelist & Minister. 2011. 236p. 27.99 *(978-1-4520-6741-4(4))* AuthorHouse.

Isbister, Colin. The Body of Christ. 2007. 196p. (ENG.). 21.99 *(978-1-60266-952-9(X))*; per. 13.99 *(978-1-60266-951-2(1))* Xulon Pr., Inc.

—Will the Real Jesus Please Stand Up? 2007. 328p. 27.99 *(978-1-60034-891-4(2))* Xulon Pr., Inc.

Isbister, Colin James. All Things in Perspective: Book 2 of the Body of Christ Series A Biblical Perspective of Attitude & Behaviour in the Christian. 2009. pap. 14.99 *(978-1-60791-560-7(X))* Xulon Pr., Inc.

Iserte, Salvador. Como Adquirir Personalidad Encantadora: How to Have a Winning Personality. (SPA.). *(978-84-7645-327-8(2)*, 223287) Clie, Editorial.

—Como Alcanzar la Libertad: How to Be Free. (SPA.). *(978-84-7645-097-0(4)*, 223157) Clie, Editorial.

—Como Alcanzar una Vida Radiante: How to Have a Happy Life. (SPA.). *(978-84-7645-090-1(7)*, 223145) Clie, Editorial.

—Como Enfrentar la Vida Con Exito: How to Succeed in Life. (SPA.). 128p. *(978-84-7228-968-0(0)*, 223040) Clie, Editorial.

—Como Ser Artifice de Tu Propio Destino: How to Be the Guide of Your Future. (SPA.). 128p. *(978-84-7228-988-8(5)*, 223069) Clie, Editorial.

—Despierte a la Vida: Wake up to Life. (SPA.). 336p. *(978-84-7228-937-6(0)*, 223012) Clie, Editorial.

—La Gran Aventura del Hombre Moderno: The Christian in the Modern World. (SPA.). *(978-84-7645-067-3(2)*, 223127) Clie, Editorial.

—El Hombre Descentrado: How to Find Yourself. (SPA.). 64p. *(978-84-7228-772-3(6)*, 220470) Clie, Editorial.

—El Mayor Bien de Mi Vida: Greatest Good in My Life. (SPA.). *(978-84-7645-263-9(2)*, 223294) Clie, Editorial.

—No Te Enganes a Timismo: Don't Deceive Yourself. (SPA.). *(978-84-7645-501-2(1)*, 223480) Clie, Editorial.

—Secreto de la Eterna Juventud: Secret of Eternal Youth. (SPA.). *(978-84-7645-499-2(6)*, 223481) Clie, Editorial.

—Secreto de la Felicidad: Secret of Happiness. (SPA.). 176p. *(978-84-7228-578-1(2)*, 220804) Clie, Editorial.

—Transformacion Mas Maravillosa (Wonderful Transformation) (SPA.). *(978-84-7645-430-5(9)*, 223389) Clie, Editorial.

Israel-Clark, Anani. Equipped to Live a Victorious Life. 2006. 104p. per. 12.95 *(978-1-933912-57-8(X))* Westview Publishing Co., Inc.

Israel, Robert. Glasgow Road. 2006. pap. 15.99 *(978-1-60034-900-3(5))* Xulon Pr., Inc.

It's a Big Deal: Faith Issues. (Real Deal Bible Studies). 88p. 12.99 *(978-0-7586-0522-1(6))* Concordia Publishing Hse.

It's Worth the Wait Student Manual. 2007. 84p. (YA). spiral bd. 9.95 *(978-1-928828-23-5(X))* Hudson Productions.

It's Your Deal: Personal Issues. (Real Deal Bible Studies). 80p. 12.99 *(978-0-7586-0264-0(2))* Concordia Publishing Hse.

It's Your Serve. 80p. 17.99 *(978-0-7586-0633-4(8))* Concordia Publishing Hse.

Ivory, Luther D. The Rhythm of Discipleship. 2008. (Foundations of Christian Faith Ser.). (ENG.). 86p. pap. 13.00 (978-0-664-50296-6(2)) Geneva Pr.
Iwas, Ignatius Zakka I. & Gorgis, Amill, eds. Essays from the Visit of Mor Ignatius Zakka I Iwas to Heidelberg. Toro, George, tr. 2010. (GER.). 89.72 (978-1-61143-225-1(1)) Gorgias Pr., LLC.
Iwuala, Damian. Managing Decision Making by Applying Biblical Perspective. 2010. 136p. (ENG.). 21.99 (978-1-4520-4035-6(4)); pap. 14.99 (978-1-4520-4034-9(6)) AuthorHouse.
Izbicki, Thomas M. Reform, Ecclesiology, & the Christian Life in the Late Middle Ages. 2008. (Variorum Collected Studies). 286p. 144.95 (978-0-7546-5948-8(8)) Ashgate Publishing Co.
Jaccard, A. Hospitality. 51p. 7.95 (978-0-88172-197-3(2)) Believers Bookshelf, Inc.
Jackaway, Clarice M. & Kidder, Adah Lyle. The Tapestry of Life: A Devotional Guidebook. 2011. 160p. 41.95 **(978-1-258-08840-8(1))** Literary Licensing, LLC.
Jacks, Noreen. Promises from the Olive Tree. 2008. (Illus.). 117p. pap. 17.99 (978-0-9799116-0-6(5)) LifeSong Pubs.
Jackson, Angela. And Then Came God. 2006. 80p. per. 10.95 (978-1-933912-37-0(5)) Westview Publishing Co., Inc.
Jackson, Bertha. Africa-A Pre-Trip Must! 2007. 64p. per. 9.99 (978-1-60266-920-8(1)) Xulon Pr., Inc.
Jackson, Chris. You... Revealed! Discovering who you are, how God Feels about you, & what it Will Take to Reach your Destiny. 2010. 202p. pap. 15.95 (978-1-4327-5856-1(X)) Outskirts Pr., Inc.
Jackson, Denise. The Road Home, 0 vols. 2008. (Illus.). 128p. 14.99 (978-1-4041-0531-7(X)) Nelson, Thomas Inc.
Jackson, Ed. Life Verses ALIVE: And you He made ALIVE — Ephesians 2:1. 2007. 240p. per. 14.95 (978-0-929292-48-9(0), 800-747-0738) Hannibal Bks.
Jackson, Etta D. Understanding Your Choice. 2009. 176p. pap. 54.99 (978-1-4389-6657-1(1)) AuthorHouse.
Jackson, Gabrielle. Not Another Teen Rally. 2007. 188p. per. 13.99 (978-1-60266-320-5(3)) Xulon Pr., Inc.
Jackson, Gene. The Pew Warmers. 2008. 192p. pap. 13.99 (978-1-60477-607-2(2)) Xulon Pr., Inc.
Jackson, Gerald. They Oughta Write That down Somewhere. 2007. 208p. 21.95 (978-0-9768698-6-3(1)) Sunset Institute Pr.
Jackson, Gordon S. The Handbook for Discovering God's Will. 2008. (Living the Letters Ser.). (ENG.). 208p. pap. 9.99 (978-1-60006-239-1(3)) NavPress Publishing Group.
Jackson, Greg F. A Pastor's Guide to Conducting a Funeral: Things Every Pastor Needs to Know, but May Have Been Afraid to Ask. 2010. 116p. pap. 12.99 (978-1-61507-150-0(4)) Cross Bks. Publishing.
Jackson, Harry R., Jr. Inlaws, Outlaws & the Functional Family: A Real-World Guide to Resolving Today's Family Issues. 2007. (ENG.). 192p. pap. 12.99 (978-1-59979-240-8(0), Creation Hse.) Charisma Media.
Jackson, Jason. Struggle Without a Cause, 1 vol. 2010. 112p. pap. 19.95 (978-1-4489-4978-6(5)) PublishAmerica, Inc.
Jackson, Jennifer. The Mourning & Grieving Process. 2008. 116p. pap. 19.95 (978-1-60703-547-3(2)) PublishAmerica, Inc.
Jackson, John. Finding Your Place in God's Plan: Forty Ways to Get There. 2009. 176p. pap. 18.00 (978-0-687-65524-3(2)) Abingdon Pr.
Jackson, Keith E. Changing Your Paradigm to the Christ Mind: Strategies for Empowerment Part 1. 2011. 88p. pap. 12.00 **(978-1-4634-0034-7(9))** AuthorHouse.
Jackson, Lisa A. Going in Circles ... 2010. 200p. pap. 15.99 (978-1-60957-637-0(3)) Xulon Pr., Inc.
Jackson, Ramonica. God Can Fix What Sin Destroys. 2008. 100p. per. 9.99 (978-1-60477-516-1(1)) Xulon Pr., Inc.
Jackson, Robert. What a Man. 2009. 72p. pap. 10.49 (978-1-4343-9778-2(5)) AuthorHouse.
Jackson, Shirkendra. His Wisdom. 2008. 64p. pap. 19.95 (978-1-4327-1912-8(2)) Outskirts Pr., Inc.
Jackson, Shirey. Giving Glory to God. 2007. 31p. per. 8.99 (978-1-59879-226-3(1)) Lifevest Publishing, Inc.
Jackson, Tamara. Days of My Life II: (here & Now) 2009. 80p. pap. 12.95 (978-1-4327-2893-9(8)) Outskirts Pr., Inc.
—"God Is Good, God Is Great!" 2008. 72p. pap. 15.99 (978-1-4257-9375-3(4)) Xlibris Corp.
Jackson, William. The Christian's Legacy. 2009. 316p. pap. (978-0-217-57380-1(0)) Books LLC.
Jacob, Sunday. Ask Anything in Christ Jesus: Reside in the Finished Blessing. 2009. 78p. pap. 12.95 (978-1-4327-3028-4(2)) Outskirts Pr., Inc.
Jacobi, R. I Will Go. 175p. 6.99 (978-1-85792-031-4(7)) Christian Focus Pubns. GBR. Dist: Spring Arbor Distributors, Inc.
Jacobs. Still Small Voice. 2nd ed. 272p. 19.00 (978-0-281-04697-3(2)) SPCK Publishing GBR. Dist: Pilgrim Pr., The/United Church Pr.
—Swift to Hear. 2nd ed. 192p. 16.00 (978-0-281-05260-8(3)) SPCK Publishing GBR. Dist: Pilgrim Pr., The/United Church Pr.
Jacobs, A. J. The Year of Living Biblically: One Man's Humble Quest to Follow the Bible as Literally as Possible. 2008. (ENG.). 416p. pap. 15.00 (978-0-7432-9143-4(4)) Simon & Schuster.
—The Year of Living Biblically: One Man's Humble Quest to Follow the Bible as Literally as Possible. l.t. ed. 2008. (Thorndike Core Ser.). (Illus.). 597p. 31.95 (978-1-4104-0507-4(9)) Thorndike Pr.
Jacobs, Alan. Looking Before & After: Testimony & the Christian Life. 2008. (Stob Lectures 2006 Ser.). 120p. pap. 14.00 (978-0-8028-4981-6(4)) Eerdmans, William B. Publishing Co.
Jacobs, Dave. Gridiron Gospel. 2009. 90p. pap. 19.95 (978-1-60679-051-9(X)) Coaches Choice.
Jacobs, Ileta. The Wonder of God. 2007. 48p. per. 16.95 (978-1-60441-059-4(0)) PublishAmerica, Inc.
Jacobs, Judy. Don't Miss Your Moment: It's Never Too Late to Live Your Best. 2008. (ENG.). 224p. pap. 14.99 (978-1-59979-233-0(8), Charisma Hse.) Charisma Media.
—Stand Strong: How to Become Confident in Your Calling, Achieve Strength Through Your Trials, & Prevail Against All Odds. 2007. (ENG.). 224p. per. 14.99 (978-1-59979-066-4(1), Charisma Hse.) Charisma Media.
Jacobson, Ami. The Favor Factor: Living Life with God's Advantage. 2007. 135p. 14.99 (978-1-59979-098-5(X), Charisma Hse.) Charisma Media.
Jafolla, Richard & Jafolla, Mary-Alice. La Busqueda y Aventuras en la Busqueda. pap. 27.95 (978-0-87159-198-2(7), Unity Hse.) Unity Schl. of Christianity.
Jahsmann, Allan Hart & Simon, Martin P. Little Visits with God. 50th anniv. ed. 2007. (Little Visits Ser.). (ENG., Illus.). 413p. (J). (gr. 2). 12.99 (978-0-7586-1374-5(1)) Concordia Publishing Hse.
Jakes, Jacqueline. Jacqueline's Spiritual Jewels. 2006. 213p. per. 14.99 (978-0-7684-2367-9(8)) Destiny Image Pubs.
Jakes, T. D. Hope for Every Moment: 365 Inspirational Thoughts for Every Day of the Year. 2007. 369p. 13.99 (978-0-7684-2424-9(0)) Destiny Image Pubs.
—Insights to Help You Survive the Peaks & Valleys: Can You Stand to Be Blessed? 2008. 172p. per. 15.99 (978-0-7684-2619-9(7)) Destiny Image Pubs.
—It's Time to Reveal What God Longs to Heal: Naked & Not Ashamed. 2008. 168p. pap. 14.99 (978-0-7684-2668-7(5)) Destiny Image Pubs.
—Let it Go: Forgive So You Can Be Forgiven. 2012. pap. **(978-1-4165-4733-4(9))**; (ENG.). 272p. 25.00 (978-1-4165-4729-7(0)) Atria Bks. (Beyond Words/Atria Bks.).
—Life Overflowing: 6 Pillars for Abundant Living. 2010. 448p. reprint ed. pap. 19.99 (978-0-7642-0798-3(9)) Bethany Hse. Pubs.
—Power for Living Tradepaper. 2009. 199p. 25.99 (978-0-7684-2838-4(6)); 335p. pap. (978-0-7684-2839-1(4)) Destiny Image Pubs.
—Release Your Anointing: Tapping the Power of the Holy Spirit in You. 2011. (ENG.). 254p. pap. 15.99 **(978-0-7684-2724-0(X))** 2008. 254p. 24.99 (978-0-7684-2654-0(5)) 2008. 190p. pap. 14.99 (978-0-7684-2655-7(3)) Destiny Image Pubs.
—Reposition Yourself Reflections: Living a Life Without Limits. 2008. (ENG.). 288p. pap. 15.00 (978-1-4165-4730-3(4), Beyond Words/Atria Bks.) Atria Bks.
—Reposition Yourself Reflections: Living a Life Without Limits. l.t. ed. 2008. (ENG.). 412p. (J). pap. 17.95 (978-1-59415-228-3(4), Walker Large Print) Cengage Gale.
—Strength for Every Moment. 2009. pap. 11.99 (978-0-7684-3130-8(1)) Destiny Image Pubs.
James, Demond. Let Love Reign. 2009. 72p. pap. 11.49 (978-1-4389-5561-2(8)) AuthorHouse.
James, Frank. The Choice Is Yours. 2007. 140p. (ENG.). 21.99 (978-1-60266-526-2(5)); per. 13.99 (978-1-60266-525-5(7)) Xulon Pr., Inc.
James, H. Large. The Local Church. 2011. 64p. pap. **(978-1-871642-32-2(9))** Gospel Folio Pr.
James, Joel. Help! I'm Confused about Dating. 2011. (Living in a Fallen World Ser.). 61p. pap. **(978-1-84625-247-1(4))** DayOne Pubns.
James, John Angell. Christian Progress. 2006. 272p. per. 23.99 (978-1-4255-2492-0(3)) MPublishing.
—Christian Progress: A Sequel to the Anxious Inquirer after Salvation. 2009. 276p. 34.99 (978-1-115-79376-6(4)); 30.99 (978-1-115-79377-3(2)); pap. 26.75 (978-1-115-79379-7(9)) BiblioBazaar.
—Christian Progress: A Sequel to the Anxious Inquirer after Salvation. 2007. (ENG.). 276p. 42.95 (978-0-548-10586-3(3)) Kessinger Publishing, LLC.
—A the True Christian Exemplified in a Series of Addresses From. 2007. (ENG.). 216p. per. 24.95 (978-1-4304-4552-4(1)) Kessinger Publishing, LLC.
—The True Christian, Exemplified in a Series of Addresses from a Pastor to His Own People. 2006. 216p. per. 20.99 (978-1-4255-1780-9(3)) MPublishing.
James, Nigel. Lessons from the Road. 2008. (ENG., Illus.). 200p. pap. 14.99 (978-1-934068-48-9(9)) Authentic Media.
James, Pastor Cyrus. The Power of Understanding the Bible. 2007. 80p. per. 16.95 (978-1-4241-8808-6(3)) PublishAmerica, Inc.
James-Roberson, Joyce E. I Can't Keep a Secret: God's Word Unfolds in Segments of Seven. 2007. 56p. per. 9.95 (978-0-595-45935-3(8)) iUniverse, Inc.
James, Thomas W. Be Reconciled! Meaningful Steps for Mending Relationships. 2007. 224p. per. 15.99 (978-0-9777053-7-5(4)) McDougal & Assocs.
James Twentier. I Must Be about My Father's Business- 2010. 344p. pap. 23.83 (978-1-4251-8169-7(4)) Trafford Publishing.
Jamieson, Alan. A Churchless Faith: Faith Journeys Beyond the Churches. 203p. 16.00 (978-0-281-05465-7(7)) SPCK Publishing GBR. Dist: Pilgrim Pr., The/United Church Pr.
Jamison, Christopher. Finding Happiness: Monastic Steps for a Fulfilling Life. 2009. 192p. 12.95 (978-0-8146-1878-3(2), Liturgical Pr. Bks.) Liturgical Pr.
Jamison-Tanchuck, F. No to Religion but Yes to God. 2009. 157p. pap. 12.99 (978-1-60604-828-3(7)) Tate Publishing & Enterprises, LLC.
Janda, Steven Andrew. The Emerald Home Run. 2011. 320p. pap. 29.95 **(978-1-60911-498-5(1)**, Strategic Bk. Publishing) AEG Literary Publishing Services, Inc.
Jane, Lisa. Angel Kisses: A Book of Comfort & Joy..., 0 vols. 2009. (Illus.). 112p. 17.99 (978-1-4041-8715-3(4)) Nelson, Thomas Inc.
Jantz, Gregory L. Gotta Have It! Freedom from Wanting Everything Right Here, Right Now. 2010. (ENG.). 272p. pap. 14.99 (978-1-4347-6624-3(1)) Cook, David C.
—How to de-Stress Your Life. 2008. 192p. 5.99 (978-0-8007-8769-1(2)) Revell.
Janway, Jolene (Butcher) & Mayfield, C. Ray. When the Cows Come Home. 2007. 136p. (ENG.). 21.99 (978-1-60477-238-8(7)); per. 13.99 (978-1-60477-237-1(9)) Xulon Pr., Inc.
Janz, Paul D. & Janz. Command of Grace: A New Theological Apologetics. 2009. (ENG.). 200p. 140.00 (978-0-567-03358-1(9), T&T Clark Int'l) Continuum International Publishing Group, Ltd. GBR. Dist: National Bk. Network.
Jaquith, Anna D. Some Things Matter... Some Things Don't: 30 Chats about Life. 2007. 192p. (YA). per. 16.99 (978-1-60185-050-8(6)) ABC Book Publishing.
Jarrard, Dan. O Lord Revive Thy Work. 2007. 133p. pap. 24.95 (978-1-4241-5050-2(7)) PublishAmerica, Inc.
Jarvis, Rose. Diamond ... A Girl's Best Friend: Lessons Learned from My Dog. 2010. 184p. pap. 14.99 (978-1-61579-802-5(1)) Xulon Pr., Inc.
Jasmine, Yvette. A Girl's Guide to Successful Living. 2009. pap. 10.99 (978-1-60791-872-1(2)) Xulon Pr., Inc.
Java, Becki. Imagine That! 2007. 208p. (ENG.). 24.99 (978-1-60266-414-2(5)); per. 14.99 (978-1-60266-413-5(7)) Xulon Pr., Inc.
Jay, Shana. Around the Corner from Hood. 2007. pap. 9.99 (978-1-60034-780-1(0)) Xulon Pr., Inc.
Jeckey, Yaw. The Word. 2006. 236p. per. 14.95 (978-1-59886-473-1(4)) Tate Publishing & Enterprises, LLC.
Jedadiah. The Perils of the Potter's Sons. 2008. 136p. pap. 10.99 (978-1-4389-0892-2(X)) AuthorHouse.
Jefferson, Lakeycia. Be Healed: Prophetic Prayers for Divine Healing. 2009. 35p. pap. 20.00 (978-0-557-13407-6(2)) Lulu Enterprises Inc.
—The Oath Protect & Defend: Prophetic Prayers for Soldiers. 2009. 43p. pap. 20.00 (978-0-557-17680-9(8)) Lulu Enterprises Inc.
Jeffery, Anna. Five Gold Rings: Powerful Influences on Prominent People. 160p. (978-0-232-52528-1(5)) Darton, Longman & Todd, Ltd.
Jeffery, Peter. All Things New. 2nd ed. 36p. (978-1-85049-003-6(1)) Whitaker Pr., The.
—All Things New: A Help for Those Beginning the Christian Life. 2008. 28p. pap. (978-1-85049-226-9(3)) Evangelical Pr.
—Meeting God: Past, Present & Future. 2007. 125p. pap. (978-0-85234-671-6(9)) Evangelical Pr.
—Moving Out: With the Christian Faith. 2007. 126p. per. (978-0-85234-609-9(3)) Evangelical Pr.
Jeffery, Sandra. Salvation for the Twenty-First Century & Beyond: A reference guide on Christian Ethics. 2010. pap. 18.95 (978-1-60494-407-5(2)) Wheatmark.
Jefferys, William H. The Mystical Companionship of Jesus. 2011. 86p. 37.95 **(978-1-258-04937-9(6))** Literary Licensing, LLC.
Jeffress, Robert. Clutter-Free Christianity: What God Really Desires for You. 2009. (ENG.). 208p. 13.99 (978-1-4000-7092-3(9), WaterBrook Pr.) Doubleday Religious Publishing Group, The.
—Second Chance, Second ACT: Turning Your Messes into Successes. 2007. (ENG.). 160p. per. 13.99 (978-1-4000-7091-6(0), WaterBrook Pr.) Doubleday Religious Publishing Group, The.
Jeffrey. Armageddon: Appointment with Destiny. pap. 12.95 (978-0-921714-00-2(9)) Spring Arbor Distributors, Inc.
Jeffries, Cheryl. Tools of the Believer: 10 Ways to Beat the Devil at His Own Game. 2007. 67p. per. 8.99 (978-1-60247-333-1(1)) Tate Publishing & Enterprises, LLC.
Jeffries, Josephine. Lost Soul. 2007. 280p. 25.99 (978-1-60477-175-6(5)); per. 15.99 (978-1-60477-174-9(7)) Xulon Pr., Inc.
Jegede, Olukayode. Victory Through Prayer. 2006. 180p. per. (978-1-894928-79-3(2)) Word Alive Pr.
Jelliff, Ernie. Just A Thought. 2010. 416p. pap. 22.99 (978-1-61579-834-6(X)) Xulon Pr., Inc.
Jenkins, Barry. Reigning As Kings. 2007. 184p. 21.99 (978-1-60266-333-5(5)); per. 13.99 (978-1-60266-332-9(7)) Xulon Pr., Inc.
Jenkins, David. Hospitality. 2007. 72p. pap. 12.00 (978-0-687-46681-8(4)); 64p. pap. 10.00 (978-0-687-46691-7(1)) Abingdon Pr.
Jenkins, Johnny. Sin Then & Now. 2007. per. 7.99 (978-1-60247-165-8(7)) Tate Publishing & Enterprises, LLC.
Jenkins, Terrance. Free Indeed: How to Be Free from Demonic Influence & Addictive Behaviors. 2006. (ENG.). 120p. per. 19.95 (978-1-4241-5042-7(6)) PublishAmerica, Inc.
Jenkins, Tonia. God Is Great: The Undeniable Truth - 52 Inspirations of Hope & Faith. 2010. (Little Book. Big Idea Ser.). (ENG.). 176p. pap. 15.00 (978-1-57826-292-2(5)) Hatherleigh Co., Ltd., The.
Jennings, Linda. Life Within the Veil. 2007. 200p. per. 14.99 (978-1-60266-403-6(X)) Xulon Pr., Inc.
Jennings, Susan. 100 K. I. S. S. es from God. 2010. 212p. pap. 20.00 (978-0-557-32720-1(2)) Lulu Enterprises Inc.
Jensen, Fred M. A Study of the Foundation of Justification. 2011. 214p. 29.99 **(978-1-4535-1137-4(7))**; pap. 19.99 **(978-1-4535-1136-7(9))** Xlibris Corp.
Jensen, Paul. Over the Edge into Truth. 2008. 148p. 19.99 (978-1-932503-76-0(5)) Insight Publishing Group.
Jensen, Paul & Hillard, Todd. Over the Edge into Truth. 2008. 148p. pap. 13.99 (978-1-932503-75-3(7)) Insight Publishing Group.
Jensen, Vern A. God Never Quits! 2011. 304p. pap. 18.99 **(978-1-61379-625-2(0))** Xulon Pr., Inc.
Jeremiah, David. Captured by Grace: No One Is Beyond the Reach of a Loving God, 0 vols. 2010. 240p. pap. 15.99 (978-0-8499-4616-5(6)) Nelson, Thomas Inc.
—Life-Changing Moments with God: Praying Scripture Every Day, 0 vols. 2007. 384p. im. lthr. 19.99 (978-1-4041-0387-0(2)) Nelson, Thomas Inc.
—Living with Confidence in a Chaotic World: What on Earth Should We Do Now?, 0 vols. 2010. 288p. pap. 15.99 (978-0-8499-4701-8(4)) 2009. 80p. pap. 9.99 (978-1-4185-4291-7(1)) Nelson, Thomas Inc.
—Sanctuary: Finding Moments of Refuge in the Presence of God. 2011. 400p. lthr. 19.99 (978-1-4003-1827-8(0)) Nelson, Thomas Inc.
—Slaying the Giants in Your Life, 0 vols. 2009. 240p. pap. 14.99 (978-0-7852-8960-9(7)) Nelson, Thomas Inc.
—Until Christ Returns: Living Faithfully Today While We Wait for Our Glorious Tomorrow, 0 vols. 2007. 224p. per. 14.99 (978-0-8499-1885-4(9)) Nelson, Thomas Inc.
—What in the World Is Going On? 10 Prophetic Clues You Cannot Afford to Ignore. l.t. ed. 2010. (ENG.). 384p. pap. 17.99 (978-1-59415-334-1(5)) Cengage Gale.
—What in the World Is Going On? 10 Prophetic Clues You Cannot Afford to Ignore, 0 vols. 2010. 288p. pap. 15.99 (978-0-7852-3117-2(X)) Nelson, Thomas Inc.
—Why the Nativity? 2009. (ENG.). 176p. pap. 9.99 (978-1-4143-3381-6(1)) Tyndale Hse. Pubs.
—The 12 Ways of Christmas, 0 vols. 2008. 128p. 14.99 (978-1-4041-8727-6(8)) Nelson, Thomas Inc.
Jeremiah, David. Living with Confidence in a Chaotic World: What on Earth Should We Do Now? l.t. ed. 2010. (ENG.). 384p. pap. 17.99 (978-1-59415-330-3(2)) Cengage Gale.
Jerubaal, Donovan & Jerubaal, Claire. The Day the Holy Spirit Blew In Vol. 1: Man Eater. 2009. 248p. pap. 15.99 (978-1-60791-878-3(1)) Xulon Pr., Inc.
Jesse, Mark A. Time of Grace: A Devotional Companion. 2010. 394p. 19.99 (978-0-7586-1913-6(8)) Concordia Publishing Hse.
Jesse, Omangbon I. Christianity! 2011. 52p. pap. 15.99 **(978-1-4568-7618-0(X))** Xlibris Corp.
Jesus, Angel B. How to Be an Angel. 2011. 208p. pap. 17.95 (978-1-4502-9086-9(8)) iUniverse, Inc.
"Jesus Got My Soul Out of Hock" pap. 12.95 (978-1-58784-065-4(0)) Survivors of Assault Recovery (SOAR).
The Jesus of Historical Interpretation. 24.00 (978-0-687-34214-3(7)) Abingdon Pr.
Jeter, Celia Stark. For Love of the Truth. 2011. pap. 20.95 **(978-0-7414-6162-9(5))** Infinity Publishing.
Jethe, Scott. Corps Wisdom: A Field Manual for Life. 2007. (ENG.). 132p. per. 14.99 (978-1-4141-0674-8(2)) Pleasant Word.
Jeub, Chris & Jeub, Wendy. Love Another Child: Children. They're blessings. Always. 2011. 148p. 30.95 (978-1-4497-1065-1(4)); pap. 13.95 (978-1-4497-1063-7(8)) Author Solutions, Inc. (WestBow Pr.).
Jeynes, William. Getting Closer to God. 2009. (978-1-60752-147-1(4)); pap. (978-1-60752-146-4(6)) Information Age Publishing, Inc.
Jimenez, Alvaro. 30 Celebraciones De La Palabra. 16p. 4.95 (978-958-607-944-0(9)) Sociedad de San Pablo COL. Dist: St Pauls/Alba Hse. Pubs.
Jimerson-Overholt, Suzy, ed. Choice: A Simple Way to Peace. 2007. 87p. pap. 21.95 (978-0-9793301-2-4(2)) Evolving Journeys Publishing Hse.
Jinkins, Michael. Called to Be Human: Letters to My Children on Living a Christian Life. 2009. 160p. pap. 15.00 (978-0-8028-6300-3(0)) Eerdmans, William B. Publishing Co.
—Invitation to Psalms. ldr.'s ed. 2008. (Short-Term Disciple Bible Studies). 56p. per. 13.65 (978-0-687-65091-0(7)) Abingdon Pr.
Jiosa, Susan Taber. The Storm Master: Letting God Take Control, 1 vol. 2009. 124p. pap. 19.95 (978-1-60836-250-9(7)) PublishAmerica, Inc.
Joanna. Are Christians the Hitlers of Today? 2009. 208p. pap. 15.99 (978-1-60791-478-5(6)) Xulon Pr., Inc.
Joo. Living Fully, Dying Well - Talking to Your Child about Life & Death, 12 pack. 2006. 13.00 (978-0-687-49051-6(0)) Abingdon Pr.
—Living Fully, Dying Well - Talking to Your Family about End of Life Issues. 2006. 13.00 (978-0-687-33366-0(0)) Abingdon Pr.
—Visiting & Supporting Friends Facing Death, 12, Pack. 2006. 13.00 (978-0-687-49061-5(8)) Abingdon Pr.
Job, Rueben. Living Fully, Dying Well. ldr.'s ed. 2006. 67p. per. 26.00 (978-0-687-46670-2(9)) Abingdon Pr.
Job, Rueben P. Living Fully, Dying Well. 2006. 41.00 (978-0-687-33356-1(3)) Abingdon Pr.
Jobe, Anthony. Blocked Blessings the Onesimus Factor. 2008. 88p. pap. 9.99 (978-1-60477-973-8(X)) Xulon Pr., Inc.
John (Jd) Zumwalt. Fairytale Christianity: Living as a Christian in the REAL World. 2009. 200p. pap. 16.95 (978-1-4401-7528-2(4)) iUniverse, Inc.
John, Jean. When God Intervenes. 2009. 80p. pap. 10.49 (978-1-4490-3859-5(X)) AuthorHouse.
John, Mevogheneobo. God's Kingdom Prosperity. 2010. 108p. pap. 10.99 (978-1-4520-7296-8(5)); 21.49 (978-1-4520-7297-5(3)) AuthorHouse.
John Paul II, pseud. Dies Domini. 96p. pap. 4.95 (978-0-8198-4486-6(1), 332-168) Pauline Bks. & Media.

C

—Stay with Us Lord. 32p. pap. 3.50 (978-0-8198-4839-0(5), 332-227) Pauline Bks. & Media.
—To the Elderly. 40p. pap. 2.50 (978-0-8198-4488-0(8), 332-169) Pauline Bks. & Media.
John, Philip. God in Christ & the Fabulous Bible. 2008. 200p. pap. 19.99 (978-1-4251-5280-2(5)) Trafford Publishing.
Johnny. Snatched. 2008. 49p. pap. 16.95 (978-1-60474-854-3(0)) PublishAmerica, Inc.
Johns, C. K. It's All in Our Heads. 2007. 112p. per. 10.99 (978-1-60266-236-0(3)) Xulon Pr., Inc.
Johns, Monique W. No More Drama in My Life. 2011. 140p. pap. 15.95 (978-1-4567-2926-4(8)) AuthorHouse.
Johnson, Adam. Adam's E-Mail Network. 2008. 63p. pap. 16.95 (978-1-60563-243-8(0)) PublishAmerica, Inc.
Johnson, Alisa Miller. Divine Moments: Letters of Encouragement. 2009. 128p. pap. (978-1-55452-385-6(0), Guardian Bks.) Essence Publishing.
Johnson, Andrew. Believe Again: A Journey Back to Faith: Book I. 2010. 104p. pap. 11.95 (978-1-4502-5663-6(5)) iUniverse, Inc.
Johnson, Annette. What's Your Motivation? Identifying & Understanding What Drives You. 2nd ed. 2010. 222p. pap. 14.95 (978-0-9744935-1-0(1)) AllWrite Advertising & Publishing.
Johnson, Anthony. To Be Determined. 2007. 164p. per. 13.99 (978-1-60477-191-6(7)) Xulon Pr., Inc.
Johnson, Barbara. The Joy Journal, 0 vols. 2009. 178p. pap. 12.99 (978-1-4002-7810-7(4)) Nelson, Thomas Inc.
—When Your Child Breaks Your Heart: Help for Hurting Moms. 2008. 176p. 5.99 (978-0-8007-8775-2(7)) Revell.
Johnson, Beni. The Happy Intercessor. 2009. 199p. pap. 16.99 (978-0-7684-2753-0(3)) Destiny Image Pubs.
Johnson, Bill. La Liberación de lo Sobrenatural: El testimonio de Jesus. 2010.Tr. of Release the Power of Jesus. (SPA.). 144p. pap. 13.99 (978-987-557-284-3(5)) Peniel, Editorial ARG. Dist: Destiny Image Pubs.
—Release the Power of Jesus. 2009. 199p. pap. 16.99 (978-0-7684-2712-7(6)) Destiny Image Pubs.
—Secrets to Imitating God: How to Redesign Your World. 2009. 199p. pap. 15.99 (978-0-7684-2828-5(9)) Destiny Image Pubs.
Johnson, Bradley C. Removing the Graveclothes: Removing hindrances inorder to pursue the Kingdom Agenda. 2009. 80p. pap. 10.95 (978-1-4401-2809-7(X)) iUniverse, Inc.
Johnson, Carmen. From the Heart: A Collection of Short Essays. 2008. 92p. pap. 15.00 (978-0-9786088-6-6(0)) True Vine Publishing Co.
Johnson, Claire. From His Heart to Our Heart. 2011. 108p. pap. 11.25 **(978-1-4567-2826-7(1))** AuthorHouse.
Johnson, Constance S. The Still Small Voice of God. 2010. pap. 15.99 (978-1-61566-774-1(1)) Tate Publishing & Enterprises, LLC.
Johnson-Coverley, Dianne L. My Heart Is Filled with Praise. 2007. pap. 9.99 (978-1-60266-884-3(1)) Xulon Pr., Inc.
Johnson, Dale A. A Rule for Community. 2009. 133p. pap. 12.96 (978-0-557-07171-5(2)) Lulu Enterprises Inc.
—Why Should We Care? 2007. 164p. pap. 19.95 (978-0-615-15415-2(8)) New Sinai Pr.
Johnson, David Lawther. Learning from My Father: Lessons on Life & Faith. 2012. pap. **(978-0-8028-6708-7(1))** Eerdmans, William B. Publishing Co.
Johnson, Dewayne. Born Again... Now What? 2011. pap. 20.99 **(978-1-61777-381-5(6))** Tate Publishing & Enterprises, LLC.
Johnson, D.M. If I Can... So Can You!!! 2009. 104p. pap. 14.95 (978-1-4327-3566-1(7)) Outskirts Pr., Inc.
Johnson, Dora E. To God's Ways from Britchier. pap. 10.99 (978-0-533-14421-1(3)) Vantage Pr., Inc.
Johnson, Florence. Speak the Word Only. 2011. 152p. pap. 17.13 **(978-1-4567-7590-2(1))** AuthorHouse.
Johnson, Granvel D. Notes to Our Sons for the Journey from Childhood to Manhood. 2010. 124p. pap. 13.99 (978-1-60957-398-0(6)) Xulon Pr., Inc.
Johnson, Gregory. The Armor of God. 2009. 79p. pap. 11.99 (978-0-557-04176-3(7)) Lulu Enterprises Inc.
Johnson, Gregory. Real Men Do Talk. 2011. 38p. pap. 16.95 **(978-1-4560-5189-1(X))** PublishAmerica, Inc.
Johnson, Ian. Our Oneness in Christ. 2006. (ENG.). 204p. per. 24.95 (978-1-4241-6035-8(9)) PublishAmerica, Inc.
Johnson, Jan. Surrendering Hunger: 365 Devotions for Wholeness. 15th rev. anniv. ed. 2009. (ENG.). 293p. (gr. 12). pap. 16.99 (978-1-55725-636-2(5)) Paraclete Pr., Inc.
Johnson, Jeffrey A. Making A Comeback. 2008. 212p. pap. 15.99 (978-1-60647-665-9(3)) Xulon Pr., Inc.
Johnson, Jeffrey D. Are You Crazy? A Good Look at Jeff & Louise. 2007. (Illus.). 40p. pap. 4.00 (978-1-55635-079-5(1), Wipf and Stock) Wipf & Stock Pubs.
Johnson, Jennifer. Dead Man Walking: Craig's story of God's amazing gift of Life! 2009. pap. 11.99 (978-1-60791-209-5(0)) Xulon Pr., Inc.
Johnson, Jessica McGregor. Remembering Perfection - Everyday Inspiration for Living Your Spirituality. 2008. 268p. pap. (978-1-905823-45-1(2)) Academy Pr. Ltd.
Johnson, Jomo K. God's Trophy. 2009. 155p. pap. 10.00 (978-0-557-11369-9(5)) Lulu Enterprises Inc.
Johnson Jr., David. Break Free from Your Breach Birth. 2008. 88p. pap. 10.99 (978-1-60647-772-4(2)) Xulon Pr., Inc.
Johnson, Judy. Get in the Ark. 2012. 76p. pap. 10.95 **(978-0-609-20021-6(6))** Ajoyin Publishing, Inc.
Johnson, Kasey. 7 Ways to Be a S. M. A. R. T. E. R. Mom. 2010. (ENG.). 192p. pap. 14.99 (978-0-8341-2552-0(8), 9780834125520) Beacon Hill Pr. of Kansas City.
Johnson, Ken. Life2: The Secret to Limitless Living. 2008. (ENG.). 144p. pap. 11.99 (978-1-59979-294-1(X), Creation Hse.) Charisma Media.
Johnson, Kevin. Choose: Steer Wide of Total Stupidity, 1 vol. 2007. (Deeper Ser.). (ENG., Illus.). 112p. pap. 7.99 (978-0-310-27493-3(1)) Zondervan.
—Follow: Walk in the Rhythm of Jesus, 1 vol. 2009. (Higher Ser.). (ENG.). 112p. pap. 8.99 (978-0-310-28264-8(0)) Zondervan.
—Soar, 1 vol. 2009. (Higher Ser.). (ENG.). 112p. pap. 8.99 (978-0-310-28267-9(5)) Zondervan.
—Thrive, 1 vol. 2009. (Higher Ser.). (ENG.). 112p. pap. 8.99 (978-0-310-28265-5(9)) Zondervan.
Johnson, Kevin A. Dust Collector: Experiencing the God Who Collects Worthless Things & Makes Them into Great Things in His Hands & for His Purpose. 2010. 144p. pap. (978-1-57736-426-9(0)) Providence Hse Pubs.
Johnson, Lynn. Healing the Kingdom Black Priest. 2010. 22.99 (978-1-61579-713-4(0)); 176p. pap. 14.99 (978-1-61579-712-7(2)) Xulon Pr., Inc.
Johnson, M. A. God's Economy: The Truth about Money - 10 Principles for Prosperity 10 Sins to Poverty. 2009. 108p. 19.99 (978-1-60791-722-9(X)); pap. 11.99 (978-1-60791-721-2(1)) Xulon Pr., Inc.
Johnson, Mary. Ministering One to Another. 2007. 148p. per. 13.99 (978-1-60266-755-6(1)) Xulon Pr., Inc.
Johnson, Myrtle. God Is My Witness. 2007. per. (978-1-59581-368-8(3), Brentwood Christian Pr.) Brentwood Communications Group.
Johnson, Nicole. Dramatic Encounters with God: Seven Life-Changing Lessons of Love. 2011. 144p. pap. 14.99 **(978-1-4002-7822-0(8))** Nelson, Thomas Inc.
Johnson, Norma Lou. From Visions of Grandeur - To Depths of Despair: Help! Is Anyone Out There? 2009. 72p. pap. 10.99 (978-1-61579-300-6(3)) Xulon Pr., Inc.
Johnson, Renee D. Franklin. Yes, Lord! Now, What? 2007. 108p. per. 10.99 (978-1-60477-189-3(5)) Xulon Pr., Inc.
Johnson, Sr. The Song of Solomon Study Guide. 2007. 120p. per. 12.99 (978-1-60266-528-6(1)) Xulon Pr., Inc.
Johnson Sr., Jeffrey A. & Omnimedia Group LLC, Glm. Dialogue with My Daughters. 2011. (ENG.). 182p. pap. 14.99 **(978-0-9838328-5-0(4))** St. Paul Pr.
Johnson, Teresa S. The Land Flowing with Milk & Honey. 2009. 136p. pap. 13.95 (978-1-4401-2853-0(7)) iUniverse, Inc.
Johnson, Tim. My Problem God: The Story of My Battle to Overcome Bone Marrow Cancer. 2009. 144p. pap. 14.99 (978-1-60791-691-8(6)) Xulon Pr., Inc.
Johnson, Vernon. One Lord, One Faith. 2008. 164p. pap. 13.95 (978-1-58617-199-5(2)) Ignatius Pr.
Johnston, E. Masters Plan. 2006. pap. (978-1-897117-42-2(6)) Gospel Folio Pr.
Johnston, Jody. Legacy of a Woman's Heart: How Will You Be Remembered? 2007. 113p. per. 14.99 (978-0-924748-75-2(3)) Milestones International Publishers.
Johnston, Joe. JWR: Jesus Would Recycle. 2008. 134p. pap. (978-0-922067-96-1(1)) Johnston Music Group.
Johnston, Kurt. God's Story: Growing in Your Faith Ten Minutes at a Time. 2009. (10 Minute Moments Ser.). 94p. pap. 6.99 (978-0-7644-6231-3(8)) Group Publishing, Inc.
Johnston-Rank. Como Aumentar Ingresos y Triunfar: How to Increase Your Earnings. (SPA.). (978-84-7645-162-5(8), 223203) Clie, Editorial.
Joiner, Reggie. The Orange Leader Handbook: A Think Orange Companion. 2010. (ENG.). 192p. pap., wbk. ed. 16.99 (978-1-4347-6435-5(4)) Cook, David C.
Joiner, Reggie, et al. The Slow Fade: Why You Matter in the Story of Twentysomethings. 2010. (Orange Ser.). (ENG.). 176p. pap. 14.99 (978-1-4347-6479-9(6)) Cook, David C.
Joly, Henri. The Psychology of the Saints. 2009. 98p. pap. 19.99 (978-1-4589-3461-1(6)) General Bks. LLC.
—The Psychology of the Saints. 2007. (ENG.). 212p. 39.95 (978-0-548-08390-1(8)) Kessinger Publishing, LLC.
Jonas, Dwight E. Food for the Soul. 2011. 162p. pap. 14.99 **(978-1-61379-834-8(2))** Xulon Pr., Inc.
Jonathon, Susan. The Sword of the Lily: Expanding Out Capacity to Love. Chosa, Jim, ed. 150p. per. (978-0-9672360-1-8(0)) Second Time Clothiers, Inc.
Jones, Barry Wayne. Where Is MY Money?, 1 vol. 2009. 56p. pap. 16.95 (978-1-4489-2282-6(8)) PublishAmerica, Inc.
Jones, Bret. Keepers at Home: A Study. 2008. 60p. pap. 16.95 (978-1-60703-981-5(8)) PublishAmerica, Inc.
Jones, Brian & Chiapperino, Frank. Getting Rid of the Gorilla Group Member Discussion Guide. 2008. (Illus.). 48p. pap., instr.'s gde. ed. 6.99 (978-0-7847-2163-6(7)) Standard Publishing.
Jones, Charles & Crisp, Mary. So? Whatever! 365 Laughs & Devotionals. 2010. 388p. pap. 24.95 (978-1-61507-176-0(8)) Cross Bks. Publishing.
Jones, Cleven L. Genesis & Life. 2010. 268p. pap. 16.99 (978-1-60957-829-9(5)) Xulon Pr., Inc.
Jones, Conrad. 8 Simple Keys to Unlocking Your Unique Greatness. 2007. 120p. per. 10.99 (978-1-60266-881-2(7)) Xulon Pr., Inc.
Jones, David. Humble Is the Way. 2007. 208p. per. 15.99 (978-0-9777053-6-8(6)) McDougal & Assocs.
—My Struggle, Your Struggle. 2007. 220p. per. 14.99 (978-1-60477-298-2(0)) Xulon Pr., Inc.
Jones, Deanna. The Faith Aren. 2007. 192p. per. 13.99 (978-1-60034-960-7(9)) Xulon Pr., Inc.
Jones, Debby & Kendall, Jackie. The Young Lady in Waiting: Developing the Heart of a Princess. 2008. 292p. pap. 9.99 (978-0-7684-2657-1(X)) Destiny Image Pubs.
Jones, Dennis R. Climbing Out of Adversity: A Story of Life's Lessons to Encourage the Heart, Awaken the Church, & Challenge the Nation. 2011. xi, 257p. E-Book **(978-1-61638-465-4(4))** Excel Bks.
Jones, Doris S. Satan's Best Kept Secret. 2008. 96p. pap. 12.95 (978-1-58169-291-4(9)) Genesis Communications, Inc.
Jones, Doug. Positioning Yourself to Receive Healing. 109p. 7.95 (978-0-89276-965-0(3), 965) Faith Library Pubns., Inc.
—Understanding the Healing Power of God. 138p. 7.95 (978-0-89276-964-3(5), 964) Faith Library Pubns., Inc.
Jones, Duane. Jesus Was a Middle Schooler Too. 2007. 84p. per. 9.99 (978-1-60477-011-7(2)) Xulon Pr., Inc.
Jones, Dwayne A. Thinking with the Wrong Head. 2009. 100p. pap. 14.95 (978-1-4120-0676-7(7)) Trafford Publishing.
Jones, Dwight. Destined to Soar. 2009. 180p. pap. 14.99 (978-1-934769-21-8(5)) McDougal & Assocs.
Jones, Gerald. Speak Those Things. 2007. 116p. per. (978-1-55452-210-1(2)); 112p. (978-1-55452-141-8(6), Guardian Bks.) Essence Publishing.
Jones, Juanita. Water Out of the Wells of Salvation. 2007. 168p. per. 14.99 (978-1-4141-0597-0(5)) Pleasant Word.
Jones, K. Biblical Emergency Leadership for First Responders. 2007. 108p. per. 16.95 (978-1-4241-9771-2(6)) PublishAmerica, Inc.
Jones, Kathleen & Eubank, Maureen. God's Word Day upon Day: Devotions for Every Season of Your Life. 2010. spiral bd. 29.99 (978-1-61566-824-3(1)) Tate Publishing & Enterprises, LLC.
Jones, Khandi. If He did it for me, He'll do it for You! 2008. 35p. pap. 8.95 (978-1-4357-3236-0(7)) Lulu Enterprises Inc.
Jones-Kimberlin, Linda. Turn up the Light. 2007. (ENG.). 76p. per. 16.95 (978-1-4241-7353-2(1)) PublishAmerica, Inc.
Jones, Kirk Byron. Holy Play: The Joyful Adventure of Unleashing Your Divine Purpose. annot. ed. 2007. (ENG.). 208p. 21.95 (978-0-7879-8452-6(3), Jossey-Bass) Wiley, John & Sons, Inc.
Jones, Lesia M. Don't Settle for Less Than What He Has for You. 2007. 100p. pap. 9.95 (978-0-615-15476-3(X)) Jones, Lesia M.
Jones, Lonetha. Master, Because You Say So I Will Do It: A Message of Hope & Encouragement. 2009. 46p. pap. 10.95 (978-1-4327-3034-5(7)) Outskirts Pr., Inc.
Jones, Marlene Stewart. Sacred Memories. 2011. 496p. 34.99 **(978-1-4568-4583-4(7))**; pap. 23.99 **(978-1-4568-4582-7(9))** Xlibris Corp.
Jones, Michael Glen. Me, God, & Our Walk: Walking in Faith in the Face of Adversity. 2007. 136p. per. 24.95 (978-1-4241-6883-5(X)) PublishAmerica, Inc.
Jones, Michael O. Agape. l.t. ed. 2007. 36p. 9.95 (978-0-9792074-6-4(0)) Kingdom Publishing Group, Inc.
Jones, Nick & Jones. Adams Dream: Human longings & the love of God. 2008. (ENG., Illus.). 160p. 19.95 (978-1-906286-10-1(8)) Mowbray, A. R. & Co., Ltd. GBR. Dist: National Bk. Network.
Jones, Noel. The Battle for the Mind: How You Can Think the Thoughts of God. 2006. 189p. per. 15.99 (978-0-7684-2374-7(0)) Destiny Image Pubs.
—Battle for the Mind Kit: How You Can Think the Thoughts of God/ Multimedia Personal Development Kit: How You Can Think the Thoughts of God/ Multimedia Personal Development Kit. 2007. pap. 99.99 (978-0-7684-2604-5(9)) Destiny Image Pubs.
Jones, R. B. Rent Heavens. pap. 2.99 (978-1-56632-080-1(1)) Revival Literature.
Jones, Robert D. Freedom from Resentment: Stopping Hurts from Turning Bitter. 2010. 24p. 3.99 (978-1-935273-66-0(3)) New Growth Pr.
—Single Parents: Daily Grace for the Hardest Job. 2008. (ENG.). 24p. 3.99 (978-1-934885-27-7(4)) New Growth Pr.
Jones, Rufus M. Some Problems of Life. 2007. (ENG.). 216p. 39.95 (978-0-548-10284-8(8)) Kessinger Publishing, LLC.
Jones, Sam. Breaking the Spirit of Addiction. 2007. 116p. per. 10.99 (978-1-60266-133-2(2)) Xulon Pr., Inc.
Jones, Samuel G. Revealed: Discovering God's Will for Our Lives. 2011. pap. 12.99 **(978-1-61777-527-7(4))** Tate Publishing & Enterprises, LLC.
Jones, Sharise. Just Do You! 2007. 84p. per. 9.99 (978-1-60266-215-5(0)) Xulon Pr., Inc.
Jones, Sharon. She Found It in the Clouds. 2007. 160p. per. 11.99 (978-1-4276-1905-1(0)) Witty Publishing.
Jones, Shiela. Pillow Talk. 2007. 80p. per. 9.99 (978-1-60266-128-8(6)) Xulon Pr., Inc.
Jones Sr., Carl L. It Isn't the Jefferson Bible. 2009. 266p. pap. 23.99 (978-0-9748266-6-0(9)) Grampa Jones's Publishing Co.
Jones, T. In the Future Will You Be Stamped by the Mark? 2011. 22p. pap. 16.95 **(978-1-4560-3711-6(0))** PublishAmerica, Inc.
Jones, Thomas A. Mind Change Moments. 2009. 197p. pap. 12.00 (978-1-57782-242-4(0)) Discipleship Pubns. International.
Jones, Tonya Christine. God Said; Trust Me. 2008. 116p. pap. 9.99 (978-0-9798890-1-1(4)) Encourage Pr.
Joosse, Andrew. Living Grace. 2007. 140p. per. (978-1-897373-04-0(X)) Word Alive Pr.
Jordan, E. Bernard. The Laws of Thinking: 20 Secrets to Using the Divine Power of Your Mind to Manifest Prosperity. 2007. (ENG.). 256p. 24.95 (978-1-4019-1796-8(8)) Hay Hse., Inc.
Jordan, Joe. Excellence in the Gifts of the Holy Spirit. 2007. pap. 13.99 (978-1-60266-229-2(0)) Xulon Pr., Inc.
—Hangin' Out with God: A Personal Journey into the World of Joy. 2008. 92p. pap. 10.99 (978-1-60791-206-4(6)) Xulon Pr., Inc.
Jordan-Lake, Joy. Why Jesus Makes Me Nervous: Ten Alarming Words of Faith. 2007. 159p. per. 15.95 (978-1-55725-520-4(2)) Paraclete Pr., Inc.
Jordan, Leslie. O Taste & See That the Lord Is Good. 2008. 112p. pap. 11.99 (978-1-4389-3553-9(6)) AuthorHouse.
Jordan, Marcia. Will You Trust Me, Even If ? 2007. 180p. per. 13.99 (978-1-60266-136-3(7)) Xulon Pr., Inc.
Jordan, Marian. The List: Figuring Out Prince Charming, the Corner Office, & Happily Ever After, 1 vol. 2009. (ENG.). 176p. pap. 11.99 (978-0-8054-4671-5(0), B&H Bks.) B&H Publishing Group.
Jordan, Phil. Make Winning Happen. 2007. pap. 19.95 (978-0-9796130-3-6(5)) Kingdom Publishing Group, Inc.
Jordan, Sharon L. Living a 5-Star Life by Design. 2008. 152p. pap. 13.99 (978-1-60647-394-8(8)) Xulon Pr., Inc.
Joseph, Angela. Women for all Seasons: Biblical Examples for Every Season of Your Life. 2010. 104p. pap. 13.95 (978-1-4327-6042-7(4)) Outskirts Pr., Inc.
Joseph B Griffo & Pastor Lee Herring. The Master's Way. 2011. 110p. pap. 19.99 **(978-1-4628-6858-2(4))** Xlibris Corp.
Joseph, Emile P. The Powerless Church of Jesus Christ: A Man's Journey from Skepticism to Resolution. 2009. (J). pap. 14.99 (978-1-60799-819-8(X)) Tate Publishing & Enterprises, LLC.
Joseph, Willie. What Spirit Do You Have. 2009. 48p. pap. 16.95 (978-1-61546-243-8(0)) PublishAmerica, Inc.
Josephs, Denise. Life 101: Keeping It Real. 2006. pap. 15.99 (978-1-60034-323-0(6)) Xulon Pr., Inc.
Joshua Micheal (.The4th), Patros. Concrete Without Threat. 2011. 50p. pap. 15.99 **(978-1-4568-3664-1(1))** Xlibris Corp.
Joyner, Rick. Breaking the Power of Evil. 2008. 334p. pap. 15.99 (978-0-7684-2618-2(9)) Destiny Image Pubs.
—La Busqueda Final, 1 vol. 2008.Tr. of Final Quest. (SPA.). 208p. (gr. 13). per. 4.99 (978-987-557-170-9(9)) Peniel, Editorial ARG. Dist: Zondervan.
—Overcoming Evil in the Last Days: Expanded Edition with Study Guide. 2009. pap. 16.99 (978-0-7684-2833-9(5)) Destiny Image Pubs.
—Visions of the Harvest. 2010. (ENG.). 232p. pap. 16.99 (978-0-7684-3150-6(6)) Destiny Image Pubs.
—Visions of the Harvest. 2007. 125p. mass mkt. 8.99 (978-1-59933-121-8(7)) MorningStar Pubns., Inc.
—Wisdom from Rick Joyner. 2010. (ENG.). 21.99 (978-0-7684-3255-8(3)); (gr. 6). pap. 16.99 (978-0-7684-3287-9(1)) Destiny Image Pubs.
Joyner, Rick & Williams, Karen Jean. The Journey Begins Study Guide. 2009. 136p. pap. 11.99 (978-1-59933-752-4(5)) MorningStar Pubns., Inc.
Juckett, Michael. Serenity of James. 2010. pap. 23.99 (978-1-61663-193-2(7)) Tate Publishing & Enterprises, LLC.
Jude, Lilian. Untold Legend of the Bat Man. 2010. 86p. pap. 15.99 (978-1-4500-5997-8(X)) Xlibris Corp.
Judkins, Joe. Circle of Submission. 2010. 100p. pap. 9.95 (978-1-935105-65-7(5)) Avid Readers Publishing Group.
Juknialis, Joseph J. Fifteen-Minute Retreats to Slow down Your World. 2008. 135p. pap. 12.95 (978-1-58459-377-5(6)) World Library Pubns.
Julian. Revelations of Divine Love. Warrack, Grace, ed. 2010. 292p. 35.16 **(978-1-169-31279-1(9))**; pap. 23.16 **(978-1-162-61919-4(8))** Kessinger Publishing, LLC.
Julian & Julian. Revelations of Divine Love. Warrack, Grace, ed. 2010. 292p. 43.95 (978-1-161-40236-0(5)) Kessinger Publishing, LLC.
Julian & Warrack, Grace Harriet. Revelations of Divine Love. 2010. 346p. pap. 32.75 (978-1-145-32826-6(1)) BiblioBazaar.
Julian, Of Norwich. Revelations of Divine Love. 2010. (Illus.). 94p. pap. 15.67 (978-1-154-83419-2(0)) General Bks. LLC.
Juliano, Carroll, et al. Facing Forgiveness: A Catholic's Guide to Letting Go of Anger & Welcoming Reconciliation. 2007. 127p. per. 10.95 (978-1-59471-122-0(4)) Ave Maria Pr.
Julie. Spiritual Fruit, Gifts, Works & Callings: Growing Your Fruit. 2011. 152p. pap. 16.95 **(978-1-4520-9886-9(7))** AuthorHouse.
Julius, Prince. You Are Valuable. 2008. 140p. pap. 14.99 (978-1-60647-717-5(X)) Xulon Pr., Inc.
Juma, Florence Akumu. All Things Work Together for Good. 2010. (978-1-926676-97-5(1)) Word Alive Pr.
Jumelle, Jean Raymond. In the Shadow of Love. 2011. 184p. 25.99 **(978-1-61379-680-1(3))** Xulon Pr., Inc.
Jung, L. Shannon. Sharing Food: Christian Practices for Enjoyment. 2006. (Illus.). 176p. per. 16.00 (978-0-8006-3792-7(5), Fortress Pr.) Augsburg Fortress, Pubs.
Jungel, Eberhard. God as the Mystery of the World: On the Foundation of the Theology of the Crucified One in the Dispute Between Theism & Atheism. Guder, Darrell L., tr. 2009. 430p. pap. 51.00 (978-1-60608-494-6(1), Wipf and Stock) Wipf & Stock Pubs.
Jurino, Diane. Marching Orders from the King: Hearing from God as We Usher in His Kingdom. 2009. 96p. pap. 16.95 (978-1-61546-781-5(5)) PublishAmerica, Inc.

Juster, Patricia. The Cry: To Rend the Heavens, Release Grace, & Prepare the Way of the Lord. 2010. pap. 11.99 (978-1-61739-008-1(9)) Tate Publishing & Enterprises, LLC.

Justine, Irene F. Pastor What's My Calling? 2008. 76p. pap. 9.99 (978-1-60647-110-4(4)) Xulon Pr., Inc.

Kabala, Charles T. The Bible: The Word of God. 2009. pap. 7.50 (978-1-61623-127-9(0)) Independent Pub.

—The Bible: The word of God Preserved. 2009. pap. 5.00 (978-1-61584-404-3(X)) Independent Pub.

Kacvinsky, Kevin M. & Herenchar, Sara Maria. Transforming Truths: Dating, Sex, & Sexuality in Light of the Culture of Life. 2008. 120p. 18.99 (978-1-60647-157-9(0)); pap. 10.99 (978-1-60266-818-8(3)) Xulon Pr., Inc.

Kahl, George. Revive Your Life! 2011. 140p. 28.95 **(978-1-4497-1857-2(4))**; pap. 11.95 **(978-1-4497-1358-9(2))** Author Solutions, Inc. (WestBow Pr.).

Kainer, Gordon. Grace & the Great Controversy. 2010. 228p. pap. 14.95 (978-0-557-55048-7(3)) Lulu Enterprises Inc.

Kaithamangalam, Thomson. Hello Rachel I am Jacob. 2010. 202p. pap. 15.99 (978-1-60957-560-1(1)) Xulon Pr., Inc.

Kaitholil, George. The Prayer Called Life. pap. 4.95 (978-0-8189-7021-4(9)) St Pauls/Alba Hse. Pubs.

Kalas, J. Ellsworth. God's Promises That Keep Us. 2010. 144p. pap. 14.95 (978-1-4267-1003-2(8)) Abingdon Pr.

Kalb, Gerald D. Reflections on a Christian Life: Sermon Nuggets & Brief Devotions from the Heartland. 2008. 116p. pap. 12.95 (978-0-595-45588-1(3)) iUniverse, Inc.

Kalellis, Peter M. Letting Go of the Baggage: A Journey Through Life's Challenges. 2007. 180p. per. 16.95 (978-0-8091-4494-5(6)) Paulist Pr.

—Why Have You Abandoned Me? Discovering God's Presence When a Father Is Absent. 2011. (ENG.). 240p. pap. 19.95 (978-0-8245-2628-3(7)) Crossroad Publishing Co., The.

Kaler, Daniel. Million Dollar Kick. 2007. 144p. per. 13.99 (978-1-60266-641-2(5)) Xulon Pr., Inc.

Kalsbeck, Deb. Eighteen Things That Zap Your Strength: Or How to Fizzle Out Faster. 2009. 84p. pap. 10.99 (978-1-61579-158-3(2)) Xulon Pr., Inc.

Kalu, Hyacinth. The Word Took Flesh: Incarnating the Christian Message in Igbo Land of Nigeria in the Light of Vatican II's Theology of Inculturation. 2011. 112p. pap. 10.95 **(978-1-4620-2540-4(4))** iUniverse, Inc.

Kamese, Donald. Mission Possible. 2011. 152p. pap. 25.50 **(978-1-4461-8143-0(X))** Lulu Enterprises Inc.

Kaminski, Rita. Flying with Ravens, 1 vol. 2009. 165p. pap. 24.95 (978-1-60836-445-9(3)) PublishAmerica, Inc.

Kammerer, Gaye. Don't Ever Say There's Not a Santa Claus, 1 vol. 2010. 198p. pap. 24.95 (978-1-4512-1402-4(2)) PublishAmerica, Inc.

Kampmann, Eric. Signposts: A Devotional. 2010. pap. 15.95 (978-1-935071-30-3(0)) WND Bks, Inc.

Kanaly, Pam. Will the Real Me Please Stand up - Let's Go Deeper: Companion Workbook. 2010. pap. 13.99 (978-1-61566-667-6(2)) Tate Publishing & Enterprises, LLC.

Kandiah, Krish. Destiny: What's Life All About?, 1 vol. 2008. (Illus.). 144p. pap. 10.99 (978-0-8254-6180-4(4), Monarch Bks.) Lion Hudson PLC GBR. Dist: Kregel Pubns.

Kandiah, Krish & Kandiah, Miriam. How to Save A Life: Understanding the Cross. 2009. (Exploring Christianity Ser.). (ENG.). 48p. mass mkt. 3.99 (978-1-85078-821-8(9)) Authentic Media.

Kane, J.M. Wounded Hearts, Broken Minds. 2007. 208p. per. 14.99 (978-1-60266-231-5(2)) Xulon Pr., Inc.

Kania. A Believable Bible: An Enlightening & Inspiring Guide to a Mature Faith. 2009. 192p. 27.99 (978-1-4389-8825-2(7)); pap. 18.99 (978-1-4389-8826-9(5)) AuthorHouse.

Karampatsos, Rrrick. Heading Toward the Final Finish Line. 2008. 204p. pap. 15.99 (978-1-60647-961-2(X)) Xulon Pr., Inc.

Karasu, T. Byram. The Spirit of Happiness: Discovering God's Purpose for Your Life. 2008. (ENG.). 304p. pap. 20.95 (978-1-4165-9872-5(3)) Simon & Schuster.

Karchner, Bryan G. Good Grief. 2010. 108p. pap. 11.99 (978-1-60957-798-8(1)) Xulon Pr., Inc.

Kami, Leona. A Su Imagen. 2007. (SPA.). 112p. per. 10.99 (978-1-60477-162-6(3)) Xulon Pr., Inc.

Karwath, Raymond Edward. Turning Dreams into Reality. 2007. 50p. per. 8.95 (978-1-59824-457-1(4)) E-BookTime LLC.

Katajala-Peltomaa, S. Gender, Miracles, & Daily Life: The Evidence of Fourteenth-Century Canonization Processes. 2009. (Studies in the history of daily Life (800-1600) Ser.). (ENG & LAT., Illus.). 312p. (C). 123.00 (978-2-503-52958-5(5)) Brepols Pubs. BEL. Dist: ISD.

Kate. Hearts of Stone. 2008. 108p. pap. 10.99 (978-1-4389-2911-8(0)) AuthorHouse.

Kate Tuckett Staff. Creation Sings Your Praise. Shilson-Thomas, Annabel, ed. 2010. (ENG.). 256p. pap. 26.99 (978-1-85311-890-6(7), Canterbury Pr. Norwich) Hymns Ancient & Modern Ltd GBR. Dist: Westminster John Knox Pr.

Kato, Julius-Kei. How Immigrant Christians Living in Mixed Cultures Interpret Their Religion: Asian-American Diasporic Hybridity & Its Implications for Hermeneutics. 2011. 372p. 129.95 **(978-0-7734-3919-1(6))** Mellen, Edwin Pr., The.

Katongole, Emmanuel & Wilson-Hartgrove, Jonathan. Mirror to the Church: Resurrecting Faith after Genocide in Rwanda, 1 vol. 2009. (ENG.). 176p. pap. 15.99 (978-0-310-28489-5(9)) Zondervan.

Katz, Art. The Temptations of Christ: A Call to Sonship & Maturity. 2008. (ENG.). 54p. pap. 5.00 (978-0-9749631-2-9(7)) Burning Bush Pr.

Katz, Howard. Seven Essential Relationships: How to Pass God's Crucial Tests. 2008. (ENG.). 176p. 15.99 (978-0-615-15825-9(0)) Believe Bks., LLC.

Kauffman, Ivan. Follow Me: A History of Christian Intentionality. 2009. (ENG.). 272p. pap. 42.50 (978-0-7188-9187-9(2)) Lutterworth Pr., The GBR. Dist: Brown, David Bk. Co., The.

Kauffman, Ivan J. Follow Me: A History of Christian Intentionality. 2008. (New Monastic Library: Resources for Radical Discipleship Ser.). 274p. pap. 30.00 (978-1-55635-258-4(1), Cascade Bks.) Wipf & Stock Pubs.

Kaya & Christiane, Muller. The Book of Angels. 2008. 392p. pap. (978-2-923097-11-4(4)) Universe/City Mikael (UCM) Publishing, Inc.

Kazmierczak, Carolyn Salmon. A Kingdom for Horses: Heartfelt Devotions That Touch the Soul of a Horse Lover & Those That Love Our Lord Jesus; Also Featuring Will Jesus Return upon a White Horse? 2007. 80p. per. 16.95 (978-1-4241-8847-5(4)) PublishAmerica, Inc.

Keach, Benjamin. The Travels of True Godliness. 216p. 2009. 23.99 (978-1-103-11992-9(3)) 2009. pap. 17.99 (978-1-103-11989-9(3)) 2008. 24.99 (978-0-559-43326-9(3)) 2008. pap. 23.75 (978-0-559-43324-5(7)) BiblioBazaar.

—The Travels of True Godliness. Malcom, Howard, ed. 2009. 220p. 39.95 (978-1-104-43223-2(4)); pap. 24.95 (978-1-104-40418-5(4)) Kessinger Publishing, LLC.

Keating, Thomas. Intimacy with God: An Introduction to Centering Prayer. 2009. (ENG.). 176p. pap. 16.95 (978-0-8245-2529-3(9)) Crossroad Publishing Co., The.

Keddy, Brian B. Grace & the Legalist Mindset. 2008. 102p. pap. 16.95 (978-1-60474-744-7(7)) PublishAmerica, Inc.

Keefauver, Larry. Hugs for Grandparents: Stories, Sayings, & Scriptures to Encourage And. 2008. (Hugs Ser.). (ENG.). 128p. pap. 10.95 (978-1-4391-2465-9(5), Howard Bks.) Howard Books.

Keenam, Claude W. The Jungle of Fear: A Reverend Alabaster Armstrong Mystery. 2011. pap. 21.99 (978-1-61739-120-0(4)) Tate Publishing & Enterprises, LLC.

Keene, Rebecca S. Stumbling Upwards. 2008. 202p. pap. 13.95 (978-0-615-26421-9(2)) Keene, Rebecca S.

Keeston, David R. The Hitch Hiker's Guide to the Gospel. 2009. 165p. pap. 21.50 (978-1-4452-1690-4(6)) Lulu Enterprises Inc.

Keim, Charles F. Prayer Can Move Your Mountains: Not for the Faint of Heart. 2010. 108p. 28.95 (978-1-4497-0697-5(5)); pap. 11.95 (978-1-4497-0696-8(7)) Author Solutions, Inc. (WestBow Pr.).

Keiran, Alan. Take Charge of Your Destiny. 2008. pap. 16.99 (978-0-7684-2735-6(5)) Destiny Image Pubs.

Keith & Megan Provance. Scripture Confessions Collection: Life-Changing Words of Faith for Everyday. 2009. 192p. pap. 9.99 (978-1-57794-978-7(1)) Harrison House Pubs.

Kell, Tricia. Attitude Determines Altitude. 2006. 192p. per. (978-1-897373-03-3(1)) Word Alive Pr.

Keller, Catherine & Schneider, Laurel, eds. Polydoxy. 2010. (ENG.). 272p. (C). 110.00 (978-0-415-78135-0(3)); pap. 39.95 (978-0-415-78136-7(1)) Routledge.

Keller, Timothy. The Prodigal God: Finding Your Place at the Table. 2009. (ENG.). 24.99 (978-0-310-32535-2(8)) Zondervan.

Kelley, Alexia & Korzen, Chris. A Nation for All: How the Catholic Vision of the Common Good Can Save America from the Politics of Division. 2008. (ENG.). 176p. 24.95 (978-0-470-25862-0(4), Jossey-Bass) Wiley, John & Sons, Inc.

Kelley, Ernest J. God-Life. 2009. 344p. 28.99 (978-1-60791-428-0(X)); pap. 18.99 (978-1-60791-427-3(1)) Xulon Pr., Inc.

Kelley, Matthew. The Restoration Project. 2007. 124p. per. 10.99 (978-1-60266-428-9(5)) Xulon Pr., Inc.

Kelley, Patrick. My Father in Me: How One Man's Life Influences Future Generations. 2010. 152p. 22.99 (978-1-4490-6356-6(X)) AuthorHouse.

Kelley, Rayola. Battle for the Soul. 164p. wbk. ed. 12.99 (978-1-59160-127-2(4)) Xulon Pr., Inc.

Kelley, Rhonda & Leavell, Jo Ann. Don't Miss the Blessing, 1 vol. 2nd ed. 2010. (ENG., Illus.). 256p. 18.95 (978-1-58980-864-5(9)) Pelican Publishing Co., Inc.

Kellough, C. S. Awakening Grace. 2006. 160p. pap. 10.00 (978-1-883928-47-6(8)) Longwood Communications.

Kelly, Alan. Real Life Christianity: 7 Basic Principles for Successful Christian Living. 2009. pap. 15.99 (978-1-60799-710-8(X)) Tate Publishing & Enterprises, LLC.

Kelly, M. J. A Call to Joy: Living in the Presence of God. Date not set. 384p. pap. 14.00 (978-0-06-064342-3(0)) HarperCollins Pubs.

Kelly, Marcy. From Sorrow to Dancing. 2008. 100p. per. 10.99 (978-1-60477-611-9(0)) Xulon Pr., Inc.

Kelsey, Kathy & Kelsey, Robert. The Keys of Faith & Hope: The Keys to the Kingdom of God Series. 2010. 200p. 26.95 (978-1-4502-0883-3(5)); pap. 16.95 (978-1-4502-0881-9(9)) iUniverse, Inc.

Kelton, Tim. From the Heart: God in You Can Change the World. 2007. 223p. per. 14.99 (978-1-60247-004-0(9)) Tate Publishing & Enterprises, LLC.

Kelzenberg, Caroll. The Choice of a Lifetime. 2011. 107p. pap. 8.95 (978-0-9831755-0-6(0)) Kelzenberg, Caroll.

Kemp, Elkan V. The Disciple Whom Jesus Loved. 2008. 248p. pap. 15.99 (978-1-4343-7205-5(7)) AuthorHouse.

Kemper, Delain. Every Teen Matters. 2009. 60p. pap. 10.99 (978-1-60477-979-0(9)) Xulon Pr., Inc.

Kemper Iii, E. J. The Proper Purpose of Pain. 2008. 55p. pap. 16.95 (978-1-4241-9736-1(8)) PublishAmerica, Inc.

Kemper, Mary Ann. Flowers for the Triumph: Flower Miracles in the Life of the Catholic Church. 2009. 283p. pap. 15.95 (978-1-4327-4808-1(4)) Outskirts Pr., Inc.

Ken, Carter. Bread in the Wilderness Spirit. 2009. 64p. pap. 8.00 (978-0-687-65586-1(2)) Abingdon Pr.

Kendall, Jackie. Free Yourself to Love: The Liberating Power of Forgiveness. 2009. (ENG.). 256p. pap. 13.99 (978-0-446-58089-2(9)) FaithWords.

Kendall, Peggy. Reboot: Refreshing Your Faith in a High-tech World. 2009. 144p. pap. 14.00 (978-0-8170-1565-7(5)) Judson Pr.

Kendall, R. T. How to Forgive Ourselves - Totally: Begin Again by Breaking Free from Past Mistakes. 2007. (ENG.). 224p. per. 14.99 (978-1-59979-173-9(0), Charisma Hse.) Charisma Media.

—The Unfailing Love of Jesus: When Things Get Tough & You Feel Alone, Discover How He Reaches Out in Answer to Your Need. 2008. (ENG.). 224p. pap. 14.99 (978-1-59979-228-6(1), Charisma Hse.) Charisma Media.

—When God Shows Up: How to Recognize the Unexpected Appearances of God in Your Life. 2008. (ENG.). 224p. pap. 14.99 (978-1-59979-342-9(3), Charisma Hse.) Charisma Media.

Kendrick, Stephen, et al. The Resolution for Men. 2011. (ENG.). 272p. pap. 14.99 (978-1-4336-7122-7(0), B&H Bks.) B&H Publishing Group.

—The Resolution for Men. Lt. ed. 2011. pap. 17.99 (978-1-59415-385-3(X)) Cengage Gale.

Kennard, Steven. A Lifestyle of Grace. 2007. 120p. 18.99 (978-1-60266-166-0(9)); per. 10.99 (978-1-60266-165-3(0)) Xulon Pr., Inc.

Kennedy, Geoffrey A. Studdert. After War, Is Faith Possible? Walters, Kerry, ed. 2008. (ENG.). 236p. pap. 38.00 (978-0-7188-9201-2(1)) Lutterworth Pr., The GBR. Dist: Brown, David Bk. Co., The.

Kennedy, Gerald. I Believe. (978-0-687-18227-5(1), Abingdon Pr.

Kennedy, James. Esto Es Vida: This Is Life. (SPA.). 128p. (978-84-7228-481-4(3), 220381) Clie, Editorial.

Kennedy, Minnie E. The Training of the Devotional Life. 2007. (ENG.). 122p. 35.95 (978-0-548-07182-3(9)) Kessinger Publishing, LLC.

Kennedy, Nancy. Girl on a Swing: Finding Rest in the Warmth of God's Smile. 2006. (ENG.). 208p. pap. 13.99 (978-1-59052-729-0(1), Multnomah) Doubleday Religious Publishing Group, The.

Kennedy, Neil. 7 Laws Which Govern Increase & Order. 2007. per. (978-0-9777039-5-1(9)) Andrews, Michael S. Publishing, LLC.

Kennedy, Philip. Twentieth-Century Theologians: A New Introduction to Modern Christian Thought. 2010. (ENG., Illus.). 384p. 98.50 (978-1-84511-955-3(X)) I. B. Tauris & Co., Ltd. GBR. Dist: Macmillan.

—Twentieth-Century Theologians: A New Introduction to Modern Christian Thought. 2010. (ENG., Illus.). 384p. pap. 34.50 (978-1-84511-956-0(8), I. B. Tauris & Co., Ltd. GBR. Dist: Macmillan.

Kennedy, Studdert. The New Man in Christ - A Book of Devotion. 2007. 256p. per. (978-1-4067-8898-3(8), Pomona Pr.) Read Bks.

Kenner, Audrey. Recognizing Satan: A Case for Exorcism in Modern Times. 2007. 256p. per. 27.95 (978-1-4241-9599-2(3)) PublishAmerica, Inc.

Kenneson, Philip D., et al. The Shape of God's Reign. 2008. (Getting Your Feet Wet Ser.). 90p. pap. 12.00 (978-1-60608-055-9(5)) Wipf & Stock Pubs.

—The Shape of Our Lives: Study One in the Ekklisia Project. 2008. (Getting Your Feet Wet Ser.). 86p. pap. 12.00 (978-1-60608-054-2(7)) Wipf & Stock Pubs.

Kent, Bernard. Forgiveness: A Process, Not an Act. 2008. 124p. per. 12.95 (978-0-9814650-1-2(3)) G Publishing LLC.

Kent, Homer A., Sr. Conquering Frontiers: A History of the Brethren Church. pap. 6.99 (978-0-88469-017-7(2)) BMH Bks.

Kent, Keri Wyatt & Wyatt, Keri. Simple Compassion: Devotions to Make a Difference in Your Neighborhood & Your World, 1 vol. 2009. (ENG.). 208p. pap. 12.99 (978-0-310-29077-3(5)) Zondervan.

Kenyon, E. W. Words That Move Mountains. 2009. mass mkt. 8.99 (978-1-60374-082-1(1), 770821) Whitaker Hse.

Keown, Mark J. What GodOs up to on Planet Earth? A No-Strings-Attached Explanation of the Christian Message. 2011. 160p. pap. 18.00 **(978-1-61097-132-4(9)**, Wipf and Stock) Wipf & Stock Pubs.

Kern, Jan. Eyes Online - Eyes on Life: A Journey Out of Online Obsession. 2008. (Live Free Book Ser.). (ENG.). 240p. (YA). pap. 12.99 (978-0-7847-2159-9(9)) Standard Publishing.

—Take a Closer Look for Women: Uncommon & Unexpected Insights to Inspire Every Area of Your Life. 2007. (ENG., Illus.). 320p. pap. 14.99 (978-1-4165-4215-5(9), Howard Bks.) Howard Books.

Kern, Pamela. The Song of the Sparrow. 2007. (Illus.). 46p. per. 10.95 (978-1-887542-57-9(4)) Book Pubs. Network.

Kerr, Graham & Kerr, Treena. Recipe for Life. 2007. (ENG.). 389p. pap. 17.95 (978-1-59415-185-9(7), Walker Large Print) Cengage Gale.

Kerr, Joel. Who Is God & Where Does He Come From. 2010. pap. 10.99 (978-1-61566-949-3(3)) Tate Publishing & Enterprises, LLC.

Kerry, Graham & Kerr, Treena. Recipe for Life: How to Change Habits That Harm into Resources That Heal. 2006. (ENG., Illus.). 256p. pap. 19.99 (978-0-8054-4068-3(2), B&H Bks.) B&H Publishing Group.

Kervin, Ron. Between God & Warriors. 2008. 172p. pap. 12.95 (978-1-59824-819-7(7)) E-BookTime LLC.

Keshgegian, Flora & Keshgegian, Flora A. God Reflected: Metaphors for Life. 2008. 192p. pap. 19.00 (978-0-8006-6254-7(7), Fortress Pr.) Augsburg Fortress, Pubs.

Keshgegian, Flora A. Time for Hope: Practices for Living in Today's World. 2006. (ENG.). 240p. 39.95 (978-0-8264-1915-6(1)) Continuum International Publishing Group, Ltd. GBR. Dist: National Bk. Network.

Keshgegian, Flora A. & Keshgegian. Time for Hope: Practices for Living in Today's World. 2008. (ENG.). 240p. pap. 24.95 (978-0-8264-2986-5(6)) Continuum International Publishing Group, Ltd. GBR. Dist: National Bk. Network.

Kessinger, Tony. The Devil Is in the Details: The Subtlety of Satan in the Complexity of Life. 2010. 292p. pap. 18.99 (978-1-61507-152-4(0)) Cross Bks. Publishing.

Kessler, M. Elizabeth. Godyssey. 2008. 228p. 31.99 (978-1-59926-342-7(4)); pap. 21.99 (978-1-59926-341-0(6)) Xlibris Corp.

Ketcham, Arthur. Letters to the Family. 2011. 146p. 40.95 **(978-1-258-09045-6(7))** Literary Licensing, LLC.

Kettle, Cynthia Anne (Caron). Community Life, Death, Life Eternity, 1 vol. 2009. 89p. pap. 16.95 (978-1-60749-909-1(6)) PublishAmerica, Inc.

Keys to Christian Living. 0.75 (978-0-89265-525-0(9)) Randall Hse. Pubns.

Khalim, Noah. The Resurrection of Noah. 2007. 226p. per. 23.95 (978-0-9787798-1-8(9)) Sun Ra Communications, Inc.

—The Second Coming. 2007. 266p. per. 18.95 (978-0-9787798-0-1(0)) Sun Ra Communications, Inc.

Khater, Ariel. O November: What if you behaved like Jesus? 2011. 198p. pap. 14.95 (978-1-4327-6564-4(7)) Outskirts Pr., Inc.

Kidd, Amanda. The Devil's Church. 2008. 95p. pap. 13.95 (978-0-7414-4624-4(3)) Infinity Publishing.

Kidd, Sue Monk. Firstlight: The Early Inspirational Writings of Sue Monk Kidd. 2006. (ENG.). 240p. 19.95 (978-0-8249-4706-4(1), GuidepostsBooks) Ideals Pubns.

—When the Heart Waits: Spiritual Direction for Life's Sacred Questions. 2006. (Plus Ser.). (ENG., Illus.). 256p. pap. 13.99 (978-0-06-114486-9(4), HarperOne) HarperCollins Pubs.

Kidd, Wanda. Out of My Ashes, I Will Rise! 2009. 196p. pap. 14.99 (978-1-60791-692-5(4)) Xulon Pr., Inc.

Kidd, Wanda D. Out of My Ashes, I Will Rise! 2009. 196p. 22.99 (978-1-60791-693-2(2)) Xulon Pr., Inc.

Kiemel, Ann. Increible! Increible! (SPA.). 112p. (978-84-7228-500-2(6), 220492) Clie, Editorial.

—Me Gusta la Palabra Imposible: I Love the Word Impossible. (SPA.). 168p. (978-84-7228-496-8(4), 220555) Clie, Editorial.

—Si . . . Yes . . . (SPA.). 136p. (978-84-7228-502-6(2), 220821) Clie, Editorial.

Kientz, Michael. Build Your Walls! Guard Your Gates! 2007. 256p. per. 15.99 (978-1-60266-453-1(6)) Xulon Pr., Inc.

Kight, Ron. Stumblin' Towards Jesus. 2011. 96p. pap. 14.99 **(978-1-61203-140-8(4))** Bottom of the Hill Publishing.

Kilfeather, Rick. Hope Beyond Diagnosis. 2010. 140p. pap. 14.99 (978-1-61579-791-2(2)) Xulon Pr., Inc.

Kilgore, Deb J. Nuggets: Words of Hope & Encouragement. 2007. (Illus.). 186p. per. 19.99 (978-0-9796583-0-3(6)) Rocks To Nuggets, LLC.

Kilgore, James. Family Touch. 2006. pap. 13.99 (978-1-60034-638-5(3)) Xulon Pr., Inc.

Killian, Betty A. Miraculous Moments. (Illus.). 125p. (Orig.). pap. 6.95 (978-0-9634748-0-3(4)) Killian Ministries.

Killian, James. Truth of Our Faith. 2011. 232p. pap. 18.95 (978-1-4502-9319-8(0)) iUniverse, Inc.

Killinger, John. If Christians Were Really Christian. 2009. 166p. 19.99 (978-0-8272-1625-9(4)); 136p. E-Book (978-0-8272-1634-1(3)); 136p. E-Book (978-0-8272-1633-4(5)) Chalice Pr.

Kim, Erica. Open My Eyes, Lord: Seeing the Spiritual World Around Us: Seeing the Spiritual World Around Us. 2009. 230p. pap. 15.00 (978-1-57782-239-4(0)) Discipleship Pubns. International.

Kim, Inseong J. Rest in His Love, Our Redeemer, Jesus Christ. Evans, Denise, ed. 2011. 140p. 22.99 **(978-1-61379-060-1(0))** Xulon Pr., Inc.

Kimanzi, Joseph. The 21 Proofs of Faith: How to Live a Victorious Christian Life. 2010. 204p. pap. 17.95 (978-1-4502-5584-4(1)) iUniverse, Inc.

Kimball, Dan. I Like Jesus but Not Christianity: Following Jesus without Following Organized Religion. 2007. 144p. pap. 9.99 (978-0-310-25413-8(3)) Zondervan.

Kimball, Edward L. Father of a Prophet. 2011. (Illus.). pap. (978-0-8425-2795-8(8), Brigham Young Univ. Studies) Brigham Young Univ.

Kimmel, Tim. Little House on the Freeway: Help for the Hurried Home. 2008. (ENG.). 272p. pap. 13.99 (978-1-59052-612-5(0), Multnomah) Doubleday Religious Publishing Group, The.

Kincaid, Rebekah. A Rainbow in the Darkness. 2007. 56p. per. 16.95 (978-1-4241-6972-6(0)) PublishAmerica, Inc.

Kincheloe, Donna. I Never Walk the Halls Alone. 2007. (ENG.). 160p. pap. 18.95 (978-1-932124-90-3(X)) ACW Pr.

King, Alveda C. Who We Are in Christ Jesus: Formerly God's Plan for the Black Man. 2008. 228p. 29.99 (978-1-4363-1546-3(8)) Xlibris Corp.

King, Barbara L. Who's Angry? 2008. 184p. per. 13.99 (978-1-60477-585-3(8)) Xulon Pr., Inc.

—Who's Sad? 2009. 144p. pap. 14.99 (978-1-60791-128-9(0)) Xulon Pr., Inc.

King, Cabell. Without Nature? A New Condition for Theology. King, Cabell & Albertson, David, eds. 2009. (ENG.). 448p. 105.00 (978-0-8232-3069-3(4)); 3rd ed. pap. 40.00 (978-0-8232-3070-9(8)) Fordham Univ. Pr.

King, Clayton. Amazing Encounters with God: Stories to Open Your Eyes to His Power. 2011. pap. 11.99 (978-0-7369-3776-4(5)) Harvest Hse. Pubs.

—Dying to Live: Abandoning Yourself to God's Bold Paradox. 2010. 176p. pap. 13.99 (978-0-7369-2653-9(4)) Harvest Hse. Pubs.

C

King, Cornell. Being Number One at Being Number Two. 2007. pap. 9.99 (978-1-60266-039-7(5)) Xulon Pr., Inc.

King, Frank. Steps to the Victorious Walk. 2007. pap. 13.99 (978-1-60034-903-4(X)) Xulon Pr., Inc.

King, John. It's a Guy Thing: the Essential Guide: Helping Guys Become Men, Husbands, & Fathers. 2006. (Illus.). 183p. per. 14.99 (978-0-7684-2371-6(6)) Destiny Image Pubs.

King, Mother Jessie. Mother May I? Yes, You May! No, You May Not! 2008. 100p. pap. 11.99 (978-0-88144-297-7(6)) Yorkshire Publishing Group.

King, Patricia. Dream Big: How the Second Half of Life Can Be the Better Half of Life. 2008. 217p. per. 15.99 (978-0-7684-2625-0(1)) Destiny Image Pubs.

King, Paul L. Finding Your Niche: 12 Keys to Opening God's Doors for Your Life. 2008. 184p. pap. 12.95 (978-0-9785352-8-5(6)) Word & Spirit Pr.

King, Robert. Jehovah Himself Has Become King. 2010. 536p. (ENG.). 33.99 (978-1-4520-2229-1(1)); pap. 14.20 (978-1-4520-2228-4(3)) AuthorHouse.

—A Place Apart: Meditations on Living the Kingdom. 160p. pap. 14.95 (978-1-55126-188-1(X), 1457) Anglican Bk. Ctr. CAN. Dist: Forward Movement Pubns.

King, Sandra. Abraham: The Traveling Man of Faith. 2011. 306p. pap. 23.95 (978-1-4327-6798-3(4)) Outskirts Pr., Inc.

—Adam & the Woman. 2008. 204p. per. 14.99 (978-1-60477-432-0(0)) Xulon Pr., Inc.

King, Tammy. When the Levee Breaks: Holding on When Life Lets Go. 2010. pap. 12.99 (978-1-61663-674-6(2)) Tate Publishing & Enterprises, LLC.

Kingsley, Frank L. Rediscovering Life: Overcoming the Suicide of a Loved One. 2011. 124p. pap. 11.95 (978-1-61507-740-3(5)) Cross Bks. Publishing.

—Rediscovering Life: Overcoming the Suicide of A Loved One. 2011. 124p. 28.95 (978-1-61507-741-0(3)) Cross Bks. Publishing.

Kinkade, Thomas. Beyond the Garden Gate. gif. ed. (Lighted Path Collection). 48p. 16.96 (978-0-7369-1118-4(9)) Harvest Hse. Pubs.

Kinnaman, Gary & Jacobs, Richard. Understanding Depression & Finding Hope. 2009. 208p. 5.99 (978-0-8007-8785-1(4)) Revell.

Kinnamon, Michae & Linn, Jan. Disciples: Reclaiming Our Identity, Reforming Our Practice. 2009. 176p. pap. 19.99 (978-0-8272-0635-9(6)) Chalice Pr.

Kirby, Barbara. God Still Speaks to Me. 2011. 58p. pap. 9.95 (978-1-4626-3554-2(7)) PublishAmerica, Inc.

Kirby, Sue & Kirby, Dale. Crypt-A-Verse. 2010. 124p. pap. 13.99 (978-1-60957-679-0(9)) Xulon Pr., Inc.

Kirk, Marilyn. Faith & Forgiveness. 2007. 140p. pap. 12.95 (978-0-9789908-9-3(7)) Ketch Publishing.

—Whose Vessel Are You? 2008. 78p. pap. 12.95 (978-0-9789908-8-6(9)) Ketch Publishing.

Kirk, Pat W., compiled by. One Touch from the Maker: Tell of all His wonderful Acts. 2008. (Illus.). 128p. per. 10.95 (978-0-9777652-1-8(0)) PuckettBrowne Publishing.

Kirk, Ronald W., et al, eds. Worship Not the Creature: Animal Rights & the Bible. 2009. (ENG., Illus.). 192p. pap. 19.99 (978-0-9824929-1-8(X)) Nordskog Publishing, Inc.

Kirking, Cheryl. What Can I Give Jesus? A Christmas Message for All Ages. 2006. (Illus.). 32p. 15.95 incl. audio compact disk (978-0-9768847-1-2(2)) Mill Hse. Pr.

Kirkland, Camp. We Shall Behold Him. pap. 1.35 (978-0-8341-9419-9(8)) Lillenas Publishing Co.

Kirkland, Carl. Reaching God's Rest: The Journey. 2006. 109p. pap. 19.95 (978-1-4241-5657-3(2)) PublishAmerica, Inc.

Kirkland, Kevin D. Broken Walls: And Those Called to Repair Them. 2009. 276p. pap. 16.99 (978-1-60791-266-8(X)) Xulon Pr., Inc.

Kirkwood-Hatchett, Queen. A General Study of the Books of the Bible. 2006. 184p. per. 19.99 (978-1-59858-258-1(5)) Dog Ear Publishing, LLC.

Kirkwood, James. Unlimited Grace. 2006. (ENG.). 21.99 (978-1-60034-711-5(8)); pap. 13.99 (978-1-60034-528-9(X)) Xulon Pr., Inc.

Kirschman, Terry. Your Shepherd: Provision, Preservation & Power. 2006. (ENG.). 223p. per. 12.95 (978-0-9770398-9-0(7)) Lifebridge Bks.

Kit, Sandy. Pups, Kittens, Birds Will Heaven Be Their Home? 2009. 394p. pap. 19.99 (978-1-4363-3264-4(8)) Xlibris Corp.

Kitchen, Robert. The Syriac Book of Steps: Syriac Text & English Translation. 2008. (Texts from Christian Late Antiquity: 12). pap. 52.00 (978-1-59333-978-4(X)) Gorgias Pr., LLC.

Kitchen, Robert, intro. The Syriac Book of Steps 2. 2010. (ENG & SYR.). pap. 61.00 (978-1-59333-980-7(1)) Gorgias Pr., LLC.

Kitchin, Doyle R. Finding God's Bearings: Navigating the Navy with Faith & Passion. 2011. pap. 16.99 (978-1-61739-553-6(6)) Tate Publishing & Enterprises, LLC.

Kitzberger, Ingrid R. Transformative Encounters: Jesus & Women Re-Viewed. 2007. 45.95 (978-1-58983-289-3(2)) Society of Biblical Literature.

Kjeldsen, Douglas & Kjeldsen, Myra. Donkeys for God. 2007. 112p. per. (978-0-9556570-8-5(3)) Epic Pr. Ltd.

Kjellman, Östen. Den Forna Seden. 2011. 346p. pap. (978-1-907166-53-2(X)); 334p. pap. (978-1-907166-52-5(1)) Arktos Media Ltd.

Klatt, D M. Grits, Rice, & Dustpan Biscuits. 2008. 184p. per. 13.99 (978-1-60477-331-6(6)) Xulon Pr., Inc.

Klein, Walter. God's Word Speaks to Homosexuality. 2007. 100p. per. 11.95 (978-1-57921-896-6(2)) WinePress Publishing.

Klemmer, Brian. My Fight with God. 2010. (ENG.). 21.99 (978-0-7684-3253-4(7)) Destiny Image Pubs.

Kleyn, Diana. Bearing Fruit: Stories about Godliness for Children. 2007. (Illus.). (J). per. 8.00 (978-1-60178-023-2(0)) Reformation Heritage Bks.

Kling, Fritz. The Meeting of the Waters: 7 Global Currents That Will Propel the Future Church, 1 vol. 2010. (ENG.). 240p. pap. 16.99 (978-1-4347-6484-3(2)) Cook, David C.

Klotzle, James. God in Our Stress: the Christian's Guide to Stress Management. 2010. 98p. pap. 14.96 (978-0-557-45402-0(6)) Lulu Enterprises Inc.

Kluka, Lucille. Eureka! the Aha Phenomenon. 2007. 108p. per. 10.99 (978-1-60266-928-4(7)) Xulon Pr., Inc.

Knappen, Ken. God's Magnificent Drama. 2008. 132p. pap. 14.99 (978-1-60647-773-1(0)) Xulon Pr., Inc.

Kneas, Maria M. Strength for Tough Times: Encouragement from God's Word. 2010. pap. (978-0-9824881-6-4(5)) Lighthouse Trails Publishing Co.

Knight, Dan. Grace Gifts: Discovering the Unique Joy God Has for You. 2011. 264p. 35.95 (978-1-4497-2853-3(7)); pap. 19.95 (978-1-4497-2849-6(9)) Author Solutions, Inc. (WestBow Pr.).

Knight, Diane S. Alive & Well: Discovering God's Presence in the Midst of Everyday Life. 2010. (978-1-77069-133-9(2)) Word Alive Pr.

Knight, Trish. Walking Miracles. 2006. 59p. per. 7.95 (978-1-59886-377-2(0)) Tate Publishing & Enterprises, LLC.

Knights, Carlene A. Casting Away Stones. 2008. 97p. pap. 16.95 (978-1-60563-496-8(4)) PublishAmerica, Inc.

Knoettner, Karen. Is Jesus Your Pearl? 2007. 152p. (ENG.). 21.99 (978-1-60266-402-9(1)); per. 13.99 (978-1-60266-401-2(3)) Xulon Pr., Inc.

Knopp, Kenn. Journey into Wisdom Everlasting: From the Epiphanic Archives. 2010. 104p. pap. 11.95 (978-1-4502-7211-7(8)) iUniverse, Inc.

Knorr, Leonard J. Restoring Righteousness. 2009. 200p. pap. 14.49 (978-1-4389-3432-7(7)) AuthorHouse.

Knowles, Victor. The One Cup Faith. 194p. pap. 5.99 (978-0-89900-380-1(X)) College Pr. Publishing Co., Inc.

Knox, Gail. Out of Controland lovin' every minute of It! 2006. pap. 13.99 (978-1-60034-705-4(3)) Xulon Pr., Inc.

Knuth, Jane. Thrift Store Graces: Finding God's Gifts in the Midst of the Mess. 2012. (ENG.). 144p. pap. 13.95 (978-0-8294-3692-1(8)) Loyola Pr.

Ko, Carmelita. Rough, Rugged & Sweet, a Journey to Destiny. 2011. 88p. pap. 15.99 (978-1-4628-5608-4(X)) Xlibris Corp.

Koch, Scott B. Light up the Dungeon... The King Descends. 2008. 276p. 26.99 (978-1-60791-125-8(6)) Xulon Pr., Inc.

Koehler, Manfred. Majoring in Life. 196p. pap. 10.99 (978-0-8307-3460-3(0), Regal Bks.) Gospel Light Pubns.

Koekemoer, Marinda. Tyd Saam Met God. 2011. 168p. pap. 19.99 (978-1-4628-6052-4(4)) Xlibris Corp.

Koester, Robert J. Gospel Motivation: More Than Jesus Died for My Sins. 2007. per. (978-0-8100-1977-5(9)) Northwestern Publishing Hse.

Kohake, But, God! 2007. (Illus.). 20p. (J). per. 7.99 (978-1-60247-031-6(6)) Tate Publishing & Enterprises, LLC.

Kohlenberger, John. Read Through the Bible in a Year. 2008. (ENG.). 80p. pap. 5.99 (978-0-8024-7167-3(6)) Moody Pubs.

Kohler, Frederick & Banks, Gregory. Planting the Seed. 2007. 164p. (ENG.). 21.99 (978-1-60266-452-4(8)); per. 13.99 (978-1-60266-451-7(X)) Xulon Pr., Inc.

Kohn, Rosemarie & Sonderbo, Susanne. Good God? God-Poisoning & God-Images. Christensen, Otto, tr. from GER. 2008. 172p. pap. 20.00 (978-1-55635-559-2(9)) Wipf & Stock Pubs.

Kohut, Geri. A Crown Awaits: A Christian Woman's Journey to Overcoming Abuse. 2010. pap. 11.99 (978-1-61663-505-3(3)) Tate Publishing & Enterprises, LLC.

Kolbell, Erik. The God of Second Chances. 2008. (ENG.). 143p. pap. 15.00 (978-0-664-23122-4(5)) Westminster John Knox Pr.

Kolbet, Paul R. Augustine & the Cure of Souls: Revising a Classical Ideal. 2009. (ND Christianity & Judaism Anitqui Ser.). (ENG.). 416p. pap. 45.00 (978-0-268-03321-7(8)) Univ. of Notre Dame Pr.

Konechny, Sandra. When God Asks You. 2007. 192p. per. (978-1-897373-07-1(4)) Word Alive Pr.

Koppel, Michael S. Open-Hearted Ministry: Play As Key to Pastoral Leadership. 2008. (Prisms Ser.). 152p. (C). pap. 17.00 (978-0-8006-6295-0(4), Fortress Pr.) Augsburg Fortress, Pubs.

Korean Class Meeting 2009. 2008. pap. 10.50 (978-0-687-64914-3(5), Cokesbury) Abingdon Pr.

Korie, Daniel. Sons of God. 2008. 152p. pap. 13.99 (978-1-60647-556-0(8)) Xulon Pr., Inc.

Kornacki, Carol. Betrayal: The Deepest Cut. 2007. (ENG.). 144p. per. 10.99 (978-1-59979-243-9(5), Creation Hse.) Charisma Media.

Kortje, David. Your Personal Battle Plan: A Study Guide for the Unseen War. 2009. 152p. pap. 12.99 (978-1-4490-4151-9(5)) AuthorHouse.

Kosak, Hellen Battle. If I Forget You, O Jerusalem. 2008. 380p. 32.99 (978-1-60647-034-3(5)); pap. 20.99 (978-1-60647-033-6(7)) Xulon Pr., Inc.

Kosicki, George W., compiled by. Mercy Minutes: Daily Gems of St. Faustina to Transform Your Prayer Life. rev. ed. 2008. (ENG., Illus.). 447p. pap. 12.95 (978-1-59614-200-8(6)) Marian Pr.

Kossie-Chernyshev, Karen. Gift Out of Africa: Bearing & Sharing the Gifts of God in You. 2009. 116p. pap. 15.95 (978-1-4327-1155-9(5)) Outskirts Pr., Inc.

Koustas, R. F. An American Idiot. 2006. pap. 13.99 (978-1-60034-382-7(1)) Xulon Pr., Inc.

Kraak, William. Ultimos Tiempos: End Times. (SPA.). 88p. (978-84-7228-214-8(7), 220920) Clie, Editorial.

Kraft, Alan. Good News for Those Trying Harder. 2008. (ENG.). 208p. pap. 14.99 (978-1-4347-9940-1(9)) Cook, David C.

Kraft, Charles H. Deep Wounds Deep Healing: Discovering the Vital Link Between Spiritual Warfare & Inner Healing. 2010. (ENG.). 304p. pap. 16.99 (978-0-8307-4713-9(3)) Gospel Light Pubns.

Kraker, Joseph & Vinnie. Vinnie Here. 2008. 212p. per. 14.99 (978-1-60477-475-7(4)) Xulon Pr., Inc.

Krallmann, Gunter. Leading with Jesus: A Handbook on Qualifications for Spiritual Leadership for Individual & Group Study. ix, 84p. pap. 5.99 (978-1-85078-329-9(2)) Authentic Media.

Kratz, Jason. Message from the Mountain. 2011. pap. 8.99 (978-1-61346-490-8(8)) Tate Publishing & Enterprises, LLC.

Krautmann, Paul. The Rich Hiker's Guide to Walking with God. 2007. 216p. (ENG.). 24.99 (978-1-60266-102-8(2)); per. 14.99 (978-1-60266-101-1(4)) Xulon Pr., Inc.

Kraybill, Ron. Restoring Those Who Help Others: Self-Care & Spirituality for Those in Danger of Burn-Out, 1 vol. 2008. (ENG.). 190p. pap. 9.95 (978-1-56148-653-3(1)) Good Bks.

Krazewski, Charles. The Pope Is Dying. pap. 6.00 (978-0-88734-836-5(X)) Players Pr., Inc.

Kreider, Larry. Conozca A Jesucristo Como Senor. 2010. (SPA.). 168p. pap. (978-1-886973-88-6(1)) House to House Pubns.

Kreider, Larry & DeGrasse, Dennis. Supernatural Living: Wisdom, Knowledge, Faith, Healing, Miracles, Prophecy, Discernment, Tongues, Interpretation. 2009. pap. 16.99 (978-0-7684-2837-7(8)) Destiny Image Pubs.

Krhin, John. You Are the Temple. 2011. 192p. pap. 14.99 (978-1-61215-500-5(6)) Xulon Pr., Inc.

Kriner, Scott. Wait & See. 2010. pap. 10.95 (978-0-7414-6129-2(3)) Infinity Publishing.

Krishnan, Sunder. Loving God with All You've Got: Reordering Your Life's Priorities & Perspectives. 2009. 218p. pap. 13.99 (978-1-60066-191-4(2)) WingSpread Publishers.

Kroeger, Catherine Clark, et al, eds. Beyond Abuse in the Christian Home: Raising Voices for Change. 2008. (House of Prisca & Aquila Ser.). 254p. pap. 28.00 (978-1-55635-086-3(4)) Wipf & Stock Pubs.

Kroeker, Ann. Not So Fast: Slow-Down Solutions for Frenzied Families. 2009. (ENG.). 240p. pap. 14.99 (978-1-4347-6888-9(0)) Cook, David C.

Krogh, Jonathan B. The Joshua Factor. 2009. 184p. 29.99 (978-1-4415-5541-0(2)); pap. 19.99 (978-1-4415-5540-3(4)) Xlibris Corp.

Krotoski, Steve. The Kingdom: How to Press into the Kingdom of God: Experiencing Heaven on Earth. 2007. 19.99 incl. audio compact disk (978-0-9779550-1-5(X), TK1AB) ACTS ONE EIGHT Publishing.

Kruckenberg, Dana S. Galatians: An Exploration of Faith & Freedom. 2011. pap. 17.99 (978-1-61739-841-4(1)) Tate Publishing & Enterprises, LLC.

Kruger, C. Across All Worlds: Jesus Inside Our Darkness. 2007. 120p. per. (978-1-57383-379-0(7), Regent College Publishing) Regent College Publishing.

Krulikowski, Claire. Living A Radical Peace: Creating Life Anew. 2006. 133p. pap. 24.95 (978-1-4241-2279-0(1)) PublishAmerica, Inc.

Kryskow, Faytene. Marked: A Generation of Dread Champions Rising to Shift Nations. 2009. pap. 17.99 (978-0-7684-2819-3(X)) Destiny Image Pubs.

Kudowor, Pastor K. E. Where Is My Joshua? 2007. 108p. per. 10.99 (978-1-60266-234-6(7)) Xulon Pr., Inc.

Kugler, Chris. Being Christian: A Journey from the Boat to the Shore, Culminating at the Cross. 2011. 120p. 28.95 (978-1-4497-2177-0(X)); pap. 11.95 (978-1-4497-2176-3(1)) Author Solutions, Inc. (WestBow Pr.).

Kuhatschek, Jack. Our Loving Father: Enjoying God's Embrace. 2007. (Walking with God (Navpress) Ser.). (ENG.). 64p. 8.99 (978-1-60006-219-3(9)) NavPress Publishing Group.

Kuhn, Bradley. What's So Special about Me? 2008. pap. 9.99 (978-1-60477-941-7(1)) Xulon Pr., Inc.

Kuhn, Elizabeth Ann. Behind the Wall. 2011. 384p. pap. 19.94 (978-1-4520-6563-2(2)) AuthorHouse.

Kuhn, Mike. Fresh Vision for the Muslim World. 2009. (ENG.). 287p. pap. 14.99 (978-1-60657-019-7(6)) Authentic Media.

Kuhrt. To Proclaim Afresh. 144p. 14.95 (978-0-281-04905-9(X)) International Publishers Marketing.

Kunneman, Brenda. The Supernatural You: Living from the Well of God's Spirit Within You. 2009. (ENG.). 240p. pap. 14.99 (978-1-59979-780-9(1), Charisma Hse.) Charisma Media.

—When Your Life Has Been Tampered With. 2008. (ENG.). 240p. pap. 14.99 (978-1-59979-280-4(X), Charisma Hse.) Charisma Media.

kunzinger, bob. Penance: Walking with the Infant. 2007. 75p. per. 12.00 (978-0-9777954-7-5(0)) All Nations Pr.

Kuranga, Abraham. Spiritual Breakfast: The Best Meal for the Day. 2010. pap. 29.99 (978-1-61566-582-2(X)) Tate Publishing & Enterprises, LLC.

Kurowski, Peter. The Seduction of Extremes: Swallowing Camels & Straining Gnats. 2006. (ENG.). 180p. per. 16.99 (978-1-4141-0644-1(0)) Pleasant Word.

Kurt, James H. The Most Holy Trinity & the the Four Corners of the Universe. 2009. 316p. pap. 15.99 (978-1-4389-3768-7(7)) AuthorHouse.

Kuyper, Abraham. Cerca de Dios: Near to God. (SPA.). 128p. (978-84-7228-006-9(3), 220150) Clie, Editorial.

Kuyper, Vicki. Wonderlust: A Spiritual Travelogue for the Adventurous Soul. 2007. (ENG., Illus.). 224p. per. 14.99 (978-1-59669-076-9(3)) New Hope Pubs.

Kwan, Hee Young. Retelling the Story of Young Adult Christians. 2009. 164p. pap. (978-3-639-14254-9(3)) VDM Verlag Dr. Mueller e.K.

Kyker-Jameson, Vicki. Sing, O Barren Woman: a Disabled Woman's Miraculous Journey To. 2007. (ENG.). 192p. per. 24.95 (978-1-4241-6544-5(X)) PublishAmerica, Inc.

Laan, Ray Vander. Faith Lessons on the Prophets & Kings of Israel Discovery Guide, 1 vol. exp. rev. ed. 2008. (Faith Lessons Ser.). (ENG.). 208p. pap. 9.99 (978-0-310-27961-7(5)) Zondervan.

Laaser, Mark. Men's L. I. F. E. Guide, Revised. 2007. per. 19.95 (978-0-9771662-2-0(8)) Freedom Every Day LLC.

—Men's L. I. F. E. Guide, XXX Church. com. 2007. per. 19.95 (978-0-9771662-6-8(0)) Freedom Every Day LLC.

Laaser, Mark R. & Cane, William. The Secret Seductress: Breaking the Destructive Cycle of Pornography. 2007. (Picking up the Pieces Ser.). 128p. 7.99 (978-1-57494-223-1(9), Serendipity Hse.) LifeWay Christian Resources.

Labberton, Mark. The Dangerous Act of Worship: Living God's Call to Justice. 2007. (ENG.). 200p. 18.00 (978-0-8308-3316-0(1), IVP Bks.) InterVarsity Pr.

Laborn, Michael Allyn. Developing Intimacy with God: ... from faith to Friendship... 2011. 202p. pap. 24.95 (978-1-4626-3474-3(5)) PublishAmerica, Inc.

Lacey, William A. Seeing with the Heart. 2009. 84p. pap. 10.99 (978-1-60791-363-4(1)) Xulon Pr., Inc.

Lachappell, Holly. Flowers of Grace. 2008. 124p. pap. 10.99 (978-1-60647-550-8(9)) Xulon Pr., Inc.

Lackie, Dennis A. How to Walk in Christ. 2010. 478p. 36.99 (978-1-60957-589-2(X)); pap. 24.99 (978-1-60957-579-3(2)) Xulon Pr., Inc.

Lacueva, Francisco. Mensajes de Siempre para los Hombres: Eternal Messages for the Modern Man. (SPA.). 128p. (978-84-7228-609-2(6), 220588) Clie, Editorial.

Lacy, Earl W. The Image of Jehovah-Elohim. 2011. 220p. pap. 24.95 (978-1-4489-5751-4(6)) PublishAmerica, Inc.

Ladd, John D. Commentary on the Book of Enoch. 2008. 440p. pap. 24.99 (978-1-60647-451-8(0)) Xulon Pr., Inc.

Ladd, Karol. A Woman's Passionate Pursuit of God: Creating a Positive & Purposeful Life. 2011. 224p. pap. 12.99 (978-0-7369-2964-6(9)) Harvest Hse. Pubs.

Ladun, Brenda. Behind the Scenes of Breast Cancer: A News Anchor Tells Her Story of Body & Soul Recovery. 2007. (ENG.). 208p. pap. 16.99 (978-1-59669-091-2(7)) New Hope Pubs.

Ladyjaye. Giggles 'N God. 2008. 80p. pap. 10.99 (978-1-60647-904-9(0)) Xulon Pr., Inc.

Lafleur, Stephen. Champion's Choice: Decision Making That Transforms Lives. 2008. 76p. pap. 9.99 (978-1-60477-728-4(1)) Xulon Pr., Inc.

Lai Meng, Wan. Israel: A Light unto the Nations. 2009. (Illus.). 392p. pap. 17.99 (978-1-4490-1253-3(1)) AuthorHouse.

Laidlaw, Anne. Know God More: Be Transformed by Greater Intimacy with Your Creator. 2009. (ENG.). 384p. pap. 16.99 (978-1-59979-723-6(2), Creation Hse.) Charisma Media.

Lain-Priestley. Unfolding Year the. 2009. 128p. pap. (978-0-281-06061-0(4)) SPCK Publishing.

Laizure, Robert & Laizure, Lisa. Are You a Part -Time Christian? Why Your Answer Could Determine Where You Will Spend Eternity! 2007. pap. 10.99 (978-1-60477-257-9(3)) Xulon Pr., Inc.

—Got Fruit? 2006. 148p. per. 13.99 (978-1-60034-770-2(3)) Xulon Pr., Inc.

—#name? 2007. (SPA.). pap. 9.99 (978-1-60034-956-0(0)) Xulon Pr., Inc.

Lake, Brian. Romancing the King. 2010. (ENG.). pap. 14.99 (978-0-7684-3268-8(5)) Destiny Image Pubs.

Lake, John G. John G. Lake on Healing. 2009. 272p. pap. 12.99 (978-1-60374-162-0(3), 771620) Whitaker Hse.

Lalli, Nicholas T. God's Provision. 27p. pap. 10.00 (978-0-9662519-9-9(7)) T.K.M. Pubns.

Lam, Paul B. The 12 Universal Principles for Success. 2008. 400p. (ENG.). 33.99 (978-1-60477-630-0(7)); per. 21.99 (978-1-60477-629-4(3)) Xulon Pr., Inc.

Lam, William. In Favor with God & Man. 2007. 76p. per. 16.95 (978-1-4241-9390-5(7)) PublishAmerica, Inc.

Lamar, James. Where Is My Israel? 2007. 140p. per. 13.99 (978-1-60477-506-8(8)) Xulon Pr., Inc.

Lamb, Deacon Dick. Heal Your Thought Life: A Re-Minder. 2008. 149p. pap. 24.95 (978-1-60563-127-1(2)) PublishAmerica, Inc.

Lambert, Eric A., Jr. The Kneeling Mind: 10 Attitudes for Victorious Living. 2007. (ENG.). 143p. pap. 12.99 (978-0-87508-869-3(4)) CLC Pubns.

Lambert, Kristen. God Blocked It! How I Overcame Sin & Adversity. 2011. pap. 10.99 (978-1-61777-302-0(6)) Tate Publishing & Enterprises, LLC.

Lambshead, Nathan. Withstanding the Storm: Becoming the Christian You Were Meant to Be. 2006. 98p. per. 9.95 (978-1-59886-407-6(6)) Tate Publishing & Enterprises, LLC.

Lamontagne, Ron. No Time to Die, 1 vol. 2009. 48p. pap. 16.95 (978-1-60703-639-5(8)) PublishAmerica, Inc.

Lance, Alisha. You Can Begin Again. 2008. 436p. pap. 21.99 (978-1-60477-455-9(X)) Xulon Pr., Inc.

Landau, Felix. No Longer Alone: My Intimate Walk with Jesus Christ. 2011. 132p. 28.95 (978-1-4497-2378-1(0)); pap. 11.95 (978-1-4497-2377-4(2)) Author Solutions, Inc. (WestBow Pr.).

Landon, William. Up from the Ashes: A pesonal search for truth in a fallen World. 2010. 396p. pap. 25.95 (978-1-4502-2972-2(7)) iUniverse, Inc.

Landreth, Rod L. The Chosen Yoke. 2008. 124p. 19.99 (978-1-60647-967-4(9)); pap. 11.99 (978-1-60647-966-7(0)) Xulon Pr., Inc.

—The Sword & the Spear: God's Perfect Plan for Defeating Satan's Spear of Death. 2010. 156p. pap. 11.95 (978-1-60911-170-0(2), Eloquent Bks.) AEG Literary Publishing Services, Inc.

Landry, Natalie. Converted by Cookies, Healed by Grace: A Story of God's Redeeming Love. 2010. 77p. pap. 9.95 (978-1-4327-6213-1(3)) Outskirts Pr., Inc.

Lane, Belden C. Ravished by Beauty: The Surprising Legacy of Reformed Spirituality. 2011. (ENG., Illus.). 328p. 29.95 (978-0-19-975508-0(6)) Oxford Univ. Pr., Inc.

Lane, Kevin. Fail-Safe for Fallacy: Every Believer Can Cut Straight to the Truth. 2009. 176p. pap. 14.99 (978-1-61579-189-7(2)) Xulon Pr., Inc.

Lane, Timothy. Family Feuds: How to Respond. 2008. (ENG.). 24p. 3.99 (978-1-934885-37-6(1)) New Growth Pr.

—Freedom from Guilt: Finding Release from Your Burdens. 2008. (ENG.). 24p. 3.99 (978-1-934885-43-7(6)) New Growth Pr.

Lane, Timothy S. & Tripp, Paul David. How People Change. 2nd ed. 2008. (ENG., Illus.). 255p. pap. 17.99 (978-1-934885-53-6(3)) New Growth Pr.

Laney, Darlene. And He Made a Woman. 2008. 96p. pap. 8.99 (978-1-58169-268-6(4)) Genesis Communications, Inc.

Lang, Dean. Vision, Adventure & Faith. 2011. 162p. pap. 19.99 (978-1-4568-9168-8(5)) Xlibris Corp.

Langenbrunner, Norm. Daily Reflections for Lent 2009. 2009. 80p. pap. 2.95 (978-0-86716-906-5(0)) Franciscan Media.

Langevin, Sharon A. Rising above Life's Obstacles: Getting to Your God-Given Destiny in One Piece! 2006. 109p. per. 10.95 (978-1-59824-330-7(6)) E-BookTime LLC.

Langford, Cdp. The Tattered Heart: A Historical Fiction Biography of Mother St. Andrew Feltin, CDP Foundress of the Sisters of Divine Providence of San Antonio, Texas. 2007. 708p. per. 33.95 (978-0-595-43639-2(0)) iUniverse, Inc.

Langford, David. A Curse, A Cradle, & A Cross. 2007. 121p. pap. 14.95 (978-0-9789908-6-2(2)); (ENG.). pap. 14.95 (978-0-9789908-7-9(0)) Ketch Publishing.

Langford, Joseph. Mother Teresa's Secret Fire: The Encounter That Changed Her Life, & How It Can Transform Your Own. 2007. (Illus.). 320p. pap. 19.95 (978-1-59276-309-2(X)) Our Sunday Visitor, Publishing Div.

Langham Arts Staff. Prom Praise Solos, Vol. 2. (978-1-85792-384-1(7)) Christian Focus Pubns. GBR. Dist: Riverside.

Langlas, James. Heart of a Warrior: 7 Ancient Secrets to a Great Life. 2012. (ENG.). 160p. (YA). pap. 15.99 (978-1-57542-388-3(X)) Free Spirit Publishing, Inc.

Lanton, Mark. The Fight Is Already Fixed: This 12 Round Fight We Call Life. 2009. pap. 11.99 (978-1-60799-453-4(4)) Tate Publishing & Enterprises, LLC.

Lanza, Melissa. In My Presence. 2010. 40p. 31.99 (978-1-4415-1704-3(9)) Xlibris Corp.

LaPorte, David. Spitting in the Wind: Uncommon Sense in a World Gone Mad. 2010. pap. 14.99 (978-1-60799-919-5(6)) Tate Publishing & Enterprises, LLC.

Lapp, John & Snyder, Arnold, eds. Mission & Migration, 1 vol. 2010. (ENG.). 284p. pap. 11.95 (978-1-56148-690-8(6)) Good Bks.

Largent, Phil. Maximum Service Bk. 1: Practical Truths for Followers of Jesus: from A-Z Book 1. 2008. 64p. 5.95 (978-0-9769622-7-4(6)) IMD Pr.

—Maximum Service Bk. 2: Practical Truths for Followers of Jesus: from A-Z Book 2. 2008. 64p. 5.95 (978-0-9769622-8-1(4)) IMD Pr.

—Maximum Service Bk. 3: Practical Truths for Followers of Jesus: from A-Z Book 3. 2008. 64p. 5.95 (978-0-9769622-9-8(2)) IMD Pr.

Larimore, Walt & Crockett, Susan A. The Honeymoon of Your Dreams: How to Plan a Beautiful Life Together. annot. ed. 2007. (ENG.). 208p. 17.99 (978-0-8307-4313-1(8)) Gospel Light Pubns.

Larkins, D. O. Happy Is the Man. pap. 4.95 (978-0-9642909-6-9(0)) Spirit of Life Christain Ctr.

Larkins, Rod. Possessed. 2010. (ENG.). 252p. pap. 14.99 (978-0-7684-3276-3(6)) Destiny Image Pubs.

Larkins, Rod W. Possessed: Living Fully Abandoned to God's Glory. 2010. 253p. (978-0-7684-3508-5(0)); (978-0-7684-3507-8(2)) Destiny Image Pubs.

Larsen, Carolyn. Daily Inspirations of Blessings. 2007. 124p. per. (978-1-86920-365-8(8)) Christian Art Pubs.

—Daily Inspirations of Love. 2007. 124p. per. (978-1-86920-364-1(X)) Christian Art Pubs.

—Daily Inspirations on Prayer. 2007. 124p. per. (978-1-86920-367-2(4)) Christian Art Pubs.

Larson, Bruce. Don de la Libertad: Setting Men Free. (SPA.). 132p. (978-84-7228-132-5(9), 220318) Clie, Editorial.

—Vida Cristiana el Crecimiento (Living in the Growing Edge) (SPA.). (978-84-7228-672-6(X), 220947) Clie, Editorial.

Larson, Jim. Disfrute Ensenando: Make Learning a Joy. (SPA.). 128p. (978-84-7228-401-2(8), 220317) Clie, Editorial.

Larson, Kenneth. Opportunity Season: How to Launch Your Life Purpose! 2006. (Illus.). 184p. per. 12.99 (978-1-59886-366-6(5)) Tate Publishing & Enterprises, LLC.

Larson, Paul. A Portrait of the Holy Spirit. 2011. 102p. pap. 10.99 (978-1-61215-829-7(3)) Xulon Pr., Inc.

Larson Reid, Ruth. Love Letters from God. 2009. 188p. pap. 14.99 (978-1-4490-1026-7(8)) AuthorHouse.

Larson, Susie. The Uncommon Woman: Making an Ordinary Life Extraordinary. 2008. (ENG.). 200p. pap. 13.99 (978-0-8024-5279-5(5)) Moody Pubs.

Larussa, Tony. Bruisec Reed. 2006. pap. 15.99 (978-1-60034-728-3(2)) Xulon Pr., Inc.

Lashua, Shereen K. Naked, Embarrassed, & Exposed? Then Put Something On. 2009. 208p. pap. 15.99 (978-1-60791-909-4(5)) Xulon Pr., Inc.

Lasiter, Cindy. Diamonds in the Rough: Learning How to Apply God's Principles for Living Through the Study of Old Testament Characters. 2009. 200p. pap. 17.99 (978-1-60791-218-7(X)) Xulon Pr., Inc.

Lassiter, Darla. Passionate Pursuit. 2009. pap. 12.99 (978-1-60799-868-2(5)) Tate Publishing & Enterprises, LLC.

Lateer, Andrew James. Maranatha: Biblical Prophecy about the End of the Age in Plain English. 2011. 320p. 37.95 (978-1-4497-2717-8(4), WestBow Pr.) Author Solutions, Inc.

Lattiboudeaire, Michael-Liberte. Phema: The Prophetic Lifestyle Magazine: the Prophetic Lifestyle Magazine. 2008. 150p. per. 5.95 (978-0-01-933037-4(5), Phema Magazine) Great House Publishing Group, The.

Laubach, Frank C. Letters by a Modern Mystic: Excerpts from Letters Written at Dansalan, Lake Lanao, Philippine Islands. 2011. 46p. 35.95 (978-1-258-08800-2(2)) Literary Licensing, LLC.

Laurie, Greg. Better Than Happiness. 2008. (ENG.). 105p. pap. 13.95 (978-0-9801831-0-8(3)) Kerygma Publishing.

—Daily Hope for Hurting Hearts: A Devotional. 2010. 313p. 24.95 (978-0-9828644-1-8(8)); pap. 14.95 (978-0-9828644-0-1(X)) Kerygma Publishing.

—Discipleship: The Road Less Taken. 2009. (ENG.). 123p. pap. 10.95 (978-0-9801831-5-0(2)) Kerygma Publishing.

—For Every Season, Vol. 3. (ENG.). 312p. 2009. 24.95 (978-0-9801831-3-9(8)) 2008. pap. 14.95 (978-0-9801831-1-5(1)) Kerygma Publishing.

—For Every Season: Volume Two. 2008. (ENG.). 312p. per. 14.95 (978-0-9777103-4-8(3)) Kerygma Publishing.

—The Greatest Stories Ever Told, Vol. 2. 2008. (ENG.). 197p. pap. 13.95 (978-0-9777103-7-9(8)) Kerygma Publishing.

—Strengthening Your Faith: Messages from the Gospel of John. 2008. (ENG.). 227p. per. 9.95 (978-0-9762400-7-5(6)) Kerygma Publishing.

—Upside down Living: A Template for Changing Ourselves & the World from the Book of Acts. 2009. (ENG.). 322p. pap. 14.95 (978-0-9801831-7-7(0)) Kerygma Publishing.

—10 Things You Should Know about God & Life. 2006. 255p. pap. 11.95 (978-1-59328-210-3(9)); (ENG.). 259p. per. 11.95 (978-0-9777103-3-1(5)) Kerygma Publishing.

Lauterbach, Craig. The Father Revealed. 160p. pap. 10.99 (978-1-58169-112-2(2), Evergreen Pr.) Genesis Communications, Inc.

LaVere, Tim. Picking up Stones. 2007. 93p. pap. 9.99 (978-1-4303-2618-2(2)) Lulu Enterprises Inc.

Law, Charles. Ezekiel Rebuffed. 2010. 600p. pap. 35.00 (978-1-4269-1339-6(7)) Trafford Publishing.

Law, Eric H. F. Finding Intimacy in a World of Fear. 2007. 14.99 (978-0-8272-1041-7(8)) Chalice Pr.

Law, Prophetess Linda D. Working God's Plan. 2007. 73p. pap. 16.95 (978-1-4241-6319-9(6)) PublishAmerica, Inc.

Law, William. A Serious Call to a Devout & Holy Life. 2010. 390p. pap. 33.75 (978-1-177-81887-2(6)); 402p. pap. 34.75 (978-1-149-54497-6(X)); 372p. pap. 32.75 (978-1-149-04521-3(3)); 368p. pap. 32.75 (978-1-142-79282-4(X)) BiblioBazaar.

—A Serious Call to a Devout & Holy Life. 2009. 246p. pap. (978-0-217-31013-0(3)); 382p. pap. (978-0-217-67388-4(0)) Books LLC.

—A Serious Call to a Devout & Holy Life. 2008. (Pure Gold Classics Ser.). (ENG., Illus.). 350p. pap. 14.99 incl. audio compact disk (978-0-88270-453-1(2)) Bridge-Logos Foundation.

—A Serious Call to a Devout & Holy Life. 2007. (ENG.). 360p. per. 17.95 (978-1-60206-792-9(9)) Cosimo, Inc.

—A Serious Call to a Devout & Holy Life. 2010. 362p. 37.56 (978-1-163-20010-0(7)); pap. 25.56 (978-1-162-77611-8(0)) Kessinger Publishing, LLC.

—A Serious Call to a Devout & Holy Life. 2007. per. 12.99 (978-1-4245-0803-7(7)) Treasures Media Inc.

Lawing, Betty. Miracles Happen When God Leads. 2006. pap. 17.99 (978-1-60034-809-9(2)) Xulon Pr., Inc.

Lawrence, Brother. Practice of the Presence of God & the. 2006. pap. 5.95 (978-1-60206-033-3(9), Cosimo Classics) Cosimo, Inc.

Lawrence Dennis & Lawrence, Dennis. A Model for Practical Christian Holiness: Bonhoeffer, Webster, & Levinas Offer Believers Assurance Needed To Be Involved in Right Actions with the Right Person at the Right Time. 2008. 112p. pap. (978-3-639-09439-8(5)) VDM Verlag Dr. Mueller e.K.

Lawrence, Hermano. La Practica de la Presencia de Dios. 2008.Tr. of Practice of the Presence of God. (SPA.). 96p. mass mkt. 5.99 (978-0-88368-012-4(2), 770122) Whitaker Hse.

Lawrence, Judith. Highway of Holiness: Soul Journey. 2011. 132p. pap. 16.00 (978-1-61097-159-1(0), Resource Pubns.) Wipf & Stock Pubs.

Lawrence, Rick. Ten Tough Things: A Bold Plunge into the Christian Life. 2009. 88p. pap. 12.99 (978-0-7644-3896-7(4)) Group Publishing, Inc.

Lawrence, Rick & Lawrence, Bev. In Pursuit of Jesus: Personal Journey: Stepping off the Beaten Path. 2007. 80p. per. 9.99 (978-0-7644-3678-9(3)) Group Publishing, Inc.

Lawrence, Susan H. Pure Emotion. 2011. 244p. pap. 23.95 (978-1-4497-1769-8(1), WestBow Pr.) Author Solutions, Inc.

Lawrence, Susan H. Pure Purpose. 2010. 228p. pap. 23.95 (978-1-4497-0074-4(8), WestBow Pr.) Author Solutions, Inc.

Lawrenz, Mel & Lawrenz. Whole Church: Leading from Fragmentation to Engagement. 2009. (Jossey-Bass Leadership Network Ser.: 31). (ENG., Illus.). 208p. 24.95 (978-0-470-25934-4(5), Jossey-Bass) Wiley, John & Sons, Inc.

Lawrie, Cheryl. Mentores. PÉrez-fÉl, Liana, tr. 2007. 55p. pap. 8.00 (978-0-88177-525-9(8)) Discipleship Resources.

Laws, Bobby T. The Positive Flow: Your Life Can Be So Much More! 2007. 184p. per. 15.95 (978-1-4327-1374-4(4)) Outskirts Pr., Inc.

Lawson, David, et al. Fatal Distractions: Conquering Destructive Temptations. 2011. (40-Minute Bible Studies). (ENG.). 112p. pap. 7.99 (978-0-307-72981-1(8), WaterBrook Pr.) Doubleday Religious Publishing Group, The.

—How to Make Choices You Won't Regret. 2009. (40-Minute Bible Studies). (ENG.). 80p. pap. 7.99 (978-0-307-45764-6(8), WaterBrook Pr.) Doubleday Religious Publishing Group, The.

Lawson, Keith. The Purpose of This Life: The Full Gospel. 2009. 116p. pap. 13.95 (978-1-4327-2398-9(7)) Outskirts Pr., Inc.

Lawson, Russ. More Stories to Touch the Heart. 2008. 196p. pap. 13.24 (978-1-4357-0986-7(1)) Lulu Enterprises Inc.

Layman, Gary. I am Light: The Prodigal Path & Beyond. 2011. 300p. 31.95 (978-1-4620-0151-4(3)); pap. 21.95 (978-1-4620-0152-1(1)) iUniverse, Inc.

Layne, William. Leakage: A story of the saving grace of Jesus Christ & deliverance from alcohol, drugs, overeating, & Self. 2006. 134p. pap. 24.95 (978-1-4241-4984-1(3)) PublishAmerica, Inc.

Lazar, Silas. Rejoice by Choice. 2009. (978-1-55452-424-2(5)) Essence Publishing.

Lazaros, Ettarose. Heaven Help Mom: And Maybe the Kids Will Help. 2007. 134p. per. 7.95 (978-1-4327-0550-3(4)) Outskirts Pr., Inc.

Lazaro's Story: The Testimony of Lazaro Nitunga. 2008. (Illus.). pap. (978-0-915143-13-9(5)) Francis Asbury Society.

Le Cossec, Clement. Verdades Biblicas (Christian Truths), Vol. 1. (SPA.). (978-84-7645-506-7(2), 223600) Clie, Editorial.

Le Courtier, Francois. Thoughts & Counsels for Women of the World. 2007. 240p. per. 21.95 (978-0-9782985-0-0(0)) Catholic Authors Pr.

Le Tissier, Anne. Prepared for Battle - Inspiring Women Every Day. 2008. 112p. (978-1-85345-471-4(0)) Crusade for World Revival.

Leadership on the OtherSide, Unfreezing Moves & Sacred Cows. 43.00 (978-0-687-01985-4(0)) Abingdon Pr.

Leadingham, Everett. Heart Soul Mind Strength: Godly Living for Today's Kingdom Christian. 2006. (Dialog Ser.). 135p. pap. 7.50 (978-0-8341-2216-1(2)); pap. 7.99 (978-0-8341-2199-7(9)) Nazarene Publishing Hse.

—In His Likeness: God's Holiness at Work in Me. 2007. 7.99 (978-0-8341-2273-4(1)) Nazarene Publishing Hse.

Leaf, Ph.D., Caroline. The Gift in You: Discovering New Life Through Gifts Hidden in Your Mind, 0 vols. 2009. 240p. 19.99 (978-0-9819567-3-2(4)) Nelson, Thomas Inc.

Learning to Use My Bible: Student. rev. ed. stu. ed. 3.95 (978-0-687-07206-4(9)) Abingdon Pr.

Leatherman, David. Something to Consider. 2006. (ENG.). 21.99 (978-1-60034-526-5(3)); pap. 13.99 (978-1-60034-525-8(5)) Xulon Pr., Inc.

Leber, Kathy. How Real Is Your God? 2006. 236p. pap. 17.99 (978-1-4141-0795-0(1)) Pleasant Word.

Lebon, Randolph. The Master of Masters. 2011. 108p. pap. 12.99 (978-1-4568-8746-9(7)) Xlibris Corp.

Lechner, Diane, et al. Jesus Comes to Us, Grade 2. 268p. tchr. ed., spiral bd. 16.95 (978-0-8198-3923-7(X)) Pauline Bks. & Media.

Lechuga, Armando. No Dejes para Manana: Don't Leave for Tomorrow. (SPA.). (978-84-7645-483-1(X), 223573) Clie, Editorial.

—Recluta de Jesus (Soldier for Jesus) Soldier for Jesus. (SPA.). (978-84-7645-273-8(X), 223334) Clie, Editorial.

Leddy, Jim. The Simple Truth. 2008. 380p. pap. 20.99 (978-1-60647-828-8(1)) Xulon Pr., Inc.

Ledewitz, Bruce. Hallowed Secularism: Theory, Belief, Practice. 2009. (ENG.). 256p. 95.00 (978-0-230-61402-4(7)) Palgrave Macmillan.

Leding, Tom. Positive Thinking Is Faith in God. 2007. pap. 10.00 (978-1-890915-18-6(1)) TLM Publishing.

—With God You Will Succeed. 2007. pap. 10.00 (978-1-890915-22-3(X)) TLM Publishing.

Lee, Curtiss F. My Shepherd. 2008. 212p. pap. 15.00 (978-1-59755-136-6(8), Advantage Inspirational) Advantage Bks.

Lee, Dolores. The 12th Day: Overcoming the Pitfalls & Delays to Abundant Living. Hicks, Patricia A., ed. 2006. per. 19.99 (978-1-933972-03-9(3)) PriorityONE Pubns.

Lee, Earl G. El Ciclo de la Vida Victoriosa: Recyled for Living. (SPA.). (978-84-7228-333-6(X), 220153) Clie, Editorial.

Lee, Marva. No More Tears: Because HE Loves Me. 2007. 21.99 (978-1-60266-078-6(6)) 2006. pap. 13.99 (978-1-60034-859-4(9)) Xulon Pr., Inc.

Lee, Patsy. I Did Not Die: (but Lived, Psalms 118. 2011. 98p. pap. 19.95 (978-1-4560-5237-9(3)) PublishAmerica, Inc.

Lee, Pastonya. When God Places You in Authority over Others. 2011. pap. 8.99 (978-1-61739-327-3(4)) Tate Publishing & Enterprises, LLC.

Lee, Rebecca. Pure in Heart Pt. 1: Who's in My Heart? 2009. 192p. pap. 12.99 (978-1-60799-468-8(2)) Tate Publishing & Enterprises, LLC.

Lee, Samuel Dongho. Meditation, Confession & Healing in Writing Testimonies. 2008. 132p. pap. 14.99 (978-1-60791-119-7(1)) Xulon Pr., Inc.

Lee, Shannon. Allow Me to Brag on My God, Jesus Christ: Therefore As It Is Written: Let Him That Boasts Boast in the Lord. 1 Corinthians 1 31. 2009. 128p. pap. 14.99 (978-1-61579-401-0(8)) Xulon Pr., Inc.

Lee, Sheri Nelson. Feel Your Way Home. 2011. 124p. pap. 19.95 (978-1-4560-6955-1(1)) PublishAmerica, Inc.

Lee, Wanda. Vive el Llamado: Haga suyo el plan de Dios para su Vida. 2007. (SPA & ENG.). 224p. pap. 12.99 (978-1-59669-073-8(9)) New Hope Pubs.

Lee, Witness. Caracter. 2008.Tr. of Character. (SPA.). pap. 5.75 (978-0-7363-3754-0(7)) Living Stream Ministry.

—Crucial Principles for the Christian Life & the Church Life. 2007. 114p. per. 7.25 (978-0-7363-3228-6(6)) Living Stream Ministry.

—The Fullness of God. 2008. per. 6.50 (978-0-7363-3535-5(8)) Living Stream Ministry.

—Guidelines for the Propagation of the Lord's Recovery. 2008. 77p. pap. 6.00 (978-0-7363-3536-2(6)) Living Stream Ministry.

—The Holy Word for Morning Revival: Closely Following the Present Vision of the Lord's Recovery. 2007. per. 5.50 (978-0-7363-3604-8(4)) Living Stream Ministry.

—The Holy Word for Morning Revival: Knowing & Caring for the Church. 2007. per. 7.25 (978-0-7363-3567-6(6)) Living Stream Ministry.

LeFlore, David, Jr. Fast Food Evangelism: A Drive-Thru Approach to Sharing Christ. Batzing, Peter, ed. 2007. (Illus.). 95p. per. 5.99 (978-0-88270-341-1(2)) Bridge-Logos Foundation.

Legair, Robert. Harmless Dream or Urgent Wake-up Call? 2007. 92p. per. 9.99 (978-1-60266-144-8(8)) Xulon Pr., Inc.

Lehman, Mark. Discover Truth. 2008. 320p. (ENG.). 27.99 (978-1-60477-440-5(1)); per. 17.99 (978-1-60477-439-9(8)) Xulon Pr., Inc.

—Fill Your Life with Love. 2007. 272p. per. 15.99 (978-1-60266-895-9(7)) Xulon Pr., Inc.

Leigh, Daniel. Truth to Life: Discover the Source of Truth & the Path to Life in Christ. 2010. 344p. pap. 18.99 (978-1-60957-411-6(7)) Xulon Pr., Inc.

Leigh, JeLinda. Message from God the Father Part III: For the Time Is at Hand. 2010. 156p. pap. 11.99 (978-1-4490-7034-2(5)) AuthorHouse.

Lein, Eve L. Faith, Hope & Love & Other Wonderful Words. Date not set. (Orig.). pap. (978-0-9655019-0-3(6)) Lein, Evelyne L.

Leininger, David E. As We Believe, So We Behave: Living the Apostles' Creed. 2008. (978-0-7880-2588-4(0)) CSS Publishing Co.

Leiphart, Tim. The Next Day: How God Still Speaks. 2011. 244p. 35.95 (978-1-4497-2610-2(0)); pap. 19.95 (978-1-4497-2609-6(7), Author Solutions, Inc. (WestBow Pr.).

Leman, Kevin. Why Your Best Is Good Enough, 1 vol. 2010. (ENG.). 256p. 6.99 (978-0-8007-8794-3(3)) Revell.

Lemaster, Phil. Philosophically Speaking: The Stories & Musings of an Appalachian Preacher, Teacher, & Psychologist. 2009. (Illus.). 340p. pap. 18.99 (978-1-61579-407-2(7)) Xulon Pr., Inc.

LeMay, Michael. Intimacy with God. 2007. 184p. per. 13.99 (978-1-60266-381-7(5)) Xulon Pr., Inc.

Lemmons, Molly. Kind of Heart. 2008. (ENG.). 294p. pap. 16.95 (978-1-933582-35-1(9)) PawPrints POD.

Lemon, Sarah. Creative Ideas for Children's Worship: Based on the Sunday Gospels. 2012. 384p. pap. 39.99 (978-1-84825-112-0(2), Canterbury Pr. Norwich) Hymns Ancient & Modern Ltd GBR. Dist: Westminster John Knox Pr.

Lenz, Bob. Grace: For Those Who Think They Don't Measure Up. 2008. pap. 14.99 (978-0-7684-2701-1(0)) Destiny Image Pubs.

Leo, Brian L. Hey God? I Got Fired! 2008. 80p. per. 9.99 (978-1-60477-695-9(1)) Xulon Pr., Inc.

Leonard, Joni. Miracles Inside. 2008. 152p. pap. 11.95 (978-1-4327-2116-9(X)) Outskirts Pr., Inc.

Leonard, Mamie Sconiers. Shut in & Win. 2008. 164p. pap. 14.99 (978-1-60647-856-1(7)) Xulon Pr., Inc.

Lerch, Harold A., Sr. Two Wrongs Don't Make a Right, but Three Lefts Do. 276p. 25.99 (978-1-59160-693-2(4)); 14.99 (978-1-59160-692-5(6)) Xulon Pr., Inc.

Leross, Biblical Counseling Therapist & Life Design Consultant Quiycinda. Intimacy with God. 2009. 99p. pap. 14.99 (978-1-60557-07216-3(6)) Lulu Enterprises Inc.

LeRoux, Pierre & Leroux, Pierre. Immanuel(God with Us)in Recovery. 2011. 216p. 25.99 (978-1-61379-381-7(2)); pap. 15.99 (978-1-61379-380-0(4)) Xulon Pr., Inc.

Leschinsky, Eric M. Starving the Flesh. 2009. (J). pap. 11.99 (978-1-60799-705-4(3)) Tate Publishing & Enterprises, LLC.

Leske, Elmore. Growing as God's People. (Illus.). 176p. stu. ed. (978-0-85910-169-1(X)) Openbook Publishers.

Lesson's I've Learned: Forsake not the Instruction from the Lord. 2007. (C). per. 12.00 (978-0-9747893-5-4(6)) Robinson, Robert.

Lester, Andrew D. Anger: Discovering Your Spiritual Ally. 2007. (ENG.). 126p. per. 15.00 (978-0-664-22499-8(7)) Westminster John Knox Pr.

Letsinger, Prophetess Bernice. Suicide: Satan's Silent Sting in the Church. 2007. 76p. per. 10.00 (978-1-4257-6053-3(8)) Xlibris Corp.

Lett, Gabe. Let's Get Together: Building Community in the Church. 2008. (Illus.). 160p. per. 12.99 (978-1-60247-893-0(7)) Tate Publishing & Enterprises, LLC.

A Letter from Aida. pap. 0.69 (978-1-56632-017-7(8)) Revival Literature.

Leuthauser, Karl & Leuthauser, Kyle. The Driving Force: Living Life & Full Speed. 2009. (Illus.). 80p. pap. 9.99 (978-0-7644-3749-6(6)) Group Publishing, Inc.

Levine, Amy-Jill. Feminist Companion to the Apocalypse of John. Robbins, Maria Mayo, ed. 2010. (Feminist Companion to the New Testament & Early Christian Writings Ser.). (ENG.). 288p. 55.00 (978-0-8264-6651-8(6)); 160.00 (978-0-8264-6650-1(8)) Continuum International Publishing Group, Ltd. GBR. (T&T Clark Int'l). Dist: National Bk. Network.

Levingston, Harold. The Modern Words of God. 2008. 344p. pap. 29.95 (978-1-60672-372-2(3)) PublishAmerica, Inc.
Levron, Teddy. 3 Essentials for Christian Living. 2007. 34p. per. 3.99 net. (978-0-9771744-1-6(7)) Just Jesus Publishing.
Lewin, Ann. Seasons of Grace: Inspirational Resources for the Christian Year. 2011. 256p. pap. 24.99 (978-1-84825-090-1(8), Canterbury Pr. Norwich) Hymns Ancient & Modern Ltd GBR. Dist: Westminster John Knox Pr.
Lewis, Albert D., Jr. The Great Spiritual War, 7 vols., Set. Incl. Vol. 1. Great Spiritual War: What Is It? 64p. pap. 4.99 (978-0-9633356-1-6(8)); Vol. 2. Great Spiritual War: Our Real Foe(s) - Who Are They? 30p. pap. 2.99 (978-0-9633356-2-3(6)); Vol. 3. Great Spiritual War: Idol Worship. 26p. pap. 2.99 (978-0-9633356-3-0(4)); Vol. 5. Great Spiritual War: The Great Tribulation. 30p. pap. 2.99 (978-0-9633356-5-4(0)); Vol. 6. Great Spiritual War: Suicide; Forgiveness; Repentance: The Weapons of Our Warfare & a Letter to the President. 38p. pap. 4.99 (978-0-9633356-6-1(9)); Vol. 7. Great Spiritual War: My Personal Testimony. 106p. pap. 8.99 (978-0-9633356-7-8(7)); Vol. 4. AIDS & Abortion. 60p. pap. 6.99 (978-0-9633356-4-7(2)); (Illus.). 1997. Set pap. 33.99 (978-0-9633356-9-2(3)) Harvest Time International, Inc.
Lewis, Candace. New Day a New Way. 2009. 128p. pap. 14.00 (978-0-88177-574-7(6)) Discipleship Resources.
Lewis, Carole. First Place. 104p. pap. 19.99 (978-0-8307-2867-1(8), Gospel Light) Gospel Light Pubns.
—Hope 4 You: God's Plan for Your Health & Happiness. (First Place 4 Health Ser.). (ENG.). 192p. 2012. pap. 14.99 (978-0-8307-6185-2(3)) 2010. 17.99 (978-0-8307-5529-5(2)) Gospel Light Pubns.
Lewis, Clifford & Rice, John R. God's Ideal Woman. 2007. (ENG.). 92p. per. 18.95 (978-1-4325-8108-4(2)) Kessinger Publishing, LLC.
Lewis, Edwin. Jesus Christ & the Human Quest. 2007. (ENG.). 388p. 48.95 (978-0-548-01900-9(2)) Kessinger Publishing, LLC.
Lewis, Gregg, et al. Take the Risk: Learning to Identify, Choose, & Live with Acceptable Risk, 1 vol. 2007. (ENG.). 240p. 19.99 (978-0-310-25973-2(8)) Zondervan.
Lewis, H. DeSantis, Sr. One Day at A Time. 2006. 31.99 (978-1-4257-4262-1(9)); pap. 21.99 (978-1-4257-4261-4(0)) Xlibris Corp.
Lewis, J. El Toque Tierno de Dios.Tr. of Tender Touch of God. (SPA.). 9.99 (978-0-7899-0331-0(8), 497395) Editorial Unilit.
Lewis, Priscilla. He Is King of Kings & Lord of Lords. 2008. pap. 9.00 (978-0-8059-7323-5(0)) Dorrance Publishing Co., Inc.
Lewis, Steve D. Step into the Fire: Simple Concepts to Enable You to Experience True Worship. 2008. 146p. pap. 24.95 (978-1-60610-727-0(5)) PublishAmerica, Inc.
Lewis, Tracy. God Is Always There: Past Your Sins & Circumstances. 2007. 169p. per. 12.99 (978-1-60247-102-3(9)) Tate Publishing & Enterprises, LLC.
Libatique, Kelly. A Toast to the Holy Ghost? a Dispassionate Look at Alcohol & the Bible. 2010. 178p. pap. 12.50 (978-1-60911-347-6(0), Eloquent Bks.) AEG Literary Publishing Services, Inc.
Libby, Bob. The Forgiveness Book. 2010. 164p. (Orig.). pap. 15.95 (978-1-4502-4280-6(4)) iUniverse, Inc.
Libby, Sharon. Through It All, He Was There: An Inspirational Story of Faith. 2009. 280p. pap. 16.99 (978-1-61579-298-6(8)) Xulon Pr., Inc.
Liberated Through Submission: God's Design for Freedom in All Relationships. 2006. 188p. per. 12.99 (978-0-7369-1887-9(6)) Harvest Hse. Pubs.
Liebe, Extraordinary Leader Robin. Diamond Life. 2009. 188p. pap. 14.97 (978-0-557-12628-6(2)) Lulu Enterprises Inc.
Liebig, Greg K., Sr. This Is It! 2007. 10.00 (978-0-8059-8886-4(6)) Dorrance Publishing Co., Inc.
Liebscher, Banning. Jesus Culture: Living a Life that Transforms the World. 2009. 218p. pap. 16.99 (978-0-7684-3100-1(X)) Destiny Image Pubs.
Liesenfeld, Stephen, ed. Coming Together in Joy: 99 Sayings by Benedict XVI. 2007. (99 Words to Live by Ser.). 99p. 14.95 (978-1-56548-273-9(5)) New City Pr.
The Life. 2009. 240p. 27.99 (978-1-117-06034-7(9)) BiblioBazaar.
Life & Hope: In Rural/Small-Town Communities. pap. 12.99 (978-0-570-09827-0(0), 20-3016) Concordia Publishing Hse.
Life Together Staff & Baker Publishing Group Staff. Deepening Life Together, Kit. 2009. (Deepening Life Together Ser.). 249.99 (978-0-8010-8674-8(4)) Baker Bks.
LifeLight for Little Ones: Caregivers Manual. pap. 7.95 (978-0-570-09251-3(5), 20-2245) Concordia Publishing Hse.
LifeLight for Little Ones: Parent Letters. pap. 3.50 (978-0-570-09252-0(3), 20-2246) Concordia Publishing Hse.
Lifelines of Love. 9.99 (978-0-7586-0256-5(1)) Concordia Publishing Hse.
Lifetogether. Fruit of the Spirit. 2011. (Deepening Life Together Ser.). (Illus.). 125p. pap. 8.99 (978-0-8010-6936-9(X)) Baker Bks.
Light, Michael D. God's Principles of Prosperity. 2009. 116p. pap. 13.99 (978-1-60791-707-6(6)) Xulon Pr., Inc.
Lilljana, Raven. Water Jars of Heaven. 2007. 224p. (ENG.). 24.99 (978-1-60266-646-7(6)); per. 14.99 (978-1-60266-645-0(8)) Xulon Pr., Inc.
Lilliea. The Sealed Book: The End of a Planetary Age. 2009. 632p. pap. 29.99 (978-1-4490-0248-0(X)) AuthorHouse.
Limatola, Patricia. A Lamp, a Light, & Victory: God's Word lights our way & gives direction to our Lives. 2009. pap. 9.99 (978-1-60696-711-9(8)) Tate Publishing & Enterprises, LLC.
Linamen, Karen. Only Nuns Change Habits Overnight: Fifty-Two Amazing Ways to Master the Art of Personal Change. 2008. (ENG., Illus.). 208p. pap. 13.99 (978-1-4000-7400-6(2), WaterBrook Pr.) Doubleday Religious Publishing Group, The.
Lindsay, Henry L. Prodigal Son, Prodigal Daughter, Come Back Home. 2009. 68p. pap. 10.99 (978-1-60791-898-1(6)) Xulon Pr., Inc.
Lindsay, Terry, compiled by. A Daring Faith in a Hazardous World: Build a Courageous Lifestyle with Lee Roberson. 2006. (Illus.). 186p. 14.99 (978-1-932307-61-0(3)) Emerald Hse. Group, Inc.
Lindsey, Coy. Perfect Wave: Reflecting God by Protecting the Earth. 2008. (ENG.). 112p. pap. 8.99 (978-0-8341-5026-3(3), 9780834150263) Beacon Hill Pr. of Kansas City.
Lindsey, Tusheena "Tee". God Transitions. 2008. 216p. pap. 14.99 (978-1-58169-290-7(0)) Genesis Communications, Inc.
Lindvall, Michael. Knowing God's Triune Story. 2010. (ENG.). pap. 12.95 (978-1-57153-149-0(1), Witherspoon Pr.) Curriculum Publishing, Presbyterian Church (U. S. A.).
Lindvall, Michael L. A Geography of God: Exploring the Christian Journey. 2007. (ENG.). 139p. per. 15.00 (978-0-664-23072-2(5)) Westminster John Knox Pr.
Lingerfelt, Gene. 10 Words That Can Change Your Life. 2007. (ENG.). 144p. 12.95 (978-0-9786581-1-3(6)) Lifebridge Bks.
Lingo, Susan L. Disciple Makers. 2008. 132p. pap. 19.99 (978-0-9760696-6-9(0)) Lingo, Susan Bks.
—Faith Finders. 2008. 132p. pap. 19.99 (978-0-9760696-7-6(9)) Lingo, Susan Bks.
—Hope Finders. 2008. 132p. pap. 19.99 (978-0-9760696-8-3(7)) Lingo, Susan Bks.
—Make & Serve. 2007. 116p. pap. 10.99 (978-0-9760696-0-7(1)) Lingo, Susan Bks.
—Value Seekers. 2008. 132p. pap. 19.99 (978-0-9760696-9-0(5)) Lingo, Susan Bks.
Link, Julie Ackerman. Above All, Love: Reflections on the Greatest Commandment. 2008. (ENG.). 240p. pap. 11.99 (978-1-57293-261-6(9)) Discovery Hse. Pubs.
Linn, Dennis, et al. Healing the Future: Personal Recovery from Societal Wounding. 2012. (978-1-61643-144-0(X)); 224p. pap. 19.95 (978-0-8091-4775-5(0)) Paulist Pr.
Lipford, Kathy. Seeking to Be A Woman of Grace. 2007. 48p. pap. 16.95 (978-1-4241-6631-2(4)) PublishAmerica, Inc.
Lipscomb, T. R. Dearest Children. 2008. 304p. pap. 19.00 (978-1-59755-128-1(7), Advantage Inspirational) Advantage Bks.
Littauer, Florence. Silver Boxes, 0 vols. 2009. 168p. pap. 11.99 (978-0-7852-9732-1(4)) Nelson, Thomas Inc.
Little, Bill. The Secret & Spirituality, 1 vol. 2008. (ENG.). 144p. pap. 12.95 (978-1-58980-591-0(7)) Pelican Publishing Co., Inc.
Little, Fletcher. A God of Another Chance. 2007. 52p. per. 9.95 (978-0-595-45051-0(2)) iUniverse, Inc.
Little, Paul E. How to Give Away Your Faith. 2008. (ENG.). 202p. per. 15.00 (978-0-8308-3421-1(4), IVP Bks.) InterVarsity Pr.
Littledale, Richard. Stale Bread: A Handbook for Speaking the Story. 2007. (Illus.). 250p. pap. (978-0-7152-0835-9(7)) Saint Andrew Pr., Ltd.
Litzman, Warren Lee, Sr. The Making of a Son. 2007. (ENG., Illus.). 82p. reprint ed. pap. 8.00 (978-0-9794765-6-3(9)) Christ-life Publishing House.
—This Then Is the Message Which We Have Heard of Him: What Exactly Is the Christ-life? 2007. 91p. pap. (978-0-9794765-0-1(X)) Christ-life Publishing House.
Lively, Peggy. Above Reproach: A Study of 1 Timothy 3. 2008. 68p. pap. 11.99 (978-1-60647-373-3(5)) Xulon Pr., Inc.
Livermore, David. What Can I Do? Making a Global Difference Right Where You Are, 1 vol. 2011. (ENG.). 208p. pap. 14.99 (978-0-310-32596-3(X)) Zondervan.
Livermore Jr., Jd. The Missing Link in God's Provisions. 2007. 176p. per. 13.99 (978-1-60266-932-1(5)) Xulon Pr., Inc.
Liversage, Jerry J. Responding 12-Step Recovery: Responding to the Truth-Recovery Through Jesus. 2009. 324p. pap. 21.99 (978-1-60791-915-5(X)) Xulon Pr., Inc.
Liversidge, Bill. Victory in Jesus: Embracing His Death & Receiving His Overcoming Life. McFarland, Ken, ed. 2007. 169p. pap. 12.95 (978-0-9793409-0-1(X)) Creative Growth Ministries.
Livigni, Matt. Journey Bread II: Five-Minute Meals for the Soul-Jesus Speaks. 2011. pap. 21.99 (978-1-61777-742-4(0)) Tate Publishing & Enterprises, LLC.
Living by the Word. Date not set. pap. 5.95 (978-0-87162-641-7(1)) Warner Pr. Pubs.
Living Water: Powerful Teachings from the International Bestselling Author of the Heavenly Man, 1 vol. 2009. (ENG.). 320p. pap. 4.49 (978-0-310-31833-0(5)) Zondervan.
Livingstone. God's Promises on Simplicity. 2008. (God's Promises Ser.). (ENG.). 160p. 3.99 (978-1-934068-98-4(5)) Authentic Media.
Livingstone, des. God's Promises on Prayer. 2008. (God's Promises Ser.). (ENG.). 160p. 3.99 (978-1-934068-96-0(9)) Authentic Media.
Llorca, Raymond. Radical Christ: A Biblical Criticism on God, Jesus & Christian Belief. 2009. 236p. 26.50 (978-1-60860-622-1(8), Eloquent Bks.) AEG Literary Publishing Services, Inc.
Loades, David. The Religious Culture of Marian England, 1 vol. 2010. (Religious Cultures in the Early Modern World Ser.). (ENG.). 224p. 99.00 (978-1-85196-921-0(7)) Pickering & Chatto Pubs., Ltd. GBR. Dist: Ashgate Publishing Co.
Lobel, Matt. Out of the Wild. 2006. pap. 13.99 (978-1-60034-765-8(7)) Xulon Pr., Inc.
Lobinger, F. Atencion Pastoral A Los Enfermos. 56p. 2.95 (978-980-350-101-3(1)) Sociedad de San Pablo COL. Dist: St Pauls/Alba Hse. Pubs.
Lochhaas, Philip H. Las Nuevas Religiones Cristianas. (Serie Respuesta).Tr. of New Christian Religions. (SPA.). 40p. pap. 2.95 (978-0-570-04940-1(7), 09-2513) Concordia Publishing Hse.
—Las Religiones Orientales. (Serie Respuesta).Tr. of Eastern Religions. (SPA.). 40p. pap. 2.95 (978-0-570-04938-8(5), 09-2511) Concordia Publishing Hse.
Locklear, Greg. Calvary & the Scarlet D. 2009. 143p. pap. 18.72 (978-0-557-11913-4(8)) Lulu Enterprises Inc.
Loeb, Daniel. Hands to War: Fighting, Weapons, & Self-Defense for Christian Families. 2010. 310p. pap. 30.00 (978-0-557-21885-1(3)) Lulu Enterprises Inc.
—Hands to War: Fighting, Weapons, & Self-Defense for Christian Families (8X11 Edition) 2010. 212p. pap. 30.00 (978-0-557-21916-2(7)) Lulu Enterprises Inc.
Lofaro, Ellie & Troccoli, Kathy. Spaghetti for the Soul: A Feast on Faith, Hope, & Love. 2008. (ENG.). 224p. pap. 13.99 (978-1-4000-7162-3(3)) Doubleday Religious Publishing Group, The.
Logan, Aja. A Single Mother's Perspective. 2007. 84p. per. 16.95 (978-1-4241-8281-7(6)) PublishAmerica, Inc.
Logan, E. James. The Language of Kings. 2011. 60p. pap. 9.95 (978-1-4620-1119-3(5)) iUniverse, Inc.
Logan, Royce. The Worship Principle. 2006. pap. 15.99 (978-1-59781-893-3(3)) Xulon Pr., Inc.
Logan, Sr. Plugging into Real Worship. 2007. pap. 10.99 (978-1-60266-011-3(5)) Xulon Pr., Inc.
Loganbill, Evangeline E. Man's Divinity. 2011. 110p. 39.95 (978-1-258-03237-1(6)) Literary Licensing, LLC.
Loggins, Robert, Sr. The Good News SOUL WINNING: Daily Devotional Journal. 2008. (Illus.). 160p. pap. 16.95 (978-0-9797899-5-3(8)) Loggins, Robert.
Lohorn, Jason L. The Gideon in You. 2011. 138p. pap. 11.95 (978-1-59330-733-2(0)) Aventine Pr.
London, Andrea. Notes for the Church: Transcribed By. 2009. 87p. pap. 9.95 (978-1-4327-4766-4(5)) Outskirts Pr., Inc.
Loney, Christie. Destination Holiness. 2010. 704p. (ENG.). 48.95 (978-1-4497-0305-9(4)); pap. 40.95 (978-1-4497-0304-2(6)) Author Solutions, Inc. (WestBow Pr.).
Long And Others, Jimmy. Emerging Culture. cd-rom 45.00 (978-0-8308-2143-3(0)) InterVarsity Pr.
Long, Charles. Where's the Power? 2007. 372p. per. 19.99 (978-1-60266-387-9(4)) Xulon Pr., Inc.
Long, Eddie L. The Elect Lady: Life's Interruptions Become Godly Opportunities. 2008. (Illus.). 191p. 19.99 (978-0-88368-281-4(8), 772814) Whitaker Hse.
Long, Fredrick J. Ancient Rhetoric & Paul's Apology: The Compositional Unity of 2 Corinthians. 2008. (Society for New Testament Studies Monograph Ser.). (ENG.). 312p. pap. 44.00 (978-0-521-07895-5(4)) Cambridge Univ. Pr.
Long, Herbert C. Built Stronger: I am what I Am. 2008. 144p. 22.99 (978-1-60791-221-7(X)); pap. 14.99 (978-1-60791-220-0(1)) Xulon Pr., Inc.
Long, Jason. The Religious Condition: Answering & Explaining Christian Reasoning. 2008. 284p. pap. 20.95 (978-1-4401-0648-4(7)) iUniverse, Inc.
Long, Laphoia V. It Was Good That I Was Afflicted. 2011. 136p. pap. 14.95 (978-1-4634-5035-9(4)) AuthorHouse.
Longenecker, Dwight & Blamires, Cyprian, eds. The Path to Rome. 10th ed. 2010. 412p. pap. (978-0-85244-729-1(9)) Gracewing, Ltd.
Longshore, Gracie. Infertility, Adoption & Say, How's the Weather? 2008. 352p. 32.99 (978-1-60647-464-8(2)); pap. 20.99 (978-1-60647-463-1(4)) Xulon Pr., Inc.
Looker, Patricia. The Search for Meaning in Nostalgia. 2006. 200p. per. 13.99 (978-1-59886-433-5(5)) Tate Publishing & Enterprises, LLC.
Looper, Patricia. Christmas Eve Stories. 2011. 192p. 22.99 (978-1-61379-061-8(9)); pap. 14.99 (978-1-61379-175-2(5)) Xulon Pr., Inc.
Lopez Beceiro, Emilia. God's Dining Room Table. 2007. 92p. per. (978-1-897373-12-5(0)) Word Alive Pr.
Lopez, Jeremy. The Power of the Eternal Now: Living in the Realm of I Am. 2011. (ENG.). 224p. pap. 14.99 (978-0-7684-3824-6(1)); 186p. (978-0-7684-3825-3(X)) Destiny Image Pubs.
Lopez, Leanette. Breaking the Cycle of Self-Doubt. 2007. 272p. per. 15.99 (978-1-60266-399-2(8)) Xulon Pr., Inc.
Lord, I'm Listening... ,but sometimes I Squawk: A Personal Devotion of Christian Growth. 2006. 24.95 (978-0-9748086-4-2(4)) Amelia Island Publishing.
Lord Jesus Christ, Will You Not Stay. 396p. 19.98 (978-0-7586-0344-9(4)) Concordia Publishing Hse.
Lord, Life Becomes More Simple. Date not set. pap. 1.25 (978-0-8341-9195-2(4), AN-2643) Lillenas Publishing Co.
Loren, Julia C. Shifting Shadows of Supernatural Power: A Prophetic Manual for Those Wanting to Move in God's Supernatural Power. 2006. 209p. per. 15.99 (978-0-7684-2369-3(4)) Destiny Image Pubs.
Lotegeluaki, Stanley O. The Holy Bible: the Refreshing . The New Four Intermediate Books Between Jude & Revelations by the Intergalactic Jesus Christ Superstar. 2011. 568p. pap. 29.63 (978-1-4567-5220-0(0)) AuthorHouse.
Lotz, Anne Graham. Expecting to See Jesus Participant's Guide with DVD: A Wake-up Call for God's People, 1 vol. 2011. (ENG.). 96p. pap., pap. 31.99 incl. DVD (978-0-310-68434-3(X)) Zondervan.
—Just Give Me Jesus. l.t. ed. 2009. (ENG.). 621p. pap. 17.99 (978-1-59415-291-7(8)) Cengage Gale.
—Just Give Me Jesus, 0 vols. 2009. 512p. pap. 16.99 (978-0-8499-2093-6(0)) Nelson, Thomas Inc.
—Pursuing More of Jesus. 2009. 108p. pap. (978-1-4158-6648-1(1)) LifeWay Christian Resources.
Louer, Chris. Generational Breakthrough. 2008. 72p. pap. 10.99 (978-1-60647-879-0(6)) Xulon Pr., Inc.
—I Hear I Obey. 2009. 84p. pap. 10.99 (978-1-60791-496-9(4)) Xulon Pr., Inc.
—The Listening Gift. 2008. 88p. pap. 10.99 (978-1-60647-804-2(4)) Xulon Pr., Inc.
—What Label Are You Wearing? 2009. 88p. pap. 10.99 (978-1-60791-494-5(8)) Xulon Pr., Inc.
Louer, Christine M. Get a Grip! on a Heavenly Perspective. 2008. 96p. pap. 9.99 (978-1-60647-370-2(0)) Xulon Pr., Inc.
Louf, Andre. The Way of Humility. 2007. (Monastic Wisdom Ser.). pap. 8.99 (978-0-87907-011-3(0)) Cistercian Pubns., Inc.
Lougee, Angela. Beyond Sonship to Friendship: How to Gain Uncommon Attention from God. 2008. 196p. pap. 13.99 (978-1-60477-948-6(9)) Xulon Pr., Inc.
Louise, Karen. My Lord & My God: Seeing God in Life's Valleys. 2011. 108p. 28.95 (978-1-4497-2887-8(1)); pap. 11.95 (978-1-4497-2886-1(3)) Author Solutions, Inc. (WestBow Pr.).
Louther, Joyce. Understanding the Seasons of God. 2007. 100p. per. 9.99 (978-1-60266-786-0(1)) Xulon Pr., Inc.
Love, Dorothy. Love Has Something to Say. 2009. 176p. pap. 14.95 (978-0-578-01285-8(5)) Love, Dorothy Exclusive.
Love, Helen Mendes. Reflections on the Upsides of Aging: Living with Joy & Purpose after Age 50. 2011. 316p. 37.95 (978-1-4497-1133-7(2)); pap. 22.95 (978-1-4497-1132-0(4)) Author Solutions, Inc. (WestBow Pr.).
Love, James R., Sr. Get over Yourself: Purposeful Kingdom Living in a Me-Centered World. 2006. (ENG.). 144p. pap. 10.99 (978-1-59979-007-7(6), Creation Hse.) Charisma Media.
Love, Ollie. Same Color. pap. 10.00 (978-1-56794-186-9(9)) Star Bible & Tract Corp.
Love, Valerie. God Is in Love with You. 2009. (ENG.). 288p. pap. 12.95 (978-1-60162-842-8(0)) Urban Bks.
Lovelace, Lygia. Time Travels & Pirate Telescopes. 2010. 292p. 35.95 (978-1-61507-265-1(9)); pap. 19.95 (978-1-61507-260-6(8)) Cross Bks. Publishing.
Lovelace, Marc. Does God Lie? 18.00 (978-0-687-09275-8(2)) Abingdon Pr.
Lovelace, Sherri. In the Midst of Spiritual Warfare. 2009. 104p. pap. 17.16 (978-0-557-05264-6(5)) Lulu Enterprises Inc.
Lovelace, Todd. Marked by Love: Helping Students Live A Life of Influence. 2010. pap. 9.99 (978-1-61566-317-0(7)) Tate Publishing & Enterprises, LLC.
Loveless, Caron Chandler. What If There Were No Sisters? A Gift Book for Sisters & Those Who Wish to Celebrate Them. 2009. (ENG., Illus.). 48p. 12.99 (978-1-4165-5198-0(0), Howard Bks.) Howard Books.
Lovely, Bea. You Bit My Brother, but You Won't Bite Me. 2007. 56p. per. 9.99 (978-1-56229-206-5(4), Christian Living Bks., Inc.) Pneuma Life Publishing, Inc.
Lovern, Sandy. Finding Your Way: A Spiritual GPS for Caregivers. 2010. (ENG.). 176p. pap. 14.99 (978-1-59669-246-6(4)) New Hope Pubs.
Low, L. F. Genuine Christianity. 2009. (ENG.). 312p. pap. 24.95 (978-1-58982-483-6(0), Millennial Mind Publishing) American Bk. Publishing Group.
Lowe, Jeff. The Kingdom of God. 2008. 128p. per. 13.99 (978-1-60477-073-5(2)) Xulon Pr., Inc.
Lowe, Jim. Achieving Your Divine Potential: Become All You Were Created to Be. 2007. 231p. 15.99 (978-0-88270-205-6(X)) Bridge-Logos Foundation.
Lowery, T. L. Walking in the Supernatural. 2007. 300p. per. 12.99 (978-0-88368-659-1(7), 776591) Whitaker Hse.
Lowney, Chris. Heroic Living: Discover Your Purpose & Change the World. 2009. (ENG.). 224p. 22.95 (978-0-8294-2442-3(3)) Loyola Pr.
Lowry, Kenneth and Deany. Not Many Wise Are Called. 2008. 116p. pap. 11.99 (978-1-60647-693-2(9)) Xulon Pr., Inc.
Lowry, Mark. The Temple of Divine Truth: Second Edition. Lowry, Montecue J., ed. 2008. 164p. 17.95 (978-1-4327-2745-1(1)); pap. 9.95 (978-1-4327-2591-4(2)) Outskirts Pr., Inc.
Lowry, Melanie E. Remember the Heights: Praying with God from the Sixth Day of Creation. 2010. pap. 14.99 (978-1-60696-330-2(9)) Tate Publishing & Enterprises, LLC.
Lowton, Steve. Journeys of the Heart & Mind. 2007. 208p. per. (978-1-906210-38-0(1)) Grosvenor Hse. Publishing Ltd.
Loy, Rod. 3 Questions: A Powerful Grid to Help You Live by the Grace of God. 2011. (ENG., Illus.). 208p. pap. 14.99 (978-1-936699-15-5(X)) Gospel Publishing Hse.
Loyola, Rodolfo. Manantial en la Ciudad: Streams in the City. (SPA.). (978-84-7645-344-5(2), 223477) Clie, Editorial.
Loyola, St. Ignatius. Thoughts of St. Ignatius Loyola for Every Day of the Year. McDougall, Alan G. & Ryan, Patrick J., trs. 2006. (ENG., Illus.). 144p. 22.00 (978-0-8232-2656-6(5)) Fordham Univ. Pr.
Loze, Dennis. Modern Christianity: God's Law or Man's Law? 2010. 232p. pap. 15.99 (978-1-4520-8026-0(7)) AuthorHouse.
Lua Kanda, Didier Vakombua Lusumbu. God S Miracles in Our Daily Life. 2011. 98p. pap. 10.99 (978-1-61379-317-6(0)) Xulon Pr., Inc.
Lucado, Max. Cada Dia Merece una Oportunidad: Despierta al Regalo de 24 Horas, 0 vols. annot. ed. 2007.Tr. of Everyday Deserves a Chance: Wake up

to the Gift of 24 Hours. (SPA.). 176p. per. 12.99 (978-1-60255-026-1(3)) Grupo Nelson.
—Come Thirsty Traveling Light Next Door Savior, 0 vols. 2008. (Lucado Classic Collection). 688p. 24.99 (978-0-8499-2103-2(1)) Nelson, Thomas Inc.
—Cure for the Common Life: Living in Your Sweet Spot. l.t. ed. 2008. (Walker Large Print Ser.). (ENG.). 350p. per. 17.95 (978-1-59415-227-6(6), Walker Large Print) Cengage Gale.
—Cure for the Common Life Small Group Study, 0 vols. 2006. 212p. per. 15.99 (978-1-4185-0605-6(2)) Nelson, Thomas Inc.
—Experiencing the Words of Jesus: Trusting His Voice, Hearing His Heart, 0 vols. 2009. 224p. pap. 19.99 (978-0-8499-2127-8(9)) Nelson, Thomas Inc.
—Facing Your Giants. l.t. ed. 2008. 331p. 30.95 (978-1-4104-0791-7(8)) Thorndike Pr.
—Facing Your Giants: Study Guide, 0 vols. 2006. 144p. per. 7.99 (978-1-4185-1415-0(2)) Nelson, Thomas Inc.
—Facing Your Giants: The God Who Made a Miracle Out of David Stands Ready to Make One Out of You, 0 vols. 2008. 256p. pap. 16.99 (978-0-8499-2102-5(3)) Nelson, Thomas Inc.
—Fearless: Imagine Your Life Without Fear, 0 vols. 2009. 240p. 24.99 (978-0-8499-2139-1(2)) Nelson, Thomas Inc.
—Fearless Small Group Discussion Guide. 128p. 2012. pap. 7.99 (**978-1-4016-7542-4(5)**) 2009. pap. 9.99 (978-1-4185-4271-9(7)) Nelson, Thomas Inc.
—A Gentle Thunder: Hearing God Through the Storm. 2012. 240p. pap. 15.99 (**978-0-8499-4733-9(2)**) Nelson, Thomas Inc.
—A Gentle Thunder: Hearing God through the Storm, 0 vols. 2009. (Bestseller Collection). 256p. 9.99 (978-0-8499-2148-3(1)) Nelson, Thomas Inc.
—He Chose the Nails: What God Did to Win Your Heart. l.t. ed. 2007. (Walker Large Print Ser.). (ENG.). 288p. per. 17.95 (978-1-59415-159-0(8), Walker Large Print) Cengage Gale.
—A Heart Like Jesus, 0 vols. 2009. 96p. pap. 9.99 (978-0-8499-2948-9(2)) Nelson, Thomas Inc.
—Imagine Your Life Without Fear, 0 vols. 2009. 64p. pap. 2.99 (978-0-8499-2020-2(5)) Nelson, Thomas Inc.
—In the Eye of the Storm. 2011. (ENG.). 240p. pap. 15.99 (**978-0-8499-4628-8(X)**) Nelson, Thomas Inc.
—Max on Life: Answers & Inspiration for Today's Questions. 2011. 256p. 24.99 (978-0-8499-4812-1(6)) Nelson, Thomas Inc.
—Max on Life: Answers & Inspiration for Today's Questions. l.t. ed. 2011. 486p. 30.99 (**978-1-4104-3867-6(8)**) Thorndike Pr.
—Max on Life (International Edition) Answers & Insights to Your Most Important Questions. 2011. 272p. pap. 15.99 (**978-0-8499-4874-9(6)**) Nelson, Thomas Inc.
—On the Anvil: Stories on Being Shaped into God's Image. 2008. (ENG.). 160p. per. 14.99 (978-1-4143-1553-9(8)) Tyndale Hse. Pubs.
—Outlive Your Life: Joining God's Plan to Change the World. 2010. (Outlive Your Life Ser.). (Illus.). 174p. pap., wbk. ed., pupil's gde. ed. (978-1-4158-6878-2(6)) LifeWay Christian Resources.
—Outlive Your Life: You Were Made to Make a Difference. 2010. 240p. 24.99 (978-0-8499-2069-1(8)) Nelson, Thomas Inc.
—Outlive Your Life: You Were Made to Make A Difference. l.t. ed. 2012. (ENG.). 355p. pap. 17.99 (**978-1-59415-416-4(3)**) Cengage Gale.
—Outlive Your Life: You Were Made to Make A Difference. 2012. 18.99 (**978-0-8499-4845-9(2)**); pap. 15.99 (**978-0-8499-4738-4(3)**) Nelson, Thomas Inc.
—El Trueno Apacible, 0 vols. 2008.Tr. of Gentle Thunder. (SPA.). 288p. pap. 16.99 (978-1-60255-253-1(3)) Grupo Nelson.
—When God Whispers Your Name. 256p. 2011. pap. 15.99 (978-0-8499-4710-0(3)) 2009. 9.99 (978-0-8499-2143-8(0)) Nelson, Thomas Inc.
—You can be everything god wants you to Be, 0 vols. 2010. 128p. 14.99 (978-0-8499-4665-3(4)) Nelson, Thomas Inc.
Lucas, Charles C. The Christian Bill of Rights. 2009. 108p. 21.49 (978-1-4389-7642-6(9)); pap. 13.99 (978-1-4389-7641-9(0)) AuthorHouse.
Lucas, Ernest. Think God, Think Science: Conversations on Life, the Universe & Faith. 2009. (ENG.). 112p. 16.99 (978-1-84227-609-9(3), Paternoster) Authentic Media.
Lucas, Ezra. The Jonah Complex: Not Forgiving People We Deem Unforgivable. 2010. 70p. pap. 15.99 (978-1-4500-6017-2(X)) Xlibris Corp.
Lucas, Irene. 30 Miracles in 30 Days: 5 Easy Steps to Co-Creating Unlimited Abundance, Healing & Health in All Areas of Your Life. 2009. 185p. pap. 15.00 incl. audio compact disk (978-1-886940-65-9(7)) Czark Mountain Publishing, Inc.
Luce, Annie. Time Together. 2011. 238p. pap. 15.99 (978-1-61215-630-9(4)) Xulon Pr., Inc.
Luce, Ron. ReCreate: Building a Culture in Your Home Stronger Than the Culture Deceiving Your Kids. (ENG.). 2010. 224p. pap. 14.99 (978-0-8307-5855-5(0)) 2008. 128p. pap. 12.99 (978-0-8307-4638-5(2)) Gospel Light Pubns.
—ReCreate Your World: Find Your Voice, Shape the Culture, Change the World. 2008. (ENG.). 144p. (J). pap. 12.99 (978-0-8307-4639-2(0)) Gospel Light Pubns.
Luchtenberg, Dick. Journey to Freedom. 2009. 252p. 26.99 (978-1-60791-704-5(1)); pap. 16.99 (978-1-60791-703-8(3)) Xulon Pr., Inc.
Luck, Kenny. Dream: Have You Caught God's Vision? 2007. (God's Man Ser.). (ENG.). 224p. per. 13.99 (978-1-57856-987-8(7), WaterBrook Pr.) Doubleday Religious Publishing Group, The.
—Dream Workbook: Have You Caught God's Vision? 2007. (God's Man Ser.). (ENG.). 160p. per. 14.99 (978-1-57856-992-2(3), WaterBrook Pr.) Doubleday Religious Publishing Group, The.
—Soar: Are You Ready to Accept God's Power? 2010. (God's Man Ser.). (ENG.). 256p. pap. 16.99 (978-1-57856-989-2(3), WaterBrook Pr.) Doubleday Religious Publishing Group, The.
Luck, Kenny & Arterburn, Stephen. Every Young Man, God's Man: Confident, Courageous, & Completely His. 2010. (Every Man Ser.). (ENG.). 320p. pap. 15.99 (978-0-307-45943-5(8), WaterBrook Pr.) Doubleday Religious Publishing Group, The.
Lucore, A. J. From Invisible: All the King's Horses Children's Biography of a Christ-Inspired Mission. 2009. 312p. pap. 18.99 (978-1-60791-252-1(X)) Xulon Pr., Inc.
Ludwick, James. The Simple Handbook: (for Christians Old & New) 2006. (ENG.). 56p. per. 16.95 (978-1-4241-4264-4(4)) PublishAmerica, Inc.
Ludwick, James R. Fundamentals of Christian Life: (in a Fallen World) 2007. 88p. per. 16.95 (978-1-4241-4707-6(7)) PublishAmerica, Inc.
Ludy, Eric. The Bravehearted Gospel: The Truth Is Worth Fighting For. 2008. 250p. pap. 13.99 (978-0-7369-2164-0(8)) Harvest Hse. Pubs.
Ludy, Leslie. Set-Apart Femininity: God's Sacred Intent for Every Young Woman. 2008. 250p. pap. 13.99 (978-0-7369-2286-9(5)) Harvest Hse. Pubs.
Ludy, Leslie & Ludy, Eric. When God Writes Your Love Story (Expanded Edition) The Ultimate Guide to Guy/Girl Relationships. exp. ed. 2009. (ENG.). 304p. pap. 14.99 (978-1-60142-165-4(6), Multnomah) Doubleday Religious Publishing Group, The.
Luedke, Robert James, creator. The Collected Eye Witness Slipcased Set. 2010. (Eye Witness Ser.). (ENG.). 390p. pap. 44.99 (978-0-9758924-8-0(7)) Head Pr. Publishing.
—Eye Witness: Unknown God. 2010. (Eye Witness Ser.). (ENG.). 128p. pap. 13.99 (978-0-9758924-7-3(9)) Head Pr. Publishing.
Lugo, Raul H. Passion for the Reign of God. 2007. 1.95 (978-0-8294-2485-0(7)) Loyola Pr.
Luka, Susan. Detoured. 2007. (ENG.). 120p. per. 10.99 (978-1-60034-915-7(3)) Xulon Pr., Inc.
Luke 2. (LifeLight Bible Studies: Course 23). pap., stu. ed. 5.50 (978-0-570-09588-0(3), 20-2747); pap. 8.99 (978-0-570-09587-3(5), 20-2745) Concordia Publishing Hse.
Lull, Howard. Unless the Lord Builds the House: Building A Strong Life. 2009. 160p. pap. 14.99 (978-1-61579-299-3(6)) Xulon Pr., Inc.
Luman, J. W. The Door unto Fulness. 2007. 157p. 15.00 (978-0-9796285-3-5(9)) International Fellowship of Covenant Ministries, The.
—The Gospel. 2007. 129p. 15.00 (978-0-9796285-7-3(1)) International Fellowship of Covenant Ministries, The.
—The Necessity of Spiritual Understanding. 2007. 127p. 15.00 (978-0-9796285-6-6(3)) International Fellowship of Covenant Ministries, The.
Lumpkin, Tamala. Dear God. 2011. 94p. pap. 10.99 (**978-1-61379-140-0(2)**) Xulon Pr., Inc.
Lundin, Roger. Believing Again: Doubt & Faith in a Secular Age. 2009. 320p. pap. 26.00 (978-0-8028-3077-7(3)) Eerdmans, William B. Publishing Co.
Lusk, Patti. God's Order. 2010. (ENG.). 192p. pap. 12.99 (978-1-61638-171-4(X), Creation Hse.) Charisma Media.
Lutchman, Bernie. Two Minute Warning. 2007. 312p. per. 17.99 (978-1-60266-561-3(3)) Xulon Pr., Inc.
Lute, Ronald K. The Spirit Within. 2010. pap. 13.99 (978-1-61566-982-0(5)) Tate Publishing & Enterprises, LLC.
Luther, Martin. Being Without Desire; the Best & Noblest Love; the Two Eyes Of. 2006. pap. 9.95 (978-1-4304-0819-2(7)) Kessinger Publishing, LLC.
—The Christ Life; True Rest in God Only; Should We Love Sin; 2006. pap. 9.95 (978-1-4304-0820-8(0)) Kessinger Publishing, LLC.
—Concerning Christian Liberty. 2010. 34p. pap. 14.14 (978-1-4432-1055-3(2)) General Bks. LLC.
—Concerning Christian Liberty. 2010. 42p. pap. 12.76 (978-1-162-65827-8(4)); 24.76 (**978-1-169-19585-1(7)**); 30.95 (978-1-161-42692-2(2)) Kessinger Publishing, LLC.
—Good & Bad Deeds & Lives; Self Renunciation; True & False. 2006. pap. 9.95 (978-1-4304-0823-9(5)) Kessinger Publishing, LLC.
—Of That Which Is Perfect; What Sin Is; Man & Adam's Fall; Man's. 2006. pap. 9.95 (978-1-4304-0822-2(7)) Kessinger Publishing, LLC.
Lutje, Leon. Rounding Home: A Chicago Cubs Fan's Guide to Ecclesiastes. 2011. pap. 16.99 (**978-1-61346-534-9(3)**) Tate Publishing & Enterprises, LLC.
Lutzer, Erwin W. Getting to No: How to Break a Stubborn Habit. 2007. (ENG.). 176p. per. 12.99 (978-0-7814-4514-6(0)) Cook, David C.
—Keep Your Dream Alive. 141p. pap. 9.99 (978-0-8307-3451-1(1), Regal Bks.) Gospel Light Pubns.
—When You've Been Wronged: Moving from Bitterness to Forgiveness. 2007. (ENG.). 176p. per. 14.99 (978-0-8024-8897-8(8)) Moody Pubs.
—When You've Been Wronged: Moving from Bitterness to Forgiveness. 2007. (ENG.). 256p. pap. 6.99 (978-0-8024-8898-5(6)) Moody Pubs.
Lutzer, Erwin W. & Lutzer, Erwin. 10 Lies about God: And the Truths That Shatter Deception, 1 vol. 2009. 256p. pap. 13.99 (978-0-8254-2945-3(5)) Kregel Pubns.
Lw: Bible Learners. 1.55 (978-0-7673-5432-5(X)) LifeWay Christian Resources.
Lw: Youth in Action. 1.55 (978-0-7673-5030-3(8)) LifeWay Christian Resources.
LW Ventures & Pathways. tchr. ed. 3.75 (978-0-7673-4272-8(0)) LifeWay Christian Resources.
Lyall, Ian. I Believe (a mini-encyclopedia of Christian Belief. 2009. 72p. pap. 12.50 (978-1-4092-6539-9(0)) Lulu Enterprises Inc.
—Words from the Pulpit. 2008. 244p. pap. 22.50 (978-1-4092-1043-6(X)) Lulu Enterprises Inc.
Lybeck, Garry L. Flirting with Potiphar's Wife. 2008. 184p. pap. 14.99 (978-1-60647-718-2(8)) Xulon Pr., Inc.
Lyle, Beth. Feed the Body - Nourish the Soul: A Hundred Easy Meal Plans & Family-Time Devotionals Devotions to Dine By. 2008. 240p. pap. 15.99 (978-1-60791-134-0(5)) Xulon Pr., Inc.
Lyle, JaNell. Men of Valor: Overcoming Fear, Doubt & Unbelief. 2007. per. 8.95 (978-0-9778261-4-8(7)) Truth Pubs.
Lyles, Darrin. Operations Power up in Christ: Overcoming the Worst of Times. 2008. 100p. pap. 12.95 (978-0-9802398-2-9(6)) Williams, Benjamin Publishing.
Lynch, Beverly A. A Meditative Journey in the Psalms & Proverbs. 2011. 410p. 34.99 (978-1-61215-481-7(6)); pap. 22.99 (978-1-61215-463-3(8)) Xulon Pr., Inc.
Lynch, Don. The Spirit & Power of Elijah: Prophetic Parallels of the Ancient Prophets & Leaders of Today. 2007. 188p. per. 15.99 (978-0-7684-2590-1(5)) Destiny Image Pubs.
Lynch, Richard. Usable Truth. 2007. (ENG.). 154p. 36.95 (978-0-548-07310-0(4)) Kessinger Publishing, LLC.
Lynes, John, et al, eds. Prism. 2008. 132p. pap. 12.00 (978-0-8298-1828-4(6)); 148p. pap. 12.00 (978-0-8298-1816-1(2)) Pilgrim Pr., The/United Church Pr.
Lynn, David, et al. Daily Directions. 2008. 144p. 21.99 (978-1-60647-001-5(9)) Xulon Pr., Inc.
Lynne, Chelle. Forged by the Fire of Adversity: Faith in Trying Times. 2009. 100p. pap. 10.99 (978-1-61579-006-7(3)) Xulon Pr., Inc.
Lyon, Mack. The Glorious Gospel. pap. 6.95 (978-0-929540-21-4(2)) Publishing Designs, Inc.
—Life, Death, & Beyond. pap. 6.95 (978-0-929540-17-7(4)) Publishing Designs, Inc.
Lyons, David & Richardson, Linda Lyons. Don't Waste the Pain: Learning to Grow Through Suffering. 2010. (Experience the Life Ser.). 272p. pap. 15.99 (978-1-61521-548-5(4)) NavPress Publishing Group.
Lyons, Gabe & Herbst, Norton. Engaging Post-Christian Culture: Our Mission in a New Context, 1 vol. 2010. (Q Society Room Ser.). (ENG.). 112p. pap., instr.'s gde. ed. 9.99 (978-0-310-32522-2(6)) Zondervan.
—The Spirituality of Science: How Science Strengthens Faith in God, 1 vol. 2010. (Q Society Room Ser.). (ENG.). 96p. pap., instr.'s gde. ed. 9.99 (978-0-310-32516-1(1)) Zondervan.
—Where You Live Matters: Developing a Vision for Your City, 1 vol. 2010. (Q Society Room Ser.). (ENG.). 112p. pap. 9.99 (978-0-310-32450-8(5)) Zondervan.
—The Whole Gospel Vol. 3: Revisiting Our Message to the World, 1 vol. 2010. (Q Society Room Ser.). (ENG.). 112p. pap., instr.'s gde. ed. 9.99 (978-0-310-32519-2(6)) Zondervan.
M' Roberts. Holier Than Thou. 2008. 220p. pap. 14.99 (978-1-60647-032-9(9)) Xulon Pr., Inc.
Mabie, Hamilton Wright. The Life of the Spirit. 2009. 376p. 26.99 (978-1-103-46997-0(5)); pap. 20.99 (978-1-103-46995-6(9)) BiblioBazaar.
—The Life of the Spirit. 2009. 174p. pap. (978-1-4589-2769-9(5)) Books LLC.
—The Life of the Spirit. 2007. (ENG.). 372p. 48.95 (978-0-548-10747-8(5)) Kessinger Publishing, LLC.
MacAloon, John J. Muscular Christianity & the Colonial & Post-Colonial World. 2007. (Sport in the Global Society Ser.). (ENG.). 216p. 130.00 (978-0-415-39074-3(5)) Routledge.
MacArthur, John. Equipados para la Batalla: Como Resistir al Enemigo de Tu Alma. Jibaja, Eduardo, tr. 2007. (SPA.). 239p. pap. 10.99 (978-0-311-46330-5(4), Editorial Mundo Hispano) Casa Bautista de Publicaciones.
—The God Who Loves, 0 vols. 2008. 272p. pap. 15.99 (978-1-4002-7794-0(9)) Nelson, Thomas Inc.
—The Gospel According to Jesus: What Is Authentic Faith?, 1 vol. 2008. (ENG.). 304p. pap. 14.99 (978-0-310-29136-7(4)) Zondervan.
—The Jesus You Can't Ignore: What You Must Learn from the Bold Confrontations of Christ. l.t. ed. 2010. (ENG.). 416p. pap. 17.99 (978-1-59415-336-5(1)) Cengage Gale.
—The Jesus You Can't Ignore: What You Must Learn from the Bold Confrontations of Christ. 2010. 272p. pap. 15.99 (978-1-4002-0297-3(3)) 2009. 128p. pap. 9.99 (978-1-4002-0229-4(9)) Nelson, Thomas Inc.
—The Jesus You Can't Ignore: What You Must Learn from the Bold Confrontations of Christ. l.t. ed. 2009. 421p. 30.50 (978-1-4104-1958-3(4)) Thorndike Pr.
—The Master's Plan for the Church. 2008. (ENG.). 320p. per. 16.99 (978-0-8024-7845-0(X)) Moody Pubs.
—Simple Christianity: Rediscover the Foundational Principles of Faith. 2009. 192p. 17.99 (978-0-8307-4698-9(6), Regal Bks.) Gospel Light Pubns.
—Slave: The Hidden Truth about Your Identity in Christ. 240p. 2012. pap. 15.99 (**978-1-4002-0429-8(1)**) 2010. 22.99 (978-1-4002-0207-2(8)) Nelson, Thomas Inc.
—The Truth War: Fighting for Certainty in an Age of Deception, 0 vols. 2008. 256p. pap. 15.99 (978-1-4002-0240-9(X)) 2007. 160p. per. 9.99 (978-1-4185-1421-1(7)) Nelson, Thomas Inc.
—Welcome to the Family, 0 vols. 2008. 144p. pap. 10.99 (978-1-4002-7793-3(0)) Nelson, Thomas Inc.
MacArthur, John, ed. & contrib. by. Think Biblically! Recovering a Christian Worldview. 2009. 368p. pap. 17.99 (978-1-4335-0398-6(0)) Crossway.
MacArthur, John F. Gospel According to Jesus: What Is Authentic Faith?, 1 vol. 20th rev. enl. ed. 2008. (ENG.). 320p. (gr. 13). pap. 19.99 (978-0-310-28729-2(4)) Zondervan.
Macaulay, Susan Schaeffer. For the Children's Sake: Foundations of Education for Home & School. 2009. 166p. pap. 14.99 (978-1-4335-0695-6(5)) Crossway.
Maccaro, Janet. How to Live Longer. 2009. (ENG.). 224p. pap. 10.99 (978-1-59979-756-4(9), Siloam Pr.) Charisma Media.
MacDonald, George. The Hope of the Gospel. 2007. (ENG.). 120p. per. (978-1-4065-3002-5(6)) Dodo Pr.
Macdonald, James. Beyond Belief: Two Thousand Years of Bad Faith in the Christian Church. 2011. 512p. 74.95 (978-0-86372-346-9(2)) Garnet Publishing, Ltd. GBR. Dist: International Publishers Marketing.
MacDonald, James. Como la Lluvia: Un Encuentro con Dios Que Te Empapara de Gozo. 2006. 210p. per. 9.99 (978-0-8054-4496-4(3), B&H Bks.) B&H Publishing Group.
—Lord, Change My Attitude: Before Its Too Late. 2008. (ENG.). 312p. per. 14.99 (978-0-8024-3439-5(8)) Moody Pubs.
Macelvay, E. K. Finding the Peace of God Though Abused. 2010. 124p. pap. 11.95 (978-1-61507-335-1(3)) Cross Bks. Publishing.
MacGuire, Meade. The Life of Victory; His Cross & Mine; Lambs among Wolves: A Trilogy. 2009. pap. (978-0-9744082-6-2(3)) Orion Publishing Co.
Machowski, Martin. Old Story New: Ten-Minute Devotions to Draw Your Family to God. 2012. (ENG.). 416p. pap. 19.99 (**978-1-936768-66-0(6)**) New Growth Pr.
Macias, Kathi. Beyond Me: Living a You-First Life in a Me-First World. 2008. (ENG.). 224p. pap. 12.99 (978-1-59669-220-6(0)) New Hope Pubs.
Mack, Lauri. Rejected yet Loved. 2010. 108p. pap. 10.95 (978-1-59330-678-6(4)) Aventine Pr.
Mack, Wayne A. Maximum Impact: Living & Loving for God's Glory. 2010. pap. (978-1-59638-204-6(X)) P & R Publishing.
Mack, Wayne A. & Howard, Deborah. "It's Not Fair!" Finding Hope When Times Are Tough. 2008. 158p. pap. 11.99 (978-1-59638-112-4(4)) P & R Publishing.
MacKie, Elsie. Far Horizons. 2011. 222p. pap. 15.99 (**978-1-61379-759-4(1)**) Xulon Pr., Inc.
MacLeod, M. Donna. Seasons of Hope Guidebook: Creating & Sustaining Catholic Bereavement Groups. 2007. 191p. per., instr.'s gde. ec. 19.95 (978-1-59471-111-4(9)) Ave Maria Pr.
—Seasons of Hope Participant Journal Four, 4 vols. 2007. 63p. pap., pupil's gde. ed. 5.95 (978-1-59471-115-2(1)) Ave Maria Pr.
—Seasons of Hope Participant Journal One, 4 vols. 2007. 63p. pap., pupil's gde. ed. 5.95 (978-1-59471-112-1(7)) Ave Maria Pr.
—Seasons of Hope Participant Journal Three, 4 vols. 2007. 63p. pap., pupil's gde. ed. 5.95 (978-1-59471-114-5(3)) Ave Maria Pr.
—Seasons of Hope Participant Journal Two, 4 vols. 2007. 63p. pap., pupil's gde. ed. 5.95 (978-1-59471-113-8(5)) Ave Maria Pr.
Macmillan, Carl. Reality of Truth. 2006. 21.99 (978-1-60034-579-1(4)) Xulon Pr., Inc.
MacMillan, Carl. Reality of Truth. 2006. pap. 13.99 (978-1-60034-579-4(6)) Xulon Pr., Inc.
MacMillan, John A. The Authority of the Believer. 2007. 174p. pap. 12.99 (978-1-60066-083-2(5)) WingSpread Publishers.
MacMillan, Rev. J. A. The Authority of the Believer: Principles set forth in the Epistle to the Ephesians. 2011. 42p. pap. 6.99 (**978-1-61720-271-1(1)**) Wilder Pubns., Ltd.
MacMillan, Rev. J. A. & MacMillan, John A. The Authority of the Intercessor. 2011. 28p. pap. 5.99 (**978-1-61720-272-8(X)**) Wilder Pubns., Ltd.
—Spiritual Authority: The Believer & the Intercessor. 2011. 68p. pap. 9.99 (**978-1-61720-273-5(8)**) Wilder Pubns., Ltd.
MacNeil, John. The Spirit-Filled Life. 2009. 78p. pap. (978-1-151-43454-8(X)) Books LLC.
—The Spirit-Filled Life. 2010. 46p. pap. 11.21 (978-1-153-65647-4(7)) General Bks. LLC.
Macomber, Debbie. God's Guest List: Welcoming Those Who Influence Our Lives. l.t. ed. 2011. 287p. 30.99 (978-1-4104-3144-8(4)) Thorndike Pr.
—One Perfect Word: One Word Can Make All the Difference. 2012. (ENG.). 224p. 22.99 (978-1-4391-9059-3(3), Howard Bks.) Howard Books.
Macy, Howard R. Stepping in the Light: Life in Joy & Power. 2006. xii, 153p. (978-0-944350-69-0(0)) Friends United Pr.
Madding, Leigh Ann. Because I Lived It: Daily Devotions from A Life Changed by God's Grace. 2010. 376p. 39.95 (978-1-4497-0430-8(1)); pap. 24.95 (978-1-4497-0429-2(8)) Author Solutions, Inc. (WestBow Pr.).
Maddox, Marilyn H. Treasures of the Heart. 2011. 358p. 22.99 (**978-1-59467-244-6(X)**) Xulon Pr., Inc.
Maeba, Lawrence Nubari. The Wonders of Life. 2011. 240p. pap. 15.99 (**978-1-61215-908-9(7)**) Xulon Pr., Inc.
Maffeo, Richard. Lessons along the Journey: No Subtitle. 2008. 136p. pap. 13.99 (978-1-60647-658-1(0)) Xulon Pr., Inc.
Magada, Jeffrey M. The Good Life: You Can Walk in God's Perfect Will. 2011. (ENG.). pap. 15.99 (978-0-7684-3097-4(6)) Destiny Image Pubs.
Magee, Marty. Ebenezer & Ninety Eight Friends. 2008. pap. 14.95 (978-0-9797863-4-1(7)) Lighthouse Publishing.
Maggiolini, Sandro. Ultimas Realidades. 96p. 2.95 (978-980-207-368-7(1)) Paulinas VEN. Dist: St Pauls/Alba Hse. Pubs.

C

Maggiori, Dee. In the Spirit: Living A Christian Life. 2011. 160p. 22.23 (978-1-4670-3939-0(X)); pap. 14.95 (978-1-4520-7995-0(1)) AuthorHouse.

Mahaffy, Jr. What Would You Do? 2007. 108p. per. 10.99 (978-1-60477-231-9(X)) Xulon Pr., Inc.

Mahan, Frederick. God Alone Is the Truth & the Way: How to Survive the Decline of America. 2008. 224p. pap. 17.95 (978-0-595-52637-6(3)) iUniverse, Inc.

Mahaney, C. J. La Vida Cruzcentrica: Lo Principal de Mantener el Evangelio. 2007. 88p. per. 2.99 (978-0-7899-1595-5(2)) Editorial Unilit.

—Worldliness: Resisting the Seduction of a Fallen World. 2008. 191p. pap. (978-1-4335-0486-0(3)) Crossway.

Mahaney, C. J., ed. Worldliness: Resisting the Seduction of a Fallen World. 2008. 192p. 12.99 (978-1-4335-0280-4(1)) Crossway.

Maiden, Glen B. The Treasure: Healing the Hurt of the Post Modern Heart. 2011. 206p. pap. 19.99 (978-1-4568-8390-4(9)) Xlibris Corp.

Main, Bruce D. Why Jesus Crossed the Road: Learning to Follow the Unconventional Travel Itinerary of a First-Century Carpenter & His Ragtag Group of Friends As They Hop Fences, Cross Borders, & Generally Go Where Most People Don't. 2010. (ENG.). 224p. pap. 13.99 (978-1-4143-2660-3(2), SaltRiver) Tyndale Hse. Pubs.

Main, Robin. Santa-Tizing: What's Wrong with Christmas And How to Clean It Up. 2008. 364p. pap. 20.99 (978-1-60791-115-9(9)) Xulon Pr., Inc.

Mair, Devan. The Devil Your Adversary. 2006. pap. 8.99 (978-1-60034-146-5(2)) Xulon Pr., Inc.

—Leaving egypt going into the promised Land. 2006. pap. 9.99 (978-1-60034-148-9(9)) Xulon Pr., Inc.

—The Triune Godhead. 2006. pap. 8.99 (978-1-60034-147-2(0)) Xulon Pr., Inc.

—Waiting on the Lord. 2006. pap. 9.99 (978-1-60034-606-4(5)) Xulon Pr., Inc.

—When God Gets Angry. 2006. pap. 9.99 (978-1-60034-607-1(3)) Xulon Pr., Inc.

Majdali, Kameel. Pass the Salt. 265p. pap. (978-1-85240-285-3(7)) Sovereign World, Ltd.

Majestic Warriors Of Prayer. 101 Confessions: For President Barack Obama, the Obama Family & the Nation. 2009. 124p. pap. 11.99 (978-1-4389-8098-0(1)) AuthorHouse.

Makuannen, Yaqob. Man Woman & Spirit. 2007. 27.95 (978-0-9801297-3-1(7)); pap. 19.95 (978-0-9801297-2-4(9)) G Publishing LLC.

Malachi, Marlene. He Is Alive! The miracles of God in my personal Life. 2009. 92p. pap. 10.95 (978-1-4327-1209-9(8)) Outskirts Pr., Inc.

—The Sheep & the Goats; the Wheat & the Chaff, Ruth & Orpah - the CHURCH & ISRAEL: A Message to His Beloved Bride! 2010. 108p. pap. 11.95 (978-1-4327-5453-2(X)) Outskirts Pr., Inc.

Malarkey, Kevin. The Boy Who Came Back from Heaven: A Remarkable Account of Miracles, Angels, & Life Beyond This World. (ENG.). 2011. 264p. pap. 15.99 (978-1-4143-3607-7(1)) 2010. 248p. 24.99 (978-1-4143-3606-0(3)) Tyndale Hse. Pubs.

Malarkey, Kevin & Malarkey, Alex. The Boy Who Came Back from Heaven: A Remarkable Account of Miracles, Angels, & Life Beyond This World. l.t. ed. 2011. 335p. pap. 17.99 (978-1-59415-387-7(6)) Cengage Gale.

Maldonado, Ana G. From Prayer to Warfare. 2007. (Illus.). 171p. 16.99 (978-1-59272-179-5(6)) GM Ministries.

Maldonado, Guillermo. The Family: Restoring the Moral Structure of the Family. 2nd ed. 2007. 162p. per. 13.99 (978-1-59272-087-3(0)) GM Ministries.

—Forgiveness: How to Deal with Offenses. 2007. 76p. per. 7.99 (978-1-59272-040-8(4)) GM Ministries.

—Inner Healing & Deliverance. 4th ed. 2007. 269p. per. 14.99 (978-1-59272-007-1(2)) GM Ministries.

Malesic, Jonathan. Secret Faith in the Public Square: An Argument for the Concealment of Christian Identity. 2009. 256p. (C). pap. 28.00 (978-1-58743-226-2(9)) Brazos Pr.

Malick, Faisal. More Glory: Open Your Heart to All of God. 2011. 240p. pap. 16.99 (978-0-7684-3089-9(5)) Destiny Image Pubs.

—Positioned to Bless: Secrets to Fulfilling Your Divine Assignment. 2008. pap. 15.99 (978-0-7684-2694-6(4)) Destiny Image Pubs.

Mallory, Pat. A godly man? who can find One? 2007. (ENG.). 21.99 (978-1-60266-031-1(X)); pap. 13.99 (978-1-60266-030-4(1)) Xulon Pr., Inc.

—I Hear My Father Calling... So What What's a Girl to Do. 2009. 88p. pap. 10.99 (978-1-60791-877-6(3)) Xulon Pr., Inc.

—Into Each Life Some Rain Must Fall... but, God! 2010. 110p. pap. 11.99 (978-1-60957-522-9(9)) Xulon Pr., Inc.

Mallory, Tammi. Fishing in the 21st Century. 2006. pap. 10.99 (978-1-60034-748-1(7)) Xulon Pr., Inc.

Mally, Sarah. Making Brothers & Sisters Best Friends Coloring Book. 2008. (Illus.). 64p. (J). 7.00 (978-0-9719405-5-0(X)) Tomorrow's Forefathers, Inc.

Malone, Avon. Press to the Prize: Studies in Philippians. pap. 7.99 (978-0-89098-107-8(8)) Twentieth Century Christian Bks.

—The Purpose & the People: God's Eternal Plan - Studies in Ephesians. pap. 7.99 (978-0-89098-139-9(6)) Twentieth Century Christian Bks.

Malone, Bette. Life's Best Philosophies: A Collection of Words of Wisdom. 2007. 275p. per. 26.95 (978-1-892076-36-6(5)) Dancing Moon Pr.

Malone, Henry. Shame: Identity Thief. 2007. (ENG.). 160p. per. 13.00 (978-0-9717065-4-5(9)) Vision Life Pubns.

Malone, Sidney. HT Be a Producer & Not Just a Consumer. 2008. 52p. 7.99 (978-1-60247-271-6(8)) Tate Publishing & Enterprises, LLC.

A Man & His World. (Discover Life Ser.). tchr. ed. 7.35 (978-1-56212-105-1(7), 153065) Faith Alive Christian Resources.

Manahzekpah, Manah. Words of Inspiration. 2009. 36p. pap. 10.75 (978-1-60693-553-8(4), Strategic Bk. Publishing) AEG Literary Publishing Services, Inc.

Mancha, Ma & Mancha, Sharon E. The Power of Intimacy with Christ: Overcoming the Obstacles that Hinder Intimacy. 2009. 108p. 21.49 (978-1-4389-9932-6(1)) AuthorHouse.

Mancha, Sharon E. The Power of Intimacy with Christ: Overcoming the Obstacles that Hinder Intimacy. 2009. 108p. pap. 12.99 (978-1-4389-9931-9(3)) AuthorHouse.

Mangan, David. God Loves You: And There's Nothing You Can Do about It. 2008. 152p. per. 12.99 (978-0-86716-839-6(0), Servant Bks.) Franciscan Media.

Mangas, Alexandria & Mangas, Janet Hommel. Oxygen for the Swimmer. 2009. 132p. pap. 14.99 (978-1-60791-603-1(7)) Xulon Pr., Inc.

Mangis, Michael W. Signature Sins: Taming Our Wayward Hearts. 2008. (ENG.). 244p. pap. 16.00 (978-0-8308-3515-7(6), IVP Bks.) InterVarsity Pr.

Mangold, Gail E. When God Calls. 2010. 102p. pap. 10.99 (978-1-60957-533-5(4)) Xulon Pr., Inc.

Manigo, Paula. The Pain I've Suffered Was Worth the Gain I've Accomplished. 2009. 84p. pap. 12.99 (978-1-4389-6807-0(8)) AuthorHouse.

Manis, Rick. FULLNESS! Living Beyond Revivals & Outpourings. 2009. 139p. pap. 14.99 (978-0-578-01689-4(3)) Empyrion Pr.

Manker, Dayton A. Invasion from Heaven. pap. 5.99 (978-0-88019-073-2(6)) Schmul Publishing Co., Inc.

Mann, Alan. Atonement for a Sinless Society: Engaging with an Emerging Culture. 2007. (ENG.). 224p. per. 19.99 (978-1-84227-355-5(8), Paternoster) Authentic Media.

Mann, Donald C. Battle Prayer for Divine Healing: Field Manual 2. 2011. 564p. 38.99 (978-1-934769-48-5(7)); pap. 29.99 (978-1-934769-46-1(0)) McDougal & Assocs.

Mann, Gerald. Common Sense Religion: Renewing Your Christian Values. 166p. (Orig.). reprint ed. pap. 9.95 (978-0-9647272-0-5(X)) Riverbend Pr.

Mann, Michael. Kairos Letters: Love Letters to Believers Behind Bars. 2011. pap. 11.99 (978-1-61346-572-1(6)) Tate Publishing & Enterprises, LLC.

Mann, Thomas W. To Taste & See: Exploring Incarnation & the Ambiguities of Faith. 2008. 160p. pap. 18.00 (978-1-55635-849-4(0)) Wipf & Stock Pubs.

Mann, Tommy. All the Law: How to Obey the Entire Law Just by Showing Love, 1 vol. 2009. 101p. pap. 16.95 (978-1-61546-642-9(8)) PublishAmerica, Inc.

Mann, Tommy. Asleep in Heaven's Nursery. 2011. pap. 10.99 (978-1-61777-557-4(6)) Tate Publishing & Enterprises, LLC.

Manning, Galen. Right Choices. 2008. 404p. 33.99 (978-1-60477-933-2(0)); pap. 21.99 (978-1-60477-932-5(2)) Xulon Pr., Inc.

Manning, James. The Manifestation of the Sons of God. 2007. 268p. per. 15.99 (978-1-60266-519-4(2)) Xulon Pr., Inc.

Manning, John W. Living Victorious in Stressful Situations Through Jesus Christ: Jesus Is the Only Way. 2009. 64p. pap. 10.49 (978-1-4389-1459-6(8)) AuthorHouse.

Manning Jones, Pamela. Full Throttle: Giving Control to God. 2006. (ENG.). 108p. per. 13.99 (978-1-4141-0757-8(9)) Pleasant Word.

Manning, Michael. The Fifteen Faces of God: A Quest to Know God Through the Parables of Jesus. 2010. (ENG.). 208p. 18.00 (978-0-385-53161-0(3), Doubleday Religion) Doubleday Religious Publishing Group, The.

Manning, T. Deering. Eye Witnesses of His Majesty. 2007. 256p. per. 15.99 (978-1-60266-216-2(9)) Xulon Pr., Inc.

Manning, Wanda. Harvesting the Fruit of the Spirit: By Wanda Manning. 2008. pap. 14.95 (978-0-9779445-7-6(3)) Zoe Life Publishing.

Manolopoulos, Mark & MANOLOPOULOS, M. If Creation Is a Gift. 2009. (SUNY series in Theology & Continental Thought Ser.). 196p. 65.00 (978-0-7914-9393-9(8)) State Univ. of New York Pr.

Manser. This Is Life In Christ. 208p. pap. 19.99 (978-0-340-65651-8(4), Hodder & Stoughton) Hodder General Publishing Div. GBR. Dist: Trafalgar Square Publishing.

—This Is Our Faith. 256p. pap. (978-0-340-65650-1(6), Hodder & Stoughton) Hodder General Publishing Div.

—This Is Our God. 256p. pap. 22.99 (978-0-340-65649-5(2), Hodder & Stoughton) Hodder General Publishing Div. GBR. Dist: Trafalgar Square Publishing.

Manskar, Steven W., intro. A Disciple's Journal: Daily Bible Reading & Guidance for Reflection: Year A. 2007. 127p. spiral bd. 12.00 (978-0-88177-517-4(7)) Discipleship Resources.

Manton, Thomas. The Works of Thomas Manton, 22 vols. reprint ed. 465.00 (978-0-404-04200-4(7)) AMS Pr., Inc.

Manton, Thomas & Kistler, Don. A Treatise of Self-Denial. 2011. (978-0-9826155-8-4(2)) Northampton Pr., The.

Manz, Charles C. The Leadership Wisdom of Jesus: Practical Lessons for Today. 2009. (Playaway Adult Nonfiction Ser.). (ENG.). 34.99 (978-1-60775-721-4(4)) Findaway World, LLC.

Maoz, Baruch. A Prophet on the Run: A Devotional Commentary on the Book of Jonah. 2008. 116p. pap. 10.99 (978-1-60647-237-8(2)) Xulon Pr., Inc.

Marburger, Michael. From Speak to Share: How God Builds a Christian. 2010. pap. 20.99 (978-1-61566-772-7(5)) Tate Publishing & Enterprises, LLC.

March, Kenneth. Is God Calling His People to Leave the un-Holy Roman Catholic Church. 2010. 116p. pap. 11.99 (978-1-60957-417-8(6)) Xulon Pr., Inc.

Marchell, Kim. My Body Is Not Ready for My Return: The First Step in the Right Direction. 2010. 163p. pap. 15.95 (978-1-4327-5424-2(6)) Outskirts Pr., Inc.

Marchell, Kim. One Member Closer to Creating the Perfect Man: The Second Step in the Right Direction. 2011. 205p. pap. 17.95 (978-1-4327-7346-5(1)) Outskirts Pr., Inc.

Margo Snyder, Jr., as told by. Looking for Angels: Volume Two. 2007. (Illus.). (J). pap. (978-0-9796172-7-0(8)) Snyder, Margo.

Margo Snyder, Margo Snyder, Jr., abr. Looking for Angels. 2009. (Illus.). pap. (978-0-9796172-5-6(1)) Snyder, Margo.

Maria. And the Word Became Flesh. 2009. 88p. pap. 10.99 (978-1-60791-649-9(5)) Xulon Pr., Inc.

Maria, Anacondia. Te Llamaron Bienaventurada/You Will Be Called Blessed, 1 vol. 2008. (SPA.). 112p. pap. 9.99 (978-0-8297-5310-3(9)) Vida Pubs.

Mariades, Helena M. Strike the Target! 2010. 428p. 34.99 (978-1-61579-293-1(7)) Xulon Pr., Inc.

Maricle, Christopher. The Jesus Priorities: 8 Essential Habits. 2007. (Illus.). 143p. per. 16.00 (978-0-8358-9914-7(4)) Upper Room Bks.

Marie, Dawn. He's Our Father. 2009. 136p. pap. 14.99 (978-1-61579-182-8(5)) Xulon Pr., Inc.

Marie, Janice. But God - I Blew It! 2007. 208p. (ENG.). 24.99 (978-1-60266-532-3(X)); per. 14.99 (978-1-60266-524-8(9)) Xulon Pr., Inc.

Marie, Natalie. Race for Your Life. 2009. pap. 7.99 (978-1-60799-066-6(0)) Tate Publishing & Enterprises, LLC.

Marinez, Tony. Answers to Tough Questions: Finding Biblical Answers to the Difficulties We Face. 2010. pap. 14.99 (978-1-61579-943-5(5)) Xulon Pr., Inc.

Marinkovich, Frank. Reviving the Spirit of Zerubbabel: Keys to Successful Jurisdictional Joining. 2008. pap. 10.99 (978-1-60647-043-5(4)) Xulon Pr., Inc.

Markett, Raymond. Count Your Blessings! 2010. 68p. pap. 12.40 (978-0-578-00085-5(7)) Four Rivers Publishing.

Markham, James Edward. Chosen in Him: Persistence Through Suffering. 2008. 168p. pap. 14.99 (978-1-60791-216-3(3)) Xulon Pr., Inc.

Markham, R. E. Ultimate Mystery. 2008. 100p. pap. 10.49 (978-1-4343-9729-4(7)) AuthorHouse.

Markland, D. Min. Women! Be Silent No More. 2009. 216p. pap. 15.99 (978-1-60791-415-0(8)) Xulon Pr., Inc.

Marks, Al. The God of Today: No Subtitle. 2008. 148p. pap. 15.99 (978-1-60647-586-7(X)) Xulon Pr., Inc.

Marks, Christian. Growing up Backwards. 2009. 116p. pap. 10.99 (978-1-4490-2082-8(8)) AuthorHouse.

Marlin, Sidney L. Woman, Yes You Can! 2011. 106p. pap. 11.99 (978-1-61379-010-6(4)) Xulon Pr., Inc.

Marnu, Michael. Making your Life A Success: Wisdom, Guidance & Strength for Life. 2011. 364p. pap. 20.47 (978-1-4567-7239-0(2)) AuthorHouse.

Marple, Norman. Worship That Speaks to the Core of Our Being. 2008. 116p. pap. (978-3-639-06317-2(1)) VDM Verlag Dr. Mueller e.K.

Marryat, Florence. For Ever & Ever. 2009. 336p. pap. (978-0-217-83690-6(9)) Books LLC.

Marshall, Carl. The Light of Innocence: Christian Living. 2010. 136p. pap. 15.95 (978-1-4327-4816-6(5)) Outskirts Pr., Inc.

Marshall, Gene W. Jacob's Dream: A Christian Inquiry into Spirit Realization. 2009. 308p. pap. 21.95 (978-1-4401-1355-0(6)) iUniverse, Inc.

Marshall, John. Faith Family & Finances - 2008. 192p. pap. 15.00 (978-0-9820475-0-7(9)) Marshall, John Ministries.

Marshall, Rob. Taking on Goliath: How to Unleash the David in All of Us. 2006. (ENG.). 204p. 27.95 (978-1-60037-027-4(6)) Morgan James Publishing.

Marshall, Warner. Empowering Teens Through God's Word! Empowering Teens for Discipleship. 2011. 140p. 24.99 (978-1-4520-6212-9(9)); pap. 14.99 (978-1-4520-6207-5(2)) AuthorHouse.

Marsullo, F. Victoria Sobre los Espiritus Malignos.Tr. of Victory over Demonic Spirits. (SPA.). pap. 6.99 (978-958-9354-16-2(5), 550053) Editorial Unilit.

Marszalek, Therese. Extraordinary Miracles in the Lives of Ordinary People: Inspiring Stories of Divine Intervention. 2007. 284p. per. 14.99 (978-1-57794-825-4(4)) Harrison House Pubs.

Marti, Sechiquita Ratliff. Wealth Comes from Within! 2011. 106p. pap. 11.99 (978-1-61215-843-3(9)) Xulon Pr., Inc.

Martin, Catherine. Drawing Strength from the Names of God. 2010. 48p. 15.99 (978-0-7369-2578-5(3)) Harvest Hse. Pubs.

Martin, Donna. Living Frugally in an Unfrugal World. 2007. 60p. 7.00 (978-0-9718589-3-0(4)) Boonstra, Piet.

Martin, G. Donovan. Double-Dog Dare: The Journey Begins Here. 2011. 172p. 30.95 (978-1-4497-3014-7(0)); pap. 13.95 (978-1-4497-3013-0(2)) Author Solutions, Inc. (WestBow Pr.).

Martin, Glen & the Journey of Faith Pastoral Staff. The Journey of Life. 2011. 196p. 33.95 (978-1-4627-0521-4(9)); pap. 17.95 (978-1-4627-0520-7(0)) Cross Bks. Publishing.

Martin, Glenn W. Out of the Darkness of Academics into the Light of Jesus Christ-A True Story of Survival to Revival. 2009. 212p. pap. 19.99 (978-1-4389-8178-9(3)) AuthorHouse.

Martin Jr., George D. But What If I Fail. 2009. 104p. pap. 11.95 (978-1-4401-4759-3(0)) iUniverse, Inc.

Martin, Kenneth Roy. Godly Management. 2011. 48p. pap. 10.99 (978-1-61379-149-3(6)) Xulon Pr., Inc.

Martin, Marcus. Saving Faith: When Faith Is an Action. 2010. pap. 8.99 (978-1-61566-304-0(5)) Tate Publishing & Enterprises, LLC.

Martin, Mearle J. Thru My Eyes: God's Truth & Testimony of a Christian. 2007. per. 7.99 (978-1-59879-397-0(7)) Lifevest Publishing, Inc.

Martin, Noelle W. When It Hurts to Brea. 2011. 96p. pap. 19.95 (978-1-4560-6612-3(9)) PublishAmerica, Inc.

Martin, Red. Odds, Ends, Tidbits & Pieces. 2008. 128p. pap. 14.99 (978-1-60647-808-0(7)) Xulon Pr., Inc.

Martin, Roslyn. The Rapture Secret: Why Are We Still Here? 2009. pap. 11.99 (978-1-60696-628-0(6)) Tate Publishing & Enterprises, LLC.

Martinez, Janice. How Do I Know There Is a Heaven? 2008. 189p. pap. 24.95 (978-1-60610-136-0(6)) PublishAmerica, Inc.

Martínez, José M. Manual de Instruccion Para Nuevos: Instruction Manual for New. (SPA.). 192p. (978-84-7228-683-2(5), 220566) Clie, Editorial.

—Por Que Aun Soy Cristiano: Why Am I a Christian. (SPA.). (978-84-7645-178-6(4), 223217) Clie, Editorial.

Martini, Carlo Maria. At Your Word. Tulloch, Andrew, tr. from ITA. 45p. pap. 4.95 (978-0-85439-638-2(1)) St. Paul Pubns. GBR. Dist: St Pauls/Alba Hse. Pubs.

Martini, Carlos Maria. Dimension Contemplativa de la Vida. (SPA.). 48p. 4.95 (978-958-607-380-6(7)) Sociedad de San Pablo COL. Dist: St Pauls/Alba Hse. Pubs.

—Effata: Abrete. (SPA.). 128p. 5.95 (978-958-607-644-9(X)) Sociedad de San Pablo COL. Dist: St Pauls/Alba Hse. Pubs.

Martling, Allan. Voices from the Heart of GodÕs Inspired Word. 2011. 122p. pap. 15.00 (978-1-61097-027-3(6), Resource Pubns.) Wipf & Stock Pubs.

Martoia, Ron. The Bible As Improv: Seeing & Living the Script in New Ways, 1 vol. 2010. (ENG.). 224p. pap. 14.99 (978-0-310-28770-4(7)) Zondervan.

Marty, Martin E. Building Cultures of Trust. 2010. 200p. pap. 22.99 (978-0-8028-6546-5(1)) Eerdmans, William B. Publishing Co.

Martyn, John R. C. Saint Leander, Archbishop of Seville: A Book on the Teaching of Nuns & a Homily in Praise of the Church. 2008. (ENG.). 192p. 68.50 (978-0-7391-2771-1(3)) Lexington Bks.

Mary Mary. Be U: Be Honest, Be Beautiful, Be Intentional, Be Strong, Be You! 2010. (ENG., Illus.). 160p. pap. 14.99 (978-1-4391-6071-8(6), Howard Bks.) Howard Books.

Mascari, Angelina Kiena. Heart Cry. 2009. 116p. pap. 11.99 (978-1-60791-563-8(4)) Xulon Pr., Inc.

Masek, Paul. All Bottled Up. 2007. (YA). pap. 9.50 (978-0-9800909-1-8(1)) Out of the Box Records, LLC.

—Stirring It Up. 2007. (YA). pap. 9.50 (978-0-9800909-0-1(3)) Out of the Box Records, LLC.

—Stirring It up & All Bottled up - Two Volume Set. 2007. (YA). 15.00 (978-0-9800909-2-5(X)) Out of the Box Records, LLC.

Mashburn, Charles L. Be Still: ... & Know That I Am God. 2010. 376p. 39.95 (978-1-4497-0793-4(9)); pap. 24.95 (978-1-4497-0792-7(0)) Author Solutions, Inc. (WestBow Pr.).

Mashburn, Travis. Living Christianity. 2007. 164p. per. 13.99 (978-1-60266-213-1(4)) Xulon Pr., Inc.

Mashni, Steve. Trees of Abraham. 2008. per. 8.00 (978-0-9798207-2-4(3)) LoJo Publishing.

Mason, Debi. Arizona Clay. 2009. 143p. pap. 11.99 (978-1-60696-488-0(7)) Tate Publishing & Enterprises, LLC.

Mason, John. Believe You Can — the Power of a Positive Attitude, 1 vol. 2010. (ENG.). 208p. 5.99 (978-0-8007-8771-4(4)) Revell.

—You Can Do It: Even If Others Say You Can't. 2008. 192p. 5.99 (978-0-8007-8772-1(2)) Revell.

Mason, Lisa. Big Life Lessons from that Still, Small Voice. 2011. pap. 10.95 (978-0-7414-6386-9(5)) Infinity Publishing.

Mason, Lynn R. Something's Wrong, Someone's Missing. 2011. 44p. pap. 16.95 (978-1-4626-3477-4(X)) PublishAmerica, Inc.

Mason, Mark. American Idols: Reaching the Starbucks Generation. 2007. 196p. pap. 14.95 (978-1-4303-0882-9(6)) Lulu Enterprises Inc.

Mason, Mike. The Mystery of Children: What Our Kids Teach Us about Childlike Faith. 2007. (ENG.). 272p. per. (978-1-57383-412-4(2), Regent College Publishing) Regent College Publishing.

Mason, Thomas O. Transforming the Valley of Grief. 2009. 132p. pap. 14.99 (978-1-60791-616-1(9)) Xulon Pr., Inc.

Massey, M. F. Narcoleptic Church: Home of Slumbering Saints. 2010. pap. 11.99 (978-1-61566-097-1(6)) Tate Publishing & Enterprises, LLC.

Mast, Gerald J. Go to Church, Change the World: Christian Community As Calling. 2011. pap. (978-0-8361-9564-4(7)) Herald Pr.

Masters, Henry L. Makin' Room in the Inn: Christmas Hospitality Through an African American Experience. 2010. 64p. 7.00 (978-1-4267-0371-3(6)) Abingdon Pr.

Masters, Peter. Steps for Guidance: In the Journey of Life. 2nd ed. 2008. 134p. pap. (978-1-870855-66-2(3)) Wakeman Trust, The.

Masters, Thomas & Uelmen, Amy. Focolare: Living a Spirituality of Unity in the United States. 2011. 224p. pap. 16.95 (978-1-56548-374-3(X)) New City Community Pr.

Matejka, Larry. The Three Life Leadership Lessons. 2006. (ENG.). 112p. per. 13.99 (978-1-4141-0831-5(1)) Pleasant Word.

Matey, John J. When Good Men Do Nothing. 2008. 96p. pap. 8.99 (978-0-9749836-6-0(7)) Faithful Life Pubs.

Mathew, Thomson K. What Will Your Tombstone Say? 2008. 272p. per. 15.99 (978-1-60477-758-1(3)) Xulon Pr., Inc.

Mathewes-Green, Frederica. The Jesus Prayer: The Ancient Desert Prayer That Tunes the Heart to God. 2009. (ENG.). 196p. (gr. 13). pap. 16.99 (978-1-55725-659-1(4)) Paraclete Pr., Inc.

Mathews, Kenneth A. Leviticus: Holy God, Holy People. 2009. (Preaching the Word Ser.). 288p. 32.99 (978-1-4335-0628-4(9)) Crossway.

Mathias, Arthur. The Continuing Works of Christ: Exposing Unbelief. 2010. (ENG.). pap. 24.95 (978-0-9720656-5-8(2)) Wellspring Publishing.

Mathis, Larry & Dufek, Todd R. Tools of the Cross: Walking with the Master Carpenter. 2011. (ENG.). 154p. pap. 16.95 (978-1-60037-735-8(1)) Morgan James Publishing.

Mathis, Lena C. Jesus the Baptizer: No Subtitle. 2008. 232p. pap. 14.99 *(978-1-60647-606-2(8)*, Crown Oak Pr.) Xulon Pr., Inc.

Mathis, Phil. God Governs: The Scriptural Relationship between Predestination And a Freed Will (And How Learning this Will Help You Make a Fortune... And Then Give It Away) 2009. 156p. pap. 14.99 *(978-1-60791-118-0(3))* Xulon Pr., Inc.

Mathis, Rick. Finding a Grace-Filled Life. 2008. 112p. pap. 9.95 *(978-0-8091-4528-7(6))* Paulist Pr.

Mathison, John Ed. Transformed Living in Tough Times. 2010. 63p. pap. 8.00 *(978-0-687-65707-0(5))* Abingdon Pr.

—Treasures of the Transformed Life 40 Day Reading Book: Satisfying Your Soul's Thirst for More. 2006. 312p. per. 18.00 *(978-0-687-33445-2(4))* Abingdon Pr.

Matlawe Khatie, Ann Mabatimi. And It Became a Reality. 2007. 112p. per. 14.95 *(978-1-4327-0503-9(2))* Outskirts Pr., Inc.

Matlock, Dian Wells. Come Walk with Me to Glory: What Being A Christian Means to Me. 2011. 236p. 28.95 ***(978-1-4620-1202-2(7))***; pap. 18.95 ***(978-1-4620-1201-5(9))*** iUniverse, Inc.

Mattera, Joseph. Kingdom Awakening. 2010. (ENG.). 204p. pap. 15.99 *(978-0-7684-3264-0(2))* Destiny Image Pubs.

—Kingdom Revolution: Bringing Change to Your Life & Beyond. 2009. pap. 16.99 *(978-0-7684-3099-8(2))* Destiny Image Pubs.

Matthews, Edward M. The Collected Works of Edward M. Matthews, 3 vols. Bekken, Dean, ed. 2007. (Illus.). Vol. 1. 240p. 37.50 *(978-0-935461-95-4(7))* Vol. 2. (ENG., 257p. 50.00 *(978-0-935461-41-1(8))* Vol. 3. (ENG., 605p. 60.00 incl. cd-rom *(978-0-935461-42-8(6))* St. Alban Pr., San Diego.

Matthews, George. EXPECTATION: Looking Beyond Your Now (Second Edition) 2010. 84p. pap. 15.00 *(978-0-557-21371-9(1))* Lulu Enterprises Inc.

Mattox, Irene Young. Patterns for Living. pap. 7.99 *(978-0-89098-405-5(0))* Twentieth Century Christian Bks.

Mattox, Robert. The Christian Employee. 2007. per. *(978-1-59581-388-6(8)*, Brentwood Christian Pr.) Brentwood Communications Group.

Maul, Derek. Get Real: A Spiritual Journey for Men: Leader's Guide. 2007. 55p. 9.00 *(978-0-8358-9924-6(1))* Upper Room Bks.

—Unmaking of a Part Time Christ. 2009. 144p. pap. 16.00 *(978-0-8358-9992-5(6))* Upper Room Bks.

Maupin, Timothy. Touches of Grace. 2010. pap. 10.99 *(978-1-61663-012-6(4))* Tate Publishing & Enterprises, LLC.

Mauro, Philip. Kingdom Heresies of S. D. Gordon. pap. 2.99 *(978-0-87377-009-5(9))* GAM Pubns.

Maurus, J. Cultive Sus Sentimientos. 128p. 6.95 *(978-958-607-745-3(4))* Sociedad de San Pablo COL. Dist: St Pauls/Alba Hse. Pubs.

Maus, Tom A. God's Messenger: Called to Deliver Holy Spirit Revelation. 2008. 112p. pap. 13.95 *(978-1-4327-3261-5(7))* Outskirts Pr., Inc.

Mavrakos, Pastor Tony. God's Prescriptions for Healing the Hurts That Hinder Your Happiness. 2011. 254p. pap. 16.99 ***(978-1-61215-586-9(3))*** Xulon Pr., Inc.

Maxey, Gary S. The Latent Power of Mammon. pap. 2.99 *(978-0-88019-159-3(7))* Schmul Publishing Co., Inc.

Maxwell, Ashley. Life Throws Many Curves; Just let God be Your Coach. 2006. pap. 10.99 *(978-1-60034-580-7(8))* Xulon Pr., Inc.

Maxwell, John C. Desert Experience, 0 vols. 2008. 192p. pap. 12.99 *(978-1-4002-7797-1(3))* Nelson, Thomas Inc.

Maxwell, Lawrence. Forty Favorite Children's Stories. 2008. (Illus.). 132p. (YA). pap. 12.95 *(978-1-57258-573-7(0))* TEACH Services, Inc.

May, Gerald G. Addiction & Grace: Love & Spirituality in the Healing of Addictions. 2007. (Insight Ser.). (ENG., Illus.). 224p. pap. 14.99 *(978-0-06-112243-9(2)*, HarperOne) HarperCollins Pubs.

May, Iva. Shepherd-Shaped: I Am My Beloved's & He Is Mine. 2007. 260p. per. 14.95 *(978-0-929292-79-3(0)*, 800-747-0738) Hannibal Bks.

May, Lee. My God, My Politics: A Discussion on Faith & Politics. 2011. 180p. pap. 15.95 ***(978-1-936780-59-4(3))*** Mill City Pr., Inc.

May, Stephanie. Created in His Image: The Beauty of a Woman. 2008. 108p. pap. 11.99 *(978-1-60791-093-0(4))* Xulon Pr., Inc.

May, Teresa D. That Front Row Seat. 2010. 116p. pap. 11.99 *(978-1-60957-304-1(8))* Xulon Pr., Inc.

Mayberry, Gail. Secrets of a More Excellent Way: Inspirational Life Lessons My Mother Taught Me. 2008. pap. *(978-1-934363-19-5(7))* Zoe Life Publishing.

Mayer, Stephen McRae. Before the Twinkling of an Eye, There Is the Voice of God. 2008. 168p. 22.99 *(978-1-60477-898-4(9))*; pap. 14.99 *(978-1-60477-897-7(0))* Xulon Pr., Inc.

Mayeski, Aaron B. Plastic Faith, 1 vol. 2010. 62p. pap. 16.95 *(978-1-61582-821-0(4))* PublishAmerica, Inc.

Mayfield, Will. Tree of Life. 2006. pap. 10.00 *(978-1-4257-1695-0(4))* Xlibris Corp.

Mayhall, Carole. Words That Hurt, Words That Heal: Speaking the Truth in Love. 2007. (Growing in Christ Ser.). (ENG.). 128p. per. 10.99 *(978-1-60006-212-4(1))* NavPress Publishing Group.

Mayo, Joyce. Abused & Abandoned. 112p. (Orig.). pap. 8.95 *(978-1-882185-35-1(8))* Cornerstone Publishing, Inc.

Mazariegos, Emilio. Aventura Apasionante de Orar. 176p. 6.95 *(978-958-607-781-1(0))* Sociedad de San Pablo COL. Dist: St Pauls/Alba Hse. Pubs.

—Huellas Del Maestro. 176p. 6.95 *(978-958-607-869-6(8))* Sociedad de San Pablo COL. Dist: St Pauls/Alba Hse. Pubs.

Mazarin, Jade. The Heart's Journey to Freedom. 2010. 160p. pap. 14.99 *(978-1-60957-140-5(1))* Xulon Pr., Inc.

Mazzella, Joseph J. Walking the Path of Love. 2010. 270p. 26.99 *(978-1-60957-378-2(1))*; pap. 16.99 *(978-1-60957-377-5(3))* Xulon Pr., Inc.

Mbugua, Eunice. Adam's Death Was Worthy: Life Had to Begin in the Deadly World. 2009. 168p. pap. 13.99 *(978-1-4389-9873-2(2))* AuthorHouse.

McAfee, Caleb. Money & the Christian: A Course in Biblical Economics. 192p. 14.99 *(978-0-9656010-0-9(5))* Dimension 4 Enterprises, Inc.

—Turning your Dreams into Reality. 96p. pap. 7.99 *(978-1-58169-127-6(0)*, Evergreen Pr.) Genesis Communications, Inc.

McAleer, Joseph. Suffer the Little Children, 1 vol. 2009. 85p. pap. 14.95 *(978-1-61582-843-2(5))* PublishAmerica, Inc.

Mcalister, Mary. Born into Royalty: A Twelve-Month Journey Through the Word of God to Discover Who You Are in Christ, & Who He Is in You! 2007. 676p. per. 39.95 *(978-1-4241-9877-1(1))* PublishAmerica, Inc.

McAnally, Bryan. Life after Death & Heaven & Hell. 2009. (Indispensable Guide to Practically Everything Ser.). (ENG., Illus.). 256p. pap. 15.99 *(978-0-8249-4773-6(8)*, Guideposts) Ideals Pubns.

—Take a Closer Look: Uncommon & Unexpected Insights That Will Change Your Life. 2007. (ENG., Illus.). 320p. pap. 14.99 *(978-1-4165-4213-1(2)*, Howard Bks.) Howard Books.

McAnally, Guy. To Hell & Beyond. 2009. 67p. pap. 10.00 *(978-0-578-03320-4(8))* Empyrion Pr.

McAndrew, Patrick J. The Bad Day of Mr. Wolf. 2nd ltd. ed. 2007. (J). per. *(978-0-9744581-2-0(0))* Wings of Joy Pubs.

McArdle, Jack. Questions I Have Been Asked & Answers I Have Given. 2008. (ENG.). 144p. pap. 19.95 *(978-1-85607-599-2(0))* Columba Pr. IRL. Dist: Dufour Editions, Inc.

McBath, B. Courtney. Living @ the Next Level: Transforming Your Life's Frustrations into Fulfillment through Friendship with God. 2010. (ENG.). 224p. pap. 15.99 *(978-1-4165-5183-6(2)*, Howard Bks.) Howard Books.

McBrayer, Ronnie. The Jesus Tribe: Following Christ in the Land of the Empire. 2011. ***(978-1-57312-592-5(X))*** Smyth & Helwys Publishing, Inc.

McBrayer, Ronnie. The Journey: Leaving Religion, Following Jesus. 2009. pap. *(978-1-57312-531-4(8))* Smyth & Helwys Publishing, Inc.

McBride, O., Alfred. Fr. Mcbride's Guide to the Bible. 2008. 303p. pap. 14.95 *(978-1-59276-480-8(0))* Our Sunday Visitor, Publishing Div.

McCall, Aaron D. Opting Out: Of the World's Economic System-I Refuse to Participate, 1 vol. 2010. 97p. pap. 16.95 *(978-1-4489-7351-4(1))* PublishAmerica, Inc.

McCarthy Peabody, Susan. Alphabet Soup for Christian Living. 2007. 104p. per. 13.95 *(978-1-58595-599-2(X))* Twenty-Third Pubns./Bayard.

McCartney, Bill. Sold Out. 2009. 402p. pap. 17.99 ***(978-0-7852-9743-7(X))*** Nelson, Thomas Inc.

McCartney, Bill & Fruh, Aaron. Two Minute Warning: Why Its Time to Honor Jewish People Before the Clock Runs Out. 2009. (SPA & ENG.). 228p. pap. 14.99 *(978-1-935265-00-9(8))* Deep River Bks.

McCartney, Colin. The Beautiful Disappointment: Discovering Who You Are Through the Trials of Life. 2008. *(978-1-894860-35-2(7))* Castle Quay Bks. Canada.

McCarty Bird, Kenneth. Diary of the Coming of a Christ-Centered Age. 2007. 186p. pap. 13.95 *(978-0-7414-3822-5(4))* Infinity Publishing.

McClendon, Bernice M. I'm in His Hands: The Lord & I. 2011. 40p. pap. 16.95 ***(978-1-4626-2491-1(X))*** PublishAmerica, Inc.

McCloud, Caspar & Lange, Linda. What Was I Thinking? 2010. (ENG.). pap. 16.99 *(978-0-7684-3263-3(4))* Destiny Image Pubs.

McClung, Floyd. Learning to Love People You Don't Like. 2006. (Discipleship Essentials Ser.). (ENG.). 172p. 11.99 *(978-1-57658-380-7(5))* YWAM Publishing.

McClure, Ronald. Angels Walking among Us. 2008. 132p. 21.99 *(978-1-60477-561-7(0))*; pap. 13.99 *(978-1-60477-560-0(2))* Xulon Pr., Inc.

McClurg, Marilyn F. The Master's Work. 2011. 124p. pap. ***(978-1-926765-48-8(6))*** Gospel Folio Pr.

McClurkin, Robert. Divine Principles in an Evil Day. 2010. 160p. pap. *(978-1-926765-15-0(X))* Gospel Folio Pr.

McCormack, Jim. St Patrick: the Real Story: As Told in His Own Words. 2008. (ENG., Illus.). 56p. pap. 14.95 *(978-1-85607-607-4(5))* Columba Pr. IRL. Dist: Dufour Editions, Inc.

McCormick, Don N. COMMISSION: Christ - CENTERED LIFE: What Could A Veterinarian Know about Christ-Centered Life? 2007. pap. 13.99 *(978-1-60266-549-1(4))* Xulon Pr., Inc.

McCormick, Mike. Mylifematters. 2008. 108p. 18.99 *(978-1-60647-339-9(5))*; pap. 10.99 *(978-1-60647-338-2(7))* Xulon Pr., Inc.

McCoy, Jim. The Christian's Unity with Christ. 2007. 232p. (ENG.). 24.99 *(978-1-60266-851-5(5))*; per. 14.99 *(978-1-60266-850-8(7))* Xulon Pr., Inc.

—Stair Steps: Steps to Ascending into the Presence & the Power of God. 2009. 192p. 22.99 *(978-1-61579-109-5(4))* Xulon Pr., Inc.

McCoy, Shannon. Help! I'm a Slave to Food. 2011. (Living in a Fallen World Ser.). 59p. pap. ***(978-1-84625-242-6(3))*** DayOne Pubns.

McCracken, Mary. A Legacy of Hope: Rescued from the Quicksand of Dysfunction. 2008. (ENG.). 144p. pap. 16.95 *(978-1-932124-93-4(4))* ACW Pr.

McCrary, Kristie. Motion: High Velocity Devotions. 2008. 152p. 22.95 *(978-0-595-48961-9(3))* iUniverse, Inc.

McCrary, Kristie K. Motion: High Velocity Devotions. 2008. 152p. pap. 12.95 *(978-0-595-46698-6(2))* iUniverse, Inc.

McCulley, Carolyn. Radical Womanhood: Feminine Faith in a Feminist World. 2008. (ENG.). 224p. pap. 14.99 *(978-0-8024-5084-5(9))* Moody Pubs.

McCullough, Jackie. Satisfaction of the Soul. 2007. 181p. per. 14.99 *(978-0-7684-2412-6(7))* Destiny Image Pubs.

McCullough, Joy D. Come to the River. 2011. 266p. pap. 16.99 ***(978-1-61379-141-7(0))*** Xulon Pr., Inc.

McCune, Kelvin M. Theology for Practical Christian Living. 2008. 412p. 33.99 *(978-1-60647-030-5(2))*; pap. 21.99 *(978-1-60647-029-9(9))* Xulon Pr., Inc.

Mcdaniel, Antonio L. The Roots of Character: Includes Character Development Exercises. 2011. 212p. 24.59 ***(978-1-4670-6182-7(4))***; pap. 14.95 ***(978-1-4670-6183-4(2))*** AuthorHouse.

McDaniel, Danielle. The Spirit of the Lesson, 1. 2006. (Illus.). 4.95 *(978-0-9654074-7-2(0))* Clay Lady's Hse. Publishing Co., The.

McDaniel, Jay B. Earth, Sky, Gods & Mortals: Developing an Ecological Spirituality. 2009. 228p. pap. 25.00 *(978-1-60608-912-5(9)*, Wipf and Stock) Wipf & Stock Pubs.

McDaniel, Linda. Chosen: Are You the One or Should I Choose Another? 2007. 206p. per. 13.99 *(978-1-59886-499-1(8))* Tate Publishing & Enterprises, LLC.

McDermott, Jerry. A Gilded Walk: The Path to Heaven. 2010. 184p. (ENG.). 26.95 *(978-1-4502-1693-7(5))*; pap. 16.95 *(978-1-4502-1691-3(9))* iUniverse, Inc.

McDermott, Patti D. Wake up My Children: Wake up God's Slumbering Bride. 2009. 344p. pap. 18.99 *(978-1-61579-590-1(1))* Xulon Pr., Inc.

McDonald, Glenn. Living Beyond the Sanctuary. 2008. pap. 14.99 *(978-1-932902-78-5(3))* FaithWalk Publishing.

McDonald, Jack. Churchman-Statesman. 2006. pap. 13.99 *(978-1-60034-706-1(1))* Xulon Pr., Inc.

McDonald, Jack & McDonald, Ruth. Under the Cloud: A Place of Safety & Security in a Chaotic World. 2011. pap. 24.99 ***(978-1-61777-286-3(0))*** Tate Publishing & Enterprises, LLC.

McDonald, James. Beyond Belief: Two Thousand Years of Bad Faith in the Christian Church. 2011. 512p. pap. 34.95 *(978-0-86372-345-2(4)*, Ithaca Pr.) Garnet Publishing, Ltd. GBR. Dist: International Publishers Marketing.

McDonald, Jessie. God's Revelations. 2007. 112p. per. 11.50 *(978-0-9755272-1-4(5))* War Horse Pubn.

McDonald, Mike. Loving (God's Way) 117p. pap. 6.99 *(978-0-89098-210-5(4))* Twentieth Century Christian Bks.

McDougal, Andrea. The Glory of God Revealed. 2008. 264p. pap. 16.99 *(978-1-934769-16-4(9))* McDougal & Assocs.

McDougal, Harold. I Can Do This! 2008. 216p. pap. 16.99 *(978-1-934769-02-7(9))* McDougal & Assocs.

McDougal, Harold B. Todo le Es Posible. Cabrera Villalon, Jose Ramiro, tr. 2009. 196p. pap. 13.99 *(978-1-58158-152-2(1))* McDougal Publishing.

McDow, Kathy J. Broken Just for You. 2007. 156p. per. 14.95 *(978-0-9772099-3-4(8))* SkrAiber Publishing Services.

McDowell, Josh. Christ up Close & Personal: 5-Part Leader Guide. 2006. 48p. DVD 9.99 *(978-1-932587-90-6(X))* Green Key Bks.

—Christ up Close & Personal / Adult Group Course Kit. 2006. pap. 159.99 incl. DVD *(978-1-932587-86-9(1))* Green Key Bks.

—En Defensa del Cristianismo II.Tr. of Ready Defense II. 9.99 *(978-0-7899-0511-6(6)*, 497516) Editorial Unilit.

—Hablemos del Sexo! (Serie Realidades - Realities Ser.).Tr. of Talking It Over. (SPA.). 32p. pap. 1.99 *(978-0-7899-0246-7(X)*, 498149) Editorial Unilit.

McDowell, Josh & Bellis, David H. La Ultima Generacion de Cristianos. Valverde, Hubert, tr. 2007. (SPA.). 176p. pap. 9.50 *(978-0-311-46321-3(5)*, Editorial Mundo Hispano) Casa Bautista de Publicaciones.

McDowell, Josh & Stewart, Ed. My Friend Is Struggling with Knowing God's Will. 2009. (ENG.). 64p. mass mkt. 4.99 *(978-1-84550-442-7(9))* Christian Focus Pubns. GBR. Dist: STL Distribution North America.

McDowell, Josh & Williams, Thomas. The Relational Word: A Biblical Design to Reclaim & Transform the Next Generation. annot. ed. 2006. 249p. per. 13.99 *(978-1-932587-83-8(7))* Green Key Bks.

McDowell, Lucinda Secrest. Role of a Lifetime: Your Part in God's Story. 2008. (ENG.). 160p. per. 12.99 *(978-0-8054-4662-3(1)*, B&H Bks.) B&H Publishing Group.

McFarland, Juli J. The Past, Present, & Future You: A Biblical Key to Overcoming Your Past, Dealing with Your Present, & Planning for Your Future. 2011. 120p. 21.99 *(978-1-4567-4933-0(1))*; pap. 15.99 *(978-1-4567-4934-7(X))* AuthorHouse.

McFarland, Ken. I Don't See It That Way: It Looks a Little Different from up Here. 2009. 127p. pap. 13.99 *(978-0-8280-2468-6(5))* Review & Herald Publishing Assn.

McFarlane, Doreen. God Speaks, Are You Listening? 2009. 98p. pap. *(978-1-55452-414-3(8))* Essence Publishing.

McGee, David. Cross the Bridge to A Better Life: Discover Your Adventure. 2010. (ENG.). 112p. 9.99 *(978-1-61638-160-8(4)*, Creation Hse.) Charisma Media.

McGee, Kenneth. Off Key: Harmonizing the Praise & Worship Debate. 2009. 136p. pap. 10.99 *(978-1-60799-659-0(6))* Tate Publishing & Enterprises, LLC.

McGee, Terrance. Divine Wisdom: Exercising My Will to Act Defends My Commitment to God. 2007. 96p. per. 11.95 *(978-1-4327-1305-3(1))* Outskirts Pr., Inc.

McGeown, Susan. Biblical Women & Who They Hooked up With. 2009. 267p. pap. 16.50 *(978-0-615-14876-2(X))* Faith Inspired Bks.

McGowan, Harriet. Jezebel in Our Midst. 2007. 132p. per. 13.99 *(978-1-60477-311-8(1))* Xulon Pr., Inc.

McGowan, Sean. Future Glory: Walking in the Power of Your God-Given Destiny. 2011. 148p. 30.95 ***(978-1-4497-2373-6(X))***; pap. 13.95 ***(978-1-4497-2372-9(1))*** Author Solutions, Inc. (WestBow Pr.).

McGrath. Handbook for Anglican Theologians. 300p. 40.00 *(978-0-281-05145-8(3))* SPCK Publishing GBR. Dist: Pilgrim Pr., The/United Church Pr.

McGrath, Mark. A Forgotten Gospel: Rediscovering a Radical, Compassionate Approach to Evangelism. 2008. 80p. per. 12.99 *(978-0-9790362-0-0(8))* McGrath Communications Group.

McGraw, Joel S. Fresh Bread from the Pastor's Table. 2009. 208p. pap. 15.99 *(978-1-61579-111-8(6))* Xulon Pr., Inc.

McGraw, Robin. Christmas in My Heart, 0 vols. 2009. 112p. 19.99 *(978-1-4041-0529-4(8))* Nelson, Thomas Inc.

—Inside My Heart: Choosing to Live with Passion & Purpose. lt. ed. 2008. (Walker Large Print Ser.). (ENG.). 294p. pap. 17.95 *(978-1-59415-221-4(7)*, Walker Large Print) Cengage Gale.

—Inside My Heart: Choosing to Live with Passion & Purpose, 0 vols. 240p. 2007. per. 14.99 *(978-0-7852-8903-6(8))* 2006. 24.99 *(978-0-7852-1836-4(X))* Nelson, Thomas Inc.

McGuiggan, Jim. Where the Spirit of the Lord Is. 2011. (ENG.). 272p. pap. 17.99 ***(978-1-4516-6568-0(7)***, Howard Bks.) Howard Books.

McGuire, Meredith B. Lived Religion: Faith & Practice in Everyday Life. 2008. (ENG., Illus.). 272p. 99.00 *(978-0-19-517262-1(0))*; pap. 19.95 *(978-0-19-536833-8(9))* Oxford Univ. Pr., Inc.

McHaney, C. W. The Prize. 2008. pap. 9.99 *(978-1-60477-950-9(0))* Xulon Pr., Inc.

McHenry, Steverson. Real Faith: The Biblical Truth. 2008. 56p. pap. 9.95 *(978-1-4327-3843-3(7))* Outskirts Pr., Inc.

McIlroy, Craig E. Pray, Practice & Prosper by Doing Business God's Way: A Daily Devotion for Business People! 2010. pap. 22.99 *(978-1-61579-746-2(7))* Xulon Pr., Inc.

McInteer, Jim Bill. Precious & Powerful - Woman of God. pap. 7.99 *(978-0-89098-109-2(4))* Twentieth Century Christian Bks.

McIntosh, D. Scott. Life Lessons Learned in the Backseat of a Ford. 2009. 120p. pap. 11.99 *(978-1-60791-413-6(1))* Xulon Pr., Inc.

McIntosh, Diane. Diary of a Glutton. 2007. 140p. pap. 12.95 *(978-1-4303-2694-6(8))* Lulu Enterprises Inc.

—Spiritual Treasure Hunt. 2010. 188p. pap. 12.50 *(978-0-557-44049-8(1))* Lulu Enterprises Inc.

McInturff, Jack. Christian Living Seven Days a Week. 2007. 224p. (ENG.). 31.99 *(978-1-4257-7730-2(9))*; per. 21.99 *(978-1-4257-7707-4(4))* Xlibris Corp.

McIntyre, David M. Al Pie de la Gloria: The Starting Place of Glory. (SPA.). 96p. *(978-84-7228-931-4(1)*, 220997) Clie, Editorial.

McIntyre, Jamison A. What He Says As We Walk. 2011. 284p. pap. 19.95 ***(978-1-4575-0019-0(1))*** Dog Ear Publishing, LLC.

Mckelvey, Marvin. Surviving A Darkroom: The Chronicles of Marvin Jovel Mckelvey Sr. 2011. 80p. 20.95 ***(978-1-4620-4962-2(1))***; pap. 10.95 ***(978-1-4620-4960-8(5))*** iUniverse, Inc.

McKelvy, Luke. Union. 2007. 116p. (ENG.). 18.99 *(978-1-60266-638-2(5))*; per. 10.99 *(978-1-60266-637-5(7))* Xulon Pr., Inc.

McKenna, David Loren & Seraydarian, Patricia McKenna. A Stroke of Grace. 2008. 116p. pap. 11.99 *(978-1-60647-795-3(1))* Xulon Pr., Inc.

McKenna, Megan. The Hour of the Tiger: Facing Our Fears. 2003. 184p. pap. 17.95 *(978-1-56548-325-5(1))* New City Pr.

—The Hour of the Tiger: Facing Our Fears. 2008. 168p. pap. 22.95 *(978-1-84730-079-9(0))* Veritas Pubns. IRL. Dist: Dufour Editions, Inc.

McKenna, Robert. Dying to Lead. 2008. 208p. 25.99 *(978-1-60647-685-7(8))*; pap. 15.99 *(978-1-60647-684-0(X))* Xulon Pr., Inc.

McKenzie III, Leroy. Living under an Open Heaven. 2008. 56p. pap. 15.01 *(978-1-4357-0853-2(9))* Lulu Enterprises Inc.

McKenzie, Jeanette. The GETTING IT RIGHT Series: Growing to Maturity in Christ: A Three-Part Series on Christian Discipleship. 2008. 164p. pap. 24.95 *(978-1-60474-556-6(8))* PublishAmerica, Inc.

McKenzie, John L. Source: What the Bible Says about the Problems of Contemporary Life. 2009. (John L. Mckenzie Reprint Ser.). 228p. pap. 25.00 *(978-1-60608-274-4(4)*, Wipf and Stock) Wipf & Stock Pubs.

McKenzie, Marvin. The Foot of the Cross. 2010. 80p. pap. 8.25 *(978-0-557-60518-7(0))* Lulu Enterprises Inc.

McKenzie, Mary D. Prayer Changed My Life. 2007. 100p. pap. 15.00 *(978-1-4303-2013-5(3))* Lulu Enterprises Inc.

McKim, Marvin R. Christian Prayers for Friends: A Guidebook for Personal Prayers. 2010. 180p. 24.99 *(978-1-4520-4832-1(0))*; (ENG.). pap. 14.49 *(978-1-4520-4833-8(9))* AuthorHouse.

McKim, Randolph Harrison. The Soul of Lee, by One of His Soldiers. 258p. reprint ed. 98.00 *(978-0-7222-9326-3(7))* Library Reprints, Inc.

McKinley, David. The Life You Were Born to Give: Why It's Better to Live Than to Receive, 0 vols. 2007. 192p. per. 12.99 *(978-0-8499-1202-3(4))* Nelson, Thomas Inc.

McKinley, Rick. This Beautiful Mess: Practicing the Presence of the Kingdom of God. 2006. (ENG.). 192p. pap. 13.99 *(978-1-59052-501-2(9)*, Multnomah) Doubleday Religious Publishing Group, The.

McKinney, Deborah. Stumbling Stilettos. 2011. 176p. pap. 24.95 ***(978-1-4626-0406-7(4))*** PublishAmerica, Inc.

McKissick Jr, Rudolph W. God's Got My Back: Spiritual Lessons from Spinal Surgery. 2009. (ENG.). 74p. pap. 10.99 *(978-0-9825303-0-6(7))* St. Paul Pr.

McKissick, Rudolph W., Jr. Nuggets by Day & Gems by Night: Thoughts & Insights from the Mind of Bishop Rudolph Mckissick. 2009. (ENG.). 138p. pap. 11.99 *(978-0-9819672-5-7(6))* St. Paul Pr.

McKnight, Rosemary Whittle. I Love Me, I Love Me Not: A Study of the Christian Woman's Self-Esteem. pap. 7.99 *(978-0-89098-203-7(1))* Twentieth Century Christian Bks.

McKnight, Scot. The Jesus Creed Devotional. 2008. 196p. pap. 14.95 *(978-1-55725-592-1(X))* Paraclete Pr., Inc.

—One. Life: Jesus Calls, We Follow, 1 vol. 2010. (ENG.). 240p. pap. 14.99 *(978-0-310-27766-8(3))* Zondervan.

—40 Days Living the Jesus Creed. 2008. (ENG.). 210p. (gr. 13). per. 15.99 *(978-1-55725-577-8(6))* Paraclete Pr., Inc.

McKone, Gwenn. God, up Close & Personal. 2010. 224p. pap. 15.99 *(978-1-58930-245-7(1))* Selah Publishing Group, LLC.

McKoy, Walter G. Making Things Better Through the Transforming Power of Jesus Christ: Study Guide. 2007. 112p. per. 7.95 *(978-1-4327-0255-7(6))* Outskirts Pr., Inc.

McLain, Heidi. Babysitting for God. 2008. 144p. pap. 14.99 *(978-1-60647-636-9(X))* Xulon Pr., Inc.

McLaren, Brian D. Everything Must Change: Jesus, Global Crises, & a Revolution of Hope, 0 vols. 2009. 336p. pap. 14.99 *(978-1-4002-8029-2(X))* Nelson, Thomas Inc.

—Naked Spirituality: A Life with God in 12 Simple Words. 2012. (ENG.). 256p. pap. 14.99 ***(978-0-06-185402-6(6)***, HarperOne) HarperCollins Pubs.

McLaren, Brian D. A New Kind of Christian: A Tale of Two Friends on a Spiritual Journey. 2008. (Jossey-Bass Leadership Network Ser.: 29). (ENG.). 324p. pap. 14.95 *(978-0-470-24840-9(8)*, Jossey-Bass) Wiley, John & Sons, Inc.

McLaughlin, Heidi. Beauty Unleashed: Transforming a Woman's Soul. annot. ed. 2007. (ENG.). 256p. per. 12.99 *(978-1-933204-40-6(0))* Deep River Bks.

McLaughlin, Megan. Sex, Gender, & Episcopal Authority in an Age of Reform, 1000-1122. 2010. (ENG., Illus.). 288p. 95.00 *(978-0-521-87005-4(4))* Cambridge Univ. Pr.

McLeod, Bob. The Grace to Recognize False Teaching. 2008. 100p. pap. 9.99 *(978-1-60477-546-4(7))* Xulon Pr., Inc.

McLeod, Bunny. God's Joyful Servant. 2010. ring bd. 5.95 *(978-0-578-05689-0(5))* F.A.K.S. Pubs LLC.

McManus, David. The Holy Spirit. 2010. 136p. pap. 14.99 *(978-1-60957-609-7(8))* Xulon Pr., Inc.

McManus, Erwin Raphael. Crave: An Exploration of the Human Spirit. 2010. (Crave Ser.). 96p. pap. *(978-1-4158-6881-2(6))* LifeWay Christian Resources.

—Unleashed: Release the Untamed Faith Within. 2011. 176p. pap. 14.99 *(978-1-4002-0254-6(X))* Nelson, Thomas Inc.

—Uprising: A Revolution of the Soul, 0 vols. 2006. (Illus.). 272p. per. 14.99 *(978-0-7852-8803-9(1))* Nelson, Thomas Inc.

—Wide Awake: The Future Is Waiting Within You, 0 vols. 2008. 272p. 19.99 *(978-0-7852-1495-3(X))* Nelson, Thomas Inc.

McManus, Mike, et al. Living Together: Myths, Risks & Answers. 2008. (ENG.). 256p. 19.99 *(978-1-4165-5098-3(4)*, Howard Bks.) Howard Books.

McManus, Paul & McManus, Tracey. The 7 Great Prayers: For a Lifetime of Hope & Blessings. 2009. (ENG.). 224p. 15.95 *(978-1-59315-549-0(2))* Vanguard Pr.

McMartin, Daniel W. Lord Please Open My Eyes. 2011. 106p. pap. 19.95 ***(978-1-4560-4193-9(2))*** PublishAmerica, Inc.

McMath, Gene. Twice Rescued: A New View of Life from the Bottom of the Cliff. 2007. 144p. per. 10.95 *(978-0-9785352-3-0(5))* Word & Spirit Pr.

McMillan, Eyana Adah. Touched with Instructions. 2011. 220p. 33.95 *(978-1-4497-0990-7(7))*; pap. 17.95 *(978-1-4497-0989-1(3))* Author Solutions, Inc. (WestBow Pr.).

McMinn, M. Tratando con los Deseos Que Usted No Puede Controlar. (Serie Realidades - Realities Ser.).Tr. of Dealing with Desires You Cannot Control. (SPA.). 28p. pap. 1.99 *(978-1-56063-999-2(7)*, 498139) Editorial Unilit.

McMinn, Mark R. Finding Our Way Home: Turning Back to What Matters Most. 2010. (ENG.). 208p. pap. 21.95 *(978-0-470-91469-4(6)*, Jossey-Bass) Wiley, John & Sons, Inc.

McMurtry, Mildred. Walls of Confinement. 2011. 62p. pap. 17.98 ***(978-0-9833544-3-7(X))*** 3G Publishing, Inc.

McNamara, Robert. In My Father's Hands. 2007. (ENG.). 21.99 *(978-1-60266-046-5(8))*; pap. 13.99 *(978-1-60266-045-8(X))* Xulon Pr., Inc.

McNaught, Doug. A Man under Authority. 2008. 78p. pap. 16.95 *(978-1-4092-0472-5(3))* Lulu Enterprises Inc.

McNeal, Reggie. Get a Life! It Is All about You. 2007. 181p. 16.99 *(978-0-8054-4299-1(5)*, B&H Bks.) B&H Publishing Group.

McNeill, Nick. God Things: How God Makes the Ordinary Extraordinary. 2011. pap. 12.99 ***(978-1-61777-129-3(5))*** Tate Publishing & Enterprises, LLC.

McNeish, Delta. Crisis: Identity. 2008. 120p. 18.99 *(978-1-60647-095-4(7))*; pap. 10.99 *(978-1-60647-094-7(9))* Xulon Pr., Inc.

McPhail, Gerald J. Ultimate Success. 2009. 76p. pap. 10.99 *(978-1-60791-256-9(2))* Xulon Pr., Inc.

McPherson, JoAnn. Mission of Love. 2011. 100p. 17.99 ***(978-1-60957-039-2(1))***; pap. 10.99 ***(978-1-60957-038-5(3))*** Xulon Pr., Inc.

McPherson, Miles. DO Something! Participant's Guide: Make Your Life Count, 1 vol. 2009. (ENG.). 80p. pap. 9.99 *(978-0-8010-7249-9(2))* Baker Bks.

—DO Something! Small Group Leader's Kit: Make Your Life Count, 1 vol. 2009. (ENG.). 49.99 *(978-0-8010-7250-5(6))* Baker Bks.

McPherson, Retha & McPherson, Aldo. A Message from God: A 12 Year Old Boy's Experience in Heaven. 2009. pap. 15.99 *(978-0-7684-3051-6(8))* Destiny Image Pubs.

McQueen, Henry. Beyond the Cross. 2009. 124p. pap. 15.95 *(978-1-4251-9187-0(8))* Trafford Publishing.

McQuilkin, Robert C. The Life of Victory & the Baptism of the Spirit. 2011. 128p. 40.95 ***(978-1-258-04880-8(9))*** Literary Licensing, LLC.

McQuoid, Jeremy. How to Set Your Heart on Fire (and Not Just on Sundays) A Call to Passionate Christian Living. 2006. (ENG.). 240p. per. 14.99 *(978-1-85078-666-5(6))* Authentic Media.

McRae. Liturgies for Journey of Life. 144p. 15.00 *(978-0-281-05277-6(8))* SPCK Publishing GBR. Dist: Pilgrim Pr., The/United Church Pr.

McRoberts, Kerry D. Following Jesus to Burning Man: Recovering the Church's Vocation. 2011. (ENG.). 120p. pap. 21.00 *(978-0-7618-5383-1(9))* Hamilton Bks.

McVeigh, Kate. Conquering Intimidation: How to Overcome the Fear That Paralyzes Your Potential. 158p. 12.95 *(978-0-89276-962-9(9)*, 962) Faith Library Pubns., Inc.

McVerry, Peter. Jesus - Social Revolutionary? 2008. (ENG.). 144p. pap. 15.95 *(978-1-84730-110-9(X))* Veritas Pubns. IRL. Dist: Dufour Editions, Inc.

McVey, Steve. A Divine Invitation: Experiencing the Romance of God's Amazing Love. 2008. 216p. per. 12.00 *(978-0-9664736-9-8(8))* Grace Walk Resources, LLC.

—The Grace Walk Experience: Enjoying Life the Way God Intends. 2008. (Illus.). 239p. per. 14.99 *(978-0-7369-2302-6(0))* Harvest Hse. Pubs.

—Walking in the Will of God: Discovering the Grace & Freedom of His Plan for You. 2009. 176p. pap. 10.99 *(978-0-7369-2639-3(9))* Harvest Hse. Pubs.

—52 Lies Heard in Church Every Sunday: And Why the Truth Is So Much Better. 2011. 256p. pap. 12.99 *(978-0-7369-3864-8(8))* Harvest Hse. Pubs.

McWilliams, David. Galatians: A Mentor Commentary. 2009. (Mentor Commentary Ser.). (ENG.). 29.99 *(978-1-84550-452-6(6)*, Mentor) Christian Focus Pubns. GBR. Dist: STL Distribution North America.

Meacham, Gari. Truly Fed: Finding Freedom from Disordered Eating. 2009. (ENG.). 192p. pap. 14.99 *(978-0-8341-2464-6(5)*, 9780834124646) Beacon Hill Pr. of Kansas City.

Mead, Matthew. The Almost Christian Discovered. 2009. 128p. pap. *(978-0-217-29309-9(3))* Books LLC.

—The Almost Christian Discovered. 2009. 134p. pap. 19.99 *(978-1-4590-0439-9(6))* General Bks. LLC.

—The Almost Christian Discovered or, the False Professor Tried And. 2007. (ENG.). 256p. per. 27.95 *(978-1-4304-4554-8(8))* Kessinger Publishing, LLC.

—The Almost Christian Discovered; or, the False Professor Tried & Cast with an Introduction by William R Williams. 2006. 256p. per. 23.99 *(978-1-4255-2263-6(7))* MPublishing.

Mead, Patrick. Lessons for the Life of Faith. 2009. 231p. pap. 15.00 *(978-0-557-05202-8(5))* Lulu Enterprises Inc.

Meador, William. The Third Trumpet - Cornelius the Centurion - Book III. 2008. 256p. pap. 18.95 *(978-0-9799297-3-1(3))* Authors' Publishing Hse.

—The Third Trumpet - Cornelius the Christian - Book Iv. 2008. 232p. pap. 17.95 *(978-0-9799297-4-8(1))* Authors' Publishing Hse.

—The Third Trumpet - Cornelius the Slave - Book I. 2008. 268p. pap. 18.95 *(978-0-9799297-1-7(7))* Authors' Publishing Hse.

—The Third Trumpet - Cornelius the Soldier - Book II. 2008. 192p. pap. 17.95 *(978-0-9799297-2-4(5))* Authors' Publishing Hse.

Meadows, James L. I Corinthians. pap. 5.50 *(978-0-89098-396-6(8))* Twentieth Century Christian Bks.

—I Timothy & Titus. pap. 5.50 *(978-0-89098-414-7(X))* Twentieth Century Christian Bks.

—Some Errors of Premillenialism Refuted. pap. 5.50 *(978-0-89098-385-0(2))* Twentieth Century Christian Bks.

Mean, Elwood. Life Is More Than a Heartbeat. 2009. 184p. 25.50 *(978-1-60693-575-0(5)*, Eloquent Bks.) AEG Literary Publishing Services, Inc.

Meaux, Reneé. God's Hands in My Business: Will He Let My Business Fail? 2009. pap. 11.99 *(978-1-60799-663-7(4))* Tate Publishing & Enterprises, LLC.

Meberg, Marilyn. God at Your Wits' End: Hope for Wherever You Are, 0 vols. 2007. 176p. per. 13.99 *(978-0-8499-1861-2(8))* Nelson, Thomas Inc.

—I'd Rather Be Laughing, 0 vols. 2008. 176p. pap. 12.99 *(978-1-4002-7798-8(1))* Nelson, Thomas Inc.

Meckenstock, Shay. The Mystery of Christ: A Radical Truth... Lived, 1. Marconette, Gennifer, ed. 2007. 192p. per. *(978-0-9794167-0-5(1))* Simple Ink, LLC.

Medearis, Angela Shelf. Ten Ingredients for a Joyous Life & Peaceful Home. 2009. (ENG.). 192p. pap. 14.95 *(978-1-891105-40-1(X))* Lake Isle Pr., Inc.

Medeiros, Judith E. The Third Testament. 2011. 120p. 29.99 ***(978-1-4568-4158-4(0))***; pap. 19.99 ***(978-1-4568-4157-7(2))*** Xlibris Corp.

Medina, Chris. I Double Dog Dare You! 2007. 208p. per. 14.99 *(978-1-60266-840-9(X))* Xulon Pr., Inc.

Meding, Gwen. Come & Rest: A Bible Study for all Who Thirst For More. 2008. 244p. pap. 19.99 *(978-1-4141-1159-9(2))* Pleasant Word.

Meditation for Prosperity. 2006. pap. 12.99 *(978-1-59781-931-2(X))* Xulon Pr., Inc.

Medley, Brenda J. Dealing with Life's Issues. 2011. 270p. 22.99 ***(978-1-59781-088-3(6))*** Xulon Pr., Inc.

Medlin, Carl. The Second Great Reformation: Man Shall Not Live by Faith Only. 2008. pap. 18.99 *(978-1-60647-645-1(9))* Xulon Pr., Inc.

Meduri, P. J. Taking the Field: A Game Plan for Sharing Christ. 2008. 152p. pap. 11.99 *(978-1-58169-275-4(7))* Genesis Communications, Inc.

Meeting the Master: Encounters with Christ Through a Series of Monologues. 2007. spiral bd. *(978-0-9779521-1-3(8))* City on a Hill, Inc.

Meier, G. Marie. Memories under the Linden Tree. 2010. 156p. pap. 14.99 *(978-1-60957-613-4(6))* Xulon Pr., Inc.

Meier, Vicki S. Strike Three & You're Not Out! Surviving Heartbreak Through God's Grace. 2010. pap. 13.99 *(978-1-61566-245-6(6))* Tate Publishing & Enterprises, LLC.

Meilaender, Gilbert. The Way That Leads There: Augustinian Reflections on the Christian Life. 2006. 172p. per. 16.00 *(978-0-8028-3213-9(X))* Eerdmans, William B. Publishing Co.

Mejia, Martin. 'Conquista' 2008. (SPA.). 136p. pap. 19.95 *(978-1-58909-515-1(4))* Bookstand Publishing.

Melancon, Darla Hannah. The Things I Learned after Being Kicked Out of Church. 2010. 160p. 24.49 *(978-1-4520-6498-7(9))*; pap. 13.99 *(978-1-4520-6497-0(0))* AuthorHouse.

Melanie, Minister. Spiritually R. A. P. E. D. 2010. 101p. pap. 14.95 *(978-1-4327-6231-5(1))* Outskirts Pr., Inc.

Melbourne, Bertram L. Called to Discipleship. 2007. pap. 1.97 *(978-0-8163-2224-4(4))* Pacific Pr. Publishing Assn.

Mellichamp, Joseph. Go Fast, Turn Left: Simple Instructions for Following Jesus. 2006. 62p. 5.00 *(978-1-4276-0200-8(X))* Aardvark Global Publishing.

Mellus, Elia Yuhanon. Book of Good Works. 2010. (SYR.). 114.56 *(978-1-61143-338-8(X))* Gorgias Pr., LLC.

Mendoza, Joseph Aurelio. Heaven on Earth: A Guide to the Kingdom. 2010. 220p. 20.49 *(978-1-4490-7113-4(9))*; pap. 17.00 *(978-1-4490-7112-7(0))* AuthorHouse.

Menear, Richard W. How to Stay Out of the City Beneath Your Feet. 2008. 324p. 27.99 *(978-1-60791-083-1(7))*; per. 17.99 *(978-1-60477-703-1(6))* Xulon Pr., Inc.

Menefee, Carmen. The Religion Trap: Religion Versus Relationship. 2007. (ENG.). 68p. per. 10.99 *(978-1-4141-0979-4(2))* Pleasant Word.

Mensah, Prince. Seven Steps to Amazing Love. 2008. 148p. 22.99 *(978-1-60647-884-4(2))*; pap. 14.99 *(978-1-60647-883-7(4))* Xulon Pr., Inc.

Mensch, Christine. Give God the Ashes. 2009. 272p. pap. *(978-1-55452-406-8(7))* Essence Publishing.

Mercado, Ricardo R. Tithes & Offering: Lessons in Giving for Children & Youth Ministries. 2009. 148p. pap. 14.99 *(978-1-61579-197-2(3))* Xulon Pr., Inc.

Mercuro, Peter. The Message: A Conversation with Christ & the events that preceded It. 2007. 220p. per. 15.95 *(978-1-59858-386-1(7))* Dog Ear Publishing, LLC.

Merideth, Gaston. Food for Thought. 2007. 172p. per. 13.99 *(978-1-60266-922-2(8))* Xulon Pr., Inc.

Merkle, Judith A. Being Faithful: Christian Commitment in Modern Society. 2010. (Ecclesiological Investigations Ser.). (ENG.). 208p. 130.00 *(978-0-567-38900-8(6)*, T&T Clark Int'l) Continuum International Publishing Group, Ltd. GBR. Dist: National Bk. Network.

Merkle, Judith A. Being Faithful: Christian Commitment in Modern Society. 2012. (Ecclesiological Investigations Ser.). (ENG.). 208p. pap. 44.95 ***(978-0-567-09504-6(5)***, T&T Clark Int'l) Continuum International Publishing Group, Ltd. GBR. Dist: National Bk. Network.

Merrifield, William L. Who Do You Say I Am? Jesus Called the Christ. 2010. pap. 24.99 *(978-1-61566-600-3(1))* Tate Publishing & Enterprises, LLC.

Merrill, Nan C. & Merrill. Journey into Love: From Fear to Freedom. 2007. (ENG., Illus.). 208p. pap. 16.95 *(978-0-8264-1904-0(6))* Continuum International Publishing Group, Ltd. GBR. Dist: National Bk. Network.

Merritt, James. In A World of... Friends, Foes & Fools: Fathers Can Teach Their Kids to Know the Difference. 2008. 220p. 24.99 *(978-1-60647-600-0(9))*; pap. 14.99 *(978-1-60647-599-7(1))* Xulon Pr., Inc.

Merten, Harold. Understanding God. 2008. 168p. pap. 24.95 *(978-1-60610-086-8(6))* PublishAmerica, Inc.

Merton, Thomas. Choosing to Love the World: On Contemplation. Montaldo, Jonathan, ed. 2008. 191p. 17.95 *(978-1-59179-804-0(3))* Sounds True, Inc.

Meshar, Roxanne. God Is Not Zeus! 2009. 160p. pap. 19.95 *(978-0-557-08739-6(2))* Lulu Enterprises Inc.

Meshler, Ed. Odd God. 2007. 188p. 21.99 *(978-1-60266-691-7(1))*; per. 13.99 *(978-1-60266-653-5(9))* Xulon Pr., Inc.

—Upward Obsession: The Principles of Pry. 2009. 232p. 25.99 *(978-1-60791-503-4(0))*; pap. 15.99 *(978-1-60791-502-7(2))* Xulon Pr., Inc.

Mesrobian, Armen Z. The Sermon on the Mount & the Sermon on the Plain. Mesrobian, Armen Z., ed. l.t. ed. 2007. (Illus.). 92p. (YA). pap. 9.95 *(978-0-9632735-5-0(8))* EPS Excel Publishing Services.

Messer, Kim, compiled by. Creative Resources for Program Directors, No. 60. 2007. (Christmas Program Builder Ser.). (ENG.). 40p. pap. 5.99 *(978-0-8341-7560-0(6)*, 083-417-5606) Lillenas Publishing Co.

Messer, Neil. Selfish Genes & Christian Ethics: Theological & Ethical Reflections of Evolutionary Biology. 2007. 280p. per. *(978-0-334-02996-0(1))* Hymns Ancient & Modern Ltd.

Messick, Paul. Postulates of Christian Faith. 2008. 111p. 12.99 *(978-0-88144-213-7(5))* Yorkshire Publishing Group.

Messick, Robert. Bullets at the Border: Unforgettable Lessons Learned from the Most Unexpected Place on Earth. 2007. 292p. per. 18.00 *(978-1-932503-71-5(4))* Insight Publishing Group.

Metcalf, Patty F. Sharing the Thoughts of an Octogenarian. 2007. *(978-1-55452-198-2(X))*; 96p. per. *(978-1-55452-197-5(1)*, Guardian Bks.) Essence Publishing.

Metekia, Pastor Fekadu. Christian Fundamentals. 2011. 164p. pap. 14.99 ***(978-1-61379-726-6(5))*** Xulon Pr., Inc.

Metekia, Pastor Fekadu & McKenzie, Lynn. Christian Fundamentals. 2015. 164p. 22.99 ***(978-1-61215-520-3(0))*** Xulon Pr., Inc.

Metrick, Rick. My I Problem with God's Word. 2009. 132p. pap. 14.99 *(978-1-61579-138-5(8))* Xulon Pr., Inc.

Mettepenningen, Jürgen. Nouvelle Theologie - New Theology: Inheritor of Modernism, Precursor of Vatican II. 2010. (ENG.). 240p. 34.95 *(978-0-567-03410-6(0))*; 130.00 *(978-0-567-03409-0(7))* Continuum International Publishing Group, Ltd. GBR. (T&T Clark Int'l). Dist: National Bk. Network.

Meyer, F. B. Amor Hasta lo Sumo: Love on the Highest Plain. (SPA.). 320p. *(978-84-7228-800-3(5)*, 220025) Clie, Editorial.

—El Camino Hacia el Lugar Santisimo: The Way to the Holiest. (SPA.). *(978-84-7645-261-5(6)*, 223319) Clie, Editorial.

—Cinco Requisitos Esenciales Vida Crist. Secrets of Christian Living. (SPA.). 112p. *(978-84-7228-564-4(2)*, 220155) Clie, Editorial.

—The Directory of the Devout Life. 2009. 130p. pap. *(978-0-217-34575-0(1))* Books LLC.

—A Good Start, with the Surmons Life Without Miracles & the Prayer of Intercession. 2011. 80p. pap. 9.99 ***(978-1-61203-263-4(X))*** Bottom of the Hill Publishing.

Meyer, F. B. Probado por Fuego: Tested by Fire. (SPA.). 272p. *(978-84-7228-795-2(5)*, 222369) Clie, Editorial.

Meyer, F. b. & Meyer, F. B. Light on Life's Duties. 2011. 86p. pap. 9.99 ***(978-1-61203-260-3(5))*** Bottom of the Hill Publishing.

Meyer, J. F. The Words of Jesus: Sin, Salvation, & Other Teachings. 2007. 289p. per. *(978-0-9799743-0-4(5))* JesusForSinners.com.

Meyer, Joyce. Conflict Free Living: How to Build Healthy Relationships for Life. 2007. (ENG.). 240p. 22.99 *(978-1-59979-062-6(9)*, Charisma Hse.) Charisma Media.

—Do Yourself a Favor... Forgive: Learn How to Take Control of Your Life Through Forgiveness. 2012. (ENG.). 208p. 19.99 ***(978-0-446-54727-7(1))***; 272p. 21.99 ***(978-1-4555-1338-3(5))*** FaithWords.

—Eat the Cookie... Buy the Shoes: Giving Yourself Permission to Lighten Up. 2010. (ENG.). 208p. 19.99 *(978-0-446-53864-0(7))* FaithWords.

—Help Me - I'm Frustrated. pap. 6.99 *(978-1-57794-012-8(1))* Rounder Records.

—How to Hear from God: Learn to Know His Voice & Make Right Decisions. 2008. (ENG.). 304p. pap. 13.99 *(978-0-446-69124-6(0))* Grand Central Publishing.

—I Dare You: Embrace Life with Passion. 2007. (ENG.). 320p. 22.99 *(978-0-446-53197-9(9))* FaithWords.

—Life in the Word Devotional. 272p. pap. 24.99 *(978-1-57794-048-7(2)*, HH2-038-5) Harrison House Pubs.

—Life in the Word Gift Set. 14.99 *(978-1-57794-044-9(X)*, IW-044) Harrison House Pubs.

—Life in the Word Journal. 160p. 7.99 *(978-1-57794-046-3(6)*, HH2-046-6) Harrison House Pubs.

—Living Beyond Your Feelings: Controlling Emotions So They Don't Control You. 2011. (ENG.). 288p. 22.99 *(978-0-446-53852-7(3))*; 352p. 24.99 *(978-1-4555-0729-0(6))* FaithWords.

—The Love Revolution. 2009. (ENG.). 272p. 21.99 *(978-0-446-53856-5(6))* FaithWords.

—Making Marriage Work. 2006. (ENG., Illus.). 320p. 22.99 *(978-0-446-57726-7(X))* Grand Central Publishing.

—Never Give Up! Relentless Determination to Overcome Life's Challenges. (ENG.). 272p. 2010. pap. 13.99 *(978-0-446-56401-4(X))* 2009. 21.99 *(978-0-446-58035-9(X))* FaithWords.

—A New Way of Living: Understanding What It Means to Be a Christian. 2006. *(978-0-446-58155-4(0))* FaithWords.

—The Power of Simple Prayer: How to Talk with God about Everything. annot. ed. 2007. (ENG.). 320p. 22.99 *(978-0-446-53196-2(0))* FaithWords.

—Power Thoughts: 12 Strategies to Win the Battle of the Mind. (ENG.). 2012. 288p. pap. 14.99 *(978-1-4555-0437-4(8))* 2010. 288p. 21.99 *(978-0-446-58036-6(8))* 2010. 432p. 23.99 *(978-0-446-57414-3(7))* FaithWords.

—La Revolución de Amor. 2009. (ENG & SPA.). 288p. pap. 12.99 *(978-0-446-56738-1(8))* FaithWords.

—The Secret to True Happiness: Enjoy Today, Embrace Tomorrow. 2008. (ENG.). 288p. 23.99 *(978-0-446-53199-3(5))* FaithWords.

—Start Your New Life Today: An Exciting New Beginning with God. 2008. (ENG.). 272p. 10.99 *(978-0-446-50965-7(5))* FaithWords.

Meyer, Joyce, frwd. If You Were God, Would You Choose You? How to Accept, Pursue, & Fulfill the Call of God on Your Life. 2007. (Illus.). 331p. 16.95 *(978-0-9725454-9-5(2))* Teach All Nations.

Meyer, Paul J. My Work Is My Ministry: They Are One & the Same. 2008. 29p. pap. 1.75 *(978-0-89811-314-3(8))* Meyer Resource Group, Inc., The.

Meyers, Robin R. Saving Jesus from the Church: How to Stop Worshiping Christ & Start Following Jesus. 2009. (ENG.). 256p. 24.99 *(978-0-06-156821-3(X)*, HarperOne) HarperCollins Pubs.

Meynell, Mark. Colossians: Confident Christianity: Six Studies for Individuals or Groups. 2010. (Good Book Guides). 48p. (YA). pap. *(978-1-906334-24-6(2))* Good Bk. Co.

Michael George, Kizito. The Dysfunctional System of Lies. 2011. 516p. pap. ***(978-3-8443-2958-2(7))*** Lambert Academic Publishing.

Michael J. Rodgers Jr. Mercy. 2010. 152p. pap. 13.99 *(978-1-4269-2507-8(7))* Trafford Publishing.

Michael-Lanier, Janeen. Journey to Love. 2009. 172p. 22.99 *(978-1-60791-596-6(0))*; pap. 14.99 *(978-1-60791-572-0(3))* Xulon Pr., Inc.

Michael, William. Reviving Common Sense: A Revelation of the Lord Jesus Christ. 2009. 108p. pap. 14.95 *(978-1-4389-3428-0(9))* AuthorHouse.

Michal, Joyce. The Confirmation of a Dream. 2007. 188p. (ENG.). 21.99 *(978-1-60477-002-5(3))*; per. 13.99 *(978-1-60477-001-8(5))* Xulon Pr., Inc.

Michel, Barbara D. Fortress of a Rebel. 540p. 29.99 *(978-1-59160-142-5(8))* Xulon Pr., Inc.
Michel, Frantz. From the Fear of Voodoo to the Fear of God. 2009. 160p. pap. 14.99 *(978-1-60791-493-8(X))* Xulon Pr., Inc.
Micklich, Thomas. Kommunikation des Glaubens: Gottesbeziehung als Kategorie praktisch-theologischer Theoriebildung. 2009. (Arbeiten zur Pastoraltheologie, Liturgik und Hymnologie Ser.). (GER., Illus.). 357p. (C). pap. 77.00 *(978-3-525-62409-8(3))* Vandenhoeck & Ruprecht GmbH & Co. KG DEU. Dist: ISD.
Miesner, Ann Morgan. God, Who Are You? 2008. 324p. pap. 20.99 *(978-1-60477-940-0(3))* Xulon Pr., Inc.
Mignogna, Michael T. Fellow Catholics: It's Time to Take That Walk in Faith! 2007. 79p. pap. 9.95 *(978-0-7414-4153-9(5))* Infinity Publishing.
Mihaylov, Stefan. Humility & Pride. 2010. 100p. pap. 11.95 *(978-1-4502-2075-0(4))* iUniverse, Inc.
Mike & Richards, Joan. Our Story. 2010. 98p. pap. 10.99 *(978-1-60957-113-9(4))* Xulon Pr., Inc.
Mike, Cynthia E. Born to Succeed, You Have the Right to Expect the Best & Receive the Best! 2009. 148p. 23.50 *(978-1-60860-231-5(1)*, Eloquent Bks.) AEG Literary Publishing Services, Inc.
Mike Luoma, Brother Zagreus. Neo-gnosis. 2008. 136p. pap. 12.95 *(978-1-4357-4280-2(X))* Lulu Enterprises Inc.
Milem Sr., Terrence L. The Last Commandment: Evangelism for All Christians, 1 vol. 2010. 108p. pap. 19.95 *(978-1-4489-4329-6(9))* PublishAmerica, Inc.
Miles, C. Austin. In the Garden. 1.05 *(978-0-7673-1013-0(6))* LifeWay Christian Resources.
Miles, Cecelia. God Can Make Lemonade Out of Life's Lemons: From Challenge to Triumph. 2011. pap. 12.99 *(978-1-61739-074-6(7))* Tate Publishing & Enterprises, LLC.
Miles, Lacarol. Mustard Seed Faith: Developing the Faith You Need to Move Mountains. 2010. 61p. pap. 11.95 *(978-1-4327-6282-7(5))* Outskirts Pr., Inc.
Miles, Sara. Jesus Freak: Feeding Healing Raising the Dead. 2010. (ENG.). 192p. 21.95 *(978-0-470-48166-0(8)*, Jossey-Bass) Wiley, John & Sons, Inc.
Miley, Dinah M. Worship Inspired from the Book of Malachi. 2008. 68p. pap. 9.99 *(978-1-60647-458-7(8))* Xulon Pr., Inc.
Miley, Jeanie. Joining Forces: Balancing Masculine & Feminine. 2008. *(978-1-57312-507-9(5))* Smyth & Helwys Publishing, Inc.
Miley, Jeanie. Joint Venture: Practical Spirituality for Everyday Pilgrims. 2011. pap. ***(978-1-57312-581-9(4))*** Smyth & Helwys Publishing, Inc.
Millar, Paul. Nothing Plus Nothing. 2008. (ENG.). 124p. 18.99 *(978-1-60477-539-6(4))* Xulon Pr., Inc.
Miller, Adrienne. The Chair of Intercession. 2007. pap. 9.99 *(978-1-60034-884-6(X))* Xulon Pr., Inc.
Miller, Calvin. Faithfulness: Cultivating Spirit-Given Character. 2008. (Fruit of the Spirit Study Guide Ser.). (ENG.). 128p. per. 9.99 *(978-1-4185-2842-3(0))* Nelson, Thomas Inc.
—Goodness: Cultivating Spirit-Given Character. 2008. (Fruit of the Spirit Study Guide Ser.). (ENG.). 128p. per. 9.99 *(978-1-4185-2839-3(0))* Nelson, Thomas Inc.
—Kindness: Cultivating Spirit-Given Character. 2008. (Fruit of the Spirit Ser.). (ENG., Illus.). 128p. per. 9.99 *(978-1-4185-2837-9(4))* Nelson, Thomas Inc.
—Patience: Cultivating Spirit-Given Character. 2008. (Fruit of the Spirit Ser.). (ENG., Illus.). 128p. per. 9.99 *(978-1-4185-2836-2(6))* Nelson, Thomas Inc.
—Peace: Cultivating Spirit-Given Character. 2008. (Fruit of the Spirit Study Guide Ser.). (ENG.). 128p. per. 9.99 *(978-1-4185-2838-6(2))* Nelson, Thomas Inc.
—Sed de Significado: Thirst for Meaning. (SPA.). 136p. *(978-84-7228-195-0(7)*, 220813) Clie, Editorial.
—Self-Control: Cultivating Spirit-Given Character, 0 vols. 2008. (Fruit of the Spirit Study Guide Ser.). (ENG.). 128p. per. 9.99 *(978-1-4185-2844-7(7))* Nelson, Thomas Inc.
Miller, Charles. A Wonderful Purpose for Living. 2006. 72p. per. 10.99 *(978-1-4141-0870-2(2))* Pleasant Word.
Miller, Craig Kennet. 7 Myths of the United Methodist Church. 2008. (Illus.). 188p. pap. 14.00 *(978-0-88177-529-7(0))* Discipleship Resources.
Miller, Donald. A Million Miles in a Thousand Years: What I Learned While Editing My Life. 2009. 283p. 19.99 *(978-0-7852-1306-2(6))* Nelson, Thomas Inc.
Miller, Donald. Searching for God Knows What. I.t. ed. 2010. (ENG.). 352p. pap. 17.99 *(978-1-59415-324-2(8))* Cengage Gale.
—Searching for God Knows What. 2010. (Playaway Adult Nonfiction Ser.). (ENG.). 59.99 ***(978-1-61587-627-3(8))*** Findaway World, LLC.
—Searching for God Knows What, 0 vols. 2010. 272p. pap. 15.99 *(978-1-4002-0275-1(2))* Nelson, Thomas Inc.
Miller, Ellen. The One Year Book of Inspiration for Girlfriends: Juggling Not-So-Perfect, Often-Crazy, but Gloriously Real Lives. 2009. (ENG.). 384p. pap. 14.99 *(978-1-4143-1938-4(X))* Tyndale Hse. Pubs.
Miller Emmons, Brenda. Dear Adversity: Choosing Hope in Christ over Despair. 2010. pap. 10.99 *(978-1-61663-595-4(9))* Tate Publishing & Enterprises, LLC.
Miller, Georgia. Making a Quilt out of Cobwebs: A Journey from Betrayal to Hope. 2007. (ENG.). 112p. per. 14.51 *(978-1-4303-0578-1(9))* Lulu Enterprises Inc.
Miller, Gerhard C. F. A Spiritual Guide to the Scientific 21st Century. (Illus.). pap. 14.95 *(978-0-533-13029-0(8))* Vantage Pr., Inc.
Miller, Gilbert. How to Get A Job & Keep It by Letting. 2006. pap. 13.99 *(978-1-60034-798-6(3))* Xulon Pr., Inc.
Miller, Holly. Life after the Games. 2007. 168p. (ENG.). 21.99 *(978-1-60266-187-5(1))*; per. 13.99 *(978-1-60266-186-8(3))* Xulon Pr., Inc.
Miller, J. R. The Best Things in Life. 2011. 120p. pap. 12.99 ***(978-1-61203-146-0(3))*** Bottom of the Hill Publishing.
—The Building of Character. 2010. (Illus.). 88p. pap. 20.00 *(978-1-154-65093-8(6))* General Bks. LLC.
—The Building of Character. 2010. 282p. pap. 22.36 *(978-1-163-90281-3(0))* 2008. 280p. 42.95 *(978-0-548-92587-4(9))* 2007. (ENG.). 280p. per. 27.95 *(978-0-548-60824-1(5))* Kessinger Publishing, LLC.
—A Cure for Care. 2011. 28p. pap. 7.99 ***(978-1-61203-155-2(2))*** Bottom of the Hill Publishing.
—The Lesson of Love. 2011. 130p. pap. 12.99 ***(978-1-61203-151-4(X))*** Bottom of the Hill Publishing.
Miller, J. r. Making the Most of Life. 2007. (ENG.). 284p. 43.95 *(978-0-548-10728-7(9))* Kessinger Publishing, LLC.
Miller, J. R. Practical Religion, a Help for the Common Days. 2011. 176p. pap. 12.99 ***(978-1-61203-177-4(3))*** Bottom of the Hill Publishing.
—Secretos de una Vida Hermosa: Secrets of a Beautiful Life. (SPA.). *(978-84-7645-007-9(9)*, 223078) Clie, Editorial.
—Secrets of a Beautiful Life. 2011. 142p. pap. 12.99 ***(978-1-61203-176-7(5))*** Bottom of the Hill Publishing.
—Strength & Beauty. 2011. 128p. pap. 12.99 ***(978-1-61203-174-3(9))*** Bottom of the Hill Publishing.
—The Wider Life. 2011. 114p. pap. 12.99 ***(978-1-61203-147-7(1))*** Bottom of the Hill Publishing.
Miller, J. r. & Miller, J. R. Garden of the Heart. 2011. 116p. pap. 14.99 ***(978-1-61203-198-9(6))*** Bottom of the Hill Publishing.
—The Glory of the Common Life. 2011. 108p. pap. 12.99 ***(978-1-61203-194-1(3))*** Bottom of the Hill Publishing.
—Go Forward. 2011. 34p. pap. 7.99 ***(978-1-61203-158-3(7))*** Bottom of the Hill Publishing.
—The Hidden Life. 2011. 76p. pap. 12.99 ***(978-1-61203-193-4(5))*** Bottom of the Hill Publishing.
—In His Steps, for Those Beginning the Christian Life. 2011. 86p. pap. 9.99 ***(978-1-61203-156-9(0))*** Bottom of the Hill Publishing.
—The Joy of Service. 2011. 118p. pap. 12.99 ***(978-1-61203-152-1(8))*** Bottom of the Hill Publishing.
—Learning to Love. 2011. 30p. pap. 7.99 ***(978-1-61203-161-3(7))*** Bottom of the Hill Publishing.
—Making the Most of Life. 2011. 136p. pap. 12.99 ***(978-1-61203-143-9(9))*** Bottom of the Hill Publishing.
—The Way of Victory. 2011. (Illus.). 54p. pap. 7.99 ***(978-1-61203-164-4(1))*** Bottom of the Hill Publishing.
Miller, James Russell. Making the Most of Life. 2008. 172p. 22.99 *(978-0-554-36666-1(5))* 2008. 172p. 25.99 *(978-0-554-27363-1(2))* 2007. (ENG.). 156p. per. 19.99 *(978-1-4346-3055-1(2))* 2007. (ENG.). 172p. per. 21.99 *(978-1-4346-3069-8(2))* BiblioBazaar.
—Making the Most of Life. 2009. 138p. pap. *(978-0-217-01424-3(0))* Books LLC.
Miller, Jim. Going Beyond Belief: Live the Adventure. 2010. 120p. pap. 12.99 *(978-1-61507-074-9(5))* Cross Bks. Publishing.
Miller, Keith. Surrender to the Spirit: The Limitless Possibilities of Yielding to the Holy Spirit. 2006. 218p. per. 14.99 *(978-0-7684-2387-7(2))* Destiny Image Pubs.
Miller, Lynn. Reflections from God's Word: A Guide to Jesus for the Family of Christ. 2008. pap. 9.99 *(978-1-60477-991-2(8))* Xulon Pr., Inc.
Miller, M. C. A Basket of Barley Loaves by the Author of the High Mountain Apart & Sacramental Sabbaths. 2006. 152p. per. 18.99 *(978-1-4255-1196-9(4))* MPublishing.
Miller, Margaret Ann. A Pearl: Formed by Adversity. 2011. 128p. pap. 11.99 ***(978-1-58930-274-7(5))*** Selah Publishing Group, LLC.
Miller, Mercedes L. Pathways to Peace: Meditations for a Tranquil Life. 2007. (ENG.). 80p. pap. 9.99 *(978-1-59979-088-6(2)*, Creation Hse.) Charisma Media.
Miller, Michael L. & Miller, Martine B. If I Had No Reward in Heaven. 2008. 240p. per. 14.99 *(978-1-60477-570-9(X))* Xulon Pr., Inc.
Miller, Mike. Family Day, a Day That America Needs Again! 2007. 80p. per. 9.99 *(978-1-60266-498-2(6))* Xulon Pr., Inc.
Miller, Norman. Beyond the Norm, 0 vols. 2009. 224p. pap. 12.99 *(978-1-59555-331-7(2))* Nelson, Thomas Inc.
Miller, Renee. Strength for the Journey: A Guide to Spiritual Practice. 2011. 144p. pap. 16.00 *(978-0-8192-2746-1(3)*, Morehouse Publishing) Church Publishing, Inc.
Miller, Rose C. Sharing a Thought with Lagniappe. 2011. 116p. pap. 19.99 ***(978-1-4568-7449-0(7))*** Xlibris Corp.
Miller, Rose Marie. Nothing Is Impossible with God: Reflections on Weakness, Faith, & Power. 2012. (ENG.). 288p. pap. 15.99 ***(978-1-936768-68-4(2))*** New Growth Pr.
Miller, Sabrina Louise. Warrior in Training: Series I. 2010. 202p. pap. 19.99 *(978-0-88144-538-1(X)*, Thorncrown Publishing) Yorkshire Publishing Group.
Miller, Samuel H. The Life of the Soul. 2011. 160p. 41.95 ***(978-1-258-09209-2(3))*** Literary Licensing, LLC.
Miller, Stephen M., ed. Los Cristianos en un Mundo Perverso. 2008. 124p. pap. 8.98 *(978-1-56344-594-1(8))* Casa Nazarena de Publicaciones.
Miller, Ted. El Me Toco: He Touched Me. (SPA.). 112p. *(978-84-7228-336-7(4)*, 220345) Clie, Editorial.
Miller, Timothy. Poised for Harvest, Braced for Backlash: Birthing New Testament Movements When Jesus Disrupts the Systems. 2009. 344p. pap. 18.99 *(978-1-61579-146-0(9))* Xulon Pr., Inc.
Miller, Vince. The Generous Life. Wonders, Paul, ed. 2011. pap. 9.95 ***(978-0-9766555-8-9(6))*** Consumed Publishing.
Miller, W. D. What Does the Lord Require of You. 2006. pap. 17.99 *(978-1-60034-427-5(5))* Xulon Pr., Inc.
Millett, Kate. Spiritual Gift of Madness: The Failure of Psychiatry & the Rise of the Mad Pride Movement. 2012. pap. ***(978-1-59477-448-5(X)***, Inner Traditions) Inner Traditions International, Ltd.
Millican, Susan A. Out of the Miry Clay. 2011. 112p. 28.95 ***(978-1-4497-2606-5(2))***; pap. 11.95 ***(978-1-4497-2605-8(4))*** Author Solutions, Inc. (WestBow Pr.).
Milligan, David. The God of Many Faiths: (A Divine Logic) 2007. 164p. per. 24.95 *(978-1-4241-8114-8(3))* PublishAmerica, Inc.
Mills, Anthony M. Saints! Have We Turned the Lighthouse into a Hell House? What Is Going on with the Church Today? 2008. 244p. pap. 14.99 *(978-1-60647-107-4(4))* Xulon Pr., Inc.
Mills, Bill. Keys to Effective Leadership: Developing Your Followership Skills. 2007. 41p. pap. 5.00 *(978-0-9709482-4-3(7))* Leadership Resources International.
Mills, Derek. The Five Doors of Faith: A Radical Biblical Christian Spirituality & Foundation for Discipleship. 2010. 112p. pap. 14.09 *(978-1-4520-9837-1(9))* AuthorHouse.
Mills, Gerrie Hyman. Oy Vey! Such a Deal! Jazzed by Faith & Chocolate Pudding. 2007. (ENG., Illus.). 256p. per. 13.99 *(978-1-59979-264-4(8)*, Creation Hse.) Charisma Media.
Mills, Jo Ann. Patterns & Promises. pap. 6.95 *(978-0-929540-13-9(1))* Publishing Designs, Inc.
Mills, Sheila L. Crossing Your Jordan in Faith: Stop Wading, Start Walking. 2010. pap. 10.99 *(978-1-60799-980-5(3))* Tate Publishing & Enterprises, LLC.
Mills, Sheri D. Doing it God's Way. 2010. 124p. pap. 11.99 *(978-1-60957-671-4(3))* Xulon Pr., Inc.
Mills, Steven C. The Kingdom Order: Living for the Future in the Present. 2011. pap. 19.99 ***(978-1-61346-029-0(5))*** Tate Publishing & Enterprises, LLC.
Mills, Tonya D. Simplifying the Christian Life. 2009. 284p. pap. 16.99 *(978-1-61579-361-7(5))* Xulon Pr., Inc.
Mills, William C. Our Father: A Prayer for Christian Living. 2008. 100p. pap. 10.95 *(978-1-933275-29-1(4)*, Orthodox Research Institute) Cocheco Falls Publishing.
Mislagle, Celia. Streams of Living Water: A Daily Guide to Devotional Meditation on God's Word. 2007. 272p. pap. 9.99 *(978-1-4259-7826-6(6))* AuthorHouse.
Milthaler, Matthew. E-Merge 2.0 Small Group Leader's Guide for Older Youth. 2007. pap. 18.00 *(978-0-687-64309-7(0))* Abingdon Pr.
—E-Merge 2.0 Small Group Leader's Guide for Younger Youth. 2007. pap. 18.00 *(978-0-687-64299-1(X))* Abingdon Pr.
—EMerge 1.0: small-group leader's guide for Younger Youth: Developing Youth as Fully Devoted Disciples. 2007. 48p. pap. 18.00 incl. cd-rom *(978-0-687-33599-2(X))* Abingdon Pr.
Milton, Michael A. What God Starts, God Completes: Gospel Hope for Hurting People. 2007. (ENG.). 160p. per. 12.99 *(978-1-84550-276-8(0))* Christian Focus Pubns. GBR. Dist: STL Distribution North America.
Miner, Anthony & Limberg, Beth. Coming Out Effects on Religious Practices of Urban Gays & Bisexuals. 2010. 84p. pap. *(978-3-8383-6640-1(9))* Lambert Academic Publishing.
Miner, Caroline Eyring. To Warm the Heart. 2011. 150p. 40.95 ***(978-1-258-07812-6(0))*** Literary Licensing, LLC.
Minnick, Christy. Hug Life. 2010. 396p. pap. 20.99 *(978-1-60957-062-0(6))* Xulon Pr., Inc.
Minor, Ayanna S. And God Speaks: Divine Expressions for the Soul with CD. 2008. 119p. pap. 15.95 *(978-0-7414-4480-6(1))* Infinity Publishing.
Minott, Avis. From Birth to New Birth. 2007. pap. 9.99 *(978-1-60266-134-9(0))* Xulon Pr., Inc.
Minter, Kelly. The Fitting Room: Putting on the Character of Christ. 2011. (ENG.). 208p. pap. 14.99 *(978-1-4347-9985-2(9))* Cook, David C.
Mirabeau, Helen Hildebrandt. The Law of Jesus Christ: Pure Values & the Ten Qualities of Jesus Christ. 2009. (Illus.). 194p. (ENG.). 134.95 *(978-1-4327-1121-4(0))*; pap. 99.95 *(978-1-4327-1119-1(9))* Outskirts Pr., Inc.
Miracle, Bob. Reflections from a Miracle. 2009. 372p. pap. 17.99 *(978-1-4490-3532-7(9))* AuthorHouse.
Misal Festivo del Pueblo de Dios: Ciclo "B"Tr. of Sunday Missal of the People of God. (SPA.). 416p. pap. 6.95 *(978-980-207-003-9(3))* Paulinas VEN. Dist: St Pauls/Alba Hse. Pubs.
Misal Festivo del Pueblo de Dios: Ciclo "C" (SPA.). 448p. pap. 6.95 *(978-980-207-017-6(3))* Paulinas VEN. Dist: St Pauls/Alba Hse. Pubs.
La Mision (The Mission) Quarter 2, Level 3. (Caminando con Jesus (Walking with Jesus) Series A). (SPA.). tchr. ed. 2.50 *(978-0-570-05144-2(4)*, 16-3802) Concordia Publishing Hse.
Missler, Nancy. Kingdom, Power & Glory: The Overcomer's Handbook. 2008. (Kingdom, Power & Glory Ser.). (Illus.). 324p. per. 16.95 *(978-0-9795136-4-0(2))* King's High Way Ministries, Inc., The.
—Reflections of His Image: God's Purpose for Your Life. 2007. (In His Likeness Ser.). (Illus.). 281p. per. 12.95 *(978-0-9760994-3-7(8))* King's High Way Ministries, Inc., The.
Missler, Nancy & Missler, Chuck. The Way of Agape Textbook: Understanding God's Love. 2009. per. 14.95 *(978-0-9752534-0-3(9))* King's High Way Ministries, Inc., The.
Mitchell, Alison. Why Did Jesus Die? 2010. 6p. (J). *(978-1-904889-77-9(8))* Good Bk. Co.
—Why Did Jesus Rise? 2010. 6p. (J). *(978-1-904889-76-2(X))* Good Bk. Co.
Mitchell, James H. A More Excellent Way. 2010. 130p. pap. 14.99 *(978-1-60957-790-2(6))* Xulon Pr., Inc.
Mitchell, Jannah A. Like a Tree Planted. 2008. 88p. pap. 9.99 *(978-1-60647-166-1(X))* Xulon Pr., Inc.
Mitchell, Julie Walker. 365 Days of Hope. 2009. 268p. pap. 16.99 *(978-1-60799-082-6(2))* Tate Publishing & Enterprises, LLC.
Mitchell, Lori. Lighting Mary's House. 2011. 88p. pap. 9.95 ***(978-1-61507-788-5(X))*** Cross Bks. Publishing.
Mitchell, Noah. The Nitty Gritty: A Discussion on Dating Issues. 2008. 109p. pap. 15.99 *(978-1-4357-4378-6(4))* Lulu Enterprises Inc.
Mitchell, Pam & Landrum, Faye. Maggots, Miracles & Me. 2007. 224p. per. 14.99 *(978-1-60477-363-7(4))* Xulon Pr., Inc.
Mitchell, Stephen. Yes, You Can: Rise from the Wreckage, 1 vol. 2009. 74p. pap. 16.95 *(978-1-60749-419-5(1))* PublishAmerica, Inc.
Mitchell, Thomas R. Cellophane. 2008. 156p. pap. 11.99 *(978-1-4343-8794-3(1))* AuthorHouse.
Mittapalli, Benjamin. Balanced Christian Home. 2011. 68p. pap. 9.95 ***(978-1-4497-1461-1(7)***, WestBow Pr.) Author Solutions, Inc.
Mittelberg, Mark. Choosing Your Faith: In a World of Spiritual Options. 2008. (ENG., Illus.). 288p. 19.99 *(978-1-4143-1579-9(1))* Tyndale Hse. Pubs.
—Faith Path Workbook: Helping Friends Find Their Way to Christ, 1 vol. 2009. (ENG.). 176p. pap. 14.99 *(978-1-4347-6513-0(X))* Cook, David C.
—Your Faith Path: Discover How to Choose Your Beliefs. 2008. (ENG.). 48p. pap. 0.99 *(978-1-4143-2045-8(0))* Tyndale Hse. Pubs.
Mittelberg, Mark, et al. Becoming a Contagious Christian: Communicating Your Faith in a Style That Fits You, 1 vol. rev. ed. 2007. (ENG.). cd-rom 26.99 *(978-0-310-25789-9(1))* Zondervan.
Mitts, E. Grace Veale. Music, Mukluks & Mulligan Stew. 2007. 308p. 27.99 *(978-1-60266-394-7(7))*; (ENG.). per. 17.99 *(978-1-60266-395-4(5))* Xulon Pr., Inc.
Mize, Charlotte. What Will Your Answer Be? pap. 6.99 *(978-0-89098-206-8(6))* Twentieth Century Christian Bks.
—Why Am I... ? pap. 7.99 *(978-0-89098-205-1(8))* Twentieth Century Christian Bks.
Mobley-Wells, Rona. God Has a Plan for You, but God Will Not Plan for You: 12 Principles for Understanding the Purpose & Power of Planning. 2009. 204p. pap. 15.99 *(978-1-60791-706-9(8))* Xulon Pr., Inc.
Moffat, Allan W. Surprised by God. 2010. ***(978-1-77069-081-3(6))*** Word Alive Pr.
Mofo, Susan. While Single & Being Purified. 2008. 196p. 24.99 *(978-1-60647-334-4(4))*; pap. 14.99 *(978-1-60647-091-6(4))* Xulon Pr., Inc.
Mohammed, Gina H. Miracles & Mustard Seeds: Little Things You Can Do to Serve the Lord. 2007. (ENG., Illus.). 144p. pap. *(978-0-9731097-1-9(8))* Candlenut Bks.
Mohrmann, Jackie. Be Still & Know That I Am God. 2008. 464p. (ENG.). 35.99 *(978-1-60477-615-7(3))*; per. 23.99 *(978-1-60477-614-0(5))* Xulon Pr., Inc.
—Digging for Gold: The Treasure in God's Word. 2009. 172p. pap. 14.99 *(978-1-61579-202-3(3))* Xulon Pr., Inc.
Moiander, Gary A. Pursuing Christ. Creating Art: Exploring Life at the Intersection of Faith & Creativity. 2011. 176p. 30.95 ***(978-1-4497-1803-9(5))***; pap. 13.95 ***(978-1-4497-1801-5(9))*** Author Solutions, Inc. (WestBow Pr.).
Molina, Joaquin G. Restoring the Gates That Prevail. 2007. (ENG., Illus.). 288p. pap. 14.99 *(978-1-59979-024-4(6)*, Creation Hse.) Charisma Media.
Molinari, Robert J. Joyce's Ark. 2008. 212p. 24.99 *(978-1-60477-608-9(0))* Xulon Pr., Inc.
Mollenkott, Virginia Ramey & Sheridan, Vanessa. Transgender Journeys. 2010. 192p. pap. 22.00 *(978-1-60899-212-6(8)*, Resource Pubns.) Wipf & Stock Pubs.
Molsberry, Robert. Tour de Faith: A Cyclist's Lessons for Living. 2007. (ENG.). 144p. per. 14.95 *(978-1-56101-316-6(1))* Cowley Pubns.
Molvaer, Reidulf. Two Making One Amor & Eros in Tandem. 2009. 184p. 29.99 *(978-1-60860-996-3(0)*, Eloquent Bks.) AEG Literary Publishing Services, Inc.
Momah, Tobe. Metrobiology - A Study of Life in the City (1st Edition) ... A Doctor's Daily Devotional. 2009. pap. 22.99 *(978-1-60791-356-6(9))* Xulon Pr., Inc.
Monbleau, Wayne. Why Is This Happening to Me? How God Brings Blessing from Our Pain. 2008. (ENG.). 210p. pap. 11.99 *(978-0-87508-773-3(6))* CLC Pubns.
Mondore, Patty. A Good Paddling! Lessons about Life, Learned on the Lake. 2007. 132p. per. *(978-0-7880-2441-2(8))* CSS Publishing Co.
Monehin, Olufemi. New Creation Reality. 2010. 98p. pap. 13.00 *(978-0-557-58093-4(5))* Lulu Enterprises Inc.
Monetti, Penny. Choose to Dance. 2008. 260p. 25.99 *(978-1-60477-323-1(5))*; pap. 16.99 *(978-1-60477-322-4(7))* Xulon Pr., Inc.
Monjurr. The Journey: Living Life Without Limits. 2010. 140p. pap. 15.49 *(978-1-4520-0706-9(3))* AuthorHouse.
Monks, Dorothy J. Treasuring Life: Befriending Death. 2008. *(978-0-8189-1260-3(X))* St Pauls/Alba Hse. Pubs.
Monks of St. Gregory's Abbey. Come Let Us Adore: St. Gregory's Abbey, 1999-2011. 2011. 188p. pap. 16.95 ***(978-1-4620-3045-3(9))*** iUniverse, Inc.
Monroe, Bill. Go. 2008. (ENG.). 144p. pap. 10.99 *(978-0-9779535-7-8(2))* 21st Century Pr.
Monroy, Juan A. Apuntando a la Torre: Aiming at the Watch Tower. (SPA.). *(978-84-7645-225-7(X)*, 223314) Clie, Editorial.
—Enfoque Evangelico a la Teologia de la Liberacion: Christian Approach to... (SPA.). *(978-84-7645-474-9(0)*, 223551) Clie, Editorial.
Monsell, Carol L. Believe. 2009. 164p. pap. 14.99 *(978-1-61579-147-7(7))* Xulon Pr., Inc.
Monster, Ann. You & I AM, 1 vol. 2010. 374p. pap. 29.95 *(978-1-60610-318-0(0))* PublishAmerica, Inc.

C

Montecino, Gina. My Search for Peace of Mind: A Compelling Autobiography. 2009. 368p. pap. 17.99 (978-1-4343-2391-0(9)) AuthorHouse.
Montgomery, Dan and Kate. The Self Compass: Charting Your Personality in Christ. 2007. 212p. pap. 25.00 (978-1-4303-2417-1(1)) Lulu Enterprises Inc.
Montgomery, David. What Do You Do When Your Spouse Is Not A Child of God? 2010. 174p. pap. 14.99 (978-1-61579-360-0(7)) Xulon Pr., Inc.
Montgomery, John. Sick of Stress: Causes, Symptoms & Remedies. 2009. (ENG.). 106p. 12.99 (978-1-59979-490-7(X), Creation Hse.) Charisma Media.
Montgomery, Mel C. The Genuine Flow. 2010. 246p. pap. 17.99 (978-1-60957-958-6(5)) Xulon Pr., Inc.
Montgomery, Susan. The Proverbs 31 Church. 2006. 84p. pap. 16.95 (978-1-4241-5601-6(7)) PublishAmerica, Inc.
Montgomery, Will. The Polar Bear. 2011. (ENG.). 268p. pap. 15.99 (978-0-9836771-9-2(0)) Mindstir Media.
Montroy, Bruce. The Doorway to the Abundant Life. 2007. (ENG.). 164p. 21.99 (978-1-60266-091-5(3)) Xulon Pr., Inc.
Moody, D. The Overcoming Life, 1 vol. 2010. (Moody Classics Ser.). (ENG.). 176p. pap. 7.99 (978-0-8024-5451-5(8)) Moody Pubs.
Moody, Dwight Lyman. El Camino Hacia el Cielo.Tr. of Heaven & How to Get There. (SPA.). 128p. (978-84-7228-945-1(1), 223019) Clie, Editorial.
—Heaven: Where it Is, its inhabitants, & how to get There. 2007. 108p. pap. 7.99 (978-0-9800270-0-6(4)) Lifelines Publishing.
—The Overcoming Life. 2007. (Pure Gold Classics Ser.). (ENG., Illus.). 408p. pap. 14.99 incl. audio compact disk (978-0-88270-400-5(1)) Bridge-Logos Foundation.
—Peregrinos Hacia el Hogar Celestial.Tr. of Way Home. (SPA.). (978-84-7228-946-8(X), 223026) Clie, Editorial.
Moody, Edward E., Jr. First Aid for Emotional Hurts: Helping People Through Difficult Times. 2008. 232p. pap. 12.99 (978-0-89265-564-9(X)) Randall Hse. Pubns.
Moody, Josh. The God-Centred Life: Insights from Jonathan Edwards for Today. 2007. (ENG.). 196p. per. (978-1-57383-386-8(X), Regent College Publishing) Regent College Publishing.
Moon, Gary W. Apprenticeship with Jesus: Learning to Live Like the Master, 1 vol. 2009. (Illus.). 256p. pap. 14.99 (978-0-8010-6841-6(X)) Baker Bks.
Mooney, David. If I Had Only Known. 2011. pap. 23.99 (978-1-61739-949-7(3)) Tate Publishing & Enterprises, LLC.
Moore, Arlie E. A Divided House. 14.95 (978-1-56794-099-2(4), C-2401) Star Bible & Tract Corp.
Moore, Beth. Believing God Day by Day: Growing Your Faith All Year Long. 2008. (ENG.). 400p. 14.99 (978-0-8054-4798-9(9)) B&H Publishing Group.
—Breaking Free Day by Day: A Year of Walking in Liberty. 2007. (ENG.). 400p. 14.99 (978-0-8054-4646-3(X)) B&H Publishing Group.
—David: 90 Days with a Heart Like His. 2006. (90 Ser.). (ENG.). 437p. 24.99 (978-0-8054-4427-8(0)) B&H Publishing Group.
—David: Seeking a Heart Like His. 2010. (ENG.). 32p. pap. 9.75 (978-1-4158-6949-9(9)); (Illus.). 240p. pap. 21.00 (978-1-4158-6948-2(0)) LifeWay Christian Resources.
—Esther: It's Tough Being a Woman. 2008. pap. 277.75 (978-1-4158-5289-7(8)) LifeWay Christian Resources.
—Get Out of That Pit: Straight Talk about God's Deliverance, 0 vols. 2009. 272p. pap. 16.99 (978-0-7852-8973-9(9)) Nelson, Thomas Inc.
—Get Out of that Pit: Straight Talk about God's Deliverance from a Former Pit-Dweller. l.t. ed. 2009. (ENG.). 299p. pap. 17.99 (978-1-59415-300-6(0)) Cengage Gale.
—Jesus: 90 Days with the One & Only. 2007. (Personal Reflections Ser.). (ENG.). 448p. 24.99 (978-0-8054-4645-6(1)) B&H Publishing Group.
—John: 90 Days with the Beloved Disciple. 2008. (ENG.). 448p. 24.99 (978-0-8054-4812-2(8)) B&H Publishing Group.
—Paul: 90 Days on His Journey of Faith, 1 vol. 2010. (Personal Reflections Ser.). (ENG.). 448p. 24.99 (978-0-8054-4934-1(5)) B&H Publishing Group.
—Stepping Up: A Journey Through the Psalms of Ascent. 2007. (Illus.). 32p. pap. 6.95 (978-1-4158-5742-7(3)); 175p. per. 12.95 (978-1-4158-5743-4(1)) LifeWay Christian Resources.
—Stepping up Leader Kit: A Journey Through the Psalms of Ascent. 2007. (Illus.). 175p. 149.95 (978-1-4158-5255-2(3)) LifeWay Christian Resources.
—When Godly People Do Ungodly Things: Arming Yourself in the Age of Seduction. l.t. ed. 2007. (Walker Large Print Ser.). (ENG.). 425p. per. 17.95 (978-1-59415-150-7(4), Walker Large Print) Cengage Gale.
Moore, Cheryl G. Living on the Edge. 2011. 84p. pap. 9.99 (978-1-4567-5199-9(9)) AuthorHouse.
Moore, David. The Last Men's Book You'll Ever Need: What the Bible Says about Guy Stuff. 2008. (ENG.). 224p. pap. 12.99 (978-0-8054-4681-4(8), B&H Bks.) B&H Publishing Group.
Moore, Derrick. It's Possible! Turn Your Dreams into Reality, 1 vol. 2008. 144p. 14.99 (978-0-8254-3359-7(2)) Kregel Pubns.
Moore, Dorothy. Lady in the Hood: An Unlikely Crusader for the Inner City. 2008. (ENG., Illus.). 144p. pap. 12.99 (978-1-59979-365-8(2), Creation Hse.) Charisma Media.
Moore, Frank. Rendezvous: A Sacred Encounter with God. 2007. (ENG., Illus.). 192p. pap. 14.99 (978-0-8341-2297-0(9), 083-412-2979) Beacon Hill Pr. of Kansas City.
Moore, J. L. Challenging Reflections on the Christian Life: Rethinking the Common Experience. 2011. 184p. pap. 13.95 (978-1-4497-1560-1(5), WestBow Pr.) Author Solutions, Inc.
Moore, James W. Have You Ever Seen a Hearse Pulling a Trailer? 2009. 148p. pap. 14.95 (978-0-687-46484-5(6)) Abingdon Pr.
—If God Is Your Co-Pilot, Swap Seats! 2009. 157p. pap. 14.99 (978-1-4267-0257-0(4)) Abingdon Pr.
—If God Is Your Co-Pilot, Swap Seats! l.t. ed. 2010. (ENG.). 256p. pap. 17.99 (978-1-59415-311-2(6)) Cengage Gale.
—Jesus' Parables about Priorities. 2008. 112p. pap. 11.50 (978-0-687-65094-1(1), Dimensions For Living) Abingdon Pr.
—Moments That Take Your Breath Away. 2008. 142p. pap. 14.95 (978-0-687-49069-1(3)) Abingdon Pr.
—Standing on the Promises or Sitting on the Premises? 2007. 173p. per. 16.00 (978-0-687-64254-0(X), Dimensions For Living) Abingdon Pr.
—When the World Takes the Wind Out of Your Sails. 2010. 160p. pap. 14.95 (978-1-4267-1135-0(2)) Abingdon Pr.
—Yes, Lord, I Have Sinned: But I Have Several Excellent Excuses. 20th anniv. ed. 2012. 128p. pap. 14.99 (978-1-4267-4097-8(2), Dimensions For Living) Abingdon Pr.
Moore, Jestine. Could God Save Someone Like Me? 2008. 80p. per. 7.99 (978-1-58169-262-4(5)) Genesis Communications, Inc.
Moore, Jim. Going the Distance. 2006. pap. 15.99 (978-1-60034-795-5(9)) Xulon Pr., Inc.
—What Is Christian Truth for You? 2007. 348p. per. 17.99 (978-1-60266-089-2(1)) Xulon Pr., Inc.
Moore, Karen. Applause for Mom. 2008. (Illus.). 87p. (978-1-86920-935-3(4)) Christian Art Pubs.
Moore, Kendrick. Setting the Standards: Where Did We Go Wrong. 2006. (ENG.). 88p. per. 16.95 (978-1-4241-5685-6(8)) PublishAmerica, Inc.
Moore, Kimberly & Paul, Heather. Going Out on a Limb. 2009. 200p. pap. 15.99 (978-1-60791-940-7(0)) Xulon Pr., Inc.
Moore, Lori A. Missing Andy: The Journey from Grief to Joy. 2010. pap. 8.99 (978-1-61566-948-6(5)) Tate Publishing & Enterprises, LLC.
Moore, Mary Sharon. Touching the Reign of God: Bringing Theological Reflection to Daily Life. 2008. 108p. pap. 13.00 (978-1-60608-197-6(7), Wipf and Stock) Wipf & Stock Pubs.
Moore, MaryAnn. Victorious Living. 2008. 444p. 33.99 (978-1-60647-423-5(5)); pap. 21.99 (978-1-60647-422-8(7)) Xulon Pr., Inc.
Moore, Pastor Curt. Return to Jesus: A Vision of Self-Giving Love. 2011. 116p. 28.95 (978-1-4497-2490-0(6)); pap. 11.95 (978-1-4497-2491-7(4)) Author Solutions, Inc. (WestBow Pr.).
Moore, Peter C. A Step Further: The Journey in Disipleship. 2011. (ENG.). 220p. pap. 14.99 (978-1-59932-263-6(3)) Advantage Media Group.
Moore, Phil. These Last Days: Children, it Is the last hour 1 John 2. 2008. 334p. pap. 29.95 (978-1-60563-359-6(3)) PublishAmerica, Inc.
Moore, Ron. Ignite. 2010. 192p. pap. 18.99 (978-1-60615-002-3(2)) WinePress Publishing.
Moore, Ronnie. Love, the Force Within: Living your best life through the power of God's Love. 2010. 68p. pap. 10.49 (978-1-4520-3121-7(5)) AuthorHouse.
Moore, Sue. Rendezvous Study Guide. 2007. 3.99 (978-0-8341-2316-8(9)) Nazarene Publishing Hse.
Moore, Thomas. God in A Box. 2011. (ENG.). 102p. pap. 8.95 (978-1-4664-3377-9(9)) CreateSpace.
Moore, William. The Elder Shall Serve the Younger. 2007. 108p. per. 10.99 (978-1-60266-164-6(2)) Xulon Pr., Inc.
Moore, William S. Living Well, Dying Well. 2008. 172p. per. 12.99 (978-1-58169-255-6(2)) Genesis Communications, Inc.
Moracho, Felix. Cristianos Hoy. 448p. 14.95 (978-958-607-266-3(5)) Sociedad de San Pablo COL. Dist: St Pauls/Alba Hse. Pubs.
Moral, José M. Incondicionalmente Amados. 2011. (SPA.). 164p. pap. 13.69 (978-1-4669-0283-1(3)) Trafford Publishing.
Moran, Mary Anne. Before I Knew You Loved Me. 2008. 128p. pap. (978-1-897373-42-2(2)) Word Alive Pr.
Moran, Wilmer. End Time Answers. 2009. 178p. 29.99 (978-1-4415-5695-0(8)); pap. 19.99 (978-1-4415-5694-3(X)) Xlibris Corp.
More Everyday Parables: Simple Stories for Spiritual Reflection. 2010. (ENG., Illus.). 144p. pap. 17.95 (978-1-55145-587-7(0)) Wood Lake Publishing, Inc. CAN. Dist: Westminster John Knox Pr.
Moreau, Elizabeth. I Believe Something! 2009. 208p. pap. 15.99 (978-1-60791-362-7(3)) Xulon Pr., Inc.
—I'm Saved, So What? 2008. 212p. pap. 14.99 (978-1-60647-058-9(2)) Xulon Pr., Inc.
Morehouse Publishing Staff. The Episcopal Handbook. 2008. (Illus.). 256p. pap. 15.00 (978-0-8192-2329-6(8), Morehouse Publishing) Church Publishing, Inc.
Moreira, Isabel & Toscano, Margaret. Hell & Its Afterlife: Historical & Contemporary Perspectives. 2010. (Illus.). 282p. 99.95 (978-0-7546-6729-2(4)) Ashgate Publishing Co.
Moreno, Jose. Vuelta Al Hogar: Return Home. (SPA.). 112p. (978-84-7228-294-0(5), 220951) Clie, Editorial.
Morey. A Christian Student's Survival Guide. 2010. 314p. pap. 21.99 (978-1-60957-424-6(9)) Xulon Pr., Inc.
Morey, Robert A. Journal of Biblical Apologetics: Vol. 10, No. 1, Vol. 10. 2007. (ENG.). per. 25.00 (978-0-9796640-0-7(4)) California Biblical Univ. and Seminary.
—Studies in the Atonement. rev. ed. 320p. reprint ed. pap. (978-0-925703-07-1(9)) Crown Pubns., Inc.
Morgan, Christopher W. & Peterson, Robert A., eds. The Glory of God. 2010. (Theology in Community Ser.: Vol. 2). 256p. 23.99 (978-1-58134-978-8(5)) Crossway.
Morgan-Cole, Trudy. Daughters of Grace: Experiencing God Through Their Stories. 2008. 17.99 (978-0-8280-2383-2(2)) Review & Herald Publishing Assn.
Morgan, Diana. Conversations at the Well: Heart-to-Heart Conversations with God. 2009. 268p. pap. 16.99 (978-1-61579-343-3(7)) Xulon Pr., Inc.
Morgan, Donell. The Call: To Hang Out with a Good God That Keeps Bad Company. 2010. pap. 12.99 (978-1-61566-757-4(1)) Tate Publishing & Enterprises, LLC.
Morgan, G. Campbell. El Discipulado Cristiano: The Christian Disciple. (SPA.). 96p. (978-84-7228-826-3(9), 220312) Clie, Editorial.
—Life Problems. 2010. (G. Campbell Morgan Reprint Ser.). (Illus.). 92p. pap. 13.00 (978-1-60899-290-4(X), Wipf and Stock) Wipf & Stock Pubs.
—The Teaching of Christ. 2010. 342p. 36.99 (978-1-117-94749-5(1)); pap. 31.75 (978-1-117-94750-1(5)) BiblioBazaar.
Morgan, George. A Spiritually Led Journey. 2008. 76p. pap. 16.95 (978-1-60703-274-8(0)) PublishAmerica, Inc.
Morgan, Hugh D. Holy God, Holy People: Take Time to Be Holy, the World Rushes On. 2007. 104p. pap. incl. audio compact disk (978-1-85049-222-1(0)) Bryntirion Pr.
Morgan, J. Charles. Jesus & the Cabin. 2011. 68p. pap. 10.57 (978-1-4269-8845-5(1)) Trafford Publishing.
Morgan, Jan. Single, Yet Not Alone. 2008. 230p. pap. 15.95 (978-0-9818168-1-4(9)) Anela Pr.
Morgan, Lady Bea. The Pastor's Wife Does Cry! 2007. (ENG.). 95p. per. (978-0-9792823-4-8(9)) Prioritybooks Pubns.
Morgan, Robert. 100 Bible Verses Everyone Should Know by Heart. 2011. pap. 0.00 (978-1-59328-326-1(1)) Graham, Billy Evangelistic Assn.
Morgan, Robert J. Simple: The Christian Life Doesn't Have to Be Complicated. 2006. (Illus.). 95p. per. (978-0-89265-562-5(3)) Randall Hse. Pubns.
—Simple. Study Guide: The Christian Life Doesn't Have to Be Complicated. 2008. 45p. pap. 6.99 (978-0-89265-558-8(5)) Randall Hse. Pubns.
—100 Bible Verses Everyone Should Know by Heart. 2010. (ENG.). 288p. pap. 14.99 (978-0-8054-4682-1(6), B&H Bks.) B&H Publishing Group.
—100 Bible Verses Everyone Should Know by Heart. l.t. ed. 2010. (ENG.). 352p. pap. 17.99 (978-1-59415-341-9(8)) Cengage Gale.
Morgan, William B., Jr. People of Integrity: Authentic Christian Living. 2008. 119p. per. 12.00 (978-0-88177-513-6(4)) Discipleship Resources.
Morgridge, Charles. The True Believer's Defence, Against Charges Preferred by Trinitarians, for not Believing in the Divinity of Christ, the Deity of Christ, the Trinity, &c. 2008. 248p. pap. 19.99 (978-0-557-02478-0(1)) Lulu Enterprises Inc.
Moriarty, Glendon & Hoffman, Louis, eds. God Image Handbook for Spiritual Counseling & Psychotherapy: Research, Theory, & Practice. 2008. 295p. 130.00 (978-0-7890-3439-7(5)); pap. 49.95 (978-0-7890-3440-3(9)) Routledge.
Morin, Jerry. An Encounter with Jehovah Tsidkenu. 2007. 196p. per. 15.99 (978-1-60266-643-6(1)) Xulon Pr., Inc.
Morley, Janet, ed. Bread of Tomorrow: Praying with the World's Poor. 224p. 13.00 (978-0-281-04559-4(3)) SPCK Publishing GBR. Dist: Pilgrim Pr., The/United Church Pr.
Morley, Patrick, et al. No Man Left Behind: How to Build & Sustain a Thriving Disciple-Making Ministry for Every Man in Your Church. 2006. (ENG., Illus.). 224p. 19.99 (978-0-8024-7549-7(3)) Moody Pubs.
Morning-Gleam: Or, the Pastor's Daughter. 2006. 236p. per. 20.99 (978-1-4255-2004-5(9)) MPublishing.
Morris (editor), Tom. Concerning Christian Liberty by Martin Luther. 2010. 111p. pap. 10.99 (978-0-557-18821-5(0)) Lulu Enterprises Inc.
Morris, Carlos A. Mensajes Mayores de los Profetas: Major Messages from the Minor. (SPA.). (978-84-7645-086-4(9), 223135) Clie, Editorial.
Morris, Jackie. The 11: 59 Experience. 2009. 152p. pap. 14.99 (978-1-60791-709-0(2)) Xulon Pr., Inc.
Morris, Jonathan. The Promise: God's Purpose & Plan for When Life Hurts. (ENG.). 240p. 2009. pap. 14.99 (978-0-06-135342-0(6)) 2008. 24.95 (978-0-06-135341-3(8)) HarperCollins Pubs. (HarperOne).
Morris, Robert Corin. Provocative Grace: The Challenge in Jesus' Words. 2006. 169p. per. 17.00 (978-0-8358-9848-5(2)) Upper Room Bks.
Morris, Tom. Making Sense Out of Death: A Grief Devotional. 2010. 66p. pap. 7.64 (978-0-557-17673-1(5)) Lulu Enterprises Inc.
Morrison, David & Morrison, Linda. Prayer & Crisis Referral Network. 2011. 120p. pap. 13.99 (978-1-61379-189-9(5)) Xulon Pr., Inc.
Morrison, H. C. Remarkable Conversions & Striking Illustrations. pap. 3.99 (978-0-88019-102-9(3)) Schmul Publishing Co., Inc.
Morrison, J. D. Justice for Truth. 2007. 164p. per. 13.99 (978-1-60477-399-6(5)) Xulon Pr., Inc.
Morrison, Jennifer Ruggiero. Learning to Forgive. 2009. 64p. pap. 10.99 (978-1-60791-751-9(3)) Xulon Pr., Inc.
Morrison, Jon. There's Something I Think You Should Know: A Youth Pastor's Last Words to His Students. 2009. 236p. 24.99 (978-1-4389-7456-9(6)); pap. 15.00 (978-1-4389-7455-2(8)) AuthorHouse.
Morrow, Sue Anne Steffey. Discernment: Acting Wisely. 2007. (Living the Good Life Together Ser.). 125.00 (978-0-687-64324-0(4)) Abingdon Pr.
—Discernment Acting Wisely: Study & Reflection Guide. 2007. (Living the Good Life Together Ser.). (Illus.). 63p. pap. 9.00 (978-0-687-64344-8(9)) Abingdon Pr.
Morse, Louise. Dementia: Frank & Linda's Story - New Understanding, New Approaches, New Hope, 1 vol. 2010. 256p. pap. 13.99 (978-1-85424-930-2(4), Monarch Bks.) Lion Hudson PLC GBR. Dist: Kregel Pubns.
Mortensen, Phil. For God So Loved the Inner-City. 2008. 316p. pap. 17.99 (978-1-60477-862-5(8)) Xulon Pr., Inc.
Morton, Gerald. Never Alone in the Back: A Paramedic's Reflections on Faith, Prayer & the Journey with God. 2011. 118p. pap. 16.95 (978-1-58275-312-6(1)) Aaron Bk. Publishing.
Morton, Verner M. Between Me & Thee. 2008. 48p. pap. 16.95 (978-1-60610-957-1(X)) PublishAmerica, Inc.
Morvant, Mark. Stop, Look, And Listen: Living the Christian Life. 2009. 112p. pap. 11.99 (978-1-60791-141-8(8)) Xulon Pr., Inc.
Morya, El. Morya I. Prophet, Mark L. & Prophet, Elizabeth Clare, eds. 356p. 14.95 (978-0-922729-78-4(6)) Summit Univ. Pr.
Moser, Jolene. Start Walking, Again. 2008. 108p. 19.99 (978-1-60791-010-7(1)); pap. 11.99 (978-1-60791-009-1(8)) Xulon Pr., Inc.
Moss, Claudette. Triumph Through Faith. 2007. (ENG.). 18.99 (978-1-60034-942-3(0)); pap. 10.99 (978-1-60034-941-6(2)) Xulon Pr., Inc.
—Womenology 101 Embrace Virtue Victoriously. 2007. 164p. (ENG.). 21.99 (978-1-60266-254-4(1)); per. 13.99 (978-1-60266-253-7(3)) Xulon Pr., Inc.
Most, Glenn W. Doubting Thomas. 2007. (Illus.). 288p. per. 21.00 (978-0-674-02561-5(X)) Harvard Univ. Pr.
Moticheck, Shawn S. Removing the Veil. 2008. 180p. pap. 24.95 (978-1-60703-786-6(6)) PublishAmerica, Inc.
Motley, James B. Spiritual Warfare. 2008. 224p. pap. 14.99 (978-1-60477-618-8(8)) Xulon Pr., Inc.
Motyer, Alec. Life 2: the Sequel: What Happens When You Die? 2008. (ENG.). 128p. pap. 10.99 (978-1-84550-343-7(0)) Christian Focus Pubns. GBR. Dist: STL Distribution North America.
Moussa, Ernestine N. Be Awake & Prepared: A Message from God Given in a Vision. 2011. 140p. 28.95 (978-1-4497-1810-7(8)); pap. 11.95 (978-1-4497-1809-1(4)) Author Solutions, Inc. (WestBow Pr.).
Mouw, Richard J. Uncommon Decency: Christian Civility in an Uncivil World. 2nd ed. 2010. (ENG.). 187p. pap. 16.00 (978-0-8308-3309-2(9), IVP Bks.) InterVarsity Pr.
Moyer, Kim. Reflections from the Journey. 2007. 96p. per. 9.99 (978-1-60266-352-7(1)) Xulon Pr., Inc.
Moyer, R. Larry. Growing in the Family: 8 Vital Relationships for the Growing Christian, 1 vol. 2009. 128p. pap. 10.99 (978-0-8254-3598-0(6)) Kregel Pubns.
Mozzo, Robinson. Demosle Un Cambio A La Vida. 112p. 5.95 (978-958-607-538-1(9)) Sociedad de San Pablo COL. Dist: St Pauls/Alba Hse. Pubs.
Mpaka, Noel. Joy of Embracing Trials. 2006. pap. 13.99 (978-1-60034-880-8(7)) Xulon Pr., Inc.
Mpouma, Paulette L. Pearls of Wisdom. 2008. 104p. pap. 10.99 (978-1-60647-842-4(7)) Xulon Pr., Inc.
—7 keys of christian life Survival. 2008. pap. 10.99 (978-1-60647-817-2(6)) Xulon Pr., Inc.
Mrkvicka, Edward F. No Innocent Affair: Making Right the Wrong of Adultery. 2011. pap. 15.99 (978-1-61777-768-4(4)) Tate Publishing & Enterprises, LLC.
Mukamuri, Ephiel. Pillars to Becoming A Strong Christian: A Handbook for Every Christian Disciple. 2007. pap. 9.99 (978-1-60266-279-7(7)) Xulon Pr., Inc.
Mulder, William H. Fellowship with God in Spirit & Truth: No Subtitle. 2008. 172p. pap. 13.99 (978-1-60647-383-2(2)) Xulon Pr., Inc.
Mullen, Bob, ed. Living in Greater Happiness Today. 87p. 6.95 (978-1-56794-226-2(1)) Star Bible & Tract Corp.
Mullen, Mark. I Miss Jesus: Motivated Instrument Sleeplessly Searching. 2010. 198p. pap. 14.99 (978-1-61579-735-6(1)) Xulon Pr., Inc.
Muller, Walter. Unchaste Deception. 2008. 193p. pap. 17.50 (978-1-4092-0829-7(X)) Lulu Enterprises Inc.
Mullings, Bert. Kingdom Empowerment: Principles to Living an Empowered Life. 2008. 148p. 21.99 (978-1-60647-641-3(6)); pap. 13.99 (978-1-60647-640-6(8)) Xulon Pr., Inc.
Mullings, Margaret C. Seeds of Hope Vol. 3: A Collection of Inspirational Writings to Encourage Hope & Healing. 2008. 200p. 25.99 (978-1-60647-960-5(1)); pap. 15.99 (978-1-60647-776-2(5)) Xulon Pr., Inc.
Mullins, Brenna L. The Chandelier, 1 vol. 2010. 92p. pap. 16.95 (978-1-4489-6277-8(3)) PublishAmerica, Inc.
Mullins, J. C. The Narrow Road to God on the Interstate of Life. 2007. 196p. per. 24.95 (978-1-4241-8979-3(9)) PublishAmerica, Inc.
Mullins, Jeffery. Mrs Christ. 2007. 124p. per. 10.99 (978-1-60266-575-0(3)) Xulon Pr., Inc.
Mulryne, Mark. 2 Timothy: Faithful to the End: Seven Studies for Individuals or Groups. 2010. (Good Book Guides). 64p. pap. (978-1-905564-56-9(2)) Good Bk. Co.
Mungovan, Timothy R. The Book of Revelation: A Clear & Precise Understanding. 2011. 248p. 26.67 (978-1-4269-6863-1(9)); pap. 16.67 (978-1-4269-6862-4(0)) Trafford Publishing.
Munoz, Hector. Alabanzas a la Palabra de Dios. 112p. 2.95 (978-950-861-141-3(3)) Sociedad de San Pablo ARG. Dist: St Pauls/Alba Hse. Pubs.
Munroe. Understanding Your Potential Expanded Edition in Special Hardcover. 2008. 256p. 32.99 (978-0-7684-2804-9(1)) Destiny Image Pubs.
Munroe, Jeff. Yes, No, Maybe So: Dealing with Doubt. (Life Wise Ser.). tchr. ed. 19.95 (978-1-56212-776-3(4), 131256) Faith Alive Christian Resources.

Munroe, Myles. Applying the Kingdom: Rediscovering the Priority of God for Mankind. 2007. 252p. 24.99 (978-0-7684-2489-8(5)) Destiny Image Pubs.
—Claves para la Soltería. 2008.Tr. of Keys for Living Single. (SPA.). per. 5.99 (978-1-60374-062-3(7)) Whitaker Hse.
—God's Big Idea: Reclaiming God's Original Purposes for Your Life. 2008. 252p. 24.99 (978-0-7684-2703-5(7)) Destiny Image Pubs.
—God's Big Idea: Reclaiming God's Original Purpose for Your Life. (Kingdom Bks.). 236p. 2009. (ENG.). pap. 11.99 (978-0-7684-3128-5(X)) 2008. pap. (978-0-7684-2729-5(0)) Destiny Image Pubs.
—Keys for Change. 2009. 157p. pap. 5.99 (978-1-60374-151-4(8)) Whitaker Hse.
—Keys for Living Single. 2008. (Keys For... Ser.). 157p. per. 5.99 (978-1-60374-032-6(5)) Whitaker Hse.
—Keys for Men. 2009. pap. 5.99 (978-1-60374-152-1(6)) Whitaker Hse.
—Keys for Women. 2009. pap. 5.99 (978-1-60374-154-5(2)) Whitaker Hse.
—Kingdom Principles. lt. ed. 2008. 228p. pap. 24.99 (978-0-7684-2770-7(3)) Destiny Image Pubs.
—Kingdom Principles: Preparing for Kingdom Experience & Expansion. 2008. 188p. pap. 14.99 (978-0-7684-2664-9(2)) 2006. 215p. 19.99 (978-0-7684-2373-0(2)) Destiny Image Pubs.
—Kingdom Principles (Spanish) 2007. pap. 13.99 (978-0-7684-2433-1(X)) Destiny Image Pubs.
—Los Principios y Beneficios del Cambio: Cumpliendo tu propósito en medio de tiempos Inciertos. 2009.Tr. of Principles & Benefits of Change: Fulfilling Your Purpose in Unsettled Times. (SPA.). pap. 11.99 (978-1-60374-159-0(3)) Whitaker Hse.
—Maximizing Your Potential Expanded Edition. 2008. pap. 15.99 (978-0-7684-2674-8(X)) Destiny Image Pubs.
—The Most Important Person on Earth: The Holy Spirit, the Heavenly Governor. 2007. 318p. 19.99 (978-0-88368-986-8(3)) Whitaker Hse.
—Overcoming Crisis: The Secrets to Thriving in Challenging Times. 2009. 199p. pap. 15.99 (978-0-7684-3052-3(6)) Destiny Image Pubs.
—Potential for Every Day: A Daily Devotional. 2009. pap. 11.99 (978-0-7684-3050-9(X)) Destiny Image Pubs.
—Purpose for Living: 365 Days to Understanding, Releasing, & Maximizing Your Potential. 2009. pap. 17.99 (978-0-7684-2846-9(7)) Destiny Image Pubs.
—Rediscovering Kingdom Worship: The Purpose & Power of Praise & Worship. exp. ed. 2010. (ENG.). pap. 16.99 (978-0-7684-3247-3(2)) Destiny Image Pubs.
—Rediscovering the Kingdom. lt. ed. 2008. 240p. pap. 24.99 (978-0-7684-2775-2(4)) Destiny Image Pubs.
—Rediscovering the Kingdom Personal Development Kit: Ancient Hope for Our 21st Century World. 2007. audio compact disk 99.99 (978-0-7684-2603-8(0)) Destiny Image Pubs.
—Releasing Your Potential: Exposing the Hidden You. 2007. (Illus.). 312p. per. 15.99 (978-0-7684-2417-1(8)) Destiny Image Pubs.
—Understanding Your Place in God's Kingdom: Your Original Purpose for Existence. 2011. 272p. pap. 16.99 (978-0-7684-4065-2(3)) Destiny Image Pubs.
Munroe, Myles. Unleash Your Purpose. 2009. 252p. pap. 15.99 (978-0-7684-2758-5(4)) Destiny Image Pubs.
—Unleash Your Purpose, 1 vol. 2010. (SPA.). 189p. pap. 13.99 (978-987-557-288-1(8)) Peniel, Editorial ARG. Dist: Destiny Image Pubs.
Munsey, Phil. Legacy Now: Why Everything about You Matters. 2007. (ENG.). 240p. 21.99 (978-1-59979-259-0(1), Charisma Hse.) Charisma Media.
Munton, Doug. Warriors in Hiding. 2008. 136p. pap. 14.99 (978-1-60647-647-5(5)) Xulon Pr., Inc.
Mupanduki, Stellah. God's Little Flock Healed: They will rise on wings like Eagles. 2010. 220p. pap. 24.00 (978-1-4520-1984-0(3)) AuthorHouse.
Murch, James. Adventuring for Christ. 360p. pap. 4.99 (978-0-89900-236-1(6)) College Pr. Publishing Co., Inc.
Murchison, Rodger. Guide for Grief. 2011. 114p. pap. 14.95 (978-1-934879-31-3(2)) Crumm, David Media, LLC.
—Guide for Grief, Color Edition. 2011. 114p. pap. 24.95 (978-1-934879-35-1(5)) Crumm, David Media, LLC.
Murdoch, Lincoln. See You at the Finish! 8 Principles of Spiritual Endurance. 2006. 94p. (YA). per. 7.99 (978-1-929478-36-1(4), 3000) Cross Training Publishing.
Murphey, Cecil. When God Turned off the Lights: True Stories of Seeking God in the Darkness. 2009. (ENG.). 224p. pap. 14.99 (978-0-8307-5155-6(6)) Gospel Light Pubns.
Murphy, Dick. Covenant Promises. 2008. 216p. pap. 15.00 (978-1-59755-108-3(2), Advantage Inspirational) Advantage Bks.
Murphy, Gannon. Reasons for the Christian Hope. 2009. (ENG., Illus.). 144p. pap. 15.99 (978-1-84550-466-3(6), Mentor) Christian Focus Pubns. GBR. Dist: STL Distribution North America.
Murphy, John A. Dumb American in A Strange Country. 2006. pap. 13.99 (978-1-60034-411-4(9)) Xulon Pr., Inc.
Murphy, Jonathan. Tony, 1 vol. 2009. 73p. pap. 14.95 (978-1-4489-8943-0(4)) PublishAmerica, Inc.
Murphy, Joseph. Christ Our Joy: The Theological Vision of Pope Benedict XVI. 2008. 216p. 19.95 (978-1-58617-182-7(8)) Ignatius Pr.
Murphy, Nikita. The Business of Life. 2011. pap. 13.95 (978-1-59581-651-1(8), Brentwood Christian Pr.) Brentwood Communications Group.
Murphy-O'Connor, Jerome. Becoming Human Together: The Pastoral Anthropology of St. Paul, Third Edition. 2009. 280p. pap. 29.95 (978-1-58983-361-6(9)) Society of Biblical Literature.
Murphy, Pat. Rescued to Rescue Personal Mission Log. 2010. 184p. pap. 17.00 (978-1-59755-253-0(4), Advantage Inspirational) Advantage Bks.
Murray, Andrew. Abide in Christ. 2009. 226p. 28.99 (978-1-116-68203-8(6)); 226p. pap. 25.75 (978-1-116-68204-5(4)); (ENG.). 224p. pap. 20.99 (978-1-116-68207-6(9), BiblioLife); (ENG.). 224p. pap. 22.99 (978-1-116-68206-9(0), BiblioLife) BiblioBazaar.
—Abide in Christ. 2008. 140p. pap. 7.99 (978-1-60459-308-2(3)) Wilder Pubns., Ltd.
—Abide in Christ: Thoughts on the Blessed Life of Fellowship with the Son of God. 2011. 178p. pap. 7.75 (978-1-61427-023-2(6)) Martino Publishing.
—Absolute Surrender. 2011. 130p. pap. 5.95 (978-1-61427-070-6(8)) Martino Publishing.
—Acerquemonos Al Senor: Let Us Draw Nigh. (SPA.). 96p. (978-84-7228-890-4(0), 220011) Clie, Editorial.
—Como Vivir en la Voluntad de Dios: How to Live in the Will of God. (SPA.). 192p. (978-84-7228-914-7(1), 222236) Clie, Editorial.
—The Deeper Christian Life. 2007. 116p. pap. 8.95 (978-1-60206-572-7(1)) Cosimo, Inc.
—The Deeper Christian Life: An Aid to Its Attainment. 2007. (Authentic Original Classic Ser.). 155p. per. 13.99 (978-0-7684-2468-3(2)) Destiny Image Pubs.
—The Master's Indwelling. 2008. 124p. 21.99 (978-0-554-37187-0(1)) 2008. 124p. 24.99 (978-0-554-27884-1(7)) 2007. (ENG.). 110p. pap. 18.99 (978-1-4346-4157-0(8)) 2007. (ENG.). 120p. pap. 19.99 (978-1-4346-4230-1(5)) BiblioBazaar.
—The Master's Indwelling. 2009. 110p. pap. (978-1-4099-6334-9(9)) Dodo Pr.
—The Master's Indwelling. 2008. 92p. pap. 8.99 (978-1-60459-588-8(4)) Wilder Pubns., Ltd.
—The New Life: Words of God for Young Disciples of Christ. 2007. (Authentic Original Classic Ser.). 260p. per. 15.99 (978-0-7684-2558-1(1)) Destiny Image Pubs.
—Permaneced en Cristo (Abide in Christ) (SPA.). 200p. (978-84-7228-524-8(3), 220684) Clie, Editorial.
—Standing in the Gap. 2009. 101p. pap. (978-1-77036-052-5(2)) Christian Art Pubs.
—The True Vine. De Rosset, Rosalie, ed. 2007. (Moody Classics Ser.). (ENG.). 160p. per. 7.99 (978-0-8024-5655-7(3)) Moody Pubs.
—Vid Verdadera (True Vine) (SPA.). 112p. (978-84-7228-619-1(3), 220945) Clie Editorial.
—The Wisdom of Andrew Murray. 2008. 332p. 24.96 (978-1-60459-309-9(1)) Wilder Pubns., Ltd.
—The Wisdom of Andrew Murray: Absolute Surrender, the Master's Indwelling, & the Prayer Life. 2008. 240p. pap. 14.99 (978-1-60459-590-1(6)) Wilder Pubns., Ltd.
—Working for God. 2009. 162p. 25.99 (978-1-116-40766-2(3)); pap. 20.75 (978-1-116-40769-3(8)); pap. 21.75 (978-1-116-40768-6(X)); 26.99 (978-1-116-40767-9(1)) BiblioBazaar.
Murray, Andrew & Stevens, Bo. Abide in Christ. 2007. (Growing Disciples Series). 176p. (978-1-4158-5213-2(8)) LifeWay Christian Resources.
Murray, David. Personal Space. 2011. 52p. pap. 10.99 (978-1-61215-822-8(6)) Xulon Pr., Inc.
Murray, David P. Christians Get Depressed Too: Hope & Help for Depressed People. 2010. pap. 10.00 (978-1-60178-100-0(8)) Reformation Heritage Bks.
Murray, Douglas. It's Time to Fly. 2011. 144p. pap. 14.99 (978-1-61379-244-5(1)) Xulon Pr., Inc.
Murray, Edward, Jr. Possessing the Land: The Devine Right to Poccession. 2006. (Illus.). per. 12.95 (978-0-9787128-1-5(1)) Palm Tree Pubns.
Murray, John. If We Only Knew... Remarkable True Stories of God's Intervention. 2009. 120p. 19.99 (978-1-61579-151-4(5)); pap. 11.99 (978-1-61579-150-7(7)) Xulon Pr., Inc.
Murray, John J. Catch the Vision: Roots of the Reformed Recovery. 2007. (Illus.). 191p. per. (978-0-85234-667-9(0)) Evangelical Pr.
Murray, Richard K. The Jesus Mood: Discovering the Treasure of Imperative Faith. 2009. 197p. pap. 14.95 (978-1-4327-2334-7(0)) Outskirts Pr., Inc.
Murray, Ted. Lessons from Nehemiah. 2008. 124p. pap. (978-0-901860-86-6(7)) Scripture Truth Pubns.
Murray, Tony. Removing the Mysteries of Christianity. 2007. 104p. per. 11.95 (978-1-59858-382-3(4)) Dog Ear Publishing, LLC.
Murrell, Adam. The Essence of the Christian Faith: A 1689 Catechism for the Twenty-First Century. 2009. 140p. pap. 17.00 (978-1-60608-487-8(9), Resource Pubns.) Wipf & Stock Pubs.
Murrell, Ed. Good Cent$ A Simple Budget for Christian Young People. 2010. 148p. pap. 13.95 (978-1-61507-206-4(3)) Cross Bks. Publishing.
Murriel, Kevin. Who's Afraid of the Journey? 8 Steps to Help You Walk in the Confidence of Christ! 2009. 316p. pap. 14.99 (978-1-61579-344-0(5)) Xulon Pr., Inc.
Murzin, Rebecca. Faith Takes Action. 2010. pap. 10.99 (978-1-61663-555-8(X)) Tate Publishing & Enterprises, LLC.
Musekura, Celestin. An Assessment of Contemporary Models of Forgiveness. 2010. (American University Studies VII: Theology & Religion Ser.). 240p. (C). 75.95 (978-1-4331-0874-7(7)) Lang, Peter Publishing, Inc.
Musgrave, Jeff. The Exchange: An Inquirer's Bible Study. 2010. viii, 62p. (978-1-60682-099-5(0)); (978-1-60682-098-8(2)) BJU Pr.
Musser, Joe. Dilema De un Esceptico: A Skeptics Quest. (SPA.). (978-84-7645-315-5(9), 223381) Clie, Editorial.
Muto, Susan A. & Van Kaam, Adrian. Divine Guidance: Seeking to Find & Follow the Will of God. pap. (978-1-880982-12-9(9)) Epiphany Assn.
Mutsambiwa, Farai. God at Work in Our Dreams. 2010. (Illus.). 56p. pap. 24.49 (978-1-4520-6148-1(3)) AuthorHouse.
Muverengwi, Phanuel. How to Add Value to Your Christian Life. 2011. 180p. pap. 14.99 (978-1-4567-3631-6(0)) AuthorHouse.
—Key Elements of Christian Success: Uncompromising Greatness. 2011. 204p. pap. 19.06 (978-1-4567-7296-3(1)) AuthorHouse.
Muzio, Miles. Foundations: The Meaning of Life. 2008. 184p. pap. 13.99 (978-1-60647-085-5(X)) Xulon Pr., Inc.
My Christian Faith. 112p. stu. ed. 16.50 (978-0-570-09798-3(3), 22-2483); 176p. tchr. ed., spiral bd. 21.00 (978-0-570-09799-0(1), 2-2484) Concordia Publishing Hse.
Myatt, Devay. Prayer Counselor: How to Have an Effective Altar Call. 2009. 76p. pap. 10.99 (978-1-61579-586-4(3)) Xulon Pr., Inc.
Myers, Bill & Wimbish, David. The Dark Side of the Supernatural: What Is of God & What Isn't, 1 vol. 2008. (ENG.). 224p. (YA). (gr. 8-11). pap. 12.99 (978-0-310-27924-2(0)) Zondervan.
Myers, Kenneth A. All God's Children & Blue Suede Shoes: Christians & Popular Culture. 2012. (Turning Point Christian Worldview Ser.: Vol. 7). 224p. pap. 17.99 (978-1-4335-2822-4(3)) Crossway.
Myers, Lois. The Other Side of Calvary. 2007. 188p. per. 13.99 (978-1-60266-820-1(5)) Xulon Pr., Inc.
Myers, Wanda J. My Soul Cries... Holy Holy Holy: Building Child-Like Faith Through Simple Inspirations. 2011. 136p. pap. 11.99 (978-1-4557-1853-4(3)) AuthorHouse.
Myles, Francis. The Powers & Dangers of Transition. 2008. 336p. per. 17.99 (978-1-60477-557-0(2)) Xulon Pr., Inc.
Myra, Harold, et al. Afterlife: 11 Core Truths to Build Your Life On, 1 vol. 2008. (Foundations Ser.). (ENG.). 80p. pap. 7.99 (978-0-310-27689-0(6)) Zondervan.
Myung, Sung-Hoon & Hong, Young-Gi, eds. Charis & Charisma: David Yonggi Cho & the Growth of Yoido Full Gospel Church. 2011. (Regnum Studies in Mission Ser.). 236p. pap. 26.00 (978-1-61097-594-0(4), Wipf and Stock) Wipf & Stock Pubs.
Nagy, Chris. Psalms & Proverbs for Dogs. 2011. 140p. 28.95 (978-1-4497-2238-8(5)); pap. 11.95 (978-1-4497-2239-5(3)) Author Solutions, Inc. (WestBow Pr.).
Najarro-DeGuzman, Olive. God's Will vs. Pain Pill. 2010. 356p. pap. 20.99 (978-1-60957-846-6(5)) Xulon Pr., Inc.
Nakazibwe, Gertrude. My Visions & Dreams. 2011. 24p. pap. 15.99 (978-1-4628-6314-3(0)) Xlibris Corp.
Nan, Miss. God at Work. 2010. 164p. pap. 14.99 (978-1-60957-547-2(4)) Xulon Pr., Inc.
Nancy, W. Reece. The Dichotomy of Power: Using Power with Intelligence & Integrity. 2010. 174p. 24.95 (978-1-935271-50-5(4)); pap. 14.95 (978-1-935271-43-7(1)) Published by Westview, Inc.
Narcisse, Olita. Renew Your Mind: With thoughts from Heaven. 2011. 70p. pap. 15.99 (978-1-4653-4030-6(0)) Xlibris Corp.
Nash, Peter J. Manifesting Heaven. 2011. (978-1-77069-280-0(0)) Word Alive Pr.
Nash, Wanda. People Need Stillness. (Illus.). 80p. pap. (978-0-232-51971-6(4)) South Asia Bks.
Nasser, David. A Call to Die: A 40 Day Journey of Fasting from the World & Feasting on God. 2008. (Illus.). 351p. 19.99 (978-0-9792479-0-3(X)) Redemptive Art Publishing.
Nataraja, Kim. Journey to the Heart: Christian Contemplation Through the Centuries. 2012. (Illus.). 352p. pap. 35.00 (978-1-57075-938-3(3)) Orbis Bks.
Naumescu, Vlad & Naumescu. Modes of Religiosity in Eastern Christianity: Religious Processes & Social Change in Ukraine. 2008. (ENG.) 250p. pap. 49.95 (978-3-8258-9908-0(X)) Lit Verlag DEU. Dist: Transaction Pubs.
Navigators Staff. Going on with Christ, 10, Pack. 2007. (Growing in Christ Ser.). (ENG.). 16p. 14.99 (978-1-60006-170-7(2)) NavPress Publishing Group.
—The Grad's Guide to Time with God: Daily Devos for a Deeper Relationship. 2009. (Hollywood Nobody Ser.). (ENG.). 176p. (YA). 14.99 (978-1-60006-436-4(1), Th1nk Bks.) NavPress Publishing Group.
Navigators, The. The Grad's Guide to Choosing Well: Wisdom for Life on Your Own. 2010. (Woman's Journey of Discipleship Ser.). 176p. (YA). 14.99 (978-1-60006-921-5(5), Th1nk Bks.) NavPress Publishing Group.
Naylor, Charles W. Heart Talks. 2007. 20.00 (978-1-60416-092-5(6)); pap. 13.00 (978-1-60416-091-8(8)) Reformation Pubs.
Naylor, Charles Wesley. Heart Talks. 2010. (Illus.). 126p. pap. 21.61 (978-1-153-81483-6(8)) General Bks. LLC.
NAZARETH, Elijah. What Is Happening? 2009. 125p. pap. 14.50 (978-1-4092-5722-6(3)) Lulu Enterprises Inc.
Ndlovu, Jairos. Beautiful People of Nations. 2007. (ENG.). 500p. per. 23.99 (978-1-60266-036-6(0)) Xulon Pr., Inc.
Ndukwe, Olo. Christian Faith & Social Transformation. 2011. 496p. pap. (978-3-8443-0802-0(4)) Lambert Academic Publishing.
Neace, Kristi. Between Friends: A Woman's Look at Mentoring God's Way. 2007. (ENG.). 92p. pap. 9.95 (978-0-929292-39-7(1), 800-747-0738, CrossHouse Publishing) Hannibal Bks.
Neal, Lee Roy. Death. 2007. pap. 10.00 (978-1-4257-6258-2(1)) Xlibris Corp.
Nee, Watchman. Changed into His Likeness. 2007. (ENG.). 161p. pap. 9.99 (978-0-87508-859-4(7)) CLC Pubns.
—Changed into His Likeness. 2007. per. 8.00 (978-1-4245-0786-3(3)) Treasures Media Inc.
—Consejos Para una Vida Santa: Thoughts for a Holy Life. (SPA.). (978-84-7645-234-9(9), 223259) Clie, Editorial.
—Consejos Sobre la Vida Cristiana: Thoughts on Christian Living. (SPA.). (978-84-7645-233-2(0), 223260) Clie, Editorial.
—The Gospel of God. 492p. per. 18.50 (978-0-87083-533-9(5), 11009001) Living Stream Ministry.
—Libros en Casete: El Misterio de Cristo. (ESP.). (978-0-7363-1489-3(X)) Living Stream Ministry.
—Libros en Casete: La vida cristiana Normal. (ESP.). (978-0-7363-0854-0(7)) Living Stream Ministry.
—The Normal Christian Life. 2008. (ENG.). 304p. per. 5.99 (978-0-8423-4710-5(0)) Tyndale Hse. Pubs.
—The Secret of Christian Living. 2008. 170p. pap. 6.50 (978-0-935008-88-3(8)) Christian Fellowship Pubs., Inc.
—El Secreto de la Vida Cristiana. 2010. (SPA.). 193p. pap. (978-0-935008-93-7(4)) Christian Fellowship Pubs., Inc.
—Sit Walk Stand with Study Guide: The Process of Christian Maturity. 2008. 96p. pap. 8.99 (978-0-87508-973-7(9)) CLC Pubns.
—Spiritual Exercise: Simplified Version of the Basic Lessons on Practical Christian Living. 2007. viii, 353p. (978-0-935008-87-6(X)) Christian Fellowship Pubs., Inc.
Neece, William C. Revival Kindling: Discipleship & Spiritual Maturity, Four. 2008. Two. 20.00 (978-1-60416-082-6(9))Volume Two. pap. 13.00 (978-1-60416-081-9(0)) Reformation Pubs.
Neely, Kirk H. When Grief Comes: Finding Strength for Today & Hope for Tomorrow. 2007. 176p. pap. 13.00 (978-0-8010-6760-0(X)) Baker Bks.
Neighbour, Ralph Webster. Student Survival Kit: An Essential Guide for New Christians. 2007. 112p. pap. (978-1-4158-5253-8(7)) LifeWay Christian Resources.
Neighbour, Randall G. The Naked Truth about Small Group Ministry: When It Won't Work & What to Do about It. 2009. (Illus.). 255p. pap. 20.99 (978-0-9788779-6-5(9)) Touch Pubns.
Neilands, L. & MacKinnon, K. A Friend for Life. 128p. 5.99 (978-1-871676-78-5(9)) Christian Focus Pubns. GBR. Dist: Spring Arbor Distributors, Inc.
Neilsons D Staff. Pride & Humility: Pride Its Cause & Its Effect & in Praise of Humility. 2008. pap. 17.99 (978-1-60477-995-0(0)) Xulon Pr., Inc.
Neinast, Helen R. Discernment: Acting Wisely. 2007. (Living the Good Life Together Ser.). 62p. pap. 12.00 (978-0-687-64334-9(1)) Abingdon Pr.
Nelson, Alan. Coached by Jesus: 31 Lifechanging Questions Asked by the Master. 2010. (ENG.). 224p. pap. 15.99 (978-1-4516-2378-9(X), Howard Bks.) Howard Books.
Nelson, Alan E. The Power of a New Attitude. 2009. 256p. 6.99 (978-0-8007-8777-6(3)) Revell.
Nelson, Ed. Growing in Grace. 2007. per. 9.95 (978-0-9791856-0-1(2)) Nelson, Ed Evangelistic Assn.
Nelson, Emmitt J. The Fruit of the Spirit. 2nd lt. ed. 87p. (Orig.). pap. 9.00 (978-0-9664896-2-0(4)) Nelson Consulting, Inc.
Nelson, Gary V. Borderland Churches: A Congregation's Introduction to Missional Living. 2008. 192p. pap. 19.99 (978-0-8272-0238-2(5)) Chalice Pr.
Nelson, Jason M. Miserable Joy: Chronic Pain in the Christian Life. 2007. per. (978-0-8100-1749-8(0)) Northwestern Publishing Hse.
Nelson, Kalvin L. The Power of Me: A Guide for Living. 2008. 60p. pap. 12.95 (978-1-4327-2034-6(1)) Outskirts Pr., Inc.
Nelson, Mary J. Hope for Tough Times, 1 vol. 2009. (ENG.). 304p. 6.99 (978-0-8007-8781-3(1)) Revell.
Nelson, Melvin. Does God Lie? 2007. 260p. per. 15.99 (978-1-60266-518-7(4)) Xulon Pr., Inc.
Nelson, Patricia H. Out of Darkness: into the Light: A Kjv Study of II Peter 1:5-9. 2011. 92p. pap. 13.95 (978-1-4497-2458-0(2), WestBow Pr.) Author Solutions, Inc.
Nelson, Toni. A Beggars Purse. 2010. pap. 10.99 (978-1-61663-117-8(1)) Tate Publishing & Enterprises, LLC.
Neser, Kris. Do you know your last Name? 2006. pap. 9.99 (978-1-60034-693-4(6)) Xulon Pr., Inc.
Neufeld, Henry E. Identifying Your Gifts & Service: Small Group Edition. 2007. 140p. per. 12.99 (978-1-893729-47-6(8)) Energion Pubns.
—When People Speak for God. 2007. per. 17.99 (978-1-893729-38-4(9)) Energion Pubns.
Never Abandoned. 2007. pap. 14.95 (978-0-9792475-2-1(7)) Good Catch Publishing.
The New First Mass Book: Mother of Pearl Boys Set. 17.25 (978-0-89942-761-4(8), B808/82B, Resurrection Pr.) Catholic Bk. Publishing Corp.
The New First Mass Book: Mother of Pearl Girls Set. 17.25 (978-0-89942-760-7(X), B808/82W, Resurrection Pr.) Catholic Bk. Publishing Corp.
The New National Baptist Hymnal: 21st Century Edition Blue Pew Bible. (978-1-58942-125-7(6)) R.H. Boyd Publishing Corp.
The New National Baptist Hymnal: 21st Century Edition Red Pew Bible. (978-1-58942-124-0(8)) R.H. Boyd Publishing Corp.
Newbern, Effie B. You're Big Enough to Understand. 2011. 78p. pap. 10.99 (978-1-60957-966-1(6)) Xulon Pr., Inc.
Newberry, Tommy. El Éxito No es Casualidad: Cambie Sus Decisiones - Cambie Su Vida. 2008.Tr. of Success Is Not an Accident: Change Your Choices; Change Your Life. (SPA., Illus.). 272p. pap. 13.99 (978-1-4143-1980-3(0), Tyndale Espanol) Tyndale Hse. Pubs.

C

—Success Is Not an Accident: Change Your Choices; Change Your Life. 2007. (ENG., Illus.). 256p. per. 13.99 *(978-1-4143-1311-5(X))* Tyndale Hse. Pubs.

Newbold, Ria C. It's Time To P.U.S.H. Be Persistent under Supernatural Heat & Give Birth to Your Ministry. 2008. 124p. pap. 10.99 *(978-1-60647-129-6(5))* Xulon Pr., Inc.

Newbrough, Jennie. At the Core: Character Determines Destiny. 2008. 140p. pap. 12.95 *(978-0-9792739-0-2(0))* Ajoyin Publishing, Inc.

Newcomb, Harvey. A Practical Directory for Young Christian Females: Being a Series of Letters from a Brother to a Younger Sister. 2007. (ENG.). 256p. pap. 21.99 *(978-1-4346-1335-6(6))*; 278p. pap. 23.99 *(978-1-4346-1387-5(9))* BiblioBazaar.

—A Practical Directory for Young Christian Females: Being a Series of Letters from a Brother to a Younger Sister. 2009. 244p. pap. *(978-1-4099-4554-3(5))* Dodo Pr.

Newell, Lisa. Defy Gravity by Walking on Water. 2006. 52p. per. 11.00 *(978-1-4120-9932-5(3))* Trafford Publishing.

Newlands. Generosity & Christian Future. 288p. 35.95 *(978-0-281-05018-5(X))* International Publishers Marketing.

Newman, Bart. Because of Baghdad: What a Father Would Say about Life, If He Didn't Come Home to Say It. 2008. 164p. pap. 13.99 *(978-1-60647-011-4(6))* Xulon Pr., Inc.

Newman, Elizabeth. Untamed Hospitality: Welcoming God & Other Strangers. annot. ed. 2007. (Christian Practice of Everyday Life Ser.). 236p. (C). pap. 25.00 *(978-1-58743-176-0(9))* Brazos Pr.

Newman, Michael. The Ultimate Operations Manual. 2006. 112p. 28.99 *(978-1-58930-170-2(6))* Selah Publishing Group, LLC.

Newman, Russell A. The Quest for Absolute Truth: Encouraging You to STAND up! So We Can Restore America. 2010. 412p. 42.95 *(978-1-61507-258-3(6))*; pap. 27.95 *(978-1-61507-257-6(8))* Cross Bks. Publishing.

Newport, Iii Walter A. Smile Lines. 2008. 120p. pap. 10.99 *(978-1-60266-672-6(5))* Xulon Pr., Inc.

Newson, Arletha. The Little Book That Could Motivate. 2007. 48p. per. 9.99 *(978-1-60266-444-9(7))* Xulon Pr., Inc.

Newton, Bensley & Newton, Thelma. Fear Not: Overcome fear through ALL the Fear Not verses in the Bible. 2010. 254p. 24.95 *(978-1-4327-5237-8(5))* Outskirts Pr., Inc.

Newton, John. A Pen Dipped in Love: Selected Letters from John Newton. 2011. 194p. pap. 16.00 ***(978-1-59925-255-1(4))*** Solid Ground Christian Bks.

Newton, Richard. Bible Blessings. 2008. 336p. 45.95 *(978-1-4369-7263-5(9))*; pap. 30.95 *(978-1-4367-8816-8(1))* Kessinger Publishing, LLC.

—Bible Blessings. 2006. 336p. per. 23.99 *(978-1-4255-3384-7(1))* MPublishing.

Newton, Sheldon. Humility & the Honor of God: Unleash the Power of Obedience to God. 2008. (ENG.). 224p. 19.99 *(978-1-59979-520-1(5)*, Creation Hse.) Charisma Media.

Ngoma, Samuel. Why Is God Silent on Mandela? The Unspoken Question about a World Icon in Relation to Christ. 2009. (ENG.). 112p. pap. 14.99 *(978-1-59979-777-9(1)*, Creation Hse.) Charisma Media.

Ngosa, Keyworth N. The Mystery of Lawlessness: The Final Dimension. 2010. 160p. pap. 14.95 *(978-1-4502-0885-7(1))* iUniverse, Inc.

Ngosa, Pastor Keyworth N. Satan's Best Kept Secrets: His Nefarious Schemes & Deepest Fears Unveiled. 2011. 256p. pap. 19.95 ***(978-1-4620-2933-4(7))*** iUniverse, Inc.

Nichol, Karl. Stepping Stones to the New Jerusalem. 2007. 128p. per. 13.99 *(978-1-60266-914-7(7))* Xulon Pr., Inc.

Nicholas, David. Whatever Happened to the Gospel? 2010. 160p. pap. 13.95 *(978-1-61507-154-8(7))* Cross Bks. Publishing.

Nicholls, Samuel. Losing My Religion. 2007. 208p. per. *(978-1-897312-08-7(3))* Adlibbed Ltd.

Nichols, Bob & Laura. Issues a Guide to Heart Health. 2007. 228p. (ENG.). 24.99 *(978-1-60477-041-4(4))*; per. 14.99 *(978-1-60477-040-7(6))* Xulon Pr., Inc.

Nichols, Bridget. Literature in Christian Perspective: Becoming Faithful Readers. (Exploring Faith Ser.). 160p. *(978-0-232-52379-9(7))* Darton, Longman & Todd, Ltd.

Nichols, David. Just for Men: A Practical Daily Devotional Guide for Men. 2007. 408p. per. 21.99 *(978-1-60266-904-8(X))* Xulon Pr., Inc.

Nichols, Ray C. Design Creation, Silenced ? 2009. pap. 14.99 *(978-1-60791-880-6(3))* Xulon Pr., Inc.

Nicol, B. J. Life As A Cactus. 2007. 180p. 21.99 *(978-1-60266-265-0(7))* Xulon Pr., Inc.

—Life As a Cactus. 2007. 180p. per. 13.99 *(978-1-60266-264-3(9))* Xulon Pr., Inc.

Nieder, John & Thompson, Thomas M. Forgive & Love Again: Healing Wounded Relationships. 2010. 208p. pap. 7.99 *(978-0-7369-2905-9(3))* Harvest Hse. Pubs.

Nielson, Janice Gerber. Mothering: Using Divine Principles. 2009. (C). pap. 11.99 *(978-1-59955-247-7(7))* Cedar Fort, Inc./CFI Distribution.

Nieman, Frank B. Two theological Tales: Light Reading for Contemplatives. 2007. 408p. per. 14.95 *(978-1-4327-0224-3(6))* Outskirts Pr., Inc.

Niequist, Shauna. Cold Tangerines: Celebrating the Extraordinary Nature of Everyday Life, 1 vol. 2007. (ENG.). 224p. (gr. 13). 18.99 *(978-0-310-27360-8(9))* Zondervan.

Nieuwendam, Andre. Pure Outreach: A Practical Handbook for Winning the Lost to Christ. 2008. 125p. pap. 19.95 *(978-1-60703-926-6(5))* PublishAmerica, Inc.

Nieuwhof, Boaz. De Weg Terug. 2007. (DUT.). 216p. per. 14.99 *(978-1-60266-118-9(9))* Xulon Pr., Inc.

Niezgoda, Frank. Fish Food: Teach Us to Fish Lord - Catching Men & Women for Christ Daily Devotional. 2009. 452p. pap. 24.99 *(978-1-61579-578-9(2))* Xulon Pr., Inc.

—Fish Food: Teach Us to Fish Lord: ?Catching Men for Christ? Daily Devotional. 2006. 386p. per. 21.50 *(978-1-60002-142-8(5)*, 3980) Mountain Valley Publishing, LLC.

Nikkel, Ron. Your Journey with Jesus: Get Ready to Change Your Life This Year. 2006. (ENG.). 224p. per. 11.99 *(978-1-84550-152-5(7))* Christian Focus Pubns. GBR. Dist: STL Distribution North America.

Niles, Bruce Alan. Running Wild: (or God Ain't Late), 1 vol. 2009. 76p. pap. 16.95 *(978-1-4489-8992-8(2))* PublishAmerica, Inc.

Nix, Echol Lee, Sr., et al. The Inspiration of the Holy Spirit. 2011. 160p. pap. 20.00 ***(978-1-60306-121-6(5)**, NewSouth Bks.)* NewSouth, Inc.

Nixon-Barr, Alice. Views of You in Shaded Hues: A Place Between Black & White. 2008. 224p. pap. 15.00 *(978-1-4343-9751-5(3))* AuthorHouse.

Nixon, Steven. Endure... 2007. 409p. pap. 20.95 *(978-0-7414-4258-1(2))* Infinity Publishing.

Nnaji, Gregory Chigozie. Fresh Spring. 2011. 148p. 24.48 ***(978-1-4634-3661-2(0))***; pap. 15.00 ***(978-1-4634-3662-9(9))*** AuthorHouse.

Noble, Alan R. Difficult Doctrines of the Christian Faith for Young People. 2011. 166p. pap. 24.95 ***(978-1-4560-0188-9(4))*** PublishAmerica, Inc.

Noble, Cheryl. Divine Communication Through Dreams & Visions. 37p. *(978-0-9700610-0-3(5))* Noble, Cheryl.

Noble, Doris. They Didn't Do What I Told Them to Do: The Diary of a Deacon's Wife. 2011. pap. 20.99 ***(978-1-61346-028-3(7))*** Tate Publishing & Enterprises, LLC.

Nocturnum, Corvis. The Satanic Life: Living the Left Hand Path, 1 vols, Vol. 1. 2007. 245p. pap. 29.95 *(978-0-9791694-4-1(5))* Diabolic Pubns.

Nolan, Tony. Faith Fuel. 2007. 128p. per. 13.99 *(978-1-60266-841-6(8))* Xulon Pr., Inc.

Norbie, Donald. This I Believe. 2010. 178p. pap. *(978-1-897117-71-2(X))* Gospel Folio Pr.

Nori, Don. You Can Pray in Tongues. 2009. 187p. pap. 15.99 *(978-0-7684-3091-2(7))* Destiny Image Pubs.

Norman, R. Stanton, ed. The Mission of Today's Church: Baptist Leaders Look at Modern Faith Issues. 2007. (Illus.). 224p. per. 16.99 *(978-0-8054-4378-3(9)*, B&H Academic) B&H Publishing Group.

Norris, Denice. Explosion: A call to arms, a call to action for the Kingdom Age Believer. 2009. 90p. pap. 12.00 *(978-0-9802398-5-0(0))* Williams, Benjamin Publishing.

Norris, Gloria. Just a Closer Walk with Thee. 2009. 140p. pap. 11.99 *(978-1-4389-2078-8(4))* AuthorHouse.

Norris, Kristopher. Pilgrim Practices: Communal Discipleship for a Missional Church. 2011. pap. ***(978-1-57312-593-2(8))*** Smyth & Helwys Publishing, Inc.

North, Bob. The Way of Life: Volume One. 2008. 188p. 26.95 *(978-0-595-69772-4(0))*; pap. 16.95 *(978-0-595-45680-2(4))* iUniverse, Inc.

Northrup, Dolores. The Unlimited God. 2008. 336p. 31.99 *(978-1-60477-597-6(1))*; per. 17.99 *(978-1-60477-596-9(3))* Xulon Pr., Inc.

Norwood, Carroll. Between Yes & Amen. 2007. 112p. (ENG.). 18.99 *(978-1-60034-945-4(5))*; per. 10.99 *(978-1-60034-944-7(7))* Xulon Pr., Inc.

Norwood, James E. Christ As Conqueror & Reconciler: Theological Implications for the Church's Role in Deliverance. 2008. 124p. 24.95 *(978-0-9785352-4-7(3))* Word & Spirit Pr.

Nothwehr, Dawn M. That They May Be One: Catholic Social Teaching on Racism, Tribalism, & Xenophobia. 2008. 272p. pap. 35.00 *(978-1-57075-793-8(3))* Orbis Bks.

N'Ovec, Marlegrecy. Double Miracles in Discovery Bay, Hong Kong. 2008. 380p. pap. 19.99 *(978-1-60647-249-1(6))* Xulon Pr., Inc.

Now That You're a Grandparent. 12.00 *(978-0-687-09554-4(9))* Abingdon Pr.

Nowak, Paul. The Way of the Christian Samurai: Reflections for Servant-Warriors of Christ. 2007. 116p. pap. 11.99 *(978-0-9772234-6-6(9))* Eternal Revolution.

Nowell, Calvin. Start Somewhere: Losing What's Weighing You down from the Inside Out. 2009. (ENG.). 224p. pap. 14.99 *(978-1-4143-2331-2(X))* Tyndale Hse. Pubs.

Nowlin, C. R. The Value of a Man, 1 vol. 2010. 72p. pap. 19.95 *(978-1-4512-0977-8(0))* PublishAmerica, Inc.

Noyd, David. Valencia STINT 2009-2010. 2010. 230p. pap. 12.20 *(978-0-557-57297-7(5))* Lulu Enterprises Inc.

Nugent, Brian. An Creideamh. 2009. (Illus.). 700p. pap. 40.96 *(978-0-9556812-3-3(5))* Lulu Enterprises Inc.

Nunley, Jan, et al. How Many Lightbulbs Does It Take to Change a Christian? A Pocket Guide to Shrinking Your Ecological Footprint. 2008. 64p. pap. 10.00 *(978-1-59627-098-5(5)*, Seabury Bks.) Church Publishing, Inc.

Nunoo, Ken. The seed Master. 2008. 462p. pap. 26.96 *(978-1-4357-1732-9(5))* Lulu Enterprises Inc.

Nurse, Winston S. Through the Knot Hole: Life Is Better on the Other Side. 2008. 160p. 25.95 *(978-1-4327-2298-2(0))*; pap. 15.95 *(978-1-4327-2113-8(5))* Outskirts Pr., Inc.

Nwankwo, Ebenezer A. Complexion, Cosmetics & the Christian. 2007. 78p. pap. 10.95 *(978-1-57258-466-2(1))* TEACH Services, Inc.

Nwawuike, Innocent. Restored to the Garden of Eden. 2009. 85p. pap. 14.95 *(978-1-4327-4050-4(4))* Outskirts Pr., Inc.

Nweke, Uche. Your Light Has Come: Powerful Truths for Walking in Your Destiny & Making Maximum Impact. 2009. 116p. pap. 10.99 *(978-1-4389-3446-4(7))* AuthorHouse.

Nwobu, Christian. In Times Like These. 2010. 140p. pap. 13.00 *(978-1-4490-9007-4(9))* AuthorHouse.

—It's Never Too Late. 2010. 64p. pap. 11.69 *(978-1-4520-0781-6(0))* AuthorHouse.

—Your Faith. 2010. 68p. pap. 11.99 *(978-1-4490-9759-2(6))* AuthorHouse.

Nyarko, Victor T. Beauty for Ashes. 2009. 122p. pap. 11.50 *(978-1-59330-605-2(9))* Aventine Pr.

Nygren, Malcolm E. Shades of Life. 2008. pap. 8.95 *(978-0-9795807-0-3(6))* 2007. 200p. 25.95 *(978-0-9795807-1-0(4))* Doxology Lane Pr.

Nyimbili, Br Frank. Getting Ready for Your Promotion. 2008. 128p. pap. 15.95 *(978-1-4327-3155-7(6))* Outskirts Pr., Inc.

Nystrom, Carolyn & Packer, J. I. Guard Us, Guide Us: Divine Leading in Life's Decisions. 2008. 272p. 17.99 *(978-0-8010-1303-4(8))* Baker Bks.

Nzokwe, Denis C. Words of This Life the Ultimate Diet. 2008. 164p. pap. 14.99 *(978-1-60791-143-2(4))* Xulon Pr., Inc.

O. Burrell, Barrington. African Caribbean Church Culture - the Evolution of Black Majority Churches in Britain. 2011. 280p. pap. ***(978-1-908447-54-8(0))*** Grosvenor Hse. Publishing Ltd.

Ó Murchú, Diarmuid. The Transformation of Desire: How Desire Became Corrupted — and How We Can Reclaim It. 2007. (Illus.). 200p. per. 20.00 *(978-1-57075-704-4(6))* Orbis Bks.

Oak, John H. Called to Awaken the Laity. 2007. (ENG.). 352p. per. 15.99 *(978-1-84550-224-9(8))* Christian Focus Pubns. GBR. Dist: STL Distribution North America.

Oakes, Duwayne E. God's Plan. 2009. 104p. pap. 15.99 *(978-1-4259-0801-0(2))* AuthorHouse.

Oaks, Marcus. Diary of a Preacher's Life: A Journey from Grace to Disgrace to Grace. 2006. mass mkt. 16.95 *(978-0-9772730-1-0(6))*; 264p. per. 22.00 *(978-0-9772730-2-7(4))* Hill & Oaks Pubs.

Oasis Church, compiled by. Stories from the Oasis. 2007. pap. 14.95 *(978-0-9792475-0-7(0))* Good Catch Publishing.

Obe, Adekunle. Kiss the Son. 2009. 80p. pap. 14.00 *(978-1-4269-0782-1(6))* Trafford Publishing.

Oberbrunner, Kary. Called: Becoming Who You Were Born to Be. 2007. 196p. per. 15.99 *(978-0-88469-087-0(3))* BMH Bks.

Obert, Dennis. In the Eye of the Storm. 2011. 260p. pap. 16.99 ***(978-1-61379-017-5(1))*** Xulon Pr., Inc.

Obi, Rowland I. Knowing Jesus. 2011. (Illus.). 144p. pap. 16.46 ***(978-1-4567-8917-6(1))*** AuthorHouse.

O'Boyle, Donna-Marie Cooper. The Domestic Church: Room by Room: A Study Guide for Mothers. 2008. 254p. pap. 18.95 *(978-1-933271-20-0(5))* Circle Pr.

O'Bryan, Amanda. Ashes of Innocence. 2011. 376p. 28.99 ***(978-1-4520-1141-7(9))***; pap. 18.99 ***(978-1-4520-1140-0(0))*** AuthorHouse.

O'C. Davis, V. Experience the Miracles of Giving. 2008. 316p. pap. 17.99 *(978-1-60477-761-1(3))* Xulon Pr., Inc.

O'Collins, Gerald. Experiencing Jesus. 128p. 10.00 *(978-0-281-04763-5(4))* SPCK Publishing GBR. Dist: Pilgrim Pr., The/United Church Pr.

O'Connell, Jim. Going the Heart's Way: Silence, Space & Stillness in Our Day. 2010. (ENG.). 157p. pap. 18.95 *(978-1-85607-650-0(4))* Columba Pr. IRL. Dist: Dufour Editions, Inc.

O'Connor, Jim. Your Divine Birthright. 2010. pap. 12.99 *(978-1-61663-371-4(9))* Tate Publishing & Enterprises, LLC.

O'Connor, Karen. It's Taken Years to Get This Old. 2010. 240p. pap. 12.99 *(978-0-7369-2953-0(3))* Harvest Hse. Pubs.

O'Connor, Kevin S. The Fire That Burns for the Last Days. 2008. 92p. pap. 14.99 *(978-0-9814532-0-0(1))* Living Waters Publishing Co.

Odam, Robert. Christian Life 101 I Wish I Knew These Things. 2008. 184p. 22.99 *(978-1-60647-579-9(7))*; pap. 14.99 *(978-1-60647-578-2(9))* Xulon Pr., Inc.

Odemene, Glory. Shekinah! 2006. (ENG.). 25.99 *(978-1-60034-061-1(X))*; pap. 15.99 *(978-1-60034-060-4(1))* Xulon Pr., Inc.

Oden, Amy. God's Welcome: Hospitality for a Gospel-Hungry World. 2008. 128p. pap. *(978-0-8298-1735-5(2))* Pilgrim Pr., The/United Church Pr.

Oden, Patrick. How Long? 2011. 268p. pap. 20.00 ***(978-1-59498-023-7(3))*** Barclay Pr., Inc.

Oden, Patrick. Just a Dance: Moving with the Holy Spirit. 2007. 274p. pap. 18.00 *(978-1-59498-012-1(8))* Barclay Pr., Inc.

Oder, Slawomir & Gaeta, Saverio. Why He Is a Saint: The Life & Faith of Pope John Paul II & the Case for Canonization. 2010. (ENG., Illus.). 190p. 22.50 *(978-0-8478-3631-4(2))* Rizzoli International Pubns., Inc.

Odhuno-Shani, Nellie. Hope for the Childless: Restoring the Ruins. 2011. 92p. pap. 10.00 ***(978-1-61204-096-7(9)**, Eloquent Bks.)* AEG Literary Publishing Services, Inc.

Odhuno-Shani, Nellie. Stand Your Ground: Perishing for Lack of Knowledge. 2010. 192p. pap. 12.95 *(978-1-60911-921-8(5)*, Eloquent Bks.) AEG Literary Publishing Services, Inc.

Odom, James. Divinely Guided. 2010. 282p. pap. 16.99 *(978-1-60957-925-8(9))* Xulon Pr., Inc.

O'Driscoll, Herbert. A Certain Life: Contemporary Meditations on the Way of Christ. 93p. (Orig.). pap. 9.95 *(978-0-919030-50-3(5)*, 1254) Anglican Bk. Ctr. CAN. Dist: Forward Movement Pubns.

—Confound Them! Diabolical Plans for the Church. 128p. pap. 13.95 *(978-1-55126-318-2(1)*, 1599) Anglican Bk. Ctr. CAN. Dist: Forward Movement Pubns.

—One Man's Journal: Unique Reflections on Contemporary Living. 160p. pap. 9.95 *(978-0-919030-89-3(0)*, 1276) Anglican Bk. Ctr. CAN. Dist: Forward Movement Pubns.

—Word Today. Vol. 2. 14.95 *(978-1-55126-332-8(7)*, 1507) Vol. 3. 18.95 *(978-1-55126-333-5(5)*, 1508)Year , Vols. 1. 14.95 *(978-1-55126-331-1(9)*, 1506) Forward Movement Pubns.

Odukoya, Bimbo. How to Handle Rejection. 2007. 64p. per. 9.99 *(978-1-60034-388-9(0))* Xulon Pr., Inc.

—Marriage: Real People, Real Problems, Wise Counsel. 2008. 212p. per. 14.99 *(978-1-60477-450-4(9))* Xulon Pr., Inc.

Odukoya, Taiwo. Get All You Want. 2010. 76p. pap. 10.99 *(978-1-61579-740-0(8))* Xulon Pr., Inc.

—Limitless. 2008. 164p. per. 13.99 *(978-1-60477-453-5(3))* Xulon Pr., Inc.

—Portrait of A Champion. 2008. 104p. per. 9.99 *(978-1-60477-452-8(5))* Xulon Pr., Inc.

—100 Nuggets of Wisdom for the Man of Sig. 2006. (ENG.). pap. 13.99 *(978-1-60034-000-0(8))* Xulon Pr., Inc.

Odunayo, Ayo. The Faith of Our Fathers. 2011. 86p. pap. 15.99 ***(978-1-4568-4599-5(3))*** Xlibris Corp.

The Odyssey of a Loving Parent: A Journey Through Art & Scripture of Jesus' Expectations for Parents. 2006. (Illus.). 114p. per. 19.99 *(978-1-59879-177-8(X))* Lifevest Publishing, Inc.

Oesch, Jackie. Making the Bible Yours: A Journey into the Heart of God. 2009. 88p. pap. 12.99 *(978-1-60791-778-6(5))* Xulon Pr., Inc.

Oferta de Vida-Calif. (Offer of Life-Calif.) (SPA.). 1.50 *(978-0-8423-6288-7(6)*, 490096) Editorial Unilit.

O'Flaherty, Edward. Sunday, Sabbath, & the Weekend: Managing Time in a Global Culture. Petersen, Rodney L. & Norton, Timothy A., eds. 2010. pap. 16.00 *(978-0-8028-6583-0(6))* Eerdmans, William B. Publishing Co.

Ogden, Alan. Highway to Hope. 2007. 216p. per. 14.99 *(978-1-60266-412-8(9))* Xulon Pr., Inc.

Ogden, Greg. The Essential Commandment: A Disciple's Guide to Loving God & Others. 2011. (Essentials Set Ser.). (ENG.). 204p. pap. 16.00 ***(978-0-8308-1088-8(9)**, IVP Conn.)* InterVarsity Pr.

Ogden, Steven. I Met God in Bermuda: Faith in the 21st Century. 2009. (ENG.). 160p. pap. 19.95 *(978-1-84694-204-4(7))* Hunt, John Publishing Ltd. GBR. Dist: National Bk. Network.

Ogenaarekhua, Mary. A Workbook for Successful Mentoring. 2007. 112p. per. 14.95 *(978-0-9791566-2-5(9))* To His Glory Publishing Co., Inc.

Ogenaarekhua, Mary J. Keys to Successful Mentoring Relationships. 2008. 204p. pap. 18.95 *(978-0-9791566-6-3(1))* To His Glory Publishing Co., Inc.

—Understanding the Power of Covenants. 2008. 204p. pap. 19.95 *(978-0-9791566-8-7(8))* To His Glory Publishing Co., Inc.

Ogilvie, Lloy. Climbing the Rainbow, 0 vols. 2008. 176p. pap. 12.99 *(978-0-8499-2878-9(8))* Nelson, Thomas Inc.

Ogle, Nellie Lane. The Great White Way. 2011. 94p. 38.95 ***(978-1-258-04482-4(X))*** Literary Licensing, LLC.

Ogunbayeje, Esther. The Valiant People of God. 2007. 180p. per. 13.99 *(978-1-60266-105-9(7))* Xulon Pr., Inc.

Ogunseitan, Sola. The Devil Plans Destruction -but I Have Planted Instructions- 2007. 108p. (ENG.). 18.99 *(978-1-60266-859-1(0))*; per. 10.99 *(978-1-60266-858-4(2))* Xulon Pr., Inc.

Ojigbani, Chris. Spiritual Warfare: For the First Time Ever, the True Meaning of Spiritual Warfare Has Been Explained! 2009. 176p. pap. 14.99 *(978-1-60791-288-0(0))* Xulon Pr., Inc.

Ojigbani, Pastor Chris. Back to Sender. 2010. 148p. pap. 14.99 *(978-1-60957-423-9(0))* Xulon Pr., Inc.

Okafor, Kelechukwu O. It Is Written: God's Word in Your Mouth Will Recreate Your World. 2011. 144p. pap. 11.95 ***(978-1-4497-2575-4(9)**, WestBow Pr.)* Author Solutions, Inc.

Okereke, Okoro Chima. Called to Marketplace Discipleship. 2011. 200p. pap. ***(978-1-84903-075-5(8))*** Schiel & Denver Publishing Ltd.

Okholm, Dennis L. Monk Habits for Everyday People: Benedictine Spirituality for Protestants. 2007. 144p. per. 15.99 *(978-1-58743-185-2(8))* Brazos Pr.

Okinedo, Clement. The Greatest Kingdom Ever: The Kingdoms of This World Have Become the Kingdoms of Our Lord & of His Christ & He Shall Reign Forever & Ever. 2010. pap. 11.99 *(978-1-61579-743-1(2))* Xulon Pr., Inc.

Okonkwo, Martins. Hidden Keys to Divine Prosperity. 2006. pap. 13.99 *(978-1-60034-548-7(4))* Xulon Pr., Inc.

Okoro, Bonaventure C. The Manual for Life. 2010. 324p. 28.99 *(978-1-60957-785-8(X))*; pap. 18.99 *(978-1-60957-436-9(2))* Xulon Pr., Inc.

Okorondu, Consolatus C. The Secret of Happiness. 2006. 12.00 *(978-0-8059-9196-3(4))* Dorrance Publishing Co., Inc.

Okoye, Samuel C. A God-Guided Life, 1 vol. 2009. (ENG.). 296p. pap. 27.95 *(978-1-60836-303-2(1))* PublishAmerica, Inc.

Okoye, T. D. Love. Rebirth the Champions! Standing in Obedient & Fear of God Are the Prerequisites of Being A Champion! 2011. 76p. pap. 28.20 ***(978-1-4567-8504-8(4))*** AuthorHouse.

Oladimeji, Elsie. Into the Master's Hand. 2008. 104p. pap. 10.99 *(978-1-60791-063-3(2))* Xulon Pr., Inc.

Olagunju, Benedicta. Where Are Your Accusers? 2008. 152p. pap. *(978-0-9551496-8-9(1))* Ministry In Art.

Olanbigbe, Evangelist K. Emmanuella. The Battle of the Mind & Power of the Tongue: No Subtitle. 2008. pap. 9.99 *(978-1-60647-170-8(8))* Xulon Pr., Inc.

O'Laughlin, Michael. Henri Nouwen: His Life & Vision. 2009. (ENG., Illus.). 140p. pap. 16.00 *(978-1-57075-822-5(0))* Orbis Bks.

Oldham, W. Dale. Give Me Tomorrow. l.t. ed. 2007. (Oldham Inspirational Library). 122p. per. 7.95 *(978-1-59317-179-7(X))* Warner Pr. Pubs.

—How to Grow Spiritually. l.t. abr. ed. 2007. (Oldham Inspirational Library). 121p. per. 7.95 *(978-1-59317-178-0(1))* Warner Pr. Pubs.

—Living Close to God. l.t. ed. 2007. (Oldham Inspirational Library). 120p. per. *(978-1-59317-177-3(3))* Warner Pr. Pubs.

Olds, Peggy. To Jesus Through Mary - the Rosary & the Mysteries. 2007. (Illus.). (J). 11.95 *(978-0-9779497-1-7(0))* VirTru Powers.

O'Leary, Daniel. Unmasking God: Revealing the Divine in the Ordinary. 2011. (ENG.). 144p. pap. 22.95 *(978-1-85607-726-2(8))* Columba Pr. IRL. Dist: Dufour Editions, Inc.

O'Leary, Jeffrey. Footprints in Time: Fulfilling God's Destiny for Your Life, 0 vols. 2006. 288p. per. 13.99 *(978-0-7852-6197-1(4))* Nelson, Thomas Inc.

O'Leary, Karen. Do Your Tears Belong to Me? 2006. pap. 13.99 *(978-1-60034-701-6(0))* Xulon Pr., Inc.

O'Leary, Terry. Prayer Chain Ministry: Equipping God's People for United Prayer. 2009. pap. 11.99 *(978-1-60604-896-2(1))* Tate Publishing & Enterprises, LLC.

Oler, Flo. Dear Dillon: The Seven Basic Truths of God. 2007. per. *(978-1-60208-052-2(6))* FBC Pubns. & Printing.

Olin, Stephen. Early Piety, the Basis of Elevated Character a Discourse to the Graduating Class of Wesleyan University, August 1850. 2006. 156p. per. 18.99 *(978-1-4255-1185-2(6))* MPublishing.

Oliogu, Duke. Plug in Your Chip. 2011. 340p. pap. 18.99 *(978-1-61215-782-5(3))* Xulon Pr., Inc.

Oliphint, K. Scott & Mays, Rod. Things That Cannot Be Shaken: Holding Fast to Your Faith in a Relativistic World. 2008. 160p. pap. 12.99 *(978-1-58134-849-1(5))* Crossway.

Oliver, David. Find Your Voice: Developing the Prophetic in You & Your Church. 2007. (ENG.). 223p. pap. 14.99 *(978-1-86024-601-2(X))* Authentic Media.

Oliver, John. Giver of Life: The Holy Spirit in Orthodox Tradition. 2011. (ENG.). 164p. (gr. 13). pap. 15.99 *(978-1-55725-675-1(6))* Paraclete Pr., Inc.

Olley, Linda. Holy Hunches. 2010. 208p. pap. *(978-1-55452-538-6(1)*, Guardian Bks.) Essence Publishing.

Oloyede, Yinka. The Birthing of a Glorious Church: How to Walk Through the Door of Your Destiny. 2010. 184p. pap. 14.49 *(978-1-4490-9284-9(5))* AuthorHouse.

Olsen, Cathy. The Call to Awakening - Messages from The Cosmos. 2007. 152p. per. 17.95 *(978-1-882918-09-6(6))* InnerCircle Publishing.

Olson, Ruth. My Gift to You: Encouragement During a Cancer Crisis. 2009. 56p. pap. 9.95 *(978-1-4401-4574-2(1))* iUniverse, Inc.

Olumide, Folake T. The Rising Sun. 2009. 84p. pap. 10.99 *(978-1-61579-355-5(0))* Xulon Pr., Inc.

—The Rising Sun: Living Each Day by the Word. 2008. pap. 9.99 *(978-1-60647-096-1(5))* Xulon Pr., Inc.

Oluniyi, Rotimi. Heart of Love for Christ Jesus. 2006. pap. 9.99 *(978-1-60034-312-4(0))* Xulon Pr., Inc.

Oluoch, Silvanus. Concerning Prosperity Gospel: A glimpse into one of the popular gospels of Today. 2011. 194p. 29.99 ***(978-1-4628-7823-9(7))***; pap. 19.99 ***(978-1-4628-7822-2(9))*** Xlibris Corp.

Oluoch, Silvanus. Holy Angels: The Facts - Clear & Specific Information on God's Invisible Agents. 2009. 212p. pap. 13.99 *(978-1-60696-632-7(4))* Tate Publishing & Enterprises, LLC.

Oluokun, Ayo. Ah Lord God! 2011. 200p. pap. 15.99 ***(978-1-61379-442-5(8))*** Xulon Pr., Inc.

Omer, Kent E. Outer Banks, a Test of Faith, 1 vol. 2009. 121p. pap. 19.95 *(978-1-60749-392-1(6))* PublishAmerica, Inc.

Omolaja, Rabiu Elijah. Thy Will O Lord. 2007. 183p. per. 12.99 *(978-1-59886-601-8(X))* Tate Publishing & Enterprises, LLC.

Omotoyinbo, Fola. Beyond the Surface. 2011. 176p. pap. 13.50 ***(978-1-4567-5603-1(6))*** AuthorHouse.

On Earth As It Is in Heaven. 2009. (ENG., Illus.). 16.99 *(978-0-615-28352-4(7))* Leaf Publishing.

O'Neal, Sean. Bridges to People. 2007. 288p. per. 15.99 *(978-1-60266-268-1(1))* Xulon Pr., Inc.

Ononuju, Kingsley. Visa to Victory. 2006. pap. 10.99 *(978-1-60034-369-8(4))* Xulon Pr., Inc.

Oommen, Siji. Redeemed to the Utmost: Holy to Fallen to Divine. 2009. 104p. pap. 10.99 *(978-1-60791-504-1(9))* Xulon Pr., Inc.

Ooten, Jerry. Is This the Man. 2011. 234p. 22.99 ***(978-1-61379-947-5(0))*** Xulon Pr., Inc.

An Operative Faith for Oppressed People. *(978-1-58942-126-4(4))* R.H. Boyd Publishing Corp.

Ord, David Robert. Your Forgotten Self: Mirrored in Jesus the Christ. 2007. (ENG.). 217p. per. 17.95 *(978-1-897238-33-2(9))* Namaste Publishing, Inc. CAN. Dist: Perseus-PGW.

Ordinario, Sadiri. Seeds among Weeds. 2011. 228p. 29.99 ***(978-1-4568-5630-4(8))***; pap. 19.99 ***(978-1-4568-5629-8(4))*** Xlibris Corp.

Organized for A Mission: A Guide for Parents & Missionaries. 2008. (Illus.). 225p. pap. 9.45 *(978-0-9788579-3-6(3))* Ricks, Marie.

Oritsejafor, Ayo. Breaking the Power of Yesterday. 2008. 332p. 28.99 *(978-1-60647-917-9(2))*; pap. 18.99 *(978-1-60647-916-2(4))* Xulon Pr., Inc.

O'Rourke, Maria Rodgers. Prepare Your Heart for a Great Christmas. 2008. 121p. 12.95 *(978-0-9800227-0-4(3))* MRO Communications, Inc.

Orozco, Keri. Quest to Freedom, 1 vol. 2009. 280p. pap. 27.95 *(978-1-60703-741-5(6))* PublishAmerica, Inc.

Orr, C. E. How to Live a Holy Life. 2009. 208p. 32.99 *(978-1-115-02120-3(6))*; 208p. 28.99 *(978-1-115-02118-0(4))*; (ENG.). 207p. pap. 22.99 *(978-1-115-02112-8(5)*, BiblioLife); (ENG.). 207p. pap. 20.99 *(978-1-115-02110-4(9)*, BiblioLife); 208p. pap. 24.75 *(978-1-115-02115-9(X))*; 208p. pap. 23.75 *(978-1-115-02114-2(1))* BiblioBazaar.

—How to Live a Holy Life. 2010. 140p. pap. *(978-1-4076-4130-0(1))* HardPr.

—How to Live a Holy Life. 2010. 106p. pap. 15.96 *(978-1-162-66684-6(6))*; 27.96 ***(978-1-169-24219-7(7))*** Kessinger Publishing, LLC.

Orr, C. e. & Orr, C. E. How to Live a Holy Life. 2010. 106p. 34.95 *(978-1-161-43549-8(2))* Kessinger Publishing, LLC.

Orr, Charles Ebert. Food for the Lambs: Or- Helps for Young Christians. 2007. (ENG.). 124p. per. 18.99 *(978-1-4346-4251-6(8))*; 132p. per. 19.99 *(978-1-4346-4252-3(6))* BiblioBazaar.

—How to Live a Holy Life. 2007. (ENG.). 144p. pap. 18.99 *(978-1-4264-5083-9(4))*; 158p. pap. 21.99 *(978-1-4264-5384-7(1))* BiblioBazaar.

—How to Live a Holy Life. 2010. 132p. pap. 9.99 ***(978-1-935785-21-7(4))*** Bottom of the Hill Publishing.

—How to Live a Holy Life. 2010. (Illus.). 76p. pap. 20.00 *(978-1-153-62945-4(3))* General Bks. LLC.

Orr, Robert D. Medical Ethics & the Faith Factor: A Handbook for Clergy & Health-Care Professionals. 2009. 520p. pap. 30.00 *(978-0-8028-6404-8(X))* Eerdmans, William B. Publishing Co.

Orr, William. Como Conocer la Voluntad de Dios: How to Know the Will of God. (SPA.). 68p. *(978-84-7228-224-7(4)*, 220165) Clie, Editorial.

—Como Vencer las Preocupaciones: How to Win over Worry. (SPA.). *(978-84-7645-337-0(8)*, 223288) Clie, Editorial.

Orrill, Toni. The Glorious Summer. 2007. (ENG.). 48p. per. 20.99 *(978-0-7618-3797-8(3))* Hamilton Bks.

Orsuto, Donna & Orsuto. Holiness. 2007. (New Century Theology Ser.). (ENG., Illus.). 224p. 34.95 *(978-0-8264-5398-3(8))* Continuum International Publishing Group, Ltd. GBR. Dist: National Bk. Network.

Ortberg, John. Know Doubt: The Importance of Embracing Uncertainty in Your Faith, 1 vol. 2009. (ENG.). 192p. pap. 12.99 *(978-0-310-32503-1(X))* Zondervan.

—The Me I Want to Be: Redeeming My Time, 1 vol. 2009. (ENG.). 204p. 19.99 *(978-0-310-27592-3(X))* Zondervan.

—When the Game Is over, It All Goes Back in the Box. (ENG.). 2009. 265p. pap. 12.99 *(978-0-310-32505-5(6))* 2007. 256p. 21.99 *(978-0-310-25350-1(0))* Zondervan.

—When the Game Is over It All Goes Back in the Box, 1 vol. 2008. (ENG.). 128p. pap. 9.99 *(978-0-310-28246-4(2))* Zondervan.

—When the Game Is over, It All Goes Back in the Box. l.t. ed. 2010. 445p. 30.99 *(978-1-4104-3045-8(6))* Thorndike Pr.

Ortberg, John, et al. Daniel, 1 vol. 2008. (New Community Bible Study Ser.). (ENG.). 96p. pap. 7.99 *(978-0-310-28053-8(2))* Zondervan.

Ortega, Jeanie. High Tech in the Bible. 2011. 88p. pap. 19.95 ***(978-1-4560-5681-0(6))*** PublishAmerica, Inc.

Ortega, Jeanie Whetstone. Earth, Alien Colony! 2009. 116p. pap. 19.99 *(978-1-4363-6815-5(4))* Xlibris Corp.

Ortega, Scott. Inspired Work: A New Testament Guide to Working with Purpose. 2011. 168p. 30.95 ***(978-1-4497-2059-9(5))***; pap. 13.95 ***(978-1-4497-2058-2(7))*** Author Solutions, Inc. (WestBow Pr.).

Ortiz, Don Daniel. The 99 Success Secrets of Jesus: How to Create Miracles in Your Life! 2007. (ENG.). 244p. 24.99 *(978-1-60034-896-9(3))*; per. 14.99 *(978-1-60034-895-2(5))* Xulon Pr., Inc. (Xulon Pr.).

Ortiz, José Luis. Aloe Ver: La Planta del Futuro. 2010. 92p. pap. 14.95 *(978-1-4389-3532-4(3))* AuthorHouse.

Ortiz, Michael Francis. Schizophrenic God. 2011. 178p. pap. 19.99 ***(978-1-4568-4959-7(X))*** Xlibris Corp.

Ortlund, Elizabeth A. Lord, Make My Life a Miracle! 2010. 148p. pap. 14.95 *(978-1-4401-9717-8(2))* iUniverse, Inc.

Oruma, Ben. God Will Turn Your Hard Place into a High Place! 2009. 80p. pap. 10.99 *(978-1-61579-585-7(5))* Xulon Pr., Inc.

Osakwe, Andy. Running with A Vision. 2007. 46p. per. 6.95 *(978-1-934449-02-8(4))* Legacy Publishing Services, Inc.

Osanna, Tulio. Rol Profetico de Maria. 160p. 6.95 *(978-958-607-309-7(2))* Sociedad de San Pablo COL. Dist: St Pauls/Alba Hse. Pubs.

Osborn, James L. These Things Matter: Defining Importance in A World of Uncertainty. 2010. pap. 12.99 *(978-1-61566-512-9(9))* Tate Publishing & Enterprises, LLC.

Osborne, Aaron. Shofar: The Instrument of God. 2008. 56p. pap. 13.95 *(978-1-4327-1179-5(2))* Outskirts Pr., Inc.

Osborne, Larry. Ten Dumb Things Smart Christians Believe. 2009. (ENG.). 224p. pap. 13.99 *(978-1-60142-150-0(8)*, Multnomah) Doubleday Religious Publishing Group, The.

Osborne, R. Scott. The Book of Blessings. 2007. 228p. per. 14.99 *(978-1-60266-744-0(6))* Xulon Pr., Inc.

Osborne, Tom. Beyond the Final Score: There's More to Life Than the Game. 2009. (ENG.). 256p. 22.99 *(978-0-8307-5111-2(4))* Gospel Light Pubns.

Osburn, Charlie & Osburn, Jeanne. Love Walks by Faith: You Got to Give It All to Jesus. 2007. pap. 14.00 *(978-0-929375-29-8(7))* Whitney, Harvey Bks. Co.

Oschmann, Carol. God Speaks in Dreams: Connect with Him & Each Other. 2009. (ENG.). 339p. pap. 22.95 *(978-1-4327-3961-4(1))* Outskirts Pr., Inc.

Osgood, Donald W. God's Silent Language: Hear His Silent Language in Unexpected Places. 2007. 160p. pap. 12.95 *(978-0-9701300-6-8(6))* Hitchhiker Bks.

O'Shea, Ginger Woods. Lifestyle Choices ... up to You! Biblical & Natural Health Guidelines for More Abundant Living. 2009. 404p. 34.99 *(978-1-61579-165-1(5))*; pap. 22.99 *(978-1-61579-164-4(7))* Xulon Pr., Inc.

Oshin, Vincent O. Biblical Christianity: From Man-Centred to a Christ-Centred Church. 2009. 228p. pap. 15.99 *(978-1-60791-285-9(6))* Xulon Pr., Inc.

Osho, Tunde. Every Day in God's Presence: Soul Food for the Christian Palate - One Hundred Days of Power-Packed Meditative Nuggets for Hearts That Cry Out to God. 2008. 240p. pap. 24.95 *(978-1-60563-833-1(1))* PublishAmerica, Inc.

Osko, Yvonne. The Unwelcome Journey. 2007. 132p. per. 13.99 *(978-1-60266-405-0(6))* Xulon Pr., Inc.

Oslington, Paul. Economics & Theology. 2013. (Routledge Frontiers of Political Economy Ser.). (ENG.). 288p. (C). 130.00 *(978-0-415-45481-0(5))* Routledge.

Ososami, Bode. Worship in Spirit & in Truth. 2008. 216p. pap. 14.49 *(978-1-4389-3419-8(X))* AuthorHouse.

O'Steen-Grant, Mae. Lavender & Peach. 2009. 255p. pap. 18.95 *(978-1-4327-3910-2(7))* Outskirts Pr., Inc.

Osteen, Joel. Become a Better You: 7 Keys to Improving Your Life Every Day. l.t. ed. 2009. (ENG.). 640p. pap. 17.99 *(978-1-59415-288-7(8))* Cengage Gale.

—Become a Better You: 7 Keys to Improving Your Life Every Day. 2010. (ENG.). 128p. 5.95 *(978-0-7624-3887-7(8))* Running Pr. Bk. Pubs.

—Become a Better You Journal: A Guide to Improving Your Life Every Day. 2008. (ENG., Illus.). 224p. 9.99 *(978-1-4165-7306-7(2)*, Free Pr.) Free Pr.

—Daily Readings from Your Best Life Now: 90 Devotions for Living at Your Full Potential. 2009. (ENG.). 320p. pap. 14.99 *(978-0-446-55010-9(8))* FaithWords.

—Every Day a Friday: How to Be Happier 7 Days a Week. 2011. 49.99 ***(978-1-61113-763-7(2)***, Sound Library) AudioGO.

—Every Day a Friday: How to Be Happier 7 Days a Week. (ENG.). 2012. 300p. pap. 15.99 ***(978-0-89296-990-6(3))*** 2011. 304p. 24.99 *(978-0-89296-991-3(1))* 2011. 480p. 26.99 *(978-1-4555-0731-3(8))* FaithWords.

—It's Your Time: Activate Your Faith, Achieve Your Dreams, & Increase in God's Favor. (ENG.). 320p. 2010. pap. 15.00 *(978-1-4391-0012-7(8))* 2009. 25.00 *(978-1-4391-0011-0(X))* Free Pr. (Free Pr.).

—It's Your Time: Activate Your Faith, Achieve Your Dreams, & Increase in God's Favor. 2012. (ENG.). 176p. 5.95 ***(978-0-7624-4418-2(5)***, Running Pr. Minature Editions) Running Pr. Bk. Pubs.

—It's Your Time: Activate Your Faith, Achieve Your Dreams, & Increase in God's Favor. l.t. ed. 2010. (ENG.). 512p. pap. 17.99 *(978-1-59415-355-6(3)*, Large Print Pr.) Thorndike Pr.

—Lo Mejor de Ti: 7 Pasos para Mejorar Tu Vida Diaria. 2007. (SPA.). 400p. pap. 16.00 *(978-1-4165-4147-9(0)*, Free Pr.) Free Pr.

Osteen, John. Becoming a Man of Unwavering Faith: With Commentary & a Foreword from Joel Osteen. 2011. 39.99 ***(978-1-61113-664-7(4)***, Sound Library) AudioGO.

Osteen, Victoria. Love Your Life: Living Happy, Healthy, & Whole. 2008. (ENG.). 240p. *(978-1-4165-9984-5(3)*, Free Pr.) Free Pr.

Oswalt, Donna. Kindled Soul Holy Fire: Lenten Meditations & Prayers. 2009. 101p. pap. 12.95 *(978-1-57736-419-1(8))* Providence Hse Pubs.

Otboc, Jam. In Enemy Territory: A Survival Manual for Believers. 2010. 108p. 28.95 *(978-1-4497-0705-7(X))*; pap. 11.95 *(978-1-4497-0703-3(3))* Author Solutions, Inc. (WestBow Pr.).

Otè, FrançOis. MinistÈ Kris la Nan Lavil Jerizalem. 2011. (HAT.). 144p. pap. 13.14 ***(978-1-4669-0122-3(5))*** Trafford Publishing.

Otwell, Patricia Anne. Guide to Ministering: To Alzheimer's Patients & Their Families. 2008. (ENG.). 296p. 79.95 *(978-0-7890-2902-7(2))*; pap. 54.50 *(978-0-7890-2903-4(0))* Routledge.

Ouellette, E. J. The Majesties of His Kingdom. 2008. 67p. pap. 16.95 *(978-1-60563-863-8(3))* PublishAmerica, Inc.

Our Life in Christ Adult Bible Study Series, Vol. 4. (Bible Studies). 6.99 *(978-0-7586-0537-5(4))* Concordia Publishing Hse.

Outreach Inc., compiled by. Faith Journal. 2008. lib. bdg. 10.95 *(978-0-9787153-1-4(1))* Outreach, Inc.

Ouweneel, W. J. What Is Election? pap. 2.25 *(978-0-88172-162-1(X))* Believers Bookshelf, Inc.

Overly, Derik. Issues of the Soul. 2010. pap. 10.99 *(978-1-61566-297-5(9))* Tate Publishing & Enterprises, LLC.

Owen, Andrew. Life Is an Obstacle Course: Wisdom from the Book of James on Living an Overcoming Life. 2008. 158p. pap. 12.99 *(978-1-905991-13-6(4))* New Wine Pr.

Owen, John. Overcoming Sin & Temptation. Kapic, Kelly M. & Taylor, Justin, eds. 2006. 464p. pap. 22.00 *(978-1-58134-649-7(2))* Crossway.

Owens, Clodine. Fight Your Way Your Truth Your Life. 2011. 272p. 35.95 ***(978-1-4497-2569-3(4))***; pap. 19.95 ***(978-1-4497-2568-6(6))*** Author Solutions, Inc. (WestBow Pr.).

Owens, Jan. Never Give Up. 2008. 220p. pap. 15.99 *(978-1-60647-876-9(1))* Xulon Pr., Inc.

Owens, Virginia Stem. Caring for Mother: A Daughter's Long Goodbye. 2007. (ENG.). 163p. per. 17.00 *(978-0-664-23152-1(7))* Westminster John Knox Pr.

—A Feast of Families. 2008. 154p. pap. 18.00 *(978-1-55635-955-2(1))* Wipf & Stock Pubs.

Owl, Esther D. Awakened: Overcoming the Conspiracy Through Faith. 2007. 176p. pap. 12.95 *(978-1-4327-0539-8(3))* Outskirts Pr., Inc.

Oyafemi, Clement K. Theological Reflections for Sundays & Solemnities of Year C. 2008. 127p. pap. 19.95 *(978-1-4357-3101-1(8))* Lulu Enterprises Inc.

Oyegun, Daniel. The Person of Melchizedek. 2008. 56p. pap. 9.99 *(978-1-60647-517-1(7))* Xulon Pr., Inc.

Oyortey, Ella. Let Go & Let God. 2010. 88p. pap. 10.49 *(978-1-4389-6390-7(4))* AuthorHouse.

Pack, David C. The True Jesus Christ - Unknown to Christianity. 2009. 276p. 30.95 *(978-1-4401-8049-1(0))*; pap. 20.95 *(978-1-4401-8047-7(4))* iUniverse, Inc.

Packer, J. & Houston, James. Revolt of the Human Spirit: Finding Authentic Faith in an Age of Rebellion. 2009. 192p. 17.99 *(978-0-8307-3901-1(7)*, Regal Bks.) Gospel Light Pubns.

Packer, J. I. Conociendo a Dios: Knowing God. (SPA.). *(978-84-7645-014-7(1)*, 223083) Clie, Editorial.

Packam, Glenn. Secondhand Jesus: Trading Rumors of God for a Firsthand Faith, 1 vol. 2009. (ENG.). 224p. pap. 14.99 *(978-1-4347-6639-7(X))* Cook, David C.

Padgett (Recorder), James E. & Babinsky (Compiler), Joseph. LITTLE BOOK of TRUTHS - Hardcover. 2009. 148p. 29.95 *(978-0-557-19518-3(7))* Lulu Enterprises Inc.

Padilla, Joseph N. Adventure the Long Walk. 2008. 264p. 25.99 *(978-1-60647-053-4(1))* Xulon Pr., Inc.

Page, Marian. Bitterness: How It Can Effect You Physically, Emotionally & Spiritually. 2006. (ENG.). 64p. per. 10.99 *(978-1-4141-0780-6(3))* Pleasant Word.

Page, Nick & Page, Claire. Celebrations: All Age Worship. 2008. (ENG.). 112p. 16.99 *(978-1-85078-746-4(8))* Authentic Media.

Page, Sue. Away with Words: Training Book on the Whole Spectrum of Christian Communication. 124p. 19.00 *(978-1-901443-04-2(3)*, Lynx) SPCK Publishing GBR. Dist: Pilgrim Pr., The/United Church Pr.

Pagitt, Doug. A Christianity Worth Believing: Hope-Filled, Open-Armed, Alive-and-Well Faith for the Left Out Left Behind, And Let Down in Us All. 2008. (ENG.). 256p. 21.95 *(978-0-7879-9812-7(5)*, Jossey-Bass) Wiley, John & Sons, Inc.

Pagitt, Doug & Pagitt. A Christianity Worth Believing: Hope-Filled, Open-Armed, Alive-and-Well Faith for the Left Out, Left Behind, & Let down in Us All. 2009. (ENG.). 256p. pap. 14.95 *(978-0-470-45534-0(9)*, Jossey-Bass) Wiley, John & Sons, Inc.

Paige, D. W. En Route to D Day: Twice Dead Plucked up by the Roots, 1 vol. 2009. 188p. pap. 24.95 *(978-1-60813-851-7(8))* PublishAmerica, Inc.

Paine, Jim. The Right of Every Christian. 2011. 182p. pap. 19.99 ***(978-1-4568-1078-8(2))*** Xlibris Corp.

Palau, Luis. Changed by Faith: Dare to Trust God with Your Broken Pieces ... & Watch What Happens. 2011. (ENG.). 240p. pap. 14.99 *(978-1-4143-3622-0(5))* Tyndale Hse. Pubs.

Pallett, Jeannie. Beckoned by the King. 2008. 160p. pap. *(978-1-897373-17-0(1))* Word Alive Pr.

Palmer, Adam. The High School Survival Guide: Making the Most of the Best Time of Your Life (So Far) 2008. (Navigators Reference Library). (ENG., Illus.). 176p. (YA). pap. 12.99 *(978-1-60006-129-5(X)*, Th1nk Bks.) NavPress Publishing Group.

Palmer, Earnest L. The New Member Training for Discipleship Manual. 2008. pap. 13.50 *(978-1-60458-338-0(X))* Instant Pub.

Palmer, Everett W. You Can Have a New Life! 2011. 126p. 40.95 ***(978-1-258-08206-2(3))*** Literary Licensing, LLC.

Palmer, H. Gene. Don't Let the Shop Go Bankrupt: A Daily Reflectional. 2009. 464p. pap. 17.95 *(978-1-4327-1041-5(9))* Outskirts Pr., Inc.

Palmer, Kelly A. Cowboy Revelations: A Voice Crying in the Wilderness. 2009. 103p. pap. 12.95 *(978-1-4327-1225-9(X))* Outskirts Pr., Inc.

Palmer, Parker J. The Promise of Paradox: A Celebration of Contradictions in the Christian Life. 2008. (ENG.). 192p. 18.95 *(978-0-7879-9696-3(3)*, Jossey-Bass) Wiley, John & Sons, Inc.

Palmer, Phoebe. The Promise of the Father. pap. 19.99 *(978-0-88019-099-2(X))* Schmul Publishing Co., Inc.

Palmer, Robert Leslie. Truth in the Eight Towers. 2011. 172p. 30.95 ***(978-1-61507-844-8(4))***; pap. 13.95 ***(978-1-61507-843-1(6))*** Cross Bks. Publishing.

Palmer-Washington, Kimberly & Palmer-Hill, Beverly. Somebody Prayed for Me. 2009. 184p. pap. 14.99 *(978-1-60791-416-7(6))* Xulon Pr., Inc.

Paluch, 'Preacher Joe'. The Dinosaur Book of Wisdom & Observations. 2008. 216p. pap. 15.99 *(978-1-60647-762-5(5))* Xulon Pr., Inc.

Penford, Michael. The Upside down Kingdom: God's Plan Is Always Opposite Ours. 2009. 64p. pap. 10.49 *(978-1-4389-5484-4(0))* AuthorHouse.

Penkau, Jason/ K. Omega Course Workbook: An Intensive 12 Session Journey Equipping You for a Lifetime of Discipleship! 2007. (Illus.). 249p. spiral bd. 29.95 *(978-0-9797141-0-8(9))* Life Spring Network.

Panko, Bill & Panko, Margaret. For God's Sake Surrender. Date not set. 100p. (Orig.). pap. 9.95 *(978-1-885342-22-5(5))* Creative Ways.

Panos, Chris. God's Spy. Logos International Staff, ed. 5th ed. 270p. reprint ed. 15.95 *(978-0-910743-07-5(X))*; pap. 5.95 *(978-0-910743-00-6(2))*; pap. 6.95 *(978-0-910743-06-8(1))* Gold Bks. International, Inc.

Panteghini, Giacomo. El Gemido de la Creacion. (SPA.). 176p. 6.95 *(978-958-607-945-7(7))* Sociedad de San Pablo ESP. Dist: St Pauls/Alba Hse. Pubs.

Pantuosco Jr., Louis. Got Questions? 2007. 216p. per. 14.99 *(978-1-60477-192-3(5))* Xulon Pr., Inc.

Paquette, Paula M. S. Devotions from Hope: Living This Day Closer to God. 2011. 112p. 28.95 ***(978-1-4497-2437-5(X))***; pap. 11.95 ***(978-1-4497-2436-8(1))*** Author Solutions, Inc. (WestBow Pr.).

Parachin, Victor M. Nine Habits of Highly Effective Christians. 2009. 80p. pap. 6.95 *(978-1-933066-11-0(3))* Catholic Bk. Publishing Corp.

C

Paraclete Press Staff, compiled by. The Paraclete Book of Balance in Life. 2010. (Paraclete Book Of Ser.). (ENG.). 128p. (gr. 13). pap. 12.99 *(978-1-55725-667-6(5))* Paraclete Pr., Inc.
—The Paraclete Book of Creativity. 2010. (Paraclete Book Of Ser.). (ENG.). 128p. (gr. 13). pap. 12.99 *(978-1-55725-666-9(7))* Paraclete Pr., Inc.
—The Paraclete Book of Hospitality. 2012. (Paraclete Book Of Ser.). (ENG.). 120p. (gr. 13). pap. 12.99 *(978-1-55725-665-2(9))* Paraclete Pr., Inc.
Paraclete Press Staff & Community of Jesus Staff. The Paraclete Psalter: A Four-Week Cycle for Daily Prayer. 2010. (ENG.). 326p. (gr. 13). im. lthr. 29.99 *(978-1-55725-663-8(2))* Paraclete Pr., Inc.
Paradiso, Gerry. The Job Factor. 2008. 73p. pap. 16.95 *(978-1-60610-505-4(1))* PublishAmerica, Inc.
Parish, Fawn. The Power of Honor: Learning to Love Well. 2007. 226p. pap. *(978-0-9798978-0-1(7))* Conversations.
Park, Chang-Won. Cultural Blending in Korean Death Rites: New Interpretive Approaches. 2011. (ENG.). 256p. pap. 44.95 ***(978-1-4411-3426-4(3))*** Continuum International Publishing Group, Ltd. GBR. Dist: National Bk. Network.
Park, Mirae. Amazing Power of Fasting. 2010. 222p. 29.99 *(978-1-4415-6461-0(6))*; pap. 19.99 *(978-1-4415-6460-3(8))* Xlibris Corp.
Park, Robert L. Reflections on Selected Scriptures: A Christian Layman's Informal Commentary. 2008. 664p. pap. 24.95 *(978-1-4327-0976-1(3))* Outskirts Pr., Inc.
Parker, Anetta. God's Grace Is Sufficient: My Personal Journey from Heartache to Hope. 2011. pap. 10.99 *(978-1-61739-319-8(3))* Tate Publishing & Enterprises, LLC.
Parker, Clyde, Jr. In the Father's Footsteps. 2006. pap. 10.99 *(978-1-59781-788-2(0))* Xulon Pr., Inc.
Parker, Diane D. Addicted to Learn from an Addiction. 2008. 55p. pap. 16.95 *(978-1-60441-994-6(6))* PublishAmerica, Inc.
Parker, Jr. The Missionary & the Devil, 1 vol. 2009. 48p. pap. 16.95 *(978-1-61582-667-4(X))* PublishAmerica, Inc.
Parker Jr., Clyde C. Come Rejoice with Me in God's Mercy! The Treasury of Clyde Parker Jr. 2011. 42p. pap. 16.95 ***(978-1-4489-2128-7(7))*** PublishAmerica, Inc.
Parker, Marguerita B. The Limitless Power of God, 1 vol. 2010. 48p. pap. 16.95 *(978-1-4489-8449-7(1))* PublishAmerica, Inc.
Parker, Michael E. Fish for All: Understanding sacrifice & God's Compassion. 2010. pap. 8.99 *(978-1-61566-091-9(7))* Tate Publishing & Enterprises, LLC.
Parker, Russ. The Wild Spirit. 144p. 10.00 *(978-0-281-04985-1(8))* SPCK Publishing GBR. Dist: Pilgrim Pr., The/United Church Pr.
Parker, Veronica. Rise up You Mighty Prophet. 2009. 288p. pap. 19.99 *(978-1-4389-6928-2(7))* AuthorHouse.
Parr, Seth. Reasonable Duty. 2008. 156p. pap. 13.99 *(978-1-60647-453-2(7))* Xulon Pr., Inc.
Parr, Susan Sherwood. Peace in the Valley. 2007. (ENG., Illus.). 140p. per. 6.95 *(978-0-9765010-7-7(4))* Word Prodns.
—Peace on the Home Front. 2007. (ENG.). 140p. pap. 6.95 *(978-0-9765010-4-6(X))* Word Prodns.
Parra, Florence Lightbourne. My Most Powerful Weapon. 2011. 88p. pap. 12.99 *(978-1-4269-3963-1(9))* Trafford Publishing.
Parrino, Frank. Fool's Gold & Other Papers: Discovering Genuine Christianity. 2006. 88p. per. 9.99 *(978-1-59886-474-8(2))* Tate Publishing & Enterprises, LLC.
Parrish, Preston & Parrish, Glenda. Finding Hope in Times of Grief. 2011. 192p. pap. 10.99 *(978-0-7369-3075-8(2))* Harvest Hse. Pubs.
Parrot. Feliz a Pesar de Todo.Tr. of How to Change a Negative Attitude. (SPA.). 212p. pap. *(978-958-9269-23-7(0))* Editorial Unilit.
Parrot, J. Edward, ed. I Am the Lady of the Rosary. (Illus.). 18p. pap. *(978-1-877905-31-5(3))* American Society for the Defense of Tradition, Family & Property, The (TFP).
Parrott, John W. The Abundant Life. 2011. 84p. 15.99 ***(978-1-4568-9926-4(0))***; pap. 12.99 ***(978-1-4568-9925-7(2))*** Xlibris Corp.
Parrott, Les & Dallas, Bill. You're Stronger Than You Think: The Power to Do What You Feel You Can't. 2012. (ENG.). 224p. pap. 15.99 ***(978-1-4143-4853-7(3))*** Tyndale Hse. Pubs.
Parry, Arthur E. Dear Father: (Praying with the Psalmist) 2007. 124p. per. 12.95 *(978-0-595-44389-5(3))* iUniverse, Inc.
Parsley, Ro. He Came, 0 vols. 2008. 224p. pap. 14.99 *(978-0-7852-9681-2(6))* Nelson, Thomas Inc.
Parsley, Rod. On the Brink: Breaking Through Every Obstacle into the Glory of God, 0 vols. 2008. 228p. pap. 14.99 *(978-0-7852-9689-8(1))* Nelson, Thomas Inc.
Parsley, Ross. Do You See What I See? Exploring the Christmas of Every Day. 2008. (ENG.). 128p. 9.99 *(978-1-4347-9939-5(5))* Cook, David C.
Parsons, D. J. Ascribing Responsibility to Abortion & Other Atrocities/the Thief on The. 2009. 116p. pap. 11.99 *(978-1-60791-512-6(X))* Xulon Pr., Inc.
Parsons, Darrell J. Release Your Words Impact Your World. 2008. (ENG.). 140p. per. 9.95 *(978-1-60273-000-7(8))* Parsons Publishing Hse.
Parsons, James C. The Living Word: Or, Bible Truths & Lessons. for the Family, the School, & the Church ... 2006. 160p. per. 18.99 *(978-1-4255-1211-8(9))* MPublishing.
Parsons, Michael & Cohen, David J. On Eagles' Wings: An Exploration of Strength in the Midst of Weakness. 2008. (ENG.). 248p. pap. 38.00 *(978-0-7188-9195-4(3))* Lutterworth Pr., The GBR. Dist: Brown, David Bk. Co., The.
Partain, Calvin. Eternal Life Vital Signs. 2007. 204p. per. 14.99 *(978-1-60266-719-8(5))* Xulon Pr., Inc.
Partin, Mark. What's Faith Got to Do with It? Everything! 2011. 108p. pap. 7.99 ***(978-1-936750-13-9(9))*** Yorkshire Publishing Group.
Partington, John. The Happiness Factor: And How to Get It. 2008. 154p. pap. *(978-1-903725-80-1(1))* New Wine Pr.
Partow, Donna. Becoming a Vessel of God's Power: Give God Thirty Days & See What He Will Do. 2007. (ENG.). 288p. pap. 13.99 *(978-1-57856-960-1(5)*, WaterBrook Pr.) Doubleday Religious Publishing Group, The.
Passmore, Tim. The Jump Journal. 2011. 386p. pap. 18.99 ***(978-0-9826127-1-2(0))*** Outcome Publishing.
Patrick, Anne. Lethal Dreams. 2010. 228p. pap. 11.95 *(978-1-936167-08-1(5))* Whimsical Pubns., LLC.
Patrick, Dan. Second Most Important Book You'll Ever Read, 0 vols. 2009. 240p. pap. 14.99 *(978-0-8499-2935-9(0))* Nelson, Thomas Inc.
Patrick, Daniel L. & Gray, T. L. God Pleasing Faith. 2011. 81p. pap. 10.00 ***(978-0-9834332-5-5(9))*** Vabella Publishing.
Patrick, Frank. A Senior Citizen's Pre-Election Workbook. 2008. 80p. pap. 11.99 *(978-1-60477-770-3(2))* Xulon Pr., Inc.
Patten-Carter, Angelleta. A Wife s Pain-Filled Heart. 2011. 72p. pap. 10.99 *(978-1-61215-479-4(4))* Xulon Pr., Inc.
Pattengale, Jerry A., et al. Straight Talk: Clear Answers about Today's Christianity. 2nd ed. 2008. (Illus.). xiv, 252p. pap. ***(978-1-931283-27-4(3))*** Triangle Publishing Co.
Patterson, Angela Marie. A Handful of Laffodils. 2011. 64p. pap. 9.95 ***(978-1-61507-737-3(5))*** Cross Bks. Publishing.
Patterson, Cheryl Denise. And So I Dance!!! 2008. pap. 16.95 *(978-1-60563-209-4(0))* PublishAmerica, Inc.
Patterson, Gerald G. Growing Better. 2008. 108p. 19.99 *(978-1-60791-062-6(4))*; pap. 11.99 *(978-1-60791-061-9(6))* Xulon Pr., Inc.
Patterson, Katrina. The Bottom Line: A Practical Everyday Message for Living Beyond the Life You've Always Dreamed Of. 2007. 238p. per. 14.99 *(978-1-60247-113-9(4))* Tate Publishing & Enterprises, LLC.
Patterson, Michelle. 24 Hours. 2009. (J). pap. 7.99 *(978-1-60799-643-9(X))* Tate Publishing & Enterprises, LLC.
Patton-Bronson, Cheryl. One Day... This Day! 2007. 288p. per. 19.95 *(978-0-615-14908-0(1))* 4 Your Spirit Productions.
Patton, Sedgewick. 12 Reasons Why No Decent, Intelligent Person Should be a Christian Fundamentalist. 2007. 65p. pap. 9.95 *(978-0-7414-3902-4(6))* Infinity Publishing.
Patty, Sandi. Falling Forward: Into His Arms of Grace, 0 vols. annot. ed. 2007. 192p. per. 14.99 *(978-0-8499-1886-5(3))* Nelson, Thomas Inc.
Patwardhan, Sheryl. Follow That Light: A happy Journey. 2009. 112p. pap. 10.99 *(978-1-4389-0944-8(6))* AuthorHouse.
Paul, John I. I. Go in Peace: A Gift of Enduring Love. Durepos, Joseph, ed. 2007. 244p. per. 12.95 *(978-0-8294-2472-0(5))* Loyola Pr.
Paul, Vincent N. Don't Be Discouraged! 2008. 124p. pap. 10.99 *(978-1-60647-240-8(2))* Xulon Pr., Inc.
—Faith Deflators! 2008. 172p. pap. 13.99 *(978-1-60647-241-5(0))* Xulon Pr., Inc.
—Your Vision & What to Do with It! Handling Your Vision Responsibly; from Conception to Realization. 2009. 136p. pap. 14.99 *(978-1-61579-118-7(3))* Xulon Pr., Inc.
Paulien, Jon. The Gospel from Patmos: Everyday Insights for Living from the Last Book of the Bible. 2007. 379p. *(978-0-8280-2092-3(2))* Review & Herald Publishing Assn.
Pauline Editions Staff. Freq Used Texts & Dates. 30p. pap. *(978-0-8198-2667-1(7)*, 332-089) Pauline Bks. & Media.
Paulk, Earl. Oh! It's Just You, Cancer. pap. 9.95 *(978-0-917595-59-2(9))* Cathedral of the Holy Spirit.
—The Prophetic Word & Your Healing. pap. 8.95 *(978-0-917595-58-5(0))* Cathedral of the Holy Spirit.
Paull, Candy & Christian Life Centre Auckland Staff. Now Is the Time: Insights for Living an Abundant Life. 2008. (ENG.). 192p. 14.99 *(978-1-59979-270-5(2))* Charisma Media.
—Today Is the Day: Everyday Insights for an Extraordinary Life. 2008. (ENG.). 192p. 14.99 *(978-1-59979-271-2(0))* Charisma Media.
Paull, Candy & Tyndale Kids Staff. 100 Great Ideas to Simplify Your Life. 2011. (ENG.). 128p. pap. 9.99 *(978-1-4143-3886-6(4))* Tyndale Hse. Pubs.
Paulsen, Heather Amel. Emotional Purity: An Affair of the Heart. 2007. 160p. pap. 13.99 *(978-1-58134-855-2(X))* Crossway.
Paulson, Mark. God's Cycle of Music: A Musician's Explanation of God's Purpose & Meaning for Our Lives. 2009. pap. *(978-1-932717-18-1(8))* Hope Publishing Hse.
Pawlak, Roman. I Am the Lord Who Heals You: A Biblical Guide to Health & Abundant Living. 2010. (YA). pap. 19.95 *(978-1-58982-632-8(9))*, Millennial Mind Publishing) American Bk. Publishing Group.
Paxson, Ruth. Rios de Agua Viva: Rivers of Living Water. (SPA.). 128p. *(978-84-7228-762-4(9)*, 222395) Clie, Editorial.
Paxton, Ruth. This Man...This Cause...This Hour. pap. 0.10 *(978-1-56632-079-5(8))* Revival Literature.
Payne, Arlen J. Consider His Word: A Daily Devotional. 2009. (J). pap. 26.99 *(978-1-60604-558-9(X))* Tate Publishing & Enterprises, LLC.
Payne, Brenda. Motherhood: Hope for Discouraged Moms. 2009. pap. *(978-1-59638-169-8(8))* P & R Publishing.
Payne, Donald. They're Just People. 2009. 160p. pap. 14.95 *(978-1-934363-72-0(3))* Zoe Life Publishing.
Payne, J. D. Missional House Churches: Reaching Our Communities with the Gospel. 2008. (ENG.). 207p. pap. 16.99 *(978-1-934068-25-0(X)*, Paternoster) Authentic Media.
Payne, Patricia Ann. The Deceit of the Church. 2008. 80p. per. 9.99 *(978-1-60477-500-6(9))* Xulon Pr., Inc.
Payton, Dave. Journal to the Truth. 2009. 320p. pap. 21.99 *(978-1-60791-687-1(8))* Xulon Pr., Inc.
Pazdan, Mary Margaret. Becoming God's Beloved in the Company of Friends: A Spirituality of the Fourth Gospel. 2007. 134p. pap. 17.00 *(978-1-55635-462-5(2)*, Cascade Bks.) Wipf & Stock Pubs.
Peabody, Larry. Job-Shadowing Daniel: Walking the Talk at Work. 2010. 202p. pap. 16.95 *(978-1-4327-5330-6(4))* Outskirts Pr., Inc.
Peace, Martha. Damsels in Distress: Biblical Solutions for Problems Women Face. 2006. 187p. per. 13.99 *(978-1-59638-038-7(1))* P & R Publishing.
Peale, Norman Vincent. Seeds of Faith. 2006. (Illus.). 48p. 19.95 *(978-0-8249-4655-5(3))* Ideals Pubns.
Peale, Norman Vincent, ed. Guideposts: Personal Messages of Inspiration & Faith. 2011. 256p. 47.95 ***(978-1-258-00538-2(7))*** Literary Licensing, LLC.
—Unlock Your Faith Power. 2011. 318p. 50.95 ***(978-1-258-01115-4(8))*** Literary Licensing, LLC.
Pearcey, Nancy. Total Truth: Liberating Christianity from Its Cultural Captivity. 2008. (Illus.). 512p. pap. 20.99 *(978-1-4335-0220-0(8))* Crossway.
Pearson, Carlton. God Is Not a Christian: How the Gospel of Inclusion Can Save Us from Religion. 2007. 224p. 24.95 *(978-1-879290-34-1(0)*, PageMill Pr.) Council Oak Bks.
—The Gospel of Inclusion: Reaching Beyond Religious Fundamentalism to the True Love of God & Self. 2007. 244p. 24.95 *(978-0-9791689-0-1(2))* Azusa Pr. International.
Pearson, Faye. Taiwan Connections: Fond Memories. 2009. 308p. pap. 18.99 *(978-1-60791-545-4(6))* Xulon Pr., Inc.
Pearson, Hewlette A. C. View from the Mountain. 2006. pap. 14.99 *(978-1-60034-810-5(6))* Xulon Pr., Inc.
Pearson, Joyce L. Breaking Bread with the Brokenhearted. 2009. 108p. pap. 11.99 *(978-1-60791-451-8(4))* Xulon Pr., Inc.
Pearson, Rodney. The Power of the Process. 2008. 152p. pap. 14.99 *(978-0-9801208-4-4(5))* You Are Loved Publishing.
Peart, Anastasia "Stacie". Battling the Spirit of Perversion. 2008. 120p. (ENG.). 18.99 *(978-1-60477-467-2(3))*; per. 10.99 *(978-1-60477-466-5(5))* Xulon Pr., Inc.
Peart, Brian L. Being Real: A Simple Way to Transform Your Life & Ministry! 2008. 48p. pap. 16.95 *(978-1-60703-535-0(9))* PublishAmerica, Inc.
Peck, Andy. A Life to Die For: Discovering Your Part in God's Story. 2007. 168p. *(978-1-85345-443-1(5))* Crusade for World Revival.
Peck, D. Sound of a Cry. 160p. reprint ed. 6.99 *(978-1-85792-134-2(8)*, Christian Focus) Christian Focus Pubns. GBR. Dist: Riverside.
Peckham, David T. 101 Thoughts from the Word: New Testament. 2008. 224p. pap. 14.49 *(978-1-4389-0852-6(0))* AuthorHouse.
Pecora, Valerie. The Seasons of My Soul. 2007. 216p. (ENG.). 24.99 *(978-1-60477-303-3(0))*; per. 14.99 *(978-1-60477-302-6(2))* Xulon Pr., Inc.
Peden, Melissa Heflin. Back to the Garden: Discovering the Kingdom of God. 2010. 164p. 22.49 *(978-1-4520-5006-5(6))*; pap. 14.99 *(978-1-4520-5007-2(4))* AuthorHouse.
Pedersen, Jeffrey P. River Reflections. 2008. 225p. pap. 24.95 *(978-1-60610-656-3(2))* PublishAmerica, Inc.
Pedersen, John. Developing Your Potential. 2011. pap. 14.99 *(978-1-61739-785-1(7))* Tate Publishing & Enterprises, LLC.
Pedersen, MaryJo. For Better, for Worse, for God: Exploring the Holy Mystery of Marriage. 2008. (ENG.). 208p. pap. 13.95 *(978-0-8294-2766-0(X))* Loyola Pr.
Pedersen, W. Todd. The Disciplines of Freedom: Moving Away from the Yardstick Gospel Toward a Life of Liberty. 2009. 160p. pap. 14.99 *(978-1-61579-624-3(X))* Xulon Pr., Inc.
Pedrini, Alirio J. Aprenda a Participar en Grupos Carismaticos. (SPA.). 200p. 7.95 *(978-958-607-586-2(9))* Sociedad de San Pablo COL. Dist: St Pauls/Alba Hse. Pubs.
Pedrone, Dino. True I D. 2008. 216p. per. 14.99 *(978-1-60477-492-4(4))* Xulon Pr., Inc.
Peel, Kathy. Desperate Households: How to Restore Order & Harmony to Your Life & Home. 2007. (ENG.). 272p. per. 14.99 *(978-1-4143-1618-5(6)*, Picket Fence Pr.) Tyndale Hse. Pubs.
Peele, Chandra. Radiant: Discovering Beauty from the Inside Out. 2007. (ENG.). 208p. (YA). pap. 14.99 *(978-1-59669-089-9(5))* New Hope Pubs.
The Peep of Day: A Series of the Earliest Religious Instruction the Infant Mind Is Capable of Receiving. 2007. (ENG.). 234p. 41.95 *(978-0-548-07513-5(1))* Kessinger Publishing, LLC.
Peery, Ken. Desires of My Heart: A Lawyer. 2009. 282p. pap. 16.99 *(978-1-61579-041-8(1))* Xulon Pr., Inc.
Pegues, Deborah Smith & Temple, Ricky. Why Smart People Make Dumb Choices. 2010. 192p. pap. 11.99 *(978-0-7369-2852-6(9))* Harvest Hse. Pubs.
Pehrson, Marnie L. You're Here for a Reason: Discover & Live Your Purpose. 2008. 248p. per. 17.95 *(978-0-9676162-7-8(1))* Backup Computer Resources.
Peikert, Jennifer. Daughters of God... ... Modesty Matters. 2011. 130p. 22.99 ***(978-1-61379-519-4(X))***; pap. 14.99 ***(978-1-61379-518-7(1))*** Xulon Pr., Inc.
Pender, Charles E. The Religion of Greed & Its Impact on African Americans: Social Engineered Progressive Geocide. 2010. 192p. pap. 15.00 *(978-1-4520-4524-5(0))* AuthorHouse.
Penn-Lewis, Jessie. Cara a Cara: Face to Face. (SPA.). *(978-84-7645-115-1(6)*, 223169) Clie, Editorial.
—Morir para Vivir: Dying to Live. (SPA.). *(978-84-7645-116-8(4)*, 223167) Clie, Editorial.
—Power for Service. pap. *(978-0-87508-951-5(8))* CLC Pubns.
Penn, William. No Cross, No Crown. 2008. 424p. 30.99 *(978-0-559-15230-6(2))*; pap. 21.99 *(978-0-559-15226-9(4))* BiblioBazaar.
—No Cross, No Crown. 2009. 214p. pap. *(978-0-217-24294-3(4))*; 274p. pap. *(978-0-217-24284-4(7))* Books LLC.
—No Cross, No Crown. 2009. 246p. pap. 20.03 *(978-0-217-84376-8(X))* General Bks. LLC.
—No Cross, No Crown; a Discourse Shewing the Nature & Discipline of the Holy Cross of Christ, & That the Denial of Self & Daily Bearing of Christ. 2006. 436p. per. 26.99 *(978-1-4255-4777-6(X))* MPublishing.
Pennock, Michael. Encountering Jesus in the New Testament. 2009. (Illus.). 332p. (YA). pap., stu. ed. 24.95 *(978-1-59471-165-7(8))* Ave Maria Pr.
Penrod, Everett. What If? 2008. 136p. per. 13.99 *(978-1-58930-210-5(9))* Selah Publishing Group, LLC.
Pensamientos (Seed Thoughts) El Tiene Cuidado (Someone Who Cares) (SPA.). 1.25 *(978-0-8423-6400-3(5)*, 497116) Editorial Unilit.
Pensamientos (Seed Thoughts) Para Papa (For My Father) (SPA.). 1.25 *(978-0-8423-6282-5(7)*, 497111) Editorial Unilit.
Pensamientos (Seed Thoughts) Un Saludo Amistoso (A Friendly Hello) (SPA.). 1.25 *(978-0-8423-6283-2(5)*, 497112) Editorial Unilit.
Perdue, Bob. Ten Life Choices: Recovering the Life You Were Always Meant to Live. 2008. 192p. pap. 12.00 *(978-0-9800877-4-1(0))* Diakonia Publishing.
Perdue, Thomas H. Passover & Sukkot. 2011. 744p. pap. 36.14 ***(978-1-4634-3695-7(5))*** AuthorHouse.
El Peregrino Ruso (The Way of the Pilgrim) (SPA.). 208p. pap. 5.95 *(978-980-350-342-0(1))* Sociedad de San Pablo VEN. Dist: St Pauls/Alba Hse. Pubs.
Peres, B. J. Reflections. 2006. 333p. per. 19.95 *(978-1-59879-163-1(X))* Lifevest Publishing, Inc.
Peretti, Frank E. Penetrando la Oscuridad, 1 vol. 2008.Tr. of Piercing the Darkness. (SPA.). 464p. (gr. 11). per. 4.99 *(978-0-8297-5229-8(3))* Vida Pubs.
Pereyra, Alexis. Bad Influences. 2009. 184p. 29.99 *(978-1-4415-0825-6(2))*; pap. 19.99 *(978-1-4415-0824-9(4))* Xlibris Corp.
Perez de Emde. Caminando Con Dios: Walking with God. (SPA.). 192p. *(978-84-7228-812-6(9)*, 220130) Clie, Editorial.
Perkins, Bill. Six Battles Every Man Must Win: ... & the Ancient Secrets You'll Need to Succeed. 2011. (ENG.). 160p. pap. 12.99 *(978-1-4143-3898-9(8))* Tyndale Hse. Pubs.
Perkins, John M. & Claiborne, Shane. Follow Me to Freedom: Leading & Following As an Ordinary Radical. 2009. (ENG.). 224p. pap. 14.99 *(978-0-8307-5120-4(3))* Gospel Light Pubns.
Perrotta, Kevin & Perrotta, Louise. Jesus Man of Prayer. 2007. (ENG.). 96p. pap. 7.95 *(978-0-8294-2327-3(3))* Loyola Pr.
Perry, Barbara. God's Call to Rise Higher in Life. 2008. 47p. pap. 9.95 *(978-0-615-22345-2(1))* Perry, Barbara A.
Perry, Martyn & Fay. Stirring the Fire: Exploring New Patterns of Ministry. 2010. pap. 12.99 *(978-1-61566-446-7(7))* Tate Publishing & Enterprises, LLC.
Perry Sr., Larry J. Jehovah, the Father of True Love. 2009. 48p. pap. 12.95 *(978-1-4489-2448-6(0))* PublishAmerica, Inc.
Persad, Derek. Keys to the Kingdom. 2009. 56p. pap. 10.99 *(978-1-60791-295-8(3))* Xulon Pr., Inc.
Personal FRAN Plan. pap. 9.95 *(978-0-88177-259-3(3)*, DR259) Discipleship Resources.
Pessoni, Douglas H. With Healing in His Wings: A Complete & Concise Presentation of God's Healing Gospel. 3rd ed. 2008. 128p. pap. *(978-0-9809191-9-6(3)*, CCB Publishing) CCB Publishing.
Peterkin, Rev. Christopher S. Man's Catastrophic Plunge into A Dead Zone. 2010. 162p. pap. 14.99 *(978-1-60957-440-6(0))* Xulon Pr., Inc.
Peters, Barbara. Special Ops Woman. 2009. 160p. pap. 14.99 *(978-1-60791-864-6(1))* Xulon Pr., Inc.
Peters, Ben. Birthing the Book Within You: Inspiration & Practical Help to Produce Your Own Book. 2007. 96p. per. 10.97 *(978-0-9789884-2-5(6))* Open Heart Ministries, International.
—Holy Passion: Desire on Fire - Igniting the Torch of Godly Passion. 2006. 108p. per. 10.99 *(978-0-9789884-0-1(X))* Open Heart Ministries, International.
Peters, Jamie & Peters, Lea. No Retreat - No Regrets. 2010. 370p. pap. 21.95 *(978-1-934749-88-3(5)*, CrossHouse Publishing) Hannibal Bks.
Peters, Ken. The Skin & the Skeleton. 2007. 104p. per. 10.97 *(978-0-9789884-1-8(8))* Open Heart Ministries, International.
Peters, Marilyn. Stripes of the Tiger: Paws for Reflection. 2007. 236p. per. 14.99 *(978-1-60266-889-8(2))* Xulon Pr., Inc.
Peters, Mark. Which Way Is Up? 2009. pap. 13.95 *(978-1-935529-39-2(0))* Intermedia Publishing Group.
Peters, Matthew. Me, Myself, & I AM: A Unique Question & Answer Book: the Story of You & God. 2008. (ENG.). 96p. 13.99 *(978-1-60142-142-5(7)*, Multnomah) Doubleday Religious Publishing Group, The.
Peters, Rob. Evangel-Lies. 2007. 180p. per. 13.99 *(978-1-60266-051-9(4))* Xulon Pr., Inc.
Petersen, Jim. Lifestyle Discipleship: Encouraging Others to Spiritual Maturity. 2007. (Katie Parker Production Ser.). (ENG., Illus.). 208p. pap. 14.99 *(978-1-60006-211-7(3))* NavPress Publishing Group.
Peterson, David H. A Firm Foundation. 2008. 196p. per. 13.99 *(978-1-60477-437-5(1))* Xulon Pr., Inc.

Peterson, Eugene. Cómete Este Libro (Eat This Book) 2011. (SPA.). pap. 12.95 (978-1-58802-621-7(3)) Editorial Patmos.
Peterson, Eugene H. The Jesus Way: A Conversation on the Ways That Jesus Is the Way. 2011. 304p. pap. 17.00 (978-0-8028-6703-2(0)) 2007. 289p. 22.00 (978-0-8028-2949-8(X)) Eerdmans, William B. Publishing Co.
Peterson, Eugene H. & Santucci, Peter. Eat This Book: Study Guide. 2006. 48p. per. 6.00 (978-0-8028-3263-4(6)) Eerdmans, William B. Publishing Co.
—The Jesus Way Study Guide. 2007. 63p. per. 6.00 (978-0-8028-4566-5(5)) Eerdmans, William B. Publishing Co.
Peterson, Margaret Kim. Keeping House: The Litany of Everyday Life. 2007. (ENG.). 192p. 21.95 (978-0-7879-7691-0(1), Jossey-Bass) Wiley, John & Sons, Inc.
Peterson, Wendy D. Memoirs of a Soldier's Wife. 2010. 160p. 24.99 (978-1-4490-2479-6(3)); pap. 18.99 (978-1-4490-2478-9(5)) AuthorHouse.
Pett, David P. Can These Bones Live. 2008. 264p. pap. 16.99 (978-1-60647-978-0(4)) Xulon Pr., Inc.
Pettingill, W. L. Estudios Sencillos sobre Juan: Believe & Live. (SPA.). (978-84-7645-169-4(5), 223196) Clie, Editorial.
Pettitt, Charles J. Lukewarm Christian to Warrior for Christ: It's Time to Prepare for Battle. 2011. 120p. pap. 14.99 (978-1-4567-6042-7(4)) AuthorHouse.
Pettys, Greg. Cure for the Incurable. 2006. pap. 13.99 (978-1-60034-616-3(2)) Xulon Pr., Inc.
Pfautsch, George E. The Wisdom of our Soul. 2010. 76p. pap. 10.95 (978-1-4520-2442-4(1)) AuthorHouse.
Pfeil, Michael E. The Fifth Seal in Sharp Focus: How Long, O Lord... ? (Revelation 6. 2010. 220p. 33.95 (978-1-61507-165-4(2)); pap. 17.95 (978-1-61507-151-7(2)) Cross Bks. Publishing.
Phan, Seamus. Contemplative Thoughts of an Asian Seminarian. 2008. 208p. 29.44 (978-0-615-20800-8(2)); pap. 12.44 (978-0-615-21169-5(0)) Fides in Adversis Ministries, Inc.
Phaneuf, Gae Stuart. Reflections of a Merry Heart. 2009. 124p. pap. 19.99 (978-1-4415-2646-5(3)) Xlibris Corp.
Pharr, David. The Beginning of Our Confidence. 71p. pap. 7.99 (978-0-89098-374-4(7)) Twentieth Century Christian Bks.
Pharr, W. Larry. How to Receive Your Needs from God. 2010. 228p. pap. 15.99 (978-1-61579-761-5(0)) Xulon Pr., Inc.
Phelan, Thomas W. & Webb, Chris. 1-2-3 Magic for Christian Parents: Effective Discipline for Children 2-12. 2007. (ENG., Illus.). 240p. pap. 14.95 (978-1-889140-24-7(4)) ParentMagic, Inc.
Phelps, Owen. The Catholic Vision for Leading Like Jesus Leader's Guide: Introducing Leadership S3 Leadership Servant, Steward, Shepherd. 2009. 8p. pap. 2.95 (978-1-59276-675-8(7)) Our Sunday Visitor, Publishing Div.
Philip, Sunny. Becoming A Person of God: Understanding the Process. 2011. 268p. 24.59 (978-1-4634-1648-5(2)); pap. 14.99 (978-1-4634-1649-2(0)) AuthorHouse.
Phillips, Charmaine. How Willing Are You: Laying A Foundation for Financial Change. 2008. 112p. pap. 10.99 (978-1-60647-390-0(5)) Xulon Pr., Inc.
Phillips, Dale. A Fall from Grace. 2011. pap. 15.99 (978-1-61807-030-2(4)) Briona Glen Publishing, LLC.
—A Fall From Grace. 2012. 35.00 (978-1-61807-031-9(2)) Briona Glen Publishing, LLC.
Phillips, Damian. Great Grace upon You. 2010. 117p. pap. 13.50 (978-0-557-29953-9(5)) Lulu Enterprises Inc.
Phillips, Douglas W. The Little Boy down the Road: Short Stories & Essays on the Beauty of Family Life. 2008. 191p. 20.00 (978-1-934554-34-0(0)) Vision Forum, Inc., The.
Phillips, J. B. Day by Day with J B Phillips: Selected Readings for Daily Reflection. 288p. 17.95 (978-1-56563-891-4(3)) Hendrickson Pubs. Marketing, LLC.
Phillips, Jennifer, ed. Ambassadors for God: Envisioning Reconciliation Rites for the 21st Century. 2010. (Liturgical Studies). 192p. pap. 26.00 (978-0-89869-654-7(2)) Church Publishing, Inc.
Phillips, Julian & Berrard, A. R. Discovering Your Hidden Power: Unleashing the Power of Words. 2009. 88p. pap. 10.99 (978-1-60791-950-6(8)) Xulon Pr., Inc.
Phillips, L. Edward & Vaughan, Billy, eds. Courage to Bear Witness: Essays in Honor of Gene L. Davenport. 2009. 170p. pap. 20.00 (978-1-60608-536-3(0), Pickwick Pubns.) Wipf & Stock Pubs.
Phillips, Lori & Willers, Lynn. Held by God: Finding Hope by Recognizing His Provision in the Midst of Suffering. 2010. 264p. pap. 19.95 (978-1-61507-241-5(1)) Cross Bks. Publishing.
Phillips, Mercidieu. Divine Repairs: Moving Towards Wholeness Through Forgiveness. 2009. 180p. 22.99 (978-1-61579-025-6(X)); pap. 14.99 (978-1-60791-760-1(2)) Xulon Pr., Inc.
Phillips, Paulette & Phillips, Ron. Faith Factor: Living Life Outside the Box. 2007. 193p. pap. 11.99 (978-0-9797268-0-4(8)) Abba's Hse. Publishing.
—Faith Factor Study Guide: Living Life Outside the Box. 2007. 56p. 7.99 (978-0-9797268-1-1(6)) Abba's Hse. Publishing.
Phillips, Raelene. Puppy in the Pulpit. 144p. pap. 9.99 (978-1-58169-125-2(4), Evergreen Pr.) Genesis Communications, Inc.
Phillips, Ryan. Fall from Grace. 2006. 455p. per. 14.99 (978-0-7684-2360-0(0)) Destiny Image Pubs.
Phillips, Vivian A. Jesus Christ Is My Lover. Date not set. (Illus.). pap. (978-1-888413-08-3(5)) Seasoning Quilting (Arts & Crafts).
—My Dog & His Bone, Vol. III. Date not set. (Illus.). pap. (978-1-888413-11-3(5)) Seasoning Quilting (Arts & Crafts).
Phillips, Wallace. All Dressed up & No Place to Go: Closed Doors at the Lord's House. 2007. 104p. pap. 12.95 (978-0-9772483-8-4(0)) Diakonia Publishing.
Phillips, William. Focal Point: Christian Views of the Everyday Life. 2007. 76p. per. 10.95 (978-1-4327-0549-7(0)) Outskirts Pr., Inc.
Philpot, Kent. El Libro de la Liberacion: The Deliverance Book. (SPA.). (978-84-7228-512-5(X), 360400) Clie, Editorial.
Phipps, Barbara. God of the Bible - God of the Church. 2007. pap. 9.99 (978-1-60034-802-0(5)) Xulon Pr., Inc.
Pickard, Donald L. Apologetics for the Working Christian: Understanding the Great Commission of Jesus Christ. 2009. 192p. pap. 14.99 (978-1-61579-626-7(6)) Xulon Pr., Inc.
Pickard, Stephen. In Between God: Theology, Community, & Discipleship. 2012. (ENG.). (C). pap. 29.95 (978-1-921817-10-6(0)) ATF Pr. AUS. Dist: Brown, David Bk. Co., The.
Pickett, Hazel. God's Perfect Way for You. 2007. (ENG.). 72p. per. 16.95 (978-1-4325-8510-5(X)) Kessinger Publishing, LLC.
Pickle, Terry K. Growing in Grace March 17. 2009. 162p. pap. 19.48 (978-0-578-01952-9(3)) Acts 20/20 Ministries.
Pierce, Bart. The Bribe of Great Price. 2007. (ENG.). 135p. per. 13.95 (978-0-9704753-5-0(7)) Gatekeeper Publishing.
Pierce, Cal. Receive Your Healing & Reclaim Your Health. 2012. E-Book (978-1-61638-703-7(3), Siloam Pr.) Charisma Media.
—Receive Your Healing & Reclaim Your Health: Partnering with the Holy Spirit for Total Transformation of Your Body, Soul & Spirit. 2012. (ENG.). 256p. pap. 15.99 (978-1-61638-483-8(2), Siloam Pr.) Charisma Media.
Pierce, Chuck D. Redeeming the Time: Get Your Life Back on Track with the God of Second Opportunities. 2009. (ENG.). 240p. pap. 14.99 (978-1-59979-378-8(4), Charisma Hse.) Charisma Media.
Pierce, Chuck D. & Pierce, Pamela J. One Thing: How to Keep Your Faith in a World of Chaos. 2006. 179p. per. 15.99 (978-0-7684-2379-2(1)) Destiny Image Pubs.
Pierce, Chuck D. & Sytsema, Rebecca Wagner. Possessing Your Inheritance: Take Hold of God's Destiny for Your Life. 2009. (ENG.). 256p. pap. 14.99 (978-0-8307-5116-7(5)) Gospel Light Pubns.
Pierce, Clifford. The Life & Times of a Civil War Reenactor. 2008. 52p. pap. 10.95 (978-0-939479-30-6(3), Backintyme) Boxes & Arrows, Inc.
Pierce, David. Don't Let Me Go: What My Daughter Taught Me about the Journey Every Parent Must Make. 2009. (ENG.). 224p. 13.99 (978-0-307-44468-4(6), WaterBrook Pr.) Doubleday Religious Publishing Group, The.
Pierce, Ronald W. Partners in Marriage & Ministry. 2011. pap. 12.99 (978-0-9820465-2-4(9)) Christians for Biblical Equality.
Pierce, Stacia. Purpose Pail. pap. 35.00 (978-1-886880-47-4(6)) Life Changers Publishing.
—Revised Planner (Purpose) pap. 59.95 (978-1-886880-27-6(1)) Life Changers Publishing.
Pierson, A. T. El Camino de la Vida Eterna: The Hearth of the Gospel. (SPA.). 192p. (978-84-7228-978-9(8), 223054) Clie, Editorial.
Pierson, John W. Sometimes Love Offends. 2010. 266p. pap. 16.99 (978-1-60957-362-1(5)) Xulon Pr., Inc.
Pierson, Mark. The Art of Curating Worship: Reshaping the Role of Worship Leader. 2010. 240p. pap. 16.99 (978-1-4514-0084-7(5), Sparkhouse Pr.) Spark Hse.
Pieterse, Hendrik, ed. Wealth, Poverty, & Economy in God's World. 2007. 76p. pap. 10.95 (978-0-938162-90-2(X)) United Methodist Board of Higher Education & Ministry.
Pinches, Charles & McDaniel, Jay B., eds. Good News for Animals? Christian Approaches to Animal Well-Being. 2008. 270p. pap. 31.00 (978-1-59244-601-8(9)) Wipf & Stock Pubs.
Pink, Arthur W. The Life of Faith. 2011. 112p. pap. 12.99 (978-1-61203-312-9(1)) Bottom of the Hill Publishing.
—Practical Christianity. 2011. 196p. pap. 18.99 (978-1-61203-337-2(7)) Bottom of the Hill Publishing.
—Profiting from the Word. 2011. 106p. pap. 9.99 (978-1-61203-336-5(9)) Bottom of the Hill Publishing.
Pink, Michael. Rainforest Strategy: The Planet's Most Successful Business Model. 2008. (ENG.). 256p. 21.99 (978-1-59979-372-6(5)) Charisma Media.
Pinkham, Lynn. Moments of Contemplation. 2007. 126p. per. 10.99 (978-1-60247-444-4(3)) Tate Publishing & Enterprises, LLC.
Pinkston, Ron. Our Father. 2009. 76p. pap. 10.99 (978-0-9796620-2-7(8)) Selah Publishing Group, LLC.
Pinto-Moura, Regina. Religious Addiction, Mental Health & Spirituality. 2008. 124p. pap. 12.99 (978-1-60266-793-8(4)) Xulon Pr., Inc.
Pinto, Santan. Discernment in Your Life. 96p. pap. 10.00 (978-1-888080-00-1(0)) ABCD Printing Co.
Piper, Don & Murphey, Cecil. 90 Minutos en el Cielo: Una Historia Real de Vida y Muerte. 2006. (SPA., Illus.). 208p. reprint ed. pap. 12.99 (978-0-8007-3174-8(3)) Revell.
Piper, Jim. The Four Essentials of Christian Living. 2007. (ENG.). 176p. per. 12.95 (978-0-9793192-3-5(4)) Lifebridge Bks.
Piper, John. The Blazing Center Study Guide: The Soul-Satisfying Supremacy of God in All Things. 2006. (ENG.). 112p. pap., stu. ed. 9.99 (978-1-59052-885-9(6), Multnomah) Doubleday Religious Publishing Group, The.
—Don't Waste Your Life. rev. ed. 2009. 192p. pap. 9.99 (978-1-4335-0632-1(7)) Crossway.
—Don't Waste Your Life Group Study SET. 2009. 320p. 39.99 (978-1-4335-0631-4(9)) Crossway.
—Don't Waste Your Life Study Guide. 2009. 128p. pap. 9.99 (978-1-4335-0633-8(5)) Crossway.
—Don't Waste Your Life Teaching: Ten Sessions with John Piper. 2007. 19.99 (978-1-58134-872-9(X)) Crossway.
—Finally Alive. 2009. (ENG.). 160p. 14.99 (978-1-84550-421-2(6)) Christian Focus Pubns. GBR. Dist: STL Distribution North America.
—God Is the Gospel: Meditations on God's Love as the Gift of Himself. 2008. (John Piper Small Group Ser.). 128p. pap. 9.99 (978-1-4335-0254-5(2)) Crossway.
—God Is the Gospel: Meditations on God's Love As the Gift of Himself. 2011. 192p. pap. 14.99 (978-1-4335-2049-5(4)) Crossway.
—Spectacular Sins: And Their Global Purpose in the Glory of Christ. 2008. 128p. 15.99 (978-1-4335-0275-0(5)) Crossway.
Piper, John & Taylor, Justin, eds. Suffering & the Sovereignty of God. 2006. (Illus.). 256p. pap. 15.99 (978-1-58134-809-5(6)) Crossway.
Pitchford, Arnold. Petals in my Pathway. (Illus.). 30p. 12.50 (978-1-56794-236-1(9)) Star Bible & Tract Corp.
Pitchford, John & Santer, Mark. Daily with God. 416p. 14.95 (978-1-85311-028-3(0)) Norwich Bks. & Music GBR. Dist: Morehouse Publishing.
Pitt, Estella Moore. After You Have Suffered a While: The Sufferings of the Righteous. Pitt, Moses O., ed. 2008. 69p. pap. 8.95 (978-0-9642764-7-5(X)) Pitt, Estella.
Pittelli, Renee. Breaking the Bonds of Adult Child Abuse: A Biblical Textbook on Abusive Narcissistic Families, How they Operate, & How to Deal with Them. 2011. 649p. pap. 25.95 (978-1-4327-6656-6(2)) Outskirts Pr., Inc.
—The Family Freeloader: A Biblical Answer for Sob Stories, con Games, & Never Having to Get off the Couch. 2009. 158p. pap. 17.95 (978-1-4327-4181-5(0)) Outskirts Pr., Inc.
—Narcissistic Predicaments: A Biblical Guide to Navigating the Schemes, Snares, & No-Win Situations Unique to Abusive Families. 2010. 368p. pap. 22.95 (978-1-4327-5044-2(5)) Outskirts Pr., Inc.
Pittman, Allison K. Saturdays with Stella: How My Dog Taught Me to Sit, Stay, & Come When God Calls. 2008. (ENG., Illus.). 176p. pap. 13.99 (978-1-60142-139-5(7), Multnomah) Doubleday Religious Publishing Group, The.
Pittman, Gail. Single & Making It. 2009. 76p. pap. 11.49 (978-1-4389-5317-0(X)) AuthorHouse.
Pivonka, Dave. Spiritual Freedom: God's Life-Changing Gift. 2008. 146p. pap. 12.99 (978-0-86716-860-0(9), Servant Bks.) Franciscan Media.
Pixler, Steve. The Greater Cause: Studies from Matthew 19. 2007. 70p. per. 12.00 (978-0-9796261-0-4(2)) Continuum Ministry Resources.
Plaiss, Mark. The Image of God: Disappearing into the Divine Nature. 2010. (IlluminationBooks). 128p. pap. 9.95 (978-0-8091-4662-8(2)) Paulist Pr.
Plant, Stephen & Wüstenberg, Ralf K., eds. Religion, Religionlessness & Contemporary Western Culture: Explorations in Dietrich Bonhoeffer's Theology. 2008. 134p. 39.95 (978-3-631-57754-7(0)) Lang, Peter GmbH, Europaischer Verlag der Wissenschaften DEU. Dist: Lang, Peter.
Plante, David E. & Plante, Lorraine M. Kids Don't Build Boats. 2011. 264p. 35.95 (978-1-61507-910-0(6)); pap. 19.95 (978-1-61507-908-7(4)) Cross Bks. Publishing.
Platt, David. Radical: Taking Back Your Faith from the American Dream. 2010. (978-1-60142-220-0(2)); (ENG.). 240p. pap. 14.99 (978-1-60142-221-7(0)) Doubleday Religious Publishing Group, The. (Multnomah).
—The Radical Question Pack, No. 10: What Is Jesus Worth to You? 2010. (ENG.). 64p. pap. 19.90 (978-1-60142-321-4(7), Multnomah) Doubleday Religious Publishing Group, The.
Platt, Rita J. Step into the Waters: Experiencing the Abundance of the Spirit. 2009. (Sword of Lyric Ser.). (ENG.). 128p. pap. 9.99 (978-1-60006-369-3(6)) NavPress Publishing Group.
Plekenpol, Chris. Faith in the Fog of War: Stories of Triumph & Tragedy in the Midst of War. 2006. (ENG., Illus.). 192p. per. 13.99 (978-1-59052-741-2(0), Multnomah) Doubleday Religious Publishing Group, The.
Pillar, Russell. The Crisis Driven Church: Discover the Cure for Crisis Living. 2007. 180p. per. 13.99 (978-0-9795480-3-1(9)) Insight Publishing Group.
Plop, Peter. God's Waiting Room. (978-0-9672726-0-3(2)) kaboom pr.
Plowman, Ginger. Heaven at Home: Establishing & Enjoying a Peaceful Home. annot. ed. 2006. 224p. per. 13.95 (978-0-9767582-4-2(5)) Shepherd Pr. Inc.
Plummer, John P. Living Mysteries: A Practical Handbook for the Independent Priest. 2010. 136p. pap. 9.95 (978-1-933993-93-5(6)) Apocryphile Pr.
Pobanz, Patty. Everlasting Peace in Your Life: God's Reminders to the World. 2007. 76p. per. 16.95 (978-1-4241-9326-4(5)) PublishAmerica, Inc.
Pohl, Christine D. Living into Community: Cultivating Practices That Sustain Us. 2012. vi, 213p. pap. (978-0-8028-4985-4(7)) Eerdmans, William B. Publishing Co.
Poinsett, Brenda. The Friendship Factor: Why Women Need Other Women. 2010. (ENG.). 208p. pap. 14.99 (978-1-59669-247-3(2)) New Hope Pubs.
Poland, Hugh. Intentional Walk: More Devotions for Baseball Fans. 2009. 160p. pap. 14.00 (978-0-8170-1543-5(4)) Judson Pr.
—The Master Carpenter: Devotions for Woodworkers. 2008. 160p. pap. 15.00 (978-0-8170-1529-9(9)) Judson Pr.
Polkinghorne, John. Scientists as Theologists. 112p. 16.00 (978-0-281-04945-5(9)) SPCK Publishing GBR. Dist: Pilgrim Pr., The/United Church Pr.
Pollard, Gar. Coming Out on Top. 2011. 144p. pap. 14.99 (978-1-60957-869-5(4)) Xulon Pr., Inc.
Pollard, Margaret Camille. God Has Plans for You: Walking in His Will. 2009. 108p. pap. 14.99 (978-1-4389-7814-7(6)) AuthorHouse.
Pollard, Ryan David. Noise of War in the Camp: Sin, False Doctrine & Corruption in the Church Today. 2009. 200p. pap. 24.95 (978-1-60836-638-2(5)) PublishAmerica, Inc.
Pollmann, Karla & Vessey, Mark, eds. Augustine & the Disciplines: From Cassiciacum to Confessions. 2007. (ENG.). 272p. pap. 45.00 (978-0-19-923004-4(8)) Oxford Univ. Pr., Inc.
Ponsonby, Simon. And the Lamb Wins: Why the End of the World Is Really Good News. 2008. (ENG.). 320p. pap. 14.99 (978-1-4347-6755-4(8)) Cook, David C.
Pontifical Council for the Laity. Dignity of Older People. 63p. pap. 2.95 (978-0-8198-1877-5(1), 332-072) Pauline Bks. & Media.
Pool, John Mark. Path of a Prophet: Understanding the Journey. 2007. 182p. per. 15.99 (978-0-7684-2442-3(9)) Destiny Image Pubs.
Poole, Matthew. A Seasonable Apology for the Christian Religion. 2009. 108p. pap. 12.95 (978-1-4401-3484-5(7)) iUniverse, Inc.
Pooler, Renee'. Who Is in Control? 2007. pap. 9.99 (978-1-59684-031-7(5)) Pathway Pr.
Poos-Benson, Stephen. The Gym Bag Bible. 2007. 144p. per. 15.99 (978-1-60266-003-8(4)) Xulon Pr., Inc.
Popcak, Gregory K. God Help Me! This Stress Is Driving Me Crazy! - Finding Balance Through God's Grace. 2010. (ENG.). 160p. pap. 15.95 (978-0-8245-2598-9(1)) Crossroad Publishing Co., The.
Popcak, Gregory K. & Popcak, Lisa A. A Marriage Made for Heaven: The Secrets of Heavenly Couplehood. 2009. (ENG.). 128p. pap., wbk. ed. 12.95 (978-0-8245-2533-0(7)); (Illus.). 49.95 (978-0-8245-2532-3(9)) Crossroad Publishing Co., The.
Popcorn Miracles: Little Reminders of God's Nearness. 2008. (Illus.). per. 12.99 (978-0-9799903-0-4(0)) Majesty Hse.
Pope, Courtney A. Apostolic Mentoring: Effective Preparation for Mantles, Assignments, & Legacies. 2011. 80p. pap. 10.00 (978-1-4567-4016-0(4)) AuthorHouse.
Pope, Radny. Life Issues: Books 1-4. 2007. per. 8.99 (978-0-9776605-5-1(9)) Life-on-Life Resources.
Pope, Randy. Life Issues: Is Jesus Christ the Only Way to God? 2007. per. 2.49 (978-0-9776605-3-7(2)) Life-on-Life Resources.
—Life Issues: Is the Bible God's Word?: Book 1. 2007. per. 2.49 (978-0-9776605-1-3(6)) Life-on-Life Resources.
—Life Issues: What Is Required to Have Eternal Life?: Book 4. 2007. per. 2.49 (978-0-9776605-4-4(0)) Life-on-Life Resources.
Pope, Robert. Salvation in Celluloid: Theology, Imagination & Film. 2007. (ENG.). 224p. 145.00 (978-0-567-03206-5(X), T&T Clark Int'l) Continuum International Publishing Group, Ltd. GBR. Dist: National Bk. Network.
Popjes, Jack. A Kick in the Pants. 2008. pap. 10.95 (978-0-938978-46-6(2)) Wycliffe Bible Translators.
Popplewell, Pat Galen. Bible Interpretation. 2009. 192p. pap. 14.99 (978-1-60791-410-5(7)) Xulon Pr., Inc.
Porter, D. Go, Deliver! (Illus.). 192p. 9.99 (978-1-85792-000-0(7)) Christian Focus Pubns. GBR. Dist: Spring Arbor Distributors, Inc.
Porter, Stephen C. Simple Answers for a World Full of Questions. 2010. (978-1-77069-085-1(9)) Word Alive Pr.
Portillo, Jose A. De Campeon de Boxeo de Espana: From Boxing to Discipleship. (SPA.). 80p. (978-84-7228-818-8(8), 220255) Clie, Editorial.
Posner, Carol. Ordinary Patriot. 2007. 108p. per. 10.99 (978-1-60266-589-7(3)) Xulon Pr., Inc.
Post, Lavon. Good Morning!! How Are My College Buddies? 2008. 460p. per. 23.99 (978-1-60477-641-6(2)) Xulon Pr., Inc.
Posthuma, David A. Made for a Mission. 2008. (ENG., Illus.). 307p. pap. 15.99 (978-0-87508-981-2(X)) CLC Pubns.
Potter, Charlotte. Spin Us a Dream. 2008. 52p. pap. 16.95 (978-1-60563-019-9(5)) PublishAmerica, Inc.
Potter, James. Soul Care. 2009. 352p. pap. 19.95 (978-1-61529-004-8(4)) Vision Publishing.
Potter, Jerold. How to Conquer. 2006. pap. 4.97 (978-1-59789-527-9(X)) Barbour Publishing, Inc.
Pound, Charlotte L. He'll Do It Again! It Is Time to Start Believing & Receiving from God. 2007. 80p. per. 10.99 (978-0-9772305-1-8(1)) R.J. Erancia Pr.
Powell, Billy. Butterflies in Heaven: What Lies Beyond the Grave? 2008. (Illus.). 247p. pap. 18.95 (978-1-934144-39-3(8)) Sphinx Publishing.
Powell, Graham & Powell, Shirley. Christian Set Yourself Free. 192p. (978-1-85240-135-1(4)) Sovereign World, Ltd.
Powell, Henry Hall. The Missing Link: A Guide to Spiritual Reality. 2008. 140p. pap. 13.99 (978-1-60647-026-8(4)) Xulon Pr., Inc.
Powell, Lawrence Raphael. It's Your Call: 7 Sure Ways to Fulfill Your Life's Purpose. 2008. 204p. 19.99 (978-0-88144-291-5(7)) Yorkshire Publishing Group.
Power, Freddie. Visions: God Speaks. 2008. 80p. pap. 26.49 (978-1-4389-3316-0(9)) AuthorHouse.
The Power of Faith Audio CD Set: Change Defeat to Victory using the ingredients of Faith. 2007. Orig. Title: Believing What I can't See. cd-rom 13.99 (978-0-9794870-0-2(5)) Cook, Phyllis.

C

The Power of Faith Paperback book & Audio CD: Change Defeat to Victory Using the Ingredients of Faith. 2007. Orig. Title: Believing what you can't See. cd-rom (978-0-9794870-2-6(1)) Cook, Phyllis.

The Power of Faith Paperback book & MP3 Audio CD: Change Defeat to Victory Using the Ingredients of Faith. 2007. Orig. Title: Believing what you can't See. (978-0-9794870-3-3(X)) Cook, Phyllis.

The Power of Holy Habits. 2.00 incl. audio (978-0-687-76224-8(3)) Abingdon Pr.

Powers, Marie. From Shame to Beauty. 2010. (Women of the Word Bible Study Ser.). (ENG.). 112p. pap. 9.99 (978-0-8307-5235-5(8)) Gospel Light Pubns.

Powers, Wade. The Covenant Divorce Recovery Leader's Handbook. 2008. 324p. pap. 20.99 (978-1-60477-428-3(2)) Xulon Pr., Inc.

Powlison, David. Facing Death with Hope: Living for What Lasts. 2008. (ENG.). 24p. 3.99 (978-1-934885-52-9(5)) New Growth Pr.

—I Just Want to Die: Replacing Suicidal Thoughts with Hope. 2010. 24p. 3.99 (978-1-935273-70-7(1)) New Growth Pr.

—Recovering from Child Abuse: Healing & Hope for Victims. 2008. (ENG.). 24p. 3.99 (978-1-934885-47-5(9)) New Growth Pr.

—Sexual Assault: Healing Steps for Victims. 2010. 30p. 3.99 (978-1-935273-78-3(7)) New Growth Pr.

Powlison, David/Arthur. The Biblical Counseling Movement: History & Context. 2009. 432p. pap. 39.99 (978-1-935273-13-4(2)) New Growth Pr.

—Life Beyond Your Parents' Mistakes: The Transforming Power of God's Love. 2009. 24p. 3.99 (978-1-935273-18-9(3)) New Growth Pr.

Practical Ways to Manage Conflict: Bible Study. (On Main Street Ser.). pap. 4.50 (978-0-570-09598-9(0), 20-2841) Concordia Publishing Hse.

Prainito, Joe. 'Living & Dying Without RegretApos. 2008. 200p. pap. 14.99 (978-1-60477-680-5(3)) Xulon Pr., Inc.

Prasch, B. Ten Steps to Serenity. 22p. pap. 1.25 (978-0-8198-7337-8(3), 332-386) Pauline Bks. & Media.

Prather, Paul. A Memory of Firelight: Selected Columns from the Lexington Herald-Leader. 2009. 186p. pap. 16.00 (978-1-936138-01-2(8)) Wind Pubns.

Pratney, Winkie. Devil Take the Youngest. 2009. 273p. pap. 18.97 (978-0-557-21791-5(1)) Lulu Enterprises Inc.

Pratt, David R. Get a Life. 2011. 84p. pap. 11.45 **(978-1-4567-2233-3(6))** AuthorHouse.

Pratt, Frances Briggs. Isn't That Just Like God? The God Who Keeps His Promises. 2010. pap. 15.99 (978-1-61579-899-5(4)) Xulon Pr., Inc.

Pratt, Jack A. Best Kept Secret in Christianity. 2008. 120p. per. 10.99 (978-1-60477-724-6(9)) Xulon Pr., Inc.

Pratt, Palmerine. Adventure in Faith. 2006. 26.95 (978-1-59330-443-0(9)); pap. 14.50 (978-1-59330-442-3(0)) Aventine Pr.

Praytor, Rich. A Stand-up Comic Sits down with Jesus: A Devotional? 2007. (ENG.). 160p. per. 12.99 (978-0-8307-4473-2(8)) Gospel Light Pubns.

Preacher, The. His Word. 2009. 48p. pap. 15.99 (978-1-4415-0820-1(1)) Xlibris Corp.

Preaching & Teaching. 2008. pap. 14.95 (978-1-59712-278-8(5)) Catawba Publishing Co.

Preece, Mary Ellen Goble. The Truth Is in the Light. 2008. 92p. pap. 16.95 (978-1-60563-325-1(9)) PublishAmerica, Inc.

Prentiss, E. Stepping Heavenward. 2008. 180p. pap. (978-1-4068-6605-6(9)) Echo Library.

—Stepping Heavenward. 2008. 436p. 51.95 (978-0-548-93959-8(4)) 2007. (ENG.). 440p. per. 36.95 (978-0-548-59147-5(4)) Kessinger Publishing, LLC.

Prentiss, Elizabeth. Aunt Jane's Hero. 2009. 280p. (gr. -1-18). 24.99 (978-1-103-23472-1(2)); pap. 18.99 (978-1-103-23469-1(2)) BiblioBazaar.

—Aunt Jane's Hero. 2009. 174p. pap. (978-0-217-68488-0(2)) Books LLC.

—Aunt Jane's Hero. 2008. 292p. 43.95 (978-1-4369-5486-0(X)); pap. 28.95 (978-1-4367-8347-7(X)) Kessinger Publishing, LLC.

—Stepping Heavenward. pap. 10.99 (978-0-87377-078-1(1)) GAM Pubns.

Prescott, Bishop Kirk D. The Soulless Harvest: The Gospel with an Agenda. 2011. 94p. pap. 19.95 **(978-1-4560-5668-1(9))** PublishAmerica, Inc.

Presler, Titus. Going Global with God: Reconciling Mission in A World of Difference. 2010. 176p. pap. 20.00 (978-0-8192-2410-1(3), Morehouse Publishing) Church Publishing, Inc.

Press, Benyamin. The Secret Joy of Repentance. 2010. 72p. pap. 19.95 (978-1-4251-5967-2(2)) Trafford Publishing.

Pressley. Collecting All My Puzzle Pieces. 2007. 8.00 (978-0-8059-6875-0(X)) Dorrance Publishing Co., Inc.

Presson, Ramon/L. When Will My Life Not Suck? Authentic Hope for the Disillusioned. 2010. pap. 15.99 (978-1-935273-80-6(9)) New Growth Pr.

Preston, John. The Money Revolution: Applying Christian Principles to Handling Your Money. 2007. (ENG.). 64p. 7.99 (978-1-85078-754-9(9)) Authentic Media.

Preston, Teresa. My Devotion, My Heart: Spiritual Encouragement from My Heart to Yours. 2010. pap. 27.99 (978-1-61566-460-3(2)) Tate Publishing & Enterprises, LLC.

Prestwood, Sherri. He Came with a Message. 2008. 224p. 25.99 (978-1-60647-707-6(2)); pap. 15.99 (978-1-60647-706-9(4)) Xulon Pr., Inc.

Pretty, Diane. God Is in the Details. 2008. 204p. 36.95 (978-1-4251-7732-4(8)) Trafford Publishing.

Prewitt-Salem, Cheryl. Abuse, Bruised but Not Broken. Date not set. mass mkt. 2.99 (978-0-89274-587-6(8), CS-587) Harrison House Pubs.

Price, Cecil. What Does Jesus Say About... Christ Speaks to Us Today. 2008. (Illus.). 1901p. 34.99 (978-0-89957-611-4(7)) AMG Pubs.

Price, Eugenia. Este o Sus Padres? Orig. Title: No Pat Answers. (SPA.). 136p. (978-84-7228-207-0(4), 220740) Clie, Editorial.

—No Dudes un Momento. Orig. Title: Never a Dull Moment. (SPA.). 128p. (978-84-7228-197-4(3), 220628) Clie, Editorial.

Price, Jack F. Finding Faith: Honest Answers about God, the Bible, & the Church Today. 2011. 122p. pap. 14.29 **(978-0-557-79721-9(7))** Lulu Enterprises Inc.

Price, James E. Three Faces of the Backslider: Runaways, Rebels & Wrong Turns. 2008. (ENG.). 56p. pap. 7.99 (978-0-9762730-4-2(7)) Vision Publishing.

Price, Kerrie. The Irresistible Urge: To pursue the call of God. 2010. 234p. pap. 14.50 (978-1-60911-761-0(1), Eloquent Bks.) AEG Literary Publishing Services, Inc.

Price, Leo. Conquering Chaos. 2006. pap. 13.99 (978-1-60034-506-7(9)) Xulon Pr., Inc.

Price, Michael A. Your Days Are Numbered: A Practical Guide to Numbers in Scripture. 2011. 224p. 29.99 **(978-1-4568-8383-6(6))**; pap. 19.99 **(978-1-4568-8382-9(8))** Xlibris Corp.

Pridgen, Ronald L. Your Biblical Rights. 2009. 160p. 25.49 (978-1-4389-4537-8(X)); pap. 15.49 (978-1-4389-4536-1(1)) AuthorHouse.

Pridmore, John. From Gangland to Promised Land. 2007. (Illus.). 239p. per. (978-0-9547321-3-4(8)) Xt3 Media.

Pries, Jeff & Ward, John. Crossing. 2007. (Liquid Ser.). (ENG., Illus.). 112p. instr.'s gde. ed. 24.99 (978-1-4185-2759-4(9)) Nelson, Thomas Inc.

—Live at Five, 0 vols. 2007. (Liquid Ser.). (ENG., Illus.). 112p. 24.99 (978-1-4185-2757-0(2)) Nelson, Thomas Inc.

—Mirror Image. 2007. (Liquid Ser.). (ENG., Illus.). 112p. 24.99 (978-1-4185-2761-7(0)) Nelson, Thomas Inc.

—The Ten, Vol. 1-5. 2008. (Liquid Ser.). (ENG.). 112p. pap., instr.'s gde. ed. 9.99 (978-1-4185-3396-0(3)) Nelson, Thomas Inc.

Primiceiro, Shannon. Hagar: Target of a Jealous Beauty Queen. 2007. (Think Bible Studies). (ENG.). 128p. (YA). per. 8.99 (978-1-60006-113-4(3), Th1nk Bks.) NavPress Publishing Group.

—Leah: Confessions of a First Runner-up. 2007. (Think Bible Studies). (ENG.). 144p. (YA). per. 8.99 (978-1-60006-112-7(5), Th1nk Bks.) NavPress Publishing Group.

—Miriam: A Go-Getter Goes Too Far. 2007. (Think Bible Studies). (ENG.). 128p. (YA). pap. 8.99 (978-1-60006-114-1(1), Th1nk Bks.) NavPress Publishing Group.

Prince, Benny. Once Saved, Always? 2008. 120p. per. 8.50 (978-0-9797106-9-8(3)) Avid Readers Publishing Group.

Prince, D. S. El Espiritu Santo en Usted.Tr. of Holy Spirit in You. (SPA.). 3.50 (978-0-7899-0118-7(8), 550085) Editorial Unilit.

—El Plan de Dios para Su Dinero.Tr. of God's Plan for Your Money. (SPA.). 3.50 (978-0-7899-0114-9(5), 550081) Editorial Unilit.

—Si Deseas lo Mejor de Parte de Dios.Tr. of If You Want God's Best. (SPA.). 3.99 (978-0-7899-0120-0(X), 550087) Editorial Unilit.

Prince, Darius. What Are You Waiting For? 2006. pap. 12.99 (978-1-60034-454-1(2)) Xulon Pr., Inc.

Prince, Derek. Cita en Jerusalen: Appointment in Jerusalem. (SPA.). 248p. (978-84-7228-360-2(7), 360091) Clie, Editorial.

—Entering the Presence of God: Moving Beyond Praise & Thanksgiving to True Worship. 2007. 173p. per. 12.99 (978-0-88368-719-2(4)) Whitaker Hse.

—Gateway to God's Blessing. 2008. 176p. pap. 11.99 (978-1-60374-052-4(X)) Whitaker Hse.

Prince, Gina. Born into Sin, Transformed into Destiny: God Can Truly Deliver You. 2010. 144p. pap. 12.99 (978-1-61638-007-6(1), Creation Hse.) Charisma Media.

Prince, Jr. Are You Listening? 2007. 68p. per. 9.99 (978-1-60266-913-0(9)) Xulon Pr., Inc.

Prindle, Shelli. Real Life Real God Real Hope! 2011. 152p. pap. 14.99 **(978-1-61215-903-4(6))** Xulon Pr., Inc.

Pringle, Phil. Dead for Nothing? What the Cross Has Done for You. 2007. 140p. per. 12.99 (978-1-57794-931-2(5)) Harrison House Pubs.

—Seven Big Things That Make Life Work: Principles for Successful Living. 2010. (ENG.). pap. 14.99 (978-0-7684-3245-9(6)) Destiny Image Pubs.

Priolo, Lou. Deception: Letting Go of Lying. 2008. pap. (978-1-59638-129-2(9)) P & R Publishing.

—Fear: Breaking Its Grip. 2009. pap. (978-1-59638-121-6(3)) P & R Publishing.

Priolo, Louis Paul. Self-Image: How to Overcome Inferiority Judgments. 2007. (Resources for Biblical Living Ser.). 32p. pap. 9.99 (978-1-59638-079-0(9)) P & R Publishing.

Priority Associates Staff. Practical Christian Living. Date not set. 149p. pap., tchr. ed. 15.00 (978-1-57902-082-8(8), 5401g) Integrated Resources.

—Practical Christian Living Vol. 1: Lessons 1-9. Date not set. 106p. 11.00 (978-1-57902-080-4(1)) Integrated Resources.

—Practical Christian Living Vol. 2: Lessons 10-18. Date not set. 218p. 6.00 (978-1-57902-081-1(X)) Integrated Resources.

Pritchard, John. Beginning Again. (Illus.). 128p. 12.00 (978-0-281-05265-3(4)) SPCK Publishing GBR. Dist: Pilgrim Pr., The/United Church Pr.

Pritchard, Ray. Stealth Attack: Protecting Yourself Against Satan's Plan to Destroy Your Life. 2007. (ENG.). 160p. per. 13.99 (978-0-8024-0989-8(X)) Moody Pubs.

Pritchett, Lee. Paradise Must Wait: A Biblical take on the Rapture. 2011. 134p. pap. 24.95 **(978-1-4560-9860-5(8))** PublishAmerica, Inc.

Prochaska, Frank. Christianity & Social Service in Modern Britain: The Disinherited Spirit. 2008. (ENG., Illus.). 228p. 45.00 (978-0-19-953979-6(0)) Oxford Univ. Pr., Inc.

Proctor, Patricia. 101 Inspirational Stories of the Sacrament of Reconciliation. 2006. (Illus.). 300p. per. 14.99 (978-0-9728447-5-8(9)) Franciscan Monastery of Saint Clare.

Proczek, Zygmunt. The Servant of Mary Immaculate: Fr. Casimir Wyszynski. (978-0-944203-27-9(2)) Marian Pr.

Prodigal, The. Penny's Miracle: Standing on His Promises, 1 vol. 2009. 63p. pap. 16.95 (978-1-4489-9994-1(4)) PublishAmerica, Inc.

Proo, Al. God's Timing: Are Your Hands Tied? 1598th ed. 2006. 256p. per. 14.99 (978-1-59886-599-8(4)) Tate Publishing & Enterprises, LLC.

Prophet, Elizabeth Clare. Los Angeles to Ayudan a Crear Milagros.Tr. of How Angels Help You Create Miracles in Your Life. (SPA.). 11.50 (978-84-605-8545-9(X)) Fundacion EFE ESP. Dist: Lectorum Pubns., Inc.

Prophetess Lori J. McKenney. Transformation. 2009. 160p. 22.70 (978-1-4389-8263-2(1)); pap. 16.99 (978-1-4389-8264-9(X)) AuthorHouse.

Prophetess Sister Mary. Heart & Soul of a Prophetess of God. 2008. 176p. pap. 16.99 (978-1-4389-2560-8(3)) AuthorHouse.

Prude, George B. Run Through It: A Spiritual Journey Through Life's Roadblocks & Obstacles. 2010. 172p. pap. 12.99 (978-1-4490-8524-7(5)) AuthorHouse.

Prudhomme, Jeff Owen. God & Being: Heidegger's Relation to Theology. (Contemporary Studies in Philosophy & the Human Sciences Ser.). (ENG.). 1p. 69.98 (978-1-57392-506-8(3), Humanity Bks.) Prometheus Bks., Pubs.

Pruitt, Brian. The Power of Dad. 2008. 136p. per. 13.99 (978-1-60477-591-4(2)) Xulon Pr., Inc.

—The Power of Dad Workbook. 2008. 76p. per. 9.99 (978-1-60477-745-1(1)) Xulon Pr., Inc.

Pryor, Denona. Confessions of A Single Woman. 2011. 128p. 28.95 **(978-1-4497-2915-8(0))**; pap. 11.95 **(978-1-4497-2914-1(2))** Author Solutions, Inc. (WestBow Pr.).

Pryor, Pastor Ted. Things Your Church Never Wants You to Know: Why Lie, When the Truth Will Do? 2008. 96p. pap. 19.99 (978-1-4343-8424-9(1)) AuthorHouse.

Psalidas, Jessica V. Everlasting Purity. 2008. 200p. pap. 14.99 (978-1-60647-362-7(X)) Xulon Pr., Inc.

Publication, Bargainhouse. Created with Purpose. 2010. 210p. pap. 13.95 (978-0-557-00902-2(2)) Lulu Enterprises Inc.

Publications, Christian Focus. CF4K Children's Resource Catalog 2007: Because you're never too young to know Jesus. 2007. (ENG.). 24p. (978-1-84550-112-9(8)) Christian Focus Pubns. GBR. Dist: STL Distribution North America.

Publications International Staff, ed. My Daily Psalms & Prayers. 2010. 384p. 6.98 (978-1-4508-0407-3(1)); bds. 10.98 (978-1-60553-897-6(3)) Publications International, Ltd.

Publishing, Barbour. Encouragement for Men. 2008. (Life's little book of Wisdom Ser.). (ENG.). 192p. pap. 4.97 (978-1-60260-204-5(2), Barbour Bks.) Barbour Publishing, Inc.

Puckett, Michael R. Off the Beaten Path: A Heartfelt Journey. 106p. pap. 14.95 (978-1-892861-00-9(3)) Vision Publishing Group.

Pugh, Toni. Next Step Touchstone Truths to A Fuller. 2006. pap. 10.95 (978-1-59330-424-9(2)) Aventine Pr.

Pultorak, Mark. Contemporary Catholic Discipleship, 1 vol. 2009. 48p. pap. 16.95 (978-1-4489-2728-9(5)) PublishAmerica, Inc.

Purifoy, Tiffany. Honor God with Your Life. 2011. 188p. pap. 16.95 **(978-1-4620-2967-9(1))** iUniverse, Inc.

Purkiss, Jeff. Squires to Knights. 2007. 160p. per. 13.99 (978-1-60477-436-8(3)) Xulon Pr., Inc.

Purroy, Marino. Como Superar el Dolor. (SPA.). 176p. 6.95 (978-958-607-155-0(3)) Sociedad de San Pablo ESP. Dist: St Pauls/Alba Hse. Pubs.

Pursel, Ronald. Fear What Is It Good For? 2007. 220p. per. 14.99 (978-1-60266-290-2(8)) Xulon Pr., Inc.

Pursley, Ovit G. Counseling with God's Word: From A to W. 2011. 224p. pap. 15.86 (978-1-4269-5015-5(2)) Trafford Publishing.

Putanu, Sara. Dreams Jesus: The Supernatural Power of His Name. 2009. 204p. pap. 15.99 (978-1-60791-931-5(1)) Xulon Pr., Inc.

Putnam, Joanne. Let's Go down to the Potter's House. 2006. 189p. pap. 13.99 (978-1-56722-693-5(0)) Word Aflame Pr.

Putnam, Ronald David. The Way to Intimacy: Men's Edition. 2007. (ENG & RUS.). pap. 15.00 (978-0-9774878-2-0(2)) Slavic Christian Ministries Publishing.

Pyle, Debbie. The Lord's Feasts: A Study of How the Old Testament Feasts Find Their Fulfillment in Jesus Christ. 2010. 112p. pap. 16.95 (978-1-61507-171-5(7)) Cross Bks. Publishing.

Pytches, David. Child No More. pap. 6.95 (978-0-340-72229-9(0), Hodder & Stoughton) Hodder General Publishing Div. GBR. Dist: Trafalgar Square Publishing.

Qualls, Ken. Just Thinking Out Loud. 2009. 180p. 22.99 (978-1-60791-398-6(4)); pap. 14.99 (978-1-60791-397-9(6)) Xulon Pr., Inc.

Quansah, Emmanuel Socrates. The Seven Ultimate Rewards. 2009. 112p. pap. 15.95 (978-1-4327-4633-9(2)) Outskirts Pr., Inc.

Queen, Chuck. A Faith Worth Living: The Dynamics of an Inclusive Gospel. 2011. 168p. pap. 19.00 (978-1-61097-187-4(6), Resource Pubns.) Wipf & Stock Pubs.

Querin, Sandra. The Prayer of Job. exp. ed. 160p. pap. 9.99 (978-1-58169-145-0(9), Evergreen Pr.) Genesis Communications, Inc.

Quinn, Jackie. At the End of Myself Redefining Strength. 2007. 108p. pap. 11.99 (978-1-60034-973-7(0)) Xulon Pr., Inc.

Quinn, Shelley. Life Affirmations: Living in the Power of God's Word. 2008. 13.99 (978-0-8163-2278-7(3)) Pacific Pr. Publishing Assn.

Quiring, Richard. Faith Is. 2010. pap. 15.99 (978-1-61579-639-7(8)) Xulon Pr., Inc.

R, Jesus S. Chavira. Vida Inspirada. 2008. pap. 9.99 (978-1-60647-039-8(6)) Xulon Pr., Inc.

Raab C.S.C., Ronald Patrick. The Unsheltered Heart: An at-Home Advent Retreat (Cycle B) 2011. 96p. 5.95 **(978-1-59471-284-5(0))** Ave Maria Pr.

Raab, Ronald Patrick. The Unsheltered Heart: An at Home Advent Retreat, Cycle A. 2010. 64p. 5.95 (978-1-59471-254-8(9)) Ave Maria Pr.

Rabak, Anthony D. Just Tell Me When You're Gonna Stick Me! 2009. 176p. pap. 14.99 (978-1-60791-615-4(0)) Xulon Pr., Inc.

Rachinski, Walter. A Kingdom Not of This World. 2011. 272p. pap. 27.95 **(978-1-4560-5335-2(3))** PublishAmerica, Inc.

Radley, Chris. By the Light of the Lord's Prayer. 2008. (Illus.). 112p. (978-1-85345-452-3(4)) Crusade for World Revival.

Radloff, Robert P. The Grace of God. 2007. 92p. per. (978-1-897373-22-4(8)) Word Alive Pr.

Rafferty, Jaime. Finding the Right Piece: Using Laughter & Faith in the Puzzle of Life. 2010. 172p. pap. 13.95 (978-1-61507-170-8(9)) Cross Bks. Publishing.

Raglin, Leonard D. Legends of the Fallen. 2009. 316p. pap. 18.99 (978-1-60791-231-6(7)) Xulon Pr., Inc.

Raiborde, Nicky. Believer's Mandate. 2007. per. 15.99 (978-1-59467-990-2(8)) Xulon Pr., Inc.

Raiborde, Nicky S. Destined to Prevail. 2008. 232p. 24.99 (978-1-60647-418-1(9)); pap. 14.99 (978-1-60647-417-4(0)) Xulon Pr., Inc.

Rainer, Thom S. & Geiger, Eric. Iglesia Simple: Como Volver al Proceso Divino de Hacer Discipulos. 2007. (SPA., Illus.). 272p. per. 12.99 (978-0-8054-4483-4(1), B&H Espanol) B&H Publishing Group.

Rainer, Thom S. & Rainer, Sam S., III. Essential Church? Reclaiming a Generation of Dropouts. 2008. (ENG.). 272p. 19.99 (978-0-8054-4392-9(4), B&H Bks.) B&H Publishing Group.

Raines, Jeffrey K. A Hospital Visit & the Compassion of Jesus Christ. 2010. 70p. pap. 12.95 (978-1-4327-5656-7(7)) Outskirts Pr., Inc.

Raines, Lissa. 8 Crucial Realities: Successful Choices for Graduates. 2010. 280p. 31.99 (978-1-61507-127-2(X)); pap. 17.95 (978-1-61507-158-6(X)) Cross Bks. Publishing.

Rainey, Barbara & Yates, Susan. Barbara & Susan's Guide to the Empty Nest: Discovering New Purpose, Passion & Your Next Great Adventure. 2008. (Illus.). 244p. 19.99 (978-1-60200-060-5(3)) FamilyLife.

Rainey, Dennis. Fear Not. 16p. (C). 1.95 (978-1-57229-006-8(4)) FamilyLife.

Ramay, Marian Edgar. The Holy Spirit in the Life & Work of the Believer. 2011. 144p. 40.95 **(978-1-258-06278-1(X))** Literary Licensing, LLC.

Rambo, Brenda. Understanding the Holy Spirit: Experience the Power. 2010. (ENG.). 128p. pap. 10.99 (978-1-61638-173-8(6), Creation Hse.) Charisma Media.

Ramcharan, C. J. A Lifetime of Knowledge: A Collection of a Lifetime of Inspiration. 2008. 94p. pap. 16.95 (978-1-60441-196-6(1)) PublishAmerica, Inc.

Ramia-Enriquez, Robert. Great Controversies of the Bible: Myth, Fact, & Fallacy. 2010. 440p. 37.95 (978-1-4502-0691-4(3)); pap. 27.95 (978-1-4502-0692-1(1)) iUniverse, Inc.

Ramm, Bernard L. Salida - Los Caminos de Dios: His Way Out. (SPA.). 192p. (978-84-7228-223-0(6), 220784) Clie, Editorial.

Ramón, Connie. In a Space of Time: Lessons to Last a Lifetime. 2009. 108p. pap. 11.99 (978-1-60791-446-4(8)) Xulon Pr., Inc.

Ramon, Don. Faith for the last Days. 2009. 176p. pap. 14.95 (978-1-4327-3089-5(4)) Outskirts Pr., Inc.

Ramos, John Castilleja Rebekah. Sovereignty Suffering Surrender: The Pathways of God. 2009. 120p. pap. 11.99 (978-1-61579-246-7(5)) Xulon Pr., Inc.

Ramos, M. Los Privilegios del Cristiano.Tr. of Christian Privileges. (SPA.). 2.50 (978-1-56063-391-4(3), 493038) Editorial Unilit.

Ramos, Sandi. He Carries Me: A Message of Hope & Understanding for the Caregivers of Terminally Ill Loved Ones. 2010. pap. 10.99 (978-1-61663-091-1(4)) Tate Publishing & Enterprises, LLC.

Ramsay, Yvonne. Come Forth & Fly. 2006. (ENG., Illus.). 176p. 17.99 (978-1-59979-052-7(1), Creation Hse.) Charisma Media.

Ramsey, Betty Jane. Power for Living: A near-Death Experience. 2007. 84p. per. 16.95 (978-1-4241-7777-6(4)) PublishAmerica, Inc.

Ramsey, John. For Your Names' Sake. 2008. 155p. pap. 11.95 (978-0-615-15651-4(7)) Ramsey, John.

Ramsey, Judy. My Experience with Jesus & Angels. 2007. (ENG.). 60p. per. 16.95 (978-1-4241-0679-0(6)) PublishAmerica, Inc.

Ramsey, Norman. Moving at the Speed of Grace: Discovering the Way God Works. 2010. pap. 17.99 (978-1-61663-501-5(0)) Tate Publishing & Enterprises, LLC.

Ramsey, Sarah Lynne. Are We There Yet? Journey into the Presence of God. 2009. 292p. pap. 14.99 (978-1-60799-462-6(3)) Tate Publishing & Enterprises, LLC.

Ramunni, Angelo Paul. Left Turn, Right Turn, U-Turn. 2011. 232p. 25.99 **(978-1-61379-366-4(9))**; pap. 15.99 **(978-1-61379-365-7(0))** Xulon Pr., Inc.

Randolph, Dwight N. Just Focus: The Light of the Creator is the Source of All Goodness. 2008. 128p. pap. 14.99 (978-1-60791-233-0(3)) Xulon Pr., Inc.

Randolph, Joshua. Behind Closed Doors: The Secrets That Lie Within. 2011. 110p. pap. 12.95 **(978-1-4327-7363-2(1))** Outskirts Pr., Inc.

Rankin, Jr. Beyond the Anointing. 2008. 76p. per. 9.99 *(978-1-60477-593-8(9))* Xulon Pr., Inc.
Ransom Books. Gut Check: Confronting Love, Work, & Manhood. 2nd ed. 2008. (ENG.). 191p. 22.95 *(978-0-615-23061-0(X))* Saab & Co., Inc.
Raphael, John. All for the Master: Reverend John Raphael. 2007. per. *(978-0-9794861-2-8(2))* Truth Pubs.
Rardon, Janell. Rock-Solid Families: Transforming an Ordinary Home into a Fortress of Faith. 2007. (ENG., Illus.). 144p. (gr. 11). per. 12.99 *(978-0-89957-036-5(4))* AMG Pubs.
Rasche, Jeffrey A. My Devotional Companion: 52 Devotions for Individuals & Groups; Ideal for Use with Adult Bible Studies & All Popular 2007-2008 Uniform Series Lesson Annuals. 2007. (My Devotional Companion Ser.). 110p. per. 12.00 *(978-0-687-64142-0(X))* Abingdon Pr.
Rashotte, Susan. Heaven's Heartbeat. 2008. 288p. per. *(978-1-55452-261-3(7))* Essence Publishing.
Rasmussen, Gerald. The Gate of Beautiful: Stories, Songs, & Reflections on Christian Life. 2009. 172p. pap. 14.95 *(978-1-4327-3676-7(0))* Outskirts Pr., Inc.
Rassamni, Jerry. From Jihad to Jesus: An Ex-Militant's Journey of Faith. 2006. (Illus.). 231p. per. 14.99 *(978-0-89957-091-4(7))* AMG Pubs.
Rathjen, Melinda, ed. Ideals Easter. 2008. (ENG., Illus.). 64p. per. 6.99 *(978-0-8249-1317-5(5))* Ideals Pubns.
Ratzinger, Joseph. What It Means to Be a Christian. Taylor, Henry, tr. from GER. 2006. 86p. 14.95 *(978-1-58617-133-9(X))* Ignatius Pr.
Raup, Chuck. Return to Eden: Restoring Your Lost Calling. 2010. 25.99 *(978-1-61579-771-4(8))*; pap. 15.99 *(978-1-61579-770-7(X))* Xulon Pr., Inc.
Rauser, Randal. Faith Lacking Understanding: Theology 'Through a Glass, Darkly' 2008. (ENG.). 208p. pap. 17.99 *(978-1-84227-547-4(X)*, Paternoster) Authentic Media.
—Finding God in the Shack. 2009. (ENG.). 173p. pap. 14.99 *(978-1-60657-032-6(3))* Authentic Media.
Raven, A. Rue des Saints. 2011. 138p. pap. 14.99 ***(978-1-61379-007-6(4))*** Xulon Pr., Inc.
Ravhudzulo, Anniekie. Embracing Life Again after the Death of a Spouse. 2011. 288p. pap. 19.99 ***(978-1-4568-4191-1(2))*** Xlibris Corp.
Ravhudzulo, Anniekie. The Foundations Are Crumbling! Women Empowerment - Strategy to Overcome Obstacles. 2010. 188p. pap. 17.00 *(978-1-4490-7726-5(9))* AuthorHouse.
Rawlings, Maurice S. Which Way Are You Going? 2008. 156p. pap. 16.99 *(978-1-60477-853-3(9))* Xulon Pr., Inc.
Rawlins, James. The Kingdom: Yesterday, Today, & Tomorrow. 2008. 100p. per. 12.95 *(978-1-933912-60-8(X))* Westview Publishing Co., Inc.
Ray, Bruce A. No Rehuses el Corregir: Withold Not Correction. (SPA.). 144p. *(978-84-7228-934-5(6)*, 223008) Clie, Editorial.
Ray, Dennis R. A W O L Christians. 2011. 114p. pap. 19.95 ***(978-1-4560-5566-0(6))*** PublishAmerica, Inc.
Ray, Veronica. I Know Myself. (Moment to Reflect Ser.). pap. 2.50 *(978-0-89486-763-7(6))* Hazelden Publishing & Educational Services.
—I'm Good Enough. (Moment to Reflect Ser.). pap. 2.50 *(978-0-89486-761-3(X))* Hazelden Publishing & Educational Services.
Rayburn, Robert Louis. Who Is the Holy Spirit: And what Does HE Do? 2010. 172p. pap. 12.00 *(978-1-4490-4217-2(1))* AuthorHouse.
Raymond, Kenneth. Life under Construction: Decisions, Decisions, Decisions. 2010. 140p. 23.95 *(978-1-4401-9235-7(9))*; (ENG.). pap. 13.95 *(978-1-4401-9233-3(2))* iUniverse, Inc.
Read, Piers Paul. Hell & Other Destinations: A Novelist's Reflections on This World & the Next. 2006. 247p. pap. 15.95 *(978-1-58617-161-2(5))* Ignatius Pr.
Read, Tim. Angels Do Not Have Wings. 2011. 92p. pap. 19.95 ***(978-1-4626-1752-4(2))*** PublishAmerica, Inc.
Reader, John. Reconstructing Practical Theology: The Impact of Globalization. 2008. (Explorations in Practical, Pastoral & Empirical Theology Ser.). (Illus.). 150p. pap. 39.95 *(978-0-7546-6660-8(3))* Ashgate Publishing Co.
Reader Resource Series. Date not set. (Orig.). pap. *(978-1-883667-09-2(7))* Christian Methodist Episcopal Church, General Board of Pubns.
Ready, Racheal. Lost in His Presence. 2006. pap. 9.99 *(978-1-60034-718-4(5))* Xulon Pr., Inc.
Reagan, D. El Plan Supremo.Tr. of Master Plan. (SPA.). 9.99 *(978-0-7899-0076-0(9)*, 492300) Editorial Unilit.
Reall, Scott. Journey to Living with Courage: Freedom from Fear, 0 vols. 2008. (Journey to Freedom Study Ser.). 112p. per. 9.99 *(978-1-4185-0772-5(5))* Nelson, Thomas Inc.
Reaves, Deborah Ruth. From Weeds to Wisdom: Extracting Spiritual Lessons from the Unlikely. 2011. pap. 12.99 *(978-1-61739-707-3(5))* Tate Publishing & Enterprises, LLC.
Recker, Matthew. Living on the Edge of Eternity. 2007. 112p. per. *(978-1-59166-769-8(0))* BJU Pr.
Redenius, Kristina. Welcome to Christianity: Born Again 101. 2011. 60p. pap. 9.95 ***(978-1-4497-2951-6(7)***, WestBow Pr.) Author Solutions, Inc.
Redgrave, Kenneth. Anxious Christians: Psychological Problems & Christian Faith. (Illus.). 192p. 14.00 *(978-0-281-05507-4(6))* SPCK Publishing GBR. Dist: Pilgrim Pr., The/United Church Pr.
Redmon, Nia. Rediscovering God's Plan for Mankind: For I Know the Plans I have for You (Jeremiah 29:11) 2008. 176p. pap. 17.95 *(978-0-9790368-3-5(6))* Petra Communications, Inc.
Redmond, Jack. People Matter to God. 2008. 80p. pap. 10.99 *(978-1-60647-838-7(9))* Xulon Pr., Inc.
—Wounded Heart. 2009. 116p. pap. 11.99 *(978-1-60791-408-2(5))* Xulon Pr., Inc.
Redmond, Stephen. So Great a Cloud: A Record of Christian Witness. 2010. (ENG.). 176p. pap. 21.95 *(978-1-84730-125-3(8))* Veritas Pubns. IRL. Dist: Dufour Editions, Inc.
Reed, Jimmie. Weathering Transition. 2006. 92p. per. 12.00 *(978-1-931178-27-3(5))* Vision Publishing.
Reed, LaVerne. Mountain Move Around. 2006. pap. 10.99 *(978-1-60034-593-2(0))* Xulon Pr., Inc.
Reed, Leslie. Thinking Well: Phimisms for the Soul. 2009. 100p. pap. 11.49 *(978-1-4389-5767-8(X))* AuthorHouse.
Reed, Robert E. Character Coins: Investing in Significance. 2009. 248p. pap. 15.99 *(978-1-60791-921-6(4))* Xulon Pr., Inc.
Rees, Erik. S. H. A. P. E. Finding & Fulfilling Your Unique Purpose for Life, 1 vol. 2008. (ENG.). 256p. pap. 14.99 *(978-0-310-29248-7(4))* Zondervan.
Rees, Ian. Faith in the Furnace: Understanding God's Purpose in the Trials of Life. 2006. 208p. per. 14.00 *(978-1-84625-044-6(7))* DayOne Pubns. GBR. Dist: STL Distribution North America.
Reese, Jeanene. Bound & Determined: Christian Men & Women in Partnership. 2010. 192p. pap. 14.99 *(978-0-89112-678-2(3)*, Leafwood Pubs.) Abilene Christian Univ. Pr.
Reese, Larry. Being Intimate with God. 2006. 176p. per. 12.99 *(978-1-58169-232-7(3))* Genesis Communications, Inc.
Reese, Leona Amacher. Vimos el Amanecer Por Segunda Vez: Siempre Es Demasiado Pronto para Huir. 2010. (SPA.). 432p. pap. 27.95 *(978-1-61764-012-4(3))* AuthorHouse.
Reese, Pastor James R. 100 Most Asked Questions about the Bible. 2011. 220p. 24.59 ***(978-1-4634-3468-7(5))***; pap. 15.79 ***(978-1-4634-3469-4(3))*** AuthorHouse.
Reeveas, India Anne. My Child, Listen. 2009. 172p. pap. 24.95 *(978-1-60813-117-4(3))* PublishAmerica, Inc.
Reeves, Melissa. God's Love. 2007. 108p. (ENG.). 18.99 *(978-1-60266-733-4(0))*; per. 10.99 *(978-1-60266-732-7(2))* Xulon Pr., Inc.
Reeves, Nancy Christine. A Match Made in Heaven: A Bible-Based Guide to Deepening Your Relationship with God. 2007. 96p. pap. 10.00 *(978-0-687-64371-4(6)*, Dimensions For Living) Abingdon Pr.
Reeves, Rodney. Spirituality According to Paul: Imitating the Apostle of Christ. 2011. (ENG.). 253p. pap. 20.00 ***(978-0-8308-3546-9(1)***, IVP Acad.) InterVarsity Pr.
Register, Margaret A. No Place for Plastic Saints: Earthquakes, Chicken Feet, & Candid Confessions of a Missionary Wife. 2009. 440p. pap. 22.99 *(978-1-60647-976-6(8))* Xulon Pr., Inc.
Rehmann, Scott & Rehmann, Elizabeth. Breaking Generational Curses- Step by Step. 2007. 120p. per. 12.56 *(978-1-4251-0806-3(3))* Trafford Publishing.
Reichert, Conrad A. Bible Foundations for Marriage & Family Living in the 21st Century. 2008. 192p. (ENG.). 21.99 *(978-1-60477-448-1(7))*; per. 13.99 *(978-1-60477-447-4(9))* Xulon Pr., Inc.
Reid, Doreen Lettsome. He's Worthy. 2008. 144p. pap. 13.99 *(978-1-60647-610-9(6))* Xulon Pr., Inc.
Reid, Joyce. The God of Miracles. 2008. 200p. pap. 21.49 *(978-1-4208-0403-4(0))* AuthorHouse.
Reimers, Robin. Jacob's Revelation. 2010. 40p. pap. 16.99 *(978-1-4389-9316-4(1))* AuthorHouse.
Reinglas, Anthony. Unleash Your Vision. 2007. 108p. (ENG.). 18.99 *(978-1-60477-259-3(X))*; per. 10.99 *(978-1-60477-258-6(1))* Xulon Pr., Inc.
Rembert, David E. What's His Name? How We Draw Closer to God by Knowing & Understanding His Names. 2009. 200p. 25.99 *(978-1-61579-261-0(9))*; pap. 15.99 *(978-1-61579-260-3(0))* Xulon Pr., Inc.
Rempel, Robert. Wanted! An Interactive Study in Getting to Know God. 56p. pap. 12.95 *(978-0-921788-55-3(X))* Kindred Productions.
—With the Arms of the Father: A Group Study in Restoring Relationships. 87p. pap. 3.95 *(978-0-921788-29-4(0))*; pap. 10.95 incl. VHS *(978-0-921788-35-5(5))* Kindred Productions.
Ren, C. H. Two Beasts Rising: Book Two of the End Times Series. 2011. 220p. 33.95 *(978-1-4497-1384-3(X))*; pap. 17.95 *(978-1-4497-1385-0(8))* Author Solutions, Inc. (WestBow Pr.).
Ren, Chiang H. At War with the Armies of Darkness. (Christian Mission Ser.). 202p. 12.00 *(978-0-7880-1606-6(7))* CSS Publishing Co.
Rendle, Gilbert R. Journey in the Wilderness: New Life for Mainline Churches. 2010. 176p. pap. 16.00 *(978-1-4267-1065-0(8))* Abingdon Pr.
Renfro, Donna. An Hour with Donn: Minute by Minute Volume I. 2009. 84p. pap. 14.99 *(978-1-4490-0132-2(7))* AuthorHouse.
Renfroe, Anita & Renfroe, John. Duets Itpe, 1 vol. 2010. 256p. pap. *(978-1-4347-0059-9(3))* Kingsway Pubns.
Renich, Jill. Tener y Retener: To Have & to Hold. (SPA.). 184p. *(978-84-7228-124-0(8)*, 220868) Clie, Editorial.
Renner, Marlane. The Elephant in my Living Room. 144p. pap. 9.99 *(978-1-58169-110-8(6)*, Evergreen Pr.) Genesis Communications, Inc.
Renner, Rick. Dressed to Kill: A Biblical Approach to Spiritual Warfare & Armor. 2007. (Illus.). 465p. 24.95 *(978-0-9779459-0-0(1))* Teach All Nations.
—Paid in Full: An In-Depth at the Defining Moments of Christ's Passion. 2008. 312p. 19.95 *(978-0-9779459-1-7(X))* Teach All Nations.
Reno, Carolyn. Almost... but Lost.Tr. of Casi... Pero Perdida. pap. 0.59 *(978-1-56632-013-9(5))* Revival Literature.
Renwick, John. Reformation to Restoration: The Restoration Ideal in Europe from the 16th to the 19th Century & the Rise of New Testament Churches in Britain & America with a Special Focus on Scotland. 2010. 168p. pap. 15.95 *(978-1-4502-2411-6(3))* iUniverse, Inc.
Replies to Essays & Reviews with a Preface by the Lord Bishop of Oxford: And Letters from the Radcliffe Observer & the Reader in Geology In. 2006. 448p. per. 26.99 *(978-1-4255-4944-2(6))* MPublishing.
Restagno, Allison C. Modern-Day Miracles: 50 Real-Life Stories of Divine Encounters, Supernatural Healings, Heaven & Hell Experiences, & More. 2011. 348p. ***(978-0-7684-3733-1(4))***; ***(978-0-7684-3732-4(6))*** Destiny Image Pubs.
Restoration Academy Staff. Urban Shepherds. 2009. 220p. pap. 15.99 *(978-1-60791-177-7(9))* Xulon Pr., Inc.
Retson, Christine. Truth or Perception. 2008. 308p. pap. 17.49 *(978-1-4343-5858-5(5))* AuthorHouse.
Retzlaff, Georg. Why the Cross? Meditations for Holy Week. 2010. 108p. pap. 12.49 *(978-1-4490-6441-9(8))* AuthorHouse.
Reuschling, Wyndy Corbin, et al. Becoming Whole & Holy: An Integrative Conversation about Christian Formation. 2011. (C). pap. 25.00 *(978-0-8010-3925-6(8))* Baker Academic.
Reuss, Edith A. Luz en la Oscuridad: A Glimpse of Sunshine. (SPA.). *(978-84-7645-214-1(4)*, 223255) Clie, Editorial.
Rev. Chancey M. Smith. All Men Are Dogs: Created to Be Kings. 2009. 124p. 21.99 *(978-1-4389-6597-0(4))*; pap. 14.99 *(978-1-4389-6598-7(2))* AuthorHouse.
Rev. J. A. Jefferson. Bible Study Guide: Man's Relationship to His Eternal God. 2009. 184p. pap. 19.49 *(978-1-4389-0411-5(8))* AuthorHouse.
Reverend Lyndon Prior Mottley. In Search of the Sabbath. 2010. 76p. pap. 10.95 *(978-1-4502-0143-8(1))* iUniverse, Inc.
Revival of Hope No 2 Wording. 2.88 *(978-0-687-03856-5(1))* Abingdon Pr.
Reyes, E. Christopher. In His Name. 2010. 696p. (ENG.). 36.49 *(978-1-4520-2149-2(X))*; pap. 25.99 *(978-1-4520-2148-5(1))* AuthorHouse.
Reyneveld, Clarence. Unlocking Galatians Again. 2008. 408p. 33.99 *(978-1-60791-019-0(5))* Xulon Pr., Inc.
Reynolds, Jim. Be My Disciples. 2010. 212p. pap. 19.99 *(978-1-4520-5364-6(2))* AuthorHouse.
Reynolds Jr., David L. God's Preparations for His Heros. 2009. 112p. 19.99 *(978-1-60791-537-9(5))* Xulon Pr., Inc.
Reynolds, Kent. The Will of God: Developing the Ability to Discern & Walk in God's Purpose for Your Life. 2008. (ENG.). 240p. 17.99 *(978-1-59979-310-8(5)*, Creation Hse.) Charisma Media.
Reynolds, Susan. The Struggling Believer. 2007. 184p. 21.99 *(978-1-60266-825-6(6))* Xulon Pr., Inc.
Rhay, Christine. The Bride Made Ready. 2011. pap. 15.95 *(978-0-7414-6257-2(5))* Infinity Publishing.
Rhea, Ronald D. How to Finish First by Being. 2008. 192p. (ENG.). 21.99 *(978-1-60266-996-3(1))*; per. 13.99 *(978-1-60266-995-6(3))* Xulon Pr., Inc.
Rhodes, Angela. Start a Ministry to Youth. (But I Don't Know How to... Ser.). 48p. pap. 4.95 *(978-0-87162-876-3(7)*, D7535) Warner Pr. Pubs.
Rhodes, Daphne A. My God; His Seasons. 2007. 102p. pap. 10.95 *(978-0-7414-4297-0(3))* Infinity Publishing.
Rhodes, Milton L. Survival at the Intersection of Faith & the Intellect: Lessons Learned from a Pastor & a Professor. 2010. (ENG.). 68p. pap. 12.49 *(978-1-4490-8288-8(2))* AuthorHouse.
Rhodes, Ron. The Middle East Conflict: What You Need to Know. 2009. (Quick Reference Guides). 3.99 *(978-0-7369-2649-2(6))* Harvest Hse. Pubs.
—The Wonder of Heaven: A Biblical Tour of Our Eternal Home. 2009. 272p. pap. 13.99 *(978-0-7369-2456-6(6))* Harvest Hse. Pubs.
Rial, Dickson H. Honey from the Rock. 2009. pap. *(978-1-61584-402-9(3))* Independent Pub.
Rica & Charles Basel. Sweet Fire. 2011. 148p. 29.99 ***(978-1-4628-9330-0(9))***; pap. 19.99 ***(978-1-4628-9331-7(7))*** Xlibris Corp.
Rice, Alice Caldwell Hegan. My Pillow Book. 17.95 *(978-0-8488-1134-1(8))* Amereon LTD.
Rice, Gary. Understanding Provision, Communication, & Death. 2008. (Gifts of Freedom Ser.). pap. 15.99 *(978-0-7684-2723-3(1))* Destiny Image Pubs.
Rice, Greg. Unwrapping Increase, Destiny, Relationships, God, & the Gifts of the Spirit: The Gifts of Freedom Book 3. 3rd rev. ed. 2009. (Gifts of Freedom Ser.). pap. 15.99 *(978-0-7684-2746-2(0))* Destiny Image Pubs.
Rice, Helen Steiner & Publishing, Barbour. Celebrating Christmas Every Day. 2009. (ENG.). 96p. 9.97 *(978-1-60260-579-4(3)*, Barbour Bks.) Barbour Publishing, Inc.
Rice, Jesse. The Church of Facebook: How the Hyperconnected Are Redefining Community, 1 vol. 2009. (ENG.). 240p. pap. 12.99 *(978-1-4347-6534-5(2))* Cook, David C.
Rice, John R. Seven Secrets of a Happy, Prosperous Christian Life. 2007. (ENG.). 68p. per. 16.95 *(978-1-4325-6616-6(4))* Kessinger Publishing, LLC.
Rice Jr., Carl. A Voice from Heaven, 1 vol. 2009. 61p. pap. 16.95 *(978-1-60703-905-1(2))* PublishAmerica, Inc.
Rice, Julie. Extreme Life Makeover. 2008. 148p. pap. 15.95 *(978-0-9821153-3-6(4))* Living Waters Publishing Co.
Rice, Wayne, ed. There's a Teenager in My House: 101 Questions Parents Ask. 2008. (ENG., Illus.). 196p. pap. 15.00 *(978-0-8308-3491-4(5)*, IVP Bks.) InterVarsity Pr.
Rich, Sharon D. C. Unity. 2008. 124p. per. 10.99 *(978-1-60477-275-3(1))* Xulon Pr., Inc.
Richard S. Hipps. The Focused Life: The Beatitudes for Everyday Living. 2009. 108p. 22.95 *(978-1-4401-8090-3(3))*; pap. 12.95 *(978-1-4401-8088-0(1))* iUniverse, Inc.
Richards, Jay W. Money, Greed, & God: Why Capitalism Is the Solution & Not the Problem. 2009. (ENG.). 272p. 24.99 *(978-0-06-137561-3(6)*, HarperOne) HarperCollins Pubs.
Richards, Michelle. Trauma to Treasure. 2008. 156p. pap. 13.99 *(978-1-60647-474-7(X))* Xulon Pr., Inc.
Richards, Mitchell. Definitive Blurs. 2010. 225p. pap. 15.00 *(978-0-557-35150-3(2))* Lulu Enterprises Inc.
Richardson, Carol. Por que Luchamos Tanto?Tr. of Why Do We Struggle So? (SPA.). pap. 8.99 *(978-1-884369-93-3(6))* McDougal Publishing Co.
Richardson, Corliss B. Treasures in the Word. 2008. 156p. 22.99 *(978-1-60647-757-1(9))*; pap. 14.99 *(978-1-60647-756-4(0))* Xulon Pr., Inc.
Richardson, Joan H. Theunion. 2011. 444p. 34.99 ***(978-1-61215-535-7(9))*** Xulon Pr., Inc.
Richardson, L. A. Kimo. When the Ordinary Won't Do! 2007. 96p. per. 9.99 *(978-1-60266-062-5(X))* Xulon Pr., Inc.
Richardson, Paul Andrew. A Certain Risk: Living Your Faith at the Edge. 2010. (ENG.). 224p. pap. 12.99 *(978-0-310-29132-9(1))* Zondervan.
Richardson, Robert. Principles of the Reformation. 102p. pap. 9.95 *(978-0-9714289-6-6(4)*, Leafwood Pubs.) Abilene Christian Univ. Pr.
Richardson, Ronald W. Becoming Your Best: A Self-Help Guide for Thinking People. 2008. (Living Well Ser.). 184p. pap. 14.99 *(978-0-8066-8052-1(0)*, Augsburg Bks.) Augsburg Fortress, Pubs.
Richardson, Sandy. Soul Hunger. 2006. (ENG.). per. 14.99 *(978-1-932124-76-7(4))* ACW Pr.
Richardson Sr, Lawrence G. Abiding in the Mountain of God: Survival Strategies for a New Breed of Leaders. 2008. 60p. per. 14.95 *(978-1-4327-2073-5(2))* Outskirts Pr., Inc.
Richardson, V. Riley & Neufeld, Henry E. Disciples: Jesus with Us. l.t. ed. 2007. 84p. per. 7.99 *(978-1-893729-49-0(4))* Energion Pubns.
Richburg, C. Natasha. The Truth about the Lie I Live. 2010. (ENG.). 184p. pap. 12.99 *(978-0-9826196-9-8(3))* St. Paul Pr.
Richesin, Terry. Ticket to Heaven. 2006. (ENG.). 21.99 *(978-1-60034-746-7(0))*; pap. 13.99 *(978-1-60034-420-6(8))* Xulon Pr., Inc.
Richey, Jr. Survival. 2008. 156p. pap. 14.99 *(978-1-60647-598-0(3))* Xulon Pr., Inc.
Richman, Larry. Learning Through Life's Trials. 2007. (ENG., Illus.). 32p. pap. 4.95 *(978-0-941846-17-2(2))* Century Publishing.
Richter, Corie. God Has a Sense of Humor. 2007. (ENG.). 144p. per. 24.95 *(978-1-4241-7362-4(0))* PublishAmerica, Inc.
Rickey, Brett. Stay in the Yard: Rethinking the Limits of Personal Freedom. 2009. (ENG.). 128p. pap. 11.99 *(978-0-8341-2437-0(8)*, 9780834124370) Beacon Hill Pr. of Kansas City.
Riddering, Teri S. Rising to Everlasting Life. 2011. 256p. pap. 16.99 ***(978-1-61379-720-4(6))*** Xulon Pr., Inc.
Ridenour, Fritz. Como Ser Cristiano en Iglesia: How to Be a Christian. (SPA.). 112p. *(978-84-7228-159-2(0)*, 220170) Clie, Editorial.
—Como Ser Cristiano en un Mundo No: How to Be a Christian. (SPA.). 104p. *(978-84-7228-147-9(7)*, 220172) Clie, Editorial.
—Cual Es la Diferencia? So What's the Difference? (SPA.). 192p. *(978-84-7228-307-7(0)*, 220222) Clie, Editorial.
—Si Yo Fuera . . . It's Your Move. (SPA.). 176p. *(978-84-7228-180-6(9)*, 220840) Clie, Editorial.
Ridley, Kirl. The Voice of God. 2008. 96p. pap. 16.50 *(978-0-557-00739-4(9))* Lulu Enterprises Inc.
Ries, Xavier. Paul's Proclamation of the Gospel. 2007. *(978-0-9773829-4-1(X)*, Simple Truths) Calvary Chapel Pasadena.
Riffe, Clinton. One Wind. 2011. 218p. pap. 15.99 ***(978-1-61379-312-1(X))*** Xulon Pr., Inc.
Riggins, Mary Beth. Saving Our Singles - 101 Ways the Church Can Reach the Single Parent. 2008. 96p. pap. 10.95 *(978-0-9816172-5-1(5))* Westview Publishing Co., Inc.
Riggs, Norma K. God's Providence & Life's Lessons. 2009. 348p. pap. 18.99 *(978-1-61579-517-8(0))* Xulon Pr., Inc.
Rigney, Donna. Abused by the Church: From Victim to Victor. 2009. 236p. pap. 15.99 *(978-1-61579-445-4(X))* Xulon Pr., Inc.
Riley, Christopher. Avoiding the Dangers of Untrue Books. 2011. 376p. pap. 29.95 ***(978-1-4560-8035-8(0))*** PublishAmerica, Inc.
Riley, Christopher. When Conscience Speaks. 2007. 181p. pap. 24.95 *(978-1-60441-685-5(8))* PublishAmerica, Inc.
Riley, Diane M. Escaping Through Prayer. 2008. 92p. pap. 11.95 *(978-0-595-51624-7(6))* iUniverse, Inc.
Riley, Joy. Get Your JOY in the Morning! 2011. pap. 12.99 *(978-1-61739-265-8(0))* Tate Publishing & Enterprises, LLC.
Rinehart, Bill. Expectantseed. 2007. pap. 10.99 *(978-1-60266-071-7(9))* Xulon Pr., Inc.
Rinehart, Joseph & Rinehart, Brenda. Moving from Judgment: How to Have an Open Heart in a Closed World. 2011. pap. 13.99 ***(978-1-61777-620-5(3))*** Tate Publishing & Enterprises, LLC.
Rinehart, Paula. What's He Really Thinking? How to Be a Relational Genius with the Man in Your Life, 0 vols. 2009. 224p. pap. 14.99 *(978-0-8499-1880-3(4))* Nelson, Thomas Inc.
Ringgold, John. Your Personal Journey into Miracle Faith. 2011. 96p. pap. 10.99 *(978-1-61215-793-1(9))* Xulon Pr., Inc.
Ringma, Charles. Resist the Powers with Jacques Ellul. 2010. *(978-1-57383-423-0(8))* Regent College Publishing.
Rinker, Roger R. On the Road To: An Amazing True Story. 2009. 212p. pap. 15.99 *(978-1-60791-773-1(4))* Xulon Pr., Inc.

C

Rios, Angel L. Arbustus. 2009. 136p. pap. 14.99 *(978-1-60791-249-1(X))* Xulon Pr., Inc.

Ripka, Chuck. God Out of the Box: How You Can Change Your World! 2007. (ENG.). 224p. 19.99 *(978-1-59979-056-5(4)*, Charisma Hse.) Charisma Media.

Ristow, Augie. Agape. 2008. 140p. pap. 13.99 *(978-1-60477-829-8(6))* Xulon Pr., Inc.

Ritari, Katja. Saints & Sinners in Early Christian Ireland: Moral Theology in the Lives of Saints Brigit & Columba. 2010. (Studia Traditionis Theologiae Ser.). (ENG.). 202p. (C). pap. 102.00 *(978-2-503-53315-5(9))* Brepols Pubs. BEL. Dist: ISD.

Ritchie, George. Regreso del Futuro (Return from Tomorrow) (SPA.). 144p. *(978-84-7228-535-4(9)*, 220752) Clie, Editorial.

Rivadeneira, Caryn Dahlstrand & Rivadeneira, Caryn D. Mama's Got a Fake I.D: How to Reveal the Real You Behind All That Mom. 2009. (ENG.). 224p. 13.99 *(978-1-4000-7493-8(2)*, WaterBrook Pr.) Doubleday Religious Publishing Group, The.

Rivera, Elisa. Thank God for Paper: Reflections of a Broken Spirit. 2008. 92p. pap. 10.49 *(978-1-4389-2126-6(8))* AuthorHouse.

Rivera, Jeannette. The Fruit of the Spirit: How They Grow in My Christian Life. 2011. 60p. pap. 15.99 ***(978-1-4628-8669-2(8))*** Xlibris Corp.

Rivera, Victor Manuel. En Busca de la Verdadera Libertad. 2010. 124p. pap. 11.99 *(978-1-60957-599-1(7))* Xulon Pr., Inc.

Rivers, Francine. Una Voz en el Viento.Tr. of Voice in the Wind. (SPA.). 526p. 14.99 *(978-0-7899-0087-6(4)*, 497468) Editorial Unilit.

Rivers, Kea. Mirror Mirror: Seeing Pass the Reflection. 2008. 116p. pap. 10.99 *(978-1-60647-024-4(8))* Xulon Pr., Inc.

Roark, M. A. Wide or Narrow: What You Believe Chooses Your Path, 1 vol. 2010. 108p. pap. 19.95 *(978-1-4489-4668-6(9))* PublishAmerica, Inc.

Robaine, Ruth. Our Christian Journey: Jesus answered, I am the way & the truth & the life. No one come to the Father except through Me. 2009. 56p. pap. 13.49 *(978-1-4389-7298-5(9))* AuthorHouse.

Robb, Corina. The Mind's Ravisher. 2007. 100p. per. 9.99 *(978-1-60266-303-9(3))* Xulon Pr., Inc.

Robbin-Coker, Olu. Manifesto: Radical Truth for a Christian Revolution. 2008. 200p. pap. 14.99 *(978-1-57658-471-2(2))* YWAM Publishing.

Robbins, Brian. The House on Neptune. 2009. 216p. pap. 15.99 *(978-1-60791-445-7(X))* Xulon Pr., Inc.

Robbins, Stephen W. Transforming Beliefs: Spiritual Guidance Through the Apostles' Creed. 2006. 138p. pap. 17.00 *(978-1-59752-631-9(2)*, Wipf and Stock) Wipf & Stock Pubs.

—Transforming Habits: Spiritual Guidance through the Sermon on the Mount. 2009. 186p. pap. 21.00 *(978-1-60608-323-9(6)*, Wipf and Stock) Wipf & Stock Pubs.

Roberson, Carroll. How to Enjoy Jesus. 2007. 144p. pap. 12.95 *(978-1-933641-24-9(X))* Bible Belt Pubns.

Roberson, Roger L. & Roberson, Roger L., Jr. The Bible & the Black Man: Breaking the Chains of Prejudice. 2007. 172p. per. 12.99 *(978-1-60247-245-7(9))* Tate Publishing & Enterprises, LLC.

Roberts, Daniel. Always Being Ready. 2009. 196p. pap. 15.99 *(978-1-934769-25-6(8))* McDougal & Assocs.

—Never Alone. 2008. 216p. pap. 15.99 *(978-1-934769-13-3(4))* McDougal & Assocs.

Roberts, Edwinna. Has God Forgotten? A Practical Guide for Christians Effected by Learning Disabilities. 2008. 128p. pap. 15.95 *(978-1-4327-3246-2(3))* Outskirts Pr., Inc.

Roberts, John. Words of Life: The Seven Spirits of God. 2010. 96p. pap. 12.99 *(978-1-4520-6945-6(X))* AuthorHouse.

Roberts, Karen Lynn. The Day God Pulled My Truck Out of the Mud: And Other True Stories. 2007. 80p. per. 9.95 *(978-0-595-47182-9(X))* iUniverse, Inc.

Roberts, Kenneth J. & Waters, Anna M. Shepherd's Pie. Date not set. 217p. (Orig.). pap. 9.95 *(978-0-9610984-4-5(9))* PAX Tapes, Inc.

Roberts, Kyle & Plimpton, Beverly. Two, Please! How to Disciple Another to Maturity in Christ. 2008. 244p. pap. 16.95 *(978-1-4389-3952-0(3))* AuthorHouse.

Roberts, Martin C. Restoration of Men: Key to the Transformation of the Nations. 2007. 148p. per. 14.95 *(978-0-595-47295-6(8))* iUniverse, Inc.

Roberts, Mattie. Theresa Johnson: The Search for Her Beloved. 2011. (ENG.). 104p. pap. 14.95 ***(978-1-4327-7959-7(1))*** Outskirts Pr., Inc.

Roberts, Ricky & Roberts, Ricky, III. What Really Matters? 2006. 78p. per. 8.95 *(978-1-59886-372-7(X))* Tate Publishing & Enterprises, LLC.

Roberts, Thomas Keith. Why God Waits for You to Pray. 2007. 152p. per. 13.99 *(978-1-60477-476-4(2))* Xulon Pr., Inc.

Roberts, U. D. Practice of Quietness. 2007. per. *(978-1-59581-355-8(1)*, Brentwood Christian Pr.) Brentwood Communications Group.

Roberts, Vaughan. Battles Christians Face. 2007. (ENG.). 144p. per. 12.99 *(978-1-85078-728-0(X))* Authentic Media.

Robertson, Cassandra. How to Submit to Your Husband Joyfully: Building a Servant's Heart Toward Your Husband. 2010. (ENG.). 80p. pap. 7.99 *(978-1-61638-152-3(3)*, Creation Hse.) Charisma Media.

Robertson, Michael. Conquerors for Christ. 2007. 220p. 24.99 *(978-1-60266-572-9(9))* 2007. 220p. per. 14.99 *(978-1-60266-571-2(0))* 2006. (ENG.). 24.99 *(978-1-60034-504-3(2))* 2006. pap. 14.99 *(978-1-60034-503-6(4))* Xulon Pr., Inc.

Robertson, Michael James. Conquerors for Christ. 2008. 256p. 26.99 *(978-1-60791-057-2(8))*; 256p. pap. 16.99 *(978-1-60791-056-5(X))*; 368p. 31.99 *(978-1-60647-188-3(0))* Xulon Pr., Inc.

—Conquerors for Christ: The Great Apostasy - Mutiny & High Treason Against Jesus Christ. 2008. 368p. pap. 19.99 *(978-1-60647-187-6(2))* Xulon Pr., Inc.

Robertson, Norman. Tithing: God's Financial Plan. pap. 6.00 *(978-0-620-10675-7(1))* Robertson, Norman Ministries.

—Walking in Victory. pap. 20.00 *(978-0-9636898-3-2(5))* Robertson, Norman Ministries.

—Winners in Christ. pap. 12.00 *(978-0-9636898-4-9(3))* Robertson, Norman Ministries.

Robertson, Pat. Bring It On, 0 vols. 2008. 352p. pap. 18.99 *(978-0-7852-9656-0(5))* Nelson, Thomas Inc.

Robinson, Andra. The Reflected Throne: The Story of a Father's Love. 2007. 48p. pap. 16.95 *(978-1-60474-021-9(3))* PublishAmerica, Inc.

Robinson, Barbara J. Travailing: A Guide to Spiritual Birthing & Breakthrough. 2011. 60p. pap. 9.95 ***(978-1-4620-2901-3(9))*** iUniverse, Inc.

Robinson, Brenda & Cason, Brooke. Restructuring Your Word Young Adult Edition. 2008. 120p. pap. 12.99 *(978-1-60647-135-7(X))* Xulon Pr., Inc.

Robinson, Brenda J. Restructuring Your World. 2007. 96p. per. 12.99 *(978-1-60477-487-0(8))* Xulon Pr., Inc.

Robinson, Chris & Robinson, Jim. Chosen in the Furnace: A Testimony of Survival & a Guide to All Those Who Desire to Be Encouragers. 2011. 180p. pap. 13.95 ***(978-1-61507-767-0(7))*** Cross Bks. Publishing.

—Chosen in the Furnace: A Testimony of Survival & A Guide to All Those Who Desire to Be Encouragers. 2011. 180p. 30.95 ***(978-1-61507-768-7(5))*** Cross Bks. Publishing.

Robinson, Connie. How Big Is Your God? 2011. 216p. pap. ***(978-1-77069-374-6(2))*** Word Alive Pr.

Robinson, Cynthia. A True Sister in the Sisterhood. 2009. 70p. pap. 15.99 *(978-1-4415-0618-4(7))* Xlibris Corp.

Robinson, Dan And Brenda J. & Cason, Labron and Brooke. Time in the Garden: Making His Heart Mine. 2010. 412p. 31.99 *(978-1-4490-5615-5(6))*; pap. 19.99 *(978-1-4490-5614-8(8))* AuthorHouse.

Robinson, Dick. More Than We Can Imagine. 2008. 144p. pap. 13.99 *(978-1-60477-848-9(2))* Xulon Pr., Inc.

Robinson, Earl. Marks of a Christian. pap. 2.99 *(978-0-88019-179-1(1))* Schmul Publishing Co., Inc.

Robinson, Edward. Physical Geography of the Holy Land. 2009. (Illus.). 270p. pap. 21.14 *(978-1-150-69297-0(9))* General Bks. LLC.

Robinson, Elaine A. These Three: The Theological Virtues of Faith, Hope, & Love. 2010. 188p. pap. 22.00 *(978-1-60899-233-1(0)*, Wipf and Stock) Wipf & Stock Pubs.

Robinson, Evangelist Chatauna. The True Road to Salvation: Get Right, Church, & Let's Go Home, 1 vol. 2009. 224p. pap. 24.95 *(978-1-60813-695-7(7))* PublishAmerica, Inc.

Robinson, Evelina M. Let's Act It Out: Character Building Skits & Plays for the Christian Community. 2007. 140p. per. 10.95 *(978-1-4327-0498-8(2))* Outskirts Pr., Inc.

Robinson, Felicita. Seven Letters to Heaven: A True Story of Faith & Answered Prayers. 2010. 124p. 23.95 *(978-1-4502-2919-7(0))*; pap. 13.95 *(978-1-4502-2920-3(4))* iUniverse, Inc.

Robinson, Glacia. Sheer Inspiration. 2010. 144p. 29.99 *(978-1-4535-4192-0(6))*; pap. 19.99 *(978-1-4535-4191-3(8))* Xlibris Corp.

Robinson, Hopie M. How to Be a Virtuous Woman in Today's Society. 2006. 182p. per. *(978-1-60002-177-0(8)*, 4081) Mountain Valley Publishing, LLC.

Robinson, Jacqueline R. Life's Lessons for the Young at Heart. 2009. 140p. pap. 14.99 *(978-1-60791-547-8(2))* Xulon Pr., Inc.

Robinson, James E. COming Home to a Place Called Hope. 2008. per. *(978-0-9742248-2-4(0))* Good Apple Pr.

Robinson, James E. & Thomas, Sherry G. A Companion Guide for Your Personal Journey to Hope. 2008. 200p. per. *(978-0-9742248-3-1(9))* Good Apple Pr.

Robinson, Janai. In His Presence: Intimate Moments Between a Woman & Her Lord. 2007. 76p. per. 16.95 *(978-1-4241-9165-9(3))* PublishAmerica, Inc.

Robinson, Joanne. When Loving Him Means Hurting Me. 2008. 144p. 22.99 *(978-1-60647-867-7(2))* Xulon Pr., Inc.

Robinson, Jon. Revelation: The Soul Story. 2010. pap. 14.99 *(978-1-61663-208-3(9))* Tate Publishing & Enterprises, LLC.

Robinson Jr., David. Lord, Make Me into an Altar. 2010. 206p. 25.99 *(978-1-61579-292-4(9))* Xulon Pr., Inc.

Robinson, Larry J. More Than the Gift. 2008. 120p. pap. 13.95 *(978-1-59330-546-8(X))* Aventine Pr.

Robinson, Linda S. The Power of Love for Me While yet a Sinner. 2008. 292p. per. 13.95 *(978-1-4327-0081-2(2))* Outskirts Pr., Inc.

Robinson, Melinda L. Living to Live Again. 2008. 176p. pap. 14.99 *(978-1-60647-546-1(0))* Xulon Pr., Inc.

Robinson, Millicent. The Journeys of Faith, Hope, & Trust. 2008. 160p. pap. 10.95 *(978-1-4327-2291-3(3))* Outskirts Pr., Inc.

Robinson, Mimsie. The Anatomy of Sexual Integrity::A Strategy for Personal Victory & Discipleship. 2008. 184p. pap. 13.99 *(978-1-60477-944-8(6))* Xulon Pr., Inc.

Robinson, Rigel B. Living in Covenant. 2009. 108p. pap. 15.99 *(978-1-4363-8036-2(7))* Xlibris Corp.

Robinson, Robert. The Authority of the Kingdom. 2007. 82p. (YA). per. *(978-0-9747893-7-8(2))* Robinson, Robert.

Robinson, Simon & Robinson, Hazel. Pickups for Hiccups: Big Solutions for Small Problems. 2008. 127p. pap. 11.99 *(978-1-84030-194-6(5)*, Ambassador International) Emerald Hse. Group, Inc.

Robinson, Tri. Rooted in Good Soil: Cultivating & Sustaining Authentic Discipleship. 2010. (Shapevine Ser.). 176p. pap. 14.99 *(978-0-8010-7253-6(0))* Baker Bks.

—Small Footprint, Big Handprint: How to Live Simply & Love Extravagantly. 2007. 159p. per. 14.99 *(978-0-9786394-8-8(0))* Ampelon Publishing, LLC.

Robison, Betty. Free to be Me, 0 vols. 2009. 208p. pap. 14.99 *(978-0-9800638-8-2(4))* Nelson, Thomas Inc.

Robison, James. The Life You're Fighting For, 0 vols. 2009. 160p. 17.99 *(978-0-9800638-7-5(6))* Nelson, Thomas Inc.

Rochester, Valeria. Holy Spirit & You. 2010. 185p. pap. 15.76 *(978-0-557-09464-6(X))* Lulu Enterprises Inc.

Rockett, S. E. Life's Not Fair, but God Is Good! 2008. 208p. per. 14.99 *(978-1-60477-594-5(7))* Xulon Pr., Inc.

Rodd, Cyril S. Thinking Things Through No. 4: Why Evil & Suffering? 112p. 9.00 *(978-0-7162-0518-0(1))* Epworth Pr., The GBR. Dist: Morehouse Publishing.

Roddick, Paul M. Faith, Reason & Common Sense: An Exploration of the Historical & Contemporary Role of Religion in Human Affairs. 2010. 336p. (ENG.). 28.49 *(978-1-4490-7333-6(6))*; pap. 17.99 *(978-1-4490-7332-9(8))* AuthorHouse.

Rodgers, Beverly & Rodgers, Tom. The Singlehood Phenomenon: 10 Brutally Honest Reasons People Aren't Getting Married. 2006. (Navigators Reference Library). (ENG.). 192p. per. 12.99 *(978-1-57683-884-6(6))* NavPress Publishing Group.

Rodgers, Felecia. Is Christ Divided? A Biblical View of the Local Church-para Church Anomaly. 2011. 164p. 30.95 ***(978-1-4497-1739-1(X))***; pap. 13.95 ***(978-1-4497-1737-7(3))*** Author Solutions, Inc. (WestBow Pr.).

Rodricks, Marie. Magnify the LORD. 2010. 216p. pap. 14.49 *(978-1-4490-0294-7(3))* AuthorHouse.

Rodriguez, Diego. Beware of that Woman, Jezebel: An Important Guide for Everyone Interested in Protecting Their Walk with God. 2007. per. 7.95 *(978-0-9788829-5-2(4))* Sound Alive Publishing.

Rodriguez, J. L. Random Reflections of A Recycled Catholic. 2009. 104p. pap. 12.95 *(978-1-4327-4918-7(8))* Outskirts Pr., Inc.

Roe, Steven, ed. Matthew: A Catholic Guide for Personal Study & Faith Sharing. 2008. (God's Living Word Ser.). 151p. pap. 12.95 *(978-1-59325-092-8(4))* Word Among Us Pr.

Roehr, Merle. There Came a Child: Insights into Christian Childcare. 2010. 108p. 21.49 *(978-1-4490-7962-8(8))*; pap. 10.99 *(978-1-4490-7961-1(X))* AuthorHouse.

Roellig, Harold F. The More Excellent Way: 2000 Years of Jesus' New Way of Life. 2006. 527p. per. 24.95 *(978-0-9779853-0-2(X))* Crucifer Pr.

Roes, Gina. The Art of Breathing. 2010. 182p. pap. 14.99 *(978-1-60957-571-7(7))* Xulon Pr., Inc.

Roger Setterdahl. View from the Barn Door. 2009. 248p. pap. 19.95 *(978-1-4269-1758-5(9))* Trafford Publishing.

Roger Walton Staff. The Reflective Disciple. 2010. (Illus.). xx, 181p. pap. *(978-0-7162-0648-4(X))* Epworth Pr., The.

Rogers, Adrian. What Every Christian Ought to Know Day by Day: Essential Truths for Growing Your Faith. 2008. (ENG.). 416p. 14.99 *(978-0-8054-4800-9(4)*, B&H Bks.) B&H Publishing Group.

Rogers, Donna M. Shattered Dreams - Wake up America Before It Is too Late! The Solution for a Nation in Crisis. 2009. 152p. pap. 14.99 *(978-1-60791-748-9(3))* Xulon Pr., Inc.

Rogers, Eddie T. Supernatural: Living under an Open Heaven. 2007. 128p. per. 12.99 *(978-0-9777053-2-0(3))* McDougal & Assocs.

Rogers, Ivan. Judas Iscariot: Revisited & Restored. 2008. 144p. pap. 14.99 *(978-1-60647-809-7(5))* Xulon Pr., Inc.

Rogers, Jonathan. Take a Closer Look for Teens: Uncommon & Unexpected Insights That Are Real, Relevant & Ready to Change Your Life. 2007. (ENG., Illus.). 320p. pap. 14.99 *(978-1-4165-4214-8(0)*, Howard Bks.) Howard Books.

Rogers, Joyce & Broadman and Holman Publishers Staff. Grace for the Widow: A Journey Through the Fog of Loss. 2009. (ENG.). 128p. pap. 10.99 *(978-0-8054-4846-7(2)*, B&H Bks.) B&H Publishing Group.

Rogers, Kathleen E. A Book of Prayers: Volume I. 2007. pap. 10.00 *(978-0-8059-7416-4(4))* Dorrance Publishing Co., Inc.

Rogers, Kevin. Just Hit the Ball: The Path from Despair to Freedom. 2009. 168p. pap. 12.99 *(978-1-60696-964-9(1))* Tate Publishing & Enterprises, LLC.

Rogers, Nicholas. Unheard Voices. 2011. 580p. pap. 23.99 ***(978-1-4568-5390-7(2))*** Xlibris Corp.

Rogers, Rich. Next Level Living: Are you ready for God's great Adventure? 2008. (ENG., Illus.). 224p. pap. 14.99 *(978-1-59979-197-5(8)*, Charisma Hse.) Charisma Media.

Rogers, Steven. Quit 'Going' to Church... 2007. 168p. per. 13.99 *(978-1-60266-176-9(6))* Xulon Pr., Inc.

Rogers, Susan. Born to Laugh. 2007. per. 7.00 *(978-0-9792422-3-6(1))* Health For The World.

Rogness, Michael. Lord, Help My Unbelief: Experiencing God Through Faith. 2008. 150p. pap. 19.00 *(978-1-60608-051-1(2))* Wipf & Stock Pubs.

Rohde, Chuck. A Taste for Fear. 2011. 166p. pap. 24.95 ***(978-1-4560-0199-5(X))*** PublishAmerica, Inc.

Roitto, Rikard. Behaving As a Christ-Believer: A Cognitive Perspective on Identity & Behavior Norms in Ephesians. 2011. pap. 39.95 ***(978-1-57506-814-5(1))*** Eisenbrauns, Inc.

Rolle, Richard. The Form of Perfect Living & Other Prose Treatises. 2011. 92p. ***(978-1-84902-359-7(X))*** Benediction Classics.

Rollins, Barbara B. A Cloud of Witnesses: Two Big Books & Us. 2011. 232p. pap. 14.00 ***(978-0-9826243-6-4(0)***, Eagle Wings Pr.) Silver Boomer Bks.

Rollins, Eugene C. Grace Is Not a Blue-Eyed Blonde: Grace Is the Joyous Unmerited Blessing of God. 2008. 164p. pap. 12.00 *(978-1-4389-2790-9(8))* AuthorHouse.

Rollins, John S. The P Attitudes. 2009. 192p. pap. 14.99 *(978-1-60791-248-4(1))* Xulon Pr., Inc.

Rollins, Peter. The Fidelity of Betrayal: Towards a Church Beyond Belief. 2008. 196p. pap. 19.95 *(978-1-55725-560-0(1))*; (ENG.). 164p. pap. 19.95 *(978-1-55275-560-0(6))* Paraclete Pr., Inc.

—How (Not) to Speak of God. 2006. (ENG., Illus.). 144p. (gr. 13). pap. 19.99 *(978-1-55725-505-1(9))* Paraclete Pr., Inc.

—Insurrection: To Believe Is Human to Doubt, Divine. 2011. (ENG.). 208p. pap. 16.00 *(978-1-4516-0900-4(0)*, Howard Bks.) Howard Books.

—The Orthodox Heretic: And Other Impossible Tales. 2009. (ENG.). 184p. (gr. 13). 19.99 *(978-1-55725-634-8(9))* Paraclete Pr., Inc.

Rollman, Kimberly. Receive Healing in Jesus Name. 2008. 148p. pap. 14.99 *(978-1-60647-348-1(4))* Xulon Pr., Inc.

Rolnick, Philip A. Person, Grace, & God. 2007. (Sacra Doctrina: Christian Theology for a Postmodern Age Ser.). 270p. per. 28.00 *(978-0-8028-4043-1(4))* Eerdmans, William B. Publishing Co.

Romauldo Turner. The Bible God's Surprising Dual Guide for Either Truth or Deception. 2009. 560p. pap. 69.50 *(978-1-4269-2358-6(9))* Trafford Publishing.

Rona, Josefino T. Divine Indwelling: Key to the Wisdom, Knowledge & Power of God from within Man. 2011. 288p. 29.99 ***(978-1-4535-9015-7(3))***; pap. 19.99 ***(978-1-4535-9014-0(5))*** Xlibris Corp.

Rongstad, L. James. La Logia (The Lodge) (Serie Respuesta). (SPA.). 40p. pap. 2.95 *(978-0-570-04943-2(1)*, 09-2539) Concordia Publishing Hse.

Root, Michael & Buckley, James Joseph. Sharper Than a Two-Edged Sword: Preaching, Teaching, & Living the Bible. Root, Michael & Buckley, James J., eds. 2008. (Illus.). 112p. pap. 16.00 *(978-0-8028-6271-6(3))* Eerdmans, William B. Publishing Co.

The Roots of Christian Freedom. 5.00 *(978-0-687-86110-1(1))* Abingdon Pr.

Roots, Rochelle. Living It Up! Four Lifestyle Keys to Help You Live the Life Jesus Came to Give. 2009. 152p. pap. 14.99 *(978-1-61579-116-3(7))* Xulon Pr., Inc.

Roper, David. Teach Us to Number Our Days. 2008. (ENG.). 288p. 14.99 *(978-1-57293-196-1(5))* Discovery Hse. Pubs.

Roper, Gayle G. A Woman & Her Emotions: What Every Woman Needs to Know. 2007. (ENG.). 192p. per. 14.99 *(978-0-8341-2325-0(8)*, 0834123258) Beacon Hill Pr. of Kansas City.

Rorie, Pastor Loretta. The Christian Family Workbook. 2011. 164p. pap. 20.58 ***(978-1-4567-9970-0(3))*** AuthorHouse.

Ros, Carolyn. Broken Dreams, Fulfilled Promises. 2007. (ENG.). 160p. per. 11.99 *(978-1-57658-457-6(7))* YWAM Publishing.

Roscher, Ellie. How Coffee Saved My Lie: And Other Stories of Stumbling to Grace. 2009. 96p. pap. 10.99 *(978-0-8272-1456-9(1))* Chalice Pr.

Rose, Barbara. Ger over Him FAST. 2009. (ENG.). 100p. pap. 19.95 *(978-0-9788955-6-3(8)*, 978-0-9788955-6-3) Rose Group, The.

—If God Hears Me, I Want an Answer! 2006. per. 19.95 *(978-0-9741457-5-4(0)*, 0974145750) Rose Group, The.

Rose, Claudia. Daughter of Spirit Daughter of Peace: A Prayer for Humanity. pap. 5.95 *(978-0-9673025-9-1(5))* Wyatt-MacKenzie Publishing.

Rose-Heim, Donna. Dream Walking. 2007. 160p. per. 12.95 *(978-1-59858-377-9(8))* Dog Ear Publishing, LLC.

Rose, Jesse. Confessions of Faith. 2009. 116p. pap. 11.99 *(978-1-60791-175-3(2))* Xulon Pr., Inc.

Rose, Linda. 40 Easy Sketches for Busy Churches. 2008. 276p. pap. 20.95 *(978-1-4092-2179-1(2))* Lulu Enterprises Inc.

Rose, Marvin. Strength for Today. 2009. 130p. pap. 21.00 *(978-0-557-24209-2(6))* Lulu Enterprises Inc.

Rose Publishing (Torrance, Calif.) Staff, contrib. by. God in Real Life: Rose Bible Basics, 1 vol. 2009. 128p. pap. *(978-1-59636-325-0(8))* Rose Publishing.

Rose Publishing Staff. Esther. 2009. 14p. 3.99 *(978-1-59636-311-3(8))* Rose Publishing.

—Pop Spirituality & the Truth: The Real Secret of a New Earth. 2009. 14p. 3.99 *(978-1-59636-315-1(0))* Rose Publishing.

—Tough Questions about Christianity. 2009. 14p. 3.99 *(978-1-59636-307-6(X))* Rose Publishing.

Roselli, Robert. The Theory of Livevolution: Great Society of the Un-dead. 2008. 440p. pap. 25.99 *(978-1-60647-281-1(X))* Xulon Pr., Inc.

Rosenau, Jeff. Transfer of Trust. 2008. 112p. pap. *(978-1-55452-304-7(4)*, Guardian Bks.) Essence Publishing.

Roseveare, Helen. Living Fellowship: Willing to Be the Third Side of A Triangle. 2008. (ENG.). 240p. pap. 10.99 *(978-1-84550-351-2(1))* Christian Focus Pubns. GBR. Dist: STL Distribution North America.

—Living Sacrifice: Willing to Be Whittled as an Arrow. 2007. (Living... Ser.). (ENG.). 144p. per. 10.99 *(978-1-84550-294-2(9))* Christian Focus Pubns. GBR. Dist: STL Distribution North America.

Rosies, Toos. Mas Preciosa Que el Oro: More Precious Than Gold. (SPA.). *(978-84-7645-371-1(X)*, 223509) Clie, Editorial.

Ross, David. A Table Before Me. 2007. 316p. (ENG.). 27.99 *(978-1-60266-207-0(X))*; per. 17.99 *(978-1-60266-206-3(1))* Xulon Pr., Inc.

Ross, Forshia. From Forgiveness to Restoration, 1. 2007. 18p. 3.00 *(978-0-9766571-1-8(2))* Treasures From the Heart.

Ross, James. Foundations: A Discipleship Textbook & Tool. 2010. 296p. pap. 22.95 (978-1-4497-0311-0(9), WestBow Pr.) Author Solutions, Inc.

Ross, Janet & McDade, Jeanice. Women of Passions: Ordinary Women Serving an Extraordinary God. 2008. 364p. pap. 19.99 (978-1-60647-246-0(1)) Xulon Pr., Inc.

Ross, Joseph C. The Way to Heaven. 2009. pap. 12.99 (978-1-60696-701-0(0)) Tate Publishing & Enterprises, LLC.

Ross, Melanie, et al. The Serious Business of Worship: Essays in Honour of Bryan D. Spinks. Jones, Simon, ed. 2010. (ENG., Illus.). 256p. 130.00 (978-0-567-03326-0(0), T&T Clark Int'l) Continuum International Publishing Group, Ltd. GBR. Dist: National Bk. Network.

Ross, Steve. Blinded: The Story of Paul the Apostle. 2008. 224p. pap. 20.00 (978-1-59627-091-6(8), Seabury Bks.) Church Publishing, Inc.

Rossi, David M. The World Before a Watching Church: The Biblical Motivation for Living the Christian Life. 2011. 220p. 33.95 **(978-1-4497-2068-1(4))**; pap. 17.95 **(978-1-4497-2069-8(2))** Author Solutions, Inc. (WestBow Pr.).

Rotelle, John. Augustine Day by Day II. 6.50 (978-0-89942-177-3(6), 176/09, Resurrection Pr.) Catholic Bk. Publishing Corp.

Rothan, Michael W. 61 Minutes: Reflections & Homilies for the Year of Luke. 2009. 232p. pap. 19.95 (978-1-4490-2028-6(3)) AuthorHouse.

Rothschild, Jennifer. Lessons I Learned in the Light: All You Need to Thrive in a Dark World. 2006. (ENG.). 224p. pap. 15.99 (978-1-59052-656-9(2), Multnomah) Doubleday Religious Publishing Group, The.

Rouse, Marc. God Uses Black Sheep: Are you God's kind of Sheep. 2009. 64p. pap. 16.95 (978-1-4327-2975-2(6)) Outskirts Pr., Inc.

Rouse, Ted. Bible Proof: Every Real Christian Needs the Real Baptism with the Holy Ghost & Power. 2009. 260p. pap. 16.99 (978-1-60791-936-0(2)) Xulon Pr., Inc.

—Eternal Security - A Deadly Web of Deception. Date not set. pap. (978-1-892239-06-8(X)) Faith's Creation Christian Fellowship.

Rowan, John Patrick. The Soul: A Translation of St. Thomas Aquinas' de Anima. 2008. 299p. pap. 25.00 (978-1-60608-256-0(6), Wipf and Stock) Wipf & Stock Pubs.

Rowe. Behold the Man. Date not set. 9.85 (978-0-89137-210-3(5)) Quality Pubns.

Rowe, Fay. Keepers of the Testimony. 2008. 164p. per. (978-1-897373-14-9(7)) Word Alive Pr.

Rowe, Sherlie. And God Sings. pap. 7.99 (978-0-89098-209-9(0)) Twentieth Century Christian Bks.

Rowe, Susan. The Amos 911 Call: Apprehending Heaven in Tumultuous Times. 2011. pap. 13.99 **(978-1-61346-481-6(9))** Tate Publishing & Enterprises, LLC.

Rowe, Tim. The Magnificent Goodness of God & How It Will Transform Your Life. 2009. 424p. pap. 25.99 (978-1-61579-515-4(4)) Xulon Pr., Inc.

Rowland, Nancy. Never the Same Again. 2009. pap. 29.99 (978-1-60696-674-7(X)) Tate Publishing & Enterprises, LLC.

Roy Hession & Revel Hession. The Calvary Road. 2009. 80p. pap. 3.49 (978-1-60386-251-6(X), Watchmaker Publishing) Wexford College Pr.

Roy Hession and Revel Hession. The Calvary Road. 2008. 60p. pap. 8.45 (978-1-60597-888-8(4), Book Jungle) Standard Pubns., Inc.

Roy Hession, Hession, et al. The Calvary Road. 2009. 80p. pap. 5.95 (978-1-60386-195-3(5), Merchant Bks.) Rough Draft Printing.

Roy, Jay Paul. Josiah's Cry. 2009. 220p. pap. 15.99 (978-1-60791-161-6(2)) Xulon Pr., Inc.

Royalty, Kathleen A. Revelations for Me. 2009. 132p. pap. 14.99 (978-1-61579-449-2(2)) Xulon Pr., Inc.

Royer, Katherine. Nursery Stories of Jesus. 2009. 52p. pap. 12.00 (978-1-60899-140-2(7), Resource Pubns.) Wipf & Stock Pubs.

Royle, Roger. Between Friends. 144p. 10.00 (978-0-281-05374-2(X)) SPCK Publishing GBR. Dist: Pilgrim Pr., The/United Church Pr.

Royster, Dennis B. Discovering Holiness from God. 2007. pap. 12.00 (978-0-8059-8735-5(5)) Dorrance Publishing Co., Inc.

Royster, Pamela. When God Turns the Page: Unlocking the Secret of God's Goodness During Seasons of Change. 2007. 128p. per. 20.00 (978-1-59268-083-2(6)) G M A Publishing & Inspiration Pr.

Ruba, Rubens. A Reasonable Faith: Can you be Smart & Believe in the Bible, God, & Faith? 2011. 124p. pap. 11.95 (978-1-4497-1406-2(4), WestBow Pr.) Author Solutions, Inc.

Rubel, David. If I Had a Hammer: Stories of Building Homes & Hope with Habitat for Humanity. 2010. (ENG., Illus.). 176p. (J). pap. 10.99 (978-0-7636-4769-8(1)) Candlewick Pr.

Rubenis, Juris & Subacs, Maris. Finding God in a Tangled World: Thoughts & Parables. 2007. (Illus.). 184p. 19.00 (978-1-55725-495-5(8)) Paraclete Pr., Inc.

Rubiano, Mauricio. Como Alcanzar La Verdadera Paz Interior. 160p. 3.95 (978-958-607-928-0(7)) Sociedad de San Pablo ARG. Dist: St Pauls/Alba Hse. Pubs.

Rubietta, Jane. Come Along: The Journey into a More Intimate Faith. 2008. (ENG.). 216p. 13.99 (978-1-4000-7352-8(9), WaterBrook Pr.) Doubleday Religious Publishing Group, The.

Rubin, Jordan S. The Great Physician's RX for Children's Health, 0 vols. 2008. 256p. 24.99 (978-0-7852-1902-6(1)) Nelson, Thomas Inc.

Rubin, Jordan S. & Rubin, Nicki. The Great Physician's Rx for Children's Health. 2008. 256p. pap. 14.99 **(978-1-4016-0398-4(X))** Nelson, Thomas Inc.

Ruddick, Morris E. The Heart of a King: The Leadership Measure of the Joseph-Daniel Calling. 2010. pap. 15.99 (978-1-61579-769-1(6)) Xulon Pr., Inc.

Ruddock, Holly S. Life in Your Losses: Transformation Through Trials. 2010. pap. 13.99 (978-1-61566-795-6(4)) Tate Publishing & Enterprises, LLC.

Rudolph, Al. Tougher Than Woodpecker Lips. 2008. 180p. 22.99 (978-1-60647-664-2(5)); pap. 14.99 (978-1-60647-663-5(7)) Xulon Pr., Inc.

Rudolph, Michael E. The Rapture-Ready Church: Living Now to Make it Then. 2009. 62p. pap. 12.95 (978-1-4327-4334-5(1)) Outskirts Pr., Inc.

Ruffin, Shenietta Monique. Does Jesus Love Me? 2011. 40p. pap. 17.00 **(978-1-4567-6522-4(1))** AuthorHouse.

Rufus, Rob. Living in the Grace of God. 2007. (ENG.). 112p. per. 10.99 (978-1-86024-605-0(2)) Authentic Media.

Ruggiero, Louis. The Tower of Deception. 2008. pap. 14.95 (978-0-9801357-2-5(9)) Tree of Life Publishing Hse.

Ruitenburg, Pieter Van. Good Old Age: Letters to Seniors. 2008. 120p. pap. 10.99 (978-1-4343-8575-8(2)) AuthorHouse.

Rumble, Gordon. Revelation: Lessons from the Last Lap Home. 2010. 388p. 28.49 (978-1-4520-0722-9(5)); pap. 19.25 (978-1-4520-0723-6(3)) AuthorHouse.

Rumsey, Ginny Fralick. Day My Life Changed Forever: A Young Widow's Perspective on Surviving the Loss of a Spouse. 2009. 56p. pap. 7.99 (978-1-60696-966-3(8)) Tate Publishing & Enterprises, LLC.

Runcorn, David. Touch Wood: Meeting the Cross in the World Today. 160p. pap. (978-0-232-51943-3(9)) South Asia Bks.

Runk, Wesley T. Jesus, the Servant King. 4.75 (978-1-55673-559-2(6)) CSS Publishing Co.

Runnels, Derek. Life & Livin' It Up: A Life of Livin' it up for God's Glory. 2011. 312p. pap. 19.95 **(978-1-4327-7200-0(7))** Outskirts Pr., Inc.

Ruotsala, Aaron Dean. Cole I Love You to the Moon & Back. 2009. 220p. pap. 15.99 (978-1-60791-444-0(1)) Xulon Pr., Inc.

Rusaw, Rick & Swanson, Eric. The Externally Focused Life. 2009. 208p. pap. 15.99 (978-0-7644-3953-7(7)) Group Publishing, Inc.

—Life on Loan: Adult Study Guide. 2007. (Illus.). 47p. pap. 6.99 (978-0-7847-1902-2(0)) Standard Publishing.

—Living a Life on Loan: Finding Grace at the Intersections. 2006. (Illus.). 251p. 19.99 (978-0-7847-1855-1(5)) Standard Publishing.

Rushnell, Squire. Divine Alignment. 2012. (ENG.). 224p. 19.99 **(978-1-4516-4856-0(1)**, Howard Bks.) Howard Books.

Rushnell, Squire. When God Winks at You: How God Speaks Directly to You Through the Power of Coincidence, 0 vols. 2006. 240p. 17.99 (978-0-7852-1892-0(0)) Nelson, Thomas Inc.

Russell, Bob & Russell, Rusty. Jesus Lord of Your Personality: Four Powerful Principles for Change. 2008. (ENG.). 144p. pap. 11.95 (978-1-4391-2464-2(7), Howard Bks.) Howard Books.

Russell, Gloria. Believe Beyond Basics. 2010. 92p. pap. 10.49 (978-1-4490-4390-2(9)) AuthorHouse.

Russell, Howie. The Wind-Driven Church: A New Day! Fresh Wind! New Breed! 21st Century Church. 2009. 120p. pap. 11.99 (978-1-61579-452-2(2)) Xulon Pr., Inc.

Russell, Janet. Benjamin! 2008. 152p. pap. 14.99 (978-1-60647-576-8(2)) Xulon Pr., Inc.

Russell, Melissa & Murrow, Jeanine. Tamar s Dress. 2010. 242p. pap. 15.99 (978-1-60957-169-6(X)) Xulon Pr., Inc.

Russell, Michelle D. An Experience Every Christian Must Have: From Darkness to Light. 2009. 90p. pap. 16.95 (978-1-60813-469-4(5)) PublishAmerica, Inc.

Russell, Paul S. Making Your Life a Christian Life: The Desert Fathers & St Francis of Assisi as Guides. 2009. 304p. pap. 15.95 (978-1-4389-2338-3(4)) AuthorHouse.

Russell, Rex. What the Bible Says about Healthy Living: 3 Principles that Will Change Your Diet & Improve Your Health. 2006. (ENG.). 288p. pap. 16.99 (978-0-8307-4349-0(9)) Gospel Light Pubns.

Russell, Robert Lloyd. Thy Will Be Done on Earth. 2008. 192p. 22.99 (978-1-60647-431-0(6)); pap. 14.99 (978-1-60647-430-3(8)) Xulon Pr., Inc.

Russell-Yarde, Peter. The Tent of the Meeting: Illustrating God's Plan of Salvation. 2011. (Illus.). 564p. pap. 31.33 (978-1-4520-9914-9(6)) AuthorHouse.

Russo, Gene. Meat & Potatoes. 2009. 124p. pap. 11.99 (978-1-61579-011-1(X)) Xulon Pr., Inc.

Ruth, Amarachi. The Demands of Christian Dicipleship in a Strong Materialistic Age. 2007. 19.95 (978-0-9701116-2-3(2)) Ruth, Amarachi.

Ruth, Simply. Lovin a Thug. 2009. 160p. pap. 14.99 (978-1-60791-543-0(X)) Xulon Pr., Inc.

Ruther, Jeremy P. Foundations of Religion. 2012. (Religion & Spirituality Ser.). 178p. 95.00 **(978-1-61324-257-5(3))** Nova Science Pubs., Inc.

Rutledge, Ron & Rutledge, Cookye. Healing Made Easy: How to Receive Your Healing. 2007. reprint ed. (978-0-9771689-0-3(5)) Rutledge, Ronald.

Ryals, Jimmy. Biblical World Ministry Park, Inc: Enter A New World of Ministry. 2009. 80p. pap. 14.95 (978-1-4327-1232-7(2)) Outskirts Pr., Inc.

Ryan, Bob. Back to the Stone Age. 2008. 132p. 21.99 (978-1-60647-214-9(3)); pap. 13.99 (978-1-60647-213-2(5)) Xulon Pr., Inc.

Ryan, G. William. Signs & Wonders. 2008. 208p. pap. (978-1-55452-267-5(6)) Essence Publishing.

Ryan, Tom. Comfort My People: Prayers & Reflections Inspired by the Venerable Matt Talbot. 2008. (ENG.). 94p. pap. 13.95 (978-1-84730-030-0(8)) Veritas Pubns. IRL. Dist: Dufour Editions, Inc.

Rybarczyk, Edmund J. Beyond Salvation: Eastern Orthodoxy & Classical Pentecostalism on Becoming Like Christ. 2006. (Paternoster Theological Monographs: Ser.). 426p. pap. 43.00 (978-1-59752-732-3(7), Wipf and Stock) Wipf & Stock Pubs.

Ryle, J. C. Are You Born Again. pap. 0.06 (978-0-87377-126-9(5)) GAM Pubns.

—Assurance: How to Know You Are a Christian. l.t. ed. 2008. (ENG.). pap. 7.99 (978-1-871676-05-1(3)) Christian Focus Pubns. GBR. Dist: STL Distribution North America.

—Nuevo Nacimiento: New Birth. (SPA.). 192p. (978-84-7228-857-7(9), 220634) Clie, Editorial.

Ryle, James. Going Through the Dry Times. 96p. pap. (978-1-85240-318-8(7)) Sovereign World, Ltd.

Rytkonen, Linda. Ready or Not, the Bridegroom Is Coming! 2011. 112p. pap. 11.99 **(978-1-61379-247-6(6))** Xulon Pr., Inc.

S. J. Letters to a Young Christian. 2007. (ENG.). 116p. per. 19.95 (978-1-4304-4570-8(X)) Kessinger Publishing, LLC.

S. J. (Sarah Jackson). Letters to a Young Christian by S J. 2006. 116p. per. 16.99 (978-1-4255-0752-7(2)) MPublishing.

Sabbath, Linda Miroslava. The Unveiling of God. 2010. 146p. pap. 12.95 (978-0-557-35414-6(5)) Lulu Enterprises Inc.

Sabin, Scott. Tending to Eden: Environmental Stewardship for God's People. 2010. 176p. pap. 18.00 (978-0-8170-1572-5(8)) Judson Pr.

Sacco, Peter Andrew. What's Your Anger Type for Christians - Good Anger Versus Bad Anger? 2007. 260p. pap. 15.95 (978-1-60145-149-1(0)) Booklocker.com, Inc.

Sachau, Eduard, ed. Three Syriac Law Codes. 2010. (SYR & GER.). pap. 44.68 (978-1-61719-189-3(2)) Gorgias Pr., LLC.

Sachse, Ron. The God Glyph. 2009. 348p. pap. 18.99 (978-1-61579-258-0(9)) Xulon Pr., Inc.

Sacred Unions, Sacred Passions: Engaging the Mystery of Friendship Between Men & Women. 2009. pap. 13.95 (978-0-9825807-0-7(3)) Faith Dance Publishing.

Sacrificial Giving. (Sacrificial Giving Program Ser.). 0.70 (978-0-8146-1230-9(X)) Liturgical Pr.

Sadlack, Emil & Otto. The Desolations of the Sanctuary. 2010. 324p. pap. 22.70 (978-0-557-27598-4(9)) Lulu Enterprises Inc.

Sadler, Carolin. The Journey: Following the Rainbow. 2008. 216p. pap. (978-1-897373-43-9(0)) Word Alive Pr.

Saer, Orlando. Iron Sharpens Iron: Leading Small Groups That Thrive. 2010. (ENG.). 144p. 10.99 (978-1-84550-575-2(1)) Christian Focus Pubns. GBR. Dist: STL Distribution North America.

Sagansay, Ely Roque. Mi Daily Devotion: 100 Days of Love, Inspirations, Encouragement, Encounter with God, Self- Evaluation, Quiet time with God, Challenges & Comfort. 2011. 240p. pap. 17.95 **(978-1-4497-1313-3(0)**, WestBow Pr.) Author Solutions, Inc.

Sahai, Kaysha. The Biblical Path to Wellness: A Simple Guide to Achieving Balance in Your Life. 2011. (ENG.). 80p. pap. 10.98 (978-1-4609-1027-6(3)) CreateSpace.

Saint Paul Brotherhood. The Treasures of the Fathers of the Church the Holy Fifty Days, Volume 4. 2007. (Illus.). 418p. per. (978-0-9721698-6-8(5)) Saint Paul Brotherhood.

Sainte-Foi, Charles. Serious Hours of a Young Lady. 2008. 144p. 21.99 (978-0-554-35450-7(0)) 2008. 144p. 24.99 (978-0-554-26147-8(2)) 2007. (ENG.). 126p. pap. 18.99 (978-1-4346-0561-0(2)) BiblioBazaar.

—Serious Hours of a Young Lady. 2010. (Illus.). 78p. pap. 20.00 (978-1-153-68692-1(9)) General Bks. LLC.

—Serious Hours of a Young Lady. 2010. 100p. pap. 15.16 (978-1-162-68349-2(X)); 27.16 **(978-1-169-23972-2(2))**; 33.95 (978-1-161-45214-3(1)) Kessinger Publishing, LLC.

—Serious Hours of a Young Lady. 2009. 124p. pap. 10.45 (978-1-4385-1998-2(2), Book Jungle) Standard Pubns., Inc.

Sainte Foi, Charles. Serious Hours of a Young Lady. Philaletes, tr. 2007. 120p. per. (978-1-4065-4279-0(2)) Dodo Pr.

Sainte-Foi, Charles. Serious Hours of a Young Lady. l.t. ed. 2007. (ENG.). 142p. pap. 19.99 (978-1-4346-0616-7(3)) BiblioBazaar.

Saith, Ray. Pas de Destruction Sans Avertissement. 2011. (FRE.). 92p. pap. 13.72 **(978-1-4567-9757-7(3))** AuthorHouse.

Salesman, P. Eliecer. Las Maravillas del Espiritu Santo.Tr. of Wonders of the Holy Spirit. (SPA.). 128p. 1.95 (978-9978-06-003-2(0)) San Pablo, Editorial ECU. Dist: St Pauls/Alba Hse. Pubs.

—Novena Biblica a Maria Auxilladora (Biblical Novena to Mary Help of Christians) (SPA.). 96p. 1.95 (978-9978-06-029-2(4)) San Pablo, Editorial ECU. Dist: St Pauls/Alba Hse. Pubs.

—Novena Biblica al Divino Nino (Biblical Novena to the Divine Child) (SPA.). 144p. 1.95 (978-9978-06-016-2(2)) San Pablo, Editorial ECU. Dist: St Pauls/Alba Hse. Pubs.

—Nuevo Viacrucis Biblico (New Biblical Stations of the Cross) (SPA.). 88p. 1.95 (978-9978-06-034-6(0)) San Pablo, Editorial ECU. Dist: St Pauls/Alba Hse. Pubs.

—Secretos para Triunfar en la Vida (Secrets for a Successful Life) (SPA.). 176p. 3.95 (978-9978-06-001-8(4)) San Pablo, Editorial ECU. Dist: St Pauls/Alba Hse. Pubs.

—100 Formulas para Llegar al Exito.Tr. of One Hundred Formulas to Be Successful. (SPA.). 192p. 2.95 (978-9978-06-011-7(1)) San Pablo, Editorial ECU. Dist: St Pauls/Alba Hse. Pubs.

Salisbury, Chuck. Living a Balanced Life: Body, Mind & Spirit. 2011. (ENG.). 162p. pap. 17.95 **(978-1-61448-008-2(7))** Morgan James Publishing.

Salvetti, Neville. The Body of Christ & Fellowship. 2011. 84p. pap. 15.99 **(978-1-4653-0051-5(1))** Xlibris Corp.

—A Discourse on Stewardship. 2011. 86p. pap. 15.99 **(978-1-4568-5440-9(2))** Xlibris Corp.

Salvetti, Neville. The Gospel of Jesus the Christ. 2010. 100p. pap. 15.99 (978-1-4535-5470-8(X)) Xlibris Corp.

Sam-Seong, Kim. Church Transition Through the Principle of 12. 2008. 376p. per. 25.00 (978-1-931178-10-5(0)) Vision Publishing.

Sama, Veronica N. N. There Is No Kingdom Without a Queen. 2008. 184p. pap. 24.95 (978-1-60441-033-4(7)) PublishAmerica, Inc.

Samlalsingh, Phillip. Deliverance: The Door to Destiny. 2007. per. 20.00 (978-1-59872-957-3(8)) Instant Pub.

Sampson, Marvin R. Protection in Dangerous Times. 2008. 92p. pap. 11.99 (978-0-88144-287-8(9)) Yorkshire Publishing Group.

Samson, Will & Samson, Lisa. Enough: Contentment in an Age of Excess, 1 vol. 2009. (ENG.). 176p. pap. 12.99 (978-0-7814-4542-9(6)) Cook, David C.

—Justice in the Burbs: Being the Hands of Jesus Wherever You Live. 2007. (Mersion: Emergent Village Resources for Communities of Faith Ser.). 208p. pap. 16.00 (978-0-8010-6809-6(6)) Baker Bks.

Samuel, Barbara, ed. The I AM Factor of Salvation. 2007. 118p. 12.00 (978-0-9796285-4-2(7)) International Fellowship of Covenant Ministries, The.

Samuelson, Christine. Healer of the Broken Heart. 2008. 148p. pap. 15.99 (978-1-60477-870-0(9)) Xulon Pr., Inc.

San Pablo. Celebremos la Eucaristia.Tr. of Let's Celebrate the Eucharist. (SPA.). 32p. 1.95 (978-958-692-025-4(9)) Sociedad de San Pablo COL. Dist: St Pauls/Alba Hse. Pubs.

—Como Confesarse Bien (How to Confess Our Sins Well) (SPA.). 16p. pap. 0.95 (978-958-607-227-4(4)) Sociedad de San Pablo COL. Dist: St Pauls/Alba Hse. Pubs.

Sanchez, Daniel, Sr. Donated by God. 2009. 76p. pap. 10.95 (978-1-4401-3361-9(1)) iUniverse, Inc.

Sanchez, Ramon M. In His Living Presence 333: Journey Science to Faith. 2008. 322p. pap. 33.00 (978-1-4251-5955-9(9)) Trafford Publishing.

Sand, Faith Annette. Adventures of Faith: Or Learning to Walk on Water. 2009. (ENG.). 200p. pap. 15.00 (978-1-932717-17-4(X)) Hope Publishing Hse.

Sanders, Heyward C. Equal Rights My Eye. 2009. 172p. pap. 16.99 (978-1-61579-161-3(2)) Xulon Pr., Inc.

Sanders, J. Oswald. A Spiritual Clinic: A Suggestive Diagnosis & Prescription for Problems in Christian Life & Service. 2011. 162p. 41.95 **(978-1-258-06178-4(3))** Literary Licensing, LLC.

Sanders, J. Oswald. Spiritual Discipleship: Principles of Following Christ for Every Believer. 2007. (Commitment to Spiritual Growth Ser.). (ENG.). 208p. per. 14.99 (978-0-8024-8251-8(1)) Moody Pubs.

Sanders, Lisa. Everyday Revelations. 2010. 107p. pap. 15.18 (978-0-557-15355-8(7)) Lulu Enterprises Inc.

Sandford, John Loren & Sandford, Paula. Life Transformed: How to Renew Your Mind, Overcome Old Habits, & Become the Person God Designed You to Be. 2009. (ENG.). 224p. pap. 14.99 (978-1-59979-600-0(7), Charisma Hse.) Charisma Media.

Sandford, Paula & Sandford, John Loren. Restoring the Christian Family: A Biblical Guide to Love, Marriage, & Parenting in a Changing World. 2009. (ENG., Illus.). 320p. pap. 14.99 (978-1-59979-465-5(9), Charisma Hse.) Charisma Media.

Sandford, William. Una Iglesia Viva: Church Alive. (SPA.). 432p. (978-84-7228-409-8(3), 220491) Clie, Editorial.

Sandidge, Jeffrey. Walking on Water: Encouragement for the Discouraged Heart. 2008. 92p. pap. 9.99 (978-1-60647-646-8(7)) Xulon Pr., Inc.

Sandiford, K. Joy. Debunking Generational Curses. 2010. 88p. pap. 11.95 (978-1-4327-5335-1(5)) Outskirts Pr., Inc.

—Letters to My Sons: Failure to Thrive. 2007. 56p. per. 12.95 (978-1-4327-0526-8(1)) Outskirts Pr., Inc.

Sandin, Steve. Make the Right Choice. 2011. 114p. pap. 11.99 **(978-1-61379-164-6(X))** Xulon Pr., Inc.

Sandling, Carly Martynia. Walking Through the Psalms of Life. 2008. 60p. pap. 9.99 (978-1-60477-256-2(5)) Xulon Pr., Inc.

Sands, Jennifer. A Treasured Faith: Refining a Heart for the Riches of Christ. 2009. (ENG.). 220p. 17.95 (978-0-9767961-3-8(9), Olive Press, The) Peak Writing, LLC.

Sandsberry, Lynne. Heart, Soul, Mind, & Strength: A Devotional on the Two Great Commandments. 2011. 184p. 30.95 **(978-1-4497-2259-3(8))**; pap. 13.95 **(978-1-4497-2258-6(X))** Author Solutions, Inc. (WestBow Pr.).

Sandtorock. Christian Meat for Christian Muscles: Part 2 - Self Esteem, Prayer, Character, Wisdom & God's Promises. 2011. 352p. pap. 23.03 **(978-1-4567-9742-3(5))** AuthorHouse.

Sandusky, Michael. Psalmwriter Journey's End: The Chronicles of David Book VI. 2011. 516p. 34.99 **(978-1-4628-6319-8(1))**; pap. 23.99 **(978-1-4628-6318-1(3))** Xlibris Corp.

Sanford, Regina N. Where Is God, Now That We Need Him?, 1 vol. 2009. 60p. pap. 16.95 (978-1-61582-846-3(X)) PublishAmerica, Inc.

Sanford, Timothy L. Losing Control & Liking It: How to Set Your Teen (and Yourself) Free. 2008. (ENG.). 192p. pap. 13.99 (978-1-58997-481-4(6)) Tyndale Hse. Pubs.

Sanford: Raven, Regina N. The Atheist Within the Christian Revealed, 1 vol. 2009. (ENG.). 49p. pap. 16.95 (978-1-60749-669-4(0)) PublishAmerica, Inc.

Sangster, William E. Pure in Heart. pap. 9.99 (978-0-88019-160-9(0)) Schmul Publishing Co., Inc.

Santangelo-Peurifoy, Abigail. Let Nothing Stand in Our Way. 2008. 108p. pap. 10.99 (978-1-60647-062-6(0)) Xulon Pr., Inc.

Santini, Pamela R. Wisdom from the King's Table. 2011. 98p. pap. 19.95 **(978-1-4560-5790-9(1))** PublishAmerica, Inc.

C

Santora, Frank. Identity Crisis: Seeing Yourself as God Sees You. 2008. (ENG.). 208p. per. 12.95 (978-0-9793192-5-9(0)) Lifebridge Bks.

—Turn It Around: A Different Direction for a New Life. 2010. (ENG.). 224p. 22.99 (978-1-4165-9757-5(3), Howard Bks.) Howard Books.

Santos, Dennis. Not So Silent Night. 2011. 84p. pap. 8.95 **(978-1-60594-741-9(5)**, Llumina Christian Bks.) Aeon Publishing Inc.

Santos, L. Holy Life: Living in Purity & Obedience to God. 2009. (ENG.). 224p. pap. 13.99 (978-1-59979-766-3(6), Creation Hse.) Charisma Media.

Santrac, Aleksandar S. An Evaluation of Alvin Plantinga's Free Will Defense: Whether Our Power to Do Bad Is Something Good. 2008. 132p. 99.95 (978-0-7734-5129-2(3)) Mellen, Edwin Pr., The.

Sargent, Tony, compiled by. Gems from Martyn Lloyd-Jones: An Anthology of Quotations from 'The Doctor' 2008. (ENG.). 160p. pap. 24.99 (978-1-84227-494-1(5), Paternoster) Authentic Media.

Sarkisian, Rick. The FAQs of Life: Practical answers to life's most probing Questions. 2008. per. 12.95 (978-0-9790825-2-8(8)) LifeWork Pr.

Satzler, Ron. How to Finish Restoring the Church of Christ. 2009. 224p. pap. 19.99 (978-1-4415-1114-0(8)) Xlibris Corp.

Saucier, Sarah Ellen Collins. Ellen, My Joy. 2008. 140p. 21.99 (978-1-60647-296-5(8)); pap. 13.99 (978-1-60477-716-1(8)) Xulon Pr., Inc.

Saunders, Joseph. The Blessed Life of Christian Singles. 2007. 60p. pap. 15.50 (978-0-615-15679-8(7)) Desktop Prepress Services.

Saunders, R. E. Bud. A Son of Shotgun Saunders. 2011. 248p. pap. 15.99 (978-1-61215-611-8(8)) Xulon Pr., Inc.

Savage Sr., Robert. The Call. 2007. 164p. per. 13.99 (978-1-60266-833-1(7)) Xulon Pr., Inc.

Savage Staff. A Letter to My Sisters: The Way Out. 2007. 100p. pap. 12.99 (978-0-9795628-0-8(5)) Savage, Voncele.

Savelle, Jerry. Called to Battle Destined to Win. 2012. (ENG.). 240p. pap. 15.99 (978-0-8307-5129-7(7)) Gospel Light Pubns.

Savoy, Judy. Aaron's Rod. 2011. 220p. pap. 19.97 **(978-0-557-89327-0(5))** Lulu Enterprises Inc.

Sawyer, Timothy A. My Email to God Bounced: The absence of God from Religion. 2011. 34p. pap. 16.95 **(978-1-4560-5627-8(1))** PublishAmerica, Inc.

Saxbee, John. No Faith in Religion. 2009. (ENG.). 224p. pap. 24.95 (978-1-84694-220-4(9)) Hunt, John Publishing Ltd. GBR. Dist: National Bk. Network.

Sayers, Dorothy L. Spiritual Writings. Loades, Ann, ed. 192p. 20.00 (978-0-281-04598-3(4)) SPCK Publishing GBR. Dist: Pilgrim Pr., The/United Church Pr.

Sayers, Mark. The Vertical Self: How Biblical Faith Can Help Us Discover Who We Are in an Age of Self Obsession, 0 vols. 2010. 224p. pap. 14.99 (978-0-8499-2000-4(0)) Nelson, Thomas Inc.

Scandrette, Mark. Soul Graffiti: Making a Life in the Way of Jesus. 2008. (ENG.). 272p. pap. 14.95 (978-0-470-27662-4(2), Jossey-Bass) Wiley, John & Sons, Inc.

Scanzoni, John. Healthy American Families: A Progressive Alternative to the Religious Right, 1 vol. 2010. 225p. 44.95 (978-0-313-38401-1(0), A2883C, Praeger Pubs.) Greenwood Publishing Group, Inc.

Scarbrough, Carol & Stone, Joyce. Christ, A Sheltering Tree Help for Losses & Caretaking. 2010. 180p. pap. 14.99 (978-1-60957-828-2(7)) Xulon Pr., Inc.

Scarbrough, Robert L. Lessons for the Heart. 2011. 104p. pap. 11.95 **(978-1-4497-1915-9(5)**, WestBow Pr.) Author Solutions, Inc.

Scazzero, Geri. I Quit: The Day I Stopped Pretending Everything Was Fine & Changed My Life, My Marriage, & My Church, 1 vol. 2010. (ENG.). 224p. pap. 14.99 (978-0-310-32196-5(4)) Zondervan.

Schaap, Cindy. The Path to a Woman's Happiness. 2007. 20.00 (978-0-9793892-4-5(0)) Christian Womanhood Pubns.

Schaap, Jack. What to Expect in the Pursuit of God. 2007. per. 18.00 (978-0-9778936-1-4(8)) Hyles Pubns.

—When Everything Isn't Black & White. 2007. (YA). per. 12.75 (978-0-9778936-3-8(4)) Hyles Pubns.

Schaap, James, ed. Speaking of Pastors: Parishioners Tell Their Stories. 2006. per. 5.00 (978-0-9753387-1-1(4)) Christian Reformed Church in North America.

Schaefer, Steve. Living in the Overlap: How Jesus' Kingdom Proclamation Can Transform Your World. 2010. 256p. pap. 19.95 (978-1-57921-968-0(3)) WinePress Publishing.

Schall, James V. The Order of Things. 2007. 275p. per. 15.95 (978-1-58617-197-1(6)) Ignatius Pr.

Schall, JoAnn K. God Heals Broken Hearts: Christians Cry Too. 2011. 60p. 24.99 **(978-1-4628-9658-5(8))**; pap. 15.99 **(978-1-4628-9657-8(X))** Xlibris Corp.

Schaper, Donna. Living Well While Doing Good. 2007. 128p. per. 14.00 (978-1-59627-047-3(0)) Church Publishing, Inc.

Schenck, Timothy E. What Size Are God's Shoes? Kids, Chaos, & the Spiritual Life. 2008. 144p. pap. 12.00 (978-0-8192-2312-8(3), Morehouse Publishing) Church Publishing, Inc.

Scheperle, Paul. How Will We Live Then: What Lies Ahead after This Life? 2010. 117p. pap. 15.67 (978-0-557-31955-8(2)) Lulu Enterprises Inc.

Scherling, J. David. Sketches of His Presence. 2008. 176p. pap. 14.99 (978-1-60647-670-3(X)) Xulon Pr., Inc.

Scherrer, Steven. The Future Kingdom of God: A Present Reality & Our Blessed Hope. 2010. 180p. 26.95 (978-1-4502-6838-7(2)); pap. 16.95 (978-1-4502-6837-0(4)) iUniverse, Inc.

Schievelbein, Ginger. Come near to God: A Personal Ministry & Self-Deliverance. 2009. 412p. pap., wbk. ed. 25.99 (978-1-61579-443-0(3)) Xulon Pr., Inc.

Schirrmacher, Thomas, ed. Calvin & World Mission. 2009. 206p. pap. (978-3-941750-20-3(8)) VTR Verlag fur Theologie und Religionswissenschaft.

Schlieker, Paul. What's Missing Inside You? 2006. pap. 16.99 (978-1-60034-518-0(2)) Xulon Pr., Inc.

Schlink, M. Basilea. Encontre la Llave Al Corazon Del Dios: I Found the Key to God's Heart. (SPA.). (978-84-7645-099-4(0), 223149) Clie, Editorial.

Schlueter, Thomas. Keeper of the Keys. 2009. (ENG.). 210p. pap. 13.95 (978-0-9704753-6-7(5)) Gatekeeper Publishing.

Schluter, Bonnie G. Love Letters from God. 2009. 200p. pap. 15.99 (978-1-61579-318-1(6)) Xulon Pr., Inc.

Schmid, Vernon. Divine Fire: Reflections on the Revelation to John. 2011. 78p. pap. 19.95 **(978-1-4626-2021-0(3))** PublishAmerica, Inc.

Schmidgall, Jane E. A Latte Love. 2008. pap. 23.99 (978-1-60477-859-5(8)) Xulon Pr., Inc.

Schmidt, Ken M. Not Afraid to Tell the Truth: Exposing Apostacy & the Conspiracy of Silence in the last Days! 2011. 804p. pap. 23.99 **(978-1-4653-3448-0(3))** Xlibris Corp.

schmidt, stan. Awaiting the King: A Devotional Commentary. 2011. 328p. pap. 19.99 (978-1-4520-8690-3(7)) AuthorHouse.

Schmidt, Wayne. Living a Holy Life. 2007. (D Ser.). (Illus.). 64p. per. 7.99 (978-0-89827-369-4(2)) Wesleyan Publishing Hse.

Schmitz, Eileen. Staying in Bounds: Straight Talk on Boundaries for Effective Ministry. 2010. 208p. pap. 25.99 (978-0-8272-3481-9(3)) Chalice Pr.

Schmul, H. E. The Gift of the Thorn. pap. 0.49 (978-0-88019-063-3(9)) Schmul Publishing Co., Inc.

Schnase, Robert. Cultivating Fruitfulness: Five Weeks of Prayer & Practice for Congregations. 2008. 94p. pap. 7.00 (978-0-687-65433-8(5)) Abingdon Pr.

Schnase, Robert C. Five Practices of Fruitful Congregations Bookmark (Package Of 25) 2008. ring bd. 4.00 (978-0-687-65793-3(8)) Abingdon Pr.

Schnase, Robert C. & Carty, Terry B. Five Practices of Fruitful Youth Ministry: A Youth Leader's Guide. 2009. 64p. pap. 7.00 (978-0-687-65776-6(8)) Abingdon Pr.

Schneider, Carolyn. I Am a Christian: The Nun, the Devil, & Martin Luther. 2010. (Studies in Lutheran History & Theology Ser.). 176p. (C). 30.00 (978-0-8006-9732-7(4), Fortress Pr.) Augsburg Fortress, Pubs.

Schneider, M. Valerie. 10 Wise & Wonderful Stories for Children: Celebrating Holidays & Holy Days. 2007. (Illus.). 60p. per. 14.95 (978-1-58595-614-2(7)) Twenty-Third Pubns./Bayard.

Schneider, Roque. Dios Es Mi Suelo. 96p. 4.95 (978-958-607-660-9(1)) Sociedad de San Pablo COL. Dist: St Pauls/Alba Hse. Pubs.

—Silencio Que He Perdido. 80p. 4.95 (978-958-607-247-2(9)) Sociedad de San Pablo COL. Dist: St Pauls/Alba Hse. Pubs.

Schneiders, Kali. Truffles from Heaven: Discovering the Sweet Gift of God's Grace. 2007. 120p. 13.99 (978-1-57921-901-7(2)) WinePress Publishing.

Schoeninger, Douglas, et al, eds. Christian Anthropology: The Nature of the Human Person, Human Brokenness & Healing. 2009. 228p. pap. 17.99 (978-1-60791-956-8(7)) Xulon Pr., Inc.

Schonborn, Christoph Cardinal & Stöckl, Barbara. Who Needs God? 2009. 200p. pap. 14.95 (978-1-58617-284-8(0)) Ignatius Pr.

Schori, Katharine Jefferts. The Heartbeat of God: Finding the Sacred in the Middle of Everything. 2010. 192p. 21.99 (978-1-59473-292-8(2)) SkyLight Paths Publishing.

Schott, Linda G. I Stand Amazed! At the Wonder of It All. pap. 7.99 (978-0-89098-133-7(7)) Twentieth Century Christian Bks.

Schreurs, Linda. Words Aptly Spoken: A Prophetic Prayer Journey to Iowa's 99 County Courthouses. 2009. 372p. pap. 20.99 (978-1-60791-948-3(6)) Xulon Pr., Inc.

Schrock, Marilyn. Wake Up, Church! The Enemy Is Within Your Gates - Astral Projection & the Church. 2009. (ENG.). 80p. 10.99 (978-1-59979-852-3(2), Creation Hse.) Charisma Media.

Schroeder, Gordon H. The New Member's Guide. rev. ed. 16p. 4.00 (978-0-8170-1436-0(5)) Judson Pr.

Schroeder, John D. This Is Christianity. ldr.'s ed. 2006. (Behind the Pages Ser.). 30p. pap. 11.00 (978-0-687-33333-2(4)) Abingdon Pr.

Schroeder, Lawson. Is Your God Too Small? How & Why We Limit God. 2007. 296p. pap. 14.95 (978-1-933641-26-3(6)) Bible Belt Pubns.

Schronce, Daveena Mcwade. Mary & Me from Ruin to Royalty. 2009. 96p. pap. 10.99 (978-1-60791-068-8(3)) Xulon Pr., Inc.

Schubitz, Kathleen. ... in His Presence: Intimate moments with your Savior. 2010. (ENG., Illus.). 156p. (YA). pap. 14.95 **(978-0-9819980-7-7(0))** RPJ & Co., Inc.

Schuller Coleman, Sheila. Mommy Grace: Erasing Your Mommy Guilt. 2009. (ENG.). 176p. 14.99 (978-0-446-54541-9(4)) FaithWords.

Schuller, Robert A. Getting Through What You're Going Through, 0 vols. 2008. 224p. pap. 14.99 (978-0-7852-8942-5(9)) Nelson, Thomas Inc.

—When You Are down to Nothing, God Is up to Something: Discovering Divine Purpose & Provision When Life Hurts. 2011. (978-0-446-69979-2(9)) FaithWords.

Schuller, Robert H. Prayer, 0 vols. 2009. 254p. pap. 13.99 (978-0-8499-2950-2(4)) Nelson, Thomas Inc.

Schultz, Doug & Esau, Ken. Let's Face It! A Group Study in the Nature of the Church. 81p. pap. 3.95 (978-0-921788-52-2(5)) Kindred Productions.

Schurr, Melanie. Transforming Truths: Modern daily Christian inspirations for growth & positive Transformation. 2008. 281p. pap. 19.50 (978-0-615-14938-7(3)) LotusBooks.net Publishing.

Schut, Jessie. Faith for Tough Times. (Friendship Ser.). stu. ed. 3.25 (978-1-56212-743-5(8), 300540) Faith Alive Christian Resources.

—Helping Each Other. (Friendship Ser.). stu. ed. 3.25 (978-1-56212-742-8(X), 300530) Faith Alive Christian Resources.

—I Believe: Getting Ready to Profess My Faith. (Reformed Faith Ser.). stu. ed. 6.95 (978-1-56212-978-1(3), 151130); mentor's hndbk. ed. 9.95 (978-1-56212-919-4(8), 151135) Faith Alive Christian Resources.

—The Ten Commandments. (Other Curriculum Resources Ser.). stu. ed. 15.25 (978-1-56212-739-8(X), 300500); 191p. 17.95 (978-1-56212-061-0(1), 300504) Faith Alive Christian Resources.

Schut, Michael. Food & Faith: Justice, Joy, & Daily Bread. 2010. 296p. pap. 20.00 (978-0-8192-2411-8(1), Morehouse Publishing) Church Publishing, Inc.

—Money & Faith: The Search for Enough. 2008. 296p. pap. 20.00 (978-0-8192-2327-2(1), Morehouse Publishing) Church Publishing, Inc.

—Simpler Living, Compassionate Life: A Christian Perspective. Schut, Michael, ed. 2009. 296p. pap. 20.00 (978-0-8192-2369-2(7), Morehouse Publishing) Church Publishing, Inc.

Schutte, Dan, et al. Into the Fields Year 2: Styles of Teaching & Learning. 2006. 128p. pap. 24.95 (978-1-58595-591-6(4)) Twenty-Third Pubns./Bayard.

Schuyler, Michael. A Life Worth Living. 2008. 108p. per. 10.99 (978-1-60477-578-5(5)) Xulon Pr., Inc.

Schwab, A. Wayne & Hall, Elizabeth S. Living the Gospel: A Guide for Individuals & Small Groups. 2010. (978-0-9717552-1-5(3)) Member Mission Pr.

Schwab, Dennis. Jesus Didn't Die on A 'HolidayApos. 2008. 164p. pap. 13.99 (978-1-60477-582-2(3)) Xulon Pr., Inc.

Schwaiger, John. In Search of a Good Fit. 2009. 112p. pap. 13.99 (978-1-60791-291-0(0)) Xulon Pr., Inc.

Schwartz, Sharon. Following the Shepherd for Life. 2008. 148p. pap. 13.99 (978-1-60647-351-1(4)) Xulon Pr., Inc.

Schwartz, Victor Lewis. Black & White: Love Is the Loudest Voice. 2010. 68p. pap. 9.95 (978-1-4502-3769-7(X)) iUniverse, Inc.

Schwarzentraub, Jeff. Challenging Christianity: For Those Who Have the Guts to Be Challenged by the Truth of Jesus Christ. 2009. 188p. 22.99 (978-1-61579-440-9(9)); pap. 14.99 (978-1-61579-305-1(4)) Xulon Pr., Inc.

Schwirzer, Jennifer Jill. Finding My Way in Milwaukee. 2007. 110p. per. 9.99 (978-0-8280-1913-2(4)) Review & Herald Publishing Assn.

Scott, Andre. Is Discipleship Possible Without Discipline? 2009. 116p. pap. 10.99 (978-1-4343-7963-4(9)) AuthorHouse.

Scott, Barbara L. From Rubble to Restoration: The Amazing Story of One Family's Terrible Undoing & Divinely Orchestrated Reconstruction. 2007. (ENG., Illus.). 144p. per. 12.99 (978-1-933204-30-7(3)) Deep River Bks.

Scott, Bryan. Don't You Dare Give up! God Wants to Teach You Something, 1 vol. 2009. 73p. pap. 16.95 (978-1-61546-614-6(2)) PublishAmerica, Inc.

Scott, Byron J. Called to Witness: Evangelism Through the Appealing Christian Life. 2008. 176p. per. 12.95 (978-1-4327-2016-2(3)) Outskirts Pr., Inc.

—The Mystery of God's Will: Living the Christian Life as Seen in Ephesians. 2007. 136p. per. 10.95 (978-1-4327-0444-5(3)) Outskirts Pr., Inc.

Scott, Claudia Denise. A Gift to Share: Simple Truths Every Human Should Know. 2011. 196p. 24.77 (978-1-4269-5819-9(6)); pap. 14.77 (978-1-4269-5818-2(8)) Trafford Publishing.

Scott, Ethel A. Unveiling Spiritual Warfare. 2008. 100p. pap. 10.99 (978-1-60647-891-2(5)) Xulon Pr., Inc.

Scott, Janet. Sin Is a Dead End Street. 2007. (Illus.). 131p. per. 12.95 (978-1-933290-84-3(6)) Tate Publishing & Enterprises, LLC.

Scott, Joyce. The Reason for My Hope: The Father's Compassion in Sickness & Death. 2008. 48p. per. 8.95 (978-1-4327-0751-4(5)) Outskirts Pr., Inc.

Scott, Kirk J. Embrace Sin: Becoming Effected by Grace. 2008. pap. 9.99 (978-1-60647-012-1(4)) Xulon Pr., Inc.

Scott, Latayne C. To Love Each Other: 1 Corinthians - 13 Studied by Love's Principles Personified. pap. 7.99 (978-0-89098-116-0(7)) Twentieth Century Christian Bks.

Scott, Leonard. Soaring with Eagles. 2006. 135p. per. 9.99 (978-1-58169-215-0(3), Gazelle Pr.) Genesis Communications, Inc.

Scott-Lowe, Janine. Inspirations: No Subtitle. 2008. 144p. pap. 13.99 (978-1-60647-585-0(1)) Xulon Pr., Inc.

—Reflections. 2007. 120p. per. 10.99 (978-1-60477-230-2(1)) Xulon Pr., Inc.

Scott, Sherry B. God in My Coffee. 2008. 152p. pap. 13.99 (978-1-60647-499-0(5)) Xulon Pr., Inc.

Scott, Steven K. The Greatest Man Who Ever Lived: Secrets for Unparalleled Success & Unshakable Happiness from the Life of Jesus. 2009. (ENG.). 368p. 19.95 (978-1-4000-7464-8(9), WaterBrook Pr.) Doubleday Religious Publishing Group, The.

—The Jesus Mission: Christ Completed Twenty-Seven Missions While on Earth - Take up the Four He Assigned to You. 2011. (ENG.). 304p. 19.99 (978-0-307-73049-7(2), WaterBrook Pr.) Doubleday Religious Publishing Group, The.

Scott, Thomas. The Force of Truth: An Authentic Narrative. 2007. (ENG.). 142p. 35.95 (978-0-548-04742-2(1)) Kessinger Publishing, LLC.

Scougal, Henry. The Life of God in the Soul of Man. Hudson, Winthrop S., ed. 2011. 96p. pap. 7.95 **(978-1-891396-78-6(1))** Martino Publishing.

—The Life of God in the Soul of Man. 2011. 46p. pap. 8.49 **(978-1-61720-194-3(4))** Wilder Pubns., Ltd.

Scougal, Henry. Life of God in the Soul of Man or the Na. 2006. pap. 21.95 (978-1-4286-6271-1(5)) Kessinger Publishing, LLC.

Scroggie, W. Como Descubrir los Secretos De: How to Discover the Secrets Of. (SPA.). 120p. (978-84-7228-742-6(4), 220171) Clie, Editorial.

—Descorriendo el Velo: The Great Unveiling. (SPA.). 160p. (978-84-7228-839-3(0), 220273) Clie, Editorial.

Scroggie, W. Graham. The Christian Life. pap. 2.49 (978-1-56632-078-8(X)) Revival Literature.

Scruggs, Cheryl & Scruggs, Jeff. I Do Again: How We Found a Second Chance at Our Marriage - And You Can Too. 2008. (ENG.). 208p. 13.99 (978-1-4000-7445-7(2), WaterBrook Pr.) Doubleday Religious Publishing Group, The.

Scully, Alladin. Exploring the Bible & Religion. 2008. 532p. pap. 34.95 (978-1-60563-253-7(8)) PublishAmerica, Inc.

Scurlock, Jan. Decorating with God: An Inspiring New Way to Decorate. 2010. pap. 11.99 (978-1-61566-249-4(9)) Tate Publishing & Enterprises, LLC.

Seager-McCraw, Theresa. Sinner to Saint. 2007. 120p. per. 10.99 (978-0-9762087-9-2(2)) Waymaker Pubs.

Seals, Thomas. The Sermon on the Mount for Modern Living. 2007. 184p. per. 15.95 (978-1-58427-212-0(0)) Guardian of Truth Foundation.

Searle, David, ed. Through the Year with William Still. 2006. 376p. 26.00 (978-0-85151-941-8(5)) Banner of Truth, The.

—Truth & Love: In a Sexually Disordered World. 2007. (ENG.). 160p. per. 7.99 (978-1-84550-227-0(2)) Christian Focus Pubns. GBR. Dist: STL Distribution North America.

Sears, G. Warren. Adventures of a Witness for Jesus. 2008. 196p. pap. 10.95 (978-0-9790221-2-8(6)) YAV.

Seaton, Debra. Idolatry of Christian Leaders. 2007. 304p. per. 17.99 (978-1-60266-437-1(4)) Xulon Pr., Inc.

Seaton, Michael R. Start with Me: A Modern Parable, 1 vol. 2009. (Start Ser.). (ENG.). 160p. pap., instr.'s gde. ed. 9.99 (978-0-310-28504-5(6)) Zondervan.

Seaton, Michael R. & Seaton, Mike. Start with Me: A Modern Parable, 1 vol. 2010. (Start Ser.). (ENG.). 176p. pap. 12.99 (978-0-310-32584-0(6)) Zondervan.

Seay, Chris, et al, retold by. The Voice from on High: God Announces His Son as Israel's Liberating King, 0 vols. 2007. (Voice Ser.). 144p. pap. 14.99 (978-0-529-12414-2(9)) Nelson, Thomas Inc.

Seay, Michael. Restoring the Glory: peculiar work for peculiar People. 2007. 92p. pap. 10.95 (978-0-7414-3723-5(6)) Infinity Publishing.

Sebastian, Gayle D. A Mother's Unconditional Love. 2010. 84p. pap. 10.99 (978-1-61579-274-0(0)) Xulon Pr., Inc.

Sebastian Meyer, Nancy. Talk Easy, Listen Hard: Real Communication for Two Really Different People. 2006. (ENG.). 208p. per. 13.99 (978-0-8024-8230-3(9)) Moody Pubs.

Sedgwick. Enterprise Culture. 208p. 27.00 (978-0-281-04576-1(3)) International Publishers Marketing.

Sedinger, Ione L. The Good News of the Apocalypse: Volume Ii: A Guided Voyage Through the New Testament. 2011. 332p. 29.95 **(978-1-4620-5809-9(4))**; pap. 19.95 **(978-1-4620-5808-2(6))** iUniverse, Inc.

Sedler, Michael D. When to Speak up & When to Shut Up. 2006. 160p. 5.99 (978-0-8007-8742-4(0)) Revell.

Seed, Hal. The God Questions Gift Edition. 2008. (ENG.). 125p. pap. 4.99 (978-0-9787153-2-8(2)) Outreach, Inc.

Seed, Hal & Grider, Dan. The God Questions: Fourth Edition. 2007. 196p. pap. 12.95 (978-0-9787153-0-4(6)) Outreach, Inc.

Segler, Franklin M. & Bradley, Randall. Christian Worship: Its Theology & Practice. 3rd ed. 2006. (ENG., Illus.). 336p. per. 29.99 (978-0-8054-4067-6(4), B&H Academic) B&H Publishing Group.

Sekulow, Jay. America V. God: Why We Must Reverse the Assault on Faith in Our Courts. 2007. 256p. pap. 14.95 (978-0-06-111668-1(8), Harper San Francisco) HarperCollins Pubs.

Selby. Rescue. 128p. 13.00 (978-0-281-04897-7(5)) SPCK Publishing GBR. Dist: Pilgrim Pr., The/United Church Pr.

Self, Cliff. Man Up: Release the Champion in You! 2009. pap. 13.99 (978-1-58169-313-3(3), Evergreen Pr.) Genesis Communications, Inc.

Sellers, Susan K. To My Friend. 2011. pap. 11.95 **(978-1-60494-606-2(7))** Wheatmark.

Sellers, Terry L. Songs of My Soul: A Personal Journey to God. 2010. pap. 11.99 (978-1-61566-589-1(7)) Tate Publishing & Enterprises, LLC.

Selmanovic, Samir. It's Really All about God: Reflections of a Muslim Atheist Jewish Christian. 2009. (ENG., Illus.). 320p. 24.95 (978-0-470-43326-3(4), Jossey-Bass) Wiley, John & Sons, Inc.

Selvaggio, Anthony. The 24/7 Christian: Practical Help from the Book of James. 2008. 175p. pap. (978-0-85234-687-7(5)) Evangelical Pr.

Semerau, Ava. And God Was Pleased. 2008. 312p. pap. 17.99 (978-1-60477-742-0(7)) Xulon Pr., Inc.

Semper, Colin. Intercessions. 90p. (978-0-264-67226-7(7), Morehouse Publishing) Church Publishing, Inc.

Senack, John Andrew. God Comes Softly. 2008. pap. 11.00 (978-0-8059-8579-5(4)) Dorrance Publishing Co., Inc.

Senander, Angela. Beyond Scandal. 2011. 144p. pap. 14.95 **(978-0-8146-3410-3(9))** Liturgical Pr.

Send a Prayer Anthem. 1.75 (978-0-687-07582-9(3)) Abingdon Pr.

Serocki, Angela K. You've Been Conned: Defying Depression by the Grace of God. 2009. (J). pap. 10.99 (978-1-60799-485-5(2)) Tate Publishing & Enterprises, LLC.

Sesley, Kenneth R. Firstfruits: God's Plan to Propel You from Poverty to Prosperity! 2009. 144p. pap. 14.99 (978-1-60791-870-7(6)) Xulon Pr., Inc.

Sessions, Robert Paul. Getting Christianity Right! What a True, Better Christianity Will Be Like. 2007. 216p. (ENG.). 27.95 (978-0-595-70145-2(0)); per. 17.95 (978-0-595-45780-9(0)) iUniverse, Inc.

Sessoms, Lamont J. A Wounded Christian in a Modern Church. 2007. 56p. per. 16.95 (978-1-4241-8980-9(2)) PublishAmerica, Inc.
Sessoms, Pastor Lamont J. Satan's Last Stand. 2011. 22p. pap. 16.95 (978-1-4626-1272-7(5)) PublishAmerica, Inc.
Settle, Mary Jane. Weighting on God: An Inspiring Story of Loss & Love. 2011. pap. 12.99 (978-1-61739-067-8(4)) Tate Publishing & Enterprises, LLC.
Seu, Andrée. We Shall Have Spring Again: Essays. 2008. 157p. pap. (978-0-9821229-2-1(6)) World & Life Bks.
Seubert, Augusto. Como Entender el Mensaje de los Profetas. 128p. 6.95 (978-958-607-260-1(6)) Sociedad de San Pablo COL. Dist: St Pauls/Alba Hse. Pubs.
Severe, Kabrena. What Kind of Girl Are You? 2009. 224p. pap. 15.99 (978-1-60791-943-8(5)) Xulon Pr., Inc.
Sevig, Julie B. Peanut Butter & Jelly Prayers. 2007. (Illus.). 96p. 18.00 (978-0-8192-2275-6(5), Morehouse Publishing) Church Publishing, Inc.
Sewell. Handbook of Theological English. (Illus.). 144p. 29.00 (978-0-281-05157-1(7)) SPCK Publishing GBR. Dist: Pilgrim Pr., The/United Church Pr.
Sewell, John H. You Are Greater Than You Know. 2011. 302p. 29.99 (978-1-4500-7228-1(3)); pap. 19.99 (978-1-4500-7227-4(5)) Xlibris Corp.
Sexton, Ralph, Sr. Bloom Where You Are Planted. 62p. pap. 9.95 (978-1-57090-074-7(4), Mountain Church) aBOOKS Distributing.
Seyfert, Jim. Toe in the Pond. 2007. 84p. per. 9.99 (978-1-60266-523-1(0)) Xulon Pr., Inc.
Seymour, F. The Return of the Sun. 2010. (Illus.). 28p. 12.49 (978-1-4520-0449-5(8)) AuthorHouse.
Seymour, Jody. Lost but Making Excellent Time: Transforming the Rat Race into a Pilgrimage. 2009. 208p. pap. 23.00 (978-1-60608-286-7(8), Resource Pubns.) Wipf & Stock Pubs.
Shackleford, William A., Sr. The Sin That Will Keep Many Church Members Out of Heaven. 2009. 180p. 22.99 (978-1-60791-173-9(6)); pap. 14.99 (978-1-60791-172-2(8)) Xulon Pr., Inc.
Shaddai, Queen Juliet El. The Kingdom-of-God Mind-Set! 2008. 324p. 29.99 (978-1-4363-3162-3(5)); pap. 19.99 (978-1-4363-3161-6(7)) Xlibris Corp.
Shafer, Barry & Novelli, Michael. Shaped by the Story: Helping Students Encounter God in a New Way, 1 vol. 2008. (ENG.). 176p. pap. 29.99 (978-0-310-27366-0(8)) Zondervan.
Shaffer, Georgia. A Gift of Mourning Glories. 214p. pap. 10.99 (978-0-8307-3429-0(5), Regal Bks.) Gospel Light Pubns.
Shakarian, Demos. La Gente Mas Feliz de la Tierra: The Happiest People on Earth. (SPA.). 240p. (978-84-7228-358-9(5), 360245) Clie, Editorial.
Shakefoot, Gustav. Dr. Peacock & His Quest to Know God. 2010. 172p. 28.00 (978-1-4269-4262-4(1)); pap. 18.00 (978-1-4269-4261-7(3)) Trafford Publishing.
Shallis, Ralph. Si Quieres Ir Lejos: So You'd Like to Go Far? (SPA.). 184p. (978-84-7228-362-6(3), 220835) Clie, Editorial.
Shambaugh, William. The Will of God. 2008. 120p. pap. 14.00 (978-0-557-02435-3(8)) Lulu Enterprises Inc.
Shanetria Peterson, Evangelist. The Greatest Part of Me & Now It's Time for Deliverance. 2007. 162p. 26.94 (978-0-615-16130-3(8)) Peterson, Shanetria.
Shank, Harold. Children Mean the World to God. pap. 12.50 (978-0-89098-184-9(1)) Twentieth Century Christian Bks.
—Loosening Your Grip: Letting Go & Living in True Security. rev. ed. (Illus.). 14.95 (978-0-9665641-8-1(9)) Welverst Co.
Shanklin, Ray. Living in the Fullness of God's Blessing. 2010. 176p. pap. 14.99 (978-0-88144-409-4(X), Thorncrown Publishing) Yorkshire Publishing Group.
Shannon, Jill. Coffee Talks with Messiah: When Intimacy Meets Revelation. 2007. 165p. per. 12.99 (978-1-58169-250-1(1), Gazelle Pr.) Genesis Communications, Inc.
—Seduction of Christianity: Overcoming the Lukewarm Spirit of the Church. 2010. (ENG.). pap. 17.99 (978-0-7684-3259-6(6)) Destiny Image Pubs.
Shannon, Matthew. Convincing the Unconvincible: A Handbook for Christians. 2009. 156p. pap. 12.95 (978-1-60844-026-9(5)) Dog Ear Publishing, LLC.
Sharing Faith with Your Child. 12.00 (978-0-687-04902-8(4)) Abingdon Pr.
Sharpe, Tracy & Sharpe, Linda V. Reaching People & Touching Lives Around the World. 2009. 136p. pap. 14.99 (978-1-60791-405-1(0)) Xulon Pr., Inc.
Sharpe, Van. The Blessings of Rejection. 2008. 156p. (ENG.). 21.99 (978-1-60477-430-6(4)); per. 13.99 (978-1-60477-429-0(0)) Xulon Pr., Inc.
Shastar, Nightrissa. Chaste Disciples 4 Christ: A Great Nation of Ladies. 2008. 85p. pap. 16.95 (978-1-60474-649-5(1)) PublishAmerica, Inc.
Shaw, Donna Kellough. A Woman of Lydi. 2009. 140p. pap. 14.99 (978-1-60791-436-5(0)) Xulon Pr., Inc.
Shaw, George Bernard. On Going to Church. Branden Bks.
—On Going to Church. 2007. (ENG.). 68p. per. 16.95 (978-0-548-59812-2(6)) Kessinger Publishing, LLC.
Shaw, Mark E. Addiction-Proof Parenting: Biblical Prevention Strategies. 2010. 212p. pap. 13.95 (978-1-885904-88-1(6)) Focus Publishing.
—The Heart of Addiction: A Biblical Perspective. 2008. 256p. pap. 13.95 (978-1-885904-68-3(1)) Focus Publishing.
—The Heart of Addiction Workbook. 2009. 88p. pap. 8.95 (978-1-885904-69-0(X)) Focus Publishing.
—Strength in Numbers: The Team Approach to Biblical Counseling. 2010. (Illus.). 147p. pap. 13.95 (978-1-885904-89-8(4)) Focus Publishing.
Shea, Chris, illus. & text. If God Used Sticky Notes? 2007. 64p. 9.99 (978-0-7369-1852-7(3)) Harvest Hse. Pubs.
—If God Used Sticky Notes for Those Who Need a Little Wisdom. 2008. 64p. 9.99 (978-0-7369-2155-8(9)) Harvest Hse. Pubs.
Sheakley, Art "Moe". Do Car Salesmen Go to Heaven? The Truth, the Whole Truth, & Nothing but the Truth about the Automobile Business. 2006. 204p. pap. 17.99 (978-1-4141-0791-2(9)) Pleasant Word.
Sheals, William L. Walking in Authority: Biblical Examples for Modern Times. 2007. 104p. per. 11.95 (978-0-595-42441-2(4)) iUniverse, Inc.
Shears, Angela R., et al. Reflections on the Shack. 2009. (Reflections from the Powder Room Ser.). 173p. pap. 11.99 (978-0-7684-3127-8(1)) Destiny Image Pubs.
Shears, Jay Allan. Perspectives of Hope. 2009. 120p. pap. 11.99 (978-1-60791-765-6(3)); 108p. 19.99 (978-1-60791-392-4(5)); 108p. pap. 11.99 (978-1-60791-391-7(7)) Xulon Pr., Inc.
Sheasby, John. The Birthright: Out of the Servant's Quarters into the Father's House, 1 vol. 2010. (ENG.). 176p. 16.99 (978-0-310-32746-2(6)) Zondervan.
Shedd, Elise. Elysium Dimension: God's Heavenly Realms. 2008. 79p. pap. 9.91 (978-1-4357-3767-7(3)) Lulu Enterprises Inc.
Sheen, Fulton J. Thoughts for Daily Living. 2008. (978-0-8189-1261-0(8), St. Pauls) St Pauls/Alba Hse. Pubs.
Sheets, Donald. El Ro de Dios.Tr. of River of God. (SPA.). 9.99 (978-0-7899-0584-0(1), 496636) Editorial Unilit.
Sheets, Dutch. Roll Away Your Stone: Living in the Power of the Risen Christ. 2008. (Illus.). 256p. pap. 13.99 (978-0-7642-0470-8(X)) Bethany Hse. Pubs.
Sheffield, Frederick R. Things They Don't Tell You Before Becoming a Christian. 2008. 228p. pap. 14.99 (978-1-60477-654-6(4)) Xulon Pr., Inc.
Sheldon, Bryan W. Messiah & the Covenants of Israel. 2010. 186p. pap. (978-1-926765-10-5(9)) Gospel Folio Pr.
Sheldon, Bryan W. More Than Just a Messiah: Jesus of Nazareth. 2011. 98p. pap. (978-1-926765-55-6(9)) Gospel Folio Pr.
Sheldon, Charles. In His Steps. 2010. pap. 0.00 (978-1-59328-276-9(1)) Graham, Billy Evangelistic Assn.
—In His Steps. 2010. pap. 4.50 (978-0-9819603-2-6(4)) Hyles Pubns.
Sheldon, Charles M. En Sus Pasos: Un Lavorito de los Lectores Por Gencraiones. 2010. (Abridged Christian Classics Ser.).Tr. of In His Steps. (SPA.). 192p. pap. 3.99 (978-1-61626-029-3(7), Casa Promesa) Barbour Publishing, Inc.
—In His Steps. 2010. 308p. pap. 10.99 (978-1-60450-810-9(8)); 176p. pap. 7.99 (978-1-60450-804-8(3)) Arc Manor. (Serenity Pubs.).
—In His Steps. 2010. 186p. pap. (978-1-4076-2694-9(9)) HardPr.
—In His Steps. 246p. 2011. 41.95 (978-1-169-84450-6(2)) 2010. 33.56 (978-1-163-21775-7(1)) 2010. pap. 21.56 (978-1-162-72053-1(0)) Kessinger Publishing, LLC.
Sheldon, Charles M. In His Steps: What Would Jesus Do? 2010. 288p. pap. 24.95 (978-0-557-46366-4(1)) Lulu Enterprises Inc.
Sheldon, Charles Monroe. In His Steps. 2010. (Illus.). 136p. pap. 22.44 (978-1-153-63075-7(3)) General Bks. LLC.
Sheldon, Jean. No Longer Naked & Ashamed: Discovering that God Is not an Abuser. 2009. (Illus.). 276p. pap. 18.95 (978-1-4327-3348-3(6)) Outskirts Pr., Inc.
Shell, J. Fit for His Service: A Life of Intensity. 2010. 168p. pap. 13.95 (978-1-61507-225-5(X)) Cross Bks. Publishing.
Shellenberger, Susie. Girl Talk with God. 2011. 240p. (YA). pap. 14.99 (978-1-4003-1700-4(2)) Nelson, Thomas Inc.
—Raising a Spiritually Strong Daughter: Guiding Her Toward a Faith That Lasts. 2009. 224p. pap. 13.99 (978-0-7642-0376-3(2)) Bethany Hse. Pubs.
Shelley, Bruce L. Church History in Plain Language: Third Edition, 0 vols. 3rd ed. 2008. 560p. pap. 29.99 (978-0-7180-2553-3(9)) Nelson, Thomas Inc.
Shelly, Rubel. The Beatitudes. pap. 8.25 (978-0-89098-473-4(5)) Twentieth Century Christian Bks.
—What Christian Living Is All About: Studies in James. pap. 7.99 (978-0-89098-023-1(3)) Twentieth Century Christian Bks.
—Young People & Their Lord. pap., tchr. ed. 7.50 (978-0-89098-041-5(1)); pap., stu. ed. 7.50 (978-0-89098-018-7(7)) Twentieth Century Christian Bks.
Shelton, Rosewitha. In the Morning, When I Rise: From Loss to Anointing. 2010. 192p. (ENG.). 30.95 (978-1-4497-0080-5(2)); pap. 13.95 (978-1-4497-0078-2(0)) Author Solutions, Inc. (WestBow Pr.).
Shenton, Michael. The New Apostolic Age. 2007. 156p. per. 13.99 (978-1-60266-201-8(0)) Xulon Pr., Inc.
SHEPHARD, C. A. T. E. R. & CUMMINGS, C. A. R. O. L. Y. N. What they want you to know, messages from beyond the Grave. 2007. 500p. per. 20.00 (978-0-9767063-1-1(8)) Cummings Pr.
Shepherd, Beverley. Created As A Woman. 2007. 126p. (978-1-85345-450-9(8)) Crusade for World Revival.
Shepherd, Eleanor. More Questions than Answers: Sharing Faith by Listening. 2010. 184p. pap. 21.00 (978-1-60899-361-1(2), Resource Pubns) Wipf & Stock Pubs.
Shepherd, Jacob A. & Shepherd, Sheri Rose. His Battle: God's Plan for Victory, 1 vol. 2010. (ENG.). 224p. 14.99 (978-0-8007-1923-4(9)) Revell.
Shepherd, Sheri Rose. Girl Talk with God Workbook/Devotional Singles: Real Answers to Real Issues Our Teens Face Everyday. 2008. (ENG.). 192p. pap. 11.99 (978-1-934384-18-3(6)) Treasure Publishing.
—His Princess Retreat Weekend. 2007. (ENG., Illus.). 192p. per. 11.99 (978-1-934384-10-7(0)) Treasure Publishing.
Shepp, Victoria. Coyote Meets Jesus: Treasures in Folktales & Scripture. 2006. (Illus.). 107p. 16.75 (978-0-88489-889-4(X)) St. Mary's Pr.
Sheriffs, Deryck. The Friendship of the Lord: An Old Testament Spirituality. 2007. xiii, 363p. (978-1-57383-396-7(7), Regent College Publishing) Regent College Publishing.
Sherlock, William. A Practical Discourse Concerning Death. 2009. 244p. 28.99 (978-1-110-12052-9(4)); pap. 25.75 (978-1-110-12050-5(8)) BiblioBazaar.
—A Practical Discourse Concerning Death. 2007. (ENG.). 242p. 41.95 (978-0-548-25745-6(0)); 244p. per. 26.95 (978-1-4326-6109-0(4)) Kessinger Publishing, LLC.
Sherman, Mary. Right the Wrong Within. 2007. 212p. per. 15.99 (978-1-60266-361-9(0)) Xulon Pr., Inc.
Sherman, Ronald G. The Three Gifts from God. 2009. 130p. pap. 13.20 (978-0-557-05535-7(0)) Lulu Enterprises Inc.
Sherrod, Fred. Shiloh's Scepter. 2010. 240p. 33.95 (978-1-61507-180-7(6)); pap. 17.95 (978-1-61507-179-1(2)) Cross Bks. Publishing.
Shiben, David. The Game of Life. 2007. 244p. pap. 24.95 (978-1-4241-9914-3(X)) PublishAmerica, Inc.
Shibley, David. Living as If Heaven Matters. 2007. (ENG.). 224p. pap. 14.99 (978-1-59979-166-1(8), Charisma Hse.) Charisma Media.
—Respuestas: Answers. (SPA.). 64p. (978-84-7228-276-6(7), 220771) Clie, Editorial.
Shibley, Shirley. Hold Tight, Pilgrim, the Best is yet to Come, 1 vol. 2010. 66p. pap. 19.95 (978-1-4512-0535-0(X)) PublishAmerica, Inc.
Shields, Bob. Crawling out of the Wormhole: The Crucifixion of Self. 2011. pap. 19.99 (978-1-61777-234-4(8)) Tate Publishing & Enterprises, LLC.
Shifflett, William. Friendly Fire: Embracing the Power of Trial. 2011. pap. 15.99 (978-1-61739-397-6(5)) Tate Publishing & Enterprises, LLC.
Shiflett, M. S. The Exceptional Man. 2006. 21.99 (978-1-60034-741-2(X)) Xulon Pr., Inc.
—Exceptional Man. 2006. pap. 13.99 (978-1-60034-740-5(1)) Xulon Pr., Inc.
Shifman, Lydia K. An Invitation to Love: Lessons in Living. 2007. 196p. pap. 15.00 (978-0-9764221-1-2(5)) faithAlivebooks.com.
Shipley, Tom. Man & Woman in Biblical Law. 2010. 287p. pap. 28.50 (978-0-557-52900-1(X)) Lulu Enterprises Inc.
Shipman, Brian. Burn, 0 vols. 2008. 196p. pap. 12.99 (978-0-7852-9686-7(7)) Nelson, Thomas Inc.
Shipman, David. Sufficient Grace. 2007. 120p. per. 10.99 (978-1-60266-072-4(7)) Xulon Pr., Inc.
Shipp, Lee. Why Live This Way When You Don't Have To? 2007. 136p. (ENG.). 21.99 (978-1-60266-418-0(8)); per. 13.99 (978-1-60266-391-6(2)) Xulon Pr., Inc.
Shirelle. Sinless Sex. 2008. 168p. per. 13.99 (978-1-60477-713-0(3)) Xulon Pr., Inc.
Shirer, Priscilla. Discerning the Voice of God: How to Recognize When He Speaks. 2006. (ENG., Illus.). 127p. pap. 15.25 (978-1-4158-3662-0(0)) LifeWay Christian Resources.
—Jonah: Navigating a Life Interrupted. 2010. 157p. pap. (978-1-4158-6849-2(2)) LifeWay Christian Resources.
—One in a Million: Journey to Your Promised Land. 2010. 224p. pap. 14.99 (978-0-8054-6476-4(X), B&H Bks.) B&H Publishing Group.
Shirley, Judy. Hold My Donut While I Check My Weight / When Your Kleenex Box Is Empty. 2007. pap. 6.99 (978-1-56722-712-3(0)) Word Aflame Pr.
Shivers, Frank R. Christian Basics 101. 2009. 180p. pap. 14.99 (978-1-60791-296-5(1)) Xulon Pr., Inc.
Shoemaker, Bonnie. Heavenly Healing. 2010. 247p. pap. 14.95 (978-1-891280-88-7(0)) CMJ Marian Pubs.
Shoemaker, Tim & Shoemaker, Cheryl. Bashed Burritos, Green Eggs: And Other Indoor/Outdoor Devotionals You Can Do with Your Kids. 2007. (Illus.). 179p. pap. 12.99 (978-1-60066-140-2(8)) WingSpread Publishers.
Shoesmith, Bernard. The Fall of Babylon. 2010. 152p. pap. 14.00 (978-1-59755-239-4(9), Advantage Inspirational) Advantage Bks.
Shoesmith, Michael D. Fallen from Grace. 2007. (ENG.). 52p. per. 16.95 (978-1-4241-6982-5(8)) PublishAmerica, Inc.
Shook, Kerry & Shook, Chris. Love at Last Sight: Thirty Days to Grow & Deepen Your Closest Relationships. 2010. (ENG.). 240p. 19.99 (978-1-4000-7380-1(4), WaterBrook Pr.) Doubleday Religious Publishing Group, The.
—Un Mes para Vivir: Treinta Días para Lograr una Vida Sin Arrepentimientos. 2008. (Vintage Espanol Ser.). (SPA & ENG.). 304p. pap. 15.95 (978-0-307-45553-6(X), Vintage) Knopf Doubleday Publishing Group.
—One Month to Live: Thirty Days to a No-Regrets Life. 2008. (ENG.). 240p. 19.99 (978-1-4000-7379-5(0)) Doubleday Religious Publishing Group, The.
—One Month to Live Devotional Journal: Your Thirty-Day Companion to a No-Regrets Life. 2008. (ENG.). 192p. 14.99 (978-0-307-45708-0(7), WaterBrook Pr.) Doubleday Religious Publishing Group, The.
—One Month to Live Guidebook: To a No-Regrets Life. 2008. (ENG.). 144p. pap. 11.99 (978-0-307-45709-7(5), WaterBrook Pr.) Doubleday Religious Publishing Group, The.
Shoop, Glenn. No More Excuses. 2007. 256p. 25.99 (978-1-60266-417-3(X)); per. 15.99 (978-1-60266-416-6(1)) Xulon Pr., Inc.
Shore, Megan. Religion & Conflict Resolution: Christianity & South Africa's Truth & Reconciliation Commission. Dickson, Joshua, ed. 2009. (Illus.). 230p. 99.95 (978-0-7546-6759-9(6)) Ashgate Publishing Co.
Short-Clark, B. Elizabeth. Consider This... 2008. 112p. pap. 11.99 (978-1-60647-714-4(5)) Xulon Pr., Inc.
Short, Courtney. God Said Wait. 2008. 224p. pap. 15.99 (978-1-58930-211-2(7)) Selah Publishing Group, LLC.
Short, Robert L. The Gospel According to Dogs: What Our Four-Legged Saints Can Teach Us. 2007. (ENG., Illus.). 128p. pap. 11.95 (978-0-06-119874-8(9), HarperOne) HarperCollins Pubs.
Shotwell, D. Yvonne. How to Quickly Grow & Identify Godly Fruit: Spiritual Path to Christian Maturity & Marriage. 2011. 108p. 22.95 (978-1-4502-9760-8(9)); pap. 12.95 (978-1-4502-9758-5(7)) iUniverse, Inc.
Shpak, Julia. Power of Plentiful Wisdom. 2010. 108p. 21.49 (978-1-4520-6475-8(X)); pap. 12.95 (978-1-4520-6474-1(1)) AuthorHouse.
Shriver, Donald W. On Second Thought: Essays Out of My Life. 2010. 224p. pap. 18.00 (978-1-59627-109-8(4), Seabury Bks.) Church Publishing, Inc.
Shropshire. Jesus Likes Me: Principles of Grace Living. 2009. 92p. pap. 16.95 (978-1-4489-9751-0(8)) PublishAmerica, Inc.
Shropshire, Richard J. The Joy of Discipleship, 1 vol. 2009. 96p. pap. 16.95 (978-1-4489-9750-3(X)) PublishAmerica, Inc.
Sider, J. Alexander & Villegas, Isaac S. Presence: Giving & Receiving God. 2011. 230p. pap. 22.00 (978-1-60899-671-1(9), Cascade Bks.) Wipf & Stock Pubs.
Siegle Drege, Ann. The Hard Work of Hope: Reflections of Ray Siegle. 2008. 208p. pap. 14.95 (978-1-880292-29-7(7)) LangMarc Publishing.
Sigmund, Richard. My Time in Heaven: A True Story of Dying & Coming Back. 2010. pap. 12.99 (978-1-60374-123-1(2)) Whitaker Hse.
Sikora, Pat J. Why Didn't You Warn Me? How to Deal with Challenging Group Members. 2007. (Small Group Help Guides). (Illus.). 96p. per. 8.99 (978-0-7847-2075-2(4)) Standard Publishing.
Silas-Thomas, Leola. And God Spoke. 2009. 178p. pap. 18.00 (978-1-4389-2943-9(9)) AuthorHouse.
Silk, David. Bee Parables. 2007. 288p. per. 15.99 (978-1-60266-219-3(3)) Xulon Pr., Inc.
Silva, Ronald M. Puppetmyst. 2008. 280p. (ENG.). 25.99 (978-1-60477-472-6(X)); per. 15.99 (978-1-60477-457-3(6)) Xulon Pr., Inc.
Silver, Maxwell. The Way to God. (978-0-8022-1569-7(6)) Philosophical Library, Inc.
Silvious, Jan. Look at It This Way: Straightforward Wisdom to Put Life in Perspective. 2008. (ENG.). 192p. pap. 12.99 (978-0-307-44492-9(9), WaterBrook Pr.) Doubleday Religious Publishing Group, The.
Simmons, Brian. Falling Away: Why Christians Lose Their Faith & What Can Be Done about It. 2008. 272p. pap. 12.99 (978-0-89112-571-6(X), Leafwood Pubs.) Abilene Christian Univ. Pr.
Simmons, Judy. Ten for Teens & Tweens: God's Laws for Life & Love. 2010. 48p. pap. 10.99 (978-1-60911-640-8(2), Eloquent Bks.) AEG Literary Publishing Services, Inc.
Simmons, Tricia. Intentional Parenting. 2008. pap. 10.99 (978-1-60477-945-5(4)) Xulon Pr., Inc.
Simms, Stewart. Words Not Spoken. 2011. 158p. pap. 12.99 (978-0-88144-167-3(8)) Yorkshire Publishing Group.
Simon-Peter, Rebekah Ellen. Green Church: Reduce, Reuse, Recycle, Rejoice! 2010. 114p. 12.50 (978-1-4267-0292-1(2)) Abingdon Pr.
Simons, Dana. The Root of the Vine: Living a Judeo-Christian Faith. 2009. pap. (978-1-61623-828-5(3)) Independent Pub.
Simora, Timothy W. Words to Live By... Food for the Soul, maybe Food for Thought. 2007. 109p. per. 10.95 (978-1-59824-505-9(6)) E-BookTime LLC.
Simplicity. 2006. per. 24.00 (978-0-9770864-3-5(7)) Plaids & Prints.
Simply Quit Drinking: An Inspirational Journey from near Death. 2008. 112p. pap. 14.95 (978-0-9816134-0-6(3), Reaching Peak Publishing) Reaching Peak, LLC.
Simply Youth Ministry, creator. Guy Talk Girl Talk, No. 2: The Cure for Cooties: 10 More Gender Specific Lessons on Everyday Issues Your Teens Face. 2009. (Illus.). 104p. pap. 29.00 (978-0-7644-6234-4(2)) Group Publishing, Inc.
Simpson, A. B. Amor en la Vida del Creyente: Walking in Love. (SPA.). 160p. (978-84-7228-708-2(4), 220022) Clie, Editorial.
—Andando en el Espiritu: Walking in the Spirit. (SPA.). 160p. (978-84-7228-855-3(2), 220033) Clie, Editorial.
—Como Vivir Vida Cristiana Abundante: How to Live an Abundant Life. (SPA.). 160p. (978-84-7228-889-8(7), 222311) Clie, Editorial.
—Danger Lines in the Deeper Life. pap. 11.99 (978-1-60066-037-5(1)) WingSpread Publishers.
—Tierra de Promision: Land of Promise. (SPA.). (978-84-7645-098-7(2), 223159) Clie, Editorial.
—La Vida de Amor del Senor (Love Life of the Lord) (SPA.). 96p. (978-84-7228-842-3(0), 222912) Clie, Editorial.
—Wholly Sanctified. 2009. 121p. pap. 11.99 (978-1-60066-042-9(8)) WingSpread Publishers.
Simpson, A. B. & Simpson, Albert Benjamin. Wholly Sanctified. 2008. 96p. per. 7.99 (978-1-59986-575-1(0)) Filiquarian Publishing, LLC.
Simpson, Alison. My Ultimate Story: A Discipleship Journal. 2007. (ULT Ser.). (Illus.). 96p. (gr. 6-12). per. 5.99 (978-0-7814-4519-1(1)) Cook, David C.
Simpson, Anise V. The Truth, the Love, & the Light! 2008. 80p. pap. 9.95 (978-0-7414-4724-1(X)) Infinity Publishing.
Simpson, Christopher Ben. The Truth Is the Way: Kierkegaard's Theologia Viatorum. 2010. (ENG.). pap. 85.00 (978-0-334-04371-3(9), SCM Pr.) Hymns Ancient & Modern Ltd GBR. Dist: Westminster John Knox Pr.
Simpson, Douglas. Looking for America: Rediscovering the Meaning of Freedom. 2012. 320p. per. 19.95 (978-1-57921-835-5(0)) WinePress Publishing.
Simpson, Jimmy V. God's Commandments: Concerning Living & Salvation as Recorded in the Holy Bible. 2006. (ENG.). 132p. per. 24.95 (978-1-4241-5528-6(2)) PublishAmerica, Inc.

C

Simpson, Ray & Lee, Brent Lyons. Emerging Downunder. 2008. (ENG.). 236p. (C). pap. 10.00 (978-1-920691-91-2(X)) ATF Pr. AUS. Dist: Brown, David Bk. Co., The.

Simpson, Robert. An Atheist in the Choir Loft. 2011. 176p. 29.99 (978-1-4628-5083-9(9)); pap. 19.99 (978-1-4628-5082-2(0)) Xlibris Corp.

Simpson, Stephen W. What Women Wish You Knew about Dating: A Single Guy's Guide to Romantic Relationships. 2008. (Illus.). 208p. pap. 12.99 (978-0-8010-6840-9(1)) Baker Bks.

Simpson, William D. Living in the Hope of My Imagination: A Compelling Story that Proves the Bible to be A Living Revelation of God. 2010. 264p. pap. 16.99 (978-0-88144-488-9(X), Thorncrown Publishing) Yorkshire Publishing Group.

Sinclair, Donna. The Spirituality of Bread. 2007. (ENG., Illus.). 160p. 34.00 (978-1-896836-85-0(2)) Northstone Publishing, Inc. CAN. Dist: Westminster John Knox Pr.

Sine, Tom. The New Conspirators: Creating the Future One Mustard Seed at a Time. 2008. (ENG.). 304p. per. 16.00 (978-0-8308-3384-9(6), IVP Bks.) InterVarsity Pr.

Sinelli, Todd A. One Simple Word. 2009. (978-1-887357-04-3(1)) Lit Torch Publishing.

Sing to the Lord. Date not set. 2.00 (978-0-687-01280-0(5)) Abingdon Pr.

Singh, Laurance. Biblical Principles & Affirmations for Successful Living. 2009. 168p. pap. 11.99 (978-1-4389-7731-7(X)) AuthorHouse.

Singletary, Jay. What about My Life? How Is Your Sex Life? 2009. 128p. pap. 14.99 (978-1-60791-954-4(0)) Xulon Pr., Inc.

Singleton, Hope Lynn. I Found God. 2011. 98p. pap. 19.95 (978-1-4626-1988-7(6)) PublishAmerica, Inc.

Singleton, Sharon. Extraordinary Journeys of Ordinary Women. 2009. 244p. pap. 14.99 (978-1-4389-9819-0(8)) AuthorHouse.

Siriano, David. Cultural Collapse of America & the Wor. 2006. (ENG.). 31.99 (978-1-60034-622-4(7)); pap. 19.99 (978-1-60034-621-7(9)) Xulon Pr., Inc.

Sisemore, John R. Basic Instructions for the Shy Disciple. 2009. pap. 10.99 (978-1-60799-060-4(1)) Tate Publishing & Enterprises, LLC.

Sisemore, Timothy A. & Sismore, Ruth. World-Proof Your Kids: Raising Children Unstained by the World. 2007. (ENG.). 208p. pap. 12.99 (978-1-84550-275-1(2)) Christian Focus Pubns. GBR. Dist: STL Distribution North America.

Sisk, Mary Lance V. Love Your Neighbor As Yourself: Blessing Your Neighborhood Through Love & Prayer. 3.00 (978-0-9664295-2-7(4), 230010) Sisk, Mary Lance V.

Sister Ross. God & Me. 2010. 52p. pap. 12.99 (978-1-4520-8127-4(1)) AuthorHouse.

Sites, Jimmy. The Pursuit of Faith. Chesbro, Brandon, ed. & photos by by. 2008. (Spiritual Outdoor Adventures Ser.). (ENG., Illus.). 96p. per. 9.99 (978-0-8054-4641-8(9), B&H Bks.) B&H Publishing Group.

Sitze, Bob. It's Not Too Late: A Field Guide to Hope. 2010. (978-1-56699-397-5(0)) Alban Institute, Inc.

Sivley, Michael Ray. A Donated Life: So That Others Can Live. 2011. 92p. pap. 9.95 (978-1-4497-1926-5(0), WestBow Pr.) Author Solutions, Inc.

Sizer, Frank. Into His Presence: How to Find the Ultimate Treasure. 2007. 238p. per. 15.99 (978-0-7684-2487-4(9)) Destiny Image Pubs.

Sizoo, Joseph R. Make Life Worth Living. 2007. (ENG.). 194p. 37.95 (978-0-548-06361-3(3)) Kessinger Publishing, LLC.

Skevington, Andrea. The Pilgrim Spirit. 2007. (ENG., Illus.). 48p. 13.95 (978-0-7459-5254-3(2)) Lion Hudson PLC GBR. Dist: Independent Pubs. Group.

Skid, Cheryl Samelson. Taking God's Word to Heart: 31-Day Devotional Journal. Lowe, Fran D., ed. 2011. 142p. pap. 15.00 (978-1-886068-45-2(3)) Fruitbearer Publishing, LLC.

Skidmore, Ed. A Place at My Father's Table. 2010. 94p. pap. 12.97 (978-0-557-46831-7(0)) Lulu Enterprises Inc.

Skidmore, Kerry A. Get Ready for Christmas. 2007. 60p. per. 9.99 (978-1-60477-007-0(4)) Xulon Pr., Inc.

Skilton, Brent. The Chains of the Prodigal Brother: How We All Became Slaves, & How Jesus Came to Set Us Free. 2010. 340p. pap. 18.99 (978-1-61579-625-0(8)) Xulon Pr., Inc.

Skinner Sullivan, Rhonda. From Desperation to Destiny. 2007. 84p. pap. 10.95 (978-0-9788545-2-2(7)) We Family Ministries.

—Recovery: More Than One Day at A Time. 2007. 94p. pap. 10.95 (978-0-9788545-3-9(5)) We Family Ministries.

Skipper, Kathy. A Rose Is God's Autograph. 2007. (YA). per. 15.20 (978-1-932583-37-3(8)) digital@batesjackson llc.

Skipper, Levi. Spiritual Avalanche: Stopping It Before It Starts. 2011. pap. 10.99 (978-1-61777-563-5(0)) Tate Publishing & Enterprises, LLC.

Skoglund, Elizabeth. Can I Talk to You? Puedo Charlar Contigo? (SPA.). 176p. (978-84-7228-511-8(1), 220730) Clie, Editorial.

Slade, Leonard A. The Season. 2011. 46p. pap. 12.99 (978-1-61215-920-1(6)) Xulon Pr., Inc.

Slater, Donald Leslie & Shaw, Kenneth. It's a Brand New Day. 2007. 52p. per. 22.95 (978-1-4327-1398-0(1)) Outskirts Pr., Inc.

Slaton, Archie. Coming to Terms with Brokenness: How to Find Comfort & Encouragement Through Things Broken. 2011. 112p. 28.95 (978-1-61507-634-5(4)); pap. 11.95 (978-1-61507-633-8(6)) Cross Bks. Publishing.

Slattery, Julianna. Beyond the Masquerade: Unveiling the Authentic You. 2007. (ENG., Illus.). 208p. per. 14.99 (978-1-58997-377-0(1)) Tyndale Hse. Pubs.

Slaughter, Alvin. Reinvent Your Life: How to Turn Your Life Around, Rediscover the Fire of Your Faith, & Get Your Power Back. 2010. (ENG.). 160p. pap. 12.99 (978-1-59979-608-6(2), Charisma Hse.) Charisma Media.

Slaughter, Carolyn. Following Jesus: Steps to a Passionate Faith. 2008. 104p. pap. 10.00 (978-0-687-64958-7(7)) Abingdon Pr.

—Following Jesus Leader's Guide: Steps to a Passionate Faith. 2008. 127p. pap. 16.00 (978-0-687-64948-8(X)) Abingdon Pr.

Slaughter, Michael B. Change the World: Study for Leadership Teams. 2010. 16p. 39.00 (978-1-4267-1012-4(7)) Abingdon Pr.

Slaughter, Sylvia. Messages from Matter: Finding God's Word in the Fundamentals of Chemistry. 2010. 164p. pap. 13.95 (978-1-61507-173-9(3)) Cross Bks. Publishing.

Sleepwalking in Church: Waking up & Staying Alert. 2011. 96p. pap. 17.00 (978-1-4567-3555-5(1)) AuthorHouse.

Sleeth, Nancy. Go Green, Save Green: A Simple Guide to Saving Time, Money, & God's Green Earth. 2009. (ENG.). 432p. pap. 14.99 (978-1-4143-2698-6(X)) Tyndale Hse. Pubs.

Slicker, K. Frederick. Seeking God's Heart: A Devotional Journey Through the Psalms. 2008. 385p. pap. 17.99 (978-0-88144-208-3(9)) Yorkshire Publishing Group.

Sloan, John. Our Faithful Friend: Embracing God's Intimacy. 2007. (Walking with God (Navpress) Ser.). (ENG.). 64p. 8.99 (978-1-57683-620-0(7)) NavPress Publishing Group.

Sloan, Karen E. Flirting with Monasticism: Finding God on Ancient Paths. 2006. (ENG., Illus.). 163p. per. 15.00 (978-0-8308-3602-4(0), IVP Bks.) InterVarsity Pr.

Sloane, J. P. and Shannon. The Christian Counselor's Guide for Restoring Virginity. 2007. pap. 15.99 (978-1-60034-981-2(1)) Xulon Pr., Inc.

Sluder, Nolan. Journey West: A Sharecropper's Son Finds His Divine Destiny And Discovers the Vast Resources God Has in Store for His Children — In this Life. 2008. 200p. 25.99 (978-1-60791-048-0(9)); pap. 15.99 (978-1-60647-885-1(0)) Xulon Pr., Inc.

Sluder, Nolan. Let the Ages Roll. 2011. 116p. 21.23 (978-1-4634-1391-0(2)); pap. 10.68 (978-1-4634-1393-4(9)) AuthorHouse.

Slusser, Jon K. Zeal for His House: Desiring the Way of Christ in How Christians Gather Today. 2011. pap. 14.99 (978-1-61739-321-1(5)) Tate Publishing & Enterprises, LLC.

Small, Brenda L. My Time to Heal. 2008. pap. (978-1-59781-766-0(X)) Xulon Pr., Inc.

Small, Mary Carlock. Excellence Is the Way: In the Service of the King of Kings. 2007. 108p. per. 9.95 (978-1-4327-0932-7(1)) Outskirts Pr., Inc.

Smalley, Gary. Change Your Heart, Change Your Life: How Changing What You Believe Will Give You the Great Life You've Always Wanted. 2012. 256p. pap. 15.99 (978-0-8499-2993-9(8)) Nelson, Thomas Inc.

Smalley, Gary & Trent, John. Leaving the Light On. 2006. 190p. pap. 12.99 (978-1-60142-029-9(3), Multnomah) Doubleday Religious Publishing Group, The.

Smalls, O. Bernard. The Soul of an Artist. 2007. 120p. pap. 13.95 (978-0-615-15409-1(3)) Smalls, Bernard.

Smatt, Janice. In All Your Ways Acknowledge God. 2008. 100p. pap. 9.99 (978-1-60647-132-6(5)) Xulon Pr., Inc.

Smerillo, Daniel J. Samuel's Advice: No Subtitle. 2008. 108p. pap. 9.99 (978-1-60647-326-9(3)) Xulon Pr., Inc.

Smiley, Tom. A Little Talk With Jesus: Conversations With the Master About Life. 2006. (ENG.). 160p. pap. 19.95 (978-0-9774223-6-4(4)) Lifebridge Bks.

Smit, Nina. A Bouquet for Mother: A Sweet Fragrance in My Life. 2007. (Illus.). 83p. (978-1-86920-754-0(8)) Christian Art Pubs.

Smit, Peter-Ben. Fellowship & Food in the Kingdom: Eschatological Meals & Scenes of Utopian Abundance in the New Testament. 2008. xv, 496p. 149.50 (978-3-16-149271-6(4)) Mohr Siebeck GmbH & Co. KG DEU. Dist: Coronet Bks.

Smith, A. E. The Souls of Desperation. 2011. 88p. pap. 9.99 (978-1-4634-4046-6(4)) AuthorHouse.

Smith, Adrian B. The Creative Christian: God & Us; Partners in Creation. 2006. (ENG.). 160p. per. 24.95 (978-1-905047-75-8(4)) Hunt, John Publishing Ltd. GBR. Dist: National Bk. Network.

Smith, Alan & Shaw, Peter. The Reflective Leader. 2011. 128p. pap. 19.99 (978-1-84825-083-3(5), Canterbury Pr. Norwich) Hymns Ancient & Modern Ltd GBR. Dist: Westminster John Knox Pr.

Smith, Allie Marie & Halliday, Judy. HEAL, Healthy Eating & Abundant Living: Your Diet-Free, Faith-Filled Guide to a Fabulous Life. 2008. pap. (978-0-7644-3735-9(6)) Group Publishing, Inc.

Smith, Betty T. Around the World in Seventy Years: Finding Healing & Fulfillment in the Pursuit of God. 2007. (ENG.). 320p. per. 14.99 (978-1-59979-282-8(6), Creation Hse.) Charisma Media.

Smith, Betty T. Beyond the Happy Ending. 2011. (ENG.). 224p. pap. 12.99 (978-1-61638-648-1(7), Creation Hse.) Charisma Media.

Smith, Bill. The Conscience of Man: Understand Its Purpose & Function. 2009. (ENG.). 144p. pap. 10.99 (978-1-59979-725-0(9), Creation Hse.) Charisma Media.

—Sunday Mornings: A Time for Reflection. 2009. 196p. 29.95 (978-1-60844-190-7(3)); pap. 14.95 (978-1-60844-148-8(2)) Dog Ear Publishing, LLC.

Smith, Bruce Ray. Winter Light: A Christian's Search for Humility. 2011. (ENG.). 152p. pap. 12.95 (978-0-9828715-8-4(9), Kalos Pr.) Doulos Resources.

Smith, Catherine. A Voice Crying in the Wilderness: Personal Testimonies. 2009. 196p. pap. 15.95 (978-1-4389-3290-3(1)) AuthorHouse.

Smith, Charles E. & Wolpers, Julie. The Road Is Filled with Bumps & Potholes: Observations on the Christian Life. 2008. 84p. pap. 10.95 (978-0-595-51662-9(9)) iUniverse, Inc.

Smith, Craig. Tough Questions - Real Answers: How Can I Know God's Will? 2008. 132p. per. 7.99 (978-0-9755135-2-1(4)) Shepherd Project Pr.

Smith, Craig H. Every Monday: Finding God on Tough Days. 2009. 176p. 25.49 (978-1-4389-3923-0(X)); pap. 15.99 (978-1-4389-3922-3(1)) AuthorHouse.

Smith, Darlene L. Down at Your Feet Oh Lord. 2009. 48p. pap. 10.49 (978-1-4490-2596-0(X)) AuthorHouse.

Smith, David. Precepts from the Psalms. 2010. 138p. pap. 12.99 (978-0-9845208-3-1(X)) Faithful Life Pubs.

Smith, David L. Divorce & Remarriage: A Primer for Christians. 2008. 118p. pap. 15.00 (978-1-55635-429-8(0)) Wipf & Stock Pubs.

Smith, Donna Tobin. Muddy Feet on the Narrow Path. 2008. 156p. 12.99 (978-1-60604-234-2(3)) Tate Publishing & Enterprises, LLC.

Smith, Dorothy. How to Be a Successful Christian in Today's Troublesome Schools. 2007. 112p. per. 12.95 (978-0-595-46190-5(5)) iUniverse, Inc.

Smith, Dudley. Growing in the Character of Christ. 2009. 129p. pap. 17.01 (978-0-557-05162-5(2)) Lulu Enterprises Inc.

—The Power of Repentance. 2009. 75p. pap. 10.98 (978-1-4116-9726-3(X)) Lulu Enterprises Inc.

Smith, Eddie. Intercesores: Como Entenderlos y Promoverlos para un Trabajo Efectivo, 1 vol. 2007. (SPA.). 170p. per. 8.99 (978-987-557-130-3(X)) Vida Pubs.

Smith, Eddie & Smith, Alice. Spiritual Advocates. 2008. (ENG.). 224p. pap. 14.99 (978-1-59979-374-0(1), Charisma Hse.) Charisma Media.

Smith, Edith. The True Identity of Adam & Eve. 2007. 68p. per. 9.99 (978-1-60266-281-0(9)) Xulon Pr., Inc.

Smith, Edward A. Fruitfulness: Seven Secrets to Getting More Out of Life. 2008. (ENG.). 80p. pap. 8.99 (978-0-9762730-3-5(9)) Vision Publishing.

Smith, Efrem. Jump: Into a Life of Further & Higher. 2010. (ENG.). 192p. pap. 14.99 (978-1-4347-6457-7(5)) Cook, David C.

Smith, Elvira. God Said, Change Your Ways of Living. 2008. pap. 13.95 (978-0-9801564-5-4(9)) Kingdom Publishing Group, Inc.

Smith, Eugene. The Twelve Jesus Chose. 2007. pap. 12.00 (978-1-931178-42-6(9)) Vision Publishing.

Smith, F. LaGard. Meeting God in Quiet Places. 2010. 288p. 9.99 (978-0-7369-3011-6(6)) Harvest Hse. Pubs.

Smith, Fred. Breakfast with Fred. Smith, Brenda A., ed. 2007. (ENG.). 192p. 14.99 (978-0-8307-4476-3(2)) Gospel Light Pubns.

Smith, Gary R. Emindcipation. 2007. 80p. per. 10.95 (978-1-4327-0616-6(0)) Outskirts Pr., Inc.

Smith, Hannah Whitall. The Christian's Secret of a Happy Life. 2007. (ENG.). 100p. per. 7.95 (978-1-933993-59-1(6)) Apocryphile Pr.

—The Christian's Secret of a Happy Life. 2010. (ENG.). 260p. pap. 26.75 (978-1-176-55123-7(X)); (ENG.). 260p. pap. 26.75 (978-1-176-54689-9(9)); 256p. pap. 26.75 (978-1-145-02243-0(X)) BiblioBazaar.

—The Christian's Secret of a Happy Life. 2009. 156p. pap. (978-0-217-57393-1(2)); 154p. pap. (978-0-217-57373-3(8)); 148p. pap. (978-0-217-57375-7(4)) Books LLC.

—The Christian's Secret of a Happy Life. reprint ed. lib. bdg. 48.00 (978-0-7426-1045-3(4)) Classic Bks.

—The Christian's Secret of a Happy Life. 2010. 240p. 41.95 (978-1-161-38182-5(1)) Kessinger Publishing, LLC.

—The Christian's Secret of a Happy Life. 2011. 200p. pap. 14.95 (978-1-4585-0036-6(5)) Univ. of Michigan Library.

—The Christian's Secret of a Happy Life, by H W S. 2006. 204p. per. 18.99 (978-1-4255-1655-0(6)) MPublishing.

—The God of All Comfort. 2010. Orig. Title: Living Confidently in God's Love. 184p. pap. 12.99 (978-1-935785-20-0(6)) Bottom of the Hill Publishing.

—The Record of a Happy Life: Being Memorials of Franklin Whitall Smith, A Student of Princeton College. by His Mother, H. W. S. 2006. 212p. per. 20.99 (978-1-4255-1758-8(7)) MPublishing.

—Secreto de la Vida Cristiana Feliz: Secret of a Happy Christian Life. (SPA.). (978-84-7645-239-4(X), 223235) Clie, Editorial.

Smith, Hannah Whitall & De Rosset, Rosalie. The Christian's Secret of a Happy Life, 1 vol. 2009. (Moody Classics Ser.). (ENG.). 240p. pap. 7.99 (978-0-8024-5656-4(1)) Moody Pubs.

Smith II, R. LaMont. Preaching to improve an economic Deprived. 2006. 23.99 (978-1-59781-608-3(6)) Xulon Pr., Inc.

Smith, James. The House That Richard Built. 2007. 120p. 18.99 (978-1-60266-726-6(8)); per. 10.99 (978-1-60266-725-9(X)) Xulon Pr., Inc.

Smith, James B. Embracing the Love of God: The Path & Promise of Christian Life. 2008. (ENG.). 192p. pap. 13.99 (978-0-06-154269-5(5), HarperOne) HarperCollins Pubs.

Smith, James Bryan. The Good & Beautiful Community: Following the Spirit, Extending Grace, Demonstrating Love. 2010. (Apprentice Ser.). (ENG.). 240p. 23.00 (978-0-8308-3533-1(4), IVP Bks.) InterVarsity Pr.

Smith, James Wesley. You Can Be Free... If You Want To! 2008. 112p. pap. 11.99 (978-1-60791-078-7(0)) Xulon Pr., Inc.

Smith, Jim. Su Increible Futuro: Your Incredible Future. (SPA.). 64p. (978-84-7228-586-6(3), 220856) Clie, Editorial.

Smith, John William. Hugs to Comfort: Stories, Sayings & Scriptures to Encourage & I. 2011. (Hugs Ser.). (ENG.). 128p. pap. 10.99 (978-1-4516-5522-3(3), Howard Bks.) Howard Books.

Smith, Joseph. Pearl of Great Price. 2007. (ENG.). 120p. 19.99 (978-1-59986-694-9(3)) 2006. pap. 9.99 (978-1-59986-966-7(7)) Filiquarian Publishing, LLC.

Smith, Joyce M. Enfrentando los Problemas de la Vida: Coping with Life's Problems. (SPA.). 64p. (978-84-7228-660-3(6), 220368) Clie, Editorial.

Smith, Kathy. Stuck on Stupid: My Story. 2007. 52p. per. 9.95 (978-0-595-46761-7(X)) iUniverse, Inc.

Smith, Kay. Pleasing God. 2008. (ENG.). 288p. pap. 14.99 (978-1-59751-085-1(8)) Word For Today, The.

Smith, Keitha & Brereton, Susan. Mothering Heights: A Novel Approach for Christian Mothers. 2009. 144p. pap. 15.00 (978-0-8170-1544-2(2)) Judson Pr.

Smith, Kelvin. Living on Target: A Lifestyle of Discipleship. 2009. (ENG.). 160p. 12.95 (978-0-9793192-4-2(2)) Lifebridge Bks.

Smith, Lee & Smith, Karen. Restoring America One Family at a Time. 2011. 180p. pap. 13.95 (978-1-4627-0633-4(9)) Cross Bks. Publishing.

Smith, Lolita H. Seasons of Life. 2009. 50p. pap. 15.99 (978-1-4415-9666-6(6)) Xlibris Corp.

Smith, Malcolm. The Power of the Blood Covenant: Uncover the Secret Strength in God's Eternal Oath. annot. ed. 2006. 295p. per. 13.99 (978-1-57794-816-2(5)) Harrison House Pubs.

Smith, Mandy. Making a Mess & Meeting God: Unruly Ideas & Everyday Experiments for Worship. 2010. (ENG.). 144p. pap. 17.99 (978-0-7847-2392-0(3)) Standard Publishing.

Smith, Mariea Calhoun. The Master Is Speaking. 2011. 120p. pap. 19.99 (978-1-4628-4780-8(3)) Xlibris Corp.

Smith, Martin L. Compass & Stars. 2007. 128p. per. 12.00 (978-1-59627-048-0(9)) Church Publishing, Inc.

Smith, Melissa. Entrapments of Lust Promiscuity Sexual I. 2006. 284p. per. (978-1-4243-3034-8(3)) Read Bks.

Smith, Norma J. Walking on Water: Manifestations of the Messiah. 2011. pap. 11.99 (978-1-61346-452-6(5)) Tate Publishing & Enterprises, LLC.

Smith, Oswald J. La Aurora Se Acerca: The Dawn is Coming. (SPA.). (978-84-7645-253-0(5), 223300) Clie, Editorial.

—Hacia un Mundo Mejor: Towards a Better World. (SPA.). (978-84-7645-291-2(8), 223299) Clie, Editorial.

Smith, Pamela. I'm Saved Now What? New Believer's Handbook. 2007. 122p. per. 15.00 (978-0-9752742-5-5(2)) Turning Point Pubns., LLC.

Smith, Pamela R. Access Granted: Entering God's Presence Through Prayer. 2009. 152p. per. (978-0-9752742-7-9(9)) Turning Point Pubns., LLC.

Smith, Paula L. Take up Your Cross. 2010. 80p. pap. 7.99 (978-0-88144-489-6(8)) Yorkshire Publishing Group.

Smith, R. Alan. Our Eyes Are on You: Building Rock-Solid Faith for Faith-Shaking Times. 2010. 184p. pap. 14.99 (978-1-61579-774-5(2)) Xulon Pr., Inc.

Smith, R. Leland. Just a S K: Our Hope. 2011. 144p. 29.99 (978-1-4628-9281-5(7)); pap. 19.99 (978-1-4628-9282-2(5)) Xlibris Corp.

Smith, Richard Dean. Freedom from Dark Forces: A Model for Spiritual Warfare. 2007. 214p. pap. 20.00 (978-0-9673142-3-5(2)) Cross Resources, Inc.

Smith, Robert. Biblical Charity. 29p. pap. 2.99 (978-0-9652883-2-3(3)) Audubon Pr. & Christian Bk. Service.

—Maintain Your Momentum: Do Not Abandon Your God-given Purpose. 2007. 84p. per. 10.99 (978-1-932503-72-2(2)) Insight Publishing Group.

Smith, Robert D. Revelation Love Is the Edification Concerning Spiritual Love in This Changing World. 2007. 30p. pap. 8.00 (978-0-8059-7151-4(3)) Dorrance Publishing Co., Inc.

Smith, Ross. Naked Illusion. 2008. 140p. pap. 14.99 (978-1-60647-317-7(4)) Xulon Pr., Inc.

Smith, Roy L. Don't Kid Yourself: Spiritual Truths from Slang Expressions. 2011. 126p. 40.95 (978-1-258-02172-6(2)) Literary Licensing, LLC.

Smith, S. Darlene. The Mirror Image. 2011. (Illus.). pap. (978-1-55452-644-4(2), Essence Publishing) Essence Publishing.

Smith, Sally Stevens. Voices from the Story. 2011. 236p. pap. 16.50 (978-1-4269-6014-7(X)) Trafford Publishing.

Smith, Stephen W. The Lazarus Life: Spiritual Transformation for Ordinary People. 2008. (ENG.). 208p. pap. 13.99 (978-1-4347-9995-1(6)) Cook, David C.

—Living the Lazarus Life: A Guidebook for Spiritual Transformation, 1 vol. 2009. (ENG.). 176p. pap. 12.99 (978-1-4347-6701-1(9)) Cook, David C.

—Soul Custody: Choosing to Care for the One & Only You, 1 vol. 2010. (ENG.). 224p. pap. 14.99 (978-1-4347-6472-0(9)) Cook, David C.

Smith-Theodore, Rachel. New Way New Life. 2008. 104p. pap. 9.99 (978-1-60647-127-2(9)) Xulon Pr., Inc.

Smith, Toby. Goofy Things Girls Do to Get Guys: Part Encouragement, Part Good Laugh. 2009. 116p. pap. 13.95 (978-1-934363-41-6(3)) Zoe Life Publishing.

Smith, Tony. The Rise & Fall of Satan 'the Accuser' 2009. 59p. pap. 14.91 (978-0-557-14593-5(7)) Lulu Enterprises Inc.

Smith, Tony M. What's Holding You Back? 2011. 82p. pap. 12.99 (978-0-9840955-8-2(6)) Godzchild Inc.

Smith, Vanessa T. A New Beginning in Christ. 2011. 50p. pap. 15.99 (978-1-4568-9671-3(7)) Xlibris Corp.

Smith, Wade C. Say Fellows- Fifty Practical Talks with Boys on Life's Big Issues. 2007. (ENG.). 134p. pap. 18.99 (978-1-4346-0856-7(5)); 152p. pap. 21.99 (978-1-4346-0883-3(2)) BiblioBazaar.

—Say Fellows- Fifty Practical Talks with Boys on Life's Big Issues. 2008. 132p. pap. (978-1-4099-3825-5(5)) Dodo Pr.

Smith, Warren B. Deceived on Purpose: The New Age Implications of the Purpose-Driven Life. 2nd ed. 2006. (ENG.). 211p. per. 14.95 (978-0-9763492-0-4(5), 866 876 3910) Mountain Stream Pr.

Smith, Whitall Hanna. The Christian's Secret to a Happy Life. 2009. 124p. pap. 7.49 (978-1-60459-760-8(7)) Wilder Pubns., Ltd.

Smith, Whitall Hannah. The God of All Comfort. 2011. 208p. pap. 17.95 ***(978-1-60444-559-6(9))*** IndoEuropeanPublishing.com.

Smith, William P. When Bad Things Happen: Thoughtful Answers to Hard Questions. 2008. (ENG.). 24p. 3.99 *(978-1-934885-41-3(X))* New Growth Pr.

Smith, William P. & Smith, Winston P. How Do I Stop Losing It with My Kids? Getting to the Heart of Your Discipline Problems. 2008. (ENG.). 24p. 3.99 *(978-1-934885-28-4(2))* New Growth Pr.

Smith, Winston. Help for Stepfamilies: Avoiding the Pitfalls & Learning to Love. 2008. (ENG.). 24p. 3.99 *(978-1-934885-30-7(4))* New Growth Pr.

Smith, Winston T. Divorce Recovery: Growing & Healing God's Way. 2008. (ENG.). 24p. 3.99 *(978-1-934885-39-0(8))* New Growth Pr.

—Rest. 2006. (Vantage Point Book Ser.). (ENG.). 22p. 3.99 *(978-0-9785567-1-6(2))* New Growth Pr.

Smith, Zachariah. My First 30 Years: A Lost-and-Found Journey of Faith, 1 vol. 2010. 66p. pap. 19.95 *(978-1-4489-4317-3(5))* PublishAmerica, Inc.

Smoak, Jeff. The Lord Struck the Child. 2011. 190p. pap. 15.99 ***(978-1-4583-8938-1(3))*** Lulu Enterprises Inc.

Smylie, Scott. 49 Declarations for Courageous Christian Living. 2007. per. *(978-0-9794263-0-6(8))* Send It Ahead Pubns.

Sneddon, Craig. GOD Used a Cigarette. 2011. pap. 17.99 ***(978-1-61777-524-6(X))*** Tate Publishing & Enterprises, LLC.

Sneed, Charles C. Moving Out of Yourself. 2006. 158p. pap. 24.95 *(978-1-4241-2140-3(X))* PublishAmerica, Inc.

Sneed, Jane. What Do You Do When Your Nickname's Job? You Gotta Have Faith. 2010. pap. 12.99 *(978-1-61663-102-4(3))* Tate Publishing & Enterprises, LLC.

Snelling, Carolyn. Ace: One in Golf & One with God. 2010. (ENG.). 112p. 13.99 *(978-1-61638-153-0(1)*, Creation Hse.) Charisma Media.

—Mulligan. 2009. 128p. 13.99 *(978-1-59779-528-9(3)*, Creation Hse.) Charisma Media.

Snook, Joseph D. Intercession: Touching God through His Promises. 2010. 176p. pap. 16.99 *(978-1-4520-0538-6(9))* AuthorHouse.

Snow, Jl. The Dreamchaser Project. 2011. 396p. pap. 20.99 ***(978-1-61379-129-5(1))*** Xulon Pr., Inc.

Snyder, C. Arnold & Peters, Galen, eds. Reading the Anabaptist Bible: Reflections for Every Day of the Year. 425p. 36.00 *(978-1-894710-25-1(8))* Pandora Pr. CAN. Dist: Herald Pr.

Snyder, John. Resenting God: Causes, Consequences, Cures. 2008. 192p. per. 18.95 *(978-0-9764256-4-9(5))* Appleseed Pr.

—Storm Rider: Surviving & Thriving after Life's Catastrophes. 2008. 248p. per. 18.95 *(978-0-9764256-5-6(3))* Appleseed Pr.

Snyder, Russell J. Emotions: The Controlling Factor in the Church. 2008. 264p. pap. 16.99 *(978-1-60791-064-0(0))* Xulon Pr., Inc.

Snyder, Thomas R. Tribulation or Raptured: The choice Is Yours! 2011. 104p. 24.99 ***(978-1-4628-7846-8(6))***; pap. 15.99 ***(978-1-4628-7845-1(8))*** Xlibris Corp.

So This Is Faith: Becoming an Authentic Disciple of Christ. 2007. (ENG.). 192p. per. 14.99 *(978-0-8341-2303-8(7)*, 083-412-3037) Beacon Hill Pr. of Kansas City.

Sobiech, Katie. Beauty from Brokenness. 2010. 220p. pap. 220.00 *(978-1-4520-1238-4(5))* AuthorHouse.

Soileau, Monica Marie Singleton. Domestic Violence: The Forgotten Victims. 2008. 128p. 21.99 *(978-1-60477-828-1(8))*; pap. 13.99 *(978-1-60477-827-4(X))* Xulon Pr., Inc.

Soles, Richard V., Jr. The Bible Belt. 2008. 127p. pap. 14.95 *(978-0-557-03212-9(1))* Lulu Enterprises Inc.

Somers, Donna. At Home in Abba's Heart. pap. 13.99 *(978-1-59781-057-9(6))* Xulon Pr., Inc.

Sommer, Alan. Take Away the Stone. 2008. 132p. pap. 13.99 *(978-1-60477-755-0(9))* Xulon Pr., Inc.

Sonia Andrews-Okwum. Enforcing God's Life in This Body. 2011. 242p. pap. ***(978-1-907011-14-6(5))*** Esteemworld Pubns.

Soniregun, Babatunde. Faith Prescription. 2007. 380p. per. 19.99 *(978-1-60266-957-4(0))* Xulon Pr., Inc.

Soniregun, Babatunde "Tunde". Faith Prescription Vol. 2: A Practical & Relevant Devotional for Your Daily Journey. 2009. 380p. pap. 20.99 *(978-1-61579-313-6(5))* Xulon Pr., Inc.

Sonnenberg, Roger. We Are Family. stu. ed. 4.50 *(978-0-570-09440-1(2)*, 20-2490) Concordia Publishing Hse.

Sookdeo, Kawal Persaud. Simple Understanding. 2009. (ENG.). 183p. *(978-1-85756-650-5(5))* Janus Publishing Co.

Sooy, Mark S. The Life of Worship: Rethink, Reform, Renew. 2006. 236p. pap. 16.95 *(978-1-60145-047-0(8))* Booklocker.com, Inc.

Sorensen, Susan & Geist, Laura. Praying Through Cancer: Set Your Heart Free from Fear: A 90-Day Devotional for Women, 0 vols. 2007. 208p. pap. 12.99 *(978-0-8499-1882-7(0))* Nelson, Thomas Inc.

Sorenson, Jack, illus. Growing up Cowboy. 2008. 32p. 15.99 *(978-0-7369-2228-9(8))* Harvest Hse. Pubs.

Sorenson, Jane. Five Minutes with God. 2011. (J). *(978-0-87239-893-1(5))* Standard Publishing.

Sorenson, Stephen, et al. God Heard Their Cry Discovery Guide, 1 vol. rev. ed. 2009. (Faith Lessons Ser.). (ENG.). 256p. pap. 9.99 *(978-0-310-29121-3(6))* Zondervan.

Sorenson, Stephen W., ed. The Best of F. B. Meyer: 120 Daily Devotions to Nurture Your Spirit & Refresh Your Soul. 2006. (Honor Classics Ser.). 192p. 14.99 *(978-1-56292-581-9(4)*, 1562925814) Cook, David C.

Sorger, Matt. Power for Life. 2011. E-Book ***(978-1-61638-569-9(3)***, Charisma Hse.) Charisma Media.

Soske, Becky. I Am Not Ashamed. 2008. 80p. pap. 16.95 *(978-1-60610-091-2(2))* PublishAmerica, Inc.

Soulek, Michael. The Resident Voice. 140p. 11.99 *(978-1-59160-235-4(1))* Xulon Pr., Inc.

Southern, Jewel. Taste & See. 2008. 59p. pap. 16.95 *(978-1-60474-103-2(1))* PublishAmerica, Inc.

Sowell, Kimberly. Journey to Significance: Becoming Women of Divine Destiny. 2008. (ENG.). 160p. pap. 12.99 *(978-1-59669-217-6(0))* New Hope Pubs.

Soyars, Andrew. Snakebit! 2007. 130p. pap. 12.99 *(978-0-615-15624-8(X))* SweetFire.

Spain, William S. God Never Wastes an Experience. 2008. 92p. pap. 12.95 *(978-0-9816883-5-7(5))* PearlStone Publishing, Inc.

Sparks, Lloyd. Detour: My Brief but Amusing Career as A Bible Smuggler. 2011. 252p. pap. 19.95 ***(978-1-4620-6040-5(4))*** iUniverse, Inc.

Spear, Gene. What Am I? 2007. 120p. per. 10.99 *(978-1-60266-197-4(9))* Xulon Pr., Inc.

Spearman, Richard. No Expiration Date. 2007. 116p. per. 10.99 *(978-1-60266-603-0(2))* Xulon Pr., Inc.

Special Touch Ministry, Inc. Compel Them to Come In: Reaching People with Disabilities through the Local Church. 2010. 256p. pap. 29.95 *(978-1-4490-7586-6(X))* AuthorHouse.

Specimen Collection. (Specialty Collections). ring bd. 250.00 *(978-1-56238-291-9(8)*, SC2-L) NCCLC.

Speck, Greg O. Sex - It's Worth Waiting For. 2007. (ENG., Illus.). 256p. (gr. 7-12). per. 12.99 *(978-0-8024-7704-0(6))* Moody Pubs.

Speck, Ralph. Is That Really What God Said? Volume One Bible Stories, Parables & Miracles Interpreted for Today's Living. 2007. 112p. per. 19.95 *(978-1-60441-070-9(1))* PublishAmerica, Inc.

Speer, Bruce. Finding Your Way through Faith: A Discipleship Training Workbook. 2011. pap. 23.99 *(978-1-61777-225-2(9))* Tate Publishing & Enterprises, LLC.

Spence, Bob. In the Beginning: The Art of Bob Spence. 2010. 48p. 29.95 *(978-0-692-00367-1(3))* Adonai Art Designs, LLC.

Spence, Jan. What Shall We Do with This Baby? 5.25 *(978-1-55673-655-1(X))* CSS Publishing Co.

Spence, Jr. The I Am Single: Single for A Season, Whole for A Lifetime, Complete for Eternity. 2009. 100p. pap. 12.99 *(978-1-4343-9977-9(X))* AuthorHouse.

Spencer, Diana. God Is Not Like That: Making Sense of Christianity: A New Look at an Old Faith. 2009. 480p. pap. 29.97 *(978-1-4269-1120-0(3))* Trafford Publishing.

—God Is Not Like That - Making Sense of Christianity: A New Look at an Old Faith. 2009. 480p. 39.97 *(978-1-4269-1463-8(6))* Trafford Publishing.

Spencer, Eddie Charles. Put Out the Fire: How to Control Your Anger Before It Destroys Your Life. 2006. (ENG.). 140p. per. 14.99 *(978-1-4141-0858-2(3))* Pleasant Word.

Spencer, Gregory. Awakening the Quieter Virtues. 2010. (ENG.). 197p. pap. 16.00 *(978-0-8308-3735-9(3)*, IVP Bks.) InterVarsity Pr.

Spencer, Jimmy. Love Without Agenda: The art of being Christian. 2009. pap. *(978-1-61623-472-0(5))* Independent Pub.

Spencer, Karen D. And God Said... Just Walk. 2007. (ENG.). 60p. per. 8.95 *(978-0-533-15424-1(3))* Vantage Pr., Inc.

Spencer, Mark D. The Challenge Victorious Living in Another Kingdom: Help for Building Strong Christians & Dynamic Communities of Faith. 2011. 252p. 26.26 ***(978-1-4269-6296-7(7))***; pap. 16.26 ***(978-1-4269-6295-0(9))*** Trafford Publishing.

Spencer, Mark D. The Cry for Spiritual Reality. 2010. 132p. 25.99 *(978-1-4269-2264-0(7))* Trafford Publishing.

Spencer, Michael. Mere Churchianity: Finding Your Way Back to Jesus-Shaped Spirituality. 2010. (ENG.). 240p. pap. 13.99 *(978-0-307-45917-6(9)*, WaterBrook Pr.) Doubleday Religious Publishing Group, The.

Spencer, Nick, et al. Christianity, Climate Change, & Sustainable Living, 1 vol. 2009. (ENG.). 288p. *(978-1-59856-229-3(0))* Hendrickson Pubs. Marketing, LLC.

Spindle, Blair. Fuel: In Depth Discipleship Bible Study. 2007. 48p. 3.99 *(978-0-8341-5016-4(6))* Beacon Hill Pr. of Kansas City.

Spinney, Robert G. Dressed to Kill: Thinking Biblically about Modest & Immodest Clothing. 2007. *(978-0-9776680-8-3(8))* Tulip Bks.

Spirit, Holy & Mahon, Carmen A. Hold On. 2008. 168p. pap. 19.99 *(978-1-4363-1780-1(0))* Xlibris Corp.

The Spiritual Garden; or, Traits of Christian Character Delineated, by Hamilton, Burder & M'Cheyne. 2006. 204p. per. 20.99 *(978-1-4255-1685-7(8))* MPublishing.

Sprague, Michael. Disaster. 2011. 272p. pap. 16.99 ***(978-1-61379-842-3(3))*** Xulon Pr., Inc.

Sprague, Michael & Schenkenberger, Roy. Disaster. 2015. 272p. 26.99 ***(978-1-61379-843-0(1))*** Xulon Pr., Inc.

Sprecher, John-Paul. Young Lions Arise: A Message to Christ's Warriors & Witnesses Around the World. 2009. 100p. pap. 10.99 *(978-1-61579-121-7(3))* Xulon Pr., Inc.

Spring, Gardiner & Kistler, Don. The Distinguishing Traits of Christian Character. 2009. *(978-0-9798579-8-0(8))* Northampton Pr., The.

Sprink, Holly. Faith Postures: Cultivating Christian Mindfulness. 2009. pap. *(978-1-57312-547-5(4))* Smyth & Helwys Publishing, Inc.

Sprouse, Nicky Dawn. The Elements of Life: Faith, Grace, Glory, Hope, Love, Mercy, Peace, Joy & Happiness, 1 vol. 2009. 105p. pap. 16.95 *(978-1-61546-629-0(0))* PublishAmerica, Inc.

Spurgeon, C. H. (Charles Haddon). The Saint & His Saviour; or, the Progress of the Soul in the Knowledge of Jesus by the Rev C H Spurgeon. 2006. 448p. per. 26.99 *(978-1-4255-4950-3(0))* MPublishing.

Spurgeon, Charles H. According to Promise. 2009. 68p. pap. *(978-1-151-41393-2(3))* Books LLC.

—All of Grace. 2007. (ENG.). 132p. per. 8.75 *(978-1-60206-436-2(9))* Cosimo, Inc.

—All of Grace, 1 vol. 2010. (Moody Classics Ser.). (ENG.). 160p. pap. 7.99 *(978-0-8024-5452-2(6))* Moody Pubs.

—Gleanings among the Sheaves. 2009. 232p. 41.95 *(978-1-104-10387-3(7))*; pap. 26.95 *(978-1-104-09109-5(7))* Kessinger Publishing, LLC.

—Lecturas Matutinas.Tr. of Morning & Evening. (SPA.). 384p. *(978-84-7228-903-1(6)*, 220535) Clie, Editorial.

—The New Park Street Pulpit, 6 vols., Set. Incl. Vols. 1 & 2. 1855-1856. 35.00 *(978-1-56186-001-2(8))*; Vols. 3 & 4. 1857-1858. 35.00 *(978-1-56186-002-9(6))*; Vols. 5 & 6. 1858-1859. 35.00 *(978-1-56186-003-6(4))*; 1975. reprint ed. reprint ed. 105.00 *(978-1-56186-000-5(X))* Pilgrim Pubns.

—Segun la Promesa.Tr. of According to Promise. (SPA.). *(978-84-7645-022-2(2)*, 223087) Clie, Editorial.

Spurling, Marshall. Ladder. 2006. pap. 17.99 *(978-1-60034-182-3(9))* Xulon Pr., Inc.

Spurling, Philip. Well, Well, Well! 2006. pap. 12.99 *(978-1-60034-116-8(0))* Xulon Pr., Inc.

St. Helen's Bishopga. John: A Small Group Bible Study. 2008. (ENG.). 304p. 12.99 *(978-1-84550-361-1(9))* Christian Focus Pubns. GBR. Dist: STL Distribution North America.

St. James, Gregory. Jesus Is No Excuse: The Words & Verses of Gregory St. James. 2007. 124p. per. 10.95 *(978-1-59824-501-1(5))* E-BookTime LLC.

St James, Jill, Jr. I'm born again... now What? 2006. *(978-0-9773982-1-8(8))* Wings of Grace Pr.

St. John, Bonnie. Live Your Joy. 2009. (ENG.). 224p. 19.99 *(978-0-446-57925-4(4))* FaithWords.

Staal, David. Words Kids Need to Hear, 1 vol. 2008. (ENG.). 144p. pap. 12.99 *(978-0-310-28098-9(2))* Zondervan.

Stacey W. Smith & Sandra L. Haner. Children of Faith: Sowing Seeds for Eternity. 2011. 256p. 29.99 ***(978-1-4500-7214-4(3))***; pap. 19.99 ***(978-1-4500-7213-7(5))*** Xlibris Corp.

Stachera, Marek. Hell: The Doorway to Heaven. 2007. 108p. per. 13.90 *(978-1-4120-9952-3(8))* Trafford Publishing.

Stadler, Lisa. Straightalk: Your Issues, Your Problems, Your Solutions. 2007. (ENG.). 192p. per. 10.99 *(978-1-84550-260-7(4))* Christian Focus Pubns. GBR. Dist: STL Distribution North America.

Stahl, David. Adventures with God. 2008. 332p. pap. 17.99 *(978-1-4389-2831-9(9))* AuthorHouse.

Stahl, Shirley. Where Do I Serve You Lord? Wherever There Is a Need! 2009. (ENG.). 144p. pap. 11.99 *(978-1-58169-085-9(1)*, Axiom Pr.) Genesis Communications, Inc.

Stam, Jeff. Welcome & Enfold: Helping New People Find Their Place in Your Church. (Training & Equipping the Team Ser.). stu. ed. 2.95 *(978-1-56212-495-3(1)*, 216590) Faith Alive Christian Resources.

Stanard, Terry. Meet the man who can change your life Forever. 2007. (Illus.). 32p. 9.95 *(978-0-9794885-0-4(8))* Art of Faith Publishing.

Standard Publishing Staff. Top Secret Rubber Stamp: A family event for your Church. 2009. (F3: Faith, Fun, Family Ser.). (ENG.). (J). 1.99 *(978-0-7847-2305-0(2))* Standard Publishing.

Standard Publishing Staff, creator. Conquering Crisis: Lessons from the Life of Job. 2007. (Encounter Bible Lessons Ser.). cd-rom 24.99 *(978-0-7847-1879-7(2))* Standard Publishing.

—Resolving Conflict: Biblical Principles for Resolving Differences. 2007. (Encounter Digital Bible Lessons Ser.). (J). cd-rom 24.99 *(978-0-7847-1887-2(3))* Standard Publishing.

—Strong Women: Learning from Old Testament Heroines. 2007. (Encounter Digital Bible Lessons Ser.). cd-rom 24.99 *(978-0-7847-1882-7(2))* Standard Publishing.

Standley, G. F. Eternal Life or Eternal Existence. 2008. 176p. pap. 14.99 *(978-1-60647-843-1(5))* Xulon Pr., Inc.

Stanford, Shane. You Can't Do EVERYthing ... So Do SOMEthing: Small Ways to Change the World. 2010. 102p. pap. 14.00 *(978-1-4267-0590-8(5))* Abingdon Pr.

Stanich, Susan. Finding Shirley. 2007. 272p. per. 15.99 *(978-1-60266-464-7(1))* Xulon Pr., Inc.

Stanko, John W. The Faith Files-Volume: The Gospels. 2008. 128p. pap. 10.99 *(978-1-58169-282-2(X))* Genesis Communications, Inc.

Stanley, Andy. Breakaway Study Guide. 2006. (Northpoint Resources Ser.). (ENG.). 112p. pap., stu. ed. 9.99 *(978-1-59052-663-7(5)*, Multnomah) Doubleday Religious Publishing Group, The.

—Faith, Hope, & Luck: Discover What You Can Expect from God, 1 vol. 2009. (ENG.). 80p. pap. 9.99 *(978-0-310-32422-5(X))* Zondervan.

—How Good Is Good Enough?, Pk. 6. 2009. (LifeChange Bks.). (ENG.). 96p. pap. 19.99 *(978-1-60142-250-7(4)*, Multnomah) Doubleday Religious Publishing Group, The.

—The Principle of the Path: How to Get from Where You Are to Where You Want to Be. 2011. 224p. pap. 15.99 *(978-0-8499-4636-3(0))* Nelson, Thomas Inc.

—Starting Point, 1 vol., Kit. 2008. (ENG.). spiral bd. 69.99 *(978-0-310-28617-2(4))* Zondervan.

—Starting Point: Find Your Place in the Story, 1 vol. 2008. (ENG.). 128p. spiral bd. 24.99 *(978-0-310-28676-9(X))* Zondervan.

—Twisting the Truth: Learning to Discern in a Culture of Deception, 1 vol. 2008. (ENG.). 96p. pap. 9.99 *(978-0-310-28766-7(9))* Zondervan.

Stanley, Brad. Unwilling to Concede: Discovering God's Redeeming Commitment in a Broken World. 2008. (ENG.). 176p. pap. 12.99 *(978-1-59979-369-6(5)*, Creation Hse.) Charisma Media.

Stanley, Charles. Surviving in an Angry World: Finding Your Way to Personal Peace. 2011. (ENG., Illus.). 256p. pap. 14.99 *(978-1-4391-9057-9(7)*, Howard Bks.) Howard Books.

Stanley, Charles & Stanley, Charles F. Listening to God, 0 vols. 2009. (Life Principles Study Ser.). 128p. pap. 9.99 *(978-1-4185-4115-6(X))* Nelson, Thomas Inc.

Stanley, Charles F. Advancing Through Adversity, 0 vols. 2008. (Life Principles Study Ser.). 128p. pap. 9.99 *(978-1-4185-3333-5(5))* Nelson, Thomas Inc.

—Cómo Sobrevivir en un Mundo llendo de Enojo: Encuentre su Camino a la paz Personal. 2010.Tr. of Surviving in an Angry World - Finding Your Way to Personal Peace. (SPA & ENG., Illus.). 272p. pap. 14.99 *(978-1-4516-0216-6(2)*, Howard Bks.) Howard Books.

—Developing Inner Strength: Living in the Joy of God's Love, 0 vols. 2008. (Life Principles Study Ser.). 128p. per. 9.99 *(978-1-4185-2815-7(3))* Nelson, Thomas Inc.

—Experiencing Forgiveness, 0 vols. 2008. (Life Principles Study Ser.). (ENG.). 128p. pap. 9.99 *(978-1-4185-3337-3(8))* Nelson, Thomas Inc.

—Finding Peace: God's Promise of a Life Free from Regret, Anxiety, & Fear, 0 vols. 2007. 240p. per. 14.99 *(978-0-7852-8860-2(0))* Nelson, Thomas Inc.

—Finding Peace: God's Promise of a Life Free from Regret, Anxiety, & Fear. l.t. ed. 2006. (Walker Large Print Ser.). (ENG.). 320p. pap. 17.95 *(978-1-59415-124-8(5)*, Walker Large Print) Cengage Gale.

—Landmines in the Path of the Believer: Avoiding the Hidden Dangers, 0 vols. 2008. 256p. pap. 14.99 *(978-1-4002-8031-5(1))* Nelson, Thomas Inc.

—Leaving a Godly Legacy: Give the Inheritance That Really Matters. 2008. (Life Principles Study Ser.). (ENG.). 128p. per. 9.99 *(978-1-4185-2818-8(8))* Nelson, Thomas Inc.

—Life Principles for the Graduate: Nine Truths for Living God's Way, 0 vols. 2009. 128p. 15.99 *(978-1-4041-8698-9(0))* Nelson, Thomas Inc.

—Living the Extraordinary Life: Nine Principles to Discover It. l.t. ed. 2008. (ENG.). 352p. pap. 17.95 *(978-1-59415-243-6(8)*, Walker Large Print) Cengage Gale.

—Living the Extraordinary Life: Nine Principles to Discover It, 0 vols. 2008. 240p. pap. 14.99 *(978-1-4002-8008-7(7))* Nelson, Thomas Inc.

—Practicing Basic Spiritual Disciplines, 0 vols. 2009. (Life Principles Study Ser.). (SPA.). 128p. pap. 9.99 *(978-1-4185-4117-0(6))* Nelson, Thomas Inc.

—Preparing for Christ's Return, 0 vols. 2009. (Life Principles Study Ser.). 128p. pap. 9.99 *(978-1-4185-4118-7(4))* Nelson, Thomas Inc.

—Protecting Your Family, 0 vols. 2008. (Life Principles Study Ser.). 128p. per. 9.99 *(978-1-4185-2813-3(7))* Nelson, Thomas Inc.

—Relying on the Holy Spirit: Experience the Joy-Filled Walk with God by Learning to Hear His Voice, 0 vols. 2008. (Life Principles Study Ser.). (ENG.). 128p. pap. 9.99 *(978-1-4185-3336-6(X))* Nelson, Thomas Inc.

—Stuck in Reverse: How to Let God Change Your Direction, 0 vols. 2008. 160p. per. 7.99 *(978-1-4002-0094-8(6))* Nelson, Thomas Inc.

—Surviving in an Angry World: Finding Your Way to Personal Peace. 2010. (ENG., Illus.). 256p. 24.00 *(978-1-4391-8356-4(2)*, Howard Bks.) Howard Books.

—Talking with God, 0 vols. 2008. (Life Principles Study Ser.). 128p. pap. 9.99 *(978-1-4185-3334-2(3))* Nelson, Thomas Inc.

Stanley, Verdree B. Spit Fire; God's Wrath. 2008. 72p. pap. 16.95 *(978-1-4327-1875-6(4))* Outskirts Pr., Inc.

Stapf, Irvin F., Jr. Not for This Life Only: A Study for Growth into Maturity as the Children of God. 2009. (J). pap. 11.99 *(978-1-60799-753-5(3))* Tate Publishing & Enterprises, LLC.

Star, J. D. God's Last Call. 2008. 516p. pap. 29.95 *(978-1-4343-8846-9(8))* AuthorHouse.

Star, Pastor & Star, Anniston. By the Book: A Collection of Faith Columns, Sermons Notes & Speeches. Cook, Anthony, ed. 2011. 436p. pap. 30.95 ***(978-1-4497-2729-1(8)***, WestBow Pr.) Author Solutions, Inc.

Starr, Frank. Sharing the Christian Faith. stu. ed. 5.75 *(978-0-570-09922-2(6)*, 20-2124) Concordia Publishing Hse.

Stassen, Glen H. A Thicker Jesus: Incarnational Discipleship in a Secular Age. 2012. (ENG.). 160p. pap. 25.00 ***(978-0-664-23817-9(3))*** Westminster John Knox Pr.

State Convention Planning Committee, compiled by. Fearless: Fierce, Equipped & Compassionate. 2009. 80p. pap. 10.00 *(978-0-9818488-4-6(2))* Ajoyin Publishing, Inc.

Statesel, Frank. Second Jewels, 1 vol. 2010. 64p. pap. 19.95 *(978-1-4512-0094-2(3))* PublishAmerica, Inc.

Stauff, Leland. Power & Control: A Biblical Expose of a Frequently Ignored Problem in the Church. 2007. pap. 12.00 *(978-0-8059-8517-7(4))* Dorrance Publishing Co., Inc.

Steagald, Thomas R. Praying for Dear Life: A Reason to Rise, Strength for the Day, Courage to Face the Night. 2006. (7 Minutes Ser.). (ENG.). 224p. pap. 12.99 *(978-1-57683-816-7(1))* NavPress Publishing Group.

Stearns, Gail J. Open Your Eyes Toward Living More Deeply in the Present. 2010. 150p. pap. 19.00 *(978-1-60899-635-3(2),* Wipf and Stock) Wipf & Stock Pubs.
Stearns, Richard. The Hole in Our Gospel: What Does God Expect of Us? The Answer That Changed My Life & Might Just Change the World. l.t. ed. 2010. 416p. pap. 17.99 *(978-1-59415-323-5(X))* Cengage Gale.
—The Hole in Our Gospel: What Does God Expect of Us? The Answer That Changed My Life & Might Just Change the World, 0 vols. 2010. 352p. pap. 15.99 *(978-0-8499-4700-1(6))* Nelson, Thomas Inc.
Stearns, Rob. Rise Up. Frusher, Stephanie, ed. 2007. 208p. per. 9.95 *(978-0-9766555-1-0(9))* Consumed Publishing.
Stearns, Robert. The Cry of Mordecai: Awakening an Esther Generation in a Haman Age. 2009. 199p. pap. 16.99 *(978-0-7684-2754-7(1))* Destiny Image Pubs.
—Impossible Dream. 2007. 16.00 *(978-0-9665831-8-2(3))* Kairos Publishing.
Stearns, Robert, ed. Watchmen Manual: A Practical Guide to Prayer for Jerusalem & Her People. 2007. pap., training bk. ed. 16.95 *(978-0-9665831-6-8(7))* Kairos Publishing.
Stearns, Robert, et al. Return to Authentic Christianity: An in-depth look at 12 Vital Issues Facing Today's Church. 2010. (ENG.). pap. 14.99 *(978-0-7684-3134-6(4))* Destiny Image Pubs.
Stecker, Chuck. Passage: Blessing Our Youth into Godly Adulthood. 2009. *(978-1-60006-458-6(2))* NavPress Publishing Group.
Stedman, Ray L. La Iglesia Resucita: Body Life. (SPA.). 164p. *(978-84-7228-174-5(4),* 220489) Clie, Editorial.
Steed, Josh. Faith & Football: A Look at Life Through A Facemask. 2009. 176p. pap. 15.99 *(978-1-4490-0365-4(6))* AuthorHouse.
Steed, Tim. Ask Me about My Vow of Silence: The Roughest 3 Minutes of My Life. 2007. 176p. per. 12.95 *(978-1-60148-000-2(8))* Xyzzy Pr.
Steeger, Robert. Conquering the Spirit of Unworthiness. 2006. pap. 9.99 *(978-1-60034-432-9(1))* Xulon Pr., Inc.
Steel, Robert. Doing Good or, the Christian in Walks of Usefulness. 2007. (ENG.). 442p. 51.95 *(978-0-548-15222-5(5))*; 444p. per. 36.95 *(978-1-4304-4586-9(6))* Kessinger Publishing, LLC.
Steele, Chris & Wetherholt, Jason. Living a Life on Loan Student Devotions. 2007. (Illus.). 92p. per. 5.99 *(978-0-7847-1885-8(7))* Standard Publishing.
Steele, Daniel. Milestone Papers. pap. 7.99 *(978-0-88019-153-1(8))* Schmul Publishing Co., Inc.
Steele, Debilynne. The Orphaned Son: From Tragedy to Triumph: One Child's Story. 2011. pap. 7.99 ***(978-1-61739-186-6(7))*** Tate Publishing & Enterprises, LLC.
Steele, Mark. Christianish: What If We're Not Really Following Jesus at All?, 1 vol. 2009. (ENG.). 272p. pap. 14.99 *(978-1-4347-6692-2(6))* Cook, David C.
—Set Apart: God's Steadfast Pursuit of You. 2009. 192p. pap. 13.99 *(978-1-57794-881-0(5))* Harrison House Pubs.
Steen, David A. God of Wonders: A Daily Devotional. 2012. ***(978-0-8280-2511-9(8))*** Review & Herald Publishing Assn.
Steen, Sandra. Who Stole My Joy? Uncover the Joy Robbers of Your Present Circumstance & Discover the Joy Builders of Your Best Life. 2007. 192p. pap. 14.99 incl. audio compact disk *(978-0-88270-343-5(9))* Bridge-Logos Foundation.
Steenhoek, Brian L. Straight from God. 2009. 328p. pap. 18.99 *(978-1-60791-540-9(5))* Xulon Pr., Inc.
Stegg, Victoria. Rebel with a Godly Call. 2009. 168p. pap. 12.00 *(978-1-4389-3445-7(9))* AuthorHouse.
Steichen, Donna. Chosen: How Christ Sent Twenty-three Surprised Converts to Replant His Vineyard. 2009. 340p. pap. 16.95 *(978-1-58617-340-1(5))* Ignatius Pr.
Steidl, Grant. Conflit. 2008. 96p. pap. 7.95 *(978-2-921905-03-9(5))* Editions le mieux-etre CAN. Dist: AtlasBooks Distribution.
Steinberg, Joseph. The Book of Y. 2008. (ENG.). 176p. 15.99 *(978-1-86024-568-8(4))* Authentic Media.
Steiner, Rudolf. The Christ Mystery in Relation to the Secret of Pentecost. 2010. 48p. pap. 12.76 *(978-1-163-18126-3(9))* 2010. 50p. 30.95 *(978-1-161-64032-8(0))* 2007. (ENG.). 48p. per. 15.95 *(978-1-4325-8220-3(8))* Kessinger Publishing, LLC.
Steinhauer, R. L. Bloody Nails Guilty Hands. 2010. (ENG.). 192p. pap. 17.99 *(978-1-4490-8486-8(9))* AuthorHouse.
Stellrecht, Terri M. How My Savior Leads Me. 2011. 192p. 30.95 ***(978-1-4497-2573-0(2))***; pap. 13.95 ***(978-1-4497-2572-3(4))*** Author Solutions, Inc. (WestBow Pr.).
Stenhouse, Everett. You don't have to wear a HALO to be a HOLY PARSON: Seven Essentials for Successful Pastoral Ministry. 2011. 144p. pap. 11.95 ***(978-1-4497-2866-3(9),*** WestBow Pr.) Author Solutions, Inc.
Stenstrom, H., et al, eds. Scandinavian Critique of Anglo-American Feminist Theology - Skandinavische Kritik angloamerikanischer feministischer Theologie - Critique scandinave de la théologie féministe Anglo-américaine. 2007. (Journal of the European Society of Women in Theological Research Ser.). (ENG.). 292p. (C). pap. 39.00 *(978-90-429-1974-7(4))* Peeters Pubs. & Booksellers BEL. Dist: Brown, David Bk. Co., The.
Stephen, Matt, ed. Pencils, Paper, & Prayer: Christian Devotions for Educators. 2010. pap. 14.99 *(978-1-61663-852-8(4))* Tate Publishing & Enterprises, LLC.
Stephens, Charles Paul. The Variety of the Spiritual Awakening: How Some of Us Found Our Way to Jesus. 2008. 164p. per. 12.95 *(978-1-4327-2096-4(1))* Outskirts Pr., Inc.
Stephens, J. Steve. The Rapture Event. 2008. 172p. 21.99 *(978-1-60477-753-6(2))*; pap. 13.99 *(978-1-60477-752-9(4))* Xulon Pr., Inc.
Stephens, Joni. More Than Enough. 2008. 80p. pap. 9.99 *(978-1-60647-045-9(0))* Xulon Pr., Inc.
Stephens, Steve. The Wounded Warrior: A Survival Guide for When You're Beat up, Burned Out, or Battle Weary. 2006. (ENG.). 224p. pap. 13.99 *(978-1-59052-705-4(4),* Multnomah) Doubleday Religious Publishing Group, The.
Stephens Velejouste, Willie M. V. The Right Mind: Utilizing the Mind as God Intended. 2011. 84p. pap. 14.99 ***(978-1-4634-2917-1(7))*** AuthorHouse.
Stephenson, Andy & Winford, Rick. Taking It to the Streets: Leader's Guide. 2011. (Illus.). 82p. pap. 16.00 ***(978-1-59317-535-1(3))*** Warner Pr. Pubs.
—Taking It to the Streets: Student's Journal. 2011. (ENG., Illus.). 131p. (YA). pap. 9.00 ***(978-1-59317-537-5(X))*** Warner Pr. Pubs.
Stephenson, Dotty. Widowhood, the Definitive Turning Point. 2007. per. 12.95 *(978-0-9772160-2-4(0))* Darling Publishing.
Stephenson, Jody. Faltering Towards Perfection: Art, Faith, & Everything in Between. 2007. (Illus.). 192p. 24.95 *(978-0-9798998-0-5(X))* Planet Eureka Springs Pr.
Stephenson, John M. Watchman, How Far Gone Is the Night? (Illus.). 246p. *(978-0-9630771-5-8(5))* Living-Faith Outreach.
Stephenson, Kenneth D. How to Explain the Trinity. 2008. 92p. pap. 10.99 *(978-1-60647-941-4(5))* Xulon Pr., Inc.
Stepp, Adrian. Step into the Light. 2008. 52p. pap. 9.95 *(978-0-595-51826-5(5))* iUniverse, Inc.
Sterrett, Lew. Life Lessons from a Horse Whisperer, 1 vol. 2010. (ENG., Illus.). 192p. pap. 13.99 *(978-0-8254-6316-7(5),* Monarch Bks.) Lion Hudson PLC GBR. Dist: Kregel Pubns.
Stetson, Chuck, ed. Creating the Better Hour: Lessons from William Wilberforce. 2007. 349p. per. 24.95 *(978-0-9796462-1-8(9))* Stroud & Hall Publishing.
Steven Scherrer Th.D. Desert Living: Contemplative Living as the Context for Contemplative Praying. 2009. 160p. 24.95 *(978-1-4401-7657-9(4))*; pap. 14.95 *(978-1-4401-7655-5(8))* iUniverse, Inc.
Stevens, Becca. Find Your Way Home: Words from the Street, Wisdom from the Heart. 2008. 119p. pap. 10.50 *(978-0-687-64705-7(3))* Abingdon Pr.
Stevens, Jimmy R. New Beginnings: The Making of a Faith Champion. 2009. 164p. pap. 13.49 *(978-1-4389-1113-7(0))* AuthorHouse.
Stevens, Kathy. My Covenant with God for Protection. 2006. 362p. per. 25.99 *(978-1-59886-401-4(7))* Tate Publishing & Enterprises, LLC.
Stevens, Leona. Dare to Grow up & Love It! 2007. 148p. per. 13.99 *(978-1-60266-876-8(0))* Xulon Pr., Inc.
Stevens, Robert Joseph. Defending the Faith Series: Catholicism vs. Fundamentalist Christianity. 2009. 100p. pap. 15.49 *(978-1-4389-3561-4(7))* AuthorHouse.
Stevenson, John W. Worshiper by Design: A Unique Look at Why We Were Created. 2009. 132p. pap. 14.99 *(978-1-61579-163-7(9))* Xulon Pr., Inc.
Stevenson, Michael A. Straight Up: The Church's Official Response to the Epidemic of Downlow Living. 2006. (ENG.). 64p. pap. 7.99 *(978-1-59979-013-8(0),* Creation Hse.) Charisma Media.
Steward, Tilly. Revival in the Land - Are You Ready for It?, Vol. 1. 2008. (ENG.). 480p. pap. 17.99 *(978-1-59979-533-1(7),* Creation Hse.) Charisma Media.
Stewart, Ann Marie. Preparing My Heart for Easter: A Woman's Journey to the Cross & Beyond. 2006. (ENG.). 144p. (gr. 11). per. 14.99 *(978-0-89957-053-2(4))* AMG Pubs.
Stewart, Bob G. Another Adultery: Dysfunction Within the House of God. 2007. 52p. per. 16.95 *(978-1-4241-6671-8(3))* PublishAmerica, Inc.
Stewart-Bull, Lydia W. Blackberry Vein. 2006. 45p. per. 8.95 *(978-1-59824-235-5(0))* E-BookTime LLC.
Stewart, Clyde A. Life Without the Father: A Man's Guide to Fatherhood. 2010. pap. 12.99 *(978-1-61566-222-7(7))* Tate Publishing & Enterprises, LLC.
Stewart, Donald. It's Still Okay to Laugh: Helping You Live A Healthier Life. 2011. 342p. pap. 24.95 ***(978-1-4327-7463-9(8))*** Outskirts Pr., Inc.
Stewart, Donald K. Honest Reflections from the Heart: Eternal Perspectives. 2010. 68p. pap. 12.95 *(978-1-4327-5638-3(9))* Outskirts Pr., Inc.
—If I Were A Demon: For Real. 2010. 355p. pap. 21.95 *(978-1-4327-6099-1(8))* Outskirts Pr., Inc.
—Spiritual Illumination: Honest Questions from the Heart. 2010. 360p. pap. 23.95 *(978-1-4327-5412-9(2))* Outskirts Pr., Inc.
Stewart, Gary P. & Demy, Timothy J. Contentment. (It Happens When Ser.). 96p. 3.99 *(978-0-8254-3678-9(8))* Kregel Pubns.
—Romance. (It Happens When Ser.). 96p. 3.99 *(978-0-8254-3681-9(8))* Kregel Pubns.
Stewart, James A. The Christian Life & How to Live It. pap. 2.49 *(978-1-56632-065-8(8))* Revival Literature.
—Come O Breath. pap. 2.99 *(978-1-56632-056-6(9))* Revival Literature.
—God's New Thing, Ambassador for Christ, Glorious Third Person. pap. 2.99 *(978-1-56632-047-4(X))* Revival Literature.
—Hallelujah! Christ Is Mine. pap. 2.49 *(978-1-56632-037-5(2))* Revival Literature.
—I Must Tell: Revival Behind the Iron Curtain. pap. 2.99 *(978-1-56632-060-3(7))* Revival Literature.
—The Lordship of Christ. pap. 1.49 *(978-1-56632-062-7(3))* Revival Literature.
Stewart, James A. & Stewart, Ruth. The Wonder of God's Tomorrow. 2.99 *(978-1-56632-028-3(3))* Revival Literature.
Stewart, LaChante. I Believe in Miracles. 2009. pap. 15.99 *(978-1-4363-8634-0(9))* Xlibris Corp.
Stewart, Pamela K. He Made a Way to Escape: Finding Freedom from an Alternative Lifestyle. 2009. 108p. pap. 11.99 *(978-1-60791-933-9(8))* Xulon Pr., Inc.
Stewart, Ruth. Our Heavenly Inheritance. 4.99 *(978-1-56632-022-1(4))*; pap. 2.99 *(978-1-56632-023-8(2))* Revival Literature.
Stewart-Sykes, Alistair. On the Two Ways: Life or Death, Light or Darkness: Foundational Texts in the Tradition. 2010. *(978-0-88141-850-7(1))* St. Vladimir's Seminary Pr.
Steyn, Hansie. The King Saul Spirit. 2009. 236p. pap. 15.99 *(978-1-60791-533-1(2))* Xulon Pr., Inc.
Stibbe, Mark. One Touch from the King Change. 2007. (ENG.). pap. 14.99 *(978-1-86024-597-8(8))* Authentic Media.
Stickney, Doris. Water Bugs & Dragonflies: Explaining Death to Young Children. 2009. *(978-0-8298-1858-1(8))* Pilgrim Pr., The/United Church Pr.
Still, William. Theological Studies in the Christian Life: Towards Spiritual Maturity, What It Is to be a Christian, Prayer, Morals, Rhythms of Rest & Work. (Collected Writings of William Still: Vol. 2). 327p. *(978-0-946068-48-7(8))* Rutherford Hse.
—Towards Spiritual Maturity: Overcoming Evil in the Christian Life. 2010. (ENG.). 96p. 9.99 *(978-1-84550-574-5(3))* Christian Focus Pubns. GBR. Dist: STL Distribution North America.
Stillingfleet, Edward. Works of Edward Stillingfleet with a Life by Richard Bentley, 6 vols. reprint ed. lib. bdg. 400.00 *(978-0-404-06270-5(9))* AMS Pr., Inc.
Stock, Jon R., et al. Inhabiting the Church: Biblical Wisdom for a New Monasticism. 2006. (New Monastic Library: Resources for Radical Discipleship: Ser.). 140p. pap. 18.00 *(978-1-59752-990-7(7),* Cascade Bks.) Wipf & Stock Pubs.
Stockdale, Jean. Proverbs & Principles for Parenting Practically Perfect Progeny: Timeless Truths for Training Tots through Teens. 2006. 192p. per. 14.95 *(978-0-929292-22-9(7),* CrossHouse Publishing) Hannibal Bks.
—Run Well, Finish Strong: Passing the Baton of Faith to the Next Generation: A study in the Book of II Timothy. 2007. 224p. pap. 16.95 *(978-0-929292-90-8(1),* CrossHouse Publishing) Hannibal Bks.
Stockpole, Robert A. Saint Peter Lives in Rome: An Anglican Discovers the Minisrty of the Pope. 2006. (ENG.). 180p. pap. 13.95 *(978-1-59614-112-4(3))* Marian Pr.
Stockstill, Larry. The Remnant: Restoring integrity in American Christianity. 2008. 192p. pap. 14.99 *(978-1-59979-363-4(6),* Charisma Hse.) Charisma Media.
Stoddard, Solomon. A Guide to Christ. 2009. 66p. pap. *(978-1-151-43697-9(6))* Books LLC.
Stoeker, Fred & Stoeker, Jasen. Hero: Becoming the Man She Desires. 2009. (ENG.). 240p. 13.99 *(978-1-4000-7109-8(7),* WaterBrook Pr.) Doubleday Religious Publishing Group, The.
Stokes, Jennifer, ed. God's Blueprint for Prayer: A Guide to Approaching God in Prayer - HIS Way. 2007. 144p. pap. *(978-0-9785308-0-8(2))* Father's Hse. Publishing.
Stokes, Jerome. You Can Do It! Now Is Your Time to Win. 2007. (ENG.). 176p. per. 12.95 *(978-0-9786581-0-6(8))* Lifebridge Bks.
Stone, Brian. Teach Your Family the Truth: Building on the Basics of the Faith. 2008. (Family Focal Point Ser.). 123p. pap. *(978-1-84625-129-0(X))* DayOne Pubns.
Stone, Darla. In Christ Alone: When Your Husband Does Not Walk with Him. 2010. pap. 11.99 *(978-1-61663-104-8(X))* Tate Publishing & Enterprises, LLC.
Stone, Gary. What If Everyone Lived Next Door to Jesus? And Other Meditations from a Missionary's Heart. 2008. pap. 19.95 *(978-1-934749-14-2(1),* 1-800-747-0738) Hannibal Bks.
Stone, Jayel. The Power to Build A Man: Empowering Women about Their Men or Future Mates. 2010. 76p. pap. 12.99 *(978-1-4520-4676-1(X))* AuthorHouse.
Stone, Perry. Angels on Assignment: God's Relentless Protection of You & Your Loved Ones. 2009. (ENG.). 176p. 15.99 *(978-1-59979-752-6(6),* Charisma Hse.) Charisma Media.
—Breaking the Jewish Code: Twelve Secrets That Will Transform Your Life, Family, Health, & Finances. 2009. (ENG.). 256p. 21.99 *(978-1-59979-467-9(5),* Charisma Hse.) Charisma Media.
—Secrets from Beyond the Grave: A Biblical Guide to the Mystery of Heaven, Hell & Eternity. 2010. (ENG.). 248p. pap. 15.99 *(978-1-61638-157-8(4),* Charisma Hse.) Charisma Media.
Stone, Samuel. The Secret to Fruitful Life. 2007. 244p. (ENG.). 24.99 *(978-1-60266-634-4(2))*; per. 14.99 *(978-1-60266-633-7(4))* Xulon Pr., Inc.
Stoner, Claire, illus. Good Friends Are Like Angels: They Add Blessings to Life. 2010. 48p. 12.99 *(978-0-7369-2582-2(1))* Harvest Hse. Pubs.
Stoner, Marcia J., ed. Live It! Being a Friend for Tweens: Building Skills for Christian Living. 2006. (Live It! Ser.). (Illus.). 63p. 15.95 *(978-0-687-49514-6(8))* Abingdon Pr.
—Live It! Building Character for Tweens: Building Skills for Christian Living. 2007. (Live It! Ser.). (Illus.). 63p. 15.95 *(978-0-687-49815-4(5))* Abingdon Pr.
—Live It! Dealing with Anger for Tweens: Building Skills for Christian Living. 2006. (Live It! Ser.). (Illus.). 63p. 15.95 *(978-0-687-49534-4(2))* Abingdon Pr.
—Live It! Growing Spiritually for Tweens: Building Skills for Christian Living. 2006. (Live It! Ser.). (Illus.). 63p. 15.95 *(978-0-687-49805-5(8))* Abingdon Pr.
—Live It! Living Positively in a Media Age for Tweens: Building Skills for Christian Living. 2006. (Live It! Ser.). (Illus.). 63p. 15.95 *(978-0-687-49785-0(X))* Abingdon Pr.
—Live It! under Pressure for Tweens: Building Skills for Christian Living. 2007. (Live It! Ser.). (Illus.). 63p. pap. 15.95 *(978-0-687-49825-3(2))* Abingdon Pr.
Stortenbecker, Jim. Christian Wake up Call. 2008. 204p. pap. 14.99 *(978-1-60647-465-5(0))* Xulon Pr., Inc.
Story, Mike. One Man's Journey: A Pastor's Progress in Discipleship. 2007. 160p. per. 14.95 *(978-0-9788201-9-0(3))* IMD Pr.
Stott, John. The Cross, 1 vol. 2009. (LifeGuide Bible Studies). (ENG.). 64p. pap. 8.00 *(978-0-8308-3127-2(4),* IVP Conn.) InterVarsity Pr.
—Your Mind Matters: The Place of the Mind in the Christian Life. 2nd ed. 2006. (IVP Classics Ser.). (ENG., Illus.). 93p. per. 7.00 *(978-0-8308-3408-2(7),* IVP Bks.) InterVarsity Pr.
Stott, John, et al. Issues Facing Christians Today, 1 vol. 4th ed. 2006. (ENG.). 512p. pap. 19.99 *(978-0-310-25269-6(5))* Zondervan.
Stoudemire, Reverend Sheldon. The Street Ministry Experience. 2011. 68p. pap. 19.95 ***(978-1-4560-7921-5(2))*** PublishAmerica, Inc.
Stouffer, Austin. 95 More for the Door. 2008. 184p. pap. *(978-1-897373-19-4(8))* Word Alive Pr.
Stout, Mark Howard. Arrowproof: What It Means to Have Faith. 2011. 208p. pap. 17.95 ***(978-1-61507-882-0(7))*** Cross Bks. Publishing.
Stowell, Joseph M. From the Front Lines: Lessons from the Trenches of Life. 2007. (ENG.). 256p. per. 13.99 *(978-1-57293-233-3(3))* Discovery Hse. Pubs.
Strachan, Owen & Sweeney, Doug. Jonathan Edwards on Beauty, 1 vol. 2010. (Essential Edwards Collection). (ENG.). 160p. pap. 9.99 *(978-0-8024-2458-7(9))* Moody Pubs.
—Jonathan Edwards on the Good Life, 1 vol. 2010. (Essential Edwards Collection). (ENG.). 160p. pap. 9.99 *(978-0-8024-2459-4(7))* Moody Pubs.
—Jonathan Edwards on True Christianity, 1 vol. 2010. (Essential Edwards Collection). (ENG.). 160p. pap. 9.99 *(978-0-8024-2460-0(0))* Moody Pubs.
Strack, Diane & Brunson, Debbie. Quiet Influence: The Romans 12:1 Woman. 2009. 92p. pap. *(978-1-60006-670-2(4))* NavPress Publishing Group.
Stradford, Katrina. Psychology 808: Knowledge of Self. 2010. 538p. pap. 68.95 *(978-0-557-20941-5(2))* Lulu Enterprises Inc.
Strain, Daniel. How Things Work. 2007. 128p. per. 13.99 *(978-1-60477-206-7(9))* Xulon Pr., Inc.
Strang, Joy, ed. By Love Transformed: A Collection of Inspirational Readings. 2006. (Illus.). 382p. 14.99 *(978-1-59185-981-9(6),* Charisma Hse.) Charisma Media.
Strength of a Black Man: Destined for Self Empowerment. 2006. *(978-0-9791406-0-0(9))* McCollum, Walter.
Strength Within Surviving by the Grace of God. 2nd rev. ed. 2008. 288p. pap. 15.00 *(978-0-615-21031-5(7))* Tyler, Roland Vincent.
Strickland, Bela C. One Wrong Bite: What Wrong Really Is, Where Evil Really Began, How to Really Get Right with God, & What We Really Gain. 2009. 140p. 22.99 *(978-1-60791-868-4(4))*; pap. 14.99 *(978-1-60791-867-7(6))* Xulon Pr., Inc.
Strickland, Jennifer. Girl Perfect: An Imperfect Girl's Journey to True Perfection (Confessions of a Former Runway Model) 2008. (ENG., Illus.). 208p. pap. 14.99 *(978-1-59979-343-6(1))* Charisma Media.
Stringer, Lillie. Burnt Barley Spared Blessing. 2010. 68p. 24.99 *(978-1-4535-2787-0(7))*; pap. 15.99 *(978-1-4535-2786-3(9))* Xlibris Corp.
Strite, Eugene. Coins Left Over. 2009. pap. 18.00 *(978-1-61584-250-6(0))* Independent Pub.
Strobel, Lee. God's Outrageous Claims: Discover What They Mean for You. l.t. ed. 2007. (Walker Large Print Ser.). (ENG.). 415p. per. 17.95 *(978-1-59415-172-9(5),* Walker Large Print) Cengage Gale.
—God's Outrageous Claims: Discover What They Mean for You, 1 vol. 2009. (ENG.). 272p. pap. 3.49 *(978-0-310-28577-9(1))* Zondervan.
Strom, Kay Marshall. The Second-Half Adventure: Don't Just Retire-Use Your Time, Skills, & Resources to Change the World. 2009. (ENG.). 144p. pap. 14.99 *(978-0-8024-7875-7(1))* Moody Pubs.
Strong, Bethany. Favorite Son. *(978-0-917250-06-4(0))* Parable Pr.
Strong, Gary. His Most Excellent Way: A Biblical Approach to Living A Life of Christ-Like Loving. 2011. 104p. 19.95 ***(978-1-4620-5653-8(9))***; pap. 9.95 ***(978-1-4620-5654-5(7))*** iUniverse, Inc.
Strong, Jeff. Mere Disciple: a spiritual guide for emerging Leaders. 2010. 184p. pap. 17.99 *(978-0-557-41973-9(5))* Lulu Enterprises Inc.
Strong, Lori. Take up the Sword of the Spirit. 67p. pap. 8.99 *(978-1-59185-278-0(1),* Creation Hse.) Charisma Media.
Strong, Terri. Inspiration for Life's Journey. 2011. 80p. pap. 9.99 ***(978-1-4634-4612-3(8))*** AuthorHouse.
Strukova, Jana. A Vocational Model of Confirmation. 2009. 236p. pap. *(978-3-639-17524-0(7))* VDM Verlag Dr. Mueller e.K.
Struthers, Marilyn F. Butterflies & Beyond: Preparing A Young Child to Cope with Grief or Loss. 2011. 44p. pap. 20.95 *(978-1-4497-1098-9(0),* WestBow Pr.) Author Solutions, Inc.
Stubbs, Len. Decision Time: A Guide to the Real Answers, Real Solutions & Real Results of Christ Centered Living. 2009. 226p. pap. 18.95 *(978-1-4401-2797-7(2))* iUniverse, Inc.
Stuckey, Jim D. A Christian's Primer & Beyond. 2011. 172p. 29.99 ***(978-1-4568-7440-7(3))***; pap. 19.99 ***(978-1-4568-7439-1(X))*** Xlibris Corp.
Stuckey, Lasonya M. Created to Prosper: Going from Just Enough to More Than Enough. 2008. 200p. 25.99 *(978-1-60791-174-6(4))*; pap. 15.99 *(978-1-60791-165-4(5))* Xulon Pr., Inc.
Studdert Kennedy, Geoffrey A. After War, Is Faith Possible? The Life & Message of Geoffrey Woodbine Willie Studdert Kennedy. Walters, Kerry, ed. 2008. 238p. pap. 26.00 *(978-1-55635-379-6(0),* Cascade Bks.) Wipf & Stock Pubs.
Studioclicks. Real-Esteem: Your children need you more than you Know! 2008. 103p. pap. 10.95 *(978-0-9792029-0-2(6))* Studioclicks.
Studt, Kimberley. Let the Glory Come Down. 2007. (ENG.). 244p. per. *(978-1-55452-146-3(7))* Essence Publishing.

Sub FBS Access Learner Guide. 11.55 *(978-0-633-05062-7(8))* LifeWay Christian Resources.
Sub FBS Advanced Bible Study Commentary. 21.95 *(978-0-633-05044-3(X))* LifeWay Christian Resources.
Sub FBS All Youth. ldr.'s ed. 18.95 *(978-0-633-05045-0(8))* LifeWay Christian Resources.
Sub FBS All Youth Leader Pack. 79.35 *(978-0-633-05077-1(6))* LifeWay Christian Resources.
Sub FBS All Youth Learner Guide. 8.75 *(978-0-633-05047-4(4))*; 9.15 *(978-0-633-05046-7(6))* LifeWay Christian Resources.
Sub FBS Collegiate Learner Guide. 11.55 *(978-0-633-05048-1(2))* LifeWay Christian Resources.
Sub FBS Grades 1-3 Learner Guide. 9.15 *(978-0-633-05049-8(0))* LifeWay Christian Resources.
Sub FBS Grades 4-6 Learner Guide. 9.15 *(978-0-633-05050-4(4))* LifeWay Christian Resources.
Sub FBS Leader Guide for Grades 1-3 And 4-6. 18.95 *(978-0-633-05051-1(2))* LifeWay Christian Resources.
Sub FBS Leader Pack for Grades 1-3 And 4-6. 79.35 *(978-0-633-05083-2(0))* LifeWay Christian Resources.
Sub FBS Life Answers Learner Guide. 9.95 *(978-0-633-05053-5(9))* LifeWay Christian Resources.
Sub FBS Life Truths. ldr.'s ed. 18.95 *(978-0-633-05054-2(7))* LifeWay Christian Resources.
Sub FBS Life Truths Learner Guide. 9.95 *(978-0-633-05055-9(5))* LifeWay Christian Resources.
Sub FBS Older Youth. ldr.'s ed. 18.95 *(978-0-633-05056-6(3))* LifeWay Christian Resources.
Sub FBS Older Youth Learner Guide. 9.15 *(978-0-633-05057-3(1))* LifeWay Christian Resources.
Sub FBS Preteen. ldr.'s ed. 18.95 *(978-0-633-05059-7(8))* LifeWay Christian Resources.
Subritzky, Bill. Victory in Jesus. 224p. pap. *(978-1-85240-324-9(1))* Sovereign World, Ltd.
Suel, Joelle. Counting the Cost: Essential Truths to Answering God's Call. 2010. pap. 9.99 *(978-1-61566-777-2(6))* Tate Publishing & Enterprises, LLC.
Suire, Pastor CeCeJo. The Wind Carries His Whisper. 2008. 120p. per. 19.95 *(978-1-60474-580-1(0))* PublishAmerica, Inc.
Sulack, Pete & Slay, Tony. Fellowshipping with His Voice. 2009. 148p. 22.99 *(978-1-60647-755-7(2))*; pap. 14.99 *(978-1-60647-754-0(4))* Xulon Pr., Inc.
Sullivan, Brad. Stepping into Manhood: A Take-Action Handbook for Men. 2008. 160p. 24.00 *(978-1-4389-2664-3(2))*; pap. 15.00 *(978-1-4389-2663-6(4))* AuthorHouse.
Sullivan, Clint. Heaven or Hell, It's Your Choice. 2009. 76p. pap. 9.95 *(978-1-60693-246-9(2)*, Eloquent Bks.) AEG Literary Publishing Services, Inc.
Sullivan, Kimberly. Questions: Choices Are What Hold Us to You, You Are What Hold Us to Our Questions. 2006. (ENG.). 60p. per. 16.95 *(978-1-4241-5397-8(2))* PublishAmerica, Inc.
Sullivan, Maria. A New Name. 2006. pap. 15.99 *(978-1-60034-697-2(9))* Xulon Pr., Inc.
Sullivan, Ralph Hilary. Do You Know What Your Son Said to Me: How Jimmy channeled his suffering into a quest to lead others to God. 2007. (Illus.). 144p. pap. 12.95 *(978-0-9796216-0-4(7))* Sullivan, Ralph.
Sullivan, Rita. Lordship Through Friendship: An Inspirational Journey. 2009. 196p. pap. 14.99 *(978-1-61579-508-6(1))* Xulon Pr., Inc.
Summers, Alvin J. Why Praise. 2008. 120p. pap. 10.99 *(978-1-60647-328-3(X))* Xulon Pr., Inc.
Summers, Jeremy & LeRoy, Matthew. Awakening Grace: Spiritual Practices to Transform Your Soul. 2012. ***(978-0-89827-431-8(1))*** Wesleyan Publishing Hse.
Summers, Oliver E. What Is God up to? - Why Earth?- Why Eternity? 2008. 380p. pap. 23.99 *(978-1-60647-635-2(1))* Xulon Pr., Inc.
Summers, Sandra. Rainbow in the Night Sky! (A Prophetic & Apostolic Vernissage) 2010. pap. 11.99 *(978-1-61579-566-6(9))* Xulon Pr., Inc.
Summers, Steve. Friendship: Exploring its Implications for the Church in Postmodernity. 2011. (ENG.). 224p. pap. 44.95 ***(978-0-567-55635-6(2)***, T&T Clark Int'l) Continuum International Publishing Group, Ltd. GBR. Dist: National Bk. Network.
Summers, Sue L. Terrible Tenderness: The Bride, a Burnt Offering. pap. 10.00 *(978-0-9676616-3-6(3))* Media Alert!
Sumrall, Abner C. Correcting Your Child in Love: A Christian Parent's Manual - A Biblical Guide for Loving Discipline. 2009. (Illus.). 124p. pap. 11.99 *(978-1-61579-262-7(7))* Xulon Pr., Inc.
Sumrall, Lester. Siempre Adelante: Run with the Vision. (SPA.). 208p. *(978-84-7228-546-0(4)*, 360755) Clie, Editorial.
Sun Clothed Woman. pap. 0.95 *(978-0-937408-08-7(5))* GMI Pubns.
Surratt, Greg. Ir-Rev-Rend: Christianity Without the Pretense, Faith Without the Façade. 2011. (ENG.). 224p. 19.99 ***(978-0-446-57212-5(8))*** FaithWords.
Surviving Hurricanes: Deliver Us from Evil. 2006. 242p. 24.95 *(978-0-9748086-2-8(8))* Amelia Island Publishing.
Susan M. Provost. Where Is God in Your Life? Three Retreats in Christian Spirituality. 2009. 420p. 31.95 *(978-1-4269-2120-9(9))*; pap. 21.95 *(978-1-4269-2119-3(5))* Trafford Publishing.
Suszek, Lynne & Suszek, Mark. First Wash the Inside: Escaping Hypocrisy - A Guidebook to Freedom in Christ. 2009. 172p. pap. 14.99 *(978-1-61579-317-4(8))* Xulon Pr., Inc.
Sutera, Henrietta. How to Live the Wonderful Christian Life. 2009. 380p. pap. 20.99 *(978-1-60647-739-7(0))* Xulon Pr., Inc.
Sutherland, Arthur. I Was a Stranger: A Christian Theology of Hospitality. 2006. 100p. pap. 14.00 *(978-0-687-06324-6(8))* Abingdon Pr.
Sutherland, Richard. Motivational Dynamics with God's Word. 2008. 164p. pap. 24.95 *(978-1-60610-549-8(3))* PublishAmerica, Inc.
Sutherlin, Wanda Marie. The Journey to Boaz: A Lifetime of Crossroads. 2007. 48p. per. 9.95 *(978-1-4327-1276-1(4))* Outskirts Pr., Inc.
Suttle, Tim. An Evangelical Social Gospel? Finding God's Story in the Midst of Extremes. 2011. 120p. pap. 15.00 ***(978-1-61097-541-4(3)***, Cascade Bks.) Wipf & Stock Pubs.
Sutton, Agneta & Sutton. Christian Bioethics. 2008. (Guides for the Perplexed Ser.). (ENG.). 192p. 110.00 *(978-0-567-03196-9(9)*, T&T Clark Int'l) Continuum International Publishing Group, Ltd. GBR. Dist: National Bk. Network.
Sutton, Edward. The Witness Protection Program for the Church. 2007. 184p. per. 13.99 *(978-1-60266-927-7(9))* Xulon Pr., Inc.
Svoboda, Melannie. In Steadfast Love: Letters on the Spiritual Life. 2007. 160p. per. 14.95 *(978-1-58595-628-9(7))* Twenty-Third Pubns./Bayard.
Swain, Alison Campbell. The Angels'healing Garden. 2011. 44p. pap. 14.99 ***(978-1-61379-046-5(5))*** Xulon Pr., Inc.
Swan, Bernadette & Swan, Kevin. Spiritual Warfare 101 Made Simple. 2008. 128p. pap. 14.99 *(978-1-60647-778-6(1))* Xulon Pr., Inc.
Swan, Terry. Soul Explorers: An Invitation to the Called Life. 2008. *(978-1-55452-315-3(X))* Essence Publishing.
Swaningson, Dan. To My Girls: Advice & Encouragement from a Father's Heart. 2010. pap. 9.99 *(978-1-61663-953-2(9))* Tate Publishing & Enterprises, LLC.
Swank, Monica L. True Dependence. 2007. 84p. pap. 16.95 *(978-1-4241-9415-5(6))* PublishAmerica, Inc.
Swann, Karen. Seven Days Verses Seven Years: The Danger of Disobeying God. 2009. 64p. pap. 10.99 *(978-1-61579-254-2(6))* Xulon Pr., Inc.
Swann, Tg. Authorized Bible of Santa Claus. 2006. pap. 10.00 *(978-1-4257-2890-8(1))* Xlibris Corp.
Swanson, C. D. Passages of Everyday Life: Through Faith: A Look at Everyday Life with God in Control. 2011. 137p. pap. 16.95 *(978-1-4327-7361-8(5))* Outskirts Pr., Inc.
Swanson, Rona. Heart of Christmas. 2010. 116p. pap. 11.95 *(978-1-61507-166-1(0))* Cross Bks. Publishing.
Swearingen, Rodger. Why Bad Things Happen to Good People. Swearingen, Rodger et al, eds. 2009. 150p. pap. 20.00 *(978-1-935444-18-3(2))* World Audience Pubs.
Sweet, Leonard. 11: Indispensable Relationships You Can't Be Without. 2008. 256p. pap. *(978-1-4347-9981-4(6)*, Madison Hse. Pubs., Inc.) Cook, David C.
Sweet, Muriel J. No Stoppin' Them Preachin' Women. 1 vol. 2009. 138p. pap. 24.95 *(978-1-61546-879-9(X))* PublishAmerica, Inc.
Sweeting, George. How to Begin the Christian Life. 2012. (ENG.). 176p. pap. 8.99 ***(978-0-8024-3582-8(3))*** Moody Pubs.
Sweezy, Loy. How to Get Out of a Tough Spot. 2007. 100p. pap. 9.99 *(978-0-9717546-2-1(4))* Sweezy, Loy B.
—Let Go or Get Dragged. 2007. 116p. pap. 12.00 *(978-0-9717546-8-3(3))* Sweezy, Loy B.
—Overcoming Bad Habits. 2007. 332p. 25.99 *(978-0-9717546-1-4(6))* Sweezy, Loy B.
Sweezy, Loy B. Encouraging Scriptures. 2008. 140p. pap. 13.99 *(978-0-9717546-4-5(0))* Sweezy, Loy B.
—365 Inspirational Quotes. 2008. 236p. pap. 14.99 *(978-0-9717546-3-8(2))* Sweezy, Loy B.
Swenson, Richard. In Search of Balance: Keys to a Stable Life. 2010. (LifeChange Ser.). (ENG.). 240p. pap. 15.99 *(978-1-60006-698-6(4))* NavPress Publishing Group.
Swenson, Richard A. The Overload Syndrome: Learning to Live Within Your Limits. 2007. (Guidebook Ser.). (ENG.). 224p. pap. 14.99 *(978-1-57683-131-1(0))* NavPress Publishing Group.
Swenson, Timothy. Stand & Confess. 2010. 98p. pap. 12.92 *(978-0-557-28806-9(1))* Lulu Enterprises Inc.
Swindoll, Charles R. Attitude: Your Most Important Choice. 26p. pap. 3.99 *(978-1-57972-213-5(X))* Insight for Living.
—Choices: Decisions That Shape Integrity. 31p. pap. 3.99 *(978-1-57972-224-1(5))* Insight for Living.
—Dealing with Defiance: God's Plan for Overcoming Rebellion. 37p. pap. 3.99 *(978-1-57972-215-9(6))* Insight for Living.
—Dear Graduate: Letters of Wisdom, 0 vols. 2008. (Illus.). 144p. 15.99 *(978-1-4041-1363-3(0))* Nelson, Thomas Inc.
—Finishing Touch, 0 vols. 2008. 640p. pap. 21.99 *(978-1-4002-7800-8(7))* Nelson, Thomas Inc.
—Frente a lo Imposible. (Serie Realidades - Realities Ser.).Tr. of Impossibilities. (SPA.). 22p. 1.79 *(978-1-56063-100-2(7)*, 498116) Editorial Unilit.
—Getting Through the Tough Stuff: It's Always Something!, 0 vols. 2006. (ENG.). 256p. per. 14.99 *(978-0-8499-1320-4(9))* Nelson, Thomas Inc.
—The Grace Awakening: Believing in Grace Is One Thing. Living It Is Another, 0 vols. 2006. 304p. per. 14.99 *(978-0-8499-1188-0(5))* Nelson, Thomas Inc.
—The Grace Awakening: Believing in grace is one thing. Living it is Another, 0 vols. 2010. 416p. pap. 16.99 *(978-1-4002-0293-5(0))* Nelson, Thomas Inc.
—A Life Well Lived Bible Companion: Discover the Rewards of an Obedient Heart, 0 vols. 2008. (Illus.). 128p. per. 9.99 *(978-1-4185-3099-0(9))* Nelson, Thomas Inc.
—Moses: A Man of Selfless Devotion. l.t. ed. 2009. (Great Lives from God's Word Ser.). (ENG.). 707p. pap. 17.99 *(978-1-59415-290-0(X))* Cengage Gale.
—Our Mediator. 35p. pap. 3.99 *(978-1-57972-226-5(1))* Insight for Living.
—Parenting: From Surviving to Thriving, 0 vols. 2006. (Illus.). 272p. 19.99 *(978-0-8499-0024-2(7))* Nelson, Thomas Inc.
—This Is No Time for Wimps! The Discipline of Durability. 31p. pap. 3.99 *(978-1-57972-233-3(4))* Insight for Living.
—When Your Comfort Zone Gets the Squeeze. 29p. pap. 3.99 *(978-1-57972-236-4(9))* Insight for Living.
Swindoll, Luci. Simple Secrets to a Happy Life. 2012. 224p. 15.99 ***(978-1-4002-0353-6(8))*** Nelson, Thomas Inc.
Swinnock, George. The Fading of the Flesh & the Flourishing of Faith. Yuille, J. Stephen, ed. 2009. 176p. pap. 10.00 *(978-1-60178-072-0(9))* Reformation Heritage Bks.
Swinski, Joe-Paul. The Battleground of Rational Fear. 2011. 82p. pap. ***(978-1-926765-30-3(3))*** Gospel Folio Pr.
Swinton, John & Payne, Richard, eds. Living Well & Dying Faithfully: Christian Practices for End-of-Life Care. 2009. 320p. pap. 25.00 *(978-0-8028-6339-3(6))* Eerdmans, William B. Publishing Co.
Swope, Korbet. Cross Training Basics. 2007. 116p. per. 10.99 *(978-1-60266-377-0(7))* Xulon Pr., Inc.
Sylvester, Gloria. Don't Miss Your Destiny. 2007. 84p. per. 9.99 *(978-1-60266-103-5(0))* Xulon Pr., Inc.
Symonds, Anna. Becoming You. 2008. 226p. *(978-1-906221-77-5(4))* Troubadour Publishing Ltd.
Synago Student Led Senior High Cell Group Training Video. 15.00 *(978-0-687-05023-9(5))* Abingdon Pr.
Synan, Vinson. Voices of Pentecost. 188p. pap. 10.99 *(978-0-8307-3513-6(5)*, Regal Bks.) Gospel Light Pubns.
Sytsma, William. Follow the Leader: Discover the Dynamic Journey of Discipleship. 2006. 211p. pap. 24.95 *(978-1-4241-5560-6(6))* PublishAmerica, Inc.
Szymanski, Helen. Christmas Through a Child's Eyes: True Stories That Capture the Wonder of the Season. 2008. (ENG.). 288p. pap. 9.95 *(978-1-59869-644-8(0))* Adams Media Corp.
Taber, Clinton E. Earth's Final Dawn. 2011. 306p. pap. 18.99 ***(978-1-61379-264-3(6))*** Xulon Pr., Inc.
Tackett, Del & Ware, Jim. Daily Travelogue: Scripture Devotional. 2007. (Illus.). x, 211p. pap. *(978-1-58997-530-9(8))* Focus on the Family Publishing.
Tackett, Roy G. Taught by the Spirit. 2007. pap. 9.99 *(978-1-60266-771-6(3))* Xulon Pr., Inc.
Tada, Joni Eareckson. Finding God in Hidden Places. 2010. 160p. 9.99 *(978-0-7369-2830-4(8))* Harvest Hse. Pubs.
—A Lifetime of Wisdom: Filled with God's Priceless Rubies, 1 vol. 2009. (ENG.). 240p. 21.99 *(978-0-310-27342-4(0))* Zondervan.
—A Place of Healing: Wrestling with the Mysteries of Suffering, Pain, & God's Sovereignty. 2010. (ENG.). 224p. 21.99 *(978-1-4347-6532-1(6))* Cook, David C.
—A Place of Healing: Wrestling with the Mysteries of Suffering, Pain, & God's Sovereignty. 2010. 216p. *(978-1-4347-0206-7(5))* Kingsway Pubns.
—31 Days Toward Passionate Faith. 2007. (31 Days Ser.). (ENG.). 176p. 12.99 *(978-1-59052-423-7(3)*, Multnomah) Doubleday Religious Publishing Group, The.
Taddeo, Daniel. The Controversy: Godliness vs. Worldliness. 2010. 213p. pap. 14.95 *(978-0-7880-2227-2(X)*, Fairway Pr.) CSS Publishing Co.
—¿Qué Es lo Derecho? ¿Qué Está Mal? Una Guía Inspiradora para Encontrar las Respuestas. 2011.Tr. of What's Right? What's Wrong? (SPA.). 146p. pap. ***(978-1-926918-79-2(7)***, CCB Publishing) CCB Publishing.
—What's Right? What's Wrong? An Inspirational Guide to Finding the Answers. 2011. 138p. pap. ***(978-1-926918-51-8(7)***, CCB Publishing) CCB Publishing.
Tadema, Rits. Living in the 3 O'Clock Position. 2007. 280p. per. 15.99 *(978-1-60266-577-4(X))* Xulon Pr., Inc.
Tadevatsi, Grigor. Book of Questions. Ghazarian, Vatche, tr. 2006. *(978-1-931834-14-8(8))*, Mayreni) Mayreni Publishing.
Taft, Donald C. The Christian Journey: The Lay Ministry Weekend. 2009. 112p. pap. 11.50 *(978-1-4389-3621-5(4))* AuthorHouse.
Tainted Mirror: An Anthology. 2007. 229p. per. 14.95 *(978-0-9786066-1-9(2)*, Passionate Pens) Pen of the Writer, LLC.
Talbot, John Michael. The World Is My Cloister: Living from the Hermit Within. 2010. 128p. pap. 16.00 *(978-1-57075-858-4(1))* Orbis Bks.
Talley, Sr. Jesus Christ Made Straight A's. 2009. 220p. 24.99 *(978-1-4490-0644-0(2))*; pap. 14.49 *(978-1-4490-0643-3(4))* AuthorHouse.
Tally, Lori. Dear God, No One Told Me: For the Grieving Soul. 2011. 164p. 29.99 ***(978-1-4653-4824-1(7))***; pap. 19.99 ***(978-1-4653-4823-4(9))*** Xlibris Corp.
Talmadge, Lewis Martin. A Christian Talks with God. 2011. 52p. pap. 15.99 ***(978-1-4568-4985-6(9))*** Xlibris Corp.
Talmage, T. De Witt. Around the Tea-Table. 2009. 242p. pap. *(978-0-217-44030-1(4))*; 298p. pap. *(978-0-217-17569-2(4))*; 256p. pap. *(978-0-217-72433-3(7))* Books LLC.
—Around the Tea-Table. 2006. pap. *(978-1-4068-0773-8(7))* Echo Library.
Talton, Lisa. Thank God for Flip-Flops. 2007. 84p. per. 16.95 *(978-1-4241-9687-6(6))* PublishAmerica, Inc.
Tan, Chantha. River of Wisdom: Process to Living under Grace. 2009. 164p. pap. 26.00 *(978-1-4389-9114-6(2))* AuthorHouse.
Tan, Tee Khoon. Give As He Pleases. 2007. 76p. per. 9.99 *(978-1-60266-681-8(4))* Xulon Pr., Inc.
Tanner, Christy. It's Not about Us, 1 vol. 2009. 78p. pap. 14.95 *(978-1-61582-010-8(8))* PublishAmerica, Inc.
Tanner, John S. Notes from an Amateur. 2011. (Illus.). 144p. 24.99 ***(978-0-8425-2801-6(6)***, Brigham Young Univ. Religious Studies Ctr.) Brigham Young Univ.
Tanner, Kathryn. Christ the Key. 2009. (Current Issues in Theology Ser.). (ENG.). 322p. 74.00 *(978-0-521-51324-1(3))*; pap. 29.99 *(978-0-521-73277-2(8))* Cambridge Univ. Pr.
Tanzella-Nitti, Giuseppe. Faith, Reason, & the Natural Sciences: The Challenge of the Natural Sciences in the Work of Theologians. 2009. (ENG.). 286p. pap. 27.00 *(978-1-934542-12-5(1))* Davies Group Pubs., The.
Tapanes, April A. The Truth about Salvation. 2007. 141p. per. 11.99 *(978-1-59886-978-1(7))* Tate Publishing & Enterprises, LLC.
Tardif, Emiliano. Vuelta al Mundo Sin Maleta.Tr. of Journeying Around the World Without Luggage. (SPA.). 288p. pap. 6.95 *(978-980-350-397-0(9))* Sociedad de San Pablo VEN. Dist: St Pauls/Alba Hse. Pubs.
Tarpley, R. Michael. Be Fruitful & Multiply: Spiritual Pregnancy. 2009. 156p. 22.99 *(978-1-4490-5205-8(3))*; pap. 12.99 *(978-1-4490-5204-1(5))* AuthorHouse.
Tarrant, Jimmy. Solitary Confinement. 2009. 132p. 24.99 *(978-1-60791-735-9(1))*; pap. 14.99 *(978-1-60791-734-2(3))* Xulon Pr., Inc.
Tashiro, Patricia. An Angel Whispered. 2011. (ENG.). 127p. pap. 14.95 ***(978-1-84694-428-4(7))*** O Bks.,John Hunt.
Tasker, John. The Way of Cain. 2010. 196p. pap. 13.34 *(978-1-4452-5084-7(5))* Lulu Enterprises Inc.
Tate, Kenneth J. The Importance of Mobilizing the Christian Church As a Family Preparation Center for Daily Christian Living. 2009. 156p. pap. 11.99 *(978-1-4490-0563-4(2))* AuthorHouse.
Tate, Mark. Tug O' War: Winning the Battle Between Good & Evil. 2011. pap. 12.99 ***(978-1-61777-766-0(8))*** Tate Publishing & Enterprises, LLC.
Tatum, John Cole. The Victory Prayer. 2011. 164p. pap. 14.99 *(978-1-61215-540-1(5))* Xulon Pr., Inc.
Tauler, John. The Following of Christ. 2007. (ENG.). 372p. 48.95 *(978-0-548-01061-7(7))* Kessinger Publishing, LLC.
Tautges, Paul. Counsel One Another: A Theology of Personal Discipleship. 2009. (Illus.). 191p. pap. *(978-1-84625-142-9(7))* DayOne Pubns.
Taybron, Sandra A. Things Happen When You Pray Just Pray. 2008. 84p. pap. 9.99 *(978-1-60647-268-2(2))* Xulon Pr., Inc.
Taylor, Beth M. My Dear Child. 2009. 228p. pap. 19.95 *(978-1-59858-571-1(1))* Dog Ear Publishing, LLC.
Taylor, Chad. The Cry of the Harvest. 2008. 148p. pap. 13.99 *(978-1-60647-208-8(9))* Xulon Pr., Inc.
Taylor, Charles L. The Marked Bible. 2008. 128p. 24.99 *(978-0-554-58031-9(4))*; 132p. 21.99 *(978-0-554-58043-2(8))*; 128p. pap. 20.75 *(978-0-554-58035-7(7))*; 128p. pap. 19.75 *(978-0-554-58041-8(1))* BiblioBazaar.
—The Marked Bible. 2007. (ENG.). 128p. 35.95 *(978-0-548-07016-1(4))* Kessinger Publishing, LLC.
Taylor, Derlin. The Parable of the Cave. 2009. 112p. 22.95 *(978-1-4401-3385-5(9))*; pap. 12.95 *(978-1-4401-3384-8(0))* iUniverse, Inc.
Taylor, Genevieve. Through It All. 2007. 120p. per. *(978-1-897373-13-2(9))* Word Alive Pr.
Taylor, Gigi Bush, ed. & des. The Rosary: Page by Page & Bead by Bead. 2008. (Illus.). 78p. spiral bd. 4.95 *(978-0-88271-053-2(2))* Regina Pr., Malhame & Co.
Taylor, Hudson. The Countdown Has Started. 2007. pap. 16.00 *(978-0-8059-8510-8(7))* Dorrance Publishing Co., Inc.
Taylor, James C. The Time of the End. 2008. 151p. pap. 12.50 *(978-1-4357-4182-9(X))* Lulu Enterprises Inc.
Taylor, Jeremy. Holy Living & Dying: With Prayers Containing the Whole Duty of a Christian. 2007. 548p. per. 28.95 *(978-1-60206-550-5(0))* Cosimo, Inc.
—The Rule & Exercises of Holy Dying. 2009. 288p. 24.99 *(978-1-103-34191-7(X))*; 288p. pap. 18.99 *(978-1-103-34190-0(1))*; 256p. 24.99 *(978-1-103-17332-7(4))*; 256p. pap. 18.99 *(978-1-103-17330-3(8))* BiblioBazaar.
—The Rule & Exercises of Holy Dying. 2009. 178p. pap. *(978-0-217-36950-3(2))*; 196p. pap. *(978-0-217-36951-0(0))*; 208p. pap. *(978-0-217-39708-7(5))*; 198p. pap. *(978-0-217-60795-7(0))*; 176p. pap. *(978-0-217-13381-4(9))* Books LLC.
—The Rule & Exercises of Holy Dying. 2008. 286p. pap. 24.00 *(978-1-60608-262-1(0)*, Wipf and Stock) Wipf & Stock Pubs.
—Rule & Exercises of Holy Living & Th. 2006. pap. 45.95 *(978-1-4286-5169-2(1))* Kessinger Publishing, LLC.
—The Rule & Exercises of Holy Living & the Rule & Exercises of Holy Dying. 2007. (ENG.). 640p. 60.95 *(978-0-548-13983-7(0))* Kessinger Publishing, LLC.
Taylor, Jeremy. The Rule & Exercises of Holy Living (in Which Are Described the Means & Instruments of Obtaining Every Virtue & the Remedies Against Every Vice, & Con. 2011. 318p. ***(978-1-84902-351-1(4))*** Benediction Classics.
Taylor, Jr. You Too Can Be Free. 2008. 116p. pap. 10.99 *(978-1-60647-148-7(1))* Xulon Pr., Inc.
Taylor, Justin. El Sufrimiento y la Soberania de Dios, 1 vol. Piper, John, ed. & abr. by. Taylor, Justin, ed. 2008.Tr. of Suffering & the Sovereignty of God. (SPA.). 280p. pap. 12.99 *(978-0-8254-1586-9(1)*, Editorial Portavoz) Kregel Pubns.
Taylor, Kenneth N. Casi Doce Anos. (SPA.). 64p. *(978-84-7228-265-0(1)*, 220143) Clie, Editorial.
Taylor, Loren T. Carpooling with God. 2008. 108p. pap. 10.99 *(978-1-60477-877-9(6))* Xulon Pr., Inc.

C

Taylor, Mark Stephen. Hiking the Trail of Truth. 2009. 332p. pap. 18.99 *(978-1-60791-407-5(7))* Xulon Pr., Inc.

Taylor, Preston. Eleven Commandments. 2007. pap. 10.99 *(978-1-60266-008-3(5))* Xulon Pr., Inc.

Taylor, R. E. Be Strong & Take Courage. 2011. ***(978-1-77069-324-1(6))*** Word Alive Pr.

Taylor, Willie. Going for the Double. 2007. 5.95 net. *(978-0-9788590-6-0(5))* Armour of Light Publishing.

Taymon, Carrie. My Stand: In & for Him. 2011. 70p. 24.99 ***(978-1-4653-5305-4(4))***; pap. 15.99 ***(978-1-4653-5304-7(6))*** Xlibris Corp.

Tchividjian, Tullian. Do I Know God? Finding Certainty in Life's Most Important Relationship. (ENG.). 224p. 2009. pap. 13.99 *(978-1-60142-218-7(0))* 2007. 16.99 *(978-1-59052-936-2(7))* Doubleday Religious Publishing Group, The. (Multnomah).

—Unfashionable: Making a Difference in the World by Being Different. (ENG.). 224p. 2012. pap. 14.99 ***(978-1-60142-410-5(8))*** 2009. 18.99 *(978-1-60142-085-5(4))* Doubleday Religious Publishing Group, The. (Multnomah).

Teague, Jonathan. Mystery of the Faith. 2007. 184p. per. *(978-1-906210-46-5(2))* Grosvenor Hse. Publishing Ltd.

Teague, Michael. Rise & Walk! Seven Steps to Purposeful Living. 2007. 100p. per. 12.99 *(978-0-9788813-0-6(3))* Peak Performance Publishing.

Tee Ashira. Where Is My Boaz? 2009. 104p. pap. 11.95 *(978-1-4401-1053-5(0))* iUniverse, Inc.

Teed, Alison. Voices Crying in the Wilderness. 2008. 276p. (ENG.). 25.99 *(978-1-60477-416-0(9))*; per. 15.99 *(978-1-60477-415-3(0))* Xulon Pr., Inc.

Teitelbaum, David E. Neat Jewish Stuff for Christians. 2010. 172p. pap. 14.99 *(978-1-60957-929-6(1))* Xulon Pr., Inc.

Tele, Tunde. Destined to Win. 2008. 56p. pap. 9.99 *(978-1-60477-789-5(3))* Xulon Pr., Inc.

Tello, Mari. Arise & Ascend. 2009. 244p. 25.99 *(978-1-60791-007-7(1))*; pap. 15.99 *(978-1-60791-006-0(3))* Xulon Pr., Inc.

Temple, E. Thurston. The Patchwork Papers. 2007. 280p. per. *(978-1-4067-8789-4(2)*, Pomona Pr.) Read Bks.

Temple, John. Help! Im Drowning in Debt. 2011. (Living in a Fallen World Ser.). 63p. pap. ***(978-1-84625-249-5(0))*** DayOne Pubns.

Temple, Sheila. Gotcha Day: A Celebration of Adoption. 2011. 44p. pap. 23.95 ***(978-1-61507-825-7(8))*** Cross Bks. Publishing.

Temple, Terri. 31 Days to a New You in Christ. 2007. 148p. per. 13.99 *(978-1-60266-220-9(7))* Xulon Pr., Inc.

Templeton, David H. Thy Will Be Done. 2007. 50p. pap. 16.95 *(978-1-60474-233-6(X))* PublishAmerica, Inc.

ten Boom, Corrie. Amazing Love: True Stories of the Power of Forgiveness. 2007. (ENG.). 122p. per. 8.99 *(978-0-87508-856-3(2))* CLC Pubns.

Ten Elshof, Gregg A. I Told Me So: Self-Deception & the Christian Life. 2009. 160p. pap. 15.00 *(978-0-8028-6411-6(2))* Eerdmans, William B. Publishing Co.

Tendongho, Jean. Walking in Dominion. 2007. 68p. per. 9.99 *(978-1-60266-863-8(9))* Xulon Pr., Inc.

Tenenbaum, Michael. Blessed Assurance? A Demonstration That Christian Fundamentalism Is Simply False. 2007. 221p. pap. 17.50 *(978-0-615-15445-9(X))* Clarity.

—Blessed Assurance? A Demonstration that Christian Fundamentalism Is Simply False. Expanded - Limited Edition. 2007. 231p. pap. 14.49 *(978-0-615-16122-8(7))* Clarity.

Tengco, C. Christmas Trees in Heaven. 2008. 60p. pap. 14.95 *(978-1-4327-3295-0(1))* Outskirts Pr., Inc.

Tennant, F. R. Sources of the Doctrines of the Fall and. 2006. pap. 33.95 *(978-1-4286-4355-0(9))* Kessinger Publishing, LLC.

Tenney, Merrill Chapin. Caminos Por Que Debe Andar Cristiano: Roads a Christian Must Travel. (SPA.). 128p. *(978-84-7228-773-0(4)*, 220135) Clie, Editorial.

Tenney, Tom. God's Eye View, 0 vols. 2008. 224p. pap. 14.99 *(978-0-8499-2882-6(6))* Nelson, Thomas Inc.

—God's Eye View Workbook, 0 vols. 2008. 224p. pap. 14.99 *(978-1-4185-3214-7(2))* Nelson, Thomas Inc.

Teresi, Josephine Ann. Nature's Inspiration ~ Words & Images to Love By. 2010. 108p. pap. 15.95 *(978-1-935125-87-7(7))* Robertson Publishing.

TerKeurst, Lysa. Becoming More: Than a Good Bible Study Girl, 1 vol. 2009. (ENG.). 192p. pap. 12.99 *(978-0-310-29325-5(1))* Zondervan.

Terkeurst, Lysa. Becoming More Than a Good Bible Study Girl, 1 vol. 2009. (ENG.). 112p. pap., instr.'s gde. ed. 9.99 *(978-0-310-32208-5(1))* Zondervan.

TerKeurst, Lysa. Made to Crave Pack: Satisfying Your Deepest Desire with God, Not Food, 1 vol. 2011. (ENG.). pap., pap. 31.99 incl. DVD *(978-0-310-65278-6(2))* Zondervan.

Ternan, Fay. Down on the Farm: Insights on Christian Living. 2009. 78p. pap. 10.95 *(978-1-4327-4020-7(2))* Outskirts Pr., Inc.

Terrasi, J. & Golematis, A. Since I Met You A Beautiful Life in Christ. 2009. pap. *(978-1-61623-842-1(9))* Independent Pub.

Terrell, Pam. Becoming Spiritual Warriors for Our Children. 2007. 84p. per. 9.99 *(978-1-60266-310-7(6))* Xulon Pr., Inc.

Terrell, Ronald & Terrell, Michael. It's All about You. 2008. 144p. (ENG.). 21.99 *(978-1-60477-346-0(4))*; per. 13.99 *(978-1-60477-345-3(6))* Xulon Pr., Inc.

Terry, Justyn. The Justifying Judgement of God: A Reassessment of the Place of Judgement in the Saving Work of Christ. 2008. (Paternoster Theological Monographs). 262p. pap. 30.00 *(978-1-55635-662-9(5))* Wipf & Stock Pubs.

Terry, Robert. The Simplicity of God's Word: Substance of Righteousness: Finding the Substance of Life in Gods Awesome Word. 2008. 132p. pap. 10.99 *(978-1-60462-751-0(4))* Tate Publishing & Enterprises, LLC.

Tessore, Dag. Fasting. 2008. 112p. per. 11.95 *(978-1-56548-282-1(4))* New City Pr.

Testa, Marcos. Yo Soy el Pan de Vida-Guia.Tr. of I Am the Bread of Life. (SPA.). 160p. 5.95 *(978-958-607-849-8(3))* Sociedad de San Pablo COL. Dist: St Pauls/Alba Hse. Pubs.

Textos Oficiales Staff. Ordinario De La Misa Altar T/Dura. 256p. 12.95 *(978-980-207-133-3(1))* Sociedad de San Pablo COL. Dist: St Pauls/Alba Hse. Pubs.

Teykl, Terry. Keys to the Kingdom: Prayers for My Workplace. 40p. ring bd. 7.00 *(978-1-57892-101-0(5))* Prayer Point Pr.

Thank You for Visiting Us! 3.50 *(978-0-687-05769-6(8))* Abingdon Pr.

Thank You for Worshiping with Us. 3.50 *(978-0-687-02695-1(4))* Abingdon Pr.

Thank You for Worshipping with Us. (SPA.). 3.50 *(978-0-687-02697-5(0))* Abingdon Pr.

Tharpe, Beverly. Topics for Today's Living. 2011. 184p. 24.50 *(978-1-4269-5254-6(6))*; pap. 14.50 *(978-1-4269-5253-1(8))* Trafford Publishing.

Thavhana, Ndivhuho. Ensnared. 2011. 134p. 29.99 ***(978-1-4568-3452-4(5))***; pap. 19.99 ***(978-1-4568-3451-7(7))*** Xlibris Corp.

The Hautman Brothers, illus. On a Wing & a Prayer: Words of Comfort to Lift Your Spirit. 2006. 64p. per. 8.99 *(978-0-7369-1794-0(2))* Harvest Hse. Pubs.

The Hopper Staff. In the Eye of the Storm. 2008. 148p. pap. 24.95 *(978-1-60474-937-3(7))* PublishAmerica, Inc.

The Saga-Oracle. Jeshua's Song. 2011. pap. 26.95 ***(978-0-7414-6543-6(4))*** Infinity Publishing.

Thel. Stairwell to Redemption: Cilla's Denouement. 2011. 102p. pap. 19.95 ***(978-1-4560-8357-1(0))*** PublishAmerica, Inc.

Theriault, Serge A. Msgr Dominique M Varlet: Originator of the Old Catholic Episcopal Succession 1678-1742. 2010. 422p. pap. 24.95 *(978-1-933993-96-6(0))* Apocryphile Pr.

Thibault, Jane Marie & Morgan, Richard. No Act of Love Is Ever Wasted: The Spirituality of Caring for Persons with Dementia. 2009. 160p. pap. 16.00 *(978-0-8358-9995-6(0))* Upper Room Bks.

Thiel, Jr. Eternity in Twelve Chapters. 2008. 168p. pap. 15.99 *(978-1-60647-310-8(7))* Xulon Pr., Inc.

Thiele, Erin. Workers@home: Making the Most of Your Time. 10th rev. ed. 2007. Orig. Title: Workers@home: Making the Most of Your Time. spiral bd. *(978-1-931800-16-7(2)*, Restore Ministries International) NarrowRoad Publishing Hse.

Thieme, R. B. Isolation of Sin: [Yu Zui Ge Jue. 2007. (CHI & ENG., Illus.). 23p. *(978-1-55764-096-3(3))* Thieme, R.B. Bible Ministries.

Thigpen, Paul. Last Words: Final Thoughts of Catholic Saints & Sinners. 2006. 219p. per. 14.99 *(978-0-86716-724-5(6)*, Servant Bks.) Franciscan Media.

—Praying the Rosary with St. Paul. 2008. 95p. pap. 7.95 *(978-1-59276-553-9(X))* Our Sunday Visitor, Publishing Div.

Things Most Surely Believed among Us. pap. 2.49 *(978-0-87377-000-2(5))* GAM Pubns.

Thiselton, Anthony C. The Hermeneutics of Doctrine. 2007. 649p. 46.00 *(978-0-8028-2681-7(4))* Eerdmans, William B. Publishing Co.

Thoene, Bodie & Thoene, Brock. Why a Shepherd? More than just a name... it is the reason he was Sent. 2007. 96p. mass mkt. 2.99 *(978-0-9770565-3-8(8))* Parable Group, The.

Thollander, Lance. Walking the Galatian Road: Moving from Law to Life. 2010. pap. 13.99 *(978-1-61663-096-6(5))* Tate Publishing & Enterprises, LLC.

Thom, Julie. Complete Activity Guide for the Christian Family: Includes the History of the Holidays. 2007. pap. 17.95 *(978-0-7414-4000-6(8))* Infinity Publishing.

Thomas & Rowinski, Jason. Beyond Self: The Imitation of Christ. 2009. (ENG.). 96p. pap. 8.99 *(978-0-8341-5032-4(8)*, 9780834150324) Beacon Hill Pr. of Kansas City.

Thomas à Kempis. Christians Pattern or A Treatise of the. 2006. pap. 28.95 *(978-1-4286-3255-4(7))* Kessinger Publishing, LLC.

Thomas, Bob Ross. The Joshua Call: Active Duty in God's Army. 2009. 156p. pap. 11.95 *(978-1-4327-3495-4(4))* Outskirts Pr., Inc.

Thomas, C. S. The Church's Biggest Secret: The World's Most Irresistable Man. 2007. 144p. per. *(978-1-84401-992-2(6))* Athena Pr.

Thomas, Carla Newbern. Prescription of Repentance. 2008. 34p. pap. 8.00 *(978-0-8059-7840-7(2))* Dorrance Publishing Co., Inc.

Thomas, Charles. Living in God's Kingdom on Earth. 2007. 228p. (ENG.). 24.99 *(978-1-60477-057-5(0))*; per. 14.99 *(978-1-60266-992-5(9))* Xulon Pr., Inc.

Thomas D. Logie. Endurance: How Faith Can Help You Win the Race. 2010. 96p. pap. *(978-1-4269-2941-0(2))* Trafford Publishing (UK) Ltd.

Thomas, Desmond A. A Man after God's Own Heart. 2008. pap. 12.99 *(978-0-9543083-1-5(X))* McDougal & Assocs.

Thomas, Gary L. & Thomas, Gary. Holy Available: What If Holiness Is about More Than What We Don't Do?: Inviting God's Presence into the Questions of Life, 1 vol. 2009. (ENG.). 272p. pap. 14.99 *(978-0-310-29200-5(X))* Zondervan.

Thomas, Geoffrey. The Sure Word of God. 2007. 127p. pap. *(978-1-85049-223-8(9))* Bryntirion Pr.

Thomas, Ian. Si Perezco, Que Perezca: If I Perish, I Perish. (SPA.). 120p. *(978-84-7228-136-3(1)*, 220834) Clie, Editorial.

Thomas, Marcus D. Reflections in the Mirror. 2007. 48p. per. 16.95 *(978-1-4241-8481-1(9))* PublishAmerica, Inc.

Thomas Nelson. When You Haven't Got a Prayer, 0 vols. 2008. 144p. pap. 10.99 *(978-1-4041-7555-6(5))* Nelson, Thomas Inc.

Thomas Nelson Publishing Staff. The Ten Offenses, 0 vols. 2008. 240p. pap. 14.99 *(978-0-7852-9729-1(4))* Nelson, Thomas Inc.

Thomas Nelson Publishing Staff, creator. Checklist for Life: 40 Days of Timeless Wisdom & Foolproof Strategies for Making the Most of Life's Challenges & Opportunities, 0 vols. abr. ed. 2007. (Checklist for Life Ser.). 192p. per. 8.99 *(978-0-7852-8891-6(0))* Nelson, Thomas Inc.

—Finding Freedom from a Broken Past: How Do I Let Go?, 0 vols. 2008. (Women of Faith Study Guides). 128p. 9.99 *(978-1-4185-2937-6(0))* Nelson, Thomas Inc.

—I Will Love You Forever, 0 vols. 2008. (Illus.). 128p. 9.99 *(978-1-4041-0504-1(2))* Nelson, Thomas Inc.

Thomas Poller, Victoria. Where Did That Come from (Revised Edition) 2009. 156p. pap. 14.94 *(978-0-557-04023-0(X))* Lulu Enterprises Inc.

Thomas, Rick. Xtreme Faith: Believing for the Impossible. 2007. (ENG.). 160p. per. 12.95 *(978-0-9774223-7-1(2))* Lifebridge Bks.

—Xtreme Favor: The Keys to Unlimited Abundance. 2007. (ENG.). 160p. pap. 12.95 *(978-0-9786581-4-4(0))* Lifebridge Bks.

Thomas, Roger. The Door That No Man Can Shut. 2008. 140p. (ENG.). 21.99 *(978-1-60477-534-1(3))*; per. 13.99 *(978-1-60477-533-4(5))* Xulon Pr., Inc.

Thomas, Rusty Lee. Kingdom Leadership Institute Manual: Raising up Leaders a Time Like This Demands. 2009. 332p. pap. 18.99 *(978-1-60799-709-2(6))* Tate Publishing & Enterprises, LLC.

Thomas, Shirley. Success Filled Living. 2007. 112p. (ENG.). 18.99 *(978-1-60266-867-6(1))*; per. 10.99 *(978-1-60266-749-5(7))* Xulon Pr., Inc.

Thomas, Taheria. Trusting in God. 2011. 54p. 24.99 ***(978-1-4628-5177-5(0))***; pap. 15.99 ***(978-1-4628-5176-8(2))*** Xlibris Corp.

Thomas Troward, Troward & Thomas Troward. The Law & the Word. 2009. 120p. pap. 5.95 *(978-1-60386-196-0(3)*, Merchant Bks.) Rough Draft Printing.

Thomas, Warren. God Is the God of Specifics. 2009. 70p. pap. 12.95 *(978-1-4327-4364-2(3))* Outskirts Pr., Inc.

Thomas, Y. R. Are Christians Being Mind Manipulated? 2007. per. 9.95 *(978-1-59872-869-9(5))* Instant Pub.

Thomas, Yemina D. To God Be the Glory: Losing Weight & Gaining Power. 2007. 112p. (ENG.). 22.95 *(978-0-595-68568-4(4))*; per. 12.95 *(978-0-595-42723-9(5))* iUniverse, Inc.

Thomas, Zach. Those Who Gathered More & Those Who Gathered Less. 2011. 84p. pap. 10.99 ***(978-1-61379-186-8(0))*** Xulon Pr., Inc.

Thompkins, Jamie. There's No Place Like Home. 2010. pap. 14.99 *(978-1-61663-491-9(X))* Tate Publishing & Enterprises, LLC.

Thompson, Brad. Macedonia, Indiana: Looking for God's Purpose Close to Home. 2008. (Illus.). 102p. per. 20.00 *(978-0-9799041-0-3(2))* Zionsville Presbyterian Church.

Thompson, Cheryl A. Whispers from My Heart: Emotional & Spiritual Healing from Childhood Sexual Assault. 2009. 468p. 36.99 *(978-1-61579-430-0(1))*; pap. 24.99 *(978-1-61579-418-8(2))* Xulon Pr., Inc.

Thompson, David W. The Stranger's Compass. 2009. 116p. pap. 11.99 *(978-1-60791-389-4(5))* Xulon Pr., Inc.

Thompson, Debra. Get off the Fence: But Be Prepared to Leave A Lot Behind. 2010. 104p. pap. 15.99 *(978-1-4500-4223-9(6))* Xlibris Corp.

Thompson, Janet. Face-to-Face with Euodia & Syntyche: From Conflict to Community. 2010. (New Hope Bible Studies for Women Ser.). (ENG.). 144p. pap. 8.99 *(978-1-59669-281-7(2))* New Hope Pubs.

—Face-to-Face with Naomi & Ruth: Together for the Journey. 2009. (New Hope Bible Studies for Women Ser.). (ENG.). 144p. pap. 8.99 *(978-1-59669-253-4(7))* New Hope Pubs.

Thompson, Keith Elijah. How to Dwell in the Secret Place of the Most High God. 2008. 208p. pap. 16.95 *(978-0-9791566-9-4(6))* To His Glory Publishing Co., Inc.

Thompson, Mary. A Boy with a Purpose: The Miraculous Healing. 2009. pap. 12.95 *(978-1-61584-276-6(4))* Independent Pub.

Thompson, Olive Ross. The Devil & I. 2011. 78p. 37.95 ***(978-1-258-07342-8(0))*** Literary Licensing, LLC.

Thompson, R. Luke. So You're A Christian, Who Knew? 2009. 168p. pap. 15.95 *(978-0-557-14025-1(0))*; (ENG.). 172p. pap. 15.95 *(978-0-557-19857-3(7))* Lulu Enterprises Inc.

Thompson, Robert V. A Voluptuous God: A Christian Heretic Speaks. 2007. (ENG.). 224p. per. 21.95 *(978-1-55145-558-7(7)*, Copperhouse) Wood Lake Publishing, Inc. CAN. Dist: Westminster John Knox Pr.

Thomson, Rachel Starr. Heart to Heart: Meeting with God in the Lord's Prayer. 2006. per. *(978-0-9739591-5-4(0))* Little Dozen Press.

Thorn, Joe. Note to Self: The Discipline of Preaching to Yourself. 2011. (Re:Lit Ser.). 144p. pap. 10.99 *(978-1-4335-2206-2(3))* Crossway.

Thornber, James. Taking off My Comfortable Clothes: Removing Religion to Find Relationship. 2010. (ENG.). 224p. pap. 16.99 *(978-1-935245-26-1(0))* HigherLife Development Services, Inc.

Thornborough, Tim. Bible Notes for Adults. 2010. (Explore Ser.). 96p. pap. *(978-1-907377-00-6(X))*; pap. *(978-1-907377-04-4(2))* Good Bk. Co.

—Time with God: Your Introduction to a Regular Time with God. 2010. (Explore Ser.). 32p. *(978-1-905564-92-7(9))* Good Bk. Co.

—Why Did Jesus Die? (Access for All) 2010. 6p. *(978-1-905564-63-7(5))* Good Bk. Co.

—Why Did Jesus Rise? (Access for All) 2010. 6p. *(978-1-905564-65-1(1))* Good Bk. Co.

Thornborough, Tim & Nodder, Marcus. The Real Christmas, 10 vols. 2010. (Christianity Explored Ser.). 16p. *(978-1-906334-31-4(5))* Good Bk. Co.

Thornton, Catherine. Coping with Serious Illness. 2008. (ENG., Illus.). 94p. pap. 13.95 *(978-1-84730-051-5(0))* Veritas Pubns. IRL. Dist: Dufour Editions, Inc.

Thornton, Charles W. Are You Listening? Jesus Teaches Holiness in the Sermon on the Mount: A Layman's View. 2007. 283p. per. 21.99 *(978-1-60247-124-5(X))* Tate Publishing & Enterprises, LLC.

Thornton, J. Treasures of the Snow. 2006. 152p. per. 12.99 *(978-0-9759049-9-2(X))* Master Pr.

Thornton, R. Scott. Inclusive Christianity: A Progressive Look at Faith. 2008. (ENG.). 189p. pap. 15.00 *(978-1-932717-16-7(1))* Hope Publishing Hse.

Thorogood, Chris. From Before the Beginning-until after the End. 2006. pap. 21.99 *(978-1-59781-882-7(8))* Xulon Pr., Inc.

Thorpe, C. A., tr. The Beginning.Tr. of Dhivehi of the People of the Island of the Minicoy, Laccadive Island. 52p. pap. *(978-1-880189-25-2(9))* God's Word to the Nations Bible Society.

Thrasher, Kenneth L. With Christ Today in Paradise. 2009. 168p. pap. 19.00 *(978-1-60608-902-6(1)*, Resource Pubns.) Wipf & Stock Pubs.

Three Simple Rules 24/7. 2008. 32p. pap., stu. ed. 7.50 *(978-1-4267-0033-0(4))* Abingdon Pr.

Three Simple Rules 24/7 Leader Guide: A Six-Week Study for Youth. 2008. pap. 7.50 *(978-1-4267-0034-7(2))* Abingdon Pr.

Threes: Resource Manual. (Illus.). tchr. ed. 89.95 *(978-0-930265-47-2(5)*, 001011) Faith Alive Christian Resources.

Thurmon, Andre. It Had to Happen: From the Pit to the Palace. 2009. 56p. pap. 15.99 *(978-1-4500-0558-6(6))* Xlibris Corp.

Thy Kingdom Come. 2009. (ENG.). 109p. pap. 11.99 *(978-0-9822177-3-3(0))* Jesus is the Answer Publishing.

Tibbits, Dick. Forgive to Life Workbook: How Forgiveness Can Save Your Life, 0 vols. 2006. 176p. per., wbk. ed. 17.99 *(978-1-59145-471-7(9))* Nelson, Thomas Inc.

—Forgive to Live: How Forgiveness Can Save Your Life, 0 vols. 2008. (Illus.). 190p. pap. 14.99 *(978-0-7852-9725-3(1))* Nelson, Thomas Inc.

Tibbitts, Lila Jane. Through the Eyes of a Child. 2008. 104p. per. 14.95 *(978-1-4327-1881-7(9))* Outskirts Pr., Inc.

Tidball, Derek. The Message of Holiness: Restoring God's Masterpiece. 2010. 313p. *(978-1-84474-411-4(6))* InterVarsity Pr.

Tidwell, Cammy & Vasso, Sheryl. Wholly Devoted. 2011. 152p. pap. 14.99 *(978-1-61215-773-3(4))* Xulon Pr., Inc.

Tietjen, Suzanne Davenport. The Sheep of His Hand: Reflections on the Psalms from a 21st Century Shepherd, 1 vol. 2009. 176p. 15.99 *(978-0-8254-6298-6(3)*, Monarch Bks.) Lion Hudson PLC GBR. Dist: Kregel Pubns.

Tiffen, Gregge. Do the Angels Take a Vacation? 2007. 15p. 13.00 *(978-0-9795160-4-7(8))* P Systems.

—Fanned Fire & Forced Love Never Did Well. 2008. 16p. 13.00 *(978-0-9795160-8-5(0))* P Systems.

Tikkun, Y. M. Call of the Shepherd. 2007. pap. 14.99 *(978-0-7684-2421-8(6))* Destiny Image Pubs.

Tiller, Darryl J. Growing into Jesus: Six Building Blocks for Life in Christ. 2008. 122p. pap. 19.95 *(978-1-60474-869-7(9))* PublishAmerica, Inc.

Tiller-Woods, Mary. Faith Confessions for the Journey. 2007. 51p. pap. 9.97 *(978-0-615-16215-7(0))* Eve of Destiny.

Tilley, Keith. The Good Soil Process: A Backyard Missional Field Guide. 2010. 147p. pap. 15.00 *(978-0-557-39646-7(8))* Lulu Enterprises Inc.

Tilley, Terrence W. The Disciples' Jesus: Christology As Reconciling Practice. 2008. (Illus.). xiv, 302p. pap. 38.00 *(978-1-57075-796-9(8))* Orbis Bks.

Tillia, Stephen F. To Live Is Christ: Principles for Christian Living: A Laymanrsquo;s Look at Philippians. 2007. 140p. per. 24.95 *(978-1-4241-9451-3(2))* PublishAmerica, Inc.

Tillis, Sheryl. Leaving My Shoes Behind. 2008. 248p. pap. 15.99 *(978-1-60647-897-4(4))* Xulon Pr., Inc.

Tillman, Rix W. The Time Sequence Bible: Reading Guide & Devotions. 2010. pap. 29.95 *(978-0-7414-6070-7(X))* Infinity Publishing.

Tilma, Mary. Ancient Book Relevant Faith. 2008. 184p. pap. 14.99 *(978-1-60647-950-6(4))* Xulon Pr., Inc.

Timbs, Lorrie L. Get off That Fence! Time Is Running Out - Which Side Are You On? 2008. 88p. per. 11.95 *(978-1-4327-0943-3(7))* Outskirts Pr., Inc.

Timeless Visual Works Llc & Jefferson, Ollie. Time will tell Stage 1. 2010. 234p. 16.95 *(978-0-615-37640-0(1))* Timeless Visual Works LLC.

Timmis, Steve & Chester, Tim. Gospel-Centred Life: Becoming the Person God Wants You to Be. 2010. (Gospel-centred Ser.). 128p. pap. *(978-1-906334-71-0(4))* Good Bk. Co.

TIMMON, NICHOLAS. You'll never fall Again. 2007. 114p. pap. 14.95 *(978-0-615-17993-3(2))* lap Worldwide Ministries.

Timmons, Steve. A Used Car Dealer's Take on Jesus Christ. 2010. pap. 9.99 *(978-1-61566-462-7(9))* Tate Publishing & Enterprises, LLC.

Timms, David. Living the Lord's Prayer, 1 vol. 2010. (ENG.). 256p. pap. 13.99 *(978-0-7642-0743-3(1))* Bethany Hse. Pubs.

Tindal, Mardi. Soul Maps: A Guide to the Mid-Life Spirit. (Illus.). 129p. pap. 15.95 *(978-1-55134-115-6(8)*, 1586) United Church Publishing Hse. CAN. Dist: Forward Movement Pubns.

Tinerino, Dennis. Supersize Your Faith: Tapping into God's Miracle Power. 2007. (Illus.). 439p. per. 14.99 *(978-0-7684-2408-9(9))* Destiny Image Pubs.

Tinker, Melvin & Buttery, Nathan. Tales of the Unexpected: The Power of Jesus' Parables. 2006. (ENG.). 144p. per. 7.99 *(978-1-84550-116-7(0))* Christian Focus Pubns. GBR. Dist: STL Distribution North America.

Tiny Triumphs. 5.88 (978-0-687-07271-2(9)) Abingdon Pr.

Tirabassi, Maren C. & Tirabassi, Maria I., eds. God in My Life: Faith Stories & How & Why We Share Them. 2008. 132p. pap. 17.00 (978-0-8298-1779-9(4)) Pilgrim Pr., The/United Church Pr.

Titus, Devi. The Table Experience: Discover What Creates Deeper, More Meaningful Relationships. 2009. 208p. 21.99 (978-1-935245-13-1(9)) HigherLife Development Services, Inc.

Tiwari, Vijai. In Search for the Truth. 2007. 264p. per. 22.50 (978-1-4251-0303-3(0)) Trafford Publishing.

To All Eternity. 128p. 21.99 (978-0-7586-0142-1(5)) Concordia Publishing Hse.

Tobin, Bishop Thomas J. Effective Faith. 2010. 176p. pap. 13.95 (978-0-9798246-9-2(9), Seraphina Pr.) Hillcrest Publishing Group, Inc.

Tobin, Eamon. How to Forgive Yourself & Others: Steps to Reconciliation. 3rd ed. 2006. 82p. per. 6.95 (978-0-7648-1532-4(6)) Liguori Pubns.

Todd Chalmers, Ora Mae. Building Lives to Our Father in Heaven: Through Prayers, Spoken Words, & Poetry. 2007. (ENG., Illus.). 132p. per. 12.95 (978-0-9801647-4-9(5)) M.O.R.E. Pubs.

Togun, Kikelomo. Steps To Walking With God. 4.95 (978-0-9721991-0-0(1)) Togun, Kikelomo I.

Toks, O. J. Rejected for a Purpose: How God Uses Rejection to Help You Find & Fulfill Your Destiny. 2010. (Illus.). 263p. pap. 15.95 (978-0-9820384-3-7(7)) Elevator Group, The.

Tolbert, Callie Roberts. Suddenly Saddened: Overcoming Devastation after Tragedy & Sudden Death. 2010. pap. 11.99 (978-1-60791-771-7(8)) Xulon Pr., Inc.

Tolbert, Malcolm. The Disturbing Galilean: Essays about Jesus. 2009. pap. (978-1-57312-530-7(X)) Smyth & Helwys Publishing, Inc.

Toledo, Thomas R. Little Big Men. 2009. 168p. pap. 14.99 (978-1-60791-076-3(4)) Xulon Pr., Inc.

Toler, Stan. Total Quality Life. 2009. 192p. 17.99 (978-0-89827-400-4(1)) Wesleyan Publishing Hse.

—Total Quality Life: Strategies for Purposeful Living. 2007. (Illus.). 160p. (978-0-89827-360-1(9)) Wesleyan Publishing Hse.

Toler, Stan & Smith, Debra White. The Harder I Laugh the Deeper I Hurt: An Honest Look at Surviving Life's Pain. 2008. (ENG.). 160p. pap. 14.99 (978-0-8341-2377-9(0), 9780834123779) Beacon Hill Pr. of Kansas City.

Toler, Stan, et al. He Still Speaks. 2008. (ENG.). 112p. pap. 12.99 (978-0-8341-2384-7(3), 9780834123847) Beacon Hill Pr. of Kansas City.

Tolhurst, James. Come Lord Jesus: Reflections on the Adve. 2006. 92p. per. (978-0-85244-020-9(0)) Gracewing, Ltd.

Toliver, Cynthia D. Come See a Man. 2011. 52p. pap. 9.95 (978-1-4502-8009-9(9)) iUniverse, Inc.

Tolstoy, Leo. A Confession. 2006. (ENG.). 108p. per. 9.95 (978-1-59818-471-6(7)) Aegypan.

—The Law of Love & the Law of Violence. 2010. (ENG.). 128p. pap. 6.95 (978-0-486-47594-3(8)) Dover Pubns., Inc.

Tomasella, Todd. Raised Up. 2009. 188p. 24.99 (978-1-4389-6825-4(6)); pap. 18.95 (978-1-4389-6824-7(8)) AuthorHouse.

Tome, Brian. Free Book: I am a fanatic about freedom. & I'm fanatical about coming at you hard in this book. I'm tired of seeing people beaten down by the world's systems & by religion. I'm sick of seeing people live safe, predictable lives while their God-given passion Dies, 0 vols. 2010. 240p. pap. 14.99 (978-0-8499-2006-6(X)) Nelson, Thomas Inc.

—Free Book - Study Guide. 0 vols. 2010. (Illus.). 128p. pap. 9.99 (978-0-8499-4655-4(7)) Nelson, Thomas Inc.

—Welcome to the Revolution: A Field Guide for New Believers, 0 vols. 2008. 192p. pap. 12.99 (978-0-8499-2005-9(1)) Nelson, Thomas Inc.

Tomlin, Graham. The Seven Deadly Sins: And How to Overcome Them. 2008. (ENG., Illus.). 192p. per. 12.95 (978-0-7459-5221-5(6)) Lion Hudson PLC GBR. Dist: Independent Pubs. Group.

Tompkins, J. D. & Beckwith, Angela. The Epidemic of the Silent Church: Domestic Violence & Church Culture, 1 vol. 2009. 48p. pap. 16.95 (978-1-60703-655-5(X)) PublishAmerica, Inc.

Tomtania, Monica M. The End-Time Daughters of the King. 2008. 300p. per. 17.99 (978-1-60477-387-3(1)) Xulon Pr., Inc.

Tondeur, Keith. Escaping from Debt. (What Christians Should Know about Ser.). 40p. pap. (978-1-85240-235-8(0)) Sovereign World, Ltd.

Toney, Joyce. Unlocking the Vault. 2007. 176p. (ENG.). 21.99 (978-1-60266-544-8(3)); per. 13.99 (978-1-60266-543-9(5)) Xulon Pr., Inc.

Toon, Peter. Credo - "I Believe" An Explanation of the Christian Creed. (Catechetical Ser.). 52p. pap., stu. ed. 3.95 (978-1-886412-07-1(3)) Preservation Pr.

Topping, Frank. An Impossible God: A Classic Meditation on the Passion. 2011. 144p. pap. 15.99 (978-1-84825-095-6(9), Canterbury Pr. Norwich) Hymns Ancient & Modern Ltd GBR. Dist: Westminster John Knox Pr.

Torrey, R. A. The Baptism with the Holy Spirit. 2009. (ENG.). 68p. pap. 16.75 (978-1-117-69746-8(0)) BiblioBazaar.

—The Baptism with the Holy Spirit. 2010. 82p. 26.36 (978-1-168-92945-7(8)); 32.95 (978-1-161-60739-0(0)) Kessinger Publishing, LLC.

—How to Succeed in the Christian Life. (ENG.). 2007. 128p. 35.95 (978-0-548-12583-0(X)) 2006. pap. 20.95 (978-1-4286-3560-9(2)) Kessinger Publishing, LLC.

Torrey, Ruben A. Vida Cristiana Triunfante (Victorious Christian Life) (SPA.). 112p. (978-84-7228-637-5(1), 220944) Clie, Editorial.

Totilo, Rebecca Park. Heal with Essential Oil: Nature's Medicine Cabinet. 2010. 262p. pap. 24.99 (978-0-9827264-0-2(6)) Rebecca at the Well Foundation.

—Heal with Oil: How to Use the Essential Oils of Ancient Scripture. 2008. 112p. pap. 14.99 (978-0-9749115-4-0(2)) Rebecca at the Well Foundation.

Tottingham, Ronald L. That Love Which Is of God. 2011. 144p. pap. 12.99 (978-1-937129-00-2(4)) Faithful Life Pubs.

Touchton, Don. Run While Reading: Spiritual Fast Food for Busy People. 2007. (ENG.). 304p. per. 29.95 (978-1-4241-6614-5(4)) PublishAmerica, Inc.

Toukonen, Elizabeth Faye. Stirring Moments in the Presence of God. 2008. 128p. pap. 10.99 (978-1-58169-270-9(6)) Genesis Communications, Inc.

Townend, Stuart. 50 Small Group Worship Ideas. 2006. (ENG.). 272p. per. 13.99 (978-1-84291-279-9(8)) Kingsway Pubns. GBR. Dist: STL Distribution North America.

Townley, Ed. The Secret According to Jesus: Living a Joyful Life. 2007. 141p. per. 18.95 (978-1-933285-91-7(5)) Brown Bks. Publishing Group.

Towns, Elmer. Praying with the Conquerors: Prayers from Joshua, Judges, & Ruth Praying the Scriptures With... (series) 2009. pap. 17.99 (978-0-7684-2843-8(2)) Destiny Image Pubs.

Towns, Elmer L. Praying the Book of Job: To Understand Trouble & Suffering. 2006. 190p. per. 15.99 (978-0-7684-2361-7(9)) Destiny Image Pubs.

Townsend, Eileen. America's Role in Revelation. 2010. 52p. pap. 28.25 (978-1-4520-2937-5(7)) AuthorHouse.

Townsend, John. Handling Difficult People: What to Do When People Try to Push Your Buttons, 0 vols. 2009. 132p. pap. 10.99 (978-1-4041-7567-9(9)) Nelson, Thomas Inc.

—Where Is God? Finding His Presence, Purpose & Power in Difficult Times. 2009. 240p. pap. 14.99 (978-0-8499-4686-8(7)) Nelson, Thomas Inc.

Townsend, John. Who's Pushing Your Buttons? Handling the Difficult People in Your Life, 0 vols. 2007. 224p. per. 14.99 (978-0-7852-8921-0(6)) Nelson, Thomas Inc.

Townsend, John, et al. Boundaries: A 9-Session Focus on Boundaries - When to Say Yes & How to Say No to Take Control of Your Life, 1 vol. 2007. (ENG.). (gr. 13). 24.99 (978-0-310-27809-2(0)) Zondervan.

Townsend, Jr. Judgement on Americ. 2008. 232p. pap. 16.95 (978-0-595-51140-2(6)) iUniverse, Inc.

Townsend, Michael J. Thinking about Preaching. 2007. 143p. per. (978-0-7162-0616-3(1)) Epworth Pr., The.

Toyne, Sandy. They Call Me Pastor Sandy. 2009. 204p. pap. 15.99 (978-1-60791-739-7(4)) Xulon Pr., Inc.

Tozer, A. w. The Best of A. W. Tozer, Book One, Vol. 1. 2007. 251p. pap. 14.99 (978-1-60066-043-6(6)) WingSpread Publishers.

Tozer, A. W. Caminamos por una Senda Marcada.Tr. of We Travel an Appointed Way. (SPA.). (978-84-7645-364-3(7), 223513) Clie, Editorial.

—The Knowledge of the Holy. 2008. (ENG.). pap. 9.99 (978-1-85078-621-4(6)) Authentic Media.

—Living as a Christian: Teachings from First Peter. 2010. (ENG.). 224p. pap. 14.99 (978-0-8307-4692-7(7)) Gospel Light Pubns.

—The Pursuit of God. 2010. 170p. pap. 8.99 (978-1-60450-777-5(2)) 2009. 102p. pap. 3.99 (978-1-60450-740-9(3)) 2008. 112p. pap. 8.99 (978-1-60450-586-3(9)) Arc Manor. (Serenity Pubs.).

—The Pursuit of God. 2010. 52p. pap. 20.00 (978-1-153-78804-5(7)) General Bks. LLC.

—The Pursuit of God. 2010. 96p. pap. 16.95 (978-1-60444-242-7(5)) IndoEuropeanPublishing.com.

—The Pursuit of God. 2010. 88p. pap. 6.90 (978-1-60942-000-0(4)) International Alliance Pro-Publishing, LLC.

—The Pursuit of God. 2009. 132p. pap. 3.95 (978-1-57898-851-8(9)) Martino Publishing.

—The Pursuit of God. 2007. 104p. 7.95 (978-1-59557-033-8(0)) Positive Action For Christ.

—The Pursuit of God. 2009. 100p. pap. 3.95 (978-1-60386-215-8(3), Merchant Bks.) Rough Draft Printing.

—The Pursuit of God. 2010. 82p. pap. 5.65 (978-1-936041-21-3(9)) Simon & Brown.

—The Pursuit of God. 2007. per. 7.52 (978-1-4245-0787-0(1)) Treasures Media Inc.

—The Pursuit of God. 2011. 80p. pap. 7.77 (978-1-936594-17-7(X)) Tribeca Bks.

—The Pursuit of God. 2008. 108p. 19.99 (978-1-60459-457-7(8)); 84p. pap. 8.99 (978-1-60459-319-8(9)) Wilder Pubns., Ltd.

Tozer, A. w. The Pursuit of God: The Human Thirst for the Divine. 2007. 121p. 16.99 (978-1-60066-054-2(1)) WingSpread Publishers.

—The Pursuit of God 31 Day Experience. 2008. (31-Day Experience Ser.). 207p. pap. 14.99 (978-1-60066-076-4(2)) WingSpread Publishers.

—The Pursuit of God Large Print Edition: The Human Thirst for the Divine. l.t. ed. 2007. 161p. pap. 12.99 (978-1-60066-168-6(8)) WingSpread Publishers.

Tozer, A. W. Pursuit of God/Pursuit of Man Devotional Readings. 19.99 (978-1-60066-130-3(0)) WingSpread Publishers.

Tozer, A. w. The Radical Cross: Living the Passion of Christ. 2009. (ENG.). 148p. pap. 11.99 (978-1-60066-226-3(9)) WingSpread Publishers.

—Set of the Sail. 2007. 172p. pap. 12.99 (978-1-60066-020-7(7)) WingSpread Publishers.

—That Incredible Christian. 2007. 170p. pap. 12.99 (978-1-60066-006-1(1)) WingSpread Publishers.

Tracey, Jean. I Will Glory in the Cross. 2009. 104p. pap. 12.99 (978-1-4251-9034-7(0)) Trafford Publishing.

Trahan, Carol. Help! I'm a Single Mom. 2011. (Living in a Fallen World Ser.). 60p. pap. (978-1-84625-244-0(X)) DayOne Pubns.

Traugott, William H. William H. Traugott. 2008. 92p. pap. 9.95 (978-0-7414-4447-9(X)) Infinity Publishing.

Travelbee, Robert. From an Outlaw to the Cross. 2008. 240p. pap. 14.99 (978-1-60647-419-8(7)) Xulon Pr., Inc.

Travis, Drake. Healing Power, Voice Activated: Discover Today Your Words Bless, Heal & Restore. 2009. (ENG.). 304p. 21.99 (978-1-59979-765-6(8), Creation Hse.) Charisma Media.

Trawick, Jr. The God of the Second Chance: For those who question whether they are Forgiven. 2011. 38p. pap. 16.95 (978-1-4560-9138-5(7)) PublishAmerica, Inc.

Treadway, Wanda. In Defense of Lifting up Jesus: Will you Stand in the Gap with Me? 2011. 64p. pap. 10.43 (978-1-4269-7555-4(4)) Trafford Publishing.

Treat, Casey. How to Be Your Best When You Feel Your Worst. 2009. (ENG.). 320p. (gr. 12-18). 16.00 (978-0-425-22565-3(8), Berkley Trade) Penguin Group (USA) Inc.

Trent, John. Chasing Skinny Rabbits: What Leads You into Emotional & Spiritual Exhaustion. 2008. (Illus.). 192p. pap. 14.99 (978-0-7852-8950-0(X)) Nelson, Thomas Inc.

—Chasing Skinny Rabbits: What Leads You into Emotional & Spiritual Exhaustion... & What Can Lead You Out, 0 vols. 2010. 208p. pap. 12.99 (978-0-7852-9784-0(7)) Nelson, Thomas Inc.

—I'd Choose You. 2011. 32p. (J). 9.99 (978-1-4003-1732-5(0)) Nelson, Thomas Inc.

—The 2-Degree Difference: How Little Things Can Change Everything. 2006. (Illus.). 243p. 19.99 (978-0-8054-3064-5(4)) B&H Publishing Group.

—The 2 Degree Difference: How Small Things Can Change Everything! 2009. (ENG.). 256p. pap. 14.99 (978-0-8054-4983-9(3), B&H Bks.) B&H Publishing Group.

Tresnak, Rick. Building the Army of God. 2009. 83p. pap. 13.95 (978-1-4327-2345-3(6)) Outskirts Pr., Inc.

Trice, Raymond D. Hidden in the Process of Time: No Subtitle. 2008. 124p. 18.99 (978-1-60477-785-7(0)); pap. 10.99 (978-1-60477-784-0(2)) Xulon Pr., Inc.

Trifault, Jean-Jacques. Among Those Born of Women There Was None Greater than John. Neuwirth, Gabriela & Trifault, Mary L., eds. 2011. (Illus.). 111p. pap. 9.99 (978-0-9797877-9-9(3)) Footsteps to Wisdom Publishing.

Trillo, Michael. What Does God Really Want? Beyond the Lies How to Overcome Stress & Live the Promised Abundant Life. 2008. 194p. pap. 14.97 (978-0-9801288-0-2(3)) Breakthrough Publishing LLC.

Trine, Ralph. What All the World's A-Seeking: Or, the Vital Law of True Life, True Greatness Power & Happiness. 2007. 96p. per. 8.99 (978-1-60459-039-5(4)) Wilder Pubns., Ltd.

—What All the World's A-Seeking: the Vital Law of True Life, True. 2006. pap. 19.95 (978-1-59605-974-0(5), Cosimo Classics) Cosimo, Inc.

Tripp, Paul & Lane, Timothy S. How People Change Participant Guide. 2007. (ENG.). 188p. spiral bd., wbk. ed. 25.00 (978-0-9762308-9-2(5)) New Growth Pr.

Tripp, Paul David. Helping Your Adopted Child: Understanding Your Child's Unique Identity. 2008. (ENG.). 24p. 3.99 (978-1-934885-31-4(2)) New Growth Pr.

—Peer Pressure: Recognizing the Warning Signs & Giving New Direction. 2008. (ENG.). 24p. 3.99 (978-1-934885-29-1(0)) New Growth Pr.

—A Quest for More: Living for Something Bigger Than You. 2007. (ENG.). 216p. per. 17.99 (978-0-9785567-4-7(7)) New Growth Pr.

Tripp, Paul David & Lane, Timothy S. How People Change Leaders Guide. ldr.'s ed. 2007. (ENG.). 220p. spiral bd. 50.00 (978-0-9770807-0-0(6)) New Growth Pr.

Tripp, Rev. Marion. Moses: Israel's Great Leader. 2011. 114p. 29.99 (978-1-4628-6385-3(X)); pap. 19.99 (978-1-4628-6384-6(1)) Xlibris Corp.

Tristam, ed. The Word of the Lord: Collects & Readings for Special Occasions. 384p. 31.50 (978-1-85311-355-0(7)) Norwich Bks. & Music GBR. Dist: Morehouse Publishing.

Trivette, Pastor Terry. Homework: Building Godly Families, with God's Word, for God's Glory. 2010. 91p. pap. 11.00 (978-0-557-59574-7(6)) Lulu Enterprises Inc.

Trogdon, Rex. He Touched Me. 2011. 130p. pap. (978-1-897117-88-0(4)) Gospel Folio Pr.

Trollinger, Sara. How to Download Your Miracle: When Answers Aren't Enough. 2009. (ENG.). 192p. pap. 14.99 (978-1-935245-15-5(5)) HigherLife Development Services, Inc.

Trotman, Dawson E. & Navigators Staff. Dawson Trotman: In His Own Words. 2011. (Growing in Christ Ser.). 240p. pap. 12.99 (978-1-61747-921-2(7)) NavPress Publishing Group.

Trotter, L. A. From Vision to Victory. pap. 10.00 (978-0-927936-86-6(0)) Vincom Pubng. Co.

Trotter, Pastor Joel C. The Side of Me That Hates God. 2008. 76p. pap. 12.95 (978-1-4389-1740-5(6)) AuthorHouse.

Troward, Thomas. The Law & the Word. 2007. (ENG.). 120p. pap. 18.99 (978-1-4346-1412-4(3)); 132p. pap. 19.99 (978-1-4346-1427-8(1)) BiblioBazaar.

—The Law & the Word. 2007. (ENG.). 112p. per. 10.95 (978-1-60206-178-1(5)) Cosimo, Inc.

—The Law & the Word. 2007. (ENG.). 120p. per. (978-1-4068-1788-1(0)) Echo Library.

—The Law & the Word. 2006. pap. 12.99 (978-1-59986-943-8(8)) Filiquarian Publishing, LLC.

Troyer, Lester. Church in Society. 2011. 276p. pap. 16.99 (978-1-61215-771-9(8)) Xulon Pr., Inc.

Trufant Harvey, Jane. Thank Him: Living Life with an Attitude of Gratitude. 2008. (Illus.). spiral bd. 9.99 (978-1-58169-279-2(X), Evergreen Pr.) Genesis Communications, Inc.

Trumper, Tim J. R. When History Teaches Us Nothing: The Recent Reformed Sonship Debate in Context. 2008. 120p. pap. 15.00 (978-1-55635-303-1(0)) Wipf & Stock Pubs.

The Trumpet Judgments. pap. 0.95 (978-0-937408-10-0(7)) GMI Pubns.

Trzaska, Lynn M. Think about It! 2011. 60p. pap. 10.99 (978-1-61379-171-4(2)) Xulon Pr., Inc.

Tsidqenuew, Yah. YHWH Exists: Placing God on trial: an indepth look at the validity & righteousness of the Hebrew Scriptures, 2 vols., Vol. 1. 2012. (Illus.). 670p. 49.00 (978-0-9753375-0-9(5)) Emmanuel Academy Publishing, Inc.

Tuck, William Powell. Facing Life's Ups & Downs: The Struggle to Be Whole. 2010. 180p. pap. (978-1-57312-561-1(X)) Smyth & Helwys Publishing, Inc.

Tucker Jr., Pastor Lewis L. Damaged Goods: The Restoring Power of the Father's Love. 2009. 92p. pap. 13.95 (978-1-4327-2872-4(5)) Outskirts Pr., Inc.

Tucker, Lance. The Last of the Last Days Anointing & Power. 2009. 210p. pap. 20.50 (978-1-4357-2491-4(7)) Lulu Enterprises Inc.

Tucker, Leon. The Brazen Altar of the Roman Letter. pap. 2.49 (978-1-56632-021-4(6)) Revival Literature.

Tucker, Mike. Every Good Thing: Satisfying Your Hunger for God. 2007. (ENG.). 160p. per. 12.99 (978-0-8127-0449-5(5)) Autumn Hse. Publishing Co.

Tucker, Rev. R. E. Crossing Rivers & Moving Mountains. 2011. 142p. 29.99 (978-1-4653-5798-4(X)); pap. 19.99 (978-1-4653-5797-7(1)) Xlibris Corp.

—A Visitation from Jesus: Orders from Headquarters' 2011. 358p. 29.99 (978-1-4653-4641-4(4)); pap. 19.99 (978-1-4653-4640-7(6)) Xlibris Corp.

Tudah, Seth. Your Confession Is your Possession. 2011. 110p. pap. 11.99 (978-1-61215-398-8(4)) Xulon Pr., Inc.

Tuff, Pastor G. I. When Destiny Calls. 2010. 141p. pap. 19.99 (978-1-4500-8939-5(9)) Xlibris Corp.

Tumbaugh, Kevin. Time Witnessing: The Truth Behind Moral Values Inspired by God's Word & How Long You Will Spend in Heaven or Hell. 2011. 152p. 30.95 (978-1-4497-1307-2(6)); pap. 13.95 (978-1-4497-1306-5(8)) Author Solutions, Inc. (WestBow Pr.).

Tumbull, Judy. Another Dimension! 2008. 148p. per. 13.99 (978-1-60477-249-4(2)) Xulon Pr., Inc.

Turner, Adrienna Dionna. The Day Begins with Christ. 2008. 224p. pap. 18.99 (978-1-4389-1901-0(8)) AuthorHouse.

Turner, Alan. Is God Finished with Israel? 2008. 132p. pap. 14.99 (978-1-60647-834-9(6)) Xulon Pr., Inc.

Turner, Allan. The Christian & Idolatry. 2006. 208p. per. 18.95 (978-0-9777350-2-0(8)) Allanita Pr.

Turner, Andrew C. Dream Walker: Steps to the Ultimate Vision for Your Future. 2006. (ENG.). 159p. per. 12.96 (978-0-9774223-3-3(X)) Lifebridge Bks.

Turner, Darrell, ed. Stress Free. 2008. pap. 30.00 (978-0-933663-03-9(X)) Shepherd News Trust.

Turner, Debbie. Whispered Thunder. 2006. pap. 15.99 (978-1-60034-871-6(8)) Xulon Pr., Inc.

Turner, Edna Washington. This Truth Must Be Told! The Untold Journey Through the Eyes of My Soul. 2011. 96p. pap. 11.95 (978-1-4620-6644-5(5)) iUniverse, Inc.

Turner, Glenn O. All Things Are Possible. 2007. (ENG.). 33.99 (978-1-60034-898-3(X)); pap. 21.99 (978-1-60034-897-6(1)) Xulon Pr., Inc.

Turner, Grace. The King's Gold: True Wealth Is Found in Deeper Places, 1 vol. 2008. 256p. pap. 11.99 (978-0-8254-6277-1(0), Monarch Bks.) Lion Hudson PLC GBR. Dist: Kregel Pubns.

Turner, Johnny. The Sacred Art: Growing Faithful Disciples in the 21st Century. 2007. (Illus.). 293p. per. 16.99 (978-1-59886-872-2(1)) Tate Publishing & Enterprises, LLC.

Turner, Joyce & Costner, Karan. Fresh Misty Dew of God's Presence. 2009. 254p. pap. 15.99 (978-1-935361-36-7(8)) Comfort Publishing Services, LLC.

Turner, Ken & Turner, Lesley. The Power of Forgiveness. 2009. (ENG.). 256p. pap. 16.95 (978-1-74110-759-3(8)) New Holland Pubs. Pty, Ltd. AUS. Dist: Tuttle Publishing.

Turner, Léon. Theology, Psychology & the Plural Self. 2008. (Ashgate Science & Religion Ser.). 238p. 99.95 (978-0-7546-6519-9(4)) Ashgate Publishing Co.

Turner, Matthew Paul. Hear No Evil: My Story of Innocence, Music, & the Holy Ghost. 2010. (ENG.). 240p. pap. 14.99 (978-1-4000-7472-3(X), WaterBrook Pr.) Doubleday Religious Publishing Group, The.

Turner, Matthew Paul & Pomarolli, Kerri. How to Ruin Your Dating Life: A Christian's Guide for Avoiding [Almost] Every Mistake in the Book. 2007. (God's Design for Sex Ser.). (ENG.). 176p. pap. 12.99 (978-1-60006-139-4(7)) NavPress Publishing Group.

Turner, Ralph. God-Life: Following Jesus & Going Deeper. 2008. 123p. pap. (978-1-905991-15-0(0)) New Wine Pr.

Turner, Verlean. Woman, by Revelation. 2007. 148p. per. 24.95 (978-0-9792074-8-8(7)) Kingdom Publishing Group, Inc.

Turpin, Amya Penny Anysia. God's Love. 2011. 48p. 24.76 (978-1-4567-2750-5(8)) AuthorHouse.

Turpin, Katherine. Branded: Adolescents Converting from Consumer Faith. 2006. (Youth Ministry Alternatives Ser.). (978-0-8298-1738-6(7)) Pilgrim Pr., The/United Church Pr.

Turrell, James. The Secret According to Jesus: No One Is Left Behind. 2007. 76p. per. 12.95 (978-0-9800824-0-1(4)) AC Publishing, A California Corp.

Tutu, Bernard. The Awesome God: Keys to finding your Purpose in Him. 2011. 138p. pap. 19.99 (978-1-4568-8113-9(2)) Xlibris Corp.

C

Tutu, Desmond & Tutu, Mpho. Made for Goodness: And Why This Makes All the Difference. l.t. ed. 2010. (ENG.). 252p. pap. 25.99 (978-0-06-194625-7(7), HarperLuxe) HarperCollins Pubs.

Tutwiler, Greg. Stand Your Ground. 2007. 103p. pap. 14.95 (978-0-615-17935-3(5)) Berean Communications.

Twells, Shirley. Just for Today. 2007. 220p. per. 14.99 (978-1-60266-266-7(5)) Xulon Pr., Inc.

Twisck, Pieter Jansz. The Thirty-Three Articles of Faith: As Published in the Martyr's Mirror. 2011. 120p. 39.95 **(978-1-258-05953-8(3))** Literary Licensing, LLC.

Two Bears, David. Lessons from the Desert: My Spiritual Walk with JESUS in the Desert. 2007. 88p. per. 14.95 (978-1-4327-1528-1(3)) Outskirts Pr., Inc.

The Two Witnesses. pap. 0.95 (978-0-937408-12-4(3)) GMI Pubns.

Tyce, Lynn. He Wrote That When. 2006. 192p. per. 13.99 (978-1-932503-65-4(X)) Insight Publishing Group.

Tyndale House Publishers Staff, prod. Devotions for Advent. 2009. (Holy Bible: Mosaic Ser.). (ENG.). 48p. pap. 1.99 (978-1-4143-3578-0(4)) Tyndale Hse. Pubs.

Tyndale House Publishers Staff & GRQ, Inc. Staff, prods. 100 Great Ideas to Be a Good Friend. 2010. (ENG.). 128p. pap. 9.99 (978-1-4143-3885-9(6)) Tyndale Hse. Pubs.

—100 Great Ideas to Relax & Reduce Stress. 2010. (ENG.). 128p. pap. 9.99 (978-1-4143-3887-3(2)) Tyndale Hse. Pubs.

Tyrrell, George. Revelations of Divine Love. 2010. (ENG.). 258p. pap. 26.75 (978-1-177-65491-3(1)) BiblioBazaar.

Tyrrell, Jamie. Prayer for Busy People. 2007. per. (978-1-931551-10-6(3)) Vital Churches Institute.

Tyrrell, Mabel. A Missionary in the Making. 2007. 168p. per. 13.99 (978-1-60266-915-4(5)) Xulon Pr., Inc.

Tyson, John R. Faith, Doubt, & Courage in 15 Great People of Faith: And What We Can Learn from Them. 2008. 140p. pap. 12.00 (978-0-687-64726-2(6)) Abingdon Pr.

Uche, Kalu O. Get the Best Out of Life. 2008. 120p. 29.99 (978-1-4257-9677-8(X)); pap. 19.99 (978-1-4257-9644-0(3)) Xlibris Corp.

Ulbredtch, Robin R. Heart to Heart: A Discipleship & Mentoring Plan. 2011. 72p. pap. 9.95 **(978-1-4497-1764-3(0)**, WestBow Pr.) Author Solutions, Inc.

Ulmer, Kenneth. The Champion in You. 2008. pap. 16.99 (978-0-7684-2741-7(X)) Destiny Image Pubs.

Umar, Pastor. How Great Is Your Fall? 2011. 128p. pap. 15.67 **(978-1-4567-8593-2(1))** AuthorHouse.

Umubyeyi, Ornella. Life Beyond Sight: Existing, not Living. 2010. 64p. pap. 9.95 (978-1-4502-3351-4(1)) iUniverse, Inc.

Under Cover Curriculum. 2007. 198.00 (978-1-933185-11-8(2)) Messenger International.

Under Cover Workbook. 2007. 14.99 (978-1-933185-10-1(4)) Messenger International.

Under Protest: A sign unto You. 2007. 81p. pap. 11.99 (978-0-9752872-0-0(6)) Blaid Drwg.

Under the Baobab Tree: Claiming Roots, Kindling Hope, Spreading God's Love. 20.00 (978-0-687-08801-0(1)) Abingdon Pr.

Under the Baobab Tree: Wholesale. 45.00 (978-0-687-03903-6(7)) Abingdon Pr.

Under the Baobab Tree: Keep the Faith, Raise up Hope, Tell of God's Love: Activity Nametag Sticker Page. pap. 0.50 (978-0-687-00747-9(X)) Abingdon Pr.

Under the Baobab Tree: Keep the Faith, Raise up Hope, Tell of God's Love: Follow-up Postcard. pap. 3.00 (978-0-687-00729-5(1)) Abingdon Pr.

Under the Baobab Tree: Keep the Faith, Raise up Hope, Tell of God's Love: Heritage Recipes, Vol. 2. pap. 2.00 (978-0-687-00808-7(5)) Abingdon Pr.

Under the Baobab Tree: Keep the Faith, Raise up Hope, Tell of God's Love: Invitation Postcard, Vol. 2. pap. 4.00 (978-0-687-00748-6(8)) Abingdon Pr.

Under the Baobab Tree: Keep the Faith, Raise up Hope, Tell of God's Love: Leader Certificate, Vol. 2. pap. 3.50 (978-0-687-00717-2(8)) Abingdon Pr.

Under the Baobab Tree: Keep the Faith, Raise up Hope, Tell of God's Love: Mobile, Vol. 2. pap. 16.00 (978-0-687-00739-4(9)) Abingdon Pr.

Under the Baobab Tree: Keep the Faith, Raise up Hope, Tell of God's Love: Registration Flyer, Vol. 2. pap. 5.00 (978-0-687-00719-6(4)) Abingdon Pr.

Under the Baobab Tree: Keep the Faith, Raise up Hope, Tell of God's Love: Reproducible Activity Sheets, Vol. 2. pap. 15.00 (978-0-687-00727-1(5)) Abingdon Pr.

Under the Baobab Tree: Keep the Faith, Raise up Hope, Tell of God's Love: Student Certificate. pap. 3.25 (978-0-687-00749-3(6)) Abingdon Pr.

Under the Baobab Tree: Keep the Faith, Raise up Hope, Tell of God's Love: Teen Leader, Vol. 2. ldr.'s ed. pap. 9.00 (978-0-687-00778-3(X)) Abingdon Pr.

Under the Baobab Tree: Keep the Faith, Raise up Hope, Tell of God's Love: Teen Student Handbook. pap., stu. ed. 4.00 (978-0-687-00757-8(7)) Abingdon Pr.

Underwood, Ed. Reborn to Be Wild: Reviving Our Radical Pursuit of Jesus, 1 vol. 2010. (ENG.). 320p. pap. 16.99 (978-1-4347-0017-9(8)) Cook, David C.

—When God Breaks Your Heart: Choosing Hope in the Midst of Faith-Shattering Circumstances. 2008. (ENG.). 224p. pap. 14.99 (978-1-4347-6751-6(5)) Cook, David C.

Underwood, Richard & Boley, Brian. Tutor Manual. 2010. (Learn2Lead Ser.). 200p. pap. (978-1-905564-69-9(4)) Good Bk. Co.

Underwood, Tina. Captive No More: Getting over You so You Can Go on with God. 2010. pap. 12.99 (978-1-61566-480-1(7)) Tate Publishing & Enterprises, LLC.

Unger, Barbara Patton. Taste the Grace: How God's Love Empowers Us to Feel Good, Do Good, & Make Good. 2009. pap. (978-1-932717-19-8(6)) Hope Publishing Hse.

Unger, Merrill F. Mas Alla de la Bola de Cristal: Beyond the Crystal Ball. (SPA.). 224p. (978-84-7228-264-3(3), 220581) Clie, Editorial.

Unilit Staff. Guia Diaria: General-Senor, Ensenanos.Tr. of Agenda: General-Lord, Teach Us. (SPA.). 1.99 (978-1-56063-550-5(9), 491408) Editorial Unilit.

Unleash Heaven's Power: Your Way of Victory Through Psalm 103. 2007. 147p. per. 11.99 (978-1-60247-309-6(9)) Tate Publishing & Enterprises, LLC.

Unveil: Beginning the process of Lust Free Living. 2nd ed. 2007. per. 14.95 (978-0-9719958-6-4(9)) LFL Group, LLC, The.

Upper Room Staff. Entering the New Testament. 2008. 96p. pap., wbk. ed. 10.00 (978-0-8358-9967-3(5)) Upper Room Bks.

Urby, Tom. Expressions of Gratitude. 2008. pap. 13.99 (978-1-60477-889-2(X)) Xulon Pr., Inc.

Urick, Steve. The Fundamentals of the Christian Faith: Biblical Basics That Everyone Should Know. 2009. 128p. pap. 13.99 (978-1-4490-0771-3(6)) AuthorHouse.

Urquhart. Anything You Ask. pap. (978-0-340-72231-2(2)); (Illus.). 220p. pap. (978-0-340-23348-1(6)) Hodder General Publishing Div. (Hodder & Stoughton).

Ussery, Vanessa Dantzler. My Be Attitude. 2010. 234p. pap. 15.99 (978-1-60957-627-1(6)) Xulon Pr., Inc.

Ussher, James. Works of James Ussher, 17 vols. Elrington, C. R. & Todd, J. H., eds. reprint ed. lib. bdg. 67.50 (978-0-404-06730-4(1)) AMS Pr., Inc.

Utuk, N. George. Finding Your Unique Pathway. 2007. 224p. per. 14.99 (978-1-60266-340-4(8)) Xulon Pr., Inc.

—You Can Stage A Comeback. 2006. pap. 13.99 (978-1-60034-381-0(3)) Xulon Pr., Inc.

Uziewe-Ogbru, Irene O. Silence Is Broken-Women Era: Hear My Cry, Almighty Father. 2011. 288p. 38.99 (978-1-4520-5662-3(5)); pap. 22.99 (978-1-4520-5663-0(3)) AuthorHouse.

Uzoma, Joel. You Are Coming Out Better. 2011. 120p. pap. 19.95 **(978-1-4560-5756-5(1))** PublishAmerica, Inc.

UZONWANNE, Francis Emeka. Catching His Attention: The secret of Success. 2008. pap. 15.99 (978-1-60647-918-6(0)) Xulon Pr., Inc.

Vaden, Richard & Vaden, Christine. Finding the Needle in the Haystack: Finding True Christian Love in Today's Society. 2011. pap. 18.99 **(978-1-61777-560-4(6))** Tate Publishing & Enterprises, LLC.

Valentine, Gemma. The Purpose for Marriage: The Spiritual Implications of the Covenant. 2008. (ENG.). 192p. pap. 12.99 (978-1-59979-601-7(5), Creation Hse.) Charisma Media.

Valentine Jr., Rev. Charles. A Cry unto the Lord. 2011. 200p. 29.99 **(978-1-4653-4159-4(5))**; pap. 19.99 **(978-1-4628-9666-0(9))** Xlibris Corp.

Valerio, Pamela S. A Walk Toward Jesus. 2010. 322p. pap. 18.99 (978-1-60957-820-6(1)) Xulon Pr., Inc.

Vallés, Carlos G. Autenticidad. 64p. 3.95 (978-958-607-852-8(3)) Sociedad de San Pablo COL. Dist: St Pauls/Alba Hse. Pubs.

—Mi Angel y Yo. 128p. 4.95 (978-958-607-968-6(6)) Sociedad de San Pablo COL. Dist: St Pauls/Alba Hse. Pubs.

—Testigos de Cristo en un Mundo Nuevo. 80p. 4.95 (978-958-607-854-2(X)) Sociedad de San Pablo COL. Dist: St Pauls/Alba Hse. Pubs.

Valmyr, William. Christianity & Culture: A Christian Perspective on Worldview Development. 2009. 216p. pap. 15.99 (978-1-60791-941-4(9)) Xulon Pr., Inc.

van Alphen, Markus. Christianity & Esotericism. 2010. 112p. pap. 20.50 (978-1-4457-6213-5(7)) Lulu Enterprises Inc.

Van Amburgh, W. A Bible for the Scientist. 2007. 54p. pap. 10.50 (978-1-4116-4708-4(4)) Lulu Enterprises Inc.

van Bavel, T. J. The Longing of the Heart: Augustine's Doctrine on Prayer. 2009. (ENG.). 175p. (C). pap. 44.00 (978-90-429-1975-4(2)) Peeters Pubs. & Booksellers BEL. Dist: Brown, David Bk. Co., The.

Van Der Merwe, Andre. Grace, the Forbidden Gospel: Jesus Tore the Veil. Religion Sewed it Back Up. 2011. 228p. 33.95 (978-1-4497-1404-8(8)); pap. 17.95 (978-1-4497-1403-1(X)) Author Solutions, Inc. (WestBow Pr.).

Van Der Watt, Jan, ed. The Bible in 40 Days for Men: Discover God's Plan for Your Life. 2007. 207p. per. (978-1-86920-798-4(X)) Christian Art Pubs.

—The Bible in 40 Days for Women: Discover God's Plan for Your Life. 2007. 207p. per. (978-1-86920-799-1(8)) Christian Art Pubs.

—The Bible in 40 Days for Youth: Discover God's Plan for Your Life. 2007. 207p. per. (978-1-86920-800-4(5)) Christian Art Pubs.

Van Dunk, M. Brian. In the House of Grace. 2010. 438p. pap. 22.99 (978-1-60957-408-6(7)) Xulon Pr., Inc.

Van-Dusen, Wilson. The Country of Spirit: Selected Writings. 140p. pap. (978-0-9626795-2-0(6)) Appleseed, J. & Co.

Van Dyke, Fred. Between Heaven & Earth: Christian Perspectives on Environmental Protection, 1 vol. 2010. (Illus.). 247p. 44.95 (978-0-313-37536-1(4), C37536, Praeger Pubs.) Greenwood Publishing Group, Inc.

Van Dyke, Henry. Joy & Power. 2007. 56p. per. (978-1-4065-4718-4(2)) Dodo Pr.

Van Hee, Jan. Think on These Things: Challenging Thoughts for Teen Girls. 2008. 72p. (YA). spiral bd. 7.95 (978-0-9766823-3-2(8)) Sable Creek Pr. LLC.

Van Impe, Rexella. Reflections. 24.95 (978-1-884137-95-2(4)) Van Impe, Jack Ministries.

van Lodenstein, Jodocus. A Spiritual Appeal to Christ's Bride. Beeke, Joel R., ed. Elshout, Bartel, tr. from DUT. 2010.Tr. of Negen Predikatien over eenige stiffen, welke zeer zelden geleerd en nog minder beoefend Worden. (Illus.). 176p. (978-1-60178-106-2(7)) Reformation Heritage Bks.

Van Loon, Michelle. Uprooted: Growing a Parable Life from the Inside Out. 2006. 173p. per. (978-1-932902-62-4(7)) FaithWalk Publishing.

Van Natta, Bruce. Saved by Angels to Share How God Talks to Everyday People. 2008. pap. 16.99 (978-0-7684-2651-9(0)) Destiny Image Pubs.

Van Riper, Nadine. Life's Journey with God. 2008. 380p. pap. 20.99 (978-1-60647-709-0(9)) Xulon Pr., Inc.

van Rooyen, Leon. Well Done! ... good & faithful Servant. 2011. 142p. pap. 15.00 **(978-1-935298-77-9(1))** Truth Pubs.

Van Ruitenburg, Pieter. Good Old Age: Letters to Seniors. 2008. 120p. 21.49 (978-1-4343-8576-5(0)) AuthorHouse.

Van Schooneveld, Amber. Hope Lives: A Journey of Restoration. 2008. (Illus.). 185p. per. 12.99 (978-0-7644-3788-5(7)) Group Publishing, Inc.

Van Tassell, Ray, Jr. Means to Christian Maturity. 2009. 208p. pap. 15.99 (978-1-60791-236-1(8)) Xulon Pr., Inc.

Van Tassell, Ray C. Who Are the Sons of God? 2009. 92p. pap. 10.99 (978-1-60791-235-4(X)) Xulon Pr., Inc.

Vance, Bennie. Vessels of Honor. 2011. 146p. pap. 14.99 (978-1-61215-767-2(X)) Xulon Pr., Inc.

Vance, Sheilah & Howard, Felicia. Creativity for Christians: How to Tell Your Story & Stories of Overcoming from the Members of One Special Church. 2010. (Illus.). 120p. pap. 15.95 (978-0-9820384-2-0(9)) Elevator Group, The.

Vandeman, George E. The Worst Sinner in Town: A Collection of Inspiring Stories. 2008. pap. (978-0-8163-2272-5(4)) Pacific Pr. Pubns.

Vander Griend, Alvin J. Disciple Making: A 10-Step Guide for Churches. 117p. pap. 20.00 incl. audio (978-1-56212-115-0(4), 216625) Faith Alive Christian Resources.

Vander, Laan. In the Dust of the Rabbi: Becoming a Disciple, 1 vol. 2006. (Faith Lessons Ser.). (ENG., Illus.). 192p. pap. 9.99 (978-0-310-27120-8(7)) Zondervan.

—Walk As Jesus Walked: Making Disciples, 1 vol. 2006. (Faith Lessons Ser.). (ENG., Illus.). 208p. pap. 9.99 (978-0-310-27117-8(7)) Zondervan.

Vanier, Jean. Befriending the Stranger: Befriending a Stranger. 2010. (Illus.). 144p. pap. 15.95 (978-0-8091-4690-1(8)) Paulist Pr.

Vann, Donna. Cambodian Adventures. 2009. (ENG., Illus.). 96p. pap. 8.99 (978-1-84550-474-8(7)) Christian Focus Pubns. GBR. Dist: STL Distribution North America.

Vanover, S. T. Satan versus GOD. 2008. 174p. pap. 14.00 (978-0-8059-7688-5(4)) Dorrance Publishing Co., Inc.

VanVonderen, Jeff. Tired of Trying to Measure Up: Getting Free from the Demands, Expectations, & Intimidation of Well-Meaning People. 2008. 208p. reprint ed. pap. 14.99 (978-0-7642-0537-8(4)) Bethany Hse. Pubs.

Varner, Kelley. Secrets of the Ascended Life. 2006. 147p. per. 14.99 (978-0-7684-2358-7(9)) Destiny Image Pubs.

Varughese, T. V. Bible & Theology Mysteries Solved! Volume One: Subtitle: Amazing Solutions to 14 of the Most Puzzling Questions. 2009. pap. 14.99 (978-1-60791-450-1(6)) Xulon Pr., Inc.

Vasholz, Robert I. Calls to Worship: A Pocket Resource. 2008. (ENG.). 144p. 14.99 (978-1-84550-338-3(4)) Christian Focus Pubns. GBR. Dist: STL Distribution North America.

Vasquez, Lacey. Because He Loved: A Story of Hope. 2011. pap. 10.99 **(978-1-61346-185-3(2))** Tate Publishing & Enterprises, LLC.

Vasquez, Ruben. God Hears All Who Call: Get Ready to Receive. 2007. 192p. per. 24.95 (978-1-4241-8555-9(6)) PublishAmerica, Inc.

Vassal, Joy. Turn Around & See the Lord. 2009. 276p. 26.99 (978-1-60647-893-6(1)); pap. 16.99 (978-1-60647-892-9(3)) Xulon Pr., Inc.

Vatel, Karen Wilson. So You're Born Again Now What? 2008. 68p. pap. 9.99 (978-1-60647-479-2(0)) Xulon Pr., Inc.

Vatican Congregations Staff. Instr Non Ordained Faith. 54p. pap. 1.95 (978-0-8198-3677-9(X), 332-133) Pauline Bks. & Media.

Vaughn, Greg. Letters from Dad. 2006. 256p. per. 12.99 (978-1-59145-382-6(8)) Nelson, Thomas Inc.

Vauk, Dennis A. Free to Minister. 2007. 100p. pap. 9.95 (978-0-615-16117-4(0)) Vauk, Dennis A.

Vazquez, Lidia. Celebremos con Jesus - Misas.Tr. of Let's Celebrate with Jesus - Masses. (SPA.). 120p. pap. 4.95 (978-950-861-381-3(5)) Sociedad de San Pablo ARG. Dist: St Pauls/Alba Hse. Pubs.

VBS 08 Adult Guide. 2007. (VBS 2008 Ser.). pap. 4.99 (978-1-4347-9948-7(4)) Cook, David C.

Veatch Sr, Don. Footsteps Toward Higher Ground. 2007. 208p. per. 15.95 (978-1-59800-940-8(0)) Outskirts Pr., Inc.

Vega Jr., Frank. Marching Orders. 2006. pap. 9.99 (978-1-60034-733-7(9)) Xulon Pr., Inc.

Velez, Lisa M. A Message to the Body of Christ: What the Spirit of the Lord Is Saying to the Churches. 2009. 294p. pap. 19.95 (978-1-4327-4160-0(8)) Outskirts Pr., Inc.

Veliquette, Timothy K. Mustard Seeds to Mansions. 2008. 112p. pap. 11.99 (978-1-60647-833-2(8)) Xulon Pr., Inc.

Vella, Carlo J. The Book of Secrets. 2011. 266p. pap. 12.99 **(978-1-61667-198-3(X))** Raider Publishing International.

Venable, Sandi. There Is Only One Great Commandment. 2008. 199p. pap. 13.50 (978-0-557-02044-7(1)) Lulu Enterprises Inc.

Vencel, Josiah. Culture Makers. 2008. 188p. per. 13.99 (978-1-60477-651-5(X)) Xulon Pr., Inc.

Veneroso, Joseph R. God in Unexpected Places: Reflections on Faith & Life from Maryknoll Magazine. 2007. (Illus.). 143p. pap. 15.00 (978-1-57075-709-9(7)) Orbis Bks.

Verheyden, Paul J. Live to Fight Another Day: Finding Purpose for God & Others Through Life-Changing Events. 2010. 232p. 24.99 (978-1-4490-6852-3(9)); pap. 19.95 (978-1-4490-6853-0(7)) AuthorHouse.

Verling Chako Priest. Paulus of Tarsus: A Man Driven by the Word. 2010. 68p. pap. 13.86 (978-1-4269-2529-0(8)) Trafford Publishing.

Vermillion, Richard. White Man in a Black Man's World. 120p. 17.99 (978-1-59160-234-7(3)) Xulon Pr., Inc.

Vermont, Ernest. Tactics of Truth. 2006. pap. 14.99 (978-1-60034-456-5(9)) Xulon Pr., Inc.

Verway, Clair. Wings of Mentridar. 2008. 352p. per. 19.99 (978-1-60477-337-8(5)) Xulon Pr., Inc.

Very Much Alive. stu. ed. 3.45 (978-0-570-00762-3(3), 22-2876); 4.45 (978-0-570-00761-6(5), 22-2875) Concordia Publishing Hse.

Vesely, David. Righteousness Exalts a Nation: God's Love Will Change America. 2009. 72p. pap. 10.99 (978-1-61579-263-4(5)) Xulon Pr., Inc.

Vestal, Joel. Dangerous Faith: Growing in God & Service to the World. 2007. (Navigators Reference Library). (ENG., Illus.). 240p. pap. 14.99 (978-1-60006-197-4(4)) NavPress Publishing Group.

Via, Joshua. The Discovery. 2008. pap. 14.99 (978-1-60647-221-7(6)) Xulon Pr., Inc.

Viars, Stephen. Putting Your Past in Its Place: Moving Forward in Freedom & Forgiveness. 2011. 256p. pap. 12.99 (978-0-7369-2739-0(5)) Harvest Hse. Pubs.

Vice, Midge. Let the Older Women Teach: Seasoned Wisdom on Love & Marriage. 2008. (ENG.). 640p. pap. 17.99 (978-1-59979-388-7(1), Creation Hse.) Charisma Media.

Vickers, Douglas. The Cross: Its Meaning & Message in a Postmodern World. 2010. 170p. pap. 20.00 (978-1-60899-429-8(5)) Wipf & Stock Pubs.

—The Texture of Truth. 2007. (ENG.). 216p. per. 15.00 (978-1-60178-009-6(5)) Reformation Heritage Bks.

Victa, Francisco I. Maximum Mentoring: The Ten Dynamic Principles That Will Impact Your Life & Relationships. 2008. 164p. pap. 13.99 (978-1-60647-678-9(5)) Xulon Pr., Inc.

Victory House Staff. Little Bit of God's Women. Date not set. pap. 5.99 (978-0-932081-44-5(4)) Victory Hse., Inc.

Vidal, V. Yinka. Closer Walk with Jesus. 2010. 492p. pap. 23.95 (978-0-9640818-4-0(9)) Lara Pubns.

Vieira, Paul. Jesus Has Left the Building. 2006. mass mkt. 16.99 (978-0-9718040-8-1(7)) Karis Publishing, Inc.

Vigeveno, H. S. El Espectador.Tr. of Listener. (SPA.). 176p. (978-84-7228-390-9(9), 220375) Clie, Editorial.

Vila, Samuel. Como Prolongar y Transformar La: How to Live Longer Here. (SPA.). 96p. (978-84-7228-718-1(1), 220221) Clie, Editorial.

—Evidencias de Fe Para Jovenes: Faith Evidences for Christian. (SPA.). 136p. (978-84-7228-952-9(4), 223023) Clie, Editorial.

—Supremo Dilema: Supreme Dilemma. (SPA.). 192p. (978-84-7228-542-2(1), 220861) Clie, Editorial.

Villafane, Eldin. Beyond Cheap Grace: A Call to Radical Discipleship, Incarnation, & Justice. 2006. 98p. per. 14.00 (978-0-8028-6323-2(X)) Eerdmans, William B. Publishing Co.

Villanueva, Stephen. We Have Been Lied To. 2008. 428p. 19.99 (978-1-60462-900-2(2)) Tate Publishing & Enterprises, LLC.

Villegas, Victor. Juegos, Habilidades y Bufonadas. 128p. 5.95 (978-958-607-698-2(9)) Sociedad de San Pablo COL. Dist: St Pauls/Alba Hse. Pubs.

Vincent A. David. He Restoreth All Things: The Elijah's Message & Today's Generation. 2009. 144p. pap. 21.99 (978-1-4389-6050-0(6)) AuthorHouse.

Vincent, Alan. Heaven on Earth: Releasing the Power of Kingdom Through You. 2008. (Kingdom Ser.). pap. 16.99 (978-0-7684-2696-0(0)) Destiny Image Pubs.

Vincent, Marvin Richardson. Amusement; a Force in Christian Training. 2006. 144p. per. 16.99 (978-1-4255-1012-1(4)) MPublishing.

Vincent, Milton. A Gospel Primer for Christians: Learning to See the Glories of God's Love. 2008. 97p. per. 10.95 (978-1-885904-67-6(3)) Focus Publishing.

Vint, Tom. Walking with Dog: What Man's Best Friend Can Teach Us about God. 2011. 108p. 22.95 **(978-1-4502-9076-0(0))**; pap. 12.95 **(978-1-4502-9077-7(9))** iUniverse, Inc.

Viola, Frank. Revise Us Again: Living from a Renewed Christian Script. 2011. (ENG.). 176p. 16.99 (978-1-4347-6865-0(1)) Cook, David C.

Virgo, Terry & Newfrontiers-USA. Enjoying God's Grace. 2008. 128p. pap. 6.50 (978-0-9814803-3-6(0)) Newfrontiers USA.

—Start: An Interactive Study Guide to Help Christians Grow in Their Faith. 2008. 148p. pap. 6.50 (978-0-9814803-1-2(4)) Newfrontiers USA.

Virkler, Henry. Speaking the Truth in Love: A Christian Approach to Assertiveness. 2009. 220p. pap. 15.99 (978-1-61579-414-0(X)) Xulon Pr., Inc.

Virtue, David W. A Vision of Hope. 160p. pap. 14.99 (978-1-870345-16-3(9)) Regnum Bks.

Vogan, Charles. Eight Fundamentals of the Christian Faith. 2007. (ENG.). 368p. per. 25.00 (978-0-615-13862-6(4)) Shenandoah Bible Ministries.

—The Measure of a Christian. 2007. 248p. pap. 20.00 (978-0-615-14570-9(1)) Shenandoah Bible Ministries.

Voice of the Martyrs. Heroic Faith: How to Live a Life of Extreme Devotion, 0 vols. 2008. 176p. pap. 12.99 (978-0-7852-9677-5(8)) Nelson, Thomas Inc.

The Voice Said Cry. 4.00 (978-0-687-86447-8(X)) Abingdon Pr.

Volf, Miroslav. Against the Tide: Love in a Time of Petty Dreams & Persisting Enmities. 2010. 222p. pap. 18.00 *(978-0-8028-6506-9(2))* Eerdmans, William B. Publishing Co.
Vollbrecht, Matthew. Blind Faith. 2010. 240p. 27.99 *(978-1-4490-7852-2(4))* AuthorHouse.
von Balthasar, Hans Urs. The Christian State of Life. 29.95 *(978-0-89870-788-5(9))* Ignatius Pr.
Von Bargen, Caroline. Living in a House of Shattered Dreams. 2007. 240p. (ENG.). 24.99 *(978-1-60266-420-3(X))*; per. 14.99 *(978-1-60266-419-7(6))* Xulon Pr., Inc.
Vonruhland. Louder Than Words. 160p. 12.95 *(978-0-281-04931-8(9))* International Publishers Marketing.
Voskamp, Ann. One Thousand Gifts: A Dare to Live Fully Right Where You Are. l.t. ed. 2012. (ENG.). 331p. 30.99 ***(978-1-4104-4905-4(X))*** Thorndike Pr.
—One Thousand Gifts: A Dare to Live Fully Right Where You Are, 1 vol. 2011. (ENG.). 224p. 16.99 *(978-0-310-32191-0(3))* Zondervan.
Vost, Kevin. Fit for Eternal Life: A Christian Approach to Working Out, Eating Right, & Building the Virtues of Fitness in Your Soul. 2007. 229p. per. *(978-1-933184-31-9(0))* Sophia Institute Pr.
Vovor, Apotre Michel. Practical Guide for Born-Again Christians. 2011. 188p. 29.99 ***(978-1-4628-5958-0(5))*** Xlibris Corp.
Voyles, David W. A Shepherd's Trial: Feeding or Fleecing the Flock of God? A Look at the Relationship that Today's Pastor has with the Congregation. 2010. 148p. 22.95 *(978-1-60911-031-4(5))*, Eloquent Bks.) AEG Literary Publishing Services, Inc.
Voysey, Sheridan. Unseen Footprints: Encountering the Divine along the Journey of Life. 2007. (Illus.). 176p. per. *(978-0-8254-6168-2(5))* Lion Hudson PLC.
Vreeland, Derek. Shape Shifters: How God Changes the Human Heart. 2008. 156p. pap. 12.95 *(978-0-9785352-9-2(4))* Word & Spirit Pr.
Vroman, M. A., ed. Sabbath Readings for the Home Circle. 2007. (ENG.). 424p. 51.95 *(978-0-548-03228-2(9))* Kessinger Publishing, LLC.
Vukich, Lee. Discipleship in Youth Ministry. 3rd ed. 2006. (C). per. *(978-1-60036-020-6(3))* Academx Publishing Services, Inc.
Vukich, Lee & Vandegriff, Steve. Protecting Your Teen from Disturbing Behaviors: Helping Your Teen Overcome Today's Issues. 2007. 130p. per. 14.99 *(978-0-89957-085-3(2))* AMG Pubs.
Wabala, Daniel. Rediscovering the Pearl of Servanthood. 2006. 138p. per. 11.95 *(978-1-59886-438-0(6))* Tate Publishing & Enterprises, LLC.
Wachold, Patty. My Courage Book. 2007. 328p. per. 17.99 *(978-1-60256-291-9(6))* Xulon Pr., Inc.
Waddell, Brian R. Letters Unsent Words Unspoken. 2008. 244p. 25.99 *(978-1-60791-073-2(X))*; pap. 15.99 *(978-1-60791-072-5(1))* Xulon Pr., Inc.
Wade, Eddie L. Everyday Faith for the Christian, & the Terminal Ill. 2011. 188p. pap. 24.95 ***(978-1-4560-3719-2(6))*** PublishAmerica, Inc.
Wade, Eddie L. Growing in God Today, 1 vol. 2010. 71p. pap. 16.95 *(978-1-4489-7281-4(7))* PublishAmerica, Inc.
Wade, Janelle. Out of Darkness. 2009. 244p. pap. 15.99 *(978-1-60791-517-1(0))* Xulon Pr., Inc.
Wade, Loron. Simply Put: What God's Been Saying All Along. 2009. 223p. pap. 14.99 *(978-0-8280-2477-8(4))* Review & Herald Publishing Assn.
Wade, Peter. Semillas Y Secretos: Cultivando las semillas de dios de grandeza y aplicando los secretos de Dios del éxito para volverse vencedores, no Víctimas. 2010. (SPA.). 196p. pap. 13.99 *(978-0-909362-35-5(1))* Positive Word Ministries Inc. AUS. Dist: Lightning Source, Inc.
Wade, Peter John. God's Principles & Your Potential: Exploring the Myth of a Capricious God & Releasing the Potential of Every Believer. 2009. 208p. pap. 13.99 *(978-0-909362-31-7(9))* Positive Word Ministries Inc. AUS. Dist: Lightning Source, Inc.
Wadell, Paul J. Happiness & the Christian Moral Life: An Introduction to Christian Ethics. 2nd ed. 2012. ***(978-1-4422-0974-9(7))***; (ENG.). 308p. 80.00 ***(978-1-4422-0972-5(0))***; (ENG.). 308p. pap. 29.95 ***(978-1-4422-0973-2(9))*** Rowman & Littlefield Publishers, Inc.
Wadsworth, Olive A. Heavenward Bound Words of Help for Young Christians by Olive a Wadsworth a Prize Book. 2006. 216p. per. 20.99 *(978-1-4255-1782-3(X))* MPublishing.
Wafer, G. Arnold. Start Right, Finish Strong: What Every Christian Should Know. 2010. pap. 21.99 *(978-1-60799-713-9(4))* Tate Publishing & Enterprises, LLC.
Waggoner, Brad J. The Shape of Faith to Come: Spiritual Formation & the Future of Discipleship. 2008. (ENG.). 336p. 19.99 *(978-0-8054-4824-5(1)*, B&H Bks.) B&H Publishing Group.
Wagner, C. Peter. Dominio. 2008. 224p. 10.99 *(978-1-59979-132-6(3)*, Casa Creacion) Charisma Media.
Wagner, E. Glenn. Fire in Your Bones! 2007. (ENG.). 160p. per. 12.95 *(978-0-9793192-1-1(8))* Lifebridge Bks.
Wagner, James K. Forgiveness: the Way of Jesus: The Proven Path to Be Forgiving & Forgiven. 2007. 152p. *(978-0-7880-2437-5(X))* CSS Publishing Co.
Wagner, Lori. A Patchwork of Freedom: True Stories. Secret Quilt Code. Hope for Today. 2010. 204p. pap. 14.95 *(978-0-9798627-7-9(9))* Affirming Faith.
Wagner, Maria. Everyones Family. 2007. 288p. 25.99 *(978-1-60477-094-0(5))*; per. 15.99 *(978-1-60477-093-3(7))* Xulon Pr., Inc.
Wahl, Marcus C. Unspeakable: Logic or Faith? 2009. 72p. pap. 10.49 *(978-1-4389-5757-9(2))* AuthorHouse.
Waite, Yvonne S. My Daily Bible Blessings from My Daily Bible Reading. 2011. 664p. pap. 30.00 ***(978-1-56848-079-4(2))*** Old Paths Pubns., Inc., The.
Waiting for the Risen Christ. 3.00 *(978-0-687-86462-1(3))* Abingdon Pr.
Waldman, Christina. You Are Not Getting Older, You Are Getting Better. 2010. pap. 10.00 *(978-0-578-05607-4(0))* Torretilla, Christina D.
Waldron, Samuel E. The End Times Made Simple: How Could Everybody Be So Wrong about Biblical Prophecy? 2007. (ENG.), 251p. pap. 19.99 *(978-1-879737-50-1(7))* Calvary Pr.
Waldron, Tom. Will I See Him Again? A Look at Pets in Heaven. 2006. (ENG.). 25.99 *(978-1-60034-689-7(8))*; pap. 15.99 *(978-1-60034-688-0(X))* Xulon Pr., Inc.
Walhout, Edwin. Christianity down to Earth: Where We Are & Where We Should Be Going. 2006. (C). per. 20.00 *(978-1-59872-615-2(3))* Instant Pub.
Walker. Telling the Story. 256p. 26.95 *(978-0-281-04726-0(X))* International Publishers Marketing.
Walker, Brenda & Ring, Karen. How to Be a Compassionate Human Being. 2008. 196p. pap. 13.99 *(978-1-60647-593-5(2))* Xulon Pr., Inc.
Walker, Brian W. Propelled by Purpose. 2009. 272p. pap. 16.99 *(978-1-60791-769-4(6))* Xulon Pr., Inc.
Walker, David. It's Time to Call a Spade a Spade. 2009. 196p. pap. 14.99 *(978-1-60791-509-6(X))* Xulon Pr., Inc.
Walker, Florine. Jesus Is Looking Down. 2007. 92p. per. 9.99 *(978-1-60034-609-5(X))* Xulon Pr., Inc.
Walker, Guy. Financial Exodus. 2008. 260p. pap. 15.99 *(978-1-60647-337-5(9))* Xulon Pr., Inc.
Walker, J. Lamah. Interview with Jesus in the Hot Tub. 2011. 170p. 29.99 ***(978-1-4628-4829-4(X))***; pap. 19.99 ***(978-1-4628-4828-7(1))*** Xlibris Corp.
Walker, Janet Marie. A Time for Praise: Devotions & Prayers That Inspire & Bring Enlightenment. 2008. (ENG.). 176p. 17.99 *(978-1-59979-368-9(7)*, Creation Hse.) Charisma Media.
Walker, Jerry. Get up & Get Moving. 2007. 144p. 21.99 *(978-1-60477-114-5(3))*; per. 13.99 *(978-1-60477-113-8(5))* Xulon Pr., Inc.
Walker, Jim. Dirty Word: The Vulgar, Offensive Languages of the Kingdom of God. 2008. 256p. pap. 20.00 *(978-0-88177-539-6(8))* Discipleship Resources.
Walker, Jon. Costly Grace: A Contemporary View of Bonhoeffer's the Cost of Discipleship. 2010. 224p. pap. 15.99 *(978-0-89112-676-8(7))*, Leafwood Pubs.) Abilene Christian Univ. Pr.
Walker, Jon. In Visible Fellowship: A Contemporary View of Bonhoeffer's Classic Work Life Together. 2011. (ENG.). pap. 13.99 ***(978-0-89112-295-1(8)***, Leafwood Pubs.) Abilene Christian Univ. Pr.
Walker, Kevin D. Different Colored Boats: Book 1, 1 vol. 2009. 175p. pap. 19.95 *(978-1-60749-635-9(6))* PublishAmerica, Inc.
Walker, Lamont. Game Over: Are You Still Playing? 2011. 80p. pap. 17.00 *(978-1-4567-2649-2(8))* AuthorHouse.
Walker, Nancy. The Forgotten Christian. 2007. 176p. per. 15.00 *(978-1-59919-034-1(6))* Elim Publishing.
Walker, Reginald. Oh God, What Am I Going to Do Now! 2010. 36p. pap. 11.99 *(978-0-557-20319-2(8))* Lulu Enterprises Inc.
Walker, Rick. The Way of the Secret Path. 2008. 352p. pap. 19.99 *(978-1-60647-358-0(1))* Xulon Pr., Inc.
Walker, Sylvia Bronner. Little Nuggets for Life's Experiences. 2011. 60p. pap. 12.00 ***(978-1-4269-6853-2(1))*** Trafford Publishing.
Walkin, Newton. Praying for Miracles. 2011. 534p. 38.99 ***(978-1-60957-041-5(3))***; pap. 26.99 ***(978-1-60957-040-8(5))*** Xulon Pr., Inc.
Wall, Gary & Fish, Susan. Is Jesus Enough? A Group Study on the Lordship of Christ. 76p. pap. 3.95 *(978-0-921788-71-3(1))* Kindred Productions.
Wallace, James A., et al. Lift up Your Hearts: Homilies & Reflections for the C Cycle. 2006. 341p. per. 19.95 *(978-0-8091-4410-5(7)*, 4410-7) Paulist Pr.
Wallace, Mark/Douglas. A Leader Like Moses: Why I Love My Pastor. 2007. (Illus.). 134p. pap. 9.99 *(978-0-9792853-0-1(5))* MBCWM Pubns.
Wallace, Reah. Know What You Sow: The Simple Guide to Alter Your Life or 8 Steps to Realizing Your Dreams. 2008. 160p. pap. 14.95 *(978-1-4389-4135-6(8))* AuthorHouse.
Wallace, Victoria. A Deluxe Assortment of God's Word. 2009. pap. 10.99 *(978-1-60696-676-1(6))* Tate Publishing & Enterprises, LLC.
Waller, Alyn. Hope for the Journey: Believing God Is Enough When the Road Gets Rough. Pollard, Laura, ed. 2011. 160p. pap. 11.99 *(978-1-936143-14-6(3))* CLC Pubns.
Waller, Alyn E. Enjoy Your Journey Devotional Journal. 2006. (ENG.). 144p. spiral bd. 10.99 *(978-0-87508-893-8(7))* CLC Pubns.
Waller, Bonnie M. Extraordinary Devotions for Ordinary People. 2008. 96p. pap. 16.95 *(978-1-60610-568-9(X))* PublishAmerica, Inc.
Waller, Ted H. Worship: Bowing at the Feet of God. pap. 7.99 *(978-0-89098-140-5(X))* Twentieth Century Christian Bks.
Walley-Daniels, Pauline. School of Mentoring & Leadership III: Somebody Cares... Cares for You ... 2009. 212p. pap. 15.99 *(978-1-60791-532-4(4))* Xulon Pr., Inc.
—School of Prophetic Deliverance. 2008. (ENG.). 272p. pap. 13.99 *(978-1-59979-548-5(5)*, Creation Hse.) Charisma Media.
Walley, Pauline. School of Mentoring & Leadership II: Progressive Achievement; 2007. pap. 13.99 *(978-1-60266-027-4(1))* Xulon Pr., Inc.
—Strategic Prayer Tactics II: Effective Deliverance Prayer Tactics - 2007. pap. 14.99 *(978-1-60266-026-7(3))* Xulon Pr., Inc.
Wallis, Jim. Rediscovering Values: On Wall Street, Main Street, & Your Street. 2010. (ENG.). 272p. 24.00 *(978-1-4391-8312-0(0)*, Howard Bks.) Howard Books.
Wallis, Paul. Men Behaving Boldly: Getting to Grips with Spirituality. 128p. 9.00 *(978-0-281-05125-0(9))* SPCK Publishing GBR. Dist: Pilgrim Pr., The/United Church Pr.
Walls, Ralph. Flowers in the Crags. 2007. 464p. (ENG.). 35.99 *(978-1-60266-868-3(X))*; per. 23.99 *(978-1-60266-082-3(4))* Xulon Pr., Inc.
Walls, Teresa D. God's Divine Purpose for Your Life. 2010. pap. 11.99 *(978-1-61566-455-9(6))* Tate Publishing & Enterprises, LLC.
Walsh, Brenda & Kuzma, Kay. Passionate Prayer Promises. 2008. *(978-0-8163-2276-3(7))* Pacific Pr. Pubns.
Walsh, Sheila. The Heartache No One Sees: Christ's Promise of Healing for a Woman's Wounded Heart, 0 vols. 2007. 272p. per. 14.99 *(978-0-8499-1855-1(3))* Nelson, Thomas Inc.
Walsh, Susan. My Father, My Father. 2008. 56p. pap. 12.50 *(978-1-59858-715-9(3))* Dog Ear Publishing, LLC.
Walston, Larry. Making Sense of Life & Death. 2010. pap. 15.99 *(978-1-61579-649-6(5))* Xulon Pr., Inc.
Walter, Pastor Jim. God Is Busy Fixing Things. 2010. pap. 14.99 *(978-1-61579-923-7(0))* Xulon Pr., Inc.
Walters, Ron. The Forgotten Scripture. 2007. 276p. per. 15.99 *(978-1-60477-411-5(8))* Xulon Pr., Inc.
Walther, C. F. W. Ley y Evangelio (Law & Gospel) Weigandt, Ernesto, tr. (SPA.). 343p. 12.99 *(978-0-570-04947-0(4)*, 09-2416) Concordia Publishing Hse.
Walton, Dennis. Are You Prepared for the Kingdom? *(978-0-9728125-0-4(4))* Faith Temple of Christ.
Walton, Grady. Thoughts Escape Me. 2011. 260p. pap. 16.99 ***(978-1-61379-136-3(4))*** Xulon Pr., Inc.
Walton, Steve. Call to Live: Vocation for Everyone. 144p. 8.00 *(978-0-281-04771-0(5))* SPCK Publishing GBR. Dist: Pilgrim Pr., The/United Church Pr.
Wansbrough, Henry. Use & Abuse of the Bible: A Brief History of Biblical Interpretation. 2010. (ENG.). 224p. 22.95 *(978-0-567-09057-7(4)*, T&T Clark Int'l) Continuum International Publishing Group, Ltd. GBR. Dist: National Bk. Network.
Warch, William. The New Thought Christian. rev. ed. 2008. (Illus.). 103p. pap. 9.95 *(978-0-87516-837-1(X)*, Devorss Pubns.) DeVorss & Co.
Ward, Angie. Where's the Proof? 2008. 232p. pap. 14.99 *(978-1-60647-065-7(5))* Xulon Pr., Inc.
Ward, Bruce Kinsey. Redeeming the Enlightenment: Christianity & the Liberal Virtues. 2010. 244p. pap. 26.00 *(978-0-8028-0761-8(5))* Eerdmans, William B. Publishing Co.
Ward, Burley. Jesus' Money Secrets. 2007. 152p. pap. 11.95 *(978-1-4116-1876-3(9))* Lulu Enterprises Inc.
Ward, C. M. Asking No Question for Conscience Sake. 2011. 28p. 35.95 ***(978-1-258-06486-0(3))*** Literary Licensing, LLC.
Ward, Hannah & Wild, Jennifer, eds. The Monastic Way: Ancient Wisdom for Contemporary Living: A Book of Daily Readings. 2007. (Illus.). 242p. 20.00 *(978-0-8028-4045-5(0))* Eerdmans, William B. Publishing Co.
Ward, Henderson. One Minute to Midnight on God's Clock. 2009. (J). pap. 23.99 *(978-1-60799-630-9(8))* Tate Publishing & Enterprises, LLC.
Ward, John & Pries, Jeff. Fork in the Road, Kit. ldr.'s ed. 2007. (Liquid Ser.). (ENG., Illus.). 112p. 24.99 *(978-1-4185-2763-1(7))* Nelson, Thomas Inc.
—Money Talks. 2008. (Liquid Ser.). (ENG.). 112p. 24.99 *(978-1-4185-2765-5(3))*; (Illus.). pap., instr.'s gde. ed. 9.99 *(978-1-4185-3355-7(6))* Nelson, Thomas Inc.
Ward-Ling, Sheilah. Your Glory Reflected: Twenty Outstanding Christians of the 20th Century. 288p. pap. 19.95 *(978-0-8189-9457-9(6))* St Pauls/Alba Hse. Pubs.
Ward, Phyllis. God's Temple: 40 Days to Total Transformation. 2008. 264p. pap. 17.99 *(978-1-60477-586-0(6))* Xulon Pr., Inc.
Ward, Waylon. Who's Your Daddy? 2009. 168p. pap. 14.99 *(978-1-60791-674-1(6))* Xulon Pr., Inc.
Warden, Jr. One Hundred Reasons Why Born Again Believers Cannot Lose Their Salvation. 2009. (Illus.). 288p. pap. 19.99 *(978-1-4343-8179-8(X))* AuthorHouse.
Wardwell, Rodney W. Green: Youth Ministry Lessons I Learned the Hard Way. 2010. pap. 10.99 *(978-1-61566-104-6(2))* Tate Publishing & Enterprises, LLC.
Ware, Henry. Formation of the Christian Character. 2009. 98p. pap. 14.14 *(978-0-217-92929-5(X))* General Bks. LLC.
—Formation of the Christian Character. 2006. 280p. per. 23.99 *(978-1-4255-2495-1(8))* MPublishing.
—Progress of the Christian Life: Being a Sequel to the Formation Of. 2007. (ENG.). 96p. per. 18.95 *(978-1-4304-4533-3(5))* Kessinger Publishing, LLC.
Ware, James. Reading the Bible As Christian Scripture: Understanding the Writers' Use of Language. 2009. 124p. pap. 14.25 *(978-1-4251-8291-5(7))* Trafford Publishing.
Warman, Steve. The Second Try. 2006. (ENG.). 143p. 12.95 *(978-0-9770398-3-8(8))* Lifebridge Bks.
Warner, Donald. Up in Your Face: God, Jeremiah Wright & Me. 2008. 400p. pap. 16.95 *(978-1-4327-3662-0(0))* Outskirts Pr., Inc.
Warner, Rob. Walking with God: Discovering a Deeper Spirituality in Prayer. xii, 211p. pap. 13.99 *(978-0-340-71015-9(2)*, Hodder & Stoughton) Hodder General Publishing Div. GBR. Dist: Trafalgar Square Publishing.
Warner, Sandy. God Speaks Through Humor & Bloopers. 2008. 106p. pap. 13.00 *(978-1-4357-2656-7(1))* Lulu Enterprises Inc.
—Intercessors Arise. 2008. 220p. pap. 14.50 *(978-0-615-21516-7(5))* SOS Pubns.
—Ministering Deliverance. 2008. 157p. pap. 13.75 *(978-1-4357-2533-1(6))* Lulu Enterprises Inc.
Warner, Vera LeRay. Embracing the Love of the Father: I am the Apple of His Eye, He Is the Core of My Being. 2008. 107p. pap. 12.95 *(978-0-7414-4534-6(4))* Infinity Publishing.
Warner, Wayne. Tocados Por Fuego (Touched by Fire) (SPA.). 184p. *(978-84-7228-437-1(9)*, 360850) Clie, Editorial.
Warr, Michael. Una Nueva Dimension. (Serie Bolsilibros - Pocket Bks.).Tr. of New Dimension. (SPA.). 80p. pap. 1.50 *(978-0-945792-91-8(3)*, 490253) Editorial Unilit.
Warr, Terry E. Image to Likeness: Living from the Inside Out. 2010. 120p. (ENG.). 21.49 *(978-1-4520-2663-3(7))*; pap. 14.99 *(978-1-4520-2662-6(9))* AuthorHouse.
—Image to Likeness Journal: Living from the Inside Out. 2010. 128p. pap. 12.99 *(978-1-4520-8516-6(1))* AuthorHouse.
Warren, Frank. The Winner's Circle: Faith That Makes You All God Planned for You to Be. 2008. (ENG.). 96p. pap. 8.99 *(978-1-59979-604-8(X)*, Creation Hse.) Charisma Media.
Warren, George R. First Cause: The Beginning of Wisdom, 1 vol. 2009. 189p. pap. 24.95 *(978-1-60672-502-3(5))* PublishAmerica, Inc.
Warren, Jeff. Live Forgiven. 2008. 200p. pap. 14.99 *(978-1-60647-486-0(3))* Xulon Pr., Inc.
Warren, Kay & Holladay, Tom. The Church: 11 Core Truths to Build Your Life On, 1 vol. 2008. (Foundations Ser.). (ENG.). 80p. pap. 7.99 *(978-0-310-27692-0(5))* Zondervan.
—Good & Evil: 11 Core Truths to Build Your Life On, 1 vol. 2008. (Foundations Ser.). (ENG.). 80p. pap. 7.99 *(978-0-310-27687-6(X))* Zondervan.
—Sanctification, 1 vol. 2008. (Foundations Ser.). (ENG.). 80p. pap. 7.99 *(978-0-310-27684-5(5))* Zondervan.
—11 Core Truths to Build Your Life On: The Second Coming, 1 vol. 2008. (Foundations Ser.). (ENG.). 80p. pap. 7.99 *(978-0-310-27695-1(0))* Zondervan.
Warren, Loanna. Healing & Deliverance Devotional. 2011. 136p. pap. 14.99 ***(978-1-61379-259-9(X))*** Xulon Pr., Inc.
Warren, Rick. Answers to Life's Toughest Questions. 2006. (ENG.). 208p. pap. 9.99 *(978-0-310-27393-6(5))* Zondervan.
—Better Together: What on Earth Are We Here For?, 1 vol. 2010. (ENG.). 96p. pap., pupil's gde. ed. 8.99 *(978-0-310-32684-7(2))* Zondervan.
—God's Answers to Life's Difficult Questions, 1 vol. (ENG.). 2009. 96p. pap., pupil's gde. ed. 8.99 *(978-0-310-32692-2(3))* 2006. 208p. 16.99 *(978-0-310-27302-8(1))* Zondervan.
—God's Power to Change Your Life. 2008. *(978-1-59328-187-8(0))* Graham, Billy Evangelistic Assn.
—God's Power to Change Your Life, 1 vol. (Living with Purpose Ser.). (ENG.). 240p. 2009. pap. 3.99 *(978-0-310-28575-5(5))* 2006. 16.99 *(978-0-310-27303-5(X))* Zondervan.
—The Hope You Need: From the Lord's Prayer. 2010. 224p. 24.99 *(978-0-310-32711-0(3))* Zondervan.
—Pdl/Purpose Driven Life Mm. 2010. 336p. mass mkt. 7.99 *(978-0-310-32839-1(X))* Zondervan.
—The Power to Change Your Life. 2006. (ENG.). 240p. pap. 9.99 *(978-0-310-27392-9(7))* Zondervan.
—Purpose Driven Life: What on Earth Am I Here For?, 1 vol. 2007. (Purpose Driven Life Ser.). (ENG.). 96p. pap., stu. ed. 8.99 *(978-0-310-27866-5(X))* Zondervan.
—The Purpose Driven Life: What on Earth Am I Here For?, 1 vol. (Purpose Driven Life Ser.). (ENG., 2007. Illus.). 336p. pap. 14.99 *(978-0-310-27699-9(3))* 2006. pap., pap. 27.96 *(978-0-310-27536-7(9))* Zondervan.
—The Purpose Driven Vision. 2007. 224p. 21.99 *(978-0-310-28117-7(2))* Zondervan.
—40 Days of Love: We Were Made for Relationships, 1 vol. 2009. (ENG.). 19.99 *(978-0-310-32685-4(0))*; 96p. pap., stu. ed. 8.99 *(978-0-310-32687-8(7))* Zondervan.
Warren, Rita. The Truth of the Matter Is. 2007. 240p. per. 14.99 *(978-1-60266-948-2(1))* Xulon Pr., Inc.
Warren, Ron. The Ladder of Trust. 2007. 268p. (ENG.). 25.99 *(978-1-60266-969-7(4))*; per. 15.99 *(978-1-60266-853-9(1))* Xulon Pr., Inc.
Warren, Shellie R. Dramaholic: Solutions for the Problem Junkie. 2006. 192p. pap. 12.99 *(978-0-9768175-6-7(X))* Relevant Media Group, Inc.
—Inside of Me: Lessons of Lust, Love & Redemption. 2008. 176p. pap. 14.95 *(978-0-9814843-7-2(9))* Simon & Brown.
Warren, Thomas S. The Alexander Antidote: Turning Conflict into A Prescription of Wholeness for the Local Church. 2011. 156p. 24.95 ***(978-1-4620-2558-9(7))***; pap. 14.95 ***(978-1-4620-2552-7(8))*** iUniverse, Inc.
Warren, Traci L. How to Balance Your Life+God+S Way. 2007. 148p. per. 15.99 *(978-1-60266-167-7(7))* Xulon Pr., Inc.
Warren, W. Thomas. Sin Less: The Christian's War Within. 2009. 208p. pap. 23.00 *(978-1-60608-942-2(0))* Wipf & Stock Pubs.
Warren-Williams, Jeanette. Out of Darkness into His Marvelous Light by the Blood of Jesus. 2008. 148p. pap. 17.95 *(978-1-4327-2806-9(7))* Outskirts Pr., Inc.
Wasco, Jan & Keating, Molly. Unlocking Our Fenced in Hearts. 2008. 164p. pap. 13.99 *(978-1-60477-868-7(7))* Xulon Pr., Inc.
Washam, Michele & Mooty, Tom. Protecting Those You Love in an X-Rated World: Blocking Harmful Media & Online Influences. 2007. x, 238p. pap. *(978-0-88270-443-2(5))* Bridge-Logos Foundation.
Washburn, Phillip S. The Mystery at the Heart of Things: Ten Sermons Embracing Both Mind & Heart. 2008. 128p. pap. 11.95 *(978-1-59858-778-4(1))* Dog Ear Publishing, LLC.
Washington, Barry S., Sr. Firstfruits: God's Plan for Your Success. 2008. 144p. pap. 13.99 *(978-0-9800877-2-7(4))* Diakonia Publishing.

C

Washington, Byron L. Memos from the Master's Desk: A Life Changing Devotional Directly from the Heart of God. 2010. pap. 12.99 (978-1-61663-357-8(3)) Tate Publishing & Enterprises, LLC.
Washington, Henry A. The first word of the Kingdom: Pictures of Repentance. 2007. per. 10.99 (978-0-9794179-0-0(2)) Washington Hse.
Washington McMillan, De'Lois. Suppose Jesus Had Thrown in the Towel & Given up on Us. 2008. 248p. pap. 15.59 (978-1-4389-2106-8(3)) AuthorHouse.
Washington, William T. The New Manifest Destiny: The Pathway to Continuous Personal Enrichment; the Roadmap to Enduring National Greatness. 2007. 187p. per. 12.99 (978-1-59886-671-1(0)) Tate Publishing & Enterprises, LLC.
Watchnight. 4.50 (978-0-687-02275-5(4)) Abingdon Pr.
Watchnight: Regular. 4.50 (978-0-687-00711-0(9)) Abingdon Pr.
Watchorn, Patricia. That They May Be One John: 11. 2008. 672p. pap. 25.99 (978-1-4389-1449-7(0)) AuthorHouse.
Water in the Wilderness: God's Provision for Our Every Need. 2008. 168p. per. 9.99 (978-0-7684-2645-8(6)) Destiny Image Pubs.
Waterbury, J. B. The Happy Christian or, Piety the Only Foundation of True And. 2007. (ENG.). 200p. per. 24.95 (978-1-4304-4556-2(4)) Kessinger Publishing, LLC.
Waters, Amy & Embry, Nichole. Unparalleled Lives, One Parallel Truth. 2007. 91p. per. 9.99 (978-1-59886-851-7(9)) Tate Publishing & Enterprises, LLC.
Waterson, Jacob. The, Book of Aquaria. 2011. (ENG.). 180p. pap. 14.95 (978-1-4327-8030-2(1)) Outskirts Pr., Inc.
Watkins, Bonnie. Little White Church in the Vale: Reflections on Small-Town Faith. 2011. 72p. pap. 9.95 (978-1-4624-0004-1(3), Inspiring Voices) Author Solutions, Inc.
Watkins, Deborah. Restoration: Raphamotion. 2008. 72p. pap. 11.99 (978-1-60477-951-6(9)) Xulon Pr., Inc.
Watkins, James. When Life Gives You Lemons Sel. 2007. 128p. pap. 11.99 (978-0-8341-2307-6(X)) Beacon Hill Pr. of Kansas City.
Watkins, Sherman. Shattered. 2011. 242p. 30.99 (978-1-58930-271-6(0)) Selah Publishing Group, LLC.
Watson, Daniel. The Word Is Worth a Thousand Pictures. 2008. (Illus.). 92p. pap. 10.99 (978-1-60647-990-2(3)) Xulon Pr., Inc.
Watson, Dominique L. Inspire Me Young. 2007. pap. 10.00 (978-0-8059-8444-6(5)) Dorrance Publishing Co., Inc.
Watson, Donna S. & Goad, Rita L. Tough Times Don't Last - Tough Women Do: Heartfelt Stories & Advice from Women of Faith about the Challenges of Life & How to Live It. 2011. pap. 19.99 (978-1-61777-164-4(3)) Tate Publishing & Enterprises, LLC.
Watson, Dorothy A. Spiritually INclined: Finding spiritual renewal in everyday Living. 2008. pap. 11.99 (978-1-60604-657-9(8)) Tate Publishing & Enterprises, LLC.
Watson, Evangelist. I Still Hear Footsteps. 2011. 78p. pap. 12.95 (978-1-936780-81-5(X)) Mill City Pr., Inc.
Watson, G. D. Coals of Fire. pap. 4.99 (978-0-88019-009-1(4)) Schmul Publishing Co., Inc.
Watson, J. D. "Doc". A Word for the Day: Key Words from the New Testament. 2006. (ENG.). 384p. (gr. 11). per. 16.99 (978-0-89957-686-2(9)) AMG Pubs.
Watson, Janell. I Believe in the Church. (Illus.). 432p. pap. (978-0-340-51823-6(5), Hodder & Stoughton) Hodder General Publishing Div.
Watson, Jason B. Satans Playbook: Identifying & Defending Against Satan's Temptations. 2011. 96p. pap. 9.95 (978-1-61507-877-6(0)) Cross Bks. Publishing.
Watson, Jimmy R. Jesus Is Still Speaking Through the Gospel of Mark. 2011. 164p. 29.99 (978-1-4568-7355-4(5)); pap. 19.99 (978-1-4568-7354-7(7)) Xlibris Corp.
Watson, Kevin M. A Blueprint for Discipleship: Wesley's General Rules as a Guide for Christian Living. 2009. 128p. pap. 15.00 (978-0-88177-556-3(8)) Discipleship Resources.
Watson, Leigh. 9 Miracles: One Mother's Amazing Journey Home after Seeing Her Son off to War. 2011. 56p. pap. 9.95 (978-1-61507-734-2(0)) Cross Bks. Publishing.
Watson, Thomas. A Divine Cordial - Romans: 28. 2007. 108p. per. 11.99 (978-1-58960-359-2(1)) Sovereign Grace Pubs., Inc.
Watson, Thomas & Kistler, Don. Heaven Taken by Storm, or, The Holy Violence a Christian Is to Put Forth in His Pursuit after Glory. 2007. iv, 143p. (978-0-9798579-3-5(7)) Northampton Pr., The.
Watson, Tommy. When God Opens a Door Run Through It. 2009. 232p. pap. 18.95 (978-1-4269-1607-6(8)) Trafford Publishing.
Watt, Eric. Daniel ~ Stand up Living in a Bow down World. 2009. 72p. pap. 10.99 (978-1-60791-678-9(9)) Xulon Pr., Inc.
Wattles, Wallace. The Wisdom of Wallace D Wattles II - Including: The Purpose Driven Life, the Law of Attraction & the Law of Opulence. 2007. 124p. (ENG.). (978-956-291-401-7(1)); per. (978-956-291-391-1(0)) Editorial Benei Noaj.
Wattley, Linda D. The Last Day of Victimization. 2008. 124p. pap. 14.00 (978-0-9802468-9-6(X)) Leading Lady Pubns.
—Something about an Angel. 2007. 240p. per. 15.99 (978-0-9798084-8-7(0)) Leading Lady Pubns.
Watts, Elliott. Christos. 2009. 58p. pap. 9.90 (978-0-557-17746-2(4)) Lulu Enterprises Inc.
Waugh, Pamela. In God's Arms. 2007. 111p. per. 10.99 (978-1-60247-239-6(4)) Tate Publishing & Enterprises, LLC.
Wax, Trevin. Holy Subversion: Allegiance to Christ in an Age of Rivals. 2010. 160p. pap. 14.99 (978-1-4335-0702-1(1)) Crossway.
Way, James A. Mounting Rareness: Characteristics of Growing Christians. 2011. 116p. 21.23 (978-1-4634-3916-3(4)); pap. 11.61 (978-1-4634-3915-6(6)) AuthorHouse.
Way, Monzell. The Audacity of Faith: A Map to Success. 2011. 108p. 26.00 (978-1-4634-3520-2(7)); pap. 16.50 (978-1-4634-3521-9(5)) AuthorHouse.
Weatherill, Martha. In Love with the Lord. 2010. 69p. pap. 12.95 (978-1-4461-6451-8(9)) Lulu Enterprises Inc.
Weathersby, Melissa. Are You Arresting Your Blessing? 2011. 132p. pap. 14.99 (978-1-61379-538-5(6)) Xulon Pr., Inc.
Weaver, J. Denny. The Nonviolent Atonement, Second Edition. 2nd ed. 2011. 376p. pap. 28.00 (978-0-8028-6437-6(5)) Eerdmans, William B. Publishing Co.
Weaver, John. Outside-in: Theological Reflections on Life. 2006. (Regent's Study Guides). (Illus.). 248p. per. (978-1-57312-472-0(9)) Smyth & Helwys Publishing, Inc.
Weaver, K. d. & Weaver, K. D. Sleeping with God: A Biblical Guide to Christian Meditation. 2011. 190p. pap. 14.95 (978-1-61434-236-6(9)) Booklocker.com, Inc.
Webb, David E. A God of Principle: Desires of your Heart. 2009. 160p. pap. 14.95 (978-1-59858-949-8(0)) Dog Ear Publishing, LLC.
Webb, Donald A. Take Bread & Cup then Serve. 2010. 159p. 24.95 (978-0-692-01157-7(9)) Eucharist Pr.
Webb, Michael. In the Cleft of the Rock. 2007. 156p. (ENG.). 21.99 (978-1-60266-302-2(5)); per. 13.99 (978-1-60266-301-5(7)) Xulon Pr., Inc.
Webb-Mitchell, Brett. Follow Me: Christian Growth on the Pilgrim's Way. 2006. 175p. per. 16.00 (978-1-59627-025-1(X)) Church Publishing, Inc.
Webb, Patrick R. Saying Yes to No: A Biblical Approach to Disagreement among Christians. 2011. pap. 9.99 (978-1-61739-498-0(X)) Tate Publishing & Enterprises, LLC.
Webb, Thomas. Beyond the Pulpit, Beyond the Church. 2006. pap. 14.99 (978-1-60034-742-9(8)) Xulon Pr., Inc.
Webber, Christopher L. Re-Inventing Marriage: What Marriage Has Been & Is & Might Be. 2007. 292p. per. 20.95 (978-0-595-45671-0(5), Backinprint.com) iUniverse, Inc.
Webber, Malcolm. Purpose: Finding & Fulfilling the Will of God for Our Lives & Churches. 2009. (ENG.). 134p. pap. 15.95 (978-1-888810-63-9(7)) Strategic Pr.
Webber, Robert. Listening to the Beliefs of Emerging Churches: Five Perspectives, 1 vol. 2007. (ENG., Illus.). 240p. pap. 16.99 (978-0-310-27135-2(5)) Zondervan.
Weber, Anthony. Learning to Jump Again: A Memoir of Grief & Hope. 2011. 164p. 30.95 (978-1-4497-2131-2(1)); pap. 13.95 (978-1-4497-2130-5(3)) Author Solutions, Inc. (WestBow Pr.).
Weber, Charles. A Little Guidebook for the Servant-Leader. 2008. 64p. pap. 10.95 (978-1-4327-2700-0(1)) Outskirts Pr., Inc.
Weber, John Michael. From Junk to Jesus, in the Blink of an Eye. 2010. 80p. pap. 15.50 (978-0-557-57242-7(8)) Lulu Enterprises Inc.
Weber, Martin. God Was There: True Stories of a Police Chaplain. 2009. 127p. pap. 12.99 (978-0-8163-2348-7(8)) Pacific Pr. Publishing Assn.
Weber, Rick. Pink Lips & Fingertips: A Lifelong Dream & the Faith to Find It. 2009. 292p. pap. 16.99 (978-1-60791-752-6(1)) Xulon Pr., Inc.
Webster. People of Power. 2008. 192p. pap. (978-0-281-06000-9(2)) SPCK Publishing.
Webster, Allen. Closet Christianity. 2007. 0.35 (978-1-933808-80-2(2)) House to House Heart to Heart Publishing, Inc.
—Does Heaven Have a Smoking Section? 2007. 0.75 (978-1-933808-76-5(4)) House to House Heart to Heart Publishing, Inc.
—Four Steps to Heaven. (Part 4) 2007. 0.35 (978-1-933808-65-9(9)) House to House Heart to Heart Publishing, Inc.
—Heaven Is Four Steps from Any Place on Earth (Part 3) 2007. 0.35 (978-1-933808-61-1(6)) House to House Heart to Heart Publishing, Inc.
Webster, Donald A. You Can Be Happy: The Search for the Satisfying Life. 2011. 152p. 41.95 (978-1-258-06294-1(1)) Literary Licensing, LLC.
Webster, Douglas D. Beatitudes: Soundtrack for the Soul. 2009. 14.95 (978-1-894667-91-3(3)) Clements Publishing.
Webster, Douglas W. Dear Mom, 0 vols. 2008. 256p. pap. 14.99 (978-1-4041-7553-2(9)) Nelson, Thomas Inc.
Webster, H. Wallace. Christ Will Build His Church: But What Is My Role? 2008. 166p. pap. 19.00 (978-1-55635-954-5(3), Resource Pubns.) Wipf & Stock Pubs.
Wedding, Paul. If You Only Knew What You Already Know. Gorzelski, Dave & Simmons, Karen, eds. 2008. (ENG.). 181p. 24.95 (978-0-89990-142-8(5)) Harmonie Park Pr.
Weekes, John S. Understanding the Existence of God. 2010. 152p. pap. 15.00 (978-1-4269-2766-9(5)) Trafford Publishing.
Weems, Stovall. Awakening: A New Approach to Faith, Fasting, & Spiritual Freedom. 2010. (ENG.). 224p. pap. 14.99 (978-0-307-45953-4(5), WaterBrook Pr.) Doubleday Religious Publishing Group, The.
Weil, Pierre. Holistica: Una Nueva Vision y Abordaje De Lo Real. 112p. 5.95 (978-958-607-700-2(4)) Sociedad de San Pablo COL. Dist: St Pauls/Alba Hse. Pubs.
—Ultimo Por Que. 96p. 3.25 (978-958-607-630-2(X)) Sociedad de San Pablo COL. Dist: St Pauls/Alba Hse. Pubs.
Weil, Roger. Foundations of the Christian Faith. 2007. 400p. per. (978-0-946462-72-8(0)) Grace Pubns. Trust.
Weiner, Jonathan E. Beyond Your Backyard Group Member Discussion Guide: Stepping Out to Serve Others. 2008. (ENG.). 48p. pap. 6.99 (978-0-7847-2174-2(2)) Standard Publishing.
Weisbach, Beverly. The Backwards Blessing: One Woman's Journey Revealing the Good Even Through Tragedy. 2010. 114p. pap. 11.99 (978-1-61579-779-0(3)) Xulon Pr., Inc.
Weiss, Janice. God Was Thinking? 2011. 220p. pap. 15.99 (978-1-61379-304-6(9)) Xulon Pr., Inc.
Weiss, LeAnn. Christmas Promises: Heavenly Gifts for the Holiday Season. 2008. (ENG.). 176p. 14.99 (978-0-8307-4697-2(8)) Gospel Light Pubns.
Weiss, Martin. Songs for the Master. 2007. (ENG.). 108p. per. 12.99 (978-1-60266-106-6(5)) Xulon Pr., Inc.
Weiss, N. E. Growing as God's People. 80p. stu. ed., wbk. ed. (978-0-85910-179-0(7), 23-0533) Openbook Publishers.
Welborn, Amy. Enciclica Sobre la Esperanza. Estenger, Vilma G., tr. 2008. (Pope Benedict XVI Ser.). 1p. 14.95 (978-1-59276-471-6(1)) Our Sunday Visitor, Publishing Div.
—Encyclical on Hope. 2008. (Pope Benedict XVI Ser.). 1p. 14.95 (978-1-59276-407-5(X)) Our Sunday Visitor, Publishing Div.
—How to Celebrate the Easter Season. 2008. 1p. 14.95 (978-1-59276-397-9(9)) Our Sunday Visitor, Publishing Div.
Welch, Bob. Making the Bond Eternal: A True Testimony. 2011. pap. 12.99 (978-1-61777-345-7(X)) Tate Publishing & Enterprises, LLC.
Welch, Edward T. Bipolar Disorder: Understanding & Help for Extreme Mood Swings. 2010. 24p. 3.99 (978-1-935273-62-2(0)) New Growth Pr.
—Crossroads: A Step-by-Step Guide Away from Addiction - Facilitator's Guide. 2008. (ENG.). 112p. pap. 17.99 (978-1-934885-93-2(2)) New Growth Pr.
—Eating Disorders: The Quest for Thinness. 2008. (ENG.). 24p. 3.99 (978-1-934885-49-9(5)) New Growth Pr.
—What Do You Think of Me? Why Do I Care? Answers to the Big Questions of Life. 2011. pap. 12.99 (978-1-935273-86-8(8)) New Growth Pr.
Welch, Leona Nicholas. God of the Parking Lot: Seeing God's Blessings & Favor in the Details of Our Lives. 2010. 58p. pap. 15.99 (978-1-4415-8367-3(X)) Xlibris Corp.
Welch, Mary. Reckoning at Dusk. pap. 3.95 (978-0-910924-41-2(4)) Macalester Park Publishing Co., Inc.
Welch, Robert S. Reaching Out: Lessons of God. 2010. pap. 11.99 (978-1-61566-808-3(X)) Tate Publishing & Enterprises, LLC.
Welcome to the Family. Date not set. pap., tchr. ed. 1.00 incl. VHS (978-0-87162-507-6(5), D0894V) Warner Pr. Pubs.
Weller-Shuck, Heidi A. Wobbly Acres: Musings of a Forty-One-Year-Old Redneck Woman. 2008. 52p. pap. 16.95 (978-1-60672-333-3(2)) PublishAmerica, Inc.
Wellman, Jack. Do Babies Go to Heaven?, Why Does God Allow Suffering? 2009. (ENG.). 58p. pap. 14.97 (978-0-557-17303-7(5)) Lulu Enterprises Inc.
Wells, A. Bruce. Making Money with God: Learning to Hear the Holy Spirit. 2011. 152p. 24.23 (978-1-4567-5743-4(1)); pap. 18.70 (978-1-4567-5744-1(X)) AuthorHouse.
Wells, Carl. The Army of God: The Church. 2008. 176p. pap. 13.99 (978-1-4389-0835-9(0)) AuthorHouse.
—Financing the Vast Expanse of the Kingdom of God. 2010. 100p. pap. 10.99 (978-1-4490-3080-3(7)) AuthorHouse.
Wells, David R. Where'd Everybody Go? A Post-Rapture & Great Tribulation Survival Manual. 2011. 126p. 22.99 (978-1-61215-854-9(4)); pap. 14.99 (978-1-61215-853-2(6)) Xulon Pr., Inc.
Wells, Jan. Joshua & the Call to Live Victoriously by Faith. 2007. pap. 15.99 (978-1-60266-066-3(2)) Xulon Pr., Inc.
Wells, M. R., et al. Four Paws from Heaven Gift Edition: Inspirational Stories for Dog Lovers. 2008. 32p. 12.99 (978-0-7369-2203-6(2)) Harvest Hse. Pubs.
Wells, Rebecca A. Spiritual Growth: A Layperson Looks at Life on the Ladder. 2007. 154p. pap. 11.95 (978-0-7414-3923-9(9)) Infinity Publishing.
Wells, Thelma. Don't Give In — God Wants You to Win! Preparing for Victory in the Battle of Life. 2009. 224p. pap. 12.99 (978-0-7369-2614-0(3)) Harvest Hse. Pubs.
—God Is Not Through with Me Yet: Holding on to the One Who Holds You Close. 2007. (ENG.). 224p. 15.99 (978-1-59052-785-6(2), Multnomah) Doubleday Religious Publishing Group, The.
Welte, Bill, ed. Real Victory for Real Life: 365 Devotional Thoughts in the Spirit of America's Keswick. 2006. (ENG.). 435p. pap. 14.99 (978-0-87508-853-2(8)) CLC Pubns.
Wendt, June. Journey Without End. 2009. 208p. pap. 14.95 (978-1-4389-7132-2(X)) AuthorHouse.
Wenger, John C. The Way of Peace. 2009. 72p. pap. 10.00 (978-1-60608-953-8(6), Wipf and Stock) Wipf & Stock Pubs.
Wentroble, Barbara. Removing the Veil of Deception: How to Recognize Lying Signs, False Wonders, & Seducing Spirits. 2009. 144p. pap. 12.99 (978-0-8007-9473-6(7)) Chosen Bks.
Wentzel, Elizabeth. Christmas. Date not set. pap. 11.50 (978-0-8488-0896-9(7)) Amereon LTD.
Wenzel, Kim & Wenzel, Kathy. Ashes to Flames: Recovery from Spiritual Burnout. 2006. 270p. pap. 16.95 (978-0-7414-3571-2(3)) Infinity Publishing.
Werner, Nathan B. Holy Ouch! God's Purpose for Pain. 2010. pap. 17.99 (978-1-61566-270-8(7)) Tate Publishing & Enterprises, LLC.
Wescott-Creel, Jeanette. In the Hand of God. 2010. pap. 12.99 (978-1-61579-721-9(1)) Xulon Pr., Inc.
Wesley, Edna. The Prelude: A Woman Named Job. 2007. 44p. pap. 8.95 (978-0-7414-4075-4(X)) Infinity Publishing.
West, Cindy. Saying Yes: Accepting God's Amazing Invitation to Artists & the Church. 2008. (ENG.). 240p. pap. 13.99 (978-1-4347-9998-2(0)) Cook, David C.
West, Matthew. Experiencing the Story of Your Life. 2012. 144p. pap. 9.99 (978-0-7369-4659-9(4)) Harvest Hse. Pubs.
—Give This Christmas Away: 101 Simple & Thoughtful Ways To. 2009. (ENG.). 112p. 9.99 (978-1-4143-3644-2(6)) Tyndale Hse. Pubs.
West, Nancey. Miracles among Us: A Look Inside the Lebanon Soup Kitchen. 2008. 184p. pap. 16.95 (978-0-595-52226-2(2)) iUniverse, Inc.
Westcott, Brooke Foss. Thoughts on Revelation & Life: Being Selections from the Writings of Brooke Foss Westcott, D. D, D. C. L. Phillips, Stephen, ed. 2007. (Illus.). 398p. pap. 34.00 (978-1-55635-752-7(4)) Wipf & Stock Pubs.
Westcott, Louise. Journey to a New Heart. 2009. 180p. pap. 14.99 (978-1-60791-604-8(5)) Xulon Pr., Inc.
Weston, Michelle. Heart of an Intercessor. 2011. 140p. pap. 14.99 (978-1-61379-315-2(4)) Xulon Pr., Inc.
Westrom, Tim. Nine Prayers of Promise. 2006. (ENG.). 80p. pap. 6.99 (978-1-59979-051-0(3), Creation Hse.) Charisma Media.
Westview, Clair. Delayed by Deceit. 2008. 312p. (ENG.). 27.99 (978-1-60477-407-8(X)); per. 17.99 (978-1-60477-406-1(1)) Xulon Pr., Inc.
Wezeman, Phyllis & Harnish, James A. Advent 2008: A Calendar of Devotions. 2008. 48p. pap. 0.65 (978-0-687-65128-3(X)) Abingdon Pr.
Wezeman, Phyllis & Harnish, John E. Advent 2008: A Calendar of Devotions. 2008. 48p. pap. 1.65 (978-0-687-65138-2(7)) Abingdon Pr.
Whalen, Brett Edward. Pilgrimage in the Middle Ages. 2011. (ENG., Illus.). 400p. (C). pap. (978-1-4426-0199-4(X)) Univ. of Toronto Pr.
What's the Big Deal? World Issues. (Real Deal Bible Studies). 88p. 12.99 (978-0-7586-0519-1(6)) Concordia Publishing Hse.
Wheadon, Denis. Back to Basics. 2006. pap. (978-0-7552-0256-0(2)) Authors OnLine, Ltd.
—Grappling with Grace. 2006. pap. (978-0-7552-0257-7(0)) Authors OnLine, Ltd.
Wheeler, Doris Speigner. The Ultimate Care Giver. 2010. 260p. pap. 16.99 (978-1-60957-450-5(8)) Xulon Pr., Inc.
—Worshiping Upsidedown & Backwards. 2011. 390p. pap. 20.99 (978-1-61215-806-8(4)) Xulon Pr., Inc.
Wheeler, Steve. Forget What? The Philippian Misconception. 2009. 262p. pap. 14.99 (978-1-60696-426-2(7)) Tate Publishing & Enterprises, LLC.
Wheeler, Tompaul. God Space: From All about Me to All about Thee. 2007. (ENG.). 378p. per. 14.99 (978-0-8280-2027-5(2)) Review & Herald Publishing Assn.
Whelchel, Lisa. Creative Correction: The Bible Study: Extraordinary Ideas for Everyday Discipline. 2008. (Illus.). 158p. pap. 16.75 (978-1-4158-2896-0(2)) LifeWay Christian Resources.
—Speaking Mom-Ese: Moments of Peace & Inspiration in the Mother Tongue, 0 vols. 2007. 240p. per. 14.99 (978-0-7852-8930-2(5)) Nelson, Thomas Inc.
Whelchel, Mary. Getting along with People @ Work. 210p. pap. 10.99 (978-0-8307-3427-6(9), Regal Bks.) Gospel Light Pubns.
Where Soul & Spirit Meet. 60.00 (978-0-687-45160-9(4)) Abingdon Pr.
Whetstone, Jason. A Husband Like Him: Becoming a Christ-Like Leader in the Home. 2007. 94p. per. 9.99 (978-1-59886-738-1(5)) Tate Publishing & Enterprises, LLC.
Whipple, Charles. Heavenly Days. 2011. 304p. 29.99 (978-1-4653-5493-8(X)); pap. 19.99 (978-1-4653-5492-1(1)) Xlibris Corp.
White, Andrew Dickson. Paying Attention to People - P. 208p. 19.95 (978-0-281-04988-2(2)) International Publishers Marketing.
White, Angel. In the Beginning God. 2009. 112p. pap. (978-1-55452-389-4(3), Guardian Bks.) Essence Publishing.
White, Angel E. In the Beginning. 2009. (978-1-55452-390-0(7)) Essence Publishing.
White, Bob. I Never Knew You. 2011. 388p. pap. 20.99 (978-1-61379-185-1(2)) Xulon Pr., Inc.
White, Charles. The Blood of Abel: Vengeance & the Grace of God. 90p. 6.95 (978-1-56794-225-5(3)) Star Bible & Tract Corp.
White, Debra. Relationship Reality Keeping It Real: Real Faith in the Real World. 2011. 100p. 24.99 (978-1-4628-8496-4(2)); pap. 15.99 (978-1-4628-8495-7(4)) Xlibris Corp.
White, Ellen G. El Conflicto de los Siglos. (SPA.). 480p. pap. (978-1-883012-94-6(5)) Remnant Pubns.
—El Conflicto de los Siglos: El Amor Bajo Ataque. Date not set. (SPA.). 480p. pap. 11.99 (978-1-883012-88-5(0)) Remnant Pubns.
—Steps to Christ for a Sanctified Life: How to Become & Remain a Christian. 2007. 128p. pap. 9.95 (978-1-883012-59-5(7)) Remnant Pubns.
—Testimonies for the Church. 2009. 248p. pap. (978-1-151-15929-8(8)) Books LLC.
—Testimonies for the Church. 2010. 138p. pap. 22.63 (978-1-154-16174-8(9)) General Bks. LLC.
White, George H. Inter Moments with God. 2007. 224p. per. 17.95 (978-0-595-47121-8(8)) iUniverse, Inc.
White, Ivery. A Journey into the Family: Nine Steps to Successful Discipleship. 2011. 136p. 21.95 (978-1-4634-0827-5(7)); pap. 15.00 (978-1-4634-0828-2(5)) AuthorHouse.
White, James. Sketches of the Christian Life & Public Labors of William Miller, Gathered from His Memoir by the Late Sylvester Bliss, & from Other Sources. 2006. 420p. per. 26.99 (978-1-4255-4580-2(7)) MPublishing.
White, James Boyd. Connecting to the Gospel: Texts, Sermons, Commentaries. 2010. 226p. pap. 25.00 (978-1-60899-135-8(0), Wipf and Stock) Wipf & Stock Pubs.

White, Jerry. Rules to Live By: 52 Principles for a Better Life. 2010. (Living the Letters Ser.). 176p. 14.99 (978-1-60006-270-4(9)) NavPress Publishing Group.

White, Jerry E. The Joseph Road: Choices That Determine Your Destiny. 2010. (Living the Letters Ser.). (ENG., Illus.). 208p. pap. 14.99 (978-1-60006-269-8(5)) NavPress Publishing Group.

White, John, Jr. The Cost of Commitment. 2006. (IVP Classics Ser.). (ENG.). 172p. per. 8.00 (978-0-8308-3404-4(4), IVP Bks.) InterVarsity Pr.

—The Fight: A Practical Handbook for Christian Living. abr. ed. 2007. (IVP Classics Ser.). (ENG.). 219p. per. 10.00 (978-0-8308-3409-9(5), IVP Bks.) InterVarsity Pr.

White, Jr. The Partial Rapture Theory E X P L a I N E D. 2008. 312p. (ENG.). 27.99 (978-1-60477-685-0(4)); per. 17.99 (978-1-60477-684-3(6)) Xulon Pr., Inc.

White, Larry. Life with God. 2008. 116p. pap. 12.99 (978-1-60647-496-9(0)) Xulon Pr., Inc.

White, Michael L. A Time for Everything: The Kevin Zimmerman Story. 2008. 112p. pap. 12.75 (978-0-9786567-4-4(1)) Parson Place Pr., LLC.

White, Pastor Patricia. Tidbits in the Lord: Words of Inspiration & Encouragement. 2008. 78p. pap. 16.95 (978-1-60441-942-9(3)) PublishAmerica, Inc.

White, Pauline. Finding Refuge in the Word of God. 2007. 84p. per. 16.95 (978-1-4241-9411-7(3)) PublishAmerica, Inc.

White, Reggie & Thomas, Andrew. Fighting the Good Fight, 0 vols. 2008. 240p. pap. 14.99 (978-0-7852-9679-9(4)) Nelson, Thomas Inc.

White, Rod. A Circle of Hope: Jesus at Work among the Next Generation of the Church. 2009. 183p. pap. 13.95 (978-1-4327-4420-5(8)) Outskirts Pr., Inc.

White, Sherry. A Life Worth Living. 2011. 184p. pap. 14.95 (978-1-60047-505-4(1)) Waste and Pr.

White, Stephen R. A Space for Belief: The Place of Theology in Faith. 2006. (ENG.). 160p. per. 26.95 (978-1-85607-521-3(4)) Columba Pr. IRL. Dist: Dufour Editions, Inc.

White, Stephen Ross. The Seeking Church: A Space for All. 2009. (ENG.). 170p. pap. 26.95 (978-1-85607-628-9(3)) Columba Pr. IRL. Dist: Dufour Editions, Inc.

White Stone Books, creator. Celebrate Teachers: Heartwarming Stories, Inspirational Sayings, & Meaningful Expressions for Teachers. 2006. (Celebrate Ser.). (Illus.). 125p. 12.99 (978-1-59379-092-9(9)) White Stone Bks.

White, Thomas. Let Me Break It down! Christianity & Living the Life. 2007. 112p. per. 13.95 (978-1-4327-0470-4(2)) Outskirts Pr., Inc.

White, V. C. A Stayed Mind: Your Journey to Peace. 2010. 88p. pap. 10.49 (978-1-4520-1387-9(X)) AuthorHouse.

White, William R. In over Our Heads: Meditations on Grace. 2007. 144p. per. 13.99 (978-0-8066-9059-9(3)) Augsburg Fortress, Pubs.

Whitefield, George. George Whitefield Daily Readings. 2010. (ENG.). 384p. im. lthr. 19.99 (978-1-84550-580-6(8), Christian Heritage) Christian Focus Pubns. GBR. Dist: STL Distribution North America.

Whitehead, James D. & Whitehead, Evelyn Eaton. Holy Eros: Recovering the Passion of God. 2009. 240p. pap. 20.00 (978-1-57075-813-3(1)) Orbis Bks.

Whitelaw, Robert. Biblical View of Sin, Guilt, Final Punishment. pap. 1.49 (978-0-87377-099-6(4)) GAM Pubns.

—Can There Be Eternal Life Apart from Christ. pap. 1.49 (978-0-87377-097-2(8)) GAM Pubns.

—Gospel + Resurrection = A Kingdom. pap. 1.49 (978-0-87377-103-0(6)) GAM Pubns.

—Gospel in the Zodiac Given at Creation. pap. 1.49 (978-0-87377-006-4(4)) GAM Pubns.

—Hell: The Abode of the Dead Between Death & the Resurrection. pap. 1.49 (978-0-87377-105-4(2)) GAM Pubns.

—Human Conception: Gift or Gamble, God or Chance. pap. 1.49 (978-0-87377-106-1(0)) GAM Pubns.

—Power of the Posterity Clause. pap. 0.39 (978-0-87377-107-8(9)) GAM Pubns.

—Progress Western Style. pap. 1.49 (978-0-87377-112-2(5)) GAM Pubns.

—Questions for Saints to Ponder. pap. 1.49 (978-0-87377-109-2(5)) GAM Pubns.

—Science & the Christian Faith. pap. 1.49 (978-0-87377-114-6(1)) GAM Pubns.

—Thirty Questions about Death & Resurrection. pap. 1.49 (978-0-87377-115-3(X)) GAM Pubns.

—Ultimate World Energy Crisis. pap. 1.49 (978-0-87377-116-0(8)) GAM Pubns.

—Voices from Scripture about the Afterlife. pap. 1.49 (978-0-87377-117-7(6)) GAM Pubns.

—Will the Ungodly Surely Perish? pap. 1.49 (978-0-87377-119-1(2)) GAM Pubns.

Whitener, Barbara. His Spirit Through Me. 2006. pap. 9.99 (978-1-60034-875-4(0)) Xulon Pr., Inc.

Whiteside, Wendy & Wilson, Faye. Food & Faith. 2009. 150p. pap. 7.00 (978-1-933663-32-6(4), WD/GBGM Bks.) General Board of Global Ministries, The United Methodist Church.

Whitfield, Jocelyn. Made in God's Image to Live for His Glory. 2011. 84p. pap. 10.99 (978-1-61379-352-7(9)) Xulon Pr., Inc.

Whitley, Katerina Katsarka. Light to the Darkness: Lessons & Carols, Public & Private. 2008. 160p. pap. 18.00 (978-0-8192-2317-3(4), Morehouse Publishing) Church Publishing, Inc.

Whitman, Allen. Chapel Talks: Teachings & Meditations to Begin or End Your Day. 2008. 305p. pap. 29.95 (978-1-60474-863-5(X)) PublishAmerica, Inc.

Whitmire, Catherine. Practicing Peace: A Devotional Walk Through the Quaker Tradition. 2007. 270p. per. 16.95 (978-1-933495-07-1(3), Sorin Bks.) Ave Maria Pr.

Whitmore, Shakeena. Doing Battle: Under Fire. 2009. 57p. pap. 14.95 (978-1-4327-3885-3(2)) Outskirts Pr., Inc.

Whittelsey, A. G. Mrs. Whittelsey's Magazine for Mothers & Daughters, 3. Lt. ed. 2007. (ENG.). 448p. pap. 28.99 (978-1-4346-1346-2(1)) BiblioBazaar.

—Mrs. Whittelsey's Magazine for Mothers & Daughters Volume III. 2007. (ENG.). 408p. pap. 26.99 (978-1-4346-1294-6(5)) BiblioBazaar.

Whittemore, William Stewart. Ransomed: Let the redeemed of the LORD say So... 2008. 96p. pap. 9.99 (978-1-60647-523-2(1)) Xulon Pr., Inc.

Whittington, Beth C. When You Find Yourself in the Belly of a Whale. 2008. pap. 14.99 (978-1-60477-939-4(X)) Xulon Pr., Inc.

Whittington, Debra. Let's Go to the Mountain. 2008. 476p. pap. 27.99 (978-1-60647-853-0(2)) Xulon Pr., Inc.

Whittington, Mark. Out of the Darkness: A Journey into the Light. 2010. pap. 14.95 (978-1-60696-884-0(X)) Tate Publishing & Enterprises, LLC.

Who in the World Can You Trust? stu. ed. 6.25 (978-1-56212-865-4(5), 154210); 9.25 (978-1-56212-866-1(3), 154215) Faith Alive Christian Resources.

Whorton, Bob. Reflective Caring - Imaginative Listening to Pastoral Experiences. 2011. 160p. pap. (978-0-281-06413-7(X)) SPCK Publishing.

Why? Answers to Weather the Storms of Life. 2006. per. 14.99 (978-0-9788041-1-4(2)) World Help Inc.

Why? Because You're Anointed! 2008. 173p. per. 9.99 (978-0-7684-2643-4(X)) Destiny Image Pubs.

Why Become Born Again? 2008. pap. (978-0-9789909-6-1(X)) True-Way Tracts.

Why Follow Jesus. 2007. per. (978-1-59916-182-2(6)) Printing Systems.

Why Has Jesus Not Returned? 2008. pap. (978-0-9799385-0-4(3)) Rockwall Publishing.

Whyte, Danita, et al. Dear Papa: Letters to My Father. 2009. (ENG.). 200p. pap. 12.99 (978-0-615-30182-2(7)) Torch Legacy Pubns.

Whyte, Horace A. Groaning or Growing. 2011. (Illus.). 132p. pap. 15.60 (978-1-4567-7721-0(1)) AuthorHouse.

Widdowson, Frederick. A Bible Believer Looks at World History. 2010. 444p. pap. 29.99 (978-0-557-55445-4(4)) Lulu Enterprises Inc.

Wiebe, Timothy. Look Inside of Me! 2007. 152p. per. 13.99 (978-1-60477-236-4(0)) Xulon Pr., Inc.

Wiedemann, Randal A. Five Minutes with Jesus: Transforming Power. 2011. 236p. 33.95 (978-1-61507-842-4(8)); pap. 17.95 (978-1-61507-841-7(X)) Cross Bks. Publishing.

Wiedenhoff, Eleanor. Not Without God. 2007. 92p. per. 9.99 (978-1-60266-827-0(2)) Xulon Pr., Inc.

Wiens, Gary & Wiens, Marie. Reaching Your Power Potential: Authority on Earth as It Is in Heaven. 2006. 261p. per. 15.00 (978-0-9786201-2-7(7)) BHM Publishing.

—Reaching Your Power Potential HB: Authority on Earth as it Is in Heaven. 2006. 19.95 (978-0-9786201-3-4(5)) BHM Publishing.

Wiersbe, Warren W. Be Successful (1 Samuel) Attaining Wealth That Money Can't Buy, 1 vol. 2010. (BE Series Commentary Ser.). (ENG.). 224p. pap. 12.99 (978-1-4347-6500-0(8)) Cook, David C.

—Expert Lifemanship: Mastering the Art of Living. 2008. (Illus.). 144p. 29.99 (978-0-87508-988-1(7)) CLC Pubns.

—Romans: How to Be Right with God, Yourself, & Others. 2008. (WBS Ser.). (ENG.). 144p. pap. 8.99 (978-0-7814-4572-6(8)) Cook, David C.

—Ruth/Esther: Doing God's Will Whatever the Cost. 2008. (Wiersbe Bible Study Ser.). (ENG.). 128p. pap. 8.99 (978-0-7814-4573-3(6)) Cook, David C.

—Who Am I? New Testament Pictures of the Christian Life. 2007. (ENG.). 160p. per. 9.99 (978-1-57293-216-6(3)) Discovery Hse. Pubs.

Wiese, Bill. 23 Minutos en el Infierno. 2006. (SPA & ENG.). 192p. per. 9.99 (978-1-59185-935-2(2), Casa Creacion) Charisma Media.

Wiggenhorn, Erica. Ezekiel: Every Life Positioned for Purpose. 2011. 252p. pap. 27.95 (978-1-61507-909-4(2)) Cross Bks. Publishing.

Wiggins, Bernetta. But First You Must Be Whole. 2008. 112p. pap. 11.95 (978-1-4327-2271-5(9)) Outskirts Pr., Inc.

Wike, Dee Dee. Good to the Last Drop: Refreshing Inspiration for Homeschool Moms & Other Busy Women. 2010. pap. 18.99 (978-1-61566-287-6(1)) Tate Publishing & Enterprises, LLC.

Wilberforce, William. A Practical View of Christianity. Belmonte, Kevin, ed. 2006. (Hendrickson Christian Classics Ser.). 294p. 8.97 (978-1-59856-140-1(5)); 11.95 (978-1-59856-122-7(7)) Hendrickson Pubs. Marketing, LLC.

Wilburn, Gary. The God I Don't Believe In: Charting a New Course for Christianity. 2007. 200p. pap. 24.95 (978-0-9701374-1-8(9)) Management Practice, Inc.

Wilcken, John. God in Our World. pap. 4.95 (978-0-8189-7007-8(3)) St Pauls/Alba Hse. Pubs.

Wilcock, Penelope. In Celebration of Simplicity: The Joy of Living Lightly, 1 vol. 2009. (ENG.). 160p. 14.99 (978-0-8254-6314-3(9), Monarch Bks.) Lion Hudson PLC GBR. Dist: Kregel Pubns.

Wilcox, Nancy. Fifty-Three Days of Silence. 2007. 220p. 24.99 (978-1-60266-893-5(0)); per. 14.99 (978-1-60266-892-8(2)) Xulon Pr., Inc.

Wilcoxon, Karen Sue. Don't Worry - I'm Here: Thoughts on Waiting on God's Plan for My Life & Knowing That the Beginning of True Faith Is the End of Anxiety, 1 vol. 2009. 48p. pap. 16.95 (978-1-60836-032-1(6)) PublishAmerica, Inc.

Wilder, John R. Behold the Lamb: Volume I. 2009. 208p. 29.99 (978-1-4415-9682-6(8)); pap. 19.99 (978-1-4415-9681-9(X)) Xlibris Corp.

Wilder, Londa. Live God's Way: Follow the Path for a Satisfying Life. 2010. (ENG.). 96p. pap. 7.99 (978-1-61638-165-3(5), Creation Hse.) Charisma Media.

Wilhite, Jud. Eyes Wide Open: See & Live the Real You. 2009. (ENG.). 208p. pap. 13.99 (978-1-60142-072-5(2), Multnomah) Doubleday Religious Publishing Group, The.

Wilkerson, David. Dejad de Apretarme el Cuello: Get Your Hands off My Throat. (SPA.). 136p. (978-84-7228-133-2(7), 220269) Clie, Editorial.

—Rojo, Verde & Violeta: Purple, Violet Squish. (SPA.). 159p. (978-84-7228-157-8(4), 220777) Clie, Editorial.

—Sexo y Drogas, Donde Te Pueden Llevar: Sex & Drugs Where Will They Lead You? (SPA.). 112p. (978-84-7228-231-5(7), 220820) Clie, Editorial.

Wilkes, James R. The Glory Walk: Living on Purpose for the Glory of God. 2010. 134p. pap. 17.00 (978-1-60899-356-7(6), Resource Pubns.) Wipf & Stock Pubs.

Wilkins, James. Milk of the Word: A Scriptural follow-up program that Works. 2007. 193p. spiral bd. (978-0-9788703-6-2(0)) Calvary Publishing.

Wilkins, Steve. Face to Face: Meditations on Friendship & Hospitality. 2nd ed. 2010. pap. (978-1-59128-066-8(4)) Canon Pr.

Wilkinson, Bruce. Secrets of the Vine Leader's Guide: Breaking Through to Abundance. 2006. (ENG., Illus.). 80p. per. 10.99 (978-1-59052-858-7(1), Multnomah) Doubleday Religious Publishing Group, The.

—You Were Born for This: Seven Keys to a Life of Predictable Miracles. 2009. (ENG.). 240p. 22.99 (978-1-60142-182-1(6), Multnomah) Doubleday Religious Publishing Group, The.

Willard, Dallas & Johnson, Jan. Renovation of the Heart in Daily Practice: Experiments in Spiritual Transformation. 2006. (Redefining Life Ser.). (ENG.). 192p. per. 14.99 (978-1-57683-809-9(9)) NavPress Publishing Group.

Willard, Dallas & Zondervan Publishing Staff. Knowing Christ Today: Why We Can Trust Spiritual Knowledge. 2009. (ENG.). 240p. 24.99 (978-0-06-088244-0(1), HarperOne) HarperCollins Pubs.

Willard, Dallas, et al. The Divine Conspiracy: Jesus' Master Class for Life, 1 vol. 2010. (ENG.). 128p. pap. 9.99 (978-0-310-32439-3(4)) Zondervan.

Willard, F. Burleigh. Overcoming with Christ. 2008. 124p. per. 10.99 (978-1-60477-222-7(0)) Xulon Pr., Inc.

Willett, Harold E. Do Christians Go to Heaven? 2009. 154p. pap. 20.00 (978-0-9790221-5-9(0)) YAV.

William, Gurnall. The Christian in Complete Armour, or, a Treatise of the Saints' War Against the Devil, Wherein a Dis. 2009. 532p. 36.99 (978-1-110-34555-7(0)); pap. 39.75 (978-1-110-34549-6(6)) BiblioBazaar.

William K. Mcelvaney. Becoming a Justice Seeking Congregation: Responding to God's Justice Initiative. 2009. 176p. 25.95 (978-1-4401-5355-6(8)); pap. 15.95 (978-1-4401-5353-2(1)) iUniverse, Inc.

Williams, A. M., ed. Conversations at Little Gidding. 2006. 416p. pap. 79.00 (978-0-521-02821-9(3)) Cambridge Univ. Pr.

Williams, Andrew. Biblical Responses. 2011. 186p. pap. 14.99 (978-1-61379-251-3(4)) Xulon Pr., Inc.

Williams, Angeline. Lemonade with God: Refreshment for the Soul of the Single Woman. 2008. 100p. pap. 9.99 (978-1-60477-530-3(0)) Xulon Pr., Inc.

Williams, Apostle J. E. REAL TALK about Sex for Christians, 1 vol. 2010. 92p. pap. 16.95 (978-1-4489-5305-9(7)) PublishAmerica, Inc.

Williams, Apostle Jesse. Becoming Who You Are in Your Thought Life: Letting Go Who You Are Not to Become Who You Are, 1 vol. 2009. 81p. pap. 16.95 (978-1-60672-625-9(0)) PublishAmerica, Inc.

Williams, Benjamin & Williams, Micah Joy. The Basics in 21 Days. 2011. pap. 12.99 (978-1-61346-119-8(4)) Tate Publishing & Enterprises, LLC.

Williams, Betty L. Don't Give up & Never Quit. 2011. 110p. pap. 19.95 (978-1-4560-5210-2(1)) PublishAmerica, Inc.

Williams, Beverly J. God's Garden. Date not set. 24p. pap. 1.25 (978-1-889552-04-0(6)) Williams, Beverly J.

Williams-Camps, Deborah. Heart Matters: Intellectual Essays for Day-to Day-Living. 2011. 106p. pap. 15.99 (978-1-4628-8500-8(4)) Xlibris Corp.

Williams, Catherine I. Christian Success Initiatives: (csi) 2008. 148p. pap. 37.99 (978-1-4389-0773-4(7)) AuthorHouse.

Williams, Clarence. Truth. 2007. 138p. pap. 12.50 (978-0-615-15214-1(7)) Williams, Clarence.

Williams, Clifford. The Wisdom of Kierkegaard: A Collection of Quotations on Faith & Life. 2009. 120p. pap. 15.00 (978-1-60608-485-4(2), Wipf and Stock) Wipf & Stock Pubs.

Williams, D. R. You Are Set Apart & Transformed! 2008. 128p. 30.99 (978-1-4257-2862-5(6)); pap. 20.99 (978-1-4257-2861-8(8)) Xlibris Corp.

Williams, Darin. His Glory: Reclaiming Dominion in the Kingdom of God. 2009. 192p. pap. 15.56 (978-1-4389-1867-9(4)) AuthorHouse.

Williams, Dave. How to Help Your Pastor Succeed: Moving from the Multitude to the Inner Circle. 2011. 197p. pap. 12.95 (978-0-938020-73-8(0)) Decapolis Publishing.

Williams, David A. Saints Alive: Word, Image, & Enactment in the Lives of the Saints. 2010. (ENG., Illus.). 240p. (C). (978-0-7735-3708-8(2)) McGill-Queen's Univ. Pr.

Williams, David T. Kenosis of God: The self-limitation of God - Father, Son, & Holy Spirit. 2009. 380p. pap. 24.95 (978-1-4401-3223-0(2)) iUniverse, Inc.

Williams, Don. Start Here: Kingdom Essentials for Christians. 2006. (ENG.). 208p. per. 14.99 (978-0-8307-4297-4(2)) Gospel Light Pubns.

Williams, Elder Carol J. A Seed for A Day: God's Word Producing Productivity. 2011. 112p. pap. 12.99 (978-1-4634-2272-1(5)) AuthorHouse.

—A Seed for a Day: God's Word Producing Productivity. 2011. 112p. 22.00 (978-1-4634-2271-4(7)) AuthorHouse.

Williams, Errica L. Faithful Fasting. 2008. 80p. pap. 9.99 (978-1-60647-405-1(7)) Xulon Pr., Inc.

Williams, Eula. Bruised but Not Broken: Hidden scars -the shattering effects of Unforgiveness. 2010. 136p. pap. 13.95 (978-1-4502-1147-5(X)) iUniverse, Inc.

Williams-Green, Beverly. Maintaining the Grade. 2011. 173p. pap. 14.95 (978-1-4327-6759-4(3)) Outskirts Pr., Inc.

Williams, Horace Blake. We Are Able. 2008. 132p. pap. 13.99 (978-1-60477-901-1(2)) Xulon Pr., Inc.

Williams, Janet S. A Focused Faith: The Songs, Psalms, & Reflections Of. 2010. 136p. 28.95 (978-1-4497-0870-2(6)); pap. 11.95 (978-1-4497-0869-6(2)) Author Solutions, Inc. (WestBow Pr.).

Williams, Jannette S. God Is. 2011. 146p. pap. 24.95 (978-1-4626-2155-2(4)) PublishAmerica, Inc.

Williams, Joe, Sr. Just Be Happy & Enjoy Life. 2009. pap. 10.99 (978-1-61566-087-2(9)) Tate Publishing & Enterprises, LLC.

Williams, Joe R. The Impact of the Holy Spirit on Mortal Man. 2006. 92p. per. 9.95 (978-1-59886-408-3(4)) Tate Publishing & Enterprises, LLC.

Williams, John. Get Yourself Baptized. 2011. 130p. pap. (978-1-926765-42-6(7)) Gospel Folio Pr.

Williams, John Lane. Grandpa Jack's Book: A Nonagenarian Minister's Wit & Wisdom. Williams, Erin D., ed. 2009. 112p. 22.95 (978-1-4401-1085-6(9)); pap. 12.95 (978-1-4401-1083-2(2)) iUniverse, Inc.

Williams, Joseph. Our Pentecostal Birthright. 2010. (ENG.). 136p. pap. 12.95 (978-1-60530-138-9(8), iTouch Pubs.) Higher Standard Enterprises, Inc.

—You're on a Mission: A 31-Day Devotional Journey Around the World. 2007. 148p. per. 11.99 (978-1-59858-417-2(0)) Dog Ear Publishing, LLC.

Williams, Joy A. Friendship Maps. 2008. 220p. pap. 15.99 (978-1-60791-021-3(7)) Xulon Pr., Inc.

Williams, Jr. Life in a Cage. 2007. (ENG.). 140p. 21.99 (978-1-60034-967-6(6)) Xulon Pr., Inc.

—The Plowboy. 2007. 184p. (ENG.). 21.99 (978-1-60477-005-6(8)); per. 13.99 (978-1-60477-004-9(X)) Xulon Pr., Inc.

Williams, Karen. The Prophetic Ministry Study Guide. 2009. 104p. pap. 12.00 (978-1-60708-281-1(0)) MorningStar Pubns., Inc.

Williams, Kevin. Turning Point: Reaching in Me... to Find Me... 2010. 152p. 20.00 (978-0-9840955-2-0(7)) Godzchild Inc.

Williams, Linda J. Church Etiquette: A Handbook for Manners & Appropriate Behavior in Church. 2009. 80p. pap. 12.99 (978-1-4389-3340-5(1)) AuthorHouse.

Williams, Lisa. Anointed Whore: A Book of Deliverance. 2008. (ENG.). 216p. pap. 17.99 (978-0-9799112-0-0(6)) Williams, Michael.

Williams, Lisa M. The Secret of Contentment. 2011. 88p. pap. 10.99 (978-1-61215-751-1(3)) Xulon Pr., Inc.

Williams, Lisha. The Joy of Christmas. 2008. 69p. pap. 12.99 (978-1-4357-5110-1(8)) Lulu Enterprises Inc.

Williams, Marcia D. Reconciliation... the Ministry of Peacemakers. 2007. 231p. pap. 19.95 (978-1-4303-1624-4(1)) Lulu Enterprises Inc.

Williams, Nancy A. A Walk in the Garden: What I Learned along the Way. 2009. 148p. 22.99 (978-1-60791-861-5(7)); pap. 14.99 (978-1-60791-860-8(9)) Xulon Pr., Inc.

Williams, Nandilyn. Lion of Judah, Roar in Me. 2006. (ENG.). 64p. 9.99 (978-1-59979-074-9(2), Creation Hse.) Charisma Media.

Williams, Pat. Who Wants to Be a Champion? 10 Building Blocks to Help You Become Everything You Can Be! 2006. (ENG.). 224p. pap. 14.99 (978-1-58229-702-6(9), Howard Bks.) Howard Books.

Williams, Pat & Denney, James. Coach Wooden: The 7 Principles That Shaped His Life & Will Change Yours. 2011. 192p. 17.99 (978-0-8007-1997-5(2)) Revell.

Williams, Pat & Denney, Jim. The Pursuit: Wisdom for the Adventure of Your Life. 2008. (ENG.). 176p. 12.99 (978-0-8307-4599-9(8)) Gospel Light Pubns.

—What Are You Living For? Investing Your Life in What Matter's Most. 2009. (ENG.). 224p. 19.99 (978-0-8307-4664-4(1)) Gospel Light Pubns.

Williams, Patricia. The Endurance of Pleasing God. 2008. 48p. pap. 16.95 (978-1-60474-914-4(8)) PublishAmerica, Inc.

Williams, Patricia A. Revealing God: A New Theology from Science & Jesus. 2008. 190p. pap. 13.95 (978-0-7414-4486-8(0)) Infinity Publishing.

Williams, Patti. Sometimes It Is All about You: Connecting the Dots Between Life & Faith. 2009. (ENG.). 96p. pap. 7.99 (978-1-59979-779-3(8), Creation Hse.) Charisma Media.

Williams, Rob. I'm Saved! Now What? The Proper Response to Salvation. 2011. 104p. pap. 11.95 (978-1-4502-6219-4(8)) iUniverse, Inc.

Williams, Ron. One Second: Ten Events That Define the History of Man. 2009. 232p. pap. 15.99 (978-1-60791-237-8(6)) Xulon Pr., Inc.

Williams, Rose. A Beginning Latin Christian Reader: De Bonis Cogitationibus. 2010. (LAT & ENG.). pap. 19.00 (978-0-86516-750-6(8)) Bolchazy-Carducci Pubs.

Williams, Shalonda. Love Walk Meditations: Back to the Basics. 2007. 80p. per. 16.95 (978-1-4241-8061-5(9)) PublishAmerica, Inc.

Williams, Sherrilyn. The Personality DNA: There Is Purpose in Your Personality. 2007. per. (978-0-9721504-9-1(8)) Understanding For Life Ministries, Inc.

Williams, Sonya L. Til Death Do Us Part. 2011. 146p. 22.99 (978-1-60034-928-7(5)) Xulon Pr., Inc.

Williams Sr., Thaddeus M. Positioning Yourself: How to Transition for Happiness, Peace, & Prosperity. 2009. 136p. 25.95 (978-1-4389-6099-9(9)); pap. 19.95 (978-1-4389-8412-4(X)) AuthorHouse.

Williams, Thomas J. Consider the Lily: A Case for Stress-Free Religion. 2011. 108p. 20.95 (978-1-4620-3502-1(7)); pap. 10.95 (978-1-4620-3503-8(5)) iUniverse, Inc.

C

Williams, Wayne. Gradualism the Stealth of Antichrist. 2007. 132p. per. 13.99 (978-1-60266-520-0(6)) Xulon Pr., Inc.
Williamson, Marty & Linkous, Bobby. God. 2008. pap. 14.99 (978-1-60266-943-7(0)) Xulon Pr., Inc.
Williamson, Richard G. How to Get along with God. 2006. 275p. pap. 27.95 (978-1-4241-4890-5(1)) PublishAmerica, Inc.
Williamson, Roy. Not Least in the Kingdom. 128p. 10.00 (978-0-281-05421-3(5)) SPCK Publishing GBR. Dist: Pilgrim Pr., The/United Church Pr.
Willimon, William H. Remember Who You Are. pap. 8.95 (978-0-687-60973-4(9)) Abingdon Pr.
Willis, Avery & Evans, Steve, compiled by. Making Disciples of Oral Learners. 2007. 140p. per. 12.95 (978-1-59919-018-1(4)) Elim Publishing.
Willis, Avery T., Jr., et al. Real-Life Discipleship Training Manual: Equipping Disciples Who Make Disciples. 2010. (Hollywood Nobody Ser.). 240p. pap. 18.99 (978-1-61521-559-1(X)) NavPress Publishing Group.
Willis, Betty. Attracting the Fruits of the Spirit. 2008. 156p. per. 13.99 (978-1-60266-655-9(5)) Xulon Pr., Inc.
Willis-Bradley, Tiffanie. 52 Weeks of Devotion: .... when the brook of life dries up, living waters still Flow. 2009. 132p. pap. 43.00 (978-1-4259-8742-8(7)) AuthorHouse.
Willis, Johnny. Living in the Rhythm of God. 2011. pap. 10.99 (978-1-61739-322-8(3)) Tate Publishing & Enterprises, LLC.
—Servant Worthy. 2010. pap. 10.99 (978-1-61566-996-7(5)) Tate Publishing & Enterprises, LLC.
Willis, Keri. Teapots & Power Tools: Effectively using the tools God has equipped you with, while taking time to Be Still & Know That He Is God. 2011. (ENG.). 138p. pap. 8.90 **(978-1-4664-5876-5(3))** CreateSpace.
Willison, John. The Afflicted Man's Companion: For the Sick & Troubled. 2009. 264p. pap. 20.00 (978-1-59925-214-8(7)) Solid Ground Christian Bks.
Willison, Rick. A Warrior's Witness: A Prayer for Godly Character in Post-Modern Times. 2008. 120p. pap. 10.99 (978-1-60647-673-4(4)) Xulon Pr., Inc.
Willman, Valerie. Victory over Cancer. 2011. 220p. 17.99 **(978-1-61379-745-7(1))** Xulon Pr., Inc.
Willmann, Robert. From Victim to Victor: A Story of Failures & Triumphs of A God-Mixed Marriage. 2011. 116p. pap. 11.95 **(978-1-4497-2212-8(1)**, WestBow Pr.) Author Solutions, Inc.
Wilson, Amy Lyles, ed. Forgiveness: Perspectives on Making Peace with Your Past. 2008. 96p. pap. 12.00 (978-0-8358-9956-7(X)) Upper Room Bks.
Wilson, Amy M. Baptized in the Holy Spirit with the Evidence of Walking in Love. 2008. pap. 16.95 (978-1-60563-475-3(1)) PublishAmerica, Inc.
Wilson, B. Min. Soar Like an Eagle, Reign Like a King. 2011. 116p. 28.95 **(978-1-61507-726-7(X))**; pap. 11.95 **(978-1-61507-725-0(1))** Cross Bks. Publishing.
Wilson, Barbara. Kiss Me Again: Restoring Lost Intimacy in Marriage. 2009. (ENG.). 224p. pap. 13.99 (978-1-60142-158-6(3), Multnomah) Doubleday Religious Publishing Group, The.
Wilson, Bill. As It Is Written, So Shall It Be. 2010. 400p. 29.99 (978-1-4500-5464-5(1)); pap. 19.99 (978-1-4500-5463-8(3)) Xlibris Corp.
Wilson, Brenda. Peeking through the Pearlies. 2009. pap. 7.99 (978-1-60799-740-5(1)) Tate Publishing & Enterprises, LLC.
Wilson-Bullock, Cassandra. Dead Christians Walking. 2011. pap. 11.99 (978-1-61739-812-4(8)) Tate Publishing & Enterprises, LLC.
Wilson, Carl W. Liberty in an Evil Age. 2008. 220p. 24.99 (978-1-60647-385-6(9)); pap. 14.99 (978-1-60647-384-9(0)) Xulon Pr., Inc.
Wilson, Christop. Passage into Discipleship. 2009. 128p. pap. 12.99 (978-0-8272-3008-8(7)) Chalice Pr.
Wilson, Daniel E. Deification & the Rule of Faith: The Communication of the Gospel in Hellenistic Culture. 2010. 292p. pap. 19.99 (978-1-61507-042-8(7)) Cross Bks. Publishing.
Wilson, Daniel P. Inspiration & Wisdom. 2011. 64p. pap. 11.24 **(978-1-4670-3854-6(7))** AuthorHouse.
Wilson, David. The Holy Spirit in the Christian Experience. 2007. 72p. per. 4.50 (978-0-9786002-4-2(X)) Wilson, David.
Wilson, Douglas. Contours of Post-Maturity: (InterVarsity Press Comes of Age) 2nd ed. 2007. pap. 7.00 (978-1-885767-20-2(X)) Canon Pr.
Wilson, Earle L. Holy & Human: Overcoming Spiritual Struggles to Live a Holy Life. 2008. 160p. 12.99 (978-0-89827-355-7(2)) Wesleyan Publishing Hse.
Wilson, Evelyn D. The Overcomers. 2008. 172p. pap. 13.99 (978-1-4343-7674-9(5)) AuthorHouse.
Wilson, Freddy B. & Armster, Joyce A. The Power of Christian Friendship. 2010. pap. 7.99 (978-1-61663-087-4(6)) Tate Publishing & Enterprises, LLC.
Wilson-Hartgrove, Jonathan. God's Economy: Redefining the Health & Wealth Gospel, 1 vol. 2009. (ENG.). 224p. pap. 14.99 (978-0-310-29337-8(5)) Zondervan.
—New Monasticism: What It Has to Say to Today's Church. 2008. 160p. pap. 15.99 (978-1-58743-224-8(2)) Brazos Pr.
—The Wisdom of Stability: Rooting Faith in a Mobile Culture. 2010. (ENG.). 164p. (gr. 13). pap. 14.99 (978-1-55725-623-2(3)) Paraclete Pr., Inc.
Wilson, Heather Gemmen, et al. When Life Doesn't Turn Out the Way You Expect: Lessons for Faith Communities. 2007. (In Sight Media Ser.). (ENG.). pap. 24.99 (978-0-8341-2332-8(0), 0834123320) Beacon Hill Pr. of Kansas City.
Wilson, James. Living as Ambassadors of Relationships: Reconciling Individuals, Families, Genders, Denominations, Cultures, Liberals & Conservatives, Jews & Gentiles, & the Generations. 2008. 350p. per. 16.99 (978-0-7684-2587-1(5)) Destiny Image Pubs.
Wilson, Jared. Your Jesus Is Too Safe: Outgrowing a Drive-Thru, Feel-Good Savior, 1 vol. 2009. 288p. pap. 13.99 (978-0-8254-3931-5(0)) Kregel Pubns.
Wilson, Jim. Principles of War: A Handbook on Strategic Evangelism. 5th ed. 2009. 104p. pap. 12.00 (978-1-59128-065-1(6)) Canon Pr.
Wilson, Kelly L. A Better Day - a Better Life. 2009. 188p. pap. 14.99 (978-1-60791-166-1(3)) Xulon Pr., Inc.
Wilson, Ken. The Christian Home by God's Design. pap. 8.95 (978-1-56794-248-4(2), C-3038) Star Bible & Tract Corp.
—Mystically Wired: Exploring New Landscapes in Prayer, 0 vols. 2010. 208p. 17.99 (978-0-8499-2001-1(9)) Nelson, Thomas Inc.
Wilson, Lawrence W. A Different Kind of Crazy: Living the Way Jesus Lived. 2007. 224p. per. 14.99 (978-0-89827-348-9(X)) Wesleyan Publishing Hse.
Wilson, Loren Henry. Free Will & Predestination: Revisited in the Twenty-first Century. 2011. 96p. 24.99 **(978-1-4628-6126-2(1))**; pap. 15.99 **(978-1-4628-6125-5(3))** Xlibris Corp.
Wilson, Mark W. Christians & Hunger. 2009. pap. (978-0-9823842-5-1(4)) NextSunday Resources.
Wilson, Matt. The Godly Path of Least Resistance. 2007. 172p. per. 13.99 (978-1-60477-033-9(3)) Xulon Pr., Inc.
Wilson, Neil S. The Daily God Book Words of Wisdom. 2009. (ENG.). 384p. pap. 14.99 (978-1-4143-3460-8(5)) Tyndale Hse. Pubs.
Wilson, Norman G., ed. Journey into Holiness: Experiencing Gods Power for Holy Living. 2010. (Illus.). 193p. pap. 12.99 (978-0-89827-225-3(4)) Wesleyan Publishing Hse.
Wilson, Pete. Plan B: What Do You Do When God Doesn't Show up the Way You Thought He Would? 2010. 256p. pap. 15.99 (978-0-8499-4650-9(6)) Nelson, Thomas Inc.
Wilson, Ray. Wisdom & Common Sense for the Young Man. 2007. 72p. per. 9.99 (978-1-60266-770-9(5)) Xulon Pr., Inc.
Wilson, William. God Vision. 2008. 68p. pap. 9.95 (978-1-4401-0494-7(8)) iUniverse, Inc.
Wit, David A. Dancing with Depression: How I'm Learning to Win the Battle & How You Can Too. 2008. 176p. pap. 14.99 (978-1-60791-053-4(5)) Xulon Pr., Inc.
Wilton, Clyde C. Wilton's Wit for Children. 2011. 240p. 26.26 **(978-1-4669-0452-1(6))**; pap. 16.26 **(978-1-4669-0450-7(X))** Trafford Publishing.
Wilton, Don. When God Prayed. 2008. (ENG.). 256p. per. 16.99 (978-0-8054-4554-1(4), B&H Bks.) B&H Publishing Group.
—When God Prayed. 2011. 0.00 (978-1-59328-310-0(5)) Graham, Billy Evangelistic Assn.
Wiltse, Vern. Walking Through a Thicket: Inspirational Thoughts above New Age & Science. Brockman, Eleanor F. & Torrans, Tom, eds. (C). 4.00 (978-1-930421-17-2(6)) BullFrog Pr.
Wiman, Carl S., Sr. Thoughts of Everyday Life, by the CEO. 2007. per. (978-1-59916-242-3(3)) Printing Systems.
Windness, Jon Post. Manifesto for the Abundant Life Church: A Modern Reformation Church Dedicated to Changed Lives in the Context of A Reasonable Faith. 2007. 60p. per. 9.95 (978-0-595-42552-5(6)) iUniverse, Inc.
Winfrey, Michelle Whitaker. Yours, Mine & God's: Giving & Receiving: All for the Love of the God & the Church. 2006. 140p. per. 16.99 (978-0-9727179-3-9(5)) Hobby Hse. Publishing Group.
Winkett, Lucy. Our Sound Is Our Wound: Contemplative Listening to a Noisy World; the Archbishop of Canterbury's Lent Book 2010. 2010. (ENG.). 160p. 19.95 (978-0-8264-3921-5(7)) Continuum International Publishing Group, Ltd. GBR. Dist: National Bk. Network.
Winslow, Eleanora. Devoured by Passion. 2008. 176p. pap. 13.99 (978-1-60647-475-4(8)) Xulon Pr., Inc.
Winslow, Octavius. Soul-Depths & Soul-Heights: An Exposition of Psalm 130. 2006. 135p. per. 12.00 (978-0-85151-935-7(0)) Banner of Truth, The.
Winslow, Octavius & Kistler, Don. The Precious Things of God. 2010. (978-0-9826155-4-6(X)) Northampton Pr., The.
Winston, Bill. The Kingdom of God in You: Discover the Greatness of God's Power Within. 2010. (ENG.). 256p. pap. 14.99 (978-1-60683-032-1(5)) 2006. 225p. 17.99 (978-1-57794-796-7(7)) Harrison House Pubs.
—The Law of Confession: Revolutionize Your Life & Rewrite Your Future with the Power of Words. 2009. 256p. 19.99 (978-1-57794-969-5(2)) Harrison House Pubs.
—Transform Your Thinking, Transform Your Life: Radically Change Your Thoughts, Your World, & Your Destiny. 2009. 256p. pap. 14.99 (978-1-57794-971-8(4)) Harrison House Pubs.
Winston Lucien Daniels. The Making of Kings: Get yourself ready for the coming Kingdom Age. 2009. 192p. 26.96 (978-1-4269-0542-1(4)); pap. 16.96 (978-1-4269-0541-4(6)) Trafford Publishing.
Winter, James F. Baptism by Toilet Water. 2010. pap. 19.99 (978-1-61663-980-8(6)) Tate Publishing & Enterprises, LLC.
Winter, Ralph D., et al. Perspectives on the World Christian Movement: A Reader. 4th ed. 2009. (978-0-87808-390-9(1)) Carey, William Library Pubs.
Winters, Fred. Reflections on Wisdom & Folly. 2010. 108p. 28.95 (978-1-61507-214-9(4)); pap. 11.95 (978-1-61507-213-2(6)) Cross Bks. Publishing.
Wintoch, Claudia. You Can Change the World. 2011. (ENG.). 176p. pap. 14.99 (978-88-96727-22-5(7)) Destiny Image Europe ITA. Dist: Destiny Image Pubs.
Wirt, Sherwood E. Despues de la Experiencia: Afterglow. (SPA.). 120p. (978-84-7228-049-6(7), 220278) Clie, Editorial.
Wisdom, Charles. A Voice from Heaven. 2006. pap. 14.99 (978-1-60034-702-3(9)) Xulon Pr., Inc.
Wisdom, or Mind, Will, & Understanding. (Tudor Facsimile Texts, Old English Plays Ser.: No. 2). reprint ed. 49.50 (978-0-404-53302-1(7)) AMS Pr., Inc.
Wise, Cristy. It's All about Jesus. 2008. 68p. per. 9.99 (978-1-60477-550-1(5)) Xulon Pr., Inc.
Wise, Daniel. Pleasant Pathways; or, [P]Ersuasives to Early Piety: Containing Explanations & Illustrations of the Beauty, Safety, & Pleasantness of A Religious. 2006. 296p. per. 23.99 (978-1-4255-2718-1(3)) MPublishing.
Wise, Darrell L. The Trust Factor: Secrets to Life's Purpose. 2011. pap. 12.99 (978-1-61739-112-5(3)) Tate Publishing & Enterprises, LLC.
Wise, Heath. Young Women's L. I. F. E. Guide. Laaser, Mark, ed. 2007. per. 19.95 (978-0-9771662-8-2(7)) Freedom Every Day LLC.
Wiseman, Cathy. In Whose Steps. 2010. 354p. pap. 19.95 (978-0-9779693-8-8(X)) Dare2Dream Books.
Wisnefske, Ned. God Hides: A Critique of Religion & A Primer for Faith. 2010. 130p. pap. 16.00 (978-1-60608-868-5(8), Pickwick Pubns.) Wipf & Stock Pubs.
Witcher, Natalie. The Devil in Your Garden: Finding Victory over Shame. 2007. 127p. per. 10.99 (978-1-60247-301-0(3)) Tate Publishing & Enterprises, LLC.
Witherspoon Sr, Barron. The Fallacy of Affinity. 2010. 188p. 29.99 (978-1-60844-511-0(9)); pap. 17.99 (978-1-60844-510-3(0)) Dog Ear Publishing, LLC.
Witte, John, Jr. Christianity & Human Rights: An Introduction. Alexander, Frank S., ed. 2010. (ENG.). 400p. pap. 29.99 (978-0-521-14374-5(8)) Cambridge Univ. Pr.
Witter, Connie. 21 Days to Discover Who You Are in Christ: Living Confident & Secure in His Unchanging Love for You. 2009. 96p. pap. 4.99 (978-1-57794-964-0(1)) Harrison House Pubs.
Wittman, Ward M. A Coach's Salvation. 2007. 164p. per. 24.95 (978-1-4241-8628-0(5)) PublishAmerica, Inc.
Wittmier, Deborah. Crowns: Five Eternal Rewards That Will Change the Way You Live Your Life. 2009. 176p. pap. 14.99 (978-1-61579-248-1(1)) Xulon Pr., Inc.
Wittstruck, Bob. Living by the Covenant. 2nd rev. ed. 2009. pap. (978-1-61584-969-7(6)) Independent Pub.
Wofford, Pastor Deborah. Believe in Yourself. 2011. 78p. 24.99 **(978-1-4628-7985-4(3))**; pap. 15.99 **(978-1-4628-7984-7(5))** Xlibris Corp.
Wolbert, Richard A. A Time of Faith, Hope, & Love. 2010. pap. 8.99 (978-1-61566-732-1(6)) Tate Publishing & Enterprises, LLC.
Woldu, Gebru. Gifts of the Holy Spirit & How to Use Them. 214p. pap. 14.99 (978-1-59185-289-6(7), Creation Hse.) Charisma Media.
Wolf, Alexys V. Looking for God: Spiritual Intimacy & a Personal Relationship with Christ. 2009. (J). pap. 20.99 (978-1-60799-854-9(8)) Tate Publishing & Enterprises, LLC.
Wolf, Tony. Go Be Jesus: Making Your Mark Through Serving Others. 2007. 148p. per. 14.95 (978-0-595-47341-0(5)) iUniverse, Inc.
Wolfe, Linden C. Captivated by Christ. 2008. 152p. pap. 13.99 (978-1-60647-369-6(7)) Xulon Pr., Inc.
Wolfe, Tim. Straight-Friendly: the Gay Believer's Life in Christ. 2010. 261p. pap. 24.00 (978-0-557-12219-6(8)) Lulu Enterprises Inc.
Wolfmueller, Bryan. Final Victory. 2010. 64p. pap. 8.99 (978-0-7586-1636-4(8)) Concordia Publishing Hse.
Wolfson, Moshe. Wellsprings of Faith. Fieldsteel, Yehoshua, tr. 180p. 22.99 (978-1-58330-526-3(2)) Feldheim Pubs.
Wolgemuth, Bobbie. Tea Parties with a Purpose: 10 Simple & Fun Party Ideas for Kids of All Ages. 2009. (ENG., Illus.). 128p. 14.99 (978-1-4165-7294-7(5), Howard Bks.) Howard Books.
Wolgemuth, Robert. Seven Things You Better Have Nailed down Before All Breaks Loose. 2008. (Illus.). 210p. pap. 14.99 (978-0-7852-8956-2(9)) Nelson, Thomas Inc.
Wolmarans, Henry. Yes You Can: Achieve Your Dreams. 2007. (ENG.). 282p. per. 16.99 (978-1-933853-51-2(4)) Tsaba Hse.
Womack, Marcella R. Living from the Soul: Awakening to Christ-Consciousness. 2010. 228p. 29.99 (978-1-4415-4887-0(4)); pap. 19.99 (978-1-4415-4886-3(6)) Xlibris Corp.
Woman Submit! Christians & Domestic Violence. 2007. per. 19.99 (978-0-9794293-0-9(7)) One Way Cafe Pr. LLC.
Woman, Thou Art Loosed! Workbook. 2006. per. 13.99 (978-0-7684-2404-1(6)) Destiny Image Pubs.
Women of Faith. Imagine, 0 vols. 2010. (Women of Faith Study Guide Ser.). 128p. spiral bd. 9.99 (978-1-4185-4186-6(9)) Nelson, Thomas Inc.
—Over the Top, 0 vols. 2010. (Women of Faith Study Guide Ser.). 128p. spiral bd. 9.99 (978-1-4185-4185-9(0)) Nelson, Thomas Inc.
Wommack, Andrew. Discover the Keys to Staying Full of God. 2008. 195p. pap. 13.99 (978-1-57794-934-3(X)) Harrison House Pubs.
—Living in the Balance of Grace & Faith: Combining Two Powerful Forces to Receive from God. 2009. (ENG.). 224p. 19.99 (978-1-57794-918-3(8)) Harrison House Pubs.
—You've Already Got It! So Quit Trying to Get It. 2006. 229p. per. 13.99 (978-1-57794-833-9(5)) Harrison House Pubs.
Wonch, Mike. Sacred Life: Spiritual Practices for Everyday Living. 2007. (Ancient Faith Ser.). (ENG.). 96p. pap. 9.99 (978-0-8341-5013-3(1), 083-415-0131) Beacon Hill Pr. of Kansas City.
Wong, Nadine. What If Your Hair Could Speak What Would It Say. 2010. 108p. pap. 11.99 (978-1-60957-324-9(2)) Xulon Pr., Inc.
Wood, Allen. Say No to Religion. 2009. 76p. pap. 10.99 (978-1-61579-004-3(7)) Xulon Pr., Inc.
Wood, Chester W. Hurt People Hurt People. 2008. 80p. pap. 12.99 (978-1-60647-835-6(4)) Xulon Pr., Inc.
Wood, Cindi. Too Blessed for This Mess: The Frazzled Female's Guide to Overcoming Stress. 2007. (ENG.). 128p. 12.99 (978-0-8054-4632-6(X), B&H Bks.) B&H Publishing Group.
Wood, Fran A. What My Dog Taught Me about God: Reconnecting with God's Love & Emerging from a Spiritual Wilderness. 2007. 208p. pap. 12.95 (978-0-9797591-0-9(2)) Lemon Tree Publishing.
Wood, Katrina. Circles. 2006. pap. 15.99 (978-1-60034-585-2(9)) Xulon Pr., Inc.
Wood, Lawrence. News to Me: Gospel Stories for the Real World. 2008. (ENG.). 201p. pap. 15.00 (978-0-664-23226-9(4)) Westminster John Knox Pr.
Wood, Shawn. Wasabi Gospel: The Startling Message of Jesus. 2009. 142p. pap. 14.00 (978-1-4267-0050-7(4)) Abingdon Pr.
Woodall, Chris. Covenant: The Basis of GodÕs Self-Disclosure. 2011. 212p. pap. 23.00 **(978-1-61097-358-8(5)**, Wipf and Stock) Wipf & Stock Pubs.
Woodard, Judith A. The Holy Spirit & You. 2008. 80p. per. 9.99 (978-1-60477-207-4(7)) Xulon Pr., Inc.
Woodbridge, Myra. Chosen of the Lord-Broken in Heart. 2008. 108p. pap. 10.99 (978-1-60647-254-5(2)) Xulon Pr., Inc.
Woodcock, Anne. Contentment: Healing the Hunger of Our Hearts: 8 Studies for Individuals or Groups. 2010. (Good Book Guides). 96p. pap. (978-1-905564-66-8(X)) Good Bk. Co.
Woodley, Deborah. The Difference it Makes Having Christ in My Life & Your Life. 2011. 88p. pap. 12.84 **(978-1-4670-3583-5(1))** AuthorHouse.
Woodman, Charles M. Quakers Find a Way: Their Discoveries in Practical Living. 2011. 280p. 47.95 **(978-1-258-03694-2(0))** Literary Licensing, LLC.
Woodruff-Brown, Loria. I Am Ready to Work Out My Issues: A Devotional Journal Workbook. Hicks, Patricia A., ed. 2006. per. 14.99 (978-1-933972-02-2(5)) PriorityONE Pubns.
Woodruff, Joseph. A Life Worth Becoming. 2007. (978-0-9797732-0-4(2)) Next Innovations.
Woodruff, Michelle M. Armed & Victorious. 2008. 136p. pap. 13.95 (978-0-7414-4640-4(5)) Infinity Publishing.
Woods, Dion. Better Than Ever: Live on a Level You Never Thought Possible. 2011. (ENG.). 160p. pap. 12.99 **(978-1-61638-657-3(6)**, Creation Hse.) Charisma Media.
Woods, Dorothy. Prison Break. 2011. 92p. 24.99 **(978-1-4628-8958-7(1))**; pap. 15.99 **(978-1-4628-8959-4(X))** Xlibris Corp.
Woods, Eddie J. Turning Points Within the Church. 2010. 312p. pap. 19.95 (978-1-4490-5080-1(8)) AuthorHouse.
Woods, LaWanda. Imprisoned for Preparation. 2007. (ENG.). 504p. per. 23.99 (978-1-60034-804-4(1)) Xulon Pr., Inc.
Woods, Michael. What Now Lord? Lord. I Have Given My Life to You. What do I do Now? 2008. 112p. pap. 11.99 (978-1-60791-178-4(7)) Xulon Pr., Inc.
Woods, Richard J. Wellness: Life, Health & Spirituality. 2009. (ENG.). 271p. pap. 24.95 (978-1-84730-092-8(8)) Veritas Pubns. IRL. Dist: Dufour Editions, Inc.
Woods, The Rev. J. C. Dante's Journey: A Field Guide to the Infernal Regions. 2009. 201p. pap. 24.95 (978-1-60672-413-2(4)) PublishAmerica, Inc.
Woodson, Ed. Six Steps to the Lord, 1 vol. 2009. 60p. pap. 16.95 (978-1-60749-326-6(8)) PublishAmerica, Inc.
Woodward, Clyde H. Preacher Without a Pulpit, 1 vol. 2009. (ENG.). 118p. pap. 19.95 (978-1-60836-665-1(0)) PublishAmerica, Inc.
Woodward, Joseph. Understanding Trials to Better Understand God. 2007. 273p. per. 20.99 (978-1-59886-468-7(8)) Tate Publishing & Enterprises, LLC.
Woodworth, Anjea. Celebrating Baptism Rememberin. 2009. 24p. pap. 5.00 (978-0-88177-575-4(4)) Discipleship Resources.
Wooten, Calvin. The Book of Love: Through the Eyes of a Child. 2008. 148p. pap. 15.99 (978-1-4343-5710-6(4)) AuthorHouse.
Word Among Us Press, ed. Bearing the Fruit of the Spirit: Prayer Journal. 2007. 224p. 13.95 (978-1-59325-107-9(6)) Word Among Us Pr.
The Word for the Wise: Making Scripture the Heart of Your Counseling Ministry. 2nd rev. ed. 2008. 248p. 16.99 (978-0-9648743-6-7(9)) Skinner, Kerry L.
Word of Life Fellowship Inc, creator. Quiet Time: One Year Daily Devotional with Commentary, 1. 2007. (Quiet Time Daily Devotionals Ser.). 421p. per. 17.99 (978-1-931235-62-4(7), TQTWC) Word of Life Fellowship, Inc.
Worden, Larry D. You Have Me. 2008. 204p. pap. 15.99 (978-1-60647-634-5(3)) Xulon Pr., Inc.
Workers Unashamed - Phase I. 2007. (ENG.). 140p. pap. (978-0-9769695-4-9(8)) Polyventure Pubns.
Workman, Dave. The Outward-Focused Life: Becoming a Servant in a Serve-Me World. 2008. 208p. pap. 15.00 (978-0-8010-7150-8(X)) Baker Bks.
Workman, Terry. The Inside Awakened. 2010. 112p. 22.95 (978-1-4401-9976-9(0)) iUniverse, Inc.
Worship Feast. 50.00 (978-0-687-07531-7(9)) Abingdon Pr.
Worship Together: Pew Edition. 773p. 13.95 (978-0-919257-24-5(0)) Kindred Productions.
Worthy, David L. The God Kind of Faith: From the Problem to the Answer. 2006. (ENG.). 176p. per. 11.95 (978-0-7414-3350-3(8)) Infinity Publishing.
Worton, Roland. Emerging Worship: Becoming a Part of the Sound & Song of Heaven. 2008. pap. 15.99 (978-0-7684-2698-4(7)) Destiny Image Pubs.
Wright, B. Alexander. Do You Know the ABCs of Your Faith? 2007. 36p. per. (978-0-9772099-4-1(6)) SkrAiber Publishing Services.
Wright, Bradley R. E. Christians Are Hate-Filled Hypocrites... & Other Lies You've Been Told: A Sociologist Shatters Myths from the Secular & Christian Media. 2010. 16.99p. pap. 14.99 (978-0-7642-0746-4(6)) Bethany Hse. Pubs.

Wright, Charles. The Benefits of Living Holy. 2009. 73p. pap. 17.95 *(978-1-4327-4041-2(5))* Outskirts Pr., Inc.
Wright, Daniel E. Iron Man Oikodome: 31 Devotions for Men. 2011. pap. 12.99 *(978-1-61663-552-7(5))* Tate Publishing & Enterprises, LLC.
Wright, Fred & Wright, Sharon. The World's Greatest Revivals: How Man's Desperation Begins Waves of Revival.... Including Yours. 2007. 285p. per. 14.99 *(978-0-7684-2591-8(3))* Destiny Image Pubs.
Wright, H. Norman. How to Overcome Discouragement: Finding Your Way Back to Hope & Happiness. 2010. pap. 12.99 *(978-0-7369-2623-2(2))* Harvest Hse. Pubs.
—Respuesta a la Depresion: Answer to Depression. (SPA.). 64p. *(978-84-7228-726-6(2), 220770)* Clie, Editorial.
—Respuesta a la Disciplina: Answer to Discipline. (SPA.). 64p. *(978-84-7228-768-6(8), 222385)* Clie, Editorial.
Wright, Jeff. Tour of Life. 2010. 64p. pap. 10.99 *(978-0-8272-3661-5(1))* Chalice Pr.
Wright, Kimberly. Bedtime Thoughts for the Christian Mom: Devotionals to Challenge & Encourage Mothers. 2011. 100p. pap. 13.95 *(978-1-4269-4577-9(9))* Trafford Publishing.
Wright, Nigel G. New Baptists, New Agenda. Beaumont, Paul, ed. 2007. (ENG.). 166p. (Orig.). pap. 14.99 *(978-1-84227-157-5(1)*, Paternoster) Authentic Media.
Wright, Regenia S. Jesus & the New Math: 2+55,000. 2009. (NANA Ser.). (ENG., Illus.). 28p. 12.99 *(978-0-9713416-8-5(0))* Sonflower Publishing.
Wright, Sabrina M. Walking in His Shadow: A Walk with God. 2008. 84p. pap. 9.99 *(978-1-60647-066-4(3))* Xulon Pr., Inc.
Wurmbrand, R. Cristo en las Prisiones Comunistas: In God's Underground. (SPA.). 332p. *(978-84-7228-479-1(4), 220206)* Clie, Editorial.
Wurmbrand, Richard. The Overcomers: Stories of Love & Strength from the Founder of the Voice of the Martyrs. 2006. 310p. per. 12.99 *(978-0-88270-206-3(8))* Bridge-Logos Foundation.
Wyatt, Bob. The Spirited Festival: (the Bachelor Preacher. 2009. pap. 14.99 *(978-1-60791-675-8(4))* Xulon Pr., Inc.
Wyatt, Steve. Stuck in a Small World: Staying on Board with Your Not-So-Unique yet Thoroughly Dysfunctional Family. 2008. (ENG.). 256p. per. 12.99 *(978-0-7847-2111-7(4))* Standard Publishing.
Wynn, Rick D. It's Not about You: A Study of the Last Church Generation Volume One. 2007. 368p. per. 19.99 *(978-1-59886-564-6(1))* Tate Publishing & Enterprises, LLC.
Wyrtzen, Christine E. Walking in Wide Places. 2010. 282p. pap. 16.99 *(978-1-60957-624-0(1))* Xulon Pr., Inc.
Wyvill, Christopher. Intolerance: The Disgrace of Christians Not the Fault of Their Religion. 2007. (ENG.). 110p. 34.95 *(978-0-548-04857-3(6))* Kessinger Publishing, LLC.
X, Vagabond. Spare the Rod, Don't Hate Your Son. 2010. 159p. pap. 12.00 *(978-0-557-57134-5(0))* Lulu Enterprises Inc.
Yaconelli, Mike & Christie, Les. When Church Kids Go Bad: How to Love & Work with Rude, Obnoxious, & Apathetic Students, 1 vol. 2008. (ENG.). 192p. pap. 16.99 *(978-0-310-27665-4(9))* Zondervan.
Yancey, Philip. Finding God in Unexpected Places. 2008. (ENG.). 304p. pap. 13.99 *(978-1-4000-7470-9(3))* Doubleday Religious Publishing Group, The.
—Finding God in Unexpected Places. 2008. (Playaway Adult Nonfiction Ser.). 64.99 *(978-1-60514-798-7(2))* Findaway World, LLC.
—Finding God in Unexpected Places. l.t. ed. 2008. 469p. (YA). 29.95 *(978-1-4104-0745-0(4))* Thorndike Pr.
—Skeptic's Guide to Faith, 1 vol. 2009. (ENG.). 272p. pap. 14.99 *(978-0-310-32502-4(1))* Zondervan.
Yancey, Rob. The Messenger: Tragedy Births Destiny. 2009. 316p. 28.99 *(978-1-60791-743-4(2))*; pap. 18.99 *(978-1-60791-742-7(4))* Xulon Pr., Inc.
Yandian, Bob. Understanding the End Times. Noble, Linda, ed. 165p. pap. *(978-1-885600-10-3(0))* Bob Yandian Ministries.
Yates, Ruby. Embrace Your Tomorrow. Today! 2007. 124p. per. 10.99 *(978-1-60266-218-6(5))* Xulon Pr., Inc.
Yeager, Joy. Embracing the Hurting Heart. 2006. pap. 12.99 *(978-1-60034-467-1(4))* Xulon Pr., Inc.
Yeatman, Algene. Storms & Faith: How God Carried Me Through the Storms, with a Review of the Great Preaching During My Life. 2008. 140p. pap. 16.99 *(978-1-60791-184-5(1))* Xulon Pr., Inc.
Yehoshua, Avram. The Lifting of the Veil: Acts 15:20-21. 2009. 268p. 22.78 *(978-1-4251-2328-4(7))* Trafford Publishing.
Yell, D. M. The Drama of Man. 2007. 200p. 24.99 *(978-1-60266-768-6(3))*; per. 14.99 *(978-1-60266-767-9(5))* Xulon Pr., Inc.
Yemane, Elias. Mephibosheth: Transformation by a Covenant Love. 2007. 181p. per. 15.99 *(978-1-60247-443-7(5))* Tate Publishing & Enterprises, LLC.
Yeomans, Lilian. His Healing Power. 2006. 304p. pap. 14.99 *(978-1-57794-819-3(X))* Harrison House Pubs.
Yglesias, José. Home Again. 176p. pap. 12.95 *(978-1-55885-354-6(5))* Arte Publico Pr.
Yisrael, Bethuel Mariael. Let My People Go: A Letter to the Captivity. 2007. pap. 23.00 *(978-0-8059-8454-5(2))* Dorrance Publishing Co., Inc.
Yisrael, Navee Yaacov. Biblical Heritage Awakening. 2011. 116p. 24.95 *(978-1-4269-4883-1(2))*; pap. 14.95 *(978-1-4269-4881-7(6))* Trafford Publishing.
Yocum, Dale M. This Present World. pap. 9.99 *(978-0-88019-194-4(5))* Schmul Publishing Co., Inc.
—True & False Tongues. 0.49 *(978-0-88019-117-3(1))* Schmul Publishing Co., Inc.
Yogananda, Param. El Yoga De Jesus. 2009. (SPA.). 160p. pap. 14.95 *(978-0-87612-024-8(9))* Self-Realization Fellowship Pubs.
Yogananda, Paramhansa. Como Conversar con Dios. (SPA.). 56p. pap. 5.00 *(978-0-87612-451-2(1))*; 2008. 8.00 *(978-0-87612-450-5(3))* Self-Realization Fellowship Pubs.
Yohannan, K. P. When We Have Failed-What Next? 2008. (ENG.). 88p. pap. 3.95 *(978-1-59589-035-1(1))* Gospel For Asia Bks.
Yoho, Joanne E. A Journey to Begin. 2008. 220p. pap. 14.95 *(978-1-934769-09-6(6))* McDougal & Assocs.
Yong-Doo, Kim. Baptize by Blazing Fire: Divine Expose of Heaven & Hell. 2009. (ENG.). 176p. pap. 12.99 *(978-1-59979-767-0(4)*, Creation Hse.) Charisma Media.
Yore, Sue. The Mystic Way in Postmodernity: Transcending Theological Boundaries in the Writings of Iris Murdoch, Denise Levertov & Annie Dillard. 2009. 334p. pap. 61.95 *(978-3-03911-536-5(7))* Lang, Peter AG GBR. Dist: Lang, Peter.
Yorkey, Mike. Teen Chat. 186p. pap. 7.99 *(978-0-8307-3504-4(6)*, Gospel Light) Gospel Light Pubns.
Yost, Georgia. How to Be Effective in God's Army. 2011. 74p. pap. 15.99 ***(978-1-4628-8651-7(5))*** Xlibris Corp.
You the Graduate. 80.00 *(978-0-687-46855-3(8))* Abingdon Pr.
You Were Made for More: The Life You Have, the Life God Wants You to Have, 1 vol. 2009. 224p. pap. 3.99 *(978-0-310-32674-8(5))* Zondervan.
Youmans, Mary & Youmans, Roger. Testimony of Two. pap. 5.95 *(978-0-910924-91-7(0))* Macalester Park Publishing Co., Inc.
Young, Annette. From Grief to Glory. 2007. 100p. per. 9.99 *(978-1-60477-197-8(6))* Xulon Pr., Inc.
Young, Carlton Joseph. Realizing Your Human Potential: A Christ Centered Approach to Life. 2010. 428p. (ENG.). 36.95 *(978-1-4502-1509-1(2))*; pap. 26.95 *(978-1-4502-1507-7(6))* iUniverse, Inc.
Young, Charles M., Jr. It's All about Him: Letting Christ Live Through You. 2008. (ENG.). 224p. 19.99 *(978-1-59979-352-8(0)*, Creation Hse.) Charisma Media.
Young, Ed. High Definition Living: Bringing Clarity to Your Life. 2007. (ENG.). 224p. pap. 16.95 *(978-1-4165-7044-8(6)*, Howard Bks.) Howard Books.
—In the Zone: How to Live in the Sweet Spot of Success. 2007. 111p. 12.99 *(978-0-9725813-8-7(3))* Creality Publishing.
—Outrageous, Contagious Joy: Five Big Questions to Help You Discover One Great Life. 2008. (ENG.). 384p. (gr. 12-18). 16.00 *(978-0-425-21908-9(9)*, Berkley Trade) Penguin Group (USA) Inc.
Young-Gi Hong, Josua. Building a House of Prayer: 18 Prayer Models for Approaching God's Throne. 2008. (ENG., Illus.). 230p. pap. 13.99 *(978-0-88270-455-5(9))* Bridge-Logos Foundation.
Young III, Arthur, et al. Godfrey Tribe: The Game of Discipleship. 2010. 244p. pap. 17.95 *(978-1-61507-254-5(3))* Cross Bks. Publishing.
Young, Jim. You Decide: Your Choices Determine Your Future, 1 vol. 2010. 50p. pap. 16.95 *(978-1-4512-0891-7(X))* PublishAmerica, Inc.
Young, Naseska C. I Know He Watches Me. 2011. 108p. pap. 19.95 ***(978-1-4626-1370-0(5))*** PublishAmerica, Inc.
Young, Paul. The Hidden Key to the Power of God. 2010. 130p. pap. 11.99 *(978-0-557-60544-6(X))* Lulu Enterprises Inc.
Young, Sarah. Dear Jesus: Seeking His Life in Your Life, 0 vols. 2007. 256p. 13.99 *(978-1-4041-0495-2(X))* Nelson, Thomas Inc.
Young, Sherri R. Your Worst Enemy Is U. 2010. 80p. pap. 10.99 *(978-1-61579-647-2(9))* Xulon Pr., Inc.
Young, Tamara. Training Your Emotions One-on-One: Working Out Your Emotions by Exercising Your Faith in Christ. 2007. 135p. per. 15.99 *(978-1-59879-305-5(5))* Lifevest Publishing, Inc.
Younger, Carol Davis. Challenges of the Christian Life: Study. 2011. pap. ***(978-1-936347-02-5(4))*** NextSunday Resources.
Your Child & Anger. 12.00 *(978-0-687-03401-7(9))* Abingdon Pr.
Your Child & Conflict. 12.00 *(978-0-687-04373-6(5))* Abingdon Pr.
Your Child & Discipline. 12.00 *(978-0-687-08889-8(5))* Abingdon Pr.
Youth Certificate of Promotion. 0.60 *(978-0-687-04984-4(9))* Abingdon Pr.
Youth Disciple Leader Packet. 15.15 *(978-0-7673-5741-8(8))* LifeWay Christian Resources.
Youth for Christ International. Faith Journey. 2008. 160p. pap. 6.99 *(978-1-60006-314-5(4))* NavPress Publishing Group.
—Influencing Others. 2008. 96p. pap. 5.99 *(978-1-60006-315-2(2))* NavPress Publishing Group.
—Reaching Out: Making a Difference in Your World. 2008. 128p. pap. 6.99 *(978-1-60006-313-8(6))* NavPress Publishing Group.
Yrigoyen, Mike. Answers to Our Questions. 2008. (ENG.). 96p. pap. 8.99 *(978-0-9800320-1-7(6))* Gatekeepers Ministries, Inc.
—The Desert & the Word. 2008. (ENG.). 224p. pap. 12.99 *(978-0-9800320-0-0(8))* Gatekeepers Ministries, Inc.
Velez, Amanda. Delivered from the Leviathan Monster: Gaining Freedom from Trauma Through God's Word. 2011. pap. 18.99 ***(978-1-61777-403-4(0))*** Tate Publishing & Enterprises, LLC.
Zacharias, Karen Spears. Will Jesus Buy Me a Double-Wide? Cause I Need More Room for My Plasma TV, 1 vol. 2010. (ENG.). 240p. 16.99 *(978-0-310-29250-0(6))* Zondervan.
Zacharias, Ravi. The Grand Weaver: How God Shapes Us Through the Events of Our Lives. 2007. (ENG.). 208p. pap. 12.99 *(978-0-310-26997-7(0))* Zondervan.
—The Grand Weaver: How God Shapes Us Through the Events of Our Lives, 1 vol. (ENG.). 208p. 2010. pap. 14.99 *(978-0-310-32495-9(5))* 2008. pap. 3.49 *(978-0-310-28584-7(4))* Zondervan.
—There Is a Plan, 1 vol. 2009. (ENG.). 96p. pap. 9.99 *(978-0-310-31849-1(1))* Zondervan.
—Vuelva A Maravillarse: Como Recuperar el Regalo Divino de Asombrarnos Que Tuvimos de Ninos. Varisco, Marta, tr. 2006. 191p. 9.00 *(978-0-311-46029-8(1)*, Editorial Mundo Hispano) Casa Bautista de Publicaciones.
—Walking from East to West: God in the Shadows, 1 vol. (ENG.). 240p. 2010. pap. 14.99 *(978-0-310-32496-6(3))* 2008. pap. 3.99 *(978-0-310-28579-3(8))* Zondervan.
Zahl, Paul F. M. Grace in Practice: A Theology of Everyday Life. 2007. 267p. per. 18.00 *(978-0-8028-2897-2(3))* Eerdmans, William B. Publishing Co.
Zannd, Brian. What to Do on the Worst Day of Your Life. 2009. (ENG.). 144p. 14.99 *(978-1-59979-726-7(7))* Charisma Media.
Zaleski, Irma. Who Is God? The Soul's Road Home. 2006. (ENG.). 144p. per. 12.95 *(978-1-59030-304-7(0)*, New Seeds Bks.) Shambhala Pubns., Inc.
Zandt, Craig Van. A Heavenly Christmas: Enjoying the Presence of Jesus Everyday; A 31-Day Family Devotional. 2010. pap. 17.99 *(978-1-61663-663-0(7))* Tate Publishing & Enterprises, LLC.
Zao, Joel. Chasing Truth: A Detailed Discussion of Paul's Letter to the Romans Chapters 1-8. 2009. 320p. pap. 18.99 *(978-1-61579-558-1(8))* Xulon Pr., Inc.
Zapico, J. Control del Anticristo: Red Mundial.Tr. of Control of the Antichrist: The Global Network. (SPA.). 5.99 *(978-0-7899-0408-9(X), 550151)* Editorial Unilit.
Zaverl, David. Established in Righteousness. 2007. 212p. per. 14.99 *(978-1-60477-098-8(8))* Xulon Pr., Inc.
Zee-Zee. Angelface I: A Man of My Dreams or Is He from God's Hands. 2010. 68p. pap. 10.49 *(978-1-4490-9674-8(3))* AuthorHouse.
Zenon, Candie. My Precious Wedding Gift. 2008. (ENG.). 64p. pap. 7.99 *(978-1-59979-091-6(2)*, Creation Hse.) Charisma Media.
Zerubbabel Press, frwd. The Spontaneous You. 2007. 128p. per. 8.00 *(978-0-9662957-6-4(5))* Zerubbabel Pr.
Zigan, Mike. Ignition. 2007. 344p. (ENG.). 27.99 *(978-1-60266-886-7(8))*; per. 17.99 *(978-1-60266-885-0(X))* Xulon Pr., Inc.
Ziglar, Zig. Actitud de Vuelo: Momentos de Inspiracion para una Vida Mejor, 1 vol. 2007. (SPA., Illus.). 250p. (gr. 11). per. 9.99 *(978-987-557-133-4(4))* Vida Pubs.
Ziglar, Zig & Reighard, Ike. The One Year Daily Insights with Zig Ziglar. 2009. (ENG.). 384p. pap. 15.99 *(978-1-4143-1941-4(X))* Tyndale Hse. Pubs.
Zimmer, Matt, compiled by. Faith Intersections: Christian Listens To... a Muslim a Scientologist a Buddhist a Mormon & Others. 2010. (ENG.). 128p. pap. 13.99 *(978-0-8341-2467-7(X), 9780834124677)* Beacon Hill Pr. of Kansas City.
Zimmerman, David A. Deliver Us from Me-Ville. 2008. (ENG.). 224p. pap. 13.99 *(978-1-4347-0009-4(7))* Cook, David C.
Zimmerman, Frank. A Painful Journey. 2007. 90p. per. 9.99 *(978-1-59886-918-7(3))* Tate Publishing & Enterprises, LLC.
Zimmerman, L. M. For Love's Sake. 2007. (ENG.). 134p. 35.95 *(978-0-548-06081-0(9))* Kessinger Publishing, LLC.
Zimmermann, Patricia. Prayer Is Power. 2008. 232p. pap. 15.99 *(978-1-60791-042-8(X))* Xulon Pr., Inc.
Zmirak, John. The Bad Catholic's Guide to the Seven Deadly Sins: A Vital Look at Virtue & Vice, with Quizzes & Activities for Saintly Self-Improvement. 2010. (Bad Catholic's Guides). (ENG.). 240p. pap. 14.95 *(978-0-8245-2585-9(X))* Crossroad Publishing Co., The.
Zompetti, Cindy. Cradling My Heart. 2007. (ENG.). 96p. per. 11.99 *(978-1-4141-0871-1(0))* Pleasant Word.
Zondervan. Activate Your Mind, 1 vol. 2011. (SPA.). 112p. pap. 8.99 ***(978-987-557-324-6(8))*** Zondervan.
—Agudeza: Sharpen Your Potential, 1 vol. 2011. (Lidere Ser.). (SPA.). 144p. pap. 8.99 ***(978-0-8297-6160-3(8))*** Vida Pubs.
Zondervan Publishing Staff. Four Views on Moving Beyond the Bible to Theology. Meadors, Gary T., ed. 2009. (Counterpoints: Bible & Theology Ser.). (ENG.). 384p. pap. 19.99 *(978-0-310-27655-5(1))* Zondervan.
—Manual: The Bible for Men, 1 vol. 2009. (ENG.). 1632p. lthr. 26.99 *(978-0-310-94101-9(6))*; lthr. 59.99 *(978-0-310-94102-6(4))*; lthr. 36.99 *(978-0-310-94099-9(0))* Zondervan.
—Streams for Teens: Thoughts on Seeking Gods Will & Direction, 1 vol. Cowman, L. B. & Reimann, Jim, eds. 2009. (ENG.). 128p. 14.99 *(978-0-310-28311-9(6))* Zondervan.
—True Identity: The Bible for Women - Becoming Who You Are in Christ. 2009. (ENG.). 1824p. lthr. 59.99 *(978-0-310-93944-3(5))*; lthr. 36.99 *(978-0-310-93891-0(0))* Zondervan.
—1001 Quotations That Connect, 1 vol. Larson, Craig Brian & Lowery, Brian, eds. 2009. (ENG.). 368p. pap. 24.99 *(978-0-310-28036-1(2))* Zondervan.
Zondervan Publishing Staff & Stanley, Charles F. Como Manejar el Temor: Confident Living in Anxious Times, 1 vol. 2006. (Guided Growth Booklets Spanish Ser.). (SPA.). 24p. pap. 1.99 *(978-0-8297-4651-8(X))* Vida Pubs.
Zuck, Roy, ed. Vital Theological Issues: Examining Enduring Issues of Theology. 2006. (Vital Issues Ser.). 232p. pap. 25.00 *(978-1-59752-681-4(9)*, Wipf and Stock) Wipf & Stock Pubs.
Zukeran, Pat. World Religions Through a Christian Worldview. 2008. 300p. pap. 17.99 *(978-1-60647-068-8(X))* Xulon Pr., Inc.
Zulu, Sika. Emotional Makeover. 2006. pap. 13.99 *(978-1-59781-829-2(1))* Xulon Pr., Inc.
Zundel, Veronica. Crying for the Light: Bible Readings & Reflections for Living with Depression, 1 vol. 2009. (ENG.). 144p. pap. 10.99 *(978-0-8254-4165-3(X))* Kregel Pubns.
Zwyghuizen, Helen. Daily Choices for Christ. 2007. (ENG.). 21.99 *(978-1-60034-947-8(1))*; pap. 13.99 *(978-1-60034-943-0(9))* Xulon Pr., Inc.
5 & 10 minute sermons from the word of God [2006]________________. 2007. per. 7.00 *(978-0-9792839-0-1(6))* Word Of God Ministry.
6 short messages to the hip-hop generation from the word of God____. 2007. (YA). 7.00 *(978-0-9792839-1-8(4))* Word Of God Ministry.
40 dayz,40 nightz & a Wake Up. 2007. per. 12.99 *(978-0-9794759-1-7(0))* lifechange publishing.
52 Exciting Discipleship Studies for Single Adults B. *(978-0-7673-9380-5(5))* LifeWay Christian Resources.
52 Exciting Discipleship Studies for Single Adults, Level B. *(978-0-7673-9382-9(1))* LifeWay Christian Resources.
Las 95 tesis de Martin Lutero y la Confesion de Augsburgo.Tr. of Luther's 95 Theses & the Augsburg Confession. (SPA.). 4.99 *(978-0-7586-0620-4(6))* Concordia Publishing Hse.
2003 (Guide) Mission 2 Auxiliary. *(978-1-58942-116-5(7))* R.H. Boyd Publishing Corp.

CHRISTIAN LIFE—ANECDOTES

Acuff, Jonathan. Stuff Christians Like, 1 vol. 2010. (ENG.). 224p. pap. 12.99 *(978-0-310-31994-8(3))* Zondervan.
A'Hearn, Blair J. The God You've Always Wanted to Believe In, 1 vol. 2010. 66p. pap. 16.95 *(978-1-60672-589-4(0))* PublishAmerica, Inc.
Babb, Martin. It's a Dog Eat Dog World & Cats Are Waiting Tables: 100 Clever, Funny, & Insightful Lessons for Life. 2006. (ENG., Illus.). 256p. pap. 12.99 *(978-1-4165-3592-8(6)*, Howard Bks.) Howard Books.
Bailey, Martha. It Hurts but I'm Okay. 2012. pap. ***(978-0-914520-54-2(7))*** Insight Pr.
Bell, James Stuart & Townsend, Susan B. A Cup of Comfort Book of Prayer: Stories & Reflections That Bring You Closer to God. 2007. (ENG.). 336p. 9.95 *(978-1-59869-345-4(X))* Adams Media Corp.
Berken, Kathleen C. Walking on a Rolling Deck: Life on the Ark. 2008. pap. 14.95 *(978-0-8146-1861-5(8))* Liturgical Pr.
Blomstrand, Doreen Wright & Koshar, Barbara J. Growing Toward God: Life Lessons Inspired by the Wonderful Words of Kids, 1 vol. 2008. 128p. pap. 10.99 *(978-0-8254-4186-8(2))* Kregel Pubns.
Boreham, F. W. All the Blessings of Life: The Best Stories of F. W. Boreham. 2007. (ENG.). 288p. pap. 18.00 *(978-0-9790334-1-4(1))* Broadbanks, John Publishing.
Boyle, Gregory. Tattoos on the Heart: The Power of Boundless Compassion. (ENG.). 240p. 2011. pap. 14.00 *(978-1-4391-5315-4(9))* 2010. 25.00 *(978-1-4391-5302-4(7))* Free Pr. (Free Pr.).
—Tatuajes en el Corazon: El Poder de la Compasión Sin Límite. Ochoa, Santiago, tr. 2010. (SPA & ENG.). 256p. pap. 16.00 *(978-1-4391-6098-5(8)*, Free Pr.) Free Pr.
Bruno, Bonnie. When God Steps In: Stories of Everyday Grace. 2007. (Illus.). 256p. per. 12.99 *(978-0-7847-2066-0(5))* Standard Publishing.
Callaway, Phil. Making Life Rich Without Any Money: Stories of Finding Joy in What Really Matters. 2009. 256p. pap. 12.99 *(978-0-7369-2631-7(3))* Harvest Hse. Pubs.
Canfield, Jack, et al. Chicken Soup for the Soul: Answered Prayers: 101 Stories of Hope, Miracles, Faith, Divine Intervention, & the Power of Prayer. 2011. (ENG.). 384p. pap. 14.95 *(978-1-935096-76-4(1))* Chicken Soup for the Soul Publishing, LLC.
Conley, Joseph F. Reflections: Musings of an Old Missionary. 2009. pap. 15.99 *(978-1-60791-574-4(X))* Xulon Pr., Inc.
Cook, William. It Happened in Brazil. 2007. pap. 10.99 *(978-1-60034-958-4(7))* Xulon Pr., Inc.
Dant, Doris R., ed. Adventures of the Soul: The Best Creative Non-fiction from BYU Studies. 2009. (Illus.). 250p. pap. *(978-0-8425-2739-2(7)*, Brigham Young Univ. Studies) Brigham Young Univ.
Encina, David. Whosoever: Finding Christ in the Book of Proverbs. 2010. pap. 23.99 *(978-1-61663-015-7(9))* Tate Publishing & Enterprises, LLC.
Fitzsimmons, Thomas C. Revisiting the Footprints in the Sand, 1 vol. 2010. 140p. pap. 24.95 *(978-1-4489-5775-0(3))* PublishAmerica, Inc.
Frisina, Susan Weston. Soul Food: Encouraging Words for the Hungry Heart. 2009. 300p. pap. 18.99 *(978-1-61579-079-1(9))* Xulon Pr., Inc.
Gentry, G. T. A Bulletproof Life. 2008. 172p. pap. 14.99 *(978-1-60647-816-5(8))* Xulon Pr., Inc.
Gray, Alice. Treasures for Women Who Hope. l.t. ed. 2007. (Walker Large Print Ser.). (ENG.). 256p. per. 16.95 *(978-1-59415-157-6(1)*, Walker Large Print) Cengage Gale.
Guideposts Associates Staff, contrib. by. Time-Out: Stories to Comfort & Inspire. 2008. (ENG.). 288p. pap. 14.99 *(978-0-8249-4756-9(8)*, Guideposts) Ideals Pubns.
Gulley, Philip. For Everything a Season: Simple Musings on Living Well. 2007. (ENG.). 224p. per. 11.95 *(978-0-06-125218-1(2)*, HarperOne) HarperCollins Pubs.
—Front Porch Tales: Warm-Hearted Stories of Family, Faith, Laughter, & Love. 2007. (ENG.). 176p. pap. 11.99 *(978-0-06-125230-3(1)*, HarperOne) HarperCollins Pubs.
—Hometown Tales: Recollections of Kindness, Peace, & Joy. 2007. (ENG.). 224p. per. 11.99 *(978-0-06-125229-7(8)*, HarperOne) HarperCollins Pubs.

—Porch Talk: Stories of Decency, Common Sense, & Other Endangered Species. (ENG.). 2009. 176p. pap. 13.99 *(978-0-06-168982-6(3)*, HarperOne) 2007. 176p. 15.95 *(978-0-06-073658-3(5)*, HarperOne) 2007. 168p. pap. 15.95 *(978-0-06-134023-9(5)*, HarperLuxe) HarperCollins Pubs.

Hamilton, Nancy. Marshmallows in the Sky: Twenty-Three Articles on Christianity Based on Life Experiences. 2010. 108p. 28.95 *(978-1-4497-0209-0(0))*; pap. 11.95 *(978-1-4497-0207-6(4))* Author Solutions, Inc. (WestBow Pr.).

Heim, Susan M. & Talcott, Karen C. Chicken Soup for the Soul - Devotional Stories for Tough Times: 101 Daily Devotions to Comfort, Encourage, & Support You in Times of Need. 2011. (ENG.). 400p. pap. 14.95 *(978-1-935096-74-0(5))* Chicken Soup for the Soul Publishing, LLC.

Hill, Jim. To Be Made Whole. 2007. 216p. per. 14.95 *(978-1-931178-16-7(X))* Vision Publishing.

Hollingsworth, Mary. Christmas Miracles. 2008. (ENG., Illus.). 240p. 17.99 *(978-0-8249-4742-2(8)*, GuidepostsBooks) Ideals Pubns.

Hollingsworth, Mary, ed. And God Said... Let There Be Laughter! Humorous & Inspiring Stories, Quotes & Quips. 2008. (ENG.). 256p. per. 14.99 *(978-0-8249-4736-1(3)*, GuidepostsBooks) Ideals Pubns.

Humes, James C. Soul Shakers: Inspiring Stories from a Presidential Speechwriter. 2007. 112p. per. 11.00 *(978-0-687-49125-4(8)*, Dimensions For Living) Abingdon Pr.

Johnson, Bill & Clark, Randy. Amazed by the Power of God: (Power Compendium, Vol. 1) 2009. pap. 14.99 *(978-0-7684-2755-4(X))* Destiny Image Pubs.

Kennedy, Nancy. Lipstick Grace: Glimpses of Life, Love, & the Quest for the Perfect Lip Gloss. 2007. (ENG.). 256p. per. 12.99 *(978-1-59052-767-2(4)*, Multnomah) Doubleday Religious Publishing Group, The.

Lindquist, N. J. & Nelles, Wendy Elaine, eds. Hot Apple Cider: Words to Stir the Heart & Warm the Soul. 2008. (ENG., Illus.). 296p. 15.99 *(978-0-9784963-0-2(2))* That's Life! Communications CAN. Dist: STL Distribution North America.

Love, Valerie. God Speaks to Me. 2011. (ENG.). 288p. 6.99 *(978-1-60162-812-1(9))* Urban Bks.

McCree, George W. Treasure Chest. 2011. (Illus.). 306p. pap. 18.99 ***(978-1-61379-466-1(5))*** Xulon Pr., Inc.

McSweeney, Margaret, compiled by. Pearl Girls: Encountering Grit, Experiencing Grace. 2009. (ENG.). 192p. pap. 12.99 *(978-0-8024-5862-9(9))* Moody Pubs.

Messecar, Cathy. The Stained Glass Pickup: Glimpses of God's Uncommon Wisdom. 2006. 128p. 10.99 *(978-0-9767790-3-2(X)*, Leafwood Pubs.) Abilene Christian Univ. Pr.

Milton, Michael & Milton, Michael A. Small Things, Big Things: Inspiring Stories of Everyday Grace. 2009. pap. *(978-1-59638-145-2(0))* P & R Publishing.

O'Bryon, Jim. I Fail to Miss Your Point. 2007. 488p. pap. 27.99 *(978-1-60034-888-4(2))* Xulon Pr., Inc.

O'Leary, Daniel J. Already Within: Divining the Hidden Spring. 2007. (ENG.). 144p. per. 22.95 *(978-1-85607-575-6(3))* Columba Pr. IRL. Dist: Dufour Editions, Inc.

Olsen, Judy C., compiled by. Angels Round About: True Stories of the Lord's Tender Mercies. 2010. 140p. pap. *(978-1-59811-948-0(6))* Covenant Communications.

Osteen, Joel. The Christmas Spirit: Memories of Family, Friends, & Faith. 2010. (ENG., Illus.). 160p. 15.99 *(978-1-4391-9833-9(0)*, Free Pr.) Free Pr.

Outcalt, Todd. The Ultimate Christian Living: Faith & Fellowship Celebrated Through Stories & Photos. 2010. (Ultimate Ser.). (ENG., Illus.). 328p. pap. 14.95 *(978-0-7573-1453-7(8))* Health Communications, Inc.

Pierce, Chonda. Roadkill on the Highway to Heaven, 1 vol. 2006. (ENG.). 208p. pap. 14.99 *(978-0-310-23527-9(8))* Zondervan.

Rodgers, Anthony. How God Restored My Life. 2007. 80p. per. 10.95 *(978-1-4327-1049-1(4))* Outskirts Pr., Inc.

Segraves, Judy. The Sun Still Shines: A Collection of 52 More Short Stories for Enjoyment, Encouragement, & Enrichment. 2007. pap. 13.99 *(978-1-56722-717-8(1))* Word Aflame Pr.

Smith, Michael W. Friends are Friends Forever, 0 vols. 2009. 256p. pap. 13.99 *(978-0-7852-9746-8(4))* Nelson, Thomas Inc.

Smith, T. A. Getting Spiritually Naked, 1 vol. 2010. 48p. pap. 16.95 *(978-1-4489-4397-5(3))* PublishAmerica, Inc.

Sonnenberg, Alaine. Shine On. 2010. pap. 10.99 *(978-1-61663-826-9(5))* Tate Publishing & Enterprises, LLC.

Steiger, Brad & Steiger, Sherry Hansen. Santa Miracles: 50 True Stories that Celebrate the Most Magical Time of the Year. 2009. (ENG.). 256p. pap. 12.95 *(978-1-59869-612-7(2))* Adams Media Corp.

Szymanski, Helen, ed. Christmas Traditions: True Stories That Celebrate the Spirit of the Season. 2009. (ENG.). 288p. pap. 10.95 *(978-1-59869-838-1(9))* Adams Media Corp.

Walker, Joseph W., III. Life Between Sundays: Living Your Life Outside Church. 2009. pap. 16.99 *(978-0-7684-2829-2(7))* Destiny Image Pubs.

We Hear the Christmas Angels: True Stories of Their Presence. 2006. (Illus.). 257p. 14.95 *(978-0-8249-4704-0(5))* Ideals Pubns.

Weaver, Andrew J. & Stapleton, Carolyn L., eds. Wells of Wisdom: Grandparents & Spiritual Journeys. 2010. 160p. pap. 18.00 *(978-1-60899-235-5(7)*, Resource Pubns.) Wipf & Stock Pubs.

Webster, Patti S. It Happened in Church: Stories of Humor from the Pulpit to the Pews. I.t. ed. 2009. 333p. 30.95 *(978-1-4104-1186-0(9))* Thorndike Pr.

Witas, Mark. Living Out Loud. 2011. *(978-0-8280-2450-1(2))* Review & Herald Publishing Assn.

Wood, Gail. Saved Twice. 2009. 92p. pap. 10.99 *(978-1-61579-434-8(4))* Xulon Pr., Inc.

Xulon Press Staff. How I Met My True Love: Inspiring Real-Life Stories of How God Unites. 2007. (ENG.). 29.95 *(978-1-60266-029-8(8))*; pap. 16.99 *(978-1-60266-028-1(X))* Xulon Pr., Inc.

—Praise Reports: Inspiring REAL-LIFE STORIES of How GOD WORKS. 2007. 24.99 *(978-1-60034-852-5(1))*; (ENG.). pap. 16.99 *(978-1-60034-963-8(3))* Xulon Pr., Inc.

CHRISTIAN LIFE—ANGLICAN AUTHORS

Anglican Church of Canada, Primate's Theological Commission, contrib. by. Turning to God: Anglicans Talk about Sin, Grace, & the Christian Life, Vol. 2. (Wrestling with God Ser.: Vol. 2). (Illus.). 106p. pap. 12.95 *(978-1-55126-344-1(0)*, 1631) Anglican Bk. Ctr. CAN. Dist: Forward Movement Pubns.

Anglican Church of Canada, Primate's Theological Commission Staff, contrib. by. Meeting God Vol. 3: Anglicans Talk about Creation, the Trinity, & the Church. 177p. pap. 21.95 *(978-1-55126-345-8(9)*, 1802) Anglican Bk. Ctr. CAN. Dist: Forward Movement Pubns.

Black, Vicki K. Welcome to Anglican Spiritual Traditions. 2010. E-Book *(978-0-8192-2722-5(6)*, Morehouse Publishing) Church Publishing, Inc.

Coverdale, Miles & Coverdale, Miles, Jr. Remains of Myles Coverdale, Bishop of Exeter: Containing Prologues to the Translation of the Bible, Treatise on Death, Hope of the Faithful, Exhortation to the Carrying of Christ's Cross, Exposition upon the Twenty-Third Psalm, Confutation of the Treatise of John Standish, Defense of a Certain Poor Christian Man, Letters, Ghostly Psalms & Spiritual Songs. Pearson, George, ed. 2007. (Parker Society: Ser.). 641p. pap. 62.00 *(978-1-55635-066-5(X)*, Wipf and Stock) Wipf & Stock Pubs.

Cowdell, Scott. Abiding Faith: Christianity Beyond Certainty, Anxiety, & Violence. 2009. 242p. pap. 27.00 *(978-1-60608-223-2(X)*, Cascade Bks.) Wipf & Stock Pubs.

Divorced Christians & the Love of God. 2.00 *(978-0-687-85280-2(3))* Abingdon Pr.

Edwards, Tilden. Embracing the Call to Spiritual Depth: Gifts for Contemplative Living. 2010. 176p. pap. 16.95 *(978-0-8091-4627-7(4))* Paulist Pr.

Frost, Bede. Art of Mental Prayer. 2007. 292p. per. *(978-1-4067-8978-2(X)*, Pierides Pr.) Read Bks.

Hein, David & Henery, Charles R., eds. Spiritual Counsel in the Anglican Tradition. 2010. 194p. pap. 22.00 *(978-1-55635-419-9(3))* Wipf & Stock Pubs.

Law, William. A Serious Call to a Devout & Holy Life: Adapted to the State & Condition of All Orders of Christians, 1 vol. 2009. (ENG.). 325p. 14.95 *(978-1-59856-385-6(8))* Hendrickson Pubs. Marketing, LLC.

—The Works of the Reverend William Law V2. 2007. (ENG.). 196p. 37.95 *(978-0-548-09168-5(4))* Kessinger Publishing, LLC.

—The Works of the Reverend William Law V5. 2007. (ENG.). 192p. 37.95 *(978-0-548-09171-5(4))* Kessinger Publishing, LLC.

—The Works of the Reverend William Law V6. 2007. (ENG.). 268p. 42.95 *(978-0-548-09172-2(2))* Kessinger Publishing, LLC.

—The Works of the Reverend William Law V7. 2007. (ENG.). 212p. 39.95 *(978-0-548-09173-9(0))* Kessinger Publishing, LLC.

Morisy, Ann. Borrowing from the Future: A Faith-Based Approach to Inter-Generational Equity. 2011. (ENG.). 240p. pap. 24.95 *(978-1-4411-2536-1(1))* Continuum International Publishing Group, Ltd. GBR. Dist: National Bk. Network.

Newman, John Henry. Life's Purpose: Wisdom from John Henry Newman. 2010. pap. 6.95 *(978-0-8198-4537-7(7))* Pauline Bks. & Media.

Sedgwick, Timothy F. The Christian Moral Life: Practices of Piety. 2008. 176p. pap. 20.00 *(978-1-59627-100-5(0)*, Seabury Bks.) Church Publishing, Inc.

Sumner, George R., et al. In Spirit & in Truth: The Challenge of Discernment for Canadian Anglicans Today. 2009. 192p. pap. *(978-1-57383-443-8(2))* Regent College Publishing.

Sweeney, Jon M. The Lure of Saints: A Protestant Experience of Catholic Tradition. 2006. (Illus.). 237p. per. 15.95 *(978-1-55725-506-8(7))* Paraclete Pr., Inc.

Taylor, John V. Matter of Life & Death. 2012. 88p. ***(978-0-334-00977-1(4)***, SCM Pr.) Hymns Ancient & Modern Ltd.

Thomas, Owen C. Christian Life & Practice: Anglican Essays. 2008. 162p. pap. 19.00 *(978-1-55635-842-5(3))* Wipf & Stock Pubs.

Westcott, Brooke Foss. The Christian Life, Manifold & One: Six Sermons Preached In. 2007. (ENG.). 84p. per. 17.95 *(978-1-4304-4583-8(1))* Kessinger Publishing, LLC.

Williams, Leslie. Night Wrestling, 0 vols. 2008. 208p. pap. 11.99 *(978-1-59554-833-7(5))* Nelson, Thomas Inc.

Winner, Lauren F. Still: Notes on a Mid-Faith Crisis. 2012. (ENG.). 256p. 24.99 ***(978-0-06-176811-8(1)***, HarperOne) HarperCollins Pubs.

Wright, N. T. After You Believe: Why Christian Character Matters. 2010. (ENG.). 304p. 24.99 *(978-0-06-173055-9(6)*, HarperOne) HarperCollins Pubs.

—Small Faith — Great God. 2010. (ENG.). 176p. 18.00 *(978-0-8308-3833-2(3)*, IVP Bks.) InterVarsity Pr.

CHRISTIAN LIFE—BAPTIST AUTHORS

Bisagno, John R. Wisdom for Life: Keys to Finishing Well. 2012. (Experience the Life Ser.). 176p. pap. 14.99 ***(978-1-61747-180-3(1))*** NavPress Publishing Group.

Blackaby, Henry. Experiencing the Cross. 2010. 176p. pap. 3.00 net. *(978-1-60142-376-4(4)*, Multnomah) Doubleday Religious Publishing Group, The.

Blackaby, Henry & Blackaby, Norman C. El Llamado de Dios: El Propósito de Dios Para Todo Creyente. 2010. (ENG.). 192p. pap. 11.99 *(978-1-59669-248-0(0))* New Hope Pubs.

Buford, Thomas. Ambushed on the Road to Glory. 11.00 *(978-0-687-82112-9(6))* Abingdon Pr.

Crawley, Winston. God's Purpose for His People. 2007. 112p. pap. 14.95 *(978-0-929292-34-2(0))* Hannibal Bks.

Crowns, Casting & Hall, Mark. Your Own Jesus: A God Insistent on Making It Personal, 1 vol. 2009. (ENG.). 176p. (YA). pap., stu. ed. 9.99 *(978-0-310-31890-3(4))* Zondervan.

Crowns, Casting & Hall, Mark L. Your Own Jesus: A God Insistent on Making It Personal, 1 vol. 2009. (ENG.). 256p. pap. 16.99 *(978-0-310-29332-3(4))* Zondervan.

Dutton, Anne. Selected Spiritual Writings of Anne Dutton: Eighteenth-Century, British-Baptist, Woman Theologian: Volume 4: Theological Works. 2007. (Baptists Ser.). (Illus.). 321p. 50.00 *(978-0-88146-029-2(X))* Mercer Univ. Pr.

Ellis, Jimmie A. Coping with Anger. 2007. 48p. per. 9.99 *(978-1-59755-147-2(3)*, Advantage Inspirational) Advantage Bks.

—Coping with Disappointment. 2007. 48p. per. 9.99 *(978-1-59755-146-5(5)*, Advantage Inspirational) Advantage Bks.

—Coping with Guilt. 2007. 48p. per. 9.99 *(978-1-59755-148-9(1)*, Advantage Inspirational) Advantage Bks.

—Coping with Loneliness. 2007. 48p. per. 9.99 *(978-1-59755-149-6(X)*, Advantage Inspirational) Advantage Bks.

—Coping with Overcoming Rejection. 2007. 48p. per. 9.99 *(978-1-59755-145-8(7)*, Advantage Inspirational) Advantage Bks.

—Coping with Promises, Principles & Problems. 2007. 48p. per. 9.99 *(978-1-59755-139-7(2)*, Advantage Inspirational) Advantage Bks.

—Coping with Rejection. 2007. 48p. per. 9.99 *(978-1-59755-144-1(9)*, Advantage Inspirational) Advantage Bks.

—Coping with the Fear Factor. 2007. 48p. per. 9.99 *(978-1-59755-140-3(6)*, Advantage Inspirational) Advantage Bks.

Falwell, Jonathan. One Great Truth: Finding Your Answers to Life. (ENG.). 208p. 2011. pap. 14.99 *(978-1-4516-4184-4(2))* 2008. 20.99 *(978-1-4165-6302-0(4))* Howard Books. (Howard Bks.).

Flynn, Leslie B. The Power of Christlike Living. 2011. 126p. 40.95 ***(978-1-258-08472-1(4))*** Literary Licensing, LLC.

Graham, Billy. Peace with God: How to Choose in the Hour of Decision. 2011. 222p. 44.95 ***(978-1-258-09851-3(2))*** Literary Licensing, LLC.

Knight, Allan & Schroeder, Gordon H. New Life: Six Studies for New Baptists. 3rd rev. ed. 2009. 72p. pap. 7.00 *(978-0-8170-1563-3(9))* Judson Pr.

Meyer, F. b. The Secret of Guidance. 2011. 80p. ***(978-1-84902-404-4(9))*** Benediction Classics.

—The Secret of Guidance. 2007. 132p. per. 9.95 *(978-1-60206-675-5(2))* Cosimo, Inc.

—The Secret of Guidance, 1 vol. 2010. (Moody Classics Ser.). (ENG.). 128p. pap. 7.99 *(978-0-8024-5454-6(2))* Moody Pubs.

—The Secret of Guidance. 2008. 76p. pap. 9.49 *(978-1-60459-583-3(3))* Wilder Pubns., Ltd.

Meyer, F. b. & Meyer, F. B. The Secret of Guidance. 2011. 88p. pap. 9.99 ***(978-1-61203-259-7(1))*** Bottom of the Hill Publishing.

Mohler, R. Albert, Jr. & Mohler Jr., R. Albert. Words from the Fire: Hearing the Voice of God in the 10 Commandments. 2009. (ENG.). 208p. 22.99 *(978-0-8024-5488-1(7))* Moody Pubs.

Moore, Beth. Believing God. 2008. (Playaway Adult Nonfiction Ser.). 54.99 *(978-1-60640-585-7(3))* Findaway World, LLC.

—Believing God. 2007. pap. *(978-1-59328-112-0(9))* Graham, Billy Evangelistic Assn.

—Breaking Free: Making Liberty in Christ a Reality in Life. I.t. ed. 2006. (Walker Large Print Ser.). (ENG.). 440p. per. 17.95 *(978-1-59415-143-9(1)*, Walker Large Print) Cengage Gale.

—Breaking Free: Making Liberty in Christ a Reality in Life. 2009. (ENG., Illus.). 239p. pap. 21.00 *(978-1-4158-6802-7(6))* LifeWay Christian Resources.

Moore, Beth & McCleskey, Dale. Breaking Free: Making Liberty in Christ a Reality in Life. 2009. (ENG.). 32p. pap. 9.75 *(978-1-4158-6803-4(4))* LifeWay Christian Resources.

Rainer, Thom S. & Rainer, Art. Simple Life: Time, Relationships, Money, God, 1 vol. 2009. 336p. 19.99 *(978-0-8054-4886-3(1))*, B&H Bks.) B&H Publishing Group.

Smith SGS, Bro. Spurgeon Library Vol 1. 2010. (ENG.). 382p. pap. *(978-0-9841731-6-7(1))* Revelation Insight Publishing Co.

—Spurgeon Library Vol 2. 2010. (ENG.). 380p. pap. *(978-0-9841731-7-4(X))* Revelation Insight Publishing Co.

Smith, William P. Living in a Dangerous World: Moving from Fear to Faith. 2011. (ENG.). 24p. 3.99 ***(978-1-936768-42-4(9))*** New Growth Pr.

Spurgeon, C. H. (Charles Haddon). Feathers for Arrows; or, Illustrations from My Note Book by C H Spurgeon. 2006. 292p. per. 23.99 *(978-1-4255-2749-5(3))* MPublishing.

Spurgeon, Charles H. God's Joy in Your Heart. 2009. Orig. Title: Words of Cheer. (ENG.). mass mkt. 7.99 *(978-0-60374-185-9(2))* Whitaker Hse.

Stanley, Charles F. Developing a Servant's Heart: Give of Yourself & Receive from God, 0 vols. 2008. (Life Principles Study Ser.). 128p. per. 9.99 *(978-1-4185-2811-9(0))* Nelson, Thomas Inc.

—How to Reach Your Full Potential for God. I.t. ed. 2011. (ENG.). 416p. pap. 17.99 *(978-1-59415-357-0(4)*, Large Print Pr.) Thorndike Pr.

—How to Reach Your Full Potential for God Study Guide, 0 vols. 2009. 112p. pap. 9.99 *(978-1-4002-0272-0(8))* Nelson, Thomas Inc.

—Sharing the Gift of Encouragement: Being Blessed by Blessing Others, 0 vols. 2008. (Life Principles Study Ser.). 128p. per. 9.99 *(978-1-4185-2812-6(9))* Nelson, Thomas Inc.

Tolbert, Malcolm. Walking with the Lord: The Relevance of First John to the Contemporary Christian Life. 2008. 124p. pap. 15.00 *(978-1-55635-945-3(4)*, Wipf and Stock) Wipf & Stock Pubs.

Watson, Joann Ford, compiled by. Selected Spiritual Writings of Anne Dutton: Eighteenth-Century, British-Baptist, Woman Theologian: Volume 6: Various Works. 2009. (Baptists Ser.). (Illus.). 320p. 50.00 *(978-0-88146-154-1(7))* Mercer Univ. Pr.

Watson, Joann Ford, ed. Selected Spiritual Writings of Anne Dutton: Eighteenth-Century, British-Baptist, Woman Theologian: Volume 5 Miscellaneous Correspondence. 2007. 360p. 50.00 *(978-0-88146-053-7(2))* Mercer Univ. Pr.

White, Reggie. God's Playbook, 0 vols. 2008. 208p. pap. 14.99 *(978-0-7852-9684-3(0))* Nelson, Thomas Inc.

CHRISTIAN LIFE—BIBLIOGRAPHY

Barnes, Howell. Is Anything Too Hard for God? 2007. pap. 9.99 *(978-1-60477-321-7(9))* Xulon Pr., Inc.

Beeke, Joel R. Contagious Christian Living. 2009. pap. *(978-1-60178-079-9(6))* Reformation Heritage Bks.

Covert, Henry G. Spiritual Reflections: A Journey Through the Scriptures, 1 vol. 2008. 200p. 39.95 *(978-0-313-35901-9(6)*, C35901, Praeger Pubs.) Greenwood Publishing Group, Inc.

Duncan, Michael. Starting Out: A Study Guide for New Believers. 2010. 192p. pap. 16.99 *(978-1-4141-1780-5(9))* Pleasant Word.

Kilgore, Kay Wheeler & Countryman, J. God's Promises for Your Every Need, 0 vols. 2006. 352p. im. lthr. 9.97 *(978-1-4041-0411-2(9))* Nelson, Thomas Inc.

Shirer, Priscilla, et al. Anointed, Transformed, Redeemed: A Study of David. 2008. (Illus.). 148p. pap. 18.00 *(978-1-4158-6585-9(X))* LifeWay Christian Resources.

CHRISTIAN LIFE—BIOGRAPHY

see Christian Biography

CHRISTIAN LIFE—CATHOLIC AUTHORS

Apostoli, Andrew. Walk Humbly with Your God: Simple Steps to a Virtuous Life. 2006. 184p. per. 12.99 *(978-0-86716-759-7(9)*, Servant Bks.) Franciscan Media.

Arias, Miguel & Perez-Rodriguez, Arturo. Saints of the Americas: Conversations with 30 Saints from 15 Countries. 2007. (ENG., Illus.). 312p. per. 13.95 *(978-0-8294-2480-5(6))* Loyola Pr.

Barry, William A. Changed Heart, Changed World: The Transforming Freedom of Friendship with God. 2011. (ENG.). 208p. pap. 14.95 *(978-0-8294-3303-6(1))* Loyola Pr.

Basile, Alex. The Complete Christian: A Guide to Living. 2010. *(978-0-8189-1325-9(8))* St Pauls.

Bauer, Gerhard. Three Minutes for the Soul: Reflections to Start the Day. 2007. (7 x 4 A Meditation a Day for a Span of Four Weeks Ser.). 69p. per. 8.95 *(978-1-56548-275-3(1))* New City Pr.

Benedict XVI, pseud. Following Christ. 2009. (Spiritual Thoughts Ser.). 132p. pap. 6.95 *(978-1-60137-056-3(3))* United States Conference of Catholic Bishops.

Beyer, Richard J. The Catholic Heart Day by Day: Uplifting Stories for Courageous Living. 2008. (ENG.). 348p. (gr. 13). pap. 16.95 *(978-1-55725-600-3(4))* Paraclete Pr., Inc.

Blondel, Maurice. Action: Essay on a Critique of Life & a Science of Practice. Blanchette, Oliva, tr. from FRE. 480p. 40.00 *(978-0-268-02177-1(5))* Univ. of Notre Dame Pr.

Bondi, Michele Elena. Your Teen Apostolate: Accepting & Sharing the Love of God. 2009. *(978-1-935356-06-6(2))* Wilderness Adventure Bks.

Bowman, Thea & Nutt, Maurice J. Thea Bowman: In My Own Words. 2009. 14.99 *(978-0-7648-1782-3(5))* Liguori Pubns.

Boylan, Eugene. Partnership with Christ: A Cistercian Retreat. 2008. xiii, 216p. pap. *(978-0-87907-016-8(1))* Cistercian Pubns., Inc.

Brother Lawrence. The Practice of the Presence of God. 2009. 50p. pap. 9.45 *(978-1-4385-1910-4(9)*, Book Jungle) Standard Pubns., Inc.

—The Practice of the Presence of God. 2009. 84p. pap. 9.95 *(978-0-578-00649-9(9))* Starving Artist Bks.

Brother, Lawrence. The Practice of the Presence of God. Edmonson, Robert, ed. 2010. (Paraclete Essentials Ser.). (ENG.). 164p. (gr. 13). pap. 14.99 *(978-1-55725-694-2(2))* Paraclete Pr., Inc.

—Practicing the Presence of God: Learn to Live Moment-by-Moment. Jones, Tony, ed. Edmonson, Robert J., tr. from FRE. 2007. (Christian Classics (Paraclete) Ser.). (ENG.). 140p. (YA). (gr. 13). per. 15.99 *(978-1-55725-465-8(6))* Paraclete Pr., Inc.

Brown, Richard C. Manage the Mess of Family Stress: Gospel Solutions for Everyday Life. 2011. *(978-0-7648-1983-4(6))* Liguori Pubns.

Byron, William J. Faith-Based Reflections on American Life. 2010. 208p. pap. 14.95 *(978-0-8091-4638-3(X))* Paulist Pr.

Camus, Jean-Pierre. The Spirit of St Francis de Sales. 2008. 432p. 30.99 *(978-0-554-32273-5(0))*; 32.99 *(978-0-554-22970-6(6))* BiblioBazaar.

—The Spirit of St Francis de Sales. 2007. 372p. per. *(978-1-4068-4190-9(0))* Echo Library.

Cantalamessa, Raniero. Contemplating the Trinity: The Path to the Abundant Christian Life. Daigle-Williamson, Marsha, tr. from ITA. 2007. (Illus.). 124p. per. 10.95 (978-1-59325-097-3(5)) Word Among Us Pr.
—Remember Jesus Christ: Responding to the Challenges of Faith in Our Time. Daigle-Williamson, Marsha, tr. from ITA. 2007. 149p. per. 11.95 (978-1-59325-109-3(2)) Word Among Us Pr.
Carroll, Kathleen. A Franciscan Christmas. 2010. (978-0-86716-986-7(9)) Franciscan Media.
Chittister, Joan. In Search of Belief. 2006. 216p. per. 16.95 (978-0-7648-1484-6(2)) Liguori Pubns.
Chittister, Joan. The Radical Christian Life: A Year with Saint Benedict. 2011. E-Book **(978-0-8146-3955-9(0))**; 160p. pap. 15.95 **(978-0-8146-3365-6(X))** Liturgical Pr.
Chittister, Joan & Kownacki, Mary Lou. In My Own Words. 2008. 14.99 (978-0-7648-1753-3(1)) Liguori Pubns.
Cirincione, Joseph A. Deep down Things: Essays on Catholic Culture. 2008. (ENG.). 206p. 68.50 (978-0-7391-2354-6(8)) Lexington Bks.
Cloutier, Annette. Praey to God. 2011. 728p. 34.99 **(978-1-4500-4238-3(4))**; pap. 23.99 **(978-1-4363-1555-5(7))** Xlibris Corp.
Coleman, Gerald D. & Pettingill, David M. Following in the Footsteps of Jesus. 2006. (Illus.). 92p. pap. 13.00 (978-1-59752-964-8(8), Wipf and Stock) Wipf & Stock Pubs.
Cook, Marshall. How to Handle Worry: A Catholic Approach. 2007. pap. 12.95 (978-0-8198-3390-7(8)) Pauline Bks. & Media.
—The How to Handle Worry Workbook: A Catholic Approach. 2007. 107p. pap. 9.95 (978-0-8198-3391-4(6)) Pauline Bks. & Media.
Crosby, Michael H. & Crosby, Michael. Finding Francis, Following Christ. 2008. 266p. per. 22.00 (978-1-57075-729-7(1)) Orbis Bks.
Dajczer, Tadeusz. The Gift of Faith. 3rd ed. 2006. 127p. pap. 14.95 (978-1-933314-13-6(3)) In the Arms of Mary Foundation.
Dalton, Denise & Berger, Mary J. Jesus Lives in Us, Grade 5. 260p. tchr. ed., spiral bd. 16.95 (978-0-8198-3932-9(9)) Pauline Bks. & Media.
D'Arcy, Brian. A Little Bit of Healing. 2011. (ENG.). 168p. pap. 21.95 (978-1-85607-688-3(1)) Columba Pr. IRL. Dist: Dufour Editions, Inc.
D'Avila-Latourrette, Victor-Antoine. Simply Living the Beatitudes. 2010. 144p. 15.99 (978-0-7648-1885-1(6)) Liguori Pubns.
de Vinck, Christopher. Fathering: Building the New Civilization of Love. (Little Mandate Books Ser.). (Illus.). 64p. pap. (978-0-921440-61-1(8)) Madonna Hse. Pubns.
DeGrocco, Joseph. Take & Eat: Living Eucharistically. 2010. 109p. pap. **(978-1-933066-12-7(1)**, Resurrection Pr.) Catholic Bk. Publishing Corp.
Denny, Randal Earl. Epidemic of Joy: A Study of Acts 13 To 16. 2007. 120p. pap. 15.00 (978-1-55635-386-4(3), Wipf and Stock) Wipf & Stock Pubs.
Doherty, Catherine. Living the Gospel Without Compromise. Orig. Title: The Gospel Without Compromise. 150p. pap. (978-0-921440-86-4(3)) Madonna Hse. Pubns.
Doherty, Catherine de Hueck. Catherine de Hueck Doherty: Essential Writings. Meconi, David, ed. 2009. (Modern Spiritual Masters Ser.). 192p. pap. 16.00 (978-1-57075-824-9(7)) Orbis Bks.
Doherty, Eddie. Getting to Know God. 145p. pap. (978-0-921440-47-5(2)) Madonna Hse. Pubns.
Donovan, Jean. The Seven Virtues: An Introduction to Catholic Life. 2007. (ENG.). 160p. pap. 19.95 (978-0-8245-2452-4(7), Herder & Herder) Crossroad Publishing Co., The.
Dooley, Mark. Why Be a Catholic? 2011. (ENG.). 136p. pap. 17.95 (978-1-4411-1042-8(9), Burns & Oates) Continuum International Publishing Group, Ltd. GBR. Dist: National Bk. Network.
Duffy, Regis A. Real Presence: Worship, Sacraments, & Commitment. 2010. 220p. pap. 24.00 (978-1-60899-610-0(7), Wipf and Stock) Wipf & Stock Pubs.
Ellard, Gerald & Burns, M. Anne. Service: Religion Essentials Series, Book 4. Schmidt, Austin G., ed. 2011. 382p. 53.95 **(978-1-258-08530-8(5))** Literary Licensing, LLC.
Enzler, Clarence J. My Other Self: Conversations with Christ on Living Your Faith. 2011. 256p. pap. 13.95 (978-0-87061-248-0(4), Christian Classic) Ave Maria Pr.
Fagin, Gerald M. Putting on the Heart of Christ: How the Spiritual Exercises Invite Us to a Virtuous Life. 2010. (ENG.). 248p. pap. 16.95 (978-0-8294-2905-3(0)) Loyola Pr.
Fielder, Brad. Destiny's Path. 2009. 216p. pap. 15.99 (978-1-60791-573-7(1)) Xulon Pr., Inc.
Fortune, Fr Stan C. F. R. & Fortuna, Stan. U Got 2 Love. 2009. (Illus.). 254p. pap. (978-1-59276-337-5(5)) Our Sunday Visitor, Publishing Div.
Francis, et al. The Writings of Francis of Assisi: Letters & Prayers. 2011. **(978-1-57659-293-9(6))**; E-Book **(978-1-57659-296-0(0))** Franciscan Institute Pubns.
Gallagher, Joseph. How to Survive Being Human. 2010. 160p. pap. 18.00 (978-1-60899-668-1(9), Wipf and Stock) Wipf & Stock Pubs.
Gallagher, Timothy M. Meditation & Contemplation: An Ignatian Guide to Prayer with Scripture. 2008. (ENG.). 112p. pap. 12.95 (978-0-8245-2488-3(8)) Crossroad Publishing Co., The.
Garber, Daniel. What Happens after Pascal's Wager: Living Faith & Rational Belief. 2009. (978-0-87462-176-1(3)) Marquette Univ. Pr.
Gendron, Mike. Two Ways to Eternity: Divine Accomplishment or Human Achievement? 2011. **(978-0-9826155-7-7(4))** Northampton Pr., The.
Goizueta, Roberto S. Christ Our Companion: A Liberation Theological Aesthetic. 2009. 160p. pap. 30.00 (978-1-57075-853-9(0)) Orbis Bks.
Goodier, Alban. The Good Galilean. 2009. Orig. Title: Jesus Christ, the Model of Manhood. pap. 11.95 (978-1-928832-60-7(1)) Sophia Institute Pr.
Gould, Meredith. The Catholic Home: Celebrations & Traditions for Holidays, Feast Days, & Every Day. 2006. (ENG.). 272p. pap. 11.99 (978-0-385-51907-6(9), Image) Doubleday Religious Publishing Group, The.
Grassi, Joseph A. Healing the Heart: The Transformational Power of Biblical Heart Imagery. 2010. 142p. pap. 18.00 (978-1-60899-380-2(9), Wipf and Stock) Wipf & Stock Pubs.
Gribble, Richard. Living as an American Catholic in the 21st Century: A Short, Self-Guided Retreat. 2011. 104p. pap. **(978-0-8091-4731-1(9))** Paulist Pr.
Groome, Thomas H. Will There Be Faith? A New Vision for Educating & Growing Disciples. 2011. (ENG.). 208p. pap. 15.99 (978-0-06-203728-2(5), HarperOne) HarperCollins Pubs.
Haase, O.F.M., Albert, Albert. This Sacred Moment: Becoming Holy Right Where You Are. 2010. (ENG.). 121p. pap. 15.00 (978-0-8308-3543-0(1), IVP Bks.) InterVarsity Pr.
Hanna, Ralph, ed. Speculum Vitae: A Reading Text, Volumes 1 And 2. 2009. (Early English Text Society Original Ser.). (Illus.). 390p. 175.00 (978-0-19-956401-9(9)) Oxford Univ. Pr., Inc.
Hartmann, Tom And Mary, et al. Gifts from Heaven: Providence in Our Family. 2012. pap. **(978-1-56548-429-0(0))** New City Community Pr.
Hayes, Mike. Googling God: The Religious Landscape of People in Their 20s And 30s. 2007. 208p. per. 16.95 (978-0-8091-4487-7(5), 4487-7) Paulist Pr.
Hellman, Waybe, et al. Writings of Francis of Assisi: Studies in Early Franciscan Sources, 4 vols., Vol. 1. 2011. 336p. 29.95 **(978-1-57659-230-4(8))** Franciscan Institute Pubns.
Hiesberger, Jean Marie. 52 Saints to Pray With. 2010. 128p. pap. 9.95 (978-0-8091-4648-2(7)) Paulist Pr.
Holnacki, Lee. El Camino: Walking to Santiago de Compostela. 2008. (ENG.). 316p. per. 23.95 (978-0-271-02795-1(9)) Pennsylvania State Univ. Pr.
Hurley, Mark J. The Unholy Ghost. (Illus.). 320p. 14.95 (978-0-87973-529-6(5)) Our Sunday Visitor, Publishing Div.
Ilibagiza, Immaculée. Led by Faith: Rising from the Ashes of the Rwandan Genocide. 2009. (ENG., Illus.). 256p. pap. 14.95 (978-1-4019-1888-0(3)) Hay Hse., Inc.
Ilibagiza, Immaculée & Erwin, Steve. Led by Faith: Rising from the Ashes of the Rwandan Genocide. 2008. (ENG., Illus.). 264p. 24.95 (978-1-4019-1887-3(5)) Hay Hse., Inc.
John P., Bequette. Christian Humanism: Creation. 2007. (ENG.). 198p. pap. 36.99 (978-0-7618-3852-4(X)) Univ. Pr. of America, Inc.
John Paul II, pseud. The John Paul II Lifeguide: Words to Live By. Rice, Ellen, ed. 2006. 124p. per. 6.00 (978-1-58731-396-7(0)) St. Augustine's Pr., Inc.
Kane, John A. Holy Mary, Mother of God: Help of All Christians. 2006. 250p. per. 14.95 (978-1-928832-98-0(9)) Sophia Institute Pr.
Kavanaugh, John F. Following Christ in a Consumer Society: The Spirituality of Cultural Resistance. 25th ed. 2006. (ENG.). 240p. (Orig.). per. 20.00 (978-1-57075-666-5(X)) Orbis Bks.
Kendzia, Mary Carol. Las 5 Preguntas de Nuestra Fe Católica: à Quién, Qué, Dónde, Cuándo, Por Qué — Y Cómo Entenderla. 2011. (SPA.). (978-0-7648-1992-6(5), Libros Liguori) Liguori Pubns.
Knuth, Jane. Thrift Store Saints: Meeting Jesus 25 at a Time. 2010. (ENG.). 176p. pap. 13.95 (978-0-8294-3301-2(5)) Loyola Pr.
Kodell OSB, Jerome. Life Lessons from the Monastery: Wisdom on Love, Prayer, Calling, & Commitment. 2010. 120p. pap. 10.95 (978-1-59325-166-6(1)) Word Among Us Pr.
Kramer, Kyle T. A Time to Plant: Life Lessons in Work, Prayer, & Dirt. 2011. 192p. pap. 15.95 (978-1-933495-26-2(X), Sorin Bks.) Ave Maria Pr.
Kreeft, Peter. Before I Go: Letters to Our Children about What Really Matters. 2007. (ENG.). 264p. 18.95 (978-1-58051-224-4(0), Sheed & Ward) Rowman & Littlefield Publishers, Inc.
—Being Catholic. (How to Talk to Your Children About . . . Ser.). 30p. pap. 1.50 (978-0-87973-682-8(8)) Our Sunday Visitor, Publishing Div.
LaBelle, Jeffrey & Kendall, Daniel. Being Catholic in a Changing World. 2009. 88p. pap. 9.95 (978-0-8091-4611-6(8)) Paulist Pr.
Lawrence, Brother. The Practice of the Presence of God: Conversations & Letters of Brother Lawrence. 2009. (ENG.). 120p. pap. 14.95 (978-1-85168-640-7(1)) Oneworld Pubns. GBR. Dist: National Bk. Network.
—The Practice of the Presence of God: The Best Rule of Holy Life. 2007. 142p. per. 13.99 (978-0-7684-2534-5(4)) Destiny Image Pubs.
—The Practice of the Presence of God: The Original 17th Century Letters & Conversations of Brother Lawrence. 2007. 64p. per. 7.99 (978-1-60266-570-5(2)) Xulon Pr., Inc.
—Spiritual Maxims of Brother Lawrence. 2008. 68p. per. 4.99 (978-1-60459-248-1(6)) Wilder Pubns., Ltd.
Leahy, Breandan. His Mass & Ours: Meditations on Living Eucharistically. 2012. pap. **(978-1-56548-448-1(7))** New City Community Pr.
Libreria Editrice Vaticana, creator. Essentials for Christian Living. 2008. 127p. pap. 6.95 (978-1-60137-020-4(2)) United States Conference of Catholic Bishops.
Liesenfeld, Stephen, ed. Coming Together in Joy: 99 Sayings by Benedict XVI. 2007. (99 Words to Live by Ser.). 99p. 14.95 (978-1-56548-273-9(5)) New City Pr.
Like a Drop in the Ocean: 99 Sayings by Mother Teresa. 2006. 99p. per. 9.95 (978-1-56548-242-5(5)) New City Pr.
Lindworsky, Johann. The Training of the Will. 188p. 2008. 37.95 (978-1-4366-8403-3(X)) 2007. (ENG.). per. 22.95 (978-1-4325-8875-5(3)) Kessinger Publishing, LLC.
Loehr, Gina. The Four Teresas. 2010. 144p. pap. 13.99 (978-0-86716-944-7(3), Servant Bks.) Franciscan Media.
Lorda, Juan Luis. The Virtues of Holiness: The Basics of the Spiritual Struggle. 2010. 138p. pap. 9.95 (978-1-59417-090-4(8)) Scepter Pubs., Inc.
Lubich, Chiara. The Art of Loving. 2010.Tr. of L'Arte D'amare. (ENG.). 144p. pap. 11.95 (978-1-56548-335-4(9)) New City Pr.
—No Thorn Without a Rose: 99 Sayings by Chiara Lubich. Ciabattinin, Julian, ed. 2008. 99p. 14.95 (978-1-56548-294-4(8)) New City Pr.
—Rays: Short Reflections on Living God's Will. 2011. pap. (978-1-56548-382-8(0)) New City Community Pr.
Lubich, Chiara & Ciabattini, Julian. No Thorn Without a Rose: 99 Sayings by Chiara Lubich. 2008. (99 Words to Live by Ser.). pap. 9.95 (978-1-56548-295-1(6)) New City Pr.
Lukefahr, Oscar. We Live: To Know, Love, & Serve God. 2010. (978-0-7648-1856-1(2)) Liguori Pubns.
Martin, Curtis. Made for More. 2008. (Illus.). 117p. pap. 9.99 (978-1-934217-49-8(2)) Ascension Pr.
Martin Descalzo, Jose Luis. Reasons for Hope. Gray, David, tr. from SPA. 2007. 176p. per. 18.00 (978-0-8006-6223-3(7), Fortress Pr.) Augsburg Fortress, Pubs.
Maurin, Peter. Easy Essays. pap. 3.95 (978-0-89979-015-2(1)) British American Bks.
McBride, Alfred. Staying Faithful Today: To God, Ourselves, One Another. 2011. pap. 13.99 (978-0-86716-989-8(3)) Franciscan Media.
McCann, Catherine. New Paths Toward the Sacred: Awakening the Awe Experience in Everyday Living. 2008. 256p. pap. 19.95 (978-0-8091-4551-5(0)) Paulist Pr.
McCarthy, David Matzko. The Good Life: Genuine Christianity for the Middle Class. 2006. (Christian Practice of Everyday Life (Wipf & Stock) Ser.). 176p. pap. 21.00 (978-1-55635-068-9(6), Wipf and Stock) Wipf & Stock Pubs.
McGrath, Michael O'Neill. This Little Light: Lessons in Living from Sr. Thea Bowman. 2008. (Illus.). 95p. 20.00 (978-1-57075-791-4(7)) Orbis Bks.
McKenna, Briege. The Power of the Sacraments. 2010. pap. (978-0-86716-982-9(6), Servant Bks.) Franciscan Media.
McLaughlin, Janice. Ostriches, Dung Beetles & Other Spiritual Masters: A Book of Wisdom from the Wild. 2009. (Illus.). 144p. pap. 18.00 (978-1-57075-842-3(5)) Orbis Bks.
McPhee, Rosalie. Mothering: Becoming the Heart of the Home. (Illus.). 64p. pap. (978-0-921440-60-4(X)) Madonna Hse. Pubns.
McSorley, Joseph. Common Sense. 2011. 144p. 40.95 **(978-1-258-06907-0(5))** Literary Licensing, LLC.
Meme, Kevin & Guhin, Jeffrey Joseph, eds. Young & Catholic in America. 2010. 144p. pap. (978-0-8091-4548-5(0)) Paulist Pr.
Merton, Thomas & Merton, Thomas. Conjectures of a Guilty Bystander. 2009. (ENG.). 384p. pap. 15.99 (978-0-385-01018-4(4)) Doubleday Religious Publishing Group, The.
Moran, Gabriel. Believing in a Revealing God: The Basis of the Christian Life. 2009. 216p. pap. 29.95 (978-0-8146-5388-3(X), Michael Glazier Bks.) Liturgical Pr.
Morneau, Robert F. A New Heart: Eleven Qualities of Holiness. 2008. 144p. pap. 12.00 (978-1-57075-801-0(8)) Orbis Bks.
Morrow, T. G. Be Holy: A Catholic's Guide to the Spiritual Life. 2009. pap. (978-0-86716-878-5(1), Servant Bks.) Franciscan Media.
Mossa, Mark. Already There: Letting God Find You. 2010. pap. (978-0-86716-765-8(3)) Franciscan Media.
Mother Teresa of Calcutta. In the Heart of the World: Thoughts, Stories, & Prayers. 2010. (ENG.). 112p. pap. 12.95 (978-1-57731-900-9(1)) New World Library.
—Mother Teresa: Come Be My Light. Kolodiejchuk, Brian, ed. lt. ed. 2008. (Wheeler Hardcover Ser.). 661p. 30.50 (978-1-59722-687-5(4), Wheeler Publishing, Inc.) Cengage Gale.
—Where There Is Love, There Is God: A Path to Closer Union with God & Greater Love for Others. 2010. (ENG.). 384p. 24.00 (978-0-385-53178-8(8), Doubleday Religion) Doubleday Religious Publishing Group, The.
Mother Teresa of Calcutta & Hutchinson, Gloria. Created for Great Things: Spiritual Writings by Mother Teresa. 2008. 136p. pap. 13.95 (978-1-56548-285-2(9)) New City Pr.
Mother Teresa of Calcutta & Kolodiejchuk, Brian. Mother Teresa: Come Be My Light. 2009. (ENG.). 416p. pap. 14.99 (978-0-307-58923-1(4), Image) Doubleday Religious Publishing Group, The.
Mueller, Joan. Living a Spirituality of Action: A Woman's Perspective. 2008. (Called to Holiness). 112p. pap. 11.95 (978-0-86716-885-3(4)) Franciscan Media.
Muto, Susan & van Kaam, Adrian. The Commandments: Ten Ways to a Happy Life & a Healthy Soul. 2007. 224p. per. 14.00 (978-1-880982-42-6(0)) Epiphany Assn.
Newman, John Henry. Life's Purpose: Wisdom from John Henry Newman. 2010. pap. 6.95 (978-0-8198-4533-7(7)) Pauline Bks. & Media.
Nixon, Don. Winning the 21st Century. 2007. 108p. per. 10.99 (978-1-60266-378-7(5)) Xulon Pr., Inc.
Nouwen, Henri J. M. Beloved: Henri Nouwen in Conversation. 2007. 52p. 20.00 incl. audio compact disk (978-0-8028-6286-0(1)) Eerdmans, William B. Publishing Co.
—The Only Necessary Thing: Living a Prayerful Life. Greer, Wendy Wilson, ed. 2008. (ENG.). 224p. pap. 15.95 (978-0-8245-2493-7(4), Crossroad 8 Avenue) Crossroad Publishing Co., The.
Nouwen, Henri J. M. A Spirituality of Living. 2012. **(978-0-8358-1089-3(7))** Upper Room Bks.
O'Boyle, Donna-Marie Cooper. Mother Teresa & Me: Ten Years of Friendship. 2009. (978-1-933271-28-6(0)) Circle Pr.
O'Keefe, Mark. Deciding to Be Christian: A Daily Commitment. 2012. **(978-0-7648-2118-9(0))** Liguori Pubns.
Ostovich, Steven T. The Courage of Faith: Some Philosophical Reflections. 2009. 172p. pap. 15.95 (978-0-8146-1872-1(3)) Liturgical Pr.
Papandrea, James L. & Papandrea, James Leonard. Spiritual Blueprint: How We Live, Work, Love, Play, & Pray. 2009. 16.99 (978-0-7648-1892-9(9)) Liguori Pubns.
Paprocki, Joe. Practice Makes Catholic: Moving from a Learned Faith to a Lived Faith. 2011. (ENG., Illus.). 216p. pap. 9.95 (978-0-8294-3322-7(8)) Loyola Pr.
Pennock, Michael Francis. Questions from Seventh Period: Doc Pennock Answers Teens' Questions on Life, Love, & the Catholic Faith. rev. ed. 2006. Orig. Title: What we really want to Know. 286p. per. 18.95 (978-1-59471-101-5(1)) Ave Maria Pr.
Phalen, John. Living the Rosary: Finding Your Life in the Mysteries. 2011. 128p. pap. 12.95 (978-1-59471-264-7(6)) Ave Maria Pr.
Philippe, Jacques. Called to Life. 2009. 117p. pap. 9.95 (978-1-59417-069-0(X)) Scepter Pubs., Inc.
Pierce, Gregory A. The World As It Should Be: Living Authentically in the Here & Now Kingdom of God. 2010. (ENG.). 160p. pap. 14.95 (978-0-8294-2909-1(3)) Loyola Pr.
Popcak, Gregory K. God Help Me! These People Are Driving Me Nuts! - Making Peace with Difficult People. 2010. (ENG.). 160p. pap. 15.95 (978-0-8245-2597-2(3)) Crossroad Publishing Co., The.
Pope Leo Xiii & Treacy, Gerald C. The Chief Duties of Christians As Citizens: Encyclical Letter of Pope Leo XIII. 2011. 40p. 35.95 **(978-1-258-06172-2(4))** Literary Licensing, LLC.
—The Chief Duties of Christians As Citizens: Sapientiae Christianae. 2011. 40p. 35.95 **(978-1-258-03936-3(2))** Literary Licensing, LLC.
Prendergast, Edith. Grace Abounds: A Call to Awaken & Renew Your Faith. 2011. 160p. pap. 12.95 (978-1-59471-259-3(X)) Ave Maria Pr.
Raphael, Maryanne. What Mother Teresa Taught Me. 2007. 206p. per. 15.95 (978-0-86716-810-5(2)) Franciscan Media.
Reinhard, Sarah. Catholic Family Fun: A Guide for the Adventurous, Overwhelmed, Creative, or Clueless. 2012. (ENG.). 176p. pap. 11.95 **(978-0-8198-1604-7(3))** Pauline Bks. & Media.
Reno, Russell R. Fighting the Noonday Devil - And Other Essays Personal & Theologicalt. 2011. 128p. pap. 16.00 (978-0-8028-6547-2(X), Eerdmans, William B. Publishing Co.
Reuter, Mary. Running with Expanded Heart: Meeting God in Everyday Life. 2010. 112p. pap. 14.95 (978-0-8146-3308-3(0)) Liturgical Pr.
Riccardi, Andrea & Community of Sant'Egidio Staff. Sant Egidio Bk of Prayer. 2009. 224p. pap. 14.95 (978-1-59471-206-7(9)) Ave Maria Pr.
Richard J. Hart, Richard J. & Hart, Richard. How Christian Are You? 2009. 224p. pap. 19.95 (978-0-8091-4579-9(0)) Paulist Pr.
Roberto, John. Living Well: Christian Practices for Everyday Life. 2009. (Illus.). (978-0-9823031-0-8(6)) Lifelongfaith Assocs.
Rohr, Richard. A Lever & a Place to Stand: The Contemplative Stance, the Active Prayer. 2011. 128p. pap. 15.00 (978-1-58768-064-9(5), HiddenSpring) Paulist Pr.
Rolheiser, Ronald. Forgotten among the Lilies: Learning to Love Beyond Our Fears. 2007. (ENG.). 336p. pap. 14.00 (978-0-385-51232-9(5), Image) Doubleday Religious Publishing Group, The.
Rothlin, Hans-Peter, ed. Overlook Much, Correct a Little: 99 Sayings by John XXIII. 2007. 99p. 14.95 (978-1-56548-261-6(1)) New City Pr
—Overlook Much, Correct a Little: 99 Sayings by John Xxooo. 2007. (99 Words to Live by Ser.). 99p. per. 9.95 (978-1-56548-255-5(7)) New City Pr.
Saint-Laurent, George E. & Saint-Laurent. Catholic Spirituality in Focus: Eight Themes of Mind & Heart. 2007. (ENG.). 160p. pap. 12.95 (978-1-55778-865-8(0)) Paragon Hse. Pubs.
Santa, Thomas M. Understanding Scrupulosity: Questions, Help, & Encouragement. rev. ed. 2007. 303p. per. 26.95 (978-0-7648-1576-8(8), Liguori/Triumph) Liguori Pubns.
Sarkisian, Rick. The LifeWork Principle Journal: A Companion to the LifeWork Principle. 2007. per. 12.95 (978-0-9790825-0-4(1)) LifeWork Pr.
Schonborn, Christoph Cardinal. With Jesus Everyday: How Believing Transforms Living. 2007. (ENG.). 192p. 19.95 (978-0-8245-2420-3(9), Crossroad) Crossroad Publishing Co., The.
Schorn, Joel. Holy Simplicity: The Little Way of Mother Teresa, Dorothy Day & Therese of Lisieux. 2008. 134p. per. 12.99 (978-0-86716-815-0(3), Servant Bks.) Franciscan Media.
Sheen, Fulton J. Walk with God: Wisdom & Guidance to Help Us in Our Daily Lives. 2008. 145p. pap. 12.95 (978-0-8189-1267-2(7)) St Pauls/Alba Hse. Pubs.
Shields, Ann. Deeper Conversion: Extraordinary Grace for Ordinary Times. 2008. 112p. per. 11.99 (978-0-86716-811-2(0), Servant Bks.) Franciscan Media.
Sirois, Celia M. Jesus Is the Promise, Grade 6, Vol. 6. 316p. tchr. ed., spiral bd. 18.95 (978-0-8198-3935-0(3)) Pauline Bks. & Media.
Smith, Claire Furia. Can I Confess by E-Mail? What Catholics May & May Not Do. 2010. (978-0-8189-1312-9(6)) St Pauls/Alba Hse. Pubs.
Socias, James. The Sacraments: Source of Our Life in Christ. 2009. (978-1-890177-92-8(X)) Midwest Theological Forum.
St Albert the Great, et al. On Cleaving to God. 2011. 38p. pap. 5.95 **(978-1-61720-335-0(1))** Wilder Pubns., Ltd.

St. Bonaventure. Works of Saint Bonaventure, 6. Date not set. pap. (978-1-57659-042-3(9)) Franciscan Institute Pubns.
Stanford, Peter & Stanford. Why I Am Still a Catholic: Essays in Faith & Perseverance. 2006. (ENG.). 154p. 23.95 (978-0-8264-9145-9(6)) Continuum International Publishing Group, Ltd. GBR. Dist: National Bk. Network.
Starr, Mirabai & Teresa. Saint Teresa of Avila: Devotions, Prayers & Living Wisdom. Starr, Mirabai, ed. 2007. (Illus.). 112p. 12.95 (978-1-59179-646-6(6), BK01214) Sounds True, Inc.
Stoltz, Eric & Tomkovicz, Vince. Ascend: The Catholic Faith for a New Generation. 2009. (Illus.). 256p. pap. 24.95 (978-0-8091-4621-5(5)) Paulist Pr.
Svoboda, Melannie. Gracious Goodness: Living Each Day in the Gifts of the Spirit. 2008. (ENG.). 120p. pap. 12.95 (978-0-8294-2719-6(8)) Loyola Pr.
Swaim, Matt. Prayer in the Digital Age. 2011. 160p. pap. 16.99 (978-0-7648-1979-7(8)) Liguori Pubns.
Swain, Sr. Mary & Thurston, Bonnie, eds. Hidden in the Same Mystery: Thomas Merton & Loretto. 2010. (ENG., Illus.). 120p. pap. 15.95 (978-1-891785-60-3(5)) Fons Vitae of Kentucky, Inc.
Taking Up Our Daily Tools. 88p. (Orig.). per. 10.00 (978-1-879934-51-1(5)) St. Andrews College Pr.
Talbot, John Michael. The Universal Monk. 2011. E-Book (978-0-8146-3951-1(8)); 230p. 19.95 (978-0-8146-3341-0(2)) Liturgical Pr.
Tardy, Jo Anne. A Light Will Rise in Darkness: Growing up Black & Catholic in New Orleans. 2006. (American Catholic Experience Ser.). (Illus.). 110p. per. 9.95 (978-0-87946-316-8(3)) ACTA Pubns.
Thigpen, Paul. Last Words: Final Thoughts of Catholic Saints & Sinners. 2006. 219p. per. 14.99 (978-0-86716-724-5(6), Servant Bks.) Franciscan Media.
Thompson, Christopher J. & Long, Steven A., eds. Reason & the Rule of Faith: Conversations in the Tradition with John Paul II. 2010. (ENG.). 200p. pap. 30.00 (978-0-7618-3963-7(1)) Univ. Pr. of America, Inc.
Tjorhom, Ola. Embodied Faith: Reflections on a Materialist Spirituality. 2009. 192p. pap. 30.00 (978-0-8028-6274-7(8)) Eerdmans, William B. Publishing Co.
Torrens, James. Dare to Commit: Say Yes in a World of Maybe. 2010. 10.99 (978-0-7648-1874-5(0)) Liguori Pubns.
Trillo, Alejandro Ortega. Vicios y Virtudes: Reeducando el Alma a Través Del Cuerpo. 2011. (SPA.). (978-0-7648-2053-3(2)) Liguori Pubns.
Tschanz, Mary K., et al. Jesus Walks with Us, Grade 4. 253p. tchr. ed., spiral bd. 16.95 (978-0-8198-3929-9(9)) Pauline Bks. & Media.
Urteaga Loidi, Jesus. Saints in the World: The Adventure of Christian Life. 3rd ed. 2009. xvii, 220p. pap. (978-1-59417-084-3(3)) Scepter Pubs., Inc.
van Zeller, Hubert. Prayer & the Will of God. 2009. viii, 156p. pap. 12.95 (978-1-933184-59-3(0)) Sophia Institute Pr.
Vanier, Jean. Jean Vanier: Essential Writings. Vanier, Jean, ed. Whitney-Brown, Carolyn, ed. & intro. by. 2008. 176p. pap. 16.00 (978-1-57075-806-5(9)) Orbis Bks.
Veneroso, Joseph R. Good News Today. 2009. 140p. pap. 15.00 (978-1-57075-809-6(3)) Orbis Bks.
Von Speyr, Adrienne. Lumina & New Lumina. 2008. 105p. pap. 8.95 (978-1-58617-222-0(0)) Ignatius Pr.
Vonier, Anscar. Christianus: The Christian Life. 2011. (ENG.). 164p. pap. 14.95 **(978-0-9830297-2-4(5))** Zaccheus Pr.
Vost, Kevin. Unearthing Your Ten Talents: A Thomistic Guide to Spiritual Growth through the Virtues & the Gifts. 2009. xxiii, 241p. pap. 13.95 (978-1-933184-41-8(8)) Sophia Institute Pr.
Wagner, Nick. The Heart of Faith: A Field Guide for Catechumens & Candidates. 2010. 120p. pap. 12.95 (978-1-58595-817-7(4)) Twenty-Third Pubns./Bayard.
Welborn, Amy. Mary & the Christian Life: Scriptural Reflections on the First Disciple. 2008. 152p. pap. 11.95 (978-1-59325-113-0(0)) Word Among Us Pr.
Yount, David. Growing in Faith: A Guide for the Reluctant Christian. 2nd rev. ed. 2008. 368p. per. 24.00 (978-1-59627-082-4(9)) Church Publishing, Inc.
Zweerman, T. H. & van den Goorbergh, E. A. Saint Francis of Assisi: A Guide for Our Times. His Biblical Spirituality. Damsté, M. S., tr. from DUT. 2007. (Fiery Arrow Ser.). (ENG.). 237p. (C). pap. 32.00 (978-90-429-1955-6(8)) Peeters Pubs. & Booksellers BEL. Dist: Brown, David Bk. Co., The.

CHRISTIAN LIFE—EARLY CHURCH, CA. 30-600

Burrus, Virginia, ed. Late Ancient Christianity. 2010. 320p. (C). pap. 24.00 (978-0-8006-9720-4(0), Fortress Pr.) Augsburg Fortress, Pubs.
Chryssavgis, John. In the Heart of the Desert: The Spirituality of the Desert Fathers & Mothers. rev. ed. 2008. (Library of Perennial Philosophy). (ENG.). 224p. pap. 19.95 (978-1-933316-56-7(X)) World Wisdom, Inc.
Cyril. Festal Letters 1-12. Amidon, Philip R., tr. from GEC. 2009. 168p. 39.95 (978-0-8132-0118-4(7)) Catholic Univ. of America Pr.
Dively Lauro, Elizabeth Ann. The Soul & Spirit of Scripture Within Origen's Exegesis. 2010. (978-1-58983-500-9(X)) Society of Biblical Literature.
Downing, F. Gerald. God with Everything: The Divine in the Discourse of the First Christian Century. 2008. 328p. (978-1-906055-25-7(4)) Sheffield Phoenix Pr.
Driver, Lisa D. Maugans. Christ at the Center: The Early Christian Era. 2009. (Westminster History of Christian Thought Ser.). (ENG.). 248p. pap. 30.00 (978-0-664-22897-2(6)) Westminster John Knox Pr.
Ferguson, Everett. Baptism in the Early Church: History, Theology, & Liturgy in the First Five Centuries. 2009. (Illus.). 984p. 60.00 (978-0-8028-2748-7(9)) Eerdmans, William B. Publishing Co.
Goettmann, Alphonse & Goettmann, Rachel. The Spiritual Wisdom & Practices of Early Christianity. Nottingham, Theodore J., tr. from FRE. rev. ed. 2006. Orig. Title: Sagesse et Pratiques du Christianisme. 144p. per. 13.95 (978-1-933275-09-3(X), Orthodox Research Institute) Cocheco Falls Publishing.
Hanna, Ralph, ed. Speculum Vitae: A Reading Text, Volumes 1 And 2. 2009. (Early English Text Society Original Ser.). (Illus.). 390p. 175.00 (978-0-19-956401-9(9)) Oxford Univ. Pr., Inc.
Hopkins, Richard R. How Greek Philosophy Corrupted the Christian Concept of God. 2009. 466p. pap. 27.99 (978-0-88290-782-6(4)) Cedar Fort, Inc./CFI Distribution.
Konstantinovsky, Julia. Evagrius Ponticus: The Making of a Gnostic. 2009. (New Critical Thinking in Religion, Theology & Biblical Studies). (Illus.). 230p. 99.95 (978-0-7546-6265-5(9)) Ashgate Publishing Co.
Krueger, Derek. Byzantine Christianity. 2010. 320p. (C). pap. 24.00 (978-0-8006-9721-1(9), Fortress Pr.) Augsburg Fortress, Pubs.
Laan, Ray Vander & Sorenson, Amanda. Early Church, 1 vol., Vol. 5. exp. rev. ed. 2008. (Faith Lessons Ser.). (ENG.). 192p. pap. 9.99 (978-0-310-27971-6(2)) Zondervan.
Luther, Martin. Making the Best Man; Real Humility; What Sin Is; Man's Troubles; 2006. pap. 12.95 (978-1-4304-0825-3(1)) Kessinger Publishing, LLC.
Smith, John Arthur. Music in Ancient Judaism & Early Christianity. 2011. (Illus.). 294p. 114.95 (978-1-4094-0907-6(4)) Ashgate Publishing Co.
St. John of the Cross. Ascent of Mount Carmel. Peers, E. Allison, ed. & tr. by. from SPA. 2008. (ENG.). 352p. pap. 11.95 (978-0-486-46837-2(2)) Dover Pubns., Inc.
Valantasis, Richard, et al. The Gospels & Christian Life in History & Practice. 2009. (ENG.). 288p. 99.00 (978-0-7425-5921-9(1)); pap. 37.50 (978-0-7425-5922-6(X)) Rowman & Littlefield Publishers, Inc.

CHRISTIAN LIFE—EPISCOPAL AUTHORS

Back, George. Christmas Joy Let Heaven & Nature Sing. 2007. (Illus.). 110p. per. 9.95 (978-0-9800520-0-8(9)) Spirit & Intelligence Pr., LLC.
Goodyear, Sarah & Weissman, Ed. Episcopal Haiku. 2007. (Illus.). 120p. per. 10.00 (978-1-59627-079-4(9)) Church Publishing, Inc.
Marshall, Paul V. Messages in the Mall: Looking at Life in 600 Words or Less. 2008. 160p. per. 16.00 (978-1-59627-081-7(0)) Church Publishing, Inc.
Rhea, Henry T. He Descended into Hell. 2011. pap. 29.99 **(978-1-61346-571-4(8))** Tate Publishing & Enterprises, LLC.

CHRISTIAN LIFE—FICTION

Abakwue, S. A. Heaven at War. 2011. 718p. 34.99 **(978-1-4628-9388-1(0))**; pap. 23.99 **(978-1-4628-9387-4(2))** Xlibris Corp.
Adams, Teresa. Mary Magdalene; My Story: My Story. 2011. 244p. 29.99 **(978-1-4628-6312-9(4))**; pap. 19.99 **(978-1-4628-6311-2(6))** Xlibris Corp.
Allen, Preston L. Jesus Boy. 2010. (ENG.). 364p. pap. 15.95 (978-1-936070-04-6(9)) Akashic Bks.
Anthony, Ross. Eddie Johnson's Ark. 2007. 152p. (YA). per. (978-0-9727894-2-4(1)) Arizona Blueberry Studios.
Ardis, Barbara. If You See an Old Lady. 2011. 40p. pap. 16.95 **(978-1-4626-4238-0(1))** PublishAmerica, Inc.
Arment, Chad. Shadows from a Veiled Creation: Classic Tales of Supernatural Fiction in the Christian Tradition. 2006. (978-1-930585-26-3(8)) Coachwhip Pubns.
Atteberry, Mark. The Caleb Quest: What You Can Learn from the Boldest Dreamer in the Bible, 0 vols. 2006. 128p. per. 12.99 (978-0-7852-8784-1(1)) Nelson, Thomas Inc.
Audi, Norman. He Who Has an Ear. 2007. 236p. per. 24.95 (978-1-4241-6415-8(X)) PublishAmerica, Inc.
Augsburger, Myron S. The Fugitive: Menno Simons, Spiritual Leader in the Free Church Movement. 2008. pap. 14.99 (978-0-8361-9409-8(8)) Herald Pr.
Austin, Lynn. A Woman's Place. 2006. 448p. pap. 14.99 (978-0-7642-2890-2(0)) Bethany Hse. Pubs.
Baird, Christopher. The Enduring Light: The Chronicles of the Raven Clan. 2011. pap. 21.99 (978-1-61739-418-8(1)) Tate Publishing & Enterprises, LLC.
Barton, Janet Lee, et al. Bayou Brides: Four Generations of Couples Are Bound by Love, Faith, & Land. l.t. ed. 2008. (Thorndike Christian Historical Fiction Ser.). 439p. 28.95 (978-1-4104-0448-0(X)) Thorndike Pr.
Bartz, Meghan. A Conquest of Knowledge: St. Augustine by Train. 2007. 52p. per. 16.95 (978-1-60441-492-9(8)) PublishAmerica, Inc.
Belton, D. W. Eve Ann. 2009. 392p. pap. 20.99 (978-1-60791-995-7(8)) Xulon Pr., Inc.
Bennett, Deborah. Keepsakes for the Soul: Volume II. 2007. 108p. per. 19.95 (978-1-60441-060-0(4)) PublishAmerica, Inc.
Benoît, Michel. The Thirteenth Apostle. Brown, Andrew, tr. from FRE. 2007. 360p. per. 12.95 (978-1-84688-028-5(9)) Pushkin Pr., Ltd. GBR. Dist: Independent Pubs. Group.
Bevere, John & Olsen, Mark Andrew. Rescued. 2007. 288p. pap. 13.99 (978-0-7642-0447-0(5)) Bethany Hse. Pubs.
Billingsley, ReShonda Tate. The Devil Is a Lie. 2009. (ENG.). 304p. pap. 15.00 (978-1-4165-7804-8(8)) Gallery Pr., The IRL. Dist: Simon & Schuster, Inc.
Bird-Faulkner, Nicole. Yet Holding On. 2006. (ENG.). 188p. per. 24.95 (978-1-4241-2187-8(6)) PublishAmerica, Inc.
Blackstock, Terri. The Heart Reader of Franklin High, 0 vols. 2008. 144p. (YA). pap. 14.99 (978-1-59554-591-6(3)) Nelson, Thomas Inc.
—True Light. l.t. ed. 2008. (Restoration Ser.: No. 3). (ENG.). 511p. pap. 16.95 (978-1-59415-216-0(0), Walker Large Print) Cengage Gale.
Boehm, Tammy. Bethanyaes Crossing. 2008. 280p. pap. 15.95 (978-1-60693-231-5(4), Eloquent Bks.) AEG Literary Publishing Services, Inc.
Bonner, Robert G. Stranded & Tempted. 2006. 204p. pap. 24.95 (978-1-4241-3996-5(1)) PublishAmerica, Inc.
Bottke, Allison. A Stitch in Time. l.t. ed. 2006. (Thorndike Christian Fiction Ser.). 533p. 28.95 (978-0-7862-9157-1(5)) Thorndike Pr.
Bowen, Steven. Inspiration Point. 2007. 172p. per. 13.95 (978-1-59858-265-9(8)) Dog Ear Publishing, LLC.
Bowman, Marcia J. Yea, Tho' I Walk: Sera's Christian Growth - Book Three. 2008. 184p. 24.99 (978-1-4259-7136-6(9)); pap. 14.49 (978-1-4259-7135-9(0)) AuthorHouse.
Bowyer, Edith M. Gabriel the Acadian. Date not set. lib. bdg. 18.95 (978-0-8488-0168-7(7)) Amereon LTD.
Bozeman, Eric. Sermons at the Water Cooler. 2007. 126p. pap. 19.95 (978-1-4241-5707-5(2)) PublishAmerica, Inc.
Breme, Chris. Hark! 2006. 190p. per. 18.99 (978-1-59879-168-6(0)) Lifevest Publishing, Inc.
Brouwer, Sigmund. Flight of Shadows. l.t. ed. 2010. 606p. 31.99 (978-1-4104-3013-7(8)) Thorndike Pr.
Bruner, Roger & Bruner, Kristi Rae. Lost in Dreams. 2011. (Altered Hearts Ser.). (ENG.). 368p. (YA). (gr. 9-12). pap. 9.99 (978-1-60260-962-4(4), Barbour Bks.) Barbour Publishing, Inc.
Bunn, Davis & Oke, Janette. The Damascus Way. 2011. (Acts of Faith Ser.). 432p. 19.99 (978-0-7642-0558-3(7)); (Acts of Faith Ser.: 3). 432p. pap. 14.99 (978-0-7642-0866-9(7)); (Illus.). 426p. **(978-1-61129-301-2(4))**; (Acts of Faith Ser.). 544p. pap. 17.99 (978-0-7642-0867-6(5)) Bethany Hse. Pubs.
Bunyan, John. The Life & Death of Mr. Badman. l.t. ed. 2006. (ENG.). 186p. pap. 21.99 (978-1-4264-0437-5(9)) BiblioBazaar.
—The Pilgrim S Progress. 2010. 350p. pap. 32.75 (978-1-149-50670-7(9)) BiblioBazaar.
—The Pilgrim S Progress. 2010. (Illus.). 192p. pap. 27.74 (978-1-154-81359-3(2)) General Bks. LLC.
—The Pilgrim's Progress. 23.95 (978-0-8488-0141-0(5)) Amereon LTD.
—The Pilgrim's Progress. 2009. 428p. (gr. 12-12). 27.99 (978-0-559-95900-4(1)); pap. 21.99 (978-0-559-95898-4(6)) BiblioBazaar.
—The Pilgrim's Progress. 2007. (ENG.). 332p. 24.95 (978-1-60206-456-0(3)); per. 9.95 (978-1-60206-455-3(5)) Cosimo, Inc.
—The Pilgrim's Progress. 2008. (Illus.). 192p. pap. (978-1-4099-2050-2(X)) Dodo Pr.
—The Pilgrim's Progress. 2009. (ENG.). 248p. pap. 11.49 (978-0-9817634-3-9(X)) Kidwell Publishing.
—The Pilgrim's Progress. 2007. (ENG.). 288p. 29.95 (978-1-4344-8405-5(X)); per. 17.95 (978-1-4344-8404-8(1)) Wildside Pr., LLC.
—Pilgrim's Progress. 2007. (ENG.). 176p. per. 7.99 (978-1-4209-2952-2(6)) Digireads.com.
—Pilgrim's Progress. Pipe, Rhona, ed. 2010. (Hodder Classics Ser.). (ENG.). 224p. pap. 14.95 (978-0-340-98015-6(X), Hodder & Stoughton) Hodder General Publishing Div. GBR. Dist: Independent Pubs. Group.
—Pilgrim's Progress. 2007. (ENG.). 468p. 52.95 (978-0-548-00310-7(6)) Kessinger Publishing, LLC.
—Pilgrim's Progress. 2008. 224p. pap. 8.99 (978-1-60459-416-0(4)) Wilder Pubns., Ltd.
—The Pilgrim's Progress. 2012. 594p. pap. 44.75 **(978-1-276-79525-8(4))** 2011. 490p. pap. 38.75 **(978-1-179-89834-6(6))** 2011. 528p. pap. 40.75 **(978-1-179-97968-7(0))** 2010. (ENG.). 292p. pap. 28.75 (978-1-172-40053-9(9)) 2010. (ENG.). 400p. pap. 34.75 (978-1-177-35720-3(8)) 2010. 646p. pap. 46.75 (978-1-177-14982-2(6)) 2010. (ENG.). 352p. pap. 32.75 (978-1-177-29232-0(7)) 2010. (ENG.). 356p. pap. 32.75 (978-1-177-54146-6(7)) 2010. (ENG.). 432p. pap. 35.75 (978-1-177-60284-6(9)) 2010. 282p. pap. 28.75 (978-1-175-75185-0(5)) 2010. 74p. pap. 17.75 (978-1-175-75178-2(2)) 2010. 378p. 38.99 (978-1-140-01690-8(3)) 2010. 192p. 30.99 (978-1-140-61430-2(4)) 2010. 430p. 41.99 (978-1-140-05063-6(X)) 2010. 378p. pap. 33.75 (978-1-140-01691-5(1)) 2010. 192p. pap. 22.75 (978-1-140-61431-9(2)) 2010. 430p. pap. 35.75 (978-1-140-05064-3(8)) 2010. 632p. pap. 45.75 (978-1-146-94461-8(6)) 2010. 616p. pap. 45.75 (978-1-147-51809-2(2)) 2010. 324p. pap. 30.75 (978-1-144-58557-8(0)) 2010. 418p. pap. 34.75 (978-1-141-90619-2(8)) 2010. 398p. (gr. 12-12). pap. 33.75 (978-1-142-14795-2(9)) 2010. 460p. (gr. 12-12). pap. 36.75 (978-1-141-88554-1(9)) 2009. (ENG.). 503p. 43.99 (978-1-117-69231-9(0)) 2009. (ENG.). 503p. pap. 30.99 (978-1-117-69233-3(7), BiblioLife) 2009. (ENG.). 503p. (gr. 12-12). pap. 38.75 (978-1-117-69232-6(9)) 2009. (ENG.). 385p. 38.99 (978-1-117-26298-7(7)) 2009. (ENG.). 385p. pap. 25.99 (978-1-117-26300-7(2), BiblioLife) 2009. (ENG.). 385p. (gr. 12-12). pap. 32.75 (978-1-117-26299-4(5)) BiblioBazaar.
—The Pilgrim's Progress. 2009. 332p. pap. (978-0-217-76615-9(3)); 244p. pap. (978-0-217-91964-7(2)); 186p. pap. (978-0-217-10363-3(4)); 184p. pap. (978-0-217-12822-3(X)); 246p. pap. (978-0-217-12824-7(6)); 214p. (gr. 12-12). pap. (978-1-4589-2922-8(1)) Books LLC.
—The Pilgrim's Progress. 2011. (Hendrickson Christian Classics Ser.). (ENG.). 270p. pap. 12.97 **(978-1-59856-675-8(X))** Hendrickson Pubs. Marketing, LLC.
—Pilgrim's Progress. 2009. 328p. (gr. 12-12). pap. 18.95 (978-1-933993-72-0(3)) Apocryphile Pr.
—Pilgrim's Progress. 2012. 622p. pap. 45.75 **(978-1-278-34431-7(4))** BiblioBazaar.
—Pilgrim's Progress. 2010. 468p. 42.36 (978-1-163-31575-0(3)); pap. 30.36 **(978-1-162-57348-9(1))** Kessinger Publishing, LLC.
—The Pilgrim's Progress. 2009. (ENG.). 336p. (gr. 12-18). pap. 7.95 (978-0-451-53129-2(9), Signet Classics) Penguin Group (USA) Inc.
—The Pilgrim's Progress. (Early Best Sellers Ser.). reprint ed. lib. bdg. 48.00 (978-0-7426-1008-8(X)) Classic Bks.
—The Pilgrim's Progress. De Rosset, Rosalie, ed. 2007. (Moody Classics Ser.). (ENG.). 224p. per. 7.99 (978-0-8024-5654-0(5)) Moody Pubs.
—The Pilgrim's Progress. Owens, W. R., ed. 2nd ed. 2009. (Oxford World's Classics Ser.). (ENG., Illus.). 400p. pap. 9.95 (978-0-19-953813-3(1)) Oxford Univ. Pr., Inc.
—Pilgrim's Progress, 2 vols., vol. 1. 2011. (Illus.). 144p. (J). pap. 14.99 **(978-1-61328-049-2(1)**, Kingstone Comics) Kingstone Media Group.
—The Pilgrim's Progress, 2 vols., vol. 2. 2011. (ENG., Illus.). 152p. (J). pap. 14.99 **(978-1-61328-050-8(5)**, Kingstone Comics) Kingstone Media Group.
—The Pilgrim's Progress: From This World to That Which Is to Come. 2011. 568p. pap. 43.75 **(978-1-245-13993-9(2))** 2011. 284p. pap. 28.75 **(978-1-175-36833-1(4))** 2011. 484p. pap. 38.75 **(978-1-175-86883-1(3))** 2010. 378p. pap. 33.75 (978-1-146-44303-6(X)) 2010. 272p. pap. 27.75 (978-1-141-71274-8(1)) 2010. 510p. (gr. 12-12). pap. 39.75 (978-1-142-30144-6(3)) BiblioBazaar.
—The Pilgrim's Progress: From this World to That Which Is to Come. 2009. 318p. (gr. 12-12). pap. 29.75 (978-1-115-82283-1(7)) BiblioBazaar.
—The Pilgrims Progress: From This World to That Which Is to Come. 2010. 370p. (gr. 12-12). pap. 32.75 (978-1-142-97773-3(0)) BiblioBazaar.
—The Pilgrim's Progress: From this world to that which is to Come. 2010. (ENG.). 420p. pap. 34.75 (978-1-177-29169-9(X)) BiblioBazaar.
—The Pilgrim's Progress: From This World to That Which Is to Come (1860) 2008. 356p. 46.95 (978-1-4374-0692-4(0)); (gr. 12-12). pap. 31.95 (978-1-4373-1975-0(0)) Kessinger Publishing, LLC.
—Pilgrim's Progress: The Accurate Revised Text. 2009. (Illus.). 224p. (gr. 12-12). pap. 16.00 (978-1-59925-217-9(1)) Solid Ground Christian Bks.
—The Pilgrim's Progress - from This World to That Which Is to Come. 2008. 372p. pap. (978-1-4437-0502-8(0)) Read Bks.
—The Pilgrim's Progress: from this World to that Which Is to Come. 2009. (ENG.). 317p. pap. 23.99 (978-1-115-82285-5(3), BiblioLife) BiblioBazaar.
—The Pilgrim's Progress from This World to That Which Is to Come. 2008. 344p. pap. (978-1-4097-6329-1(3)) Read Bks.
—The Pilgrim's Progress from This World to That Which Is to Come. 2011. 220p. pap. 24.75 **(978-1-174-51446-3(9))** 2010. (ENG.). 404p. pap. 34.75 (978-1-171-53530-0(9)) 2010. 456p. pap. 36.75 (978-1-178-22811-3(8)) 2010. (ENG.). 444p. pap. 36.75 (978-1-176-30893-0(9)) 2010. 470p. pap. 37.75 (978-1-175-76312-9(8)) 2010. 370p. pap. 32.75 (978-1-175-75179-9(0)) 2010. 436p. pap. 35.75 (978-1-175-76313-6(6)) 2010. 540p. pap. 40.75 (978-1-170-53991-0(2), Gale ECCO, Print Editions) 2010. 186p. pap. 22.75 (978-1-147-18840-0(8)) 2010. 358p. pap. 32.75 (978-1-147-94505-8(5)) 2010. 410p. pap. 34.75 (978-1-147-93318-5(9)) 2010. 536p. pap. 40.75 (978-1-143-64812-0(9)) BiblioBazaar.
—The Pilgrim's Progress from This World to That Which Is to Come. 2009. 414p. pap. (978-0-217-76175-8(5)); 192p. pap. (978-0-217-76178-9(X)) Books LLC.
—The Pilgrim's Progress from This World to That Which Is to Come. 2010. 194p. pap. 15.33 (978-1-154-81360-9(6)); 96p. pap. 15.36 (978-1-154-06924-2(9)); 270p. pap. 15.57 (978-1-152-57741-1(7)) General Bks. LLC.
—The Pilgrim's Progress from this World to that Which Is to Come. 2009. 280p. 34.95 (978-0-557-00339-6(3)); (ENG.). pap. 19.95 (978-0-557-00338-9(5)) Lulu Enterprises Inc.
—The Pilgrim's Progress, from This World, to That Which Is to Come. 2010. 350p. pap. 32.75 (978-1-177-11845-3(9)); 352p. pap. 32.75 (978-1-142-49127-7(7)) BiblioBazaar.
—The Pilgrim's Progress, from This World, to That Which Is to Come. 2009. 200p. pap. (978-1-150-30090-5(6)) Books LLC.
—The Pilgrim's Progress from This World to That Which Is to Come. 2011. 334p. pap. 31.75 **(978-1-172-89555-7(4))** 2010. 340p. pap. 31.75 (978-1-175-76310-5(1)) 2010. 450p. pap. 36.75 (978-1-148-18670-2(0)) 2010. 540p. pap. 40.75 (978-1-143-81841-7(5)) 2010. 430p. pap. 35.75 (978-1-142-12081-8(3)) BiblioBazaar.
—Pilgrim's Progress from This World to That Which Is to Come. 2010. 196p. pap. 19.99 (978-1-150-86769-9(8)) General Bks. LLC.
—The Pilgrim's Progress from this world to that which is to Come. 2010. (ENG.). 356p. pap. 32.75 **(978-1-178-45822-0(9))** BiblioBazaar.
—The Pilgrim's Progress from This World to That Which Is to Come; by John Bunyan with Illustrations from Designs by J D Watson. 2006. 496p. per. 29.99 (978-1-4255-5514-6(4)) MPublishing.
—The Pilgrim's Progress from This World to That Which Is to Come Delivered. 2009. (ENG.). 294p. 34.99 (978-1-117-05143-7(9)) BiblioBazaar.
—The Pilgrim's Progress from This World to That Which Is to Come Delivered under the Similitude of a Dream by John Bunyan the Text Divided into Chap. 2006. 488p. per. 29.99 (978-1-4255-5418-7(0)) MPublishing.
—El Progreso del Peregrino: Un Lavorito de los Lectores Por Gencraiones. 2010. (Abridged Christian Classics Ser.).Tr. of Pilgrim's Progress. (SPA.). 192p. pap. 3.99 (978-1-61626-030-9(0), Casa Promesa) Barbour Publishing, Inc.
Bunyan, John & Barnard, Frederick. The Pilgrim's Progress. 2010. 280p. pap. 27.75 (978-1-175-75177-5(4)) BiblioBazaar.
—The Pilgrim's Progress from This World to That Which Is to Come. 2010. (ENG.). 394p. pap. 33.75 (978-1-176-28769-3(9)) BiblioBazaar.
—The Pilgrim's Progress, from This World to That Which Is to Come. 2010. 332p. pap. 31.75 (978-1-171-85416-6(1)) BiblioBazaar.
Bunyan, John & Cheever, George Barrell. The Pilgrim's Progress. 2010. 556p. pap. 42.75 (978-1-146-51235-0(X)) BiblioBazaar.

Bunyan, John & Gilbert, John. The Pilgrim's Progress from This World to That Which Is to Come. 2010. 446p. pap. 36.75 (978-1-142-29418-2(8)) BiblioBazaar.

Bunyan, John & Hale, Edward Everett. The Pilgrim's Progress. 2010. 134p. pap. 20.75 (978-1-175-98199-8(0)) BiblioBazaar.

Bunyan, John & Landels, William. The Pilgrim's Progress. 2011. 404p. pap. 34.75 (978-1-174-97178-5(9)) BiblioBazaar.

Bunyan, John & Lydon, A. F. 1836-1917. The Pilgrim's Progress: From this world to that which is to Come. 2010. (ENG.). 224p. pap. 25.75 (978-1-176-23658-5(X)) BiblioBazaar.

Bunyan, John & Lydon, Alexander Francis. The Pilgrim's Progress from This World to That Which Is to Come. 2010. 368p. pap. 32.75 (978-1-143-18146-7(8)) BiblioBazaar.

Bunyan, John & Offor, George. The Pilgrim's Progress: From this world to that which is to Come. 2010. (ENG.). 372p. pap. 32.75 (978-1-177-29261-0(0)) BiblioBazaar.

Bunyan, John & Scott, Thomas. The Pilgrim's Progress. 2011. 398p. pap. 33.75 (978-1-179-97568-9(5)) 2010. 350p. (gr. 12-12). pap. 32.75 (978-1-141-99416-8(X)) BiblioBazaar.

Bunyan, John & Scott, Thomas. The Pilgrim's Progress from This World to That Which Is to Come. 2010. 380p. pap. 33.75 (978-1-178-22864-9(9)); 386p. pap. 33.75 (978-1-175-75180-5(4)) BiblioBazaar.

Bunyan, John & Strang, William. The Pilgrim's Progress from This World to That Which Is to Come. 2010. 388p. pap. 33.75 (978-1-175-99329-8(8)) BiblioBazaar.

Bunyan, John & Venables, Edmund. The Pilgrim's Progress from This World to That Which Is to Come. 2010. (ENG.). 324p. pap. 30.75 (978-1-171-53766-3(2)) BiblioBazaar.

Bunyan, John & Walton, Izaak. Pilgrim's Progress. 2011. 434p. pap. 35.75 (978-1-173-54148-4(9)) 2010. 458p. (gr. 12-12). pap. 36.75 (978-1-144-62455-0(X)) 2010. 442p. (gr. 12-12). pap. 35.75 (978-1-142-35067-3(3)) BiblioBazaar.

Bunyan, John, et al. The Pilgrim's Progress. 2011. 204p. pap. 24.75 (978-1-179-97388-3(7)) 2011. 596p. pap. 44.75 (978-1-172-75673-5(2)) 2010. (ENG.). 594p. pap. 44.75 (978-1-171-54630-6(0)) 2010. (ENG.). 448p. pap. 36.75 (978-1-178-01251-4(4)) 2010. 620p. pap. 45.75 (978-1-148-57943-6(5)) BiblioBazaar.

—The Pilgrim's Progress: From This World to That Which Is to Come. Lovik, C. J., ed. 2009. 240p. 26.99 (978-1-4335-0699-4(8)) Crossway.

—The Pilgrim's Progress from This World to That Which Is to Come. 2010. (ENG.). 210p. pap. 24.75 (978-1-177-29187-3(8)) BiblioBazaar.

Bunyan, John, et al. The Pilgrim's Progress from This World to That Which Is to Come; 2011. 212p. pap. 24.75 (978-1-179-98082-9(4)) BiblioBazaar.

Bunyan, John Jr. & Bunyan, John. The Pilgrim's Progress. 2010. 524p. pap. 40.75 (978-1-174-93336-3(4)) BiblioBazaar.

—The Pilgrim's Progress: From This World, to That Which Is to Come. 2010. 492p. pap. 38.75 (978-1-142-47494-2(1)) BiblioBazaar.

—The Pilgrim's Progress from This World to That Which Is to Come. 2010. (ENG.). 394p. pap. 33.75 (978-1-174-92190-2(0)); 408p. pap. 34.75 (978-1-174-92188-9(9)) BiblioBazaar.

Bunyan, John Jr., et al. Pilgrim's Progress. 2010. 430p. pap. 35.75 (978-1-145-35483-8(1)) BiblioBazaar.

Bunyan, John Jr., et al. The Pilgrim's Progress from This World to That Which Is to Come. 2010. 574p. pap. 43.75 (978-1-178-29037-0(9)); (ENG.). 418p. pap. 34.75 (978-1-174-92189-6(7)) BiblioBazaar.

Burney, Claudia Mair. The Exorsistah. 2010. (ENG.). 336p. mass mkt. 7.99 (978-1-4516-1093-2(9), Pocket Star) Pocket Star.

Caine, Hall. The Christian (German Edition) 2009. 552p. 29.99 (978-1-103-10311-9(3)) 2009. 552p. pap. 23.99 (978-1-103-10308-9(3)) 2008. 616p. 38.99 (978-0-554-24264-4(8)) 2008. 616p. 34.99 (978-0-554-33567-4(0)) 2007. (ENG.). 614p. pap. 33.99 (978-1-4264-6129-3(1)) BiblioBazaar.

—The Christian (German Edition) 2009. 222p. pap. (978-1-4588-6752-0(8)) Books LLC.

—The Christian (German Edition) reprint ed. lib. bdg. 48.00 (978-0-7426-1082-8(9)) Classic Bks.

—The Christian (German Edition) 2006. (ENG.). pap. (978-1-4065-1128-4(5)) Dodo Pr.

—The Christian (German Edition) 2007. (ENG.). 546p. 57.95 (978-0-548-06831-1(3)) Kessinger Publishing, LLC.

Cantrell, Julie. Into the Free. 2012. (ENG.). 368p. pap. 12.99 (978-0-7814-0424-2(X)) Cook, David C.

Cherry, Kittredge. At the Cross. 2008. 312p. per. 18.95 (978-1-933993-42-3(1)) Androgyne Bks.

Chi, Charlie. Letters to My Friends from Christ: The Journey to Your Soul. 2009. pap. 13.99 (978-1-61566-020-9(8)) Tate Publishing & Enterprises, LLC.

Chiappa, Patti Leudeman. Sara's Journey: A Novel. 2010. pap. 14.99 (978-1-61663-299-1(2)) Tate Publishing & Enterprises, LLC.

Chick, Jack T. This Was Your Life. 2007. (LAO.). 0.16 (978-0-7589-0678-6(1), 1736) Chick Pubns., Inc.

Combs, Leon. A Search for Reality. 2007. 176p. (ENG.). 21.99 (978-1-60266-967-3(8)); per. 13.99 (978-1-60266-966-6(X)) Xulon Pr., Inc.

Conte, Josue Raul. The Stones Cry Out! 2006. 425p. per. 21.95 (978-1-60002-147-3(6), 4091) Mountain Valley Publishing, LLC.

Crews, T. Joshua Abel. 2007. 92p. per. 16.95 (978-1-4241-7743-1(X)) PublishAmerica, Inc.

Crossing, Joan. Jezebel's Wings. 2007. 54p. pap. 16.95 (978-1-4241-8846-8(6)) PublishAmerica, Inc.

Cummins, Maria. Mabel Vaughan. 2010. 508p. pap. 29.95 (978-1-4290-4464-6(0)) Applewood Bks.

Daniel, Elizabeth. Reconciled. 2007. 368p. per. 19.99 (978-1-60266-482-1(X)) Xulon Pr., Inc.

Darby, Nazara. God Has a Plan for Our Lives & Not Manaes Plan: Grace's Story. 2008. 68p. pap. 21.00 (978-1-4389-2051-1(2)) AuthorHouse.

Davis, Anita. Fumble: Mitch & Mia's Story. 2009. 126p. pap. 11.95 (978-1-4327-4740-4(1)) Outskirts Pr., Inc.

Davis, Brenda. Because They Love Me? 2007. 76p. per. 16.95 (978-1-60441-477-6(4)) PublishAmerica, Inc.

Davis, Bryan. Eye of Oracle. 2006. 400p. (J). pap. 14.99 (978-0-89957-870-5(5)) AMG Pubs.

Dekker, Ted. Chaos, 0 vols. 2010. (Books of History Chronicles: Bk. 4). 256p. pap. 9.99 (978-1-59554-862-7(9)) Nelson, Thomas Inc.

—Chosen, 0 vols. 2010. (Books of History Chronicles: Bk. 1). 272p. (YA). pap. 9.99 (978-1-59554-859-7(9)) Nelson, Thomas Inc.

—Renegade, 0 vols. 2010. (Books of History Chronicles: Bk. 3). 288p. pap. 9.99 (978-1-59554-861-0(0)) Nelson, Thomas Inc.

Denny, Ewan. Loving on the Edge. 2008. 120p. pap. 9.99 (978-0-9551496-7-2(3)) Ministry In Art GBR. Dist: STL Distribution North America.

Doherty, Catherine. Not Without Parables: Stories of Yesterday, Today & Eternity. 2nd alt. ed. (Illus.). 187p. pap. (978-0-921440-16-1(2)) Madonna Hse. Pubns.

Downs, Tim. Plague Maker, 0 vols. 2006. 416p. per. 15.99 (978-1-59554-235-9(3)) Nelson, Thomas Inc.

Dubrova, Oksana. Empyrean Love. 2009. 236p. pap. 15.95 (978-1-4401-6510-8(6)) iUniverse, Inc.

Eastham, Earl A. The Adrian Assignment, 1 vol. 2010. 134p. pap. 24.95 (978-1-4489-4267-1(5)) PublishAmerica, Inc.

Ellis, Jamellah. That Faith, That Trust, That Love. 2007. (ENG.). 384p. mass mkt. 6.99 (978-0-345-49497-9(0), One World/Ballantine) Random House Publishing Group.

Eom, Jacob Y. My Brother My Lord. 2007. (KOR.). 128p. per. 13.99 (978-1-60477-134-3(8)) Xulon Pr., Inc.

Finley, Martha. Christmas with Grandma Elsie. 2010. (ENG.). 324p. pap. 30.75 (978-1-143-97372-7(0)) BiblioBazaar.

—Christmas with Grandma Elsie. 2009. 148p. pap. (978-1-150-34013-0(4)) Books LLC.

—Christmas with Grandma Elsie. 2010. 130p. pap. 21.89 (978-1-153-59562-9(1)) General Bks. LLC

—Christmas with Grandma Elsie. 2010. (Elsie Dinsmore Collection Ser.). (ENG.). 234p. (J). pap. 7.95 (978-1-59856-414-3(5)) Hendrickson Pubs. Marketing, LLC.

—Christmas with Grandma Elsie. 2010. 324p. 36.76 (978-1-164-34655-5(5)); pap. 24.76 (978-1-163-94701-2(6)) Kessinger Publishing, LLC.

—Elsie's Girlhood. 2008. 300p. 25.99 (978-0-554-32464-7(4)); 28.99 (978-0-554-23161-7(1)) BiblioBazaar.

—Elsie's Girlhood. 2007. (ENG.). 292p. per. (978-1-4065-4308-7(X)) Dodo Pr.

—Elsie's Girlhood. 2009. (Original Elsie Classics Ser.). (ENG., Illus.). 316p. (J). pap. 7.95 (978-1-59856-402-0(1)) Hendrickson Pubs. Marketing, LLC.

—The Two Elsies. l.t. ed. 2006. (ENG.). 210p. pap. 22.99 (978-1-4264-7097-4(5)); Bk. 10. 190p. pap. 19.99 (978-1-4264-7021-9(5)) BiblioBazaar.

Flanagan, Crystal. 10 Seconds from Glory. 2010. pap. 12.99 (978-1-61663-688-3(2)) Tate Publishing & Enterprises, LLC.

Flowers, Pastor Jacqueline. Where Are the Men? 2011. 276p. pap. 14.95 (978-0-9634196-4-4(1), Llumina Christian Bks.) Aeon Publishing Inc.

Freeman, Mary E. Wilkins. Jerome, a Poor Man. 2009. 272p. pap. (978-0-217-49624-7(5)) Books LLC.

—Jerome, a Poor Man. 2007. (ENG.). 444p. per. (978-1-4065-6045-9(6)) Dodo Pr.

Gaede, Kenya. The Great Sacrifice: A Thriller. 2011. pap. 25.99 (978-1-61663-881-8(8)) Tate Publishing & Enterprises, LLC.

Golden, Ray. Christiana's Secret: The Lost Treasure of Dead Man's Gulch. 2009. 160p. 23.50 (978-1-60693-596-5(8), Eloquent Bks.) AEG Literary Publishing Services, Inc.

Griggs, Vanessa Davis. If Memory Serves. 2008. (ENG.). 320p. 15.00 (978-0-7582-1735-3(6), Dafina) Kensington Publishing Corp.

Gulley, Philip. Almost Friends: A Harmony Novel. 2007. (ENG., Illus.). 224p. pap. 12.95 (978-0-06-089730-7(9), HarperOne) HarperCollins Pubs.

Hafer, Todd & Hafer, Jedd. From Bad to Worse: A Novel with Girls. 2007. (Bad Idea Ser.). (ENG., Illus.). 272p. (YA). per. 12.99 (978-1-57683-970-6(2)) NavPress Publishing Group.

Haslam, Gerald W. Grace Period. 2006. (Western Literature Ser.). (ENG.). 300p. 24.95 (978-0-87417-679-7(4)) Univ. of Nevada Pr.

Herman, Kathy. The Grand Scheme. l.t. ed. 2009. (Phantom Hollow Ser.). 560p. 29.95 (978-1-4104-1281-2(4)) Thorndike Pr.

Howe, Bridget S. If the West Falls... Globalization, the End of America & Biblical Prophecy. 2011. 348p. 39.95 (978-1-4497-2181-7(8)); pap. 24.95 (978-1-4497-2180-0(X)) Author Solutions, Inc. (WestBow Pr.).

Hurston, Zora Neale. Moses, Man of the Mountain. 2008. (P. S. Ser.). (ENG.). 352p. pap. 13.99 (978-0-06-169514-8(9), HarperPerennial) HarperCollins Pubs.

Ingels, Keith. The Copper Scroll. 2011. pap. 12.99 (978-1-61739-559-8(5)) Tate Publishing & Enterprises, LLC.

Jackson, Neta. The Yada Yada Prayer Group Gets Real. l.t. ed. 2008. (Yada Yada Prayer Group Ser.). (ENG.). 576p. pap. 31.95 (978-1-59415-259-7(4), Walker Large Print) Cengage Gale.

—The Yada Yada Prayer Group Gets Real. l.t. ed. 2008. (Yada Yada Prayer Group Ser.). 575p. 31.95 (978-1-4104-0797-9(7)) Thorndike Pr.

Jenkins, Jerry B. Seclusion Point, 0 vols. 2009. (Renegade Spirit Ser.). 256p. (YA). pap. 14.99 (978-1-59554-839-9(4)) Nelson, Thomas Inc.

Jenkins, Jerry B. & Perrodin, John. The Tattooed Rats. 2008. 240p. (YA). pap. 9.99 (978-1-59554-413-1(5)) Nelson, Thomas Inc.

John Jr. After 30 Minutes in Hell a Man Came from the Darkness to the Light: Volume 1. 2011. 58p. pap. 15.99 (978-1-4568-7979-2(0)) Xlibris Corp.

Johnson, Ashley. Children of Wrath. 2008. 300p. pap. 17.50 (978-1-84799-984-9(0)) Lulu Enterprises Inc.

Johnson, Vera L. In the Beginning. 2007. 86p. pap. 10.00 (978-0-8059-7576-5(4)) Dorrance Publishing Co., Inc.

Jones, Alicia Hill. Blessings of Purpose. 2007. pap. 12.95 (978-0-9794646-0-7(9)) Destiny 11 Pubns.

Jones, Annie. The Sisterhood of the Queen Mamas. l.t. ed. 2007. (Center Point Premier Fiction Large Print) Ser.). 302p. 31.95 (978-1-58547-911-5(X)) Ctr. Point Large Print.

Jones, Brandi. A New Way. 2011. 156p. pap. 14.99 (978-1-61379-176-9(3)) Xulon Pr., Inc.

Jr., John. After 30 Minutes in Hell a Man Came from the Darkness to the Light: Volume 1. 2011. 58p. 24.99 (978-1-4568-7980-8(4)) Xlibris Corp.

Kingsbury, Karen. Family. l.t. ed. 2007. (Firstborn Ser.). (ENG.). 507p. per. 16.95 (978-1-59415-188-0(1), Walker Large Print) Cengage Gale.

—Family. rev. l.t. ed. 2007. (Firstborn Ser.). 509p. 30.95 (978-0-7862-9611-8(9)) Thorndike Pr.

—Found. l.t. ed. 2007. (Firstborn Ser.). (ENG.). 519p. per. 16.95 (978-1-59415-182-8(2), Walker Large Print) Cengage Gale.

—Found. l.t. rev. ed. 2007. (Firstborn Ser.). 521p. 30.95 (978-0-7862-9302-5(0)) Thorndike Pr.

—Learning. l.t. ed. 2011. (Bailey Flanigan Ser.: No. 2). pap. 17.99 (978-1-59415-391-4(4)) Cengage Gale.

—Rejoice. l.t. ed. 2006. (Redemption Ser.). (ENG.). 495p. per. 15.95 (978-1-59415-119-4(9), Walker Large Print) Cengage Gale.

—Reunion. l.t. ed. 2006. (Redemption Ser.). (ENG.). 530p. per. 15.95 (978-1-59415-120-0(2), Walker Large Print) Cengage Gale.

Kingsbury, Karen & Smalley, Gary. Rejoice. 2009. (Redemption Ser.: 4). (ENG.). 384p. pap. 12.99 (978-1-4143-3303-8(X)) Tyndale Hse. Pubs.

—Reunion. 2009. (Redemption Ser.: 5). (ENG.). 400p. pap. 12.99 (978-1-4143-3304-5(8)) Tyndale Hse. Pubs.

Laake, Winter. The Satanic Paradigm. 2010. 240p. 31.51 (978-0-557-31310-5(4)); pap. 15.00 (978-0-557-38196-8(7)) Lulu Enterprises Inc.

Lawhead, Stephen R. The Sword & the Flame. 2011. (Dragon King Trilogy Ser.). 368p. pap. 9.99 (978-1-59554-959-4(5)) Nelson, Thomas Inc.

Lecomte, Eva. Paua the Waldensian. W. M. Strong, tr. 2007. (ENG.). 168p. pap. 19.99 (978-1-4264-2128-0(1)); 166p. pap. 21.99 (978-1-4264-2196-9(6)) BiblioBazaar.

Lee, Casey. Kingdom Come: Volume One. 2010. 396p. 42.95 (978-1-4497-0357-2(X)); pap. 27.95 (978-1-4497-0555-8(3)) Author Solutions, Inc. (WestBow Pr.).

Lehn, Sydney vom. Dare to Imagine. 144p. pap. 2.95 (978-0-88028-217-8(7), 1569) Forward Movement Pubns.

Leigh, Tamara. Perfecting Kate. 2007. (Tamara Leigh Ser.). (ENG.). 416p. per. 12.99 (978-1-59052-927-0(8), Multnomah Fiction) Doubleday Religious Publishing Group, The.

Leonard Smith. After the Flood. 2009. 252p. 26.95 (978-1-4401-8439-0(9)); pap. 16.95 (978-1-4401-8438-3(0)) iUniverse, Inc.

Lewis, Sherri. The List. 2011. (ENG.). 304p. 6.99 (978-1-60162-892-3(7)) Urban Bks.

Lewis, Sherri L. Dance into Destiny. 2008. (ENG.). 288p. 14.95 (978-1-60162-950-0(8)) Urban Bks.

Logsdon, Gene. Pope Mary: And the Church of Almighty Good Food. 2011. 200p. 24.95 (978-0-9789676-4-2(X)) Wicker Pk. Pr., Ltd.

Longfellow, Ki. The Secret Magdalene. 2007. (ENG., Illus.). 448p. per. 14.95 (978-0-307-34667-4(6), Three Rivers Pr.) Crown Publishing Group.

Lopez, Heidi Jo. The Knights Revealed. 2011. pap. 21.99 (978-1-61739-165-1(4)) Tate Publishing & Enterprises, LLC.

Lost & Found. 2008. 274p. (YA). per. 15.95 (978-0-9778564-0-4(2)) Iluzhions Publishing.

MacDonald, George. Ranald Bannerman's Boyhood. 2007. (ENG.). 250p. pap. 22.99 (978-1-4264-3515-7(0)); 216p. pap. 20.99 (978-1-4264-3480-8(4)) BiblioBazaar.

—Ranald Bannerman's Boyhood. 2007. (Illus.). 256p. per. (978-1-4065-3017-9(4)) Dodo Pr.

—Ranald Bannerman's Boyhood. 2007. (ENG.). 392p. per. 33.95 (978-0-548-79305-3(0)) Kessinger Publishing, LLC.

—Salted with Fire. 2007. (ENG.). 152p. per. 10.95 (978-1-60312-315-0(6)); 24.95 (978-1-60312-733-2(X)) Aegypan.

—Salted with Fire. 2006. 182p. pap. 19.99 (978-1-4264-3407-5(3)) 2007. (ENG.). 202p. pap. 22.99 (978-1-4264-3457-0(X)) BiblioBazaar.

—Salted with Fire. 2007. (ENG.). 184p. per. (978-1-4065-3020-9(4)) Dodo Pr.

Mackel, Kathryn. Outriders, 0 vols. 2007. (Birthright Project Ser.). 268p. (YA). (gr. 8-13). pap. 9.99 (978-1-59554-403-2(8)) Nelson, Thomas Inc.

Macomber, Debbie. The Shop on Blossom Street. 2010. (ENG.). 400p. mass mkt. (978-0-7783-2882-7(1), 0778328821, Mira Bks.) Harlequin Enterprises, Ltd.

Mae, Terry. An Illogical, Improbable, Incredible Love: Finding True Love, the Second Time Around. 2010. 323p. pap. 14.95 (978-1-4327-6242-1(7)) Outskirts Pr., Inc.

Martha Finley. Grandmother Elsie. l.t. ed. 2007. (ENG.). 208p. pap. 22.99 (978-1-4264-8305-9(8)) BiblioBazaar.

Martin, Charles. Maggie. l.t. ed. 2007. (Center Point Premier Fiction (Large Print) Ser.). 335p. 31.95 (978-1-58547-884-2(9)) Ctr. Point Large Print.

Mayo Anderson, Marilyn. Sheena's Dreams. 2011. (ENG.). 288p. 6.99 (978-1-60162-813-8(7)) Urban Bks.

McBride, Gordon. Flying to Tombstone. 2009. (ENG.). pap. 18.99 (978-1-59092-727-4(3)) Orchard House Pr.

McClain, Paul. The Valley of the Giants. 2008. 488p. per. 23.99 (978-1-60477-491-7(6)) Xulon Pr., Inc.

McCoy, Glenn. It Seemed Like the End. 2007. 204p. per. 14.99 (978-1-60266-740-2(3)) Xulon Pr., Inc.

McGeown, Susan. Rules for Survival. 2007. 292p. pap. 17.50 (978-0-615-14407-8(1)) Faith Inspired Bks.

McMullen, John William. Poor Souls. Billings, Melanie, ed. 2006. pap. 13.95 (978-1-59374-716-9(0)) Whiskey Creek Pr., LLC.

McNichol, John. The Emperor of North Americ. 2011. 472p. pap. 13.99 (978-1-936453-07-8(X)) Bezalel Bks.

Mesterton, Esther. Hidden Passage: Lost in a Canyon Paradise & Bound by Sin, Will They Find Their Way Home & to the Savior Who Can Set Them Free? 2007. 264p. per. 20.99 (978-1-60247-561-8(X)) Tate Publishing & Enterprises, LLC.

Meyer, Frank. America's Choice: Tragedy or Triumph. 2007. 358p. pap. 18.95 (978-0-7414-4072-3(5)) Infinity Publishing.

Millman, Selena. Christmas with Ty. 2009. 51p. pap. 14.06 (978-0-578-00564-5(6)) Millman, Selena.

Mills, DiAnn, et al. Brothers of the Outlaw Trail: Four Women Surrender Their Hearts to Men with Questionable Pasts. l.t. ed. 2008. (Thorndike Christian Historical Fiction Ser.). 447p. 28.95 (978-1-4104-0449-7(8)) Thorndike Pr.

Montague, Darryl L. Agape: Chapter Two- the Inner Circle. 2007. Tr. of 255. per. 14.95 (978-0-9765843-2-2(8)) Precious Seeds Media Group.

Moore, J. F. Linside Farm. 2007. 352p. 46.95 (978-0-548-54828-8(5)); (ENG.). per. 31.95 (978-0-548-49152-2(6)) Kessinger Publishing, LLC.

—Linside Farm. 2006. 360p. per. 26.99 (978-1-4255-3707-4(3)) MPublishing.

—Linside Farm. 2008. 352p. pap. (978-1-4097-0587-1(0)) Read Bks.

Moore, Stephanie Perry. Chasing Faith. rev. l.t. ed. 2007. (Thorndike African-American Ser.). 495p. 29.95 (978-0-7862-9722-1(0)) Thorndike Pr.

—God Wants You to Shine: A Novelzine¿. 2007. (Faith Thomas Ser.). 144p. (YA). pap. 11.99 (978-0-7369-1920-3(1)) Harvest Hse. Pubs.

Moubarak, Victor. Visions. 2007. 228p. per. 14.99 (978-1-60477-032-2(5)) Xulon Pr., Inc.

Murray, Nicholas. Parish & Other Pencilings by Kirwan [Pseud]. 2006. 288p. per. 23.99 (978-1-4255-2601-6(2)) MPublishing.

Not Easily Broken. l.t. ed. 2007. (Center Point Premier Fiction (Large Print) Ser.). 318p. lib. bdg. 31.95 (978-1-58547-940-5(3)) Ctr. Point Large Print.

Ntihemuka, Patty Froese. Mary: Call Me Blessed: the Story of an Unwed Mother. 2008. 248p. pap. 17.99 (978-0-8127-0484-6(3)) Review & Herald Publishing Assn.

O'Brien, Sonia. Epicenter: A Novel. 2008. 248p. pap. (978-1-59811-598-7(7)) Covenant Communications.

O'Gorman, Angie. The Book of Sins. 2010. 234p. pap. 18.95 (978-1-935514-32-9(6)) Plain View Pr.

Old, Kenneth G. A Boy & His Lunch: Tales about Sharing - the DFerence It Can Make. 2006. 282p. per. 21.99 (978-1-59886-572-1(2)) Tate Publishing & Enterprises, LLC.

Packer, Jeanne. Olive: A Fictional Account of the Life of Olive Ann Oatman. 2010. 220p. 24.99 (978-1-4520-1467-8(1)); pap. 14.49 (978-1-4520-1466-1(3)) AuthorHouse.

Pansy. Tip Lewis & His Lamp. l.t. ed. 2007. (ENG.). 174p. pap. 21.99 (978-1-4264-3652-9(1)); 148p. pap. 18.99 (978-1-4264-3601-7(7)) BiblioBazaar.

—Tip Lewis & His Lamp. 2006. (ENG.). pap. (978-1-4068-2305-9(8)) Echo Library.

Paro, Martin. Truth & Consequences. 2007. 246p. per. 18.99 (978-1-59886-889-0(6)) Tate Publishing & Enterprises, LLC.

Parr, Delia. A Hearth in Candlewood. l.t. ed. 2007. (Candlewood Trilogy). 431p. 27.95 (978-1-4104-0290-5(8)) Thorndike Pr.

Pena, Marianne. No Mercy: Whispers from Hell. 2010. 592p. 39.95 (978-1-4502-0866-6(5)); pap. 29.95 (978-1-4502-0864-2(9)) iUniverse, Inc.

Peterson, Tracie. The Coming Storm. l.t. ed. 2007. (Heirs of Montana Ser.: Vol. 2). 569p. 28.95 (978-0-7862-9742-9(5)) Thorndike Pr.

—Under the Northern Lights. 2006. (Alaskan Quest Ser.: 2). 384p. pap. 14.99 (978-0-7642-2774-5(2)) Bethany Hse. Pubs.

Phillips, Jenny. The Parable of the Golden Pathway. 2010. (978-1-60641-651-8(0)) Deseret Bk. Co.

Phillips, Marc. The Legend of Sander Grant. 2009. (ENG.). 220p. pap. 13.95 (978-1-84659-064-1(7), Telegram Bks.) Saqi Bks. GBR. Dist: Consortium Bk. Sales & Distribution.

Pittman, Allison K. Stealing Home. 2009. (ENG.). 352p. pap. 13.99 (978-1-60142-136-4(2), Multnomah) Doubleday Religious Publishing Group, The.

Pneuman, Angela. Home Remedies. 2007. (Harvest Original Ser.). (ENG.). 240p. pap. 14.00 *(978-0-15-603075-5(6),* Mariner Bks.) Houghton Mifflin Harcourt Trade & Reference Pubs.
Poland, Shirley Gunstream. Hearing the Silent Cries. 2008. 124p. pap. 11.99 *(978-1-60647-919-3(9))* Xulon Pr., Inc.
Poor, Myrtle. My Lonesome Domain. 2008. 91p. pap. 16.95 *(978-1-60672-614-3(5))* PublishAmerica, Inc.
Porter, Cheryl. Never Alone: Battling the Devil in the City of Angels. 2009. (YA). *(978-0-8280-2471-6(5))* Review & Herald Publishing Assn.
Powell, Omar. Getting Out the Game: A Novel Based on True Events & Experiences. 2007. 288p. per. 17.95 *(978-1-4327-0973-0(9))* Outskirts Pr., Inc.
Prescott, Urban. The Day the Thunder Died. 2011. pap. 24.99 *(978-1-61739-157-6(3))* Tate Publishing & Enterprises, LLC.
Ragland, Thomas. Jesus Gnosis Story of Simon by Philip. 2009. 104p. pap. 12.99 *(978-1-4269-1365-5(6))* Trafford Publishing.
Raney, Deborah. Remember to Forget. 2007. (ENG.). 368p. pap. 13.00 *(978-1-58229-643-2(X),* Howard Bks.) Howard Books.
Reagan, Becky. The Manger. 2009. 200p. 26.99 *(978-1-4389-3615-4(X))*; pap. 14.95 *(978-1-4389-3614-7(1))* AuthorHouse.
Refuge. 2009. pap. 12.99 *(978-1-56722-736-9(8))* Word Aflame Pr.
Richards, Scott & Card, Orson Scott. Zanna's Gift: A Life in Christmases. 2008. (ENG.). 144p. 5.99 *(978-0-7653-5835-6(2),* Forge Bks.) Doherty, Tom Assocs., LLC.
Richmond, Legh. The Annals of the Poor. 2008. 188p. 22.99 *(978-0-554-36741-5(6))* 2008. 188p. 25.99 *(978-0-554-27438-6(8))* 2007. 170p. pap. 19.99 *(978-1-4346-3224-1(5))* 2007. (ENG.). 186p. pap. 21.99 *(978-1-4346-3225-8(3))* BiblioBazaar.
—The Annals of the Poor. 2007. (ENG.). 180p. 42.99 *(978-1-4280-7538-2(0))*; per. 35.99 *(978-1-4280-7540-5(2))* IndyPublish.com.
Ricks, M. Awesome Wonder: The Gift of Remembrance. 2007. 168p. per. 24.95 *(978-1-4241-8487-3(8))* PublishAmerica, Inc.
Riley, Lila. Ruby or Heart of Gold. 2007. (ENG.). 108p. 33.95 *(978-0-548-06630-0(2))* Kessinger Publishing, LLC.
Robb, R. E. The Light in Dorky Walker. 2011. 160p. 27.99 ***(978-1-4670-4287-1(0))***; pap. 16.95 ***(978-1-4670-4288-8(9))*** AuthorHouse.
Samson, Lisa. Goodbye, Hollywood Nobody. 2008. (Hollywood Nobody Ser.). (ENG.). 192p. (YA). pap. 12.99 *(978-1-60006-222-3(9),* Th1nk Bks.) NavPress Publishing Group.
Sauls, Debra. So-Called Christians. 2006. 48p. pap. 16.95 *(978-1-4241-3298-0(3))* PublishAmerica, Inc.
Schimel, Chris. Touch One: How Much Is One Soul Worth to God? 2007. (ENG.). 176p. pap. 12.99 *(978-1-59979-181-4(1),* Creation Hse.) Charisma Media.
Sheldon, Charles. In His Steps. 2007. 204p. per. 12.95 *(978-1-933993-58-4(8))* Apocryphile Pr.
Shivers, John. Broken Spirit. 2006. (ENG., Illus.). 344p. 14.00 *(978-1-933341-06-4(8))* CRM.
Siegrist, Audrey. The Upward Way. 2009. (Illus.). 416p. 13.30 *(978-0-7399-2410-5(9))* Rod & Staff Pubs., Inc.
Simons, Joe. Last Chance. 2009. pap. 10.99 *(978-1-60799-245-5(0))* Tate Publishing & Enterprises, LLC.
Smith, Dayshawn. Mizuki Dragon Warrior. 2011. 140p. pap. 19.99 ***(978-1-4628-6143-9(1))*** Xlibris Corp.
Snelling, Lauraine. A Promise for Ellie. 2006. (Daughters of Blessing Ser.: 1). 320p. pap. 12.99 *(978-0-7642-2809-4(9))* Bethany Hse. Pubs.
—A Promise for Ellie. l.t. ed. 2006. (Thorndike Christian Romance Ser.). 497p. 28.95 *(978-0-7862-9159-5(1))* Thorndike Pr.
Snow, Laura. Trading Pain for Pain. 2007. 156p. per. 14.99 *(978-1-60247-119-1(3))* Tate Publishing & Enterprises, LLC.
Stimpson, Michelle. Someone to Watch over Me. l.t. ed. 2011. 503p. 31.99 ***(978-1-4104-4019-8(2))*** Thorndike Pr.
Tate, Kimberly Cash. Heavenly Places. 2008. 359p. per. 13.99 *(978-1-57794-857-5(2))* Harrison House Pubs.
Terry, Wayne Glenn. Holy Infinite God. 2011. 690p. pap. 15.95 ***(978-1-4626-2826-1(5))*** PublishAmerica, Inc.
Teykl, Terry. Mosquito on an Elephants Rump. 135p. 8.00 *(978-1-57892-103-4(1))* Prayer Point Pr.
Toler, Stan & Smith, Debra White. The Richest Person in the World: A Modern-Day Parable. 2007. 157p. 12.99 *(978-0-7369-2043-8(9))* Harvest Hse. Pubs.
Vaughn, Edward. Cumberland County: A Bite of the Apple. 2010. 252p. pap. 14.49 *(978-1-4520-4296-1(9))* AuthorHouse.
Vought, Edward & Vought, Eunice. They Call Me Nuisance. 2010. 167p. pap. 9.95 *(978-1-4327-5746-5(6))* Outskirts Pr., Inc.
Walters, Del. The Jesus Seed. 2010. 368p. pap. 22.99 *(978-1-4520-6231-0(5))* AuthorHouse.
Walton, O. F. Christie's Old Organ. 2009. 60p. pap. *(978-1-151-67731-0(0))* Books LLC.
Warner, Susan. Hills of the Shatemuc. 2008. 644p. 34.99 *(978-0-554-38604-1(6))* 2008. 644p. 38.99 *(978-0-554-29301-1(3))* 2007. (ENG.). 572p. per. 30.99 *(978-1-4346-7336-7(0))* 2007. (ENG.). 642p. per. 33.99 *(978-1-4346-7337-4(5))* BiblioBazaar.
—The Wide, Wide World. 2012. 694p. pap. 48.75 ***(978-1-277-06799-6(6))*** 2010. 584p. pap. 44.75 *(978-1-178-42798-1(6))* 2010. 538p. pap. 40.75 *(978-1-177-67561-1(7))* 2010. 598p. pap. 44.75 *(978-1-177-80126-3(4))* 2010. 362p. pap. 32.75 *(978-1-147-56562-1(7))* 2010. 702p. pap. 48.75 *(978-1-144-13728-9(4))* 2010. 362p. pap. 32.75 *(978-1-144-96417-5(2))* 2010. 342p. pap. 31.75 *(978-1-142-60385-4(7))* 2010. 342p. pap. 31.75 *(978-1-142-18666-1(0))* 2010. 534p. pap. 40.75 *(978-1-142-21806-5(6))* BiblioBazaar.
—The Wide, Wide World. 2010. (Illus.). 446p. pap. 51.32 *(978-1-153-81198-9(7))* General Bks. LLC.
—The Wide Wide World. 2010. 586p. 44.99 *(978-1-140-13751-1(4))*; pap. 44.75 *(978-1-140-13752-8(2))* BiblioBazaar.
—The Wide Wide World. 2009. 564p. pap. 21.00 ***(978-85-62022-69-2(1))*** Endeavor Bks./Mountain States Litho.
—The Wide Wide World. 2010. 484p. pap. 14.90 ***(978-1-60942-056-7(X))*** International Alliance For Women in Music.
Warner, Susan & Wetherell, Elizabeth. Hills of the Shatemuc. 2007. 216p. per. 14.95 *(978-1-60312-367-9(9))*; (ENG.). 216p. 26.95 *(978-1-60312-705-9(4))*; 272p. per. 15.95 *(978-1-60312-329-7(6))*; (ENG.). 272p. 29.95 *(978-1-60312-747-9(X))* Aegypan.
Warner, Susan Bogert. The Wide, Wide World. 2012. 438p. pap. 35.75 ***(978-1-277-07601-1(4))*** 2011. 456p. pap. 36.75 ***(978-1-179-30692-6(9))*** BiblioBazaar.
—The Wide, Wide World. 2009. 236p. pap. *(978-0-217-64684-0(0))* Books LLC.
Warren, Susan May. The Perfect Match. 2009. (Deep Haven Ser.). (ENG.). 352p. pap. 12.99 *(978-1-4143-1385-6(3))* Tyndale Hse. Pubs.
Wayne, Jimmy. Paper Angels: A Novel. 2011. (ENG., Illus.). 304p. 19.99 *(978-1-4516-0619-5(2),* Howard Bks.) Howard Books.
Weatherby, Kent. Rising from Bethany: The Story of Lazarus. 2010. pap. 15.99 *(978-1-61663-302-8(6))* Tate Publishing & Enterprises, LLC.
Weber, Carl. The First Lady. 2008. (ENG.). 288p. 15.00 *(978-0-7582-1576-5(2),* Dafina) Kensington Publishing Corp.
West, R. Grantham. Ad 2040: Clear & Present Danger. 2011. 352p. 29.99 ***(978-1-4568-7777-4(1))***; pap. 19.99 ***(978-1-4568-7776-7(3))*** Xlibris Corp.
Wetherell, Elizabeth. The Wide, Wide World. 2008. 336p. 28.99 *(978-0-559-88119-0(3))*; pap. 30.75 *(978-0-559-88118-3(5))* BiblioBazaar.
—The Wide, Wide World. 2008. 740p. pap. *(978-1-4065-7599-6(2))* Dodo Pr.
—The Wide, Wide World. 2008. 584p. 58.95 *(978-0-548-99900-4(7))* 2007. (ENG.). 588p. per. 43.95 *(978-0-548-64753-0(4))* Kessinger Publishing, LLC.
Wetherell, Elizabeth & Warner, Susan. The Wide, Wide World. 2008. 528p. 55.95 *(978-1-4366-6884-2(0))*; pap. 40.95 *(978-0-548-89457-6(4))* Kessinger Publishing, LLC.
What Would Jesus Do. 3.99 *(978-1-57748-294-9(8))* Barbour Publishing, Inc.
Wheeler, Joe. Christmas in My Heart: A treasury of old-fashioned Christmas Stories, 16, 16. 2007. (Christmas in My Heart Ser.: 16). (Illus.). 128p. pap. 11.99 *(978-0-8280-2029-9(9))* Review & Herald Publishing Assn.
Whitlow, Robert. Greater Love. 2010. (Tides of Truth Ser.). 400p. pap. 15.99 *(978-1-59554-450-6(X))* Nelson, Thomas Inc.
Wick, Lori. White Chocolate Moments. l.t. ed. 2008. (Walker Large Print Ser.). (ENG.). 352p. per. 17.95 *(978-1-59415-190-3(3),* Walker Large Print) Cengage Gale.
—White Chocolate Moments. 2006. 359p. per. 13.99 *(978-0-7369-1780-3(2))* Harvest Hse. Pubs.
—White Chocolate Moments. l.t. ed. 2007. (Thorndike Christian Romance Ser.). 529p. 28.95 *(978-0-7862-9613-2(5))* Thorndike Pr.
Williams, Betty. Throughout Life's Journey: Stay in the House of God. 2007. 76p. per. 16.95 *(978-1-4241-9308-0(7))* PublishAmerica, Inc.
Williams, Sabriena. Wait on the Lord, I Say Wait. 2008. 192p. pap. 16.95 *(978-0-9821153-1-2(8))* Living Waters Publishing Co.
Wilson, Pamela. Backside of the Desert. 2007. 340p. per. 14.95 *(978-0-9779375-1-6(8))* Voices Bks. & Publishing.
Winston, Selena. The First Lady. 2010. 196p. pap. 13.95 *(978-1-4327-6289-6(3))* Outskirts Pr., Inc.
Winter, David J. The Fall & Rise. 2011. 400p. pap. 19.95 *(978-1-60830-034-1(X),* 37477, Aberdeen Bay) Champion Writers, Inc.
Young, Ryan. Climbing Veritas Mountain: One Man's Journey with the Lord. 2010. 124p. 19.95 *(978-1-4502-1944-0(6))*; pap. 9.95 *(978-1-4502-1942-6(X))* iUniverse, Inc.

CHRISTIAN LIFE—JUVENILE LITERATURE

Burns, Jim. Fresh Ideas 10: Intense Illustrations. 161p. 17.99 *(978-0-8307-2920-3(8),* Gospel Light) Gospel Light Pubns.
Munger, Robert Boyd & Nystrom, Carolyn. My Heart — Christ's Home Retold for Children. 2010. (IVP Booklets Ser.). (ENG.). 32p. (J). 1.50 *(978-0-87784-031-2(8))*; 12.99 *(978-0-8308-3395-5(1))* InterVarsity Pr. (IVP Bks.).
Roche, Maite. My First Prayers for My Family. 2010. 14p. 6.99 *(978-1-58617-504-7(1))* Ignatius Pr.
Stark Muyskens, Nancy. For What? 2010. 26p. pap. 12.95 *(978-1-60844-288-1(8))* Dog Ear Publishing, LLC.

CHRISTIAN LIFE—LUTHERAN AUTHORS

Augsburg Fortress, creator. The Lutheran Handbook II. 2007. (Illus.). 304p. per. 14.99 *(978-0-8066-7037-9(1))* Augsburg Fortress, Pubs.
Bloomquist, Karen L., ed. Theological Practices That Matter. 2010. (ENG.). 180p. pap. 15.00 *(978-1-932688-43-6(9),* Lutheran Univ. Pr.) Kirk Hse. Pubs.
Cooey, Paula M. Willing the Good: Jesus, Dissent, & Desire. 2006. (Illus.). 232p. per. 21.00 *(978-0-8006-3664-7(3),* Fortress Pr.) Augsburg Fortress, Pubs.
Gooch, John O. Being a Christian in the Wesleyan Tradition: Belonging, Believing, Living, Growing. 2009. 126p. pap. *(978-0-88177-559-4(2))* Discipleship Resources.
Kierkegaard, Soren. Christian Discourses & the Crisis & a Crisis in the Life of an Actress, Vol. 17. Perkins, Robert L., ed. 2007. (International Kierkegaard Commentary Ser.: Volume 17). (Illus.). 382p. 50.00 *(978-0-88146-031-5(1))* Mercer Univ. Pr.
Kierkegaard, Soren. Discourses at the Communion on Fridays. Walsh, Sylvia, tr. from DAN. 2011. (Indiana Series in the Philosophy of Religion Ser.). (ENG.). 168p. 29.95 *(978-0-253-35673-4(3),* 0253356733) Indiana Univ. Pr.
Kierkegaard, Soren & Kierkegaard, Soren. Christian Discourses: The Crisis & a Crisis in the Life of an Actress. 2009. (Kierkegaard's Writings). (ENG., Illus.). 512p. (C). pap. 45.00 *(978-0-691-14078-0(2))* Princeton Univ. Pr.
Kierkegaard, Soren & Kierkegaard, Soren. Three Discourses on Imaged Occasions. 2009. (Kierkegaard's Writings). (ENG.). 198p. (C). pap. 25.95 *(978-0-691-14074-2(X))* Princeton Univ. Pr.
Kierkegaard, Soren & Pattison, George. Spiritual Writings: A New Translation & Selection. 2010. (ENG.). 304p. pap. 15.99 *(978-0-06-187599-1(6),* HarperPerennial) HarperCollins Pubs.
Kierkegaard, Soren, et al. Upbuilding Discourses in Various Spirits. 2009. (Kierkegaard's Writings: Vol. 15). (ENG., Illus.). 464p. (C). pap. 35.00 *(978-0-691-14077-3(4))* Princeton Univ. Pr.
Levison, John R. Filled with the Spirit. 2009. 500p. 45.00 *(978-0-8028-6372-0(8))* Eerdmans, William B. Publishing Co.
Otte, Hans & Schneider, Hans. Frömmigkeit Oder Theologie: Johann Arndt und Die "Vier Bucher Vom Wahren Christentum" 2007. (Studien Zur Kirchengeschichte Niedersachsens Ser.). (GER., Illus.). 435p. (C). 77.00 *(978-3-89971-386-2(9))* Vandenhoeck & Ruprecht GmbH & Co. KG DEU. Dist: ISD.
Plass, Ewald M., compiled by. What Luther Says. 16th ed. 2006. (ENG.). 1667p. 39.99 *(978-0-7586-1295-3(8))* Concordia Publishing Hse.
Tilley, Janice. Barb Letters. 2007. 112p. per. *(978-1-55452-125-8(4),* Guardian Bks.) Essence Publishing.

CHRISTIAN LIFE—MENNONITE AUTHORS

Augsburger, David. Caring Enough to Confront: How to Understand & Express Your Deepest Feelings Towards Others. 2009. (ENG.). 192p. pap. 12.99 *(978-0-8307-4649-1(8))* Gospel Light Pubns.
Brunk, Truman H. The Singing Junk-Man: Stories of Grace & Hope & Humor. 2010. *(978-1-931038-62-1(7))* Cascadia Publishing Hse., LLC.
Burkholder, David G. Free Indeed! 2009. 272p. 10.20 *(978-0-7399-2409-9(5))* Rod & Staff Pubs., Inc.
Hiele, Gerke van, et al. Encountering the Eternal One: A Guide for Mennonite Churches. 119p. 14.50 *(978-1-894710-75-6(4))* Pandora Pr. CAN. Dist: Herald Pr.
Houser, Gordon. Present Tense: A Mennonite Spirituality. 2011. 174p. pap. 16.95 ***(978-1-931038-90-4(2))*** Cascadia Publishing Hse., LLC.
Kraybill, Donald B. The Upside-Down Kingdom. 2011. pap. ***(978-0-8361-9513-2(2))*** Herald Pr.
Kreider, Alan. Social Holiness: A Way of Living for God's Nation. 2008. (Illus.). 300p. pap. 33.00 *(978-1-55635-848-7(2))* Wipf & Stock Pubs.
Lee, Robert & Lee, Nancy V., eds. Making Sense of the Journey: The Geography of Our Faith. 2009. (ACRS Memoirs Ser.: 1). (Illus.). 352p. pap. 21.95 *(978-1-931038-71-3(6))* Cascadia Publishing Hse., LLC.
Martin, Isaac D. The Christian's Social Responsibility. 2010. 87p. pap. 3.85 *(978-0-7399-2421-1(4))* Rod & Staff Pubs., Inc.
Weaver, Paul M. "More Than Conquerors" 2008. 224p. 9.00 *(978-0-7399-2392-4(7))* Rod & Staff Pubs., Inc.

CHRISTIAN LIFE—METHODIST AUTHORS

Abingdon Press, ed. Time Handbook. 2009. 96p. pap. 12.00 *(978-0-687-65328-7(2))* Abingdon Pr.
Coyner, Michael J., et al. A Year with John Wesley & Our Methodist Values. 2008. 64p. pap. 5.00 *(978-0-88177-550-1(9))* Upper Room Bks.
Day, R. Pat. When All Hell Breaks Loose: Weathering the Storms of Life. 2011. 144p. pap. 12.00 *(978-1-4267-1890-8(X))* Abingdon Pr.
Dunnam, Maxie. Going on to Salvation: A Study of Wesleyan Beliefs. rev. ed. 2008. 157p. pap. 13.00 *(978-0-687-65313-3(4))* Abingdon Pr.
Hollies, Linda H. Jesus & Those Bodacious Women: Life Lessons from One Sister to Another. 10th anniv. ed. 2007. 268p. (Orig.). per. 14.00 *(978-0-8298-1776-8(X))* Pilgrim Pr., The/United Church Pr.
Hudson, Trevor. The Serenity Prayer: A Simple Prayer to Enrich Your Life. 2012. ***(978-0-8358-1094-4(1))*** Upper Room Bks.
Job, Rueben P. Three Simple Rules: A Wesleyan Way of Living. 2007. (Illus.). 80p. bds. 5.99 *(978-0-687-64966-2(8))* Abingdon Pr.
—Three Simple Rules (Korean) A Wesleyan Way of Living. 2008. 80p. pap. 4.25 *(978-0-687-65453-6(X))* Abingdon Pr.
—Three Simple Rules (Portuguese) 2008. pap. 4.00 *(978-1-4267-0021-7(0))* Abingdon Pr.
—Three Simple Rules (Spanish) Tres reglas Sencillas. 2008. pap. 4.25 *(978-0-687-65493-2(9))* Abingdon Pr.
—Three Simple Rules That Will Change the World. 2009. 92p. pap. 8.95 *(978-1-4267-0026-2(1))* Abingdon Pr.
Messer, Donald, ed. Cherishing Life & Love: Reflections of Paul Murphy. 2009. 148p. pap. 13.95 *(978-0-9819921-0-5(2))* Rider Green Bk. Pubs.
Moore, James. Jesus' Parables about Discipleship. 2009. 112p. pap. 11.50 *(978-0-687-64695-1(2))* Abingdon Pr.
Moore, James W. Lord, Give Me Patience, & Give It to Me Right Now! 2010. pap. 14.00 *(978-1-4267-0760-5(6))* Abingdon Pr.
—Rich in the Things That Count the Most. 2006. 126p. per. 14.99 *(978-0-687-49010-3(3),* Dimensions For Living) Abingdon Pr.
Rasmus, Rudy. Touch: Pressing Against the Wounds of a Broken World, 0 vols. 2008. (Illus.). 256p. per. 14.99 *(978-0-8499-1985-5(1))* Nelson, Thomas Inc.
Rose, Tim. The Nearest: Devotion not Devotions. 2011. (ENG.). 175p. pap. 19.95 *(978-1-84694-508-3(9))* O Bks., John Hunt.
Schnase, Robert C. Five Practices of Fruitful Living. 2010. 168p. 16.00 *(978-1-4267-0880-0(7))* Abingdon Pr.
—Forty Days of Fruitful Living: Practicing a Life of Grace. 2010. 104p. pap. 12.00 *(978-1-4267-1594-5(3))* Abingdon Pr.
Slaughter, Michael. Christmas Is Not Your Birthday: Experience the Joy of Living & Giving like Jesus. 2011. 112p. pap. 12.00 *(978-1-4267-2735-1(6))* Abingdon Pr.
Uda, Joan A. At the Water's Edge II: God's grace in everyday Life. 2008. 214p. pap. 14.99 *(978-0-9798270-1-3(9))* Rice Universe Publishing.
Wolf, Carlene. The Power of the Word: -Spiritual Guidance for the Journey of Your Life. 2008. (Illus.). 804p. *(978-1-60800-000-5(1))* LifeReloaded.

CHRISTIAN LIFE—MIDDLE AGES, 600-1500

Bertelsmeier-Kierst, Christa, ed. Elisabeth von Thüringen und die neue Frömmigkeit in Europa. 2008. (Kulturgeschichtliche Beiträge zum Mittelalter und zur frühen Neuzeit Ser.). 350p. pap. 81.95 *(978-3-631-56992-4(0))* Lang, Peter GmbH, Europäischer Verlag der Wissenschaften DEU. Dist: Lang, Peter.
Fliegel, Stephen J. Sacred Meaning in the Christian Art of the Middle Ages. 2009. (The Sacred Landmarks Ser.). (Illus.). 19.95 *(978-0-9638675-5-1(5))* Levin College of Urban Affairs, Cleveland State Univ.
Ghosh, Kantik & Gillespie, Vincent, eds. After Arundel: Religious Writing in Fifteenth-century England. 2012. (Medieval Church Studies). (ENG, FRE & LAT., Illus.). 657p. (C). 196.00 ***(978-2-503-53402-2(3))*** Brepols Pubs. BEL. Dist: ISD.
Ingram, John K. The Earliest English Translation of the First Three Books of the de Imitatione Christi. 2007. (ENG.). 328p. 45.95 *(978-0-548-05161-0(5))* Kessinger Publishing, LLC.
Krueger, Derek. Byzantine Christianity. 2010. 320p. (C). pap. 24.00 *(978-0-8006-9721-1(9),* Fortress Pr.) Augsburg Fortress, Pubs.
McAvoy, Liz Herbert, ed. The Anchoritic Traditions of Medieval Europe. 2010. 256p. 90.00 *(978-1-84383-520-2(7),* Boydell Press) Boydell & Brewer, Ltd. GBR. Dist: Boydell & Brewer, Inc.

CHRISTIAN LIFE—MORMON AUTHORS

Alder, Shannon L. 300 Questions to Ask Your Parents Before It's Too Late. 2011. pap. 11.99 *(978-0-88290-978-3(9))* Cedar Fort, Inc./CFI Distribution.
Allen, S. C. Drought Amidst the Flood. 2010. 132p. pap. 16.00 *(978-1-58982-767-7(8),* Millennial Mind Publishing) American Bk. Publishing Group.
Alston, Burns. Running on Empty. 2008. pap. 12.99 *(978-1-59955-106-7(3))* Cedar Fort, Inc./CFI Distribution.
Anderson, Richard P. Your Divine Purpose: Discovering God's Plan for You. 2008. xi, 196p. *(978-1-59811-518-5(9))* Covenant Communications.
Barkdull, Larry. Rescuing Wayward Children. 2009. xiii, 288p. *(978-1-59811-733-2(5),* Debolsillo) Covenant Communications, Inc.
Bassett, Doug. How to Lengthen Your Stride: Without Getting a Hernia. 2009. pap. 11.99 *(978-1-59955-291-0(4))* Cedar Fort, Inc./CFI Distribution.
Beckert, Charles B. & Brinley, Derry L. A Balanced Life: Living the Hula Hoop Principle. 2006. (Illus.). 118p. per. 10.99 *(978-1-55517-943-4(6))* Cedar Fort, Inc./CFI Distribution.
Bednar, David A. Increase in Learning. 2011. ***(978-1-60908-943-6(X))*** Deseret Bk. Co.
Belcher, Kris. Facing the Son: Eliminating the Spiritual Light Blockers in Your Life. 2011. viii, 120p. pap. 8.99 net. *(978-1-60908-066-2(1))* Deseret Bk. Co.
Benedict, Jeff. The Mormon Way of Doing Business: How Eight Western Boys Reached the Top of Corporate America. 2008. (ENG., Illus.). 256p. pap. 15.99 *(978-0-446-69635-7(8),* Business Plus) Grand Central Publishing.
Bowman, David. Dude! Don't Be a Lemuel! 2011. (YA). pap. 11.99 ***(978-1-59955-943-8(9))*** Cedar Fort, Inc./CFI Distribution.
Boyack, Merrilee Browne. In Trying Times, Just Keep Trying! 2010. x, 148p. *(978-1-60641-597-9(2))* Deseret Bk. Co.
Brown, Randall J. Experiencing Christ: Coming to Know Your Savior. 2009. pap. 11.99 *(978-0-88290-959-2(2))* Cedar Fort, Inc./CFI Distribution.
Burbidge, Clark. Life on the Narrow Path. 2011. 144p. pap. 10.99 *(978-1-59955-457-0(7),* Bonneville Bks.) Cedar Fort, Inc./CFI Distribution.
Bushman, John S. Impractical Grace. 2011. pap. 13.99 *(978-1-59955-475-4(5))* Cedar Fort, Inc./CFI Distribution.
Bytheway, John. Golf: Lessons I Learned While Looking for My Ball. 2008. 17.95 *(978-1-59038-909-6(3))* Deseret Bk. Co.
—I Hope You Know How Much I Love You! And Other Advice for a Happier Life. 2011. 64p. 10.99 *(978-1-60641-947-2(1))* Deseret Bk. Co.
—When Times Are Tough: 5 Scriptures That Will Help You Get Through Almost Anything. 2010. 176p. pap. 10.99 *(978-1-60641-848-2(3))* Deseret Bk. Co.
Carver, Timothy L. That's Faith! 2009. 102p. pap. 8.99 *(978-1-59955-237-8(X))* Cedar Fort, Inc./CFI Distribution.
Christianson, Jack R. & Bassett, K. Douglas. Life Lessons from the Book of Mormon. 2007. 245p. per. 16.99 *(978-1-59955-079-4(2))* Cedar Fort, Inc./CFI Distribution.
Christianson, Jack R., et al. Where Can I Turn for Peace? 2009. (Illus.). 102p. *(978-1-59811-863-6(3))* Covenant Communications.

Cramer, Steven A. Reaching Higher: Twenty-Five Ways to Feel Better about Yourself. 2008. pap. 12.99 *(978-1-59955-122-7(5))* Cedar Fort, Inc./CFI Distribution.

Dalton, Elaine S. A Return to Virtue. 2011. (Illus.). xviii, 141p. (YA). 22.99 ***(978-1-60908-924-5(3))*** Deseret Bk. Co.

Dant, Doris R., ed. Adventures of the Soul: The Best Creative Non-fiction from BYU Studies. 2009. (Illus.). 250p. pap. *(978-0-8425-2739-2(7)*, Brigham Young Univ. Studies) Brigham Young Univ.

Dew, Sheri. God Wants a Powerful People. 2007. 240p. 18.95 *(978-1-59038-813-6(5))* Deseret Bk. Co.

—Saying It Like It Is. 2009. 160p. 17.95 *(978-1-60641-087-5(3))* Deseret Bk. Co.

DiGirolamo, Vincent. Principles with Promise: For members of the Church of Jesus Christ of Latter Day Saints. 2007. 880p. 79.00 *(978-0-9786815-0-0(9))* Celestine Publishing, LLC.

—Principles with Promise: For Members of the Church of Jesus Christ of Latter-day Saints. 2008. 769p. pap. 39.95 *(978-0-9786815-5-5(X))* Celestine Publishing, LLC.

—Principles with Promise: Old Testament, New Testament. 2008. 469p. pap. 29.95 *(978-0-9786815-4-8(1))* 2007. 400p. 49.00 *(978-0-9786815-1-7(7))* Celestine Publishing, LLC.

Eaton, Robert I. Digging Deeper: Understanding & Applying Life-Changing Doctrines from the Book of Mormon. 2006. (Illus.). xi, 192p. 25.95 *(978-1-59038-618-7(3))* Deseret Bk. Co.

Edmunds, Mary El. MEE Speaks. 2008. 192p. pap. 12.95 *(978-1-59038-887-7(9))* Deseret Bk. Co.

Edmunds, Mary Ellen. Keeping It Together in a Pull-Apart World. 2007. 64p. 9.95 *(978-1-59038-754-2(6))* Deseret Bk. Co.

Eyring, Henry B. Because He First Loved Us. 2006. 272p. pap. 7.99 *(978-1-59038-637-8(X))* Deseret Bk. Co.

Featherstone, Vaughn J. The Light of Hope. 2007. 197p. *(978-1-59811-455-3(7))* Covenant Communications.

Ferrell, James. The Holy Secret. 2008. 224p. 24.99 *(978-1-59038-718-4(X))* Deseret Bk. Co.

Freeman, Emily. Love Life, & See Good Days: A How-to Book on Happiness. 2011. (Illus.). vi, 138p. 15.99 *(978-1-60908-742-5(9))* Deseret Bk. Co.

—The Promise of Enough: Seven Principles of True Abundance. 2009. 21.95 *(978-1-60641-143-8(8))* Deseret Bk. Co.

—21 Days Closer to Christ. 2007. 21.99 *(978-1-59038-802-0(X))* Deseret Bk. Co.

Hafen, Bruce C. Spiritually Anchored in Unsettled Times. 2009. (Illus.). xi, 132p. 17.95 *(978-1-60641-069-1(5))* Deseret Bk. Co.

Hales, Robert D. Return with Light & Honor: Four Phases of Our Mortal Journey Home. 2010. 27.99 *(978-1-57008-769-1(5))* Deseret Bk. Co.

Hinckley, Kevin. Burying Our Swords: How Christ Can Remove Rebellion from Our Hearts. 2008. 160p. 21.95 *(978-1-59038-961-4(1))* Deseret Bk. Co.

Holzapfel, Richard. He Will Give You Rest. 2010. 32p. 18.99 *(978-1-60641-667-9(7))* Deseret Bk. Co.

Hughes, Dean. The Cost of Winning: Coming in First Across the Wrong Finish Line. 2008. *(978-1-59038-910-2(7))* Deseret Bk. Co.

Hunt, Cynthia Ann. The Gethsemane Map: Journey to Healing Relationships & Overcoming Fear. 2007. (Illus.). xii, 139p. pap. *(978-0-615-13778-0(4))* Hunt, Cynthia.

Kapp, Ardeth G. Doing What We Came to Do: Living a Life of Love. 2011. 15.99 *(978-1-60908-743-2(7))* Deseret Bk. Co.

—The Joy of Believing. 2007. 80p. 14.95 *(978-1-59038-809-9(7))* Deseret Bk. Co.

Kimball, Edward L. The Teachings of Spencer W. Kimball. 2006. 688p. pap. 25.00 *(978-1-57008-938-1(8))* Desert Bks.

Linford, Marilynne Todd. Sister to Sister. 2009. 183p. pap. *(978-1-59811-803-2(X))* Covenant Communications.

—We Are Sisters: Inspiration for Women. 2007. vi, 181p. *(978-1-59811-345-7(3))* Covenant Communications.

Mackert, Brian. Illegitimate: How a Loving God Rescued a Son of Polygamy. 2009. (Playaway Adult Nonfiction Ser.). (ENG.). 59.99 *(978-1-61545-977-3(4))* Findaway World, LLC.

Mangum, Alan. Agents unto Themselves. 2007. pap. 15.99 *(978-1-59955-095-4(4))* Cedar Fort, Inc./CFI Distribution.

Maxwell, Neal. The Neal A. Maxwell Quote Book, ILLUS Editon. 2009. 448p. 49.99 *(978-1-60641-026-4(1))* Deseret Bk. Co.

—Not My Will, but Thine. 2008. 192p. pap. 12.95 *(978-1-59038-875-4(5))* Deseret Bk. Co.

Maxwell, Neal A. The Promise of Discipleship. 2010. 160p. pap. 13.99 *(978-1-60641-645-7(6))* Deseret Bk. Co.

McKay, David Oman. Treasures of Life. Middlemiss, Clare, ed. 2011. 574p. 63.95 ***(978-1-258-07711-2(6))*** Literary Licensing, LLC.

McLean, Michael. From God's Arms to My Arms to Yours. 2007. (Illus.). 48p. 16.95 incl. audio compact disk *(978-1-59038-493-0(8)*, Shadow Mountain) Deseret Bk. Co.

—Mission to Be Happy. 2009. *(978-1-60641-203-9(5))* Deseret Bk. Co.

Millet, Robert. Are We There Yet? 2010. 168p. pap. 17.99 *(978-1-60641-252-7(3))* Deseret Bk. Co.

—Grace Works. 2007. 176p. pap. 13.95 *(978-1-59038-760-3(0))* Deseret Bk. Co.

Millett, Robert. Men of Influence: The Potential of the Priesthood to Lift the World. 2009. 144p. 18.95 *(978-1-60641-095-0(4))* Deseret Bk. Co.

Moore, Richard G. 12 Keys to Developing Spiritual Maturity: Achieving Our Divine Potential. 2006. 131p. per. 10.99 *(978-1-55517-942-7(8))* Cedar Fort, Inc./CFI Distribution.

Nelson, Kim. Getting Past If Only. 2010. 36p. pap. 14.99 *(978-1-60641-664-8(2))* Deseret Bk. Co.

Nelson, Russell Marion. Hope in Our Hearts. 2009. *(978-1-60641-201-5(9))* Deseret Bk. Co.

Nelson, Wendy Watson. Change Your Questions, Change Your Life. 2009. *(978-1-59038-598-2(5))* Deseret Bk. Co.

—Rock Solid Relationships: Strengthening Personal Relationships with Wisdom from the Scriptures. 2010. *(978-1-60641-728-7(2))* Deseret Bk. Co.

Nelson, Zane. 13 Common Mistakes for Making Life Miserable. 2006. pap. 14.99 *(978-1-55517-948-9(7))* Cedar Fort, Inc./CFI Distribution.

Newell, Lloyd D. Virtue & the Abundant Life. 2012. xv, 341p. pap. ***(978-1-60908-064-8(5))*** Deseret Bk. Co.

Nibley, Peston. L D S Adventure Stories. Nibley, Peston, ed. 2011. 222p. 44.95 ***(978-1-258-02541-0(8))*** Literary Licensing, LLC.

Norcia Mason, Sharon. Gratitude's Transcending Power. 2006. pap. 11.99 *(978-0-9788849-0-1(6))* Mason, Sharon.

Oaks, Dallin H. Life's Lessons Learned. 2011. 21.99 ***(978-1-60908-931-3(6))*** Deseret Bk. Co.

Oaks, Kristen. A Single Voice. 2008. 224p. pap. 17.95 *(978-1-59038-859-4(3))* Deseret Bk. Co.

Okazaki, Chieko. What a Friend We Have in Jesus. 2008. 160p. 16.95 *(978-1-59038-855-6(0))* Deseret Bk. Co.

Olsen, Judy C., compiled by. Angels Round About: True Stories of the Lord's Tender Mercies. 2010. 140p. pap. *(978-1-59811-948-0(6))* Covenant Communications.

Olson, Camille Fronk. Too Much to Carry Alone, Time Out Classics. 2009. 64p. 9.95 *(978-1-60641-036-3(9))* Deseret Bk. Co.

O'Reilly, Sidne. The Twelve Week Challenge: Lay a Foundation for Your Success. 2007. pap. 12.99 *(978-1-59955-083-1(0))* Cedar Fort, Inc./CFI Distribution.

Orme, Gilbert Charles. Short Talks, Anyone? V1-2. 2011. 172p. 42.95 ***(978-1-258-07902-4(X))*** Literary Licensing, LLC.

Packham, E. Richard. Enabled by the Power of Christ. 2008. pap. 12.99 *(978-1-59955-227-9(2))* Cedar Fort, Inc./CFI Distribution.

Packham, Richard. Born of the Spirit. 2008. 92p. pap. 9.99 *(978-1-59955-197-5(7))* Cedar Fort, Inc./CFI Distribution.

Parry, Donald & Parry, Jay. Understanding Isaiah. 2009. 672p. pap. 27.99 *(978-1-60641-081-3(4))* Deseret Bk. Co.

Perry, L. Tom. Family Ties: A Message for Fathers. 2011. 15.99 *(978-1-60908-768-5(2))* Deseret Bk. Co.

Pinegar, Ed J. & Allen, Richard J. On the Bright Side: Feeling Good When Things Seem Bad. 2010. 202p. pap. *(978-1-59811-917-6(6))* Covenant Communications.

Poelman, Anne Os. The Simeon Solution. 2008. 160p. pap. 14.95 *(978-1-59038-886-4(7))* Deseret Bk. Co.

Porter, Bruce D. The King of Kings. 2007. pap. 15.95 *(978-1-59038-815-0(1))* Deseret Bk. Co.

Rasmus, Carolyn J. Simplify: A Guide to Caring for the Soul. 2007. ix, 166p. *(978-1-59038-623-1(X))* Deseret Bk. Co.

Read, Teena. The ABC's of Being LDS: Living the "Mormon" Lifestyle. 2008. pap. 12.99 *(978-1-59955-220-0(5))* Cedar Fort, Inc./CFI Distribution.

Riddle, Lori. Choose to Believe, Live to Receive. 2008. pap. 8.99 *(978-1-59955-177-7(2))* Cedar Fort, Inc./CFI Distribution.

Rife, Richard C. The Divine Virtues: 14 Values to Live By. 2010. pap. 12.99 *(978-1-59955-390-0(2))* Cedar Fort, Inc./CFI Distribution.

—Honoring Christmas in My Heart. 2009. pap. 6.99 *(978-1-59955-314-6(7))* Cedar Fort, Inc./CFI Distribution.

Robinson, Jodi Marie. Women of Virtue. 2009. pap. 12.99 *(978-1-59955-255-2(8))* Cedar Fort, Inc./CFI Distribution.

Robinson, Joy, compiled by. Tender Mercies: Stories to Stir the Soul. 2008. pap. 17.99 *(978-0-88290-848-9(0))* Cedar Fort, Inc./CFI Distribution.

Scott, Richard G. Finding Peace, Happiness & Joy. 2007. 25.95 *(978-1-57008-752-3(0))* Deseret Bk. Co.

—Finding Peace, Happiness, & Joy. 2010. 352p. pap. 17.99 *(978-1-60641-672-3(3))* Deseret Bk. Co.

Shaffer, Kimberly S., compiled by. The Ready Resource for Relief Society, Volume Two: Teachings of Presidents of the Church: Spencer W Kimball. 2006. 142p. per. 11.99 *(978-1-55517-981-6(9)*, Cedar Fort, Inc.) Cedar Fort, Inc./CFI Distribution.

Slater, Mary (Study). The Golden Link: A Novel Based on the Life of Mustafa Kemal. 2011. 424p. 56.95 ***(978-1-258-08585-8(2))*** Literary Licensing, LLC.

Stawski, Willard. That Ye May Prosper: Meaningful Lessons from the Book of Mormon. 2007. 167p. per. 12.99 *(978-1-59955-030-5(X))* Cedar Fort, Inc./CFI Distribution.

Stewart, Ora Pate. From Where I Stood. 2011. 104p. 39.95 ***(978-1-258-07329-9(3))*** Literary Licensing, LLC.

Swift, Charles & Strathearn, Gaye. Living the Book of Mormon: The 36th Annual Sidney B. Sperry Symposium. 2007. 25.95 *(978-1-59038-799-3(6))* Deseret Bk. Co.

Tanner, Obert C. Christ's Ideals for Living. 2011. 484p. 58.95 ***(978-1-258-00219-0(1))*** Literary Licensing, LLC.

Taylor, Gary G. RX for Emotional Headaches. 2007. pap. 12.99 *(978-1-59955-066-4(0))* Cedar Fort, Inc./CFI Distribution.

Theler, Jaime. Enjoying the Journey: Steps to Finding Joy Now. 2008. 157p. pap. 12.99 *(978-0-88290-839-7(1))* Cedar Fort, Inc./CFI Distribution.

Uchtdorf, Dieter F. Your Happily Ever After. 2011. (Illus.). 64p. 14.99 ***(978-1-60641-652-5(9))*** Deseret Bk. Co.

Ulrich, Wendy. Weakness Is Not Sin: The Liberating Distinction That Awakens Our Strengths. 2009. 15.95 *(978-1-60641-139-1(X))* Deseret Bk. Co.

Wamsley, Denise. The Christmas Experiment. 2010. 192p. pap. 13.99 *(978-0-88290-975-2(4))* Cedar Fort, Inc./CFI Distribution.

Watts, Emily. I Hate It When Exercise Is the Answer: A Fitness Program for the Soul. 2009. 14.95 *(978-1-60641-107-0(1))* Deseret Bk. Co.

Wilcox, S. Michael. Time Out for Women Classics. 2011. 58p. 6.59 net. *(978-1-60908-067-9(X))* Deseret Bk. Co.

Wille, Gregory R. Happiness 101. 2008. pap. 10.99 *(978-0-88290-950-9(9))* Cedar Fort, Inc./CFI Distribution.

Wirthlin, Joseph B. Press On: Messages on Faith, Hope, & Charity. 2007. 288p. 21.95 *(978-1-59038-834-1(8))* Deseret Bk. Co.

Wood, Robert S. The Complete Christian. 2007. 208p. 19.95 *(978-1-59038-750-4(3))* Deseret Bk. Co.

Woodger, Mary Jane. Gifts of Self Esteem. 2007. 179p. per. 14.99 *(978-1-59955-020-6(2))* Cedar Fort, Inc./CFI Distribution.

Zobell Jr., Albert L., ed. Modern Parables. 2011. 120p. 39.95 ***(978-1-258-02883-1(2))*** Literary Licensing, LLC.

The 2007 BYU Religious Education Student Symposium. 2007. 200p. pap. 10.95 *(978-0-8425-2685-2(4)*, Brigham Young Univ. Religious Studies Ctr.) Brigham Young Univ.

CHRISTIAN LIFE—ORTHODOX EASTERN AUTHORS

Mathewes-Green, Frederica. At the Corner of East & Now: A Modern Life in Ancient Christian Orthodoxy. 2009. pap. 16.95 *(978-1-888212-34-1(9))* Conciliar Pr.

Raphaela. Becoming Icons of Christ. 2011. ***(978-0-88141-391-5(7))*** St. Vladimir's Seminary Pr.

Webber, Meletios. Bread & Water, Wine & Oil: An Orthodox Christian Experience of God. 2007. 208p. per. 15.95 *(978-1-888212-91-4(8))* Conciliar Pr.

Zacharias. The Hidden Man of the Heart (1 Peter 3: The Cultivation of the Heart in Orthodox Christian Anthropology. Veniamin, Christopher, ed. 2008. 203p. pap. 19.95 *(978-0-9800207-1-7(9))* Mount Thabor Publishing.

CHRISTIAN LIFE—PICTORIAL WORKS

Campbelljones, Brenda & Campbelljones, Franklin. Journey of Spirit Walk of Faith: Our Relationship with God. 2010. 168p. pap. 17.99 *(978-1-4490-4692-7(4))* AuthorHouse.

CHRISTIAN LIFE—POETRY

Angerstein, Stanley. He Is Able: I Am Willing. 2009. 56p. pap. 10.99 *(978-1-61579-216-0(3))* Xulon Pr., Inc.

Anonymous. Flocks Feed Feast: But He Was Wounded for Our Transgressions, He Was Bruised for Our Iniquities - The Chastisement of Our Peace Was upon Him; & with His Stripes We Are Healed. Isaiah 53:5. 2009. 84p. pap. 10.99 *(978-1-60791-775-5(0))* Xulon Pr., Inc.

Antisdel, Vera J. From the Heart. 2011. 140p. pap. 19.99 ***(978-1-4568-4265-9(X))*** Xlibris Corp.

Aragon, Nora D. Song in My Heart: Worshiping God Every Day Through Devotion & Inspiration. 2009. 228p. pap. 15.99 *(978-1-61579-205-4(8))* Xulon Pr., Inc.

Arcemont, Connie. Paradigm of Love. 2007. 60p. per. 16.95 *(978-1-4241-7678-6(6))* PublishAmerica, Inc.

Autry, Samuel Jackson. Peace, Joy, & More. 2007. 73p. pap. 5.92 *(978-1-4303-1756-2(6))* Lulu Enterprises Inc.

Bagwell, Ray E. Transgressions: (Book of Christian Poetry), 1 vol. 2009. 61p. pap. 12.95 *(978-1-61546-074-8(8))* PublishAmerica, Inc.

Balduff, Neva. Uncommon Prayers for an All-too-Common Journey: One Woman's Faith in a Time of Doubt. 2010. pap. 10.99 *(978-1-61566-911-0(6))* Tate Publishing & Enterprises, LLC.

Barber-Dorris (West), Kimberly. I am on my Way. 2008. 51p. pap. 20.49 *(978-1-4357-5279-5(1))* Lulu Enterprises Inc.

Bartlett-Bettger, M. Marie. Poetic Journey Through an Artist Soul. 2011. 48p. pap. 10.99 ***(978-1-61379-351-0(0))*** Xulon Pr., Inc.

Bartlett, Beverly H. The Lord's Garden. 2009. pap. 17.99 *(978-1-60799-249-3(3))* Tate Publishing & Enterprises, LLC.

Baumgaertner, Jill, ed. Imago Dei: Poems from Christianity & Literature. 2012. (ENG.). 224p. pap. 17.99 ***(978-0-89112-321-7(0)***, ACU Pr.) Abilene Christian Univ. Pr.

Bell, Miss Nina. Milestones & Hardships. 2008. 54p. pap. 16.95 *(978-1-4241-8776-8(1))* PublishAmerica, Inc.

Berrigan, Daniel. The Discipline of the Mountain: Dante's Purgatorio in a Nuclear World. 2007. (Daniel Berrigan Reprint Ser.). (Illus.). 144p. pap. 17.00 *(978-1-55635-470-0(3))* Wipf & Stock Pubs.

Boudreau, Bobby A. Messages for Mankind. 2010. 12p. 10.99 *(978-1-4520-1780-8(8))* AuthorHouse.

Bowers, Shereeda L. Empowered for Purpose: From Pain to Promise, 1 vol. 2010. 76p. pap. 16.95 *(978-1-4489-9639-1(2))* PublishAmerica, Inc.

Boyden, Christopher. Questions in the Balance. 2011. 200p. pap. 15.99 ***(978-1-61379-282-7(4))*** Xulon Pr., Inc.

Brown, Antron-Reshaud. Bohemian Rebel Naked & Exposed, Vol. 1. 2007. 131p. pap. 11.95 *(978-0-615-14660-7(0))* Brown, Antron Reshaud.

Brown, Claiborne. The Book of Love towards God: Biblical Poems. 2010. 52p. pap. 10.00 *(978-1-4269-4692-9(9))* Trafford Publishing.

Burns, Hope E. Biblical Truths in Poetry. 2011. 204p. 30.00 ***(978-1-4269-7092-4(7))***; pap. 20.00 ***(978-1-4269-7091-7(9))*** Trafford Publishing.

Bush, Pamela Mae Rhew. Unto the Lord: Poetic Words of Faith, Love & Prayer. 2008. 76p. pap. 8.95 *(978-0-557-01242-8(2))* Lulu Enterprises Inc.

Carlson, David P. Angel Cloud Poetry. 2011. 48p. pap. 8.10 ***(978-1-4269-9362-6(5))*** Trafford Publishing.

Carlson, Melissa. When the Rains Descend. 2008. 56p. pap. 8.95 *(978-1-59858-841-5(9))* Dog Ear Publishing, LLC.

Carpenter, Patricia L. "Poems & 'Blessings' to Enrich Your Life!" 2007. 296p. per. 19.99 *(978-1-4257-7995-5(6))* Xlibris Corp.

—Poems & Thoughts About: 'living' in his Presence! 2007. 128p. per. 19.99 *(978-1-4257-8122-4(5))* Xlibris Corp.

—Poems & Thoughts To: Stay 'true' to the savior ~ no matter What! 2007. 308p. per. 19.99 *(978-1-4257-8051-7(2))* Xlibris Corp.

Carpenter-Williams, Patricia. Collection of Work. 2007. pap. 11.00 *(978-0-8059-8644-0(8))* Dorrance Publishing Co., Inc.

Caswell, Jonathan. Spirit-Led Limericks & Other Christian Poetry. 2011. 90p. pap. 19.95 ***(978-1-4560-9841-4(1))*** PublishAmerica, Inc.

Chamberlain, Letha Christina. Run Straight to Greatest Mystery, 1 vol. 2010. 165p. pap. 24.95 *(978-1-60836-284-4(1))* PublishAmerica, Inc.

Chaucer, Geoffrey. The Selected Canterbury Tales: A New Verse Translation. Fisher, Sheila, tr. (ENG & ENM.). 2012. 800p. pap. 18.95 ***(978-0-393-34178-2(X)***, 34178) 2011. 816p. 35.00 *(978-0-393-07945-6(7)*, 7945) Norton, W. W. & Co., Inc.

Chillemi, Stacey. Keep the Faith: To Live & Be Heard from the Heavens Above. 2007. 71p. pap. 15.96 *(978-1-4116-2845-8(4))* Lulu Enterprises Inc.

Cofield, Michael. The Greatest Spiritual Gift: (Poems of Praise & Compassion), 1 vol. 2010. 108p. pap. 19.95 *(978-1-4489-6693-6(0))* PublishAmerica, Inc.

Coleman, Rhonda Carol. God's Words Thru a Friend. 2009. 74p. pap. 14.95 *(978-1-60749-670-0(4))* PublishAmerica, Inc.

Coleman, Tamala J. Spiritual Expressions. 2007. 72p. per. 10.95 *(978-1-4327-0859-7(7))* Outskirts Pr., Inc.

Collins, An. Divine Songs & Meditations. Stewart, Stanley N., ed. 2011. 56p. 36.95 ***(978-1-258-01960-0(4))*** Literary Licensing, LLC.

Cook, Tammy L. In Rhymes of Trouble: For the Broken Hearted, Lonely, & Overwhelmed. 2010. 56p. pap. 10.49 *(978-1-4490-8152-2(5))* AuthorHouse.

Cooper, Sue. Touching Soul: Devotional Poems & Words of Inspiration on God, Religion, & Yoga. 2010. (ENG.). 208p. 12.95 *(978-1-56589-255-2(0))* Crystal Clarity Pubs.

Curtis, Angela. From Mourning to Morning: 2006. pap. 9.99 *(978-1-60034-683-5(9))* Xulon Pr., Inc.

D., Diamond. Unheard Words, 1 vol. 2009. 73p. pap. 16.95 *(978-1-60749-437-9(X))* PublishAmerica, Inc.

Dailey, Christy Diann. Our Heavenly Son. 2007. 88p. per. 16.95 *(978-1-4241-8067-7(8))* PublishAmerica, Inc.

Dangelo, Cornell. The Light of Truth: The Alpha & Omega. 2007. 424p. pap. 7.77 *(978-1-4343-2119-0(3))* AuthorHouse.

Davis, Christopher. Transformed the New Life. 2011. 58p. pap. 16.95 ***(978-1-4626-2238-2(0))*** PublishAmerica, Inc.

DeLaCruz, Diana. Of the Cross. 2011. 126p. pap. 14.99 ***(978-1-61379-363-3(4))***; 74p. pap. 10.99 ***(978-1-61379-294-0(8))*** Xulon Pr., Inc.

Divers, Betty S. My Soul Cries Out. 2008. 136p. pap. 71.99 *(978-1-4363-3735-9(6))* Xlibris Corp.

Dominguez, Ilusión Guzmán. Passages from My Life. 2009. 64p. pap. 10.99 *(978-1-61579-500-0(6))* Xulon Pr., Inc.

E., Kevin. Timely Rhymes. 2011. 172p. pap. 24.95 ***(978-1-4626-3739-3(6))*** PublishAmerica, Inc.

Eady, H. T. The Blood Song. 2011. 188p. pap. 14.99 ***(978-1-61379-216-2(6))*** Xulon Pr., Inc.

Edwards, Rita Vaughan. From Lessons to Blessings, 1 vol. 2010. 98p. pap. 19.95 *(978-1-4489-4320-3(5))* PublishAmerica, Inc.

Evans, Josie V. A Spirit That Looks down & Calls Me a Living Soul. 2008. 81p. pap. 16.95 *(978-1-60672-126-1(7))* PublishAmerica, Inc.

Fann, David M. Walking with God. 2009. 100p. pap. 10.99 *(978-1-61579-232-0(5))* Xulon Pr., Inc.

Farina, Susie. Words from the Inner Chamber. 2007. 120p. per. 10.99 *(978-1-60266-900-0(7))* Xulon Pr., Inc.

Fleming, Mozell. Arrivals, Departures, & Flights of Fancy. 2008. 107p. pap. 16.95 *(978-1-60610-214-5(1))* PublishAmerica, Inc.

Ford, Deborah S. The Unction Of: One Witness, One Servant. 2007. 34p. pap. 8.00 *(978-0-8059-7694-6(9))* Dorrance Publishing Co., Inc.

Francois, Doris. Tell It as You See It: My Earlier Expressions; God's Interceding Grace. 2010. 92p. pap. 12.00 *(978-1-4269-3053-9(4))* Trafford Publishing.

French, Stewart. From Heaven & Back Again: A Collections of Poems & Musings on the Christian Faith. 2011. 128p. pap. 13.32 *(978-1-4567-7297-0(X))* AuthorHouse.

French, Stewart. More of the Same: Further Poems & Thoughts on the Christian Faith & Life in General. 2011. 136p. pap. 13.32 ***(978-1-4567-8376-1(9))*** AuthorHouse.

Garland, Maurice T. Spiritually Inspired Poems. 2007. 212p. per. 13.95 *(978-1-4327-0993-8(3))* Outskirts Pr., Inc.

Garrett, Alma. All Things New. 2011. 112p. 21.23 ***(978-1-4634-4030-5(8))***; pap. 12.01 ***(978-1-4634-4029-9(4))*** AuthorHouse.

Gilmore, Kelvin. Poetic Persuasions. 2009. 76p. pap. 14.95 *(978-1-60749-542-0(2))* PublishAmerica, Inc.

Glover. Engaging Thoughts: Inspirational Expressions to Motivate Your Day. 2009. 112p. 24.05 *(978-1-4490-2448-2(3))*; pap. 14.95 *(978-1-4490-2447-5(5))* AuthorHouse.

Goins, Terri A. Daybreak: A Christian Anthology. 2010. 356p. 32.00 *(978-1-4269-3067-6(4))*; pap. 22.00 *(978-1-4269-3066-9(6))* Trafford Publishing.

Gordon, Bessie L. Life Is Full of It. 2006. 41p. per. 10.95 *(978-1-60002-244-9(8), 4312)* Mountain Valley Publishing, LLC.

Gossett, Gary. Two Kinds of Love from God Above. 2008. 124p. 26.99 *(978-0-88144-300-4(X))* Yorkshire Publishing Group.

Gray, Shawn Lyn. Through One Boy's Eyes, 1 vol. 2010. 80p. pap. 19.95 *(978-1-4489-3929-9(1))* PublishAmerica, Inc.

Greer, Cathi. Chaos to Grace. 2008. 108p. pap. 19.95 *(978-1-60672-943-4(8))* PublishAmerica, Inc.

Haddad, S. K. Celtic Saints & the English Church. 2010. 170p. pap. *(978-1-85756-775-5(7))* Janus Publishing Co.

Hanna, Ralph, ed. Speculum Vitae: A Reading Text, Volumes 1 And 2. 2009. (Early English Text Society Original Ser.). (Illus.). 390p. 175.00 *(978-0-19-956401-9(9))* Oxford Univ. Pr., Inc.

Harring-Duhart, Mary Ann. On Broken Pieces Sweat & Tears. 2011. 176p. pap. 20.50 ***(978-1-257-37693-3(4))*** Lulu Enterprises Inc.

Hayden, Maggie. Poetry for Christ, 1 vol. 2010. 76p. pap. 19.95 *(978-1-4512-9323-4(2))* PublishAmerica, Inc.

Hayes, Lacresha Nicole. BeComing: My Personal Memoirs. 2007. 152p. per. 17.99 *(978-0-9798154-3-0(6))* Living Waters Publishing Co.

Henderson, Steven G. Flesh Love & Spirit: Cries of a Sinner, Joys of a Saint. 2007. 196p. per. 16.95 *(978-0-595-46674-0(5))* iUniverse, Inc.

Hightower, Shontel D. No More Tears I'm All Grown Up. 2010. 76p. pap. 10.49 *(978-1-4490-8533-9(4))* AuthorHouse.

Hill, Susan. Words That Rock Your Soul . the Spiritual Journey Continues! 2008. 184p. pap. 25.50 *(978-1-4092-3188-2(7))* Lulu Enterprises Inc.

—Words That Rock Your Soul A Poetic Journey from Birth to Death & Beyond. 2008. 120p. pap. 19.95 *(978-1-4092-3062-5(7))* Lulu Enterprises Inc.

—Words That Rock Your Soul A Poetic Journey from Birth to Death & Beyond . by Susan Hill COLOUR VERSION. 2008. 120p. pap. 56.95 *(978-1-4092-3211-7(5))* Lulu Enterprises Inc.

Humphries, Darlene C. Free to Be Me. 2011. 88p. pap. 15.49 ***(978-1-4567-2792-5(3))*** AuthorHouse.

Jacobs, Sherry. Midst of Angels. 2011. 28p. pap. 15.99 ***(978-1-4568-6106-3(9))*** Xlibris Corp.

James, Alvin. Poems from God to Me to You. 2010. 148p. pap. 11.99 *(978-1-4520-0066-4(2))* AuthorHouse.

Jbw. To God with Love: A Collection of Selected Poems. 2009. 170p. pap. 19.95 *(978-1-61546-456-2(5))* PublishAmerica, Inc.

Jeter, Denise. Apples of Gold. 2009. 388p. pap. 20.99 *(978-1-61579-391-4(7))* Xulon Pr., Inc.

Johnson, Faith. Inspirations by Faith. 2007. 132p. per. 13.99 *(978-1-60266-162-2(6))* Xulon Pr., Inc.

Johnson-Medland, N. Thomas. Entering the Stream: Poems about Union. 2011. 156p. pap. 18.00 *(978-1-61097-139-3(6),* Resource Pubns.) Wipf & Stock Pubs.

Johnson-Medland, N. Thomas. From the Belly of the Whale: Poems of the Male Soul. 2011. 134p. pap. 17.00 ***(978-1-61097-415-8(8),*** Resource Pubns.) Wipf & Stock Pubs.

Johnson, Sharyl Lynn. God Is Speakingâ¿ Can You Hear Him, 1 vol. 2010. 50p. pap. 16.95 *(978-1-4512-8693-9(7))* PublishAmerica, Inc.

Jones, Richard O. Storm Shelter Poems for the Children of God: Christian Poetry for all Occasions. 2010. 132p. 21.95 *(978-1-4502-3747-5(9))*; pap. 11.95 *(978-1-4502-3748-2(7))* iUniverse, Inc.

Jordan, Stephannie. The God Who Cares. 2008. pap. 19.95 *(978-1-934363-05-8(7))* Zoe Life Publishing.

Kalevik, Marlene. Gold Nuggets. 2007. 128p. per. *(978-1-55452-196-8(3),* Guardian Bks.) Essence Publishing.

Kiehl, Craig. Poems & Prayers from the Heart. 2009. 128p. pap. 14.99 *(978-1-60791-432-7(8))* Xulon Pr., Inc.

Kilday, Faye. Angels Speaking: Poems for Guidance & Inspiration. 2008. 116p. pap. 12.95 *(978-1-4092-0759-7(5))* Lulu Enterprises Inc.

King, Arlene Fay. A Spoken Word: Christian poems to inspire, exalt, & Comfort. 2010. pap. 7.99 *(978-1-61663-455-1(3))* Tate Publishing & Enterprises, LLC.

King, Toni. Christian Poetry for Married Couples. 2008. 144p. per. *(978-1-55452-255-2(2))* Essence Publishing.

Kizzee, Bobbie. Simple Rhymes for Places in Time. 2010. 128p. 29.99 *(978-1-4415-9104-3(4))*; pap. 19.99 *(978-1-4415-9103-6(6))* Xlibris Corp.

Korich, Jason M. Through Him: A Book of Inspirational Poems, 1 vol. 2010. 54p. pap. 16.95 *(978-1-60610-828-4(X))* PublishAmerica, Inc.

Kosek, Jill. His Words, My Pen, Your Heart, 1 vol. 2010. 118p. pap. 19.95 *(978-1-4489-4208-4(X))* PublishAmerica, Inc.

Langland, William. Piers Plowman: A New Translation of the B-text. Schmidt, A. V. C., tr. from ENM. 2009. (Oxford World's Classics Ser.). (ENG.). 416p. 14.95 *(978-0-19-955526-0(5))* Oxford Univ. Pr., Inc.

Lennon, Pat. Singing in the Valley. 2008. 128p. pap. 14.99 *(978-1-60647-802-8(8))* Xulon Pr., Inc.

Leslie, Belle Anne. Precious Lord, Take My Hand: Poems of Encouragement. 2009. 128p. pap. 12.00 *(978-1-4490-4968-3(0))* AuthorHouse.

Logospilgrim. A light burden: my life as an Orthodox Christian. 2009. 100p. pap. 15.00 *(978-0-557-04857-1(5))* Lulu Enterprises Inc.

Long, Alice Catherine Prince. Psalms Straight from the Heart: Inspirational Poems, Scriptures, & Prayers. 2010. 96p. pap. 10.49 *(978-1-4520-5411-7(8))* AuthorHouse.

Luginbuhl, Frank. Grand Dad's Book of Verse: Volume 1: Expanding the View of the Christian Life & the Lack Thereof. 2007. 60p. per. 16.95 *(978-1-4241-7763-9(4))* PublishAmerica, Inc.

Lundell, Gerry O. My Poetry My Therapy: A Potpourri of Poetry. 2009. 84p. pap. 10.99 *(978-1-60791-834-9(X))* Xulon Pr., Inc.

Lynn, G. G. God Is Love: Inspired Poetry about the Joyful Life God Wants Us to Live. 2008. 72p. pap. 10.95 *(978-1-4343-8427-0(6))* AuthorHouse.

Lynn, Megan. An Eye for Life Poetry. 2011. 170p. pap. 19.99 ***(978-1-4568-8436-9(0))*** Xlibris Corp.

MacKifield, Missionary Alberta. Expressions from the Heart: Divinely Inspired Poetry. 2010. 40p. pap. 16.99 *(978-1-4389-7499-6(X))* AuthorHouse.

Madjemite, Dorene. Quagmires. 2008. 100p. pap. 16.95 *(978-1-60813-063-4(0))* PublishAmerica, Inc.

Malisa, Vanessa. The Lord's Poems, 1 vol. 2010. 62p. pap. 19.95 *(978-1-4489-4341-8(8))* PublishAmerica, Inc.

Mann, Jeanette. Pearls of Wisdom. 2010. 150p. pap. *(978-1-904444-00-8(8))* Apex Publishing Ltd., Essex.

Mason, Vanessa. God Still Answers in the Midst of It All, 1 vol. 2010. 56p. pap. 16.95 *(978-1-4489-3337-2(4))* PublishAmerica, Inc.

Mateus, Isabel Maria. My thoughts & Memories. 2007. 49p. pap. 9.95 *(978-0-615-17480-8(9))* Crossover Ministries.

Matrisch, Ron. Because of Him. 2009. 152p. pap. 11.99 *(978-1-4490-3210-4(9))* AuthorHouse.

McCauley, Trevor T. The Paper Sail: Words of Faith & Inspiration. 2010. 108p. 28.95 *(978-1-61507-183-8(0))*; pap. 11.95 *(978-1-61507-182-1(2))* Cross Bks. Publishing.

McClain, Frances. I'm Amazed at God's Grace. 2008. 96p. pap. 16.95 *(978-1-60563-748-8(3))* PublishAmerica, Inc.

Mckibben. The Lord Is Always There: My Book of Poems. 2008. 120p. pap. 12.99 *(978-1-60477-638-6(2))* Xulon Pr., Inc.

Millette, Lois. Saved & Sanctified: A Poetic Companion to the New Testament. 2010. pap. 26.99 *(978-1-61663-083-6(3))* Tate Publishing & Enterprises, LLC.

Milton, John. Paradise Lost & Paradise Regained. l.t. ed. 2011. pap. 23.99 *(978-1-4104-3584-2(9),* Kennebec Large Print) Cengage Gale.

Mobley, Samuel G. Inspirations from Above. 2011. pap. 9.99 ***(978-1-61777-546-8(0))*** Tate Publishing & Enterprises, LLC.

Moore, Gabriel. Red Ink Poetry. 2008. 132p. pap. 13.99 *(978-1-60647-426-6(X))* Xulon Pr., Inc.

Morneau, Robert F. A Splash of Sunshine: And Other Glimpses of Grace. 2011. 144p. 15.00 *(978-1-57075-930-7(8))* Orbis Bks.

Nieken, Nancy. Poems to Cuddle With: No Subtitle. 2008. 84p. pap. 9.99 *(978-1-60647-521-8(5))* Xulon Pr., Inc.

Norton, Sherry. Chains Broken: With Seeds of Faith Sown & Watered by the Holy Spirit. 2011. 196p. pap. 17.95 ***(978-1-4497-2489-4(2),*** WestBow Pr.) Author Solutions, Inc.

Obeng, Michael Y. Therapeutic Psalm(s) 2011. 388p. pap. 20.99 *(978-1-61215-599-9(5))* Xulon Pr., Inc.

O'Brien, Dermot. Seasons of Light: A Collection of Haiku. 2011. (ENG., Illus.). 80p. pap. 9.95 *(978-1-84730-240-3(8))* Veritas Pubns. IRL. Dist: Dufour Editions, Inc.

Olivo, Helen Brennan. Flowers of Faith: Inspirational Poems. 2007. 52p. per. 10.95 *(978-1-4327-1023-1(0))* Outskirts Pr., Inc.

O'Neill, Jerry R. Out from the Shadows: Poetic Portraits of Faith. 2007. (Illus.). 184p. pap. 21.00 *(978-1-55635-177-8(1),* Resource Pubns.) Wipf & Stock Pubs.

Overbay, Edward. From Jesus' Heart to My Heart to Your Heart. 2011. 268p. 24.59 *(978-1-4567-4399-4(6))*; pap. 14.03 *(978-1-4567-4400-7(3))* AuthorHouse.

Patton, Kenneth L. Recognition: Sonnets on the Mysticism of Human Love. 2011. 108p. 39.95 ***(978-1-258-03507-5(3))*** Literary Licensing, LLC.

Pearson, Carol Lynn. The Sweet, Still Waters of Home: Inspiration for Mothers from the 23rd Psalm. 2011. 64p. 12.99 *(978-1-59955-802-8(5),* Bonneville Bks.) Cedar Fort, Inc./CFI Distribution.

Pendergrass, Joan Exum. To Honor My Father, 1 vol. 2010. 72p. pap. 19.95 *(978-1-4512-8686-1(4))* PublishAmerica, Inc.

Pickett, Evelyn Faith. Psalms of Faith. 2011. 62p. pap. 15.99 ***(978-1-4628-7029-5(5))*** Xlibris Corp.

Piepenhagen, Jacqueline. Heavenly Angels among Us. 2010. 92p. pap. 9.95 *(978-1-4502-4128-1(X))* iUniverse, Inc.

Pierce Jr Ii, David. The Uncensored Gospel: The Eternal G. 2010. 112p. 21.99 *(978-1-4490-7130-1(9))* AuthorHouse.

Pitilli, Loretta. Creating Our Pilgrimage. 2007. pap. 0.00 *(978-0-9801565-0-8(5))* SimplyWrite Pr.

Podvojsky, Ron. The Great I AM 50 Great Christian Poems. 2007. 58p. pap. 6.96 *(978-1-4357-0100-7(3))* Lulu Enterprises Inc.

Potter, Dorian Petersen. Praising Through Poetry. 2011. 148p. pap. 18.97 ***(978-1-257-06282-9(4))*** Lulu Enterprises Inc.

Pruitt, Lonnie E. Prayer Is Our Power. 2008. 100p. pap. 13.95 *(978-1-4327-3269-1(2))* Outskirts Pr., Inc.

Reinert, Richard Shane. He's the Pen, I'm the Paper. 2009. 228p. pap. 15.99 *(978-1-61579-130-9(2))* Xulon Pr., Inc.

Richards, Benita Smith. I Believe in Miracles. 2010. 308p. pap. 15.49 *(978-1-4520-0845-5(0))* AuthorHouse.

Richinson, Rich. A New Life: A Gift from Your Guardian Angel. 2008. pap. 14.95 *(978-0-9800615-0-5(4))* A New Life Publishing.

Rodriguez, Erica Mary. Another Chance. 2011. 72p. pap. 27.00 ***(978-1-4567-4964-4(1))*** AuthorHouse.

Russom, Steven. Hidden Treasures: A Journey of the Heart. 2010. 99p. pap. 19.99 *(978-0-557-55603-8(1))* Lulu Enterprises Inc.

Sander, Timothy. Here among the Hypnotized. 2010. 100p. pap. 9.95 *(978-1-4502-1786-6(9))* iUniverse, Inc.

Sanford, Mary. Scent from Heaven: Fragrance for the Soul. 2011. 112p. 21.23 *(978-1-4567-1697-4(2))*; pap. 10.68 *(978-1-4567-1695-0(6))* AuthorHouse.

Sarno, Sheila L. He Loves Me! A Book of Prayers, Prose & Poetry. 2008. 24p. pap. *(978-1-55452-292-7(7),* Guardian Bks.) Essence Publishing.

Sawatzky, Lee Mark. Searching for Good. 2011. 186p. pap. 19.99 ***(978-1-4628-8408-7(3))*** Xlibris Corp.

Schetzsle, Ed. From the Poet's Hand: Life Lessons. 2007. 53p. per. 10.99 *(978-1-60247-081-1(2))* Tate Publishing & Enterprises, LLC.

Sidney, Philip & Sidney, Mary. The Sidney Psalter: The Psalms of Sir Philip & Mary Sidney. Hamlin, Hannibal et al, eds. 2009. (Oxford World's Classics Ser.). (ENG.). 336p. pap. 18.95 *(978-0-19-921793-9(9))* Oxford Univ. Pr., Inc.

Sinclair, Sarah. Tell Them about Me. 2007. 56p. per. 16.95 *(978-1-4241-5935-2(0))* PublishAmerica, Inc.

Slone, Trevor "Unashamed". Poetry & Wisdom about Life, Love, & What Really Matters. 2010. 212p. pap. 18.99 *(978-1-4490-9781-3(2))* AuthorHouse.

Smithson, Hazel D. Views of Life. 2007. 51p. pap. *(978-0-7951-8794-0(7))* Watermark Pr.

Songer, Daniel R. Jesus' Poetic Song: Inspirational Christian Song Lyrics & Poems. 2009. 188p. pap. 18.49 *(978-1-4389-7972-4(X))* AuthorHouse.

Strawn, Kathryn A. Hope's Garden: Inspirational Poetry for Growing Your Faith. 2006. (ENG.). 76p. per. 11.99 *(978-1-4141-0690-8(4))* Pleasant Word.

Sustaita, Velia. God's ABCs, 1 vol. 2009. 76p. pap. 14.95 *(978-1-61582-764-0(1))* PublishAmerica, Inc.

Taylor, Joy S. Findings: My Journey to Joy: A Collection of Poems. 2007. (Illus.). 102p. per. 9.99 *(978-1-60247-033-0(2))* Tate Publishing & Enterprises, LLC.

The Prophetic Poetess. Pass the Salt! Spiritual Poetry, Prophetic Messages & Empowering Quotes to Awaken the Conscience & Revive the Spirit! 2010. 320p. pap. 17.99 *(978-1-4490-6197-5(4))* AuthorHouse.

Thomas, Valerie. ?Ç£Lord Have Mercy, Mercy on Me?Ç¥: Poetry for the Entire Family. 2010. 138p. pap. 12.95 *(978-1-4327-6331-2(8))* Outskirts Pr., Inc.

Thompson, Carol Ann. Reason & Rhyme. 2010. 176p. pap. 13.95 *(978-1-4497-0375-2(5),* WestBow Pr.) Author Solutions, Inc.

Thomson, James. The City of Dreadful Night, & Other Poems. 2008. 240p. pap. *(978-1-904999-72-0(7))* Kennedy & Boyd.

Time Flies: My First Thirty Years. 2006. pap. 29.95 *(978-0-9791191-0-1(3))* Time Flies Ministries.

Truetomyself. Poems of True Emotions: Poetry from the heart to the Heart, 1 vol. 2010. 63p. pap. 16.95 *(978-1-4489-6180-1(7))* PublishAmerica, Inc.

Turner, Shirley A. Catch the Spirit & Be Set Free. 2011. 118p. pap. 11.99 ***(978-1-61379-240-7(9))*** Xulon Pr., Inc.

Tyler, Louise. Through the Eyes of a Poet. 2008. 116p. 19.99 *(978-1-60791-075-6(6))*; pap. 11.99 *(978-1-60791-074-9(8))* Xulon Pr., Inc.

Weidenweber, Don. Confessions of an Agnostic Believer. 2009. (ENG.). 198p. 13.99 *(978-0-9816514-5-3(3))* Last Chapter Publishing.

Wheeler, Angela. Looking for God. 2010. 115p. pap. 10.00 *(978-0-557-57893-1(0))* Lulu Enterprises Inc.

Whetstone, Carol A. All for Him: Poems & Prayers of Perseverance. 2007. 132p. per. 13.95 *(978-0-595-44927-9(1))* iUniverse, Inc.

Words to His Servant. 2006. pap. 9.99 *(978-1-59781-865-0(8))* Xulon Pr., Inc.

Wright, Chuck. Finding God Beneath the Ashes. 2009. (Illus.). 164p. 25.70 *(978-1-4269-1499-7(7))*; pap. 15.70 *(978-1-4251-8311-0(5))* Trafford Publishing.

Wright-Noble, Sylvia. Making Sense of Life Through Poetry. 2007. 68p. per. 16.95 *(978-1-60441-152-2(X))* PublishAmerica, Inc.

Young, James O. My Sheep Know My Voice: Anointed Poetry. 2010. 108p. (ENG.). 21.49 *(978-1-4490-9228-3(4))*; pap. 10.99 *(978-1-4490-9227-6(6))* AuthorHouse.

CHRISTIAN LIFE—PRESBYTERIAN AUTHORS

Cootsona, Greg. Say Yes to No: Using the Power of No to Create the Best in Life, Work, & Love. 2009. (ENG.). 176p. pap. 12.95 *(978-0-385-52573-2(7))* Knopf Doubleday Publishing Group.

Edwards, Robert B., Jr. Living up in a down World: Living Life Grace Fully ! 2008. 148p. pap. 14.95 *(978-0-595-46374-9(6))* iUniverse, Inc.

Ferguson, Sinclair B. In Christ Alone: Living the Gospel Centered Life. 2007. 243p. *(978-1-56769-089-7(0))* Reformation Pubns.

Flavel, John. Triumphing over Sinful Fear. Yuille, J. Stephen, ed. 2011. 144p. pap. *(978-1-60178-132-1(6))* Reformation Heritage Bks.

Keller, Timothy. Counterfeit Gods: The Empty Promises of Money, Sex, & Power, & the Only Hope That Matters. 2009. (ENG.). 240p. (gr. 12-18). 19.95 *(978-0-525-95136-0(9),* Dutton Adult) Penguin Group (USA) Inc.

—Counterfeit Gods: The Empty Promises of Money, Sex, & Power, & the Only Hope that Matters. 2011. (ENG.). 240p. (gr. 12). 15.00 *(978-1-59448-549-7(6),* Riverhead Trade (Paperbacks)) Penguin Group (USA) Inc.

Kennedy, D. James. Delighting God. 186p. pap. 9.99 *(978-0-8307-3413-9(9),* Regal Bks.) Gospel Light Pubns.

Labberton, Mark. The Dangerous Act of Loving Your Neighbor: Seeing Others Through the Eyes of Jesus. 2010. (ENG.). 236p. 20.00 *(978-0-8308-3840-0(6),* IVP Bks.) InterVarsity Pr.

McRae, Rhonda. What My Golden Retriever Taught Me about God. 2010. *(978-1-59638-163-6(9))* P & R Publishing.

Miller, C. John. Accepting God's Forgiveness: Believing in God's Love for You. 2011. (ENG.). 24p. 3.99 ***(978-1-936768-49-3(6))*** New Growth Pr.

Miller, J. r. & Miller, J. R. Living Without Worry. 2011. 118p. pap. 12.99 ***(978-1-61203-150-7(1))*** Bottom of the Hill Publishing.

Orr, Charles Ebert. How to Live a Holy Life. 2008. 160p. 22.99 *(978-0-554-33152-2(7))*; 25.99 *(978-0-554-23849-4(7))* BiblioBazaar.

—How to Live a Holy Life. 2007. 104p. per. *(978-1-4068-1793-5(7))* Echo Library.

Ortberg, John. God Is Closer Than You Think: If God Is Always with Us, Why Is He So Hard to Find? l.t. ed. 2008. (Walker Large Print Ser.). (ENG.). 336p. per. 17.95 *(978-1-59415-134-7(2),* Walker Large Print) Cengage Gale.

—When the Game Is over, It All Goes Back in the Box, 1 vol. 2009. (ENG.). 256p. pap. 3.99 *(978-0-310-28662-2(X))* Zondervan.

Pond, Clifford. For Starters: An Introduction to Christianity. 32p. wbk. ed. 4.99 *(978-0-946462-45-2(3))* Grace Pubns. Trust GBR. Dist: Evangelical Pr.

Rutherford, Samuel. The King in His Beauty: The Piety of Samuel Rutherford. Vogan, Matthew, ed. & intro. by. 2011. (Illus.). pap. 10.00 *(978-1-60178-125-3(3))* Reformation Heritage Bks.

Selvaggio, Anthony T. & Selvaggio, Anthony T. 7 Toxic Ideas Polluting Your Mind. 2011. 126p. pap. ***(978-1-59638-196-4(5))*** P & R Publishing.

Sittser, Gerald L. Love One Another: Becoming the Church Jesus Longs For. 2008. (ENG.). 189p. pap. 15.00 *(978-0-8308-3449-5(4),* IVP Bks.) InterVarsity Pr.

CHRISTIAN LIFE—REFORMED AUTHORS

Beeke, Joel R. Walking as He Walked. 2007. per. *(978-1-60178-010-2(9))* Reformation Heritage Bks.

DeYoung, Kevin. Just Do Something: How to Make a Decision Without Dreams, Visions, Fleeces, Open Doors, Random Bible Verses, Casting Lots, Liver Shivers, Writing in the Sky, Etc, 1 vol. 2009. (ENG.). 128p. pap. 10.99 *(978-0-8024-5838-4(6))* Moody Pubs.

Meyers, Robin R. Saving Jesus from the Church: How to Stop Worshiping Christ & Start Following Jesus. 2010. (ENG.). 256p. pap. 14.99 *(978-0-06-156822-0(8),* HarperOne) HarperCollins Pubs.

Murray, Andrew. Abiding in Christ. 2010. pap. 0.00 *(978-1-59328-270-7(2))* Graham, Billy Evangelistic Assn.

—Absolute Surrender. 2007. (ENG.). 144p. 24.95 *(978-1-60206-998-5(0))*; per. 8.95 *(978-1-60206-573-4(X))* Cosimo, Inc.

—Absolute Surrender. 2007. (ENG.). 132p. per. 6.99 *(978-1-59986-656-7(0))* Filiquarian Publishing, LLC.

—Absolute Surrender. 2009. 116p. pap. 7.00 *(978-1-60039-150-7(8))* Lamp Post Inc.

—Absolute Surrender. 2007. per. 7.42 *(978-1-4245-0785-6(5))* Treasures Media Inc.

—Absolute Surrender. 2008. 80p. pap. 5.95 *(978-1-60459-587-1(6))* Wilder Pubns., Ltd.

—Daily in His Presence: A Classic Devotional from One of the Most Powerful Voices of the Nineteenth Century. 2011. (ENG.). 400p. pap. 16.99 *(978-1-60142-403-7(5),* Multnomah) Doubleday Religious Publishing Group, The.

—Essential Works of Andrew Murray. rev. ed. 2008. (ENG.). 1408p. pap. 24.99 *(978-1-60260-210-6(7),* Barbour Bks.) Barbour Publishing, Inc.

Pond, Clifford. For Starters: An Introduction to Christianity. 32p. wbk. ed. 4.99 *(978-0-946462-45-2(3))* Grace Pubns. Trust GBR. Dist: Evangelical Pr.

Selvaggio, Anthony T. & Selvaggio, Anthony T. 7 Toxic Ideas Polluting Your Mind. 2011. 126p. pap. ***(978-1-59638-196-4(5))*** P & R Publishing.

Sproul, R. C. Classic Teachings on the Nature of God, 1 vol. 2010. (ENG., Illus.). 600p. 24.95 *(978-1-59856-468-6(4))* Hendrickson Pubs. Marketing, LLC.

—Five Things Every Christian Needs to Grow. 2nd ed. 2008. 135p. 15.00 *(978-1-56769-103-0(X),* Reformation Trust Publishing) Ligonier Ministries.

ten Boom, Corrie. Reflexiones Sobre la Gloria de Dios: Meditaciones Ineditas de la Autora de Refugio Secreto, 1 vol. 2006. (SPA.). 128p. (gr. 11). 7.99 *(978-0-8297-4500-9(9))* Vida Pubs.

CHRISTIAN LIFE—SEVENTH DAY ADVENTIST AUTHORS

Batchelor, Doug. Who Do You Think You Are? Finding the Right Life Through Real Faith. 2010. pap. 1.99 *(978-0-8163-2415-6(8))* Pacific Pr. Publishing Assn.

Blake, Chris. Searching for a God to Love: The One You Always Wanted Is Really There. 2008. 255p. pap. 13.99 *(978-0-8163-2304-3(6))* Pacific Pr. Publishing Assn.

—Swimming Against the Current: Living for the God You Love. 2007. (Illus.). 287p. 9.97 *(978-0-8163-2141-4(8))* Pacific Pr. Publishing Assn.

Bullon, Alejandro. Knowing Jesus Is Everything. 2009. 88p. pap. 12.99 *(978-0-8280-2381-8(6))* Review & Herald Publishing Assn.

Burkeen, Charles. A Place for Us Guys. 2007. 127p. 5.97 *(978-0-8163-2193-3(0))* Pacific Pr. Publishing Assn.

Camacho Garcia, Carlos. Changed: Real Lives in a Real World. 2009. (Illus.). 128p. pap. 1.99 *(978-0-8163-9322-0(2))* Pacific Pr. Publishing Assn.

Dickerson, Ed. Grounds for Belief: The Place Brought Them Together, the Discussion Changed Them Forever. 2007. 5.97 *(978-0-8163-2184-1(1))* Pacific Pr. Publishing Assn.

Finley, Mark. End-Time Living: Essential Truths for Troubled Times. 2006. 1.99 *(978-0-8163-2174-2(4))* Pacific Pr. Publishing Assn.

Fitzgerald, Troy. 20 Questions God Wants to Ask You: Life-Changing Encounters with the Divine. 2008. 14.99 *(978-0-8163-2275-6(9))* Pacific Pr. Publishing Assn.

Fitzgerald, Troy Eric. Discovering God's Will: A Practical Guide To. 2007. 143p. 12.99 *(978-0-8163-2180-3(9))* Pacific Pr. Publishing Assn.

Gibson, Ty. A God Named Desire. 2010. (Illus.). 192p. 17.99 *(978-0-8163-2397-5(6))* Pacific Pr. Publishing Assn.

Goldstein, Clifford. Life Without Limits: Powerful Truths That Bring Hope & Meaning. 2007. *(978-0-8280-2059-6(0))* Autumn Hse. Publishing Co.

Handysides, Allan. Living Praise: A Sound Mind, a Healthy Body, a Grateful Heart. 2009. 152p. pap. 11.99 *(978-0-8280-2497-6(9))* Review & Herald Publishing Assn.

Hohnberger, Jim. Come, Walk with Me: Are You Waiting for God or Is God Waiting for You? 2011. (Illus.). 159p. 16.99 ***(978-0-8163-2414-9(X))*** Pacific Pr. Publishing Assn.

—Men of Power: Reclaiming Your Legacy. 2007. (Illus.). 223p. 16.99 *(978-0-8163-2191-9(4))* Pacific Pr. Publishing Assn.

Jones, Mike. Sometimes I Don't Feel Like a Christian: Everyone Struggles, but Failure Isn't Final. 2010. 14.99 *(978-0-8163-2381-4(X))* Pacific Pr. Publishing Assn.

Loredo, De la. The Race: An Allegory. 2012. ***(978-0-8280-2638-3(6))*** Review & Herald Publishing Assn.

Martin, A. Allan, et al. God Encounters: Pursuing a 24/7 Experience of Jesus. 2009. 192p. pap. 14.99 *(978-0-8163-2339-5(9))* Pacific Pr. Publishing Assn.

Milward, Arthur A. It's Going to Be All Right: More True Stories Of. 2012. ***(978-0-8280-2563-8(0))*** Review & Herald Publishing Assn.

Moore, Ralph. Question God: The Anatomy of an Asking Christian. 2008. 70p. pap. 10.95 *(978-1-57258-509-6(9))* TEACH Services, Inc.

Morales-Gudmundsson, Lourdes. I Forgive You, But- We Know We Should, Why Is It So Hard? 2007. 13.99 *(978-0-8163-2201-5(5))* Pacific Pr. Publishing Assn.

—52 Short Reflections from I Forgive You, But- Forgiveness. 2007. 111p. 4.97 *(978-0-8163-2244-2(9))* Pacific Pr. Publishing Assn.

Schilt, W. Clarence & Schilt, Stephen. A Life to Die For: Discover the Secret of Christ's Transforming Power. 2009. pap. 17.99 *(978-0-8163-2308-1(9))* Pacific Pr. Publishing Assn.

Smith, Dennis Edwin. 40 Days: Prayers & Devotions. 2012. ***(978-0-8280-2575-1(4))*** Review & Herald Publishing Assn.

White, Ellen G. True Revival: The Church's Greatest Need: Selections from the Writings of Ellen G. White. 2010. *(978-0-8280-2572-0(X))* Review & Herald Publishing Assn.

Yoon, Won K. Context & Continuity: The Korean Adventist Church in North America & Its Future Generations. 2008. (Illus.). 242p. pap. 21.99 *(978-1-883925-60-4(6))* Andrews Univ. Pr.

CHRISTIAN LIFE—STUDY AND TEACHING

Abingdon Press Staff. 3 Essential Teacher Resources. 35.00 *(978-0-687-09785-2(1))* Abingdon Pr.

Abingdon Youth, creator. Emerge 1. 0: Developing Youth as Fully Devoted Disciples: Small-Group Leader's Guide for Older Youth. 2007. 48p. pap. 18.00 incl. cd-rom *(978-0-687-64120-8(9))* Abingdon Pr.

Alexander-Reindorf, Deaconess Floria. I Exist in All Planes at the Same Time: Anthology Three, Volume Two. 2010. 360p. pap. 33.95 *(978-1-4401-7162-8(9))* iUniverse, Inc.

Anderson, C. Thomas. Wisdom Wins, Vol. 2. 2007. per. 7.95 *(978-1-58588-018-8(3))* Winword Publishing.

Benedict XVI, pseud. Coming Together in Joy: 99 Sayings by Benedict XVI. Liesenfeld, Stephen, ed. 2008. 99p. pap. 9.95 *(978-1-56548-274-6(3))* New City Pr.

Burns, Jim. Parents & Family. 2010. (Uncommon Ser.). (ENG.). 208p. (gr. 9-12). pap. 14.99 *(978-0-8307-5097-9(5))* Gospel Light Pubns.

Bynum, Juanita. My Inheritance. 32p. 1.49 *(978-1-56229-145-7(9)*, Christian Living Bks., Inc.) Pneuma Life Publishing, Inc.

Campillo, Fernando. Manual para Grupos de Discipulado: Manual for Discipleship Groups. (SPA.). *(978-84-7645-210-3(1)*, 223268) Clie, Editorial.

Case, Steve L. Caffeine & Cash. 2009. *(978-0-8298-1845-1(6))* Pilgrim Pr., The/United Church Pr.

—Caffeine & Chutzpah. 2009. *(978-0-8298-1844-4(8))* Pilgrim Pr., The/United Church Pr.

—Caffeine & Courage. 2009. *(978-0-8298-1843-7(X))* Pilgrim Pr., The/United Church Pr.

Chandler, Julia. You Shall Receive Power. 2007. 108p. per. 10.99 *(978-1-60034-878-5(5))* Xulon Pr., Inc.

Cooper, Barry & Shammas, Sam. English Made Easy. 2010. (Christianity Explored Ser.). 64p. pap., pupil's gde. ed. *(978-1-904889-36-6(0))*; 96p. pap. *(978-1-904889-35-9(2))* Good Bk. Co.

Deuink, James W., ed. Preparing the Christian Schools for the 21st Century. 8.95 *(978-0-89084-585-1(9)*, 055293) BJU Pr.

Dios Elige a Su Pueblo (God Chooses His People) Quarter 1, Level 3. (Caminando con Jesus (Walking with Jesus) Series B). (SPA.). tchr. ed. 2.50 *(978-0-570-05146-6(0)*, 16-3901) Concordia Publishing Hse.

Dios Me Da Su Palabra (God Gives Me His Word) Quarter 1, Level 2. (Caminando con Jesus (Walking with Jesus) Series A). (SPA.). tchr. ed. 3.50 *(978-0-570-05126-8(6)*, 16-2801) Concordia Publishing Hse.

Dios Me Dio Relaciones (God Gave Me Relationships) Quarter 3, Level 1. (Caminando con Jesus (Walking with Jesus) Series B). (SPA.). tchr. ed. 2.50 *(978-0-570-05106-0(1)*, 16-1903) Concordia Publishing Hse.

Dios Me Dio un Cuerpo (God Gave Me a Body) Quarter 2, Level 1. (Caminando con Jesus (Walking with Jesus) Series B). (SPA.). tchr. ed. 2.50 *(978-0-570-05105-3(3)*, 16-1902) Concordia Publishing Hse.

Dios Me Dio un Mundo (God Gave Me a World) Quarter 1, Level 1. (Caminando con Jesus (Walking with Jesus) Series B). (SPA.). tchr. ed. 2.50 *(978-0-570-05104-6(5)*, 16-1901) Concordia Publishing Hse.

Dios Prepara a Su Pueblo (God Prepares His People) Quarter 2, Level 3. (Caminando con Jesus (Walking with Jesus) Series B). (SPA.). tchr. ed. 3.50 *(978-0-570-05147-3(9)*, 16-3902) Concordia Publishing Hse.

Disciple II nto the Word into the World. tchr. ed. 5.00 *(978-0-687-75633-9(2))* Abingdon Pr.

Downing, Simon. World Empire & the Return of Jesus Christ. 2011. 530p. 43.99 ***(978-1-61379-845-4(8))*** Xulon Pr., Inc.

El Espiritu Santo (The Holy Spirit) Quarter 1, Level 3. (Caminando con Jesus (Walking with Jesus) Series A). (SPA.). tchr. ed. 3.50 *(978-0-570-05143-5(6)*, 16-3801) Concordia Publishing Hse.

Est Bib Lifeway Para Escol Del 1 Al 6 Grados Ayudas Para la Ensen. 16.50 *(978-0-7673-4450-0(2))* LifeWay Christian Resources.

Est Bib Lifeway Para Escol Del 1 Al 6 Grados Manual Para el Lider. 2.95 *(978-0-7673-4632-0(7))* LifeWay Christian Resources.

Estudios Biblicos Lifeway Para Adultos Ayudas Para la Ensenanza. 13.00 *(978-0-7673-4492-0(8))* LifeWay Christian Resources.

Etbs: Youth Teacher. 3.75 *(978-0-7673-5198-0(3))* LifeWay Christian Resources.

Exodus 1. ldr.'s ed. (LifeLight Bible Studies: Course 10). 6.50 *(978-0-570-09278-0(7)*, 20-2290) Concordia Publishing Hse.

Exploring God's Word: Grade 1 - Teacher Kit. (Voyages Ser.). 225.00 incl. audio, cd-rom *(978-0-570-00258-1(3)*, 57-0110) Concordia Publishing Hse.

Exploring God's Word: Grade 2 - Teacher Kit. (Voyages Ser.). 215.00 incl. audio, cd-rom *(978-0-570-00263-5(X)*, 57-0210) Concordia Publishing Hse.

Exploring God's Word: Grade 3 - Teacher Kit. (Voyages Ser.). 190.00 incl. audio, cd-rom *(978-0-570-00268-0(0)*, 57-0310) Concordia Publishing Hse.

Exploring God's Word: Kindergarten - Teacher Kit. (Voyages Ser.). per. 225.00 incl. audio, cd-rom *(978-0-570-00250-5(8)*, 57-0010) Concordia Publishing Hse.

Exploring God's Word: Teacher Kit - Preschool. (Voyages Ser.). tchr. ed., spiral bd. 195.00 incl. audio, cd-rom *(978-0-570-00306-9(7)*, 57-1110) Concordia Publishing Hse.

FBS: Children's Teacher. 3.00 *(978-0-7673-4037-3(X))* LifeWay Christian Resources.

FBS Adult Teacher. 3.35 *(978-0-7673-4831-7(1))* LifeWay Christian Resources.

FBS Children Teaching Kit. 11.95 *(978-0-7673-4137-0(6))* LifeWay Christian Resources.

FBS Estudios Biblicos Lifeway Para Preescolares, Ayudas Para La. 18.95 *(978-0-7673-4478-4(2))* LifeWay Christian Resources.

FBS Kindergarten Connection Learner Guide. 1.60 *(978-0-7673-5556-8(3))* LifeWay Christian Resources.

FBS Preschool Teacher. 12.42 *(978-0-7673-4109-7(0))* LifeWay Christian Resources.

First Place 4 Health (Organization) Staff & First Place 4 Health. Daily Victory, Daily Joy. 2009. (First Place 4 Health Ser.). (ENG.). 224p. 19.99 *(978-0-8307-4724-5(9))* Gospel Light Pubns.

Fleming, Melvin. Faith-Based Mentoring: Mission-POSSIBLE. 2007. 56p. per. 11.99 *(978-1-60266-330-5(0))* Xulon Pr., Inc.

George, B. Crecer en Gracia.Tr. of Growing in Grace. 8.99 *(978-1-56063-695-3(5)*, 492890) Editorial Unilit.

Godfrey, Pastor I. K. Miracles at Calvary Cross: Do you need a Miracle? 2011. 52p. pap. 16.95 ***(978-1-4560-7003-8(7))*** PublishAmerica, Inc.

Gospel Light Publications Staff. Baby Beginnings Teacher's Guide with CD-ROM: 0-18 Months. 2008. (ENG.). 104p. pap. 14.99 *(978-0-8307-4496-1(7))* Gospel Light Pubns.

—Baby Beginnings Teacher's Guide with CD-ROM: 18 to 36 Months. 2008. (ENG.). 104p. 14.99 *(978-0-8307-4669-9(2))* Gospel Light Pubns.

Harris, Janice L., et al. Discovering A Christlike Character (Book 4) CHRISTIAN SCHOOL Edition: Student Workbook. Snyder, Barb, ed. 2007. (Illus.). 196p. spiral bd., wbk. ed. 19.95 *(978-1-930547-51-3(X))* Deeper Roots Pubns. & Media.

—Discovering A Christlike Character (Book 4) CHRISTIAN SCHOOL Edition: TEACHER's Guide. Snyder, Barb & Harris, JoAnna, eds. 2007. (Illus.). 282p. tchr. ed., spiral bd. 28.95 *(978-1-930547-50-6(1))* Deeper Roots Pubns. & Media.

—Discovering A Christlike Character (Book 4) HOME SCHOOL Edition: TEACHER's Guide - Snyder, Barb, ed. 2007. (Illus.). 334p. tchr. ed., spiral bd. 28.95 *(978-1-930547-62-9(5))* Deeper Roots Pubns. & Media.

—Discovering A Christlike Character (Book 4) HOME SCHOOL: Student Workbook- Snyder, Barb & Harris, JoAnna, eds. 2007. (Illus.). 296p. spiral bd., wbk. ed. 19.95 *(978-1-930547-63-6(3))* Deeper Roots Pubns. & Media.

Henderson, Warren/Allen. The Fruitful Bough: Affirming Biblical Manhood Teacher's Guide. 2008. 40p. 10.95 *(978-0-9795387-6-6(9))* Henderson, Warren.

Henley, Karyn. Play: Building Relationships. (Children's Ministry Folders). tchr. ed. 2.99 *(978-0-7847-0683-1(2)*, 42233) Standard Publishing.

—Scripture Memory. (Children's Ministry Folders). tchr. ed. 2.99 *(978-0-7847-0689-3(1)*, 42239) Standard Publishing.

—Young Children: What Are They Like? (Children's Ministry Folders). tchr. ed. 2.99 *(978-0-7847-0682-4(4)*, 42232) Standard Publishing.

Higgins, Rupert & Cooper, Barry. Discipleship Explored Starter Pack. 2010. (Discipleship Explored Ser.). pap. *(978-1-906334-40-6(4))* Good Bk. Co.

Holladay, Tom, et al. Holy Spirit: Small Group Study, 1 vol. 2008. (Foundations Ser.). (ENG., Illus.). 80p. pap. 6.99 *(978-0-310-27676-0(4))* Zondervan.

Isenhower, Valerie K. & Todd, Judith A. Listen for God's Leading: A Workbook for Corporate Spiritual Discernment. 2009. 128p. pap. 15.00 *(978-0-8358-9985-7(3))* Upper Room Bks.

Kendzia, Mary Carol. The 5 W's of Our Catholic Faith: Who, What, When, Where, Why ... & How We Live It. 2011. *(978-0-7648-1986-5(0))* Liguori Pubns.

Knight, Allan & Schroeder, Gordon H. New Life: Six Studies for New Baptists. 3rd rev. ed. 2009. 72p. pap. 7.00 *(978-0-8170-1563-3(9))* Judson Pr.

Langford, Andy & Ralls, Mark. Is This All There Is? And Other Big Questions about God & Life. 2009. 192p. pap. 15.00 *(978-1-4267-0039-2(3)*, Abingdon Press) Abingdon Pr.

Lee, Witness. The Knowledge of Life. 216p. per. 8.25 *(978-0-87083-014-3(7)*, 07010001) Living Stream Ministry.

Living in Christ: Teacher Guide. 124p. tchr. ed. 17.95 *(978-0-7586-0466-8(1))* Concordia Publishing Hse.

Low, L. F. Genuine Christianity: Study Manual & Facilitators Guide. 2012. *(978-1-58982-773-8(2)*, Millennial Mind Publishing) American Bk. Publishing Group.

Luther, Servant of God: Teacher Guide. 128p. tchr. ed. 19.75 *(978-0-7586-0464-4(5))* Concordia Publishing Hse.

Lw: Youth in Action Teacher. 3.75 *(978-0-7673-5058-7(8))* LifeWay Christian Resources.

Lw: Youth in Discovery Teacher. 3.75 *(978-0-7673-5170-6(3))* LifeWay Christian Resources.

LW Directions. tchr. ed. 3.76 *(978-0-7673-4408-1(1))* LifeWay Christian Resources.

LW Pursuits Teacher Edition. 3.75 *(978-0-7673-4590-3(8))* LifeWay Christian Resources.

Lynn, David & Davis, Rick. 52 Discussions to Confirm the Faith of Your Teenagers, 1 vol. 2009. (TalkSheets Ser.). (ENG.). 128p. pap. 14.99 *(978-0-310-66873-2(5))* Zondervan.

Mi Dios es Amor (My God Is Love) Quarter 2, Level 1. (Caminando con Jesus (Walking with Jesus) Series A). tchr. ed. 3.50 *(978-0-570-05102-2(9)*, 16-1802) Concordia Publishing Hse.

Milthaler, Matthew. E-Merge 2. 0 Small Group Leader's Guide for Older Youth. 2007. pap. 18.00 *(978-0-687-64309-7(0))* Abingdon Pr.

—EMerge 1. 0: Developing Youth as Fully Devoted Disciples. 2007. 48p. 60.00 *(978-0-687-49005-9(7))* Abingdon Pr.

Morgan, G. Campbell. Principios Basicos de la Vida: Basics of Christian Living. (SPA.). 80p. *(978-84-7228-845-4(5)*, 220712) Clie, Editorial.

Moy, Randy & Moy, Nancy. Covenant Partnership. 2009. 288p. pap. 16.99 *(978-1-60791-906-3(0))* Xulon Pr., Inc.

My Life in Jesus. 80p. tchr. ed. 19.50 *(978-0-570-00759-3(3)*, 22-2873) Concordia Publishing Hse.

Ogden, Greg. Discipleship Essentials: A Guide to Building Your Life in Christ. 2007. (Essentials Set Ser.). (ENG.). 237p. per. 18.00 *(978-0-8308-1087-1(0)*, IVP Conn.) InterVarsity Pr.

One Room Sunday School Teacher Guide: Spring. tchr. ed. 12.00 *(978-0-687-03598-4(8))* Abingdon Pr.

One Room Sunday School Teacher Guide: Winter. tchr. ed. 10.50 *(978-0-687-03597-7(X))* Abingdon Pr.

One Year Foundational Course in Christianity for Ages 4-8: 12 Topics of the Chistian Faith. l.t. ed. 2007. (Illus.). 432p. (J). spiral bd. 89.00 *(978-0-9795662-0-2(7))* Foundations Publishing.

Ortberg, John, et al. New Community Series Library, ZCS, 1 vol. 2008. (New Community Bible Study Ser.). pap., pap., pap. 83.88 *(978-0-310-65025-6(9))* Zondervan.

El Pecado (Sin) Quarter 1, Level 2. (Caminando con Jesus (Walking with Jesus) Series B). (SPA.). tchr. ed. 3.50 *(978-0-570-05129-9(0)*, 16-2901) Concordia Publishing Hse.

Pennock, Michael. Your Life in Christ: Foundations of Catholic Morality. 2008. (Illus.). 288p. (YA). pap. 24.95 *(978-1-59471-123-7(2))* Ave Maria Pr.

—Your Life in Christ: Foundations of Catholic Morality: Teacher's Wraparound Edition. 2007. (Illus.). 333p. pap. 26.95 *(978-1-59471-124-4(0))* Ave Maria Pr.

Powell, Kara. The Christian Life. Powell, Kara, ed. 2009. (Uncommon Ser.). (ENG., Illus.). 192p. (J). pap. 14.99 *(978-0-8307-4642-2(0))* Gospel Light Pubns.

Powell, Kara, ed. Parents & Family. 2010. (Uncommon Ser.). (ENG.). 192p. (J). (gr. 7-9). pap. 14.99 *(978-0-8307-5099-3(1))* Gospel Light Pubns.

Pratt, James. On the Way to Zoraster's House: (Esoteric Psychology) 2007. 140p. per. 13.95 *(978-0-595-42529-7(1))* iUniverse, Inc.

Robinson, Christine C., et al. Heart to Heart: Fourteen Gatherings for Reflection & Sharing. 2009. (ENG.). 1p. pap. 14.00 *(978-1-55896-550-8(5)*, Skinner Hse. Bks.) Unitarian Universalist Assn.

Rosales, Raymond S. It's about Mission! Ventures & Views of a Pilgrim in Hispanic Ministry. 344p. pap. 14.95 *(978-0-570-09974-1(9)*, 16-6034) Concordia Publishing Hse.

Scanlon, Paul. Crossing Over: Getting to the Best Life Yet, 0 vols. 2007. 176p. per. 13.99 *(978-1-59951-017-0(0))* Nelson, Thomas Inc.

Schutte, Dan, et al. Into the Fields: Basic Catechetical Skills & Attitudes, Year 1. 2006. (Illus.). 128p. pap. 24.95 *(978-1-58595-590-9(6))* Twenty-Third Pubns./Bayard.

Sheets, Dutch. Authority in Prayer: Praying with Power & Purpose. 2007. 192p. pap. 14.99 *(978-0-7642-0406-7(8))* Bethany Hse. Pubs.

Sherlin, Keith A. How Can God Be All-Powerful & Totally Loving When He Planned a World with Sin & Suffering? A Reformed Evangelical Dispensational Theodicy, 1 vol. 2009. 127p. pap. 19.95 *(978-1-60610-680-8(5))* PublishAmerica, Inc.

Solo Dios Salva (Only God Saves) Quarter 3, Level 3. (Caminando con Jesus (Walking with Jesus) Series B). (SPA.). tchr. ed. 2.50 *(978-0-570-05148-0(7)*, 16-3903) Concordia Publishing Hse.

Stanbrough, David L. What about Santa Claus & Christians at Christmas? How to Teach Your Children the Real Meaning of Christmas - from the Bible. 2008. 60p. pap. 10.95 *(978-1-4327-2892-2(X))* Outskirts Pr., Inc.

Stoltzfus, Tony. A Leader's Life Purpose Handbook: Calling & Destiny Discovery Tools for Christian Life Coaching. 2009. (Illus.). 284p. pap. 23.99 *(978-0-9794163-7-8(X))* Coach22 Bookstore LLC.

Stoner, Marcia J., ed. Live It! Living Positively in a Media Age for Tweens: Building Skills for Christian Living. 2006. (Live It! Ser.). (Illus.). 63p. 15.95 *(978-0-687-49785-0(X))* Abingdon Pr.

Sub FBS 1st & 2Nd Graders Teaching Pictures. 45.15 *(978-0-633-05073-3(3))* LifeWay Christian Resources.

Sub FBS 3rd & 4th Graders Teaching Pictures. 45.15 *(978-0-633-05075-7(X))* LifeWay Christian Resources.

Sub FBS Access. ldr.'s ed. 79.35 *(978-0-633-05090-0(3))*; 18.95 *(978-0-633-05063-4(6))* LifeWay Christian Resources.

Sub FBS Adult. ldr.'s ed. 79.35 *(978-0-633-05076-4(8))*; 18.95 *(978-0-633-05039-9(3))* LifeWay Christian Resources.

Sub FBS Life Answers. ldr.'s ed. 18.95 *(978-0-633-05052-8(0))* LifeWay Christian Resources.

Sub FBS Life Answers Leader Pack. 81.15 *(978-0-633-05084-9(9))* LifeWay Christian Resources.

Sub FBS Pathways Learner Guide. 9.55 *(978-0-633-05058-0(X))* LifeWay Christian Resources.

Summit Ministries Staff. Lightbearers. 3rd ed. 2008. 286p. pap., wbk. ed. *(978-0-936163-12-3(7))* Summit Pr. CO.

—Lightbearers: Home School Curriculum Teaching Materials. 3rd ed. 2008. *(978-0-936163-26-0(7))* Summit Pr. CO.

Tan, Soo-Inn & Smith, Gordon T. Courage & Calling. 2008. 96p. per. *(978-1-57383-410-0(6)*, Regent College Publishing) Regent College Publishing.

Tanner, Obert C. Christ's Ideals for Living. 2011. 484p. 58.95 ***(978-1-258-00219-0(1))*** Literary Licensing, LLC.

Thornborough, Tim. Discipleship Explored. 2010. 40p. pap., pupil's gde. ed. *(978-1-906334-89-5(7))*; 96p. pap. *(978-1-906334-85-7(4))* Good Bk. Co.

Thornborough, Tim & Fee, Kerry. Discipleship Explored. 2010. 40p. pap., pupil's gde. ed. *(978-1-906334-84-0(6))* Good Bk. Co.

Tice, Rico & Cooper, Barry. Christianity Explored. 2010. (Christianity Explored Ser.). (SPA.). 60p. pap., pupil's gde. ed. *(978-1-906334-58-1(7))*; pap. *(978-1-906334-59-8(5))* Good Bk. Co.

Wallace, Susan Helen. Jesus Loves Us, Grade 1. 252p. tchr. ed., spiral bd. 16.95 *(978-0-8198-3920-6(5))* Pauline Bks. & Media.

Weiss, N. E. According to Plan. 96p. tchr. ed. *(978-0-85910-316-9(1))* Openbook Publishers.

WILLHAUCK. Living in Gods Light. pap. 8.50 *(978-0-687-02197-0(9))* Abingdon Pr.

Williams, Alton. The Harvest Discipleship Study Guide. 2007. per. *(978-0-9797019-3-1(7))* Understanding For Life Ministries, Inc.

Wommack, Andrew. War Is Over: God Is Not Mad, So Stop Struggling with Sin & Judgment. 2008. 224p. pap. 14.99 *(978-1-57794-935-0(8))* Harrison House Pubs.

Wright, Una. For Children Only, Volume II: A Book of Object Lessons for Young Children. 2009. 100p. pap. 12.85 *(978-1-4269-1622-9(1))* Trafford Publishing.

Yandian, Bob. Colossians. Noble, Linda, ed. 146p. *(978-1-885600-08-0(9))* Bob Yandian Ministries.

—Grace - From Here to Eternity: Grace for Living, Dying & Eternity. Willis, Leanna, ed. 110p. *(978-1-885600-07-3(0))* Bob Yandian Ministries.

CHRISTIAN LITERATURE

see also Catholic Literature; Christian Poetry; Christianity and Literature; Devotional Literature; Papal Documents; Prayers; Sermons

Allen, Joseph J., ed. And He Leads Them: The Mind & Heart of Philip Saliba. 459p. pap. 20.00 *(978-1-888212-29-7(2))* Conciliar Pr.

Bankston, Terry. The Templum. 2007. 76p. per. 16.95 *(978-1-60441-347-2(6))* PublishAmerica, Inc.

Bawden, Charles R. A Tract for the Buryats. Walravens, Hartmut, ed. 2009. (Abhandlungen Für Die Kunde des Morgenlandes Ser.). (ENG., Illus.). 105p. (C). pap. 51.00 *(978-3-447-05990-9(7))* Harrassowitz, Otto Verlag DEU. Dist: ISD.

Blackwell, Madison G. Two Witnesses. 2010. pap. 9.99 *(978-1-61566-645-4(1))* Tate Publishing & Enterprises, LLC.

Clayton, Mary & Magennis, Hugh. The Old English Lives of St. Margaret. 2006. (Cambridge Studies in Anglo-Saxon England Ser.). (ENG.). 252p. pap. 53.00 *(978-0-521-03267-4(9))* Cambridge Univ. Pr.

Cole, Leona J. Prince of the House of David. 2011. 260p. 35.95 ***(978-1-4497-2311-8(X)***, WestBow Pr.) Author Solutions, Inc.

Crawford, Raymond I. E. Out of Love: A Computer Nerd. 2009. pap. 18.99 *(978-1-60791-812-7(9))* Xulon Pr., Inc.

Culbertson, Kimberly M., et al, eds. Relief: A Christian Literary Expression Issue 3. 2. 2009. 160p. pap. 14.95 *(978-0-9792284-5-2(X))* ccPublishing, NFP.

Denn, George. Hey by George! 2007. 164p. (ENG.). 21.99 *(978-1-60266-298-8(3))*; per. 13.99 *(978-1-60266-297-1(5))* Xulon Pr., Inc.

Duran, Angelica. The Age of Milton & the Scientific Revolution. 2006. (Medieval & Renaissance Texts & Studies). (Illus.). 349p. 58.00 *(978-0-8207-0386-2(9))* Duquesne Univ. Pr.

Edwards, Judson. Blissful Affliction: The Ministry & Misery of Writing. 2011. pap. ***(978-1-57312-594-9(6))*** Smyth & Helwys Publishing, Inc.

Elias Boudinot, Vol. 35. *(978-0-404-60935-1(X))* AMS Pr., Inc.

Elias Smith: Selected Writings, Vol. 34. *(978-0-404-60934-4(1))* AMS Pr., Inc.

Ellis, Joyce K. & Shaw, Tammie Edington. Writing So Heaven Will Be Different: 35 Years of Encouraging Stories from the Write-to-Publish Conference. 2008. 136p. pap. 14.99 *(978-1-4141-1198-8(3))* Pleasant Word.

Ethan Smith: Selected Writings, Vol. 36. *(978-0-404-60936-8(8))* AMS Pr., Inc.

Faithwriters.Com. FaithWriters - Eternally Blessed. 2007. pap. 17.99 *(978-1-59781-115-6(7))* Xulon Pr., Inc.

Faithwriters.com. Faithwriters - Hidden in the Hymns. 2007. 300p. pap. 19.99 *(978-1-4141-1069-1(3))* Pleasant Word.

Foster, Richard & Yancey, Philip. A Syllable of Water: Twenty Writers of Faith Reflect upon Their Art. Griffin, Emilie, ed. 2008. 240p. pap. 20.00 *(978-1-55725-566-2(0))* Paraclete Pr., Inc.

Fox, George. The Works of George Fox. 2010. 514p. pap. 39.75 *(978-1-142-22577-3(1))*; 466p. pap. 37.75 *(978-1-141-88602-9(2))*; 358p. pap. 32.75 *(978-1-142-20507-2(X))* BiblioBazaar.

—The Works of George Fox. 2009. 336p. pap. *(978-1-150-79206-9(X))*; 344p. pap. *(978-0-217-28650-3(X))*; 358p. pap. *(978-0-217-28652-7(6))*; 554p. pap. *(978-0-217-40270-5(4))*; 316p. pap. *(978-0-217-61466-5(3))*; 578p. pap. *(978-0-217-76357-8(X))*; 520p. pap. *(978-0-217-64286-6(1))*; 322p. pap. *(978-0-217-64292-7(6))*; 486p. pap. *(978-1-4589-4244-9(9))* Books LLC.

—The Works of George Fox. 2009. 346p. pap. 24.10 *(978-1-150-19407-8(3))* General Bks. LLC.

George Duffield: Selected Works, Vol. 39. *(978-0-404-60939-9(2))* AMS Pr., Inc.

Gerhart, Mary. The Christianity Reader. Gerhart, Mary & Udoh, Fabian E., eds. 2007. (ENG., Illus.). 856p. per. 45.00 *(978-0-226-28959-5(1))* Univ. of Chicago Pr.

Gerhart, Mary & Udoh, Fabian E., eds. The Christianity Reader. 2007. (ENG.). 800p. 102.50 *(978-0-226-28958-8(3))* Univ. of Chicago Pr.

Giles, Paul. American Catholic Arts & Fictions: Culture, Ideology, Aesthetics. 2008. (Cambridge Studies in American Literature & Culture Ser.). (ENG.). 564p. pap. 74.00 *(978-0-521-05773-8(6))* Cambridge Univ. Pr.

Grattan, Andrew. Christ' A Portrait of the Writer as an English Benedictine Novice. 2011. 176p. pap. 15.95 ***(978-1-4620-4262-3(7))*** iUniverse, Inc.

Grube, George W. More - What the Church Fathers Say About ..., 3 vols., Vol. 3. 2007. (ENG., Illus.). 207p. 17.95 *(978-1-933654-09-6(0))* Light & Life Publishing Co.

Hanna, Ralph. The English Manuscripts of Richard Rolle: A Descriptive Catalogue. 2010. (University of Exeter Press - Exeter Medieval Texts & Studies). (Illus.). 264p. 140.00 *(978-0-85989-820-1(2))* Univ. of Exeter Pr. GBR. Dist: Chicago Distribution Ctr.

Havergal, Frances Ridley & Chalkley, David L. Valuable Selections from the Writings of Frances Ridley Havergal. 2009. (Illus.). 96p. pap. ***(978-0-9817321-8-3(6))*** Granted Ministries Pr.

Hendrix, Scott H. Early Protestant Spirituality. 2009. (Classics of Western Spirituality Ser.). 368p. 39.95 *(978-0-8091-0566-3(7))*; pap. 29.95 *(978-0-8091-4211-8(2))* Paulist Pr.

Hesson, Carolyn/J, ed. Christian Writer's Compass: From Ideas to Publication & Marketing. 2010. (ENG.). pap. *(978-0-9708451-9-1(7))* Opine Publishing.

Holder, Arthur. Christian Spirituality: The Classics. 2009. (ENG.). 392p. (C). 90.00 *(978-0-415-77601-1(5))* Routledge.

Hone, Ed & Coll, Roisin, eds. All Together: Creative Prayer with Children. 2009. (ENG.). 126p. pap. 21.95 *(978-1-84730-179-6(7))* Veritas Pubns. IRL. Dist: Dufour Editions, Inc.

Hupp, David A. Christian Evangelism Printing: A How to Do it Guide for in Home Printers & Desktop Publishers. 2009. pap. *(978-1-61623-753-0(8))* Independent Pub.

Intervarsity Press. The Ivp Pocket Reference Series. 11p. pap. 81.00 *(978-0-8308-2700-8(5))* InterVarsity Pr.

Jones, David. Friars' Tales. 2011. (Manchester Medieval Sources Ser.). (ENG.). 272p. pap. 34.95 *(978-0-7190-8425-6(3))* Manchester Univ. Pr. GBR. Dist: Macmillan.

—Friars's Tales. 2011. (Manchester Medieval Sources Ser.). (ENG.). 272p. 95.00 *(978-0-7190-8424-9(5))* Manchester Univ. Pr. GBR. Dist: Macmillan.

Jovceva, Marija, et al, eds. Berlinski Sbornik: Ein kirchenslavisches Denkmal mittelbulgarischer Redaktion des beginnenden 14. Jahrhunderts erganzt aus weiteren handschriftlichen Quellen. 2006. (Schriften der Balkan-Kommission Ser.). (GER.). 456p. (C). pap. 126.00 *(978-3-7001-3578-4(5))* Austrian Academy of Sciences Press AUT. Dist: Brown, David Bk. Co., The.

Kamil, Murad. Catalogue of the Manuscripts Newly Found in the Monastery of St. Mary Deipara in the Nitrian Desert. 2010. (SYR.). 84.80 *(978-1-61143-049-3(6))* Gorgias Pr., LLC.

Kelly, W. Collections of Selected Pamphlets. pap. 7.95 *(978-0-88172-093-8(3))* Believers Bookshelf, Inc.

Koop, Doug. Northern Lights: An Anthology of Contemporary Christian Writing in Canada. Rempel-Burkholder, Byron & Dueck, Dora, eds. 2008. (ENG.). 256p. pap. 24.95 *(978-0-470-15526-4(4)*, Wiley) Wiley, John & Sons, Inc.

Kurian, George Thomas & Smith, James D., III, eds. The Encyclopedia of Christian Literature, 2 vols. 2010. (ENG.). 732p. 189.00 *(978-0-8108-6987-5(X))* Scarecrow Pr., Inc.

Le Peau, Andrew T. & Doll, Linda. Heart. Soul. Mind. Strength: An Anecdotal History of InterVarsity Press, 1947-2007. 2006. (ENG.). 232p. pap. 18.00 *(978-0-8308-3369-6(2)*, IVP Bks.) InterVarsity Pr.

Livingstone Corporation Staff, ed. Take My Heart, O God: Riches from the Greatest Christian Women Writers of All Time, 1 vol. 2010. (ENG.). 384p. 14.99 *(978-0-310-32747-9(4))* Zondervan.

Lyman Beecher: Selected Works, Vol. 37. *(978-0-404-60937-5(6))* AMS Pr., Inc.

Mawhinney, Bruce. Preaching with Freshness, 1 vol. 2008. (Preaching with Ser.). 264p. pap. 15.99 *(978-0-8254-3449-5(1))* Kregel Pubns.

Mentzer, Leon. Amen! A Simple Guide to Self-Marketing Your Christian Book. 2007. 151p. per. 12.99 *(978-1-60247-467-3(2))* Tate Publishing & Enterprises, LLC.

Mills, Kevin. The Prodigal Sign: A Parable of Criticism. 2009. (Critical Inventions Ser.). (ENG., 167p. Illus.). pap. 27.50 *(978-1-84519-155-9(2))*; 52.50 *(978-1-84519-154-2(4))* Sussex Academic Pr. GBR. Dist: International Specialized Bk. Services.

Of Granada, Louis & de Caussade, Jean-Pierre. The Sinner's Guide & Abandonment to Divine Providence. Bob, Brother, ed. 2011. 208p. pap. 12.95 ***(978-1-934335-48-2(7))*** WordWright.biz, Inc.

Olasky, Marvin. Telling the Truth: How to Revitalize Christian Journalism. 2010. 304p. pap. 33.00 *(978-1-60899-898-2(3)*, Wipf and Stock) Wipf & Stock Pubs.

Ono, Shoko & Scahill, John. The Katherine Group: A Three Manuscript Parallel Text: Seinte Katerine, Seinte Marherete, Seinte Iuliene, & Hali Meihad, with Wordlists. 2011. (Studies in English Medieval Language & Literature Ser.). (ENM.). 386p. 86.95 *(978-3-631-61172-2(2))* Lang, Peter GmbH, Europaischer Verlag der Wissenschaften DEU. Dist: Lang, Peter.

Otten, Willemien, et al. How the West Was Won: Essays on the Literary Imagination, the Canon, & the Christian Middle Ages. 2010. (Illus.). 422p. *(978-90-04-18496-1(1))* BRILL.

Parker, Margaret. The Spanish Santa Catalina de Alejandría: The Many Lives of a Saint's Life. 2010. (Estudios de Literatura Medieval Ser.: 7). 208p. lib. bdg. 24.95 *(978-1-58871-174-8(9)*, Juan de la Cuesta-Hispanic Monographs) LinguaText, Ltd.

Pearson, Linda Sedrick & Fenton, Cathy Sedrick. New Every Morning. 2008. 184p. pap. 14.96 *(978-1-4357-5041-8(1))* Lulu Enterprises Inc.

Perkins, Robert L., ed. International Kierkegaard Commentary: The Point of View, Volume 22. 2010. (IKC Ser.). 248p. 50.00 *(978-0-88146-213-5(6))* Mercer Univ. Pr.

Pink, Arthur W. Writings of Arthur W Pink from Booklets & Pamphlets. 2011. 170p. pap. 16.99 ***(978-1-61203-346-4(6))*** Bottom of the Hill Publishing.

Powell, Susan. A Critical Edition of John Mirk's Festial, edited from British Library MS Cotton Claudius A. II: Volume 1, 2 vols. 2010. (Early English Text Society Original Ser.). (ENM & ENG., Illus.). 550p. 130.00 *(978-0-19-957849-8(4))* Oxford Univ. Pr., Inc.

Randall House Publications, creator. Celebrate Easter: Easter Sketches & Plays for Your Church. 2009. 116p. spiral bd. 19.99 *(978-0-89265-589-2(5))* Randall Hse. Pubns.

Rein, Nathan. The Chancery of God: Protestant Print, Polemic & Propaganda Against the Empire, Magdeburg, 1546-1551. 2008. (St Andrews Studies in Reformation History Ser.). (Illus.). 282p. 124.95 *(978-0-7546-5686-9(1))* Ashgate Publishing Co.

Representative Writings, 1840-1860, Vol. 41. *(978-0-404-60941-2(4))* AMS Pr., Inc.

Richardson, Jan L. In the Sanctuary of Women: Daily Prayers & Readings. 2010. (Illus.). 332p. 22.00 *(978-0-8358-1030-2(5))* Upper Room Bks.

Rigg, A. G. A History of Anglo-Latin Literature, 1066-1422. 2006. (ENG.). 436p. (C). pap. 79.00 *(978-0-521-03041-0(2))* Cambridge Univ. Pr.

Robinson, Jacqueline R. Life's Lessons for the Young at Heart. 2009. 140p. pap. 14.99 *(978-1-60791-547-8(2))* Xulon Pr., Inc.

Rushforth, Rebecca. Saints in English Kalendars Before Ad 1100. 2010. (Henry Bradshaw Society Ser.: Volume 117). 144p. 99.00 *(978-1-870252-23-2(3))* Bradshaw, Henry Society GBR. Dist: Boydell & Brewer, Inc.

Shriver, Donald W. On Second Thought: Essays Out of My Life. 2010. 224p. pap. 18.00 *(978-1-59627-109-8(4)*, Seabury Bks.) Church Publishing, Inc.

Smalko, Emilia. It's Time to Act! Working to Re-Humanize the Fetus in A New Era of Promising New Solutions & Alternatives to Abortion: 2011. 174p. pap. 21.95 ***(978-1-4327-7134-8(5))*** Outskirts Pr., Inc.

Somerset, Fiona. Four Wycliffite Dialogues. 2010. (Early English Text Society Original Ser.). (ENG., Illus.). 350p. 110.00 *(978-0-19-957848-1(6))* Oxford Univ. Pr., Inc.

Sperk, Klaus, ed. Medieval English saints' Legends. (English Texts). (ENG.). VII, 136p. 210.00 ***(978-3-11-212762-9(5))*** De Gruyter, Mouton DEU. Dist: de Gruyter, Walter GmbH & Co. KG.

Spurgeon, Charles H. Lectures to My Students. 2009. 212p. 23.99 *(978-1-103-32277-0(X))*; pap. 17.99 *(978-1-103-32276-3(1))* BiblioBazaar.

St. John, Raymond A. Explorations in Literature. 3rd ed. 2007. (Illus.). xxiii, 623p. pap. *(978-1-59166-502-1(7))* BJU Pr.

Steinbrecher, John. Letters Direct from Heaven: A Comfort to the Oppressed & Warning to the Oppressor. 2011. 188p. 42.95 ***(978-1-258-09454-6(1))*** Literary Licensing, LLC.

Stewart, James A. The Divine Library. pap. 2.49 *(978-1-56632-040-5(2))* Revival Literature.

Stewart, James A., selected by. Treasure House of Good Books. pap. 1.50 *(978-1-56632-064-1(X))* Revival Literature.

Stuart, Sally. Christian Writers' Market Guide 2009. 2009. (ENG.). 560p. pap. 34.99 *(978-0-307-44643-5(3))* Doubleday Religious Publishing Group, The.

Stuart, Sally E. Christian Writers' Market Guide 2008: The Essential Reference Tool for the Christian Writer. 2008. (Christian Writer's Market Guide Ser.). (ENG.). 640p. pap. 34.99 *(978-1-4000-7461-7(4))* Doubleday Religious Publishing Group, The.

Ten Harmsel, Larry & Van Til, Reinder. An Eerdmans Century: 1911-2011. 2011. 192p. 20.00 ***(978-0-8028-6658-5(1))*** Eerdmans, William B. Publishing Co.

Valadez, Diego. Retorica Cristiana. (SPA & LAT., Illus.). lxi, 863p. 35.99 *(978-968-16-3047-8(5))* Fondo de Cultura Economica USA.

Van Dyke, Henry. The Spirit of Christmas. 2009. 68p. pap. 16.75 *(978-1-110-60645-0(1))* BiblioBazaar.

—The Spirit of Christmas. 2007. (ENG.). 64p. per. 16.95 *(978-0-548-71862-9(8))* Kessinger Publishing, LLC.

Von Habsburg, Maximilian. Catholic & Proptestant Translations of the Imitatio Christi: From Late Medieval Classic to Early Modern Bestseller. 2011. (St Andrews Studies in Reformation History Ser.). 376p. 134.95 ***(978-0-7546-6765-0(0))*** Ashgate Publishing Co.

Wagner, Debra. Good News: The Best Religion Writing in North America. 2006. 165p. per. 14.00 *(978-1-59627-028-2(4))* Church Publishing, Inc.

Welch & Babbs, Liz. Celtic Treasure: Unearthing the Riches of Celtic Spirituality. 2009. (ENG., Illus.). 80p. 9.95 *(978-0-7459-5355-7(7))* Lion Hudson PLC GBR. Dist: Independent Pubs. Group.

Wellhausen, J. Das Evangelium Lucae: Ubersetzt und Erklart. 2009. 142p. pap. 12.00 *(978-1-60608-756-5(8)*, Wipf and Stock) Wipf & Stock Pubs.

William Miller: Selected Works, Vol. 40. *(978-0-404-60940-5(6))* AMS Pr., Inc.

Wolfe, Gregory, ed. Bearing the Mystery: Twenty Years of Image. 2009. (ENG., Illus.). 446p. 30.00 *(978-0-8028-6464-2(3))* Eerdmans, William B. Publishing Co.

CHRISTIAN LITERATURE—BIBLIOGRAPHY

Petersen, William J. & Petersen, Randy. 100 Christian Books That Changed the Century. 2007. 222p. per. 10.95 *(978-1-60126-043-7(1))* Masthof Pr.

Rainey, David. Faith Reads: A Selective Guide to Christian Nonfiction, 1 vol. 2008. 388p. 55.00 *(978-1-59158-602-9(X)*, LU8602) Libraries Unlimited, Inc.

Tischler, Nancy M. Encyclopedia of Contemporary Christian Fiction: From C. S. Lewis to Left Behind, 1 vol. 2009. 400p. 95.00 *(978-0-313-34568-5(6)*, GR4568, Greenwood Pr.) Greenwood Publishing Group, Inc.

CHRISTIAN LITERATURE—HISTORY AND CRITICISM

Andrews, James, ed. Rhetoric, Religion, & the Roots of Identity in British Colonial America: A Rhetorical History of the United States, Volume 1. 2007. (Rhetorical History of the United States Ser.). (ENG.). 372p. 189.00 *(978-0-87013-782-2(4))* Michigan State Univ. Pr.

Andræ, Eric R. & Giertz, Bo. A Hammer for God: Bo Giertz: Lectures from the Centennial Symposia, & Selected Essays by the Bishop. 2010. 342p. ***(978-0-9789129-7-0(7))***; pap. ***(978-0-9789129-8-7(5))*** Lutheran Legacy Inc.

Badir, Patricia. The Maudlin Impression: English Literary Images of Mary Magdalene, 1550-1700. 2009. (ND Reformations: Medieval & Early Modern Ser.). (ENG.). 304p. pap. 38.00 *(978-0-268-02215-0(1))* Univ. of Notre Dame Pr.

Bailey, Julius. Race Patriotism: Protest & Print Culture in the A.M.E. Church. 2012. (ENG., Illus.). 192p. 47.00 ***(978-1-57233-845-6(8))*** Univ. of Tennessee Pr.

Bequette, John P. Rhetoric in the Monastic Tradition: A Textual Study. 2012. (C). 79.95 ***(978-1-4331-1797-8(5))*** Lang, Peter Publishing, Inc.

Beverslius, John. C.S. Lewis & the Search for Rational Religion: Revised & Updated Edition. 2nd ed. 2007. (ENG.). 1p. pap. 21.98 *(978-1-59102-531-3(1))* Prometheus Bks., Pubs.

Biggs, Frederick M. Sources of Anglo-Saxon Literary Culture: The Apocrypha. 2007. pap. 12.00 *(978-1-58044-119-3(X))* Medieval Institute Pubns.

Boggel, Sandra. Metadiscourse in Middle English & Early Modern English Religious Texts: A Corpus-based Study. 2009. (English Corpus Linguistics Ser.). (Illus.). 248p. 69.95 *(978-3-631-58986-1(7))* Lang, Peter GmbH, Europaischer Verlag der Wissenschaften DEU. Dist: Lang, Peter.

Borries, Ekkehard. Schwesternspiegel im 15. Jahrhundert: Gattungskonstitution - Editionen - Untersuchungen. 2008.Tr. of Specula sororum. 15th Century Books of Behaviour & Etiquette for Sisters. (GER.). XIII, 540p. 217.00 *(978-3-11-020070-6(8))* De Gruyter, Walter Inc.

Branch, Lori. Rituals of Spontaneity: Sentiment & Secularism from Free Prayer to Wordsworth. 2006. (Illus.). 362p. 44.95 *(978-1-932792-11-9(2))* Baylor Univ. Pr.

Brennan, Herbie. Through the Wardrobe: Your Favorite Authors on C. S. Lewis' Chronicles of Narnia. 2010. (ENG.). 200p. (J). (gr. 6-11). pap. 12.95 *(978-1-935251-68-2(6))* BenBella Bks.

Brooke, George J. & Romer, Thomas, eds. Ancient & Modern Scriptural Historiography/L'Historiographie Biblique Ancienne et Moderne. 2007. (Bibliotheca Ephemeridum Theologicarum Lovaniensium Ser.). (ENG.). 372p. (C). pap. 109.00 *(978-90-429-1969-3(8))* Peeters Pubs. & Booksellers BEL. Dist: Brown, David Bk. Co., The.

Brown, John. John Bunyan: His Life Times & Work. 3rd ed. 2007. (Illus.). 522p. pap. 45.00 *(978-1-55635-219-5(0)*, Wipf and Stock) Wipf & Stock Pubs.

—John Bunyan His Life Times & Work. 2006. (Illus.). pap. 40.95 *(978-1-4286-5050-3(4))* Kessinger Publishing, LLC.

Bunyan, John. All-in-One Curriculum for the Pilgrim's Progress. 2006. (Illus.). 496p. 39.99 incl. cd-rom *(978-1-893345-77-5(7))* Answers in Genesis Ministries.

Byer, Silvia Giovanardi. Celestial Crusades & Wars in Heaven. 2008. 128p. pap. *(978-3-639-05950-2(6))* VDM Verlag Dr. Mueller e.K.

Cadwallader, Robyn. Three Methods for Reading the Thirteenth-Century Seinte Marherete: Archetypal, Semiotic, & Deconstructionist. 2008. 397p. *(978-0-7734-4840-7(3))* Mellen, Edwin Pr., The.

Cairns, William. The Religion of Dr Johnson & Other Essays. 2007. 152p. per. *(978-1-4067-8806-8(6)*, Pomona Pr.) Read Bks.

Callow, Simon. Dickens' Christmas: A Victorian Celebration. 2009. (ENG., Illus.). 160p. pap. 19.95 *(978-0-7112-3031-6(5))* Lincoln, Frances Ltd. GBR. Dist: Perseus-PGW.

Camden, Vera J., ed. Trauma & Transformation: The Political Progress of John Bunyan. 2007. (ENG.). 200p. 55.00 *(978-0-8047-5785-0(2))* Stanford Univ. Pr.

Campbell, Gordon, et al. Milton & the Manuscript of de Doctrina Christiana. 2008. (ENG., Illus.). 208p. 110.00 *(978-0-19-929649-1(9))* Oxford Univ. Pr., Inc.

Campbell, Kirsty. Call to Read. 2010. (ENG.). 336p. pap. 38.00 *(978-0-268-02306-5(9))* Univ. of Notre Dame Pr.

Carruthers & Carruthers, Jo. Secularizing Scripture: Protestantism, Englishness & Literature. 2011. (New Directions in Religion & Literature Ser.). (ENG.). 160p. 90.00 *(978-0-8264-3913-0(6))*; pap. 27.95 *(978-0-8264-3321-3(9))* Continuum International Publishing Group, Ltd. GBR. Dist: National Bk. Network.

Carter, Grayson, ed. Sehnsucht: the C. S. Lewis Journal. 2011. 232p. pap. 26.00 *(978-1-61097-324-3(0)*, Wipf and Stock) Wipf & Stock Pubs.

Casiday, Augustine M. Evagruis Ponticus. 2006. (Early Church Fathers Ser.). (Illus.). 250p. per. 37.95 *(978-0-415-32447-2(5))* Routledge.

Castagna, Valentina. Re-Reading Margery Kempe in the 21st Century. 2011. 102p. pap. *(978-3-0343-0642-3(3))* Lang, Peter.

Coleman, T. W. English Mystics of the Fourteenth Century 1938. 2007. (ENG.). 174p. 37.95 *(978-0-548-05566-3(1))* Kessinger Publishing, LLC.

Collins, Joseph B. Christian Mysticism in the Elizabethan Age: With its Background in Mystical Methodology. 2008. 265p. pap. 23.00 *(978-1-60608-282-9(5)*, Wipf and Stock) Wipf & Stock Pubs.

Corbett, Tony. The Laity, the Church & the Mystery Plays: A Drama of Belonging. 2009. 262p. 74.50 *(978-1-84682-153-0(3))* Four Courts Pr. IRL. Dist: International Specialized Bk. Services.

Cousins, A. D. Companion to Thomas More. Grace, Damian, ed. 2009. (ENG.). 253p. 58.00 *(978-1-61147-420-6(5))* Fairleigh Dickinson Univ. Pr.

Cousins, A. D. & Grace, Damian. A Companion to Thomas More. 2009. 58.00 *(978-0-8386-4215-3(2))* Fairleigh Dickinson Univ. Pr.

Craun, Edwin D. Ethics & Power in Medieval English Reformist Writing. 2010. (Cambridge Studies in Medieval Literature Ser.). (ENG.). 232p. 85.00 *(978-0-521-19932-2(8))* Cambridge Univ. Pr.

Cunningham, Richard B. C. S. Lewis: Defender of the Faith. 2008. (C. S. Lewis Secondary Studies Ser.). 226p. pap. 25.00 *(978-1-55635-922-4(5)*, Wipf and Stock) Wipf & Stock Pubs.

Curtright, Travis. The One Thomas More. 2012. ***(978-0-8132-1995-0(7))*** Catholic Univ. of America Pr.

Darby, Peter. Bede & the End of Time. 2012. (Studies in Early Medieval Britain Ser.). 276p. 124.95 ***(978-1-4094-3048-3(0))*** Ashgate Publishing Co.

Davis, Christian R. Reading for Redemption: Practical Christian Criticism. 2011. 130p. pap. 16.00 *(978-1-61097-064-8(0)*, Wipf and Stock) Wipf & Stock Pubs.

DeGregorio, Scott, ed. The Cambridge Companion to Bede. 2010. (Cambridge Companions to Literature Ser.). (ENG., Illus.). 302p. (C). pap. 32.99 *(978-0-521-73073-0(2))* Cambridge Univ. Pr.

Di Gangi, Mariano. Great Themes in Puritan Preaching. 2007. (Illus.). 138p. 28.99 *(978-1-894400-26-8(7))* Sola Scriptura.

Dobranski, Stephen B. & Rumrich, John P., eds. Milton & Heresy. 2009. (ENG.). 284p. pap. 38.99 *(978-0-521-10093-9(3))* Cambridge Univ. Pr.

Doerksen, Daniel W. Picturing Religious Experience: George Herbert, Calvin, & the Scriptures. 2011. (ENG.). 256p. 75.00 ***(978-1-61149-356-6(0))*** Univ. of Delaware Pr.

Duke, Roger D. & Newton, Phil A., eds. Venture All for God: Piety in the Writings of John Bunyan. 2011. (Illus.). pap. 10.00 ***(978-1-60178-153-6(9))*** Reformation Heritage Bks.

Dummer, Jürgen, et al. Philologia Sacra et Profana: Ausgewählte Beiträge Zur Antike und Zu Ihrer Wirkungsgeschichte. 2006. (Altertumswissenschaftliches Kolloquium. Interdisziplinare Studien zur Antike und zu ihrem Nachleben (AwK) Ser.). (GER., Illus.). 408p. (C). 94.00 *(978-3-515-08663-9(3))* Steiner, Franz Verlag Wiesbaden GmbH DEU. Dist: Brown, David Bk. Co., The.

Dunan-Page, Anne. The Cambridge Companion to Bunyan. 2010. (Cambridge Companions to Literature Ser.). (ENG.). 212p. pap. 29.99 *(978-0-521-73308-3(1))* Cambridge Univ. Pr.

Dunan-Page, Anne, ed. The Cambridge Companion to Bunyan. 2010. (Cambridge Companions to Literature Ser.). (ENG.). 212p. 85.00 *(978-0-521-51526-9(2))* Cambridge Univ. Pr.

Duncan, Conrad Garfield. Burning the Flags of Extremism. 2011. 136p. pap. 11.95 *(978-1-4497-1301-0(7)*, WestBow Pr.) Author Solutions, Inc.

Dyas, Dee & Thomson, R. M. The Bury Bible. 2008. (Illus.). 102p. pap. 170.00 *(978-1-84384-066-4(9)*, D. S. Brewer) Boydell & Brewer, Ltd. GBR. Dist: Boydell & Brewer, Inc.

Efthymiadis, Stephanos. Hagiography in Byzantium: Literature Social History & Cult. 2011. (Variorum Collected Studies). (Illus.). 374p. 165.00 ***(978-1-4094-3016-2(2))*** Ashgate Publishing Co.

Esolen, Anthony. Ironies of Faith: The Laughter at the Heart of Christian Literature. 2007. (Illus.). 350p. per. 18.00 *(978-1-933859-31-6(8))* ISI Bks.

Fox, Michael & Sharma, Manish, eds. Old Englitерature & the Old Testament. 2011. (Toronto Anglo-Saxon Ser.). (Illus.). 400p. ***(978-0-8020-9854-2(1))*** Univ. of Toronto Pr.

Frakes, Jerold C. Contextualizing the Muslim Other in Medieval Judeo-Christian Discourse. Frakes, Jerold C., ed. 2011. (New Middle Ages Ser.). (ENG., Illus.). 224p. 85.00 *(978-0-230-11143-1(2))* Palgrave Macmillan.

Freeman, Thomas S. & Evenden, Elizabeth. Religion & the Book in Early Modern England: The Making of John Foxe's 'Book of Martyrs' 2011. (Cambridge Studies in Early Modern British History Ser.). (ENG., Illus.). 402p. 99.00 *(978-0-521-83349-3(3))* Cambridge Univ. Pr.

Froude, James. Bunyan. 2007. (ENG.). 188p. 37.95 *(978-0-548-05027-9(9))* Kessinger Publishing, LLC.

Froude, James Anthony. Bunyan. 2011. (Cambridge Library Collection - English Men of Letters Ser.). (ENG.). 194p. pap. 19.99 ***(978-1-108-03466-1(7))*** Cambridge Univ. Pr.

Fudge, John D. Commerce & Print in the Early Reformation. 2007. (Northern World Ser.). (Illus.). 289p. *(978-90-04-15662-3(3))* BRILL.

Gaarden, Bonnie. The Christian Goddess: Archetype & Theology in the Fantasies of George MacDonald. 2011. (ENG.). 224p. 65.00 *(978-1-61147-008-6(0))* Fairleigh Dickinson Univ. Pr.

Gandolfo, Anita. Faith & Fiction: Christian Literature in America Today, 1 vol. 2007. 208p. 44.95 *(978-0-275-99196-8(2)*, C9196, Praeger Pubs.) Greenwood Publishing Group, Inc.

Gerould, Gordon Hall. Saints' Legends. 2009. 220p. pap. 19.99 *(978-1-150-70260-0(5))* General Bks. LLC.

—Saints' Legends. 2008. 402p. 49.95 *(978-1-4365-6679-7(7))* 2007. (ENG.). 404p. per. 34.95 *(978-0-548-75217-3(6))* Kessinger Publishing, LLC.

Ghosh, Kantik & Gillespie, Vincent, eds. After Arundel: Religious Writing in Fifteenth-century England. 2012. (Medieval Church Studies). (ENG, FRE & LAT., Illus.). 657p. (C). 196.00 ***(978-2-503-53402-2(3))*** Brepols Pubs. BEL. Dist: ISD.

Giacomini, Michela P. Sir Richard Blackmore & the Bible: A Reading of His Physico-Theological Poems. 2006. (ENG.). 184p. pap. 41.99 *(978-0-7618-3560-8(1))* Univ. Pr. of America, Inc.

Gillespie, Vincent. Looking in Holy Books: Essays on Late-Medieval Religious Writing in England. 2008. (University of Wales - Religion & Culture in the Middle Ages Ser.). 272p. 110.00 *(978-0-7083-1858-4(4))*; pap. 39.95 *(978-0-7083-1857-7(6))* Univ. of Wales Pr. GBR. Dist: Chicago Distribution Ctr.

Grafton, Anthony & Williams, Megan. Christianity & the Transformation of the Book: Origen, Eusebius, & the Library of Caesarea. 2008. (Illus.). 384p. pap. 21.00 *(978-0-674-03048-0(6)*, Belknap Pr.) Harvard Univ. Pr.

Green, Roger P. H. Latin Epics of the New Testament: Juvencus, Sedulius, Arator. 2007. (ENG.). 464p. 150.00 *(978-0-19-928457-3(1))* Oxford Univ. Pr., Inc.

Hamilton, James. Our Christian Classics V3: Readings from the Best Divines With. 2007. (ENG.). 432p. per. 36.95 *(978-1-4304-4551-7(3))* Kessinger Publishing, LLC.

Hannay, Margaret Patterson. C. S. Lewis: A Map of His Worlds. 2009. (C. S. Lewis Secondary Studies Ser.). 314p. pap. 35.00 *(978-1-60608-410-6(0)*, Wipf and Stock) Wipf & Stock Pubs.

Hardy, Elizabeth Baird. Milton, Spenser & the Chronicles of Narnia: Literary Sources for the C. S. Lewis Novels. 2006. (ENG.). 196p. per. 35.00 *(978-0-7864-2876-2(7))* McFarland & Co., Inc. Pubs.

Hardy, Grant. Understanding the Book of Mormon: A Reader's Guide, 1 vol. 2010. (ENG.). 336p. 29.95 *(978-0-19-973170-1(5))* Oxford Univ. Pr., Inc.

Hass, Andrew, et al. The Oxford Handbook of English Literature & Theology. 2007. (Oxford Handbooks Ser.). (ENG.). 908p. 175.00 *(978-0-19-927197-9(6))* Oxford Univ. Pr., Inc.

Hayes, Mary. Divine Ventriloquism in Medieval English Literature: Power, Anxiety, Subversion. 2011. (New Middle Ages Ser.). (ENG.). 260p. 85.00 *(978-0-230-10899-8(7))* Palgrave Macmillan.

Heidl, Gyorgy & Somos, R., eds. Origeniana Nona: Origen & the Religious Practice of His Time. 2009. (Bibliotheca Ephemeridum Theologicarum Lovaniensium Ser.). (ENG.). 752p. (C). pap. 138.00 *(978-90-429-2234-1(6))* Peeters Pubs. & Booksellers BEL. Dist: Brown, David Bk. Co., The.

Hill, Geoffrey. Collected Critical Writings. Haynes, Kenneth, ed. 2009. (ENG.). 832p. pap. 34.95 *(978-0-19-923448-6(5))* Oxford Univ. Pr., Inc.

Hill-Vasquez, Heather. Sacred Players: The Politics of Response in the Middle English Religious Drama. 2007. 229p. 64.95 *(978-0-8132-1497-9(1))* Catholic Univ. of America Pr.

Holmes, Emily A. & Farley, Wendy. Women, Writing, Theology: Transforming a Tradition of Exclusion. 2011. (ENG.). 330p. pap. 39.95 *(978-1-60258-376-4(5))* Baylor Univ. Pr.

Jacobs, Alan. The Narnian: The Life & Imagination of C. S. Lewis. (Plus Ser.). (ENG., Illus.). 2008. 384p. pap. 14.95 *(978-0-06-144872-0(9)*, HarperOne) 2006. 368p. per. 14.95 *(978-0-06-087269-4(1)*, Harper San Francisco) HarperCollins Pubs.

Kabir, Ananya Jahanara. Paradise, Death & Doomsday in Anglo-Saxon Literature. 2006. (Cambridge Studies in Anglo-Saxon England Ser.). (ENG.). 224p. pap. 42.00 *(978-0-521-03060-1(9))* Cambridge Univ. Pr.

Kerby-Fulton, Kathryn. Books under Suspicion: Censorship & tolerance of Revelatory Writing in Late Medieval England. 2011. (ENG., Illus.). 616p. pap. 35.00 ***(978-0-268-03323-1(4))*** Univ. of Notre Dame Pr.

Kibbey, Ann. The Interpretation of Material Shapes in Puritanism: A Study of Rhetoric, Prejudice, & Violence. 2009. (Cambridge Studies in American Literature & Culture Ser.). (ENG.). 216p. pap. 31.99 *(978-0-521-10788-4(1))* Cambridge Univ. Pr.

Knott, John R. Discourses of Martyrdom in English Literature, 1563-1694. 2010. (ENG., Illus.). 304p. pap. 33.99 *(978-0-521-13158-2(8))* Cambridge Univ. Pr.

Krondorfer, Bjorn. Male Confessions: Intimate Revelations & the Religious Imagination. 2009. (ENG., Illus.). 312p. 70.00 *(978-0-8047-6899-3(4))*; pap. 24.95 *(978-0-8047-6900-6(1))* Stanford Univ. Pr.

Kullmann, Dorothea. The Church & Vernacular Literature in Medieval France. 2009. (Studies & Texts). (FRE & ENG., Illus.). vi, 296p. 75.00 *(978-0-88844-165-2(7))* Pontifical Institute of Mediaeval Studies, Dept. of Pubns. CAN. Dist: Univ. of Toronto Pr.

Lewin, Ann. Love Is the Meaning: Growing in Faith with Julian of Norwich. 2010. (ENG.). ix, 67p. pap. 13.99 *(978-1-84825-050-5(9)*, Canterbury Pr. Norwich) Hymns Ancient & Modern Ltd GBR. Dist: Westminster John Knox Pr.

Lewis, C. S. The Complete C. S. Lewis Signature Classics. 2007. (ENG., Illus.). 1088p. pap. 29.99 *(978-0-06-120849-2(3)*, HarperOne) HarperCollins Pubs.

Magennis, Hugh & Swan, Mary, eds. A Companion to Ælfric. 2009. (Brill's Companions to the Christian Tradition Ser.). 480p. *(978-90-04-17681-2(0))* BRILL.

Magennis, Hugh & Wilcox, Jonathan, eds. The Power of Words: Anglo-Saxon Studies Presented to Donald G. Scragg on His Seventieth Birthday. 2006. (Medieval European Studies: VIII). (ENG., Illus.). 434p. per. 44.95 *(978-1-933202-15-0(7))* West Virginia Univ. Pr.

Mahan, Henry. The Works of Henry Mahan. 2008. 484p. 37.36 *(978-1-4357-0619-4(6))*; (ENG.). 616p. 42.64 *(978-1-4357-0623-1(4))*; (ENG.). 628p. 43.50 *(978-1-4357-0621-7(8))* Lulu Enterprises Inc.

McAvoy, Liz Herbert, ed. Rhetoric of the Anchorhold: Space, Place & Body Within Discourses of Enclosure. 2008. (University of Wales - Religion & Culture in the Middle Ages Ser.). (Illus.). 224p. 85.00 *(978-0-7083-2130-0(5))* Univ. of Wales Pr. GBR. Dist: Chicago Distribution Ctr.

McColman, Carl. The Lion, the Mouse, & the Dawn Treader: Spiritual Lessons from C. S. Lewis's Narnia. 2011. (ENG.). 144p. pap. 14.99 *(978-1-55725-887-8(2))* Paraclete Pr., Inc.

McIlhenny, Albert. The New Restorationists: A Critique of Frank Viola & George Barna's Pagan Christianity? 2010. 68p. pap. 8.36 *(978-0-557-46221-6(5))* Lulu Enterprises Inc.

Mearns, James. The Canticles of the Christian Church: Eastern & Western, in Early & Medieval Times. 2012. (ENG.). 122p. pap. 40.00 ***(978-1-107-63823-5(2))*** Cambridge Univ. Pr.

Merton, Thomas. Echoing Silence: Thomas Merton on the Vocation of Writing. Inchausti, Robert, ed. 2007. (ENG.). 224p. per. 18.95 *(978-1-59030-348-1(2)*, New Seeds Bks.) Shambhala Pubns., Inc.

Metlake, George. Life & Writings of St Columban. 2006. pap. 28.95 *(978-1-4286-3724-5(9))* Kessinger Publishing, LLC.

Miller, Stephen. The Peculiar Life of Sundays. 2008. 320p. 27.95 *(978-0-674-03168-5(7))* Harvard Univ. Pr.

Millet, Olivier, ed. Jean Calvin: Institution de la religion Chretienne(1541), 2 vols. 2008. (Textes Litteraires Francais Ser.). (FRE.). 1814p. (C). pap. 130.00 *(978-2-600-01240-9(0))* Droz, Librairie CHE. Dist: Brown, David Bk. Co., The.

Morgan, David T. The New Brothers Grimm & Their Left Behind Fairy Tales. 2006. (Illus.). 222p. per. 20.00 *(978-0-88146-036-0(2))* Mercer Univ. Pr.

Morrison, Tessa. Isaac Newton's Temple of Solomon & His Reconstruction of Sacred Architecture. 2010. (ENG., Illus.). xix, 186p. 99.00 *(978-3-0348-0045-7(2)*, 3034800452) Birkhauser Verlag AG CHE. Dist: Springer.

Mueller, William R. John Donne: Preacher. 2011. 276p. 47.95 ***(978-1-258-07732-7(9))*** Literary Licensing, LLC.

Murphy, G. Ronald. Gemstone of Paradise: The Holy Grail in Wolfram's Parzival. 2010. (ENG.). 256p. pap. 24.95 *(978-0-19-974759-7(8))* Oxford Univ. Pr., Inc.

Murphy-O'Connor, J., et al. Celebrating Paul: Festschrift in Honor of Jerome Murphy-O'Connor, O.P., & Joseph A. Fitzmyer, S.J. 2012. ***(978-0-915170-47-0(7))*** Catholic Biblical Assn. of America.

Naudé, Piet. Neither Calendar nor Clock: Perspectives on the Belhar Confession. 2010. pap. 25.00 *(978-0-8028-6259-4(4))* Eerdmans, William B. Publishing Co.

Overing, Gillian R. & Lees, Clare A. Double Agents: Women & Clerical Culture in Anglo-Saxon England. 2010. (University of Wales Press - Religion & Culture in the Middle Ages Ser.). (ENG.). 256p. 85.00 *(978-0-7083-2183-6(6))* Univ. of Wales Pr. GBR. Dist: Chicago Distribution Ctr.

Owens, W. R. & Sim, Stuart, eds. Reception,Appropriation, Recollection: Bunyan's Pilgrim's Progress. 2007. (Religious & Discourse Ser.: Vol. 33). 253p. (C). pap. 61.95 *(978-0-8204-7983-5(7))* Lang, Peter Publishing, Inc.

Papandrea, James Leonard. Reading the Early Church Fathers: From the Didache to Nicaea. 2012. 352p. pap. 24.95 ***(978-0-8091-4751-9(3))*** Paulist Pr.

Papazian, Mary A., ed. The Sacred & Profane in English Renaissance Literature. 2008. (Illus.). 384p. 75.00 *(978-0-87413-025-6(5))* Univ. of Delaware Pr.

Patterson, Mary Hampson. Domesticating the Reformation: Protestant Best Sellers, Private Devotion, & the Revolution of English Piety. 2007. 449p. *(978-0-8386-4109-5(1))* Fairleigh Dickinson Univ. Pr.

Payer, Pierre J. Sex & the New Medieval Literature of Confession, 1150-1300. 2009. (Studies & Texts). (ENG.). ix, 249p. 75.00 *(978-0-88844-163-8(0))* Pontifical Institute of Mediaeval Studies, Dept. of Pubns. CAN. Dist: Univ. of Toronto Pr.

Peters, Kate. Print Culture & the Early Quakers. 2009. (Cambridge Studies in Early Modern British History Ser.). (ENG., Illus.). 292p. pap. 51.00 *(978-0-521-09312-5(0))* Cambridge Univ. Pr.

Pezzini, Domenico. The Translation of Religious Texts in the Middle Ages: Tracts & Rules, Hymns & Saints' Lives. 2008. (Linguistic Insights. Studies in Language & Communication Ser.). 428p. pap. *(978-3-03911-600-3(2))* Lang, Peter.

Robinett, P. A. As the Waters Cover the Se. 2008. 124p. pap. 19.95 *(978-1-878411-07-5(1))* Aesculapius Pr.

Roth, John K. Masterplots II. 2007. 96.00 *(978-1-58765-383-4(4))*; 96.00 *(978-1-58765-381-0(8))*; 96.00 *(978-1-58765-380-3(X))*; 96.00 *(978-1-58765-382-7(6))* Salem Pr., Inc.

Roy, Neil & Rutherford, Janet, eds. Benedict XVI & the Sacred Liturgy. 2010. 210p. 45.00 *(978-1-84682-254-4(8))* Four Courts Pr. IRL. Dist: International Specialized Bk. Services.

Rütten, Tanja. How to Do Things with Texts: Patterns of Instruction in Religious Discourse 1350-1700. 2011. (English Corpus Linguistics Ser.). (Illus.). 260p. 76.95 *(978-3-631-61802-8(6))* Lang, Peter GmbH, Europaischer Verlag der Wissenschaften DEU. Dist: Lang, Peter.

Salter, Elisabeth. Vernacularity in England & Wales, C. 1300-1550. Wicker, Helen, ed. 2011. (Utrecht Studies in Medieval Literacy Ser.). (ENG., Illus.). 335p. (C). 102.00 *(978-2-503-52883-0(X))* Brepols Pubs. BEL. Dist: ISD.

Scheck, Helene. Reform & Resistance: Formations of Female Subjectivity in Early Medieval Ecclesiastical Culture. 2008. (SUNY Series in Medieval Studies). (Illus.). xii, 238p. (C). 70.00 *(978-0-7914-7483-9(6))* State Univ. of New York Pr.

Schmitt, Jean-Claude. The Conversion of Herman the Jew: Autobiography, History, & Fiction in the Twelfth Century. Novikoff, Alex J., tr. from FRE. 2010. (Middle Ages Ser.). (Illus.). 320p. (C). 59.95 *(978-0-8122-4254-6(8))* Univ. of Pennsylvania Pr.

Shaheen, Naseeb. Biblical References in Shakespeare's Plays. 2011. (ENG.). 880p. 125.00 ***(978-1-61149-358-0(7))*** Univ. of Delaware Pr.

Skinner, Christopher W. What Are They Saying about the Gospel of Thomas? 2012. ***(978-1-61643-136-5(9))***; 144p. pap. ***(978-0-8091-4761-8(0))*** Paulist Pr.

Soergel, Philip M. Miracles & the Protestant Imagination: The Evangelical Wonder Book in Reformation Germany, 1 vol. 2012. (Oxford Studies in Historical Theology Ser.). (ENG., Illus.). 272p. 65.00 ***(978-0-19-984466-1(6))*** Oxford Univ. Pr., Inc.

Spargo, Tamsin. John Bunyan. 2011. (Writers & Their Work Ser.). (C). (ENG.). 80.00 *(978-0-7463-1049-6(8))*; pap. 26.00 *(978-0-7463-0982-7(1))* Northcote Hse. Publishers, Ltd. GBR. Dist: Brown, David Bk. Co., The.

Stewart, Jon. Patristic & Medieval Tradition. 2008. (Kierkegaard Research: Sources, Reception & Resources Ser.). 350p. 134.95 *(978-0-7546-6391-1(4))* Ashgate Publishing Co.

Styler, Rebecca. Literary Theology by Women Writers of the Nineteenth Century. 2010. (Nineteenth Century Ser.). (Illus.). 190p. 99.95 *(978-0-7546-6735-3(9))* Ashgate Publishing Co.

Sweeney, Anne & Sweeney, Anne R. Robert Southwell: Snow in Arcadia: Redrawing the English Lyric Landscape, 1586-1595. 2007. (ENG.). 328p. 84.00 *(978-0-7190-7418-9(5))* Manchester Univ. Pr. GBR. Dist: Macmillan.

Szwarc, Krzysztof. Jezus Chrystus-Osoba I Czyn: Romano Guardiniego Chrystologia Personalistyczna. 2008. (POL.). 524p. *(978-83-7363-737-5(0))* Katolicki Uniwersytet Lubelski, Wydawnictwo.

Tinkle, Theresa. Gender & Power in Medieval Exegesis. 2010. (New Middle Ages Ser.). (ENG.). 212p. 84.00 *(978-0-230-10435-8(5))* Palgrave Macmillan.

Vance, Norman. The Sinews of the Spirit: The Ideal of Christian Manliness in Victorian Literature & Religious Thought. 2010. (ENG., Illus.). 256p. pap. 38.99 *(978-0-521-12860-5(9))* Cambridge Univ. Pr.

Waller, George M., ed. Puritanism in Early Americ: Problems in American Civilization. 2011. 126p. 40.95 ***(978-1-258-03579-2(0))*** Literary Licensing, LLC.

Walsh, Chad. The Literary Legacy of C. S. Lewis. 2008. (C. S. Lewis Secondary Studies Ser.). 282p. pap. 31.00 *(978-1-55635-884-5(9)*, Wipf and Stock) Wipf & Stock Pubs.

Walsh, Milton. Second Friends: C. S. Lewis & Ronald Knox in Conversation. 2008. 350p. pap. 16.95 *(978-1-58617-240-4(9))* Ignatius Pr.

Walsh, Richard G. Three Versions of Judas. 2010. (BibleWorld Ser.). (ENG.). 224p. (C). 100.00 *(978-1-84553-701-2(7))*; pap. 34.95 *(978-1-84553-702-9(5))* Equinox Publishing Ltd. GBR. Dist: ISD.

Warren, Nancy. Embodied Word: Female Spiritualities, Contested Orthodoxies, & English Religious Cultures, 1350-1700. 2010. (ND Reformations: Medieval & Early Modern Ser.). (ENG., Illus.). 352p. pap. 36.00 *(978-0-268-04420-6(1))* Univ. of Notre Dame Pr.

Wetmore, Kevin J., ed. Catholic Theatre & Drama: Critical Essays. 2010. (ENG., Illus.). 235p. pap. 55.00 *(978-0-7864-4741-1(9))* McFarland & Co., Inc. Pubs.

Wheeler, Michael. The Old Enemies: Catholic & Protestant in Nineteenth-Century English Culture. 2011. (ENG.). 370p. pap. 45.00 *(978-0-521-29281-8(6))* Cambridge Univ. Pr.

Wolfe, Gregory. Beauty Will Save World: Recovering the Human in an Ideological Age. 2011. (ENG., Illus.). 320p. 29.95 *(978-1-933859-88-0(1))* ISI Bks.

Zettersten, Arne. Double Worlds & Creative Process: Language & Life. 2011. (ENG., Illus.). 256p. 85.00 *(978-0-230-62314-9(X))* Palgrave Macmillan.

CHRISTIAN LITERATURE, EARLY

Augustine, Saint. The Confessions. 2006. (ENG.). pap. *(978-1-4065-1000-3(9))* Dodo Pr.

—The Confessions of Saint Augustine. 2008. 468p. per. 9.99 *(978-1-59986-572-0(6))* Filiquarian Publishing, LLC.

—The Confessions of Saint Augustine. Blaiklock, E. M., tr. from LAT. 2010. (Hodder Classics Ser.). (ENG.). 304p. pap. 12.95 *(978-0-340-98012-5(5)*, Hodder & Stoughton) Hodder General Publishing Div. GBR. Dist: Independent Pubs. Group.

—The Confessions of Saint Augustine. 2008. 208p. pap. 7.99 *(978-1-60459-407-2(1))* Wilder Pubns., Ltd.

Augustine, St. Augustine, Later Works: Library of Christian Classics, V8. Burnaby, John & Baillie, John, eds. 2011. 360p. 51.95 ***(978-1-258-09926-8(8))*** Literary Licensing, LLC.

Bagnall, Roger S. Early Christian Books in Egypt. 2009. (ENG., Illus.). 136p. (C). 30.95 *(978-0-691-14026-1(X))* Princeton Univ. Pr.

Bernard of Clairvaux. Treatises I: Apologia, Precept & Dispensation. (Cistercian Fathers Ser.: No. 1). 190p. 7.95 *(978-0-87907-101-1(X))* Cistercian Pubns., Inc.

Biblia Patristica: Index des Citations et Allusions Bibliques Dans la LittéRature Patristique. -6 ;p. *(978-2-222-01802-5(1))* Bow Historical Bks.

Bingham, D. Jeffrey. Early Christian Thought. 2010. (Routledge Religion Companions Ser.). (ENG.). 360p. (C). 155.00 *(978-0-415-44225-1(7))* Routledge.

Blumell, Lincoln H. Lettered Christians: Christians, Letters, & Late Antique Oxyrhynchus. 2012. (New Testament Tools, Studies & Documents Ser.: Vol. 39). (ENG., Illus.). xiii, 427p. ***(978-90-04-18095-6(8))*** BRILL.

Bremmer, J. N., ed. The Pseudo-Clementines. 2010. (Studies on Early Christian Apocrypha Ser.). (ENG.). 357p. (C). pap. 70.00 *(978-90-429-2269-3(9))* Peeters Pubs. & Booksellers BEL. Dist: Brown, David Bk. Co., The.

Budge, E. A. Wallis, ed. Coptic Martyrdoms, Etc. in the Dialect of Upper Egypt. (Coptic Texts Ser.: Vol. 4). (Illus.). reprint ed. 76.50 *(978-0-404-11554-8(3))* AMS Pr., Inc.

—Miscellaneous Coptic Texts in the Dialect of Upper Egypt, 2 vols. (Coptic Texts Ser.: Vol. 5). (Illus.). reprint ed. 150.00 *(978-0-404-11555-5(1))* AMS Pr., Inc.

Burghardt, Walter J. The Didache; the Epistle of Barnabas; the Epistles & the Martyrdom of St Polycarp; the Fragments of Papias; the Epistle of Diognetus. Burghardt, Walter J. et al, eds. 2011. 240p. 46.95 ***(978-1-258-04163-2(4))*** Literary Licensing, LLC.

Carol, Ann. Early Christian Writers: The Pageant of Literature. 2011. 222p. 44.95 ***(978-1-258-01879-5(9))*** Literary Licensing, LLC.

Clement of Alexandria. Clement of Alexandria, Miscellanies Book VII: The Greek Text with Introduction, Translation, Notes, Dissertations & Indices. Hort, Fenton John Anthony & Mayor, Joseph Bickersteth, eds. 2010. (Cambridge Library Collection - Religion Ser.). (ENG.). 572p. pap. 39.99 *(978-1-108-00754-2(6))* Cambridge Univ. Pr.

Cole, Leona J. Prince of the House of David. 2011. 260p. pap. 19.95 ***(978-1-4497-2309-5(8)***, WestBow Pr.) Author Solutions, Inc.

Colless, Brian E., tr. from SYR. The Wisdom of the Pearlers: An Anthology of Syriac Christian Mysticism. 2007. (Cistercian Studies). 240p. per. *(978-0-87907-316-9(0))* Cistercian Pubns., Inc.

Conybeare, F. C., ed. The Apology & Acts of Apollonius: And Other Monuments of Early Christianity. 2007. 368p. pap. 35.00 *(978-1-55635-275-1(1)*, Wipf and Stock) Wipf & Stock Pubs.

Creeds Councils & Controversies-Spck. 30.00 *(978-0-687-85177-5(7))* Abingdon Pr.

De Kelaita, Joseph. The Paradise of Eden. 2009. (SYR.). 110.00 *(978-1-60724-333-5(4))* Gorgias Pr., LLC.

Downing, F. Gerald. God with Everything: The Divine in the Discourse of the First Christian Century. 2008. 328p. *(978-1-906055-25-7(4))* Sheffield Phoenix Pr.

Frend, W. H. C. & Stevenson, J., eds. Creeds, Councils & Controversies: Documents Illustrating the History of the Church, AD 337-461. 2012. 504p. (C). pap. 45.00 ***(978-0-8010-3970-6(3))*** Baker Academic.

—A New Eusebius: Documents Illustrating the History of the Church to AD 337. 2012. 504p. (C). pap. 45.00 ***(978-0-8010-3971-3(1))*** Baker Academic.

Freund, Stefan. Laktanz, Diuinae institutiones , Buch 7: de uita Beata: Einleitung, Text, Übersetzung und Kommentar. 2009. (Texte und Kommentare Ser.).Tr. of Lactantius, Diuinae institutiones , Book 7: de uita beata . Introduction, text, translation & Commentary. (GER & LAT.). X, 707p. 165.00 *(978-3-11-019345-9(0))* De Gruyter, Walter Inc.

Freund, Stefan. Laktanz. Divinae institutiones . Buch 7: de vita Beata: Einleitung, Text, Ãœbersetzung und Kommentar. 2009. (Texte und Kommentare Ser.).Tr. of Lactantius, Diuinae institutiones , Book 7: de uita beata . Introduction, text, translation & Commentary. (GER & LAT.). X, 707p. 252.00 ***(978-3-11-173726-3(8))*** De Gruyter, Walter Inc.

Halton, Thomas P. Hermias, Gentilium Philosophorum Irrisio. 2009. 46p. pap. 6.00 *(978-1-60608-632-2(4)*, Wipf and Stock) Wipf & Stock Pubs.

Harris, J. Rendel. Hermas in Arcadia & Other Essays. 2007. 87p. pap. 14.00 *(978-1-55635-061-0(9)*, Wipf and Stock) Wipf & Stock Pubs.

Hefele, Charles Joseph. Patrum Apostolicorum Opera. 2011. 340p. pap. 29.00 *(978-1-60608-189-1(6)*, Wipf and Stock) Wipf & Stock Pubs.

Heine, Ronald E. Reading the Old Testament with the Ancient Church: Exploring the Formation of Early Christian Thought. 2007. (Evangelical Ressourcement Ser.). 208p. (C). pap. 24.00 *(978-0-8010-2777-2(2))* Baker Academic.

Hill, Charles E. & Kruger, Michael J. The Early Text of the New Testament. 2012. (ENG.). 448p. 175.00 ***(978-0-19-956636-5(4))*** Oxford Univ. Pr., Inc.

Holmes, Michael W., et al. The Apostolic Fathers: Greek Texts & English Translations. Holmes, Michael W., ed. 3rd ed. 2007. (Illus.). 832p. (C). 44.99 *(978-0-8010-3468-8(X))* Baker Academic.

Irenaeus. The Writings of Irenaeus. Roberts, Alexander & Donaldson, James, eds. 2007. 276p. per. 18.95 *(978-1-933993-47-8(2))* Apocryphile Pr.

Joslyn-Siemiatkoski, Daniel & Joslyn-Siemiatkoski, Dani. Christian Memories of the Maccabean Martyrs. 2009. (ENG.). 272p. 89.00 *(978-0-230-60279-3(7))* Palgrave Macmillan.

C

Kraus, Thomas J. Ad Fontes: Original Manuscripts & Their Significance for Studying Early Christianity - Selected Essays. 2007. (Texts & Editions for New Testament Study Ser.). (MUL., Illus.). 304p. *(978-90-04-16182-5(1))* BRILL.

Kraus, Thomas J. & Nicklas, Tobias. Early Christian Manuscripts: Examples of Applied Method & Approach. 2010. (Texts & Editions for New Testament Study Ser.). *(978-90-04-18265-3(9))* BRILL.

La Porta, S. Two Anonymous Sets of Scholia on Dionysius the Areopagite's Heavenly Hierarchy (Scriptores Armeniaci 29) 2008. (Corpus Scriptorum Christianorum Orientalium Ser.). (ENG.). 124p. (C). pap. 76.00 *(978-90-429-1918-1(3))* Peeters Pubs. & Booksellers BEL. Dist: Brown, David Bk. Co., The.

—Two Anonymous Sets of Scholia on Dionysius the Areopagite's Heavenly Hierarchy (Scriptores Armeniaci 30) 2008. (Corpus Scriptorum Christianorum Orientalium Ser.). (ENG.). 157p. (C). pap. 70.00 *(978-90-429-1919-8(1))* Peeters Pubs. & Booksellers BEL. Dist: Brown, David Bk. Co., The.

Moody Publishing Staff & Moody Publishing. The Apostolic Fathers, 1 vol. 2009. (Moody Classics Ser.). (ENG.). 320p. pap. 8.99 *(978-0-8024-5659-5(6))* Moody Pubs.

Oulton, John Ernest Leonard. Alexandrian Christianity: Selected Translations of Clement & Origen. Chadwick, Henry, ed. 2011. 470p. 57.95 ***(978-1-258-01421-6(1))*** Literary Licensing, LLC.

Overbeck, J. Josephus. S. Ephraemi Syri, Rabulae Episcopi Edesseni, Balaei, Aliorumque Opera Selecta. 2006. (SYR.). 500p. 98.00 *(978-1-59333-517-5(2))* Gorgias Pr., LLC.

Paulinus, et al. Carmina. 2006. (Bibliotheca scriptorum Graecorum et Romanorum Teubneriana (BT) Ser.). (LAT.). XXX, 38p. *(978-3-598-71323-1(1))* Teubner, B.G. GmbH.

Petermann, Julius Heinrich. The Great Treasure or Great Book, commonly called the Book of Adam, the Mandaeans' work of highest Authority: Thesaurus sive Liber Magnus, vulgo Liber Adami appellatus, opus Mandaeorum summi Ponderis. 2006. (Gorgias Mandean Studies: 2). 780p. 268.00 *(978-1-59333-525-0(3))* Gorgias Pr., LLC.

Porter, Stanley, et al, eds. Journal of Greco-Roman Christianity & Judaism. 2007. 248p. *(978-1-905048-58-8(0))* Sheffield Phoenix Pr.

Porter, Stanley E. Journal of Greco-Roman Christianity & Judaism. 2008. 236p. *(978-1-906055-28-8(9))* Sheffield Phoenix Pr.

Porter, Stanley E., et al, eds. Journal of Greco-Roman Christianity & Judaism. 2011. 208p. ***(978-1-907534-18-8(0))*** 2010. 244p. *(978-1-906055-83-7(1))* Sheffield Phoenix Pr.

Rankin, David. Athenagoras: Philosopher & Theologian. 2009. 202p. 99.95 *(978-0-7546-6604-2(2))* Ashgate Publishing Co.

Sandnes, Karl Olav. The Gospel "According to Homer & Virgil" Cento & Canon. 2011. XII, 280p. *(978-90-04-18718-4(9))* BRILL.

Schaff, Philip. The Oldest Church Manual Called the Teaching of the Twelve Apostles: The Didache & Kindred Documents in the Oringal, with Translations & Discussions of Post-Apostolic Teaching, Baptism, Worship, & Discipline, & with Illustrations & Facsimiles of the Jerusalem Manuscript. 2008. 311p. pap. 26.00 *(978-1-60608-301-7(5)*, Wipf and Stock) Wipf & Stock Pubs.

Schwiebert, Jonathan & Schwiebert. Knowledge & the Coming Kingdom: The Didache's Meal Ritual & Its Place in Early Christianity. 2008. (Library of New Testament Studies). (ENG.). 304p. 130.00 *(978-0-567-04575-1(7)*, T&T Clark Int'l) Continuum International Publishing Group, Ltd. GBR. Dist: National Bk. Network.

Sisebut. King Sisebut & the Culture of Visigothic Spain, with Translations of the Lives of Saint Desiderius of Vienne & Saint Masona of Mérida: Vita Vel Passio Sancti Desiderii a Sisebuto Rege Composita & Vita Sancti Masonae Emeretensis. Martyn, John R. C., tr. from LAT. & intro. by. 2008. (LAT & ENG.). 248p. 109.95 *(978-0-7734-5033-2(5))* Mellen, Edwin Pr., The.

Smith, Andrew W. The Fallowfield Carol: Or the Adventure of Messrs. Wiggin & Clarke, Concerning Their Search for an Ancient Carol of Christm. 2010. pap. 11.99 *(978-1-61566-250-0(2))* Tate Publishing & Enterprises, LLC.

Valentina, Peshkova. The Book of Hermes - the Key to the Secret Doctrine. 2007. (RUS.). 388p. 26.95 *(978-1-4327-1822-0(3))*; per. 19.95 *(978-1-4327-0849-8(X))* Outskirts Pr., Inc.

Westerhoff, Matthias. Das Paulusverständnis im Liber Graduum. 2008. (Patristische Texte und Studien Ser.).Tr. of Did the Author of the 'Book of Steps' Understand Paul? (GER.). XIV, 260p. 119.00 *(978-3-11-020732-3(X))* De Gruyter, Walter Inc.

Whitacre, Rodney A. A Patristic Greek Reader. 2007. (GEC & ENG.). 279p. per. *(978-1-59856-043-5(3))* Hendrickson Pubs. Marketing, LLC.

Williams, D. H., ed. Tradition, Scripture, & Interpretation: A Sourcebook of the Ancient Church. 2006. (Evangelical Ressourcement Ser.). 192p. (C). pap. 22.00 *(978-0-8010-3164-9(8))* Baker Academic.

CHRISTIAN LITERATURE, EARLY (COLLECTIONS)

Here are entered collections of writings of Christian authors to the time of Gregory the Great in the West, and John of Damascus in the East.

see also Apologetics—Early Church, ca. 30-600; Apostolic Fathers; Bible—Quotations, Early; Church Orders, Ancient; Fathers of the Church; Jesus Christ—Biography—Apocryphal and Legendary Literature; Jesus Christ—Trial; Latin Literature, Medieval and Modern; Literature, Medieval; Liturgies, Early Christian; Martyrologies; Scholia

Assemani, Stephen Evodius & Benedictus, Peter, eds. The Works of St. Ephrem the Syrian. 2010. (LAT.). 946.56 *(978-1-60724-824-8(7))*; 946.56 *(978-1-60724-823-1(9))*; 946.56 *(978-1-60724-825-5(5))*; 946.56 *(978-1-60724-822-4(0))*; 946.56 *(978-1-60724-826-2(3))*; 946.56 *(978-1-60724-827-9(1))* Gorgias Pr., LLC.

Barone, Joe, et al. Living in the Light: 22 Creative Components Including Services, Dialogues, Monologues, Skits, Dramas, Mediations, & a Litany. 2008. 137p. per. 27.95 *(978-0-7880-2502-0(3))* CSS Publishing Co.

Edersheim, Alfred. The Abridged Edersheim. 2009. 498p. pap. 23.99 *(978-1-4415-5467-3(X))* Xlibris Corp.

Fox, George. The Journal of George Fox 2 Part Set: A Revised Edition, 2 vols. Nickalls, John L., ed. 2010. (Cambridge Library Collection - Religion Ser.). (ENG.). 844p. pap. 60.00 *(978-1-108-01611-7(1))* Cambridge Univ. Pr.

Schaff, Philip, ed. Nicene & Post-Nicene Fathers: Second Series Volume I - Eusebius. 2007. 644p. (ENG.). 37.95 *(978-1-60206-508-6(X))*; per. 26.95 *(978-1-60206-507-9(1))* Cosimo, Inc.

—Nicene & Post-Nicene Fathers: Second Series Volume III Theodoret, Jerome, Gennadius, Rufinus. 2007. 612p. 32.95 *(978-1-60206-512-3(8))* Cosimo, Inc.

Williams, Michael. An Anthology of Classic Christian Literature. 2007. (ENG.). 482p. 53.95 *(978-0-548-05793-3(1))* Kessinger Publishing, LLC.

CHRISTIAN LITERATURE, EARLY—BIBLIOGRAPHY

Kessel, G. & Pinggera, K. A Bibliography of Syriac Ascetic & Mystical Literature. 2011. (Eastern Christian Studies). (ENG & MUL.). 224p. (C). pap. 70.00 *(978-90-429-2457-4(8))* Peeters Pubs. & Booksellers BEL. Dist: Brown, David Bk. Co., The.

Menzies, Allan, ed. The Ante-Nicene Fathers: Volume IX - Recently Discovered Additions to Early Christian Literature. 2007. 544p. pap. 24.95 *(978-1-60206-485-0(7))* Cosimo, Inc.

Roberts, Alexander. AnteNicene Fathers V2 Fathers of the Sec. 2006. pap. 45.95 *(978-1-4286-1282-2(3))* Kessinger Publishing, LLC.

Roberts, Alexander & Donaldson, James, eds. The Writings of the Ante-Nicene Fathers. 2007. 616p. per. 24.95 *(978-1-933993-44-7(8))* Apocryphile Pr.

CHRISTIAN LITERATURE, EARLY—HISTORY AND CRITICISM

Allen, Pauline & Sim, David C., eds. Ancient Jewish & Christian Texts as Crisis Management Literature: Thematic Studies from the Centre for Early Christian Studies. 2012. (ENG.). 224p. 110.00 ***(978-0-567-28102-9(7)***, T&T Clark Int'l) Continuum International Publishing Group, Ltd. GBR. Dist: National Bk. Network.

Amar, J. P., ed. The Syriac Vita Tradition of Ephrem the Syrian, 2 vols. 2011. (Corpus Scriptorum Christianorum Orientalium Ser.). (ENG.). (C). 104p. pap. 102.00 ***(978-90-429-2331-7(8))***; 118p. pap. 94.00 ***(978-90-429-2332-4(6))*** Peeters Pubs. & Booksellers BEL. Dist: Brown, David Bk. Co., The.

Aune, David Edward & Fotopoulos, John. The New Testament & Early Christian Literature in Greco-Roman Context: Studies in Honor of David E. Aune. 2006. (Supplements to Novum Testamentum Ser.: Vol. 122). (Illus.). 468p. *(978-90-04-14304-3(1))* BRILL.

Bertaina, David. Christian & Muslim Dialogues. 2011. 114.00 *(978-1-61143-920-5(5))* 2010. pap. 37.24 *(978-1-61719-941-7(9))* Gorgias Pr., LLC.

Bull, George. Defensio Fidei Nicaenae, Vol. 1: A Defence of the Nicene Creed, out of the Extant Writings of the Catholick Doctors, Who Flourished During the Three First Centuries of the Christian Church; in which also Is incidentally Vindicated the Creed of Constantinople; Concerning the Holy Ghost. 2008. 390p. pap. 32.00 *(978-1-60608-137-2(3)*, Wipf and Stock) Wipf & Stock Pubs.

Czachesz, Istvan. The Grotesque Body in Early Christian Discourse: Hell, Scatology, & Metamorphosis. 2012. (BibleWorld Ser.). (ENG.). 224p. (C). 95.00 ***(978-1-84553-885-9(4))*** Equinox Publishing Ltd. GBR. Dist: ISD.

—The Grotesque Body in Early Christian Literature: Hell, Scatology & Metamorphosis. 2012. (BibleWorld Ser.). (ENG.). 192p. (C). pap. 35.00 ***(978-1-84553-886-6(2))*** Equinox Publishing Ltd. GBR. Dist: Brown, David Bk. Co., The.

De Lagarde, Paul Anton, intro. The Pseudo-Clementine Recognitions & Homilies (10-14) in Syriac. 2010. (SYR.). 102.56 *(978-1-60724-941-2(3))* Gorgias Pr., LLC.

Dennis, Walker. Clericist Catholic Authors & the Crystallization of Historical Memory of WW1 in Lebanonist- Particularist Discourse, 1918-1922. 2011. (SPA.). 106.00 *(978-1-4632-0021-3(8))* Gorgias Pr., LLC.

Eberhart, Christian. Ritual & Metaphor: Sacrifice in the Bible. 2011. ***(978-1-58983-601-3(4))***; ***(978-1-58983-602-0(2))*** Society of Biblical Literature.

Evans, Craig A. & Zacharias, Daniel H., eds. Jewish & Christian Scripture as Artifact & Canon. 2011. (ENG.). 338p. pap. 55.00 ***(978-0-567-29329-9(7)***, T&T Clark Int'l) Continuum International Publishing Group, Ltd. GBR. Dist: National Bk. Network.

Foster, Paul & Foster. The Writings of the Apostolic Fathers. 2007. (ENG.). 178p. 35.95 *(978-0-567-03106-8(3)*, T&T Clark Int'l) Continuum International Publishing Group, Ltd. GBR. Dist: National Bk. Network.

Foster, Russell J. The Writings of the Apostolic Fathers. 2007. (ENG.). 184p. 130.00 *(978-0-567-03105-1(5)*, T&T Clark Int'l) Continuum International Publishing Group, Ltd. GBR. Dist: National Bk. Network.

Giere, S. D. A New Glimpse of Day One: Intertextuality, History of Interpretation, & Genesis 1. 1-5. 2009. (Beihefte zur Zeitschrift für die neutestamentliche Wissenschaft und die Kunde der älteren Kirche Ser.). (ENG.). XVII, 359p. 140.00 *(978-3-11-022433-7(X))*; 210.00 ***(978-3-11-174148-2(6))*** De Gruyter, Walter Inc.

Grupner, Axel & Wolter, Michael, eds. Moses in Biblical & Extra-Biblical Traditions. 2007. (Beihefte Zur Zeitschrift Für Die Alttestamentliche Wissenschaft Ser.). (ENG., Illus.). VIII, 277p. 140.00 *(978-3-11-019460-9(0))* De Gruyter, Walter Inc.

Gunn, Cate. Ancrene Wisse & Vernacular Spirit - From Pastoral Literature to Vernacular Spirituality. 2008. (University of Wales Press - Religion & Culture in the Middle Ages Ser.). 208p. 85.00 *(978-0-7083-2034-1(1))* Univ. of Wales Pr. GBR. Dist: Chicago Distribution Ctr.

Haines-Eitzen, Kim. The Gendered Palimpsest: Women, Writing, & Representation in Early Christianity, 1 vol. 2011. (ENG., Illus.). 214p. 65.00 *(978-0-19-517129-7(2))* Oxford Univ. Pr., Inc.

Hardouin, Jean. The Prolegomena of Jean Hardouin. Detering, Hermann, ed. 2010. 210p. pap. 20.50 *(978-3-8391-8381-6(2))* Bks. on Demand.

Hosang, Boddens. Establishing Boundaries: Christian-Jewish Relations in Early Council Texts & the Writings of Church Fathers. 2010. 204p. *(978-90-04-18255-4(1))* BRILL.

Hunt, Hannah. Clothed in the Body Asceticism the Body & the Spiritual in the Late Antique Era. 2012. (Ashgate Studies in Philosophy & Theology in Late Antiquity Ser.). 224p. 99.95 ***(978-1-4094-0914-4(7))*** Ashgate Publishing Co.

Jensen, Carsten Selch, et al. Crusading & Chronicle Writing in the Medieval Baltic Frontier: A Companion to the Chronicle of Henry of Livonia. 2011. (Illus.). 522p. 134.95 ***(978-0-7546-6627-1(1))*** Ashgate Publishing Co.

Jourdan, Fabienne. Orphée et les Chrétiens: La Réception du Mythe D'Orphée Dans la Littérature Chrétienne Grecque des Cinq Premiers Siecles. (Anagoge Ser.). (FRE., Illus.). (C). 2011. 478p. pap. 68.00 ***(978-2-251-18111-0(3))*** 2010. 488p. pap. 68.00 ***(978-2-251-18110-3(5))*** Societe d'edition Les Belles lettres FRA. Dist: ISD.

Kaye, John. Some Account of the Writings & Opinions of Clement of Alexandri. 2007. 484p. 53.95 *(978-0-548-19655-7(9))* Kessinger Publishing, LLC.

—Some Account of the Writings & Opinions of Clement of Alexandria. 2007. 488p. per. 38.95 *(978-1-4325-0398-7(7))* Kessinger Publishing, LLC.

Kennedy, George Alexander. Greek Rhetoric under Christian Emperors. 2008. 358p. pap. 39.00 *(978-1-55635-980-4(2))* Wipf & Stock Pubs.

Kessel, G. & Pinggera, K. A Bibliography of Syriac Ascetic & Mystical Literature. 2011. (Eastern Christian Studies). (ENG & MUL.). 224p. (C). pap. 70.00 *(978-90-429-2457-4(8))* Peeters Pubs. & Booksellers BEL. Dist: Brown, David Bk. Co., The.

King, D. The Syriac Versions of the Writings of Cyril of Alexandria: A Study in Translation Technique. 2008. (Corpus Scriptorum Christianorum Orientalium Ser.). (ENG.). 614p. (C). pap. 174.00 *(978-90-429-1999-0(X))* Peeters Pubs. & Booksellers BEL. Dist: Brown, David Bk. Co., The.

Klingshirn, William E. & Safran, Linda. The Early Christian Book. (Cua Studies in Early Christianity Ser.). (Illus.). 314p. 2008. per. 29.95 *(978-0-8132-1531-0(5))* 2007. 39.95 *(978-0-8132-1486-3(6))* Catholic Univ. of America Pr.

Koester, Helmut, et al. Trajectories Through Early Christianity. 2006. 310p. pap. 30.00 *(978-1-59752-736-1(X)*, Wipf and Stock) Wipf & Stock Pubs.

Krueger, Derek. Writing & Holiness: The Practice of Authorship in the Early Christian East. 2011. (Divinations: Rereading Late Ancient Religion Ser.). (Illus.). 312p. (C). pap. 27.50 *(978-0-8122-2147-3(8))* Univ. of Pennsylvania Pr.

La Porta, S. The Armenian Scholia on Dionysius the Areopagite: Studies on their Literary & Philological Tradition. 2008. (Corpus Scriptorum Christianorum Orientalium Ser.). (ENG.). 149p. (C). pap. 76.00 *(978-90-429-1920-4(5))* Peeters Pubs. & Booksellers BEL. Dist: Brown, David Bk. Co., The.

Leemans, Johan, et al, eds. Reading Patristic Texts on Social Ethics: Issues & Challenges for Twenty-First-Century Christian Social Thought. 2011. (ENG.). 288p. 34.95 *(978-0-8132-1859-5(4))* Catholic Univ. of America Pr.

Levine, Amy Jill. A Feminist Companion to Patristic Literature. 2008. (Feminist Companion to the New Testament & Early Christian Writings Ser.). (ENG., Illus.). 256p. 49.95 *(978-0-567-04555-3(2))*; 160.00 *(978-0-567-04554-6(4))* Continuum International Publishing Group, Ltd. GBR. (T&T Clark Int'l). Dist: National Bk. Network.

Louth, Andrew. Patrology: The Eastern Fathers from the Council of Chalcedon to John of Damascus. Di Berardino, Angelo, ed. Walford, Adrian, tr. 2nd ed. 2008. (ENG.). 736p. 166.00 *(978-0-227-17265-0(5))*; pap. 105.00 *(978-0-227-17264-3(7))* Clarke, James Co., Ltd. GBR. Dist: Brown, David Bk. Co., The.

Martin, Dale B. New Testament History & Literature. 2012. (Open Yale Courses Ser.). (ENG., Illus.). 464p. pap. 18.00 ***(978-0-300-18085-5(3))*** Yale Univ. Pr.

Mülke, Markus. Der Autor und sein Text: Die Verfälschung des Originals im Urteil antiker Autoren. 2008. (Untersuchungen zur antiken Literatur und Geschichte Ser.). (GER.). 419p. 147.00 *(978-3-11-020250-2(6))* De Gruyter, Walter Inc.

Oesterley, Hermann. Gesta Romanorum. 2009. 768p. pap. 52.75 *(978-1-116-56987-2(6))*; 41.99 *(978-1-116-56985-8(X))*; 48.99 *(978-1-116-56984-1(1))* BiblioBazaar.

—Gesta Romanorum. 2009. 392p. pap. *(978-0-217-96003-8(0))* Books LLC.

Pfleiderer, Otto. Primitive Christianity V4: Its Writings & Teachings in Their Historical. Montgomery, W., tr. 2007. pap. 42.95 *(978-1-4304-4975-1(6))* Kessinger Publishing, LLC.

Pierce, Chad T. Spirits & the Proclamation of Christ: 1 Peter 3:18-22 in Light of Sin & Punishment Traditions in Early Jewish & Christian Literature. 2011. (Wissenschaftliche Untersuchungen zum Neuen Testament Ser.). 289p. pap. 137.50 ***(978-3-16-150858-5(0))*** Mohr Siebeck GmbH & Co. KG DEU. Dist: Coronet Bks.

Remer, Gary. Humanism & the Rhetoric of Toleration. 2008. (ENG.). 332p. per. 27.95 *(978-0-271-02811-8(4))* Pennsylvania State Univ. Pr.

Roberts, Alexander & Donaldson, James, eds. The Writings of the Apostolic Fathers. 2007. 160p. per. 14.95 *(978-1-933993-45-4(6))* Apocryphile Pr.

Ruzer, Serge & Kofsky, Aryeh. Syriac Idiosyncrasies: Theology & Hermeneutics in Early Syriac Literature. 2010. (Jerusalem Studies in Religion & Culture Ser.). 188p. *(978-90-04-18498-5(8))* BRILL.

Scheck, Helene. Reform & Resistance: Formations of Female Subjectivity in Early Medieval Ecclesiastical Culture. 2009. (SUNY Series in Medieval Studies). 224p. pap. 24.95 *(978-0-7914-7484-6(4)*, Suny Pr.) State Univ. of New York Pr.

Sim, David & Repschinski, Boris. Matthew & His Christian Contemporaries. 2008. (Library of New Testament Studies, the Ser.). (ENG.). 222p. 130.00 *(978-0-567-04453-2(X)*, T&T Clark Int'l) Continuum International Publishing Group, Ltd. GBR. Dist: National Bk. Network.

Stone, Michael E., et al, eds. Noah & His Book(S) 2010. (ENG.). 394p. pap. 45.95 *(978-1-58983-488-0(7))* Society of Biblical Literature.

Stringer, Martin. Rethinking the Origins of the Eucharist. 2011. (SCM Studies in Worship & Liturgy Ser.). (ENG.). 300p. pap. 75.00 *(978-0-334-04214-3(3)*, SCM Pr.) Hymns Ancient & Modern Ltd GBR. Dist: Westminster John Knox Pr.

Sturdy, J. V. M. Redrawing the Boundaries: The Date of Early Christian Literature. Knight, Jonathan, ed. 2008. (BibleWorld Ser.). (ENG.). 192p. (C). per. 34.95 *(978-1-84553-302-1(X))* Equinox Publishing Ltd. GBR. Dist: ISD.

Sturdy, J. V. M. & Knight, Jonathan. Redrawing the Boundaries: The Date of Early Christian Literature. 2008. (BibleWorld Ser.). (ENG.). 192p. (C). 99.95 *(978-1-84553-301-4(1))* Equinox Publishing Ltd. GBR. Dist: ISD.

Theissen, Gerd. The New Testament: A Literary History. Maloney, Linda M., tr. from GER. 2011. 304p. (C). 49.00 *(978-0-8006-9785-3(5)*, Fortress Pr.) Augsburg Fortress, Pubs.

Toepel, A. Die Adam- und Seth-Legenden im Syrischen Buch der Schatzhöhle. eine quellenkritische Untersuchung. 2006. (Corpus Scriptorum Christianorum Orientalium Ser.). (ENG.). 259p. (C). pap. 124.00 *(978-90-429-1739-2(3))* Peeters Pubs. & Booksellers BEL. Dist: Brown, David Bk. Co., The.

VanderKam, James C. Enoch: A Man for All Generations. 2008. (ENG.). 324p. pap. 29.95 *(978-1-57003-796-2(5))* Univ. of South Carolina Pr.

Wilson, Robert M. Studies in the Gospel of Thomas. (Orthodoxies & Heresies in the Early Church Ser.). reprint ed. 23.00 *(978-0-404-62374-6(3))* AMS Pr., Inc.

Wright, Charles D. The Irish Tradition in Old English Literature. 2006. (Cambridge Studies in Anglo-Saxon England Ser.: Vol. 6). (ENG.). 336p. pap. 63.00 *(978-0-521-03211-7(3))* Cambridge Univ. Pr.

Young, Frances, et al, eds. The Cambridge History of Early Christian Literature. 2007. (ENG., Illus.). 566p. (C). per. 38.00 *(978-0-521-69750-7(6))* Cambridge Univ. Pr.

Young, Robin Darling & Aune, David E., eds. Reading Religions in the Ancient World: Essays Presented to Robert Mcqueen Grant on His 90th Birthday. 2007. (Novum Testamentum Supplements Ser.). (Illus.). 305p. *(978-90-04-16196-2(1))* BRILL.

Zellentin, Holger Michael. Rabbinic Parodies of Jewish & Christian Literature. 2011. (Texts & Studies in Ancient Judaism, No. 139 Ser.). 284p. 197.50 *(978-3-16-150647-5(2))* Mohr Siebeck GmbH & Co. KG DEU. Dist: Coronet Bks.

CHRISTIAN LITERATURE FOR CHILDREN

Adams, Jessie. A Guide to the Spiritual Development of Children: Seventeen Subjects Every Christian Parent Needs to Focus Upon. 2010. 112p. pap. 11.95 *(978-1-61507-175-3(X))* Cross Bks. Publishing.

Ewers, Hans-Heino. Fundamental Concepts of Childrens Literature Research. 2012. (ENG., Illus.). 186p. (C). pap. 39.95 ***(978-0-415-89648-1(7))*** Routledge.

Mantemach, Janaan. Really Good Books for Kids: A Guide for Catechists & Parents. 2007. 126p. per. 14.95 *(978-0-8091-4396-2(8)*, 4396-8) Paulist Pr.

CHRISTIAN MINISTRY

see Clergy—Office

CHRISTIAN MUSIC

see Church Music

CHRISTIAN MUSIC, CONTEMPORARY

see Contemporary Christian Music

CHRISTIAN NAMES

see Names, Personal

CHRISTIAN PATRON SAINTS

Here are entered works on Christian saints as patrons or protectors of persons, trades, churches, organizations, institutions, countries, etc., or on Christian saints whose protection is invoked against given evils.

Calamari, Barbara & DiPasqua, Sandra. Patron Saints: A Feast of Holy Cards. 2007. (ENG., Illus.). 160p. 27.50 *(978-0-8109-9402-7(X))* Abrams.

Daughters of St. Paul Staff. Patron Saints. 70p. pap. 1.95 *(978-0-8198-5859-7(5)*, 332-269) Pauline Bks. & Media.

Dunne, William P., ed. Is It a Saint's Name? over 3000 Christian Names for Boys & Girls. 2011. 50p. 35.95 ***(978-1-258-02819-0(0))*** Literary Licensing, LLC.

Lastra, Yolanda, et al. Adoring the Saints: Fiestas in Central Mexico. 2009. (ENG., Illus.). 219p. 55.00 *(978-0-292-71980-4(9))* Univ. of Texas Pr.

McGrane, Janice. Saints to Lean On: Spiritual Companions for Illness & Disability. 2006. 167p. per. 13.95 *(978-0-86716-595-1(2))* Franciscan Media.

Mornin, Edward & Mornin, Lorna. Saints of California: A Guide to Places & Their Patrons. 2009. (ENG., Illus.). 192p. pap. 19.95 *(978-0-89236-984-3(1))* Oxford Univ. Pr., Inc.

Pescador, Juan Javier. Crossing Borders with the Santo Niño de Atocha. 2009. (ENG., Illus.). 280p. 34.95 *(978-0-8263-4709-1(6))* Univ. of New Mexico Pr.

Rowe, Erin Kathleen. Saint & Nation: Santiago, Teresa of Avila, & Plural Identities in Early Modern Spain. 2011. (ENG.). 296p. 74.95 *(978-0-271-03773-8(3))* Pennsylvania State Univ. Pr.

CHRISTIAN PILGRIMS AND PILGRIMAGES
see Pilgrims and Pilgrimages

CHRISTIAN POETRY
see also Carols; Hymns

Adderley, Alison Patricia. Destined to go over not Under: How to Weather the Storms of Life & Live Victoriously. 2009. 184p. pap. 15.95 (978-1-4327-3717-7(1)) Outskirts Pr., Inc.

Addison, Jr. The Psalms of Joel. 2007. 220p. per. 16.99 (978-1-60266-615-3(6)) Xulon Pr., Inc.

Allen, Patricia. Gifted Moments. 2007. 204p. per. 14.99 (978-1-60477-124-4(0)) Xulon Pr., Inc.

Almudevar, Antonio. Mas Arriba: Poetry for the Christian Church. (SPA.). 416p. (978-84-7228-791-4(2), 222345) Clie, Editorial.

Arcemont, Connie Lou. You're Home Now. 2008. 84p. pap. 16.95 (978-1-60563-356-5(9)) PublishAmerica, Inc.

Artifex, Latet. Weather of Me. 2008. 108p. pap. 16.95 (978-1-60441-192-8(9)) PublishAmerica, Inc.

Austin, Victoria. Infected. 2008. pap. 16.95 (978-1-60563-661-0(4)) PublishAmerica, Inc.

Bartosh, Sister Joan, et al. Poems Prayers & Blessings: From the Hearts of Chaplains. 2011. (Illus.). 48p. pap. 17.99 (978-0-9834637-0-2(0)) Artpacks.

Batchelor, Mary, compiled by. The Lion Christian Poetry Collection. 573p. pap. 24.00 (978-0-7459-5057-0(4), Lion) Lion Hudson PLC GBR. Dist: Trafalgar Square Publishing.

Bauscher, David. An Anthology of Spiritual Poetry & Meditations. 2008. 39p. pap. 18.95 (978-1-4357-4284-0(2)) Lulu Enterprises Inc.

Birkett, Maureen. To God Be the Glory: A Book of Christian Poetry. 2008. 112p. pap. 10.95 (978-1-4327-1961-6(0)) Outskirts Pr., Inc.

Bishop of Tracheia, Paul. A Hymn of Praise for Celtic Saints & Other Poems. 2010. 92p. pap. (978-1-84748-758-2(0)) Athena Pr.

Bowman, Lisa Ag. God's Amazing Love. 2011. 252p. pap. 16.99 (978-1-61379-135-6(6)) Xulon Pr., Inc.

Brigh Cassidy, Sister Mary. Gifts of Her Spirit. 2008. 96p. pap. 20.00 (978-0-9790247-5-7(7)) Artpacks.

Brown, Angela. Flowetry. 2006. 42p. per. 7.95 (978-1-60002-266-1(9), 4184) Mountain Valley Publishing, LLC.

Brown, Dallas. The Spirit Leads Home. 2008. 104p. pap. 16.95 (978-1-60703-410-0(7)) PublishAmerica, Inc.

Burkholder, Carolyn. A Nod to God: His Lighter Side in Verse. 2010. 128p. pap. 11.95 (978-1-4502-6583-6(9)) iUniverse, Inc.

Burton, Mother Frances. The Gospel in Poems. 2008. 79p. pap. 16.95 (978-1-60563-684-9(3)) PublishAmerica, Inc.

Busch Jr, Horace R. The Altar Boy: An Anthology of poetry & writings by a Catholic & former altar Boy. 2007. 80p. per. 7.95 (978-1-4327-1788-9(X)) Outskirts Pr., Inc.

Cahill, Lori Mulder. The Journey Continues. 2008. pap. 12.99 (978-1-60647-702-1(1)) Xulon Pr., Inc.

Callahan, Deborah. Memory Verses to Live By. 2007. 352p. per. 19.99 (978-1-60034-922-5(6)) Xulon Pr., Inc.

Cameron, Jozetta. Divine Revelations: Inspirational Poems. 2007. 152p. per. 13.99 (978-1-60266-367-1(X)) Xulon Pr., Inc.

Camper, Larry L. If You Faint Not. 2009. 108p. pap. 11.99 (978-1-60791-367-2(4)) Xulon Pr., Inc.

Campisano, Lori. The Scent of Water. 2008. 224p. pap. 14.00 (978-1-57921-945-1(4)) WinePress Publishing.

Chandler, Melissa Leigh. Truth & Life. 2008. 108p. 18.99 (978-1-60477-802-1(4)); pap. 10.99 (978-1-60477-801-4(6)) Xulon Pr., Inc.

Chansky, Norman M. Essence of the Psalms: Poems Inspired by the Sacred Text. 2008. 128p. pap. 16.00 (978-1-55635-500-4(9), Resource Pubns.) Wipf & Stock Pubs.

Chapman, L. Irene. A Pilgrims Psalms of Praise. 2008. 348p. pap. 19.99 (978-1-4363-8706-4(X)) Xlibris Corp.

Chaucer, Geoffrey. The Canterbury Tales. Raffel, Burton, tr. from ENM. abr. ed. 2008. (ENG.). 672p. 36.00 (978-0-679-64355-5(9)) Random House Publishing Group.

—Chaucer's Canterbury Pilgrims, Retold by Katharine Lee Bates; Illustrated by Angus MacDonall, with Color Plates by Milo Winter. 2006. (Illus.). 316p. per. 23.99 (978-1-4255-2968-0(2)) MPublishing.

Chesnut, M. Kathleen. Dancing into Joy: A spiraling Easter Dance. 2006. pap. 14.95 (978-0-9785090-0-2(5)) DewSpirit Publishing.

Chiappara-Bennett, Lucia. Strangers in the Night of Poetry. 2008. 60p. pap. 15.99 (978-1-4363-5406-6(4)) Xlibris Corp.

Cisneroz, Yolanda. I Will Prevail over My Enemies. 2007. 108p. per. 14.95 (978-1-4327-0390-5(0)) Outskirts Pr., Inc.

Clemoes, Peter. Interactions of Thought & Language in Old English Poetry. 2006. (Cambridge Studies in Anglo-Saxon England Ser.). (ENG.). 544p. pap. 95.00 (978-0-521-03516-3(3)) Cambridge Univ. Pr.

Clie Staff. Antologia de la Poesia Cristiana: Anthology of Christian Poetry. (SPA.). (978-84-7645-047-5(8), 223107) Clie, Editorial.

Cole, Antoinette. Christian Confessions: A Book of Poems. 2011. 56p. pap. 9.99 (978-1-4634-2611-8(9)) AuthorHouse.

Cole, Jack. 4004 BC. 2008. 108p. pap. 10.95 (978-0-7414-4562-9(X)) Infinity Publishing.

Covington, Pat. Cleansed by the Blood. 2008. 160p. pap. 11.99 (978-1-4389-1668-2(X)) AuthorHouse.

Covington, Ralph. Footsteps on A Gym Floor. 2007. per. 10.00 (978-0-9797339-0-1(1)) Poetic Proverbs.

Crane, Chris. The One-Word Answer in a Two-Faced World. 2007. 200p. per. 24.95 (978-1-4241-6787-6(6)) PublishAmerica, Inc.

Crockett, Kim. His Hand Is Stretched Out Still. 2007. 70p. pap. 9.95 (978-0-7414-4432-5(1)) Infinity Publishing.

Crombie, Elizabeth G. God's Journey of Love for the Human Heart. 2008. 79p. pap. 16.95 (978-1-60672-113-1(5)) PublishAmerica, Inc.

Crumbley, Gene. Bible Stories in Rhyme. 2008. 184p. 29.99 (978-0-88144-288-5(7)) Yorkshire Publishing Group.

Da Todi, Jacopone. The God-Madness. Daly, Pádraig, tr. from ITA. 2008. 80p. per. (978-1-904556-86-2(8)) Dedalus Ltd.

DaPoet, LadyVee. Clenched Teeth Smiling. 2008. 96p. pap. 12.00 (978-1-4343-9849-9(8)) AuthorHouse.

Davis, Kathy. Scatter Joy, Lend a Hand, Pray for Peace, Understand: 75 Simple Ways to Celebrate the Holidays. 2008. (ENG.). 64p. 9.99 (978-0-7407-7331-0(3)) Andrews McMeel Publishing.

Dean, Sandra. A Garden in My Heart. 2007. (Illus.). 97p. per. 12.95 (978-0-931563-27-0(5), Wish Bk. Pr.) Wishing Room, Inc., The.

Del Busto, Perez. Poesias: Christian Poetry. (SPA.). (978-84-7645-193-9(8), 223245) Clie, Editorial.

Destefano, James. Poems from the Heart, Conversations with God. 2006. 136p. per. 11.99 (978-1-59858-164-5(3)) Dog Ear Publishing, LLC.

Dixon, Richard A. A Prayer As a Poem for Each Day. 2008. 388p. per. 19.99 (978-1-60477-646-1(3)) Xulon Pr., Inc.

Downey, David G. Modern Poets & Christian Teaching: Richard Watson Gilder, Edwin Markham, Edward Rowland Sill. 2007. 192p. 37.95 (978-0-548-52738-2(5)); (ENG.). per. 22.95 (978-0-548-49982-5(9)) Kessinger Publishing, LLC.

Durbin, Billie. Whispers of God. 2010. 112p. pap. 11.95 (978-1-4497-0245-8(7), WestBow Pr.) Author Solutions, Inc.

Ebama, Nya. Letters from God. 2006. 104p. per. 9.99 (978-1-58930-172-6(2)) Selah Publishing Group, LLC.

Elkins, Christy. The Dusty Road. 2010. 43p. pap. 20.00 (978-0-557-23494-3(8)) Lulu Enterprises Inc.

Farnsworth-Simpson, Patricia Ann. Windows of Light. 2008. 176p. pap. 18.95 (978-0-615-19123-2(1)) P.F.P. Pubs.

Ferguson, Satara P. Handmade by God. 2009. 76p. pap. 11.49 (978-1-4389-2377-2(5)) AuthorHouse.

Gall, Abby. Trees of Righteousness. 2008. 164p. pap. 13.99 (978-1-60477-855-7(5)) Xulon Pr., Inc.

Gammie, Theo-Jane. Look up! Live Up! 2010. 120p. pap. 11.99 (978-1-60957-527-4(X)) Xulon Pr., Inc.

Gentry, Reginald L. Minister G's Book of Poetry. 2008. 62p. pap. 16.95 (978-1-60563-327-5(5)) PublishAmerica, Inc.

Gilbert, Paula. Street Preacher: Poems. 2008. 156p. pap. 14.95 (978-1-4327-3713-9(9)) Outskirts Pr., Inc.

Glover, Geraldine M. Poems Indicated & Inspired by God, 1 vol. 2009. 73p. pap. 16.95 (978-1-60813-177-8(7)) PublishAmerica, Inc.

Glover, Sherri R. Expressions of My Own Heart. 2007. 80p. per. 13.95 (978-1-4327-1010-1(9)) Outskirts Pr., Inc.

Glover, Virginia. Wow: Words of Wisdom. 2011. 428p. 34.99 (978-1-4653-4736-7(4)); pap. 23.99 (978-1-4653-4735-0(6)) Xlibris Corp.

Gorby, John Paul. Tend the Garden: Stories & testimonies about how inspirational poetry can change people's Lives. 2007. 180p. per. 24.95 (978-1-4241-9986-0(7)) PublishAmerica, Inc.

Grant, Juanita. My Heart Knows. 2008. 136p. per. 13.99 (978-1-60477-242-5(5)) Xulon Pr., Inc.

Greene, William F. Religious Poems. 2011. 178p. 29.99 (978-1-4628-5664-0(0)); pap. 19.99 (978-1-4628-5663-3(2)) Xlibris Corp.

Handley, Ana Magdalene. Rejoice in the Lord Always. 2011. 96p. pap. 15.99 (978-1-4628-7124-7(0)) Xlibris Corp.

Harper, Diana. Speak Softly, Lord: [Poetry of Faith]. 2008. 62p. pap. 16.95 (978-1-60563-228-5(7)) PublishAmerica, Inc.

Harper, Frances Ellen Watkins. Idylls of the Bible. 2009. 68p. pap. 16.95 (978-1-120-62956-2(X)) Kessinger Publishing, LLC.

Harver, Laura. Exposed to Healing. 2007. 140p. per. 13.99 (978-1-60034-994-2(3)) Xulon Pr., Inc.

Havergal, Frances Ridley & Chalkley, David L. Valuable Selections from the Writings of Frances Ridley Havergal. 2009. (Illus.). 96p. pap. (978-0-9817321-8-3(6)) Granted Ministries Pr.

Helgeson, Jan. Dusty Roads & Dandelions. 2007. 116p. per. 10.99 (978-1-60266-286-5(X)) Xulon Pr., Inc.

Helt, Evelyn "Sis". Poems Alive. 2006. per. 0.25 net. (978-0-9744581-1-3(2)) Wings of Joy Pubs.

Heno, Christy Colby. My Tummy Talked in Church Today. 2007. (Illus.). 128p. per. 10.00 (978-0-687-49011-0(1), Dimensions For Living) Abingdon Pr.

Hightower, Shontel D. I'm Still Standing. 2009. 52p. pap. 15.00 (978-1-4389-5323-6(2)) AuthorHouse.

Hoffmann, Deanna. Spirit to Spirit: Poetic Prayers, Praises, And Meditations. 2009. 444p. pap. 22.99 (978-1-60791-222-4(8)) Xulon Pr., Inc.

Holden, Reginald O. Heart to Heart, Volume 1. 2007. 72p. per. 9.95 (978-1-4327-0857-3(0)) Outskirts Pr., Inc.

Hollenbeak, Joy. The Rough Cross. 2008. 144p. pap. 24.95 (978-1-60610-495-8(0)) PublishAmerica, Inc.

Hood, Gayla Dewan. Messages from God. 2008. 88p. pap. 10.99 (978-1-60647-446-4(4)) Xulon Pr., Inc.

Housden, Roger. For Lovers of God Everywhere: Poems of the Christian Mystics. 2009. (ENG.). 200p. 19.95 (978-1-4019-2384-6(4)) Hay Hse., Inc.

Hudgens, Meosha L. Me, Myself & I Seeking God. 2010. 120p. (ENG.). 21.49 (978-1-4389-9652-3(7)); pap. 10.99 (978-1-4389-8913-6(X)) AuthorHouse.

In the House of the Father. 2007. 105p. per. 10.95 (978-1-60002-193-0(X), 4064) Mountain Valley Publishing, LLC.

Ironfield, Holly. Words of Wisdom. 2008. 428p. pap. 24.99 (978-1-60647-294-1(1)) Xulon Pr., Inc.

Irwin, Wayne. It's All about You, Lord. 2006. 112p. per. 10.95 (978-1-933912-29-5(4)) Westview Publishing Co., Inc.

Jackson, Bertha. Are You Listening to His Voice? 2007. 124p. (ENG.). 18.99 (978-1-60477-069-8(4)); per. 10.99 (978-1-60266-919-2(8)) Xulon Pr., Inc.

Jackson, Sandra. From the Heart: Pages of My Mind. 2008. 132p. pap. 12.15 (978-1-4389-1433-6(4)) AuthorHouse.

Jackson, Thaddeus. The Power of Positive Poetry. 2007. 184p. per. 13.99 (978-1-60266-335-0(1)) Xulon Pr., Inc.

Janicik, Tom. Your Gift of Grace. 2008. (Illus.). 212p. pap. 16.99 (978-1-60647-146-3(5)) Xulon Pr., Inc.

Jones-Kimberlin, Linda. Poetic Journey into the Fire of Light: Turn up the Light II, 1 vol. 2009. 94p. pap. 16.95 (978-1-60813-625-4(6)) PublishAmerica, Inc.

Jones, Yvette A. Revelations in the Scroll of the Book it Is Written of Me. 2010. 100p. pap. 12.95 (978-1-4327-6087-8(4)) Outskirts Pr., Inc.

Kamurasi, Richard. The Spiritual Mirror for the Soul: Devotional Prayer Poems of the Soul on Hope, Encouragement & Prosperity. 2007. 188p. (ENG.). 30.99 (978-1-4257-3885-3(0)); per. 20.99 (978-1-4257-3884-6(2)) Xlibris Corp.

Kidd, Vickie M. Blossoms of the Heart. 2008. 52p. pap. 16.95 (978-1-60610-036-3(X)) PublishAmerica, Inc.

Kiesling, Ralph W. More Reflecting Thoughts, 1 vol. 2009. 121p. pap. 19.95 (978-1-60813-922-4(0)) PublishAmerica, Inc.

La Shea A Stanard. To God Be the Glory. 2010. 52p. pap. 10.95 (978-1-4502-1401-8(0)) iUniverse, Inc.

Lanay. Psalms of a Black Woman: Modern Expressions of Love, Life, Encouragement & Praise Using Diverse Topics for All Occasions. 2008. 83p. pap. 16.95 (978-1-60813-354-3(0)) PublishAmerica, Inc.

Langland, William & Fowler, David C. Piers Plowman: The A Version. Vaughan, Míceál F., ed. 2011. (ENG.). 208p. (C). (gr. 13-17). 50.00 (978-1-4214-0139-3(8)); pap. 20.00 (978-1-4214-0140-9(1)) Johns Hopkins Univ. Pr.

Lauer, Al. Buried Treasures. 2008. 76p. pap. 9.00 (978-0-8059-7752-0(8)) Dorrance Publishing Co., Inc.

Lee, Jeffrey. God Has the Last Word! 2007. 136p. per. 24.95 (978-1-4241-8745-4(1)) PublishAmerica, Inc.

Lee, John B. Under the Weight of Heaven: Writing from the Abbey of Gethsemani. 2008. (ENG., Illus.). 90p. pap. 15.95 (978-0-88753-453-9(8)) Black Moss Pr. CAN. Dist: LitDistCo.

Lewis Jr., Marvin. The Language of My Imagination. 2008. 128p. pap. 14.99 (978-1-60647-560-7(6)) Xulon Pr., Inc.

Life, Liberty, & the Lord: Poetic Parables. 2008. pap. (978-0-9819254-0-0(5)) Marion (ME) Enterprises LLC.

Littles, Wanda Thomas. Come Sunday Morning. 2008. 132p. pap. 13.99 (978-1-60647-488-4(X)) Xulon Pr., Inc.

Loveless, Caron Chandler. What If There Were No Teachers? A Gift Book for Teachers & Those Who Wish to Celebrate Them. 2008. (ENG., Illus.). 48p. 12.99 (978-1-4165-5197-3(2), Howard Bks.) Howard Books.

Lutes, Joy. Work in Progress. 2008. 136p. pap. 13.99 (978-1-60647-526-3(6)) Xulon Pr., Inc.

MacDonald, George. A Book of Strife in the Form of the Diary of an Old Soul. 2007. 96p. per. (978-1-4065-2990-6(7)) Dodo Pr.

—The Diary of an Old Soul [Hardcover Edition]. 2007. 128p. 19.99 (978-1-59986-596-6(3)) Filiquarian Publishing, LLC.

Magennis, Hugh. Images of Community in Old English Poetry. 2006. (Cambridge Studies in Anglo-Saxon England Ser.). (ENG.). 224p. pap. 42.00 (978-0-521-03184-4(2)) Cambridge Univ. Pr.

Majeska, Judith. Walking Through - 2007. 48p. per. 9.99 (978-1-60477-388-0(X)) Xulon Pr., Inc.

Malara, Joseph. God's Clarity Through Poetry. 2007. 172p. per. (978-1-55452-212-5(9)) Essence Publishing.

Mandel, Shirley. Midnight Flower: An anthology of contemporary christian Poems. 2007. 64p. per. 12.50 (978-1-4303-2258-0(6)) Lulu Enterprises Inc.

Marie, Tricia. Beyond to Better Things. 2008. 80p. pap. 16.95 (978-1-60703-252-6(X)) PublishAmerica, Inc.

Massie, Richard. You Are Not Alone. 2010. 152p. pap. 11.99 (978-1-4490-6841-7(3)) AuthorHouse.

McAdoo, Tara. Glorious Expressions. 2007. 108p. (ENG.). 18.99 (978-1-60266-344-2(0)); per. 10.99 (978-1-60266-343-5(2)) Xulon Pr., Inc.

McCowan Nevills, Jennifer. Love Conquers All. 2008. (ENG., Illus.). 50p. pap. 12.99 (978-0-9655792-8-5(X)) Don Paul Publishing, LLC.

McDonnell, Kilian. Wrestling with God. 2011. 80p. pap. 10.95 (978-0-9740992-8-6(7)) St. John's Univ. Pr.

McGee, Doris. Heart Transplant: A spiritual & inspiring book of poetry & Images. 2008. 72p. pap. 24.99 (978-1-4343-7489-9(0)) AuthorHouse.

McKee, John A. Poems of Hope. 2008. 104p. pap. 10.99 (978-1-58930-224-2(9)) Selah Publishing Group, LLC.

Menkin, Peter Obl Cam Osb. Seasons of Faith: Religious & Spiritual Poetry. 2011. 94p. pap. 15.99 (978-1-4628-8068-3(1)) Xlibris Corp.

Michelle, Tenicka. Life's Cycles. 2008. 140p. 21.99 (978-1-60477-954-7(3)); pap. 13.99 (978-1-60477-953-0(5)) Xulon Pr., Inc.

Miller, Maury. Psalm Songs: Poetic Meditations on the Psalms. 2010. 164p. 30.95 (978-1-4497-0403-2(4)); pap. 13.95 (978-1-4497-0404-9(2)) Author Solutions, Inc. (WestBow Pr.).

Moore, Jean R. Bread & butter christmas Poems. 2008. 97p. pap. 16.96 (978-1-4357-1781-7(3)) Lulu Enterprises Inc.

Morales, Jr. Inspirational Poetry. 2008. 108p. 18.99 (978-1-60647-439-6(1)); pap. 10.99 (978-1-60647-438-9(3)) Xulon Pr., Inc.

Murray, Jef, illus. Divining Divinity: A Book of Poems. 2008. 56p. 10.95 (978-0-9768580-1-0(0)) Kaufmann Publishing.

Murray, Molly. The Poetics of Conversion in Early Modern English Literature: Verse & Change from Donne to Dryden. 2011. (ENG.). 218p. pap. 45.00 (978-1-107-40282-9(4)) Cambridge Univ. Pr.

Nabors, Amanda. Sweet Whispers of Love Divine. 2008. (ENG.). 108p. pap. 13.95 (978-0-9816483-5-4(5)) Prioritybooks Pubns.

Newman, Cardinal John Henry & Egan, Maurice. The Dream of Gerontius. 2007. 80p. per. 8.50 (978-1-60206-803-2(8)) Cosimo, Inc.

Newman, John Henry. Verses on Various Occasions. 352p. 2008. 46.95 (978-1-4365-8873-7(1)) 2007. (ENG.). per. 31.95 (978-0-548-80052-2(9)) Kessinger Publishing, LLC.

Niki, J. Reaching Out in Troubled Times, 1. gif. ed. 2006. (Illus.). 64p. per. 11.99 (978-0-9790442-1-2(9), 02) J.Niki Enterprises, LLC.

Nuño, Daniel. Ofrenda Poetica: Poetic Offering. (SPA.). 312p. (978-84-7228-886-7(2), 222351) Clie, Editorial.

—Poesias para la Iglesia Cristiana: Poems for the Christian Church. (SPA.). 384p. (978-84-7228-271-1(6), 220700) Clie, Editorial.

O'Brien, Patricia. Psalms, Poems & Musings. 2008. pap. 24.95 (978-1-4241-8784-3(2)) PublishAmerica, Inc.

O'Murchu, Diarmuid. Jesus in the Power of Poetry: A New Voice for Gospel Truth. 2009. (ENG.). 224p. pap. 19.95 (978-0-8245-2521-7(3)) Crossroad Publishing Co., The.

Orchard, Andy. The Poetic Art of Aldhelm. 2006. (Cambridge Studies in Anglo-Saxon England Ser.). (ENG.). 332p. pap. 63.00 (978-0-521-03457-9(4)) Cambridge Univ. Pr.

Osborne, Michael E. Enduring Hope: A Collection of Christian Poetry. 2008. 414p. pap. 29.95 (978-1-60610-286-2(9)) PublishAmerica, Inc.

Owens, Jr John. The Inspirational Book of Poetry. 2008. 144p. pap. 13.99 (978-1-60477-499-3(1)) Xulon Pr., Inc.

Parks, Hannah. Under His Wings. 2008. 236p. pap. 14.99 (978-1-60647-031-2(0)) Xulon Pr., Inc.

Patterson, Erik. Father of Two Children, Child of One God: Poems, Thoughts & Prayers. 2010. 220p. 29.99 (978-1-4500-6771-3(9)); pap. 19.99 (978-1-4500-6770-6(0)) Xlibris Corp.

Patterson, William. Lessons of the Learned. 2008. 76p. pap. 6.08 (978-1-4357-4529-2(9)) Lulu Enterprises Inc.

Patton, Anthony. Poetic Dreams. 2007. 64p. per. 9.99 (978-1-60266-930-7(9)) Xulon Pr., Inc.

Paulinus, et al. Carmina. 2006. (Bibliotheca scriptorum Graecorum et Romanorum Teubneriana (BT) Ser.). (LAT.). XXX, 38p. (978-3-598-71323-1(1)) Teubner, B.G. GmbH.

Payne, Toya. State of Affairs. 2008. 164p. 22.99 (978-1-60647-484-6(7)); pap. 14.99 (978-1-60647-483-9(9)) Xulon Pr., Inc.

Pestone, Margaret. September Soliloquy. 2008. 80p. pap. 10.00 (978-1-4257-6007-6(4)) Xlibris Corp.

Pierce, K. M. Faith, Death & Randomness. 2007. 56p. pap. 8.99 (978-0-615-15985-0(0)) Saeligstone.

Pike, Albert L. Searching for Salvation: From Brokenness to Wholeness. 2009. (Illus.). 64p. pap. 15.95 (978-1-4327-3398-8(2)) Outskirts Pr., Inc.

Pisacane, Julie. Pages of My Heart: A Biblically Inspired Collection of Treasured Poems & Devotionals. 2007. 94p. pap. 16.95 (978-1-4241-9814-6(3)) PublishAmerica, Inc.

Redman, Nathan. Bloodwork. 2007. 384p. per. 22.99 (978-1-60477-355-2(3)) Xulon Pr., Inc.

Reynolds, Michael. The 21st Century Psalms. 2008. 62p. pap. 34.95 (978-0-557-00148-4(X)) Lulu Enterprises Inc.

Robin, Tabitha. Soulful Ink: Faith in the Cross of Christ. 2007. 199p. pap. 24.95 (978-1-4241-8763-8(X)) PublishAmerica, Inc.

Rodriguez, Zobeida. Mensajes en Poesia: Messages in Poetry. (SPA., Illus.). 183p. (978-84-7645-479-4(1), 223563) Clie, Editorial.

Roland, Joe E. E. Some Things I Know about Angels, Both Large & Small. 2007. 34p. 16.00 (978-0-8059-7557-4(8)) Dorrance Publishing Co., Inc.

Rubi, Joe. Tangerine Scorpions: A Collection of Breaths Before Stung Alive. 2007. 148p. per. 24.95 (978-1-4241-8972-4(1)) PublishAmerica, Inc.

Russell, Joyce. Romans Paraphrased in Stanza. 2008. 192p. pap. 16.99 (978-1-60791-002-2(0)) Xulon Pr., Inc.

Sabater Fortea, Juan Bautista. Sound Declarations. 2008. 66p. pap. 16.95 (978-0-557-01212-1(0)) Lulu Enterprises Inc.

Sandra M. Dowd, M. Dowd, et al. Heavenly Inspirations of Faith, Hope, & Love. 2010. 156p. pap. 13.95 (978-1-4497-0097-3(7), WestBow Pr.) Author Solutions, Inc.

Sawatzky, Lee Mark. Searching for Good. 2011. 186p. 29.99 (978-1-4628-8546-6(2)) Xlibris Corp.

Scales, Mary. Crying Out to God. 2008. 55p. pap. 16.95 (978-1-60703-135-2(3)) PublishAmerica, Inc.

C

Schefer, Leopold. The World-Priest Tr from the German of Leopold Schefer, by Charles T Brooks. 2006. 392p. per. 26.99 *(978-1-4255-4164-4(X))* MPublishing.
Schueler, Douglas. Love Notes Life Notes. 2007. 152p. per. 13.99 *(978-1-60266-289-6(4))* Xulon Pr., Inc.
Schurrer, Brian. Leviathan's Beat. 2008. 105p. pap. 16.95 *(978-1-60672-346-3(4))* PublishAmerica, Inc.
Sedulius, et al. Sedulii Opera Omnia: Una Cum Excerptis Ex Remigii Expositione in Sedulii Paschale Carmen. 2007. (Corpus Scriptorum Christianorum Orientalium Ser.). (LAT.). xlvii, 532p. (C). 78.00 *(978-3-7001-3681-1(1))* Austrian Academy of Sciences Press AUT. Dist: Brown, David Bk. Co., The.
Severance, Jim. Spiritual Reflections Through Prayers of Poetry. 2008. 124p. per. 10.99 *(978-1-60477-417-7(7))* Xulon Pr., Inc.
Shaw, Brent. Distillations. 2007. 160p. (ENG.). 21.99 *(978-1-60477-135-0(6))*; per. 13.99 *(978-1-60477-129-9(1))* Xulon Pr., Inc.
Shaw, Luci. Accompanied by Angels: Poems of the Incarnation. 2006. 98p. per. 15.00 *(978-0-8028-2987-0(2))* Eerdmans, William B. Publishing Co.
Shrum, Estelle. He Is the Word: Scriptural Poetry That Anwers Biblical Questions. 2006. 179p. pap. 24.95 *(978-1-4241-4526-3(0))* PublishAmerica, Inc.
Simpson, Pat, et al. Precious Prayers. 2008. 190p. pap. 20.95 *(978-1-4357-2588-1(3))* Lulu Enterprises Inc.
Slaughter, Darlene. Words to the Wise. 2011. 70p. pap. 15.99 ***(978-1-4568-7839-9(5))*** Xlibris Corp.
Sledge, Marie. Lord, Come Sit with Me a While. 2008. 102p. pap. 16.95 *(978-1-60672-037-0(6))* PublishAmerica, Inc.
Smyth, Sandy. Journey to Wholeness. 2009. 236p. pap. 15.99 *(978-1-60791-406-8(9))* Xulon Pr., Inc.
Stanfield, Dan. Faithful Strengths. 2008. 56p. pap. 16.95 *(978-1-60474-086-8(8))* PublishAmerica, Inc.
Strickland, Diana. Mercies of God. 2008. 63p. pap. 16.95 *(978-1-60703-484-1(0))* PublishAmerica, Inc.
Strickland, Gwen. Reflections of God's Love & Mercy. 2008. 110p. pap. 19.95 *(978-1-60610-115-5(3))* PublishAmerica, Inc.
Strunk, William, Jr. Juliana. 180p. 2008. 37.95 *(978-1-4365-7804-2(3))* 2007. (ENG.). per. 22.95 *(978-0-548-79829-4(X))* Kessinger Publishing, LLC.
Tasso, Torquato. Jerusalem Delivered. 2008. 424p. pap. 21.99 *(978-1-59547-733-0(0))* NuVision Pubns., LLC.
Thompson, Anne B. The Northern Homily Cycle. 2008. pap. 20.00 *(978-1-58044-126-1(2))* Medieval Institute Pubns.
Thompson, Patara. Loving Him. 2007. pap. 9.99 *(978-1-60034-950-8(1))* Xulon Pr., Inc.
Tittmann, Catherine. The God of the Universe Dances in Trees. 2007. 148p. per. 14.95 *(978-0-595-43540-1(8))* iUniverse, Inc.
Todd, M. Leanne. The Truth, the Whole Truth, & Nothing but the Truth, so Help Me GOD. 2008. 244p. pap. 24.95 *(978-1-60703-335-6(6))* PublishAmerica, Inc.
Tohline, Veda. Poems of Faith for Daily Living. 2007. 256p. (ENG.). 25.99 *(978-1-60266-912-3(0))*; per. 15.99 *(978-1-60266-911-6(2))* Xulon Pr., Inc.
Tozer, A. w. The Christian Book of Mystical Verse. 2011. 168p. pap. 9.50 ***(978-1-61427-015-7(5))*** Martino Publishing.
—The Christian Book of Mystical Verse. 2011. 204p. 19.99 ***(978-1-61720-175-2(8))***; pap. 9.99 ***(978-1-61720-172-1(3))*** Wilder Pubns., Ltd.
Tozer, A. w. & et al. The Christian Book of Mystical Verse. 2010. 168p. pap. 13.99 *(978-1-57898-885-3(3))* Martino Publishing.
Traylor, Christina. The Gift of Psalms. 2008. 44p. pap. 15.95 *(978-1-4327-2844-1(X))* Outskirts Pr., Inc.
Trementozzi, David. Light for the Dark Night. 2008. 124p. 18.99 *(978-1-60791-153-1(1))* Xulon Pr., Inc.
Van Seters, T. To Know Him. 2006. 172p. per. 12.99 *(978-1-59886-589-9(7))* Tate Publishing & Enterprises, LLC.
Vassell, Kamille. From My Heart to You. 2010. 156p. pap. 12.95 *(978-1-4502-2776-6(7))* iUniverse, Inc.
Vida, Marco Girolamo & Vida, M. Christiad. Gardner, James, tr. from LAT. 2009. (I Tatti Renaissance Library: 39). Orig. Title: Christiados libri Sex. (LAT & ENG.). 496p. 29.95 *(978-0-674-03408-2(2))* Harvard Univ. Pr.
Vile, Ralph. Let the Bells Ring Out on Christmas Morning. 2008. 124p. per. 10.99 *(978-1-60477-610-2(2))* Xulon Pr., Inc.
—We Are His Poets. 2007. 228p. per. 14.99 *(978-1-60477-140-4(2))* Xulon Pr., Inc.
Von Christ, Wilhelm & Paranikas, M. Anthologia Graeca Carminum Christianorum. 2010. 426p. pap. 35.75 *(978-1-148-13991-3(5))* BiblioBazaar.
Von Christ, Wilhelm & Paranikas, Matthaios. Anthologia Graeca Carminum Christianorum. 2010. 422p. pap. 34.75 *(978-1-143-05349-8(4))* BiblioBazaar.
Wace. La Vie de Sainte Marguerite. 2010. 192p. pap. 23.75 *(978-1-141-43990-4(5))* BiblioBazaar.
Wace. La Vie de sainte Marguerite. Keller, Hans-Erich, ed. (Beihefte zur Zeitschrift fur romanische Philologie Ser.). (FRE.). 333p. 210.00 ***(978-3-11-179507-2(1))*** De Gruyter, Walter Inc.
Wace, Robert & Joly, Aristide. La Vie de Sainte Marguerite. 180p. 2010. 30.36 *(978-1-166-82642-0(2))* 2010. pap. 18.36 *(978-1-166-73448-0(X))* 2009. 37.95 *(978-1-120-54185-7(9))* 2009. pap. 22.95 *(978-1-120-44988-7(X))* Kessinger Publishing, LLC.
Walden, Constance V. Time Without End: Poetry Celebrating Jesus Christ & His Promise of Eternal Life. 2010. 128p. pap. 11.95 *(978-1-4502-4106-9(9))* iUniverse, Inc.
Waldenville, John. God's Revelations to Me. 2007. 504p. per. 34.95 *(978-1-4241-6309-0(9))* PublishAmerica, Inc.
Walker, Kyle. Ripples of Reflections. 2008. 257p. pap. 27.95 *(978-1-60474-679-2(3))* PublishAmerica, Inc.
Ward, Jean Elizabeth. Adam & Eve: the Poem. 2008. 148p. pap. 23.50 *(978-1-4357-3212-4(X))* Lulu Enterprises Inc.
Wells, Tracee Y. Heavenly Inspirations Manifested. 2007. (ENG.). 104p. per. 10.99 *(978-1-59932-050-2(9))* Advantage Media Group.
White, Nicole. God Spoke & I Wrote. 2006. (ENG.). 76p. per. 16.95 *(978-1-4241-2191-5(4))* PublishAmerica, Inc.
Williams, Prophetess Darlene G. Dedication to Christ the Wounds. 2008. 249p. pap. 24.95 *(978-1-60610-364-7(4))* PublishAmerica, Inc.
Wisdom, Robert W. God Be My Anchor. 2008. 64p. pap. 16.95 *(978-1-60703-690-6(8))* PublishAmerica, Inc.
Witherington, Ben, III. The Living Legacy: The Soul in Paraphrase, the Heart in Pilgrimage. 2008. (Illus.). 312p. pap. 34.00 *(978-1-55635-895-1(4))* Wipf & Stock Pubs.
Wolberg, Kristine A. "All Possible Art" George Herbert's the Country Parson. 2008. 168p. (C). 43.50 *(978-0-8386-4170-5(9))* Fairleigh Dickinson Univ. Pr.
Wolf, Marc. Solar Reign I: The Fruitful Spirit Has. 2006. 97p. pap. 16.95 *(978-1-4241-3322-2(X))* PublishAmerica, Inc.
Wood, Philip "Chip" Cowboy Poet. To the Glory of God. 2011. pap. 14.99 ***(978-1-61346-260-7(3))*** Tate Publishing & Enterprises, LLC.
Wright, Richard J. Odyssey. 2008. 88p. pap. 10.95 *(978-1-4327-3118-2(1))* Outskirts Pr., Inc.
Yarbrough, Robert. Is Anything Too Hard for God? 2006. 12.00 *(978-0-8059-8338-8(4))* Dorrance Publishing Co., Inc.
Yisrael, Michelle R. She Speaks Psalms, 1 vol. 2009. 134p. pap. 24.95 *(978-1-60813-056-6(8))* PublishAmerica, Inc.

CHRISTIAN POETRY—HISTORY AND CRITICISM

Adams, Robert, ed. London, British Library, MS Lansdowne 398 & Oxford, Bodleian Library. 2011. (Seenet Ser.: Volume 10). cd-rom 99.00 *(978-1-84384-093-0(6))*, D. S. Brewer) Boydell & Brewer, Ltd. GBR. Dist: Boydell & Brewer, Inc.
Blevins, Jacob. Re-Reading Thomas Traherne: A Collection of New Critical Essays. 2007. (C). *(978-0-86698-370-9(8))* Arizona State Univ., Arizona Ctr. for Medieval & Renaissance Studies.
Browning, Elizabeth Barrett. Essays on the Greek Christian Poets & the English Poets by Elizabeth Barrett Browning. 2006. 236p. per. 20.99 *(978-1-4255-2029-8(4))* MPublishing.
Calabrese, Michael, et al, eds. The Piers Plowman Electronic Archive: 6. San Marino, Huntington Library MS 128 (Hm & Hm2) 2009. (Seenet Ser.: Volume 7). cd-rom 130.00 *(978-1-84384-091-6(X)*, D. S. Brewer) Boydell & Brewer, Ltd. GBR. Dist: Boydell & Brewer, Inc.
Charlesworth, James H. The Earliest Christian Hymnbook. 2011. (ENG.). 172p. pap. 38.00 *(978-0-227-17355-8(4))* Clarke, James Co., Ltd. GBR. Dist: Brown, David Bk. Co., The.
Charlesworth, James H., tr. The Earliest Christian Hymnbook. 2009. 172p. pap. 20.00 *(978-1-60608-646-9(4)*, Cascade Bks.) Wipf & Stock Pubs.
Cheikho, Louis. Arabic Christian Poets Before & after Islam. 2006. (Christianity in the Islamic World Ser.: 1). 1445p. 312.00 *(978-1-59333-536-6(9))* Gorgias Pr., LLC.
Cruickshank, Frances. Verse & Poetics in George Herbert & John Donne. 2010. (Illus.). 146p. 99.95 *(978-1-4094-0480-4(3))* Ashgate Publishing Co.
DiPasquale, Theresa & DiPasquale, Theresa M. Refiguring the Sacred Feminine: The Poems of John Donne, Aemilia Lanyer, & John Milton. 2008. 320p. lib. bdg. 60.00 *(978-0-8207-0405-0(9))* Duquesne Univ. Pr.
Dixon, James Main. Matthew Arnold. 2009. 104p. pap. *(978-0-217-78203-6(5))* Books LLC.
Dockray-Miller, Mary. Saints Edith & AEthelthryth: Princesses, Miracle Workers, & their Late Medieval Audience: the Wilton Chronicle & the Wilton Life of St. AEthelthryth. 2009. (Medieval Women: Texts & Contexts Ser.). (ENG & ENM., Illus.). 476p. (C). 138.00 *(978-2-503-52836-6(8))* Brepols Pubs. BEL. Dist: ISD.
Easson, Angus. G. M. Hopkins. (Routledge Guides to Literature Ser.). 2011. (ENG.). 240p. pap. 26.95 *(978-0-415-27324-4(2))* 2008. xii, 223p. 95.00 *(978-0-415-27323-7(4))* Routledge.
Feeney, Joseph J., et al. Soundings. 2006. 38.00 *(978-0-916101-56-5(8))* St. Joseph's Univ. Pr.
Fein, Susanna Greer. My Wyl & My Wrytyng: Essays on John the Blind Audelay. 2009. 50.00 *(978-1-58044-135-3(1))*; pap. 25.00 *(978-1-58044-136-0(X))* Medieval Institute Pubns.
Franke, William. Poetry & Apocalypse: Theological Disclosures of Poetic Language. 2008. (ENG.). 232p. 60.00 *(978-0-8047-5910-6(3))* Stanford Univ. Pr.
Gardner, Thomas. John in the Company of Poets: The Gospel in Literary Imagination. 2011. (Studies in Christianity & Literature Ser.). (ENG.). 236p. 69.95 *(978-1-60258-315-3(3))* Baylor Univ. Pr.
Groff, Kent Ira. Facing East, Praying West: Poetic Reflections on the Spiritual Exercises. 2010. 112p. pap. 12.95 *(978-0-8091-4628-4(2))* Paulist Pr.
Henriksen, Erin. Milton & the Reformation Aesthetics of the Passion. 2009. 214p. *(978-90-04-18032-1(X))* BRILL.
Hessel-Robinson, Timothy. The Reverend Edward Taylor's Sacramental Meditations on the Song of Songs: The Erotic Devotion of an American Puritan. 2011. (ENG.). 240p. 119.95 ***(978-0-7734-3921-4(8))*** Mellen, Edwin Pr., The.
Hill, Norma Ferguson. Dr. Martin Luther King Jr. 's Chronicle & Creative Poems. 2007. pap. 9.00 *(978-0-8059-8624-2(3))* Dorrance Publishing Co., Inc.
Hopkins, Gerard Manley. Gerard Manley Hopkins: The Major Works. Phillips, Catherine, ed. & intro. by. 2009. (Oxford World's Classics Ser.). (ENG.). 480p. pap. 15.95 *(978-0-19-953885-0(9))* Oxford Univ. Pr., Inc.
Hume, Anthea. Edmund Spenser: Protestant Poet. 2008. (ENG.). 212p. pap. 32.99 *(978-0-521-09160-2(8))* Cambridge Univ. Pr.
Huppe, Bernard Felix. Doctrine & Poetry: Augustine's Influence on Old English Poetry. 2011. 258p. 47.95 ***(978-1-258-00256-5(6))*** Literary Licensing, LLC.
Jones, Henry Festing. Browning as a Philosophical & Religious Teacher. 2006. (ENG.). 266p. pap. 21.99 *(978-1-4264-7087-5(8))*; 300p. pap. 23.99 *(978-1-4264-7163-6(7))* BiblioBazaar.
Kane, George, ed. Piers Plowman: The A Version. rev. ed. (ENM & ENG.). 484p. *(978-0-485-11339-6(2))* Continuum International Publishing Group, Ltd.
Karkov, Catherine E. Text & Picture in Anglo-Saxon England: Narrative Strategies in the Junius 11 Manuscript. 2009. (Cambridge Studies in Anglo-Saxon England Ser.). (ENG., Illus.). 288p. pap. 38.99 *(978-0-521-09306-4(6))* Cambridge Univ. Pr.
Keiser, Albert. The Influence of Christianity on the Vocabulary of Old English Poetry. 2009. (ENG.). 153p. 30.99 *(978-1-117-22834-1(7))*; pap. 20.75 *(978-1-117-22835-8(5))* BiblioBazaar.
—The Influence of Christianity on the Vocabulary of Old English Poetry. 2007. (ENG.). 152p. 36.95 *(978-0-548-15554-7(2))*; 156p. per. 21.95 *(978-1-4304-4993-5(4))* Kessinger Publishing, LLC.
Kolbrener, William. Milton's Warring Angels: A Study of Critical Engagements. 2008. (ENG.). 228p. (C). pap. 31.99 *(978-0-521-10182-0(4))* Cambridge Univ. Pr.
Kowalik, Barbara. Betwixt Engelaunde & Englene Londe: Dialogic Poetics in Early English Religious Lyric. 2011. (Studies in English Medieval Language & Literature Ser.). 258p. 72.95 *(978-3-631-61695-6(3))* Lang, Peter GmbH, Europaischer Verlag der Wissenschaften DEU. Dist: Lang, Peter.
Kuchar, Gary. The Poetry of Religious Sorrow in Early Modern England. (ENG.). 254p. 2011. pap. 35.99 *(978-0-521-17442-8(2))* 2008. 97.99 *(978-0-521-89669-6(X))* Cambridge Univ. Pr.
Laing, Jeanie M. Notes on Superstition & Folk Lore. 2008. 116p. 21.99 *(978-0-559-43436-5(7))*; pap. 19.75 *(978-0-559-43435-8(9))* BiblioBazaar.
—Notes on Superstition & Folk Lore. 2008. 112p. 34.95 *(978-1-4371-7462-5(0))*; pap. 19.95 *(978-1-4370-4270-2(8))* Kessinger Publishing, LLC.
Mahan, David C. An Unexpected Light: Theology & Witness in the Poetry & Thought of Charles Williams, Micheal O'Siadhail, & Geoffrey Hill. 2008. (Princeton Theological Monographs). 246p. pap. 27.00 *(978-1-55635-507-3(6)*, Pickwick Pubns.) Wipf & Stock Pubs.
Mannani, Manijeh. Divine Deviants: The Dialectics of Devotion in the Poetry of Donne & Rumi. 2007. (C). 66.95 *(978-0-8204-8859-2(3))* Lang, Peter Publishing, Inc.
McAloon, Francis. The Language of Poetry As a Form of Prayer: The Theo-Poetic Aesthetics of Gerard Manley Hopkins. 2008. 260p. 109.95 *(978-0-7734-5022-6(X))* Mellen, Edwin Pr., The.
Mengozzi, A., ed. Religious Poetry in Vernacular Syriac from Northern Iraq (17th-20th Centuries). an Anthology. 2011. (Corpus Scriptorum Christianorum Orientalium Ser.). (ENG.). (C). 163p. pap. 87.00 ***(978-90-429-2277-8(X))***; 129p. pap. 94.00 ***(978-90-429-2276-1(1))*** Peeters Pubs. & Booksellers BEL. Dist: Brown, David Bk. Co., The.
Meyer, Kinereth & Deshen, Rachel Salmon. Reading the Underthought: Jewish Hermeneutics & the Christian Poetry of Hopkins & Eliot. 2010. 314p. 69.95 *(978-0-8132-1742-0(3))* Catholic Univ. of America Pr.
Miller, Greg & Miller. George Herbert's Holy Patterns: Reforming Individuals in Community. 2007. (Continuum Literary Studies). (ENG., Illus.). 192p. 135.00 *(978-0-8264-2807-3(X))* Continuum International Publishing Group, Ltd. GBR. Dist: National Bk. Network.
Morris, Richard, ed. Cursor Mundi Pt. V: A Northumbrian Poem of the XIVth Century. 2006. (Early English Text Society Original Ser.: Volume 68). 330p. per. 70.00 *(978-1-84384-103-6(7))* Early English Text Society (EETS) GBR. Dist: Boydell & Brewer, Inc.
Nichols, Aidan. The Poet as Believer: A Theological Study of Paul Claudel. 2011. (Ashgate Studies in Theology, Imagination & the Arts Ser.). 288p. 99.95 *(978-1-4094-2685-1(8))* Ashgate Publishing Co.
O'Daly, Gerard. Days Linked by Song: Prudentius' Cathemerinon. 2012. (ENG & LAT.). 432p. 185.00 ***(978-0-19-926395-0(7))*** Oxford Univ. Pr., Inc.
Oldcorn, Anthony, et al, eds. Purgatorio. (Illus.). 412p. 2008. per. 29.95 *(978-0-520-25056-7(7))* 2007. 60.00 *(978-0-520-25055-0(9))* Univ. of California Pr.
Roberts, Michael John & Roberts, Michael. The Humblest Sparrow: The Poetry of Venantius Fortunatus. 2009. (ENG., Illus.). 376p. (C). 90.00 *(978-0-472-11683-6(5))* Univ. of Michigan Pr.
Roe, Dinah. Christina Rossetti's Faithful Imagination: The Devotional Poetry & Prose. annot. ed. 2007. (ENG.). 248p. 84.00 *(978-0-230-00507-5(1))* Palgrave Macmillan.
Rowe, Karen E. Saint & Singer: Edward Taylor's Typology & the Poetics of Meditation. 2009. (Cambridge Studies in American Literature & Culture Ser.). (ENG.). 360p. (C). pap. 50.00 *(978-0-521-10819-5(5))* Cambridge Univ. Pr.
Scheinberg, Cynthia. Women's Poetry & Religion in Victorian England: Jewish Identity & Christian Culture. 2009. (Cambridge Studies in Nineteenth-Century Literature & Culture Ser.). (ENG.). 296p. pap. 41.00 *(978-0-521-09983-7(8))* Cambridge Univ. Pr.
Schwartz, Regina. Sacramental Poetics at the Dawn of Secularism: When God Left the World. 2008. (Cultural Memory in the Present Ser.). (ENG.). 216p. 60.00 *(978-0-8047-5667-9(8))*; pap. 19.95 *(978-0-8047-5833-8(6))* Stanford Univ. Pr.
Schwartz, Regina M. Remembering & Repeating: Biblical Creation in Paradise Lost. 2011. (ENG.). 156p. pap. 24.99 *(978-0-521-17729-0(4))* Cambridge Univ. Pr.
Simpson, Ken. Spiritual Architecture & Paradise Regained: Milton's Literary Ecclesiology. 2007. (Medieval & Renaissance Literary Studies). 320p. 58.00 *(978-0-8207-0391-6(5))* Duquesne Univ. Pr.
Singleton, Marion White. God's Courtier: Configuring a Different Grace in George Herbert's Temple. 2009. (ENG.). 272p. pap. 36.99 *(978-0-521-10795-2(4))* Cambridge Univ. Pr.
Smock, Frederick. Pax Intrantibus: A Meditation on the Poetry of Thomas Merton. 2007. (ENG.). 96p. 25.00 *(978-0-9721144-6-2(7)*, Broadstone Bks.) Broadstone Media LLC.
Smyser, William Emory. Tennyson. 2008. 210p. 39.95 *(978-1-4365-1251-0(4))* 2007. (ENG.). 212p. per. 24.95 *(978-0-548-74338-6(X))* Kessinger Publishing, LLC.
Spurr, Barry. See the Virgin Blest: The Virgin Mary in English Poetry. 2007. (ENG., Illus.). 272p. 89.00 *(978-1-4039-7492-1(6))* Palgrave Macmillan.
Theben, Judith. Die mystische Lyrik des 14. und 15. Jahrhunderts: Untersuchungen - Texte - Repertorium. 2010. (Kulturtopographie des alemannischen Raums Ser.).Tr. of Mystical Verse of the 14th & 15th Centuries. Analyses â€" Texts â€" Repertorium. (GER., Illus.). XII, 586p. *(978-3-484-89501-0(2))* Verlag Max Niemeyer.
Twomey, Lesley K. The Serpent & the Rose: The Immaculate Conception & Hispanic Poetry in the Late Medieval Period. 2008. (Studies in Medieval & Reformation Traditions: History, Culture, Religion, Ideas). 1333p. (C). *(978-90-04-16595-3(9))* BRILL.
Urbanski, Piotr, tr. Pietas Humanistica: Neo-Latin Religious Poetry in Poland in European Context. 2006. (Illus.). 310p. pap. 57.95 *(978-0-8204-9870-6(X))* Lang, Peter Publishing, Inc.
Waldron, Robert. Walking with Gerard Manley Hopkins: A Poet's Journey. 2011. 144p. pap. 11.95 ***(978-0-8091-4739-7(4))*** Paulist Pr.
Ward, Jean. Christian Poetry in the Post-Christian Day: Geoffrey Hill, R. S. Thomas, Elizabeth Jennings. 2009. 304p. pap. 74.95 *(978-3-631-58012-7(6))* Lang, Peter GmbH, Europaischer Verlag der Wissenschaften DEU. Dist: Lang, Peter.
Westcott, Brooke Foss. An Appreciation of the Late Christina Georgina Rossetti. 2009. 28p. pap. 15.75 *(978-1-113-26233-2(8))* BiblioBazaar.
—An Appreciation of the Late Christina Georgina Rossetti. 2009. 82p. pap. *(978-1-4588-0781-6(9))* Books LLC.
—An Appreciation of the Late Christina Georgina Rossetti. 2009. 28p. pap. 15.95 *(978-1-104-01055-3(0))* Kessinger Publishing, LLC.
Yeager, Robert F. On John Gower: Essays at the Millennium. 2006. (Studies in Medieval Culture). 40.00 *(978-1-58044-098-1(3))*; 20.00 *(978-1-58044-099-8(1))* Medieval Institute Pubns.
Zeeman, Nicolette. 'Piers Plowman' & the Medieval Discourse of Desire. 2009. (Cambridge Studies in Medieval Literature Ser.). (ENG., Illus.). 328p. pap. 36.99 *(978-0-521-12298-6(8))* Cambridge Univ. Pr.

CHRISTIAN POPULAR MUSIC

see Contemporary Christian Music

CHRISTIAN PRIESTHOOD

see Priesthood

CHRISTIAN RECONSTRUCTIONISM

see Dominion Theology

CHRISTIAN REFORMED CHURCH

The CRC & You. (Bibles Ser.). 1.00 *(978-1-56212-704-6(7)*, 165400) Faith Alive Christian Resources.
De Jong, James A. Henry J. Kuiper: Shaping the Christian Reformed Church, 1907-1962, Vol. 55. 2007. (Historical Series of the Reformed Church in America: No. 55). (Illus.). 270p. per. 28.00 *(978-0-8028-2585-8(0))* Eerdmans, William B. Publishing Co.
Greenway, Roger S. & Leder, Arie C. For God So Loved the World: Essays in Honour of Roger S. Greenway. 2006. (ENG.). pap. *(978-1-55306-983-6(8))* Essence Publishing.
Haarsma, Deborah B. & Haarsma, Loren D. Origins: A Reformed Look at Creation, Design, & Evolution. 2007. *(978-1-59255-227-6(7))* Faith Alive Christian Resources.
—Origins: Christian Perspectives on Creation, Evolution, & Intelligent Design. 2nd ed. 2011. *(978-1-59255-573-4(X))* Faith Alive Christian Resources.
Hoezee, Scott. Grace Through Every Generation: The Ongoing Story of the Christian Reformed Church in North America. 2006. (Illus.). 128p. pap. 6.95 *(978-1-59255-294-8(3))* Faith Alive Christian Resources.
Hyde, Daniel. With Heart & Mouth: An Exposition of the Belgic Confession. 2008. 560p. 30.00 *(978-0-9793677-5-5(1))* Reformed Fellowship, Inc.
Klumpenhower, Gary. Native Gems for His Crown. 2007. 208p. pap. *(978-0-9792739-2-6(7))* Ajoyin Publishing, Inc.
Krabbendam, Hans. Freedom on the Horizon: Dutch Immigration to America, 1840-1940. Boonstra, Harry & Sheeres, Gerrit, trs. from DUT. 2009. 432p. pap. 32.00 *(978-0-8028-6545-8(3))* Eerdmans, William B. Publishing Co.
Selles, Kurt D. A New Way of Belonging: Covenant Theology, China, & the Christian Reformed Church, 1921-1951. 2010. pap. 28.00 *(978-0-8028-6662-2(X))* Eerdmans, William B. Publishing Co.
Smidt, Corwin, et al. Divided by a Common Heritage: The Christian Reformed Church & the Reformed Church in America at the Beginning of the New

Millennium. 2006. (Historical Series of the Reformed Church in America: 54). (Illus.). 226p. per. 24.00 (978-0-8028-0385-6(7)) Eerdmans, William B. Publishing Co.
Suk, John D. Not Sure: A Pastor's Journey from Faith to Doubt. 2011. 213p. pap. 18.00 (978-0-8028-6650-9(6)) Eerdmans, William B. Publishing Co.
Tamminga, Louis M. The Elder's Handbook. 2008. (978-1-59255-460-7(1)) Faith Alive Christian Resources.
Vos, Geerhardus. Grace & Glory: Sermons Preached in Chapel at Princeton Seminary. 2007. 164p. per. 15.00 (978-1-59925-127-1(2)) Solid Ground Christian Bks.
Wiersma, Lori & VanDyke, Connie Kuiper. The Deacon's Handbook. 2009. (978-1-59255-458-4(X)) Faith Alive Christian Resources.

CHRISTIAN SAINTS

see Saints

CHRISTIAN SCIENCE

see also Boston (Mass.)—First Church of Christ, Scientist; Mental Healing; Spiritual Healing

Adams, Joseph. A Christian Science Exposition of the Atonement. 2007. (ENG.). 92p. per. 18.95 (978-1-4304-4590-6(4)) Kessinger Publishing, LLC.
Atkins, Gaius. Modern Religious Cults & Movements. 2009. 123.00 (978-1-60724-296-3(6)) Gorgias Pr., LLC.
Atkins, Gaius Glenn. Modern Religious Cults & Movements. 2008. 280p. 28.99 (978-0-554-25822-5(6)) 2008. 280p. 25.99 (978-0-554-35125-4(0)) 2007. (ENG.). 246p. pap. 20.99 (978-1-4264-9555-7(2)) BiblioBazaar.
—Modern Religious Cults & Movements. 2007. (ENG.). 372p. 48.95 (978-0-548-13110-7(4)) 2006. pap. 33.95 (978-1-4286-4159-4(9)) Kessinger Publishing, LLC.
Barrington, A. H. Anti Christian Cults 1898. 2007. (ENG.). 170p. 37.95 (978-0-548-05506-9(8)) Kessinger Publishing, LLC.
Bellwald, A. M. Christian Science & the Catholic Faith. 2007. (ENG.). 286p. 43.95 (978-0-548-03926-7(7)) Kessinger Publishing, LLC.
The Bookmark Medley, Volume 1. 2007. kivar 19.95 (978-0-930227-87-6(5)) Bookmark, The.
Brown, William Leon. Christian Science Falsely So Called. 2007. (ENG.). 116p. 34.95 (978-0-548-09333-7(4)) Kessinger Publishing, LLC.
Burroughs, Dillon, et al, compiled by. Comparing Christianity with the Cults. rev. ed. 2007. (ENG.). 18p. 2.50 (978-0-8024-8212-9(0)) Moody Pubs.
DeWaters, Lillian. The Christ Within: A Study of the Absolute. 2007. 252p. per. 19.95 (978-1-60206-193-4(9)) Cosimo, Inc.
Dresser, Horatio W. The Quimby Manuscripts. 2007. 448p. per. 27.95 (978-1-60206-214-6(5)) Cosimo, Inc.
Eddy, Mary. Science & Health. 2009. (Amer Philosophy, Religion Ser.). (ENG.). 600p. pap. 34.95 (978-1-4290-1864-7(X)) Applewood Bks.
Eddy, Mary Baker. Christian Science vs. Pantheism. 15p. reprint ed. pap. 5.00 (978-0-87952-054-0(X)) Eddy, The Writings of Mary Baker.
—Church Manual: Of the First Church of Christ, Scientist, in Boston, Massachusetts. 138p. reprint ed. 18.00 (978-0-87952-084-7(1)) Eddy, The Writings of Mary Baker.
—The First Church of Christ, Scientist, & Miscellany. 366p. reprint ed. pap. 16.00 (978-0-87952-041-0(8)) Eddy, The Writings of Mary Baker.
—Miscellaneous Writings, 1883-1896. 471p. reprint ed. pap. 16.00 (978-0-87952-040-3(X)) Eddy, The Writings of Mary Baker.
—No & Yes. 46p. pap. 5.00 (978-0-87952-237-7(2)) Eddy, The Writings of Mary Baker.
—No & Yes. 2009. 48p. pap. (978-0-217-24290-5(1)); pap. (978-0-217-51954-0(7)); pap. (978-0-217-51952-6(0)) Books LLC.
—The People's Idea of God: It's Effect on Health & Christianity. 14p. pap. 5.00 (978-0-87952-235-3(6)) Eddy, The Writings of Mary Baker.
—Poetical Works of Mary Baker Eddy. 2011. 156p. 41.95 (978-1-258-03161-9(2)) Literary Licensing, LLC.
—Prose Works, Other Than Science & Health with Key to the Scriptures. 1268p. reprint ed. 55.00 (978-0-87952-074-8(4)) Eddy, The Writings of Mary Baker.
—Pulpit & Press. 2009. 66p. pap. (978-0-217-53762-9(6)) Books LLC.
—Pulpit & Press. 90p. reprint ed. pap. 10.00 (978-0-87952-046-5(9)) Eddy, The Writings of Mary Baker.
—Retrospection & Introspection. 2009. 104p. pap. 18.75 (978-1-115-99162-9(0)) BiblioBazaar.
—Retrospection & Introspection. 2009. 56p. pap. (978-0-217-04145-4(0)) Books LLC.
—Retrospection & Introspection. 95p. reprint ed. pap. 10.00 (978-0-87952-044-1(2)) Eddy, The Writings of Mary Baker.
—Rudimental Divine Science. 17p. pap. 5.00 (978-0-87952-059-5(0)) Eddy, The Writings of Mary Baker.
—Rudimental Divine Science. 2009. 28p. pap. 15.75 (978-1-113-36610-8(9)) BiblioBazaar.
—Science & Health: With Key to the Scriptures. 2010. 728p. pap. 50.75 (978-1-147-55615-5(6)); 722p. pap. 49.75 (978-1-147-25200-2(9)); 684p. pap. 48.75 (978-1-145-04081-6(0)); 728p. pap. 50.75 (978-1-143-93154-3(8)); 718p. pap. 49.75 (978-1-145-34704-5(5)) BiblioBazaar.
—Science & Health: With key to the Scriptures. 2010. (ENG.). 724p. pap. 50.75 (978-1-177-30723-9(5)); 604p. pap. 45.75 (978-1-177-21079-9(7)) BiblioBazaar.
—Science & Health with Key to the Scriptures. 2010. 694p. pap. 48.75 (978-1-148-22492-3(0)); 724p. pap. 50.75 (978-1-148-30018-4(X)) BiblioBazaar.
—Science & Health with Key to the Scriptures. 2011. (ENG.). 322p. pap. 11.99 (978-1-4209-3810-4(X)) Digireads.com.
—Science & Health, with Key to the Scriptures. 2010. 730p. pap. 50.75 (978-1-146-41038-0(7)) 2010. 692p. pap. 48.75 (978-1-146-56512-7(7)) 2010. 694p. pap. 48.75 (978-1-148-05876-4(1)) 2010. 600p. pap. 44.75 (978-1-146-83205-2(2)) 2010. 690p. pap. 48.75 (978-1-148-17892-9(9)) 2008. 508p. 32.99 (978-0-554-39861-7(3)) 2008. 368p. 29.99 (978-0-554-35396-8(2)) 2008. 508p. 35.99 (978-0-554-30558-5(5)) 2008. 368p. 31.99 (978-0-554-26093-8(X)) BiblioBazaar.
—Science & Health, with Key to the Scriptures. 2009. 366p. pap. (978-0-217-54661-4(7)) Books LLC.
—Science & Health, with Key to the Scriptures. 2010. (Illus.). 504p. pap. 56.61 (978-1-153-68596-2(5)) General Bks. LLC.
—Science & Health; with Key to the Scriptures. 2009. 394p. pap. (978-1-150-28623-0(7)) Books LLC.
—Science & Health with Key to the Scriptures. (Early Best Sellers Ser.). reprint ed. lib. bdg. 48.00 (978-0-7426-1021-7(7)) Classic Bks.
—Science & Health, with Key to the Scriptures. lt. ed. 2008. (ENG.). Vol. 1. 366p. pap. 26.99 (978-1-4346-0446-0(2)) Vol. 2. 506p. pap. 39.75 (978-1-4375-0573-3(2)) BiblioBazaar.
—Unity of Good. 2011. 68p. pap. 7.99 (978-1-61203-172-9(2)) Bottom of the Hill Publishing.
—Unity of Good. 2006. pap. 17.95 (978-1-4286-3590-6(4)) Kessinger Publishing, LLC.
—Unity of Good. 2007. (ENG.). 256p. per. (978-1-4067-7417-7(0)) Read Bks.
—Unity of Good. 2007. (ENG.). 56p. pap. 8.45 (978-1-60424-353-6(8)), Book Jungle) Standard Pubns., Inc.
—Unity of Good. 64p. reprint ed. pap. 5.00 (978-0-87952-053-3(1)) Eddy, The Writings of Mary Baker.
Gaius Glenn Atkins. Modern Religious Cults & Movements. lt. ed. 2007. (ENG.). 278p. pap. 23.99 (978-1-4264-9936-4(1)) BiblioBazaar.
Gimbel, Steven. Einstein's Jewish Science: Physics at the Intersection of Politics & Religion. 2012. (ENG.). 256p. 24.95 (978-1-4214-0554-4(7)) Johns Hopkins Univ. Pr.
Greenhouse, Lucia. Fathermothergod: My Journey Out of Christian Science. 2012. (ENG.). 304p. pap. 15.00 (978-0-307-72093-1(4)) Broadway Bks.
—Fathermothergod: My Journey Out of Christian Science. 2011. (ENG.). 320p. 25.00 (978-0-307-72092-4(6), Crown) Crown Publishing Group.
Harm, Frederick R. Las Religiones Ciencia. (Serie Respuesta).Tr. of Science Religions. (SPA.). 40p. pap. 2.95 (978-0-570-04941-8(5), 09-2514) Concordia Publishing Hse.
Hopkins, Emma. High Mysticism. 2007. 380p. 36.95 (978-1-60206-922-0(0)); per. 22.95 (978-1-60206-210-8(2)) Cosimo, Inc.
—Scientific Christian Mental Practice. 2007. 280p. per. 10.95 (978-1-60206-197-2(1)) Cosimo, Inc.
Hulsey, Michael. Healing... the Children's Bread: Understanding Your Covenant Right to Be Healed. 2006. 12.00 (978-0-9787246-1-0(5)) Restoring Hearts Ministries.
Huse, Sibyl Marvin. Essays on Divine Metaphysics. 2011. 160p. 41.95 (978-1-258-02341-6(5)) Literary Licensing, LLC.
Johnston, Julia M. The Science of Celestial Being. 2007. kivar 16.95 (978-0-930227-86-9(7)) Bookmark, The.
Kimball, Edward A. Lectures & Articles on Christian Science. 2007. (ENG.). 488p. 53.95 (978-0-548-06306-4(0)) Kessinger Publishing, LLC.
Kratzer, G. A. Dominion Within. 2007. (ENG.). 232p. 41.95 (978-0-548-07754-2(1)) Kessinger Publishing, LLC.
Kratzer, Glenn A. Spiritual Man. 2007. (ENG.). 228p. 41.95 (978-0-548-08772-5(5)) Kessinger Publishing, LLC.
Lee, Charles Hamilton. Divine Direction or Chaos? 2011. 98p. 38.95 (978-1-258-06981-0(4)) Literary Licensing, LLC.
Messer, Mary Burt. The Science of Society: The Identity of Each As Godlike Embracing All. 2011. 248p. 46.95 (978-1-258-07348-0(X)) Literary Licensing, LLC.
Michell, Deidre. Christian Science: Women, Healing, & the Church. 2009. (ENG.). 242p. pap. 35.99 (978-0-7618-4574-4(7)) Univ. Pr. of America, Inc.
Moll, Albert. Christian Science, Medicine, & Occultism. Rebman, F. J., tr. 2007. (ENG.). 48p. per. 15.95 (978-1-4304-4536-4(X)) Kessinger Publishing, LLC.
Moses, Alfred Geiger. Jewish Science: Divine Healing in Judaism. Shannon, William F., ed. 2011. (ENG.). 124p. pap. 9.95 (978-0-9843040-3-5(7)) Hudson Mohawk Pr.
Pengelly, Nick. Don't Forget the Angels. 2007. 167p. per. 13.99 (978-88-89127-30-8(9)) Destiny Image Europe ITA. Dist: Destiny Image Pubs.
Podmore, Frank. Mesmerism & Christian Science: A Short History of Mental Healing. 2011. (Cambridge Library Collection - Spiritualism & Esoteric Knowledge Ser.). (ENG.). 328p. pap. 24.99 (978-1-108-07246-5(1)) Cambridge Univ. Pr.
Roberts, Oral. The Healing Stream. Montgomery, G. H., ed. 2011. 80p. 37.95 (978-1-258-00496-5(8)) Literary Licensing, LLC.
Seward, Theodore F. How to Get Acquainted with God the Meani. 2006. pap. 21.95 (978-1-4286-3615-6(3)) Kessinger Publishing, LLC.
Simmons, Evangelist Mary F. Divine Healing + Divine Health = A Divine Life: The Three d's. 2010. 68p. pap. 15.00 (978-1-4490-6670-3(4)) AuthorHouse.
Smith, Mamie. The Unfolding of a Rose. 2009. 144p. 22.50 (978-1-60860-058-8(0), Strategic Bk. Publishing) AEG Literary Publishing Services, Inc.
Spangler, Helen. Man's Relationship to God. 2007. kivar 19.95 (978-0-930227-85-2(9)) Bookmark, The.
Steiger, H. W. Christian Science & Philosophy. (978-0-8022-1637-3(4)) Philosophical Library, Inc.
Stetson, Augusta E. Reminiscences, Sermons & Correspondence V1: Proving Adherence. 2007. (ENG.). 632p. per. 45.95 (978-1-4304-4609-5(9)) Kessinger Publishing, LLC.
Twain, Mark, pseud. Christian Science. 2009. 214p. 26.99 (978-1-60512-388-2(9)); pap. 13.99 (978-1-60512-488-9(5)) Akasha Publishing, LLC. (Akasha Classics).
—Christian Science. 2008. 280p. 25.99 (978-0-559-25566-3(7)) 2008. 280p. pap. 26.75 (978-0-559-25563-2(2)) 2008. 216p. 27.99 (978-0-559-29548-0(2)) 2008. 216p. 24.99 (978-0-554-38851-9(0)) 2007. (ENG.). 196p. pap. 19.99 (978-1-4346-7874-4(1)) 2007. (ENG.). 212p. pap. 22.99 (978-1-4346-7875-1(X)) BiblioBazaar.
—Christian Science. 2009. 152p. pap. (978-0-217-45733-0(9)); 146p. pap. (978-1-4590-4216-2(6)) Books LLC.
—Christian Science. 2009. 172p. pap. (978-1-4065-7115-8(6)) Dodo Pr.
—Christian Science. 2009. 172p. pap. 12.99 (978-1-61534-081-1(5)) EZreads Pubns., LLC.
—Christian Science. 2010. 144p. pap. (978-1-4068-5528-9(6)) Echo Library.
—Christian Science. 2010. 110p. pap. 20.03 (978-1-153-59552-0(4)) General Bks. LLC.
Waldschmidt-Nelson, Britta. Christian Science im Lande Luthers: Eine amerikanische Religionsgemeinschaft in Deutschland, 1894-2009. 2009. (Transatlantische Historische Studien (THS) Ser.). (GER., Illus.). 296p. (C). 64.00 (978-3-515-09380-4(X)) Steiner, Franz Verlag Wiesbaden GmbH DEU. Dist: Brown, David Bk. Co., The.
Walter, William W. The Healing of Pierpont Whitney. 2007. (ENG.). 232p. 41.95 (978-0-548-08946-0(9)) Kessinger Publishing, LLC.
Winslow, Wentworth Byro. God Is Doing It. 2006. pap. 19.95 (978-1-4286-5350-4(3)) Kessinger Publishing, LLC.
—God Will Do It. 2006. pap. 20.95 (978-1-4286-4070-2(3)) Kessinger Publishing, LLC.
Wood, Henry. New Thought Simplified How to Gain Harmo. 2006. pap. 24.95 (978-1-4286-3952-2(7)) Kessinger Publishing, LLC.
Young, Vash. No Thank You. 2011. 198p. 44.95 (978-1-258-07976-5(3)) Literary Licensing, LLC.
21st Century Science & Health with Key to the Scriptures: A revision of Science & Health by Mary Baker Eddy. 2008. 600p. pap. 45.00 (978-0-9795454-1-2(2)) Neutrino Publishing.

CHRISTIAN SCIENCE—HISTORY

Eddy, Mary Baker. Message to the Mother Church for 1900. 15p. reprint ed. pap. 5.00 (978-0-87952-055-7(8)) Eddy, The Writings of Mary Baker.
—Message to the Mother Church for 1901. 35p. reprint ed. pap. 5.00 (978-0-87952-056-4(6)) Eddy, The Writings of Mary Baker.
—Message to the Mother Church for 1902. 20p. reprint ed. pap. 5.00 (978-0-87952-057-1(4)) Eddy, The Writings of Mary Baker.
Milmine, Georgine. The Life of Mary Baker G. Eddy & the History of Christian Science. 495p. reprint ed. 74.00 (978-0-7950-1471-0(6)) New Library Press LLC.
Smillie, Paul. In Defense of Mary Baker Eddy & the Remnant of Her Seed: A Compilation of His Articles. 2007. (ENG.). 356p. pap. 24.99 (978-1-4196-7824-0(8)) CreateSpace.

CHRISTIAN SECTS

see also Anglican Communion; Armenian Church; Bruderhof Communities; Catholic Church; Catholic Church—Societies, etc.; Christian Science; Christian Union; Churches of Christ; Clapham Sect; Communicatio in Sacris; Congregational Churches; Eastern Churches; Ecumenical Movement; Free Churches; Fundamentalist Churches; General Convention of the Christian Church; Harmonists; Heresies and Heretics; Holiness Churches; Huguenots; Interdenominational Cooperation; Jacobites (Syrian Christians); Jansenists; Lutheran Church; Mennonites; Methodist Church; Mormon Church; New Jerusalem Church; Old Believers; Patarines; Plymouth Brethren; Presbyterian Church; Protestant Churches; Restoration Movement (Christianity); Shakers; Society of Friends; Unification Church; United Church of Christ

Angerson, John, photos by. Love, Power, Sacrifice: Life with the Jesus Army. 2008. (ENG., Illus.). 64p. (978-1-904587-48-4(8)) Lewis, Dewi Media, Ltd.
Ball, Bryan W. The Seventh Day Men: Sabbatarians & Sabbatarianism in England & Wales, 1600-1800. 2009. (ENG., Illus.). 468p. pap. 58.00 (978-0-227-17311-4(2)) Clarke, James Co., Ltd. GBR. Dist: Brown, David Bk. Co., The.
Beeke, Joel R. The Heritage Reformed Congregations: Who We Are & What We Believe. 2007. (978-1-60178-024-9(9)) Reformation Heritage Bks.
Binkley, Timothy, et al. A Higher Moral & Spiritual Stand: Selected Writings of Milton Wright. Binkley, Timothy, ed. 2009. (Pietist & Wesleyan Studies). (ENG., Illus.). 278p. pap. 48.00 (978-0-8108-6060-5(0)) Scarecrow Pr., Inc.
Bloom, Harold. The American Religion. 2006. 305p. per. 20.00 (978-0-9787210-0-8(4)) Hartley, Chu Pubs.
Blunt, John Henry. Dictionary of Sects, Heresies, Ecclesiastical Parties, & Schools of Religious Thought. 2008. (Gorgias Reference Classics Ser.: 2). 138.00 (978-1-59333-796-4(5)) Gorgias Pr., LLC.
Bonney, Richard & Trim, D. J. B., eds. Persecution & Pluralism: Calvinists & Religious Minorities in Early Modern Europe 1550-1700, Vol. 2. 2006. (Studies in the History of Religious & Political Pluralism Ser.). 326p. (C). pap. 63.95 (978-3-03910-570-0(1)) International Academic Pubs.
—Persecution & Pluralism: Calvinists & Religious Minorities in Early Modern Europe 1550-1700, Vol. 2. 2006. (Studies in the History of Religious & Political Pluralism Ser.). 326p. (C). pap. (978-0-8204-7597-4(1)) Lang, Peter AG.
Bruschi, Caterina. The Wandering Heretics of Languedoc. 2011. (Cambridge Studies in Medieval Life & Thought: Fourth Ser.). (ENG.). 232p. pap. 39.99 (978-0-521-18227-0(1)) Cambridge Univ. Pr.
Burnett, Amy Nelson. The Eucharistic Pamphlets of Andreas Bodenstein von Karlstadt. 2011. 304p. pap. 39.95 (978-1-935503-16-3(2)) Truman State Univ. Pr.
Carter, Kate B. Denominations That Base Their Beliefs on the Teachings of Joseph Smith, the Mormon Prophet. 2011. 72p. 36.95 (978-1-258-00261-9(2)) Literary Licensing, LLC.
Chiovaro, Francesco & Fenili, J. Robert. The History of the Congregation of the Most Holy Redeemer. 2010. (978-0-7648-1978-0(X)) Liguori Pubns.
Chrysostomos, et al. Orthodox Insights: A Collection of Short Questions & Answers on Liturgical Practice & Orthodox Worship, 2 vols. 2009. (978-0-911165-84-5(3)); (978-0-911165-82-1(7)); (978-0-911165-83-8(5)) Ctr. for Traditionalist Orthodox Studies.
Collins, Paul M. & Ensign-George, Barry. Denomination: Assessing an Ecclesiological Category. Collins, Paul M. & Ensign-George, Barry, eds. 2011. (Ecclesiological Investigations Ser.). (ENG.). 192p. 110.00 (978-0-567-13131-7(9), T&T Clark Int'l) Continuum International Publishing Group, Ltd. GBR. Dist: National Bk. Network.
Commins, Gary. Becoming Bridges: The Spirit & Practice of Diversity. 2007. (ENG., Illus.). 160p. per. 14.95 (978-1-56101-294-7(7)) Cowley Pubns.
Cook, R. Franklin. Paul Orjala: The Man, the Mission. 2009. (ENG.). 96p. pap. 9.99 (978-0-8341-2461-5(0), 9780834124615) Beacon Hill Pr. of Kansas City.
—Vistas: The Changing Face of Nazarene Missions. 2009. (ENG.). 96p. pap. 9.99 (978-0-8341-2462-2(9), 9780834124622) Beacon Hill Pr. of Kansas City.
Courtney, Steve. Joseph Hopkins Twichell: The Life & Times of Mark Twain's Closest Friend. 2010. (ENG., Illus.). 368p. pap. 24.95 (978-0-8203-3617-6(3)) Univ. of Georgia Pr.
Coutta, Ramsey. Divine Institutions. 2006. (ENG.). 23.99 (978-1-60034-356-8(2)); pap. 13.99 (978-1-60034-355-1(4)) Xulon Pr., Inc.
Dingel, Irene. Kirche und Regionalbewußtsein in der Frühen Neuzeit: Konfessionell bestimmte Identifikationsprozesse in den Territorien. Dingel, Irene, ed. 2009. (GER.). 203p. 52.00 (978-3-374-02637-1(0)) Evangelische Verlagsanstalt GmbH DEU. Dist: Eisenbrauns, Inc.
Ellingson, Stephen. The Megachurch & the Mainline: Remaking Religious Tradition in the Twenty-First Century. 2007. 256p. 52.50 (978-0-226-20489-5(8)); per. 22.50 (978-0-226-20490-1(1)) Univ. of Chicago Pr.
Evert, Jason. Purity 365: Daily Reflections on True Love. 2009. pap. (978-0-86716-936-2(2), Servant Bks.) Franciscan Media.
Foley, Thomas W. Faces of Faith: A History of the First Order of Indian Sisters. 2008. pap. (978-1-885938-39-8(X)) Cathedral Foundation Pr.
Gerloff, Roswith I. H. A Plea for British Black Theologies, 2 Volumes: The Black Church Movement in Britain in Its Transatlantic Cultural & Theological Interaction with Special Reference to the Pentecostal Oneness (Apostolic) & Sabbatarian Movements. 2010. 1130p. pap. 135.00 (978-1-60899-667-4(0), Wipf and Stock) Wipf & Stock Pubs.
—A Plea for British Black Theologies, Volume 1: The Black Church Movement in Britain in Its Transatlantic Cultural & Theological Interaction with Special Reference to the Pentecostal Oneness (Apostolic) & Sabbatarian Movements. 2010. 466p. pap. 61.00 (978-1-60899-665-0(4), Wipf and Stock) Wipf & Stock Pubs.
—A Plea for British Black Theologies, Volume 2: The Black Church Movement in Britain in Its Transatlantic Cultural & Theological Interaction with Special Reference to the Pentecostal Oneness (Apostolic) & Sabbatarian Movements. 2010. 678p. pap. 75.00 (978-1-60899-666-7(2), Wipf and Stock) Wipf & Stock Pubs.
Gray-Reeves, Mary & Perham, Michael. The Hospitality of God: Emerging Worship for a Missional Church. 2011. pap. (978-1-59627-140-1(X), Seabury Bks.) Church Publishing, Inc.
Hamilton, Adam. Christianity's Family Tree Leader's Guide: What Other Christians Believe & Why. ldr.'s ed. 2007. (Illus.). 133p. 12.00 (978-0-687-49116-2(9)) Abingdon Pr.
Hamilton, Adam & Carter, Kenneth H., Jr. Christianity's Family Tree Leader's Guide: What Other Christians Believe & Why. ldr.'s ed. 2007. 20p. 35.00 (978-0-687-49275-6(0)) Abingdon Pr.
Hamilton, Adam & Sharpe, Sally D. Christianity's Family Tree Leader's Guide: What Other Christians Believe & Why. 2007. 96p. pap. 11.00 (978-0-687-46671-9(7)) Abingdon Pr.
Handbook of Denominations. 10th ed. 16.00 (978-0-687-01479-8(4)) Abingdon Pr.
Ingersol, Stan, et al. Our Watchword & Song: The Centennial History of the Church of the Nazarene. 2009. (ENG.). 736p. pap. 69.99 (978-0-8341-2444-8(0), 9780834124448) Beacon Hill Pr. of Kansas City.
Jain, Poornima. Religious Sects & Social Development: A Comparative Study of Jains, Christians, & Sikhs. 2010. 216p. 45.00 (978-81-316-0262-1(1)) Rawat Pubns. IND. Dist: International Specialized Bk. Services.

C

Jamison-Tanchuck, F. No to Religion but Yes to God. 2009. 157p. pap. 12.99 *(978-1-60604-828-3(7))* Tate Publishing & Enterprises, LLC.

Jones, Rufus M. The Church's Debt to Heretics. 2007. (ENG.). 256p. 42.95 *(978-0-548-10258-9(9))* Kessinger Publishing, LLC.

—The Church's Debt to Heretics. 2008. 256p. pap. 26.00 *(978-1-59752-888-7(9))* Wipf & Stock Pubs.

Jones, Thomas A. In Seach of a City: An Autobiographical Perspective on a Remarkable but Controversial Movement. 2007. (Illus.). 231p. pap. 16.00 *(978-1-57782-221-9(8))* Discipleship Pubns. International.

Jullien, F. Le monachisme en Perse: La reforme d'Abraham le Grand, pere des moines de L'Orient. 2008. (Corpus Scriptorum Christianorum Orientalium Ser.). (FRE., Illus.). 293p. (C). pap. 96.00 *(978-90-429-2090-3(4))* Peeters Pubs. & Booksellers BEL. Dist: Brown, David Bk. Co., The.

Koehn, Philip. Choosing your Religion. 2009. 658p. pap. 36.50 *(978-0-557-07567-6(X))* Lulu Enterprises Inc.

Kostenberger, Andreas J. & Kruger, Michael J. The Heresy of Orthodoxy: How Contemporary Culture's Fascination with Diversity Has Reshaped Our Understanding of Early Christianity. 2010. 256p. pap. 17.99 *(978-1-4335-0143-2(0))* Crossway.

Lichti, James Irvin. Houses on the Sand? Pacifist Denominations in Nazi Germany. 2006. (Studies in Modern European History: Vol. 51). 78.95 *(978-0-8204-6731-3(6))* Lang, Peter Publishing, Inc.

Lindner, Eileen, ed. Yearbook of AMER & Canadia. 2009. 464p. pap. 55.00 *(978-0-687-65880-0(2))* Abingdon Pr.

—Yearbook of American & Canadian Churches 2010. 2010. pap. 55.00 *(978-0-687-46686-3(5))* Abingdon Pr.

Lindner, Eileen W., ed. Yearbook of American & Canadian Churches. 75th ed. 2007. (Yearbook of American & Canadian Churches Ser.). 439p. per. 50.00 *(978-0-687-33569-5(8))* Abingdon Pr.

—Yearbook of American & Canadian Churches 2008. 2008. pap. 52.00 *(978-0-687-65149-8(2))* Abingdon Pr.

Littell, Franklin Hamlin & Littell, Franklin. From State Church to Pluralism: A Protestant Interpretation of Religion in American History. 2007. (ENG.). 192p. pap. 19.95 *(978-0-202-30921-7(5))* Aldine Transaction.

Mattox, Mickey Leland & Roeber, A. G. Changing Churches: An Orthodox, Catholic, & Lutheran Theological Conversation. 2012. pap. ***(978-0-8028-6694-3(8))*** Eerdmans, William B. Publishing Co.

McLaren, Brian D., et al, eds. The Justice Project, 1 vol. 2009. (Emersion). 288p. 21.99 *(978-0-8010-1328-7(3))* Baker Bks.

Mead, Frank Spencer & Hill, Samuel S. Handbook of Denominations in the United States. 13th ed. 2010. 432p. instr.'s hndbk. ed. 24.00 *(978-1-4267-0048-4(2))* Abingdon Pr.

Moltmann, Jurgen. A Broad Place. Kohl, Margaret, tr. from GER. 2007. (Illus.). 412p. 29.00 *(978-0-8006-6214-1(8)*, Fortress Pr.) Augsburg Fortress, Pubs.

Moore, Rosemary. The History of the Life of Thomas Ellwood: Written by Himself. 2010. (Sacred Literature Trust Ser.). (ENG.). 240p. pap. 27.95 *(978-0-300-16514-2(5))* Yale Univ. Pr.

Mullin, Robert Bruce & Richey, Russell E. Reimagining Denominationalism: Interpretive Essays, 1 vol. 2011. (Religion in America Ser.). 336p. pap. 29.95 *(978-0-19-976745-8(9))* Oxford Univ. Pr., Inc.

Regan, Ethna. Theology & the Boundary Discourse of Human Rights. 2010. (ENG.). 256p. pap. 44.95 *(978-1-58901-642-2(4))* Georgetown Univ. Pr.

Regev, Eyal. Sectarianism in Qumran: A Cross-Cultural Perspective. (Religion & Society Ser.). (ENG.). XVIII, 438p. 255.00 ***(978-3-11-182278-5(8))***; 2007. 154.00 *(978-3-11-019332-9(9))* De Gruyter, Walter Inc.

Reiterman, Tim. Raven: The Untold Story of the Rev. Jim Jones & His People. 2008. (ENG., Illus.). 688p. (gr. 12-18). 18.95 *(978-1-58542-678-2(4)*, Tarcher) Penguin Group (USA) Inc.

Roberts, Zach T. Baptist Stories of Emergence. 2009. pap. *(978-1-57312-551-2(2))* Smyth & Helwys Publishing, Inc.

Schilling, A. M. Die Anbetung der Magier und die Taufe der Sasaniden: Zur Geistesgeschichte des iranischen Christentums in der Spatantike. 2008. (Corpus Scriptorum Christianorum Orientalium Ser.). (GER.). 376p. (C). pap. 124.00 *(978-90-429-1815-3(2))* Peeters Pubs. & Booksellers BEL. Dist: Brown, David Bk. Co., The.

Slocum, Robert Boak. Light in a Burning-Glass: A Systematic Presentation of Austin Farrer's Theology. 2007. (Illus.). 132p. 34.95 *(978-1-57003-669-9(1))* Univ. of South Carolina Pr.

Smith, David M., ed. The Heads of Religious Houses: England & Wales, III. 1377-1540. 2011. (Heads of Religious Houses Ser.). (ENG.). 912p. pap. 98.00 *(978-0-521-36993-0(2))* Cambridge Univ. Pr.

Smith, John Howard. The Perfect Rule of the Christian Religion: A History of Sandemanianism in the Eighteenth Century. 2009. ix, 236p. pap. 24.95 *(978-1-4384-2508-5(2))*; 240p. 70.00 *(978-1-4384-2507-8(4))* State Univ. of New York Pr.

St. Teresa of Avila. Autobiography of St. Teresa of Avila. 2010. (ENG.). 352p. pap. 10.95 *(978-0-486-47598-1(0))* Dover Pubns., Inc.

Trickler, C. Jack. A Layman's Guide To: Why Are There So Many Christian Denominations? 2010. 292p. 25.99 *(978-1-4490-4578-4(2))* AuthorHouse.

Van Amberg, Joel. A Real Presence: Religious & Social Dynamics of the Eucharistic Conflicts in Early Modern Augsburg, 1520-1530. 2011. (ENG.). X, 270p. ***(978-90-04-21698-3(7))*** BRILL.

Van Gelder, Craig. The Missional Church & Denominations: Helping Congregations Develop a Missional Identity. 2008. (Illus.). 288p. pap. 26.00 *(978-0-8028-6358-4(2))* Eerdmans, William B. Publishing Co.

Wood, Tom. 27 Main Street. 2010. 238p. pap. *(978-0-9552920-8-8(5))* Red Hen Publishing.

Zdero, Rad. Letters to the House Church Movement. 2011. 168p. pap. 14.99 ***(978-1-61379-022-9(8))*** Xulon Pr., Inc.

CHRISTIAN SOCIAL THEORY

see Christian Sociology

CHRISTIAN SOCIALISM

Berdiaev, Nikolai & Lowrie, Donald A. The Fate of Man in the Modern World. 3rd ed. 2009. pap. *(978-1-59731-263-9(0))* Perennis, Sophia.

Bradstock, Andrew. Radical Religion in Cromwell's England: A Concise History from the English Civil War to the End of the Commonwealth. 2011. (International Library of Historical Studies). (ENG., Illus.). 224p. 88.00 *(978-1-84511-764-1(6))*; pap. 28.00 *(978-1-84511-765-8(4))* I. B. Tauris & Co., Ltd. GBR. Dist: Macmillan.

Bronstein, Jamie. John Francis Bray: Transatlantic Radical. (ENG.). 206p. 2010. 70.00 *(978-0-85036-603-7(8))* 2009. pap. 29.95 *(978-0-85036-604-4(6))* Merlin Pr. Ltd. GBR. Dist: Independent Pubs. Group.

Burton, John & McCabe, Eileen. We Don't Do God: Blair's Religious Belief & its Consequences. 2009. (ENG., Illus.). 256p. 22.95 *(978-1-84706-352-6(7))* Continuum International Publishing Group, Ltd. GBR. Dist: National Bk. Network.

Crowther, Kathleen. Adam & Eve in the Protestant Reformation. 2010. (ENG., Illus.). 304p. 85.00 *(978-0-521-19236-1(6))* Cambridge Univ. Pr.

Geoghegan, Vincent. Socialism & Religion. 2011. (Routledge Studies in Social & Political Thought Ser.). (ENG.). 256p. 125.00 *(978-0-415-66828-6(X))* Routledge.

Gladden, Washington. Tools & the Man: Property & Industry under the Christian Law. 2010. 322p. pap. 30.75 *(978-1-142-09700-4(5))* 2010. 324p. pap. 30.75 *(978-1-142-68791-5(0))* 2008. 320p. 28.99 *(978-0-559-58982-9(4))* 2008. 320p. pap. 29.75 *(978-0-559-58979-9(4))* BiblioBazaar.

—Tools & the Man: Property & Industry under the Christian Law. 320p. 2010. 36.76 *(978-1-163-42976-1(7))* 2010. pap. 24.76 *(978-1-162-96356-3(5))* 2007. (ENG.). 45.95 *(978-0-548-12254-9(7))* Kessinger Publishing, LLC.

Kuyper, Abraham Jr. & Kuyper, Abraham. The Problem of Poverty. 2011. 94p. ***(978-0-932914-87-3(X))*** Dordt College Pr.

Masterman, N. C. John Malcolm Ludlow: The Builder of Christian Socialism. 2008. (ENG.). 312p. pap. 42.00 *(978-0-521-07695-1(1))* Cambridge Univ. Pr.

Mitchell, Daria, ed. Greed, Lust & Power: Franciscan Strategies for Building a More Just World. 2010. (ENG.). 72p. pap. 14.00 ***(978-1-57659-220-5(0))*** Franciscan Institute Pubns.

Murry, John M. Defence of Democracy. 2006. 320p. per. *(978-1-4067-3134-7(X)*, Hesperides Pr.) Read Bks.

Raven, Charles E. Christian Socialism, 1848-1854. 2009. 410p. 30.99 *(978-1-113-92570-1(1))*; 32.99 *(978-1-113-92571-8(X))*; pap. 27.99 *(978-1-113-92568-8(X))*; pap. 21.99 *(978-1-113-92566-4(3))* BiblioBazaar.

Thompson, Joseph P. The Workman: His False Friends & His True Friends. 2008. 260p. pap. 20.00 *(978-1-59925-201-8(5))* Solid Ground Christian Bks.

CHRISTIAN SOCIOLOGY

Here are entered works on the sociology of Christian denominations and general Christian social theory. Works on the efforts of the church to deal with social problems are entered under Church and Social Problems.

see also Dominion Theology; Power (Theology); Social Gospel

Abbott, Lyman. Christianity & Social Problems. 2010. 396p. pap. 33.75 *(978-1-177-14369-1(0))* 2010. 382p. 38.99 *(978-1-140-39152-4(6))* 2010. 398p. pap. 33.75 *(978-1-148-71362-5(X))* 2010. 382p. pap. 33.75 *(978-1-140-39153-1(4))* 2010. 386p. pap. 33.75 *(978-1-141-91271-1(6))* 2008. 384p. 29.99 *(978-0-559-68889-8(X))* 2008. 384p. pap. 32.75 *(978-0-559-68884-3(9))* BiblioBazaar.

—Christianity & Social Problems. 2009. 184p. pap. 19.99 *(978-1-150-54657-0(3))* General Bks. LLC.

—Christianity & Social Problems. 384p. 2010. 39.16 *(978-1-163-41881-9(1))* 2007. (ENG.). 48.95 *(978-0-548-11138-3(3))* Kessinger Publishing, LLC.

—Christianity & Social Problems. 2008. 388p. pap. *(978-1-4097-9968-9(9))* Read Bks.

Abraham, Martin. Evangelium und Kirchengestalt: Reformatorisches Kirchenverständnis heute. (Theologische Bibliothek Töpelmann Ser.).Tr. of Gospel & the Shape of the Church. A Reformational Understanding of the Church Today. (GER.). XV, 601p. 300.00 ***(978-3-11-181861-0(6))***; 2007. 182.00 *(978-3-11-019444-9(9))* De Gruyter, Walter Inc.

Allen, John L. The Future Church: How Ten Trends Are Revolutionizing the Catholic Church. 2012. (ENG.). 480p. pap. 16.00 ***(978-0-385-52039-3(5)***, Image) Doubleday Religious Publishing Group, The.

Allen, John L., Jr. The Future Church: How Ten Trends Are Revolutionizing the Catholic Church. 2009. (ENG.). 480p. 28.00 *(978-0-385-52038-6(7))* Knopf Doubleday Publishing Group.

Andelson, Robert V. Imputed Rights: An Essay in Christian Social Theory. 2nd ed. 2011. (ENG.). 192p. 32.95 *(978-0-85683-278-9(2))*; pap. 19.95 *(978-0-85683-272-7(3))* Shepheard-Walwyn Pubs., Ltd. GBR. Dist: Independent Pubs. Group.

Anderson, Carl. A Civilization of Love: What Every Catholic Can Do to Transform the World. 2009. (ENG.). 240p. pap. 13.99 *(978-0-06-133532-7(0)*, HarperOne) HarperCollins Pubs.

—Civilization of Love: What Every Catholic Can Do to Transform the World. 2008. 224p. 19.95 *(978-0-06-133531-0(2)*, HarperOne) HarperCollins Pubs.

Andreae, Johann. Christianopolis: An Ideal of the 17th Century. Held, Felix, tr. 2007. 312p. per. 21.95 *(978-1-60206-886-5(0))* Cosimo, Inc.

Babson, Roger W. New Tasks for Old Churches: Studies of T. 2006. pap. 22.95 *(978-1-4286-4761-9(9))* Kessinger Publishing, LLC.

Baker, Christopher & Reader, John, eds. Entering the New Theological Space: Blurred Encounters of Faith, Politics & Community. 2009. (Explorations in Practical, Pastoral & Empirical Theology Ser.). (Illus.). 256p. 114.95 *(978-0-7546-6339-3(6))* Ashgate Publishing Co.

Baker, Doug P. Covenant & Community: Our Role as the Image of God. 2008. 158p. pap. 18.00 *(978-1-55635-203-4(4))* Wipf & Stock Pubs.

Barentsen, Jack. Emerging Leadership in the Pauline Mission: A Social Identity Perspective on Local Leadership Development in Corinth & Ephesus. 2011. (Princeton Theological Monographs). 396p. pap. 44.00 ***(978-1-61097-244-4(9)***, Pickwick Pubns.) Wipf & Stock Pubs.

Barrera, Albino. Economic Compulsion & Christian Ethics. 2007. (New Studies in Christian Ethics Ser.). (ENG.). 268p. pap. 55.00 *(978-0-521-04357-1(3))* Cambridge Univ. Pr.

Barrett, Edward. Persons & Liberal Democracy: The Ethical & Political Thought of Karol Wojtyla/John Paul II. 2010. (ENG.). 158p. 60.00 *(978-0-7391-2114-6(6))* Lexington Bks.

Baum, Gregory. Religion & Alienation: A Theological Reading of Sociology. 2nd ed. 2007. 258p. *(978-2-89507-800-5(9))* Novalis Publishing.

Benestad, J. Brian. Church, State, & Society. 2011. 456p. 54.95 *(978-0-8132-1800-7(4))* Catholic Univ. of America Pr.

—Church, State, & Society: An Introduction to Catholic Social Doctrine. 2011. 456p. pap. 34.95 *(978-0-8132-1801-4(2))* Catholic Univ. of America Pr.

Berdyaev, Nicholas. Fate of Man in the Modern World. 2006. 136p. per. *(978-1-4067-3430-0(6)*, Hesperides Pr.) Read Bks.

Berger, Rose Marie. Who Killed Donte Manning? The Myth & Spirit of an American Neighborhood. 2009. *(978-1-934074-40-4(3))* Apprentice Hse.

Beutel, Harald. Die Sozialtheologie Thomas Chalmers (1780-1847) und Ihre Bedeutung Für Die Freikirchen: Eine Studie Zur Diakonie der Erweckungsbewegung. 2007. (Arbeiten zur Pastoraltheologie, Liturgik und Hymnologie Ser.). (GER., Illus.). 320p. (C). pap. 81.00 *(978-3-525-62396-1(8))* Vandenhoeck & Ruprecht GmbH & Co. KG DEU. Dist: ISD.

Bielo, James. Words upon the Word: An Ethnography of Evangelical Group Bible Study. 2009. (ENG.). 208p. 70.00 *(978-0-8147-9121-9(2))*; pap. 21.00 *(978-0-8147-9122-6(0))* New York Univ. Pr.

Bielo, James S., ed. The Social Life of Scriptures: Cross-Cultural Perspectives on Biblicism. 2009. (Signifying (on)Scriptures Ser.). (ENG., Illus.). 272p. (C). 72.00 *(978-0-8135-4605-6(2))*; pap. 28.95 *(978-0-8135-4606-3(0))* Rutgers Univ. Pr.

Bigelow, Herbert S. The Religion of Revolution. 2007. (ENG.). 118p. 34.95 *(978-0-548-01810-1(3))* Kessinger Publishing, LLC.

Birch, Charles, et al, eds. Liberating Life: Contemporary Approaches to Ecological Theology. 2007. 304p. pap. 33.00 *(978-1-55635-187-7(9)*, Wipf and Stock) Wipf & Stock Pubs.

Bradford, Amory Howe. Heredity & Christian Problems. 2010. reprint ed. 304p. pap. 29.75 *(978-1-177-94413-7(8))*; 304p. pap. 29.75 *(978-1-144-61920-4(3))*; 306p. pap. 29.75 ***(978-1-141-94433-0(2))*** BiblioBazaar.

—Heredity & Christian Problems. 2009. 142p. pap. *(978-0-217-48330-8(5))* Books LLC.

—Heredity & Christian Problems. 296p. reprint ed. 2010. 35.16 ***(978-1-163-43099-6(4))*** 2010. pap. 23.16 ***(978-1-162-96414-0(6))*** 2007. (ENG.). 43.95 *(978-0-548-12381-2(0))* Kessinger Publishing, LLC.

Brady, Bernard V. Essential Catholic Social Thought. 2008. 294p. pap. 26.00 *(978-1-57075-756-3(9))* Orbis Bks.

Brittain, Christopher Craig. The Weight of Objectivity. 2010. 204p. pap. *(978-3-8383-5033-2(2))* Lambert Academic Publishing.

Brown, Callum G. Religion & Society in Twentieth-Century Britain. 2006. (Religion, Politics & Society in Britain Ser.). (ENG., Illus.). 360p. (C). per. 50.20 *(978-0-582-47289-1(X))* Longman Publishing Group.

Bruehl, Charles P. The Pope's Plan for Social Reconstruction. 10.00 *(978-0-8159-6507-7(9))* Devin-Adair Pubs., Inc.

Budde, Michael L. The Borders of Baptism: Identities, Allegiances, & the Church. 2011. (Theopolitical Visions: Ser.). 204p. pap. 22.00 ***(978-1-61097-135-5(3)***, Cascade Bks.) Wipf & Stock Pubs.

Burbach, Christiane & Heckmann, Friedrich. Generationenfragen: Theologische Perspektiven Zur Gesellschaft des 21. Jahrhunderts. 2007. (GER.). 189p. (C). pap. 36.00 *(978-3-525-60433-5(5))* Vandenhoeck & Ruprecht GmbH & Co. KG DEU. Dist: ISD.

Cadorette, Curt. Catholicism in Social & Historical Contexts: An Introduction. 2010. 288p. pap. 20.00 *(978-1-57075-872-0(7))* Orbis Bks.

Cannon, Mae Elise. Social Justice Handbook: Small Steps for a Better World. 2009. (BridgeLeader Partnership Ser.). (ENG.). 304p. pap. 20.00 *(978-0-8308-3715-1(9)*, IVP Bks.) InterVarsity Pr.

Carlson, Edgar M. The Church & the Public Conscience: Christian Responsibility in Public. 2011. 116p. 39.95 ***(978-1-258-04770-2(5))*** Literary Licensing, LLC.

Carroll, Jackson W., et al, eds. Handbook for Congregational Studies. 192p. (Orig.). 21.00 *(978-0-687-16562-9(8))* Abingdon Pr.

Cassidy, Eoin G., ed. The Common Good in an Unequal World: Reflections on the Compendium of the Social Doctrine of the Church. 2007. (ENG., Illus.). 218p. pap. 23.95 *(978-1-84730-056-0(1))* Veritas Pubns. IRL. Dist: Dufour Editions, Inc.

Chalmers, Thomas. The Christian & Civic Economy of Large Towns V1. 2007. (ENG.). 360p. 46.95 *(978-0-548-15220-1(9))*; 364p. per. 31.95 *(978-1-4304-4581-4(5))* Kessinger Publishing, LLC.

Chapman. Living the Magnificat: Affirming Catholicism in a Broken World. Chapman, Mark, ed. 2007. (Affirming Catholicism Ser.). (ENG.). 144p. 24.95 *(978-1-906286-06-4(X))* Mowbray, A. R. & Co., Ltd. GBR. Dist: National Bk. Network.

Chung, Paul & Duchrow, Ulrich. Liberating Lutheran Theology: Freedom for Justice & Solidarity in a Global Context. 2011. (Studies in Lutheran History & Theology Ser.). 256p. (C). 33.00 *(978-0-8006-9778-5(2)*, Fortress Pr.) Augsburg Fortress, Pubs.

Cleary, Maureen. Management Dilemmas in Catholic Human Service: Health Care, Welfare, & Education. 2007. (Illus.). 304p. *(978-0-7734-5462-0(4))* Mellen, Edwin Pr., The.

Collins, Chuck & Wright, Mary. The Moral Measure of the Economy. 2007. (Illus.). 222p. per. 20.00 *(978-1-57075-693-1(7))* Orbis Bks.

Colwell, Stephen. New Themes for the Protestant Clergy. 2009. (Illus.). 198p. pap. 19.99 *(978-1-150-36469-3(6))* General Bks. LLC.

—New Themes for the Protestant Clergy: Creeds Without Charity, theology Without Humanity, & Protestantism Without Christianity ... 2006. 420p. per. 26.99 *(978-1-4255-4498-0(3))* MPublishing.

Colwell, Stephen, abr. New Themes for the Protestant Clergy. 2009. (Amer Philosophy, Religion Ser.). (ENG.). 420p. pap. 25.95 *(978-1-4290-1843-2(7))* Applewood Bks.

Corkery, Padraig. Companion to the Compendium of the Social Doctrine of the Church. 2008. (ENG.). 124p. pap. 16.95 *(978-1-85390-959-7(9))* Veritas Pubns. IRL. Dist: Dufour Editions, Inc.

Coulter, Michael L., et al. Catholic Social Thought, Social Science, & Social Policy, 2 vols. 2007. (ENG.). 1192p. 174.00 *(978-0-8108-5906-7(8))* Scarecrow Pr., Inc.

Cram101 Textbook Reviews & Cram101 Textbook Reviews. Outlines & Highlights for Social Ethics in the Making: Interpreting an American Tradition by Gary J. Dorrien, ISBN. 2011. 262p. pap. 31.95 ***(978-1-61461-600-9(0))*** Cram101 Inc.

Cranage, David Herbert Somerset. The War & Unity: Being Lectures Delivered at the Local Lectures Sum. 2007. 138p. pap. 18.99 *(978-1-4264-9489-5(0))*; 152p. pap. 21.99 *(978-1-4264-9870-1(5))* BiblioBazaar.

Creasey, Maurice A. Collected Essays of Maurice Creasey, 1912-2004: The Social Thought of a Quaker Thinker. 2011. (Illus.). 504p. 149.95 *(978-0-7734-1493-8(2))* Mellen, Edwin Pr., The.

Curran, Charles E. The Social Mission of the U. S. Catholic Church: A Theological Perspective. 2010. (Moral Traditions Ser.). (ENG.). 208p. pap. 29.95 *(978-1-58901-743-6(9))* Georgetown Univ. Pr.

Dahnelt, Rainer. Funktion und Gottesbegriff: Der Einfluss der Religionssoziologie auf die Theologie am Beispiel von Niklas Luhmann und Falk Wagner. 2009. viii, 263p. *(978-3-374-02659-3(1))* Evangelische Verlagsanstalt GmbH.

Daniel, Wallace L. The Orthodox Church & Civil Society in Russia. 2006. (Eugenia & Hugh M. Stewart '26 Series on Eastern Europe). (ENG., Illus.). 270p. 29.95 *(978-1-58544-523-3(1))* Texas A&M Univ. Pr.

Davies, Douglas J. & Guest, Mathew. Bishops, Wives & Children: Spiritual Capital Across the Generations. 2007. (Illus.). 228p. 99.95 *(978-0-7546-5485-8(0))* Ashgate Publishing Co.

Dawson, Christopher. The Judgment of the Nations. 2011. (Worlds of Christopher Dawson Ser.). 200p. pap. 24.95 ***(978-0-8132-1880-9(2))*** Catholic Univ. of America Pr.

Dommen, Edward & Bratt, James D., eds. John Calvin Rediscovered: The Impact of His Social & Economic Thought. 2007. (Princeton Theological Seminary Studies in Reformed Theology & History Ser.). (ENG.). 161p. per. 30.00 *(978-0-664-23227-6(2))* Westminster John Knox Pr.

Dorrien, Gary. Social Ethics in the Making: Interpreting an American Tradition. 2010. (ENG.). 752p. pap. 46.95 *(978-1-4443-3730-3(0)*, Wiley-Blackwell) Wiley, John & Sons, Inc.

Dorrien, Gary J. Reconstructing the Common Good: Theology & the Social Order. 2008. 230p. pap. 26.00 *(978-1-59244-949-1(2))* Wipf & Stock Pubs.

—Social Ethics in the Making: Interpreting an American Tradition. 2008. (ENG., Illus.). 752p. 164.95 *(978-1-4051-8687-2(9)*, Wiley-Blackwell) Wiley, John & Sons, Inc.

Drinkwater, F. Money & Social Justice. 2007. 92p. per. 14.45 *(978-0-9782985-5-5(1))* Catholic Authors Pr.

Dulles, Avery Robert. Church & Society: The Laurence J. Mcginley Lectures, 1988-2007. 3rd ed. 2008. (ENG.). 546p. 45.00 *(978-0-8232-2862-1(2))* Fordham Univ. Pr.

Ekelund, Robert B., Jr., et al. The Marketplace of Christianity. 2006. (ENG., Illus.). 368p. (gr. 17). 31.95 *(978-0-262-05082-1(X))* MIT Pr.

Eliot, T. S. Christianity & Culture. 2007. (ENG.). 208p. per. *(978-1-4067-5858-0(2))* Read Bks.

Ellis, Marc H. Peter Maurin. 2010. (Catholic Worker Reprint Ser.). (Illus.). 204p. pap. 23.00 *(978-1-60899-060-3(5)*, Wipf and Stock) Wipf & Stock Pubs.

Ely, Richard. Social Aspects of Christianity. 2009. pap. 50.70 *(978-1-60724-301-4(6))* Gorgias Pr., LLC.

Enrique Dussell Staff. Politics of Liberation: A Critical Global History, Vol. 1. 2nd ed. 2011. x, 166p. pap. ***(978-0-334-04186-3(4)***, SCM Pr.) Hymns Ancient & Modern Ltd.

Evans, Bernard F. Lazarus at the Table: Catholic & Social Justice. 2006. (Michael Glazier Bks.). 125p. per. 15.95 *(978-0-8146-5114-8(3))* Liturgical Pr.

Ferret, Richard/Bowen. Charisma & Routinisation in a Millennialist Community: Seventh-day Adventist Identity. 2008. 376p. 119.95 *(978-0-7734-4862-9(4))* Mellen, Edwin Pr., The.

Fimister, Alan. Robert Schuman: Neo Scholastic Humanism & the Re-Unification of Europe. 2008. 278p. 55.95 *(978-90-5201-439-5(6))* PIE - Peter Lang BEL. Dist: Lang, Peter.

Finn, Daniel K. The Moral Dynamics of Economic Life: An Extension & Critique of Caritas in Veritate. 2012. E-Book *(978-0-19-985834-7(9))* Oxford Univ. Pr., Inc.

Finn, Daniel K., ed. The Moral Dynamics of Economic Life: An Extension & Critique of Caritas in Veritate, 1 vol. 2012. (ENG.). 192p. pap. 29.95 *(978-0-19-985835-4(7))* Oxford Univ. Pr., Inc.

Finn, Daniel K., ed. The True Wealth of Nations: Catholic Social Thought & Economic Life. 2010. (ENG., Illus.). 336p. pap. 35.00 *(978-0-19-973982-0(X))* Oxford Univ. Pr., Inc.

Flanagan, Kieran. Sociology in Theology: Reflexivity & Belief. 2007. (ENG.). 256p. 100.00 *(978-0-230-00265-4(X))* Palgrave Macmillan.

Forrester, Duncan B. Forrester on Christian Ethics: Collected Writings on Christianity India & the Social Order. 2010. (Ashgate Contemporary Thinkers on Religion: Collected Works Ser.). 536p. 144.95 *(978-0-7546-6438-3(4))* Ashgate Publishing Co.

Fountain, David. Let Conscience Speak. 32p. pap. 0.99 *(978-0-85479-810-0(2))* Revival Literature.

Friesen, Steven, et al, eds. Corinth in Context: Comparative Studies on Religion & Society. 2010. XXVI, 518p. pap. *(978-90-04-18211-0(X))* BRILL.

Garrigan, Siobhan. The Real Peace Process: Worship, Politics, & the End of Sectarianism. 2010. (Religion & Violence Ser.). (ENG.). 240p. (C). 99.95 *(978-1-84553-693-0(2))*; pap. 34.95 *(978-1-84553-694-7(0))* Equinox Publishing Ltd. GBR. Dist: ISD.

Gates, Jamie & Middendorf, Jon. Living Justice: Revolutionary Compassion in a Broken World. 2007. (Undercurrent Ser.). (ENG.). 96p. pap. 8.99 *(978-0-8341-5019-5(0)*, 0834150190) Beacon Hill Pr. of Kansas City.

Genilo, Eric Marcelo O. John Cuthbert Ford, SJ: Moral Theologian at the End of the Manualist ERA. 2007. (Moral Traditions Ser.). (ENG.). 240p. 49.95 *(978-1-58901-181-6(3))* Georgetown Univ. Pr.

George, Francis. God in Action: How Faith in God Can Address the Challenges of the World. 2011. 240p. 22.99 *(978-0-307-59026-8(7)*, Doubleday Religion) Doubleday Religious Publishing Group, The.

Gill, Robin. Theology in a Social Context Vol. 1: Sociological Theology. 2012. (Ashgate Contemporary Ecclesiology Ser.). 196p. 99.95 *(978-1-4094-2595-3(9))*; pap. 39.95 *(978-1-4094-2594-6(0))* Ashgate Publishing Co.

Gladden, Washington. Christianity & Socialism. 2009. 72p. pap. 14.14 *(978-1-151-61443-8(2))* General Bks. LLC.

—Christianity & Socialism. 2007. (ENG.). 246p. 41.95 *(978-0-548-15531-8(3))*; pap. 26.95 *(978-1-4304-4963-8(2))* Kessinger Publishing, LLC.

—Social Salvation. 2008. 252p. 25.99 *(978-0-559-48205-2(1))*; pap. 25.75 *(978-0-559-48201-4(9))* BiblioBazaar.

—Social Salvation. 2009. 104p. pap. 19.99 *(978-1-151-69719-6(2))* General Bks. LLC.

—Social Salvation. 2009. 252p. 41.95 *(978-1-104-20819-6(9))*; pap. 26.95 *(978-1-4374-9554-6(0))* Kessinger Publishing, LLC.

—Tools & the Man: Property & Industry under the Christian Law. 2010. 324p. pap. 30.75 *(978-1-142-68791-5(0))* 2010. 322p. pap. 30.75 *(978-1-142-09700-4(5))* 2008. 320p. 28.99 *(978-0-559-58982-9(4))* 2008. 320p. pap. 29.75 *(978-0-559-58979-9(4))* BiblioBazaar.

—Tools & the Man: Property & Industry under the Christian Law. 320p. 2010. 36.76 *(978-1-163-42976-1(7))* 2010. pap. 24.76 *(978-1-162-96356-3(5))* 2007. (ENG.). 45.95 *(978-0-548-12254-9(7))* Kessinger Publishing, LLC.

Gomez, Ricardo. The Mission of God in Latin America. 2010. (Illus.). 244p. pap. 35.00 *(978-1-60947-003-6(6))* Emeth Pr.

Goudzwaard, Bob, et al. Hope in Troubled Times: A New Vision for Confronting Global Crises. 2007. (Illus.). 256p. (C). pap. 22.00 *(978-0-8010-3248-6(2))* Baker Academic.

Grant, Stanley. In Defense of A Nation. 2011. 180p. 30.95 *(978-1-4497-2918-9(5))*; pap. 13.95 *(978-1-4497-2917-2(7))* Author Solutions, Inc. (WestBow Pr.).

Greaney, Michael D. In Defense of Human Dignity: Essays on the Just Third Way: A Natural Law Perspective. 2008. x, 303p. pap. *(978-0-944997-02-4(3))* Ctr. for Economic & Social Justice.

Greenway, Roger S. & Leder, Arie C. For God So Loved the World: Essays in Honour of Roger S. Greenway. 2006. (ENG.). pap. *(978-1-55306-983-6(8))* Essence Publishing.

Haavik, Kristof. The Socialist Christian. 2007. 184p. per. 24.95 *(978-1-4241-9764-4(3))* PublishAmerica, Inc.

Harmon Sr., E. Ken. Growing God's Kingdom. 2008. 124p. pap. 10.99 *(978-1-60477-972-1(1))* Xulon Pr., Inc.

Harris, Samuel Smith. The Relation of Christianity to Civil Society. 2009. 226p. pap. 25.75 *(978-1-115-99829-1(3))* BiblioBazaar.

—The Relation of Christianity to Civil Society. 2007. (ENG.). 222p. 39.95 *(978-0-548-15551-6(8))*; pap. 24.95 *(978-1-4304-4990-4(X))* Kessinger Publishing, LLC.

Harvey, Barry. Can These Bones Live? A Catholic Baptist Engagement with Ecclesiology, Hermeneutics, & Social Theory. 2008. 304p. (C). pap. 28.00 *(978-1-58743-081-7(9))* Brazos Pr.

Hayes, Mary Dolores. Various Group Mind Theories: Viewed in T. 2006. pap. 24.95 *(978-1-4286-6144-8(1))* Kessinger Publishing, LLC.

Heddendorf, Russell & Vos, Matthew. Hidden Threads: A Christian Critique of Sociological Theory. 2009. (ENG.). 256p. pap. 36.99 *(978-0-7618-4901-8(7))* 2nd ed. 2010. xii, 242p. E-Book *(978-0-7618-4902-5(5))* Univ. Pr. of America, Inc.

Helms, John Michael. Hoping Liberia: Stories of Civil War from Africa's First Republic. 2009. pap. *(978-1-57312-544-4(X))* Smyth & Helwys Publishing, Inc.

Hendricks, Obery M., Jr. The Universe Bends Toward Justice: Radical Reflections on the Bible, the Church, & the Body Politic. 2011. 192p. pap. 22.00 *(978-1-57075-940-6(5))* Orbis Bks.

Henson, James. A Schaefferian Sociology. 2009. 104p. pap. *(978-3-639-03549-0(6))* VDM Verlag Dr. Mueller e.K.

Hermkens, Anna-Karina, et al, eds. Moved by Mary: The Power of Pilgrimage in the Modern World. 2009. (Illus.). 282p. 114.95 *(978-0-7546-6789-6(8))*; pap. 29.95 *(978-0-7546-6792-6(8))* Ashgate Publishing Co.

Herron, George. The Christian State: A Political Vision of Christ. 2007. (ENG.). 214p. 39.95 *(978-0-548-05205-1(0))* Kessinger Publishing, LLC.

Hobgood, Mary Elizabeth & Hobgood, Mary E. Dismantling Privilege: An Ethics of Accountability. 2009. xi, 210p. *(978-0-8298-1823-9(5))* Pilgrim Pr., The/United Church Pr.

Hodgkin, Henry T. Christian Revolution an Essay on the Met. 2006. pap. 28.95 *(978-1-4286-3618-7(8))* Kessinger Publishing, LLC.

Hornsby-Smith, Michael P. An Introduction to Catholic Social Thought. 2006. (Introduction to Religion Ser.). (ENG., Illus.). (C). 402p. 104.00 *(978-0-521-86339-1(2))*; 400p. per. 40.00 *(978-0-521-68199-5(5))* Cambridge Univ. Pr.

Hummel, Rev Dr Cynthia Huling & Hummel, Rev. Cynthia Huling. The Lord Is Like a Firefighter. 2011. 48p. pap. 18.10 *(978-0-557-30779-1(1))* Lulu Enterprises Inc.

II. (1951-1958) 2009.Tr. of Berlin Lectures III. (GER.). LXVIII, 422p. 235.00 *(978-3-11-020531-2(9))* De Gruyter, Walter Inc.

Ilo, Stan Chu. The Church & Development in Africa: Aid & Development from the Perspective of Catholic Social Ethics. 2011. (African Christian Studies). 342p. pap. 38.00 *(978-1-60899-779-4(0)*, Pickwick Pubns.) Wipf & Stock Pubs.

Ingleby, Jonathan. Beyond Empire: Postcolonialism & Mission in a Global Context. 2010. 300p. pap. 15.49 *(978-1-4490-8230-7(0))* AuthorHouse.

Johnson, Dale A. Why Should We Care? 2007. 164p. pap. 19.95 *(978-0-615-15415-2(8))* New Sinai Pr.

Johnson, M. L. Overcoming Racism Through the Gospel. 2007. 424p. per. 21.99 *(978-1-60266-300-8(9))* Xulon Pr., Inc.

Johnson, Talmage C. Life's Intimate Relationships. 2007. (ENG.). 204p. 39.95 *(978-0-548-06327-9(3))* Kessinger Publishing, LLC.

Judge, E. A. & Scholer, David M. Social Distinctives of the Christians in the First Century: Pivotal Essays. 2008. 232p. pap. *(978-1-56563-880-8(8))*, Hendrickson Pubs. Marketing, LLC.

Kavanaugh, John F. Following Christ in a Consumer Society: The Spirituality of Cultural Resistance. 25th ed. 2006. (ENG.). 240p. (Orig.). per. 20.00 *(978-1-57075-666-5(X))* Orbis Bks.

Kerwin, Donald & Gerschutz, J. R. And You Welcomed Me: Migration & Catholic Social Teaching. 2009. (ENG.). 192p. 68.50 *(978-0-7391-4099-4(X))*; pap. 28.50 *(978-0-7391-4100-7(7))* Lexington Bks.

Klostermeier, Birgit. Das unternehmerische Selbst der Kirche: Eine Diskursanalyse. 2011. (Praktische Theologie im Wissenschaftsdiskurs Ser.). (GER.). XVIII, 394p. 126.00 *(978-3-11-025952-0(4))* De Gruyter, Walter Inc.

Kotre, John. The View from the Border: Why Catholics Leave the Church & Why They Stay. 2009. (ENG., Illus.). 283p. pap. 24.95 *(978-0-202-36307-3(4))* Aldine Transaction.

Krason, Stephen M. The Public Order & the Sacred Order: Contemporary Issues, Catholic Social Thought, & the Western & American Traditions, 2 vols. 2009. (Catholic Social Thought Ser.: 2 Volumes). (ENG.). 1144p. (gr. 17). 210.00 *(978-0-8108-6396-5(0))* Scarecrow Pr., Inc.

Kraus, C. Norman. The Authentic Witness: Credibility & Authority. 2010. (Illus.). 200p. pap. 23.00 *(978-1-60899-230-0(6))* Wipf & Stock Pubs.

Krier, Mich. The Challenge & Spirituality of Catholic Social Teaching: Revised Edition. 2011. 272p. pap. 22.00 *(978-1-57075-945-1(6))* Orbis Bks.

Labanow, Cory E. Evangelicalism & the Emerging Church: A Congregational Study of a Vineyard Church. 2009. (Explorations in Practical, Pastoral & Empirical Theology Ser.). 156p. 89.95 *(978-0-7546-6450-5(3))* Ashgate Publishing Co.

Laski, John. Capitalism & Christianity: A Moral & Ethical Struggle. 2008. 108p. pap. 16.95 *(978-1-60441-624-4(6))* PublishAmerica, Inc.

Lee, Michael E. Bearing the Weight of Salvation: The Soteriology of Ignacio Ellacuria. 2009. (ENG.). 256p. pap. 34.95 *(978-0-8245-2421-0(7))* Crossroad Publishing Co., The.

Leemans, Johan, et al, eds. Reading Patristic Texts on Social Ethics: Issues & Challenges for Twenty-First-Century Christian Social Thought. 2011. (ENG.). 288p. 34.95 *(978-0-8132-1859-5(4))* Catholic Univ. of America Pr.

Leo XIII. On the Condition of the Working Classes: Rerum Novarum. 56p. pap. 3.50 *(978-0-8198-1492-0(X)*, 332-037) Pauline Bks. & Media.

Lewis, Albert D., Jr. The Great Spiritual War, 7 vols., Set. Incl. Vol. 1. Great Spiritual War: What Is It? 64p. pap. 4.99 *(978-0-9633356-1-6(8))*; Vol. 2. Great Spiritual War: Our Real Foe(s) - Who Are They? 30p. pap. 2.99 *(978-0-9633356-2-3(6))*; Vol. 3. Great Spiritual War: Idol Worship. 26p. pap. 2.99 *(978-0-9633356-3-0(4))*; Vol. 5. Great Spiritual War: The Great Tribulation. 30p. pap. 2.99 *(978-0-9633356-5-4(0))*; Vol. 6. Great Spiritual War: Suicide; Forgiveness; Repentance: The Weapons of Our Warfare & a Letter to the President. 38p. pap. 4.99 *(978-0-9633356-6-1(9))*; Vol. 7. Great Spiritual War: My Personal Testimony. 106p. pap. 8.99 *(978-0-9633356-7-8(7))*; Vol. 4. AIDS & Abortion. 60p. pap. 6.99 *(978-0-9633356-4-7(2))*; (Illus.). 1997. Set pap. 33.99 *(978-0-9633356-9-2(3))* Harvest Time International, Inc.

Liacopulos, George P. Church & Society: Orthodox Christian Perspectives, Past Experiences, & Modern Challenges. 2007. *(978-0-9774610-6-6(8))*; pap. *(978-0-9774610-5-9(X))* Somerset Hall Pr.

Liebeschuetz, J. H. W. G. Ambrose & John Chrysostom: Clerics between Desert & Empire. 2011. (ENG.). 320p. 110.00 *(978-0-19-959664-5(6))* Oxford Univ. Pr., Inc.

Lower, Michael. Employee Participation in Governance: A Legal & Ethical Analysis. 2010. (ENG.). 234p. 99.00 *(978-0-521-86284-4(1))* Cambridge Univ. Pr.

Lukenbill, David. Capital Punishment & Catholic Social Teaching: A Tradition of Support. 2009. (Illus.). 121p. pap. 14.95 *(978-0-9791670-7-2(8))*, LampStand Foundation, The.

Macarthur, Kathleen Walker. The Economic Ethics of John Wesley. 2011. 168p. 41.95 *(978-1-258-00698-3(7))* Literary Licensing, LLC.

Mack, Burton L. Christian Mentality: The Entanglements of Power, Violence & Fear. 2011. (Religion in culture: studies in social contest & Construction Ser.). (ENG.). 198p. (C). 99.95 *(978-1-84553-894-1(3))* Equinox Publishing Ltd. GBR. Dist: ISD.

—Christian Mentality: The Entanglements of Power, Violence, & Fear. 2011. (Religion in culture: studies in social contest & Construction Ser.). (ENG.). 198p. (C). pap. 29.95 *(978-1-84553-895-8(1))* Equinox Publishing Ltd. GBR. Dist: ISD.

Magariño, Aurelio. Justicia Social en un Mundo Injusto: La Iglesia Como Agente de Cambio. 2009. (SPA.). 168p. *(978-0-7586-1901-3(4))* Concordia Publishing Hse.

Mangalwadi, Vishal. Truth & Transformation. 2009. 256p. pap. 17.99 *(978-1-57658-512-2(3))* YWAM Publishing.

Martin, David Lozell. The Breaking of the Image: A Sociology O. 2006. (ENG.). 224p. per. *(978-1-57383-382-0(7)*, Regent College Publishing) Regent College Publishing.

Massaro, Thomas. Living Justice: Catholic Social Teaching in Action. 2nd ed. 2011. (ENG.). 210p. pap. 21.95 *(978-1-4422-1013-4(3))* Rowman & Littlefield Publishers, Inc.

Mathews, Shailer, et al. Building a Moral Reserve: Or the Civic Responsibilities of the Christian Citizen. 2011. 126p. 40.95 *(978-1-258-06612-3(2))* Literary Licensing, LLC.

Matz, B. J. Patristic Sources & Catholic Social Teaching: A Forgotten Dimension - A Textual, Historical, & Rhetorical Analysis of Patristic Source Citations in the Church's Social Documents. 2008. (Annua Nuntia Lovaniensia Ser.). (ENG.). 166p. (C). pap. 60.00 *(978-90-429-2029-3(7))* Peeters Pubs. & Booksellers BEL. Dist: Brown, David Bk. Co., The.

Mayblin, Maya. Gender, Catholicism, & Morality in Brazil: Virtuous Husbands, Powerful Wives. 2010. (Contemporary Anthropology of Religion Ser.). (ENG., Illus.). 224p. 84.00 *(978-0-230-62312-5(3))* Palgrave Macmillan.

Maynard, Jane Frances, et al. Pastoral Bearings: Lived Religion & Pastoral Theology. 2010. (ENG.). 310p. 83.99 *(978-0-7391-2360-7(2))* Lexington Bks.

McCarthy, David Matzko. The Good Life: Genuine Christianity for the Middle Class. 2006. (Christian Practice of Everyday Life (Wipf & Stock) Ser.). 176p. pap. 21.00 *(978-1-55635-068-9(6))*, Wipf and Stock) Wipf & Stock Pubs.

McCarthy, David Matzko & Baker Publishing. The Heart of Catholic Social Teaching: Its Origin & Contemporary Significance, 1 vol. McCarthy, David Matzko, ed. 2009. 224p. pap. 26.00 *(978-1-58743-248-4(X))* Brazos Pr.

McCarthy, George E. & Rhodes, Royal W. Eclipse of Justice: Ethics, Economics, & the Lost Traditions of American Catholicism. 2008. 304p. pap. 33.00 *(978-1-60608-248-5(5))* Wipf & Stock Pubs.

McCurley, Foster R., ed. Social Ministry in the Lutheran Tradition. 2008. 190p. pap. 22.00 *(978-0-8006-2129-2(8)*, Fortress Pr.) Augsburg Fortress, Pubs.

McDonagh, Francis, ed. Dom Helder Camara: Essential Writings. 2009. 160p. pap. 16.00 *(978-1-57075-823-2(9))* Orbis Bks.

McDonald, Daniel, ed. Catholic Social Teaching in Global Perspective. 2010. 240p. pap. 26.00 *(978-1-57075-896-6(4))* Orbis Bks.

McGinnis, James. Activities for Catholic Social Teaching: A Resource Guide for Teachers & Youth Ministers. 2006. (Illus.). 219p. per. 19.95 *(978-1-59471-067-4(8))* Ave Maria Pr.

McHugh, F. P. Catholic Social Thought: Renovating the Tradition: A Keyguide to Resources. 2008. (Annua Nuntia Lovaniensia Ser.). (ENG.). 393p. (C). pap. 70.00 *(978-90-429-1963-1(9))* Peeters Pubs. & Booksellers BEL. Dist: Brown, David Bk. Co., The.

McKanan, Dan. The Catholic Worker after Dorothy: Practicing the Works of Mercy in a New Generation. 2008. 236p. per. 19.95 *(978-0-8146-3187-4(8)*, Liturgical Pr. Bks.) Liturgical Pr.

McLaughlin, Janice. Ostriches, Dung Beetles & Other Spiritual Masters: A Book of Wisdom from the Wild. 2009. (Illus.). 144p. pap. 18.00 *(978-1-57075-842-3(5))* Orbis Bks.

McNabb, OP, Fr. Vincent, Vincent. Nazareth or Social Chaos. 2010. (ENG., Illus.). 96p. pap. 19.95 *(978-1-932528-19-0(9))* IHS Pr.

McVerry, Peter. Jesus - Social Revolutionary? 2008. (ENG.). 144p. pap. 15.95 *(978-1-84730-110-9(X))* Veritas Pubns. IRL. Dist: Dufour Editions, Inc.

Medaille, John C. Vocation of Business: Social Justice in the Marketplace. 2007. (ENG.). 374p. pap. 65.00 *(978-0-8264-2809-7(6))* Continuum International Publishing Group, Ltd. GBR. Dist: National Bk. Network.

Mike Luoma, Brother Zagreus. Neo-gnosis. 2008. 136p. pap. 12.95 *(978-1-4357-4280-2(X))* Lulu Enterprises Inc.

Miller, J. Bleecker. Leo Xiii & Modern Civilization. 2007. (ENG.). 196p. 37.95 *(978-0-548-14614-9(4))* 2006. pap. 22.95 *(978-1-4286-5946-9(3))* Kessinger Publishing, LLC.

—Leo Xiii & Modern Civilization. 2008. 192p. pap. *(978-1-4086-7698-1(2))* Read Bks.

Monahan, Susanne C., et al. Sociology of Religion. 2006. pap. 10.95 *(978-1-4288-1658-9(5))* Cram101 Inc.

—Sociology of Religion: A Reader. 2nd ed. 2010. (ENG.). 400p. (C). pap. 80.20 *(978-0-205-71082-9(4)*, Prentice Hall) Prentice Hall PTR.

Mondragon, Carlos. Like Leaven Dough: Protestant Social Thought in Latin America, 1920-1950. 2010. (ENG.). 186p. 60.00 *(978-1-61147-056-7(0))* Fairleigh Dickinson Univ. Pr.

Montgomery, Robert. The Spread of Religions: A Social Scientific Theory Based on the Spread of Buddhism, Christianity & Islam. 2007. 372p. per. 20.00 *(978-1-59899-086-7(1))* Long Dash Publishing.

Moreno, Antonio F. Church, State, & Civil Society in Postauthoritarian Philippines: Narratives of Engaged Citizenship. 2008. 372p. (C). pap. 39.00 *(978-971-550-494-2(9))* Univ. of Hawaii Pr.

Mowbray, Donald. Pain & Suffering in Medieval Theology: Academic Debates at the University of Paris in the Thirteenth Century. 2009. 204p. 99.00 *(978-1-84383-461-8(8)*, Boydell Press) Boydell & Brewer, Ltd. GBR. Dist: Boydell & Brewer, Inc.

Myers, Joseph R. Organic Community: Creating a Place Where People Naturally Connect. 2007. (Mersion: Emergent Village Resources for Communities of Faith Ser.). 192p. pap. 14.00 *(978-0-8010-6598-9(4))* Baker Bks.

Nearing, Scott. Social Religion: an Interpretation of Christianity in Terms of Modern. 2007. (ENG.). 248p. per. 26.95 *(978-1-4304-4288-2(3))* Kessinger Publishing, LLC.

Nelson-Pallmeyer, Jack. Authentic Hope: It's the End of the World As We Know It but Soft Landings Are Possible. 2012. (ENG.). 176p. pap. 22.00 *(978-1-57075-957-4(X))* Orbis Bks.

Neuhaus, Richard J. Doing Well & Doing Good: The Challenge to the Christian Capitalist. 2012. (ENG.). 320p. pap. 15.00 *(978-0-307-95560-9(5)*, Image) Doubleday Religious Publishing Group, The.

Neusner, Jacob, et al. Judaic & Christian Visions of the Social Order: Describing, Analyzing & Comparing Systems of the Formative Age. 2011. (Jacob Neusner Series: Religion/Social Order Ser.). (ENG.). 388p. pap. 38.95 *(978-0-7618-5635-1(8))* Univ. Pr. of America, Inc.

Newell, Edward J. Education Has Nothing to Do with Theology: James Michael Lee's Social Science Religious Instruction. 2006. (Princeton Theological Monographs). 130p. pap. 17.00 *(978-1-59752-527-5(8)*, Pickwick Pubns.) Wipf & Stock Pubs.

Newlands, George & Smith, Allen. Hospitable God: The Transformative Dream. 2010. 252p. 99.95 *(978-0-7546-6560-1(7))* Ashgate Publishing Co.

Ntarangwi, Mwenda. Jesus & Ubuntu: Exploring the Social Impact of Christianity in Africa. 2011. *(978-1-59221-842-4(3))*; pap. *(978-1-59221-843-1(1))* Africa World Pr.

Obelkevich, James. Religion & the People, 800-1700. 2011. (ENG.). 341p. pap. 40.00 *(978-0-8078-9740-9(X))* Univ. of North Carolina Pr.

Obikwelu, Polycarp Chuks. Contextual Application of Christian Social Teaching on Political Ethics: In the Light of the Pronouncements of the Bishops of Africa & Madagascar in the Era of Globalisation with Particular Reference to English-Speaking Sub-Saharan Africa, Vol. 838. 2006. (European University Studies: Vol. 23). xxi,426p. pap. 76.95 *(978-0-8204-8733-5(3))* Lang, Peter Publishing, Inc.

Obodoechina, Uchechukwu. The Imperative of Self-Reliance for the Churches in Africa: A Study in Christian Social Ethics, Vol. 873. 2006. (European University Studies Ser.: Vol. 23). xx,354p. pap. 62.95 *(978-0-8204-8730-4(9))* Lang, Peter Publishing, Inc.

O'Brien, David J. & Shannon, Thomas A., eds. Catholic Social Thought: The Documentary Heritage. 2010. 824p. pap. 30.00 *(978-1-57075-891-1(3))* Orbis Bks.

O'Donnell, Bill & O'Donnell, Mary. Father Bill: Reflections of a Beloved Rebel. 2009. *(978-1-881896-33-3(1))* Pacific View Pr.

Orobator, Agbonkhianmeghe E. Reconciliation, Justice, & Peace: The Second African Synod. 2011. 304p. pap. 40.00 *(978-1-57075-916-1(2))* Orbis Bks.

Ortberg, John, et al. 1 & 2 Samuel: Growing a Heart for God, 1 vol. 2008. (New Community Bible Study Ser.). (ENG.). 96p. pap. 7.99 *(978-0-310-28049-1(4))* Zondervan.

Osgniach, Augustine J. Christian State. 2006. pap. 33.95 *(978-1-4286-5749-6(5))* Kessinger Publishing, LLC.

Palacios, Joseph M. & Palacios, Joseph Martin. The Catholic Social Imagination: Activism & the Just Society in Mexico & the United States. 2007. (Morality & Society Ser.). (Illus.). 320p. (ENG.). 70.00 *(978-0-226-64500-1(2))*; per. 30.00 *(978-0-226-64501-8(0))* Univ. of Chicago Pr.

Parker, Kathleen. Sacred Service in Civic Space. 2007. 368p. pap. 18.00 *(978-0-9795589-0-0(5))* Meadville Lombard Theological Schl. Pr.

Pennock, Michael. Catholic Social Teaching: Learning & Living Justice. 2007. (Illus.). 282p. stu. ed., per. 24.95 *(978-1-59471-102-2(X))*; 290p. tchr. ed., per. *(978-1-59471-103-9(8))* Ave Maria Pr.

C

Pérez Prieto, Victorino & Prieto, Victorino Pérez. Más Allá de la Fragmentación de la Teología: El Saber y la Vida: Raimon Panikkar. 2008. (SPA.). 341p. *(978-84-9876-150-4(6))* Tirant lo Blanch.

Perkins, Anna Kasafi. Justice As Equality: Michael Manley's Caribbean Vision of Justice. 2010. x, 154p. *(978-1-4331-1036-8(9))* Lang, Peter GmbH, Europaischer Verlag der Wissenschaften.

Pickard, Stephen. In Between God: Theology, Community, & Discipleship. 2012. (ENG.). (C). pap. 29.95 ***(978-1-921817-10-6(0))*** ATF Pr. AUS. Dist: Brown, David Bk. Co., The.

Pierson, Paul Everett. The Dynamics of Christian Mission: History Through a Missiological Perspective. 2009. 364p. pap. *(978-0-86585-006-4(2),* Debolsillo) Carey, William International Univ. Pr.

Pius XI. On Social Reconstruction: Quadragesimo Anno. 75p. pap. 1.25 *(978-0-8198-6926-5(0))* Pauline Bks. & Media.

Poloma, Margaret & Green, John. The Assemblies of God: Godly Love & the Revitalization of American Pentecostalism. 2010. (ENG.). 272p. 47.00 *(978-0-8147-6783-2(4))* New York Univ. Pr.

Pontifical Council For Justice Staff. Compendium of the Social Doctrine Church. 2006. pap. *(978-0-86012-436-8(3))* Continuum International Publishing Group, Ltd.

Pope Pius XI. Atheistic Communism: Encyclical Letter of His Holiness Pope Pius XI. 2011. 34p. 35.95 ***(978-1-258-05942-2(8))*** Literary Licensing, LLC.

Preston, Ronald H. Confusions in Christian Social Ethics: Problems for Geneva & Rome. 2011. 224p. ***(978-0-334-02573-3(7),*** SCM Pr.) Hymns Ancient & Modern Ltd.

Radosh, Daniel. Rapture Ready! Adventures in the Parallel Universe of Christian Pop Culture. 2010. (ENG.). 320p. pap. 15.95 *(978-1-59376-281-0(X),* Soft Skull Pr.) Counterpoint LLC.

Rauschenbusch, Walter. Christianity & the Social Crisis. 2010. 456p. pap. 36.75 *(978-1-177-14428-5(X))* 2010. (ENG.). 454p. pap. 36.75 *(978-1-176-54748-3(8))* 2010. 448p. pap. 36.75 *(978-1-144-15600-6(9))* 2010. 454p. pap. 36.75 *(978-1-144-20681-7(2))* 2010. 450p. pap. 36.75 *(978-1-142-59716-0(4))* 2010. 456p. pap. 36.75 *(978-1-142-16281-8(8))* 2009. 448p. 41.99 *(978-1-113-65332-1(9))* 2009. 448p. pap. 34.99 *(978-1-113-65330-7(2))* 2009. 448p. 34.99 *(978-1-113-65336-9(1))* 2009. 448p. pap. 36.75 *(978-1-113-65335-2(3))* 2009. 448p. pap. 35.75 *(978-1-113-65333-8(7))* 2009. 448p. pap. 35.75 *(978-1-113-65326-0(4))* 2009. 448p. pap. 36.75 *(978-1-113-65328-4(0))* 2009. (ENG.). 446p. pap. 28.99 *(978-1-113-65331-4(0),* BiblioLife) 2009. (ENG.). 446p. pap. 28.99 *(978-1-113-65324-6(8),* BiblioLife) 2009. (ENG.). 446p. pap. 26.99 *(978-1-113-65329-1(9),* BiblioLife) BiblioBazaar.

—Christianity & the Social Crisis. 2009. 256p. pap. *(978-1-4590-4241-4(7))* Books LLC.

—Christianity & the Social Crisis. 2007. (ENG.). 444p. 51.95 *(978-0-548-15529-5(1));* pap. 36.95 *(978-1-4304-4960-7(8))* Kessinger Publishing, LLC.

—Christianity & the Social Crisis. 2007. pap. ***(978-1-4067-5864-1(7))*** Read Bks.

—Christianity & the Social Crisis in the 21st Century: The Classic That Woke up the Church. 2008. 400p. pap. 14.95 *(978-0-06-149726-1(6),* HarperOne) HarperCollins Pubs.

—A Gospel for the Social Awakening: Selections from the Writings of Walter Rauschenbusch. 2008. 187p. pap. 16.00 *(978-1-60608-034-4(2))* Wipf & Stock Pubs.

Rauschenbusch, Walter. The Social Principles of Jesus. 2012. 214p. pap. 24.75 ***(978-1-276-67184-2(9))*** 2011. 214p. pap. 24.75 ***(978-1-179-88367-0(5))*** 2010. (ENG.). 212p. pap. 24.75 *(978-1-177-62141-0(X))* 2010. 214p. pap. 24.75 *(978-1-141-44497-7(6))* BiblioBazaar.

—The Social Principles of Jesus. 2009. 134p. pap. *(978-1-4589-3621-9(X))* Books LLC.

—The Social Principles of Jesus. 2010. (Illus.). 116p. pap. 20.68 *(978-1-153-82262-6(8))* General Bks. LLC.

—The Social Principles of Jesus. 2010. 214p. 31.96 ***(978-1-163-49145-4(4))*** 2010. 214p. pap. 19.96 ***(978-1-163-08871-5(4))*** 2007. (ENG.). 212p. 39.95 *(978-0-548-18806-4(8))* 2007. (ENG.). 216p. per. 24.95 *(978-1-4304-9203-0(1))* Kessinger Publishing, LLC.

—The Social Principles of Jesus. 2010. 262p. pap. 19.95 *(978-1-935758-04-4(7))* WordStream Publishing, LLC.

Reynalds, Jeremy. Homeless in the City Ii: A Mission of Love. 2010. 224p. 33.95 *(978-1-4497-0365-3(8));* pap. 17.95 *(978-1-4497-0364-6(X))* Author Solutions, Inc. (WestBow Pr.).

Rivera, Mayra. The Touch of Transcendence: A Postcolonial Theology of God. 2007. (ENG.). 186p. per. 25.00 *(978-0-664-23073-9(3))* Westminster John Knox Pr.

Rourke, Thomas. The Social & Political Thought of Benedict XVI. 2010. (ENG.). 158p. 57.99 *(978-0-7391-4280-6(1))* Lexington Bks.

Rourke, Thomas R. The Social & Political Thought of Benedict XVI. 2011. (ENG.). 160p. pap. 24.95 *(978-0-7391-4281-3(X))* Lexington Bks.

Ruether, Rosemary Radford. Christianity & Social Systems: Historical Constructions & Ethical Challenges. 2008. (ENG.). 310p. 85.00 *(978-0-7425-4642-4(X));* pap. 32.95 *(978-0-7425-4643-1(8))* Rowman & Littlefield Publishers, Inc.

Ruge-Jones, Philip. Cross in Tensions: Luther's Theology of the Cross as Theolgico-Social Critique. 2008. (Princeton Theological Monographs). (Illus.). 220p. pap. 23.00 *(978-1-55635-522-6(X),* Pickwick Pubns.) Wipf & Stock Pubs.

Ruggiero, Vincent Ryan. The Practice of Loving Kindness: A Guide to Spiritual Fulfillment & Social Harmony. 2006. 152p. per. 13.95 *(978-1-56548-254-8(9))* New City Pr.

Rutledge, Fleming. Condemned into Redemption: The Meaning of the Crucifixion of Jesus for Today's World. *(978-0-8028-3890-2(1))* Eerdmans, William B. Publishing Co.

Saracino, Michele. Being about Borders: A Christian Anthropology of Difference. 2011. x, 153p. pap. 29.95 *(978-0-8146-5710-2(9));* E-Book *(978-0-8146-8005-6(4))* Liturgical Pr.

Schmidt, Charles. The Social Results of Early Christianity. Thorpe, tr. 2008. 512p. 55.95 *(978-1-4365-4593-8(5))* 2007. (ENG.). 516p. per. 40.95 *(978-0-548-70248-2(9))* Kessinger Publishing, LLC.

Schor, Adam M. Theodoret's People: Social Networks & Religious Conflict in Late Roman Syria. 2011. (Transformation of the Classical Heritage Ser.). (ENG., Illus.). 320p. 49.95 *(978-0-520-26862-3(8))* Univ. of California Pr.

Schwartz, Avraham. Jewish Secret of Wealth According to Th. 2006. (ENG & SPA., Illus.). 176p. per. *(978-956-291-348-5(1))* Editorial Benei Noaj.

Scott, Peter. Theology, Ideology & Liberation. 2008. (Cambridge Studies in Ideology & Religion Ser.). 288p. pap. 38.99 *(978-0-521-07229-8(8))* Cambridge Univ. Pr.

Scott, R. B. Y. & Vlastos, Gregory, eds. Towards the Christian Revolution. 2007. (ENG.). 268p. 42.95 *(978-0-548-11555-8(9))* Kessinger Publishing, LLC.

Shahan, Michael, ed. A Report from the Front Lines: Conversations on Public Theology: A Festschrift in Honor of Robert Benne. 2008. 184p. pap. 30.00 *(978-0-8028-4863-5(X))* Eerdmans, William B. Publishing Co.

Singer, Anna M. Walter Rauschenbusch & His Contribution to Social Christianity. 2007. 136p. pap. 16.00 *(978-1-55635-417-5(7),* Wipf and Stock) Wipf & Stock Pubs.

Stelzle, Charles. The Social Application of Religion. 2009. 144p. 21.99 *(978-0-554-40143-0(6));* pap. 20.75 *(978-0-554-40140-9(1))* BiblioBazaar.

—The Social Application of Religion. 2009. 64p. pap. 14.14 *(978-1-4589-9939-9(4))* General Bks. LLC.

—The Social Application of Religion. 2008. 139p. pap. 12.00 *(978-1-60608-136-5(5),* Wipf and Stock) Wipf & Stock Pubs.

Stelzle, Charles, et al. The Social Application of Religion: the Merrick Lectures For 1907-08. 2007. (ENG.). 144p. per. 20.95 *(978-1-4304-4291-2(3))* Kessinger Publishing, LLC.

Stoddart, Eric. Theological Perspectives on A Surveillance Society: Watching & Being Watched. 2011. (Explorations in Practical, Pastoral & Empirical Theology Ser.). 206p. 99.95 *(978-0-7546-6797-1(9))* Ashgate Publishing Co.

Stoops, John Dashiell. The Kingdom of Jesus. 2011. 198p. 42.95 ***(978-1-258-08187-4(3))*** Literary Licensing, LLC.

Storrar, William, et al. A World for All? Global Civil Society in Political Theory & Trinitarian Theology. 2011. 376p. pap. 35.00 *(978-0-8028-2742-5(X))* Eerdmans, William B. Publishing Co.

Sullins, David & Blasi, Anthony J., eds. Catholic Social Thought: American Reflections on the Compendium. 2008. (ENG.). 218p. 68.50 *(978-0-7391-2311-9(4))* Lexington Bks.

Taysom, Stephen C. Shakers, Mormons, & Religious Worlds: Conflicting Visions, Contested Boundaries. 2010. (Religion in North America Ser.). (ENG.). 280p. 34.95 *(978-0-253-35540-9(0),* 0253355400) Indiana Univ. Pr.

Terry, Peter. A Prophet in Modern Times. 2008. 380p. pap. 25.95 *(978-1-4357-1495-3(4))* Lulu Enterprises Inc.

Thompson, E. H., tr. from LAT. Andreae, J. V. (1619) Christianopolis. 2010. (International Archives of the History of Ideas / archives internationales d'histoire des Idées Ser.). 352p. pap. 269.00 *(978-90-481-5236-0(4),* 9048152364) Springer.

Thompson, J. Milburn. Introducing Catholic Social Thought. 2010. 208p. pap. 22.00 *(978-1-57075-862-1(X))* Orbis Bks.

TICE. Inside the Mormon Mind: The Social Psychology of Mormonism ASHFORD UNIVERSITY. 2009. (ENG.). (C). pap. 23.60 *(978-0-558-09781-3(2))* Pearson Learning Solutions.

Tickle, Phyllis. The Great Emergence: How Christianity Is Changing & Why. 2008. (Mersion: Emergent Village Resources for Communities of Faith Ser.). (Illus.). 176p. 17.99 *(978-0-8010-1313-3(5))* Baker Bks.

Tirimanaa, Cssr, Vimal. Catholic Teaching on Violence, War & Peace in Our Contemporary World: A Collection of Essays. 2007. 171p. per. 5.00 *(978-81-7086-373-1(2))* ATF Pr. AUS. Dist: International Publishers Marketing.

Titus, Craig Steven. The Person & the Polis: Faith & Values Within the Secular State. 2007. (John Henry Cardinal Newman Lectures: Vol. 1). 187p. per. 29.95 *(978-0-9773103-0-2(2))* Institute for the Psychological Science Pr., The.

Trainor, Brian. Christ, Society & the State. 2012. (ENG.). 614p. (C). pap. 40.50 *(978-1-921511-58-5(3))* ATF Pr. AUS. Dist: Brown, David Bk. Co., The.

Tuzik, Robert L. Reynold Hillenbrand: The Reform of the Catholic Liturgy & the Call to Social Action. 2010. (Illus.). xi, 226p. pap. *(978-1-59525-030-8(1))* Hillenbrand Bks.

Ullucci, Daniel C. The Christian Rejection of Animal Sacrifice, 1 vol. 2011. (ENG.). 256p. 74.00 ***(978-0-19-979170-5(8))*** Oxford Univ. Pr., Inc.

Umoren, Anthony Iffen. Paul & Power Christology: Exegesis & Theology of Romans 1:3-4 in Relation to Popular Power Christology in an African Context. 2007. XV, 207p. pap. 46.95 *(978-3-631-57554-3(8))* Lang, Peter Publishing, Inc.

United Methodist Committee on Relief, contrib. by. A Plan for Christian Casework in Disaster Recover. 53p. *(978-1-890569-09-9(7))* General Board of Global Ministries, The United Methodist Church.

Urwin, E. C. Religion in Planned Society. 2007. 84p. per. *(978-1-4067-8856-3(2),* Pomona Pr.) Read Bks.

Van Amberg, Joel. A Real Presence: Religious & Social Dynamics of the Eucharistic Conflicts in Early Modern Augsburg, 1520-1530. 2011. (ENG.). X, 270p. ***(978-90-04-21698-3(7))*** BRILL.

VanDrunen, David. Natural Law & the Two Kingdoms: A Study in the Development of Reformed Social Thought. 2009. 480p. pap. 35.00 *(978-0-8028-6443-7(0))* Eerdmans, William B. Publishing Co.

Verstraeten, Johan, ed. Scrutinizing the Signs of the Times in the Light of the Gospel. 2007. (Bibliotheca Ephemeridum Theologicarum Lovaniensium Ser.). (ENG.). 334p. (C). pap. 108.00 *(978-90-429-1978-5(7))* Peeters Pubs. & Booksellers BEL. Dist: Brown, David Bk. Co., The.

Vetter, Herbert F. James Luther Adams: Prophet to the Powerful. 2009. 251p. pap. 24.95 *(978-0-615-25994-9(4))* Harvard Square Library.

Vila, Samuel. Religion Al Alcance del Pueblo: Religion for the People. (SPA.). 232p. *(978-84-7228-007-6(1),* 220759) Clie, Editorial.

Wagner, C. Peter. Dominion! How Kingdom Action Can Change the World. 2010. 224p. pap. 14.99 *(978-0-8007-9469-9(9))* Chosen Bks.

Ward, Louis B. & Coughlin, Charles E. Father Charles E Coughlin: An Authorized Biography. 2011. 380p. 53.95 ***(978-1-258-00259-6(0))*** Literary Licensing, LLC.

Weber, Max. The Protestant Ethic & the Spirit of Capitalism. 2006. pap. 8.95 *(978-1-4288-1499-8(X))* Cram101 Inc.

—The Protestant Ethic & the Spirit of Capitalism. Swedberg, Richard, ed. 2009. (Norton Critical Editions Ser.). (ENG.). 312p. (C). pap. 14.00 net. *(978-0-393-93068-9(8),* 93068) Norton, W. W. & Co., Inc.

Weigel, George. Against the Grain: Christianity & Democracy, War & Peace. 2008. (ENG.). 352p. 24.95 *(978-0-8245-2448-7(9),* Crossroad 8 Avenue) Crossroad Publishing Co., The.

Wheatley, Alan B. Patronage in Early Christianity: Its Use & Transformation from Jesus to Paul of Samosata. 2011. (Princeton Theological Monographs). 212p. pap. 23.00 ***(978-1-59752-587-9(1),*** Pickwick Pubns.) Wipf & Stock Pubs.

Williams, Thomas D. The World as It Could Be: Catholic Social Thought for a New Generation. 2011. (ENG.). 240p. pap. 24.95 *(978-0-8245-2666-5(X))* Crossroad Publishing Co., The.

Windley-Daoust, Jerry & Kilmartin, Lorraine. Living Justice & Peace 2008: Catholic Social Teaching in Practice. 2nd ed. 2008. (Illus.). 336p. pap. 26.25 *(978-0-88489-985-3(3))* St. Mary's Pr.

Withrow, Lisa R. Alienation & Connection: Suffering in a Global Age. 2011. ***(978-0-7391-3707-9(7));*** (ENG.). 192p. 60.00 ***(978-0-7391-3705-5(0))*** Lexington Bks.

Woods, Thomas E. Beyond Distributism. 2008. 79p. pap. *(978-1-880595-29-9(X))* Acton Institute for the Study of Religion & Liberty.

Wylie Kellermann, Bill. Seasons of Faith & Conscience: Explorations in Liturgical Direct Action. 2008. 246p. pap. 27.00 *(978-1-55635-923-1(3),* Wipf and Stock) Wipf & Stock Pubs.

Zafirovski, Milan. Destiny of Modern Societies: The Calvinist Predestination of a New Society. 2011. (Studies in Critical Social Sciences Ser.). (ENG.). 622p. pap. 36.00 ***(978-1-60846-125-7(4))*** Haymarket Bks.

Zafirovski, Milan & Zafirovski. The 'Destiny' of Modern Societies: The Calvinist 'Predestination' of a New Society. 2009. 624p. *(978-90-04-17629-4(2))* BRILL.

Zondervan. Issues Facing Christians Today, 1 vol. 2011. (Grandes oportunidades y retos para el cristianismo Hoy Ser.). (SPA.). 288p. pap. 8.99 ***(978-0-8297-6201-3(9));*** 224p. pap. 8.99 ***(978-0-8297-6197-9(7));*** 208p. pap. 8.99 ***(978-0-8297-6199-3(3));*** 160p. pap. 8.99 ***(978-0-8297-6195-5(0))*** Zondervan.

CHRISTIAN SOCIOLOGY—BIBLICAL TEACHING

see Sociology, Biblical

CHRISTIAN SOCIOLOGY—HISTORY

Brehmer, Karl. Wilhelm Emmanuel von Ketteler (1811-1877) Arbeiterbischof und Sozialethiker: Auf den Spuren einer zeitlosen Modernität. 2009. (GER., Illus.). 165p. *(978-3-7954-2135-9(7))* Schnell und Steiner GmbH, Verlag.

Chalcraft, David & Chalcraft. Max Weber & the Sociology of Biblical Social Worlds. 2013. (Library of Hebrew Bible/Old Testament Studies, the Ser.). (ENG.). 224p. 120.00 *(978-0-567-02758-0(9),* T&T Clark Int'l) Continuum International Publishing Group, Ltd. GBR. Dist: National Bk. Network.

Curran, Charles E. The Social Mission of the U.S. Catholic Church: A Theological Perspective. 2011. xi, 196p. ***(978-1-58901-717-7(X))*** Georgetown Univ. Pr.

Dodaro, Robert. Christ & the Just Society in the Thought of Augustine. 2008. (ENG.). 264p. pap. 37.99 *(978-0-521-06964-9(5))* Cambridge Univ. Pr.

Ekelund, Robert B., Jr., et al. The Marketplace of Christianity. 2008. (ENG., Illus.). 368p. (gr. 17). pap. 15.95 *(978-0-262-55071-0(7))* MIT Pr.

Friesen, Steven J., et al. Corinth in Context: Comparative Studies on Religion & Society. 2010. (Illus.). 500p. *(978-90-04-18197-7(0))* BRILL.

Graf, Friedrich Wilhelm. Fachmenschenfreundschaft: Studien zu Weber und Troeltsch. 2012. (Troeltsch-Studien. Neue Folge Ser.).Tr. of Scholarly Friendship. Studies on Weber & Troeltsch. (GER.). 360p. (gr. 17). E-Book 168.00 ***(978-3-11-174576-3(7))*** De Gruyter, Walter Inc.

Graf, Friedrich Wilhelm. Fachmenschenfreundschaft: Studien zu Weber und Troeltsch. Troeltsch-Studien. Neue Folge 3. 2010. (Troeltsch-Studien. Neue Folge Ser.).Tr. of Scholarly Friendship. Studies on Weber & Troeltsch. (GER.). 360p. 112.00 *(978-3-11-024553-0(1))* De Gruyter, Walter Inc.

Greaves, Richard L. Society & Religion in Elizabethan England. 2009. 944p. pap. 60.00 *(978-0-8166-5776-6(9))* Univ. of Minnesota Pr.

Harris, Mark W. Elite: Uncovering Classism in Unitarian Universalist History. 2011. v, 154p. pap. 10.00 ***(978-1-55896-573-7(4),*** Skinner Hse. Bks.) Unitarian Universalist Assn.

Kenworthy, Scott M. The Heart of Russia: Trinity-Sergius, Monasticism, & Society after 1825. 2010. (Woodrow Wilson Center Book Ser.). (ENG., Illus.). 544p. 74.00 *(978-0-19-973613-3(8))* Oxford Univ. Pr., Inc.

Mondragón, Carlos. Like Leaven in the Dough: Protestant Social Thought in Latin America, 1920-1950. 2010. *(978-0-8386-4273-3(X))* Fairleigh Dickinson Univ. Pr.

Morgan, D. Densil. Span of the Cross: Christian Religion & Society in Wales, 1914-2000. 2nd ed. 2011. (ENG., Illus.). 310p. pap. 40.00 *(978-0-7083-2397-7(9))* Univ. of Wales Pr. GBR. Dist: Chicago Distribution Ctr.

Sarris, Peter, et al. An Age of Saints? Power, Conflict, & Dissent in Early Medieval Christianity. 2011. 256p. *(978-90-04-20660-1(4))* BRILL.

Snell, K. D. M. & Ell, Paul S. Rival Jerusalems: The Geography of Victorian Religion. 2009. (ENG., Illus.). 516p. pap. 58.00 *(978-0-521-12122-4(1))* Cambridge Univ. Pr.

Talbott, Rick F. Jesus, Paul, & Power: Rhetoric, Ritual, & Metaphor in Ancient Mediterranean Christianity. 2010. 218p. pap. 24.00 *(978-1-59752-448-3(4),* Cascade Bks.) Wipf & Stock Pubs.

Waterman, A. M. C. Revolution, Economics & Religion: Christian Political Economy, 1798-1833. 2006. (ENG., Illus.). 328p. pap. 69.00 *(978-0-521-03038-0(2))* Cambridge Univ. Pr.

Watson, Francis. Paul, Judaism, & the Gentiles: Beyond the New Perspective. 2007. 400p. per. 32.00 *(978-0-8028-4020-2(5))* Eerdmans, William B. Publishing Co.

Williams, Ritva H. Stewards, Prophets, Keepers of the Word: Leadership in the Early Church. 2006. 228p. per. 24.95 *(978-1-56563-949-2(9))* Hendrickson Pubs. Marketing, LLC.

CHRISTIAN SOCIOLOGY—STUDY AND TEACHING

Bergman, Roger. Catholic Social Learning: Educating the Faith That Does Justice. 2011. (ENG., Illus.). 160p. pap. 24.00 *(978-0-8232-3329-8(4));* 3rd ed. 75.00 *(978-0-8232-3328-1(6))* Fordham Univ. Pr.

CHRISTIAN STEWARDSHIP

Here are entered works on the duty of the individual Christian to contribute time, talents, and material possessions in the service of God. Works on the duty of the individual Christian to contribute financially to the church are entered under Christian Giving. Works on the solicitation and administration of church funds are entered under Church Finance.

see also Christian Giving

Abingdon Press, creator. Treasures of the Transformed Life: Satisfying Your Soul's Thirst for More. ldr.'s ed. 2006. 56p. pap. 11.00 *(978-0-687-33465-0(9))* Abingdon Pr.

Acton Institute for the Study of Religion and Liberty Staff, contrib. by. Environmental Stewardship in the Judeo-Christian Tradition: Jewish, Catholic & Protestant Wisdom on the Environment. 2007. (ENG., Illus.). 119p. pap. 9.95 *(978-1-880595-15-2(X))* Acton Institute for the Study of Religion & Liberty.

Acton Institute for the Study of Religion and Liberty Staff, et al. Effective Stewardship: Doing What Matters Most, 1 vol. 2009. (ENG.). 96p. pap. 7.99 *(978-0-310-32229-0(4))* Zondervan.

Anslinger, Leisa. Living Catholic Stewardship: A Call to Serve. 2009. 1p. 14.95 *(978-1-59276-705-2(2))* Our Sunday Visitor, Publishing Div.

—Viviendo la Corresponsabilidad Catolica: Un Llamado a Servir. Estenger, Vilma G., tr. 2009. (SPA.). 1p. 14.95 *(978-1-59276-706-9(0))* Our Sunday Visitor, Publishing Div.

Anslinger, Leisa & Shepp, Victoria. Forming Generous Hearts: Stewardship Planning for Lifelong Faith Formation. 2007. 146p. per. 14.95 *(978-1-58595-642-5(2))* Twenty-Third Pubns./Bayard.

Anton, Ronald. God's Seven Ways to Ease Suffering. 2007. 480p. per. 26.99 *(978-1-60477-267-8(0))* Xulon Pr., Inc.

Arthur, David & Arthur, Kay. Money & Possessions. 2009. (40-Minute Bible Studies). (ENG.). 104p. pap. 7.99 *(978-0-307-45768-4(0),* WaterBrook Pr.) Doubleday Religious Publishing Group, The.

Bebslin. Tithing & Winning Souls: Sharing the Good News to Others. 2008. 100p. pap. 10.99 *(978-1-60647-896-7(6))* Xulon Pr., Inc.

Binz, Stephen J. Stewardship of the Earth. 2007. (Threshold Bible Study Ser.). (Illus.). 129p. per. 12.95 *(978-1-58595-373-8(3))* Twenty-Third Pubns./Bayard.

Black, Suzy. Faith & Finance: Creating Godly Wealth in A Worldly System. 2009. 164p. pap. 14.99 *(978-1-60791-660-4(6))* Xulon Pr., Inc.

Borg, Richard A. The Chief Steward. 2008. 408p. pap. 21.99 *(978-1-60477-507-5(6))* Xulon Pr., Inc.

Branson, Mary Kinney. Spending God's Money. 2006. per. *(978-0-9779407-6-9(4))* Father's Pr., LLC.

Brott, Rich. All the Financial Scriptures in the Bible with Commentary. 2008. 364p. per. 24.99 *(978-1-60185-004-1(2))* ABC Book Publishing.

—A Biblical Perspective on Tithing & Giving: A Believer's Stewardship Guide. 2008. 172p. per. 16.99 *(978-1-60185-000-3(X))* ABC Book Publishing.

—How to Receive Prosperity & Provision: 17 Biblical Principles You Must Know. 2008. 296p. per. 19.99 *(978-1-60185-005-8(0))* ABC Book Publishing.

—Prosperity Has A Purpose: 27 Biblical Principles to Understand. 2008. 288p. per. 19.99 *(978-1-60185-006-5(9))* ABC Book Publishing.

—15 Biblical Responsibilities Leading to Financial Wisdom. 2008. 120p. per. 14.99 *(978-1-60185-010-2(7))* ABC Book Publishing.

Brown, Edward R. Our Father's World: Mobilizing the Church to Care for Creation. 2nd ed. 2008. (ENG.). 203p. pap. 15.00 *(978-0-8308-3484-6(2),* IVP Bks.) InterVarsity Pr.

Carter, Doug. Raising More Than Money: Redefining Generosity, Reflecting God's Heart, 0 vols. 2007. 224p. 24.99 *(978-1-4185-1957-5(X))* Nelson, Thomas Inc.

Case, Steve. Living Stewardship [Older Youth]. 2011. 83p. pap. 12.95 *(978-1-84694-575-5(5))* O Bks.,John Hunt.

Celia, Dan. All for the Master: Relections on the Stewardship of Our Gifts, 0 vols. 2008. 128p. pap. 12.98 *(978-0-7852-8969-2(0))* Nelson, Thomas Inc.

Christensen, Joshua. Consider the Ant: 3 Keys to Biblical Prosperity. 2010. pap. 15.99 *(978-1-61663-196-3(1))* Tate Publishing & Enterprises, LLC.

Christopher, J. Clif. Not Your Parents' Offering Plate: A New Vision for Financial Stewardship. 2008. (Illus.). 123p. pap. 14.00 *(978-0-687-64853-5(X))* Abingdon Pr.

Clark, Sereno D. The Faithful Steward. 2007. 68p. per. *(978-1-4065-1383-7(0))* Dodo Pr.

—The Faithful Steward. 2007. 72p. per. *(978-1-4068-4624-9(4))* Echo Library.

Clark, Wayne B. Beyond Fundraising: A Complete Guide to Congregational Stewardship. 2007. pap. 20.00 *(978-1-55896-523-2(8))* Unitarian Universalist Assn.

Clements, C. Justin. Time, Talent, & Treasure: Reflections on the U. S. Bishops' Model for Parish Stewardship. 2006. 112p. per. 14.95 *(978-0-7648-1500-3(8))* Liguori Pubns.

Conrad, Alphin Carl. The Divine Economy: A Study in Stewardship. 2011. 168p. 41.95 ***(978-1-258-04835-8(3))*** Literary Licensing, LLC.

Conyers, David Ellis. Stewardship on Steroids: Increase Your Cash Flow, Build Wealth & Become A Great Christian Steward. 2011. 220p. 29.99 ***(978-1-4567-9403-3(5))***; pap. 24.99 ***(978-1-4567-9404-0(3))*** AuthorHouse.

Cooke, Parsons. The Divine Law of Beneficence. 2009. 358p. pap. 31.75 *(978-1-116-09507-4(6))*; pap. 32.75 *(978-1-116-09506-7(8))* BiblioBazaar.

—The Divine Law of Beneficence. 2008. 364p. 46.95 *(978-0-548-96249-7(9))* 2007. (ENG.). 368p. per. 31.95 *(978-0-548-63792-0(X))* Kessinger Publishing, LLC.

—The Divine Law of Beneficence. 2006. 364p. per. 26.99 *(978-1-4255-3709-8(X))* MPublishing.

Crown Financial Ministries, creator. Rich Man & Lazarus. 2009. (God Provides Ser.). 25.00 *(978-1-56427-262-1(1))* Crown Financial Ministries, Inc.

Deffenbaugh, Daniel. Learning the Language of the Fields: Tilling & Keeping as Christian Vocation. 2006. (ENG.). 176p. per. 14.95 *(978-1-56101-282-4(3))* Cowley Pubns.

Druhe, Marilyn. Living Stewardship [Daily Life]. 2011. 87p. pap. 12.95 *(978-1-84694-571-7(2))* O Bks.,John Hunt.

Edwards, Denis. Ecology at the Heart of Faith. 2006. 146p. per. 26.00 *(978-1-57075-665-8(1))* Orbis Bks.

Eristhee, Thomas. The Church Revealed. 2007. 128p. per. *(978-1-55452-157-9(2))* Essence Publishing.

Everett, Stephen. The New Testament Principle of Kingdom Stewardship. 2008. 284p. pap. 16.99 *(978-0-7684-2649-6(9))* Destiny Image Pubs.

Foster, Charles. Steward: Living as Disciples in Everyday Life Session Videos. 89.95 *(978-0-687-09964-1(1))* Abingdon Pr.

—Steward: Living as Disciples in Everyday Life Training Video. 29.95 *(978-0-687-09974-0(9))* Abingdon Pr.

Gaddis, Todd. Money & More: The Quest for Generous Living. 2007. 128p. per. *(978-1-55452-200-2(5))*, Guardian Bks.) Essence Publishing.

Galan, Vicente. Mayordomia en la Vida del Creyente: Stewardship in Christian Life. (SPA.). 48p. *(978-84-7228-807-2(2)*, 220597) Clie, Editorial.

Gardner, Tom. The Desires of Your Heart. 2007. (ENG.). 208p. pap. 12.99 *(978-1-59979-080-0(7)*, Creation Hse.) Charisma Media.

Gooch, Margaret. Voices of the Volunteers - an Exploration of the Influences That Volunteer Experiences Have on the Resilience & Sustainability of Catchment Groups I. 2008. 288p. pap. *(978-3-639-00275-1(X))* VDM Verlag Dr. Mueller e.K.

Gottlieb, Roger S. A Greener Faith: Religious Environmentalism & Our Planet's Future. 2009. (ENG.). 312p. pap. 19.95 *(978-0-19-539620-1(0))* Oxford Univ. Pr., Inc.

—Religion & the Environment V1, 4 vols. 2010. (Illus.). *(978-0-415-55821-1(2))* Routledge.

—Religion & the Environment V2, 4 vols. 2010. (Illus.). *(978-0-415-55820-4(4))* Routledge.

—Religion & the Environment V3, 4 vols. 2010. (Illus.). *(978-0-415-55819-8(0))* Routledge.

—Religion & the Environment V4, 4 vols. 2010. (Illus.). *(978-0-415-55818-1(2))* Routledge.

Gottlieb, Roger S., ed. Religion & the Environment, 4 vols. 2010. (Illus.). 1552p. 1295.00 *(978-0-415-55451-0(9))* Routledge.

Guidelines for Leading Your Congregation 2009-2012 - Stewardship: Yes, It's about Money, but a whole Lot More — Using God's Resources Responsibly. 2008. 2.95 *(978-0-687-64911-2(0))* Abingdon Pr.

Halteman, James. The Clashing Worlds of Economics & Faith. annot. ed. 2007. 224p. pap. 24.00 *(978-1-55635-170-9(4)*, Wipf and Stock) Wipf & Stock Pubs.

Hart, John. Sacramental Commons: Christian Ecological Ethics. 2006. (Nature's Meaning Ser.). (ENG.). 274p. 92.00 *(978-0-7425-4599-1(7))*; per. 29.95 *(978-0-7425-4605-9(5))* Rowman & Littlefield Publishers, Inc.

Heerspink, Robert. The Joy of Generosity: Stewardship Resources for Your Church: Devotions. (Stewardship Ser.). 13.75 *(978-1-56212-797-8(7)*, 151465) Faith Alive Christian Resources.

Hill, Mike. Biblical Financial Wisdom. 2008. 184p. pap. 15.96 *(978-0-557-01029-5(2))* Lulu Enterprises Inc.

Hines, Mack T. Developing Stewardship: Emphasis on Substance among the Congregants of St. Paul Baptist Church. 2007. 68p. pap. 20.00 *(978-0-8059-7543-7(8))* Dorrance Publishing Co., Inc.

Horak, Edmund. The Money Moment: How to Encourage A Lifestyle of Giving. 2010. pap. 14.99 *(978-1-61566-647-8(8))* Tate Publishing & Enterprises, LLC.

Hosenfeld, Charlene A. Eco-Faith: Creating & Sustaining Green Congregations. 2009. 215p. pap. 20.00 *(978-0-8298-1818-5(9))* Pilgrim Pr., The/United Church Pr.

Hussein, Bedru & Miller, Lynn. Stewardship for All? Two Believers - One from a Poor Country, One from a Rich Country - Speak from Their Settings, 1 vol. 2007. (ENG.). 104p. per. 6.95 *(978-1-56148-584-0(5))* Good Bks.

International Catholic Stewardship Council. Investing in Our Parish Brochure. (Parish Stewardship Program Ser.). 0.35 *(978-0-8146-2179-0(1))* Liturgical Pr.

—Sharing God's Gifts Brochure. (Parish Stewardship Program Ser.). 0.35 *(978-0-8146-2176-9(7))* Liturgical Pr.

—Sharing Our Time & Talents Brochure. (Parish Stewardship Program Ser.). 0.35 *(978-0-8146-2177-6(5))* Liturgical Pr.

—Supporting Our Faith Community Brochure. (Parish Stewardship Program Ser.). 0.35 *(978-0-8146-2178-3(3))* Liturgical Pr.

Johnson, Kelly S. The Fear of Beggars: Stewardship & Poverty in Christian Ethics. 2007. (Eerdmans Ekklesia Ser.). 236p. per. 20.00 *(978-0-8028-0378-8(4))* Eerdmans, William B. Publishing Co.

Jones, Clifford A., Sr. Star Book for Stewardship. 2012. (ENG.). 224p. 15.99 ***(978-0-8170-1665-4(1))*** Judson Pr.

Jorgenson, Allen G. Awe & Expectation. 2010. (Illus.). 146p. pap. 18.00 *(978-1-60608-795-4(9)*, Wipf and Stock) Wipf & Stock Pubs.

The Joy of Generosity: Stewardship Resources for Your Church. (Stewardship Ser.). 37.75 *(978-1-56212-796-1(9)*, 151460) Faith Alive Christian Resources.

Kacher, Larry. Behold I Am A Disciple of Jesus Christ. 2007. 100p. pap. 12.95 *(978-1-4327-0110-9(X))* Outskirts Pr., Inc.

Katz, Robert & Katz, Jamie. A Guide to Christian Financial Planning & Stories of Stewardship. 2006. (Money Came by the House the Other Day Ser.). 158p. pap. 12.95 *(978-1-932021-50-9(7))* DC Pr. LLC.

Keithahn, Mary. Living Stewardship [Older Children]. 2011. 96p. pap. 12.95 *(978-1-84694-574-8(7))* O Bks.,John Hunt.

Kiiru, MacMillan. Mobilizing & Managing Resources. 2009. 264p. pap. 24.99 *(978-9966-20-181-2(5))* Evangel Publishing Hse.

Kiouachoglou, Anastasios. Tithing, Giving & the New Testament. 2008. 104p. pap. 10.99 *(978-1-60791-114-2(0))* Xulon Pr., Inc.

Lawrence, Robert. The Basics for the Journey of a Lifetime: Following the Savior. 2011. 92p. pap. 13.95 ***(978-1-61507-750-2(2))*** Cross Bks. Publishing.

Leavell, Frank H. Training in Stewardship. 2007. (ENG.). 112p. 34.95 *(978-0-548-03129-2(0))* Kessinger Publishing, LLC.

Leggett, Donald. Money: Burden or Blessing? 2007. 84p. per. *(978-1-894667-86-9(7))* Clements Publishing.

Ligon, Dwight. Five Fold Ministry Rip-off Artists. 2007. 64p. per. 16.95 *(978-1-4241-8475-0(4))* PublishAmerica, Inc.

Lingerfelt, Gene. 80-10-10: Everyman's Road to Riches. 2009. (ENG.). 144p. 12.95 *(978-0-9824145-4-5(4))* Lifebridge Bks.

Logan-Nowlin, Kim. Refusing a Direct Order. 2007. 172p. per. 13.99 *(978-1-60266-068-7(9))* Xulon Pr., Inc.

Lucado, Max. Becoming Money Smart, 0 vols. 2007. (Max on Life Ser.). (Illus.). 64p. 9.99 *(978-1-4041-0490-7(9))* Nelson, Thomas Inc.

March, W. Eugene. God's Land on Loan: Israel, Palestine, & the World. 2007. (ENG.). 131p. per. 17.00 *(978-0-664-23151-4(9))* Westminster John Knox Pr.

Mathison. Transformed Life: Realizing Your Church's Full Stewardship Potential. 2006. 78.00 *(978-0-687-33435-3(7))* Abingdon Pr.

Mathison, John Ed, contrib. by. Treasures of the Transformed Life Participant's Workbook: Satisfying Your Soul's Thirst for More. 2006. 56p. pap. 4.50 *(978-0-687-33455-1(1))* Abingdon Pr.

McCalep, George & McCalep, Sadie. Blessed, Healed & Delivered. 2006. 376p. 25.00 *(978-1-891773-77-8(1))* Orman Pr.

McCullar, Michael D. Stewardship: A Way of Living. 2009. pap. *(978-0-9821806-9-3(1))* NextSunday Resources.

McDonald, Walter E. Parenting with a Purpose. 2010. 276p. 26.99 *(978-1-60957-307-2(2))* Xulon Pr., Inc.

McDuff, Mallory. Sacred Acts: How Chruches are Working to Protect Earth's Climate. 2012. (ENG., Illus.). 288p. pap. 17.95 ***(978-0-86571-700-8(1)***, 9780865717008) New Society Pubs., Ltd. CAN. Dist: Consortium Bk. Sales & Distribution.

McDuff, Mallory D. Natural Saints: How People of Faith Are Working to Save God's Earth, 1 vol. 2010. (ENG., Illus.). 240p. 26.00 *(978-0-19-537957-0(8))* Oxford Univ. Pr., Inc.

McKinley, David. The Life You Were Born to Give: Why It's Better to Live Than to Receive, 0 vols. 2007. 192p. per. 12.99 *(978-0-8499-1202-3(4))* Nelson, Thomas Inc.

Metzger, James A. Consumption & Wealth in Luke's Travel Narrative. 2007. (Biblical Interpretation Ser.). 218p. *(978-90-04-16261-7(5))* BRILL.

Meyer, Paul J. & Preissler, Scott. Master Keys of Stewardship: Truths That Guide Our Actions as Stewards. 2007. 30p. pap. 1.75 *(978-0-89811-337-2(7))* Meyer Resource Group, Inc., The.

Miller, Herb. New Consecration Sunday Stewardship Program. rev. ed. 2007. (Illus.). 64p. 8.75 *(978-0-687-64447-6(X))* Abingdon Pr.

—New Consecration Sunday Stewardship Program & Guest. ldr.'s rev. ed. 2007. (Illus.). 80p. pap. 33.00 *(978-0-687-64437-7(2))* Abingdon Pr.

Milton, Michael A. Giving as an Act of Worship. 2006. (Faith for Living: Ser.). 24p. pap. 2.50 *(978-1-59752-712-5(2)*, Wipf and Stock) Wipf & Stock Pubs.

Moser, Ingrid Friesen. Body Talk: Speaking the Words of Health. 2007. pap. 12.00 *(978-0-8361-9370-1(9))* Herald Pr.

Mosser, David N. Stewardship Services. 2007. (Just in Time! (Abingdon Press) Ser.). 102p. per. 12.00 *(978-0-687-33516-9(7))* Abingdon Pr.

Moyers, Bill. Welcome to Doomsday. 2006. (New York Review Books Collection). (ENG.). 56p. pap. 7.95 *(978-1-59017-209-4(4))* New York Review of Bks., Inc., The.

Nichols, B. Ann. Tithes: The Extortion of the Body of Christ. 2006. 153p. per. 12.95 *(978-1-59886-293-5(6))* Tate Publishing & Enterprises, LLC.

Olson, Raymond M. Stewards Appointed: Ten Studies in Christian Stewardship Based on Luther's Small Catechism. 2011. 148p. 40.95 ***(978-1-258-04044-4(1))*** Literary Licensing, LLC.

Pedersen, W. Todd. The Disciplines of Freedom: Moving Away from the Yardstick Gospel Toward a Life of Liberty. 2009. 160p. pap. 14.99 *(978-1-61579-624-3(X))* Xulon Pr., Inc.

Perdue, Lisa. One Tenth: A Scriptural Guide to Giving. 2007. 120p. per. 9.95 *(978-1-4327-0560-2(1))* Outskirts Pr., Inc.

Phillips, Jack. Cycles of Discipleship: A Stewardship Program for the Local Church. 2007. 300.00 incl. cd-rom *(978-0-88177-497-9(9))* Upper Room Bks.

Piat, Stephane-Joseph. Riches & the Spirit. Oligny, Paul J., tr. 2011. 254p. 46.95 ***(978-1-258-04201-1(0))*** Literary Licensing, LLC.

Reader Resource Series. Date not set. (Orig.). pap. *(978-1-883667-09-2(7))* Christian Methodist Episcopal Church, General Board of Pubns.

Reeves, Michael & Tyler, Jennifer. Extravagant Generosity: The Heart of Giving. 2011. 64p. 35.00 *(978-1-4267-2856-3(5))* Abingdon Pr.

Robertson, C. K. Transforming Stewardship. Lemler James, ed. 2009. (Transformations Ser.). 176p. pap. 16.00 *(978-0-89869-607-3(0))* Church Publishing, Inc.

Robison, James. True Prosperity: Truth Matters. 2006. E-Book 9.99 *(978-1-4143-0501-1(X))* Tyndale Hse. Pubs.

Ronsvalle, John & Ronsvalle, Sylvia. The State of Church Giving Through 2005: Abolition of the Institutional Enslavement of Overseas Missions. 2007. 168p. pap. 30.00 *(978-0-9679633-7-2(0))* Empty Tomb, Inc.

Ronsvalle, John L. & Ronsvalle, Sylvia. The State of Church Giving Through 2004: Will We Will? 16th ed. 2006. pap. 28.00 *(978-0-9679633-6-5(2))* Empty Tomb, Inc.

Rusaw, Rick & Swanson, Eric. The Externally Focused Life. 2009. 208p. pap. 15.99 *(978-0-7644-3953-7(7))* Group Publishing, Inc.

Sansano, Ricardo. Privilegio de Diezmar & Ofrendar: Privilege of Tithing. (SPA.). 64p. *(978-84-7228-645-0(2)*, 220718) Clie, Editorial.

Schnase, Robert. Extravagant Generosity. 2008. 32p. pap. 7.00 *(978-1-4267-0005-7(9))* Abingdon Pr.

Schwartzentraub, Betsy. Afire with God: Becoming Spirited Stewards. 2007. (Illus.). 115p. per. 13.00 *(978-0-88177-520-4(7))* Discipleship Resources.

Shiplett, Gary R. A New Paradigm for Funding Ministry: How to Grow Giving in the Church, 1 vol. 2009. 132p. pap. 19.95 *(978-1-60703-136-9(1))* PublishAmerica, Inc.

Smith, Meisha. Joy & Truth of Tithing. 2007. 84p. per. 9.99 *(978-1-60266-158-5(8))* Xulon Pr., Inc.

Smotherman, Glen. Stewart Shipp of Peachtree Corners: Stewardship Messages. 2007. (ENG.). 112p. per. 13.99 *(978-1-4141-0821-6(4))* Pleasant Word.

Sowell, Evelyn. Living Stewardship [Young Adults]. 2011. 83p. pap. 12.95 *(978-1-84694-577-9(1))* O Bks.,John Hunt.

Speer, William. God's Rule for Christian Giving. 2009. 276p. 34.99 *(978-1-115-43667-0(8))*; 30.99 *(978-1-115-43664-9(3))*; pap. 27.75 *(978-1-115-43663-2(5))*; pap. 26.75 *(978-1-115-43661-8(9))* BiblioBazaar.

—God's Rule for Christian Giving. 2006. 276p. per. 23.99 *(978-1-4255-2494-4(X))* MPublishing.

—Gods Rule for Christian Giving: a Practical Essay on the Science Of. 2007. (ENG.). 276p. per. 27.95 *(978-1-4304-4567-8(X))* Kessinger Publishing, LLC.

Stafford, Bill. The Adventure of Spirit Filled Giving. 2007. pap. 10.99 *(978-1-60477-117-6(8))* Xulon Pr., Inc.

Stanley, Charles F. Understanding Financial Stewardship, 0 vols. 2008. (Life Principles Study Ser.). (ENG.). 128p. pap. 9.99 *(978-1-4185-3335-9(1))* Nelson, Thomas Inc.

Stewardship. 0.75 *(978-0-89265-535-9(6))* Randall Hse. Pubns.

Subalusky, Pam. Matters of Life & Dirt: Finding Fun & Fulfillment in Land Stewardship. 2007. (ENG.). 198p. pap. 10.00 *(978-1-4196-6640-7(1))* CreateSpace.

Thompson, Marvin G. Stealing the Tithe: The Cursed Nation, Biblical Stewardship, A Crisis of Faith. 2009. 118p. pap. 19.95 *(978-1-4489-2614-5(9))* PublishAmerica, Inc.

Tompkins, J. D. & Beckwith, Angela. The Epidemic of the Silent Church: Domestic Violence & Church Culture, 1 vol. 2009. 48p. pap. 16.95 *(978-1-60703-655-5(X))* PublishAmerica, Inc.

Toney, Joyce. The Noahide Laws: 2007. 92p. per. 10.99 *(978-1-60266-107-3(3))* Xulon Pr., Inc.

Tucker, Paul M. Christian Stewardship. pap. 4.99 *(978-0-89098-503-8(0))* Twentieth Century Christian Bks.

Vallet, Ronald E. Congregations at the Crossroads: Remembering to Be Households of God. 2006. 256p. pap. 27.00 *(978-1-59752-875-7(7)*, Wipf and Stock) Wipf & Stock Pubs.

van Rooyen, Leon. Well Done! ... good & faithful Servant. 2011. 142p. pap. 15.00 ***(978-1-935298-77-9(1))*** Truth Pubs.

Vincent, Mark. A Christian View of Money: Celebrating God's Generosity. 3rd ed. 2006. 142p. pap. 17.00 *(978-1-55635-131-0(3)*, Wipf and Stock) Wipf & Stock Pubs.

Whitmore, Mike. Accountable to God: Biblical Stewardship. 2007. 187p. per. 12.99 *(978-1-59886-532-5(3))* Tate Publishing & Enterprises, LLC.

Wilkinson, Bruce. The God Pocket: He Owns It - You Carry It - Suddenly, Everything Changes. 2011. 144p. 12.99 *(978-1-60142-185-2(0)*, Multnomah) Doubleday Religious Publishing Group, The.

Wilkinson, Bruce & Kopp, David. The God Pocket: He Owns It, You Carry It: Suddenly, Everything Changes. 2011. ***(978-0-307-71384-1(9))***; ***(978-1-60142-413-6(2))*** Doubleday Religious Publishing Group, The. (Multnomah).

Williamson, Roy. Not Least in the Kingdom. 128p. 10.00 *(978-0-281-05421-3(5))* SPCK Publishing GBR. Dist: Pilgrim Pr., The/United Church Pr.

Wood, Debbie. A FIT Life: Biblically Based Life Improvement. 2009. pap. 23.99 *(978-1-60799-945-4(5))* Tate Publishing & Enterprises, LLC.

Wretlind, Dennis O. Shekels, Dollars & Sense: A Biblical Theology of Financial Stewardship. 2006. 112p. per. 15.50 *(978-1-4120-9981-3(1))* Trafford Publishing.

Zech, Charles. Best Practices in Parish Stewardship. 2008. per. 24.95 *(978-1-59276-492-1(4))* Our Sunday Visitor, Publishing Div.

CHRISTIAN STEWARDSHIP—SERMONS

Mosser, David N. The Stewardship Companion: Lectionary Resources for Preaching. 2007. (ENG.). 249p. per. 25.00 *(978-0-664-22993-1(X))* Westminster John Knox Pr.

Sweetser, Terry & Milnor, Susan. The Abundance of Our Faith: Award-Winning Sermons on Giving, Plus Suggestions for Group Discussion. 2006. x, 212p. pap. 16.00 *(978-1-55896-516-4(5)*, Skinner Hse. Bks.) Unitarian Universalist Assn.

CHRISTIAN STEWARDSHIP—STUDY AND TEACHING

Block, Dale J. Healthcare Stewardship. 2009. 280p. 30.95 *(978-0-595-50223-3(7))*; pap. 20.95 *(978-0-595-51032-0(9))* iUniverse, Inc.

Hamilton, Adam. Enough: Stewardship Program Guide: Discovering Joy Through Simplicity & Generosity. 2009. 128p. 29.00 *(978-1-4267-0287-7(6))* Abingdon Pr.

Vallet, Ronald E. Stewards of the Gospel: Reforming Theological Education. 2011. 304p. pap. 32.00 ***(978-0-8028-6616-5(6))*** Eerdmans, William B. Publishing Co.

CHRISTIAN SYMBOLISM

see Christian Art and Symbolism

CHRISTIAN THEOLOGIANS

see Theologians

CHRISTIAN UNION

Here are entered works on prospective and actual mergers within and across denominational lines. Works on a movement generally dated from the Edinburgh Missionary Conference of 1910 to the formation of the World Council of Churches in 1948 for the purpose of church cooperation and unity are entered under Ecumenical Movement. Works on unity as one of the "marks" of the church are entered under Church—Unity. Works on religious activities planned and conducted cooperatively by two or more Christian sects are entered under Interdenominational Cooperation.

see also Communicatio in Sacris; Ecumenical Movement; Interdenominational Cooperation

American Institute of Christian Philosophy. Christ & the Church: Essays concerning the Church & the Unification of Christendom. reprint ed. 2011. 332p. pap. 31.75 ***(978-1-175-27625-4(1))*** 2009. 324p. 36.99 *(978-1-117-67038-6(4))* 2009. (ENG.). 323p. pap. 23.99 *(978-1-117-67040-9(6)*, BiblioLife) 2009. 324p. pap. 29.75 *(978-1-117-67039-3(2))* BiblioBazaar.

Anderson, H. George, et al. Living Together as Lutherans: Unity Within Diversity. 2007. 80p. per. 9.99 *(978-0-8066-8034-7(2)*, Augsburg Bks.) Augsburg Fortress, Pubs.

Appleby, David. Black Bartholomew's Day: Preaching, Polemic & Restoration Nonconformity. 2008. (Politics, Culture & Society in Early Modern Britain Ser.). (ENG.). 272p. 89.00 *(978-0-7190-7561-2(0))* Manchester Univ. Pr. GBR. Dist: Macmillan.

Borght, Ed A. J. G. van der. The Unity of the Church: A Theological State of the Art & Beyond. 2009. 358p. *(978-90-04-17968-4(2))* BRILL.

Brigham, Erin. Sustaining the Hope for Unity: Ecumenical Dialogue in a Postmodern World. 2012. ***(978-0-8146-6022-3(4))*** Liturgical Pr.

Chung, Paul S. Christian Spirituality & Ethical Life. 2010. (Illus.). 178p. pap. 20.00 *(978-1-55635-790-9(7)*, Pickwick Pubns.) Wipf & Stock Pubs.

Church Unity: Harding Preachers' Forum 1995. pap. 8.99 *(978-0-89225-455-2(6))* Gospel Advocate Co., Inc.

Cranage, David Herbert Somerset. The War & Unity: Being Lectures Delivered at the Local Lectures Sum. 2007. 138p. pap. 18.99 *(978-1-4254-9489-5(0))*; 152p. pap. 21.99 *(978-1-4264-9870-1(5))* BiblioBazaar.

Davenport, John Sidney. Christian Unity & Its Recovery. 2007. (ENG.). 122p. 35.95 *(978-0-548-15188-4(1))*; 124p. per. 20.95 *(978-1-4304-4546-3(7))* Kessinger Publishing, LLC.

—Christian Unity & Its Recovery. 2006. (ENG.). 120p. per. 16.99 *(978-1-4255-0849-4(9))* MPublishing.

DeVille, Adam A. J. Orthodoxy & the Roman Papacy: Ut Unum Sint & the Prospects of East-West Unity. 2011. (ENG.). 280p. pap. 38.00 *(978-0-268-02607-3(6))* Univ. of Notre Dame Pr.

C

DFollinger, Johann Joseph Ignaz von. Lectures on the Reunion of the Churches. 2006. 212p. per. 20.99 *(978-1-4255-1778-6(1))* MPublishing.

Documents on Christian Unity. reprint ed. 150.00 *(978-0-7222-2153-2(3))* Library Reprints, Inc.

Echeverria, Eduardo J. Dialogue of Love. 2009. 280p. pap. 31.00 *(978-1-60608-176-1(4),* Wipf and Stock) Wipf & Stock Pubs.

Ellis, Tom. Judah Inherits Christianity. 2008. (ENG.). pap. 13.95 *(978-0-533-15790-7(0))* Vantage Pr., Inc.

Evans, Gillian R. Method in Ecumenical Theology: The Lessons So Far. 2009. (ENG.). 248p. pap. 34.99 *(978-0-521-09395-8(3))* Cambridge Univ. Pr.

Ewer, Ferdinand Cartwright. Sermons on the Failure of Protestantism & on Catholocity by the Rev Ferdinand C Ewer. 2006. 172p. per. 18.99 *(978-1-4255-1357-3(3))* MPublishing.

Fewson, Michael. Will the Real Church Stand up. 2006. pap. 13.99 *(978-1-60034-453-4(4))* Xulon Pr., Inc.

Fitch, John. Anglican Eirenicon: The Concept of Churchmanship in the Quest for Christian Unity. 2009. (Illus.). 284p. pap. 38.00 *(978-0-7188-9212-8(7))* Lutherworth Pr., The GBR. Dist: Brown, David Bk. Co., The.

Foster, John. Then & Now: The Historic Church & the Younger Churches. 2007. 188p. per. *(978-1-4067-8861-7(9),* Pomona Pr.) Read Bks.

Fries, Heinrich & Rahner, Karl. Unity of the Churches: An Actual Possibility. Gritsch, Ruth C. L. & Gritsch, Eric W., trs. 2009. 158p. pap. 18.00 *(978-1-55635-758-9(3),* Wipf and Stock) Wipf & Stock Pubs.

Fuller, Reginald Dean. The Mustard Seed Church: A Call to Church Mission & Reform. 2010. 374p. pap. 20.99 *(978-1-61579-697-7(5))* Xulon Pr., Inc.

Geffert, Bryn. Eastern Orthodox & Anglicans: Diplomacy, Theology, & the Politics of Interwar Ecumenism. 2009. (ENG., Illus.). 560p. 60.00 *(978-0-268-02975-3(X))* Univ. of Notre Dame Pr.

Gros, Jeffrey, et al. Growth in Agreement III: International Dialogue Texts & Agreed Statements, 1998-2005. Gros, Jeffrey et al, eds. 2008. (Faith & Order Paper Ser.). 615p. per. 65.00 *(978-0-8028-6229-7(2))* Eerdmans, William B. Publishing Co.

—Growth in Agreement III: International Dialogue Texts & Agreed Statements, 1998-2005. 2007. 615p. pap. *(978-2-8254-1511-5(1))* World Council of Churches/Conseil Oecumenique des Eglises CHE. Dist: International Specialized Bk. Services.

Hesperides. Can the Churches Unite? World Conference on Faith & Order. 2007. 248p. per. *(978-1-4067-5688-3(1),* Hesperides Pr.) Read Bks.

Ho Yan Au, Connie. Grassroots Unity in the Charismatic Renewal. 2011. 298p. pap. 33.00 *(978-1-60899-561-5(5),* Wipf and Stock) Wipf & Stock Pubs.

Hogan, Linda & Thiessen, Gesa Elsbeth. Ecumenical Ecclesiology: Unity, Diversity & Otherness in a Fragmented World. Thiessen, Gesa Elsbeth, ed. 2011. (Ecclesiological Investigations Ser.). (ENG.). 260p. pap. 44.95 *(978-0-567-61834-4(X),* T&T Clark Int'l) Continuum International Publishing Group, Ltd. GBR. Dist: National Bk. Network.

Iakovos & Constantelos, Demetrios J. That They May Be One: Position Papers, Essays, Homilies, & Prayers on Christian Unity. 2007. *(978-1-885652-99-7(2));* pap. *(978-1-885652-98-0(4))* Holy Cross Orthodox Pr.

Kasper, Walter, prod. Harvesting the Fruits: Basic Aspects of Christian Faith in Ecumenical Dialogue. 2009. (ENG.). 224p. 17.95 *(978-1-4411-6272-4(0))* Continuum International Publishing Group, Ltd. GBR. Dist: National Bk. Network.

Lathrop, John P. Answer the Prayer of Jesus: A Call for Biblical Unity. 2011. (House of Prisca & Aquila Ser.). 128p. pap. 16.00 *(978-1-60899-392-5(2),* Wipf and Stock) Wipf & Stock Pubs.

Locke, Kenneth A. The Church in Anglian Theology: An Historical, Theological & Ecumenical Exploration. 2009. (Illus.). 232p. 99.95 *(978-0-7546-6530-4(5))* Ashgate Publishing Co.

Logan, Samuel T., Jr., ed. Confronting Kingdom Challenges: A Call to Global Christians to Carry the Burden Together. 2007. (Illus.). 256p. pap. 15.99 *(978-1-58134-863-7(0))* Crossway.

Lovell, George & Richardson, Neil. Sustaining Preachers & Preaching: A Practical Guide. 2011. (ENG., Illus.). 264p. 120.00 *(978-0-567-18141-1(3));* pap. 34.95 *(978-0-567-50785-3(8))* Continuum International Publishing Group, Ltd. GBR. (T&T Clark Int'l). Dist: National Bk. Network.

Lubich, Chiara. Living Dialogue: Steps on the Way to Communion among Christians. 2009. (ENG.). 88p. pap. 9.95 *(978-1-56548-326-2(X))* New City Pr.

Lunn, Henry Simpson. Chapters from My Life with Special Reference to Reunion. 2007. (ENG.). 450p. 52.95 *(978-0-548-04586-2(0))* Kessinger Publishing, LLC.

Newbigin, Lesslie. The Reunion of the Church, Revised Edition: A Defence of the South India Scheme. 2011. 220p. pap. 25.00 ***(978-1-61097-512-4(X),*** Wipf and Stock) Wipf & Stock Pubs.

Nugent, John, ed. Radical Ecumenicity: Pursuing Unity & Continuity after John Howard Yoder. 2010. 240p. pap. 25.00 *(978-0-89112-042-1(4),* ACU Pr.) Abilene Christian Univ. Pr.

Presbyterian National Union Convention Minutes & Phonographic Report. 2006. 164p. per. 18.99 *(978-1-4255-1213-2(5))* MPublishing.

Puglisi, J. F. How Can the Petrine Ministry Be a Service to the Unity of the Universal Church? 2010. 379p. pap. 40.00 *(978-0-8028-4862-8(1))* Eerdmans, William B. Publishing Co.

Radner, Ephraim & Turner, Philip. The Fate of Communion: The Agony of Anglicanism & the Future of a Global Church. 2007. 306p. per. 25.00 *(978-0-8028-6327-0(2))* Eerdmans, William B. Publishing Co.

Reath, Mary. Rome & Canterbury: The Elusive Search for Unity. spiral bd. *(978-0-7425-5279-1(9));* 2007. (ENG., Illus.). 160p. 21.95 *(978-0-7425-5278-4(0))* Rowman & Littlefield Publishers, Inc.

Ren, C. H. Christianity & the Future: Book One of the End Times Series. 2011. 224p. pap. 17.95 *(978-1-4497-1381-2(5),* WestBow Pr.) Author Solutions, Inc.

Robbins, Anna M., ed. Ecumenical & Eclectic: The Unity of the Church in the Contemporary World: Essays in Honour of Alan P. F. Sell. 2007. (Studies in Christian History & Thought Ser.). (Illus.). 338p. pap. 40.00 *(978-1-55635-478-6(9),* Wipf and Stock) Wipf & Stock Pubs.

Samuel Simon. The Church of the Redeemer, As Developed Within the General Synod of the Lutheran Church in America with a Historic Outline from the Apostolic Age T. 2006. 288p. per. 23.99 *(978-1-4255-2650-4(0))* MPublishing.

Schneider, Theodor & Wenz, Gunther. Das Kirchliche Amt in Apostolischer Nachfolge. (Dialog der Kirchen Ser.). (GER.). (C). 2008. 310p. pap. 48.00 *(978-3-525-56936-8(9))* 2006. 423p. pap. 48.00 *(978-3-525-56934-4(3))* Vandenhoeck & Ruprecht GmbH & Co. KG DEU. Dist: ISD.

Schwenk, James L. Catholic Spirit: Wesley, Whitefield, & the Quest for Evangelical Unity in Eighteenth-Century British Methodism. 2008. (Revitalization: Explorations in World Christian Movements Ser.). (ENG.). 158p. per. 47.00 *(978-0-8108-5837-4(1))* Scarecrow Pr., Inc.

Stow, Baron. Christian Brotherhood: A Letter to the Hon. Heman Lincoln... . 2006. 220p. per. 20.99 *(978-1-4255-1831-8(1))* MPublishing.

Taraqji, Marcel & Ibrahim, Gregorios, trs. The Vienna Dialogue. 2009. (ARA.). 100.00 *(978-1-60724-268-0(0));* 95.00 *(978-1-60724-267-3(2))* Gorgias Pr., LLC.

Thomas, Norman E. Missions & Unity: Lessons from History, 1792Ntilde;2010. 2010. (American Society of Missiology Ser.). 346p. pap. 39.00 *(978-1-60899-602-5(6),* Cascade Bks.) Wipf & Stock Pubs.

Thompson, Alan. One Lord, One People: The Unity of the Church in Acts in Its Literary Setting. 2008. (Library of New Testament Studies). (ENG.). 240p. 130.00 *(978-0-567-04559-1(5),* T&T Clark Int'l) Continuum International Publishing Group, Ltd. GBR. Dist: National Bk. Network.

Tomberlin, Jim & Bird, Warren. Better Together: Making Church Mergers Work. 2012. (Jossey-Bass Leadership Network Ser.: 62). (ENG.). 272p. 24.95 ***(978-1-118-13130-5(4),*** Jossey-Bass) Wiley, John & Sons, Inc.

Turfa, Arthur. Lost Opportunity yet Seed Bed for Later Discussion - the Council of Ferarra-Florence As a Springboard for Encounters Between Western & Eastern Chris. 2008. 212p. pap. 78.00 *(978-3-8364-9877-7(4))* VDM Verlag Dr. Mueller e.K.

Vondey, Wolfgang, ed. Pentecostalism & Christian Unity: Ecumenical Documents & Critical Assessments. 2010. 304p. pap. 33.00 *(978-1-60899-077-1(X),* Pickwick Pubns.) Wipf & Stock Pubs.

Walsh, Albert J. D. Learning the Grammar of an Ecumenical Faith. 2009. 136p. pap. *(978-3-639-20179-6(5))* VDM Verlag Dr. Mueller e.K.

Winfield, Flora. Growing Together. 160p. 19.00 *(978-0-281-05348-3(0))* SPCK Publishing GBR. Dist: Pilgrim Pr., The/United Church Pr.

Witsell, William Postell. Our Church: One Through the Ages. 2007. (ENG.). 172p. 37.95 *(978-0-548-06492-4(X))* Kessinger Publishing, LLC.

CHRISTIAN UNION—CATHOLIC CHURCH

Attridge, M. S. & Skira, J. Z., eds. In God's Hands: Essays on the Church & Ecumenism in Honour of Michael A. Fahey, S. J. 2006. (Bibliotheca Ephemeridum Theologicarum Lovaniensium Ser.: Vol. 199). (ENG.). 314p. (C). pap. 131.00 *(978-90-429-1830-6(6))* Peeters Pubs. & Booksellers BEL. Dist: Brown, David Bk. Co., The.

Bliss, Frederick M. Catholic & Ecumenical: History. 2nd ed. 2007. (ENG.). 208p. pap. 28.95 *(978-0-7425-5257-9(8))* Rowman & Littlefield Publishers, Inc.

—Catholic & Ecumenical: History & Hope: Why the Catholic Church Is Ecumenical & What She Is Doing about It. 2nd ed. 2007. (Sheed & Ward Book Ser.). (ENG.). 208p. 88.00 *(978-0-7425-5256-2(X))* Rowman & Littlefield Publishers, Inc.

Crabtree, J. Russell. The Fly in the Ointment: Why Denominations Aren't Helping Their Congregations & How They Can. 2008. (Illus.). 192p. pap. 18.00 *(978-0-89869-606-6(2))* Church Publishing, Inc.

Dawson, Christopher & Kollar, Rene. The Movement Towards Christian Unity in the Nineteenth Century. 2006. pap. *(978-0-9773909-0-8(X))* St. Vincent Archabbey Pubns.

Doherty, Catherine. Poustinia: Encountering God in Silence, Solitude & Prayer. 3rd rev. ed. (Madonna House Classics Ser.). 210p. pap. *(978-0-921440-54-3(5))* Madonna Hse. Pubns.

Fehring, Richard J. & Notare, Theresa. Human Fertility: Where Faith & Science Meet: Proceedings of an Interdisciplinary Conference, August 11 & 12, 2006, Washington, DC. 2008. (C). pap. *(978-0-87462-732-9(X))* Marquette Univ. Pr.

Lehner, Ulrich, ed. Beda Mayr, Vertheidigung der katholischen Religion (1789) Sammt einem Anhange von der Möglichkeit einer Vereinigung zwischen unserer, und der Evangelisch-Lutherischen Kirche. 2009. (Brill's Studies in Intellectual History). (GER & ENG.). 434p. *(978-90-04-17318-7(8))* BRILL.

Murray, Paul, ed. Receptive Ecumenism & the Call to Catholic Learning: Exploring a Way for Contemporary Ecumenism. 2008. (ENG.). 464p. 110.00 *(978-0-19-921645-1(2))* Oxford Univ. Pr., Inc.

Quinn, John R. The Reform of the Papacy: The Costly Call to Christian Unity. 2007. (Ut Unim Sint Ser.). (ENG.). 192p. pap. 14.95 *(978-0-8245-2404-3(7),* Crossroad) Crossroad Publishing Co., The.

Tavard, George H. Vatican II & the Ecumenical Way. 2007. 155p. (C). pap. *(978-0-87462-729-9(X))* Marquette Univ. Pr.

Vereb, Jerome M. Because He Was a German! Cardinal Bea & the Origins of Roman Catholic Engagement in the Ecumenical Movement. 2006. 332p. 35.00 *(978-0-8028-2885-9(X))* Eerdmans, William B. Publishing Co.

Woznicki, Andrew. The Transcendent Mystery of Man: A Global Approach to Ecumenism. 2006. (Illus.). 414p. lib. bdg. 79.95 *(978-1-933146-15-7(X))* Academica Pr., LLC.

CHRISTIAN UNION—HISTORY

Bliss, Frederick M. Catholic & Ecumenical: History. 2nd ed. 2007. (ENG.). 208p. pap. 28.95 *(978-0-7425-5257-9(8))* Rowman & Littlefield Publishers, Inc.

—Catholic & Ecumenical: History & Hope: Why the Catholic Church Is Ecumenical & What She Is Doing about It. 2nd ed. 2007. (Sheed & Ward Book Ser.). (ENG.). 208p. 88.00 *(978-0-7425-5256-2(X))* Rowman & Littlefield Publishers, Inc.

Davies, Noel A. A History of Ecumenism in Wales, 1956-1990. 2008. (University of Wales - Bangor History of Religion Ser.). 192p. 85.00 *(978-0-7083-2150-8(X))* Univ. of Wales Pr. GBR. Dist: Chicago Distribution Ctr.

Macy, Paul Griswold. If It Be of God: The Story of the World Council of Churches. 2011. 192p. 42.95 ***(978-1-258-02921-0(9))*** Literary Licensing, LLC.

Norgren, William A. Faith & Order in the U.S.A: A Brief History of Studies & Relationships. 2011. 104p. pap. 20.00 *(978-0-8028-6599-1(2))* Eerdmans, William B. Publishing Co.

Rogers, Francis M. The Quest for Eastern Christians: Travels & Rumor in the Age of Discovery. 2009. (ENG.). 240p. pap. 50.00 *(978-0-8166-5861-9(7))* Univ. of Minnesota Pr.

CHRISTIAN UNION—ORTHODOX EASTERN CHURCH

Attridge, M. S. & Skira, J. Z., eds. In God's Hands: Essays on the Church & Ecumenism in Honour of Michael A. Fahey, S. J. 2006. (Bibliotheca Ephemeridum Theologicarum Lovaniensium Ser.: Vol. 199). (ENG.). 314p. (C). pap. 131.00 *(978-90-429-1830-6(6))* Peeters Pubs. & Booksellers BEL. Dist: Brown, David Bk. Co., The.

Bartholomew, Ecumenical Patriarch. Speaking the Truth in Love: Theological & Spiritual Exhortations of Ecumenical Patriarch Bartholomew. Chryssavgis, John, ed. 2nd ed. 2010. (Orthodox Christianity & Contemporary Thought Ser.). (ENG.). 464p. 37.00 *(978-0-8232-3337-3(5))* Fordham Univ. Pr.

FitzGerald, Thomas E. & Gratsias, Emmanuel. Restoring the Unity in Faith: The Orthodox-Oriental Orthodox Theological Dialogue: An Introduction with Texts. 2008. *(978-1-885652-93-5(3))* Holy Cross Orthodox Pr.

Yossa, Kenneth. Common Heritage, Divided Communion: The Declines & Advances of Inter-Orthodox Relations from Chalcedon to Chambésy. 2009. 286p. 12.00 *(978-1-60724-067-9(X))* Gorgias Pr., LLC.

CHRISTIAN UNION AND THE LORD'S SUPPER

see Lord's Supper and Christian Union

CHRISTIAN WOMEN

see also Amish Women; Catholic Women; Mormon Women; Quaker Women

Abingdon Women Preaching Annl Series 1 Software. 29.95 *(978-0-687-05719-1(1))* Abingdon Pr.

Abingdon Women Preaching Annl Series 1-Year C Window Software. 29.95 *(978-0-687-05695-8(0))* Abingdon Pr.

Adams, Lynn Fox. God Needs Me: Living with Dysautonomia. 2009. pap. 14.99 *(978-1-60799-592-0(1))* Tate Publishing & Enterprises, LLC.

Akins, Harold Deane Thomason. Founded on the Rock, Jesus Christ: Autobiography of the Co-Founder & History of the Renowned Savannah Christian Preparatory School. 2007. (Illus.). 200p. pap. *(978-0-9724224-5-1(5))* Bonaventure Bks.

Alexander, Estrelda & Yong, Amos, eds. Philip's Daughters: Women in Pentecostal-Charismatic Leadership. 2008. (Princeton Theological Monographs). 260p. pap. 27.00 *(978-1-55635-832-6(6),* Pickwick Pubns.) Wipf & Stock Pubs.

Alexander, Karyn. Mad at God. 2010. 266p. pap. 16.99 *(978-1-60957-250-1(5))* Xulon Pr., Inc.

Alexander, Laronda & Raley, Lisa. Love's Response: Reconnecting to God through Healing of Emotional Wounds. 2010. 236p. pap. 14.99 *(978-1-4490-4508-1(1))* AuthorHouse.

Allen, I. Fountaine. Purposefully Made. 2008. 104p. per. 14.95 *(978-1-4327-1930-2(0))* Outskirts Pr., Inc.

Allen, Susan & Stoeker, Brenda. The Healing Choice: How to Move Beyond Betrayal. 2008. (ENG.). 256p. pap. 13.99 *(978-1-4000-7425-9(8))* Doubleday Religious Publishing Group, The.

—The Healing Choice Guidebook: Move Beyond Betrayal. 2008. (ENG.). 160p. pap. 10.99 *(978-1-4000-7426-6(6))* Doubleday Religious Publishing Group, The.

Allen, Valerie. I Am Inspired: The Beginning. 2009. 50p. pap. 12.95 *(978-1-4327-2904-2(7))* Outskirts Pr., Inc.

Alpha. God's Master Plan for Humanity. 2011. 72p. pap. 10.72 ***(978-1-4269-7392-5(6))*** Trafford Publishing.

Alsdorf, Debbie. Deeper: Living in the Reality of God's Love. 2008. 224p. pap. 12.99 *(978-0-8007-3215-8(4))* Revell.

—A Different Kind of Wild: Is Your Faith Too Tame? 2009. 207p. pap. 12.99 *(978-0-8007-3366-7(5))* Revell.

Alston, Marie, et al. A Month of Miracles: 30 Stories of the Unmistakable Presence of God. 2008. (ENG.). 160p. 14.99 *(978-1-59669-209-1(X))* New Hope Pubs.

Alsup, Wendy & Alsup, Wendy Horger. Practical Theology for Women: How Knowing God Makes a Difference in Our Daily Lives. 2008. (Re:Lit Ser.). 160p. pap. 11.99 *(978-1-4335-0209-5(7))* Crossway.

Amariah, Esther. Mercy & Grace: Victory Through Hardships. 2011. 188p. 30.95 ***(978-1-4497-1539-7(7));*** pap. 13.95 ***(978-1-4497-1538-0(9))*** Author Solutions, Inc. (WestBow Pr.).

Amey, Lakevia. Predator: Why fabulous Christian women can't find love in today's Church. 2011. (ENG.). 184p. pap. 15.00 ***(978-1-4664-3569-8(0))*** CreateSpace.

Anderson, M. Rosalie. Hungered: Living One Day at a Time - the Diary of a Missionary. 2008. 101p. pap. 16.95 *(978-1-60441-877-4(X))* PublishAmerica, Inc.

Anderson, Olyer. The Bible Is Right & Somebody's Wrong! 2007. 76p. per. 16.95 *(978-1-4241-8298-5(0))* PublishAmerica, Inc.

Andreasen, Joy. Whispers of Joy: Messages from an Unseen World. 2010. 212p. pap. 14.95 *(978-1-4327-6021-2(1))* Outskirts Pr., Inc.

Antillon, Ramona. Ashleigh: God's Miracle Baby: For with God Nothing Shall Be Impossible. 2011. 108p. 22.50 ***(978-1-4634-1775-8(6));*** pap. 14.99 ***(978-1-4634-1776-5(4))*** AuthorHouse.

Arbiser, Pola. Give Me the Children: How A Christian Woman Saved A Jewish Family During the Holocaust. 2010. 244p. pap. 25.95 *(978-1-4502-5180-8(3))* iUniverse, Inc.

Armato, James Joseph. Woman, Don't Be Stoopid! The Christian Women's Guide on Why They Shouldn't Marry or Even Date Unsaved Men, Waiting for a Spouse, & What They Should Look for in a Man Because They Desperately Need It! 2009. 500p. pap. 24.99 *(978-1-61579-210-8(4))* Xulon Pr., Inc.

Armstrong, Kristin. Work in Progress: An Unfinished Woman's Guide to Grace. 2009. (ENG.). 240p. 18.99 *(978-0-446-19800-4(5))* FaithWords.

Arterburn, Stephen & Ethridge, Shannon. Every Young Woman's Battle: Guarding Your Mind, Heart, & Body in a Sex-Saturated World. 2009. (Every Man Ser.). (ENG.). 304p. pap. 15.99 *(978-0-307-45800-1(8),* WaterBrook Pr.) Doubleday Religious Publishing Group, The.

Arthur, Kay, et al, contrib. by. Faithful Abundant True Weekend Retreat & Study Guide: Three Lives Going Deeper Still. 2010. (Faithful, Abundant, True Ser.). (Illus.). 155p. pap. *(978-1-4158-6898-0(0))* LifeWay Christian Resources.

Arthur, Kay, et al. Youniquely Woman: Becoming Who God Designed You to Be. 2008. (Illus.). 234p. pap. 13.99 *(978-0-7369-1726-1(8))* Harvest Hse. Pubs.

Aspin, Dee. Lord of the Ringless. 2008. 392p. pap. 19.99 *(978-1-60477-711-6(7))* Xulon Pr., Inc.

Atteberry, Mark. So Much More Than Sexy. 2009. (ENG.). 208p. pap. 14.99 *(978-0-7847-2119-3(X))* Standard Publishing.

Aughtmon, Susanna Foth. My Bangs Look Good & Other Lies I Tell Myself: The Tired Supergirl's Search for Truth, 1 vol. 2010. (ENG.). 192p. pap. 12.99 *(978-0-8007-3418-3(1))* Revell.

Augustine, Sue. Sanity Secrets for Stressed-Out Women: Energize & Renew Your Life. 2009. (Illus.). 288p. pap. 12.99 *(978-0-7369-2417-7(5))* Harvest Hse. Pubs.

Bailey, Martha. It Hurts but I'm Okay. 2012. pap. ***(978-0-914520-54-2(7))*** Insight Pr.

Bailey, Martha. Putting My Dress-Up Clothes Away: Because Big Girls Live in the Real World. 2007. *(978-0-914520-47-4(4))* Insight Pr.

Bailey, Mary. Jesus My Son: Mary's Journal of Jesus' Early Life. 2010. 208p. pap. 14.99 *(978-1-4490-6493-8(0))* AuthorHouse.

Baker Publishing Group Staff. Moments of Peace for a Woman's Heart. 2008. 384p. 14.99 *(978-0-7642-0550-7(1))* Bethany Hse. Pubs.

Ballestero, Shelly. Beauty by God: Inside-Out Secrets for Every Woman. 2009. (ENG., Illus.). 224p. pap. 15.99 *(978-0-8307-4684-2(6))* Gospel Light Pubns.

Balloy, Magdalene Patricia. Beyond the Darkness: My Transforming Journey with Jesus. 2010. 172p. 25.95 *(978-1-4502-5690-2(2));* pap. 15.95 *(978-1-4502-5689-6(9))* iUniverse, Inc.

Banister, Christa Ann. Around the World in 80 Dates: Confessions of a Christian Serial Dater. 2007. (Growing in Christ Ser.). (ENG.). 288p. per. 12.99 *(978-1-60006-177-6(X))* NavPress Publishing Group.

Barnes, Emilie. The One-Minute Home Organizer: Making Your Home Beautiful & Your Life Clutter Free. 2007. 144p. pap. 9.99 *(978-0-7369-2134-3(6))* Harvest Hse. Pubs.

—Quiet Moments Alone with God: A Devotional for Women. 2009. 288p. 9.99 *(978-0-7369-2256-2(3))* Harvest Hse. Pubs.

—Walk with Me Today, Lord: Inspiring Devotions for Women. 2008. 224p. pap. 11.99 *(978-0-7369-2348-4(9))* Harvest Hse. Pubs.

—365 Things Every Woman Should Know. 2010. 224p. pap. 7.99 *(978-0-7369-2851-9(0))* Harvest Hse. Pubs.

Barrett, Cynthia D. Why Me Lord. 2011. 116p. pap. 11.99 *(978-1-61215-569-2(3))* Xulon Pr., Inc.

Barrett, Mary. Celebrate: Just Live It. 2011. 192p. pap. 16.95 *(978-1-4502-9489-8(8))* iUniverse, Inc.

Barron, Christie. Governing Girls: Rehabilitation in the Age of Risk. 2012. 170p. pap. 19.95 ***(978-1-55266-436-0(8))*** Fernwood Publishing Co., Ltd. CAN. Dist: Independent Pubs. Group.

Barton, Ruth Haley. Longing for More: A Woman's Path to Transformation in Christ. 2007. (Transforming Center Set Ser.). (ENG.). 251p. per. 16.00 *(978-0-8308-3506-5(7),* IVP Bks.) InterVarsity Pr.

Beach, Shelly. The Silent Seduction of Self-Talk: Conforming Deadly Thought Patterns to the Word of God, 1 vol. 2009. (ENG.). 196p. pap. 13.99 *(978-0-8024-5077-7(6))* Moody Pubs.

Beard, Kathleen. Into the Mist: Journey into Dementia. 2011. 240p. pap. 17.95 *(978-1-4497-1207-5(X),* WestBow Pr.) Author Solutions, Inc.

The Beauty of Mentoring: Growing Through Change. (Christian Women's Bible Study Ser.). pap. 8.99 *(978-0-570-06882-5(5),* 20-3042) Concordia Publishing Hse.

The Beauty of Simplicity: When Less Is More. (Christian Women's Bible Study Ser.). pap. 8.99 *(978-0-570-06881-5(9),* 20-3045) Concordia Publishing Hse.

Belton, Cheryl. Rightly Dividing the Word of Truth, 1 vol. 2009. 139p. pap. 24.95 (978-1-60836-799-3(1)) PublishAmerica, Inc.

Benedict, Marie-Solange. Child of a Mountainous Land. 2007. 312p. (ENG.). 27.99 (978-1-60477-128-2(3)); per. 17.99 (978-1-60477-127-5(5)) Xulon Pr., Inc.

Bennett, Tammy. 101 Makeover Minutes. 2007. 240p. pap. 11.99 (978-0-7369-1992-0(9)) Harvest Hse. Pubs.

Beresford, Jennifer. Creating Confidence in Women: A Handbook for Women in Churches. (Illus.). 112p. 13.00 (978-0-281-05146-5(1)) SPCK Publishing GBR. Dist: Pilgrim Pr., The/United Church Pr.

Bergren, Lisa T. The Busy Mom's Devotional: Ten Minutes a Week to a Life of Devotion. 2007. (ENG.). 224p. pap. 14.99 (978-1-4000-7246-0(8), WaterBrook Pr.) Doubleday Religious Publishing Group, The.

Bergren, Lisa T. & Price, Rebecca. What Women Want: The Life You Crave & How God Satisfies. 2007. (ENG.). 320p. pap. 13.99 (978-1-4000-7245-3(X), WaterBrook Pr.) Doubleday Religious Publishing Group, The.

Bergstrom, Patricia. Welcome to My World: A Place I'll Always Remember. 2009. 157p. pap. 15.03 (978-0-557-09604-6(9)) Lulu Enterprises Inc.

Berry, Jan. Ritual Making Women: Shaping Rites for Changing Lives. 2009. (Gender, Theology & Spirituality Ser.). (ENG.). 256p. (C). 99.95 (978-1-84553-414-1(X)); pap. 34.95 (978-1-84553-415-8(8)) Equinox Publishing Ltd. GBR. Dist: ISD.

Berthelson, Sarah. Walking in the Wilderness of Fear. 2010. 90p. pap. 10.99 (978-1-60957-194-8(0)) Xulon Pr., Inc.

Best, Carolyn. Sonlight for Living: Health for the Spiritual Life. 2009. 64p. pap. 10.99 (978-1-61579-217-7(1)) Xulon Pr., Inc.

Betts, Doreen A. A Wave of the Baton. 2011. 256p. pap. 16.99 (978-1-61379-252-0(2)) Xulon Pr., Inc.

Bevere, Lisa. Be Angry, but Don't Blow It! Maintaining Your Passion Without Losing Your Cool, 0 vols. 2007. 208p. per. 14.99 (978-0-7852-8918-0(6)) Nelson, Thomas Inc.

—Fight Like a Girl: The Power of Being a Woman. 2008. (ENG.). 240p. pap. 11.99 (978-0-446-69468-1(1)) FaithWords.

—Lioness Arising: Wake up & Change Your World. (ENG.). 240p. 2011. pap. 14.99 (978-0-307-45779-0(6)) 2010. 19.99 (978-0-307-45778-3(8)) Doubleday Religious Publishing Group, The. (WaterBrook Pr.).

Bgtkaren. How Me, Myself & I Formed a Self-Help Group. 2009. 68p. pap. 10.99 (978-1-61507-084-8(2)) Cross Bks. Publishing.

Bingham, Derick. Ruth: A foreigner Redeemed. 2008. 60p. pap. (978-1-897117-72-9(8)) Gospel Folio Pr.

Blackaby, Henry & Webb, Carrie Blackaby. Prepared to Be God's Vessel: How God Can Use an Obedient Life to Bless Others, 0 vols. 2007. 224p. per. 14.99 (978-0-7852-8861-9(9)) Nelson, Thomas Inc.

Blackmer, Robert B. Miracles from God, 1 vol. 2009. 143p. pap. 24.95 (978-1-4489-9136-5(6)) PublishAmerica, Inc.

Blackmon, Valerie. The Making of a Woman: Discovering the Life-Giver Within You. 2010. pap. 15.99 (978-1-61579-882-7(X)) Xulon Pr., Inc.

Blair D, Andrea L. Cross-Examined. 2011. 152p. 30.95 (978-1-4497-2189-3(3)); pap. 13.95 (978-1-4497-2188-6(5)) Author Solutions, Inc. (WestBow Pr.).

Blievernicht, Melanie. Divorce Is Only Human: My Journey with God Through Divorce. 2010. 184p. pap. 17.95 (978-1-935271-42-0(3)) Published by Westview, Inc.

Boaz, Sarai. We Let the Dogs Out. 2009. 52p. pap. 9.95 (978-1-4401-3331-2(X)) iUniverse, Inc.

Bond, Janet. Janet's Silent Prayers. 2009. 48p. pap. 16.95 (978-1-60836-932-4(3)) PublishAmerica, Inc.

Booher, Dianna. The Esther Effect, 0 vols. 2008. 144p. pap. 15.99 (978-0-7852-9675-1(1)) Nelson, Thomas Inc.

Bostrom, Kathleen. Making Space for the Spirit: 100 Simple Ways to Nurture Your Soul. 2010. (ENG.). 98p. pap. 13.00 (978-0-664-23462-1(3)) Westminster John Knox Pr.

Bourke, Dale Hanson. Embracing Your Second Calling: Find Passion & Purpose for the Rest of Your Life. 2010. 240p. pap. 16.99 (978-0-8499-4697-4(2)) Nelson, Thomas Inc.

Bourne, Fumiko/Tanahara. Mama, Mama, Don't Die: A Child's Eye-Witness-History of the Battle of Okinawa! 2007. (Illus.). 80p. pap. 5.95 (978-0-9797319-0-7(9)) Bourne Enterprises.

Boyack, Merrilee Browne. Toss the Guilt & Catch the Joy: A Woman's Guide to a Better Life. 2008. viii, 200p. pap. (978-1-59038-925-6(5)) Deseret Bk. Co.

Braendel, Shari. Good Girls Don't Have to Dress Bad: Every Woman, 1 vol. 2010. (ENG.). 192p. pap., pupl's gde. ed. 14.99 (978-0-310-32601-4(X)) Zondervan.

Bray, Wendy. True Confidence - Inspiring Women Every Day. 2008. 112p. (978-1-85345-470-7(2)) Crusade for World Revival.

Brazelton, Kate. Pathway to Purpose for Women, 1 vol. 2008. (ENG.). 256p. pap. 14.99 (978-0-310-29249-4(2)) Zondervan.

Brenda Waggoner. The Velveteen Woman: Becoming Real Through God's Transforming Love. 2009. 216p. 27.95 (978-1-4401-6770-6(2)); pap. 17.95 (978-1-4401-6768-3(0)) iUniverse, Inc.

Brestin, Dee. A Woman of Moderation: Breaking the Chains of Poor Eating Habits. 2007. (Dee Brestins Ser.). (ENG.). 144p. per. 10.99 (978-0-7814-4445-3(4)) Cook, David C.

Bright, Dee. The Divine Romance: Going to God with the Longings Only He Can Fulfill. 2008. 224p. pap. 12.99 (978-0-8007-3225-7(1)) Revell.

Bright-Fey, J. A Morning Cup of Prayer for Women. 2006. (978-1-58173-596-3(0)) Crane Hill Pubs.

Bright-Fey, John A. A Morning Cup of Prayer for Friends: A Daily Guided Devotional for a Lifetime of Inspiration & Peace. 2006. (Morning Cup Ser.). (ENG., Illus.). 80p. spiral bd. (978-1-57587-263-6(3)) Crane Hill Pubs.

—A Morning Cup of Prayer for Women: A Daily Guided Devotional for a Lifetime of Inspiration & Peace. 2006. (Morning Cup Ser.). (ENG., Illus.). 80p. spiral bd. (978-1-57587-266-7(8)) Crane Hill Pubs.

Brittingham, Margaret. Mom from down Under: A Book of Answered Prayer. 2011. pap. 10.99 (978-1-61739-544-4(7)) Tate Publishing & Enterprises, LLC.

Broadman and Holman Publishers Staff, prod. Bible Promises for Women. 2008. (ENG.). 128p. pap. 3.99 (978-0-8054-4769-9(5), B&H Bks.) B&H Publishing Group.

Broadway-Tetrick, Lynda. A Princess in God's Kingdom. 2009. pap. 8.99 (978-1-60799-644-6(8)) Tate Publishing & Enterprises, LLC.

Brock, Anita & Newman, Gail. Mileage, Memories & Mishaps: True Tales of Joyful Life Journeys. 2006. 180p. pap. 14.99 (978-1-59755-036-9(1), Advantage Inspirational) Advantage Bks.

Brodersen, Cheryl. When a Woman Lets Go of the Lies: Discovering the Truth about Who You Are in God's Eyes. 2012. pap. 12.99 (978-0-7369-4942-2(9)) Harvest Hse. Pubs.

Brodersen, Cheryl & Brodersen, Cheryl. When a Woman Lets Go of Her Fears: The Amazing Power of Trusting God. 2010. 208p. pap. 13.99 (978-0-7369-2792-5(1)) Harvest Hse. Pubs.

Broling, Janet. What Can One Woman Do? The Historic New York City Women's Prayer Summits. 2008. (ENG., Illus.). 240p. 19.95 (978-1-932458-56-5(5)) Bronze Bow Publishing.

Brooks, Joel & Hammond, Michelle McKinney. What Women Don't Know (And Men Don't Tell You) The Unspoken Rules of Finding Lasting Love. 2009. (ENG.). 208p. pap. 8.99 (978-0-307-45850-6(4)) Doubleday Religious Publishing Group, The.

Broom, Laura Love. The Whisper of Truth, 1 vol. 2010. 122p. pap. 19.95 (978-1-4512-1435-2(9)) PublishAmerica, Inc.

Brown, Mamie Dell. Born to Be a Blessing. 2009. 32p. pap. 12.99 (978-1-4490-3575-4(2)) AuthorHouse.

Brownback, Lydia. Contentment: A Godly Woman's Adornment. 2008. (On-the-Go Devotionals Ser.). 112p. pap. 10.99 (978-1-58134-958-0(0)) Crossway.

—Joy: A Godly Woman's Adornment. 2010. (On-the-Go Devotionals Ser.). 112p. pap. 10.99 (978-1-4335-1301-5(3)) Crossway.

—Purity: A Godly Woman's Adornment. 2010. (On-the-Go Devotionals Ser.). 136p. pap. 10.99 (978-1-4335-1298-8(X)) Crossway.

—Trust: A Godly Woman's Adornment. 2008. (On-the-Go Devotionals Ser.). 128p. pap. 10.99 (978-1-58134-957-3(2)) Crossway.

Bryan, Ruth. Handfuls of Purpose: Gleanings from the Inner Life of Ruth Bryan. 2006. (ENG.). 496p. per. 28.00 (978-1-60178-003-4(6)) Reformation Heritage Bks.

Burdett-Coutts, Angela Georgina. Woman's Mission. 2009. 426p. pap. (978-0-217-41952-9(6)) Books LLC.

Burgess, Gloria D. The Journey. 2008. (ENG.). 340p. pap. 29.95 (978-1-58982-452-2(0), Millennial Mind Publishing) American Bk. Publishing Group.

Burke, Leanne. The Fight of My Life the Purpose of My Pain. 2009. 155p. 23.50 (978-1-60860-030-4(0), Strategic Bk. Publishing) AEG Literary Publishing Services, Inc.

Burns, Zorina A. Tattoo Love. 2009. 96p. pap. 10.99 (978-1-60791-781-6(5)) Xulon Pr., Inc.

Burton, Valorie. Successful Women Think Differently: 9 Habits to Make You Happier, Healthier, & More Resilient. 2012. 208p. pap. 12.99 (978-0-7369-3856-3(7)) Harvest Hse. Pubs.

Butcher, Carmen Acevedo. A Little Daily Wisdom: Christian Women Mystics. 2008. (Illus.). 311p. pap. 14.95 (978-1-55725-586-0(5)) Paraclete Pr., Inc.

Butt, Sheila, et al. We Bow Down: Women Look at Worship. pap. 8.95 (978-0-929540-28-3(X)) Publishing Designs, Inc.

Cadwallader, Robyn. Three Methods for Reading the Thirteenth-Century Seinte Marherete: Archetypal, Semiotic, & Deconstructionist. 2008. 397p. (978-0-7734-4840-7(3)) Mellen, Edwin Pr., The.

Caine, Christine. Can I Have & Do It All, Please? 2009. 192p. pap. (978-0-9805187-1-9(7)) Equip & Empower Ministries.

Caldwell, Barbara A. Through This 21st Century: Let Others Witness Christ's Love Through Your Actions. 2010. 48p. pap. 9.95 (978-1-4269-2325-8(2)) Trafford Publishing.

Camerer, Lori Kallander. His Still Small Voice. 2008. 168p. 34.95 (978-1-4327-0710-1(8)) Outskirts Pr., Inc.

Campbell, Micca. An Untroubled Heart: Finding a Faith That Is Stronger Than All My Fears, 1 vol. 2009. (ENG.). 240p. pap. 14.99 (978-1-4347-6797-4(3)) Cook, David C.

Cantelow, AliceAnn. Shepherd's Gate: how God built a refuge for women & children. 2007. 120p. pap. 7.99 (978-0-9787281-9-9(X)) LBMG Music.

Capozzi, Ruth Joy. With Tender Hand: Abuse Is Not Love / Love Is Not Abuse. 2011. 108p. 28.95 (978-1-4497-1818-3(3)); pap. 9.95 (978-1-4497-1816-9(7)) Author Solutions, Inc. (WestBow Pr.).

Carlin, Joyce. A Time to Be Deborah. 2009. 134p. pap. 17.00 (978-1-60608-288-1(4), Resource Pubns.) Wipf & Stock Pubs.

Carlisle, Evangelist Dee. I Learned Worship: Through the Things I've Suffered. 2009. 156p. 22.49 (978-1-4490-2177-1(8)); pap. 13.99 (978-1-4490-2176-4(X)) AuthorHouse.

Carr, Rita. My Journey Home: There Is Hope for Single-Parent Families & Hurting Women. 2010. (ENG.). 144p. pap. 10.99 (978-1-61638-158-5(2), Creation Hse.) Charisma Media.

Carradine, Sheree. The joy & the pain of the single christian?? Woman: Lead us not into temptation, but deliver us from all Evil. 2009. 314p. pap. 20.95 (978-1-4327-4456-4(9)) Outskirts Pr., Inc.

Carrell, Laura. The 12 W's of the Christian Woman: Maintaining Balance in Your Walk with God. 2010. 189p. pap. 10.95 (978-1-4327-5960-5(4)) Outskirts Pr., Inc.

Carter, Donna. 10 Smart Things Women Can Do to Build a Better Life. 2007. 160p. pap. 10.99 (978-0-7369-2039-1(0)) Harvest Hse. Pubs.

Carter, Koby A. Overthrowing Jezebel: Ask Me How I Know! 2010. 112p. 21.49 (978-1-4520-3691-5(8)); pap. 13.49 (978-1-4520-3690-8(X)) AuthorHouse.

Carter, Tarran. Emotionally Wounded Spiritually Strong: Victim No More — 7 Healing Prescriptions. 2011. pap. 14.99 (978-1-61663-448-3(0)) Tate Publishing & Enterprises, LLC.

Carver-Jackson, Karen. Dancing While in the Valley: In the Valleys We Grow. 2010. pap. 11.99 (978-1-61566-842-7(X)) Tate Publishing & Enterprises, LLC.

Cathcart, Sandy. Wild Woman: A Daughter's Search for A Father's Love. 2011. 152p. 30.95 (978-1-4497-2514-3(7)); pap. 13.95 (978-1-4497-2513-6(9)) Author Solutions, Inc. (WestBow Pr.).

Catherine of Siena. Little Talks with God. Carrigan, Henry L., Jr., ed. 2007. 144p. per. 9.95 (978-1-55725-531-0(8)) Paraclete Pr., Inc.

Cawthorne Crafton, Barbara. Some Things You Just Have to Live With: Musings on Middle Age. 2007. 176p. pap. 13.00 (978-0-8192-2291-6(7), Morehouse Publishing) Church Publishing, Inc.

Chainey, Billie. Heavenly Seduction - My Induction into a Bizarre Sex Cult. 2009. 378p. pap. 27.97 (978-0-557-07878-3(4)) Lulu Enterprises Inc.

Chan, Zenobia C. Y. Silenced Women. 2009. 167p. 49.00 (978-1-60692-199-9(1)) Nova Science Pubs., Inc.

Chanski, Mark. Womanly Dominion: More Than a Gentle & Quite Spirit. 2008. 240p. pap. 19.99 (978-1-879737-60-0(4)) Calvary Pr.

Chapman, Annie. Letting Go of Anger: How to Get Your Emotions under Control. 2010. 208p. pap. 11.99 (978-0-7369-2473-3(6)) Harvest Hse. Pubs.

—Overcoming Negative Emotions: God's Path to Becoming a Positive Woman. 2011. (Illus.). 192p. pap. 11.99 (978-0-7369-2863-2(4)) Harvest Hse. Pubs.

Chargois, Paige Lanier. Certain Women Called by Christ: Biblical Realities for Today. 2008. (ENG.). 176p. per. 12.99 (978-1-59669-200-8(6)) New Hope Pubs.

Charisma House Staff, contrib. by. From Our Hearts to Yours: Amazing Experiences & Heartfelt Insights from Women Revealing God's Love for You. 2008. (ENG.). 144p. 14.99 (978-1-59979-229-3(X), Charisma Hse.) Charisma Media.

Chastain, A. Ruth. Frontier Girl: True Soldier of the Cross. 2008. (Illus.). 184p. pap. 12.99 (978-1-60462-814-2(6)) Tate Publishing & Enterprises, LLC.

Chole, Alicia Britt. Intimate Conversations: Devotions to Nurture a Woman's Soul, 1 vol. 2009. 160p. pap. 12.99 (978-0-8007-3289-9(8)) Revell.

Christian Art Gifts, creator. A Mother - A Gift from God. 2010. 79p. (978-1-77036-434-9(X)) Christian Art Pubs.

Clairmont, Patsy. I Second That Emotion: Untangling Our Zany Feelings. 2011. 192p. pap. 15.99 (978-0-7852-9841-0(X)) Nelson, Thomas Inc.

—Kaleidoscope of Proverbs: Bits & Pieces Held to the Light, 0 vols. 2010. 208p. 16.99 (978-1-4002-0270-6(1)) Nelson, Thomas Inc.

—Wof: Finding God in the Broken Places, 0 vols. 2008. (Women of Faith Study Guide Ser.). 128p. pap. 9.99 (978-1-4185-3220-8(7)) Nelson, Thomas Inc.

Clark, Diane. Influence of Godly Women. 2008. 93p. per. 20.00 (978-0-9715548-2-5(X)) Victoriously Free! Publishing.

Clark, Linda M. Awaken the Leader in You: 10 Life Essentials for Women in Leadership. 2009. 256p. pap. 12.99 (978-1-59669-221-3(9)) New Hope Pubs.

Clarkson, Sally. Dancing with My Father: How God Leads Us into a Life of Grace & Joy. 2010. (ENG.). 224p. pap. 13.99 (978-0-307-45706-6(0), WaterBrook Pr.) Doubleday Religious Publishing Group, The.

Claus, Mary T. Mary's Little Star. 2011. 111p. pap. 12.95 (978-1-4327-7293-2(7)) Outskirts Pr., Inc.

Clayton, Brenda. Desperate Wives: Help & Hope for Women Considering Separation or Divorce. 2006. (ENG.). 192p. per. 14.99 (978-0-8341-2238-3(3), 083-412-2383) Beacon Hill Pr. of Kansas City.

Clinton, Julie & Byers, Mary M. Extraordinary Women: Secrets to Discovering the Dream God Created for You. 2007. 256p. 19.99 (978-0-7369-2110-7(9)) Harvest Hse. Pubs.

Clinton, Julie & Clinton, Timothy E. A Woman's Path to Emotional Freedom: God's Promise of Hope & Healing. 2010. 224p. pap. 12.99 (978-0-7369-2996-7(7)) Harvest Hse. Pubs.

Coates, Jan. Set Free: God's Healing Power for Abuse Survivors & Those Who Love Them. 2007. 184p. per. 13.99 (978-1-57921-912-3(8)) WinePress Publishing.

Cobb, Nancy. Suitcase Carrier for God. 2007. 185p. pap. 24.95 (978-1-4241-9398-1(2)) PublishAmerica, Inc.

Coffey, Cara Ann. Uncovered No More: Clothed by God. 2011. pap. 16.99 (978-1-61739-555-0(2)) Tate Publishing & Enterprises, LLC.

Cohick, Lynn H. & Smith, James. Women in the World of the Earliest Christians: Illuminating Ancient Ways of Life. 2009. (Illus.). 352p. (C). pap. 26.99 (978-0-8010-3172-4(9)) Baker Academic.

Coker, Elizabeth. F a I T H Faithful Actions Initiated Through Him: A Twelve Week Discipleship Course for Women. 2010. 220p. pap. 17.95 (978-1-61507-266-8(7)) Cross Bks. Publishing.

Cole, Addie, BA. Faith Conquers Determination. 2011. 64p. pap. 15.00 (978-1-4567-1367-4(6)) AuthorHouse.

Cole, Sabrina B. Tragedy into Blessings, 1 vol. 2010. 48p. pap. 16.95 (978-1-4489-9035-1(1)) PublishAmerica, Inc.

Collier-Thomas, Bettye. Jesus, Jobs, & Justice: African American Women & Religion. 2010. (ENG., Illus.). 736p. 37.50 (978-1-4000-4420-7(0), Knopf) Knopf Doubleday Publishing Group.

Collins, Ace. Stories Behind Women of Extraordinary Faith, 1 vol. 2008. (ENG.). 240p. 15.99 (978-0-310-26316-6(6)) Zondervan.

Companjen, Anneke. Singing Through the Night: Courageous Stories of Faith from Women in the Persecuted Church. 2007. 304p. pap. 14.99 (978-0-8007-3198-4(0)) Revell.

Compton, Madonna Sophia, et al. Women Saints: 365 Daily Readings. 2006. (ENG.). 544p. pap. 19.95 (978-0-8245-2413-5(6), Crossroad) Crossroad Publishing Co., The.

Cook, Lupita -Luna. Deliverance Out of Egypt: Time to Break the Chains from Physical Abuse, Mental Abuse & Suicidal Abuse! Time to do it Gods Way! 2011. 64p. pap. 10.43 (978-1-4269-7658-2(5)) Trafford Publishing.

Cooper, Mable Lee. Escape, Faith & Courage of Lou Bertha Flanagan. 2009. 636p. pap. 35.95 (978-1-4401-3145-5(7)) iUniverse, Inc.

Coppedge, Beth & Charalambakis, Fedra. Lydia Prayer Guide: Becoming Women of Prayer. 2007. (Illus.). 16p. pap. 2.00 (978-0-915143-07-8(0)) Francis Asbury Society.

Cornelison, Jane. An Ordinary Woman. 2009. 32p. pap. 12.75 (978-0-557-06453-3(8)) Lulu Enterprises Inc.

Couch, Donna / Erickson. Together but Alone: When God Means Something Different to Your Spouse. 2008. 117p. pap. 11.95 (978-0-86716-852-5(8)) Franciscan Media.

Coughlin, Paul. Unleashing Courageous Faith: The Hidden Power of a Man's Soul. 2009. 288p. 19.99 (978-0-7642-0577-4(3)) Bethany Hse. Pubs.

Coughlin, Paul & Degler, Jennifer D. No More Christian Nice Girl: When Just Being Nice — Instead of Good — Hurts You, Your Family, & Your Friends. 2010. 192p. pap. 14.99 (978-0-7642-0769-3(5)) Bethany Hse. Pubs.

Counselet, Counselor. Born to Testify. 2011. 196p. pap. 24.95 (978-1-4560-7510-1(1)) PublishAmerica, Inc.

Covington, Debbie Sutton. If I Will. 2010. 104p. pap. 10.99 (978-1-60957-561-8(X)) Xulon Pr., Inc.

Craig, Leigh Ann. Wandering Women & Holy Matrons: Women As Pilgrims in the Later Middle Ages. 2009. (978-90-04-17426-9(5)) BRILL.

Crane, Demetrius M. A Love Affair with the Lord. 2012. (978-1-55452-769-4(4)) Essence Publishing.

Currington, Rebecca & Webb, Joan. Bendiciones para Cada Día: Refeigerio Espirtual para Mujeres. 2010. (Spiritual Refreshment Ser.).Tr. of Everyday Blessings. (ENG & SPA.). 224p. pap. 4.99 (978-1-60260-870-2(9), Casa Promesa) Barbour Publishing, Inc.

Cutler, Mary. The First Gleam of Dawn. 2007. 344p. per. 17.99 (978-1-60477-403-0(7)) Xulon Pr., Inc.

Cutsforth, Norma Harker. From Egypt to low: A Journey of Faith. 2011. 298p. pap. 27.95 (978-1-4626-1975-7(4)) PublishAmerica, Inc.

Cynewulf. The Elene of Cynewulf. 2008. 52p. per. (978-1-4065-8602-2(1)) Dodo Pr.

Da Cunha, Cesaltina. A Cowgirl & Her Horse: A Young Girl's Walk with God. 2011. pap. 14.99 (978-1-61777-769-1(2)) Tate Publishing & Enterprises, LLC.

Danielle, Deanna. An Ordinary Person, an Extraordinary Gift. 2011. 188p. 30.95 (978-1-4497-0541-1(3)); pap. 13.95 (978-1-4497-0540-4(5)) Author Solutions, Inc. (WestBow Pr.).

Daniels, Kimberly. Spiritual Housekeeping. 2011. E-Book (978-1-61638-570-5(7), Charisma Hse.) Charisma Media.

Darby, Jo Ann. MGFL! Much Girlfriend Love: Nuggets of Encouragement for the Christian Girlfriend's Heart & Soul. 2011. (ENG.). 152p. pap. 12.95 (978-1-886057-35-7(4)) Warren Publishing, Inc.

Darrah, Victoria Wilson. Journey to Healing for the Brokenhearted: Holding on to Heaven While You Go Through Hell. 2009. 384p. 32.99 (978-1-60791-746-5(7)); pap. 20.99 (978-1-60791-745-8(9)) Xulon Pr., Inc.

David C. Griffin, Lpc Bcpcc & Griffin, David. Date Smart to Marry for Life: Divorce Prevention for Single Christian Women. 2010. 120p. pap. 11.95 (978-1-4497-0035-5(7), WestBow Pr.) Author Solutions, Inc.

David C. Griffin, Lpc Bcpcc, et al. Date Smart to Marry for Life: Divorce Prevention for Single Christian Women. 2010. (ENG.). 120p. 28.95 (978-1-4497-0036-2(5), WestBow Pr.) Author Solutions, Inc.

Davis, Anna L. The College Precipice. 2008. 128p. 21.99 (978-1-60647-318-4(2)); pap. 13.99 (978-1-60477-846-5(6)) Xulon Pr., Inc.

Davis, Evelyn Rose. Equipped to Serve: How God Used a Sinner's Journey Through the Fire to Grow the Kingdom. 2007. 96p. per. 9.99 (978-1-60247-338-6(2)) Tate Publishing & Enterprises, LLC.

Davis, Gail. Not Afraid to Tell Who I Was Because I Know Who I Am. 2011. 92p. pap. 14.99 (978-1-4634-1208-1(8)) AuthorHouse.

Davis, Rachelle. Letters to My Sisters. 2011. pap. 11.95 (978-0-7414-6566-5(3)) Infinity Publishing.

Davis, Susan. In Love with the Whirlwind: When God Takes Your Heart by Storm. 2010. 120p. pap. 14.99 (978-1-4490-8856-9(2)) AuthorHouse.

De Theo, Nolita W. La Mujer de Sus Sueños. 2007. (ENG & SPA.). 172p. 8.99 (978-1-59979-107-4(2), Casa Creacion) Charisma Media.

Dehart, Paige. Unmasked: One Soul's Journey from Anonymity to Identity. 2007. 295p. per. 22.99 (978-1-59886-736-7(9)) Tate Publishing & Enterprises, LLC.

DeMoss, Nancy Leigh. A Place of Quiet Rest: Finding Intimacy with God Through a Daily Devotional Life. 2013. (ENG.). 288p. pap. 14.99 (978-0-8024-6642-6(7)) Moody Pubs.

C

DeMoss, Nancy Leigh, ed. Becoming God's True Woman. 2nd ed. 2008. 208p. pap. 15.99 (978-1-4335-0366-5(2)) Crossway.

DeMuth, Mary E. Beautiful Battle: A Woman's Guide to Spiritual Warfare. 2012. 240p. pap. 13.99 (978-0-7369-4380-2(3)) Harvest Hse. Pubs.

Denas, Treva. When God Came Calling: A Story of Undeserving Mercy & Grace. 2010. pap. 10.99 (978-1-61566-266-1(9)) Tate Publishing & Enterprises, LLC.

Denzey, Nicola. The Bone Gatherers: The Lost Worlds of Early Christian Women. (ENG.). 2008. 312p. pap. 18.00 (978-0-8070-1309-0(9)) 2007. 300p. (978-0-8070-1308-3(0)) Beacon Pr.

Desmond, Janell Haworth. My Heart Will Always Cry: A Mother's Journey of Hope & Healing for Her Hurting Heart. 2011. 116p. pap. 28.95 (978-1-4497-1605-9(9)); pap. 11.95 (978-1-4497-1604-2(0)) Author Solutions, Inc. (WestBow Pr.).

DeVries, Kelly. Joan of Arc: A Military Leader. 2011. (ENG., Illus.). 252p. pap. 16.95 (978-0-7524-6061-1(7)) History Pr. Ltd., The GBR. Dist: Independent Pubs. Group.

Diamond, Susan Ward. The Daily Grind: God with Your Coffee. 2011. 172p. 24.99 (978-1-4567-5213-2(8)); pap. 17.99 (978-1-4567-5214-9(6)) AuthorHouse.

Dillman, Rena Blake. In Sickness & in Health. 2010. 88p. pap. 14.00 (978-1-4490-7984-0(9)) AuthorHouse.

Dillow, Linda. Satisfy My Thirsty Soul: For I Am Desperate for Your Presence. 2007. (Quiet Times for the Heart Ser.). (ENG.). 304p. per. 15.99 (978-1-57683-390-2(9)) NavPress Publishing Group.

Dillow, Linda & Pintus, Lorraine. Intimate Issues: Twenty-One Questions Christian Women Ask about Sex. 2009. (ENG.). 304p. pap. 14.99 (978-0-307-44494-3(5), WaterBrook Pr.) Doubleday Religious Publishing Group, The.

Dilmore, Don. God, Hold Me While I Cry: How God Used Others to Bless Anna's Life. 2011. 200p. pap. 15.99 (978-1-4567-4503-5(4)) AuthorHouse.

DiMarco, Hayley. The Woman of Mystery: Unveiling the Secret to True Romance. 2009. (ENG.). 192p. pap. 14.99 (978-1-4143-2468-5(5)) Tyndale Hse. Pubs.

DiMickele, Susan. Chasing Superwoman: A Working Mom's Adventures in Life & Faith, 1 vol. 2010. (ENG.). 224p. pap. 14.99 (978-1-4347-6462-1(1)) Cook, David C.

DiMickele, Susan M. Chasing Superwoman: A Working Mom's Adventures in Life & Faith. 2010. 224p. E-Book (978-0-7814-0450-1(9)) Kingsway Pubns.

Ditchfield, Christin. A Way with Words: What Women Should Know about the Power They Possess. 2010. 176p. pap. 12.99 (978-1-4335-0284-2(4)) Crossway.

Ditrick, Eleanor & Chap. Flutter By. 2008. 292p. pap. 16.00 (978-1-59858-792-0(7)) Dog Ear Publishing, LLC.

Dixon, Sandy. You Are Washed in the Water of the Word. 2008. 152p. pap. 13.99 (978-1-60477-697-3(8)) Xulon Pr., Inc.

Dollar, Taffi L. Your Spiritual Makeover: Experience the Beauty of a Balanced Life: Spirit, Soul & Body. 224p. 2010. pap. 13.99 (978-1-57794-974-9(9)) 2007. 19.99 (978-1-57794-914-5(5)) Harrison House Pubs.

Donaldson, James. Woman: Her Position & Influence in Ancient Greece & Rome, & Among Early Christians. 278p. reprint ed. 98.00 (978-0-7222-1516-6(9)) Library Reprints, Inc.

Downing, Bessie. In My Father's House. 2010. (ENG.). 172p. pap. 14.00 (978-1-4349-0539-0(X)) Dorrance Publishing Co., Inc.

Draper, T. Shanae. I'm No Supermodel!, 1 vol. 2010. 80p. pap. 19.95 (978-1-61546-998-7(2)) PublishAmerica, Inc.

Duckworth, M. La Mujer Decidida.Tr. of Decisive Woman. 6.99 (978-1-56063-636-6(X), 495103) Editorial Unilit.

Dunbar, Agnes B. C. A Dictionary of Saintly Women, 2 Vols. reprint ed. 250.00 (978-0-7222-1729-0(3)) Library Reprints, Inc.

Dutton, Anne. A Heart Renewed. 2008. 80p. pap. 11.99 (978-1-60647-303-0(4)) Xulon Pr., Inc.

Eckert, Kim Gaines. Stronger Than You Think: Becoming Whole Without Having to Be Perfect - A Woman's Guide. 2007. (ENG.). 241p. per. 16.00 (978-0-8308-3373-3(0), IVP Bks.) InterVarsity Pr.

Eckert, Ruth. Life after Heroin. 2010. 36p. pap. 8.99 (978-0-88144-240-3(2)) Yorkshire Publishing Group.

Eckles, Janet. Simply Salsa: Dancing Without Fear at God's Fiesta. 2011. 160p. pap. 13.99 (978-0-8170-1701-9(1)) Judson Pr.

Eden, Dawn. The Thrill of the Chaste: Finding Fulfillment While Keeping Your Clothes On, 0 vols. 2006. 224p. per. 13.99 (978-0-8499-1311-2(X)) Nelson, Thomas Inc.

Edwards, Marva J. Bound to Be Free: Breaking Free from Domestic Violence. 2010. 124p. (ENG.). 23.50 (978-1-4490-8517-9(2)); pap. 13.99 (978-1-4490-8513-1(X)) AuthorHouse.

Edwards, Sue. Proverbs: Ancient Wisdom for a Postmodern World, 1 vol. 2007. (Sue Edwards Inductive Bible Study Ser.). 96p. pap. 12.99 (978-0-8254-2548-6(4)); pap. 12.99 (978-0-8254-2547-9(6)) Kregel Pubns.

Egan, Gwendolyn & Egan, Dorothy "Dori". Shattered Secrets: Gwendolyn's Journey Through the Dark World of Multiple Personalities. 2011. 188p. pap. 13.95 (978-1-61507-727-4(8)) Cross Bks. Publishing.

Ehman, Karen. The Complete Guide to Getting & Staying Organized: Manage Your Time, Eliminate Clutter & Experience Order, Keep Your Family First. 2008. 219p. per. 12.99 (978-0-7369-2074-2(9)) Harvest Hse. Pubs.

—A Life That Says Welcome: Simple Ways to Open Your Heart & Home to Others. 2006. 240p. pap. 13.99 (978-0-8007-3139-7(5)) Revell.

Eldar, Dorthy Murray. Whispers from God. 2011. 348p. pap. 18.99 (978-1-61215-459-6(X)) Xulon Pr., Inc.

Eldredge, John & Eldredge, Stasi. Captivating: Unveiling the Mystery of a Woman's Soul. l.t. ed. 2007. (ENG.). 356p. (J). pap. 16.95 (978-1-59415-110-1(5), Walker Large Print) Cengage Gale.

—Captivating: Unveiling the Mystery of a Woman's Soul. 2011. 256p. pap. 16.99 (978-1-4002-0038-2(5)) Nelson, Thomas Inc.

Elizabeth Clare Prophet. Preparation for My Mission. 2009. 428p. pap. 26.95 (978-1-4401-7394-3(X)) iUniverse, Inc.

Elledge, Dawn. Dawn-Ings: The Journey of a Lifetime. 2010. 218p. pap. 15.99 (978-1-61579-701-1(7)) Xulon Pr., Inc.

Ellis, Wendy. The Hands of Time: A Passionate Look at Mentoring God's Way. 2010. 124p. 21.95 (978-1-60976-281-0(9), Strategic Bk. Publishing) AEG Literary Publishing Services, Inc.

Ellison, Edna. Stronger Still: A Woman's Guide to Turning Your Hurt into Healing for Others. 2007. (ENG., Illus.). 224p. per. 14.99 (978-1-59669-090-5(9)) New Hope Pubs.

Ethridge, Shannon. Completely His: Loving Jesus Without Limits. 2008. (ENG.). 224p. 13.99 (978-1-4000-7492-1(4)) Doubleday Religious Publishing Group, The.

—Every Woman's Battle: Discovering God's Plan for Sexual & Emotional Fulfillment. 2009. (Every Man Ser.). (ENG.). 288p. pap. 14.99 (978-0-307-45798-1(2), WaterBrook Pr.) Doubleday Religious Publishing Group, The.

—Every Woman's Marriage: Igniting the Joy & Passion You Both Desire. 2010. (Every Man Ser.). (ENG.). 320p. pap. 15.99 (978-0-307-45857-5(1), WaterBrook Pr.) Doubleday Religious Publishing Group, The.

Evans, Linda L. Will You Sparkle in the Light: An End-of-the-Age Crash Course in the Supernatural & Spiritual Things of God. 2011. 320p. pap. 22.95 (978-1-4497-1959-3(7), WestBow Pr.) Author Solutions, Inc.

Evans, Samantha. Love Letters to Miscarried Moms: Written in the midst of my grief so that you will not be alone in Yours. 2011. 128p. 28.95 (978-1-4497-1004-0(2)); pap. 11.95 (978-1-4497-1002-6(6)) Author Solutions, Inc. (WestBow Pr.).

Faithful, I. M. The Road to Visions, Dreams & Miracles. 2011. 88p. 24.99 (978-1-4568-6110-0(7)); pap. 15.99 (978-1-4568-6109-4(3)) Xlibris Corp.

Fawley, Carla Rae. Serendipity! 30 Day Devotional. 2011. 80p. pap. 12.99 (978-1-4634-2065-9(X)) AuthorHouse.

Ferguson, Mindy. Hugs Bible Reflections for Women: 52 Inspirational Studies & Stories to Draw You Closer to God. 2009. (ENG., Illus.). 224p. pap. 14.99 (978-1-4165-8722-4(5), Howard Bks.) Howard Books.

Ferguson, Shirley. No Longer Bound. 2008. 64p. pap. 10.99 (978-1-60647-993-3(8)) Xulon Pr., Inc.

Ferree, Mamie C. No Stones: Women Redeemed from Sexual Addiction. 2010. (ENG.). 276p. pap. 20.00 (978-0-8308-3740-3(X), IVP Bks.) InterVarsity Pr.

First Place 4 Health. Balanced Living. 2010. (First Place Ser.). (ENG.). 256p. 19.99 (978-0-8307-5396-3(6)) Gospel Light Pubns.

—Healthy Summer Living. 2009. (First Place Ser.). (ENG.). 192p. pap. 14.99 (978-0-8307-4722-1(2)) Gospel Light Pubns.

First Place 4 Health & First Place 4 Health. Celebrate Success. 2009. (First Place Ser.). (ENG.). 256p. 19.99 (978-0-8307-4755-9(9)) Gospel Light Pubns.

Fitzpatrick, Carol Lynn. 365 One-Minute Meditations from Daily Wisdom for Women. 2009. (One minute Meditations Ser.). (ENG.). 384p. pap. 9.99 (978-1-60260-371-4(5), Barbour Bks.) Barbour Publishing, Inc.

Fitzpatrick, Elyse. Comforts from the Cross: Celebrating the Gospel One Day at a Time. 2009. 146p. (978-1-4335-0556-0(8)) Crossway.

Fitzpatrick, Elyse M. Because He Loves Me: How Christ Transforms Our Daily Life. 2010. 224p. pap. 15.99 (978-1-4335-1951-2(8)) Crossway.

—Comforts from the Cross: Celebrating the Gospel One Day at a Time. 2011. 152p. pap. 14.99 (978-1-4335-2821-7(5)) Crossway.

Flaaten, Rosemary. A Woman & Her Relationships: Transforming the Way We Connect. 2007. (ENG.). 192p. per. 14.99 (978-0-8341-2338-0(X), 083-412-338X) Beacon Hill Pr. of Kansas City.

—A Woman & Her Workplace: Building Healthy Relationships from 9 To 5. 2010. (ENG.). 192p. pap. 14.99 (978-0-8341-2523-0(4), 9780834125230) Beacon Hill Pr. of Kansas City.

Floch, Carol. The Single Mom's Devotional: A Book of 52 Practical & Encouraging Devotions. 2009. (ENG.). 176p. pap. 12.99 (978-0-8307-5161-7(0)) Gospel Light Pubns.

Flory, Susy. So Long, Status Quo: What I Learned from Women Who Changed the World. 2009. (ENG.). 160p. pap. 13.99 (978-0-8341-2438-7(6), 9780834124387) Beacon Hill Pr. of Kansas City.

Floyd, Heidi. In a Word: Quiet Little Thoughts About God. 2011. 128p. pap. 9.99 (978-0-7586-2727-8(0)) Concordia Publishing Hse.

Fortener, Dorathea. A Life of Promise: Surviving Adversity through Faith. 2009. pap. 23.99 (978-1-60799-417-6(8)) Tate Publishing & Enterprises, LLC.

Foxworth Holman, Debra. Thanks to Jesus, I Am Still Here: My not so Private Journey. 2009. 108p. 24.99 (978-1-4490-0936-6(0)); pap. 15.99 (978-1-4490-0938-0(7)) AuthorHouse.

Frahm-Arp, Maria. Professional Women in South African Pentecostal Charismatic Churches. 2009. (Studies of Religion in Africa Ser.). 296p. (978-90-04-16875-6(3)) BRILL.

Frisina, Susan Weston. Soul Food: Encouraging Words for the Hungry Heart. 2009. 300p. pap. 18.99 (978-1-61579-079-1(9)) Xulon Pr., Inc.

Frone, Barbara. My Journey with God. 2010. 108p. (ENG.). 28.95 (978-1-4497-0137-6(X)); pap. 11.95 (978-1-4497-0135-2(3)) Author Solutions, Inc. (WestBow Pr.).

Gabrielson, Sarah. Love God, Live Life. 2011. 96p. pap. 10.99 (978-1-61379-704-4(4)) Xulon Pr., Inc.

Gallington, Edna M. Watching from the Shadows: Through Eyes of Passion, 24 Biblical Women Tell Their Stories. 2010. 120p. (ENG.). 28.95 (978-1-4497-0255-7(4)); pap. 11.95 (978-1-4497-0254-0(6)) Author Solutions, Inc. (WestBow Pr.).

Garrison, Brenda. Princess Unaware: Finding the Fabulous in Every Day. 2009. (ENG.). 288p. pap. 14.99 (978-0-7847-2118-6(1)) Standard Publishing.

Garza, Crystal. The Modest Heart. 2007. 108p. per. 10.99 (978-1-60477-276-0(X)) Xulon Pr., Inc.

Gass, Kim Wilkins. In Daddy's Arms: Being a Preacher's Kid Becoming a Child of Jesus the Miraculous. 2009. 324p. pap. 18.99 (978-1-60791-227-9(9)) Xulon Pr., Inc.

George, Denise. What Women Wish Pastors Knew: Understanding the Hopes, Hurts, Needs, & Dreams of Women in the Church, 1 vol. 2007. (ENG., Illus.). 208p. 16.99 (978-0-310-26930-4(X)) Zondervan.

George, Elizabeth. Breaking the Worry Habit... Forever! God's Plan for Lasting Peace of Mind. l.t. ed. 2009. (ENG.). 320p. pap. 17.99 (978-1-59415-302-0(7)) Cengage Gale.

—Breaking the Worry Habit... Forever! God's Plan for Lasting Peace of Mind. 2009. 272p. pap. 12.99 (978-0-7369-1927-2(9)) Harvest Hse. Pubs.

—Finding God's Path Through Your Trials Growth & Study Guide. 2007. 160p. pap. 8.99 (978-0-7369-1652-3(0)) Harvest Hse. Pubs.

—Following God with All Your Heart: Believing & Living God's Plan for You. 2008. 250p. pap. 13.99 (978-0-7369-0504-6(9)) Harvest Hse. Pubs.

—A Woman after God's Own Heart. 303p. 2007. (Illus.). 17.99 (978-0-7369-2046-9(3)) 2006. per. 13.99 (978-0-7369-1883-1(3)) Harvest Hse. Pubs.

—A Woman after God's Own Heart: Growth & Study Guide. 2006. (Illus.). 175p. per. 8.99 (978-0-7369-1884-8(1)) Harvest Hse. Pubs.

—A Woman after God's Own Heart — A Daily Devotional. 2007. 384p. pap. 13.99 (978-0-7369-2081-0(1)) Harvest Hse. Pubs.

—A Woman after God's Own Heart(r) Collection. 2006. 816p. pap. 26.97 (978-0-7369-1882-4(5)) Harvest Hse. Pubs.

—Womans High Calling: 10 Ways to Live Out God's Plan for Your Life. 2011. 304p. pap. 13.99 (978-0-7369-3027-2(2)) Harvest Hse. Pubs.

—A Young Woman after God's Own Heart: A Devotional. 2008. 149p. (YA). (gr. 7-12). 9.99 (978-0-7369-2297-5(0)) Harvest Hse. Pubs.

Georgia Yates Blount & Olivia Sebastian. From God the Promise: Memoir of a Holy Woman. 2009. 312p. 29.95 (978-1-4389-7033-2(1)); pap. 23.95 (978-1-4389-7034-9(X)) AuthorHouse.

Gibbs, Terri, compiled by. Glimmers of Grace: Sparkling Reminders to Encourage You, 0 vols. 2008. (Women of Faith Ser.). (Illus.). 128p. 12.99 (978-1-4041-0478-5(X)) Nelson, Thomas Inc.

Gibson, Jean. Seasons of Womanhood: Stories of despair & Hope. 2007. (ENG.). 155p. 14.99 (978-1-86024-627-2(3)) Authentic Media.

Giles, Elizabeth (Liz). A Beginner's Journey, 1 vol. 2010. 83p. pap. 16.95 (978-1-4489-8594-4(3)) PublishAmerica, Inc.

Glahn, Sandra. Cappuccino with Colossians. 2007. (Coffee Cup Bible Studies). (ENG.). 176p. spiral bd. 12.99 (978-0-89957-234-5(0)) AMG Pubs.

—Premium Roast with Ruth. 2007. (Coffee Cup Bible Studies). (ENG.). 176p. (gr. 11). spiral bd. 12.99 (978-0-89957-236-9(7)) AMG Pubs.

Godfrey, Erika R. Single Ladies, C L a P Your Hands - Celebrating Life Always Praising. 2008. 80p. pap. 10.99 (978-1-60647-759-5(5)) Xulon Pr., Inc.

Godley, Pamela. Gods Pearl. 2006. pap. 10.99 (978-1-60034-482-4(8)) Xulon Pr., Inc.

Goldstone, Nancy. The Maid & the Queen: The Secret History of Joan of Arc. 2012. (ENG.). 320p. (gr. 12). 26.95 (978-0-670-02333-2(7), Viking Adult) Penguin Group (USA) Inc.

Gonzales, Adelaida M. My Amazing Journey with God. 2009. 84p. pap. 10.99 (978-1-61579-601-4(0)) Xulon Pr., Inc.

Goodboy, Eadie. A Woman after God's Heart. 2010. (Women of the Word Bible Study Ser.). (ENG.). 128p. pap. 9.99 (978-0-8307-5233-1(1)) Gospel Light Pubns.

Goode, Christee T. Thirty Something. 2007. 104p. per. 9.99 (978-1-59886-620-9(6)) Tate Publishing & Enterprises, LLC.

Graves, Lori. Chasing the Light: ... a Journey Through the Healing. 2010. 128p. 24.50 (978-1-4269-3873-3(X)); pap. 14.50 (978-1-4269-3872-6(1)) Trafford Publishing.

Gray, Alice. Small Acts of Grace: You Can Make a Difference in Everday, Ordinary Ways, 0 vols. 2006. 208p. per. 10.99 (978-0-8499-0448-6(X)) Nelson, Thomas Inc.

—Treasures for Women Who Hope. l.t. ed. 2007. (Walker Large Print Ser.). (ENG.). 256p. per. 16.95 (978-1-59415-157-6(1), Walker Large Print) Cengage Gale.

Green, Bishop Jackie. The Hurt Lady: Spiritual Warfare Manual. 2009. 408p. 28.49 (978-1-4389-3708-3(3)); pap. 17.99 (978-1-4389-3707-6(5)) AuthorHouse.

Green, Janelle. This Earthly Tent: Me, God & MS. 2008. 124p. pap. 11.99 (978-1-60647-612-3(2)) Xulon Pr., Inc.

Greiner, Laura & Escobar, Kathy. Refresh: Sharing Stories. Building Faith. 2007. (ENG.). 160p. pap. 14.99 (978-1-59669-069-1(0)) New Hope Pubs.

Greiner, Laura & Kohring, Sharon. Rendezvous Joy Ride Philippians: Bible Study Leader Guide. 2007. (Illus.). 96p. pap. 24.99 incl. cd-rom (978-0-7644-3512-6(4)) Group Publishing, Inc.

—Rendezvous Joy Ride Phillipians: Personal Guidebook for Bible Study. 2007. (Illus.). 80p. per. 7.99 (978-0-7644-3511-9(6)) Group Publishing, Inc.

Greiner, Laura Ross. TruthDare: Dare to Live the Truth You Believe, 1 vol. 2010. 144p. pap. 11.99 (978-0-8254-2738-1(X)) Kregel Pubns.

Gresh, Dannah. Five Little Questions: That Reveal the Life God Designed for You, 0 vols. 2007. (Illus.). 208p. per. 13.99 (978-0-7852-1244-7(2)) Nelson, Thomas Inc.

—Five Little Questions That Reveal the Life God Designed for You Guided Meditation Journal, 0 vols. 2007. (Illus.). 128p. per. 9.99 (978-1-4185-2834-8(X)) Nelson, Thomas Inc.

Griffin, Lashae. Faith in the Midst of Adversity. 2011. pap. 11.95 (978-0-7414-6659-4(7)) Infinity Publishing.

Griffith, Marilynn, compiled by. SistahFaith: Real Stories of Pain, Truth, & Triumph. 2010. (ENG.). 240p. pap. 14.99 (978-1-4391-5277-5(2), Howard Bks.) Howard Books.

Griffiths, Fiona J. The Garden of Delights: Reform & Renaissance for Women in the Twelfth Century. 2006. (Middle Ages Ser.). (Illus.). 412p. (C). 69.95 (978-0-8122-3960-7(1)) Univ. of Pennsylvania Pr.

Group Publishing, compiled by. Simply Relevant Chocolate Boutique: Relational Bible Series for Women. 2007. (Illus.). 80p. per. 9.99 (978-0-7644-3445-7(4)) Group Publishing, Inc.

—Simply Relevant Heart Spa: Relational Bible Series for Women. 2007. (Illus.). 80p. per. 9.99 (978-0-7644-3444-0(6)) Group Publishing, Inc.

Guthrie, Nancy. Hoping for Something Better: Refusing to Settle for Life as Usual. 2007. (ENG.). 240p. per. 14.99 (978-1-4143-1307-8(1), SaltRiver) Tyndale Hse. Pubs.

Hale, Cynthia. I'm a Piece of Work! Sisters Shaped by God. 2010. 144p. pap. 16.00 (978-0-8170-1571-8(X)) Judson Pr.

Hall, Josie. Durbin Memoirs. 2011. 70p. 24.99 (978-1-4628-5862-0(7)); pap. 15.99 (978-1-4628-5861-3(9)) Xlibris Corp.

Hall, Lula. Call Me Abar or Call Me Eve: Redefining the Female Gender. 2011. 192p. pap. 16.95 (978-1-4670-6117-9(4)) AuthorHouse.

Hall-Williams, Shirley. No Place for a Woman: Examining Leadership in the Church. 2010. pap. 10.99 (978-1-61663-779-8(X)) Tate Publishing & Enterprises, LLC.

Hallman, Barbara Anne. Hands that Hold Hearts: Contemplating the Outreach of Love. 2011. 68p. pap. 24.45 (978-1-4497-1161-0(8), WestBow Pr.) Author Solutions, Inc.

Hamilton, Nancy. Pieces of My Life. 2009. pap. 9.99 (978-1-60799-823-5(8)) Tate Publishing & Enterprises, LLC.

Hammond, Michelle McKinney. The Diva Principle. l.t. ed. 28.95 (978-0-7862-7161-0(2), Large Print Pr.) Thorndike Pr.

—Divanomics: How to Still Be Fabulous When You're Broke. 2010. (ENG.). 272p. pap. 12.99 (978-1-4143-3382-3(X)) Tyndale Hse. Pubs.

—How to Avoid the 10 Mistakes Single Women Make. 2006. 206p. per. 12.99 (978-0-7369-1391-1(2)) Harvest Hse. Pubs.

—The Real Skinny on Losing It: True Confessions & Divine Revelations of a Former Yo-Yo Dieter. 2010. (ENG.). 224p. pap. 12.99 (978-1-4143-3383-0(8)) Tyndale Hse. Pubs.

Hamon, Jane. The Deborah Company: Becoming a Woman Who Makes a Difference. 2007. 313p. per. 15.99 (978-0-7684-2426-3(7)) Destiny Image Pubs.

Haney, Joy. Passing the Mantle. 2006. 207p. pap. 14.99 (978-1-56722-700-0(7)) Word Aflame Pr.

Harling, Becky. Rewriting Your Emotional Script: Erase Old Messages, Embrace New Attitudes. 2008. (Growing in Christ Ser.). (ENG.). 240p. pap. 14.99 (978-1-60006-188-2(5)) NavPress Publishing Group.

Harmon, Joan. Woman of Warfare. 2010. 116p. pap. 11.95 (978-1-4497-0413-1(1), WestBow Pr.) Author Solutions, Inc.

Harper, Chris. Inspiration Vitamin for Christian Mothers. 2011. 60p. pap. 12.99 (978-1-4634-0160-3(4)) AuthorHouse.

Harper, Lisa. What the Bible Is All about for Women: A Book of 66 Devotions. 2007. (ENG.). 224p. per. 14.99 (978-0-8307-4406-0(1)) Gospel Light Pubns.

Harper Ms, Carolyn. Why Didnt Anybody Ever Tell Me about Thi. 2006. (ENG.). 24.99 (978-1-60034-905-8(6)); pap. 14.99 (978-1-60034-904-1(8)) Xulon Pr., Inc.

Harrell, Sheena. How God Delivered Me from a Spirit of Fear. 2008. 72p. pap. 10.99 (978-1-60791-121-0(3)) Xulon Pr., Inc.

Harris, Frances S. Straight Talk on God's Undying Love for His Unique Women. 2011. 52p. pap. 15.99 (978-1-4568-4682-4(5)) Xlibris Corp.

Harris, Laura Leigh. Wanted: God's Women for America - Adventure Group (Booklet 10), 12 vols., Vol. 10. 2007. 32p. stu. ed. 6.99 (978-0-9797389-0-6(3)) Jeremiah's Tree Adventures LLC.

—Wanted: God's Women for America - Adventure Group (Booklet 11), 12 vols., Vol. 11. 2007. 32p. stu. ed. 6.99 (978-0-9797389-1-3(1)) Jeremiah's Tree Adventures LLC.

—Wanted: God's Women for America - Adventure Group (Booklet 12), 12 vols., Vol. 12. 2007. 34p. 6.99 (978-0-9797389-2-0(X)) Jeremiah's Tree Adventures LLC.

—Wanted: God's Women for America - Adventure Group (Leader's Guide) 2007. 32p. ldr.'s hndbk. ed. 6.99 (978-0-9797389-3-7(8)) Jeremiah's Tree Adventures LLC.

Harris, S. K. Walt. 2010. 159p. pap. 19.99 (978-1-4500-9602-7(6)) Xlibris Corp.

Harvest House Publishers. Walking with God in the Quiet Places: Devotions for Women. 2009. 272p. 9.99 (978-0-7369-2798-7(0)) Harvest Hse. Pubs.

Harvey, Evangelist Elaine. I Am a Survivor. 2009. 80p. pap. 10.99 (978-1-60791-698-7(3)) Xulon Pr., Inc.

Hasak, Jan. Mourning Has Broken. 2008. 304p. pap. 17.99 (978-1-60647-252-1(6)) Xulon Pr., Inc.

Hauser, Penny Mary. Broken by Addiction, Blessed by God. 2010. 16.99 *(978-0-7648-1893-6(7))* Liguori Pubns.

Hayden, Londa. Date, Pray, Wait. 2011. 118p. pap. 19.95 ***(978-1-4560-1154-3(5))*** PublishAmerica, Inc.

Heald, Cynthia. Becoming a Woman of Faith: Fixing our eyes on Jesus, the author & perfecter of faith. Hebrews 12:2. 2009. (Becoming a Woman Of ... Ser.). (ENG.). 112p. pap. 9.99 *(978-1-61521-021-3(0))* NavPress Publishing Group.

—Drawing near to the Heart of God: Encouragement for Your Lifetime Journey. 2011. (NavPress Devotional Readers Ser.). 272p. pap. 14.99 ***(978-1-61521-622-2(7))*** NavPress Publishing Group.

—Life Promises for Women: Inspirational Scriptures & Devotional Thoughts. 2011. (ENG.). 224p. 9.99 *(978-1-4143-3729-6(9))* Tyndale Hse. Pubs.

—Uncommon Beauty: 7 Qualities of a Beautiful Woman. 2007. (ENG.). 208p. per. 12.99 *(978-1-4143-0085-6(9))* Tyndale Hse. Pubs.

Heidish, Marcy. Defiant Daughters: Christian Women of Conscience. 2010. 256p. pap. 16.99 *(978-0-7648-1950-6(X))* Liguori Pubns.

Heim, Joanne. Misplacing God: And Finding Him Again, 1 vol. 2009. 160p. pap. 11.99 *(978-0-8254-2759-6(2))* Kregel Pubns.

Helen Robertson, Robertson, et al. A Miraculous Experience: Will You Take the Time to Have One? 2010. 180p. pap. 13.95 *(978-1-4497-0064-5(0),* WestBow Pr.) Author Solutions, Inc.

Hemm, Cindi, et al. Miracle on Southwest Boulevard: Eugene Field Elementary the Remarkable True Story of One Woman's Perseverance & Faith to Change the World, One Child at A Time. A Study in Community Schools. How to Turn A Low Performing School into A Place of Academic Ex. 2011. 144p. 28.95 *(978-1-4497-1454-3(4))*; pap. 11.95 *(978-1-4497-1452-9(8))* Author Solutions, Inc. (WestBow Pr.).

Henderson, Betty. Divine Service: A Woman's Bible Study. 2010. viii, 152p. pap. *(978-1-60682-158-9(X))* BJU Pr.

Henderson, Carol, ed. Wide Open Spaces: Women Exploring Call through Stories & Reflections. 2011. (ENG.). 176p. pap. 14.95 *(978-1-84694-563-2(1))* O Bks.,John Hunt.

Henry, Lorraine. Flip Side of a Coin. 2010. 116p. pap. 12.99 *(978-1-4490-5344-4(0))* AuthorHouse.

Hensel, Sylvia. From the Heart of A Woman: Love Letters to My Lord. 2011. 124p. 28.95 ***(978-1-4497-2761-1(1))***; pap. 11.95 ***(978-1-4497-2760-4(3))*** Author Solutions, Inc. (WestBow Pr.).

Hensley, Cathy. Morning Came Suddenly. 2010. 120p. pap. 10.99 *(978-1-4490-9745-5(6))* AuthorHouse.

her Children, Collected by. A Collection of Ethel Layman Schlossnagle's Inspirations. 2010. 55p. pap. 19.50 *(978-0-557-35619-5(9))* Lulu Enterprises Inc.

Herbert, Beulah. Self Perception of Tamil Christian Women. 2010. 348p. pap. *(978-3-639-25030-5(3))*; 384p. pap. *(978-3-639-15582-2(3))* VDM Verlag Dr. Mueller e.K.

Hicks, Patricia. Tests, Trials, & Testimonies. 2011. 286p. pap. 16.99 *(978-1-61215-752-8(1))* Xulon Pr., Inc.

Higgs, Liz Curtis. Embrace Grace: Welcome to the Forgiven Life. 2006. (ENG., Illus.). 160p. 13.99 *(978-1-4000-7218-7(2),* WaterBrook Pr.) Doubleday Religious Publishing Group, The.

—Slightly Bad Girls of the Bible: Flawed Women Loved by a Flawless God. l.t. ed. 2009. (ENG.). 480p. pap. 17.95 *(978-1-59415-244-3(6),* Walker Large Print) Cengage Gale.

—Slightly Bad Girls of the Bible: Flawed Women Loved by a Flawless God. 2007. (ENG.). 288p. pap. 13.99 *(978-1-4000-7212-5(3),* WaterBrook Pr.) Doubleday Religious Publishing Group, The.

Hill, Zakiyyah. Descendants of Tamar. 2007. 132p. per. 13.99 *(978-1-60477-099-5(6))* Xulon Pr., Inc.

Hines, Pamela. The Fabric of a Woman: Investing in You - Body, Soul, & Spirit. 2009. pap. 12.99 *(978-1-60374-126-2(7))* Whitaker Hse.

—A Wife's Prayer: Seeking God's Best for Your Husband. 2007. 174p. per. 12.99 *(978-0-88368-204-3(4))* Whitaker Hse.

Hislop, Bev. Shepherding Women in Pain: Real Women, Real Issues & What You Need to Know to Truly Help, 1 vol. 2010. (ENG.). 384p. pap. 14.99 *(978-0-8024-7705-7(4))* Moody Pubs.

Hobgood, Debra. In These Shoes. 2010. 384p. 28.49 *(978-1-4520-5655-5(2))*; pap. 17.99 *(978-1-4520-5646-3(3))* AuthorHouse.

Hodasi, Jacquelyne K. The Woman Inside. 2008. 75p. pap. 16.95 *(978-1-60474-830-7(3))* PublishAmerica, Inc.

Hogue, Donna Kay. Divorce Happens... even to Christians! Healing begins with Chocolate Cake. 2007. 118p. pap. 12.00 *(978-0-9776181-1-8(0))* Oasis Printing.

Hollies, Linda H. Beloved, You Can Win! Strategies for Walking Your Talk. 2008. 144p. 16.00 *(978-0-8298-1792-8(1))* Pilgrim Pr., The/United Church Pr.

Hollis, Heidi. Jesus Is No Joke: A True Story of an Unlikely Witness Who Saw Jesus. 2008. 188p. pap. 16.95 *(978-0-615-19005-1(7))* Level Head Publishing.

Hoover, Mae. The Journey to & from the Mountain. 2010. 212p. pap. 15.99 *(978-1-60957-626-4(8))* Xulon Pr., Inc.

Horn, Sara. God Strong: The Military Wife's Spiritual Survival Guide, 1 vol. 2010. (ENG.). 240p. pap. 14.99 *(978-0-310-29402-3(9))* Zondervan.

Horst, Tamyra. Praying Like Crazy for Your Husband. 2010. pap. 12.99 *(978-0-8163-2425-5(5))* Pacific Pr. Publishing Assn.

Houston, Bobbie. I'll Have What She's Having: The Ultimate Compliment to Any Woman Daring to Change Her World, 0 vols. 2008. (Illus.). 192p. pap. 14.99 *(978-0-8499-1977-0(0))* Nelson, Thomas Inc.

Howard, Annie Louise. The Sharecroppers Daughter. 2008. 84p. pap. 15.99 *(978-1-4363-2529-5(3))* Xlibris Corp.

Howard Books Staff. My Pocket Prayer Partner for Women. 2007. (ENG., Illus.). 224p. pap. 15.99 *(978-1-4165-4217-9(5),* Howard Bks.) Howard Books.

Howard, Chrys. Motivationals for Mom: Inspiring You to Be All You Can Be. 2011. (ENG.). 176p. pap. 12.99 ***(978-1-4516-6567-3(9),*** Howard Bks.) Howard Books.

Howard, Judy. Heavenly Patchwork II: Quilt Stories to Warm Your Heart. 2007. (Illus.). 182p. 14.95 *(978-0-9762375-2-5(0))* Dorcas Publishing.

Howard, Ruth Gordon. Energy for God's Women! 5 Steps to Restore the Energy, Joy, & Balance to Your Life. 2007. 155p. pap. *(978-0-9791489-0-3(1))* Mission Hills Publishing.

Howard, Sara M. Tuesday s Grace. 2011. 222p. pap. 15.99 *(978-1-61215-589-0(8))* Xulon Pr., Inc.

Howe, Michele. Still Going It Alone: Mothering with Faith & Finesse When the Children Have Grown. 2009. 130p. pap. 14.95 *(978-1-59856-241-5(X))* Hendrickson Pubs. Marketing, LLC.

Howell, Sarah L. Ephesians: Finding True Love. 2008. (Heart Stealers Bible Studies). (ENG.). 160p. (gr. 11). per. 12.99 *(978-0-89957-111-9(5))* AMG Pubs.

Hsu, Lily M. The Unforgettable Memoirs. 2011. 394p. pap. 20.99 *(978-1-61215-787-0(4))* Xulon Pr., Inc.

Hubbard, Jill. The Secrets Women Keep: What Women Hide & the Truth That Brings Them Freedom, 0 vols. 2008. 256p. pap. 14.99 *(978-0-7852-2816-5(0))* Nelson, Thomas Inc.

Hull, Patsy. An Arranged Departure: From a Mere Sharecropper to an Angel Escort to Heaven; One Christian Woman's Difficult Journey Through Life. 2006. (ENG.). 56p. per. 16.95 *(978-1-4241-5827-0(3))* PublishAmerica, Inc.

Hunt, Susan. Prayers of the Bible: Equipping Women to Call on God in Truth. 2011. pap. ***(978-1-59638-387-6(9))*** P & R Publishing.

Hyatt, Susan C. A Biographical Dictionary of Christian Women. 1000p. 35.00 *(978-1-888435-10-8(0))* Hyatt International Ministries, Inc.

I Must Be Alive: I Smell Coffee. 2009. pap. 12.99 *(978-1-56722-737-6(6))* Word Aflame Pr.

Ieron, Julie-Allyson & Allyson-Ieron, Julie. Transformed Women in the Bible: Explore Real Life Issues. Experience Real Life Change. 2006. (Sisters in Faith Bible Ser.). 80p. per. 7.99 *(978-0-89827-339-7(0))* Wesleyan Publishing Hse.

Inspirio Staff. Laughter for a Woman's Soul: Revive Your Spirit with Women of Faith, 1 vol. deluxe ed. 2007. (... for a Woman's Soul Ser.). (ENG., Illus.). 208p. lthr. 14.99 *(978-0-310-81912-7(1))* Inspirio.

Isham, Lindsey Nicole & Isham, Lindsey. No Sex in the City: One Virgin's Confessions on Love, Lust, Dating, & Waiting, 1 vol. 2009. 176p. pap. 12.99 *(978-0-8254-2906-4(4))* Kregel Pubns.

J Countryman, creator. The Sweet Talk of Success! How 35 Amazing Women Overcame Major Challenges in Life, 0 vols. 2007. (Illus.). 224p. pap. 12.99 *(978-1-4041-0408-2(9))* Nelson, Thomas Inc.

Jackie. Saved, Single, & Sexy. 2011. 46p. pap. 16.95 ***(978-1-4560-4320-9(X))*** PublishAmerica, Inc.

Jakes, Serita & Jakes, T. D. Speak to Women, 3 vols. in 1. 2006. 416p. 17.99 *(978-0-7642-0301-5(0))* Bethany Hse. Pubs.

Jakes, T. D. The Devotional Writings of T.D. Jakes. 2007. 480p. *(978-0-88486-420-2(0),* Inspirational Pr.) BBS Publishing Corp.

—Woman, Thou Art Loosed! Devotional. 2007. 256p. pap. 13.99 *(978-0-7642-0450-0(5))* Bethany Hse. Pubs.

James, Carolyn Custis. Understanding Purpose, 0 vols. 2006. (Women of Faith Study Guides). 144p. per. 9.99 *(978-1-4185-0711-4(3))* Nelson, Thomas Inc.

James, Carolyn Custis & James, Carolyn C. Lost Women of the Bible: The Women We Thought We Knew, 1 vol. 2008. (ENG., Illus.). 240p. pap. 14.99 *(978-0-310-28525-0(9))* Zondervan.

James, John Angell. Female Piety. 2006. 464p. per. 29.99 *(978-1-4255-5104-9(1))* MPublishing.

James, Sabatina. My Fight for Faith & Freedom. 2010. 240p. 21.95 *(978-1-60747-718-1(1))* Phoenix Bks., Inc.

Jane & Rebecca. Why Me, Oh Lord, Why Me? 2009. 208p. pap. 13.95 *(978-1-4327-4146-4(2))* Outskirts Pr., Inc.

Jaynes, Sharon. Becoming Spiritually Beautiful: Seeing Yourself from God's Perspective. 2010. 224p. pap. 12.99 *(978-0-7369-2679-9(8))* Harvest Hse. Pubs.

—Experience the Ultimate Makeover: Discovering God's Transforming Power. 2007. (Illus.). 222p. per. 12.99 *(978-0-7369-1813-8(2))* Harvest Hse. Pubs.

—"I'm Not Good Enough"... & Other Lies Women Tell Themselves. 2009. 240p. pap. 13.99 *(978-0-7369-1870-1(1))* Harvest Hse. Pubs.

—The Power of a Woman's Words: Speaking Life & Encouragement into Your Relationships. 2007. 240p. pap. 13.99 *(978-0-7369-1869-5(8))* Harvest Hse. Pubs.

—Your Scars Are Beautiful to God: Finding Peace & Purpose in the Hurts of Your Past. annot. ed. 2006. 240p. per. 13.99 *(978-0-7369-1610-3(5))* Harvest Hse. Pubs.

Jaynes, Sharon, et al. Trusting God: A Girlfriends in God Faith Adventure. 2011. (ENG.). 288p. pap. 14.99 *(978-1-60142-393-1(4),* Multnomah) Doubleday Religious Publishing Group, The.

Jenkins, Brenda. How My Mother Became My Guardian Angel. 2011. 280p. 29.99 ***(978-1-4568-3371-8(5))***; pap. 19.99 ***(978-1-4568-3370-1(7))*** Xlibris Corp.

Johnson, Becky Freeman. It's Fun to Be Your Friend. 2007. (Heartlite Stories Ser.). 120p. 9.99 *(978-0-7369-1805-3(1))* Harvest Hse. Pubs.

—It's Fun to Be Your Sister. 2007. (Heartlite Stories Ser.). 107p. 9.99 *(978-0-7369-1804-6(3))* Harvest Hse. Pubs.

Johnson, Beni & Cooke, Shae. Beautiful One: A Walk in Deeper Intimacy with the One Who Created Us. 2010. 212p. *(978-0-7684-3439-2(4))*; *(978-0-7684-3438-5(6))* Destiny Image Pubs.

Johnson, Beni, et al. Beautiful One: A Walk in Deeper Intimacy with the One Who Created Us. 2010. (ENG.). 212p. pap. 16.99 *(978-0-7684-3249-7(9))* Destiny Image Pubs.

Johnson, Nicole. Fresh-Brewed Life: A Stirring Invitation to Wake up Your Soul. 2011. 224p. pap. 15.99 *(978-1-4002-0315-4(5))* Nelson, Thomas Inc.

—Fresh Brewed Life Study Guide, 0 vols. 2009. 48p. pap. 9.99 *(978-1-4185-3226-0(6))* Nelson, Thomas Inc.

—Keeping a Princess Heart: In a Not-So-Fairy-Tale World, 0 vols. 2007. 208p. per. 13.99 *(978-0-8499-1881-0(2))* Nelson, Thomas Inc.

Jones, Anne. By His Hand. 2007. 124p. per. 10.99 *(978-1-60034-872-3(6))* Xulon Pr., Inc.

Jones, Barbara S. Through the Valleys. 2006. 153p. pap. 13.95 *(978-0-7414-3291-9(9))* Infinity Publishing.

Jones, Beneth Peters. Filling the Empty Places. 2007. (Illus.). 238p. per. *(978-1-59166-781-0(X))* BJU Pr.

Jones, Bret. Keepers at Home: A Study. 2008. 60p. pap. 16.95 *(978-1-60703-981-5(8))* PublishAmerica, Inc.

Jones, Ian, et al, eds. Women & Ordination in the Christian Churches: International Perspectives. 2012. (ENG.). 256p. pap. 44.95 ***(978-0-567-17615-8(0),*** T&T Clark Int'l) Continuum International Publishing Group, Ltd. GBR. Dist: National Bk. Network.

Jones, Nick & Jones. Women & Ordination in the Christian Churches: International Perspectives. 2008. (ENG.). 256p. 140.00 *(978-0-567-03154-9(3),* T&T Clark Int'l) Continuum International Publishing Group, Ltd. GBR. Dist: National Bk. Network.

Jones, Sharise. Just Do You! 2007. 84p. per. 9.99 *(978-1-60266-215-5(0))* Xulon Pr., Inc.

Jones, Yvonne. Sexy, Sassy, Sanctified Woman. 2009. (YA). pap. 20.00 *(978-1-60458-540-7(4))* Instant Pub.

Jordan, Marian. The List: Figuring Out Prince Charming, the Corner Office, & Happily Ever After, 1 vol. 2009. (ENG.). 176p. pap. 11.99 *(978-0-8054-4671-5(0),* B&H Bks.) B&H Publishing Group.

Jordan, Rebecca Barlow. For Women: Heart to Heart Encouragement, 1 vol. 2010. (Day-Votions Ser.). (ENG.). 160p. 12.99 *(978-0-310-32203-0(0))* Zondervan.

—Mothers: Heart to Heart Encouragement, 1 vol. 2010. (Day-Votions Ser.). (ENG.). 144p. 12.99 *(978-0-310-32204-7(9))* Zondervan.

Jordan, Rhonie L. Called to Run, 1 vol. 2009. 101p. pap. 16.95 *(978-1-4489-9700-8(3))* PublishAmerica, Inc.

Joseph, Angela. Women for all Seasons: Biblical Examples for Every Season of Your Life. 2010. 104p. pap. 13.95 *(978-1-4327-6042-7(4))* Outskirts Pr., Inc.

Judy Foster. Let Yourself Go & Be Free from Emotional & Abusive Relationships. 2010. 164p. pap. 15.95 *(978-1-4502-0112-4(1))* iUniverse, Inc.

Kasik, Dot Radius & Aalagaard, Ann. Actions Mightier Than Boastings. 2009. 146p. pap. 15.00 *(978-1-934582-15-2(8))* Back Channel Pr.

Kassian, Mary A. Girls Gone Wise Companion Guide. 2012. (ENG., Illus.). 128p. pap. 9.99 ***(978-0-8024-5156-9(X))*** Moody Pubs.

Kassian, Mary A. Girls Gone Wise in a World Gone Wild, 1 vol. 2010. (ENG.). 272p. pap. 14.99 *(978-0-8024-5154-5(3))* Moody Pubs.

Keene, Lorie Looney. Pull up a Chair: You, Me, & the Gospel of John. 2008. (ENG.). 192p. pap. 12.99 *(978-1-59669-202-2(2))* New Hope Pubs.

Kehrli, Jackie. Becoming a woman of God. 2010. 127p. pap. 9.98 *(978-0-557-14468-6(X))* Lulu Enterprises Inc.

Kelley, Rhonda H. Personal Holiness: A Biblical Study for Developing a Holy Lifestyle. rev. ed. 2010. (Woman's Guide Ser.). (ENG.). 176p. pap. 14.99 *(978-1-59669-257-2(X))* New Hope Pubs.

—Spiritual Wellness: A Personal Study of Colossians. rev. ed. 2010. (Woman's Guide Ser.). (ENG.). 176p. pap. 14.99 *(978-1-59669-259-6(6))* New Hope Pubs.

—True Contentment: A Biblical Study for Achieving Satisfaction in Life. rev. ed. 2010. (Woman's Guide Ser.). (ENG.). 176p. pap. 14.99 *(978-1-59669-260-2(X))* New Hope Pubs.

Kennedy, Nancy. Lipstick Grace: Glimpses of Life, Love, & the Quest for the Perfect Lip Gloss. 2007. (ENG.). 256p. per. 12.99 *(978-1-59052-767-2(4),* Multnomah) Doubleday Religious Publishing Group, The.

Kidder, Virelle. Meet Me at the Well: Take a Month & Water Your Soul. 2008. (ENG.). 240p. per. 13.99 *(978-0-8024-4861-3(5))* Moody Pubs.

Kimmel, June. A Life Surrendered. 2007. 98p. per. 6.95 *(978-1-59166-728-5(3))* BJU Pr.

—My Heart Restored. 2009. *(978-1-59166-925-8(1))* BJU Pr.

King, Jennifer. The One Year Mini for Busy Women. 2007. (ENG., Illus.). 384p. 12.99 *(978-1-4143-1477-8(9))* Tyndale Hse. Pubs.

Kingery, Naomi. Sugar Free Me. 2008. 180p. pap. 13.99 *(978-1-60477-849-6(0))* Xulon Pr., Inc.

Kinsey, Lanette. Mostly Martha. 2006. 127p. pap. 11.99 *(978-1-56722-696-6(5))* Word Aflame Pr.

Kirby, Barbara. God Still Speaks to Me. 2011. 58p. pap. 9.95 ***(978-1-4626-3554-2(7))*** PublishAmerica, Inc.

Kirk-Duggan, Cheryl A. & Torjesen, Karen Jo, eds. Women & Christianity, 1 vol. 2009. (Women & Religion in the World Ser.). 300p. 44.95 *(978-0-275-99155-5(5),* C9155, Praeger Pubs.) Greenwood Publishing Group, Inc.

Knight, Jennie S. Feminist Mysticism & Images of God: A Practical Theology. 2011. pap. ***(978-0-8272-1050-9(7))*** Chalice Pr.

Kohut, Geri. A Crown Awaits: A Christian Woman's Journey to Overcoming Abuse. 2010. pap. 11.99 *(978-1-61663-505-3(3))* Tate Publishing & Enterprises, LLC.

Kok, Elsa. A Woman with a Past, a God with a Future: Embracing God's Transforming Love. 2006. (ENG., Illus.). 160p. per. 12.99 *(978-1-59669-001-1(1))* New Hope Pubs.

Kramer, Heidi. Through the Fear: Inspiring Stories of Christian Women & Cancer. 2007. spiral bd. 15.00 *(978-0-615-14153-4(6))* Life Inspired Speaking.

Kuhn, Elizabeth Ann. Behind the Wall. 2011. 384p. 36.49 ***(978-1-4634-0911-1(7))***; pap. 19.94 ***(978-1-4520-6563-2(2))*** AuthorHouse.

Kullberg, Kelly Monroe, et al. Ruby Slippers: How the Soul of a Woman Brings Her Home, 1 vol. 2008. (ENG.). 224p. pap. 14.99 *(978-0-310-28952-4(1))* Zondervan.

Labeach, Nicole. A Woman's True Purpose: Live Like You Matter. 2007. (ENG.). 224p. per. 19.99 *(978-1-4022-0730-3(1))* Sourcebooks, Inc.

Lacy, Kendra. Pockets of Light. 2011. 120p. pap. 19.99 ***(978-1-4628-9375-1(9))*** Xlibris Corp.

Ladd, Karol. The Power of a Positive Mom & the Power of a Positive Woman. annot. ed. 2006. (ENG.). 544p. pap. 16.99 *(978-1-4165-4169-1(1),* Howard Bks.) Howard Books.

—Thrive, Don't Simply Survive: Passionately Live the Life You Didn't Plan. 2009. (ENG.). 256p. pap. 14.99 *(978-1-4165-8049-2(2),* Howard Bks.) Howard Books.

—Unfailing Love: A Woman's Walk Through First John. 2012. (Positive Woman Connection Ser.). 240p. pap. 12.99 ***(978-0-7369-2977-6(0))*** Harvest Hse. Pubs.

Ladd, Karol. A Woman's Passionate Pursuit of God: Creating a Positive & Purposeful Life. 2011. 224p. pap. 12.99 *(978-0-7369-2964-6(9))* Harvest Hse. Pubs.

Lamb, Peggy. A Month of Sundays & Then Some. 2010. 120p. pap. 11.95 *(978-1-4497-0786-6(6),* WestBow Pr.) Author Solutions, Inc.

Lambert, Frances. For His Glory: A Book of Remembrance Survivor from Judgement to Life. 2011. pap. 14.95 ***(978-0-7414-6379-1(2))*** Infinity Publishing.

Lane, Elizabeth. A Most Unlikely Servant. 2006. pap. 13.99 *(978-1-60034-521-0(2))* Xulon Pr., Inc.

Larson, Susie. Alone in Marriage: Encouragement for the Times When It's All up to You. 2007. (ENG.). 224p. per. 13.99 *(978-0-8024-5278-8(7))* Moody Pubs.

—The Uncommon Woman: Making an Ordinary Life Extraordinary. 2008. (ENG.). 200p. pap. 13.99 *(978-0-8024-5279-5(5))* Moody Pubs.

Le Tissier, Anne. Prepared for Battle - Inspiring Women Every Day. 2008. 112p. *(978-1-85345-471-4(0))* Crusade for World Revival.

Leigh, Silvia Lia. Sing Deborah Sing. 2009. pap. 14.99 *(978-1-60791-365-8(8))* Xulon Pr., Inc.

Leonard, Lynn Cochrane. Not by Chance: God's Coincidental Guidance of My Life. 2010. 160p. pap. 13.95 *(978-1-4497-0679-1(7),* WestBow Pr.) Author Solutions, Inc.

Levasheff, Christina Adelseck. Eyes that See: Judson's Story of Hope in Suffering. 2010. pap. 16.99 *(978-1-60799-993-5(5))* Tate Publishing & Enterprises, LLC.

Lewis, Carole & Symank, Cara. The Mother Daughter Legacy: How a Mother's Love Shapes a Daughter's Life. 2008. (ENG.). 200p. pap. 10.99 *(978-0-8307-3339-2(6))* Gospel Light Pubns.

Linamen, Karen. Only Nuns Change Habits Overnight: Fifty-Two Amazing Ways to Master the Art of Personal Change. 2008. (ENG., Illus.). 208p. pap. 13.99 *(978-1-4000-7400-6(2),* WaterBrook Pr.) Doubleday Religious Publishing Group, The.

—A Waist Is a Terrible Thing to Mind: Loving Your Body, Accepting Yourself, & Living Without Regret. 2010. (ENG.). 208p. pap. 13.99 *(978-1-4000-7401-3(0),* WaterBrook Pr.) Doubleday Religious Publishing Group, The.

Linamen, Karen Scalf. A Waist Is a Terrible Thing to Mind: Loving Your Body, Accepting Yourself, & Living without Regret. l.t. ed. 2010. (ENG.). 288p. pap. 17.99 *(978-1-59415-326-6(4))* Cengage Gale.

Ling, Georgia Curtis. What's in the Bible for Women: Life's Questions, God's Answers. Richards, Larry, ed. 2007. (Illus.). 352p. pap. 17.99 *(978-0-7642-0383-1(5))* Bethany Hse. Pubs.

Lit 'n' Lattes: Adding Faith & Fun to Your Book Club. 2008. pap. *(978-0-7644-3714-4(3))* Group Publishing, Inc.

Liutbirg & Hathumoda. Anchoress & Abbess in Ninth-Century Saxony: The Lives of Liutbirga of Wendhausen & Hathumoda of Gandersheim. 2009. (Illus.). 216p. pap. 29.95 *(978-0-8132-1569-3(2))* Catholic Univ. of America Pr.

Livingstone Corporation Staff, ed. Take My Heart, Oh God: Riches from the Greatest Christian Women Writers of All Time, 1 vol. 2010. (ENG.). 384p. 14.99 *(978-0-310-32747-9(4))* Zondervan.

Lloyd, Jennifer M. Women & the Shaping of British Methodism: Persistent Preachers, 1807-1907. 2010. (ENG., Illus.). 336p. 89.95 *(978-0-7190-7885-9(7))* Manchester Univ. Pr. GBR. Dist: Macmillan.

Loehr, Gina. Choosing Beauty: A 30-Day Spiritual Makeover for Women. 2009. xi, 116p. pap. 12.99 *(978-0-86716-921-8(4))* Franciscan Media.

—Real Women, Real Saints: Friends for Your Spiritual Journey. 2008. 165p. pap. *(978-0-86716-858-7(7))* Franciscan Media.

Long, Eddie L. The Elect Lady: Life's Interruptions Become Godly Opportunities. 2008. (Illus.). 191p. 19.99 *(978-0-88368-281-4(8), 772814)* Whitaker Hse.
—The Elect Lady Workbook. 2008. 166p. per. 14.99 *(978-1-60374-024-1(4), 770241)* Whitaker Hse.
Long, Jennifer D. On the Road 2 Recover. 2011. 120p. 21.99 ***(978-1-4567-6205-6(2))*** AuthorHouse.
Long, Kaye Fussell. From Tragedy to Triumph. 2011. 112p. 28.95 ***(978-1-61507-809-7(6))***; pap. 11.95 ***(978-1-61507-808-0(8))*** Cross Bks. Publishing.
Lonon, Tanjo C. Dressing in the Beauty of Holiness: The Wardrobe of the Christian Woman. 2011. 108p. 21.99 ***(978-1-4634-4900-1(3))***; pap. 12.99 ***(978-1-4634-4901-8(1))*** AuthorHouse.
Love, Melanie Amos. Journeywords: For a Woman. 2009. 154p. pap. 14.99 *(978-1-61579-020-3(9))* Xulon Pr., Inc.
Love, Valerie. God Speaks to Me. 2011. (ENG.). 288p. 6.99 *(978-1-60162-812-1(9))* Urban Bks.
Lovingsworth, Ra Kelly. Broken into Wholeness: The Beauty of Truth. 2008. pap. 14.99 *(978-1-60647-007-7(8),* Crown Oak Pr.) Xulon Pr., Inc.
Lowden, Leigh. With True Affection, Millie B. A Story of Friendship & God's Grace. 2009. pap. 10.99 *(978-1-60791-712-0(2))* Xulon Pr., Inc.
Loy D.D., Gary. La Teología Mujerista: A Christian Minister Examines the Mujerista Theology of Ada María Isasi-Díaz. 2009. 69p. pap. 8.00 *(978-0-557-03451-2(5))* Lulu Enterprises Inc.
Lucas, John. Memorial Sketch of the Life & Public W. 2006. pap. 27.95 *(978-1-4286-6031-1(3))* Kessinger Publishing, LLC.
Lucy, Jennifer. Dried Tears: A Woman's Guide to Overcoming. 2011. 100p. pap. 14.95 ***(978-0-9840955-7-5(8))*** Godzchild Inc.
Ludy, Leslie. The Lost Art of True Beauty: The Set-Apart Girl's Guide to Feminine Grace. 2010. 176p. pap. 10.99 *(978-0-7369-2290-6(3))* Harvest Hse. Pubs.
—Sacred Singleness: The Set-Apart Girl's Guide to Purpose & Fulfillment. 2009. 192p. pap. 12.99 *(978-0-7369-2288-3(1))* Harvest Hse. Pubs.
Lutz, Jessie G. Pioneer Chinese Christian Women: Gender, Christianity, & Social Mobility. 2010. (ENG.). 1p. 85.00 *(978-1-61146-061-2(1))* Lehigh Univ. Pr.
Lutz, Jessie Gregory. Pioneer Chinese Christian Women: Gender, Christianity, & Social Mobility. 2010. (Illus.). 444p. 85.00 *(978-0-9801496-8-5(1))* Lehigh Univ. Pr.
Lyda, Hope. One Minute with God for Women. 2008. 143p. per. 5.99 *(978-0-7369-2167-1(2))* Harvest Hse. Pubs.
—Tea Light Moments to Refresh Your Day. 2009. 144p. pap. 6.99 *(978-0-7369-2408-5(6))* Harvest Hse. Pubs.
Lyn, Tami. Raising Stephen: One Day at a Time. 2008. 100p. pap. 11.00 *(978-1-59755-137-3(6),* Advantage Inspirational) Advantage Bks.
M., Linda. Alone, but Never Alone: One Woman's Journey to Spiritual Enlightment. 2011. 104p. pap. 13.95 ***(978-1-4634-2417-6(5))*** AuthorHouse.
Ma B. The Apostle's Wife. 2008. 48p. pap. 16.95 *(978-1-60703-331-8(3))* PublishAmerica, Inc.
MacArthur, John. Twelve Extraordinary Women: How God Shaped Women of the Bible, & What He Wants to Do with You, 0 vols. 2008. 240p. pap. 15.99 *(978-1-4002-8028-5(1))* Nelson, Thomas Inc.
—Twelve Extraordinary Women: How God Shaped Women of the Bible, & What He Wants to Do with You. l.t. ed. 2006. (Thorndike Inspirational Ser.). 358p. 27.95 *(978-0-7862-8845-8(0))* Thorndike Pr.
—Twelve Extraordinary Women: How God Shaped Women of the Bible & What He Wants to Do with You. l.t. ed. 2007. (ENG.). 330p. (J). pap. 17.95 *(978-1-59415-155-2(5),* Walker Large Print) Cengage Gale.
Mack, Phyllis. Heart Religion in the British Enlightenment: Gender & Emotion in Early Methodism. 2011. (ENG., Illus.). 342p. pap. 65.00 *(978-0-521-29036-4(8))* Cambridge Univ. Pr.
MacKenzie, Catherine. Christian Heroines: Just Like You? 2009. (ENG.). 176p. pap. 6.99 *(978-1-84550-460-1(7))* Christian Focus Pubns. GBR. Dist: STL Distribution North America.
Macomber, Debbie. God's Guest List: Welcoming Those Who Influence Our Lives. 2010. (ENG.). 208p. 23.00 *(978-1-4391-0896-3(X),* Howard Bks.) Howard Books.
—Knit Together: Discover God's Pattern for Your Life. l.t. ed. 2008. (ENG.). 389p. (YA). pap. 16.95 *(978-1-59415-260-3(8),* Walker Large Print) Cengage Gale.
—Knit Together: Discover God's Pattern for Your Life. 2008. (ENG.). 240p. pap. 13.99 *(978-0-446-69968-6(3))* FaithWords.
—Knit Together: Discover God's Pattern for Your Life. l.t. ed. 2008. 389p. 30.50 *(978-1-4104-0798-6(5))* Thorndike Pr.
Maggio, Jennifer Barnes. Overwhelmed: The Life of a Single Mom. 2010. pap. 13.99 *(978-1-61663-361-5(1))* Tate Publishing & Enterprises, LLC.
Mahaney, Carolyn, et al. Shopping for Time: How to Do It All & Not Be Overwhelmed. 2007. 96p. pap. 12.99 *(978-1-58134-913-9(0))* Crossway.
Maltby, Tammy. Confessions of a Good Christian Girl: The Secrets Women Keep & the Grace That Saves Them, 0 vols. 2008. 288p. per. 14.99 *(978-0-7852-8941-8(0))* Nelson, Thomas Inc.
Mangion, Carmen M. Contested Identities: Catholic Women Religious in Nineteenth-Century England & Wales. 2008. (ENG., Illus.). 296p. 89.00 *(978-0-7190-7627-5(7))* Manchester Univ. Pr. GBR. Dist: Macmillan.
Mansfield, Stephen. WHERE HAS OPRAH TAKEN US? International Edition: The Religious Influence of the World's Most Famous Woman. 2011. 272p. pap. 15.99 ***(978-0-7852-3710-5(0))*** Nelson, Thomas Inc.
Marchiano, Bruce. Jesus, the Man Who Loved Women: He Treasures, Esteems, & Delights in You. 2008. (ENG.). 224p. pap. 14.99 *(978-1-4165-4397-8(X),* Howard Bks.) Howard Books.
Marker, Gary. Imperial Saint: The Cult of St. Catherine & the Dawn of Female Rule in Russia. 2007. (Illus.). 327p. 42.00 *(978-0-87580-375-3(X))* Northern Illinois Univ. Pr.
Markham, Tonya. Shifting Sands: A Young Woman's Struggle for Faith & Acceptance. 2010. pap. 10.99 *(978-1-61566-976-9(0))* Tate Publishing & Enterprises, LLC.
Marlin, Sidney L. Woman, Yes You Can! 2011. 106p. pap. 11.99 *(978-1-61379-010-6(4))* Xulon Pr., Inc.
Maryon, Diana. O Love How Deep. 2011. 536p. 44.95 ***(978-1-4497-2121-3(4))***; pap. 34.95 ***(978-1-4497-2120-6(6))*** Author Solutions, Inc. (WestBow Pr.).
Mason, Lynn D. Mourning to Morning. 2009. 324p. pap. 18.99 *(978-1-61579-297-9(X))* Xulon Pr., Inc.
Matsunobu, Iris. A Story to Be Told. 2011. 56p. pap. 9.95 *(978-1-4497-1355-3(6),* WestBow Pr.) Author Solutions, Inc.
Matutu, Bryan. The Blooming Rose: A tribute to Rose Sibusisiwe MATUTU 1. 03. 53 To 3. 12. 07. 2009. 240p. pap. 19.13 *(978-1-4251-9075-0(8))* Trafford Publishing.
Maxie, Wendy Fields. Heart Writer: A Writing Companion for the Christian Woman. 2011. 112p. pap. *(978-1-55452-601-7(9),* Guardian Bks.) Essence Publishing.
Mazzoni, Cristina & Mazzoni. The Women in God's Kitchen: Cooking, Eating, & Spiritual Writing. 2006. (ENG.). 232p. pap. 24.95 *(978-0-8264-1912-5(7))* Continuum International Publishing Group, Ltd. GBR. Dist: National Bk. Network.
Mcalister, Mary Alice. Seventy Years in Mississippi a Look Back. 2011. 100p. pap. 19.95 ***(978-1-4560-0673-0(8))*** PublishAmerica, Inc.
McCain Edd, Emma. How to Recognize a Deadbeat: 101 Red Flags for Single Christian Women. 2011. 78p. pap. 12.95 ***(978-1-61434-450-6(7))*** Booklocker.com, Inc.
McCaskill, Jane. God Makes No Mistakes. 2008. 272p. pap. 15.99 *(978-1-60477-863-2(6))* Xulon Pr., Inc.
McCoy, Anna. Mujer, Actúa Ahora: Aprende, inicia, y vive tu Sueño. 2009.Tr. of Woman, Act Now: Learn, Launch, & Live Your Dream. (SPA.). 304p. pap. 10.99 *(978-1-60374-088-3(0))* Whitaker Hse.
—Woman, Act Now: Learn, Launch, & Live Your Dream. 304p. 2009. pap. 12.99 *(978-1-60374-087-6(2))* 2008. (ENG.). 19.99 *(978-1-60374-068-5(6))* Whitaker Hse.
McCray, Joe A. Miracles Never Cease, 1 vol. 2010. 54p. pap. 16.95 *(978-1-4489-5132-1(1))* PublishAmerica, Inc.
McCulley, Carolyn. Radical Womanhood: Feminine Faith in a Feminist World. 2008. (ENG.). 224p. pap. 14.99 *(978-0-8024-5084-5(9))* Moody Pubs.
McDowell, Lucinda Secrest. Quilts from Heaven: Parables from the Patchwork of Life. 2007. (Illus.). 178p. 14.99 *(978-0-8054-4435-3(1))* B&H Publishing Group.
—Role of a Lifetime: Your Part in God's Story. 2008. (ENG.). 160p. per. 12.99 *(978-0-8054-4662-3(1),* B&H Bks.) B&H Publishing Group.
McGraw, Robin. From My Heart to Yours: Life Lessons on Faith, Family, & Friendship, 0 vols. 2007. (Illus.). 160p. 16.99 *(978-1-4041-0521-8(2))* Nelson, Thomas Inc.
McGuirk, Nancy. Rest Assured: Devotions for Souls in a Restless World. 2007. (ENG.). 256p. 14.99 *(978-0-8054-4541-1(2),* B&H Bks.) B&H Publishing Group.
McIntosh, Helen B. Messages to Myself: Overcoming a Distorted Self-Image. 2009. (ENG.). 160p. pap. 13.99 *(978-0-8341-2456-1(4),* 9780834124561) Beacon Hill Pr. of Kansas City.
McKinney, Leslie Ann. Accepted in the Beloved: A Devotional Bible Study for Women on Finding Healing & Wholeness in God's Love. 2008. (House of Prisca & Aquila Ser.). 56p. pap. 10.00 *(978-1-55635-936-1(5))* Wipf & Stock Pubs.
McMenamin, Cindi. When a Woman Overcomes Life's Hurts. 2012. 224p. pap. 12.99 ***(978-0-7369-4858-6(9))*** Harvest Hse. Pubs.
—When Women Walk Alone — A 31 Day Devotional Companion. 2008. 128p. pap. 5.99 *(978-0-7369-2283-8(0))* Harvest Hse. Pubs.
—Women on the Edge. 2010. 208p. pap. 12.99 *(978-0-7369-2652-2(6))* Harvest Hse. Pubs.
McSweeney, Margaret, compiled by. Pearl Girls: Encountering Grit, Experiencing Grace. 2009. (ENG.). 192p. pap. 12.99 *(978-0-8024-5862-9(9))* Moody Pubs.
Meagher, George T. & Kasper, Mary. With Attentive Ear & Courageous Heart: A Biography of Mother Mary Kasper, Foundress of the Poor Handmaids of Jesus Christ. 2011. 282p. 47.95 ***(978-1-258-09026-5(0))*** Literary Licensing, LLC.
Meberg, Marilyn. Tell Me Everything: How You Can Heal from the Secrets You Thought You'd Never Share, 0 vols. 2010. 240p. 19.99 *(978-1-4002-0274-4(4))* Nelson, Thomas Inc.
Meeder, Kim. Fierce Beauty: Choosing to Stand for What Matters Most. 2011. (ENG.). 192p. pap. 13.99 *(978-1-60142-203-3(2),* Multnomah) Doubleday Religious Publishing Group, The.
Meeks, Paulette Carnnetar. The Best for Last: One Woman's Unusual Tale of Life & Love. 2009. pap. 14.99 *(978-1-60799-878-5(5))* Tate Publishing & Enterprises, LLC.
Meeuwsen, Terry. Just Between Friends, 0 vols. 2008. 144p. pap. 9.99 *(978-0-7852-9698-0(0))* Nelson, Thomas Inc.
Mellon, Joelle. The Virgin Mary in the Perceptions of Women: Mother, Protector & Queen since the Middle Ages. 2008. (ENG., Illus.). 219p. pap. 35.00 *(978-0-7864-3502-9(X))* McFarland & Co., Inc. Pubs.
Menéndez Antuña, Luis. Mujer y poder en el Cristianismo Antiguo. 2008. 245p. pap. 27.95 *(978-1-84799-065-5(7))* Lulu Enterprises Inc.
Mesanko, Kerin Lee. Broken Beads on My Moccasins. 2009. 162p. pap. 14.99 *(978-1-60791-912-4(5))* Xulon Pr., Inc.
Meyer, Joyce. Be Your Best. 2008. 128p. pap. 11.99 *(978-0-446-54517-4(1))* FaithWords.
—The Confident Woman: Start Today Living Boldly & Without Fear. 2010. (ENG.). 272p. pap. 13.99 *(978-0-446-55840-2(0))* FaithWords.
—Living Beyond Your Feelings: Controlling Emotions So They Don't Control You. 2011. (ENG.). 288p. 22.99 *(978-0-446-53852-7(3))*; 352p. 24.99 *(978-1-4555-0729-0(6))* FaithWords.
—100 Ways to Simplify Your Life. 2008. (ENG.). 192p. 16.99 *(978-0-446-19416-7(6))*; 240p. pap. 16.99 *(978-0-446-50939-8(6))* FaithWords.
Mhlaba, Nathi. Fearlessly Single: Diary of A Single Christian Woman. 2011. 76p. pap. 9.95 ***(978-1-4497-2369-9(1),*** WestBow Pr.) Author Solutions, Inc.
Miller, Adrienne L. Misery Loves Company, but God Loves Us More. 2009. 308p. pap. 18.99 *(978-1-61579-090-6(X))* Xulon Pr., Inc.
Miller, Holly. Life after the Games. 2007. 168p. (ENG.). 21.99 *(978-1-60266-187-5(1))*; per. 13.99 *(978-1-60266-186-8(3))* Xulon Pr., Inc.
Miller, Kathy Collard. Partly Cloudy with Scattered Worries: Finding Peace in All Kinds of Weather. 2010. pap. 15.99 *(978-1-61579-753-0(X))* Xulon Pr., Inc.
Miller, Sally. The Bible Is a Girl's Best Friend: Experiencing a Fresh Encounter with God's Word. 2007. 224p. pap. 12.99 *(978-0-7369-2029-2(3))* Harvest Hse. Pubs.
Miller, Sally & Mueller, Cheri. Play with Me: Two Friends on a Spiritual Journey with Kids. 2006. 210p. per. *(978-1-932902-61-7(9))* FaithWalk Publishing.
Mills, Lucinda. Let Yesterday Go: Finding Grace in the Midst of the Storm. 2011. pap. 19.99 *(978-1-61739-722-6(9))* Tate Publishing & Enterprises, LLC.
Minnis, Alastair & Voaden, Rosalynn. Yale Companion to Medieval Holy Women in the Christain Tradition. 2009. (ENG.). 480p. 59.95 *(978-0-300-11301-3(3))* Yale Univ. Pr.
Mitchell, A. A. Open Your Eyes to the Calling. 2010. 108p. 21.49 *(978-1-4520-4806-2(1))*; (ENG.). pap. 10.99 *(978-1-4520-4807-9(X))* AuthorHouse.
Mitchell, Joyce. Soul Spa: Spiritual Therapy for Women in Leadership. 2009. (ENG.). 176p. pap. 12.99 *(978-1-59669-269-5(3))* New Hope Pubs.
Moberg, Marlys Taege. The Heart of Jesus: Women in the Gospel of Luke. 2009. 52p. pap., wbk. ed. 5.99 *(978-0-7586-1661-6(9))*; 48p. pap. 8.99 *(978-0-7586-1660-9(0))* Concordia Publishing Hse.
Mobley, Fay. Women of Vice & Virtue. 2007. 68p. per. 8.95 *(978-1-58427-217-5(1))* Guardian of Truth Foundation.
Moll, Minister. New Beginning's Ministry. 2010. 292p. pap. 18.50 *(978-1-4490-7127-1(9))* AuthorHouse.
Montecristo, J. The Girl That Wouldn't Die, 1 vol. 2010. 53p. pap. 16.95 *(978-1-4489-5992-1(6))* PublishAmerica, Inc.
Montgomery, Scott B. St. Ursula & the Eleven Thousand Virgins of Cologne: Relics, Reliquaries & the Visual Culture of Group Sanctity in Late Medieval Europe. 2009. (Illus.). 207p. pap. 60.95 *(978-3-03911-852-6(8))* Lang, Peter AG GBR. Dist: Lang, Peter.
Moore, Beth. Esther: It's Tough Being a Woman. 2008. pap. 277.75 *(978-1-4158-5289-7(8))* LifeWay Christian Resources.
—Hasta Luego, Inseguridad: Has Sido una Mala Amiga. 2010.Tr. of So Long, Insecurity: You've Been a Bad Friend to Us. (SPA.). 368p. pap. 14.99 *(978-1-4143-3475-2(3))* Tyndale Hse. Pubs.
—So Long, Insecurity: You've Been a Bad Friend to Us. l.t. ed. 2011. (ENG.). 461p. 30.99 *(978-1-4104-3400-5(1))* Thorndike Pr.
—So Long, Insecurity: You've Been a Bad Friend to Us. 2010. (ENG.). 368p. 24.99 *(978-1-4143-3472-1(9))* Tyndale Hse. Pubs.
—So Long, Insecurity Group Experience. 2011. (ENG.). 112p. pap. 14.99 *(978-1-4143-4990-9(4))* Tyndale Hse. Pubs.
—So Long, Insecurity Group Experience Leader's Guide. 2011. (ENG.). 128p. pap. 16.99 *(978-1-4143-4991-6(2))* Tyndale Hse. Pubs.
—A Woman's Heart: God's Dwelling Place. 2007. (Illus.). 222p. per. 14.95 *(978-1-4158-5581-2(1))* LifeWay Christian Resources.
—A Woman's Heart Leader's Guide: God's Dwelling Place. 2007. 31p. pap. 6.95 *(978-1-4158-5579-9(X))* LifeWay Christian Resources.
Moore, Karen. Hugs for Aunts: Stories, Sayings, & Scriptures to Encourage & Inspire. 2007. (Hugs Ser.). (ENG., Illus.). 128p. 11.99 *(978-1-4165-4180-6(2),* Howard Bks.) Howard Books.
Morgan, Elisa. She Did What She Could (SDWSC) Five Words of Jesus That Will Change Your Life. 2009. (ENG.). 144p. 9.99 *(978-1-4143-3378-6(1))* Tyndale Hse. Pubs.
Morris, Shelita L. God Favors Me. 2010. 126p. 29.99 *(978-1-4535-2952-2(7))*; pap. 19.99 *(978-1-4535-2951-5(9))* Xlibris Corp.
Moston, Marcia. Call of A Coward. 2011. 148p. 30.95 ***(978-1-4497-1998-2(8))***; pap. 13.95 ***(978-1-4497-1996-8(1))*** Author Solutions, Inc. (WestBow Pr.).
Mueller, Ella Numrich. Life in Germany During World War II: From Padew in Galizien, Poland to America. 2008. 116p. pap. 13.99 *(978-1-4389-1078-9(9))* AuthorHouse.
Murchsion, Maureen. War Child: Memories of a World War II Childhood. 2009. (Adventures Ser.). (ENG., Illus.). 112p. 7.99 *(978-1-84550-538-7(7))* Christian Focus Pubns. GBR. Dist: STL Distribution North America.
Muse, Marilyn. Women Need to Connect. 2011. 152p. pap. 24.95 ***(978-1-4560-6782-3(6))*** PublishAmerica, Inc.
Myers, Brenda M. Walking the Tightrope without a Grace Net. 2010. 112p. pap. 12.95 *(978-1-4502-3763-5(0))* iUniverse, Inc.
Myers, Kristen. Coffee with the Savior: A Bible Study for Women. 2010. (Lutheran Difference Ser.). 128p. pap. 8.99 *(978-0-7586-1755-2(0))* Concordia Publishing Hse.
Nappa, Amy. Thirsty: Meeting Jesus at Your Deepest Need. 2008. (Redefining Life Ser.). (ENG.). 224p. pap. 14.99 *(978-1-60006-093-9(5))* NavPress Publishing Group.
Neuharth, Grace Ann & Winters-Gutierrez, Wanda. Family Secrets: Letters to My Granddaughters. 2010. pap. 14.99 *(978-1-61566-133-6(6))* Tate Publishing & Enterprises, LLC.
Newcombe, Amy. Searching for God. 2011. 148p. pap. 12.95 ***(978-1-4620-4583-9(9))*** iUniverse, Inc.
Newman, Ivy Julease. A Space Called Chastity: A Message to Unmarried Women on God, Sex, & Relationships. 2010. 108p. 22.95 *(978-1-4502-2413-0(X))*; (ENG.). pap. 12.95 *(978-1-4502-2415-4(6))* iUniverse, Inc.
Newman, Suzanne. Treasures in Heaven. 2011. 60p. pap. 12.19 ***(978-1-4567-9790-4(5))*** AuthorHouse.
Newton, Linda. Better Than Jewels: 31 Days of Biblical Insight for a Woman Seeking God. 2009. 136p. 12.95 *(978-1-59317-369-2(5))* Warner Pr. Pubs.
—Sapphires from Psalms: 31 Gems of Encouragement for a Woman Seeking God. 2010. 136p. 12.95 *(978-1-59317-511-5(6))* Warner Pr. Pubs.
Nicodem, Deborah Lee. Detoured by Divorce: Finding God's Way Through & Beyond. 2007. 160p. pap. 12.99 *(978-1-58134-865-1(7))* Crossway.
Nielsen, Brandee. Unforgotten. 2011. 116p. 28.95 ***(978-1-4497-2191-6(5))***; pap. 11.95 ***(978-1-4497-2192-3(3))*** Author Solutions, Inc. (WestBow Pr.).
Niles, Success D. O. Revelations of Life: The Hard Way, 1 vol. 2009. 48p. pap. 16.95 *(978-1-60749-189-7(3))* PublishAmerica, Inc.
NIV Busy Mom's Bible, Find: Time - Walmart, 1 vol. 2009. 1152p. lthr. 24.99 *(978-0-310-94890-2(8))* Zondervan.
Noble, Doris. They Didn't Do What I Told Them to Do: The Diary of a Deacon's Wife. 2011. pap. 20.99 ***(978-1-61346-028-3(7))*** Tate Publishing & Enterprises, LLC.
Norton, Joan & Starbird, Margaret. 14 Steps to Awaken the Sacred Feminine: Women in the Circle of Mary Magdalene. 2009. (ENG.). 1p. pap. 14.00 *(978-1-59143-091-9(7))* Bear & Co.
Obey, Crystal. Refined by Fire Discovering Victory Thro. 2006. pap. 15.00 *(978-1-59268-080-1(1))* G M A Publishing & Inspiration Pr.
—Refined by Fire Secrets of Becoming A Ch. 2006. pap. 15.00 *(978-1-59268-079-5(8))* G M A Publishing & Inspiration Pr.
Obey, Crystal & Obey, Anthony, compiled by. Refined by Fire: Defining Moments of Phenomenal Women. 2007. 132p. per. 15.00 *(978-1-59268-082-5(8))* G M A Publishing & Inspiration Pr.
Okwata, Esther. More & More Veils Lifted from My Face: God's Mercy for the Penitent. 2010. 172p. pap. 59.99 *(978-1-4490-7145-5(7))* AuthorHouse.
Olsen, Rachel, ed. God's Purpose for Every Woman: A P31 Women's Devotional. 2007. 367p. per. 14.99 *(978-0-7369-2064-3(1))* Harvest Hse. Pubs.
Olson, Anna Dee. Growing up Amish: Insider Secrets from One Woman's Inspirational Journey. 2008. (ENG.). 138p. pap. 14.95 *(978-1-60037-334-3(8))* Morgan James Publishing.
Omartian, Stormie. Just Enough Light for the Step I'm on Book of Prayers. 2008. 125p. per. 6.99 *(978-0-7369-2391-0(8))* Harvest Hse. Pubs.
—The Power of a Praying Wife. deluxe ed. 2007. 208p. 16.99 *(978-0-7369-1989-0(9))* Harvest Hse. Pubs.
—The Power of a Praying Woman. 2007. 253p. per. 13.99 *(978-0-7369-1926-5(0))*; 256p. pap. 16.99 *(978-0-7369-2205-0(9))* Harvest Hse. Pubs.
—The Power of a Praying Woman: A Bible Study Workbook for Video Curriculum. 2006. (Power of a Praying Series! Ser.). (Illus.). 151p. per. 14.95 *(978-1-933376-46-2(5))* Sampson Resources.
—The Power of a Praying Woman: Leader Guide for Video Curriculum. 2006. (Illus.). 40p. pap. 8.95 *(978-1-933376-47-9(3))* Sampson Resources.
—The Power of a Praying Woman: Leader Kit. 2006. audio compact disk 279.00 *(978-1-933376-45-5(7))* Sampson Resources.
—The Power of a Praying Woman: Prayer & Study Guide. 2007. 216p. per. 8.99 *(978-0-7369-1987-6(2))* Harvest Hse. Pubs.
—The Power of a Praying Woman Book of Prayers. 2007. 127p. per. 6.99 *(978-0-7369-1988-3(0))* Harvest Hse. Pubs.
Orevillo-Montenegro, Muriel. The Jesus of Asian Women. 2007. (Faith & Cultures Ser.). 270p. per. 24.00 *(978-1-57075-533-0(7))* Orbis Bks.
Ortiz, Sandra K. Last Dance: A Story of Great Faith & Courage. 2008. 104p. pap. 10.99 *(978-1-60791-162-3(0))* Xulon Pr., Inc.
Osherow, Michele. Biblical Women's Voices in Early Modern England. 2009. (Women & Gender in the Early Modern World Ser.). (Illus.). 202p. 99.95 *(978-0-7546-6674-5(3))* Ashgate Publishing Co.
Osteen, Victoria. Love Your Life: Living Happy, Healthy, & Whole. 2009. (ENG.). 240p. pap. 15.00 *(978-0-7432-9698-4(2),* Free Pr.) Free Pr.
—Love Your Life: Living Happy, Healthy, & Whole. l.t. ed. 2009. (ENG.). 307p. pap. 17.95 *(978-1-59415-285-6(3))* Thorndike Pr.
Ousley, Pamela D. Tiaras, Mirrors, & Truth: Releasing a Woman's Princess Identity. 2010. 196p. pap. 17.95 *(978-1-61507-190-6(3))* Cross Bks. Publishing.
—Tiaras, Mirrors & Truth: Releasing a Woman's Princess Identity. 2010. 196p. 33.95 *(978-1-61507-191-3(1))* Cross Bks. Publishing.
Pallister, John. A Brief Memoir of Mrs Jane Pallister, of Preston near Hull. 2007. pap. 16.95 *(978-1-4304-6986-5(2))* Kessinger Publishing, LLC.
Park, Jung Eun Sophia. A Hermeneutic on Dislocation As Experience: Creating a Borderland, Constructing a Hybrid Identity. 2012. viii, 137p.

(978-1-4331-1594-3(8)); E-Book (978-1-4539-0190-8(6)) Lang, Peter GmbH, Europaischer Verlag der Wissenschaften.

Parrott, Ele. Transforming Together: Authentic Spiritual Mentoring, 1 vol. 2009. (ENG.). 176p. pap. 13.99 (978-0-8024-6661-7(3)) Moody Pubs.

Partow, Donna. Becoming a Vessel of God's Power: Give God Thirty Days & See What He Will Do. 2007. (ENG.). 288p. pap. 13.99 (978-1-57856-960-1(5), WaterBrook Pr.) Doubleday Religious Publishing Group, The.

—Becoming the Woman God Wants Me to Be: A 90-Day Guide to Living the Proverbs 31 Life. 2008. 352p. pap. 13.99 (978-0-8007-3072-7(0)) Revell.

—Let Your Life Count: Make a Difference Right Where You Are. 2006. (ENG.). 256p. per. 12.99 (978-1-57856-959-5(1), WaterBrook Pr.) Doubleday Religious Publishing Group, The.

—This Isn't the Life I Signed up For: A 10-Week Journey to Hope & Healing. 2010. (ENG.). 288p. reprint ed. pap. 13.99 (978-0-7642-0791-4(1)) Bethany Hse. Pubs.

Patterson, Dorothy Kelly. BeAttitudes for Women: Wisdom from Heaven for Life on Earth. 2008. 272p. pap. 29.00 (978-1-60608-012-2(1)) Wipf & Stock Pubs.

Payton, Doris. Jewels Shining in Darkness: Jewels in the Kingdom of God. 2009. 92p. pap. 10.99 (978-1-61579-520-8(0)) Xulon Pr., Inc.

Peace, Martha. Damsels in Distress: Biblical Solutions for Problems Women Face. 2006. 187p. per. 13.99 (978-1-59638-038-7(1)) P & R Publishing.

Pearl, Debi. Creada para Ser su Ayuda Idonea: Descubre Como Puede Dios Hacer Glorioso Tu Matrimonio. 2006. (SPA & ENG., Illus.). 295p. pap. 12.00 (978-1-892112-87-3(6)) No Greater Joy Ministries, Inc.

—The Help Meets Journey: A Yearly Companion Journal for Created to Be His Help Meet. 2008. (ENG.). 184p. spiral bd. 10.95 (978-1-892112-88-0(4)) No Greater Joy Ministries, Inc.

Pearson, Veronica M. Comfort for the Weary Heart. 2009. 76p. pap. 10.99 (978-1-61579-439-3(5)) Xulon Pr., Inc.

Pecora, Valerie. The Seasons of My Soul. 2007. 216p. (ENG.). 24.99 (978-1-60477-303-3(0)); per. 14.99 (978-1-60477-302-6(2)) Xulon Pr., Inc.

Peters, Barbara. Special Ops Woman. 2009. 160p. pap. 14.99 (978-1-60791-864-6(1)) Xulon Pr., Inc.

Peters, Christine. Patterns of Piety: Women, Gender & Religion in Late Medieval & Reformation England. 2009. (Cambridge Studies in Early Modern British History Ser.). (ENG., Illus.). 412p. pap. 53.00 (978-0-521-09344-6(9)) Cambridge Univ. Pr.

Petty, Gretchen. What on Earth! Spiritual Encounters That Made Me Believe. 2010. pap. 12.99 (978-1-61566-624-9(9)) Tate Publishing & Enterprises, LLC.

Pier Angela Belton. Who Are You Wearing? I'm Wearing an Original by God. 2009. 156p. pap. 14.95 (978-1-4401-5419-5(8)) iUniverse, Inc.

Platz, Ann. Queen Esther's Reflection: A Portrait of Grace, Courage, & Excellence. 2007. (ENG.). 224p. per. 12.99 (978-1-59669-012-7(7)) New Hope Pubs.

Poinsett, Brenda. The Friendship Factor: Why Women Need Other Women. 2010. (ENG.). 208p. pap. 14.99 (978-1-59669-247-3(2)) New Hope Pubs.

Polimino, Jennifer & Warren, Carolyn. Praying Through Your Pregnancy: An Inspirational Week-by-Week Guide for Moms-to-Be. 2010. (ENG.). 192p. pap. 14.99 (978-0-8307-5577-6(2)) Gospel Light Pubns.

Posa, Charlotte. To Women with Love: Walking Away from the Abuse. Lowe, Fran D., ed. 2011. 168p. lib. bdg. 15.00 (978-1-886068-52-0(6)) Fruitbearer Publishing, LLC.

Pratt, Cinthia W. Fearfully Female & Wonderfully Woman: Becoming All that God Created. 2011. 200p. 33.95 (978-1-4497-1677-6(6)); pap. 17.95 (978-1-4497-1675-2(X)) Author Solutions, Inc. (WestBow Pr.).

Praying with Celtic Holy Women. 2007. 20.00 (978-0-9793767-2-6(6)) SOFIA.

Prentiss, E. Stepping Heavenward. 2008. 180p. pap. (978-1-4068-6605-6(9)) Echo Library.

—Stepping Heavenward. 2008. 436p. 51.95 (978-0-548-93959-8(4)) 2007. (ENG.). 440p. per. 36.95 (978-0-548-59147-5(4)) Kessinger Publishing, LLC.

Primm, Sonia Lovell. The Adventures of a Sheltered Life. 2007. (Illus.). 245p. per. 14.99 (978-1-59886-887-6(X)) Tate Publishing & Enterprises, LLC.

Prophet, Elizabeth Clare. Preparation for My Mission. 2009. 428p. 36.95 (978-1-4401-7396-7(6)) iUniverse, Inc.

Prophet, Erin. Prophet's Daughter. 2010. (ENG., Illus.). 304p. pap. 14.95 (978-1-59921-972-1(7), Lyons Pr.) Globe Pequot Pr., The.

Pryor, Liz. What Did I Do Wrong? What to Do When You Don't Know Why the Friendship Is Over. 2011. (ENG.). 208p. pap. 14.00 (978-1-4516-4965-9(7), Free Pr.) Free Pr.

Pughe, Roberta Mary & Sohl, Paula Anema. Resurrecting Eve: Women of Faith Challenge the Fundamentalist Agenda. 2007. (ENG., Illus.). 236p. per. 16.95 (978-1-883991-70-8(6)) White Cloud Pr.

—Resurrecting Eve: Women of Faith Unveil the Fundamentalist Agenda. 2007. pap. (978-1-883391-70-6(9)) White Cloud Pr.

Purcell, Joan M. At His Feet: Five Bible Studies for Women. 2010. 144p. pap. 13.49 (978-1-4520-8387-2(8)) AuthorHouse.

Raphael Burns, Helena. He Speaks to You. 2012. (ENG.). 384p. pap. 10.95 (978-0-8198-3419-5(X)) Pauline Bks. & Media.

Ratcliff-Rondeau, Nancy. Peace, Power, Perseverance, & Prophecy. 2010. 79p. pap. 14.00 (978-0-557-30363-2(X)) Lulu Enterprises Inc.

Rathmell, Susan Reneau. From His Hands to Mine: Leaning on God through the First Year of Motherhood, 1 vol. 2010. 144p. pap. 24.95 (978-1-4489-4977-9(7)) PublishAmerica, Inc.

Ray, Charles. Mrs. C. H. Spurgeon: A Biography of Susannah Spurgeon. 2006. per. 5.00 (978-1-60208-018-8(6)) FBC Pubns. & Printing.

Ray, Crystol T. My Sistahs, You'Re Chasing the Wrong Man. 2008. 52p. pap. 16.95 (978-1-60474-938-0(5)) PublishAmerica, Inc.

Reed, LaVerne. Mountain Move Around. 2006. pap. 10.99 (978-1-60034-598-2(0)) Xulon Pr., Inc.

Reimer, Kathie & Whittle, Lisa. The 7 Hardest Things God Asks a Woman to Do. annot. ed. 2007. 189p. per. 12.99 (978-0-9767582-5-9(3)) Shepherd Pr. Inc.

Renner, Nancy K. Trials & Tribulations of Being a Redhead: Bullied, Taunted & Teased for being a Redhead. 2011. 68p. pap. 9.95 (978-1-4497-2028-5(5), WestBow Pr.) Author Solutions, Inc.

Rhea, Rhonda. The Purse-uit of Holiness: Learning to Imitate the Master Designer. 2008. 240p. pap. 12.99 (978-0-8007-3253-0(7)) Revell.

Rich, Ronda. What Southern Women Know about Faith: Kitchen Table Stories & Back Porch Comfort, 1 vol. 2010. (ENG.). 224p. pap. 14.99 (978-0-310-29186-2(0)) Zondervan.

Richardson, Jan L. In the Sanctuary of Women: Daily Prayers & Readings. 2010. (Illus.). 332p. 22.00 (978-0-8358-1030-2(5)) Upper Room Bks.

Ricks, Eric F. Woman, God Made You a Queen for Life. 2008. 112p. pap. 12.99 (978-0-9818753-0-9(0)) Leading Lady Pubns.

Ridpath, Marcia, et al. Real Women: In the Middle of Real Life. 2007. 176p. per. 16.95 (978-0-595-46306-0(1)) iUniverse, Inc.

Rinehart, Paula. Better Than My Dreams: Finding What You Long for Where You Might Not Think to Look, 0 vols. 2007. 256p. per. 14.99 (978-0-8499-1867-4(7)) Nelson, Thomas Inc.

Ris, Diane, et al. Saint Mother Theodore GuéRin: Woman of Providence. 2011. 324p. pap. 22.99 (978-1-4567-3605-7(1)) AuthorHouse.

Roberts, Mattie. Theresa Johnson: The Search for Her Beloved. 2011. (ENG.). 104p. pap. 14.95 (978-1-4327-7959-7(1)) Outskirts Pr., Inc.

Robertson, Annette. Love & Acceptance. 2009. pap. 13.99 (978-1-60799-760-3(6)) Tate Publishing & Enterprises, LLC.

Robertson, Helen. A Miraculous Experience: Will You Take the Time to Have One? 2010. 180p. 30.95 (978-1-4497-0066-9(7), WestBow Pr.) Author Solutions, Inc.

Robertson, Jean. A Place of My Own: A Memoir. 2010. 202p. pap. 15.99 (978-1-61579-757-8(2)) Xulon Pr., Inc.

Robertson, Nancy. Christian Sisterhood, Race Relations, & the YWCA, 1906-46. 2010. (Women in American History Ser.). (ENG., Illus.). 304p. pap. 25.00 (978-0-252-07710-4(5)) Univ. of Illinois Pr.

Robinson, Cynthia. A True Sister in the Sisterhood. 2009. 70p. pap. 15.99 (978-1-4415-0618-4(7)) Xlibris Corp.

Rocha-Pierce, Ann. My Mother, the Wife, the Grandmother, the Mystic. 2008. 112p. 29.99 (978-1-4389-2841-8(6)); pap. 19.99 (978-1-4389-2466-3(6)) AuthorHouse.

Rodricks, Marie. Magnify the LORD. 2010. 216p. pap. 14.49 (978-1-4490-0294-7(3)) AuthorHouse.

Rodriquez, Camille. When I Die: On Being, Living, & Having the Last Word. 2011. pap. 10.99 (978-1-61739-643-4(5)) Tate Publishing & Enterprises, LLC.

Rogers, Roni. Oh! Jesus, Help Me over the Hump of My Rainbow. 2008. 188p. 29.99 (978-1-4363-4514-9(6)); pap. 19.99 (978-1-4363-4513-2(8)) Xlibris Corp.

Rose-Deane, Vilma M. Tried but Not Tired! A True Story. 2011. 64p. pap. 9.95 (978-1-4502-8202-4(4)) iUniverse, Inc.

Rose, Margaret, et al, eds. Lifting Women's Voices: Prayers to Change the World. 2009. 416p. 25.00 (978-0-8192-2323-4(9), Morehouse Publishing) Church Publishing, Inc.

Rossman, Teresa Marie. Her Own Words. 2011. 298p. pap. 16.99 (978-1-61379-344-2(8)) Xulon Pr., Inc.

Rothschild, Jennifer. Self Talk, Soul Talk: What to Say When You Talk to Yourself. 2007. 192p. pap. 12.99 (978-0-7369-2072-8(2)) Harvest Hse. Pubs.

Roush, Christine. Swimming Upstream. 2009. 116p. pap. 15.00 (978-1-60844-020-7(6)) Dog Ear Publishing, LLC.

Rowe, Eleanor. The Desperate Search. 2007. 212p. per. 14.99 (978-1-60266-612-2(1)) Xulon Pr., Inc.

Rowley, Trudy Kay. When the Redbud Blooms. 2011. 160p. pap. 14.99 (978-1-61215-626-2(6)) Xulon Pr., Inc.

Rubial García, Antonio. Profetisas y Solitarios: Espacios y Mensajes de una Religión Dirigida Por Ermitaños y Beatas Laicos en Las Ciudades de Nueva Espana. 2006. (Historia Ser.). (SPA., Illus.). 258p. pap. 23.99 (978-968-16-7984-2(9)) Fondo de Cultura Económcia.

Rushing, Rita Jones. "silly Women" 2009. 108p. pap. 15.99 (978-1-4415-4745-3(2)) Xlibris Corp.

Ryder, O. Faye. Walking on the Right Side of God: One Woman's Spiritual Journey. 2010. pap. 12.99 (978-1-61566-957-8(4)) Tate Publishing & Enterprises, LLC.

Sainte Foi, Charles. Serious Hours of a Young Lady. Philaletes, tr. 2007. 120p. per. (978-1-4065-4279-0(2)) Dodo Pr.

Salisbury, Judy & Geisler, Norman. Reasons for Faith: A Common Sense Guide for Christian Women. 2011. 218p. pap. 24.00 (978-1-61097-172-0(8), Wipf and Stock) Wipf & Stock Pubs.

Sanders, Laura. Scattered Memories. 2011. 76p. pap. 19.95 (978-1-4512-7697-8(4)) PublishAmerica, Inc.

Sandford, Paula. Healing for a Woman's Emotions: Released from Damaging Thoughts & Feelings. annot. ed. 2006. (ACE & ENG.). 224p. pap. 14.99 (978-1-59979-054-1(8), Charisma Hse.) Charisma Media.

Sanok, Catherine. Her Life Historical: Exemplarity & Female Saints' Lives in Late Medieval England. 2007. (Middle Ages Ser.). (Illus.). 280p. (C). 65.00 (978-0-8122-3986-7(5)) Univ. of Pennsylvania Pr.

Savoy, Judy. The Wall. 2011. 106p. pap. 10.99 (978-0-557-80048-3(X)) Lulu Enterprises Inc.

Schaap, Cindy. The Path to a Woman's Happiness. 2007. 20.00 (978-0-9793892-4-5(0)) Christian Womanhood Pubns.

Schaberg, Jane & Schaberg. Mary Magdalene Understood. 2006. (ENG.). 176p. pap. 14.95 (978-0-8264-1899-9(6)) Continuum International Publishing Group, Ltd. GBR. Dist: National Bk. Network.

Scheppmann, Susanne. Embraced by the Father: Finding Grace in the Names of God. 2010. (ENG.). 224p. pap. 14.99 (978-1-59669-244-2(8)) New Hope Pubs.

—Perplexing Proverbs-A Bible Study for Women: Following God Christian Living Series. 2007. (Following God Ser.). (ENG.). 192p. (gr. 11). pap. 14.99 (978-0-89957-247-5(2)) AMG Pubs.

Schley-Florence, Mildred. A Fight to Be Heard: My Soul Cried Out. 2011. 52p. pap. 9.95 (978-1-4502-9426-3(X)) iUniverse, Inc.

Schmidt, Melinda, et al. Daily Seeds from Women Who Walk in Faith. 2008. (ENG.). 416p. 14.99 (978-0-8024-7561-9(2)) Moody Pubs.

Schrock, Mary. The Greater Inheritance: The tru story of one Amish family's journey to the Truth. 2009. 150p. pap. 13.95 (978-1-935298-24-3(0)) Truth Pubs.

Schweitzer, Carol L. Schnabl. The Stranger's Voice: Julia Kristeva's Relevance for a Pastoral Theology for Women Struggling with Depression. 2010. (Practical Theology Ser.). 228p. (C). 74.95 (978-1-4331-0884-6(4)) Lang, Peter Publishing, Inc.

Scurnaci, Dondi. Career Moves: How to Plan for Success, Create Value for Your Organization, & Make Yourself Indispensable No Matter Where You Work. 2010. (ENG.). 256p. 21.99 (978-1-59979-857-8(3)) Charisma Media.

—Ready, Set... Grow! How to Rediscover Your Passion, Overcome Your Fears, & Create the Life You've Always Wanted. 2009. (ENG.). 256p. 21.99 (978-1-59979-466-2(7)) Charisma Media.

Scurnaci, Dondi. A Softer Strength. 2011. E-Book (978-1-61638-575-0(8), Charisma Hse.) Charisma Media.

Seed, Zoe A. Choices Not Chosen: A Journey Through Brokenness. 2009. 212p. pap. 15.99 (978-1-60791-673-4(8)) Xulon Pr., Inc.

Seibert, Virginia Ozue. Nurturing Journey's from Both Sides of the Veil. 2009. 252p. 29.95 (978-1-60844-364-2(7)); pap. 15.95 (978-1-60844-329-1(9)) Dog Ear Publishing, LLC.

Sell, Colleen. A Cup of Comfort for Christian Women: Stories that celebrate your faith & trust in God. 2011. (ENG.). 336p. 14.95 (978-1-4405-1118-9(7)) Adams Media Corp.

Sennett, Linda. The Restoration of a Woman's Soul: The Transformation of a Woman's Soul from Death to Life. 2011. 128p. 22.99 (978-1-4567-2570-9(X)); pap. 13.99 (978-1-4567-2571-6(8)) AuthorHouse.

The Service of Women in the Church. (Touchpoint Ser.). 30p. pap. 2.99 (978-0-570-09560-6(3), 20-2504); 40p. pap., stu. ed. 2.99 (978-0-570-09559-0(X), 20-2503) Concordia Publishing Hse.

Shaddai, Queen Juliet El. Woman, You Are God's Most Precious Vessel Filled with Treasures & Miracles! 2008. 200p. 29.99 (978-1-4363-3168-5(4)); pap. 19.99 (978-1-4363-3167-8(6)) Xlibris Corp.

Shanklin, Charesse. Torn. 2010. 160p. (ENG.). 25.99 (978-1-4520-0735-9(7)); pap. 19.99 (978-1-4520-0734-2(9)) AuthorHouse.

Sharp, Kathy Chapman. Life's Too Short to Miss the Big Picture for Women: Making the Most of What's Most Important. 2011. 224p. pap. 14.99 (978-0-89112-282-1(6), Leafwood Pubs.) Abilene Christian Univ. Pr.

Sharpe, Sally D. & Davis-Carroll, Hilda. 365 Meditations for Mothers by Mothers. 2007. 264p. pap. 16.00 (978-0-687-49255-8(6), Dimensions For Living) Abingdon Pr.

Shastar, Nightrissa. Chaste Disciples 4 Christ: A Great Nation of Ladies. 2008. 85p. pap. 16.95 (978-1-60474-649-5(1)) PublishAmerica, Inc.

Shaw, Jane. Octavia, Daughter of God: The Story of a Female Messiah & Her Followers. 2011. (Illus.). 432p. 35.00 (978-0-300-17615-5(5)) Yale Univ. Pr.

Shepherd, Sheri Rose. Fit for My King: His Princess 30-Day Diet Plan & Devotional. 2009. 208p. 14.99 (978-0-8007-1916-6(6)) Revell.

—His Princess Bride: Love Letters from Your Prince. 2009. 208p. 13.99 (978-0-8007-1915-9(8)) Revell.

Sherrer, Quin & Garlock, Ruthanne B. A Woman's Guide to Spiritual Warfare: Protect Your Home, Family & Friends from Spiritual Darkness. 2010. (ENG.). 208p. pap. 14.99 (978-0-8307-4748-1(6)) Gospel Light Pubns.

Shirer, Priscilla. The Resolution for Women. 2011. (ENG.). 288p. pap. 14.99 (978-1-4336-7401-3(7), B&H Bks.) B&H Publishing Group.

—The Resolution for Women. Lt. ed. 2011. pap. 17.99 (978-1-59415-386-0(8)) Cengage Gale.

Shirer, Priscilla, et al. Anointed, Transformed, Redeemed: A Study of David. 2008. (Illus.). 148p. pap. 18.00 (978-1-4158-6585-9(X)) LifeWay Christian Resources.

Sigmon, Roger R. Sleeping with the Angels. 2011. 116p. 28.95 (978-1-4627-0550-4(2)); pap. 11.95 (978-1-4627-0549-8(9)) Cross Bks. Publishing.

Sill. Encounters in Quest of Christian Womanhood: The Basel Mission in Pre- & Early Colonial Ghana. 2010. (Studies in Christian Mission Ser.). 418p. (978-90-04-18450-3(3)) BRILL.

Sill, Ulrike. Encounters in Quest of Christian Womanhood: The Basel Mission in Pre- & Early Colonial Ghana. 2010. (978-90-04-18888-4(6)) BRILL.

Silvas, et al. Macrina the Younger, Philosopher of God. 2008. (Medieval Women: Texts & Contexts Ser.). (ENG & GRE., Illus.). 264p. (C). 102.00 (978-2-503-52390-3(0)) Brepols Pubs. BEL. Dist: ISD.

Silvious, Jan. Smart Girls Think Twice: Making Wise Choices When It Counts, 0 vols. 2008. 224p. pap. 14.99 (978-0-7852-2815-8(2)) Nelson, Thomas Inc.

Skelton, Vonda. Seeing Through the Lies: Unmasking the Myths Women Believe. 2008. (ENG.). 176p. per. 12.99 (978-0-8307-4501-2(7)) Gospel Light Pubns.

Slattery, Kathryn. Lost & Found: One Daughter's Story of Amazing Grace. 2008. 223p. 17.99 (978-0-8249-4734-7(7), GuidepostsBooks) Ideals Pubns.

Slaughter, Sena. I March to the Tune of a Different Drummer. 2011. 64p. pap. 19.95 (978-1-4512-7723-4(7)) PublishAmerica, Inc.

Smalley, Erin & Oliver, Carrie. Grown-Up Girlfriends: Finding & Keeping Real Friends in the Real World. 2007. (ENG.). 240p. per. 13.99 (978-1-4143-0809-8(4)) Tyndale Hse. Pubs.

Smith, Gwen. Broken into Beautiful: Let God Restore Your Wounded Heart. 2008. 250p. pap. 12.99 (978-0-7369-2317-0(9)) Harvest Hse. Pubs.

Smith, Michelle. From Lesbianism to Grace: The Power of Change. 2009. pap. 10.99 (978-1-60799-842-6(4)) Tate Publishing & Enterprises, LLC.

Smith, W. D. Women & Womb: A Journey Through the Transfer of a Destiny, 1 vol. 2010. 168p. pap. 24.95 (978-1-4489-4334-0(5)) PublishAmerica, Inc.

Smith, Yolanda Y. Women's Spirituality & Education in the Black Church. 2012. (Black Religion/Womanist Thought/Social Justice Ser.). (ENG., Illus.). 256p. 85.00 (978-0-230-61833-6(2)) Palgrave Macmillan.

Snidow, Chris. Joan of Arc & the God of the Bible. 2006. 164p. per. 14.95 (978-0-595-39255-1(5)) iUniverse, Inc.

Snow, Rhonda. The Prison Gates Are Broken. 2007. 184p. per. 13.99 (978-1-60266-318-3(1)) Xulon Pr., Inc.

Sober, Melody. Vova Story. 2010. 108p. pap. 10.99 (978-1-4490-5679-7(2)) AuthorHouse.

Soraya. Broken-But Not Destroyed: In Search for God. 2009. 236p. pap. 15.99 (978-1-61579-068-5(3)) Xulon Pr., Inc.

Sowell, Kimberly. Journey to Significance: Becoming Women of Divine Destiny. 2008. (ENG.). 160p. pap. 12.99 (978-1-59669-217-6(0)) New Hope Pubs.

Sowell, Kimberly & Ellison, Edna. Women of the Covenant: Spiritual Wisdom from Women of the Bible. 2009. (New Hope Bible Studies for Women Ser.). (ENG.). 144p. pap. 8.99 (978-1-59669-270-1(7)) New Hope Pubs.

Spellman, Lynne. Unbolting the Dark, A Memoir. 2011. (ENG.). 104p. pap. 22.95 (978-0-7618-5584-2(X)) Hamilton Bks.

Spruell, Carlene K. Life with My Son: A Mother's Journey Thro. 2006. 128p. per. 13.95 (978-0-595-40479-7(0)) iUniverse, Inc.

St. James, Rebecca. Pure: A 90-Day Devotional for the Mind, Body, & Spirit. 2008. (ENG.). 272p. pap. 13.99 (978-0-446-50041-8(0)) FaithWords.

Stafford, Nancy. Beauty by the Book: Seeing Yourself as God Sees You. 2006. (ENG.). 240p. pap. 16.99 (978-1-59052-981-2(2), Multnomah) Doubleday Religious Publishing Group, The.

Stanfill, Brenda Richie. Fatal Errors. 2007. 125p. pap. 19.95 (978-1-60441-646-0(X)) PublishAmerica, Inc.

Starbuck, Margot. Unsqueezed: Springing Free from Skinny Jeans, Nose Jobs, Highlights & Stilettos. 2010. (ENG.). 237p. pap. 16.00 (978-0-8308-3616-1(0), IVP Bks.) InterVarsity Pr.

Staveley, Lilian. A Christian Woman's Secret: A Modern-Day Journey to God. 2009. (ENG.). 168p. pap. 17.95 (978-1-933316-58-1(6)) World Wisdom, Inc.

Stephan, Scott. Redeeming the Southern Family: Evangelical Women & Domestic Devotion in the Antebellum South. (ENG.). 320p. 2011. pap. 24.95 (978-0-8203-3980-1(6)) 2008. lib. bdg. 44.95 (978-0-8203-3222-2(4)) Univ. of Georgia Pr.

Stevens, Becca. Find Your Way Home: Words from the Street, Wisdom from the Heart. 2008. 119p. pap. 10.50 (978-0-687-64705-7(3)) Abingdon Pr.

Stewart, Ian M. Mary Stephens Corbishley Mbe: A Biography of Her Life & Work at Her Oral Schools for Deaf Children in Cuckfield, East Sussex, the Uk. 2010. (Illus.). 160p. pap. 12.38 (978-1-4520-6855-8(0)) AuthorHouse.

Stoeker, Fred & Stoeker, Brenda. Every Heart Restored: A Wife's Guide to Healing in the Wake of a Husband's Sexual Sin. 2010. (Every Man Ser.). (ENG.). 352p. pap. 15.99 (978-0-307-45942-8(X), WaterBrook Pr.) Doubleday Religious Publishing Group, The.

Strack, Diane & Brunson, Debbie. Quiet Influence: The Romans 12:1 Woman. 2009. 92p. pap. (978-1-60006-670-2(4)) NavPress Publishing Group.

Strack, Diane R. New Start for Single Moms, 0 vols. 2007. (Illus.). 128p. per. 9.99 (978-1-4185-2801-0(3)) Nelson, Thomas Inc.

—New Start for Single Moms Kit, 0 vols. 2007. 99.99 (978-1-4185-2853-9(6)) Nelson, Thomas Inc.

Stroud, Marion. Dear God, It's Me & It's Urgent: Prayers for Every Season of a Woman's Life. 2008. (ENG.). 224p. 14.99 (978-1-57293-272-2(4)) Discovery Hse. Pubs.

Sweet, Katrina L. Silent Screams from Within: A Woman's Story of Tragedy to Triumph. 2011. 128p. 19.95 (978-1-936513-30-7(7)); pap. 10.95 (978-1-936513-29-1(3)) PearlStone Publishing, Inc.

Swenson, Amber Abee. Bible Moms: Life Lessons from Mothers in the Bible. 2007. (ENG.). 158p. per. 12.99 (978-1-933204-39-0(7)) Deep River Bks.

Sylvest, Martha. Mary Claire's Dream. 2008. 284p. 26.99 (978-1-60647-798-4(6)); pap. 16.99 (978-1-60647-797-7(8)) Xulon Pr., Inc.

Syswerda, Jean E. The Women's Devotional Guide to the Bible: A One-Year Plan for Studying, Praying, & Responding to God's Word. 2012. 384p. pap. 15.99 (978-0-8499-2977-9(6)) Nelson, Thomas Inc.

Taber, Shirin. Wanting All the Right Things: Finding a Spiritual, Balanced, & Fulfilled Life. 2006. 186p. per. 13.99 (978-0-9776167-9-4(7)) Relevant Media Group, Inc.

Taege, Marlys. The Heart of Jesus: Women in the Gospel of Luke. 2009. 224p. pap. 12.99 (978-0-7586-1659-3(7)) Concordia Publishing Hse.

Taylor, Larissa Juliet. The Virgin Warrior: The Life & Death of Joan of Arc. 2010. (Illus.). 280p. pap. 20.00 *(978-0-300-16895-2(0))* Yale Univ. Pr.

Taylor, Thérèse & Taylor. Bernadette of Lourdes: Her life, death & visions: new anniversary Edition. 2nd rev. ed. 2008. (ENG., Illus.). 372p. 19.95 *(978-0-8264-2085-5(0),* Burns & Oates) Continuum International Publishing Group, Ltd. GBR. Dist: National Bk. Network.

Taylor Williams, Debbie. If God Is in Control, Why Am I a Basket Case? Extraordinary Choices for a JoyFilled Life. rev. ed. 2011. (ENG.). 224p. pap. 14.99 *(978-1-59669-337-1(1))* New Hope Pubs.

TerKeurst, Lysa. Becoming More: Than a Good Bible Study Girl, 1 vol. 2009. (ENG.). 192p. pap. 12.99 *(978-0-310-29325-5(1))* Zondervan.

Terkeurst, Lysa. Becoming More Than a Good Bible Study Girl, 1 vol. 2009. (ENG.). 112p. pap., instr.'s gde. ed. 9.99 *(978-0-310-32208-5(1))* Zondervan.

TerKeurst, Lysa. Made to Crave: Satisfying Your Deepest Desire with God, Not Food. (ENG.). 2011. 24.99 *(978-0-310-67154-1(X))* 2010. 192p. pap. 14.99 *(978-0-310-29326-2(X))* Zondervan.

—Made to Crave Pack: Satisfying Your Deepest Desire with God, Not Food, 1 vol. 2011. (ENG.). pap., pap. 31.99 incl. DVD *(978-0-310-65278-6(2))* Zondervan.

—Made to Crave Participant's Guide: Satisfying Your Deepest Desire with God, Not Food. 2011. (ENG.). 96p. pap. 9.99 *(978-0-310-67155-8(8))* Zondervan.

—What Happens When Women Say Yes to God: Experiencing Life in Extraordinary Ways. 2007. 154p. per. 10.99 *(978-0-7369-1922-7(8))* Harvest Hse. Pubs.

Thacker-Brown, Cheryl. The Re-Making of an Addict. 2011. 120p. 24.95 ***(978-1-4567-5601-7(X))***; pap. 16.95 ***(978-1-4567-5602-4(8))*** AuthorHouse.

Thomas, Amelia M. Me. James, E. A., ed. 2nd ed. 2011. (Illus.). 112p. pap. 18.95 ***(978-1-931671-38-5(9))*** FM Publishing Co.

Thomas, Angela. Do You Know Who I Am? And Other Brave Questions Women Ask. 2010. (ENG.). 240p. pap. 14.99 *(978-1-4391-6070-1(8),* Howard Bks.) Howard Books.

—Do You Think I'm Beautiful? Answering the Question Every Woman Asks. 2007. 143p. per. 10.95 *(978-1-4158-6048-9(3))* LifeWay Christian Resources.

—Do You Think I'm Beautiful? Leader Kit: Answering the Question Every Woman Asks. 2007. 149.95 incl. DVD *(978-1-4158-5286-6(3))* LifeWay Christian Resources.

Thomas Nelson. AMAZING FREEDOM (9 inner packs Of 4) 2010. pap. 5.99 *(978-1-4002-8103-9(2))* Nelson, Thomas Inc.

Thomas Nelson Publishing Staff. The Woman's Study Bible: Second Edition, 0 vols. 2nd ed. 2008. 1888p. im. lthr. 69.99 *(978-0-7180-2534-2(2))*; im. lthr. 79.99 *(978-0-7180-2535-9(0))* Nelson, Thomas Inc.

Thompson, Debi. Here Comes the Bride but Is She Ready??? 2007. 120p. per. 10.99 *(978-1-60477-349-1(9))* Xulon Pr., Inc.

Thompson, Grant. The Southern! Witness in the Natural & Spiritual, 1 vol. 2010. 82p. pap. 19.95 *(978-1-4489-4028-8(1))* PublishAmerica, Inc.

Thompson, Janet. Face-to-Face with Elizabeth & Mary: Generation to Generation. 2010. (New Hope Bible Studies for Women Ser.). (ENG.). 144p. pap. 8.99 *(978-1-59669-252-7(9))* New Hope Pubs.

—Face-to-Face with Mary & Martha: Sisters in Christ. 2009. (New Hope Bible Studies for Women Ser.). (ENG.). 144p. pap. 8.99 *(978-1-59669-254-1(5))* New Hope Pubs.

—Face-to-Face with Naomi & Ruth: Together for the Journey. 2009. (New Hope Bible Studies for Women Ser.). (ENG.). 144p. pap. 8.99 *(978-1-59669-253-4(7))* New Hope Pubs.

Thompson, Janice & Hanna, Janice. Everyday Joy. 2009. (Spiritual Refreshment Ser.). (ENG.). 224p. pap. 7.99 *(978-1-60260-346-2(4),* Barbour Bks.) Barbour Publishing, Inc.

Thompson, Lady Robin. The Making of A Proverbs 31 Woman. 2011. 80p. pap. 20.00 ***(978-1-4567-9769-0(7))*** AuthorHouse.

Tiso, Ruth. Woman Come Out of the Shadow. 2010. (ENG.). 56p. pap. *(978-1-907629-10-5(6))* ShieldCrest.

Torres-Reyes, Debra Roberts. Negroes, Flies & Wet Toilet Paper: Confessions of a Preacher's Daughter: Losing My Religion & Finding God. 2011. 316p. 32.95 *(978-1-4502-1903-7(9))*; pap. 22.95 *(978-1-4502-1901-3(2))* iUniverse, Inc.

Townsend, Karen. It All Started When I Stopped Using Lotion: One Woman's Journey from Chaos to Calm. Coleman, Valerie J. Lewis, ed. 2011. 128p. pap. 12.95 ***(978-0-9817436-5-3(X))*** Queen V Publishing - Ohio.

Tracy, Pamela Kaye. Promesas para Cada Día: Refrigerio Espiritual paraa Mujeres. 2010. (Spiritual Refreshment for Women Ser.).Tr. of Everyday Promises. (ENG & SPA.). 224p. pap. 4.99 *(978-1-60260-868-9(7),* Casa Promesa) Barbour Publishing, Inc.

Treat, Janet. Following the Shepherd. 2011. 124p. pap. 11.95 ***(978-1-4497-2201-2(6),*** WestBow Pr.) Author Solutions, Inc.

Trotter, Henrietta. Divine Interventions. 2010. 280p. 25.99 *(978-1-4520-6815-2(1))*; pap. 15.49 *(978-1-4520-6816-9(X))* AuthorHouse.

Tukes, Catherine F. Vessels of Honor: Fit for the Master's Use. 2010. 103p. pap. 10.95 *(978-1-4327-5224-8(3))* Outskirts Pr., Inc.

Turpin, Joanne. Women in Church History: 21 Stories for 21 Centuries. 2007. 232p. per. 14.95 *(978-0-86716-776-4(9))* Franciscan Media.

Twigg, Nancy. From Clutter to Clarity: Simplifying Life from the Inside Out. 2007. 192p. pap. 12.99 *(978-0-7847-2110-0(6))* Standard Publishing.

Tye, Diane. Baking as Biography: A Life Story in Recipes. 2010. 288p. (ENG.). (C). *(978-0-7735-3724-8(4))*; pap. *(978-0-7735-3725-5(2))* McGill-Queen's Univ. Pr.

Ulrich, Isolde. The Romance of Kilimanjaro: The Anatomy of a Midlife Crisis Series. 2011. pap. 19.99 ***(978-1-61346-496-0(7))*** Tate Publishing & Enterprises, LLC.

Valentine, Scott R. Barefoot & Pregnant: The Socialization of the Educated Korean Woman. 2007. per. 19.95 *(978-0-9704006-3-5(2))* Bound & Determined Pubs.

Van Berkel, Connie L. Choose High Road Victories: For Christian Women in the Workplace. 2006. (ENG.). 236p. per. 17.99 *(978-1-4141-0785-1(4))* Pleasant Word.

Verriett, Tamara. A Call for the Daughters of Zion. 2006. per. 12.95 *(978-0-9742207-9-6(5))* KNB Pubns., LLC.

Voges, Aletha. My Will, God's Response: God's Will, My Response: A Memoir of Losing A Loved One. 2010. pap. 13.99 *(978-1-61566-269-2(3))* Tate Publishing & Enterprises, LLC.

Von Oven, Amy E. Still in My Arms. 2011. 156p. 23.25 ***(978-1-4567-4865-4(3))***; pap. 13.70 ***(978-1-4567-4866-1(1))*** AuthorHouse.

Voudrie, Krista. Convictions of a Young Girl's Heart: What Every Young Christian Woman Struggles With. 2007. 57p. pap. 16.95 *(978-1-60441-411-0(1))* PublishAmerica, Inc.

W., Joye. Walking Through the 'C' Word: A Victorious Journey Through Cancer, Divorce & Despair. 2008. 132p. pap. 11.95 *(978-1-4327-2561-7(0))* Outskirts Pr., Inc.

Waddell, Marshele Carter. Hope for the Home Front: Winning the Emotional & Spiritual Battles of a Military Wife. 2006. (ENG.). 176p. per. 12.99 *(978-1-59669-032-5(1))* New Hope Pubs.

Wagner, Holly. Warrior Chicks: Rising Strong, Beautiful & Confident. 2007. (ENG.). 208p. per. 14.99 *(978-0-8307-4480-0(0))* Gospel Light Pubns.

Walsh, Christine. The Cult of St Katherine in Early Medieval Europe. 2007. (Church, Faith & Culture in the Medieval West Ser.). (Illus.). 244p. 124.95 *(978-0-7546-5861-0(9))* Ashgate Publishing Co.

Walsh, Joseph. What Would You Die for Persuas Passion. 2006. 164p. per. 14.95 *(978-1-934074-02-2(0))* Apprentice Hse.

Walsh, Sheila. Beautiful Things Happen When a Woman Trusts God, 0 vols. 2010. 288p. 21.99 *(978-1-4002-0243-0(4))* Nelson, Thomas Inc.

—Get off Your Knees & Pray. l.t. ed. 2010. (ENG.). 352p. pap. 17.99 *(978-1-59415-289-4(6))* Cengage Gale.

—Get off Your Knees & Pray, 0 vols. 2010. 240p. pap. 14.99 *(978-1-4002-0253-9(1))* Nelson, Thomas Inc.

—God Has a Dream for Your Life, 0 vols. 2009. 224p. pap. 14.99 *(978-1-4002-8035-3(4))* Nelson, Thomas Inc.

—I'm Not Wonder Woman, but God Made Me Wonderful!, 0 vols. 2008. (Women of Faith Ser.). 240p. per. 14.99 *(978-1-4002-0200-3(0))* Nelson, Thomas Inc.

—Let Go: Live Free of the Burdens All Women Know. 2011. 288p. pap. 15.99 *(978-1-4002-0302-4(3))* 2009. 256p. 21.99 *(978-0-8499-0135-5(9))* Nelson, Thomas Inc.

—Let Go: Live Free of the Burdens All Women Know. l.t. ed. 2011. (ENG.). 384p. pap. 17.99 *(978-1-59415-356-3(6),* Large Print Pr.) Thorndike Pr.

Warren, Frank. The Winner's Circle: Faith That Makes You All God Planned for You to Be. 2008. (ENG.). 96p. pap. 8.99 *(978-1-59979-604-8(X),* Creation Hse.) Charisma Media.

Warren, Nancy. Embodied Word: Female Spiritualities, Contested Orthodoxies, & English Religious Cultures, 1350-1700. 2010. (ND Reformations: Medieval & Early Modern Ser.). (ENG., Illus.). 352p. pap. 36.00 *(978-0-268-04420-6(1))* Univ. of Notre Dame Pr.

Wasoba, Karen. Lord, Shut Me up! Anger Management for Christians. 2007. 216p. per. 17.95 *(978-1-58736-763-2(7))* Wheatmark.

Watters, Candice. Get Married: What Women Can Do to Help It Happen. 2008. (ENG., Illus.). 208p. per. 12.99 *(978-0-8024-5829-2(7))* Moody Pubs.

Weatherly, Lori Clark. Facets of Life. 2011. 142p. pap. 14.99 ***(978-1-61379-146-2(1))*** Xulon Pr., Inc.

Weaver, Joanna. Having a Mary Heart in a Martha World: Finding Intimacy with God in the Busyness of Life. gif. ed. 2007. (ENG., Illus.). 288p. 19.99 *(978-1-4000-7403-7(7),* WaterBrook Pr.) Doubleday Religious Publishing Group, The.

—Having a Mary Spirit: Allowing God to Change Us from the Inside Out. l.t. ed. 2007. (Walker Large Print Ser.). (ENG.). 529p. per. 17.95 *(978-1-59415-176-7(8),* Walker Large Print) Cengage Gale.

—Having a Mary Spirit: Allowing God to Change Us from the Inside Out. 2006. (ENG.). 288p. pap. 14.99 *(978-1-4000-7247-7(6),* WaterBrook Pr.) Doubleday Religious Publishing Group, The.

Webb, Joan & Webb, Joan C. It's A Wonderful Imperfect Life: Daily Encouragement for Women Who Strive Too Hard to Make It Just Right. 2009. (ENG.). 192p. pap. 12.99 *(978-0-8307-4801-3(6))* Gospel Light Pubns.

Webster, Jessica Anne. Overcoming Life's Battles with Jesus: Fighting the Storm from Within. 2011. 80p. 20.95 ***(978-1-4620-3867-1(0))***; pap. 10.95 ***(978-1-4620-3868-8(9))*** iUniverse, Inc.

Weidner, Robin. Secure in Heart: Overcoming Insecurity in a Woman's Life. 2010. 327p. pap. 16.00 *(978-1-57782-250-9(1))* Discipleship Pubns. International.

Weigand, Vilma. Creating & Singing Faith: An Immigrant's Compelling & Inspiring True Story. 2010. 233p. pap. 14.95 *(978-1-4327-5599-7(4))* Outskirts Pr., Inc.

West, Marion Bond. Praying for My Life. 2006. 288p. 17.95 *(978-0-8249-4705-7(3),* GuidepostsBooks) Ideals Pubns.

Whelchel, Lisa. Taking Care of the Me in Mommy: Becoming a Better Mom: Spirit, Body & Soul, 0 vols. 2007. 304p. per. 14.99 *(978-0-7852-8929-6(1))* Nelson, Thomas Inc.

White, Caroline, ed. & tr. Lives of Roman Christian Women. 2010. (ENG., Illus.). 288p. (gr. 12-18). 16.00 *(978-0-14-144193-1(3),* Penguin Classics) Penguin Group (USA) Inc.

White, Rebecca J. From the Barstool to the Pulpit. 2008. 188p. pap. 19.99 *(978-0-9818753-3-0(5))* Leading Lady Pubns.

Whittle, Lisa. Behind Those Eyes: What's Really Going on Inside the Souls of Women, 0 vols. 2008. 240p. pap. 14.99 *(978-0-7852-2813-4(6))* Nelson, Thomas Inc.

Wier, Kim. Are You Talking to Me? 169p. pap. 10.99 *(978-0-8307-3382-8(5),* Regal Bks.) Gospel Light Pubns.

—Get a Life! 176p. pap. 10.99 *(978-0-8307-3426-9(0),* Regal Bks.) Gospel Light Pubns.

Wiitala, Geri Colozzi. Scripture Exposes the Errors of Fundamentalists Mentality. 2011. 84p. pap. 19.95 ***(978-1-4560-7735-8(X))*** PublishAmerica, Inc.

Wilbanks, Monika. The Universal Sisterhood: And Women Shall Lead. 2011. pap. 13.99 ***(978-1-61739-942-8(6))*** Tate Publishing & Enterprises, LLC.

Wilkinson, Helena. Finding Freedom. 2007. 126p. pap. *(978-1-85345-451-6(6))* Crusade for World Revival.

Williams, Debbie Taylor. The Plan A Woman in a Plan B World: What to Do When Life Doesn't Go According to Plan. 2010. 14.99 *(978-0-89112-641-6(4),* Leafwood Pubs.) Abilene Christian Univ. Pr.

Williams, Joyce, compiled by. My Faith Still Holds. l.t. ed. 2007. (Walker Large Print Ser.). (ENG.). 239p. per. 15.95 *(978-1-59415-167-5(9),* Walker Large Print) Cengage Gale.

Williams, Patricia. The Endurance of Pleasing God. 2008. 48p. pap. 16.95 *(978-1-60474-914-4(8))* PublishAmerica, Inc.

Wilson, Gladys Blews. Standing in the Gap. 2011. 272p. pap. 19.95 ***(978-1-4497-2105-3(2),*** WestBow Pr.) Author Solutions, Inc.

Wilson, Meg. Hope after Betrayal: Healing When Sexual Addiction Invades Your Marriage, 1 vol. 2007. 160p. pap. 10.99 *(978-0-8254-3935-3(3))* Kregel Pubns.

Wilson, Stina. Breaking Up: He's Just Not That into God. 2007. 128p. pap. 9.99 *(978-0-8254-3937-7(X))* Kregel Pubns.

Windle, K. A Joyful Life, 1 vol. 2010. 48p. pap. 16.95 *(978-1-4489-4949-6(1))* PublishAmerica, Inc.

Winifred, Avis. REACH for the Visionary Woman of God: With the Father, Son, & Holy Spirit I Can Do All Things. 2010. 148p. pap. 13.95 *(978-1-4497-0342-4(9),* WestBow Pr.) Author Solutions, Inc.

Winslow, Octavius. Life in Jesus. 2011. (ENG.). 430p. pap. 25.95 ***(978-1-4585-0003-8(9))*** Univ. of Michigan Library.

Winter, Deanne. Hope: Live Life... 2009. 176p. pap. 11.99 *(978-1-4389-4184-4(6))* AuthorHouse.

A Woman & Her Relationships, DVD + Book: Lessons for Faith Communities. 2009. (ENG.). pap. 24.99 *(978-0-8341-2447-9(5),* 9780834124479) Beacon Hill Pr. of Kansas City.

Women of Faith. Nothing Is Impossible: A Women of Faith Devotional, 0 vols. 2010. 256p. 15.99 *(978-1-4002-0242-3(6))* Nelson, Thomas Inc.

Women of Faith, creator. Amazing Freedom, 0 vols. 2007. (Women of Faith Study Guides). 144p. per. 9.99 *(978-1-4185-2637-5(1))* Nelson, Thomas Inc.

Woodard, Gayle. It's My Prerogative. 2007. pap. 15.99 *(978-1-934769-07-2(X))* McDougal & Assocs.

Wootton, Janet. This Is Our Song: Womens Hymn Writing. 2010. (ENG.). 216p. pap. 50.00 *(978-0-7162-0655-2(2))* Epworth Pr., The. GBR. Dist: Westminster John Knox Pr.

Wright, H. Norman. Healing for the Father Wound: A Trusted Christian Counselor Offers Time-Tested Advice. 2008. 192p. pap. 13.99 *(978-0-7642-0535-4(8))* Bethany Hse. Pubs.

Yarbough, Delores Byrd Finger. This Little Light of Mine. 2010. 112p. 22.95 *(978-1-4502-0833-8(9))*; pap. 12.95 *(978-1-4502-0832-1(0))* iUniverse, Inc.

Young, Carol Ann. Mother, Please Don't Throw My Life Away: The cry of the unborn & the voices of those longing to be Heard. 2008. 96p. pap. 12.95 *(978-1-4327-3149-6(1))* Outskirts Pr., Inc.

Young, Sarah. Biblical Womanhood: Nine Studies for Individuals or Groups. 2010. 64p. pap. *(978-1-904889-07-6(7))* Good Bk. Co.

Zondervan. Made to Crave, Case Of 24: Satisfying Your Deepest Desire with God, Not Food, 1 vol. 2011. pap. 351.68 ***(978-0-310-31546-9(8))*** Zondervan.

Zondervan Publishing Staff. Devotions to Go, 1 vol. 2009. (ENG.). 192p. Vol. 3. 12.99 *(978-0-310-82282-0(3))* Vol. 4. 12.99 *(978-0-310-82283-7(1))* Zondervan.

—True Identity: The Bible for Women - Becoming Who You Are in Christ. 2009. (ENG.). 1824p. lthr. 24.99 *(978-0-310-93897-2(X))*; lthr. 59.99 *(978-0-310-93944-3(5))*; lthr. 36.99 *(978-0-310-93891-0(0))* Zondervan.

100+ ways God Shows Me He Loves Me. 2007. pap. 10.00 *(978-0-9793892-5-2(9))* Christian Womanhood Pubns.

2003 Guide for Y. W. A. & Junior Mission. *(978-1-58942-121-9(3))* R.H. Boyd Publishing Corp.

CHRISTIAN YEAR

see Church Year

CHRISTIANITY

Here are entered works on the Christian religion including its origin, beliefs, practices and influence treated collectively. Works on the institutional history of the church are entered under Church History.

see also Christian Civilization; Church History; Communism and Christianity; Jesus Christ; Messianic Judaism; Pentecostalism; Protestantism; Theology; Women in Christianity

also headings beginning with the word Christian and Church; and names of Christian churches and sects, e.g. Catholic Church; Lutheran Church; Huguenots

A. Collection of Devotions By the Clergy of Christ Episcopal Church. The Blessing of A Ginkgo Tree: A Collection of Devotions by the Clergy of Christ Episcopal Church. 2010. 192p. pap. 14.25 *(978-1-4567-0079-9(0))* AuthorHouse.

Abbas & Abbas. Children of Abraham/les Enfants D'Abraham. 2007. (ENG & FRE., Illus.). 239p. pap. *(978-2-916355-01-6(4))* Editions Intervalles.

ABBE Scientist Research Division Staff. Religion of Jesus -Modern Views & Reports: Index, Reference & Medical Analysis of New Research Information. 2008. 160p. ring bd. 69.95 *(978-0-7883-4677-4(6))* ABBE Pubs. Assn. of Washington, D.C.

Abbott, Lyman. The Evolution of Christianity. 2008. 167p. 28.99 *(978-0-554-65372-3(9))*; 108p. 25.99 *(978-0-554-65381-5(8))*; 272p. pap. 26.75 *(978-0-554-65376-1(1))*; 272p. pap. 27.75 *(978-0-554-65373-0(7))* BiblioBazaar.

—The Evolution of Christianity, Vol. 1. 2009. (Cambridge Library Collection - Religion Ser.). (ENG.). 272p. pap. 23.99 *(978-1-108-00019-2(3))* Cambridge Univ. Pr.

—The Evolution of Christianity. 2007. 272p. 42.95 *(978-0-548-11135-2(9))* Kessinger Publishing, LLC.

—The Great Companion. 2009. 160p. 26.99 *(978-1-110-46477-7(0))*; pap. 20.75 *(978-1-110-46472-2(X))* BiblioBazaar.

—The Great Companion. 2007. (ENG.). 164p. 36.95 *(978-0-548-09619-2(8))* Kessinger Publishing, LLC.

—What Christianity Means to Me: A Spiritual Autobiography. 2007. (ENG.). 208p. 39.95 *(978-0-548-10764-5(5))* Kessinger Publishing, LLC.

Abebe, Lulsegged. Christian Councils As Agents of Reconciliation & Change. 2009. 228p. pap. *(978-3-639-07748-3(2))* VDM Verlag Dr. Mueller e.K.

Abraham, Michael. Repent the Secondary Sin & Receive Your True Power to Get Wealth from God: (subtitle Is the provisions column, too Long) 2007. 176p. per. 24.95 *(978-1-4241-7705-9(7))* PublishAmerica, Inc.

Absolute Victory. pap. 4.99 *(978-0-89274-542-5(8),* ABD-001) Harrison House Pubs.

Absolute Victory. 2008. (ENG.). lib. bdg. 10.00 *(978-1-56267-641-4(5))* Victory Christian Ctr.

Ackermann, C. The Christian Element in Plato & the Platonic Philosophy. Asbury, Samuel Ralph, tr. 2007. (ENG.). 286p. 43.95 *(978-0-548-15213-3(6))*; 288p. per. 28.95 *(978-1-4304-4572-2(6))* Kessinger Publishing, LLC.

The Act & Testimony. 2010. pap. 18.16 *(978-1-61143-169-8(7))* Gorgias Pr., LLC.

Acuff, Jesse. Old Covenant, New Covenant: The Case Against Legalism. 2011. pap. 20.99 ***(978-1-61739-873-5(X))*** Tate Publishing & Enterprises, LLC.

Adair, James R. Introducing Christianity. 2008. (World Religions Ser.). (Illus.). 498p. 130.00 *(978-0-415-77211-2(7),* 0415772117); 512p. pap. 36.95 *(978-0-415-77212-9(5),* 0415772125) Routledge.

Adams, Sebastian. Adams Synchronological Chart or Map of History. 2008. (Illus.). 31p. pap. 6.99 *(978-0-89051-535-8(2))* Master Bks.

Adams, Wes & Hughey, Rhonda. Revival: Its Present Relevance & Coming Role at the End of the Age. annot. ed. 2010. (ENG.). 246p. pap. 15.99 *(978-0-9826018-4-6(0))* Oasis Hse.

Adebiyi, Apostle Emmanuel. Spiritual Communication. 2011. 264p. 29.99 ***(978-1-4568-8195-5(7))***; pap. 19.99 ***(978-1-4568-8194-8(9))*** Xlibris Corp.

Adler, Mortimer J. How to Prove There Is a God: Mortimer J. Adler's Writings & Thoughts about God. Dzugan, Ken, ed. 2011. (ENG.). 320p. pap. 29.95 *(978-0-8126-9689-9(1))* Open Court Publishing Co.

Adogame, Afeosemime U. Christianity in Africa & the African Diaspora: The Appropriation of a Scattered Heritage. Gerloff, Roswith & Hock, Klaus, eds. 2009. (ENG.). 368p. 150.00 *(978-1-84706-317-5(9))* Continuum International Publishing Group, Ltd. GBR. Dist: National Bk. Network.

Adrian B. Smith Staff. God, Energy & the Field. 2009. (ENG.). 160p. pap. 19.95 *(978-1-84694-135-1(0))* Hunt, John Publishing Ltd. GBR. Dist: National Bk. Network.

Afanasiev, Nicholas. The Church of the Holy Spirit. Plekon, Michael, ed. Permiakov, Vitaly, tr. from RUS. 2007. (ENG., Illus.). 416p. 45.00 *(978-0-268-02030-9(2))* Univ. of Notre Dame Pr.

Afonso, A. V., ed. Indian Christianity. 2009. (Illus.). 542p. 125.00 *(978-81-87586-41-8(9))* Centre for Studies in Civilizations IND. Dist: Coronet Bks.

Agee, Dorothy Martin. Revelation for God's Children. 2010. pap. 12.99 *(978-1-61663-350-9(6))* Tate Publishing & Enterprises, LLC.

Agina, Harry N. The Invasion of the Funky Pastors: Church Business at War with African Culture. 2010. 140p. 26.95 *(978-1-4490-8120-1(7))*; pap. 16.95 *(978-1-4490-8119-5(3))* AuthorHouse.

Agogoe, Meshack Kwesi. Compromise: Perverting the word of God. 2011. 102p. pap. 15.99 ***(978-1-4568-4901-6(8))*** Xlibris Corp.

Ahern, Kevin. The Radical Bible. 2009. 172p. pap. 12.00 *(978-1-57075-816-4(6))* Orbis Bks.

Ajala-Immanuel, Sarah. Fleece My Sheep? The Unprecedented Tragedy of the Church in Bed with a Sinful World. 2011. 140p. pap. 15.66 *(978-1-4567-7669-5(X))* AuthorHouse.

Ajibola, Babatunde Ezekiel. Christhood for Mankind. 2008. 381p. pap. 42.50 *(978-1-4092-1302-4(1))* Lulu Enterprises Inc.

Al Morris. Civilisation Hijacked: Rescuing Jesus from Christianity & the human spirit from Bondage. 2009. 244p. pap. 19.95 *(978-1-4401-8242-6(6))* iUniverse, Inc.

Albera, Dionigi & Couroucli, Maria, eds. Sharing Sacred Spaces in the Mediterranean: Christians, Muslims, & Jews at Shrines & Sanctuaries. 2012. (New Anthropologies of Europe Ser.). (ENG., Illus.). 290p. 70.00 *(978-0-253-35633-8(4),* 0253356334); pap. 24.95 *(978-0-253-22317-3(2),* 0253223172) Indiana Univ. Pr.

Albert, Damon. Pure Vessels A Handbook for Reviving Biblical Christianity in the Heart of Today's Cultural Christian. 2010. 127p. pap. 13.00 *(978-0-557-32728-7(8))* Lulu Enterprises Inc.

Albright, Kendall. Timeless Truth's for Believers. 2011. 196p. 29.99 ***(978-1-4628-6812-4(6))***; pap. 19.99 ***(978-1-4628-6811-7(8))*** Xlibris Corp.

Albro, John A. The Life of Thomas Shepard. 2009. 326p. 32.99 *(978-1-115-29940-4(9))*; 36.99 *(978-1-115-29941-1(7))*; pap. 31.75 *(978-1-115-29939-6(5))* BiblioBazaar.

—The Life of Thomas Shepard. 2008. 322p. 45.95 *(978-1-4366-4813-4(0))* 2008. 324p. pap. 30.95 *(978-0-548-85333-7(9))* 2007. (ENG.). 324p. 45.95 *(978-0-548-37067-4(2))* 2007. (ENG.). 324p. per. 30.95 *(978-0-548-31377-0(6))* Kessinger Publishing, LLC.

Alexis, Jonas E. Christianity's Dangerous Idea: How the Christian Principle & Spirit Offer the Best Explanation for Life & Why Other Alternatives Fail: Volume One. 2010. 704p. (ENG.). 36.49 *(978-1-4520-0612-3(1))*; pap. 25.99 *(978-1-4520-0611-6(3))* AuthorHouse.

Allaway, Al. E-Praise 4 Gifting. 2008. 280p. pap. 22.50 *(978-0-615-16362-8(9))* Allawaybooks.com.

Allington, William. The Truthfulness of Christianity Demonstrated & Illustrated. 2006. (Illus.). 124p. per. 16.99 *(978-1-4255-0848-7(0))* MPublishing.

Almaroof, B. S. Reality of Lucifer. 2011. 60p. pap. 12.10 *(978-1-4567-7316-8(X))* AuthorHouse.

Alokan, Olusegun Ayodeji Peter. Joseph Babalola & the Growth of Indigenous Pentecostalism in Nigeri. 2011. 140p. pap. ***(978-3-8454-0763-0(8))*** Lambert Academic Publishing.

Althouse, Larry & Althouse, Valere. Sixty Days with Luke: A New Devotional-Study Excursion through the Third Gospel. 2010. 248p. 28.95 *(978-1-4269-4676-9(7))* Trafford Publishing.

Ambridge, Rev L. N. Path of Life. 2011. 200p. pap. 19.99 ***(978-1-4568-8628-8(2))*** Xlibris Corp.

Amitay, Ory. From Alexander to Jesus. 2010. (Hellenistic Culture & Society Ser.). (ENG.). 260p. 49.95 *(978-0-520-26636-0(6))* Univ. of California Pr.

Amos, Catherine. The Holy Spirit - She Is with Us: A Book of Revelation & Hope. 2011. 102p. 24.95 *(978-1-4327-6836-2(0))*; (ENG.). pap. 16.95 *(978-1-4327-7001-3(2))* Outskirts Pr., Inc.

And the Two. Date not set. pap. *(978-0-87162-297-6(1))* Warner Pr. Pubs.

Anderson. Free Grace Soteriology. 2010. 384p. pap. 20.99 *(978-1-61579-208-5(2))* Xulon Pr., Inc.

Anderson, Charlie. Where Have All the Men Gone. 2011. 92p. pap. 15.99 ***(978-1-4568-4019-8(3))*** Xlibris Corp.

Anderson, David R. Free Grace Soteriology. 2010. 32.99 *(978-1-61579-733-2(5))* Xulon Pr., Inc.

Anderson, H. Winston. Looking Forward. 2010. 244p. pap. 19.95 *(978-1-4401-9244-9(8))* iUniverse, Inc.

Anderson, Marjorie Elaine. A Christian Soldier's Declaration of Faith. 2009. 76p. pap. 10.99 *(978-1-4490-3597-6(3))* AuthorHouse.

Anderson, Robert. The Silence of God. 2007. 224p. per. 17.95 *(978-1-60206-217-7(X))* Cosimo, Inc.

—The Silence of God. 2011. 232p. pap. 6.35 ***(978-1-61427-039-3(2))*** Martino Publishing.

Andre', Michelle. My Damascus. 2010. 124p. 21.49 *(978-1-4520-2188-1(0))*; pap. 10.99 *(978-1-4520-2187-4(2))* AuthorHouse.

Andrews Sr., James R. The Plan of Salvation. 2008. 48p. pap. 16.95 *(978-1-60441-218-5(6))* PublishAmerica, Inc.

Angelina, Lisa. Nothing Hidden. 13.60 *(978-1-930586-11-6(6))* American Bk. Publishing Group.

Ankerberg, John & Burroughs, Dillon. How Do We Know God Exists?, 8, Bk 3. 2008. (Contender's Bible Study Ser.). (ENG.). 112p. (gr. 11). pap. 7.99 *(978-0-89957-781-4(4))* AMG Pubs.

—How Do We Know the Bible Is True?, 8, Bk 1. 2008. (Contender's Bible Study Ser.). (ENG.). 112p. (gr. 11). pap. 7.99 *(978-0-89957-779-1(2))* AMG Pubs.

Ann, Bridgette. Now Is the Time! Kingdom Minded. 2011. 152p. pap. 19.95 ***(978-1-4497-1357-7(2))***, WestBow Pr.) Author Solutions, Inc.

Annan, George Kingsley. 7 Keys to Fulfilling Your Dream. 2010. 126p. pap. 14.99 *(978-1-60957-268-6(8))* Xulon Pr., Inc.

Anoitings & Mantles. pap. 6.00 *(978-0-940763-09-8(5))* DuFresne, Ed Ministries.

Anonymous. Certaine Sermons or Homilies Appointed to Be Read in Churches in Thetime of Queen Elizabeth I. 2010. 434p. pap. 24.95 *(978-1-933993-89-8(8))* Apocryphile Pr.

Antai, Sunday. Unzipped! An Exposé on Left-Handed Christianity. 2011. 200p. pap. 17.95 ***(978-1-4497-1879-4(5))***, WestBow Pr.) Author Solutions, Inc.

Antoine, Wanda Conway. Identity Theft: Using the Name of Jesus Without Permission. 2011. pap. 8.99 *(978-1-61739-979-4(5))* Tate Publishing & Enterprises, LLC.

Antonina. Generational Curse of Unforgiveness Towards Women & Empowering the Body of Chr. 2008. pap. 14.99 *(978-1-60034-830-3(0))* Xulon Pr., Inc.

Archer, Michael J. The Resurrection Myth. 2009. 51p. pap. 19.84 *(978-0-557-00261-0(3))* Lulu Enterprises Inc.

Armstrong, Tad. It's Ok to Say God: Prelude to A Constitutional Renaissance. 2011. 368p. 39.95 ***(978-1-4497-2987-5(8))***; pap. 24.95 ***(978-1-4497-2986-8(X))*** Author Solutions, Inc. (WestBow Pr.).

Arnold, Kay Bell. Ministry from A Bed, 1 vol. 2010. 50p. pap. 16.95 *(978-1-4489-4319-7(1))* PublishAmerica, Inc.

Arnold, Scott R. I Used to be A Dumpster Diver but Jesus Set Me Free. 2010. pap. 24.99 *(978-1-61566-941-7(8))* Tate Publishing & Enterprises, LLC.

Arthur W. Pink. The Sovereignty of God. 2011. 236p. pap. 5.89 ***(978-1-60386-420-6(2)***, Watchmaker Publishing) Wexford College Pr.

Ashbury, Michael. Exposé of the Secret Vatican Vault. 2011. 242p. pap. 24.95 ***(978-1-4560-4175-5(4))*** PublishAmerica, Inc.

Ashcroft, Mary Ellen. Dogspell: The Gospel According to Dog. 2008. 112p. 18.00 *(978-1-59627-093-0(4)*, Seabury Bks.) Church Publishing, Inc.

Ashford, Brynn Taylor. Welcome to the Fresh-Squeezed Life Café: Fresh-Squeezed Life Available Daily. Always Open. Come In! 2010. 172p. pap. 19.95 *(978-1-4497-0278-6(3)*, WestBow Pr.) Author Solutions, Inc.

Ashmore, Ray. Let Your Light Shine. 2010. 149p. pap. 15.95 *(978-0-557-39225-4(X))* Lulu Enterprises Inc.

Asiamah, Kodzo. A Dormant Conscience Never Learns, 1 vol. 2009. 225p. pap. 24.95 *(978-1-61582-781-7(1))* PublishAmerica, Inc.

Asomugha, Lilian I. Are You Living in Someone Else s Mind. 2010. 86p. pap. 10.99 *(978-1-60957-534-2(2))* Xulon Pr., Inc.

Astor-Aguilera, Miguel Angel. The Maya World of Communicating Objects: Quadripartite Crosses, Trees, & Stones. 2011. (ENG., Illus.). 350p. 75.00 *(978-0-8263-4763-3(0))* Univ. of New Mexico Pr.

Atkinson, William W. Mystic Christianity: The Inner Teachings of the Master. 2009. 232p. pap. 29.95 *(978-1-60444-024-9(4))* IndoEuropeanPublishing.com.

Aubrey, Roger. Discovering God. 2008. 180p. pap. 13.99 *(978-1-60647-364-1(6))* Xulon Pr., Inc.

Austin, Denise. Kingdom-Minded People: Christian Identity & the Contributions of Chinese Business Christians: Christian Identity & the Contributions of Chinese Business Christians. 2011. (Global Pentecostal & Charismatic Studies). (Illus.). 249p. ***(978-90-04-20402-7(4))*** BRILL.

Austin, Michael. Lost Relation: Finding Humanity & God - After the Party. 2009. 168p. pap. 14.99 *(978-1-60791-978-0(8))* Xulon Pr., Inc.

Ayers, Ken. The Ten Minute Tribulation: The Final 7 Years. 2011. 136p. 24.99 ***(978-1-4634-2292-9(X))***; pap. 17.99 ***(978-1-4567-5529-4(3))*** AuthorHouse.

Ayres, Lewis & Twomey, D. Vincent, eds. The Mystery of the Holy Trinity in the Fathers of the Church: Proceedings of the Fourth International Patristic Conference, Maynooth. 2007. (Irish Theological Quarterly Ser.). 199p. 65.00 *(978-1-85182-859-3(1))* Four Courts Pr. IRL. Dist: International Specialized Bk. Services.

Azurdia, Arturo G. Connected Christianity: Engaging Culture Without Compromise. 2009. (ENG., Illus.). 96p. pap. 9.99 *(978-1-84550-468-7(2))* Christian Focus Pubns. GBR. Dist: STL Distribution North America.

B. Maureen Gaglardi. What the Devil Is Happening? 2010. 150p. 29.99 *(978-1-4535-2677-4(3))*; pap. 19.99 *(978-1-4535-2676-7(5))* Xlibris Corp.

A Baby Is Coming/ un niño Viene. 2010. pap. 3.00 *(978-1-4267-1413-9(0))* Abingdon Pr.

Backstrom, Joel. What it's All About! 2011. 62p. pap. 10.99 ***(978-1-61379-511-8(4))*** Xulon Pr., Inc.

Bailey, Edward I., contrib. by. Implicit Religion in Contemporary Society. vii, 302p. *(978-3-89271-694-5(3))* Deutscher Studien Verlag GmbH.

Baker, Anthony D. Diagonal Advance: Perfection in Christian Theology. 2011. (Veritas Ser.). 348p. pap. 39.00 ***(978-1-61097-815-6(3)***, Cascade Bks.) Wipf & Stock Pubs.

Baker, William J. Playing with God: Religion & Modern Sport. 2007. (Illus.). 336p. 29.95 *(978-0-674-02421-2(4))* Harvard Univ. Pr.

Ball, Andrew. Return to God Alone: Questioning Christianity. 2011. 396p. pap. 21.93 ***(978-1-4567-7641-1(X))*** AuthorHouse.

Balz, Horst Robert, et al. Theologische Realenzyklopädie. (GER., Illus.). 2007. XI, 772p. lthr. 363.00 *(978-3-11-019078-6(8))* 2006. XI, 693p. lthr. 335.00 *(978-3-11-018384-9(6))* De Gruyter, Walter Inc.

Banks, Kathryn & Bossier, Philiep G., eds. Commonplace Culture in Western Europe in the Early Modern Period II: Consolidation of Godgiven Power. 2011. (Groningen Studies in Cultural Change Ser.). (ENG.). 211p. (C). 70.00 *(978-90-429-2475-8(6))* Peeters Pubs. & Booksellers BEL. Dist: Brown, David Bk. Co., The.

Bar Hebraeus, Gregory. The Barn of Mysteries. 2010. (SYR.). 149.96 *(978-1-61143-246-6(4))* Gorgias Pr., LLC.

—The Chronography of Bar Hebraeus. 2010. (SYR.). 146.72 *(978-1-61143-208-4(1))* Gorgias Pr., LLC.

Barbara Esch Shisler, Esch Shisler & Shisler, Barbara. To Buy a Field: Unearthing Spiritual Treasure. 2010. 96p. pap. 9.95 *(978-1-4497-0058-4(6)*, WestBow Pr.) Author Solutions, Inc.

Barber, Michael. Should Christianity Abandon the Doctrine. 2006. 264p. per. 25.95 *(978-1-58112-940-3(8))* Universal Pubs.

BarCharts, Inc. Comparative Religion: Christianity. 2011. (ENG.). 6p. 5.95 ***(978-1-4232-1639-1(3))*** Barcharts, Inc.

Barclay, William. Insights - The Lord's Prayer: What the Bible Tells Us about the Lord's Prayer. 2011. (Insights Ser.). 80p. pap. 12.50 ***(978-0-7152-0859-5(4))*** Saint Andrew Pr., Ltd. GBR. Dist: Westminster John Knox Pr.

Bardas, Theodor. Learning about the Reality of God. 2007. 172p. per. 24.95 *(978-1-4241-7478-2(3))* PublishAmerica, Inc.

Baring-Gould, Sabine. The Origin & Development of Religious Belief. 2009. 252p. pap. *(978-0-217-09947-9(5))*; 344p. pap. *(978-0-217-36232-0(X))* Books LLC.

—The Origin & Development of Religious Belief. 2009. 238p. pap. 20.12 *(978-1-4589-9775-3(8))* General Bks. LLC.

Barksdale, Annie. Power to Remain in the House of the Lord. 2008. 82p. pap. 16.95 *(978-1-60441-099-0(X))* PublishAmerica, Inc.

Barnes, Albert. Miscellaneous Essays & Reviews by Albert Barnes. 2006. 376p. per. 26.99 *(978-1-4255-3957-3(2))*; (ENG.). per. 26.99 *(978-1-4255-3958-0(0))* MPublishing.

Barnes, Corey L. Christ's Two Wills in Scholastic Thought: The Christology of Aquinas & Its Historical Contexts. 2012. (Studies & Texts). (ENG.). 366p. 85.00 ***(978-0-88844-178-2(9))*** Pontifical Institute of Mediaeval Studies, Dept. of Pubns. CAN. Dist: Univ. of Toronto Pr.

Barrett-Smith, Becky. Forgiveness & the Gospel of His Salvation. 2011. 90p. pap. 15.99 ***(978-1-4535-3534-9(9))*** Xlibris Corp.

Barry, F. R. Christianity & the New World an Approa. 2006. pap. 30.95 *(978-1-4286-6000-7(3))* Kessinger Publishing, LLC.

Barwell, Daniel. Little Church Has Grown. 2006. (ENG.). 31.99 *(978-1-60034-497-8(6))*; pap. 19.99 *(978-1-60034-496-1(8))* Xulon Pr., Inc.

Bass, Michael R. Gospel of Grace. 2008. 204p. pap. 14.99 *(978-1-60477-857-1(1))* Xulon Pr., Inc.

Batzler, Louis Richard. You Are Immortal! The Words & Deeds of Jesus about Eternal Life: A Postmodern Exploration. 2008. 275p. pap. 27.95 *(978-1-60563-323-7(2))* PublishAmerica, Inc.

Baugh, Alexander L., ed. Days Never to Be Forgotten: Oliver Cowdery. 2009. (Illus.). 415p. *(978-0-8425-2742-2(7)*, Brigham Young Univ. Religious Studies Ctr.) Brigham Young Univ.

Bauman, Chad M. Christian Identity & Dalit Religion in Hindu India, 1868-1947. 2008. (Studies in the History of Christian Missions). 288p. pap. 40.00 *(978-0-8028-6276-1(4))* Eerdmans, William B. Publishing Co.

Bayles, Chuck D. Love Never Fails: God's Strategy for Winning. 2011. 148p. 29.99 ***(978-1-4628-6809-4(6))***; pap. 19.99 ***(978-1-4628-6808-7(8))*** Xlibris Corp.

Beam, Jack. The God Awful Truth about Heaven. 2008. 95p. 9.95 *(978-0-9796749-1-4(3))* Flanders Fields Pr.

Beamon, Sylvia. Royston Cave: Used by Saints or Sinners? 2011. (ENG., Illus.). 316p. pap. 33.00 ***(978-0-9557400-0-8(2))*** Temple Pubns., The GBR. Dist: SCB Distributors.

Bearman, Alan. A North Atlantic Puritan. 2010. 324p. pap. *(978-3-8383-4569-7(X))* Lambert Academic Publishing.

Beauchene, Valerie A. The Paralysis of Unforgiveness: Sexual Abuse & Other Crippling Violations. 2007. (Wonders of Practical Christianity: A Teaching Ser.). 93p. per. 12.99 *(978-1-59879-418-2(3))* Lifevest Publishing, Inc.

Bediako, Kwame. Theology & Identity: The Impact of Culture upon Christian Thought in the Second Century & in Modern Africa. xviii, 507p. pap. 33.99 *(978-1-870345-10-1(X))* Regnum Bks.

Beecher, Henry, abr. New Star Papers. 2009. (Amer Philosophy, Religion Ser.). (ENG.). 412p. pap. 25.95 *(978-1-4290-1982-8(4))* Applewood Bks.

Beecher, Henry Ward. New Star Papers; or, Views & Experiences of Religious Subjects by Henry Ward Beecher. 2006. 412p. per. 26.99 *(978-1-4255-4382-2(0))* MPublishing.

—Star Papers. 2009. (Amer Philosophy, Religion Ser.). (ENG.). 364p. pap. 22.95 *(978-1-4290-1904-0(2))* Applewood Bks.

Belcher, Joseph. Sketches from Life; or, Illustrations of the Influence of Christianity. 2006. 548p. per. 29.99 *(978-1-4255-6043-0(1))* MPublishing.

Bell-Ranske, Jutta. The Meaning of Christianity & the Spirit Behind All Symbols - 2006. pap. 12.95 *(978-1-4286-7089-1(0))* Kessinger Publishing, LLC.

Bell, Rob. Drops Like Stars. 2012. (ENG.). 144p. pap. 12.99 ***(978-0-06-219728-3(2)***, HarperOne) HarperCollins Pubs.

Belmonte, Kevin. The Quotable Chesterton: The Wit & Wisdom of G. K. Chesterton. 2011. 336p. pap. 15.99 *(978-1-59555-205-1(7))* Nelson, Thomas Inc.

Ben, Naja & Moussa Sy. And You Shall Be a Blessing: Encountering People of Other Cultures & Religions. 2011. 162p. pap. ***(978-3-941750-46-3(1))*** VTR Verlag fur Theologie und Religionswissenschaft.

Bender, Keith. Despiritualized Church. 2009. 312p. pap. *(978-1-886940-52-9(5))* Ozark Mountain Publishing, Inc.

Benedict, Gerald S., ed. Celtic Wisdom: The Poetry & Prose of a Mystic Tradition. 2008. (Sacred Wisdom Ser.). (ENG.). 192p. 8.95 *(978-1-905857-87-6(X)*, Watkins Publishing) Duncan Baird Pubs. GBR. Dist: Sterling Publishing Co., Inc.

Benedict XVI, pseud. Questions & Answers. 2008. 175p. 14.95 *(978-1-59276-439-6(8))* Our Sunday Visitor, Publishing Div.

Bensly, R. L. & Kennett, Robert H., eds. The Epistles of S. Clement to the Corinthians in Syriac. 2010. (SYR.). pap. 27.52 *(978-1-61143-610-5(9))* Gorgias Pr., LLC.

Benson, P. R. Yet a More Excellent Way: An Essay on the Theory & Practice of the Christian Religion. 2007. (ENG.). 250p. 41.95 *(978-0-548-15000-9(1))*; 250p. 41.95 *(978-0-548-15023-8(0))*; 252p. per. 26.95 *(978-1-4304-4326-1(X))*; 252p. per. 26.95 *(978-1-4304-4354-4(5))* Kessinger Publishing, LLC.

Benson, Richard & Benson, Cindy. Secretos Mormones no Quieren. 2011.Tr. of Secrets Mormons Don¿t Want You to Know. 208p. pap. 11.95 ***(978-0-7589-0653-3(6))*** Chick Pubns., Inc.

Bentley Hart, David. The Story of Christianity. 2012. (ENG., Illus.). 256p. 29.95 ***(978-1-84724-845-9(4))*** Quercus GBR. Dist: Independent Pubs. Group.

Bequette, John P. Rhetoric in the Monastic Tradition: A Textual Study. 2012. (C). 79.95 ***(978-1-4331-1797-8(5))*** Lang, Peter Publishing, Inc.

Berdoe, Edward. Browning & the Christian Faith. 2008. 256p. 25.99 *(978-0-559-61616-7(3))*; pap. 25.75 *(978-0-559-61614-3(7))* BiblioBazaar.

—Browning & the Christian Faith. 2009. 144p. pap. *(978-0-217-69315-8(6))*; pap. *(978-1-4590-5133-1(5))*; pap. *(978-1-4590-5130-0(0))* Books LLC.

Berg, Holger. Military Occupation under the Eyes of the Lord: Studies in Erfurt during the Thirty Years War. 2010. (Forschungen Zur Kirchen- und Dogmengeschichte Ser.). (ENG., Illus.). 395p. (C). 96.00 *(978-3-525-56455-4(4))* Vandenhoeck & Ruprecht GmbH & Co. KG DEU. Dist: ISD.

Berger, Peter L., ed. Between Relativism & Fundamentalism: Religious Resources for a Middle Position. 2009. 224p. pap. 17.00 *(978-0-8028-6387-4(6))* Eerdmans, William B. Publishing Co.

Bergsma, William. Planet Earth in Peril. 2011. 534p. 38.99 ***(978-1-61379-276-6(X))***; pap. 26.99 ***(978-1-61379-275-9(1))*** Xulon Pr., Inc.

Bernard, A. R. Happiness Is... Simple Steps to a Life of Joy. 2011. (ENG.). 224p. pap. 15.99 *(978-1-4516-2922-4(2)*, Touchstone) Touchstone.

Bernwall, Bernie. What Wouldn't Jesus Do? Four Decades of Christian Influence in America. 2011. pap. 12.99 ***(978-1-61739-959-6(0))*** Tate Publishing & Enterprises, LLC.

Berry, Donald. Through a Glass Darkly: The Ambiguity of the Christian Tradition. 2006. (ENG.). 96p. per. 29.50 *(978-0-7618-3547-9(4))* Univ. Pr. of America, Inc.

Bethune, Ava. God gives all things at the proper Time. 2010. 144p. pap. 14.99 *(978-1-60957-565-6(2))* Xulon Pr., Inc.

Bevere, John. Honor's Reward Curriculum. 2007. 198.00 *(978-1-933185-35-4(X))* Messenger International.

—Honor's Reward Devotional Workbook. 2007. pap. 15.99 *(978-1-933185-34-7(1))* Messenger International.

Bingham, Jane. Christianity. 2007. (Atlas of World Faiths/Arcturus Ser.). (Illus.). 48p. (YA). (gr. 7-12). lib. bdg. 32.80 *(978-1-59920-054-5(6))* Black Rabbit Bks.

Blanchard, John. The Complete Gathered Gold: A Treasury of Quotations for Christians. 2006. 703p. *(978-0-85234-644-0(1))* Evangelical Pr.

Blankenship, Lawrence L. The Divine Law: Religion & Christianity. 2010. 124p. pap. 13.95 *(978-1-4502-6179-1(5))* iUniverse, Inc.

Bloesch, Donald G. Christian Foundations, 4 vols. 97.96 *(978-0-8308-8140-6(9))* InterVarsity Pr.

Blue, Ken & Swan, Alden. The Gospel Uncensored: How Only Grace Leads to Freedom. 2010. 220p. 33.95 *(978-1-4497-0455-1(7))*; pap. 17.95 *(978-1-4497-0454-4(9))* Author Solutions, Inc. (WestBow Pr.).

Blumenfeld, Warren J., et al, eds. An Investigation of Christian Privilege & Religious Oppression in the United States. 2008. 184p. *(978-90-8790-677-1(3))*; pap. *(978-90-8790-676-4(5))* Sense Pubs.

Blunt, John Henry. Dictionary of Sects, Heresies, Ecclesiastical Parties, & Schools of Religious Thought. 2008. (Gorgias Reference Classics Ser.: 2). 138.00 *(978-1-59333-796-4(5))* Gorgias Pr., LLC.

Bockmuehl, Markus & Stroumsa, Guy G., eds. Paradise in Antiquity: Jewish & Christian Views. 2010. (ENG.). 272p. 95.00 *(978-0-521-11786-9(0))* Cambridge Univ. Pr.

Boddu, Suvarna Kumar. Persistence & Change: A Study of the Impact of Christianity on the Tribes of East Godavari District. 2011. 200p. 32.07 ***(978-1-4567-8072-2(7))***; pap. 17.09 ***(978-1-4567-8071-5(9))*** AuthorHouse.

Bogeatzes, A. S. Knowing & Living Your Orthodox Christian Faith: A Guide to Faith & Worship. 2010. 224p. pap. 17.95 *(978-1-4497-0434-6(4)*, WestBow Pr.) Author Solutions, Inc.

Bohannon, Richard R. The Organization & Leadership of the First Century Church: A Study. 2011. 152p. 30.95 *(978-1-4497-1343-0(2))*; pap. 13.95 *(978-1-4497-1342-3(4))* Author Solutions, Inc. (WestBow Pr.).

Bolde, Bill. Lead the Way. 2010. 294p. pap. 16.99 *(978-1-60957-662-2(4))* Xulon Pr., Inc.

Bolt, John & Bavinck, Herman. Essays on Religion, Science, & Society. Bolt, John, ed. ed. Sheeres, Gerrit & Boonstra, Harry, trs. from DUT. 2008. (Illus.). 304p. (C). 39.99 *(978-0-8010-3241-7(5))* Baker Academic.

Borg, Marcus J. Speaking Christian: Why Christian Words Have Lost Their Meaning & Power - And How They Can Be Restored. 2012. (ENG.). 256p. pap. 14.99 ***(978-0-06-197658-2(X)***, HarperOne) HarperCollins Pubs.

Borg, Marcus J. & Scorer, Tim. Living the Heart of Christianity: A Guide to Putting Your Faith into Action. 2006. (ENG.). 176p. pap. 15.99 *(978-0-06-111842-5(7)*, HarperOne) HarperCollins Pubs.

Bortolazzo, Paul. The Coming of the Son of Man: After the Tribulation of Those Days. 2007. (Watchman Ser.). 397p. per. 21.99 *(978-1-60247-101-6(0))* Tate Publishing & Enterprises, LLC.

Boston, Paulette. Traveling under Concealed Orders: A School Almost Left Behind. 2006. xiii, 164p. per. 16.95 *(978-0-9787788-4-2(7))* LUMEN-US Pubns.

Boswell, Carroll W. Caleb's Eye: A Spy's Journey Through Genesis. 2011. 404p. pap. 24.00 ***(978-1-4634-3052-8(3))*** AuthorHouse.

Bott, Michael S. God s Ways with Man. 2011. 372p. pap. 20.99 *(978-1-61215-794-8(7))* Xulon Pr., Inc.

Botzet, Lee. A Heart for God's Glory. 2007. (ENG.). 252p. per. 15.99 *(978-1-60266-115-8(4))* Xulon Pr., Inc.

Bovines, Julie. Got God? 2010. 200p. pap. 15.99 *(978-1-60957-489-5(3))* Xulon Pr., Inc.

Bowden, John. A Chronology of World Christianity. 2008. (ENG., Illus.). 544p. 80.00 *(978-0-8264-9633-1(4))* Continuum International Publishing Group, Ltd. GBR. Dist: National Bk. Network.

Bowne, Borden P. Studies in Christianity. reprint ed. 28.50 *(978-0-404-59075-8(6))* AMS Pr., Inc.

Boyd, Darlene R. Worth More Than Diamonds. 2010. 52p. pap. 15.50 *(978-0-557-43148-9(4))* Lulu Enterprises Inc.

Brace, Charles Lorin. Gesta Christi: Or a History of Humane Pr. 2006. pap. 42.95 *(978-1-4286-5938-4(2))* Kessinger Publishing, LLC.

Brackney, William H. Historical Dictionary of Radical Christianity. 2012. (Historical Dictionaries of Religions, Philosophies & Movements Ser.). (ENG.). 368p. 100.00 ***(978-0-8108-7179-3(3))*** Scarecrow Pr., Inc.

Brackney, William H. Studying Christianity: The Critical Issues. 2010. (Studying World Religions Ser.). (ENG., Illus.). 192p. 80.00 *(978-0-8264-9885-4(X))* Continuum International Publishing Group, Ltd. GBR. Dist: National Bk. Network.

Brackney, William H. & Brackney. Studying Christianity: The Critical Issues. 2010. (Studying World Religions Ser.). (ENG., Illus.). 192p. 24.95 *(978-0-8264-9886-1(8))* Continuum International Publishing Group, Ltd. GBR. Dist: National Bk. Network.

Bradley, Mark. Iran & Christianity: Historical Identity & Present Relevance. (ENG., Illus.). 210p. 2011. pap. 44.95 ***(978-1-4411-1167-8(0))*** 2009. 130.00 *(978-1-84706-027-3(7))* Continuum International Publishing Group, Ltd. GBR. Dist: National Bk. Network.

Brague, Remi. The Law of God: The Philosophical History of an Idea. Cochrane, Lydia G., tr. from FRE. (ENG.). 384p. 2008. pap. 22.50 *(978-0-226-07079-7(4))* 2007. 37.50 *(978-0-226-07078-0(6))* Univ. of Chicago Pr.

Brantley M Div, T. Charles. Even Christians Use the Bathroom - Reality Christianity: Simul Iustus et Pecator (Both Justified & Sinner) 2008. 244p. pap. 14.95 *(978-1-4327-2516-7(5))* Outskirts Pr., Inc.

Bread for the Wilderness, Wine for the Journey: The Miracle of Prayer & Meditation. 144p. reprint ed. pap. 14.95 *(978-1-887730-06-8(0))* Intermundia Pr., LLC., The.

Breese, Daryl & D'Aoust, Gerald. God's Steed- Key to World Peace. 2011. 234p. pap. 85.50 ***(978-1-4583-9062-2(4))*** Lulu Enterprises Inc.

Brekus, Catherine A. & Gilpin, W. Clark. American Christianities: A History of Dominance & Diversity. 2011. (ENG., Illus.). 528p. 75.00 *(978-0-8078-3515-9(3))*; pap. 34.95 *(978-0-8078-7213-0(X))* Univ. of North Carolina Pr.

Bremer, Thomas. Religion & the Conceptual Boundary in Central & Eastern Europe: Encounters of Faiths. Bremer, Thomas, ed. 2008. (Studies in Central & Eastern Europe Ser.). (ENG.). 256p. 95.00 *(978-0-230-55076-6(2))* Palgrave Macmillan.

Brennan, David Paul. Understanding the Light. 2010. 120p. pap. 14.99 *(978-0-557-56727-0(0))* Lulu Enterprises Inc.

Brian, Wills. 10 Hours to Live. 2010. pap. 12.99 *(978-1-60374-243-6(3))* Whitaker Hse.

Brickett, Maryann. America - Yes We Are a Christian Nation. 2011. 220p. pap. 15.99 *(978-1-61215-922-5(2))* Xulon Pr., Inc.

Bridwell, Edward E. The Pathology of Hyperbolic Religion. 2011. pap. 10.99 ***(978-1-61777-204-7(6))*** Tate Publishing & Enterprises, LLC.

Bright, Bill. Discover God Bible Study: Number 2. 2007. (Illus.). 75p. per. 9.99 *(978-0-7644-3555-3(8))* Group Publishing, Inc.

Broadley, Robert. Christianity a Divine Revelation: a Defense of the Christian Religion. 2007. pap. 20.95 *(978-1-4304-4966-9(7))* Kessinger Publishing, LLC.

Brock, Sebastian P. Spirituality in the Syriac Tradition. 2010. 98.48 *(978-1-61143-558-0(7))* Gorgias Pr., LLC.

Brod, Max. Paganism - Christianity - Judaism: A Confession of Faith. Wolfe, William, tr. from GER. 2nd ed. 2010. (Judaic Studies Ser.). (ENG.). 288p. pap. 35.00 *(978-0-8173-5663-7(0))* Univ. of Alabama Pr.

Bromell, Poiette McGill. Saved & Sexual A Survival Guide for Pastors' Wives. 2010. 79p. pap. 12.00 *(978-0-557-21391-7(6))* Lulu Enterprises Inc.

Brougham, James P. Power-Filled Words That Change Lives. 2008. 117p. pap. 12.95 *(978-0-615-20156-6(3))* Brougham, James P.

Brown, Arthur I. Footprints of God. 2007. (ENG.). 248p. 41.95 *(978-0-548-10805-5(6))* Kessinger Publishing, LLC.

Brown, Dave. Simple Christianity. 2007. 340p. per. 17.99 *(978-1-60266-214-8(2))* Xulon Pr., Inc.

Brown, Eleanor. Prayer: The Essentials. 2011. 60p. pap. 19.95 ***(978-1-4560-7974-1(3))*** PublishAmerica, Inc.

Brown, Kay Wiley. Born Again Truths. 2011. 296p. pap. 16.99 *(978-1-61215-814-3(5))* Xulon Pr., Inc.

Brown, L. Duane. What Is the Apostasy? 2010. 232p. pap. 15.99 *(978-0-9845208-1-7(3))* Faithful Life Pubs.

Brown, Pastor Jeff. Stories from Jesus: The Parables, 1 vol. 2010. 194p. pap. 24.95 *(978-1-4489-7764-2(9))* PublishAmerica, Inc.

Brown, Rebecca K. L. T. Frog: Learning to Fully Rely on God. 2009. 253p. pap. 19.95 *(978-1-4327-3561-6(6))* Outskirts Pr., Inc.

Brown, Richard C. Help Your Child Make Friends & Be a Friend. 2012. ***(978-0-7648-2083-0(4))*** Liguori Pubns.

Brown, Robert H., III. Tradition Versus Truth. 2008. 112p. per. 10.95 *(978-1-4327-1932-6(7))* Outskirts Pr., Inc.

Brown, Stewart J. & Tackett, Timothy, eds. Enlightenment, Reawakening & Revolution 1660-1815. 2007. (Cambridge History of Christianity Ser.: Vol. 7). (ENG., Illus.). 694p. 242.00 *(978-0-521-81605-2(X))* Cambridge Univ. Pr.

Brownell, Rick. Recovering Our Lost Theology: The Sovereign Grace of God. 2011. pap. 21.99 ***(978-1-61777-612-0(2))*** Tate Publishing & Enterprises, LLC.

Bruinsma, Reinder. Key Words of the Christian Faith. 2008. 141p. pap. 11.99 *(978-0-8280-2340-5(9))* Review & Herald Publishing Assn.

Bruun, M. & Cowling, David, eds. Commonplace Culture in Western Europe in the Early Modern Period I. Reformation, Counter-Reformation & Revolt. 2011. (Groningen Studies in Cultural Change Ser.). (ENG.). 278p. (C). 70.00 *(978-90-429-2474-1(8))* Peeters Pubs. & Booksellers BEL. Dist: Brown, David Bk. Co., The.

Bryan, William Jennings. In His Image. 2008. 216p. 27.99 *(978-0-554-24376-4(8))* 2008. 216p. 24.99 *(978-0-554-33679-4(0))* 2006. (ENG.). 212p. pap. 22.99 *(978-1-4264-6467-6(3))* BiblioBazaar.

—In His Image. 2007. 264p. 42.95 *(978-0-548-01704-3(2))* Kessinger Publishing, LLC.

—In His Image. 2009. 180p. pap. 12.95 *(978-1-4385-1578-6(2))*, Book Jungle) Standard Pubns., Inc.

Bryant, Delmar De Forest. The Changing of Water into Wine. 2006. pap. 9.95 *(978-1-4286-7518-6(3))* Kessinger Publishing, LLC.

—The Creative Principle. 2006. pap. 9.95 *(978-1-4286-7526-1(4))* Kessinger Publishing, LLC.

—The Future of the Regenerate Race. 2006. pap. 9.95 *(978-1-4286-7531-5(0))* Kessinger Publishing, LLC.

—The Garden & the Gods. 2006. pap. 9.95 *(978-1-4286-7515-5(9))* Kessinger Publishing, LLC.

—The Gold Fish. 2006. pap. 9.95 *(978-1-4286-7521-6(3))* Kessinger Publishing, LLC.

—The Lost Word. 2006. pap. 9.95 *(978-1-4286-7525-4(6))* Kessinger Publishing, LLC.

—Luz the Resurrection Bone. 2006. pap. 9.95 *(978-1-4286-7529-2(9))* Kessinger Publishing, LLC.

—The Mystery of Christ & the New Church. 2006. pap. 9.95 *(978-1-4286-7516-2(7))* Kessinger Publishing, LLC.

—The Prayer That Prevails. 2006. pap. 9.95 *(978-1-4286-7524-7(8))* Kessinger Publishing, LLC.

—The Saintly Image. 2006. pap. 9.95 *(978-1-4286-7522-3(1))* Kessinger Publishing, LLC.

—Serpent & the Devil. 2006. pap. 9.95 *(978-1-4286-7520-9(5))* Kessinger Publishing, LLC.

—Sin & Its Remedy. 2006. pap. 9.95 *(978-1-4286-7530-8(2))* Kessinger Publishing, LLC.

—The Stone the Builders Rejected. 2006. pap. 9.95 *(978-1-4286-7517-9(5))* Kessinger Publishing, LLC.

—The Sun Clothed Woman. 2006. pap. 12.95 *(978-1-4286-7540-7(X))* Kessinger Publishing, LLC.

—The Tree of Life. 2006. pap. 9.95 *(978-1-4286-7527-8(2))* Kessinger Publishing, LLC.

—The Unborn Souls. 2006. pap. 9.95 *(978-1-4286-7523-0(X))* Kessinger Publishing, LLC.

—The Water of Regeneration. 2006. pap. 9.95 *(978-1-4286-7528-5(0))* Kessinger Publishing, LLC.

Bryce, Bruce E. Grandpa's Code. 2011. 160p. 30.95 ***(978-1-4497-2613-3(5))***; pap. 13.95 ***(978-1-4497-2612-6(7))*** Author Solutions, Inc. (WestBow Pr.).

Buck, Terrie. Knowing the Truth, 1 vol. 2010. 124p. pap. 19.95 *(978-1-4489-3406-5(0))* PublishAmerica, Inc.

Buckridan, Rakib. The Bible & Christianity: Their impending Demise & a Forward-Looking Plea. 2010. 592p. pap. 38.95 *(978-1-60860-305-3(9))*, Eloquent Bks.) AEG Literary Publishing Services, Inc.

Bunae, Atinuke. Press on, Ms Margaret! 2010. 84p. 24.99 *(978-1-4415-4958-7(7))*; pap. 15.99 *(978-1-4415-4957-0(9))* Xlibris Corp.

Bunge, Marcia J., ed. Children, Adults, & Shared Responsibilities: Jewish, Christian & Muslim Perspectives. 2012. (ENG.). 320p. 95.00 ***(978-1-107-01114-4(0))*** Cambridge Univ. Pr.

Burbach, Christiane & Heckmann, Friedrich. Generationenfragen: Theologische Perspektiven Zur Gesellschaft des 21. Jahrhunderts. 2007. (GER.). 189p. (C). pap. 36.00 *(978-3-525-60433-5(5))* Vandenhoeck & Ruprecht GmbH & Co. KG DEU. Dist: ISD.

Burdette, Dallas R. Biblical Preaching & Teaching: Series of Specialized Studies from Psalms ? Revelation ? Hebrews. 2010. 36.99 *(978-1-61579-729-5(7))*; pap. 24.99 *(978-1-61579-728-8(9))* Xulon Pr., Inc.

Burger, Constance. Resume' of a Woman. 2007. 197p. pap. 18.51 *(978-0-615-16976-7(7))* Burger, Constance.

Burgess, Richard. Nigeria's Christian Revolution: The Civil War Revival & Its Pentecostal Progeny (1967-2006) 2008. (Regnum Studies in Mission Ser.). 376p. pap. 45.00 *(978-1-60608-020-7(2))* Wipf & Stock Pubs.

—Nigeria's Christian Revolution: The Civil War Revival & Its Pentecostal Progeny, 1967-2006. 2008. (ENG., Illus.). 247p. 40.99 *(978-1-870345-63-7(0)*, Paternoster) Authentic Media.

Burke, Jonathan. Sleeping in the Dust. 2010. 145p. pap. 12.50 *(978-0-557-67285-1(6))* Lulu Enterprises Inc.

Burns, Deborah R. Script ure Notes Journal. 2010. 132p. pap. 14.99 *(978-1-60957-433-8(8))* Xulon Pr., Inc.

Burns, M. P. Credo: the Battered Bride: One Catholic looks at the Church he Loves. 2008. 348p. pap. 27.50 *(978-1-4092-1184-6(3))* Lulu Enterprises Inc.

Bush, L. C. Brown. Faith to Find a Job. 2010. 214p. pap. 15.99 *(978-1-60957-844-2(9))* Xulon Pr., Inc.

Buswell, Robert E., Jr. & Lee, Timothy S., eds. Christianity in Korea. 2007. 408p. per. 26.00 *(978-0-8248-3206-3(X))* Univ. of Hawaii Pr.

Butkiewicz, Eleanor. Restoring the Broken Walls of Past Generations: Discovering the Forgotten Ministry of Jesus Christ. 2011. pap. 20.99 ***(978-1-61739-665-6(6))*** Tate Publishing & Enterprises, LLC.

Butler, Margaret A. Faith Walks: Weekly Devotionals for the Growing Christian. 2011. pap. 15.99 *(978-1-61739-251-1(0))* Tate Publishing & Enterprises, LLC.

Byle, Ann. Christianity for Skeptics: A Conversation for Thinking People. 2007. pap. 19.99 *(978-1-932902-70-9(8))* FaithWalk Publishing.

C. Paul Puckett. Liberalization & Apostasy of Americ. 2009. 72p. pap. 10.49 *(978-1-4389-9887-9(2))* AuthorHouse.

Cafferky, Michael. Management: A Faith-Based Perspective. 2011. (ENG., Illus.). 648p. (C). 166.67 ***(978-0-13-605834-2(5)***, Prentice Hall) Prentice Hall PTR.

Caird, John. The Fundamental Ideas of Christianity, 2 vols., Set. (Gifford Lectures: 1892-93, 1895-96). reprint ed. 74.50 *(978-0-404-60460-8(9))* AMS Pr., Inc.

—The Fundamental Ideas of Christianity. 2009. 304p. 25.99 *(978-1-103-82233-1(0))*; pap. 19.99 *(978-1-103-82228-7(4))* BiblioBazaar.

—The Fundamental Ideas of Christianity. 2009. 144p. pap. *(978-1-150-60531-4(6))* Books LLC.

Caldwell, Robert. Christianity Explained to a Hindu: Or Christianity & Hinduism Compared. Compiled from Bishop Caldwell, Rev. Nehemiah Goreh, Krishna Mohun Banerjea, 2008. 72p. pap. 26.45 *(978-1-4097-0009-8(7))* Audubon Pr. & Christian Bk. Service.

Callahan, Sidney. Called to Happiness: Where Faith & Psychology Meet. 2011. 168p. pap. 20.00 *(978-1-57075-918-5(9))* Orbis Bks.

Calvin, John. John Calvin on the Christian Faith. McNeill, John T., ed. 2011. 252p. 46.95 ***(978-1-258-02797-1(6))*** Literary Licensing, LLC.

Cannaday, Lee Thomas. The Testimony. 2011. 64p. pap. 14.50 ***(978-1-4634-4883-7(X))*** AuthorHouse.

Caplow, Theodore, et al. All Faithful People: Change & Continuity in Middletown's Religion. 2009. (ENG.). 392p. pap. 60.00 *(978-0-8166-5720-9(3))* Univ. of Minnesota Pr.

Carlson, Paul R. The Empty Pew: Why Americans are Abandoning the Churches. 2009. 307p. pap. 19.95 *(978-1-4327-4083-2(0))* Outskirts Pr., Inc.

Carlson, William G., et al, eds. The Pietist Impulse in Christianity. 2012. (ENG.). 366p. (C). pap. 50.00 ***(978-0-227-68000-1(6))*** Clarke, James Co., Ltd. GBR. Dist: Brown, David Bk. Co., The.

Carlsson, Leif. Round Trips to Heaven. 2008. 404p. pap. *(978-3-8364-7254-8(6))* VDM Verlag Dr. Mueller e.K.

Carman. Riot Manual. Date not set. pap. 4.99 *(978-0-917143-46-5(9))* Sparrow Corp., The.

Carpenter, Edward. Pagan & Christian Creeds. 2008. 268p. 28.99 *(978-0-554-21426-9(1))* 2008. 268p. 25.99 *(978-0-554-30729-9(4))* 2006. (ENG.). 266p. pap. 23.99 *(978-1-4264-0153-4(1))* BiblioBazaar.

—Pagan & Christian Creeds Their Origin. 2007. pap. *(978-1-4065-1291-5(5))* Dodo Pr.

Carroll, Beverly. From Glimpses to Glory: Your Vision Becomes Reality. 2011. 136p. pap. 13.00 ***(978-1-4583-2814-4(7))*** Lulu Enterprises Inc.

Carson, Timothy L. Your Calling as a Christian. 2007. (Your Calling As... Ser.). 88p. per. 9.99 *(978-0-8272-4413-9(4))* Chalice Pr.

Carter, Currin. The Big Bang, Dinosaurs, & Jesus: Essays on the Evolution of Christianity. 2011. pap. 10.99 ***(978-1-61346-521-9(1))*** Tate Publishing & Enterprises, LLC.

Carter, Roger W. The Force of Creation, Salvation & Judgement. 2011. 276p. pap. 19.95 *(978-1-4497-1072-9(7))*, WestBow Pr.) Author Solutions, Inc.

Caspi, Mishael M. & Neu-Sokol, Gerda. The Legend of Elijah in Judaism, Christianity, Islam, & Literature: A Study in Comparative Religion. 2009. 312p. 119.95 *(978-0-7734-4726-4(1))* Mellen, Edwin Pr., The.

Castillo, Sharman. The Lie. 2012. (ENG.). 132p. pap. 15.00 *(978-1-4404-0041-4(5))* CreateSpace.

Cburnett, The Scribe. A Parallel Guide to the Scriptures: ~ it Is Written ~. 2011. 160p. 24.99 ***(978-1-4634-0972-2(9))***; pap. 16.95 ***(978-1-4634-0973-9(7))*** AuthorHouse.

Chadwick, Henry, ed. Not Angels but Anglicans: An Illustrated History of Christianity in the British Isles. 2010. (ENG., Illus.). 320p. pap. 35.00 *(978-1-85311-878-4(8)*, Canterbury Pr. Norwich) Hymns Ancient & Modern Ltd GBR. Dist: Westminster John Knox Pr.

Chapman, C. L. Rightly Dividing the Word of Truth. 2010. 272p. 24.95 *(978-1-4269-3919-8(1))*; pap. 14.95 *(978-1-4269-3918-1(3))* Trafford Publishing.

Chappell, Brian. The Ultimate Threshold Dialogue. 2010. 76p. pap. *(978-3-8383-8039-1(8))* Lambert Academic Publishing.

Charles, Daniel. Christianity: A Bible-based & Crystal Clear Presentation. 2009. 428p. 32.50 *(978-1-60693-508-8(9)*, Eloquent Bks.) AEG Literary Publishing Services, Inc.

Charles, Joseph G. Names of Jesus from A to Z. 2010. 70p. pap. 10.99 *(978-1-60957-249-5(1))* Xulon Pr., Inc.

Charles, R. H., ed. The Book of the Secrets of Enoch. Morfill, W.R., tr. 2007. (ENG.). 148p. 35.95 *(978-0-548-10798-0(X))* Kessinger Publishing, LLC.

Charles, Robert H. A Critical History of the Doctrine of a Future Life, in Israel, in Judaism, & in Christianity. reprint ed. 38.50 *(978-0-404-18455-1(3))* AMS Pr., Inc.

Chase, Dr Dylan M. & Chase, Dylan M. Protect This Temple. 2010. 116p. pap. 11.99 *(978-1-60957-443-7(5))* Xulon Pr., Inc.

Chazuka, Mercy. Grace: The Gospel Basics That Every Christian Should Know. 2011. 188p. 26.95 ***(978-1-4620-1509-2(3))***; pap. 16.95 ***(978-1-4620-1507-8(7))*** iUniverse, Inc.

Cheshire, Michael. How to Knock over A 7-Eleven: And Other Ministry Training. 2011. 172p. pap. 13.95 ***(978-1-4497-2737-6(9))***, WestBow Pr.) Author Solutions, Inc.

Chester, Tim. Closing the Window: Steps to Living Porn Free. 2010. (ENG.). 151p. pap. 15.00 *(978-0-8308-3842-4(2)*, IVP Bks.) InterVarsity Pr.

Chesterton, G. K. Defiant Joy: The Remarkable Life & Impact of G. K. Chesterton. 2011. 336p. pap. 16.99 *(978-1-59555-201-3(4))* Nelson, Thomas Inc.

—Orthodoxy. Date not set. 160p. 160.00 *(978-0-8488-2648-2(5))* Amereon LTD.

—Orthodoxy. reprint ed. lib. bdg. 98.00 *(978-0-7426-3013-0(7))* Classic Bks.

—Orthodoxy. 2007. 184p. per. 9.95 *(978-1-59462-817-7(3)*, Book Jungle) Standard Pubns., Inc.

Chiles, Paul. Rose of Calcutta. 2010. 122p. 19.99 *(978-1-60957-259-4(9))* Xulon Pr., Inc.

Chinaka, Francis. The School of God's Presence. 2010. 126p. pap. 14.99 ***(978-1-61215-010-9(1))*** Xulon Pr., Inc.

Chipman, Bill. The Pieces Fit: Christianity Contemplated. 2011. 168p. 30.95 ***(978-1-4497-2025-4(0))***; pap. 13.95 ***(978-1-4497-2024-7(2))*** Author Solutions, Inc. (WestBow Pr.).

Chitpakdee, Anikamarn. Lamin Sanneh on Missiological Approach to Religious Pluralism. 2010. 160p. pap. *(978-3-8383-7966-1(7))* Lambert Academic Publishing.

Cho, Paul Hang-Sik. Eschatology & Ecology: Experiences of the Korean Church. 2011. (Regnum Studies in Global Christianity Ser.). 272p. pap. 30.00 ***(978-1-61097-435-6(2)***, Wipf and Stock) Wipf & Stock Pubs.

Choi, Meesaeng Lee. The Rise of Korean Holiness Church in Relation to the American Holiness Movement: Wesley's "Scriptual Holiness" & the "Fourfold Gospel" 2008. (Revitalization: Explorations in World Christian Movements Ser.). (ENG.). 176p. per. 47.00 *(978-0-8108-5816-9(9))* Scarecrow Pr., Inc.

Chrisitan Religion Series. Date not set. (Christian Religion Ser.). (Orig.). pap. 4.50 *(978-1-881309-09-3(6))* Orchid Land Pubns.

Christian, Ian Michael. The Saving of America: Spiritually. 2010. 224p. pap. 21.95 *(978-0-557-40189-5(5))* Lulu Enterprises Inc.

Christian Vision Literature Staff. What the Bible Says about Satan. 2008. 196p. pap. 18.95 *(978-1-4357-0678-1(1))* Lulu Enterprises Inc.

Christianity & Modern Thought. 2009. 148p. pap. *(978-1-4588-1961-1(2))* Books LLC.

Christianity & Modern Thought. 2006. 316p. per. 23.99 *(978-1-4255-3001-3(X))* MPublishing.

Christianity Explored Staff. CY Handbook: A Seven-Step Journey Through the Life of Jesus. 2nd rev. ed. 2010. (Christianity Explored Ser.). (SPA.). 48p. (YA). pap. *(978-1-907377-14-3(X))* Good Bk. Co.

—CY Nano - Handbook: A Seven-Step Journey Through the Life of Jesus. 2010. (Christianity Explored Ser.). (SPA.). 48p. (YA). pap. *(978-1-907377-15-0(8))* Good Bk. Co.

—CY Sample Pack: A Seven-Step Journey Through the Life of Jesus. 2010. (Christianity Explored Ser.). (YA). pap. *(978-1-907377-23-5(9))* Good Bk. Co.

—CY Starter Pack: A Seven-Step Journey Through the Life of Jesus. 2010. (Christianity Explored Ser.). (YA). pap. *(978-1-907377-32-7(8))* Good Bk. Co.

Christodonte, Marcos, Sr. Lords of His Majesty. 2009. 118p. pap. 18.09 *(978-0-615-24667-3(2))* Lords of His Majesty.

Chryssides, George D. Christianity Today, Vol. No. 2. 2010. (Religion Today Ser.). (ENG., Illus.). 192p. 24.95 *(978-1-84706-542-1(2))* Continuum International Publishing Group, Ltd. GBR. Dist: National Bk. Network.

—Christianity Today: An Introduction. 2010. (Religion Today Ser.). (ENG., Illus.). 192p. 80.00 *(978-1-84706-541-4(4))* Continuum International Publishing Group, Ltd. GBR. Dist: National Bk. Network.

Chryssides, George D. & Wilkins, Margaret Z. Christians in the Twenty-First Century. 2011. (ENG., Illus.). 481p. (C). 99.95 *(978-1-84553-212-3(0))*; pap. 34.95 *(978-1-84553-213-0(9))* Equinox Publishing Ltd. GBR. Dist: ISD.

CHUKU, U. C. H. E. E. P. H. R. A. I. M. Customary Christianity: Antichrist by Default. 2007. 244p. (ENG.). 28.95 *(978-0-595-68748-0(2))*; per. 18.95 *(978-0-595-44463-2(6))* iUniverse, Inc.

Chukwuocha, A. C. & Chukwuocha, A. The War Within: Christians & Inner Conflicts, 1 vol. 2009. (ENG.). 144p. pap. 16.99 *(978-9966-805-39-3(7))* Zondervan.

Chung, Paul S., et al, eds. Asian Contextual Theology for the Third Millennium: A Theology of Minjung in Fourth-Eye Formation. Chung, Paul S., tr. 2006. (Princeton Theological Monographs). 372p. pap. 35.00 *(978-1-55635-044-3(9)*, Pickwick Pubns.) Wipf & Stock Pubs.

Clarke, James Freeman. Steps of Belief; or, Rational Christianity Maintained Against Atheism, Free Religion, & Romanism by James Freeman Clarke. 2006. 324p. per. 23.99 *(978-1-4255-3155-3(5))* MPublishing.

Clarke, Richard. A Whisper of God: Essays on Post-Catholic Ireland & the Christian Future. 2007. (ENG.). 136p. per. 18.95 *(978-1-85607-536-7(2))* Columba Pr. IRL. Dist: Dufour Editions, Inc.

Clemmer, Edward Joseph. Gospel (on the Road to) Emmaus. 2011. 712p. pap. 31.68 *(978-1-4567-7378-6(X))* AuthorHouse.

Clinton, John L. Come to Me. 2007. pap. 12.00 *(978-0-9801357-0-1(2))* Tree of Life Publishing Hse.

Cloud, Ira. Genesis & Exodus in a Nutshell. 2011. pap. 7.99 ***(978-1-61777-880-3(X))*** Tate Publishing & Enterprises, LLC.

Cochran, Noal B. King of Thorns, 1 vol. 2009. 56p. pap. 16.95 *(978-1-60813-997-2(2))* PublishAmerica, Inc.

Coe, George Albert. The Religion of a Mature Mind. 2009. 174p. pap. 19.99 *(978-1-4589-3626-4(0))* General Bks. LLC.

—The Religion of a Mature Mind. 2007. (ENG.). 444p. 51.95 *(978-0-548-09141-8(2))* Kessinger Publishing, LLC.

Coffeen, Don S. The Rescue: Old Testament Boot Camp for a New Testament War. 2010. pap. 16.99 *(978-1-61663-607-4(6))* Tate Publishing & Enterprises, LLC.

Cole, Janie. Yielded & Submitted. 2011. 120p. 23.99 ***(978-1-4670-6656-3(7))***; pap. 16.95 ***(978-1-4670-6657-0(5))*** AuthorHouse.

Cole, Martin. Connecting You with God's Word. 2010. (Engage Ser.). (YA). 8p. *(978-1-906334-23-9(4))*; 128p. pap. *(978-1-906334-04-8(8))*; 128p. pap. *(978-1-906334-06-2(4))*; 128p. pap. *(978-1-906334-08-6(0))*; 128p. pap. *(978-1-906334-03-1(X))*; 128p. pap. *(978-1-906334-07-9(2))*; 128p. pap. *(978-1-906334-05-5(6))* Good Bk. Co.

Cole-Tuner, Ronald, ed. Design & Destiny: Jewish & Christian Perspectives on Human Germline Modification. 2008. (Basic Bioethics Ser.). (ENG.). 248p. (gr. 17). per. 23.00 *(978-0-262-53301-0(4))* MIT Pr.

Cole-Turner, Ronald, ed. Design & Destiny: Jewish & Christian Perspectives on Human Germline Modification. 2008. (Basic Bioethics Ser.). (ENG.). 248p. (gr. 17). 58.00 *(978-0-262-03373-2(9))* MIT Pr.

Coleson, Joseph E. Care of Creation: Christian Voices on God, Humanity, & the Environment. 2010. 201p. pap. *(978-0-89827-451-6(6))* Wesleyan Publishing Hse.

Collins, Florence O. Inside-Out Christianity. pap. 6.50 *(978-0-89098-135-1(3))* Twentieth Century Christian Bks.

Collins Winn, Christian T., et al, eds. The Pietist Impulse in Christianity. 2011. (Princeton Theological Monographs). 366p. pap. 40.00 ***(978-1-60608-327-7(9)**,* Pickwick Pubns.) Wipf & Stock Pubs.

Colvert, Gavin T., ed. The Renewal of Civilization. 2010. 300p. 24.95 *(978-0-9669226-9-1(7))* American Maritain Assn., Inc.

Company, Css Publishing, compiled by. Lectionary Tales for the Pulpit, Series Vii, Cycle B for the Revised Common Lectionary. 2011. (Illus.). 196p. pap. 19.95 ***(978-0-7880-2665-2(8))*** CSS Publishing.

Compendio de la Religion Cristiana. (ENG & SPA.). 63p. pap. 3.00 *(978-1-55883-022-6(7)*, 603210) Libros Desafio.

Conant, William C. Narratives of Remarkable Conversions & Revival Incidents with an Introduction by Henry Ward Beecher. 2006. 468p. per. 29.99 *(978-1-4255-5202-2(1))* MPublishing.

Congregation for Cath Educatio Staff. Consecrated Persons & Mission. 72p. pap. 4.95 *(978-0-8198-1563-7(2)*, 332-046) Pauline Bks. & Media.

Congregation Catholic Ed Staff. Cath Sch Threshold 3rd Millenn. 22p. pap. 2.50 *(978-0-8198-1552-1(7)*, 332-040) Pauline Bks. & Media.

Conner, K.J. Name of God. 192p. pap. *(978-0-949829-12-2(9))* Acacia Pr.

Conners, Kevin. Is Hell the Only Difference? Demanding Sanctification in the Pretentious Church. 2011. 120p. 28.95 ***(978-1-4497-1224-2(X))***; pap. 11.95 ***(978-1-4497-1222-8(3))*** Author Solutions, Inc. (WestBow Pr.).

Connor, John. Diamonds for the Bride. 2008. 536p. 63.50 *(978-1-84799-173-7(4))* Lulu Enterprises Inc.

Conway, Eamonn. Rahner: A Guide for the Perplexed. 2012. (Guides for the Perplexed Ser.). (ENG.). 176p. 110.00 *(978-0-567-03440-3(2))*; pap. 24.95 *(978-0-567-03441-0(0))* Continuum International Publishing Group, Ltd. GBR. (T&T Clark Int'l). Dist: National Bk. Network.

Conway, Moncure Daniel. Christianity. 2007. (ENG.). 148p. 35.95 *(978-0-548-15526-4(7))*; pap. 20.95 *(978-1-4304-4957-7(8))* Kessinger Publishing, LLC.

Cook, John Granger. Roman Attitudes Toward the Christians: From Claudius to Hadrian. 2010. (Illus.). 378p. 197.50 *(978-3-16-150553-9(0))* Mohr Siebeck GmbH & Co. KG DEU. Dist: Coronet Bks.

Cooke, Phil. Branding Faith: Why Some Churches & Non-Profits Make a Difference & Other's Don't. 2008. (ENG.). 224p. 17.99 *(978-0-8307-4563-0(7))* Gospel Light Pubns.

Cooke, Steven W. Conversations with a Masterpiece: Miracles & Medical Marvels! 2008. 148p. pap. 13.99 *(978-1-60477-573-0(4))* Xulon Pr., Inc.

Cooling, Christian Vision for State Education. 226p. *(978-0-281-04758-1(8))* SPCK Publishing.

Cooney, Jonathan. The Lord Is My Shepherd, Etc. 2008. 360p. per. *(978-3-8364-3476-8(8))* VDM Verlag Dr. Mueller e.K.

Cooper, Barbara M. Evangelical Christians in the Muslim Sahel. 2010. (African Systems of Thought Ser.). (ENG., Illus.). 480p. pap. 24.95 *(978-0-253-22233-6(8)*, 0253222338) Indiana Univ. Pr.

Cooper, Craig. How to Be a Religious Demon. 2011. 64p. pap. 7.95 ***(978-1-4357-9229-6(7))*** Lulu Enterprises Inc.

Cooper, Edith Fairman. It's All about Jesus: Observations of a Former Seventh-Day Adventist. 2007. 476p. per. 29.95 *(978-1-4241-5934-5(2))* PublishAmerica, Inc.

Cooper, Eric. Daddy I Miss You. 2011. 132p. pap. 14.99 ***(978-1-61379-258-2(1))*** Xulon Pr., Inc.

Cooper, Kate & Gregory, Jeremy, eds. Elite & Popular Religion. 2006. (Studies in Church History Ser.: Volume 42). (Illus.). 456p. 80.00 *(978-0-9546809-2-3(8))* Ecclesiastical History Society GBR. Dist: Boydell & Brewer, Inc.

Corbett, Julia Mitchell, ed. Through a Glass Darkly: Readings on the Concept of God. 144p. 10.95 *(978-0-687-41894-7(1))* Abingdon Pr.

Cordon, Gary L. Sr. Your Guide to Biblical Fasting. 2011. 122p. 29.99 ***(978-1-4568-2903-2(3))*** Xlibris Corp.

Cormack, Don. Killing Fields Living Fields. 2009. (ENG., Illus.). 464p. 13.99 *(978-1-84550-511-0(5))* Christian Focus Pubns. GBR. Dist: STL Distribution North America.

Cornwall, Judson. Things You Don't Know about Heaven. 2007. (ENG.). 192p. pap. 12.99 *(978-1-59979-096-1(3)*, Charisma House) Charisma Media.

Corrigan, John, et al. Jews, Christians, Muslims: A Comparative Introduction to Monotheistic Religions. 2nd ed. 2011. (ENG., Illus.). 408p. (C). pap. 85.00 *(978-0-205-01825-3(4)*, Prentice Hall) Prentice Hall PTR.

Costello, Elaine. Religious Signing: A Comprehensive Guide for All Faiths. 2009. (ENG.). 352p. pap. 22.00 *(978-0-553-38619-6(0))* Random House Publishing Group.

Cotter, Elizabeth M. The General Chapter in a Religous Institute: With Particular Reference to IBVM Loreto Branch. 2008. 380p. pap. 90.95 *(978-3-03911-414-6(X))* Lang, Peter AG GBR. Dist: Lang, Peter.

Coulton, G. G. Christ, St Francis & To-day. 2010. (Cambridge Library Collection - History Ser.). (ENG.). 220p. pap. 22.99 *(978-1-108-01039-9(3))* Cambridge Univ. Pr.

Cox, Harvey. When Jesus Came to Harvard: Making Moral Choices Today. 2006. (ENG.). 352p. pap. 29.95 *(978-0-618-71054-6(X))* Houghton Mifflin Harcourt Publishing Co.

Cox, John. Googling God. 2008. 272p. per. 12.99 *(978-0-7369-2127-5(3))* Harvest Hse. Pubs.

Cram101 Textbook Reviews Staff. Outlines & Highlights for Introduction to Christianity by Mary Jo Weaver, David Brakke, Isbn: 9780495097266. 2009. 64p. pap. 27.95 *(978-1-4288-9290-3(7))* Cram101 Inc.

—Outlines & Highlights for Medieval Christianity: A Peoples History of Christianity, Vol. 4 by Daniel E. Bornstein (Editor), ISBN. 2009. 58p. pap. 26.95 *(978-1-4288-9291-0(5))* Cram101 Inc.

Craughwell, Thomas J. This Saint Will Change Your Life. 2011. (ENG., Illus.). 480p. pap. 19.95 *(978-1-59474-528-7(5))* Quirk Bks.

Crichton, J. D. Celebrating the Word. 176p. pap. 14.95 *(978-1-85607-123-9(5))* International Scholars Pubns.

Critser, Sherman L. & Miller, David L. Equipping the Church for Difficult Times: A training manual based on the Book of Revelation. 2009. 148p. pap. 14.99 *(978-1-60791-659-8(2))* Xulon Pr., Inc.

Cronkhite, Elizabeth. The ACIM Mentor Articles: Answers for Students of A Course in Miracles. 2010. 370p. pap. 21.00 *(978-0-557-45794-6(7))* Lulu Enterprises Inc.

Crookall, Stan. Drawing Souls to Christ. 2009. 288p. pap. 16.99 *(978-1-60791-381-8(X))* Xulon Pr., Inc.

Cross, F. L. & Livingstone, E. A., eds. Dictionary of the Christian Church. 2007. 1786p. per. 49.95 *(978-1-59856-250-7(9))* Hendrickson Pubs. Marketing, LLC.

Cross, John R. The Stranger on the Road to Emmaus. l.t. ed. 2009. pap. *(978-1-890082-71-0(6))* 4th rev. ed. 2008. pap. *(978-1-890082-54-3(6))* GoodSeed International.

Crowe, Philip. Strange Design: Exploring the Ways of God. 160p. 16.00 *(978-1-85311-326-0(3))* Norwich Bks. & Music GBR. Dist: Morehouse Publishing.

Cruttwell, Charles Thomas. Saxon Church & the Norman Conquest. 2006. pap. 28.95 *(978-1-4286-3881-5(4))* Kessinger Publishing, LLC.

Cullen, Timothy R., ed. Modern Analysis of Religious Practices. 2011. ***(978-1-61324-259-9(X))*** Nova Science Pubs., Inc.

Culliver, Jerome J. Two Gospels: One Total Truth; the Other A Total Deception. 2011. 223p. pap. 19.95 *(978-1-4327-6542-2(6))* Outskirts Pr., Inc.

Culp, Kristine A. Vulnerability & Glory: A Theological Account. 2010. (ENG.). 224p. pap. 30.00 *(978-0-664-23522-2(0))* Westminster John Knox Pr.

Cultural Research Services Staff. The Marketing of Christianity: The Evolution of Early Christian Doctrine. (ICR Monographs: No. 39). 25p. 8.00 *(978-0-904674-31-6(2)*, MAOC1) Institute for Cultural Research, The GBR. Dist: I S H K.

Cummings, George. The Christs of God. 2011. 148p. 24.95 *(978-1-4502-8813-2(8))*; pap. 14.95 *(978-1-4502-8814-9(6))* iUniverse, Inc.

Cummings, P. H. A Defense of the Supreme God. 2011. 46p. 35.95 ***(978-1-258-06147-0(3))*** Literary Licensing, LLC.

Cunningham, William R. Beyond the Hype: Pursuing the Truth of Christianity. 2007. 120p. (ENG.). 22.95 *(978-0-595-69611-6(2))*; per. 12.95 *(978-0-595-42755-0(3))* iUniverse, Inc.

Cupitt, D. Crisis of Moral Authority. 2012. 159p. pap. ***(978-0-334-01958-9(3)***, SCM Pr.) Hymns Ancient & Modern Ltd.

Curtis, Larry L. Ramblings of a Middle-aged Christian. 2010. 130p. pap. 14.99 *(978-1-60957-583-0(0))* Xulon Pr., Inc.

Cuss, Spart A. The Mark of the Beast Revealed: The Real Meaning of Your Credit Score. 2011. 156p. pap. 14.95 ***(978-1-4620-1524-5(7))*** iUniverse, Inc.

C.V.L. Is Jesus Christ God? 2009. 336p. pap. 25.50 *(978-0-557-02354-7(8))* Lulu Enterprises Inc.

Daggers, Jenny. Postcolonial Theology of Religions: Particularity & Pluralism in World Christianity. 2012. (ENG.). 224p. (C). 115.00 *(978-0-415-61040-7(0))*; pap. 39.95 *(978-0-415-61043-8(5))* Routledge.

Dales, Douglas. This Is My Faith: A Personal Confirmation. (Illus.). 96p. pap. 10.50 *(978-1-85311-333-8(6))* Norwich Bks. & Music GBR. Dist: Morehouse Publishing.

Dalton, Lucius M. The Lord Will Provide. 2011. 116p. 21.23 *(978-1-4567-3722-1(8))*; pap. 13.73 *(978-1-4567-3721-4(X))* AuthorHouse.

Daly, Gerald Michael. The Miracle Children. 2010. 344p. pap. 24.95 *(978-1-4497-0502-2(2)*, WestBow Pr.) Author Solutions, Inc.

D'Ambrosio-Crabtree, Gayle. Secondhand Hope. 2008. 96p. pap. 12.99 *(978-1-4357-1271-3(4))* Lulu Enterprises Inc.

Darin Bowler. God: A Long Time Ago in a Galilean Far, Far Away. 2010. 112p. pap. 14.95 *(978-1-4269-2419-4(4))* Trafford Publishing.

Darling, Dallas M. The Other Side of Christianity. 2008. 192p. pap. 15.99 *(978-1-60647-522-5(3))* Xulon Pr., Inc.

Darr, D. C. The Religion of Man vs. the Word of God: How Man Makes God Conform to Man's Image. 2010. pap. 10.99 *(978-1-61663-222-9(4))* Tate Publishing & Enterprises, LLC.

Daughrity, Dyron B. The Changing World of Christianity: The Global History of a Borderless Religion. 2010. (Illus.). 304p. (C). 129.95 *(978-1-4331-0523-4(3))*; pap. 34.95 *(978-1-4331-0452-7(0))* Lang, Peter Publishing, Inc.

Daughters of St Paul. Devotion to Sacred Heart. 22p. pap. 1.25 *(978-0-8198-1858-4(5)*, 332-067) Pauline Bks. & Media.

—Devotion to St Patrick. 22p. pap. *(978-0-8198-1853-9(4)*, 332-066) Pauline Bks. & Media.

—Devotions to St Dymphna. 14p. pap. *(978-0-8198-1850-8(X)*, 332-065) Pauline Bks. & Media.

Davenport, Gene L. Though the Mountains Tremble: Biblical Reflections on Contemporary Society. 2009. 218p. pap. 24.00 *(978-1-55635-562-2(9)*, Wipf and Stock) Wipf & Stock Pubs.

Davidson, Don. The Eternal Perspective: Essays on the Truths of Christianity by a Former Skeptic. 2007. 191p. pap. 24.95 *(978-1-4241-9941-9(7))* PublishAmerica, Inc.

Davies, Donald T. The Calling. 2009. 332p. pap. 18.99 *(978-1-60791-198-2(1))* Xulon Pr., Inc.

Davies, Philip R. Tribute to Geza Vermes: Essays on Jewish & Christian Literature & History. White, Richard T., ed. 2009. (Library of Hebrew Bible/Old Testament Studies, the Ser.). (ENG.). 406p. 65.00 *(978-0-567-19151-9(6)*, T&T Clark) Continuum International Publishing Group, Ltd. GBR. Dist: National Bk. Network.

Davies, Tom. Through Fields of Gold: A Pilgrimage from Berlin to Rome. (Illus.). 196p. 25.00 *(978-0-281-05358-2(8))* SPCK Publishing GBR. Dist: Pilgrim Pr., The/United Church Pr.

Davies, Wells. The Embattled but Empowered Community: Comparing Understandings of Spiritual Power in Argentine Popular & Pentecostal Cosmologies. 2010. (Global Pentecostal & Charismatic Studies). (Illus.). 314p. *(978-90-04-17830-4(9))* BRILL.

Davis, Forrest. Let Us Create God in Our Own Image: Christianity's Revolving Throne. 2010. 216p. 24.99 *(978-1-4520-6605-9(1))*; pap. 14.49 *(978-1-4520-6604-2(3))* AuthorHouse.

Davis, George B. Oprah Theology: A Comparative Analysis of Oprah Winfrey's Worldview of Christianity & Biblical Christianity. 2011. 168p. 30.95 ***(978-1-61507-849-3(5))***; pap. 13.95 ***(978-1-61507-848-6(7))*** Cross Bks. Publishing.

Davis, Gerald. A Cause & A Cure for Unanswered Prayer & Blessings Not Received. 2007. 72p. per. 9.50 *(978-0-9777039-7-5(5)*, VisionQuest Publishing) Andrews, Michael S. Publishing, LLC.

Davis, Jeanne, et al, eds. Worship Resources Year B: Beginning Advent 2011 up to Advent 2012. 2011. 240p. pap. 21.95 ***(978-0-8309-1514-9(1)***, Herald Publishing Hse.) Herald Publishing Hse.

Davison, Andrew, ed. Imaginative Apologetics: Theology, Philosophy & the Catholic Tradition. 2011. (ENG.). 256p. pap. 29.99 *(978-0-334-04352-2(2)*, SCM Pr.) Hymns Ancient & Modern Ltd GBR. Dist: Westminster John Knox Pr.

Dawkins, Shay. The Good News: How Revealing Delusions in Christianity Will Bring Peace to All: Dawkins Truth: Volume 1. 2011. (ENG.). 135p. pap. 16.95 ***(978-1-4327-7761-6(0))*** Outskirts Pr., Inc.

Dawson, Christopher. The Judgment of the Nations. 2011. (Works of Christopher Dawson Ser.). 200p. pap. 24.95 ***(978-0-8132-1880-9(2))*** Catholic Univ. of America Pr.

Day, Albert Edward. The Faith We Live. 2007. (ENG.). 176p. 37.95 *(978-0-548-08312-3(6))* Kessinger Publishing, LLC.

De Chateaubriand, Viscount. Genius of Christianity or the Spirit and. 2006. pap. 52.95 *(978-1-4286-3505-0(X))* Kessinger Publishing, LLC.

De Flavigny, Marie-Catherine Sophie. A Catholic Mother Speaks to Her Children. Booton, Debra, ed. 2011. 256p. pap. 15.95 *(978-1-4327-5767-9(4))* Outskirts Pr., Inc.

De Haan, Mart. Been Thinking About: Coming Together Around the Ideas & Issues That Divide Us. 2007. (ENG.). 352p. per. 12.99 *(978-1-57293-208-1(2))* Discovery Hse. Pubs.

De Pressense, E. The Ancient World & Christianity 1900. Holmden, Annie Harwood, tr. 2007. (ENG.). 508p. 55.95 *(978-0-548-05568-7(8))* Kessinger Publishing, LLC.

de Roos, Herman. Spiritualiteit en Zingeving. 2010. (DUT.). 225p. pap. 32.95 *(978-1-4457-6750-5(3))* Lulu Enterprises Inc.

de Wesselow, Thomas. The Sign. 2012. (ENG., Illus.). 464p. (gr. 12). 28.95 ***(978-0-525-95365-4(5)**,* Dutton Adult) Penguin Group (USA) Inc.

Deacon, A. Theological Graffiti. 2011. 88p. pap. 12.95 *(978-0-533-16339-7(0))* Vantage Pr., Inc.

The Death of a Legacy of Error: The Revelation of the Body of Christ. 2011. 120p. pap. 10.95 ***(978-1-4620-3782-7(8))*** iUniverse, Inc.

Decret, François. Early Christianity in North Africa. 2011. (ENG.). 240p. pap. 38.00 *(978-0-227-17356-5(2))* Clarke, James Co., Ltd. GBR. Dist: Brown, David Bk. Co., The.

—Early Christianity in North Africa. Smither, Edward L., tr. 2009. 240p. pap. 26.00 *(978-1-55635-692-6(7)*, Cascade Bks.) Wipf & Stock Pubs.

Defining Dogma Assumption. 32p. pap. *(978-0-8198-0748-9(6)*, 332-004) Pauline Bks. & Media.

Dehandschutter, Boudewijn & Dehandschutter, B. Polycarpiana: Studies on Martyrdom & Persecution in Early Christianity: Collected Essays. Leemans, J., ed. 2007. (Bibliotheca Ephemeridum Theologicarum Lovaniensium Ser.). (ENG.). 286p. (C). pap. 108.00 *(978-90-429-1993-8(0))* Peeters Pubs. & Booksellers BEL. Dist: Brown, David Bk. Co., The.

Dekoven, Stan. The Laws of Christ. 2010. 54p. pap. 10.00 *(978-1-61529-002-4(8))* Vision Publishing.

Delotavo, Alan J. Back to the Original Church: The Secret Behind Church Movements. 2010. 112p. pap. 14.00 *(978-1-55635-566-0(1)*, Resource Pubns.) Wipf & Stock Pubs.

Dembski, William. The End of Christianity: Finding a Good God in an Evil World. 1 vol. 2009. (ENG.). 254p. 22.99 *(978-0-8054-2743-1(0)*, B&H Academic) B&H Publishing Group.

Denman, William F. Mediation-A Scriptural & Christian Perspective. 2007. 176p. per. 24.95 *(978-1-4241-8337-1(5))* PublishAmerica, Inc.

Denomme, Jean. Where Is This God of Yours? For Those Who Wonder ... 2010. 200p. 26.95 *(978-1-4502-3346-0(5))*; pap. 16.95 *(978-1-4502-3345-3(7))* iUniverse, Inc.

Depoortere, Frederiek. Badiou & Theology. 2009. (Philosophy & Theology Ser.). (ENG.). 168p. 24.95 *(978-0-567-03262-1(0))*; 120.00 *(978-0-567-03261-4(2))* Continuum International Publishing Group, Ltd. GBR. (T&T Clark Int'l). Dist: National Bk. Network.

Derby, Timothy C. Seven Spiritual Mistakes Christian Parents Make: And How You Can Avoid Them. 2009. 140p. pap. *(978-0-9729465-7-5(8))* Nicole-Ashley Publishing.

DeVaughn, Vaughn E., Sr. The Devaughn Code: For the Truth's Sake. 2007. 88p. per. 12.95 *(978-1-56167-982-9(8))* American Literary Pr.

Dew, Sheri. Saying It Like It Is. 2009. 160p. 17.95 *(978-1-60641-087-5(3))* Deseret Bk. Co.

C

Dickie, Robert L. Authentic Christianity 101. 2007. 47p. pap. *(978-0-85234-672-3(7))* Evangelical Pr.

Dickson, E. Dale. 1 + 1 = 1: The Greatest Equation Ever Written. 2007. 165p. per. 12.99 *(978-1-60247-141-2(X))* Tate Publishing & Enterprises, LLC.

Dillard, Lanchelle. What's Love Got to Do with It Everything! An Inspirational Step by Step Guide for Everyone. 2009. 68p. pap. 15.49 *(978-1-4389-3529-4(3))* AuthorHouse.

Dinkins, Baynard. Hell Is Full of Good People. 160p. pap. 10.99 *(978-1-58169-129-0(7)*, Evergreen Pr.) Genesis Communications, Inc.

Dinsmore, Jim. It Seems to Me: An Attempt to Talk Sense about the Bible. 2011. 124p. 28.95 ***(978-1-4497-1719-3(5)**,* WestBow Pr.) Author Solutions, Inc.

Direction for Our Times, "Anne". Volume Four: Part 1: Jesus the King Part 2: Heaven Speaks to Priests Part 3: Jesus Speaks to Sinners, Vol IV. 2007. (ENG.). 128p. per. 5.00 *(978-0-9766841-3-8(6))* Direction for our Times.

—Volume Seven: Greetings from Heaven, Vol. 7. 2007. (ENG.). 122p. per. 5.00 *(978-0-9766841-6-9(0))* Direction for our Times.

—Volume Three: God the Father Speaks to His Children & the Blessed Mother Speaks to Her Bishops & Priests, Vol. III. 2007. (ENG.). 124p. per. 5.00 *(978-0-9766841-2-1(8))* Direction for our Times.

Dodgen, Esther Carls. A Bouquet of Flowers: Inspiration Gathered from My Spiritual Garden. 2010. 252p. pap. 18.95 *(978-1-4490-5147-1(2))* AuthorHouse.

Dods, Marcus. Mohammed Buddha & Christ Four Lectures. 2006. pap. 27.95 *(978-1-4286-3439-8(8))* Kessinger Publishing, LLC.

Dolan, Michael Francis. Where Have All the Catholics Gone? 2010. 160p. 24.95 *(978-1-4502-6118-0(3))*; pap. 14.95 *(978-1-4502-6120-3(5))* iUniverse, Inc.

Doles, Jeff. Miracles & Manifestations of the Holy Spirit in the History of the Church. 2007. 280p. pap. 24.95 *(978-0-9744748-9-2(4))* Walking Barefoot Ministries.

Dollison, Denise. My Beloved. 2006. pap. 9.99 *(978-1-60034-483-1(6))* Xulon Pr., Inc.

Donaldson, James, ed. The Apocryphal Gospels, Acts, & Revelations,. Walker, Alexander & Roberts, Alexander, trs. 2010. 148.52 *(978-1-61719-739-0(4))* Gorgias Pr., LLC.

D.O.S. Jesus the Greatest Architecture. 2011. 100p. pap. 19.95 ***(978-1-4560-7770-9(8))*** PublishAmerica, Inc.

Dougill, John. In Search of Japan's Hidden Christians: A Story of Suppression, Secrecy & Survival. 2012. (ENG., Illus.). 272p. 22.95 ***(978-4-8053-1147-9(9))*** Tuttle Publishing.

Douthat, Ross. Bad Religion: How We Became a Nation of Heretics. 2012. (ENG.). 352p. 26.00 ***(978-1-4391-7830-0(5)**,* Free Pr.) Free Pr.

Dowling, Maelruain & Dowling, Elizabeth. Lorrha-Stowe Missal & the Hours of Bangor. 2008. 463p. pap. 30.00 *(978-0-557-00229-0(X))* Lulu Enterprises Inc.

Dressler, Craig. Never Fail: Strategies for Success. 2011. *(978-1-58982-787-5(2))* American Bk. Publishing Group.

Drummond, Henry. The Program of Christianity. 2011. 40p. pap. 7.99 ***(978-1-61203-222-1(2))*** Bottom of the Hill Publishing.

Drummond, Henry. The Program of Christianity an Address. 2007. (ENG.). 308p. 43.95 *(978-0-548-03197-1(5))* Kessinger Publishing, LLC.

Drummond, James. Via, Veritas, Vita: Lectures on "Christianity in Its Most Simple & Intelligible Form" 2nd ed. (Hibbert Lectures: 1894). reprint ed. 31.50 *(978-0-404-60412-7(9))* AMS Pr., Inc.

Duè, Andrea, et al. Atlas Historico del Cristianismo (Historical Atlas of Christianity) (SPA.). 324p. 89.95 *(978-84-285-2090-4(9))* San Pablo Ediciones ESP. Dist: St Pauls/Alba Hse. Pubs.

Dunbar, David Michael. Dosing Froggy: Who Died & Made You God? 2010. (Illus.). 352p. pap. 18.95 *(978-1-4327-5924-7(8))* Outskirts Pr., Inc.

Duncan, Apostle J. Vernon. Come Buy Without Money: Advanced Techniques in Kingdom Financing. 2011. 168p. pap. 20.30 ***(978-1-4567-7852-1(8))*** AuthorHouse.

Duncan, Donnell. Faith Science: Where Faith & the Scientific Method Collide. 2011. pap. 19.99 *(978-1-61739-006-7(2))* Tate Publishing & Enterprises, LLC.

Dunigan, William. Reviving the Dead Church by the Way of Reminiscing the Day of Pentecost. 2007. 156p. per. 24.95 *(978-1-4241-6541-4(5))* PublishAmerica, Inc.

Dunlop, L. C. Cornbread Christianity. 2008. 302p. pap. 16.95 *(978-0-7414-4492-9(5))* Infinity Publishing.

Durgin, David W. The Christian Way. 2011. 396p. pap. 27.95 (978-1-4497-2749-9(2), WestBow Pr.) Author Solutions, Inc.

Dyas, Dee, ed. The English Parish Church through the Centuries: Daily Life & Spirituality, Art & Architecture, Literature & Music. 2010. (ENG., Illus.). (C). 29.95 (978-0-9550673-2-7(4)) Christianity and Culture Project GBR. Dist: Brown, David Bk. Co., The.

Ebuziem, Cajetan E. Doing Ministry in the Igbo Context: Towards an Emerging Model & Method for the Church in Africa. 2010. (Bible & Theology in Africa Ser.). 288p. (C). 80.95 (978-1-4331-1154-9(3)) Lang, Peter Publishing, Inc.

Eckfeldt, Edgar L. The Christian Legacy: Taming Brutish Human Nature in Western Civilization. 2011. (ENG.). 560p. pap. 35.95 (978-0-89226-106-2(4)) Paragon Hse. Pubs.

Edge, Henry T. Theosophy & Christianity. 2010. 120p. pap. 15.96 (978-1-163-13391-0(4)) 2009. 122p. 34.95 (978-1-104-83436-4(7)) 2007. (ENG.). 120p. per. 19.95 (978-1-4304-8291-8(5)) Kessinger Publishing, LLC.

Edwards, Joel. An Agenda for Change, 1 vol. 2008. (ENG.). 144p. pap. 12.99 (978-0-310-28371-3(X)) Zondervan.

—An Agenda for Change: A Global Call for Spiritual & Social Transformation, 1 vol. 2008. (ENG., Illus.). 144p. (gr. 13). 14.99 (978-0-310-28400-0(7)) Zondervan.

Edwards, Jon C. Rational Faith: Observations of Christianity by a Non-Authority on the Subject. 2011. 44p. pap. 16.95 (978-1-4626-2892-6(3)) PublishAmerica, Inc.

Edwards, Judson. Making the Good News Good Again: Recovering the Wonder of the Gospel. 2009. pap. (978-1-57312-529-1(6)) Smyth & Helwys Publishing, Inc.

Eedle, Arthur. Seven Steps to Bethlehem. 2010. 214p. pap. 25.50 (978-1-4092-1069-6(3)) Lulu Enterprises Inc.

—Showdown. 2008. 225p. pap. 21.50 (978-1-4092-1404-5(4)) Lulu Enterprises Inc.

—Unless the Lord build the House. 2010. 318p. pap. 21.50 (978-1-4092-1871-5(6)) Lulu Enterprises Inc.

Egbewoh, Paul. The Invisible - the Only True God. 2008. 361p. 42.49 (978-1-4357-2720-5(7)); 44.49 (978-1-4357-2719-9(3)); pap. 27.49 (978-1-4357-2124-1(1)) Lulu Enterprises Inc.

Ekelund, Robert B., Jr. & Tollison, Robert D. Economic Origins of Roman Christianity. 2011. (ENG., Illus.). 288p. 45.00 (978-0-226-20002-6(7)) Univ. of Chicago Pr.

Ekelund, Robert B., Jr., et al. The Marketplace of Christianity. 2008. (ENG., Illus.). 368p. (gr. 17). pap. 15.95 (978-0-262-55071-0(7)) MIT Pr.

Ekstrand, Donald W. Christianity. 2008. 368p. 31.99 (978-1-60647-137-1(6)) Xulon Pr., Inc.

—Christianity: The Pursuit of Divine Truth. 2008. 368p. pap. 19.99 (978-1-60477-929-5(2)) Xulon Pr., Inc.

Ekunwe, Ebun. They Are New Every Morning: That you may declare the praises of Him who called you out of darkness into His Wonderful Light, 1 vol. 2010. 123p. pap. 19.95 (978-1-4489-6244-0(7)) PublishAmerica, Inc.

Ekwugha, Maurice. Gospel of Deliverance. 2008. pap. 19.99 (978-1-60647-099-2(X)) Xulon Pr., Inc.

Éla, Jean-Marc. My Faith as an African. Brown, John Pairman & Perry, Susan, trs. 2009. 208p. pap. 23.00 (978-1-60608-623-0(5), Wipf and Stock) Wipf & Stock Pubs.

Eldred, Timothy. Pray 21: Discovery Guide. 2007. (ENG.). 126p. 10.99 (978-0-9796551-0-4(2)) Christian Endeavor International.

Ellingsen, Mark. Sin Bravely: A Joyful Alternative to a Purpose-Driven Life. 2009. (ENG.). 160p. pap. 17.95 (978-0-8264-2964-3(5)) Continuum International Publishing Group, Ltd. GBR. Dist: National Bk. Network.

Elliott, Melvin W. Genesis One: God's Table of Contents to the Bible. 2011. pap. 15.99 (978-1-61663-590-9(8)) Tate Publishing & Enterprises, LLC.

Elmore, Joe. Highlighted for Life: The Bible Says. 2007. (978-0-9799233-4-0(4)) Elmore, Joe.

Elstub, Colin. Contradiction & Controversy in the Bible. 2008. 163p. pap. 13.95 (978-1-4092-3661-0(7)) Lulu Enterprises Inc.

Embry, Adam. Help! I Can't Get Motivated. 2011. (Living in a Fallen World Ser.). 63p. pap. (978-1-84625-248-8(2)) DayOne Pubns.

English, George Bethune. Five Pebbles from the Brook. 2007. 108p. per. (978-1-4065-2545-8(6)) Dodo Pr.

—Five Pebbles from the Brook. 2009. 76p. pap. (978-1-4068-5178-6(7)) Echo Library.

Engs, Ruth Clifford, ed. Conversations in the Abbey: Senior monks of Saint Meinrad reflect on their Lives. 2007. 384p. per. 18.95 (978-0-87029-411-2(3)) Booklocker.com, Inc.

Ensign, Rebecca. Oleand: The Guardian Angel. 2007. 120p. per. 12.95 (978-1-886769-34-2(6)) Gold Leaf Pr.

Ephraim, Bryan. Rejected. 2009. 452p. pap. 20.49 (978-1-4389-6900-8(7)) AuthorHouse.

Epperson, Ian. Love Songs for the Apocalypse. 2010. 144p. pap. 12.49 (978-1-4490-6581-2(3)) AuthorHouse.

Erhinenta, Palmer. God's Redemption to Mankind: His Redeeming Spirit of Salvation. 2008. 80p. pap. 15.49 (978-1-4389-3511-9(0)) AuthorHouse.

Eriksen, Annelin. Gender, Christianity & Change in Vanuatu: An Analysis of Social Movements in North Ambrym. 2007. (Anthropology & Cultural History in Asia & the Indo-Pacific Ser.). 216p. 114.95 (978-0-7546-7209-8(3)) Ashgate Publishing Co.

Eristhee, Thomas. Now You Are Saved. 2007. 48p. per. (978-1-55452-158-6(0)) Essence Publishing.

Erlich, Haggai. Islam & Christianity in the Horn of Africa: Somalia, Ethiopia, Sudan. 2010. 200p. 49.95 (978-1-58826-713-9(X)) Rienner, Lynne Pubs.

Escobar, Mark. Thorns & Thistles: Pathways to Discipleship Cycle B. 2011. 286p. pap. 16.95 (978-1-4327-7126-3(4)) Outskirts Pr., Inc.

Esler, Philip F. Sex, Wives, & Warriors: Reading Biblical Narrative with its Ancient Audience. 2012. (ENG.). 420p. (C). pap. 60.00 (978-0-227-67991-3(1)) Clarke, James Co., Ltd. GBR. Dist: Brown, David Bk. Co., The.

Esposito, John L., frwd. Children of Abraham: Judaism, Christianity, Islam. 2006. (Princeton Classic Editions Ser.). (ENG.). 264p. (C). per. 19.95 (978-0-691-12769-9(7)) Princeton Univ. Pr.

Evans, Charles G. B. Is Jesus God? An Examination & Refutation of Popular Cultic Views. 2010. 203p. pap. 13.95 (978-1-4327-6290-2(7)) Outskirts Pr., Inc.

Evans, Craig A., ed. Encyclopedia of the Historical Jesus. 2008. (ENG.). 752p. (C). 195.00 (978-0-415-97569-8(7)) Routledge.

—Routledge Encyclopedia of the Historical Jesus. 2010. (ENG.). 752p. (C). pap. 65.00 (978-0-415-88088-6(2)) Routledge.

Evans, Craig A. & Zacharias, Daniel H., eds. 'What Does the Scripture Say?' Studies in the Function of Scripture in Early Judaism & Christianity: The Synoptic Gospels, 2 vols. 2012. (Library of New Testament Studies). (ENG.). 288p. 120.00 (978-0-567-38350-1(4), T&T Clark Int'l) Continuum International Publishing Group, Ltd. GBR. Dist: National Bk. Network.

Evans, G. R. The History of Christian Europe. (ENG., Illus.). 224p. 2011. pap. 19.95 (978-0-7459-5382-3(4)) 2009. 34.95 (978-0-7459-5265-9(8)) Lion Hudson PLC GBR. Dist: Independent Pubs. Group.

Evbuomwan. The Glory of Unity. 2009. 100p. pap. 10.49 (978-1-4389-3717-5(2)) AuthorHouse.

Fabyan, Pastor Steve. 42nd Generation the XGeneration. 2007. 88p. 16.95 (978-1-4241-5897-3(4)) PublishAmerica, Inc.

Fagerburg, Frank B. Is This Religion? 2007. (ENG.). 190p. 37.95 (978-0-548-06252-4(8)) Kessinger Publishing, LLC.

Fahlbusch, J.;, E.;;; Pelikan & Lochman, J. M., eds. The Encyclopedia of Christianity, Volume 5 Volume 5 (Si-Z), 5 vols. 2008. 896p. (978-90-04-14596-2(6)) BRILL.

Fahlbusch, Erwin, et al, eds. The Encyclopedia of Christianity: Volume 5: Si-Z, 5 vols., 5. 2008. (Encyclopedia of Christianity Ser.). 866p. 100.00 (978-0-8028-2417-2(X)) Eerdmans, William B. Publishing Co.

Falke, Cassandra. Intersections in Christianity & Critical Theory. Falke, Cassandra, ed. 2010. (ENG.). 208p. 84.00 (978-0-230-23480-2(1)) Palgrave Macmillan.

Farhadian, Charles E. Christianity, Islam & Nationalism in Indonesia. 2009. 236p. pap. 39.95 (978-0-415-54669-0(9)) Routledge.

Farley, William P. Gospel-Powered Humility. 2011. pap. (978-1-59638-240-4(6)) P & R Publishing.

Farooq, Asad. Jesus & Moses in India. 2011. 408p. 32.95 (978-1-4502-8263-5(6)); pap. 22.95 (978-1-4502-8261-1(X)) iUniverse, Inc.

Faulkes, Irene. Truth, Grace & Power. 2010. 168p. pap. 19.99 (978-1-4535-2733-7(8)) Xlibris Corp.

Faurot, Randal. The Pilgrim's Progress from the City of Destruction to the Celestial City of Refuge, from a Gospel Stand-Point, Containing Interviews with Sectarians. 2006. 224p. per. 20.99 (978-1-4255-1878-3(8)) MPublishing.

Ferguson, Richard. A Real-Life Christian Spiritual Journey. 2011. 312p. 31.95 (978-1-4620-1674-7(X)); pap. 21.95 (978-1-4620-1672-3(3)) iUniverse, Inc.

Feuerbach, Ludwig. The Essence of Christianity. 2008. (Philosophical Classics Ser.). (ENG.). 304p. pap. 10.95 (978-0-486-45421-4(5)) Dover Pubns., Inc.

Fiedler, Klaus. The Story of Faith Missions: From Hudson Taylor to Present Day Africa. 2011. 428p. pap. 49.00 (978-1-61097-478-3(6), Wipf and Stock) Wipf & Stock Pubs.

Fiedler, Nick. The Hopeful Skeptic: Revisiting Christianity from the Outside. 2009. (ENG.). 175p. pap. 16.00 (978-0-8308-3727-4(2), IVP Bks.) InterVarsity Pr.

Fields, Doug & McGill, Matt. Small Group Start to Finish. 2006. 193p. pap. 49.00 incl. cd-rom (978-0-7644-6005-0(6)) Group Publishing, Inc.

Finnamore, Alice. The Glory of Being: A Biblical Journey into Abundance. 2010. 196p. pap. 20.00 (978-1-4269-1665-6(5)) Trafford Publishing.

Fischer, Moritz. Pfingstbewegung zwischen Fragilität und Empowerment: Beobachtungen zur Pfingstkirche »Nzambe Malamu« mit ihren transnationalen Verpflechtungen. 2011. (Kirche, Konfession, Religion Ser.). (GER., Illus.). 349p. (C). 68.00 (978-3-89971-843-0(7)) Vandenhoeck & Ruprecht GmbH & Co. KG DEU. Dist: ISD.

Fisher, Christopher L. Human Significance in Theology & the Natural Sciences: An Ecumenical Perspective with Reference to Pannenberg, Rahner, & Zizioulas. 2010. (Princeton Theological Monographs). 368p. pap. 40.00 (978-1-60608-053-5(9), Pickwick Pubns.) Wipf & Stock Pubs.

Fisher, Edward. Marrow of Modern Divinity. 2009. (ENG.). 390p. 29.99 (978-1-84550-479-3(8)) Christian Focus Pubns. GBR. Dist: STL Distribution North America.

Fisk, Basil C. Understanding Christian History. 2010. (Illus.). 392p. pap. (978-0-7552-1262-0(2)) Authors OnLine, Ltd.

Flancher, Arlene & Hanson, Laurie J., eds. The Funny Shape of Faith: Devotions for the Rest of Us. 2007. (Illus.). 359p. per. 14.99 (978-0-8066-5761-5(8)) Augsburg Fortress, Pubs.

Flanders, Christopher L. About Face: Rethinking Face for 21st Century Mission. 2011. (American Society of Missiology Monograph Ser.). 322p. pap. 35.00 (978-1-60899-523-3(2), Pickwick Pubns.) Wipf & Stock Pubs.

Flatt, John. Loreto Day School Sealdah. 2010. 156p. pap. 19.95 (978-1-4092-3791-4(5)) Lulu Enterprises Inc.

Flint, Roy. The Narrow Path. 2011. 136p. pap. 16.95 (978-1-4497-1041-5(7), WestBow Pr.) Author Solutions, Inc.

Flower, Marilyn O. The Woman Clothed by the Sun with the Moon under Her Feet. 2010. 208p. pap. (978-3-8383-8270-8(6)) Lambert Academic Publishing.

Floyd, Charlene. Christian Voices: Journeys Through Faith & Politics in Contemporary American Protestantism. 2007. 184p. 44.95 (978-0-275-99002-2(8), C9002, Praeger Pubs.) Greenwood Publishing Group, Inc.

Fontana, David. Is Christianity Good for You? 2011. (ENG.). 252p. pap. 22.95 (978-1-84694-441-3(4)) Hunt, John Publishing Ltd. GBR. Dist: National Bk. Network.

Ford, John & Ford, Katherine. When Evil Reigns: The Timeline of the Antichrist's Imminent Rise to Power. 2011. pap. 19.99 (978-1-61663-661-6(0)) Tate Publishing & Enterprises, LLC.

Ford, Juanita. Life in the Blood. 2009. 36p. pap. 16.99 (978-1-4490-3843-4(3)) AuthorHouse.

Fortson, Tom. Manhood: Let the Truth Be Told. 2008. (ENG.). 144p. pap. 11.99 (978-0-8024-7761-3(5)) Moody Pubs.

Fosdick, Harry Emerson. Christianity & Progress. 2009. 250p. pap. 24.99 (978-0-559-65695-8(5)) 2009. 250p. pap. 25.75 (978-0-559-65692-7(0)) 2008. 152p. 24.99 (978-0-554-29859-7(7)) 2008. 152p. 21.99 (978-0-554-39162-5(7)) 2007. (ENG.). 134p. pap. 18.99 (978-1-4346-8589-6(6)) 2007. (ENG.). 148p. pap. 19.99 (978-1-4346-8590-2(X)) BiblioBazaar.

—Christianity & Progress. 2007. (ENG.). 248p. 41.95 (978-0-548-12315-7(2)) Kessinger Publishing, LLC.

Foster, Elizabeth. The Perfect Gift. 2011. 108p. 28.95 (978-1-4497-0919-8(2)); pap. 11.95 (978-1-4497-0917-4(6)) Author Solutions, Inc. (WestBow Pr.).

Fountain, Samuel. Jesus, a Man for All Time. 2008. 280p. 27.50 (978-1-60693-091-5(5), Eloquent Bks.) AEG Literary Publishing Services, Inc.

Fowler, Ruth & Bassett, B. J. A Touch of Grace. 2011. 120p. pap. 11.99 (978-1-61215-574-6(X)) Xulon Pr., Inc.

Franke, John. Manifold Witness: The Plurality of Truth. 2009. (Living Theology Ser.). 152p. pap. 18.00 (978-0-687-49195-7(9), Abingdon Press) Abingdon Pr.

Franklin, Daniel P. Christians in Hell: Is Your Faith Merely False Hope? 2010. pap. 12.99 (978-1-61663-457-5(X)) Tate Publishing & Enterprises, LLC.

Franklin, Jentezen. The Fasting Edge Journal: A Personal 21-Day Guide. 2012. (ENG.). 128p. pap. 14.99 (978-1-61638-850-8(1), Charisma Hse.) Charisma Media.

Franklin, Sharlette. Why Storms Are Needed. 2007. 90p. pap. 16.50 (978-0-615-17669-7(0)) Franklin, Sharlette M.

Frechette, Richard. Haiti: The God of Tough Places, the Lord of Burnt Men. 2010. (ENG.). 144p. 29.95 (978-1-4128-1420-1(0)) Transaction Pubs.

Free Thought & Christian Faith. 2007. (ENG.). 146p. 35.95 (978-0-548-05155-9(0)) Kessinger Publishing, LLC.

Freidzon, Claudio. De gloria en Gloria, 0 vols. 2010. (SPA.). 384p. pap. 16.99 (978-1-60255-428-3(5)) Grupo Nelson.

French, Lachlen. Breath of Light. 2010. 480p. pap. (978-0-9814278-6-7(3)) Kima Global Pubs.

Friedman, Lauri S. Christianity. 2007. (Introducing Issues with Opposing Viewpoints Ser.). (ENG., Illus.). 167p. (J). (gr. 3-7). lib. bdg. 35.75 (978-0-7377-3874-2(X), Greenhaven Pr., Inc.) Cengage Gale.

Friendship Christmas Book & Easter Book. (Other Curriculum Resources Ser.). 39.95 (978-1-56212-904-0(X), 301410); 39.95 (978-1-56212-903-3(1), 301400) Faith Alive Christian Resources.

Friesen, Paul. A Second Look at First Impressions: A Layperson's Practical Bible Study Manual. 2008. 84p. pap. 8.95 (978-0-595-53099-1(0)) iUniverse, Inc.

Frost, Michael & Hirsch, Alan. Rejesus: A Wild Messiah for a Missional Church. 2009. (Illus.). 240p. pap. 19.95 (978-1-59856-228-6(2)) Hendrickson Pubs. Marketing, LLC.

Frye, John. Christianity. Bartlett, Cynthia, ed. 2009. (ENG., Illus.). pap., stu. ed. 37.50 (978-1-4085-0455-0(3)) Nelson Thornes Ltd. GBR. Dist: Trans-Atlantic Pubns., Inc.

Fulghum, Charles. Sermons of A Psychiatrist. 2011. 156p. pap. 11.70 (978-1-4567-3647-7(7)) AuthorHouse.

Furey, Debbie. The Rapture: Behold, the Bridegroom Cometh! 2010. pap. 12.99 (978-1-61663-630-2(0)) Tate Publishing & Enterprises, LLC.

Gabriel, Ruben. A Divine Word from a Revelation: God Is Longing for the World to Listen to His Message. 2010. pap. 16.99 (978-1-61663-490-2(1)) Tate Publishing & Enterprises, LLC.

Gadol, Kohen Ben. Last Sounding of Shofar. 2010. pap. 24.95 (978-0-7414-6126-1(9)) Infinity Publishing.

Galloway, Tommy. The Cure for Common Christianity. 2007. 124p. (ENG.). 18.99 (978-1-60266-315-2(7)); per. 10.99 (978-1-60266-314-5(9)) Xulon Pr., Inc.

Galluzzo, James S. The Spirituality of Mary Magdelene. 2008. 116p. pap. 12.95 (978-0-595-49581-8(8)) iUniverse, Inc.

Gamble, Matthew M. Tested, Tried & Justified. 2011. 64p. pap. 15.99 (978-1-4670-3934-5(9)) AuthorHouse.

Ganda, Friday. The Unfinished Journey with my Lord. 2010. 112p. pap. 11.99 (978-1-60957-344-7(7)) Xulon Pr., Inc.

Garcia, Ehud M. The Wisdom of James. 2008. 208p. pap. 15.99 (978-1-60647-914-8(8)) Xulon Pr., Inc.

Garland-Hill, Marlene L. Slavery & Christianity the Untold Story. 2009. 226p. pap. 25.00 (978-1-61529-006-2(0)) Vision Publishing.

Garret, G. Douglas. The French Theology Of 911. 2011. 58p. pap. 16.95 (978-1-4560-9731-8(8)) PublishAmerica, Inc.

Gasser, Georg, ed. Personal Identity & Resurrection: How Do We Survive Our Death? 2010. 294p. 99.95 (978-1-4094-0494-1(3)); (Illus.). 99.95 (978-1-4094-0493-4(5)) Ashgate Publishing Co.

Gathogo, Julius. African Hospitality from a Missiological Perspective. 2011. 184p. pap. (978-3-8443-0006-2(6)) Lambert Academic Publishing.

—The Pangs of Birth in African Christianity. 2011. 476p. pap. (978-3-8443-0606-4(4)) Lambert Academic Publishing.

Geaves, Ron & Vaughan-Williams, Rebecca. Key Words in Christianity. 2006. (ENG.). 152p. per. 9.95 (978-1-58901-126-7(0)) Georgetown Univ. Pr.

Geis, Robert. The Christ from Death Arisen. 2008. (ENG.). 268p. pap. 44.50 (978-0-7618-4077-0(X)) Univ. Pr. of America, Inc.

Gelfer, Joseph, ed. The Best of Journal of Men, Masculinities & Spirituality. 2010. 116.00 (978-1-61143-003-5(8)) Gorgias Pr., LLC.

Genger, Ross W. The Holy Club. 2011. 244p. pap. 15.99 (978-1-61379-865-2(2)) Xulon Pr., Inc.

Gentry, Sharon Hayes. The Wreck: A Journey of Emotional Healing, 1 vol. 2010. 102p. pap. 16.95 (978-1-4489-6138-2(6)) PublishAmerica, Inc.

George, Bob. Classic Christianity: Life's Too Short to Miss the Real Thing. 2010. 192p. pap. 12.99 (978-0-7369-2673-7(9)) Harvest Hse. Pubs.

—Classic Christianity Study Guide: Life's Too Short to Miss the Real Thing. 2010. 128p. pap. 8.99 (978-0-7369-2915-8(0)) Harvest Hse. Pubs.

George, Gregg. Christians Can't Lose: Exploring the Existence of God & Refuting Evolution (and other False World Views) 2011. 116p. 28.95 (978-1-4627-0528-3(6)); pap. 11.95 (978-1-4627-0527-6(8)) Cross Bks. Publishing.

George, Robert L. The Trinity's Weak Links Revealed: A chain Is only as strong as it's weakest Link. 2007. 200p. per. 16.95 (978-0-595-44288-1(9)) iUniverse, Inc.

Gerald, Claudine. The Soldier. 2007. per. 8.99 (978-1-934333-01-3(8)) Eagle Bk. Bindery.

Gerloff, Roswith & Hock, Klaus. Christianity in Africa & the African Diaspora: The Appropriation of a Scattered Heritage. Gerloff, Roswith & Hock, Klaus, eds. Adogame, Afe, ed. 2011. (ENG.). 368p. pap. 49.95 (978-1-4411-2330-5(X)) Continuum International Publishing Group, Ltd. GBR. Dist: National Bk. Network.

Gifford, Paul. African Christianity: Its Public Role in Uganda & Other African Countries. viii, 368p. (978-9970-02-170-3(2)) Fountain Pubs. Ltd. UGA. Dist: Michigan State Univ. Pr.

—Christianity, Politics, & Public Life in Kenya. 2009. (Columbia/Hurst Ser.). (ENG.). 276p. (gr. 17). 90.00 (978-0-231-15442-0(9)) Columbia Univ. Pr.

Gilbert, S. J. Choose to Win: Tools to Empower You on the Playing Field of Life. 2011. pap. 12.99 (978-1-61739-080-7(1)) Tate Publishing & Enterprises, LLC.

Gill, Adele M. 7 Pathways to Hope. 2011. (978-1-58982-605-6(4), Millennial Mind Publishing) American Bk. Publishing Group.

Giner-Sorolla, Hilary. A Christian's Treasury of Trees & Plants. 2011. 144p. pap. 47.95 (978-1-4497-0711-8(4), WestBow Pr.) Author Solutions, Inc.

Gipson, Danny & Gipson, David. David & Danny's Heavenly Devotionals. 2010. 396p. 31.99 (978-1-4520-2619-0(X)); pap. 22.99 (978-1-4520-2618-3(1)) AuthorHouse.

Gjerde, Jon. Catholicism & the Shaping of 19th Century America. Kang, S. Deborah, ed. (ENG., Illus.). 2012. 292p. pap. 32.99 (978-0-521-27966-6(6)) 2011. 304p. 99.00 (978-1-107-01024-6(1)) Cambridge Univ. Pr.

Gladden, Washington. Recollections. 2009. 456p. 42.99 (978-1-115-38310-3(8)); 35.99 (978-1-115-38308-0(6)); pap. 36.75 (978-1-115-38307-3(8)) BiblioBazaar.

—Recollections. 2010. 208p. pap. 25.57 (978-1-151-83487-4(4)) 2009. 282p. pap. 20.68 (978-0-217-98011-1(2)) General Bks. LLC.

Glanzer, Perry L. & Ream, Todd C. Christianity & Moral Identity in Higher Education. 2009. (ENG.). 288p. 89.00 (978-0-230-61240-2(7)) Palgrave Macmillan.

God Almighty. Scribe of Righteousness. 2011. 68p. pap. 15.67 (978-1-4567-7770-8(X)) AuthorHouse.

Godawa, Brian. Hollywood Worldviews: Watching Films with Wisdom & Discernment, 1 vol. enl. ed. 2009. (ENG.). 260p. pap. 16.00 (978-0-8308-3713-7(2), IVP Bks.) InterVarsity Pr.

God's Holy Words. 2009. 128p. pap. 10.99 (978-1-4389-9660-8(8)) AuthorHouse.

Goheen, Michael W. & Bartholomew, Craig G. Living at the Crossroads: An Introduction to Christian Worldview. 2008. (Illus.). 224p. (C). pap. 19.99 (978-0-8010-3140-3(0)) Baker Academic.

Goines, R. L. Angelic Encounter: El. 2010. 190p. pap. 14.99 (978-1-60957-793-3(0)) Xulon Pr., Inc.

Gold, Lorna. New Financial Horizons: The Emergence of an Economy of Communion. 2010. 184p. pap. 16.95 (978-1-56548-354-5(5)) New City Community Pr.

Goldman, Shalom L. Zeal for Zion: Christians, Jews, & the Idea of the Promised Land. 2010. (ENG., Illus.). 384p. 35.00 (978-0-8078-3344-5(4)) Univ. of North Carolina Pr.

Goldstein, Clifford. Life Without Limits: Powerful Truths That Bring Meaning & Hope. 2007. (978-0-8280-2058-9(2)) Autumn Hse. Publishing Co.

González, Justo L. Breve Historia de las Doctrinas Cristianas. 2007. 244p. per. 20.00 (978-0-687-49090-5(1)) Abingdon Pr.

Gonzalo, Jorge. The Truth of Christ. 2007. 22.00 (978-0-9767789-7-4(1)) Hudson Bks.

Goodman, Paul L. It's Never Too Late to Finish Well: Or Too Early to Start. 2008. 168p. 26.29 (978-1-4251-7486-6(8)) Trafford Publishing.

Goossaert, Vincent & Palmer, David A. The Religious Question in Modern China. 2011. 480p. 40.00 *(978-0-226-30416-8(7))* Univ. of Chicago Pr.
Goossen, Gayle. Rock the World: An Interactive Study of Our Faith Heritage. 48p. pap. 12.95 *(978-0-921788-28-7(2))* Kindred Productions.
Gorder, A. Christian Van. Christianity in Persia & the Status of Non-Muslims in Modern Iran. 2010. (ENG., Illus.). 352p. 83.99 *(978-0-7391-3609-6(7))* Lexington Bks.
Gordon, Elizabeth. Creator of My Heart: A New Heart Is What I Need. 2011. 144p. 28.95 *(978-1-4497-0971-6(0))*; pap. 11.95 *(978-1-4497-0969-3(9))* Author Solutions, Inc. (WestBow Pr.).
Gordon, George A. Aspects of the Infinite Mystery. 2009. 376p. 26.99 *(978-1-103-80205-0(4))*; pap. 20.99 *(978-1-103-80194-7(5))* BiblioBazaar.
—Aspects of the Infinite Mystery. 2007. (ENG.). 370p. 48.95 *(978-0-548-01235-2(0))* Kessinger Publishing, LLC.
Gordon, Patricia. Transitions & Memories. 2007. 113p. per. 10.99 *(978-1-59886-755-8(5))* Tate Publishing & Enterprises, LLC.
Gordon, S. D. Quiet Talks with World Winners. 2008. 196p. 22.99 *(978-0-554-33700-5(2))* 2008. 196p. 25.99 *(978-0-554-24397-9(0))* 2006. (ENG.). 176p. pap. 19.99 *(978-1-4264-6415-7(0))* 2006. (ENG.). 194p. pap. 21.99 *(978-1-4264-6489-8(4))* BiblioBazaar.
—Quiet Talks with World Winners. 2007. (ENG.). 128p. per. *(978-1-4068-6239-3(8))* Echo Library.
Gore, Bruce W. Historical & Chronological Context of the Bible. 2010. 640p. pap. 34.95 *(978-1-4269-4359-1(8))* Trafford Publishing.
Gouldson, Phil. We Ought to Explain: Practical Notes for New Churchgoers. 2009. 56p. pap. *(978-1-84748-559-5(6))* Athena Pr.
Govan, Glenda L. Deception: The Deceptive Work of the Adversary. 2010. 63p. pap. 12.95 *(978-1-4327-4286-7(8))* Outskirts Pr., Inc.
Graham, Carol. Azariah of Dornakal. 2007. 132p. per. *(978-1-4067-8810-5(4))*, Pomona Pr.) Read Bks.
Graham, Elaine L. Grace Jantzen: Redeeming the Present. 2009. 282p. 114.95 *(978-0-7546-6823-7(1))*; pap. 34.95 *(978-0-7546-6824-4(X))* Ashgate Publishing Co.
Graham, John. May I Borrow That Deck of Cards: (an Interesting Story & Inspirational Study) 2011. 152p. 29.99 ***(978-1-4628-8520-6(9))***; pap. 19.99 ***(978-1-4628-8519-0(5))*** Xlibris Corp.
Grant, Colin. The Reading & Preaching of the Scriptures in the Worship of the Christian Church, Volume 7, 7 vols. 2010. 734p. 45.00 *(978-0-8028-1771-6(8))* Eerdmans, William B. Publishing Co.
Green, Hollis. Why Christianity Fails in America. 2007. 244p. per. 14.95 *(978-0-9796019-1-0(6))* Global Education Advance.
Green, Ken & Green, Bernard. Christianity in Ancient Rome: The First Three Centuries. 2010. (ENG.). 272p. 29.95 *(978-0-567-03250-8(7))*, T&T Clark Int'l) Continuum International Publishing Group, Ltd. GBR. Dist: National Bk. Network.
Gregory, B. L. God Is... ... God's Purpose for Me Through the Number 12. 2010. 100p. pap. 12.00 *(978-1-4343-9796-6(3))* AuthorHouse.
Grenham, Thomas, ed. Who Do You Say I Am? Opportunies & Challenges for Pastoral Ministry. 2009. (ENG.). 128p. pap. 22.95 *(978-1-84730-173-4(8))* Veritas Pubns. IRL. Dist: Dufour Editions, Inc.
Gresham, Sylvia L. Destined for Greater Things. 2007. *(978-0-9794861-1-1(4))* Truth Pubs.
Grey, Mary. An Earthful of Glory. 112p. 10.99 *(978-0-281-04833-5(9))* International Publishers Marketing.
—Praying with Augustine. 2nd ed. 128p. 8.00 *(978-0-281-05119-9(4))* SPCK Publishing GBR. Dist: Pilgrim Pr., The/United Church Pr.
Grier, Albert C. The Truth Way. 2007. per. 14.95 *(978-1-59872-880-4(6))* Instant Pub.
Griffin, Debra L. Why Judas Was Born to Betray Jesus. 2010. 124p. 23.95 *(978-1-4502-1783-5(4))*; pap. 13.95 *(978-1-4502-1781-1(8))* iUniverse, Inc.
Griffin, Justin. The Truth about Images of Jesus & the 2nd Commandment. 2006. 147p. per. 11.99 *(978-1-59886-554-7(4))* Tate Publishing & Enterprises, LLC.
Griffith, Brian. Correcting Jesus: 2000 Years of Changing the Story. 2009. (ENG.). 336p. pap. 16.95 *(978-1-935259-02-2(4))* Exterminating Angel Pr.
Griffiths, Paul J. Lying: An Augustinian Theology of Duplicity. 2010. 254p. pap. 28.00 *(978-1-60899-491-5(0))* Wipf & Stock Pubs.
Griggs, Denise I. Biblical Creation: As Told by the Wise & Majestic Oak Tree. 2008. 48p. pap. 8.49 *(978-0-615-25198-1(6))* Glass Tree Bks.
Griggs, Sr. Behold the King & His Kingdom! 2007. 160p. 21.99 *(978-1-60266-540-8(0))*; per. 13.99 *(978-1-60266-539-2(7))* Xulon Pr., Inc.
Griswold, Frank T. Praying Our Days: A Guide & Companion. 2009. 196p. 20.00 *(978-0-8192-2359-3(X))*, Morehouse Publishing) Church Publishing, Inc.
Groh, John E. Rubbing God's Ear with His Promises: A Year's Prayers. 2009. 364p. pap. 22.70 *(978-1-4389-5802-6(1))* AuthorHouse.
Groody, Daniel G. & Campese, Gioacchino, eds. A Promised Land, a Perilous Journey: Theological Perspectives on Migration. 2008. (ENG., Illus.). 352p. pap. 32.00 *(978-0-268-02973-9(3))* Univ. of Notre Dame Pr.
Groppe, Elizabeth. Eating & Drinking. 2011. 136p. pap. 15.00 *(978-0-8006-9809-6(6))*, Augsburg Fortress) Augsburg Fortress, Pubs.
Grounds, Vernon C. Revolution & the Christian Faith: An Evangelical Perspective. 2007. 240p. pap. 26.00 *(978-1-55635-375-8(8))*, Wipf and Stock) Wipf & Stock Pubs.
Grove, Daisy E. The Mystery Teaching of the Bible. 2007. (ENG.). 126p. 35.95 *(978-0-548-00665-8(2))* Kessinger Publishing, LLC.
Groves, Laura Lee. I'm Outnumbered! One Mom's Lessons in the Lively Art of Raising Boys, 1 vol. 2010. 192p. pap. 12.99 *(978-0-8254-2739-8(8))* Kregel Pubns.
Guia del Votante para Cristianos Devotos. 2006. 0.40 *(978-1-888992-93-9(X))* Catholic Answers, Inc.
Gunn, Angus M. Intelligent Design & Fundamentalist Opposition to Evolution. 2006. (ENG., Illus.). 215p. per. 35.00 *(978-0-7864-2743-7(4))* McFarland & Co., Inc. Pubs.
Haag, John W. Is Christianity Just Another Religion? 2011. 212p. pap. 15.99 ***(978-1-61379-238-4(7))*** Xulon Pr., Inc.
Hach, Robert. The Passion & Persuasion. 2011. 120p. pap. 19.99 ***(978-1-4535-6293-2(1))*** Xlibris Corp.
Hage, Wolfgang. Syriac Christianity in the East. 2010. 91.28 *(978-1-61143-557-3(9))* Gorgias Pr., LLC.
Hagee, John. Can America Survive? 10 Prophetic Signs That We Are the Terminal Generation. Lt. ed. 2011. (ENG.). 547p. pap. 17.99 *(978-1-59415-373-0(6))* Cengage Gale.
—Can America Survive? 10 Prophetic Signs That We Are the Terminal Generation. 2010. (ENG.). 288p. 22.99 *(978-1-4391-8985-6(4))*, Howard Bks.) Howard Books.
Hagemeyer, Jenny. Touch Me Guide to Healing: It's Time to Heal the Church to Heal the World. 2011. 212p. pap. 18.95 ***(978-1-4620-4669-0(X))*** iUniverse, Inc.
Haggart, G. P. The Infernal Truth, Series 2: Familiars, Wizards & Witches. 2008. 24p. 15.95 *(978-1-4357-1433-5(4))* Lulu Enterprises Inc.
Haines, Charles Regina. Christianity & Islam in Spain. 2006. pap. *(978-1-4068-1085-1(1))* Echo Library.
Haines, Charles Reginald. Christianity & Islam in Spain. 2008. 212p. 24.99 *(978-0-554-36182-6(5))* 2008. 212p. 27.99 *(978-0-554-26879-8(5))* 2007. (ENG.). 182p. pap. 19.99 *(978-1-4346-2074-3(3))* 2007. 208p. 22.99 *(978-1-4346-2075-0(1))* BiblioBazaar.
Halbertsma, T. H. F. Early Christian Remains of Inner Mongolia: Discovery, Reconstruction & Appropriation. 2008. (Sinica Leidensia Ser.). (Illus.). 400p. *(978-90-04-16708-7(0))* BRILL.
Hale, Elnader. I Gotta Have It. 2009. 174p. pap. 19.96 *(978-0-557-06239-3(X))* Lulu Enterprises Inc.
Hale, Rosemary Drage. Christianity. 2009. (Understanding Religions Ser.). (YA). (gr. 7-12). 31.95 *(978-1-4358-5621-9(X))* Rosen Publishing Group, Inc., The.
—Understanding Christianity: Origins, Beliefs, Practices, Holy Texts, Sacred Places. 2010. (ENG., Illus.). 112p. pap. 9.95 *(978-1-907486-15-9(1))*, Watkins Publishing) Duncan Baird Pubs. GBR. Dist: Sterling Publishing Co., Inc.
Hall, Al A. Why Christianity? Fundamental Principles & Beliefs. 2008. (ENG.). 176p. pap. 12.99 *(978-1-59979-483-9(7))*, Creation Hse.) Charisma Media.
Hall-Williams, Shirley. No Place for a Woman: Examining Leadership in the Church. 2010. pap. 10.99 *(978-1-61663-779-8(X))* Tate Publishing & Enterprises, LLC.
Hallett, Garth. Theology Within the Bounds of Language: A Methodological Tour. 2011. 256p. 75.00 *(978-1-4384-3369-1(7))* State Univ. of New York Pr.
Ham, Ken, ed. The New Answers Book: Over 25 Questions on Creation/Evolution & the Bible. 2007. (Illus.). 378p. per. 14.99 *(978-0-89051-509-9(3))* Master Bks.
Hamblin, David A. Unveiling the Mysteries of the Last Days: Systematic Prophecy from Genesis to Revelation. 2010. pap. 28.99 *(978-1-61566-876-2(4))* Tate Publishing & Enterprises, LLC.
Hamburger, Jeffrey F., ed. Leaves from Paradise: The Cult of John the Evangelist at the Dominican Convent of Paradies Bei Soest. 2008. (Houghton Library Studies: 2). (Illus.). 200p. pap. 35.00 *(978-0-9765472-8-0(7))* Harvard Univ. Pr.
Hamby, Damon. Kingdom Principles: Christianity in Action. 2011. pap. 10.99 *(978-1-61739-182-8(4))* Tate Publishing & Enterprises, LLC.
Hamilton, Chris. A Message of Hope for Mankind: CREATING the NEW PLANET EARTH Includes Channelling from Astara. 2011. 240p. pap. 19.99 ***(978-1-4568-8283-9(X))*** Xlibris Corp.
Hamilton, Gavin. El Discurso Del Monte Olivete: The Olivet Discourse. (SPA.). 213p. *(978-84-7228-019-9(5))*, 220315) Clie, Editorial.
Hamm, George H. Christianity Snoozes While God Chooses!!!, 1 vol. 2010. 138p. pap. 24.95 *(978-1-4489-2719-7(6))* PublishAmerica, Inc.
Hampsch, John H. Mary, Our Tainted Nature's Solitary Boast. 24p. pap. 1.25 *(978-1-57918-087-4(6)*, 7172) Queenship Publishing Co.
Hanciles, Jehu J. Beyond Christendom: Globalization, African Migration, & the Transformation of the West. 2008. (Illus.). 448p. pap. 35.00 *(978-1-57075-790-7(9))*, Orbis Bks.
Hannah, John D. How Do We Glorify God? 2008. (Basics of the Reformed Faith Ser.). 44p. pap. *(978-1-59638-082-0(9))* P & R Publishing.
Hannan, Peter. Nine Faces of God. 2nd rev. ed. 2008. (ENG.). 185p. pap. 29.95 *(978-1-85607-596-1(6))*, Columba Pr. IRL. Dist: Dufour Editions, Inc.
Hannington, Muweesi. Death & Funeral Rites in Ugand. 2010. 124p. pap. *(978-3-639-27464-6(4))* VDM Verlag Dr. Mueller e.K.
Hansen, Bruce. 'All of You Are One' The Social Vision of Gal 3.28, 1 Cor 12.13 & Col 3.11. 2010. (Library of New Testament Studies, the Ser.). (ENG.). 256p. 120.00 *(978-0-567-13604-6(3))*, T&T Clark Int'l) Continuum International Publishing Group, Ltd. GBR. Dist: National Bk. Network.
Hanson, Marty & Kriva, William A. Life Pearls. 2010. 116p. pap. 11.95 *(978-1-4497-0280-9(5))*, WestBow Pr.) Author Solutions, Inc.
Harber, Jane E. Here... Have A Miracle: Experiencing Rest & Refreshing in This Harried, Hurried World. 2010. pap. 13.99 *(978-1-61566-314-9(2))* Tate Publishing & Enterprises, LLC.
—Walking Toward the Light: A Study for New Believers & Veteran Christians. 2011. pap. 15.99 *(978-1-61739-297-9(9))* Tate Publishing & Enterprises, LLC.
Hargrave, A. T. I See Dead Churches: And Their Coming Resurrection. 2011. pap. 15.99 *(978-1-61663-743-9(9))* Tate Publishing & Enterprises, LLC.
Hariankis, Stylianos. The Infallibility of the Church in Orthodox Theology. Kariatlis, Philip, tr. from GEC. 2008. (ENG.). 276p. (C). per. 18.00 *(978-1-920691-98-1(7))*, ATF Imprint) ATF Pr. AUS. Dist: Brown, David Bk. Co., The.
Harinck, George, et al, eds. Breaches & Bridges: Reformed Subcultures in the Netherlands, Germany & the United States. (VU Studies on Protestant History: Vol. 4). (Illus.). 166p. (C). pap. 45.00 *(978-90-5383-695-8(0))* VU Univ. Pr. NLD. Dist: Independent Pubs. Group.
Harisun, Marelle. Power, Theology & Ecclesiology in Practice. 2011. 428p. pap. ***(978-3-8383-3838-5(3))*** Lambert Academic Publishing.
Harmon, Tom. Lord, Teach Us to Pray. 2011. 104p. pap. 12.95 ***(978-1-60920-016-9(0))*** Ajoyin Publishing, Inc.
Harrington, Peter. 10 FAQ's of New Christians. 48p. 19.95 *(978-0-88177-304-0(2))* Discipleship Resources.
Harrington, Todd. Resonating the Gospel Within a Post Christian Culture. 2008. 132p. pap. *(978-3-639-01382-5(4))* VDM Verlag Dr. Mueller e.K.
Harris, Ramona. Awakening the Mystic in You: Messages of Light from the Christian Mystics. 2010. (ENG.). 140p. pap. 23.00 *(978-0-7618-5363-3(4))* Hamilton Bks.
Harrison, Orest Andrew. God Christian Names: A Reference Manual Containing 1,475 of the Most Commonly Used Names, Descriptions, & Expressions Identifying the Great Deity, the Creator of Heaven & Earth. 2011. (ENG.). 171p. pap. 19.95 ***(978-1-4327-7149-2(3))*** Outskirts Pr., Inc.
Harrison, Victoria S. Religion & Modern Thought. 2007. (Scm Core Text Ser.). 408p. per. *(978-0-334-04126-9(0))* Hymns Ancient & Modern Ltd.
Hart, David Bentley. Atheist Delusions: The Christian Revolution & Its Fashionable Enemies. 2010. (ENG.). 272p. pap. 17.00 *(978-0-300-16429-9(7))* Yale Univ. Pr.
Hart, David Bentley. The Story of Christianity: An Illustrated History of 2000 Years of the Christian Faith. 2012. (ENG., Illus.). 256p. 22.95 ***(978-0-85738-342-6(6))*** Quercus GBR. Dist: Independent Pubs. Group.
Hart, R. C. Longings of the Heart. 2010. 52p. pap. 20.95 *(978-1-4497-0828-3(5))*, WestBow Pr.) Author Solutions, Inc.
Hartman, John E. Letters to Laodicea: A Call to Repentance for Evangelical America. 2011. 164p. 30.95 *(978-1-4497-1081-1(6))*; pap. 13.95 *(978-1-4497-1080-4(8))* Author Solutions, Inc. (WestBow Pr.).
Hartman, Roger. Unfolding the Mysteries of Revelation. 2010. 200p. pap. 15.99 *(978-1-60957-597-7(0))* Xulon Pr., Inc.
Harton, F. P. Life in Christ. 2007. 124p. per. *(978-1-4067-8837-2(6))*, Pomona Pr.) Read Bks.
Harvey, Susan Ashbrook & Hunter, David G. The Oxford Handbook of Early Christian Studies. Harvey, Susan Ashbrook & Hunter, David, eds. 2008. (Oxford Handbooks Ser.). (ENG., Illus.). 800p. 165.00 *(978-0-19-927156-6(9))* Oxford Univ. Pr., Inc.
Hashemifard, Mirahmad. Shenakht-E Donya-Ye Gharb. 2011. (ENG & PER., Illus.). 676p. 65.00 *(978-1-4490-9664-9(6))*; pap. 53.00 *(978-1-4490-9663-2(8))* AuthorHouse.
Hashimifard, Mir Ahmad. Shinakht-I Dunya-Yi Gharb. 2010. (Illus.). 670p. *(978-1-4490-9665-6(4))* AuthorHouse.
Haslam, William. From Death to Life: Twenty Years of my Ministry. 2007. 252p. per. *(978-1-4065-3350-7(5))* Dodo Pr.
Hathcock, David B. The Eternal Purpose. 2011. 152p. 25.01 ***(978-1-4567-6088-5(2))***; pap. 17.55 ***(978-1-4567-6089-2(0))*** AuthorHouse.
Haththotuwa, Minoli. Just Say the Word. 2010. 186p. pap. 14.99 *(978-1-60957-509-0(1))* Xulon Pr., Inc.
Hatmaker, Patricia. Satan Is a Wimp When You Stand on the Power of God. 2007. (ENG.). 120p. per. 10.95 *(978-0-7414-3802-7(X))* Infinity Publishing.
Hattaway, Paul & Yun, Brother. Yun: The Illustrated Story of the Heavenly Man. 2006. (Illus.). 128p. pap. 11.99 *(978-0-8254-6128-6(6))*, Monarch Bks.) Lion Hudson PLC GBR. Dist: Kregel Pubns.
Hatten, Douglas. The Recognitions of Clement. 2008. 343p. pap. 26.95 *(978-0-615-18002-1(7))* Hatten, Douglas.
Hauerwas, Stanley. Christian Existence Today: Essays on Church, World, & Living in Between. 2010. 282p. pap. 31.00 *(978-1-60899-710-7(3))*, Wipf and Stock) Wipf & Stock Pubs.
Hawks, A. J. Living in a Grey World: Rediscovering the Black & White Truth of the Word. 2010. pap. 10.99 *(978-1-61566-401-6(7))* Tate Publishing & Enterprises, LLC.
Hayes, Norvel. Worship: More Than Just A Song. 2010. 128p. pap. 10.99 *(978-1-60683-003-1(1))* Harrison House Pubs.
Haynes, William F. & Kelly, Geffrey B. Is There A God in Health Care? Toward A New Spirituality of Medicine. 2010. 246p. pap. 27.00 *(978-1-60899-753-4(7))*, Wipf and Stock) Wipf & Stock Pubs.
Heath, Gordon L. Doing Church History: A User-Friendly Introduction to Researching the History of Christianity. 2008. 108p. pap. *(978-1-894667-90-6(5))* Clements Publishing.
Hebblethwaite, Brian. Essence of Christianity. 224p. 19.00 *(978-0-281-04815-1(0))* SPCK Publishing GBR. Dist: Pilgrim Pr., The/United Church Pr.
—In Defence of Christianity. 2006. (ENG.). 208p. per. 30.00 *(978-0-19-921075-6(6))* Oxford Univ. Pr., Inc.
Heckman, Garth. Dedicate: 14 Event-Driven Student Ministry Outlines. 2009. (On the Altar Ser.). (ENG.). 128p. (YA). pap. 16.99 *(978-0-7847-2266-4(8))* Standard Publishing.
Hedstrom, Kurt. A Chance Encounter with the Law. 2011. pap. 29.99 *(978-1-61663-010-2(8))* Tate Publishing & Enterprises, LLC.
Heflin, Stuart E. The Goshen Dilemma. 2011. 76p. pap. 9.99 ***(978-1-4567-6609-2(0))*** AuthorHouse.
Heft, James L., ed. Passing on the Faith: Transforming Traditions for the Next Generation of Jews, Christians, & Muslims. 4th ed. 2007. (Abrahamic Dialogues Ser.). (ENG., Illus.). 334p. 65.00 *(978-0-8232-2647-4(6))*; per. 28.00 *(978-0-8232-2648-1(4))* Fordham Univ. Pr.
Heim, Karl. Christian Faith & Natural Sciences. 15.00 *(978-0-8446-0690-3(1))* Smith, Peter Pub., Inc.
Hein, Marvin. On the Shoulders of Giants: A Group Study in Our Faith Heritage. 73p. pap. 3.95 *(978-0-921788-27-0(4))*; pap. 8.95 incl. VHS *(978-0-921788-34-8(7))* Kindred Productions.
Helms, Selah & Kahler, Susan. Small Talks on Big Questions: A Manual to Help Explain Christian Doctrine. 2007. 304p. per. 30.00 *(978-1-59925-109-7(4))* Solid Ground Christian Bks.
Help Hassle Free Events. Date not set. pap. 2.99 *(978-0-87162-611-0(X))*, E5300S) Warner Pr. Pubs.
Hemenway, Joanne. Forget Them Not: A Holistic Guide to Prison Ministry. 2010. 184p. pap. 21.00 *(978-1-60899-320-8(5))*, Wipf and Stock) Wipf & Stock Pubs.
Henderson, Alaric. So Built We the People. 2011. 70p. 24.99 ***(978-1-4568-9623-2(7))***; pap. 15.99 ***(978-1-4568-9622-5(9))*** Xlibris Corp.
Henderson, Warren. Hiding God: The Ambition of World Religion. 2007. 160p. per. 10.95 *(978-0-9795387-1-1(8))* Henderson, Warren.
Henley, Karyn. Communicating with Young Children. (Children's Ministry Folders). tchr. ed. 2.99 *(978-0-7847-0686-2(7))*, 42236) Standard Publishing.
Henry & Teske, R. J. Henry of Ghent's Summa: The Questions on God's Unity & Simplicity (Articles 25-30) 2006. (Dallas Medieval Texts & Translations Ser.: Vol. 6). (LAT & ENG., Illus.). 388p. (C). pap. 66.00 *(978-90-429-1811-5(X))* Peeters Pubs. & Booksellers BEL. Dist: Brown, David Bk. Co., The.
Henry Drummond. The Greatest Thing in the World & Other Addresses. 2009. 80p. pap. 3.95 *(978-1-60386-221-9(8))*, Merchant Bks.) Rough Draft Printing.
Henry, Jerome A. The and Word Ladder. 2011. 346p. pap. 18.99 ***(978-1-61379-633-7(1))*** Xulon Pr., Inc.
Herd, Jared Howard. More Lost Than Found: Finding a Way Back to Faith. 2011. 208p. pap. 15.99 *(978-1-4002-0303-1(1))* Nelson, Thomas Inc.
Heredia, Carlos I. Meditemos la Pasion del Senor.Tr. of Let's Meditate the Passion of the Lord. (SPA.). 80p. pap. 2.95 *(978-950-861-343-1(2))* Sociedad de San Pablo ARG. Dist: St Pauls/Alba Hse. Pubs.
Herford, R. Travers. Christianity in Talmud & Midrash. 2010. (Illus.). 198p. pap. 24.19 *(978-1-154-66240-5(3))* General Bks. LLC.
—Christianity in Talmud & Midrash. 2006. *(978-0-88125-930-8(6))* Ktav Publishing Hse., Inc.
Herring. Introduction to the History of Christian. 2006. 288p. pap. *(978-0-8264-6738-6(5))* Continuum International Publishing Group, Ltd.
Herring, George. Introduction to the History of Christianity: From the Early Church to the Enlightenment. 2006. (ENG., Illus.). 288p. 49.95 *(978-0-8264-6737-9(7))*, Burns & Oates) Continuum International Publishing Group, Ltd. GBR. Dist: National Bk. Network.
—Modern Christianity: An Introductory History. 2016. (ENG.). 352p. 29.95 *(978-1-84706-001-3(3))*; 95.00 *(978-1-84706-000-6(5))* Continuum International Publishing Group, Ltd. GBR. Dist: National Bk. Network.
Hertz, Solange. On the Contrary. 2011. 322p. pap. 19.95 ***(978-0-9842365-3-4(8))*** Tumblar Hse.
Hess, Cynthia. Sites of Violence, Sites of Grace: Christian Nonviolence & the Traumatized Self. 2008. (ENG.). 178p. 62.99 *(978-0-7391-1945-7(1))* Lexington Bks.
Hester, Angela. These Words are Gods' Words. 2011. 176p. pap. 11.70 *(978-1-4567-0143-7(6))* AuthorHouse
Hewitt, Hugh. A Guide to Christian Ambition: Using Career, Politics, & Culture to Influence the World, 0 vols. 2006. 224p. pap. 13.99 *(978-0-7852-8871-8(6))* Nelson, Thomas Inc.
Hibbard, E. J. The Two Laws: Object, Function, & Duration of Each. 2006. 80p. per. 10.95 *(978-1-57258-474-7(2)*, 945-6335) TEACH Services, Inc.
Hicks-Drake, Bertha. Wisdom Hidden in A Mystery A Love Story. 2007. pap. 13.99 *(978-1-60034-825-9(4))* Xulon Pr., Inc.
Highful, Kyle. St Basil's Address to Young Men. 2007. 88p. per. *(978-3-8364-3434-8(2))* VDM Verlag Dr. Mueller e.K.
Hild, L. Brian. The Unbiased Truth: Using God's Word to Break down Walls of Division Between Churches. 2007. 116p. per. 10.99 *(978-1-59886-631-5(1))* Tate Publishing & Enterprises, LLC.
Hill, Jason E. More Than Words: Moving Beyond Lip-Service Christianity to True Faith. 2011. 184p. pap. 13.95 ***(978-1-4497-1776-6(4))***; 30.95 ***(978-1-4497-1778-0(0))*** Author Solutions, Inc. (WestBow Pr.).
Hill, R. A. P. The Interregnum. 2011. (ENG.). 168p. pap. 19.99 *(978-1-107-64810-4(6))* Cambridge Univ. Pr.
Hill, Samuel S., Jr. The South & the North in American Religion. 2007. (Mercer University Lamar Memorial Lectures). (ENG.). 168p. per. 22.95 *(978-0-8203-3131-7(7))* Univ. of Georgia Pr.
Hilliard, Donald, Jr. How Daddy can make a Difference. 16p. pap. 1.99 *(978-1-58169-071-2(1))*, Evergreen Pr.) Genesis Communications, Inc.
Hillis, Newell Dwight. The Influence of Christ in Modern Life Being a Study of the New Problems of the Church in American Society. 2007. (ENG.). 428p. 51.95 *(978-0-548-01029-7(3))* Kessinger Publishing, LLC.
Hochstrasser, Josef. Religion ist heilbar: Glaube, Schule, Fussball. Diese drei. Aus der Sicht eines Agnostikers. 2007. 221p. *(978-3-7296-0736-1(7))* Zytglogge Verlag AG Bern.

C

Hodges, Houston. The Lessons. 2010. 230p. pap. 19.70 *(978-0-557-22187-5(0))* Lulu Enterprises Inc.

Hodgson, Janet. Making the Sign of the Cross: A Creative Resource for Seasonal Worship, Retreats & Quiet Days. 2010. (ENG., Illus.). 128p. pap. 34.99 *(978-1-84825-006-2(1)*, Canterbury Pr. Norwich) Hymns Ancient & Modern Ltd GBR. Dist: Westminster John Knox Pr.

Hokkanen, Markku. Medicine & Scottish Missionaries in the Northern Malawi Region, 1875-1930: Quests for Health in a Colonial Society. 2007. (Illus.). 680p. *(978-0-7734-5341-8(5))* Mellen, Edwin Pr., The.

Holbach, Paul Henri Thiry. Christianity Unveiled. 2009. 78p. pap. *(978-1-151-45372-3(2))* Books LLC.

Holding, James. The Impossible Faith. 2007. 112p. per. 10.99 *(978-1-60266-084-7(0))* Xulon Pr., Inc.

Holding, James Patrick. Blowing the Doors Off! A Defense Manual for Christian Students. 2008. pap. 22.99 *(978-1-60647-991-9(1))* Xulon Pr., Inc.

Holl, Karl. The Distinctive Elements in Christianity. Hope, Norman V., tr. 2006. 80p. pap. 11.00 *(978-1-59752-950-1(8)*, Wipf and Stock) Wipf & Stock Pubs.

Holladay, Tom, et al. God, 1 vol. 2008. (Foundations Ser.). (ENG., Illus.). 80p. (gr. 13). pap., instr.'s gde. ed. 6.99 *(978-0-310-27672-2(1))* Zondervan.

—Jesus: 11 Core Truths to Build Your Life On, 1 vol. 2008. (Foundations Ser.). (ENG., Illus.). 80p. (gr. 13). pap., stu. ed., instr.'s gde. ed. 6.99 *(978-0-310-27674-6(8))* Zondervan.

—Salvation: 4 Sessions, 1 vol. 2008. (Foundations Ser.). (ENG., Illus.). 80p. (gr. 13). pap., instr.'s gde. ed. 6.99 *(978-0-310-27682-1(9))* Zondervan.

Holland, Shawn L. Voted Most Likely Not to Succeed but, Godâ¿ !, 1 vol. 2010. 60p. pap. 19.95 *(978-1-4489-4970-0(X))* PublishAmerica, Inc.

Holman, Joe E. Project Bible Truth. 2010. 406p. pap. 24.24 *(978-0-615-23722-0(3))* Holman, Joe E.

Holmes, Jack H. Real Christianity: The New Covenant. Bradley, Annette, ed. unabr. ed. pap., tchr. ed. 18.00 *(978-0-9707166-1-3(3))* Cadcepts Publishing.

Holmes, Phoebe Marie. Citizenship in the Postwar Kingdom of God. 2007. (ENG.). 140p. 35.95 *(978-0-548-05938-8(1))* Kessinger Publishing, LLC.

Holt, David E. Abc's of Ministry: Choosing it - Learning It - Doing it - after It. 2008. 188p. pap. 14.95 *(978-1-60693-087-8(7)*, Strategic Bk. Publishing) AEG Literary Publishing Services, Inc.

Holton, M. Jan. Building the Resilient Community: Lessons from the Lost Boys of Sudan. 2010. 186p. pap. 21.00 *(978-1-60899-245-4(4)*, Cascade Bks.) Wipf & Stock Pubs.

Hooks, Gavin W. The Message of Pain: A Whisper of Hope. 2011. 272p. 35.95 *(978-1-4497-0952-5(4))*; pap. 19.95 *(978-1-4497-0951-8(6))* Author Solutions, Inc. (WestBow Pr.).

Horn, Thomas. The Researchers Library of Ancient Texts: Volume One the Apocrypha Includes the Books of Enoch, Jasher, & Jubilees. 2011. (ENG.). 584p. pap. 29.95 ***(978-0-9836216-9-0(1))*** Anomalos Publishing, LLC.

Hort, Fenton John Anthony. The Way, the Truth, the Life: The Hulsean Lectures For 1871. 2010. (Cambridge Library Collection - Religion Ser.). (ENG.). 268p. pap. 23.99 *(978-1-108-00701-6(5))* Cambridge Univ. Pr.

Hosey, LaToya M. Forever Sisters. 2010. 528p. pap. 26.99 *(978-1-60957-665-3(9))* Xulon Pr., Inc.

Hotz, Kendra G., et al. What Do Our Neighbors Believe? Questions & Answers onJudaism, Christianity, & Islam. 2006. (ENG.). 159p. per. 17.00 *(978-0-664-23065-4(2))* Westminster John Knox Pr.

Houck, Russ. Epidemic: Examing the Infected Roots of Judaism & Christianity. 2009. pap. 19.99 *(978-1-61623-123-1(8))* Independent Pub.

Hovde, Howard. A Dream that Came to Life: The History of the Laity Lodge Retreat Center. 2007. pap. 17.00 *(978-1-57312-487-4(7))* Smyth & Helwys Publishing, Inc.

Howard, Josef A. Turning Your Mess into A Message. 2011. 168p. 22.23 *(978-1-4520-7890-8(4))*; pap. 11.70 *(978-1-4520-7889-2(0))* AuthorHouse.

Howard, Marcos L. Arqueolog a b Blica. 2010. 102p. pap. 12.99 *(978-1-60957-831-2(7))* Xulon Pr., Inc.

Howard, Richard C. The King Describes His Kingdom. Date not set. *(978-0-9628091-9-4(5))* Naioth Sound & Publishing Co.

Howe, Quincy. Tertullian of Africa: The origin of Christian thought in the West. 2010. 108p. pap. 12.95 *(978-1-4502-5843-2(3))* iUniverse, Inc.

Howe, Tankred. Vandalen, Barbaren und Arianer Bei Victor Von Vita. 2007. (Studien zur Alten Geschichte Ser.). (GER.). 411p. (C). 87.00 ***(978-3-938032-17-6(0))*** Antike, Verlag, e.K. DEU. Dist: ISD.

Howell, James C. Introducing Christianity: Exploring the Bible, Faith, & Life. 2009. (ENG.). 208p. pap. 17.00 *(978-0-664-23297-9(3))* Westminster John Knox Pr.

Hryn, Halyna, ed. Churches & States: Studies on the History of Christianity in Ukraine. 2011. (Harvard Papers in Ukrainian Studies). (ENG.). 440p. pap. 29.95 *(978-1-932650-06-8(7))* Harvard Ukrainian Research Institute.

Huggins, Sid. Morning will Come. 2006. pap. 15.99 *(978-1-60034-775-7(4))* Xulon Pr., Inc.

Human Rights Watch (Organization) Staff, contrib. by. Montagnard Christians in Vietnam: A Case Study in Religious Repression. 2011. (Illus.). 28p. pap. ***(978-1-56432-755-0(8))*** Human Rights Watch.

Hummer/Pastor, Evangelist/Servant of Christ Jesus, Ann. The Kingdom of the Supernatural: Basic Instructions before Leaving Earth. 2010. 108p. 28.95 *(978-1-4497-0628-9(2))*; pap. 11.95 *(978-1-4497-0627-2(4))* Author Solutions, Inc. (WestBow Pr.).

Hunt, Thomas E. "the Christian Soldier" 2011. 138p. 29.99 ***(978-1-4535-6060-0(2))***; pap. 19.99 ***(978-1-4535-6059-4(9))*** Xlibris Corp.

Hunter, Alan & Chan, Kim-kwong. Protestantism in Contemporary China. 2007. (Cambridge Studies in Ideology & Religion Ser.). (ENG., Illus.). 316p. pap. 61.00 *(978-0-521-04691-6(2))* Cambridge Univ. Pr.

Hunter, James Davison. To Change the World: The Irony, Tragedy, & Possibility of Christianity in the Late Modern World, 1 vol. 2010. (ENG., Illus.). 368p. 27.95 *(978-0-19-973080-3(6))* Oxford Univ. Pr., Inc.

Hushbeck, Elgin L., Jr. Christianity & Secularism. 3rd ed. 2007. Orig. Title: Consider Christianity, Volume 2: Evidence for the Christian Faith. 220p. reprint ed. per. 16.99 *(978-1-893729-52-0(4))* Energion Pubns.

—Evidence for the Bible. 3rd ed. 2007. Orig. Title: Consider Christianity, Volume 1: Evidence for the Bible. 212p. per. 16.99 *(978-1-893729-51-3(6))* Energion Pubns.

Hutchings, Noah W. The Dark Side of the Purpose Driven Church. 2007. 192p. pap. 13.95 *(978-1-933641-00-3(2))* Bible Belt Pubns.

Hutchins, Charles A. Fifty Days. 2006. 12.00 *(978-0-8059-8257-2(4))* Dorrance Publishing Co., Inc.

Hutchison, Joyce & Rupp, Joyce. Now That Youve Gone Home. 2009. 128p. pap. 10.95 *(978-1-59471-215-9(8))* Ave Maria Pr.

Huxley, Thomas Henry. Christianity & Agnosticism: A Controversy. 2006. pap. 22.95 *(978-1-4286-4292-8(7))* Kessinger Publishing, LLC.

Hyde, John. What's the Problem with Jesus? 2008. 224p. pap. 16.95 *(978-0-9821153-0-5(X))* Living Waters Publishing Co.

Hylson-Smith, Kenneth. To the Ends of the Earth: The Globalization of Christianity. 2007. (ENG.). 240p. per. 23.99 *(978-1-84227-475-0(9)*, Paternoster) Authentic Media.

Ianakieva, Nadia. The Red Dress Decision: True Stories of a Life Filled with God's Miracles. 2010. pap. 15.99 *(978-1-61663-168-0(6))* Tate Publishing & Enterprises, LLC.

Ike, Jude Chikodi. The Church as Locus of Man's Encounter with God: A Study of the Theology of Otto Semmelroth & its Implication for the Church in Africa. 2011. (Europäische Hochschulschriften. Reihe 23: Theologie Ser.). 388p. pap. 90.95 *(978-3-631-61709-0(7))* Lang, Peter GmbH, Europaischer Verlag der Wissenschaften DEU. Dist: Lang, Peter.

Inbaraj, Lamech. Charismatic Movement: Unmistakable Agent of Wholesome Transformation. 2010. 272p. pap. *(978-3-639-24284-3(X))* VDM Verlag Dr. Mueller e.K.

The Inclusive Pulpit Journal. 2007. 19.95 *(978-0-9638451-3-9(6))* Community Church Pr.

Ingram, Harvey. Adam, Israel, & Jesus. 2009. *(978-1-55452-229-3(3))*; (ENG.). 320p. pap. *(978-1-55452-228-6(5)*, Guardian Bks.) Essence Publishing.

Innocent, Mimose. Under the King?ÇÖs Wings: Hiding, Living, Resting. 2011. 87p. 33.95 ***(978-1-4327-6700-6(3))*** Outskirts Pr., Inc.

Isbell, Raymond E. Essays on Selected Christian Topics. 2011. 272p. 28.99 *(978-1-4520-6735-3(X))*; pap. 15.99 *(978-1-4520-6736-0(8))* AuthorHouse.

—Paul, God's Evangelist & Minister. 2011. 236p. 27.99 *(978-1-4520-6741-4(4))* AuthorHouse.

Isbister, Colin James. How to Be A Lousy Christian in 12 Easy Lessons: Book 3 of the Body of Christ Series A Biblical Perspective of Attitude & Behaviour in the Christian. 2009. pap. 14.99 *(978-1-60791-564-5(2))* Xulon Pr., Inc.

Iverson, Donald William. Higher Metaphysics: A Treatise on Esoteric Christianity. 2011. 106p. 39.95 ***(978-1-258-01276-2(6))*** Literary Licensing, LLC.

Iwasiuk, Gosta. The Jesus Gene: How Religion Is Setting Us up for the Next Mass Extermination. 2008. (Illus.). 170p. pap. *(978-0-9763928-1-1(X))* Cutting Edge Publishing.

Jacik, Rob. Them Demons Is Tricky. 2010. 180p. pap. 16.95 *(978-0-557-15327-5(1))* Lulu Enterprises Inc.

Jackson, Earl. The Sons of God & the Nephilim. 2008. 150p. pap. 13.95 *(978-0-557-03312-6(8))* Lulu Enterprises Inc.

Jackson, Hawea. Relationship Between the Church & State & Church & Culture. 2010. 76p. pap. *(978-3-8383-6996-9(3))* Lambert Academic Publishing.

Jackson, Jennifer Lynn. Jaclyn's Gift: Dear God She Prayed. 2008. 136p. pap. 16.95 *(978-1-4327-3697-2(3))* Outskirts Pr., Inc.

Jackson MBA, Sharon Wright. Strands of Black Pearls, 1 vol. 2010. 52p. pap. 16.95 *(978-1-4489-5504-6(1))* PublishAmerica, Inc.

Jackson-Perry, Cheryl. The Holy Spirit in You. 2008. 140p. pap. 14.95 *(978-0-615-20232-7(2))* Chanelco Publishing Co.

Jacobs, Alan. When Jesus Lived in India: The Quest for the Aquarian Gospel - The Mystery of the Missing Years. 2009. (ENG.). 224p. pap. 19.95 *(978-1-906787-29-5(8)*, Watkins Publishing) Duncan Baird Pubs. GBR. Dist: Sterling Publishing Co., Inc.

Jacobs, Andre. Why the Bible Cannot Be the Word of God. 2011. 116p. 23.23 ***(978-1-4567-2275-3(1))***; pap. 16.95 ***(978-1-4567-2276-0(X))*** AuthorHouse.

Jacobsen, Douglas. The World's Christians: Who They Are, Where They Are, & How They Got There. 2011. (ENG., Illus.). 416p. 94.95 *(978-1-4051-8889-0(8))*; pap. 39.95 *(978-1-4051-8887-6(1))* Wiley, John & Sons, Inc. (Wiley-Blackwell).

Jakes, T. D. The T. D. Jakes Relationship Bible: Life Lessons on Relationships from the Inspired Word of God. 2011. (ENG., Illus.). 1584p. 39.99 *(978-1-4391-7278-0(1)*, Beyond Words/Atria Bks.) Atria Bks.

—64 Lessons for a Life Without Limits. 2011. (ENG.). 256p. 13.99 *(978-1-4516-2524-0(3)*, Beyond Words/Atria Bks.) Atria Bks.

James, Gatty. Prayers 'n' the Hood: The Scope of God, His Answering of Prayers & Hoods in the Americas. 2007. per. 14.95 *(978-0-9786872-0-5(5))* James Management Consulting, Inc.

James, Loren. The Cross Was Hell. 2006. pap. 14.95 *(978-0-9785845-1-1(1)*, 24) Loving Fire Publishing.

Janes, Lewis G. A Study of Primitive Christianity. 2009. 324p. 32.99 *(978-1-116-21918-0(2))*; 324p. pap. 30.75 *(978-1-116-21919-7(0))*; 324p. pap. 29.75 *(978-1-116-21920-3(4))*; (ENG.). 322p. pap. 23.99 *(978-1-116-21922-7(0)*, BiblioLife); (ENG.). 322p. pap. 24.99 *(978-1-116-21921-0(2)*, BiblioLife) BiblioBazaar.

Jarrell, Michael. I Hate Religion. 2011. (ENG.). 112p. 15.95 ***(978-1-936417-27-8(8))*** Pilot Communications Group, Inc.

Jean, Lois. Stepping Out in Faith. 2009. 56p. pap. 12.79 *(978-0-557-06484-7(8))* Lulu Enterprises Inc.

Jen, Dixson. Christianity & Me What You Need to Kn. 2007. 376p. pap. 19.95 *(978-1-4327-0043-0(X))* Outskirts Pr., Inc.

Jenkins, Bervin. The Art of Warfare: The Battle Series. 2011. 66p. 24.99 ***(978-1-4628-2988-0(0))***; pap. 15.99 ***(978-1-4628-2987-3(2))*** Xlibris Corp.

Jenkins, Philip. The Next Christendom: The Coming of Global Christianity, 1 vol. 3rd ed. 2011. (ENG., Illus.). 400p. pap. 15.95 *(978-0-19-976746-5(7))* Oxford Univ. Pr., Inc.

Jensen, John W. It's All about Jesus. 2008. 108p. pap. 19.95 *(978-1-60703-524-4(3))* PublishAmerica, Inc.

Jeong, Yang-Cun. Koreanische Immigrationsgemeinden in der Bundesrepublik Deutschland: Die Entstehung, Entwicklung und Zukunft der koreanischen protestantischen Immigrationsgemeinden in der Bundesrepublik Deutschland Seit 1963. 2008. (IC - Studien zur interkulturellen Geschichte des Christentums. Etudes d'histoire interculturelle de christianisme. Studies in the Intercultural History of Christianity Ser.). (GER.). 250p. pap. 65.95 *(978-3-631-57713-4(3))* Lang, Peter GmbH, Europaischer Verlag der Wissenschaften DEU. Dist: Lang, Peter.

Jersak, Bradley. Her Gates Will Never Be Shut. 2009. 234p. pap. 26.00 *(978-1-60608-882-1(3)*, Wipf and Stock) Wipf & Stock Pubs.

, Jerusalem, Jerusalem. Seven Years close to the Lord. 2009. 170p. pap. 19.95 *(978-0-557-06925-5(4))* Lulu Enterprises Inc.

Jinarajadasa, C. Christ & Buddha & Other Sketches. 2007. (ENG.). 108p. 34.95 *(978-0-548-00671-9(7))* Kessinger Publishing, LLC.

Jinkins, Michael. Called to Be Human: Letters to My Children on Living a Christian Life. 2009. 160p. pap. 15.00 *(978-0-8028-6300-3(0))* Eerdmans, William B. Publishing Co.

John Paul II, pseud. Cert Aspect Celebr Sac Penance. 16p. pap. 1.95 *(978-0-8198-4821-5(2)*, 332-212) Pauline Bks. & Media.

—Dawn of a New Era. 32p. pap. *(978-0-8198-6949-4(X)*, 332-320) Pauline Bks. & Media.

Johnson, Dale A. Jesus on the Silk Road. 2008. 125p. pap. 18.50 *(978-1-4357-3986-4(8))* Lulu Enterprises Inc.

Johnson, Elias Henry. The Religious Use of Imagination. 2009. 240p. 23.99 *(978-0-559-95916-5(8))*; pap. 17.99 *(978-0-559-95915-8(X))* BiblioBazaar.

—The Religious Use of Imagination. 2007. (ENG.). 234p. 41.95 *(978-0-548-15750-3(2))*; pap. 26.95 *(978-1-4304-5237-9(4))* Kessinger Publishing, LLC.

Johnson, Elizabeth A. & Johnson. Quest for the Living God: Mapping Frontiers in the Theology of God. 2007. (ENG., Illus.). 248p. 27.95 *(978-0-8264-1770-1(1))* Continuum International Publishing Group, Ltd. GBR. Dist: National Bk. Network.

Johnson, Franklyn Tyrone. Lessons Learned: Along Life's River. 2010. 252p. pap. 15.99 *(978-1-4520-5892-4(X))* AuthorHouse.

Johnson, Galen. Prisoner of Conscience: John Bunyan on Self, Community, & Christian Faith. 2007. (Studies in Christian History & Thought: Ser.). 260p. pap. 27.00 *(978-1-59752-094-2(2)*, Wipf and Stock) Wipf & Stock Pubs.

Johnson, Jeffrey D. The Descent of God: The Ancient Message: Exodus 19, 20. 2007. 20p. pap. 3.00 *(978-1-55635-078-8(3)*, Wipf and Stock) Wipf & Stock Pubs.

—The Silent God: Why God Does Not Speak. 2007. 12p. pap. 2.00 *(978-1-55635-077-1(5)*, Wipf and Stock) Wipf & Stock Pubs.

Johnson, Melissa Z. Healing Bible Ointments & Perfumes Just for You. 2011. 88p. pap. 28.17 ***(978-1-4269-6211-0(8))*** Trafford Publishing.

Johnson, Steve. Atlas of Global Christianity. Johnson, Todd M. & Ross, Kenneth R., eds. 2010. (ENG., Illus.). 400p. (gr. 17). 250.00 *(978-0-7486-3267-1(0))* Edinburgh Univ. Pr. GBR. Dist: Columbia Univ. Pr.

Johnson, Teresa Ann. The God, Who Hears. 2010. 132p. pap. 14.99 *(978-1-60957-658-5(6))* Xulon Pr., Inc.

Johnstone, Patrick. The Future of the Global Church: History, Trends, & Possibilities. 2011. (ENG.). 256p. 39.99 ***(978-1-60657-132-3(X))*** Authentic Media.

Jón Hnefill Aðalsteinsson & Jakob S. Jónsson. Hið Mystíska X. 2009. (ICE., Illus.). 280p. pap. *(978-9979-54-842-3(8))* Haskolautgafan.

Jonas, Glenn & Lopez, Kathryn. Christianity: A Biblical, Historical, & Theological Guide for Students. 2010. (Illus.). 320p. pap. 35.00 *(978-0-88146-204-3(7))* Mercer Univ. Pr.

Jonas, Hensworth W. C. Dancing with Idolatry. 2009. 148p. pap. 14.99 *(978-1-60791-731-1(9))* Xulon Pr., Inc.

Jones, David A. A Biblical Guide to Caregiving. 2011. 284p. pap. 24.99 ***(978-1-4583-9600-6(2))*** Lulu Enterprises Inc.

Jones, Joshua H. Biblical Truth & Outdoor Lies: Devotions for the Christian Outdoorsman. 2007. 236p. pap. 21.95 *(978-1-4303-2265-8(9))* Lulu Enterprises Inc.

Jones, L. Gregory & Musekura, Célestin. Forgiving As We've Been Forgiven: Community Practices for Making Peace. 2010. (Resources for Reconciliation Ser.). (ENG.). 140p. pap. 15.00 *(978-0-8308-3455-6(9)*, IVP Bks.) InterVarsity Pr.

Jones, Paul E. Being a Gay Christian in a Hostile World. 2010. 54p. pap. 12.00 *(978-0-557-06315-4(9))* Lulu Enterprises Inc.

Jones, Robert A. Turning the World Right Side Up: Claiming the Earth for Christ. 2011. 92p. pap. 11.95 *(978-1-4502-7967-3(8))* iUniverse, Inc.

Jones, Toby. The Way of Jesus: Re-Forming Spiritual Communities in a Post-Church Age. 2010. 154p. pap. 18.00 *(978-1-60899-152-5(0)*, Resource Pubns.) Wipf & Stock Pubs.

Jordan, David J. An Offering of Wine - an Introductory Exploration of the Role of Wine in the Hebrew Bible & Ancient Judaism Through the Examination of the Semantics. 2008. 232p. per. *(978-3-8364-3508-6(X))* VDM Verlag Dr. Mueller e.K.

Jordan, David Starr. The Religion of a Sensible American. 2009. 48p. pap. *(978-0-217-84597-7(5))* Books LLC.

—The Religion of a Sensible American. 2007. (ENG.). 84p. per. 17.95 *(978-1-4304-4301-8(4))* Kessinger Publishing, LLC.

Jorgensen, Jonas Adelin. Jesus Imandars & Christ Bhaktas: Two Case Studies of Interreligious Hermeneutics & Identity in Global Christianity. 2008. xii, 481p. pap. 107.95 *(978-3-631-58486-6(5))* Lang, Peter GmbH, Europaischer Verlag der Wissenschaften DEU. Dist: Lang, Peter.

Josephus, Flavius. Collected Works of Flavius Josephus. 2008. 180p. 25.99 *(978-0-554-27846-9(4))* 2008. 180p. 22.99 *(978-0-554-37149-8(9))* 2007. (ENG.). 156p. pap. 19.99 *(978-1-4346-4125-0(2))* BiblioBazaar.

Jowah, Larry Enoch. Righteousness by Faith. 2007. 120p. per. 19.95 *(978-1-4241-0021-7(6))* PublishAmerica, Inc.

Joyner, Rick. The Power to Change the World: The Welsh & Azusa Street Revivals. 2006. 208p. per. 8.99 *(978-1-929371-72-3(1))* MorningStar Pubns., Inc.

Juan, Ellen Li. Intangible Inheritance: A Lyrical Memoir. 2011. 98p. 38.95 ***(978-1-258-08761-6(8))*** Literary Licensing, LLC.

Judge, Mark. A Tremor of Bliss: Sex, Catholicism, & Rock 'n' Roll. 2010. (ENG.). 208p. pap. 14.00 *(978-0-385-51920-5(6)*, Doubleday Religion) Doubleday Religious Publishing Group, The.

Jumpa, James J. Does It Really Happen This Way. 2008. 248p. pap. 14.99 *(978-1-60647-322-1(0))* Xulon Pr., Inc.

Just Call Me Bob: The Wit & Wisdom of Robert W. Funk. 2007. (Illus.). 199p. per. 20.00 *(978-1-59815-005-6(7))* Polebridge Pr.

K.Champlin, Miriam. Constant Fellowship: A Handbook on Scripture Meditation. 2011. pap. 12.99 ***(978-1-61346-145-7(3))*** Tate Publishing & Enterprises, LLC.

Kagoya, Miria. The Christian Concept of God in Ugand. 2010. 96p. pap. *(978-3-639-22748-2(4))* VDM Verlag Dr. Mueller e.K.

Kaiser, Robert Blair. A Church in Search of Itself: Benedict XVI & the Battle for the Future. 2007. (Vintage Ser.). (ENG., Illus.). 304p. pap. 13.95 *(978-0-307-27814-2(X)*, Vintage) Knopf Doubleday Publishing Group.

Kallestad, Walt & Cole, Shawn-Marie. Reign Down: Change Your Life Through the Gift of Repentance. 2008. (ENG.). 272p. 18.99 *(978-1-4165-6271-9(0)*, Howard Bks.) Howard Books.

Kalu, Ogbu. African Christianity: An African Story. 2007. *(978-1-59221-580-5(7))*; 480p. pap. *(978-1-59221-581-2(5))* Africa World Pr.

—African Pentacostalism. 2008. (ENG., Illus.). 352p. 99.00 *(978-0-19-534000-6(0))* Oxford Univ. Pr., Inc.

—African Pentecostalism: An Introduction. 2008. (ENG., Illus.). 352p. pap. 24.95 *(978-0-19-533999-4(1))* Oxford Univ. Pr., Inc.

Kalu, Ogbu, et al. African Christianity: Mission, Ferment, & Trauma. 2010. *(978-1-59221-776-2(1))*; 694p. pap. *(978-1-59221-777-9(X))* Africa World Pr.

Kalu, Ogbu U. & Low, Alaine, eds. Interpreting Contemporary Christianity: Global Processes & Local Identities. 2008. 368p. pap. 45.00 *(978-0-8028-6242-6(X))* Eerdmans, William B. Publishing Co.

Kampmann, Eric. Signposts: A Devotional. 2010. pap. 15.95 *(978-1-935071-30-3(0))* WND Bks, Inc.

Kandiah, Krish & Kandiah, Miriam. How to Save A Life: Understanding the Cross. 2009. (Exploring Christianity Ser.). (ENG.). 48p. mass mkt. 3.99 *(978-1-85078-821-8(9))* Authentic Media.

Kangosa, Guy-Angelo. Die Bedeutung der Jesaja-Zitate für die lukanische Christologie: Eine exegetische Untersuchung mit Ausblick auf den afrikanischen Kontext. 2008. (Europäische Hochschulschriften. Reihe 23: Theologie Ser.). 240p. pap. 61.95 *(978-3-631-57686-1(2))* Lang, Peter GmbH, Europaischer Verlag der Wissenschaften DEU. Dist: Lang, Peter.

Kania, Walter. A Credible Christianity. 2010. 204p. 26.99 *(978-1-4520-2831-6(1))* AuthorHouse.

—A Credible Christianity: Saving Jesus from the Church. 2010. 208p. pap. 16.99 *(978-1-4520-2832-3(X))* AuthorHouse.

Kapfer, Richard. And God Said... A Christian Study of Ecology & the Care of God's Creation. pap. 3.99 *(978-0-570-09347-3(3)*, 20-2403) Concordia Publishing Hse.

Karchner, Roberta. Growing Wings - Lessons for Earthbound Christians. 2011. 108p. 28.95 ***(978-1-4497-2632-4(1))***; pap. 11.95 ***(978-1-4497-2631-7(3))*** Author Solutions, Inc. (WestBow Pr.).

Kasomo, Daniel W. African Spirituality: An Introduction. 2011. 256p. pap. ***(978-3-8443-3071-7(2))*** Lambert Academic Publishing.

Kay, David. The Semitic Religions - Hebrew, Jewish, Christian & Moslem. 2008. 228p. *(978-1-4437-3262-8(1))* 2007. 224p. per. *(978-1-4067-8844-0(9))* Read Bks. (Pomona Pr.).

Keen, Ralph. Christian Tradition. 2008. (ENG.). 400p. pap. 64.95 *(978-0-7425-6089-5(9))* Rowman & Littlefield Publishers, Inc.

Keller, Timothy. The Prodigal God. 2011. (ENG.). 176p. (gr. 12). 14.00 *(978-1-59448-402-5(3)*, Riverhead Trade (Paperbacks)) Penguin Group (USA) Inc.

—The Prodigal God: Finding Your Place at the Table. 2009. (ENG.). 80p. pap. 9.99 *(978-0-310-32536-9(6))* Zondervan.

—The Prodigal God: Recovering the Heart of the Christian Faith. 2008. (ENG.). 160p. (gr. 12-18). 19.95 *(978-0-525-95079-0(6)*, Dutton Adult) Penguin Group (USA) Inc.

—The Prodigal God Curriculum Kit: Finding Your Place at the Table, 1 vol. 2009. (ENG.). pap. 54.99 *(978-0-310-32075-3(5))* Zondervan.

Kemp, Bishop Otis L. Walking with God. 2010. 48p. pap. 15.99 *(978-1-4415-7230-1(9))* Xlibris Corp.

Kennedy, Darren. Providence & Personalism: Karl Barth in Conversation with Austin Farrerm John Macmurray & Vincent Brümmer. 2011. (Illus.). 328p. pap. 68.95 ***(978-3-0343-0735-2(7))*** Lang, Peter AG GBR. Dist: Lang, Peter.

Kennedy, David M. You Voted for Who? And You Call Yourself A Christian? 2011. 135p. 29.95 ***(978-0-9828950-7-8(0))*** Entry Way Publishing.

Kennedy, Philip. Christianity: An Introduction. 2011. (I. B. Tauris Introductions to Religion Ser.). (ENG., Illus.). 288p. 85.00 *(978-1-84885-382-9(3))*; pap. 25.00 *(978-1-84885-383-6(1))* I. B. Tauris & Co., Ltd. GBR. Dist: Macmillan.

Kennedy, W. H. The Last Great War. 2011. 112p. pap. 11.95 *(978-1-4497-1405-5(6)*, WestBow Pr.) Author Solutions, Inc.

Kensky, Meira. Trying Man, Trying God: The Divine Courtroom in Early Jewish & Christian Literature. 2010. (Illus.). 392p. pap. 157.50 *(978-3-16-150409-9(7))* Mohr Siebeck GmbH & Co. KG DEU. Dist: Coronet Bks.

Kerrigan, Jason. Restoring the Biblical Christ Is Jesus. 2007. 272p. 27.95 *(978-1-4327-0369-1(2))* Outskirts Pr., Inc.

Kevin W. Shorter. Church Search: How to Get Your Ministry to Show up in Search Engines. 2010. (Illus.). 80p. pap. 9.95 *(978-1-4497-0107-9(8)*, WestBow Pr.) Author Solutions, Inc.

Khek Gee Lim, Francis, ed. Christianity in Contemporary China. 2012. (ENG., Illus.). 272p. (C). 145.00 ***(978-0-415-52846-7(1))*** Routledge.

Kilpatrick, Bob & Kilpatrick, Joel. The Art of Being You: How to Live as God's Masterpiece, 1 vol. 2010. (ENG.). 224p. 18.99 *(978-0-310-32544-4(7))* Zondervan.

Kim, Heup Young, et al, eds. Asian & Oceanic Christianities in Conversation: Exploring Theological Identities at Home & in Diaspora. 2011. (ENG., Illus.). 239p. pap. 67.00 *(978-90-420-3298-9(7))* Rodopi.

Kim, Kirsteen, et al. Christianity as World Religion. 2008. (ENG., Illus.). 282p. 39.95 *(978-0-8264-9841-0(8))* Continuum International Publishing Group, Ltd. GBR. Dist: National Bk. Network.

King, Henry Churchill. Letters on the Greatness & Simplicity of the Christian Faith. 2009. 208p. 23.99 *(978-1-103-91817-1(6))*; pap. 17.99 *(978-1-103-91811-9(7))* BiblioBazaar.

—Letters on the Greatness & Simplicity of the Christian Faith. 2007. (ENG.). 208p. 39.95 *(978-0-548-15236-2(5))*; per. 24.95 *(978-1-4304-4603-3(X))* Kessinger Publishing, LLC.

King, Michael Lee. The Greatest Mystery Ever Revealed: The Mystery of the Will of God: the Image of God. Book 1. 2011. 152p. pap. 15.04 ***(978-1-4634-1237-1(1))*** AuthorHouse.

—The Greatest Mystery Ever Revealed: the Mystery of the Will of God: Growing in Grace. Book 2. 2011. 268p. pap. 15.95 ***(978-1-4634-1250-0(9))*** AuthorHouse.

Kingdom Scribes Publishing. A Letter to the Angels: A Guide to the Future Direction of the Church. 2007. 101p. pap. 12.99 *(978-0-9797134-2-2(0))* Kingdom Scribes Publishing, LLC.

—Stay in Your Lane: Understanding Gifts & Offices. 2007. 75p. pap. 11.99 *(978-0-9797134-1-5(2))* Kingdom Scribes Publishing, LLC.

Kingsford, Anna. The Hermetic Kabbalah of Anna Kingsford. 2007. 231p. pap. 26.50 *(978-1-84753-313-5(2))* Lulu Enterprises Inc.

Kinnamon, Michael, ed. Together We Pray. 2006. 400p. pap. 28.00 *(978-2-8254-1360-9(7))* World Council of Churches/Conseil Oecumenique des Eglises CHE. Dist: International Specialized Bk. Services.

Kisau, Mumo P. Inclusiveness of Christianity. 2010. 252p. pap. *(978-3-8383-5046-2(4))* Lambert Academic Publishing.

Kizilos, Tolly. God & the Problem of Evil. 2008. 100p. pap. 9.95 *(978-1-4357-1272-0(2))* Lulu Enterprises Inc.

Klick, Jeffrey A. Generational Impact: A Vision for the Family. 2011. pap. 13.99 *(978-1-61739-536-9(6))* Tate Publishing & Enterprises, LLC.

Klopper, Maki. Your Godly Standing Place. 2010. 126p. pap. 19.99 *(978-1-4535-3594-3(2))* Xlibris Corp.

Kloster, John. Tomorrow's Christian Church, 1 vol. 2009. 140p. pap. 24.95 *(978-1-4489-2000-6(0))* PublishAmerica, Inc.

Knepp, Judy. Unite My Heart: A hands-on approach to wholeness & Deliverance. 2010. pap. 17.99 *(978-1-61663-200-7(3))* Tate Publishing & Enterprises, LLC.

Knight, George R. The Apocalyptic Vision & the Neutering of Adventism. 2008. pap. 10.99 *(978-0-8280-2385-6(9))* Review & Herald Publishing Assn.

Knight, Sherrie C. The Dividing Line: The Difference Between Discernment & Deception. 2011. 164p. 30.95 *(978-1-4497-1140-5(5))*; pap. 13.95 *(978-1-4497-1138-2(3))* Author Solutions, Inc. (WestBow Pr.).

Knippel, Charles T. Self-righteousness: Our Greatest Danger. 2007. 147p. pap. 11.50 *(978-0-615-15879-2(X))* Knippel, Charles T.

Knowles, Denell A. Defining Moment: A Faith Tested. 2008. pap. 9.99 *(978-1-60647-164-7(3))* Xulon Pr., Inc.

Knysh, Alexander D., et al. Judaism, Christianity, & Islam: A Sourcebook. rev. ed. 2007. (ENG.). 398p. pap. 33.80 *(978-0-7575-4764-5(8))* Kendall Hunt Publishing Co.

Koch, Andrew M. & Gates, Paul Henry. Medieval America: Cultural Influences of Christianity in the Law & Public Policy. 2012. ***(978-0-7391-7283-4(2))*** Lexington Bks.

Kodl-Squires, Ellen. Messages from Above: Christian Inspirational Verse to Uplift You, 1 vol. 2010. 115p. pap. 19.95 *(978-1-60474-281-7(X))* PublishAmerica, Inc.

Koehler, Edward W. A. A Summary of Christian Doctrine. 2nd rev. ed. 352p. 26.99 *(978-0-570-03860-3(X)*, 12-2813) Concordia Publishing Hse.

Koepping. World Christianity. 2010. 1600p. 1295.00 *(978-0-415-46827-5(2))*; Vol. 1. 400p. *(978-0-415-47291-3(1))*; Vol. 2. 400p. *(978-0-415-47290-6(3))*; Vol. 3. 400p. *(978-0-415-47289-0(X))*; Vol. 4. 400p. *(978-0-415-47288-3(1))* Routledge.

Kohler, Eike. MIT Absicht: Rhetorisch: Seelsorge in der Gemeinschaft der Kirche. 2006. (Arbeiten zur Pastoraltheologie, Liturgik und Hymnologie Ser.). (GER., Illus.). 320p. (C). pap. 84.00 *(978-3-525-62389-3(5))* Vandenhoeck & Ruprecht GmbH & Co. KG DEU. Dist: ISD.

Kolbell, Erik. The God of Second Chances. 2008. (ENG.). 143p. pap. 15.00 *(978-0-664-23122-4(5))* Westminster John Knox Pr.

Kolini, Emmanuel M. & Holmes, Peter R. Christ Walks Where Evil Reigned: Responding to the Rwandan Genocide. 2008. (ENG.). 218p. per. 16.99 *(978-1-934068-41-0(1))* Authentic Media.

Kollar, Charles A. Solution-Focused Pastoral Conseling: An Effective Short-Term Approach for Getting People Back on Track, 1 vol. ed. 2011. (ENG.). 272p. 24.99 *(978-0-310-32929-9(9))* Zondervan.

Koncel, Ed. Views from the Pew, Pulpit & Women Religious. 2010. 166p. 29.99 *(978-1-4535-3691-9(4))*; pap. 19.99 *(978-1-4535-3690-2(6))* Xlibris Corp.

Kosanke, Monsignor Charles G. & Watson Manhardt, Laurie. Come & See: Isaiah. 2011. 221p. 19.95 ***(978-1-931018-75-3(8))*** Emmaus Road Publishing.

Kosicki, George W. Now Is the Time for Mercy. 2011. (Illus.). 122p. pap. 14.95 ***(978-1-59614-232-9(4))*** Marian Pr.

Kozelsky, Mara. Christianizing Crimea: Shaping Sacred Space in the Russian Empire & Beyond. 2009. (ENG., Illus.). 288p. 42.00 *(978-0-87580-412-5(8))* Northern Illinois Univ. Pr.

Kozyra, Anna. How I Was Grafted In: Your Personal Journal Recording Your Christian Legacy... Past, Present & Future. 2011. 68p. pap. 13.95 ***(978-1-4497-2966-0(5)***, WestBow Pr.) Author Solutions, Inc.

Kramer, Mark A. A Stir in the Waters. 2011. 292p. 26.99 *(978-1-61215-902-7(8))*; pap. 16.99 *(978-1-61215-901-0(X))* Xulon Pr., Inc.

Kreider, Alan. The Change of Conversion & the Origin of Christendom. 2007. 142p. pap. 18.00 *(978-1-55635-393-2(6)*, Wipf and Stock) Wipf & Stock Pubs.

Kronen, John & Reitan, Eric. God's Final Victory: A Comparative Philosophical Case for Universalism. 2011. (Continuum Studies in Philosophy of Religion Ser.). (ENG.). 256p. 120.00 ***(978-1-4411-3065-5(9))*** Continuum International Publishing Group, Ltd. GBR. Dist: National Bk. Network.

Kubilus, Derek & Priebe, Jonathan. The Real War on Terror: Waging Holy War in the Peaceful Kingdom. 2007. 126p. pap. 16.00 *(978-1-55635-153-2(4)*, Wipf and Stock) Wipf & Stock Pubs.

Kugler, Chris. Being Christian: A Journey from the Boat to the Shore, Culminating at the Cross. 2011. 120p. 28.95 ***(978-1-4497-2177-0(X))***; pap. 11.95 ***(978-1-4497-2176-3(1))*** Author Solutions, Inc. (WestBow Pr.).

Kuhn, Alvin Boyd. A Rebirth for Christianity: The Spiritual Meaning of Christ. 2nd ed. 2008. (ENG.). 280p. pap. 14.95 *(978-0-8356-0838-1(7)*, Quest Bks.) Theosophical Publishing Hse.

Kujur, Joseph Marianus & Robinson, Rowena, eds. Margins of Faith: Dalit & Tribal Christianity in India. 2010. 320p. (C). 39.95 *(978-81-321-0467-4(6)*, B04674C) SAGE Pubns., Inc.

Küng, Hans. Disputed Truth Vol. 2: Memoirs, Volume 2. 2008. (ENG., Illus.). 576p. 34.95 *(978-0-8264-9910-3(4))* Continuum International Publishing Group, Ltd. GBR. Dist: National Bk. Network.

Kurian, George Thomas, ed. The Encyclopedia of Christian Civilization, 4 vols., Vol. 4 Set. 2012. (ENG., Illus.). 2790p. 595.00 *(978-1-4051-5762-9(3)*, Wiley-Blackwell) Wiley, John & Sons, Inc.

—Nelson's Dictionary of Christianity: The Authoritative Resource on the Christian World, 0 vols. 2009. 784p. pap. 27.99 *(978-1-4185-3228-4(2))* Nelson, Thomas Inc.

Kurts, Paul. Trinitarian Letters: Your Adoption & Inclusion in the Life of God. 2011. 248p. pap. 19.95 *(978-1-4497-0940-2(0)*, WestBow Pr.) Author Solutions, Inc.

Kusema, Wellingtone Garati. The Believers' Companion: A Concise Topical Handbook on Doctrine in the African Apostolic Church. 2011. 410p. pap. 14.99 ***(978-0-9557546-1-6(5))*** Heritage Pr.

Kwenda, Nina E. Hurt No More America! 2010. 314p. pap. 15.99 *(978-1-60957-500-7(8))* Xulon Pr., Inc.

Lackey, P. R. The Tyranny of the Trinity: The Orthodox Cover-up. 2008. 408p. pap. 17.99 *(978-1-4343-0711-8(5))* AuthorHouse.

Lackner, Joseph H. Virtues for Mission. 90p. pap. 3.00 *(978-0-9704376-4-8(1))* North American Ctr. for Marianist Studies.

Lagarde, Paul de. Collected Works. 2010. (GRE & LAT.). 265.92 *(978-1-61719-026-1(8))*; 265.92 *(978-1-61719-028-5(4))*; 265.92 *(978-1-61719-027-8(6))* Gorgias Pr., LLC.

Laidacker, Wayne. What Part of Christianity Don't You Understand. 2011. 108p. 21.23 ***(978-1-4520-4541-2(0))***; pap. 10.99 ***(978-1-4520-4540-5(2))*** AuthorHouse.

Laizure, Robert & Laizure, Lisa. Jesus said WHAT? What He said it means to follow Him... 2007. pap. 13.99 *(978-1-60266-829-4(9))* Xulon Pr., Inc.

Lake, S. D. The Pagans Are Revolting. 2010. 128p. 23.95 *(978-1-4502-4391-9(6))*; pap. 13.95 *(978-1-4502-4389-6(4))* iUniverse, Inc.

Lambert, Malcolm. Christians & Pagans: The Conversion of Britain from Alban to Bede. 2010. (ENG., Illus.). 336p. 50.00 *(978-0-300-11908-4(9))* Yale Univ. Pr.

Landers, Macon. Revival. 2009. pap. 11.99 *(978-1-60696-305-0(8))* Tate Publishing & Enterprises, LLC.

Landon, William. Leviathan: The relation between organized religion & Christianity. 2007. 256p. per. 19.95 *(978-0-595-44582-0(9))* iUniverse, Inc.

Landy, Francis. Hosea. 2011. 230p. pap. ***(978-1-905048-99-1(8))*** Sheffield Phoenix Pr.

Lane, Donna E. & Lane, Hayden J. Restored Christianity. 2007. 252p. pap. 20.95 *(978-1-59299-296-6(X))* Inkwater Pr.

Lane, Thomas B. Reading & Understanding the Gospels: Who Jesus Is, What He Teaches, & the Beginning of Christianity. 2011. 584p. pap. 27.95 ***(978-1-4327-6823-2(9))*** Outskirts Pr., Inc.

Langford, Thomas A. The Christian Academic: Exercising Faith in the University Setting. 2007. 328p. pap. 16.95 *(978-0-9789908-5-5(4))* Ketch Publishing.

Laniak, Timothy S. Finding the Lost Images of God: Uncover the Ancient Culture, Discover Hidden Meanings, 1 vol. 2012. (Ancient Context, Ancient Faith Ser.). (ENG.). 128p. pap. 14.99 *(978-0-310-32474-4(2))* Zondervan.

Larue, Joseph. Handbook for the Saints. 2011. 108p. pap. 16.95 ***(978-1-58275-311-9(3))*** Aaron Bk. Publishing.

Lateer, Andrew James. Maranatha: Biblical Prophecy about the End of the Age in Plain English. 2011. 320p. 37.95 ***(978-1-4497-2717-8(4))***; pap. 22.95 ***(978-1-4497-2716-1(6))*** Author Solutions, Inc. (WestBow Pr.).

Lathem, Warren. Our Father... I Believe. 2010. 111p. pap. 12.00 *(978-0-557-44161-7(7))* Lulu Enterprises Inc.

Lauck, Jon K. Prairie Republic: The Political Culture of Dakota Territory, 1879-1889. 2010. (ENG.). 256p. (C). 32.95 *(978-0-8061-4110-7(7))* Univ. of Oklahoma Pr.

Laugrand, Frederic & Oosten, Jarich G. Inuit Shamanism & Christianity: Transitions & Transformations in the Twentieth Century. 2010. (McGill-Queen's Native & Northern Ser.). (Illus.). 467p. (C). *(978-0-7735-3589-3(6))*; (ENG., pap. *(978-0-7735-3590-9(X))* McGill-Queen's Univ. Pr.

LaVere, Pastor Tim. You Are Not Autistic! 2008. 73p. pap. 16.95 *(978-1-4241-8688-4(9))* PublishAmerica, Inc.

Law, William. A Practical Treatise upon Christian Perfection. 2009. 200p. pap. *(978-0-217-66512-4(8))* Books LLC.

—A Practical Treatise upon Christian Perfection. 2009. 68p. pap. 14.14 *(978-1-4590-1523-4(1))*; 208p. pap. 19.99 *(978-1-4590-1520-3(7))* General Bks. LLC.

Lawson, Marc. It; S the End of the Church as We Know It: The 166 Factor. 2007. 317p. per. 15.99 *(978-0-7684-2499-7(2))* Destiny Image Pubs.

Leadbeater, C. W. The Christian Creed. 2010. 184p. 37.95 *(978-1-161-35096-8(9))* Kessinger Publishing, LLC.

Leadingham, Everett. Mosaic of Faith: Piecing Together Our Christian Story. 2007. 7.99 *(978-0-8341-2285-7(5))*; pap. 7.50 *(978-0-8341-2286-4(3))* Nazarene Publishing Hse.

Leathers, Chonnette. Die to Live: He Who Has an Ear, Let Him Hear What the Spirit Is Saying to the Church. 2011. pap. 12.99 ***(978-1-61739-960-2(4))*** Tate Publishing & Enterprises, LLC.

Leaves, Nigel. Religion under Attack: Getting Theology Right. 2011. 240p. pap. 20.00 *(978-1-59815-027-8(8))* Polebridge Pr.

LeBlanc, Roger. My Dogma Ran over Your Karm. 2007. 148p. per. 13.99 *(978-1-60266-623-8(7))* Xulon Pr., Inc.

Lee, Samuel. Rediscovering Japan, Reintroducing Christendom: Two Thousand Years of Christian History in Japan. 2010. (ENG.). 210p. pap. 31.50 *(978-0-7618-4949-0(1))* Hamilton Bks.

Lees, Jim. Promise for America. 2010. 154p. pap. 14.99 *(978-1-60957-956-2(9))* Xulon Pr., Inc.

Leftow, Brian. Time & Eternity. 2009. (Cornell Studies in the Philosophy of Religion). 392p. pap. 36.95 *(978-0-8014-7522-1(8))* Cornell Univ. Pr.

Lemler, James. Transforming Congregations. 2008. (Transformations Ser.). 192p. pap. 16.00 *(978-0-89869-584-7(8))* Church Publishing, Inc.

Lennox, John C. God's Undertaker: Has Science Buried God? 2009. (ENG.). 224p. pap. 14.95 *(978-0-7459-5371-7(9))* Lion Hudson PLC GBR. Dist: Independent Pubs. Group.

Lepati, Malibo Don. A Warning to the Christy. 2011. 166p. pap. 8.99 ***(978-1-61667-285-0(4))*** Raider Publishing International.

Leustean, Lucian, ed. Eastern Christianity & the Cold War 1945-91. 2011. (ENG.). 384p. (C). pap. 44.95 ***(978-0-415-67336-5(4))*** Routledge.

—Representing Religion in the European Union. 2012. (Routledge Studies in Religion & Politics Ser.). (ENG., Illus.). 256p. (C). 130.00 ***(978-0-415-68504-7(4))*** Routledge.

Leuze, Reinhard. Das Christentum: Grundriss einer monotheistischen Religion. 2010. (Forschungen Zur Systematischen und Okumenischen Theologie Ser.). (GER.). 204p. (C). 98.00 *(978-3-525-56358-8(2))* Vandenhoeck & Ruprecht GmbH & Co. KG DEU. Dist: ISD.

Lever, A. B. And God Said. 2007. 332p. per. 17.99 *(978-1-60477-115-2(1))* Xulon Pr., Inc.

Lewis, C. S. Mere Christianity Gift Edition. 2012. (ENG.). 320p. 34.99 ***(978-0-06-135021-4(4)***, HarperOne) HarperCollins Pubs.

Lewis, Michael E. A Theology of Suffering & Difficulty: Corporate & Personal Aspects. 2007. 282p. pap. 28.00 *(978-1-59752-993-8(1)*, Wipf and Stock) Wipf & Stock Pubs.

Lewis, R. M. A System for Memorizing God's Word. 2008. 120p. pap. 13.95 *(978-1-4357-0672-9(2))* Lulu Enterprises Inc.

Lian, Xi. Redeemed by Fire: The Rise of Popular Christianity in Modern China. 2010. (ENG., Illus.). 352p. (C). 45.00 *(978-0-300-12339-5(6))* Yale Univ. Pr.

Libby, David J., et al, eds. Affect & Power: Essays on Sex, Slavery, Race, & Religion. 2007. (ENG.). 256p. per. 25.00 *(978-1-934110-33-1(7))* Univ. Pr. of Mississippi.

Life Magazine Editors. Life Jesus: An Illustrated Biography. 2012. (ENG., Illus.). 112p. 29.95 *(978-1-60320-174-2(2))* Time Home Entertainment, Inc.

Lim, Swee Hong. Giving Voice to Asian Christians. 2008. 344p. pap. *(978-3-639-06074-4(1))* VDM Verlag Dr. Mueller e.K.

Lin, Zichun. Duo Yuan Xing Han Yu Shen Xue Quan Shi: A Polyphonic View on Sino-Christian Theology. 2008. *(978-7-80254-081-1(X))* China Religion and Culture Publishing Hse.

Lisle, Jason. Discerning Truth. 2010. pap. 10.99 *(978-0-89051-594-5(8))* Master Bks.

Livingstone, E. A., ed. The Concise Oxford Dictionary of the Christian Church. 2nd rev. ed. 2006. (Oxford Paperback Reference Ser.). (ENG.). 672p. per. 21.95 *(978-0-19-861442-5(X))* Oxford Univ. Pr., Inc.

Lloyd, Enel. Aliens & Men. 2011. 312p. pap. 18.99 *(978-1-61215-921-8(4))* Xulon Pr., Inc.

Lloyd-Jones, Martyn. Magnify the Lord: Luke 14655. 2011. (ENG.). 112p. 9.99 ***(978-1-84550-754-1(1)***, Christian Heritage) Christian Focus Pubns. GBR. Dist: STL Distribution North America.

Locke, Robert T. The Forgotten Blessing. 2007. 248p. per. 24.95 *(978-1-60441-328-1(X))* PublishAmerica, Inc.

Lockhart, Douglas. Going Beyond the Jesus Story: An Examination of Christian Belioef, Mystical Experience & the Ongoing Development of Conscious Awareness. 2011. (ENG.). 391p. pap. 29.95 *(978-1-84694-465-9(1))* Hunt, John Publishing Ltd. GBR. Dist: National Bk. Network.

Logan, F. Donald. A History of the Church in the Middle Ages. 2nd rev. ed. 2012. (ENG., Illus.). 360p. (C). 130.00 *(978-0-415-66993-1(6))*; pap. 37.95 *(978-0-415-66994-8(4))* Routledge.

Loisy, Alfred. The Gospel & the Church. 2012. 116p. pap. 19.75 ***(978-1-277-76070-5(5))*** BiblioBazaar.

—The Gospel & the Church. Home, Christopher, tr. 2010. 312p. 36.76 ***(978-1-164-33826-0(9))*** 2010. 314p. pap. 24.76 ***(978-1-164-02874-1(X))*** 2008. 312p. 45.95 *(978-1-4365-2596-1(9))* 2007. (ENG.). 312p. per. 30.95 *(978-0-548-72950-2(6))* Kessinger Publishing, LLC.

Loisy, Alfred Firmin. The Gospel & the Church. 2012. 302p. pap. 29.75 ***(978-1-278-00855-4(1))*** 2010. 318p. pap. 30.75 *(978-1-148-15741-2(7))* 2010. 322p. pap. 30.75 *(978-1-142-19294-5(6))* 2009. 292p. 30.99 *(978-1-115-82037-0(0))* 2009. 292p. 34.99 *(978-1-115-82036-3(2))* 2009. 292p. pap. 28.75 *(978-1-115-82038-7(9))* 2009. 292p. pap. 27.75 *(978-1-115-82039-4(7))* 2009. (ENG.). 290p. pap. 21.99 *(978-1-115-82041-7(9)*, BiblioLife) BiblioBazaar.

—The Gospel & the Church. 2009. 106p. pap. *(978-0-217-08051-4(0))* Books LLC.

Loisy, Alfred Firmin & Home, Christopher. The Gospel & the Church. 2010. (ENG.). 292p. pap. 28.75 *(978-1-143-97800-5(5))*; (ENG.). 314p. pap. 30.75 *(978-1-177-64144-9(5))*; 292p. pap. 28.75 *(978-1-178-16879-2(4))*; 292p. pap. 28.75 *(978-1-141-00402-7(X))* BiblioBazaar.

Loisy, Alfred Firmin, et al. The Gospel & the Church. 2010. 322p. pap. 30.75 *(978-1-178-22222-7(5))* BiblioBazaar.

Longenecker, Dwight. More Christianity: Finding the Fullness of the Faith - Expanded Revised Edition. 2010. 275p. pap. 16.95 *(978-1-58617-342-5(1))* Ignatius Pr.

Lopez, Raul E. A City Set on A Hill. 2011. 302p. pap. 18.99 *(978-1-61215-804-4(8))* Xulon Pr., Inc.

Lomes, Herman. Salvation Weekly: The Theological Activist. 2011. 180p. pap. 19.99 ***(978-1-4568-9788-8(8))*** Xlibris Corp.

Lotegeluaki, Stanley. Jesus Christ Is Lord & Is Worshipped in Infinite Multiple Universes Throughout Infinity. 2011. 812p. pap. 36.14 *(978-1-4520-9890-6(5))* AuthorHouse.

Lotegeluaki, Stanley O. Africa: Intergalactic Federation of African Tribes: The Christian Kingdom of Jesus Christ. Kush the Land of 10,000 Tribes Swarming Through Space in a Quintillion Universes- the Promised Land. 2011. 784p. pap. 36.14 ***(978-1-4634-1177-0(4))*** AuthorHouse.

Love, Christopher & Kistler, Don. The Natural Man's Condition: A True Map of Man's Miserable Estate by Nature, Considered Either in the State of Nature or Grace. 2010. *(978-0-9826155-0-8(7))* Northampton Pr., The.

Love, Dean. It'll Work If You Work It. 2007. 120p. per. 10.99 *(978-1-60266-484-5(6))* Xulon Pr., Inc.

Lovett, Joseph. The Good News: The World's One True Religion. 2007. pap. 10.00 *(978-0-8059-7902-2(6))* Dorrance Publishing Co., Inc.

Loyd, Roger. Common Sense Christianity, 1 vol. 2009. 48p. pap. 16.95 *(978-1-61546-389-3(5))* PublishAmerica, Inc.

Lucado, Max. It's Not about Me: Rescue from the Life We Thought Would Make Us Happy. 2011. 176p. 18.99 *(978-0-8499-4709-4(X))* Nelson, Thomas Inc.

Lucas, Kemba Jarena. At the Cross Witness Yarn: Winifred's Witness. 2010. 154p. pap. 19.99 *(978-0-557-23122-5(1))* Lulu Enterprises Inc.

—Ten Prayers by A Satisfied Woman: A Prophetic Prayer Collection for Women. 2008. 96p. pap. 17.99 *(978-1-4357-5580-2(4))* Lulu Enterprises Inc.

Ludy, Eric. The Bravehearted Gospel: The Truth Is Worth Fighting For. 2008. 250p. pap. 13.99 *(978-0-7369-2164-0(8))* Harvest Hse. Pubs.

Lukings, Tim. Fruit Loose & Fancy Tree. 2009. 188p. pap. 14.99 *(978-1-60791-600-0(2))* Xulon Pr., Inc.

Lund, James & Jackson, Peb. A Dangerous Faith: True Stories of Answering the Call to Adventure. 2008. (ENG.). 224p. pap. 13.99 *(978-1-4000-7345-0(6))* Doubleday Religious Publishing Group, The.

C

Lynn, David. More High School TalkSheets, Epic Old Testament Stories: 52 Ready-to-Use Discussions, 1 vol. 2012. (TalkSheets Ser.). (ENG.). 128p. pap. 14.99 (978-0-310-88938-0(3)) Zondervan.

Lynn, David & Davis, Rick. 52 Discussions to Confirm the Faith of Your Teenagers, 1 vol. 2009. (TalkSheets Ser.). (ENG.). 128p. pap. 14.99 (978-0-310-66873-2(5)) Zondervan.

Lyons, Gabe & Fermi Project Staff. UnChristian: Change the Perception. 2009. (Society Room Ser.). 70.00 (978-0-8010-0317-2(2)) Baker Bks.

M, Winston. You Have All Been Fooled. 2010. 140p. pap. 12.00 (978-1-60911-618-7(6), Eloquent Bks.) AEG Literary Publishing Services, Inc.

MacDonald. The Thomas Book near Death, a Quest & a New Gospel by the Twin Brother of Jesus. 2010. 254p. 26.50 (978-1-60860-819-5(0), Eloquent Bks.) AEG Literary Publishing Services, Inc.

Mack, Barbara Ann Mary. The Present Testament Volume Five Melodies from Heaven. 2011. 136p. pap. 15.90 (978-1-4634-2188-5(5)) AuthorHouse.

Mack, Burton L. Myth & the Christian Nation: A Social Theory of Religion. 2008. (Religion in Culture: Studies in Social Contest & Construction Ser.). (ENG.). 304p. (C). 99.95 (978-1-84553-372-4(0)); pap. 34.95 (978-1-84553-373-1(9)) Equinox Publishing Ltd. GBR. Dist: ISD.

MacKinnon, Ben. Green Bean Spirituality. 2008. 108p. pap. 10.95 (978-1-59858-842-2(7)) Dog Ear Publishing, LLC.

Macleod, Norman. Parish Papers. 2006. 340p. per. 23.99 (978-1-4255-3414-1(7)) MPublishing.

Macloed, Norman. Parish Papers. 2007. 222p. pap. 20.99 (978-1-4264-6193-4(3)) 2006. (ENG.). 248p. pap. 22.99 (978-1-4264-6248-1(4)) BiblioBazaar.

MacMillan, Robert. When God Calls a Woman. 2011. 330p. pap. 27.05 (978-1-60746-565-2(5)) FastPrncil, Inc.

Maina, Grace. Nun's Daughter. 2010. 262p. pap. 19.99 (978-1-4535-1444-3(9)) Xlibris Corp.

Makwasha, Gift M. The Repression, Resistance, & Revival of the Ancestor Cult in the Shona Churches of Zimbabwe: A Study of the Persistence of a Traditional Religious Belief. 2010. v, 416p. 129.95 (978-0-7734-3682-4(0)) Mellen, Edwin Pr., The.

Mann, Donald C. Discovering Our Redemption. 2011. 576p. 38.99 (978-1-934769-51-5(7)); pap. 29.99 (978-1-934769-50-8(9)) McDougal & Assocs.

Mannion. The Routledge Companion to the Christian Church. 2010. (Routledge Companions Ser.). (ENG.). 704p. (C). pap. 50.00 (978-0-415-56768-8(8)) Routledge.

Manus, Samuel E. Nuggets of Truth. 2011. 140p. pap. 11.95 (978-1-4497-2005-6(6), WestBow Pr.) Author Solutions, Inc.

Maposa, Richard S. 'de-Colonization Extended to African Theology' 2011. 64p. pap. (978-3-8443-9709-3(4)) Lambert Academic Publishing.

Marcus, Cesar Leo. Kabbalah Judeo-Christian the Divine Logic. 2007. 186p. pap. 24.99 (978-1-4303-0826-3(5)) Lulu Enterprises Inc.

Marcus, John. Misconceptions of Christianity: How the Bible Proves All Things. 2010. pap. 18.99 (978-1-61663-739-2(0)) Tate Publishing & Enterprises, LLC.

Mark, Harry. Christians Belong to Israel. 2007. 80p. per. 13.99 (978-1-60266-587-3(7)) Xulon Pr., Inc.

Marti, Kurt, et al. Notizen und Details: 1964-2007. 2010. (GER.). 1422p. (978-3-290-17541-2(3)) Theologischer Verlag Zurich, AG, TVZ.

Martin, Luther & Bach, Eugene. Back to the Jerusalem of Th East: The Underground House Church of North Korea. 2011. mass mkt. 17.99 (978-1-936533-10-7(3)) Fifth Estate, Inc.

Martin, Walter, et al. The Kingdom of the Occult, 0 vols. 2008. 752p. 29.99 (978-1-4185-1644-4(9)) Nelson, Thomas Inc.

Martinez, Naomi Westbrook. God Always Makes Sense: An Illuminating Study of the Book of Job. 2011. pap. 13.99 (978-1-61777-018-0(3)) Tate Publishing & Enterprises, LLC.

Mason, Bernice M. Bible Prophecy Worth Repeating! 2011. 108p. pap. 15.99 (978-1-4568-6585-6(4)) Xlibris Corp.

Mason, Mike. Champagne for the Soul: Celebrating God's Gift of Joy. 2006. (ENG.). 208p. per. (978-1-57383-390-5(8), Regent College Publishing) Regent College Publishing.

Masters, Peter. The Faith: Great Christian Truths. 2006. 119p. per. (978-1-870855-54-9(X)) Wakeman Trust, The.

Mather, Paul, et al. Missional Communities: The Rise of the Post-Congregational Church. 2011. (Jossey-Bass Leadership Network Ser.: 55). (ENG.). 192p. 24.95 (978-0-470-63345-8(X), Jossey-Bass) Wiley, John & Sons, Inc.

Mathews, Aidan. In the Poorer Quarters. 2008. (ENG.). 224p. pap. 23.95 (978-1-84730-027-0(8)) Veritas Pubns. IRL. Dist: Dufour Editions, Inc.

Mathews, Laura Wright. Love Letters to the Beloved: Seven Churches. 2010. 68p. pap. 10.49 (978-1-4520-4494-1(5)) AuthorHouse.

Mathiesen, Gaylan Kent. A Theology of Mission: Examining the Challenges & Opportunities in Northeast Asia. 2007. (ENG.). 224p. pap. 16.00 (978-1-932688-26-9(9), Lutheran Univ. Pr.) Kirk Hse. Pubs.

Matthee, Johan. Christenskap Wetenskap en Die Bybel: 'n moet lees boek vir elke Christen. 2011. 204p. 29.99 (978-1-4568-8835-0(8)); pap. 19.99 (978-1-4568-8834-3(X)) Xlibris Corp.

Mauro, Philip. Champion of Kingdom. pap. 2.99 (978-0-87377-047-7(1)) GAM Pubns.

Maze, Scott. Theodorus Frelinghuysen's Evangelism: Catalyst to the First Great Awakening. 2011. pap. (978-1-60178-123-9(7)) Reformation Heritage Bks.

Mbano, Dunstan M. Ecclesiological Trends in the Catholic & Protestant Churches & Their Significance for the Church in Africa: A Study of Selected Texts. 2008. (Europäische Hochschulschriften. Reihe 23: Theologie Ser.). 324p. pap. 81.95 (978-3-631-58497-2(0)) Lang, Peter GmbH, Europaischer Verlag der Wissenschaften DEU. Dist: Lang, Peter.

McAfee, David G. Disproving Christianity & Other Secular Writings (2nd edition, Revised) 2011. (ENG.). 168p. pap. 13.99 (978-0-9564276-8-7(5)) Dangerous Little Bks. GBR. Dist: Lean Marketing Pr.

McCain, Paul Timothy, ed. Concordia: The Lutheran Confessions. 2011. (ENG.). 1036p. pap. 44.99 (978-0-7586-3063-6(8)) Concordia Publishing Hse.

McCarroll, Thomas. Secrets of the Cults. 2009. 206p. 25.50 (978-1-60693-958-1(0), Eloquent Bks.) AEG Literary Publishing Services, Inc.

McClendon, Phillip. Reflections. 2010. 158p. 29.99 (978-1-4535-0482-6(6)); pap. 19.99 (978-1-4535-0481-9(8)) Xlibris Corp.

McCosh, James. The Method of the Divine Government: Physical & Moral. 2nd ed. 2009. (Cambridge Library Collection - Religion Ser.). 556p. pap. 39.99 (978-1-108-00414-5(8)) Cambridge Univ. Pr.

McCracken, John. Politics & Christianity in Malawi 1875-1940 3rd Edition: The Impact of the Livingstonia Mission in the Northern Province. 3rd ed. 2008. 380p. pap. (978-99908-87-50-1(0)) Kachere Series, Bks. on Religion, Theology & Society in Malawi MWI. Dist: Michigan State Univ. Pr.

McDermott, Jerry. A Gilded Walk: The Path to Heaven. 2010. 184p. (ENG.). 26.95 (978-1-4502-1693-7(5)); pap. 16.95 (978-1-4502-1691-3(9)) iUniverse, Inc.

McDonald, Lee Martin, ed. 'Noncanonical' Religious Texts in Early Judaism & Early Christianity. 2012. (Jewish & Christian Text Ser.). (ENG.). 264p. 120.00 (978-0-567-12419-7(3), T&T Clark Int'l) Continuum International Publishing Group, Ltd. GBR. Dist: National Bk. Network.

McDowell, Josh. Is Christ Really God? Adult Group 8 Session. ldr.'s ed. 2007. 125p. 17.99 (978-1-932587-96-8(9)) Green Key Bks.

—Is Christ Really God? Adult Group DVD 5 Part. ldr.'s ed. 2007. 65p. 9.99 (978-1-932587-97-5(7)) Green Key Bks.

—Is Christ Really God? Youth DVD 5 Part. ldr.'s ed. 2007. 65p. (YA). (978-1-60098-000-8(7)) Green Key Bks.

—Is Christ Really God? Youth Group 8 Session. ldr.'s ed. 2007. 125p. (YA). 17.99 (978-1-932587-99-9(3)) Green Key Bks.

McDowell, Josh, et al. O God: A Dialogue on Truth & Oprah's Spirituality. 2009. 128p. pap. 14.99 (978-1-935071-17-4(3)) WND Bks, Inc.

McFall-Perkins, Betty Lou. A Heap of Broken Vessels. 2006. 37p. pap. 8.95 (978-0-7414-3502-6(0)) Infinity Publishing.

McFarland, Ken. I Don't See It That Way: It Looks a Little Different from up Here. 2009. 127p. pap. 13.99 (978-0-8280-2468-6(5)) Review & Herald Publishing Assn.

McIntosh, Diane. Spiritual Treasure Hunt. 2010. 188p. pap. 12.50 (978-0-557-44049-8(1)) Lulu Enterprises Inc.

McIntyre, Ralph. The First Resurrection. 2007. 204p. per. 14.99 (978-1-60477-039-1(2)) Xulon Pr., Inc.

McKinney, Edward. Gorbachev to Spark Armageddon. 2011. 408p. pap. 37.95 (978-1-257-67269-1(X)) Lulu Enterprises Inc.

McLellan, John. Political Christianity - P. 256p. 25.00 (978-0-281-04921-9(1)) SPCK Publishing GBR. Dist: Pilgrim Pr., The/United Church Pr.

McLennan, Scotty. Jesus Was a Liberal: Reclaiming Christianity for All. 2009. (ENG.). 272p. 27.00 (978-0-230-61429-1(9)) Palgrave Macmillan.

McLeod, Frank E. Whatcha' See? Are You Getting Used to the Dark? 2010. 134p. 22.50 (978-1-60911-141-0(9), Eloquent Bks.) AEG Literary Publishing Services, Inc.

McLin, Chance. EModeTIONS: Hot Chocolate Chats with God. 2011. 152p. 30.95 (978-1-4497-1244-0(4)); pap. 13.95 (978-1-4497-1242-6(8)) Author Solutions, Inc. (WestBow Pr.).

McLoughlin, William Gerald. The Cherokees & Christianity, 1794-1870: Essays on Acculturation & Cultural Persistence. Conser, Walter H., ed. 2008. (ENG.). 368p. per. 26.95 (978-0-8203-3138-6(4)) Univ. of Georgia Pr.

McMahon, C. Matthew. A Heart for Reformation. 2007. per. 22.95 net. (978-0-9765336-9-6(3)) Puritan Pubns.

McManus, Agnes & Perry, Carol. Called & Sent: A Brief History of the Society of Saint Ursula. 2009. (Illus.). iii, 212p. E-Book (978-1-4401-2980-3(0)) iUniverse, Inc.

McMinn, Mark R. & Campbell, Clark D. Integrative Psychotherapy: Toward a Comprehensive Christian Approach. 2007. (Christian Association for Psychological Studies Partnership Book Ser.). (ENG., Illus.). 405p. 30.00 (978-0-8308-2830-2(3), IVP Acad.) InterVarsity Pr.

McNeal, Reggie & McNeal. Missional Renaissance: Changing the Scorecard for the Church. 2009. (Jossey-Bass Leadership Network Ser.: 28). (ENG.). 224p. 24.95 (978-0-470-24344-2(9), Jossey-Bass) Wiley, John & Sons, Inc.

McQuoid, Elizabeth. One People: Living Out God's Story. 2007. (Spring Harvest Bible Studies). (ENG., Illus.). 80p. pap. 6.99 (978-1-85078-758-7(1)) Authentic Media.

Mead, Matthew. The Trumpet of Truth: One God, One Faith One choice. & the Lies of Christianity. 2011. 124p. pap. 13.99 (978-1-4567-1985-2(8)) AuthorHouse.

Mead, Sidney E. The Lively Experiment: The Shaping of Christianity in America. 2007. 240p. pap. 26.00 (978-1-55635-276-8(X), Wipf and Stock) Wipf & Stock Pubs.

Meadows, James L. Different Religions (Churches) pap. 5.50 (978-0-89098-380-5(1)) Twentieth Century Christian Bks.

Mees, Michael & Wrye, Gabriel. Heaven Come Down: Serpent Handlers, Sinners, & the Electrifying Spirit. 2012. (ENG., Illus.). 144p. 24.95 (978-1-935950-01-1(0)) Bazillion Points.

Meiers, Jim. The Angry Cross: The Murder of Jesus, 1 vol. 2010. 198p. pap. 24.95 (978-1-4489-3922-0(4)) PublishAmerica, Inc.

Meijers, Marja. Grace of Giving: Turning the Key to Enter & Experience Fullness of Life. 2011. pap. 10.99 (978-1-61739-078-4(X)) Tate Publishing & Enterprises, LLC.

Mejia, Jairo. Christianity Reformed from its Roots: A Life Centered in God. 2008. 338p. 33.95 (978-0-595-70949-6(4)); pap. 23.95 (978-0-595-47242-0(7)) iUniverse, Inc.

Melé, Domènec & Dierksmeier, Claus, eds. Reciprocity & the Logic of Gift: Business Challenges of the Encyclical Letter. 2012. (Humanism in Business Ser.). (ENG., Illus.). 280p. 95.00 (978-0-230-29682-4(3)) Palgrave Macmillan.

Melgosa, Julián. Mental & Emotional Health. 2010. 128p. pap. 7.97 (978-0-8163-2416-3(6)) Pacific Pr. Publishing Assn.

Melloni, Alberto & Soskice, Janet Martin, eds. Rethinking Europe. 2010. 140p. pap. (978-0-334-03078-2(1), SCM Pr.) Hymns Ancient & Modern Ltd.

Mendum, J. P. & Bennett, D. M., prods. Revelations of Antichrist: Christ & Christianity. 432p. pap. 8.00 (978-0-944379-33-2(8)) CPA Bk. Pub.

Menegon, Eugenio. Ancestors, Virgins, & Friars: Christianity As a Local Religion in Late Imperial China. 2010. (Harvard-Yenching Institute Monograph Ser.: 69). (Illus.). 450p. 49.95 (978-0-674-03596-6(8)) Harvard Univ., Asia Ctr.

Meshler, Ed. Upward Obsession: The Principles of Pry. 2009. 232p. 25.99 (978-1-60791-503-4(0)); pap. 15.99 (978-1-60791-502-7(2)) Xulon Pr., Inc.

Messervy-Norman, J.G. One in the hand of God. 2008. 28p. 13.50 (978-1-84799-460-8(1)) Lulu Enterprises Inc.

Methroduthu, John A. Glorious Bride. 2008. 52p. pap. 15.99 (978-1-4363-2329-1(0)) Xlibris Corp.

Metswamere, Mosebodi Betty. A, Girl Uncovering the Joy of Heaven: The Silence & Happiness in Zion. 2011. (ENG.). 138p. pap. 16.95 (978-1-4327-7162-1(0)) Outskirts Pr., Inc.

Meyer, John. Romans. 2010. 170p. pap. 16.99 (978-1-60957-789-6(2)) Xulon Pr., Inc.

Meyer, Joyce. Look Great, Feel Great: 12 Keys to Enjoying a Healthy Life Now. 2008. (ENG.). 240p. pap. 13.99 (978-0-446-50491-1(2)) FaithWords.

Meyers, Robin. The Underground Church: Reclaiming the Subversive Way of Jesus. 2012. (ENG.). 288p. 24.95 (978-1-118-06159-6(4), Jossey-Bass) Wiley, John & Sons, Inc.

Michael George, Kizito. Judithising Christ? 2011. 356p. pap. (978-3-8443-9598-3(9)) Lambert Academic Publishing.

—The Witchcraft of the Ti. 2011. 572p. pap. (978-3-8443-9022-3(7)) Lambert Academic Publishing.

Michailidis, Rev. Andreas. The Creed. 2011. 220p. pap. 15.99 (978-1-61379-158-5(5)) Xulon Pr., Inc.

Middleton, Paul. Martyrdom: A Guide for the Perplexed. 2011. (Guides for the Perplexed Ser.). (ENG.). 224p. 80.00 (978-0-567-03217-1(5), T&T Clark Int'l) Continuum International Publishing Group, Ltd. GBR. Dist: National Bk. Network.

Mignogna, Michael T. Fellow Catholics It's Time to Get Out if the Boat! 2006. 79p. pap. 9.95 (978-0-7414-3685-6(X)) Infinity Publishing.

Mikhail, Labib. Polytheism & Oneness: In Islam & Christianity. Mikhail, Labib, ed. 2009. 530p. 25.00 (978-1-890297-25-1(9)); pap. 20.00 (978-1-890297-26-8(7)) Blessed Hope Ministry.

Mikicic, M. Anton. God Is Redundant. 2010. 208p. pap. 17.50 (978-1-60844-180-8(6)) Dog Ear Publishing, LLC.

Mikkelsen, Hans Vium. Reconciled Humanity: Karl Barth in Dialogue. 2010. pap. 30.00 (978-0-8028-6363-8(9)) Eerdmans, William B. Publishing Co.

Miller, Barbara B. Mighty Inspiration: Love Letters from God. 2009. 124p. 22.50 (978-1-60693-880-5(0), Eloquent Bks.) AEG Literary Publishing Services, Inc.

Miller, Calvin. The Path of Celtic Prayer: An Ancient Way to Everyday Joy. 2007. (ENG.). 170p. 18.00 (978-0-8308-3504-1(0), IVP Bks.) InterVarsity Pr.

Miller, Eric. Hope in a Scattering Time: A Life of Christopher Lasch. 2010. 420p. 32.00 (978-0-8028-1769-3(6)) Eerdmans, William B. Publishing Co.

Miller, Gordon, ed. & photos by. Wisdom of the Earth: Visions of an Ecological Faith, 2 vols., Set. (Wisdom of the Earth Ser.: Vol. 1). (Illus.). (Orig.). pap. (978-0-9647007-0-3(0)) Green Rock Pr.

Miller, Nicholas P. The Religious Roots of the First Amendment: Dissenting Protestantism & the Separation of Church & State. 2012. (ENG.). 272p. 35.00 (978-0-19-985836-1(5)) Oxford Univ. Pr., Inc.

Miller, Robert J., ed. The Complete Gospels. 4th ed. 2010. (ENG.). 484p. pap. 35.00 (978-1-59815-018-6(9)) Polebridge Pr.

Miller, Wayne A. The Growing of Christianity: A Different Perspective. 2008. 153p. pap. 24.95 (978-1-60610-403-3(9)) PublishAmerica, Inc.

Mills, Charles D. Adventism Going Two Ways: Where Are You? 2011. (ENG.). 258p. pap. 24.95 (978-1-4327-7506-3(5)) Outskirts Pr., Inc.

Mingana, Alphonse. The Early Spread of Christianity in Central Asia & the Far East. 2010. pap. 25.12 (978-1-61719-589-1(8)) Gorgias Pr., LLC.

Mishmash, Scott A. I Am That I Am: An in-Depth Study of the Believer's Spirit-Led Walk. 2011. pap. 10.99 (978-1-61663-483-4(9)) Tate Publishing & Enterprises, LLC.

Mitchell-Hemphill, Lynda. God Has Said. 2010. 96p. pap. 11.95 (978-1-4502-3349-1(X)) iUniverse, Inc.

Mitchell, Phyllis. The Old Covered Wagon: An Inspirational Adventure Story. 2011. 68p. pap. 9.95 (978-1-4497-1623-3(7), WestBow Pr.) Author Solutions, Inc.

Mitchell, Susan Catherine. Through the Valley: The Way of the Cross for the End of Life. 2009. (ENG.). 72p. pap. 11.95 (978-1-84730-174-1(6)) Veritas Pubns. IRL. Dist: Dufour Editions, Inc.

Mittelstadt, Martin W. & Sutton, Geoffrey W., eds. Forgiveness, Reconciliation, & Restoration: Mulitdisciplinary Studies from A Pentecostal Perspective. 2010. (Pentecostals, Peacemaking, & Social Justice: Ser.). 266p. pap. 29.00 (978-1-60899-194-5(6), Pickwick Pubns.) Wipf & Stock Pubs.

Miyamoto, Arata. Embodied Cross: Intercontextual Reading of Theologia Crucis. 2010. 166p. pap. 19.00 (978-1-60899-149-5(0), Wipf and Stock) Wipf & Stock Pubs.

Moon, W. Jay. African Proverbs Reveal Christianity in Culture: A Narrative Portrayal of Builsa Proverbs Contextualizing Christianity in Ghana. 2009. (American Society of Missiology Monograph Ser.). 234p. pap. 26.00 (978-1-60608-553-0(0), Pickwick Pubns.) Wipf & Stock Pubs.

Moore, Chevelle R. The Healing of a Nation: Through the Ties That Bind Us Together. 2007. 72p. per. 8.99 (978-1-59886-517-2(X)) Tate Publishing & Enterprises, LLC.

Moore, Ed. Prayer Force One: Uniting America's Praying Majority: Across America. 2007. per. 11.99 (978-0-9624843-1-5(8)) Christchurch Pubns.

Moore, Peter C. A Step Further: The Journey in Discipleship. 2011. (ENG.). 220p. pap. 14.99 (978-1-59932-263-6(3)) Advantage Media Group.

Moore, Ray A. Soldier of God: MacArthur's Attempt to Christianize Japan. 2011. ix, 167p. (978-1-878282-94-1(8)); pap. (978-1-878282-79-8(4)) St. Johann Pr.

Moore, T. L. Ed on My Shoulder. 2008. 96p. pap. 9.99 (978-1-60477-810-6(5)) Xulon Pr., Inc.

Moorhen, Tristan. I Can Fly, but Only at Night. 2008. 152p. pap. 13.95 (978-1-4357-0916-4(0)) Lulu Enterprises Inc.

Moosbach, Carola. Traces of Heaven. 128p. 13.00 (978-0-281-05394-0(4)) SPCK Publishing GBR. Dist: Pilgrim Pr., The/United Church Pr.

Moracho, Felix. Iniciacion Cristiana & Devocionario Popular. (SPA.). 160p. 6.95 (978-958-607-329-5(7)) Sociedad de San Pablo ESP. Dist: St Pauls/Alba Hse. Pubs.

Morfill, W.R., tr. The Book of the Secrets of Enoch. 2007. 164p. per. 11.45 (978-1-59462-667-8(7), Book Jungle) Standard Pubns., Inc.

Morgan, David. The Sacred Heart of Jesus: The Visual Evolution of a Devotion. 2009. (Meertens Ethnology Cahier Ser.). 50p. pap. (978-90-8964-019-2(3), Leiden Univ. Pr.) Amsterdam Univ. Pr.

Morgan, Ian Charles. 21st Century Church. 2010. 160p. pap. 19.99 (978-0-557-30023-5(1)) Lulu Enterprises Inc.

Morgan-Thomas, Victoria. Incest, Rape, & Rage. 2010. 248p. pap. 15.99 (978-1-60957-447-5(8)) Xulon Pr., Inc.

Morris, John H. Contemporary Creed: Reasonable Pathways Through the Problems of Christian Beliefs & Ethics. 2012. (ENG.). 214p. pap. 16.95 (978-1-78099-079-8(0)) Hunt, John Publishing Ltd. GBR. Dist: National Bk. Network.

Morris, Kevin L. & Chesterton, G. K. The Truest Fairy Tale: An Anthology of the Religious Writings of G. K. Chesterton. 2007. (ENG.). 244p. pap. 40.00 (978-0-7188-3061-8(X)) Lutherworth Pr., The. GBR. Dist: Brown, David Bk. Co., The.

Morris, Tom. Someone Died Now What? A Youth Pastor's Survival Guide. 2010. 316p. 35.99 (978-0-557-49557-3(1)) Lulu Enterprises Inc.

Morris, Victoria. The Waitress of Life: 10 Contemporary Christian Scenes. 2011. 66p. pap. 8.65 (978-1-60746-428-0(4)) FastPrncil, Inc.

moshe, ben david. On the Gate of Rome. 2008. 526p. 49.49 (978-1-4092-2748-9(0)) Lulu Enterprises Inc.

Mosley, Doyle. Expressions of the Heart. 2007. pap. 13.99 (978-1-60477-290-6(5)) Xulon Pr., Inc.

Motloung, Josiah. Soul Winning. 2006. (ENG.). 96p. per. (978-1-84401-478-1(9)) Athena Pr.

Moule. Forgiveness & Reconciliation. 260p. 36.00 (978-0-281-05139-7(9)) SPCK Publishing GBR. Dist: Pilgrim Pr., The/United Church Pr.

Moxom, Philip Stafford. From Jerusalem to Nicea. 2010. 134.84 (978-1-61143-354-8(1)) Gorgias Pr., LLC.

Mtata, Kenneth, ed. Dignity of Work: Theological & Interdisciplinary Perspectives. 2012. (ENG.). 112p. pap. 15.00 (978-1-932688-68-9(4), Lutheran Univ. Pr.) Kirk Hse. Pubs.

Mueller, Walt. 99 Thoughts for Parents of Teenagers: The Truth on Raising Teenagers from Parents Who Have Been There. 2011. pap. (978-0-7644-4869-0(2)) Group Publishing, Inc.

Muhammad, Malchezedek. The Prophetic Seal of the Sacred 360 Degree Circle. 2010. 216p. pap. 35.00 (978-1-4490-1949-5(8)) AuthorHouse.

Muldoon, Tim. A Saint for All Reasons: A Pocket Bible of 100 Saints for Every Situation. 2010. 128p. pap. 13.99 (978-0-8437-1381-7(X)) Hammond World Atlas Corp.

Müller, Retief. African Pilgrimage: Ritual Travel in South Africa's Christianity of Zion. 2011. 222p. 99.95 (978-1-4094-3082-7(0)) Ashgate Publishing Co.

Munger, Scott. Rethinking God: Undoing the Damage. 2007. 214p. per. 14.99 (978-0-89957-038-9(0)) AMG Pubs.

Munn, Gerald E. Congruent Parallels, Living Infinity~Living God: An Answer to Atheism. 2011. 206p. pap. 24.95 (978-1-4327-6617-7(1)) Outskirts Pr., Inc.

Munyon, J. L. How Good Is My Bible? 2010. 44p. pap. 11.95 (978-1-4327-6159-2(5)) Outskirts Pr., Inc.

Murdock, Mike. 7 Laws You Must Honor to Have Uncommon Success: Master 7 Mentorship Program. 2009. 60p. (978-1-56394-420-8(0)) Wisdom International, Inc.

Murphy, Bill. Basic Help to Confess. 32p. pap. 1.25 (978-0-8198-1156-1(4), 332-021) Pauline Bks. & Media.

Murphy, Gannon, ed. American Theological Inquiry, Volume Four, Issue One: A Biannual Journal of Theology, Culture, & History. 2011. 112p. pap. 14.00 (978-1-61097-231-4(7), Wipf and Stock) Wipf & Stock Pubs.

—American Theological Inquiry, Volume Three, Issue One: A Biannual Journal of Theology, Culture, & History. 2010. 204p. pap. 22.00 *(978-1-60899-397-0(3),* Wipf and Stock) Wipf & Stock Pubs.
—American Theological Inquiry, Volume Two, Issue One: Biannual Journal of Theology, Culture, & History. 2009. 202p. pap. 22.00 *(978-1-60608-459-5(3),* Wipf and Stock) Wipf & Stock Pubs.
—American Theological Inquiry, Volume Two, Issue Two. 2009. 146p. pap. 18.00 *(978-1-60899-000-9(1),* Wipf and Stock) Wipf & Stock Pubs.
Murphy, Gannon, et al, eds. American Theological Inquiry Vol. 1: A Biannual Journal of Theology, Culture, & History. 2008. (Illus.). 184p. pap. 21.00 *(978-1-60608-095-5(4))* Wipf & Stock Pubs.
Murphy, John Robin. Be Transformed: New Life Awaits. 2007. 181p. per. 12.99 *(978-0-9788715-0-5(2))* Rock House Way Pr.
Murphy, Nancey & Knight, Christopher C., eds. Human Identity at the Intersection of Science, Technology & Religion. 2010. (Ashgate Science & Religion Ser.). (Illus.). 254p. 99.95 *(978-1-4094-1050-8(1))* Ashgate Publishing Co.
Murray, Andrew. The Believer's New Life. 2007. per. 13.98 *(978-1-4245-0808-2(8))* Treasures Media Inc.
—Teach Me to Pray. 2011. (Classic Insights Ser.). (ENG.). 384p. 14.99 *(978-1-61626-351-5(2),* Barbour Bks.) Barbour Publishing, Inc.
—Waiting on God. 2007. (ENG.). 138p. pap. 8.99 *(978-0-87508-854-9(6))* CLC Pubns.
—Waiting on God. 2008. 88p. pap. 7.49 *(978-1-60459-320-4(2))* Wilder Pubns., Ltd.
Murray, Iain H. A Scottish Christian Heritage. 2006. (Illus.). 403p. 28.00 *(978-0-85151-930-2(X))* Banner of Truth, The.
Murray, Stephen Butler. Reclaiming Divine Wrath: A History of a Christian Doctrine & Its Interpretation. 2011. (Studies in Theology, Society & Culture Ser.). (ENG.). 303p. pap. 66.95 ***(978-3-0343-0703-1(9))*** Lang, Peter AG GBR. Dist: Lang, Peter.
Musya, Justus K. Inculturating the Eucharist in Afric. 2011. 96p. pap. ***(978-3-8443-1847-0(X))*** Lambert Academic Publishing.
Naidoo, Thillayvel. Long Walk to Enlightenment. 2010. 420p. pap. 33.00 *(978-1-4349-9808-8(8),* RoseDog Bks.) Dorrance Publishing Co., Inc.
Nan, Miss. God at Work. 2010. 164p. pap. 14.99 *(978-1-60957-547-2(4))* Xulon Pr., Inc.
Neal, Donovan. The Gospel Explained. 2010. 56p. pap. 12.00 *(978-0-557-39077-9(X))* Lulu Enterprises Inc.
Neborak, Sonja. Thoughts in the Atomic Age. 2011. 156p. 41.95 ***(978-1-258-07918-5(6))*** Literary Licensing, LLC.
Nelson, David. Life Giving Wisdom. 2011. 113p. pap. 12.95 ***(978-1-4327-7215-4(5))*** Outskirts Pr., Inc.
Neufeld, Dennis & Sterling, Rick. The Spirit of the Church. 2007. 196p. per. 12.99 *(978-1-59886-481-6(5))* Tate Publishing & Enterprises, LLC.
Newbigin. Faith & Power. 192p. 19.00 *(978-0-281-05153-3(4))* SPCK Publishing GBR. Dist: Pilgrim Pr., The/United Church Pr.
Newman, John Henry. Discussions & Arguments on Various Subjects. 2008. 422p. 51.95 *(978-1-4365-3956-2(0))* 2007. (ENG.). 424p. per. 36.95 *(978-0-548-74034-7(8))* Kessinger Publishing, LLC.
—Discussions & Arguments on Various Subjects. 2007. (ENG.). 416p. per. *(978-1-4067-8363-6(3))* Read Bks.
Newton, Barbara & Driscoll, Ellen Newton. When Christians Divorce: A Self-Help Book for Victims of Divorce. 2006. 113p. per. 10.99 *(978-1-59886-550-9(1))* Tate Publishing & Enterprises, LLC.
Nicholls, Cherub. The Legitimacy of the Holy Bible as a Legal Instrument. 2007. (ENG.). 120p. 18.99 *(978-1-60034-651-4(0));* per. 10.99 *(978-1-60034-650-7(2))* Xulon Pr., Inc.
Niebuhr, Reinhold. Does Civilization Need Religion? A Study in the Social Resources & Limitations of Religion in Modern Life. 2010. 242p. pap. 21.00 *(978-1-60899-800-5(2),* Wipf and Stock) Wipf & Stock Pubs.
Nielson, Claus Bager. A War Canoe Heading for Christianity. 2007. (Intervention Press Ser.). (ENG., Illus.). 24p. pap. 19.95 *(978-87-89825-77-9(2))* Left Coast Pr., Inc.
Nisl, Joanne. House of Healing: Biblical Keys that Unlock Heaven's Door to Healing. 2011. pap. 10.99 *(978-1-61739-971-8(X))* Tate Publishing & Enterprises, LLC.
Nnaji, Gregory Chigozie. Like A Little Child. 2011. 108p. 23.58 ***(978-1-4634-3664-3(5));*** pap. 14.08 ***(978-1-4634-3665-0(3))*** AuthorHouse.
Nnanyelugo, Samuel. The Mystery of Christ. 2008. 384p. pap. 25.48 *(978-1-4357-0725-2(7))* Lulu Enterprises Inc.
Noebel, David A. Worldviews in Collision. 2008. 560p. pap. 17.99 *(978-0-7369-2198-5(2))* Harvest Hse. Pubs.
Nordeide, Saebjorg Walaker. The Viking Age as a Period of Religious Transformation: The Christianization of Norway from AD 560 To 1150/1200. 2012. (Studies in Viking & Medieval Scandinavia Ser.). (ENG., Illus.). 355p. (C). 116.00 *(978-2-503-53480-0(5))* Brepols Pubs. BEL. Dist: ISD.
Norman, Archie. Soul Survival. 2011. 136p. 21.23 ***(978-1-4567-6342-8(3));*** pap. 14.99 ***(978-1-4567-6340-4(7))*** AuthorHouse.
Nurnberger, Klaus. Richard Dawkins' God Delusion. 2010. 220p. 29.99 *(978-1-4500-5983-1(X));* pap. 19.99 *(978-1-4500-5982-4(1))* Xlibris Corp.
Nuss, Donald R. The Anatomies of God, the Bible, & Religion: Decoding the Old & New Testaments. 2010. 600p. 43.95 *(978-1-4502-5013-9(0));* pap. 33.95 *(978-1-4502-5012-2(2))* iUniverse, Inc.
Nuziard, Jeff. Stop the Madness... What I Hate about Religion. 2009. 148p. pap. 14.99 *(978-1-61579-098-2(5))* Xulon Pr., Inc.
Nwaogwugwu, Cletus Chukwuemeka. Ancestor Christology: A Christian Evaluation of the Ancestral Cult in the Traditional Religion of the Sub-Saharan Africa. 2011. 596p. 43.95 *(978-1-4502-6228-6(7));* pap. 33.95 *(978-1-4502-6227-9(9))* iUniverse, Inc.
Ó Murchú, Diarmuid. Ancestral Grace: Meeting God in Our Human Story. 2008. xv, 270p. pap. 22.00 *(978-1-57075-794-5(1))* Orbis Bks.
Obe, Adekunle. The Glory of the Son. 2010. 202p. pap. 20.95 *(978-1-4327-6379-4(2))* Outskirts Pr., Inc.
—The Pattern Son. 2008. 78p. pap. 13.18 *(978-1-4251-6828-5(0))* Trafford Publishing.
O'Brien, George Dennis. God & the New Haven Railway: And Why Neither One Is Doing Very Well. 2008. (ENG.). 184p. pap. 18.00 *(978-0-268-03730-7(2))* Univ. of Notre Dame Pr.
O'Brien, Mary Elizabeth. Servant Leadership in Nursing: Spirituality & Practice in Contemporary Healthcare. rev. ed. 2010. (Illus.). 355p. pap. 49.95 *(978-0-7637-7485-1(5))* Jones & Bartlett Learning, LLC.
—Spirituality in Nursing: Standing on Holy Ground. 3rd rev. ed. 2007. (ENG.). 423p. pap. 76.95 *(978-0-7637-4648-3(7))* Jones & Bartlett Learning, LLC.
—Spirituality in Nursing 4E. 4th rev. ed. 2010. 432p. pap. 73.95 *(978-0-7637-9650-1(6))* Jones & Bartlett Learning, LLC.
Obwoge, Hezekiah. Church & Development. 2010. 224p. pap. *(978-3-8383-5157-5(6))* Lambert Academic Publishing.
O'Connor, Dennis P. Bridges of Faith: Building a Relationship with a Sister Parish. 2007. 195p. per. 19.95 *(978-0-86716-584-5(7))* Franciscan Media.
—Bridges of Faith: Building a Relationship with a Sister Parish: A Personal Journal. 2007. 80p. per. 4.95 *(978-0-86716-794-8(7))* Franciscan Media.
O'Connor, Karen. The Golden Years Ain't for Wimps: Humorous Stories for Your Senior Moments. l.t. ed. 2008. (ENG.). 320p. (YA). pap. 17.95 *(978-1-59415-246-7(2),* Walker Large Print) Cengage Gale.
Oddy, Jeremy. Christian Fellowship. 2009. 60p. pap. *(978-3-639-15850-2(4))* VDM Verlag Dr. Mueller e.K.
Oden, Thomas C. Classic Christianity: A Systematic Theology. 2009. (ENG.). 900p. 39.99 *(978-0-06-144971-0(7),* HarperOne) HarperCollins Pubs.
—How Africa Shaped the Christian Mind: Rediscovering the African Seedbed of Western Christianity. (Early African Christianity Set Ser.). (ENG.). 204p. 2010. pap. 17.00 *(978-0-8308-3705-2(1),* IVP Acad.) 2007. (Illus.). 22.00 *(978-0-8308-2875-3(3),* IVP Bks.) InterVarsity Pr.
Odhiambo, George. Faces of Christianity. 2011. 152p. pap. ***(978-3-8443-1652-0(3))*** Lambert Academic Publishing.
O'Donnell, Tim. A View from the Back Pew: God, Religion & Our Personal Quest for Truth. 2011. (ENG.). 280p. pap. 15.95 *(978-0-9845344-1-8(5))* Linchpin Publishing, LLC.
Ofori-Tano, Kwasi. Assurance in Christ's Weeping. 2011. 90p. 24.99 ***(978-1-4568-4840-8(2));*** pap. 15.99 ***(978-1-4568-4839-2(9))*** Xlibris Corp.
Ogle, Nellie Lane. The Great White Way. 2011. 94p. 38.95 ***(978-1-258-04482-4(X))*** Literary Licensing, LLC.
Ogungbile, David O. & Akinade, Akintunde, eds. Creativity & Change in Nigerian Christianity. 2006. 392p. *(978-978-8422-22-8(5))* Malthouse Press Ltd, Nigeria NGA. Dist: Michigan State Univ. Pr.
Oldridge, Darren. The Devil: A Very Short Introduction. 2012. (Very Short Introductions Ser.). (ENG., Illus.). 144p. pap. 11.95 ***(978-0-19-958099-6(5))*** Oxford Univ. Pr., Inc.
Olfert, Rebecca A. The First & Greatest. 2011. 128p. pap. 14.99 ***(978-1-61215-841-9(2))*** Xulon Pr., Inc.
Olmstead, Albert Ten Eyck. The Mid-Third Century of the Christian Era II: Classical Philology, V37, No. 4, October 1942. 2011. 28p. 35.95 ***(978-1-258-09665-6(X))*** Literary Licensing, LLC.
Omoth, David. Writings of Jesus Christ. 2009. 110p. pap. 14.90 *(978-0-557-09524-7(7))* Lulu Enterprises Inc.
O'Murchu, Diarmuid. Christianity's Dangerous Memory: A Rediscovery of the Revolutionary Jesus. 2011. (ENG.). 216p. pap. 19.95 *(978-0-8245-2678-8(3))* Crossroad Publishing Co., The.
Onagbola, Al'samawa'Al. Thechristians' God Exposed: A Woman Scientist Is God. 2011. 161p. pap. 18.95 ***(978-1-4327-7165-2(5))*** Outskirts Pr., Inc.
Osagie, Peter A. You Are Born Again, Now What? 2010. 76p. pap. 10.00 *(978-0-557-41912-8(3))* Lulu Enterprises Inc.
Osborne, Josh. Christian Without the Quotations: A Novel Idea. 2010. 218p. pap. 11.95 *(978-1-4327-4901-9(3))* Outskirts Pr., Inc.
Oshin, Vincent O. Biblical Christianity: From Man-Centred to a Christ-Centred Church. 2009. 228p. pap. 15.99 *(978-1-60791-285-9(6))* Xulon Pr., Inc.
Osteen, Joel. Daily Readings from Your Best Life Now: 90 Devotions for Living at Your Full Potential. 2009. (ENG.). 320p. pap. 14.99 *(978-0-446-55010-9(8))* FaithWords.
Osteen, Joel. Every Day a Friday Journal: How to Be Happier 7 Days a Week. 2012. (ENG.). 256p. 11.99 ***(978-0-89296-981-4(4))*** FaithWords.
Overseas Missionary Fellowship, creator. A Christian's Pocket Guide to the Japanese. 2008. (ENG.). 74p. pap. 4.99 *(978-1-84550-316-1(3))* Christian Focus Pubns. GBR. Dist: STL Distribution North America.
Owens, LaVerne. Gambling with God's Grace & Mercy. 2007. 144p. per. 13.99 *(978-1-60266-497-5(8))* Xulon Pr., Inc.
Pace, Joe II & Pace, Joe. Simple Christianity. 2009. pap. 9.99 *(978-1-60696-696-9(0))* Tate Publishing & Enterprises, LLC.
Pace, M. J. God Is in the Sabbath. 2011. pap. 8.99 *(978-1-61739-911-4(6))* Tate Publishing & Enterprises, LLC.
Paeth, Scott. Exodus Church & Civil Society: Public Theology & Social Theory in the Work of Jürgen Moltmann. 2008. (New Critical Thinking in Religion, Theology & Biblical Studies). 232p. 99.95 *(978-0-7546-6201-3(2))* Ashgate Publishing Co.
Paharik, James. The Long Journey: In Search of Justice & Peace in Jerusalem. 2009. 152p. pap. 14.95 *(978-0-8146-3221-5(1))* Liturgical Pr.
Palmer, Kelly. No Bull: A Common Sense, Bible-Based Approach to Issues Facing Christianity Today. 2011. pap. 11.99 *(978-1-61739-734-9(2))* Tate Publishing & Enterprises, LLC.
Palmer, Parker J. The Promise of Paradox: A Celebration of Contradictions in the Christian Life. 2008. (ENG.). 192p. 18.95 *(978-0-7879-9696-3(3),* Jossey-Bass) Wiley, John & Sons, Inc.
Palmer, Roo. Dale. Forbearing Secrets. 2010. 330p. pap. 26.00 *(978-1-4092-9858-8(2))* Lulu Enterprises Inc.
Parenti, Michael. God & His Demons. 2010. (ENG.). 240p. 25.00 *(978-1-61614-177-6(8))* Prometheus Bks., Pubs.
Paris, Peter J. Religion & Poverty: Pan-African Perspectives. 2009. (ENG., Illus.). 384p. 94.95 *(978-0-8223-4356-1(8));* pap. 26.95 *(978-0-8223-4378-3(9))* Duke Univ. Pr.
Parlette, Ralph. The University of Hard Knocks. 2008. 184p. 22.99 *(978-0-559-64802-1(2));* 184p. pap. 21.75 *(978-0-559-64798-7(0));* 124p. 21.99 *(978-0-554-30851-7(7));* 124p. 24.99 *(978-0-554-21548-8(9))* BiblioBazaar.
—The University of Hard Knocks. 2007. (ENG.). 120p. per. *(978-1-4065-4087-1(0))* Dodo Pr.
—The University of Hard Knocks. 2008. (ENG.). 108p. pap. 9.45 *(978-1-4385-0266-3(4),* Book Jungle) Standard Pubns., Inc.
Parr, Susan Sherwood. The Prayer Workshop: Results Through Scriptural & Specific Prayer. 2006. (ENG., Illus.). 146p. pap. 9.95 *(978-0-9728590-9-7(8))* Word Prodns.
Parrino, Frank. Fool's Gold & Other Papers: Discovering Genuine Christianity. 2006. 88p. per. 9.99 *(978-1-59886-474-8(2))* Tate Publishing & Enterprises, LLC.
Parrott, JoAnn. The Sonshine Tree. 2007. 112p. (ENG.). 18.99 *(978-1-60266-627-6(X));* per. 10.99 *(978-1-60266-626-9(1))* Xulon Pr., Inc.
Parsons, D. J. Ascribing Responsibility to Abortion & Other Atrocities/the Thief on The. 2009. 116p. 19.99 *(978-1-60791-513-3(8))* Xulon Pr., Inc.
Parsons, John Denham. Our Sun-God: Or Christianity Before Christ. 2007. (ENG.). 212p. per. 18.95 *(978-1-58509-297-0(5))* Book Tree, The.
Partee, Milt. Christianity in Crisis: A wake-up call for the Church. 2010. 88p. pap. 10.95 *(978-1-4490-8535-3(0))* AuthorHouse.
Pascual, Dennis Mark. The Branches Fallen from the Vine Looking at the lives of christians in these last days & how to really Live. 2010. 61p. pap. 10.45 *(978-0-557-42101-5(2))* Lulu Enterprises Inc.
Pasquini, John J. Christian History: The First Five Hundred Years. 2011. 276p. pap. 27.95 ***(978-1-4626-0545-3(1))*** PublishAmerica, Inc.
Patrick J. Amer. The Five Commandments of Jesus: A New Approach to Christianity. 2009. 192p. pap. 16.95 *(978-1-4401-6224-4(7))* iUniverse, Inc.
Patrick, St. Confession of St Patrick & Related Texts Including His Epistle to the Christian Subjects of the Tyrant Coroticus, St Fiech's Metrical Life of St. 2011. 108p. ***(978-1-84902-574-4(6))*** Benediction Classics.
Patton, Guy. Masters of Deception: Murder & Intrigue in the World of Occult Politics. 2008. (ENG.). 350p. pap. 19.95 *(978-1-931882-88-0(6))* Adventures Unlimited Pr.
Paul, VI. Credo the People of God. 16p. pap. *(978-0-8198-1495-1(4),* 332-038) Pauline Bks. & Media.
—Dec on Procured Abortion. 27p. pap. *(978-0-8198-1847-8(X),* 332-063) Pauline Bks. & Media.
—Decr on Priestly Training. 20p. pap. *(978-0-8198-1834-8(8),* 332-055) Pauline Bks. & Media.
Paul Veliyathil. God Is Plural: Sermons for an Emerging Church. 2010. 344p. pap. 22.95 *(978-1-4401-9576-1(5))* iUniverse, Inc.
Payne, Brian. Exposing Christianity: My Way of Sharing an Alternative to the Church's Truth. 2007. 76p. per. 16.95 *(978-1-4241-9413-1(X))* PublishAmerica, Inc.
Pearsall, Minister F. Irving. Traditionalism of Life: Reformation Towards Restoration. 2011. 100p. pap. 11.65 *(978-1-4269-5479-5(4))* Trafford Publishing.
Pearson, John. Vindiciae Epistolarum Sancti Ignatii, 2 vols. (Library of Anglo-Catholic Theology: No. 16). reprint ed. 57.50 *(978-0-404-52140-0(1))* AMS Pr., Inc.
Peek, Susan. A Soldier Surrenders: The Conversion of Saint Camillus de Lellis. 2007. 190p. per. 14.95 *(978-1-58617-118-6(6))* Ignatius Pr.
Peele, Billy. God's Blessings: The Wit & Wisdom of a Retired Country Preacher. 2006. 13.00 *(978-0-8059-9182-6(4))* Dorrance Publishing Co., Inc.
Peltier, Richard. A Symposium of Christian Beliefs. 2010. 230p. pap. 15.99 *(978-1-60957-552-6(0))* Xulon Pr., Inc.
Pennel, Joe E. God, Cornbread, & Elvis: Pondering the Things of Everyday Life. 2008. (ENG.). 236p. pap. 14.95 *(978-1-934314-38-8(2))* Common Thread Media, LLC.
Penner, Todd C. & Vander Stichele, Caroline. Mapping Gender in Ancient Religious Discourses. 2010. *(978-1-58983-495-8(X))* Society of Biblical Literature.
Perdue, Thomas H. Second Blessing. 2011. 744p. pap. 36.14 ***(978-1-4634-3698-8(X))*** AuthorHouse.
Perrin. Studying Christian Spirituality. 2007. 368p. 35.95 *(978-0-415-39474-1(0))* Routledge.
Perrin, ed. Studying Christian Spirituality. 2007. (ENG.). 368p. (C). 130.00 *(978-0-415-39473-4(2))* Routledge.
Peters, F. E. The Voice, the Word, the Books: The Scared Scripture of the Jews, Christians & Muslims. 2007. (ENG., Illus.). 320p. (C). 29.95 *(978-0-691-13112-2(0))* Princeton Univ. Pr.
Petersen, Randy. 99 Bible Promises for Tough Times. 2009. (99 Ways Ser.). (ENG.). 112p. pap. 5.99 *(978-0-307-45838-4(5),* WaterBrook Pr.) Doubleday Religious Publishing Group, The.
Pettis, Deborah. Living under the Influence. 2010. 46p. pap. 9.95 *(978-1-4327-5742-7(3))* Outskirts Pr., Inc.
Phan, Peter C., ed. Christianities in Asia. 2010. (Blackwell Guides to Global Christianity Ser.: 1). (ENG., Illus.). 290p. 94.95 *(978-1-4051-6089-6(6));* 288p. pap. 37.95 *(978-1-4051-6090-2(X))* Wiley, John & Sons, Inc. (Wiley-Blackwell).
Phillips, L. Edward. The Ritual Kiss in Early Christian Worship. 2009. 88.00 *(978-1-60724-387-8(3))* Gorgias Pr., LLC.
Philpot, John. The Examinations & Writings of John Philpot. 2009. 284p. pap. 25.69 *(978-0-217-79738-2(5))* General Bks. LLC.
Picknett, Lynn & Prince, Clive. The Turin Shroud: How Da Vinci Fooled History. 2007. (ENG., Illus.). 304p. per. 14.00 *(978-0-7432-9217-7(0),* Touchstone) Touchstone.
Pierson, John W. Sometimes Love Offends. 2010. 266p. pap. 16.99 *(978-1-60957-362-1(5))* Xulon Pr., Inc.
Piironen, Henry M. The Holy Life of Christianity: The Workbook on Demystifying the Christian Ethics of the Holy Life in the New Testament. 2008. 480p. pap. 40.95 *(978-1-4401-0427-5(1))* iUniverse, Inc.
Pillsbury, Curtis. The Oracles of God... or the Words of Men? What Is Your Attitude toward the Living Word? 2010. pap. 17.99 *(978-1-61663-468-1(5))* Tate Publishing & Enterprises, LLC.
Ping, Bob. Changing of the Gods: The Future of Judeo-Christian-Islamic Religion in a Postmodern World. 2010. 628p. 33.99 *(978-1-4490-8710-4(8))* AuthorHouse.
Pink, Arthur Walkington & Kistler, Don. Studies on Saving Faith. 2010. viii, 209p. *(978-0-9826155-1-5(5))* Northampton Pr., The.
Pinno, A. Arthur. God Is! 2011. 296p. 26.99 *(978-1-61215-621-7(5));* pap. 16.99 *(978-1-61215-620-0(7))* Xulon Pr., Inc.
Pinos, Johnny F. Discover Life! 2009. 124p. pap. 11.99 *(978-1-60791-747-2(5))* Xulon Pr., Inc.
Piper, Don & Murphey, Cecil. Heaven Is Real: Lessons on Earthly Joy — From the Man Who Spent 90 Minutes in Heaven. l.t. ed. 2009. 358p. 30.50 *(978-1-4104-1210-2(5))* Thorndike Pr.
Pittman, Sr. The Sign of Christ's Return. 2008. 324p. pap. 22.95 *(978-1-4401-0398-8(4))* iUniverse, Inc.
Pius XII, pseud & Aquas, Hauretis. Devotion Sac Heart/Pius XII. 46p. pap. 1.50 *(978-0-8198-1844-7(5),* 332-061) Pauline Bks. & Media.
Plummer, John P. Living Mysteries: A Practical Handbook for the Independent Priest. 2010. 136p. pap. 9.95 *(978-1-933993-93-5(6))* Apocryphile Pr.
Pluta, Leonard. Father of Thousand Orphans. 2011. 880p. pap. 32.99 ***(978-1-61379-206-3(9))*** Xulon Pr., Inc.
Poirier, John C. The Tongues of Angels: The Concept of Angelic Languages in Classical Jewish & Christian Texts. 2010. (Illus.). XI, 224p. pap. 117.50 *(978-3-16-150569-0(7))* Mohr Siebeck GmbH & Co. KG DEU. Dist: Coronet Bks.
Pollefeyt, Didier & Bieringer, Reimund, eds. Paul & Judaism: Crosscurrents in Pauline Exegesis & the Study of Jewish-Christian Relations. 2012. (ENG.). 272p. 110.00 ***(978-0-567-07280-1(0),*** T&T Clark Int'l) Continuum International Publishing Group, Ltd. GBR. Dist: National Bk. Network.
Pollington, Stephen. The Elder Gods: The Otherworld of Early England. 2011. (ENG., Illus.). 536p. (C). pap. 65.00 ***(978-1-898281-64-1(5))*** Anglo-Saxon Bks. GBR. Dist: Brown, David Bk. Co., The.
Pollock, A. J. The Savior - Sinless, et Tempted. 16p. pap. 0.50 *(978-0-88172-158-4(1))* Believers Bookshelf, Inc.
Pontius, John. Following the Light of Christ into His Presence. 2011. pap. 16.99 *(978-1-55517-358-6(6))* Cedar Fort, Inc./CFI Distribution.
Popcak, Gregory K. The Life God Wants You to Have: Discovering the Divine Plan When Human Plans Fail. 2011. (ENG.). 208p. pap. 18.95 *(978-0-8245-2696-2(1))* Crossroad Publishing Co., The.
Porter, Wendy, ed. McMaster Journal of Theology & Ministry, Volume 9. 2009. 160p. pap. 18.00 *(978-1-60608-398-7(8),* Pickwick Pubns.) Wipf & Stock Pubs.
Potter, Andrew. Simply Heaven: As it Appears from Genesis Through Revelation. 2011. pap. 19.99 ***(978-1-61777-388-4(3))*** Tate Publishing & Enterprises, LLC.
Potts, Amy. Sponges. 2008. 48p. pap. 16.95 *(978-1-60474-080-6(9))* PublishAmerica, Inc.
Powell, Samuel M. Discovering Our Christian Faith: An Introduction to Theology. 2008. (ENG.). 352p. 44.99 *(978-0-8341-2354-0(1),* 083-412-3541) Beacon Hill Pr. of Kansas City.
Powers, Dave. Finding the Strength. 2008. 56p. pap. 17.50 *(978-0-615-17809-7(X))* Harvest Publishing.
—Why Christians Believe. 2008. 104p. pap. 18.50 *(978-0-615-17810-3(3))* Harvest Publishing.
Powley, Mark. Consumer Detox: Less Stuff More Life, 1 vol. 2010. (ENG.). 272p. pap. 14.99 *(978-0-310-32475-1(0))* Zondervan.
Pratt, Charles Edgar. Paganism in Christianity: A New Testament for Rational Believers. 2011. 256p. 47.95 ***(978-1-258-04190-8(1))*** Literary Licensing, LLC.
Pretcow, Ct. Christianity Debugged. 2009. pap. *(978-1-61623-698-4(1))* Independent Pub.

Price, Reynolds. Letter to a Godchild: Concerning Faith. 2007. (ENG., Illus.). 112p. pap. 10.95 *(978-1-4165-8803-0(5)*, Scribner) Simon & Schuster.

Price, Roger. God's Gift of Wisdom: Using God's Council to Your Advantage. 2009. 52p. pap. 12.95 *(978-1-4327-4748-0(7))* Outskirts Pr., Inc.

Pride, Fred. The Blossoming of Christianity: From the Supernatural to the Natural. 2011. 606p. 34.99 ***(978-1-4628-5045-7(6))***; pap. 23.99 ***(978-1-4628-5044-0(8))*** Xlibris Corp.

Pridham, Arthur. Notes & Reflections on the Epistle to the Romans. 2008. 428p. 51.95 *(978-1-4372-6765-5(3))*; 424p. pap. 36.95 *(978-1-4371-4132-0(3))* Kessinger Publishing, LLC.

Pringle, Phil. But God. 2008. (ENG.). 224p. pap. 14.99 *(978-1-59979-367-2(9))* Charisma Media.

Priolo, Lou. Bitterness: The Root That Pollutes. 2008. pap. *(978-1-59638-130-8(2))* P & R Publishing.

Procter-Murphy, Jeff & Felten, David. Living the Questions: An Introduction to Progressive Christianity. 2012. (ENG.). 400p. pap. 17.99 ***(978-0-06-210936-1(7)***, HarperOne) HarperCollins Pubs.

Putnik, Noel. The Pious Impiety of Agrippa's Magic. 2010. 80p. pap. *(978-3-639-24046-7(4))* VDM Verlag Dr. Mueller e.K.

Pym, Val. The Other Bible Code: Unlocking the Glorious Destiny of the Church of Jesus Christ. 2010. 148p. pap. 14.95 *(978-1-4502-4132-8(8))* iUniverse, Inc.

Quakkelaar, Dan. God's Choice: A Layman's Perspective on Predestination & Election. 2009. 109p. pap. 13.95 *(978-1-4327-3900-3(X))* Outskirts Pr., Inc.

Rabast, Jochen. Angels in Luggage. 2010. 98p. pap. *(978-3-8391-2340-9(2))* Books on Demand GmbH.

Radner, Ephraim & Turner, Philip. The Fate of Communion: The Agony of Anglicanism & the Future of a Global Church. 2007. 306p. per. 25.00 *(978-0-8028-6327-0(2))* Eerdmans, William B. Publishing Co.

Raffensperger, Christian. Reimagining Europe: Kievan Rus' in the Medieval World. 2012. (Harvard Historical Studies: 177). (ENG., Illus.). 340p. 55.00 ***(978-0-674-06384-6(8))*** Harvard Univ. Pr.

Raguin, Virginia Chieffo, et al. Pilgrimage & Faith: Buddhism, Christianity & Islam. 2010. *(978-1-932476-47-7(4))*; pap. *(978-1-932476-48-4(2))* Serindia Pubns., Inc.

Rajkumar, Peniel. Dalit Theology & the Dalit Liberation: Problems , Paradigms & Possibilities. 2010. (New Critical Thinking in Religion, Theology & Biblical Studies). 218p. 99.95 *(978-0-7546-6513-7(5))* Ashgate Publishing Co.

Ramos, M. Los Privilegios del Cristiano.Tr. of Christian Privileges. (SPA.). 2.50 *(978-1-56063-391-4(3)*, 493038) Editorial Unilit.

Ranganayi, Clorisa. A King among Jesse's Men. 2008. 64p. pap. 13.50 *(978-1-84426-505-3(6))* Upfront Publishing Ltd. GBR. Dist: Printondemand-worldwide.com.

Rashdall, Hastings. Philosophy & Religion - Six Lectures Delivered at Cambridge. 2007. 208p. per. *(978-1-4067-8834-1(1)*, Pomona Pr.) Read Bks.

Rassam, Suha. Christianity in Iraq, New Edition. 2010. 320p. pap. *(978-0-85244-738-3(8))* Gracewing, Ltd.

Rast, Jeff. Free His People! Pursuing a More Biblical View of the People of God. 2008. 176p. pap. 12.45 *(978-1-4389-1721-4(X))* AuthorHouse.

Rathbun, Russell E. D. NuChristian: Finding Faith in a New Generation. 2009. 192p. pap. 15.00 *(978-0-8170-1549-7(3))* Judson Pr.

Raya, Joseph. Theophany: And Sacraments of Initiation. 198p. pap. *(978-0-921440-37-6(5))* Madonna Hse. Pubns.

Raya, Joseph M. Theotokos, Bearer of God: Mary, Mother of Our Lord God & Saviour Jesus Christ. 138p. pap. *(978-0-921440-40-6(5))* Madonna Hse. Pubns.

Reece, Erik. An American Gospel: On Family, History, & the Kingdom of God. 2010. (ENG.). 240p. (gr. 12-18). 15.00 *(978-1-59448-445-2(7)*, Riverhead Trade (Paperbacks)) Penguin Group (USA) Inc.

Reed, James. Over 200 Questions & Answers. 2007. 420p. per. 21.99 *(978-1-60477-048-3(1))* Xulon Pr., Inc.

Reed, John M. Crusading Against Athens. 2011. 166p. 29.99 ***(978-1-4653-3639-2(7))***; pap. 19.99 ***(978-1-4653-3638-5(9))*** Xlibris Corp.

Reem, A. D. What If Jesus Christ Was an Alien! 2011. 212p. pap. 9.99 ***(978-1-61667-187-7(4))*** Raider Publishing International.

Regesh, John Ben. Saint Paul, the First Antichrist. 2009. 180p. 24.50 *(978-1-60860-266-7(4)*, Eloquent Bks.) AEG Literary Publishing Services, Inc.

Reid, Alvin L. Join the Movement: God Is Calling You to Change the World. 2007. 160p. pap. 10.99 *(978-0-8254-3652-9(4))* Kregel Pubns.

Reid, Gordon & Tyler, S. AS Edexcel Religious Studies. 2009. (Illus.). pap. 29.50 *(978-1-84489-441-3(X))* Hodder Education GBR. Dist: Trans-Atlantic Pubns., Inc.

Reisinger, John. An Appointment You Will Keep. pap. 0.06 *(978-0-87377-125-2(7))* GAM Pubns.

Ren, C. H. Christianity & the Future: Book One of the End Times Series. 2011. 224p. 33.95 *(978-1-4497-1382-9(3)*, WestBow Pr.) Author Solutions, Inc.

Renault, Paul. A question of God's Will. 2007. per. 14.95 *(978-1-934379-05-9(0))* Printmedia Bks.

Replies to Essays & Reviews with a Preface by the Lord Bishop of Oxford: And Letters from the Radcliffe Observer & the Reader in Geology In. 2006. 448p. per. 26.99 *(978-1-4255-4944-2(6))* MPublishing.

Retzlaff, Georg. What Jesus Taught & Why it Matters: Towards A Christianity with No Other Foundation but Christ. 2010. 128p. pap. 11.95 *(978-1-4520-7718-5(5))* AuthorHouse.

Reynolds, John T. Will the Real Church Please Stand. 2011. 100p. 24.99 ***(978-1-4628-9978-4(1))***; pap. 15.99 ***(978-1-4628-9977-7(3))*** Xlibris Corp.

Rhea, Henry T. He Descended into Hell. 2011. pap. 29.99 ***(978-1-61346-571-4(8))*** Tate Publishing & Enterprises, LLC.

Rhodes, Wil. P. E. R. S. O. N. A. L. Ministry Profile. 2009. 294p. pap. 29.95 *(978-0-557-10141-2(7))* Lulu Enterprises Inc.

Riccardi, Constantino Vincent. Christ & Freedom. 2010. 282p. pap. 30.00 *(978-1-60899-709-1(X)*, Wipf and Stock) Wipf & Stock Pubs.

Rich, Cynthia Holder. The Fifohazana: Madagascar's Indigenous Christian Movement. 2008. 300p. 109.95 *(978-1-60497-581-9(4))* Cambria Pr.

Rich, Cynthia Holder. Indigenous Christianity in Madagascar: The Power to Heal in Community. 2011. xx, 188p. (C). 76.95 ***(978-1-4331-1416-8(X))*** Lang, Peter Publishing, Inc.

Richards, George W. Beyond Fundamentalism & Modernism: The Gospel of God. 2007. (ENG.). 346p. 46.95 *(978-0-548-05846-6(6))* Kessinger Publishing, LLC.

Richardson, Robert F. Justice Pending: The Revelation of God's Inconvenient Truth. 2010. 424p. 42.95 *(978-1-4497-0362-2(3))*; pap. 27.95 *(978-1-4497-0361-5(5))* Author Solutions, Inc. (WestBow Pr.).

Richie, John D. The Myths of Christianity. 2006. (ENG.). 268p. per. 15.95 *(978-1-59800-837-1(4))* Outskirts Pr., Inc.

Richison, Grant C. Certainty: A Place to Stand. 2010. ***(978-1-894860-62-8(4))*** BayRidge Bks.

Ricoeur, Paul. Living up to Death. Pellauer, David, tr. from FRE. 2009. (ENG., Illus.). 132p. 22.50 *(978-0-226-71349-6(0))* Univ. of Chicago Pr.

Riell, Howard Michael. Enoch & the Book of Comfort - Light for the Darkness to Come. 2011. 284p. pap. 15.95 ***(978-1-60264-721-3(6))*** Virtualbookworm.com Publishing, Inc.

Riter, Mike. 2033 When the Creator Returns. 2011. 240p. 31.99 ***(978-1-4568-1867-8(8))***; pap. 21.99 ***(978-1-4568-1866-1(X))*** Xlibris Corp.

Rivera, Victor Manuel. En Busca de la Verdadera Libertad. 2010. 124p. pap. 11.99 *(978-1-60957-599-1(7))* Xulon Pr., Inc.

Roark, M. A. Wide or Narrow: What You Believe Chooses Your Path, 1 vol. 2010. 108p. pap. 19.95 *(978-1-4489-4668-6(9))* PublishAmerica, Inc.

Robert, Morritt. Christian Epigraphy: Early Christian Epitaphs & Inscriptions & History of Their Preservation. 2011. 424p. pap. ***(978-3-639-34233-8(X))*** VDM Verlag Dr. Mueller e.K.

Roberts, Bob J. Glocalization: How Followers of Jesus Engage the New Flat World, 1 vol. 2007. (ENG., Illus.). 208p. 18.99 *(978-0-310-26718-8(8))* Zondervan.

Roberts, Lynn. Lost & Found. 2011. 144p. pap. 13.70 ***(978-1-4567-6883-6(2))*** AuthorHouse.

Robertson, S. & Robertson, B. Mission to India. 2010. 216p. pap. 39.47 *(978-1-4269-1269-6(2))* Trafford Publishing.

Robertson, Stan. Why Was That Tree in the Garden, Anyway? 2009. 400p. pap. 24.95 *(978-1-58982-528-4(4)*, Millennial Mind Publishing) American Bk. Publishing Group.

Robin, Tabitha. Controversy in the Church: the Truth Revealed. 2008. 59p. pap. 8.01 *(978-1-4357-4035-8(1))* Lulu Enterprises Inc.

Robinson, Frank B. The God Nobody Knows. 2007. (ENG.). 228p. 41.95 *(978-0-548-08839-5(X))* Kessinger Publishing, LLC.

Rodd, Cyril S. Thinking Things Through No. 5: Is There Life After Death? 128p. 10.00 *(978-0-7162-0520-3(3))* Epworth Pr., The GBR. Dist: Morehouse Publishing.

Rodriguez, Angel M. Spanning the Abyss: How the Atonement Brings Humanity & God Together. 2008. 10.99 *(978-0-8280-2357-3(3))* Review & Herald Publishing Assn.

Rodriguez, Samuel. Path of Miracles: The Seven Life-Changing Principles That Lead to Purpose & Fulfillment. 2010. (ENG.). 272p. (gr. 12-18). 15.00 *(978-0-451-22883-3(9)*, Celebra) Penguin Group (USA) Inc.

Rogers, D. R. The Weeping Merchants. 2008. 120p. pap. 14.95 *(978-1-4357-3639-9(7))* Lulu Enterprises Inc.

Rogers, Glenn. The Simplified New Testament Study Bible. 2010. 636p. pap. 45.00 *(978-0-9792072-9-7(0))* Mission & Ministry Resources.

Romanow, Beverly E. One Mother's Story. 2011. ***(978-1-77069-270-1(3))*** Word Alive Pr.

Roscoe, Hugh. Occultism & Christianity: A Restatement of Faith. 2007. (ENG.). 168p. 36.95 *(978-0-548-05587-8(4))* Kessinger Publishing, LLC.

Rosen, Ruthe. Never Give Up: How to Find Hope & Purpose in Adversity. 2011. 200p. pap. 16.95 ***(978-1-879384-86-6(8))*** Cypress Hse.

Ross, Robert R. Thus Saith the Lord God of Israel, Let My People Go! 2006. per. 12.95 *(978-0-9787801-0-4(8))* CSM Technical Institute.

Rothwell, Malcolm. Sense & Nonsense: Conversations with a clown about spiritual Things. 2011. 300p. pap. 18.73 *(978-1-4567-7010-5(1))* AuthorHouse.

Rottier, Debbie. A Cup of Cold Water: Hospitality at Its Best. 2nd ed. 2012. (Illus.). 176p. pap. 19.99 ***(978-1-57658-715-7(0))*** YWAM Publishing.

Royce, Josiah. William James & Other Essays on the Ph. 2006. pap. 30.95 *(978-1-4286-3784-9(2))* Kessinger Publishing, LLC.

Royston, Julia A. Frontline Worshipper. 2011. 92p. pap. 10.00 ***(978-0-9818135-7-8(7))*** BK Royston Publishing.

Rubin, M. Medieval Christianity in Practice. 2009. (Princeton Readings in Religions Ser.). (ENG., Illus.). 360p. (C). pap. 27.95 *(978-0-691-09059-7(9))* Princeton Univ. Pr.

Ruge-Jones, Philip. The Word of the Cross in a World of Glory. 2008. (Lutheran Voices Ser.). 96p. per. 11.99 *(978-0-8066-8005-7(9)*, Augsburg Fortress) Augsburg Fortress, Pubs.

Rush, John A. Failed God: Fractured Myth in a Fragile World. 2008. (ENG., Illus.). 472p. pap. 28.95 *(978-1-58394-274-1(2)*, Frog Ltd.) North Atlantic Bks.

Rush, Stephen & Hamilton, Reid H. Better Get It in Your Soul: What Liturgists Can Learn from Jazz. 2008. 176p. pap. 18.00 *(978-0-89869-574-8(0))* Church Publishing, Inc.

Russell, Mark A. Lessons in Christianity from Man's Best Friend: Man's Best Friend Teaches One How to Become Better Companion & Friend for God. 2011. 152p. pap. 13.50 ***(978-1-4634-2234-9(2))*** AuthorHouse.

Russell, Thomas Arthur. Comparative Christianity: A Student's Guide to a Religion & Its Diverse Traditions. 2010. pap. 34.95 *(978-1-59942-877-2(6))* Universal Pubs.

Ryniker, Robert K. 20 Years of Faith. 2008. 108p. 29.99 *(978-1-4363-1274-5(4))*; pap. 19.99 *(978-1-4363-1273-8(6))* Xlibris Corp.

Sabbath, R. Sacred Tropes: Tanakh, New Testament, & Qur'an as Literature & Culture. 2009. (Biblical Interpretation Ser.). 544p. *(978-90-04-17752-9(3))* BRILL.

Salazar, Teresa. A Trumpet Blast. 2010. 57p. pap. 8.00 *(978-0-557-67862-4(5))* Lulu Enterprises Inc.

Salmonson, Marilyn. Voice of Encouraging Thoughts. 2007. (Illus.). 238p. per. 26.99 *(978-1-59886-417-5(3))* Tate Publishing & Enterprises, LLC.

Saltzgiver, Ty. Considering Christianity. Date not set. 2.50 *(978-0-9616562-1-8(2))* Salt Resources, Inc.

Salvetti, Neville. Who Is Jesus the Christ. 2011. 62p. pap. 15.99 ***(978-1-4653-0036-2(8))*** Xlibris Corp.

Samellas, Antigone. Alienation: The Experience of the Eastern Mediterranean, 50-600 A. D. 2010. 556p. pap. *(978-3-03911-789-5(0))* Lang, Peter.

Samman, Khaldoun. Cities of God & Nationalism: Mecca, Jerusalem, & Rome as Contested World Cities. 2007. (ENG.). 290p. 125.00 *(978-1-59451-293-3(0))*; per. 39.95 *(978-1-59451-294-0(9))* Paradigm Pubs.

Sampson, Fay. Visions & Voyages: The Story of Celtic Spirituality. 2009. (ENG., Illus.). 192p. pap. 16.95 *(978-0-7459-5235-2(6))* Lion Hudson PLC GBR. Dist: Independent Pubs. Group.

Sampson, Philip, et al, eds. Faith & Modernity. 2011. 352p. pap. 39.00 ***(978-1-61097-590-2(1)***, Wipf and Stock) Wipf & Stock Pubs.

Sanders, Anthony R. 90 Days: A Journal Between You & God. 2011. 246p. 15.99 *(978-1-61379-028-1(7))*; pap. 15.99 *(978-1-61379-027-4(9))* Xulon Pr., Inc.

Sandford, R. Loren. The Prophetic Church: Wielding the Power to Change the World. 2009. 224p. pap. 17.00 *(978-0-8007-9462-0(1))* Chosen Bks.

Sanneh, Lamin O. & Akinade, Akintunde E. A New Day: Essays on World Christianity in Honor of Lamin Sanneh. 2010. 338p. (C). 84.95 *(978-1-4331-0456-5(3))* Lang, Peter Publishing, Inc.

Santoro, Nicholas J. Mary in Our Life: Atlas of the Names & Titles of Mary, the Mother of Jesus, & Their Place in Marian Devotion. 2011. 772p. pap. 55.95 ***(978-1-4620-4021-6(7))*** iUniverse, Inc.

Saunders, Gartrell. A Poignant Place in Him. 2010. 118p. pap. 11.99 *(978-1-60957-604-2(7))* Xulon Pr., Inc.

Saunders, Stan. Permission Granted: Liberation & Motivation for Spectator Churchgoers. 2011. pap. 10.99 *(978-1-61739-931-2(0))* Tate Publishing & Enterprises, LLC.

Saward, John. Sweet & Blessed Country: The Christian Hope for Heaven. 2008. (ENG.). 208p. pap. 19.95 *(978-0-19-954366-3(6))* Oxford Univ. Pr., Inc.

Saxton, Jeff. The New Pharisee. 2010. 264p. 26.75 *(978-1-60693-976-5(9)*, Strategic Bk. Publishing) AEG Literary Publishing Services, Inc.

Scantlebury, Michael. Kingdom Advancing Prayer Volume 3. 2006. 240p. per. *(978-1-894928-80-9(6))* Word Alive Pr.

Schaeffer, Francis A. The Mark of the Christian. 2nd ed. 2006. (IVP Classics Ser.). (ENG.). 63p. (Orig.). per. 6.00 *(978-0-8308-3407-5(9)*, IVP Bks.) InterVarsity Pr.

Schatkin, Andrew. Essays on the Christian Worldview & Others Political, Literary, & Philosophical. 2010. (ENG.). 134p. pap. 22.50 *(978-0-7618-5343-5(X))* Hamilton Bks.

Schillebeeckx, Edward. World & Church: Schillebeeckx Collected Works 4. 2013. (ENG.). 272p. 110.00 ***(978-0-567-05422-7(5)***, T&T Clark Int'l) Continuum International Publishing Group, Ltd. GBR. Dist: National Bk. Network.

Schlatter, Victor. Showdown of the Gods. 176p. pap. 9.99 *(978-1-58169-121-4(1)*, Evergreen Pr.) Genesis Communications, Inc.

Schlink, M. Basilea. Patmos, Cuando los Cielos Se Abrieron: Patmos: When the Heavens Opened. (SPA.). 160p. *(978-84-7228-240-7(6)*, 220673) Clie, Editorial.

Schoenecker, R. W. Agnus Dei: From the works of Maria Valtorta. 2010. 582p. pap. 29.95 *(978-1-4327-6166-0(8))* Outskirts Pr., Inc.

Schultz, Doug & Esau, Ken. Let's Face It! A Group Study in the Nature of the Church. 81p. pap. 3.95 *(978-0-921788-52-2(5))* Kindred Productions.

Schumacher, John N. Growth & Decline: Essays on Philippine Church History. 2010. 302p. pap. 43.00 *(978-971-550-588-8(0))* Univ. of the Philippines Pr. PHL. Dist: Univ. of Hawaii Pr.

Schuon, Frithjof. Christianity/Islam: Perspectives on Esoteric Ecumenism, a New Translation with Selected Letters. 2008. (ENG., Illus.). 256p. pap. 19.95 *(978-1-933316-49-9(7))* World Wisdom, Inc.

Schwindt, Bernie. Lost at Sea. 2010. pap. 11.95 *(978-0-7414-5813-1(6))* Infinity Publishing.

Scott, Janet. What Canst Thou Say? Towards a Quaker Theology. 2007. 100p. per. *(978-0-901689-74-0(2))* Quaker Books.

Scott, Lynne. A Sign for Life. 2008. 128p. pap. 11.99 *(978-1-4343-3872-3(X))* AuthorHouse.

Scott, Thomas. Essays on the Most Important Subjects in Religion. 2009. 376p. 31.99 *(978-1-115-71248-4(9))*; pap. 20.99 *(978-1-115-71251-4(9))* BiblioBazaar.

—Essays on the Most Important Subjects in Religion. 2009. 306p. pap. *(978-0-217-71518-8(4))* Books LLC.

—Essays on the Most Important Subjects in Religion. 2009. 262p. pap. 21.24 *(978-0-217-71521-8(4))* General Bks. LLC.

—Essays on the Most Important Subjects in Religion. 2007. (ENG.). 370p. 48.95 *(978-0-548-14990-4(9))*; 372p. per. 33.95 *(978-1-4304-4316-2(2))* Kessinger Publishing, LLC.

Scougal, Henry. The Life of God in the Soul of Man. Hudson, Winthrop S., ed. 2011. 96p. pap. 7.95 ***(978-1-891396-78-6(1))*** Martino Publishing.

See, Alva B. Naked Before God: Out of Darkness unto Light. 2011. pap. 22.99 *(978-1-61739-097-5(6))* Tate Publishing & Enterprises, LLC.

Sellars, Roy Wood. The Next Step in Religion. 2011. 154p. pap. 12.99 ***(978-1-61203-917-6(0))*** Bottom of the Hill Publishing.

Setiawan, Mohamad Nur Kholis & Djaka Soetapa. Meniti Kalam Kerukunan: Beberapa Istilah Dalam Islam Dan Kristen. 2010. (IND., Illus.). *(978-979-687-756-0(2))* BPK GUNUNG MULIA.

Settje, David. Faith & War: How Christians Debated the Cold & Vietnam Wars. 2011. (ENG.). 244p. 39.00 *(978-0-8147-4133-7(9))* New York Univ. Pr.

Settje, David E. Faith & War: How Christians Debated the Cold & Vietnam Wars. 2011. E-Book *(978-0-8147-4134-4(7))* New York Univ. Pr.

Sexton. What Volcano Will Soon Erupt & Shake the Whole World? 48p. pap. 9.95 *(978-1-57090-082-2(5)*, Mountain Church) aBOOKS Distributing.

Seyfried, Elise. Unhaling: on God, Grace & a Perfectly Imperfect Life. 2010. 160p. pap. 19.51 *(978-0-578-05056-0(0))* Venia Pr.

Seymour, C. A Theodicy of Hell. 2010. (Studies in Philosophy & Religion Ser.). 224p. pap. 149.00 *(978-90-481-5478-4(2)*, 9048154782) Springer.

Shaird, Mary K. Vying for Second Place: Living in submission to Christ. 2009. 157p. pap. 16.99 *(978-0-557-15281-0(X))* Lulu Enterprises Inc.

Shanks, Herschel. Christianity & Rabbinic Judaism. 2nd ed. 2011. (ENG.). 480p. (C). pap. 46.67 ***(978-0-205-85916-0(X)***, Prentice Hall) Prentice Hall PTR.

Shark, Carson. Jesus Birth: [6 B. C.] [1 A. D.] [6 A. D.]. 2011. 264p. 29.95 ***(978-1-4620-5803-7(5))***; pap. 19.95 ***(978-1-4620-5801-3(9))*** iUniverse, Inc.

Shaw, Donna Kellough. A Woman of Lydi. 2009. 140p. pap. 14.99 *(978-1-60791-436-5(0))* Xulon Pr., Inc.

Shaw, Philip A. & Petts, David. Pagan & Christian: Religious Change in Early Medieval Europe. 2011. (Duckworth Debates in Archaeology Ser.). (Illus.). 144p. pap. 24.95 *(978-0-7156-3754-8(1))* Duckworth Publishers GBR. Dist: International Publishers Marketing.

Shea, Suzanne Strempek & Strempek Shea, Suzanne. Sundays in America: A Yearlong Road Trip in Search of Christian Faith. 2009. (ENG.). 324p. pap. 16.00 *(978-0-8070-7225-7(7))* Beacon Pr.

Shean, John F. Soldiering for God: Christianity & the Roman Army. 2010. xviii, 452p. *(978-90-04-18731-3(6))* BRILL.

Sheets, Dutch. Intercessory Prayer. 2008. (Beginner's Guide To Ser.). (ENG.). 192p. per. 12.99 *(978-0-8307-4539-5(4))* Gospel Light Pubns.

Shemer, Ze'ev. The Answer: Does Religion Really Matter? 2011. 176p. pap. 15.95 *(978-1-4502-8773-9(5))* iUniverse, Inc.

Shepard, D. Introducing the Lambeth Bible: A Study of Text & Imagery. 2007. (ENG., Illus.). 320p. (C). 152.00 *(978-2-503-51511-3(8))* Brepols Pubs. BEL. Dist: ISD.

Shipe, Ernest. Seven Words of Love: A Love Letter from Golgotha to Your Heart. 2010. 124p. 23.95 *(978-1-4502-1307-3(3))*; pap. 13.95 *(978-1-4502-1305-9(7))* iUniverse, Inc.

Shomuyiwa, Oladayo. Unlocking the Spirit of Excellence: A Guide to an Excellent Life in God, 1 vol. 2010. 162p. pap. 24.95 *(978-1-4489-7826-7(2))* PublishAmerica, Inc.

Showalter, Richard & Showalter, Jewel. A Silk Road Pilgrimage: Discovering the Church of the East. 2009. pap. 12.99 *(978-0-8361-9477-7(2))* Herald Pr.

Shubin, Daniel H. Heavenly Relationships. 2008. 239p. pap. 16.99 *(978-0-557-02371-4(8))* Lulu Enterprises Inc.

Shuman, Joel James & Owens, L. Roger, eds. Wendell Berry & Religion: Heaven's Earthly Life. 2009. (Culture of the Land Ser.). (ENG., Illus.). 272p. 40.00 *(978-0-8131-2555-8(3))* Univ. Pr. of Kentucky.

Shupe, Bob G. The Little Brown Church in the Vale ... When Did the Lights Go Out? 2008. pap. 13.95 *(978-1-60494-137-1(5))* Wheatmark.

Shuping, Isaiah. The Mind of God. 2007. 120p. pap. 17.95 *(978-1-84753-119-3(9))* Lulu Enterprises Inc.

Sibbes, Richard. Bruised Reed & A Description of Christ. 2010. 232p. pap. 20.00 *(978-1-4466-4003-6(5))* Lulu Enterprises Inc.

Siedell, Daniel A. God in the Gallery: A Christian Embrace of Modern Art. 2008. (Cultural Exegesis Ser.). (Illus.). 192p. (C). pap. 25.00 *(978-0-8010-3184-7(2))* Baker Academic.

Silié, Edwin. It's NOT about Me! Preaching to the Man in the Mirror. 2011. 180p. 30.95 ***(978-1-4497-1388-1(2))***; pap. 13.95 ***(978-1-4497-1387-4(4))*** Author Solutions, Inc. (WestBow Pr.).

Silva, Mike. Would You Like Fries with That?, 0 vols. 2008. 132p. pap. 9.99 *(978-0-7852-9648-5(4))* Nelson, Thomas Inc.

Sim, John. God Revealed in John. 2011. 226p. 29.99 ***(978-1-4568-0796-2(X))*** Xlibris Corp.

Simmons, Brandon. Christianity: Are You Addicted? 2009. 60p. pap. 10.49 *(978-1-4389-5664-0(9))* AuthorHouse.

Simpson, A. B. Practical Christianity. 2009. 115p. pap. 11.99 *(978-1-60066-088-7(6))* WingSpread Publishers.

Singh, Laurance. Biblical Principles & Affirmations for Successful Living. 2009. 168p. pap. 11.99 *(978-1-4389-7731-7(X))* AuthorHouse.

Singley, Sharon. Born of Adam Born of God. 2010. 107p. pap. 9.99 *(978-0-557-33525-1(6))* Lulu Enterprises Inc.

Siniossoglou, Niketas. Plato & Theodoret: The Christian Appropriation of Platonic Philosophy & the Hellenic Intellectual Resistance. 2011. (Cambridge Classical Studies). (ENG.). 280p. pap. 36.99 (978-0-521-30065-0(7)) Cambridge Univ. Pr.

—Radical Platonism in Byzantium: Illumination & Utopia in Gemistos Plethon. 2011. (Cambridge Classical Studies). (ENG., Illus.). 470p. 120.00 (978-1-107-01303-2(8)) Cambridge Univ. Pr.

Six Short Messages to the Hip Hop Generation from the Word of God. 2008. 36p. (YA). (978-0-9792839-4-9(9)) Word Of God Ministry.

Skelton, Stephen. InSight: Harry Potter Guide Book. 2010. (ENG.). 28p. 2.99 (978-0-9827891-6-2(5)) Primetime Parable Ministries.

Slattery, Dennis Patrick. Day-to-Day Dante: Exploring Personal Myth through the Divine Comedy. 2011. 404p. 35.95 (978-1-4502-8365-6(9)); pap. 25.95 (978-1-4502-8363-2(2)) iUniverse, Inc.

Smith, D. Sc. Assault on Tradition: The Decline of Christianity & Western Civilization. 2011. 150p. pap. 24.95 **(978-1-4512-4061-0(9))** PublishAmerica, Inc.

Smith, Dana. One Truth, One Hope, One Salvation. 2010. 105p. pap. 12.95 (978-0-557-55106-4(4)) Lulu Enterprises Inc.

Smith, David. Bible Lessons from Our Pets. 2011. (ENG.). 144p. mass mkt. 12.95 **(978-1-936417-25-4(1))** Pilot Communications Group, Inc.

Smith, E. Elaine. Demolition in Progress: Exposing the Enemy. 2008. 84p. pap. 16.95 (978-1-60474-386-9(7)) PublishAmerica, Inc.

Smith, George P. The Christian Religion & Biotechnology: A Search for Principled Decision-making. 2010. (International Library of Ethics, Law, & the New Medicine Ser.). xx, 254p. pap. 219.00 (978-90-481-6808-8(2), 9048168082) Springer.

Smith, Harold "Chris". The Splendor of God's Word!!! 2006. 336p. per. 18.95 (978-1-59824-367-3(5)) E-BookTime LLC.

Smith, Huston. The Soul of Christianity: Restoring the Great Tradition. 2006. (Plus Ser.). (ENG.). 208p. pap. 14.99 (978-0-06-085835-3(4), HarperOne) HarperCollins Pubs.

Smith, J. Translated Hallelujahs: A Linguistic & Exegetical Commentary on Select Septuagint Psalms. 2011. (Contributions to Biblical Exegesis & Theology Ser.). (ENG.). 300p. (C). pap. 56.00 (978-90-429-2384-3(9)) Peeters Pubs. & Booksellers BEL. Dist: Brown, David Bk. Co., The.

Smith, James K. A. The Devil Reads Derrida - & Other Essays on the University, the Church, Politics, & the Arts. 2009. 192p. pap. 18.00 (978-0-8028-6407-9(4)) Eerdmans, William B. Publishing Co.

Smith, Joseph Nathan. The Generations of Noah. 2008. 128p. pap. 16.99 (978-0-615-19309-0(9)) Smith, Joseph Nathan.

Smith, Lisa. Tuesday's Girl. 2011. 64p. pap. 9.95 (978-1-4497-0760-6(2), WestBow Pr.) Author Solutions, Inc.

Smith, Paul R. Integral Christianity: The Spirit's Call to Evolve. 2011. (ENG., Illus.). 408p. 24.95 (978-1-55778-891-7(X)) Paragon Hse. Pubs.

Solovyov, Vladimir. A Solovyov Anthology. 2nd ed. (RUS & ENG.). 250p. (978-1-901157-19-2(9)) St. Austin Pr.

Solovyov, Vladimir Sergeyevich. Freedom, Faith, & Dogma: Essays by V.S. Soloviev on Christianity & Judaism. 2008. vii, 251p. (C). 70.00 (978-0-7914-7535-5(2)) State Univ. of New York Pr.

Sompayrac. Experimental Christianity. 2010. 144p. pap. 11.95 (978-1-59330-682-3(2)) Aventine Pr.

Sozo, Joshua. Divine Insurrection. 2008. 483p. pap. 32.50 (978-1-4303-1619-0(5)) Lulu Enterprises Inc.

Spurr, Barry. Anglo-Catholic in Religion: T. S. Eliot & Christianity. 2010. (ENG., Illus.). 340p. pap. 53.00 (978-0-7188-3073-1(3)) Lutterworth Pr., The GBR. Dist: Brown, David Bk. Co., The.

St Rose, J. Lambert. Helen & Her Sister Haiti: A theological reflection on the social, historical,economic, religious, political & national consciousness with a call T. 2011. 404p. 29.99 **(978-1-4634-3538-7(X))** AuthorHouse.

Stafford, Gilbert W. Signals at the Crossroads: The Church of God in the 21st Century. 2011. (ENG.). 254p. pap. 17.95 **(978-1-59317-544-3(2))** Warner Pr. Pubs.

Stalder, S. J. Our Hebraic Roots: Digging into the Purpose of God's Celebrations. 2011. pap. 12.99 **(978-1-61777-227-6(5))** Tate Publishing & Enterprises, LLC.

Stalker, James. The Atonement. 2008. 157p. pap. 19.95 (978-0-557-00807-0(7)) Lulu Enterprises Inc.

Standish, Colin D. & Standish, Russell R. The Everlasting Gospel. 2007. 368p. per. 16.95 (978-0-923309-23-7(3)) Hartland Pubns.

Standish, Colin D. & Russell R. The 144,000 the Great Multitude & the Return of Jesus. 2007. 352p. per. 16.95 (978-0-923309-95-4(0)) Hartland Pubns.

Stanley, Charles F. The Power of God's Love: A 31-Day Devotional to Encounter the Father's Greatest Gift, 0 vols. 2008. 160p. pap. 7.99 (978-1-4002-0093-1(8)) Nelson, Thomas Inc.

Stanley, Joseph. The Paschal Mystery: Devotions for Lent & Easter. 2011. 164p. pap. 13.95 (978-1-4497-0500-8(6), WestBow Pr.) Author Solutions, Inc.

Stark, Rodney. The Triumph of Christianity: How the Jesus Movement Became the World's Largest Religion. 2011. (ENG.). 272p. 27.99 (978-0-06-200768-1(8), HarperOne) HarperCollins Pubs.

Starkey, A. Denise. The Shame That Lingers: A Survivor-Centered Critique of Catholic Sin-Talk. 2009. (American University Studies VII: Theology & Religion Ser.). 216p. (C). 39.95 (978-1-4331-0676-7(0)) Lang, Peter Publishing, Inc.

Starr, Brian D. Major Saints Ancestry. 2010. 258p. pap. 19.99 (978-1-4535-4094-7(6)) Xlibris Corp.

Starr, Chloe & Starr. Reading Christian Scriptures in China. 2008. (ENG.). 240p. 130.00 (978-0-567-03292-8(2), T&T Clark Int'l) Continuum International Publishing Group, Ltd. GBR. Dist: National Bk. Network.

Starr, G. A., ed. Christianity Not as Old as the Creation: The Last of Defoe's Performances, 1 vol. 2011. (Pickering Masters Ser.). (ENG.). 160p. 125.00 (978-1-84893-191-6(3)) Pickering & Chatto Pubs., Ltd. GBR. Dist: Ashgate Publishing Co.

Steed, Josh. Faith & Football: A Look at Life Through A Facemask. 2009. 176p. 24.99 (978-1-4490-1369-1(4)) AuthorHouse.

Stefon, Matt. Christianity: History, Belief, & Practice. 2011. (Illus.). xvii, 384p. lib. bdg. 70.50 (978-1-61530-493-6(2)) Rosen Publishing Group, Inc., The.

Steiner, Rudolf. Christ & the Human Soul. 2011. 50p. 36.95 **(978-1-258-00629-7(4))** Literary Licensing, LLC.

Steiner, Rudolf. Christianity As Mystical Fact. Welburn, Andrew J., tr. from GER. & pref. by. 5th ed. 2006. (Classics in Anthroposophy Ser.: 8). 256p. pap. 17.95 (978-0-88010-436-4(8)) SteinerBooks, Inc.

Stekeler-Weithofer, Pirmin. Sinn. 2011. (Grundthemen Philosophie Ser.).Tr. of Meaning. (GER.). 217p. pap. 28.00 **(978-3-11-025415-0(8))** De Gruyter, Walter Inc.

Stevens, Kent. DANIEL: Touchstone of Prophecy. 2008. 300p. pap. 17.50 (978-1-4357-3387-9(8)) Lulu Enterprises Inc.

Stewart, Donald K. Theologically Speaking & Much More: Conscious Theological Reflections for Ordinary, Everyday People. 2011. (ENG.). 394p. pap. 23.95 **(978-1-4327-7873-6(0))** Outskirts Pr., Inc.

Stibbe, Mark W. G. Guide to Christian Belief. 2007. (Questions of Faith Ser.). (Illus.). 143p. pap. 14.95 (978-1-59856-224-8(X)); pap. 9.97 (978-1-59856-328-3(9)) Hendrickson Pubs. Marketing, LLC.

Stone, Eric A. Religion & Human Survival: An Essay. 13p. (C). lib. bdg. 7.95 (978-0-9631937-1-1(6)) BioPsychology Pr.

Stone, Perry F. Nightmare along Pennsylvania Avenue: Prophetic Insight into America's Role in the Coming End Times. 2009. (ENG.). 336p. 21.99 (978-1-59979-860-8(3), Frontline) Charisma Media.

Stott, John. Basic Christianity. 2006. (IVP Classics Ser.). (ENG.). 180p. per. 6.00 (978-0-8308-3403-7(6), IVP Bks.) InterVarsity Pr.

—Basic Christianity. 2012. (IVP Classics Ser.). (ENG.). 192p. pap. 6.00 **(978-0-8308-3413-6(3)**, IVP Bks.) InterVarsity Pr.

Stott, John. Basic Christianity. 50th anniv. ed. 2008. 176p. pap. 8.00 (978-0-8028-6463-5(5)) Eerdmans, William B. Publishing Co.

Strachan, Owen & Sweeney, Doug. Jonathan Edwards on Heaven & Hell, 1 vol. 2010. (Essential Edwards Collection). (ENG.). 160p. pap. 9.99 (978-0-8024-2461-7(9)) Moody Pubs.

Strom, Andrew. The Out-of-Church Christians. 2008. 116p. pap. 9.88 (978-0-9799073-5-7(7)) RevivalSchl.

Strutz, Richard. Transforming Truth. 2010. 180p. pap. 12.95 (978-1-4327-5677-2(X)) Outskirts Pr., Inc.

Stuart, Moses. Letters on the Eternal Generation of the Son of God. 2010. 174p. pap. 13.99 (978-0-557-55586-1(2)) Lulu Enterprises Inc.

Stuart, Tony. What the Bible Says about Your Body. 2007. pap. 19.99 (978-1-60034-869-3(6)) Xulon Pr., Inc.

Stuchbery, Ian. Experiencing God in a Secular World. 2011. (ENG.). 90p. pap. 17.95 (978-0-7618-5498-2(3)) Hamilton Bks.

Stumpf, Christoph & Zaborowski, Holger, eds. Church as Politeia: The Political Self-Understanding of Christianity. Proceedings of a Becket Institute Conference at the University of Oxford, 28 September - ' October 2000. (Arbeiten zur Kirchengeschichte Ser.). XII, 352p. 255.00 **(978-3-11-187474-6(5))** De Gruyter, Walter Inc.

Suba, Abd'Isho. The Pearl. 2010. (SYR.). 98.24 (978-1-61143-346-3(0)) Gorgias Pr., LLC

Sullivan, Jan. Forever Family. 2008. 116p. pap. 10.99 (978-1-60647-482-2(0)) Xulon Pr., Inc.

Summerville, Rosey. Divinity: How to Partake in the Divine Nature of Jesus Christ. 2011. pap. 11.99 **(978-1-61777-570-3(3))** Tate Publishing & Enterprises, LLC.

Swanson, Reuben J. Bread? or Crumbs? A Collection of Sermons for Advent, Christmas, Epiphany, & Pentecost. 2007. 378p. pap. 42.00 (978-1-55635-194-5(1), Resource Pubns.) Wipf & Stock Pubs.

Swedenborg, Emanuel. Heaven & Its Wonders & Hell: From Things Heard & Seen. 2008. 476p. pap. (978-1-4097-1321-0(0)) Read Bks.

—The True Christian Religion. 2009. 268p. pap. (978-1-4589-0834-6(8)); 384p. pap. (978-0-217-64171-5(7)) Books LLC.

Sweet, Danice. Consider It Joy. 2007. 116p. per. 16.95 (978-0-9768083-9-8(0)) Pearson Publishing Co.

Sweet, Leonard, ed. The Church of the Perfect Storm. 2008. 187p. per. 17.00 (978-0-687-65089-7(5)) Abingdon Pr.

Tackett, Del & Ware, Jim. Daily Travelogue: Scripture Devotional. 2007. (Illus.). x, 211p. pap. (978-1-58997-530-9(8)) Focus on the Family Publishing.

Takeuchi, S. J. Osamu & Takeuchi, S. J. Conscience & Culture. 2010. 228p. pap. (978-3-8383-5782-9(5)) Lambert Academic Publishing.

Tanabe, Jennifer P. The Words of David S. C. Kim: Let Us Learn from the Past. 2010. 321p. pap. 24.95 (978-0-557-28334-7(5)) Lulu Enterprises Inc.

Taneti, James Elisha. History of the Telugu Christians: A Bibliography. 2011. xii, 109p. E-Book **(978-0-8108-7509-8(8))** Scarecrow Pr., Inc.

Taniguchi, Masaharu. Truth of Life: Book of General Principles, Vol. 1. 2nd ed. 2006. Orig. Title: Seimei No Jisso, Tochuban, Vol. 1. pap. 11.00 (978-0-9661797-0-5(6)) Seicho-No-Ie, Inc.

Taylor, Charles L. The Marked Bible. 2008. 132p. 21.99 (978-0-554-58043-2(8)); 128p. 24.99 (978-0-554-58031-9(4)); 128p. pap. 19.75 (978-0-554-58041-8(1)); 128p. pap. 20.75 (978-0-554-58035-7(7)) BiblioBazaar.

—The Marked Bible. 2007. (ENG.). 128p. 35.95 (978-0-548-07016-1(4)) Kessinger Publishing, LLC.

Taylor, Qiana Renee'. Pure Beauty: What I could not seeä¿ My Story, 1 vol. 2010. 48p. pap. 16.95 (978-1-4489-3300-6(5)) PublishAmerica, Inc.

Taylor, Tracy Carol. 60 Christian Traits. 2011. pap. 14.99 (978-1-61739-148-4(4)) Tate Publishing & Enterprises, LLC.

Temple, William. The Faith & Modern Thought - Six Lectures. 2007. 188p. per. (978-1-4067-8826-6(0), Pomona Pr.) Read Bks.

Terpstra, John. Skin Boat: Acts of Faith & Other Navigations. 2009. (ENG.). 160p. pap. (978-1-55447-079-2(X)) Gaspereau Pr.

Terrell, Richard. Christ, Faith, & the Holocaust. 2011. 184p. pap. 13.95 (978-1-4497-0912-9(5), WestBow Pr.) Author Solutions, Inc.

Terry, Thomas C. Don't Get Bit by the Viper: Exposing & Destroying the Antichrist Spirit. 2007. pap. 10.99 (978-1-60477-283-8(2)) Xulon Pr., Inc.

The Servants. Christianity-Seed of Truth: The True Foundations of Eternal Life. 2011. 196p. pap. 24.95 **(978-1-4560-3667-6(X))** PublishAmerica, Inc.

Theriault, Serge A. Msgr Dominique M Varlet: Originator of the Old Catholic Episcopal Succession 1678-1742. 2010. 422p. pap. 24.95 (978-1-933993-96-6(0)) Apocryphile Pr.

Theriot, D. M. Words to Live By: Reflections on God's Word. 2011. 64p. pap. 9.95 **(978-1-4497-2223-4(7)**, WestBow Pr.) Author Solutions, Inc.

Thibodeaux, Mark E. God's Voice Within: The Ignatian Way to Discover God's Will. 2010. (ENG.). 242p. pap. 14.95 (978-0-8294-2861-2(5)) Loyola Pr.

Thiering, Barbara. Jesus the Man: Decoding the Real Story of Jesus & Mary Magdalene. 2006. (ENG., Illus.). 464p. per. 15.00 (978-1-4165-4138-7(1), Beyond Words/Atria Bks.) Atria Bks.

Thistlethwaite, Susan Brooks, ed. Interfaith Just Peacemaking: Jewish, Christian, & Muslim Perspectives on the New Paradigm of Peace & War. 2011. (ENG., Illus.). 272p. 85.00 **(978-0-230-33989-7(1))** Palgrave Macmillan.

Thomas, C. L. The Four Pillars of Evangelism: Simple Steps to Help Any Child of God Evangelize Just Like Jesus. 2011. 220p. pap. 24.95 **(978-1-4634-3935-4(0))** AuthorHouse.

Thomas, David. Christian Doctrines in Islamic Theology. 2008. 384p. (978-90-04-16935-7(0)) BRILL.

Thomas, Derek. What Is Providence? 2008. (978-1-59638-092-9(6)) P & R Publishing.

Thomas, John N. Sacred Light: Following the Paschal Journey. 2008. 64p. 34.95 (978-0-9801529-0-6(9)) Thomas, John Photography, Inc.

Thomas, Lashundra D. So What's up with This Christianity Thing, Anyway? 2011. 72p. pap. 20.00 **(978-1-4490-8006-8(5))** AuthorHouse.

Thomas, Mahila. Book of Refutations against the Claims of the Pope. 2010. (ARC.). 90.80 (978-1-61143-350-0(9)) Gorgias Pr., LLC.

Thomas Nelson. AMAZING FREEDOM (9 inner packs Of 4) 2010. pap. 5.99 (978-1-4002-8103-9(2)) Nelson, Thomas Inc.

Thomas, Sylvia A. Tough Skin. 2006. per. 10.00 (978-0-9752851-6-9(5)) Amani Publishing, LLC.

Thomas, W. Griffith. Progreso Del Cristiano: Let Us Go On. (SPA.). 200p. (978-84-7228-856-0(0), 220727) Clie, Editorial.

Thompson, E. H., tr. from LAT. Andreae, J. V. (1619) Christianopolis. 2010. (International Archives of the History of Ideas / archives internationales d'histoire des Idées Ser.). 352p. pap. 269.00 (978-90-481-5236-0(4), 9048152364) Springer.

Thompson, Mark D. A Sure Ground on Which to Stand: The Relation of Authority & Interpretive Method in Luther's Approach to Scripture. 2006. (Studies in Christian History & Thought Ser.). (ENG.). 333p. per. 39.99 (978-1-84227-145-2(8), Paternoster) Authentic Media.

—A Sure Ground on Which to Stand: The Relation of Authority & Interpretive Method in Luther's Approach to Scripture. 2007. (Studies in Christian History & Thought Ser.). 362p. pap. 36.00 (978-1-59752-734-7(3), Wipf and Stock) Wipf & Stock Pubs.

Thornborough, Tim & Laferton, Carl. The Real Easter, 10 vols. 2010. (Christianity Explored Ser.). 16p. (978-1-906334-65-9(X)) Good Bk. Co.

Thorne, Sinclair L. The Price of Pastoral Care & Dealing with the Vision for the Church. 2010. 128p. pap. 14.99 (978-1-60957-467-3(2)) Xulon Pr., Inc.

Thornton, Norman. Searching for Christianity. 2011. (ENG.). 258p. pap. 27.18 **(978-1-906791-72-8(4))** Arena Bks. GBR. Dist: Lightning Source UK, Ltd.

Thornton, R. Scott. Inclusive Christianity: A Progressive Look at Faith. 2008. (ENG.). 189p. pap. 15.00 (978-1-932717-16-7(1)) Hope Publishing Hse.

Thurber, Bill. A Moment of Truth. 2007. 336p. per. 17.99 (978-1-60477-034-6(1)) Xulon Pr., Inc.

—A Moment of Truth John: 16. 2007. 336p. 27.99 (978-1-60477-035-3(X)) Xulon Pr., Inc.

Thurlow, Vicky. Changing the Face of God: Undoing the Damage of Religious & Abusive Programming. 2008. 264p. 25.95 (978-0-9816480-1-9(0)); (ENG., Illus.). 260p. per. 14.95 (978-0-9816480-0-2(2)) DVT Investments, LLC.

Tice, Rico & Cooper, Barry. The Real Jesus, 10 vols. 2010. (Christianity Explored Ser.). 16p. (978-1-904889-88-5(3)) Good Bk. Co.

Timanoff, Morris. A Messiah Called Winnie. 2010. 251p. pap. 16.04 (978-0-557-19358-5(3)) Lulu Enterprises Inc.

Timberlake-Linton, Marjorie Daun. Embracing Truth in Times of Adversity: Learning How to Listen & Trust Divine Guidance. 2011. 464p. 34.95 **(978-1-4620-1749-2(5))**; pap. 24.95 **(978-1-4620-1748-5(7))** iUniverse, Inc.

Timbs, Lorrie L. A Marked Soul. 2011. 80p. pap. 19.95 **(978-1-4626-2269-6(0))** PublishAmerica, Inc.

Todeschi, Kevin J. God in Real Life. 2009. 206p. 15.95 (978-0-87604-584-8(0)) A.R.E. Pr.

Tomlinson, Matt & Tomlinson, M. In God's Image: The Metaculture of Fijian Christianity. 2009. (Anthropology of Christianity Ser.). (ENG., Illus.). 261p. 55.00 (978-0-520-25777-1(4)); pap. 24.95 (978-0-520-25778-8(2)) Univ. of California Pr.

Tondeur, Keith. Your Money & Your Life: Learning How to Handle Money God's Way. 176p. 11.00 (978-0-281-04943-1(2)) SPCK Publishing GBR. Dist: Pilgrim Pr., The/United Church Pr.

Toney, Joyce. The Noahide Laws: 2007. 92p. per. 10.99 (978-1-60266-107-3(3)) Xulon Pr., Inc.

Tong, Joy Kooi-Chin. Overseas Chinese Christian Entrepreneurs in Modern China: A Case Study of the Influence of Christian Ethics on Business Life. 2012. (Key Issues in Modern Sociology Ser.). (Illus.). 180p. 99.00 **(978-0-85728-353-5(7))** Anthem Pr. GBR. Dist: Books International, Inc.

Toppar, Emefa. Beyond the Shame. 2011. 34p. pap. 14.95 **(978-1-4457-8939-2(6))** Lulu Enterprises Inc.

Tosti, John. The Book of Ittai. 2010. 233p. pap. 16.99 (978-0-557-48344-0(1)) Lulu Enterprises Inc.

Townsend, Luther Tracy. The Arena & the Throne. 2006. 268p. per. 23.99 (978-1-4255-2406-7(0)) MPublishing.

Townsend, Michael. Thinking Things Through No. 2: Worship. 112p. 10.00 (978-0-7162-0513-5(0)) Epworth Pr., The GBR. Dist: Morehouse Publishing.

Townsend, Pastor L. Fitzjerald. Learn of Me: Simple Theology for Learning Christ & Being Saved. 2011. 106p. pap. 12.95 **(978-1-4567-4996-5(X))** AuthorHouse.

Tozer, A. w. God's Pursuit of Man. 2007. 138p. pap. 12.99 (978-1-60066-184-6(X)) WingSpread Publishers.

Tozer, A. W. Reclaiming Christianity: A Call to Authentic Faith. 2009. (ENG.). 224p. pap. 14.99 (978-0-8307-4690-3(0)) Gospel Light Pubns.

Traill, Ian. Who Am I? 2008. 212p. pap. 21.00 (978-1-931178-51-8(8)) Vision Publishing.

Trickler, C. Jack. A Layman's Guide To: Why Are There So Many Christian Denominations? 2010. 292p. 25.99 (978-1-4490-4578-4(2)) AuthorHouse.

Troeltsch, Ernst. Funf Vortrage Zu Religion und Geschichtsphilosophie Fur England und Schottland. der Historismus und Seine Uberwindung (1924)/Christian Thought. Its History & Application (1923) 2006. (GER & ENG., Illus.). XVI, 268p. 189.00 (978-3-11-018232-3(7)) De Gruyter, Walter Inc.

Troy, Aidan. Out of the Shadow: Responding to Suicide. 2010. (ENG.). 140p. pap. 12.95 (978-1-84730-175-8(4)) Veritas Pubns. IRL. Dist: Dufour Editions, Inc.

Trueman, Carl R. Minority Report: Unpopular Thoughts on Everything from Ancient Christianity to Zen-Calvinism. 2007. (ENG.). 222p. per. 17.99 (978-1-84550-317-8(1), Mentor) Christian Focus Pubns. GBR. Dist: STL Distribution North America.

—Reformation: Yesterday, Today & Tomorrow. 100p. 8.99 (978-1-85049-175-0(5)) Bryntirion Pr. GBR. Dist: Spring Arbor Distributors, Inc.

Tsichlis, Michael George. For the Hope of Humanity: The Doctrine of the Dormition of the Theotokos in Orthodox Christian Tradition. 2011. 100p. pap. 9.95 **(978-1-4620-3487-1(X))** iUniverse, Inc.

Tunstall, Jim. The Seed of the Woman: The Story of an Ancient Prophecy Fulfilled. 2011. 192p. pap. 18.50 **(978-1-4520-9062-7(9))** AuthorHouse.

Turner, Allan. The Christian & Calvinism. 2007. 204p. pap. 18.95 (978-0-9777350-3-7(6)) Allanita Pr.

Turner, John W. The Key. 2010. pap. 13.99 (978-1-61566-350-7(9)) Tate Publishing & Enterprises, LLC.

Tutt, Mary Lou. Whispers of God: Creative Lover. 2011. 268p. 24.59 **(978-1-4567-6017-5(3))**; pap. 14.03 **(978-1-4567-6018-2(1))** AuthorHouse.

Tyler, Sarah & Reid, Gordon. Religion & Life: Based on a Study of Christianity & Islam. 2009. (Illus.). 128p. pap. 20.00 (978-0-340-98716-2(2)) Hodder Education GBR. Dist: Trans-Atlantic Pubns., Inc.

Tyler, Sarah K. & Reid, Gordon. Advanced Religious Studies (2Nd Edition) 2008. 504p. pap. 67.50 (978-0-340-95931-2(2)) Hodder Education GBR. Dist: Trans-Atlantic Pubns., Inc.

Umar, Pastor. Emergence of the Priests: God's End Time Army. 2011. 288p. pap. 20.38 **(978-1-4567-8588-8(5))** AuthorHouse.

Unamuno, Miguel de. Tragic Sense of Life. 2007. (ENG.). 302p. pap. 23.99 (978-1-4346-2494-9(3)); 340p. pap. 24.99 (978-1-4346-2536-6(2)) BiblioBazaar.

—Tragic Sense of Life. Flitch, J. E. Crawford, tr. 2007. (ENG.). 288p. per. (978-1-4065-5044-3(2)) Dodo Pr.

Ungar, Paul. The Mystery of Christian Faith: A Tangible Union with the Invisible God - An Apologetic on the Borderline of Theology, Medicine, & Philosophy. 2007. (ENG., Illus.). 424p. per. 59.99 (978-0-7618-3957-6(7)) Univ. Pr. of America, Inc.

Upchurch, Thomas Adams. Christian Nation? The United States in Popular Perception & Historical Reality, 1 vol. 2010. 198p. 44.95 (978-0-313-38642-8(0), A3081C, Praeger Pubs.) Greenwood Publishing Group, Inc.

Ussher, James. A Body of Divinity: The Sum & Substance of Christian Religion. 2007. 488p. per. 35.00 (978-1-59925-118-9(3)) Solid Ground Christian Bks.

Ustorf, Werner. Robinson Crusoe tries again: Missiology & European Constructions of 'Self' & 'Other' in a Global World 1789 - 2010. Loffler, Roland, ed. 2010. (Research in Contemporary Religion Ser.). (ENG.). 271p. (C). 95.00 (978-3-525-60444-1(0)) Vandenhoeck & Ruprecht GmbH & Co. KG DEU. Dist: ISD.

C

Vainio, Olli-Pekka. Beyond Fideism: Negotiable Religious Identities. 2010. (Transcending Boundaries in Philosophy & Theology Ser.). (Illus.). 196p. 89.95 *(978-1-4094-0679-2(2))* Ashgate Publishing Co.

Valantasis, Richard. The Making of the Self: Ancient & Modern Asceticism. 2008. 336p. pap. 37.00 *(978-1-55635-286-7(7))* Wipf & Stock Pubs.

Van Allen, Bob. Issues in Christianity. 2011. pap. 15.99 *(978-1-61739-530-7(7))* Tate Publishing & Enterprises, LLC.

van Beek, Huibert, ed. Revisioning Christian Unity. 2009. (Studies in Global Christianity Ser.). 320p. pap. 35.00 *(978-1-60899-109-9(1)*, Wipf and Stock) Wipf & Stock Pubs.

van der Ploeg, J. P. M. The Book of Judith. 2010. 91.04 *(978-1-61143-559-7(5))* Gorgias Pr., LLC.

Van Hook, Susan Michelle. Elijah: Hearing God in the Midst of Life's Drama. 2011. 152p. pap. 19.95 ***(978-1-4497-2439-9(6)***, WestBow Pr.) Author Solutions, Inc.

van Rensburg, Ewald. God Bless Africa: Nkosi Sikelel IAfrika. 2011. 288p. pap. 17.95 *(978-0-7963-1081-1(5))* NB Pubs. Ltd. ZAF. Dist: International Publishers Marketing.

Vanessa A. Jackson Austin. Refreshments for the Heart: God's Treasure Chest. 2009. 124p. pap. 17.99 *(978-1-4389-4268-1(0))* AuthorHouse.

Vanity, Vanity-American Christianity: Chasing the Wind. 2007. 253p. per. 14.99 *(978-1-59886-838-8(1))* Tate Publishing & Enterprises, LLC.

VanSickle, Elizabeth Paige. Conversations with God. 2009. (ENG.). 646p. 45.84 *(978-0-557-04954-7(7))*; 647p. pap. 28.88 *(978-0-557-04937-0(7))* Lulu Enterprises Inc.

Varghese, Baby. Baptism & Chrismation in the Syriac Tradition. 2011. pap. 31.10 ***(978-1-4632-0049-7(8))*** Gorgias Pr., LLC.

Varner, writer Gary R. Magic, Witchcraft, Pagans & Christians: A Study in the Suppression of Belief & the Rise of Christianity. 2010. 108p. pap. 11.50 *(978-0-557-39932-1(7))* Lulu Enterprises Inc.

Vass, Larry Ivan. A Reformed View of the Sovereignty of God in a Postmodern World. 2007. 302p. pap. 29.95 *(978-1-4241-9653-1(1))* PublishAmerica, Inc.

Vatican, II. Decr Apostolate of Laity. 40p. pap. 3.50 *(978-0-8198-1836-2(4)*, 332-056) Pauline Bks. & Media.

—Decr Church Eastern Rite. 15p. pap. *(978-0-8198-1837-9(2)*, 332-057) Pauline Bks. & Media.

—Decr Media Social Commun. 24p. pap. 1.95 *(978-0-8198-1838-6(0)*, 332-058) Pauline Bks. & Media.

Vattimo, Gianni, et al. After the Death of God. Robbins, Jeffrey W., ed. 2009. (Insurrections: Critical Studies in Religion, Politics, & Culture Ser.). (ENG.). 216p. (gr. 17). pap. 18.50 *(978-0-231-14125-3(4))* Columbia Univ. Pr.

Vaughan, Robert. The Causes of the Corruption of Christianity. 2009. 200p. pap. 19.99 *(978-1-4589-1222-0(1))* General Bks. LLC.

Vaughn, Gary L. Tune up Your Marriage. 2009. 160p. 17.95 *(978-1-59317-370-8(9))* Warner Pr. Pubs.

Vaux, Kenneth L. Ministry on the Edge: Reflections of an Interfaith Pioneer, Civil Rights Advocate, & the First Bioethicist. 2010. 284p. pap. 31.00 *(978-1-60899-506-6(2))* Wipf & Stock Pubs.

Velarde, Robert. Conversations with C. S. Lewis: Imaginative Discussions about Life, Christianity & God. 2008. (ENG.). 187p. pap. 15.00 *(978-0-8308-3483-9(4)*, IVP Bks.) InterVarsity Pr.

Venter, Tertius Hj. A Lemoncode Sceptic & Orange Answers. 2011. 88p. pap. 12.10 *(978-1-4567-7066-2(7))* AuthorHouse.

Via, Rick L. God Still Moves. 2008. 124p. 18.99 *(978-1-60647-505-8(3))*; pap. 10.99 *(978-1-60647-504-1(5))* Xulon Pr., Inc.

Vinje, Renate. When Silence Is Not Golden. 2008. 400p. pap. 19.99 *(978-1-4363-2806-7(3))* Xlibris Corp.

Vitcavich, Michael. Deciduous Belief: Letting Go of the Old You so the New You Can Embrace a Healthy & Meaningful Relationship with God & Others. 2011. 408p. pap. 27.95 ***(978-1-61507-692-5(1))*** Cross Bks. Publishing.

Voerding, Philip. The Trouble with Christianity: A Concise Outline of Christian History. 2009. 176p. 24.99 *(978-1-4389-8944-0(X))*; pap. 14.99 *(978-1-4389-8924-2(5))* AuthorHouse.

Wade, Frank. Transforming Scripture. 2008. (Transformations Ser.). 160p. pap. 16.00 *(978-0-89869-594-6(5))* Church Publishing, Inc.

Wade, Loron. Simply Put: What God's Been Saying All Along. 2009. 223p. pap. 14.99 *(978-0-8280-2477-8(4))* Review & Herald Publishing Assn.

Waggoner, Robert L. Christianity or Humanism: BLURB: Which Will You Choose? 2007. *(978-0-929540-67-2(0))* Publishing Designs, Inc.

Waite, D. A. The First 200 Questions Answered by Dr D a Waite. 2010. 178p. pap. 14.00 *(978-1-56848-066-4(0))* Old Paths Pubns., Inc., The.

Waite, D. A. The Third 200 Questions Answered by Dr D a Waite. 2011. 202p. pap. 15.00 ***(978-1-56848-074-9(1))*** Old Paths Pubns., Inc., The.

Waite, D. A. Jr. & Waite, D. A. The Fourth 200 Questions Answered. 2011. 172p. pap. 14.00 ***(978-1-56848-077-0(6))*** Old Paths Pubns., Inc., The.

Waite, D. A. Jr. & Waite, D. A. The Second 200 Questions Answered. 2010. 178p. pap. 14.00 *(978-1-56848-070-1(9))* Old Paths Pubns., Inc., The.

Wakefield, Dan. The Hijacking of Jesus: How the Religious Right Distorts Christianity & Promotes Prejudice & Hate. 2007. (ENG.). 208p. per. 14.95 *(978-1-56025-956-5(6))* Basic Bks.

Walker, Scott. Understanding Christianity. 11.00 *(978-0-687-82716-9(7))* Abingdon Pr.

Wallace, Peter G. The Long European Reformation. 2nd rev. ed. 2012. (European History in Perspective Ser.). (ENG., Illus.). 320p. (C). 95.00 ***(978-0-230-57482-3(3))***; pap. 32.00 ***(978-0-230-57483-0(1))*** Palgrave Macmillan.

Walters, Glenn. The Student Body. 2011. 188p. 26.99 ***(978-1-61215-390-2(9))*** Xulon Pr., Inc.

Walters, Wendy K., ed. Blood Covenant: What Jesus Really Did for Us: Walk of Death. 2008. 112p. pap. *(978-0-9799879-8-4(9))* Palm Tree Pubns.

Ward, J. w. g. & Ward, J. W. G. The God We Need. 2008. 160p. pap. 18.00 *(978-1-59752-522-0(7)*, Wipf and Stock) Wipf & Stock Pubs.

Ward, Keith. Christianity: A Beginner's Guide. 2007. (Beginners Guide (Oneworld) Ser.). (ENG.). 208p. per. 14.95 *(978-1-85168-539-4(1))* Oneworld Pubns. GBR. Dist: National Bk. Network.

Ward, Robin. A Guide to Christianity. 2007. 96p. pap. *(978-0-281-05896-9(2))* SPCK Publishing.

Ward, William G. The Ideal of a Christian Church Considered in Comparison with Existing Practice. 612p. 2008. 59.95 *(978-1-4365-4951-6(5))* 2007. (ENG.). per. 44.95 *(978-0-548-69703-0(5))* Kessinger Publishing, LLC.

Wariboko, Waibinte E. Race & the Civilizing Mission: The Impliations for the Framing of Blackness & African Personhood. 2010. 146p. pap. *(978-1-59221-770-0(2))* Africa World Pr.

Warren, Hunter. Think Like God. 2008. pap. 15.99 *(978-0-7684-2710-3(X))* Destiny Image Pubs.

Warren, William Loyal. Jesus' Rapture Is Coming Soon! The Coming Rapture of Jesus! 2010. 272p. pap. 20.95 *(978-1-4502-3381-1(3))* iUniverse, Inc.

Warrington Jr, Bernard. Going Beyond Measure — Intrepidity: A 40-day devotional towards your spiritual transformation, health & Growth. 2009. 92p. pap. 14.95 *(978-1-4327-4167-9(5))* Outskirts Pr., Inc.

Warshaw, Steven. Discovering History Vol. 2: Traditional African Religions (Christianity) & History. Date not set. (Illus.). pap. 24.95 *(978-0-87297-062-5(0))* Diablo Pr., Inc.

Waskow, Arthur, et al. The Tent of Abraham: Stories of Hope & Peace for Jews, Christians, & Muslims. 2007. (ENG.). 240p. per. 17.00 *(978-0-8070-7729-0(1))* Beacon Pr.

Waterland, Daniel. Works of Daniel Waterland, 11 vols. Von Mildert, William, ed. reprint ed. 215.00 *(978-0-404-06860-8(X))* AMS Pr., Inc.

Waters, Tracie Seattle. God's Hand Was in it All: Through the Lord We Can All Pull Through. 2010. 128p. pap. 13.95 *(978-1-4502-5759-6(3))* iUniverse, Inc.

Watkins, Tiffany. The Sexual Abuse of Youth Within the Church. 2008. 72p. per. 13.95 *(978-1-4327-1897-8(5))* Outskirts Pr., Inc.

Watson, Allen D. & Bliss, Wesley F. Miracles. 2009. 160p. pap. 14.99 *(978-1-61579-114-9(0))* Xulon Pr., Inc.

Watson, John. Christianity & Idealism: the Christian Ideal of Life in Its Relations To. 2007. pap. 30.95 *(978-1-4304-4969-0(1))* Kessinger Publishing, LLC.

Watton, Victor. Christianity: Bullet Guides. 2012. (Bullet Guides). (ENG.). 120p. pap. 6.95 ***(978-1-4441-3494-0(9)***, Hodder & Stoughton) Hodder General Publishing Div. GBR. Dist: Independent Pubs. Group.

Watton, Victor W. & Kolka, Daine. Christianity. 2nd ed. 2009. (Illus.). 112p. (gr. 10-12). pap. 38.50 *(978-0-340-98678-3(6))* Hodder Education GBR. Dist: Trans-Atlantic Pubns., Inc.

Weaver, Andrew J. & Messer, Donald E., eds. Connected Spirits. 2010. 160p. pap. 18.00 *(978-1-60899-210-2(1)*, Resource Pubns.) Wipf & Stock Pubs.

Weaver, Mary Jo & Brakke, David. Introduction to Christianity. 4th rev. ed. 2008. (ENG.). 304p. (C). per. 128.95 *(978-0-495-09726-6(8))* Wadsworth.

Webber, Christopher. Welcome to the Christian Faith. 2011. E-Book ***(978-0-8192-2744-7(7)***, Morehouse Publishing) Church Publishing, Inc.

Webster, Charlie. Revitalizing Christianity. 2011. 248p. ***(978-1-77067-414-1(4))***; pap. ***(978-1-77067-415-8(2))*** FriesenPress.

Weeks, Lena Pittman. God Given Messages. 2007. (ENG.). 242p. 41.95 *(978-0-548-06125-1(4))* Kessinger Publishing, LLC.

Weiss, Dennis D. Acts: An in-Depth Study. 2011. 120p. 28.95 ***(978-1-4627-0526-9(X))***; pap. 11.95 ***(978-1-4627-0525-2(1))*** Cross Bks. Publishing.

Welch, Edward. Running Scared: Fear, Worry, & the God of Rest. 2007. (ENG.). 324p. per. 15.99 *(978-0-9785567-5-4(5))* New Growth Pr.

Wells, Carl. The Christian Betrayal of the United States 2010. 252p. pap. 15.99 *(978-1-4520-5295-3(6))* AuthorHouse.

Wells, Carl. Christianity for Rich People. 2011. 112p. pap. 13.00 ***(978-1-4567-6886-7(7))*** AuthorHouse.

Wells, George Albert. Cutting Jesus down to Size: What Higher Criticism Has Achieved & Where It Leaves Christianity. 2009. (ENG.). 384p. pap. 44.95 *(978-0-8126-9656-1(5))* Open Court Publishing Co.

Wenger, Jay L. Toward the Mind of Christ: The Perspective of an Experimental Psychologist. 2008. 260p. pap. 14.95 *(978-1-60126-141-0(1))* Masthof Pr.

Wergland, Glendyne R. Sisters in the Faith: Shaker Women & Equality of the Sexes. 2011. (Illus.). 248p. pap. 26.95 *(978-1-55849-863-1(X))*; lib. bdg. 80.00 *(978-1-55849-862-4(1))* Univ. of Massachusetts Pr.

Wessels, Anton. Europe. 2012. (Illus.). ix, 242p. pap. ***(978-0-334-02569-6(9)***, SCM Pr.) Hymns Ancient & Modern Ltd.

West, Steve. Philosophical Dialogues on the Christian Faith: Discussions on the Arguments, Evidence, & Truth of Christianity. 2007. 118p. pap. 15.00 *(978-1-55635-142-6(9))* Wipf & Stock Pubs.

West, William Robert. Unconditional Immortality. 2008. 364p. pap. 22.95 *(978-0-7414-4620-6(0))* Infinity Publishing.

Westcott, Brooke Foss. Thoughts on Revelation & Life: Being Selections from the Writings of Brooke Foss Westcott, D. D, D. C. L. Phillips, Stephen, ed. 2007. (Illus.). 398p. pap. 34.00 *(978-1-55635-752-7(4))* Wipf & Stock Pubs.

Wetzel, Klaus. Kirchengeschichte Asiens. 2010. 682p. pap. *(978-3-941750-25-8(9))* VTR Verlag fur Theologie und Religionswissenschaft.

Whately, Richard. Essays on Some of the Peculiarities of the Christian Religion. 2009. 198p. pap. 19.99 *(978-0-217-71452-5(8))* General Bks. LLC.

—Essays on Some of the Peculiarities of the Christian Religion. 2007. (ENG.). 392p. 48.95 *(978-0-548-14997-3(6))*; 396p. per. 33.95 *(978-1-4304-4323-0(5))* Kessinger Publishing, LLC.

—Essays on Some of the Peculiarities of the Christian Religion. 2008. (ENG.). 304p. per. *(978-1-4086-6205-2(1))* Read Bks.

Whipple, Charles. What Do You Know. 2010. 232p. 34.95 *(978-0-557-44890-6(5))* Lulu Enterprises Inc.

Whitehead, John Wallace. Where Is God in His Church? 2011. 188p. 30.95 ***(978-1-4497-1869-5(8))***; pap. 13.95 ***(978-1-4497-1868-8(X))*** Author Solutions, Inc. (WestBow Pr.).

Whitelaw, Robert. Christ's Ministry from Baptism to Pentecost. pap. 0.39 *(978-0-87377-098-9(6))* GAM Pubns.

Whitt, Bill. God All Around: 31 Places to Find the Fingerprints of God in Your Life. 2008. 200p. pap. 14.95 *(978-1-4357-2324-5(4))* Lulu Enterprises Inc.

Wickwire, Daniel. 100 Questions about the Bible & the Qur'an. 2011. 160p. 30.95 ***(978-1-4497-2689-8(5))***; pap. 13.95 ***(978-1-4497-2688-1(7))*** Author Solutions, Inc. (WestBow Pr.).

Wiebe, Martha M. When Religion Makes No(N) Sense. 2011. ***(978-1-77069-272-5(X))*** Word Alive Pr.

WIJSEN, Frans & SCHREITER, Robert, eds. Global Christianity: Contested Claims. 2007. 232p. per. 62.00 *(978-90-420-2192-1(6))* Rodopi.

Wilberforce, William. A Practical View of the Prevailing Religious System. 2011. 202p. pap. 16.99 ***(978-1-61203-285-6(0))*** Bottom of the Hill Publishing.

Wilberforce, William & Beltz, Bob. Real Christianity: The Book That Helped End Slavery in England. 2006. (ENG.). 208p. per. 14.99 *(978-0-8307-4311-7(1))* Gospel Light Pubns.

Wilk, Karen. Don't Invite Them to Church: Moving from a Come & See to a Go & Be Church. 2010. 128p. *(978-1-59255-531-4(4))* Faith Alive Christian Resources.

Wilkes, Baron. A Journey in Time. 2007. 66p. pap. 16.95 *(978-1-4241-9349-3(4))* PublishAmerica, Inc.

William Jennings Bryan. In HIS000000 Image. 2007. 192p. pap. 19.99 *(978-1-4264-6393-8(6))* BiblioBazaar.

Williams, Allan. A Black Man's Worth. 2009. 320p. pap. 17.99 *(978-1-4490-3003-2(3))* AuthorHouse.

Williams, Betty L. Stop! Hold on & Listen to God, 1 vol. 2010. 146p. pap. 24.95 *(978-1-4489-4187-2(3))* PublishAmerica, Inc.

Williams, Blake. Creating a Christian Americ. 2008. 184p. pap. *(978-3-639-11110-1(9))* VDM Verlag Dr. Mueller e.K.

Williams, K. A. The error of Job. 2006. per. *(978-0-9785262-0-7(1))* Williams, Keith.

Williams, Louise. Christian Bumper Stickers. 2011. 50p. pap. 15.99 ***(978-1-4568-8164-1(7))*** Xlibris Corp.

Williams, Nancy. A Way of Life: Removing the Mask. 2009. 222p. pap. 21.95 *(978-1-4327-3209-7(9))* Outskirts Pr., Inc.

Williamson, Roy. Joyful Uncertainty. 128p. 10.00 *(978-0-281-05248-6(4))* SPCK Publishing GBR. Dist: Pilgrim Pr., The/United Church Pr.

Willis, Jay Thomas. God, or Balance in the Universe. 2006. (ENG.). 104p. per. 10.95 *(978-0-7414-3641-2(8))* Infinity Publishing.

Willis, Johnny. Preparing the Church for the End Times. 2011. pap. 11.99 *(978-1-61739-318-1(5))* Tate Publishing & Enterprises, LLC.

—When Morning Comes. 2010. pap. 10.99 *(978-1-61663-363-9(8))* Tate Publishing & Enterprises, LLC.

Wilsey, John D. One Nation under God? An Evangelical Critique of Christian America. 2011. 226p. pap. 25.00 ***(978-1-60899-792-3(8)***, Pickwick Pubns.) Wipf & Stock Pubs.

Wilson, Charles Reagan. Baptized in Blood: The Religion of the Lost Cause, 1865-1920. 2nd ed. 2009. (ENG.). 264p. pap. 24.95 *(978-0-8203-3425-7(1))* Univ. of Georgia Pr.

Wilson, David. Behold the Lamb, the Last Hours of Christ's Life. 2007. 110p. per. 6.25 *(978-0-9786002-2-8(3))* Wilson, David.

Wilson, Edward. Giving Birth to an Anointed Ministry. 2008. 75p. pap. 14.95 *(978-0-615-18015-1(9))* Edward Wilson.

Winter, David & Winter, David. Christianity. 2009. (One-Stop Ser.). (ENG., Illus.). 128p. instr.'s gde. ed. 19.95 *(978-0-7459-5323-6(9))* Lion Hudson PLC GBR. Dist: Independent Pubs. Group.

Winters, April A. Determined Growth 2: Season of Change. 2011. 96p. pap. 10.25 ***(978-1-4670-3374-9(X))*** AuthorHouse.

with Gaye Lisby, Tim Snider. Victorious Living Becoming a Comeback Kid in a Knock-down World. 2010. 255p. pap. 15.98 *(978-0-557-30856-9(9))* Lulu Enterprises Inc.

Witham, Larry. A City upon a Hill: How Sermons Changed the Course of American History. 336p. 2008. pap. 15.95 *(978-0-06-133812-0(5))* 2007. (Illus.). (gr. 13). 24.95 *(978-0-06-085427-0(8))* HarperCollins Pubs. (HarperOne).

Wolf, Alexys. What Was God Thinking? 2007. 164p. pap. 12.99 *(978-1-58169-256-3(0))* Genesis Communications, Inc.

Wolfe, Linden C. Captivated by the King & His Kingdom: A Personal Encounter with the Sermon on the Mount. 2010. 116p. 28.95 *(978-1-61507-582-9(8))*; pap. 11.95 *(978-1-61507-341-2(8))* Cross Bks. Publishing.

Wolsey, Roger. Kissing Fish. 2011. 398p. 29.99 ***(978-1-4568-3941-3(1))***; pap. 19.99 ***(978-1-4568-3940-6(3))*** Xlibris Corp.

Wommack, Andrew. War Is Over: God Is Not Mad, So Stop Struggling with Sin & Judgment. 2008. 224p. pap. 14.99 *(978-1-57794-935-0(8))* Harrison House Pubs.

Wong, Cliff & Kwong, Andrew. A Biblical Perspective on How to Handle Worry & Fear. 2010. pap. 16.99 *(978-1-61579-922-0(2))* Xulon Pr., Inc.

Wood, Frank L. The Layman's Galilean. 2007. (ENG.). 178p. 37.95 *(978-0-548-06970-7(0))* Kessinger Publishing, LLC.

Woodall, R. Woody. Choices. 2010. 48p. pap. 10.95 *(978-0-557-41891-6(7))* Lulu Enterprises Inc.

Woodard, William P. Religions in Japan: Buddhism, Shinto, Christianity. Bunce, William K., ed. 2011. 208p. 44.95 ***(978-1-258-03836-6(6))*** Literary Licensing, LLC.

Woodhead, Linda. Christianity. 2010. (Brief Insight Ser.). (ENG., Illus.). 224p. 14.95 *(978-1-4027-7534-5(2))* Sterling Publishing Co., Inc.

Woodrow, Brian M. Both Ways Work Together. 2009. 68p. pap. 14.25 *(978-1-60860-150-9(1)*, Strategic Bk. Publishing) AEG Literary Publishing Services, Inc.

Woods, Dorothy. Spiritual Boot Camp Manual. 2010. 48p. pap. 15.99 *(978-1-4535-3803-6(8))* Xlibris Corp.

Woods, Rob. Fishing Every Day. 2011. 68p. pap. 14.99 ***(978-1-4634-3388-8(3))*** AuthorHouse.

Woolsey, Edwin L. The Voice of Seven Thunders: Shadows of Things to Come. 2011. 248p. 26.59 ***(978-1-4634-0629-5(0))***; pap. 16.95 ***(978-1-4634-0630-1(4))*** AuthorHouse.

Wragg, Jerry. Exemplary Spiritual Leadership: Facing the Challenges, Escaping the Dangers. 2010. (Ministry & Mission Ser.). 153p. pap. *(978-1-84625-200-6(8))* DayOne Pubns.

Wright, J. Robert. A Companion to Bede. 2008. (Illus.). 144p. 25.00 *(978-0-8028-6309-6(4))* Eerdmans, William B. Publishing Co.

Wright, N. T. Surprised by Hope: Rethinking Heaven, the Resurrection, & the Mission of the Church. 2008. (ENG.). 352p. 24.99 *(978-0-06-155182-6(1)*, HarperOne) HarperCollins Pubs.

Wright, Robin M. & Vilaça, Aparecida. Native Christians: Modes & Effects of Christianity among Indigenous Peoples of the Americas. 2009. (Vitality of Indigenous Religions Ser.). (Illus.). 266p. 114.95 *(978-0-7546-6355-3(8))* Ashgate Publishing Co.

Yager, Michael. The God Manifesto: How Jews, Christians, & Muslims Can Return to Their God. 2007. 84p. per. 10.95 *(978-0-595-44562-2(4))* iUniverse, Inc.

Yancey, Philip. What Good Is God? In Search of a Faith That Matters. (ENG.). 2012. 304p. pap. 14.99 ***(978-0-446-55984-3(9))*** 2010. 304p. 23.99 *(978-0-446-55985-0(7))* 2010. 448p. 25.99 *(978-0-446-57416-7(3))* FaithWords.

Yarhouse, Mark A. & Sells, James N. Family Therapies: A Comprehensive Christian Appraisal. 2008. (Christian Association for Psychological Studies Partnership Book Ser.). (ENG.). 511p. 35.00 *(978-0-8308-2805-0(2)*, IVP Acad.) InterVarsity Pr.

Yeo, K. K. Musing with Confucius & Paul: Toward a Chinese Christian Theology. 2008. 508p. pap. 55.00 *(978-1-55635-488-5(6))* Wipf & Stock Pubs.

Yeo, Khiok-Khng. Musing with Confucius & Paul: Toward a Chinese Christian Theology. 2008. (ENG.). 508p. pap. 58.00 *(978-0-227-17283-4(3))* Clarke, James Co., Ltd. GBR. Dist: Brown, David Bk. Co., The.

Yoder, Anna. As Far Back As I Can Remember. 2007. 220p. per. *(978-1-897373-11-8(2))* Word Alive Pr.

Yoder, John Howard & Nugent, John C. The End of Sacrifice: The Capital Punishment Writings of John Howard Yoder. 2011. 286p. pap. ***(978-0-8361-9464-7(0))*** Herald Pr.

Yogananda, Paramhansa. La Ciencia de la Religion.Tr. of Science of Religion. (SPA.). pap. 8.00 *(978-0-87612-007-1(9))* Self-Realization Fellowship Pubs.

—The Yoga of Jesus: Understanding the Hidden Teachings of the Gospels. 2007. (Illus.). 147p. per. 14.00 *(978-0-87612-556-4(9))* Self-Realization Fellowship Pubs.

Yopp, Christopher. Gilgal: A Journey Through Lent. 2011. pap. 12.99 *(978-1-61663-111-6(2))* Tate Publishing & Enterprises, LLC.

Young, John. Christianity: An Introduction. 5th ed. 2011. (Teach Yourself Ser.). (ENG.). 416p. pap. 16.95 *(978-1-4441-0511-7(6)*, Hodder & Stoughton) Hodder General Publishing Div. GBR. Dist: Independent Pubs. Group.

Young, K. M. Jb Rotherham's Nt Book & Letters of John: The Beloved of Messiah. 2011. 210p. pap. 19.99 ***(978-1-4415-4210-6(8))*** Xlibris Corp.

Young, Richard Fox, ed. India & the Indianness of Christianity: Essays on Understanding, Historical, Theological, & Bibliographical, in Honor of Robert Eric Frykenberg. 2009. (ENG., Illus.). 280p. pap. 45.00 *(978-0-8028-6392-8(2))* Eerdmans, William B. Publishing Co.

Yuna, Jeffrey M. God Speaks: Hearing the Voice of God. 2011. 104p. pap. 11.95 ***(978-1-4497-2648-5(8)***, WestBow Pr.) Author Solutions, Inc.

Zacharias, Ravi. The Lamb & the Fuhrer: Jesus Talks with Hitler. 2009. (Great Conversations Ser.). (ENG.). 96p. pap. 11.99 *(978-1-60142-320-7(9)*, Multnomah) Doubleday Religious Publishing Group, The.

Zahl, Paul F.M. 2000 Years of Amazing Grace: The Story & Meaning of the Christian Faith. 2006. (ENG.). 480p. 26.95 *(978-0-7425-5276-0(4))* Rowman & Littlefield Publishers, Inc.

Zomber, Michael. Jesus & the Samurai: The Shining Religion & the Samurai. 2009. 48p. pap. 9.95 *(978-1-4401-7684-5(1))* iUniverse, Inc.

Zukeran, Patrick. Unless I See Is There Enough Evidence to Believe? 2011. 208p. 33.95 ***(978-1-4627-0621-1(5))***; pap. 17.95 ***(978-1-4627-0620-4(7))*** Cross Bks. Publishing.

1st Evangelical Lutheran Church. Through These Doors & Beyond. 2011. 96p. pap. 9.99 ***(978-1-4634-5985-7(8))*** AuthorHouse.

CHRISTIANITY—APOLOGETIC WORKS

see Apologetics

CHRISTIANITY—BIBLIOGRAPHY

Gerhart, Mary. The Christianity Reader. Gerhart, Mary & Udoh, Fabian E., eds. 2007. (ENG., Illus.). 856p. per. 45.00 *(978-0-226-28959-5(1))* Univ. of Chicago Pr.

Gerhart, Mary & Udoh, Fabian E., eds. The Christianity Reader. 2007. (ENG.). 800p. 102.50 *(978-0-226-28958-8(3))* Univ. of Chicago Pr.

Rainey, David. Faith Reads: A Selective Guide to Christian Nonfiction, 1 vol. 2008. 388p. 55.00 *(978-1-59158-602-9(X)*, LU8602) Libraries Unlimited, Inc.

Taneti, James. History of the Telugu Christians: A Bibliography. 2011. (ATLA Bibliography Ser.). (ENG.). 122p. 70.00 *(978-0-8108-7243-1(9))* Scarecrow Pr., Inc.

CHRISTIANITY—BIOGRAPHY

see Christian Biography

CHRISTIANITY—COMMUNICATION

see Communication—Religious Aspects—Christianity

CHRISTIANITY—CONTROVERSIAL LITERATURE

see also Secularism

Alexandrova, Alena, et al, eds. Re-Treating Religion: Deconstructing Christianity with Jean-Luc Nancy. 2012. (Perspectives in Continental Philosophy Ser.). (ENG.). 404p. 125.00 ***(978-0-8232-3464-6(9))*** Fordham Univ. Pr.

Arya, Ravi Prakash. Unraveling the Mysteries of Jesus the Christ. 2011. 152p. pap. ***(978-3-8454-0613-8(5))*** Lambert Academic Publishing.

Atrott, Hans. Jesus' Bluff: The Universal Scandal of the World (M. Magnes), 1 vol. 2009. (ENG.). 583p. pap. 34.95 *(978-1-61582-816-6(8))* PublishAmerica, Inc.

Attwell, Lionel. JESUS CHRIST the COUNTERFEIT CHRISTIAN MESSIAH - incorporating What Really Happened in the Garden of Eden & God, genes & Evil. 2007. 318p. pap. 39.95 *(978-1-84799-863-7(1))* Lulu Enterprises Inc.

Bakunin, Mikhail. God & the State. 2009. pap. 8.75 *(978-0-9737827-7-6(3))* Black Cat Pr. CAN. Dist: AK Pr. Distribution.

Barbalho, Valquirio. The Third & Last Testament. 2009. 680p. pap. 25.99 *(978-1-4389-5097-6(7))* AuthorHouse.

Barker, James. Song of Solomon. 2009. 130p. pap. 11.99 *(978-0-9824931-4-4(2))* Faithful Life Pubs.

Bates, Steve. Bible Crusade. 2007. 200p. (ENG.). 24.99 *(978-1-60034-778-8(9))*; per. 14.99 *(978-1-60034-777-1(0))* Xulon Pr., Inc.

Berger, David. The Jewish-Christian Debate in the High Middle Ages: A Critical Edition of the Nizzahon Vetus. 2008. 616p. pap. 60.00 *(978-1-59740-545-4(0))* ACLS Humanities E-Book.

Blyth, Philip Gledstanes. Christianity & Tradition. 2008. 228p. 24.99 *(978-0-559-83146-1(3))*; pap. 24.75 *(978-0-559-83142-3(0))* BiblioBazaar.

—Christianity & Tradition. 2009. 114p. pap. *(978-0-217-81255-9(4))* Books LLC.

—Christianity & Tradition. 2007. (ENG.). 224p. 39.95 *(978-0-548-15543-1(7))*; pap. 24.95 *(978-1-4304-4980-5(2))* Kessinger Publishing, LLC.

Borg, Marcus J. The God We Never Knew: Beyond Dogmatic Religion to A More Authenthic Contemporary Faith. 2006. (Plus Ser.). 208p. pap. 13.95 *(978-0-06-114491-2(6)*, Harper San Francisco) HarperCollins Pubs.

Bradley, David. An Introduction to the Urantia Revelation. 3rd rev. ed. 2008. Orig. Title: An Introduction to the Urantia Book Revelation. (ENG., Illus.). 120p. pap. 15.95 *(978-0-9663270-2-1(0))* White Egret Pubns.

Braude, Morris. Conscience on Trial: Three Public Religious Disputations Between Christians & Jews in the Thirteenth & Fifteenth Centuries. 2011. 148p. 40.95 ***(978-1-258-01561-9(7))*** Literary Licensing, LLC.

Butler, Samuel. The Fair Haven. 2008. 212p. 24.99 *(978-0-554-31287-3(5))* 2008. 212p. 27.99 *(978-0-554-21984-4(0))* 2006. (ENG.). 222p. pap. 20.99 *(978-1-4264-1378-0(5))* 2006. (ENG.). 210p. pap. 22.99 *(978-1-4264-1431-2(5))* BiblioBazaar.

—The Fair Haven. 2009. 166p. pap. *(978-0-217-29323-5(9))* Books LLC.

—The Fair Haven. 2008. 204p. pap. *(978-1-4065-9561-1(6))* Dodo Pr.

The Case Against the Case for Christ: A New Testament Scholar Refutes Lee Strobel. 2009. 256p. pap. *(978-1-57884-005-2(8))* American Atheist Pr.

Chazan, Robert. Fashioning Jewish Identity in Medieval Western Christendom. 2009. (ENG.). 396p. pap. 51.00 *(978-0-521-10056-4(9))* Cambridge Univ. Pr.

Church, Philip, et al, eds. The Gospel & the Land of Promise: Christian Approaches to the Land of the Bible. 2011. 202p. pap. 22.00 ***(978-1-60899-545-5(3)***, Pickwick Pubns.) Wipf & Stock Pubs.

Clark, George. The Bible Revisited II: Beyond the Bible. 2009. 129p. pap. 14.95 *(978-1-4327-3852-5(6))* Outskirts Pr., Inc.

Cobb, Tyrone W. It Is Written. 2010. 396p. pap. 20.99 *(978-1-61579-965-7(6))* Xulon Pr., Inc.

Collins, Anthony. A Discourse of the Grounds & Reasons of the Christian Religion. 2009. 182p. pap. *(978-1-150-42289-8(0))* Books LLC.

Cook, Henry. The Why of Our Faith. 2007. 96p. per. *(978-1-4067-8816-7(3)*, Pomona Pr.) Read Bks.

Cresswell, Peter. Jesus the Terrorist. 2010. (ENG., Illus.). 440p. pap. 29.95 *(978-1-84694-274-7(8))* Hunt, John Publishing Ltd. GBR. Dist: National Bk. Network.

Devisch, Ignaas, et al. Re-treating Religion: Deconstructing Christianity with Jean-Luc Nancy. Alexandrova, Alena, ed. 2012. (Perspectives in Continental Philosophy Ser.). (ENG.). 404p. pap. 30.00 ***(978-0-8232-3465-3(7))*** Fordham Univ. Pr.

Ehrman, Bart D. Forged: Writing in the Name of God — Why the Bible's Authors Are Not Who We Think They Are. 2012. (ENG.). 256p. pap. 15.99 ***(978-0-06-201262-3(2)***, HarperOne) HarperCollins Pubs.

—Jesus, Interrupted: Revealing the Hidden Contradictions in the Bible (and Why We Don't Know about Them) 2009. (ENG.). 256p. 25.99 *(978-0-06-117393-6(2)*, HarperOne) HarperCollins Pubs.

—Jesus, Interrupted: Revealing the Hidden Contradictions in the Bible (And Why We Don't Know about Them) 2010. (ENG.). 304p. pap. 15.99 *(978-0-06-117394-3(0)*, HarperOne) HarperCollins Pubs.

Emperor Julian. The an Edict Forbidding the Christians to Teach the Literature Of. 2006. pap. 9.95 *(978-1-4286-8599-4(5))* Kessinger Publishing, LLC.

Faber, M. D. Becoming God's Children: Religion's Infantilizing Process, 1 vol. 2010. 208p. 44.95 *(978-0-313-38226-0(3)*, A2650C) Greenwood Publishing Group, Inc.

Feuerbach, Ludwig. The Essence of Christianity. Evans [George Eliot], Marian, tr. 2011. (Cambridge Library Collection - Philosophy Ser.). (ENG.). 366p. pap. 29.99 ***(978-1-108-04031-0(4))*** Cambridge Univ. Pr.

Fitzgerald, David. Nailed: Ten Christian Myths That Show Jesus Never Existed at All. 2010. 246p. pap. 24.95 *(978-0-557-70991-5(1))* Lulu Enterprises Inc.

Foster, S. P. Melancholy Duty: The Hume-Gibbon Attack on Christianity. 2010. (International Archives of the History of Ideas / archives internationales d'histoire des Idées Ser.). 372p. pap. 279.00 *(978-90-481-4933-9(9)*, 9048149339) Springer.

Gaebelein, Arno C. El Cristianismo Es Religion? Christianity: Is It a Religion? (SPA.). *(978-84-7645-012-3(5)*, 223076) Clie, Editorial.

Giles, Chauncey. Church of the New Jerusalem What It Is W. 2006. pap. 15.95 *(978-1-4286-3425-1(8))* Kessinger Publishing, LLC.

Graves, Kersey. The A Comparison of the Miraculous & Immaculate Conception Of. 2006. pap. 12.95 *(978-1-4286-8878-0(1))* Kessinger Publishing, LLC.

—Logical or Common Sense View of the Doctrine of Divine Incarnation. 2006. pap. 12.95 *(978-1-4286-8875-9(7))* Kessinger Publishing, LLC.

—The Origin of Baptism by Water, Fire, Blood, & the Holy Ghost - 2006. pap. 12.95 *(978-1-4286-8874-2(9))* Kessinger Publishing, LLC.

—Sacred Cycles Explaining the Advent of the Gods, the Master Key To. 2006. pap. 12.95 *(978-1-4286-8879-7(X))* Kessinger Publishing, LLC.

—The World's Sixteen Crucified Saviors. 2008. 400p. 31.99 *(978-0-554-29618-0(7))*; 29.99 *(978-0-554-38921-9(5))* BiblioBazaar.

—The World's Sixteen Crucified Saviors. 2009. 256p. pap. *(978-1-150-79346-2(5))* Books LLC.

—The World's Sixteen Crucified Saviors. 2009. 326p. 38.99 *(978-1-59547-091-1(3))* NuVision Pubns., LLC.

—The World's Sixteen Crucified Saviors: Christianity before Christ. 2007. 436p. per. 14.45 *(978-1-60206-280-1(3))* Cosimo, Inc.

Hacker, John D. Church of Christ Viewed in the Midst of. 2006. pap. 33.95 *(978-1-4286-5348-1(1))* Kessinger Publishing, LLC.

Harwood, William. Dictionary of Contemporary Mythology Third Edition 2011. Strozier, M. Stefan & Torke, Kyle, eds. 2011. (Illus.). 602p. 45.00 ***(978-1-935444-78-7(6))*** World Audience Pubs.

Havemann, Daniel. Der 'Apostel der Rache' Nietzsches Paulusdeutung. (Monographien und Texte zur Nietzsche-Forschung Ser.). (GER.). X, 312p. 255.00 ***(978-3-11-187634-4(9))*** De Gruyter, Walter Inc.

Hill, Stephen. Defying Ignorance: Exposing Christianity's Most Popular Myths. 2007. 152p. per. 24.95 *(978-1-60441-554-4(1))* PublishAmerica, Inc.

Ingersoll, Robert Green. Lectures & Essays: A Selection. 2007. (ENG.). 158p. 36.95 *(978-0-548-15723-7(5))*; pap. 21.95 *(978-1-4304-5203-4(X))* Kessinger Publishing, LLC.

Jacobs, Thornwell. For Heretics Only. 2011. 322p. 50.95 ***(978-1-258-06999-5(7))*** Literary Licensing, LLC.

Jay, Les. Catholics are NOT Christians. 2007. 140p. pap. 14.99 *(978-0-9785571-0-2(7))* Witty Publishing.

Jeffrey, Grant R. The Signature of God, Revised Edition: Conclusive Proof that Every Teaching, Every Command, Every Promise in the Bible Is True. l.t. ed. 2010. (ENG.). 416p. pap. 17.99 *(978-1-59415-338-9(8))* Cengage Gale.

Joe, Billie. Fodder to Chew On: Book Two. 2011. 76p. pap. 13.49 ***(978-1-4634-0573-1(1))*** AuthorHouse.

Jones, Thomas A. In Seach of a City: An Autobiographical Perspective on a Remarkable but Controversial Movement. 2007. (Illus.). 231p. pap. 16.00 *(978-1-57782-221-9(8))* Discipleship Pubns. International.

Kelsey, Graves. The World's Sixteen Crucified Saviors. 2007. 328p. per. 19.99 *(978-1-59547-780-4(2))* NuVision Pubns., LLC.

Kenyon, J. Forbidden Religion: Suppressed Heresies of the West. 2006. (ENG., Illus.). 1p. per. 18.00 *(978-1-59143-067-4(4))* Inner Traditions International, Ltd.

Lasker, Daniel. Jewish Philosophical Polemics Against Christianity in the Middle Ages: With a New Introduction. 2nd ed. 2007. 318p. pap. 29.95 *(978-1-904113-51-5(6))* Littman Library of Jewish Civilization, The GBR. Dist: International Specialized Bk. Services.

Last Prophets. Secrets of the Holy Bible. 2011. 612p. 50.99 *(978-1-4567-1165-8(2))*; pap. 34.99 *(978-1-4567-1164-1(4))* AuthorHouse.

Lefavi Sosc, Robert. The 2: 4 Solution. 2008. 76p. pap. 14.95 *(978-1-60145-575-8(5))* Booklocker.com, Inc.

Levieils, Xavier. Contra Christianos: La Critique Sociale et Religieuse du Christianisme des Origenes Au Concile de Nicee (45-325) 2007. (Beihefte Zur Zeitschrift Für Die Neutestamentliche Wissenschaft und Die Kunde der älteren Kirche Ser.). (FRE.). XIII, 548p. 196.00 *(978-3-11-019554-5(2))* De Gruyter, Walter Inc.

Loftus, John. The Christian Delusion: Why Faith Fails. 2010. (ENG.). 1p. pap. 21.00 *(978-1-61614-168-4(9))* Prometheus Bks., Pubs.

Loftus, John W. Why I Became an Atheist: A Former Preacher Rejects Christianity. 2012. (ENG.). 480p. pap. 21.00 ***(978-1-61614-577-4(3))*** Prometheus Bks., Pubs.

Loftus, John W., ed. The End of Christianity. 2011. (ENG.). 435p. pap. 21.00 *(978-1-61614-413-5(0))* Prometheus Bks., Pubs.

Massey, Gerald. Gerald Massey's Lectures. 2008. 292p. pap. 22.95 *(978-1-58509-322-9(X))* Book Tree, The.

Mayer, Stephen McRae. Before the Twinkling of an Eye, There Are the Ways of God. 2008. 364p. 32.99 *(978-1-60477-900-4(4))*; pap. 20.99 *(978-1-60477-899-1(7))* Xulon Pr., Inc.

Mc Sweeney, Richard. A Jesus of Nazareth. 2007. 316p. 48.95 *(978-1-84799-030-3(4))* Lulu Enterprises Inc.

McQueen, Henry. Beyond the Cross. 2009. 124p. pap. 15.95 *(978-1-4251-9187-0(8))* Trafford Publishing.

Meslier, Jean. Testament. Shreve, Michael, tr. from FRE. 2009. (ENG.). 580p. 32.00 *(978-1-59102-749-2(7))* Prometheus Bks., Pubs.

Mike Luoma, Brother Zagreus. Neo-gnosis. 2008. 136p. pap. 12.95 *(978-1-4357-4280-2(X))* Lulu Enterprises Inc.

The Myth of Nazareth: The Invented Town of Jesus. 2007. (Illus.). per. 19.50 *(978-0-9794078-0-2(X))* Kevalin Pr.

Nietzsche, Friedrich Wilhelm. The Anti-Christ. 2011. 86p. pap. 7.77 *(978-1-936594-26-9(9)*, SoHo Bks.) Tribeca Bks.

—The Antichrist. 2007. (ENG.). 120p. per. 5.99 *(978-1-59986-631-4(5))* Filiquarian Publishing, LLC.

—The Antichrist. 2008. 108p. pap. 5.90 *(978-1-60459-326-6(1))* Wilder Pubns., Ltd.

—The Antichrist. Mencken, H. L., tr. 2008. 108p. 19.99 *(978-1-60459-327-3(X))* Wilder Pubns., Ltd.

—Der Antichrist: Versuch einer Kritik des Christentums. 2006. pap. *(978-1-4068-3460-4(2))* Echo Library.

Obeng, Kwadwo. We Are All Africans; Exposing the Negative Influence of the Judeo-Christian-Islamic Religions on Africans. 2009. 796p. pap. 85.95 *(978-1-935097-31-0(8))* Hillcrest Publishing Group, Inc.

Onfray, Michel. Atheist Manifesto: The Case Against Christianity, Judaism, & Islam. 2011. (ENG.). 264p. pap. 14.95 *(978-1-61145-009-8(X)*, 611008, Arcade Publishing) Skyhorse Publishing Co., Inc.

Packer, James S. Saints, Sinners, & Christian History: The Contradictions of the Christian Past. 2008. 230p. pap. 16.99 *(978-1-59955-137-1(3))* Cedar Fort, Inc./CFI Distribution.

Pendleton, J. Distinctive Principles of Baptists. 2006. 256p. per. 27.00 *(978-1-57978-544-4(1))* Baptist Standard Bearer, Inc.

Popovich, Phyllis. Shrouded in Darkness. 2008. 252p. pap. 14.49 *(978-1-4343-9230-5(9))* AuthorHouse.

Powell, Larry & Self, William R. Holy Murder: Abraham, Isaac, & the Rhetoric of Sacrifice. 2006. (ENG., Illus.). 202p. per. 36.99 *(978-0-7618-3578-3(4)*, Univ. Pr. of America, Inc.

Price, Robert M. Jesus Is Dead. 2007. pap. 18.00 *(978-1-57884-000-7(7))* American Atheist Pr.

—The Reason Driven Life: What Am I Here on Earth For? 2006. (ENG., Illus.). 1p. 26.98 *(978-1-59102-476-7(5))* Prometheus Bks., Pubs.

Reif, Jennifer. The Holy Book of Mary Magdalene: The Path of the Grail Steward. 2008. 180p. pap. 16.95 *(978-0-595-52243-9(2))* iUniverse, Inc.

Remsberg, John. The Christ Myth - a Critical Review & Analysis of the Evidence of His Existence. 2007. 328p. per. 24.99 *(978-1-59547-933-4(3))* NuVision Pubns., LLC.

Riell, Howard M. Enoch & the Book of Coincidences III: Promise. 2006. 134p. per. 14.95 *(978-1-58939-927-3(7))* Virtualbookworm.com Publishing, Inc.

Sanchez, Cheryl. Jesus Is Not the Reason for the Season. 2009. 92p. pap. 15.96 *(978-0-557-15243-8(7))* Lulu Enterprises Inc.

Schmitz, Rolf P. Jakob Ben Reuben: Kriege Gottes: Milchamot Hash-Shem. 2011. (Judentum und Umwelt. Realms of Judaism Ser.). 232p. 69.95 *(978-3-631-59496-4(8))* Lang, Peter GmbH, Europaischer Verlag der Wissenschaften DEU. Dist: Lang, Peter.

Servetus, Michael. The Restoration of Christianity: An English Translation of Christianismi Restitutio, 1553 by Michael Servetus. Hoffman, Christopher & Hillar, Marian, trs. from SPA. 440p. 129.95 *(978-0-7734-5520-7(5))* Mellen, Edwin Pr., The.

—Treatise Concerning the Supernatural Regeneration & the Kingdom of the Antichrist. Hoffman, Christopher A. & Hillar, Marian, trs. from LAT. 2008. 316p. 119.95 *(978-0-7734-5047-9(5))* Mellen, Edwin Pr., The.

—Treatise on Faith & Justice of Christ's Kingdom. Hoffman, Christopher A. & Hillar, Marian, trs. from LAT. 2008. 124p. 89.95 *(978-0-7734-5067-7(X))* Mellen, Edwin Pr., The.

Servetus, Michael & Hoffman, Christopher A. Thirty Letters to Calvin, Preacher to the Genevans: And Sixty Signs of the Kingdom of the Antichrist & His Revelation Which Is Now at Hand: (From the Restoration of Christianity, 1553) 2010. lxxxvi, 175p. 109.95 *(978-0-7734-1316-0(2))* Mellen, Edwin Pr., The.

Sharpe, R. A. Forgiveness: How Religion Endangers Morality. 2007. (Societas Ser.). (ENG.). 130p. pap. 17.90 *(978-1-84540-083-5(6))* Imprint Academic GBR. Dist: Ingram Pub. Services.

Shelley, Percy Bysshe. The Necessity of Atheism. reprint ed. lib. bdg. 98.00 *(978-0-7426-2116-9(2))* Classic Bks.

Simpson, Marvin. The Book of Satan: Prince of Earth, 1 vol. 2009. 161p. pap. 24.95 *(978-1-60813-278-2(1))* PublishAmerica, Inc.

Sinclair, Upton. The Profits of Religion. (ENG.). 232p. 2008. per. 16.95 *(978-1-60312-441-6(1))* 2007. 28.95 *(978-1-60312-619-9(8))* Aegypan.

—The Profits of Religion. 2008. 284p. 28.99 *(978-0-554-25952-9(4))*; 25.99 *(978-0-554-35255-8(9))* BiblioBazaar.

—The Profits of Religion. 2009. 164p. pap. *(978-0-217-28288-8(1))* Books LLC.

—The Profits of Religion. 2006. pap. *(978-1-4068-0569-7(6))* Echo Library.

—The Profits of Religion. 2007. (ENG.). 324p. *(978-1-934568-25-5(2))* Synergy International of The Americas, Ltd.

—The Profits of Religion: An Essay in Economic Interpretation. 2009. 324p. 25.99 *(978-1-103-18955-7(7))* 2009. 324p. pap. 19.99 *(978-1-103-18954-0(9))* 5th ed. 2007. (ENG.). 250p. pap. 20.99 *(978-1-4346-0072-1(6))* 5th l.t. ed. 2007. 280p. pap. 23.99 *(978-1-4346-0157-5(9))* BiblioBazaar.

—The Profits of Religion: An Essay in Economic Interpretation. 2007. 228p. per. *(978-1-4065-5380-2(8))* Dodo Pr.

—The Profits of Religion: An Essay in Economic Interpretation, 315. 315p. reprint ed. 98.00 *(978-0-7222-2115-0(0))* Library Reprints, Inc.

Sledge, Allison. The Quintessential Jesus of Nazareth: An Astrological Interpretation of the Messiah's Natal Chart. 2011. 344p. 28.28 ***(978-1-4634-7420-1(2))***; pap. 17.72 ***(978-1-4634-7421-8(0))*** AuthorHouse.

Sloat, John W. Moving Beyond the Christian Myth: The Next Step in Our Spiritual Evolution. 2011. (ENG., Illus.). 148p. pap. ***(978-1-926918-94-5(0)***, CCB Publishing) CCB Publishing.

Smith, Andrew Phillip. The Gnostics: History, Tradition, Scriptures, Influence. 2008. (ENG.). 256p. pap. 14.95 *(978-1-905857-78-4(0)*, Watkins Publishing) Duncan Baird Pubs. GBR. Dist: Sterling Publishing Co., Inc.

Spong, John Shelby. Jesus for the Non-Religious. 2008. 336p. per. 14.99 *(978-0-06-077841-5(5)*, HarperOne) HarperCollins Pubs.

Sprinkle, Joe M. 'The Book of the Covenant' A Literary Approach. 2009. (Library of Hebrew Bible/Old Testament Studies, the Ser.). (ENG.). 224p. 39.95 *(978-0-567-32481-8(8)*, T&T Clark) Continuum International Publishing Group, Ltd. GBR. Dist: National Bk. Network.

Stenger, Victor J. God & the Folly of Faith. 2012. (ENG.). 375p. pap. 20.00 ***(978-1-61614-599-6(4))*** Prometheus Bks., Pubs.

Stenhouse, Fanny. Expose of Polygamy: A Lady's Life among the Mormons. DeSimone, Linda Wilcox, ed. 2008. (Life Writings of Frontier Women Ser.). (ENG., Illus.). 200p. 29.95 *(978-0-87421-713-1(X)*, Utah State Univ. Pr.) Univ. Pr. of Colorado.

Talmage, T. De Witt. Around the Tea-Table. 2008. 284p. 28.99 *(978-0-554-27096-8(X))* 2007. (ENG.). 262p. pap. 21.99 *(978-1-4346-2496-3(X))* BiblioBazaar.

—Around the Tea-Table. 2007. (ENG.). 240p. per. *(978-1-4065-4880-8(4))* Dodo Pr.

—Around the Tea-Table. 2007. (ENG.). 502p. 53.95 *(978-0-548-25561-2(X))*; 504p. per. 38.95 *(978-1-4326-5909-7(X))* Kessinger Publishing, LLC.

Taylor, Robert. The Eleusinian Mysteries Are Entirely the Same As the Christian. 2006. pap. 9.95 *(978-1-4304-2687-5(X))* Kessinger Publishing, LLC.

Taylor, Thomas, tr. The Arguments of the Emperor Julian Against the Christians: To Which Are Added Extracts from Other Works of Julian Relative to Christians. 2007. 119p. pap. 15.00 *(978-1-55635-164-8(X)*, Wipf and Stock) Wipf & Stock Pubs.

Tolstoy, Leo. The Kingdom of God Is Within You. l.t. ed. 2006. 310p. pap. 24.99 *(978-1-4264-1700-9(4))* BiblioBazaar.

—The Kingdom of God Is Within You. Garnett, Constance, tr. from RUS. 2006. (Dover Value Editions Ser.). (ENG., Illus.). 352p. per. 12.95 *(978-0-486-45138-1(0))* Dover Pubns., Inc.

Vayro, Ian Ross. They Lied to Us in Sunday School. 2006. (Illus.). 428p. pap. *(978-0-9756878-6-4(7)*, 305-024) Joshua Bks.

Voltaire. God & Human Beings: First English Translation. Shreve, Michael, tr. from FRE. 2010. (ENG.). 152p. pap. 18.00 *(978-1-61614-178-3(6))* Prometheus Bks., Pubs.

Warne, Floyd Lawrence. Christianity: A Critique of Religious Doctrine. 2011. 116p. 39.95 ***(978-1-258-07292-6(0))*** Literary Licensing, LLC.

Whitehouse, Maggy. The Marriage of Jesus: The Lost Wife of the Hidden Years. 2007. (ENG.). 260p. per. 19.95 *(978-1-84694-008-8(7))* O Bks.,John Hunt.

CHRISTIANITY—ESSENCE, GENIUS, NATURE

see also Demythologization

Atkinson, Mark. Unveiling the Great Mystery of the First Century Church Volume One Paperback. 2007. 296p. pap. 27.50 *(978-1-84799-925-2(5))* Lulu Enterprises Inc.

Batterson, Mark. Primal: A Quest for the Lost Soul of Christianity. 2010. (ENG.). 208p. pap. 13.99 *(978-1-60142-357-3(8)*, Multnomah) Doubleday Religious Publishing Group, The.

Blyth, Philip Gledstanes. Christianity & Tradition. 2008. 228p. 24.99 *(978-0-559-83146-1(3))*; pap. 24.75 *(978-0-559-83142-3(0))* BiblioBazaar.

—Christianity & Tradition. 2009. 114p. pap. *(978-0-217-81255-9(4))* Books LLC.

—Christianity & Tradition. 2007. (ENG.). 224p. 39.95 *(978-0-548-15543-1(7))*; pap. 24.95 *(978-1-4304-4980-5(2))* Kessinger Publishing, LLC.

Bowman, John Wick. The Religion of Maturity. 2007. (ENG.). 334p. 45.95 *(978-0-548-07101-4(2))* Kessinger Publishing, LLC.

Brightwell Sr., Claude. Everybody Ought to Know Who Jesus Is. 2008. 56p. pap. 9.95 *(978-1-4327-3684-2(1))* Outskirts Pr., Inc.

Brunton, Lauder. Truth & Delusion. 2006. pap. 15.95 *(978-1-4286-3914-0(4))* Kessinger Publishing, LLC.

Bulgakov, Sergei Nikolaevich & Jakim, Boris. Relics & Miracles: Two Theological Essays. 2011. 128p. pap. 24.00 ***(978-0-8028-6531-1(3))*** Eerdmans, William B. Publishing Co.

Capetz, Paul E. Christian Faith as Religion: A Study in the Theologies of Calvin & Schleiermacher. 2011. 340p. pap. 38.00 ***(978-1-61097-141-6(8)**, Wipf and Stock)* Wipf & Stock Pubs.

Chesterton & Chesterton, G. K. Orthodoxy. 2007. (B&N Library of Essential Reading Ser.). (ENG.). 176p. pap. 8.95 *(978-0-7607-8631-4(3))* Barnes & Noble, Inc.

Chesterton, G. K. Orthodoxy. 2011. 142p. pap. 12.99 ***(978-1-61203-253-5(2))*** Bottom of the Hill Publishing.

—Orthodoxy. l.t. ed. 2006. pap. *(978-1-4068-2223-6(X))* Echo Library.

—Orthodoxy: The classic of Christian Apologetics. 2010. 172p. pap. 14.95 *(978-1-60444-082-9(1))* IndoEuropeanPublishing.com.

Collier, Robert Laird. Meditations on the Essence of Christianity, by R Laird Collier. 2006. 144p. per. 16.99 *(978-1-4255-1058-9(2))* MPublishing.

Colquhoun, Lady. Worlds Religion As Contrasted with Genui. 2006. pap. 24.95 *(978-1-4286-3497-8(5))* Kessinger Publishing, LLC.

Colson, Charles & Fickett, Harold. The Faith: What Christians Believe, Why They Believe It, & Why It Matters. 2008. (ENG.). 176p. pap. 12.99 *(978-0-310-27604-3(7))* Zondervan.

Colson, Charles, et al. The Faith: What Christians Believe, Why They Believe It, & Why It Matters, 1 vol. 2008. (ENG.). 176p. 18.99 *(978-0-310-27603-6(9))* Zondervan.

Colson, Charles W. The Faith Curriculum Kit. 2008. (ENG.). pap. 52.99 *(978-0-310-29373-6(1))* Zondervan.

Cooper, Alison. Facts about Christianity. 2010. (World Religions Ser.). (ENG.). 48p. (YA). lib. bdg. 26.50 *(978-1-61532-320-3(1)*, Rosen Central) Rosen Publishing Group, Inc., The.

Davis, Dale Ralph. The House That Jesus Built. 2007. (ENG.). 64p. pap. 4.99 *(978-1-84550-312-3(0))* Christian Focus Pubns. GBR. Dist: STL Distribution North America.

Drew, Charles D. A Journey Worth Taking: Finding Your Purpose in This World. 2007. 270p. per. *(978-1-59638-042-4(X))* P & R Publishing.

Drummond, Henry. The Program of Christianity. 2011. 40p. pap. 7.99 ***(978-1-61203-222-1(2))*** Bottom of the Hill Publishing.

—The Program of Christianity. 2008. 48p. per. 7.99 *(978-1-60459-174-3(9))* Wilder Pubns., Ltd.

Drury, Keith. Common Ground. 2008. 187p. pap. 13.99 *(978-0-89827-354-0(4))* Wesleyan Publishing Hse.

D'Souza, Dinesh. Lo Grandioso del Cristianismo. 2009. Orig. Title: What's So Great about Christianity. (SPA.). 400p. pap. 13.99 *(978-1-4143-2978-9(4)*, Tyndale Espanol) Tyndale Hse. Pubs.

—What's So Great about Christianity. 2007. (ENG.). 348p. 27.95 *(978-1-59698-517-9(8))* Regnery Publishing, Inc., An Eagle Publishing Co.

—What's So Great about Christianity. 2008. (ENG.). 368p. pap. 14.99 *(978-1-4143-2601-6(7))* Tyndale Hse. Pubs.

—What's So Great about Christianity Study Guide: Your Guide to Answering the New Atheists. 2009. (ENG.). 144p. pap. 7.99 *(978-1-4143-3210-9(6))* Tyndale Hse. Pubs.

Eaton, Arthur Wentworth Hamilton. The Heart of the Creeds: Historical Religion in the Light of Modern. 2007. (ENG.). 212p. per. 24.95 *(978-1-4304-4347-6(2))* Kessinger Publishing, LLC.

Ewbank, J. Robert. John Wesley, Natural Man, & The 'Isms' 2009. 198p. pap. 23.00 *(978-1-60608-578-3(6)*, Resource Pubns.) Wipf & Stock Pubs.

The Faith, Session 1: What Christians Believe, Why They Believe It, & Why It Matters, 1 vol. 2009. 2.99 *(978-0-310-79209-3(6))* Zondervan.

The Faith, Session 2: What Christians Believe, Why They Believe It, & Why It Matters, 1 vol. 2009. 2.99 *(978-0-310-79210-9(X))* Zondervan.

The Faith, Session 3: What Christians Believe, Why They Believe It, & Why It Matters, 1 vol. 2009. 2.99 *(978-0-310-79211-6(8))* Zondervan.

The Faith, Session 4: What Christians Believe, Why They Believe It, & Why It Matters, 1 vol. 2009. 2.99 *(978-0-310-79212-3(6))* Zondervan.

The Faith, Session 5: What Christians Believe, Why They Believe It, & Why It Matters, 1 vol. 2009. 2.99 *(978-0-310-79213-0(4))* Zondervan.

The Faith, Session 6: What Christians Believe, Why They Believe It, & Why It Matters, 1 vol. 2009. 2.99 *(978-0-310-79214-7(2))* Zondervan.

Guite, Malcolm. What Do Christians Believe? Belonging & Belief in Modern Christianity. 2008. (ENG.). 144p. per. 9.95 *(978-0-8027-1640-8(7))* Walker & Co.

Gulley, Philip. The Evolution of Faith: How God Is Creating a Better Christianity. (ENG.). 2012. 224p. pap. 14.99 ***(978-0-06-168993-2(9)**, HarperOne)* 2011. 256p. 24.99 *(978-0-06-073660-6(7)*, HarperOne) 2011. 256p. pap. 24.99 *(978-0-06-206527-8(0)*, HarperLuxe) HarperCollins Pubs.

Harnack, Adolf. What Is Christianity? Saunders, Thomas Bailey, tr. 2011. 312p. pap. 14.95 ***(978-1-61427-016-4(3))*** Martino Publishing.

Harnack, Adolph. What Is Christianity? 15.00 *(978-0-8446-2208-8(7))* Smith, Peter Pub., Inc.

—What Is Christianity? Sixteen Lectures delivered in the University of Berlin 1899-1900. Saunders, Thomas Bailey, tr. 2006. 312p. per. 24.95 *(978-1-58509-272-7(X))* Book Tree, The.

Hauerwas, Stanley. Working with Words: On Learning to Speak Christian. 2011. 340p. pap. 37.00 *(978-1-60899-968-2(8)*, Cascade Bks.) Wipf & Stock Pubs.

Hick, John. The Second Christianity. 2009. 140p. pap. 17.00 *(978-1-60608-986-6(2)*, Wipf and Stock) Wipf & Stock Pubs.

Howard, Kathy. God's Truth Revealed: Biblical Foundations for the Christian Faith. 2010. (ENG.). 192p. pap. 14.99 *(978-1-59669-268-8(5))* New Hope Pubs.

Howie, Carl G. God in the Eternal Present. 2011. 128p. 40.95 ***(978-1-258-02803-9(4))*** Literary Licensing, LLC.

Huntington, F. D. The Fitness of Christianity to Man. 2007. (ENG.). 136p. 35.95 *(978-0-548-14612-5(8))* 2006. pap. 20.95 *(978-1-4286-5943-8(9))* Kessinger Publishing, LLC.

Leithart, Peter J. Deep Comedy: Trinity, Tragedy, & Hope in Western Literature. 2006. (ENG.). 159p. pap. 15.00 *(978-1-59128-027-9(3))* Canon Pr.

Leland, John. Advantage & Necessity of Christian Rev. 2006. pap. 42.95 *(978-1-4286-4196-9(3))*; (ENG.). pap. 40.95 *(978-1-4286-4254-6(4))* Kessinger Publishing, LLC.

Mackey, James P. Christianity & Creation: The Essence of the Christian Faith & Its Future among Religions. 2006. (ENG.). 424p. 160.00 *(978-0-8264-1895-1(3))*; pap. 49.95 *(978-0-8264-1907-1(0))* Continuum International Publishing Group, Ltd. GBR. Dist: National Bk. Network.

Meyers, Robin R. Saving Jesus from the Church: How to Stop Worshiping Christ & Start Following Jesus. 2010. (ENG.). 256p. pap. 14.99 *(978-0-06-156822-0(8)*, HarperOne) HarperCollins Pubs.

Moore, James W. Faith Is the Answer, but What Are the Questions? 2007. 141p. per. 14.95 *(978-0-687-64673-9(1)*, Dimensions For Living) Abingdon Pr.

Moran, Gabriel. Uniqueness: Problem or Paradox in Jewish & Christian Traditions. 2008. 166p. pap. 21.00 *(978-1-60608-232-4(9)*, Wipf and Stock) Wipf & Stock Pubs.

Motyer, J. A. & van den Toren, Benno. Christian Belief. 2009. (ENG.). 224p. pap., instr.'s gde. ed. 9.95 *(978-0-7459-5214-7(3))* Lion Hudson PLC GBR. Dist: Independent Pubs. Group.

Newbigin, Lesslie. A Faith for this One World. 2011. 128p. pap. 18.00 ***(978-1-61097-709-8(2)**, Wipf and Stock)* Wipf & Stock Pubs.

Newbigin, Lesslie. The Finality of Christ. 2009. 120p. pap. 15.00 *(978-1-60608-581-3(6)*, Wipf and Stock) Wipf & Stock Pubs.

Northbourne, Lord. Of the Land & the Spirit: The Essential Lord Northbourne on Ecology & Religion. 2008. (Perennial Philosophy Ser.). (ENG.). 272p. pap. 19.95 *(978-1-933316-61-1(6))* World Wisdom, Inc.

Nygren, Anders. Essence of Christianity: Two Essays. Watson, Philip S., tr. 2009. 128p. pap. 16.00 *(978-1-60608-716-9(9)*, Wipf and Stock) Wipf & Stock Pubs.

Rivage-Seul, Michael. The Emperor's God: Imperial Misunderstandings of Christianity Pbk. 2008. (Illus.). 210p. (C). pap. 24.00 *(978-1-933567-17-4(1))* Institute for Economic Democracy Pr., Inc.

Rosenquist D. D., Bradford Mark. The New Christian Handbook: A Manual for New Believers, 1 vol. 2009. 155p. pap. 19.95 *(978-1-61546-039-7(X))* PublishAmerica, Inc.

Royce, Josiah. The Problem of Christianity. 2008. 452p. 30.99 *(978-0-559-86276-2(8))*; pap. 35.75 *(978-0-559-86275-5(X))* BiblioBazaar.

—The Problem of Christianity. 2009. 170p. pap. *(978-1-4589-3386-7(5))* Books LLC.

Simmons, Henry M. New Tables of Stone & Other Essays. 2007. (ENG.). 334p. 45.95 *(978-0-548-06456-6(3))* Kessinger Publishing, LLC.

Simpson, Albert B. The Fourfold Gospel: Jesus as Savior, Sanctifier, Healer & Coming King Audio Excerpts CD. 2007. (Pure Gold Classics). (Illus.). 339p. pap. 14.99 incl. audio compact disk *(978-0-88270-336-7(6))* Bridge-Logos Foundation.

Simpson, P. Carnegie. The Fact of Christ: A Series of Lectures. 2007. (ENG.). 212p. 39.95 *(978-0-548-09954-4(5))* Kessinger Publishing, LLC.

So, Damon W. K. The Forgotten Jesus & the Trinity You Never Knew. 2010. (Illus.). 254p. pap. 28.00 *(978-1-60899-631-5(X)*, Wipf and Stock) Wipf & Stock Pubs.

Speer, Robert E. Seeking the Mind of Christ. 2011. 186p. 42.95 ***(978-1-258-10467-2(9))*** Literary Licensing, LLC.

Thomson, William. Aids to Faith; a Series of Theological Essays by Several Writers Being a Reply to Essays & Reviews Ed by William Thomson. 2006. 544p. (ENG.). per. 29.99 *(978-1-4255-6026-3(1))*; per. 29.99 *(978-1-4255-6025-6(3))* MPublishing.

Tolstoy, Leo. The Kingdom of God Is Within You. l.t. ed. 2006. 310p. pap. 24.99 *(978-1-4264-1700-9(4))* BiblioBazaar.

—The Kingdom of God Is Within You. Garnett, Constance, tr. from RUS. 2006. (Dover Value Editions Ser.). (ENG., Illus.). 352p. per. 12.95 *(978-0-486-45138-1(0))* Dover Pubns., Inc.

Towns, Elmer. Core Christianity: What Is Christianity All About? 2007. (ENG.). 160p. per. 12.99 *(978-0-89957-109-6(3))* AMG Pubs.

Trench, Richard Chenevix. The Fitness of Holy Scripture for Unfolding the Spiritual Life of Men II Christ the Desire of All Nations, or, the Unconscious Prophecies of Heathen. 2006. 268p. per. 23.99 *(978-1-4255-2370-1(6))* MPublishing.

Wardle, Timothy. The Jerusalem Temple & Early Christian Identity. 2010. (Illus.). 298p. pap. 137.50 *(978-3-16-150568-3(9))* Mohr Siebeck GmbH & Co. KG DEU. Dist: Coronet Bks.

Wilken, Robert L. The Myth of Christian Beginnings. 2009. 232p. pap. 26.00 *(978-1-60608-693-3(6)*, Wipf and Stock) Wipf & Stock Pubs.

Zahnd, Brian. Beauty Will Save the World: Rediscovering the Allure & Mystery of Christianity. 2012. xviii, 234p. E-Book ***(978-1-61638-641-2(X))**;* (ENG.). 256p. pap. 15.99 ***(978-1-61638-585-9(5))*** Charisma Media. (Charisma Hse.).

CHRISTIANITY—EVIDENCES

see Apologetics

CHRISTIANITY—HISTORY

see Church History

CHRISTIANITY—JUVENILE LITERATURE

Camesecca, Leigh. What Are the Promises I Make at Baptism? 2011. 32p. 17.99 *(978-1-60641-953-3(6))* Deseret Bk. Co.

Doane, Linda. God Had A Plan for Me. 2010. 60p. pap. 9.95 *(978-1-4502-2385-0(0))* iUniverse, Inc.

MacKenzie, Carine. The Life of Jesus. 2011. (ENG., Illus.). 64p. 10.99 ***(978-1-84550-749-7(5))*** Christian Focus Pubns. GBR. Dist: STL Distribution North America.

Roche, Maite. My First Prayers for Christmas. 2010. 14p. 6.99 *(978-1-58617-505-4(X))* Ignatius Pr.

Stark Muyskens, Nancy. For What? 2010. 26p. pap. 12.95 *(978-1-60844-288-1(8))* Dog Ear Publishing, LLC.

CHRISTIANITY—MISCELLANEA

Albrecht, Greg. Between Religious Rocks & Life's Hard Places: 101 Answers to Tough Questions about What You Believe, 0 vols. 2007. 224p. per. 16.99 *(978-0-529-12228-5(6))* Nelson, Thomas Inc.

Barrera, Navas. Formacion de un Desafiador: Making a Christian Challenger. (SPA.). *(978-84-7645-365-0(5)*, 223441) Clie, Editorial.

Bittinger, Marvin. The Faith Equation: A Mathematical Journey in Christianity. 2009. (ENG.). 300p. 19.99 *(978-0-9816514-3-9(7))* Last Chapter Publishing.

Blanski, Tyler. Mud & Poetry: Love, Sex, & the Sacred. 2010. 208p. 16.95 *(978-1-935205-09-8(9))* Fresh Air Bks.

Borg, Marcus J. The God We Never Knew: Beyond Dogmatic Religion to A More Authentic Contemporary Faith. 2006. (Plus Ser.). 208p. pap. 13.95 *(978-0-06-114491-2(6)*, Harper San Francisco) HarperCollins Pubs.

Brooks, C. Harry & Charles, Ernest. Christianity & Autosuggestion. 2007. (ENG.). 160p. 36.95 *(978-0-548-07740-5(1))* Kessinger Publishing, LLC.

Brooks, Ronald M. & Geisler, Norman L. When Skeptics Ask: A Handbook on Christian Evidences. 2008. (Illus.). 352p. pap. 19.99 *(978-0-8010-7164-5(X))* Baker Bks.

Busacker, John. 8 Questions God Can't Answer. 2009. (ENG.). 144p. pap. 14.95 *(978-0-578-01501-9(3))* Life-Worth, LLC.

Courtauld, George. Who, When & What the Hell: A Mass of Fascinating Facts about Christianity. 2012. (ENG.). 160p. 12.95 ***(978-1-903071-37-3(2))*** Bene Factum Publishing, Ltd. GBR. Dist: Independent Pubs. Group.

El Cristiano de Rodillas: The Kneeling Christian. (SPA.). 160p. *(978-84-7228-521-7(9)*, 220204) Clie, Editorial.

Dirks, Jerald. What You Weren't Taught in Sunday School. 2011. ***(978-1-59008-069-6(6))*** amana pubns.

Gates, Elexie L. Truth in Focus, 1 vol. 2009. 73p. pap. 16.95 *(978-1-4489-2462-2(6))* PublishAmerica, Inc.

Gibbons, Eric. Christian Voodoo: A Guide to Luck, Omens, Recipes for Homemade Miracles, & Exorcism. 2007. (Illus.). 128p. pap. 14.95 *(978-0-7643-2566-3(3))* Schiffer Publishing, Ltd.

Goldingay, John. Key Questions about Christian Faith: Old Testament Answers. 2010. *(978-1-59856-430-3(7))* Hendrickson Pubs. Marketing, LLC.

Gomez, Enrique. Cristianismo Frente a las Sectas: Christianity vs. the Cults. (SPA.). *(978-84-7645-422-0(8)*, 223329) Clie, Editorial.

Jackson Case. Forjadores Del Cristianismo - Tomo I: Makers of Christianity - I. (SPA.). *(978-84-7645-227-1(6)*, 223315) Clie, Editorial.

Jackson, Gordon S. OJesus Does Stand-up,O & Other Satires. 2009. 114p. pap. 19.00 *(978-1-60899-038-2(9)*, Resource Pubns.) Wipf & Stock Pubs.

Jeffress, Robert. Outrageous Truth... Seven Absolutes You Can Still Believe. 2008. (ENG.). 256p. pap. 14.99 *(978-1-4000-7494-5(0))* Doubleday Religious Publishing Group, The.

Kenyon, J. Forbidden Religion: Suppressed Heresies of the West. 2006. (ENG., Illus.). 1p. per. 18.00 *(978-1-59143-067-4(4))* Inner Traditions International, Ltd.

Logos. Christian History Library in Libronix. 2007. cd-rom 129.95 *(978-0-912498-55-3(2))* Foundation for American Christian Education.

McCollister, John C. The Christian Book of Why. 2010. 360p. pap. 19.95 *(978-0-8246-0484-4(9))* David, Jonathan Pubs., Inc.

McDowell, Josh & Johnson, Kevin. The Awesome Book of Bible Answers for Kids. 2011. 160p. pap. 11.99 *(978-0-7369-2872-4(3))* Harvest Hse. Pubs.

McNeil, John. Forjadores Del Cristianismo - Tomo II: Makers of Christianity - II. (SPA.). *(978-84-7645-228-8(4)*, 223316) Clie, Editorial.

Minirth, Frank B. & Minirth, Frank. A Brilliant Mind: Proven Ways to Increase Your Brainpower. 2007. 192p. pap. 12.99 *(978-0-8007-3187-8(5))* Revell.

Pauls, Tim. You Ask about Faith: Questions Teens Are Asking. 2008. 10.49 *(978-0-7586-1493-3(4))* Concordia Publishing Hse.

Plass, Adrian. Bacon Sandwiches & Salvation: A Humorous Antidote for the Pharisee in All of Us. 2008. (ENG.). 257p. pap. 14.99 *(978-1-934068-76-2(4))* Authentic Media.

Prakasha, Padma Aon. The Christ Blueprint: 13 Keys to Christ Consciousness. 2010. (ENG.). 376p. pap. 18.95 *(978-1-55643-884-4(2))* North Atlantic Bks.

Rose Publishing Staff. Tough Questions about Christianity. 2009. 14p. 3.99 *(978-1-59636-307-6(X))* Rose Publishing.

Rubenis, Juris & Subacs, Maris. Finding God in a Tangled World: Thoughts & Parables. 2007. (Illus.). 184p. 19.00 *(978-1-55725-495-5(8))* Paraclete Pr., Inc.

Schulenburg, Brian. What's the Deal With... ? 500 Questions Today's Students Are Asking about the Biggest Issues in Life, 1 vol. 2007. (Quick Questions Ser.). (ENG.). 144p. pap. 10.99 *(978-0-310-27364-6(1))* Zondervan.

Tolstoy, Leo. Leo Tolstoy: Spiritual Writings. Moore, Charles E., ed. 2006. (Modern Spiritual Masters Ser.). 207p. per. 17.00 *(978-1-57075-673-3(2))* Orbis Bks.

Webster, Patti S. It Happened in Church: Stories of Humor from the Pulpit to the Pews. l.t. ed. 2009. 333p. 30.95 *(978-1-4104-1186-0(9))* Thorndike Pr.

Wilkens, Steve. The Original Dr. Steve's Almanac of Christian Trivia: A Miscellany of Oddities, Instructional Anecdotes, Little-Known Facts & Occasional Frivolity. 2007. (ENG., Illus.). 162p. per. 12.00 *(978-0-8308-3438-9(9))* InterVarsity Pr.

Williams, Donald T. The Devil's Dictionary of the Christian Faith. 2008. 128p. pap. 16.99 *(978-0-8272-0638-0(0))* Chalice Pr.

Zacharias, Ravi & Geisler, Norman L., eds. Quien Creo A Dios? Y Respuestas A Mas de 100 Preguntas Acerca de Cuestiones de Fe, 1 vol. 2007. (SPA.). 301p. per. 12.99 *(978-0-8297-4890-1(3))* Zondervan.

CHRISTIANITY—ORIGIN

see also Church—Foundation

Adeola, Moses O. The Origin of Christianity. 2009. 140p. 22.50 *(978-1-60860-186-8(2)*, Strategic Bk. Publishing) AEG Literary Publishing Services, Inc.

Aguirre Monasterio, Rafael. Del Movimiento de Jesús a la Iglesia Cristiana: Ensayo de Exégesis Sociológica Del Cristianismo Primitivo. 2009. (Agora Ser.: Vol. 4). (SPA.). 243p. *(978-84-8169-927-2(6))* Verbo Divino, Editorial.

Bird, Michael F. & Crossley, James G. How Did Christianity Begin? A Believer & Non-Believer Examine the Evidence. 2008. 224p. pap. 19.95 *(978-1-59856-341-2(6))* Hendrickson Pubs. Marketing, LLC.

Boyarin, Daniel. Border Lines: The Partition of Judaeo-Christianity. 2006. (Divinations: Rereading Late Ancient Religion Ser.). 392p. (C). per. 26.50 *(978-0-8122-1986-9(4))* Univ. of Pennsylvania Pr.

Brandon, S. G. F. The Fall of Jerusalem & the Christian Church. 2010. 314p. pap. 36.00 *(978-1-60899-747-3(2)*, Wipf and Stock) Wipf & Stock Pubs.

Capes, David B., et al, eds. Israel's God & Rebecca's Children: Christology & Community in Early Judaism & Christianity: Essays in Honor of Larry W. Hurtado & Alan F. Segal. 2007. (Illus.). 510p. 79.95 *(978-1-60258-026-8(X))* Baylor Univ. Pr.

Casey, Maurice. Judaism, Jewish Identities, & the Gospel Tradition: Essays in Honour of Maurice Casey. Crossley, James G., ed. 2010. (BibleWorld Ser.). (ENG.). 240p. (C). 39.95 *(978-1-84553-284-0(8))*; 99.95 *(978-1-84553-283-3(X))* Equinox Publishing Ltd. GBR. Dist: ISD.

Collins, John J. & Evans, Craig A., eds. Christian Beginnings & the Dead Sea Scrolls. 2006. (Acadia Studies in Bible & Theology Ser.). 144p. (C). pap. 18.00 *(978-0-8010-2837-3(X))* Baker Academic.

Corley, Kathleen E. Maranatha: Women's Funerary Rituals & Christian Origins. 2010. 280p. (C). 35.00 *(978-0-8006-6236-3(9)*, Fortress Pr.) Augsburg Fortress, Pubs.

Cresswell, Peter. Jesus the Terrorist. 2010. (ENG., Illus.). 440p. pap. 29.95 *(978-1-84694-274-7(8))* Hunt, John Publishing Ltd. GBR. Dist: National Bk. Network.

Crossley, James G. Jesus in an Age of Terror: Scholarly Projects for a New American Century. 2008. (BibleWorld Ser.). (ENG.). 284p. (C). 99.95 *(978-1-84553-429-5(8))*; pap. 34.95 *(978-1-84553-430-1(1))* Equinox Publishing Ltd. GBR. Dist: ISD.

—Why Christianity Happened: A Sociohistorical Account of Christian Origins (26-50 CE) 2006. (ENG.). 232p. per. 30.00 *(978-0-664-23094-4(6))* Westminster John Knox Pr.

Falcao, Luis Miguel. The Reawakening of Consciousness. 2009. 330p. pap. *(978-0-9814117-3-6(8))* Kima Global Pubs.

Gadalla, Moustafa. The Ancient Egyptian Roots of Christianity. 2007. (Illus.). 192p. pap. 12.95 *(978-1-931446-29-7(5))* Tehuti Research Foundation.

Gould, Meredith. Why Is There a Menorah on the Altar? Jewish Roots of Christian Worship. 2009. 176p. pap. 20.00 *(978-1-59627-117-3(5)*, Seabury Bks.) Church Publishing, Inc.

Graystone, Geoffrey. The Dead Sea Scrolls & the Originality of Christ. 2011. 122p. 40.95 ***(978-1-258-01596-1(X))*** Literary Licensing, LLC.

Hanges, James Constantine. Christ, the Image of the Church: The Construction of a New Cosmology & the Rise of Christianity. 2006. (ENG.). 284p. pap. 24.00 *(978-1-888570-95-3(4))* Davies Group Pubs., The.

Hanson, Kenneth. Blood Kin of Jesus: James & the Lost Jewish Church. 2009. (ENG., Illus.). 248p. pap. 20.00 *(978-1-57178-224-3(9))* Council Oak Bks.

Hilhorst, Anthony, et al, eds. Flores Florentino: Dead Sea Scrolls & Other Early Jewish Studies in Honour of Florentino Garcia Martinez. 2007. (Supplements to the Journal for the Study of Judaism Ser.). (ITA, FRE, SPA & ENG., Illus.). 836p. lib. bdg. *(978-90-04-16292-1(5))* BRILL.

Huch, Larry. La Bendición Torá: Revelando el misterio, impartiendo el Milagro. 2009.Tr. of Torah Blessing: Revealing the Mystery, Releasing the Miracle. (SPA.). pap. 10.99 *(978-1-60374-156-9(9))* Whitaker Hse.

—The Torah Blessing: Revealing the Mystery, Releasing the Miracle. 2009. 208p. pap. 13.99 *(978-1-60374-118-7(6)*, 771187) Whitaker Hse.

Huller, Stephan. The Real Messiah: The Throne of St. Mark & the True Origins of Christianity. 2011. (ENG.). 288p. pap. 17.95 *(978-1-907486-64-7(X)*, Watkins Publishing) Duncan Baird Pubs. GBR. Dist: Sterling Publishing Co., Inc.

Hurtado, Larry W. The Earliest Christian Artifacts: Manuscripts & Christian Origins. 2006. (Illus.). 248p. per. 20.00 *(978-0-8028-2895-8(7))* Eerdmans, William B. Publishing Co.

Instone-Brewer, David. Traditions of the Rabbis from the Era of the New Testament: Feasts & Sabbaths: Passover & Atonement, 6 vols., 2A. 2007. (HEB & ENG.). 400p. 60.00 *(978-0-8028-4763-8(3))* Eerdmans, William B. Publishing Co.

Jabbar, Malik H. The Biggest Lie Ever Told, 4th Edition. 4th exp. rev. ed. 2006. per. 9.95 *(978-1-57154-007-2(5))* Rare Bks. Distributors.

Jaffé, Dan. Studies in Rabbinic Judaism & Early Christianity: Text & Context. 2010. (Ancient Judaism & Early Christianity Ser.). (FRE & ENG.). 248p. *(978-90-04-18410-7(4))* BRILL.

Kaiseratt, Harold. Our False Christianity: How it Started. 2010. pap. 12.95 *(978-0-533-16353-3(6))* Vantage Pr., Inc.
Kautsky, Karl. Foundations of Christianity: A study in Christian Origins. 2007. 288p. per. *(978-0-902869-93-6(0))* International Marxist Grp. (IMG).
Knight, Jonathan. Christian Origins. 2008. (ENG.). 472p. 39.95 *(978-0-567-03351-2(1)*, T&T Clark Int'l) Continuum International Publishing Group, Ltd. GBR. Dist: National Bk. Network.
Knohl, Israel & Knohl. Messiahs & Resurrection in 'the Gabriel Revelation' 2009. (Robert & Arlene Kogod Library of Judaic Studies, the Ser.). (ENG & HEB., Illus.). 144p. 29.95 *(978-0-8264-2507-2(0))*; 100.00 *(978-0-8264-4669-5(8))* Continuum International Publishing Group, Ltd. GBR. Dist: National Bk. Network.
Kohn, Risa Levitt & Moore, Rebecca. A Portable God: The Origin of Judaism & Christianity. 2007. (ENG., Illus.). 220p. 75.00 *(978-0-7425-4464-2(8))*; per. 24.95 *(978-0-7425-4465-9(6))* Rowman & Littlefield Publishers, Inc.
Kraus, Thomas J. Ad Fontes: Original Manuscripts & Their Significance for Studying Early Christianity - Selected Essays. 2007. (Texts & Editions for New Testament Study Ser.). (MUL., Illus.). 304p. *(978-90-04-16182-5(1))* BRILL.
Laan, Ray Vander. Promised Land, 1 vol., Vol. 1. rev. exp. ed. 2008. (Faith Lessons Ser.). (ENG.). 160p. pap. 9.99 *(978-0-310-27957-0(7))* Zondervan.
—Walking with God in the Desert, 1 vol. 2010. (Faith Lessons Ser.). (ENG.). 336p. pap. 10.99 *(978-0-310-32993-0(0))* Zondervan.
Laan, Ray Vander & Sorenson, Amanda. Early Church, 1 vol., Vol. 5. exp. rev. ed. 2008. (Faith Lessons Ser.). (ENG.). 192p. pap. 9.99 *(978-0-310-27971-6(2))* Zondervan.
Larson, Martin A. The Religion of the Occident: Or the Origin & Development or the Essene Christian Faith. 2011. 732p. 71.95 ***(978-1-258-01017-1(8))*** Literary Licensing, LLC.
Lawson, R. S. Death by Deception. 2010. 88p. pap. 10.95 *(978-1-4502-1463-6(0))* iUniverse, Inc.
Lazarus, William P. & Sullivan, Mark. Comparative Religion for Dummies. 2008. (ENG., Illus.). 366p. pap. 19.99 *(978-0-470-23065-7(7)*, For Dummies) Wiley, John & Sons, Inc.
Lillie, Arthur. Buddha & Buddhism. 2010. (ENG.). 244p. pap. 26.75 *(978-1-176-23317-1(3))* 2009. 236p. 28.99 *(978-1-110-41807-7(8))* 2009. 236p. pap. 25.75 *(978-1-110-41805-3(1))* 2009. (ENG.). 234p. pap. 20.99 *(978-1-110-41802-2(7)*, BiblioLife) 2009. (ENG.). 234p. pap. 22.99 *(978-1-110-41804-5(3)*, BiblioLife) 2009. 236p. 23.99 *(978-1-103-01944-1(9))* 2009. 236p. pap. 17.99 *(978-1-103-01942-7(2))* BiblioBazaar.
—Buddha & Buddhism. 2010. (Illus.). 108p. pap. 13.78 *(978-1-154-65055-6(3))*; 126p. pap. 16.31 *(978-1-150-87285-3(3))* General Bks. LLC.
—Buddha & Buddhism. 2010. 236p. 41.95 *(978-1-161-36650-1(4))* Kessinger Publishing, LLC.
Luomanen, Petri & Pyysiäinen, Ilkka, eds. Explaining Christian Origins & Early Judaism: Contributions from Cognitive & Social Science. 2007. (Biblical Interpretation Ser.). (Illus.). 312p. *(978-90-04-16329-4(8))* BRILL.
Lyda, Hap C. S. History of Biblical Christianity: An Introductory Study of Beginning Christianity & the New Testament. 2006. *(978-0-9630629-6-3(4))* 21st Century Pr.
Mason, Steve & Helfield, Michael W. Josephus, Judea, & Christian Origins: Methods & Categories. 2009. 450p. pap. *(978-1-59856-254-5(1))* Hendrickson Pubs. Marketing, LLC.
Milavec, Aaron. Salvation Is from the Jews (John 4:22) Saving Grace in Judaism & Messianic Hope in Christianity. 2007. (Michael Glazier Bks.). 201p. per. 23.95 *(978-0-8146-5989-2(6))* Liturgical Pr.
Moel, Dennis. The Shadow of the Temple: Jerusalem in Jesus' Day. 2008. (Illus.). 212p. pap. 16.99 *(978-1-60477-635-5(8))* Xulon Pr., Inc.
Ocansey, James K. Jesus Christ: The Missing Years & the Mysteries. 2007. 144p. 23.95 *(978-0-595-69058-9(0))*; per. 13.95 *(978-0-595-44890-6(9))* iUniverse, Inc.
Oegema, Gerbern S. & Charlesworth, James H., eds. The Pseudepigrapha & Christian Origins: Essays from the Studiorum Novi Testamenti Societas. 2011. (ENG.). 312p. pap. 49.95 ***(978-0-567-43054-0(5)***, T&T Clark Int'l) Continuum International Publishing Group, Ltd. GBR. Dist: National Bk. Network.
Oegema, Gerbern S. & Oegema. Pseudepigrapha & Christian Origins: Essays from the Studiorum Novi Testamenti Societas. Charlesworth, James H., ed. 2008. (Jewish & Christian Text Ser.). (ENG.). 312p. 140.00 *(978-0-567-02719-1(8)*, T&T Clark Int'l) Continuum International Publishing Group, Ltd. GBR. Dist: National Bk. Network.
Porter, Stanley E., ed. The Messiah in the Old & New Testaments. 2007. (McMaster New Testament Studies). 268p. per. 29.00 *(978-0-8028-0766-3(6))* Eerdmans, William B. Publishing Co.
Raisanen, Heikki. The Rise of Christian Beliefs: The Thought World of Early Christians. 2009. 432p. (C). pap. 39.00 *(978-0-8006-6266-0(0)*, Fortress Pr.) Augsburg Fortress, Pubs.
Reimarus, Hermann Samuel. Reimarus: Fragments. Talbert, Charles H., ed. Fraser, Ralph S., tr. 2009. 290p. pap. 33.00 *(978-1-60608-891-3(2)*, Wipf and Stock) Wipf & Stock Pubs.
Royalty, Robert M. The Origin of Heresy. 2012. (Routledge Studies in Religion Ser.). (ENG.). 272p. (C). 125.00 ***(978-0-415-53694-3(4))*** Routledge.
Sagovsky, Nicholas. Ecumenism, Christian Origins & the Practice of Communion. 2008. (ENG.). 232p. (C). pap. 36.00 *(978-0-521-09053-7(9))* Cambridge Univ. Pr.
Sausa, Don. The Jesus Tomb: Is It Fact or Fiction? Scholars Chime In. 2007. per. 21.95 *(978-0-9788346-9-2(0))* Vision Pr., The.
Shillington, V. George. Jesus & Paul Before Christianity: Their World & Work in Retrospect. 2011. (ENG., Illus.). 244p. pap. 27.00 ***(978-1-60899-694-0(8)***, Cascade Bks.) Wipf & Stock Pubs.
Skarsaune, Oskar. In the Shadow of the Temple: Jewish Influences on Early Christianity. 2008. (ENG.). 455p. pap. 28.00 *(978-0-8308-2844-9(3)*, IVP Acad.) InterVarsity Pr.
Smith, William Benjamin. The Birth of the Gospel: A Study of the Origin & Purport of the Primitive Allegory of the Jesus. Gulick, Addison, ed. 2011. 256p. 47.95 ***(978-1-258-07524-8(5))*** Literary Licensing, LLC.
Still, Todd D., ed. Jesus & Paul Reconnected: Fresh Pathways into an Old Debate. 2007. 184p. pap. 22.00 *(978-0-8028-3149-1(4))* Eerdmans, William B. Publishing Co.
Tabor, James D. The Jesus Dynasty: The Hidden History of Jesus, His Royal Family, & the Birth of Christianity. 2007. (ENG., Illus.). 400p. pap. 16.00 *(978-0-7432-8724-1(X))* Simon & Schuster.
—Paul & Jesus: How the Apostle Transformed Christianity. 2012. (ENG., Illus.). 320p. 26.00 *(978-1-4391-2331-7(4))* Simon & Schuster.
Taylor, Robert. The Diegesis. 2009. 384p. pap. *(978-1-4589-1409-5(7))* Books LLC.
Theissen, Gerd. Von Jesus zur urchristlichen Zeichenwelt: Neutestamentliche Grenzgänge im Dialog. 2011. (Novum Testamentum et Orbis Antiquus/Studien zur Umwelt des Neuen Testaments (NTOA/StUNT) Ser.). (GER.). 237p. (C). 81.00 *(978-3-525-55023-6(5))* Vandenhoeck & Ruprecht GmbH & Co. KG DEU. Dist: ISD.
Theodore, James. Cultivating the Cook's Garden: The Classic Guide to Organic Gourmet Gardening. 2010. 200p. pap. 18.00 *(978-1-57178-223-6(0))* Council Oak Bks.
Vande Kappelle, Robert P. Into Thin Places: One ManÕs Search for the Center. 2011. 432p. pap. 48.00 *(978-1-61097-093-8(4)*, Resource Pubns.) Wipf & Stock Pubs.

CHRISTIANITY—PHILOSOPHY

see also Philosophical Theology; Transcendence of God

Abbott, Lorraine. Philosophy Through Christianity: For OCR B GCSE Religious Studies. 2nd ed. 2009. (Illus.). 120p. pap. 35.00 *(978-0-340-98411-6(2))* Hodder Education GBR. Dist: Trans-Atlantic Pubns., Inc.
Act as If... 2007. per. 12.00 *(978-0-9636136-1-5(8))* A1 Organizing.
Adams, Graham. Christ & the Other: In Dialogue with Hick & Newbigin. 2010. 216p. 99.95 *(978-1-4094-0028-8(X))* Ashgate Publishing Co.
Alan And Mary Israel. The Voice of the Lord: From his Initiated Word. 2010. 216p. pap. 17.95 *(978-1-4502-1144-4(5))* iUniverse, Inc.
Allison, C. FitzSimons. Trust in an Age of Arrogance. 2011. (ENG.). 200p. pap. 36.25 *(978-0-7188-9236-4(4))* Lutterworth Pr., The GBR. Dist: Printondemand-worldwide.com.
—Trust in an Age of Arrogance. 2009. 200p. pap. 23.00 *(978-1-60608-555-4(7)*, Wipf and Stock) Wipf & Stock Pubs.
Ankerberg, John & Burroughs, Dillon. Why Does God Allow Suffering & Evil?, 8, Bk 4. 2008. (Contender's Bible Study Ser.). (ENG.). 112p. (gr. 11). pap. 7.99 *(978-0-89957-782-1(2))* AMG Pubs.
Anscombe, G. E. M. Faith in a Hard Ground: Essays on Religion, Philosophy & Ethics. Geach, Mary & Gormally, Luke, eds. 2008. (St Andrews Studies in Philosophy & Public Affairs Ser.). (ENG.). 250p. 80.00 *(978-1-84540-143-6(3))* Imprint Academic GBR. Dist: Ingram Pub. Services.
Athanasopoulos, C. The Presence of God in Eastern Orthodoxy: Divine Essence & Divine Energies. 2012. (ENG.). (C). pap. 50.00 ***(978-0-227-17386-2(4))*** Clarke, James Co., Ltd. GBR. Dist: Brown, David Bk. Co., The.
Auser, Wallace. Dissing God: The Myth of Religious Neutrality in a Secular Progressive Culture. 2007. 147p. per. 14.99 *(978-0-89957-110-2(7))* AMG Pubs.
Azkoul, Michael. God, immortality & freedom of the will according to the church Fathers: A Philosophy of Spiritual Cognition. 2006. 232p. *(978-0-7734-5640-2(6))* Mellen, Edwin Pr., The.
Baggett, John F. & Baggett, John. Seeing Through the Eyes of Jesus: His Revolutionary View of Reality & His Transcendent Significance for Faith. 2008. 392p. pap. 32.00 *(978-0-8028-6340-9(X))* Eerdmans, William B. Publishing Co.
Barge, Laura Inez Deavenport. Exploring Worldviews in Literature: From William Wordsworth to Edward Albee. 2009. pap. 19.95 *(978-0-89112-538-9(8)*, ACU Pr.) Abilene Christian Univ. Pr.
Barnett, Christopher B. Kierkegaard Pietism & Holiness. 2011. (New Critical Thinking in Religion, Theology & Biblical Studies). 242p. 89.95 *(978-1-4094-1156-7(7))* Ashgate Publishing Co.
Berdiaev, Nikolai & Reavey, George. The Meaning of History. 2nd ed. 2009. pap. *(978-1-59731-257-8(6))* Perennis, Sophia.
Bergin, Liam, ed. According to Your Word: Proceedings of a Conference Held on Saturday 4 March 2006 at the Pontifical College Rome to Honour Desmond Cardinal Connell on His Eightieth Birthday. 2007. 168p. (C). 55.00 *(978-1-84682-083-0(9))* Four Courts Pr. IRL. Dist: International Specialized Bk. Services.
Beyer, Jason A. A Comparison of Judeo-Christian Theism & Philosophical Naturalism As Explanatory Worldviews. 2007. 232p. *(978-0-7734-5322-7(9))* Mellen, Edwin Pr., The.
Bianchi, Joseph M. Common Faith, Common Culture: How Christianity Defeats Paganism. 2007. (ENG.). 112p. per. 15.95 *(978-1-59925-089-2(6))* Calvary Pr.
Black, John Sutherland. The Christian Consciousness: Its Relation to Evolution in Morals And. 2007. (ENG.). 260p. per. 27.95 *(978-1-4304-4553-1(X))* Kessinger Publishing, LLC.
Blood, Barry E. Giving Voice to the Silent Pulpit: A layman explores the differences between Popular & Academic Christianity. 2011. 112p. pap. 14.00 ***(978-1-61097-298-7(8)***, Resource Pubns.) Wipf & Stock Pubs.
Boa, Kenneth & Turner, John Alan. Hearts & Minds: Raising Your Child with a Christian View of the World. 2006. (ENG.). 256p. pap. 14.99 *(978-1-4143-0164-8(2))* Tyndale Hse. Pubs.
Boer, Roland. Criticism of Theology: Marxism & Theology III. 2012. (Historical Materialism Book Ser.). (ENG., Illus.). 358p. pap. 28.00 ***(978-1-60846-197-4(1))*** Haymarket Bks.
Boer, Roland. Criticism of Theology: On Marxism & Theology III. 2010. (Historical Materialism Book Ser.). 368p. *(978-90-04-18974-4(2))* BRILL.
Boeve, Lieven & Brabant, Christophe. Between Philosophy & Theology: Contemporary Interpretations of Christianity. 2010. (Illus.). 250p. 99.95 *(978-1-4094-0060-8(3))* Ashgate Publishing Co.
Boley, Brian. What Do Evangelical Christians Believe? 2007 400p. pap. 29.95 *(978-0-615-14461-0(6))* Oddparts Pr.
Bonzo, J. Matthew & Stevens, Michael Roger. After Worldview: Christian Higher Education in Postmodern Worlds. 2009. 131p. pap. *(978-0-932914-74-3(8))* Dordt College Pr.
Borishade, Ola. Gentlemen, Start Your Engines! 2011. 196p. pap. 14.99 *(978-1-4567-3864-8(X))* AuthorHouse.
Bradshaw, David. Aristotle East & West: Metaphysics & the Division of Christendom. 2007. (ENG.). 312p. pap. 46.00 *(978-0-521-03556-9(2))* Cambridge Univ. Pr.
Brown, Rev. Lawrence C. Sr. The Waiting Room. 2011. 54p. 24.99 ***(978-1-4628-8622-7(1))***; pap. 15.99 ***(978-1-4628-6246-7(2))*** Xlibris Corp.
Browning, Don S. Reviving Christian Humanism: The New Conversation on Spirituality, Theology, & Psychology. 2009. (Theology & the Sciences Ser.). 176p. (C). pap. 24.00 *(978-0-8006-9626-9(3)*, Fortress Pr.) Augsburg Fortress, Pubs.
Brüntrup, Godehard & Tacelli, R. K., eds. The Rationality of Theism. 2010. (Studies in Philosophy & Religion Ser.). 288p. pap. 160.00 *(978-90-481-5268-1(2)*, 9048152682) Springer.
Bryant, Jeffrey C. Full Spectrum Prosperity. 2009. 96p. pap. 10.75 *(978-1-4343-8429-4(2))* AuthorHouse.
Bryant Sr., Darryl J. Discipleship Boot Camp for the Kingdom of God. 2011. 374p. pap. 23.99 ***(978-1-61379-200-1(X))*** Xulon Pr., Inc.
Butterfield, Herbert. Christianity & History. 2009. 158p. 23.00 *(978-1-59740-339-9(3))*; 156p. pap. 16.00 *(978-1-59740-340-5(7))* ACLS Humanities E-Book.
Camus, Albert. Christian Metaphysics & Neoplatonism. Srigley, Ronald D., tr. from FRE. & intro. by. 2007. (Eric Voegelin Institute in Political Philosophy: Studies in Ser.). (ENG.). 160p. (C). 29.95 *(978-0-8262-1753-0(2))* Univ. of Missouri Pr.
Cappelø, Niels Jørgen, et al, eds. Kierkegaard's Late Writings. 2010. (ENG & GER.). XI, 509p. 238.00 *(978-3-11-022301-9(5))* De Gruyter, Walter Inc.
—Kierkegaard's Late Writings: [Print + Online]. 2010. (ENG & GER.). 285.00 *(978-3-11-022303-3(1))* De Gruyter, Walter Inc.
Caputo, John D. & Vattimo, Gianni. After the Death of God. Robbins, Jeffrey W., ed. 2007. (Insurrections: Critical Studies in Religion, Politics, & Culture Ser.). (ENG., Illus.). 216p. (gr. 17). 35.00 *(978-0-231-14124-6(6))* Columbia Univ. Pr.
Carlisle, Clare. Kierkegaard's 'Fear & Trembling' 2010. (Reader's Guides). (ENG.). 192p. 80.00 *(978-1-84706-460-8(4))* Continuum International Publishing Group, Ltd. GBR. Dist: National Bk. Network.
—Kierkegaard's Fear & Trembling. 2010. (Reader's Guides). (ENG.). 192p. 24.95 *(978-1-84706-461-5(2))* Continuum International Publishing Group, Ltd. GBR. Dist: National Bk. Network.
Carnell, Edward John, ed. A Philosophy of the Christian Religion. 2007. (Edward Carnell Library). 526p. pap. 58.00 *(978-1-55635-621-6(8))* Wipf & Stock Pubs.
Casey, Robert Pierce. Clement of Alexandria & the Beginnings of Christian Platonism. 2007. per. 37.70 *(978-1-59333-874-9(0))* Gorgias Pr., LLC.
Châtelet, François, et al. La révolution sans Modèle. (Archontes Ser.). (GER.). 188p. 135.00 ***(978-3-11-104856-7(X))*** De Gruyter, Mouton DEU. Dist: de Gruyter, Walter GmbH & Co. KG.
Church, Maggie, comment & compiled by. God's Taking Names. 2007. (Illus.). 34p. 7.95 *(978-0-9798169-0-1(4))* CMSI.
Clark, Gillian. Body & Gender Soul & Reason in Late Antiquity. 2011. (Variorum Collected Studies). (Illus.). 346p. 154.95 *(978-1-4094-2375-1(1))* Ashgate Publishing Co.
Coakley, Sarah & Stang, Charles M., eds. Re-Thinking Dionysius the Areopagite. 2009. (Directions in Modern Theology Ser.). (ENG.). 240p. pap. 34.95 *(978-1-4051-8089-4(7)*, Wiley-Blackwell) Wiley, John & Sons, Inc.
Colton, Charles. Core Christianity. 2006. (ENG.). 23.99 *(978-1-60034-350-6(3))*; pap. 13.99 *(978-1-60034-349-0(X))* Xulon Pr., Inc.
Copan, Paul. Loving Wisdom: Christian Philosophy of Religion. 2007. 214p. per. 24.99 *(978-0-8272-2139-0(8))* Chalice Pr.
Cosgrove, Mark P. Foundations of Christian Thought: Faith, Learning, & the Christian Worldview, 1 vol. 2006. (Illus.). 192p. pap. 15.99 *(978-0-8254-2434-2(8))* Kregel Pubns.
Cowan, Steven B., et al. The Love of Wisdom: A Christian Introduction to Philosophy, 1 vol. 2009. (ENG.). 480p. 34.99 *(978-0-8054-4770-5(9)*, B&H Academic) B&H Publishing Group.
Cram101 Textbook Reviews & Cram101 Textbook Reviews. Outlines & Highlights for Reason & Religious Belief by Michael Peterson, Isbn: 9780195335996 0195335996. 2011. 120p. pap. 28.95 ***(978-1-61812-071-7(9))*** Cram101 Inc.
Crisp, Oliver D., et al. Theology & Philosophy: Faith & Reason. Crisp, Oliver D. et al, eds. 2012. (Religion & the University Ser.). (ENG.). 256p. 120.00 *(978-0-567-41033-7(1)*, T&T Clark Int'l) Continuum International Publishing Group, Ltd. GBR. Dist: National Bk. Network.
Cross, Charles. We Each Get a Turn. 2009. 292p. 25.95 *(978-1-4401-3483-8(9))* iUniverse, Inc.
Crossan, John Dominic. Four Other Gospels: Shadows on the Contour of Canon. 2008. 208p. pap. 23.00 *(978-1-55635-820-3(2))* Wipf & Stock Pubs.
Dalton, Terry L. Does God Advocate the Secret ? 2008. pap. 16.95 *(978-1-4241-8916-8(0))* PublishAmerica, Inc.
Daniel, David Mills. Briefly: Kierkegaard's Fear & Trembling. 2007. (Briefly (Scm Press) Ser.). 95p. per. *(978-0-334-04130-6(9))* Hymns Ancient & Modern Ltd.
Delany, Vincent John. The Finger of God: How God's Existence Impacts upon Humanity. 2009. (ENG.). 188p. pap. 19.95 *(978-1-898595-54-0(2))* Sussex Academic Pr. GBR. Dist: International Specialized Bk. Services.
Delio, Ilia. Christ in Evolution. 2008. 228p. pap. 22.00 *(978-1-57075-777-8(1))* Orbis Bks.
Depoortere, Frederiek. Christ in Postmodern Philosophy: Gianni Vattimo, Rene Girard, & Slavoj Zizek. 2008. (ENG., Illus.). 176p. 24.95 *(978-0-567-03332-1(5)*, T&T Clark Int') Continuum International Publishing Group, Ltd. GBR. Dist: National Bk. Network.
Diederich, Brian. Christ: the Dark Years Historical Edition. 2010. 125p. pap. 10.99 *(978-0-578-00913-1(7))* Diederich, Brian D.
Digeser, Elizabeth Depalma. A Threat to Public Piety: Christians, Platonists, & the Great Persecution. 2012. (ENG.). 240p. 45.00 *(978-0-8014-4181-3(1))* Cornell Univ. Pr.
Dillon, John M. The Platonic Heritage: Further Studies in the History of Platonism & Early Christianity. 2012. (Variorum Collected Studies). 336p. 165.00 ***(978-1-4094-4662-0(X))*** Ashgate Publishing Co.
Dittrich, Constance. Augustinus, ein Lehrer des Abendlandes: Einführung und Dokumente. Dittrich, Constance et al, eds. 2009. (Schriften der Universitätsbibliothek Eichstätt Ser.). (GER.). 136p. pap. 30.00 *(978-3-447-05923-7(0))* Harrassowitz, Otto Verlag DEU. Dist: ISD.
Dole, Andrew & Chignell, Andrew, eds. God & the Ethics of Belief: New Essays in Philosophy of Religion. 2009. (ENG.). 296p. (C). pap. 42.00 *(978-0-521-11841-5(7))* Cambridge Univ. Pr.
Donini, Pierluigi. Commentary & Tradition: Aristotelianism, Platonism, & Post-Hellenistic Philosophy. Bonazzi, Mauro & Sharples, Robert W., eds. 2010. (Commentaria in Aristotelem Graeca et Byzantina Ser.). (ENG, FRE & ITA.). 466p. 182.00 *(978-3-11-021872-5(0))* De Gruyter, Walter Inc.
English, Adam C. The Possibility of Christian Philosophy: Maurice Blondel at the Intersection of Theology & Philosophy. (Routledge Radical Orthodoxy Ser.). 2012. (ENG.). 160p. (C). pap. 42.95 ***(978-0-415-54196-1(4))*** 2007. 144p. 145.00 *(978-0-415-77041-5(6))* Routledge.
English, Adam C. Theology Remixed: Christianity as Story, Game, Language, Culture. 2010. (ENG.). 208p. pap. 20.00 *(978-0-8308-3874-5(0)*, IVP Acad.) InterVarsity Pr.
Fairbairn, A. M. The Philosophy of the Christian Religion. 2007. (ENG.). 610p. 59.95 *(978-0-548-14954-6(2))*; 612p. per. 44.95 *(978-1-4304-4270-7(0))* Kessinger Publishing, LLC.
Fiedler, Robert R. Good & Evil Volume Iii: The Eve of Annihilation. 2011. 188p. pap. 22.95 ***(978-1-4620-3112-2(9))*** iUniverse, Inc.
Fisher, Timothy. It's a Sign! Seeing Jesus in the Ordinary. 2006. (ENG.). 136p. per. 24.95 *(978-1-4241-5531-6(2))* PublishAmerica, Inc.
Flanagan, John A. A Healing Word: Finding Inner Peace Through Scripture. 2009. (ENG.). 104p. pap. 16.95 *(978-1-84730-160-4(6))* Veritas Pubns. IRL. Dist: Dufour Editions, Inc.
Franck, Didier. Nietzsche & the Shadow of God. Bergo, Bettina & Farah, Philippe, trs. from FRE. 2012. (ENG.). 438p. pap. 34.95 ***(978-0-8101-2666-4(4))*** Northwestern Univ. Pr.
Furtak, Rick Anthony, ed. Kierkegaard's 'Concluding Unscientific Postscript' A Critical Guide. 2010. (Cambridge Critical Guides). (ENG.). 272p. 85.00 *(978-0-521-89798-3(X))* Cambridge Univ. Pr.
Gabriel, Merigala. Subjectivity & Religious Truth in the Philosophy of Soren Kierkegaard. 2010. (Mercer Kierkegaard Ser.). 224p. pap. 30.00 *(978-0-88146-170-1(9))* Mercer Univ. Pr.
Geldhof, Joris. Revelation, Reason & Reality: Theological Encounters with Jaspers, Schelling & Baader. 2007. (Studies in Philosophical Theology Ser.). 200p. (C). pap. 57.00 *(978-90-429-1929-7(9))* Peeters Pubs. & Booksellers BEL. Dist: Brown, David Bk. Co., The.
Gilman, James. Faith, Reason, & Compassion: A Philosophy of the Christian Faith. 2007. (ENG.). 168p. 73.00 *(978-0-7425-5270-8(5))*; per. 24.95 *(978-0-7425-5271-5(3))* Rowman & Littlefield Publishers, Inc.
Gilson, Etienne. The Gilson Lectures on Thomas Aquinas. 2008. (Etienne Gilson Ser.). (ENG.). pap. 29.95 *(978-0-88844-730-2(2))* Pontifical Institute of Mediaeval Studies, Dept. of Pubns. CAN. Dist: Univ. of Toronto Pr.
Gilson, fnof;tienne. Medieval Essays. Colbert, James G., tr. 2011. 234p. pap. 26.00 ***(978-1-60899-387-1(6)***, Cascade Bks.) Wipf & Stock Pubs.
Glimpel, Christoph. Gottesgedanke und Autonome Vernunft: Eine Kritisch-Konstruktive Auseinandersetzung MIT Den Philosophischen Grundlagen der Theologie Wolfhart Pannenbergs. 2007. (GER.). 302p. (C). 62.00 *(978-3-89971-363-3(X))* Vandenhoeck & Ruprecht GmbH & Co. KG DEU. Dist: ISD.
Graner, James. Christianity & the Enlightenment Thi. 2006. 98p. pap. 16.95 *(978-1-4241-4168-5(0))* PublishAmerica, Inc.
Greene. The Philosophy of Jesus: (Revelation Faith Philosophy) 2009. 176p. 22.49 *(978-1-4389-5577-3(4))*; pap. 11.99 *(978-1-4389-5576-6(6))* AuthorHouse.

C

Gushee, David P. Only Human: Christian Reflections on the Journey Toward Wholeness. 2010. (Enduring Questions in Christian Life Ser.: 6). (ENG., Illus.). 256p. pap. 24.95 (978-0-470-88961-9(6), Jossey-Bass) Wiley, John & Sons, Inc.

Habermas, Gary. Philosophy, Miracles, & the Resurrection of Jesus. 2006. (C). per. (978-1-60036-050-3(5)) Academx Publishing Services, Inc.

Habermas, Gary R., et al, eds. C. S. Lewis as Philosopher: Truth, Goodness & Beauty. 2008. (ENG., Illus.). 268p. pap. 23.00 (978-0-8308-2808-1(7), IVP Acad.) InterVarsity Pr.

Hall, David W. & Padgett, Marvin. Calvin & Culture: Exploring a Worldview. 2010. pap. (978-1-59638-098-1(5)) P & R Publishing.

Hamer, Gary. The Greatest Lie Ever Told: Revealing the Truth to a Deceived World. 2009. pap. 18.99 (978-1-61566-143-5(3)) Tate Publishing & Enterprises, LLC.

Hannay, Alastair. Kierkegaard: Concluding Unscientific Postscript. 2009. (Cambridge Texts in the History of Philosophy Ser.). (ENG.). 582p. (C). 108.00 (978-0-521-88247-7(8)); pap. 42.00 (978-0-521-70910-1(5)) Cambridge Univ. Pr.

Harnack, Adolf. Christianity & History. 2009. 70p. pap. 16.75 (978-1-110-83387-0(3)) BiblioBazaar.

—Christianity & History. Saunders, Thomas Bailey, tr. 2007. pap. 16.95 (978-1-4304-4977-5(2)) Kessinger Publishing, LLC.

Harris, A. D. Woe Be unto the Prophets! 2007. 88p. per. 9.99 (978-1-60266-431-9(5)) Xulon Pr., Inc.

Henson, James. A Schaefferian Sociology. 2009. 104p. pap. (978-3-639-03549-0(6)) VDM Verlag Dr. Mueller e.K.

Hermann, Deuser. Was ist Wahrheit anderes als ein Leben für eine Idee? Kierkegaards Existenzdenken und die Inspiration des Pragmatismus -Gesammelte Aufsätze zur Theologie und Religionsphilosophie. Cappelø, Niels Jørgen & Kleinert, Markus, eds. 2011.Tr. of What Is Truth Other Than a Life for an Idea? Kierkegaardâ€(tm)S Existential Thinking & the Inspiration of Pragmatism. Collected Essays on Theology & Philosophy of Religion. (GER & ENG.). 580p. 182.00 (978-3-11-022807-6(6)) De Gruyter, Walter Inc.

Hodgson, Leonard. Towards a Christian Philosophy. 2007. 196p. per. (978-1-4067-8796-2(5), Pomona Pr.) Read Bks.

Hoffecker, W. Andrew, ed. Revolutions in Worldview: Understanding the Flow of Western Thought. 2007. (Illus.). 424p. per. 29.99 (978-0-87552-573-0(3)) P & R Publishing.

Idew, Eyam. The Excalibur of Christ: The Diary of the Master Disciple. 2011. 280p. 25.99 **(978-1-4520-8049-9(6))**; pap. 17.49 **(978-1-4520-8048-2(8))** AuthorHouse.

Žižek, Slavoj & Milbank, John. The Monstrosity of Christ: Paradox or Dialectic? Davis, Creston, ed. 2011. (Short Circuits Ser.). (ENG.). 320p. (gr. 17). pap. 13.95 (978-0-262-51620-4(9)) MIT Pr.

J. K. Fausnight. Going Godless: Rediscovering Spirituality in a Material World. 2010. 276p. pap. 20.95 (978-1-4502-0503-0(8)) iUniverse, Inc.

Jantzen, G. M. Death & Invention Modernity. 2008. (Death & the Displacement of Beauty Ser.). 224p. 37.95 (978-0-415-29035-7(X)); 120.00 (978-0-415-29034-0(1)) Routledge.

Jean-Marie, Vivaldi. Kierkegaard: History & Eternal Happiness. 2008. (ENG.). 142p. pap. 29.50 (978-0-7618-4145-6(8)) Univ. Pr. of America, Inc.

Johnson, Aaron P. Ethnicity & Argument in Eusebius' Praeparatio Evangelica. 2006. (Oxford Early Christian Studies). (ENG.). 288p. 125.00 (978-0-19-929613-2(8)) Oxford Univ. Pr., Inc.

Jones, Richard H. For the Glory of God: The Role of Christianity in the Rise & Development of Modern Science, the History of Christian Ideas & Control Beliefs in Science. 2011. (ENG.). 176p. pap. 27.95 **(978-0-7618-5566-8(1))** Univ. Pr. of America, Inc.

Jordan, Jeffrey. Philosophy of Religion: The Key Thinkers. 2011. (Key Thinkers Ser.). (ENG.). 200p. 100.00 (978-1-4411-0994-1(3)) Continuum International Publishing Group, Ltd. GBR. Dist: National Bk. Network.

Jordan, Jeffrey J., ed. Philosophy of Religion: The Key Thinkers. 2011. (Key Thinkers Ser.). (ENG.). 200p. 29.95 (978-1-4411-9215-8(8)) Continuum International Publishing Group, Ltd. GBR. Dist: National Bk. Network.

Kaftan, Julius. The Truth of the Christian Religion V2. 2007. (ENG.). 456p. 52.95 (978-0-548-09342-9(3)) Kessinger Publishing, LLC.

Kaldellis, Anthony. The Christian Parthenon: Classicism & Pilgrimage in Byzantine Athens. 2009. (ENG., Illus.). 268p. 107.00 (978-0-521-88228-6(1)) Cambridge Univ. Pr.

Kane, J.M. Wounded Hearts, Broken Minds. 2007. 208p. per. 14.99 (978-1-60266-231-5(2)) Xulon Pr., Inc.

Kidus, Gebre Menfes. Mystery & Meaning: Christian Philosophy & Orthodox Meditations, 1 vol. 2010. 292p. pap. 27.95 (978-1-60836-006-2(7)) PublishAmerica, Inc.

Kierkegaard, S. Ren & Kierkegaard, Soren. Selected Essays. Bellinger, Charles K. & Hollander, L. M., trs. 2011. 192p. pap. **(978-1-84902-457-0(X))** Benediction Classics.

Kierkegaard, Soren. Fear & Trembling. 2008. 92p. pap. 7.49 (978-1-60459-318-1(0)) Wilder Pubns., Ltd.

Kierkegaard, Soren, et al, eds. Fear & Trembling. Walsh, Sylvia, tr. from DAN. 2006. (Cambridge Texts in the History of Philosophy Ser.). (ENG.). 190p. (C). per. 22.00 (978-0-521-61269-2(1)) Cambridge Univ. Pr.

Kimpel, Ben F. Religious Faith, Language, & Knowledge: A Philosophical Preface to Theology. 2011. 172p. 42.95 **(978-1-258-07340-4(4))** Literary Licensing, LLC.

King, Henry Churchill. The Seeming Unreality of the Spiritual Life. 2009. 164p. 25.99 (978-0-559-07953-5(2)) 2009. 164p. 22.99 (978-0-559-07968-9(0)) 2009. 164p. pap. 20.75 (978-0-559-07964-1(8)) 2009. 164p. pap. 21.75 (978-0-559-07957-3(5)) 2008. 268p. 25.99 (978-0-559-60554-3(4)) 2008. 268p. pap. 26.75 (978-0-559-60551-2(X)) BiblioBazaar.

—The Seeming Unreality of the Spiritual Life. 2009. 152p. pap. (978-0-217-10491-3(6)) Books LLC.

—The Seeming Unreality of the Spiritual Life. 2007. (ENG.). 262p. 42.95 (978-0-548-01848-4(0)) Kessinger Publishing, LLC.

Kirkpatrick, Matthew D. Attacks on Christendom in a World Come of Age: Kierkegaard, Bonhoeffer, & the Question of Religionless Christianity. 2011. (Princeton Theological Monographs). 258p. pap. 28.00 **(978-1-60899-550-9(X)**, Pickwick Pubns.) Wipf & Stock Pubs.

Kotsko. Zizek & Theology. 2008. (Philosophy & Theology Ser.). (ENG.). 182p. 29.95 (978-0-567-03245-4(0), T&T Clark Int'l) Continuum International Publishing Group, Ltd. GBR. Dist: National Bk. Network.

Kotsko, Adam. Zizek & Theology. 2008. (Philosophy & Theology Ser.). (ENG.). 182p. 120.00 (978-0-567-03244-7(2), T&T Clark Int'l) Continuum International Publishing Group, Ltd. GBR. Dist: National Bk. Network.

Kreeft, Peter. The Philosophy of Jesus. 2007. 168p. 17.00 (978-1-58731-635-7(8)) St. Augustine's Pr., Inc.

Lampe, Peter & Brawley, Robert L. New Testament Theology in a Secular World: A Constructivist Work in Christian Apologetics. Lampe, Peter & Brawley, Robert L., trs. from GER. 2012. (ENG.). 224p. 130.00 (978-0-567-32417-7(6)); pap. 39.95 (978-0-567-38888-9(3)) Continuum International Publishing Group, Ltd. GBR. (T&T Clark Int'l). Dist: National Bk. Network.

Laurence, Seth. The Spirit of Meta-Physical Paradox. 2009. 170p. (978-0-7552-1184-5(7)); pap. (978-0-7552-1183-8(9)) Authors OnLine, Ltd.

Leckey, Dolores, ed. Monika K Hellwig. 2010. 144p. pap. 19.95 (978-0-8146-5696-9(X)) Liturgical Pr.

Leedy, Randy. Love Not the World: Winning the War Against Worldliness. 2012. **(978-1-60682-041-4(9))** BJU Pr.

Liebe, Extraordinary Leader Robin. The Pharisee Philosophy. 2010. 322p. pap. 18.00 (978-0-557-24163-7(4)) Lulu Enterprises Inc.

Lightbody, Brian & DeRoo, Neal, eds. The Logic of Incarnation: James K. A. Smith's Critique of Postmodern Religion. 2008. 252p. pap. 28.00 (978-1-55635-969-9(1), Pickwick Pubns.) Wipf & Stock Pubs.

Littrell, James D. The Turning Tide: Adventures in Philosophy. 2007. 540p. pap. 27.95 (978-1-58597-426-9(9)) 2006. 27.95 (978-1-58597-414-6(5)) Leathers Publishing.

Lodyzhenskii, Mitrofan Vasilevich. Light Invisible: Satisfying the Thirst for Happiness. of Novo Divievo, Mother Magdelena, tr. from RUS. 2011. (ENG.). 280p. pap. 24.95 (978-0-88465-187-1(8)) Holy Trinity Monastery.

Lopez, Antonio. Spirit's Gift: The Metaphysical Insight of Claude Bruaire. 2006. 262p. 74.95 (978-0-8132-1443-6(2)) Catholic Univ. of America Pr.

Mack, Burton L. Christian Mentality: The Entanglements of Power, Violence & Fear. 2011. (Religion in culture: studies in social contest & Construction Ser.). (ENG.). 198p. (C). 99.95 (978-1-84553-894-1(3)) Equinox Publishing Ltd. GBR. Dist: ISD.

—Christian Mentality: The Entanglements of Power, Violence, & Fear. 2011. (Religion in culture: studies in social contest & Construction Ser.). (ENG.). 198p. (C). pap. 29.95 (978-1-84553-895-8(1)) Equinox Publishing Ltd. GBR. Dist: ISD.

Marion, Jean-Luc. The Visible & the Revealed. Gschwandtner, Christina M., tr. from FRE. 3rd ed. 2008. (Perspectives in Continental Philosophy Ser.). (ENG.). 188p. 70.00 (978-0-8232-2883-6(5)); pap. 28.00 (978-0-8232-2884-3(3)) Fordham Univ. Pr.

Mather, Cotton. The Christian Philosopher. 2009. 184p. pap. (978-0-217-94900-2(2)) Books LLC.

McCabe, Gerard. Intending Communion. 2010. 228p. pap. (978-3-639-24445-8(1)) VDM Verlag Dr. Mueller e.K.

McLaren, Brian D. Everything Must Change: Jesus, Global Crises, & a Revolution of Hope, 0 vols. 2009. 336p. pap. 14.99 (978-1-4002-8029-2(X)) Nelson, Thomas Inc.

McLeod-Harrison, Mark S. Apologizing for God: The Importance of Living in History. 2011. 166p. pap. 19.00 (978-1-60899-766-4(9), Cascade Bks.) Wipf & Stock Pubs.

Meaney, Marie Cabaud. Simone Weil's Apologetic Use of Literature: Her Christological Interpretations of Ancient Greek Texts. 2008. (Oxford Modern Languages & Literature Monographs). (ENG.). 288p. 110.00 (978-0-19-921245-3(7)) Oxford Univ. Pr., Inc.

Meek, Esther Lightcap. Loving to Know: Covenant Epistemology. 2011. 534p. pap. 49.00 **(978-1-60899-928-6(9)**, Cascade Bks.) Wipf & Stock Pubs.

Mehl, Roger. The Condition of the Christian Philosopher. 2011. 222p. pap. 42.50 (978-0-227-17375-6(9)) Clarke, James Co., Ltd. GBR. Dist: Brown, David Bk. Co., The.

Mekkes, J. P. A. Creation, Revelation, & Philosophy. 2010. pap. (978-0-932914-83-5(7)) Dordt College Pr.

Menssen, Sandra & Sullivan, Thomas D. The Agnostic Inquirer: Revelation from a Philosophical Standpoint. 2007. 331p. per. 35.00 (978-0-8028-0394-8(6)) Eerdmans, William B. Publishing Co.

Meredith SJ, Anthony. Christian Philosophy in the Early Church. 2012. (ENG.). 184p. 80.00 **(978-0-567-27860-9(3))**; pap. 24.95 **(978-0-567-30818-4(9))** Continuum International Publishing Group, Ltd. GBR. (T&T Clark Int'l). Dist: National Bk. Network.

The Metaphysics of Capital. 2006. 130p. per. 18.00 (978-0-9789902-0-6(X)) Intertheory Pr.

Miller, Carl Wallace. A Scientist's Approach to Religion. 2007. (ENG.). 134p. 35.95 (978-0-548-05725-4(7)) Kessinger Publishing, LLC.

Moloney, Patrick. Gunna Dan: An angel for Everyone. 2010. 208p. 33.95 (978-1-4497-0744-6(0)); pap. 17.95 (978-1-4497-0741-5(6)) Author Solutions, Inc. (WestBow Pr.).

Mooren, Thomas. Freedom Through Subjugation: The Good Shepherd According to Foucault, the West, the Chinese & the Church. 2011. 168p. 39.95 **(978-3-643-90030-2(9))** Lit Verlag DEU. Dist: Transaction Pubs.

Moreland, James Porter & Moreland, J. P. Kingdom Triangle: Recover the Christian Mind, Renovate the Soul, Restore the Spirit's Power, 1 vol. 2007. (ENG.). 240p. 19.99 (978-0-310-27432-2(X)) Zondervan.

Mössner, Nicola, et al, eds. Richard Swimburne: Christian Philosophy in a Modern World. 2009. (ENG.). 226p. pap. 39.95 (978-3-86838-004-0(3)) Ontos Verlag DEU. Dist: Transaction Pubs.

Nagell, Edward. Destiny: Volume Three: Christianity, the Do-It-Yourself Religion. 2006. 269p. pap. 15.95 (978-0-7414-3694-8(9)) Infinity Publishing.

Nwagwu, Mary Gerard Anna. Theology & Methodology of Canon Law. 2006. 251p. per. 25.49 (978-1-59879-188-4(5)) Lifevest Publishing, Inc.

Nygren, Anders. Meaning & Method: Prolegomena to a Scientific Philosophy of Religion & a Scientific Theology. Watson, Philip S., tr. 2009. 428p. pap. 51.00 (978-1-60608-770-1(3), Wipf and Stock) Wipf & Stock Pubs.

O'Brien, John A. Truths Men Live By: A Philosophy of Religions & Life. 2007. (ENG.). 442p. 51.95 (978-0-548-07287-5(6)) Kessinger Publishing, LLC.

O'Donnell, Phillip. Dinosaurs: Dead or Alive? 2006. pap. 10.99 (978-1-60034-262-2(0)) Xulon Pr., Inc.

Oliphint, K. Scott & Tipton, Lane G., eds. Revelation & Reason: New Essays in Reformed Apologetics. 2007. 336p. per. 24.99 (978-0-87552-596-9(2)) P & R Publishing.

Olree, Andy G. The Choice Principle: The Biblical Case for Legal Toleration. 2006. (ENG.). 274p. per. 44.50 (978-0-7618-3453-3(2)) Univ. Pr. of America, Inc.

Ouweneel, W. J. What Is the Christian's Hope? 53p. pap. 2.95 (978-0-88172-116-4(6)) Believers Bookshelf, Inc.

Pate, C. Marvin. From Plato to Jesus: What Does Philosophy Have to Do with Theology?, 1 vol. 2011. 352p. pap. 29.99 (978-0-8254-3391-7(6)) Kregel Pubns.

Pearcey, Nancy. Total Truth: Liberating Christianity from Its Cultural Captivity. 2008. (Illus.). 512p. pap. 20.99 (978-1-4335-0220-0(8)) Crossway.

Peery, Rebekah S. Nietzsche, Philosopher of the Perilous Perhaps. 2008. 32.95 (978-0-87586-643-7(3)); pap. 22.95 (978-0-87586-642-0(5)) Algora Publishing.

Perkins, Arthur. Family of God: Essays on the Christian Trinity & the Scripture Which Presents God to Mankind. 2006. (Illus.). 395p. per. 14.95 (978-0-9777848-1-3(9)) Hyperthoughts.com, LLC.

Perkins, Robert L., ed. Kierkegaard's Fear & Trembling: Critical Appraisals. 2009. (Kierkegaard Classic Studies). 264p. pap. 28.00 (978-1-60608-886-9(6), Wipf and Stock) Wipf & Stock Pubs.

Peterson, Michael, et al. Reason & Religious Belief: An Introduction to the Philosophy of Religion. 4th ed. 2008. (ENG.). 368p. (Orig.). (C). pap. 59.95 (978-0-19-533599-6(6)) Oxford Univ. Pr., Inc.

Phillips, D. Z. Whose God? Which Tradition? The Nature of Belief in God. 2008. 184p. 99.95 (978-0-7546-6018-7(4)) Ashgate Publishing Co.

Pieper, Josef. The Platonic Myths. Farrelly, Dan, tr. from GER. 2011. (ENG.). 96p. pap. 11.00 (978-1-58731-637-1(4)); 19.00 (978-1-58731-636-4(6)) St. Augustine's Pr., Inc.

Price, Robert. The Antidote for War & Discontent: How Wisdom, Knowledge, & Human Nature Can Change Us. 2009. 180p. 26.95 (978-0-595-62705-9(6)); pap. 16.95 (978-0-595-52474-7(5)) iUniverse, Inc.

Purdy, Hayward. The Biggest Lies in History. 2007. 29.00 (978-0-8059-8901-4(3)) Dorrance Publishing Co., Inc.

Ramsey, Ian & Gill, Jerry. Christian Empiricism: Studies in Philosophy & Religion. 2009. (ENG.). 260p. pap. 48.00 (978-0-227-17291-9(4)) Clarke, James Co., Ltd. GBR. Dist: Brown, David Bk. Co., The.

Ramsey, Ian T. Freedom & Immortality: The Forwood Lectures in the University of Liverpool 1957. 2011. (Ian T. Ramsey Reprint Ser.). 158p. pap. 18.00 **(978-1-61097-213-0(9)**, Wipf and Stock) Wipf & Stock Pubs.

—Religious Language: An Empirical Placing of Theological Phrases. 2011. (Ian T. Ramsey Reprint Ser.). 192p. pap. 22.00 **(978-1-61097-212-3(0)**, Wipf and Stock) Wipf & Stock Pubs.

Robinson, Mike A. One Way to God: Christian Philosophy & Presuppositional Apologetics Examine World Religions. 2008. 208p. pap. 9.95 (978-1-4327-2295-1(6)) Outskirts Pr., Inc.

Rogers, Henry. Reason & Faith; Their Claims & Conflicts. 2007. 80p. per. (978-1-4068-3996-8(5)) Echo Library.

Royce, Josiah. The Problem of Christianity. 2008. 452p. 30.99 (978-0-559-86276-2(8)); pap. 35.75 (978-0-559-86275-5(X)) BiblioBazaar.

—The Problem of Christianity. 2009. 170p. pap. (978-1-4589-3386-7(5)) Books LLC.

Sabatier, Auguste. Outlines of a Philosophy of Religion Based on Psychology & History. 2009. 164p. pap. (978-1-4588-9428-1(2)) Books LLC.

—Outlines of a Philosophy of Religion Based on Psychology & History. 2007. (ENG.). 362p. 46.95 (978-0-548-14991-1(7)); 364p. per. 31.95 (978-1-4304-4317-9(0)) Kessinger Publishing, LLC.

Savary, Louis M. Telhard de Chardin-the Divine Milieu Explained: A Spirituality for the 21st Century. 2007. 288p. pap. 19.95 (978-0-8091-4484-6(0), 4484-6) Paulist Pr.

Schmidt-Biggemann, Wilhelm. Philosophia Perennis: Historical Outlines of Western Spirituality in Ancient, Medieval & Early Modern Thought. 2010. (International Archives of the History of Ideas / archives internationales d'histoire des Idées Ser.). xix, 496p. pap. 379.00 (978-90-481-6782-1(5), 9048167825) Springer.

Scott, David & Scott. The Mind of Christ. 2007. (ENG.). 170p. 23.95 (978-0-8264-9074-2(3)) Continuum International Publishing Group, Ltd. GBR. Dist: National Bk. Network.

Simpson, A. B. Cristianismo Practico: Practical Christianity. (SPA.). (978-84-7228-932-1(X), 223007) Clie, Editorial.

Simut, Corneliu C. Traditionalism & Radicalism in the History of Christian Thought. 2010. (ENG.). 240p. 89.00 (978-0-230-10558-4(0)) Palgrave Macmillan.

Smith, James K. A. & Stassen, Glen. Desiring the Kingdom: Worship, Worldview, & Cultural Formation. 2009. (Cultural Liturgies Ser.). (C). pap. 21.99 (978-0-8010-3577-7(5)) Baker Academic.

Sproul, R. C. The Consequences of Ideas: Understanding the Concepts That Shaped Our World. 2009. (Illus.). 224p. E-Book (978-1-4335-1162-2(2)) Crossway.

Sproul, R. c. & Sproul, R. C. The Consequences of Ideas: Understanding the Concepts That Shaped Our World. 2009. 224p. pap. 15.99 (978-1-4335-0314-6(X)) Crossway.

St. Siddious. Requiem for the Living: The Philosphical Principles of St. Siddious. 2007. 84p. per. 16.95 (978-1-4241-7808-7(8)) PublishAmerica, Inc.

Stanford, Miles J. Principio de la Posicion: Principle of Position. (SPA.). 104p. (978-84-7228-439-5(5), 220715) Clie, Editorial.

Stang, Charles M. Apophasis & Pseudonymity in Dionysius the Areopagite: No Longer I. 2012. (Oxford Early Christian Studies). (ENG.). 272p. 110.00 **(978-0-19-964042-3(4))** Oxford Univ. Pr., Inc.

Steiger, H. W. Christian Science & Philosophy. (978-0-8022-1637-3(4)) Philosophical Library, Inc.

Steinbronn, Anthony J. Worldviews: A Christian Response to Religious Pluralism. 2007. (ENG.). 270p. per. 16.99 (978-0-7586-0598-6(6)) Concordia Publishing Hse.

Stewart, Jon, ed. Mynster's: Rationalism, Supernaturalism & the Debate about Mediation. 2009. 683p. 95.00 (978-87-635-3096-5(1)) Museum Tusculanum Pr. DNK. Dist: Chicago Distribution Ctr.

Sunshine, Glenn S. & Sunshine, Glenn. Why You Think the Way You Do: The Story of Western Worldviews from Rome to Home, 1 vol. 2009. (ENG.). 208p. (C). pap. 14.99 (978-0-310-29230-2(1)) Zondervan.

Sweetman, Robert. In the Phrygian Mode: Neo-Calvinism, Antiquity, & the Lamentations of Reformational Philosophy. (ENG.). 336p. 2012. 69.95 (978-0-7618-3020-7(0)) 2007. per. 47.50 (978-0-7618-3021-4(9)) Univ. Pr. of America, Inc.

Tatakis, Basil. Christian Philosophy in the Patristic & Byzantine Tradition. Dragas, George, ed. 2007. 364p. 32.95 (978-1-933275-17-8(0)); pap. 22.95 (978-1-933275-16-1(2)) Cocheco Falls Publishing. (Orthodox Research Institute).

Thwaytes, John. Lucifer, Bright Son of the Dawn. 2011. 152p. 31.35 **(978-1-4567-9796-6(4))**; pap. 16.46 **(978-1-4567-9794-2(8))** AuthorHouse.

Timpe, Kevin. Arguing about Religion. 2009. (ENG.). 648p. pap. 50.00 (978-0-415-98862-9(4)) Routledge.

Tomlin. Provocative Church 3rd Ne. 3rd ed. 2009. (Illus.). 192p. pap. (978-0-281-06006-1(1)) SPCK Publishing.

Ure, Adam. Vasilii Rozanov & the Creation: The Edenic Vision & the Rejection of Eschatology. 2011. (ENG.). 288p. 110.00 (978-1-4411-5494-1(9)) Continuum International Publishing Group, Ltd. GBR. Dist: National Bk. Network.

Van Til, Cornelius. Apologetics. 2011. 104p. 39.95 **(978-1-258-06705-2(6))** Literary Licensing, LLC.

Vassányi, Miklós. Anima Mundi: the Rise of the World Soul Theory: The Rise of the World Soul Theory. 2010. (International Archives of the History of Ideas / archives internationales d'histoire des Idées Ser.). 10p. 189.00 (978-90-481-8795-9(8), 9048187958) Springer.

Vattimo, Gianni & Girard, René. Christianity, Truth, & Weakening Faith: A Dialogue. Antonello, Pierpaolo, ed. McCuaig, William, tr. from ITA. 2010. (ENG.). 136p. (gr. 17). 18.50 (978-0-231-14828-3(3)) Columbia Univ. Pr.

Veenstra, Jan R. Christian Humanism. MacDonald, A. A. & von Martels, Z. R. W. M., eds. 2009. (Studies in Medieval & Reformation Traditions: History, Culture, Religion, Ideas). (GER & ENG., Illus.). 538p. (978-90-04-17631-7(4)) BRILL.

Vest, Norvene. Re-Visioning Theology: A Mythic Approach to Religion. 2011. 224p. pap. 19.95 (978-0-8091-4688-8(6)) Paulist Pr.

Vincelette, Alan Roy. Recent Catholic Philosophy: The Twentieth Century. 2011. pap. (978-0-87462-803-6(2)) Marquette Univ. Pr.

von Hildebrand, Dietrich. The Nature of Love. Crosby, John F., tr. from GER. 2009. (ENG.). 432p. 40.00 (978-1-58731-560-2(2)) St. Augustine's Pr., Inc.

Walker, J. Lamah. The Illiberal Manifesto: Expulsion from the Garden of Eden. 2011. 234p. 29.99 **(978-1-4628-4826-3(5))**; pap. 19.99 **(978-1-4628-4825-6(7))** Xlibris Corp.

Walker, W. L. Christian Theism & a Spiritual Monism: God, Freedom & Immortality in View of Monistic Evolution. 2007. (ENG.). 500p. 53.95 (978-0-548-09071-8(8)) Kessinger Publishing, LLC.

—Christian Theism & a Spiritual Monism: God, Freedom & Immortality in View of Monistic Evolution. 2007. 496p. per. (978-1-4067-8823-5(6), Pomona Pr.) Read Bks.

Wallace-Hadrill, D. S. Christian Antioch: A Study of Early Christian Thought in the East. 2009. (ENG.). 232p. pap. 34.99 *(978-0-521-09435-8(4))* Cambridge Univ. Pr.

Walsh, Sylvia. Kierkegaard: Thinking Christianly in an Existential Mode. 2009. (Christian Theology in Context Ser.). (ENG.). 248p. 110.00 *(978-0-19-920835-7(2))*; pap. 35.00 *(978-0-19-920836-4(0))* Oxford Univ. Pr., Inc.

—Living Christianly: Kierkegaard's Dialectic of Christian Existence. 2008. (ENG.). 216p. pap. 25.00 *(978-0-271-02764-7(9))* Pennsylvania State Univ. Pr.

Ward, Keith. The Philosopher & the Gospels: Jesus Through the Lens of Philosophy. 2012. (ENG.). 192p. pap. 17.95 ***(978-0-7459-5562-9(2))*** Lion Hudson PLC GBR. Dist: Independent Pubs. Group.

Werther, David & Linville, Mark D. Philosophy & the Christian Worldview: Analysis, Assessment & Development. Werther, David & Linville, Mark D., eds. 2012. (Continuum Studies in Philosophy of Religion Ser.). (ENG.). 288p. 120.00 *(978-1-4411-0869-2(6))* Continuum International Publishing Group, Ltd. GBR. Dist: National Bk. Network.

White, Roberta & Lynch, Jeff. The Bible — Word of God or Word of Man? 2011. 96p. pap. 10.95 ***(978-1-4634-2670-5(4))*** AuthorHouse.

Wilkens, Steve & Sanford, Mark L. Hidden Worldviews: Eight Cultural Stories That Shape Our Lives. 2009. (ENG.). 218p. pap. 22.00 *(978-0-8308-3854-7(6))*, IVP Acad.) InterVarsity Pr.

Williams, Clifford. The Divided Soul. 2009. 108p. pap. 14.00 *(978-1-60608-735-0(5))*, Wipf and Stock) Wipf & Stock Pubs.

Woodworth, Ron. The Destiny Series Vol. 1: For Such a Time as This: Lessons in Discernment for the Thinking Christian. 2007. (ENG.). 352p. per. 21.99 *(978-1-4141-0838-4(9))* Pleasant Word.

Zizek, Slavoj & Milbank, John. The Monstrosity of Christ: Paradox or Dialectic? Davis, Creston, ed. 2009. (Short Circuits Ser.). (ENG.). 320p. (gr. 17). 28.95 *(978-0-262-01271-3(5))* MIT Pr.

Zycinski, Jozef. God & Post-Modern Thought: Philosophical Issues in the Contemporary Critique of Modernity. 2010. pap. *(978-1-56518-267-7(7))* Council for Research in Values & Philosophy.

CHRISTIANITY—POETRY

see Christian Poetry

CHRISTIANITY—POLITY

see Church Polity

CHRISTIANITY—PSYCHOLOGY

Allender, Dan B. The Wounded Heart: Hope for Adult Victims of Childhood Sexual Abuse. 2008. (Real Life Stuff for Women Ser.). (ENG.). 272p. pap. 16.99 *(978-1-60006-307-7(1))* NavPress Publishing Group.

Ascano, R. P. & Ascano, S. L. Spiritual Adoption. 2011. 271p. pap. 14.99 *(978-1-935906-37-7(2))* Intermedia Publishing Group.

Bellostas, J. Cristianismo y Psicologia en la Educa: Christianity & Psychology in Ed. (SPA.). *(978-84-7645-507-4(0)*, 223587) Clie, Editorial.

Bloomer, George G. Authority Abusers. 2008. (ENG.). 204p. 19.99 *(978-1-60374-046-3(5))* Whitaker Hse.

The Bondage Makers. 2006. pap. 9.99 *(978-1-60034-274-5(4))* Xulon Pr., Inc.

Brittain, Angela K. The Don't Forget to Look up Workbook: Uncovering the Root of Anxiety, Panic & Fear. 2008. 64p. pap. 8.95 *(978-0-9662003-1-7(4))* Brittain Communications.

Brown, Warren S. & Strawn, Brad D. The Physical Nature of Christian Life: Neuroscience, Psychology, & the Church. 2012. (ENG., Illus.). 200p. (C). 95.00 ***(978-0-521-51593-1(9))***; pap. 27.99 ***(978-0-521-73421-9(5))*** Cambridge Univ. Pr.

Byers, Andrew. Faith Without Illusions: Following Jesus as a Cynic-Saint. 2011. (ENG.). 224p. pap. 17.00 *(978-0-8308-3618-5(7))*, IVP Bks.) InterVarsity Pr.

Cabezas, Rita. Psicoterapia Cristiana (Christian Psychotherapy) (SPA.). *(978-84-7645-310-0(8)*, 223429) Clie, Editorial.

Canty, Helen. Eclipse of the Heart. 2008. 159p. 19.95 *(978-1-934363-21-8(9))* Zoe Life Publishing.

Capps, Donald. Jesus the Village Psychiatrist. 2008. (ENG.). 145p. pap. 20.00 *(978-0-664-23240-5(X))* Westminster John Knox Pr.

Coe, John & Hall, Todd W. Psychology in the Spirit: Contours of a Transformational Psychology. 2010. (Christian Worldview Integration Ser.). (ENG.). 446p. pap. 30.00 *(978-0-8308-2813-5(3))*, IVP Acad.) InterVarsity Pr.

Cohen, Charles Lloyd. God's Caress: The Psychology of Puritan Religious Experience. 2008. 328p. pap. 32.00 *(978-1-59740-525-6(6))* ACLS Humanities E-Book.

Cooper, Terry. Don Browning & Psychology: Interpreting the Horizons of Our Lives. 2011. 240p. pap. 30.00 *(978-0-88146-254-8(3))* Mercer Univ. Pr.

Cox, David. Jung & St Paul: A Study of the Doctrine of Justification by Faith & Its Relation to the Concept of Individuation. 2011. 370p. 53.95 ***(978-1-258-03047-6(0))*** Literary Licensing, LLC.

Cupitt, Don. New Great Story. 2010. 120p. pap. 19.00 *(978-1-59815-026-1(X))* Polebridge Pr.

Dueck, Alvin & Ulanov, Ann Belford. The Living God & Our Living Psyche: What Christians Can Learn from Carl Jung. 2008. 111p. per. 15.00 *(978-0-8028-2467-7(6))* Eerdmans, William B. Publishing Co.

Entwistle, David N. Integrative Approaches to Psychology & Christianity: An Introduction to Worldview Issues, Philosophical Foundations, & Models of Integration. 2nd ed. 2010. 340p. pap. 35.00 *(978-1-55635-944-6(6))* Wipf & Stock Pubs.

Faber, M. D. Becoming God's Children: Religion's Infantilizing Process, 1 vol. 2010. 208p. 44.95 *(978-0-313-38226-0(3)*, A2650C) Greenwood Publishing Group, Inc.

Flanagan, Eileen. The Wisdom to Know the Difference: When to Make a Change-And When to Let Go. 2010. (ENG.). 288p. (gr. 12). 15.95 *(978-1-58542-829-8(9))*, Tarcher) Penguin Group (USA) Inc.

Ghaly, Ramsis F. Christianity & the Brain: Patients Stories: 100 Stories of Hope, Faith & Courage. 2010. 304p. 31.95 *(978-1-4502-4042-0(9))*; (ENG.). pap. 21.95 *(978-1-4502-4043-7(7))* iUniverse, Inc.

Hoffman, Marie T. Toward Mutual Recognition: Relational Psychoanalysis & the Christian Narrative. 2010. (Relational Perspectives Book Ser.). (ENG.). 278p. (C). pap. 37.95 *(978-0-415-99914-4(6))*; 120.00 *(978-0-415-99913-7(8))* Routledge.

Hunt, Dave & McMahon, T. A. Psychology & the Church: Critical Questions, Crucial Answers. 2007. (ENG., Illus.). 256p. pap. 25.99 *(978-1-928660-61-3(4))* Berean Call, The.

Jeffery, H. B. What Seek Ye? 2007. (ENG.). 108p. 34.95 *(978-0-548-08466-3(1))* Kessinger Publishing, LLC.

Johnson, Eric L. Foundations for Soul Care: A Christian Psychology Proposal. 2007. (ENG., Illus.). 716p. 45.00 *(978-0-8308-2567-7(3))*, IVP Acad.) InterVarsity Pr.

Jones, Stanton L. & Butman, Richard E. Modern Psychotherapies: A Comprehensive Christian Appraisal. 2nd rev. ed. 2011. (Christian Association for Psychological Studies Partnership Book Ser.). (ENG.). 496p. 35.00 ***(978-0-8308-2852-4(4))***, IVP Acad.) InterVarsity Pr.

Kotre, John. The View from the Border: Why Catholics Leave the Church & Why They Stay. 2009. (ENG., Illus.). 283p. pap. 24.95 *(978-0-202-36307-3(4))* Aldine Transaction.

Kristeva, Julia. This Incredible Need to Believe. Brahic, Beverley Bie, tr. from ITA. 2011. (European Perspectives: a Series in Social Thought & Cultural Criticism Ser.). (ENG.). 136p. (gr. 17). pap. 14.95 ***(978-0-231-14785-9(6))*** Columbia Univ. Pr.

—This Incredible Need to Believe. 2009. *(978-82-311-4784-3(5))* Columbia Univ. Pr.

—This Incredible Need to Believe. Brahic, Beverley Bie, tr. from ITA. 2009. (European Perspectives: a Series in Social Thought & Cultural Criticism Ser.). (ENG.). 136p. (gr. 17). 19.95 *(978-0-231-14784-2(8))* Columbia Univ. Pr.

Leadingham, Everett. Heart Soul Mind Strength: Godly Living for Today's Kingdom Christian. 2006. (Dialog Ser.). 135p. pap. 7.50 *(978-0-8341-2216-1(2))*; pap. 7.99 *(978-0-8341-2199-7(9))* Nazarene Publishing Hse.

Linn, Dennis, et al. Healing the Future: Personal Recovery from Societal Wounding. 2012. ***(978-1-61643-144-0(X))***; 224p. pap. 19.95 ***(978-0-8091-4775-5(0))*** Paulist Pr.

Luomanen, Petri & Pyysiäinen, Ilkka, eds. Explaining Christian Origins & Early Judaism: Contributions from Cognitive & Social Science. 2007. (Biblical Interpretation Ser.). (Illus.). 312p. *(978-90-04-16329-4(8))* BRILL.

Mahill, Wendy J. Embracing a Feeling Heart. 2011. 190p. pap. 16.99 ***(978-1-61379-148-6(8))*** Xulon Pr., Inc.

Mike Harris. A Journey of Self-Discovery: Combining Biblical Principles with Psychology. 2010. 72p. pap. 10.95 *(978-1-4502-1326-4(X))* iUniverse, Inc.

Montgomery, Dan. Compass Psychotheology Where Psychology. 2007. 280p. pap. 29.95 *(978-1-84728-178-4(8))* Lulu Enterprises Inc.

—COMPASS THERAPY: Christian Psychology in Action. 2008. 320p. pap. 34.95 *(978-0-557-02288-5(6))* Lulu Enterprises Inc.

Moore, Jestne. Could God Save Someone Like Me? 2008. 80p. per. 7.99 *(978-1-58169-262-4(5))* Genesis Communications, Inc.

Newell, William L. Desire in René Girard & Jesus. 2012. (ENG.). 254p. (gr. 17). 65.00 ***(978-0-7391-7109-7(7))*** Lexington Bks.

Pennock, Dee. Path to Sanity: Lessons from Ancient Holy Counselors on How to Have a Sound Mind. 2010. (Illus.). 216p. pap. 15.95 *(978-1-933654-26-3(0))* Light & Life Publishing Co.

Peterson, James. Changing Human Nature: Ecology, Ethics, Genes, & God. 2010. 264p. pap. 18.00 *(978-0-8028-6549-6(6))* Eerdmans, William B. Publishing Co.

Powlison, David/Arthur. The Biblical Counseling Movement: History & Context. 2009. 432p. pap. 39.99 *(978-1-935273-13-4(2))* New Growth Pr.

Reimers, Adrian J. The Soul of the Person: A Contemporary Philosophical Psychology. 2006. 301p. 64.95 *(978-0-8132-1453-5(X))* Catholic Univ. of America Pr.

Richo, David. How to Be an Adult in Faith & Spirituality. 2011. 176p. pap. 16.95 *(978-0-8091-4691-8(6))* Paulist Pr.

Rowe, John. The Second Fall: Existential Christianity. 2011. 96p. pap. 15.95 ***(978-0-9846177-3-9(6)***, Advocate Hse.) A Cappela Publishing.

Rush, Vincent E. We Will Be Like Him: Growing Toward God at Every Age of Life. 2008. (Illus.). 134p. per. 14.95 *(978-0-8091-4511-9(1)*, 4511-9) Paulist Pr.

Schwirzer, Jennifer Jill. 13 Weeks to Peace: Allowing Jesus to Heal Your Heart & Mind. 2011. pap. 15.99 ***(978-0-8163-2494-1(8))*** Pacific Pr. Publishing Assn.

Seybold, Kevin S. Explorations in Neurosciences Psychology & Religion. 2007. (Ashgate Science & Religion Ser.). (Illus.). 174p. 99.95 *(978-0-7546-5563-3(6))* Ashgate Publishing Co.

Stevenson, Darryl H., et al, eds. Psychology & Christianity Integration: Seminal Works that Shaped the Movement. 2007. 64.95 *(978-0-9792237-1-6(7))*; pap. 39.95 *(978-0-9792237-0-9(9))* Christian Assn. for Psychological Studies, Inc.

Timpe, Kevin. Arguing about Religion. 2009. (Arguing about Philosophy Ser.). (ENG.). 648p. 150.00 *(978-0-415-98861-2(6))* Routledge.

Walker, Rick. The Way of the Secret Path. 2008. 352p. pap. 19.99 *(978-1-60647-358-0(1))* Xulon Pr., Inc.

Watts, Fraser, ed. Jesus & Psychology. 2007. (ENG., Illus.). 224p. (C). per. 19.95 *(978-1-59947-124-2(8))* Templeton Pr.

White, Christopher G. Unsettled Minds: Psychology & the American Search for Spiritual Assurance, 1830-1940. 2008. (Illus.). 278p. 50.00 *(978-0-520-25679-8(4))* Univ. of California Pr.

Whitfield, Geoffrey Victor. The Prenatal Psychology of Frank Lake & the Origins of Sin & Human Dysfunction. 2007. 144p. per. 29.00 *(978-0-9797935-0-9(5))* Emeth Pr.

Woodward, John B. Man As Spirit, Soul, & Body: A Study of Biblical Psychology. 2nd ed. 2007. pap. *(978-1-931527-63-7(6))* Grace Ministries.

CHRISTIANITY—RELATIONS

see Christianity and Other Religions

CHRISTIANITY—RENEWAL

see Church Renewal

CHRISTIANITY—UNION BETWEEN CHURCHES

see Christian Union

CHRISTIANITY—EARLY CHURCH, CA. 30-600

Bright, Pamela. The Book of Rules of Tyconius: Its Purpose & Inner Logic. 2009. (ND Christianity & Judaism Antiqui Ser.). (ENG.). 208p. pap. 30.00 *(978-0-268-02219-8(4))* Univ. of Notre Dame Pr.

Bunge, Gabriel. Despondency: The Spiritual Teaching of Evagrius Ponticus on Acedia. 2012. ***(978-0-88141-394-6(1))*** St. Vladimir's Seminary Pr.

Canfield, Leon H. The Early Persecutions of the Christians. (Columbia University, Studies in the Social Sciences: No. 136). reprint ed. 37.50 *(978-0-404-51136-4(8))* AMS Pr., Inc.

Conti, Marco, ed. Priscillian of Avila: Complete Works. 2010. (Oxford Early Christian Studies). (ENG.). 328p. 175.00 *(978-0-19-956737-9(9))* Oxford Univ. Pr., Inc.

Denzey, Nicola. The Bone Gatherers: The Lost Worlds of Early Christian Women, 1 vol. 2007. (History Ser.). (ENG.). 300p. *(978-0-8070-1308-3(0))* Beacon Pr.

Dodaro, Robert. Christ & the Just Society in the Thought of Augustine. 2008. (ENG.). 264p. pap. 37.99 *(978-0-521-06964-9(5))* Cambridge Univ. Pr.

Dunning, Benjamin H. Specters of Paul: Sexual Difference in Early Christian Thought. 2011. (Divinations: Rereading Late Ancient Religion Ser.). 264p. (C). 55.00 *(978-0-8122-4307-9(2))* Univ. of Pennsylvania Pr.

Fischer, Bob & Fischer, Robert. The Ways of the Way: Restoring the Jewish Roots of the Modern Church. 2009. (ENG.). 368p. 23.99 *(978-1-59979-763-2(1)*, Creation Hse.) Charisma Media.

Flebbe, Jochen. Solus Deus: Untersuchungen zur Rede von Gott im Brief des Paulus an die Römer. 2008. (Beihefte Zur Zeitschrift Für Die Neutestamentliche Wissenschaft und Die Kunde der älteren Kirche Ser.). (GER.). XIII, 509p. 175.00 *(978-3-11-020217-5(4))* De Gruyter, Walter Inc.

Fredriksen, Paula. Sin: The Early History of an Idea. 2012. (ENG., Illus.). 208p. 24.95 ***(978-0-691-12890-0(1))*** Princeton Univ. Pr.

Khalil, Ihab. Worlds Apart: Selected Essays on Ancient Egyptian & Early Christian Thought. 2009. (Illus.). 136p. 23.95 *(978-1-4401-1719-0(5))*; pap. 13.95 *(978-1-4401-1718-3(7))* iUniverse, Inc.

Massey, Lesly F. Women & the New Testament: An Analysis of Scripture in Light of New Testament Era Culture. alt. ed. 2012. (ENG.). 160p. pap. 25.00 ***(978-0-7864-6772-3(X))*** McFarland & Co., Inc. Pubs.

Neander, Augustus. The History of the Christian Religion & Church During the First Three Centuries. Rose, Henry, tr. 2007. (ENG.). 116p. per. 12.75 *(978-1-60206-331-0(1))* Cosimo, Inc.

Neusner, Jacob. Judaism & Christianity in the Age of Constantine: History, Messiah, Israel, & the Initial Confrontation. 2008. (Chicago Studies in the History of Judaism Ser.). 262p. per. 30.00 *(978-0-226-57653-4(1))* Univ. of Chicago Pr.

PressensT, Edmond de. The Early Years of Christianity by E de Pressenst Tr by Annie Harwood. 2006. 544p. per. 29.99 *(978-1-4255-6029-4(6))* MPublishing.

Purves, George T. The Testimony of Justin Martyr to Early Christianity. 2010. 316p. 36.99 *(978-1-117-94647-4(9))*; pap. 29.75 *(978-1-117-94648-1(7))* BiblioBazaar.

Schmidt, Charles. The Social Results of Early Christianity. Thorpe, tr. 2008. 512p. 55.95 *(978-1-4365-4593-8(5))* 2007. (ENG.). 516p. per. 40.95 *(978-0-548-70248-2(9))* Kessinger Publishing, LLC.

Swete, H. B. The Holy Spirit in the Ancient Church: A Study of Christian Teaching in the Age of the Fathers. (Orthodoxies & Heresies in the Early Church Ser.). reprint ed. 42.50 *(978-0-404-62395-1(6))* AMS Pr., Inc.

Vivian, Tim & Athanassakis, Apostolos N. Becoming Fire: Through the Year with the Desert Fathers & Mothers. 2008. pap. *(978-0-87907-525-5(2))* Cistercian Pubns., Inc.

Von Harnack, Adolf. The Expansion of Christianity in the First Three Centuries, Vol. I. Moffatt, James, ed. 494p. reprint ed. 26.00 *(978-0-8290-0530-1(7))* Irvington Pubs.

Webb, Ruth. Demons & Dancers: Performance in Late Antiquity. 2009. (Illus.). 318p. 49.00 *(978-0-674-03192-0(X))* Harvard Univ. Pr.

Woodward, Ernest L. Christianity & Nationalism in the Later Roman Empire. (Orthodoxies & Heresies in the Early Church Ser.). reprint ed. 32.50 *(978-0-404-62398-2(0))* AMS Pr., Inc.

Workman, Herbert B. Christian Thought to the Reformation. 2010. 274p. 34.99 *(978-1-140-30564-4(6))*; pap. 27.75 *(978-1-140-30565-1(4))* BiblioBazaar.

—Christian Thought to the Reformation. 2007. (ENG.). 270p. 42.95 *(978-0-548-15207-2(1))*; 272p. per. 27.95 *(978-1-4304-4565-4(3))* Kessinger Publishing, LLC.

CHRISTIANITY—MIDDLE AGES, 600-1500

Ames, Christine Caldwell. Righteous Persecution: Inquisition, Dominicans, & Christianity in the Middle Ages. 2008. (Middle Ages Ser.). 320p. (C). 59.95 *(978-0-8122-4133-4(9))* Univ. of Pennsylvania Pr.

Denery II, Dallas G. Seeing & Being Seen in the Later Medieval World: Optics, Theology & Religious Life. 2009. (Cambridge Studies in Medieval Life & Thought: Fourth Ser.). (ENG.). 220p. (C). pap. 31.99 *(978-0-521-10893-5(4))* Cambridge Univ. Pr.

Hames, Harvey J. Like Angels on Jacob's Ladder: Abraham Abulafia, the Franciscans & Joachimism. 2008. (Illus.). 171p. 50.00 *(978-0-7914-7271-2(X))* State Univ. of New York Pr.

Hamm, Berndt. Media Salutis: Gnaden- und Heilsmedien in der abendländischen Religiosität des Mittelalters und der Frühen Neuzeit. Leppin, Volker & Schneider-Ludorff, Gury, eds. 2011. (Spatmittelalter, Humanismus Reformation Ser.). (GER.). 247p. 167.50 ***(978-3-16-150672-7(3))*** Mohr Siebeck GmbH & Co. KG DEU. Dist: Coronet Bks.

Rubin, M. Medieval Christianity in Practice. 2009. (Princeton Readings in Religions Ser.). (ENG., Illus.). 360p. (C). 85.00 *(978-0-691-09058-0(0))* Princeton Univ. Pr.

Toy, John, ed. English Saints in the Medieval Liturgies of Scandinavian Churches. 2009. (Henry Bradshaw Society Subsidia Ser.: Volume 6). (Illus.). 250p. 90.00 *(978-1-870252-46-1(2))* Bradshaw, Henry Society GBR. Dist: Boydell & Brewer, Inc.

Workman, Herbert B. Christian Thought to the Reformation. 2010. 274p. 34.99 *(978-1-140-30564-4(6))*; pap. 27.75 *(978-1-140-30565-1(4))* BiblioBazaar.

—Christian Thought to the Reformation. 2007. (ENG.). 270p. 42.95 *(978-0-548-15207-2(1))*; 272p. per. 27.95 *(978-1-4304-4565-4(3))* Kessinger Publishing, LLC.

CHRISTIANITY—16TH CENTURY

Guerrero. El Viaje de Hierusalem. Calcraft, ed. Date not set. (Hispanic Text Ser.: No. 37). (SPA & ENG., Illus.). 119p. pap. 17.95 *(978-0-85989-235-3(2))* Univ. of Exeter Pr. GBR. Dist: Brown, David Bk. Co., The.

Workman, Herbert B. Christian Thought to the Reformation. 2010. 274p. 34.99 *(978-1-140-30564-4(6))*; pap. 27.75 *(978-1-140-30565-1(4))* BiblioBazaar.

—Christian Thought to the Reformation. 2007. (ENG.). 270p. 42.95 *(978-0-548-15207-2(1))*; 272p. per. 27.95 *(978-1-4304-4565-4(3))* Kessinger Publishing, LLC.

CHRISTIANITY—17TH CENTURY

Hall, Bishop. The Art of Divine Meditation. 2007. 80p. per. 8.25 *(978-1-58960-362-2(1))* Sovereign Grace Pubs., Inc.

CHRISTIANITY—18TH CENTURY

Laamann, Lars P. Christian Heretics in Late Imperial China: Christian Inculturation & State Control, 1720-1850. 2007. (Routledge Studies in the Modern History of Asia: Vol. 40). (Illus.). 204p. 160.00 *(978-0-415-29779-0(6))* Routledge.

CHRISTIANITY—19TH CENTURY

Cunningham, William. Christian Civilization with Special Reference to India. 2007. (ENG.). 164p. per. 21.95 *(978-1-4304-4584-5(X))* Kessinger Publishing, LLC.

Drummond, Henry. The Program of Christianity: an Address. 2007. pap. 16.95 *(978-1-4304-4962-1(4))* Kessinger Publishing, LLC.

Laamann, Lars P. Christian Heretics in Late Imperial China: Christian Inculturation & State Control, 1720-1850. 2007. (Routledge Studies in the Modern History of Asia: Vol. 40). (Illus.). 204p. 160.00 *(978-0-415-29779-0(6))* Routledge.

Pullen, Henry William. Modern Christianity, a Civilized Heathenism by the Author of the Fight at Dame Europa's Schoo. 2006. 168p. per. 18.99 *(978-1-4255-1301-6(8))* MPublishing.

Tolstoy, Leo. The Kingdom of God Is Within You. 2009. 272p. pap. 8.99 *(978-1-60450-351-7(3))* Arc Manor.

—The Kingdom of God Is Within You. 2008. 312p. 29.99 *(978-0-554-22080-2(6))* 2008. 312p. 28.99 *(978-0-554-31383-2(9))* 2006. 324p. pap. 23.99 *(978-1-4264-1612-5(1))* BiblioBazaar.

—The Kingdom of God Is Within You. 2009. 142p. pap. *(978-1-4589-5334-6(3))* Books LLC.

—The Kingdom of God Is Within You. Wiener, Leo, tr. 2007. (ENG.). 384p. 28.95 *(978-1-60206-746-2(5))* Cosimo, Inc.

—The Kingdom of God Is Within You. Garnett, Constance, tr. 2007. (ENG.). 316p. per. *(978-1-4065-2091-0(8))* Dodo Pr

—The Kingdom of God Is Within You. 2008. 244p. pap. 9.99 *(978-1-60459-406-5(3))* Wilder Pubns., Ltd.

Webster, John C. B. A Social History of Christianity: Northwest India Since 1800. 2007. (ENG., Illus.). 408p. 55.00 *(978-0-19-569045-3(1))* Oxford Univ. Pr., Inc.

CHRISTIANITY—20TH CENTURY

see also Death of God Theology

Abbott, Lyman. Letters to Unknown Friends. 2007. (ENG.). 180p. 37.95 *(978-0-548-08693-3(1))* Kessinger Publishing, LLC.

—Letters to Unknown Friends. 2008. 180p. pap. *(978-1-4097-6853-1(8))* Read Bks.

Abingdon. Faces on Faith - Frederick Beuchner, Marion Wright Edelman, Gustavo Gutierrez: Classic Interviews with 20th-Century Leaders. 2008. cd-rom 25.00 *(978-0-687-65333-1(9))* Abingdon Pr.

—Faces on Faith - Joan Chittister, Marcus Borg, James Lawson: Classic Interviews with 20th-Century Leaders. 2008. cd-rom 25.00 *(978-0-687-65353-9(3))* Abingdon Pr.

—Faces on Faith: Desmond Tutu, Parker Palmer, Adele Gonzales: Classic Interviews with 20th-Century Leaders. 2008. cd-rom 25.00 *(978-0-687-65402-4(5))* Abingdon Pr.

—Faces on Faith: Huston Smith, Rita Nakashima Brock, Chaim Potok: Classic Interviews with 20th-Century Leaders. 2008. cd-rom 25.00 (978-0-687-65343-0(6)) Abingdon Pr.

Adler, Bill. Ask Billy Graham: The World's Best-Loved Preacher Answers Your Most Important Questions. 2007. 256p. per. 13.99 **(978-0-8499-1982-4(7))** Nelson, Thomas Inc.

Adler, Bill, Sr., compiled by. Ask Billy Graham: The World's Best-Loved Preacher Answers Your Most Important Questions, 0 vols. 2010. 256p. pap. 14.99 (978-0-7852-9789-5(8)) Nelson, Thomas Inc.

Akenson, Donald Harman. God's Peoples: Covenant & Land in South Africa, Israel, & Ulster. (ENG.). 416p. (978-0-7735-0940-5(2)) McGill-Queen's Univ. Pr.

Angurell, Benjamin. Altar de la Unidad: The Altar of Unity. (SPA.). (978-84-7645-223-3(3), 223270) Clie, Editorial.

Barth, Karl. Word of God Word of Man. Horton, Douglas, tr. 2008. 37.50 (978-0-8446-1599-8(4)) Smith, Peter Pub., Inc.

Bednarowski, Mary. Twentieth-Century Global Christianity. 2010. 320p. (C). pap. 24.00 (978-0-8006-9725-9(1), Fortress Pr.) Augsburg Fortress, Pubs.

Blamires, Harry. Where Do We Stand? a Christian Response. 2006. 172p. per. (978-1-57383-316-5(9), Regent College Publishing) Regent College Publishing.

Bosanquet, Bernard. What Religion Is. 2009. 94p. pap. 18.95 (978-1-104-52850-8(9)) Kessinger Publishing, LLC.

Bunch, David. Prayer & Prophecy: The Essential Kenneth Leech. Bunch, David & Ritchie, Angus, eds. 2009. 256p. pap. 30.00 (978-1-59627-115-9(9), Seabury Bks.) Church Publishing, Inc.

Campbell, Will D. Writings on Reconciliation & Resistance. Goode, Richard C., ed. 2010. 237p. pap. 28.00 (978-1-60608-128-0(4)) Cascade Bks.

Carver, Thomas Nixon. The Religion Worth Having. 2009. 56p. pap. (978-0-217-36766-0(6)) Books LLC.

—The Religion Worth Having. 2007. (ENG.). 148p. 35.95 (978-0-548-14962-1(3)); 152p. per. 20.95 (978-1-4304-4278-3(6)) Kessinger Publishing, LLC.

Cassidy, Michael. Christianity for the Open-Minded. 2006. (IVP Booklets Ser.). (ENG.). 48p. 1.50 (978-0-87784-038-1(5), IVP Bks.) InterVarsity Pr.

Cohu, J. R. Vital Problems of Religion. 2007. 304p. per. (978-1-4067-9671-1(9), Pomona Pr.) Read Bks.

Cook, Richard R. & Pao, David W., eds. After Imperialism: Christian Identity in China & the Global Evangelical Movement. 2011. (Studies in Chinese Christianity Ser.). 256p. pap. 28.00 **(978-1-60899-336-9(1)**, Pickwick Pubns.) Wipf & Stock Pubs.

Cox, Harvey. The Future of Faith. 2010. (ENG.). 256p. pap. 15.99 (978-0-06-175553-8(2), HarperOne) HarperCollins Pubs.

—The Future of Faith: The Rise & Fall of Beliefs & the Coming Age of the Spirit. 2009. (ENG.). 256p. 24.99 (978-0-06-175552-1(4), HarperOne) HarperCollins Pubs.

Crane, Frank. Lame & Lovely: Essays on Religion for Modern Minds. 2007. (ENG.). 212p. per. 24.95 (978-1-4304-4333-9(2)) Kessinger Publishing, LLC.

Crawford, Dan D. A Thirst for Souls: The Life of Evangelist Percy B. Crawford (1902-1960) 2010. (ENG., Illus.). 363p. pap. 19.95 (978-1-57591-148-9(5)) Susquehanna Univ. Pr.

Davies, Noel & Conway, Martin. World Christianity in the 20th Century. 2008. (Scm Core Text Ser.). 308p. pap. (978-0-334-04043-9(4)) Hymns Ancient & Modern Ltd.

Elliott, Charles. Memory & Salvation. 352p. pap. (978-0-232-52141-2(7)) South Asia Bks.

Farhadian, Charles E., ed. Introducing World Christianity. 2012. (ENG.). 292p. 84.95 (978-1-4051-8249-2(0), Wiley-Blackwell) Wiley, John & Sons, Inc.

—Introducing World Christianity. 2012. (ENG.). 292p. pap. 39.95 (978-1-4051-8248-5(2), Wiley-Blackwell) Wiley, John & Sons, Inc.

Faunce, William Herbert Perry. What Does Christianity Mean? 2007. (ENG.). 242p. 41.95 (978-0-548-15535-6(6)); pap. 26.95 (978-1-4304-4971-3(3)) Kessinger Publishing, LLC.

Gabriel, Ralph H. Christianity & Modern Thought. Brown, Charles R., ed. 212p. 2010. 31.96 (978-1-163-38658-3(8)) 2007. (ENG.). 39.95 (978-0-548-07741-2(X)) Kessinger Publishing, LLC.

Gager, Leroy. Segundo Exodo: Second Exodus. (SPA.). 448p. (978-84-7228-911-6(7), 222406) Clie, Editorial.

Garnett, Jane, et al, eds. Redefining Christian Britain: Post 1945 Perspectives. 2007. 308p. per. (978-0-334-04092-7(2)) Hymns Ancient & Modern Ltd.

Glover, T. R. Jesus in the Experience of Men. 2007. (ENG.). 262p. 42.95 (978-0-548-01028-0(5)) Kessinger Publishing, LLC.

Guinness, Os. The Last Christian on Earth: Uncover the Enemy's Plot to Undermine the Church. 2010. (ENG.). 256p. pap. 14.99 (978-0-8307-5125-9(4)) Gospel Light Pubns.

Hall, Charles Cuthbert. Christian Belief Interpreted by Christian Experience: Lectures Delivered. 2007. (ENG.). 300p. per. 28.95 (978-1-4304-4535-7(1)) Kessinger Publishing, LLC.

—The Universal Elements of the Christian Religion: an Attempt To. 2007. (ENG.). 308p. per. 28.95 (978-1-4304-4314-8(6)) Kessinger Publishing, LLC.

Inge, William Ralph. Truth & Falsehood in Religion: Six Lectures Delivered at Cambridge in the Lent Term, 1903. 2007. (ENG.). 188p. per. 22.95 (978-1-4304-4272-1(7)) Kessinger Publishing, LLC.

—Truth & Falsehood in Religion Six Lec. 2007. 188p. per. (978-1-4067-8885-3(6), Pomona Pr.) Read Bks.

Jenson, Robert W. A Religion Against Itself. 2009. 128p. pap. 16.00 (978-1-60899-141-9(5), Wipf and Stock) Wipf & Stock Pubs.

Joers, Lawrence E. God Is My Captain. 2007. (ENG.). 176p. 37.95 (978-0-548-08054-2(2)) Kessinger Publishing, LLC.

Jon Sobrino Staff. Concilium 2005/3: Christianity in Crisis? 2011. 142p. pap. **(978-0-334-03084-3(6)**, SCM Pr.) Hymns Ancient & Modern Ltd.

Kelly, Howard A. A Scientific Man & the Bible a Personal Testimony. 2007. (ENG.). 156p. 36.95 (978-0-548-03248-0(3)) Kessinger Publishing, LLC.

Koschorke, Klaus, ed. Falling Walls: The Year 1989/90 as a Turning Point in the History of World Christianity / Einsturzende Mauern: das Jahr 1989/90 als Epochenjahr in der Geschichte des Weltchristentums. 2009. (Studien zur Aussereuropaischen Christentumsgeschichte (Asien Ser.). (ENG & GER.). 451p. (C). pap. 81.00 (978-3-447-05995-4(8)) Harrassowitz, Otto Verlag DEU. Dist: ISD.

Lewis, C. S. The Screwtape Letters. 2009. (ENG.). 256p. 29.99 (978-0-06-170818-3(6), HarperOne) HarperCollins Pubs.

Lewis, J. P. The Divine Order & the Immortalization of Man: A Treatise on God's Practical Demonstration of Life & Immortality. 2011. 176p. 42.95 **(978-1-258-04440-4(4))** Literary Licensing, LLC.

Lurie, David H. Pacto, el Holocausto & la Semana 70: Covenant, the Holocaust & the 70th Week. (SPA.). (978-84-7645-446-6(5), 223455) Clie, Editorial.

Martinez, J. M. Los Cristianos en el Mundo Hoy: Christians in the Contemporary. (SPA.). (978-84-7645-244-8(6), 223283) Clie, Editorial.

Mathews, Shailer. Creative Christianity: The Cole Lectures For 1934. 2011. 168p. 41.95 **(978-1-258-01723-1(7))** Literary Licensing, LLC.

Mathews, Shailer. The Gospel & the Modern Man. 2009. 346p. 32.99 (978-1-115-52780-4(0)) 2009. 346p. 36.99 (978-1-115-52779-8(7)) 2009. 346p. 36.99 (978-1-115-52785-9(1)) 2009. 346p. pap. 31.75 (978-1-115-52788-0(6)) 2009. 346p. pap. 32.75 (978-1-115-52787-3(8)) 2009. 348p. 25.99 (978-1-103-58242-6(9)) 2009. 348p. pap. 19.99 (978-1-103-58241-9(0)) 2008. 348p. 28.99 (978-0-559-77638-0(1)) 2008. 348p. pap. 31.75 (978-0-559-77634-2(9)) BiblioBazaar.

—The Gospel & the Modern Man. 2009. 150p. pap. (978-0-217-08053-8(7)); 150p. pap. (978-0-217-89242-1(6)); 146p. pap. (978-0-217-58583-5(3)) Books LLC.

—The Gospel & the Modern Man. 2009. 150p. pap. 19.99 (978-1-4588-7770-3(1)) General Bks. LLC.

Newbigin, Lesslie. Honest Religion for Secular Man. 2011. 160p. pap. 19.00 **(978-1-61097-583-4(9)**, Wipf and Stock) Wipf & Stock Pubs.

Noll, Mark A. What Ever Happened to Christian Canada. 2007. (ENG.). 60p. per. (978-1-57383-405-6(X), Regent College Publishing) Regent College Publishing.

Nunez, E. A. & Taylor, W. D. Crisis & Hope in Latin America: An Evangelical Perspective. (Illus.). xvi, 528p. pap. (978-1-900890-01-4(1)) WEF GBR. Dist: O. M. Literature.

Orchard, W. E. The Outlook for Religion. 2007. 280p. per. (978-1-4067-8807-5(4), Pomona Pr.) Read Bks.

Ratzinger, Joseph & Schall, James. Faith & the Future. 2009. 160p. pap. 14.95 (978-1-58617-219-0(0)) Ignatius Pr.

Rauschenbusch, Walter. Dare We Be Christians. 2009. 64p. pap. 13.99 (978-1-103-78412-7(9)) BiblioBazaar.

—Dare We Be Christians. 2007. (ENG.). 64p. per. 16.95 (978-0-548-71377-8(4)) Kessinger Publishing, LLC.

Ritcher, Scott. Letters to Saint Clinton. 2007. 190p. pap. 13.95 (978-0-615-13898-5(5)) K Composite Media.

Sanneh, Lamin. Disciples of All Nations: Pillars of World Christianity. 2007. (Oxford Studies in World Christianity Ser.). (ENG., Illus.). 368p. per. 19.95 (978-0-19-518961-2(2)) Oxford Univ. Pr., Inc.

Ser Evangelico Hoy: Being a Christian in the Twentieth Century. (SPA.). (978-84-7645-316-2(7), 223453) Clie, Editorial.

Sperry, W. L. Disciplines of Liberty the Faith & con. 2006. pap. 22.95 (978-1-4286-3610-1(2)) Kessinger Publishing, LLC.

Thomas, Owen C. Christian Life & Practice: Anglican Essays. 2008. 162p. pap. 19.00 (978-1-55635-842-5(3)) Wipf & Stock Pubs.

Thompson, James W. The Church in Exile: God's Counterculture in a Non-Christian World. 2011. 160p. pap. 12.99 (978-0-89112-273-9(7), Leafwood Pubs.) Abilene Christian Univ. Pr.

Tillich, Paul. The Irrelevance & Relevance of the Christian Message. Foster, Durwood, ed. 2007. 104p. pap. 13.00 (978-1-55635-211-9(5), Wipf and Stock) Wipf & Stock Pubs.

Urwin, E. C. Religion in Planned Society. 2007. 84p. per. (978-1-4067-8856-3(2), Pomona Pr.) Read Bks.

Veldman, Meine. H F Kohlbrugge & Karl Barth on the Word of God And 'Man' 2010. 168p. pap. (978-3-8383-0240-9(0)) Lambert Academic Publishing.

Vrooman, William A. Progressive Christianity: A Study of the Old Faith & the New Reformation. 2007. (ENG.). 386p. 48.95 (978-0-548-06561-7(6)) Kessinger Publishing, LLC.

Waddell, Peter Hately. Christianity As an Ideal. 2007. (ENG.). 216p. 39.95 (978-0-548-15533-2(X)); pap. 24.95 (978-1-4304-4967-6(5)) Kessinger Publishing, LLC.

Watson, John. The Mind of the Master. 2009. 348p. 36.99 (978-1-116-05185-8(0)); 32.99 (978-1-116-05186-5(9)); pap. 32.75 (978-1-116-05187-2(7)) BiblioBazaar.

Watson, John & Maclaren, Ian. The Mind of the Master. 2007. (ENG.). 344p. 46.95 (978-0-548-01826-2(X)) Kessinger Publishing, LLC.

Watson, John & Maclaren], [Ian. The Mind of the Master. 2010. 120.92 (978-1-61719-262-3(7)) Gorgias Pr., LLC.

Wyand, Fred B., ed. Religion & the Church Tomorrow. 2007. (ENG.). 220p. 39.95 (978-0-548-06595-2(0)) Kessinger Publishing, LLC.

CHRISTIANITY—21ST CENTURY

Adeney, Miriam. Kingdom Without Borders: The Untold Story of Global Christianity, 1 vol. 2009. (ENG.). 295p. pap. 18.00 (978-0-8308-3849-3(X), IVP Bks.) InterVarsity Pr.

Avant, John. If God Were Real: A Journey into a Faith That Matters. 2009. (ENG.). 224p. pap. 14.99 (978-1-4165-8779-8(9), Howard Bks.) Howard Books.

Bass, Diana Butler. Christianity after Religion: The End of Church & the Birth of a New Spiritual Awakening. 2012. (ENG.). 272p. 25.99 **(978-0-06-200373-7(9)**, HarperOne) HarperCollins Pubs.

Blood, Barry E. Giving Voice to the Silent Pulpit: A layman explores the differences between Popular & Academic Christianity. 2011. 112p. pap. 14.00 **(978-1-61097-298-7(8)**, Resource Pubns.) Wipf & Stock Pubs.

Brech, Ronald. Christianity for the Twenty-first Century? A Personal Exposition of the Drama of Christ. 2008. 184p. pap. (978-1-84748-399-7(2)) Athena Pr.

Broadman and Holman Publishers Staff & Broadman and Holman. Evangelicals Engaging Emergent: A Discussion of the Emergent Church Movement, 1 vol. Henard, William & Greenway, Adam, eds. 2009. (ENG.). 352p. pap. 24.99 (978-0-8054-4739-2(3), B&H Academic) B&H Publishing Group.

Buchanan, Patrick J. Suicide of a Superpower: Will America Survive To 2025? (ENG.). 496p. 2012. pap. 15.99 **(978-1-250-00411-6(X)**, St. Martin's Griffin) 2011. 27.99 (978-0-312-57997-5(7), Dunne, Thomas Bks.) St. Martin's Pr.

Callen, Barry L. Caught Between Truths: The Central Paradoxes of Christian Faith. 2007. per. 29.00 (978-0-9776555-5-7(5)) Emeth Pr.

Conway, Jan. The Finisher: A New Path for Your Second Half. 2009. pap. 13.95 (978-1-935529-10-1(2)) Intermedia Publishing Group.

Cox, Harvey. The Future of Faith. 2010. (ENG.). 256p. pap. 15.99 (978-0-06-175553-8(2), HarperOne) HarperCollins Pubs.

—The Future of Faith: The Rise & Fall of Beliefs & the Coming Age of the Spirit. 2009. (ENG.). 256p. 24.99 (978-0-06-175552-1(4), HarperOne) HarperCollins Pubs.

DeYoung, Kevin & Kluck, Ted. Why We're Not Emergent: By Two Guys Who Should Be. 2008. (ENG.). 256p. pap. 14.99 (978-0-8024-5834-6(3)) Moody Pubs.

Elnes, Eric. Asphalt Jesus: Finding a New Christian Faith along the Highways of America. 2007. (ENG., Illus.). 256p. 22.95 (978-0-7879-8608-7(9), Jossey-Bass) Wiley, John & Sons, Inc.

Equale, Tony. An Unknown God: Essays in Pursuit of the Sacred. 2009. 317p. (ENG.). (978-1-933567-27-3(9)); pap. 25.00 (978-1-933567-26-6(0)) Institute for Economic Democracy Pr., Inc.

Farhadian, Charles E., ed. Introducing World Christianity. 2012. (ENG.). 292p. 84.95 (978-1-4051-8249-2(0), Wiley-Blackwell) Wiley, John & Sons, Inc.

—Introducing World Christianity. 2012. (ENG.). 292p. pap. 39.95 (978-1-4051-8248-5(2), Wiley-Blackwell) Wiley, John & Sons, Inc.

Frost, Michael & Hirsch, Alan. ReJesus: A Wild Messiah for a Missional Church. 2009. (Illus.). 240p. pap. (978-1-921202-91-9(2)) Hendrickson Pubs. Marketing, LLC.

Gardner, Clinton C. Beyond Belief: Discovering Christianity's New Paradigm. 2008. pap. (978-1-935052-02-9(0)) White River Pr.

Garnett, Jane, et al, eds. Redefining Christian Britain: Post 1945 Perspectives. 2007. 308p. per. (978-0-334-04092-7(2)) Hymns Ancient & Modern Ltd.

Gates, Everett. Helping You Is Killing Me: The Armorbearers Call to Serve. 2008. pap. 13.99 (978-1-60647-295-8(X)) Xulon Pr., Inc.

Geering, Lloyd. Coming Back to Earth: From Gods, to God, to Gaia. 2009. xv, 221p. (978-1-59815-016-2(2)) Polebridge Pr.

Gibbons, Dave. The Monkey & the Fish, 1 vol. 2009. (Leadership Network Innovation Ser.). (ENG.). 224p. pap. 18.99 (978-0-310-27602-9(0)) Zondervan.

Goodwin, Janelle. Reflections - My Journey of Becoming a Lady of Virtue. 2010. 147p. pap. 19.95 (978-0-557-31092-0(X)) Lulu Enterprises Inc.

Guinness, Os. The Last Christian on Earth: Uncover the Enemy's Plot to Undermine the Church. 2010. (ENG.). 256p. pap. 14.99 (978-0-8307-5125-9(4)) Gospel Light Pubns.

Herringshaw, Mark. The Karma of Jesus, 1 vol. 2009. 208p. pap. 13.99 (978-0-7642-0734-1(2)) Bethany Hse. Pubs.

Hylton, Jim. The Supernatural Skyline: Where Heaven Touches Earth. 2010. 302p. **(978-0-7684-3449-1(1))**; **(978-0-7684-3450-7(5))** Destiny Image Pubs.

Jeske, Christine. Into the Mud: Inspiration for Everday Activists: True Stories of South Africa, 1 vol. 2010. (ENG.). 208p. pap. 13.99 (978-0-8024-5879-7(3)) Moody Pubs.

Jon Sobrino Staff. Concilium 2005/3: Christianity in Crisis? 2011. 142p. pap. **(978-0-334-03084-3(6)**, SCM Pr.) Hymns Ancient & Modern Ltd.

Jones, Tony & Jones. The New Christians: Dispatches from the Emergent Frontier. 2009. (ENG.). 288p. pap. 14.95 (978-0-470-45539-5(X), Jossey-Bass) Wiley, John & Sons, Inc.

Lyons, Gabe. The Next Christians: The Good News about the End of Christian America. 2010. (ENG.). 240p. 19.99 (978-0-385-52984-6(8), Doubleday Religion) Doubleday Religious Publishing Group, The.

McClure, Joshua A. Can These Bones Live? The Miraculous story of what can happen to a church that follows God's Vision. 2006. 250p. 14.95 (978-1-59886-472-4(6)) Tate Publishing & Enterprises, LLC.

Miller, Robert J. The Future of the Christian Tradition. 2007. 264p. per. (978-1-59815-000-1(6)) Polebridge Pr.

Murchison, William. Mortal Follies: Episcopalians & the Decline of Mainstream Christianity. 2009. (ENG.). 288p. 25.95 (978-1-59403-230-1(0)) Encounter Bks.

Neuhaus, Richard John. American Babylon: Notes of a Christian Exile. 2010. (ENG.). 288p. (gr. 9). pap. 16.95 (978-0-465-02071-3(2)) Basic Bks.

Olsen, Glenn W. The Turn to Transcendence: The Role of Religion in the Twenty-First Century. 2010. (ENG.). 404p. 49.95 (978-0-8132-1740-6(7)) Catholic Univ. of America Pr.

O'Malley, Steven J., ed. World Revitalization Movements. 2011. pap. 35.00 **(978-1-60947-018-0(4))** Emeth Pr.

Pagitt, Doug. A Christianity Worth Believing: Hope-Filled, Open-Armed, Alive-and-Well Faith for the Left Out Left Behind, And Let Down in Us All. 2008. (ENG.). 256p. 21.95 (978-0-7879-9812-7(5), Jossey-Bass) Wiley, John & Sons, Inc.

Pagitt, Doug & Pagitt. A Christianity Worth Believing: Hope-Filled, Open-Armed, Alive-and-Well Faith for the Left Out, Left Behind, & Let down in Us All. 2009. (ENG.). 256p. pap. 14.95 (978-0-470-45534-0(9), Jossey-Bass) Wiley, John & Sons, Inc.

Piatt, Christian & Piatt, Amy. MySpace to Sacred Space: God for a New Generation. 2007. 167p. per. 19.99 (978-0-8272-2334-9(X)) Chalice Pr.

Poloma, Margaret & Hood, Ralph W., Jr. Blood & Fire: Godly Love in a Pentecostal Emerging Church. 2008. (ENG.). 304p. (C). 45.00 (978-0-8147-6748-1(6)) New York Univ. Pr.

Rathbun, Russell. Post-Rapture Radio: Lost Writings from a Failed Revolution. 2008. (ENG.). 208p. pap. 14.95 (978-0-470-29272-3(5), Jossey-Bass) Wiley, John & Sons, Inc.

Reynolds, Alan. A Troubled Faith. 2006. 192p. per. (978-1-894928-98-4(9)) Word Alive Pr.

Robinson, Martin. Metavista: Bible, Church & Mission in an Age of Imagination. 2008. (Faith in an Emerging Culture Ser.). (ENG., Illus.). 256p. pap. 23.99 (978-1-84227-506-1(2), Paternoster) Authentic Media.

Rwengabo, Sabastiano. Beyond the Spiritual. 2011. 188p. pap. **(978-3-8433-8896-2(2))** Lambert Academic Publishing.

Sanneh, Lamin. Disciples of All Nations: Pillars of World Christianity. 2007. (Oxford Studies in World Christianity Ser.). (ENG., Illus.). 368p. per. 19.95 (978-0-19-518961-2(2)) Oxford Univ. Pr., Inc.

Sinclair, Scott Gamb. An Introduction to Christianity for a New Millennium. 2008. (ENG.). 176p. 62.99 (978-0-7391-2466-6(8)); pap. 26.50 (978-0-7391-2467-3(6)) Lexington Bks.

Sine, Tom. The New Conspirators: Creating the Future One Mustard Seed at a Time. 2008. (ENG.). 304p. per. 16.00 (978-0-8308-3384-9(6), IVP Bks.) InterVarsity Pr.

Smith, Robert. Cross Examination. 2007. 340p. per. (978-1-897117-37-8(X)) Gospel Folio Pr.

Standish, Colin D. & Standish, Russell R. Postmodernism & the Decline of Christianity. 2007. (ENG.). 160p. per. 13.95 (978-0-923309-71-8(3)) Hartland Pubns.

Stenhouse, John & Knowles, Brett, eds. Christianity in the Post Secular West. 2007. (Illus.). 290p. per. 20.00 (978-1-920691-75-2(8)) ATF Pr. AUS. Dist: International Publishers Marketing.

Stiller, Karen & Metzger, Willard. Going Missional. 2010. 184p. pap. (978-1-77069-021-9(2)) Word Alive Pr.

Stoner, Timothy J. The God Who Smokes: Scandalous Meditations on Faith. 2008. (Living the Letters Ser.). (ENG.). 320p. pap. 14.99 (978-1-60006-247-6(4)) NavPress Publishing Group.

Tickle, Phyllis. The Great Emergence: How Christianity Is Changing & Why. 2012. (Illus.). 172p. pap. 14.99 (978-0-8010-7102-7(X)) Baker Bks.

Voerman, Jan. The Hidden Agenda. 2006. 202p. per. 17.95 (978-1-57258-451-8(3), 945-6312) TEACH Services, Inc.

Walker, Jim. Dirty Word: The Vulgar, Offensive Languages of the Kingdom of God. 2008. 256p. pap. 20.00 (978-0-88177-539-6(8)) Discipleship Resources.

Wilson, Douglas. Heaven Misplaced: Christ's Kingdom on Earth. 2008. (ENG.). 19.00 (978-1-59128-051-4(6)) Canon Pr.

CHRISTIANITY AND ANTISEMITISM

Alsleben-Baumann, Claudia. Synagoga - Typologien eines christlich-kultivierten Antijudaismus: Einsichten und Auswege im Fokus anamnetischer Religionspädagogik. 2009. (Übergänge. Studien zur Evangelischen und Katholischen Theologie/Religionspädagogik Ser.). (GER.). 200p. pap. 56.95 (978-3-631-58576-4(4)) Lang, Peter GmbH, Europaischer Verlag der Wissenschaften DEU. Dist: Lang, Peter.

Anidjar, Gil. Semites: Race, Religion, Literature. 2007. (Cultural Memory in the Present Ser.). (ENG.). 160p. 55.00 (978-0-8047-5694-5(5)); per. 19.95 (978-0-8047-5695-2(3)) Stanford Univ. Pr.

Ben-Dror, Graciela. Argentina, 1933-1945. 2009. (Studies in Antisemitism Ser.). (ENG.). 278p. 55.00 (978-0-8032-1889-5(3)) Univ. of Nebraska Pr.

Berger, David. Persecution, Polemic, & Dialogue: Essays in Jewish-Christian Relations. 2010. (Judaism & Jewish Life Ser.). (ENG.). 450p. 45.00 (978-1-934843-76-5(8)) Academic Studies Pr.

Biale, David. Blood & Belief: The Circulation of a Symbol Between Jews & Christians. (Illus.). 2008. 316p. pap. 25.95 (978-0-520-25798-6(7)) 2007. 299p. 55.00 (978-0-520-25304-9(3)) Univ. of California Pr.

Blaschke, Olaf. Offenders or Victims? German Jews & the Causes of Modern Catholic Antisemitism. 2009. (Studies in Antisemitism Ser.). (ENG.). 232p. 50.00 (978-0-8032-2522-0(9)) Univ. of Nebraska Pr.

Blech, Arthur. The Causes of Anti-Semitism: A Critique of the Bible. rev. ed. 2006. (ENG.). 1p. per. 21.98 (978-1-59102-446-0(3)) Prometheus Bks., Pubs.

—The Causes of Anti-Semitism: A Critique of the Bible. 2010. 512p. 29.95 (978-1-59079-068-7(5)) Select Bks.
Connelly, John. From Enemy to Brother: The Revolution in Catholic Teaching on the Jews, 1933-1965. 2012. (ENG.). 384p. 35.00 (978-0-674-05782-1(1)) Harvard Univ. Pr.
Coppa, Frank J. The Papacy, the Jews, & the Holocaust. 2008. 373p. pap. 34.95 (978-0-8132-1547-1(1)) Catholic Univ. of America Pr.
Cymet, David. History vs. Apologetics: The Holocaust, the Third Reich, & the Catholic Church. 2010. (ENG., Illus.). 510p. 94.50 (978-0-7391-3293-7(8)) Lexington Bks.
—History vs Apologetics: The Holocaust, the Third Reich, & the Catholic Church. 2011. (ENG.). 510p. pap. 39.95 (978-0-7391-3294-4(6)) Lexington Bks.
Dietrich, Donald. God & Humanity in Auschwitz: Jewish-Christian Relations & Sanctioned Murder. 2008. (ENG.). 367p. pap. 29.95 (978-1-4128-0858-3(8)) Transaction Pubs.
Donaldson, Terence L. Jews & Anti-Judaism in the New Testament: Decision Points & Divergent Interpretations. 2010. (ENG.). 192p. (C). pap. 24.95 (978-1-60258-263-7(7)) Baylor Univ. Pr.
Fattorini, Emma. Hitler, Mussolini & the Vatican: Pope Pius XI & the Speech That Was Never Made. 2011. (ENG.). 220p. 25.00 (978-0-7456-4488-2(0)) Polity Pr. GBR. Dist: Wiley, John & Sons, Inc.
Feldman, Egal. Catholics & Jews in Twentieth-Century America. 2006. 344p. per. 21.00 (978-0-252-07385-4(1)) Univ. of Illinois Pr.
Gerdmar, Anders. Roots of Theological Anti-Semitism: German Biblical Interpretation & the Jews, from Herder & Semler to Kittel & Bultmann. 2010. (Illus.). 678p. pap. (978-90-04-18621-7(2)) 2008. 668p. (978-90-04-16851-0(6)) BRILL.
Gray, Ronald. Jesus's Gospel of Love & the Holocaust. 2008. 72p. pap. (978-1-84748-294-5(5)) Athena Pr.
Gritsch, Eric W. Martin Luther's Anti-Semitism: Against His Better Judgment. 2011. pap. 25.00 (978-0-8028-6676-9(X)) Eerdmans, William B. Publishing Co.
Hanebrink, Paul A. In Defense of Christian Hungary: Religion, Nationalism, & Antisemitism, 1890-1944. (Illus.). 2009. 272p. pap. 25.95 (978-0-8014-7530-6(9)) 2006. 255p. 54.95 (978-0-8014-4485-2(3)) Cornell Univ. Pr.
Harper, Carol. Through the Eye of a Needle. 2007. 121p. per. 10.99 (978-1-59886-865-4(9)) Tate Publishing & Enterprises, LLC.
Heinz, Daniel, ed. Freikirchen und Juden im »Dritten Reich«: Instrumentalisierte Heilsgeschichte, antisemitische Vorurteile und verdrängte Schuld. 2011. (Kirche, Konfession, Religion Ser.). (GER.). 343p. (C). 68.00 (978-3-89971-690-0(6)) Vandenhoeck & Ruprecht GmbH & Co. KG DEU. Dist: ISD.
Horner, Barry E. Future Israel: Why Christian Anti-Judaism Must Be Challenged. Clendenen, E. Ray, ed. annot. ed. 2007. (New American Commentary Studies in Bible & Theology Ser.). (ENG.). 400p. 19.99 (978-0-8054-4627-2(3), B&H Academic) B&H Publishing Group.
Idinopulos, Thomas A. Betrayal of Spirit: Jew-hatred, the Holocaust, & Christianity. 2008. (ENG.). 244p. pap. 24.00 (978-1-888570-96-0(2)) Davies Group Pubs., The.
Johnson, Hannah. Blood Libel: The Ritual Murder Accusation at the Limit of Jewish History. 2012. (ENG.). 250p. (C). 70.00 (978-0-472-11835-9(8)) Univ. of Michigan Pr.
Keller, Zsolt. Der Blutruf: Eine schweizerische Wirkungsgeschichte 1900-1950. 2006. (GER.). 200p. (C). pap. 36.00 (978-3-525-55328-2(5)) Vandenhoeck & Ruprecht GmbH & Co. KG DEU. Dist: ISD.
Livak, Leonid. The Jewish Persona in the European Imagination: A Case of Russian Literature. 2010. (Stanford Studies in Jewish History & C Ser.). (ENG., Illus.). 512p. 60.00 (978-0-8047-7055-2(7)) Stanford Univ. Pr.
Martin, Regis. The Suffering of Love: Christ's Descent into the Hell of Human Hopelessness. 2007. 254p. pap. 16.95 (978-1-58617-105-6(4)) Ignatius Pr.
Michael, Robert. A History of Catholic Antisemitism: The Dark Side of the Church. (ENG.). 292p. 2011. pap. 28.00 (978-0-230-11131-8(9)) 2008. 100.00 (978-0-230-60388-2(2)) Palgrave Macmillan.
—Holy Hatred: Christianity, Antisemitism, & the Holocaust. annot. ed. 2006. (ENG.). 256p. pap. 30.00 (978-1-4039-7472-3(1)) Palgrave Macmillan.
Michael, Robert & Michael, Robert T. Holy Hatred: Christianity, Antisemitism, & the Holocaust. annot. ed. 2006. (ENG.). 256p. 95.00 (978-1-4039-7471-6(3)) Palgrave Macmillan.
Millman, Richard. La Question Juive Entre les Deux Guerres: Ligues de Droite et Antisémitisme en France. (FRE.). 338p. (978-2-200-21166-0(X)) Armand, Colin.
Nelson, Riley H. Replacement Theology: Dishonesty? Envy? Covetousness? Conceitedness? Presumptuousness? Ignorance? or, Blasphemy? 2008. 148p. pap. 15.99 (978-1-60477-952-3(7)) Xulon Pr., Inc.
Perry, Marvin B., et al, eds. Antisemitic Myths: A Historical & Contemporary Anthology. 2008. (ENG.). 384p. pap. 27.00 (978-0-253-21950-3(7), 0253219507) Indiana Univ. Pr.
Probst, Christopher J. Demonizing the Jews: Luther & the Protestant Church in Nazi Germany. 2012. (ENG., Illus.). 270p. 70.00 (978-0-253-00098-9(X), 025300098X); pap. 25.00 (978-0-253-00100-9(5), 0253001005) Indiana Univ. Pr.
Rancour-Laferriere, Daniel. The Sign of the Cross: From Golgotha to Genocide. 2011. (ENG.). 313p. 39.95 (978-1-4128-1133-0(3)) Transaction Pubs.
Rudin, James. Christians & Jews — Faith to Faith: Tragic History, Promising Present, Fragile Future. 2010. 224p. 24.99 (978-1-58023-432-0(1)) Jewish Lights Publishing.
Shepardson, Christine C. Anti-Judaism & Christian Orthodoxy: Ephrem's Hymns in Fourth-Century Syria. 2008. 208p. (C). 34.95 (978-0-8132-1536-5(6)) Catholic Univ. of America Pr.
Spear, Sonja. Jesus the Jew. 2009. 204p. pap. (978-3-639-17600-1(6)) VDM Verlag Dr. Mueller e.K.
Spector, Sheila A. Romanticism & the Jewish Question: Nationalism, Religion, Individualism. 2011. (Illus.). 242p. 99.95 (978-0-7546-6880-0(0)) Ashgate Publishing Co.
Spicer, Kevin P., ed. Antisemitism, Christian Ambivalence, & the Holocaust. 2007. (ENG.). 360p. 20.00 (978-0-253-34873-9(0), 0253348730) Indiana Univ. Pr.
Unterseher, Lisa A. The Mark of Cain & the Jews. 2009. 98.00 (978-1-59333-896-1(1)) Gorgias Pr., LLC.
Wilson, Barrie. How Jesus Became Christian. 2009. (ENG.). 336p. pap. (978-0-679-31494-3(6), Vintage Canada) Random Hse. of Canada, Ltd. CAN. Dist: Random Hse., Inc.
—How Jesus Became Christian. 2009. (ENG.). 336p. pap. 17.99 (978-0-312-36189-1(0), St. Martin's Griffin) St. Martin's Pr.

CHRISTIANITY AND ATHEISM

see also Communism and Christianity

Andrews, Edgar. Who Made God? Searching for a Theory of Everything. 2009. 305p. (978-0-85234-707-2(3)) Evangelical Pr.
Austin, Michael. Dawkins' Dilemmas. 2008. 160p. per. 13.99 (978-1-60477-666-9(8)) Xulon Pr., Inc.
Bloch, Ernst. Atheism in Christianity: The Religion of the Exodus & the Kingdom. Swann, J. T., tr. from GER. 2nd ed. 2009. (ENG.). 304p. 100.00 (978-1-84467-371-1(5), 844371); pap. 26.95 (978-1-84467-394-0(4), 844394) Verso Bks. GBR. Dist: Norton, W. W. & Co., Inc.
Chamberlain, Paul. Why People Don't Believe: Confronting Seven Challenges to Christian Faith. 2011. 176p. pap. 14.99 (978-0-8010-1377-5(1)) Baker Bks.
Comfort, Ray. How to Know God Exists: Scientific Proof of God. 2008. 192p. per. 12.99 (978-0-88270-432-6(X)) Bridge-Logos Foundation.
—You Can Lead an Atheist to Evidence, but You Can't Make Him Think: Answers to Questions from Angry Skeptics. 2009. 160p. 22.95 (978-1-935071-06-8(6)) WND Bks, Inc.
Craig, William Lane & Meister, Chad, eds. God Is Great, God Is Good: Why Believing in God Is Reasonable & Responsible. 2009. (ENG., Illus.). 265p. pap. 19.00 (978-0-8308-3726-7(4), IVP Bks.) InterVarsity Pr.
Crean, Thomas. God Is No Delusion: A Refutation of Richard Dawkins. 2007. 160p. pap. 12.95 (978-1-58617-231-2(X)) Ignatius Pr.
David, Andrew, et al, eds. 'God Is Dead' & I Don't Feel So Good Myself. 2009. 208p. pap. 23.00 (978-1-60608-531-8(X), Cascade Bks.) Wipf & Stock Pubs.
Davis, Mike. The Atheist's Bible Companion to the New Testament: A Comprehensive Guide to Christian Bible Contradictions. 2009. 462p. pap. 28.95 (978-1-4327-4864-7(5)) Outskirts Pr., Inc.
—The Atheist's Introduction to the New Testament: How the Bible Undermines the Basic Teachings of Christianity. 2008. 184p. pap. 18.95 (978-1-4327-2691-1(9)) Outskirts Pr., Inc.
Deltenbeck, Monika, et al. Could Jesus Walk on Water? 164 Questions & Answers about the Faith. 2007. (Illus.). 181p. per. 15.00 (978-1-58768-040-3(8), 040-3, HiddenSpring) Paulist Pr.
Donovan, Paul. Happily Godless: A Young Adult's Guide to Atheism. 2007. 163p. pap. 24.95 (978-1-4241-9963-1(8)) PublishAmerica, Inc.
Eagleton, Terry. Reason, Faith, & Revolution: Reflections on the God Debate. (Terry Lectures Ser.). (ENG.). 200p. 2010. pap. 16.00 (978-0-300-16453-4(X)) 2009. 25.00 (978-0-300-15179-4(9)) Yale Univ. Pr.
Eberstadt, Mary. The Loser Letters. 2010. 130p. pap. 10.95 (978-1-58617-431-6(2)) Ignatius Pr.
The End of Reason: A Response to the New Atheists, 1 vol. 2009. 144p. pap. 3.49 (978-0-310-32670-0(2)) Zondervan.
Fay, Ele. A Dove Flies: Why I Became A Christian. 2008. 196p. pap. 13.99 (978-1-60647-622-2(X)) Xulon Pr., Inc.
Ferguson, Paul. God & the Atheist: A Lawyer Assesses the Evidence for the Existence of God. 2007. 103p. per. 12.99 (978-1-932307-72-6(9), Ambassador International) Emerald Hse. Group, Inc.
Fergusson, David. Faith & Its Critics: A Conversation. (ENG.). 208p. 2011. pap. 18.85 (978-0-19-958568-7(7)) 2009. 35.00 (978-0-19-956938-0(X)) Oxford Univ. Pr., Inc.
Fernald, Daniel Horace. Atheism Answered. 2008. 108p. pap. 11.99 (978-1-60647-694-9(7)) Xulon Pr., Inc.
Ganssle, Gregory E. A Reasonable God: Engaging the New Face of Atheism. 2009. (ENG.). 165p. pap. 24.95 (978-1-60258-241-5(6)) Baylor Univ. Pr.
Gates, Todd Allen. Dialogue with a Christian Proselytizer. 2006. 328p. pap. 17.95 (978-1-60145-089-0(3)) Booklocker.com, Inc.
Gisburne, Nick. The Atheists Are Revolting! 2007. 216p. pap. 17.99 (978-1-4303-1442-4(7)) Lulu Enterprises Inc.
Hahn, Scott & Wiker, Benjamin. Answering the New Atheism: Dismantling Dawkins' Case Against God. 2008. 151p. pap. 12.95 (978-1-931018-48-7(0)) Emmaus Road Publishing.
Hitchens, Christopher & Wilson, Douglas. Is Christianity Good for the World? 72p. 2009. pap. 7.00 (978-1-59128-069-9(9)) 2008. (ENG.). 12.00 (978-1-59128-053-8(2)) Canon Pr.
—Is Christianity Good for the World? A Debate. 2008. (ENG.). 72p. (978-0-7710-4118-1(7), McClelland & Stewart) McClelland & Stewart CAN. Dist: Random Hse., Inc.
Jones, Kathleen. Challenging Richard Dawkins. 2008. 221p. pap. 14.99 (978-1-85311-841-8(9)) Canterbury Pr.
Lennox, John. Gunning for God: A Critique of the New Atheism. 2011. (ENG., Illus.). 248p. pap. 14.95 (978-0-7459-5322-9(0)) Lion Hudson PLC GBR. Dist: Independent Pubs. Group.
Loftus, John W. Why I Became an Atheist: A Former Preacher Rejects Christianity. 2012. (ENG.). 480p. pap. 21.00 (978-1-61614-577-4(3)) Prometheus Bks., Pubs.
Meynell, Hugo Anthony. The Epistemological Argument Against Atheism: Why a Knowledge of God Is Implied in Everything We Know. 2012. l, 248p. 139.95 (978-0-7734-1566-9(1)) Mellen, Edwin Pr., The.
Moffat, Russel. Atheists Can Be Wankers Too! A Foot Soldier's Response to the Four Horsemen. 2009. 212p. pap. 14.49 (978-1-4389-5185-0(X)) AuthorHouse.
Mohler, Albert R., Jr. & Mohler Jr., R. Albert. Atheism Remix: A Christian Confronts the New Atheists. 2008. 112p. 15.99 (978-1-4335-0497-5(9)) Crossway.
Morrow, Jonathan & McDowell, Sean. Is God Just a Human Invention? And Seventeen Other Questions Raised by the New Atheists, 1 vol. 2010. 304p. pap. 16.99 (978-0-8254-3654-3(0)) Kregel Pubns.
Myers, David G. A Friendly Letter to Skeptics & Atheists: Musings on Why God Is Good & Faith Isn't Evil. 2008. (ENG., Illus.). 160p. 16.95 (978-0-470-29027-9(7), Jossey-Bass) Wiley, John & Sons, Inc.
Nall, James. Practical Atheism in Denying the Agency of Providence Detected & Exposed by Rev James Nall. 2006. 144p. per. 16.99 (978-1-4255-1063-3(9)) MPublishing.
Ordway, Holly. Not God's Type: A Rational Academic Finds a Radical Faith, 1 vol. 2010. (ENG.). 160p. pap. 13.99 (978-0-8024-3194-3(1)) Moody Pubs.
Randall, H. W. Five Voices. 2010. 496p. pap. 20.49 (978-1-4520-1104-2(4)) AuthorHouse.
Riskas, Thomas. Deconstructing Mormonism: An Analysis & Assessment of the Mormon Faith. 2011. 784p. mass mkt. 29.95 (978-1-57884-007-6(4)) American Atheist Pr.
Robertson, James. Old Truths & Modern Speculations. 2007. (ENG.). 356p. 46.95 (978-0-548-11382-0(3)) Kessinger Publishing, LLC.
Sanford: Raven, Regina N. The Atheist Within the Christian Revealed, 1 vol. 2009. (ENG.). 49p. pap. 16.95 (978-1-60749-669-4(0)) PublishAmerica, Inc.
Schaeffer, Frank. Patience with God: Faith for People Who Don't Like Religion (or Atheism) 2010. (ENG.). 256p. pap. 14.95 (978-0-306-81922-3(8)) Da Capo Pr., Inc.
Selmanovic, Samir. It's Really All about God: How Islam, Atheism, & Judaism Made Me a Better Christian. 2011. (ENG.). 304p. pap. 15.95 (978-0-470-92341-2(5), Jossey-Bass) Wiley, John & Sons, Inc.
Shook, John R. The God Debates: A 21st Century Guide for Atheists & Believers (and Everyone in Between) 2010. (ENG., Illus.). 256p. 87.95 (978-1-4443-3641-2(X), Wiley-Blackwell) Wiley, John & Sons, Inc.
—The God Debates: A 21st Century Guide for Atheists & Believers (And Everyone in Between) 2010. (ENG., Illus.). 256p. pap. 26.95 (978-1-4443-3642-9(8), Wiley-Blackwell) Wiley, John & Sons, Inc.
Sire, James W. & Peraino, Carl. Deepest Differences: A Christian-Atheist Dialogue, 1 vol. 2009. (ENG.). 203p. pap. 15.00 (978-0-8308-3358-0(7), IVP Bks.) InterVarsity Pr.
Smalley, David. Baptized Atheist. 2010. 200p. pap. 18.00 (978-1-57884-008-3(2)) American Atheist Pr.
Stenger, Victor J. The New Atheism: Taking a Stand for Science & Reason. 2009. (ENG., Illus.). 250p. pap. 19.00 (978-1-59102-751-5(9)) Prometheus Bks., Pubs.
Tullis, Stuart N. Why? Addressing Our Most Foundational Question. 2008. 168p. pap. 13.99 (978-1-60647-291-0(7)) Xulon Pr., Inc.
Vetter, Herbert F. Is God Necessary? No! & Yes! 2007. 121p. pap. 12.95 (978-0-615-16046-7(8)) Harvard Square Library.
Zacharias, Ravi K. & Zacharias, Ravi. The End of Reason: A Response to the New Atheists. 2008. (ENG.). 112p. 12.99 (978-0-310-28251-8(9)) Zondervan.

CHRISTIANITY AND COMMUNISM

see Communism and Christianity

CHRISTIANITY AND CULTURE

Abbott, Matt. Behind the Scenes. 2007. 176p. per. 13.99 (978-1-60477-235-7(2)) Xulon Pr., Inc.
Adams, Frank Kwesi. Odwira & the Gospel: A Study of the Asante Odwira Festival & Its Significance for Christianity in Ghana. 2011. (Regnum Studies in Mission Ser.). 256p. pap. 28.00 (978-1-61097-439-4(5), Wipf and Stock) Wipf & Stock Pubs.
Adefila, Johnson Ajibade. Was Christianity a Means of the Deafricanization & Social Control of Slaves? A Comparison of the Response of Free West Africans to Christianity with the Response of African Slaves in the United States. 2011. (ENG.). 184p. 109.95 (978-0-7734-3955-9(2)) Mellen, Edwin Pr., The.
Adeney, Frances S. Graceful Evangelism: Christian Witness in a Complex World. 2010. (C). pap. 22.00 (978-0-8010-3185-4(0)) Baker Academic.
Albala, Ken & Eden, Trudy, eds. Food & Faith in Christian Culture. 2011. (Arts & Traditions of the Table: Perspectives on Culinary History Ser.). (ENG., Illus.). 280p. (gr. 17). 79.50 (978-0-231-14996-9(4)) Columbia Univ. Pr.
Anastaplo, George. Christian Heritage: Problems & Prospects. 2010. (ENG.). 464p. 99.99 (978-0-7391-3597-6(X)); pap. 45.50 (978-0-7391-3598-3(8)) Lexington Bks.
Anderson, David A. Gracism: The Art of Inclusion. 2010. (BridgeLeader Partnership Ser.). (ENG.). 168p. pap. 15.00 (978-0-8308-3737-3(X), IVP Bks.) InterVarsity Pr.
Angelov, Dimiter G. Church & Society in Late Byzantium. 2009. 40.00 (978-1-58044-142-1(4)); 20.00 (978-1-58044-143-8(2)) Medieval Institute Pubns.
Ankerberg, John, et al. The Facts on Halloween. 2008. (Facts on Ser.). 96p. mass mkt. 5.99 (978-0-7369-2219-7(9)) Harvest Hse. Pubs.
Aquino, Maria Pilar & Rosado-Nunes, Maria Jose, eds. Feminist Intercultural Theology: Latina Explorations for a Just World. 2007. (Studies in Latino/A Catholicism). 270p. per. 35.00 (978-1-57075-741-9(0)) Orbis Bks.
Arbour, Linda Marie. Tales Out of School: A Challenge to Catholic Educators. 2011. 260p. pap. 19.95 (978-1-4502-8909-2(6)) iUniverse, Inc.
Arbuckle, Gerald A. Culture, Inculturation, & Theologians: A Postmodern Critique. 2010. 24.95 (978-0-8146-5458-3(4)) Liturgical Pr.
Armerding, Carl Edwin, et al. The Bible in World Christian Perspective: Studies in Honor of Carl Edwin Armerding. 2008. (978-1-57383-432-2(7)) Regent College Publishing.
ATF Press, creator. Rainbow Spirit Theology: Toward an Australian Aboriginal Theology. 2011. (ENG., Illus.). 97p. (C). per. 5.00 (978-1-920691-80-8(4)) ATF Pr. AUS. Dist: Brown, David Bk. Co., The.
Athanassiadi, Polymnia. Vers la Pensée Unique: La Montée de L'intolérance Dans L'Antiquité Tardive. 2010. (Histoire Ser.). (FRE.). 192p. (C). pap. 38.00 (978-2-251-38100-8(7)) Societe d'edition Les Belles lettres FRA. Dist: ISD.
Bacon, Leonard. The American Church a Discourse in Behalf of the American Home Missionary Society, Preached in the Cities of New York & Brooklyn, May, 1852 by Rev. 2011. 26p. pap. 11.99 (978-1-4181-9232-7(5)) MPublishing.
Baehr, Theodore & Boone, Pat. Culture-Wise Family: Upholding Christian Values in a Mass-Media World. 2007. (ENG., Illus.). 256p. pap. 16.99 (978-0-8307-4355-1(3)) Gospel Light Pubns.
Bahr, Howard M. The Navajo as Seen by the Franciscans, 1920-1950: A Sourcebook. 2nd ed. 2011. (Native American Resources Ser.). (ENG.). 682p. (gr. 17). 95.00 (978-0-8108-6752-9(4)) Scarecrow Pr., Inc.
Barber, John. The Road from Eden: Studies in Christianity & Culture. (Illus.). 2009. (ENG.). 586p. pap. (978-1-933146-71-3(0)) 2007. 684p. lib. bdg. (978-1-933146-34-8(6)) Academica Pr., LLC.
Basile, Alex. Finding Faith in a Godless World: A Catholic Path to God. 2008. (978-0-8189-1265-8(0)) St Pauls/Alba Hse. Pubs.
Battle Michael. Ubuntu: I in You & You in Me. 2009. 176p. pap. 18.00 (978-1-59627-111-1(6), Seabury Bks.) Church Publishing, Inc.
Battle, Michael. Ubuntu: I in You & You in Me. 2009. 176p. 25.00 (978-1-59627-113-5(2), Seabury Bks.) Church Publishing, Inc.
Bediako, Kwame. Theology & Identity: The Impact of Culture upon Christian Thought in the Second Century & in Modern Africa. 2011. (Regnum Studies in Mission Ser.). 526p. pap. 63.00 (978-1-61097-440-0(9), Wipf and Stock) Wipf & Stock Pubs.
Bell, Rob. Velvet Elvis. 2012. (ENG.). 208p. pap. 14.99 (978-0-06-219721-4(5), HarperOne) HarperCollins Pubs.
Bergler, Thomas E. The Juvenilization of American Christianity. 2012. pap. (978-0-8028-6684-4(0)) Eerdmans, William B. Publishing Co.
Beutler, Johannes, et al, eds. More Than a Passover: Inculturation in the Supper Narratives of the New Testament. (Illus.). 395p. pap. 82.95 (978-3-631-56575-9(5)) Lang, Peter GmbH, Europaischer Verlag der Wissenschaften DEU. Dist: Lang, Peter Publishing, Inc.
Bevans, Stephen B. Contextual Theology in the Twenty-First Century. 2012. (ENG.). 154p. (C). pap. 30.00 (978-0-276-79982-2(8)) Clarke, James Co., Ltd. GBR. Dist: Brown, David Bk. Co., The.
—Mission & Culture: The Louis J. Luzbetak Lectures. 2012. (ENG., Illus.). 192p. 40.00 (978-1-57075-965-9(0)) Orbis Bks.
Bevans, Stephen B. & Schroeder, Roger P. Prophetic Dialogue: Reflections on Christian Mission Today. 2011. 208p. 35.00 (978-1-57075-911-6(1)) Orbis Bks.
Black, Fiona C. The Recycled Bible: Autobiography, Culture, & the Space Between. 2006. (SBL - Semeia Studies). (Illus.). 218p. (978-90-04-13088-3(8)) BRILL.
Boa, Kenneth. Unchanging Faith in a Changing World, 0 vols. 2008. 420p. pap. 21.99 (978-0-7852-9697-3(2)) Nelson, Thomas Inc.
Bodily Affections produced by Religious Excitement. 2010. pap. 18.04 (978-1-61143-162-9(X)) Gorgias Pr., LLC.
Boeve, Lieven. God Interrupts History: Theology in a Time of Upheaval. 2007. (ENG., Illus.). 224p. pap. 35.95 (978-0-8264-2813-4(4)) Continuum International Publishing Group, Ltd. GBR. Dist: National Bk. Network.
Bonk, Jonathan J. Missions & Money: Affluence as a Missionary Problem... Revisited. rev. exp. ed. 2007. (American Society of Missiology Ser.: 41). 272p. per. 27.00 (978-1-57075-650-4(3)) Orbis Bks.
Bower, Matt. Standing by the Pillar. 2008. (ENG.). 248p. 24.99 (978-1-60477-511-2(4)) Xulon Pr., Inc.
Boyce-Tillman, June. Unconventional Wisdom. 2007. (Gender, Theology & Spirituality Ser.). (ENG., Illus.). 224p. (C). 99.95 (978-1-84553-099-0(3)); pap. 29.95 (978-1-84553-100-3(0)) Equinox Publishing Ltd. GBR. Dist: ISD.
Bramadat, Paul & Seljak, David, eds. Christianity & Ethnicity in Canada, Vol. 2. 2008. 448p. (978-0-8020-9875-7(4)); (Illus.). pap. (978-0-8020-9584-8(4)) Univ. of Toronto Pr.
Breen, Tom. The Messiah Formerly Known as Jesus: Dispatches from the Intersection of Christianity & Pop Culture. 2008. 227p. pap. 19.95 (978-1-60258-019-0(7)) Baylor Univ. Pr.

Brelsford, Theodore & Rogers, P. Alice, eds. Contextualizing Theological Education. 2008. (Illus.). 196p. pap. 28.00 *(978-0-8298-1784-3(0))* Pilgrim Pr., The/United Church Pr.

Broadman and Holman Publishers Staff & Broadman and Holman. MissionShift: Global Mission Issues in the Third Millennium, 1 vol. Hesselgrave, David & Stetzer, Ed, eds. 2010. (ENG.). 432p. pap. 26.99 *(978-0-8054-4537-4(4),* B&H Academic) B&H Publishing Group.

Brundin, Abigail & Treherne, Matthew. Forms of Faith in Sixteenth-Century Italy. 2009. (Catholic Christendom, 1300-1700 Ser.). (Illus.). 274p. 124.95 *(978-0-7546-6555-7(0))* Ashgate Publishing Co.

Budden, Chris. Following Jesus in Invaded Space. 2011. (ENG.). 256p. pap. 37.50 *(978-0-227-17358-9(9))* Clarke, James Co., Ltd. GBR. Dist: Brown, David Bk. Co., The.

—Following Jesus in Invaded Space: Doing Theology on Aboriginal Land. 2009. (Princeton Theological Monographs). 190p. pap. 22.00 *(978-1-60608-608-7(1),* Pickwick Pubns.) Wipf & Stock Pubs.

Burns. Christian Worship: Postcolonial Perspectives. 2011. (Cross Cultural Theologies Ser.). (ENG.). 188p. (C). pap. 29.95 *(978-1-84553-408-0(5))* Equinox Publishing Ltd. GBR. Dist: ISD.

Burton, Michael C. Deep Roots: The African/Black Contribution to Christianity. 2008. 124p. pap. 10.95 *(978-1-4401-0323-0(2))* iUniverse, Inc.

Buxton, Graham. Celebrating Life: Beyond the Sacred-Secular Divide. 2007. (ENG., Illus.). 220p. pap. 19.99 *(978-1-84227-507-8(0),* Paternoster) Authentic Media.

Campolo, Anthony. Red Letter Christians. 2007. *(978-0-8307-4618-7(8),* Regal Bks.) Gospel Light Pubns.

Campolo, Tony. Red Letter Christians: A Citizen's Guide to Faith & Politics. 2008. (ENG., Illus.). 256p. 19.99 *(978-0-8307-4529-6(7))* Gospel Light Pubns.

Camuti, Paul. Sound the Alarm. 2008. 84p. pap. 11.99 *(978-1-60647-379-5(4))* Xulon Pr., Inc.

Cannell, Fenella, ed. The Anthropology of Christianity. annot. ed. 2006. (ENG., Illus.). 384p. per. 26.95 *(978-0-8223-3646-4(4))* Duke Univ. Pr.

Cannell, Fenella, ed. & contrib. by. The Anthropology of Christianity. 2006. (ENG., Illus.). 384p. 94.95 *(978-0-8223-3608-2(1))* Duke Univ. Pr.

Cao, Nanlai. Constructing China's Jerusalem: Christians, Power, & Place in Contemporary Wenzhou. 2010. (Contemporary Issues in Asia & Pacific Ser.). (ENG., Illus.). 232p. 55.00 *(978-0-8047-7080-4(8))*; pap. 21.95 *(978-0-8047-7360-7(2))* Stanford Univ. Pr.

Capes, David B. & Charles, J. Daryl, eds. Thriving in Babylon: Essays in Honor of A. J. Conyers. 2010. (Princeton Theological Monographs). 426p. pap. 47.00 *(978-1-60608-956-9(0),* Pickwick Pubns.) Wipf & Stock Pubs.

Carpenter, Joel A. Walking Together: Christian Thinking & Public Life in South Africa. 2012. (ENG.). 416p. pap. 28.99 ***(978-0-89112-315-6(6))*** Abilene Christian Univ. Pr.

Carson, D. A. Christ & Culture Revisited. 2008. 240p. 24.00 *(978-0-8028-3174-3(5))* Eerdmans, William B. Publishing Co.

Carter, Craig A. Rethinking Christ & Culture: A Post-Christendom Perspective. 2007. 224p. (C). pap. 22.00 *(978-1-58743-159-3(9))* Brazos Pr.

Case, Jay Riley. An Unpredictable Gospel: American Evangelicals & World Christianity, 1812-1920. 2012. (ENG., Illus.). 328p. 99.00 ***(978-0-19-977232-2(0))***; pap. 24.95 ***(978-0-19-977231-5(2))*** Oxford Univ. Pr., Inc.

Cassidy, Laurie & O'Connell, Maureen H. Religion, Economics, & Culture in Conflict & Conversation: College Theology Society Annual Volume 56 2010. 2011. (Illus.). 256p. pap. 35.00 *(978-1-57075-913-0(8))* Orbis Bks.

Cheon, Byung-Suk. Zur Entwicklung und Begrundung der Koreanischen Indigenisierungstheologie. (Beitrage zur theologischen Urteilsfindung Ser.: Vol. 12). (GER.). 217p. 30.95 *(978-3-631-50182-5(X))* Lang, Peter Publishing, Inc.

Cheong, Pauline Hope. Digital Religion, Social Media & Culture: Perspectives, Practices & Futures. 2012. (Digital Formations Ser.). (Illus.). (C). 340p. pap. 129.95 ***(978-1-4331-1475-5(5))***; 344p. pap. 36.95 ***(978-1-4331-1474-8(7))*** Lang, Peter Publishing, Inc.

Cherry, Mark J., ed. The Death of Metaphysics; the Death of Culture: Epistemology, Metaphysics, & Morality. 2006. (Philosophical Studies in Contemporary Culture Ser.). XXI, 279p. 169.00 *(978-1-4020-4620-9(0),* 1402046200) Springer.

Chin, Catherine M. Grammar & Christianity in the Late Roman World. 2007. (Divinations: Rereading Late Ancient Religion Ser.). 280p. (C). 69.95 *(978-0-8122-4035-1(9))* Univ. of Pennsylvania Pr.

Christianity Today International Staff, creator. Engaging the Culture, 0 vols. 2008. (Christianity Today Study Ser.). 176p. pap. 9.99 *(978-1-4185-3423-3(4))* Nelson, Thomas Inc.

—Faith & Work, 0 vols. 2008. (Christianity Today Study Ser.). 160p. pap. 9.99 *(978-1-4185-3425-7(0))* Nelson, Thomas Inc.

Chua, Liana. The Christianity of Culture: Conversion, Ethnic Citizenship, & the Matter of Religion in Malaysian Borneo. 2011. (Contemporary Anthropology of Religion Ser.). (ENG., Illus.). 274p. 90.00 ***(978-0-230-12046-4(6))*** Palgrave Macmillan.

Chukwu, Donatus Oluwa. The Church As the Extended Family of God. 2011. 214p. 29.99 ***(978-1-4568-0511-1(8))***; pap. 19.99 ***(978-1-4568-0510-4(X))*** Xlibris Corp.

Chung, Paul S. The Cave & the Butterfly: An Intercultural Theory of Interpretation & Religion in the Public Sphere. 2010. 316p. pap. 35.00 *(978-1-60608-530-1(1),* Cascade Bks.) Wipf & Stock Pubs.

Claffey, Patrick. Christian Churches in Dahomey-Benin: A Study of Their Socio-Political Role. 2007. (Studies of Religion in Africa Ser.). (Illus.). 328p. *(978-90-04-15572-5(4))* BRILL.

Clapp, Rodney. Johnny Cash & the Great American Contradiction: Christianity & the Battle for the Soul of a Nation. 2008. (ENG.). 159p. pap. 17.00 *(978-0-664-23088-3(1))* Westminster John Knox Pr.

Clegg, Tom & Bird, Warren. Missing in America: Making an Eternal Difference in the World Next Door. 2007. 195p. per. 14.99 *(978-0-7644-3563-8(9))* Group Publishing, Inc.

Cobb, John B. Spiritual Bankruptcy: A Prophetic Call to Action. 2010. 192p. pap. 19.00 *(978-1-4267-0295-2(7))* Abingdon Pr.

Cobb Jr., John B., ed. Resistance: The New Role of Progressive Christians. 2008. (ENG.). 328p. pap. 20.00 *(978-0-664-23287-0(6))* Westminster John Knox Pr.

Cole, Neil. Church 3. 0: Upgrades for the Future of the Church. 2010. (Jossey-Bass Leadership Network Ser.: 49). (ENG., Illus.). 304p. 24.95 *(978-0-470-52945-4(8),* Jossey-Bass) Wiley, John & Sons, Inc.

Collins, Christopher. Homeland Mythology: Biblical Narratives in American Culture. 2007. (ENG.). 264p. 29.95 *(978-0-271-02993-1(5))* Pennsylvania State Univ. Pr.

Collins, Paul M. Christian Inculturation in India. 2007. (Liturgy, Worship & Society Ser.). (Illus.). 252p. 114.95 *(978-0-7546-6076-7(1))* Ashgate Publishing Co.

Conser, Walter H. & Payne, Rodger M., eds. Southern Crossroads: Perspectives on Religion & Culture. 2008. (Religion in the South Ser.). (ENG., Illus.). 390p. 60.00 *(978-0-8131-2494-0(8))* Univ. Pr. of Kentucky.

Conyers, A. J. The Listening Heart: Vocation & the Crisis of Modern Culture. 2009. (ENG.). 232p. pap. 29.95 *(978-1-60258-183-8(5))* Baylor Univ. Pr.

Cosgrove, Mark P. Foundations of Christian Thought: Faith, Learning, & the Christian Worldview, 1 vol. 2006. (Illus.). 192p. pap. 15.99 *(978-0-8254-2434-2(8))* Kregel Pubns.

Cossa, Jost. African Renaissance & Higher Education: A View Through the Lenses of Christian Higher Education. 2008. 88p. pap. *(978-3-639-08733-8(X))* VDM Verlag Dr. Mueller e.K.

Cowan, Bainard, ed. Gained Horizons: Regensburg & the Enlargement of Reason. 2011. (ENG.). 176p. pap. 17.00 *(978-1-58731-325-7(1))* St. Augustine's Pr., Inc.

Craven, S. Michael. Uncompromised Faith: Overcoming Our Culturalized Christianity. 2009. (Navigators Reference Library). (ENG.). 224p. (YA). pap. 12.99 *(978-1-60006-362-6(4))* NavPress Publishing Group.

Creary, Nicholas M. Domesticating a Religious Import: The Jesuits & the Inculturation of the Catholic Church in Zimbabwe, 1879-1980. 2nd ed. 2011. (ENG., Illus.). 280p. 48.00 *(978-0-8232-3334-2(0))* Fordham Univ. Pr.

Crossan, John Dominic. God & Empire: Jesus Against Rome, Then & Now. 2007. (ENG.). 256p. 22.95 *(978-0-06-084323-6(3),* HarperOne) HarperCollins Pubs.

Crossan, John Dominic & Crossan, John D. God & Empire: Jesus Against Rome, Then & Now. 2008. (ENG.). 272p. pap. 13.99 *(978-0-06-085831-5(1),* HarperOne) HarperCollins Pubs.

Crouch, Andy. Culture Making: Recovering Our Creative Calling. 2008. (ENG.). 288p. 22.00 *(978-0-8308-3394-8(3),* IVP Bks.) InterVarsity Pr.

Cruchley-Jones, Peter, ed. God at Ground Level: Reappraising Church Decline in the UK Through the Experience of Grass Roots Communities & Situations. 2007. 132p. pap. 32.95 *(978-3-631-57494-2(0))* Lang, Peter Publishing, Inc.

Cusveller, Bart, et al. The Matrix Reformed: Science Fiction, Technology, & Christian Philosophy. 2011. 150p. ***(978-0-932914-90-3(X))*** Dordt College Pr.

Danz, Christian & Schüssler, Werner, eds. Paul Tillichs Theologie der Kultur: Aspekte - Probleme - Perspektiven. 2011. (Tillich Research Ser.). (GER & ENG.). X, 506p. 112.00 ***(978-3-11-026236-0(3))*** De Gruyter, Walter Inc.

Dark, David. The Sacredness of Questioning Everything, 1 vol. 2009. (ENG.). 256p. pap. 15.99 *(978-0-310-28618-9(2))* Zondervan.

Dawson, Christopher. The Formation of Christendom. 2008. 320p. (C). pap. 17.95 *(978-1-58617-239-8(5))* Ignatius Pr.

Dean, Jeffrey. The Fight of Your Life: Why Your Teen Is at Risk & What Only You Can Do about It. 2009. (ENG.). 224p. pap. 13.99 *(978-1-60142-110-4(9),* Multnomah) Doubleday Religious Publishing Group, The.

Denton-Borhaug, Kelly. U. S. War-culture, Sacrifice & Salvation. 2011. (Religion & Violence Ser.). (ENG.). 290p. (C). pap. 29.95 *(978-1-84553-711-1(4))* Equinox Publishing Ltd. GBR. Dist: ISD.

—U. S. War-Culture, Sacrifice, & Salvation. 2011. (Religion & Violence Ser.). (ENG.). 290p. (C). 99.95 *(978-1-84553-710-4(6))* Equinox Publishing Ltd. GBR. Dist: ISD.

Dixit, Rajkumar. Branded Faith. 2010. (Illus.). 180p. pap. 21.00 *(978-1-60899-559-2(3),* Wipf and Stock) Wipf & Stock Pubs.

Don Cupitt Staff. Meaning of the West: An Apologia for Secular Christianity. 2011. x, 171p. pap. ***(978-0-334-04202-0(X),*** SCM Pr.) Hymns Ancient & Modern Ltd.

Donaldson, Amy M. We Want to Believe: Faith & Gospel in the X-files. 2011. 256p. pap. 28.00 ***(978-1-60608-361-1(9),*** Cascade Bks.) Wipf & Stock Pubs.

Douglas, Lois McKinney, et al. Encountering Missionary Life & Work: Preparing for Intercultural Ministry. 2008. (Encountering Mission Ser.). (Illus.). 416p. (C). pap. 32.00 *(978-0-8010-2659-1(8))* Baker Academic.

Downey, Deane E. D. & Porter, Stanley E., eds. Christian Worldview & the Academic Disciplines: Crossing the Academy. 2009. (McMaster Divinity College Press General Ser.). 542p. pap. 53.00 *(978-1-60608-529-5(8),* Pickwick Pubns.) Wipf & Stock Pubs.

Dowsett, Rose. Global Mission: Reflections & Case Studies in Contextualization for the Whole Church. 2011. ***(978-0-87808-532-3(7))***; (Illus.). xi, 216p. ***(978-0-87808-619-1(6))*** Carey, William Library Pubs.

Draper, Brian. Searching 4 Faith. 2007. (Questions of Faith Ser.). (Illus.). 156p. pap. 14.95 *(978-1-59856-137-1(5))* Hendrickson Pubs. Marketing, LLC.

Dube, Jimmy G. A Socio-Political Agenda for the Twenty-First Century Zimbabwean Church: Empowering the Excluded. 2006. 220p. *(978-0-7734-5577-1(9))* Mellen, Edwin Pr., The.

Duffy, Regis A. An American Emmaus. 2010. 192p. pap. 21.00 *(978-1-60899-534-9(8),* Wipf and Stock) Wipf & Stock Pubs.

Dunn, Dennis J. The Struggle: Religion & the Rise of Global Civilization. 2010. *(978-1-60497-720-2(5))* Cambria Pr.

Dupre, Louis. Religion & the Rise of Modern Culture. 2008. (Erasmus Institute Bks.). (ENG.). 128p. pap. 25.00 *(978-0-268-02594-6(0))* Univ. of Notre Dame Pr.

Early, John D. Maya & Catholic Cultures in Crisis. 2012. (ENG., Illus.). 416p. 74.95 ***(978-0-8130-4013-4(2))*** Univ. Pr. of Florida.

Early, John D. The Maya & Catholicism: An Encounter of Worldviews, 311 vols. 2006. (ENG., Illus.). 320p. 59.95 *(978-0-8130-3025-8(0))* Univ. Pr. of Florida.

Ebelebe, Charles A. Africa & the New Face of Mission: A Critical Assessment of the Legacy of the Irish Spiritans among the Igbo of Southeastern Nigeria. 2009. (Illus.). xviii, 242p. E-Book *(978-0-7618-4597-3(6))* Univ. Pr. of America, Inc.

Eckhardt, John. Ordinary People Extraordinary Power: Be Activated to Heal, Deliver, Prophesy, Preach, & Demonstrate God's Kingdom. 2010. (ENG.). 224p. pap. 14.99 *(978-1-61638-166-0(3),* Charisma Hse.) Charisma Media.

Edwards, Gene. The Organic Church vs the New Testament Church. 2007. per. 9.95 *(978-0-9778033-1-6(7))* Seedsowers, The.

Ellul, Jacques. The Subversion of Christianity. Bromiley, Geoffrey W., tr. 2011. (Jacques Ellul Legacy Ser.). 216p. pap. 25.00 ***(978-1-60608-974-3(9),*** Wipf and Stock) Wipf & Stock Pubs.

Elwell, J. Sage. Crisis of Transcendence: A Theology of Digital Art & Culture. 2010. (ENG.). 210p. 60.00 *(978-0-7391-4108-3(2))* Lexington Bks.

—Crisis of Transcendence: A Theology of Digital Art & Culture. 2011. E-Book *(978-0-7391-4110-6(4))* Lexington Bks.

Engelke, Matthew & Tomlinson, Matt, eds. The Limits of Meaning: Case Studies in the Anthropology of Christianity. 2007. 252p. 27.95 *(978-1-84545-507-1(X))* Berghahn Bks., Inc.

Englund, Harri, ed. Christianity & Public Culture in Africa. 2011. (Cambridge Centre of African Studies). (ENG.). 240p. 49.95 *(978-0-8214-1945-8(5))* Ohio Univ. Pr.

Espin, Orlando O. Grace & Humanness: Theological Reflections Because of Culture. 2007. 145p. per. 26.00 *(978-1-57075-730-3(5))* Orbis Bks.

Estes, Douglas C. Simchurch: Being the Church in the Virtual World, 1 vol. 2009. (ENG.). 256p. pap. 16.99 *(978-0-310-28784-1(7))* Zondervan.

Eze, Damian Onwuegbuchulam. The Eucharist as Orikonso: A Study in Eucharistic Ecclesiology from an Igbo Perspective. 2008. (Europäische Hochschulschriften. Reihe 23: Theologie Ser.). 312p. pap. 74.95 *(978-3-631-57883-4(0))* Lang, Peter GmbH, Europaischer Verlag der Wissenschaften DEU. Dist: Lang, Peter.

Ezeh, Everest. Christian Culture. 2011. 384p. pap. 20.99 ***(978-1-61215-546-3(4))*** Xulon Pr., Inc.

Ferguson, Dave, et al. The Big Idea: Focus the Message — Multiply the Impact, 1 vol. 2007. (Leadership Network Innovation Ser.). (ENG., Illus.). 208p. pap. 18.99 *(978-0-310-27241-0(6))* Zondervan.

Fessenden, Tracy. Culture & Redemption: Religion, the Secular, & American Literature. 2006. (ENG., Illus.). 352p. (C). 42.00 *(978-0-691-04963-2(7))* Princeton Univ. Pr.

Fisher, Linford D. The Indian Great Awakening: Religion & the Shaping of Native Cultures in Early America, 1 vol. 2012. (ENG., Illus.). 312p. 34.95 ***(978-0-19-974004-8(6))*** Oxford Univ. Pr., Inc.

Flanders, Christopher L. About Face: Rethinking Face for 21st Century Mission. 2011. (American Society of Missiology Monograph Ser.). 322p. pap. 35.00 *(978-1-60899-523-3(2),* Pickwick Pubns.) Wipf & Stock Pubs.

Friedli, Richard. Intercultural Perceptions & Prospects of World Christianity. 2010. (FRE, GER & ENG.). 140p. *(978-3-631-61462-4(4))* Lang, Peter Publishing, Inc.

Friedman, Terry. The Eighteenth-Century Church in Britian. 2011. (Paul Mellon Centre for Studies in Britis Ser.). (ENG., Illus.). 800p. 100.00 *(978-0-300-15908-0(0))* Yale Univ. Pr.

Frost, Michael. Exiles: Living Missionally in a Post-Christian Culture. 2006. (Illus.). 333p. per. 19.95 *(978-1-56563-670-5(8))* Hendrickson Pubs. Marketing, LLC.

Fulton, Robert. Legacy: The Belief in Immortality & the Logic of Culture. 2011. *(978-1-58982-812-4(7))* American Bk. Publishing Group.

Gallagher, Sharon, ed. Where Faith Meets Culture. 2009. 240p. pap. 24.00 *(978-1-60899-144-0(X),* Cascade Bks.) Wipf & Stock Pubs.

Garces-Foley, Kathleen. Crossing the Ethnic Divide: The Multiethnic Church on a Mission, 1 vol. 2011. (Aar Academy Ser.). 194p. pap. 24.95 *(978-0-19-979680-9(7))* Oxford Univ. Pr., Inc.

Geering, Lloyd. Coming Back to Earth: From Gods, to God, to Gaia. 2009. xv, 221p. *(978-1-59815-016-2(2))* Polebridge Pr.

Giago, Tim. Children Left Behind: The Dark Legacy of Indian Mission Boarding Schools. 2006. (Illus.). 166p. per. *(978-1-57416-086-4(9))* Clear Light Pubs.

Gibson, Dan, et al, compiled by. Besides the Bible: 100 Books that Have, Should, or Will Create Christian Culture. 2010. (ENG.). 270p. pap. 14.99 *(978-1-60657-091-3(9),* Authentic Bibles) Authentic Media.

Gilley, Gary. This Little Church Had None: A Church in Search of the Truth. 2009. 272p. pap. *(978-0-85234-708-9(1))* Evangelical Pr.

Gitari, David, ed. Anglican Liturgical Inculturation in Africa. 2009. 88.00 *(978-1-60724-380-9(6))* Gorgias Pr., LLC.

Goodwin. World Christianity in Local Context Vol. 1: Essays in Memory of David A. Kerr, 1 vol. Goodwin, Stephen R., ed. 2009. (ENG., Illus.). 262p. 130.00 *(978-1-84706-510-0(4))* Continuum International Publishing Group, Ltd. GBR. Dist: National Bk. Network.

Gort, Jerald D., et al, eds. Crossroad Discourses between Christianity & Culture. 2010. (Illus.). 652p. 189.00 *(978-90-420-2863-0(7))* Rodopi.

Gort, Jerald D., et al. Crossroad Discourses Between Christianity & Culture. 2010. 652p. pap. 87.00 *(978-90-420-2865-4(3))* Rodopi.

Grabner-Haider, Anton & Maier, Johann. Kulturgeschichte des frühen Christentums: Von 100 bis 500 n.Chr. 2008. (GER.). 232p. (C). 54.00 *(978-3-525-54003-9(5))* Vandenhoeck & Ruprecht GmbH & Co. KG DEU. Dist: ISD.

Graf, Friedrich Wilhelm, et al, eds. Rezensionen und Kritiken. 2007. (GER.). XX, 928p. 335.00 *(978-3-11-019304-6(3))* De Gruyter, Walter Inc.

Graves, Joshua. The Feast: How to Serve Jesus in a Famished World. 2009. 208p. 14.99 *(978-0-89112-639-3(2),* Leafwood Pubs.) Abilene Christian Univ. Pr.

Grier, Derek. Out of Africa: I Thought Christianity Was a White Man's Religion until I Met Christ. (Orig.). pap. 7.95 *(978-0-9632116-9-9(2))* Ham Publishing Co.

Griffith, Sidney H. The Church in the Shadow of the Mosque: Christians & Muslims in the World of Islam. (Jews, Christians, & Muslims from the Ancient to the Modern World Ser.). (ENG., Illus.). 248p. (C). 2010. pap. 25.95 *(978-0-691-14628-7(4))* 2007. 45.00 *(978-0-691-13015-6(9))* Princeton Univ. Pr.

Halik, Tomas. Night of the Confessor: Christian Faith in an Age of Uncertainty. 2012. (ENG.). 240p. pap. 13.00 ***(978-0-385-52452-0(8),*** Image) Doubleday Religious Publishing Group, The.

Hall, David W. & Padgett, Marvin. Calvin & Culture: Exploring a Worldview. 2010. pap. *(978-1-59638-098-1(5))* P & R Publishing.

Halverson, James L. Contesting Christendom: Readings in Medieval Religion & Culture. 2007. (ENG.). 254p. 85.00 *(978-0-7425-5471-9(6))*; per. 29.95 *(978-0-7425-5472-6(4))* Rowman & Littlefield Publishers, Inc.

Hamilton, Adam. Seeing Gray: Where Faith & Politics Meet Participant Study Guide. 2009. 109p. 12.00 *(978-1-4267-0754-4(1))* Abingdon Pr.

—Seeing Gray in a World of Black & White: Thoughts on Religion, Morality, & Politics. 2008. 242p. pap. 22.95 *(978-0-687-64969-3(2))* Abingdon Pr.

Hand, Brian R. Upright Downtime: Biblical Wisdom for Entertainment Choices. 2008. *(978-1-59166-856-5(5))* BJU Pr.

Haney, T. Ronald. M u s i n g S: Essays on Faith versus Culture. 2009. 240p. 29.99 *(978-1-4415-9909-4(6))*; pap. 19.99 *(978-1-4415-9908-7(8))* Xlibris Corp.

Hansen, Collin, et al. Where Faith & Culture Meet Participant's Guide, 1 vol. 2007. (Intersect / Culture Ser.). (ENG.). 96p. (gr. 13). pap. 9.99 *(978-0-310-28096-5(6))* Zondervan.

Harrington, Todd. Resonating the Gospel Within a Post Christian Culture. 2008. 132p. pap. *(978-3-639-01382-5(4))* VDM Verlag Dr. Mueller e.K.

Harris, Antipas. For Such A Time as This: Re-imaging practical theology for independent pentecostal Churches. 2010. (ENG.). 188p. pap. 35.00 *(978-1-60947-000-5(1))* Emeth Pr.

Harvey, Paul. Moses, Jesus, & the Trickster in the Evangelical South. 2012. (Mercer University Lamar Memorial Lectures). (ENG.). 200p. 28.95 ***(978-0-8203-3411-0(1))*** Univ. of Georgia Pr.

Healy, Nicholas J. & Schindler, D. C. Being Holy in the World: Theology & Culture in the Thought of David L. Schindler. 2011. pap. 34.00 *(978-0-8028-6554-0(2))* Eerdmans, William B. Publishing Co.

Heard, A. B. Your Best Life Later. 2007. 196p. per. 13.99 *(978-1-60266-674-0(1))* Xulon Pr., Inc.

Hederman, Mark Patrick. Dancing with Dinosaurs: A Spirituality for the 21st Century. 2011. (ENG.). 100p. pap. 17.95 ***(978-1-85607-735-4(7))*** Columba Pr. IRL. Dist: Dufour Editions, Inc.

Hegeman, David Bruce. Plowing in Hope: Toward a Biblical Theology of Culture. 2nd ed. 2007. (ENG.). pap. 12.00 *(978-1-59128-049-1(4))* Canon Pr.

Heie, Harold & King, Michael A., eds. Mutual Treasure: Seeking Better Ways for Christians & Culture to Converse. 2009. 208p. pap. 19.95 *(978-1-931038-57-7(0))* Cascadia Publishing Hse., LLC.

Heneis, Julia. Inkulturation und ihre Relevanz für die Sozialarbeit mit AfrikanerInnen in Wien: Am Beispiel der afrikanischen katholischen Gemeinde. 2010. (Europäische Hochschulschriften. Reihe 22: Soziologie Ser.). (GER.). 120p. pap. 21.95 *(978-3-631-59961-7(7))* Lang, Peter GmbH, Europaischer Verlag der Wissenschaften DEU. Dist: Lang, Peter.

Heyndrikx, Marcel. Towards Another Future: On the Christian Faith & Its Shape Between Yesterday & Tomorrow. 2006. (Louvain Theological & Pastoral Monographs: Vol. 34). (ENG.). x, 358p. (C). pap. 42.00 *(978-90-429-1774-3(1))* Peeters Pubs. & Booksellers BEL. Dist: Brown, David Bk. Co., The.

Hill, Robert W. The Color of Sabbath: Proclamations & Prayers for New Beginnings. 2007. pap. *(978-1-932717-13-6(7))* Hope Publishing Hse.

Hillman, Os. Change Agent. 2011. E-Book ***(978-1-61638-567-5(7),*** Charisma Hse.) Charisma Media.

Hipps, Shane. Flickeringpixels: How Technology Shapes Your Faith. 2009. (ENG.). 208p. 16.99 *(978-0-310-29321-7(9))* Zondervan.

Hoch, Ronald E. & Smith, David P. Old School, New Clothes: The Cultural Blindness of Christian Education. 2011. 166p. pap. 19.00 ***(978-1-61097-161-4(2),*** Wipf and Stock) Wipf & Stock Pubs.

Hoke, Steve & Taylor, Bill. Global Mission Handbook: A Guide for Crosscultural Service. 2009. (ENG.). 303p. pap. 20.00 *(978-0-8308-3717-5(5)*, IVP Bks.) InterVarsity Pr.
Holeton, David, ed. Liturgical Inculturation in the Anglican Communion. 2009. 88.00 *(978-1-60724-369-4(5))* Gorgias Pr., LLC.
Hopper, David H. Divine Transcendence & the Culture of Change. 2010. 272p. pap. 35.00 *(978-0-8028-6505-2(4))* Eerdmans, William B. Publishing Co.
Houle, Robert. Making African Christianity: Africans Reimagining Their Faith in Colonial South Africa. 2011. (ENG.). 332p. 80.00 *(978-1-61146-081-0(6))* Lehigh Univ. Pr.
Howell, Brian M. Christianity in the Local Context: Southern Baptists in the Philippines. 2008. (Contemporary Anthropology of Religion Ser.). (ENG., Illus.). 272p. 95.00 *(978-0-230-60661-6(X))* Palgrave Macmillan.
Howell, Brian M. & Zehner, Edwin. Power & Identity in the Global Church: Six Contemporary Cases. 2009. *(978-0-87808-513-2(0))* Carey, William Library Pubs.
Hughes, Dewi Arwel. Ethnic Identity from the Margins: A Christian Perspective. 2011. *(978-0-87808-459-3(2))* Carey, William Library Pubs.
Hughes, Gerard J. Fidelity without Fundamentalism: A Dialogue with Tradition. 2010. (Illus.). 176p. pap. 15.95 *(978-0-8091-4724-3(6))* Paulist Pr.
Hunt, John & Penwell, Dan, eds. AMG's Handi-Reference World Religions & Cults. 2008. (AMG Handi-Reference Ser.). (ENG.). 800p. pap. 9.99 *(978-0-89957-113-3(1))* AMG Pubs.
Hunt, Robert A. The Gospel among the Nations: A Documentary History of Inculturation ASM #46. 2010. 400p. pap. 35.00 *(978-1-57075-874-4(3))* Orbis Bks.
Ilo, Stan Chu, et al, eds. The Church as Salt & Light: Path to an African Ecclesiology of Abundant Life. 2011. (African Christian Studies). 192p. pap. 22.00 ***(978-1-61097-100-3(0)***, Pickwick Pubns.) Wipf & Stock Pubs.
—The Church in Africa as Salt & Light: Path to an African Ecclesiology of Abundant Life. 2012. (ENG.). 192p. (C). pap. 35.00 ***(978-0-227-68008-7(1))*** Clarke, James Co., Ltd. GBR. Dist: Brown, David Bk. Co., The.
Irarrázaval, Diego. Inculturation: New Dawn of the Church in Latin America. Berryman, Phillip, tr. 2008.Tr. of Inculturacion: Amanecer Eclesial en America Latina. 146p. pap. 18.00 *(978-1-55635-831-9(8))* Wipf & Stock Pubs.
Isaac, Gordon L. Left Behind or Left Befuddled: The Subtle Dangers of Popularizing the End Times. 2008. pap. 16.95 *(978-0-8146-2420-3(0))* Liturgical Pr.
Jacobsen, Knut A. & Raj, Selva J. South Asian Christian Diaspora: Invisible Diaspora in Europe & North America. Jacobsen, Knut A. & Raj, Selva J., eds. 2008. (Illus.). 284p. 114.95 *(978-0-7546-6261-7(6))* Ashgate Publishing Co.
Jagessar, Michael N. & Burns, Stephen. Christian Worship: Postcolonial Perspectives. 2011. (Cross Cultural Theologies Ser.). (ENG.). 188p. (C). 99.95 *(978-1-84553-407-3(7))* Equinox Publishing Ltd. GBR. Dist: ISD.
Jahn, Curtis A., ed. Here We Stand: A Confessional Christian Study of Worldviews. 2010. 360p. pap. *(978-0-8100-2229-4(X))* Northwestern Publishing Hse.
Jenkins, Philip. The New Faces of Christianity: Believing the Bible in the Global South. 272p. 2008. (ENG.). pap. 15.95 *(978-0-19-536851-2(7))* 2006. 26.00 *(978-0-19-530065-9(3))* Oxford Univ. Pr., Inc.
Jennings, Brian K. Leading Virtue: A Model for the Contextualisation of Christian Ethics. 2009. (IC - Studien zur interkulturellen Geschichte des Christentums. Etudes d'histoire interculturelle de christianisme. Studies in the Intercultural History of Christianity Ser.). 154p. 47.95 *(978-3-631-59300-4(7))* Lang, Peter GmbH, Europaischer Verlag der Wissenschaften DEU. Dist: Lang, Peter.
Jeremiah, David. I Never Thought I'd See the Day! Culture at the Crossroads. 2011. 44.99 ***(978-1-61113-275-5(4)***, Sound Library) AudioGO.
—I Never Thought I'd See the Day! Culture at the Crossroads. 2012. (ENG.). 352p. pap. 14.99 ***(978-0-446-56596-7(2))*** 2012. (SPA.). 352p. pap. 12.99 *(978-1-4555-0431-2(9))* 2011. (ENG.). 352p. 24.99 *(978-0-446-56595-0(4))* 2011. (ENG.). 480p. 26.99 *(978-1-4555-0734-4(2))* FaithWords.
Jethani, Skye. The Divine Commodity: Discovering a Faith Beyond Consumer Christianity, 1 vol. 2009. (ENG.). 192p. 18.99 *(978-0-310-28375-1(2))* Zondervan.
Jewett, Robert, et al, eds. The Bible & the American Future. 2009. 306p. pap. 34.00 *(978-1-60608-993-4(5)*, Cascade Bks.) Wipf & Stock Pubs.
Jeynes, William & Martinez, Enedina. Christianity, Education, & Modern Society. 2007. *(978-1-59311-737-5(X))*; (ENG.). 312p. (C). per. *(978-1-59311-736-8(1))* Information Age Publishing, Inc.
John Holdsworth Staff. Lies, Sex & Politicians: Communicating the Old Testament in Contemporary Culture. 2011. 178p. pap. ***(978-0-334-04340-9(9)***, SCM Pr.) Hymns Ancient & Modern Ltd.
John P., Bequette. Christian Humanism: Creation. 2007. (ENG.). 198p. pap. 36.99 *(978-0-7618-3852-4(X))* Univ. Pr. of America, Inc.
Jorgensen, Jonas Adelin. Jesus Imandars & Christ Bhaktas: Two Case Studies of Interreligious Hermeneutics & Identity in Global Christianity. 2008. xii, 481p. pap. 107.95 *(978-3-631-58486-6(5))* Lang, Peter GmbH, Europaischer Verlag der Wissenschaften DEU. Dist: Lang, Peter.
Judge, E. A. Jerusalem & Athens: Cultural Transformation in Late Antiquity. Nobbs, Alanna, ed. 2010. (Illus.). 364p. 197.50 *(978-3-16-150572-0(7))* Mohr Siebeck GmbH & Co. KG DEU. Dist: Coronet Bks.
Kabus, Wolfgang, ed. Popularmusik und Kirche: Geistreiche Klänge - Sinnliche Orte. 2008. (Friedensauer Schriftenreihe. C: Musik - Kirche - Kultur Ser.). 180p. pap. 56.95 *(978-3-631-57721-9(4))* Lang, Peter GmbH, Europaischer Verlag der Wissenschaften DEU. Dist: Lang, Peter.
Kadaliyil, Abraham. Toward a Relational Spirit Ecclesiology in Asi. 2009. 224p. pap. *(978-3-639-13498-8(2))* VDM Verlag Dr. Mueller e.K.
Kallenberg, Brad J. God & Gadgets: Following Jesus in a Technological Age. 2010. 188p. pap. 22.00 *(978-1-60899-399-4(X)*, Cascade Bks.) Wipf & Stock Pubs.
Kauffman, J. Timothy. Reconnecting the Church. 2010. 234p. pap. 19.99 *(978-1-4500-8718-6(3))* Xlibris Corp.
Kennedy, Thomas Frank. Inculturation & the Church in North America. Kennedy, T. Frank, ed. 2007. (Boston College Church in the 21st Century Ser.). (ENG., Illus.). 256p. pap. 24.95 *(978-0-8245-2438-8(1)*, Herder & Herder) Crossroad Publishing Co., The.
Kettle, David J. Western Culture in Gospel Context: Towards the Conversion of the West: Theological Bearings for Mission & Spirituality. 2011. 396p. pap. 44.00 ***(978-1-61097-184-3(1)***, Cascade Bks.) Wipf & Stock Pubs.
Kierkegaard, Soren. The Moment & Late Writings. 2009. (Kierkegaard's Writings: Vol. 23). (ENG., Illus.). 712p. (C). pap. 60.00 *(978-0-691-14081-0(2))* Princeton Univ. Pr.
Kim, Eunjoo Mary. Preaching in an Age of Globalization. 2010. (ENG.). 176p. pap. 25.00 *(978-0-664-23369-3(4))* Westminster John Knox Pr.
Kim, Paul Mantae. The Puberty Ritual in Sri Lanka: A Comparative Exploration of Perceptions & Attitudes between Buddhists & Christians. 2011. (Illus.). xiv, 241p. (C). 79.95 ***(978-1-4331-1462-5(3))*** Lang, Peter Publishing, Inc.
King, Alveda C. Who We Are in Christ Jesus: Formerly God's Plan for the Black Man. 2008. 228p. pap. 19.99 *(978-1-4363-0599-0(3))* Xlibris Corp.
Kirk, J. Andrew. The Future of Reason, Science & Faith: Following Modernity & Postmodernity. 2007. (Transcending Boundaries in Philosophy & Theology Ser.). 266p. 114.95 *(978-0-7546-5882-5(1))* Ashgate Publishing Co.
Knight, Frances. Church in the Nineteenth Century. 2008. (I. B. Tauris History of the Christian Church Ser.). (ENG.). 256p. 42.00 *(978-1-85043-899-1(4))* I. B. Tauris & Co., Ltd. GBR. Dist: Macmillan.

Koch, Andrew M. & Gates, Paul Henry. Medieval America: Cultural Influences of Christianity in the Law & Public Policy. 2012. ***(978-0-7391-7283-4(2))*** Lexington Bks.
Krabill, James R. & Murray, Stuart. Forming Christian Habits in Post-Christendom: The Legacy of Alan & Eleanor Kreider. 2011. pap. ***(978-0-8361-9602-3(3))*** Herald Pr.
Kraft, Charles H. Worldview for Christian Witness. 2007. *(978-0-87808-520-0(3))* Carey, William Library Pubs.
Kuehne, Dale S. Sex & the iWorld: Rethinking Relationship Beyond an Age of Individualism. 2009. 160p. (C). pap. 19.99 *(978-0-8010-3587-6(2))* Baker Academic.
Lara, Jaime. Christian Texts for Aztecs: Art & Liturgy in Colonial Mexico. 2008. (ENG., Illus.). 336p. 75.00 *(978-0-268-03379-8(X))* Univ. of Notre Dame Pr.
Larkin, Brian. The Very Nature of God: Baroque Catholicism & Religious Reform in Bourbon Mexico City. 2010. (ENG., Illus.). 326p. (C). pap. 27.95 *(978-0-8263-4834-0(3))* Univ. of New Mexico Pr.
Leithart, Peter J. & Barach, John, eds. The Glory of Kings: A Festschrift for James B. Jordan. 2011. 366p. pap. 40.00 ***(978-1-60899-680-3(8)***, Pickwick Pubns.) Wipf & Stock Pubs.
Levieils, Xavier. Contra Christianos: La Critique Sociale et Religieuse du Christianisme des Origenes Au Concile de Nicee (45-325) 2007. (Beihefte Zur Zeitschrift Für Die Neutestamentliche Wissenschaft und Die Kunde der älteren Kirche Ser.). (FRE.). XIII, 548p. 196.00 *(978-3-11-019554-5(2))* De Gruyter, Walter Inc.
Levy, Ian, et al, eds. A Companion to the Eucharist in the Middle Ages. 2011. (Brill's Companions to the Christian Tradition Ser.). (Illus.). xvii, 640p. ***(978-90-04-20141-5(6))*** BRILL.
Linn, Dennis, et al. Healing the Future: Personal Recovery from Societal Wounding. 2012. ***(978-1-61643-144-0(X))***; 224p. pap. 19.95 ***(978-0-8091-4775-5(0))*** Paulist Pr.
Long, D. Stephen. Theology & Culture: A Guide to the Discussion. 2007. (Cascade Companions: Ser.). 124p. pap. 17.00 *(978-1-55635-052-8(X))* Wipf & Stock Pubs.
Long, Stephen D. Theology & Culture: A Guide to the Discussion. 2010. (ENG.). 124p. pap. 38.00 *(978-0-227-17325-1(2))* Clarke, James Co., Ltd. GBR. Dist: Brown, David Bk. Co., The.
Luhr, Eileen & Luhr, E. Witnessing Suburbia: Conservatives & Christian Youth Culture. 2009. (ENG., Illus.). 280p. 50.00 *(978-0-520-25594-4(1))*; pap. 21.95 *(978-0-520-25596-8(8))* Univ. of California Pr.
MacArthur, John. Right Thinking in a World Gone Wrong: A Biblical Response to Today's Most Controversial Issues. 2009. 272p. pap. 14.99 *(978-0-7369-2643-0(7))* Harvest Hse. Pubs.
Mack, Burton L. Christian Mentality: The Entanglements of Power, Violence & Fear. 2011. (Religion in culture: studies in social contest & Construction Ser.). (ENG.). 198p. (C). 99.95 *(978-1-84553-894-1(3))* Equinox Publishing Ltd. GBR. Dist: ISD.
—Christian Mentality: The Entanglements of Power, Violence, & Fear. 2011. (Religion in culture: studies in social contest & Construction Ser.). (ENG.). 198p. (C). pap. 29.95 *(978-1-84553-895-8(1))* Equinox Publishing Ltd. GBR. Dist: ISD.
Maffly-Kipp, Laurie F., et al, eds. Practicing Protestants: Histories of Christian Life in America, 1630-1965. 2006. (Lived Religions Ser.). (ENG., Illus.). 376p. (C). (gr. 13-17). pap. 28.00 *(978-0-8018-8362-0(8))* Johns Hopkins Univ. Pr.
—Practicing Protestants Vol. 3: Histories of Christian Life in America, 1630-1965. 2006. (Lived Religions Ser.). (ENG., Illus.). 376p. (C). (gr. 13-17). 62.00 *(978-0-8018-8361-3(X))* Johns Hopkins Univ. Pr.
Mangalwadi, Vishal. Truth & Transformation. 2009. 256p. pap. 17.99 *(978-1-57658-512-2(3))* YWAM Publishing.
Mann, Janice. Romanesque Architecture & Its Sculptural Decoration in Christian Spain, 1000-1120: Exploring Frontiers & Defining Identities. 2009. (ENG., Illus.). 300p. *(978-0-8020-9324-0(8))* Univ. of Toronto Pr.
Marks, John. Reasons to Believe: One Man's Journey among the Evangelicals & the Faith He Left Behind. 2009. 400p. pap. 15.99 *(978-0-06-083277-3(0)*, HarperPerennial) HarperCollins Pubs.
Marti, Gerardo. Hollywood Faith: Holiness, Prosperity, & Ambition in a Los Angeles Church. 2008. (ENG.). 288p. (C). pap. 25.95 *(978-0-8135-4349-9(5))* Rutgers Univ. Pr.
—A Mosaic of Believers: Diversity & Innovation in a Multiethnic Church. 2009. (ENG.). 264p. pap. 22.95 *(978-0-253-20343-4(0)*, 0253203430) Indiana Univ. Pr.
Martin, Joel & Nicholas, Mark A., eds. Native Americans, Christianity, & the Reshaping of the American Religious Landscape. 2010. (ENG., Illus.). 336p. 75.00 *(978-0-8078-3406-0(8))* Univ. of North Carolina Pr.
Martin, Joel W. & Nicholas, Mark A., eds. Native Americans, Christianity, & the Reshaping of the American Religious Landscape. 2010. (ENG., Illus.). 336p. pap. 27.95 *(978-0-8078-7145-4(1))* Univ. of North Carolina Pr.
Martin, Kathleen J. Indigenous Symbols & Practices in the Catholic Church: Visual Culture Missionization & Appropriation. 2010. (Vitality of Indigenous Religions Ser.). (Illus.). 300p. 99.95 *(978-0-7546-6631-8(X))* Ashgate Publishing Co.
Matheny, Paul Duane. Contextual Theology. 2012. (ENG.). 146p. (C). pap. 30.00 ***(978-0-227-68012-4(X))*** Clarke, James Co., Ltd. GBR. Dist: Brown, David Bk. Co., The.
—Contextual Theology: The Drama of Our Times. 2011. 146p. pap. 18.00 ***(978-1-60899-967-5(X)***, Pickwick Pubns.) Wipf & Stock Pubs.
Maxwell, Chris & Standard Publishing Staff. Season One: Episodes 40-52. Cain, Kristi & Derico, Laura, eds. ldr.'s ed. 2008. (Faith Cafe Ser.). (ENG., Illus.). 64p. pap. 14.99 *(978-0-7847-2207-7(2))* Standard Publishing.
—Season One: Episodes 40-52 - Participant's Guide. Cain, Kristi & Derico, Laura, eds. 2008. (Faith Cafe Ser.). (ENG., Illus.). 32p. pap. 3.99 *(978-0-7847-2208-4(0))* Standard Publishing.
McBrayer, Ronnie. The Jesus Tribe: Following Christ in the Land of the Empire. 2011. ***(978-1-57312-592-5(X))*** Smyth & Helwys Publishing, Inc.
McCullough, Kevin. Musclehead Revolution: Overturning Liberalism with Commonsense Thinking. 2006. 201p. 19.99 *(978-0-7369-1730-8(6))* Harvest Hse. Pubs.
McDonald, Daniel, ed. Catholic Social Teaching in Global Perspective. 2010. 240p. pap. 26.00 *(978-1-57075-896-6(4))* Orbis Bks.
McDonald, Lee Martin, et al. From Biblical Criticism to Biblical Faith: Essays in Honor of Lee Martin Mcdonald. 2007. 450p. 45.00 *(978-0-88146-052-0(4))* Mercer Univ. Pr.
McEachern, Claire & Shuger, Debora, eds. Religion & Culture in Renaissance England. 2006. (ENG.). 308p. pap. 61.00 *(978-0-521-03488-3(4))* Cambridge Univ. Pr.
McElvaine, Robert S. Grand Theft Jesus: The Hijacking of Religion in America. 2009. (ENG.). 336p. pap. 13.95 *(978-0-307-39580-1(4)* Three Rivers Pr.) Crown Publishing Group.
McGough, Michael. A Field Guide to the Culture Wars: The Battle over Values from the Campaign Trail to the Classroom, 1 vol. 2008. (Religion, Politics, & Public Life under the auspices of the Leonard E. Greenberg Center for the Study of Religion in Public Life, Trinity College, Hartford CT Ser.). 164p. 34.95 *(978-0-313-35107-5(4)*, C35107, Praeger Pubs.) Greenwood Publishing Group, Inc.
McKenzie, John L. The Civilization of Christianity. 2009. (John L. Mckenzie Reprints Ser.). 264p. pap. 29.00 *(978-1-60608-043-6(1))* Wipf & Stock Pubs.

McLynn, Neil. Christian politics & religious culture in late Antiquity. 2009. (Variorum Collected Studies). (Illus.). 334p. 154.95 *(978-0-7546-5992-1(5))* Ashgate Publishing Co.
McNeil, Lou F. Recovering American Catholic Inculturation: John England's Jacksonian Populism & Romanticist Adaptation. 2008. (ENG.). 270p. 68.50 *(978-0-7391-2453-6(6))* Lexington Bks.
Merchant, Dan. Lord, Save Us from Your Followers: Why Is the Gospel of Love Dividing America?, 0 vols. 2008. (Illus.). 240p. 19.99 *(978-0-8499-1993-0(2))* Nelson, Thomas Inc.
Miles, Margaret R. Bodies in Society: Essays on Christianity in Contemporary Culture. 2008. 242p. pap. 27.00 *(978-1-55635-421-2(5))* Wipf & Stock Pubs.
Miller, Donald Eugene, et al, eds. Overcoming Violence in Asia: The Role of the Church in Seeking Cultures of Peace. 2011. 294p. pap. 23.95 *(978-1-931038-89-8(9))* Cascadia Publishing Hse., LLC.
Milton, Michael A. Cooperation Without Compromise: Faithful Gospel Witness in a Pluralistic Setting. 2007. 20p. pap. 3.50 *(978-1-55635-390-1(1)*, Wipf and Stock) Wipf & Stock Pubs.
Minor, Robert N. When Religion Is an Addiction. 2007. 168p. per. 14.95 *(978-0-9709581-2-9(9))* HumanityWorks!
Mohler, R. Albert. Culture Shift. 2009. 192p. pap. 0.82 *(978-1-60142-251-4(2)*, Multnomah) Doubleday Religious Publishing Group, The.
—Culture Shift: The Battle for the Moral Heart of America. 2011. (ENG.). 208p. pap. 12.99 *(978-1-60142-381-8(0)*, Multnomah) Doubleday Religious Publishing Group, The.
Moon, W. Jay. African Proverbs Reveal Christianity in Culture: A Narrative Portrayal of Builsa Proverbs Contextualizing Christianity in Ghana. 2009. (American Society of Missiology Monograph Ser.). 234p. pap. 26.00 *(978-1-60608-553-0(0)*, Pickwick Pubns.) Wipf & Stock Pubs.
Moore, Wes. Forcefully Advancing: The Last Hope for America & American Christianity. 2010. pap. 21.99 *(978-1-61566-730-7(X))* Tate Publishing & Enterprises, LLC.
Moschella, Mary Clark. Ethnography As a Pastoral Practice: An Introduction. 2008. *(978-0-8298-1774-4(3))* Pilgrim Pr., The/United Church Pr.
Moxnes, Halvor. Jesus Beyond Nationalism: Constructing the Historical Jesus in a Period of Cultural Complexity. Blanton, Ward & Crossley, James G., eds. 2009. (Bible World Ser.). (ENG.). 188p. (C). 99.95 *(978-1-84553-410-3(7))* Equinox Publishing Ltd. GBR. Dist: ISD.
Moxnes, Halvor, et al, eds. Jesus Beyond Nationalism: Constructing the Historical Jesus in a Period of Cultural Complexity. 2009. (Bible World Ser.). (ENG.). 188p. (C). pap. 35.00 *(978-1-84553-411-0(5))* Equinox Publishing Ltd. GBR. Dist: ISD.
Muchimba, Felix. Liberating the African Soul: Comparing African & Western Christian Music & Worship Styles. 2008. (ENG.). 156p. per. 14.99 *(978-1-934068-42-7(X))* Authentic Media.
Muehlhoff, Tim & Lewis, Todd V. Authentic Communication: Christian Speech Engaging Culture, 1 vol. 2010. (Christian Worldview Integration Ser.). (ENG.). 219p. pap. 18.00 *(978-0-8308-2815-9(X)*, IVP Acad.) InterVarsity Pr.
Neckebrouck, V. Entre le global et le Local: Inculturation et changement Social. 2007. (Annua Nuntia Lovaniensia Ser.). (ENG.). 198p. (C). pap. 65.00 *(978-90-429-1960-0(4))* Peeters Pubs & Booksellers BEL. Dist: Brown, David Bk. Co., The.
Neusner, Jacob, et al. Judaic & Christian Visions of the Social Order: Describing, Analyzing & Comparing Systems of the Formative Age. 2011. (Jacob Neusner Series: Religion/Social Order Ser.). (ENG.). 388p. pap. 38.95 ***(978-0-7618-5635-1(8))*** Univ. Pr. of America, Inc.
Nichols, Stephen J. Jesus Made in America: A Cultural History from the Puritans to the Passion of the Christ. 2008. (ENG.). 237p. pap. 20.00 *(978-0-8308-2849-4(4)*, IVP Acad.) InterVarsity Pr.
Nkansah-Obrempong, James. Visual Theology. 2010. 296p. pap. *(978-3-639-23087-1(6))* VDM Verlag Dr. Mueller e.K.
Noble, Ivana. Theological Interpretation of Culture in Post-Communist Context: Central & East European Search for Roots. 2010. 242p. 99.95 *(978-1-4094-0007-3(7))* Ashgate Publishing Co.
Nolan, Albert. Hope in an Age of Despair. Muyebe, Stan, ed. 2009. 192p. pap. 18.00 *(978-1-57075-835-5(2))* Orbis Bks.
Nwankpa, Ph. D. Understanding Cultural Perspectives, God's Word, & Missions: A Powerful Tool for Theologizing. 2009. 296p. pap. 15.49 *(978-1-4389-4924-6(3))* AuthorHouse.
Okorie, George Maduakolam. The Integral Salvation of the Human Person in Ecclesia in Africa: A case study of the theological implications among the Igbo in Nigeria. 2008. (Europäische Hochschulschriften. Reihe 23: Theologie Ser.). 482p. pap. 107.95 *(978-3-631-57647-2(1))* Lang, Peter GmbH, Europaischer Verlag der Wissenschaften DEU. Dist: Lang, Peter.
Oliphint, K. Scott & Mays, Rod. Things That Cannot Be Shaken: Holding Fast to Your Faith in a Relativistic World. 2008. 160p. pap. 12.99 *(978-1-58134-849-1(5))* Crossway.
Oliver, Jose R. Caciques & Cemi Idols: The Web Spun by Taino Rulers Between Hispaniola & Puerto Rico. 2009. (Caribbean Archaeology & Ethnohistory Ser.). (ENG.). 432p. pap. 34.95 *(978-0-8173-5515-9(4))*; (Illus.). 59.00 *(978-0-8173-1636-5(1))* Univ. of Alabama Pr.
Olsen, Glenn W. On the Road to Emmaus: The Catholic Dialogue with America & Modernity. 2012. (ENG.). 320p. 69.95 ***(978-0-8132-1954-7(X))*** Catholic Univ. of America Pr.
Olsen, Glenn W. The Turn to Transcendence: The Role of Religion in the Twenty-First Century. 2010. (ENG.). 404p. 49.95 *(978-0-8132-1740-6(7))* Catholic Univ. of America Pr.
Olson, Duane. Issues in Contemporary Christian Thought: A Fortress Introduction. 2011. 312p. (C). pap. 25.00 *(978-0-8006-9665-8(4)*, Fortress Pr.) Augsburg Fortress, Pubs.
Olson, Joseph W. Jesuit Inculturation in the New World: Experiments in Missions of 16th, 17th, & 18th Centuries. 2008. 304p. pap. 21.95 *(978-1-4327-3828-0(3))* Outskirts Pr., Inc.
onen, T. S. Communication & Conversion in Northern Cameroon: The Dii people & Norwegian Missionaries, 1934-1960. 2009. (Studies in Christian Mission Ser.). (Illus.). xiv, 234p. *(978-90-04-17754-3(X))* BRILL.
Orevillo-Montenegro, Muriel. The Jesus of Asian Women. 2007. (Faith & Cultures Ser.). 270p. per. 24.00 *(978-1-57075-533-0(7))* Orbis Bks.
Ormerod, Neil J. & Clifton, Shane. Globalization & the Mission of the Church. (ENG.). 2011. 228p. pap. 44.95 ***(978-0-567-34907-1(1))*** 2010. 240p. 130.00 *(978-0-567-26183-0(2))* Continuum International Publishing Group, Ltd. GBR. (T&T Clark Int'l). Dist: National Bk. Network.
Ott, John S. & Jones, Anna Trumbore, eds. The Bishop Reformed: Studies on Episcopal Power & Culture in the Central Middle Ages. 2007. (Church, Faith & Culture in the Medieval West Ser.). (Illus.). 296p. 124.95 *(978-0-7546-5765-1(5))* Ashgate Publishing Co.
Pagitt, Doug. Church in the Inventive Age. 2010. 128p. pap. 14.99 *(978-1-4514-0085-4(3)*, Sparkhouse Pr.) Spark Hse.
Pahl, Jon. Empire of Sacrifice: The Religious Origins of American Violence. 2010. (ENG., Illus.). 288p. 35.00 *(978-0-8147-6762-7(1))* New York Univ. Pr.
—Shopping Malls & Other Sacred Spaces: Putting God in Place. 2008. 288p. pap. 32.00 *(978-1-60608-397-0(X)*, Wipf and Stock) Wipf & Stock Pubs.
Parsley, Rod. Living on Our Heads: Righting an Upside-Down Culture. 2010. (ENG.). 224p. 22.99 *(978-1-61638-188-2(4)*, Frontline) Charisma Media.
Pavey, Stephen. Theologies of Power & Crisis: Envisioning / Embodying Christianity in Hong Kong. 2011. (American Society of Missiology Monograph

C

Ser.). 148p. pap. 18.00 (978-1-60899-513-4(5), Pickwick Pubns.) Wipf & Stock Pubs.

Payne, Franklin E. (Ed). Worldview Book. 2010. 459p. pap. 24.99 (978-0-557-32228-2(6)) Lulu Enterprises Inc.

Pears. Doing Contextual Theology. 2009. viii, 196p. pap. 34.95 (978-0-415-41705-1(8)); 100.00 (978-0-415-41704-4(X)) Routledge.

Pearson, Thomas & Pearson, T. Missions & Conversions: Creating the Montagnard-Dega Refugee Community. 2009. (Contemporary Anthropology of Religion Ser.). (ENG., Illus.). 256p. 100.00 (978-0-230-61536-6(8)) Palgrave Macmillan.

Penyak, Lee M. & Petrie, Walter J., eds. Religion & Society in Latin America: Interpretive Essays from Conquest to Present. 2009. (Illus.). 304p. pap. 40.00 (978-1-57075-850-8(6)) Orbis Bks.

Perkins, Robert L., ed. The Moment & Late Writings: International Kierkegaard Commentary Volume 23. 2009. 248p. 50.00 (978-0-88146-160-2(1)) Mercer Univ. Pr.

Pete Ward Staff. Theological Reflections & Cultural Studies. 2011. viii, 204p. pap. (978-0-334-04165-8(1), SCM Pr.) Hymns Ancient & Modern Ltd.

Peter, Val J. Seven Secular Challenges Facing 21st-Century Catholics. 2009. 208p. pap. 17.95 (978-0-8091-4570-6(7)) Paulist Pr.

Peterson, Eugene H. The Jesus Way: A Conversation on the Ways That Jesus Is the Way. 2011. 304p. pap. 17.00 (978-0-8028-6703-2(0)) 2007. 289p. 22.00 (978-0-8028-2949-8(X)) Eerdmans, William B. Publishing Co.

Peterson, Eugene H. & Santucci, Peter. The Jesus Way Study Guide. 2007. 63p. per. 6.00 (978-0-8028-4566-5(5)) Eerdmans, William B. Publishing Co.

Philip Sheldrake Staff. George Herbert: Ccsst. 2010. viii, 178p. pap. (978-1-85311-948-4(2), Morehouse Publishing) Church Publishing, Inc.

Platt, Christian & Platt, Amy. MySpace to Sacred Space: God for a New Generation. 2007. 167p. per. 19.99 (978-0-8272-2334-9(X)) Chalice Pr.

Pierson, Paul Everett. The Dynamics of Christian Mission: History Through a Missiological Perspective. 2009. 364p. pap. (978-0-86585-006-4(2), Debolsillo) Carey, William International Univ. Pr.

Platt, David. Radical: Taking Back Your Faith from the American Dream. 2010. (978-1-60142-220-0(2)); (ENG.). 240p. pap. 14.99 (978-1-60142-221-7(0)) Doubleday Religious Publishing Group, The. (Multnomah).

Plumer, Eric A. The Catholic Church & American Culture: Why the Claims of Dan Brown Strike a Chord. 2009. 340p. pap. 25.00 (978-1-58966-135-6(4)) Univ. of Scranton Pr.

Pointer, Richard W. Encounters of the Spirit: Native Americans & European Colonial Religion. 2007. (Religion in North America Ser.). (ENG.). 312p. 39.95 (978-0-253-34912-5(5), 0253349125) Indiana Univ. Pr.

Pope, David J. Interrupting Behavioral Evolution: An Essay. 2006. xx, 76p. (978-0-9779189-2-8(0)) Walden Hse. Publishing.

Prior. Gospel & Culture in Vanuatu, Vol. 4. 2007. 292p. pap. 5.00 (978-1-920691-69-1(3)) ATF Pr. AUS. Dist: International Publishers Marketing.

Rathbun, Russell. Post-Rapture Radio: Lost Writings from a Failed Revolution. 2008. (ENG.). 208p. pap. 14.95 (978-0-470-29272-3(5), Jossey-Bass) Wiley, John & Sons, Inc.

Rebecca, E. & Zorach. Idols in the Age of Art: Objects Devotions & Early Modern World. Cole, Michael W., ed. 2009. (Objects, Devotions & the Early Modern World Ser.). (Illus.). 384p. 124.95 (978-0-7546-5290-8(4)) Ashgate Publishing Co.

Recinos, Harold. Wading Through Many Voices: Toward a Theology of Public Conversation. 2011. (ENG.). 392p. (gr. 17). 64.95 (978-1-4422-0583-3(0)) Rowman & Littlefield Publishers, Inc.

Recinos, Harold J. Wading Through Many Voices: Toward a Theology of Public Conversation. 2011. (978-1-4422-0585-7(7)) Rowman & Littlefield Publishers, Inc.

Reid, Gregory R. Trojan Church. 2008. 208p. pap. 15.99 (978-1-60647-733-5(1)) Xulon Pr., Inc.

Richardson, Miles. Being-in-Christ & Putting Death in Its Place: An Anthropologist's Account of Christian Performance in Spanish America & the American South. 2006. (Illus.). 414p. per. 19.95 (978-0-8071-3204-3(7)) Louisiana State Univ. Pr.

Robinson, Bob. Christians Meeting Hindus: An Analysis & Theological Critique of the Hindu-Christian Encounter in India. 2011. (Regnum Studies in Mission Ser.). 416p. pap. 47.00 (978-1-61097-596-4(0), Wipf and Stock) Wipf & Stock Pubs.

Robison, James & Richards, Jay W. Indivisible: Restoring Faith, Family, & Freedom Before It's Too Late. 2012. (ENG.). 256p. pap. 14.99 (978-1-4555-0314-8(2)); 384p. 21.99 (978-1-4555-0312-4(6), 1337900) FaithWords.

Robison, James & Richards Jay, W. Indivisible: Restoring Faith, Family, & Freedom Before It's Too Late. l.t. ed. 2012. (ENG.). 571p. pap. 17.99 (978-1-59415-441-6(4)) Cengage Gale.

Rodriguez, Jeanette & Fortier, Ted. Cultural Memory: Resistance, Faith, & Identity. 2007. (ENG., Illus.). 172p. pap. 16.95 (978-0-292-71664-3(8)) Univ. of Texas Pr.

Rogers, Glenn. North American Cross-Cultural Church Planting. 2008. 256p. pap. 23.95 (978-0-9792072-2-8(3)) Mission & Ministry Resources.

—Understanding American Culture: The Theological & Philosophical Shaping of the American Worldview. 2007. pap. 21.95 (978-0-9774396-9-0(0)) Mission & Ministry Resources.

Rolheiser, Ronald. Secularity & the Gospel: Being Missionaries to Our Children. 2006. (ENG.). 240p. pap. 24.95 (978-0-8245-2412-8(8)) Crossroad Publishing Co., The.

Rook, Russell D. Rhyming Hope & History: Theology & Culture in the Work of Robert Jenson. 2011. 240p. pap. 26.00 (978-1-60899-600-1(X), Pickwick Pubns.) Wipf & Stock Pubs.

Rosman, Doreen. Evangelicals & Culture. 2012. (ENG.). 198p. (C). pap. 39.00 (978-0-227-68034-6(0)) Clarke, James Co., Ltd. GBR. Dist: Brown, David Bk. Co., The.

Rosman, Doreen. Evangelicals & Culture: Second Edition. 2011. 198p. pap. 23.00 (978-1-61097-328-1(3), Pickwick Pubns.) Wipf & Stock Pubs.

Rottenberg, Isaac C. Judaism, Christianity, Paganism: A Judeo-Christian Worldview & Its Cultural Implications. 2007. 197p. (978-0-9773852-1-8(3)) Hebraic Heritage Pr.

Rowell, John. To Give or Not to Give? Rethinking Dependency, Restoring Generosity, & Redefining Sustainability. 2007. (ENG., Illus.). 286p. per. 16.99 (978-1-932805-86-4(9)) Authentic Media.

Ruge-Jones, Philip. The Word of the Cross in a World of Glory. 2008. (Lutheran Voices Ser.). 96p. per. 11.99 (978-0-8066-8005-7(9), Augsburg Fortress) Augsburg Fortress, Pubs.

Rutler, George W. A Crisis of Saints: The Call to Heroic Faith in an Unheroic World. 2nd ed. 2009. (ENG.). 224p. pap. 19.95 (978-0-8245-2525-5(6)) Crossroad Publishing Co., The.

Rwengabo, Sabastiano. Beyond the Spiritual. 2011. 188p. pap. (978-3-8433-8896-2(2)) Lambert Academic Publishing.

Samuel, Vinay & Hauser, Albrecht, eds. Proclaiming Christ in Christ's Way: Studies in Integral Mission: Essays Presented to Walter Arnold on the Occasion of His 60th Birthday. 2007. 228p. pap. 25.00 (978-1-59752-860-3(9), Wipf and Stock) Wipf & Stock Pubs.

Sawyer, John F. A., ed. The Bible & Culture. 2006. (ENG., Illus.). 564p. 119.95 (978-1-4051-0136-3(9), Wiley-Blackwell) Wiley, John & Sons, Inc.

Sayers, Mark. The Trouble with Paris: Following Jesus in a World of Plastic Promises, 0 vols. 2008. (Illus.). 224p. pap. 14.99 (978-0-8499-1999-2(1)) Nelson, Thomas Inc.

Sayers, Mark & Lawhead, Stephen R. The Trouble with Paris Participant's Guide, 0 vols. 2008. 128p. pap., stu. ed. 9.99 (978-1-4185-3339-7(4)) Nelson, Thomas Inc.

Scarborough, Rick. Enough Is Enough: A Practical Guide to Political Action at the Local, State, & National Level. 2008. (ENG.). 272p. pap. 14.99 (978-1-59979-389-4(X), Frontline) Charisma Media.

Schindler, Jeanne Heffernan. Christianity & Civil Society: Catholic & Neo-Calvinist Perspectives. 2008. (ENG.). 214p. 68.50 (978-0-7391-0884-0(0)) Lexington Bks.

Scott, Michael W. The Severed Snake: Matrilineages, Making Place, & a Melanesian Christianity in Southeast Solomon Islands. 2007. (Carolina Academic Press Ritual Studies Monographs). 414p. pap. 45.00 (978-1-59460-153-8(4)) Carolina Academic Pr.

Scruton, Roger. Culture Counts: Faith & Feeling in a World Besieged. 2007. (Brief Encounters Ser.). (ENG.). 120p. 20.00 (978-1-59403-194-6(0)) Encounter Bks.

Seasoltz, R. Kevin. A Virtuous Church: Catholic Theology, Ethics, & Liturgy for the 21st Century. 2012. (ENG.). 288p. pap. 38.00 (978-1-57075-973-4(1)) Orbis Bks.

Seton Hall University & Scigliano, Anthony. Christianity & Culture. rev. ed. 2011. (ENG.). 336p. pap. 41.95 (978-0-7575-7626-3(5)) Kendall Hunt Publishing Co.

Shank, David A. & Krabill, James R. Mission from the Margins: Selected Writings from the Life & Ministry of David A. Shank. 2010. (Illus.). vii, 351p. (978-0-936273-44-0(5)) Herald Pr.

Sherrill, Michael J., ed. Missio Dei #13 Spanish: On Becoming A Missional Church in Japan. 2007.Tr. of Como Ser una Iglesia Misional en Japon. (SPA., Illus.). 28p. 3.95 (978-1-933845-07-4(4), Mission Focus) Mennonite Mission Network.

Shuler, Randy. Hand Me a Dr Pepper, Please: A Fresh Look at the Issue of Christians & Social Drinking. 2010. pap. 12.99 (978-1-61566-590-7(0)) Tate Publishing & Enterprises, LLC.

Simpson, Charles. Inside the Churches of Christ: The Reflection of a Former Pharisee on What Every Christian Should Know about the Nondenomination Denomination. 2009. 308p. 25.99 (978-1-4389-0140-4(2)); pap. 17.00 (978-1-4389-0139-8(9)) AuthorHouse.

Sine, Tom. The New Conspirators: Creating the Future One Mustard Seed at a Time. 2008. (ENG.). 304p. per. 16.00 (978-0-8308-3384-9(6), IVP Bks.) InterVarsity Pr.

Singh, David Emmanuel, ed. Christianity & Cultures: Shaping Christian Thinking in Context. 2008. (Regnum Studies in Mission Ser.). 276p. pap. 32.00 (978-1-60608-315-4(5), Wipf and Stock) Wipf & Stock Pubs.

Smilde, David. Reason to Believe: Cultural Agency in Latin American Evangelicalism. 2007. (Anthropology of Christianity Ser.). (Illus.). 262p. 60.00 (978-0-520-24942-4(9)); per. 26.95 (978-0-520-24943-1(7)) Univ. of California Pr.

Smiley, D. M. Africa - The Womb of God. 10.00 (978-0-9724025-0-7(0)) New Covenant Fellowship International.

Smith, David I. Learning from the Stranger: Christian Faith & Cultural Diversity. 2009. (ENG., Illus.). 200p. pap. 20.00 (978-0-8028-2463-9(3)) Eerdmans, William B. Publishing Co.

Smith, James K. A. & Stassen, Glen. Desiring the Kingdom: Worship, Worldview, & Cultural Formation. 2009. (Cultural Liturgies Ser.). (C). pap. 21.99 (978-0-8010-3577-7(5)) Baker Academic.

Sniegocki, John. Catholic Social Teaching & Economic Globalization: The Quest for Alternatives. 2009. pap. 37.00 (978-0-87462-744-2(3)) Marquette Univ. Pr.

Sommerfeldt, John. Christianity in Culture: A Historical Quest. 2009. (ENG.). 262p. pap. 36.99 (978-0-7618-4671-0(9)) Univ. Pr. of America, Inc.

Stackhouse, John G. Making the Best of It: Following Christ in the Real World, 1 vol. 2011. (ENG.). 384p. pap. 19.95 (978-0-19-984394-7(5)) Oxford Univ. Pr., Inc.

Stackhouse, John G. & Stackhouse, John G., Jr. Making the Best of It: Following Christ in the Real World. 2008. (ENG.). 384p. 27.95 (978-0-19-517358-1(9)) Oxford Univ. Pr., Inc.

Staub, Dick. The Culturally Savvy Christian: A Manifesto for Deepening Faith & Enriching Popular Culture in an Age of Christianity - Lite. 2008. (ENG.). 256p. pap. 14.95 (978-0-470-34403-3(2), Jossey-Bass) Wiley, John & Sons, Inc.

Stockel, H. Henrietta. Salvation Through Slavery: Chiricahua Apaches & Priests on the Spanish Colonial Frontier. 2008. (ENG., Illus.). 191p. (C). 29.95 (978-0-8263-4325-3(2)) Univ. of New Mexico Pr.

Stroumsa, Guy G. Kanon und Kultur: Zwei Studien zur Hermeneutik des antiken Christentums. (Hans-Lietzmann-Vorlesungen Ser.). (GER.). XXV, 66p. 45.00 (978-3-11-177273-8(X)) De Gruyter, Walter Inc.

Stults, Donald Le Roy. Grasping Truth & Reality: Lesslie Newbigin's Theology of Mission to the Western World. 2008. 308p. pap. 34.00 (978-1-55635-723-7(0), Wipf and Stock) Wipf & Stock Pubs.

Sugden, Chris. Gospel, Culture, & Transformation: A Reprint with a New Introduction of Part Two of Seeking the Asian Face of Jesus. 2011. (Regnum Studies in Mission Ser.). 160p. pap. 18.00 (978-1-61097-484-4(0), Wipf and Stock) Wipf & Stock Pubs.

Sugirtharajah, R. S., ed. Voices from the Margin: Interpreting the Bible in the Third World. 3rd rev. exp. ed. 2006. 506p. per. 35.00 (978-1-57075-686-3(4)) Orbis Bks.

Sweet, Leonard. So Beautiful: Divine Design for Life & the Church. 2009. (ENG.). 304p. pap. 16.99 (978-1-4347-9979-1(4)) Cook, David C.

Swidler, Leonard. Club Modernity for Reluctant Christians. 2011. (ENG.). 160p. pap. 17.95 (978-0-931214-12-7(2)) Ecumenical Pr.

Takenaka, Masao. God Is Rice. 2009. 90p. pap. 13.00 (978-1-60608-892-0(0), Wipf and Stock) Wipf & Stock Pubs.

Tamel, J. A. Reluctant Horses, Broken Bridges, Magic Feathers, & a Tossed Salad. 2007. 192p. per. 13.99 (978-1-60266-790-7(X)) Xulon Pr., Inc.

Tedesco, Robert J. Snowballs Taking Chances: A Biblical Examination of Modern Christianity. 2007. 251p. per. 14.99 (978-1-59886-362-8(2)) Tate Publishing & Enterprises, LLC.

Tenery, Robert M. & Sells, J. Steve. For Such a Time As This: Five Steps to a Spirit-Powered Church. 2010. 164p. 30.95 (978-1-61507-230-9(6)); pap. 13.95 (978-1-61507-229-3(2)) Cross Bks. Publishing.

Thomas, R. Murray. Manitou & God: North-American Indian Religions & Christian Culture, 1 vol. 2007. (Illus.). 292p. 49.95 (978-0-313-34779-5(4), C34779, Praeger Pubs.) Greenwood Publishing Group, Inc.

Thompson, Billy M. Sodom & Gomorrah in America. 2007. 88p. per. 9.95 (978-1-4327-0304-2(8)) Outskirts Pr., Inc.

Thompson, Jack. Out of Harm's Way. 2006. xviii, 234p. pap. 19.99 (978-1-4143-0443-4(9)) Tyndale Hse. Pubs.

Thong, Chan Kei. Faith of Our Fathers: God in Ancient China. 2007. (CHI., Illus.). 265p. pap. 20.00 (978-0-9796269-6-0(0)) Leadership Development International.

Thong, Chan Kei, et al. Finding God in Ancient China: How the Ancient Chinese Worshiped the God of the Bible, 1 vol. 2009. (ENG.). 352p. pap. 24.99 (978-0-310-29238-8(7)) Zondervan.

Tillich, Paul. The Irrelevance & Relevance of the Christian Message. Foster, Durwood, ed. 2007. 104p. pap. 13.00 (978-1-55635-211-9(5), Wipf and Stock) Wipf & Stock Pubs.

Tinker, George E. American Indian Liberation: A Theology of Sovereignty. 2008. vi, 170p. pap. 22.00 (978-1-57075-805-8(0)) Orbis Bks.

Titus, Craig Steven, ed. Christianity & the West: Interaction & Impact in Art & Culture, John Henry Cardinal Newman Lecture. 2009. (John Henry Cardinal Newman Lecture Ser.). (Illus.). 168p. pap. 24.95 (978-0-9773103-2-6(9)) Institute for the Psychological Science Pr., The.

—On Wings of Faith & Reason: The Christian Difference in Culture & Science. 2008. (John Henry Cardinal Newman Lectures). 155p. pap. 24.95 (978-0-9773103-3-3(7)) Institute for the Psychological Science Pr., The.

Todd, Matthew R. S. Historical Attitudes That Have Shaped the Church's Use of the Arts. 2010. 188p. pap. (978-1-926676-68-5(8)) Word Alive Pr.

Toler, Stan. ReThink Your Life: A Diet for the Mind. 2008. 249p. 19.99 (978-0-89827-373-1(0)) Wesleyan Publishing Hse.

Tomlinson, Matt & Engelke, Matthew, eds. The Limits of Meaning: Case Studies in the Anthropology of Christianity. 2006. 252p. (C). 90.00 (978-1-84545-170-7(8)) Berghahn Bks., Inc.

Tovey, Phillip. Inculturation: The Eucharist in Africa. 2009. 88.00 (978-1-60724-362-5(8)) Gorgias Pr., LLC.

Trueman, Carl R. Fools Rush in Where Monkeys Fear to Tread: Taking Aim at Everyone. 2012. xiii, 241p. pap. (978-1-59638-405-7(0)) P & R Publishing.

Tubenzele, Philippe Kanku. L'Afrique est a Construire: La Responsabilite Spirituelle. (FRE.). 252p. pap. 44.95 (978-3-03911-427-6(1)) Lang, Peter Publishing, Inc.

Turpin, Katherine. Branded: Adolescents Converting from Consumer Faith. 2006. (Youth Ministry Alternatives Ser.). (978-0-8298-1738-6(7)) Pilgrim Pr., The/United Church Pr.

Ullman, Brett. Media, Faith, Culture: Connecting Our Ancient Faith with Our Modern World. 2011. (978-1-77069-140-7(5)) Word Alive Pr.

Ustorf, Werner. Robinson Crusoe tries again: Missiology & European Constructions of 'Self' & 'Other' in a Global World 1789 - 2010. Loffler, Roland, ed. 2010. (Research in Contemporary Religion Ser.). (ENG.). 271p. (C). 95.00 (978-3-525-60444-1(0)) Vandenhoeck & Ruprecht GmbH & Co. KG DEU. Dist: ISD.

Valmyr, William. Christianity & Culture: A Christian Perspective on Worldview Development. 2009. 216p. pap. 15.99 (978-1-60791-941-4(9)) Xulon Pr., Inc.

Vande Kappelle, Robert P. Into Thin Places: One ManÕs Search for the Center. 2011. 432p. pap. 48.00 (978-1-61097-093-8(4), Resource Pubns.) Wipf & Stock Pubs.

Vanhoozer, Kevin J., et al, eds. Everyday Theology: How to Read Cultural Texts & Interpret Trends. annot. ed. 2007. (Cultural Exegesis Ser.). 288p. (C). pap. 23.99 (978-0-8010-3167-0(2)) Baker Academic.

Vattimo, Gianni & Girard, René. Christianity, Truth, & Weakening Faith: A Dialogue. Antonello, Pierpaolo, ed. McCuaig, William, tr. from ITA. 2010. (ENG.). 136p. (gr. 17). 18.50 (978-0-231-14828-3(3)) Columbia Univ. Pr.

Villegas, Diana. The Christian Path in a Pluralistic World & the Study of Spirituality. 2012. E-Book (978-0-7391-6813-4(4)) Lexington Bks.

Villegas, Diana L. The Christian Path in a Pluralistic World & the Study of Spirituality. 2011. (ENG.). 130p. (gr. 17). 55.00 (978-0-7391-6812-7(6)) Lexington Bks.

Vollmer, Matthias. Fortuna Diagrammatica: Das Rad der Fortuna als bildhafte Verschlüsselung der Schrift de consolatione philosophiae des Boethius. 2009. (Apeliotes. Studien zur Kulturgeschichte und Theologie Ser.). (GER., Illus.). 342p. pap. 74.95 (978-3-631-57949-7(7)) Lang, Peter GmbH, Europaischer Verlag der Wissenschaften DEU. Dist: Lang, Peter.

Wang, Aiming. Church in China: Faith, Ethics, Structure: The Heritage of the Reformation for the Future of the Church in China. 2009. 590p. pap. (978-3-03911-814-4(5)) Lang, Peter.

Wariboko, Waibinte E. Ruined by "Race" Afro-Caribbean Missionaries & the Evangelization of Southern Nigeria, 1895-1925. 2006. (Illus.). xv, 261p. (978-1-59221-439-6(8)); 278p. pap. (978-1-59221-440-2(1)) Africa World Pr.

Watkins, Ralph C. The Gospel Remix: Reaching the Hip Hop Generation. 2007. 148p. per. 15.00 (978-0-8170-1507-7(8)) Judson Pr.

Weaver, Alain Epp. States of Exile: Visions of Diaspora, Witness, & Return. 2008. (Illus.). 215p. pap. 19.99 (978-0-8361-9422-7(5)) Herald Pr.

Wendland, Ernst. Galu Wamkota. 2007. 512p. (C). pap. (978-99908-87-05-1(5)) Kachere Series, Bks. on Religion, Theology & Society in Malawi MWI. Dist: Michigan State Univ. Pr.

Wenger, Tisa. We Have a Religion: The 1920s Pueblo Indian Dance Controversy & American Religious Freedom. 2009. (ENG., Illus.). 336p. 62.95 (978-0-8078-3262-2(6)) Univ. of North Carolina Pr.

Wenger, Tisa & Wenger, Tisa Joy. We Have a Religion: The 1920s Pueblo Indian Dance Controversy & American Religious Freedom. 2009. (ENG., Illus.). 336p. pap. 23.95 (978-0-8078-5935-3(4)) Univ. of North Carolina Pr.

White, James Emery. Christ among the Dragons: Finding Our Way Through Cultural Challenges. 2010. (ENG.). 190p. 17.00 (978-0-8308-3312-2(9), IVP Bks.) InterVarsity Pr.

Wilhite, Jud & Taaffe, Bill. Uncensored Grace: Stories of Hope from the Streets of Vegas. 2008. (ENG.). 240p. 13.99 (978-1-60142-146-3(X), Multnomah) Doubleday Religious Publishing Group, The.

Wilkens, Hermann. Kata Markon. (GER.). 116p. 28.95 (978-3-631-34879-6(7)) Lang, Peter Publishing, Inc.

Wilkens, Steve & Sanford, Mark L. Hidden Worldviews: Eight Cultural Stories That Shape Our Lives. 2009. (ENG.). 218p. pap. 22.00 (978-0-8308-3854-7(6), IVP Acad.) InterVarsity Pr.

Wilkens, Tom & Wilkens, Kim. Un-American Activities: Countercultural Themes in Christianity. 2009. xix, 331p. (978-0-7880-2230-2(X), Fairway Pr.) CSS Publishing Co.

Williams, Scott. Church Diversity: We Are Church Diversity! 2011. 190p. (978-0-89221-703-8(0)) New Leaf Pr., Inc.

Woods, Thomas E., Jr. & Woods, Jr., Thomas E., Thomas E. The Church Confronts Modernity: Catholic Intellectuals & the Progressive Era. 2006. (Religion & American Culture Ser.). (ENG.). 304p. (gr. 17). pap. 27.00 (978-0-231-13187-2(9)) Columbia Univ. Pr.

Woodyard, David. The Church in the Time of Empire. 2011. (ENG.). 167p. pap. 16.95 (978-1-84694-595-3(X)) O Bks., John Hunt.

Wright, N. T. The Gospel & Our Culture: Nashotah House Studies No. 1. 2007. 36p. 7.50 (978-0-9792243-0-0(6)) Nashotah Hse.

Yai-Chow, Teresa Wong, et al. The Cosmos in Becoming. 2009. 250p. pap. 18.00 (978-1-920691-94-3(4)) ATF Pr. AUS. Dist: International Publishers Marketing.

York, Joe. With Signs Following: Photographs from the Southern Religious Roadside. 2007. (ENG., Illus.). 67p. 25.00 (978-1-57806-975-0(0)) Univ. Pr. of Mississippi.

Young, Frances M. Biblical Exegesis & the Formation of Christian Culture. 2007. (ENG.). 340p. pap. 69.00 (978-0-521-04513-1(4)) Cambridge Univ. Pr.

Young, Robin Darling & Aune, David E., eds. Reading Religions in the Ancient World: Essays Presented to Robert Mcqueen Grant on His 90th Birthday. 2007. (Novum Testamentum Supplements Ser.). (Illus.). 305p. (978-90-04-16196-2(1)) BRILL.

CHRISTIANITY AND DEMOCRACY

see Democracy—Religious Aspects—Christianity

CHRISTIANITY AND ECONOMICS
see also Christian Sociology; Christian Stewardship; Church and Labor; Communism and Christianity

Beed, Clive & Beed, Cara. Alternatives to Economics: Christian Socio-Economic Perspectives. 2006. (ENG.). 408p. per. 57.99 *(978-0-7618-3398-7(6))* Univ. Pr. of America, Inc.

Budde, Michael L. & Brimlow, Robert W. Christianity Incorporated: How Big Business Is Buying the Church. 2007. 192p. pap. 22.00 *(978-1-55635-245-4(X)*, Wipf and Stock) Wipf & Stock Pubs.

Ekelund, Robert B., Jr., et al. The Marketplace of Christianity. 2006. (ENG., Illus.). 368p. (gr. 17). 31.95 *(978-0-262-05082-1(X))* MIT Pr.

Fleet, Bruce. The Solomon Secret: 7 Principles of Financial Success from King Solomon, History's Wealthiest Man. 2010. (ENG.). 160p. (gr. 12). 13.95 *(978-1-58542-818-2(3)*, Tarcher) Penguin Group (USA) Inc.

Griffin, Linda. Christians in Business. 2007. pap. 8.00 *(978-0-8059-7530-7(6))* Dorrance Publishing Co., Inc.

Harper, Ian R. & Gregg, Samuel, eds. Christian Theology & Market Economics. 2008. 240p. 119.00 *(978-1-84720-377-9(9))* Elgar, Edward Publishing, Inc.

Hartropp, Andrew. What Is Economic Justice? Biblical & Secular Perspectives Contrasted. 2008. (Paternoster Theological Monographs). 256p. pap. 29.00 *(978-1-55635-866-1(0))* Wipf & Stock Pubs.

Kimelman, Nancy J. Common Cents: How the Economy Really Works — from the Global Market to the Supermarket. (ENG.). 288p. 2010. pap. 14.95 *(978-1-4027-7122-4(3))* 2008. 19.95 *(978-1-4027-5256-8(3))* Sterling Publishing Co., Inc.

McAfee, Caleb. Money & the Christian: A Course in Biblical Economics. 192p. 14.99 *(978-0-9656010-0-9(5))* Dimension 4 Enterprises, Inc.

McLeod, Andrew. Holy Cooperation! Building Graceful Economies. 2008. 140p. pap. 17.00 *(978-1-55635-635-3(8))* Wipf & Stock Pubs.

Nixon, Don. Winning the 21st Century. 2007. 108p. per. 10.99 *(978-1-60266-378-7(5))* Xulon Pr., Inc.

Slaughter, Michael B. Upside Living in a Downside Economy. 2009. 96p. pap. 8.00 *(978-1-4267-0305-8(8))* Abingdon Pr.

Tawney, Richard H. Religion & the Rise of Capitalism. 2008. 32.00 *(978-0-8446-1446-5(7))* Smith, Peter Pub., Inc.

CHRISTIANITY AND INTERNATIONAL AFFAIRS

Aaltola, Mika. Sowing the Seeds of Sacred: Political Religion of Contemporary World Order & American ERA. 2008. (International Relations Studies Ser.). (Illus.). 216p. *(978-90-04-16563-2(0))* BRILL.

Butler, Jennifer S. Born Again: The Christian Right Globalized. 2006. (ENG.). 224p. per. 24.95 *(978-0-7453-2242-1(5))* Pluto Pr. GBR. Dist: Macmillan.

The Churches in International Affairs: Reports 2003-2006. 2007. 453p. pap. 29.50 *(978-2-8254-1514-5(6))* World Council of Churches/Conseil Oecumenique des Eglises CHE. Dist: International Specialized Bk. Services.

Cohen, Raymond & Westbrook, Raymond. Isaiah's Vision of Peace in Biblical & Modern International Relations: Swords into Plowshares. 2008. (Culture & Religion in International Relations Ser.). (ENG., Illus.). 304p. 100.00 *(978-1-4039-7735-9(6))* Palgrave Macmillan.

Dittmer, Jason & Sturm, Tristan. Mapping the End Times: American Evangelical Geopolitics & Apocalyptic Visions. 2010. (Critical Geopolitics Ser.). (Illus.). 280p. 119.95 *(978-0-7546-7601-0(3))*; pap. 44.95 *(978-1-4094-0083-7(2))* Ashgate Publishing Co.

Evans, Mike. The Final Move Beyond Iraq: The Final Solution While the World Sleeps. 2007. (ENG., Illus.). 360p. pap. 14.99 *(978-1-59979-188-3(9)*, Frontline) Charisma Media.

Hartch, Todd. Missionaries of the State: The Summer Institute of Linguistics, State Formation, & Indigenous Mexico, 1935-1985. 2006. (Illus.). 272p. 39.95 *(978-0-8173-1515-3(2))* Univ. of Alabama Pr.

Horsley, Richard A., ed. In the Shadow of Empire: Reclaiming the Bible as a History of Faithful Resistance. 2008. (ENG.). 192p. pap. 25.00 *(978-0-664-23232-0(9))* Westminster John Knox Pr.

Kirkemo, Ron. Embraced & Engaged. 2009. 282p. pap. 31.00 *(978-1-60608-335-2(X)*, Wipf and Stock) Wipf & Stock Pubs.

Ngwana, Timothy P. Religion in World Affairs. 2007. 88p. per. 15.99 *(978-1-4257-7481-3(4))* Xlibris Corp.

Rees, Wyn, et al. British Foreign Policy & the Anglican Church: Christian Engagement with the Contemporary World. 2008. (Illus.). 172p. pap. 39.95 *(978-0-7546-6037-8(0))* Ashgate Publishing Co.

Ross, Wyn. British Foreign Policy & the Anglican Church: Christian Engagement with the Contemporary World. Blewett, Timothy & Hyde-Price, Adrian, eds. 2008. (Illus.). 172p. 99.95 *(978-0-7546-6035-4(4))* Ashgate Publishing Co.

Schlabach, Gerald W., ed. Just Policing, Not War: An Alternative Response to World Violence. 2007. 255p. per. 27.95 *(978-0-8146-5221-3(2))* Liturgical Pr.

Stone, Ronald & Stone. Prophetic Realism: Beyond Militarism & Pacifism in an Age of Terror. 2007. (ENG.). 208p. pap. 26.95 *(978-0-567-02675-0(2)*, T&T Clark Int'l) Continuum International Publishing Group, Ltd. GBR. Dist: National Bk. Network.

Wylie Kellermann, Bill. Seasons of Faith & Conscience: Explorations in Liturgical Direct Action. 2008. 246p. pap. 27.00 *(978-1-55635-923-1(3)*, Wipf and Stock) Wipf & Stock Pubs.

CHRISTIANITY AND JUSTICE

Arthur, Gordon. Law Liberty & Church: Authority & Justice in the Major Churches in England. 2006. (Ashgate New Critical Thinking in Religion, Theology, & Biblical Studies). 222p. 99.95 *(978-0-7546-5437-7(0))* Ashgate Publishing Co.

Basil, The Great. On Social Justice. 2009. 112p. 14.00 *(978-0-88141-053-2(5))* St. Vladimir's Seminary Pr.

Belousek, Darrin W. Snyder. Atonement, Justice, & Peace: The Message of the Cross & the Mission of the Church. 2011. pap. 55.00 ***(978-0-8028-6642-4(5))*** Eerdmans, William B. Publishing Co.

Benedict XVI, pseud. La Caridad en la Verdad: Caritas in Veritate. 2009. (Carta Enciclica Ser.). (SPA.). 94p. pap. 6.95 *(978-1-60137-806-4(8))* United States Conference of Catholic Bishops.

—Charity in Truth: Caritas in Veritate: Encyclical Letter. 2009. 93p. pap. 6.95 *(978-1-60137-049-5(0))* United States Conference of Catholic Bishops.

Bibbs, Alvin C. Crazy Enough to Care: Changing Your World Through Compassion, Justice & Racial Reconciliation, 1 vol. 2009. (Willow Creek Resources Ser.). (ENG.). 150p. pap. 16.00 *(978-0-8308-2115-0(5)*, IVP Conn.) InterVarsity Pr.

Boers, Arthur Paul. Justice That Heals: A Biblical Vision for Victims & Offenders. 2008. (Restorative Justice Classics Ser.). 176p. pap. 20.00 *(978-1-55635-786-2(9))* Wipf & Stock Pubs.

Boreczky, Elemér. John Wyclif's Discourse on Dominion in Community. 2007. (Studies in the History of Christian Traditions). x, 323p. *(978-90-04-16349-2(2))* BRILL.

Bovati, Pietro. Re-establishing Justice: Legal Terms, Concepts & Procedures in the Hebrew Bible. 2009. (Library of Hebrew Bible/Old Testament Studies, the Ser.). (ENG.). 478p. 75.00 *(978-0-567-05265-0(6)*, T&T Clark) Continuum International Publishing Group, Ltd. GBR. Dist: National Bk. Network.

Cannon, Mae Elise. Social Justice Handbook: Small Steps for a Better World. 2009. (BridgeLeader Partnership Ser.). (ENG.). 304p. pap. 20.00 *(978-0-8308-3715-1(9)*, IVP Bks.) InterVarsity Pr.

Capper, Brian. Jesus & the Poor. 2012. (ENG.). 272p. 130.00 *(978-0-567-03086-3(5))*; pap. 33.95 *(978-0-567-03087-0(3))* Continuum International Publishing Group, Ltd. GBR. (T&T Clark Int'). Dist: National Bk. Network.

Chung, Paul S. Christian Mission & a Diakonia of Reconciliation: A Global Reframing of Justification & Justice. 2008. (ENG.). 212p. pap. 30.00 *(978-1-932688-36-8(6)*, Lutheran Univ. Pr.) Kirk Hse. Pubs.

Connelly, Douglas. Good & Evil. 2008. (LifeGuide Bible Studies). (ENG.). 60p. pap. 8.00 *(978-0-8308-3130-2(4)*, IVP Conn.) InterVarsity Pr.

Cooper, Ben. Just Love: Why God Must Punish Sin. 2010. (Illus.). 128p. pap. *(978-1-904889-54-0(9))* Good Bk. Co.

Cullen. Catholic Social Justice: Theological & Practical Explorations. Hoose, Bernard & Mannion, Gerard, eds. 2007. (ENG.). 272p. 41.95 *(978-0-567-04542-3(0))* Continuum International Publishing Group, Ltd. GBR. Dist: National Bk. Network.

DeYoung, Curtiss Paul. Coming Together in the 21st Century: The Bible's Message in an Age of Diversity. 2009. 252p. pap. 19.00 *(978-0-8170-1564-0(7))* Judson Pr.

Dodaro, Robert. Christ & the Just Society in the Thought of Augustine. 2008. (ENG.). 264p. pap. 37.99 *(978-0-521-06964-9(5))* Cambridge Univ. Pr.

Duffy, Michael. Catholic Social Thought & the Promotion of Justice. 2008. 204p. pap. *(978-3-639-03766-1(9))* VDM Verlag Dr. Mueller e.K.

Dykstra, Laurel & Myers, Ched, eds. Liberating Biblical Study: Scholarship, Art, & Action in Honor of the Center & Library for the Bible & Social Justice. 2011. (Center & Library for the Bible & Social Justice Ser.). 278p. pap. 31.00 ***(978-1-61097-401-1(8)***, Cascade Bks.) Wipf & Stock Pubs.

Fancher, Mark. I Ain't Got Tired Yet: The Spiritual Battles of Enslaved African Christians & their Descendants. 2010. pap. 15.00 *(978-0-615-37842-8(0))* Mark P. Fancher.

Gates, Jamie & Middendorf, Jon. Living Justice: Revolutionary Compassion in a Broken World. 2007. (Undercurrent Ser.). (ENG.). 96p. pap. 8.99 *(978-0-8341-5019-5(0)*, 0834150190) Beacon Hill Pr. of Kansas City.

Greaney, Michael D. In Defense of Human Dignity: Essays on the Just Third Way: A Natural Law Perspective. 2008. x, 303p. pap. *(978-0-944997-02-4(3))* Ctr. for Economic & Social Justice.

Groody, Daniel G. Globalization, Spirituality, & Justice: Navigating the Path to Peace. 2007. (Theology in Global Perspective Ser.). (Illus.). 280p. per. 28.00 *(978-1-57075-696-2(1))* Orbis Bks.

Guzder, Deena. Divine Rebels: American Christian Activists for Social Justice. 2011. (ENG.). 320p. pap. 16.95 *(978-1-56976-264-6(3)*, Hill, Lawrence Bks.) Chicago Review Pr., Inc.

Hancock, Jim & International Justice Mission. The Justice Mission: A Video-Enhanced Curriculum Reflecting the Heart of God for the Oppressed of the World, 1 vol. 2006. (ENG.). (gr. 13). pap. 37.99 incl. DVD *(978-0-310-27707-1(8))* Zondervan.

Hartropp, Andrew. What Is Economic Justice? Biblical & Secular Perspectives Contrasted. 2008. (Paternoster Theological Monographs). 256p. pap. 29.00 *(978-1-55635-866-1(0))* Wipf & Stock Pubs.

Haugen, Gary A. Good News about Injustice: A Witness of Courage in a Hurting World, 1 vol. 10th rev. ed. 2009. (ENG., Illus.). 273p. pap. 16.00 *(978-0-8308-3710-6(8)*, IVP Bks.) InterVarsity Pr.

Heagle, John. Justice Rising: The Emerging Biblical Vision. 2010. 240p. pap. 22.00 *(978-1-57075-884-3(0))* Orbis Bks.

Hiers, Richard H. Justice & Compassion in Biblical Law. 2009. (ENG.). 256p. 120.00 *(978-0-567-29789-1(6))*; pap. 34.95 *(978-0-567-26909-6(4))* Continuum International Publishing Group, Ltd. GBR. (T&T Clark Int'l). Dist: National Bk. Network.

Hondagneu-Sotelo, Pierrette, ed. Religion & Social Justice for Immigrants. 2006. (ENG.). 256p. 68.00 *(978-0-8135-3908-9(0))*; per. 25.95 *(978-0-8135-3909-6(9))* Rutgers Univ. Pr.

Horsley, Richard A. Covenant Economics: A Biblical Vision of Justice for All. 2009. (ENG.). 176p. pap. 25.00 *(978-0-664-23395-2(3))* Westminster John Knox Pr.

Ipgrave, Michael. Justice & Rights: Christian & Muslim Perspectives. 2009. (ENG.). 192p. pap. 24.95 *(978-1-58901-489-3(8))* Georgetown Univ. Pr.

Jackson, Timothy P. The Priority of Love: Christian Charity & Social Justice. 2009. (New Forum Bks.). (ENG., Illus.). 248p. (C). pap. 22.95 *(978-0-691-14428-3(1))* Princeton Univ. Pr.

Johnson, Byron R. More God, Less Crime: How Religion & Faith-Based Approaches Reduce Crime & Foster Hope. 2011. (ENG.). 288p. 26.95 *(978-1-59947-373-4(9))* Templeton Pr.

Kammer, Fred. Faith. Works. Wonders: An Insider's Guide to Catholic Charities. 2009. 220p. pap. 24.00 *(978-1-60608-927-9(7)*, Pickwick Pubns.) Wipf & Stock Pubs.

—Salted with Fire: Spirituality for the Faithjustice Journey. 2008. 154p. pap. 18.00 *(978-1-55635-998-9(5)*, Wipf and Stock) Wipf & Stock Pubs.

Keller, Timothy. Every Good Endeavor: Connecting Your Work to God's Plan for the World. 2012. (ENG.). 288p. (gr. 12). 25.95 ***(978-0-525-95270-1(5)***, Dutton Adult) Penguin Group (USA) Inc.

Kemeny, P. C., ed. Church, State & Public Justice: Five Views. 2007. (Spectrum Multiview Book Ser.). (ENG.). 254p. per. 19.00 *(978-0-8308-2796-1(X)*, IVP Acad.) InterVarsity Pr.

Larson, Susie. Embracing Your Freedom: A Personal Experience of God's Heart for Justice. 2009. (ENG.). 288p. pap. 13.99 *(978-0-8024-5280-1(9))* Moody Pubs.

Long, Michael G., ed. Resist! Christian Dissent for the 21st Century. 2008. 216p. pap. 18.00 *(978-1-57075-800-3(X))* Orbis Bks.

Magariño, Aurelio. Justicia Social en un Mundo Injusto: La Iglesia Como Agente de Cambio. 2009. (SPA.). 168p. ***(978-0-7586-1901-3(4))*** Concordia Publishing Hse.

Marsh, Charles & Perkins, John M. Welcoming Justice: God's Movement Toward Beloved Community. 2009. (Resources for Reconciliation Ser.). (ENG.). 140p. pap. 15.00 *(978-0-8308-3453-2(2)*, IVP Bks.) InterVarsity Pr.

Massingale, Bryan N. Racial Justice & the Catholic Church. 2010. 240p. pap. 26.00 *(978-1-57075-776-1(3))* Orbis Bks.

McIlroy, David. A Biblical View of Law & Justice. 2007. (ENG.). 272p. per. 39.99 *(978-1-84227-267-1(5)*, Paternoster) Authentic Media.

McLaren, Brian D., et al, eds. The Justice Project, 1 vol. 2009. (Emersion). 288p. 21.99 *(978-0-8010-1328-7(3))* Baker Bks.

Nelson, Alan. The Only Alternative: Christian Nonviolent Peacemakers in America. 2008. 190p. pap. 22.00 *(978-1-55635-262-1(X)*, Wipf and Stock) Wipf & Stock Pubs.

O'Donnell, Bill & O'Donnell, Mary. Father Bill: Reflections of a Beloved Rebel. 2009. *(978-1-881896-33-3(1))* Pacific View Pr.

Oliver, Willard M. Catholic Perspectives on Crime & Criminal Justice. 2008. (ENG.). 294p. 78.99 *(978-0-7391-1747-7(5))* Lexington Bks.

Peery, Ken. Desires of My Heart: A Lawyer. 2009. 282p. pap. 16.99 *(978-1-61579-041-8(1))* Xulon Pr., Inc.

Pilavachi, Mike & Hoeksma, Liza. When Necessary Use Words: Changing Lives Through Worship, Justice & Evangelism. 2007. (ENG.). 160p. per. 12.99 *(978-0-8307-3814-4(2))* Gospel Light Pubns.

Presa, Neal D., ed. That They May All Be One: Celebrating the World Communion of Reformed Churches. 2010. (ENG.). 200p. pap. 20.00 *(978-0-664-23572-7(7))* Westminster John Knox Pr.

Puza, Richard & Doe, Norman. Religion & Law in Dialogue: Convenantal & Non-convenantal Cooperation between State & Religion in Europe. Proceedings of the Conference Tubingen 18-21 November 2004 - Actes du Colloque Tubingen 18-21 Novembre 2004. Doe, N. & Fuza, R., eds. 2006. (ENG & FRE.). 298p. (C). pap. 66.00 *(978-90-429-1705-7(9))* Peeters Pubs. & Booksellers BEL. Dist: Brown, David Bk. Co., The.

Rigby, Cynthia. Promotion of Social Righteousness. 2010. (ENG.). pap. 16.95 *(978-1-57153-064-6(9)*, Witherspoon Pr.) Curriculum Publishing, Presbyterian Church (U. S. A.).

Ruis, David & Giles, Doug. The Justice God Is Seeking. 2007. (ENG.). 144p. pap. 12.99 *(978-0-8307-3915-8(7)*, Regal Bks.) Gospel Light Pubns.

Sanders, Cheryl J. Ministry at the Margins: The Prophetic Mission of Women, Youth & the Poor. 2009. 144p. (Orig.). pap. 18.00 *(978-1-60608-760-2(6)*, Wipf and Stock) Wipf & Stock Pubs.

Scaperlanda, Michael A. & Collett, Teresa S. Recovering Self-Evident Truths: Catholic Perspectives on American Law. 2007. 403p. per. 39.95 *(978-0-8132-1482-5(3))* Catholic Univ. of America Pr.

Schutt, Michael P. Redeeming Law: Christian Calling & the Legal Profession. 2007. (ENG.). 290p. per. 24.00 *(978-0-8308-2599-8(1)*, IVP Acad.) InterVarsity Pr.

Schwendeman, Jill. When Youth Lead: Intergenerational Social Justice Ministry. 2007. ix, 139p. pap. 15.00 *(978-1-55896-520-1(3))* Unitarian Universalist Assn.

Scott, Margaret. The Eucharist & Social Justice. 2009. 156p. pap. 16.95 *(978-0-8091-4566-9(9))* Paulist Pr.

Shick, Stephen M. Be the Change: Poems, Prayers, & Meditations for Peacemakers & Justice Seekers. 2009. pap. 12.00 *(978-1-55896-549-2(1)*, Skinner Hse. Bks.) Unitarian Universalist Assn.

Shytov, Alexander Nikolaevich. Conscience & Love in Making Judicial Decisions. 2010. (Law & Philosophy Library). 260p. pap. 179.00 *(978-90-481-5889-8(3)*, 9048158893) Springer.

Skotnicki, Andrew. Criminal Justice & the Catholic Church. 2007. (ENG.). 174p. 70.00 *(978-0-7425-5202-9(0))*; pap. 24.95 *(978-0-7425-5203-6(9))* Rowman & Littlefield Publishers, Inc.

Smith, Christine Marie, ed. Preaching Justice: Ethnic & Cultural Perspectives. 2008. 174p. pap. 20.00 *(978-1-60608-142-6(X)*, Wipf and Stock) Wipf & Stock Pubs.

Stassen, Glen Harold. Just Peacemaking: The New Paradigm for the Ethics of Peace & War. 2008. *(978-0-8298-1793-5(X))* Pilgrim Pr., The/United Church Pr.

Talley, Alan J. Christian Morality & Justice. 2009. (Illus.). 122p. spiral bd., instr.'s gde. ed. 26.25 *(978-0-88489-766-8(4))* St. Mary's Pr.

Tu, Stephen. Pro-Life Pulpit: Preaching & the Challenge of Abortion. 2011. 170p. pap. 20.00 ***(978-1-61097-357-1(7)***, Wipf and Stock) Wipf & Stock Pubs.

Uhalde, Kevin. Expectations of Justice in the Age of Augustine. annot. ed. 2007. 248p. (C). 65.00 *(978-0-8122-3987-4(3))* Univ. of Pennsylvania Pr.

Vennard, Jane. Embracing the World: Praying for Justice & Peace. 2008. (ENG.). 176p. pap. 19.95 *(978-0-470-39076-4(X)*, Jossey-Bass) Wiley, John & Sons, Inc.

Vera Mendez, Juan Antonio. Palabra con filo Liberador: De la conciencia solidaria a la transformacion Social. 2009. (SPA., Illus.). 142p. 15.00 *(978-1-61505-022-2(1))* Publicaciones Gaviota.

Windley-Daoust, Jerry & Kilmartin, Lorraine. Living Justice & Peace 2008: Catholic Social Teaching in Practice. 2nd ed. 2008. (Illus.). 336p. pap. 26.25 *(978-0-88489-985-3(3))* St. Mary's Pr.

Wolterstorff, Nicholas. Justice: Rights & Wrongs. (ENG.). 416p. (C). 2010. pap. 25.95 *(978-0-691-14630-0(6))* 2007. 52.50 *(978-0-691-12967-9(3))* Princeton Univ. Pr.

—Justice in Love. 2011. 35.00 *(978-0-8028-6615-8(8))* Eerdmans, William B. Publishing Co.

Worthington, Everett L., Jr. A Just Forgiveness: Responsible Healing Without Excusing Injustice. 2009. (ENG.). 252p. pap. 17.00 *(978-0-8308-3701-4(9)*, IVP Bks.) InterVarsity Pr.

Wright, N. T. Evil & the Justice of God. 2006. (ENG.). 176p. 18.00 *(978-0-8308-3398-6(6)*, IVP Bks.) InterVarsity Pr.

Yankoski, Mike & Yankoski, Danae. Zealous Love: A Practical Guide to Social Justice, 1 vol. 2009. (ENG.). 240p. pap. 16.99 *(978-0-310-29076-6(7))* Zondervan.

CHRISTIANITY AND LAW
see Religion and Law

CHRISTIANITY AND LITERATURE
see also Christian Literature

Achinstein, Sharon. Literature & Dissent in Milton's England. 2008. (ENG., Illus.). 316p. pap. 42.00 *(978-0-521-05070-8(7))* Cambridge Univ. Pr.

Ainsworth, David. Milton & the Spiritual Reader. 2010. 244p. pap. 39.95 *(978-0-415-88390-0(3))* Routledge.

Atkins, G. Douglas. Literary Paths to Religious Understanding: Essays on Dryden, Pope, Keats, George Eliot, Joyce, T. S. Eliot, & E. B. White. 2009. (ENG.). 196p. 89.00 *(978-0-230-62147-3(3))* Palgrave Macmillan.

Badir, Patricia. The Maudlin Impression: English Literary Images of Mary Magdalene, 1550-1700. 2009. (ND Reformations: Medieval & Early Modern Ser.). (ENG.). 304p. pap. 38.00 *(978-0-268-02215-0(1))* Univ. of Notre Dame Pr.

Baker, Christopher Paul. Religion in the Age of Shakespeare, 1 vol. 2007. (Age of Shakespeare Ser.). (Illus.). 264p. 75.00 *(978-0-313-33636-2(9)*, GR3636, Greenwood Pr.) Greenwood Publishing Group, Inc.

Beauregard, David N. Catholic Theology in Shakespeare's Plays. 2007. 226p. 49.50 *(978-0-87413-002-7(6))* Univ. of Delaware Pr.

Blanton, Virginia & Scheck, Helene. Intertexts: Studies in Anglo-Saxon Culture Presented to Paul E. Szarmach. 2007. *(978-0-86698-382-2(1))* Arizona State Univ., Arizona Ctr. for Medieval & Renaissance Studies.

Branch, Lori. Rituals of Spontaneity: Sentiment & Secularism from Free Prayer to Wordsworth. 2006. (Illus.). 362p. 44.95 *(978-1-932792-11-9(2))* Baylor Univ. Pr.

Brown, John. John Bunyan: His Life Times & Work. 3rd ed. 2007. (Illus.). 522p. pap. 45.00 *(978-1-55635-219-5(0)*, Wipf and Stock) Wipf & Stock Pubs.

—John Bunyan His Life Times & Work. 2006. (Illus.). pap. 40.95 *(978-1-4286-5050-3(4))* Kessinger Publishing, LLC.

Bruner, Kurt & Bruner, Olivia. Twilight Phenomenon: Forbidden Fruit or Thirst-Quenching Fantasy? 2009. 173p. pap. 14.99 *(978-0-7684-3136-0(0))* Destiny Image Pubs.

Buccola, Regina & Hopkins, Lisa, eds. Marian Moments in Early Modern British Drama. 2007. (Studies in Performance & Early Modern Drama Ser.). 198p. 99.95 *(978-0-7546-5637-1(3))* Ashgate Publishing Co.

Bunyan, John. All-in-One Curriculum for the Pilgrim's Progress. 2006. (Illus.). 496p. 39.99 incl. cd-rom *(978-1-893345-77-5(7))* Answers in Genesis Ministries.

Bush, Harold K. Mark Twain & the Spiritual Crisis of His Age. 2007. (Studies in American Literary Realism & Naturalism). (Illus.). 360p. 47.50 *(978-0-8173-1538-2(1))* Univ. of Alabama Pr.

Bush, Harold K., Jr. Mark Twain & the Spiritual Crisis of His Age. 2008. (Amer Lit Realism & Naturalism Ser.). (ENG., Illus.). 352p. pap. 29.95 *(978-0-8173-5548-7(0))* Univ. of Alabama Pr.

Cairns, William. The Religion of Dr Johnson & Other Essays. 2007. 152p. per. *(978-1-4067-8806-8(6)*, Pomona Pr.) Read Bks.

Clarke, Peter & Methuen, Charlotte, eds. The Church & Literature. 2012. (Studies in Church History Ser.: Volume 48). (Illus.). 528p. 80.00

(978-0-9546809-9-2(5)) Ecclesiastical History Society GBR. Dist: Boydell & Brewer, Inc.

Colon, Susan E. Victorian Parables. 2012. (New Directions in Religion & Literature Ser.). (ENG.). 176p. 100.00 (978-0-8264-4348-9(6)); pap. 29.95 (978-1-4411-4650-2(4)) Continuum International Publishing Group, Ltd. GBR. Dist: National Bk. Network.

Corelle, Laurel Snow. A Poet's High Argument: Elizabeth Bishop & Christianity. 2008. (Illus.). 152p. 34.95 (978-1-57003-762-7(0)) Univ. of South Carolina Pr.

Courtmanche, Jason Charles. How Nathaniel Hawthorne's Narratives Are Shaped by Sin: His Use of Biblical Typology in His Four Major Works. 2008. 268p. 109.95 (978-0-7734-5017-2(3)) Mellen, Edwin Pr., The.

Cowan, Louise & Guinness, Os, eds. Invitation to the Classics: A Guide to Books You've Always Wanted to Read. 2006. (Masterworks Ser.). (Illus.). 384p. pap. 24.99 (978-0-8010-6810-2(X)) Baker Bks.

Cox, John D. The Devil & the Sacred in English Drama, 1350-1642. 2006. (ENG., Illus.). 268p. pap. 53.00 (978-0-521-03118-9(4)) Cambridge Univ. Pr.

Davidson, Clifford. Festivals & Plays in Late Medieval Britain. 2007. (Illus.). 216p. 99.95 (978-0-7546-6052-1(4)) Ashgate Publishing Co.

Downey, Deane E. D. & Porter, Stanley E., eds. Christian Worldview & the Academic Disciplines: Crossing the Academy. 2009. (McMaster Divinity College Press General Ser.). 542p. pap. 53.00 (978-1-60608-529-5(8), Pickwick Pubns.) Wipf & Stock Pubs.

Dunan-Page, Anne. The Cambridge Companion to Bunyan. 2010. (Cambridge Companions to Literature Ser.). (ENG.). 212p. pap. 29.99 (978-0-521-73308-3(1)) Cambridge Univ. Pr.

Dunan-Page, Anne, ed. The Cambridge Companion to Bunyan. 2010. (Cambridge Companions to Literature Ser.). (ENG.). 212p. 85.00 (978-0-521-51526-9(2)) Cambridge Univ. Pr.

Dyas, Dee & Thomson, R. M. The Bury Bible. 2008. (Illus.). 102p. pap. 170.00 (978-1-84384-066-4(9), D. S. Brewer) Boydell & Brewer, Ltd. GBR. Dist: Boydell & Brewer, Inc.

Ellenzweig, Sarah. The Fringes of Belief: English Literature, Ancient Heresy, & the Politics of Freethinking, 1660-1760. 2008. (ENG.). 256p. 60.00 (978-0-8047-5877-2(8)) Stanford Univ. Pr.

Ellis, Jim. From Malt to Marriage: Nursery Rhymes & the Tales They Tell. 2007. (978-1-933197-37-1(4)) Orange Frazer Pr.

Fox, Michael & Sharma, Manish, eds. Old Engliterature & the Old Testament. 2011. (Toronto Anglo-Saxon Ser.). (Illus.). 400p. **(978-0-8020-9854-2(1))** Univ. of Toronto Pr.

Franke, William. Poetry & Apocalypse: Theological Disclosures of Poetic Language. 2008. (ENG.). 232p. 60.00 (978-0-8047-5910-6(3)) Stanford Univ. Pr.

Froude, James. Bunyan. 2007. (ENG.). 188p. 37.95 (978-0-548-05027-9(9)) Kessinger Publishing, LLC.

Froude, James Anthony. Bunyan. 2011. (Cambridge Library Collection - English Men of Letters Ser.). (ENG.). 194p. pap. 19.99 **(978-1-108-03466-1(7))** Cambridge Univ. Pr.

Gaarden, Bonnie. The Christian Goddess: Archetype & Theology in the Fantasies of George MacDonald. 2011. (ENG.). 224p. 65.00 (978-1-61147-008-6(0)) Fairleigh Dickinson Univ. Pr.

Gandolfo, Anita. Faith & Fiction: Christian Literature in America Today, 1 vol. 2007. 208p. 44.95 (978-0-275-99196-8(2), C9196, Praeger Pubs.) Greenwood Publishing Group, Inc.

Giacomini, Michela P. Sir Richard Blackmore & the Bible: A Reading of His Physico-Theological Poems. 2006. (ENG.). 184p. pap. 41.99 (978-0-7618-3560-8(1)) Univ. Pr. of America, Inc.

Giannone, Richard. Flannery O'Connor, Hermit Novelist: With a New Preface by the Author. 2010. 312p. pap. 29.95 (978-1-57003-910-2(0)) Univ. of South Carolina Pr.

Giles, Paul. American Catholic Arts & Fictions: Culture, Ideology, Aesthetics. 2008. (Cambridge Studies in American Literature & Culture Ser.). (ENG.). 564p. pap. 74.00 (978-0-521-05773-8(6)) Cambridge Univ. Pr.

González, Eduardo. Cuba & the Fall: Christian Text & Queer Narrative in the Fiction of José Lezama Lima & Reinaldo Arenas. 2010. (New World Studies). (ENG., Illus.). 320p. (C). (gr. 13-17). pap. 32.50 (978-0-8139-2982-8(2)); (gr. 17). 69.50 (978-0-8139-2981-1(4)) Univ. Pr. of Virginia.

Gretlund, Jan No & Westarp, Karl-He, eds. Flannery O'Connors Radical Reality. 2007. 216p. pap. 21.95 (978-1-57003-717-7(5)) Univ. of South Carolina Pr.

Grey, Mary & Forde. Lantern & the Looking Glass. 190p. 16.00 (978-0-281-04906-6(8)) SPCK Publishing GBR. Dist: Pilgrim Pr., The/United Church Pr.

Guibbory, Achsah. Ceremony & Community from Herbert to Milton: Literature, Religion, & Cultural Conflict in Seventeenth-Century England. 2006. (ENG.). 292p. pap. 58.00 (978-0-521-03244-5(X)) Cambridge Univ. Pr.

—Christian Identity, Jews, & Israel in 17th-Century England. 2010. (ENG., Illus.). 344p. 110.00 (978-0-19-955716-5(0)) Oxford Univ. Pr., Inc.

Guite, Malcolm. Faith, Hope & Poetry: Theology & the Poetic Imagination. 2010. (Ashgate Studies in Theology, Imagination & the Arts Ser.). 268p. 99.95 (978-0-7546-6906-7(8)) Ashgate Publishing Co.

Hamlin, Hannibal. Psalm Culture & Early Modern English Literature. 2007. (ENG.). 304p. pap. 63.00 (978-0-521-03706-8(9)) Cambridge Univ. Pr.

Hammond, Jeffrey A. The American Puritan Elegy: A Literary & Cultural Study. 2008. (Cambridge Studies in American Literature & Culture Ser.). (ENG.). 284p. pap. 53.00 (978-0-521-10381-7(9)) Cambridge Univ. Pr.

Hardy, Clarence. James Balwins God. 2009. (ENG.). 168p. pap. 19.95 (978-1-57233-692-6(7)) Univ. of Tennessee Pr.

Hass, Andrew, et al. The Oxford Handbook of English Literature & Theology. 2007. (Oxford Handbooks Ser.). (ENG.). 908p. 175.00 (978-0-19-927197-9(6)) Oxford Univ. Pr., Inc.

Hill, Wm. Thomas, ed. Lonely without God: Graham Greene's Quixotic Journey of Faith. 2007. lib. bdg. (978-1-933146-39-3(7)) Academica Pr., LLC.

Hume, Anthea. Edmund Spenser: Protestant Poet. 2008. (ENG.). 212p. pap. 32.99 (978-0-521-09160-2(8)) Cambridge Univ. Pr.

Isaac, Gordon L. Left Behind or Left Befuddled: The Subtle Dangers of Popularizing the End Times. 2008. pap. 16.95 (978-0-8146-2420-3(0)) Liturgical Pr.

Jackson, Kenneth S. & Marotti, Arthur F., eds. Shakespeare & Religion: Early Modern & Postmodern Perspectives. 2011. (ENG.). 304p. pap. 38.00 (978-0-268-03270-8(X)) Univ. of Notre Dame Pr.

Jacobs, Alan. The Narnian: The Life & Imagination of C. S. Lewis. (Plus Ser.). (ENG., Illus.). 2008. 384p. pap. 14.95 (978-0-06-144872-0(9), HarperOne) 2006. 368p. per. 14.95 (978-0-06-087269-4(1), Harper San Francisco) HarperCollins Pubs.

—Wayfaring: Essays Pleasant & Unpleasant. 2010. 167p. pap. 18.00 (978-0-8028-6568-7(2)) Eerdmans, William B. Publishing Co.

Jasper, David. Rhetoric, Power, & Community. 2009. (David Jasper Reprint Ser.). 184p. pap. 21.00 (978-1-60608-831-9(9), Wipf and Stock) Wipf & Stock Pubs.

—The Study of Literature & Religion. 2009. (David Jasper Reprint Ser.). 178p. pap. 20.00 (978-1-60608-832-6(7), Wipf and Stock) Wipf & Stock Pubs.

Jasper, David, ed. Postmodernism, Literature, & the Future of Theology. 2009. (David Jasper Reprint Ser.). 204p. pap. 23.00 (978-1-60608-829-6(7), Wipf and Stock) Wipf & Stock Pubs.

Jasper, David & Allen, Smith. Between Truth & Fiction: A Narrative Reader in Literature & Theology. 2010. (ENG.). 300p. pap. 55.00 (978-0-334-04192-4(9), SCM Pr.) Hymns Ancient & Modern Ltd GBR. Dist: Westminster John Knox Pr.

Jasper, David & Crowder, Colin, eds. European Literature & Theology in the Twentieth Century. 2009. (David Jasper Reprint Ser.). 202p. pap. 23.00 (978-1-60608-830-2(0), Wipf and Stock) Wipf & Stock Pubs.

Jasper, David & Smith, Allen, eds. Between Truth & Fiction: A Narrative Reader in Literature & Theology. 2010. (ENG.). 192p. (C). pap. 39.95 (978-1-60258-319-1(6)) Baylor Univ. Pr.

Jeffrey, David Lyle & Maillet, Gregory P. Christianity & Literature: Philosophical Foundations & Critical Practice. 2011. (Christian Worldview Integration Ser.). (ENG.). 336p. pap. 24.00 (978-0-8308-2817-3(6), IVP Acad.) InterVarsity Pr.

Jensen, Phebe. Religion & Revelry in Shakespeare's Festive World. 2009. (ENG., Illus.). 280p. 98.00 (978-0-521-50639-7(5)) Cambridge Univ. Pr.

Kabir, Ananya Jahanara. Paradise, Death & Doomsday in Anglo-Saxon Literature. 2006. (Cambridge Studies in Anglo-Saxon England Ser.). (ENG.). 224p. pap. 42.00 (978-0-521-03060-1(9)) Cambridge Univ. Pr.

Keiser, Albert. The Influence of Christianity on the Vocabulary of Old English Poetry. 2009. (ENG.). 153p. 30.99 (978-1-117-22834-1(7)); pap. 20.75 (978-1-117-22835-8(5)) BiblioBazaar.

—The Influence of Christianity on the Vocabulary of Old English Poetry. 2007. (ENG.). 152p. 36.95 (978-0-548-15554-7(2)); 156p. per. 21.95 (978-1-4304-4993-5(4)) Kessinger Publishing, LLC.

Kerry, Paul E. The Ring & the Cross: Christianity & the Lord of the Rings. 2010. (ENG.). 310p. 80.00 (978-1-61147-064-2(1)) Fairleigh Dickinson Univ. Pr.

—The Ring & the Cross: Christianity & the Writings of J.R.R. Tolkien. 2010. (978-0-8386-4224-5(1)) Fairleigh Dickinson Univ. Pr.

Knott, John R. Discourses of Martyrdom in English Literature, 1563-1694. 2010. (ENG., Illus.). 304p. pap. 33.99 (978-0-521-13158-2(8)) Cambridge Univ. Pr.

Kowalik, Barbara. Betwixt Engelaunde & Englene Londe: Dialogic Poetics in Early English Religious Lyric. 2011. (Studies in English Medieval Language & Literature Ser.). 258p. 72.95 (978-3-631-61695-6(3)) Lang, Peter GmbH, Europaischer Verlag der Wissenschaften DEU. Dist: Lang, Peter.

Lee, Maurice S. Uncertain Chances: Science, Skepticism, & Belief in Nineteenth-Century American Literature, 1 vol. 2011. (ENG.). 256p. 65.00 (978-0-19-979757-8(9)) Oxford Univ. Pr., Inc.

Leigh, S.J., David J. Apocalyptic Patterns in Twentieth-Century Fiction. 2008. (ENG.). 288p. pap. 28.00 (978-0-268-03380-4(3)) Univ. of Notre Dame Pr.

Leithart, Peter J. Deep Comedy: Trinity, Tragedy, & Hope in Western Literature. 2006. (ENG.). 159p. pap. 15.00 (978-1-59128-027-9(3)) Canon Pr.

Loewenstein, David. Representing Revolution in Milton & his Contemporaries: Religion, Politics, & Polemics in Radical Puritanism. 2007. (ENG., Illus.). 428p. pap. 60.00 (978-0-521-03298-8(9)) Cambridge Univ. Pr.

Loewenstein, David & Marshall, John, eds. Heresy, Literature & Politics in Early Modern English Culture. 2009. 332p. pap. 42.00 (978-0-521-12685-4(1)) Cambridge Univ. Pr.

Lowe, Peter. Christian Romanticism: T. S. Eliot's Response to Percy Shelley. 2006. 84.95 (978-1-934043-34-9(6)) Cambria Pr.

Lundin, Roger, ed. Invisible Conversations: Religion in the Literature of America. 2009. (ENG.). 205p. 39.95 (978-1-60258-147-0(9)) Baylor Univ. Pr.

Markos, Louis. From Achilles to Christ: Why Christians Should Read the Pagan Classics. 2007. (ENG., Illus.). 264p. per. 24.00 (978-0-8308-2593-6(2), IVP Acad.) InterVarsity Pr.

Martin, Catherine Gimelli. Milton among the Puritans: The Case for Historical Revisionism. 2010. (Illus.). 378p. 99.95 (978-1-4094-0856-7(6)) Ashgate Publishing Co.

Marx, Walter. Transfer des Sakralen: Die Säkularisierung christlicher Denkformen, Motive und Gebräuche in Cervantes' Don Quijote. 2008. (Europäische Hochschulschriften. Reihe 24: Ibero-Romanische Sprachen und Literaturen Ser.). 314p. pap. 74.95 (978-3-631-58155-1(6)) Lang, Peter GmbH, Europaischer Verlag der Wissenschaften DEU. Dist: Lang, Peter.

Mase-Hasegawa, Emi. Christ in Japanese Culture: Theological Themes in Shusaku Endo's Literary Works. 2008. (Brill's Japanese Studies Library Ser.). 248p. (978-90-04-16596-0(7)) BRILL.

May, Cedrick. Evangelism & Resistance in the Black Atlantic, 1760-1835. 2008. (ENG.). 168p. 39.95 (978-0-8203-2798-3(0)) Univ. of Georgia Pr.

Mayer, Jean-Christophe. Shakespeare's Hybrid Faith: History, Religion & the Stage. 2006. (Early Modern Literature in History Ser.). (ENG., Illus.). 248p. 84.00 (978-0-230-00525-9(X)) Palgrave Macmillan.

McAloon, Francis. The Language of Poetry As a Form of Prayer: The Theo-Poetic Aesthetics of Gerard Manley Hopkins. 2008. 260p. 109.95 (978-0-7734-5022-6(X)) Mellen, Edwin Pr., The.

McMullen, Joanne Halleran & Peede, Jon Parrish, eds. Inside the Church of Flannery O'Connor: Sacrament, Sacramental, & the Sacred in Her Fiction. 2008. 232p. pap. 22.95 (978-0-88146-138-1(5)) Mercer Univ. Pr.

Miller, Greg & Miller. George Herbert's Holy Patterns: Reforming Individuals in Community. 2007. (Continuum Literary Studies). (ENG., Illus.). 192p. 135.00 (978-0-8264-2807-3(X)) Continuum International Publishing Group, Ltd. GBR. Dist: National Bk. Network.

Mounsey, Chris. Being the Body of Christ: Towards a Twentieth-Century Homosexual Theology for the Anglican Church. 2012. (Gender, Theology & Spirituality Ser.). (ENG.). 224p. (C). 99.95 (978-1-84553-951-1(6)); pap. 29.95 (978-1-84553-952-8(4)) Equinox Publishing Ltd. GBR. Dist: Brown, David Bk. Co., The.

Nisly, Lamar. Wingless Chickens, Bayou Catholics, & Pilgrim Wayfarers: Constructions of Audience & Tone in O'Connor, Percy, & Gautreaux. 2011. (Flannery O'Connor Ser.). (Illus.). 256p. 35.00 (978-0-88146-214-2(4)) Mercer Univ. Pr.

Nowak, Maciej. Koncepcja Dziejów W Powiesciach Historycznych: Teodor Jeske-Choinski, Zofia Kossak, Hanna Malewska. 2009. (POL.). 347p. (978-83-7363-804-4(0)) Katolicki Uniwersytet Lubelski, Wydawnictwo.

Oddie, William. Chesterton & the Romance of Orthodoxy: The Making of GKC, 1874-1908. 2010. (ENG.). 416p. pap. 29.95 (978-0-19-958201-3(7)) Oxford Univ. Pr., Inc.

O'Gorman, Farrell. Peculiar Crossroads: Flannery O'Connor, Walker Percy, & Catholic Vision in Postwar Southern Fiction. 2007. (Southern Literary Studies). 272p. pap. 22.95 (978-0-8071-3335-4(3)) Louisiana State Univ. Pr.

Otten, Willemien, et al. How the West Was Won: Essays on the Literary Imagination, the Canon, & the Christian Middle Ages. 2010. (Illus.). 422p. (978-90-04-18496-1(1)) BRILL.

Parker, John. The Aesthetics of Antichrist: From Christian Drama to Christopher Marlowe. 2007. 252p. 39.95 (978-0-8014-4519-4(1)) Cornell Univ. Pr.

Pearce, Joseph. The Quest for Shakespeare. 2008. 216p. 21.95 (978-1-58617-224-4(7)) Ignatius Pr.

Perkin, J. Russell. Theology & the Victorian Novel. 2009. (ENG.). 273p. (C). (978-0-7735-3606-7(X)) McGill-Queen's Univ. Pr.

Peters, Kate. Print Culture & the Early Quakers. 2009. (Cambridge Studies in Early Modern British History Ser.). (ENG., Illus.). 292p. pap. 51.00 (978-0-521-09312-5(0)) Cambridge Univ. Pr.

Potts, Willard. Joyce & the Two Irelands. 2010. (Literary Modernism Ser.). (ENG.). 232p. pap. 25.00 (978-0-292-71885-2(3)) Univ. of Texas Pr.

Ramsey, G. Lee, Jr. Preachers & Misfits, Prophets & Thieves: The Minister in Southern Fiction. 2008. (ENG.). 208p. pap. 20.00 (978-0-664-23224-5(8)) Westminster John Knox Pr.

Remer, Gary. Humanism & the Rhetoric of Toleration. 2008. (ENG.). 332p. per. 27.95 (978-0-271-02811-8(4)) Pennsylvania State Univ. Pr.

Rhodes, Ron. Unlocking the Mysteries of The Lost Symbol. 2009. pap. (978-0-7369-1886-2(8)) Harvest Hse. Pubs.

Richardson, Marianna Edwards & Thackeray, Christine. Latter-Day Truths in Narnia Dr. Marianna Edwards Richardson & Christine Edwards Thackeray. 2008. 15.99 (978-1-59955-193-7(4)) Cedar Fort, Inc./CFI Distribution.

Roberts, Dave. The Twilight Gospel: The Spiritual Roots of the Stephenie Meyer Vampire Saga, 1 vol. 2009. (ENG., Illus.). 160p. pap. 12.99 (978-1-85424-976-0(2), Monarch Bks.) Lion Hudson PLC GBR. Dist: Kregel Pubns.

Roberts, Michael John & Roberts, Michael. The Humblest Sparrow: The Poetry of Venantius Fortunatus. 2009. (ENG., Illus.). 376p. (C). 90.00 (978-0-472-11683-6(5)) Univ. of Michigan Pr.

Roberts, Robert C., et al. Finding a Common Thread: Reading Great Texts from Homer to O'Connor. 2012. (ENG.). 456p. (C). pap. 35.00 **(978-1-58731-254-0(9))** St. Augustine's Pr., Inc.

Roe, Dinah. Christina Rossetti's Faithful Imagination: The Devotional Poetry & Prose. annot. ed. 2007. (ENG.). 248p. 84.00 (978-0-230-00507-5(1)) Palgrave Macmillan.

Scheck, Helene. Reform & Resistance: Formations of Female Subjectivity in Early Medieval Ecclesiastical Culture. 2009. (SUNY Series in Medieval Studies). 224p. pap. 24.95 (978-0-7914-7484-6(4), Suny Pr.) State Univ. of New York Pr.

Scheinberg, Cynthia. Women's Poetry & Religion in Victorian England: Jewish Identity & Christian Culture. 2009. (Cambridge Studies in Nineteenth-Century Literature & Culture Ser.). (ENG.). 296p. pap. 41.00 (978-0-521-09983-7(8)) Cambridge Univ. Pr.

Schwartz, Regina. Sacramental Poetics at the Dawn of Secularism: When God Left the World. 2008. (Cultural Memory in the Present Ser.). (ENG.). 216p. 60.00 (978-0-8047-5667-9(8)); pap. 19.95 (978-0-8047-5833-8(6)) Stanford Univ. Pr.

Seed, John. Dissenting Histories: Politics, History & Memory in Eighteenth-Century England. 2009. (ENG.). 192p. (gr. 17). 100.00 (978-0-7486-2151-4(2)) Edinburgh Univ. Pr. GBR. Dist: Columbia Univ. Pr.

Shaheen, Naseeb. Biblical References in Shakespeare's Plays. 2011. (ENG.). 880p. 125.00 **(978-1-61149-358-0(7))** Univ. of Delaware Pr.

Short, Robert L. The Parables of Dr. Seuss. 2008. (ENG., Illus.). 95p. pap. 15.00 (978-0-664-23047-0(4)) Westminster John Knox Pr.

Shuger, Debora Kuller. The Renaissance Bible: Scholarship, Sacrifice, & Subjectivity. 2010. (ENG., Illus.). 313p. (C). pap. 39.95 (978-1-60258-309-2(9)) Baylor Univ. Pr.

Sinfield, Alan. Literature in Protestant England, 1560-1660. 2009. (Routledge Revivals Ser.). (ENG.). 160p. 120.00 (978-0-415-55290-5(7)) Routledge.

—Literature in Protestant England 1560-1660 (Routledge Revivals) 2009. 172p. pap. 39.95 (978-0-415-55997-3(9)) Routledge.

Spargo, Tamsin. John Bunyan. 2011. (Writers & Their Work Ser.). (C). (ENG.). 80.00 (978-0-7463-1049-6(8)); pap. 26.00 (978-0-7463-0982-7(1)) Northcote Hse. Publishers, Ltd. GBR. Dist: Brown, David Bk. Co., The.

Spencer, Jamie. Fictional Religion: Keeping the New Testament New. 2011. 164p. pap. 18.00 **(978-1-59815-032-2(4))** Polebridge Pr.

Stapleton, Julia. Christianity, Patriotism, & Nationhood: The England of G. K. Chesterton. 2009. (ENG., Illus.). 250p. 83.99 (978-0-7391-2613-4(X)); pap. 34.99 (978-0-7391-2614-1(8)) Lexington Bks.

Stein, William Bysshe. Hawthorne's Faust: A Study of the Devil Archetype. 2011. 182p. 42.95 **(978-1-258-02412-3(8))** Literary Licensing, LLC.

Streete, Adrian. Protestantism & Drama in Early Modern England. 2009. (ENG.). 308p. 103.00 (978-0-521-76017-1(8)) Cambridge Univ. Pr.

Sturch, Richard. Four Christian Fantasists a Study of the Fantastic Writings of George MacDonald, Charles Williams, C S Lewis & J R R Tolkien. 2007. 148p. per. (978-3-905703-04-7(1)) Walking Tree Pubs.

Sykes, John D. Flannery O'Connor, Walker Percy, & the Aesthetic of Revelation. 2007. (ENG.). 208p. (C). 39.95 (978-0-8262-1757-8(5)) Univ. of Missouri Pr.

Targoff, Ramie. John Donne, Body & Soul. (ENG., Illus.). 2009. 232p. pap. 20.00 (978-0-226-78964-4(0)) 2008. 208p. 30.00 (978-0-226-78963-7(2)) Univ. of Chicago Pr.

Taylor, Jefferey H. Four Levels of Meaning in the York Cycle of Mystery Plays: A Study in Medieval Allegory. 2006. 128p. (C). 89.95 (978-0-7734-5578-8(7)) Mellen, Edwin Pr., The.

Treanor, Lucia. The Symmetrical Patterning in Franciscan Writings of the Late Middle Ages: A Study of the Palindromic Structuring of Language. 2011. (ENG.). 272p. 119.95 **(978-0-7734-2535-4(7))** Mellen, Edwin Pr., The.

Tuck, William Powell. The Left Behind Fantasy: The Theology Behind the Left Behind Tales. 2010. 166p. pap. 19.00 (978-1-60899-277-5(2), Resource Pubns.) Wipf & Stock Pubs.

Vos, Nelvin. Inter-Actions: Relationships of Religion & Drama. 2009. (ENG.). 204p. pap. 31.50 (978-0-7618-4469-3(4)) Univ. Pr. of America, Inc.

Waldmeir, John C. Cathedrals of Bone: The Role of the Body in Contemporary Catholic Literature. 3rd ed. 2009. (ENG.). 224p. 55.00 (978-0-8232-3060-0(0)) Fordham Univ. Pr.

Walrath, Douglas Alan. Displacing the Divine: The Minister in the Mirror of American Fiction. 2010. (Religion & American Culture Ser.). (ENG., Illus.). 400p. (gr. 17). 55.00 (978-0-231-15106-1(3)) Columbia Univ. Pr.

Wheeler, Michael. The Old Enemies: Catholic & Protestant in Nineteenth-Century English Culture. 2011. (ENG.). 370p. pap. 45.00 (978-0-521-29281-8(6)) Cambridge Univ. Pr.

White, Laura Mooneyham. Jane Austen's Anglicanism. 2011. (Illus.). 228p. 89.95 (978-1-4094-1863-4(4)) Ashgate Publishing Co.

Wich-Schwarz, Johannes. Transformation of Language & Religion in Rainer Maria Rilke. 2011. 172p. (C). 73.95 **(978-1-4331-1481-6(X))** Lang, Peter Publishing, Inc.

Wright, Andrew. Christianity & Critical Realism: Ambiguity, Truth & Theological Literacy. 2012. (New Studies in Critical Realism & Spirituality Ser.). (ENG.). 352p. 160.00 **(978-0-415-53957-9(9))** Routledge.

Zettersten, Arne. Double Worlds & Creative Process: Language & Life. 2011. (ENG., Illus.). 256p. 85.00 (978-0-230-62314-9(X)) Palgrave Macmillan.

CHRISTIANITY AND MEDICINE

see Medicine—Religious Aspects

CHRISTIANITY AND OTHER RELIGIONS

Abrahamsen, Valerie A. Goddess & God: A Holy Tension in the First Christian Centuries. 2006. (Marco Polo Monographs: 10). (Illus.). 270p. (C). 39.95 (978-0-9719496-3-8(8), Marco Polo Monographs) Shangri-La Pubns.

Adams, Graham. Christ & the Other: In Dialogue with Hick & Newbigin. 2010. 216p. 99.95 (978-1-4094-0028-8(X)) Ashgate Publishing Co.

Adogame, Afe, et al. African Traditions in the Study of Religion in Africa Emerging Trends Indigenous Spirituality & the Interface with Other World Religions. 2012. (Vitality of Indigenous Religions Ser.). (Illus.). 240p. 99.95 **(978-1-4094-1970-9(3))** Ashgate Publishing Co.

Almond, Ian. Two Faiths, One Banner: When Muslims Marched with Christians across Europe's Battlegrounds. 2011. (Illus.). 256p. pap. 19.95 (978-0-674-06176-7(4)) Harvard Univ. Pr.

Anderson, Don. For Heaven's Sake: Who Is Jesus? 2006. 125p. per. 9.95 (978-1-60002-139-8(5), 3976) Mountain Valley Publishing, LLC.

Angus, S. The Environment of Early Christianity. 2009. 254p. 34.99 (978-1-115-27340-4(X)); 30.99 (978-1-115-27339-8(6)); pap. 25.75 (978-1-115-27337-4(X)); pap. 26.75 (978-1-115-27338-1(8)) BiblioBazaar.

Angus, Samuel. The Environment of Early Christianity. 2009. 148p. pap. (978-1-150-51227-8(X)) Books LLC.

Ankerberg, John & Burroughs, Dillon. How Is Christianity Different from Other Religions?, 8, Bk 2. 2008. (Contender's Bible Study Ser.). (ENG.). 112p. (gr. 11). pap. 7.99 (978-0-89957-780-7(6)) AMG Pubs.

Apel, William D. Signs of Peace: The Interfaith Letters of Thomas Merton. 2006. (Illus.). 202p. per. 22.00 (978-1-57075-681-8(3)) Orbis Bks.

Ariarajah, S. Wesley. The Bible & People of Other Faiths. 2009. 86p. (Orig.). pap. 12.00 (978-1-60608-908-8(0)) Wipf & Stock Pubs.

Arya, Ravi Prakash. Unraveling the Mysteries of Jesus the Christ. 2011. 152p. pap. (978-3-8454-0613-8(5)) Lambert Academic Publishing.

Asbridge, Thomas. The Crusades: The Authoritative History of the War for the Holy Land. 2011. (ENG.). 384p. pap. 19.99 (978-0-06-078729-5(5), Ecco) HarperCollins Pubs.

Athanassiadi, Polymnia. Vers la Pensée Unique: La Montée de L'intolérance Dans L'Antiquité Tardive. 2010. (Histoire Ser.). (FRE.). 192p. (C). pap. 38.00 (978-2-251-38100-8(7)) Societe d'edition Les Belles lettres FRA. Dist: ISD.

Balmer, Brice H. Meeting Our Multifaith Neighbors. 2006. (Illus.). 196p. per. 14.99 (978-0-8361-9339-8(3)) Herald Pr.

Barker, Gregory A. & Gregg, Stephen E. Jesus Beyond Christianity: The Classic Texts. 2010. (ENG.). 256p. 29.95 (978-0-19-955344-0(0)) Oxford Univ. Pr., Inc.

Barnes, Michael. Interreligious Learning: Dialogue, Spirituality & the Christian Imagination. 2011. (ENG.). 306p. 95.00 (978-1-107-01284-4(8)) Cambridge Univ. Pr.

Barron, Ds. Gnospel. 2007. 80p. per. 17.95 (978-1-59800-989-7(3)) Outskirts Pr., Inc.

Bartlett, W. B. Islam's War Against the Crusaders. 2009. (ENG., Illus.). 288p. 36.95 (978-0-7524-4681-3(9)) History Pr. Ltd.,The GBR. Dist: Independent Pubs. Group.

BeDuhn, Jason & Mirecki, Paul, eds. Frontiers of Faith: The Christian Encounter with Manichaeism in the Acts of Archelaus. 2007. (Nag Hammadi & Manichaean Studies). 192p. (978-90-04-16180-1(5)) BRILL.

Beekmann, Sharon. Enticed by the Light: The Terrifying Story of One Woman's Encounter with the New Age. 2011. 202p. pap. 22.00 (978-1-61097-151-5(5), Resource Pubns.) Wipf & Stock Pubs.

Bekele, Serawit. Hybridized Religious Practices. 2010. 72p. pap. (978-3-639-23294-3(1)) VDM Verlag Dr. Mueller e.K.

Benoît, Standaert. Sharing Sacred Space. 2009. 144p. pap. 19.95 (978-0-8146-3280-2(7), Liturgical Pr. Bks.) Liturgical Pr.

Berend, Nora. At the Gate of Christendom: Jews, Muslims & 'Pagans' in Medieval Hungary, C. 1000 - C. 1300. 2006. (Cambridge Studies in Medieval Life & Thought). (ENG., Illus.). 364p. pap. 74.00 (978-0-521-02720-5(9)) Cambridge Univ. Pr.

Béthune, Pierre-François de. Interreligious Hospitality: The Fulfillment of Dialogue. 2010. 21.95 (978-0-8146-3305-2(6)) Liturgical Pr.

Blake, Kenneth. God thanks for saving Me. 2009. 199p. pap. 21.34 (978-1-4357-5145-3(0)) Lulu Enterprises Inc.

Bock, Darrell L. The Missing Gospels: Unearthing the Truth Behind Alternative Christianities, 0 vols. 2007. 256p. per. 14.99 (978-0-7852-8906-7(2)) Nelson, Thomas Inc.

Boesel, Chris. Risking Proclamation, Respecting Difference: Christian Faith, Imperialistic Discourse & Abraham. 2010. (ENG.). 305p. (C). pap. 43.00 (978-0-227-17314-5(7)) Clarke, James Co., Ltd. GBR. Dist: Brown, David Bk. Co., The.

Boteler, Lori. Truth & Love in Religions. 2008. per. 25.00 (978-0-9798207-3-1(1)) LoJo Publishing.

Brighton, Simon & Welbourn, Terry. Echoes of the Goddess: A Quest for the Sacred Feminine in the British Landscape. 2010. (ENG., Illus.). 256p. 32.95 (978-0-7110-3419-8(2)) Allan, Ian Publishing GBR. Dist: BookMasters Distribution Services (BDS).

Brill, Alan. Judaism & Other Religions: Models of Understanding. 2010. (ENG.). 292p. 89.00 (978-0-230-62226-5(7)) Palgrave Macmillan.

Brockman, David R. No Longer the Same: Religious Others & the Liberation of Christian Theology. 2010. (New Approaches to Religion & Power Ser.). (ENG.). 208p. 89.00 (978-0-230-10855-4(5)) Palgrave Macmillan.

Brown, Brian, et al. Augustine & World Religions. 2008. (Augustine in Conversation: Tradition & Innovation Ser.). (ENG.). 310p. pap. 34.99 (978-0-7391-2580-9(X)) Lexington Bks.

Bruner, Kurt D. Oprah's Jesus: The Rise of Spirituality Without Religion. 2010. 151p. (978-0-7684-3434-7(3)); (978-0-7684-3435-4(1)) Destiny Image Pubs.

Cameron, Alan. The Last Pagans of Rome, 1 vol. 2010. (ENG., Illus.). 912p. 85.00 (978-0-19-974727-6(X)) Oxford Univ. Pr., Inc.

Campbell, Cynthia M. A Multitude of Blessings: A Christian Approach to Religious Diversity. 2006. (ENG.). 118p. per. 17.00 (978-0-664-22956-6(5)) Westminster John Knox Pr.

Campbell, Joan Cecelia. Phoebe: Patron & Emissary. 2009. pap. 3.50 (978-0-8146-5281-7(6)) Liturgical Pr.

Carafano, Vinnie. Reaching a Lost World: Cults & World Religions. 2010. (ENG.). 176p. (YA). 14.99 (978-1-57658-499-6(2)) YWAM Publishing.

Carpenter, Edward. Pagan & Christian Creeds. 2010. pap. 54.40 (978-1-61719-332-3(1)) Gorgias Pr., LLC.

—Pagan & Christian Creeds: Their Origin & Meaning. 2011. 324p. pap. 30.75 (978-1-179-05716-3(3)) 2010. 328p. pap. 30.75 (978-1-142-15609-1(5)) 2009. (ENG.). 320p. 36.99 (978-1-117-20866-4(4)) 2009. (ENG.). 320p. pap. 29.75 (978-1-117-20867-1(2)) BiblioBazaar.

—Pagan & Christian Creeds: Their Origin & Meaning. 2007. (ENG.). 192p. per. (978-1-4068-4393-4(8)) Echo Library.

—Pagan & Christian Creeds: Their Origin & Meaning. 2012. 328p. pap. (978-1-290-39164-1(5)) HardPr.

—Pagan & Christian Creeds: Their Origin & Meaning. 2010. 316p. 36.76 (978-1-169-31876-2(2)) pap. 24.76 (978-1-162-56086-1(X)); 45.95 (978-1-161-35050-0(0)) Kessinger Publishing, LLC.

—Pagan & Christian Creeds: Their Origin & Meaning. 2009. 242p. 34.99 (978-1-59547-501-5(X)) 2007. (ENG.). 244p. per. 17.99 (978-1-59547-763-7(2)) NuVision Pubns., LLC.

—Pagan & Christian Creeds: Their Origin & Meaning. 2011. 276p. pap. (978-3-8424-4006-7(5)) Tredition GmbH.

—Pagan & Christian Creeds: Their origin & Meaning. 2010. (ENG.). 322p. pap. 30.75 (978-1-176-97149-3(2)) BiblioBazaar.

—Pagan & Christian Creeds: Their origin & Meaning. 2010. 216p. pap. (978-1-4076-1445-8(2)) HardPr.

—Pagan & Christian Creeds; Their Origin & Meaning. 2010. (Illus.). 168p. pap. 25.51 (978-1-153-67602-1(8)) General Bks. LLC.

Carr, Matthew. Blood & Faith: The Purging of Muslim Spain. 2011. (ENG., Illus.). 368p. pap. 19.95 (978-1-59558-640-7(7)) New Pr., The.

Cathcart, Mark. Charis - the Human Voice of the Holy Bible. 2010. (ENG.). 150p. pap. 16.95 (978-1-84694-356-0(6)) Hunt, John Publishing Ltd. GBR. Dist: National Bk. Network.

Cattoi, Thomas. Divine Contingency: Theologies of Divine Embodiment in Maximos the Confessor & Tsong kha Pa. 2008. 105.00 (978-1-59333-970-8(4)) Gorgias Pr., LLC.

Chenique, François & Rangdreul, Christian. Souvenirs Métaphysiques D'Orient et D'Occident. 2009. (FRE.). 233p. (978-2-296-08564-0(4)) Harmattan Pr.

Chesterton, G. K. The Everlasting Man. 2011. 224p. pap. 12.99 (978-1-61203-254-2(0)) Bottom of the Hill Publishing.

—The Everlasting Man. 2008. (ENG.). 232p. per. (978-1-4065-9100-2(9)) Dodo Pr.

—The Everlasting Man. 2007. (Dover Books on Western Philosophy Ser.). (ENG.). 288p. per. 9.95 (978-0-486-46036-9(3)) Dover Pubns., Inc.

—The Everlasting Man. 2007. 262p. per. 14.95 (978-1-59856-016-9(6)) Hendrickson Pubs. Marketing, LLC.

—The Everlasting Man. 2008. 180p. 29.99 (978-1-60459-247-4(8)); per. 8.99 (978-1-60459-246-7(X)) Wilder Pubns., Ltd.

Chung, Paul S. The Cave & the Butterfly: An Intercultural Theory of Interpretation & Religion in the Public Sphere. 2010. 316p. pap. 35.00 (978-1-60608-530-1(1), Cascade Bks.) Wipf & Stock Pubs.

Chung, S. & Chung, Paul S. Constructing Irregular Theology: Bamboo & Minjung in East Asian Perspective. 2009. (Studies in Systematic Theology Ser.). (978-90-04-17417-7(6)) BRILL.

Clarke, Clifton & Yong, Amos. Global Renewal, Religious Pluralism, & the Great Commission: Towards a Renewal Theology of Mission & Interreligious Encounter. 2011. (978-0-9819582-8-6(1)) Emeth Pr.

Clarke, James Freeman. Ten Great Religions: An Essay in Comparative Theology. l.t. ed. 2007. (ENG.). 568p. pap. 32.99 (978-1-4264-8211-3(6)) BiblioBazaar.

—Ten Great Religions: An Essay in Comparative Theology. 2007. (ENG.). 544p. 57.95 (978-0-548-08262-1(6)); 57.95 (978-0-548-11354-7(8)) Kessinger Publishing, LLC.

—Ten Great Religions; an Essay in Comparative Theology; a Comparison of All Religions, by James Freeman Clarke + Part. 2006. 456p. per. 29.99 (978-1-4255-5074-5(6)) MPublishing.

—Ten Great Religions; an Essay in Comparative Theology, by James Freeman Clarke + Part. 2006. 544p. per. 29.99 (978-1-4255-6024-9(5)) MPublishing.

Cobb, Gary. Three Religions One Temple Mount. 2007. 396p. per. 22.99 (978-1-60266-558-3(3)) Xulon Pr., Inc.

Comfort, Ray. World Religions in a Nutshell. 2008. (Illus.). 176p. 14.99 (978-0-88270-669-6(1)) Bridge-Logos Foundation.

Corduan, Winfried. A Tapestry of Faiths: The Common Threads Between Christianity & World Religions. 2009. 248p. pap. 27.00 (978-1-60608-841-8(6), Wipf and Stock) Wipf & Stock Pubs.

Cornille, Catherine, ed. Many Mansions? Multiple Religious Belonging & Christian Identity. 2010. 158p. pap. 19.00 (978-1-60899-453-3(8), Wipf and Stock) Wipf & Stock Pubs.

Cory, Steven & Burroughs, Dillon, compiled by. Comparing Christianity with World Religions. rev. ed. 2007. (ENG.). 22p. 1.99 (978-0-8024-8213-6(9)) Moody Pubs.

Cosgrove, Mark P. Foundations of Christian Thought: Faith, Learning, & the Christian Worldview, 1 vol. 2006. (Illus.). 192p. pap. 15.99 (978-0-8254-2434-2(8)) Kregel Pubns.

Cotham, Perry C. One World, Many Neighbors: A Christian Perspective on Worldviews. 2008. 268p. (978-0-89112-522-8(1)) Abilene Christian Univ. Pr.

Cracknell, Kenneth. In Good & Generous Faith: Christian Responses to Religious Pluralism. 2012. 300p. pap. (978-0-7162-0596-8(3)) Saint Andrew Pr., Ltd.

Cyprian of Carthage. On the Church: Select Letters, Bk.33. 2007. (ENG.). 250p. pap. 20.00 (978-0-88141-313-7(5)) St. Vladimir's Seminary Pr.

De Give, Bernard. A Trappist Meeting Monks from Tibet. 2010. (Illus.). 356p. pap. (978-0-85244-535-8(0)) Gracewing, Ltd.

Dewick, E. C. The Christian Attitude to Other Religions. 2011. (ENG.). 232p. pap. 22.99 (978-0-521-24260-8(6)) Cambridge Univ. Pr.

Dorhauer, John & Culver, Sheldon. Steeplejacking: How the Christian Right Is Hijacking Mainstream Religion. 2007. (ENG.). 200p. per. 14.95 (978-0-9771972-8-6(X)) Ig Publishing, Inc.

Driscoll, Mark. On Who Is God? 2008. (Book You'll Actually Read Ser.). 88p. pap. 9.99 (978-1-4335-0136-4(8)) Crossway.

Dueck, Alvin & Reimer, Kevin. A Peaceable Psychology: Christian Therapy in a World of Many Cultures, 1 vol. 2009. (ENG.). 288p. (C). pap. 25.00 (978-1-58743-105-0(X)) Brazos Pr.

Early, John D. Maya & Catholic Cultures in Crisis. 2012. (ENG., Illus.). 416p. 74.95 (978-0-8130-4013-4(2)) Univ. Pr. of Florida.

Early, John D. The Maya & Catholicism: An Encounter of Worldviews, 311 vols. 2006. (ENG., Illus.). 320p. 59.95 (978-0-8130-3025-8(0)) Univ. Pr. of Florida.

Edelheit, Amos. Ficino, Pico, & Savonarola: The Evolution of Humanist Theology 1461/2-1498. 2008. (Medieval Mediterranean Ser.: Vol. 78). 640p. (978-90-04-16667-7(X)) BRILL.

Ederamulla, Siri. Yativarayaku Dutu Kitu Himi Ha Sinlaka Kitu Sasna. 2010. 168p. (978-955-30-2688-0(5), Library of Congress — New Delhi Overseas Office) Godage, S. & Brothers.

Ehlke, Roland Cap. Speaking the Truth in Love to Jehovah's Witnesses. 2008. (978-0-8100-2059-7(9)) Northwestern Publishing Hse.

Engberg, Jakob. Impulsore Chresto: Opposition to Christianity in the Roman Empire c. 50-250 AD. 2007. 349p. pap. 68.95 (978-3-631-56778-4(2)) Lang, Peter GmbH, Europaischer Verlag der Wissenschaften DEU. Dist: Lang, Peter Publishing, Inc.

Estakhr, Mehdi. The Place of Zoroaster in History, Book 1, Book 2: Using the Cult of Personality as a Literary Source of Authority. 2012. (ENG.). 912p. 199.95 (978-0-7734-2608-5(6)) Mellen, Edwin Pr., The.

Ewbank, J. Robert. John Wesley, Natural Man, & The 'Isms' 2009. 198p. pap. 23.00 (978-1-60608-578-3(6), Resource Pubns.) Wipf & Stock Pubs.

Ezegbobelu, Edmund Emeka. Challenges of Interreligious Dialogue: Between the Christian & the Muslim Communities in Nigeria. 2009. (Europäische Hochschulschriften. Reihe 23: Theologie Ser.). 294p. pap. 72.95 (978-3-631-58993-9(X)) Lang, Peter GmbH, Europaischer Verlag der Wissenschaften DEU. Dist: Lang, Peter.

Fagan, Geraldine. Believing in Russia - Religious Policy after Communism. 2012. (Routledge Contemporary Russia & Eastern Europe Ser.). (ENG., Illus.). 288p. (C). 160.00 (978-0-415-49002-3(2)) Routledge.

Farhadian, Charles E., ed. Introducing World Christianity. 2012. (ENG.). 292p. 84.95 (978-1-4051-8249-2(0), Wiley-Blackwell) Wiley, John & Sons, Inc.

—Introducing World Christianity. 2012. (ENG.). 292p. pap. 39.95 (978-1-4051-8248-5(2), Wiley-Blackwell) Wiley, John & Sons, Inc.

Feldmeier, Peter. Encounters in Faith: Christianity in Interreligious Dialogue. 2011. (ENG.). 326p. (C). pap. 31.95 (978-1-59982-031-6(5)) St. Mary's Pr.

Finney, Charles G. The Character, Claims & Practical Workings of Freemasonry. 292p. (Orig.). 2008. 43.95 (978-1-4366-7492-8(1)) 2007. (ENG.). per. 28.95 (978-1-4325-6696-8(2)) Kessinger Publishing, LLC.

Fisher, Linford D. The Indian Great Awakening: Religion & the Shaping of Native Cultures in Early America, 1 vol. 2012. (ENG., Illus.). 312p. 34.95 (978-0-19-974004-8(6)) Oxford Univ. Pr., Inc.

Flynn, Paul. Waking up from Syncretism: The Power of Pure Worship. 2008. 240p. pap. 14.99 (978-1-60647-013-8(2)) Xulon Pr., Inc.

Ford, John & Katherine. What If I'm Right? 2009. 288p. pap. 13.99 (978-1-60696-633-4(2)) Tate Publishing & Enterprises, LLC.

Frank F. Ellinwood. Oriental Religions & Christianity: A Course of Lectures Delivered on the Ely Foundati. l.t. ed. 2007. (ENG.). 312p. pap. 24.99 (978-1-4264-8299-1(X)) BiblioBazaar.

Gabra, Gawdat & Takla, Hany N., eds. Christianity & Monasticism in Upper Egypt: Volume 1: Akhmim & Sohag. 2008. (ENG., Illus.). 288p. 39.50 (978-977-416-122-3(X)) American Univ. in Cairo Pr. EGY. Dist: Oxford Univ. Pr., Inc.

Geller, Pamela. Stop the Islamization of America: A Practical Guide to the Resistance. 2011. 192p. 25.95 (978-1-936488-36-0(1)) WND Bks, Inc.

Gerald W. VanCe, A. B. The Unpaved Road: My Search for an Intellectually Respectable Religion. 2009. 76p. pap. 12.50 (978-1-4343-4858-6(X)) AuthorHouse.

Gilbert, George Holley. Greek Thought in the New Testament. 2011. 216p. 44.95 (978-1-258-01921-1(3)) Literary Licensing, LLC.

Glover, T. R. The Influence of Christ in the Ancient World. 2012. (ENG.). 130p. pap. 39.99 (978-1-107-67021-1(7)) Cambridge Univ. Pr.

—The Influence of Christ in the Ancient World. 2007. (ENG.). 130p. 35.95 (978-0-548-01538-4(4)) Kessinger Publishing, LLC.

Godsey, R. Kirby. Is God a Christian? Creating a Community of Conversation. 2011. 256p. 19.95 (978-0-88146-242-5(X)); (ENG.). E-Book 15.00 (978-0-88146-248-7(9)) Mercer Univ. Pr.

Goldsmith, Mike. What about Other Faiths? 128p. pap. 8.99 (978-0-340-74543-4(6), Hodder & Stoughton) Hodder General Publishing Div. GBR. Dist: Trafalgar Square Publishing.

Gorski, Eugene F. Theology of Religions: A Sourcebook for Interreligious Study. 2008. 336p. pap. 24.95 (978-0-8091-4533-1(2)) Paulist Pr.

Goussetis, Alexander. Encountering World Religions: An Orthodox Christian Perspective & Parish Study Guide. 2008. (ENG.). 144p. pap. 15.95 (978-1-933654-22-5(8)) Light & Life Publishing Co.

Gozzi, Paulo. Como Lidiar con las Sectas (How to Deal with the Sects) (SPA.). 144p. 6.95 (978-958-607-743-9(8)) Sociedad de San Pablo COL. Dist: St Pauls/Alba Hse. Pubs.

Graves, Kersey. The Bible of Bibles. 2009. 346p. pap. (978-1-4589-0996-1(4)) Books LLC.

—The Bible of Bibles. 2007. (ENG.). 388p. per. 18.45 (978-1-60206-258-0(7)) Cosimo, Inc.

Hahn, Johannes, et al. From Temple to Church: Destruction & Renewal of Local Cultic Topography in Late Antiquity. 2008. (Religions in the Graeco-Roman World Ser.: Vol. 163). (GER & ENG., Illus.). xi, 378p. (C). (978-90-04-13141-5(8)) BRILL.

Haight, Roger & Haight. The Future of Christology. 2007. (ENG.). 224p. pap. 29.95 (978-0-8264-2927-8(0)) Continuum International Publishing Group, Ltd. GBR. Dist: National Bk. Network.

Hanegraaff, Hank. The Bible Answer Book for Students, 0 vols. 2007. (Illus.). 256p. 14.99 (978-1-4041-0450-1(0)) Nelson, Thomas Inc.

Hanna, Nabil I. Promises Fulfilled: Christianity, Islam, & the Baha'i Faith. 2010. (978-1-931847-77-3(0)) Baha'i Publishing Trust, U.S.

Harland, Philip A. Dynamics of Identity in the World of the Early Christians. 2009. (ENG., Illus.). 256p. 110.00 (978-0-567-61328-8(3)); pap. 34.95 (978-0-567-11146-3(6)) Continuum International Publishing Group, Ltd. GBR. (T&T Clark Int'l). Dist: National Bk. Network.

Hart, William David. Black Religion: Malcolm X, Julius Lester, & Jan Willis. 2010. (ENG.). 244p. pap. 29.00 (978-0-230-10721-2(4)) Palgrave Macmillan.

Heft, James. Catholicism & Interreligious Dialogue, 1 vol. 2011. (ENG.). 240p. 99.00 (978-0-19-982787-9(7)); pap. 29.95 (978-0-19-982789-3(3)) Oxford Univ. Pr., Inc.

Hentsch, Ariane, et al, eds. Changing the Present, Dreaming the Future: A Critical Moment in Interreligious Dialogue. 2006. 154p. (C). pap. 15.50 (978-2-8254-1490-3(5)) World Council of Churches/Conseil Oecumenique des Eglises CHE. Dist: International Specialized Bk. Services.

Herringshaw, Mark. The Karma of Jesus, 1 vol. 2009. 208p. pap. 13.99 (978-0-7642-0734-1(2)) Bethany Hse. Pubs.

Hick, John. Dialogues in the Philosophy of Religion. 2010. (ENG.). 256p. pap. 33.95 (978-0-230-25283-7(4)) Palgrave Macmillan.

—The Second Christianity. 2009. 140p. pap. 17.00 (978-1-60608-986-6(2), Wipf and Stock) Wipf & Stock Pubs.

Hiebert, Paul G. Transforming Worldviews: An Anthropological Understanding of How People Change. 2008. (Illus.). 368p. (C). pap. 24.99 (978-0-8010-2705-5(5)) Baker Academic.

Hillman, Eugene. Many Paths: A Catholic Approach to Religious Pluralism. 2008. 108p. (Orig.). pap. 13.00 (978-1-55635-993-4(4), Wipf and Stock) Wipf & Stock Pubs.

Hughes, Veronica. The Pearl of Great Price: The Spiritual Journey of a New Age Seeker to the Light of Christ & the Eastern Orthodox Church. 2010. 200p. 33.95 (978-1-4497-0661-6(4)); pap. 17.95 (978-1-4497-0660-9(6)) Author Solutions, Inc. (WestBow Pr.).

Hunt, Dave. Yoga & the Body of Christ: What Position Should Christians Hold? 2007. (ENG.). 170p. per. 9.99 (978-1-928660-48-4(7)) Berean Call, The.

Hunt, John. Pantheism & Christianity. 2009. 358p. pap. (978-1-4588-9608-7(0)) Books LLC.

Huntington, F. D. The Fitness of Christianity to Man. 2007. (ENG.). 136p. 35.95 (978-0-548-14612-5(8)) 2006. pap. 20.95 (978-1-4286-5943-8(9)) Kessinger Publishing, LLC.

Hyde, Walter Woodburn. Paganism to Christianity in the Roman Empire. 2011. 304p. 48.95 (978-1-258-03900-4(1)) Literary Licensing, LLC.

—Paganism to Christianity in the Roman Empire. 2008. 296p. pap. 25.00 (978-1-60608-349-9(X)) Wipf & Stock Pubs.

Ingham, Michael. Mansions of the Spirit: The Gospel in a Multi-Faith World. 167p. pap. 10.95 (978-1-55126-185-0(5), 1447) Forward Movement Pubns.

Jackson, Lisa A. Going in Circles ... 2010. 200p. pap. 15.99 (978-1-60957-637-0(3)) Xulon Pr., Inc.

Jacolliot, Louis. The Bible in India. 2010. 328p. pap. 24.95 (978-0-557-35161-9(8)) Lulu Enterprises Inc.

Jahn, Curtis A., ed. Here We Stand: A Confessional Christian Study of Worldviews. 2010. 360p. pap. (978-0-8100-2229-4(X)) Northwestern Publishing Hse.

James Freeman Clarke. Ten Great Religions: An Essay in Comparative Theology. 2007. (ENG.). 508p. pap. 30.99 (978-1-4264-8139-0(X)) BiblioBazaar.

Jansen, Katherin L. & Rubin, Miri, eds. Charisma & Religious Authority: Jewish, Christian & Muslim Preaching, 1200-1500. 2010. (Europa Sacra Ser.). (ENG, ARA & HEB., Illus.). 260p. (C). 87.00 (978-2-503-52859-5(7)) Brepols Pubs. BEL. Dist: ISD.

Jean, Yanick. Ahobobo: On the Sacramental Imagination in West Africa, Bénin, 2006-2008. 2010. (ENG.). 132p. pap. 22.00 (978-0-7618-5365-7(0)) Univ. Pr. of America, Inc.

John Morrison. New Ideas in India During the Nineteenth Century: A Study of Social Political & Religious Develo. l.t. ed. 2007. (ENG.). 198p. pap. 21.99 (978-1-4264-7745-4(7)) BiblioBazaar.

Johnsrud Zorgati, Ragnhild. Pluralism in the Middle Ages: Hybrid Identities, Conversion, & Mixed Marriages in Medieval Iberia. 2011. (Routledge Research in Medieval Studies). (ENG.). 228p. (C). 125.00 (978-0-415-88131-9(5)) Routledge.

Kahlos, Maijastina. Debate & Dialogue: Christian & Pagan Cultures C. 360-430. 2007. (New Critical Thinking in Religion, Theology & Biblical Studies). 224p. 99.95 (978-0-7546-5713-2(2)) Ashgate Publishing Co.

Keown, Mark J. What GodÕs up to on Planet Earth? A No-Strings-Attached Explanation of the Christian Message. 2011. 160p. pap. 18.00 (978-1-61097-132-4(9), Wipf and Stock) Wipf & Stock Pubs.

Khera, Mandeep. Why? Answers to Life's Most Important Question. 2008. (Illus.). xi, 129p. (978-1-4389-1031-4(2)) AuthorHouse.

Kim, Grace Ji-Sun. The Holy Spirit, Chi, & the Other: A Model of Global Intercultural Pneumatology. 2011. (ENG., Illus.). 240p. 85.00 *(978-0-230-12030-3(X))* Palgrave Macmillan.

Kirkwood, Neville. Just Who Is God? 2008. pap. 14.95 *(978-0-9797863-7-2(1))* Lighthouse Publishing.

Koch, Kurt E. Ocultismo & Cura de Almas: Christian Counseling on Ocultism. (SPA.). *(978-84-7228-784-6(X),* 220637) Clie, Editorial.

Kombo, James Henry Owino. The Doctrine of God in African Christian Thought: The Holy Trinity, Theological Hermeneutics & the African Intellectual Culture. 2007. (Studies in Reformed Theology Ser.). 298p. *(978-90-04-15804-7(9))* BRILL.

König, Andrea, ed. Christliche Existenz in einer überwiegend nicht-christlichen Umgebung: Situationsbeschreibung, Initiativen und Perspektiven für die Zukunft. 2008. (Glaube und Denken. Jahrbuch der Karl-Heim-Gesellschaft Ser.). (GER & ENG., Illus.). 420p. pap. 99.95 *(978-3-631-58300-5(1))* Lang, Peter GmbH, Europaischer Verlag der Wissenschaften DEU. Dist: Lang, Peter.

Krotz, Douglas Roper. The Man Who Sent the Magi. 2011. 274p. pap. 19.95 *(978-1-935529-87-3(0))* Intermedia Publishing Group.

Kujawa-Holbrook, Sheryl A. God Beyond Borders: Congregations Building Interreligious Community. 2012. ***(978-1-56699-416-3(0))*** Alban Institute, Inc.

Lai, Pan-Chiu & Lam, Jason, eds. Sino-Christian Theology: A Theological Qua Cultural Movement in Contemporary China. 2010. (IC - Studien zur interkulturellen Geschichte des Christentums. Etudes d'histoire interculturelle de christianisme. Studies in the Intercultural History of Christianity Ser.). 248p. 69.95 *(978-3-631-60435-9(1))* Lang, Peter GmbH, Europaischer Verlag der Wissenschaften DEU. Dist: Lang, Peter.

Larisa Seklitova & Ludmila Strelnikova. The Soul & Secrets of Its Structure. 2011. 394p. 29.99 ***(978-1-4568-9834-2(5))***; pap. 19.99 ***(978-1-4568-9833-5(7))*** Xlibris Corp.

Lawrenz, Mel. I Want to Believe: Finding Your Way in an Age of Many Faiths. 2008. (ENG., Illus.). 256p. 16.99 *(978-0-8307-4452-7(5))* Gospel Light Pubns.

Lee, Mikyung. Public Dialogue Between Church & Others. 2009. 296p. pap. *(978-3-639-11217-7(2))* VDM Verlag Dr. Mueller e.K.

Leopold, G., ed. Christianity & Theosophy Harmonized Being a Series of Questions Addressed to the Founders of Christianity on the above Subjects with Their Answers. 2007. (ENG.). 270p. 42.95 *(978-0-548-00684-9(9))* Kessinger Publishing, LLC.

Lepard, Brian D. In the Glory of the Father: The Baha'i Faith & Christianity. 2008. x, 246p. *(978-1-931847-34-6(7))* Baha'i Publishing Trust, U.S.

Leunk, Thea Nyhoff. Which Way to God? A Christian Look at World Religions. 2008. 106p. pap. 19.95 *(978-1-59255-428-7(8))* Faith Alive Christian Resources.

Liepert, David. Muslim, Christian & Jew: Finding a Path to Peace Our Faiths Can Share. 2010. (ENG.). 320p. pap. 15.95 *(978-0-9813882-0-5(5))* Faith of Life Pubng. CAN. Dist: SCB Distributors.

Lindbeck, George. The Nature of Doctrine: Religion & Theology in a Postliberal Age. 25th anniv. ed. 2009. (ENG.). 200p. pap. 30.00 *(978-0-664-23335-8(X))* Westminster John Knox Pr.

Lindenfeld, David F. & Richardson, Miles, eds. Beyond Conversion & Syncretism: Indigenous Encounters with Missionary Christianity, 1800-2000. 2011. (ENG.). 328p. 95.00 ***(978-0-85745-217-7(7))*** Berghahn Bks., Inc.

Lowndes, Judith. The Complete Multifaith Resource for Primary Re. 2011. (ENG., Illus.). 136p. pap. 47.95 *(978-0-415-66868-2(9))*; 144p. pap. 47.95 *(978-0-415-66867-5(0))* Routledge.

Mackey, James P. Christianity & Creation: The Essence of the Christian Faith & Its Future among Religions. 2006. (ENG.). 424p. 160.00 *(978-0-8264-1895-1(3))*; pap. 49.95 *(978-0-8264-1907-1(0))* Continuum International Publishing Group, Ltd. GBR. Dist: National Bk. Network.

Madsen, William. Christo-Paganism: A Study of Mexican Religious Syncretism. 2011. 76p. 37.95 ***(978-1-258-02011-8(4))*** Literary Licensing, LLC.

Magesa, Laurenti. African Religion in the Dialogue Debate: From Intolerance to Coexistence. 2011. (ENG.). 208p. pap. 27.95 *(978-3-643-90018-0(X))* Lit Verlag DEU. Dist: Transaction Pubs.

Major Religions of the World .... Revisited. 2008. 247p. 28.95 *(978-1-934927-02-1(3))* W R F Publishing Co.

March, W. Eugene. God's Tapestry: Reading the Bible in a World of Religious Diversity. 2009. (ENG.). 160p. pap. 15.00 *(978-0-664-23360-0(0))* Westminster John Knox Pr.

Martin, Carlos G. Christianity among the Religions of the World. 2007. (ENG., Illus.). 455p. per. 62.99 *(978-0-7618-3793-0(0))* Univ. Pr. of America, Inc.

Martin, Richard C. & Witte, John, Jr., eds. Sharing the Book: Religious Perspectives on the Rights & Wrongs of Proselytism. 2008. 442p. pap. 51.00 *(978-1-59244-904-0(2))* Wipf & Stock Pubs.

Massey, Gerald. The Historical Jesus, & the Mythical C. 2006. pap. 16.95 *(978-1-59605-989-4(3),* Cosimo Classics) Cosimo, Inc.

—The Natural Genesis. 2007. (ENG.). 544p. 39.95 *(978-1-60206-850-6(X))*; 568p. 39.95 *(978-1-60206-849-0(6))* Cosimo, Inc.

—The Natural Genesis - 2007. 568p. per. 29.95 *(978-1-60206-084-5(3))*; (ENG.). 544p. per. 29.95 *(978-1-60206-085-2(1))* Cosimo, Inc.

—The Natural Genesis. (African Studies). reprint ed. 75.00 *(978-0-938818-80-9(5))* ECA Assocs.

Mastrocinque, Attilio. Des Mysteres de Mithra aux Mysteres de Jesus. 2009. (Potsdamer Altertumswissenschaftliche Beitrage (PAwB) Ser.). (FRE., Illus.). 128p. (C). pap. 59.00 *(978-3-515-09250-0(1))* Steiner, Franz Verlag Wiesbaden GmbH DEU. Dist: Brown, David Bk. Co., The.

Masuku, Francis G. The Encounter Between Christian & Traditional African Spiritualities in Malawi. 2007. 396p. 119.95 *(978-0-7734-5248-0(6))* Mellen, Edwin Pr., The.

Maurice, Frederick Denison. The Religions of the World & Their Relations to Christianity. 2010. (Cambridge Library Collection - Religion Ser.). (ENG.). 284p. pap. 23.99 *(978-1-108-00793-1(7))* Cambridge Univ. Pr.

McAnally, Bryan. World Religions & What People Believe. 2009. (Indispensable Guide to Practically Everything Ser.). (ENG., Illus.). 256p. pap. 15.99 *(978-0-8249-4770-5(3))* Ideals Pubns.

McDaniel, Jay B. With Roots & Wings. 2009. 254p. pap. 28.00 *(978-1-60608-842-5(4),* Wipf and Stock) Wipf & Stock Pubs.

McDermott, Gerald R. God's Rivals: Why Has God Allowed Different Religions? Insights from the Bible & the Early Church. 2007. (ENG., Illus.). 181p. per. 18.00 *(978-0-8308-2564-6(9),* IVP Acad.) InterVarsity Pr.

McDowell, Josh & Hostetler, Bob. The Deceivers. 2006. 176p. (YA). pap. 10.99 *(978-1-60098-013-8(9))* Green Key Bks.

McGoldrick, James. Christianity & Its Competitors: The New Faces of Old Heresy. 2006. (ENG.). 208p. per. 10.99 *(978-1-84550-140-2(3))* Christian Focus Pubns. GBR. Dist: STL Distribution North America.

McIlhenny, Albert. The New Restorationists: A Critique of Frank Viola & George Barna's Pagan Christianity? 2010. 68p. pap. 8.36 *(978-0-557-46221-6(5))* Lulu Enterprises Inc.

McKinney, S. B. G. The Science & Art of Religion. 2007. (ENG.). 490p. 53.95 *(978-0-548-14964-5(X))*; 492p. per. 38.95 *(978-1-4304-4260-6(8))* Kessinger Publishing, LLC.

McLeod-Harrison, Mark S. Make/Believing the World(s) Toward a Christian Ontological Pluralism. 2009. (McGill-Queen's Studies in the History of Ideas Ser.). 386p. (C). *(978-0-7735-3593-0(4))* McGill-Queen's Univ. Pr.

—Repairing Eden: Humility, Mysticism, & the Existential Problem of Religious Diversity. 2007. (ENG.). 168p. (C). per. *(978-0-7735-3059-1(2))* McGill-Queen's Univ. Pr.

Mehta, Shyam. Christianity: German Edition. 2010. (GER.). 185p. pap. 27.50 *(978-1-4092-9146-6(4))* Lulu Enterprises Inc.

—Christianity: Italian Edition. 2010. (ITA.). 172p. pap. 26.95 *(978-1-4092-9229-6(0))* Lulu Enterprises Inc.

—Christianity: Portuguese Edition. 2010. (POR.). 174p. pap. 26.95 *(978-1-4092-9205-0(3))* Lulu Enterprises Inc.

Melville, Henry. Ancient Dates & Celestial Points Revealed by Means of the Median. 2006. pap. 12.95 *(978-1-4304-1305-9(0))* Kessinger Publishing, LLC.

—The Birth of Christ Revealed by Means of the Median & Persian. 2006. pap. 12.95 *(978-1-4304-1306-6(9))* Kessinger Publishing, LLC.

—The Death of Christ Revealed by Means of the Median & Persian. 2006. pap. 9.95 *(978-1-4304-1302-8(6))* Kessinger Publishing, LLC.

—Masonic Ceremonies Revealed by Means of the Median & Persian. 2006. pap. 12.95 *(978-1-4304-1304-2(2))* Kessinger Publishing, LLC.

Merivale, Charles. The Conversion of the Roman Empire; the Boyle Lectures for the Year 1864, Delivered at the Chapel Royal, Whitehall, by Charles Merivale. 2006. 276p. per. 23.99 *(978-1-4255-2500-2(8))* MPublishing.

Merton, Thomas. On Eastern Meditation. Thurston, Bonnie, ed. 2012. (ENG.). 80p. pap. 13.95 ***(978-0-8112-1994-5(1),*** 21994) New Directions Publishing Corp.

Middelmann, Udo W. Christianity Versus Fatalistic Religions in the War Against Poverty. 2008. (ENG.). 225p. pap. 17.99 *(978-1-934068-28-1(4),* Paternoster) Authentic Media.

Miles, Todd. A God of Many Understandings? The Gospel & Theology of Religions, 1 vol. 2010. (ENG.). 416p. pap. 29.99 *(978-0-8054-4822-1(5),* B&H Academic) B&H Publishing Group.

Miller, Darrow L. Emancipating the World: A Christian Response to Radical Islam & Fundamentalist Atheism. 2012. ***(978-1-57658-716-4(9))*** YWAM Publishing.

Miller, Michael St. A. Reshaping the Contextual Vision in Caribbean Theology: Theoretical Foundations for Theology Which Is Contextual, Pluralistic, & Dialectical. 2007. (ENG.). 414p. 89.50 *(978-0-7618-3784-8(1))*; per. 57.99 *(978-0-7618-3785-5(X))* Univ. Pr. of America, Inc.

Morgan, Christopher W. & Peterson, Robert A., eds. Faith Comes by Hearing: A Response to Inclusivism. 2008. (ENG.). 270p. per. 23.00 *(978-0-8308-2590-5(8),* IVP Acad.) InterVarsity Pr.

Morris, Jonathan. God Wants You Happy: From Self-Help to God's Help. 2011. (ENG.). 240p. 24.99 *(978-0-06-191356-3(1),* HarperOne) HarperCollins Pubs.

Morrison, John. New Ideas in India During the Nineteenth Century. 2008. 200p. 25.99 *(978-0-554-24920-9(0))*; 22.99 *(978-0-554-34223-8(5))* BiblioBazaar.

—New Ideas in India During the Nineteenth Century. 2008. 164p. pap. *(978-1-4099-0396-3(6))* Dodo Pr.

Mortensen, Viggo & Nielsen, Andreas Østerlund. Walk Humbly with the Lord: Church & Mission Engaging Plurality. 2010. 336p. pap. 45.00 *(978-0-8028-6630-1(1))* Eerdmans, William B. Publishing Co.

Mosher, Lucinda. Loss: Understanding America's Religious Diversity. 2007. (Faith in the Neighborhood Ser.). 208p. per. 19.00 *(978-1-59627-059-6(4),* Seabury Bks.) Church Publishing, Inc.

Muck, Terry & Adeney, Frances S. Christianity Encountering World Religions: The Practice of Mission in the Twenty-First Century. 2009. (Encountering Mission Ser.). (Illus.). 416p. (C). pap. 30.00 *(978-0-8010-2660-7(1))* Baker Academic.

Mudge, Lewis S., et al. The Gift of Responsibility: The Promise of Dialogue among Christians, Jews, & Muslims. 2008. (ENG.). 328p. pap. 24.95 *(978-0-8264-2839-4(6))* Continuum International Publishing Group, Ltd. GBR. Dist: National Bk. Network.

Murray, Abdu H. & Murray, Abdu. Apocalypse Later: Why the Gospel of Peace Must Trump the Politics of Prophecy in the Middle East, 1 vol. 2009. 208p. pap. 13.99 *(978-0-8254-2978-1(1))* Kregel Pubns.

Nachtigall, Patrick. Passport of Faith: A Christian's Encounter with World Religions. 2007. (ENG.). 316p. per. 16.95 *(978-1-59317-130-8(7))* Warner Pr. Pubs.

Ncozana, Silas S. The Spirit Dimension in African Christianity: A Pastoral Study among the Tumbuka People of Northern Malawi. 2006. (Illus.). 207p. pap. 29.95 *(978-99908-81-03-5(0))* Kachere Series, Bks. on Religion, Theology & Society in Malawi MWI. Dist: Michigan State Univ. Pr.

Newbigin, Lesslie. A Faith for this One World. 2011. 128p. pap. 18.00 ***(978-1-61097-709-8(2),*** Wipf and Stock) Wipf & Stock Pubs.

Newbigin, Lesslie. The Finality of Christ. 2009. 120p. pap. 15.00 *(978-1-60608-581-3(6),* Wipf and Stock) Wipf & Stock Pubs.

Nicholson, Hugh. Comparative Theology & the Problem of Religious Rivalry, 1 vol. 2011. (AAR Reflection & Theory in the Study of Religion Ser.). (ENG.). 344p. 74.00 *(978-0-19-977286-5(X))* Oxford Univ. Pr., Inc.

Numrich, Paul David. The Faith Next Door: American Christians & Their New Religious Neighbors. 2009. (ENG., Illus.). 184p. 25.00 *(978-0-19-538621-9(3))* Oxford Univ. Pr., Inc.

Ochs, Peter & Johnson, William Stacy, eds. Crisis, Call, & Leadership in the Abrahamic Traditions. 2009. (ENG.). 288p. 95.00 *(978-0-230-61825-1(1))* Palgrave Macmillan.

Oliver, Jose R. Caciques & Cemi Idols: The Web Spun by Taino Rulers Between Hispaniola & Puerto Rico. 2009. (Caribbean Archaeology & Ethnohistory Ser.). (ENG.). 432p. pap. 34.95 *(978-0-8173-5515-9(4))*; (Illus.). 59.00 *(978-0-8173-1636-5(1))* Univ. of Alabama Pr.

O'Mahony, Anthony, ed. Christianity & Jerusalem. 2010. 340p. pap. *(978-0-85244-646-1(2))* Gracewing, Ltd.

Pack, David C. The True Jesus Christ - Unknown to Christianity. 2009. 276p. 30.95 *(978-1-4401-8049-1(0))*; pap. 20.95 *(978-1-4401-8047-7(4))* iUniverse, Inc.

Paffenroth, Kim. Augustine & World Religions. Brown, Brian & Doody, John A., eds. 2008. (Augustine in Conversation: Tradition & Innovation Ser.). (ENG.). 310p. 89.50 *(978-0-7391-2579-3(6))* Lexington Bks.

Paintner, Christine Valters. Lectio Divina — the Sacred Art: Transforming Words & Images into Heart-Centered Prayer. 2011. 192p. pap. 16.99 *(978-1-59473-300-0(7))* SkyLight Paths Publishing.

Parton, Craig A. Religion on Trial. 2008. (ENG.). 114p. (C). pap. 33.00 *(978-0-7188-9220-3(8))* Lutterworth Pr., The GBR. Dist: Brown, David Bk. Co., The.

—Religion on Trial. 2008. 114p. pap. 14.00 *(978-1-55635-715-2(X),* Wipf and Stock) Wipf & Stock Pubs.

Pearson, Carlton. God Is Not a Christian, nor a Jew, Muslim, Hindu... God Dwells with Us, in Us, Around Us, as Us. 2010. (ENG.). 304p. 25.00 *(978-1-4165-8443-8(9),* Beyond Words/Atria Bks.) Atria Bks.

—God Is Not a Christian, nor a Jew, Muslim, Hindu... God Dwells with Us, in Us, Around Us, As Us. 2011. (ENG.). 304p. pap. 15.00 *(978-1-4165-8444-5(7),* Beyond Words/Atria Bks.) Atria Bks.

Pearson, Thomas & Pearson, T. Missions & Conversions: Creating the Montagnard-Dega Refugee Community. 2009. (Contemporary Anthropology of Religion Ser.). (ENG., Illus.). 256p. 100.00 *(978-0-230-61536-6(8))* Palgrave Macmillan.

Peters, William. Jil Hid Gie: Discover the Secret to Your Soul. 2009. 398p. 49.99 *(978-0-692-00460-9(2))* Jil Hid Gie Foundation.

Pointer, Richard W. Encounters of the Spirit: Native Americans & European Colonial Religion. 2007. (Religion in North America Ser.). (ENG.). 312p. 39.95 *(978-0-253-34912-5(5),* 0253349125) Indiana Univ. Pr.

Pope, Randy. Life Issues: Do Non-Christians Really Deserve Eternal Punishment? 2007. per. 2.49 *(978-0-9776605-2-0(4))* Life-on-Life Resources.

Pratt, Douglas. The Church & Other Faiths: The World Council of Churches, the Vatican, & Interreligious Dialogue. 2010. (ENG.). 386p. pap. *(978-3-0343-0454-2(4))* Lang, Peter.

Rassam, Suha. Christianity in Iraq, New Edition. 2010. 320p. pap. *(978-0-85244-738-3(8))* Gracewing, Ltd.

Reid, Gilbert. A Christian's Appreciation of Other Faiths. 2009. 150p. pap. *(978-1-151-16462-9(3))* Books LLC.

—A Christian's Appreciation of Other Faiths. 2010. (Illus.). 138p. pap. 15.89 *(978-1-154-66268-9(3))* 2009. 152p. pap. 19.99 *(978-0-217-42425-7(2))* General Bks. LLC.

Rhodes, Daniel. Burst World Religions: Short-Term Teen Studies, 5 pack. 2009. 24 + coverp. 8.00 *(978-0-687-65971-5(X))* Abingdon Pr.

—Burst World Religions Leader's Guide: Short-Term Teen Studies. 2009. 82p. 11.00 *(978-0-687-65972-2(8))* Abingdon Pr.

Richie, Tony. Speaking by the Spirit: A Pentecostal Model for Interreligious Dialogue. 2011. 370p. pap. 45.00 *(978-1-60947-014-2(1))* Emeth Pr.

Riley-Smith, Jonathan. The Crusades, Christianity, & Islam. 2008. (Bampton Lectures in America Ser.). (ENG., Illus.). 136p. (gr. 17). 26.50 *(978-0-231-14624-1(8))* Columbia Univ. Pr.

—The Crusades, Christianity, & Islam. 2011. (Bampton Lectures in America Ser.). (ENG.). 136p. (gr. 17). pap. 19.50 *(978-0-231-14625-8(6))* Columbia Univ. Pr.

Robinson, Michael. There Are Moral Absolutes How to Be Abs. 2006. 160p. pap. 10.95 *(978-1-59800-766-4(1))* Outskirts Pr., Inc.

Robinson, Mike A. One Way to God: Christian Philosophy & Presuppositional Apologetics Examine World Religions. 2008. 208p. pap. 9.95 *(978-1-4327-2295-1(6))* Outskirts Pr., Inc.

Rose Publishing Staff. Christianity, Cults & Religions. 2008. (Rose Bible Basics Ser.). (ENG., Illus.). 112p. pap. 12.99 *(978-1-59636-202-4(2))* Rose Publishing.

Rummel, Erika. Biblical Humanism & Scholasticism in the Age of Erasmus. 2008. (Brill's Companions to the Christian Tradition Ser.: Vol. 9). 352p. (C). *(978-90-04-14573-3(7))* BRILL.

Ryad, U. Islamic Reformism & Christianity: A Critical Reading of the Works of Mu?ammad Rash?d Ri?? & His Associates (1898-1935) 2009. (History of Christian-Muslim Relations Ser.). (Illus.). xiv, 387p. *(978-90-04-17911-0(9))* BRILL.

Ryan, Thomas. Interreligious Prayer: A Christian Guide. 2008. 85p. per. 12.95 *(978-0-8091-4513-3(8),* 4513-3) Paulist Pr.

Sabbah, Patriarch Michel. Faithful Witness: On Reconciliation & Peace in the Holy Land. Christiansen, S.J., Drew, Drew, ed. 2009. 208p. pap. 24.95 *(978-1-56548-307-1(3))* New City Pr.

Samkutty, V J & Samkutty. The Samaritan Mission in Acts, Vol. 328. 2006. (Library of New Testament Studies: Vol. 328). (ENG., Illus.). 272p. 180.00 *(978-0-567-04464-8(5),* T&T Clark Int'l) Continuum International Publishing Group, Ltd. GBR. Dist: National Bk. Network.

Scandrette, Mark. Soul Graffiti: Making a Life in the Way of Jesus. 2008. (ENG.). 272p. pap. 14.95 *(978-0-470-27662-4(2),* Jossey-Bass) Wiley, John & Sons, Inc.

Scarfe Beckett, Katharine. Anglo-Saxon Perceptions of the Islamic World. 2008. (Cambridge Studies in Anglo-Saxon England Ser.). (ENG.). 288p. pap. 36.99 *(978-0-521-05438-6(9))* Cambridge Univ. Pr.

Schweiker, William. Dust That Breathes: Christian Faith & the New Humanisms. 2010. (Challenges in Contemporary Theology Ser.). (ENG.). 256p. 119.95 *(978-1-4443-3535-4(9),* Wiley-Blackwell) Wiley, John & Sons, Inc.

Scott, Dan. Faith to Faith: A Conversation about Christianity & World Religions. 2008. (ConversantLife.com Ser.). 250p. pap. 13.99 *(978-0-7369-2350-7(0))* Harvest Hse. Pubs.

Selmanovic, Samir. It's Really All about God: How Islam, Atheism, & Judaism Made Me a Better Christian. 2011. (ENG.). 304p. pap. 15.95 *(978-0-470-92341-2(5),* Jossey-Bass) Wiley, John & Sons, Inc.

Setiawan, Mohamad Nur Kholis & Djaka Soetapa. Meniti Kalam Kerukunan: Beberapa Istilah Dalam Islam Dan Kristen. 2010. (IND., Illus.). *(978-979-687-756-0(2))* BPK GUNUNG MULIA.

Sheldon, Henry C. The Mystery Religions & the New Testament. 2010. 160p. pap. 17.95 *(978-0-557-50416-9(3))* Lulu Enterprises Inc.

Shepherd, Arthur Pearce. Anthroposophy & the Christian Churches. 2011. 20p. 35.95 ***(978-1-258-00124-7(1))*** Literary Licensing, LLC.

Simpson, Charles. Inside the Churches of Christ: The Reflection of a Former Pharisee on What Every Christian Should Know about the Nondenomination Denomination. 2009. 308p. 25.99 *(978-1-4389-0140-4(2))*; pap. 17.00 *(978-1-4389-0139-8(9))* AuthorHouse.

Sims, Bryan. Christianity & Worldview Analysis. 2009. 152p. pap. *(978-3-639-13358-5(7))* VDM Verlag Dr. Mueller e.K.

Sit, Kwan-Yuk Claire. The Lord's Prayer: An Eastern Perspective. 2008. 192p. pap. 20.00 *(978-0-88010-596-5(8))* SteinerBooks, Inc.

Smith, Warren. A Wonderful Deception: The Further New Age Implications of the Purpose Driven Movement. 2009. pap. 14.95 *(978-0-9824881-0-2(6))* Lighthouse Trails Publishing Co.

Sparks, Adam. One of a Kind. 2009. 352p. pap. 39.00 *(978-1-60608-345-1(7),* Pickwick Pubns.) Wipf & Stock Pubs.

Spencer, Robert R. Religion of Peace? Why Christianity Is & Islam Isn't. 2007. (ENG.). 264p. 27.95 *(978-1-59698-515-5(1))* Regnery Publishing, Inc., An Eagle Publishing Co.

St. Clair, Adelina. The Path of a Christian Witch. 2010. (ENG.). 216p. pap. 15.95 *(978-0-7387-1982-5(X))* Llewellyn Pubns.

Standard Publishing Staff. Examining Religions. 2006. cd-rom 24.99 *(978-0-7847-1877-3(6))* Standard Publishing.

Steinbronn, Anthony J. Worldviews: A Christian Response to Religious Pluralism. 2007. (ENG.). 270p. per. 16.99 *(978-0-7586-0598-6(6))* Concordia Publishing Hse.

Steiner, Rudolf. Renewing Christian Religious Work: Courses for Priests, 1. Post, Marsha, tr. from GER. 2010. (Collected Works of Rudolf Steiner: 342). (Illus.). 328p. pap. 30.00 *(978-0-88010-622-1(0))* SteinerBooks, Inc.

Steinkerchner, Scott. Beyond Agreement: Interreligious Dialogue amid Persistent Differences. 2010. (ENG.). 206p. (gr. 17). 55.00 *(978-1-4422-0642-7(X))* Rowman & Littlefield Publishers, Inc.

—Beyond Agreement: Interreligious Dialogue amid Perspective Differences. 2010. *(978-1-4422-0644-1(6))* Rowman & Littlefield Publishers, Inc.

Stott, John. Christian Mission in the Modern World, 1 vol. 2008. (IVP Classics Ser.). (ENG.). 192p. pap. 8.00 *(978-0-8308-3411-2(7),* IVP Bks.) InterVarsity Pr.

Strange, Daniel. The Possibility of Salvation among the Unevangelized: An Analysis of Inclusivism in Recent Evangelical Theology. 2006. (Biblical & Theological Monographs). (ENG., Illus.). 380p. per. 44.99 *(978-1-84227-047-9(8),* Paternoster) Authentic Media.

Stroumsa, Guy G. The End of Sacrifice: Religious Transformations in Late Antiquity. Emanuel, Susan, tr. from FRE. 2009. (ENG.). 160p. 32.00 *(978-0-226-77738-2(3))* Univ. of Chicago Pr.

Sung-hae, Kim. Encounters: The New Religions of Korea & Christianity. 2009. pap. 35.00 *(978-89-954424-9-4(2))* RAS-KB KOR. Dist: Cheng & Tsui Co.

Swidler, Leonard & Mojzes, Paul, eds. The Uniqueness of Jesus: A Dialogue with Paul F. Knitter. 2008. 206p. pap. 23.00 *(978-1-55635-652-0(8))* Wipf & Stock Pubs.

Swindoll, Charles R. Religions of the World Passport. 2007. 7.99 *(978-1-57972-759-8(X))* Insight for Living.

Tavárez, David. The Invisible War: Indigenous Devotions, Discipline, & Dissent in Colonial Mexico. 2011. (ENG., Illus.). 400p. 65.00 *(978-0-8047-7328-7(9))* Stanford Univ. Pr.

Theile, Notto R. Who Can Stop the Wind? Travels in the Borderland Between East & West. 2010. 9.95 *(978-0-8146-3329-8(3))*; E-Book 14.95 *(978-0-8146-3934-4(8))* Liturgical Pr.

Thomas, R. Murray. Manitou & God: North-American Indian Religions & Christian Culture, 1 vol. 2007. (Illus.). 292p. 49.95 *(978-0-313-34779-5(4)*, C34779, Praeger Pubs.) Greenwood Publishing Group, Inc.

Thompson, Livingstone A. A Protestant Theology of Religious Pluralism. 2009. 413p. pap. 69.95 *(978-3-03911-875-5(7))* Lang, Peter AG GBR. Dist: Lang, Peter.

Thomson, Edward. Our Oriental Missions. 2006. 276p. per. 23.99 *(978-1-4255-2502-6(4))* MPublishing.

Timmerman, Christiane, et al, eds. Faith-Based Radicalism: Christianity, Islam & Judaism Between Constructive Activism & Destructive Fanaticism. 309p. pap. 44.95 *(978-90-5201-050-2(1))* Lang, Peter Publishing, Inc.

Timmerman, Christiane & Segaert, Barbara, eds. How to Conquer the Barriers to Intercultural Dialogue: Christianity, Islam & Judaism. 3rd ed. 2007. (Gods, Humans & Religions Ser.: Vol. 5). 240p. pap. 41.95 *(978-90-5201-373-2(X))* Lang, Peter Publishing, Inc.

Tinker, George E. American Indian Liberation: A Theology of Sovereignty. 2008. vi, 170p. pap. 22.00 *(978-1-57075-805-8(0))* Orbis Bks.

Trask, Paul. The Long Way Home: Moving from a Pseudo-Christian Cult into Genuine Christianity. 2006. per. 10.00 *(978-0-9707160-7-1(9))* Refiner's Fire Ministries.

Tutu, Desmond. God Is Not a Christian: And Other Provocations. 2011. (ENG.). 256p. 23.99 *(978-0-06-187462-8(0)*, HarperOne) HarperCollins Pubs.

Tyler, Aaron. Islam, the West, & Tolerance: Conceiving Coexistence. 2008. (ENG.). 240p. 89.00 *(978-0-230-60546-6(X))* Palgrave Macmillan.

Tyner, M. J. Did Jesus Rise from the Dead? 2007. per. 1.00 *(978-0-9789909-1-6(9))* True-Way Tracts.

Ullucci, Daniel C. The Christian Rejection of Animal Sacrifice, 1 vol. 2011. (ENG.). 256p. 74.00 ***(978-0-19-979170-5(8))*** Oxford Univ. Pr., Inc.

Urantia Foundation Staff, ed. The Urantia Book: Revealing the Mysteries of God, the Universe, Jesus, & Ourselves. 2008. (ENG.). 2097p. 27.95 *(978-0-911560-07-7(6))*; pap. 22.95 *(978-0-911560-51-0(3))* Urantia Foundation.

Urick, Steve. Major Cults & False World Religions. 2011. 368p. pap. 19.99 *(978-1-4520-7156-5(X))* AuthorHouse.

Ustorf, Werner. Robinson Crusoe tries again: Missiology & European Constructions of 'Self' & 'Other' in a Global World 1789 - 2010. Loffler, Roland, ed. 2010. (Research in Contemporary Religion Ser.). (ENG.). 271p. (C). 95.00 *(978-3-525-60444-1(0))* Vandenhoeck & Ruprecht GmbH & Co. KG DEU. Dist: ISD.

van Wiele, J. Faith & Culture: The Construction of a Christian Identity in Interaction with the Other World Religions in Education. 2008. (Annua Nuntia Lovaniensia Ser.). (ENG.). 234p. (C). pap. 76.00 *(978-90-429-1931-0(0))* Peeters Pubs. & Booksellers BEL. Dist: Brown, David Bk. Co., The.

Vande Kappelle, Robert P. Into Thin Places: One ManÕs Search for the Center. 2011. 432p. pap. 48.00 *(978-1-61097-093-8(4)*, Resource Pubns.) Wipf & Stock Pubs.

VanDerwall, Francis W. The Enduring Quest, a Christian's Attempt to Explain Other Religions, Jesus, & Christian Practices: A Textbook. 2009. 318p. 29.50 *(978-1-60860-491-3(8)*, Eloquent Bks.) AEG Literary Publishing Services, Inc.

Vanier, Jean. Encountering 'the Other' 2006. 62p. per. 8.95 *(978-0-8091-4409-9(3)*, 4409-3) Paulist Pr.

Vejrup Nielsen, M. Sin & Selfish Genes. 2010. (Studies in Philosophical Theology Ser.). 286p. (C). pap. 70.00 *(978-90-429-2263-1(X))* Peeters Pubs. & Booksellers BEL. Dist: Brown, David Bk. Co., The.

Walker, Bruce. The Swastika Against the Cross. 2008. 104p. pap. 19.95 *(978-1-4327-2169-5(0))* Outskirts Pr., Inc.

Webber, Robert E. Who Gets to Narrate the World? Contending for the Christian Story in an Age of Rivals. 2008. (ENG.). 137p. pap. 15.00 *(978-0-8308-3481-5(8)*, IVP Bks.) InterVarsity Pr.

Wendland, Ernst. Galu Wamkota. 2007. 512p. (C). pap. *(978-99908-87-05-1(5))* Kachere Series, Bks. on Religion, Theology & Society in Malawi MWI. Dist: Michigan State Univ. Pr.

Wenger, Tisa. We Have a Religion: The 1920s Pueblo Indian Dance Controversy & American Religious Freedom. 2009. (ENG., Illus.). 336p. 62.95 *(978-0-8078-3262-2(6))* Univ. of North Carolina Pr.

Wenger, Tisa & Wenger, Tisa Joy. We Have a Religion: The 1920s Pueblo Indian Dance Controversy & American Religious Freedom. 2009. (ENG., Illus.). 336p. pap. 23.95 *(978-0-8078-5935-3(4))* Univ. of North Carolina Pr.

Wood, Nicholas J. Faiths & Faithfulness. 2009. (Paternoster Theological Monographs). 238p. pap. 27.00 *(978-1-60899-159-4(8)*, Wipf and Stock) Wipf & Stock Pubs.

Wood, Simon A. Christian Criticisms, Islamic Proofs: Rashid Rida's Modernist Defense of Islam. 2012. (ENG.). 248p. pap. 30.00 *(978-1-85168-671-1(1))* Oneworld Pubns. GBR. Dist: National Bk. Network.

Wright, Brian. Brigid: Goddess, Druidess & Saint. 2009. (ENG., Illus.). 256p. pap. 32.95 *(978-0-7524-4865-7(X))* History Pr. Ltd., The GBR. Dist: Independent Pubs. Group.

Wuthnow, Robert. America & the Challenges of Religious Diversity. 2007. (ENG.). 416p. (C). per. 29.95 *(978-0-691-13411-6(1))* Princeton Univ. Pr.

Yai-Chow, Teresa Wong, et al. The Cosmos in Becoming. 2009. 250p. pap. 18.00 *(978-1-920691-94-3(4))* ATF Pr. AUS. Dist: International Publishers Marketing.

Yamase, Shinji. The Impact of Christianity on Colonial Maya, Ancient Mexico, China, & Japan: How a Monotheistic Religion Was Received by Several Pagan Societies. 2008. (Illus.). 436p. 129.95 *(978-0-7734-5145-2(5))* Mellen, Edwin Pr., The.

Yungen, Ray. For Many Shall Come in My Name: How the Ancient Wisdom Is Drawing Millions of People into Mystical Experiences & Preparing the World for the End of the Age. 2nd ed. 2007. (ENG.). 224p. per. 12.95 *(978-0-9721512-9-0(X))* Lighthouse Trails Publishing Co.

Zacharias, Ravi. Beyond Opinion: Living the Faith We Defend, 0 vols. 2010. 384p. pap. 15.99 *(978-0-8499-4653-0(0))* Nelson, Thomas Inc.

Zukeran, Pat. World Religions Through a Christian Worldview. 2008. 300p. pap. 17.99 *(978-1-60647-068-8(X))* Xulon Pr., Inc.

CHRISTIANITY AND OTHER RELIGIONS—BUDDHISM

see also Catholic Church—Relations—Buddhism

Anonymous. The Dhammapad: With Explanatory Notes & A Short Essay on Buddha's Thought. 2011. 150p. 41.95 ***(978-1-258-04307-0(6))*** Literary Licensing, LLC.

Appleton, George. On the Eightfold Path: Christian Presence amid Buddhism. 2011. 156p. 41.95 ***(978-1-258-00787-4(8))*** Literary Licensing, LLC.

Blackburn, Anne M. Locations of Buddhism: Colonialism & Modernity in Sri Lanka. 2010. (Buddhism & Modernity Ser.). (ENG., Illus.). 256p. 45.00 *(978-0-226-05507-7(8))* Univ. of Chicago Pr.

Burnett, David. The Spirit of Buddhism: A Christian Perspective on Buddhist Thought. 2007. (Illus.). 352p. pap. 16.99 *(978-0-8254-6145-3(6)*, Monarch Bks.) Lion Hudson PLC GBR. Dist: Kregel Pubns.

Carter, John Ross. In the Company of Friends: Exploring Faith & Understanding with Buddhists & Christians. 2012. (ENG.). 368p. 85.00 ***(978-1-4384-4279-2(3))*** State Univ. of New York Pr.

Carus, Paul. Buddha, the Gospel. 252p. 2009. 34.99 *(978-1-59547-518-3(4))* 2007. per. 19.99 *(978-1-59547-941-9(4))* NuVision Pubns., LLC.

—Buddhism & Its Christian Critics. 2010. (ENG.). 330p. pap. 31.75 *(978-1-177-47983-7(4))* 2010. (ENG.). 340p. pap. 31.75 *(978-1-176-23344-7(0))* 2010. (ENG.). 334p. pap. 31.75 *(978-1-176-36971-9(7))* 2010. 322p. pap. 30.75 *(978-1-175-04115-9(7))* 2010. 332p. 36.99 *(978-1-140-19126-1(8))* 2010. 332p. pap. 31.75 *(978-1-140-19127-8(6))* 2010. 340p. pap. 31.75 *(978-1-144-59635-2(1))* 2010. 338p. pap. 31.75 *(978-1-142-21491-3(5))* 2008. 323p. 28.99 *(978-0-559-60281-8(2))* 2008. 328p. pap. 30.75 *(978-0-559-60279-5(0))* BiblioBazaar.

—Buddhism & Its Christian Critics. 2009. (Illus.). 174p. pap. 19.99 *(978-1-150-43259-0(4))* General Bks. LLC.

—Buddhism & Its Christian Critics. 2010. 324p. 36.76 *(978-1-163-31925-3(2))* 2010. 324p. pap. 24.76 *(978-1-162-80326-5(6))* 2007. (ENG.). 322p. 45.95 *(978-0-548-00691-7(1))* Kessinger Publishing, LLC.

Cioccolanti, Steve. From Buddha to Jesus: An Insider's View of Buddhism & Christianity, 1 vol. 2010. (ENG., Illus.). 256p. pap. 13.99 *(978-1-85424-956-2(8)*, Monarch Bks.) Lion Hudson PLC GBR. Dist: Kregel Pubns.

De Neui, Paul H. Communicating Christ in Asian Cities: Urban Issues in Buddhist Contexts. 2009. x, 297p. *(978-0-87808-007-6(4))* Carey, William Library Pubs.

—Complexities of Money & Missions in Asia. 2011. ***(978-0-87808-038-0(4))*** Carey, William Library Pubs.

—Family & Faith in Asia: The Missional Impact of Social Networks. 2009. *(978-0-87808-022-9(8))* Carey, William Library Pubs.

—Suffering: Christian Reflections on Buddhist Dukkha. 2011. *(978-0-87808-024-3(4))* Carey, William Library Pubs.

De Neui, Paul H. & Lim, David. Communicating Christ Through Story & Song: Orality in Buddhist Contexts. 2007. *(978-0-87808-511-8(4))* Carey, William Library Pubs.

Derbolav, Josef, et al. Search for a New Humanity: A Dialogue. Gage, Richard L., ed. 2008. (Echoes & Reflections Ser.). (ENG.). 276p. 42.00 *(978-1-84511-598-2(8))* I. B. Tauris & Co., Ltd. GBR. Dist: Macmillan.

Didier, Hugues. Les Portugais Au Tibet: Les Premières Relations Jésuites, 1624-1635. (FRE., Illus.). 382p. *(978-2-906462-31-1(4))* Chandeigne, Editions.

Dods, Marcus. Mohammed, Buddha & Christ. 2009. 100p. pap. *(978-1-151-63622-5(3))* Books LLC.

Drew, Rose. Buddhist & Christian? An Exploration of Dual Belonging. 2011. (Routledge Critical Studies in Buddhism Ser.). (ENG.). 288p. (C). 140.00 *(978-0-415-61123-7(7))* Routledge.

Du Boulay, Shirley, selected by. Swami Abhishiktananda: Essential Writings. 2007. (Modern Spiritual Masters Ser.). 205p. per. 18.00 *(978-1-57075-695-5(3))* Orbis Bks.

Edmunds, Albert J. Buddhist & Christian Gospels Being Gos. 2006. pap. 27.95 *(978-1-4286-3844-0(X))* Kessinger Publishing, LLC.

Goddard, Dwight. Was Jesus Influenced by Buddhism: A Comparative Study of the Lives & Thoughts of Gautama & Jesus. 2011. 256p. 47.95 ***(978-1-258-05865-4(0))*** Literary Licensing, LLC.

Goddard, Dwight. Was Jesus Influenced by Buddhism? a Comparative Study of the Lives & Thoughts of Gautama & Jesus. 2007. 260p. per. 19.45 *(978-1-60206-281-8(1))* Cosimo, Inc.

Hanh, Thich Nhat. Volviendo a Casa. (SPA.). 184p. *(978-84-95456-47-2(8)*, 86934) Ediciones Oniro S.A.

Hardy, R. Spence. Christianity & Buddhism Compared. 2007. (ENG.). 144p. 35.95 *(978-0-548-15542-4(9))*; pap. 20.95 *(978-1-4304-4979-9(9))* Kessinger Publishing, LLC.

Harris, Elizabeth. Theravada Buddhism & the British Encounter: Religious, Missionary & Colonial Experience in Nineteenth Century Sri Lanka. 2009. 280p. pap. 39.95 *(978-0-415-54442-9(4))* Routledge.

Heisig, J. W. & Kim, S., eds. Monasticism Buddhist & Christian: The Korean Experience. 2008. (Louvain Theological & Pastoral Monographs). 201p. (C). pap. 32.00 *(978-90-429-2060-6(2))* Peeters Pubs. & Booksellers BEL. Dist: Brown, David Bk. Co., The.

Ingram, Paul O. Buddhist-Christian Dialogue in an Age of Science. 2007. (ENG.). 168p. per. 19.95 *(978-0-7425-6215-8(8))*; 65.00 *(978-0-7425-6214-1(X))* Rowman & Littlefield Publishers, Inc.

—The Process of Buddhist-Christian Dialogue. 2011. (ENG.). 149p. pap. 36.00 *(978-0-227-17369-5(4))* Clarke, James Co., Ltd. GBR. Dist: Brown, David Bk. Co., The.

—The Process of Buddhist-Christian Dialogue. 2009. 162p. pap. 18.00 *(978-1-60608-554-7(9)*, Cascade Bks.) Wipf & Stock Pubs.

Ingram, Paul O. Theological Reflections at the Boundaries. 2011. 188p. pap. 22.00 ***(978-1-61097-405-9(0)***, Cascade Bks.) Wipf & Stock Pubs.

Ingram, Paul O., ed. Buddhist-Christian Dialogue: Mutual Renewal & Transformation. 2007. 254p. pap. 28.00 *(978-1-55635-391-9(2)*, Wipf and Stock) Wipf & Stock Pubs.

Jäger, Stefan S. Glaube und Religiöse Rede Bei Tillich und Im Shin-Buddhismus: Eine Religionshermeneutische Studie. 2011. (Tillich Research Ser.). (GER.). XX, 614p. 140.00 ***(978-3-11-026875-1(2))*** De Gruyter, Walter Inc.

Keenan, John P. Grounding Our Faith in a Pluralist World: With a little help from Nagarjuna. 2008. 136p. pap. 17.00 *(978-1-55635-997-2(7)*, Wipf and Stock) Wipf & Stock Pubs.

King, Winston L. Buddhism & Christianity: Some Bridges of Understanding. 2008. (Routledge Library Editions: Buddhism Ser.). (ENG.). 4p. (C). 165.00 *(978-0-415-46110-8(3))* Routledge.

Knitter, Paul F. Without Buddha I Could Not Be a Christian. 2009. (ENG.). 336p. pap. 22.95 *(978-1-85168-673-5(8))* Oneworld Pubns. GBR. Dist: National Bk. Network.

Lefebure, Leo D. & Feldmeier, Peter. The Path of Wisdom: A Christian Commentary on the Dhammapada. 2011. x, 379p. ***(978-90-429-2330-0(X))*** Eerdmans, William B. Publishing Co.

Lillie, Arthur. The Influence of Buddhism on Primitive Christianity. 2010. 196p. pap. 19.95 *(978-0-557-47270-3(9))* Lulu Enterprises Inc.

Lim, David & De Neui, Paul H. Communicating Christ in the Buddhist World. 2007. 280p. *(978-0-87808-510-1(6))* Carey, William Library Pubs.

Lounibos, John B. Self-Emptying of Christ & the Christian: Three Essays on Kenosis. 2011. 132p. pap. 16.00 ***(978-1-61097-189-8(2)***, Wipf and Stock) Wipf & Stock Pubs.

Mabry, John R. The Way of Thomas: Nine Insights for Enlightened Living from the Secret Sayings of Jesus. 2006. (ENG.). 196p. per. 19.95 *(978-1-84694-030-9(3))* Hunt, John Publishing Ltd. GBR. Dist: National Bk. Network.

Mac, Mary. The OUTRAGEOUS JOY Journey: Where Abraham meets the Buddha & you meet Yourself. 2010. 348p. pap. 19.97 *(978-1-4452-2173-1(X))* Lulu Enterprises Inc.

MacGregor, Kirk R. A Comparative Study of Adjustments to Social Catastrophes in Christianity & Buddhism: The Black Death in Europe & the Kamakura Takeover in Japan As Causes of Religious Reform. 2011. 400p. 129.95 ***(978-0-7734-1549-2(1))*** Mellen, Edwin Pr., The.

Miyamoto, Arata. Embodied Cross: Intercontextual Reading of Theologia Crucis. 2010. 166p. pap. 19.00 *(978-1-60899-149-5(0)*, Wipf and Stock) Wipf & Stock Pubs.

Monier-Williams, Monier. Buddhism, in Its Connection with Brahmanism & Hinduism & in Contrast with Christianity 2nd ed. reprint ed. 57.50 *(978-0-404-17349-4(7))* AMS Pr., Inc.

Paradisian Publications. The buddhist essene gospel of jesus volume II: The New Age Essene & Maha Bodhi Renaissance. 2007. 107p. per. 14.00 *(978-0-9725877-2-3(1))* Paradisian Pubns.

Paul Carus. The Gospel of Budh. 2011. (Illus.). 336p. pap. 7.89 ***(978-1-60386-397-1(4)***, Watchmaker Publishing) Wexford College Pr.

Peerman, Gordon. Blessed Relief: What Christians Can Learn from Buddhists about Suffering. 2008. 208p. pap. 16.99 *(978-1-59473-252-2(3))* SkyLight Paths Publishing.

Roach, Michael & McNally, Christie. The Eastern Path to Heaven: A Guide to Happiness from the Teachings of Jesus in Tibet. 2008. 160p. pap. 16.00 *(978-1-59627-097-8(7)*, Seabury Bks.) Church Publishing, Inc.

Roebert, Donovan. The Gospel for Buddhists & the Dharma for Christians. 2009. 338p. pap. 37.00 *(978-1-60608-040-5(7)*, Resource Pubns.) Wipf & Stock Pubs.

Skelton, Tommy. Christianity, Buddhism & Zen: A Look Outside the Box. 2007. 136p. per. 24.95 *(978-1-4241-4944-5(4))* PublishAmerica, Inc.

Snook, Stewart. Christ More Powerful: Analogies of Christ in Non-Christian Religions. 2011. 108p. 21.23 ***(978-1-4567-1122-1(9))***; pap. 10.68 ***(978-1-4567-1123-8(7))*** AuthorHouse.

Strand, Clark. How to Believe in God: Whether You Believe in Religion or Not. 2009. (ENG.). 256p. 24.95 *(978-0-7679-2069-8(4))* Knopf Doubleday Publishing Group.

Streeter, Burnett Hillman. The Buddha & the Christ: An Exploration of the Meaning of the Universe & the Purpose of Human Life 1933. 2007. (ENG.). 348p. 46.95 *(978-0-548-05520-5(3))* Kessinger Publishing, LLC.

Thompson, Ross. Buddhist Christianity: A Passionate Openness. 2010. (ENG., Illus.). 313p. pap. 24.95 *(978-1-84694-336-2(1))* Hunt, John Publishing Ltd. GBR. Dist: National Bk. Network.

Trebor. Christianity, Sect of Judaism or Buddhism? 2010. 202p. pap. 19.99 *(978-1-4535-1449-8(X))* Xlibris Corp.

Yandell, Keith & Netland, Harold. Buddhism: A Christian Exploration & Appraisal, 1 vol. 2009. (ENG., Illus.). 230p. pap. 22.00 *(978-0-8308-3855-4(4)*, IVP Acad.) InterVarsity Pr.

Zacharias, Ravi. The Lotus & the Cross: Jesus Talks with Buddha. 2010. (Great Conversations Ser.). (ENG.). 96p. pap. 11.99 *(978-1-60142-318-4(7)*, Multnomah) Doubleday Religious Publishing Group, The.

CHRISTIANITY AND OTHER RELIGIONS—CONFUCIANISM

Huang, Z. Confronting Confucian Understandings of the Christian Doctrine of Salvation: A Systematic Theological Analysis of the Basic Problems in the Confucian-Christian Dialogue. 2009. (Studies in Systematic Theology Ser.). *(978-90-04-17726-0(4))* BRILL.

Lee, Chung Soon. Christian-Confucian Spirituality in Kore. 2008. 216p. pap. *(978-3-639-10652-7(0))* VDM Verlag Dr. Mueller e.K.

Thong, Chan Kei. Faith of Our Fathers: God in Ancient China. 2007. (CHI., Illus.). 265p. pap. 20.00 *(978-0-9796269-0-6(7))* Leadership Development International.

Thong, Chan Kei, et al. Finding God in Ancient China: How the Ancient Chinese Worshiped the God of the Bible, 1 vol. 2009. (ENG.). 352p. pap. 24.99 *(978-0-310-29238-8(7))* Zondervan.

CHRISTIANITY AND OTHER RELIGIONS—DRUIDISM

Virpiranta, Mika. Struggles of Sun Against Thunder. 2011. 154p. pap. 41.90 ***(978-952-498-495-9(4))*** Bks. on Demand.

CHRISTIANITY AND OTHER RELIGIONS—GREEK

Johnson, Luke Timothy. Among the Gentiles: Greco-Roman Religion & Christianity. 2010. (Anchor Yale Bible Reference Library). (ENG.). 480p. pap. 22.00 *(978-0-300-16810-5(1))* Yale Univ. Pr.

Markos, Louis. From Achilles to Christ: Why Christians Should Read the Pagan Classics. 2007. (ENG., Illus.). 264p. per. 24.00 *(978-0-8308-2593-6(2)*, IVP Acad.) InterVarsity Pr.

Papadogiannakis, Yannis. Christianity & Hellenism in the Fifth-Century Greek East: Theodoret's Apologetics Against the Greeks in Context. 2012. (Hellenic Studies Ser.). (ENG., Illus.). 200p. pap. 19.95 *(978-0-674-06067-8(9))* Harvard Univ., Ctr. for Hellenic Studies.

Patte, Daniel, et al, eds. Greek Patristic & Eastern Orthodox Interpretations of Romans, Vol. 9. 2013. (Romans Through History & Culture Ser.). (ENG.). 224p. pap. 39.95 *(978-0-567-48092-7(5)*, T&T Clark Int'l) Continuum International Publishing Group, Ltd. GBR. Dist: National Bk. Network.

Priestly, Joseph. The Imperfection of Socrates' Ideas Concerning Piety & Virtue In. 2006. pap. 9.95 *(978-1-4304-1794-1(3))* Kessinger Publishing, LLC.

Stenger, Jan. Hellenische Identität in der Spätantike: Pagane Autoren und Ihr Unbehagen an der eigenen Zeit. 2009. (Untersuchungen zur antiken Literatur und Geschichte Ser.).Tr. of Experience of Crisis & Literature in Late Antiquity. Greek Authors & their Concern for their own Times. (GER.). X, 424p. 210.00 ***(978-3-11-173190-2(1))*** De Gruyter, Walter Inc.

Stenger, Jan. Hellenische Identität in der Spätantike: Pagane Autoren und Ihr Unbehagen an der eigenen Zeit. 2009. (Untersuchungen zur antiken Literatur und Geschichte Ser.).Tr. of Experience of Crisis & Literature in Late Antiquity. Greek Authors & their Concern for their own Times. (GER.). X, 424p. 140.00 *(978-3-11-021328-7(1))* De Gruyter, Walter Inc.

CHRISTIANITY AND OTHER RELIGIONS—HINDUISM

Abrams, Bahia. The Other Half of My Soul. 2007. 360p. 24.00 *(978-0-9789548-3-3(1))*; pap. 18.00 *(978-0-9789548-4-0(X))* Grateful Steps.

Ballantyne, James. Christianity Contrasted with Hindu Philosophy an Essay. 2007. (ENG.). 282p. 43.95 *(978-0-548-05102-3(X))* Kessinger Publishing, LLC.

Burnett, David G. & Burnett, David. The Spirit of Hinduism: A Christian Perspective on Hindu Life & Thought. 2nd ed. 2007. (Illus.). 304p. pap. 16.99 *(978-0-8254-6110-1(3)*, Monarch Bks.) Lion Hudson PLC GBR. Dist: Kregel Pubns.

Chatterji, Mohini M. The Bhagavad Gita or the Lord's Lay with References to the Christian Scriptures. 2007. (ENG.). 310p. 45.95 *(978-0-548-04167-3(9))* Kessinger Publishing, LLC.

Clooney, Francis. Divine Mother, Blessed Mother: Hindu Goddesses & the Virgin Mary, 1 vol. 2010. (ENG.). 288p. pap. 24.95 *(978-0-19-973873-1(4))* Oxford Univ. Pr., Inc.

—Hindu God, Christian God: How Reason Helps Break down the Boundaries between Religions, 1 vol. 2010. 220p. pap. 24.95 *(978-0-19-973872-4(6))* Oxford Univ. Pr., Inc.

Clooney, Francis X. Comparative Theology: Deep Learning Across Religious Borders. 2010. (ENG.). 200p. 99.95 *(978-1-4051-7973-7(2))*; pap. 32.95 *(978-1-4051-7974-4(0))* Wiley, John & Sons, Inc. (Wiley-Blackwell).

Clooney, S. J. New Comparative Theology: Interreligious Insights from the Next Generation. Francis X, ed. 2010. (ENG.). 232p. pap. 29.95 *(978-0-567-14137-8(3)*, T&T Clark Int'l) Continuum International Publishing Group, Ltd. GBR. Dist: National Bk. Network.

Clooney, S. J. & Francis X, eds. New Comparative Theology: Interreligious Insights from the Next Generation. 2010. (ENG.). 232p. 100.00

C

(978-0-567-31048-4(5), T&T Clark Int'l) Continuum International Publishing Group, Ltd. GBR. Dist: National Bk. Network.

Cornille, C. The Song Divine: Christian Commentaries on the Bhagavad Gita. 2006. (Christian Commentaries on Non-Christian Sacred Texts Ser.: Vol. 1). vi, 219p. *(978-90-429-1769-9(5))* Peeters Pubs. & Booksellers.

Cornille, Catherine, ed. Song Divine: Christian Commentaries on the Bhagavad Gita. 2006. (Christian Commentaries on Non-Christian Sacred Texts). 219p. pap. 40.00 *(978-0-8028-4016-5(7))* Eerdmans, William B. Publishing Co.

Farquhar, J. N. Crown of Hinduism. 2006. 472p. per. *(978-1-4067-2630-5(3)*, Hesperides Pr.) Read Bks.

Karingadayil, Santhosh Thomas. From Darkness to Light: The Concept of Salvation in the Perspectives of Thomas Aquinas & Sankara. 2011. (Europäische Hochschulschriften. Reihe 23: Theologie Ser.). 310p. pap. 76.95 *(978-3-631-61890-5(5))* Lang, Peter GmbH, Europäischer Verlag der Wissenschaften DEU. Dist: Lang, Peter.

Klostermaier, Klaus K. Hindu & Christian in Vrindaban. 128p. pap. 14.00 *(978-0-334-00616-9(3))* Hymns Ancient & Modern Ltd GBR. Dist: Trinity Pr. International.

Largen, Kristin J. Baby Krishna, Infant Christ: A Comparative Theology of Salvation. 2011. 240p. pap. 30.00 *(978-1-57075-932-1(4))* Orbis Bks.

Pérez Prieto, Victorino & Prieto, Victorino Pérez. Más Allá de la Fragmentación de la Teología: El Saber y la Vida: Raimon Panikkar. 2008. (SPA.). 341p. *(978-84-9876-150-4(6))* Tirant lo Blanch.

Pitt, Malcolm. Introducing Hinduism. 2011. 66p. 36.95 ***(978-1-258-02373-7(3))*** Literary Licensing, LLC.

Richard, H. L. Hinduism: A Brief Look at the Theology, Scriptures, & Social System, with Comments on the Gospel in India. 2007. 61p. *(978-0-87808-514-9(9))* Carey, William Library Pubs.

Robinson, Bob. Christians Meeting Hindus: An Analysis & Theological Critique of the Hindu-Christian Encounter in India. 2011. (Regnum Studies in Mission Ser.). 416p. pap. 47.00 ***(978-1-61097-596-4(0)***, Wipf and Stock) Wipf & Stock Pubs.

Rynne, Terrence J. Gandhi & Jesus: The Saving Power of Nonviolence. 2008. 228p. pap. 20.00 *(978-1-57075-766-2(6))* Orbis Bks.

Sharma, Arvind. Christianity for Hindus. 2010. 109p. pap. *(978-81-246-0540-0(8)*, Library of Congress — New Delhi Overseas Office) D. K. Print World (P) Ltd.

Sheridan, Daniel P. Loving God: Krsna & Christ: A Christian Commentary on the Narada Sutras. 2008. (Christian Commentaries on Non-Christian Sacred Texts). 216p. pap. 46.00 *(978-0-8028-6282-2(9))* Eerdmans, William B. Publishing Co.

Sheveland, John. Piety & Responsibility: Patterns of Unity in Karl Rahner Karl Bath & Vedanta Deshika. 2011. (New Critical Thinking in Religion, Theology & Biblical Studies). 224p. 89.95 *(978-1-4094-0905-2(8))* Ashgate Publishing Co.

Smart, Ninian. The Yogi & the Devotee (Routledge Revivals) 2011. (Routledge Revivals Ser.). (ENG.). 178p. 110.00 *(978-0-415-68236-7(3))* Routledge.

Snook, Stewart. Christ More Powerful: Analogies of Christ in Non-Christian Religions. 2011. 108p. 21.23 ***(978-1-4567-1122-1(9))***; pap. 10.68 ***(978-1-4567-1123-8(7))*** AuthorHouse.

Swami Akhikananda. Hindu View of Christ. *(978-0-8022-0012-9(5))* Philosophical Library, Inc.

Sydnor, Jon Paul. Ramanuja & Schleiermacher: Toward a Constructive Comparative Theology. 2012. (ENG.). 238p. (C). pap. 45.00 ***(978-0-227-68024-7(3))*** Clarke, James Co., Ltd. GBR. Dist: Brown, David Bk. Co., The.

—Ramanuja & Schleiermacher: Toward a Constructive Comparative Theology. 2011. (Princeton Theological Monographs). 238p. pap. 26.00 ***(978-1-60899-308-6(6)***, Pickwick Pubns.) Wipf & Stock Pubs.

Vemuri, Raj. From Hinduism to Christ: A Former Hindu Brahmin Looks at World Religions & the Powerful Truths of the Christian Faith. 2009. 292p. pap. 18.99 *(978-1-4141-1493-4(1))* Pleasant Word.

Yogananda, Swami. Super Advanced Course Number One Lessons 1 To. 2007. 180p. per. 14.95 *(978-1-933993-50-8(2))* Apocryphile Pr.

CHRISTIANITY AND OTHER RELIGIONS—ISLAM

see also Jesus Christ—Islamic Interpretations; Missions to Muslims

A, Abdullahi. From Islam to Christianity: Muhammad in the Bible Facts or Fiction. 2008. 101p. pap. 16.95 *(978-1-4092-0833-4(8))* Lulu Enterprises Inc.

Abbott, Daniel H. Revolutionary Strategies in Early Christianity: 4th Generation Warfare (4GW) Against the Roman Empire, & the Counterinsurgency (COIN) Campaign to Sa. 2008. 48p. pap. 19.16 *(978-1-934840-36-8(X))* Nimble Bks. LLC.

Abdel Razaq, S. S. Neo-Muslim Intellectuals in the West & their Contributions to Islamic Thought & the Formation of Western Islam: An Exploratory Investigation of the Religious & Literary Activities of Western Neo-Muslim Intellectuals. 2008. (New Religious Identities in the Western World Ser.). (ENG.). 338p. (C). pap. 65.00 *(978-90-429-2112-2(9))* Peeters Pubs. & Booksellers BEL. Dist: Brown, David Bk. Co., The.

Abdullah, Naeem. Islam: A Favor to Humanity. 2009. 130p. pap. 18.95 *(978-1-4327-4338-3(4))* Outskirts Pr., Inc.

Abell, Irwin. Jesus Versus Allah. 2007. (ENG.). 300p. per. 16.95 *(978-0-7414-3781-5(3))* Infinity Publishing.

Aboona, Hirmis. Assyrians, Kurds, & Ottomans: Intercommunal Relations on the Periphery of the Ottoman Empire. 2008. 344p. 109.95 *(978-1-60497-583-3(0))* Cambria Pr.

Abu Groon, Sheikh Elnayyal. The All-Embracing Message of Islam: Fi Rihab Al-Risalah. 2009. 68p. pap. 10.95 *(978-1-4327-3601-9(9))* Outskirts Pr., Inc.

Abu-Nimer/Augsburger, et al. Peace-Building by, Between, & Beyond Muslims & Evangelical Christians. Abu-Nimer, Moha & Augsburger, Dav, eds. 2009. (ENG.). 324p. 83.99 *(978-0-7391-3521-1(X))* Lexington Bks.

Ahlstrand, Kajsa, ed. Non-Muslims in Muslim Majority Societies - with Focus on the Middle East & Pakistan. 2009. (Church of Sweden Research Ser.). 174p. pap. 20.00 *(978-1-60608-609-4(X)*, Pickwick Pubns.) Wipf & Stock Pubs.

Akbari, Suzanne Conklin. Idols in the East: European Representations of Islam & the Orient, 1100-1450. 2009. (Illus.). 336p. 49.95 *(978-0-8014-4807-2(7))* Cornell Univ. Pr.

al-Jabbar, Abd. Critique of Christian Origins. Reynolds, Gabriel Said & Samir, Samir Khalil, trs. from ARA. 2010. (Brigham Young University - Islamic Translation Ser.). (ARA & ENG.). 249p. 37.95 *(978-0-8425-2715-6(X)*, Brigham Young Univ. Pr.) Brigham Young Univ.

AL-SHARIF, William. Christianity, Islam & Secular Criticism. 2010. 219p. pap. 27.50 *(978-1-4457-8079-5(8))* Lulu Enterprises Inc.

Ali, Daniel. Out of Islam: Free at Last. 2007. 162p. per. 12.99 *(978-1-59886-761-9(X))* Tate Publishing & Enterprises, LLC.

Ali, Maulvi Muhammad. Muhammad & Christ. 2007. (Analecta Gorgiana Ser.: 41). per. 39.00 *(978-1-59333-726-1(4))* Gorgias Pr., LLC.

Ali, Muhammad. Muhammad & Christ. 2010. pap. 35.20 *(978-1-61719-640-9(1))* Gorgias Pr., LLC.

Almirzanah, Syafaatun. When Mystic Masters Meet: Towards a New Matrix for Christian-Muslim Dialogue. 2011. (ENG.). 252p. pap. 16.95 *(978-1-935295-12-9(8))* Blue Dome Pr.

Almond, Ian. Two Faiths, One Banner: When Muslims Marched with Christians Across Europe's Battlegrounds. 2009. (Illus.). 256p. 29.95 *(978-0-674-03397-9(3))* Harvard Univ. Pr.

Anderson, Christian S. What Every Christian Should Know about Islam. 2008. 148p. pap. 14.99 *(978-1-60647-442-6(1))* Xulon Pr., Inc.

Ankerberg, John & Caner, Emir. The Truth about Islam & Women. 2009. (Truth about Islam Ser.). 80p. pap. 7.99 *(978-0-7369-2503-7(1))* Harvest Hse. Pubs.

Ankerberg, John, et al. The Truth about Islam & Jesus. 2009. (Truth about Islam Ser.). 80p. pap. 7.99 *(978-0-7369-2502-0(3))* Harvest Hse. Pubs.

Awodeyi, Jonah. This Jesus - Torah, Gospel & Quran. 2010. 86p. pap. 8.50 *(978-1-4457-6544-0(6))* Lulu Enterprises Inc.

Azbell, Frederick J. Organized Religion Is... Blind, Leading the Blind. 2010. 232p. pap. 16.99 *(978-1-4520-5367-7(7))* AuthorHouse.

Baile, Mohamed Wa. Beyond the Clash of Civilizations: A New Cultural Synthesis for Muslims in the West. 2011. 200p. 26.95 ***(978-1-4620-3422-2(5))***; pap. 16.95 ***(978-1-4620-3420-8(9))*** iUniverse, Inc.

Bakos, Gergely Tibor. On Faith, Rationality, & the Other in the Late Middle Ages: A Study of Nicholas of Cusa's Manuductive Approach to Islam. 2010. (Princeton Theological Monographs). 360p. pap. 40.00 *(978-1-60608-342-0(2)*, Pickwick Pubns.) Wipf & Stock Pubs.

Barto, Linda iLham. The Bible & the Qur'an at the Edge of Renaissance: A Judeo-Christian-Muslim Compass to a World of Peace. 2009. 272p. pap. 18.95 *(978-1-934937-88-4(6))* Mill City Pr., Inc.

Beaumont, I. Mark. Christology in Dialogue with Muslims: A Critical Analysis of Christian Presentations of Christ for Muslims from the Ninth & Twentieth Centuries. 2011. (Regnum Studies in Mission: Ser.). 260p. pap. 29.00 ***(978-1-61097-593-3(6)***, Wipf and Stock) Wipf & Stock Pubs.

Becker, C. & Chaytor, H. Christianity & Islam. 2009. pap. 44.20 *(978-1-60724-274-1(5))* Gorgias Pr., LLC.

Becker, C. H. Christianity & Islam. 2009. 122p. 24.99 *(978-1-110-90667-3(6))*; (ENG.). 120p. pap. 18.99 *(978-1-110-90661-1(7)*, BiblioLife); (ENG.). 120p. pap. 19.99 *(978-1-110-90663-5(3)*, BiblioLife); 122p. pap. 19.75 *(978-1-110-90665-9(X))* BiblioBazaar.

—Christianity & Islam. Chaytor, H. J., tr. 2011. 82p. pap. 9.99 ***(978-1-61203-930-5(8))*** Bottom of the Hill Publishing.

—Christianity & Islam. 2010. 48p. pap. *(978-1-4076-1205-8(0))* HardPr.

—Christianity & Islam. 2007. (ENG.). 120p. per. *(978-1-4067-5859-7(0))* Read Bks.

Becker, C. h. & Becker, C. H. Christianity & Islam. 2010. 36p. pap. 14.14 *(978-1-153-59550-6(8))* General Bks. LLC.

Becker, Carl Heinrich. Christianity & Islam. 2008. 124p. 21.99 *(978-0-559-74015-2(8))*; pap. 19.75 *(978-0-559-74012-1(3))* BiblioBazaar.

—Christianity & Islam. 2007. (ENG.). 120p. 34.95 *(978-0-548-15525-7(9))*; pap. 19.95 *(978-1-4304-4956-0(X))* Kessinger Publishing, LLC.

Bell, Steve. Grace for Muslims? The Journey from Fear to Faith. 2007. (ENG.). 176p. per. 14.99 *(978-1-85078-664-1(X))* Authentic Media.

Ben-Chanan, Ami. Qur'an-Bible Comparison: A Topical Study of the Two Most Influential & Respectful Books in Western & Middle Eastern Civilizations. 2011. 424p. pap. 18.33 *(978-1-4269-5492-4(1))* Trafford Publishing.

Bennett, Clinton. Victorian Images of Islam. 2010. 105.68 *(978-1-60724-673-2(2))* Gorgias Pr., LLC.

Bennett, Clinton & Bennett. Understanding Christian-Muslim Relations: Past & Present. 2008. (ENG.). 272p. 130.00 *(978-0-8264-8782-7(3))*; (Illus.). 39.95 *(978-0-8264-8783-4(1))* Continuum International Publishing Group, Ltd. GBR. Dist: National Bk. Network.

Berman, Paul. The Flight of the Intellectuals: The Controversy over Islam & the Press. 2010. 304p. 26.00 *(978-1-933633-51-0(4))* Melville Hse. Publishing.

—The Flight of the Intellectuals: The Controversy over Islamism & the Press. 2011. 320p. pap. 16.95 *(978-1-935554-44-8(1))* Melville Hse. Publishing.

Bertaina, David. Christian & Muslim Dialogues. 2011. 114.00 *(978-1-61143-920-5(5))* 2010. pap. 37.24 *(978-1-61719-941-7(9))* Gorgias Pr., LLC.

Bethmann, Erich W. Bridge to Islam: A Study of the Religious Forces of Islam & Christianity in the near East. 2011. 320p. 50.95 ***(978-1-258-01726-2(1))*** Literary Licensing, LLC.

Blyden, Edward Wilmot. Christianity, Islam & the Negro Race. (African Heritage Classical Research Studies). 407p. reprint ed. 40.00 *(978-0-938818-36-6(8))* ECA Assocs.

Bobrick, Benson. The Caliph's Splendor: Islam & the West in the Golden Age of Baghdad. 2012. (ENG., Illus.). 288p. 28.00 ***(978-1-4165-6762-2(3))*** Simon & Schuster.

Boer, Jan H. Christians: Why We Reject Muslim Law. 2008. 528p. per. *(978-1-55452-217-0(X))* Essence Publishing.

Bradley, Mark. Iran: Open Hearts in a Closed Land. 2007. (ENG.). 116p. per. 9.99 *(978-1-85078-770-9(0))* Authentic Media.

Bradley, Scott A. Christianity vs. Islam: An Examination over the Black Religious Debate. Divers, Consuelo, ed. 47p. (Orig.). (C). pap. 4.95 *(978-0-9636928-2-5(8))* Rivers of Life Ministry.

Brown, Norman O. The Challenge of Islam: The Prophetic Tradition. Neu, Jerome, ed. 2009. (ENG.). 164p. pap. 14.95 *(978-1-55643-802-8(8))* North Atlantic Bks.

Burman, Thomas E. Reading the Qur'an in Latin Christendom, 1140-1560. 2009. (Material Texts). (Illus.). 328p. (C). pap. 24.95 *(978-0-8122-2062-9(5))* Univ. of Pennsylvania Pr.

—Reading the Quran in Latin Christendom, 1140-1560. 2007. (Material Texts). (ENG., Illus.). 328p. (C). 59.95 *(978-0-8122-4018-4(9))* Univ. of Pennsylvania Pr.

Burns, Robert A. Christianity, Islam, & the West. 2011. (ENG.). 150p. pap. 26.95 ***(978-0-7618-5559-0(9))*** Univ. Pr. of America, Inc.

Caner, Ergun Mehmet & Caner, Emir Fethi. Unveiling Islam: An Insider's Look at Muslim Life & Beliefs, 1 vol. rev. ed. 2009. 288p. pap. 15.99 *(978-0-8254-2428-1(3))* Kregel Pubns.

Cearley, Gary. Thou Shalt Not Bear False Witness: The T. 2006. 200p. pap. 22.40 *(978-1-84728-731-1(X))* Lulu Enterprises Inc.

Chandler, Paul Gordon. Pilgrims of Christ on the Muslim Road: Exploring a New Path Between Two Faiths. 2008. (ENG.). 224p. pap. 19.95 *(978-0-7425-6603-3(X))* Rowman & Littlefield Publishers, Inc.

Chapman, Colin G. Cross & Crescent: Responding to the Challenge of Islam. 2nd rev. ed. 2008. (ENG.). 400p. per. 18.00 *(978-0-8308-3485-3(0)*, IVP Bks.) InterVarsity Pr.

Chatrath, Nick. Reaching Muslims: A One-Stop Guide for Christians, 1 vol. 2011. (Illus.). 160p. pap. 12.99 *(978-0-85721-014-2(9)*, Monarch Bks.) Lion Hudson PLC GBR. Dist: Kregel Pubns.

Cliff, Nigel. Holy War: How Vasco da Gama's Epic Voyages Turned the Tide in a Centuries-Old Clash of Civilizations. (ENG.). 2012. 352p. pap. 17.99 ***(978-0-06-173513-4(2)***, HarperPerennial) 2011. 560p. 29.99 *(978-0-06-173512-7(4))* HarperCollins Pubs.

Coakley, Sarah & Ward, Frances. Fear & Friendship: Anglicans Engaging with Islam. Coakley, Sarah & Ward, Frances, eds. 2012. (ENG.). 224p. pap. 22.95 *(978-1-4411-0149-5(7))* Continuum International Publishing Group, Ltd. GBR. Dist: National Bk. Network.

Conference upon Missionary Work for the Mohammedans. 2010. 87.08 *(978-1-61719-207-4(4))* Gorgias Pr., LLC.

Conlon, John R. Islam: And the Clash with Christianity. 2008. 184p. pap. 16.99 *(978-1-4141-1234-3(3))* Pleasant Word.

Cooper, Barbara M. Evangelical Christians in the Muslim Sahel. 2010. (African Systems of Thought Ser.). (ENG., Illus.). 480p. pap. 24.95 *(978-0-253-22233-6(8)*, 0253222338) Indiana Univ. Pr.

Cooper, Barbara MacGowan & Cooper, Barbara. Evangelical Christians in the Muslim Sahel. 2006. (African Systems of Thought Ser.). (ENG., Illus.). 480p. 49.95 *(978-0-253-34739-8(4)*, 0253347394) Indiana Univ. Pr.

Corwin, Gary. The Desert Is Alive: Streams of Living Water from Muscat to Marrakech. 2007. (ENG., Illus.). 168p. per. 14.99 *(978-1-85078-697-9(6))* Authentic Media.

Cragg, Kenneth. A Christian-Muslim Inter-Text Now: From Anathemata to Theme. 2010. 248p. pap. 30.00 *(978-1-901764-50-5(8))* International Publishers Marketing.

Cragg, Kenneth B. Christians & Muslims: From History to Healing. 2011. 240p. 28.95 ***(978-1-4502-8520-9(1))***; pap. 18.95 ***(978-1-4502-8519-3(8))*** iUniverse, Inc.

Crowley, Roger. Empires of the Sea: The Siege of Malta, the Battle of Lepanto, & the Contest for the Center of the World. 2009. (ENG., Illus.). 368p. pap. 16.00 *(978-0-8129-7764-6(5)*, Random Hse. Trade Paperbacks) Random House Publishing Group.

Dada, Isaiah. Defribillation of Peace. 2009. 152p. pap. *(978-3-639-15934-9(9))* VDM Verlag Dr. Mueller e.K.

Dardess, George. Do We Worship the Same God? Comparing the Bible & the Qur'an. 2006. 166p. per. 12.95 *(978-0-86716-731-3(9))* Franciscan Media.

Dardess, George & Mich, Marvin L. Krier. In the Spirit of St. Francis & the Sultan: Catholics andMuslims Working Together for the Common Good. 2011. (Illus.). 224p. pap. 20.00 *(978-1-57075-907-9(3))* Orbis Bks.

Dardess, George & Rosenthal, Peggy. Reclaiming Beauty for the Good of the World: Muslim & Christian Creativity as Moral Power. 2010. (ENG., Illus.). 280p. pap. 22.95 *(978-1-891785-61-0(3))* Fons Vitae of Kentucky, Inc.

De Bunsen, Ernest. Islam or True Christianity: Including a Chapter on Mahomed's Place. 2007. pap. 22.95 *(978-1-4304-4972-0(1))* Kessinger Publishing, LLC.

De Mattei, Roberto. Holy War, Just War: Islam & Christendom at War. 2007. 92p. pap. 12.95 *(978-0-9720616-5-0(7)*, Chronicles Pr.) Rockford Institute, The.

Domnwachukwu, Chinaka Samuel. Incessant Warfare: A Critical History of Spiritual Warfare Through the Ages. 2011. 288p. 35.95 ***(978-1-4627-0569-6(3))***; pap. 19.95 ***(978-1-4627-0568-9(5))*** Cross Bks. Publishing.

Dorman, Harry Gaylord. Toward Understanding Islam Contemporary. 2006. pap. 21.95 *(978-1-4286-5475-4(5))* Kessinger Publishing, LLC.

Echevarria, Ana & Beagles, Martin. The Moorish Guard of the Kings of Castile (1410-1467) 2008. (Illus.). 384p. *(978-90-04-17110-7(X))* BRILL.

Echeverri Uruburu, Gonzalo. Nostradamus & the Apocalyptic War Between Islam & West: Villegas Prophecy. 2006. (ENG., Illus.). 352p. per. 16.95 *(978-958-8293-04-2(9))* Villegas Editores S.A. COL. Dist: Independent Pubs. Group.

El-Ansary, Waleed & Linnan, David, eds. Muslim & Christian Understanding: Theory & Application of a Common Word. 2010. (ENG., Illus.). 300p. 100.00 *(978-0-230-10370-2(7))* Palgrave Macmillan.

El-Ansary, Waleed & Linnan, David K., eds. Muslim & Christian Understanding: Theory & Application of a Common Word. 2010. (ENG., Illus.). 300p. pap. 29.00 *(978-0-230-10442-6(8))* Palgrave Macmillan.

Ellul, Max J. The Sword & the Green Cross: The Saga of the Knights of Saint Lazarus from the Crusades to the 21st Century. 2011. 396p. 28.28 *(978-1-4567-1420-8(1))*; pap. 17.72 *(978-1-4567-1421-5(X))* AuthorHouse.

Erlich, Haggai. Islam & Christianity in the Horn of Africa: Somalia, Ethiopia, Sudan. 2010. 200p. 49.95 *(978-1-58826-713-9(X))* Rienner, Lynne Pubs.

Faith under Fire#8482; 3: Tough Faith Questions, Session 3: Four Sessions on Forgiveness, Suffering, the Trinity, & Islam, 1 vol. 2009. (Zondervangroupware Small Group Edition Ser.). 4.99 *(978-0-310-79870-5(1))*; 2.99 *(978-0-310-79860-6(4))*; 4.99 *(978-0-310-79865-1(5))* Zondervan.

Faith under Fire#8482; 3: Tough Faith Questions, Session 4: Four Sessions on Forgiveness, Suffering, the Trinity, & Islam, 1 vol. 2009. (Zondervangroupware Small Group Edition Ser.). (ENG.). 2.99 *(978-0-310-79866-8(3))*; 2.99 *(978-0-310-79861-3(2))*; (ENG.). 4.99 *(978-0-310-79871-2(X))* Zondervan.

Forsey, Alicia McNary. Queen Isabella Sforza Szapolyai of Transylvania & Sultan Suleyman of the Ottoman Empire: A Case of Sixteenth-Century Muslim-Christian Collaboration. 2009. (Illus.). 180p. 99.95 *(978-0-7734-4653-3(2))* Mellen, Edwin Pr., The.

Forstel, Karl. Schriften zum Islam von Arethas und Euthymios Zigabenos und Fragmente der griechischen Koranubersetzung. Griechisch-deutsche Textausgabe. 2009. (Corpus Islamo-Christianum Ser.). (GER & GEC.). 128p. (C). pap. 54.00 *(978-3-447-05904-6(4))* Harrassowitz, Otto Verlag DEU. Dist: ISD.

Francisco, Adam S. & Francisco, Adam. Martin Luther & Islam: A Study in Sixteenth-Century Polemics & Apologetics. 2007. (History of Christian-Muslim Relations Ser.). 262p. *(978-90-04-16043-9(4))* BRILL.

Funk, Mary Margaret. Islam Is... . An Experience of Dialogue & Devotion. 2nd ed. 2008. 155p. pap. 14.00 *(978-1-59056-125-6(2))* Lantern Bks.

Gabriel, Theodore. Christian Minorities in an Islamic State: The Pakistan Experience. 2007. (Illus.). 132p. 89.95 *(978-0-7546-6024-8(9))*; pap. 39.95 *(978-0-7546-6036-1(2))* Ashgate Publishing Co.

Gairdner, W.H.T. The Rebuke of Islam. 2009. 100.48 *(978-1-60724-411-0(X))* Gorgias Pr., LLC.

Galvan (Abu Noah), Abu Noah Ibrahim Ibn Mika'eel Jason. Art Thou That Prophet? 2008. 188p. pap. 18.40 *(978-0-557-00033-3(5))* Lulu Enterprises Inc.

Garcia-Oliver, Ferran. The Valley of the Six Mosques: Work & Life in Medieval Valldigna. 2012. (Medieval Countryside Ser.). (ENG., Illus.). 404p. (C). 138.00 *(978-2-503-53130-4(X))* Brepols Pubs. BEL. Dist: ISD.

Gauss, James F. Islam & Christianity: A Revealing Contrast. 2009. 389p. pap. 15.99 *(978-0-88270-611-5(X))* Bridge-Logos Foundation.

George, Ron. Newer Paths in Muslim-Christian Understanding. 2007. 380p. per. 19.99 *(978-1-60266-997-0(X))* Xulon Pr., Inc.

Ghattas, Raouf, et al. A Christian Guide to the Qur'an: Building Bridges in Muslim Evangelism, 1 vol. 2009. 448p. pap. 24.99 *(978-0-8254-2688-9(X))* Kregel Pubns.

Goodwin. World Christianity in Local Context Vol. 1: Essays in Memory of David A. Kerr, 1 vol. Goodwin, Stephen R., ed. 2009. (ENG., Illus.). 262p. 130.00 *(978-1-84706-510-0(4))* Continuum International Publishing Group, Ltd. GBR. Dist: National Bk. Network.

Goodwin, Stephen R. World Christianity in Muslim Encounter Vol. 2: Essays in Memory of David A. Kerr, 2 vols. 2009. (ENG., Illus.). 384p. 170.00 *(978-1-84706-511-7(2))* Continuum International Publishing Group, Ltd. GBR. Dist: National Bk. Network.

Goodwin, Stephen R. & Goodwin. World Christianity in Local Context & Muslim Encounter 2 VOLUME SET: Essays in Memory of David A. Kerr, 2 vols. 2009. (ENG., Illus.). 576p. 260.00 *(978-0-8264-1099-3(5))* Continuum International Publishing Group, Ltd. GBR. Dist: National Bk. Network.

Gotteil, Richard J. H. A Christian Bahira Legend. 2010. (ARA.). pap. 30.88 *(978-1-61143-334-0(7))* Gorgias Pr., LLC.

Greear, J. D. Breaking the Islam Code: Understanding the Soul Questions of Every Muslim. 2010. 176p. pap. 11.99 *(978-0-7369-2638-6(0))* Harvest Hse. Pubs.

Griffith, Sidney H. The Church in the Shadow of the Mosque: Christians & Muslims in the World of Islam. (Jews, Christians, & Muslims from the Ancient to the Modern World Ser.). (ENG., Illus.). 248p. (C). 2010. pap. 25.95

(978-0-691-14628-7(4)) 2007. 45.00 (978-0-691-13015-5(9)) Princeton Univ. Pr.

—Syriac Writers on Muslims & the Religious Challenge of Islam. 2010. 86.24 (978-1-61143-562-7(5)) Gorgias Pr., LLC.

Griswold, Eliza. The Tenth Parallel: Dispatches from the Fault Line Between Christianity & Islam. 2010. (ENG., Illus.). 336p. 27.00 (978-0-374-27318-7(9)) Farrar, Straus & Giroux.

—The Tenth Parallel: Dispatches from the Fault Line Between Christianity & Islam. 2011. (ENG.). 336p. pap. 16.00 (978-0-312-56936-5(X)) Picador.

Gualini, Muhammad Muddassir Silvio. Muslims & Christians Divided under the Same God? 2011. (Illus.). 272p. pap. 18.81 (978-1-4490-7505-7(3)) AuthorHouse.

Gwynn, Murl Edward. Conflict: Christianity's Love vs. Islam's Submission. 2011. 220p. 27.95 (978-1-4620-3485-7(3)); pap. 17.95 (978-1-4620-3486-4(1)) iUniverse, Inc.

Hakim, Nasir. Paradigm Shift - What Every Student of Messenger Elijah Muhammad Should Know. 2010. (ENG.). 142p. pap. 14.95 (978-1-884855-37-5(7)) Secretarius MEMPS Pubns.

Hamdani, Syed Nisar Hussain. Istiqbal-E-Imam Mahdi: (Welcoming the Savior - Imam Mahdi) 2009. 256p. pap. 14.72 (978-1-4389-4303-9(2)) AuthorHouse.

Hansen, B. Dale. Light about God & Man. 2007. 506p. pap. 22.95 (978-0-7414-4144-7(6)) Infinity Publishing.

Hasan, Israr. Believers & Brothers: A History of Uneasy Relationship. 2009. 328p. pap. 19.99 (978-1-4389-4445-6(4)) AuthorHouse.

Haven, Christine J. Conveyance of Eternal Love. 2007. 597p. pap. 34.38 (978-0-615-17990-2(8)) Owl Creek Pr.

Heazell, F. N., et al, eds. Kurds & Christians. 2010. 115.76 (978-1-61719-842-7(0)) Gorgias Pr., LLC.

Heck, Paul L. Common Ground: Islam, Christianity, & Religious Pluralism. 2009. (ENG., Illus.). 240p. pap. 26.95 (978-1-58901-507-4(X)) Georgetown Univ. Pr.

Hinze, Wesley. Social Trust, Trust in Muslims, & American Religion. 2009. 56p. pap. (978-3-639-17778-7(9)) VDM Verlag Dr. Mueller e.K.

Hitchcock, David. Are the Teachings of the Lord Jesus Christ & the Prophet Muhammad Reconcilable? As Presented to Dublin Metropolitan University. 2009. 180p. pap. 14.49 (978-1-4389-5198-0(1)) AuthorHouse.

Holden, Andrew. Religious Cohesion in Times of Conflict: Christian-Muslim Relations in Segregated Towns. 2009. (ENG.). 224p. 130.00 (978-1-84706-535-3(X)) Continuum International Publishing Group, Ltd. GBR. Dist: National Bk. Network.

Holden, Andrew & Holden. Religious Cohesion in Times of Conflict: Christian-Muslim Relations in Segregated Towns. 2009. (ENG.). 224p. 34.95 (978-1-84706-536-0(8)) Continuum International Publishing Group, Ltd. GBR. Dist: National Bk. Network.

Hooper, Baron. Three Sides of Truth, 1 vol. 2010. 82p. pap. 19.95 (978-1-60703-152-9(3)) PublishAmerica, Inc.

Hoskins, Edward J. A Muslim's Heart: What Every Christian Needs to Know to Share Christ with Muslims. 2007. (Beginning the Walk Ser.). (ENG.). 80p. pap. 8.99 (978-0-9672480-6-6(X)) NavPress Publishing Group.

Hunter, Erica C. D. & Healey, John, eds. The Christian Heritage of Iraq. 2009. 107.00 (978-1-60724-111-9(0)) Gorgias Pr., LLC.

Ibrahim, Gregorios. Accepting the Other. 2009. (ARA.). 118.00 (978-1-60724-263-5(X)) Gorgias Pr., LLC.

Idliby, Ranya, et al. The Faith Club: A Muslim, a Christian, a Jew — Three Women Search for Understanding. rev. l.t. ed. 2007. (Thorndike Inspirational Ser.). 521p. 29.95 (978-0-7862-9336-0(5)) Thorndike Pr.

Institute Of Islamic Studies, ed. Islam & Christianity. 2009. 54p. pap. (978-3-941750-91-3(7)) VTR Verlag fur Theologie und Religionswissenschaft.

—Jesus & Muhammad As Founders of Religion. 2009. 54p. pap. (978-3-941750-92-0(5)) VTR Verlag fur Theologie und Religionswissenschaft.

Ioan, Ovidiu. Muslime und Araber Bei Isojahb III. (649-659) 2009. (Gottinger Orientforschungen. I. Reihe: Syriaca Ser.). (GER.). 145p. (C). pap. 54.00 (978-3-447-05861-2(7)) Harrassowitz, Otto Verlag DEU. Dist: ISD.

Ipgrave, Michael, ed. Building a Better Bridge: Muslims, Christians & the Common Good. 2008. (ENG.). 200p. pap. 24.95 (978-1-58901-221-9(6)) Georgetown Univ. Pr.

Ipgrave, Michael & Marshall, David, eds. Humanity: Christian & Muslim Perspectives. 2011. (ENG.). 176p. pap. 24.95 (978-1-58901-716-0(1)) Georgetown Univ. Pr.

Isaacs-Martin, Wendy. A Violent Origin: A Girardian Analysis of the Scapegoating of Ali Ibn Abu Talib in Shi'ite Tradition. 2010. 208p. pap. (978-3-8383-0005-4(X)) Lambert Academic Publishing.

Isom-Verhaaren, Christine. Allies with the Infidel: The Ottoman & French Alliance in the Sixteenth Century. 2011. (Library of Ottoman Studies). (ENG., Illus.). 304p. 95.00 (978-1-84885-728-5(4), Tauris Academic Studies) I. B. Tauris & Co., Ltd. GBR. Dist: Macmillan.

Jabbour, Nabeel T. The Crescent Through the Eyes of the Cross: Insights from an Arab Christian. 2008. (Experiencing God Ser.). (ENG.). 272p. per. 14.99 (978-1-60006-195-0(8)) NavPress Publishing Group.

—Unshackled & Growing. 2007. (Guidebook Ser.). (ENG., Illus.). 248p. pap. 12.99 (978-0-9729023-2-8(5)) NavPress Publishing Group.

James-Sow, Linnette. What's So Different about Islam? My Experience of the Christian World & the Islamic World. 2009. 56p. pap. 9.99 (978-1-60860-324-4(5), Eloquent Bks.) AEG Literary Publishing Services, Inc.

Janssen, Al, et al. Secret Believers: What Happens When Muslims Believe in Christ. 2008. 272p. pap. 15.99 (978-0-8007-3264-6(2)) Revell.

Jenkins, Philip. God's Continent: Christianity, Islam, & Europe's Religious Crisis. 2009. (ENG.). 352p. pap. 16.95 (978-0-19-538462-8(8)) Oxford Univ. Pr., Inc.

Jesus, Israel. The War of Armageddon: Its Jesus versus Allah. 2009. 100p. pap. 10.00 (978-1-60693-889-8(4), Strategic Bk. Publishing) AEG Literary Publishing Services, Inc.

Joe, Hoo Ie. Theological Method of Contextual Theology. 2010. 96p. pap. (978-3-639-23501-2(0)) VDM Verlag Dr. Mueller e.K.

Johnson, Dale A. Monk George & his Debate with Muslims. 2008. 50p. pap. 15.50 (978-1-4357-4006-8(8)) Lulu Enterprises Inc.

Johnston, David L. Earth, Empire, & Sacred Text: Muslims & Christians As Trustees of Creation. 2010. (Comparative Islamic Studies Ser.). (ENG.). 652p. (C). 110.00 (978-1-84553-225-3(2)) Equinox Publishing Ltd. GBR. Dist: ISD.

Jukko, Risto. Trinity in Unity in Christian-Muslim Relations: The Work of the Pontifical Council for Interreligious Dialogue. 2007. (History of Christian-Muslim Relations Ser.). 384p. (978-90-04-15862-7(6)) BRILL.

Kateregga, Badru D. & Shenk, David W. A Muslim & a Christian in Dialogue. 2011. Orig. Title: Islam & Christianity: A Muslim & a Christian Response. pap. (978-0-8361-9619-1(8)) Herald Pr.

Kaufmann, Thomas. Türckenbüchlein: Zur Christlichen Wahrnehmung "Türkischer Religion" in Spätmittelalter und Reformation. 2008. (Forschungen Zur Kirchen- und Dogmengeschichte Ser.). (GER., Illus.). 299p. (C). 84.00 (978-3-525-55222-3(X)) Vandenhoeck & Ruprecht GmbH & Co. KG DEU. Dist: ISD.

Kedar, Benjamin Z. Franks, Muslims & Oriental Christians in the Latin Levant: Studies in Frontier Acculturation. 2006. (Variorum Collected Studies Series: CS868 Ser.). (Illus.). 336p. 154.95 (978-0-7546-5912-9(7)) Ashgate Publishing Co.

Kennedy, Hugh. The Byzantine & Early Islamic near East. 2006. (Variorum Collected Studies). (Illus.). 288p. 150.00 (978-0-7546-5909-9(7)) Ashgate Publishing Co.

Kepnes, Steven & Koshul, Basit Bilal, eds. Scripture, Reason, & the Contemporary Islam-West Encounter: Studying the Other, Understanding the Self. 2007. (ENG.). 248p. 89.00 (978-1-4039-7535-5(3)) Palgrave Macmillan.

Khimjee, Husein. The Attributes of God in the Monotheistic Faiths of Judeo-Christian & Islamic Traditions. 2011. 108p. pap. 11.95 (978-1-4620-4613-3(4)) iUniverse, Inc.

Kidd, Thomas & Kidd, Thomas S. American Christians & Islam: Evangelical Culture & Muslims from the Colonial Period to the Age of Global Terrorism. 2008. (ENG., Illus.). 224p. (C). 31.95 (978-0-691-13349-2(2)) Princeton Univ. Pr.

King, Isaac. Complete Assurance to Enter into Heaven: A Great Eye-Opener for Muslims & Christians. 2010. 176p. pap. 19.95 (978-1-4327-5430-3(0)) Outskirts Pr., Inc.

King, Margaret. 'Isa Shall be a Sign of the Hour. 2006. per. 45.00 (978-0-9790351-0-4(4)) Susiana Pr.

Kirk, J. Andrew. Civilisations in Conflict? Islam, the West & Christian Faith. 2011. (Regnum Studies in Mission Ser.). 234p. pap. 26.00 (978-1-61097-442-4(5), Wipf and Stock) Wipf & Stock Pubs.

Kreeft, Peter. Between Allah & Jesus: What Christians Can Learn from Muslims. 2010. (ENG.). 188p. pap. 16.00 (978-0-8308-3746-5(9), IVP Bks.) InterVarsity Pr.

Krikorian, Hohannes K. Islam & Christianity Face to Face. 2011. 72p. 36.95 (978-1-258-08864-4(9)) Literary Licensing, LLC.

Krstic, Tijana. Contested Conversions to Islam: Narratives of Religious Change in the Early Modern Ottoman Empire. 2011. (ENG., Illus.). 280p. 60.00 (978-0-8047-7317-1(3)) Stanford Univ. Pr.

Lassner, Jacob. Jews, Christians, & the Abode of Islam: Modern Scholarship, Medieval Realities. 2012. (ENG.). 336p. 45.00 (978-0-226-47107-5(1)) Univ. of Chicago Pr.

Lawson, Todd. The Crucifixion & the Qur'an: A Study in the History of Muslim Thought. 2009. (ENG.). 256p. pap. 29.95 (978-1-85168-635-3(5)) Oneworld Pubns. GBR. Dist: National Bk. Network.

Legenhausen, Al-Hajj Muhammad, tr. from ARA. Jesus: Through the Qur'an & Shi'ite Narrations. 2007. (ENG.). 437p. per. 18.00 (978-1-879402-14-0(9)) Tahrike Tarsile Quran, Inc.

Leirvik, Oddbjorn. Human Conscience & Muslim-Christian Relations: Modern Egyptian Thinkers on Al-Damir. 2006. (Routledge Islamic Studies). 310p. 160.00 (978-0-415-38566-4(0)) Routledge.

—Images of Jesus Christ in Islam. 2nd ed. 2010. (ENG.). 304p. 34.95 (978-1-4411-8160-2(1)); 120.00 (978-1-4411-7739-1(6)) Continuum International Publishing Group, Ltd. GBR. Dist: National Bk. Network.

MacLean, Gerald & Matar, Nabil. Britain & the Islamic World, 1558-1713. 2011. (ENG., Illus.). 304p. 65.00 (978-0-19-920318-5(0)) Oxford Univ. Pr., Inc.

Madrigal, Carlos. Explaining the Trinity to Muslims: A Personal Reflection on the Biblical Teaching in Light of the Theological Criteria of Islam. 2011. (978-0-87808-525-5(4)) Carey, William Library Pubs.

Majid, Anouar. We Are All Moors: Ending Centuries of Crusades Against Muslims & Other Minorities. 2012. 224p. pap. 20.00 (978-0-8166-6080-3(8)) 2009. (ENG.). 240p. 24.95 (978-0-8166-6079-7(4)) Univ. of Minnesota Pr.

Makdisi, Ussama. Artillery of Heaven: American Missionaries & the Failed Conversion of the Middle East. (United States in the World Ser.). (Illus.). 2009. 280p. pap. 19.95 (978-0-8014-7575-7(9)) 2007. 262p. 60.95 (978-0-8014-4621-4(X)) Cornell Univ. Pr.

Malik, Habib C. Islamism & the Future of the Christians of the Middle East. 2010. (Hoover Inst Press Publication Ser.). E-Book 9.95 (978-0-8179-1096-9(4)) Hoover Institution Pr.

Markham, Ian S. Engaging with Bediuzzaman Said Nursi: A Model of Interfaith Dialogue. 2009. 188p. 99.95 (978-0-7546-6931-9(9)) Ashgate Publishing Co.

Marshall, David, ed. Communicating the Word: Revelation, Translation, & Interpretation in Christianity & Islam. 2011. (Illus.). 208p. pap. 24.95 (978-1-58901-784-9(6)) Georgetown Univ. Pr.

McElveen, Floyd C. & Mcelveen, Floyd C. Islam Exposed: Islam 101 & what it means to America. Are we in danger? Are Muslims a real threat to our Freedom? Bilbo, Greg, ed. 2011. 46p. pap. 2.95 (978-0-9831983-0-7(6)) Big Mac Pubs.

McGarvey, Kathleen. Muslim & Christian Women in Dialogue: The Case of Northern Nigeria. 2008. 450p. pap. 95.95 (978-3-03911-417-7(4)) Lang, Peter AG GBR. Dist: Lang, Peter.

McGee, Martin. Christian Martyrs for a Muslim People. 2008. 224p. pap. 18.95 (978-0-8091-4539-3(1)) Paulist Pr.

Medearis, Carl. Muslims, Christians, & Jesus: Gaining Understanding & Building Relationships. 2008. 192p. pap. 14.99 (978-0-7642-0567-5(6)) Bethany Hse. Pubs.

—Muslims, Christians & Jesus: Gaining Understanding & Building Relationships, 1 vol. 2011. (ENG.). 96p. 31.99 (978-0-310-89488-9(3)); 24.99 (978-0-310-89085-0(3)) Zondervan.

Michel, Thomas F. & Omar, Irfan A. A Christian View of Islam: Essays on Dialogue by Thomas F. Michel. 2010. 240p. pap. (978-1-57075-860-7(3)) Orbis Bks.

Muir, Sir William K. C. S. I. Ll. D. D. C. L. The Apology of Al Kindy, Written at the Court of Al Mâmûn. 2011. 224p. pap. 19.99 (978-1-4568-2188-3(1)) Xlibris Corp.

Mujiburrahman. Feeling Threatened. 2006. (ISIM Dissertations Ser.). 428p. pap. (978-90-5356-938-2(3), Leiden Univ. Pr.) Amsterdam Univ. Pr.

Muldoon, James, ed. Travellers, Intellectuals, & the World Beyond Medieval Europe. 2010. (Expansion of Latin Europe, 1000-1500 Ser.). (Illus.). 406p. 175.00 (978-0-7546-5974-7(7)) Ashgate Publishing Co.

Musk, Bill A. The Certainty Trap: Can Christians & Muslims Afford the Luxury of Fundamentalism? 2007. (978-0-87808-519-4(X)) Carey, William Library Pubs.

Nader Pourhassan. God's Scripture: A Faithful Comparison - What Jews, Christians, & Muslims Must Know. 2009. 372p. pap. 24.95 (978-1-4401-8679-0(0)) iUniverse, Inc.

Naeem, Tahir. Islamic System - a Brief Overview: (in the light of modern Social Sciences) 2011. 90p. 24.99 (978-1-4535-7064-7(0)); pap. 15.99 (978-1-4535-7063-0(2)) Xlibris Corp.

Nazir-Ali, Michael. Frontiers in Muslim-Christian Encounter. 2007. 192p. pap. 22.00 (978-1-59752-914-3(1), Wipf and Stock) Wipf & Stock Pubs.

Neale, William Henry. The Mohammedan System of Theology: A Compendious Survey of the History & Doctrines of Islamism Contrasted with Christianity. 2007. (ENG.). 280p. 42.95 (978-0-548-15310-9(8)); pap. 27.95 (978-1-4304-4693-4(5)) Kessinger Publishing, LLC.

Netton, Ian Richard. Islam, Christianity & Tradition: A Comparative Exploration. 2007. (ENG., Illus.). 256p. (gr. 17). pap. 40.00 (978-0-7486-2392-1(2)) Edinburgh Univ. Pr. GBR. Dist: Columbia Univ. Pr.

Netton, Richard & Netton, Ian Richard. Islam, Christianity & Tradition: A Comparative Exploration. 2007. (ENG., Illus.). 256p. (gr. 17). 130.00 (978-0-7486-2391-4(4)) Edinburgh Univ. Pr. GBR. Dist: Columbia Univ. Pr.

Obermann, Julian. Islamic Origins: A Study in Background & Foundation. 2011. 68p. 36.95 (978-1-258-07414-2(1)) Literary Licensing, LLC.

O'Mahony, Anthony & Loosley, Emma, eds. Christian Responses to Islam: Muslim-Christian Relations in the Modern World. 2008. (ENG., Illus.). 264p. 89.00 (978-0-7190-7637-9(0)) Manchester Univ. Pr. GBR. Dist: Macmillan.

O'Mahony, Anthony & Loosley, Emma, eds. Christian Responses to Islam: Muslim-Christian Relations in The Modern World. 2012. (ENG., Illus.). 256p. pap. 24.95 (978-0-7190-8668-7(X)) Manchester Univ. Pr. GBR. Dist: Macmillan.

Omar, Irfan, ed. A Muslim View of Christianity: Essays on Dialogue. annot. ed. 2007. (Fate Meets Faith Ser.). 264p. per. 28.00 (978-1-57075-690-0(2)) Orbis Bks.

Orji, Cyril U. Ethnic & Religious Conflict in Africa: An Analysis of Bias, Decline, & Conversion Based on the Works of Bernard Lonergan. 2008. pap. (978-0-87462-736-7(2)) Marquette Univ. Pr.

orr, eldon. Confirming the Glory of the Everlasting Gospel! 2009. 79p. pap. 7.00 (978-1-4357-2502-7(6)) Lulu Enterprises Inc.

O'Shea, Hayley. Dialogue Between Muslim & Christian. 2009. (ARA & ENG., Illus.). 116p. pap. 12.49 (978-1-4389-1207-3(2)) AuthorHouse.

Pagden, Anthony. Worlds at War: The 2,500 - Year Struggle Between East & West. (ENG., Illus.). 576p. pap. (978-0-19-956977-9(0)) Oxford Univ. Pr., Inc.

—Worlds at War: The 2,500-Year Struggle Between East & West. 2009. (ENG., Illus.). 656p. pap. 18.00 (978-0-8129-6890-3(5), Random Hse. Trade Paperbacks) Random House Publishing Group.

—Worlds at War: The 2,500-Year Struggle Between East & West. 2008. (ENG., Illus.). 656p. 35.00 (978-1-4000-6067-2(2)) Random Hse., Inc.

Papademetriou, George C. Two Traditions, One Space: Orthodox Christians & Muslims in Dialogue. 2010. (978-1-935244-06-6(X)) Somerset Hall Pr.

Paris, Derrick. For the Love of Eve-il, 1 vol. 2010. 56p. pap. 16.95 (978-1-61546-795-2(5)) PublishAmerica, Inc.

Parshall, Phil. La Fortaleza y el Fuego: Christ & Muslims. (SPA.). (978-84-7645-055-0(9), 223118) Clie, Editorial.

Pat (Patrick J. Roelle, Sr.). Christians under Siege. 2009. 512p. 30.99 (978-1-4490-3082-7(3)); pap. 20.49 (978-1-4490-3083-4(1)) AuthorHouse.

Patey, Cecil. Obama in Cairo: When Christians & Moslems Meet. 2009. 176p. pap. 17.50 (978-1-4490-0570-2(5)) AuthorHouse.

Paul-Magidi, James. Beyond the Quran. 2011. 434p. pap. 22.99 (978-1-61215-796-2(3)) Xulon Pr., Inc.

Peters, F. E. Jesus & Muhammad: Parallel Tracks, Parallel Lives. 2010. (ENG.). 304p. 24.95 (978-0-19-974746-7(6)) Oxford Univ. Pr., Inc.

Philippsohn, Ludwig. The Development of the Religious Idea in Judaism, Christianity And. 2007. pap. 28.95 (978-1-4304-4995-9(0)) Kessinger Publishing, LLC.

Phillips, Walter. Brothers Kept Apart: Examining the Christian & Islamic religious barriers that have divided Christians & Muslims for over 1,300 Years. 2009. 208p. 27.95 (978-1-4401-1612-4(1)); pap. 17.95 (978-1-4401-1610-0(5)) iUniverse, Inc.

Pourhassan, Nader. God's Scripture: A Faithful Comparison — What Jews, Christians, & Muslims Must Know. 2009. 372p. 34.95 (978-1-4401-8681-3(2)) iUniverse, Inc.

Presentation of Christianity to Muslims. 2010. 97.04 (978-1-61719-003-2(9)) Gorgias Pr., LLC.

Prince Ghazi Bin Muhammad, et al, contrib. by. Sophi: The Journal of Traditional Studies, Volume 15, Number 2. 2010. 178p. pap. 17.95 (978-0-9798429-6-2(4)) Foundation for Traditional Studies.

Pye, Michael, et al, eds. Religious Harmony. 2006. (Religion & Reason Ser.: Vol. 45). (ENG., Illus.). X, 363p. 154.00 (978-3-11-018847-9(3)) De Gruyter, Walter Inc.

Qaimmaqami, Abbas Husayni. Europäischer Islam oder Islam in Europa? Erfahrungen und Ansichten eines Ayatollahs in Europa. 2010. (GER., Illus.). 227p. (978-3-89930-282-0(6)) Schiler, Hans.

Quinn, Frederick. The Sum of All Heresies: The Image of Islam in Western Thought. 2007. (ENG., Illus.). 232p. 29.95 (978-0-19-532563-8(X)) Oxford Univ. Pr., Inc.

Rabiipour, Saiid. Farewell to Islam. 2009. 348p. pap. 18.99 (978-1-61579-513-0(8)) Xulon Pr., Inc.

Rasmussen, Lissi, ed. Bridges Instead of Walls: Christian-Muslim Interaction in Denmark, Indonesia & Nigeria. 2007. (ENG.). 197p. pap. 20.00 (978-1-932688-29-0(3), Lutheran Univ. Pr.) Kirk Hse. Pubs.

Ratliff, Walter R. Pilgrims on the Silk Road: A Muslim-Christian Encounter in Khiva. 2009. (Illus.). 312p. pap. 34.00 (978-1-60608-133-4(0)) Wipf & Stock Pubs.

Reedijk, Rachel. Roots & Routes: Identity Construction & the Jewish-Christian-Muslim Dialogue. 2010. (Illus.). 376p. pap. 116.00 (978-90-420-2839-5(4)) Rodopi.

Reeves, Minou & Stewart, P. J. Muhammad in Europe. 2011. 308p. 38.95 (978-1-85964-123-1(7)) Garnet Publishing, Ltd. GBR. Dist: International Publishers Marketing.

Register, Ray. Dialogue & Interfaith Witness with Muslims. 2007. 116p. per. 9.95 (978-0-9796019-3-4(2)) Global Education Advance.

Renard, John. Islam & Christianity: Theological Themes in Comparative Perspective. 2011. (ENG.). 322p. 60.00 (978-0-520-25508-1(9)); pap. 24.95 (978-0-520-26678-0(1)) Univ. of California Pr.

Richardson, Don. Secrets of the Koran: Revealing Insights into Islam's Holy Bible. 2008. (ENG.). 272p. pap. 16.99 (978-0-8307-3123-7(7)) Gospel Light Pubns.

Richardson, Joel. The Islamic Antichrist: The Shocking Truth about the Real Nature of the Beast. 2nd ed. 2009. 304p. 25.95 (978-1-935071-12-9(2)) WND Bks, Inc.

Ridgeon, Lloyd. Islamic Interpretations of Christianity. 2010. pap. 39.95 (978-0-415-58706-8(9)) Routledge.

Robson, James. Christ in Islam. 2006. (ENG.). 136p. per. 11.95 (978-0-9745667-8-8(0)) Bardic Pr.

—Christ in Islam. 2009. 100p. pap. 18.75 (978-0-559-12469-3(4)); pap. 13.99 (978-0-559-12475-4(9)) BiblioBazaar.

—Christ in Islam. 2009. pap. 44.20 (978-1-60724-299-4(0)) Gorgias Pr., LLC.

Rogerson, Barnaby. The Last Crusaders: The Hundred-Year Battle for the Center of the World. (ENG.). 512p. (gr. 12). 2011. 19.95 (978-1-59020-440-5(9)) 2010. 35.00 (978-1-59020-286-9(4)) Overlook Pr., The.

Roosenberg, Tim & Lale, Tim. Islam & Christianity: The Coming Holy War. 2011. (978-0-8280-2592-8(4)) Review & Herald Publishing Assn.

Rosenberg, Joel C. Dentro de la Revolución: Cómo los Partidarios de la Yihad, de Jefferson y de Jesús Luchan para Dominar el Medio Oriente y Transformar el Mundo. 2009.Tr. of Inside the Revolution: Inside the Revolution. (SPA.). 608p. pap. 9.99 (978-1-4143-1934-6(7), Tyndale Espanol) Tyndale Hse. Pubs.

Rushby, Kevin. Paradise: A History of the Idea That Rules the World. 2006. (ENG., Illus.). 272p. per. 15.95 (978-0-7867-1910-5(9)) Basic Bks.

Salama, Mohammad R. Islam, Orientalism & Intellectual History: Modernity & the Politics of Exclusion since Ibn. 2011. (Library of Middle East History Ser.). (ENG., Illus.). 304p. 96.00 (978-1-84885-005-7(0), Tauris Academic Studies) I. B. Tauris & Co., Ltd. GBR. Dist: Macmillan.

Saldana, Stephanie. The Bread of Angels: A Journey to Love & Faith. 2011. 320p. pap. 15.00 (978-0-307-28046-6(2), Anchor) Knopf Doubleday Publishing Group.

Saleh, Walid, ed. In Defense of the Bible: A Critical Edition & an Introduction to Al-Biqa's Bible Treatise. 2008. (Illus.). 232p. (C). (978-90-04-16857-2(5)) BRILL.

Sanneh, Lamin. Jesus & the Cross: Reflections of Christians from Islamic Contexts. Singh, David Emmanuel, ed. 2008. (Global Theological Voices Ser.). 242p. pap. 27.00 (978-1-60608-021-4(0), Wipf and Stock) Wipf & Stock Pubs.

Schmitz, Bertram. Paulus und der Koran. 2010. (GER.). 212p. (C). pap. 32.00 (978-3-525-51007-0(1)) Vandenhoeck & Ruprecht GmbH & Co. KG DEU. Dist: ISD.

Schneider, Heinrich. Der Christlich-Muslimische Dialog: Voraussetzungen, Erfahrungen, Probleme. 2007. (GER.). 180p. *(978-3-205-77689-5(5))* Bohlau Verlag Gmbh & Cie.

Shah, Hashmat. Out of Pakistan: A Testimony of the Miraculous Hand of God in My Life. 2011. 128p. 21.23 ***(978-1-4634-2509-8(0))***; pap. 11.99 ***(978-1-4634-2510-4(4))*** AuthorHouse.

Siddiqui, Mona, ed. The Routledge Reader in Christian-Muslim Relations. 2012. (ENG.). (C). 416p. pap. 49.95 *(978-0-415-68556-6(7))*; 320p. 125.00 *(978-0-415-68554-2(0))* Routledge.

Siljander, Mark D. & Mann, John David. A Deadly Misunderstanding: A Congressman's Quest to Bridge the Muslim-Christian Divide. 2008. (ENG.). 272p. 24.99 *(978-0-06-143828-8(6)*, HarperOne) HarperCollins Pubs.

Sinaga, Martin L. & Sinn, Simone, eds. Freedom & Responsibility: Christian & Muslim Explorations. 2010. 156p. pap. 16.00 *(978-1-932688-50-4(1)*, Lutheran Univ. Pr.) Kirk Hse. Pubs.

Smith, Henry Preserved. The Bible & Islam or, the Influence of the Old & New Testaments. 2007. (ENG.). 328p. per. 30.95 *(978-1-4304-4352-0(9))* Kessinger Publishing, LLC.

Smith, Jane Idleman. Muslims, Christians, & the Challenge of Interfaith Dialogue. 2007. (ENG.). 192p. 29.99 *(978-0-19-530731-3(3))* Oxford Univ. Pr., Inc.

Smith, R. Bosworth. Mohammed & Mohammedanism 1876. 2007. (ENG.). 404p. 49.95 *(978-0-548-05430-7(4))* Kessinger Publishing, LLC.

Smith, Reginald. Mohammed & Mohammedanism. 2007. (ENG.). 274p. 42.95 *(978-0-548-05250-1(6))* Kessinger Publishing, LLC.

Snook, Stewart. Christ More Powerful: Analogies of Christ in Non-Christian Religions. 2011. 108p. 21.23 ***(978-1-4567-1122-1(9))***; pap. 10.68 ***(978-1-4567-1123-8(7))*** AuthorHouse.

Soares, Benjamin F., ed. Muslim-Christian Encounters in Africa. 2006. (Islam in Africa Ser.). (Illus.). 308p. *(978-90-04-15264-9(4))* BRILL.

Sookhdeo, Patrick. The Challenge of Islam to the Church & Its Mission. 2nd ed. 2008. (ENG.). 193p. 19.99 *(978-0-9787141-5-4(6))* Isaac Publishing.

—The Challenge of Islam to the Church & its Mission. 2nd ed. 2009. (ENG.). 193p. pap. 14.99 *(978-0-9787141-8-5(0))* Isaac Publishing.

—A Christian's Pocket Guide to Islam. 2010. (ENG.). 144p. mass mkt. 6.99 *(978-1-84550-572-1(7))* 96p. reprint ed. pap. 2.99 *(978-1-85792-699-6(4)*, Christian Focus) Christian Focus Pubns. GBR. Dist: STL Distribution North America, Riverside.

—Faith, Power & Territory. 2008. (ENG & ARA., Illus.). 368p. 20.00 *(978-0-9787141-3-0(X))* Isaac Publishing.

Sperber, Jutta. Christians & Muslims: The Dialogue Activities of the World Council of Churches & their Theological Foundation. (Theologische Bibliothek Töpelmann Ser.). (ENG.). X, 484p. 374.00 ***(978-3-11-177324-7(8))*** De Gruyter, Walter Inc.

Stark, Rodney. God's Battalions: The Case for the Crusades. (ENG., 288p. 2010. Illus.). pap. 14.99 *(978-0-06-158260-8(3))* 2009. 24.99 *(978-0-06-158261-5(1))* HarperCollins Pubs. (HarperOne).

Stephens, W. R. W. Christianity & Islam. 2009. 94.24 *(978-1-60724-412-7(8))* Gorgias Pr., LLC.

Stoddart, William, compiled by. What Do the Religions Say about Each Other? Christian Attitudes towards Islam; Islamic Attitudes towards Christianity. 2008. 136p. pap. 16.95 *(978-1-59731-089-5(1))* Perennis, Sophia.

Strong, Cynthia A. & Page, Meg. A Worldview Approach to Ministry among Muslim Women. 2007. *(978-0-87808-370-1(7))* Carey, William Library Pubs.

Sturrup, Cassandra. From Jihad to Jesus: How a Destiny Unfolds & Truth Is Revealed. 2010. 128p. pap. 14.99 *(978-1-61579-654-0(1))* Xulon Pr., Inc.

Tharp, John W. The Quran: God's Word or Satan's Great Deception? 2011. 176p. pap. 15.95 *(978-1-4620-0749-3(X))*; pap. 15.95 *(978-1-4620-0750-9(3))* iUniverse, Inc.

Thomas, D. R. & Roggema, B. Christian-Muslim Relations. A Bibliographical History. Volume 1 (600-900) 2009. (Christian-Muslim Relations. A Bibliographical History Ser.). 944p. *(978-90-04-16975-3(X))* BRILL.

Thomas, David. The Bible in Arab Christianity. 2006. (History of Christian-Muslim Relations Ser.: Vol. 6). (Illus.). 444p. *(978-90-04-15558-9(9))* BRILL.

—Christian Doctrines in Islamic Theology. 2008. 384p. *(978-90-04-16935-7(0))* BRILL.

Thompson, Livingstone A. A Formula for Conversation: Christians & Muslims in Dialogue. 2007. (ENG.). 112p. pap. 26.50 *(978-0-7618-3639-1(X))* Univ. Pr. of America, Inc.

Tolan, John Victor. Sons of Ishmael: Muslims Through European Eyes in the Middle Ages. 2008. (ENG., Illus.). 256p. 65.00 *(978-0-8130-3222-1(9))* Univ. Pr. of Florida.

Torrance, David W. & Taylor, George. Israel, God's Servant: God's Key to the Redemption of the World. 2008. (ENG.). 224p. per. 19.99 *(978-1-84227-554-2(2)*, Paternoster) Authentic Media.

Tramm, T. W. From Abraham to Armageddon. 2009. 295p. pap. 16.95 *(978-0-615-25534-7(5))* Tramm, T.W.

Troll, Christian W. Dialogue & Difference: Clarity in Christian-Muslim Relations. Marshall, David, tr. from GER. 2009. 192p. pap. 34.00 *(978-1-57075-856-0(5))* Orbis Bks.

Troll, Christian W. Muslims Ask, Christians Answer. 2012. xi, 146p. pap. ***(978-1-56548-430-6(4))*** New City Community Pr.

Umar, Imam Warith-Deen. Yahvehism. 2011. 330p. 29.99 ***(978-1-4568-1852-4(X))***; pap. 19.99 ***(978-1-4568-1851-7(1))*** Xlibris Corp.

Van Gorder, Christian. Muslim-Christian Relations in Central Asia. 2008. (Illus.). XIV, 210p. 170.00 *(978-0-415-77608-0(2))* Routledge.

van Gorder, Christian. Muslim-Christian Relations in Central Asia. 2012. (ENG., Illus.). 224p. (C). pap. 42.95 ***(978-0-415-53322-5(8))*** Routledge.

Vaux, Kenneth L. Journey into an Interfaith World: Jews, Christians, & Muslims in a World Come of Age. 2010. 276p. pap. 31.00 *(978-1-60899-540-0(2))* Wipf & Stock Pubs.

Volf, Miroslav. Allah: A Christian Response. (ENG.). 2012. 336p. pap. 15.99 ***(978-0-06-192708-9(2))*** 2011. 256p. 25.99 *(978-0-06-192707-2(4))* HarperCollins Pubs. (HarperOne).

Volf, Miroslav, et al, eds. A Common Word: Muslims & Christians on Loving God & Neighbor. 2009. 258p. pap. 14.00 *(978-0-8028-6380-5(9))* Eerdmans, William B. Publishing Co.

Ward, Mariel. Penetrating the Stronghold of Islam: An Insider's Perspective from a Bible Translation Team. 2008. (ENG.). 174p. pap. 12.99 *(978-1-59979-486-0(1)*, Creation Hse.) Charisma Media.

Watt, W. M. & Watt, W. Montgomery. Islam & Christianity Today: A Contribution to Dialogue. 2007. 176p. 175.00 *(978-0-415-44670-9(8))* Routledge.

Webb, Mohammed. Yankee Muslim. 2006. 324p. 35.00 *(978-0-89370-819-1(4))*; (ENG.). per. 19.95 *(978-0-89370-919-8(0))* Wildside Pr., LLC. (Borgo Pr.).

Wessels, Antonie. Muslims & the West: Can They Be Integrated? Bowden, John, tr. from DUT. 2006. (ENG.). 198p. (C). pap. 45.00 *(978-90-429-1684-5(2))* Peeters Pubs. & Booksellers BEL. Dist: Brown, David Bk. Co., The.

Weyer, Robert Van De. Shared Well: A Concise Guide to Relations Between Islam & the West. (Illus.). 160p. pap. 15.95 *(978-1-57488-608-5(8))* Potomac Bks., Inc.

Wickwire, Daniel. Has the Bible Been Changed? As Is Claimed by Muslims. 2011. 112p. 28.95 ***(978-1-4497-2692-8(5))***; pap. 11.95 ***(978-1-4497-2691-1(7))*** Author Solutions, Inc. (WestBow Pr.).

Wiertzema, John. The Coming Judgment of Islam. 2007. 168p. (ENG.). 21.99 *(978-1-60266-501-9(X))*; per. 13.99 *(978-1-60266-500-2(1))* Xulon Pr., Inc.

Williams, Rowan, et al, contrib. by. A Common Word. 2009. 166p. pap. 17.95 *(978-0-9798429-4-8(8))* Foundation for Traditional Studies.

—Sophi. 2009. 216p. pap. 17.95 *(978-0-9798429-3-1(X))* Foundation for Traditional Studies.

Winkler, Dietmar. Syriac Churches Encountering Islam. 2010. pap. 34.00 *(978-1-61143-001-1(1))* Gorgias Pr., LLC.

Winkler, Lewis E. Contemporary Muslim & Christian Responses to Religious Plurality: Wolfhart Pannenberg in Dialogue with Abdulaziz Sachedina. 2012. (ENG.). 350p. pap. 45.00 ***(978-0-227-68026-1(X))*** Clarke, James Co., Ltd. GBR. Dist: Brown, David Bk. Co., The.

Woodberry, J. & Basselin, Robin, eds. Resources for Peacemaking in Muslim-Christian Relations: Contributions from the Conflict Transformation Project. 2006. 152p. per. 22.00 *(978-1-881266-25-9(7))* Fuller Seminary Pr.

Woodberry, John Dudley & Reisacher, Evelyne A. Toward Respectful Understanding & Witness among Muslims: Essays in Honor of J. Dudley Woodberry. 2011. ***(978-0-87808-018-2(X))*** Carey, William Library Pubs.

Worschech, Udo. «Ich will Ismael segnen»: Gemeinsame Wurzeln in Christentum und Islam. 2011. (Friedensauer Schriftenreihe. Reihe A: Theologie Ser.). 154p. 47.95 *(978-3-631-60644-5(3))* Lang, Peter GmbH, Europaischer Verlag der Wissenschaften DEU. Dist: Lang, Peter.

Yasin, Ibn. The Authenticity of the Gospel of Barnabas. 2011. 130p. 29.99 ***(978-1-4568-5453-9(4))***; pap. 19.99 ***(978-1-4568-5452-2(6))*** Xlibris Corp.

Yoosuf, Abraham Kevork. The Religion of Mohammed & Christian Sufferings. 2011. 87.08 *(978-1-61143-915-1(9))* Gorgias Pr., LLC.

Zahniser, A. H. Mathias. The Mission & Death of Jesus in Islam & Christianity. 2008. 288p. pap. 35.00 *(978-1-57075-807-2(7))* Orbis Bks.

Zaidi, Ali. Islam, Modernity, & the Human Sciences. 2011. (ENG.). 234p. 85.00 *(978-0-230-11035-9(5))* Palgrave Macmillan.

Zebiri, Kate. British Muslim Converts: Choosing Alternative Lives. 2007. 304p. per. 39.95 *(978-1-85168-546-2(4))* Oneworld Pubns. GBR. Dist: National Bk. Network.

Zegers, Frans J. L. Is Allah God? 2008. 132p. pap. 23.95 *(978-1-4092-0122-9(8))* Lulu Enterprises Inc.

Zinner, Samuel. The Abrahamic Archetype: Conceptual & Historical Relationships Between Judaism, Christianity & Islam. 2012. 175p. 29.95 ***(978-1-901383-41-6(5))*** Archetype GBR. Dist: Midpoint Trade Bks., Inc.

CHRISTIANITY AND OTHER RELIGIONS—JUDAISM

see also Christianity and Antisemitism; Judaism (Christian Theology); Missions to Jews

Abulafia, Anna. Christian Jewish Relations 1000-1300: Jews in the Service of Medieval Christendom. 2011. (Medieval World Ser.). (ENG., Illus.). 288p. (C). pap. 38.80 *(978-0-582-82296-2(3))* Longman Publishing Group.

Allen, Ethan. An introduction to hebrew customs of the Bible. 2008. 86p. pap. 16.87 *(978-1-4357-1301-7(X))* Lulu Enterprises Inc.

Aus, Roger David. The Death, Burial, & Resurrection of Jesus & the Death, Burial, & Translation of Moses in Judaic Tradition. 2008. (Studies in Judaism Ser.). (ENG.). 352p. pap. 52.50 *(978-0-7618-4087-9(7))* Univ. Pr. of America, Inc.

Avery-Peck, Alan J. & Neusner, Jacob. Judaism & Christianity: New Directions for Dialogue & Understanding. 2009. *(978-90-04-17938-7(0))* BRILL.

Azbell, Frederick J. Organized Religion Is... Blind, Leading the Blind. 2010. 232p. pap. 16.99 *(978-1-4520-5367-7(7))* AuthorHouse.

Baker, Todd D. Matthew 27: 25. 2008. 76p. pap. 10.95 *(978-0-595-53073-1(7))* iUniverse, Inc.

Bale, Anthony. Feeling Persecuted: Christians, Jews & Images of Violence in the Middle Ages. 2010. (ENG., Illus.). 240p. 45.00 *(978-1-86189-761-9(8))* Reaktion Bks., Ltd. GBR. Dist: Chicago Distribution Ctr.

Barclay, John M. G. & Sweet, John Philip McMurdo, eds. Early Christian Thought in its Jewish Context. 2007. (ENG., Illus.). 316p. pap. 61.00 *(978-0-521-04412-7(X))* Cambridge Univ. Pr.

Barth, Roderich, et al, eds. Christentum und Judentum: Akten des Kongresses der Internationalen Schleiermacher-Gesellschaft in Halle, März 2009. 2011. (Schleiermacher-Archiv Ser.). (GER.). XII, 638p. 196.00 *(978-3-11-022052-0(0))* De Gruyter, Walter Inc.

Beckwith, Roger. Daily & Weekly Worship: From Jewish to Christian. 2009. 88.00 *(978-1-60724-346-5(6))* Gorgias Pr., LLC.

Berger, David. Persecution, Polemic, & Dialogue: Essays in Jewish-Christian Relations. 2010. (Judaism & Jewish Life Ser.). (ENG.). 450p. 45.00 *(978-1-934843-76-5(8))* Academic Studies Pr.

Biale, David. Blood & Belief: The Circulation of a Symbol Between Jews & Christians. 2007. (Illus.). 299p. 55.00 *(978-0-520-25304-9(3))* Univ. of California Pr.

Bierman, Dominiquae. Yes! 2008. 212p. 25.99 *(978-1-60647-988-9(1))*; pap. 15.99 *(978-1-60647-987-2(3))* Xulon Pr., Inc.

Blumenkranz, B. Juifs et Chretiens dans le Monde Occidental 430-1096. 2006. (Collection de la Revue des Études Juives Ser.). (ENG.). 440p. (C). pap. 93.00 *(978-90-429-1879-5(9))* Peeters Pubs. & Booksellers BEL. Dist: Brown, David Bk. Co., The.

Blumenkranz, Bernhard. Les Auteurs Chretiens Latins du Moyen Age: Sur les Juifs et le Judaisme. 2007. (Collection de la Revue des Études Juives Ser.). (FRE & ENG.). 304p. (C). pap. 66.00 *(978-90-429-1878-8(0))* Peeters Pubs. & Booksellers BEL. Dist: Brown, David Bk. Co., The.

Bodian, Miriam. Dying in the Law of Moses: Crypto-Jewish Martyrdom in the Iberian World. 2007. (Modern Jewish Experience Ser.). (ENG., Illus.). 304p. 35.00 *(978-0-253-34861-6(7)*, 0253348617) Indiana Univ. Pr.

Boesel, Chris. Risking Proclamation, Respecting Difference: Christian Faith, Imperialistic Discourse, & Abraham. 2007. 306p. pap. 33.00 *(978-1-55635-523-3(8))* Wipf & Stock Pubs.

Boguslawski, Steven C. Thomas Aquinas on the Jews: Insights into His Commentary on Romans 9-11. 2008. (Stimulus Bks.). 145p. per. 18.95 *(978-0-8091-4233-0(3))* Paulist Pr.

Böttrich, Christfried & Thomanek, Judith, eds. Zwischen Zensur und Selbstbesinnung: Christliche Rezeptionen des Judentums. 2009. (Greifswalder theologische Forschungen Ser.). (GER., Illus.). 396p. 95.95 *(978-3-631-58863-5(1))* Lang, Peter GmbH, Europaischer Verlag der Wissenschaften DEU. Dist: Lang, Peter.

Boys, Mary C. & Lee, Sara S. Christians & Jews in Dialogue: Learning in the Presence of the Other. 2008. 240p. pap. 18.99 *(978-1-59473-254-6(X))* 2006. 220p. 21.99 *(978-1-59473-144-0(6))* SkyLight Paths Publishing.

Braude, Morris. Conscience on Trial: Three Public Religious Disputations Between Christians & Jews in the Thirteenth & Fifteenth Centuries. 2011. 148p. 40.95 ***(978-1-258-01561-9(7))*** Literary Licensing, LLC.

Bright, Pamela. The Book of Rules of Tyconius: Its Purpose & Inner Logic. 2009. (ND Christianity & Judaism Anitqui Ser.). (ENG.). 208p. pap. 30.00 *(978-0-268-02219-8(4))* Univ. of Notre Dame Pr.

Broadhead, Edwin K. Jewish Ways of Following Jesus: Redrawing the Religious Map of Antiquity. 2010. (Wissenschaftliche Untersuchungen zum Neuen Testament, No. 266 Ser.). (Illus.). 459p. 257.50 *(978-3-16-150304-7(X))* Mohr Siebeck GmbH & Co. KG DEU. Dist: Coronet Bks.

Brooks, Douglas A., ed. Milton & the Jews. 2008. (ENG.). 240p. 103.00 *(978-0-521-88883-7(2))* Cambridge Univ. Pr.

Burkitt, F. C, et al. Early & Later Jewish Influence on Christianity: Essays on Hebrew Influence on Religion, Language & Literature. 2007. (Analecta Gorgiana Ser.: 38). per. 29.00 *(978-1-59333-692-9(6))* Gorgias Pr., LLC.

Campbell, William S. Paul & the Creation of Christian Identity. 2008. (T&T Clark Biblical Studies). (ENG.). 218p. 44.95 *(978-0-567-03367-3(8)*, T&T Clark Int'l) Continuum International Publishing Group, Ltd. GBR. Dist: National Bk. Network.

Carlebach, Elisheva. Palaces of Time: Jewish Calendar & Culture in Early Modern Europe. 2011. (Illus.). 304p. 35.00 *(978-0-674-05254-3(4)*, Belknap Pr.) Harvard Univ. Pr.

Carlebach, Elisheva & Schacter, Jacob J., eds. New Perspectives on Jewish-Christian Relations. 2011. (ENG., Illus.). XII, 548p. ***(978-90-04-22117-8(4))*** BRILL.

Casey, Maurice. Judaism, Jewish Identities, & the Gospel Tradition: Essays in Honour of Maurice Casey. Crossley, James G., ed. 2010. (BibleWorld Ser.). (ENG.). 240p. (C). 39.95 *(978-1-84553-284-0(8))*; 99.95 *(978-1-84553-283-3(X))* Equinox Publishing Ltd. GBR. Dist: ISD.

Center for Learning Staff. Jewish-Christian Relations in Light of the Holocaust: Teacher Manual. 2006. (Religion Ser.). 160p. (YA). spiral bd. 29.95 *(978-1-56077-742-7(7))* Center for Learning, The.

—Jewish-Christian Relations in Light of the Holocaust, Student Book. 2006. (Religion Ser.). 172p. (YA). spiral bd. 12.95 *(978-1-56077-755-7(9))* Center for Learning, The.

Chafets, Zev. A Match Made in Heaven: American Jews, Christian Zionists, & One Man's Exploration of the Weird & Wonderful Judeo-Evangelical Alliance. 2008. 240p. pap. 13.95 *(978-0-06-089059-9(2)*, HarperPerennial) HarperCollins Pubs.

Chazan, Robert. Reassessing Jewish Life in Medieval Europe. 2010. (ENG.). 288p. (C). 85.00 *(978-0-521-76304-2(5))*; pap. 28.99 *(978-0-521-14543-5(0))* Cambridge Univ. Pr.

Cohen, Mark R. Under Crescent & Cross. 2008. (ENG.). 320p. (C). pap. 26.95 *(978-0-691-13931-9(8))* Princeton Univ. Pr.

Conte, Joseph F. Judaeo-Christian Kabbalah: (Part One - not a Subtitle) 2006. 319p. pap. 29.95 *(978-1-4241-0630-1(3))* PublishAmerica, Inc.

—Judaeo-Christian Kabbalah: (Part Two - not a Subtitle) 2006. 605p. pap. 39.95 *(978-1-4241-2897-6(8))* PublishAmerica, Inc.

Crü, et al. Die pseudepigraphen Briefe an die Gemeinde in Thessaloniki: Studien zu ihrer Abfassung und zur jüdisch-christlichen Sozialgeschichte. 2010. (GER.). 336p. pap. *(978-3-17-021149-0(8))* Kohlhammer, W., GmbH.

D'Abrera, A. Y., ed. The Tribunal of Zaragoza & Crypto-Judaism 1484-1515. 2008. (Europa Sacra Ser.). (ENG, LAT & SPA., Illus.). 242p. (C). 102.00 *(978-2-503-52472-6(9))* Brepols Pubs. BEL. Dist: ISD.

Dacy, Marianne. The Separation of Early Christianity from Judaism. 2010. *(978-1-60497-700-4(0))* Cambria Pr.

Dauermann, Stuart. Christians & Jews Together. 2008. (Messiah & Christians Ser.). 42p. pap. 6.00 *(978-1-60608-403-8(8)*, Wipf and Stock) Wipf & Stock Pubs.

David, Leb. Apples & Oranges. 2008. 144p. pap. 12.95 *(978-1-934527-09-2(2))* Torah Aura Productions.

Debono-De-Laurentis, M. The Forgotten Roots. 2008. 316p. 30.95 *(978-1-4251-7167-4(2))* Trafford Publishing.

Deeg, Alexander, et al, eds. Preaching in Judaism & Christianity: Encounters & Developments from Biblical Times to Modernity. 2008. (Studia Judaica Ser.). (ENG.). X, 247p. 168.00 ***(978-3-11-916624-9(3))*** De Gruyter, Walter Inc.

Deeg, Alexander, et al. Preaching in Judaism & Christianity: Encounters & Developments from Biblical Times to Modernity. 2008. (Studia Judaica Ser.). (ENG., Illus.). X, 247p. 112.00 *(978-3-11-019665-8(4))* De Gruyter, Walter Inc.

Deutsch, Yaacov & Aronsky, Avi. Judaism in Christian Eyes: Early Modern Description of Jews & Judaism, 1 vol. 2012. (ENG., Illus.). 352p. 74.00 ***(978-0-19-975653-7(8))*** Oxford Univ. Pr., Inc.

Dickow, Cheryl. Our Jewish Roots: A Catholic Woman's Guide to Fulfillment Today by Connecting with her Past. 2010. 204p. pap. 14.99 *(978-0-9823388-8-9(0))* Bezalel Bks.

Dietrich, Donald. God & Humanity in Auschwitz: Jewish-Christian Relations & Sanctioned Murder. 2008. (ENG.). 367p. pap. 29.95 *(978-1-4128-0858-3(8))* Transaction Pubs.

Dohrmann, Natalie B. & Stern, David, eds. Jewish Biblical Interpretation & Cultural Exchange: Comparative Exegesis in Context. 2008. (Jewish Culture & Contexts Ser.). (Illus.). 352p. (C). 69.95 *(978-0-8122-4074-0(X))* Univ. of Pennsylvania Pr.

Dunn, James D. G. Parting of the Ways. 2nd ed. 2011. 218p. pap. ***(978-0-334-02999-1(6)***, SCM Pr.) Hymns Ancient & Modern Ltd.

Dureau, Yona. Francesco Giorgio's de Harmonia Mundi. 2011. (Illus.). 704p. 169.95 ***(978-0-7734-1582-9(3))*** Mellen, Edwin Pr., The.

Dynner, Glenn, ed. Holy Dissent: Jewish & Christian Mystics in Eastern Europe. 2011. 44.95 *(978-0-8143-3517-8(9))* Wayne State Univ. Pr.

Echols, Eldred. The Things That Remain. 126p. pap. 7.95 *(978-1-56794-243-9(1)*, C-3029) Star Bible & Tract Corp.

Erasmus, Desiderius & Hovingh, Pieter Frans. Vi-7 Ordinis Sexti Tomus Septimus: Annotationes in Epistolam Ad Romanos. 2011. (LAT, ENG & GRE., Illus.). XII, 420p. ***(978-90-04-20338-9(9))*** BRILL.

Evans, Roger Steven. Issues of New Testament Anti-Judaism: Son of Man, Deicide, & Divine Predetermination. 2008. (ENG.). 120p. pap. 26.50 *(978-0-7618-4143-2(1))* Univ. Pr. of America, Inc.

Fairweather, William. The Background of the Gospels. 2009. 288p. pap. *(978-0-217-57197-5(2))* Books LLC.

Fischer, Bob & Fischer, Robert. The Ways of the Way: Restoring the Jewish Roots of the Modern Church. 2009. (ENG.). 368p. 23.99 *(978-1-59979-763-2(1)*, Creation Hse.) Charisma Media.

Frassetto, Michael. Christian Attitudes Toward the Jews in the Middle Ages: A Casebook. 2012. (ENG.). 304p. pap. 42.95 ***(978-0-415-54262-3(6))*** 2006. 222p. 126.00 *(978-0-415-97827-9(0))* Routledge.

Fredriksen, Paula. Augustine & the Jews: A Christian Defense of Jews & Judaism. 2010. 528p. pap. 20.00 *(978-0-300-16628-6(1))* Yale Univ. Pr.

Garber, Zev, ed. The Jewish Jesus: Revelation, Reflection, Reclamation. 2011. (Shofar Supplements in Jewish Studies). (Illus.). 405p. pap. 59.95 *(978-1-55753-579-5(5))* Purdue Univ. Pr.

Gavin, Frank. Aphraates & the Jews: A Study of the Controversial Homilies of the Persian Sage in their Relation to Jewish Thought. 2007. (Analecta Gorgiana Ser.: 29). per. 29.00 *(978-1-59333-620-2(9))* Gorgias Pr., LLC.

Gerdmar, Anders. Roots of Theological Anti-Semitism: German Biblical Interpretation & the Jews, from Herder & Semler to Kittel & Bultmann. 2010. (Illus.). 678p. pap. *(978-90-04-18621-7(2))* 2008. 668p. *(978-90-04-16851-0(6))* BRILL.

Glaser, Eliane. Judaism Without Jews: Philosemitism & Christian Polemic in Early Modern England. 2007. (ENG.). 224p. 95.00 *(978-0-230-50774-6(3))* Palgrave Macmillan.

Gompertz, Ron. Chrismukkah: Everything You Need to Know to Celebrate the Hybrid Holiday. (ENG., Illus.). 144p. 2009. pap. 10.95 *(978-1-58479-770-8(3))* 2006. 17.95 *(978-1-58479-558-2(1))* Stewart, Tabori & Chang.

Gottlieb, Michah, ed. Moses Mendelssohn: Writings on Judaism, Christianity, & the Bible. 2011. (Tauber Institute Series for the Study of European Jewry & the Brandeis Library of Modern Jewish Thought Ser.). 296p. (C). 85.00 *(978-1-58465-684-5(0))*; (ENG.). pap. 26.00 *(978-1-58465-685-2(9))* Univ. Pr. of New England. (Brandeis University Press).

Gruen, George & Gruen, Jean. Let's Witness to Jews: A Practical Guide for Sharing Your Faith- an Individual or Small Group Study. 2009. pap. 14.99 *(978-1-60799-260-8(4))* Tate Publishing & Enterprises, LLC.

Grypeou, E. & Spurling, H. The Exegetical Encounter between Jews & Christians in Late Antiquity. 2009. (Jewish & Christian Perspectives Ser.). (978-90-04-17727-7(2)) BRILL.

Guetta, Alessandro. Philosophy & Kabbalah: Elijah Benamozegh & the Reconciliation of Western Thought & Jewish Esotericism. Kahan, Helena, tr. from ITA. 2010. (SUNY series in Contemporary Jewish Thought Ser.). 246p. pap. 24.95 (978-0-7914-7576-8(X), Suny Pr.) State Univ. of New York Pr.

Guetta, Alessandro & Kahan, Helena. Philosophy & Kabbalah: Elijah Benamozegh & the Reconciliation of Western Thought & Jewish Esotericism. Kahan, Helena, tr. from ITA. 2009. 224p. 65.00 (978-0-7914-7575-1(1)) State Univ. of New York Pr.

Guibbory, Achsah. Christian Identity, Jews, & Israel in 17th-Century England. 2010. (ENG., Illus.). 344p. 110.00 (978-0-19-955716-5(0)) Oxford Univ. Pr., Inc.

Gushee, David P., et al. Jewish-Christian Dialogue: Drawing Honey from the Rock. Berger, Alan L. & Patterson, David, eds. 2008. (ENG.). 322p. pap. 19.95 (978-1-55778-856-6(1)) Paragon Hse. Pubs.

HaCohen, Ran. Reclaiming the Hebrew Bible: German-Jewish Reception of Biblical Criticism. Engel, Michelle, tr. (Studia Judaica Ser.). 2011. (ENG., Illus.). 250p. 196.00 (978-3-11-214252-3(7)) 2010. 280p. 126.00 (978-3-11-024756-5(9)) De Gruyter, Walter Inc.

Hagee, John. In Defense of Israel: The Bible's Mandate for Supporting the Jewish State. rev. ed. 2007. (ENG.). 256p. per. 14.99 (978-1-59979-210-1(9), Frontline) Charisma Media.

Hagee, John & Fuchs, Sarah. In Defense of Israel. 2009. 200p. pap. 25.00 (978-965-229-440-1(3)) Gefen Publishing Hse., Ltd ISR. Dist: Strauss Consultants.

Hamdani, Syed Nisar Hussain. Istiqbal-E-Imam Mahdi: (Welcoming the Savior - Imam Mahdi) 2009. 256p. pap. 14.72 (978-1-4389-4303-9(2)) AuthorHouse.

Hansen, B. Dale. Light about God & Man. 2007. 506p. pap. 22.95 (978-0-7414-4144-7(6)) Infinity Publishing.

Harkins, Franklin T., ed. Transforming Relations: Essays on Jews & Christians throughout History in Honor of Michael A. Signer. 2010. (ENG., Illus.). 480p. 50.00 (978-0-268-03090-2(1)) Univ. of Notre Dame Pr.

Harrington, Daniel J. The Synoptic Gospels Set Free: Preaching without Anti-Semitism. 2009. (Stimulus Bks.). (Illus.). 256p. pap. 19.95 (978-0-8091-4583-6(9)) Paulist Pr.

Harris, J. Rendel. Testimonies, Part II. 2009. 150p. pap. 13.00 (978-1-60608-508-0(5), Wipf and Stock) Wipf & Stock Pubs.

—Testimonies: Volume 1. 2011. (Cambridge Library Collection - Religion Ser.). (ENG.). 150p. pap. 19.99 (978-1-108-03969-7(3)) Cambridge Univ. Pr.

—Testimonies: Volume 2. 2011. (Cambridge Library Collection - Religion Ser.). (ENG.). 162p. pap. 19.99 (978-1-108-03970-3(7)) Cambridge Univ. Pr.

Harshbarger, Luther H. & Mourant, John A. Judaism & Christianity: Perspectives & Traditions. 490p. reprint ed. (978-0-8290-0294-2(4)); pap. (978-0-8290-0295-9(2)) Irvington Pubs.

Hart, Lewis A. A Jewish Reply to Christian Evangelists. 2009. 254p. 30.99 (978-1-113-61256-4(8)); pap. 26.75 (978-1-113-61255-7(X)); pap. 25.75 (978-1-113-61254-0(1)) BiblioBazaar.

—A Jewish Reply to Christian Evangelists. 2007. (ENG.). 250p. 41.95 (978-0-548-03934-2(8)) Kessinger Publishing, LLC.

Hart, Mitchell. Jewish Blood: Reality & metaphor in history, religion & Culture. Hart, Mitchell, ed. 2009. (Routledge Jewish Studies Ser.). (ENG., Illus.). 240p. (C). 120.00 (978-0-415-47749-9(2)) Routledge.

Hartman, Craig. Through Jewish Eyes. 2010. x, 196p. (978-1-59166-953-1(7)) BJU Pr.

Hasan, Israr. Believers & Brothers: A History of Uneasy Relationship. 2009. 328p. pap. 19.99 (978-1-4389-4445-6(4)) AuthorHouse.

Hasselhoff, Görge K., ed. Die Entdeckung des Christentums in der Wissenschaft des Judentums. (Studia Judaica Ser.).Tr. of Discovery of Christianity in the Science of Judaism. (GER.). 2011. VIII, 351p. 196.00 (978-3-11-214551-7(8)) 2010. 300p. 126.00 (978-3-11-024628-5(7)) De Gruyter, Walter Inc.

Helfgott, Benjamin W. The Doctrine of Election in Tannaitic Literature. 2011. 220p. 44.95 (978-1-258-07908-6(9)) Literary Licensing, LLC.

Heschel, Susannah, ed. Abraham Joshua Heschel: Essential Writings. 2011. 200p. pap. 20.00 (978-1-57075-919-2(7)) Orbis Bks.

Hoffman, Michael. Judaism Discovered: A Study of the Anti-Biblical Reli. 2008. (HEB, GER & ENG., Illus.). 1102p. 55.00 (978-0-9703784-5-3(9)) Independent History & Research Co., The.

Hofmann, Norbert J. & Sievers, Joseph. The Catholic Church & the Jewish People: Recent Reflections from Rome. Cunningham, Philip A., ed. 2nd ed. 2007. (Abrahamic Dialogues Ser.). (ENG.). 256p. 55.00 (978-0-8232-2805-8(3)) Fordham Univ. Pr.

Holladay, Carl R., et al. Scripture & Traditions: Essays on Early Judaism & Christianity in Honor of Carl R. Holladay. 2008. (978-90-04-16747-6(1)) BRILL.

Horbury, William & Horbury. Jews & Christians. 2006. (Academic Paperback Ser.). (ENG.). 352p. 65.00 (978-0-567-04223-1(5), T&T Clark Int'l) Continuum International Publishing Group, Ltd. GBR. Dist: National Bk. Network.

Horowitz, Elliott. Reckless Rites: Purim & the Legacy of Jewish Violence. 2008. (Jews, Christians, & Muslims from the Ancient to the Modern World Ser.). (ENG., Illus.). 360p. (C). pap. 26.95 (978-0-691-13824-4(9)) Princeton Univ. Pr.

Hosang, Boddens. Establishing Boundaries: Christian-Jewish Relations in Early Council Texts & the Writings of Church Fathers. 2010. 204p. (978-90-04-18255-4(1)) BRILL.

Howell, Timothy D. The Matthean Beatitudes in Their Jewish Origins: A Literary & Speech Act Analysis. 2011. (C). 89.95 (978-1-4331-1545-5(X)) Lang, Peter Publishing, Inc.

Huch, Larry. La Bendición Torá: Revelando el misterio, impartiendo el Milagro. 2009.Tr. of Torah Blessing: Revealing the Mystery, Releasing the Miracle. (SPA.). pap. 10.99 (978-1-60374-156-9(9)) Whitaker Hse.

—The Torah Blessing: Revealing the Mystery, Releasing the Miracle. 2009. 208p. pap. 13.99 (978-1-60374-118-7(6), 771187) Whitaker Hse.

Idinopulos, Thomas A. Betrayal of Spirit: Jew-hatred, the Holocaust, & Christianity. 2008. (ENG.). 244p. pap. 24.00 (978-1-888570-96-0(2)) Davies Group Pubs., The.

Idliby, Ranya, et al. The Faith Club: A Muslim, a Christian, a Jew - Three Women Search for Understanding. 2007. (ENG.). 416p. pap. 15.99 (978-0-7432-9048-7(8), Free Pr.) Free Pr.

—The Faith Club: A Muslim, a Christian, a Jew — Three Women Search for Understanding. l.t. ed. 2007. (Walker Large Print Ser.). (ENG.). 575p. per. 17.95 (978-1-59415-199-6(7), Walker Large Print) Cengage Gale.

—The Faith Club: A Muslim, a Christian, a Jew — Three Women Search for Understanding. rev. l.t. ed. 2007. (Thorndike Inspirational Ser.). 521p. 29.95 (978-0-7862-9336-0(5)) Thorndike Pr.

Inbari, Motti. Jewish Fundamentalism & the Temple: Who Will Build the Third Temple? 2009. (SUNY Series in Israeli Studies). 224p. pap. 29.95 (978-1-4384-2624-2(0)) State Univ. of New York Pr.

Jacobs, Steven, et al. Maven in Blue Jeans: A Festschrift in Honor of Zev Garber. 2009. (Illus.). 513p. pap. 59.95 (978-1-55753-521-4(3)) Purdue Univ. Pr.

Jacobsen, Anders-Christian & Ulrich, Jorg, eds. Critique & Apologetics: Jews, Christians & Pagans in Antiquity. 2009. (Early Christianity in the Context of Antiquity Ser.). 304p. 64.95 (978-3-631-58011-0(8)) Lang, Peter GmbH, Europäischer Verlag der Wissenschaften DEU. Dist: Lang, Peter.

Jaffé, Dan. Studies in Rabbinic Judaism & Early Christianity: Text & Context. 2010. (Ancient Judaism & Early Christianity Ser.). (FRE & ENG.). 248p. (978-90-04-18410-7(4)) BRILL.

Jewish Educational Media. The Rebbe Speaks - Yud Tes Kislev. cd-rom 20.00 (978-0-8266-9983-1(9)) Kehot Pubn. Society.

Johnson, Jeffrey D. Unlocked Treasures: Contemplative Aspects of Faith. 2011. 126p. pap. 16.00 (978-1-61097-150-8(7), Wipf and Stock) Wipf & Stock Pubs.

Johnson, Maria Poggi. Strangers & Neighbors: What I Have Learned about Christianity by Living among Orthodox Jews, 0 vols. 2006. 160p. pap. 13.99 (978-0-8499-1151-4(6)) Nelson, Thomas Inc.

Joslyn-Siemiatkoski, Daniel & Joslyn-Siemiatkoski, Dani. Christian Memories of the Maccabean Martyrs. 2009. (ENG.). 272p. 89.00 (978-0-230-60279-3(7)) Palgrave Macmillan.

Justice, Dmin. Gifts for the Gods: Pagan & Christian Sacrifices. 2008. 96p. pap. 11.95 (978-1-4401-1416-8(1)) iUniverse, Inc.

Kaplan, Debra. Beyond Expulsion: Jews, Christians, & Reformation Strasbourg. 2011. (Stanford Studies in Jewish History & C Ser.). (ENG., Illus.). 272p. 60.00 (978-0-8047-7442-0(0)) Stanford Univ. Pr.

Kasimow, Harold, ed. No Religion Is an Island: Abraham Joshua Heschel & Interreligious Dialogue. 2009. 224p. (Orig.). pap. 25.00 (978-1-60608-341-3(4), Wipf and Stock) Wipf & Stock Pubs.

Kessler, Edward. An Introduction to Jewish-Christian Relations. 2010. (Introduction to Religion Ser.). (ENG., Illus.). 264p. (C). 100.00 (978-0-521-87976-7(0)); pap. 31.00 (978-0-521-70562-2(2)) Cambridge Univ. Pr.

Kessler, Edward & Wenborn, Neil, eds. A Dictionary of Jewish-Christian Relations. 2008. (ENG., Illus.). 544p. pap. 31.99 (978-0-521-73078-5(3)) Cambridge Univ. Pr.

Kim, Lloyd. Polemic in the Book of Hebrews: Anti-Judaism, Anti-Semitism, Supersessionism? 2006. (Princeton Theological Monographs). 236p. pap. 25.00 (978-1-59752-839-9(0), Pickwick Pubns.) Wipf & Stock Pubs.

Kinzer, Mark S. Israel's Messiah & the People of God: A Vision for Messianic Jewish Covenant Fidelity. 2012. (ENG.). 250p. pap. 39.00 (978-0-7188-9260-9(7)) Lutherworth Pr., The GBR. Dist: Brown, David Bk. Co., The.

—Israel's Messiah & the People of God: A Vision for Messianic Jewish Covenant Fidelity. Rosner, Jennifer, ed. 2011. 250p. pap. 28.00 (978-1-60608-883-8(1), Cascade Bks.) Wipf & Stock Pubs.

Kleinmann, Yvonne, ed. Kommunikation durch symbolische Akte: Religiöse Heterogenität und politische Herrschaft in Polen-Litauen. 2010. (Forschungen zur Geschichte und Kultur des Ostlichen Mitteleuropa (FGKOM) Ser.). (GER., Illus.). 305p. (C). 72.00 (978-3-515-09419-1(9)) Steiner, Franz Verlag Wiesbaden GmbH DEU. Dist: Brown, David Bk. Co., The.

Klepper, Deeana Copeland. The Insight of Unbelievers: Nicholas of Lyra & Christian Reading of Jewish Text in the Later Middle Ages. (Jewish Culture & Contexts Ser.). (Illus.). 240p. (C). 2008. pap. 24.95 (978-0-8122-2021-6(8)) 2007. 59.95 (978-0-8122-3991-1(1)) Univ. of Pennsylvania Pr.

Knight, Jonathan. Christian Origins. 2008. (ENG.). 472p. 39.95 (978-0-567-03351-2(1), T&T Clark Int'l) Continuum International Publishing Group, Ltd. GBR. Dist: National Bk. Network.

Kogan, Michael S. Opening the Covenant: A Jewish Theology of Christianity. 2007. (ENG.). 304p. 39.95 (978-0-19-511259-7(8)) Oxford Univ. Pr., Inc.

Kogman-Appel, Katrin & Meyer, Mati, eds. Between Judaism & Christianity: Art Historical Essays in Honor of Elisheva (Elisabeth) Revel-Neher. 2008. (Medieval Mediterranean Ser.). 394p. (C). (978-90-04-17106-0(1)) BRILL.

Kohn, Risa Levitt & Moore, Rebecca. A Portable God: The Origin of Judaism & Christianity. 2007. (ENG., Illus.). 220p. 75.00 (978-0-7425-4464-2(8)); per. 24.95 (978-0-7425-4465-9(6)) Rowman & Littlefield Publishers, Inc.

Könighofer, Martina. The New Ship of Zion: Dynamic Diaspora Dimensions of the African Hebrew Israelites of Jerusalem. 2011. (ENG.). 144p. pap. 29.50 (978-3-8258-1055-9(0)) Lit Verlag DEU. Dist: Transaction Pubs.

Kupor, Robert. Jesus the Misunderstood Jew: What the New Testament Really Says about the Man from Nazareth. 2007. 216p. 27.95 (978-0-595-69314-6(8)); per. 17.95 (978-0-595-42404-7(X)) iUniverse, Inc.

Lang, Ariella. Converting a Nation: A Modern Inquisition & the Unification of Italy. 2008. (Studies in European Culture & History Ser.). (ENG.). 248p. 95.00 (978-0-230-60672-2(5)) Palgrave Macmillan.

Langer, Ruth. Cursing the Christians? A History of the Birkat Haminim, 1 vol. 2011. (ENG.). 400p. 74.00 (978-0-19-978317-5(9)) Oxford Univ. Pr., Inc.

Lasker, Daniel. Jewish Philosophical Polemics Against Christianity in the Middle Ages: With a New Introduction. 2nd ed. 2007. 318p. pap. 29.95 (978-1-904113-51-5(6)) Littman Library of Jewish Civilization, The GBR. Dist: International Specialized Bk. Services.

Leeser, Isaac, abr. The Jews & the Mosaic Law. 2009. (Amer Philosophy, Religion Ser.). (ENG.). 296p. pap. 19.95 (978-1-4290-1912-5(3)) Applewood Bks.

Lenzen, Verena, ed. Erinnerung als Herkunft der Zukunft: Zum Jubiläumssymposium des Instituts für Jüdisch-Christliche Forschung an der Universität Luzern (17.-19. September 2006) 2008. (Judaica et Christiana Ser.). 169p. pap. (978-3-03911-502-0(2)) Lang, Peter.

Leonhard, Clemens. The Jewish Pesach & the Origins of the Christian Easter: Open Questions in Current Research. (Studia Judaica Ser.). (ENG.). XI, 507p. 300.00 (978-3-11-185035-1(8)); 2006. 182.00 (978-3-11-018857-8(0)) De Gruyter, Walter Inc.

Levering, Matthew. Jewish-Christian Dialogue & the Life of Wisdom: Engagements with the Theology of David Novak. (ENG.). 2011. 220p. pap. 44.95 (978-1-4411-8063-6(X)) 2010. 224p. 120.00 (978-1-4411-3364-9(X)) Continuum International Publishing Group, Ltd. GBR. Dist: National Bk. Network.

Leveils, Xavier. Contra Christianos: La Critique Sociale et Religieuse du Christianisme des Origenes Au Concile de Nicee (45-325) 2007. (Beihefte Zur Zeitschrift Für Die Neutestamentliche Wissenschaft und Die Kunde der älteren Kirche Ser.). (FRE.). XIII, 548p. 196.00 (978-3-11-019554-5(2)) De Gruyter, Walter Inc.

Levine, Amy-Jill. The Misunderstood Jew: The Church & the Scandal of the Jewish Jesus. (ENG.). 2007. 256p. pap. 13.99 (978-0-06-113778-5(2)) 2006. 240p. 24.95 (978-0-06-078966-4(2)) HarperCollins Pubs. (HarperOne).

Livesey, Nina E. Circumcision as a Malleable Symbol: Early Jewish Treatments of Circumcision. 2010. (Illus.). 207p. pap. 97.50 (978-3-16-150628-4(6)) Mohr Siebeck GmbH & Co. KG DEU. Dist: Coronet Bks.

Lohr, Joel N. Chosen & Unchosen: Conceptions of Election in the Pentateuch & Jewish-Christian Interpretation. 2009. xviii, 254p. 39.50 (978-1-57506-171-9(6)) Eisenbrauns, Inc.

Lucass, Shirley. The Concept of the Messiah in the Scriptures of Judaism & Christianity. 2011. (Library of Second Temple Studies). (ENG.). 256p. 110.00 (978-0-567-58384-0(8), T&T Clark Int'l) Continuum International Publishing Group, Ltd. GBR. Dist: National Bk. Network.

Ludlow, Morwenna. The Early Church: The I. B. Tauris History of the Christian Church. 2009. (I. B. Tauris History of the Christian Church Ser.). (ENG., Illus.). 256p. 42.00 (978-1-84511-366-7(7)) I. B. Tauris & Co., Ltd. GBR. Dist: Macmillan.

Lustiger, Jean-Marie. The Promise. 2007. 168p. pap. 18.00 (978-0-8028-0771-7(2)) Eerdmans, William B. Publishing Co.

Lustiger, Jean-Marie & Duchesne, Jean. Cardinal Jean-Marie Lustiger on Christians & Jews. 2010. (Stimulus Bks.). 192p. pap. 16.95 (978-0-8091-4353-5(4)) Paulist Pr.

Mabry, John R. The Way of Thomas: Nine Insights for Enlightened Living from the Secret Sayings of Jesus. 2006. (ENG.). 196p. per. 19.95 (978-1-84694-030-9(3)) Hunt, John Publishing Ltd. GBR. Dist: National Bk. Network.

Maduro, Otto, ed. Judaism, Christianity, & Liberation: An Agenda for Dialogue. 2009. 160p. pap. 18.00 (978-1-60608-234-8(5)) Wipf & Stock Pubs.

Majid, Anouar. We Are All Moors: Ending Centuries of Crusades Against Muslims & Other Minorities. 2012. 224p. pap. 20.00 (978-0-8166-6080-3(8)) 2009. (ENG.). 240p. 24.95 (978-0-8166-6079-7(4)) Univ. of Minnesota Pr.

Malkiel, David & Malkiel, David Joshua. Reconstructing Ashkenaz: The Human Face of Franco-German Jewry, 1000-1250. 2008. (Stanford Studies in Jewish History & C Ser.). (ENG.). 376p. 65.00 (978-0-8047-5950-2(2)) Stanford Univ. Pr.

Maoz, Moshe. The Meeting of Civilizations: Muslim, Christian, & Jewish. Ma'oz, Moshe, ed. 2009. (ENG.). 264p. 65.00 (978-1-84519-287-7(7)) Sussex Academic Pr. GBR. Dist: International Specialized Bk. Services.

Ma'oz, Moshe, ed. The Meeting of Civilizations: Muslim, Christian, & Jewish. 2010. 280p. pap. 34.50 (978-1-84519-395-9(4)) Sussex Academic Pr. GBR. Dist: International Specialized Bk. Services.

Marcus, César Leo. Kabbalah Judeo-Cristiana: El plan Divino. 2006. (SPA.). pap. 19.50 (978-1-59835-016-6(1), CBH Bks.) Cambridge BrickHouse, Inc.

Marcus, Cesar Leo. Kabbalah Judeo Cristiana la Lógica Divina. 2007. 150p. pap. 19.50 (978-1-4303-1043-3(X)) Lulu Enterprises Inc.

Marquardt, Friedrich-Wilhelm. Theological Audacities: Selected Essays. Pangritz, Andreas, ed. Chung, Paul S., ed. & tr. by. from GER. McCord, Don, tr. from GER. 2010. (Princeton Theological Monographs). 278p. pap. 31.00 (978-1-60608-943-9(9), Pickwick Pubns.) Wipf & Stock Pubs.

Martyr, Justin. The Writings of Justin Martyr. Roberts, Alexander & Donaldson, James, eds. 2007. 152p. per. 14.95 (978-1-933993-46-1(4)) Apocryphile Pr.

Mayo, Philip L. Those Who Call Themselves Jews: The Church & Judaism in the Apocalypse of John. 2006. (Princeton Theological Monographs). 218p. pap. 24.00 (978-1-59752-558-9(8), Pickwick Pubns.) Wipf & Stock Pubs.

McGrath, James F. The Only True God: Early Christian Monotheism in Its Jewish Context. 2009. (ENG.). 168p. 42.00 (978-0-252-03418-3(X)) Univ. of Illinois Pr.

McTernan, John & Singer, Tovia. Rabbi vs. Chaplain: Is Jesus Israel's Promised Messiah? 2007. 96p. pap. 11.95 (978-1-933641-27-0(4)) Bible Belt Pubns.

Merkley, Paul Charles. Christian Attitudes Towards the State of Israel. 2007. (McGill-Queen's Studies in the History of Religion Ser.). (ENG.). 284p. per. (978-0-7735-3255-7(2)) McGill-Queen's Univ. Pr.

Michael, Robert. Holy Hatred: Christianity, Antisemitism, & the Holocaust. annot. ed. 2006. (ENG.). 256p. pap. 30.00 (978-1-4039-7472-3(1)) Palgrave Macmillan.

Michael, Robert & Michael, Robert T. Holy Hatred: Christianity, Antisemitism, & the Holocaust. annot. ed. 2006. (ENG.). 256p. 95.00 (978-1-4039-7471-6(3)) Palgrave Macmillan.

Michel, Thomas, ed. Friends on the Way: Jesuits Encounter Contemporary Judaism. 3rd ed. 2007. (Abrahamic Dialogues Ser.). (ENG.). 176p. 65.00 (978-0-8232-2811-9(8)) Fordham Univ. Pr.

Milavec, Aaron. Salvation Is from the Jews (John 4:22) Saving Grace in Judaism & Messianic Hope in Christianity. 2007. (Michael Glazier Bks.). 201p. per. 23.95 (978-0-8146-5989-2(6)) Liturgical Pr.

Mills, Lawrence H. Avesta Eschatology: Compared with the Books of Daniel & Revelations. 2010. 90p. 33.95 (978-1-161-60565-5(7)) Kessinger Publishing, LLC.

Milson, David. Art & Architecture of the Synagogue in Late Antique Palestine: In the Shadow of the Church. 2006. (Ancient Judaism & Early Christianity Ser.). (Illus.). 579p. (978-90-04-15186-4(9)) BRILL.

Mittleman, Alan L., et al, eds. Uneasy Allies? Evangelical & Jewish Relations. 2007. (ENG., Illus.). 288p. per. 31.50 (978-0-7391-1966-2(4)) Lexington Bks.

Mittleman/Johnson/Is. Uneasy Allies? Evangelical & Jewish Relations. 2007. (ENG.). 288p. 68.50 (978-0-7391-1965-5(6)) Lexington Bks.

Moel, Dennis. The Shadow of the Temple: Jerusalem in Jesus' Day. 2008. (Illus.). 212p. pap. 16.99 (978-1-60477-635-5(8)) Xulon Pr., Inc.

Moore, Daniel F. Jesus, an Emerging Jewish Mosaic: Jewish Perspectives, Post-Holocaust. 2012. (ENG.). 344p. pap. 55.00 (978-0-567-11855-4(X), T&T Clark Int'l) Continuum International Publishing Group, Ltd. GBR. Dist: National Bk. Network.

Moore, Daniel F. & Moore. Jesus, an Emerging Jewish Mosaic: Jewish Perspectives, Post-Holocaust. 2008. (Jewish & Christian Texts in Contexts & Related Studies). (ENG.). 344p. 155.00 (978-0-567-02738-2(4), T&T Clark Int'l) Continuum International Publishing Group, Ltd. GBR. Dist: National Bk. Network.

Moore, George. Christian Writers on Judaism: Nineteen Centuries of Apologetics & Polemics. 2007. 64p. per. 29.00 (978-1-59333-864-0(3)) Gorgias Pr., LLC.

Moran, Gabriel. Uniqueness: Problem or Paradox in Jewish & Christian Traditions. 2008. 166p. pap. 21.00 (978-1-60608-232-4(9), Wipf and Stock) Wipf & Stock Pubs.

Moyaert, M. & Pollefeyt, D., eds. Never Revoked: Nostra Aetate as Ongoing Challenge for Jewish-Christian Dialogue. 2010. (Louvain Theological & Pastoral Monographs). (ENG.). 186p. (C). pap. 41.00 (978-90-429-2236-5(2)) Peeters Pubs. & Booksellers BEL. Dist: Brown, David Bk. Co., The.

Moyaert, Marianne. Never Revoked: Nostra Aetate as Ongoing Challenge for Jewish-Christian Dialogue. Didier, Pollefeyt, ed. 2010. 186p. pap. 53.00 (978-0-8028-6571-7(2)) Eerdmans, William B. Publishing Co.

Nelson, Riley H. Replacement Theology: Dishonesty? Envy? Covetousness? Conceitedness? Presumptuousness? Ignorance? or, Blasphemy? 2008. 148p. pap. 15.99 (978-1-60477-952-3(7)) Xulon Pr., Inc.

Neusner, Jacob. Telling Tales: Making Sense of Christian & Judaic Nonsense: the Urgency & Basis for Judeo-Christian Dialogue. 2007. 176p. pap. 20.00 (978-1-55635-487-8(8)) Wipf & Stock Pubs.

Newman, Louis I. Jewish Influence on Christian Reform Movements. (Columbia University, Oriental Studies: No. 23). reprint ed. 45.00 (978-0-404-50513-4(9)) AMS Pr., Inc.

Obirek, Stanisaw. Obrzeza Katolicyzmu. 2008. (POL.). 217p. (978-83-61053-11-8(5)) Forum Naukowe, Wydawnictwo, Holding Edukacyjny-Pietrzyk, Pawel, Spolka.

Oesterley, W. O. E. The Doctrine of the Last Things: Jewish & Christian. 2008. (ENG.). 128p. pap. 19.75 (978-1-4375-1955-6(5)); 144p. pap. 21.75 (978-1-4375-1956-3(3)) BiblioBazaar.

Paget, James Carleton. Jews, Christians & Jewish Christians in Antiquity. 2010. (Illus.). 548p. 257.50 (978-3-16-150312-2(0)) Mohr Siebeck GmbH & Co. KG DEU. Dist: Coronet Bks.

Palmisano, Joseph. Beyond the Walls: Abraham Joshua Heschel & Edith Stein on the Significance of Empathy for Jewish-Christian Dialogue. 2012. (Aar academy Ser.). (ENG.). 208p. 74.00 (978-0-19-992502-5(X)) Oxford Univ. Pr., Inc.

Parkes, James William. The Conflict of the Church & the Synagogue: A Study in the Origins of Antisemitism. 2008. 456p. pap. 45.00 (978-1-59740-504-1(3)) ACLS Humanities E-Book.

Pastor Angelo McCutchen, Angelo McCutche & Pastor Angelo McCutchen. Why Christians Should Understand the Jewish Roots of Their Faith. 2009. 64p. pap. 15.49 (978-1-4389-6793-6(4)) AuthorHouse.

Patey, Cecil. Obama in Cairo: When Christians & Moslems Meet. 2009. 176p. pap. 17.50 (978-1-4490-0570-2(5)) AuthorHouse.

C

Philippsohn, Ludwig. The Development of the Religious Idea in Judaism, Christianity And. 2007. pap. 28.95 *(978-1-4304-4995-9(0))* Kessinger Publishing, LLC.

Poorthuis, Marcel & Schwartz, Joshua, eds. Interaction between Judaism & Christianity in History, Religion, Art, & Literature. 2008. (Jewish & Christian Perspectives Ser.). 640p. *(978-90-04-17150-3(9))* BRILL.

Porter, Stanley, et al, eds. Journal of Greco-Roman Christianity & Judaism. 2007. 248p. *(978-1-905048-58-8(0))* Sheffield Phoenix Pr.

Porter, Stanley E. Journal of Greco-Roman Christianity & Judaism. 2008. 236p. *(978-1-906055-28-8(9))* Sheffield Phoenix Pr.

Porter, Stanley E., et al, eds. Journal of Greco-Roman Christianity & Judaism. 2011. 208p. ***(978-1-907534-18-8(0))*** 2010. 244p. *(978-1-906055-83-7(1))* Sheffield Phoenix Pr.

Pranaitis, I. B. Talmud Unmasked the Secret Rabbinical Te. 2006. pap. 18.95 *(978-1-4286-5414-3(3))* Kessinger Publishing, LLC.

Price, R. El Secreto de los Rollos del Mar Muerto.Tr. of Secret of Dead Sea Scrolls. (SPA.). *(978-0-7899-0424-9(1),* 498655) Editorial Unilit.

Rabbi Michael Mayersohn. Are We Sinners? Christian & Jewish Beliefs on Sin & Evil. 2009. 128p. pap. 13.95 *(978-1-4401-6911-3(X))* iUniverse, Inc.

Reedijk, Rachel. Roots & Routes: Identity Construction & the Jewish-Christian-Muslim Dialogue. 2010. (Illus.). 376p. pap. 116.00 *(978-90-420-2839-5(4))* Rodopi.

Resnick, Irven M. Marks of Distinction: Christian Perspectives of Jews in the High Middle Ages. 2012. (ENG.). 400p. 69.95 ***(978-0-8132-1969-1(8))*** Catholic Univ. of America Pr.

Riell, Howard Michael. Enoch & the Book of Coincidences IV: Star & Cross. 2007. 156p. per. 14.95 *(978-1-58939-985-3(4))* Virtualbookworm.com Publishing, Inc.

Rizzi, Marco. Hadrian & the Christians. 2010. (Millennium-Studien / Millennium Studies).Tr. of Hadrian & the Christians. (ITA & ENG., Illus.). 186p. 98.00 *(978-3-11-022470-2(4))* De Gruyter, Walter Inc.

Rizzi, Marco, ed. Hadrian & the Christians. 2011. (Millennium-Studien / Millennium Studies).Tr. of Hadrian & the Christians. (ENG & ITA., Illus.). VI, 186p. 154.00 ***(978-3-11-916286-9(8))*** De Gruyter, Walter Inc.

Robinson, Thomas A. Ignatius of Antioch & the Parting of the Ways: Early Jewish-Christian Relations. 2009. xiv, 285p. *(978-1-59856-323-8(8))* Hendrickson Pubs. Marketing, LLC.

Rosenstock-Huessy, Eugen, ed. Judaism Despite Christianity: The 1916 Wartime Correspondence Between Eugen Rosenstock-Huessy & Franz Rosenzweig. 2011. (ENG., Illus.). 224p. pap. 22.50 *(978-0-226-72801-8(3))* Univ. of Chicago Pr.

Roth, Sid. The Incomplete Church: Unifying God's Children. 2007. 173p. per. 15.99 *(978-0-7684-2437-9(2))* Destiny Image Pubs.

Rowland, Christopher. Christian Origins. 2nd ed. 480p. 32.00 *(978-0-281-05366-7(9))* SPCK Publishing GBR. Dist: Pilgrim Pr., The/United Church Pr.

Royalty, Robert M. The Origin of Heresy. 2012. (Routledge Studies in Religion Ser.). (ENG.). 272p. (C). 125.00 ***(978-0-415-53694-3(4))*** Routledge.

Rubin, Dominic. Holy Russia, Sacred Israel: Jewish-Christian Encounters in Russian Religious Thought. 2010. (Reference Library of Jewish Intellectual History Ser.). (ENG.). 570p. 55.00 *(978-1-934843-79-6(2))* Academic Studies Pr.

Ruderman, David B. Connecting the Covenants: Judaism & the Search for Christian Identity in Eighteenth-Century England. 2007. (Jewish Culture & Contexts Ser.). 152p. (C). 59.95 *(978-0-8122-4016-0(2))* Univ. of Pennsylvania Pr.

Rudin, James. Christians & Jews — Faith to Faith: Tragic History, Promising Present, Fragile Future. 2010. 224p. 24.99 *(978-1-58023-432-0(1))* Jewish Lights Publishing.

Russell, Peter J. Heterodoxy Within Second-Temple Judaism & Sectarian Diversity Within the Early Church: A Correlative Study. 2008. 482p. *(978-0-7734-4938-1(8))* Mellen, Edwin Pr., The.

Rutgers, L. V. Making Myths: Jews in Early Christian Identity Formation. 2009. (ENG.). 159p. (C). pap. 32.00 *(978-90-429-2240-2(0))* Peeters Pubs. & Booksellers BEL. Dist: Brown, David Bk. Co., The.

Ruzer, Serge. Mapping the New Testament: Early Christian Writings as a Witness for Jewish Biblical Exegesis. 2007. (Jewish & Christian Perspectives Ser.). 254p. *(978-90-04-15892-4(8))* BRILL.

Sandgren, Leo Dupree. Vines Intertwined: A History of Jews & Christians from the Babylonian Exile to the Advent of Islam, 1 vol. 2010. (ENG., Illus.). 700p. *(978-1-59856-083-1(2))* Hendrickson Pubs. Marketing, LLC.

Sandmel, Samuel. We Jews & Jesus: Exploring Theological Differences for Mutual Understanding. 2006. 164p. reprint ed. per. 16.99 *(978-1-59473-208-9(6))* SkyLight Paths Publishing.

Sandt, Hubertus Waltherus Maria van de. Matthew, James, & Didache: Three Related Documents in Their Jewish & Christian Setting. Zangenberg, Jurgen, ed. 2008. 488p. *(978-90-04-15748-4(4))* BRILL.

Schäfer, Peter. Jewish Jesus - How Judaism & Christianity Shaped Each Other. 2012. (ENG., Illus.). 352p. (C). 35.00 ***(978-0-691-15390-2(6))*** Princeton Univ. Pr.

Schendowich, Naomi, tr. from GER. The Historical Writings of Joseph of Rosheim: Leader of Jewry in Early Modern Germany. 2006. (Studies in European Judaism: Vol. 12). (HEB., Illus.). *(978-90-04-15349-3(7))* BRILL.

Schoolman, Leonard A. The Changing Christian World: A Brief Introduction for Jews. 2008. 163p. pap. 16.99 *(978-1-58023-344-6(9))* Jewish Lights Publishing.

Schultz-Aldrich, Janice L., ed. "Truth" Is a Divine Name: Hitherto Unpublished Papers of Edward A. Synan, 1918-1997. 2010. (Illus.). 298p. pap. 81.00 *(978-90-420-3154-8(9))* Rodopi.

Schultz, Kevin M. Tri-Faith America: How Catholics & Jews Held Postwar America to Its Protestant Promise, 1 vol. 2011. (ENG., Illus.). 288p. 34.95 *(978-0-19-533176-9(1))* Oxford Univ. Pr., Inc.

Schwarz, Berthold & Stadelmann, Helge, eds. Christen, Juden und die Zukunft Israels: Beiträge zur Israellehre aus Geschichte und Theologie. 2008. (Edition Israelogie Ser.). (GRE & GER.). 348p. 35.95 *(978-3-631-58138-4(6))* Lang, Peter GmbH, Europäischer Verlag der Wissenschaften DEU. Dist: Lang, Peter.

Scott, Walter, Sr. Religious Discourses by a Layman. 2006. pap. 17.95 *(978-1-4286-5148-7(9))* Kessinger Publishing, LLC.

Seidman, Naomi. Faithful Renderings: Jewish-Christian Difference & the Politics of Translation. 2006. (Afterlives of the Bible Ser.). 312p. 60.00 *(978-0-226-74505-3(8));* per. 25.00 *(978-0-226-74506-0(6))* Univ. of Chicago Pr.

Shalev-Eyni. Jews among Christians: Hebrew Book Illumination from Lake Constance. 2010. (Studies in Medieval & Early Renaissance Art History Ser.). (ENG., Illus.). 227p. (C). 160.00 *(978-1-905375-09-7(3))* Brepols Pubs. BEL. Dist: Brown, David Bk. Co., The.

Shamir, Avner. Christian Conceptions of Jewish Books: The Pfefferkorn Affair. 2011. 130p. pap. 25.00 *(978-87-635-0772-1(2))* Museum Tusculanum Pr. DNK. Dist: Chicago Distribution Ctr.

Sherman, Franklin, ed. Bridges: The Road to Reconciliation, Vol. 1. 2011. (Stimulus Book Ser.). 464p. pap. 29.95 *(978-0-8091-4732-8(7))* Paulist Pr.

Sibley, Jim R. Mishkan 52: Death, Trials & Triumph: Excerpts from 19th Century Missionary Writings. 2007. 79p. pap. 12.00 *(978-0-9798503-0-1(4))* Pasche Pr.

—Mishkan 53: Salvation & the Jewish People. 2007. 66p. pap. 12.00 *(978-0-9798503-1-8(2))* Pasche Pr.

—Mishkan 54: Jewish Evangelism, Muslim Evangelism. 2008. 82p. pap. 12.00 *(978-0-9798503-2-5(0))* Pasche Pr.

—Mishkan 55: Israel & the Land. 2008. 75p. pap. 12.00 *(978-0-9798503-3-2(9))* Pasche Pr.

Signer, Michael A., ed. Coming Together for the Sake of God: Contributions to Jewish-Christian Dialogue from Post-Holocaust Germany. 2007. 173p. per. 19.95 *(978-0-8146-5167-4(4))* Liturgical Pr.

Silver, David. A slow train Coming. 2007. 210p. pap. 25.50 *(978-1-84799-726-5(0))* Lulu Enterprises Inc.

Skarsaune, Oskar. In the Shadow of the Temple: Jewish Influences on Early Christianity. 2008. (ENG.). 455p. pap. 28.00 *(978-0-8308-2844-9(3),* IVP Acad.) InterVarsity Pr.

Small, Joseph D. & Rosenthal, Gil. Let Us Reason Together: Christian & Jews in Conversation. 2010. (ENG.). pap. 16.95 *(978-1-57153-211-4(0),* Witherspoon Pr.) Curriculum Publishing, Presbyterian Church (U. S. A.).

Snook, Stewart. Christ More Powerful: Analogies of Christ in Non-Christian Religions. 2011. 108p. 21.23 ***(978-1-4567-1122-1(9))***; pap. 10.68 ***(978-1-4567-1123-8(7))*** AuthorHouse.

Soloviev, V. S. Freedom, Faith, & Dogma. 2009. 240p. pap. 24.95 *(978-0-7914-7536-2(0),* Suny Pr.) State Univ. of New York Pr.

Solovyov, Vladimir Sergeyevich. Freedom, Faith, & Dogma: Essays by V.S. Soloviev on Christianity & Judaism. 2008. vii, 251p. (C). 70.00 *(978-0-7914-7535-5(2))* State Univ. of New York Pr.

Spear, Sonja. Jesus the Jew. 2009. 204p. pap. *(978-3-639-17600-1(6))* VDM Verlag Dr. Mueller e.K.

Stading, Mark. For Whom Does Thy Kingdom Come? 2007. 572p. pap. 49.95 *(978-1-4303-1090-7(1))* Lulu Enterprises Inc.

Stanton, Graham N. & Stroumsa, Guy G., eds. Tolerance & Intolerance in Early Judaism & Christianity. 2008. (ENG.). 388p. pap. 46.00 *(978-0-521-05057-9(X))* Cambridge Univ. Pr.

Stendahl, Krister. Meanings: The Bible as Document & as Guide. 2nd ed. 2008. 272p. pap. 25.00 *(978-0-8006-6366-7(7))* Augsburg Fortress, Pubs.

Stone, Perry. Breaking the Jewish Code: Twelve Secrets That Will Transform Your Life, Family, Health, & Finances. 2009. (ENG.). 256p. 21.99 *(978-1-59979-467-9(5),* Charisma Hse.) Charisma Media.

Synan, Edward A. The Popes & the Jews in the Middle Ages. 2008. 264p. pap. 26.00 *(978-1-59740-505-8(1))* ACLS Humanities E-Book.

Tartakoff, Paola. Between Christian & Jew: Conversion & Inquisition in the Crown of Aragon, 1250-1391. 2012. (Middle Ages Ser.). (Illus.). 264p. (C). 55.00 ***(978-0-8122-4421-2(4))*** Univ. of Pennsylvania Pr.

Thienhaus, Ole J. Jewish-Christian Dialogue: The Example of Gilbert Crispin. 2006. (ENG.). 204p. per. 24.95 *(978-1-4241-0740-7(7))* PublishAmerica, Inc.

Trebor. Christianity, Sect of Judaism or Buddhism? 2010. 202p. pap. 19.99 *(978-1-4535-1449-8(X))* Xlibris Corp.

Tripp, Gilbert. Major World Religions & Modern Cults (Compared with the Holy Bible) 2010. 196p. pap. 14.95 *(978-1-4327-5457-0(2))* Outskirts Pr., Inc.

Tyson, Joseph B. Images of Judaism in Luke-Acts. 2010. pap. 24.94 *(978-1-57003-963-8(1))* Univ. of South Carolina Pr.

Umar, Imam Warith-Deen. Yahvehism. 2011. 330p. 29.99 ***(978-1-4568-1852-4(X))***; pap. 19.99 ***(978-1-4568-1851-7(1))*** Xlibris Corp.

Unterseher, Lisa A. The Mark of Cain & the Jews. 2009. 98.00 *(978-1-59333-896-1(1))* Gorgias Pr., LLC.

Vaux, Kenneth L. Journey into an Interfaith World: Jews, Christians, & Muslims in a World Come of Age. 2010. 276p. pap. 31.00 *(978-1-60899-540-0(2))* Wipf & Stock Pubs.

Vose, Robin. Dominicans, Muslims & Jews in the Medieval Crown of Aragon. 2009. (Cambridge Studies in Medieval Life & Thought: Fourth Ser.). (ENG., Illus.). 310p. 102.00 *(978-0-521-88643-7(0))* Cambridge Univ. Pr.

Walton, Michael Thomson. Anthonius Margaritha & the Jewish Faith: Jewish Life & Conversion in Sixteenth-Century Germany. 2012. ***(978-0-8143-3800-1(3))*** Wayne State Univ. Pr.

Whitelaw, Robert. Biblical Return of Israel. pap. 1.49 *(978-0-87377-095-8(1))* GAM Pubns.

Wyse, Marion. Variations on the Messianic Theme: A Case Study of Interfaith Dialogue. 2009. (ENG.). 264p. 49.00 *(978-1-934843-47-5(4))* Academic Studies Pr.

Yoder, John Howard. The Jewish-Christian Schism Revisited. Cartwright, Michael G. & Ochs, Peter, eds. 2008. (Theology in a Postcritical Key Ser.). 290p. pap. 34.99 *(978-0-8361-9475-3(6))* Herald Pr.

Zangenberg, Jurgen & Sandt, Hubertus Waltherus Maria van de. Matthew, James, & Didache: Three Related Documents in Their Jewish & Christian Setting. 2008. 54.95 *(978-1-58983-358-6(9))* Society of Biblical Literature.

Zinguer, Ilana, et al, eds. Hebraic Aspects of the Renaissance: Sources & Encounters. 2011. (Brill's Series in Jewish Studies). (ENG & FRE.). XII, 296p. ***(978-90-04-21255-8(8))*** BRILL.

Zinner, Samuel. The Abrahamic Archetype: Conceptual & Historical Relationships Between Judaism, Christianity & Islam. 2012. 175p. 29.95 ***(978-1-901383-41-6(5))*** Archetype GBR. Dist: Midpoint Trade Bks., Inc.

CHRISTIANITY AND OTHER RELIGIONS—SHINTO

Snook, Stewart. Christ More Powerful: Analogies of Christ in Non-Christian Religions. 2011. 108p. 21.23 ***(978-1-4567-1122-1(9))***; pap. 10.68 ***(978-1-4567-1123-8(7))*** AuthorHouse.

CHRISTIANITY AND PARAPSYCHOLOGY

Taylor, Robert. Syntagma of the Evidences of the Christian Religion. 2010. 206p. pap. 24.75 *(978-1-178-27343-4(1));* 130p. pap. 20.75 *(978-1-149-04971-6(5))* BiblioBazaar.

—Syntagma of the Evidences of the Christian Religion. 2010. 130p. pap. 11.85 *(978-1-151-03874-6(1))* 2010. 102p. pap. 11.85 *(978-1-154-86407-6(3))* 2009. 116p. pap. 19.99 *(978-1-150-29010-7(2))* General Bks. LLC.

Wheless, Joseph. Forgery in Christianity. 2007. (ENG.). 440p. per. 24.95 *(978-1-60206-264-1(1))* Cosimo, Inc.

Zaravinos, Demitrios. The Modern Day Vampire Hunter's Guidebook of D. Zaravinos. 2010. 191p. pap. 14.00 *(978-0-557-66475-7(6))* Lulu Enterprises Inc.

CHRISTIANITY AND PHILOSOPHY

see Philosophy and Religion

CHRISTIANITY AND POLITICS

see also Church and International Organization

Aaltola, Mika. Sowing the Seeds of Sacred: Political Religion of Contemporary World Order & American ERA. 2008. (International Relations Studies Ser.). (Illus.). 216p. *(978-90-04-16563-2(0))* BRILL.

Aguilar, Mario I. A Social History of the Catholic Church in Chile: The Second Period of the Pinochet Government 1980-1990. 2006. 282p. (C). 109.95 *(978-0-7734-5653-2(8))* Mellen, Edwin Pr., The.

Aikman, David. Jesus in Beijing: How Christianity Is Transforming China & Changing the Global Balance of Power. 2006. (ENG., Illus.). 418p. per. 16.95 *(978-1-59698-025-9(7))* Regnery Publishing, Inc., An Eagle Publishing Co.

Alexander, Peter Lawrence. Lessons in Governing: The Inseparable Relationship Between God, Man & Government. Gaus, Andy, tr. 2011. 406p. pap. 29.95 ***(978-0-939067-76-3(5))*** Alexander Publishing.

Allen, Brooke. Moral Minority: Our Skeptical Founding Fathers. (ENG.). 256p. 2007. per. 14.95 *(978-1-56663-751-0(1))* 2006. 24.95 *(978-1-56663-675-9(2))* Dee, Ivan R. Pub.

Altermatt, Urs. Konfession, Nation und Rom: Essays zur Kulturgeschichte der Schweiz im 19. und 20. Jahrhundert. 2009. (GER.). 442p. *(978-3-7193-1457-6(X))* Huber & Co., AG, Verlag.

Andersen, Svend. Macht aus Liebe: Zur Rekonstruktion einer lutherischen politischen Ethik. 2010. (Theologische Bibliothek Töpelmann Ser.).Tr. of Power from Love. Reconstructing a Lutheran Political Ethics. (GER.). XII, 329p. 112.00 *(978-3-11-021629-5(9))* De Gruyter, Walter Inc.

Antila, Jaakko Olavi. "Politiikka on Kirkossa" Keskustapuolueen Kirkkopoliittisten Tavoitteiden Muotoutuminen Vuosina 1966-1978. 2010. (Illus.). 478p. pap. *(978-952-5031-57-7(8))* Suomen kirkkohistoriallinen seura.

Autry Jr., George. Malice Cloaked in Liberty. 2007. pap. 19.99 *(978-1-60477-382-8(0))* Xulon Pr., Inc.

Baker, Hunter. The End of Secularism. 2009. 224p. pap. 17.99 *(978-1-4335-0654-3(8))* Crossway.

Barnes, Julian & Barnes, Timothy. Constantine: Dynasty, Religion & Power in the Later Roman Empire. 2011. (Blackwell Ancient Lives Ser.: 16). (ENG., Illus.). 288p. 128.95 *(978-1-4051-1727-2(3),* Wiley-Blackwell) Wiley, John & Sons, Inc.

Barrett, Edward. Persons & Liberal Democracy: The Ethical & Political Thought of Karol Wojtyla/John Paul II. 2010. (ENG.). 158p. 60.00 *(978-0-7391-2114-6(6))* Lexington Bks.

Barrett, Rob. Disloyalty & Destruction: Religion & Politics in Deuteronomy & the Modern World. 2009. (Library of Hebrew Bible/Old Testament Studies, the Ser.). (ENG.). 304p. 130.00 *(978-0-567-61414-8(X),* T&T Clark Int'l) Continuum International Publishing Group, Ltd. GBR. Dist: National Bk. Network.

Bauckham, Richard. The Bible in Politics, Second Edition: How to Read the Bible Politically. 2nd ed. 2011. (ENG.). 192p. pap. 25.00 *(978-0-664-23708-0(8))* Westminster John Knox Pr.

Bauerschmidt, Frederick Christian. Julian of Norwich & the Mystical Body Politic of Christ. 2008. (ND Studies Spirituality & Theology Ser.). (ENG.). 304p. per. 35.00 *(978-0-268-02208-2(9))* Univ. of Notre Dame Pr.

Beach-Verhey, Timothy A. Robust Liberalism: H. Richard Niebuhr & the Ethics of American Public Life. 2011. (ENG.). 320p. 49.95 *(978-1-60258-252-1(1))* Baylor Univ. Pr.

Bebbington, David W. The Nonconformist Conscience. 2009. (ENG.). 208p. 122.00 *(978-0-415-55554-8(X))* Routledge.

Beckwith, Francis J. Politics for Christians: Statecraft as Soulcraft. 2010. (Christian Worldview Integration Ser.). (ENG.). 175p. pap. 18.00 *(978-0-8308-2814-2(1),* IVP Acad.) InterVarsity Pr.

Bell, C. Stephen. God's Way, Not Politics: Please, Let God Be God! 2011. 72p. pap. 9.95 ***(978-1-4497-2278-4(4),*** WestBow Pr.) Author Solutions, Inc.

Bell, James. A War of Religion: Dissenters, Anglicans & the American Revolution. 2008. (Studies in Modern History Ser.). (ENG., Illus.). 352p. 95.00 *(978-0-230-54297-6(2))* Palgrave Macmillan.

Benbow, Mark. Leading Them to the Promised Land: Woodrow Wilson, Covenant Theology, & the Mexican Revolution, 1913-1915. 2011. 49.00 *(978-1-60635-025-6(0))* Kent State Univ. Pr.

Benne, Robert. Good & Bad Ways to Think about Religion & Politics. 2010. 120p. pap. 14.00 *(978-0-8028-6364-5(7))* Eerdmans, William B. Publishing Co.

Bennett, Douglas. The Minimization of the Gospel. 2009. 181p. pap. 13.99 *(978-0-557-01997-7(4))* Lulu Enterprises Inc.

Bennette, Rebecca Ayako. Fighting for the Soul of Germany: The Catholic Struggle for Inclusion after Unification. 2012. (Harvard Historical Studies: 178). (ENG., Illus.). 380p. 49.95 ***(978-0-674-06563-5(8))*** Harvard Univ. Pr.

Benson, Bruce Ellis & Heltzel, Peter Goodwin, eds. Evangelicals & Empire: Christian Alternatives to the Political Status Quo. 2008. 336p. pap. 32.00 *(978-1-58743-235-4(8))* Brazos Pr.

Berend, Nora, ed. Christianization & the Rise of Christian Monarchy: Scandinavia, Central Europe & Rus' C. 900-1200. 2007. (ENG., Illus.). 458p. 105.00 *(978-0-521-87616-2(8))* Cambridge Univ. Pr.

Berlinerblau, Jacques. Thumpin' It: The Use & Abuse of the Bible in Today's Presidential Politics. 2007. (ENG.). 190p. pap. 17.00 *(978-0-664-23173-6(X))* Westminster John Knox Pr.

Besier, Gerhard, et al. Glaube, Freiheit, Diktatur in Europa und Den USA: Festschrift Für Gerhard Besier Zum 60. Geburtstag. 2007. (GER., Illus.). 894p. (C). 111.00 *(978-3-525-35089-8(9))* Vandenhoeck & Ruprecht GmbH & Co. KG DEU. Dist: ISD.

Billington, Hardy. The Election by Faith In '04. 2006. (Illus.). 205p. 19.95 *(978-1-59886-573-8(0))* Tate Publishing & Enterprises, LLC.

Bivins, Jason C. Religion of Fear: The Politics of Horror in Conservative Evangelicalism. 2008. (ENG., Illus.). 336p. 27.95 *(978-0-19-534081-5(7))* Oxford Univ. Pr., Inc.

Black, Amy E. Beyond Left & Right: Helping Christians Make Sense of American Politics. 2008. 256p. pap. 15.99 *(978-0-8010-6726-6(X))* Baker Bks.

Blair, Robert. The Great Omission: Amazing Ways the Church Muddles the Message: How to Get It Right & Tell It Right. 2007. 303p. per. *(978-0-7880-2442-9(6))* CSS Publishing Co.

Bloomquist, Karen L., ed. Being the Church in the Midst of Empire: Trinitarian Reflections. 2007. (ENG.). 284p. pap. 18.00 *(978-1-932688-33-7(1),* Lutheran Univ. Pr.) Kirk Hse. Pubs.

Boer, Roland. Political Grace: The Revolutionary Theology of John Calvin. 2009. (ENG.). 176p. pap. 25.00 *(978-0-664-23393-8(7))* Westminster John Knox Pr.

Bothwell, Cecil. The Prince of War: Billy Graham's Crusade for a Wholly Christian Empire. 2007. 216p. 2nd rev. ed. (J). per. 16.00 *(978-0-9700125-7-9(8))* 3rd rev. ed. (ENG.). lib. bdg. 24.00 *(978-0-9700125-8-6(6))* Brave Ulysses Bks.

Bourne, Richard. Seek the Peace of the City: Christian Political Criticism as Public, Realist, & Transformative. 2009. (Theopolitical Visions Ser.). 329p. pap. 38.00 *(978-1-55635-642-1(0))* Cascade Bks.

Boyack, Connor. Latter-day Liberty: A Gospel Approach to Government & Politics. 2011. 288p. pap. 17.99 ***(978-1-59955-934-6(X))*** Bonneville B.V. NLD. Dist: Cedar Fort, Inc./CFI Distribution.

Boyo, Bernard. Theology & Politics: The Role of the Church. 2010. 292p. pap. *(978-3-8383-0104-4(8))* Lambert Academic Publishing.

Bradstock. Faith in the Revolution. 208p. 31.95 *(978-0-281-05067-3(8))* International Publishers Marketing.

Brehmer, Karl. Wilhelm Emmanuel von Ketteler (1811-1877) Arbeiterbischof und Sozialethiker: Auf den Spuren einer zeitlosen Modernität. 2009. (GER., Illus.). 165p. *(978-3-7954-2135-9(7))* Schnell und Steiner GmbH, Verlag.

Brennan, Brian. The Good Steward: Ernest C. Manning Story, 1 vol. 2009. (ENG., Illus.). 240p. 24.95 *(978-1-897252-16-1(1))* Fitzhenry & Whiteside, Ltd. CAN. Dist: Ingram Pub. Services.

Brennan, Sean. The Politics of Religion in Soviet Occupied Germany: The Case of Berlin-Brandenburg, 1945-1949. 2011. (ENG.). 256p. 70.00 ***(978-0-7391-5125-9(8))*** Lexington Bks.

—The Politics of Religion in Soviet-Occupied Germany: The Case of Berlin-Brandenburg, 1945-1949. 2011. ***(978-0-7391-5127-3(4))*** Lexington Bks.

Bretherton, Luke. Christianity & Contemporary Politics: The Conditions & Possibilites of Faithful Witness. 2010. (ENG.). 272p. 99.95 *(978-1-4051-9968-1(7));* pap. 42.95 *(978-1-4051-9969-8(5))* Wiley, John & Sons, Inc. (Wiley-Blackwell).

Brint, Steven & Schroedel, Jean Reith, eds. Evangelicals & Democracy in America, Volume 1: Religion & Society. 2011. (ENG., Illus.). 373p. pap. 29.95 ***(978-0-87154-011-9(8))*** Russell Sage Foundation.

—Evangelicals & Democracy in America, Volume 2: Religion & Politics. 2011. (ENG., Illus.). 373p. pap. 29.95 ***(978-0-87154-012-6(6))*** Russell Sage Foundation.

Brint, Steven G. & Schroedel, Jean Reith. Evangelicals & American Democracy, 2 vols. 2009. *(978-0-87154-067-6(3))* Russell Sage Foundation.

—Evangelicals & Democracy in America, 2 vols. 2009. *(978-0-87154-068-3(1))* Russell Sage Foundation.

Broers. Politics & Religion in Napoleonic Italy. 2007. 256p. 34.00 *(978-0-415-44394-4(6))* Routledge.

Brog, David & Fuchs, Sarah. Standing with Israel. 2009. 264p. pap. 25.00 *(978-965-229-428-9(4))* Gefen Publishing Hse., Ltd ISR. Dist: Strauss Consultants.

Brown, Callum G. Religion & Society in Twentieth-Century Britain. 2006. (Religion, Politics & Society in Britain Ser.). (ENG., Illus.). 360p. (C). per. 50.20 *(978-0-582-47289-1(X))* Longman Publishing Group.

Brown, Wesley Haddon & Penner, Peter F. Christian Perspectives on the Israeli-Palestinian Conflict. 2008. 238p. *(978-3-937896-57-1(0))* Neufeld, David.

Bruce, Steve. Paisley: Religion & Politics in Northern Ireland. (ENG.). 2009. 312p. pap. 27.95 *(978-0-19-956571-9(6))* 2007. (Illus.). 288p. 60.00 *(978-0-19-928102-2(5))* Oxford Univ. Pr., Inc.

—Religion & Politics in the United Kingdom. 2011. (Routledge Studies in Religion & Politics Ser.). (ENG., Illus.). 208p. (C). 130.00 *(978-0-415-66492-9(6))* Routledge.

Budde, Michael L. The Borders of Baptism: Identities, Allegiances, & the Church. 2011. (Theopolitical Visions: Ser.). 204p. pap. 22.00 ***(978-1-61097-135-5(3)***, Cascade Bks.) Wipf & Stock Pubs.

Burack, Cynthia. Sin, Sex, & Democracy: Antigay Rhetoric & the Christian Right. 2008. 224p. (C). 74.50 *(978-0-7914-7405-1(4))*; (Illus.). 187p. pap. 29.95 *(978-0-7914-7406-8(2))* State Univ. of New York Pr.

Burleigh, Michael. Sacred Causes: The Clash of Religion & Politics, from the Great War to the War on Terror. 2007. (Illus.). 576p. 27.95 *(978-0-06-058095-7(X))* HarperCollins Pubs.

Burnell, Joel. Poetry, Providence, & Patriotism. 2009. (Princeton Theological Monographs). 320p. pap. 35.00 *(978-1-60608-042-9(3)*, Pickwick Pubns.) Wipf & Stock Pubs.

Burt, Robert A. In the Whirlwind: God & Humanity in Conflict. 2012. (ENG.). 400p. 29.95 ***(978-0-674-06566-6(2))*** Harvard Univ. Pr.

Butler, Matthew, ed. Faith & Impiety in Revolutionary Mexico. 2007. (Studies of the Americas Ser.). (ENG.). 304p. 100.00 *(978-1-4039-8381-7(X))* Palgrave Macmillan.

Buzalka, Juraj & Buzalka. Nation & Religion: The Politics of Commemorations in South-East Poland. 2008. (ENG., Illus.). 256p. pap. 49.95 *(978-3-8258-9907-3(1))* Lit Verlag DEU. Dist: Transaction Pubs.

Cafardi, Nicholas P. Voting & Holiness: Catholic Perspectives on Political Participation. 2012. 265p. ***(978-1-61643-140-2(7))*** Paulist Pr.

Cafardi, Nicholas P., ed. Voting & Holiness: Catholic Perspectives on Political Participation. 2012. 272p. pap. 24.95 ***(978-0-8091-4767-0(X))*** Paulist Pr.

Campbell, Will D. Writings on Reconciliation & Resistance. Goode, Richard C., ed. 2010. 237p. pap. 28.00 *(978-1-60608-128-0(4))* Cascade Bks.

Campolo, Tony. Is Jesus a Democrat or a Republican?, 0 vols. 2009. 208p. pap. 11.99 *(978-0-8499-2927-4(X))* Nelson, Thomas Inc.

—Letters to a Young Evangelical: The Art of Mentoring. 2008. (ENG.). 288p. pap. 13.95 *(978-0-465-00354-9(0))* Basic Bks.

Canfield, Jeff. When Church & Government Collide. 2011. 184p. pap. 13.99 ***(978-1-58930-273-0(7))*** Selah Publishing Group, LLC.

Carey, Hilary M. Empires of Religion. 2008. (ENG.). 352p. 100.00 *(978-0-230-20880-3(0))* Palgrave Macmillan.

—God's Empire: Religion & Colonialism in the British World, C.1801-1908. 2011. (ENG., Illus.). 448p. 99.00 *(978-0-521-19410-5(5))* Cambridge Univ. Pr.

Carlin, David. Can a Catholic Be a Democrat: How the Party I Loved Became the Enemy of My Religion. 2007. 221p. per. 14.95 *(978-1-933184-19-7(1))* Sophia Institute Pr.

Carney, William H. How Would Jesus Vote? A Biblical Perspective on Today's Hot Political Issues. 2006. (ENG.). 80p. pap. 6.99 *(978-1-59979-077-0(7)*, Creation Hse.) Charisma Media.

Carpenter, Joel A. Walking Together: Christian Thinking & Public Life in South Africa. 2012. (ENG.). 416p. pap. 28.99 ***(978-0-89112-315-6(6))*** Abilene Christian Univ. Pr.

Carter, Jimmy. Our Endangered Values: America's Moral Crisis. 2006. (ENG.). 224p. pap. 15.00 *(978-0-7432-8501-8(8))* Simon & Schuster.

Case, Linda Carol Harms. An American Legacy of Patriotic Prayers: Blessings of Liberty, Volume 1. 2008. 712p. pap. 44.95 *(978-1-58736-654-3(1))* Wheatmark.

—An American Legacy of Patriotic Prayers: Blessings of Liberty, Volume 2. 2008. pap. 43.95 *(978-1-60494-007-7(7))* Wheatmark.

Casey, Michael W. The Rhetoric of Sir Garfield Todd: Christian Imagination & the Dream of an African Democracy. 2007. (Studies in Rhetoric & Religion: Vol. 2). (Illus.). 436p. 54.95 *(978-1-932792-86-7(4))* Baylor Univ. Pr.

Chaput, Charles J. Render unto Caesar: Serving the Nation by Living Our Catholic Beliefs in Political Life. 2009. (ENG.). 272p. pap. 14.00 *(978-0-385-52229-8(0)*, Image) Doubleday Religious Publishing Group, The.

—Render unto Caesar: Serving the Nation by Living Our Catholic Beliefs in Political Life. 2008. (ENG.). 272p. 21.95 *(978-0-385-52228-1(2))* Knopf Doubleday Publishing Group.

Chavura, Stephen A. Tudor Protestant Political Thought, 1547-1603. 2011. XIV, 252p. ***(978-90-04-20632-8(9))*** BRILL.

Chrissidis, Nikolaos A., et al, eds. Religion & Identity in Russia & the Soviet Union: A Festschrift for Paul Bushkovitch. 2011. (Illus.). 282p. 31.95 *(978-0-89357-379-9(5))* Slavica Pubs.

Christianity Today International Staff, creator. Politics, 0 vols. 2008. (Christianity Today Study Ser.). 128p. pap. 9.99 *(978-1-4185-3426-4(9))* Nelson, Thomas Inc.

Christoyannopoulos, Alexandre. Christian Anarchism: A Political Commentary on the Gospel. abr. ed. 2011. (ENG.). 250p. pap. 34.90 ***(978-1-84540-247-1(2))*** Imprint Academic GBR. Dist: Ingram Pub. Services.

Chung, Paul S. Karl Barth: God's Word in Action. 2008. 520p. pap. 55.00 *(978-1-55635-527-1(0))* Wipf & Stock Pubs.

Church, Forrest. So Help Me God: The Founding Fathers & the First Great Battle over Church & State. 2008. (ENG.). 540p. pap. 27.95 *(978-0-15-603487-6(5)*, Mariner Bks.) Houghton Mifflin Harcourt Trade & Reference Pubs.

Citizen, A. A Time to Stand: Restoring God to America. 2007. (ENG.). 160p. per. 12.95 *(978-0-615-16280-5(0))* Time To Stand, A.

Claffey, Patrick. Christian Churches in Dahomey-Benin: A Study of Their Socio-Political Role. 2007. (Studies of Religion in Africa Ser.). (Illus.). 328p. *(978-90-04-15572-5(4))* BRILL.

Claiborne, Shane & Haw, Chris. Jesus for President: Politics for Ordinary Radicals, 1 vol. 2008. (ENG., Illus.). 176p. pap. 16.99 *(978-0-310-27842-9(2))* Zondervan.

Clements, Keith. The Moot Papers: Faith, Freedom & Society, 1938-1944. 2010. (ENG., Illus.). 752p. 295.00 *(978-0-567-03257-7(4)*, T&T Clark Int'l) Continuum International Publishing Group, Ltd. GBR. Dist: National Bk. Network.

Close, Christopher. The Negotiated Reformation: Imperial Cities & the Politics of Urban Reform, 1525-1550. 2009. (ENG., Illus.). 296p. 95.00 *(978-0-521-76020-1(8))* Cambridge Univ. Pr.

Clouse, Robert G., et al, eds. The Cross & the Flag. 2007. 260p. pap. 29.00 *(978-1-55635-431-1(2))* Wipf & Stock Pubs.

Coleman, John & Coleman, John Aloysius. Christian Political Ethics. 2007. (Ethikon Series in Comparative Ethics). 289p. 66.00 *(978-0-691-13140-5(6))* Princeton Univ. Pr.

Coleman, John Aloysius. Christian Political Ethics. Coleman, John A., ed. 2007. (Ethikon Series in Comparative Ethics). (ENG.). 308p. (C). per. 26.95 *(978-0-691-13481-9(2))* Princeton Univ. Pr.

Collier-Thomas, Bettye. Jesus, Jobs, & Justice: African American Women & Religion. 2010. (ENG., Illus.). 736p. 37.50 *(978-1-4000-4420-7(0)*, Knopf) Knopf Doubleday Publishing Group.

Collins, Christopher. Homeland Mythology: Biblical Narratives in American Culture. 2007. (ENG.). 264p. 29.95 *(978-0-271-02993-1(5))* Pennsylvania State Univ. Pr.

Colson, Charles W. & Colson, Charles. God & Government: An Insider's View on the Boundaries Between Faith & Politics, 1 vol. rev. ed. 2007. (ENG.). 448p. pap. 14.99 *(978-0-310-27764-4(7))* Zondervan.

The Commands of Men: Why the Republican Party Is So Wrong, According to God's Word, Law & New Covenant. 2008. 553p. pap. 18.95 *(978-0-9789965-7-4(7))* Wayfarer Pr., LLC.

Conger, Kimberly H. The Christian Right in Republican State Politics. 2009. (ENG.). 216p. 89.00 *(978-0-230-62079-7(5))* Palgrave Macmillan.

Connolly, William E. Capitalism & Christianity, American Style. 2008. (ENG.). 192p. 79.95 *(978-0-8223-4249-6(9))*; pap. 22.95 *(978-0-8223-4272-4(3))* Duke Univ. Pr.

Coppa, Frank J. The Policies & Politics of Pope Pius Xii: Between Diplomacy & Morality. 2011. (C). pap. 36.95 ***(978-1-4331-0521-0(7))*** Lang, Peter Publishing, Inc.

Costambeys, Marios. Power & Patronage in Early Medieval Italy: Local Society, Italian Politics & the Abbey of Farfa, C. 700-900. 2011. (Cambridge Studies in Medieval Life & Thought: Fourth Ser.). (ENG.). 410p. pap. 50.00 *(978-0-521-17830-3(4))* Cambridge Univ. Pr.

Cox, Meg. Cynicism & Hope: Reclaiming Discipleship in a Postdemocratic Society. 2008. 136p. pap. 17.00 *(978-1-60608-214-0(0)*, Cascade Bks.) Wipf & Stock Pubs.

Crossan, John Dominic. God & Empire: Jesus Against Rome, Then & Now. 2007. (ENG.). 256p. 22.95 *(978-0-06-084323-6(3)*, HarperOne) HarperCollins Pubs.

Crossan, John Dominic & Crossan, John D. God & Empire: Jesus Against Rome, Then & Now. 2008. (ENG.). 272p. pap. 13.99 *(978-0-06-085831-5(1)*, HarperOne) HarperCollins Pubs.

Crouter, Richard. Reinhold Niebuhr: On Politics, Religion, & Christian Faith, 1 vol. 2010. (ENG.). 208p. pap. 19.95 *(978-0-19-537968-6(3))* Oxford Univ. Pr., Inc.

Curry, Lisa G. Catholicism & the Clan MacDonell of Glengarry: Religion & Politics in the Highlands of Scotland, 1650-1750. 2008. 280p. 109.95 *(978-0-7734-5233-6(8))* Mellen, Edwin Pr., The.

Curtis, Maurice. Challenge to Democracy: Militant Catholicism in Modern Ireland. 2010. (ENG., Illus.). 256p. pap. 24.95 ***(978-1-84588-969-2(X))*** History Pr. Ltd.,The GBR. Dist: Independent Pubs. Group.

Daniel, Wallace L. The Orthodox Church & Civil Society in Russia. 2006. (Eugenia & Hugh M. Stewart '26 Series on Eastern Europe). (ENG., Illus.). 270p. 29.95 *(978-1-58544-523-3(1))* Texas A&M Univ. Pr.

Davis, Paul. The Bible & the Constitution. 2007. per. *(978-1-60208-050-8(X))* FBC Pubns. & Printing.

Dawson, Christopher. The Judgment of the Nations. 2011. (Worlds of Christopher Dawson Ser.). 200p. pap. 24.95 ***(978-0-8132-1880-9(2))*** Catholic Univ. of America Pr.

Dawson, Jane E. A. The Politics of Religion in the Age of Mary, Queen of Scots: The Earl of Argyll & the Struggle for Britain & Ireland. 2007. (Cambridge Studies in Early Modern British History Ser.). (ENG., Illus.). 276p. pap. 56.00 *(978-0-521-03749-5(2))* Cambridge Univ. Pr.

Deace, Steven. Without a Vision the People Perish. 2007. 276p. per. 15.99 *(978-1-60266-642-9(3))* Xulon Pr., Inc.

Denton, Robert. Studies of Identity in the 2008 Presidential Campaign. 2010. (Lexington Studies in Political Communication Ser.). (ENG.). 252p. 78.99 *(978-0-7391-4102-1(3))*; pap. 31.50 *(978-0-7391-4103-8(1))* Lexington Bks.

Derrig, M. God Save Me from Your People. 2007. 132p. pap. 24.95 *(978-1-4241-4055-8(2))* PublishAmerica, Inc.

Dershowitz, Alan M. Blasphemy: How the Religious Right Is Hijacking Our Declaration of Independence. 2008. (ENG.). 208p. pap. 15.95 *(978-0-470-28168-0(5)*, Wiley) Wiley, John & Sons, Inc.

—Blasphemy: How the Religious Right Is Hijacking the Declaration of Independence. 2007. (ENG.). 208p. 22.95 *(978-0-470-08455-7(3)*, Wiley) Wiley, John & Sons, Inc.

Dienst, Karl. Politik und Religionskultur in Hessen und Nassau zwischen 'Staatsumbruch' (1918) und 'nationaler Revolution' (1933) Ursachen und Folgen. 2010. (Theion. Studien zur Religionskultur - Studies in Religious Culture Ser.). (GER.). 310p. 79.95 *(978-3-631-60469-4(6))* Lang, Peter GmbH, Europaischer Verlag der Wissenschaften DEU. Dist: Lang, Peter.

DiIulio, John J., Jr. Godly Republic. 2007. 528p. pap. 24.95 *(978-0-520-90421-7(4))* Univ. of California Pr.

—Godly Republic: A Centrist Blueprint for America's Faith-Based Future. 2008. (Wildavsky Forum Ser.). 328p. pap. 24.95 *(978-0-520-25800-6(2))* Univ. of California Pr.

—Godly Republic: A Centrist Blueprint for America's Faith-Based Future. 2007. (Wildavsky Forum Ser.). 309p. 40.00 *(978-0-520-25414-5(7))* Univ. of California Pr.

Dionne, E. J., Jr. Souled Out: Reclaiming Faith & Politics after the Religious Right. (ENG.). 264p. 2009. pap. 18.95 *(978-0-691-14329-3(3))* 2008. (C). 24.95 *(978-0-691-13458-1(8))* Princeton Univ. Pr.

Dittmer, Jason & Sturm, Tristan. Mapping the End Times: American Evangelical Geopolitics & Apocalyptic Visions. 2010. (Critical Geopolitics Ser.). (Illus.). 280p. 119.95 *(978-0-7546-7601-0(3))*; pap. 44.95 *(978-1-4094-0083-7(2))* Ashgate Publishing Co.

Djupe, Paul A. & Gilbert, Christopher P. The Political Influence of Churches. 2008. (Cambridge Studies in Social Theory, Religion & Politics Ser.). (ENG., Illus.). 294p. 88.00 *(978-0-521-87165-5(4))*; pap. 23.99 *(978-0-521-69219-9(9))* Cambridge Univ. Pr.

Doerksen, Paul G. Beyond Suspicion: Post-Christian Protestant Political Theology in John Howard Yoder & Oliver O'Donovan. 2010. (Paternoster Theological Monographs). 246p. pap. 28.00 *(978-1-60899-439-7(2)*, Wipf and Stock) Wipf & Stock Pubs.

Doerksen, Paul G. & Koop, Karl, eds. The Church Made Strange for the Nations: Essays in Ecclesiology & Political Theology. 2011. (Princeton Theological Monographs). 204p. pap. 22.00 ***(978-1-60899-398-7(1)***, Pickwick Pubns.) Wipf & Stock Pubs.

Domenico, Roy P. & Hanley, Mark Y., eds. Encyclopedia of Modern Christian Politics. 2006. (Illus.). 712p. 199.95 *(978-0-313-32362-1(3)*, GR2362, Greenwood Pr.) Greenwood Publishing Group, Inc.

Dooyeweerd, Herman, et al. The Struggle for a Christian Politics: An Essay in Grounding the Calvinistic Worldview in Its Law-Idea. 2009. xiii, 316p. *(978-0-7734-4895-7(0))* Mellen, Edwin Pr., The.

Dosendrode, S. & Dosenrode-Lynge, Sören Zibrandt von. Christianity & Resistance in the 20th Century: From Kaj Munk & Dietrich Bonhoeffer to Desmond Tutu. 2008. (International Studies in Religion & Society). 265p. (C). *(978-90-04-17126-8(6))* BRILL.

Douglas, Mark. Believing Aloud: Reflections on Being Religious in the Public Square. 2010. 198p. pap. 23.00 *(978-1-60899-247-8(0)*, Cascade Bks.) Wipf & Stock Pubs.

Drew, Charles D. Body Broken: Can Republicans & Democrats Sit in the Same Pew? 2012. (ENG.). 192p. pap. 15.99 *(978-1-936768-30-1(5))* New Growth Pr.

Drogus, Carol Ann & Stewart-Gambino, Hannah. Activist Faith: Grassroots Women in Democratic Brazil & Chile. 2008. (ENG.). 272p. pap. 30.00 *(978-0-271-02550-6(6))* Pennsylvania State Univ. Pr.

Dube, Jimmy G. A Socio-Political Agenda for the Twenty-First Century Zimbabwean Church: Empowering the Excluded. 2006. 220p. *(978-0-7734-5577-1(9))* Mellen, Edwin Pr., The.

Dunn, Charles W. The Future of Religion in American Politics. Dunn, Charles W., ed. 2009. (ENG., Illus.). 288p. 30.00 *(978-0-8131-2516-9(2))* Univ. Pr. of Kentucky.

Dyson, R. W., ed. & tr. from LAT. Sedulius Scottus, de Rectoribus Christianis. 2010. (LAT & ENG.). 202p. 90.00 *(978-1-84383-566-0(5)*, Boydell Press) Boydell & Brewer, Ltd. GBR. Dist: Boydell & Brewer, Inc.

Edgar, Bob. Middle Church: Reclaiming the Moral Values of the Faithful Majority from the Religious Right. 2007. (ENG.). 272p. pap. 15.00 *(978-0-7432-8950-4(1))* Simon & Schuster.

Edwards, Mark & Edwards, Mark Thomas. The Right of the Protestant Left. 2012. (ENG., Illus.). 288p. 85.00 ***(978-1-137-01989-9(1))*** Palgrave Macmillan.

Ehrensperger, Kathy. Paul & the Dynamics of Power: Communication & Interaction in the Early Christ-Movement. 2007. (Library of New Testament Studies, the Ser.). (ENG.). 250p. 140.00 *(978-0-567-04374-0(6)*, T&T Clark Int'l) Continuum International Publishing Group, Ltd. GBR. Dist: National Bk. Network.

Ellingsen, Mark. When Did Jesus Become Republican? Rescuing Our Country & Our Values from the Right — Strategies for a Post-Bush America. 2007. (ENG.). 224p. 24.95 *(978-0-7425-5224-1(1))* Rowman & Littlefield Publishers, Inc.

Ellul, Jacques. Anarchy & Christianity. Bromiley, Geoffrey W., tr. 2011. (Jacques Ellul Legacy Ser.). 114p. pap. 15.00 ***(978-1-60608-971-2(4)***, Wipf and Stock) Wipf & Stock Pubs.

Elmore, A. E. Lincoln's Gettysburg Address: Echoes of the Bible & Book of Common Prayer. 2nd ed. 2009. (ENG., Illus.). 280p. 32.95 *(978-0-8093-2951-9(4))* Southern Illinois Univ. Pr.

Emeghara, Nkem Goodluck L. Baptism, Power & the Miraculous in Contemporary Nigerian Christianity. 2011. 120p. pap. 13.32 *(978-1-4520-9899-9(9))* AuthorHouse.

Englund, Harri, ed. Christianity & Public Culture in Africa. 2011. (Cambridge Centre of African Studies). (ENG.). 240p. 49.95 *(978-0-8214-1945-8(5))* Ohio Univ. Pr.

Erb, Peter C. The Correspondence of Henry Edward Manning & William Ewart Gladstone, 1844-1853, Vol. 2. 2012. (ENG.). 640p. 180.00 *(978-0-19-957733-0(1))* Oxford Univ. Pr., Inc.

—The Correspondence of Henry Edward Manning & William Ewart Gladstone, 1861-1875, Vol. 3. 2012. (ENG.). 640p. 180.00 *(978-0-19-957734-7(X))* Oxford Univ. Pr., Inc.

Erb, Peter C., ed. The Correspondence of Henry Edward Manning & William Ewart Gladstone, 1833-1844, Vol. 1. 2012. (ENG.). 640p. 180.00 *(978-0-19-957732-3(3))* Oxford Univ. Pr., Inc.

—The Correspondence of Henry Edward Manning & William Ewart Gladstone, 1882-1891, Vol. 4. 2012. (ENG.). 640p. 180.00 *(978-0-19-957735-4(8))* Oxford Univ. Pr., Inc.

Eshete, Tibebe. The Evangelical Movement in Ethiopia: Resistance & Resilience. 2009. (ENG.). 525p. (C). 59.95 *(978-1-60258-002-2(2))* Baylor Univ. Pr.

Evans, Bernard F. Vote Catholic? Beyond the Political Din. 2008. 98p. per. 9.95 *(978-0-8146-2946-8(6)*, Liturgical Pr. Bks.) Liturgical Pr.

Faircloth, Sean. Attack of the Theocrats! How the Religious Right Harms Us All, & What We Can Do about It. 2012. pap. ***(978-0-9844932-5-8(5))***; 168p. 21.95 ***(978-0-9844932-4-1(7))*** Pitchstone LLC.

Farhadian, Charles E., ed. Introducing World Christianity. 2012. (ENG.). 292p. 84.95 *(978-1-4051-8249-2(0)*, Wiley-Blackwell) Wiley, John & Sons, Inc.

—Introducing World Christianity. 2012. (ENG.). 292p. pap. 39.95 *(978-1-4051-8248-5(2)*, Wiley-Blackwell) Wiley, John & Sons, Inc.

Fea, John. Was America Founded as a Christian Nation? A Historical Introduction. 2011. (ENG., Illus.). 304p. pap. 30.00 *(978-0-664-23504-8(2))* Westminster John Knox Pr.

Fillmore, Cynthia. Satan, Saints, & Heretics. 2009. 248p. pap. *(978-3-639-16805-1(4))* VDM Verlag Dr. Mueller e.K.

Fitch, David. The End of Evangelicalism? Discerning a New Faithfulness for Mission: Towards an Evangelical Political Theology. 2011. (Theopolitical Visions Ser.). 252p. pap. 28.00 *(978-1-60608-684-1(7)*, Cascade Bks.) Wipf & Stock Pubs.

Flippen, J. Brooks. Jimmy Carter, the Politics of Family, & the Rise of the Religious Right. 2011. (Since 1970: Histories of Contemporary America Ser.). (ENG., Illus.). 456p. 69.95 *(978-0-8203-3769-2(2))*; pap. 26.95 *(978-0-8203-3770-8(6))* Univ. of Georgia Pr.

Ford, Alan. James Ussher: Theology, History, & Politics in Early-Modern Ireland & England. 2007. (ENG.). 336p. 135.00 *(978-0-19-927444-4(4))* Oxford Univ. Pr., Inc.

Formicola, Jo Renee. The Politics of Values: Games Political Strategists Play. 2008. (ENG.). 210p. 70.00 *(978-0-7425-3973-0(3))*; per. 24.95 *(978-0-7425-3974-7(1))* Rowman & Littlefield Publishers, Inc.

Forster, Greg. The Contested Public Square: The Crisis of Christianity & Politics. 2008. (ENG.). 254p. pap. 24.00 *(978-0-8308-2880-7(X)*, IVP Acad.) InterVarsity Pr.

Foster, Craig L. A Different God? Mitt Romney, the Religious Right, & the Mormon Question. 2008. 70.00 *(978-1-58958-118-0(0))*; pap. 24.95 *(978-1-58958-117-3(2))* Kofford, Greg Books, Inc.

Fox, Larry. A Biblical Perspective of Self-Defense & Civil Disobedience. 2009. 120p. pap. 11.99 *(978-1-61579-602-1(9))* Xulon Pr., Inc.

Frame, Tom. Anglicans in Australia. 2007. (ENG.). 304p. pap. 35.95 *(978-0-86840-830-9(1)*, UNSW Press) NewSouth Publishing AUS. Dist: Independent Pubs. Group.

Freston, Paul. Evangelical Christianity & Democracy in Latin America. 2008. (ENG., Illus.). 256p. 99.00 *(978-0-19-517476-2(3))*; pap. 24.95 *(978-0-19-530803-7(4))* Oxford Univ. Pr., Inc.

Frontline Books Staff, contrib. by. Make Your Vote Count: What the Bible Says about 21 Key Political Issues for 2012: From the Publisher of Frontline Books. 2011. E-Book ***(978-1-61638-581-1(2))*** DPMJ Publishing.

Frontline Books Staff, contrib. by. Make Your Vote Count: What the Bible Says about 25 Key Political Issues. 2007. (ENG.). 96p. per. 9.99 *(978-1-59979-292-7(3)*, Frontline) Charisma Media.

Gallagher, Paul. Citizens of Heaven, Residents of the Earth. 2008. 212p. pap. *(978-3-639-07077-4(1))* VDM Verlag Dr. Mueller e.K.

Gamwell, Franklin I. By the People, for the People. 2009. 152p. pap. 17.00 (978-1-60608-321-5(X), Wipf and Stock) Wipf & Stock Pubs.

Gandal, Keith. Class Representation in Modern Fiction & Film. annot. ed. 2007. (ENG.). 240p. 95.00 (978-1-4039-7792-2(5)) Palgrave Macmillan.

Ganiel, Gladys. Evangelicalism & Conflict in Northern Ireland. 2008. (Contemporary Anthropology of Religion Ser.). (ENG.). 224p. 84.00 (978-0-230-60539-8(7)) Palgrave Macmillan.

Gardner, John E. The Three Rs: The View of a Common Man. 2008. 168p. pap. 14.95 (978-1-59858-596-4(7)) Dog Ear Publishing, LLC.

Garrard-Burnett, Virginia. Terror in the Land of the Holy Spirit: Guatemala under General Efrain Rios Montt, 1982-1983, 1 vol. 2010. (Religion & Global Politics Ser.). (ENG., Illus.). 288p. 55.00 (978-0-19-537964-8(0)) Oxford Univ. Pr., Inc.

Geoghegan, Vincent. Socialism & Religion. 2011. (Routledge Studies in Social & Political Thought Ser.). (ENG.). 256p. 125.00 (978-0-415-66828-6(X)) Routledge.

Gibbs, Nancy & Duffy, Michael. The Preacher & the Presidents: Billy Graham in the White House. 2008. (ENG., Illus.). 448p. pap. 14.99 (978-1-59995-104-1(5)) Center St.

—The Preacher & the Presidents: Billy Graham in the White House. l.t. ed. 2008. (Thorndike Nonfiction Ser.). (Illus.). 797p. 32.95 (978-1-4104-0381-0(5)) Thorndike Pr.

Gibson, William & Cornwall, Robert D., eds. Religion Politics & Dissent 1660-1832: Essays in Honour of James E. Bradley (Ebk) 2010. 268p. 119.95 (978-0-7546-6384-3(1)) Ashgate Publishing Co.

Gifford, Paul. Christianity, Politics, & Public Life in Kenya. 2009. (Columbia/Hurst Ser.). (ENG.). 276p. (gr. 17). 90.00 (978-0-231-15442-0(9)) Columbia Univ. Pr.

Gingrich, Bob. In Their Own Words. 2006. 25.99 (978-1-60034-620-0(0)) Xulon Pr., Inc.

—In THEIR OWN WORDS: Founding Fathers & the Bible. 2006. pap. 15.99 (978-1-60034-619-4(7)) Xulon Pr., Inc.

God & the Constitution: Christianity & American Politics. Date not set. (978-0-7425-2249-7(0)) Rowman & Littlefield Publishers, Inc.

Goldberg, Michelle. Kingdom Coming: The Rise of Christian Nationalism. annot. ed. 2007. (ENG.). 256p. per. 14.95 (978-0-393-32976-6(3), 32976) Norton, W. W. & Co., Inc.

Gorenfeld, John. Bad Moon Rising: How Reverend Moon Created the Washington Times, Seduced the Religious Right, & Built an American Kingdom. 2008. (ENG.). 329p. 24.95 (978-0-9794822-3-6(2)) PoliPointPress, LLC.

Gorman, Robert. Toward the Common Good: A Catholic Critique of the Discipline of Political Science. 2011. (Catholic Social Thought Ser.). (ENG.). 194p. (gr. 17). 65.00 (978-0-8108-7796-2(1)) Scarecrow Pr., Inc.

Gottwald. Bible & Liberation. 584p. 45.00 (978-0-281-04719-2(7)) International Publishers Marketing.

Gragg, Rod. By the Hand of Providence: How Faith Shaped the American Revolution. (ENG.). 304p. 2012. pap. 14.99 (978-1-4516-2352-9(6)) 2011. 24.99 (978-1-4165-9630-1(5)) Howard Books. (Howard Bks.).

Gragg, Rod. Forged in Faith: How Faith Shaped the Birth of the Nation 1607-1776. 2011. (ENG.). 272p. pap. 14.99 (978-1-4516-2350-5(X), Howard Bks.) Howard Books.

Graham, Gordon. The Kuyper Center Review. 2010. x, 150p. 24.00 (978-0-8028-6491-8(0)) Eerdmans, William B. Publishing Co.

Griffin, David Ray. Christian Faith & the Truth Behind 9/11: A Call to Reflection & Action. 2006. (ENG.). 246p. per. 40.00 (978-0-664-23117-0(9)) Westminster John Knox Pr.

Gross, Artie. In the Light of Scripture: Why Christians Shouldn't Vote for Liberals. 2008. pap. 14.99 (978-1-60604-787-3(6)) Tate Publishing & Enterprises, LLC.

Guerra, Marc D. Christians as Political Animals: Taking the Measure of Modernity & Modern Democracy. 2010. (ENG.). 26.95 (978-1-933859-92-7(X)) ISI Bks.

Gushee, David P. The Future of Faith in American Politics: The Public Witness of the Evangelical Center. 2008. 358p. per. 29.95 (978-1-60258-071-8(5)) Baylor Univ. Pr.

Gutterman, David S. Prophetic Politics: Christian Social Movements & American Democracy. 2006. 222p. per. 22.95 (978-0-8014-7338-8(1), ILR Pr.) Cornell Univ. Pr.

Haar, Gerrie ter. How God Became African: African Spirituality & Western Secular Thought. 2009. 136p. (C). 34.95 (978-0-8122-4173-0(8)) Univ. of Pennsylvania Pr.

Haavik, Kristof. The Socialist Christian. 2007. 184p. per. 24.95 (978-1-4241-9764-4(3)) PublishAmerica, Inc.

Hall, David W. Calvin in the Public Square: Liberal Democracies, Rights, & Civil Liberties. 2009. pap. (978-1-59638-099-8(3)) P & R Publishing.

Hamilton, Adam. Seeing Gray: Where Faith & Politics Meet Participant Study Guide. 2009. 109p. 12.00 (978-1-4267-0754-4(1)) Abingdon Pr.

—Seeing Gray in a World of Black & White: Thoughts on Religion, Morality, & Politics. 2008. 242p. pap. 22.95 (978-0-687-64969-3(2)) Abingdon Pr.

Hanebrink, Paul A. In Defense of Christian Hungary: Religion, Nationalism, & Antisemitism, 1890-1944. (Illus.). 2009. 272p. pap. 25.95 (978-0-8014-7530-6(9)) 2006. 255p. 54.95 (978-0-8014-4485-2(3)) Cornell Univ. Pr.

Hanna, Judith Lynne. Naked Truth: Strip Clubs, Democracy, & a Christian Right. 2012. E-Book (978-0-292-73575-0(8)); (ENG., Illus.). 350p. 55.00 (978-0-292-72911-7(1)); (ENG., Illus.). 350p. pap. 24.95 (978-0-292-73576-7(6)) Univ. of Texas Pr.

Hansen, Susan. Religion & Reaction: The Secular Political Challenge to the Religious Right. 2011. (ENG.). 216p. (gr. 17). 60.00 (978-1-4422-1105-6(9)) Rowman & Littlefield Publishers, Inc.

Hanson, Buddy. The Christian Prince. 2007. 332p. pap. 19.95 (978-0-9771773-6-3(X)) Hanson Group.

Hanson, Paul D. Political Engagement as Biblical Mandate. 2009. 168p. pap. 19.00 (978-1-55635-515-8(7), Cascade Bks.) Wipf & Stock Pubs.

Harink, Douglas, ed. Paul, Philosophy, & the Theopolitical Vision: Critical Engagements with Agamben, Badiou, Zizek, & Others. 2010. (Theopolitical Visions Ser.). 350p. pap. 39.00 (978-1-60608-662-9(6), Cascade Bks.) Wipf & Stock Pubs.

Harper, Lisa Sharon. Evangelical Does Not Equal Republican... or Democrat. 2008. (Does Not Equal Ser.). (ENG.). 242p. 24.95 (978-1-59558-419-9(6), 955419) New Pr., The.

Harris, Matthew & Kidd, Thomas, eds. The Founding Fathers & the Debate over Religion in Revolutionary America: A History in Documents, 1 vol. 2011. (ENG., Illus.). 206p. (C). pap. 19.95 (978-0-19-532650-5(4)) Oxford Univ. Pr., Inc.

Harris, Sam. Letter to a Christian Nation. 2008. (Vintage Ser.). (ENG.). 144p. pap. 12.95 (978-0-307-27877-7(8), Vintage) Knopf Doubleday Publishing Group.

Harris, Susan K. God's Arbiters: Americans & the Philippines, 1898-1902, 1 vol. 2011. (Imagining the Americas Ser.). (ENG., Illus.). 288p. 35.00 (978-0-19-974010-9(0)) Oxford Univ. Pr., Inc.

Hart, Darryl G. A Secular Faith: Why Christianity Favors the Separation of Church & State. 2006. (ENG.). 288p. 26.95 (978-1-56663-576-9(4)) Dee, Ivan R. Pub.

Hastings, Derek. Catholicism & the Roots of Nazism: Religious Identity & National Socialism, 1 vol. (ENG., Illus.). 2011. 312p. pap. 21.95 (978-0-19-984345-9(7)) 2009. 320p. 29.95 (978-0-19-539024-7(5)) Oxford Univ. Pr., Inc.

Hauerwas, Stanley M. & Coles, Romand. Christianity, Democracy, & the Radical Ordinary: Conversations Between a Radical Democrat & a Christian. 2008. (ENG.). 378p. (C). pap. 43.00 (978-0-7188-9217-3(8)) Lutterworth Pr., The GBR. Dist: Brown, David Bk. Co., The.

—Christianity, Democracy, & the Radical Ordinary: Conversations between a Radical Democrat & a Christian. 2007. (Theopolitical Visions Ser.). 378p. pap. 39.00 (978-1-55635-297-3(2)) Wipf & Stock Pubs.

Haynes, Michael. The Key Is to Be. 2010. 116p. pap. 12.95 (978-0-557-33434-6(9)) Lulu Enterprises Inc.

Heck, Gene W. God, Governance, & Economic Man: The Lessons of the Founders as Derived from Economic History. 2009. (ENG.). 326p. 41.99 (978-0-7618-4816-5(9)) Univ. Pr. of America, Inc.

Heclo, Hugh. Christianity & American Democracy. 2009. (Alexis de Tocqueville Lectures on American Politics Ser.). 312p. pap. 20.00 (978-0-674-03230-9(6)) Harvard Univ. Pr.

Heide, Gale. Domesticated Glory. 2010. 182p. pap. 21.00 (978-1-60608-537-0(9), Pickwick Pubns.) Wipf & Stock Pubs.

Henderson, Jerry. Where Are the Peacemakers: Commentaries. 2012. (ENG.). 112p. pap. 24.95 (978-0-7618-5516-3(5)) Hamilton Bks.

Hendricks, Obery M., Jr. The Universe Bends Toward Justice: Radical Reflections on the Bible, the Church, & the Body Politic. 2011. 192p. pap. 22.00 (978-1-57075-940-6(5)) Orbis Bks.

Herndon, Jeffrey C. Eric Voegelin & the Problem of Christian Political Order. 2007. (Eric Voegelin Institute Series in Political Philosophy). (ENG.). 208p. (C). 39.95 (978-0-8262-1737-0(0)) Univ. of Missouri Pr.

Herrick, Samantha Kahn. Imagining the Sacred Past: Hagiography & Power in Early Normandy. 2007. (Harvard Historical Studies: 156). (Illus.). 272p. 57.50 (978-0-674-02443-4(5)) Harvard Univ. Pr.

Hesse, O. & van Oort, J., eds. Christentum und Politik in der Alten Kirche. 2009. (Patristic Studies). (GER.). 154p. (C). pap. 55.00 (978-90-429-2165-8(X)) Peeters Pubs. & Booksellers BEL. Dist: Brown, David Bk. Co., The.

Heyer, Kristin E., et al. Catholics & Politics: The Dynamic Tension Between Faith & Power. Heyer, Kristin E. et al, eds. 2008. (Religion & Politics Ser.). (ENG., Illus.). 248p. 44.95 (978-1-58901-216-5(X)); pap. 29.95 (978-1-58901-215-8(1)) Georgetown Univ. Pr.

Hocking, W. E., et al. Church & the New World Mind: The Drake Lectures for 1944. (Essay Index Reprint Ser.). reprint ed. 20.95 (978-0-8369-9698-2(4)) Ayer Co. Pubs., Inc.

Hoffmann, Michael. Die französischen Konservativen in der katholischen Provinz: Parteigenese und politische Kultur im Doubs (1900-1930) 2008. (Moderne Geschichte und Politik Ser.). (GER., Illus.). 196p. pap. 56.95 (978-3-631-58166-7(1)) Lang, Peter GmbH, Europaischer Verlag der Wissenschaften DEU. Dist: Lang, Peter.

Hollingworth, Miles. Pilgrim City: St. Augustine of Hippo & His Innovation in Political Thought. 2010. (ENG.). 256p. 120.00 (978-0-567-31002-6(7), T&T Clark Int'l) Continuum International Publishing Group, Ltd. GBR. Dist: National Bk. Network.

—Pilgrim City: St Augustine of Hippo & His Innovation in Political Thought. 2010. (ENG.). 256p. 34.95 (978-0-567-48010-1(0), T&T Clark Int'l) Continuum International Publishing Group, Ltd. GBR. Dist: National Bk. Network.

Horsley, Richard A., ed. In the Shadow of Empire: Reclaiming the Bible as a History of Faithful Resistance. 2008. (ENG.). 192p. pap. 25.00 (978-0-664-23232-0(9)) Westminster John Knox Pr.

Howard, John A. Christianity: Lifeblood of America's Free Society (1620-1945) 2011. 140p. 28.95 (978-1-61507-859-2(2)); pap. 11.95 (978-1-61507-858-5(4)) Cross Bks. Publishing.

Hudson, Deal W. Onward, Christian Soldiers: The Growing Political Power of Catholics & Evangelicals in the United States. 2010. (ENG.). 352p. pap. 21.99 (978-1-4165-2446-5(0), Threshold Editions) Threshold Editions.

Hughes, Richard T. Christian America & the Kingdom of God. 2009. (ENG.). 232p. (gr. 14). 30.95 (978-0-252-03285-1(3)) Univ. of Illinois Pr.

Hunter, Joel C. A New Kind of Conservative. 2008. (ENG.). 224p. 19.99 (978-0-8307-4533-3(5)) Gospel Light Pubns.

—Right Wing, Wrong Bird: Why the Tactics of the Religious Right Won't Fly with Most Conservative Christians. 2007. (ENG.). 190p. per. 14.99 (978-0-9786783-0-2(3)) Northland, A Church Distributed.

Hutson, James H. Church & State in America: The First Two Centuries. 2007. (Cambridge Essential Histories Ser.). (ENG.). 222p. per. 23.99 (978-0-521-68343-2(2)); 220p. 73.99 (978-0-521-86493-0(3)) Cambridge Univ. Pr.

Idestrscaron;m, Jonas, ed. For the Sake of the World. 2009. (Church of Sweden Research Ser.). 156p. pap. 18.00 (978-1-60899-108-2(3), Pickwick Pubns.) Wipf & Stock Pubs.

Inboden, William. Religion & American Foreign Policy, 1945-1960: The Soul of Containment. 2010. (ENG.). 368p. pap. 28.00 (978-0-521-15630-1(0)) Cambridge Univ. Pr.

Inboden, William Charles, III. Religion & American Foreign Policy, 1945-1960: The Soul of Containment. 2008. (ENG.). 372p. 90.00 (978-0-521-51347-0(2)) Cambridge Univ. Pr.

Iskander, Elizabeth. Sectarian Conflict in Egypt: Coptic Media, Identity & Representation. 2012. (Routledge Studies in Middle Eastern Politics Ser.). (ENG.). 240p. (C). 135.00 (978-0-415-69578-7(3)) Routledge.

Jantzen, Kyle. Faith & Fatherland: Parish Politics in Hitler's Germany. 2008. 256p. (C). pap. 22.00 (978-0-8006-2358-6(4), Fortress Pr.) Augsburg Fortress, Pubs.

Jewett, Robert, et al, eds. The Bible & the American Future. 2009. 306p. pap. 34.00 (978-1-60608-993-4(5), Cascade Bks.) Wipf & Stock Pubs.

Joireman, Sandra, ed. Church, State, & Citizen: Christian Approaches to Political Engagement. 2009. (ENG.). 200p. pap. 24.95 (978-0-19-537845-0(8)) Oxford Univ. Pr., Inc.

Joireman, Sandra Fullerton, ed. Church, State, & Citizen: Christian Approaches to Political Engagement. 2009. (ENG.). 200p. 99.00 (978-0-19-537846-7(6)) Oxford Univ. Pr., Inc.

Josephson, Peter & Holder, R. Ward. The Irony of Barack Obama: Barack Obama Reinhold Niebuhr & the Problem of Christian Statecraft. 2012. 228p. 99.95 (978-1-4094-4212-7(8)) Ashgate Publishing Co.

Kabati, Jean-Daniel. The Role of Churches in Rebuilding Community Relations. 2010. 164p. pap. (978-3-8383-5871-0(6)) Lambert Academic Publishing.

Kaiser, Wolfram. Christian Democracy & the Origins of European Union. 2007. (New Studies in European History Ser.). (ENG.). 388p. 107.00 (978-0-521-88310-8(5)) Cambridge Univ. Pr.

Kasischke, Tanja Martina. Wo keine Regierung existiert, gibt es keinen Gott: Zivilreligion im antebellum Amerika am Beispiel der Gemeinschaft der Shaker. 2008. 260p. pap. 65.95 (978-3-631-58181-0(5)) Lang, Peter GmbH, Europaischer Verlag der Wissenschaften DEU. Dist: Lang, Peter.

Katongole, Emmanuel. The Sacrifice of Africa: A Political Theology for Africa. 2010. 200p. pap. 16.00 (978-0-8028-6268-6(3)) Eerdmans, William B. Publishing Co.

Kenny, Mary. Crown & Shamrock: Love & Hate Between Ireland & the British Monarchy. 2010. (ENG., Illus.). 410p. pap. 34.95 (978-1-905494-98-9(X)) New Island Books IRL. Dist: Dufour Editions, Inc.

Kern, Sally. The Stoning of Sally Kern. 2011. E-Book (978-1-61638-438-8(7)) DPMJ Publishing.

Kerr, Nathan R. Christ, History & Apocalyptic: The Politics of Christian Mission. 2008. (Theopolitical Visions Ser.). 222p. pap. 28.00 (978-1-60608-199-0(3)) Wipf & Stock Pubs.

Kester, Scott J. The Haunted Philosophe: James Madison, Republicanism, & Slavery. 2008. (ENG.). 128p. 57.99 (978-0-7391-2174-0(X)) Lexington Bks.

Kidd, Thomas S. God of Liberty: A Religious History of the American Revolution. 2010. (ENG.). 304p. (gr. 8). 26.95 (978-0-465-00235-1(8)) Basic Bks.

Kidd, Thomas S. God of Liberty: A Religious History of the American Revolution. 2012. (ENG.). 320p. (gr. 8). pap. 16.99 (978-0-465-02890-0(X)) Basic Bks.

Kieser, Hans-Lukas. Nearest East: American Millenialism & Mission to the Middle East. 2010. (Politics History & Social Chan Ser.). (ENG.). 224p. 59.50 (978-1-4399-0222-6(4)) Temple Univ. Pr.

Kimball, Charles. When Religion Becomes Lethal: The Explosive Mix of Politics & Religion in Judaism, Christianity, & Islam. 2011. (ENG., Illus.). 272p. 27.95 (978-0-470-58190-2(5), Jossey-Bass) Wiley, John & Sons, Inc.

Kirk, J. Andrew. Civilisations in Conflict? Islam, the West & Christian Faith. 2011. (Regnum Studies in Mission Ser.). 234p. pap. 26.00 (978-1-61097-442-4(5), Wipf and Stock) Wipf & Stock Pubs.

Kirk, Stephen. Satan as Barack Obama. 2011. 92p. pap. 11.95 (978-1-4567-6384-8(9)) AuthorHouse.

Kirwan, Michael. Political Theology: An Introduction. 2009. 192p. (C). pap. 22.00 (978-0-8006-6367-4(5), Fortress Pr.) Augsburg Fortress, Pubs.

Kittredge, Cynthia. The Bible in the Public Square: Reading the Signs of the Times. Aitken, Ellen Bradshaw, ed. 2008. 274p. (C). 27.00 (978-0-8006-3859-7(X), Fortress Pr.) Augsburg Fortress, Pubs.

Koch, Andrew M. & Gates, Paul Henry. Medieval America: Cultural Influences of Christianity in the Law & Public Policy. 2012. (978-0-7391-7283-4(2)) Lexington Bks.

Kosek, Joseph Kip. Acts of Conscience: Christian Nonviolence & Modern American Democracy. (Columbia Studies in Contemporary American History Ser.). (ENG., Illus.). 376p. (gr. 17). 2011. pap. 26.50 (978-0-231-14419-3(9)) 2009. 55.00 (978-0-231-14418-6(0)) Columbia Univ. Pr.

Kotsko, Adam. Politics of Redemption: The Social Logic of Salvation. 2010. (ENG.). 224p. 34.95 (978-0-567-18566-2(4)); 120.00 (978-0-567-52588-8(0)) Continuum International Publishing Group, Ltd. GBR. (T&T Clark Int'l). Dist: National Bk. Network.

Krason, Stephen M. The Public Order & the Sacred Order: Contemporary Issues, Catholic Social Thought, & the Western & American Traditions, 2 vols. 2009. (Catholic Social Thought Ser.: 2 Volumes). (ENG.). 1144p. (gr. 17). 210.00 (978-0-8108-6396-5(0)) Scarecrow Pr., Inc.

Kunter, Katharina. Erfüllte Hoffnungen und zerbrochene Träume: Evangelische Kirchen in Deutschland im Spannungsfeld von Demokratie und Sozialismus (1980-1993) 2006. (Arbeiten Zur Kirchlichen Zeitgeschichte Ser.). (GER.). 346p. (C). 89.00 (978-3-525-55745-7(0)) Vandenhoeck & Ruprecht GmbH & Co. KG DEU. Dist: ISD.

Lacorne, Denis. Religion in America: A Political History. Holoch, George, tr. from FRE. 2011. (Religion, Culture, & Public Life Ser.). (ENG., Illus.). 248p. (gr. 17). 29.50 (978-0-231-15100-9(4)) Columbia Univ. Pr.

Lambert, Frank. Religion in American Politics. 2008. (ENG.). 304p. (C). 24.95 (978-0-691-12833-7(2)) Princeton Univ. Pr.

—Religion in American Politics: A Short History. 2010. (ENG.). 304p. (C). pap. 18.95 (978-0-691-14613-3(6)) Princeton Univ. Pr.

Larkin, Emmet. The Roman Catholic Church & the Home Rule Movement in Ireland, 1870-1874. 2011. (ENG.). 440p. pap. 50.00 (978-0-8078-6560-6(5)) Univ. of North Carolina Pr.

Larson, James S. Is God a Republican? Essays from a Christian Viewpoint. 2011. (Religion & Spirituality Ser.). 79p. pap. 43.00 (978-1-61209-679-7(4)) Nova Science Pubs., Inc.

Laski, John. Capitalism & Christianity: A Moral & Ethical Struggle. 2008. 108p. pap. 16.95 (978-1-60441-624-4(6)) PublishAmerica, Inc.

Leech, Kenneth. The Sky Is Red: Discerning the Signs of the Times. 2nd ed. 296p. pap. 26.00 (978-0-232-52499-4(8)) Abingdon Pr.

Leland, John, et al. De Viris Illustribus: Of Famous Men. 2010. (Studies & Texts). (LAT & ENG.). 498p. 95.00 (978-0-88844-170-6(3)) Pontifical Institute of Mediaeval Studies, Dept. of Pubns. CAN. Dist: Univ. of Toronto Pr.

Lerner, Michael. The Left Hand of God: Healing America's Political & Spiritual Crisis. 2007. 416p. pap. 14.95 (978-0-06-114662-6(5), HarperOne) HarperCollins Pubs.

Leustean, Dr, Lucian N & Leustean, Lucian. Orthodoxy & the Cold War: Religion & Political Power in Romania, 1947-65. 2009. (ENG., Illus.). 288p. 89.00 (978-0-230-21801-7(6)) Palgrave Macmillan.

Lewis, Ted. Electing Not to Vote: Christian Reflections on Reasons for Not Voting. Lewis, Ted, ed. 2008. 140p. pap. 17.00 (978-1-55635-227-0(1), Cascade Bks.) Wipf & Stock Pubs.

Llywelyn, Dorian. Toward a Catholic Theology of Nationality. 2010. (ENG.). 342p. 83.99 (978-0-7391-4089-5(2)) Lexington Bks.

Loewenstein, David & Marshall, John, eds. Heresy, Literature & Politics in Early Modern English Culture. 2009. 332p. pap. 42.00 (978-0-521-12685-4(1)) Cambridge Univ. Pr.

London, Samuel G., Jr. Seventh-Day Adventists & the Civil Rights Movement. 2009. (ENG.). 192p. 55.00 (978-1-60473-272-6(5)) Univ. Pr. of Mississippi.

Long, D. Stephen & Fox, Nancy Ruth. Calculated Futures: Theology, Ethics, & Economics. 2007. 245p. per. 34.95 (978-1-60258-014-5(6)) Baylor Univ. Pr.

Long, Michael G. & Long, Michael G. God & Country? Diverse Perspectives on Christianity & Patriotism. Sadd, Tracy Wenger, ed. 2007. (ENG.). 304p. 89.00 (978-1-4039-7300-9(8)) Palgrave Macmillan.

Lovin, Robin W. Christian Realism & the New Realities. 2008. (ENG.). 240p. 89.00 (978-0-521-84194-8(1)); 248p. pap. 30.99 (978-0-521-60300-3(5)) Cambridge Univ. Pr.

Luebke, David M., et al, eds. Conversion & the Politics of Religion in Early Modern Germany. 2012. (ENG.). 220p. 70.00 (978-0-85745-375-4(0)) Berghahn Bks., Inc.

Luebke, David Martin. Conversion & the Politics of Religion in Early Modern Germany. 2012. E-Book (978-0-85745-376-1(9)) Berghahn Bks., Inc.

Lumsdaine, David Halloran. Evangelical Christianity & Democracy in Asia. 2009. (ENG., Illus.). 352p. pap. 29.95 (978-0-19-530825-9(5)) Oxford Univ. Pr., Inc.

Lutzer, Erwin W. Is God on America's Side? The Surprising Answer & How It Affects Our Future. 2009. (ENG.). 112p. pap. 6.99 (978-0-8024-8952-4(4)) Moody Pubs.

—When a Nation Forgets God: 7 Lessons We Must Learn from Nazi Germany, 1 vol. 2009. (ENG.). 160p. pap. 8.99 (978-0-8024-4656-5(6)) Moody Pubs.

Magee, Malcolm D. What the World Should Be: Woodrow Wilson & the Crafting of a Faith-Based Foreign Policy. 2008. (ENG.). 200p. 39.95 (978-1-60258-070-1(7)) Baylor Univ. Pr.

Maguire, Moira J. Precarious Childhood in Post-Independence Ireland. 2012. (ENG.). 272p. pap. 28.95 (978-0-7190-8774-5(0)) Manchester Univ. Pr. GBR. Dist: Macmillan.

Mahmood, Sohail. Growing Influence of Evangelical Christianity on the Policies of Us. 2010. 64p. pap. (978-3-8383-2146-2(4)) Lambert Academic Publishing.

Main, Darren. Hearts & Minds: Talking to Christians about Homosexuality. 2008. (ENG., Illus.). 160p. pap. 14.95 (978-1-84409-145-4(7)) Findhorn Pr. GBR. Dist: Independent Pubs. Group.

Malick, Faisal. The Political Spirit: Subtitle: How Political Spirits Control & Govern People — and How You Can Overcome Them. 2008. 237p. pap. 17.99 (978-0-7684-2733-2(9)) Destiny Image Pubs.

Maritain, Jacques. Christianity, Democracy, & the American Ideal: A Jacques Maritain Reader. Kelly, James P., III, ed. 2006. (Illus.). 133p. per. (978-1-933184-01-2(9)) Sophia Institute Pr.

Marker, Gary. Imperial Saint: The cult of st. catherine & the dawn of female rule in Russia. 2011. (ENG., Illus.). 327p. pap. 26.00 (978-0-87580-666-2(X)) Northern Illinois Univ. Pr.

Marlin, George J. Narcissist Nation: Reflections of a Blue-State Conservative. 2011. 208p. 30.00 (978-1-58731-565-7(3)); pap. 18.00 (978-1-58731-566-4(1)) St. Augustine's Pr., Inc.

Marsden, Lee. For God's Sake: The Christian Right & US Foreign Policy. 2008. (ENG.). 237p. 100.00 (978-1-84277-884-5(6)); pap. 32.00 (978-1-84277-885-2(4)) Zed Bks., Ltd. GBR. Dist: Macmillan.

Marsh, Charles. Wayward Christian Soldiers: Freeing the Gospel from Political Captivity. (ENG.). 256p. 2008. pap. 14.95 (978-0-19-537603-6(X)) 2007. 25.00 (978-0-19-530720-7(8)) Oxford Univ. Pr., Inc.

Marshall, Ellen Ott. Christians in the Public Square: Faith That Transforms Politics. 2008. 133p. pap. 18.00 (978-0-687-64698-2(7)) Abingdon Pr.

Marshall, Ruth A. Political Spiritualities: The Pentecostal Revolution in Nigeria. 2009. (ENG.). 360p. 65.00 (978-0-226-50712-5(2)); pap. 24.00 (978-0-226-50713-2(0)) Univ. of Chicago Pr.

Martin, David. The Future of Christianity: Reflections on Violence & Democracy Religion & Secularisation. 2010. (Illus.). 240p. 99.95 (978-1-4094-0658-7(X)); pap. 29.95 (978-1-4094-0669-3(5)) Ashgate Publishing Co.

Matey, John J. When Good Men Do Nothing. 2008. 96p. pap. 8.99 (978-0-9749836-6-0(7)) Faithful Life Pubs.

Mathewes, Charles T. The Republic of Grace: Augustinian Thoughts for Dark Times. 2010. 280p. pap. 20.00 (978-0-8028-6508-3(9)) Eerdmans, William B. Publishing Co.

—A Theology of Public Life. (Cambridge Studies in Christian Doctrine Ser.). (ENG.). 384p. 2008. pap. 39.99 (978-0-521-53990-6(0)) 2007. 110.00 (978-0-521-83226-7(8)) Cambridge Univ. Pr.

McCallum, Fiona. Christian Religious Leadership in the Middle East: The Political Role of the Patriarch. 2010. vi, 298p. (978-0-7734-3704-3(5)) Mellen, Edwin Pr., The.

McCullough, Kevin. Musclehead Revolution: Overturning Liberalism with Commonsense Thinking. 2006. 201p. 19.99 (978-0-7369-1730-8(6)) Harvest Hse. Pubs.

McCullough, Peter. Sermons at Court: Politics & Religion in Elizabethan & Jacobean Preaching. 2011. (Cambridge Studies in Early Modern British History Ser.). (ENG., Illus.). 256p. pap. 37.99 (978-0-521-02205-7(3)) Cambridge Univ. Pr.

McDaniel, Eric L. Politics in the Pews: The Political Mobilization of Black Churches. 2008. (Politics of Race & Ethnicity Ser.). (ENG., Illus.). 224p. (C). 80.00 (978-0-472-07046-6(0)); pap. 26.95 (978-0-472-05046-8(X)) Univ. of Michigan Pr.

McDermott, Michael J. Faithful Citizen, Faithful Catholic: Informing Your Conscience & Your Vote. 2007. 38p. pap. 7.25 (978-0-88489-980-8(2)) St. Mary's Pr.

McDonald, Marci. The Armageddon Factor: The Rise of Christian Nationalism in Canada. 2011. (ENG.). 464p. pap. 19.50 (978-0-307-35647-5(7), Vintage Canada) Random Hse. of Canada, Ltd. CAN. Dist: Random Hse., Inc.

McDowell, Stephen & Beliles, Mark. The American Dream: Jamestown & the Planting of the American Christian Republic. 2007. 140p. pap. 10.95 (978-1-887456-20-3(1)) Providence Foundation.

McGough, Michael. A Field Guide to the Culture Wars: The Battle over Values from the Campaign Trail to the Classroom, 1 vol. 2008. (Religion, Politics, & Public Life under the auspices of the Leonard E. Greenberg Center for the Study of Religion in Public Life, Trinity College, Hartford, CT Ser.). 164p. 34.95 (978-0-313-35107-5(4), C35107, Praeger Pubs.) Greenwood Publishing Group, Inc.

McGraw, Bryan T. Faith in Politics: Religion & Liberal Democracy. 2010. (ENG.). 330p. 95.00 (978-0-521-11333-5(4)); 336p. pap. 33.99 (978-0-521-13042-4(5)) Cambridge Univ. Pr.

McLynn, Neil. Christian politics & religious culture in late Antiquity. 2009. (Variorum Collected Studies). (Illus.). 334p. 154.95 (978-0-7546-5992-1(5)) Ashgate Publishing Co.

McMickle, Marvin A., ed. The Audacity of Faith: Christian Leaders Reflect on the Election of Barack Obama. 2009. 192p. pap. 17.00 (978-0-8170-1554-1(X)) Judson Pr.

Meacham, Jon. American Gospel: God, the Founding Fathers, & the Making of a Nation. 2007. (ENG., Illus.). 448p. per. 16.00 (978-0-8129-7666-3(5), Random Hse. Trade Paperbacks) Random House Publishing Group.

Meier, Heinrich. Leo Strauss & the Theologico-Political Problem. Brainard, Marcus, tr. from GER. 2006. (Modern European Philosophy Ser.). (ENG.). 206p. per. 27.99 (978-0-521-69945-7(2)) Cambridge Univ. Pr.

—The Lesson of Carl Schmitt: Four Chapters on the Distinction between Political Theology & Political Philosophy, Expanded Edition. Brainard, Marcus & Berman, Robert, trs. from GER. 2011. (Illus.). 240p. pap. 25.00 (978-0-226-51886-2(8)) Univ. of Chicago Pr.

Meissner, Joshua. The Perjured City. 2008. 120p. pap. (978-3-639-06166-6(7)) VDM Verlag Dr. Mueller e.K.

Metz, Johann Baptist. Faith in History & Society: Toward a Practical Fundamental Theology. Ashley, J. Matthew, ed. & tr. by. from GER. 2007. (ENG.). 304p. pap. 34.00 (978-0-8245-2554-5(X), Herder & Herder) Crossroad Publishing Co., The.

Meyers, Robin. Why the Christian Right Is Wrong: A Minister's Manifesto for Taking Back Your Faith, Your Flag, Your Future. 2008. (ENG.). 224p. pap. 14.95 (978-0-470-18463-9(9), Jossey-Bass) Wiley, John & Sons, Inc.

Miller, Richard W., ed. We Hold These Truths: Catholicism & American Political Life. 2008. 137p. per. 14.95 (978-0-7648-1720-5(5)) Liguori Pubns.

Moen, Matthew C. The Transformation of the Christian Right in The 1980s. 2nd ed. 2008. (ENG., Illus.). 224p. pap. 27.50 (978-0-8173-5532-6(4)) Univ. of Alabama Pr.

Mohler, R. Albert. Culture Shift. 2009. 192p. pap. 0.82 (978-1-60142-251-4(2), Multnomah) Doubleday Religious Publishing Group, The.

—Culture Shift: The Battle for the Moral Heart of America. 2011. (ENG.). 208p. pap. 12.99 (978-1-60142-381-8(0), Multnomah) Doubleday Religious Publishing Group, The.

Monsma, Steve. Healing for a Broken World: Christian Perspectives on Public Policy. 2008. 224p. pap. 16.99 (978-1-58134-961-0(0)) Crossway.

Montalban, Manuel Vazquez. Y Dios Entro en la Habana. (SPA., Illus.). 716p. 29.95 (978-84-03-59494-4(1)) Aguilar, S. A. de Ediciones-Grupo Santillana ESP. Dist: Santillana USA Publishing Co., Inc.

Montover, Nathan. Luther's Revolution: The Political & Temporal Dimensions of Luthers Doctrine of the Prie. 2012. (ENG.). 164p. (C). pap. 30.00 (978-0-227-68014-8(6)) Clarke, James Co., Ltd. GBR. Dist: Brown, David Bk. Co., The.

—Luther's Revolution: The Political Dimensions of Martin Luther's Universal Priesthood. 2011. (Princeton Theological Monographs). 164p. pap. 19.00 (978-1-60899-993-4(9), Pickwick Pubns.) Wipf & Stock Pubs.

Moore, Scott H. The Limits of Liberal Democracy: Politics & Religion at the End of Modernity, 1 vol. 2009. (ENG.). 161p. pap. 18.00 (978-0-8308-2893-7(1), IVP Acad.) InterVarsity Pr.

Morley, Felix. Christian History of the Constitution of the United States of America V1. Hall, Verna M. & Montgomery, Joseph Allan, eds. 2011. 540p. 62.95 (978-1-258-01739-2(3)) Literary Licensing, LLC.

Muñoz, Vincent Phillip. God & the Founders: Madison, Washington, & Jefferson. 2009. (ENG., Illus.). 252p. 92.00 (978-0-521-51515-3(7)); pap. 26.99 (978-0-521-73579-7(3)) Cambridge Univ. Pr.

Murphy, Andrew R. Prodigal Nation: Moral Decline & Divine Punishment from New England To 9/11, 1 vol. 2011. (ENG.). 248p. pap. 19.95 (978-0-19-977527-9(3)) Oxford Univ. Pr., Inc.

Murphy, James. America, Let's Get Real & Truthful. 2006. 108p. pap. 19.95 (978-1-4241-4195-1(8)) PublishAmerica, Inc.

Nelsen, Jerry. Stepping Through Troubled Times: Our Christian Walk in the Midst of Political Turmoil. 2011. 192p. 30.95 (978-1-4497-2337-8(3)); pap. 13.95 (978-1-4497-2336-1(5)) Author Solutions, Inc. (WestBow Pr.).

Nelson-Pallmeyer, Jack & Nelson-Pallmeyer. Saving Christianity from Empire. 2007. (ENG.). 192p. pap. 24.95 (978-0-8264-2830-1(4)) Continuum International Publishing Group, Ltd. GBR. Dist: National Bk. Network.

New Covenant Press. Blood Guilt: Christian Responses to America's War on Terror. 2011. 534p. 29.95 (978-0-9833753-1-9(3)) New Covenant Pr.

Newell, Edmund & Foster, Claire, eds. Worlds We Live In: Dialogues with Rowan Williams. (Illus.). 144p. (978-0-232-52614-1(1)) Darton, Longman & Todd, Ltd.

Nicolay, Polly. We the People, Taking America Back. 2008. 248p. (ENG.). 24.99 (978-1-60477-019-3(8)); per. 14.99 (978-1-60477-018-6(X)) Xulon Pr., Inc.

Noll, Mark A. & Harlow, Luke E., eds. Religion & American Politics: From the Colonial Period to the Present. 2nd ed. 2007. (Illus.). 520p. 99.00 (978-0-19-531714-5(9)); (ENG., 480p. per. 25.00 (978-0-19-531715-2(7)) Oxford Univ. Pr., Inc.

Obikwelu, Polycarp Chuks. Contextual Application of Christian Social Teaching on Political Ethics: In the Light of the Pronouncements of the Bishops of Africa & Madagascar in the Era of Globalisation with Particular Reference to English-Speaking Sub-Saharan Africa, Vol. 838. 2006. (European University Studies: Vol. 23). xxi,426p. pap. 76.95 (978-0-8204-8733-5(3)) Lang, Peter Publishing, Inc.

Oladipo, Caleb Oluremi. The Will to Arise: Theological & Political Themes in African Christianity & the Renewal of Faith & Identity. 2006. 272p. (C). pap. 32.95 (978-0-8204-6389-6(2)) Lang, Peter Publishing, Inc.

O'Leary, Brad. America's War on Christianity. 2010. pap. 12.95 (978-1-935071-24-2(6)) WND Bks, Inc.

Oller, Jan P. Gods, Guns, & Fear. 2009. 376p. pap. 17.99 (978-1-4389-4163-9(3)) AuthorHouse.

Olsen, Glenn W. On the Road to Emmaus: The Catholic Dialogue with America & Modernity. 2012. (ENG.). 320p. 69.95 (978-0-8132-1954-7(X)) Catholic Univ. of America Pr.

O'Mahony, D., ed. Political & Social Philosophy. 2009. IV, 268p. 122.00 (978-0-415-55570-8(1)) Routledge.

O'Neill, Kevin. City of God: Christian Citizenship in Postwar Guatemala. 2009. (Anthropology of Christianity Ser.). (ENG.). 312p. 55.00 (978-0-520-26062-7(7)); pap. 24.95 (978-0-520-26063-4(5)) Univ. of California Pr.

O'Neill, Thomas. Two Masters. 2009. 48p. pap. 15.99 (978-1-4415-0688-7(8)) Xlibris Corp.

Opa, Peter. Jesus Would Vote for a Black President. 2008. 179p. pap. 15.50 (978-1-4357-1060-3(6)) Lulu Enterprises Inc.

Osborn, Ronald E. Anarchy & Apocalypse: Essays on Faith, Violence, & Theodicy. 2010. 174p. pap. 20.00 (978-1-60608-962-0(5), Cascade Bks.) Wipf & Stock Pubs.

Overton, Roger N., ed. God & Governing. 2009. 144p. pap. 18.00 (978-1-60608-774-9(6), Pickwick Pubns.) Wipf & Stock Pubs.

Pabst, Adrian. The Crisis of Global Capitalism: Pope Benedict XVIS Social Encyclical & the Future of Politic. 2012. (ENG.). 304p. (C). pap. 45.00 (978-0-227-68016-2(2)) Clarke, James Co., Ltd. GBR. Dist: Brown, David Bk. Co., The.

Pagan, Peter, et al. The Human Person & a Culture of Freedom. 2009. 390p. (978-0-9669226-7-7(0)) American Maritain Assn., Inc.

Papkova, Irina. The Orthodox Church & Russian Politics. 2011. (Woodrow Wilson Center Book Ser.). (ENG.). 265p. 65.00 (978-0-19-979114-9(7)) Oxford Univ. Pr., Inc.

Park, Chung-Shin. Protestantism & Politics in Korea. 2009. (ENG.). 320p. pap. 30.00 (978-0-295-98930-3(0)) Univ. of Washington Pr.

Parkin, Jon. Taming the Leviathan: The Reception of the Political & Religious Ideas of Thomas Hobbes in England 1640-1700. 2007. (Ideas in Context Ser.). (ENG.). 472p. 132.00 (978-0-521-87735-0(0)) Cambridge Univ. Pr.

—Taming the Leviathan: The Reception of the Political & Religious Ideas of Thomas Hobbes in England, 1640-1700. 2010. (Ideas in Context Ser.). (ENG.). 470p. pap. 40.00 (978-0-521-16831-1(7)) Cambridge Univ. Pr.

Parry, Ken, ed. The Blackwell Companion to Eastern Christianity. (Wiley-Blackwell Companions to Religion Ser.: 31). (ENG., Illus.). 528p. 2010. pap. 49.95 (978-1-4443-3361-9(5)) 2007. 188.95 (978-0-631-23423-4(3)) Wiley, John & Sons, Inc. (Wiley-Blackwell).

Paske, Gerald. Why the Fundamentalist Right Is so Fundamentally Wrong. 2006. 130p. per. 22.95 (978-0-922993-60-4(2)) Marquette Bks., LLC.

Patterson, Eric D. Christianity & Power Politics Today: Christian Realism & Contemporary Political Dilemmas. Patterson, Eric, ed. 2008. (ENG., Illus.). 196p. 84.00 (978-0-230-60264-9(9)) Palgrave Macmillan.

Pavey, Stephen. Theologies of Power & Crisis: Envisioning / Embodying Christianity in Hong Kong. 2011. (American Society of Missiology Monograph Ser.). 148p. pap. 18.00 (978-1-60899-513-4(5), Pickwick Pubns.) Wipf & Stock Pubs.

Payne, Daniel P. The Revival of Political Hesychasm in Contemporary Orthodox Thought: The Political Hesychasm of John Romanides & Christos Yannaras. 2011. (ENG.). 334p. 80.00 (978-0-7391-4720-7(X)) Lexington Bks.

Pecknold, C. C. Christianity & Politics. 2010. (Cascade Companions Ser.). 196p. pap. 23.00 (978-1-55635-242-3(5), Cascade Bks.) Wipf & Stock Pubs.

Pell, George. God & Caesar: Selected Essays on Religion, Politics, & Society. Casey, M. A., ed. 2007. 189p. per. 29.95 (978-0-8132-1503-7(X)) Catholic Univ. of America Pr.

Pera, Marcello. Why We Should Call Ourselves Christians: The Religious Roots of Free Societies. 2011. (ENG.). 220p. 23.95 (978-1-59403-564-7(4)) Encounter Bks.

Perkins, Mary Anne. Christendom & European Identity: The Legacy of a Grand Narrative Since 1789. (Religion & Society Ser.). (ENG.). XII, 385p. 225.00 (978-3-11-185288-1(1)) De Gruyter, Walter Inc.

Perreau-saussin, Emilie. Catholicism & Democracy: An Essay in the History of Political Thought. 2012. (ENG.). 200p. (C). 45.00 (978-0-691-15394-0(9)) Princeton Univ. Pr.

Pett, David P. Can These Bones Live. 2008. 264p. pap. 16.99 (978-1-60647-978-0(4)) Xulon Pr., Inc.

Phillips, Kevin. American Theocracy: The Peril & Politics of Radical Religion, Oil, & Borrowed Money in the 21st Century. 2007. (ENG.). 480p. (gr. 12-18). 17.00 (978-0-14-303828-3(1), Penguin (Non-Classics)) Penguin Group (USA) Inc.

Posner, Sarah. God's Profits: Faith, Fraud, & the Republican Crusade for Values Voters. 2008. (ENG.). 207p. 19.95 (978-0-9794822-1-2(5)) PoliPointPress, LLC.

Press, Bill. How the Republicans Stole Religion: Why the Religious Right Is Wrong about Faith & Politics & What We Can Do to Make It Right. 2006. (ENG.). 288p. pap. 14.95 (978-0-385-51604-4(5), Three Leaves) Doubleday Religious Publishing Group, The.

Prud'homme, Joseph Gilbert. Faith & Politics in America: From Jamestown to the Civil War. 2011. 285p. 80.95 (978-1-4331-0582-1(9)) Lang, Peter Publishing, Inc.

Radanovich, George. The and New World Order Is the Old World Order. 2011. 22.99 (978-1-61379-263-6(8)); 162p. pap. 14.99 (978-1-61379-262-9(X)) Xulon Pr., Inc.

Ranger, T. O. Evangelical Christianity & Democracy in Africa. 2008. (ENG.). 288p. pap. 29.95 (978-0-19-530802-0(6)) Oxford Univ. Pr., Inc.

Ranger, Terence O., ed. Evangelical Christianity & Democracy in Africa. 2008. (ENG.). 288p. 99.00 (978-0-19-517477-9(1)) Oxford Univ. Pr., Inc.

Ratzinger, Joseph. The Church, Ecumenism, & Politics. 2008. 250p. 19.95 (978-1-58617-217-6(4)) Ignatius Pr.

Reardon, Lawrence C., et al, eds. The Catholic Church & the Nation-State: Comparative Perspectives. 2006. (Religion & Politics Ser.). (ENG.). 298p. per. 26.95 (978-1-58901-115-1(5)) Georgetown Univ. Pr.

—The Catholic Church & the Nation-State: Comparative Perspectives. 2006. (Religion & Politics Ser.). (ENG.). 298p. 49.95 (978-1-58901-114-4(7)) Georgetown Univ. Pr.

Redekop, John H. Politics under God. 2007. 223p. per. 11.99 (978-0-8361-9355-8(5)) Herald Pr.

Rees, Wyn, et al. British Foreign Policy & the Anglican Church: Christian Engagement with the Contemporary World. 2008. (Illus.). 172p. pap. 39.95 (978-0-7546-6037-8(0)) Ashgate Publishing Co.

Richters, Katja. The Post-Soviet Russian Orthodox Church: Politics, Culture & Greater Russia. 2012. (Routledge Contemporary Russia & Eastern Europe Ser.). (ENG., Illus.). 224p. (C). 140.00 (978-0-415-66933-7(2)) Routledge.

Riswold, Caryn D. Two Reformers: Martin Luther & Mary Daly as Political Theologians. 2007. (Illus.). 216p. pap. 24.00 (978-1-59752-826-9(9)) Wipf & Stock Pubs.

Robbins, Jeff. The Sleeping Giant Has Awoken: The New Politics of Religion in the United States. Magee, Neal, ed. 2008. (ENG.). 248p. 100.00 (978-0-8264-2968-1(8)); pap. 29.95 (978-0-8264-2969-8(6)) Continuum International Publishing Group, Ltd. GBR. Dist: National Bk. Network.

Robertson, Pat. Courting Disaster, 0 vols. 2008. 320p. pap. 14.99 (978-0-7852-9730-7(8)) Nelson, Thomas Inc.

Robison, James & Richards, Jay W. Indivisible: Restoring Faith, Family, & Freedom Before It's Too Late. 2012. (ENG.). 256p. pap. 14.99 (978-1-4555-0314-8(2)); 384p. 21.99 (978-1-4555-0312-4(6), 1337900) FaithWords.

Robison, James & Richards Jay, W. Indivisible: Restoring Faith, Family, & Freedom Before It's Too Late. l.t. ed. 2012. (ENG.). 571p. pap. 17.99 (978-1-59415-441-6(4)) Cengage Gale.

Robson, Laura. Colonialism & Christianity in Mandate Palestine. 2011. (Illus.). 256p. E-Book (978-0-292-73548-4(0)); (ENG., 55.00 (978-0-292-72653-6(8)) Univ. of Texas Pr.

Romocea, Cristian. Church & State: Religious Nationalism & State Identification in Post-Communist Romania. 2011. (ENG.). 272p. 120.00 (978-1-4411-6857-3(5)) Continuum International Publishing Group, Ltd. GBR. Dist: National Bk. Network.

Rosenberg, Joel C. Dentro de la Revolución: Cómo los Partidarios de la Yihad, de Jefferson y de Jesús Luchan para Dominar el Medio Oriente y Transformar el Mundo. 2009.Tr. of Inside the Revolution: Inside the Revolution. (SPA.). 608p. pap. 9.99 (978-1-4143-1934-6(7), Tyndale Espanol) Tyndale Hse. Pubs.

Ross, Wyn. British Foreign Policy & the Anglican Church: Christian Engagement with the Contemporary World. Blewett, Timothy & Hyde-Price, Adrian, eds. 2008. (Illus.). 172p. 99.95 (978-0-7546-6035-4(4)) Ashgate Publishing Co.

Rourke, Thomas. The Social & Political Thought of Benedict XVI. 2010. (ENG.). 158p. 57.99 (978-0-7391-4280-6(1)) Lexington Bks.

Rourke, Thomas R. The Social & Political Thought of Benedict XVI. 2011. (ENG.). 160p. pap. 24.95 (978-0-7391-4281-3(X)) Lexington Bks.

Rudin, Rabbi James. The Baptizing of America: The Religious Right's Plans for the Rest of Us. 2006. (ENG.). 336p. per. 16.95 (978-1-56025-893-3(4)) Basic Bks.

Ruotsila, Markku. The Origins of Christian Anti-Internationalism: Conservative Evangelicals & the League of Nations. 2nd rev. ed. 2007. (Religion & Politics Ser.). (ENG.). 256p. 49.95 (978-1-58901-190-8(2)); per. 19.95 (978-1-58901-191-5(0)) Georgetown Univ. Pr.

Rwengabo, Sabastiano. Beyond the Spiritual. 2011. 188p. pap. (978-3-8433-8896-2(2)) Lambert Academic Publishing.

Ryden, David. Is the Good Book Good Enough? Evangelical Perspectives on Public Policy. 2010. (ENG.). 298p. 70.00 (978-0-7391-5059-7(6)) Lexington Bks.

Ryden, David K. Is the Good Book Good Enough? Evangelical Perspectives on Public Policy. 2010. (978-0-7391-5061-0(8)) Lexington Bks.

Sageng, Hans. Kingdom Come Now. 2008. (Illus.). 152p. per. 14.95 (978-0-9797710-3-3(X)) Along The Way.

Sahayadoss, Santhosh J. Martin Luther on Social & Political Issues: His Relevance for Church & Society in India. 2006. 250p. pap. (978-0-8204-8720-5(1)); pap. (978-3-631-55679-5(9)) Lang, Peter AG.

Sandoz, Ellis. Republicanism, Religion, & the Soul of America. 2006. (Eric Voegelin Institute Series in Political Philosophy Ser.). (ENG.). 248p. (C). per. 24.95 (978-0-8262-1726-4(5)); (Illus.). 44.95 (978-0-8262-1674-8(9)) Univ. of Missouri Pr.

Scarborough, Rick. Enough Is Enough: A Practical Guide to Political Action at the Local, State, & National Level. 2008. (ENG.). 272p. pap. 14.99 (978-1-59979-389-4(X), Frontline) Charisma Media.

Schäfer, Axel R. Countercultural Conservatives: American Evangelicalism from the Postwar Revival to the New Christian Right. 2011. (Studies in American Thought & Culture Ser.). (ENG., Illus.). 264p. pap. 29.95 (978-0-299-28524-1(3)) Univ. of Wisconsin Pr.

Schall, James V. The Mind That Is Catholic: Philosophical & Political Essays. 2008. 352p. pap. 34.95 (978-0-8132-1541-9(2)) Catholic Univ. of America Pr.

Schei, Kenneth A. Rescuing Jesus (and America) from the Religious Right. 2007. ring bd. 14.95 (978-0-926491-02-1(4)) Synthesis.

Schindler, Jeanne Heffernan. Christianity & Civil Society: Catholic & Neo-Calvinist Perspectives. 2008. (ENG.). 214p. 68.50 (978-0-7391-0884-0(0)) Lexington Bks.

Schröter, Susanne. Christianity in Indonesia: Perspectives of Power. 2011. 424p. pap. 49.95 (978-3-643-10798-5(6)) Lit Verlag DEU. Dist: Transaction Pubs.

Schultz, Daniel. Changing the Script: An Authentically Faithful & Authentically Progressive Political Theology for the 21st Century. 2010. (ENG.). 220p. pap. 15.95 (978-1-935439-14-1(6)) Ig Publishing, Inc.

Settje, David E. Lutherans & the Longest War: Adrift on a Sea of Doubt about the Cold & Vietnam Wars, 1964-1975. 2006. (ENG.). 232p. 57.99 (978-0-7391-1531-2(6)); pap. 27.50 (978-0-7391-1532-9(4)) Lexington Bks.

Shahan, Michael, ed. A Report from the Front Lines: Conversations on Public Theology: A Festschrift in Honor of Robert Benne. 2008. 184p. pap. 30.00 (978-0-8028-4863-5(X)) Eerdmans, William B. Publishing Co.

Shanks, Andrew. Hegel's Political Theology. 2008. (ENG.). 252p. pap. 34.99 (978-0-521-08806-0(2)) Cambridge Univ. Pr.

Sharlet, Jeff. The Family: The Secret Fundamentalism at the Heart of American Power. 2009. 464p. pap. 15.99 (978-0-06-056005-8(3), HarperPerennial) 2008. (ENG.). 352p. 25.95 (978-0-06-055979-3(9)) HarperCollins Pubs.

Sheffield, Anthony & Josiah, Barak. The United States, Law, Government, Religion, Christianity, & Illegalities: God, Creator, Supreme Judge, Divine Providence, Lord Jesus Christ - No Man, No Government, No False Religion Is to Be Before or Oppose God, His Rightness, His Provided Rights. 2011. 420p. pap. 38.95 (978-1-4497-1824-4(8), WestBow Pr.) Author Solutions, Inc.

Shields, Jon A. The Democratic Virtues of the Christian Right. 2009. (ENG., Illus.). 216p. (C). 31.95 (978-0-691-13740-7(4)) Princeton Univ. Pr.

Shoemaker, H. Stephen. Being Christian in an Almost Chosen Nation: Thinking about Faith & Politics. 2006. 172p. per. 16.00 (978-0-687-33423-0(3)) Abingdon Pr.

Shorris, Earl. The Politics of Heaven: America in Fearful Times. 2007. (ENG.). 384p. 25.95 (978-0-393-05963-2(4), 5963) Norton, W. W. & Co., Inc.

Shubin, Daniel H. Militarist Christendom & the Gospel of the Prince of Peace. 2006. 289p. per. 16.95 (978-1-60002-260-9(X), 4146) Mountain Valley Publishing, LLC.

—Militarist Christendom & the Gospel of the Prince of Peace. 2006. (ENG.). 280p. pap. 16.00 (978-0-9662757-2-8(1)) Shubin, Daniel H.

Sider, Ronald J. I Am Not a Social Activist: The Prism Essays. 2007. pap. 16.99 (978-0-8361-9396-1(2)) Herald Pr.

—The Scandal of Evangelical Politics: Why Are Christians Missing the Chance to Really Change the World? 2008. 282p. pap. 20.00 (978-0-8010-6837-9(1)) Baker Bks.

Simons, Greg, frwd. The Role of the Russian Orthodox Church in Russia since 1990: Changing Dynamics of Politics & Religion. 2009. vii, 240p. 109.95 (978-0-7734-4703-5(2)) Mellen, Edwin Pr., The.

Skar, Brian. Evangeliberal: Following Jesus from the near Left. Grosinger, Paula, ed. 2006. per. 12.95 (978-0-9788649-0-3(5)) Skar Publishing.

Smidt, Corwin E., et al. Pews, Prayers, & Participation: Religion & Civic Responsibility in America. 2008. (Religion & Politics Ser.). (ENG., Illus.). 296p. 44.95 (978-1-58901-218-9(6)); pap. 26.95 (978-1-58901-217-2(8)) Georgetown Univ. Pr.

Smith, Gary Scott. Faith & the Presidency from George Washington to George W. Bush. 2009. (ENG.). 680p. pap. 24.95 (978-0-19-539596-9(4)) Oxford Univ. Pr., Inc.

Smith, Gregory Allen. Politics in the Parish: The Political Influence of Catholic Priests. 2nd rev. ed. 2008. (Religion & Politics Ser.). (ENG.). 272p. pap. 26.95 (978-1-58901-193-9(7)) Georgetown Univ. Pr.

Smith, R. Drew. Freedom's Distant Shores: American Protestants & Post-Colonial Alliances with Africa. annot. ed. 2006. 325p. per. 34.95 (978-1-932792-37-9(6)) Baylor Univ. Pr.

Smith, Ted A. The New Measures: A Theological History of Democratic Practice. 2007. (ENG., Illus.). 356p. 107.99 (978-0-521-87131-0(X)) Cambridge Univ. Pr.

Somerville, Henry. Studies in the Catholic Social Movement. 2011. (ENG., Illus.). 128p. pap. 20.95 (978-1-932528-18-3(0)) IHS Pr.

Spannenberger, Norbert. Die Katholische Kirche in Ungarn 1918-1939: Positionierung Im Politischen System und "Katholische Renaissance" 2006. (HUN & GER., Illus.). 211p. (C). 52.00 (978-3-515-08668-4(4)) Steiner, Franz Verlag Wiesbaden GmbH DEU. Dist: Brown, David Bk. Co., The.

Stanley, Louie. A Political Christian Says: (Politically Proper): Short articles designed to help readers think for themselves; an alternative to today's political reporting from one Christian perspective.: (It Is okay for Christians to be Political), 1 vol. 2010. 120p. pap. 19.95 (978-1-4489-5247-2(6)) PublishAmerica, Inc.

Stephens, Randall J. & Giberson, Karl W. The Anointed: Evangelical Truth in a Secular Age. 2011. (ENG., Illus.). 384p. 29.95 (978-0-674-04818-8(0), Belknap Pr.) Harvard Univ. Pr.

Sterne, Evelyn Savidge. Ballots & Bibles: Ethnic Politics & the Catholic Church in Providence. 2008. (Cushwa Center Studies of Catholicism in Twentieth-Century America). 320p. pap. 22.95 (978-0-8014-7497-2(3)) Cornell Univ. Pr.

Steven, Martin. Christianity & Party Politics: Keeping the Faith. 2011. (Routledge Studies in Religion & Politics Ser.). (ENG., Illus.). 184p. (C). 130.00 (978-0-415-55660-6(0)) Routledge.

Stone, Ronald & Stone. Prophetic Realism: Beyond Militarism & Pacifism in an Age of Terror. 2007. (ENG.). 208p. pap. 26.95 (978-0-567-02675-0(2), T&T Clark Int'l) Continuum International Publishing Group, Ltd. GBR. Dist: National Bk. Network.

Strasser, Ulrike. State of Virginity: Gender, Religion, & Politics in an Early Modern Catholic State. 2006. (Social History, Popular Culture & Politics in Germany Ser.). (ENG., Illus.). 264p. per. 22.95 (978-0-472-03215-0(1)) Univ. of Michigan Pr.

Strehle, Stephen. The Egalitarian Spirit of Christianity: The Sacred Roots of American & British Government. 2008. (ENG.). 320p. 49.95 (978-1-4128-0816-3(2)) Transaction Pubs.

Suarez, Ray. The Holy Vote: The Politics of Faith in America. 2007. (ENG.). 320p. per. 15.99 (978-0-06-082998-8(2), HarperPerennial) HarperCollins Pubs.

Sullivan, Amy. The Party Faithful: How & Why Democrats Are Closing the God Gap. 2008. (ENG.). 272p. 25.00 (978-0-7432-9786-8(5), Scribner) Scribner.

Tamadonfar, Mehran & Jelen, Ted G. The Role of Religion in Affecting Regime Change: A Study of Secularization & Charismatic Leadership in Poland & Iran. 2011. 99.95 (978-0-7734-1479-2(7)) Mellen, Edwin Pr., The.

The World Famous Anonymous Author Staff. The Man from Tennessee. 2007. 184p. (ENG.). 21.99 (978-1-60477-481-8(9)); per. 13.99 (978-1-60477-480-1(0)) Xulon Pr., Inc.

Thomasius, Christian. Essays on the Church, State, & Politics. 2007. (Natural Law & Enlightenment Classics Ser.). (ENG.). 327p. (C). (gr. 12). pap. 14.50 (978-0-86597-499-9(3)) Liberty Fund, Inc.

—Essays on the Church, State, & Politics. 2007. (Natural Law & Enlightenment Classics Ser.). (ENG.). 327p. (C). (gr. 12). 24.00 (978-0-86597-498-2(5)) Liberty Fund, Inc.

Thompson, Alden L. Beyond Common Ground: Why Liberals & Conservatives Need Each Other. 2009. 254p. pap. 16.99 (978-0-8163-2340-1(2)) Pacific Pr. Publishing Assn.

Thompson, Augustine Op. Revival Preachers & Politics in Thirteenth Century Italy: The Great Devotion Of 1233. 2010. 258p. pap. 28.00 (978-1-60899-494-6(5), Wipf and Stock) Wipf & Stock Pubs.

Thompson, Mary V. In the Hands of a Good Providence: Religion in the Life of George Washington. 2008. (ENG., Illus.). 272p. 29.95 (978-0-8139-2763-3(3)) Univ. Pr. of Virginia.

Titus, Craig Steven. The Person & the Polis: Faith & Values Within the Secular State. 2007. (John Henry Cardinal Newman Lectures: Vol. 1). 187p. per. 29.95 (978-0-9773103-0-2(2)) Institute for the Psychological Science Pr., The.

Torr, James D. How Does Religion Influence Politics? annot. ed. 2008. (At Issue Ser.). (ENG.). 111p. (YA). (gr. 10-12). 22.50 (978-0-7377-3426-3(4), Greenhaven Pr., Inc.) Cengage Gale.

Townsend, Verlane. Jesus, How Would He Vote? 2008. 68p. pap. 10.99 (978-0-88144-296-0(8)) Yorkshire Publishing Group.

Trainor, Brian. Christ, Society & the State. 2012. (ENG.). 614p. (C). pap. 40.50 (978-1-921511-58-5(3)) ATF Pr. AUS. Dist: Brown, David Bk. Co., The.

Trueman, Carl R. Republocrat: Confessions of a Liberal Conservative. 2010. 128p. pap. 9.99 (978-1-59638-183-4(3)) P & R Publishing.

Trumper, Tim J. R. Preaching & Politics: Engagement without Compromise. 2009. 118p. pap. 15.00 (978-1-60608-008-5(3), Wipf and Stock) Wipf & Stock Pubs.

Tutino, Stefania. Empire of Souls: Robert Bellarmine & the Christian Commonwealth. 2010. (Oxford Studies in Historical Theology Ser.). (ENG.). 384p. 74.00 (978-0-19-974053-6(4)) Oxford Univ. Pr., Inc.

—Law & Conscience: Catholicism in Early Modern England 1570-1625. 2007. (Catholic Christendom, 1300-1700 Ser.). 268p. 124.95 (978-0-7546-5771-2(X)) Ashgate Publishing Co.

—Thomas White & the Blackloists: Between Politics & Theology During the English Civil War. 2008. (Catholic Christendom, 1300-1700 Ser.). 228p. 124.95 (978-0-7546-5817-7(1)) Ashgate Publishing Co.

Twesigye, Emmanuel K. Religion, Politics & Cults in East Africa: God's Warriors & Saints. 2010. (Bible & Theology in Africa Ser.). 280p. (C). 78.95 (978-1-4331-0995-9(6)); pap. 39.95 (978-1-4331-1112-9(8)) Lang, Peter Publishing, Inc.

Upchurch, Thomas Adams. Christian Nation? The United States in Popular Perception & Historical Reality, 1 vol. 2010. 198p. 44.95 (978-0-313-38642-8(0), A3081C, Praeger Pubs.) Greenwood Publishing Group, Inc.

Utter, Glenn H. Mainline Christians & U. S. Public Policy: A Reference Handbook, 1 vol. 2007. (Contemporary World Issues Ser.). 336p. 55.00 (978-1-59884-000-1(2), MACHVA1C) ABC-CLIO, LLC.

Voorhis, Horace Jeremiah & Brooks, Phillips. The Christian in Politics. 2011. 146p. 40.95 (978-1-258-10090-2(8)) Literary Licensing, LLC.

Wallace, W. Jason. Catholics Slaveholders & Dilem. 2010. (ENG.). 208p. pap. 30.00 (978-0-268-04421-3(X)) Univ. of Notre Dame Pr.

Wallis, Jim. God's Politics: Why the Right Gets It Wrong & the Left Doesn't Get It. annot. ed. 2006. (Plus Ser.). (ENG.). 432p. pap. 14.99 (978-0-06-083447-0(1), HarperOne) HarperCollins Pubs.

—The Great Awakening: Seven Ways to Change the World. 2009. (ENG.). 352p. pap. 15.99 (978-0-06-144488-3(X), HarperOne) HarperCollins Pubs.

Walz, Jeffrey S. & Montreal, Steven R. Lutheran Pastors & Politics: Issues in the Public Square. 2007. (ENG.). 190p. per. 29.99 (978-0-7586-0046-2(1)) Concordia Publishing Hse.

Wampler, Dee. One Nation under God: A Trial Lawyer Exposes the Myth of the Separation Between Church & State. 2008. (Illus.). 24.99 (978-1-58169-284-6(6), Evergreen Pr.) Genesis Communications, Inc.

Ward, Graham. The Politics of Discipleship: Becoming Postmaterial Citizens. 2009. (Church & Postmodern Culture Ser.). 304p. (C). pap. 25.00 (978-0-8010-3158-8(3)) Baker Academic.

Warner, Tom & Between the Lines Staff. Losing Control: Canada's Social Conservatives in the Age of Rights. 2010. 300p. pap. 29.95 (978-1-897071-41-0(8)) Between the Lines CAN. Dist: Univ. of Toronto Pr.

Waterman, A. M. C. Revolution, Economics & Religion: Christian Political Economy, 1798-1833. 2006. (ENG., Illus.). 328p. pap. 69.00 (978-0-521-03038-0(2)) Cambridge Univ. Pr.

Waters, Brent. The Family in Christian Social & Political Thought. 2007. (Oxford Studies in Theological Ethics Ser.). (ENG.). 336p. 135.00 (978-0-19-927196-2(8)) Oxford Univ. Pr., Inc.

Weaver, Alain Epp. States of Exile: Visions of Diaspora, Witness, & Return. 2008. (Illus.). 215p. pap. 19.99 (978-0-8361-9422-7(5)) Herald Pr.

Webster, Phil. 1776 Faith. 2009. 236p. pap. 15.99 (978-1-61579-415-7(8)) Xulon Pr., Inc.

—1776 Faith: The Christian Worldview of the Signers of the Declaration of Independence. 2009. 236p. 25.99 (978-1-61579-425-6(5)) Xulon Pr., Inc.

Wilcox, Clyde & Robinson, Carin. Onward Christian Soldiers? The Religious Right in American Politics. 4th ed. 2010. (Dilemmas in American Politics Ser.). (ENG., Illus.). 264p. (C). pap. 32.00 (978-0-8133-4453-9(0)) Westview Pr.

Williams, Freya S. Pray Before You Vote: Jesus Is not a Democrat or a Republican. Jesus Is Lord! 2007. (ENG.). 196p. per. 14.99 (978-1-59755-117-5(1), Advantage Inspirational) Advantage Bks.

Wills, Garry. Bush's Fringe Government. 2006. (ENG.). 56p. pap. 7.95 (978-1-59017-210-6(8)) New York Review of Bks., Inc., The.

—Under God: Religion & American Politics. 2007. (ENG.). 448p. pap. 16.00 (978-1-4165-4335-0(X)) Simon & Schuster.

Wilsey, John D. One Nation under God? An Evangelical Critique of Christian America. 2011. 226p. pap. 25.00 (978-1-60899-792-3(8), Pickwick Pubns.) Wipf & Stock Pubs.

Wilson, J. Matthew, ed. From Pews to Polling Places: Faith & Politics in the American Religious Mosaic. 2007. (Religion & Politics Ser.). (ENG., Illus.). 336p. 49.95 (978-1-58901-173-1(2)); pap. 29.95 (978-1-58901-172-4(4)) Georgetown Univ. Pr.

Wilson, Michael. Death of a Politician. 2011. 224p. pap. 15.99 (978-1-61379-503-3(3)) Xulon Pr., Inc.

Winters, Michael Sean. God's Right Hand: How Jerry Falwell Made God a Republican & Baptized the American Right. 2012. (ENG.). 384p. 28.99 (978-0-06-197067-2(0), HarperOne) HarperCollins Pubs.

Wisnewski, Jesse. American Crossroads: The Intersection of Christianity & Democracy. 2011. 106p. pap. 13.00 (978-1-61097-607-7(X), Resource Pubns.) Wipf & Stock Pubs.

Wood, Philip. 'We have no king but Christ' Christian Political Thought in Greater Syria on the Eve of the Arab Conquest (C. 400-585) 2011. (ENG., Illus.). 350p. 110.00 (978-0-19-958849-7(X)) Oxford Univ. Pr., Inc.

Woodyard, David. The Church in the Time of Empire. 2011. (ENG.). 167p. pap. 16.95 (978-1-84694-595-3(X)) O Bks. John Hunt.

Woolley, Richard. The Ethical Foundations of Socialism: The Influence of William Temple & R.H. Tawney on New Labour. 2007. 228p. 109.95 (978-0-7734-5283-1(4)) Mellen, Edwin Pr., The.

Wright, George. Religion, Politics & Thomas Hobbes. 2010. (International Archives of the History of Ideas / archives internationales d'histoire des Idées Ser.). (Illus.). xiv, 357p. pap. 249.00 (978-90-481-7132-3(6), 9048171326) Springer.

Wright, Luke Savin Herrick. Samuel Taylor Coleridge & the Anglican Church. 2010. (ENG.). 312p. pap. 35.00 (978-0-268-04418-3(X)) Univ. of Notre Dame Pr.

Wright, Russell O. Chronology of Religious Life in America. 2009. (ENG.). 232p. pap. 35.00 (978-0-7864-4004-7(X)) McFarland & Co., Inc. Pubs.

Wüstenberg, Ralf K. The Political Dimension of Reconciliation: A Theological Analysis of Ways of Dealing with Guilt During the Transition to Democracy in South Africa & (East) Germany. Lundell, Randi H., tr. from GER. 2009. 458p. pap. 50.00 (978-0-8028-2824-8(8)) Eerdmans, William B. Publishing Co.

Wylie Kellermann, Bill. Seasons of Faith & Conscience: Explorations in Liturgical Direct Action. 2008. 246p. pap. 27.00 (978-1-55635-923-1(3), Wipf and Stock) Wipf & Stock Pubs.

Yoder, Nathan E. & Scheppard, Carol A. Exiles in the Empire: Believers Church Perspectives on Politics: Papers Presented at the Twelfth Believers Church Conference, September 2004. 266p. 25.75 (978-1-894710-68-8(1)) Pandora Pr. CAN. Dist: Herald Pr.

York, Tripp. Living on Hope While Living in Babylon: e Christian Anarchists of the 20th Century. 2009. (ENG.). 136p. pap. 42.50 (978-0-7188-9202-9(X)) Lutterworth Pr., The GBR. Dist: Brown, David Bk. Co., The.

—Living on Hope While Living in Babylon: The Christian Anarchists of the 20th Century. 2009. 138p. pap. 17.00 (978-1-55635-685-8(4), Wipf and Stock) Wipf & Stock Pubs.

Zafirovski, Milan. The Protestant Ethic & the Spirit of Authoritarianism: Puritanism, Democracy, & Society. (ENG., Illus.). xx, 337p. 2010. pap. 129.00 (978-1-4419-2381-3(0), 1441923810) 2007. 129.00 (978-0-387-49320-6(4), 0387493204) Springer.

Zieba, Maciej. Papal Economics: The Catholic Church on Democratic Capitalism, from Rerum Novarum to Caritas in Veritate. 2012. (Culture of Enterprise Ser.). (ENG.). 26.95 (978-1-933859-97-2(0)) ISI Bks.

CHRISTIANITY AND PROGRESS

see Progress—Religious Aspects—Christianity

CHRISTIANITY AND REVOLUTION

see Revolutions—Religious Aspects

CHRISTIANITY AND SCIENCE

see Religion and Science

CHRISTIANITY AND THE ARTS

see also Christianity and Literature

Ballian, Anna. Relics of the Past: Treasusres of the Greek Orthodox Church & the Population Exchange. 2011. (ENG & FRE., Illus.). 232p. pap. 42.50 (978-88-7439-575-0(2)) 5 Continents ITA. Dist: Hachette Bk. Group.

Barker, Sebastian, et al. Rowan Williams' Theology of Art & Other Essays. 2009. 87p. (978-0-7734-4861-2(6)) Mellen, Edwin Pr., The.

Bernier, Ronald R., ed. Beyond Belief. 2010. (Illus.). 150p. pap. 19.00 (978-1-60899-087-0(7), Pickwick Pubns.) Wipf & Stock Pubs.

Borromeo, Federico. Sacred Painting. Museum. 2010. (I Tatti Renaissance Library: 44). (LAT & ENG., Illus.). 336p. 29.95 (978-0-674-04758-7(3)) Harvard Univ. Pr.

Bosco, Louis. Images of the Unseen: The Mysteries of Life Revealed in Sacred Art. 2011. (978-0-8189-1336-5(3)) St Pauls.

Bradley, J. 'You Shall surely not Die' The Concepts of Sin & Death as Expressed in the Manuscript Art of Northwestern Europe, C. 800-1200, 2 vols. 2008. (Illus.). 448p. (978-90-04-16910-4(5)) BRILL.

Brown, David. God & Grace of Body: Sacrament in Ordinary. 2007. (ENG., Illus.). 464p. 75.00 (978-0-19-923182-9(6)) Oxford Univ. Pr., Inc.

Brown, Frank Burch. Inclusive yet Discerning: Navigating Worship Artfully. 2009. (Illus.). 176p. pap. 20.00 (978-0-8028-6256-3(X)) Eerdmans, William B. Publishing Co.

Brown, Kate. Sense of the Sacramental. (Illus.). 224p. 25.00 (978-0-281-04849-6(5)) SPCK Publishing GBR. Dist: Pilgrim Pr., The/United Church Pr.

Cavarnos, Constantine. Byzantine Sacred Art. 2011. 132p. 40.95 (978-1-258-06676-5(9)) Literary Licensing, LLC.

De Gruchy, John W. Christianity, Art & Transformation: Theological Aesthetics in the Struggle for Justice. 2008. (ENG., Illus.). 288p. pap. 41.00 (978-0-521-08950-0(6)) Cambridge Univ. Pr.

Drotz, Dallas. The Picture of Scripture. 2010. 67p. pap. 31.99 (978-0-557-70848-2(6)) Lulu Enterprises Inc.

Dyrness, William A. Senses of the Soul: Art & the Visual in Christian Worship. 2008. (Art for Faith's Sake: Ser.). 198p. pap. 23.00 (978-1-55635-864-7(4), Cascade Bks.) Wipf & Stock Pubs.

Eck, Xander van & Van Eck, Xander. Clandestine Splendor: Paintings for the Catholic Church in the Dutch Republic. 2008. (ENG., Illus.). 368p. 100.00 (978-90-400-8468-3(8)) Waanders B.V., Uitgeverij NLD. Dist: National Bk. Network.

Elwell, J. Sage. Crisis of Transcendence: A Theology of Digital Art & Culture. 2010. (ENG.). 210p. 60.00 (978-0-7391-4108-3(2)) Lexington Bks.

—Crisis of Transcendence: A Theology of Digital Art & Culture. 2011. E-Book (978-0-7391-4110-6(4)) Lexington Bks.

Forte, Bruno. The Portal of Beauty: Towards a Theology of Aesthetics. Glenday, David & McPartlan, Paul, trs. from ITA. 2008.Tr. of porta della bellezza: per un'estetica Teologica. 130p. pap. 30.00 (978-0-8028-3280-1(6)) Eerdmans, William B. Publishing Co.

Godawa, Brian. Word Pictures: Knowing God Through Story & Imagination, 1 vol. 2009. (ENG.). 208p. pap. 16.00 (978-0-8308-3709-0(4), IVP Bks.) InterVarsity Pr.

González-Andrieu, Cecilia. Bridge to Wonder: Art as a Gospel of Beauty. 2012. (ENG.). 250p. (C). 29.95 (978-1-60258-351-1(X)) Baylor Univ. Pr.

Horner, Grant. Meaning at the Movies: Becoming a Discerning Viewer. 2010. 224p. pap. 16.99 (978-1-4335-1228-5(9)) Crossway.

Horowitz, Deborah E., et al. Ethiopian Art. 2006. (ENG., Illus.). 30.00 (978-1-903942-02-4(0)) Third Millenium Publishing GBR. Dist: National Bk. Network.

Jasper, David. The Sacred Community: Art, Sacrament, & the People of God. 2012. (ENG., Illus.). 240p. 39.95 (978-1-60258-558-4(X)) Baylor Univ. Pr.

Jeffrey, David Lyle. Houses of the Interpreter: Reading Scripture, Reading Culture. 2009. (ENG.). 300p. (C). pap. 49.95 (978-1-60258-239-2(4)) Baylor Univ. Pr.

Jensen, Robin Margaret & Vrudny, Kimberly J. Visual Theology: Forming & Transforming the Community Through the Arts. 2009. pap. 39.95 (978-0-8146-5399-9(5)) Liturgical Pr.

Kirkpatrick, Katherine, editor. A Circle of Friends: Remembering Madeleine L'Engle (second Edition) 2010. 224p. pap. 20.00 (978-0-557-22788-4(7)) Lulu Enterprises Inc.

—A Circle of Friends: Remembering Madeleine L'Engle. 2010. 224p. pap. 74.00 (978-0-557-18532-0(7)) Lulu Enterprises Inc.

Krahn, Karmen & James, Leslie. Proclamation by Design: The Visual Arts in Worship. 2007. pap. (978-0-8361-9402-9(0)) Faith & Life Pr.

Kumler, Aden. Translating Truth: Ambitious Images & Religious Knowledge in Late Medieval France & England. 2011. (ENG., Illus.). 290p. 65.00 (978-0-300-16493-0(9)) Yale Univ. Pr.

Kupfer, Marcia, ed. The Passion Story: From Visual Representation to Social Drama. 2008. (ENG., Illus.). 272p. (C). 90.00 (978-0-271-03307-5(X)) Pennsylvania State Univ. Pr.

Kupfer, Marcia A. The Passion Story: From Visual Representation to Social Drama. 2011. (ENG.). 306p. pap. 44.95 (978-0-271-03343-3(6)) Pennsylvania State Univ. Pr.

Luz, Manuel. Imagine That: Discovering Your Unique Role as a Christian Artist. 2009. (ENG.). 184p. pap. 14.99 (978-0-8024-2450-1(3)) Moody Pubs.

Mochizuki, Mia M. The Netherlandish Image after Iconoclasm, 1566-1672: Material Religion in the Dutch Golden Age. 2008. (Illus.). 424p. 144.95 (978-0-7546-6104-7(0)) Ashgate Publishing Co.

Moffitt, John F. Painterly Perspective & Piety: Religious Uses of the Vanishing Point, from the 15th to the 18th Century. 2008. (ENG., Illus.). 320p. pap. 45.00 (978-0-7864-3505-0(4)) McFarland & Co., Inc. Pubs.

Moore, James W. Christianity & the Arts. pap. (978-0-86187-803-1(5), Thoemmes Continuum) Continuum International Publishing Group, Ltd.

Nichols, Aidan. Lost in Wonder: Essays on Liturgy & the Arts. 2011. 194p. 89.95 (978-1-4094-3161-9(4)) Ashgate Publishing Co.

Noble, Ivana. Theological Interpretation of Culture in Post-Communist Context: Central & East European Search for Roots. 2010. 242p. 99.95 (978-1-4094-0007-3(7)) Ashgate Publishing Co.

Noland, Rory. The Worshiping Artist: Equipping You & Your Ministry Team to Lead Others in Worship, 1 vol. 2007. (ENG., Illus.). 224p. pap. 18.99 (978-0-310-27334-9(X)) Zondervan.

Orenduff, Lai-Kent Chew. The Transformation of Catholic Religious Art in the Twentieth Century: Father Marie-Alain Couturier & the Church at Assy, France. 2008. (Illus.). 212p. 109.95 (978-0-7734-4985-5(X)) Mellen, Edwin Pr., The.

Pope Pius Xii & Pizzardo, Joseph. The Function of Art, Addresses of Pope Pius Xii: On Sacred Art, Instruction of the Supreme Sacred Congregation of the Holy Office. 2011. 12p. pap. 35.95 **(978-1-258-04844-0(2))** Literary Licensing, LLC.
Raguin, Virginia Chieffo. Art, Piety & Destruction in the Christian West, 1500-1700. 2010. (Visual Culture in Early Modernity Ser.). (Illus.). 238p. 109.95 *(978-0-7546-6946-3(7))* Ashgate Publishing Co.
Rook, Russell D. Rhyming Hope & History: Theology & Culture in the Work of Robert Jenson. 2011. 240p. pap. 26.00 **(978-1-60899-600-1(X)**, Pickwick Pubns.) Wipf & Stock Pubs.
Rookmaaker, Hans R. Art Needs No Justification. 2010. 64p. pap. *(978-1-57383-441-4(6))* Regent College Publishing.
Seerveld, Calvin. Rainbows for the Fallen World. pap. 16.99 *(978-1-900507-32-5(3))* Solway GBR. Dist: O. M. Literature.
Shaw, Luci. Breath for the Bones, 0 vols. 2009. 224p. pap. 13.99 *(978-0-8499-2964-9(4))* Nelson, Thomas Inc.
Spencer, William David & Spencer, Aida B. God Through the Looking Glass: Glimpses from the Arts. (Illus.). 208p. pap. 21.99 *(978-1-900507-85-1(4))* Solway GBR. Dist: O. M. Literature.
Sullivan, Michael. Windows into the Light: A Lenten Journey of Stories & Art. 2008. (Illus.). 144p. pap. 18.00 *(978-0-8192-2322-7(0)*, Morehouse Publishing) Church Publishing, Inc.
Taylor, W. David O., ed. For the Beauty of the Church: Casting a Vision for the Arts, 1 vol. 2010. (ENG.). 208p. pap. 15.99 *(978-0-8010-7191-1(7))* Baker Bks.
Todd, Matthew R. S. Historical Attitudes That Have Shaped the Church's Use of the Arts. 2010. 188p. pap. *(978-1-926676-68-5(8))* Word Alive Pr.
Treier, Daniel J., et al, eds. The Beauty of God: Theology & the Arts. 2007. (ENG., Illus.). 233p. per. 22.00 *(978-0-8308-2843-2(5)*, IVP Acad.) InterVarsity Pr.
Valters Paintner, Christine & Beckman, Betsey. Awakening the Creative Spirit: Bringing the Arts to Spiritual Direction. 2010. (Spiritual Directors International Ser.). 256p. pap. 24.00 *(978-0-8192-2371-5(9)*, Morehouse Publishing) Church Publishing, Inc.
Wooddell, Joseph D. The Beauty of the Faith: Using Aesthetics for Christian Apologetics. 2010. 130p. pap. 16.00 *(978-1-60608-195-2(0)*, Wipf and Stock) Wipf & Stock Pubs.

CHRISTIANITY AND THE WORLD
see Church and the World

CHRISTIANITY AND WAR
see War—Religious Aspects

CHRISTIANITY IN LITERATURE
Adelman, Janet. Blood Relations: Christian & Jew in the Merchant of Venice. 2008. 224p. 35.00 *(978-0-226-00681-9(6))* Univ. of Chicago Pr.
Atkins, G. Douglas. Literary Paths to Religious Understanding: Essays on Dryden, Pope, Keats, George Eliot, Joyce, T. S. Eliot, & E. B. White. 2009. (ENG.). 196p. 89.00 *(978-0-230-62147-3(3))* Palgrave Macmillan.
Barge, Laura Inez Deavenport. Exploring Worldviews in Literature: From William Wordsworth to Edward Albee. 2009. pap. 19.95 *(978-0-89112-538-9(8)*, ACU Pr.) Abilene Christian Univ. Pr.
Bell, Luke. Baptizing Harry Potter: A Christian Reading of J. K. Rowling. 2010. (Illus.). 240p. pap. 16.00 *(978-1-58768-058-8(0)*, HiddenSpring) Paulist Pr.
Bell, Shirley. The Da Vinci Code: the Background Explained. 2008. 135p. pap. 15.95 *(978-1-84799-638-1(8))* Lulu Enterprises Inc.
Brown, Kevin. They Love to Tell the Story: Five Contemporary Novelists Take on the Gospels. 2008. *(978-1-933483-15-3(6))* Kennesaw State Univ. Pr.
Bueno, Lorenzo Fernandez & Urresti, Mariano Fernandez. Keys to the Da Vinci Code: The Hidden Lineage of Jesus & Other Mysteries. 2010. (Illus.). 188p. 19.95 *(978-1-59079-101-1(0))* Select Bks.
Burstein, Dan & De Keijzer, Arne. Inside Angels & Demons: The Story Behind the International Bestseller. 2009. (ENG.). 544p. 7.99 *(978-1-59315-489-9(5))* Vanguard Pr.
Callow, Simon. Dickens' Christmas: A Victorian Celebration. 2009. (ENG., Illus.). 160p. pap. 19.95 *(978-0-7112-3031-6(5))* Lincoln, Frances Ltd. GBR. Dist: Perseus-PGW.
Carpentier Brown, Nancy. The Mystery of Harry Potter: A Catholic Family Guide. 2007. (Illus.). 175p. per. 12.95 *(978-1-59276-398-6(7))* Our Sunday Visitor, Publishing Div.
Chernaik, Warren L. The Poet's Time: Politics & Religion in the Work of Andrew Marvell. 2010. (ENG.). 260p. pap. 38.99 *(978-0-521-12933-6(8))* Cambridge Univ. Pr.
Clarke, Peter & Methuen, Charlotte, eds. The Church & Literature. 2012. (Studies in Church History Ser.: Volume 48). (Illus.). 528p. 80.00 **(978-0-9546809-9-2(5))** Ecclesiastical History Society GBR. Dist: Boydell & Brewer, Inc.
Colon, Susan E. Victorian Parables. 2012. (New Directions in Religion & Literature Ser.). (ENG.). 176p. 100.00 *(978-0-8264-4348-9(6))*; pap. 29.95 *(978-1-4411-4650-2(4))* Continuum International Publishing Group, Ltd. GBR. Dist: National Bk. Network.
Crowe, Marian E. Aiming at Heaven, Getting the Earth: The English Catholic Novel Today. 2007. (ENG.). 420p. 120.99 *(978-0-7391-1640-1(1))*; per. 40.99 *(978-0-7391-1641-8(X))* Lexington Bks.
Davies, Trevor H. Spiritual Voices in Modern Literature. 2009. 312p. 32.99 *(978-1-113-90316-7(3))* BiblioBazaar.
—Spiritual Voices in Modern Literature. 2009. 118p. pap. *(978-0-217-55990-4(5))* Books LLC.
—Spiritual Voices in Modern Literature. 2008. 310p. 45.95 *(978-1-4365-6112-9(4))* 2007. (ENG.). 312p. per. 30.95 *(978-0-548-75165-7(X))* Kessinger Publishing, LLC.
—Spiritual Voices in Modern Literature. 2007. (ENG.). 312p. per. *(978-1-4067-7116-9(3))* Read Bks.
De Souza, Francis. Shredding the Da Vinci Code & Vindicating the Deity of Christ. 2007. 340p. per. 12.95 *(978-1-4327-0496-4(6))* Outskirts Pr., Inc.
Dillon, John F. & McKeel, William J. Response to the DaVinci Code As Impression Management. 2007. (ENG.). 172p. (C). 94.95 *(978-1-934043-68-4(0))* Cambria Pr.
Field, Rosalind, et al, eds. Christianity & Romance in Medieval England. 2010. (Christianity & Culture: Issues in Teaching/Research Ser.: Volume 3). (Illus.). 226p. 90.00 *(978-1-84384-219-4(X)*, D. S. Brewer) Boydell & Brewer, Ltd. GBR. Dist: Boydell & Brewer, Inc.
Fussell, Edwin Sill. The Catholic Side of Henry James. 2009. (Cambridge Studies in American Literature & Culture Ser.). (ENG.). 192p. pap. 33.00 *(978-0-521-10658-8(5))* Cambridge Univ. Pr.
Gandolfo, Anita. Faith & Fiction: Christian Literature in America Today, 1 vol. 2007. 208p. 44.95 *(978-0-275-99196-8(2)*, C9196, Praeger Pubs.) Greenwood Publishing Group, Inc.
Garrett, Greg. One Fine Potion: The Literary Magic of Harry Potter. 2010. (ENG.). 160p. pap. 19.95 *(978-1-60258-198-2(3))* Baylor Univ. Pr.
Granger, John. How Harry Cast His Spell: The Meaning Behind the Mania for J. K. Rowling's Bestselling Books. 3rd ed. 2008. (ENG.). 304p. pap. 14.99 *(978-1-4143-2188-2(0)*, SaltRiver) Tyndale Hse. Pubs.
Gray, F. Elizabeth. Christian & Lyric Tradition in Victorian Women's Poetry. 2009. (Routledge Studies in Nineteenth Century Literature Ser.). (ENG.). 274p. (C). 125.00 *(978-0-415-80586-5(4))* Routledge.
Hassel, R. Chris, Jr. Faith & Folly in Shakespeare's Romantic Comedies. 2011. (ENG.). 272p. pap. 24.95 **(978-0-8203-3853-8(2))** Univ. of Georgia Pr.
Henky, Daniele & Hurley, Robert, eds. Traces de spiritualité en littérature de Jeunesse. 2009. (Recherches en littérature et spiritualité Ser.: Vol. 16). (FRE, GER & ENG., Illus.). 213p. pap. *(978-3-0343-0018-6(2))* Lang, Peter.
Ingram, John. Beyond Da Vinci: The True Bride of Christ. 2010. 156p. pap. 22.49 *(978-1-4520-2327-4(1))* AuthorHouse.
Jasper, David, ed. Postmodernism, Literature, & the Future of Theology. 2009. (David Jasper Reprint Ser.). 204p. pap. 23.00 *(978-1-60608-829-6(7)*, Wipf and Stock) Wipf & Stock Pubs.
Jasper, David & Allen, Smith. Between Truth & Fiction: A Narrative Reader in Literature & Theology. 2010. (ENG.). 300p. pap. 55.00 *(978-0-334-04192-4(9)*, SCM Pr.) Hymns Ancient & Modern Ltd GBR. Dist: Westminster John Knox Pr.
Jasper, David & Crowder, Colin, eds. European Literature & Theology in the Twentieth Century. 2009. (David Jasper Reprint Ser.). 202p. pap. 23.00 *(978-1-60608-830-2(0)*, Wipf and Stock) Wipf & Stock Pubs.
Jasper, David & Smith, Allen, eds. Between Truth & Fiction: A Narrative Reader in Literature & Theology. 2010. (ENG.). 192p. (C). pap. 39.95 *(978-1-60258-319-1(6))* Baylor Univ. Pr.
Jeffrey, David Lyle & Maillet, Gregory P. Christianity & Literature: Philosophical Foundations & Critical Practice. 2011. (Christian Worldview Integration Ser.). (ENG.). 336p. pap. 24.00 *(978-0-8308-2817-3(6)*, IVP Acad.) InterVarsity Pr.
Kephart, Christine. The Catherian Cathedral: Gothic Cathedral Iconography in Willa Cather's Fiction. 2011. (ENG., Illus.). 164p. 60.00 *(978-1-61147-016-1(1))* Fairleigh Dickinson Univ. Pr.
Kerry, Paul E. The Ring & the Cross: Christianity & the Lord of the Rings. 2010. (ENG.). 310p. 80.00 *(978-1-61147-064-2(1))* Fairleigh Dickinson Univ. Pr.
—The Ring & the Cross: Christianity & the Writings of J.R.R Tolkien. 2010. *(978-0-8386-4224-5(1))* Fairleigh Dickinson Univ. Pr.
King, Walter N. Hamlet's Search for Meaning. 2011. (ENG.). 192p. pap. 22.95 *(978-0-8203-3855-2(9))* Univ. of Georgia Pr.
Mahan, David C. An Unexpected Light: Theology & Witness in the Poetry of Charles Williams, Micheal O'Siadhail, & Geoffrey Hill. 2010. (ENG.). 246p. pap. 42.50 *(978-0-227-17336-7(8))* Clarke, James Co., Ltd. GBR. Dist: Brown, David Bk. Co., The.
Matthews, Honor. Character & Symbol in Shakespeare's Plays: A Study of Certain Christian & Pre-Christian Elements in Their Structure & Imagery. 2009. (Cambridge Library Collection - Literary Studies). (ENG.). 224p. pap. 22.99 *(978-1-108-00235-6(8))* Cambridge Univ. Pr.
McInnis, Jeff. Shadows & Chivalry: C. S. Lewis & George MacDonald on Suffering, Evil, & Goodness. 2008. (Studies in Christian History & Thought Ser.). 332p. pap. 39.00 *(978-1-55635-665-0(X))* Wipf & Stock Pubs.
McInnis, Jeff, ed. Shadows & Chivalry: C.S. Lewis & George MacDonald on Suffering, Evil, & Goodness. 2007. (Studies in Christian History & Thought Ser.). 307p. pap. 33.99 *(978-1-84227-430-9(9)*, Paternoster) Authentic Media.
McMullen, Joanne Halleran & Peede, Jon Parrish, eds. Inside the Church of Flannery O'Connor: Sacrament, Sacramental, & the Sacred in Her Fiction. 2008. 232p. pap. 22.95 *(978-0-88146-138-1(5))* Mercer Univ. Pr.
Middleton, Darren J. N. Broken Hallelujah: Nikos Kazantzakis & Christian Theology. 2006. (ENG.). 174p. 78.99 *(978-0-7391-1927-3(3))* Lexington Bks.
Middleton, Darren J. N., ed. Mother Tongue Theologies. 2009. 252p. pap. 28.00 *(978-1-55635-965-1(9)*, Pickwick Pubns.) Wipf & Stock Pubs.
Murray, Molly. The Poetics of Conversion in Early Modern English Literature: Verse & Change from Donne to Dryden. 2011. (ENG.). 218p. pap. 45.00 *(978-1-107-40282-9(4))* Cambridge Univ. Pr.
Nicola, Metropolitan Bishoy. The Real Holy Grail: An Orthodox Response to Dan Brown's Deceptions in Angles & Demons & the Da Vinci Code. 2007. 188p. per. 15.95 *(978-1-933275-14-7(6)*, Orthodox Research Institute) Cocheco Falls Publishing.
Olson, Roger E. Finding God in the Shack: Seeking Truth in a Story of Evil & Redemption, 1 vol. 2009. (ENG.). 160p. pap. 15.00 *(978-0-8308-3708-3(6)*, IVP Bks.) InterVarsity Pr.
Perkin, J. Russell. Theology & the Victorian Novel. 2009. (ENG.). 273p. (C). *(978-0-7735-3606-7(X))* McGill-Queen's Univ. Pr.
Persaud, Christopher H. K. The Da Vinci Code Revisited: A conclusive refutation of the sinister, widespread Lie. 2010. 346p. 29.99 *(978-1-4500-3488-3(8))*; pap. 19.99 *(978-1-4500-3487-6(X))* Xlibris Corp.
Roe, Dinah. Christina Rossetti's Faithful Imagination: The Devotional Poetry & Prose. annot. ed. 2007. (ENG.). 248p. 84.00 *(978-0-230-00507-5(1))* Palgrave Macmillan.
Rogers, Tom. 'God of Rescue' John Berryman & Christianity. 2011. 435p. pap. 82.95 *(978-3-03910-748-3(8))* Lang, Peter AG GBR. Dist: Lang, Peter.
Root, Jerry. C. S. Lewis & a Problem of Evil: An Investigation of a Pervasive Theme. 2010. (ENG.). 284p. (C). pap. 48.00 *(978-0-227-17338-1(4))* Clarke, James Co., Ltd. GBR. Dist: Brown, David Bk. Co., The.
—C. S. Lewis & a Problem of Evil: An Investigation of a Pervasive Theme. 2008. (Princeton Theological Monographs). 308p. pap. 32.00 *(978-1-55635-720-6(6)*, Pickwick Pubns.) Wipf & Stock Pubs.
Rossow, Francis C. Gospel Patterns in Literature: Familiar Truths in Unexpected Places. 2008. (ENG.). 194p. pap. 16.00 *(978-1-932688-31-3(5)*, Lutheran Univ. Pr.) Kirk Hse. Pubs.
Ryken, Leland & Mead, Marjorie Lamp. A Reader's Guide to Caspian: A Journey into C. S. Lewis's Narnia. 2008. (ENG., Illus.). 172p. pap. 15.00 *(978-0-8308-3499-0(0)*, IVP Bks.) InterVarsity Pr.
Shullenberger, William. Lady in the Labyrinth: Milton's Comus as Initiation. 2008. (ENG.). 360p. 67.50 *(978-1-61147-387-2(X))*; 361p. 67.50 *(978-0-8386-4174-3(1))* Fairleigh Dickinson Univ. Pr.
Spencer, Michael. Understanding Four Quartets as a Religious Poem: How T.S. Eliot Uses Symbols & Rhythms to Plumb Mystical Meaning. 2008. 148p. 99.95 *(978-0-7734-5058-5(0))* Mellen, Edwin Pr., The.
Srigley, Ronald D. Albert Camus' Critique of Modernity. 2011. (ENG., Illus.). 202p. (C). (gr. 13). 60.00 *(978-0-8262-1924-4(1))* Univ. of Missouri Pr.
Srigley, Susan, ed. Dark Faith: New Essays on Flannery O'Connor's the Violent Bear It Away. 2012. (ENG.). 232p. pap. 28.00 **(978-0-268-04138-0(5))** Univ. of Notre Dame Pr.
Stevens, Jennifer. The Historical Jesus & the Literary Imagination 1860-1920. 2010. (Liverpool University Press - English Association Monographs). (ENG.). 312p. 95.00 *(978-1-84631-470-4(4))* Liverpool Univ. Pr. GBR. Dist: Chicago Distribution Ctr.
Tate, Andrew. Contemporary Fiction & Christianity. 2010. (Continuum Literary Studies). (ENG.). 168p. 44.95 *(978-1-4411-6175-8(9))* Continuum International Publishing Group, Ltd. GBR. Dist: National Bk. Network.
Theodorou, George. Black & White, & Brown: The Da Vinci Code Deception. 2006. 96p. pap. 15.95 *(978-1-59800-577-6(4))* Outskirts Pr., Inc.
Thompson, Diane Oenning. The Brothers Karamazov & the Poetics of Memory. 2009. (Cambridge Studies in Russian Literature Ser.). (ENG.). 380p. pap. 42.00 *(978-0-521-11147-8(1))* Cambridge Univ. Pr.
Vahanian, Gabriel. Wait Without Idols. 2010. 256p. pap. 28.00 *(978-1-60899-148-8(2)*, Wipf and Stock) Wipf & Stock Pubs.
Valkeakari, Tuire. Religious Idiom & the African American Novel, 1952-1998. 2007. (ENG.). 272p. 59.95 *(978-0-8130-3055-5(2))* Univ. Pr. of Florida.
Vere, Pete & Miesel, Sandra. Pied Piper of Atheism: Philip Pullman & Children's Fantasy. 2008. 104p. per. 9.95 *(978-1-58617-255-8(7))* Ignatius Pr.
Ware, Jim. Finding God in the Hobbit. 2006. (ENG.). 208p. 14.99 *(978-1-4143-0596-7(6)*, SaltRiver) Tyndale Hse. Pubs.
Wetmore, Kevin J., ed. Catholic Theatre & Drama: Critical Essays. 2010. (ENG., Illus.). 235p. pap. 55.00 *(978-0-7864-4741-1(9))* McFarland & Co., Inc. Pubs.
White, Laura Mooneyham. Jane Austen's Anglicanism. 2011. (Illus.). 228p. 89.95 *(978-1-4094-1863-4(4))* Ashgate Publishing Co.
Williams, Thomas. Following Prince Caspian: Further Encounters with the Lion of Narnia, 0 vols. 2008. 64p. pap. 2.99 *(978-0-8499-1997-8(5))* Nelson, Thomas Inc.
Wilson, Douglas & Miller, Jared. What I Learned in Narnia. 2011. (J). pap. *(978-1-59128-079-8(6))* Canon Pr.
Wood, Ralph C. Chesterton: The Nightmare Goodness of God. 2011. (Making of Christian Imagination Ser.). (ENG.). 358p. 34.95 *(978-1-60258-161-6(4))* Baylor Univ. Pr.
Yeager, Robert F. On John Gower: Essays at the Millennium. 2006. (Studies in Medieval Culture). 40.00 *(978-1-58044-098-1(3))*; 20.00 *(978-1-58044-099-8(1))* Medieval Institute Pubns.

CHRISTIANS
see also Catholics; Jewish Christians; Nuns; Protestants
Abbas & Abbas. Children of Abraham/les Enfants D'Abraham. 2007. (ENG & FRE., Illus.). 239p. pap. *(978-2-916355-01-6(4))* Editions Intervalles.
Arthur, James, et al. Education, Politics & Religion: Reconciling the Civic & the Sacred in Education. 2010. (ENG., Illus.). 176p. (C). pap. 39.95 *(978-0-415-56549-3(9))* Routledge.
—Education Politics & Religion Arthur: Reconciling the Civil & the Sacred in Education. 2010. (ENG., Illus.). 176p. (C). 120.00 *(978-0-415-56548-6(0)*, Routledge) Taylor & Francis Group GBR. Dist: Taylor & Francis Group.
Ascough, Richard S., et al. Associations in the Greco-Roman World: A Sourcebook. 2012. (ENG., Illus.). 430p. (C). pap. 39.95 **(978-1-60258-374-0(9))** Baylor Univ. Pr.
Beckwith, Francis J. Politics for Christians: Statecraft as Soulcraft. 2010. (Christian Worldview Integration Ser.). (ENG.). 175p. pap. 18.00 *(978-0-8308-2814-2(1)*, IVP Acad.) InterVarsity Pr.
Bell, Michel A. The New Managing God's Money: The Basics: Become a Good Manager of God's Resources. 3rd ed. 2007. (Illus.). 422p. 20.00 *(978-0-9735902-2-7(X))* Bell, Michel A. CAN. Dist: WinePress Publishing.
Blumhofer. People of Faith: A History of Western Christianity a History of Western Christianity. 2010. (ENG.). 272p. 69.95 *(978-1-4051-3248-0(5))*; pap. 26.95 *(978-1-4051-3249-7(3))* Wiley, John & Sons, Inc. (Wiley-Blackwell).
Brandt, Gareth. Under Construction: Reframing Men's Spirituality. 2009. (Illus.). 225p. 13.99 **(978-0-8361-9502-6(7))** Herald Pr.
Bretherton, Luke. Christianity & Contemporary Politics: The Conditions & Possibilites of Faithful Witness. 2010. (ENG.). 272p. 99.95 *(978-1-4051-9968-1(7))*; pap. 42.95 *(978-1-4051-9969-8(5))* Wiley, John & Sons, Inc. (Wiley-Blackwell).
Brinton, Henry G. The Welcoming Congregation: Roots & Fruits of Christian Hospitality. 2012. (ENG.). 152p. pap. 17.00 **(978-0-664-23700-4(2))** Westminster John Knox Pr.
Burchett, Author Walter, BA. Heavenly angel lay lay explains the difference between a cold christian & a Backslider. 2007. 49p. pap. 14.95 *(978-0-615-17483-9(3))* Crossover Ministries.
Burdette, Dallas R. Old Texts Through New Eyes. 2009. 504p. 36.99 *(978-1-60791-379-5(8))*; pap. 24.99 *(978-1-60791-377-1(1))* Xulon Pr., Inc.
Chandler, Floyd Vernon. Beyond the Grave. 2009. 206p. pap. 23.00 *(978-1-60608-938-5(2)*, Resource Pubns.) Wipf & Stock Pubs.
College 101: Campus Life for Christians. 2010. 224p. pap. 9.99 *(978-0-7586-1906-8(5))* Concordia Publishing Hse.
Crosson, Russ. Eight Important Money Decisions for Every Couple. 2012. pap. **(978-0-7369-4622-3(5))** Harvest Hse. Pubs.
Denton, William. Who Are Christians? a Discourse, Delivered in Music Hall, Boston, Mass., by William Denton. 2011. 34p. pap. 11.99 **(978-1-4181-9449-9(2))** MPublishing.
Djupe, Paul A. & Gilbert, Christopher P. The Political Influence of Churches. 2008. (Cambridge Studies in Social Theory, Religion & Politics Ser.). (ENG., Illus.). 294p. 88.00 *(978-0-521-87165-5(4))*; pap. 23.99 *(978-0-521-69219-9(9))* Cambridge Univ. Pr.
Duncan, Michael. Starting Out: A Study Guide for New Believers. 2010. 192p. pap. 16.99 *(978-1-4141-1780-5(9))* Pleasant Word.
Dungy, Tony & Whitaker, Nathan. UnCommon: Finding Your Path to Significance. l.t. ed. 2011. 393p. 30.99 *(978-1-4104-3380-0(3))* Thorndike Pr.
Eldredge, John. Fathered by God: Learning What Your Dad Could Never Teach You, 0 vols. 2009. 240p. pap. 15.99 *(978-1-4002-8027-8(3))* Nelson, Thomas Inc.
English, Don. Alpha, Omega, Alpha. 2010. pap. 17.99 *(978-1-61566-909-7(4))* Tate Publishing & Enterprises, LLC.
Faxon, Darrel. So What if Christians Lose the Culture War? 2006. (ENG.). 168p. per. 15.99 *(978-1-4141-0689-2(0))* Pleasant Word.
Fierbaugh, Stephen. Surviving Celibacy. 2009. 162p. pap. 15.98 *(978-0-578-04608-2(3))* Fierbaugh, Stephen.
Fusco, Daniel. Ahead of the Curve: Preparing the Church for Post-Postmodernism. 2011. pap. 9.99 *(978-1-61739-441-6(6))* Tate Publishing & Enterprises, LLC.
Gerloff, Roswith I. H. A Plea for British Black Theologies, 2 Volumes: The Black Church Movement in Britain in Its Transatlantic Cultural & Theological Interaction with Special Reference to the Pentecostal Oneness (Apostolic) & Sabbatarian Movements. 2010. 1130p. pap. 135.00 *(978-1-60899-667-4(0)*, Wipf and Stock) Wipf & Stock Pubs.
—A Plea for British Black Theologies, Volume 1: The Black Church Movement in Britain in Its Transatlantic Cultural & Theological Interaction with Special Reference to the Pentecostal Oneness (Apostolic) & Sabbatarian Movements. 2010. 466p. pap. 61.00 *(978-1-60899-665-0(4)*, Wipf and Stock) Wipf & Stock Pubs.
—A Plea for British Black Theologies, Volume 2: The Black Church Movement in Britain in Its Transatlantic Cultural & Theological Interaction with Special Reference to the Pentecostal Oneness (Apostolic) & Sabbatarian Movements. 2010. 678p. pap. 75.00 *(978-1-60899-666-7(2)*, Wipf and Stock) Wipf & Stock Pubs.
Green, Tony A. D. Twelve Reasons Christians Don't Grow Even in Good Churches! 2007. 116p. (ENG.). 18.99 *(978-1-60266-925-3(2))*; per. 10.99 *(978-1-60266-924-6(4))* Xulon Pr., Inc.
Groseclose, Win. No Nice Christians! 2010. (ENG.). 150p. pap. 12.49 *(978-0-557-39378-7(7))* Lulu Enterprises Inc.
Gross, Artie. In the Light of Scripture: Why Christians Shouldn't Vote for Liberals. 2008. pap. 14.99 *(978-1-60604-787-3(6))* Tate Publishing & Enterprises, LLC.
Herrera, Robert A. Mystics in Spite of Themselves: Four Saints & the Worlds They Didn't Leave. 2010. 136p. pap. 12.99 *(978-0-8028-4861-1(3))* Eerdmans, William B. Publishing Co.
Hobbs, Reginald. A Biblical Perspective on the First African-American President. 2009. 68p. pap. 10.49 *(978-1-4389-7867-3(7))* AuthorHouse.
Holum, Kenneth G. & Lapin, Hayim. Shaping the Middle East: Jews, Christians, & Muslims in an Age of Transition, 400-800 C.E. 2011. *(978-1-934309-31-5(1))* Univ. Pr. of Maryland.

C

Houston, James M. Letters of Faith Through the Seasons Vol. 1: A Treasury of Great Christian's Correspondence. 2006. (ENG.). 333p. 19.99 *(978-1-56292-749-3(3)*, 1562927493) Cook, David C.

Jacobsen, Douglas. The World's Christians: Who They Are, Where They Are, & How They Got There. 2011. (ENG., Illus.). 416p. 94.95 *(978-1-4051-8889-0(8)*, Wiley-Blackwell) Wiley, John & Sons, Inc.

Jibben, Ken. Emerge: Leaders to Continue a Life of Vision & Purpose. 2009. 198p. pap. 13.95 *(978-1-4327-3951-5(4))* Outskirts Pr., Inc.

Kanshimike, Wellington. When God Made an Opportunity Cost: The Economy of God's Love. 2009. (J). pap. 14.99 *(978-1-60696-499-6(2))* Tate Publishing & Enterprises, LLC.

Kemodle, Peter Jefferson. Lives of Christian Ministers. 2009. 494p. 53.95 *(978-1-120-38888-9(0))*; pap. 38.95 *(978-1-120-31878-7(5))* Kessinger Publishing, LLC.

Kiraz, George, ed. Hugoye: Journal of Syriac Studies. 2010. pap. 77.00 *(978-1-60724-672-5(4))* Gorgias Pr., LLC.

Kitchen, Robert. The Syriac Book of Steps: Syriac Text & English Translation. 2008. (Texts from Christian Late Antiquity: 12). pap. 52.00 *(978-1-59333-978-4(X))* Gorgias Pr., LLC.

Klemp, Nathaniel J. The Morality of Spin: Virtue & Vice in Political Rhetoric & the Christian Right. 2012. ***(978-1-4422-1054-7(0))***; (ENG.). 210p. (gr. 17). 70.00 ***(978-1-4422-1052-3(4))*** Rowman & Littlefield Publishers, Inc.

Kuehne, Dale S. Sex & the iWorld: Rethinking Relationship Beyond an Age of Individualism. 2009. 160p. (C). pap. 19.99 *(978-0-8010-3587-6(2))* Baker Academic.

Kuzma, Kay & Walsh, Brenda. Prayer Promises for Kids: More Than 100 Promises to Pray, Claim, & Believe. 2009. (J). 11.99 *(978-0-8163-2343-2(7))* Pacific Pr. Publishing Assn.

Lanzano, Stanley F. True Places: A Lowcountry Preacher, His Church, & His People. 2009. (ENG.). 124p. 19.95 *(978-1-57003-851-8(1))* Univ. of South Carolina Pr.

Lyda, Ed. Final Approach: Why Did America Turn Against God? 2010. pap. 11.99 *(978-1-61579-820-9(X))* Xulon Pr., Inc.

Madsen, Louise. Christian Community: An Introduction. 40p. pap. 3.95 *(978-0-86315-220-7(1)*, 1913) Floris Bks. GBR. Dist: SteinerBooks, Inc.

Maso, Gerson. Through the Valley: The Journey of an African Refugee. 2011. 108p. pap. 11.95 ***(978-1-61507-860-8(6))*** Cross Bks. Publishing.

Massey, M. F. Narcoleptic Church: Home of Slumbering Saints. 2010. pap. 11.99 *(978-1-61566-097-1(6))* Tate Publishing & Enterprises, LLC.

May, Melanie A. Jerusalem Testament: Palestinian Christians Speak, 1988-2008. 2009. 176p. pap. 22.00 *(978-0-8028-6485-7(6))* Eerdmans, William B. Publishing Co.

Moyer, R. Larry. 31 Days to Living as a New Believer, 1 vol. 2009. 112p. pap. 9.99 *(978-0-8254-3571-3(4))* Kregel Pubns.

Naaman, Paul. The Maronites: The Origins of an Antiochene Church: A Historical & Geographical Study of the Fifth to Seventh Centuries. 2011. pap. 24.95 *(978-0-87907-243-8(1))* Cistercian Pubns., Inc.

Nevada Lister-Kassa. Planting a Seed of Faith. 2009. 56p. pap. 9.95 *(978-1-4401-8534-2(4))* iUniverse, Inc.

Oosting, Kenneth W. The Christian's Guide to Effective Personal Management, Second Edition. 2009. 252p. pap. 28.00 *(978-1-55635-110-5(0)*, Wipf and Stock) Wipf & Stock Pubs.

Pecknold, C. C. Christianity & Politics. 2010. (Cascade Companions Ser.). 196p. pap. 23.00 *(978-1-55635-242-3(5)*, Cascade Bks.) Wipf & Stock Pubs.

Pelton, Robert W. America A Christian Nation? Here Are the Facts. 2008. 328p. pap. 16.95 *(978-0-7414-3777-8(5))* Infinity Publishing.

Perkins, Bill. Seis Batallas Que Todo Hombre Debe Ganar: Y los Antiguos Secretos para Triunfar. 2008. Orig. Title: Six Battles Every Man Must Win. (SPA.). 144p. pap. 9.99 *(978-1-4143-2397-8(2)*, Tyndale Espanol) Tyndale Hse. Pubs.

Phillips, Richard D. The Masculine Mandate: God's Calling to Men. 2009. *(978-1-56769-120-7(X))* Reformation Pubs.

Purcell, Joan M. Memoirs of a Woman in Politics: Spiritual Struggle. 2009. 316p. pap. 15.99 *(978-1-4389-0468-9(1))* AuthorHouse.

Riley-Smith, Jonathan & Riley-Smith, Jonathan Simon Christopher. Crusaders & Settlers in the Latin East. 2008. (Variorum Collected Studies). (Illus.). 378p. 165.00 *(978-0-7546-5967-9(4))* Ashgate Publishing Co.

Robertson, Brandan. To the Beat of a Different Drum. . 2009. 70p. pap. 10.80 *(978-0-557-14699-4(2))* Lulu Enterprises Inc.

Rock, Stephen. Faith & Foreign Policy: The Views & Influence of U. S. Christians & Christian Organizations. 2011. (ENG., Illus.). 232p. 100.00 *(978-0-8264-2030-5(3))*; pap. 29.95 *(978-0-8264-2320-7(5))* Continuum International Publishing Group, Ltd. GBR. Dist: National Bk. Network.

Rote, Kyle, Jr. & Pettigrew, Ph.D., Joe. Living Life in the Zone: A 40-Day Spiritual Gameplan for Men, 0 vols. 2009. 352p. pap. 14.99 *(978-0-8499-4652-3(2))* Nelson, Thomas Inc.

Russell, Paul S. Making Your Life a Christian Life: The Desert Fathers & St Francis of Assisi as Guides. 2009. 304p. pap. 15.95 *(978-1-4389-2338-3(4))* AuthorHouse.

Sharpe, Sally. 365 More Meditations for Teens. 2009. 283p. pap. 16.00 *(978-1-4267-0258-7(2))* Abingdon Pr.

Shires, Preston. Hippies of the Religious Right. 2007. (ENG.). 275p. per. 29.95 *(978-1-932792-57-7(0))* Baylor Univ. Pr.

Sigloh, Jane. Like Trees Walking: In the Second Half of Life. 2007. (ENG.). 144p. per. 13.95 *(978-1-56101-290-9(4))* Cowley Pubns.

Smith, Christian, et al. Passing the Plate: Why American Christians Don't Give Away More Money. 2008. (ENG., Illus.). 240p. 24.95 *(978-0-19-533711-2(5))* Oxford Univ. Pr., Inc.

Smith, Leonard. The Unitarians: A Short History. 2nd ed. 2008. (Illus.). 208p. pap. 25.00 *(978-0-9816402-0-4(6))* Blackstone Editions.

Smith, Winston T. Help! My Spouse Committed Adultery: First Steps for Dealing with Betrayal. 2008. 24p. 3.99 *(978-1-934885-38-3(X))* New Growth Pr.

Spykerman, Stephen J. Christians & Jews - the Two Faces of Israel. 2010. 228p. pap. 15.99 *(978-1-60957-539-7(3))* Xulon Pr., Inc.

Standard Publishing Staff. F3 Name Tag: A family event for your Church. 2009. (F3: Faith, Fun, Family Ser.). (ENG.). (J). 4.99 *(978-0-7847-2311-1(7))* Standard Publishing.

—Huddle up Family Cards: A family event for your Church. 2009. (F3: Faith, Fun, Family Ser.). (ENG.). (J). 2.99 *(978-0-7847-2334-0(6))* Standard Publishing.

—Huddle up Placemats: A family event for your Church. 2009. (F3: Faith, Fun, Family Ser.). (ENG.). (J). 4.99 *(978-0-7847-2308-1(7))* Standard Publishing.

—Huddle up Rubber Stamp: A family event for your Church. 2009. (F3: Faith, Fun, Family Ser.). (ENG.). (J). 1.99 *(978-0-7847-2309-8(5))* Standard Publishing.

—Outback Adventure Family Cards: A family event for your Church. 2009. (F3: Faith, Fun, Family Ser.). (ENG.). (J). 2.99 *(978-0-7847-2310-4(9))* Standard Publishing.

—Outback Adventure Placemats: A family event for your Church. 2009. (F3: Faith, Fun, Family Ser.). (ENG.). (J). 4.99 *(978-0-7847-2306-7(0))* Standard Publishing.

—Outback Adventure Rubber Stamp: A family event for your Church. 2009. (F3: Faith, Fun, Family Ser.). (ENG.). (J). 1.99 *(978-0-7847-2307-4(9))* Standard Publishing.

—Top Secret Family Cards: A family event for your Church. 2009. (F3: Faith, Fun, Family Ser.). (ENG.). (J). 2.99 *(978-0-7847-2312-8(5))* Standard Publishing.

Sunami, Christopher. Hero for Christ: 30 Ways to Be More Like Mother Teresa, Martin Luther King, Jr. , & Twenty Other World-Changing Christians. 2008. (Illus.). 256p. pap. 16.95 *(978-0-9702438-2-9(0)*, Kitoba Bks.) Nimbus, Inc.

Sweeting, George. The Joys of Successful Aging: Living Your Days to the Fullest. 2008. (ENG.). 160p. pap. 14.99 *(978-0-8024-7290-8(7))* Moody Pubs.

Tierney, William. The Christian Secret: How to Build More Than Abundance from a Christian Perspective. 2009. 268p. 24.99 *(978-1-4490-2569-4(2))*; pap. 17.24 *(978-1-4490-2568-7(4))* AuthorHouse.

Tomlinson, Daniel A. A Woman's Silent Testimony: How Pregnancy Enlivens Biblical Truths. 2010. pap. 21.99 *(978-1-61566-692-8(3))* Tate Publishing & Enterprises, LLC.

Trebilco, Paul. Self-designations & Group Identity in the New Testament. 2011. (ENG., Illus.). 392p. 99.00 ***(978-1-107-01299-8(6))*** Cambridge Univ. Pr.

Tucker, Cynthia Grant. No Silent Witness: Three Generations of Unitarian Wives & Daughters, 1 vol. 2010. (Religion in America Ser.). (ENG., Illus.). 256p. 29.95 *(978-0-19-539020-9(2))* Oxford Univ. Pr., Inc.

Vetere, Joseph. The Genesis Diet. 2012. E-Book ***(978-1-61638-701-3(7)***, Siloam Pr.) Charisma Media.

—The Genesis Diet: A Complete Wellness Program to Help You Get Well, Be Well, & Stay Well. 2012. (ENG.). 256p. pap. 15.99 ***(978-1-61638-495-1(6)***, Siloam Pr.) Charisma Media.

Waggadore, Ray & Waggadore, Maxine. What Happens When Christians Follow False Teachers & False Prophets, 1 vol. 2009. 73p. pap. 16.95 *(978-1-60836-401-5(1))* PublishAmerica, Inc.

Walters, J. & Wilmoth, Logan, eds. Index to Hugoye: Journal of Syriac Studies. 2011. pap. 30.80 ***(978-1-4632-0078-7(1))*** Gorgias Pr., LLC.

Wendland, Mike. The Online Christian. Niederquell, Mike, ed. Date not set. (Illus.). 150p. pap. 18.95 *(978-1-889966-01-4(0))* Cyberspacebooks.

Wills, Lawrence M. Not God's People: Insiders & Outsiders in the Biblical World. 2008. (Religion in the Modern World Ser.). (ENG.). 268p. pap. 27.95 *(978-0-7425-6250-9(6))*; (Illus.). 80.00 *(978-0-7425-6249-3(2))* Rowman & Littlefield Publishers, Inc.

Yancey, George. Compromising Scholarship: Religious & Political Bias in American Higher Education. 2011. (ENG., Illus.). 250p. 34.95 *(978-1-60258-268-2(8))* Baylor Univ. Pr.

York, Tripp. Living on Hope While Living in Babylon: e Christian Anarchists of the 20th Century. 2009. (ENG.). 136p. pap. 42.50 *(978-0-7188-9202-9(X))* Lutherworth Pr., The GBR. Dist: Brown, David Bk. Co., The.

Zuccaro, Ron. Heaven, Iron & I: The Ron Martinelli Story. 2010. (ENG., Illus.). 145p. pap. 15.95 ***(978-0-615-41750-9(7))*** Tribute Hse. Publishing.

Zukeran, Pat. World Religions Through a Christian Worldview. 2008. 300p. pap. 17.99 *(978-1-60647-068-8(X))* Xulon Pr., Inc.

CHRISTIANS—BIOGRAPHY

see Christian Biography

CHRISTIANS—PERSECUTIONS

see Persecution

CHRISTIANS—TRAVEL

Castillo, Joe. The Christian B&B Directory. 2006. 430p. pap. 12.95 *(978-0-9770428-0-7(4))* William & Warren, Inc.

Euben, Roxanne L. Journeys to the Other Shore: Muslim & Western Travelers in Search of Knowledge. 2008. (Princeton Studies in Muslim Politics Ser.). (ENG.). 328p. (C). pap. 24.95 *(978-0-691-13840-4(0))* Princeton Univ. Pr.

CHRISTIANS—AFRICA

Adeola, Moses. Cultural & Religious Dilemma of Africans: In the Diaspora. 2006. per. 16.95 *(978-0-9787788-0-4(4))* LUMEN-US Pubns.

Baraza, Patrick Wanakuta. Rival Claims for the Soul of Africa. 2007. (Illus.). 88p. pap. 10.95 *(978-1-934454-02-2(8))* Hillcrest Publishing Group, Inc.

Bediako, Kwame. Theology & Identity: The Impact of Culture upon Christian Thought in the Second Century & in Modern Africa. 2011. (Regnum Studies in Mission Ser.). 526p. pap. 63.00 ***(978-1-61097-440-0(9)***, Wipf and Stock) Wipf & Stock Pubs.

Blyden, Edward Wilmot. Christianity, Islam & the Negro Race. (African Heritage Classical Research Studies). 407p. reprint ed. 40.00 *(978-0-938818-36-6(8))* ECA Assocs.

Carpenter, Joel A. Walking Together: Christian Thinking & Public Life in South Africa. 2012. (ENG.). 416p. pap. 28.99 ***(978-0-89112-315-6(6))*** Abilene Christian Univ. Pr.

Carretta, Vincent & Reese, Ty M., eds. The Life & Letters of Philip Quaque, the First African Anglican Missionary. 2010. (Race in the Atlantic World, 1700-1900 Ser.). (ENG., Illus.). 240p. 39.95 *(978-0-8203-3319-9(0))* Univ. of Georgia Pr.

Conteh, Prince Sorie. Major Religions of Sierra Leone: An Overview. 2011. 132p. pap. 19.99 ***(978-1-4568-9786-4(1))*** Xlibris Corp.

Daneel, M. L. Zionism & Faith-Healing in Rhodesia: Aspects of African Independent Churches. February, V. A., tr. (Communications Ser.). (ENG.). 64p. 210.00 ***(978-3-11-187489-0(3))*** De Gruyter, Mouton DEU. Dist: de Gruyter, Walter GmbH & Co. KG.

Davis, Rebecca. With Two Hands: Stories of God at work in Ethiopia. 2010. (ENG., Illus.). 176p. 8.99 *(978-1-84550-539-4(5))* Christian Focus Pubns. GBR. Dist: STL Distribution North America.

Englund, Harri, ed. Christianity & Public Culture in Africa. 2011. (Cambridge Centre of African Studies). (ENG.). 240p. 49.95 *(978-0-8214-1945-8(5))* Ohio Univ. Pr.

Gifford, Paul. African Christianity: Its Public Role in Uganda & Other African Countries. viii, 368p. *(978-9970-02-170-3(2))* Fountain Pubs. Ltd. UGA. Dist: Michigan State Univ. Pr.

Human Rights Watch (Organization) Staff, contrib. by. Arbitrary Killings by Security Forces: Submission to the Investigative Bodies on the November 28-29, 2008 Violence in Jos, Plateau State, Nigeria. 2009. (Illus.). 26p. pap. ***(978-1-56432-474-0(5))*** Human Rights Watch.

Kirsch. Spirits & Letters: Reading, Writing & Charisma in African Christianity. 2008. (Illus.). 288p. 90.00 *(978-1-84545-483-8(9))* Berghahn Bks., Inc.

Kscaron;nig, Adrio. Here Am I! A Christian Reflection on God. 2011. 248p. pap. 27.00 ***(978-1-61097-555-1(3)***, Wipf and Stock) Wipf & Stock Pubs.

Nwaogwugwu, Cletus Chukwuemeka. Ancestor Christology: A Christian Evaluation of the Ancestral Cult in the Traditional Religion of the Sub-Saharan Africa. 2011. 596p. 43.95 *(978-1-4502-6228-6(7))*; pap. 33.95 *(978-1-4502-6227-9(9))* iUniverse, Inc.

O'Donovan, Wilbur. Biblical Christianity in African Perspective. 2009. (ENG.). 358p. pap. *(978-1-60126-205-9(1))* Masthof Pr.

Shaw, Brent D. Sacred Violence: African Christians & Sectarian Hatred in the Age of Augustine. 2011. (ENG., Illus.). 930p. 160.00 *(978-0-521-19605-5(1))*; pap. 65.00 *(978-0-521-12725-7(4))* Cambridge Univ. Pr.

Soares, Benjamin F., ed. Muslim-Christian Encounters in Africa. 2006. (Islam in Africa Ser.). (Illus.). 308p. *(978-90-04-15264-9(4))* BRILL.

Timm, Stefan. Das christlich-koptische Agypten in arabischer Zeit (Teil 1: A-C): eine Sammlung christlicher Statten in Agypten in arabischer Zeit, unter Ausschlua von Alexandria, Kairo, des Apa-Mena-Klosters, der Sketis und der Sinai-Region. 2007. (Tubinger Atlas des Vorderen Orients (TAVO) Ser.). (GER.). 494p. (C). pap. 126.00 *(978-3-88226-208-7(7))* Reichert, Ludwig Dr. DEU. Dist: Brown, David Bk. Co., The.

CHRISTIANS—ASIA

Brock, Sebastian P. Spirituality in the Syriac Tradition. 2010. 98.48 *(978-1-61143-558-0(7))* Gorgias Pr., LLC.

Johnson, Dale A. Jesus on the Silk Road. 2008. 125p. pap. 18.50 *(978-1-4357-3986-4(8))* Lulu Enterprises Inc.

Jongeneel, Jan A. B. & Liu, Jiafeng, eds. Christian Presence & Progress in North-East Asia: Historical & Comparative Studies. 2011. (IC - Studien zur interkulturellen Geschichte des Christentums. Etudes d'histoire interculturelle de christianisme. Studies in the Intercultural History of Christianity Ser.). 256p. 69.95 *(978-3-631-61115-9(3))* Lang, Peter GmbH, Europaischer Verlag der Wissenschaften DEU. Dist: Lang, Peter.

Lillie, Arthur. Buddha & Buddhism. 2010. (ENG.). 244p. pap. 26.75 *(978-1-176-23317-1(3))* 2009. 236p. 28.99 *(978-1-110-41807-7(8))* 2009. 236p. pap. 25.75 *(978-1-110-41805-3(1))* 2009. (ENG.). 234p. pap. 22.99 *(978-1-110-41804-6(3)*, BiblioLife) 2009. (ENG.). 234p. pap. 20.99 *(978-1-110-41802-2(7)*, BiblioLife) 2009. 236p. 23.99 *(978-1-103-01944-1(9))* 2009. 236p. pap. 17.99 *(978-1-103-01942-7(2))* BiblioBazaar.

—Buddha & Buddhism. 2010. (Illus.). 108p. pap. 13.78 *(978-1-154-65055-6(3))*; 126p. pap. 16.31 *(978-1-150-87285-3(3))* General Bks. LLC.

—Buddha & Buddhism. 2010. 236p. 41.95 *(978-1-161-36650-1(4))* Kessinger Publishing, LLC.

McCormick, Michael. Charlemagne's Survey of the Holy Land: Wealth, Personnel, & Buildings of a Mediterranean Church Between Antiquity & the Middle Ages. 2011. (Dumbarton Oaks Medieval Humanities Ser.). (ENG., Illus.). 310p. 39.95 *(978-0-88402-363-0(X))* Dumbarton Oaks.

van Gorder, Christian. Muslim-Christian Relations in Central Asia. 2012. (ENG., Illus.). 224p. (C). pap. 42.95 ***(978-0-415-53322-5(8))*** Routledge.

Wilson, Chris. Ethno-Religious Violence in Indonesia: From Soil to God. 2008. (Illus.). 256p. 170.00 *(978-0-415-45380-6(1))* Routledge.

CHRISTIANS—CHINA

Aikman, David. Jesus in Beijing: How Christianity Is Transforming China & Changing the Global Balance of Power. 2006. (ENG., Illus.). 418p. per. 16.95 *(978-1-59698-025-9(7))* Regnery Publishing, Inc., An Eagle Publishing Co.

Austin, Denise. Kingdom-Minded People: Christian Identity & the Contributions of Chinese Business Christians: Christian Identity & the Contributions of Chinese Business Christians. 2011. (Global Pentecostal & Charismatic Studies). (Illus.). 249p. ***(978-90-04-20402-7(4))*** BRILL.

Charbonnier, Jean. Christians in China. 2006. 700p. pap. 24.95 *(978-0-89870-916-2(4))* Ignatius Pr.

Falkenstine, Mike. The Chinese Puzzle: Putting the Pieces Together for a Deeper Understanding of China & Her Church. 2008. pap. 13.99 *(978-1-60647-143-2(0))* Xulon Pr., Inc.

Fallman, Fredrik. Salvation & Modernity: Intellectuals & Faith in Contemporary China. 2008. (ENG.). 180p. pap. 34.99 *(978-0-7618-4090-9(7))* Univ. Pr. of America, Inc.

Goh, Nai Lat. Friendship with Jesus. 2010. 184p. pap. *(978-3-639-24479-3(6))* VDM Verlag Dr. Mueller e.K.

Gu Chang-Sheng. Awaken: Memoirs of a Chinese Historian. 2009. 228p. 25.99 *(978-1-4490-0618-1(3))*; pap. 14.99 *(978-1-4490-0617-4(5))* AuthorHouse.

Hattaway, Paul. China's Christian Martyrs, 1 vol. 2007. (Illus.). 496p. pap. 16.99 *(978-0-8254-6127-9(8)*, Monarch Bks.) Lion Hudson PLC GBR. Dist: Kregel Pubns.

Henderson, Elsa. Wise Men Seek Him. 2011. 66p. pap. 10.99 ***(978-1-61379-293-3(X))*** Xulon Pr., Inc.

Moule, A. C. Christians in China. 2010. pap. 60.40 *(978-1-61143-605-1(2))* Gorgias Pr., LLC.

Yeo, K. K. Musing with Confucius & Paul: Toward a Chinese Christian Theology. 2008. 508p. pap. 55.00 *(978-1-55635-488-5(6))* Wipf & Stock Pubs.

CHRISTIANS—EUROPE

Briggs, John H. Y., ed. A Dictionary of European Baptist Life & Thought. 2009. (Studies in Baptist History & Thought Ser.). 566p. pap. 69.00 *(978-1-60899-165-5(2)*, Wipf and Stock) Wipf & Stock Pubs.

De Ruiter, Bert. Sharing Lives: Overcoming Our Fear of Islam. 2010. 226p. pap. *(978-3-941750-22-7(4))* VTR Verlag fur Theologie und Religionswissenschaft.

Emilianides, Achilles, ed. Religious Freedom in the European Union: The Application of the European Convention on Religious Freedom in the European Union: the Application of the European Convention on Human Rights in the European Union. Proceedings of the 19th Meeting of the European Consortium for Church & State Resear. 2011. (ENG & FRE.). 418p. (C). pap. 78.00 *(978-90-429-2243-3(5))* Peeters Pubs. & Booksellers BEL. Dist: Brown, David Bk. Co., The.

Ermatinger, James W. Daily Life of Christians in Ancient Rome, 1 vol. 2006. (Greenwood Press Daily Life Through History Ser.). (Illus.). 224p. 49.95 *(978-0-313-33564-8(8)*, GR3564, Greenwood Pr.) Greenwood Publishing Group, Inc.

Jeffery, Patricia. Migrants & Refugees: Muslim & Christian Pakistani families in Bristol. 2010. (ENG., Illus.). 232p. pap. 22.99 *(978-0-521-14124-6(9))* Cambridge Univ. Pr.

Jones, Ian. The Local Church & Generational Change in Birmingham, 1945-2000. 2012. (Royal Historical Society Studies in History New Ser.: Volume 84). (Illus.). 208p. 80.00 ***(978-0-86193-317-4(6))*** Royal Historical Society GBR. Dist: Boydell & Brewer, Inc.

Juterczenka, Sünne. Über Gott und die Welt: Endzeitvisionen, Reformdebatten und die europäische Quäkermission in der Frühen Neuzeit. Veröffentlichungen des Max-Planck-Instituts für Geschichte. 2008. (Veröffentlichungen des Max-Planck-Instituts Für Geschichte Ser.). (GER., Illus.). 367p. (C). 83.00 *(978-3-525-35458-2(4))* Vandenhoeck & Ruprecht GmbH & Co. KG DEU. Dist: ISD.

Perkins, Judith. Roman Imperial Identities in the Early Christian Era. 2010. 214p. pap. 39.95 *(978-0-415-59488-2(X))* Routledge.

Riccardi, Andrea & Community of Sant'Egidio Staff. Sant Egidio Bk of Prayer. 2009. 224p. pap. 14.95 *(978-1-59471-206-7(9))* Ave Maria Pr.

Subak, Susan Elisabeth. Rescue & Flight: American Relief Workers Who Defied the Nazis. 2010. (ENG., Illus.). 342p. 40.00 *(978-0-8032-2525-1(3))* Univ. of Nebraska Pr.

Werner, Yvonne Maria. Christian Masculinity: Men & Religion in Northern Europe in the 19th & 20th Centuries. 2012. (ENG., Illus.). 322p. pap. 49.00 ***(978-90-5867-873-7(3))*** Leuven Univ. Pr. BEL. Dist: Cornell Univ. Pr.

Yuille, J. Stephen. Puritan Spirituality: The Fear of God in the Affective Theology of George Swinnock. 2008. (Studies in Christian History & Thought Ser.). (ENG.). 262p. 39.99 *(978-1-84227-562-7(3)*, Paternoster) Authentic Media.

CHRISTIANS—GERMANY

Bretschneider, Karl Gottlieb. Apology for the Modern Theology of Protestant Germany. 2007. (ENG.). 92p. per. 18.95 *(978-1-4304-4336-0(7))* Kessinger Publishing, LLC.

Keller, Ursula E. Reflections of My Life. 2007. 100p. per. 9.99 *(978-1-60477-343-9(X))* Xulon Pr., Inc.

Schmithals, Walter. Karl Johann Philipp Spitta: Briefe an seine Braut (1836-1837) Schmithals, Walter, ed. 2008. (GER.). 165p. (C). 35.00 *(978-3-525-55783-9(3))* Vandenhoeck & Ruprecht GmbH & Co. KG DEU. Dist: ISD.

CHRISTIANS—INDIA

Asimi, A. D. The Christian Minority in Pakistan. 2010. 208p. pap. *(978-1-77069-005-9(0))* Word Alive Pr.

Mackenzie, G. T. Christianity in Travancore. 2010. 96.08 (978-1-61719-179-4(5)) Gorgias Pr., LLC.

Nag, Chitta Ranjan. Mizo Society in Transition. (C). 28.00 (978-0-7069-6963-4(4)) Vikas Publishing Hse. Private, Ltd. IND. Dist: South Asia Bks.

Phyllis, Thompson. Sadhu Sundar Singh. 2007. (ENG.). 1p. pap. 12.99 (978-1-85078-656-6(9)) Authentic Media.

Sahayamary, Sr. Prophets for Today. 2011. 168p. pap. (978-3-8443-2896-7(3)) Lambert Academic Publishing.

Taneti, James Elisha. History of the Telugu Christians: A Bibliography. 2011. xii, 109p. E-Book (978-0-8108-7509-8(8)) Scarecrow Pr., Inc.

Vallavanthara, Antony. India in 1500 Ad. 2010. 95.00 (978-1-60724-770-8(4)) Gorgias Pr., LLC.

CHRISTIANS—JAPAN

Dougill, John. In Search of Japan's Hidden Christians: A Story of Suppression, Secrecy & Survival. 2012. (ENG., Illus.). 272p. 22.95 (978-4-8053-1147-9(9)) Tuttle Publishing.

Phillips, James M. From the Rising of the Sun: Christians & Society in Contemporary Japan. 2011. 320p. (Orig.). pap. 37.00 (978-1-61097-557-5(X), Wipf and Stock) Wipf & Stock Pubs.

CHRISTIANS—KOREA

Lee, Kyung Sook & Park, Kyung Mi, eds. Korean Feminists in Conversation with the Bible, Church & Society. 2011. 144p. (978-1-906055-71-4(8)) Sheffield Phoenix Pr.

Sung-hae, Kim. Encounters: The New Religions of Korea & Christianity. 2009. pap. 35.00 (978-89-954424-9-4(2)) RAS-KB KOR. Dist: Cheng & Tsui Co.

CHRISTIANS—LATIN AMERICA

Clymer, Donald R. Meditations on the Beatitudes: Lessons from the Margins. 2011. (978-1-931038-85-0(6)) Cascadia Publishing Hse., LLC.

Prieto, Jaime. Mennonites in Latin America: Historical Sketches. 2009. (978-1-889239-05-7(4)) Bethel College.

—Menonitas en América Latina: Bosquejos Históricos. 2009. (SPA.). (978-1-889239-06-4(2)) Bethel College.

Unilit Staff. Guia Diaria: Colombia-Dios Bendiga-Patria.Tr. of Agenda: Colombia-God Bless Our Country. (SPA.). 1.99 (978-1-56063-552-9(5), 491410) Editorial Unilit.

—Guia Diaria: Dios Bendiga a Puerto Rico.Tr. of Agenda: God Bless Puerto Rico. (SPA.). 1.99 (978-1-56063-558-1(4), 491411) Editorial Unilit.

CHRISTIANS—MIDDLE EAST

Aboona, Hirmis. Assyrians, Kurds, & Ottomans: Intercommunal Relations on the Periphery of the Ottoman Empire. 2008. 344p. 109.95 (978-1-60497-583-3(0)) Cambria Pr.

Ameer, John Pierre. Assyrians in Yonkers: Reminiscences of a Community. 2008. pap. 79.00 (978-1-59333-745-2(0)) Gorgias Pr., LLC.

Bailey, Betty Jane & Bailey, Martin J. Who Are the Christians in the Middle East? Second Edition. 2nd ed. 2010. 243p. pap. 20.00 (978-0-8028-6595-3(X)) Eerdmans, William B. Publishing Co.

Cutts. Christians under the Crescent in Asia. 2006. 78.00 (978-1-59333-405-5(2)) Gorgias Pr., LLC.

Dalrymple, William. From the Holy Mountain. 2012. (Vintage Ser.). (ENG., Illus.). 512p. pap. 16.95 (978-0-307-94889-2(7), Vintage) Knopf Doubleday Publishing Group.

Dass, Ramsay. Middle East Christians: The Untold Story. 2008. 332p. pap. 19.95 (978-0-9815162-9-5(7)) Second Time Media & Communications.

Haar Romeny, R. B. ter. Religious Origins of Nations? The Christian Communities of the Middle East. 2009. 384p. (978-90-04-17375-0(7)) BRILL.

Hoospianmer, Roubik, as told by. An Unusual Story: The True, Sad, Quirky & Even Funny Tale of a Christian's Survival in Modern-Day Iran, 1 vol. 2009. 61p. pap. 16.95 (978-1-60672-699-0(4)) PublishAmerica, Inc.

Jenkins, John P. The Lost History of Christianity: The Thousand-Year Golden Age of the Church in the Middle East, Africa, & Asia — And How It Died. 2008. (ENG.). 336p. 26.95 (978-0-06-147280-0(8), HarperOne) HarperCollins Pubs.

Kildani, Hanna Said. Modern Christianity in the Holy Land: Development of the Structure of Churches & the Growth Of...: Translated by George Musleh. 2010. xviii, 719p. (978-1-4490-5286-7(X)) AuthorHouse.

Kildani, Rev. Hanna. Modern Christianity in the Holy Land: Development of the Structure of Churches & the Growth of Christian Institutions in Jordan & Palestine. 2010. 740p. (ENG.). 46.99 (978-1-4490-5285-0(1)); pap. 33.49 (978-1-4490-5284-3(3)) AuthorHouse.

Kuruvilla, Samuel J. Radical Christianity in Palestinian & Israel: Liberation & Theology in the Middle East. 2012. (Library of Modern Religion Ser.: No. 19). (ENG., Illus.). 320p. 95.00 (978-1-84885-551-9(6), Tauris Academic Studies) I. B. Tauris & Co., Ltd. GBR. Dist: Macmillan.

Madden, Richard Robert. The Turkish Empire V2: in Its Relations with Christianity & Civilization. 2007. pap. 38.95 (978-1-4304-5000-9(2)) Kessinger Publishing, LLC.

Malik, Habib C. Islamism & the Future of the Christians in the Middle East. 2010. (Hoover inst press Publication). (ENG.). 66p. pap. 9.95 (978-0-8179-1095-2(6)) Hoover Institution Pr.

Mansour, Botrus. When Your Neighbor Is the Savior. 2011. (978-1-932717-23-5(4)) Hope Publishing Hse.

McGahern, Una. Christian Palestinians in the Israeli State. 2011. (Durham Modern Middle East & Islamic World Ser.). (ENG., Illus.). 216p. (C). 140.00 (978-0-415-60571-7(7)) Routledge.

Pilch, John J. Stephen: Paul & the Hellenist Israelites. 2008. (Paul's Social Network: Brothers & Sisters in Faith Ser.). 87p. per. 9.95 (978-0-8146-5229-9(8), Liturgical Pr. Bks.) Liturgical Pr.

Shahbaz, Yonan. The Rage of Islam: An Account of the Massacres of Christians by the Turks in Persia. 2006. 68.00 (978-1-59333-411-6(7)) Gorgias Pr., LLC.

Stephanous, Andrea Zaki. Political Islam, Citizenship, & Minorities: The Future of Arab Christians in the Islamic Middle East. 2010. (ENG.). 254p. pap. 37.50 (978-0-7618-5213-1(1)) Univ. Pr. of America, Inc.

Timmerman, Christiane & Leman, Johan, eds. In-Between Spaces: Christian & Muslim Minorities in Transition in Europe & the Middle East. 2009. 284p. pap. 56.95 (978-90-5201-565-1(1)) PIE - Peter Lang BEL. Dist: Lang, Peter.

CHRISTIANS—OCEANIA

Van Dusen, Henry P. They Found the Church There - the Armed Forces Discover Christian Missions in the Pacific. 2007. 132p. per. (978-1-4067-8791-7(4), Pomona Pr.) Read Bks.

CHRISTIANS—PAKISTAN

Gabriel, Theodore. Christian Minorities in an Islamic State: The Pakistan Experience. 2007. (Illus.). 132p. 89.95 (978-0-7546-6024-8(9)); pap. 39.95 (978-0-7546-6036-1(2)) Ashgate Publishing Co.

Walbridge, Linda. The Christians of Pakistan. 2009. 262p. pap. 39.95 (978-0-415-57086-6(3)) Routledge.

CHRISTIANS—SOVIET UNION

Benson, David. Milagros en Moscu: Miracles in Moscow. (SPA.). 328p. (978-84-7228-261-2(9), 220593) Clie, Editorial.

Brumfield, William C. & Velimirovic, Milos M., eds. Christianity & the Arts in Russia. 2008. (ENG., Illus.). 268p. pap. 31.99 (978-0-521-08923-4(9)) Cambridge Univ. Pr.

Olema, A. History of Evangelical Christianity in Russia. 8.99 (978-1-56632-082-5(8)) Revival Literature.

CHRISTIANS—SPAIN

Baruque, Julio Valdeon & Valdeón Baruque, Julio. Cristianos, Judíos, y Musulmanes. 2007. 182p. 24.95 (978-84-8432-757-8(4)) Critica Editorial ESP. Dist: Planeta Publishing Corp.

Burns, Robert I. Muslims Christians, & Jews in the Crusader Kingdom of Valencia: Societies in Symbiosis. 2009. (Cambridge Iberian & Latin American Studies). (ENG., Illus.). 388p. pap. 51.00 (978-0-521-09518-1(2)) Cambridge Univ. Pr.

Catlos, Brian A. The Victors & the Vanquished: Christians & Muslims of Catalonia & Aragon, 1050-1300. 2007. (Cambridge Studies in Medieval Life & Thought). (ENG., Illus.). 480p. pap. 61.00 (978-0-521-03644-3(5)) Cambridge Univ. Pr.

Grieve, Patricia E. The Eve of Spain: Myths of Origins in the History of Christian, Muslim, & Jewish Conflict. 2009. (ENG., Illus.). 328p. (gr. 17). 63.00 (978-0-8018-9036-9(5)) Johns Hopkins Univ. Pr.

Hitchcock, Richard. Mozarabs in Medieval & Early Modern Spain: Identities & Influences. 2008. (Illus.). 172p. 99.95 (978-0-7546-6314-0(0)) Ashgate Publishing Co.

Lowney, Chris. A Vanished World: Muslims, Christians, & Jews in Medieval Spain. 2006. (ENG., Illus.). 352p. per. 19.99 (978-0-19-531191-4(4)) Oxford Univ. Pr., Inc.

CHRISTIANS—TURKEY

Karabash, A. Naman & Gorgis, Amill. Shed Blood. Toro, George, tr. 2010. (GER.). 97.04 (978-1-61143-243-5(X)) Gorgias Pr., LLC.

Naayem, Joseph & Bryce, Lord. Shall this Nation Die? 2010. 126.80 (978-1-61719-041-4(1)) Gorgias Pr., LLC.

Ozil, Ayse. Orthodox Christians in the Late Ottoman Empire. 2012. (SOAS/Routledge Studies on the Middle East Ser.). (ENG.). 240p. (C). 125.00 (978-0-415-68263-3(0)) Routledge.

Tellbe, Mikael. Christ-Believers in Ephesus: A Textual Analysis of Early Christian Identity Formation in a Local Perspective. 2009. (Wissenschaftliche Untersuchungen zum Neuen Testament Ser.). (Illus.). 361p. 177.50 (978-3-16-150048-0(2)) Mohr Siebeck GmbH & Co. KG DEU. Dist: Coronet Bks.

Trigona-Harany, Benjamin. The Ottoman Süryânî from 1908 To 1914. 2010. 110.12 (978-1-60724-069-3(6)) Gorgias Pr., LLC.

CHRISTIANS, JEWISH

see Jewish Christians

CHRISTIANS OF ST. JOHN

see Mandaeans

CHRISTIE, AGATHA, 1891-1976

Cade, Jared. Agatha Christie & the Eleven Missing Days. (ENG., Illus.). 3rd ed. 2006. 256p. per. 19.95 (978-0-7206-1280-6(2)) 4th rev. ed. 2011. 300p. pap. 19.95 (978-0-7206-1390-2(6)) Owen, Peter Ltd. GBR. Dist: Independent Pubs. Group.

Christie, Agatha. An Autobiography. 2012. (ENG.). 560p. pap. 16.99 (978-0-06-220457-8(2), William Morrow Paperbacks) HarperCollins Pubs.

Christie, Agatha. Autobiography. 2011. (ENG., Illus.). 544p. 29.99 (978-0-06-207359-4(1)) HarperCollins Pubs.

Curran, John. Agatha Christie, Murder in the Making: More Stories & Secrets from Her Notebooks. 2011. 432p. 25.99 (978-0-06-206542-1(4)) HarperCollins Pubs.

—Agatha Christie: Murder in the Making: More Stories & Secrets from Her Notebooks. 2012. 432p. pap. 16.99 (978-0-06-206543-8(2), William Morrow Paperbacks) HarperCollins Pubs.

Curran, John. Agatha Christie's Secret Notebooks: Fifty Years of Mysteries in the Making. 496p. 2011. pap. 16.99 (978-0-06-198837-0(5), Harper Paperbacks) 2010. (Illus.). 25.99 (978-0-06-198836-3(7)) HarperCollins Pubs.

Escott, John. Agatha Christie, Woman of Mystery. Oxford University Press Staff, ed. 3rd ed. 2008. (ENG., Illus.). 64p. pap. 9.38 (978-0-19-479050-5(9)) Oxford Univ. Pr., Inc.

Gerald, Michael C. The Poisonous Pen of Agatha Christie. 2011. (ENG., Illus.). 288p. pap. 25.00 (978-0-292-72864-6(6)) Univ. of Texas Pr.

Hack, Richard. The Duchess of Death: The Biography of Agatha Christie. 2009. (Illus.). 396p. 25.95 (978-1-59777-620-2(3)) Phoenix Bks., Inc.

Holgate, Mike. Agatha Christie's True Crime Inspirations: Stranger Than Fiction. 2011. (ENG., Illus.). 128p. pap. 15.95 (978-0-7524-5539-6(7)) History Pr. Ltd.,The GBR. Dist: Independent Pubs. Group.

Macaskill, Hilary. Agatha Christie at Home. 2009. (ENG., Illus.). 144p. 40.00 (978-0-7112-3029-3(3)) Lincoln, Frances Ltd. GBR. Dist: Perseus-PGW.

Makinen, Merja. Agatha Christie: Investigating Femininity. 2006. (Crime Files Ser.). (ENG.). 224p. 84.00 (978-1-4039-4171-8(8)) Palgrave Macmillan.

Norman, Andrew. Agatha Christie: The Finished Portrait. 2007. (ENG., Illus.). 224p. 29.95 (978-0-7524-3990-7(1)) History Pr. Ltd.,The GBR. Dist: Independent Pubs. Group.

Riviere, Francois. Agatha Christie's England. (GER.). (978-3-8067-2809-5(7)) Gerstenberg DEU. Dist: International Bk. Import Service, Inc.

—Footsteps of Agatha Christie. (Illus.). 157p. 29.95 (978-0-09-185212-2(9)) Random Hse. GBR. Dist: Trafalgar Square Publishing.

Thompson, Laura. Agatha Christie: Das faszinierende Leben der großen Kriminalschriftstellerin. 2009. (ENG.). 544p. pap. 14.95 (978-0-7553-1488-1(3)) Headline Bk. Publishing GBR. Dist: Independent Pubs. Group.

York, R. A. & York, Richard. Agatha Christie: Power & Illusion. 2007. (Crime Files Ser.). (ENG.). 232p. 95.00 (978-0-230-52501-6(6)) Palgrave Macmillan.

Zemboy, James. The Detective Novels of Agatha Christie: A Reader's Guide. 2008. (ENG.). 448p. 75.00 (978-0-7864-3914-0(9)) McFarland & Co., Inc. Pubs.

CHRISTIE, JOHN REGINALD HALLIDAY, 1899?-1953

Marston, Edward. John Christie. 2008. (Crime Archive Ser.). (Illus.). 128p. 5.00 (978-1-905615-16-2(7)) National Archives (PRO), The GBR. Dist: International Publishers Marketing.

CHRISTIE, JULIE, 1940-

Ewbank, Tim & Hildred, Stafford. Julie Christie: The Biography. 2nd ed. 2009. (ENG., Illus.). 272p. 24.95 (978-0-233-00255-2(3)) Andre Deutsch GBR. Dist: Independent Pubs. Group.

CHRISTIE, WILLIAM

Christie, Thomas, et al. Brother of Mine: The Civil War Letters of Thomas & William Christie. 2010. E-Book (978-0-87351-810-9(1)) Minnesota Historical Society Pr.

Smith, Hampton, ed. Brother of Mine: The Civil War Letters of Thomas & William Christie. 2010. (ENG.). 336p. pap. 19.95 (978-0-87351-781-2(4)) Minnesota Historical Society Pr.

CHRISTINA, OF MARKYATE, SAINT, 1096-1160

Talbot, C. H. The Life of Christina of Markyate. Fanous, Samuel & Leyser, Henrietta, eds. 2010. (Oxford World's Classics Ser.). (ENG., Illus.). 144p. pap. 15.95 (978-0-19-955605-2(9)) Oxford Univ. Pr., Inc.

CHRISTMAS

see also Christmas Decorations; Christmas Sermons; Jesus Christ—Nativity

Adams, Rosemary. Historic Photos of Christmas in Chicago. 2008. (Historic Photos Ser.). (ENG.). 205p. 39.95 (978-1-59652-511-5(8)) Turner Publishing Co.

Adams, Rosemary K. Remembering Christmas in Chicago. 2010. (Remembering Ser.). (ENG., Illus.). 134p. pap. 16.95 (978-1-59652-696-9(3)) Turner Publishing Co.

Alvarez, C. Diane. Tumbleweed Christmas 2011. 24p. pap. 14.39 (978-1-4567-9968-7(1)) AuthorHouse.

Anonymus. Keep Calm at Christmas. 2012. (Keep Calm & Carry On Ser.). (ENG.). 160p. 8.95 (978-0-09-194505-3(4)) Ebury Publishing GBR. Dist: Independent Pubs. Group.

Armstrong, Neil. Christmas in Nineteenth-Century England. 2011. (ENG., Illus.). 208p. 95.00 (978-0-7190-7759-3(1)) Manchester Univ. Pr. GBR. Dist: Macmillan.

Artley, Bob. Bob Artley's Country Christmas: As Remembered by a Former Kid. rev. ed. 2006. (ENG., Illus.). 40p. 9.95 (978-0-7603-2652-7(5), 0760326525, Voyageur Pr) MBI Publishing Co. LLC.

Ashton, John. A Righte Merrie Christmasse!!! 2009. 228p. pap. (978-1-84830-217-4(7), Wildhem Pr.) Echo Library.

Ayo, Nicholas. St. Nicholas in America: Christmas Holy Day & Holiday. 2006. per. 14.95 (978-0-9776458-1-7(9)) Corby Books.

Back, George. Christmas Joy Let Heaven & Nature Sing. 2007. (Illus.). 110p. per. 9.95 (978-0-9800520-0-8(9)) Spirit & Intelligence Pr., LLC.

Ballowe, James. Christmas in Illinois. 2010. (ENG., Illus.). 224p. 29.95 (978-0-252-03442-8(2)) Univ. of Illinois Pr.

Basile, Alex. A Christmas with Christ: Finding Joy Each December. 2011. (978-0-8189-1338-9(X)) St. Paul Pubns.

Bendit, Phoebe D. The Reality of Christmas: A Study in Mythology. 2011. 16p. pap. 35.95 (978-1-258-05007-8(2)) Literary Licensing, LLC.

Benevides, Kerrie. The Christmas Heart. 2007. 64p. per. 11.99 (978-1-60477-185-5(2)) Xulon Pr., Inc.

Bennett, Arnold. The Feast of St Friend: A Christmas Book. 2007. 60p. per. (978-1-4065-4781-8(6)) Dodo Pr.

—The Feast of St Friend: A Christmas Book. 2007. (ENG.). 124p. 35.95 (978-0-548-11445-2(5)) Kessinger Publishing, LLC.

—Friendship & Happiness. 2009. 48p. pap. (978-1-4099-7565-6(7)) Dodo Pr.

Billhaltom. Some Assembly Required: A Daddy's Christmas Book. 2009. pap. 15.00 (978-1-61623-616-8(7)) Independent Pub.

Boone, Pat. The Real Christmas. 2011. 62p. 36.95 (978-1-258-04910-2(4)) Literary Licensing, LLC.

Bosch, Henry, et al. Christmas: Quiet Moments for the Season. 2007. (Strength for the Soul from Our Daily Bread Ser.). (ENG.). 128p. per. 5.99 (978-1-57293-259-3(7)) Discovery Hse. Pubs.

Brady, Steve. The Incredible Journey: Christmas from Genesis to Jesus. 2011. 200p. pap. (978-0-85746-003-5(X)) Bible Reading Fellowship.

Brennan, Rebecca. Southern Living Big Book of Christmas. 2009. (Illus.). 416p. (978-0-8487-3290-5(1)) Oxmoor Hse. Inc.

Brown, Cameron. Christmas Facts, Figures & Fun. 2006. (Illus.). 96p. 5.95 (978-1-904332-27-5(7)) Sterling Publishing Co., Inc.

Butler, Carolyn. Under African Skies: Reflections for Advent & Christmas. 2011. 96p. pap. 9.95 (978-0-7963-0850-4(0)) NB Pubs. Ltd. ZAF. Dist: International Publishers Marketing.

Butler, Dori Hillestad. Christmas: Season of Peace & Joy. 2006. (First Facts Ser.). (ENG., Illus.). 24p. (gr. 1-2). 24.65 (978-0-7368-6394-0(X), First Facts) Capstone Pr., Inc.

Called: Pastoral Letters to Young Timothys. 2008. pap. 12.95 (978-0-9798778-1-0(4)) Christian Word Bks.

Carne, David. 7 Ways to Get Ready for Jesus' Birthday. 2007. (ENG.). 18.95 (978-1-932773-90-3(8)) Marian Pr.

Canfield, Jack L. & Hansen, Mark Victor. A Chicken Soup for the Soul Christmas. 2007. (Chicken Soup Ser.). (ENG., Illus.). 288p. pap. 14.95 (978-0-7573-0646-4(2)) Health Communications, Inc.

—Chicken Soup for the Soul the Book of Christmas Virtues: Inspirational Stories to Warm the Heart. 2007. (Chicken Soup for the Soul Ser.). (ENG.). 272p. pap. 14.95 (978-0-7573-0691-4(8)) Health Communications, Inc.

Canfield, Jack L., et al. Chicken Soup for the Soul: Christmas Cheer: Stories about the Love, Inspiration, & Joy of Christmas. 2008. (Chicken Soup for the Soul Ser.). (ENG.). 380p. pap. 14.95 (978-1-935096-15-3(X)) Chicken Soup for the Soul Publishing, LLC.

Carriage House Staff. Christmas Memories. deluxe ed. 17.95 (978-0-89786-031-4(4)); 17.95 (978-0-89786-032-1(2)) Carriage Hse. Pubns., Ltd.

Carroll, Kathleen. A Franciscan Christmas. 2010. (978-0-86716-986-7(9)) Franciscan Media.

Cartwright, Ran & Cartwright, Christene. A Little Christmas Magic, 1 vol. 2010. 128p. pap. 19.95 (978-1-4512-0470-4(1)) PublishAmerica, Inc.

Cates, Tim, contrib. by. Glory in the Highest: A New Hallelujah. 2010. (ENG.). 128p. pap. 8.99 (978-0-8341-7778-9(1), 9780834177789) Allegis Pubns.

Celano, Peter, ed. Christmas with the Holy Fathers. 2008. (ENG.). 121p. (gr. 13). 19.95 (978-1-55725-603-4(9)) Paraclete Pr., Inc.

Center for the Study of C. S. Lewis and Friends Staff, contrib. by. Advent & Christmas Wisdom. 2007. 114p. per. 10.99 (978-0-7648-1628-4(4)) Liguori Pubns.

Christie, Agatha. Star over Bethlehem: Poems & Holiday Stories. 2011. (ENG.). 80p. pap. 12.99 (978-0-06-207430-0(X), William Morrow Paperbacks) HarperCollins Pubs.

Christie, Judy Pace. Hurry Less, Worry Less at Christmastime: Having the Holiday Season You Long For. 2007. 126p. per. 14.99 (978-0-687-49086-8(3), Dimensions For Living) Abingdon Pr.

Christmas A to Z. 2007. 320p. pap. 14.99 (978-1-4185-2943-7(5)) Nelson, Thomas Inc.

Christmas Card Value Assortment. 2009. pap. (978-1-60260-598-5(X), Barbour Bks.) Barbour Publishing, Inc.

Christmas Family Fun. rev. ed. 9.95 (978-1-57229-025-9(0)) FamilyLife.

Christmas in Paris & the Provinces. 2008. 80p. (J). (978-0-7166-0812-7(X)) World Bk., Inc.

Christmas in Spain & Its Capital, Madrid. 2009. (978-0-7166-0814-1(6)) World Bk., Inc.

Churcher, John & Bishop, Ted. Advent to Epiphany. 2010. 80p. pap. 10.50 (978-1-4461-4398-8(8)) Lulu Enterprises Inc.

Clara A. Urann, Mary P. Pringle and. The Celebration of Christmas in Europe & America: Yuletide Traditions from Many Lands. 2009. 100p. pap. 11.95 (978-0-557-00051-7(3)) Lulu Enterprises Inc.

Coates, Linda & Kelly, Leslie S. The Twelve Days of Christmas: A Guide to an Old Tradition with a New Purpose. 2009. pap. 19.99 (978-1-60696-260-2(4)) Tate Publishing & Enterprises, LLC.

Cockrell, Lucinda, compiled by. A Victorian Christmas: Sentiments & Sounds of a Bygone Era, 0 vols. 2008. (Illus.). 64p. 14.99 (978-1-4041-0507-2(7)) Nelson, Thomas Inc.

Coffey, Tim, illus. Celebrating the Spirit of Christmas. 2007. 64p. 10.99 (978-0-7369-2103-9(6)) Harvest Hse. Pubs.

Collins, Ace. Ace Collins Christmas Boxed Set, 1 vol. 2007. (ENG.). pap., pap., pap. 24.99 (978-0-310-28112-2(1)) Zondervan.

Conceptis Puzzles. Christmas Sudoku. 2010. (ENG.). 96p. spiral bd. 8.95 (978-1-4027-7498-0(2), Puzzlewright) Sterling Publishing Co., Inc.

Cormier, Jay. Waiting in Joyful Hope. 2011. 112p. pap. 2.00 (978-0-8146-3361-8(7)) Liturgical Pr.

C

—Waiting in Joyful Hope: Daily Reflections for Advent & Christmas 2007-2008 Year A. 2007. 101p. per. 2.00 *(978-0-8146-3080-8(4)*, Liturgical Pr. Bks.) Liturgical Pr.

Cormier, Jay. Waiting in Joyful Hope Large Print. 2011. 112p. pap. 5.95 ***(978-0-8146-3398-4(6))*** Liturgical Pr.

Cox, Ronald B. The Journey to Bethlehem. 2011. 60p. pap. 9.95 ***(978-1-4620-4191-6(4))*** iUniverse, Inc.

Crafton, Barbara Cawthorne. Mary & Her Miracle: The Christmas Story Retold. 2007. (Illus.). 112p. 18.00 *(978-0-8192-2148-3(1)*, Morehouse Publishing) Church Publishing, Inc.

Crowder, Bill. Windows on Christmas. 2007. (ENG., Illus.). 128p. per. 11.99 *(978-1-57293-228-9(7))* Discovery Hse. Pubs.

Cuddihy, Kevin & Metcalfe, Phillip. Christmas's Most Wanted: The Top 10 Book of Kris Kringles, Merry Jingles, & Holiday Cheer. 2006. (Illus.). 304p. 7.98 *(978-1-57866-159-6(5)*, Galahad Bks.) BBS Publishing Corp.

Dahlstrom, Carol Field. Merry Christmas Ideas: 225 Projects for Crafting, Cookie-Baking, Gift Giving, Decoeating, & Merry-Making. 2007. 160p. pap. 24.95 *(978-0-9768446-6-2(4))* Dahlstrom, Carol Field Inc.

Darragh, Kathleen. 12 Days of Christmas. 2006. (Illus.). 27p. (J). 9.95 *(978-0-87946-319-9(8))* ACTA Pubns.

Dawson, W. F. Christmas: Its Origin & Associations. 2010. 380p. 39.16 *(978-1-169-77742-2(2))* Kessinger Publishing, LLC.

Dawson, W. f. & Dawson, W. F. Christmas: Its Origin & Associations. 2010. 380p. 48.95 *(978-1-161-38051-4(5))* Kessinger Publishing, LLC.

de Sturtz, Maria Ester H. & de Perez, Ursula S. Manos a la Obra: La Iglesia Celebra. (SPA.). 32p. 6.99 *(978-0-7586-0498-9(X))* Concordia Publishing Hse.

dePaola, Tomie. Christmas Remembered. 2009. (ENG.). 96p. (J). (gr. -1-18). pap. 9.99 *(978-0-14-241481-1(6)*, Puffin) Penguin Group (USA) Inc.

Dickens, Charles & Ross, Alice. A Christmas Dinner by Charles Dickens. 2008. (ENG.). 88p. 24.95 *(978-1-933176-10-9(5))* Red Rock Pr., Inc.

Dickmann, Nancy. Navidad. 2011. (Fiestas Ser.). (SPA.). 24p. (gr. -1-1). 21.99 *(978-1-4329-5377-5(X)*, Bellota) Heinemann-Raintree.

Doherty, Catherine. Donkey Bells: Advent & Christmas. 156p. pap. *(978-0-921440-38-3(3))* Madonna Hse. Pubns.

Douglas, Hugh, compiled by. A Right Royal Christmas: An Anthology. 2011. (ENG., Illus.). 160p. pap. 14.95 ***(978-0-7524-6431-2(0))*** History Pr. Ltd., The GBR. Dist: Independent Pubs. Group.

Doyle, Marian I. Christmas Long Ago. 2006. (Illus.). 112p. pap. 19.95 *(978-0-7643-2357-7(1))* Schiffer Publishing, Ltd.

Dudley, Martin. A Herald Voice: The Work of God in Advent & Christmas. 160p. 12.00 *(978-0-281-05280-6(8))* SPCK Publishing GBR. Dist: Pilgrim Pr., The/United Church Pr.

Dunnam, Maxie D. The Grace-Filled Life: 52 Devotions to Warm Your Heart & Guide Your Path. 2010. 175p. pap. 12.00 *(978-1-4267-0682-0(0))* Abingdon Pr.

Dunphy, Hubert M. Christmas Every Christmas. (Illus.). reprint ed. 17.00 *(978-1-930873-22-3(0))* Neumann Pr., The.

Dunphy, John J. From Christmas to Twelfth Night in Southern Illinois. 2010. (ENG., Illus.). 144p. pap. 19.99 *(978-1-59629-913-9(4))* History Pr., The.

Ecclesia Bible Society Staff, ed. Son of the Most High. 2006. 144p. 16.99 *(978-0-529-12348-0(7))* Nelson, Thomas Inc.

Edwards, Larry D. The Christian Holy Days: The Biblical Account of Christmas, Passion Week, Easter, Ascension, & Pentecost. 2010. 34.99 *(978-1-61579-709-7(2))*; 404p. pap. 22.99 *(978-1-61579-710-3(6))* Xulon Pr., Inc.

Edworthy, Niall. The Curious World of Christmas: Celebrating All That Is Weird, Wonderful, & Festive. 2008. (ENG., Illus.). 192p. (gr. 12-18). 16.95 *(978-0-399-53457-7(1)*, Perigee Trade) Penguin Group (USA) Inc.

Engelbreit, Mary. Do You Believe? A Pocket Treasure Book for Christmas. gif. ed. 2006. (ENG., Illus.). 32p. 9.95 *(978-0-7407-6287-1(7))* Andrews McMeel Publishing.

Estes, Steven D. A Better December: Proverbs to Brighten Christmas. 2012. (ENG.). 96p. pap. 9.99 ***(978-1-936768-67-7(4))*** New Growth Pr.

Fadness, Arley K. Blueprints for Advent & Christmas: Dynamic Sketches, Scenes, & Scripts for the Season. 2008. (Illus.). 168p. pap. *(978-0-7880-2556-3(2))* CSS Publishing Co.

Favourite Christmas Songs & Stories. (Illus.). 47p. 19.95 *(978-1-85479-328-7(4))* O'Mara, Michael Bks., Ltd. GBR. Dist: Trans-Atlantic Pubns., Inc.

Fawcett, Brian. A Blue Spruce Christmas. 2010. (ENG., Illus.). 120p. 24.00 *(978-1-897151-94-5(2))* Cormorant Bks. Inc. CAN. Dist: Univ. of Toronto Pr.

Featherstone, Vaughn J. The Light of Hope. 2007. 197p. *(978-1-59811-455-3(7))* Covenant Communications.

Ferguson, Norman. I See ... Xmas. 2008. (ENG., Illus.). 112p. pap. 13.95 *(978-1-906032-39-5(4))* Anova Bks. GBR. Dist: Independent Pubs. Group.

Fimbel, Mary Ellen. The Amazing Giving Tree Secret: A Story of Kindness, Love, & Joy. 2011. 32p. pap. 13.95 ***(978-1-4627-0644-0(4))*** Cross Bks. Publishing.

Finley, Mitch. Season of Promises: Praying Through Advent with Julian of Norwich, Thomas ç Kempis, Caryll Houselander, Thomas Merton, Brother Lawrence, Max Picard. 2010. 64p. pap. 9.00 *(978-1-60899-263-8(2)*, Wipf and Stock) Wipf & Stock Pubs.

The First Christmas. 5.00 *(978-0-687-02674-6(1))* Abingdon Pr.

Foote, Carol. A Reel Meaning for Christmas: Finding Yourself in the Classic Christmas Films. 2007. 68p. per. 14.99 *(978-1-4141-0552-9(5))* Pleasant Word.

Forbes, Bruce David. Christmas: A Candid History. (Illus.). 2008. 188p. pap. 16.95 *(978-0-520-25802-0(9))* 2007. 179p. 29.95 *(978-0-520-25104-5(0))* Univ. of California Pr.

Francis. Advent & Christmas Wisdom from Saint Francis of Assisi: Daily Scripture & Prayers Together with Saint Francis of Assisi's Own Words. 2008. 10.99 *(978-0-7648-1756-4(6))* Liguori Pubns.

Frederick, Chuck. Spirit of the Lights. LeMay, Konnie, ed. 2011. pap. 16.95 *(978-0-942235-11-1(8))* Lake Superior Port Cities, Inc.

Freeman, Emily. A Christ-Centered Christmas. 2010. (Illus.). 96p. pap. 10.99 *(978-1-60641-839-0(4))* Deseret Bk. Co.

Garvey, John. A Great Light: Helping Families Find Meaning at Christmas. 2008. (ENG.). 96p. pap. 15.95 *(978-1-84730-062-1(8))* Veritas Pubns. IRL. Dist: Dufour Editions, Inc.

Gibson, Cay. Christmas Mosaic: An Illustrated Book Study for Christmas. 2007. 210p. (J). spiral bd. 19.99 *(978-0-9798469-1-5(9))* Hillside Education.

The Gift of Christmas Presence. 2007. 6.00 *(978-0-687-64381-3(3))* Abingdon Pr.

Gompertz, Ron. Chrismukkah: Everything You Need to Know to Celebrate the Hybrid Holiday. (ENG., Illus.). 144p. 2009. pap. 10.95 *(978-1-58479-770-8(3))* 2006. 17.95 *(978-1-58479-558-2(1))* Stewart, Tabori & Chang.

Gorey, Edward, Illus. The Twelve Terrors of Christmas. 2006. 32p. 9.95 *(978-0-7649-3710-1(3)*, A128) Pomegranate Communications, Inc.

Gospel Light, compiled by. A Christmas Wonderland: Stories, Verse & Thoughts to Cheer Your Heart. 2006. (ENG., Illus.). 224p. 14.99 *(978-0-8307-4202-8(6))* Gospel Light Pubns.

Green, Jonathan. A Christmas Miscellany: Everything You Always Wanted to Know about Christmas. 2009. (Books of Miscellany Ser.). (ENG., Illus.). 184p. 14.95 *(978-1-60239-757-6(0)*, 239757) Skyhorse Publishing Co., Inc.

Green, Maxine. Christmas, the Celebration of Satan's Birthday. 111p. pap. 8.95 *(978-0-9633722-1-5(1))* Fowler Enterprises.

Green Tiger Press Staff. We Wish You A Crazy Christmas: Strange Christmas Cards Postcard Book. 2011. (ENG., Illus.). 30p. pap. 9.95 *(978-1-59583-446-1(X)*, Darling & Co.) Laughing Elephant.

Greenfield, Stephen. We wish you a retro Christmas. 2008. 196p. pap. 18.95 *(978-1-4092-4675-6(2))* Lulu Enterprises Inc.

Greive, Bradley Trevor. Every Day Is Christmas. 2011. (ENG.). 120p. pap. 4.99 ***(978-1-4494-1409-2(5))*** Andrews McMeel Publishing.

Group Publishing, creator. A Night in Bethlehem: A Hands-on Holy Land Experience. 2007. 39.99 *(978-0-7644-3659-8(7))* Group Publishing, Inc.

—A Night in Bethlehem: A Hands-on Holy Land Experience: Director Manual. 2007. 223p. per. 39.99 *(978-0-7644-3593-5(0))* Group Publishing, Inc.

Gruchow, Diane. These My Christmas Dreams. 2008. 140p. pap. 13.99 *(978-1-60647-256-9(9))* Xulon Pr., Inc.

Gulevich, Tanya. Christmas from A to Z. abr. rev. ed. 2011. (ENG., Illus.). 573p. (gr. 6). pap. 24.95 *(978-0-7808-1244-4(1))* KWS Pubs.

Guttman, Peter. Christmas in America: A Photographic Celebration of the Holiday Season. (Illus.). 176p. 2007. 24.95 *(978-1-60239-066-9(5))* 2nd ed. 2011. (ENG., 24.95 *(978-1-61608-096-9(5)*, 608096) Skyhorse Publishing Co., Inc.

Hall, Manly P. Story of Christmas. pap. 4.95 *(978-0-89314-379-4(0))* Philosophical Research Society, Inc.

Hanby-Robie, Sharon. A Simple Christmas: A Faith-Filled Guide to a Meaningful & Stress-Free Christmas. 2006. (Spirit of Simple Living Ser.). (ENG., Illus.). 200p. pap. 14.95 *(978-0-8249-4703-3(7))* Ideals Pubns.

Harding, Nathan & Harding, William. Christmas-the way it used to Be. 2010. 47p. pap. 6.14 *(978-0-557-62099-9(6))* Lulu Enterprises Inc.

Harry, Lou & Tobias, Todd, eds. Indy Men's Magazine Presents the X-Mas Men: Holiday Reflections. 2006. pap. 13.95 *(978-0-87195-199-1(1))* Indiana Historical Society.

Hartl, Alfred. We Have Seen a Great Light: 99 Sayings on Christmas. 2007. pap. 9.95 *(978-1-56548-271-5(9))* New City Pr.

Harvey, Anne, compiled by. Waiting for Santa: An Anthology of Childhood Christmases. 2010. (ENG., Illus.). 160p. pap. 14.95 *(978-0-7524-5806-9(X))* History Pr. Ltd., The GBR. Dist: Independent Pubs. Group.

Hayden, Christopher. O Come, Let Us Adore: Exploring the Crib at Christmas. 2011. (ENG.). 112p. pap. 15.95 *(978-1-84730-247-2(5))* Veritas Pubns. IRL. Dist: Dufour Editions, Inc.

Heath, Marian Russell, ed. A Christmas Garland. 2011. (ENG., Illus.). 128p. 20.00 ***(978-0-486-48091-6(7))*** Dover Pubns., Inc.

Heinz, Donald. Christmas: A Celebration of Christian Culture. 2006. (ENG.). 40.00 *(978-0-300-10866-8(4))* Yale Univ. Pr.

—Christmas: Festival of Incarnation. 2010. 256p. 29.00 *(978-0-8006-9733-4(2)*, Fortress Pr.) Augsburg Fortress, Pubs.

Hervey, Thomas K. The Book of Christmas. (Myth, Legend & Folklore Ser.). (Illus.). 224p. pap. 6.95 *(978-1-84022-506-8(8))* Wordsworth Editions, Ltd. GBR. Dist: Advanced Global Distribution Services.

Hisey, Belinda & Sineva, Natasha. Pocketboy's Gift: The True Meaning of Christmas. 14.95 *(978-0-9645748-1-6(0))*; pap. 7.95 *(978-0-9645748-2-3(9))* Pocketboy Bks.

Hollis, Tim. Christmas Wishes: A Catalog of Vintage Holiday Treats & Treasures. 2010. (ENG., Illus.). 192p. 24.95 *(978-0-8117-0507-3(2))* Stackpole Bks.

Holtz, Albert. From Holidays to Holy Days: A Benedictine Walk Through Advent. 2008. 136p. pap. 16.00 *(978-0-8192-2316-6(6)*, Morehouse Publishing) Church Publishing, Inc.

Hottes, Alfred Carl. 1001 Christmas Facts & Fancies 1937. 2007. (ENG.). 308p. 43.95 *(978-0-548-05374-4(X))* Kessinger Publishing, LLC.

Howse, Jennifer. Boxing Day: Canadian Celebrations. 2010. (Illus.). 24p. pap. *(978-1-77071-638-4(6))* Weigl Educational Pubs. Ltd.

Huckabee, Mike. A Simple Christmas: Twelve Stories That Celebrate the True Holiday Spirit. (ENG.). (gr. 12). 2012. 240p. pap. 15.00 ***(978-1-59523-098-0(X))*** 2009. 160p. 22.95 *(978-1-59523-062-1(9))* Penguin Group (USA) Inc. (Sentinel).

Huntsman, Eric D. Good Tidings of Great Joy: An Advent Celebration of the Savior's Birth. 2011. 160p. 27.99 ***(978-1-60641-659-4(6))*** Deseret Bk. Co.

Husted, Benjamin R. Christmas Out of the Advent Box: Reclaiming Christmas for Fun, Faith, & Family. 2006. (ENG., Illus.). 111p. per. 9.99 *(978-1-933204-28-4(1))* Deep River Bks.

Ideals Christmas. 2008. (ENG.). 64p. pap. 6.99 *(978-0-8249-1320-5(5))* Ideals Pubns.

Ideals Editors, ed. Christmas Ideals 2009 & Christmas Recipes. 2009. (ENG.). 64p. pap. 8.99 *(978-0-8249-1323-6(X))* Ideals Pubns.

Ideals Publications Inc. Staff, creator. Ideals Christmas. 2006. (Ideals Christmas Ser.). (Illus.). 64p. per. 6.95 *(978-0-8249-1311-3(6))* Ideals Pubns.

Janvier, A. Thomas. The Christmas Kalends of Provence & Some Other Provencal Festivals. 2007. 120p. 41.99 *(978-1-4280-7487-3(2))*; per. 34.99 *(978-1-4280-7483-5(X))* IndyPublish.com.

Jarrett, Vicky, ed. A Christmas Treasury: A Collection of Joyful Holiday Readings. 2006. 96p. mass mkt. 5.95 *(978-0-9779681-0-7(3)*, Our State Magazine) Mann Media, Inc.

Jeffrey, Yvonne. The Everything Family Christmas Book: Stories, Songs, Recipes, Crafts, Traditions, & More. 2008. (ENG.). 448p. pap. 15.95 *(978-1-59869-561-8(4))* Adams Media Corp.

Jennison, Christopher. All Aboard for Christmas. 2009. (ENG.). 128p. (J). 25.00 *(978-1-4379-6995-5(X))* DIANE Publishing Co.

Jeremiah, David. The 12 Ways of Christmas, 0 vols. 2008. 128p. 14.99 *(978-1-4041-8727-6(8))* Nelson, Thomas Inc.

John Paul II, pseud. Advent & Christmas Wisdom from Pope John Paul II: Daily Scripture & Prayers Together with Pope John Paul II's Own Words, 1 vol. 2006. (Advent & Christmas Wisdom Ser.). (Illus.). 112p. per. 9.95 *(978-0-7648-1510-2(5))* Liguori Pubns.

Joiner, F. Belton. Advent, Christmas, & Epiphany Services. 2010. 97p. pap. 12.00 *(978-1-4267-0680-6(4))* Abingdon Pr.

Jones, Rufus M. The Shepherd Who Missed the Manger: A Christmas Story. 2011. 30p. 35.95 ***(978-1-258-05401-4(9))*** Literary Licensing, LLC.

Joy of Christmas with Angela Lansbury. 17.95 *(978-1-57008-935-0(3)*, Bookcraft, Inc.) Deseret Bk. Co.

Kapp, Ardeth G. The Joy of Believing. 2007. 80p. 14.95 *(978-1-59038-809-9(7))* Deseret Bk. Co.

Karoub, Ginny. Mulberry Lane. 2008. 36p. 8.99 *(978-1-60247-519-9(9))* Tate Publishing & Enterprises, LLC.

Kazek, Kelly. Christmas Tales of Alabama. 2011. 128p. pap. 12.99 ***(978-1-60949-155-0(6))*** History Pr., The.

Kealen, Erin. Memories of Christmas: A Christmas Program. 2007. 32p. pap. *(978-0-87227-824-0(7))* Regular Baptist Pr.

Kellogg, Alice M. Christmas Entertainments: Containing Fancy Drills, Acrostics, Motion Songs, Tableaux, Short Plays, & Recitations in Costume for Children of Five to Fifteen Years. 2008. 148p. pap. 13.95 *(978-1-4357-3325-1(8))* Lulu Enterprises Inc.

Kelly, Joseph F. The Feast of Christmas. 2010. E-Book *(978-0-8146-3932-0(1))*; 136p. pap. 14.95 *(978-0-8146-3325-0(0))* Liturgical Pr.

Killinger, Anne Kathryn. An Inner Journey to Christmas: An Advent Devotional. 2010. 112p. pap. 14.99 *(978-0-8272-1638-9(6))* Chalice Pr.

King, Heidi Tyline. The Christmas Book: Creative Ideas for Making the Holidays Memorable. 2011. (ENG.). 160p. pap. 16.95 *(978-1-61628-149-6(9))* Weldon Owen, Inc.

Kingsbury, Karen. A Treasury of Christmas Miracles: True Stories of God's Presence Today. rev. ed. 2007. (ENG.). 176p. 13.99 *(978-0-446-19392-4(5))* FaithWords.

Kirking, Cheryl. What Can I Give Jesus? A Christmas Message for All Ages. 2006. (Illus.). 32p. 15.95 incl. audio compact disk *(978-0-9768847-1-2(2))* Mill Hse. Pr.

Kissinger, Barbara Hallman. Christmas Merrymaking, 1 vol. 2007. (ENG., Illus.). 128p. 19.95 *(978-1-58980-482-1(1))* Pelican Publishing Co., Inc.

Kostyal, Karen & Colonial Williamsburg Foundation. Christmas in Williamsburg: 300 Years of Family Traditions. 2011. (ENG., Illus.). 64p. (J). (gr. k-12). 17.95 *(978-1-4263-0867-3(1))*; lib. bdg. 27.90 *(978-1-4263-0868-0(X))* National Geographic Society. (National Geographic Children's Bks.).

Larsen, Melissa K. Dare to Believe in the Man in the Red Suit. 2009. 48p. pap. 17.49 *(978-1-4490-4134-2(5))* AuthorHouse.

Laurie, Greg. His Christmas Presence. 2007. (ENG.). 143p. 12.95 *(978-0-9777103-8-6(6))* Kerygma Publishing.

Leisure Arts & Leisure Arts designers. Creating the Happiest of Holidays, Book 2, Bk. 2. 2nd ed. 2010. (ENG.). 160p. pap. 19.95 *(978-1-60900-012-7(9))* Leisure Arts, Inc.

Leith, John H. May You Have A Merry Christmas: And the Best New Year Ever! Goodloe, James C., ed. 2010. 112p. pap. 14.00 *(978-1-60899-423-6(6)*, Resource Pubns.) Wipf & Stock Pubs.

Lennox, Doug. Now You Know Christmas: The Little Book of Answers. 2007. (Now You Know Ser.). (ENG., Illus.). 96p. pap. 9.99 *(978-1-55002-745-7(X)*, Dundurn Pr.) Dundurn CAN. Dist: Ingram Pub. Services.

Lester, Meera. Why Does Santa Wear Red? And 100 Other Christmas Curiousities Unwrapped. 2007. (ENG., Illus.). 256p. per. 9.95 *(978-1-59869-457-4(X))* Adams Media Corp.

Life Staff. Picture Puzzle Christmas, Set. 2010. (ENG., Illus.). 400p. pap. 29.95 *(978-1-60320-346-3(X))* Time Home Entertainment, Inc.

Liguori, Alfonso Maria de'. Advent & Christmas Wisdom from Saint Alphonsus Liguori: Daily Scripture & Prayers Together with Saint Alphonsus Liguori's Own Words. 2011. *(978-0-7648-1909-4(7))* Liguori Pubns.

Linsley, Leslie. A Nantucket Christmas. 2006. (ENG., Illus.). 108p. per. 19.99 *(978-0-8212-5807-1(9))* Bulfinch.

Littlefield, Bruce. Merry Christmas, America: Celebrating the Holiday Across the U. S. A. 2007. (Illus.). 144p. pap. 19.95 *(978-0-06-134829-7(5)*, Collins Design) HarperCollins Pubs.

Livingood, J., et al, eds. Christmas I Remember Best. (Illus.). *(978-0-910901-00-0(7))*; pap. 5.95 *(978-0-910901-01-7(5))* Deseret News Publishing Co.

Logan, Ben. Christmas Remembered. 2010. (ENG.). 208p. 17.99 *(978-0-7603-3853-7(1)*, 0760338531, Voyageur Pr) MBI Publishing Co. LLC.

Lowe, Scott C., ed. Christmas - Philosophy for Everyone: Better Than a Lump of Coal. 2010. (Philosophy for Everyone Ser.: 5). (ENG., Illus.). 256p. pap. 19.95 *(978-1-4443-3090-8(X)*, Wiley-Blackwell) Wiley, John & Sons, Inc.

Loxton, Howard. Christmas. 39.00 *(978-1-56696-141-7(6))* Jackdaw Pubns.

Macdonogh, Steve. Green & Gold: Wren Boys of Dingle. (Illus.). 96p. 3.50 *(978-0-86322-041-8(X))* Penguin Group (USA) Inc.

MacKinnon, Chris. The Story of Christmas. 2008. 112p. pap. 12.00 *(978-1-4357-2980-3(3))* Lulu Enterprises Inc.

Madison Square Garden Entertainment. Radio City Christmas Spectacular. 2009. (Illus.). 46p. *(978-0-615-28843-7(X))* Madison Square Garden LP.

Magill, John, et al. Christmas in New Orleans, 1 vol. 2009. (ENG., Illus.). 240p. 39.95 *(978-1-58980-560-6(7))* Pelican Publishing Co., Inc.

Main, Robin. Santa-Tizing: What's Wrong with Christmas And How to Clean It Up. 2008. 364p. pap. 20.99 *(978-1-60791-115-9(9))* Xulon Pr., Inc.

McCormack, Derek. Christmas Days: From Fake Snow to Santalands - The Things That Make Christmas Christmas. 2010. (ENG., Illus.). 320p. pap. 12.95 *(978-0-88784-839-1(7))* House of Anansi Pr. CAN. Dist: Perseus-PGW.

McCullough, David. In the Dark Streets Shineth: A 1941 Christmas Eve Story. 2010. 56p. 19.99 *(978-1-60641-831-4(9)*, Shadow Mountain) Deseret Bk. Co.

McGraw, Robin. Christmas in My Heart, 0 vols. 2009. 112p. 19.99 *(978-1-4041-0529-4(8))* Nelson, Thomas Inc.

McKenna, Megan. Advent, Christmas, & Epiphany: Stories & Reflections on the Sunday Readings. 2008. 256p. pap. 19.95 *(978-1-56548-300-2(6))* New City Pr.

McKinley, Rick, et al. Advent Conspiracy: Can Christmas Still Change the World?, 1 vol. 2009. (ENG.). 160p. pap. 12.99 *(978-0-310-32452-2(1))* Zondervan.

Meeks, Blair Gilmer. Expecting the Unexpected: An Advent Devotional Guide. 2006. 125p. per. 15.00 *(978-0-8358-1004-3(6))* Upper Room Bks.

Michael O'Mara Books UK. A Gift Book for Christmas. 2010. (ENG.). 64p. 4.95 *(978-1-84317-408-0(1))* O'Mara, Michael Bks., Ltd. GBR. Dist: Independent Pubs. Group.

Miles, Clement A. Christmas in Ritual & Tradition, Christian & Pagan. 2009. 420p. 30.99 *(978-0-559-06062-5(9))*; 32.99 *(978-0-559-06047-2(5))*; pap. 33.75 *(978-0-559-06058-8(0))*; pap. 34.75 *(978-0-559-06050-2(5))* BiblioBazaar.

—Christmas in Ritual & Tradition, Christian & Pagan. 2008. 416p. 24.95 *(978-1-4344-7377-6(5))*; pap. 14.95 *(978-1-4344-7376-9(7))* Wildside Pr., LLC.

Millard-Brawn, Madge. What My Mother Told Me. 2009. 128p. pap. 21.50 *(978-0-9559740-0-7(3))* Brawn, Madge GBR. Dist: Lulu Enterprises Inc.

Miller, Calvin. The Christ of Christmas: Readings for Advent - 31 Days of Devotions. 2006. (ENG.). 144p. 9.99 *(978-0-8054-4419-3(X)*, B&H Bks.) B&H Publishing Group.

Miller, J. r. & Miller, J. R. Christmas Making. 2011. 34p. pap. 7.99 ***(978-1-61203-154-5(4))*** Bottom of the Hill Publishing.

Miller, W. David. The Call of Christmas on the Human Heart. 2011. 338p. pap. 18.99 ***(978-1-61379-196-7(8))*** Xulon Pr., Inc.

Mitchell, Michael D. The Two Sides of Santa. 2011. 44p. pap. 11.95 ***(978-1-4327-5781-6(4))*** Outskirts Pr., Inc.

Moore, James W. The Miracle of Christmas: An Advent Study for Adults. 2006. 39p. pap. 6.50 *(978-0-687-33236-6(2))* Abingdon Pr.

Moore, Mary G. Advent of Understanding: Facing the First Christmas after the Death of a Loved One. 2007. 93p. per. 5.95 *(978-1-933066-07-3(5)*, Resurrection Pr.) Catholic Bk. Publishing Corp.

Morneau, Robert. Waiting in Joyful Hope Advent & Christmas 2009-2010. 2009. 112p. pap. 2.00 *(978-0-8146-3082-2(0)*, Liturgical Pr. Bks.) Liturgical Pr.

Mr. Wishmadoo Xmas Wish. 12.95 *(978-0-9718438-1-3(3))* Wall Hse. Publishing Co.

Murphey, Cecil & Gibson, Marley. Christmas Miracles. 2009. (ENG.). 256p. 14.99 *(978-0-312-58983-7(2))* St. Martin's Pr.

—The Spirit of Christmas. 2011. (ENG.). 208p. 14.99 *(978-0-312-64501-4(5))* St. Martin's Pr.

Nelson, Russell M. Wise Men & Women Still Adore Him. 2010. 12p. pap. ***(978-1-60641-835-2(1)***, Wiley-Blackwell) Deseret Bk. Co.

Neumuller, Anders. God Jul: A Swedish Christmas. 2009. (ENG., Illus.). 96p. 19.95 *(978-1-60239-755-2(4)*, 239755) Skyhorse Publishing Co., Inc.

Osteen, Joel. The Christmas Spirit: Memories of Family, Friends, & Faith. 2010. (ENG., Illus.). 160p. 15.99 *(978-1-4391-9833-9(0)*, Free Pr.) Free Pr.

Page, Sally. The Flower Shop Christmas: Christmas in a Country Flower Shop. 2007. (ENG., Illus.). 192p. 34.95 *(978-0-9719552-8-8(X))* Source Bk. Pubns.

Papa, Carrie. The Brightest Star of All: And Other Christmas Stories. 2008. 80p. pap. 8.00 *(978-0-687-64813-9(0))* Abingdon Pr.

Patton, Kathryn. The Wonder of Christmas. 2006. (ENG., Illus.). 126p. (J). 19.95 (978-0-8249-5877-0(2)) Ideals Pubns.

Peale, Norman Vincent. My Christmas Treasury. Date not set. 160p. 15.00 (978-0-88365-928-1(X), Galahad Bks.) BBS Publishing Corp.

Perry, Joe. Christmas in Germany: A Cultural History. 2010. (ENG., Illus.). 424p. 49.95 (978-0-8078-3364-3(9)) Univ. of North Carolina Pr.

Perry, Marta. Naomi's Christmas. 2012. (Pleasant Valley Ser.). (ENG.). (gr. 12). pap. 14.00 **(978-0-425-25329-8(5)**, Berkley Trade) Penguin Group (USA) Inc.

Peterson, Eugene H. My First Message the Christmas Story. 2008. (Living the Letters Ser.). 24p. (J). 12.99 (978-1-60006-276-6(8)) Message Bks. AUS. Dist: NavPress Publishing Group.

Pickens, Jennifer B. Christmas at the White House. 2009. (ENG., Illus.). 408p. 49.95 (978-0-615-28764-5(6)) Fife & Drum Pr.

Plaut, Joshua Eli. A Kosher Christmas:: 'tis the Season to Be Jewish. 2012. 240p. 68.00 **(978-0-8135-5379-5(2))**; pap. 22.95 **(978-0-8135-5380-1(6))** Rutgers Univ. Pr.

Pringle, Mary P. & Urann, Clara A. Yule-Tide in Many Lands. 2010. (Illus.). 84p. pap. (978-1-4068-5723-7(3)) Echo Library.

Pringle, Mary Poague. Yule-Tide in Many Lands. 2010. (Illus.). 56p. pap. 20.00 (978-1-153-74513-0(5)); 54p. pap. 17.50 (978-1-152-14692-1(0)) General Bks. LLC.

Pringle, Mary Poague & Urann, Clara A. Yule-Tide in Many Lands. 2010. 238p. pap. 26.75 (978-1-177-11535-3(2)) 2008. 120p. 21.99 (978-0-554-39705-4(6)) 2008. 120p. 24.99 (978-0-554-30402-1(3)) BiblioBazaar.

Publications International Staff, ed. Armchair Digest: Christmas Unwrapped. 2010. 320p. 10.98 (978-1-60553-913-3(9)) Publications International, Ltd.

Puzzle Society Staff. Christmas Logic: 100 Puzzles. 2010. (ENG.). 144p. pap. 7.99 (978-0-7407-9960-0(6)) Andrews McMeel Publishing.

—Christmas Word Roundup: 100 Puzzles. 2010. (ENG.). 128p. pap. 7.99 (978-0-7407-9958-7(4)) Andrews McMeel Publishing.

—Pocket Posh Christmas Brain Games - 100 Puzzles. 2010. (ENG.). 128p. pap. 7.99 (978-0-7407-9961-7(4)) Andrews McMeel Publishing.

—Pocket Posh Christmas Sudoku - 100 Puzzles. 2010. (ENG.). 128p. pap. 7.99 (978-0-7407-9956-3(8)) Andrews McMeel Publishing.

Ratsch, Christian & Muller-Ebeling, Claudia. Pagan Christmas: The Plants, Spirits, & Rituals at the Origins of Yuletide. Lueders, Katja & Lorenzo, Rafael, trs. from GER. 2006. (ENG., Illus.). 1p. pap. 29.95 (978-1-59477-092-0(1)) Inner Traditions International, Ltd.

Raya, Joseph M. Christmas: Birth of Our Lord God & Saviour, Jesus Christ. 140p. (978-0-921440-45-1(6)) Madonna Hse. Pubns.

Reed, Robert M. Christmas Postcards: A Collector's Guide. 2007. (Illus.). 176p. pap. 29.95 (978-0-7643-2689-9(9)) Schiffer Publishing, Ltd.

Reminisce Christmas. 2010. (Illus.). 208p. **(978-0-89821-834-3(9))** Reiman Pubns., L.P.

Ricks, Patricia W. The Christmas Spirit. Date not set. mass mkt. (978-0-449-22403-8(1), Fawcett) Random House Publishing Group.

Rife, Richard C. Honoring Christmas in My Heart. 2009. pap. 6.99 (978-1-59955-314-6(7)) Cedar Fort, Inc./CFI Distribution.

Ritson, Darren. W. Ghosts at Christmas. 2010. (ENG., Illus.). 144p. pap. 14.95 (978-0-7524-5767-3(5)) History Pr. Ltd., The GBR. Dist: Independent Pubs. Group.

Rockwell, Norman. Norman Rockwell's Christmas Book. rev. ed. 2009. (ENG., Illus.). 224p. 24.95 (978-0-8109-8262-8(5)) Abrams.

Rogers, Thomas. Advent, Christmas, Epiphany. (Church Year Bible Study Series B). pap., stu. ed. 5.50 (978-0-570-09450-0(X), 20-2568); pap. 5.50 (978-0-570-09451-7(8), 20-2569) Concordia Publishing Hse.

Sams, Ferrol. Christmas Gift! 2010. 112p. 25.00 (978-0-88146-211-1(X)) Mercer Univ. Pr.

Sanchez, Cheryl. Jesus Is Not the Reason for the Season. 2009. 92p. pap. 15.96 (978-0-557-15243-8(7)) Lulu Enterprises Inc.

Sander, Jennifer Basye, et al. Green Christmas: How to Have a Joyous, Eco-Friendly Holiday Season. 2008. (ENG.). 192p. pap. 7.95 (978-1-60550-041-6(0)) Adams Media Corp.

Santos, Dennis. Not So Silent Night. 2011. 84p. pap. 8.95 **(978-1-60594-741-9(5)**, Llumina Christian Bks.) Aeon Publishing Inc.

Schauffler, Robert Haven, Editor. CHRISTMAS: Its Origin, Celebration & Significance as Related in Prose & Verse. 2008. 240p. pap. 19.95 (978-1-4357-3324-4(X)) Lulu Enterprises Inc.

Schauffler, Robert Haven. Christmas: Its origin, celebration & significance as related in prose & Verse. 2010. (ENG.). 356p. pap. 32.75 (978-1-176-54660-8(0)) BiblioBazaar.

—Christmas Its Origin, Celebration & Significance As Related in Prose & Verse. 2010. (Illus.). 148p. pap. 23.65 (978-1-153-59557-5(5)) General Bks. LLC.

Scheidies, Carolyn R. Heart of Christmas. 2008. 51p. pap. 28.38 (978-0-557-00324-2(5)) Lulu Enterprises Inc.

Seeley, Mary Evans. Season's Greetings from the White House: The Collection of Presidential Christmas Cards, Messages & Gifts. 6th ed. 2007. 272p. 40.00 (978-0-9657684-7-4(3)) Presidential Christmas, A.

Selby, Anna. The Victorian Christmas. 2008. (Illus.). 224p. 39.95 (978-1-84468-028-3(2)) Pen & Sword Bks. Ltd. GBR. Dist: Casemate Pubs. & Bk. Distributors, LLC.

Sell, Colleen. A Cup of Comfort for Christmas: Stories That Celebrate the Warmth, Joy, & Wonder of the Holiday. 2nd ed. 2007. (ENG.). 336p. per. 9.95 (978-1-59869-658-5(0)) Adams Media Corp.

Shea, Chris, illus. Merry Christmas with Love. 2008. 64p. 9.99 (978-1-4003-1410-2(0)) Nelson, Thomas Inc.

Shoemaker, Alfred Lewis, et al. Christmas in Pennsylvania: A Folk-Cultural Study. 50th ed. 2009. (ENG., Illus.). 224p. 24.95 (978-0-8117-0506-6(4)) Stackpole Bks.

Slaughter, Michael. Christmas Is Not Your Birthday: Experience the Joy of Living & Giving like Jesus. 2011. 112p. pap. 12.00 (978-1-4267-2735-1(6)) Abingdon Pr.

Slotterback, Carole S. The Psychology of Santa. 2009. (Illus.). xi, 121p. 59.00 (978-1-60692-700-7(0)) Nova Science Pubs., Inc.

Smart, William B. The Three Levels of Christmas: An Invitation to Celebrate the Christ All Year Long. 2007. pap. 12.95 (978-1-59038-803-7(8)) Deseret Bk. Co.

Smith, Chuck, as told by. The Christmas Story: God's Unspeakable Gift. 2006. (Illus.). 112p. 12.99 (978-1-932941-91-3(6)) Word For Today, The.

Spadafori, Gina & Bice, Jeanne. Christmas: The Best Experts' Advice for a Memorable Season with Stories & Photos of Holiday Magic. 2008. (Ultimate Ser.). (ENG., Illus.). 304p. pap. 14.95 (978-0-7573-0754-6(X)) Health Communications, Inc.

Spangler, Ann. Immanuel: Praying the Names of God Through the Christmas Season, 1 vol. 2007. (ENG.). 144p. 14.99 (978-0-310-27614-2(4)) Zondervan.

Stansfield, Anita. By the Light of a Star: True Christmas Stories. 2008. 26p. pap. (978-1-59811-406-5(9), Debolsillo) Covenant Communications, Inc.

Stauffer, Jeanne. A Family Christmas: Handmade Gifts & Heartfelt Stories. 2007. (Illus.). 176p. (978-1-59217-186-6(9), House of White Birches, Inc.) Annie's Publishing, LLC.

Steiger, Brad & Steiger, Sherry Hansen. Christmas Miracles: Inspirational True Stories of Holiday Magic. 2008. (ENG.). 240p. pap. 12.95 (978-1-60550-017-1(8)) Adams Media Corp.

—Santa Miracles: 50 True Stories that Celebrate the Most Magical Time of the Year. 2009. (ENG.). 256p. pap. 12.95 (978-1-59869-612-7(2)) Adams Media Corp.

Steiner, Rudolf. The Christmas Imagination. 2011. 16p. pap. 35.95 **(978-1-258-02440-6(3))** Literary Licensing, LLC.

Stocks, Linda Nelson & Nelson, Linda L. Sleigh Bells Ring. gif. ed. 2006. (ENG., Illus.). 80p. 9.95 (978-0-7407-6073-0(4)) Andrews McMeel Publishing.

Storrings, Michael. A Very New York Christmas. 2008. (ENG., Illus.). 96p. 19.95 (978-0-312-37705-2(3)) St. Martin's Pr.

Stuever, Hank. Tinsel: A Search for America's Christmas Present. 2010. (ENG.). 352p. pap. 14.95 (978-0-547-39456-5(X), Mariner Bks.) Houghton Mifflin Harcourt Trade & Reference Pubs.

Sullivan, Ed & Precht, Betty Sullivan. Christmas with Ed Sullivan. 2011. 290p. 48.95 **(978-1-258-07352-6(5))** Literary Licensing, LLC.

Sullivan, Robert. Flight of the Reindeer: The True Story of Santa Claus & His Christmas Mission. 2010. (ENG., Illus.). 96p. (J). (gr. 4-7). 22.95 (978-1-61608-151-5(1), 608151) Skyhorse Publishing Co., Inc.

Summers Bridgewater. Christmas Trivia: Fun & Fascinating Facts about Christmas. 2011. 100p. 9.95 (978-0-9827732-8-4(5)) Summers Bridgewater Pr. Inc., The.

Swindoll, Charles R. A Bethlehem Christmas: Celebrating the Joyful Season, 0 vols. 2007. (Illus.). 192p. 14.99 (978-1-4041-0468-6(2)) Nelson, Thomas Inc.

Szymanski, Helen. Classic Christmas: True Stories of Holiday Cheer & Goodwill. 2006. (ENG.). 288p. per. 12.95 (978-1-59337-520-1(4)) Adams Media Corp.

Szymanski, Helen, ed. Christmas Traditions: True Stories That Celebrate the Spirit of the Season. 2009. (ENG.). 288p. pap. 10.95 (978-1-59869-838-1(9)) Adams Media Corp.

Tabori Fried, Natasha & Tabori, Lena, eds. The Christmas Almanac: Every Thing You Need for a Perfect Holiday! rev. ed. 2009. (ENG., Illus.). 240p. 27.50 (978-1-59962-069-5(3), Welcome Bks.) Welcome Enterprises, Inc.

Tarkington, Booth. Beasley's Christmas Party. 2009. 110p. (gr. 4-7). 24.99 (978-1-60512-386-8(2)); pap. 10.99 (978-1-60512-486-5(9)) Akasha Publishing, LLC. (Akasha Classics).

—Beasley's Christmas Party. 2008. (gr. 4-7). 150p. pap. 19.75 (978-0-554-85995-8(5)); 153p. pap. 19.75 (978-0-554-85993-4(9)) BiblioBazaar.

—Beasley's Christmas Party. 2008. 112p. 34.95 (978-1-4368-8697-0(X)) 2008. 108p. 34.95 (978-1-4365-7418-1(8)) 2008. 112p. pap. 19.95 (978-1-4367-8624-9(X)) 2007. (ENG.). 108p. per. 19.95 (978-0-548-78566-9(X)) 2007. (ENG.). 108p. (gr. 4-7). 34.95 (978-0-548-01191-1(5)) Kessinger Publishing, LLC.

—Beasley's Christmas Party. 2007. (ENG.). 108p. (gr. 4-7). per. (978-1-4067-1885-0(8)) Read Bks.

—Beasley's Christmas Party. 2008. 112p. 24.95 (978-1-4344-7576-3(X)); pap. 14.95 (978-1-4344-7575-6(1)) Wildside Pr., LLC.

Taylor, Nancy S. Baby's First Christmas. (Illus.). 50p. 15.95 (978-0-937745-16-8(2)) Traditions Pr.

Tempelman-Kluit, Anne, ed. Sleds, Sleighs & Snow: A Canadian Christmas Carol. 2007. (ENG., Illus.). 292p. pap. 19.95 (978-1-55285-905-6(3)) Whitecap Bks., Ltd. CAN. Dist: Midpoint Trade Bks., Inc.

They Came to the Manger: Heart-Warming Christmas Tales of Creatures Great & Small. 2010. 224p. 14.99 (978-0-8249-4819-1(X), GuidepostsBooks) Ideals Pubns.

Thibodeaux, Kathy. A Christmas Dream. 2007. (Illus.). 68p. (J). 25.00 (978-0-9799864-0-6(0)) Magnificat! Publishing Co.

Thomas. Advent & Christmas Wisdom from St. Thomas Aquinas. 2009. 10.99 (978-0-7648-1819-6(8)) Liguori Pubns.

Thomas, Bruce. First Christmas Present: Why Were Those First Three Gifts so Special? 2006. 12p. pap. 9.95 (978-83-330-0000-3(2)) First Christmas Project.

Thomas, Dylan. A Child's Christmas in Wales. 2009. (ENG., Illus.). 64p. pap. 9.95 (978-0-8112-1731-6(0), 21731) New Directions Publishing Corp.

Thomas, Nancy Smith. Moravian Christmas in the South. 2007. (ENG., Illus.). 184p. 34.95 (978-0-8078-3181-6(6)) Univ. of North Carolina Pr.

Thomas Nelson Publishing Staff, creator. Christmas A to Z: Unwrapping the Wonder of Seasonal Words & Phrases, 0 vols. 2007. (Illus.). 208p. 19.99 (978-1-4185-2796-9(3)) Nelson, Thomas Inc.

Thompson, Jim. The St Nicholas Solution. 2009. 112p. pap. 11.95 (978-1-4401-3345-9(X)) iUniverse, Inc.

Thornborough, Tim & Nodder, Marcus. The Real Christmas, 10 vols. 2010. (Christianity Explored Ser.). 16p. (978-1-906334-31-4(5)) Good Bk. Co.

Tille, Alexander. Yule & Christmas. 2009. 194p. pap. (978-0-217-65715-0(X)) Books LLC.

—Yule & Christmas. 2009. 196p. pap. 19.99 (978-1-4590-1078-9(7)) General Bks. LLC.

Time-Life Books Staff, contrib. by. The Book of Christmas. (Illus.). 144p. 20.00 (978-1-84447-180-5(2)) Time Life Value GBR. Dist: Mercury Bks. Ltd.

Tolhurst, James. Come Lord Jesus: Reflections on the Adve. 2006. 92p. per. (978-0-85244-020-9(0)) Gracewing, Ltd.

Travers, Sam. Christmas in the Old West: A Historical Scrapbook. (Illus.). 304p. pap. 28.00 (978-0-87842-460-3(1), 674) Mountain Pr. Publishing Co., Inc.

Van Dyke, Henry. The First Christmas Tree. 2009. 78p. pap. 16.75 (978-1-110-45354-2(X)) BiblioBazaar.

—The First Christmas Tree. 2007. 48p. per. (978-1-4065-4714-6(X)) Dodo Pr.

—The Spirit of Christmas. 2009. 68p. pap. 16.75 (978-1-110-60645-0(1)) BiblioBazaar.

—The Spirit of Christmas. 2007. (ENG.). 64p. per. 16.95 (978-0-548-71862-9(8)) Kessinger Publishing, LLC.

—What Peace Means, & the Spirit of Christmas. 2007. 68p. per. (978-1-4065-4727-6(1)) Dodo Pr.

Van Orden, Betty. The Twelve Days of Christmas: Ideas for a More Meaningful Holiday Season. 2007. 162p. per. 12.99 (978-1-59955-050-3(4)) Cedar Fort, Inc./CFI Distribution.

—The Twelve Days of Christmas Encore! 2009. pap. 10.99 (978-1-59955-338-2(4)) Cedar Fort, Inc./CFI Distribution.

Verbrugge, Verlyn D. A Not-So-Silent Night: The Unheard Story of Christmas & Why It Matters, 1 vol. 2009. 104p. pap. 9.99 (978-0-8254-3909-4(4)) Kregel Pubns.

Waggoner, Susan. Christmas Memories: Gifts, Activities, Fads, & Fancies, 1920s-1960s. 2009. (ENG., Illus.). 112p. 17.95 (978-1-58479-789-0(4)) Stewart, Tabori & Chang.

—Have Yourself a Very Vintage Christmas: Crafts, Decorating Tips, & Recipes, 1920s-1960s. 2011. (ENG., Illus.). 144p. 19.95 (978-1-58479-923-8(4)) Stewart, Tabori & Chang.

—Under the Tree: The Toys & Treats That Made Christmas Special, 1930-1970. 2007. (ENG., Illus.). 112p. 18.95 (978-1-58479-641-1(3)) Stewart, Tabori & Chang.

Walmsley, Denise. The Christmas Experiment. 2010. 192p. pap. 13.99 (978-0-88290-975-2(4)) Cedar Fort, Inc./CFI Distribution.

Warren, Rick. The Purpose of Christmas. 2008. (ENG., Illus.). 144p. 17.99 (978-1-4165-5900-9(0), Howard Bks.) Howard Books.

—The Purpose of Christmas, 1 vol. 2008. (ENG.). 64p. pap., stu. ed. 6.99 (978-0-310-31855-2(6)) Zondervan.

We Have Seen a Great Light: 99 Sayings on Christmas. 2007. 99p. 14.95 (978-1-56548-270-8(0)) New City Pr.

Weatherhead, A. Kingsley. Charlie's Christmas Letter. 2010. (Illus.). 80p. pap. 11.00 (978-1-60899-699-5(9), Resource Pubns.) Wipf & Stock Pubs.

Weatherhead, L. G. Christmas & the Christ. 2011. 32p. 35.95 **(978-1-258-00143-8(8))** Literary Licensing, LLC.

Weber, Susan. Christmas in Santa Fe, 1 vol. rev. exp. ed. 2011. (ENG., Illus.). 104p. 19.99 **(978-1-4236-2338-0(X))** Gibbs Smith, Publisher.

Webster, Douglas. A Christmas Journey. 2007. 120p. per. (978-1-894667-87-6(5)) Clements Publishing.

Weintraub, Stanley. General Washington's Christmas Farewell: A Mount Vernon Homecoming 1783. 2007. (ENG.). 224p. pap. 16.95 (978-1-4165-6789-9(5), Free Pr.) Free Pr.

Weintraub, Stanley. Pearl Harbor Christmas: A World at War, December 1941. 2012. (ENG., Illus.). 224p. pap. 14.00 **(978-0-306-82153-0(2))** Da Capo Pr., Inc.

Weiss, LeAnn. Christmas Promises: Heavenly Gifts for the Holiday Season. 2008. (ENG.). 176p. 14.99 (978-0-8307-4697-2(8)) Gospel Light Pubns.

Weller, Alan. Vintage Christmas. 2010. (Dover Pictura Electronic Clip Art Ser.). (ENG., Illus.). 128p. pap. 39.95 (978-0-486-99014-9(1)) Dover Pubns., Inc.

Wentzel, Elizabeth. Christmas. Date not set. pap. 11.50 (978-0-8488-0896-9(7)) Amereon LTD.

West, Matthew. Give This Christmas Away: 101 Simple & Thoughtful Ways To. 2009. (ENG.). 112p. 9.99 (978-1-4143-3644-2(6)) Tyndale Hse. Pubs.

Whiteley, Sheila. Christmas, Ideology & Popular Culture. 2008. (ENG., Illus.). 208p. (gr. 17). 120.00 (978-0-7486-2808-7(8)); pap. 35.00 (978-0-7486-2809-4(6)) Edinburgh Univ. Pr. GBR. Dist: Columbia Univ. Pr.

Will, Julianne M. Los Doce Días de Navidad: Celebrando Este Tiempo Como Catolicos. Estenger, Vilma G., tr. 2009. (SPA.). 1p. 14.95 (978-1-59276-718-2(4)) Our Sunday Visitor, Publishing Div.

—The Twelve Days of Christmas: Celebrating the Season as Catholics. 2009. 1p. 14.95 (978-1-59276-717-5(6)) Our Sunday Visitor, Publishing Div.

Willes, Laura F. Christmas with the Prophets. 2010. 21.99 (978-1-60641-828-4(9)) Deseret Bk. Co.

Williams, Dustin. A Carol to My King: A Tribute to Christmas. 2007. 124p. pap. 9.95 (978-0-615-17582-9(1)) Gibson Heritage, LLC.

Williams, Lisha. The Joy of Christmas. 2008. 69p. pap. 12.99 (978-1-4357-5110-1(8)) Lulu Enterprises Inc.

Williams, Marilyn. Advent Devotions, Keeping Christ in Your Christmas. 2009. 58p. pap. 24.00 (978-0-557-11659-1(7)) Lulu Enterprises Inc.

—Advent Family Devotions: Keeping Christ in Christmas. 2010. 112p. 28.95 (978-1-4497-0824-5(2)); pap. 11.95 (978-1-4497-0823-8(4)) Author Solutions, Inc. (WestBow Pr.).

Williams, Rowan, et al. Darkness Yielding: Liturgies, Prayers & Reflections for Christmas, Holy Week & Easter. 2008. 321p. pap. 24.99 (978-1-85311-844-9(3)) Canterbury Pr.

Winter, Nicholas. The Christmas Box. 2009. (Book-in-A-Box Ser.). (ENG., Illus.). 160p. 14.95 (978-1-85906-178-7(8)) Connections Bk. Publishing, Ltd. GBR. Dist: Red Wheel/Weiser.

Wintersteen, Benjamin & Browne, Katherine E., frwds. An Ethnographic Study of Papadjab, an Afro-Caribbean Devil Dancer: The Christmas Street Festival in St. Lucia. 2010. (ENG., Illus.). 180p. 99.95 (978-0-7734-3688-6(X)) Mellen, Edwin Pr., The.

Wojina, Lisa. Bathroom Book of Christmas Trivia: Stories, Weird Facts & Folklore Behind Holiday Traditions from Around the World. 2007. (Bathroom Book Of... Ser.). (ENG., Illus.). 224p. per. (978-1-897278-14-7(4)) Blue Bike Bks.

World Book, Inc. Staff. Christmas in Germany. 18.50 (978-0-7166-0854-7(5)) World Bk., Inc.

World Book, Inc Staff, contrib. by. Christmas in Austria & Its Capital, Vienna. 2007. (978-0-7166-0810-3(3)) World Bk., Inc.

—Christmas in Holland. 2011. **(978-0-7166-0821-9(9))** World Bk., Inc.

World Book, Inc Staff, contrib. by. Christmas on the Emerald Isle. 2010. 1696p. 22.00 (978-0-7166-0818-9(9)) World Bk., Inc.

World Book, Inc. Staff, ed. Christmas in Ireland. (978-0-7166-0855-4(3)) World Bk., Inc.

World Publishing Staff. Christmas Moments: Readings for the Christmas Season. (God's Word Ser.). pap. 2.99 (978-0-529-10474-8(1)) Nelson, Thomas Inc.

Wren, Brian & Wren, Brian A. Advent, Christmas, & Epiphany: Liturgies & Prayers for Public Worship. 2008. (ENG., Illus.). 240p. pap. 30.00 (978-0-664-23309-9(0)) Westminster John Knox Pr.

Wright, Christine. More Christmas Wrapped up. 2008. pap. (978-1-84427-261-7(3)) Scripture Union.

Wright, Ralph. Living the Days of Advent & the Christmas Season 2008. 2008. 48p. pap. 3.95 (978-0-8091-4519-5(7)) Paulist Pr.

CHRISTMAS—DRAMA

see Christmas Plays

CHRISTMAS—JUVENILE LITERATURE

Roche, Maite. My First Prayers for Christmas. 2010. 14p. 6.99 (978-1-58617-505-4(X)) Ignatius Pr.

CHRISTMAS—MEDITATIONS

Almquist, Curtis G. The Twelve Days of Christmas: Unwrapping the Gifts. 2006. (ENG.). 80p. per. 13.95 (978-1-56101-293-0(9)) Cowley Pubns.

Andrew, Gawrych, ed. Gift of Hope. 2009. 96p. pap. 3.50 (978-1-59471-221-0(2)) Ave Maria Pr.

Arnold, Eberhard, et al. When the Time Was Fulfilled: Christmas Meditations. 2nd ed. 2007. xxv, 141p. (978-0-87486-940-8(4)) Plough Publishing Hse.

Arthur, Ginny, ed. Best of Blessings: Advent, Christmas, & Epiphany. 152p. pap. 19.95 (978-1-55126-220-8(7), 1509) Forward Movement Pubns.

Blanchard, John. Why on Earth Did Jesus Come? 2009. 40p. pap. (978-0-85234-706-5(5)) Evangelical Pr.

Bonhoeffer, Dietrich. God Is in the Manger: Reflections on Advent & Christmas. 2012. (ENG.). 112p. 16.00 **(978-0-664-23887-2(4))** Westminster John Knox Pr.

Bonhoeffer, Dietrich & Riess, Jana. God Is in the Manger: Reflections on Advent & Christmas. 2010. (ENG.). 96p. pap. 13.00 (978-0-664-23429-4(1)) Westminster John Knox Pr.

Bullion, Joyce. Pray It Forward. 2007. pap. 13.99 (978-1-60266-512-5(5), Crown Oak Pr.) Xulon Pr., Inc.

Bullis, Marty A. The Miraculous Journey: Anticipating God in the Christmas Season. 2007. (ENG.). 144p. 14.99 (978-0-8307-4278-3(6)) Gospel Light Pubns.

Chilcote, Paul Wesley. Come Thou Long-Expected Jesus: Advent & Christmas with Charles Wesley. 2007. 128p. per. 14.00 (978-0-8192-2250-3(X), Morehouse Publishing) Church Publishing, Inc.

Christmas Prayers. Date not set. 1.25 (978-0-88271-524-7(0), 10200) Regina Pr., Malhame & Co.

Claus, Santa & Finley, Mitch. The True Meaning of Christmas. 2008. (ENG.). 106p. 12.95 (978-0-8245-2499-9(3)) Crossroad Publishing Co., The.

Collings, Michael R. All Calm, All Bright: Christmas Meditations. 2nd ed. Date not set. 100p. pap. 15.00 (978-1-886405-57-8(3)) White Crow Pr.

D'Avila-Latourrette, Victor-Antoine. A Monastery Journey to Christmas. 2011. (Illus.). 208p. **(978-0-7648-2081-6(8))** Liguori Pubns.

Finley, Jeanne Torrence. Blessings of the Manger Student: An Advent Study Based on the Revised Common Lectionary. 2010. (Sftcs Ser.). pap. 7.00 (978-0-687-46696-2(2)) Abingdon Pr.

C

Fisher, Susan, ed. Looking, Longing & Living: Readying Ourselves for Advent. 2007. 60p. per. (978-1-57383-416-2(5), Regent College Publishing) Regent College Publishing.

Gleddiesmith, Stacey. Welcoming the Stranger: Readying Ourselves for Christmas. 2010. **(978-1-57383-452-0(1))** Regent College Publishing.

Gleddiesmith, Stacey, ed. God with Us, Always. 2008. 60p. pap. (978-1-57383-430-8(0)) Regent College Publishing.

Griffin, James A. Christmas Joy. 2007. 82p. (978-0-8189-1257-3(X), St. Pauls) St Pauls/Alba Hse. Pubs.

Guthrie, Nancy. Come, Thou Long Expected Jesus: Experiencing the Peace & Promise of Christmas. 2008. 142p. (978-1-4335-0418-1(9)) Crossway.

Hanegraaff, Hank. The Heart of Christmas: A Devotional for the Season, 0 vols. 2009. 128p. 14.99 (978-1-4041-8758-0(8)) Nelson, Thomas Inc.

Hemrich-Skomer, Denise & Tyrtania, Joachim. Let the Children Come: A Family Guide to the Liturgy of the Word Cycle A. 2007. 64p. (J). per. 6.95 (978-0-9787087-1-9(7)) Bound by Grace Pr., LLC.

Jars of Clay. Peace Is Here: Christmas Reflections. 2007. (Illus.). 57p. (978-1-894160-08-7(8)) Gray Matters Pr.

Lucado, Max, et al. The Glory of Christmas, 0 vols. collector's ed. 2009. 160p. 15.99 (978-1-4041-8759-7(6)) Nelson, Thomas Inc.

McKenna, Megan. Advent, Christmas, & Epiphany: Stories & Reflections on the Daily Readings. 2008. 256p. pap. 19.95 (978-1-56548-301-9(4)) New City Pr.

—Advent, Christmas & Epiphany: Stories & Reflections on the Sunday & Daily Readings. 2008. 512p. pap. 39.90 (978-1-56548-302-6(2)) New City Pr.

Merton Institute for Contemplative Living Staff. Advent & Christmas. Montaldo, Jonathan & Toth, Robert G., eds. 2010. (Illus.). 64p. 5.95 (978-1-59471-195-4(X)) Ave Maria Pr.

Nancy, Guthrie. Come, Thou Long-Expected Jesus: Experiencing the Peace & Promise of Christmas. Guthrie, Nancy, ed. 2008. 144p. pap. 12.99 (978-1-4335-0180-7(5)) Crossway.

Pennoyer, Greg & Wolfe, Gregory, eds. God With Us: Rediscovering the Meaning of Christmas. 2007. 164p. (978-1-57725-541-3(0)) Paraclete Pr.

Phillips, Dennis. God with Us: Reflections on the Christmas Story. 2006. (ENG.). 76p. per. 9.95 (978-0-7414-3546-0(2)) Infinity Publishing.

Ratzinger, Joseph. The Blessing of Christmas: Meditations for the Season. 2007. 110p. 14.95 (978-1-58617-172-8(0)) Ignatius Pr.

Rhodes, Ray. Family Worship for the Christmas Season. 2007. 120p. per. 12.00 (978-1-59925-129-5(9)) Solid Ground Christian Bks.

Roberts, Oral. Christ near You. 2011. 34p. 35.95 **(978-1-258-00142-1(X))** Literary Licensing, LLC.

Santa Claus. The True Meaning of Christmas. 2008. (978-0-8245-2442-5(X)) Crossroad Publishing Co., The.

Schneider, Richard H., et al. Guideposts for the Spirit: Christmas Stories of Faith. 2007. 282p. per. 9.99 (978-0-8249-4728-6(2), GuidepostsBooks) Ideals Pubns.

Shea, John. Starlight: Beholding the Christmas Miracle All Year Long. 2006. 269p. 18.95 (978-0-87946-322-9(8)); per. 14.95 (978-0-87946-313-7(9)) ACTA Pubns.

Smith, John. Hugs for the Holidays: Stories, Sayings, & Scriptures to Encourage & Inspire. 2011. (Hugs Ser.). (ENG., Illus.). 160p. pap. 9.99 (978-1-4516-4895-9(2), Howard Bks.) Howard Books.

the Daughters of St. Paul. Advent Grace: Daily Gospel Reflections. 2009. 128p. pap. 7.95 (978-0-8198-0787-8(7)) Pauline Bks. & Media.

Tyrtania, Joachim & Hemrich-Skomer, Denise. Let the Children Come: A Family Guide to the Liturgy of the Word. 2006. 65p. (J). per. 6.95 (978-0-9787087-0-2(9)) Bound by Grace Pr., LLC.

Webber, Christopher L. Advent with Evelyn Underhill. 2006. 96p. per. 13.00 (978-0-8192-2221-3(6), Morehouse Publishing) Church Publishing, Inc.

Wilke, Julia Kitchens Trust, et al. Christmas: the Good, the Bad, & the Ugly: An Advent Study for Adults. 2010. 48p. pap. 7.00 (978-0-687-66034-6(3)) Abingdon Pr.

Williams, Jane. Approaching Christmas. 2006. (Illus.). 128p. 14.95 (978-0-8198-0780-9(X)) Pauline Bks. & Media.

Wolfe, Gregory, et al, eds. God with Us: Rediscovering the Meaning of Christmas. 2007. (Illus.). 185p. 29.95 (978-1-55725-541-9(5)) Paraclete Pr., Inc.

CHRISTMAS—POETRY

see also Carols

Christmas Program Builder No. 61: Creative Resources for Program Directors. 2008. (ENG.). 32p. pap. 5.99 (978-0-8341-7628-7(9), 0834176289) Lillenas Publishing Co.

Collings, Michael R. All Calm, All Bright: Christmas Offerings. 2007. (ENG.). 148p. (Orig.). per. 13.99 (978-1-4344-0172-4(3)) Wildside Pr., LLC.

Decock, John E. Poetic Meditations. 2011. 64p. 20.43 **(978-1-4269-7490-8(6))**; pap. 10.43 **(978-1-4269-7489-2(2))** Trafford Publishing.

Donkersgoed, Dwayne. Hay & Holly: Poems of Christmas & the Christmas Season. 2007. 84p. per. 16.95 (978-1-4241-8309-8(X)) PublishAmerica, Inc.

Evelyn-Hall, Rose P. A Christmas Collage: A Selection of Poems for the Christmas Season, Including an Ode to Joseph - A Special Tribute to A Special Father. 2009. 64p. pap. 10.99 (978-1-60791-897-4(8)) Xulon Pr., Inc.

Frost, Robert. Prophets Really Prophesy As Mystics: The Commentators Merely by Statistics. 2011. 12p. pap. 35.95 **(978-1-258-03502-0(2))** Literary Licensing, LLC.

Hopper, Edward. The Fire on the Hearth in Sleepy Hollows a Christmas Poem of the Olden Time by Edward Hopper. 2006. 108p. per. 16.99 (978-1-4255-0700-8(X)) MPublishing.

Ideals Publications Inc. Staff. Ideals Christmas. 2007. (Ideals Christmas Ser.). (Illus.). 64p. per. 6.99 (978-0-8249-1316-8(7), Ideals) Ideals Pubns.

Martin, Charles. The Divine Eraser: A Book of Christian Poems. 2010. pap. 15.99 (978-1-61663-027-0(2)) Tate Publishing & Enterprises, LLC.

Mitchell, William. Tribute to the Advent. 2009. 92p. pap. 12.95 (978-0-557-08306-0(0)) Lulu Enterprises Inc.

Morris, Harrison S. In the Yule-Log Glow-Book III: Christmas Poems from 'round the World. 2007. 168p. pap. 19.99 (978-1-4346-6188-3(1)); (ENG.). 192p. pap. 21.99 (978-1-4346-6189-0(X)) BiblioBazaar.

Morris, Harrison S. & Frank P. Mahony. In the Yule-Log Glow Book II: Christmas Tales from Round the World. 2007. (ENG.). 148p. pap. 18.99 (978-1-4264-9569-4(2)); 166p. pap. 21.99 (978-1-4264-9950-0(7)) BiblioBazaar.

Morris, Harrison S. & Morris, Harrison S. In the Yule-Log Glow, Book I Christmas Tales from 'Round the World. 2010. (Illus.). 86p. pap. 20.00 (978-1-153-63167-9(9)) General Bks. LLC.

Morris, Harrison Smith. In the Yule Log Glow Book I: Christmas Tales from Round the World. 2007. 142p. pap. 18.99 (978-1-4264-9421-5(1)); (ENG.). 154p. pap. 21.99 (978-1-4264-9802-2(0)) BiblioBazaar.

Morrissey, Anne. Santa's Adventures: Preparations for the Christmas Flight 2007, 2009 2010. 2011. 28p. pap. 11.32 **(978-1-4567-4363-5(5))** AuthorHouse.

New Directions Staff & Thomas, K. Christmas Poems. Hayes, Albert M. & Laughlin, James, eds. gif. ed. 2009. (ENG.). 96p. pap. 11.95 (978-0-8112-1808-5(2), 21808) New Directions Publishing Corp.

NiBlack, Patricia A. Christmas Poems & Prayers. 2007. (Illus.). 38p. (J). 7.00 (978-0-9801524-0-1(2)) Freehand Publishing Desk, LLC.

Sail, Erica & Sail, Lawrence. Songs of the Darkness. 2011. (ENG., Illus.). 48p. pap. 22.95 (978-1-904634-98-0(2)) Enitharmon Pr. GBR. Dist: Dufour Editions, Inc.

Schauffler, Robert Haven. Christmas. 2008. 336p. pap. 28.99 (978-0-554-35064-6(5)); 29.99 (978-0-554-25761-7(0)) BiblioBazaar.

—Christmas: Its Origin, Celebration & Significance as Related in Prose & Verse. 2007. (ENG.). 290p. pap. 21.99 (978-1-4264-9492-5(0)); 332p. pap. 24.99 (978-1-4264-9873-2(X)) BiblioBazaar.

Schauffler, Robert Haven, ed. Christmas. 2007. 252p. per. (978-1-4065-3888-5(4)) Dodo Pr.

Simonis, George. Christmas. 2008. 118p. pap. 15.95 (978-1-4357-3839-3(X)) Lulu Enterprises Inc.

St. Nicholas No. 2 December 1877 Vol. 5: No. 2 December 1877. l.t. ed. 2007. (ENG.). 272p. pap. 23.99 (978-1-4264-8635-7(9)); 244p. pap. 20.99 (978-1-4264-8578-7(6)) BiblioBazaar.

Thompson, John David. On Holiday. 2007. pap. 20.00 (978-0-9720717-5-8(X)) Palindrome Publishing of Iowa.

Warren, Patti. Christmas Inspiratons, Vol. 1. 2007. 21p. pap. 3.00 (978-0-9728227-1-8(2)) Unique Publishing.

Zitzelsberger, James N. Clancy's Christmas Stampede: And Other Christmas Story-Poems. 2010. 80p. pap. 8.95 (978-0-615-38705-5(5)) Moki Lane Publishing.

CHRISTMAS—SONGS AND MUSIC

see Christmas Music

CHRISTMAS BOOKS

see Christmas; Christmas Plays; Christmas Stories; Gift Books

CHRISTMAS CARDS

Ames, Kenneth L. American Christmas Cards, 1900-1960. 2011. (ENG., Illus.). 320p. pap. 40.00 (978-0-300-17687-2(2)) Yale Univ. Pr.

Balchin, Judy & Pinder, Polly. Papercrafts for Christmas: Making Cards & Decorations. 2008. (ENG., Illus.). 144p. pap. 19.95 (978-1-84448-317-4(7)) Search Pr., Ltd. GBR. Dist: Independent Pubs. Group.

Denk, Margaret. The Christmas Cat Book. 2006. (Celebration (Red Rock Press) Ser.). (ENG., Illus.). 64p. 9.95 (978-1-933176-07-9(5)) Red Rock Pr., Inc.

—The Christmas Dog Book. 2006. (Celebration (Red Rock Press) Ser.). (ENG., Illus.). 64p. 9.95 (978-1-933176-08-6(3)) Red Rock Pr., Inc.

Gilmore, Agatha E. Santa Comes to Town. 2007. (Celebration (Red Rock Press) Ser.). (ENG., Illus.). 64p. 9.95 (978-1-933176-14-7(8)) Red Rock Pr., Inc.

Lundy, Brook & Mitchell, Duncan. Merry Christmas, Even If You Don't Buy This Book: 45 Cards for Expressing All Your Christmas Wishes If You Have Any. 2009. (ENG., Illus.). 96p. pap. 9.95 (978-1-4027-6809-5(5)) Sterling Publishing Co., Inc.

Pinsky, Nina. The Christmas Flower Book. 2007. (Celebration (Red Rock Press) Ser.). (ENG., Illus.). 64p. 9.95 (978-1-933176-12-3(1)) Red Rock Pr., Inc.

Roy, Warren. A Life Story in 50 Christmas Cards: 1945-2003. 2007. (ENG., Illus.). 122p. per. (978-1-896209-85-2(8)) Bayeux Arts, Inc.

Viebrock, Clint. The Christmas Animal Book. 2007. (Celebration (Red Rock Press) Ser.). (ENG., Illus.). 64p. 9.95 (978-1-933176-11-6(3)) Red Rock Pr., Inc.

Weller, Alan. Dover CardCrafter Studio: Christmas Cards. 2011. (ENG.). 48p. pap. 19.95 (978-0-486-99143-6(1)) Dover Pubns., Inc.

CHRISTMAS CAROLS

see Carols

CHRISTMAS COOKING

Atkinson, Catherine, et al. The Spirit of Christmas: Traditional Recipes, Crafts & Carols. 2009. (ENG., Illus.). 128p. pap. 17.95 (978-1-84773-640-6(8)) New Holland Pubs., Ltd. GBR. Dist: Sterling Publishing Co., Inc.

Barbour Publishing, creator. Bakin' up Cookies & Love. 2006. (Christmas at Home with Mary & Martha Ser.). (Illus.). 156p. per. 3.97 (978-1-59789-430-2(3), Barbour Bks.) Barbour Publishing, Inc.

—Cookin' up Traditional Dishes & Faith. 2006. (Christmas at Home with Mary & Martha Ser.). (Illus.). 142p. per. 3.97 (978-1-59789-433-3(8), Barbour Bks.) Barbour Publishing, Inc.

—Dishin' up Desserts & Hope. 2006. (Christmas at Home with Mary & Martha Ser.). (Illus.). 157p. per. 3.97 (978-1-59789-432-6(X), Barbour Bks.) Barbour Publishing, Inc.

—Stirrin' up Chocolate & Joy. 2006. (Christmas at Home with Mary & Martha Ser.). (Illus.). 142p. per. 3.97 (978-1-59789-431-9(1), Barbour Bks.) Barbour Publishing, Inc.

Bell, Annie. Gorgeous Christmas. 2010. (ENG.). 192p. pap. 19.95 (978-1-906868-07-9(7)) Cathie, Kyle Ltd. GBR. Dist: National Bk. Network.

Better Homes and Gardens Books Staff. Best of Christmas Ideas. 2009. (Better Homes & Gardens Crafts Ser.: 12). (ENG., Illus.). 192p. pap. 14.99 (978-0-470-50395-9(5), Wiley) Wiley, John & Sons, Inc.

Betty Crocker. Betty Crocker Christmas Cookies Groc Ed. 2011. 160p. spiral bd. 9.99 **(978-1-118-12042-2(6)**, Betty Crocker) Wiley, John & Sons, Inc.

Betty Crocker Editors. Christmas Cook Book. 2nd ed. 2010. (ENG., Illus.). 352p. pap. 19.95 (978-0-470-87403-5(1), Betty Crocker) Wiley, John & Sons, Inc.

Bice, Jeanne. Jeanne Bice's Quacker Factory Christmas: Simple Recipes, Fabulous Parties & Decorations to Put Sparkle, Not Stress, into Your Season. 2006. (Quacker Factory Ser.). (ENG., Illus.). 256p. pap. 19.95 (978-0-7573-0574-0(1)) Health Communications, Inc.

Bordon, David & Winters, Tom. Everything Christmas. 2010. (ENG., Illus.). 320p. 14.99 (978-0-307-72929-3(X), WaterBrook Pr.) Doubleday Religious Publishing Group, The.

Bowers, Sharon. A Very Candy Christmas: Recipes & Projects for Parents & Children to Make Together. 2012. (Illus.). 176p. 19.95 **(978-1-61769-000-6(7))** Stewart, Tabori & Chang.

Brennan, Rebecca. Southern Living Big Book of Christmas. 2009. (Illus.). 416p. **(978-0-8487-3290-5(1))** Oxmoor Hse., Inc.

Brown, Ellen. Gluten-Free Christmas Cookies. 2011. (ENG.). 128p. pap. 14.95 (978-1-60433-239-1(5)) Cider Mill Pr. Bk. Pubs., LLC.

Calvert, Jo, et al. Complete Christmas Book: The All-You-Need Guide to a Memorable Christmas with Recipes, Crafts & Decorating Ideas. 2007. (ENG., Illus.). 240p. 24.95 (978-0-9738355-7-1(5)) Transcontinental Bks. CAN. Dist: Random Hse., Inc.

Christmas Cooking. Date not set. (Essentials Collection Cooking). 96p. 5.98 (978-1-4054-1519-4(3)) Parragon, Inc.

Christmas Cooking from the Heart: Fresh & Simple. 2009. (Illus.). 160p. **(978-0-696-24227-4(3))** Meredith Bks.

Christmas Cooking from the Heart: Simple to Sensational. 2007. (Illus.). 160p. (978-0-696-23558-0(7)) Meredith Bks.

Christmas Food. 2008. 96p. (978-1-4075-3394-0(0)) Parragon, Inc.

Christmasd Cookies & Bars. 2008. (Cooking Ser.). 96p. (978-1-4075-2097-1(0)) Parragon, Inc.

Cook, Sian, et al. Women's Institute Complete Christmas: Over 130 Recipes for a Perfect Christmas. 2010. (ENG., Illus.). 192p. pap. 23.95 (978-0-85720-028-0(3)) Simon & Schuster, Ltd. GBR. Dist: Independent Pubs. Group.

Country Christmas. 2007. audio compact disk (978-5-557-58299-5(1)) Alpha Omega Publications.

Country Living Editors. Country Living Merry & Bright: 301 Festive Ideas for Celebrating Christmas. 2009. (ENG., Illus.). 224p. pap. 19.95 (978-1-58816-782-8(8)) Hearst Communications, Inc.

Country Living Magazine Editors. Country Living Merry & Bright: 125 Festive Ideas for Celebrating Christmas. 2011. (ENG., Illus.). 128p. spiral bd. 12.95 (978-1-58816-907-5(3)) Hearst Communications, Inc.

Dahlstrom, Carol Field. Merry Christmas Ideas: 225 Projects for Crafting, Cookie-Baking, Gift Giving, Decoeating, & Merry-Making. 2007. 160p. 24.95 (978-0-9768446-6-2(4)) Dahlstrom, Carol Field Inc.

—Simply Christmas: Renew the Spirit - 201 Easy Crafts, Food & Decorating Ideas. (Illus.). 192p. pap. 11.95 (978-0-9679764-1-9(3), Brave Ink Pr.) Dahlstrom, Carol Field Inc.

Day, Martha. Classic Cooking for Christmas: A Seasonal Collection of over 100 Festive Recipes Shown in More Than 450 Tempting Photographs. 2010. (ENG., Illus.). 160p. pap. 19.99 (978-1-84476-837-0(6)) Anness Publishing GBR. Dist: National Bk. Network.

Deen, Paula. Christmas with Paula Deen: Recipes & Stories from My Favorite Holiday. 2007. (ENG., Illus.). 224p. 23.00 (978-0-7432-9286-3(3)) Simon & Schuster.

Desaulniers, Marcel. I'm Dreaming of a Chocolate Christmas. 2007. (ENG., Illus.). 224p. 29.95 (978-0-7645-9900-2(3), Wiley) Wiley, John & Sons, Inc.

Dickens, Charles & Ross, Alice. A Christmas Dinner by Charles Dickens. 2008. (ENG.). 88p. 24.95 (978-1-933176-10-9(5)) Red Rock Pr., Inc.

Downey, Donna, et al. The Partridge & the Pear: A Collection of Recipes for the Twelve Days of Christmas. 2007. (Illus.). 119p. (978-0-9786878-0-9(9)) Free Esprits.

Dunn, Alan. Alan Dunn's Christmas Cakes. 2010. (ENG., Illus.). 112p. 19.95 (978-1-84773-771-7(4)) New Holland Pubs., Ltd. GBR. Dist: Sterling Publishing Co., Inc.

Ebinger, Virginia Nylander. Aguinaldos: Christmas Customs, Music, & Foods of the Spanish-Speaking Countries of the Americas. 2009. 280p. pap. 29.95 (978-0-86534-689-5(5)) Sunstone Pr.

Edgerton, Amy, et al. Christmas with Southern Living 2007. Brennan, Rebecca, ed. rev. ed. 2007. (Christmas with Southern Living Ser.). (ENG., Illus.). 192p. 29.95 (978-0-8487-3152-6(2)) Oxmoor Hse., Inc.

Elf, Buddy The. Santa's Ultimate Recipes. 2008. 64p. pap. 31.99 (978-1-4363-7561-0(4)) Xlibris Corp.

Farrow, Joanna. Creative Christmas Cakes. (Illus.). 80p. 8.95 (978-1-85391-484-3(3)) Merehurst, Ltd. GBR. Dist: Tuttle Publishing.

Food and Wine Magazine Editors. Holiday Collection. Date not set. (Illus.). 304p. 23.95 (978-0-916103-18-7(8)) American Express Food & Wine Magazine Corp.

Garramone, Dominic. 'Tis the Season to be Baking: Christmas Reflections & Bread Recipes. 2007. (Illus.). 96p. pap. 12.00 (978-1-933370-05-7(X)) Reedy Pr.

Gilpin, R. Christmas Cooking. 1p. pap. 6.95 (978-0-7945-0217-1(2)) EDC Publishing.

Ginsburg, Arthur & Cogin. Mr. Food Christmas Made Easy: Recipes, Tips & Edible Gifts for a Stress-Free Holiday. 2010. 186p. 21.95 (978-0-9755396-0-6(4)) Cogin, Inc.

Good Housekeeping Editors, ed. The Great Christmas Cookie Swap Cookbook: 60 Large-Batch Recipes to Bake & Share. 2009. (ENG., Illus.). 160p. spiral bd. 12.95 (978-1-58816-757-6(7)) Hearst Communications, Inc.

Good, Phyllis Pellman. Fix-It & Forget-It Christmas Cookbook: 600 Slow Cooker Holiday Recipes, 1 vol. 2010. (ENG.). 284p. spiral bd. 18.95 (978-1-56148-702-8(3)); 24.95 (978-1-56148-703-5(1)); pap. 18.95 (978-1-56148-701-1(5)) Good Bks.

Gooseberry Patch. Christmas, Bk. 10. 10th ed. 2008. (Christmas Ser.). (ENG., Illus.). 160p. 27.95 (978-0-8487-3226-4(X)) Oxmoor Hse., Inc.

—Christmas Cookie Jar. 2008. (ENG., Illus.). 224p. 16.95 (978-1-933494-59-3(X)) Gooseberry Patch.

—Christmas with Family & Friends Cookbook. 2009. (ENG., Illus.). 224p. 16.95 (978-1-933494-76-0(X)) Gooseberry Patch.

—Cozy Country Christmas Cookbook: Heartfelt Holiday Memories, the Tastiest Recipes & Homespun Holiday Gifts to Delight Family & Friends. 2006. (ENG., Illus.). 224p. 16.95 (978-1-931890-89-2(7)) Gooseberry Patch.

—Gooseberry Patch Christmas. (ENG., Illus.). 160p. Bk. 9. 9th rev. ed. 2007. per. 19.95 (978-1-60140-634-7(7), Gooseberry Patch)Bk. 10. 10th ed. 2008. pap. 19.95 (978-0-8487-3237-0(5)) Oxmoor Hse., Inc.

—Gooseberry Patch Christmas Bk. 9: Our Tastiest Christmas Recipes, Gifts to Make & Give, & Fresh Ideas That Make the Season Sparkle! 9th rev. ed. 2007. (Christmas Ser.). (ENG., Illus.). 160p. 27.95 (978-1-60140-231-8(7), Gooseberry Patch) Oxmoor Hse., Inc.

—Gooseberry Patch Christmas All Through the House: Over 600 Holiday Recipes, Cheery Crafts & Easy-to-Make Gifts for Flurries of Fun. 2011. (ENG., Illus.). 512p. pap. 24.95 (978-0-8487-3454-1(8)) Oxmoor Hse., Inc.

—Gooseberry Patch Christmas, Book 11. 11th ed. 2009. (ENG.). 160p. 29.95 (978-0-8487-3279-0(0), Gooseberry Patch) Oxmoor Hse., Inc.

—Our Favorite Christmas Recipes Cookbook. 2009. (ENG., Illus.). 126p. spiral bd. 7.95 (978-1-933494-48-7(4)) Gooseberry Patch.

—Very Merry Christmas Cookbook: Over 185 Tried & True Recipes, Scrumptious Menu Ideas & Clever How-To's for a Magical Christmas. rev. ed. 2007. (ENG., Illus.). 160p. 27.95 (978-0-8487-3180-9(8), Gooseberry Patch) Oxmoor Hse., Inc.

—Very Merry Christmas Cookbook: Over 185 Tried & True Recipes, Scrumptious Menu Ideas & Clever How-To's for a Magical Christmas! rev. ed. 2007. (ENG., Illus.). 160p. pap. 19.95 (978-0-8487-3181-6(6), Gooseberry Patch) Oxmoor Hse., Inc.

Gooseberry Patch, ed. 101 Christmas Recipes. 2009. (ENG., Illus.). 112p. spiral bd. 14.95 (978-1-933494-77-7(8)) Gooseberry Patch.

Gooseberry Patch, ed. & des. Gooseberry Patch Farmhouse Style: Fresh ideas, recipes & decorations to share with family & Friends. 2007. 40p. 10.95 (978-1-60140-247-9(3)) Leisure Arts, Inc.

Gooseberry Patch (Firm) Staff, contrib. by. Christmas Classics: Recipes for a Very Merry Christmas. 2009. (Illus.). 32p. pap. **(978-1-933494-91-3(3))** Gooseberry Patch.

Gooseberry Patcha Staff. Gooseberry Patch Christmas Bk. 13: Recipes, Projects & Gift Ideas. 2011. (ENG., Illus.). 160p. pap. 19.95 (978-0-8487-3428-2(9)) Oxmoor Hse., Inc.

Greenberg, Margie & Greenberg, Abbey. The Flour Pot Christmas Cookie Book: Creating Edible Works of Art for the Holidays. 2009. (ENG.). 136p. 16.95 (978-0-7624-3554-8(2)) Running Pr. Bk. Pubs.

Guinn, Jeff. Santa's North Pole Cookbook: Classic Christmas Recipes from Saint Nicholas Himself. (ENG., 272p. (gr. 12). 2012. Illus.). pap. 12.00 **(978-0-399-16064-6(7))** 2007. 19.95 (978-1-58542-589-1(3)) Penguin Group (USA) Inc. (Tarcher).

Hamlyn All Color Staff. 200 Christmas Recipes: Hamlyn All Color. 2010. (ENG., Illus.). 240p. pap. 7.99 (978-0-600-62165-2(0), Hamlyn) Octopus Publishing Group GBR. Dist: Hachette Bk. Group.

Holley, Emma. 500 Christmas Recipes: Make Christmas special with this comprehensive collection of classic festive recipes, shown in more than 500 inspirational Photographs. 2011. (ENG., Illus.). 256p. 35.00 (978-0-7548-2080-2(7)) Anness Publishing GBR. Dist: National Bk. Network.

Hood, Karen Jean Matsko. Christmas Delights Cookbook: A Collection of Christmas Recipes. 2008. (Delights Ser.). 22.95 (978-1-59434-975-1(4)); 29.95 (978-1-59434-974-4(6)) Whispering Pine Pr. International, Inc.

—Christmas Delights Cookbook: A Collection of Christmas Recipes, Cookbook Delights Series. Whispering Pine Press International, ed. 2010. (ENG.). 224p. per. 19.95 (978-1-59434-157-1(5)) Whispering Pine Pr. International, Inc.

—Christmas Delights Cookbook: A Collection of Christmas Recipes, Cookbook Delights Series. 2008. 320p. 19.95 (978-1-59434-159-5(1)); 24.95

(978-1-59434-156-4(7)); spiral bd. 19.95 (978-1-59434-158-8(3)); (ENG.). ring bd. 24.95 (978-1-59434-160-1(5)); cd-rom 13.95 (978-1-59434-161-8(3)) Whispering Pine Pr. International, Inc.

—Christmas Delights Cookbook, Volume II: A Collection of Christmas Recipes, Vol. 2. 2008. (Delights Ser.). 320p. 22.95 (978-1-59434-508-1(2)) Whispering Pine Pr. International, Inc.

—Christmas Delights Cookbook, Volume II: A Collection of Christmas Recipes, Volume II, Vol. 2. 2008. (Delights Ser.). 320p. 19.95 (978-1-59434-503-6(1)); 22.95 (978-1-59434-504-3(X)); pap. 24.95 (978-1-59434-500-5(7)); spiral bd. 19.95 (978-1-59434-502-9(3)); 320p. per. 19.95 (978-1-59434-501-2(5)); ring bd. 24.95 (978-1-59434-507-4(4)); 320p. cd-rom 13.95 (978-1-59434-505-0(8)) Whispering Pine Pr. International, Inc.

—Hood & Matsko Family Favorite Christmas Sweets: Our Favorite Christmas Sweets Recipes. 2007. ring bd. 24.95 (978-1-59649-677-4(0)); 320p. per. 22.95 (978-1-59649-842-6(0)) Whispering Pine Pr. International, Inc.

Hopley, Claire. The History of Christmas Food & Feasts. 2009. (Illus.). 224p. 50.00 (978-1-84468-065-8(7)) Pen & Sword Bks. Ltd. GBR. Dist: Casemate Pubs. & Bk. Distributors, LLC.

Jarrett, Vicky, ed. A Christmas Treasury: A Collection of Joyful Holiday Readings. 2006. 96p. mass mkt. 5.95 (978-0-9779681-0-7(3), Our State Magazine) Mann Media, Inc.

Kindbud, Seymour. The Happy (Happy!!!) Holiday Pot Cookie Swap Cookbook: Burst: Don't bogart the cookies, Man! 2011. (ENG.). 176p. pap. 12.95 (978-1-60433-238-4(7)) Cider Mill Pr. Bk. Pubs., LLC.

King, Heidi Tyline. Home for the Holidays: Creative Ideas for Making the Holidays Memorable. 2007. (Illus.). 159p. 25.00 (978-1-934533-01-7(7)) Gold Street Pr.

Kirchsteiger, Ernst. Swedish Christmas Traditions: A Smorgasbord of Scandinavian Recipes, Crafts, & Other Holiday Delights. 2010. (ENG., Illus.). 128p. 19.95 (978-1-61608-052-5(3), 608052) Skyhorse Publishing Co., Inc.

Kohart, Georgia. Heart & Hearth: Christmas on the Farm. 2007. (Illus.). 250p. spiral bd. 21.95 (978-0-9706348-3-2(8)) Heritage Heart Farm.

Lagerlof, Selma. Scandinavian Christmas: Essays & Stories, Recipes & Traditions. Schense, Deb, ed. 2011. (Illus.). 96p. pap. 14.95 **(978-1-932043-73-0(X))** Penfield Bks.

Lawson, Nigella. Nigella Christmas: Food Family Friends Festivities. 2009. 288p. 35.00 (978-1-4013-2336-3(7)) Hyperion Pr.

Leisure Arts & Leisure Arts designers. Creating the Happiest of Holidays, Book 2, Bk. 2. 2nd ed. 2010. (ENG.). 160p. pap. 19.95 (978-1-60900-012-7(9)) Leisure Arts, Inc.

Leisure Arts Staff, ed. Creating the Happiest of Holidays, Vol. 2. 2009. (ENG.). 160p. pap. 19.95 (978-1-60140-884-6(6)) Leisure Arts, Inc.

—Spirit of Christmas Bk 20 Special Anniv, Vol. 20. 20th rev. anniv. ed. 2006. (ENG., Illus.). 192p. 29.95 (978-1-57486-529-5(3)) Leisure Arts, Inc.

Lester, Meera. Why Does Santa Wear Red? And 100 Other Christmas Curiousities Unwrapped. 2007. (ENG., Illus.). 256p. per. 9.95 (978-1-59869-457-4(X)) Adams Media Corp.

Lindsey, Jordan. The Merry Mayhem Holiday Recipe Book Of 2007. 2007. 50p. pap. 7.00 (978-0-615-17837-0(5)) Lindsey, Jordan.

Lion House. Lion House Christmas. 2006. (Illus.). 154p. 26.99 (978-1-59038-615-6(9)) Deseret Bk. Co.

Macomber, Debbie. Debbie Macomber's Christmas Cookbook: Favorite Recipes & Holiday Traditions from My Home to Yours. 2011. (ENG.). 240p. 29.95 (978-0-373-89239-6(X)) Harlequin Enterprises, Ltd. CAN. Dist: Simon & Schuster, Inc.

Maltby, Tammy. The Christmas Kitchen: The Gathering Place for Making Memories. 2009. (ENG., Illus.). 132p. 14.99 (978-1-4165-8765-1(9), Howard Bks.) Howard Books.

Martin, James. Masterclass: Make Your Home Cooking Easier. 2011. (ENG., Illus.). 224p. 34.95 (978-0-00-729472-5(7)) HarperCollins Pubs. Ltd. GBR. Dist: Independent Pubs. Group.

Maxwell, Robert. Mom's Thanksgiving & Christmas Best: Bob's in the Kitchen. 2009. 68p. pap. 21.95 (978-1-4327-2301-9(4)) Outskirts Pr., Inc.

McDonald, Ralph J., illus. Cooking up a Classic Christmas: Santa's Secrets for an Unforgettable Holiday! 2006. 111p. 17.95 (978-0-87197-526-3(2), FRP) Southwestern Publishing Group, Inc.

Meisner, Kimberly. Victoria 500 Christmas Ideas: Celebrate the Season in Splendor. 2009. (ENG., Illus.). 480p. 24.95 (978-1-58816-766-8(6)) Hearst Communications, Inc.

Messecar, Cathy. A Scrapbook of Christmas Firsts: Stories to warm your heart & tips to simplify your Holidays. 2008. 160p. 16.99 (978-0-89112-564-8(7), Leafwood Pubs.) Abilene Christian Univ. Pr.

Nargi, Lela, ed. Christmas on the Farm: A Collection of Favorite Recipes, Stories, Gift Ideas, & Decorating Tips from the Farmer's Wife. 2011. (ENG., Illus.). 224p. 17.99 **(978-0-7603-4102-5(8)**, 0760341028, Voyageur Pr) MBI Publishing Co. LLC.

Nilsen, Angela, ed. 101 Christmas Dishes: Tried-and-Tested Recipes. 2007. (Good Food 101 Ser.). (ENG., Illus.). 216p. pap. 9.95 (978-0-563-53929-2(1)) BBC Worldwide GBR. Dist: Independent Pubs. Group.

Our State's Christmas Kitchen. 2009. (ENG.). spiral bd. (978-0-9779681-5-2(4), Our State Magazine) Mann Media, Inc.

Paré, Jean. Gifts from the Family Kitchen: 2-In-1 Cookbook Collection. 2008. (978-1-897069-89-9(8)) Recipe Factory, Inc.

Patch, Gooseberry. Christmas in the Country Cookbook: Family Recipes, Merry Gifts from the Kitchen, & Sweet Holiday Memories to Celebrate the Simple Joys of the Season. 2007. (ENG., Illus.). 224p. 16.95 (978-1-933494-23-4(9)) Gooseberry Patch.

—Christmas Kitchen Cookbook. 2008. (ENG., Illus.). 224p. 16.95 (978-1-933494-54-8(9)) Gooseberry Patch.

—Gooseberry Patch Christmas Bk. 13: Recipes, Projects & Gift Ideas. 2011. (ENG., Illus.). 160p. 29.95 (978-0-8487-3427-5(0)) Oxmoor Hse., Inc.

Pearlman, Ann & Bayer, Mary Beth. The Christmas Cookie Club: All the Rules & Delicious Recipes to Start Your Own Holiday Cookie Club. 2010. (ENG., Illus.). 240p. pap., wbk. ed. 15.00 (978-1-4391-5954-5(8), Beyond Words/Atria Bks.) Atria Bks.

Peterson, Valerie & Fryer, Janice. Cookie Craft Christmas: Dozens of Decorating Ideas for a Sweet Holiday. 2009. (ENG., Illus.). 169p. 14.95 (978-1-60342-440-0(7), 1603424407) Workman Publishing Co., Inc.

Press, Cider Mill. Holiday Shots: Christmas Concoctions That Will Really Get You in the Holiday Mood. 2011. (ENG.). 144p. pap. 12.95 (978-1-60433-241-4(7)) Cider Mill Pr. Bk. Pubs., LLC.

Publications International Staff. Concealed Spiral Oster Creative Entertaining. 2008. (Illus.). 160p. spiral bd. 10.98 (978-1-4127-9941-6(4)) Publications International, Ltd.

Publications International Staff, ed. 100 Best Holiday Cookies. 2007. spiral bd. 12.98 (978-1-4127-2546-0(1)) Publications International, Ltd.

Rather, Rebecca & Oresman, Alison. The Pastry Queen Christmas: Big-Hearted Holiday Entertaining, Texas Style. 2007. (ENG., Illus.). 240p. 32.50 (978-1-58008-790-2(6)) Ten Speed Pr.

Rigg, Annie. Christmas Cooking with Kids. 2011. (ENG.). 128p. (978-1-84975-025-7(4)) Ryland Peters & Small.

Rodgers, Rick. Christmas 101: Celebrate the Holiday Season from Christmas to New Year's. 2007. (ENG.). 192p. per. 15.95 (978-0-06-122734-9(X), Morrow, William Cookbooks) HarperCollins Pubs.

Russell, Don. Christmas Beer: The Cheeriest, Tastiest, & Most Unusual Holiday Brews. 2008. (ENG., Illus.). 208p. 7.95 (978-0-7893-1796-4(6)) Universe Publishing.

Smith, Della. Della's Happy Christmas. 2009. (ENG., Illus.). 312p. 45.00 (978-0-09-193306-7(4)) Ebury Publishing GBR. Dist: Independent Pubs. Group.

Southern Living Magazine Editors. Christmas with Southern Living 2009. 2009. (ENG.). 192p. 29.95 (978-0-8487-3282-0(0)) Oxmoor Hse., Inc.

—Christmas with Southern Living 2010: Great Recipes - Easy Entertaining - Festive Decorations - Gift Ideas. 2010. (ENG., Illus.). 192p. 29.95 (978-0-8487-3346-9(0)) Oxmoor Hse., Inc.

—Christmas with Southern Living 2011: Savor * Entertain * Decorate * Share. 2011. (ENG., Illus.). 192p. 29.95 (978-0-8487-3463-3(7)) Oxmoor Hse., Inc.

—Cooking for Christmas: Favorite Holiday Recipes to Share with Family & Friends. 2011. (ENG.). 288p. pap. 24.95 (978-0-8487-3582-1(X)) Oxmoor Hse., Inc

Southern Living Ultimate Christmas: Festive Holiday Decorations, Favorite Seasonal Recipes & Easy Entertaining Ideas. 2011. (Illus.). 416p. **(978-0-8487-3450-3(5))** Oxmoor Hse., Inc.

Stancliffe, Sarah. The Christian Aid Book of Simple Feasts: Cooking for a Crowd Through the Christian Year. 2008. (Christian Aid Ser.). (Illus.). 234p. pap. 14.99 (978-1-85311-836-4(2)) Canterbury Pr.

Stauffer, Jeanne. A Family Christmas: Handmade Gifts & Heartfelt Stories. 2007. (Illus.). 176p. (978-1-59217-186-6(9), House of White Birches, Inc.) Annie's Publishing, LLC.

Stone, Michelle. Merry Christmas from Kentucky: Recipes for the Season. 2007. (Illus.). 160p. 21.95 (978-0-913383-98-8(8)) McClanahan Publishing Hse., Inc.

Sunset Books Staff & Gooseberry Patch. Christmas All Through the House: Over 600 Holiday Recipes, Cheery Crafts & Easy-to-Make Gifts for Flurries of Fun! 2008. (ENG., Illus.). 512p. spiral bd. 29.95 (978-0-8487-3252-3(9)) Oxmoor Hse., Inc.

Sunset Books Staff & Leisure Arts Staff. Christmas Traditions. 2008. (ENG.). 160p. 27.95 (978-1-60140-832-7(3)) Leisure Arts, Inc.

Sunset Books Staff & Southern Living Foods Staff. Christmas Cookbook: All-New Ultimate Holiday Entertaining Guide. 2008. (ENG.). 288p. 29.95 (978-0-8487-3229-5(4)) Oxmoor Hse., Inc.

Tabori, Lena, ed. The Little Big Book of Christmas. 2011. (ENG., Illus.). 352p. 24.95 (978-1-59962-100-5(2), Welcome Bks.) Welcome Enterprises, Inc.

Talbot, K. R. & Hammari, Kimiko Christensen. Christmas Games & Goodies. 2008. 16p. pap. 2.99 (978-1-59955-180-7(2)) Cedar Fort, Inc./CFI Distribution.

Telemundo & Izturriaga, Maria Alecia. Telemundo Presenta - Celebraciones: En Casa con las Estrellas de Telemundo. 2007. (SPA., Illus.). 320p. pap. 19.99 (978-1-4165-5502-5(1), Beyond Words/Atria Bks.) Atria Bks.

Thompson, Serena. The Farm Chicks Christmas: Merry Ideas for the Holidays. 2010. (ENG., Illus.). 128p. 27.95 (978-1-58816-521-3(3)) Hearst Communications, Inc.

Trimmings. 2007. 132p. 24.95 (978-1-60140-589-0(8)) Leisure Arts, Inc.

Voth, Norma Jost. The Festive Christmas Cookbook: Cakes, Cookies & Breads. 2008. 304p. pap. 12.95 (978-0-88486-438-7(3)) Bristol Park Bks.

Vync, Grunes Van, et al. Very Merry Cookie Party: How to Plan & Host a Christmas Cookie Exchange. 2010. (ENG., Illus.). 248p. pap. 19.95 (978-0-8118-6675-0(0)) Chronicle Bks. LLC.

Westland, Pamela. The Best Ever Christmas: 100 practical ways to make a perfect Celebration. 2010. (ENG., Illus.). 128p. pap. 17.99 (978-1-84476-805-9(8)) Anness Publishing GBR. Dist: National Bk. Network.

Williams, Chuck, et al. Christmas Gifts from the Kitchen. 2009. (ENG.). 112p. 18.95 (978-0-8487-3295-0(2)) Oxmoor Hse., Inc.

Wilson, Dede. Baker's Field Guide to Christmas Cookies. 2011. (Baker's FG Ser.). (ENG., Illus.). 176p. pap. 14.95 (978-1-55832-751-1(7)) Harvard Common Pr.

Zwirn, Lisa B. Christmas Cookies: 50 Recipes to Treasure for the Holiday Season. 2008. (ENG., Illus.). 144p. 16.99 (978-0-06-137696-2(5), Morrow, William Cookbooks) HarperCollins Pubs.

CHRISTMAS DECORATIONS

see also Christmas Trees

Andrews, Lynne. Christmas Blessings. 2007. (Illus.). 36p. 12.95 (978-1-934539-02-6(3)) Viking Woodcrafts, Inc.

Atkinson, Catherine, et al. The Spirit of Christmas: Traditional Recipes, Crafts & Carols. 2009. (ENG., Illus.). 128p. pap. 17.95 (978-1-84773-640-6(8)) New Holland Pubs., Ltd. GBR. Dist: Sterling Publishing Co., Inc.

Balchin, Judy & Pinder, Polly. Papercrafts for Christmas: Making Cards & Decorations. 2008. (ENG., Illus.). 144p. pap. 19.95 (978-1-84448-317-4(7)) Search Pr., Ltd. GBR. Dist: Independent Pubs. Group.

Barseghian, Tina. A Homemade Christmas: Creative Ideas for an Earth-Friendly, Frugal, Festive Holiday. 2010. (ENG.). 128p. pap. 14.95 (978-0-373-89222-8(5)) Harlequin Enterprises, Ltd. CAN. Dist: Simon & Schuster, Inc.

Beane Henry, Cynthia. Remembering Christmas or the Advent of Christmas in 24 Recollections. 2010. 62p. pap. 32.60 (978-0-557-24942-8(2)) Lulu Enterprises Inc.

Bell, Carolyn. Christmas Decorating: How to Make & Decorate Your Own Festive Cards, Baubles, Wreaths, Candles, Stockings, Crackers & Tree Decorations. 2008. (ENG., Illus.). 96p. pap. 9.99 (978-1-84476-591-1(1)) Anness Publishing GBR. Dist: National Bk. Network.

Bellman, Sheryll. Through the Shopping Glass: A Century of New York Christmas Windows. gif. ed. 2006. (ENG., Illus.). 96p. 12.98 (978-0-7893-1550-2(5), Rizzoli Universe Promotional Bks.) Rizzoli International Pubns., Inc.

Bellows, Melina Gerosa. The Fun Book for Christmas: New Ways to Have Fun for the Holidays. 2009. (ENG.). 96p. 9.99 (978-0-7407-8581-8(8)) Andrews McMeel Publishing.

Benjamin, Per, et al. Christmas: Creativity with Flowers. 2007. (ENG., Illus.). 96p. (978-90-5856-207-4(7), Stichting Kunstboak (Acc)) Antique Collectors' Club.

—Christmas Emotions. 2007. (ENG., Illus.). 160p. 80.00 (978-90-5856-240-1(9), Stichting Kunstboak (Acc)) Antique Collectors' Club GBR. Dist: National Bk. Network.

Better Homes and Gardens Books Staff. Best of Christmas Ideas. 2009. (Better Homes & Gardens Crafts Ser.: 12). (ENG., Illus.). 192p. pap. 14.99 (978-0-470-50395-9(5), Wiley) Wiley, John & Sons, Inc.

Bice, Jeanne. Jeanne Bice's Quacker Factory Christmas: Simple Recipes, Fabulous Parties & Decorations to Put Sparkle, Not Stress, into Your Season. 2006. (Quacker Factory Ser.). (ENG., Illus.). 256p. pap. 19.95 (978-0-7573-0574-0(1)) Health Communications, Inc.

Bowers, Sharon. A Very Candy Christmas: Recipes & Projects for Parents & Children to Make Together. 2012. (Illus.). 176p. 19.95 **(978-1-61769-000-6(7))** Stewart, Tabori & Chang.

Brennan, Rebecca. Southern Living Big Book of Christmas. 2009. (Illus.). 416p. **(978-0-8487-3290-5(1))** Oxmoor Hse., Inc.

Brennan, Rebecca, et al, eds. Christmas with Southern Living 2008: Great Recipes - Easy Entertaining - Festive Decorations - Gift Ideas. 2008. (Christmas with Southern Living Ser.). (ENG., Illus.). 192p. 29.95 (978-0-8487-3228-8(6)) Oxmoor Hse., Inc.

Brenner, Robert. Christmas, 1940-1959: A Collector's Guide to Decorations & Customs. 2007. (Schiffer Book for Collectors Ser.). (Illus.). 160p. pap. 29.95 (978-0-7643-2672-1(4)) Schiffer Publishing, Ltd.

Brucker, Virginia. Gifts from the Heart: Simple Ways to Make Your Family's Christmas More Meaningful. 2007. (ENG., Illus.). 336p. per. (978-1-897178-30-0(1)) Insomniac Pr.

Bula, Melinda. Candy Cane Lane: Quilts & More to Sweeten the Holidays. 2009. (ENG., Illus.). 32p. pap. (978-1-56477-924-3(6)) Martingale & Co.

Calvert, Jo, et al. Complete Christmas Book: The All-You-Need Guide to a Memorable Christmas with Recipes, Crafts & Decorating Ideas. 2007. (ENG., Illus.). 240p. 24.95 (978-0-9738355-7-1(5)) Transcontinental Bks. CAN. Dist: Random Hse., Inc.

Carestio, Amanda. Fa la la la Felt: 45 Handmade Holiday Decorations. 2010. (ENG.). 132p. pap. 14.95 (978-1-60059-615-5(0)) Lark Bks.

Carestio, Amanda. Pretty in Patchwork: Holidays: 30+ Holiday Patchwork Projects to Piece, Stitch, & Love. 2012. (Pretty in Patchwork Ser.). (ENG., Illus.). 128p. pap. 19.95 **(978-1-4547-0279-5(6))** Lark Bks.

Carlson, Melody. Let Them Eat Fruitcake. 2008. (86B Ser.). (ENG.). 320p. pap. 14.99 (978-1-58919-106-8(4)) Cook, David C.

Chase, Karen. Paddy Paws & Friends Presents Christmas. Date not set. (Illus.). 60p. pap. 9.95 (978-1-57377-052-1(3), 01988402248) Eas'l Pubns.

The Christment Tree Pattern Book Vol. 2: Twenty-One Christian Ornaments for Your Christmas Tree, Vol. 2. (Illus.). 107p. pap. 10.95 (978-1-56608-047-7(9), A-B226) Meriwether Publishing, Ltd.

Clare Youngs. Christmas Crafting in No Time. 2011. (ENG., Illus.). 176p. pap. 24.95 (978-1-907563-78-2(4)) CICO Bks. GBR. Dist: Ryland Peters & Small.

Country Christmas. 2007. audio compact disk (978-5-557-58299-5(1)) Alpha Omega Publications.

Country Living Editors. Country Living Merry & Bright: 301 Festive Ideas for Celebrating Christmas. 2009. (ENG., Illus.). 224p. pap. 19.95 (978-1-58816-782-8(8)) Hearst Communications, Inc.

Country Living Magazine Editors. Country Living Merry & Bright: 125 Festive Ideas for Celebrating Christmas. 2011. (ENG., Illus.). 128p. spiral bd. 12.95 (978-1-58816-907-5(3)) Hearst Communications, Inc.

Crafthouse Press Staff & Search Press Staff. Christmas: Festive Perforated Papers, Stickers & Designs-All in One Book! 2008. (ENG., Illus.). 96p. pap. 15.95 (978-1-84448-319-8(3)) Search Pr., Ltd. GBR. Dist: Independent Pubs. Group.

Crow, Judy & Chamberlain, Glenda, eds. Christmas Traditions in Plastic Canvas. 2010. (ENG., Illus.). 176p. 24.95 (978-1-57367-336-5(6)) Annie's Publishing, LLC.

Dahlstrom, Carol Field. Merry Christmas Ideas: 225 Projects for Crafting, Cookie-Baking, Gift Giving, Decoeating & Merry-Making. 2007. 160p. 24.95 (978-0-9768446-6-2(4)) Dahlstrom, Carol Field Inc.

—Simply Christmas: Renew the Spirit - 201 Easy Crafts, Food & Decorating Ideas. (Illus.). 192p. pap. 11.95 (978-0-9679764-1-9(3), Brave Ink Pr.) Dahlstrom, Carol Field Inc.

Dickerson, C. D., et al. A Nativity from Naples: Presepe Sculpture of the Eighteenth Century. 2008. (Illus.). ix, 115p. (978-0-912804-49-1(1)) Kimbell Art Museum.

DRG Publishing Staff. In the Nick of Time. 2010. (ENG., Illus.). 34p. pap. 8.95 (978-1-59217-303-7(9)) Annie's Publishing, LLC.

Dunkley, Diana. Christmas in Miniature: Festive Projects & Decorating Ideas for the Holidays. 2006. (ENG., Illus.). 128p. 24.95 (978-1-4027-1030-8(5), Chapelle) Sterling Publishing Co., Inc.

Edgerton, Amy, et al. Christmas with Southern Living 2007. Brennan, Rebecca, ed. rev. ed. 2007. (Christmas with Southern Living Ser.). (ENG., Illus.). 192p. 29.95 (978-0-8487-3152-6(2)) Oxmoor Hse., Inc.

Evelegh, Tessa. Home-Made Christmas. 2009. (ENG., Illus.). 128p. 19.95 (978-1-906525-82-8(X)) CICO Bks. GBR. Dist: Ryland Peters & Small.

Finnanger, Tone. Tilda's Summer Ideas. 2011. (ENG., Illus.). 48p. pap. 6.99 (978-0-7153-3864-3(1)) David & Charles Pubs. GBR. Dist: F&W Media, Inc.

Garrity, Mary Carol. Nell Hill's O Christmas Tree. 2009. (ENG.). 144p. 29.99 (978-0-7407-7397-6(6)) Andrews McMeel Publishing.

Goble, Fiona. Knitivity: Create Your Own Christmas Scene. 2011. (ENG.). 80p. pap. 16.99 (978-1-4494-0365-2(4)) Andrews McMeel Publishing.

—Twas the Knits Before Christmas. 2011. (ENG.). 64p. 16.99 (978-0-7641-6459-0(7)) Barron's Educational Series, Inc.

Goldsmith, Becky & Jenkins, Linda. Quilt a New Christmas. 2011. (ENG., Illus.). 96p. pap. 27.95 (978-1-60705-177-0(X)) C & T Publishing.

Goodluck, Rina/Lynn, prod. Holiday Bazaar 2007-08 ~ Pacific Northwest. 2007. 10.25 net. (978-1-881005-54-4(2)) Gail's Guides.

Gooseberry Patch. Christmas, Bk. 10. 10th ed. 2008. (Christmas Ser.). (ENG., Illus.). 160p. 27.95 (978-0-8487-3226-4(X)) Oxmoor Hse., Inc.

—Gooseberry Patch Christmas, Bk. 10. 10th ed. 2008. (Christmas Ser.). (ENG., Illus.). 160p. pap. 19.95 (978-0-8487-3237-0(5)) Oxmoor Hse., Inc.

—Gooseberry Patch Christmas All Through the House: Over 600 Holiday Recipes, Cheery Crafts & Easy-to-Make Gifts for Flurries of Fun. 2011. (ENG., Illus.). 512p. pap. 24.95 (978-0-8487-3454-1(8)) Oxmoor Hse., Inc.

Gooseberry Patch, ed. & des. Gooseberry Patch Farmhouse Style: Fresh ideas, recipes & decorations to share with family & Friends. 2007. 40p. 10.95 (978-1-60140-247-9(3)) Leisure Arts, Inc.

Gooseberry Patcha Staff. Gooseberry Patch Christmas Bk. 13: Recipes, Projects & Gift Ideas. 2011. (ENG., Illus.). 160p. pap. 19.95 (978-0-8487-3428-2(9)) Oxmoor Hse., Inc.

Govan, James L. Art of the Creche: Nativities from Around the World. 2007. (ENG., Illus.). 208p. 34.95 (978-1-85894-402-9(3)) Merrell Pubs. Ltd. GBR. Dist: Perseus Distribution.

Greenfield, Stephen. We wish you a retro Christmas. 2008. 196p. pap. 18.95 (978-1-4092-4675-6(2)) Lulu Enterprises Inc.

Group Publishing, creator. Decorating Places: Transform Your Church into a Rocky Mountain Ranch. 2007. DVD, cd-rom 14.99 (978-5-558-03218-5(9)) Group Publishing, Inc.

Hardy, Emma. Tree Top Decorations. 2008. (ENG., Illus.). 96p. 15.95 (978-1-906094-87-4(X)) CICO Bks. GBR. Dist: Ryland Peters & Small.

—Tree Top Decorations. 2009. (Illus.). 96p. (978-1-906094-78-2(0)) Ryland Peters & Small.

Hickey, Mary. Comfort & Joy: 14 Quilts for Christmas. 2007. (That Patchwork Place Ser.). (ENG., Illus.). 112p. per. 27.95 (978-1-56477-763-8(4), That Patchwork Place) Martingale & Co.

High, David & del Pozzo, Ralph. Christmasland. 2006. (Illus.). 128p. 9.95 (978-0-06-115000-5(2), Collins Design) HarperCollins Pubs.

Hittle, Karina. Christmas with Artful Offerings: Delicious Cookie-Cutter Designs for Quilting, Sewing, & Punchneedle. 2007. (That Patchwork Place Ser.). (ENG., Illus.). 96p. per. 24.95 (978-1-56477-777-5(4), That Patchwork Place) Martingale & Co.

Hobbs, Anna. Glorious Christmas Crafts: A Treasury of Wonderful Creations for the Holiday Season. 2010. (ENG., Illus.). 144p. 19.95 (978-1-897330-26-5(X)) Madison Pr. Bks. CAN. Dist: Independent Pubs. Group.

Holm, Heather. Discovering the Magic of Christmas: 75 Ways to Make Your Holidays More Meaningful. 2008. 192p. pap. 13.99 (978-1-59955-182-1(9)) Cedar Fort, Inc./CFI Distribution.

Ita, Sam. Christmas Tree In-a-Box (BAF) 2007. (ENG., Illus.). 80p. (gr. 1). pap. 14.95 (978-1-4027-5416-6(7)) Sterling Publishing Co., Inc.

Jerome, Louie. Christmas Tree. 2009. 40p. pap. 16.50 *(978-1-4092-8727-8(0))* Lulu Enterprises Inc.

Johansen, Linda. Fast, Fun & Easy Christmas Decorations: Festive Fabric Keepsakes to Create & Embellish. 2006. (ENG., Illus.). 64p. pap. 16.95 *(978-1-57120-340-3(0))* C & T Publishing.

King, Heidi Tyline. Home for the Holidays: Creative Ideas for Making the Holidays Memorable. 2007. (Illus.). 159p. 25.00 *(978-1-934533-01-7(7))* Gold Street Pr.

Kooler, Donna. Donna Kooler's Stocking Collection: 15 of Donna's Favorite Cross Stich Christmas Stockings. Kooler Design Studi, ed. 2nd rev. ed. 2010. (ENG.). 96p. pap. 22.95 *(978-1-60140-503-6(0))* Leisure Arts, Inc.

Leisure Arts. Debbie Mumm(r): Joy Joy Joy. 2008. (ENG.). 96p. pap. 19.95 *(978-1-60140-648-4(7))* Leisure Arts, Inc.

Leisure Arts & Leisure Arts designers. Creating the Happiest of Holidays, Book 2, Bk. 2. 2nd ed. 2010. (ENG.). 160p. pap. 19.95 *(978-1-60900-012-7(9))* Leisure Arts, Inc.

Leisure Arts Inc, ed. Bears & Blossoms Christmas. 2007. 44p. 10.95 *(978-1-60140-425-1(5))* Leisure Arts, Inc.

Leisure Arts Staff, ed. Creating the Happiest of Holidays, Vol. 2. 2009. (ENG.). 160p. pap. 19.95 *(978-1-60140-884-6(6))* Leisure Arts, Inc.

Lester, Meera. Why Does Santa Wear Red? And 100 Other Christmas Curiousities Unwrapped. 2007. (ENG., Illus.). 256p. per. 9.95 *(978-1-59869-457-4(X))* Adams Media Corp.

Linsley, Leslie. A Nantucket Christmas. 2006. (ENG., Illus.). 108p. per. 19.99 *(978-0-8212-5807-1(9))* Bulfinch.

Lose, Patrick. A Patrick Lose Christmas: Whimsical Projects to Deck the Halls. 2008. (ENG.). 64p. pap. 29.95 *(978-1-57120-339-7(7))* C & T Publishing.

Lundberg, Helene S. Swedish Christmas Crafts. 2008. (ENG., Illus.). 96p. 14.95 *(978-1-60239-330-1(3))* Skyhorse Publishing Co., Inc.

Manwaring, Loraine & Nelsen, Susan. Holiday Wrappings: Quilts to Welcome the Season. 2008. (ENG., Illus.). 32p. pap. 16.95 *(978-1-56477-862-8(2)*, That Patchwork Place) Martingale & Co.

Marshall, Katerin. Gran Libro de la Cocina Navidena.Tr. of Great Book of Christmas Cooking. (SPA.). 6.98 *(978-970-606-062-4(6))* Libra Pubs., Inc.

Martin, Dick. Best of Dick Martin - Christmas. 2006. (ENG.). 96p. pap. 16.95 *(978-1-57486-211-9(1))* Leisure Arts, Inc.

Matela, Bobbie. Knit Noel. 2007. 176p. 24.95 *(978-1-59217-174-3(5))* Annie's Publishing, LLC.

McCormack, Derek. Christmas Days: From Fake Snow to Santalands - The Things That Make Christmas Christmas. 2010. (ENG., Illus.). 320p. pap. 12.95 *(978-0-88784-839-1(7))* House of Anansi Pr. CAN. Dist: Perseus-PGW.

McGuiggan, Amy Whorf, frwd. Christmas in New England: A Treasury of Traditions, from the Yule Log & the Christmas Tree to Flying Santa & the Enchanted Village. 2006. (ENG., Illus.). 192p. per. 19.95 *(978-1-889833-98-9(3))* Commonwealth Editions.

McMillan, Patricia & McMillan, Katharine. Christmas at Historic Houses. 2010. (Illus.). 224p. 45.00 *(978-0-7643-3559-4(6))* Schiffer Publishing, Ltd.

McMillan, Patricia Hart. Delicious Christmas Decorations at Historic Houses & Your Home. 2011. (Illus.). 96p. 19.99 ***(978-0-7643-3726-0(2)***, Schiffer Publishing Ltd) Schiffer Publishing, Ltd.

McMillan, Patricia Hart & McMillan, Katharine Kaye. Decorating for Christmas at Historic Houses. 2011. (Illus.). 224p. 45.00 ***(978-0-7643-3839-7(0)***, Schiffer Publishing Ltd) Schiffer Publishing, Ltd.

Meisner, Kimberly. Victoria 500 Christmas Ideas: Celebrate the Season in Splendor. 2009. (ENG., Illus.). 480p. 24.95 *(978-1-58816-766-8(6))* Hearst Communications, Inc.

Messecar, Cathy. A Scrapbook of Christmas Firsts: Stories to warm your heart & tips to simplify your Holidays. 2008. 160p. 16.99 *(978-0-89112-564-8(7)*, Leafwood Pubs.) Abilene Christian Univ. Pr.

Milligan, Lynda & Smith, Nancy. Christmas with Possibilities: 15 Quilted Holiday Projects. 2010. (ENG., Illus.). 80p. pap. 22.95 *(978-1-57120-939-9(5))* C & T Publishing.

Montroll, John. Easy Christmas Origami. 2006. (Dover Origami Papercraft Ser.). (ENG., Illus.). 48p. pap. 3.95 *(978-0-486-45024-7(4))* Dover Pubns., Inc.

Morrison, Mary. Christmas Jewelry. 3rd rev. ed. 2009. (Illus.). 160p. (Orig.). pap. 19.99 *(978-0-7643-3365-1(8))* Schiffer Publishing, Ltd.

Nargi, Lela, ed. Christmas on the Farm: A Collection of Favorite Recipes, Stories, Gift Ideas, & Decorating Tips from the Farmer's Wife. 2011. (ENG., Illus.). 224p. 17.99 ***(978-0-7603-4102-5(8)***, 0760341028, Voyageur Pr) MBI Publishing Co. LLC.

Nerjordet, Arne, et al. 55 Christmas Balls to Knit: Colorful Festive Ornaments — Tree Decorations, Centerpieces, Wreaths, Window Dressings. 2011. (ENG.). 140p. 24.95 *(978-1-57076-487-5(5))* Trafalgar Square Bks.

Nguyen, Duy & Nguyen, Tramy. Holiday Origami on the Fl[i]pside. 2008. (Illus.). 367p. ***(978-1-4027-3884-5(6)***, Sterling Innovation) Sterling Publishing Co., Inc.

Overlook Press Staff & Nonesuch Press Staff. The Great American Christmas Book. 2007. (ENG.). 356p. (gr. 12). 17.95 *(978-1-58567-982-9(8))* Overlook Pr., The.

Overman, Kathy M. Fun Family Christmas Devotions: Advent Guide for Busy Parents. 2007. per. 19.95 *(978-0-9743425-6-6(4))* Ablaze Pubns.

Page, Sally. The Flower Shop Christmas: Christmas in a Country Flower Shop. 2007. (ENG., Illus.). 192p. 34.95 *(978-0-9719552-8-8(X))* Source Bk. Pubns.

Patch, Gooseberry. Christmas in the Country Cookbook: Family Recipes, Merry Gifts from the Kitchen, & Sweet Holiday Memories to Celebrate the Simple Joys of the Season. 2007. (ENG., Illus.). 224p. 16.95 *(978-1-933494-23-4(9))* Gooseberry Patch.

—Christmas Kitchen Cookbook. 2008. (ENG., Illus.). 224p. 16.95 *(978-1-933494-54-8(9))* Gooseberry Patch.

—Gooseberry Patch Christmas Bk. 13: Recipes, Projects & Gift Ideas. 2011. (ENG., Illus.). 160p. 29.95 *(978-0-8487-3427-5(0))* Oxmoor Hse., Inc.

Peterson, Valerie & Fryer, Janice. Cookie Craft Christmas: Dozens of Decorating Ideas for a Sweet Holiday. 2009. (ENG., Illus.). 169p. 14.95 *(978-1-60342-440-0(7)*, 1603424407) Workman Publishing Co., Inc.

Pierce, Val. Mini Christmas Crochet. 2011. (Twenty to Make Ser.). (ENG., Illus.). 48p. pap. 9.95 *(978-1-84448-740-0(7))* Search Pr., Ltd. GBR. Dist: Independent Pubs. Group.

Poole, Jeannine. More Than a Gift: Creating Meaningful Memories. 2010. 116p. 21.49 *(978-1-4520-3928-2(3))*; (ENG.). pap. 12.95 *(978-1-4520-3929-9(1))* AuthorHouse.

Regan, Patrick. An Old-Fashioned Christmas. 2008. (ENG., Illus.). 72p. 9.99 *(978-0-7407-7384-6(4))* Andrews McMeel Publishing.

Sargant, Pam. Christmas Survival Kit. 2007. 56p. pap. 30.95 *(978-1-4357-0344-5(8))* Lulu Enterprises Inc.

Scott, Elizabeth M. Christmas Tree. 2009. 36p. pap. 15.00 *(978-1-4490-4218-9(X))* AuthorHouse.

Scroll Saw Woodworking and Crafts Editors, ed. Big Book of Christmas Ornaments & Decorations: 38 Favorite Projects & Patterns. 2011. (Best of Scroll Saw W Ser.). (ENG., Illus.). 160p. pap. 19.95 *(978-1-56523-606-6(8))* Fox Chapel Publishing Co., Inc.

Smith, Chuck & Smith, Chuck, Jr. Planet Christmas: The World's Most Extreme Christmas Decorations! 2006. (Illus.). 144p. 9.95 *(978-1-84340-325-8(0)*, Collins & Brown) Anova Bks. GBR. Dist: Sterling Publishing Co., Inc.

Smith, Travis. Kitschmasland! Christmas Decor from the 1950s to The 1970s. 2nd rev. ed. 2008. (Illus.). 160p. pap. 29.99 *(978-0-7643-2978-4(2))* Schiffer Publishing, Ltd.

Southern Living Magazine Editors. Christmas with Southern Living 2010: Great Recipes - Easy Entertaining - Festive Decorations - Gift Ideas. 2010. (ENG., Illus.). 192p. 29.95 *(978-0-8487-3346-9(0))* Oxmoor Hse., Inc.

—Christmas with Southern Living 2011: Savor * Entertain * Decorate * Share. 2011. (ENG., Illus.). 192p. 29.95 *(978-0-8487-3463-3(7))* Oxmoor Hse., Inc.

Southern Living Ultimate Christmas: Festive Holiday Decorations, Favorite Seasonal Recipes & Easy Entertaining Ideas. 2011. (Illus.). 416p. ***(978-0-8487-3450-3(5))*** Oxmoor Hse., Inc.

Stauffer, Jeanne. A Family Christmas: Handmade Gifts & Heartfelt Stories. 2007. (Illus.). 176p. *(978-1-59217-186-6(9)*, House of White Birches, Inc.) Annie's Publishing, LLC.

Stauffer, Jeanne & Hatch, Sandra L. Holly Jolly Christmas Quilting. 2007. (Illus.). 175p. *(978-1-59217-184-2(2)*, House of White Birches, Inc.) Annie's Publishing, LLC.

Stratford, Susan & Stratford, Sue. Mini Christmas Knits. 2011. (Twenty to Make Ser.). (ENG., Illus.). 48p. pap. 9.95 *(978-1-84448-722-6(9))* Search Pr., Ltd. GBR. Dist: Independent Pubs. Group.

Sunset Books Staff & Gooseberry Patch. Christmas All Through the House: Over 600 Holiday Recipes, Cheery Crafts & Easy-to-Make Gifts for Flurries of Fun! 2008. (ENG., Illus.). 512p. spiral bd. 29.95 *(978-0-8487-3252-3(9))* Oxmoor Hse., Inc.

Sunset Books Staff & Leisure Arts Staff. Christmas Traditions. 2008. (ENG.). 160p. 27.95 *(978-1-60140-832-7(3))* Leisure Arts, Inc.

Swinson, Antonia. Creating Your Perfect Christmas. 2006. (ENG., Illus.). 112p. *(978-1-84597-256-1(2))* Ryland Peters & Small.

Swinson, Antonia & Pell, Sania. Creating Your Perfect Christmas Stylish Ideas & Step-By-Step Projects for the Festive Season. 2006. (Illus.). 111p. *(978-1-84597-255-4(4))* Ryland Peters & Small.

Taylor, Cheryl Almgren. Deck the Halls: Quilts to Celebrate Christmas. 2009. (ENG., Illus.). 96p. pap. *(978-1-56477-910-6(6))* Martingale & Co.

Taylor, Terry. A Very Beaded Christmas: 46 Projects that Glitter, Twinkle & Shine. 2009. (ENG., Illus.). 132p. pap. 17.95 *(978-1-60059-393-2(3)*, 1304883) Lark Bks.

Thompson, Jim. The St Nicholas Solution. 2009. 112p. pap. 11.95 *(978-1-4401-3345-9(X))* iUniverse, Inc.

Thompson, Serena. The Farm Chicks Christmas: Merry Ideas for the Holidays. 2010. (ENG., Illus.). 128p. 27.95 *(978-1-58816-521-3(3))* Hearst Communications, Inc.

Trebilco, Joyce Anne. Christmas Musings: To Illuminate What We Celebrate. 2011. pap. 9.99 ***(978-1-61739-271-9(5))*** Tate Publishing & Enterprises, LLC.

Trimmings. 2007. 132p. 24.95 *(978-1-60140-589-0(8))* Leisure Arts, Inc.

Waggoner, Susan. Have Yourself a Very Vintage Christmas: Crafts, Decorating Tips, & Recipes, 1920s-1960s. 2011. (ENG., Illus.). 144p. 19.95 *(978-1-58479-923-8(4))* Stewart, Tabori & Chang.

Wecker-Frisch, Janet. Panels & Patchwork Celebrate a Cozy Christmas: Featuring the Camp Christmas fabric collection by Janet Wecker-Frisch. Landauer Corporation Staff, ed. 2006. (Illus.). 48p. pap. 8.95 *(978-1-890621-56-8(0))* Landauer Publishing, LLC.

Weiland, Barbara. Sew It for Christmas. 2007. (Illus.). 176p. 24.95 *(978-1-59217-167-5(2))* Annie's Publishing, LLC.

Weller, Alan. Christmas Vector Motifs. 2011. (Dover Electronic Clip Art Ser.). (ENG.). 48p. pap. 19.95 *(978-0-486-99161-0(X))* Dover Pubns., Inc.

Westland, Pamela. The Best Ever Christmas: 100 practical ways to make a perfect Celebration. 2010. (ENG., Illus.). 128p. pap. 17.99 *(978-1-84476-805-9(8))* Anness Publishing GBR. Dist: National Bk. Network.

Willms, Heather & Willms, Elissa. Christmas Quilts from Hopscotch: Warm & Cozy, Merry & Bright. 2008. (ENG.). 80p. pap. 24.95 *(978-1-56477-868-0(1)*, That Patchwork Place) Martingale & Co.

Wood, Dorothy. Make Me I'm Yours... Christmas: Over 20 Fun Festive Projects. 2011. (ENG., Illus.). 128p. pap. 14.99 *(978-0-7153-3896-4(X))* David & Charles Pubs. GBR. Dist: F&W Media, Inc.

Woodcarving Illustrated Staff, ed. Handcarved Christmas: 36 Beloved Ornaments, Decorations, & Gifts. 2011. (Best of Woodcarving Ser.). (ENG., Illus.). 144p. pap. 19.95 *(978-1-56523-605-9(X))* Fox Chapel Publishing Co., Inc.

Zieg, Tom. 300 Christian & Inspirational Patterns for Scroll Saw Woodworking. 2nd rev. expurg. ed. 2009. (ENG.). 192p. pap. 19.95 *(978-1-56523-430-7(8))* Fox Chapel Publishing Co., Inc.

CHRISTMAS IN ART

Dover, ed. Merry Christmas CD-ROM & Book. 2009. (Dover Electronic Clip Art Ser.). (ENG.). 48p. pap. 19.95 *(978-0-486-99050-7(8))* Dover Pubns., Inc.

Hawksworth, Peggy. Christmas with the Postcard Artists 1898-1940. 2008. pap. 113.89 *(978-1-4251-1750-4(3))* Trafford Publishing.

Kissinger, Barbara Hallman. Christmas Merrymaking, 1 vol. 2007. (ENG., Illus.). 128p. 19.95 *(978-1-58980-482-1(1))* Pelican Publishing Co., Inc.

Lantos, James. Christmas. Lantos, James & Lantos, Jim, eds. 2009. (Applewood's Pictorial America Ser.). (ENG.). 56p. pap. 9.95 *(978-1-60889-005-7(8))* Applewood Bks.

Rockwell, Norman. Norman Rockwell's Christmas Book. rev. ed. 2009. (ENG., Illus.). 224p. 24.95 *(978-0-8109-8262-8(5))* Abrams.

Vedrenne, Penny. Christmas: A Book of Stencils. 2007. 76p. pap. 19.95 *(978-1-4303-1242-0(4))* Lulu Enterprises Inc.

Zimanski, Diane & Scheidler, Adrea. Twelve Days of Christmas. 2006. (ENG.). 36p. per. 17.95 *(978-1-59800-591-2(X))* Outskirts Pr., Inc.

CHRISTMAS ISLAND

Dennis, Simone. Truncated Travel: Life in the Migration Exclusion Zone on Christmas Island, Indian Ocean, Australia. 2008. xxxii, 213p. 99.95 *(978-1-60497-510-9(5))* Cambria Pr.

CHRISTMAS MUSIC

see also Carols

Adore Him: A Christmas Worship Experience. 2007. (ENG., Illus.). 168p. pap. 8.99 *(978-0-8341-7562-4(2)*, 0834175622) Lillenas Publishing Co.

Agay, Denes, ed. The Joy of Popular Christmas Songs. 2010. 64p. pap. 14.99 *(978-0-8256-8114-1(6)*, 0825681146, Yorktown Music) Music Sales Corp.

—The Joy of Popular Christmas Songs: Piano Solo. 2010. (ENG.). pap. 14.99 *(978-1-4234-9516-1(0)*, 1423495160, Yorktown Music) Music Sales Corp.

Albrecht, Sally & Althouse, Jay. North Pole Star: The Search for the Most Talented Reindeer of Them All. 2007. (ENG.). 60p. pap. 19.95 *(978-0-7390-4749-1(3))* Alfred Publishing Co., Inc.

Albrecht, Sally K., et al. Fiesta! the Legend of the Poinsettia: A Christmas Mini-Musical for Unison Voices, based on a Mexican Folk Tale (Kit), Book & CD. 2011. 64p. pap. 64.99 *(978-0-7390-8046-7(6))* Alfred Publishing Co., Inc.

—Fiesta! the Legend of the Poinsettia: A Christmas Mini-Musical for Unison Voices, based on a Mexican Folk Tale (Teacher's Handbook) 2011. (ENG.). 64p. pap. 34.99 *(978-0-7390-8044-3(X))* Alfred Publishing Co., Inc.

Alexander, Dennis. Especially for Christmas, Book 1: 8 Christmas Favorites Arranged for Early Intermediate to Intermediate Pianists. 2008. (Especially for Christmas Ser.). (ENG.). 24p. pap. 6.95 *(978-0-7390-5576-2(3))* Alfred Publishing Co., Inc.

—Especially for Christmas, Book 2: 8 Christmas Favorites Arranged for Intermediate Pianists. 2008. (Especially for Christmas Ser.). (ENG.). 24p. pap. 6.95 *(978-0-7390-5577-9(1))* Alfred Publishing Co., Inc.

—Especially for Christmas, Book 3: 8 Christmas Favorites Arranged for Late Intermediate Pianists. 2008. (Especially for Christmas Ser.). (ENG.). 24p. pap. 6.95 *(978-0-7390-5578-6(X))* Alfred Publishing Co., Inc.

Alexander, Dennis, et al. Premier Piano Course Christmas, Bk 5. 2011. (Premier Piano Course Ser.). 24p. pap. 6.99 ***(978-0-7390-7553-1(5))*** Alfred Publishing Co., Inc.

—Premier Piano Course Christmas, Bk 6. 2011. (Premier Piano Course Ser.). 24p. pap. 6.99 ***(978-0-7390-7554-8(3))*** Alfred Publishing Co., Inc.

Alexander, Dennis, et al. Premier Piano Course Christmas, Bk 1A. 2008. (Premier Piano Course Ser.). (ENG.). 24p. pap. 6.95 *(978-0-7390-5491-8(0))* Alfred Publishing Co., Inc.

—Premier Piano Course Christmas, Bk 1B. 2008. (Premier Piano Course Ser.). (ENG.). 24p. pap. 6.99 *(978-0-7390-5492-5(9))* Alfred Publishing Co., Inc.

—Premier Piano Course Christmas, Bk 2A. 2008. (Premier Piano Course Ser.). (ENG.). 24p. pap. 6.95 *(978-0-7390-5504-5(6))* Alfred Publishing Co., Inc.

—Premier Piano Course Christmas, Bk 2B. 2008. (Premier Piano Course Ser.). (ENG.). 24p. pap. 6.95 *(978-0-7390-5505-2(4))* Alfred Publishing Co., Inc.

—Premier Piano Course Christmas, Bk 4. 2009. (Premier Piano Course Ser.). (ENG.). 24p. pap. 6.95 *(978-0-7390-6150-3(X))* Alfred Publishing Co., Inc.

Alfred Publishing, creator. Christmas Banjo. 2010. (Just for Fun (Alfred) Ser.). (ENG.). 128p. pap. 16.99 *(978-0-7390-6975-2(6))* Alfred Publishing Co., Inc.

—Christmas Guitar. 2010. (Just for Fun (Alfred) Ser.). (ENG.). 128p. pap. 16.99 *(978-0-7390-6972-1(1))* Alfred Publishing Co., Inc.

—Christmas Mandolin. 2010. (Just for Fun (Alfred) Ser.). (ENG.). 120p. pap. 16.99 *(978-0-7390-6974-5(8))* Alfred Publishing Co., Inc.

—Christmas Ukulele. 2010. (Just for Fun (Alfred) Ser.). (ENG.). 120p. pap. 16.99 *(978-0-7390-6973-8(X))* Alfred Publishing Co., Inc.

Alfred Publishing, ed. Christmas Instrumental Solos — Popular Christmas Songs: Alto Sax. 2007. (ENG.). 20p. pap. 12.95 *(978-0-7390-4868-9(6))* Alfred Publishing Co., Inc.

—Christmas Instrumental Solos — Popular Christmas Songs: Cello (with Piano Acc.) 2007. (ENG.). 64p. pap. 14.95 *(978-0-7390-4876-4(7))* Alfred Publishing Co., Inc.

—Christmas Instrumental Solos — Popular Christmas Songs: Clarinet. 2007. (ENG.). 20p. pap. 12.95 *(978-0-7390-4867-2(8))* Alfred Publishing Co., Inc.

—Christmas Instrumental Solos — Popular Christmas Songs: Horn in F. 2007. (ENG.). 20p. pap. 12.95 *(978-0-7390-4871-9(6))* Alfred Publishing Co., Inc.

—Christmas Instrumental Solos — Popular Christmas Songs: Piano Acc. 2007. (ENG.). 44p. pap. 12.95 *(978-0-7390-4873-3(2))* Alfred Publishing Co., Inc.

—Christmas Instrumental Solos — Popular Christmas Songs: Trombone. 2007. (ENG.). 20p. pap. 12.95 *(978-0-7390-4872-6(4))* Alfred Publishing Co., Inc.

—Christmas Instrumental Solos — Popular Christmas Songs: Trumpet. 2007. (ENG.). 20p. pap. 12.95 *(978-0-7390-4870-2(8))* Alfred Publishing Co., Inc.

—Christmas Instrumental Solos — Popular Christmas Songs: Viola (with Piano Acc.) 2007. (ENG.). 64p. pap. 14.95 *(978-0-7390-4875-7(9))* Alfred Publishing Co., Inc.

—Christmas Instrumental Solos — Popular Christmas Songs: Violin (with Piano Acc.) 2007. (ENG.). 64p. pap. 14.95 *(978-0-7390-4874-0(0))* Alfred Publishing Co., Inc.

—A Stained Glass Christmas with Heavenly Carols: Piano/Vocal/Chords. 2007. (ENG.). 80p. pap. 12.95 *(978-0-7390-4901-3(1))* Alfred Publishing Co., Inc.

—5 Finger Christmas Fun: 11 Delightful Melodies Arranged for Piano with Optional Duet Accompaniments. 2008. (5 Finger Ser.). (ENG.). 32p. pap. 8.95 *(978-0-7390-5551-9(8))* Alfred Publishing Co., Inc.

Alfred Publishing Staff. The Best Easy Book of Christmas Guitar: Over 100 Christmas Favorites Including a Special Easy Solo Guitar TAB Section! 2008. (ENG.). 152p. pap. 19.95 *(978-0-7390-5525-0(9))* Alfred Publishing Co., Inc.

—Christmas Hits Sheet Music Playlist: Piano/Vocal/Chords. 2008. (Playlist Ser.). (ENG.). 240p. pap. 19.95 *(978-0-7390-5594-6(1))* Alfred Publishing Co., Inc.

—Christmas Jazzin' About: Piano / Keyboard , Book & CD. rev. ed. 2010. (Faber Edition: Jazzin' About Ser.). (ENG.). pap. 11.25 *(978-0-571-53404-3(X))* Faber & Faber, Ltd. GBR. Dist: Alfred Publishing Co., Inc.

—Christmas Song Essentials: Piano/Vocal/Chords. 2007. (ENG., Illus.). 172p. pap. 16.95 *(978-0-7390-4898-6(8))* Alfred Publishing Co., Inc.

—Classic FM — Christmas Favorites. 2010. (Faber Edition Ser.). (ENG.). pap. 13.80 *(978-0-571-53480-7(5))* Faber & Faber, Ltd. GBR. Dist: Alfred Publishing Co., Inc.

—Easy Christmas Carols Instrumental Solos: Alto Sax, Book & CD. 2011. (Easy Instrumental Solos Ser.). (ENG.). 16p. pap. 9.99 ***(978-0-7390-8395-6(3))*** Alfred Publishing Co., Inc.

—Easy Christmas Carols Instrumental Solos: Clarinet, Book & CD. 2011. (Easy Instrumental Solos Ser.). (ENG.). 16p. pap. 9.99 ***(978-0-7390-8394-9(5))*** Alfred Publishing Co., Inc.

—Easy Christmas Carols Instrumental Solos: Flute, Book & CD. 2011. (Easy Instrumental Solos Ser.). (ENG.). 16p. pap. 9.99 ***(978-0-7390-8393-2(7))*** Alfred Publishing Co., Inc.

—Easy Christmas Carols Instrumental Solos: Horn in F, Book & CD. 2011. (Easy Instrumental Solos Ser.). (ENG.). 16p. pap. 9.99 ***(978-0-7390-8398-7(8))*** Alfred Publishing Co., Inc.

—Easy Christmas Carols Instrumental Solos: Piano Acc. , Book & CD. 2011. (Easy Instrumental Solos Ser.). (ENG.). 56p. pap. 12.99 ***(978-0-7390-8400-7(3))*** Alfred Publishing Co., Inc.

—Easy Christmas Carols Instrumental Solos: Tenor Sax, Book & CD. 2011. (Easy Instrumental Solos Ser.). (ENG.). 16p. pap. 9.99 ***(978-0-7390-8396-3(1))*** Alfred Publishing Co., Inc.

—Easy Christmas Carols Instrumental Solos: Trombone, Book & CD. 2011. (Easy Instrumental Solos Ser.). (ENG.). 16p. pap. 9.99 ***(978-0-7390-8399-4(6))*** Alfred Publishing Co., Inc.

—Easy Christmas Carols Instrumental Solos: Trumpet, Book & CD. 2011. (Easy Instrumental Solos Ser.). (ENG.). 16p. pap. 9.99 ***(978-0-7390-8397-0(X))*** Alfred Publishing Co., Inc.

—Easy Christmas Carols Instrumental Solos for Strings: Cello, Book & CD. 2011. (Easy Instrumental Solos Ser.). (ENG.). 72p. pap. 14.99 ***(978-0-7390-8403-8(8))*** Alfred Publishing Co., Inc.

—Easy Christmas Carols Instrumental Solos for Strings: Viola, Book & CD. 2011. (Easy Instrumental Solos Ser.). (ENG.). 72p. pap. 14.99 ***(978-0-7390-8402-1(X))*** Alfred Publishing Co., Inc.

—Easy Christmas Carols Instrumental Solos for Strings: Violin, Book & CD. 2011. (Easy Instrumental Solos Ser.). (ENG.). 72p. pap. 14.99 ***(978-0-7390-8401-4(1))*** Alfred Publishing Co., Inc.

—Easy Christmas Instrumental Solos for Strings, Level 1: Cello, Book & CD. 2009. (Easy Instrumental Solos Ser.). (ENG.). 60p. pap. 14.95 *(978-0-7390-6229-6(8))* Alfred Publishing Co., Inc.

—Easy Christmas Instrumental Solos for Strings, Level 1: Viola, Book & CD. 2009. (Easy Instrumental Solos Ser.). (ENG.). 60p. pap. 14.95 *(978-0-7390-6228-9(X))* Alfred Publishing Co., Inc.

—Easy Christmas Instrumental Solos for Strings, Level 1: Violin, Book & CD. 2009. (Easy Instrumental Solos Ser.). (ENG.). 60p. pap. 14.95 *(978-0-7390-6227-2(1))* Alfred Publishing Co., Inc.

—Easy Christmas Instrumental Solos, Level 1: Alto Sax, Book & CD. 2009. (Easy Instrumental Solos Ser.). (ENG.). 16p. pap. 9.95 *(978-0-7390-6221-0(2))* Alfred Publishing Co., Inc.

—Easy Christmas Instrumental Solos, Level 1: Clarinet, Book & CD. 2009. (Easy Instrumental Solos Ser.). (ENG.). 16p. pap. 9.95 *(978-0-7390-6220-3(4))* Alfred Publishing Co., Inc.

—Easy Christmas Instrumental Solos, Level 1: Flute, Book & CD. 2009. (Easy Instrumental Solos Ser.). (ENG.). 16p. pap. 9.95 *(978-0-7390-6219-7(0))* Alfred Publishing Co., Inc.

—Easy Christmas Instrumental Solos, Level 1: Horn in F, Book & CD. 2009. (Easy Instrumental Solos Ser.). (ENG.). 16p. pap. 9.95 (978-0-7390-6224-1(7)) Alfred Publishing Co., Inc.

—Easy Christmas Instrumental Solos, Level 1: Piano Acc. , Book & CD. 2009. (Easy Instrumental Solos Ser.). (ENG.). 44p. pap. 12.95 (978-0-7390-6226-5(3)) Alfred Publishing Co., Inc.

—Easy Christmas Instrumental Solos, Level 1: Tenor Sax, Book & CD. 2009. (Easy Instrumental Solos Ser.). (ENG.). 16p. pap. 9.95 (978-0-7390-6222-7(0)) Alfred Publishing Co., Inc.

—Easy Christmas Instrumental Solos, Level 1: Trombone, Book & CD. 2009. (Easy Instrumental Solos Ser.). (ENG.). 16p. pap. 9.95 (978-0-7390-6225-8(5)) Alfred Publishing Co., Inc.

—Easy Christmas Instrumental Solos, Level 1: Trumpet, Book & CD. 2009. (Easy Instrumental Solos Ser.). (ENG.). 16p. pap. 9.95 (978-0-7390-6223-4(9)) Alfred Publishing Co., Inc.

—Elf: the Broadway Musical — Selections: Piano/Vocal. 2011. (ENG.). 112p. pap. 19.99 **(978-0-7390-8475-5(5))** Alfred Publishing Co., Inc.

—Hit the Keys! Christmas Favorites: (Piano/Vocal/Guitar) 2011. (Hit the Keys! Ser.). 204p. pap. 19.99 **(978-0-7390-8300-0(7))** Alfred Publishing Co., Inc.

—My First Pop Christmas Songs: Pending. 2009. (My First... Ser.). (ENG.). 24p. pap. 7.95 (978-0-7390-6261-6(1)) Alfred Publishing Co., Inc.

—Piano Stylings of Classic Christmas Carols. Shanaphy, Edward, ed. 2011. (Ekay Edition Ser.). (ENG.). pap. 16.95 **(978-1-929006-66-3(7))** Alfred Publishing Co., Inc.

—Premier Piano Course Christmas, Bk 3. 2009. (Premier Piano Course Ser.). (ENG.). 24p. pap. 6.95 (978-0-7390-6149-7(6)) Alfred Publishing Co., Inc.

—See, Sing & Play Christmas Fingerstyle Guitar: Pending, Book & DVD. 2009. (ENG.). 32p. pap. 21.95 (978-0-7390-6248-7(4)) Alfred Publishing Co., Inc.

—See, Sing & Play Christmas for Guitar: The Easiest Way to Learn 7 Essential Christmas Songs on Guitar. 2008. (ENG.). 24p. pap. 16.95 (978-0-7390-4845-0(7)) Alfred Publishing Co., Inc.

—Sunday Morning Organist, Vol 1: Solos for Christmas. 2009. (Alfred's Classic Editions Ser.). (ENG.). 120p. pap. 17.95 (978-0-7390-6208-1(5)) Alfred Publishing Co., Inc.

—Susan Boyle — the Gift: Piano/Vocal/Guitar. 2011. 48p. pap. 14.99 (978-0-7390-7785-6(6)) Alfred Publishing Co., Inc.

—This Holy Night: 12 Christmas Classics for Guitar (Guitar TAB), Book & CD. 2011. 56p. pap. 16.99 **(978-0-7390-8248-5(5))** Alfred Publishing Co., Inc.

—Top 10 Popular Christmas. 2011. (Top 10 Ser.). 40p. pap. 8.99 **(978-0-7390-8139-6(X))** Alfred Publishing Co., Inc.

—Top 50 Christmas Hits: Easy Piano. 2009. (Top 50 Ser.). (ENG.). 148p. pap. 17.95 (978-0-7390-6213-5(1)) Alfred Publishing Co., Inc.

—The Ultimate Song Pages Christmas — A to Z: Piano/Vocal/Chords. 2009. (Ultimate Song Pages Ser.). (ENG.). 720p. pap. 27.95 (978-0-7390-6282-1(4)) Alfred Publishing Co., Inc.

—Ultimate Vocal Sing-along Christmas: Female Voice, Book & Enhanced CD. 2008. (Ultimate Play-along Ser.). (ENG.). 32p. pap. 12.95 (978-0-7390-5601-1(8)) Alfred Publishing Co., Inc.

—Ultimate Vocal Sing-along Christmas: Male Voice, Book & Enhanced CD. 2008. (Ultimate Play-along Ser.). (ENG.). 36p. pap. 12.95 (978-0-7390-5602-8(6)) Alfred Publishing Co., Inc.

—The World's Best Guitar Songbook. 2008. (Best Guitar Songbook Ser.). (ENG.). 280p. pap. 24.95 (978-0-7390-5507-6(0)) Alfred Publishing Co., Inc.

—World's Greatest Christmas Music: Piano/Vocal/Chords. 2009. (World's Greatest Ser.). (ENG.). 232p. pap. 19.95 (978-0-7390-6284-5(0)) Alfred Publishing Co., Inc.

—World's Most Beloved Christmas Songs: Piano/Vocal/Chords. 2008. (ENG.). 272p. pap. 24.95 (978-0-7390-5593-9(3)) Alfred Publishing Co., Inc.

—10 for 10 Sheet Music Christmas: Easy Piano Solos. 2009. (10 for 10 Sheet Music Ser.). (ENG.). 32p. pap. 10.00 (978-0-7390-6169-5(0)) Alfred Publishing Co., Inc.

—10 for 10 Sheet Music Christmas Favorites: Piano/Vocal/Chords. 2008. (10 for 10 Sheet Music Ser.). (ENG.). 48p. pap. 9.99 (978-0-7390-5595-3(X)) Alfred Publishing Co., Inc.

Alfred Publishing Staff. 40 Sheet Music Bestsellers — Christmas Songs: Piano/Vocal/Guitar. 2011. (40 Sheet Music Bestsellers Ser.). 168p. pap. 16.99 **(978-0-7390-8189-1(6))** Alfred Publishing Co., Inc.

Amsco Publications, creator. Christmas Favorites: Playalong for Alto Saxophone. 2007. (CenterStage Ser.). (ENG., Illus.). 32p. pap. 12.95 incl. audio compact disk (978-0-8256-3569-4(1), 0825635691) Music Sales Corp.

—Christmas Favorites: Playalong for Clarinet. 2007. (CenterStage Ser.). (ENG.). 32p. pap. 12.95 incl. audio compact disk (978-0-8256-3570-0(5), 0825635705) Music Sales Corp.

—Christmas Favorites: Playalong for Flute. 2007. (CenterStage Ser.). (ENG.). 32p. pap. 12.95 incl. audio compact disk (978-0-8256-3571-7(3), 0825635713) Music Sales Corp.

—Christmas Favorites: Playalong for Trumpet. 2007. (CenterStage Ser.). (ENG.). 32p. pap. 12.95 incl. audio compact disk (978-0-8256-3572-4(1), 0825635721) Music Sales Corp.

—Christmas Favorites: Playalong for Violin. 2007. (Christmas Favorites Ser.). (ENG.). 32p. pap. 12.95 incl. audio compact disk (978-0-8256-3573-1(X), 082563573X) Music Sales Corp.

Anders, Roger D. Thirty-Seven Songs & Choruses: For Sunday School, Vacation Bible School, or Special Children Services. 2010. pap. 8.99 (978-1-60799-589-0(1)) Tate Publishing & Enterprises, LLC.

Andrews, Lee, contrib. by. Mel Bay Presents Dobro Christmas Songbook, 1 vol. 2007. (ENG.). 32p. pap. 7.95 (978-0-7866-7620-0(5)) Mel Bay Pubns., Inc.

Arnold, Jeff. Christmas Standards: 27 Chord Melody Arrangements in Standard Notation & Tablature (Jazz Guitar) 2006. (ENG.). 56p. pap. 12.95 (978-1-4234-1429-2(2), 1423414292) Leonard, Hal Corp.

Baker, Kenneth. Complete Keyboard Player Christmas Songs. (Illus.). 40p. pap. 7.95 (978-0-8256-1159-8(5), AM65954) Music Sales Corp.

BarlowGirl. BarlowGirl - Home for Christmas. 2008. (ENG.). 128p. pap. 16.95 (978-1-4234-6879-0(1), 1423468791) Leonard, Hal Corp.

Baumgartner, Eric. Teaching Little Fingers to Play Christmas Favorites: A Christmas Book for the Earliest Beginner. 2006. (ENG.). 31p. pap. 12.99 incl. audio compact disk (978-1-4234-1692-0(9), 1423416929); 32p. pap. 6.99 (978-1-4234-1691-3(0), 1423416910) Willis Music Co.

—Teaching Little Fingers to Play More Christmas Favorites: Mid-Elementary Piano Supplement. 2006. (ENG.). 40p. pap. 12.99 incl. audio compact disk (978-1-4234-1694-4(5), 1423416945); (Illus.). pap. 6.99 (978-1-4234-1693-7(7), 1423416937) Willis Music Co.

Beck, Andy, et al. The Animals' Christmas Tree: A Tree-mendous Mini-Musical for Unison & 2-Part Voices (Kit), Book & CD. 2008. (ENG.). 56p. pap. 64.99 (978-0-7390-5071-2(0)) Alfred Publishing Co., Inc.

—The Animals' Christmas Tree: A Tree-mendous Mini-Musical for Unison & 2-Part Voices (Teacher's Handbook) 2008. (ENG.). 56p. pap. 34.99 (978-0-7390-5069-9(9)) Alfred Publishing Co., Inc.

—Nanny Claus — the North Pole Nanny: A Magical Christmas Musical for Unison & 2-Part Voices (Director's Score), Score. 2009. (ENG.). 84p. pap. 19.95 (978-0-7390-5843-5(6)) Alfred Publishing Co., Inc.

—Nanny Claus — the North Pole Nanny: A Magical Christmas Musical for Unison & 2-Part Voices (Performance Pack), Kit. 2009. (ENG.). pap. 99.95 (978-0-7390-5846-6(0)) Alfred Publishing Co., Inc.

—Nanny Claus — the North Pole Nanny: A Magical Christmas Musical for Unison & 2-Part Voices (Preview Pack), Book & CD. 2009. (ENG.). pap. 17.95 (978-0-7390-5845-9(2)) Alfred Publishing Co., Inc.

—Nanny Claus — the North Pole Nanny: A Magical Christmas Musical for Unison & 2-Part Voices (Student 5-Pack), 5 Books. 2009. (ENG.). pap. 27.50 (978-0-7390-5844-2(4)) Alfred Publishing Co., Inc.

Bell-Krasner, Laurel. Soul. 2009. 60p. pap. 9.95 (978-1-4401-7090-4(8)) iUniverse, Inc.

Belmo & Marsh, Garry. The Beatles Christmas Book: Everywhere It's Christmas. 2011. (ENG.). 228p. pap. 35.95 (978-1-926592-25-1(5)) Collector's Guide Publishing, Inc. CAN. Dist: Independent Pubs. Group.

Beloff, Jim. Jumpin' Jim's Happy Holidays. 2006. (ENG.). 56p. pap. 14.95 (978-1-4234-2249-5(X), 142342249X) Leonard, Hal Corp.

Bennett, Tony, contrib. by. A Swingin' Christmas: Featuring the Count Basie Big Band (Piano/Vocal/Chords) 2009. (ENG.). 48p. pap. 14.95 (978-0-7390-6111-4(9)) Alfred Publishing Co., Inc.

Berlin, Irving. White Christmas. 2010. (ENG.). 10p. pap. 6.99 incl. audio compact disk (978-1-4234-9511-6(X), 142349511X) Leonard, Hal Corp.

—White Christmas: The Musical. 2008. (ENG.). 72p. pap. 16.95 (978-1-4234-6350-4(1), 1423463501) Leonard, Hal Corp.

Berry, Cindy. O Little Town of Bethlehem: Carols for the Christ Child. 2011. (ENG.). 40p. pap. 15.99 **(978-0-8341-7910-3(5)**, 9780834179103) Lillenas Publishing Co.

Berry, Cindy. What Can I Play for Christmas? 10 Easily Prepared Piano Arrangements. 2009. (Sacred Performer Collections). (ENG.). 40p. pap. 12.95 (978-0-7390-6393-4(6)) Alfred Publishing Co., Inc.

Blessings of Christmas. 2007. audio compact disk (978-5-557-58510-1(9)) Alpha Omega Publications.

Bob Dylan - Christmas in the Heart. 2009. (ENG.). pap. 17.99 (978-1-4234-9022-7(3), 1423490223); 56p. pap. 17.99 (978-0-8256-3730-8(9), 0825637309) Music Sales Corp.

Bober, Melody. Christmas Memories. 2007. (ENG.). 24p. pap. 6.95 (978-0-7390-4915-0(1)); pap. 6.95 (978-0-7390-4914-3(3)); pap. 6.95 (978-0-7390-4916-7(X)) Alfred Publishing Co., Inc.

—Christmas Memories for Two, Bk 1. 2011. (Memories Ser.). 32p. pap. 7.99 **(978-0-7390-8301-7(5))** Alfred Publishing Co., Inc.

—Christmas Memories for Two, Bk 2. 2011. (Memories Ser.). 40p. pap. 7.99 **(978-0-7390-8302-4(3))** Alfred Publishing Co., Inc.

—Christmas Memories for Two, Bk 3. 2011. (Memories Ser.). 36p. pap. 7.99 **(978-0-7390-8303-1(1))** Alfred Publishing Co., Inc.

—Popular Christmas Memories, Bk 1: 9 Early Intermediate to Intermediate Piano Arrangements of the Season's Most Popular Songs. 2009. 24p. pap. 6.95 (978-0-7390-6394-1(4)) Alfred Publishing Co., Inc.

—Popular Christmas Memories, Bk 2: 9 Intermediate Piano Arrangements of the Season's Most Popular Songs. 2009. (ENG.). 24p. pap. 6.95 (978-0-7390-6395-8(2)) Alfred Publishing Co., Inc.

—Popular Christmas Memories, Bk 3: 8 Late Intermediate Piano Arrangements of the Season's Most Popular Songs. 2009. (ENG.). 24p. pap. 6.95 (978-0-7390-6396-5(0)) Alfred Publishing Co., Inc.

—Repeat the Sounding Joy! Christmas Medleys for Piano Solo. 2009. (ENG.). 48p. pap. 15.99 (978-0-8341-7702-4(1), 9780834177024) Lillenas Publishing Co.

Bober, Melody, contrib. by. A Contemporary Christmas: Early Advanced Piano: 9 Arrangements of Contemporary Christian & Classic Favorites. 2008. (Alfred's Sacred Performer Collections). (ENG.). 48p. pap. 12.95 (978-0-7390-5315-7(9)) Alfred Publishing Co., Inc.

Boesiger, R. Kevin. A Silent Night Brings New Light: SATB with Opt. Solos. 2011. 11p. pap. 1.95 **(978-1-4291-2527-7(6))** Lorenz Corp., The.

Boston Music Company & Hal Leonard Corporation Staff, creators. Beginning Christmas for Piano. 2008. (ENG.). 32p. pap. 9.95 (978-0-8256-3683-7(3), 0825636833) Music Sales Corp.

Brentwood-Benson Music Publishing Staff, creator. Jars of Clay Christmas Songs. 2007. 95p. per. 14.95 (978-5-557-52191-8(7), Brentwood-Benson Music Publishing, Inc.) Brentwood Music, Inc.

Brickman, Jim & Coates, Dan. The Essential Jim Brickman: Christmas. 2009 (Essential Jim Brickman Ser.). (ENG.). 60p. pap. 19.95 (978-0-7390-6271-5(9)) Alfred Publishing Co., Inc.

Bryce Inman, ed. 25 Christmas Favorites: From Today's Top Artists. 2008. (ENG.). 192p. pap. 24.95 (978-1-4234-6724-3(8), 1423467248) Leonard, Hal Corp.

Burlingham, Jan, illus. & adapted by. The Friendly Beasts: A Medieval French Carol. 2009. 28p. (J). 14.95 (978-0-8091-6742-5(5), Ambassador Bks.) Paulist Pr.

Canticos de Navidad: Songs for Christmas. (SPA.). 148p. (978-84-7228-192-9(2), 226076) Clie, Editorial.

Celtic Woman. A Christmas Celebration: Piano/Vocal/Chords. 2008. (ENG.). 96p. pap. 21.95 (978-0-7390-5680-6(8)) Alfred Publishing Co., Inc.

Chandler, Paul-Gordon. Songs in Waiting: Spiritual Reflections on Christ's Birth. 2009. (Illus.). 128p. 20.00 (978-0-8192-2360-9(3), Morehouse Publishing) Church Publishing, Inc.

Cherwien, David M. Let the People Sing! A Keyboardist's Creative & Practical Guide to Engaging God's People in Meaningful Song. 179p. spiral bd. 24.00 (978-0-570-01354-9(2), 99-1666) Concordia Publishing Hse.

Chilcott, Bob. Bob Chilcott Carols 2: 10 carol arrangements for mixed Voices. 2009. 72p. pap. 12.95 (978-0-19-336507-0(3)) Oxford Univ. Pr., Inc.

Choplin, Pepper. Fall on Your Knees: SAB with Opt. Orchestra. 2011. 11p. pap. 1.95 **(978-1-4291-2560-4(8))** Lorenz Corp., The.

—Fall on Your Knees: SATB with Opt. Orchestra. 2011. 11p. pap. 1.95 **(978-1-4291-2559-8(4))** Lorenz Corp., The.

Christmas. 2009. (ENG., Illus.). pap. 3.00 (978-0-9823352-1-5(0)) Branches of Ivy Bks.

Christmas from the Realms of Glory: Bebo Norman. 2007. 79p. per. 14.95 (978-5-557-52190-1(9), Brentwood-Benson Music Publishing, Inc.) Brentwood Music, Inc.

Christmas Is a Birthday: A Musical for Senior Adult Choir. 2008. (ENG.). 88p. pap. 7.99 (978-0-8341-7645-4(9), 9780834176454) Lillenas Publishing Co.

Christmas Mosaic: A Festival of Carols for Any Choir. 2009. (ENG.). 104p. pap. 6.99 (978-0-8341-7694-2(7), 9780834176942) Lillenas Publishing Co.

A Christmas Offering: A Praise & Worship Celebration for Any Choir. 2008. (ENG.). 96p. pap. 6.99 (978-0-8341-7643-0(2), 0834176432) Lillenas Publishing Co.

Christmas Program Builder No. 61: Creative Resources for Program Directors. 2008. (ENG.). 32p. pap. 5.99 (978-0-8341-7628-7(9), 0834176289) Lillenas Publishing Co.

Christmas Songs. (Easy Keyboard Library). 48p. 9.95 (978-1-85909-173-9(3), Warner Bros. Pubns.) Alfred Publishing Co., Inc.

Clancy, Ronald M. Best-Loved Christmas Carols: The Stories Behind Twenty-Five Yuletide Favorites. 2006. (ENG., Illus.). 112p. 19.95 (978-1-4027-4187-6(1)) Sterling Publishing Co., Inc.

Coates, Dan. The Christmas Songbook: For Easy Piano. 2007. (ENG.). 144p. pap. 18.95 (978-0-7390-4736-1(1)) Alfred Publishing Co., Inc.

—The Hilarious Holiday Songbook: For Easy Piano. 2008. (ENG.). 72p. pap. 14.95 (978-0-7390-5592-2(5)) Alfred Publishing Co., Inc.

Coates, Dan, contrib. by. Simply Christmas: 30 Favorite Christmas Songs & Carols. 2008. (Simply Ser.). (ENG.). 80p. pap. 12.95 (978-0-7390-5183-2(0)) Alfred Publishing Co., Inc.

—The World's Most-Beloved Christmas Songs: 60 Heart-Warming Holiday Favorites. 2010. (ENG.). 176p. pap. 19.99 (978-0-7390-7340-7(0)) Alfred Publishing Co., Inc.

Come & Adore Him: A Christmas Musical for Senior Adult Choir. 2011. (ENG.). 88p. pap. 7.99 **(978-0-8341-7900-4(8)**, 9780834179004) Lillenas Publishing Co.

Crowder, Band, David. David Crowder*Band - Oh for Joy. 2011. (ENG.). 66p. pap. 16.99 **(978-1-4584-1794-7(8)**, 1458417948) Leonard, Hal Corp.

Cuddihy, Kevin & Metcalfe, Phillip. Christmas's Most Wanted: The Top 10 Book of Kris Kringles, Merry Jingles, & Holiday Cheer. 2006. (Illus.). 304p. 7.98 (978-1-57866-159-6(5), Galahad Bks.) BBS Publishing Corp.

Curry, Craig. Christmas Themes & Variations: Creative Settings for Solo Piano. 2008. (ENG.). 56p. pap. 16.95 (978-1-4234-6719-9(1), 1423467191) Leonard, Hal Corp.

Curry, Craig. A Jazz-Inspired Christmas: Solo Piano Arrangements with Optional Bass & Drum Parts, Book & CD. 2011. (Sacred Performer Collections). (ENG.). 40p. pap. 14.99 **(978-0-7390-8141-9(1))** Alfred Publishing Co., Inc.

Curry, Craig, et al. Snow Falling on Ivory: Seasonal Piano Solos with Optional Instruments. 2008. (ENG.). 88p. pap. 24.95 (978-1-59235-262-3(6), 1592352626, Glory Sound) Shawnee Pr., Inc.

Cutshall, Eric. Mandolin Christmas. 2008. (ENG.). 64p. pap. 9.95 (978-1-57424-242-3(3), 1574242423) Centerstream Publishing.

Das Weihnachtsoratorium. Buch + CD. 2006. (ENG., Illus.). 91p. 14.95 incl. lp (978-3-937406-70-1(0)) Edel Classica Gmbh.

Davis, Chip. Mannheim Steamroller Christmas. 2008. (ENG.). 192p. pap. 14.95 (978-1-4391-5259-1(4)) Pocket Books.

—Mannheim Steamroller Christmas: The Season for Joy, 0 vols. 2007. (Illus.). 64p. 14.99 (978-1-4041-0511-9(5)) Nelson, Thomas Inc.

Davis, Geron & Nolde, Pam. Hallelujah, Jesus Is Born: Christmas with Geron Davis; SATB. 2008. 140p. pap. 7.95 (978-5-557-40890-5(8), Brentwood-Benson Music Publishing, Inc.) Brentwood Music, Inc.

DeVries, John, contrib. by. Christmas at Bethlehem Gulch: An 'Old West' Children's Musical about the Coming of the Savior. 2007. (ENG., Illus.). 120p. pap. 7.99 (978-0-8341-7558-7(4), 0834175584) Lillenas Publishing Co.

Don't Be Scared! A Simple Christmas Music Program for Preschoolers. 2009. (ENG.). 40p. pap. 19.99 (978-0-8341-7700-0(5), 9780834177000) Lillenas Publishing Co.

Down from His Glory: The Love Story of Christmas. 2011. (ENG.). 144p. pap. 8.99 **(978-0-8341-7898-4(2)**, 9780834178984) Lillenas Publishing Co.

Duncan, Heather. Songs of Heather's Harmony. 2010. 92p. pap. 10.75 (978-0-557-47433-2(7)) Lulu Enterprises Inc.

Duren, Cliff, creator. A Love to Save the World: A Christmas Celebration of Invitation & Redemption. 2007. (Easy 2 Excel Flexible Ser.). (ENG., Illus.). 76p. pap. 19.99 (978-0-8341-7563-1(0), 0834175630) Lillenas Publishing Co.

Ebinger, Virginia Nylander. Aguinaldos: Christmas Customs, Music, & Foods of the Spanish-Speaking Countries of the Americas. 2009. 280p. pap. 29.95 (978-0-86534-689-5(5)) Sunstone Pr.

Elvis Christmas. 2008. (ENG.). 88p. pap. 17.99 (978-1-4234-5650-6(5), 1423456505) Leonard, Hal Corp.

Emmanuel Has Come: A Christmas Worship Presentation in Unison/2-Part. 2011. (ENG.). 48p. pap. 5.99 **(978-0-8341-7901-1(6)**, 9780834179011) Lillenas Publishing Co.

Enya. Enya - & Winter Came. 2009. (ENG.). 56p. pap. 17.99 (978-1-4234-7014-4(1), 1423470141) Leonard, Hal Corp.

Esmond, Doug. Irish You a Merry Christmas: The Many Moods of Celtic Christmas Arranged for Solo Guitar. 2010. (ENG.). 32p. pap. 15.99 incl. audio compact disk (978-1-57424-259-1(8), 1574242598) Centerstream Publishing.

Esmond, James Douglas. ASAP Christmas for Guitar: Learn How to Play the Fingerstyle Way. 2011. (ENG.). 24p. pap. 14.99 incl. audio compact disk **(978-1-57424-272-0(5)**, 1574242725) Centerstream Publishing.

Etheridge, Melissa. Melissa Etheridge - A New Thought for Christmas. 2009. (ENG.). 72p. pap. 16.99 (978-1-4234-8252-9(2), 1423482522) Leonard, Hal Corp.

Faber, Nancy. Joy to the World: The Collaborative Artist Chamber Music Series. 2011. (ENG.). 24p. pap. 9.95 **(978-1-61677-706-7(0)**, 1616777060) Faber Piano Adventures(r).

—Silent Night: The Collaborative Artist Chamber Music Series. 2011. (ENG.). 8p. pap. 9.95 **(978-1-61677-707-4(9)**, 1616777079) Faber Piano Adventures(r).

Faber, Nancy & Faber, Randall. My First Piano Adventure Christmas - Book A: Pre-Reading. 2010. (ENG.). 16p. pap. 4.95 (978-1-61677-625-1(0), 1616776250) Faber Piano Adventures(r).

—My First Piano Adventure Christmas - Book B: Steps on the Staff. 2010. (ENG.). 20p. pap. 5.50 (978-1-61677-626-8(9), 1616776269) Faber Piano Adventures(r).

—My First Piano Adventure Christmas - Book C: Skips on the Staff. 2010. (ENG.). 20p. pap. 5.50 (978-1-61677-627-5(7), 1616776277) Faber Piano Adventures(r).

Fettke, Tom, contrib. by. God Is with Us: SATB Choral Score, Choral Score. 2011. 104p. pap. 8.99 **(978-0-7390-8251-5(5))** Alfred Publishing Co., Inc.

—Messiah Christmas Suite: SAB & Solo with Opt. Orchestra or Instrumental Ensemble. 2011. 15p. pap. 1.95 **(978-1-4291-2486-7(5))** Lorenz Corp., The.

—Messiah Christmas Suite -SATB. 2011. 15p. pap. 1.95 **(978-1-4291-2485-0(7))** Lorenz Corp., The.

Fettke, Tom & Sherberg, Jon. Time of Wonder. 49.95 (978-0-7673-1223-3(6)) LifeWay Christian Resources.

Flauhaus, Rod, photos by. Jim Brickman: Homecoming. 2007. (ENG., Illus.). 72p. pap. 16.95 (978-0-7390-4944-0(5)) Alfred Publishing Co., Inc.

Fox, Daniel. World's Greatest Christmas Songs: 65 of the World's Most Popular & Best Loved Traditional & Contemporary Christmas Songs. rev. ed. 2008. (World's Greatest Ser.). (ENG.). 144p. pap. 17.95 (978-0-7390-5585-4(2)) Alfred Publishing Co., Inc.

Gallina, Jill & Gallina, Michael. Silent Mice, Holy Mice. 2011. (ENG.). 56p. pap. 49.99 (978-1-4584-0016-1(6), 1458400166, Glory Sound) Shawnee Pr., Inc.

—The Tale of the Drowsy Shepherd. 2007. (ENG.). 24p. pap. 24.95 (978-1-59235-172-5(7), 1592351727) Leonard, Hal Corp.

—The Tale of the Drowsy Shepherd. 2007. (ENG.). 40p. pap. 24.95 (978-1-59235-171-8(9), 1592351719) Shawnee Pr., Inc.

Garden, John. The Christmas Carol Dance Book. 2010. 76p. pap. 29.99 (978-1-4452-6444-8(7)) Lulu Enterprises Inc.

George, Jeannette Clift. An A. D. Player's Christmas: Production Pack. pap. 60.50 (978-0-8341-9911-8(4)) Lillenas Publishing Co.

Gerou, Tom. 5 Finger Christmas Classics: 14 Timeless Themes Arranged for Piano with Optional Duet Accompaniments. 2009. (5 Finger Ser.). (ENG.). 32p. pap. 8.95 (978-0-7390-6398-9(7)) Alfred Publishing Co., Inc.

—5 Finger Christmas Hits: 10 Holiday Favorites Arranged for Piano with Optional Duet Accompaniments. 2007. (5 Finger Ser.). (ENG.). 32p. pap. 8.99 (978-0-7390-4823-8(6)) Alfred Publishing Co., Inc.

Gift of Love: A Contemporary Christmas Worship Experience. 2009. (ENG.). 152p. pap. 9.99 (978-0-8341-7735-2(8), 9780834177352) Lillenas Publishing Co.

Giglio, Louie, contrib. by. Indescribable. 2008. audio compact disk 14.99 (978-5-557-44623-5(0)) Point of Grace Entertainment Group.

Giles, Gordon. O Come Emmanuel: A Musical Tour of Daily Readings for Advent & Christmas. 2006. (ENG.). 168p. (gr. 13). per. 16.99 (978-1-55725-515-0(6)) Paraclete Pr., Inc.

Goss, Louise & Holland, Sam. The Music Tree Christmas: 4 Solos & 2 Duets for Student & Teacher. 2007. (ENG.). 16p. pap. 6.95 *(978-0-7390-4912-9(7))* Alfred Publishing Co., Inc.
—The Music Tree Christmas: 6 Solos & 1 Duet for Student & Teacher. 2007. (ENG.). 16p. pap. 6.95 *(978-0-7390-4911-2(9))* Alfred Publishing Co., Inc.
Gramann, Fred. A la Nanita Nana: 2 or 3 Octaves (Handbells or Handchimes), Level 2. 2011. 10p. pap. 4.50 ***(978-1-4291-2362-4(1))*** Lorenz Corp., The.
The Great Gift Exchange: An Easy-to-sing, Easy-to-stage Kids' Christmas Musical about the Saving Gift of Jesus. 2009. (ENG.). 64p. pap. 5.99 *(978-0-8341-7699-7(8)*, 9780834176997) Lillenas Publishing Co.
Guaraldi, Vince. A Charlie Brown Christmas. 2006. (Jazz Play-along Ser.). (ENG.). 64p. pap. 16.99 incl. audio compact disk *(978-1-4234-1390-5(3)*, 1423413903) Leonard, Hal Corp.
—A Charlie Brown Christmas: Beginning Piano Solos. 2008. (ENG.). 32p. pap. 12.99 *(978-1-4234-5648-3(3)*, 1423456483) Leonard, Hal Corp.
—Peanuts: Alto Sax. 2010. (ENG.). 24p. pap. 12.99 incl. audio compact disk *(978-1-4234-8688-6(9)*, 1423486889) Leonard, Hal Corp.
—Peanuts: Flute. 2010. (ENG.). 24p. pap. 12.99 incl. audio compact disk *(978-1-4234-8686-2(2)*, 1423486862) Leonard, Hal Corp.
—Peanuts: Horn. 2010. (ENG.). 24p. pap. 12.99 incl. audio compact disk *(978-1-4234-8691-6(9)*, 1423486919) Leonard, Hal Corp.
—Peanuts: Trombone. 2010. (ENG.). 24p. pap. 12.99 incl. audio compact disk *(978-1-4234-8692-3(7)*, 1423486927) Leonard, Hal Corp.
—Peanuts: Viola. 2010. (ENG.). 24p. pap. 12.99 incl. audio compact disk *(978-1-4234-8694-7(3)*, 1423486943) Leonard, Hal Corp.
Haase, Ernie & Signature Sound. Every Light That Shines at Christmas. 2009. (ENG.). 120p. pap. 19.99 *(978-0-8341-7777-2(3)*, 9780834177772) Lillenas Publishing Co.
Hakes, Derek K. He Is Born! 2 or 3 Octaves, Level 2+ 2011. 8p. pap. 4.50 ***(978-1-4291-2326-6(5))*** Lorenz Corp., The.
Hal Leonard. Chris Tomlin - Glory in the Highest: Christmas Songs of Worship, 1 vol. 2010. (ENG.). 112p. pap. 16.99 *(978-1-935288-08-4(3)*, 1935288083) Leonard, Hal Corp.
Hal Leonard Corp. Big Christmas Collection: Jazz Play-along Volume 162. 2011. (ENG.). 136p. pap. 24.99 incl. audio compact disk ***(978-1-4584-0842-6(6)***, 1458408426) Leonard, Hal Corp.
—Christmas Songs. 2011. (ENG.). 144p. pap. 12.99 ***(978-1-4584-1159-4(1)***, 1458411591) Leonard, Hal Corp.
—Christmas Strumming: Ukulele Play-along Volume 11. 2011. (ENG.). 16p. pap. 12.99 incl. audio compact disk ***(978-1-4584-1003-0(X)***, 145841003X) Leonard, Hal Corp.
—Easy Pop Christmas Melodies: Book Only. 2011. (ENG.). 24p. pap. 6.99 ***(978-1-4584-0796-2(9)***, 1458407969) Leonard, Hal Corp.
—Easy Pop Christmas Melodies: Book/CD Pack. 2011. (ENG.). 24p. pap. 14.99 incl. audio compact disk ***(978-1-4584-0795-5(0)***, 1458407950) Leonard, Hal Corp.
—Glee: The Music - The Christmas Album. 2011. (ENG.). 80p. pap. 14.99 ***(978-1-4584-0820-4(5)***, 1458408205) Leonard, Hal Corp.
—Glee: the Music - the Christmas Album. 2011. (ENG.). 88p. pap. 16.99 ***(978-1-4584-0819-8(1)***, 1458408191) Leonard, Hal Corp.
Hal Leonard Corp. The Holly & the Ivory. 2011. (ENG.). 76p. pap. 16.95 *(978-1-4584-0254-7(1)*, 1458402541) Shawnee Pr., Inc.
Hal Leonard Corp., creator. All the Best Songs of Praise & Worship 3: More Contemporary Favorites. 2009. (ENG.). 298p. spiral bd. 19.99 *(978-0-8341-7708-6(0)*, 9780834177086) Lillenas Publishing Co.
—Anthology of Christmas Songs - Gold Edition. 2010. (ENG.). 352p. pap. 27.00 *(978-1-4234-9381-5(8)*, 1423493818) Leonard, Hal Corp.
—Christmas: Easy Pieces for Acoustic Guitar. 2010. 24p. pap. 12.99 incl. audio compact disk *(978-1-84938-327-1(8)*, 1849383278) Music Sales Corp.
—Christmas at the Manger. 2010. (ENG.). 64p. pap. 10.99 *(978-1-4234-8001-3(5)*, 1423480015) Leonard, Hal Corp.
—Christmas at the Movies. 2011. (ENG.). 56p. pap. 12.99 ***(978-1-4584-0774-0(8)***, 1458407748) Leonard, Hal Corp.
—Christmas Ballads - Audition Songs for Male & Female Singers. 2010. (ENG.). 48p. pap. 14.99 incl. audio compact disk *(978-1-4234-9495-9(4)*, 1423494954) Music Sales Corp.
—Christmas Blues: Blues Play-along Volume 11. 2010. (ENG.). 72p. pap. 12.99 incl. audio compact disk *(978-1-4234-9471-3(7)*, 1423494717) Leonard, Hal Corp.
—Christmas Carols. 2011. (ENG.). 152p. pap. 14.99 ***(978-1-4584-1100-6(1)***, 1458411001) Leonard, Hal Corp.
—Christmas Carols for Easy Classical Guitar. 2010. (ENG.). 40p. pap. 9.99 incl. audio compact disk *(978-1-60378-248-7(6)*, 1603782486) Cherry Lane Music Co.
—Christmas Cheer: Piano Play-along Volume 98. 2010. (ENG.). 32p. pap. 14.99 incl. audio compact disk *(978-1-4234-9470-6(9)*, 1423494709) Leonard, Hal Corp.
—Christmas Classic Favorites. 2010. (ENG.). 88p. pap. 12.99 *(978-1-4234-9477-5(6)*, 1423494776) Leonard, Hal Corp.
—Christmas Classics: Beginning Piano Solo Play-along Volume 5. 2011. (ENG.). 16p. pap. 14.99 incl. audio compact disk ***(978-1-4584-0829-7(9)***, 1458408299) Leonard, Hal Corp.
—Christmas Classics: Essential Elements Guitar Ensembles Mid-Intermediate Level. 2011. (ENG.). 32p. pap. 9.99 ***(978-1-4584-1005-4(6)***, 1458410056) Leonard, Hal Corp.
—Christmas Classics: Hal Leonard Recorder Songbook. 2010. (ENG.). 16p. (J). pap. 6.99 *(978-1-4234-9479-9(2)*, 1423494792) Leonard, Hal Corp.
—Christmas Favorites: Harmonica Play-along Volume 16. 2010. (ENG.). 24p. pap. 14.99 incl. audio compact disk *(978-1-4234-9464-5(4)*, 1423494644) Leonard, Hal Corp.
—Christmas Favorites: Violin Play-along Volume 17. 2010. (ENG.). 16p. pap. 14.99 incl. audio compact disk *(978-1-4234-9472-0(5)*, 1423494725) Leonard, Hal Corp.
—Christmas Favorites for Accordion. 2006. (ENG., Illus.). 64p. pap. 9.95 *(978-1-4234-1433-9(0)*, 1423414330) Leonard, Hal Corp.
—Christmas Hits: Beginning Piano Solo Play-along Volume 4. 2011. (ENG.). 16p. pap. 14.99 incl. audio compact disk ***(978-1-4584-0828-0(0)***, 1458408280) Leonard, Hal Corp.
—Christmas Songs: Ukulele Play-along Series Volume 5. 2010. (ENG.). 24p. pap. 12.99 incl. audio compact disk *(978-1-4234-9474-4(1)*, 1423494741) Leonard, Hal Corp.
—Fingerpicking Christmas Classics: 15 Songs Arranged for Solo Guitar in Notes & Tablature. 2010. (ENG.). 48p. pap. 7.99 *(978-1-4234-9465-2(2)*, 1423494652) Leonard, Hal Corp.
—Great Songs of Christmas. 2010. (ENG.). 200p. pap. 17.99 *(978-1-60378-256-2(7)*, 1603782567) Cherry Lane Music Co.
—More Christmas Piano Solos - Level 1: Hal Leonard Student Piano Library. 2010. (ENG.). 24p. pap. 12.99 incl. audio compact disk *(978-1-4234-9326-6(5)*, 1423493265) Leonard, Hal Corp.
—More Christmas Piano Solos - Level 2: Hal Leonard Student Piano Library. 2010. (ENG.). 32p. pap. 12.99 incl. audio compact disk *(978-1-4234-9327-3(3)*, 1423493273) Leonard, Hal Corp.
—More Christmas Piano Solos - Level 3: Hal Leonard Student Piano Library. 2010. (ENG.). 40p. pap. 12.99 incl. audio compact disk *(978-1-4234-9328-0(1)*, 1423493281) Leonard, Hal Corp.
—More Christmas Piano Solos - Level 4: Hal Leonard Student Piano Library. 2010. (ENG.). 40p. pap. 12.99 incl. audio compact disk *(978-1-4234-9329-7(X)*, 142349329X) Leonard, Hal Corp.
—More Christmas Piano Solos - Level 5: Hal Leonard Student Piano Library. 2010. (ENG.). 32p. pap. 12.99 incl. audio compact disk *(978-1-4234-9330-3(3)*, 1423493303) Leonard, Hal Corp.
—More Christmas Piano Solos - Prestaff Level: Hal Leonard Student Piano Library. 2010. (ENG.). 16p. pap. 10.99 incl. audio compact disk *(978-1-4234-9325-9(7)*, 1423493257) Leonard, Hal Corp.
—The Most Requested Christmas Songs. 2011. (ENG.). 258p. pap. 19.99 ***(978-1-4584-1274-4(1)***, 1458412741) Cherry Lane Music Co.
—Piano Recital Showcase: Christmas Eve Solos: 10 Christmas Favorites at an Intermediate Level. 2011. (ENG.). 40p. pap. 8.99 ***(978-1-4584-1183-9(4)***, 1458411834) Leonard, Hal Corp.
—The Real Christmas Book Play-along, Vol. A-G. 2011. (ENG.). 4p. pap. 24.99 ***(978-1-4584-1551-6(1)***, 1458415511) Leonard, Hal Corp.
—The Real Christmas Book Play-along, Vol. H-M. 2011. (ENG.). 4p. pap. 24.99 ***(978-1-4584-1552-3(X)***, 145841552X) Leonard, Hal Corp.
—The Real Christmas Book Play-along, Vol. N-Y. 2011. (ENG.). 4p. pap. 24.99 ***(978-1-4584-1553-0(8)***, 1458415538) Leonard, Hal Corp.
—The World's Greatest Christmas Carols: Stories & Music of the Best Loved Carols. 2007. (ENG.). 63p. pap. 14.95 incl. audio compact disk *(978-1-59235-178-7(6)*, 1592351786) Shawnee Pr., Inc.
—The 4 Chord Songbook: Strum & Sing Series. 2010. (ENG.). 112p. pap. 10.99 *(978-1-60378-251-7(6)*, 1603782516) Cherry Lane Music Co.
Hal Leonard Corporation Staff. Christmas Carols: 10 Holiday Favorites. 2007. (Jazz Play-along Ser.). (ENG.). 80p. pap. 14.95 incl. audio compact disk *(978-1-4234-3165-7(0)*, 1423431650) Leonard, Hal Corp.
Hal Leonard Corporation Staff, creator. Baching Around the Christmas Tree: Alto Sax. 2008. (ENG.). 24p. pap. 10.95 incl. audio compact disk *(978-1-60378-075-9(0)*, 1603780750) Cherry Lane Music Co.
—Baching Around the Christmas Tree: Cello. 2008. (ENG.). 24p. pap. 10.95 incl. audio compact disk *(978-1-60378-071-1(8)*, 1603780718) Cherry Lane Music Co.
—Baching Around the Christmas Tree: Clarinet. 2008. (ENG.). 24p. pap. 10.95 incl. audio compact disk *(978-1-60378-068-1(8)*, 1603780688) Cherry Lane Music Co.
—Baching Around the Christmas Tree: F Horn. 2008. (ENG.). 24p. pap. 10.95 incl. audio compact disk *(978-1-60378-073-5(4)*, 1603780734) Cherry Lane Music Co.
—Baching Around the Christmas Tree: Tenor Sax. 2008. (ENG.). 24p. pap. 10.95 incl. audio compact disk *(978-1-60378-076-6(9)*, 1603780769) Cherry Lane Music Co.
—Baching Around the Christmas Tree: Trombone. 2008. (ENG.). 24p. pap. 10.95 incl. audio compact disk *(978-1-60378-074-2(2)*, 1603780742) Cherry Lane Music Co.
—Baching Around the Christmas Tree: Trumpet. 2008. (ENG.). 24p. pap. 10.95 incl. audio compact disk *(978-1-60378-072-8(6)*, 1603780726) Cherry Lane Music Co.
—Baching Around the Christmas Tree: Viola. 2008. (ENG.). 24p. pap. 10.95 incl. audio compact disk *(978-1-60378-070-4(X)*, 160378070X) Cherry Lane Music Co.
—Baching Around the Christmas Tree: Violin. 2008. (ENG.). 24p. pap. 10.95 incl. audio compact disk *(978-1-60378-069-8(6)*, 1603780696) Cherry Lane Music Co.
—Big Book of Christmas Songs: Alto Sax. 2006. (ENG.). 144p. pap. 14.95 *(978-1-4234-1368-4(7)*, 1423413687) Leonard, Hal Corp.
—Big Book of Christmas Songs: Cello. 2006. (ENG.). 144p. pap. 14.95 *(978-1-4234-1375-2(X)*, 142341375X) Leonard, Hal Corp.
—Big Book of Christmas Songs: Flute. 2006. (ENG.). 144p. pap. 14.95 *(978-1-4234-1364-6(4)*, 1423413644) Leonard, Hal Corp.
—Big Book of Christmas Songs: Horn. 2006. (ENG.). 146p. pap. 14.95 *(978-1-4234-1371-4(7)*, 1423413717) Leonard, Hal Corp.
—Big Book of Christmas Songs: Tenor Sax. 2006. (ENG.). 144p. pap. 14.95 *(978-1-4234-1369-1(5)*, 1423413695) Leonard, Hal Corp.
—Big Book of Christmas Songs: Trombone. 2006. (ENG.). 144p. pap. 14.95 *(978-1-4234-1372-1(5)*, 1423413725) Leonard, Hal Corp.
—Big Book of Christmas Songs: Trumpet. 2006. (ENG.). 144p. pap. 14.95 *(978-1-4234-1370-7(9)*, 1423413709) Leonard, Hal Corp.
—Big Book of Christmas Songs - Violin. 2006. (ENG.). 146p. pap. 14.95 *(978-1-4234-1373-8(3)*, 1423413733) Leonard, Hal Corp.
—Big Book of Christmas Songs for Clarinet: Clarinet. 2006. (ENG.). 144p. pap. 14.95 *(978-1-4234-1367-7(9)*, 1423413679) Leonard, Hal Corp.
—Charlie Brown Christmas: Easy Piano CD Play-along Volume 29. 2009. (ENG.). 40p. pap. 14.99 incl. audio compact disk *(978-1-4234-8300-7(6)*, 1423483006) Leonard, Hal Corp.
—A Charlie Brown Christmas Vol. 34: Piano Play-along. 2006. (Piano Play-along Ser.). (ENG., Illus.). 32p. pap. 15.95 incl. audio compact disk *(978-0-634-09998-4(1)*, 0634099981) Leonard, Hal Corp.
—Christian Christmas Favorites. 2007. (ENG.). 56p. pap. 12.95 *(978-1-4234-3160-2(X)*, 142343160X) Leonard, Hal Corp.
—Christmas Carols: Clarinet. 2006. (ENG.). 24p. pap. 10.95 incl. audio compact disk *(978-1-4234-1354-7(7)*, 1423413547) Leonard, Hal Corp.
—Christmas Carols: Easy Piano CD Play-along Volume 28. 2009. (ENG.). 32p. pap. 14.99 incl. audio compact disk *(978-1-4234-8298-7(0)*, 1423482980) Leonard, Hal Corp.
—Christmas Carols: Harmonica Play-along Volume 11. 2009. (ENG.). 24p. pap. 12.99 incl. audio compact disk *(978-1-4234-8259-8(X)*, 142348259X) Leonard, Hal Corp.
—Christmas Carols: Piano Duet Play-along Volume 24. 2008. (ENG.). 64p. pap. 14.95 incl. audio compact disk *(978-1-4234-5671-1(8)*, 1423456718) Leonard, Hal Corp.
—Christmas Carols: Pro Vocal Male/Female Edition Volume 7. 2009. (ENG.). 12p. pap. 14.99 incl. audio compact disk *(978-1-4234-8322-9(7)*, 1423483227) Leonard, Hal Corp.
—Christmas Carols: Sing with the Choir Volume 13. 2009. (ENG.). 40p. pap. 14.99 incl. audio compact disk *(978-1-4234-8480-6(0)*, 1423484800) Leonard, Hal Corp.
—Christmas Carols: Violin Play-along Volume 5. 2006. (ENG.). 16p. pap. 14.99 incl. audio compact disk *(978-1-4234-1381-3(4)*, 1423413814) Leonard, Hal Corp.
—Christmas Carols: Volume 9. 2007. (Play with the CD Piano Ser.). (ENG.). 64p. pap. 19.95 incl. audio compact disk *(978-1-4234-5196-9(1)*, 1423451961) Leonard, Hal Corp.
—Christmas Carols for Mandolin. 2006. (ENG.). 56p. pap. 8.95 *(978-1-4234-1398-1(9)*, 1423413989) Leonard, Hal Corp.
—Christmas Carols for Ukulele. 2008. (ENG.). 48p. pap. 7.95 *(978-1-4234-5651-3(3)*, 1423456513) Leonard, Hal Corp.
—Christmas Classics. (ENG.). 2008. 40p. pap. 6.95 *(978-1-4234-5647-6(5)*, 1423456475) 2007. 64p. pap. 14.95 incl. audio compact disk *(978-1-4234-3162-6(6)*, 1423431626) Leonard, Hal Corp.
—Christmas Classics for Bass: 20 Melodies Arranged for 4-String Electric Bass. 2007. (ENG.). 56p. pap. 9.95 *(978-1-4234-3158-9(8)*, 1423431588) Leonard, Hal Corp.
—Christmas Favorites: Sing with the Choir Volume 10. 2008. (ENG.). 46p. pap. 14.95 incl. audio compact disk *(978-1-4234-5814-2(1)*, 1423458141) Leonard, Hal Corp.
—Christmas Favorites Vol. 2: Play with the CD - Guitar. 2006. (ENG.). 56p. pap. 19.95 incl. audio compact disk *(978-1-4234-1767-5(4)*, 1423417674) Leonard, Hal Corp.
—Christmas Favorites - Alto Sax: Big Band Play-along Volume 5. 2008. (ENG.). 24p. pap. 14.95 incl. audio compact disk *(978-1-4234-5849-4(4)*, 1423458494) Leonard, Hal Corp.
—Christmas Favorites - Bass: Big Band Play-along Volume 5. 2008. (ENG.). 24p. pap. 14.95 incl. audio compact disk *(978-1-4234-5855-5(9)*, 1423458559) Leonard, Hal Corp.
—Christmas Favorites - Drums: Big Band Play-along Volume 5. 2008. (ENG.). 24p. pap. 14.95 incl. audio compact disk *(978-1-4234-5856-2(7)*, 1423458567) Leonard, Hal Corp.
—Christmas Favorites - Guitar: Big Band Play-along Volume 5. 2008. (ENG.). 24p. pap. 14.95 incl. audio compact disk *(978-1-4234-5853-1(2)*, 1423458532) Leonard, Hal Corp.
—Christmas Favorites - Piano: Big Band Play-along Volume 5. 2008. (ENG.). 40p. pap. 14.95 incl. audio compact disk *(978-1-4234-5854-8(0)*, 1423458540) Leonard, Hal Corp.
—Christmas Favorites - Tenor Sax: Big Band Play-along Volume 5. 2008. (ENG.). 24p. pap. 14.95 incl. audio compact disk *(978-1-4234-5850-0(8)*, 1423458508) Leonard, Hal Corp.
—Christmas Favorites - Trombone: Big Band Play-along Volume 5. 2008. (ENG.). 24p. pap. 14.95 incl. audio compact disk *(978-1-4234-5852-4(4)*, 1423458524) Leonard, Hal Corp.
—Christmas Favorites - Trumpet: Big Band Play-along Volume 5. 2008. (ENG.). 24p. pap. 14.95 incl. audio compact disk *(978-1-4234-5851-7(6)*, 1423458516) Leonard, Hal Corp.
—Christmas Favorites for Mandolin. 2007. (ENG.). 48p. pap. 8.95 *(978-1-4234-1399-8(7)*, 1423413997) Leonard, Hal Corp.
—Christmas Favorites for Two. 2006. (ENG.). 80p. pap. 10.95 *(978-1-4234-1366-0(0)*, 1423413660) Leonard, Hal Corp.
—Christmas for Two: Piano Duet Play-along Volume 37. 2009. (ENG.). 64p. pap. 14.99 incl. audio compact disk *(978-1-4234-8012-9(0)*, 1423480120) Leonard, Hal Corp.
—Christmas Guitar Collection: 20 Songs Arranged for Solo Fingerstyle Guitar. 2007. (ENG.). 65p. pap. 17.95 incl. audio compact disk *(978-1-4234-3154-1(5)*, 1423431545) Leonard, Hal Corp.
—Christmas Hits. (Keyboard Play-along Ser.). (ENG., 2007. Illus.). 48p. pap. 14.95 incl. audio compact disk *(978-1-4234-3376-7(9)*, 1423433769) 2006. 64p. pap. 19.95 incl. audio compact disk *(978-1-4234-1764-4(X)*, 142341764X) Leonard, Hal Corp.
—Christmas Hits: Alto Sax. 2009. (ENG.). 16p. pap. 12.99 incl. audio compact disk *(978-1-4234-8344-1(8)*, 1423483448) Leonard, Hal Corp.
—Christmas Hits: Bass Play-along Volume 33. 2009. (ENG.). 24p. pap. 12.99 incl. audio compact disk *(978-1-4234-8258-1(1)*, 1423482581) Leonard, Hal Corp.
—Christmas Hits: Cello. 2009. (ENG.). 16p. pap. 12.99 incl. audio compact disk *(978-1-4234-8351-9(0)*, 1423483510) Leonard, Hal Corp.
—Christmas Hits: Clarinet. 2009. (ENG.). 16p. pap. 12.99 incl. audio compact disk *(978-1-4234-8343-4(X)*, 142348343X) Leonard, Hal Corp.
—Christmas Hits: Flute. 2009. (ENG.). 16p. pap. 12.99 incl. audio compact disk *(978-1-4234-8342-7(1)*, 1423483421) Leonard, Hal Corp.
—Christmas Hits: Horn. 2009. (ENG.). 16p. pap. 12.99 incl. audio compact disk *(978-1-4234-8347-2(2)*, 1423483472) Leonard, Hal Corp.
—Christmas Hits: Pro Vocal Men's Edition Volume 42. 2008. (ENG.). 30p. pap. 15.95 incl. audio compact disk *(978-1-4234-5821-0(4)*, 1423458214) Leonard, Hal Corp.
—Christmas Hits: Pro Vocal Women's Edition Volume 39. 2008. (ENG.). 40p. pap. 15.95 incl. audio compact disk *(978-1-4234-5820-3(6)*, 1423458206) Leonard, Hal Corp.
—Christmas Hits: Tenor Sax. 2009. (ENG.). 16p. pap. 12.99 incl. audio compact disk *(978-1-4234-8345-8(6)*, 1423483456) Leonard, Hal Corp.
—Christmas Hits: Trombone. 2009. (ENG.). 16p. pap. 12.99 incl. audio compact disk *(978-1-4234-8348-9(0)*, 1423483480) Leonard, Hal Corp.
—Christmas Hits: Trumpet. 2009. (ENG.). 16p. pap. 12.99 incl. audio compact disk *(978-1-4234-8346-5(4)*, 1423483464) Leonard, Hal Corp.
—Christmas Hits: Viola. 2009. (ENG.). 16p. pap. 12.99 incl. audio compact disk *(978-1-4234-8350-2(2)*, 1423483502) Leonard, Hal Corp.
—Christmas Hits: Violin. 2009. (ENG.). 16p. pap. 12.99 incl. audio compact disk *(978-1-4234-8349-6(9)*, 1423483499) Leonard, Hal Corp.
—Christmas Hits Vol. 1: Play with the CD - Guitar. 2006. (ENG.). 48p. pap. 19.95 incl. audio compact disk *(978-1-4234-1766-8(6)*, 1423417666) Leonard, Hal Corp.
—Christmas Peace: 30 Inspirational Songs of the Season. 2009. (ENG.). 184p. pap. 16.99 *(978-1-4234-8000-6(7)*, 1423480007) Leonard, Hal Corp.
—Christmas Piano Solos: John Thompson's Modern Course for the Piano. 2008. (ENG.). 48p. pap. 14.95 incl. audio compact disk *(978-1-4234-5698-8(X)*, 142345698X) Willis Music Co.
—Christmas Piano Solos - Fifth Grade: John Thompson's Modern Course for the Piano. 2008. (ENG.). 48p. pap. 9.95 *(978-1-4234-5693-3(9)*, 1423456939) Willis Music Co.
—Christmas Piano Solos - First Grade: John Thompson's Modern Course for the Piano. 2008. (ENG.). 32p. pap. 6.99 *(978-1-4234-5689-6(0)*, 1423456890); pap. 10.95 incl. audio compact disk *(978-1-4234-5694-0(7)*, 1423456947) Willis Music Co.
—Christmas Piano Solos - Fourth Grade: John Thompson's Modern Course for the Piano. 2008. (ENG.). 40p. pap. 12.95 incl. audio compact disk *(978-1-4234-5697-1(1)*, 1423456971); pap. 7.95 *(978-1-4234-5692-6(0)*, 1423456920) Willis Music Co.
—Christmas Piano Solos - Second Grade. 2008. (ENG.). 32p. pap. 10.95 incl. audio compact disk *(978-1-4234-5695-7(5)*, 1423456955) Willis Music Co.
—Christmas Piano Solos - Second Grade: John Thompson's Modern Course for the Piano. 2008. (ENG.). 32p. pap. 6.95 *(978-1-4234-5690-2(4)*, 1423456904) Willis Music Co.
—Christmas Piano Solos - Third Grade: John Thompson's Modern Course for the Piano. 2008. (ENG.). 40p. pap. 7.95 *(978-1-4234-5691-9(2)*, 1423456912); pap. 12.95 incl. audio compact disk *(978-1-4234-5696-4(3)*, 1423456963) Willis Music Co.
—Christmas Songs: 15 Holiday Hits Arranged for Three or More Guitarists. 2007. (ENG.). 32p. pap. 9.95 *(978-1-4234-3159-6(6)*, 1423431596) Leonard, Hal Corp.
—Christmas Songs: Budget Books. 2008. (ENG.). 304p. pap. 12.99 *(978-1-4234-5645-2(9)*, 1423456459) Leonard, Hal Corp.
—Christmas Songs: Easy Piano Solo. 2007. (ENG.). 48p. pap. 8.99 *(978-1-4234-3178-7(2)*, 1423431782) Leonard, Hal Corp.
—Christmas Songs: Easy Rhythm Guitar Series Volume 11. 2008. (ENG.). 24p. pap. 14.95 incl. audio compact disk *(978-1-4234-5654-4(8)*, 1423456548) Leonard, Hal Corp.
—Christmas Songs for Banjo. 2007. (ENG.). 56p. pap. 7.95 *(978-1-4234-1397-4(0)*, 1423413970) Leonard, Hal Corp.
—Christmas Songs for Bass: 24 Melodies Arranged for 4-String Electric Bass. 2007. (ENG.). 48p. per. 9.95 *(978-1-4234-3157-2(X)*, 142343157X) Leonard, Hal Corp.

—Christmas Songs for Viola. 2006. (ENG.). 146p. pap. 14.95 *(978-1-4234-1374-5(1)*, 1423413741) Leonard, Hal Corp.

—Christmas Strumming: Easy Rhythm Guitar Series Volume 12. 2009. (ENG.). 24p. pap. 14.99 incl. audio compact disk *(978-1-4234-8254-3(9)*, 1423482549) Leonard, Hal Corp.

—Christmas Time Is Here: Sing with the Choir Volume 11. 2008. (ENG.). 48p. pap. 14.95 incl. audio compact disk *(978-1-4234-5815-9(X)*, 142345815X) Leonard, Hal Corp.

—Christmas Tradition: 7 Arrangements for Brass Quintet - Conductor's Score. 2008. (ENG.). 32p. pap. 16.95 *(978-1-4234-6378-8(1)*, 1423463781) Leonard, Hal Corp.

—Christmas Tradition: 7 Arrangements for Brass Quintet - Horn in F. 2008. (ENG.). 16p. pap. 8.95 *(978-1-4234-6381-8(1)*, 1423463811) Leonard, Hal Corp.

—Christmas Tradition: 7 Arrangements for Brass Quintet - Trombone. 2008. (ENG.). 16p. pap. 8.95 *(978-1-4234-6382-5(X)*, 142346382X) Leonard, Hal Corp.

—Christmas Tradition: 7 Arrangements for Brass Quintet - Trumpet I in B-flat. 2008. (ENG.). 16p. pap. 8.95 *(978-1-4234-6379-5(X)*, 142346379X) Leonard, Hal Corp.

—Christmas Tradition: 7 Arrangements for Brass Quintet - Trumpet II in B-flat. 2008. (ENG.). 16p. pap. 8.95 *(978-1-4234-6380-1(3)*, 1423463803) Leonard, Hal Corp.

—Christmas Tradition: 7 Arrangements for Brass Quintet - Tuba. 2008. (ENG.). 16p. pap. 8.95 *(978-1-4234-6383-2(8)*, 1423463838) Leonard, Hal Corp.

—Contemporary Christian Christmas. 2006. (ENG.). 80p. pap. 12.95 *(978-1-4234-1365-3(2)*, 1423413652) Leonard, Hal Corp.

—Cool Christmas: Jazz Play-along Volume 111. 2009. (ENG.). 72p. pap. 15.99 incl. audio compact disk *(978-1-4234-8253-6(0)*, 1423482530) Leonard, Hal Corp.

—Disney's Princess Christmas Album. 2008. (ENG.). 64p. pap. 12.95 *(978-1-4234-5649-0(1)*, 1423456491) Leonard, Hal Corp.

—Holiday Hits. 2006. (Easy Piano Play-along Ser.). (ENG.). 38p. pap. 14.95 incl. audio compact disk *(978-1-4234-1350-9(4)*, 1423413504) Leonard, Hal Corp.

—More Christmas Piano Solos: For All Piano Methods. 2009. (ENG.). 16p. pap. 6.99 *(978-1-4234-8360-1(X)*, 142348360X) Leonard, Hal Corp.

—More Christmas Piano Solos - Level 1: Hal Leonard Student Piano Library. 2009. (ENG.). 24p. pap. 6.99 *(978-1-4234-8361-8(8)*, 1423483618) Leonard, Hal Corp.

—More Christmas Piano Solos - Level 2: Hal Leonard Student Piano Library. 2009. (ENG.). 32p. pap. 6.99 *(978-1-4234-8362-5(6)*, 1423483626) Leonard, Hal Corp.

—More Christmas Piano Solos - Level 3: Hal Leonard Student Piano Library. 2009. (ENG.). 40p. pap. 6.99 *(978-1-4234-8363-2(4)*, 1423483634) Leonard, Hal Corp.

—More Christmas Piano Solos - Level 4: Hal Leonard Student Piano Library. 2009. (ENG.). 40p. pap. 7.99 *(978-1-4234-8364-9(2)*, 1423483642) Leonard, Hal Corp.

—More Christmas Piano Solos - Level 5: Hal Leonard Student Piano Library. 2009. (ENG.). 32p. pap. 7.99 *(978-1-4234-8365-6(0)*, 1423483650) Leonard, Hal Corp.

—The Real Christmas Book. 2009. (ENG.). 216p. pap. 25.00 *(978-1-4234-8250-5(6)*, 1423482506); pap. 25.00 *(978-1-4234-8249-9(2)*, 1423482492) Leonard, Hal Corp.

—The Real Christmas Book: Bass Clef Edition. 2009. (ENG.). 216p. pap. 25.00 *(978-1-4234-8261-1(1)*, 1423482611) Leonard, Hal Corp.

—The Real Christmas Book: C Edition, 1 vol. 2008. (ENG.). 216p. pap. 25.00 *(978-1-4234-3387-3(4)*, 1423433874) Leonard, Hal Corp.

—Teaching Little Fingers to Play Christmas Classics. 2009. (ENG.). 24p. pap. 12.99 incl. audio compact disk *(978-1-4234-8021-1(X)*, 142348021X); 22p. pap. 6.99 *(978-1-4234-8022-8(8)*, 1423480228) Willis Music Co.

—Teaching Little Fingers to Play More Christmas Classics. 2010. (ENG.). 32p. pap. 12.99 incl. audio compact disk *(978-1-4234-8023-5(6)*, 1423480236); pap. 6.99 *(978-1-4234-8024-2(4)*, 1423480244) Willis Music Co.

—The Ultimate Christmas Guitar Songbook: The Complete Resource for Every Guitar Player! 2007. (ENG.). 224p. per. 19.95 *(978-1-4234-3195-4(2)*, 1423431952) Leonard, Hal Corp.

—A Very Merry Contemporary Christmas: 25 Seasonal Favorites. 2007. (ENG.). 200p. pap. 24.95 *(978-1-4234-5525-7(8)*, 1423455258) Leonard, Hal Corp.

—A Very Special Christmas. 2008. (ENG.). 48p. pap. 6.95 *(978-1-4234-5646-9(7)*, 1423456467) Leonard, Hal Corp.

—A Very Special Christmas: Piano, Vocal, Guitar. 2007. (ENG.). 176p. per. 15.99 *(978-1-4234-3164-0(2)*, 1423431642) Leonard, Hal Corp.

—Worship Songs for Kids Songbook: With Easy Instructions. 2008. (ENG.). 24p. (J). (gr. -1-3). pap. 9.95 *(978-1-4234-3461-0(7)*, 1423434617) Leonard, Hal Corp.

—50 Christmas Piano Solos. 2008. (ENG.). 194p. pap. 16.95 *(978-1-4234-5652-0(1)*, 1423456521) Leonard, Hal Corp.

Hal Leonard Corporation Staff, ed. The Christmas Caroling Songbook, 1 vol. 2006. (ENG.). 96p. pap. 9.99 *(978-1-4234-1419-3(5)*, 1423414195) Leonard, Hal Corp.

Hal Leonard Publications Staff. Christmas Carols: Essential Songs Series, 1 vol. 2009. (ENG.). 248p. pap. 19.99 *(978-1-4234-8251-2(4)*, 1423482514) Leonard, Hal Corp.

Handel, George Frideric. Messiah at Christmas: Bb Trumpet. 2007. (ENG.). 20p. pap. 12.95 incl. audio compact disk *(978-90-431-2594-9(6)*, 9043125946) Leonard, Hal Corp.

—Messiah at Christmas: Eb Alto Saxophone. 2007. (ENG.). 20p. pap. 12.95 incl. audio compact disk *(978-90-431-2593-2(8)*, 9043125938) Leonard, Hal Corp.

—Messiah at Christmas: F/Eb Horn. 2007. (ENG.). 32p. pap. 12.95 incl. audio compact disk *(978-90-431-2595-6(4)*, 9043125954) Leonard, Hal Corp.

—Messiah at Christmas: Flute/Oboe/Mallet Percussion. 2007. (ENG.). 20p. pap. 12.95 incl. audio compact disk *(978-90-431-2591-8(1)*, 9043125911) Leonard, Hal Corp.

—Messiah at Christmas: Piano Accompaniment. 2007. (ENG.). 56p. pap. 9.95 *(978-90-431-2597-0(0)*, 9043125970) Leonard, Hal Corp.

—Messiah at Christmas: Trombone/Euphonium BC/TC/Bassoon. 2007. (ENG.). 32p. pap. 12.95 incl. audio compact disk *(978-90-431-2596-3(2)*, 9043125962) Leonard, Hal Corp.

Handel, George Frideric & Sanborn, Jan. Christmas with Handel's Messiah: Artistic Settings of Selections from the Masterful Oratorio by George Frideric Handel. 2011. (Sacred Performer Collections). (ENG.). 32p. pap. 10.99 ***(978-0-7390-7888-4(7))*** Alfred Publishing Co., Inc.

Harnsberger, L. C. Christmas Favorites for Recorder. 2007. (ENG.). 24p. pap. 5.99 *(978-0-7390-4918-1(6))* Alfred Publishing Co., Inc.

Hartsell, Randall. Christmas Creations: 11 Seasonal Piano Solos. 2009. (ENG.). 32p. pap. 6.99 *(978-1-4234-8010-5(4)*, 1423480104) Willis Music Co.

Hartsell, Randall. More Christmas Creations: 9 Seasonal Piano Solos. 2011. (ENG.). 32p. pap. 6.99 ***(978-1-4584-1086-3(2)***, 1458410862) Willis Music Co.

Hayes, Mark, et al. Christmas Evergreens: Timeless Piano Arrangements of Classic Carols. 2007. (ENG.). 72p. pap. 18.95 *(978-1-59235-175-6(1)*, 1592351751) Shawnee Pr., Inc.

Hayes, Mark. Popular Performer Christmas Classics. 2011. (Popular Performer Ser.). (ENG.). 52p. pap. 12.99 ***(978-0-7390-8288-1(4))*** Alfred Publishing Co., Inc.

Healey, Bruce. Season of Carols: Easy Solo Cello & Piano. 2007. (ENG.). 44p. pap. 9.95 *(978-1-4234-2625-7(8)*, 1423426258) Leonard, Hal Corp.

—Season of Carols: Easy Solo Viola & Piano. 2007. (ENG.). 44p. pap. 9.95 *(978-1-4234-2624-0(X)*, 142342624X) Leonard, Hal Corp.

Heaven on Earth: A Christmas Musical for Every Choir. 2011. (ENG.). 108p. pap. 6.99 ***(978-0-8341-7899-1(0)***, 9780834178991) Lillenas Publishing Co.

Help! My Kids Have to Sing at Christmas: Kids Songs for Every Christmas Occasion. 2011. (ENG.). 56p. pap. 19.99 ***(978-0-8341-8115-1(0)***, 9780834181151) Lillenas Publishing Co.

Hendrickson Publishers, creator. A Classic Christmas Caroling Songbook: 30 Sing-along Favorites. 2011. (ENG.). pap. 9.95 incl. audio compact disk ***(978-1-59856-933-9(3))*** Hendrickson Pubs. Marketing, LLC.

Henges, Greg & Hal Leonard Publications Staff. Christmas Piano Songs for Dummies, 1 vol. Gulla, Bob, ed. 2008. (ENG.). 208p. pap. 19.95 *(978-1-4234-2325-6(9)*, 1423423259) Leonard, Hal Corp.

Hofheins, Nathan. A Christmas Overture: Score for Picc. 2, 2. Eh. 2. Bass- Cl. 2 — 4. 3. 3. 1 — 5perc. Timp — Harp. Cel — Org — Str. 2010. 24p. spiral bd. 100.00 *(978-0-19-380506-4(5))* Oxford Univ. Pr., Inc.

Hogan, Ed. Creative Carols for String Quartet Vol. 2: Traditional Carols with a Popular Twist. 2011. (ENG.). 32p. pap. 59.99 ***(978-0-8341-7816-8(8)***, 9780834178168) Lillenas Publishing Co.

—Creative Carols for String Quartet, Volume 1: Traditional Carols with a Popular Twist. 2010. (ENG.). 36p. pap. 59.99 *(978-0-8341-7815-1(X)*, 9780834178151) Lillenas Publishing Co.

—Creative Carols for Trombone: Traditional Carols with a Popular Twist. 2010. (ENG.). 28p. cd-rom 29.99 *(978-0-8341-7807-6(9)*, 0834178079) Lillenas Publishing Co.

—Creative Carols for Trumpet: Traditional Carols with a Popular Twist. 2010. (ENG.). 28p. cd-rom 29.99 *(978-0-8341-7806-9(0)*, 0834178060) Lillenas Publishing Co.

—Creative Carols for Violin: Traditional Carols with a Popular Twist. 2010. (ENG.). 28p. cd-rom 29.99 *(978-0-8341-7809-0(5)*, 0834178095) Lillenas Publishing Co.

—Creative Carols for Woodwind Trio, Volume 1: Traditional Carols with a Popular Twist. 2010. (ENG.). 40p. cd-rom 59.99 *(978-0-8341-7813-7(3)*, 0834178133) Lillenas Publishing Co.

Immanuel: An Advent Collection. 2007. (ENG., Illus.). 72p. pap. 4.99 *(978-0-8341-7554-9(1)*, 0834175541) Lillenas Publishing Co.

Janszen, Matthew. A Seasoned Christmas: Advanced Piano Solo. 2009. (ENG.). 56p. pap. 14.99 incl. audio compact disk *(978-1-4234-8376-2(6)*, 1423483766) Leonard, Hal Corp.

Jars of Clay. Bebo Norman - From the Realms of Glory: Difficulty - Moderate. 2007. (ENG.). 80p. pap. 15.99 *(978-1-59802-103-5(6)*, 1598021036) Brentwood Music, Inc.

Jesus: Light of the World: A Simple Christmas Music Program for Preschoolers. 2008. (ENG.). 32p. pap. 9.99 *(978-0-8341-7648-5(3)*, 9780834176485) Lillenas Publishing Co.

Johnson, Victor C. Christ the Babe Is Lord of All: SATB/SAB with Opt. Flute. 2011. 8p. pap. 1.85 ***(978-1-4291-2556-7(X))*** Lorenz Corp., The.

—Listen, Children, Hear the Angels Sing! SATB Divisi, a Capella, with Opt. Solo. 2011. 8p. pap. 1.85 ***(978-1-4291-2583-3(7))*** Lorenz Corp., The.

Johnston, Paul. Jazz Performer — Christmas. 2011. (Jazz Performer Ser.). (ENG.). 40p. pap. 12.99 ***(978-0-7390-8289-8(2))*** Alfred Publishing Co., Inc.

Joseph M. Martin. Season of Wonders: Celebrating the Miracle of Christmas. 2007. (ENG.). 100p. pap. 7.95 *(978-1-59235-170-1(0)*, 1592351700, Flammer, Harold Music) Shawnee Pr., Inc.

—Tapestry of Light: A Celtic Christmas Celebration. 2011. (ENG.). 104p. pap. 8.95 *(978-1-61780-868-5(7)*, 1617808687, Flammer, Harold Music) Shawnee Pr., Inc.

—Winter's Grace: A Cantata for Christmas. 2010. (ENG.). 104p. pap. 8.95 *(978-1-4234-7773-0(1)*, 1423477731, Flammer, Harold Music) Shawnee Pr., Inc.

Joseph M. Martin & Joseph M. Martin. Tapestry of Light. 2011. (ENG.). 1p. pap. 59.99 ***(978-1-4584-0023-9(9)***, 1458400239); 104p. pap. 8.95 ***(978-1-4584-0301-8(7)***, 1458403017) Shawnee Pr., Inc. (Flammer, Harold Music).

Josh Groban - Noel. 2008. (ENG.). 88p. pap. 16.95 *(978-1-4234-5685-8(8)*, 1423456858) Leonard, Hal Corp.

Josh Groban - Noël. 2008. (ENG.). 96p. pap. 17.99 *(978-1-4234-5684-1(X)*, 142345684X) Leonard, Hal Corp.

Joy to the World. Date not set. 5.95 *(978-0-88271-572-8(0)*, 10206) Regina Pr., Malhame & Co.

Joyce, Anna, ed. Christmas Songs. 2009. (Take the Lead Ser.). 19p. pap. incl. audio compact disk *(978-1-84328-830-5(3))* International Music Pubns. Ltd.

Kellogg, Alice Maude. Christmas Entertainments. 2007. 108p. per. *(978-1-4068-1985-4(9))* Echo Library.

Kendall, Michelle. A Book of Mormon Christmas. 2011. (J). 15.99 *(978-1-59955-508-9(5))* Cedar Fort, Inc./CFI Distribution.

Kern, Philip, contrib. by. Christmas Favorites Book 2, Bk. 2. 2006. (Hal Leonard Student Piano Library Adult Piano Method). (ENG.). 32p. pap. 12.99 incl. audio compact disk *(978-1-4234-1583-1(3)*, 1423415833) Leonard, Hal Corp.

Keveren, Phillip, et al. Christmas Favorites, Bk. 2. 2006. (Hal Leonard Student Piano Library Adult Piano Method). (ENG.). 32p. pap. 12.95 incl. disk *(978-1-4234-1584-8(1)*, 1423415841) Leonard, Hal Corp.

Keveren, Phillip. Christmas Medleys: The Phillip Keveren Series. 2007. (ENG.). 72p. pap. 10.95 *(978-1-4234-2673-8(8)*, 1423426738) Leonard, Hal Corp.

—Christmas Time Is Here. 2006. (ENG.). 55p. pap. 12.99 *(978-1-4234-1412-4(8)*, 1423414128) Leonard, Hal Corp.

—Christmas Worship Medleys: The Phillip Keveren Series. 2008. (ENG.). 64p. pap. 12.99 *(978-1-4234-5676-6(9)*, 1423456769) Leonard, Hal Corp.

—Holiday Favorites. 2006. (ENG.). 56p. pap. 12.95 *(978-1-4234-1413-1(6)*, 1423414136) Leonard, Hal Corp.

—Santa Swings: Phillip Keveren Series. 2010. (ENG.). 64p. pap. 12.99 *(978-1-4234-9551-2(9)*, 1423495519) Leonard, Hal Corp.

—Yuletide Jazz: 20 Christmas Favorites. 2009. (ENG.). 64p. pap. 17.99 incl. audio compact disk *(978-1-4234-8263-5(8)*, 1423482638) Leonard, Hal Corp.

Koerts, James. Wondrous Christmas: 11 Contemporary Arrangements of Traditional Christmas Melodies. 2010. (Sacred Performer Collections). (ENG.). 48p. pap. 12.99 *(978-0-7390-7558-6(6))* Alfred Publishing Co., Inc.

Labenske, Victor. Now Proclaim Messiah's Birth: 10 Fresh Interpretations of Classic Christmas Melodies. 2007. (Sacred Performer Collections Ser.). (ENG.). 48p. pap. 12.99 *(978-0-7390-4913-6(5))* Alfred Publishing Co., Inc.

Lamb, Linda R. Good Christian Friends, Rejoice! 3, 4 or 5 Octaves with Opt Handchimes (2 Octaves). Level 3. 2011. 7p. pap. 4.50 ***(978-1-4291-2327-3(3))*** Lorenz Corp., The.

Lanz, David. David Lanz - Christmas Eve. 2008. (ENG.). 80p. pap. 12.95 *(978-1-4234-4176-2(1)*, 1423441761) Leonard, Hal Corp.

Larson, Lloyd. Images of Christmas. 2006. (ENG.). 40p. pap. 14.95 *(978-0-634-09146-9(8)*, 0634091468) Bock, Fred Music Co., Inc.

Larson, Lloyd, contrib. by. Joy of Every Longing Heart: SATB with Opt. C-Instrument & Cello. 2011. 11p. pap. 1.95 ***(978-1-4291-2584-0(5))*** Lorenz Corp., The.

Lee, Guy. Easy Christmas Guitar. 2007. 20p. (YA). spiral bd. 5.99 *(978-0-9747795-4-6(7))* Guytar Publishing.

Legacy of Love: A Kids' Christmas Musical about Lasting Love. 2009. (ENG.). 96p. pap. 7.99 *(978-0-8341-7698-0(X)*, 9780834176980) Lillenas Publishing Co.

Lehman, Clayton. Sacred Music for Christmas. 2010. 93p. pap. 25.00 *(978-0-578-04320-3(3))* Harmonies for Life.

L'Estrange, Alexander. A Christmas Special. 2010. (Faber Edition: Choral Basics Ser.). (ENG.). pap. 5.50 *(978-0-571-52370-2(6))* Faber & Faber, Ltd. GBR. Dist: Alfred Publishing Co., Inc.

The Light Before Christmas: A Musical about the Light of the World. 2011. (ENG.). 64p. pap. 7.99 ***(978-0-8341-7903-5(2)***, 9780834179035) Lillenas Publishing Co.

Limbaugh, Matt. Who's the Little Baby? SATB or Two-Part Mixed with Opt. Percussion. 2011. 12p. pap. 1.95 ***(978-1-4291-2535-2(7))*** Lorenz Corp., The.

—Who's the Little Baby? Unison or Two-Part with Opt. Percussion. 2011. 12p. pap. 1.95 ***(978-1-4291-2551-2(9))*** Lorenz Corp., The.

Line, Lorie. Lorie Line: A Special Christmas Collection. 20th anniv. ed. 2009. (ENG.). 104p. pap. 34.95 *(978-1-891195-25-9(5)*, 1891195255) Leonard, Hal Corp.

—Lorie Line - Christmas Around the World. 2008. 88p. pap. 34.95 *(978-1-4234-6639-0(X)*, 142346639X); pap. 34.95 *(978-1-891195-22-8(0)*, 1891195220) Leonard, Hal Corp.

—Lorie Line - Christmas Bells Are Ringing! 2011. (ENG.). 104p. pap. 34.95 ***(978-1-891195-31-0(X)***, 189119531X) Leonard, Hal Corp.

—Lorie Line - Making Spirits Bright: A Holiday Book. 2010. (ENG.). 100p. pap. 34.95 *(978-1-61774-292-7(9)*, 1617742929) Leonard, Hal Corp.

—Lorie Line - the Glory of Christmas. 2007. (ENG.). 94p. pap. 34.95 *(978-1-4234-5475-5(8)*, 1423454758) Leonard, Hal Corp.

Linn, Jennifer. Christmas Impressions: Nine Traditional Carols for Piano Solo. 2007. (Composer Showcase Ser.). (ENG.). 32p. per. 6.99 *(978-1-4234-3168-8(5)*, 1423431685) Leonard, Hal Corp.

A Love to Save the World: A Christmas Celebration of Invitation & Redemption. 2007. (Easy 2 Excel Ser.). (ENG., Illus.). 64p. pap. 5.99 *(978-0-8341-7557-0(6)*, 0834175576) Lillenas Publishing Co.

Lowe, Marilyn. Christmas Music Book 1 for Music Moves for Piano. 2007. 40p. (J). spiral bd. 17.95 *(978-1-57999-632-1(9)*, G-7054) G I A Pubns., Inc.

—Christmas Music Book 2 for Music Moves for Piano. 2007. 40p. (J). spiral bd. 9.95 *(978-1-57999-633-8(7)*, G-7055) G I A Pubns., Inc.

Macgimsey, Robert. Sweet Little Jesus Boy: SATB with Opt. Orchestra. 2011. 11p. pap. 2.10 ***(978-1-4291-2473-7(3))*** Lorenz Corp., The.

Madison Square Garden Entertainment. Radio City Christmas Spectacular. 2009. (Illus.). 148p. *(978-1-59591-050-9(6))* Madison Square Garden LP.

Mannheim Steamroller. Mannheim Steamroller: Christmas Song. 2008. (ENG.). 64p. pap. 16.95 *(978-1-4234-5290-4(9)*, 1423452909) Leonard, Hal Corp.

Martin, Hugh & Blane, Ralph. Have Yourself a Merry Little Christmas: For Brass Quintet. 2011. (ENG.). 8p. pap. 30.00 ***(978-1-4584-1500-4(7)***, 1458415007) Leonard, Hal Corp.

Martin, Joseph M. Winter's Grace. 2010. (ENG.). 104p. pap. 16.99 *(978-1-4234-7774-7(X)*, 142347774X) Shawnee Pr., Inc.

Martin, Pamela. Echo Christmas Joy: SATB with Opt. Orchestra or Instrumental Ensemble. 2011. 11p. pap. 1.95 ***(978-1-4291-2479-9(2))*** Lorenz Corp., The.

Matz, Carol. Famous & Fun Pop Christmas, Bk 1. 2011. (Famous & Fun Ser.). (ENG.). 24p. pap. 7.99 ***(978-0-7390-8290-4(6))*** Alfred Publishing Co., Inc.

—Famous & Fun Pop Christmas, Bk 2. 2011. (Famous & Fun Ser.). 24p. pap. 7.99 ***(978-0-7390-8291-1(4))*** Alfred Publishing Co., Inc.

—Famous & Fun Pop Christmas, Bk 3. 2011. (Famous & Fun Ser.). 24p. pap. 7.99 ***(978-0-7390-8292-8(2))*** Alfred Publishing Co., Inc.

Mauldin, Russell & Fettke, Tom, contrib. by. The Promised Hope: ... starts with a baby's first Cry. 2010. (ENG.). 112p. pap. 7.99 *(978-0-8341-7779-6(X)*, 9780834177796) Lillenas Publishing Co.

Mauldin, Steve, contrib. by. Beautiful Star: A Southern Gospel Senior Adult Christmas Musical. Lt. ed. 2010. (ENG.). 77p. pap. 7.99 *(978-0-8341-7781-9(1)*, 9780834177819) Lillenas Publishing Co.

McDonald, Mary, contrib. by. O Come to Set Us Free: SATB with Opt. Acoustic Bass & Drumset or Bongos. 2011. 8p. pap. 1.85 ***(978-1-4291-2567-3(5))*** Lorenz Corp., The.

McGinnis, Edward D. Songs & Signs of Jesus the Messiah. 2010. 68p. pap. 25.30 *(978-0-557-54262-8(6))* Lulu Enterprises Inc.

Merrill, Bob & Styne, Jule. Mr. Magoo's Christmas Carol: Sheet Music from the First Animated Christmas Special. 2011. (ENG.). 44p. pap. 14.99 ***(978-0-7390-7663-7(9))*** Alfred Publishing Co., Inc.

Messer, Kim, compiled by. Creative Resources for Program Directors, No. 60. 2007. (Christmas Program Builder Ser.). (ENG.). 40p. pap. 5.99 *(978-0-8341-7560-0(6)*, 083-417-5606) Lillenas Publishing Co.

Michael Buble - Christmas. 2011. (ENG.). 112p. pap. 16.99 ***(978-1-4584-1918-7(5)***, 1458419185) Leonard, Hal Corp.

Michael Buble - Let It Snow. 2009. (ENG.). 32p. pap. 10.99 *(978-1-4234-8255-0(7)*, 1423482557) Leonard, Hal Corp.

Miller, Carolyn. Merry Christmas! 8 Simple Solos for the Season. 2011. (ENG.). 16p. pap. 6.99 ***(978-1-4584-0803-7(5)***, 1458408035) Willis Music Co.

Miller, Carolyn & Thompson, John. First Christmas Duets: 1 Piano, 4 Hands/Early Elementary Level. 2010. (ENG.). 40p. pap. 6.99 *(978-1-4234-9520-8(9)*, 1423495209) Willis Music Co.

Miller, Donald. Christmas Strings: Viola, Violin 3 & Ensemble Score, 1 vol. 2007. (ENG., Illus.). 68p. pap. 9.95 *(978-0-7866-7560-9(8))* Mel Bay Pubns., Inc.

—Christmas Strings: Violin 1 & 2 with Piano Accompaniment: Solo, 1 vol. 2007. (ENG.). 52p. pap. 9.95 *(978-0-7866-7558-6(6))* Mel Bay Pubns., Inc.

—Mel Bay Presents Christmas Strings: Cello & Bass with Piano Accompaniment: for Solo Ensemble, 1 vol. 2007. (ENG., Illus.). 60p. pap. 9.95 *(978-0-7866-7559-3(4))* Mel Bay Pubns., Inc.

MMO, creator. Christmas Memories: Sing or Play-along to Your Favorite Christmas Songs. 2006. (ENG., Illus.). 40p. pap. 14.98 incl. audio compact disk *(978-1-59615-218-2(4)*, 1596152184) Music Minus One.

Moyer, Geff. One Toy for Christmas. 2011. 7.50 ***(978-1-61588-230-4(8))*** Heuer Publishing LLC.

Nagata, Chika, contrib. by. Christmas Ukulele, Hawaiian Style. 2006. (ENG., Illus.). 32p. pap. 19.99 incl. audio compact disk *(978-1-57424-207-2(5)*, 1574242075) Centerstream Publishing.

The Name... Jesus: A Christmas Musical Celebrating Emmanuel, the King of Kings. 2008. (ENG.). 136p. pap. 8.99 *(978-0-8341-7644-7(0)*, 0834176440) Lillenas Publishing Co.

Nickerson, Ross, contrib. by. Christmas Music for Banjo Made Easy, 1 vol. 2007. (ENG., Illus.). 32p. pap. 14.95 *(978-0-7866-7702-3(3))* Mel Bay Pubns., Inc.

Niles, John Jacob. Christmas Songs & Carols Pack: High Voice. 2008. (ENG.). 48p. pap. 19.95 incl. audio compact disk *(978-1-4234-3694-2(6)*, 1423436946, G Schirmer, Inc.) Leonard, Hal Corp.

—Christmas Songs & Carols Pack: Low Voice. 2008. (ENG.). 48p. pap. 19.95 incl. audio compact disk *(978-1-4234-3695-9(4)*, 1423436954, G Schirmer, Inc.) Leonard, Hal Corp.

Nolan, Douglas. A Song Is Born: A Cantata for Christmas. 2008. (ENG.). 56p. pap. 7.95 *(978-1-59235-260-9(X)*, 159235260X) Shawnee Pr., Inc.

Norman, Bebo. Jars of Clay: Christmas Songs. 2007. (ENG.). 96p. pap. 15.99 *(978-1-59802-102-8(8)*, 1598021028) Brentwood Music, Inc.

Norman, Edward W. The Light Celestial: A Christmas Choir Cantata. 2011. 66p. pap. 36.95 ***(978-1-258-03256-2(2))*** Literary Licensing, LLC.

C

Norton, Christopher. American Popular Piano - Christmas: Level 2. Smith, Scott McBride, ed. 2008. (ENG.). 20p. pap. 6.25 *(978-1-897379-46-2(3)*, 1897379463) Novus Via Music Group Inc. CAN. Dist: Leonard, Hal Corp.

O Holy Child of Bethlehem: Christmas Carols Arranged for Solo Piano. 2008. (ENG.). 48p. pap. 15.99 *(978-0-8341-7647-8(5)*, 9780834176478) Lillenas Publishing Co.

Pace, Cynthia. Easy Christmas Melodies Piano: With Duet Accompaniments. 2007. (ENG.). 32p. pap. 12.95 incl. audio compact disk *(978-1-4234-2603-5(7)*, 1423426037) Leonard, Hal Corp.

Page, Anna Laura, et al. A Christmas Carol — Scrooge in Bethlehem (A Musical for Children Based upon a Story by Charles Dickens) Director's Score, Score. 2008. (ENG.). 32p. pap. 24.95 *(978-0-7390-5060-6(5))* Alfred Publishing Co., Inc.

—A Christmas Carol — Scrooge in Bethlehem (A Musical for Children Based upon a Story by Charles Dickens) Performance Pack, Score & 10 Books. 2008. (ENG.). pap. 64.95 *(978-0-7390-5065-1(6))* Alfred Publishing Co., Inc.

—A Christmas Carol — Scrooge in Bethlehem (A Musical for Children Based upon a Story by Charles Dickens) Preview Pack, Book & CD. 2008. (ENG.). pap. 16.95 *(978-0-7390-5064-4(8))* Alfred Publishing Co., Inc.

—A Christmas Carol — Scrooge in Bethlehem (A Musical for Children Based upon a Story by Charles Dickens) Singer's Edition 5-Pack, 5 Books. 2008. (ENG.). pap. 22.50 *(978-0-7390-5061-3(3))* Alfred Publishing Co., Inc.

Parks, Marty. O for a Dozen Tongues to Sing - Gospel Hymns: Six Ready-to-Sing Anthems for Two-part Mixed Voices. 2009. spiral bd. 29.95 *(978-1-4267-0016-3(4))* Abingdon Pr.

—Once upon a Miracle: A Christmas Musical for Senior Adult Choir. 2007. (ENG., Illus.). 80p. pap. 7.99 *(978-0-8341-7556-3(8)*, 0834175568) Lillenas Publishing Co.

Parks, Marty, creator. He Is Born - Emmanuel! A Christmas Presentation of 5 Songs in Unison/2-Part. 2010. (ENG.). 36p. pap. 5.99 *(978-0-8341-7780-2(3)*, 9780834177802) Lillenas Publishing Co.

Pearl, David. Mozart Meets Santa. 2006. (ENG.). 48p. pap. 10.95 *(978-1-57560-898-3(7)*, 1575608987) Cherry Lane Music Co.

Peck, Rebecca J. & Kirkland, Kirk, told to. Be Not Afraid: A Christmas Musical Proclaiming That Hope is Here. 2007. (ENG., Illus.). 128p. pap. 8.99 *(978-0-8341-7555-6(X)*, 083417555X) Allegis Pubns.

Pethel, Stan. He Is Born, the Divine Christ Child: Christmas Portraits Arranged for Solo Piano. 2007. (ENG., Illus.). 48p. pap. 15.99 *(978-0-8341-7582-2(7)*, 0834175827) Lillenas Publishing Co.

Prince of Peace: A Christmas Presentation of 5 Songs in Unison/2-Part. 2008. (ENG.). 32p. pap. 5.99 *(978-0-8341-7659-1(9)*, 9780834176591) Lillenas Publishing Co.

Prins, Matthew. In Quiet Joy: 3, 4 or 5 Octaves (Handbells or Handchimes), Level 2+ 2011. 7p. pap. 4.50 ***(978-1-4291-2360-0(5))*** Lorenz Corp., The.

Publications International Staff. Christmas Lights & Music Treasury. 2009. (SPA.). 160p. (J). bds. 16.98 *(978-1-4127-2756-3(1)*, PIL Kids) Publications International, Ltd.

Ramage, Heather, ed. The Christmas Classics. 2008. (ENG.). 136p. pap. 29.95 incl. audio compact disk *(978-0-8256-3647-9(7)*, 0825636477) Music Sales Corp.

Rejino, Mona. Merry Christmas Medleys: Intermediate Level Composer Showcase. 2009. (ENG.). 24p. pap. 7.99 *(978-1-4234-8515-5(7)*, 1423485157) Leonard, Hal Corp.

Renfrow, Kenon D. Popular Performer It's Time for Christmas: The Best Christmas Hits & Traditional Holiday Selections. 2009. (Popular Performer Ser.). (ENG.). 48p. pap. 12.95 *(978-0-7390-6400-9(2))* Alfred Publishing Co., Inc.

River, David. The Divine Romance - the Song of Jesus & His Bride. 2008. 116p. pap. 10.99 *(978-1-60647-116-6(3))* Xulon Pr., Inc.

Robb, John Donald. Hispanic Folk Songs of New Mexico: With Selected Songs Collected, Transcribed, & Arranged for Voice with Piano or Guitar Accompaniment. rev. ed. 2008. (ENG., Illus.). 98p. spiral bd. 29.95 *(978-0-8263-4434-2(8))* Univ. of New Mexico Pr.

Rocherolle, Eugenie. Candlelight Christmas: The Eugenie Rocherolle Series. 2008. (ENG.). 24p. pap. 14.99 incl. audio compact disk *(978-1-4234-6168-5(1)*, 1423461681) Leonard, Hal Corp.

Rollin, Catherine. Dances for Christmas Bk. 2: 6 Intermediate Christmas Favorites Arranged in Dance Styles. 2008. (Dances for Christmas Ser.). 24p. pap. 6.95 *(978-0-7390-5627-1(1))* Alfred Publishing Co., Inc.

—Dances for Christmas, Bk 1: 6 Early Intermediate to Intermediate Christmas Favorites Arranged in Dance Styles. 2008. (Dances for Christmas Ser.). (ENG.). 24p. pap. 6.95 *(978-0-7390-5626-4(3))* Alfred Publishing Co., Inc.

Rollins, Jack & Nelson, Steve. Frosty the Snow Man: For Brass Quintet. 2011. (ENG.). 12p. pap. 30.00 ***(978-1-4584-1499-1(X)***, 145841499X) Leonard, Hal Corp.

Rouse, Jay. Cool Shades of Christmas: Holiday Jazz. 2007. (ENG.). 64p. pap. 14.95 *(978-1-4234-5524-0(X)*, 142345524X) Leonard, Hal Corp.

Ruth, Anita, ed. The Glory of Christmas: A Holiday Book. 2009. (Illus.). 94p. pap. 34.95 *(978-1-891195-19-8(0))* Leonard, Hal Corp.

Ryan, Michael. Prayer at the Manger: 2 or 3 Octaves (Handbells or Handchimes), Level 2. 2011. 8p. pap. 4.50 ***(978-1-4291-2365-5(6))*** Lorenz Corp., The.

Sanborn, Jan, contrib. by. Popular Performer: Christmas: The Best Christmas Hits from the Holiday Season. 2007. (Popular Performer Ser.). (ENG.). 40p. pap. 12.95 *(978-0-7390-4636-4(5))* Alfred Publishing Co., Inc.

Schram, Ruth Elaine, contrib. by. Follow the Christmas Star: Two-Part Any Combination with Opt. Percussion. 2011. 15p. pap. 1.95 ***(978-0-7877-0652-4(3))*** Lorenz Corp., The.

Schram, Scott. The Last Noel: A Christmas Musical for Children. 2007. (ENG.). pap. 16.95 *(978-0-7390-4486-5(9))*; pap. 22.50 *(978-0-7390-4483-4(4))* Alfred Publishing Co., Inc.

A Season for Joy: A Christmas Presentation of 5 Songs in Unison/2-Part. 2009. (ENG.). 32p. pap. 5.99 *(978-0-8341-7695-9(5)*, 9780834176959) Lillenas Publishing Co.

A Season of Joy. 4.95 incl. audio compact disk *(978-0-687-36343-8(8))* Abingdon Pr.

Setliff, Carolyn C. Christmas for Elizabeth: 12 Early Elementary Solos with Optional Accompaniment. 2006. (ENG.). 32p. pap. 6.95 *(978-1-4234-1437-7(3)*, 1423414373) Willis Music Co.

—Christmas Time: 7 Mid to Later Intermediate Piano Solos. 2006. (ENG.). 32p. pap. 6.95 *(978-1-4234-1438-4(1)*, 1423414381) Willis Music Co.

Shackley, Larry, contrib. by. Christmas Proclamations! Brass Solos for Trumpet, Horn, Trombone, or Baritone T. C. 2011. 64p. audio compact disk 19.95 ***(978-1-4291-2563-5(2))*** Lorenz Corp., The.

—The Moon & Stars Were Shining: SATB with Opt. Instrumental Ensemble. 2011. 11p. pap. 1.95 ***(978-1-4291-2578-9(0))*** Lorenz Corp., The.

Shafferman, Jean Anne. Simple Sacred Songs for Children: 6 Delightfully Easy Songs for Unison or 2-Part with Reproducible Song Sheets. 2007. (ENG.). 36p. pap. 37.95 *(978-0-7390-4799-6(X))*; pap. 14.95 *(978-0-7390-4798-9(1))* Alfred Publishing Co., Inc.

Sinatra, Frank. Frank Sinatra Christmas Collection. 2008. (ENG.). 58p. pap. 14.99 *(978-1-4234-6353-5(6)*, 1423463536) Leonard, Hal Corp.

—Frank Sinatra Christmas Collection: Easy Piano. 2008. (ENG.). 48p. pap. 12.99 *(978-1-4234-6362-7(5)*, 1423463625) Leonard, Hal Corp.

—132. Frank Sinatra Christmas Collection: E-Z Play Today #132. 2008. (ENG.). 40p. pap. 9.99 *(978-1-4234-6363-4(3)*, 1423463633) Leonard, Hal Corp.

Slattery, Paul. Big Christmas Songbook. 2008. (ENG.). 96p. pap. 12.95 incl. audio compact disk *(978-1-84772-566-0(X)*, 184772566X) Music Sales Corp.

Smith, Rollin, ed. Easy Organ Christmas Album: Seasonal Classics for Use in Church & Recital by Bach, Brahms, Franck, Pachelbel & Others. 2006. (Dover Music for Organ Ser.). (ENG.). 112p. per. 9.95 *(978-0-486-45286-9(7))* Dover Pubns., Inc.

Smith, Scott McBride, ed. American Popular Piano - Christmas: Level 1. 2008. (ENG.). 16p. pap. 5.95 *(978-1-897379-45-5(5)*, 1897379455) Novus Via Music Group Inc. CAN. Dist: Leonard, Hal Corp.

—American Popular Piano - Christmas: Level 4. 2009. (ENG.). 22p. pap. 6.95 *(978-1-897379-48-6(X)*, 189737948X) Novus Via Music Group Inc. CAN. Dist: Leonard, Hal Corp.

—American Popular Piano - Christmas: Level 5. 2009. (ENG.). 22p. pap. 6.95 *(978-1-897379-49-3(8)*, 1897379498) Novus Via Music Group Inc. CAN. Dist: Leonard, Hal Corp.

Springer, Mike. Not Just Another Christmas Book, Bk 1: 9 Jazzy Piano Solos with Optional CD Accompaniments, Book & CD. 2011. (Not Just Another Ser.). 24p. pap. 8.99 ***(978-0-7390-8114-3(4))*** Alfred Publishing Co., Inc.

—Not Just Another Christmas Book, Bk 2: 9 Jazzy Piano Solos with Optional CD Accompaniments, Book & CD. 2011. (Not Just Another Ser.). 24p. pap. 8.99 ***(978-0-7390-8115-0(2))*** Alfred Publishing Co., Inc.

—Not Just Another Christmas Book, Bk 3: 8 Jazzy Piano Solos with Optional CD Accompaniments, Book & CD. 2011. (Not Just Another Ser.). 28p. pap. 8.99 ***(978-0-7390-8116-7(0))*** Alfred Publishing Co., Inc.

Sprunger, Ron & Sprunger, Linda. What Child Is This? Christmas Organ & Piano Duets. 2011. (ENG.). 88p. pap. 18.99 ***(978-0-8341-7914-1(8)***, 9780834179141) Lillenas Publishing Co.

Sterling, Cindy & Curry, Sheldon. A Simple Christmas Pageant: Bulletin Insert, Sheet. 2009. (ENG.). pap. 8.00 *(978-0-7390-6300-2(6))* Alfred Publishing Co., Inc.

—A Simple Christmas Pageant: SATB Director's Score, Choral Score. 2009. (ENG.). 32p. pap. 25.00 *(978-0-7390-6294-4(8))* Alfred Publishing Co., Inc.

—A Simple Christmas Pageant: Singer's Edition. 2009. (ENG.). 20p. pap. 3.95 *(978-0-7390-6299-9(9))* Alfred Publishing Co., Inc.

Sterling, Robert, contrib. by & creator. Peace on Earth: A Christmas Musical; SATB. 2007. 127p. pap. 8.95 *(978-5-557-78134-3(X)*, Word Music) Word Entertainment.

Stewart, Kevin. A Mighty Fortress Is Our God: 3, 4 or 5 Octaves, Level 3. 2011. 8p. pap. 4.50 ***(978-1-4291-2330-3(3))*** Lorenz Corp., The.

Takahashi, Masa. Christmas Carols: Jazz Guitar Chord Melody Solos. 2010. (ENG.). 40p. pap. 12.99 *(978-1-4234-9478-2(4)*, 1423494784) Leonard, Hal Corp.

Tchaikovsky, Peter Il'yich. A Classical Christmas: 3, 4, 5 or 6 Octaves with Opt. Handchimes (2, 3 or 4 Octaves) & Sleighbells, Level 4. 2011. 8p. pap. 4.95 ***(978-1-4291-2341-9(9))*** Lorenz Corp., The.

Tchaikovsky, Peter Il'yich. The Nutcracker Suite Vol. 2082. 2009. (ENG.). 72p. pap. 15.99 incl. audio compact disk *(978-1-4234-8323-6(5)*, 1423483235, G Schirmer, Inc.) Leonard, Hal Corp.

These Are Special Times: Piano/Vocal/Chords. 2008. (ENG.). 100p. pap. 21.95 *(978-0-7390-5400-0(7))* Alfred Publishing Co., Inc.

Thomas Nelson Publishing Staff, et al. A Baby Changes Everything, 0 vols. 2008. 64p. 15.99 *(978-1-4041-8734-4(0))* Nelson, Thomas Inc.

Tomlin, Chris. Chris Tomlin - Glory in the Highest: Christmas Songs of Worship. 2010. (ENG.). 64p. pap. 14.99 *(978-1-4234-9480-5(6)*, 1423494806) Leonard, Hal Corp.

Tornquist, Carol. Christmas Carols for Today: 10 Contemporary Arrangements of Traditional Carols. 2009. (Sacred Performer Collections). (ENG.). 40p. pap. 12.99 *(978-0-7390-6301-9(4))* Alfred Publishing Co., Inc.

—I Can Play! Praise. 2008. (ENG.). 96p. pap. 14.95 *(978-1-4234-4580-7(5)*, 1423445805) Leonard, Hal Corp.

—Medleys for Blended Worship — Christmas. 2011. (Sacred Performer Collections). 40p. pap. 12.99 ***(978-0-7390-7318-6(4))*** Alfred Publishing Co., Inc.

Tornquist, Carol. Top 25 Christmas Songs for Solo Piano. 2008. (ENG.). 96p. pap. 19.95 *(978-1-4234-6723-6(X)*, 142346723X) Leonard, Hal Corp.

Tornquist, Carol, ed. Piano Christmas: The Complete Christmas Collection. 2006. (ENG., Illus.). 248p. pap. 29.95 *(978-1-4234-2397-3(6)*, 1423423976) Leonard, Hal Corp.

Trans-Siberian Orchestra. The Lost Christmas Eve: Piano/Vocal/Chords. 2008. (ENG.). 156p. pap. 21.95 *(978-0-7390-5396-6(5))* Alfred Publishing Co., Inc.

Treasury of Christmas. 2007. audio compact disk *(978-5-557-58301-5(7))* Alpha Omega Publications.

Tsitsaros, Christos. Fantasia on Polish Christmas Carols: A Medley of Seven Traditional Kolendy for Late Intermediate Piano. 2011. (ENG.). 16p. pap. 6.99 ***(978-1-4584-1188-4(5)***, 1458411885) Leonard, Hal Corp.

Ultimate Christmas. 2008. 224p. *(978-1-4054-9488-5(3))* Parragon, Inc.

Vandall, Robert D. Celebrated Christmas Duets, Bk 1: 5 Christmas Favorites Arranged for Late Elementary Pianists. 2008. (Celebrated Christmas Duets Ser.). (ENG.). 24p. pap. 6.95 *(978-0-7390-5628-8(X))* Alfred Publishing Co., Inc.

—Celebrated Christmas Duets, Bk 2: 5 Christmas Favorites Arranged for Early Intermediate Pianists. 2008. (Celebrated Christmas Duets Ser.). (ENG.). 28p. pap. 7.50 *(978-0-7390-5629-5(8))* Alfred Publishing Co., Inc.

—Celebrated Christmas Duets, Bk 3: 5 Christmas Favorites Arranged for Early Intermediate to Intermediate Pianists. 2008. (Celebrated Christmas Duets Ser.). (ENG.). 28p. pap. 7.50 *(978-0-7390-5630-1(1))* Alfred Publishing Co., Inc.

—Celebrated Christmas Solos: 8 Christmas Favorites Arranged for Early Intermediate to Intermediate Pianists. 2007. (Celebrated Ser.). (ENG.). 24p. pap. 6.99 *(978-0-7390-4902-0(X))* Alfred Publishing Co., Inc.

—Celebrated Christmas Solos: 8 Christmas Favorites Arranged for Intermediate to Late Intermediate Pianists. 2007. (Celebrated Ser.). (ENG.). 24p. pap. 6.99 *(978-0-7390-4903-7(8))* Alfred Publishing Co., Inc.

Wagner, Douglas E. Christmas Bells Overture, Handbell Part: 3, 4 or 5 Octaves & Keyboard or Concert Band, Level 3. 2011. 11p. pap. 4.95 ***(978-1-4291-2335-8(4))*** Lorenz Corp., The.

—Christmas Bells Overture, Keyboard/Handbell Score: 3, 4 or 5 Octaves & Keyboard or Concert Band, Level 3. 2011. 20p. pap. 7.95 ***(978-1-4291-2334-1(6))*** Lorenz Corp., The.

—The Rose of Bethlehem: SATB with Opt. Instrumental Ensemble. 2011. 12p. pap. 1.95 ***(978-1-4291-2476-8(8))*** Lorenz Corp., The.

We Celebrate the King: A Christmas Worship Collection. 2011. (ENG.). 116p. pap. 8.99 ***(978-0-8341-7902-8(4)***, 9780834179028) Lillenas Publishing Co.

Wedgwood, P. Needle. Christmas Cobweb Book/Cd Spotlight. 2009. (Faber Edition Ser.). (ENG.). 32p. pap. 22.25 *(978-0-571-52294-1(7))* Faber & Faber, Ltd. GBR. Dist: Alfred Publishing Co., Inc.

Wedgwood, Pam. Recorderworld Christmas. 2009. (Faber Edition: RecorderWorld Ser.). (ENG.). 16p. pap. 7.25 *(978-0-571-52355-9(2))* Faber & Faber, Ltd. GBR. Dist: Alfred Publishing Co., Inc.

White, Marilyn. O Holy Child of Bethlehem: Christmas Carols Arranged for Solo Piano. 2008. (ENG.). 48p. pap. 14.99 *(978-1-4234-6151-7(7)*, 1423461517) Lillenas Publishing Co.

WILBERG, Mack. Rest in Me(Suo-Gân) 2009. 8p. pap. 1.85 *(978-0-19-386989-9(6))* Oxford Univ. Pr., Inc.

Willard, Karen E. An American Christmas Harp. 2009. pap. *(978-1-61584-532-3(1))* Independent Pub.

Williams, Andy. Andy Williams - Christmas Collection: Original Keys for Singers. 2010. (ENG.). 120p. pap. 17.99 *(978-1-4234-9603-8(5)*, 1423496035) Leonard, Hal Corp.

Wolaver, Bill. 17 Contemporary Christian Christmas Hits, Vol. 2. 2006. (ENG.). 64p. pap. 15.99 *(978-1-59802-079-3(X)*, 159802079X) Brentwood Music, Inc.

Worley, Karla. On This Very Night: A Christmas Musical for Every Choir. 2007. (Illus.). 118p. pap. 7.95 *(978-5-557-77126-9(3)*, Word Music) Word Entertainment.

101 Strings Orchestra, contrib. by. Treasury of Christmas. 2007. audio compact disk *(978-5-558-03355-7(X))* Alpha Omega Publications.

CHRISTMAS MUSIC—HISTORY AND CRITICISM

Griffin, Pam. The Sounds of Christmas. 2011. pap. 2.99 ***(978-1-59955-923-0(4)***, Bonneville Bks.) Cedar Fort, Inc./CFI Distribution.

Nobbman, Dale. The Ultimate Christmas Music Companion Fact Book. 2007. (ENG.). 152p. pap. 19.99 *(978-1-57424-228-7(8)*, 1574242288) Centerstream Publishing.

Slover, Tim. Messiah: The Little-Known Story of Handel's Beloved Oratorio. 2007. (ENG., Illus.). 80p. 19.95 *(978-1-934393-05-5(3))* Silverleaf Pr.

CHRISTMAS PANTOMIME

see Pantomime (Christmas Entertainment)

CHRISTMAS PLAYS

see also Pantomime (Christmas Entertainment)

Anderson, Dean A. & Tkach, Rod. I Spy Christmas: Three Christmas Plays Plus a Candlelight Service. 2008. 67p. *(978-0-7880-2551-8(1))* CSS Publishing Co.

Birney, David. A Christmas Pudding. 2008. 72p. per. 7.50 *(978-0-573-65125-0(6))* French, Samuel Inc.

Christmas Program Builder No. 61: Creative Resources for Program Directors. 2008. (ENG.). 32p. pap. 5.99 *(978-0-8341-7628-7(9)*, 0834176289) Lillenas Publishing Co.

Cook, Pat. If It's Monday, This Must Be Christmas. 2007. pap. 6.50 *(978-1-58342-402-5(4))* Dramatic Publishing Co.

Dickens, Charles. A Christmas Carol: Play. 2008. (ENG.). 96p. (Orig.). pap. 18.95 *(978-1-85459-987-2(9))* Theatre Communications Group, Inc.

Hare, Walter Ben. The White Christmas & Other Merry Christmas Plays. 2007. (Illus.). 228p. per. *(978-1-4065-2345-4(3))* Dodo Pr.

Harwood, A. C., tr. Christmas Plays from Oberufer: The Paradise Play, the Shepherds Play, the Kings Play. 2007. (Illus.). 119p. per. *(978-1-85584-184-0(3))* Sophia Bks.

Hewitt, Keith. Nativity Dramas: Four Nontraditional Christmas Plays for All Ages. 2007. 106p. per. 12.95 *(978-0-7880-2483-2(3))* CSS Publishing Co.

Hill, Helen, et al. The Saintons Go to Bethlehem. 2011. 66p. 36.95 ***(978-1-258-08557-5(7))*** Literary Licensing, LLC.

Lee, Nate. Long Wait for A Messiah. 2009. (Efs Ser.). 6.00 *(978-0-687-46683-2(0))* Abingdon Pr.

McKinney, Joshua L. His First Noel. 2007. pap. 5.99 *(978-0-89265-588-5(7))* Randall Hse. Pubns.

Meyers, Elaina, compiled by. Christmas Programs for the Church. 2007. (Christmas Program Bks.). (Illus.). 64p. per. 7.99 *(978-0-7847-1943-5(8))* Standard Publishing.

—Standard Christmas Progam Book. 2007. 48p. pap. 6.99 *(978-0-7847-1942-8(X))* Standard Publishing.

Ramirez, Frank. Come All Ye Faithful: Three Christmas Plays. 2008. (Illus.). 64p. *(978-0-7880-2485-6(X))* CSS Publishing Co.

Randall House Publications, creator. Celebrate Christmas, Volume 1: Christmas Sketches & Plays for Your Church. 2007. 116p. spiral bd. 19.99 *(978-0-89265-586-1(0))* Randall Hse. Pubns.

Sayers, Dorothy L. He That Should Come. 2011. 102p. pap. 14.00 ***(978-1-61097-022-8(5)***, Wipf and Stock) Wipf & Stock Pubs.

Smith, Jeff. Yule Fuel: Cool Drama Scripts for Christmas. 2008. (ENG.). 48p. pap. 19.99 *(978-0-8341-7654-6(8)*, 9780834176546) Lillenas Publishing Co.

Standard Publishing Staff. Christmas Programs for the Church. 2009. (Holiday Program Bks.). (ENG.). 48p. (J). pap. 6.99 *(978-0-7847-2265-7(X))* Standard Publishing.

Van Zandt, Billy & Rhodes, Amy. A Night at the Nutcracker. 2008. (Illus.). 82p. per. 7.50 *(978-0-573-65238-7(4))* French, Samuel Inc.

Williams, John. Welcome Prince of Peace! a Christmas Play. 2011. 60p. pap. ***(978-1-926765-60-0(5))*** Gospel Folio Pr.

Wra, Rhonda, ed. More Christmas on Stage: An Anthology of Royalty-Free Christmas Plays. 2008. (Illus.). 318p. pap. *(978-1-56608-151-1(3))* Meriwether Publishing, Ltd.

CHRISTMAS SERMONS

Boice, James Montgommery. The King Has Come: The Real Message of Christmas. 2008. (ENG.). pap. 10.99 *(978-1-84550-366-6(X))* Christian Focus Pubns. GBR. Dist: STL Distribution North America.

Cloud, Olivia, ed. Joy to the World: Inspirational Christmas Messages from America's Pr. 2013. (ENG.). 416p. pap. 24.99 *(978-1-4516-5633-6(5)*, Beyond Words/Atria Bks.) Atria Bks.

Cloud, Olivia M. & Cloud, Olivia, eds. Joy to the World: Inspirational Christmas Messages from America's Preachers. 2006. (ENG.). 416p. 25.00 *(978-1-4165-4000-7(8)*, Beyond Words/Atria Bks.) Atria Bks.

Concordia Pulpit. Sermons for Advent & Christmas. 2008. (Selections from Concordia Pulpit Resources Ser.). 168p. pap. 16.99 incl. cd-rom *(978-0-7586-1379-0(2))* Concordia Publishing Hse.

Guthrie, Nancy. Come, Thou Long Expected Jesus: Experiencing the Peace & Promise of Christmas. 2008. 142p. pap. ***(978-1-4335-0418-1(9))*** Crossway.

Guthrie, Thomas. The Angels' Song. 2008. 58p. pap. *(978-1-4099-5814-7(0))* Dodo Pr.

—The Angels' Song. 2009. 144p. 35.95 *(978-1-104-42202-8(6))*; pap. 20.95 *(978-1-104-38170-7(2))* Kessinger Publishing, LLC.

Jacob. Jacob of Sarug's Homilies on the Nativity. 2010. (SYR & ENG.). ix, 243p. ***(978-1-60724-139-3(0))*** Gorgias Pr., LLC.

Leinenweber, John, ed. Bernard of Clairvaux: Sermons for Advent & the Christmas Season. Edmonds, Irene et al, trs. from LAT. 2007. (Cistercian Fathers Ser.). 202p. per. 24.95 *(978-0-87907-451-7(5)*, CF051P) Cistercian Pubns., Inc.

Merton, Thomas & Guerric. The Christmas Sermons of Blessed Guerric of Igny. Sister Rose Of Lima, tr. 2011. 66p. 36.95 ***(978-1-258-04469-5(2))*** Literary Licensing, LLC.

Motter, Alton M. Preaching the Nativity: Nineteen Great Sermons for Advent, Christmas, & Epiphany. Motter, Alton M., ed. 2011. 148p. 40.95 ***(978-1-258-03072-8(1))*** Literary Licensing, LLC.

Murray, Scott R. Away in a Manger: Resources for Advent & Christmas Preaching & Worship. 2008. 34.99 *(978-0-7586-1448-3(9))* Concordia Publishing Hse.

Nancy, Guthrie. Come, Thou Long-Expected Jesus: Experiencing the Peace & Promise of Christmas. Guthrie, Nancy, ed. 2008. 144p. pap. 12.99 *(978-1-4335-0180-7(5))* Crossway.

Proclus, St., et al. On the Incarnation of the Lord. 2011. 26p. 35.95 ***(978-1-258-03387-3(9))*** Literary Licensing, LLC.

Radecke, Mark William. Love's Pure Light: Christmas Candlelight Sermons & Service. 2008. *(978-0-7880-2559-4(7))* CSS Publishing Co.

Richards, H. M. S. Christmas Catechism. 2011. 128p. 40.95 ***(978-1-258-06615-4(7))*** Literary Licensing, LLC.

The check digit for ISBN-10 appears in parentheses after the full ISBN-13

Tuck, William Powell. Christmas Is for the Young... Whatever Their Age: 16 Christmas Sermon Stories. 2007. 172p. per. (978-0-7880-2486-3(8)) CSS Publishing Co.

CHRISTMAS STORIES

Alfred Publishing Staff. The Carol Singer's Carol: Choral Octavo. 2011. (Faber Edition: Choral Signature Ser.). (ENG.). pap. 3.95 **(978-0-571-53671-9(9))** Faber & Faber, Ltd. GBR. Dist: Alfred Publishing Co., Inc.

Barbour Publishing Staff. A Read-Aloud Family Christmas: A Collection of Classic Christmas Stories. 2009. (Value Bks.). (ENG.). 160p. pap. 1.99 (978-1-60260-383-7(9), Barbour Bks.) Barbour Publishing, Inc.

Bethlehem Writers Group. A Christmas Sampler: Sweet, Funny, & Strange Holiday Tales. 2009. 236p. 29.95 (978-1-60844-111-2(3)); pap. 14.95 (978-1-60844-110-5(5)) Dog Ear Publishing, LLC.

Buttars, Robyn. Christmas Rose. 2008. 96p. pap. 8.95 (978-1-59038-988-1(3), Shadow Mountain) Deseret Bk. Co.

Chesser, Barbara Russell. Keeping Christmas Vol. 2: Stories to Warm Your Heart Throughout the Year. 2011. (ENG.). 112p. 17.95 **(978-1-936417-16-2(2))** Pilot Communications Group, Inc.

Chik, Grace K. Seasons Blessings for You: A Collection of Christmas Stories. 2010. **(978-1-77069-082-0(4))** Word Alive Pr.

Christie, Agatha. Star over Bethlehem: Poems & Holiday Stories. 2011. (ENG.). 80p. pap. 12.99 (978-0-06-207430-0(X), William Morrow Paperbacks) HarperCollins Pubs.

Christmas Stocking Tales. Date not set. (Illus.). 100p. spiral bd. 18.00 (978-1-885351-11-1(9)) Cheval International.

Christmas Story. (VIE.). 16p. 1.50 (978-0-570-05178-7(9), 16-6062) Concordia Publishing Hse.

A Christmas Treasury. 2010. (ENG.). 148p. 14.95 (978-1-59936-020-1(9)) Granite Publishing & Distribution.

Culbertson, Kimberly M., et al, eds. Relief: A Christian Literary Expression Volume 3 Issue 1. 2009. 186p. pap. 14.95 (978-0-9792284-3-8(3)) coPublishing, NFP.

Deseret Book Company Staff, contrib. by. Sharing Christmas: Stories for the Season. 2008. (Illus.). 112p. 21.95 (978-1-59038-969-0(7)) Deseret Bk. Co.

Dickens, Charles. Christmas Books. 2009. 306p. 25.99 (978-1-110-00608-3(X)); pap. 19.99 (978-1-110-00606-9(3)) BiblioBazaar.

—Christmas Books. 2009. 126p. pap. (978-0-217-45767-5(3)); 192p. pap. (978-1-4590-4263-6(8)) Books LLC.

—Christmas Books. 2008. 452p. (gr. 12-12). (978-1-4437-3404-2(7), Hesperides Pr.) Read Bks.

—Christmas Books. 2010. (Fine Edition Ser.). (ENG.). 416p. 26.95 (978-0-9558818-2-4(X)) Whites / White's Books Ltd. GBR. Dist: Independent Pubs. Group.

—A Christmas Carol: And Other Christmas Books. Douglas-Fairhurst, Robert, ed. 2006. (Oxford World's Classics Hardcovers Ser.). (ENG., Illus.). 496p. 25.00 (978-0-19-920474-8(6)) Oxford Univ. Pr., Inc.

—A Christmas Carol & Other Christmas Books. 2009. (ENG.). 440p. 18.00 (978-0-307-27175-4(7), Everyman's Library) Knopf Doubleday Publishing Group.

Feather, Jane, et al. Snowy Night with a Stranger. 2008. (ENG.). 416p. mass mkt. 7.99 (978-1-4165-7822-2(6), Pocket Star) Pocket Star.

Gibbs, Betty, et al, eds. Taking off the Tinsel. pap. 12.95 (978-1-895836-19-6(0)) River Bks. CAN. Dist: Coteau Bks.

Godfrey, Thomas, ed. Murder for Christmas. 2007. (Illus.). 465p. 9.99 (978-0-7858-2307-0(7), Castle Bks., Inc.) Book Sales, Inc.

Green, Jane, et al. This Christmas. 2009. (ENG.). 352p. 15.00 (978-0-7582-3488-9(0)) Kensington Publishing Corp.

Guinn, Jeff. The Autobiography of Santa Claus. 2006. (Illus.). 287p. reprint ed. 18.00 (978-1-4223-5264-9(1)) DIANE Publishing Co.

—The Autobiography of Santa Claus. 2006. (ENG., Illus.). 304p. (gr. 12-18). 11.95 (978-1-58542-448-1(X), Tarcher) Penguin Group (USA) Inc.

Hansen, Jennie L., et al. The Spirit of Christmas: Stories of the Season: Fictional Christmas Stories by Beloved LDS Authors. 2008. 140p. pap. (978-1-59811-581-9(2), Deboisilio) Covenant Communications, Inc.

Harris, Charlaine & Kelner, Toni L. P., eds. Wolfsbane & Mistletoe: Hair-Raising Holiday Tales. 2010. (ENG.). 352p. (gr. 12). 15.00 (978-0-441-01762-1(2), Ace Trade) Penguin Group (USA) Inc.

Henry, O., et al. Texas Christmas Tales. 2011. (ENG., Illus.). 108p. pap. 8.95 **(978-1-892588-21-0(8))** Great Texas Line Pr.

Hollingsworth, Mary. Christmas Miracles. 2008. (ENG., Illus.). 240p. 17.99 (978-0-8249-4742-2(8), GuidepostsBooks) Ideals Pubns.

Hugh Lauter Levin Associates, Inc.Staff & Barron, Kacey, eds. Family Christmas Treasures: A Celebration of Art & Stories. 2008. (ENG., Illus.). 240p. 35.00 (978-0-7893-9971-7(7)) Universe Publishing.

InkerMen Staff, contrib. by. Cold Turkey: A Christmas Selection. 2009. (Illus.). 144p. pap. (978-0-9556259-5-4(5)) Inkermen Pr.

Irving, Washington. Old Christmas. 2008. (ENG., Illus.). 200p. pap. 14.95 (978-1-4290-1668-1(X)) Applewood Bks.

Kauffman, Donna, et al. Kissing Santa Claus. 2010. (ENG.). 320p. 6.99 (978-0-7582-3865-6(1), Brava) Kensington Publishing Corp.

Kendall, Michelle. A Book of Mormon Christmas. 2011. (J). 15.99 (978-1-59955-508-9(5)) Cedar Fort, Inc./CFI Distribution.

Lagerlof, Selma. Scandinavian Christmas: Essays & Stories, Recipes & Traditions. Schense, Deb, ed. 2011. (Illus.). 96p. pap. 14.95 **(978-1-932043-73-0(X))** Penfield Bks.

Langford, David. A Curse, A Cradle, & A Cross. 2007. 121p. (ENG.). pap. 14.95 (978-0-9789908-7-9(0)); pap. 14.95 (978-0-9789908-6-2(2)) Ketch Publishing.

Lewis, Linda M. Dickens, His Parables, & His Reader. 2012. (ENG.). 312p. (C). (gr. 13). 60.00 (978-0-8262-1947-3(0)) Univ. of Missouri Pr.

Long, Judy & Payton, Thomas, eds. Southern Christmas: Literary Classics of the Holidays. 2006. (ENG.). 224p. pap. 15.95 (978-1-892514-08-0(7)) Hill Street Pr., LLC.

Mary Roberts Rinehart. The Truce of God. 2010. 100p. pap. 3.49 (978-1-60386-361-2(3), Watchmaker Publishing) Wexford College Pr.

McCord, Charline R. & Tucker, Judy H., eds. Christmas Memories from Mississippi. 2010. (ENG.). 192p. 28.00 (978-1-60473-755-4(7)) Univ. Pr. of Mississippi.

—Christmas Stories from the South's Best Writers, 1 vol. 2008. (ENG., Illus.). 208p. 15.95 (978-1-58980-600-9(X)) Pelican Publishing Co., Inc.

Michaels, Fern & Lamb, Cathy. Holiday Magic. l.t. ed. 2010. (ENG.). 34.99 (978-1-4104-3166-0(5), Wheeler Publishing, Inc.) Cengage Gale.

Michaels, Fern, et al. Holiday Magic. 2010. (ENG.). 384p. 7.99 (978-1-4201-0835-4(2), Zebra Bks.) Kensington Publishing Corp.

—Snow Angels. 2009. (ENG.). 384p. pap. 7.99 (978-1-4201-0364-9(4), Zebra Bks.) Kensington Publishing Corp.

Moore, Tara & Commonwealth Universities Association London Staff. Victorian Christmas in Print. 2009. (Nineteenth-Century Major Lives & Letters Ser.). (ENG., Illus.). 208p. 89.00 (978-0-230-61654-7(2)) Palgrave Macmillan.

Morris, Harrison S. & Frank P. Mahony. In the Yule-Log Glow Book II: Christmas Tales from Round the World. 2007. (ENG.). 148p. pap. 18.99 (978-1-4264-9569-4(2)); 166p. pap. 21.99 (978-1-4264-9950-0(7)) BiblioBazaar.

Morris, Harrison S. & Morris, Harrison S. In the Yule-Log Glow, Book I Christmas Tales from 'Round the World. 2010. (Illus.). 86p. pap. 20.00 (978-1-153-63167-9(9)) General Bks. LLC.

Morris, Harrison Smith. In the Yule Log Glow Book I: Christmas Tales from Round the World. 2007. 142p. pap. 18.99 (978-1-4264-9421-5(1)); (ENG.). 154p. pap. 21.99 (978-1-4264-9802-2(0)) BiblioBazaar.

Neely, Kirk H. & Kern, June Neely, illus. Comfort & Joy: Nine Stories for Christmas. 2006. (978-1-891885-50-1(2)); pap. (978-1-891885-49-5(9)) Hub City Writers Project.

Newell, Lloyd & Newell, Karmel. A Christmas Treasury for Latter-day Saint Families. 2007. 128p. 21.95 (978-1-59038-807-5(0)) Deseret Bk. Co.

O'Rourke, P. J. The Dreaded Feast: Writers on Enduring the Holidays. Plimpton, Taylor & Clarke, Michele, eds. 2009. (ENG.). 208p. 15.95 (978-0-8109-8265-9(X), Abrams Image) Abrams.

Papa, Carrie. The Brightest Star of All: And Other Christmas Stories. 2008. 80p. pap. 8.00 (978-0-687-64813-9(0)) Abingdon Pr.

Park, John Edgar. The Christmas Heretic & Other Stories. 2011. 94p. 38.95 **(978-1-258-04287-5(8))** Literary Licensing, LLC.

Reed, Shelby, et al. On Santa's Naughty List. 2008. (Ellora's Cave Ser.). (ENG.). 304p. pap. 19.99 (978-1-4165-7764-5(5)) Pocket Books.

—Red Hot Holidays. 2009. (Ellora's Cave Ser.). (ENG.). 288p. pap. 14.00 (978-1-4391-4870-9(8)) Gallery Pr., The IRL. Dist: Simon & Schuster, Inc.

Rhodes, Eric Foster. Going Home for Christmas: 34 Stories Set in the Christmas Season. 2009. 228p. pap. 16.95 (978-1-4490-2964-7(7)) AuthorHouse.

Romp, Billy & Urbanska, Wanda. Christmas on Jane Street: A True Story. 2008. 160p. pap. 12.95 (978-0-06-162642-5(2), Harper Paperbacks) HarperCollins Pubs.

Rousseau, Emile A., Jr. The Night I Almost Missed: And Other Stories about the Birth of Christ. 2007. 92p. per. 12.99 (978-0-924748-79-0(6)) Milestones International Publishers.

Saint Nicholas. 2009. (Illus.). 16p. pap. 8.95 (978-0-9746996-9-1(1)) Eastern Slope Publisher.

Schleiermacher, Friedrich. Christmas Eve Celebration: A Dialogue. Tice, Terrence N., tr. from GER. 2010. 146p. pap. 18.00 (978-1-60608-961-3(7), Cascade Bks.) Wipf & Stock Pubs.

Sexton, Ralph, Sr. Sick Chickens. 90p. pap. 9.95 (978-1-57090-073-0(6), Mountain Church) aBOOKS Distributing.

Smith, John. Hugs for the Holidays: Stories, Sayings, & Scriptures to Encourage & Inspire. 2011. (Hugs Ser.). (ENG., Illus.). 160p. pap. 9.99 (978-1-4516-4895-9(2), Howard Bks.) Howard Books.

Smith, Tammy Robinson, compiled by. Christmas Blooms. 2008. 120p. pap. 12.95 (978-0-9767793-7-7(4)) Mountain Girl Pr.

Standard Publishing Staff, creator. The Greatest Christmas Stories of All Time: Timeless Classics That Celebrate the Season. 2006. 320p. 24.99 (978-0-7847-1953-4(5)) Standard Publishing.

Standiford, Les. The Man Who Invented Christmas: How Charles Dickens's A Christmas Carol Rescued His Career & Revived Our Holiday Spirits. 2011. (ENG.). 256p. pap. 14.99 **(978-0-307-40579-1(6))** Broadway Bks.

Tesdell, Diana Secker, ed. Christmas Stories. 2007. (ENG.). 400p. 15.00 (978-0-307-26717-7(2), Everyman's Library) Knopf Doubleday Publishing Group.

Toner, Gerald R. Lipstick Like Lindsay's & Other Christmas Stories, 1 vol. (ENG., Illus.). 112p. 16.95 (978-0-88289-809-4(4)) Pelican Publishing Co., Inc.

Van Dyke, Henry. The First Christmas Tree: And the Story of the Other Wise Man. 2008. (ENG., Illus.). 128p. 12.95 (978-0-486-46874-7(7)) Dover Pubns., Inc.

Wagenknecht, Edward. Fireside Book of Christmas Stories. lib. bdg. 36.95 (978-0-8488-1897-5(0)) Amereon LTD.

Watson, Calvin Glenn. Who Was That Baby? A Christmas Story. 2010. 79p. pap. 13.95 (978-1-4327-5971-1(X)) Outskirts Pr., Inc.

Weale, David. An Island Christmas Reader. (Illus.). 96p. pap. 12.95 (978-0-9698606-0-0(9)) Acorn Pr., The CAN. Dist: Goose Lane Editions.

Wheeler, Joe L., ed. Christmas in My Heart Book 15. 2006. (Christmas in My Heart Ser.: 15). (Illus.). 127p. per. 11.99 (978-0-8280-2008-4(6)) Review & Herald Publishing Assn.

Will, Julianne M. Adviento: Maneras Sencillas de Prepararse para el Nacimiento de Jesus. Estenger, Vilma G., tr. 2009. (SPA.). 1p. 14.95 (978-1-59276-715-1(X)) Our Sunday Visitor, Publishing Div.

CHRISTMAS TREES

see also Christmas Decorations

Armstrong, Nancy. The Rockefeller Center Christmas Tree Gift Set: The History & Lore of theWorld's Most Famous Evergreen. Lewis, Alexandra, ed. 2010. (ENG., Illus.). 160p. 14.95 (978-1-60433-101-1(1)) Cider Mill Pr. Bk. Pubs., LLC.

The Christmant Tree Pattern Book Vol. 2: Twenty-One Christian Ornaments for Your Christmas Tree, Vol. 2. (Illus.). 107p. pap. 10.95 (978-1-56608-047-7(9), A-B226) Meriwether Publishing, Ltd.

Foley, Daniel J. The Christmas Tree: An Evergreen Garland Filled with History, Folklore, Symbolism, Traditions, Legends & Stories. 2011. 162p. 41.95 **(978-1-258-00733-1(9))** Literary Licensing, LLC.

Hewitt, James. The Christmas Tree. 2007. 88p. pap. 15.00 (978-1-4303-0820-1(6)) Lulu Enterprises Inc.

Jerome, Louie. Christmas Tree. 2009. 40p. pap. 16.50 (978-1-4092-8727-8(0)) Lulu Enterprises Inc.

Lawrence, James E. How to Grow & Sell Christmas Trees. 2011. 176p. 42.95 **(978-1-258-02533-5(7))** Literary Licensing, LLC.

Lewis, Alexandra. Grow Your Own Rockefeller Center Christmas Tree. 2010. (ENG.). 72p. 14.95 (978-1-60433-199-8(2)) Cider Mill Pr. Bk. Pubs., LLC.

Mohr, Angela. Making Gourd Ornaments. 2007. (Illus.). 64p. pap. 12.95 (978-0-7643-2716-2(X)) Schiffer Publishing, Ltd.

Neuschel, Frederick H. Lives & Legends of the Christmas Tree Ships. 2007. (ENG., Illus.). 288p. 24.95 (978-0-472-11623-2(1)) Univ. of Michigan Pr.

—Lives & Legends of the Christmas Tree Ships. 2009. (ENG., Illus.). 288p. pap. 18.95 (978-0-472-03366-9(2)) Univ. of Michigan Pr.

O'Connor, Martha, text. The Tree at Rockefeller Center: A Holiday Tradition. 2007. (Illus.). 143p. (978-1-59591-048-6(4)) Melcher Media.

Russell, Frank C. Carving Songbird Ornaments with Power. 2008. 80p. pap. 16.99 (978-0-7643-3135-0(3)) Schiffer Publishing, Ltd.

Scott, Elizabeth M. Christmas Tree. 2009. 36p. pap. 15.00 (978-1-4490-4218-9(X)) AuthorHouse.

Wray, Robert D. Christmas Trees for Pleasure & Profit. 4th ed. 2008. (ENG.). 160p. 45.00 (978-0-8135-4416-8(5)); pap. 21.95 (978-0-8135-4417-5(3)) Rutgers Univ. Pr.

CHRISTO, 1935-

Chernow, Burt. Christo & Jeanne-Claude. Date not set. pap. (978-0-312-30251-1(7), St. Martin's Griffin) St. Martin's Pr.

Christo & Jean-Claude. Christo & Jeanne-Claude: the Mastaba / over the River. 2010. (ENG., Illus.). 116p. pap. 35.00 (978-84-343-1193-0(3)) Poligrafa, Ediciones, S. A. ESP. Dist: D.A.P./Distributed Art Pubs.

Christo & Jeanne Claude. Christo & Jeanne-Claude: Early Works 1958-64. 2010. (ENG & GER., Illus.). 192p. pap. 35.00 (978-3-941100-79-4(3)) DruckVerlag Kettler GmbH DEU. Dist: D.A.P./Distributed Art Pubs.

Goldberger, Paul & Christo, Jeanne-Claude. Christo & Jeanne-Claude: The complete life & work of Christo & Jeanne-Claude. 2010. (ENG., Illus.). 700p. 1500.00 (978-3-8365-0664-9(5)) TASCHEN DEU. Dist: Ingram Pub. Services.

O'Doherty, Brian. Christo & Jeanne-Claude: Remembering the Running Fence, Sonoma & Marin Counties, California, 1972-1976. 2010. (ENG., Illus.). 173p. 49.95 (978-0-520-26646-9(3)) Univ. of California Pr.

Philippi, Simone, ed. Christo & Jeanne-Claude: Over the River. 2008. (ENG., Illus.). 180p. 49.99 (978-3-8365-0665-3(3)) TASCHEN DEU. Dist: Ingram Pub. Services.

CHRISTOLOGY

see Jesus Christ

CHROMATIC ABERRATION (OPTICS)

see Lenses

CHROMATIC ALTERATION (MUSIC)

see Musica Ficta

CHROMATIC VISION

see Color Vision

CHROMATICISM (MUSIC)

see also Musica Ficta

Burnett, Henry & Nitzberg, Roy. A New Theory of Tonality: Composition Chromaticism & the Development Process. 2007. (Illus.). 430p. 124.95 (978-0-7546-5162-8(2)) Ashgate Publishing Co.

Kopp, David. Chromatic Transformations in Nineteenth-Century Music. 2006. (Cambridge Studies in Music Theory & Analysis Ser.). (ENG., Illus.). 292p pap. 58.00 (978-0-521-02849-3(3)) Cambridge Univ. Pr.

CHROMATICS

see Color

CHROMATIN

Banfalvi, Gaspar. Apoptotic Chromatin Changes. 2009. (ENG., Illus.). xii, 412p. 209.00 (978-1-4020-9560-3(0)) Springer.

Chellappan, S. P. Chromatin Protocols. 2nd ed. 2009. (Methods in Molecular Biology Ser.). (Illus.). 400p. 139.00 (978-1-58829-873-7(6)) Humana Pr.

Collas, Philippe, ed. Chromatin Immunoprecipitation Assays: Methods & Protocols. 2009. (Methods in Molecular Biology Ser.). (ENG., Illus.). ix, 258p. 149.00 (978-1-60327-413-5(8), 1603274138) Humana Pr.

Dame, Remus T. & Dorman, Charles J., eds. Bacterial Chromatin. 2010. (ENG., Illus.). x, 448p. 199.00 (978-90-481-3472-4(2), 9048134722) Springer.

Ferguson-Smith, Anne, et al. Epigenomics. 2008. (ENG., Illus.). xiv, 442p. 229.00 (978-1-4020-9186-5(9), 1402091869) Springer.

Koorsen, Gerrit. The Binding of Linker Histone H5 to Dna & Chromatin. 2010. 188p. pap. (978-3-639-22210-4(5)) VDM Verlag Dr. Mueller e.K.

Kundu, Tapas K. & Dasgupta, Dipak, eds. Chromatin & Disease. (Subcellular Biochemistry Ser.). xiv, 458p. 2010. pap. 219.00 (978-90-481-7374-7(4), 9048173744) 2007. (C). 219.00 (978-1-4020-5465-5(3), 1402054653) Springer.

Laurent, Brehon. Chromatin Dynamics in Cellular Function. 2010. (Results & Problems in Cell Differentiation Ser.). (Illus.). viii, 151p. pap. 109.00 (978-3-642-07024-2(8), 3642070248) Springer.

Morse, Randall H., ed. Chromatin Remodeling: Methods & Protocols. 2011. (Methods in Molecular Biology Ser.). (ENG., Illus.). xii, 453p. 139.00 **(978-1-61779-476-6(7)**, 1617794767) Humana Pr.

Tariq, Muhammad. Molecular Analysis of Transcriptional Gene Silencing in Arabidopsis. 2010. 116p. pap. (978-3-639-25673-4(5)) VDM Verlag Dr. Mueller e.K.

Tollefsbol, Trygve O., ed. Epigenetics Protocols. (Methods in Molecular Biology Ser.). (Illus.). 2010. 320p. pap. 149.00 (978-1-61737-501-9(2), 1617375012) 2nd ed. 2011. (ENG., xi, 332p. 139.00 **(978-1-61779-315-8(9)**, 1617793159) Humana Pr.

CHROMATOGRAPHIC ANALYSIS

see also Gas Chromatography; Gel Permeation Chromatography; Liquid Chromatography; Thin Layer Chromatography

Albertsson, Ann-Christine. Chromatography for Sustainable Polymeric Materials: Renewable, Degradable, & Recyclable. 2008. (Advances in Polymer Science Ser.). (Illus.). 191p. 269.00 (978-3-540-78762-4(3)) Springer.

Albertsson, Ann-Christine & Hakkarainen, Minna. Chromatography for Sustainable Polymeric Materials: Renewable, Degradable & Recyclable. 2010. (Advances in Polymer Science Ser.). (Illus.). xii, 191p. pap. 269.00 (978-3-642-09756-0(1), 3642097561) Springer.

Ali, Imran, et al. Nanochromatography & Nanocapillary Electrophoresis: Pharmaceutical & Environmental Analyses. 2009. (ENG., Illus.). 270p. 99.95 (978-0-470-17851-5(5), Wiley) Wiley, John & Sons, Inc.

Banki, Mahmoud Reza. Fast & Cheap Protein Purification. 2009. 140p. pap. (978-3-639-15443-6(6)) VDM Verlag Dr. Mueller e.K.

Bertholf, Roger & Winecker, Ruth, eds. Chromatographic Methods in Clinical Chemistry & Toxicology. 2007. (ENG., Illus.). 308p. 195.00 (978-0-470-02309-9(0), Wiley) Wiley, John & Sons, Inc.

Bhattacharyya, Lokesh & Rohrer, Jeffrey S. Applications of Ion Chromatography in the Analysis of Pharmaceutical & Biological Products. 2012. (ENG.). 476p. 125.00 **(978-0-470-46709-1(6)**, Wiley) Wiley, John & Sons, Inc.

Bliesner, David M. Validating Chromatographic Methods: A Practical Guide. 2006. (ENG., Illus.). 304p. 105.00 (978-0-471-74147-3(7), Wiley-Interscience) Wiley, John & Sons, Inc.

Carta, Giorgio & Jungbauer, Alois. Protein Chromatography: Process Development & Scale-up. 2010. (ENG., Illus.). 364p. 130.00 (978-3-527-31819-3(4), Wiley-VCH) Wiley, John & Sons, Inc.

Cazes, Jack. Encyclopedia of Chromatography, 3 vols. 3rd ed. 2010. (ENG., Illus.). 800p. Vol. 2. (978-1-4200-8481-8(X)) Vol. 3. (978-1-4200-8482-5(8)) CRC Pr. LLC.

—Encyclopedia of Chromatography, 3 vols., Set. 3rd rev. ed. 2009. (ENG., Illus.). 2850p. 690.00 (978-1-4200-8459-7(3), CRC Press) Taylor & Francis Group GBR. Dist: Taylor & Francis Group.

—Encyclopedia of Chromatography, Third Edition - Volume 1, 3 vols. 3rd ed. 2010. (Illus.). 800p. (978-1-4200-8480-1(1)) CRC Pr. LLC.

Cecchi, Teresa. Ion-Pair Chromatography & Related Techniques. 2009. (Analytical Chemistry Ser.). (ENG., Illus.). 215p. 133.95 (978-1-4398-0096-6(0), CRC Press) Taylor & Francis Group GBR. Dist: Taylor & Francis Group.

Churms, Shirley C. & Ravenscroft, Neil. Chromatographic Analysis of Carbohydrates. 2008. (Illus.). 420p. 159.95 (978-0-8493-7068-7(X)) CRC Pr. LLC.

Cserháti, Tibor. Chromatography of Aroma Compounds & Fragrances. 2010. (ENG., Illus.). xii, 392p. 199.00 (978-3-642-01655-4(3), 3642016553) Springer.

—Multivariate Methods in Chromatography: A Practical Guide. 2008. (ENG., Illus.). 352p. 200.00 (978-0-470-05820-6(X), Wiley) Wiley, John & Sons, Inc.

Dasgupta, Amitava. Advances in Chromatographic Techniques for Therapeutic Drug Monitoring. 2009. (ENG., Illus.). 475p. 174.95 (978-1-4200-6758-3(3), CRC Press) Taylor & Francis Group GBR. Dist: Taylor & Francis Group.

Elwood, John T., ed. Biomedical Chromatography. 2010. (Chemical Engineering Methods & Technology Ser.). (Illus.). ix, 178p. 59.00 (978-1-60741-291-5(3) Nova Biomedical Bks.) Nova Science Pubs., Inc.

Ettre, Leslie S. Chapters in the Evolution of Chromatography. Hinshaw, John V., ed. 2008. (Illus.). 473p. 124.00 (978-1-86094-943-2(6)) Imperial College Pr. GBR. Dist: World Scientific Publishing Co., Inc.

C

Freitag, Ruth, ed. Modern Advances in Chromatography. 2011. (Advances in Biochemical Engineering Biotechnology Ser.). (ENG., Illus.). xii, 271p. pap. 329.00 *(978-3-642-07706-7(4),* 3642077064) Springer.
Fritz, James S. & Gjerde, Douglas T. Ion Chromatography. 4th ed. 2009. (ENG., Illus.). 394p. 200.00 *(978-3-527-32052-3(0),* Wiley-VCH) Wiley, John & Sons, Inc.
Gehrke, Charles W. & Wixom, Robert L., eds. Chromatography: A Science of Discovery. 2010. (ENG., Illus.). 410p. 99.95 *(978-0-470-28345-5(9),* Wiley) Wiley, John & Sons, Inc.
Gottschalk, Uwe, ed. Process Scale Purification of Antibodies. 2009. (ENG., Illus.). 456p. 122.00 *(978-0-470-20962-2(3),* Wiley-Interscience) Wiley, John & Sons, Inc.
Grinberg, Nelu & Grushka, Eli, eds. Advances in Chromatography, Vol. 45. 2006. (Advances in Chromatography Ser.). (ENG., Illus.). 285p. 195.95 *(978-1-57444-735-4(1),* CRC Press) Taylor & Francis Group GBR. Dist: Taylor & Francis Group.
Grushka, Eli & Grinberg, Nelu, eds. Advances in Chromatography. (Advances in Chromatography Ser.). (ENG., Illus.). Vol. 48. 2009. 422p. 205.95 *(978-1-4200-8453-5(4))* Vol. 49. 2011. 461p. 229.95 *(978-1-4398-4091-7(1))* Vol. 50. 2012. 465p. 229.95 *(978-1-4398-5844-8(6))* Taylor & Francis Group GBR. (CRC Press). Dist: Taylor & Francis Group.
—Advances in Chromatography, Volume 46. 2007. (Advances in Chromatography Ser.). (ENG., Illus.). 488p. 195.95 *(978-1-4200-6025-6(2),* CRC Press) Taylor & Francis Group GBR. Dist: Taylor & Francis Group.
—Advances in Chromatography, Volume 47. 2009. (Advances in Chromatography Ser.). (ENG., Illus.). 462p. 195.95 *(978-1-4200-6036-2(8),* CRC Press) Taylor & Francis Group GBR. Dist: Taylor & Francis Group.
Gupta, Mool C. & Ballato, John, eds. The Handbook of Photonics, Vol.3 2nd rev. ed. 2006. (ENG., Illus.). 1040p. 179.95 *(978-0-8493-3095-7(5),* CRC Press) Taylor & Francis Group GBR. Dist: Taylor & Francis Group.
Hagel, Lars, et al. Handbook of Process Chromatography: Development, Manufacturing, Validation & Economics. 2nd ed. 2007. (ENG., Illus.). 382p. 180.00 *(978-0-12-374023-6(1),* Academic Pr.) Elsevier Science & Technology Bks.
Hostettmann, K., et al. Preparative Chromatography Techniques: Applications in Natural Product Isolation. 2nd ed. 2010. (ENG., Illus.). xi, 244p. pap. 249.00 *(978-3-642-08288-7(2),* 3642082882) Springer.
Hyötyläinen, Tuulia, ed. Comprehensive Two-Dimensional Chromatography. 2012. (ENG., Illus.). 380p. 199.00 *(978-3-642-10731-3(1),* 3642107311) Springer.
Khopkar, S. M. Solvent Extraction Separation of Elements with Liquid Ion Exchangers. 2009. (Illus.). 280p. *(978-1-906574-22-2(7))* New Age Science, Ltd.
Kissinger, P. T. Electrochemical Detection in HPLC & HPCE. Date not set. (Chromatographic Science Ser.). *(978-0-8247-0019-5(8))* Dekker, Marcel Inc.
Maithani, Mukesh. Simultaneous Estimation of Drugs by Rp-Hplc. 2011. 140p. pap. ***(978-3-8433-7515-3(1))*** Lambert Academic Publishing.
Marion, Steven. The Effect of Silica Surface Chemistry in Rp-Lc of Steroid Compounds. 2009. 108p. pap. *(978-3-639-15187-9(9))* VDM Verlag Dr. Mueller e.K.
Mattiasson, B., ed. Expanded Bed Chromatography. 2010. 250p. pap. 199.00 *(978-90-481-5380-0(8),* 9048153808) Springer.
Mazurek Mariusz Staff. Forced-Flow Planar Chromatography. 2009. 400p. 169.95 *(978-1-57444-546-6(4))* CRC Pr. LLC.
McMahon, Robert J., ed. Avidin-Biotin Interactions: Methods & Applications. (Methods in Molecular Biology Ser.). (Illus.). 2010. xiv, 232p. pap. 119.00 *(978-1-61737-657-3(4),* 1617376574) 2008. 232p. 119.00 *(978-1-58829-583-5(4))* Humana Pr.
Miller, James M. Chromatography: Concepts & Contrasts. 2nd ed. 2009. (ENG., Illus.). 520p. pap. 94.95 *(978-0-470-53025-2(1),* Wiley-Interscience) Wiley, John & Sons, Inc.
Mondello, Luigi, ed. Comprehensive Chromatography in Combination with Mass Spectrometry. 2011. (Wiley - Interscience Series on Mass Spectrometry Ser.: 36). (ENG., Illus.). 496p. 125.00 *(978-0-470-43407-9(4),* Wiley) Wiley, John & Sons, Inc.
Nesterenko, Pavel, et al. High Performance Chelation Ion Chromatography. 2010. (RSC Chromatography Monographs). (ENG., Illus.). 316p. (C). 160.00 ***(978-1-84973-041-9(5))*** Royal Society of Chemistry, The GBR. Dist: Ingram Pub. Services.
Nguyen, Anh Mai. Preparation of MacRoporous Monoliths for Use in Liquid Chromatography. 2010. 108p. pap. *(978-3-8383-2234-6(7))* Lambert Academic Publishing.
Ozkan, Sibel A. Electroanalytical Methods in Pharmaceutical Analysis & Their Validation. 2011. (ENG., Illus.). 350p. 99.75 net. *(978-0-9664286-7-4(6))* HNB Publishing.
Picó, Yolanda. LC-MS for Pesticide Analysis in Food & the Environment. 2010. (Wiley - Interscience Series on Mass Spectrometry Ser.). (ENG.). 512p. 120.00 *(978-0-470-09846-2(5),* Wiley-Interscience) Wiley, John & Sons, Inc.
Podzimek, Stepan. Light Scattering, Size Exclusion Chromatography & Asymmetric Flow Field Flow Fractionation: Powerful Tools for the Characterization of Polymers, Proteins & Nanoparticles. 2011. (ENG., Illus.). 372p. 105.00 *(978-0-470-38617-0(7),* Wiley) Wiley, John & Sons, Inc.
Poole, Colin. Handbook of Methods & Instrumentation in Separation Science, 2 vols., Vol. 1. 2009. (ENG., Illus.). 880p. 165.00 *(978-0-12-375095-2(4),* Academic Pr.) Elsevier Science & Technology Bks.
—Handbook of Methods & Instrumentation in Separation Science, 2 vols., Vol. 2. 2009. (ENG., Illus.). 1294p. 165.00 *(978-0-12-375094-5(6),* Academic Pr.) Elsevier Science & Technology Bks.
Pyell, Ute, ed. Electrokinetic Chromatography: Theory, Instrumentation & Applications. 2006. (ENG., Illus.). 552p. 315.00 *(978-0-470-87102-7(4),* Wiley) Wiley, John & Sons, Inc.
Ramos, Lourdes, ed. Comprehensive two dimensional gas Chromatography. 2009. (Comprehensive Analytical Chemistry Ser.: 55). (ENG., Illus.). 328p. 275.00 *(978-0-444-53237-4(4),* Elsevier Science) Elsevier Science & Technology Bks.
Rayne, Richard C., ed. Neurotransmitter Methods. 2010. (Methods in Molecular Biology Ser.). 288p. pap. 139.00 *(978-1-61737-023-6(1),* 1617370231) Humana Pr.
Risby, Terence & Sehnert, Shelley. Chromatographic Analysis of the Environment. 3rd exp. rev. ed. Date not set. (Chromatographic Science Ser.). (Illus.). *(978-0-8247-9456-9(7),* 9456-7) Dekker, Marcel Inc.
Shalliker, R. Andrew, ed. Hyphenated & Alternative Methods of Detection in Chromatography. 2011. (Chromatographic Science Ser.). (ENG., Illus.). 308p. 169.95 *(978-0-8493-9077-7(X),* CRC Press) Taylor & Francis Group GBR. Dist: Taylor & Francis Group.
Sharma, Rakesh & Dhingra, Shuchi. Functionalized Silica Gel As Metal Scavenger, Sensor, & Catalyst. 2011. 276p. pap. ***(978-3-8443-1991-0(3))*** Lambert Academic Publishing.
Silwal, Indira. Characterization of Unknown Chemicals. 2010. 168p. pap. *(978-3-639-14160-3(1))* VDM Verlag Dr. Mueller e.K.
Simpson, Richard J., et al, eds. Basic Methods in Protein Purification & Analysis: A Laboratory Manual. 2008. (ENG., Illus.). 436p. 162.00 *(978-0-87969-868-3(3));* pap. 97.00 *(978-0-87969-867-6(5))* Cold Spring Harbor Laboratory Pr.
Suomi, Johanna. Mekc-Ms & Biological Matrices. 2010. 96p. pap. *(978-3-8383-4988-6(1))* Lambert Academic Publishing.
Takahashi, Nobuhiro, et al. Proteomic Biology Using LC-MS: Large Scale Analysis of Cellular Dynamics & Function. 2007. (Wiley - Interscience Series on Mass Spectrometry Ser.: 15). (ENG., Illus.). 262p. 99.95 *(978-0-471-66258-7(5),* Wiley-Interscience) Wiley, John & Sons, Inc.
Venn, Richard F., ed. Principles & Practice of Bioanalysis. 2nd rev. ed. 2008. (ENG., Illus.). 344p. 99.95 *(978-0-8493-3857-1(3),* CRC Press) Taylor & Francis Group GBR. Dist: Taylor & Francis Group.
Wagner, Hildebert, et al, eds. Chromatographic Fingerprint Analysis of Herbal Medicines: Thin-Layer & High Performance Liquid Chromatography of Chinese Drugs, 2 vols. 2nd ed. 2011. (ENG., Illus.). xl, 1024p. 319.00 *(978-3-7091-0762-1(8),* 3709107628) Springer.
Walls, Dermot & Loughran, Sinéad T., eds. Protein Chromatography: Methods & Protocols. 2010. (Methods in Molecular Biology Ser.). (Illus.). x, 527p. 139.00 *(978-1-60761-912-3(1),* 1607619121) Humana Pr.
Yamamoto Shuichi Staff. Ion Exchange Chromatography of Proteins. 2nd ed. 2009. 450p. 169.95 *(978-1-57444-767-5(X))* CRC Pr. LLC.
Zachariou, Michael. Affinity Chromatography: Methods & Protocols. Zachariou, Michael, ed. 2nd ed. 2007. (Methods in Molecular Biology Ser.). (Illus.). 343p. 129.00 *(978-1-58829-659-7(8))* Humana Pr.
Zachariou, Michael, ed. Affinity Chromatography: Methods & Protocols. 2nd ed. 2010. (Methods in Molecular Biology Ser.). (Illus.). xii, 348p. pap. 129.00 *(978-1-61737-701-3(5),* 1617377015) Humana Pr.
Zehnacker, Anne, ed. Chiral Recognition in the Gas Phase. 2010. (ENG., Illus.). 247p. 99.95 *(978-1-4200-8227-2(2),* CRC Press) Taylor & Francis Group GBR. Dist: Taylor & Francis Group.

CHROMATOGRAPHY
see Chromatographic Analysis

CHROMATOGRAPHY, THIN LAYER
see Thin Layer Chromatography

CHROMATOPHORES
see also Chloroplasts

Fietz, Susanne. Phytoplankton Pigments in Lake Baikal. 2008. 204p. pap. *(978-3-8364-8933-1(3))* VDM Verlag Dr. Mueller e.K.
Parker, George Howard. Animal Colour Changes & their Neurohumours: A Survey of Investigations 1910-1943. 2012. (ENG.). 388p. pap. 39.99 ***(978-1-107-61325-6(6))*** Cambridge Univ. Pr.

CHROMIUM

Abhilash, et al. Chromium Biosorption by Fungus. 2011. 84p. pap. ***(978-3-8443-8975-3(X))*** Lambert Academic Publishing.
Hamid, Rehana, et al. Antioxidative Efficiency of Brassica Juncea Exposed to Chromium Stress. 2011. 68p. pap. ***(978-3-8454-1939-8(3))*** Lambert Academic Publishing.
Ionescu-Gabor, Sorin. Recrystallisation Annealing of Martensitic Chromium Steel Strip. 2010. 132p. pap. *(978-3-639-23103-8(1))* VDM Verlag Dr. Mueller e.K.
Kurniawan, Tonni Agustiono. Removal of Toxic Cr(VI) from Wastewater. 2012. ***(978-1-62081-025-5(5))*** Nova Science Pubs., Inc.
Mahmood, Tariq & Zia Qureshi, Irfan. Thyroid Gland & Chromium Toxicity. 2010. 132p. pap. *(978-3-639-25661-1(1))* VDM Verlag Dr. Mueller e.K.
McLeod, Malcolm Noell. Lifting Your Depression, 1 vol. 2009. (ENG.). 224p. pap. 18.95 *(978-1-59120-245-5(0))* Basic Health Pubns., Inc.
Murria, María José Balart, ed. Management of Hazardous Residues Containing Cr(VI) 2011. (Waste & Waste Management Ser.). 388p. 80.00 *(978-1-61668-267-5(1))* Nova Science Pubs., Inc.
Roza, Greg. Chromium. 2008. (Understanding the Elements of the Periodic Table Ser.). (Illus.). 48p. (YA). (gr. 5-9). lib. bdg. 26.50 *(978-1-4042-1411-8(9))* Rosen Publishing Group, Inc., The.
Salden, Margaret P. Chromium: Environmental, Medical & Materials Studies. 2011. (Series: Chemical Engineering Methods & Technology Ser.). (Illus.). xiii, 384p. 129.00 *(978-1-61122-656-0(2))* Nova Science Pubs., Inc.
Sundaram, S. & Raghavan, P. S. Chromium -VI Reagents: Synthetic Applications: Synthetic Applications. 2011. (SpringerBriefs in Molecular Science Ser.). (ENG., Illus.). xii, 66p. pap. 49.95 *(978-3-642-20816-4(9),* 3642208169) Springer.
Technology Research Editors, ed. Chromium: Health & Pollution Issues, 2007 Ed. 2007. pap. 128.50 *(978-1-60030-407-1(9),* Search-In-Print) CSA Journal Division.
Thiravetyan, Philip & Suksabye, Parinda. Treatment of Chromium Contamination in the Environment. 2011. (Chemistry Research & Applications Ser.). pap. 43.00 *(978-1-61209-291-1(8))* Nova Science Pubs., Inc.
Vincent, John, ed. The Nutritional Biochemistry of Chromium(III) 2007. (ENG., Illus.). 292p. 210.00 *(978-0-444-53071-4(1),* Elsevier Science) Elsevier Science & Technology Bks.
World Health Organization. Inorganic Chromium (III) Compounds. 2009. (Concise International Chemical Assessment Document No 76 Ser.). (ENG.). 102p. pap. 24.00 *(978-92-4-153076-7(6))* World Health Organization.

CHROMODYNAMICS, QUANTUM
see Quantum Chromodynamics

CHROMOLITHOGRAPHS
see Chromolithography

CHROMOLITHOGRAPHY
see also Color Prints

Hollander, Joel A. Coloured Political Lithographs as Irish Propaganda: Warrior Artists & the Battle for Home Rule, 1879-1886. 2006. (Illus.). 304p. 119.95 *(978-0-7734-5671-6(6))* Mellen, Edwin Pr., The.

CHROMOPHOTOGRAPHY
see Color Photography

CHROMOSOME ABNORMALITIES
see also Human Chromosome Abnormalities; Karyotypes

Arrieta, Isabel, ed. Fragile Sites: New Discoveries & Changing Perspectives. 2007. 359p. (C). 79.00 *(978-1-60021-504-9(1))* Nova Science Pubs., Inc.
Epstein, Charles J. The Consequences of Chromosome Imbalance: Principles, Mechanisms, & Models. 2007. (Developmental & Cell Biology Ser.). (ENG.). 512p. pap. 100.00 *(978-0-521-03809-6(X))* Cambridge Univ. Pr.
Gloscow, Eleanor J. New Research on Genomic Instability. 2006. 302p. 129.00 *(978-1-60021-320-5(0))* Nova Science Pubs., Inc.
Nasheuer, H. P., ed. Genome Stability & Human Diseases. 2009. (Subcellular Biochemistry Ser.). (ENG., Illus.). xvi, 340p. 269.00 *(978-90-481-3470-0(6),* 9048134706) Springer.
Obe, G. & Natarajan, A. T., eds. Chromosome Aberrations, Vol. 104. (Illus.). 394p. reprint ed. *(978-3-8055-7767-0(2))* Karger, S. AG.
Reddy, Pr. Chromosome Damage by Environmental Agent. 2006. 140p. per. *(978-1-4067-1418-0(6),* Hesperides Pr.) Read Bks.
Richardson, Rebecca. Craig Richardson: A Life Worth Living, with Disabilities. 2011. 287p. pap. 19.95 ***(978-1-4327-7479-0(4))*** Outskirts Pr., Inc.
Ross, Judith L. & Mazzocco, Michèle M., eds. Neurogenetic Developmental Disorders: Variation of Manifestation in Childhood. 2007. (Issues in Clinical & Cognitive Neuropsychology Ser.). (ENG., Illus.). 524p. (gr. 17). 60.00 *(978-0-262-13480-4(2))* MIT Pr.
Shamina, Natalya V. 2nd Pollen Formation: 40 Cytological Mechanisms of Nuclear Meiotic Restitution. 2010. (Botanical Research & Practices Ser.). 109p. pap. 43.00 *(978-1-61668-976-6(5),* Nova Novinka) Nova Science Pubs., Inc.
Tassone, Flora & Berry-Kravis, Elizabeth M., eds. The Fragile X-Associated Tremor Ataxia Syndrome (FXTAS) 2010. (ENG., Illus.). xvi, 188p. 139.00 *(978-1-4419-5804-4(5),* 1441958045) Springer.
Wang, Pei. Statistical Methods for Cgh Array Analysis. 2010. 38p. pap. *(978-3-639-11406-5(X))* VDM Verlag Dr. Mueller e.K.
Wayda, Kornelia Emma. Foetal Nuchal Translucency. 2011. 100p. pap. ***(978-3-8443-1921-7(2))*** Lambert Academic Publishing.

CHROMOSOME MAPPING
see Gene Mapping

CHROMOSOME NUMBERS
see also Aneuploidy; Polyploidy

Bajaj, Y., ed. Haploids in Crop Improvement I, Vol. 1. 2008. (Biotechnology in Agriculture & Forestry Ser.). (Illus.). xx, 549p. 689.00 *(978-3-540-50798-7(1))* Springer.
Hu, Han, et al. Thermal Spray Fundamentals: From Powder to Part. 2009. (Illus.). x, 211p. 189.00 *(978-0-387-28319-7(6))* Springer.
Jain, S. Mohan, et al, eds. In vitro Haploid Production in Higher Plants: Volume 1: Fundamental Aspects & Methods. 2010. (Current Plant Science & Biotechnology in Agriculture Ser.). (Illus.). 368p. pap. 309.00 *(978-90-481-4579-9(1),* 9048145791) Springer.
—In vitro Haploid Production in Higher Plants: Volume 2: Applications. 2010. (Current Plant Science & Biotechnology in Agriculture Ser.). (Illus.). 440p. pap. 429.00 *(978-90-481-4580-5(5),* 9048145805) Springer.
—In vitro Haploid Production in Higher Plants: Volume 3: Important Selected Plants. 2010. (Current Plant Science & Biotechnology in Agriculture Ser.). (Illus.). 320p. pap. 339.00 *(978-90-481-4581-2(3),* 9048145813) Springer.
—In vitro Haploid Production in Higher Plants: Volume 4: Cereals. 2010. (Current Plant Science & Biotechnology in Agriculture Ser.). (Illus.). 220p. pap. 269.00 *(978-90-481-4682-6(8),* 9048146828) Springer.
—In vitro Haploid Production in Higher Plants: Volume 5: Oil, Ornamental & Miscellaneous Plants. 2010. (Current Plant Science & Biotechnology in Agriculture Ser.). (Illus.). 240p. pap. 229.00 *(978-90-481-4683-3(6),* 9048146836) Springer.
Moore, D. M., ed. Flora Europaea Check-List & Chromosome Index. 2009. (Flora Europaea Ser.). (ENG.). 436p. pap. 55.00 *(978-0-521-10573-6(0))* Cambridge Univ. Pr.
Palmer, Constantine E. Don, et al. Haploids in Crop Improvement II. 2010. (Biotechnology in Agriculture & Forestry Ser.). (Illus.). xv, 318p. pap. 319.00 *(978-3-642-06073-1(0),* 3642060730) Springer.

CHROMOSOMES
see also Chromosome Abnormalities; Chromosome Numbers; Genetics; Human Chromosomes; Karyokinesis; Karyotypes; Linkage (Genetics); Sex Chromosomes; Translocation (Genetics)

Balbas, Paulina & Lorence, Argelia, eds. Recombinant Gene Expression: Reviews & Protocols. 2nd ed. 2010. (Methods in Molecular Biology Ser.). (Illus.). 494p. pap. 159.00 *(978-1-61737-460-9(1),* 1617374601) Humana Pr.
Bartone, John C., ed. Drinking Water with Chromosome Fragments (Micronuclei) with Index & Medical Analysis of New Research Information for All Nations. 2006. (Illus.). 160p. 69.95 *(978-0-7883-4746-7(2),* 0-7883-4746-7) ABBE Pubs. Assn. of Washington, D.C.
Bass, Hank W. & Birchler, James A. Plant Cytogenetics: Genome Structure & Chromosome Function. 2009. (Plant Genetics & Genomics: Crops & Models Ser.). (Illus.). 500p. 209.00 *(978-0-387-70868-3(5))* Springer.
Birchler, James A. Plant Chromosome Engineering. 2011. (Illus.). xi, 329p. E-Book ***(978-1-61737-957-4(3))*** Humana Pr.
Camacho, Juan Pedro M., ed. B Chromosomes in the Eukaryote Genome, Vol. 106. (Cytogenetic & Genome Research Ser.: Vol. 160, Nos. 2-4). (Illus.). 274p. reprint ed. *(978-3-8055-7807-3(5))* Karger, S. AG.
Davis, Greg & Kayser, Kevin J., eds. Chromosomal Mutagenesis. 2010. (Methods in Molecular Biology Ser.). (Illus.). xvi, 236p. pap. 119.00 *(978-1-61737-833-1(X),* 161737833X) Humana Pr.
Davis, Gregory D. & Kayser, Kevin J., eds. Chromosomal Mutagenesis. 2007. (Methods in Molecular Biology Ser.). (Illus.). 235p. 119.00 *(978-1-58829-899-7(X),* 158829899X) Humana Pr.
De Wulf, Peter & Earnshaw, William C. The Kinetochore: From Molecular Discoveries to Cancer Therapy. 2008. (ENG., Illus.). xiv, 514p. 149.00 *(978-0-387-69073-5(5),* 0387690735) Springer.
Eddy, E. Mitchell & Griswold, Michael D., eds. Testicular Chromosome Structure & Gene Expression. 2008. (Annals of the New York Academy of Sciences Ser.: Vol. 1411). (ENG., Illus.). 300p. per. 145.95 *(978-1-57331-693-4(8),* Wiley-Blackwell) Wiley, John & Sons, Inc.
Egel, Richard & Lankenau, Dirk-Henner. Recombination & Meiosis: Crossing-over & Disjunction. 2010. (Genome Dynamics & Stability Ser.). (Illus.). xvi, 365p. pap. 279.00 *(978-3-642-09459-0(7),* 3642094597) Springer.
—Recombination & Meiosis: Models, Means, & Evolution. 2010. (Genome Dynamics & Stability Ser.). (Illus.). xxii, 390p. pap. 299.00 *(978-3-642-08850-6(3),* 3642088503) Springer.
Farzana, Perveen & Abbasi, Fida M. In Situ Hybridization for Analysis of Rice Plant Genomic Constitution: In Situ Hybridization for the Analysis of Genomic Constitution of Rice Plants. 2011. 60p. pap. ***(978-3-639-34123-2(6))*** VDM Verlag Dr. Mueller e.K.
Fukui, Kiichi & Ushiki, Tatsuo, eds. Chromosome Nanoscience & Technology. 2007. (ENG., Illus.). 288p. 157.95 *(978-1-4200-4491-1(5),* CRC Press) Taylor & Francis Group GBR. Dist: Taylor & Francis Group.
G, Archana. Phonological Accuracy Measures in down's Syndrome. 2011. 104p. pap. ***(978-3-8443-8731-5(5))*** Lambert Academic Publishing.
Griffin, D. & Bridger, J., eds. International Chromosome Conference: 15th Conference, London, September 2004, Vol. 107. (Illus.). 140p. pap. *(978-3-8055-7815-8(6))* Karger, S. AG.
Houben, A., ed. Chromosome Structure & Function. 2009. (Illus.). 180p. *(978-3-8055-9212-3(4))* Karger, S. AG.
Jeanteur, Philippe, ed. Regulation of Alternative Splicing. 2010. (Progress in Molecular & Subcellular Biology Ser.). (Illus.). xiii, 192p. pap. 269.00 *(978-3-642-07858-3(3),* 3642078583) Springer.
Keeney, Scott, ed. Meiosis: Volume 2, Cytological Methods, 2 vols. 2009. (Methods in Molecular Biology Ser.). (ENG., Illus.). x, 438p. 159.00 *(978-1-60761-102-8(3),* 1607611023) Humana Pr.
Khan, Imtiaz Ahmed. Homoeologous Chromosome Recombination in Triticeae. 2010. 184p. pap. *(978-3-639-24679-7(9))* VDM Verlag Dr. Mueller e.K.
Korf, Bruce R. Medical Genetics at a Glance. 2nd rev. ed. 2007. (At a Glance Ser.). (ENG., Illus.). 168p. per. 44.95 *(978-1-4051-4846-7(2),* Wiley-Blackwell) Wiley, John & Sons, Inc.
Krupp, Guido & Parwaresch, Reza, eds. Telomerases, Telomeres & Cancer. 2010. (Molecular Biology Intelligence Unit Ser.). 426p. pap. 279.00 *(978-1-4419-3391-1(3),* 1441933913) Springer.
Lezhava, Teimuraz. Human Chromosomes & Aging. 2009. (Illus.). 177p. pap. 49.00 *(978-1-60456-471-6(7),* Nova Biomedical Bks.) Nova Science Pubs., Inc.
Liehr, Thomas. Small Supernumerary Marker Chromosomes (sSMC) A Guide for Human Geneticists & Clinicians. 2011. (ENG., Illus.). xx, 220p. 69.95 *(978-3-642-20765-5(0),* 3642207650) Springer.

Lima-De-Faria. Praise of Chromosome Folly. 2008. 380p. 88.00 (978-981-281-479-1(5)); pap. 54.00 (978-981-281-094-6(3)) World Scientific Publishing Co., Inc.

Lima-de-Faria, A. One Hundred Years of Chromosome Research & What Remains to be Learned. 2010. 228p. pap. 169.00 (978-90-481-6350-2(1), 9048163501) Springer.

Lue, Neal & Autexier, Chantal. Telomerases: Chemistry, Biology & Clinical Applications. 2012. (ENG.). 318p. 125.00 (978-0-470-59204-5(4), Wiley) Wiley, John & Sons, Inc.

MacKenzie, Alasdair, ed. YAC Protocols. 2nd ed. 2010. (Methods in Molecular Biology Ser.). (Illus.). 224p. pap. 119.00 (978-1-61737-673-3(6), 1617376736) Humana Pr.

Mancini, Leonardo, ed. Telomeres: Function, Shortening & Lengthening. 2009. (Illus.). xvii, 478p. 129.00 (978-1-60692-350-4(1)) Nova Science Pubs., Inc.

Martins, Cesar, et al. Animal Genomes under the Focus of Cytogenetics. 2011. (Genetics - Research & Issues Ser.). (Illus.). vi, 160p. 69.00 (978-1-61209-390-1(6)) Nova Science Pubs., Inc.

Meksem, Khalid & Kahl, Guenter, eds. The Handbook of Plant Mutation Screening: Mining of Natural & Induced Alleles. 2010. (Molecular Plant Biology Ser.). (ENG., Illus.). 460p. 229.95 (978-3-527-32604-4(9), Wiley-VCH) Wiley, John & Sons, Inc.

Nosek, Jozef & Tomáska, Lubomir. Origin & Evolution of Telomeres. Nosek, Jozef & Tomáska, Lubomir, eds. 2008. (Molecular Biology Intelligence Unit Ser.). (978-1-58706-309-1(3)) Landes Bioscience.

Novikov, Dmitri. High Resolution Imaging of Polytene Chromosomes. 2009. 96p. pap. (978-3-639-12924-3(5)) VDM Verlag Dr. Mueller e.K.

O'Brien, Stephen J., et al. Atlas of Mammalian Chromosomes. 2006. (ENG., Illus.). 714p. 475.00 (978-0-471-35015-6(X), Wiley-Liss) Wiley, John & Sons, Inc.

Osterman, Andrei L. & Gerdes, Svetlana, eds. Microbial Gene Essentiality: Protocols & Bioinformatics. 2007. (Methods in Molecular Biology Ser.). (Illus.). 400p. 139.00 (978-1-58829-378-7(5), 1588293785) Humana Pr.

Qureshi, Shumila, et al. Cytological Analysis of Allium Cepa L. 2010. 80p. pap. (978-3-639-24734-3(5)) VDM Verlag Dr. Mueller e.K.

Rahal, Rami. Cdk Control of Mitotic Progression. 2010. 200p. pap. (978-3-8383-2082-3(4)) Lambert Academic Publishing.

Rudolph, K. Lenhard. Telomeres & Telomerase in Ageing, Disease, & Cancer: Molecular Mechanisms of Adult Stem Cell Ageing. Rudolph, K. Lenhard, ed. 2007. (ENG., Illus.). xiv, 330p. 239.00 (978-3-540-73708-7(1), 3540737081) Springer.

Rudolph, K. Lenhard, ed. Telomeres & Telomerase in Aging, Disease, & Cancer: Molecular Mechanisms of Adult Stem Cell Ageing. 2010. (ENG., Illus.). xiv, 330p. pap. 239.00 (978-3-642-09288-6(8), 3642092888) Springer.

Schmid, M. & Nanda, Indrajit, eds. Chromosomes Today: Volume 14. 2010. (ENG.). xvi, 274p. pap. 163.00 (978-90-481-5855-3(9), 9048158559) Springer.

Schulz, Jacob H., ed. Genetic Recombination Research Progress. 2008. (Illus.). xiii, 385p. (C). 185.00 (978-1-60456-482-2(2)) Nova Science Pubs., Inc.

Schwartz, Edward. Microbial Megaplasmids. 2009. (Microbiology Monographs). (ENG., Illus.). x, 348p. 239.00 (978-3-540-85466-1(5)) Springer.

Songyang, Zhou, ed. Telomeres & Telomerase: Methods & Protocols. 2nd ed. 2011. (Methods in Molecular Biology Ser.). (Illus.). x, 191p. 119.00 (978-1-61779-091-1(5), 1617790915) Humana Pr.

Tollefsbol, Trygve O., ed. Epigenetics Protocols. (Methods in Molecular Biology Ser.). (Illus.). 2010. 320p. pap. 149.00 (978-1-61737-501-9(2), 1617375012) 2nd ed. 2011. (ENG., xi, 332p. 139.00 **(978-1-61779-315-8(9)**, 1617793159) Humana Pr.

Tsubouchi, Hideo, ed. DNA Recombination: Methods & Protocols. 2011. (Methods in Molecular Biology Ser.). (Illus.). xiv, 565p. 159.00 (978-1-61779-128-4(8), 1617791288) Humana Pr.

Ugarkovic, Durdica. Centromere: Structure & Evolution. Ugarkovic, Durdica, ed. 2009. (Progress in Molecular & Subcellular Biology Ser.). (ENG., Illus.). x, 183p. 169.00 (978-3-642-00181-9(5), 3642001815) Springer.

Vasarhelyi, Krisztina. Chromosome Rearrangement Breakpoint Hot Spots in Humans. 2011. 140p. pap. **(978-3-8443-3492-0(0))** Lambert Academic Publishing.

Weitao, Tao & Nordstrom, Kurt. The Cycle of Escherichia Coli Chromosomes & Plasmids. 2010. 108p. pap. (978-3-639-25232-3(2)) VDM Verlag Dr. Mueller e.K.

Zhao, Shaying & Stodolsky, Marvin, eds. Bacterial Artificial Chromosomes: Volume 1: Library Construction, Physical Mapping, & Sequencing. 2010. (Methods in Molecular Biology Ser.). (Illus.). 384p. pap. 129.00 (978-1-61737-288-9(9), 1617372889) Humana Pr.

—Bacterial Artificial Chromosomes: Volume 2: Functional Studies. 2010. (Methods in Molecular Biology Ser.). (Illus.). 344p. pap. 149.00 (978-1-61737-289-6(7), 1617372897) Humana Pr.

CHROMOSPHERIC ERUPTIONS

see Solar Flares

CHROMOTHERAPY

see Color—Therapeutic Use

CHROMOXYLOGRAPHY

see Color Prints

CHRONIC ACTIVE HEPATITIS

Diehl, A. M., et al, eds. Chronic Hepatitis Metabolic, Cholestatic, Viral & Autoimmune. 2007. (Falk Symposium Ser.). 272p. 229.00 (978-1-4020-6522-4(1)) Springer.

Hirschfield, Gideon & Heathcote, Jenny. Autoimmune Hepatitis: A Guide for Practicing Clinicians. 2011. (Clinical Gastroenterology Ser.). (Illus.). 400p. 189.00 **(978-1-60761-568-2(1)**, 1607615681) Humana Pr.

Kumada, H., et al, eds. Chronic Hepatitis C in Asia: Epidemiology, Pathophysiology, Hepatocellular Carcinoma & Treatment. (Intervirology 2006, Vol. 49, No. 1-2 Ser.). (Illus.). 120p. (978-3-8055-8017-5(7)) Karger, S. AG.

CHRONIC DISEASES

see also Chronic Fatigue Syndrome; Chronic Pain; Chronic Renal Failure

Adeyi, Olusoji, et al. Public Policy & the Challenge of Chronic Noncommunicable Diseases. 2007. (Directions in Development Ser.). (ENG., Illus.). 208p. per. 30.00 (978-0-8213-7044-5(8), 9780821370445) World Bank Pubns.

Aggarwal, Bharat B., et al, eds. Inflammation Life Style & Chronic Diseases. 2011. (Oxidative Stress & Disease Ser.). (ENG., Illus.). 504p. 149.95 (978-1-4398-3989-8(1), CRC Press) Taylor & Francis Group GBR. Dist: Taylor & Francis Group.

Ahmedzai, Sam H., et al. Supportive Care in Respiratory Disease. 2nd ed. 2012. (ENG., Illus.). 412p. 135.00 **(978-0-19-959176-3(8))** Oxford Univ. Pr., Inc.

Albrecht, Urs, ed. The Circadian Clock. 2010. (Protein Reviews Ser.). (ENG., Illus.). xi, 300p. 159.00 (978-1-4419-1261-9(4), 1441912614) Springer.

American College of Sports Medicine Staff, et al. ACSM's Exercise Management for Persons with Chronic Diseases & Disabilities. 3rd ed. 2009. (ENG., Illus.). 456p. 72.00 (978-0-7360-7433-9(3)) Human Kinetics Pubs.

Atwood, Joan. Handbook of Family Therapy & Chronic Illness (tent.) Gallo, Concetta, ed. 2008. 85.00 (978-0-7890-3387-1(9)) Routledge.

Badura, Bernhard, et al, eds. Fehlzeiten-Report 2006: Chronische Krankheiten. 2006. (Fehlzeiten-Report). (Illus.). XVI, 456p. pap. 48.95 (978-3-540-34367-7(9), 3540343679) Springer.

Bährer-Kohler, Sabine & Krebs-Roubicek, Eva, eds. Self Management of Chronic Disease: Alzheimer's Disease. 2009. (ENG., Illus.). xiv, 158p. pap. 79.95 (978-3-642-00325-7(7)) Springer.

Bailey, Beatrice. Farewell, My Friend. Allen, Wendy et al, eds. 2008. 203p. pap. 19.95 (978-0-9801520-0-5(3)) Bailey, Beatrice Toney.

Bakris, George L. & Bomback, Andrew S. Chronic Kidney Disease (Ckd) & Hypertension Essentials. rev. ed. 2010. 148p. pap. 28.95 (978-0-7637-8136-1(3)) Jones & Bartlett Learning, LLC.

Bales & Ritchie, eds. Handbook of Clinical Nutrition & Aging. 2nd ed. 2008. (Nutrition & Health Ser.) (Illus.). 500p. 189.00 (978-1-60327-384-8(0)) Springer.

Bales, Connie W. & Ritchie, Christine Seel. Handbook of Clinical Nutrition & Aging. 2nd ed. 2009. (Illus.). xxvii, 668p. (978-1-60327-385-5(9)) Humana Pr.

Barber, Kimberly. The Role of Chronic Illness in Mental Wellbeing. 2010. 120p. pap. (978-3-8383-0229-4(X)) Lambert Academic Publishing.

Bell, Iris R. Getting Whole, Getting Well: Healing Holistically from Chronic Illness. 2008. (ENG.). pap. 14.95 (978-1-60037-387-9(9)) Morgan James Publishing.

Benzon, Honorio T., et al. Practical Management of Pain. Benzon, Honorio T. et al, eds. 4th ed. 2008. (ENG., Illus.). 1344p. 274.00 (978-0-323-04184-3(1), Mosby) Elsevier - Health Sciences Div.

Berbari, Adel E. & Mancia, Giuseppe, eds. Cardiorenal Syndrome: Mechanisms, Risk & Treatment. 2010. (ENG., Illus.). 450p. 219.00 (978-88-470-1462-6(X), 884701462X) Springer.

Beukelman, David R., et al, eds. Augmentative Communication Strategies for Adults with Acute or Chronic Medical Conditions. 2007. (Illus.). 418p. pap. 59.95 incl. cd-rom (978-1-55766-875-2(2)) Brookes, Paul H. Publishing Co.

Bigelsen, Harvey. Doctors Are More Harmful Than Germs: How Surgery Can Be Hazardous to Your Health - And What to Do about It. 2011. (ENG., Illus.). 264p. pap. 17.95 (978-1-55643-958-2(X)) North Atlantic Bks.

Birenbaum, Arnold. Remaking Chronic Care in the Age of Health Care Reform: Changes for Lower Cost, Higher Quality Treatment, 1 vol. 2011. 205p. 48.00 (978-0-313-39888-9(7), A3659C); E-Book **(978-0-313-39889-6(5)**, Praeger Pubs.) Greenwood Publishing Group, Inc.

Bodach, Diane LaRae. Straw into Gold: Illness, Loss, & Hardship As a Path to Inner Peace. 340p. 2012. E-Book (978-1-57733-332-6(2,) 2011. pap. 19.95 (978-1-57733-223-7(7)) Blue Dolphin Publishing, Inc.

Bricker, J. Timothy, et al, eds. Adults with Childhood Illnesses: Considerations for Practice. 2011. (Health, Medicine & Human Development Ser.). (ENG., Illus.). XXII, 299p. 210.00 **(978-3-11-916189-3(6))**; 140.00 **(978-3-11-025521-8(9))** De Gruyter, Walter Inc.

Brown, Wayne. Alone in My Universe: Struggling with an Orphan Disease in an Unsympathetic World. 2011. 344p. 33.95 (978-1-4502-9593-2(2)); pap. 23.95 (978-1-4502-9592-5(4)) iUniverse, Inc.

Bruera, Eduardo, et al. Textbook of Palliative Medicine. 2009. (ENG., Illus.). xxxi, 1095p. pap. 99.50 (978-0-340-96624-2(6)) Hodder Arnold Pubs.

Busse, R., et al. Tackling Chronic Disease in Europe: Strategies, Interventions & Challenges. 2010. (Observatory Studies Ser.). (ENG., Illus.). 131p. pap. 36.00 (978-92-890-4192-8(7)) World Health Organization.

Cadena, Cirilo H. GarcíA, et al, eds. Chronic Diseases & Medication-Adherence Behaviors: Psychological Research in Ibero-American Countries. 2012. (Health Psychology Research Focus Ser.). 246p. 140.00 **(978-1-61470-639-7(5))** Nova Science Pubs., Inc.

Carter, Brian S., et al, eds. Palliative Care for Infants, Children, & Adolescents: A Practical Handbook. 2nd ed. 2011. (ENG., Illus.). 560p. (gr. 17). 70.00 (978-1-4214-0148-5(7)); pap. 35.00 (978-1-4214-0149-2(5)) Johns Hopkins Univ. Pr.

Cazzola, Mario, et al, eds. Chronic Obstructive Pulmonary Disease: Outcomes & Biomarkers. 2009. ring bd. 229.95 (978-1-4200-8460-3(7), Informa Healthcare) Taylor & Francis Group GBR. Dist: Taylor & Francis Group.

Challem, Jack. The Inflammation Syndrome: Your Nutrition Plan for Great Health, Weight Loss & Pain-Free Living. 2nd rev. ed. 2010. (ENG., Illus.). 272p. pap. 14.95 (978-0-470-44085-8(6), Wiley) Wiley, John & Sons, Inc.

Chan, Fong, et al. Understanding Psychosocial Adjustment to Chronic Illness & Disability: A Handbook for Evidence-Based Practitioners in Rehabilitation. 2009. (Illus.). xvii, 584p. (978-0-8261-2386-2(4)) Springer.

Clotfelter, Kevin D. Who Writes a Book Because They're Angry?, 1 vol. 2009. 49p. pap. 16.95 (978-1-60813-940-8(9)) PublishAmerica, Inc.

Cohen, Richard M. Strong at the Broken Places: Voices of Illness, a Chorus of Hope. 2009. (ENG.). 352p. pap. 14.99 (978-0-06-076312-1(4), HarperPerennial) HarperCollins Pubs.

Collins, Gary R. Usted Puede Hacer la Diferencia.Tr. of You Can Make a Difference. (SPA.). 295p. (978-1-56063-506-2(1)) Editorial Unilit.

Colp, Ralph, Jr. Darwin's Illness. 2008. (ENG.). 368p. 44.95 (978-0-8130-3231-3(8)) Univ. Pr. of Florida.

Committee on Living Well with Chronic Disease: Public Action to Reduce Disability and Improve Functioning and Quality of Life & Institute of Medicine. Living Well with Chronic Illness: A Call for Public Health Action. 2012. (ENG.). 330p. pap. 61.75 **(978-0-309-22127-6(7))** National Academies Pr.

Committee on Qualification of Biomarkers and Surrogate Endpoints in Chronic Disease & Institute of Medicine. Perspectives on Biomarker & Surrogate Endpoint Evaluation: Discussion Forum Summary. 2011. (ENG.). 140p. pap. 33.75 (978-0-309-16324-8(2)) National Academies Pr.

Committee on Qualifications of Biomarkers and Surrogate Endpoints in Chronic Disease & Institute of Medicine. Evaluation of Biomarkers & Surrogate Endpoints in Chronic Disease. 2010. (ENG.). 336p. pap. 47.00 (978-0-309-15129-0(5)) National Academies Pr.

Cotter, Caitlin. There Is Something You Should Know. 2010. 60p. pap. (978-3-8383-5308-1(0)) Lambert Academic Publishing.

Coughlin, Steven S. Post-Traumatic Stress Disorder & Chronic Health Conditions. 2012. **(978-0-87553-016-1(8))** American Public Health Assn.

Cram101 Textbook Reviews & Cram101 Textbook Reviews. Outlines & Highlights for Chronic Graft Versus Host Disease: Interdisciplinary Management by Steven Z. Pavletic Edited by Georgia B. Vogelsang, ISBN. 2011. 160p. pap. 29.95 **(978-1-61461-217-9(X))** Cram101 Inc.

—Outlines & Highlights for Lifestyle Modifications in Pharmacotherapy by Thomas L Lenz. 2011. 100p. pap. 27.95 **(978-1-61830-822-1(X))** Cram101 Inc.

Cummings, Sherry M. & Kropf, Nancy P. Handbook of Psychosocial Interventions with Older Adults: Evidence-Based Approaches. 2008. (Journal of Gerontological Social Work Ser.: No. 50). (978-0-7890-3831-9(5)); 362p. (978-0-7890-3829-6(3)); 362p. (978-0-7890-3830-2(7)) Haworth Pr., Inc., The.

Cutler, David M. Health at Older Ages: The Causes & Consequences of Declining Disability among the Elderly. Wise, David A., ed. 2009. (National Bureau of Economic Research Conference Report). (Illus.). 336p. 115.00 (978-0-226-13231-0(5)) Univ. of Chicago Pr.

D'Arcy, Yvonne M. Compact Clinical Guide to Chronic Pain Management: Evidence-Based Approach for Primary Care. 2010. (Illus.). 240p. (978-0-8261-0540-0(8)) Springer Publishing Co., Inc.

Dickman, Andrew & Simpson, Karen H., eds. Chronic Pain. 2008. (Oxford Pain Management Library Ser.). (Illus.). 152p. pap. 24.95 (978-0-19-923028-0(5)) Oxford Univ. Pr., Inc.

Din, Ahmad, et al. Barley ß-Glucan: Functional Beverage for Chronic Diseases Management. 2011. 160p. pap. **(978-3-8443-0782-5(6))** Lambert Academic Publishing.

Dite, P., et al, eds. From Chronic Inflammation to Cancer: Falk Symposium 173 June 4-5, 2010, Brno. 2010. (Illus.). 128p. (978-3-8055-9653-4(7)) Karger, S. AG.

—From Chronic Inflammation to Cancer Vol. 28, Nos. 4-5: Falk Symposium 173, Brno, June 2010. Special Issue: Digestive Diseases 2010. 2010. (Illus.). 128p. pap. (978-3-8055-9611-4(1)) Karger, S. AG.

Dorland, John & McColl, Mary. Emerging Approaches to Chronic Disease Management in Primary Health Care. 2007. (School of Policy Studies). (ENG., Illus.). 224p. (C). per. 34.95 (978-1-55339-130-2(6)) Queen's Univ., Schl. of Policy Studies CAN. Dist: McGill-Queen's Univ. Pr.

Douglas, Donna-Beth. Hope on the Horizon: Breakthrough Natural Solutions for Preventing & Reversing Chronic Disease. alt. ed. 2006. 252p. pap. 29.95 (978-0-9789290-0-8(4)) Chancellor Publishing.

Downs, Alan. Untitled Book On Dysthymia. Date not set. mass mkt. (978-0-312-98613-1(0), St. Martin's Paperbacks) St. Martin's Pr.

Ekeanyanwu, Chukwuma & NWANKWO, Olisa. Nutritional Pharmacology of Dietary Phytochemicals. 2011. 144p. pap. **(978-3-8433-9334-8(6))** Lambert Academic Publishing.

Essex, Dana. Adaptation to Chronic Illness. 2010. 96p. pap. (978-3-8383-6563-3(1)) Lambert Academic Publishing.

Estwick, David. Eating Patterns & Chronic Disease: Introducing 'the Living Healthy System' 2007. 106p. pap. 13.00 (978-0-8059-7419-5(9)) Dorrance Publishing Co., Inc.

Falvo, Donna. Medical & Psychosocial Aspects of Chronic Illness & Disability. 3rd rev. ed. 2007. 572p. pap. 121.95 (978-0-7637-5766-3(7)) 4th ed. 2010. 693p. pap. 110.95 (978-1-4496-2570-2(3)) Jones & Bartlett Learning, LLC.

Falvo, Donna R. Medical & Psychosocial Aspects of Chronic Illness & Disability. 4th rev. ed. 2008. (Illus.). 693p. 97.95 (978-0-7637-4461-8(1)) Jones & Bartlett Learning, LLC.

Field, Marilyn J. & Jette, Alan M., eds. The Future of Disability in America. 2007. (ENG., Illus.). 618p. 59.95 (978-0-309-10472-2(6)) National Academies Pr.

Finestone, Hillel M. The Pain Detective, Every Ache Tells a Story: Understanding How Stress & Emotional Hurt Become Chronic Physical Pain, 1 vol. 2009. (Praeger Series on Contemporary Health & Living Ser.). (Illus.). 227p. 44.95 (978-0-313-35993-4(8), C35993, Praeger Pubs.) Greenwood Publishing Group, Inc.

Flanagan, Steven R., et al. Medical Aspects of Disability: A Handbook for the Rehabilitation Professional. 4th ed. 2010. xvii, 761p. (978-0-8261-2783-9(5)); (978-0-8261-2784-6(3)) Springer.

Flick, Uwe & Röhnsch, Gundula. Gesundheit auf der Straße: Gesundheitsvorstellungen und Umgang mit Krankheit im Kontext von Jugendobdachlosigkeit. 2008. (Illus.). 287p. pap. (978-3-7799-1973-5(7)) Juventa Verlag GmbH.

Freye, Enno. Acquired Mitochondropathy - A New Paradigm in Western Medicine Explaining Chronic Diseases: The Safety Guide for Prevention & Therapy of Chronic Ailments. 2011. (ENG., Illus.). x, 392p. 209.00 **(978-94-007-2035-0(1)**, 9400720351) Springer.

Garrison, Susan E. Understanding Medicare's NCCI Edits: Logic & Interpretation of the Edits. 2009. 119.95 (978-1-60359-196-6(6)) American Medical Assn.

Gerhart, Ursula C. & Marley, James A. Caring for the Chronically Mentally Ill. 2nd ed. 2010. (ENG.). (C). pap. 70.95 (978-0-534-64246-4(2)) Brooks/Cole.

Ginès, Pere, et al, eds. Chronic Liver Failure: Mechanisms & Management. 2010. (Clinical Gastroenterology Ser.). (Illus.). xviii, 590p. 239.00 (978-1-60761-865-2(6), 1607618656) Humana Pr.

González, Virginia, et al. Tomando Control de Su Salud: Una Guia para el Manejo de Las Enfermedades del Corazon, Diabetes, Asma, Bronquitis, Enfisema y Otros Problemas Cronicos. 2nd ed. 2007. (SPA & ENG., Illus.). 392p. pap. 18.95 (978-1-933503-09-7(2)) Bull Publishing Co.

Green, Ken. The End of Stigma? 2008. 192p. 140.00 (978-0-415-37624-2(6)); pap. 43.95 (978-0-415-37625-9(4)) Routledge.

Greenberg, Tamara McClintock. When Someone You Love Has a Chronic Illness: Hope & Help for Those Providing Support. 2012. pap. 13.99 **(978-1-59955-939-1(0)**, Plain Sight Publishing) Cedar Fort, Inc./CFI Distribution.

Greene, Jeremy A. Prescribing by Numbers: Drugs & the Definition of Disease. 2008. (ENG., Illus.). 336p. (gr. 17). pap. 26.00 (978-0-8018-9100-7(0)) Johns Hopkins Univ. Pr.

Grey House Publishing, creator. The Complete Directory for People with Chronic Illness. 8th ed. 2007. (Complete Directory for People with Chronic Illness Ser.). 912p. per. 165.00 (978-1-59237-183-9(3)) Grey Hse. Publishing.

Gully, James Manby. WaterCure in Chronic Diseases. 2006. pap. 36.95 (978-1-4286-4268-3(4)) Kessinger Publishing, LLC.

Harpham, Wendy Schlessel & Harpham, Wendy. Happiness in a Storm: Facing Illness & Embracing Life as a Healthy Survivor. 2006. (ENG.). 400p. per. 18.95 (978-0-393-32905-6(4), 32905) Norton, W. W. & Co., Inc.

Harris, Randall E. Inflammation in the Pathogenesis of Chronic Diseases: The COX-2 Controversy. 2007. (Subcellular Biochemistry Ser.). (Illus.). 340p. 229.00 (978-1-4020-5687-1(7)) Springer.

Hewitt-Taylor, Jaqui. Children with Complex & Continuing Health Needs: The Experiences of Children, Families & Care Staff. 2007. (ENG.). 240p. pap. (978-1-84310-502-2(0)) Kingsley, Jessica Ltd.

Hill, Pamela. Common Skin Diseases: A Handbook for the Aesthetician. 2007. (ENG., Illus.). 288p. (C). per. 56.95 (978-1-4018-8170-2(X), Milady Publishing Co.) Delmar Cengage Learning.

Hoffmann, Erik C. Health-Related Quality of Life. 2009. (Public Health in the 21st Century Ser.). (Illus.). xii, 192p. 129.00 (978-1-60741-723-1(5), Nova Biomedical Bks.) Nova Science Pubs., Inc.

Holtackers, Thomas R. It Takes Courage: Coping with Chronic Illness. 2007. 192p. 15.99 (978-0-9789333-0-2(3), Courage Pr.) M S S U X, Unlimited.

Impact of Duplex Scanning in the Management of Chronic. 26.50 (978-91-554-4995-7(6)) Almqvist & Wiksell International SWE. Dist: Coronet Bks.

Irwig, Les, et al. Evidence-Based Medical Monitoring: From Principles to Practice. Irwig, Les et al, eds. 2008. (Evidence-Based Medicine Ser.). (ENG., Illus.). 376p. pap. 111.95 (978-1-4051-5399-7(7)) Wiley, John & Sons, Inc.

Jaff, Jennifer. Friday Tired: A Feminist Rant on Healthcare in America in the 21st Century. 2007. 132p. (ENG.). 23.95 (978-0-595-69016-9(5)); per. 13.95 (978-0-595-44850-0(X)) iUniverse, Inc

Jain. Chronic Pain. rev. ed. 2010. 165p. pap. 22.95 (978-0-7637-8604-5(7)) Jones & Bartlett Learning, LLC.

Jensen, Mark P. Hypnosis for Chronic Pain Management: Therapist Guide, 1 vol. 2011. (Treatments That Work Ser.). (Illus.). 304p. pap. 45.00 (978-0-19-977237-7(1)) Oxford Univ. Pr., Inc.

John, Walter. Solace: How Caregivers & Others Can Relate, Listen, & Respond Effectively to a Chronically Ill Person. 2011. (ENG.). 224p. pap. 14.95 (978-1-933503-62-2(9)) Bull Publishing Co.

Kash, Peter Morgan, et al. Freedom from Disease: The Breakthrough Approach to Preventing Cancer, Heart Disease, Alzheimer's, & Depression by Controlling Insulin. 2009. (ENG.). 272p. pap. 14.95 (978-0-312-35870-9(9), St. Martin's Griffin) St. Martin's Pr.

Kearney, Mark, ed. Chronic Heart Failure. 2009. (Oxford Cardiology Library). (Illus.). 144p. pap. 24.95 (978-0-19-954233-8(3)) Oxford Univ. Pr., Inc.

Kendall-Tackett, Kathleen A., et al, eds. The Psychoneuroimmunology of Chronic Disease: Exploring the Links Between Inflammation, Stress, & Illness. 2009. (Illus.). x, 263p. 59.95 (978-1-4338-0476-2(X)) American Psychological Assn.

Kingsbury, Leigh Ann Creaney. People Planning Ahead: A Guide to Communicating Healthcare & End of Life Wishes. 2008. (978-0-940898-98-1(5)) American Assn. on Intellectual & Developmental Disabilities.

Knapp, Karl. Raw Emotion. 2011. 84p. pap. 41.99 **(978-1-4568-4124-9(6))** Xlibris Corp.

Knotkova, Helena, et al, eds. Neural Plasticity in Chronic Pain. 2011. **(978-1-61324-657-3(9))** Nova Science Pubs., Inc.

Krueger, Hans, et al. The Health Impact of Smoking & Obesity & What to Do about It. 2007. (Illus.). 352p. (ENG.). (978-0-8020-9200-7(4)); pap. (978-0-8020-9441-4(4)) Univ. of Toronto Pr.

Larsen, Pamala D. & Lubkin, Ilene Morof. Chronic Illness: Impact & Intervention. 8th ed. 2011. 716p. 96.95 **(978-1-4496-4905-0(X))** Jones & Bartlett Learning, LLC.

Leo, Raphael J. Clinical Manual of Pain Management in Psychiatry. 2007. 267p. per. 64.00 (978-1-58562-275-7(3)) American Psychiatric Publishing, Inc.

Lerner, Barron H. When Illness Goes Public: Celebrity Patients & How We Look at Medicine. 2009. (ENG., Illus.). 352p. pap. 19.95 (978-0-8018-9227-1(9)) Johns Hopkins Univ. Pr.

Livneh, Hanoch, ed. Coping with Chronic Illness & Disability: Theoretical, Empirical, & Clinical Aspects. 2007. (ENG., Illus.). xxvi, 430p. 109.00 (978-0-387-48668-0(2), 0387486682) Springer.

Lollar, Donald, ed. Launching into Adulthood: An Integrated Response to Support Transition of Youth with Chronic Health Conditions & Disabilities. 2010. (Illus.). 256p. 44.95 (978-1-59857-102-8(8)) Brookes, Paul H. Publishing Co.

Lopatin, Edward J. Manage Your Chronic Illness, Your Life Depends on It: One hundred recommendations to help prevent illness & to manage your physicians, hospital Stay. 2011. 128p. 29.99 **(978-1-4628-4743-3(9))**; pap. 19.99 **(978-1-4628-4742-6(0))** Xlibris Corp.

Lorig, Kate, et al. Living a Healthy Life with Chronic Conditions: For Ongoing Physical & Mental Health Conditions. 2007. (ENG.). 408p. pap. 18.95 (978-1-933503-08-0(4)) Bull Publishing Co.

—Living a Healthy Life with Chronic Conditions: Self-Management of Heart Disease, Fatigue, Arthritis, Worry, Diabetes, Frustration, Asthma, Pain, Emphysema, & Others. 3rd ed. 2006. (ENG., Illus.). 384p. pap. 18.95 (978-1-933503-01-1(7)) Bull Publishing Co.

Manderson, Lenore & Smith-Morris, Carolyn, eds. Chronic Conditions, Fluid States: Chronicity & the Anthropology of Illness. 2010. (Studies in Medical Anthropology Ser.). (ENG., Illus.). 336p. 75.00 (978-0-8135-4746-6(6)) Rutgers Univ. Pr.

Marcus, Dawn A. Chronic Pain: A Primary Care Guide to Practical Management. 2nd ed. 2008. (Current Clinical Practice Ser.). (Illus.). 438p. 129.00 (978-1-60327-464-7(2)) Humana Pr.

—Headache & Chronic Pain Syndromes: The Case-Based Guide to Targeted Assessment & Treatment. 2006. (Current Clinical Practice Ser.). (Illus.). 209p. 119.00 (978-1-58829-745-7(4), 1588297454) Humana Pr.

Margereson, Carl & Trenoweth, Steve, eds. Developing Holistic Care for Long-Term Conditions. 2009. (ENG., Illus.). 370p. 135.00 (978-0-415-46080-4(8)) Routledge.

Mars, Laura, ed. Complete Directory for People with Chronic Illness. 2011. 2500p. pap. 165.00 (978-1-59237-741-1(6)) Grey Hse. Publishing.

Mars-Proietti, Laura, ed. Complete Directory for People with Chronic Illness: 2009/10. 9th rev. ed. 2009. 1200p. pap. 165.00 (978-1-59237-415-1(8)) Grey Hse. Publishing.

Martensen, Robert. A Life Worth Living: A Doctor's Reflections on Illness in a High-Tech Era. 2009. (ENG., Illus.). 240p. pap. 14.00 (978-0-374-53203-1(6)) Farrar, Straus & Giroux.

Martinez, Fernando J. & Wedzicha, Jadwiga Anna. Chronic Obstructive Pulmonary Disease Exacerbations. Wedzicha, Wisia & Martinez, Fernando J., eds. Wedzicha, Jadwiga A., ed. 2008. (ENG., Illus.). 456p. 250.00 (978-1-4200-7086-6(X), Informa Healthcare) Taylor & Francis Group GBR. Dist: Taylor & Francis Group.

Martirosyan, Danik M. Functional Foods for Chronic Diseases. 2006. per. 59.00 (978-0-9767535-2-0(9)) D & A Inc.

Martz, Erin & Livneh, Hanoch, eds. Coping with Chronic Illness & Disability: Theoretical, Empirical, & Clinical Aspects. 2010. (ENG., Illus.). xxvi, 430p. pap. 109.00 (978-1-4419-4308-8(0), 1441943080) Springer.

McColl, Mary Ann & Dorland, John. Emerging Approaches to Chronic Disease Management in Primary Health Care. 2007. (School of Policy Studies). (ENG., Illus.). 224p. (C). 95.00 (978-1-55339-131-9(4)) Queen's Univ., Schl. of Policy Studies CAN. Dist: McGill-Queen's Univ. Pr.

Mete, ed. Economic Implications of Chronic Illness & Disability in Eastern Europe & the Former Soviet Union. 2008. (ENG., Illus.). 152p. per. 25.00 (978-0-8213-7337-8(4), 9780821373378) World Bank Pubns.

Meyer, Maria M. & Derr, Paula. Chronic Lung Disease: A Guide for Caregivers. 2007. (Comfort of Home Ser.). (ENG., Illus.). 360p. per. 24.95 (978-0-9787903-1-8(6)) CareTrust Pubns., LLC.

Miles, Ann. Chronic Conditions, Fluid States: Chronicity & the Anthropology of Illness. Manderson, Lenore & Smith-Morris, Carolyn, eds. 2010. (Studies in Medical Anthropology Ser.). (ENG., Illus.). 336p. pap. 29.95 (978-0-8135-4747-3(4)) Rutgers Univ. Pr.

Milham, Samuel. Dirty Electricity: Electrification & the Diseases of Civilization. 2010. 120p. 22.95 (978-1-4502-3822-9(X)); pap. 12.95 (978-1-4502-3821-2(1)) iUniverse, Inc.

Miller, Maria & Miller, Daniel. My American Dream: One Woman's Journey Living with a Chronic Disease. 2010. 192p. 24.99 (978-1-4520-7699-7(5)); pap. 18.99 (978-1-4520-7698-0(7)) AuthorHouse.

Molla, Michael T. & Madans, Jennifer H. Life Expectancy, Free of Chronic Condition-Induced Activity Limitations among White & Black Americans, 2000-2006. 2010. (978-0-8406-0645-7(1)) National Ctr. for Health Statistics.

Montenegro, Mary. Pelvic Pain: Causes, Symptoms & Treatments. 2011. (Human Anatomy & Physiology Pain & its Origins, Diagnosis & Treatments Ser.). 241p. 95.00 **(978-1-61324-656-6(0))** Nova Science Pubs., Inc.

Morewitz, Stephen. Chronic Diseases & Health Care: New Trends in Diabetes, Arthritis, Osteoporosis, Fibromyalgia, Low Back Pain, Cardiovascular Disease, & Cancer. 2010. (ENG.). x, 376p. pap. 99.00 (978-1-4419-3953-1(9), 1441939539) Springer.

Morewitz, Stephen & Goldstein, Mark L. Aging & Chronic Disorders. 2010. (ENG.). xiv, 236p. pap. 59.95 (978-1-4419-4362-0(5), 1441943625) Springer.

Morewitz, Stephen J. & Goldstein, Mark L. Aging & Chronic Disorders. 2007. (ENG.). xiv, 236p. 59.95 (978-0-387-70856-0(1), 0387708561) Springer.

Moss, Pamela. Contesting Illness: Processes & Practices. Teghtsoonian, Katherine & Moss, Pamela, eds. 2008. (ENG.). 368p. pap. (978-0-8020-9365-3(5)) Univ. of Toronto Pr.

Nack, Adina. Damaged Goods? Women Living with Incurable Sexually Transmitted Diseases. 2008. (ENG., Illus.). 264p. (C). 66.50 (978-1-59213-707-7(5)); pap. 23.95 (978-1-59213-708-4(3)) Temple Univ. Pr.

Naschitz, Jochanan E., ed. Challenges in Acute Geriatric Care. 2009. 79.00 (978-1-60741-309-7(4)) Nova Science Pubs., Inc.

Natelson, Benjamin H. Your Symptoms Are Real: What to Do When Your Doctor Says Nothing Is Wrong. 2007. (ENG., Illus.). 288p. 24.95 (978-0-471-74028-5(4), Wiley) Wiley, John & Sons, Inc.

Newman. Chronic Illness: A Psychosocia. 2008. 192p. (C). 119.95 (978-0-335-21942-1(X), 9780335219421); pap. 39.95 (978-0-335-21941-4(1), 9780335219414) McGraw-Hill Education GBR. (Open University Pr.). Dist: McGraw-Hill Cos., The.

Niel-Asher, Simeon. The Concise Book of Trigger Points, Revised Edition. rev. ed. 2008. (ENG., Illus.). 216p. pap. 29.95 (978-1-55643-745-8(5)) North Atlantic Bks.

Nolte, E. ., et al. Managing Chronic Conditions: Experience in Eight Countries. 2009. (EURO Nonserial Publication Ser.). (ENG., Illus.). 198p. pap. 48.00 (978-92-890-4294-9(X)) World Health Organization.

Norman, Robert A. & Ruescher, Linda. Chronic Illness. 2009. 178p. pap. 22.95 (978-0-7637-7764-7(1)) Jones & Bartlett Learning, LLC.

Northrop, Dorothy E., et al. Health Insurance Resources: A Guide for People with Chronic Disease & Disability. 2nd ed. 2006. (Health Insurance Resources: A Guide for People with Chronic Disease Ser.). (ENG., Illus.). 232p. per. 26.95 (978-1-932603-34-7(4)) Demos Medical Publishing, LLC.

Nuovo, Jim, ed. Chronic Disease Management. 2006. (Illus.). 371p. per. 84.95 (978-0-387-32927-7(7), 0387329277) Springer.

O'Donohue, William T. Behavioral Approaches to Chronic Disease in Adolescence: A Guide to Integrative Care. 2009. (ENG., Illus.). xii, 354p. 179.00 (978-0-387-87686-3(3), 0387876863) Springer.

Otis, John. Managing Chronic Pain: A Cognitive-Behavioral Therapy Approach Workbook. 2007. (Treatments That Work Ser.). (ENG., Illus.). 144p. pap., wbk. ed. 27.95 (978-0-19-532917-9(1)) Oxford Univ. Pr., Inc.

Otis, John D. Managing Chronic Pain: A Cognitive-Behavioral Therapy Approach. 2007. (Treatments That Work Ser.). (ENG., Illus.). 128p. (C). per., instr.'s gde. ed. 37.95 (978-0-19-532916-2(3)) Oxford Univ. Pr., Inc.

Paterson, Barbara L., et al, eds. Translating Chronic Illness Research into Practice. 2010. (ENG., Illus.). 224p. pap. 47.99 (978-1-4051-5965-4(0), Wiley-Blackwell) Wiley, John & Sons, Inc.

Paterson, Grace. Boundary Infostructures for Chronic Disease. 2008. 192p. pap. (978-3-639-02539-2(3)) VDM Verlag Dr. Mueller e.K.

Perez, Carlos Ayan. Aerobic Exercise in Special Populations. Carral, Jose Maria Cancela & Martinez, Silvia Varela, eds. 2010. (Sports & Athletics Preparation, Performance, & Psychology Ser.). 111p. pap. 43.00 (978-1-60876-697-0(7)) Nova Science Pubs., Inc.

Phaswana-Mafuya, Nancy & Tassiopoulos, Dimitri. Non-Communicable Diseases (NCDs) in Developing Countries. 2011. (Series: Public Health in the 21st Century Ser.). (Illus.). 262p. 95.00 (978-1-61209-996-5(3)) Nova Science Pubs., Inc.

Pool, Robert. Nutrigenomics & Beyond: Informing the Future - Workshop Summary. 2007. (ENG., Illus.). 90p. pap. 21.00 (978-0-309-10489-0(0)) National Academies Pr.

Randall, Sue & Ford, Helen, eds. Long Term Conditions: A Guide for Nurses & Healthcare Professionals. 2011. (ENG., Illus.). 344p. pap. 41.99 (978-1-4443-3249-0(X), Wiley-Blackwell) Wiley, John & Sons, Inc.

Rea, William J. Reversibility of Chronic Degenerative Disease: Diagnostic Considerations. 2012. (ENG., Illus.). 442p. 139.95 **(978-1-4398-1346-1(9)**, CRC Press) Taylor & Francis Group GBR. Dist: Taylor & Francis Group.

—Reversibility of Chronic Degenerative Disease & Hypersensitivity Vol. 1: Regulating Mechanisms. 2010. (ENG., Illus.). 594p. 139.95 (978-1-4398-1342-3(6), CRC Press) Taylor & Francis Group GBR. Dist: Taylor & Francis Group.

—Reversibility of Chronic Generative Disease & Hypersensitivity Vol. 2: Clinical Manifestations. 2012. (ENG., Illus.). 442p. 139.95 (978-1-4398-1343-0(4), CRC Press) Taylor & Francis Group GBR. Dist: Taylor & Francis Group.

Remington, Patrick L., et al. Chronic Disease Epidemiology & Control. 3rd ed. 2009. (978-0-87553-192-2(X)) American Public Health Assn.

Rennard, Stephen I., et al, eds. Clinical Management of Chronic Obstructive Pulmonary Disease. 2nd rev. ed. 2007. (Lung Biology in Health & Disease Ser.: Vol. 222). (ENG., Illus.). 608p. 300.00 (978-0-8493-7587-3(8), Informa Healthcare) Taylor & Francis Group GBR. Dist: Taylor & Francis Group.

Ritsatakis, A. & Maka, P. Gaining Health. 2009. (EURO NON SERIAL PUBLICATIONS Ser.). 272p. pap. 60.00 (978-92-890-4179-9(X)) World Health Organization.

Roach, Helmtrud I., et al, eds. Epigenetic Aspects of Chronic Diseases. 2011. (ENG., Illus.). xviii, 238p. 169.00 (978-1-84882-643-4(5), 1848826435) Springer.

Roitman, Jeff & La Fontaine, Tom. The Exercise Professional's Guide to Optimizing Health: Strategies for Preventing & Reducing Chronic Disease. 2011. (ENG., Illus.). 288p. pap. 46.99 (978-0-7817-7548-9(5)) Lippincott Williams & Wilkins.

Ronco, C. & Levin, N. W., eds. Advances in Chronic Kidney Disease 2008: 10th International Conference on Dialysis, Cancun, January 2008 Including Abstracts: Special Issue: Blood Purification 2008, Vol. 26, No. 1. 2008. (Illus.). 132p. (C). pap. (978-3-8055-8467-8(9)) Karger, S. AG.

Rones, Ramel. Sunset Tai Chi: Simplified Tai Chi for Relaxation & Longevity. 2011. 360p. pap. 20.95 (978-1-59439-212-2(9)) YMAA Pubn. Ctr.

Rushing, Pattie. Skin for Skin: A Woman's Journey Through Ulcerative Colitis. 2009. 194p. pap. 24.95 (978-1-60813-976-7(X)) PublishAmerica, Inc.

Ryan, W. C. On Eagles' Wings: A Memoir about Faith,Courage & Patriotism. 2011. 200p. 15.95 (978-0-9713703-0-2(3)) Crown, Thomas Publishing.

Sage, Crystal. Heal Beneath the Surface: Become Your Own Best Healer Using True Healing Solutions. 2011. 316p. pap. 29.99 **(978-1-4567-1238-9(1))** AuthorHouse.

Sage, Nigel, et al. CBT for Chronic Illness & Palliative Care: A Workbook & Toolkit. 2008. (ENG., Illus.). 386p. pap. 71.95 (978-0-470-51707-9(7), Wiley-Interscience) Wiley, John & Sons, Inc.

Saito, Shigeru. Chronic Total Occlusions. Saito, Shigeru & Waksman, Ron, eds. 2009. (ENG., Illus.). 256p. 146.95 (978-1-4051-5703-2(8), Wiley-Blackwell) Wiley, John & Sons, Inc.

Salusky, Isidro B., ed. Accumulation of Metals & Minerals in Chronic Kidney Disease, Vol. 23. (Illus.). (978-3-8055-7934-6(9)) Karger, S. AG.

Sands, Roberta G. & Gellis, Zvi D. Clinical Social Work Practice in Behavioral Mental Health: Toward Evidence-Based Practice. 3rd rev. ed. 2010. (ENG.). 368p. (C). pap. 129.80 (978-0-205-82016-0(6), Prentice Hall) Prentice Hall PTR.

Satterfield, Jason M. A Cognitive-Behavioral Approach to the Beginning of the End of Life: Minding the Body. 2008. (Treatments That Work Ser.). (ENG., Illus.). 256p. pap. 42.95 (978-0-19-534163-8(5)) Oxford Univ. Pr., Inc.

—Minding the Body Workbook. 2008. (Treatments That Work Ser.). (ENG., Illus.). 208p. pap. 27.95 (978-0-19-534164-5(3)) Oxford Univ. Pr., Inc.

Saxton, John, ed. Exercise & Chronic Disease. 2011. (ENG., Illus.). 400p. (C). 150.00 (978-0-415-49860-9(0)); pap. 63.95 (978-0-415-49861-6(9)) Routledge.

Schatman, Michael E., ed. Ethical Issues in Chronic Pain Management. 2007. (Pain Management Ser.: Vol. 1). (ENG., Illus.). 328p. 250.00 (978-0-8493-9268-9(3), Informa Healthcare) Taylor & Francis Group GBR. Dist: Taylor & Francis Group.

Schatman, Michael E. & Campbell, Alexandra, eds. Chronic Pain Management: Guidelines for Multidisciplinary Program Development. 2007. (Pain Management Ser.: Vol. 3). (Illus.). 284p. 100.00 (978-1-4200-4512-3(1), Informa Healthcare) Taylor & Francis Group GBR. Dist: Taylor & Francis Group.

Schattner, Ami & Knobler, Hilla, eds. Metabolic Aspects of Chronic Liver Disease. 2008. (Illus.). 362p. 185.00 (978-1-60021-201-7(8)) Nova Science Pubs., Inc.

Schneider, Jennifer. Chronic Pain: The Complete Health Guide to the Causes & Treatment of Chronic Pain. 2nd ed. 2009. (Living With Ser.). (ENG., Illus.). 400p. pap. 16.95 (978-1-57826-285-4(2)) Hatherleigh Co., Ltd., The.

Schraeder, Cheryl & Shelton, Paul S., eds. Comprehensive Care Coordination for Chronically Ill Adults. 2011. (ENG., Illus.). 488p. pap. 64.99 **(978-0-8138-1194-9(5)**, Wiley-Blackwell) Wiley, John & Sons, Inc.

Schumm, Darla & Stoltzfus, Michael. Disability & Religious Diversity: Cross-Cultural & Inter-Religious Perspectives. 2011. (ENG., Illus.). 272p. 90.00 (978-0-230-11973-4(5)) Palgrave Macmillan.

Shannon, Joyce Brennfleck. Disease Management Sourcebook. 2008. (Health Reference Ser.). (Illus.). 622p. (C). 87.00 (978-0-7808-1002-0(3)) Omnigraphics, Inc.

Shimizu, Ichiro. Female Hepatology: Favorable Role of Female Factors in Chronic Liver Disease. 2009. (Hepatology Research & Clinical Developments Ser.). 9.00 (978-1-60741-692-0(1), Nova Biomedical Bks.) Nova Science Pubs., Inc.

Shoskes, Daniel A., ed. Chronic Prostatitis/Chronic Pelvic Pain Syndrome. (Current Clinical Urology Ser.). (Illus.). 2010. xiii, 278p. pap. 109.00 (978-1-61737-926-0(3), 1617379263) 2008. 278p. 99.00 (978-1-934115-27-5(4)) Humana Pr.

Slavin, K. V., ed. Peripheral Nerve Stimulation. 2011. (Progress in Neurological Surgery Ser.). (Illus.). 224p. (978-3-8055-9488-2(7)) Karger, S. AG.

Sperry, Len. Treatment of Chronic Medical Conditions: Cognitive-Behavioral Therapy Strategies & Integrative Treatment Protocols. 2008. 248p. 49.95 (978-1-4338-0389-5(5)) American Psychological Assn.

Springhouse Publishing Company Staff, ed. Chronic Disorders. 2008. (Incredibly Easy! Ser.). (ENG., Illus.). 384p. pap. 31.99 (978-0-7817-8688-1(6)) Lippincott Williams & Wilkins.

Stein, Andrew. Longing for Nothingness: Resistance, Denial, & the Place of Death in the Nursing Home. 2010. (ENG.). 194p. 57.99 (978-0-7657-0577-8(X), Aronson, Jason) Rowman & Littlefield Publishers, Inc.

Stephens, C.N.C., Patricia. Reversing Chronic Disease: A Journey Back to Health. 2010. pap. 14.99 (978-1-61566-197-8(2)) Tate Publishing & Enterprises, LLC.

Stuckler, David & Siegel, Karen. Sick Societies: Responding to the Global Challenge of Chronic Disease. 2011. (ENG., Illus.). 374p. 75.00 (978-0-19-957440-7(5)) Oxford Univ. Pr., Inc.

Suzana, Almoosawi. Polyphenols in Green Coffee Bean & Chocolate: Effect on Glucoregulatory Biomarkers Blood Pressure & Lipid Profile in Obesity. 2011. 304p. pap. **(978-3-639-33931-4(2))** VDM Verlag Dr. Mueller e.K.

Svenstrup, Jå Rgen & Svanholm, Gitte. Seize Life. 2011. 154p. pap. 29.90 **(978-87-7114-268-6(1))** Bks. on Demand.

Szabo, Jason. Incurable & Intolerable: Chronic Disease & Slow Death in Nineteenth-Century France. 2009. (ENG., Illus.). 310p. (C). 49.95 (978-0-8135-4545-5(5)) Rutgers Univ. Pr.

Taylor, Renee R. Cognitive Behavioral Therapy for Chronic Illness & Disability. 2010. (ENG., Illus.). xiv, 378p. pap. 79.95 (978-1-4419-3785-8(4), 1441937854) Springer.

Teghtsoonian, Katherine & Moss, Pamela, eds. Contesting Illness: Processes & Practices. 2008. (ENG.). 368p. pap. (978-0-8020-9512-1(7)) Univ. of Toronto Pr.

Temple, Norman J., et al, eds. Nutritional Health: Strategies for Disease Prevention. 2nd ed. 2010. (Nutrition & Health Ser.). (Illus.). 488p. pap. 119.00 (978-1-61737-580-4(2), 1617375802) Humana Pr.

Templet, Allison. Instructor Guide for the Textbook of Functional Medicine. 2007. (Illus.). cd-rom 75.00 (978-0-9773713-1-0(X)) Institute for Functional Medicine, The.

Trafton, Jodie Anne & Gordon, William P., eds. Best Practices in the Behavioral Management of Chronic Disease Volume I: Neuropsychiatric Disorders. 2007. (Illus.). 473p. pap. 80.00 (978-1-932745-15-3(7)) Institute for Disease Mgmt.

—Best Practices in the Behavioral Management of Chronic Disease Volume II: Other Medical Disorders. 2007. (Illus.). 434p. pap. 80.00 (978-1-932745-32-0(7)) Institute for Disease Mgmt.

—Best Practices in the Behavioral Management of Health from Preconception to Adolescence. 2008. (Illus.). 565p. pap. (978-1-932745-46-7(7)) Institute for Disease Mgmt.

Ventling, C. D., ed. Body Psychotherapy in Progressive & Chronic Disorders. (Illus.). (978-3-8055-7448-8(7)) Karger, S. AG.

Vercellini, Paolo, ed. Chronic Pelvic Pain. 2011. (GIP - Gynaecology in Practice Ser.: 6). (ENG., Illus.). 196p. pap. 83.95 (978-1-4443-3066-3(7), Wiley-Blackwell) Wiley, John & Sons, Inc.

Verma, Anju. An Integrated Approach for Ontology Based Personalized Modeling. 2010. 256p. pap. (978-3-8383-5153-7(3)) Lambert Academic Publishing.

Von Korff, Michael, et al, eds. Global Perspectives on Mental-Physical Comorbidity in the WHO World Mental Health Surveys. 2009. (ENG., Illus.). 340p. 126.00 (978-0-521-19959-9(X)) Cambridge Univ. Pr.

Wild, Chris, et al. Molecular Epidemiology of Chronic Diseases. 2008. (ENG., Illus.). 384p. 145.00 (978-0-470-02743-1(6), Wiley) Wiley, John & Sons, Inc.

Williamson, Peggie. Exercise for Special Populations. 2010. (ENG.). 448p. pap. 60.99 (978-0-7817-9779-5(9)) Lippincott Williams & Wilkins.

World Health Organization. Global Status Report on Noncommunicable Diseases 2010. 2011. (Nonserial Publication Ser.). (ENG.). 162p. pap. 48.00 **(978-92-4-156422-9(9))** World Health Organization.

—Prioritized Research Agenda for Prevention & Control of Noncommunicable Diseases. 2011. (Nonserial Publication Ser.). (ENG.). 55p. pap. 24.00 **(978-92-4-156420-5(2))** World Health Organization.

World Health Organization: Regional Office for the Western Pacific. Noncommunicable disease & Poverty: The need for pro-poor strategies in the Western Pacific Region; a Review. 2007. (WPRO Nonserial Publication Ser.). (ENG., Illus.). 92p. pap. 18.00 (978-92-9061-234-6(7)) World Health Organization.

World Health Organization: Regional Office For The Western Pacific. Noncommunicable Disease Risk Factors & Socioeconomic Inequalities: What Are the Links?; A Multicountry Analysis of Noncommunicable Disease Surveillance Data. 2011. 100p. pap. 18.00 (978-92-9061-474-6(9)) World Health Organization.

Yehuda, Shlomo & Mostofsky, David I., eds. Nutrients, Stress & Medical Disorders. 2010. (Nutrition & Health Ser.). (ENG., Illus.). 448p. pap. 189.00 (978-1-61737-566-8(7), 1617375667) Humana Pr.

CHRONIC DISEASES—NURSING

Boult, Chad. Guided Care: A New Nurse-Physician Partnership in Chronic Care. 2009. (Illus.). 200p. (978-0-8261-4411-9(X)) Springer.

Clarke, Victoria & Walsh, Andrew, eds. Fundamentals of Mental Health Nursing. 2009. (ENG., Illus.). 320p. pap. 59.99 (978-0-19-954774-6(2)) Oxford Univ. Pr., Inc.

Elster, Elizabeth J. Power Through Pain: Living with Reflex Neurovascular Dystrophy. 2007. 112p. per. 12.95 (978-0-595-43716-0(8)) iUniverse, Inc.

Lubkin, Ilene & Larsen, Pamala. Chronic Illness: Impact & Intervention. 7th rev. ed. 2008. 634p. 86.95 (978-0-7637-5126-5(X)) Jones & Bartlett Learning, LLC.

Lubkin, Ilene Morof & Larsen, Pamala D. Chronic Illness Impact & Interventions. 5th ed. 2006. pap. 10.95 (978-1-4288-1683-1(6)) Cram101 Inc.

Newman, Stanton, et al. Chronic Physical Illness: Self-Management & Behavioural Interventions. 2008. (ENG., Illus.). 240p. (C). pap. 49.00 (978-0-335-21786-1(9), 0335217869) McGraw-Hill Education GBR. Dist: McGraw-Hill Cos., The.

Snoddon, Janet. Case Management of Long Term Conditions: Principles & Practice for Nurses. 2010. (ENG.). 224p. pap. 52.99 *(978-1-4051-8005-4(6),* Wiley-Blackwell) Wiley, John & Sons, Inc.

Steed, Liz, et al. Chronic Physical Illness: Self-Management & Behavioural Interventions. 2008. (ENG., Illus.). 240p. (C). 127.00 *(978-0-335-21787-8(7),* 0335217877) McGraw-Hill Education GBR. Dist: McGraw-Hill Cos., The.

Wright, Kerri, et al. Long Term Conditions: Nursing Care & Management. 2011. (ENG., Illus.). 304p. pap. 46.99 *(978-1-4051-8338-3(1),* Wiley-Blackwell) Wiley, John & Sons, Inc.

CHRONIC DISEASES IN CHILDREN

Bandy, Roberta. A Mother's Search for Meaning: The Dance Goes On. 2nd ed. 2009. 9.99 *(978-0-7586-1777-4(1))* Concordia Publishing Hse.

Dempsey, Sharon. Extreme Parenting: Parenting Your Child with a Chronic Illness. 2008. (ENG.). 176p. pap. *(978-1-84310-619-7(1))* Kingsley, Jessica Ltd.

Donoghue, Elaine A. & Kraft, Colleen A. Managing Chronic Health Needs in Child Care & Schools: A Quick Reference Guide. 2009. (ENG.). 214p. pap. 47.00 *(978-1-58110-299-4(2))* American Academy of Pediatrics.

Falduto-Huspen, Laurie. Unveiled: An Unexpected Life. 2010. 200p. pap. 19.95 *(978-1-4490-3430-6(6))* AuthorHouse.

Hewitt-Taylor, Jaquelina. Providing Support at Home for Children & Young People Who Have Complex Health Needs. 2008. (ENG.). 216p. pap. 60.99 *(978-0-470-51731-4(X),* Wiley) Wiley, John & Sons, Inc.

Jackson Allen, Patricia, et al. Primary Care of the Child with a Chronic Condition. 5th ed. 2009. (ENG., Illus.). 880p. (C). 86.95 *(978-0-323-05877-3(9),* Mosby) Elsevier - Health Sciences Div.

Lambert, Beth & Kobliner, Victoria. A Compromised Generation: The Epidemic of Chronic Illness in America's Children. 2010. (ENG.). 358p. pap. 18.95 *(978-1-59181-096-4(5))* Sentient Pubns.

Morewitz, Stephen & Goldstein, Mark L. Chronic Disorders in Children & Adolescents. 2011. (ENG.). xiii, 282p. 169.00 *(978-1-4419-9763-0(6),* 1441997636) Springer.

Omar, Hatim, et al, eds. Adolescence & Chronic Illness. A Public Health Concern. 2010. (Health & Human Development (Joav Merrick - Series Editor - National Institute of Child Health & Human Development, Ministry of Social Affairs, Jerusalem) Ser.). (Illus.). x, 477p. 195.00 *(978-1-60876-628-4(4))* Nova Science Pubs., Inc.

CHRONIC FATIGUE SYNDROME

see also Epstein-Barr Virus Diseases

Adams, Alison. Chronic Fatigue, ME, & Fibromyalgia: The Natural Recovery Plan. 2010. (ENG.). 256p. pap. 19.95 *(978-1-906787-76-9(X),* Watkins Publishing) Duncan Baird Pubs. GBR. Dist: Sterling Publishing Co., Inc.

Allenby, Sasha. Joyful Recovery from Chronic Fatigue Syndrome/Me. 2008. (Illus.). 172p. 23.50 *(978-1-60693-145-5(8),* Strategic Bk. Publishing) AEG Literary Publishing Services, Inc.

Ann, Sheryl. Blue Highway Sunshine Route: Daily Reader for Those with Fibromyalgia & Chronic Fatigue Syndrome, 1 vol. 2010. 498p. pap. 29.95 *(978-1-60813-860-9(7))* PublishAmerica, Inc.

Bell, David. Andrea's Revolver. 2009. 115p. pap. 21.50 *(978-1-4452-2161-8(6))* Lulu Enterprises Inc.

Bell, David S. Cellular Hypoxia & Neuro-Immune Fatigue. 2007. 100p. pap. 14.95 *(978-1-59594-179-4(7),* Wingspan Pr.) WingSpan Publishing.

—Faces of CFS: Case Histories of Chronic Fatigue Syndrome. pap. 25.00 *(978-0-9707702-0-2(0))* MZR Publishing.

Bested, Alison C. & Logan, Alan C. Hope & Help for Chronic Fatigue Syndrome & Fibromyalgia. 2008. (Illus.). 254p. per. 18.95 *(978-1-58182-465-0(3),* Cumberland Hse.) Sourcebooks, Inc.

Bested, Alison C., et al. Hope & Help for Chronic Fatigue Syndrome & Fibromyalgia. 2nd ed. 2008. (ENG., Illus.). 286p. pap. 23.99 *(978-1-58182-670-8(2),* Cumberland Hse.) Sourcebooks, Inc.

Bharadvaj, Daivati. Natural Treatments for Chronic Fatigue Syndrome, 1 vol. 2007. (Complementary & Alternative Medicine Ser.). (Illus.). 216p. 44.95 *(978-0-275-99374-0(4),* C9374, Praeger Pubs.) Greenwood Publishing Group, Inc.

Blucher, Peter & Lynch, Alastair. Taking Nothing for Granted: A Sportsman's Fight Against Chronic Fatigue. 2008. 384p. *(978-0-7322-8811-2(6),* HarperSports) HarperCollins Pubs. Australia.

Brady, Tami. Strategies: A Chronic Fatigue Syndrome & Fibromyalgia Journey. 2008. 168p. per. 17.95 *(978-1-932690-48-4(4))* Loving Healing Pr., Inc.

Campling, Frankie & Sharpe, Michael. Chronic Fatigue Syndrome. 2nd ed. 2008. (Facts Ser.). (ENG., Illus.). 224p. pap. 24.95 *(978-0-19-923316-8(0))* Oxford Univ. Pr., Inc.

Chalder, Trudie A. Coping with Chronic Fatigue. (Illus.). x, 70p. *(978-0-85969-685-2(5),* Sheldon Press) SPCK Publishing.

Challem, Jack. No More Fatigue: Why You're So Tired & What You Can Do about It. 2011. (ENG., Illus.). 288p. 25.95 *(978-0-470-52545-6(2),* Wiley) Wiley, John & Sons, Inc.

Colbert, Don. The New Bible Cure for Chronic Fatigue & Fibromyalgia. 2011. E-Book ***(978-1-61638-430-2(1),*** Siloam Pr.) Charisma Media.

Cooper, Celeste. Integrative Therapies for Fibromyalgia, Chronic Fatigue Syndrome, & Myofascial Pain. 2010. (ENG.). 1p. pap. 34.95 *(978-1-59477-323-5(8),* Healing Arts Pr.) Inner Traditions International, Ltd.

Craggs-Hinton, Christine. The Chronic Fatigue Healing Diet. 128p. *(978-0-85969-878-8(5),* Sheldon Press) SPCK Publishing.

Downing-Orr, Kristina. Beating Chronic Fatigue: Your Step-by-Step Guide to Complete Recovery. 2013. (ENG., Illus.). 240p. pap. 13.95 ***(978-0-7499-4093-5(X))*** Piatkus Bks. GBR. Dist: Independent Pubs. Group.

Downing-Orr, Kristina. Beating Chronic Fatigue: Your Step-by-Step Guide to Complete Recovery. 2011. (ENG., Illus.). 240p. pap., instr.'s gde. ed. 14.95 *(978-0-7499-4098-0(0))* Piatkus Bks. GBR. Dist: Independent Pubs. Group.

Fernie. Coping Better Chron Fatigue Syndrome. 2009. (Karnac Self Help Ser.). (Illus.). 156p. pap. 26.95 *(978-1-85575-537-6(8))* Karnac Bks. GBR. Dist: Stylus Publishing, LLC.

Fowler, Nancy & Ball, Lisa. Chronic Fatigue & Fibromyalgia: From F.I.N.E. (Frustrated, Irritated, Nauseated, Exhausted) to Feeling Better. 2010. 214p. 18.00 *(978-1-882883-68-4(3))* Idyll Arbor, Inc.

Hickmott, Olive. Recover Your Energy. 2009. (Illus.). 144p. pap. *(978-1-904312-57-4(8))* MX Publishing, Ltd.

Hyde, Byron. Missed Diagnoses Myalgic Encephalomyelitis & Chronic Fatigue Syndrome Second Edition. 2010. 146p. pap. 27.50 *(978-0-557-32517-7(X))* Lulu Enterprises Inc.

Johnson, Susan K. Medically Unexplained Illness: Gender & Biopsychosocial Implications. 2007. 280p. 49.95 *(978-0-9792125-8-1(8))* American Psychological Assn.

Kidd, Pam. I Have Cfs but I Don't Look Sick. 2011. 98p. pap. 19.95 ***(978-1-4560-3532-7(0))*** PublishAmerica, Inc.

Kilcoyne, Martha. Defeat Chronic Fatigue Syndrome: An Eight Step Protocol. 2007. per. 11.95 *(978-0-9794769-3-8(3))* Adlbooks.com.

King, Roger. Love & Fatigue in America. 2012. (ENG.). 254p. 26.95 ***(978-0-299-28720-7(3))*** Univ. of Wisconsin Pr.

Kinsella. Cognitive Behavioural Therapy for Chronic Fatigue Syndrome. 2007. (ENG., Illus.). 184p. (C). 47.50 *(978-0-415-43612-0(5))* Routledge.

Kinsella, Philip. Cognitive Behavioural Therapy for Chronic Fatigue Syndrome: A Guide for Clinicians. 2007. (ENG., Illus.). 184p. (C). 110.00 *(978-1-58391-737-4(3))* Routledge.

Lisman, Susan R. & Dougherty, Karla. Chronic Fatigue Syndrome for Dummies. 2007. (ENG.). 384p. per. 21.99 *(978-0-470-11772-9(9),* For Dummies) Wiley, John & Sons, Inc.

Montpetit, Lucie. Breaking Free from Persistent Fatigue. 2012. (ENG.). 272p. pap. ***(978-1-84819-101-3(4))*** Kingsley, Jessica Ltd.

Murphree, Rodger. Treating & Beating Fibromyalgi. 2008. 414p. pap. 19.95 *(978-0-9728938-4-8(9))* Harrison & Hampton Publishing.

Natelson, Benjamin H. Your Symptoms Are Real: What to Do When Your Doctor Says Nothing Is Wrong. 2007. (ENG., Illus.). 288p. 24.95 *(978-0-471-74028-5(4),* Wiley) Wiley, John & Sons, Inc.

Pall, Martin L. Explaining Unexplained Illnesses: Disease Paradigm for Chronic Fatigue Syndrome, Multiple Chemical Sensitivity, Fibromyalgia, Post-Traumatic Stress Disorder, Gulf War Syndrome, & Others. 2007. (Illus.). 446p. per. 100.00 *(978-0-7890-2389-6(X),* Informa Healthcare) Taylor & Francis Group.

—Explaining 'unexplained Illnesses' Potential Paradigm for Chronic Fatigue Syndrome, Multiple Chemical Sensitivity, Fibromyalgia, Post-Traumatic Stress Disorder, & Gulf War Syndrome. 2007. (Illus.). 535p. 89.95 *(978-0-7890-2388-9(1),* Informa Healthcare) Taylor & Francis Group.

parks, peggy j. Chronic fatigue Syndrome. 2011. (Compact Research Ser.). (YA). (gr. 7-12). lib. bdg. 37.27 ***(978-1-60152-228-3(2))*** ReferencePoint Pr., Inc.

Penn, Georgiana. The Many Languages & Peaces of God. 2007. 244p. per. 25.00 *(978-0-9796866-0-3(1))* Alabaster Bk. Pub.

Powlison, David. I'm Exhausted: What to Do When You're Always Tired. 2010. 24p. 3.99 *(978-1-935273-72-1(8))* New Growth Pr.

Rubin, Jordan S. & Brasco, Joseph. GPRX for Fibromyalgia & Chronic Fatigue, 0 vols. 2007. (Great Physician's Rx Ser.). 128p. 9.99 *(978-0-7852-1913-2(7))* Nelson, Thomas Inc.

Skelly, Mari & Walker, Helen. Alternative Treatments for Fibromyalgia & Chronic Fatigue Syndrome. 2nd ed. 2006. (ENG., Illus.). 288p. per. 17.95 *(978-0-89793-472-5(5))* Hunter Hse., Inc.

Steefel, Lorraine. What Nurses Know... Chronic Fatigue Syndrome: The Answers You Need from the People You Trust. 2011. (What Nurses Know... Ser.). (ENG.). 190p. pap. 16.95 *(978-1-932603-87-3(5))* Demos Medical Publishing, LLC.

Stremecki, Annette. Diary of a Medical Nightmare. 2008. 228p. pap. 19.95 *(978-1-4251-7021-9(8))* Trafford Publishing.

Svoboda, Edita & Zelenjcik, Kristof. Chronic Fatigue Syndrome: Symptoms, Causes & Prevention. 2010. (Immune System Disorders Ser.). 201p. 98.00 *(978-1-60741-493-3(7),* Nova Biomedical Bks.) Nova Science Pubs., Inc.

Teitelbaum, Jacob. From Fatigued to Fantastic! A Clinically Proven Program to Regain Vibrant Health & Overcome Chronic Fatigue & Fibromyalgia. 3rd rev. ed. 2007. (ENG., Illus.). 448p. (gr. 12-18). 17.00 *(978-1-58333-289-4(8),* Avery) Penguin Group (USA) Inc.

Turp, Elizabeth. Chronic Fatigue Syndrome/ME: Support for Family & Friends. 2010. (ENG.). 240p. pap. *(978-1-84905-141-5(0))* Kingsley, Jessica Ltd.

Watanabe, Y., et al, eds. Fatigue Science for Human Health. 2010. (ENG.). xiv, 236p. pap. 99.00 *(978-4-431-99830-3(6),* 4431998306) Springer.

Watanabe, Yasuyoshi, et al. eds. Fatigue Science for Human Health. 2007. (ENG.). xiv, 236p. 99.00 *(978-4-431-73463-5(5),* 4431734635) Springer.

CHRONIC PAIN

Here are entered works on pain that persists over a long period of time. Works on pain that is difficult to control are entered under Intractable Pain.

Abaci, Peter. Take Charge of Your Chronic Pain: The Latest Research, Cutting Edge Tools, & Alternative Treatments for Feeling Better. 2009. (ENG., Illus.). 296p. pap. 16.95 *(978-0-7627-5409-0(5))* Globe Pequot Pr., The.

Bailey, Kari. Patient Endurance. 2011. 140p. pap. 14.99 ***(978-1-61215-828-0(5))*** Xulon Pr., Inc.

Ballantyne, Jane C., et al, eds. Bonica's Management of Pain. 4th rev. ed. 2009. (ENG., Illus.). 2064p. 329.99 *(978-0-7817-6827-6(6))* Lippincott Williams & Wilkins.

Berger, Ann, ed. Myths & Facts about Chronic Cancer Pain. 2006. (Illus.). 32p. pap. 10.95 *(978-1-891483-45-5(5))* PRR, Inc.

Bogduk, Nikolai & McGuirk, Brian. Management of Acute & Chronic Neck Pain: An Evidence-based Approach. 2006. (Pain Research & Clinical Management Ser.: 17). (ENG., Illus.). 196p. 99.95 *(978-0-444-50846-1(5),* Elsevier) Elsevier - Health Sciences Div.

Brennan, James. Chronic Pain & Working Women of Berkshire County. 2008. 224p. pap. *(978-3-639-00822-7(7))* VDM Verlag Dr. Mueller e.K.

Brown, Ronald S. Clinician's Guide to Diagnosis & Treatment of Chronic Orofacial Pain. 2009. 70p. pap. 29.95 *(978-1-936176-04-5(1))* American Academy of Oral Medicine.

Central Recovery Press, The Editors of. My Pain Recovery Journal. 2011. (ENG.). 204p. pap. 19.95 *(978-0-9799869-7-0(4))* Central Recovery Pr.

Chaitow, Leon & Lovegrove Jones, Ruth. Chronic Pelvic Pain & Dysfunction: Practical Physical Medicine. 2nd ed. 2011. (ENG., Illus.). 544p. pap. 74.95 ***(978-0-7020-3532-6(7),*** Churchill Livingstone) Elsevier - Health Sciences Div.

Chikly, Bruno. Silent Waves, Theory & Practice of Lymph Drainage Therapy: With Applications for Lymphedema, Chronic Pain, & Inflammation. (Illus.). 450p. suppl. ed. 65.00 *(978-0-9700530-6-0(1))* Upledger Institute, The.

Clark, M. R. & Treisman, G. J., eds. Chronic Pain & Addiction. 2011. (Advances in Psychosomatic Medicine Ser.). (Illus.). 166p. *(978-3-8055-9725-8(8))* Karger, S. AG.

Clark, M. R. & Treisman, Glenn J. Chronic Pain & Addiction. 2011. (Illus.). v, 165p. E-Book *(978-3-8055-9726-5(6))* Karger, S. AG.

Cochran, Robert T., Jr. Understanding Chronic Pain: A Doctor Talks to His Patients. 2nd exp. ed. 2007. (ENG., Illus.). 200p. per. 18.95 *(978-1-57736-395-8(7))* Turner Publishing Co.

Committee on Advancing Pain Research, Care, and Education & Institute of Medicine. Relieving Pain in America: A Blueprint for Transforming Prevention, Care, Education, & Research. 2011. (ENG.). 382p. 59.95 ***(978-0-309-21484-1(X))*** National Academies Pr.

Cousins, Michael & Gallagher, Rollin. Fast Facts: Fast Facts: Chronic & cancer Pain. 2nd rev. ed. 2011. (ENG., Illus.). 168p. pap. 25.00 ***(978-1-905832-85-9(0))*** Health Pr., Ltd. GBR. Dist: BookMasters Distribution Services (BDS).

Cram101 Textbook Reviews. Outlines & Highlights for Bonicas Management of Pain by Scott Fishman. Isbn: 9780781768276. 2011. 542p. pap. 38.95 ***(978-1-61461-444-9(X))*** Cram101 Inc.

Croft, Peter, et al. Chronic Pain Epidemiology: From Aetiology to Public Health. 2010. (ENG., Illus.). 368p. pap. 98.50 *(978-0-19-923576-6(7))* Oxford Univ. Pr., Inc.

D'Arcy, Yvonne M. Compact Clinical Guide to Chronic Pain Management: An Evidence-Based Approach for Nurses. 2011. (Illus.). x, 358p. E-Book ***(978-0-8261-0548-6(3))*** Springer Publishing Co., Inc.

D'Arcy, Yvonne M. Compact Clinical Guide to Chronic Pain Management: Evidence-Based Approach for Primary Care. 2010. (Illus.). 240p. *(978-0-8261-0540-0(8))* Springer Publishing Co., Inc.

Dickman, Andrew & Simpson, Karen H., eds. Chronic Pain. 2008. (Oxford Pain Management Library Ser.). (Illus.). 152p. pap. 24.95 *(978-0-19-923028-0(5))* Oxford Univ. Pr., Inc.

Egoscue, Pete & Gittines, Roger. Pain Free Living: The Egoscue Method for Strength, Harmony, & Happiness. 2011. (ENG., Illus.). 176p. 17.95 *(978-1-4027-8643-3(3))* Sterling Publishing Co., Inc.

Elster, Elizabeth J. Power Through Pain: Living with Reflex Neurovascular Dystrophy. 2007. 112p. per. 12.95 *(978-0-595-43716-0(8))* iUniverse, Inc.

Emlet, Michael R. Chronic Pain: Living by Faith When Your Body Hurts. 2010. 24p. 3.99 *(978-1-935273-64-6(7))* New Growth Pr.

Faguet, Guy B. Pain Control & Drug Policy: A Time for Change, 1 vol. 2010. (Illus.). 238p. 44.95 *(978-0-313-38280-2(8),* A2685C, Praeger Pubs.) Greenwood Publishing Group, Inc.

Fehmi, Les & Robbins, Jim. Dissolving Pain: Simple Brain-Training Exercises for Overcoming Chronic Pain. 2010. (ENG., Illus.). 224p. pap. 17.95 *(978-1-59030-780-9(1),* Trumpeter) Shambhala Pubns., Inc.

Field, Beverly J. & Swarm, Robert A. Chronic Pain. 2008. (Advances in Psychotherapy — Evidence-Based Practice Ser.: Vol. 11). (Illus.). 112p. pap. 29.80 *(978-0-88937-320-4(5))* Hogrefe Publishing.

Flor, Herta & Turk, Dennis C. Chronic Pain: An Integrated Biobehavioral Approach. 2011. ***(978-0-931092-90-9(5))*** IASI Pr.

Fox, Steven M. Chronic Pain in Small Animal Medicine. 2009. (ENG., Illus.). 256p. 84.95 *(978-1-84076-124-5(5))* Manson Publishing, Ltd. GBR. Dist: Thieme Medical Pubs., Inc.

Ganapathy, Sugantha & Chan, Vincent W. S. Regional Analgesia & Acute Pain Management, an Issue of Anesthesiology Clinics. 2011. (Clinics: Surgery Ser.: 29-2). (ENG., Illus.). 192p. 105.00 *(978-1-4377-2426-4(4),* Saunders) Elsevier - Health Sciences Div.

Gardner-Nix, Jackie. The Mindfulness Solution to Pain: Step-by-Step Techniques for Chronic Pain Management. 2nd rev. ed. 2009. (ENG., Illus.). 224p. pap. 18.95 *(978-1-57224-581-5(6))* New Harbinger Pubns.

Gartrell, Margaret. Older People Coping with Chronic Pain. 2010. 232p. pap. *(978-3-8383-3896-5(0))* Lambert Academic Publishing.

Giordano, James. Complementary & Integrative Approaches to Chronic Pain. 2008. 400p. (C). 99.95 *(978-0-7637-3820-4(4))* Jones & Bartlett Learning, LLC.

Giordano, James, ed. Maldynia: Multidisciplinary Perspectives on the Illness of Chronic Pain. 2010. (ENG., Illus.). 280p. 149.95 *(978-1-4398-3630-9(2),* CRC Press) Taylor & Francis Group GBR. Dist: Taylor & Francis Group.

Gould, Harry J. Understanding Pain: What It Is, Why It Happens, & How It's Managed. 2006. (American Academy of Neurology Ser.). (ENG., Illus.). 192p. per. 21.95 *(978-1-932603-58-3(1))* Demos Medical Publishing, LLC.

Greco, Tony. Meditations for Pain Recovery: A Holistic Approach. 2010. (ENG.). 400p. pap. 16.95 *(978-0-9818482-8-0(1))* Central Recovery Pr.

Gregory, Mark A. My Pain Angel. 2010. 120p. 21.49 *(978-1-4490-6137-1(0));* 128p. pap. 10.99 *(978-1-4490-6136-4(2))* AuthorHouse.

Grinstead, Stephen F. Addiction-Free Pain Management Recovery Guide: Managing Pain & Medication in Recovery. 2nd ed. 2008. (ENG.). pap. 15.00 *(978-0-8309-1376-3(9),* Independence Pr.) Herald Publishing Hse.

—Managing Pain & Coexisting Disorders: Using the Addiction-Free Pain Management System. 2007. pap. 15.00 *(978-0-8309-1347-3(5),* Independence Pr.) Herald Publishing Hse.

Hains, Bryan. Cell-Based Therapy for Chronic Neuropathic Pain after Cns Injury. 2011. 264p. pap. ***(978-3-8443-2697-0(9))*** Lambert Academic Publishing.

Hakim, Alan J., et al, eds. Hypermobility, Fibromyalgia & Chronic Pain. 2010. (ENG., Illus.). 336p. pap. 89.95 *(978-0-7020-3005-5(8),* Churchill Livingstone) Elsevier - Health Sciences Div.

Hasenbring, Monika I., et al, eds. From Acute to Chronic Back Pain: Risk Factors, Mechanisms, & Clinical Implications. 2012. (ENG., Illus.). 624p. 165.00 ***(978-0-19-955890-2(6))*** Oxford Univ. Pr., Inc.

Hemmenway, Nicole. No, It Is Not in My Head: The Journey of A Chronic Pain Survivor from Wheelchair to Marathon. 2010. (ENG.). 252p. pap. 19.95 *(978-1-60037-699-3(1))* Morgan James Publishing.

Heshusius, Lous. Inside Chronic Pain: An Intimate & Critical Account. 2009. (Culture & Politics of Health Care Work Ser.). 200p. 24.95 *(978-0-8014-4796-9(8))* Cornell Univ. Pr.

Jay, Gary W. Chronic Pain. 2007. (ENG., Illus.). 314p. 200.00 *(978-0-8493-3046-9(7))* CRC Pr. LLC.

Jensen, Mark P. Hypnosis for Chronic Pain Management: Therapist Guide, 1 vol. 2011. (Treatments That Work Ser.). (Illus.). 304p. pap. 45.00 *(978-0-19-977237-7(1))* Oxford Univ. Pr., Inc.

—Hypnosis for Chronic Pain Management: Workbook, 1 vol. 2011. (Treatments That Work Ser.). (Illus.). 160p. pap. 29.95 *(978-0-19-977238-4(X))* Oxford Univ. Pr., Inc.

Katz, Nathaniel P., et al. Managing Chronic Pain with Opioids in Primary Care. 2007. (Illus.). 72p. spiral bd. *(978-0-9740093-1-5(8))* Inflexxion, Inc.

Knotkova, Helena, et al, eds. Neural Plasticity in Chronic Pain. 2011. ***(978-1-61324-657-3(9))*** Nova Science Pubs., Inc.

Knotkova, Helena, et al, eds. Pain. Brain Stimulation in the Treatment of Pain. 2010. (Disability Studies (Joav Merrick - Series Editor - National Institute of Child Health & Human Development, Ministry of Social Affairs, Jerusalem Ser.). 89.00 *(978-1-60876-690-1(X))* Nova Science Pubs., Inc.

Lee, John & Baranowski, Andrew. Long-Term Pain: A Guide to Practical Management. 2007. (ENG., Illus.). 104p. pap. 27.50 *(978-0-19-921415-0(8),* Oxford Univ. Pr., Inc.

Leo, Raphael J. Clinical Manual of Pain Management in Psychiatry. 2007. 267p. per. 64.00 *(978-1-58562-275-7(3))* American Psychiatric Publishing, Inc.

Lyrakos, George N. Role of Dispositional Optimism in Health Related Quality of Life among Health Care Professionals with Musculoskeletal Pain. 2011. (Muscular System - Anatomy, Functions & Injuries Ser.). pap. 43.00 *(978-1-61761-109-4(3),* Nova Biomedical Bks.) Nova Science Pubs., Inc.

Manderson, Lenore & Smith-Morris, Carolyn, eds. Chronic Conditions, Fluid States: Chronicity & the Anthropology of Illness. 2010. (Studies in Medical Anthropology Ser.). (ENG., Illus.). 336p. 75.00 *(978-0-8135-4746-6(6))* Rutgers Univ. Pr.

Marcus, Dawn A. Chronic Pain: A Primary Care Guide to Practical Management. 2nd ed. 2008. (Current Clinical Practice Ser.). (Illus.). 438p. 129.00 *(978-1-60327-464-7(2))* Humana Pr.

—Headache & Chronic Pain Syndromes: The Case-Based Guide to Targeted Assessment & Treatment. 2006. (Current Clinical Practice Ser.). (Illus.). 209p. 119.00 *(978-1-58829-745-7(4),* 1588297454) Humana Pr.

Mayer, Emeran A. & Bushnell, M. Catherine, eds. Functional Pain Syndromes: Presentation & Pathophysiology. 2009. pap. 95.00 *(978-0-931092-75-6(2))* International Assn. for the Study of Pain/IASP Pr.

McClain, Brenda C. & Suresh, Santhanam, eds. Handbook of Pediatric Chronic Pain: Current Science & Integrative Practice. 2011. (Perspectives on Pain in Psychology Ser.). (ENG., Illus.). xv, 413p. 169.00 *(978-1-4419-0349-5(6),* 1441903496) Springer.

McGonigal, Kelly. Yoga for Pain Relief: Simple Practices to Calm Your Mind & Heal Your Chronic Pain. 2009. (New Harbinger Whole-Body Healing Ser.). (ENG., Illus.). 200p. pap. 21.95 *(978-1-57224-689-8(8))* New Harbinger Pubns.

Miles, Ann. Chronic Conditions, Fluid States: Chronicity & the Anthropology of Illness. Manderson, Lenore & Smith-Morris, Carolyn, eds. 2010. (Studies in Medical Anthropology Ser.). (ENG., Illus.). 336p. pap. 29.95 *(978-0-8135-4747-3(4))* Rutgers Univ. Pr.

Namerow, Norman S. The Handbook of Chronic Pain Rehabilitation: A Guide to Providing Comprehensive Care. Richeimer, Steven H., ed. 2008. (Contemporary Pain Medicine Ser.). 250p. 125.00 *(978-1-58829-762-4(4),* 1588297624) Humana Pr.

Otis, John. Managing Chronic Pain: A Cognitive-Behavioral Therapy Approach Workbook. 2007. (Treatments That Work Ser.). (ENG., Illus.). 144p. pap., wbk. ed. 27.95 *(978-0-19-532917-9(1))* Oxford Univ. Pr., Inc.

Otis, John D. Managing Chronic Pain: A Cognitive-Behavioral Therapy Approach. 2007. (Treatments That Work Ser.). (ENG., Illus.). 128p. (C). per., instr.'s gde. ed. 37.95 *(978-0-19-532916-2(3))* Oxford Univ. Pr., Inc.

Parks, Tim. Teach Us to Sit Still: A Skeptic's Search for Health & Healing. 2011. (ENG.). 336p. 25.99 *(978-1-60961-158-3(6))* Rodale Pr., Inc.

Patnaik, Gourishankar. The Aging Knee. 2010. 72p. pap. *(978-3-639-26869-0(5))* VDM Verlag Dr. Mueller e.K.

Phillips, Maggie. Reversing Chronic Pain: A 10-Point All-Natural Plan for Lasting Relief. 2007. (ENG., Illus.). 256p. pap. 17.95 *(978-1-55643-676-5(9))* North Atlantic Bks.

Pike, Lois V. Healing Hope. 2008. 164p. pap. 15.95 *(978-1-4401-0336-0(4))* iUniverse, Inc.

Pohl, Mel, et al. Pain Recovery for Families: How to Find Balance When Someone Else's Chronic Pain Becomes Your Problem Too. 2010. (ENG.). 220p. pap. 20.95 *(978-0-9818482-3-5(0))* Central Recovery Pr.

Pollard, Steven W. Chronic Pain: A Self-Help Guide: A Two-Part Book of My Journey with Chronic Pain & Part 2: A Self-Help Guide for Coping with Chronic Pain. 2011. 262p. pap. 16.95 ***(978-1-4620-3034-7(3))*** iUniverse, Inc.

Pratt, Maureen. Beyond Pain: Job, Jesus & Joy. 2010. pap. 14.95 *(978-1-58595-786-6(0))* Twenty-Third Pubns./Bayard.

Rashiq, Saifudin, et al, eds. Chronic Pain: A Health Policy Perspective. 2008. (Health Care & Disease Management Ser.: 10). (ENG., Illus.). 346p. 129.95 *(978-3-527-32382-1(1)*, Wiley-VCH) Wiley, John & Sons, Inc.

Reese, Hazel Lucretia. A Sexy 60's Woman: With a New Attitude & Still She Does Not Complain. 2011. 106p. pap. 19.95 ***(978-1-4626-0328-2(9))*** PublishAmerica, Inc.

Richeimer, Steven H. & Namerow, Norman S., eds. The Handbook of Chronic Pain Rehabilitation: A Guide to Providing Comprehensive Care. 2006. (Contemporary Pain Medicine Ser.). 250p. 125.00 *(978-1-59745-345-5(5))* Humana Pr.

Rothbart, Brian A. & Penzabene, Linda F. Forever Free from Chronic Pain: The Pain Sufferer's Guide to Getting Your Life Back. 2009. 260p. 34.95 *(978-1-60005-128-9(6))* Happy About.

Roy, Ranjan. Chronic Pain & Family: A Clinical Perspective. 2010. (ENG.). x, 158p. pap. 69.95 *(978-1-4419-2128-4(1)*, 1441921281) Springer.

—Psychosocial Interventions for Chronic Pain: In Search of Evidence. 2008. (ENG.). xiii, 177p. 189.00 *(978-0-387-76295-1(7)*, 0387762957) Springer.

—Psychosocial Interventions for Chronic Pain: In Search of Evidence. 2010. (ENG.). xiii, 177p. pap. 189.00 *(978-1-4419-2616-6(X)*, 144192616X) Springer.

—Social Relations & Chronic Pain. 2010. (Springer Series in Rehabilitation & Health Ser.). 172p. pap. 119.00 *(978-1-4419-3350-8(6)*, 1441933506) Springer.

Schatman, Michael E., ed. Ethical Issues in Chronic Pain Management. 2007. (Pain Management Ser.: Vol. 1). (ENG., Illus.). 328p. 250.00 *(978-0-8493-9268-9(3)*, Informa Healthcare) Taylor & Francis Group GBR. Dist: Taylor & Francis Group.

Schatman, Michael E. & Campbell, Alexandra, eds. Chronic Pain Management: Guidelines for Multidisciplinary Program Development. 2007. (Pain Management Ser.: Vol. 3). (Illus.). 284p. 100.00 *(978-1-4200-4512-3(1)*, Informa Healthcare) Taylor & Francis Group GBR. Dist: Taylor & Francis Group.

Schneider, Jennifer. Chronic Pain: The Complete Health Guide to the Causes & Treatment of Chronic Pain. 2nd ed. 2009. (Living With Ser.). (ENG., Illus.). 400p. pap. 16.95 *(978-1-57826-285-4(2))* Hatherleigh Co., Ltd., The.

Schnitzer, Stephen. Chronic Pain Survival Tricks & Self-Help Techniques: A Survivor's Manual by One Who Knows. 2011. 140p. 23.95 ***(978-1-4620-0163-7(7))***; pap. 13.95 ***(978-1-4620-0162-0(9))*** iUniverse, Inc.

Shakhshir, Patricia. The Lived Experience of Latinas Who Listen to Music for Chronic Pain. 2010. 68p. pap. *(978-3-639-23425-1(1))* VDM Verlag Dr. Mueller e.K.

Stahl, Stephen M., et al. Chronic Pain & Fibromyalgia. 2009. (Stahl's Illustrated Ser.). (ENG., Illus.). 176p. pap. 39.99 *(978-0-521-13322-7(X))* Cambridge Univ. Pr.

Stannard, Cathy, et al, eds. Evidence-Based Chronic Pain Management. 5th ed. 2010. (Evidence-Based Medicine Ser.). (ENG., Illus.). 464p. 220.95 *(978-1-4051-5291-4(5))* Wiley, John & Sons, Inc.

Szallasi, Arpad, ed. Analgesia. 2010. (Methods in Molecular Biology Ser.). (Illus.). 528p. 189.00 *(978-1-60327-322-0(0)*, 1603273220) Humana Pr.

Versagi, Charlotte Michael. Step-by-Step Massage Therapy Protocols for Common Conditions. 2011. (LWW Massage Therapy & Bodywork Educational Ser.). (ENG., Illus.). 352p. pap. 54.95 *(978-0-7817-8715-4(7))* Lippincott Williams & Wilkins.

Vierck, Charles J., Jr., et al. Chronic Pain for Dummies. 2008. (ENG., Illus.). 384p. pap. 19.99 *(978-0-471-75140-3(5)*, For Dummies) Wiley, John & Sons, Inc.

Webster, Lynn R. & Dove, Beth. Avoiding Opioid Abuse While Managing Pain: A Guide for Practitioners. 2007. (Illus.). 202p. per. *(978-0-9624814-8-2(3))* Sunrise River Pr.

Wilder, Lauren. Healing Prayers: Prayers & Reflective Wisdom to Recognize the Effects of Chronic Pain. 2009. 60p. pap. 9.95 *(978-1-4401-4589-6(X))* iUniverse, Inc.

Wilson, Peter, et al. Chronic Pain, 4 vols. 2nd ed. 2008. (ENG., Illus.). 728p. 198.50 *(978-0-340-94008-2(5)*, Hodder Arnold) Hodder Education GBR. Dist: Oxford Univ. Pr., Inc.

World Health Organization. WHO Guidelines on Pharmacological Treatment of Persisting Pain in Children with Medical Illnesses. 2012. 250p. pap. 30.00 *(978-92-4-154812-0(6))* World Health Organization.

Wright, H. Norman & Ellis, Lynn. Coping with Chronic Pain & Illness. 2010. 240p. pap. 12.99 *(978-0-7369-2706-2(9))* Harvest Hse. Pubs.

Wright/jonniewright, Jonnie, 2nd. Choices: Managing Chronic Pain. 2008. 88p. per. 9.99 *(978-0-9768950-1-5(3))* Wright, Jonnie.

CHRONIC PAIN—POPULAR WORKS

Argoff, Charles & Galer, Bradley S. Defeat Chronic Pain Now! Groundbreaking Strategies for Eliminating the Pain of Arthritis, Back & Neck Conditions, Migraines, Diabetic Neuropathy, & Chronic Illness. 2010. (ENG., Illus.). 272p. pap. 21.99 *(978-1-59233-407-0(5)*, 1592334075) Quayside.

Bacci, Ingrid lorch. Effortless Pain Relief: A Guide to Self-Healing from Chronic Pain. 2007. (ENG.). 272p. pap. 18.95 *(978-1-4165-8451-3(X)*, Free Pr.) Free Pr.

Barrett, Deborah, ed. Pain Tracking: Your Personal Guide to Living Well with Chronic Pain. 2012. (ENG., Illus.). 375p. pap. 20.00 ***(978-1-61614-513-2(7))*** Prometheus Bks., Pubs.

Barsky, Arthur J. & Deans, Emily C. Feeling Better: A 6-Week Mind-Body Program to Ease Your Chronic Symptoms. 2007. (ENG.). 256p. pap. 13.95 *(978-0-06-076614-6(X)*, William Morrow Paperbacks) HarperCollins Pubs.

Brady, Scott & Proctor, William. Pain Free for Life: The 6-Week Cure for Chronic Pain — Without Surgery or Drugs. 2011. (ENG., Illus.). 304p. 27.99 *(978-0-446-57761-8(8))* Center St.

Burch, Vidyamala. Living Well with Pain & Illness: The Mindful Way to Free Yourself from Suffering. unabr. ed. 2010. 304p. pap. 15.95 *(978-1-59179-747-0(0))* Sounds True, Inc.

Cochran, Robert T., Jr. Curing Chronic Pain: Stories of Hope & Healing. 2009. (Florida Trilogy: Bk. 3). (ENG.). 338p. pap. 19.95 *(978-1-57736-412-2(0))* Turner Publishing Co.

Crosson, Denise, et al. Pain Recovery: How to Find Balance & Reduce Suffering from Chronic Pain. 2009. (ENG., Illus.). 193p. pap., wbk. ed. 20.95 *(978-0-9799869-9-4(0))* Central Recovery Pr.

DeLaune, Valerie. Pain Relief with Trigger Point Self-Help. 2011. (ENG., Illus.). 336p. pap. 29.95 ***(978-1-58394-400-4(1))*** North Atlantic Bks.

Gildenberg, Philip L. & DeVaul, Richard A. Let's Talk Chronic Pain: A Manual for Patients & Physicians. 2013. (ENG., Illus.). 200p. pap. 59.95 *(978-3-642-11845-6(3)*, 3642118453) Springer.

Harrar, Sari. Your New Pain Prescription: From Migraines to Arthritis, Ulcers to Cancer Pain, Find Relief at Last with Customized Treatment Plans for More Than 60 Common Chronic Pain Conditions. 2011. *(978-1-60529-132-1(3))* Rodale Pr., Inc.

Jain. Chronic Pain. rev. ed. 2010. 165p. pap. 22.95 *(978-0-7637-8604-5(7))* Jones & Bartlett Learning, LLC.

Kloth, David, et al. Pain-Wise: A Patient's Guide to Pain Management. 2011. (ENG., Illus.). 160p. pap. 15.00 ***(978-1-57826-408-7(1))*** Hatherleigh Co., Ltd., The.

Leal, Liza H. Cupid's Challenge. 2011. (ENG.). 120p. pap. 14.95 *(978-1-59687-874-7(6))* IBks., Inc.

Lewandowski, Michael J. The Chronic Pain Care Workbook: A Self-Treatment Approach to Pain Relief Using the Behavioral Assessment of Pain Questionnaire. 2006. (Workbook Ser.). (ENG., Illus.). 240p. per., wbk. ed. 28.95 *(978-1-57224-470-2(4))* New Harbinger Pubns.

Nicholas, Michael, et al. Manage Your Pain: Practical & Positive Ways of Adapting to Chronic Pain. 2006. (Illus.). 224p. reprint ed. per. 14.95 *(978-0-285-63679-8(0))* Souvenir Pr. Ltd. GBR. Dist: Independent Pubs. Group.

Peterson, Martha. Move Without Pain. 2012. (ENG., Illus.). 160p. pap. 19.95 *(978-1-4027-7459-1(1))* Sterling Publishing Co., Inc.

Plews-Ogan, Margaret, et al. Choosing Wisdom: The Path Through Adversity. 2012. (ENG.). (C). 19.95 ***(978-1-59947-395-6(X))*** Templeton Pr.

Pohl, Mel. A Day Without Pain. rev. ed. 2011. (ENG.). 264p. pap. 15.95 *(978-1-936290-62-8(6))* Central Recovery Pr.

Rengo-Kocher, Rebecca. Beyond Chronic Pain: A Get-Well Guidebook for Soothing Chronic Pain of the Body, Mind & Spirit. 2006. 96p. spiral bd. 19.99 *(978-0-9787957-0-2(9))* Beyond Publishing.

Sadler, Jan. Pain Relief Without Drugs: A Self-Help Guide for Chronic Pain & Trauma. 3rd ed. 2007. (ENG., Illus.). 1p. 19.95 *(978-1-59477-151-4(0)*, Healing Arts Pr.) Inner Traditions International, Ltd.

Teaman, Blake H. 10 Simple Solutions to Chronic Pain: How to Stop Pain from Controlling Your Life. 2007. (New Harbinger Ten Simple Solutions Ser.). (ENG.). 192p. per. 15.95 *(978-1-57224-482-5(8))* New Harbinger Pubns.

CHRONIC RENAL FAILURE

Bakris, George L., ed. The Kidney in Heart Failure. 2012. (ENG., Illus.). xii, 248p. 209.00 ***(978-1-4614-3693-5(1)***, 1461436931) Springer.

—Managing the Kidney when the Heart Is Failing. 2012. (ENG., Illus.). x, 114p. pap. 49.95 ***(978-1-4614-3690-4(7)***, 1461436907) Springer.

Bakris, George L. & Bomback, Andrew S. Chronic Kidney Disease (Ckd) & Hypertension Essentials. rev. ed. 2010. 148p. pap. 28.95 *(978-0-7637-8136-1(3))* Jones & Bartlett Learning, LLC.

Bell, Melissa. Heart & Soul. 2010. (ENG., Illus.). 260p. 26.95 *(978-1-84454-921-4(6))* Blake, John Publishing, Ltd. GBR. Dist: Independent Pubs. Group.

Bellomo, R. & Bonventre, J., eds. Acute Kidney Injury - Scientific Evidence Driving Change in Patient Management. 2008. (Illus.). 120p. pap. *(978-3-8055-8646-7(9))* Karger, S. AG.

Borm Bruckmeier Publishing, ed. DARF pocket Tool: Dose Adjustment in Renal Failure. 2007. 9.95 *(978-1-59103-803-0(0))* Bruckmeier, Borm Publishing, LLC.

Brown, Edwina, et al. End of Life Care in Nephrology: From Advanced Disease to Bereavement. 2007. (Oxford Specialist Handbooks in End of Life Care Ser.). (ENG., Illus.). 352p. 79.95 *(978-0-19-921105-0(1))* Oxford Univ. Pr., Inc.

Cram101 Textbook Reviews & Cram101 Textbook Reviews. Outlines & Highlights for Review of Hemodialysis for Nurses & Dialysis Personnel by Judith Z Kallenbach, Isbn: 9780323028714. 2011. 100p. pap. 27.95 ***(978-1-61461-374-9(5))*** Cram101 Inc.

Daugirdas, John T. Handbook of Chronic Kidney Disease Management. 2011. (Lippincott Williams & Wilkins Handbook Ser.). (ENG., Illus.). 656p. pap. 64.99 *(978-1-58255-893-6(0))* Lippincott Williams & Wilkins.

El Nahas, Meguid & Levin, Adeera, eds. Chronic Kidney Disease: A Practical Guide to Understanding & Management. 2010. (Oxford Clinical Nephrology Ser.). (ENG., Illus.). 208p. pap. 79.95 *(978-0-19-954931-3(1))* Oxford Univ. Pr., Inc.

Halper, Thomas. The Misfortunes of Others: End-Stage Renal Disease in the United Kingdom. 2009. (Studies in Philosophy & Health Policy Ser.). (ENG.). 232p. pap. 36.99 *(978-0-521-11572-8(8))* Cambridge Univ. Pr.

Henrich, William L. & Henrich, William L. Principles & Practice of Dialysis. 4th rev. ed. 2009. (ENG., Illus.). 752p. 99.00 *(978-0-7817-8163-3(9))* Lippincott Williams & Wilkins.

Henry, Mitchell L. Vascular Access for Hemodialysis-X. 2007. *(978-1-56625-950-7(9))* Precept Pr.

Himmelfarb, Jonathan & Sayegh, Mohamed H. Chronic Kidney Disease, Dialysis, & Transplantation: A Companion to Brenner & Rector's the Kidney. 3rd ed. 2010. (ENG., Illus.). 760p. 195.00 *(978-1-4377-0987-2(7)*, Saunders) Elsevier - Health Sciences Div.

Hsu, Chen H., ed. Calcium & Phosphate Metabolism Management in Chronic Renal Disease. 2010. (ENG., Illus.). xii, 188p. pap. 139.00 *(978-1-4419-4122-0(3)*, 1441941223) Springer.

Ishikawa, Isao. Exercise-Induced Acute Renal Failure: Acute Renal Failure with Severe Loin Pain & Patchy Renal Ischemia after Anaerobic Exercise. 2007. (ENG., Illus.). 108p. 99.00 *(978-4-431-69483-0(8)*, 4431694838) Springer.

Kallenbach, Judith Z. Review of Hemodialysis for Nurses & Dialysis Personnel. 8th ed. 2011. (ENG., Illus.). 432p. pap. 59.95 *(978-0-323-07702-6(1)*, Mosby) Elsevier - Health Sciences Div.

Kariuki, Anastacia. Dietary Inadequacies in Chronic Renal Disease in Developing Countries. 2011. 140p. pap. ***(978-3-8433-8024-9(4))*** Lambert Academic Publishing.

Kellum, John A., et al. Continuous Renal Replacement Therapy, 1 vol. 2009. (ENG., Illus.). 288p. pap. 39.95 *(978-0-19-539278-4(7))* Oxford Univ. Pr., Inc.

Kjellstrand, C. M. & Dossetor, J. B., eds. Ethical Problems in Dialysis & Transplantation. 2010. (Developments in Nephrology Ser.). (ENG.). 264p. pap. 258.00 *(978-90-481-4131-9(1)*, 9048141311) Springer.

Kopple, Joel D., et al, eds. Nutritional Management of Renal Disease. 2012. (ENG.). 650p. 119.95 ***(978-0-12-391934-2(7)***, Academic Pr.) Elsevier Science & Technology Bks.

L. Walters, Kevan. Brother to Brother: The Miracle of Family. 2010. pap. 16.99 *(978-1-61663-344-8(1))* Tate Publishing & Enterprises, LLC.

Levin, N. W., et al, eds. Advances in Chronic Kidney Disease 2009: 11th International Conference on Dialysis, Las Vegas, Nev. , January 2009. 2009. (Illus.). 158p. pap. *(978-3-8055-9031-0(8))* Karger, S. AG.

Levy, Jeremy, et al. Oxford Handbook of Dialysis. 3rd ed. 2009. (Oxford Handbooks Ser.). (ENG., Illus.). 984p. 54.95 *(978-0-19-923528-5(7))* Oxford Univ. Pr., Inc.

Mallappallil, Mary C. & Friedman, Eli A. Present & Future Therapies for End-Stage Renal Disease. 2010. 204p. 96.00 *(978-981-4280-02-0(X))* World Scientific Publishing Co., Inc.

Mancuso, Dominick W. Progress in Kidney Transplantation. 2006. (Illus.). 175p. 129.00 *(978-1-60021-312-0(X))* Nova Science Pubs., Inc.

Mehta, R. L., ed. CRRT 2006 - a Multimedia Conference Compilation: Including Abstracts of the 1st to 11th International Conferences on Continuous Renal Replacement Therapies, San Diego, Calif. , 1995-2006. incl. cd-rom *(978-3-8055-8108-0(4))* Karger, S. AG.

Mitch, W. E., ed. Nutritional Therapy in Patients with Chronic Kidney Disease: Protein-Restricted Diets Supplemented with Keto/Amino Acids: International Advisory Board Meeting 2006: Abstracts: Supplement Issue: American Journal of Nephrology 2006, Vol. 26, Suppl. 1. (Illus.). 28p. pap. *(978-3-8055-8247-6(1))* Karger, S. AG.

Morris, Peter & Knechtle, Stuart J. Kidney Transplantation: Principles & Practice. 6th ed. 2008. (ENG., Illus.). 872p. 297.00 *(978-1-4160-3343-1(2)*, Saunders) Elsevier - Health Sciences Div.

Offer, Daniel, et al. Dialysis Without Fear: A Guide to Living Well on Dialysis for Patients & Their Families. 2007. (ENG.). 304p. per. 17.95 *(978-0-19-530995-9(2))* Oxford Univ. Pr., Inc.

Patient Safety & Quality Issues in End Stage Renal Disease Treatment: Hearing Before the Committee on Ways & Means, U.S. House of Representatives, One Hundred Ninth Congress, Second Session, December 6, 2006. 2007. (Illus.). iii, 94p. *(978-0-16-078967-0(2)*, 552-070-36085-9) United States Government Printing Office.

Peitzman, Steven J. Dropsy, Dialysis, Transplant: A Short History of Failing Kidneys. 2007. (Johns Hopkins Biographies of Disease Ser.). (ENG., Illus.). 240p. 24.95 *(978-0-8018-8734-5(8))* Johns Hopkins Univ. Pr.

Rettig, Richard, et al. Chronic Kidney Disease: A Quiet Revolution in Nephrology. 2010. 94p. pap. 20.00 *(978-0-8330-4972-8(0)*, tr-826) RAND Corp., The.

Rich, Deborah. A Kidney Through Faith. 2008. 56p. pap. 16.95 *(978-1-60441-126-3(0))* PublishAmerica, Inc.

Ronco, C., et al, eds. Fluid Overload: Diagnosis & Management. 2010. (Contributions to Nephrology Ser.). (ENG., Illus.). 244p. *(978-3-8055-9416-5(X))* Karger, S. AG.

Ronco, C. & Levin, N. W., eds. Advances in Chronic Kidney Disease 2007: 9th International Conference on Dialysis, Austin, Tex. , January 2007: Special Issue: Blood Purification 2007, Vol. 25, No. 1. (Illus.). 124p. pap. *(978-3-8055-8237-7(4))* Karger, S. AG.

Ronco, C., et al. Cardiovascular Disorders in Hemodialysis, Vol. 149. (Contributions to Nephrology Ser.: Vol. 149). (Illus.). *(978-3-8055-7938-4(1))* Karger, S. AG.

Slaughter, Mark S. Cardiac Surgery in Chronic Renal Failure. Cohn, Lawrence, ed. 2007. (ENG., Illus.). 112p. 99.95 *(978-1-4051-3132-2(2)*, Wiley-Blackwell) Wiley, John & Sons, Inc.

Stamopoulos, Dimosthenis, et al. Magnetically-Assisted Hemodialysis: A New Strategy for Treatment of End Stage Renal Disease. 2008. (Illus.). xii, 95p. pap. 89.00 *(978-1-60456-681-9(7))* Nova Science Pubs., Inc.

CHRONICALLY ILL

see also Lepers

Agronin, Marc. How We Age: A Doctor's Journey into the Heart of Growing Old. 2012. (ENG.). 320p. pap. 15.00 ***(978-0-7382-1558-7(9))*** Da Capo Pr., Inc.

Atwood, Joan & Gallo, Concetta. Family Therapy & Chronic Illness. 2009. (ENG.). 230p. 39.95 *(978-0-202-36335-6(X))* Aldine Transaction.

Bailey, Elisabeth Tova. The Sound of a Wild Snail Eating: A True Story. 2010. (ENG.). 208p. 18.95 *(978-1-56512-606-0(8)*, 1565126068) Algonquin Bks. of Chapel Hill.

Baker, Barbara. Coping with Long-Term Illness. ix, 118p. *(978-0-85969-844-3(0)*, Sheldon Press) SPCK Publishing.

Bell, Iris R. Getting Whole, Getting Well: Healing Holistically from Chronic Illness. 2008. (ENG.). pap. 14.95 *(978-1-60037-387-9(9))* Morgan James Publishing.

Bernhard, Toni. How to Be Sick: A Buddhist-Inspired Guide for the Chronically Ill & Their Caregivers. 2010. (ENG.). 216p. pap. 15.95 *(978-0-86171-626-5(4))* Wisdom Pubns.

Boult, Chad. Guided Care: A New Nurse-Physician Partnership in Chronic Care. 2009. (Illus.). 200p. *(978-0-8261-4411-9(X))* Springer.

Bouvard, Marguerite Guzman & Bouvard, Marguerite. Healing: A Life with Chronic Illness. 2007. (ENG.). 160p. pap. 19.95 *(978-1-58465-623-4(9))* Univ. Pr. of New England.

Brill, Alida & Lockshin, Michael D. Dancing at the River's Edge: A Patient & Her Doctor Negotiate Life with Chronic Illness. 3rd ed. (ENG.). 2010. 264p. pap. 16.95 *(978-0-9824332-7-0(1))* 2009. 224p. 23.95 *(978-0-9801394-0-2(6))* Schaffner Pr., Inc.

Carrier, Judith. Managing Long-Term Conditions & Chronic Illness in Primary Care: A Guide to Good Practice. 2009. (ENG., Illus.). 224p. 140.00 *(978-0-415-45087-4(X))*; pap. 43.95 *(978-0-415-45088-1(8))* Routledge.

Chillemi, Stacey. Epilepsy You're Not Alone. 2010. 273p. 39.95 *(978-1-4357-2973-5(0))* Lulu Enterprises Inc.

Cohen, Richard M. Strong at the Broken Places: Voices of Illness, a Chorus of Hope. 2009. (ENG.). 352p. pap. 14.99 *(978-0-06-076312-1(4)*, HarperPerennial) HarperCollins Pubs.

Cox, Robin A. F. & Palmer, Keith. Fitness for Work: The Medical Aspects. Brown, Ian, ed. 4th rev. ed. 2007. (ENG., Illus.). 760p. pap. 95.00 *(978-0-19-921565-2(0))* Oxford Univ. Pr., Inc.

Cupitt. Reaching Out: The Psychology of Assertive Outreach. 2009. (ENG., Illus.). 272p. (C). 39.95 *(978-0-415-45407-0(7))*; 105.00 *(978-0-415-45406-3(9))* Routledge.

Delgado Gaitan, Concha. Prickly Cactus: Finding Sacred Meaning in Chronic Illness. 2009. pap. 14.95 *(978-1-879384-76-7(0))* Cypress Hse.

Dickman, Andrew & Simpson, Karen H., eds. Chronic Pain. 2008. (Oxford Pain Management Library Ser.). (Illus.). 152p. pap. 24.95 *(978-0-19-923028-0(5))* Oxford Univ. Pr., Inc.

Dillard, Judy L. The Beauty of Pain: My experience & practical advice for Christians with chronic Illness. 2008. 92p. pap. 10.95 *(978-1-4327-2669-0(2))* Outskirts Pr., Inc.

Dukes, Thomas. Sugar Blood Jesus: A Memoir of Faith, Madness & Cream Gravy. 2009. 167p. pap. 19.95 *(978-1-878009-61-6(3)*, OSL Pubns.) Order of Saint Luke.

Earle, Mary C. Days of Grace: Meditation & Practices for Living with Illness. 2009. 128p. pap. 12.00 *(978-0-8192-2364-7(6)*, Morehouse Publishing) Church Publishing, Inc.

Edwards, Laurie. A Life Disrupted: Getting Real about Chronic Illness in Your Twenties & Thirties. 2008. (ENG.). 288p. pap. 14.99 *(978-0-8027-1649-1(0))* Walker & Co.

Eshowsky, Myron. Peace with Cancer: Shamanism as a Spiritual Approach to Healing. 2010. 186p. pap. 20.00 *(978-0-9793865-0-3(0))* Shoshana Pubns.

Falvo, Donna. Medical & Psychosocial Aspects of Chronic Illness & Disability. 3rd rev. ed. 2007. 572p. pap. 121.95 *(978-0-7637-5766-3(7))* 4th ed. 2010. 693p. pap. 110.95 *(978-1-4496-2570-2(3))* Jones & Bartlett Learning, LLC.

Falvo, Donna R. Medical & Psychosocial Aspects of Chronic Illness & Disability. 4th rev. ed. 2008. (Illus.). 693p. 97.95 (978-0-7637-4461-8(1)) Jones & Bartlett Learning, LLC.

Fiennes, William. The Music Room: A Memoir. 2010. (ENG.). 216p. pap. 14.95 (978-0-393-33878-2(9), 33878) Norton, W. W. & Co., Inc.

Frank, David & Mooney, Bernard. Hypnosis & Counselling in the Treatment of Cancer & Chronic Illness. 2007. Orig. Title: Hypnosis & Counselling in the Treatment of Chronic Illness. 160p. pap. (978-1-84590-080-9(4)) Crown Hse. Publishing.

Ganda, Kanchan. Dentist's Guide to Medical Conditions & Complications. 2008. (ENG., Illus.). 552p. pap., instr.'s gde. ed. 94.99 (978-0-8138-0926-7(6), Wiley-Blackwell) Wiley, John & Sons, Inc.

Gerhart, Ursula C. & Marley, James A. Caring for the Chronically Mentally Ill. 2nd ed. 2010. (ENG.). (C). pap. 70.95 (978-0-534-64246-4(2)) Brooks/Cole.

Gibbs, Lisa. When the Whole 'Bloke' Thing Starts to Crumble - Men's Access to Chronic Illness Self Management Programs. 2008. 224p. pap. (978-3-639-05072-1(X)) VDM Verlag Dr. Mueller e.K.

Graf, Ellen. The Natural Laws of Good Luck: A Memoir of an Unlikely Marriage. 2011. (ENG.). 272p. pap. 15.95 (978-1-59030-833-2(6), Trumpeter) Shambhala Pubns., Inc.

Greenberg, Tamara McClintock. The Psychological Impact of Acute & Chronic Illness: A Practical Guide for Primary Care Physicians. 2006. (Illus.). 176p. per. 49.95 (978-0-387-33682-4(6), 0387336826) Springer.

Greenberg, Tamara McClintock. When Someone You Love Has a Chronic Illness: Hope & Help for Those Providing Support. 2012. pap. 13.99 (978-1-59955-939-1(0), Plain Sight Publishing) Cedar Fort, Inc./CFI Distribution.

Harpham, Wendy Schlessel & Harpham, Wendy. Happiness in a Storm: Facing Illness & Embracing Life as a Healthy Survivor. 2006. (ENG.). 400p. per. 18.95 (978-0-393-32905-6(4), 32905) Norton, W. W. & Co., Inc.

Heise, Kenan. He Writes about Us: An Autobiography of a Chicago Journalist. 2012. (ENG.). 336p. pap. 18.95 (978-1-936863-17-4(0), Marion Street Pr.) Acorn Guild Pr., LLC.

Hillman, Anne & Chapparo, Chris. Living a Meaningful Life with Chronic Illness. 2008. 368p. pap. (978-3-8364-9512-7(0)) VDM Verlag Dr. Mueller e.K.

Jaff, Jennifer. Friday Tired: A Feminist Rant on Healthcare in America in the 21st Century. 2007. 132p. (ENG.). 23.95 (978-0-595-69016-9(5)); per. 13.95 (978-0-595-44850-0(X)) iUniverse, Inc.

John, Walter. Solace: How Caregivers & Others Can Relate, Listen, & Respond Effectively to a Chronically Ill Person. 2011. (ENG.). 224p. pap. 14.95 (978-1-933503-62-2(9)) Bull Publishing Co.

Johnson, Hugh, et al. How I Got My Wiggle Back: A Memoir of Healing. 2012. (ENG., Illus.). 288p. 25.95 (978-1-118-01933-7(4)) Wiley, John & Sons, Inc.

Kaufman, Miriam, et al. The Ultimate Guide to Sex & Disability: For All of Us Who Live with Disabilities, Chronic Pain, & Illness. 2nd ed. 2007. (ENG., Illus.). 360p. per. 18.95 (978-1-57344-304-3(2)) Cleis Pr.

Kiel, Donna. He Was There Even When I Was Unaware & So Was Ms. 2009. 108p. 19.99 (978-1-60791-422-8(0)); pap. 11.99 (978-1-60791-421-1(2)) Xulon Pr., Inc.

Koralek, Jenny. Mother, Do Not Weep for Me: A Son's Life Remembered with Joy. 2010. (ENG.). 250p. pap. 13.95 (978-1-59675-034-0(0), Morning Light Pr.

Krämer, Olaf. Nonverbale Seelsorge im Kontext stationärer Pflege: Analysen, Beobachtungen und Poimenische Postulate. 2011. (Europäische Hochschulschriften. Reihe 23: Theologie Ser.). (GER.). 414p. pap. 93.95 (978-3-631-61831-8(X)) Lang, Peter GmbH, Europaischer Verlag der Wissenschaften DEU. Dist: Lang, Peter.

Kroll, Thilo. Focus on Disability: Trends in Research & Application. 2007. 89.00 (978-1-60021-792-0(3), Nova Biomedical Bks.) Nova Science Pubs., Inc.

Kuenstler, Aletha T. Chronic Illness: Facing Its Challenges. 2011. 184p. pap. 14.99 (978-1-61215-905-8(2)) Xulon Pr., Inc.

Lazarus. COPD: Principles, Diagnosis & Therapy. Date not set. 406p. (978-0-7216-1020-7(X)) Harcourt Health Sciences Group.

Lippmann, Sylvia. Don't Let Chronic Illness Stand in Your Way: The Coach Approach to Reaching Your Full Potential. 2008. 160p. per. 11.95 (978-1-59330-515-4(X)) Aventine Pr.

Little, James W., et al. Little & Falace's Dental Management of the Medically Compromised Patient. 8th ed. 2012. (ENG., Illus.). 736p. (C). pap. 84.95 (978-0-323-08028-6(6), Mosby) Elsevier - Health Sciences Div.

Lubkin, Ilene & Larsen, Pamala. Chronic Illness: Impact & Intervention. 7th rev. ed. 2008. 634p. 86.95 (978-0-7637-5126-5(X)) Jones & Bartlett Learning, LLC.

Malone, Mary. Tough Diagnosing, Murphy's Law, & the Trouble That Comes with Them. 2010. 156p. pap. 11.99 (978-1-4520-7516-7(6)) AuthorHouse.

Margereson, Carl & Trenoweth, Steve, eds. Developing Holistic Care for Long-Term Conditions. 2009. (ENG., Illus.). 384p. (C). 45.95 (978-0-415-46081-1(6)) Routledge.

McWhirter, Kathy. Walking A Fine Line: Pressing on Through Chronic Illness. 2009. 264p. pap. 21.00 (978-1-4251-8665-4(3)) Trafford Publishing.

Miller-Day, Michelle A. Family Communication, Connections, & Health Transitions. 2010. (Health Communication Ser.). 464p. (C). 149.95 (978-1-4331-1069-6(5)); pap. 49.95 (978-1-4331-1068-9(7)) Lang, Peter Publishing, Inc.

Miller, Maria & Miller, Daniel. Mi Sueño Americano: El Viaje de una Mujer Viviendo con una Enfermedad Crónica. 2010. (SPA.). 148p. 24.99 (978-1-4520-9245-4(1)); pap. 18.99 (978-1-4520-9246-1(X)) AuthorHouse.

Morewitz, Stephen. Chronic Diseases & Health Care: New Trends in Diabetes, Arthritis, Osteoporosis, Fibromyalgia, Low Back Pain, Cardiovascular Disease, & Cancer. 2010. (ENG.). x, 376p. pap. 99.00 (978-1-4419-3953-1(9), 1441939539) Springer.

Moss, Pamela. Contesting Illness: Processes & Practices. Teghtsoonian, Katherine & Moss, Pamela, eds. 2008. (ENG.). 368p. (978-0-8020-9365-3(5)) Univ. of Toronto Pr.

Nauert, Rick. Telehealth Consumer-Provider Interaction. 2009. 220p. pap. (978-3-639-16474-9(1)) VDM Verlag Dr. Mueller e.K.

Nicol, Jane. Nursing Adults with Long Term Conditions. 2011. (ENG., Illus.). 176p. pap. (978-0-85725-441-2(3)) Learning Matters Ltd.

Nolte, Ellen & McKee, Martin. Caring for People with Chronic Conditions: A Health System Perspective. 2008. (ENG., Illus.). 288p. (C). 152.00 (978-0-335-23369-4(4), 0335233694); pap. 62.00 (978-0-335-23370-0(8), 0335233708) McGraw-Hill Education GBR. Dist: McGraw-Hill Cos., The.

Northrop, Dorothy E., et al. Health Insurance Resources: A Guide for People with Chronic Disease & Disability. 2nd ed. 2006. (Health Insurance Resources: A Guide for People with Chronic Disease Ser.). (ENG., Illus.). 232p. per. 26.95 (978-1-932603-34-7(4)) Demos Medical Publishing, LLC.

ODell, Courtney. Mothers with Multiple Sclerosis. 2008. 92p. pap. (978-3-639-01181-4(3)) VDM Verlag Dr. Mueller e.K.

Organisation for Economic Co-operation and Development Staff. Maladie, Invalidité et Travail: Surmonter les Obstacles (Vol. 2): Australie, Espagne, Luxembourg et Royaume-Uni. 2007. pap. 63.00 (978-92-64-03817-2(5)) Organization for Economic Cooperation & Development.

—Sickness, Disability & Work: Breaking the Barriers (Vol. 2): Australia, Luxembourg, Spain & the United Kingdom. 2007. pap. 49.00 (978-92-64-03815-8(9)) Organization for Economic Cooperation & Development.

—Sickness, Disability & Work: Denmark, Finland, Ireland & the Netherlands. 2008. (Illus.). 204p. pap. 63.00 (978-92-64-04968-0(1)) Organization for Economic Cooperation & Development.

Patarca-Montero, Roberto. Chronic Illness, Fatigue, & Debilitation: The Stem Cell Link: What Does the Literature Say? 2006. 265p. 59.95 (978-0-7890-2502-9(7)); pap. 39.95 (978-0-7890-2503-6(5)) Haworth Pr., Inc., The. (Haworth Medical Pr.).

Prasher, Vee P. & Kerr, Mike P. Epilepsy & Intellectual Disabilities. 2008. (Illus.). 180p. 119.00 (978-1-84800-258-6(0)) Springer.

Rea, William J. Reversibility of Chronic Generative Disease & Hypersensitivity Vol. 2: Clinical Manifestations. 2012. (ENG., Illus.). 442p. 139.95 (978-1-4398-1343-0(4), CRC Press) Taylor & Francis Group GBR. Dist: Taylor & Francis Group.

Rhodus, Nelson L. Clinician's Guide Medically Complex Dental Patients. 2009. 142p. pap. 29.95 (978-1-936176-05-2(X)) American Academy of Oral Medicine.

Robichaud, Trish, et al. After the Diagnosis: the Journey Beyond. 2009. 112p. pap. 17.88 (978-0-557-05903-4(8)) Lulu Enterprises Inc.

Schraeder, Cheryl & Shelton, Paul S., eds. Comprehensive Care Coordination for Chronically Ill Adults. 2011. (ENG., Illus.). 488p. pap. 64.99 (978-0-8138-1194-9(5), Wiley-Blackwell) Wiley, John & Sons, Inc.

Sheehy, Gail. Passages in Caregiving: Turning Chaos into Confidence. (ENG.). 2011. 416p. pap. 16.99 (978-0-06-166121-1(X), Harper Paperbacks) 2010. 368p. 27.99 (978-0-06-166120-4(1), Morrow, William & Co.) HarperCollins Pubs.

—Passages in Caregiving: Turning Chaos into Confidence. Lg. ed. 2010. (ENG.). 732p. 33.99 (978-1-4104-2989-6(X)) Thorndike Pr.

Silva, Telma. Radiation Narratives & Illness. 2009. 200p. pap. (978-3-639-17417-5(8)) VDM Verlag Dr. Mueller e.K.

Snoddon, Janet. Case Management of Long Term Conditions: Principles & Practice for Nurses. 2010. (ENG.). 224p. pap. 52.99 (978-1-4051-8005-4(6), Wiley-Blackwell) Wiley, John & Sons, Inc.

Stockdale, Brenda. You Can Beat the Odds: The Surprising Factors Behind Chronic Illness & Cancer. 2009. (ENG.). 272p. pap. 18.95 (978-1-59181-079-7(5)) Sentient Pubns.

Sullivan, Jackie. Pastoral Care to Younger Adults in Long-Term Care. 2007. (ENG., Illus.). 220p. 135.00 (978-0-7890-2941-6(3)) Routledge.

—Pastoral Care with Young & Midlife Adults in Long-Term Care. 2007. (ENG., Illus.). 220p. per. 31.95 (978-0-7890-2942-3(1)) Routledge.

Teghtsoonian, Katherine & Moss, Pamela, eds. Contesting Illness: Processes & Practices. 2008. (ENG.). 368p. pap. (978-0-8020-9512-1(7)) Univ. of Toronto Pr.

Tohme, George F. Lifestyle Makeover for Diabetics & Pre-Diabetics: 5 Lifesaving Action Steps You Must Take Now to Prevent, Manage or Reverse Diabetes & Its Deadly Complications. 2008. 306p. pap. 29.95 (978-0-9791215-1-7(5)) Lifestyle Makeover Pr.

When I Am Weak, Then I Am Strong: Keeping Faith through Adversities. 2011. 148p. 30.95 (978-1-4497-2204-3(0)); pap. 13.95 (978-1-4497-2203-6(2)) Author Solutions, Inc. (WestBow Pr.).

Wolfe-Jenson, Kate. Dancing with Monsters: Chronic Illness as Creative Transformation. 2008. 168p. 25.95 (978-0-595-51086-3(9)); pap. 15.95 (978-0-595-43566-1(1)) iUniverse, Inc.

CHRONICALLY ILL—HOME CARE

Altschuler, Jenny. Counselling & Psychotherapy for Families Facing Illness & Death. Frosh, Stephen, ed. 2nd rev. ed. 2012. (Basic Texts in Counselling & Psychotherapy Ser.). (ENG., Illus.). 208p. pap. 32.95 (978-0-230-52100-1(2)) Palgrave Macmillan.

Clotfelter, Kevin D. Who Writes a Book Because They're Angry?, 1 vol. 2009. 49p. pap. 16.95 (978-1-60813-940-8(9)) PublishAmerica, Inc.

Levine, Carol & Murray, Thomas H., eds. The Cultures of Caregiving: Conflict & Common Ground among Families, Health Professionals & Policy Makers. 2007. (ENG., Illus.). 216p. (gr. 17). per. 25.00 (978-0-8018-8771-0(2)) Johns Hopkins Univ. Pr.

Mathew, Lucy, et al. The Comfort of Home for Chronic Liver Disease: A Guide for Caregivers. 2009. (Comfort of Home Ser.). (ENG., Illus.). 360p. pap. 24.95 (978-0-9787903-2-5(4)) CareTrust Pubns., LLC.

Meyer, Maria M. & Derr, Paula. The Comfort of Home for Chronic Heart Failure: A Guide for Caregivers. 2008. (Comfort of Home Ser.). (ENG., Illus.). 360p. pap. 24.95 (978-0-9787903-3-2(2)) CareTrust Pubns., LLC.

Shenkman, Martin. Estate Planning for People with a Chronic Condition or Disability. 2009. (ENG.). 200p. pap. 21.95 (978-1-932603-66-8(2)) Demos Medical Publishing, LLC.

Votroubek, Wendy & Tabacco, Aaron. Pediatric Home Care for Nurses: A Family-Centered Approach. 3rd rev. ed. 2009. 748p. pap. 133.95 (978-0-7637-5586-7(9)) Jones & Bartlett Learning, LLC.

CHRONICALLY ILL—MENTAL HEALTH

Barr, Jr. A Patient's Voice: Inspiring & Practical Advice about Living with Chronic Health Conditions, Such As Cancer & Sarcoidosis, & Achieving Positive Re. 2009. 256p. pap. 19.95 (978-1-4401-1988-0(0)) iUniverse, Inc.

DeYoung, Eric M. How to Live a Happy, Healthy, Wealthy & Safe Life! The Missing Links in Conventional Medicine. 2011. 116p. pap. 14.95 (978-1-4269-5309-5(7)) Trafford Publishing.

Elster, Elizabeth J. Power Through Pain: Living with Reflex Neurovascular Dystrophy. 2007. 112p. per. 12.95 (978-0-595-43716-0(8)) iUniverse, Inc.

Furer, Patricia, et al. Treating Health Anxiety & Fear of Death: A Practitioner's Guide. 2006. (Series in Anxiety & Related Disorders Ser.). (Illus.). 268p. 69.95 (978-0-387-35144-5(2), 0387351442) Springer.

Harvey, I. Shevon. Temple of Care. 2008. 156p. per. (978-3-8364-3524-6(1)) VDM Verlag Dr. Mueller e.K.

Sperry, Len. Treatment of Chronic Medical Conditions: Cognitive-Behavioral Therapy Strategies & Integrative Treatment Protocols. 2008. 248p. 49.95 (978-1-4338-0389-5(5)) American Psychological Assn.

Taylor, Renee R. Cognitive Behavioral Therapy for Chronic Illness & Disability. 2010. (ENG., Illus.). xiv, 378p. pap. 79.95 (978-1-4419-3785-8(4), 1441937854) Springer.

Wolf, Msw. I Still Dream Big: Stories of Teens Living with Chronic Illness. 2009. 160p. pap. 13.99 (978-1-4490-3096-4(3)) AuthorHouse.

CHRONICALLY ILL CHILDREN

see also Chronic Diseases in Children

Bandy, Roberta. A Mother's Search for Meaning: The Dance Goes On. 2nd ed. 2009. 9.99 (978-0-7586-1777-4(1)) Concordia Publishing Hse.

Brown, Ronald T., et al. Chronic Illness in Children & Adolescents. 2007. (Advances in Psychotherapy — Evidence-Based Practice Ser.: Vol. 9). (Illus.). 86p. pap. 29.80 (978-0-88937-319-8(1)) Hogrefe Publishing.

Castillo, Christine L. Children with Complex Medical Issues in Schools: Neuropsychological Descriptions & Interventions. 2008. (Illus.). 79.00 (978-0-8261-2472-2(0)) Springer Publishing Co., Inc.

Chatelle, Melody. Journeys of Heartache & Grace: Conversations & Life Lessons from Young People with Serious Illnesses. 2008. xxix, 221p. (978-1-880292-34-1(3)) LangMarc Publishing.

Cline, Foster & Greene, Lisa C. Parenting Children with Health Issues & Special Needs: Love & Logic Essentials for Raising Happy, Healthier Kids. 2010. 105p. pap. 7.95 (978-1-935326-04-5(X)) Love & Logic Institute, Inc.

Cline, Foster W. & Greene, Lisa C. Parenting Children with Health Issues: Essential Tools, Tips, & Tactics for Raising Kids with Chronic Illness, Medical Conditions & Special Healthcare Needs. 2007. (Illus.). 384p. per. 24.95 (978-1-930429-89-5(4)) Love & Logic Institute, Inc.

Dempsey, Sharon. Extreme Parenting: Parenting Your Child with a Chronic Illness. 2008. (ENG.). 176p. pap. (978-1-84310-619-7(1)) Kingsley, Jessica Ltd.

Donoghue, Elaine A. & Kraft, Colleen A. Managing Chronic Health Needs in Child Care & Schools: A Quick Reference Guide. 2009. (ENG.). 214p. pap. 47.00 (978-1-58110-299-4(2)) American Academy of Pediatrics.

Greco, Tony. Meditations for Pain Recovery: A Holistic Approach. 2010. (ENG.). 400p. pap. 16.95 (978-0-9818482-8-0(1)) Central Recovery Pr.

Hernandez, Geri. Medically Fragile Training Manual. 2010. pap. 18.99 (978-1-61566-258-6(8)) Tate Publishing & Enterprises, LLC.

Hewitt-Taylor, Jaquelina. Providing Support at Home for Children & Young People Who Have Complex Health Needs. 2008. (ENG.). 216p. pap. 60.99 (978-0-470-51731-4(X), Wiley) Wiley, John & Sons, Inc.

Hewitt-Taylor, Jaqui. Children with Complex & Continuing Health Needs: The Experiences of Children, Families & Care Staff. 2007. (ENG.). 240p. pap. (978-1-84310-502-2(0)) Kingsley, Jessica Ltd.

Kelly, Jill. Without a Word: How a Boy's Unspoken Love Changed Everything. 2010. (ENG., Illus.). 272p. 23.99 (978-0-446-56337-6(4)) FaithWords.

Luginbuehl-Oelhafen, Ruth/R. Art Therapy with Chronic Physically Ill Adolescents: Exploring the Effectiveness of Medical Art Therapy as a Complementary Treatment. 2009. 220p. pap. 37.95 (978-0-398-07857-7(2)) Thomas, Charles C. Pub., Ltd.

Mattingly, Cheryl. The Paradox of Hope: Journeys Through a Clinical Borderland. 2010. (ENG.). 291p. 60.00 (978-0-520-26734-3(6)); pap. 26.95 (978-0-520-26735-0(4)) Univ. of California Pr.

McCarroll, Elizabeth M. Links Between Children's Health & Social Competence with Peers. 2009. 120p. pap. (978-3-639-17311-6(2)) VDM Verlag Dr. Mueller e.K.

National Center for Health Statistics (U.S.) Staff, contrib. by. Design & Operation of the National Survey of Adoptive Parents of Children with Special Health Care Needs, 2008. 2010. (978-0-8406-0634-1(6)) National Ctr. for Health Statistics.

Pepin, Ricki. God's Health Plan - the Audacious Journey to a Better Life. 2007. 308p. 27.99 (978-1-60266-699-3(7)) Xulon Pr., Inc.

Philo, Jolene. A Different Dream for My Child: Meditations for Parents of Critically or Chronically Ill Children. 2009. (ENG.). 272p. pap. 10.99 (978-1-57293-307-1(0)) Discovery Hse. Pubs.

Reston, James Jr. Fragile Innocence: A Father's Memoir of His Daughter's Courageous Journey. 2007. (ENG.). 272p. pap. 13.95 (978-1-4000-8244-5(7), Three Rivers Pr.) Crown Publishing Group.

Riddick-Grisham, Susan & Deming, Laura, eds. Pediatric Life Care Planning & Case Management, Second Edition. 2nd rev. ed. 2011. (ENG., Illus.). 1051p. 159.95 (978-1-4398-0358-5(7), CRC Press) Taylor & Francis Group GBR. Dist: Taylor & Francis Group.

Schabecoff, Philip & Schabecoff, Alice. Poisoned for Profit: How Toxins Are Making Our Children Chronically Ill — With New Information on What We Can Do. 2010. (ENG.). 368p. pap. 17.95 (978-1-60358-256-8(8)) Chelsea Green Publishing.

Snyder, Leigh. Stars in the Sand: Finding the Light of the Lord in Unexpected Places. 2011. (ENG.). 128p. pap. 11.95 (978-1-4620-2731-6(8)) iUniverse, Inc.

Valentine, Fay, ed. Nursing Care of Children & Young People with Chronic Illness. 2007. (ENG., Illus.). 280p. per. 66.99 (978-1-4051-4402-5(5), Wiley-Blackwell) Wiley, John & Sons, Inc.

Vickers, Margaret H. Working & Caring for a Child with Chronic Illness: Disconnected & Doing It All. 2006. (ENG.). 256p. 100.00 (978-1-4039-9767-8(5)) Palgrave Macmillan.

Votroubek, Wendy & Tabacco, Aaron. Pediatric Home Care for Nurses: A Family-Centered Approach. 3rd rev. ed. 2009. 748p. pap. 133.95 (978-0-7637-5586-7(9)) Jones & Bartlett Learning, LLC.

CHRONICLE OF MOREA

Shawcross, Teresa. The Chronicle of Morea: Historiography in Crusader Greece. 2009. (Oxford Studies in Byzantium Ser.). (ENG., Illus.). 418p. 150.00 (978-0-19-955700-4(4)) Oxford Univ. Pr., Inc.

CHRONICLE PLAY

see Historical Drama

CHRONOBIOLOGY

Here are entered works on time-related events in biological systems, such as development, growth, aging, cyclic phenomena, and biorhythms.

see also Biological Rhythms

Bissonette, John A. & Storch, Ilse, eds. Temporal Dimensions of Landscape Ecology: Wildlife Responses to Variable Resources. 2007. (Illus.). 284p. per. 59.95 (978-0-387-45445-0(4)); x, 286p. 129.00 (978-0-387-45444-3(6), 0387454446) Springer.

Léglise, Anne-Laure. Progress in Circadian Rhythm Research. 2008. (Illus.). 129.00 (978-1-60021-876-7(8)) Nova Science Pubs., Inc.

Naylor, Ernest. Chronobiology of Marine Organisms. 2010. (ENG., Illus.). 252p. (C). 78.00 (978-0-521-76053-9(4)) Cambridge Univ. Pr.

Redfern, Peter H. & Lemmer, B., eds. Physiology & Pharmacology of Biological Rhythms. 2010. (Handbook of Experimental Pharmacology Ser.). (Illus.). xxiv, 668p. pap. 729.00 (978-3-642-08265-8(3), 3642082653) Springer.

Stillman, Bruce & Stewart, David, eds. Clocks & Rhythms, Vol. LXXII. 2008. (ENG., Illus.). 674p. 310.00 (978-0-87969-822-5(5)); pap. 126.00 (978-0-87969-823-2(3)) Cold Spring Harbor Laboratory Pr.

Ulijaszek, S. J. & Strickland, S. S., eds. Seasonality & Human Ecology. 2009. (Society for the Study of Human Biology Symposium Ser.). (ENG., Illus.). 264p. pap. 53.00 (978-0-521-10304-6(5)) Cambridge Univ. Pr.

Youan, Bi-Botti C. Chronopharmaceutics: Science & Technology for Biological Rhythm Guided Therapy & Prevention of Diseases. Youan, Bi-Botti C., ed. 2009. (ENG., Illus.). 384p. 122.00 (978-0-471-74343-9(7), Wiley) Wiley, John & Sons, Inc.

CHRONOGRAMS

see Anagrams

CHRONOLOGY

see also Almanacs; Calendar; Clocks and Watches; Dendrochronology; Geological Time; Hindu Chronology; Jewish Chronology; Maya Chronology; Months; Radioactive Dating; Time

Bachle, Anna Elisabeth & Deger-Jalkotzy, Sigrid, eds. LH III C Chronology & Synchronisms III: LH III C Late & the transition to the Early Iron Age. Proceedings of the International Workshop held at the Austrian Academy of Sciences at Vienna, February 23rd And 24th 2007. 2009. (Denkschriften der Phil. -Hist. Klasse Ser.). (ENG., Illus.). 408p. (C). pap. 116.00 (978-3-7001-6598-9(6)) Austrian Academy of Sciences Press AUT. Dist: Brown, David Bk. Co., The.

Callender, Craig. Introducing Time. 2010. (Introducing Ser.). (ENG., Illus.). 176p. 9.95 (978-1-84831-120-6(6)) Totem Bks. GBR. Dist: Consortium Bk. Sales & Distribution.

Couzens, Reginald C. The Stories of the Months & Days. 2008. 112p. (gr. 4-7). 21.99 (978-0-554-39609-5(2)) 2008. 112p. (gr. 4-7). 24.99 (978-0-554-30306-2(X)) 2007. (ENG.). 100p. per. 16.99

(978-1-4346-9822-3(X)) 2007. (ENG.). 108p. per. 19.99 (978-1-4346-9823-0(8)) BiblioBazaar.

Gibbs, Errol A. & Grey, Philip A. Thoughts to Enlighten & Empower the Mind: 2001 Questions & Philosophical Thoughts to Inspire, Enlighten, & Empower Our World to Limitless Heights. 2011. 268p. 24.95 **(978-1-4567-4070-2(9))**; pap. 16.95 **(978-1-4567-4071-9(7))** AuthorHouse.

Langdon, Stephen H. Babylonian Menologies & the Semitic Calendars. (Ancient Mesopotamian Texts & Studies). reprint ed. 32.50 (978-0-404-18192-5(9)) AMS Pr., Inc.

Machette, Michael N., et al. Terrestrial Cosmogenic-Nuclide Dating of Alluvial Fans in Death Valley, California. 2008. (Illus.). v, 44p. (978-1-4113-2187-8(1)) United States Geological Survey.

Nott, Josiah Clark. Types of Mankind. 2008. 508p. 39.95 (978-1-4255-9663-7(0)) MPublishing.

—Types of Mankind V. 2008. 280p. 39.95 (978-1-4255-9664-4(9)) MPublishing.

Poisson, Sara. Silent Voices from the Past: A Chronicle of the Almshouse of Sullivan County. 2010. 116p. pap. 12.95 (978-1-4502-5907-1(3)) iUniverse, Inc.

Suski, P. M. The Year Names of China & Japan. 2010. (ENG.). 64p. 75.00 (978-0-415-59417-2(0)) Routledge.

CHRONOLOGY, ASSYRO-BABYLONIAN

Parker, Richard A. & Dubberstein, Waldo H. Babylonian Chronology: 626 B. C. - A. D. 75. 2007. (Illus.). 60p. pap. 12.00 (978-1-55635-453-3(3), Wipf and Stock) Wipf & Stock Pubs.

Pruzsinszky, Regine (Eds). Mesopotamian Chronology of the 2nd Millenium B. C. an Introduction to the Textual Evidence & Related Chronological Issues. 2009. (Denkschriften der Gesamtakademie Ser.). (ENG.). 232p. (C). pap. 72.00 (978-3-7001-6504-0(8)) Austrian Academy of Sciences Press AUT. Dist: Brown, David Bk. Co., The.

CHRONOLOGY, BIBLICAL

see Bible—Chronology

CHRONOLOGY, ECCLESIASTICAL

see Church History—Chronology

CHRONOLOGY, EGYPTIAN

Ashton, John & Down, David. Unwrapping the Pharaohs: How Egyptian Archaeology Confirms the Biblical Timeline. 2006. (Illus.). 218p. 34.99 (978-0-89051-468-9(2)) Master Bks.

Barta, Miroslav & Vymazalova, Hana, eds. Chronology & Archaeology in Ancient Egypt: The Third Millennium BC. 2008. (ENG.). 319p. (C). 100.00 (978-80-7308-245-1(4)) Czech Institute of Egyptology CZE. Dist: Brown, David Bk. Co., The.

Bennett, C. Alexandria & the Moon: An Investigation into the Lunar Macedonian Calendar of Ptolemaic Egypt. 2011. (Studia Hellenistica Ser.). (ENG.). 276p. (C). pap. 99.00 **(978-90-429-2505-2(1))** Peeters Pubs. & Booksellers BEL. Dist: Brown, David Bk. Co., The.

Hornung, Erik. The Egyptian Amduat: The Book of the Hidden Chamber. Warburton, David, tr. 2007. (ENG., Illus.). 446p. 95.00 (978-3-9522608-4-5(3)) Daimon Verlag CHE. Dist: AtlasBooks Distribution.

Krauss, Rolf, et al, eds. Ancient Egyptian Chronology. 2006. (Handbook of Oriental Studies: Vol. 83). (Illus.). 517p. (978-90-04-11385-5(1)) BRILL.

CHRONOLOGY, GREEK

Bennett, C. Alexandria & the Moon: An Investigation into the Lunar Macedonian Calendar of Ptolemaic Egypt. 2011. (Studia Hellenistica Ser.). (ENG.). 276p. (C). pap. 99.00 **(978-90-429-2505-2(1))** Peeters Pubs. & Booksellers BEL. Dist: Brown, David Bk. Co., The.

CHRONOLOGY, HINDU

see Hindu Chronology

CHRONOLOGY, HISTORICAL

see also Calendar; Calendars

also subdivision History—Chronology under names of countries, e.g. United States—History—Chronology

Acosta & Acosta, Ray. Revolutionary Days: A Chronology of the Mexican Revolution. 3910. (ENG.). 264p. 29.95 (978-0-9816637-1-5(0)) Editorial Mazatlan.

Adams, Sebastian. Adams' Chart of History: A Chronology of Ancient, Modern, & Biblical History. 2007. 21p. pap. (978-0-89051-513-6(1)) Master Bks.

—Adams' Synchronological Chart or Map of History. 2007. (Illus.). 21p. 37.99 (978-0-89051-505-1(0)) Master Bks.

Al-Biruni. The Chronology of Ancient Nations. Sachau, Edward C., ed. xvi, 464p. reprint ed. lib. bdg. 90.00 (978-0-89241-178-8(3)) Caratzas, Aristide D. Pub.

Censorinus & Censorinus. The Birthday Book. Parker, Holt N., tr. from LAT. 2007. (Illus.). 120p. 30.00 (978-0-226-09974-3(1)) Univ. of Chicago Pr.

Chapman, Arthur & Cooper, Hilary, eds. Constructing History 11-19. 2009. (Illus.). 176p. 112.00 (978-1-84787-187-9(9), B71879C); pap. 48.00 (978-1-84787-188-6(7), B71879P) SAGE Pubns., Ltd. GBR. Dist: SAGE Pubns., Inc.

Chapman, Michael E. Historian's Companion: Chronologies, Glossaries, Readings, Style Guide. 2008. 368p. (978-0-9786597-1-4(6)) Trebarwyth Pr.

Colton, Joel, et al. A History of the Modern World. 10th ed. 2007. (Illus.). xxxii, 1259p. (978-0-07-310748-6(4)); (978-0-07-310692-2(5)) McGraw-Hill Cos., The.

Dalal, Roshen. The Illustrated Timeline of the History of the World. 2011. (History Timelines Ser.). (Illus.). 277p. (YA). (gr. 7-12). lib. bdg. 47.95 (978-1-4488-4797-6(4)) Rosen Publishing Group, Inc., The.

Diacu, Florin. The Lost Millennium: History's Timetables under Siege. 2nd ed. 2011. (ENG., Illus.). 248p. (gr. 17). 60.00 **(978-1-4214-0287-1(4))**; pap. 25.00 **(978-1-4214-0288-8(2))** Johns Hopkins Univ. Pr.

Eder, Walter & Renger, Johannes, eds. Chronologies of the Ancient World: Names, Dates & Dynasties. Henkelman, Wouter F. M., tr. from GER. 2006. (Brill's New Pauly - Supplements Ser.). 363p. (978-90-04-15320-2(9)) BRILL.

Flexner, Doris & Flexner, Stuart Berg. The Pessimist's Guide to History: An Irresistible Compendium of Catastrophes, Barbarities, Massacres, & Mayhem - From 14 Billion Years Ago to 2007. 3rd ed. 2008. (ENG.). 512p. pap. 14.99 (978-0-06-143101-2(X), HarperPerennial) HarperCollins Pubs.

Forrest, Glen C., et al. The Illustrated Timeline of Military History. 2011. (History Timelines Ser.). (Illus.). 232p. (YA). (gr. 7-12). lib. bdg. 47.95 (978-1-4488-4794-5(X)) Rosen Publishing Group, Inc., The.

"God's Friend". A Christian Chronology of History: A Time Line of Human History from a Christian Prospective. 2011. 172p. pap. 13.96 (978-1-4269-5603-4(7)) Trafford Publishing.

Gregory, John Milton. The Hand-Book of History & Chronology Embracing Modern History, Both European & American, for the 16th, 17th, 18th & 19th Centuries for Studen. 2006. 196p. per. 18.99 (978-1-4255-1585-0(1)) MPublishing.

Hilliam, David. Monarchs, Murderers & Mistresses. 2007. 352p. pap. (978-0-7509-4804-3(3)) History Pr. Ltd.,The.

Jacobson, Judy. History for Genealogists: Using Chronological Time Lines to Find & Understand Your Ancestors. 2009. 296p. pap. 29.95 (978-0-8063-5439-2(9)) Clearfield Co.

Kerr, Gordon. Timeline History of the World. 2008. (Illus.). 164p. (978-0-7088-0674-6(0)) Futura Publications.

Napoleoni, Loretta. 10 Years That Shook the World: A Timeline of Events From 2001. 2012. (ENG., Illus.). 182p. pap. 12.95 **(978-1-60980-413-8(9))** Seven Stories Pr.

Nobel. Timelines. Date not set. (C). pap. 2.76 (978-0-395-90328-5(9)) CENGAGE Learning.

A Political Chronology of the World. 2011. (ENG.). 1008p. 675.00 (978-1-85743-577-1(X)) Routledge.

Rosenberg, Daniel & Grafton, Anthony. Cartographies of Time: A History of the Timeline. 2012. (ENG., Illus.). 272p. pap. 35.00 **(978-1-61689-058-2(4))** Princeton Architectural Pr.

Rosenberg, Daniel, et al. Cartographies of Time: A History of the Timeline. 2010. (ENG., Illus.). 272p. 50.00 (978-1-56898-763-7(3)) Princeton Architectural Pr.

Sayce, A. H., ed. Ancient Empires of the East: Herodotos I-III. 2010. (Cambridge Library Collection - Classics Ser.). 540p. pap. 39.99 (978-1-108-01096-2(2)) Cambridge Univ. Pr.

Singleton, Esther. The World's Great Events: An Indexed History of the World from B. C. 4004 to A. D. 1908, Volume 2. 2010. 520p. pap. 39.75 (978-1-142-51697-0(0)) BiblioBazaar.

Summon, Parminder Singh. Summon's Compendium of Days: An Essential Digest of Daily History, Biography, Philosophy, Customs & Traditions, Curiosities of Human Nature, & Learned Discourse Designed to Inspire & Entertain. 2007. (Illus.). 408p. per. 29.00 (978-1-59627-057-2(8), Seabury Bks.) Church Publishing, Inc.

Synchronology of the Principal Events in Sacred & Profane History from the Creation of Man to the Present. 2007. (ENG.). 322p. 45.95 (978-0-548-03915-1(1)) Kessinger Publishing, LLC.

Tischer, Gene J. Why You Were Born: The chronological story of your existence from the beginning of creation to Now. 2010. 108p. 21.23 (978-1-4520-9000-9(9)); pap. 10.68 (978-1-4520-9001-6(7)) AuthorHouse.

Truhart, Peter. Regents of Nations: Index, 5 vols. 2nd ed. 2006. (Regents of Nations Ser.: Vol. 5). 134.00 (978-3-598-21547-6(9)) Saur, K. G. Verlag GmbH & Co. DEU. Dist: Saur, K. G. Verlag GmbH & Co.

Tucker, Spencer C., ed. A Global Chronology of Conflict: From the Ancient World to the Modern Middle East, 6 vols. 2009. (Illus.). 2777p. 395.00 (978-1-85109-667-1(1), CHRMHC) ABC-CLIO, LLC.

Ussher, James. The Annals of the World. 2007. (Illus.). 960p. per. (978-0-89051-510-5(7)) Master Bks.

Vincent, Benjamin. Haydn's Dictionary of Dates & Universal Information: Relating to All Ages & Nations. 2008. (Gorgias Reference Classics Ser.: 3). 156.00 (978-1-59333-797-1(3)) Gorgias Pr., LLC.

Walker, William T. Term Paper Resource Guide to Nineteenth-Century World History, 1 vol. 2009. (Term Paper Resource Guides). 397p. 65.00 (978-0-313-35404-5(9), GR5404) Greenwood Publishing Group, Inc.

Wallraff, Martin. Julius Africanus und Die Christliche Weltchronik: Julius Africanus und Die Christliche Weltchronistik. 2006. (Texte und Untersuchungen Zur Geschichte der Altchristlichen Literatur Ser.). (ITA, GER & ENG., Illus.). VIII, 346p. 154.00 (978-3-11-019105-9(9)) De Gruyter, Walter Inc.

Wechsler, Robert. Day by Day in Jewish Sports History. 2007. 39.50 (978-0-88125-969-8(1)) Ktav Publishing Hse., Inc.

CHRONOLOGY, JEWISH

see Jewish Chronology

CHRONOLOGY, MAYA

see Maya Chronology

CHRONOLOGY, ROMAN

Feeney, D. C. Caesar's Calendar: Ancient Time & the Beginnings of History. 2007. (Sather Classical Lectures). (Illus.). 372p. 45.00 (978-0-520-25119-9(9)) Univ. of California Pr.

Feeney, Denis. Caesar's Calendar: Ancient Time & the Beginnings of History. 2008. (Sather Classical Lectures). (ENG., Illus.). 392p. pap. 21.95 (978-0-520-25801-3(0)) Univ. of California Pr.

Rupke, J. Revolutionizing Time - the History of the Roman Calendar. 2011. 240p. 149.95 (978-1-4443-9653-9(6), Wiley-Blackwell) Wiley, John & Sons, Inc.

Rupke, Jorg. The Roman Calendar from Numa to Constantine: Time, History, & the Fasti. Richardson, David M. B., tr. from GER. 2011. (ENG., Illus.). 240p. 149.95 (978-0-470-65508-5(9), Wiley-Blackwell) Wiley, John & Sons, Inc.

CHRONOLOGY, SUMERIAN

see Chronology, Assyro-Babylonian

CHRONOMETERS

Betts, Jonathan. Harrison: Eine Uhr zur Bestimmung des Längengrads. 2nd ed. 2007. (ENG., Illus.). 96p. pap. 16.95 (978-0-948065-81-1(8)) National Maritime Museum GBR. Dist: Independent Pubs. Group.

Betts, Jonathan D. Keeping Time: The Story of the Marine Chronometer. deluxe ed. (Illus.). 224p. 150.00 (978-0-917376-50-4(1)) Mariners Museum.

Cronin, John. Marine Chronometers, 1 vol. 2010. (ENG., Illus.). 112p. 29.95 (978-1-84797-185-2(7)) Crowood Pr., Ltd. GBR. Dist: Independent Pubs. Group.

Sobel, Dava. Longitude: The True Story of a Lone Genius Who Solved the Greatest Scientific Problem of His Time. 10th ed. 2007. (ENG., Illus.). 208p. per. 14.00 (978-0-8027-1529-6(X)) Walker & Co.

CHRONOMETRY, MENTAL

see Time Perception

CHRONOPHOTOGRAPHY

see also Cinematography

Adam, Hans Christian. Edward Muybridge: The Complete Locomotion Photographs. 2010. (FRE, GER & ENG., Illus.). 872p. 69.99 (978-3-8365-0941-1(5)) TASCHEN DEU. Dist: Ingram Pub. Services.

Grochau, Marcos Hexsel. An Integrated Approach to Improve Time-Lapse Seismic Interpretation. 2010. 136p. pap. (978-3-8383-2211-7(8)) Lambert Academic Publishing.

Hogg, James, et al. Sequences: Contemporary Chronophotography & Experimental Digital Art. 2009. (ImageTime Ser.). (ENG., Illus.). 256p. (gr. 17). pap. 34.50 (978-1-905674-76-3(7)) Wallflower Pr. GBR. Dist: Columbia Univ. Pr.

CHRYSANTHEMUMS

Herrington, Arthur. The Chrysanthemum. 2008. (Gardening in America Ser.). (ENG.). 172p. pap. 13.95 (978-1-4290-1286-7(2)) Applewood Bks.

CHRYSIPPUS, CA. 280-207 OR 6 B.C.

Jedan, Christoph. Stoic Virtues: Chrysippus & the Religious Character of Stoic Ethics. 2012. (ENG.). 244p. pap. 44.95 **(978-1-4411-9794-8(X))** Continuum International Publishing Group, Ltd. GBR. Dist: National Bk. Network.

Jedan, Christoph & Jedan. Stoic Virtues: Chrysippus & the Religious Character of Stoic Ethics. 2010. (Continuum Studies in Ancient Philosophy Ser.). (ENG., Illus.). 256p. 120.00 (978-1-4411-1252-1(9)) Continuum International Publishing Group, Ltd. GBR. Dist: National Bk. Network.

Løkke, HÃ¥vard. Early Stoic Epistemology. 2012. (Studies in the History of Philosophy of Mind Ser.). (ENG.). 250p. 139.00 **(978-94-007-2152-4(8)**, 9400721528) Springer.

CHRYSLER AUTOMOBILE

see also Dodge Automobile; Plymouth Automobile

Ackerson, Robert. PT Cruiser: Chrysler's Classic Design for a Modern Age. 2007. (ENG., Illus.). 208p. pap. (978-1-84584-039-6(9), 1845840399) Veloce Publishing Ltd. GBR. Dist: MBI Distribution Services/Quayside Distribution.

Chilton. Chilton Chrysler Service Manuals, 2012 Edition, Vol. 1 And 2, 2 vols. 2012. (ENG.). 2130p. 149.95 **(978-1-133-62576-6(2))** Delmar Cengage Learning.

Chilton, (Chilton). Chilton Chrysler Service Manual, 2010 Edition (2 Volume Set) 2010. (ENG.). 2016p. 149.95 (978-1-111-03654-6(3)) Delmar Cengage Learning.

Chilton Automotive Editorial Staff. Chilton Daimler Chrysler Service Manual 2008, Vol. 1 & 2, Set. 2007. (ENG.). 2400p. 149.95 (978-1-4283-2204-2(3)) Delmar Cengage Learning.

—Chrysler Compact, 1987-95. 448p. pap. 16.95 (978-0-8019-8678-9(8)) Nichols Publishing Co.

—Chrysler Mid-Size, 1981-95. 448p. pap. 16.95 (978-0-8019-8677-2(X)) Nichols Publishing Co.

Finkbeiner, Andrew. Mopar B-Body Performance Upgrades 1962-1979. 2012. (Illus.). 144p. pap. 24.95 **(978-1-934709-30-6(1))** CarTech, Inc.

Finkbeiner, Andy. How to Build Max-Performance Mopar Big Blocks. 2009. 144p. pap. 24.95 (978-1-934709-03-0(4), S-A Design) CarTech, Inc.

Freund, Ken. Chrysler 300 Dodge Charger & Magnum 2005 Thru 2009. 2010. (Haynes Repair Manual Ser.). (ENG., Illus.). 320p. pap. 26.95 (978-1-56392-855-0(8), 1563928558) Haynes Manuals, Inc.

Genat, Robert. Hemi: The Ultimate American V-8. (ENG.). 168p. 2009. 14.99 (978-0-7858-2584-5(3), 0785825843, Crestline) 2007. (Illus.). pap. 24.95 (978-0-7603-2747-0(5), 0760327475, Motorbooks) MBI Publishing Co. LLC.

—Mopar Muscle: Fifty Years: Dodge, Plymouth & Chrysler Performance. 2006. (ENG., Illus.). 384p. pap. 24.95 (978-0-7603-2679-4(7), 0760326797, Motorbooks) MBI Publishing Co. LLC.

Godfrey, Eric. Chrysler LH-Series: 1998 Thru 2004. 2010. (ENG.). 400p. pap. 29.95 (978-1-56392-733-1(0)) Haynes,Chilton.

Grist, Peter. Virgil Exner, Visioneer: The Official Biography of Virgil M. Exner, Designer Extraordinaire. 2007. (ENG., Illus.). 160p. 49.95 (978-1-84584-118-8(2), 1845841182) Veloce Publishing Ltd. GBR. Dist: MBI Distribution Services/Quayside Distribution.

Hamilton, Joe L. Chilton's Chrysler 300/Charger/Magnum: 2005-07 Repair Manual. 2008. (ENG., Illus.). 384p. pap. 29.95 (978-1-56392-685-3(7)) Haynes,Chilton.

—Chrysler 300 & Dodge Charger & Magnum: 2005 - 2009. 2011. (ENG., Illus.). 384p. pap. 29.95 (978-1-56392-911-3(2)) Haynes,Chilton.

Haynes, John. Dodge Caravan Chrysler Voyager & Town & Country: 2003 Thru 2007. 2010. (ENG., Illus.). 304p. pap. 26.95 (978-1-56392-850-5(7), 1563928507) Haynes Manuals, Inc.

Haynes Manuals Editors, ed. Chrysler LHS,Concorde,300M,Dodge Intrepid, 1998-2004. 2009. (Haynes Repair Manual Ser.). (ENG., Illus.). 320p. pap. 26.95 (978-1-56392-732-4(2), 1563927322) Haynes Manuals, Inc.

Holmstrom, Darwin. Hemi Muscle Cars. 2008. (ENG., Illus.). 336p. 50.00 (978-0-7603-3172-9(3), 0760331723, Motorbooks) MBI Publishing Co. LLC.

Maddox, Robert. Chrysler PT Cruiser: 2001 Thru 2009. 2010. (ENG.). 400p. pap. 29.95 (978-1-56392-799-7(3)) Haynes,Chilton.

Masters, Timothy & Lehto, Steve. Drawn to Injustice: The Wrongful Conviction of Timothy Masters. 2012. (ENG.). 448p. (gr. 12). pap. 9.99 **(978-0-425-24792-1(9)**, Berkley) Penguin Group (USA) Inc.

McCausey, Greg, photos by. Dodge Daytona & Chrysler Laser: The Definitive History 1984-1993. 2007. (Illus.). 184p. 25.00 (978-1-4251-2382-6(1)) Trafford Publishing.

Mccausey, Gregory. Chrysler Front Wheel Drive Performance: 1983-1992. 2009. pap. 19.00 (978-1-61584-912-3(2)) Independent Pub.

Na. How to Rebuild the Big-Block Mopar. 2012. (ENG., Illus.). 144p. pap. 24.95 **(978-1-934709-37-5(9))** CarTech, Inc.

Narus, Don. Chrysler- the Golden Age 1940-1949. 2009. 130p. pap. 22.95 (978-0-578-01121-9(2)) New Albany Bks.

—Chrysler's Land Yacht-Twon & Country Convertibles 1942-1986. 2009. pap. 22.95 (978-1-61623-211-5(0)) Independent Pub.

Nedbal, Richard. How to Build Max-Performance Hemi Engines. 2009. (Illus.). 144p. pap. 24.95 (978-1-932494-95-2(2), S-A Design) CarTech, Inc.

Ramifications of Auto Industry Bankruptcies: Hearing Before the Subcommittee on Commercial & Administrative Law of the Committee on the Judiciary, House of Representatives, One Hundred Eleventh Congress, First Session, July 22, 2009. 2010. (Illus.). iv, 282p. (978-0-16-085324-1(9), 552-070-40654-9) United States Government Printing Office.

Robinson, Jon G. Standard Catalog of 1950s Chrysler. 2006. (ENG., Illus.). 224p. per. 24.99 (978-0-89689-249-1(2), Antique Trader) Krause Pubns.

Rockwell, David G. We Were the Ramchargers: Inside Drag Racing's Legendary Team. 2009. 39.95 (978-0-7680-1932-2(X)) SAE Intl.

Schild, Jim & Schild, James J. Proving Ground: A History of Dodge, Chrysler, & Plymouth Racing. 2009. (ENG., Illus.). 192p. 40.00 (978-0-7603-3458-4(7), 0760334587, Motorbooks) MBI Publishing Co. LLC.

Shepard, Larry. How to Rebuild & Modify Chrysler 426 Hemi Engines: New Technology for 1964 to 1971 Classic Hemis & Today's Modern Crate Engines. 2007. (ENG., Illus.). 240p. (gr. 12-18). 19.95 (978-1-55788-525-8(7), HP Trade) Penguin Group (USA) Inc.

—The Mopar Six-Pack Engine Handbook: How to Rebuild & Modify the 440 6-Barrel & 340 6-Barrel or Convert Your la Small-Block (318-360 C. I.), Mopar Big Block (383-440 C. I.) or Magnum (5. 2L-5. 9L) to 6-Barrel Induction. 2008. (ENG., Illus.). 256p. (gr. 12-18). 19.95 (978-1-55788-528-9(1), HP Trade) Penguin Group (USA) Inc.

Szilagyi, Jim. How to Build Big-Inch Mopar Small Blocks. 2007. (ENG., Illus.). 144p. pap. 24.95 (978-1-932494-57-0(X), S-A Design) CarTech, Inc.

Thacker, Tony & Fetherston, David. Chrysler Concept Cars 1940-1970. 2008. (Chrysler Ser.). (Illus.). 142p. pap. 24.95 (978-1-932494-70-9(7)) CarTech, Inc.

Weertman, Willem L. Chrysler Engines 1922-1998. 2007. 69.95 (978-0-7680-1642-0(8)) SAE Intl.

Wegmann, John. Chrysler Caravan, Voyager, & Town & Country: 2003 Thru 2007. 2010. (ENG., Illus.). 384p. pap. 29.95 (978-1-56392-857-4(4)) Haynes,Chilton.

Yanik, Anthony J. Maxwell Motor & the Making of Chrysler Corporation. 2009. (Illus.). 189p. 34.95 (978-0-8143-3423-2(7)) Wayne State Univ. Pr.

Young, Tony. Chrysler, Dodge, Plymouth Muscle. 2007. 12.99 (978-0-7603-3204-7(5)) MBI Publishing Co. LLC.

CHRYSLER CORPORATION

Clark, Jennifer. Mondo Agnelli: Fiat, Chrysler, & the Power of a Dynasty. 2011. (ENG., Illus.). 368p. 29.95 **(978-1-118-01852-1(4)**, Wiley) Wiley, John & Sons, Inc.

GM & Chrysler Dealership Closures: Protecting Dealers & Consumers: Hearing Before the Committee on Commerce, Science, & Transportation, United States Senate, One Hundred Eleventh Congress, First Session, June 3, 2009. 2010. (Illus.). iv, 130p. **(978-0-16-087147-4(6)**, 552-070-41990-0) United States Government Printing Office.

Grist, Peter. Virgil Exner, Visioneer: The Official Biography of Virgil M. Exner, Designer Extraordinaire. 2007. (ENG., Illus.). 160p. 49.95 (978-1-84584-118-8(2), 1845841182) Veloce Publishing Ltd. GBR. Dist: MBI Distribution Services/Quayside Distribution.

Kousakis, James S. & Leonard, John Peter. General Motors & Chrysler: Assistance & Exit from the Troubled Asset Relief Program. 2012. **(978-1-61942-072-4(4))** Nova Science Pubs., Inc.

Lehto, Steve. Chrysler's Turbine Car: The Rise & Fall of Detroit's Coolest Creation. (ENG.). 2012. 240p. pap. 16.95 **(978-1-61374-345-4(9))** 2010. (Illus.). 224p. 24.95 *(978-1-56976-549-4(9))* Chicago Review Pr., Inc.
Narus, Don. Steering Wheels & Dashboards 1939-1949 Chrysler Corporation. 2007. 123p. pap. 22.95 *(978-0-615-17145-6(1))* New Albany Bks.
Oversight of TARP Assistance to the Automobile Industry: Field Hearing Before the Congressional Oversight Panel, One Hundred Eleventh Congress, First Session, Hearing Held in Detroit, Michigan, July 27, 2009. 2009. (Illus.). iii, 150p. *(978-0-16-084597-0(1)*, 552-070-40103-2) United States Government Printing Office.
teNeues. 125 Years of Automobiles: Illustrated Chronicle of Daimler AG. 2010. (Illus.). 304p. 59.95 *(978-3-8327-9442-2(5))* teNeues Publishing Co.
Vlasic, Bill. Once upon a Car: The Fall & Resurrection of America's Big Three Auto Makers — GM, Ford, & Chrysler. 2012. (ENG.). 400p. pap. 15.99 **(978-0-06-184563-5(9)**, William Morrow Paperbacks) 2011. 394p. E-Book 21.99 **(978-0-06-204222-4(X)**, Morrow, William & Co.) 2011. (ENG.). 400p. 26.99 *(978-0-06-184562-8(0)*, Morrow, William & Co.) 2011. (ENG.). 624p. pap. 26.99 *(978-0-06-208860-4(2)*, HarperLuxe) HarperCollins Pubs.
Yanik, Anthony J. Maxwell Motor & the Making of Chrysler Corporation. 2009. (Illus.). 189p. 34.95 *(978-0-8143-3423-2(7))* Wayne State Univ. Pr.

CHRYSOMELIDAE

Ciegler, Janet. Leaf & Seed Beetles of South Carolina (Coleoptera: Biota of South Carolina, Volume 4. 2007. (Biota of South Carolina Ser.). (Illus.). 252p. per. 40.00 *(978-0-9753471-8-8(7))* Clemson Univ. Public Service Publishing.
Jolivet, P. & Santiago-Blay, J. A. Research on Chrysomelidae, Volume 1 Volume One. 2008. 384p. *(978-90-04-15204-5(0))* BRILL.

CHRYSOPHYCEAE

Duff, K., et al. Atlas of Chrysophycean Cysts: Volume I. 2011. (Developments in Hydrobiology Ser.). (ENG.). 200p. pap. 299.00 *(978-90-481-4450-1(7)*, 9048144507) Springer.
Kristiansen, Jorgen & Andersen, Robert A., eds. Chrysophytes: Aspects & Problems. 2011. (ENG.). 351p. pap. 39.99 *(978-0-521-18007-8(4))* Cambridge Univ. Pr.
Sandgren, Craig D., et al, eds. Chrysophyte Algae: Ecology, Phylogeny & Development. 2009. (ENG., Illus.). 416p. pap. 74.00 *(978-0-521-10241-4(3))* Cambridge Univ. Pr.

CHRYSOSTOM, JOHN, SAINT, D. 407

see John Chrysostom, Saint, D. 407

CHRYSOTILE

see Serpentine

CHUANG-TZU

Palmer, Martin. The Book of Chuang Tzu. Palmer, Martin et al, trs. from CHI. rev. ed. 2007. (ENG., Illus.). 352p. (gr. 12-18). 16.00 *(978-0-14-045537-3(X)*, Penguin Classics) Penguin Group (USA) Inc.
Wilson, Carol A. Still Point of the Turning World. 2009. 304p. pap. 18.95 *(978-1-60237-296-2(9))* Amber Lotus Publishing.

CHUKCHI

Bogoras, Waldemar. Chukchee Mythology. 2009. 228p. 27.99 *(978-0-559-13230-8(1))*; 23.99 *(978-0-559-13241-4(7))*; pap. 24.75 *(978-0-559-13238-4(7))*; pap. 22.99 *(978-0-559-13233-9(6))* BiblioBazaar.

CHUNG-KUO KUNG CHAN TANG

Biographiq. Mao Zedong - the Great Helmsman. 2008. 76p. pap. 9.99 *(978-1-59986-036-7(8)*, Biographiq) Filiquarian Publishing, LLC.
May, Jennifer. Sources of Authority. 2011. 344p. pap. **(978-3-8381-2534-3(7))** Südwestdeutscher Verlag für Hochschulschriften AG & Co. KG.
McGregor, Richard. The Party: The Secret World of China's Communist Rulers. 2012. (ENG.). 336p. pap. 16.99 *(978-0-06-170876-3(3)*, HarperPerennial) HarperCollins Pubs.
Sleeboom-Faulkner, Margaret. The Chinese Academy of Social Sciences (CASS) Shaping the Reforms, Academia & China (1977-2003) 2006. 300p. *(978-90-04-15323-3(3))* BRILL.
Tse-Tung, Mao. Chinese Revolution & the Communist Party of Chin. 2011. 34p. 35.95 **(978-1-258-00288-6(4))** Literary Licensing, LLC.
Wang, Laidi. Zhong Gong Chuang Shi Ren Fang Tan Lu. 2008. (Zhen Xiang Xi Lie Ser.: Vol. 43). (CHI., Illus.). 339p. *(978-1-932138-63-4(3))* Mirror Bks. USA.
Xing, Ming & Li, Peiguang. Dang Yuan Gan Bu Xue Li Lun 2009: Danyuan Ganbu Xue Lilun 2009. 2009. (Illus.). *(978-7-5051-1718-1(1))* Red Flag Pr.
Ying, Esther Cheo. Black Country to Red China: One Girl's Journey from War-Torn England to Revolutionary China. 2009. (ENG., Illus.). 190p. pap. 14.95 *(978-0-09-953603-1(X))* Random Hse. GBR. Dist: Independent Pubs. Group.

CHUNNEL (ENGLAND AND FRANCE)

see Channel Tunnel (England and France)

CHURCH, BENJAMIN, 1734-1776

Nathaniel Philbrick. Mayflower: A Story of Courage, Community, & War. l.t. ed. 2007. (ENG.). 752p. (J). pap. 15.95 *(978-1-59413-186-8(4)*, Large Print Pr.) Thorndike Pr.

CHURCH, FREDERICK EDWIN, 1826-1900

Carr, Carr. Frederic Edwin Church. 2008. 112p. 50.00 *(978-1-974162-17-8(6))* Univ. Pr. of New England.
Carr, Gerald L. Frederic Edwin Church: Romantic Landscapes & Seascapes. 2008. (ENG., Illus.). 136p. 50.00 *(978-0-9741621-7-1(5))* Adelson Galleries, Inc.
Kornhauser, Elizabeth Mankin & Manthorne, Katherine. Fern Hunting among Picturesque Mountains: Frederic Edwin Church in Jamaica. 2010. (Olana Collection Ser.). (Illus.). 80p. 24.95 *(978-0-8014-4920-8(0))* Cornell Univ. Pr.
Navas Sanz de Santamaria, Pablo. The Journey of Frederic Edwin Church through Colombia & Ecuador April - October 1853. 2010. (SPA & ENG.). 192p. 69.95 *(978-958-8306-26-1(4))* Villegas Editores S.A. COL. Dist: Independent Pubs. Group.
Ryan, James Anthony. Frederic Church's Olana: Architecture & Landscape as Art. 2011. (Illus.). 104p. pap. 17.95 *(978-1-883789-28-2(1))* Black Dome Pr. Corp.
Wilmerding, John. Maine Sublime: Frederic Edwin Church's Landscapes of Mount Desert & Mount Katahdin. 2012. (Olana Collection Ser.). (ENG.). 80p. 24.95 **(978-0-8014-5103-4(5))** Cornell Univ. Pr.

CHURCH, WILLIAM CONANT, 1836-1917

Bigelow, Donald N. William Conant Church & the Army & Navy Journal. (Columbia University, Studies in the Social Sciences: No. 576). reprint ed. 27.50 *(978-0-404-51576-8(2))* AMS Pr., Inc.

CHURCH

see also Christian Union; Christianity; Church Work; Communion of Saints; Ecumenical Movement; Jesus Christ—Mystical Body; Language Question in the Church; Mission of the Church; Priesthood, Universal; Salvation Outside the Catholic Church; Salvation Outside the Church

Abbey, Richard. The City of God & the Church-Makers; 2006. 340p. per. 23.99 *(978-1-4255-3495-0(3))* MPublishing.
Addison, Cynthia. Mamma Said. 2009. 52p. pap. 15.49 *(978-1-4389-4060-1(2))* AuthorHouse.
Attridge, M. S. & Skira, J. Z., eds. In God's Hands: Essays on the Church & Ecumenism in Honour of Michael A. Fahey, S. J. 2006. (Bibliotheca Ephemeridum Theologicarum Lovaniensium Ser.: Vol. 199). (ENG.). 314p. (C). pap. 131.00 *(978-90-429-1830-6(6))* Peeters Pubs. & Booksellers BEL. Dist: Brown, David Bk. Co., The.
Avis, Paul D. L., ed. The Christian Church: An Introduction to the Major Traditions. 240p. 29.00 *(978-0-281-05246-2(8))* SPCK Publishing GBR. Dist: Pilgrim Pr., The/United Church Pr.
Babson, Roger W. Future of the Churches Historic & Econ. 2006. pap. 19.95 *(978-1-4286-5021-3(0))* Kessinger Publishing, LLC.
Badcock, Gary D. The House Where God Lives: The Doctrine of the Church. 2009. 382p. pap. 36.00 *(978-0-8028-4582-5(7))* Eerdmans, William B. Publishing Co.
Baldwin, Amanda Mae Gary. Lost Souls Sitting on the Pew. 2011. 40p. pap. 13.95 **(978-1-4497-1160-3(X)**, WestBow Pr.) Author Solutions, Inc.
Baldwin, Lewis V. The Voice of Conscience: The Church in the Mind of Martin Luther King, Jr, 1 vol. 2010. (ENG., Illus.). 368p. pap. 29.95 *(978-0-19-538030-9(4))* Oxford Univ. Pr., Inc.
Barnes, Albert. Miscellaneous Essays & Reviews by Albert Barnes. 2006. 376p. per. 26.99 *(978-1-4255-3957-3(2))*; (ENG.). per. 26.99 *(978-1-4255-3958-0(0))* MPublishing.
Bathrellos, Demetrios. The Theology of John Zizioulas: Personhood & the Church. Knight, Douglas, ed. 2007. 216p. 99.95 *(978-0-7546-5430-8(3))* Ashgate Publishing Co.
Beach, Nancy & Groeschel, Craig. It: How Churches & Leaders Can Get It & Keep It: How Churches & Leaders Can Get It & Keep It, 1 vol. 2008. (ENG.). 160p. 18.99 *(978-0-310-28682-0(4))* Zondervan.
Belcher, Jim. Deep Church: A Third Way Beyond Emerging & Traditional. 2009. (ENG.). 233p. pap. 17.00 *(978-0-8308-3716-8(7)*, IVP Bks.) InterVarsity Pr.
Bernard, Daniel. The Church at Its Best. 2007. 176p. pap. 12.99 *(978-1-58169-254-9(4))* Genesis Communications, Inc.
Bidwell, Kevin J. The Church as the Image of the Trinity: A Critical Evaluation of Miroslav VolfÕs Ecclesial Model. 2011. (WEST Theological Monograph Ser.). 282p. pap. 31.00 **(978-1-61097-373-1(9)**, Wipf and Stock) Wipf & Stock Pubs.
Billy Graham Evangelistic Association, prod. Preparing Your Church for New Christians. 2008. (Christian Growth Ser.). 31p. pap. 1.95 *(978-0-89066-305-9(X)*, 6305X) World Wide Pubns.
Blanchard, Ken & Hodges, Phil. The Most Loving Place in Town: A Modern Day Parable for the Church. 2010. 208p. pap. 14.99 *(978-0-8499-4704-9(9))* Nelson, Thomas Inc.
Boal, Tim. Building Authentic Community: Enjoying Christ's Church in a Postmodern Age. 2006. 236p. per. 13.99 *(978-0-88469-307-9(4))* BMH Bks.
Bruinsma, Reinder. The Body of Christ: An Adventist Understanding of the Church. 2009. 222p. 19.99 *(978-0-8280-2488-4(X))* Review & Herald Publishing Assn.
Buchanan, John M. A New Church for a New World. 2008. (Foundations of Christian Faith Ser.). (ENG.). 92p. pap. 13.00 *(978-0-664-50141-9(9))* Geneva Pr.
Buckenmaier, Achim. Universale Kirche vor Ort: Zum Verhältnis von Universalkirche und Ortskirche. 2009. (GER.). 444p. *(978-3-7917-2193-4(3))* Pustet, Friedrich GmbH & Co. KG.
Campbell, R. K. The Church of the Living God. pap. 6.95 *(978-0-88172-007-5(0))* Believers Bookshelf, Inc.
Chester, Tim & Timmis, Steve. Total Church: A Radical Reshaping Around Gospel & Community. 2008. (Re:Lit Ser.). 224p. pap. 15.99 *(978-1-4335-0208-8(9))* Crossway.
Conner, Benjamin T. Practicing Witness. 2011. 136p. pap. 16.00 *(978-0-8028-6611-0(5))* Eerdmans, William B. Publishing Co.
Cooley, W. L. The Nature of the Church. 2006. per. *(978-1-60208-001-0(1))* FBC Pubns. & Printing.
Counted, Victor. Church in Cyberspace. 2010. 72p. pap. *(978-3-8383-7707-0(9))* Lambert Academic Publishing.
Coverson, Robert James. God's Super-Natural Prescriptions: Volume I. 2008. 112p. 21.49 *(978-1-4389-2059-7(8))*; pap. 10.99 *(978-1-4389-2058-0(X))* AuthorHouse.
Crabb, Larry. Real Church: Does it exist? Can I find It? 2009. 224p. pap. 14.99 *(978-0-7852-9827-4(4))* Nelson, Thomas Inc.
Cramer, Jared C. Safeguarded by Glory: Michael Ramsey's Ecclesiology & the Struggles of Contemporary Anglicanism. 2010. (ENG.). 172p. 60.00 *(978-0-7391-4271-4(2))* Lexington Bks.
Cross, F. L. & Livingstone, E. A., eds. Dictionary of the Christian Church. 2007. 1786p. per. 49.95 *(978-1-59856-250-7(9))* Hendrickson Pubs. Marketing, LLC.
Davis, Phillip M. The Vision Casting Church. Date not set. *(978-0-9652262-2-6(0))* Orman Pr.
Davison, Andrew. For the Parish: A Critique of Fresh Expressions. 2010. (ENG.). xi, 251p. pap. 35.00 *(978-0-334-04365-2(4)*, SCM Pr.) Hymns Ancient & Modern Ltd GBR. Dist: Westminster John Knox Pr.
Dees, Doug. Resymbol: Guide to Rethink, Redefine, & Release the Church. 2010. 168p. pap. 14.99 *(978-1-935245-11-7(2))* HigherLife Development Services, Inc.
Dekoven, Stan. Setting the House in Order. 2009. 108p. pap. 15.00 *(978-1-931178-02-0(X))* Vision Publishing.
Delotavo, Alan J. Back to the Original Church: The Secret Behind Church Movements. 2010. 112p. pap. 14.00 *(978-1-55635-566-0(1)*, Resource Pubns.) Wipf & Stock Pubs.
DeMott, Nancy, et al. Holy Places: Matching Sacred Space with Mission & Message. 2007. *(978-1-56699-345-6(8))* Alban Institute, Inc.
Dever, Mark. 12 Challenges Churches Face. 2008. 192p. 17.99 *(978-1-58134-944-3(0))* Crossway.
Dodd, C. H. History & the Gospel. 2008. 192p. *(978-1-4437-3250-5(8))* 2007. 188p. per. *(978-1-4067-8804-4(X))* Read Bks. (Pomona Pr.).
Drane, John. An A - Z of the Missional Church. 2012. (A-Z of the Missional Church Ser.). 144p. pap. 19.99 *(978-1-84825-064-2(9)*, Canterbury Pr. Norwich) Hymns Ancient & Modern Ltd GBR. Dist: Westminster John Knox Pr.
Driscoll, Mark & Breshears, Gerry. Vintage Church: Timeless Truths & Timely Methods. (Re:Lit:Vintage Jesus Ser.). 336p. 2012. pap. 17.99 **(978-1-4335-2758-6(8))** 2008. 21.99 *(978-1-4335-0130-2(9))* Crossway.
Dula, Peter. Cavell, Companionship, & Christian Theology. 2010. (AAR Reflection & Theory in the Study of Religion Ser.). (ENG.). 272p. 65.00 *(978-0-19-539503-7(4))* Oxford Univ. Pr., Inc.
Ellens, J. Harold. Honest Faith for Our Time: Truth-Telling about the Bible, the Creed, & the Church. 2010. 194p. pap. 22.00 *(978-1-60899-708-4(1)*, Pickwick Pubns.) Wipf & Stock Pubs.
Fackre, Gabriel J. The Church: Signs of the Spirit & Signs of the Times. 2006. (Christian Story, a Pastoral Systematics Ser.: Vol. 5). 185p. per. 22.00 *(978-0-8028-3392-1(6))* Eerdmans, William B. Publishing Co.
Fajfr, Ruth S. The Prototype Church. pap. 2.49 *(978-1-56632-029-0(1))* Revival Literature.
Fakes, Dennis. C h u r c H: A vision of what the church could Be. 2008. 84p. pap. 10.95 *(978-0-595-52845-5(7))* iUniverse, Inc.
Fletcher, Paul. Disciplining the Divine: Toward an (Im)Political Theology. 2009. 218p. 99.95 *(978-0-7546-6716-2(2))*; pap. 39.95 *(978-0-7546-6722-3(7))* Ashgate Publishing Co.
Frangipane, Francis. When Many Are One: How to Lay Aside Our Differences & Come Together as the House of God. 2009. (ENG.). 224p. pap. 14.99 *(978-1-59979-529-4(9)*, Charisma Hse.) Charisma Media.
Friesen, Dwight J. Thy Kingdom Connected: What the Church Can Learn from Facebook, the Internet, & Other Networks, 1 vol. 2009. (Emersion). (ENG.). 192p. pap. 14.99 *(978-0-8010-7163-8(1))* Baker Bks.
Gaillardetz, Richard R. Ecclesiology for a Global Church: A People Called & Sent. 2008. (Theology in Global Perspective Ser.). 312p. pap. 30.00 *(978-1-57075-769-3(0))* Orbis Bks.
Giertz, Bo. ChristÕS Church: Her Biblical Roots, Her Dramatic History, Her Saving Presence, Her Glorious Future. Andr3/4, Hans, tr. 2010. 208p. pap. 23.00 *(978-1-60899-703-9(0)*, Resource Pubns.) Wipf & Stock Pubs.
González Faus, José Ignacio. Builders of Community: Rethinking Ecclesiastical Ministry. 2012. (ENG.). 176p. lib. bdg. 21.99 *(978-1-934996-25-6(4)*, Convivium Press) Convivium Pr., Inc.
Good, Jack. The Dishonest Church. 2008. (ENG.). 256p. pap. 17.00 *(978-1-878282-07-1(7))* St. Johann Pr.
Gould, Meredith. The Word Made Fresh: Communicating Church & Faith Today. 2008. 192p. pap. 22.00 *(978-0-8192-2285-5(2)*, Morehouse Publishing) Church Publishing, Inc.
Gustafson, James M. Treasure in Earthen Vessels: The Church As Human Community. 2008. (Library of Theological Ethics Ser.). (ENG.). 176p. pap. 25.00 *(978-0-664-23296-2(5))* Westminster John Knox Pr.
Hahn, Scott & Socias, James. The Church: Sacrament of Salvation. 2009. *(978-1-936045-09-9(5))* Midwest Theological Forum.
Hall, Timothy J. Church, Go to Hell! Please? A Call for Revival! Plus 53 Bonus Articles from the Heart. 2009. 336p. pap. 18.99 *(978-1-60791-219-4(8))* Xulon Pr., Inc.
Halley, Charles. The Heart of the Matter: Changing the World God's Way. 2006. 179p. per. 19.99 *(978-0-8272-1452-1(9))* Chalice Pr.
Hamilton, Elaine Martens. Church on the Couch: Does the Church Need Therapy?, 1 vol. 2008. (ENG.). 176p. pap. 14.99 *(978-0-310-28391-1(4))* Zondervan.
Hammett, Edward H. Reaching People under 40 While Keeping People Over 60: Being Church for All Generations. 2007. (Columbia Partnership Leadership Ser.). 180p. per. 24.99 *(978-0-8272-3254-9(3))* Chalice Pr.
Harcum, E. Rae. Saving Our Church: Five Systemic Diseases Pose a Vital Mission for the Organized Church. 2009. xiv, 129p. E-Book *(978-0-7618-4699-4(9))* Hamilton Bks.
Harper, Brad & Metzger, Paul Louis. Exploring Ecclesiology: An Evangelical & Ecumenical Introduction, 1 vol. 2009. 352p. (C). pap. 26.99 *(978-1-58743-173-9(4))* Brazos Pr.
Harvey, Barry. Can These Bones Live? A Catholic Baptist Engagement with Ecclesiology, Hermeneutics, & Social Theory. 2008. 304p. (C). pap. 28.00 *(978-1-58743-081-7(9))* Brazos Pr.
Harvey, D. D. La Iglesia: The Church. (SPA.). 272p. *(978-84-7228-679-5(7)*, 220483) Clie, Editorial.
Haudel, Matthias. Die Selbsterschließung des dreieinigen Gottes: Grundlage eines ökumenischen Offenbarungs-, Gottes- und Kirchenverständnisses. 2006. (Forschungen Zur Systematischen und Okumenischen Theologie Ser.). (GER.). 640p. (C). 104.00 *(978-3-525-56338-0(8))* Vandenhoeck & Ruprecht GmbH & Co. KG DEU. Dist: ISD.
Haymes, Brian. On Being the Church: Revisionist Baptist Identity. 2009. (Studies in Baptist History & Thought Ser.). 236p. pap. 27.00 *(978-1-60608-598-1(0)*, Wipf and Stock) Wipf & Stock Pubs.
Heath, Elaine A. & Kisker, Scott T. Longing for Spring. 2011. (ENG.). 116p. pap. 31.25 *(978-0-7188-9242-5(9))* Lutherworth Pr., The GBR. Dist: Printondemand-worldwide.com.
Heim, Maximilian Heinrich. Joseph Ratzinger: Life in the Church & Living Theology: Fundamentals of Ecclesiology. Miller, Michael J., tr. from GER. 2007. 614p. 29.95 *(978-1-58617-149-0(6))* Ignatius Pr.
Henderson, Gladys B. Dilapidated Houses: My Vision of the Laodicean Church Today. 2008. 32p. pap. 8.00 *(978-0-8059-7176-7(9))* Dorrance Publishing Co., Inc.
Henderson, Jim & Casper, Matt. Jim & Casper Go to Church: Frank Conversation about Faith, Churches, & Well-Meaning Christians. 2007. (ENG.). 208p. 16.99 *(978-1-4143-1331-3(4)*, BarnaBks.) Tyndale Hse. Pubs.
Hirsch, Alan. The Forgotten Ways: Reactivating the Missional Church. 2009. (Illus.). 304p. pap. 19.99 *(978-1-58743-164-7(5))* Brazos Pr.
Hirsch, Alan & Altclass, Darryn. The Forgotten Ways Handbook: A Practical Guide for Developing Missional Churches, 1 vol. 2009. 224p. pap. 13.99 *(978-1-58743-249-1(8))* Brazos Pr.
Hirsch, Alan & Hirsch, Debra. Untamed: Reactivating a Missional Form of Discipleship, 1 vol. 2010. (Shapevine Ser.). (ENG.). 208p. pap. 14.99 *(978-0-8010-1343-0(7))* Baker Bks.
Hocking, W. E., et al. Church & the New World Mind: The Drake Lectures for 1944. (Essay Index Reprint Ser.). reprint ed. 20.95 *(978-0-8369-9698-2(4))* Ayer Co. Pubs., Inc.
Horton, Michael Scott. People & Place: A Covenant Ecclesiology. 2008. (ENG.). 336p. pap. 35.00 *(978-0-664-23071-5(7))* Westminster John Knox Pr.
Hubbard, David A. Iglesias: Quien las Necesita?: Churches, Who Needs Them? (SPA.). 128p. *(978-84-7228-254-4(6)*, 220485) Clie, Editorial.
Ihsen, Florian. Eine Kirche in der Liturgie: Zur ekklesiologischen Relevanz ökumenischer Gottesdienstgemeinschaft. 2010. (Forschungen Zur Systematischen und Okumenischen Theologie Ser.). (GER.). 313p. (C). 96.00 *(978-3-525-56360-1(4))* Vandenhoeck & Ruprecht GmbH & Co. KG DEU. Dist: ISD.
Izuzquiza, Daniel. Rooted in Jesus Christ: Toward a Radical Ecclesiology. 2009. (Illus.). 304p. pap. 35.00 *(978-0-8028-6279-2(9))* Eerdmans, William B. Publishing Co.
Johnson, Kim Allan. The Team: God's Vision for His Church Is Greater Than You Ever Thought Possible. 2007. 4.97 *(978-0-8163-2203-9(1))* Pacific Pr. Publishing Assn.
Johnston, Rick. Church Life Course. 2011. 192p. pap. 26.50 **(978-1-4461-6033-6(5))** Lulu Enterprises Inc.
Kariatlis, Philip. Church As Communion: The Gift & Goal of Koinonia. 2010. (ENG.). 288p. (C). pap. 27.00 **(978-1-921817-08-3(9))** ATF Pr. AUS. Dist: Brown, David Bk. Co., The.
Katz, Art & Volk, Paul. The Spirit of Truth. 2008. 105p. reprint ed. pap. 10.00 *(978-0-9749631-1-2(9))* Burning Bush Pr.
Kauffman, J. Timothy. Reconnecting the Church. 2010. 234p. 29.99 *(978-1-4500-8719-3(1))* Xlibris Corp.
Kimbrough, S. T., Jr., ed. Orthodox & Wesleyan Ecclesiology. 2007. 300p. 20.00 *(978-0-88141-268-0(6))* St. Vladimir's Seminary Pr.
Kirkpatrick, Matthew D. Attacks on Christendom in a World Come of Age: Kierkegaard, Bonhoeffer, & the Question of Religionless Christianity. 2011. (Princeton Theological Monographs). 258p. pap. 28.00 **(978-1-60899-550-9(X)**, Pickwick Pubns.) Wipf & Stock Pubs.
Kluck, Ted & DeYoung, Kevin. Why We Love the Church: In Praise of Institutions & Organized Religion. 2009. (ENG.). 240p. pap. 14.99 *(978-0-8024-5837-7(8))* Moody Pubs.
Komonchak, Joseph A. Who Are the Church? 2008. (Père Marquette Lecture in Theology Ser.). (C). *(978-0-87462-588-2(2))* Marquette Univ. Pr.
Kraus, C. Norman. The Authentic Witness: Credibility & Authority. 2010. (Illus.). 200p. pap. 23.00 *(978-1-60899-230-0(6))* Wipf & Stock Pubs.
Kydd, Ronald A. N. Finding Pieces of the Puzzle: A Fresh Look at the Christian Story. 2011. 284p. pap. 31.00 **(978-1-60608-567-7(0)**, Wipf and Stock) Wipf & Stock Pubs.
La Due, William J. The Trinity Guide to the Christian Church. 2006. (ENG.). 176p. pap. 29.95 *(978-0-8264-1950-7(X))* Continuum International Publishing Group, Ltd. GBR. Dist: National Bk. Network.

C

Lam, Joseph & Lam Cong, Joseph Quy. Theologische Verwandtschaft: Augustinus Von Hippo und Joseph Ratzinger/Papst Benedikt XVI. 2009. (GER.). 268p. *(978-3-429-03077-3(3))* Echter Wuerzburg.

Leith, John H. The Church: A Believing Fellowship. 2011. 204p. pap. 23.00 ***(978-1-61097-570-4(7)***, Wipf and Stock) Wipf & Stock Pubs.

Liederbach, Mark & Reid, Alvin L. The Convergent Church: Missional Worshipers in an Emerging Culture, 1 vol. 2009. 304p. pap. 19.99 *(978-0-8254-3645-1(1))* Kregel Pubns.

Locke, Kenneth A. The Church in Anglian Theology: An Historical, Theological & Ecumenical Exploration. 2009. (Illus.). 232p. 99.95 *(978-0-7546-6530-4(5))* Ashgate Publishing Co.

Mackay, John A. Ecumenics. 2009. (ENG.). 304p. pap. 19.99 *(978-1-4391-9402-7(5))* Simon & Schuster.

Mannion, Gerard. Ecclesiology & Postmodernity: Questions for the Church in Our Time. 2007. 249p. per. 29.95 *(978-0-8146-5223-7(9))* Liturgical Pr.

Mannion, Gerard, ed. Church & Religious 'Other' 2011. (ENG.). 314p. pap. 44.95 ***(978-0-567-43391-6(9)***, T&T Clark Int'l) Continuum International Publishing Group, Ltd. GBR. Dist: National Bk. Network.

Mannion, Gerard & Mannion. Church & Religious 'Other' 2008. (Ecclesiological Investigations Ser.). (ENG.). 314p. 130.00 *(978-0-567-03286-7(8)*, T&T Clark Int'l) Continuum International Publishing Group, Ltd. GBR. Dist: National Bk. Network.

Mannion, Gerard, et al. Christian Community Now: Ecclesiological Investigations. 2008. (Ecclesiological Investigations Ser.). (ENG.). 224p. 130.00 *(978-0-567-03242-3(6)*, T&T Clark Int'l) Continuum International Publishing Group, Ltd. GBR. Dist: National Bk. Network.

Mansini, Guy. The Word Has Dwelt among Us: Explorations in Theology. 2008. ix, 276p. pap. *(978-1-932589-45-0(7))* Ave Maria Univ.

McClung, Floyd. You See Bones, I See an Army: Changing the Way We Do Church. 2008. (ENG.). 255p. *(978-1-57658-438-5(0))* YWAM Publishing.

McGehee, J. Pittman & Thomas, Damon. The Invisible Church: Finding Spirituality Where You Are, 1 vol. 2008. (Psychology, Religion, & Spirituality Ser.). 160p. 34.95 *(978-0-313-36530-0(X)*, C36530, Praeger Pubs.) Greenwood Publishing Group, Inc.

McIntosh, Gary. Here Today, There Tomorrow: Unleashing Your Church's Potential. 2010. *(978-0-89827-422-6(2))* Wesleyan Publishing Hse.

McKay, Bobbie. When God Becomes Real: Stories of Presence, Models of Church. 2008. ix, 83p. pap. *(978-0-913552-71-1(2))* Exploration Pr.

McQuilken, Robertson. The Five Smooth Stones: Essential Principles for Biblical Ministry. 2007. (ENG., Illus.). 240p. per. 14.99 *(978-0-8054-4518-3(8)*, B&H Bks.) B&H Publishing Group.

Mehta, Hemant. I Sold My Soul on EBay: Viewing Faith through an Atheist's Eyes. 2007. (ENG.). 224p. pap. 13.99 *(978-1-4000-7347-4(2)*, WaterBrook Pr.) Doubleday Religious Publishing Group, The.

Metzger, Paul Louis. Consuming Jesus: Beyond Race & Class Divisions in a Consumer Church. 2007. 184p. pap. 16.00 *(978-0-8028-3068-5(4))* Eerdmans, William B. Publishing Co.

Meyers, Patty. Live, Learn, Pass It On! The Practical Benefits of Generations Growing Together in Faith. 2007. 141p. per. 13.00 *(978-0-88177-469-6(3))* Discipleship Resources.

Milne, Bruce. Dynamic Diversity: Bridging Class, Age, Race & Gender in the Church. 2007. (ENG.). 190p. per. 17.00 *(978-0-8308-2806-7(0)*, IVP Acad.) InterVarsity Pr.

Moody, J. My Church Its Characteristics & Perpet. 2006. 348p. per. 34.00 *(978-1-57978-523-9(9))* Baptist Standard Bearer, Inc.

Moran, Gabriel. Believing in a Revealing God: The Basis of the Christian Life. 2009. 216p. pap. 29.95 *(978-0-8146-5388-3(X)*, Michael Glazier Bks.) Liturgical Pr.

Morey, Tim. Embodying Our Faith: Becoming a Living, Sharing, Practicing Church. 2009. (ENG.). 197p. pap. 16.00 *(978-0-8308-3729-8(9)*, IVP Bks.) InterVarsity Pr.

Mulyanegara, Riza. Church Marketing. 2010. 268p. pap. *(978-3-8383-4967-1(9))* Lambert Academic Publishing.

Nee, Watchman. Church Affairs. 244p. pap. 9.25 *(978-0-87083-378-6(2)*, 08003001) Living Stream Ministry.

—La Iglesia Gloriosa: The Glorious Church. (SPA.). 192p. *(978-84-7228-799-0(8)*, 220482) Clie, Editorial.

—La Iglesia Normal: The Normal Church. (SPA.). *(978-84-7228-798-3(X)*, 220484) Clie, Editorial.

Newbigin, Lesslie. The Household of God: Lectures on the Nature of Church. 2008. 156p. pap. 18.00 *(978-1-60608-222-5(1)*, Wipf and Stock) Wipf & Stock Pubs.

Newlands, George M. The Church of God. 2008. (Traces of Liberality: the George Newlands Reprint Ser.). 132p. pap. 16.00 *(978-1-55635-917-0(9))* Wipf & Stock Pubs.

Niebuhr, H. Richard. The Responsibility of the Church for Society & Other Essays. Culp, Kristine A., ed. 2008. (Library of Theological Ethics Ser.). (ENG.). 155p. pap. 30.00 *(978-0-664-23048-7(2))* Westminster John Knox Pr.

Nugent, John, ed. Radical Ecumenicity: Pursuing Unity & Continuity after John Howard Yoder. 2010. 240p. pap. 25.00 *(978-0-89112-042-1(4)*, ACU Pr.) Abilene Christian Univ. Pr.

Oakland Roger. Faith Undone: The Emerging Church... a New Reformation or an End-Time Deception. 2007. 263p. per. *(978-0-9791315-1-6(0))* Lighthouse Trails Publishing Co.

Oh, Gwang Seok. John Wesley's Ecclesiology: A Study in Its Sources & Development. 2007. (Revitalization: Explorations in World Christian Movements Ser.). (ENG.). 324p. per. 58.00 *(978-0-8108-5964-7(5))* Scarecrow Pr., Inc.

Osborne, B. A Theology of the Church for the Third Millennium: A Franciscan Approach. 2009. (Studies in Systematic Theology Ser.). *(978-90-04-17657-7(8))* BRILL.

Oshin, Vincent O. Biblical Christianity: From Man-Centred to a Christ-Centred Church. 2009. 228p. pap. 15.99 *(978-1-60791-285-9(6))* Xulon Pr., Inc.

Paeth, Scott. Exodus Church & Civil Society: Public Theology & Social Theory in the Work of Jürgen Moltmann. 2008. (New Critical Thinking in Religion, Theology & Biblical Studies). 232p. 99.95 *(978-0-7546-6201-3(2))* Ashgate Publishing Co.

Paga, Larry J. Communicating with God. 2008. 148p. pap. 11.99 *(978-1-58169-263-1(3))* Genesis Communications, Inc.

Pearle, Bob. The Vanishing Church: Searching for Significance in the 21st Century. 2009. 148p. pap. 14.95 *(978-1-934749-39-5(7)*, 800-747-0738) Hannibal Bks.

Percy, Martyn. Belief, Practice & the Church: Unattended Moments. 2010. (Explorations in Practical, Pastoral & Empirical Theology Ser.). 204p. pap. 39.95 *(978-0-7546-6605-9(0))* Ashgate Publishing Co.

—Shaping the Church: The Promise of Implicit Theology. 2010. (Explorations in Practical, Pastoral & Empirical Theology Ser.). (Illus.). 204p. 99.95 *(978-0-7546-6600-4(X))* Ashgate Publishing Co.

Pierce, Chuck D. & Sytsema, Rebecca Wagner. The Future War of the Church: How We Can Defeat Lawlessness & Bring God's Order to the Earth. 2007. (ENG.). 320p. per. 16.99 *(978-0-8307-4414-5(2))* Gospel Light Pubns.

Platt, David. Radical Together: Unleashing the People of God for the Purpose of God. 2011. (ENG.). 176p. pap. 14.99 *(978-1-60142-372-6(1)*, Multnomah) Doubleday Religious Publishing Group, The.

Porter, Lawrence B. A Guide to the Church: Its Origin & Nature, Its Mission & Its Ministries. 2008. *(978-0-8189-1255-9(3))* St Pauls/Alba Hse. Pubs.

Ramsey, Michael. The Gospel & the Catholic Church, 1 vol. 2009. (ENG.). 249p. 16.95 *(978-1-59856-389-4(0))* Hendrickson Pubs. Marketing, LLC.

—The Gospel & the Catholic Church. 2008. 248p. pap. 27.00 *(978-1-60608-245-4(0)*, Wipf and Stock) Wipf & Stock Pubs.

Reed, T. L. Church Folkz, 1 vol. 2010. 116p. pap. 19.95 *(978-1-4489-7011-7(3))* PublishAmerica, Inc.

Rescher, Nicholas. Church's Thesis after 70 Years. Olszewski, Adam et al, eds. 2007. (ENG.). 551p. (gr. 11). 159.95 *(978-3-938793-09-1(0))* Ontos Verlag DEU. Dist: Transaction Pubs.

Rhody, Donald. Portraits of the Church: Reflections & Considerations of God's Design. 2011. pap. 22.99 ***(978-1-61346-085-6(6))*** Tate Publishing & Enterprises, LLC.

Rieger, Hans-Martin. Theologie als Funktion der Kirche: Eine Systematisch-Theologische Untersuchung zum Verhaltnis von Theologie und Kirche in der Moderne. 2007. (Theologische Bibliothek Töpelmann Ser.). (GER.). XI, 556p. 182.00 *(978-3-11-019949-9(1))* De Gruyter, Walter Inc.

Salvetti, Neville. Who Is Jesus the Christ. 2011. 62p. pap. 15.99 ***(978-1-4653-0036-2(8))*** Xlibris Corp.

Scheid, Edward G. Catholic Teaching on Church. 2010. viii, 75p. pap. ***(978-1-56077-902-5(0))*** Center for Learning, The.

Shoop, Marcia W. Mount. Let the Bones Dance: Embodiment & the Body of Christ. 2010. (ENG.). 184p. pap. 30.00 *(978-0-664-23412-6(7))* Westminster John Knox Pr.

Sider, J. Alexander. To See History Doxologically: History & Holiness in John Howard Yoder's Ecclesiology. 2011. 224p. pap. 28.00 *(978-0-8028-6573-1(9))* Eerdmans, William B. Publishing Co.

Sjogren, Steve. Making a Good Church Great: Becoming a Community God Calls Home. 2010. (ENG.). 192p. 19.99 *(978-0-8307-4662-0(5))* Gospel Light Pubns.

Smit, Peter-Ben. Old Catholic & Philippine Independent Ecclesiologies in History: The Catholic Church in Every Place. 2011. (Brill's Series in Church History Ser.). XIV, 548p. ***(978-90-04-20647-2(7))*** BRILL.

Smith, Paul R. Integral Christianity: The Spirit's Call to Evolve. 2011. (ENG., Illus.). 408p. 24.95 *(978-1-55778-891-7(X))* Paragon Hse. Pubs.

Stott, John. The Living Church: Convictions of a Lifelong Pastor. 2007. (ENG.). 180p. 17.00 *(978-0-8308-3486-0(9)*, IVP Bks.) InterVarsity Pr.

Strivens, Robert. Which Church? 2007. 172p. per. *(978-0-85234-668-6(9))* Evangelical Pr.

Summers, Steve. Friendship: Exploring Its Implications for the Church in Postmodernity. 2010. (Ecclesiological Investigations Ser.). (ENG.). 224p. 130.00 *(978-0-567-49064-3(5)*, T&T Clark Int'l) Continuum International Publishing Group, Ltd. GBR. Dist: National Bk. Network.

Summers, Steve. Friendship: Exploring Its Implications for the Church in Postmodernity. 2011. (ENG.). 224p. pap. 44.95 ***(978-0-567-55635-6(2)***, T&T Clark Int'l) Continuum International Publishing Group, Ltd. GBR. Dist: National Bk. Network.

Sutherland, Martin. Peace, Toleration & Decay: The Ecclesiology of Later Stuart Dissent. 2007. (Studies in Christian History & Thought: Ser.). 246p. pap. 26.00 *(978-1-59752-791-0(2)*, Wipf and Stock) Wipf & Stock Pubs.

Tayler, John. A Retrospect of the Religious Life of England. 2007. (ENG.). 382p. 48.95 *(978-0-548-05253-2(0))* Kessinger Publishing, LLC.

Thiessen, Gesa Elsbeth. Ecumenical Ecclesiology: Unity, Diversity & Otherness in a Fragmented World. Hogan, Linda, ed. & frwd. by. 2009. (Ecclesiological Investigations Ser.). 272p. 130.00 *(978-0-567-00913-5(0)*, T&T Clark Int'l) Continuum International Publishing Group, Ltd. GBR. Dist: National Bk. Network.

Thomas, Jesse. Church & the Kingdom A New Testament S. 2006. 328p. per. 33.00 *(978-1-57978-521-5(2))* Baptist Standard Bearer, Inc.

Thompson, George B. Church on the Edge of Somewhere: Ministry, Marginality, & the Future. 2007. *(978-1-56699-348-7(2))* Alban Institute, Inc.

Towns, Elmer L. What's Right with the Church: A Manifesto of Hope. 2009. (ENG.). 224p. 17.99 *(978-0-8307-5134-1(3))* Gospel Light Pubns.

Tozer, A. W. Reclaiming Christianity: A Call to Authentic Faith. 2009. (ENG.). 224p. pap. 14.99 *(978-0-8307-4690-3(0))* Gospel Light Pubns.

Treacy, Gerald C. Heaven's Beginning: A Simplified Edition of the Encyclical Mystici Corporis Christi, the Mystical Body of Christ, by Pope Pius XII. 2011. 34p. 35.95 ***(978-1-258-02576-2(0))*** Literary Licensing, LLC.

Tserklevych, Natalia. The Knowledge of God & Participation in the Trinitarian Community. 2008. 100p. pap. *(978-3-639-00715-2(8))* VDM Verlag Dr. Mueller e.K.

Vallet, Ronald E. Congregations at the Crossroads: Remembering to Be Households of God. 2006. 256p. pap. 27.00 *(978-1-59752-875-7(7)*, Wipf and Stock) Wipf & Stock Pubs.

Van Gelder, Craig. The Missional Church in Context: Helping Congregations Develop Contextual Ministry. Van Gelder, Craig, ed. 2007. (Missional Church Ser.). (Illus.). 243p. per. 20.00 *(978-0-8028-4567-2(3))* Eerdmans, William B. Publishing Co.

Van Loon, Michelle. The Church for Skeptics: A Conversation for Thinking People. 2007. pap. *(978-1-932902-71-6(6))* FaithWalk Publishing.

Vanderwell, Howard. The Church of All Ages: Generations Worshiping Together. 2007. *(978-1-56699-358-6(X))* Alban Institute, Inc.

Velez, Lisa M. A Message to the Body of Christ: What the Spirit of the Lord Is Saying to the Churches. 2009. 294p. pap. 19.95 *(978-1-4327-4160-0(8))* Outskirts Pr., Inc.

Vondey, Wolfgang. People of Bread: Rediscovering Ecclesiology. 2008. 448p. pap. 29.95 *(978-0-8091-4559-1(6))* Paulist Pr.

Washington Gladden. The Church & Modern Life. 2007. (ENG.). 126p. pap. 18.99 *(978-1-4264-6032-6(5))*; 138p. pap. 19.99 *(978-1-4264-6398-3(7))* BiblioBazaar.

Watson, Natalie. Introducing Feminist Ecclesiology. 2008. 135p. pap. 21.00 *(978-1-60608-160-0(8)*, Wipf and Stock) Wipf & Stock Pubs.

White, Stephen Ross. The Seeking Church: A Space for All. 2009. (ENG.). 170p. pap. 26.95 *(978-1-85607-628-9(8))* Columba Pr. IRL. Dist: Dufour Editions, Inc.

White, Thomas. Selected Writings of James Madison Pendl. 2006. 468p. per. 40.00 *(978-1-57978-046-3(6))*; (ENG.). 488p. per. 40.00 *(978-1-57978-048-7(2))*; (ENG.). 460p. per. 40.00 *(978-1-57978-047-0(4))* Baptist Standard Bearer, Inc.

Williams, Donald T. The Devil's Dictionary of the Christian Faith. 2008. 128p. pap. 16.99 *(978-0-8272-0638-0(0))* Chalice Pr.

Willis, Johnny. Preparing the Church for the End Times. 2011. pap. 11.99 *(978-1-61739-318-1(5))* Tate Publishing & Enterprises, LLC.

Wilson-Hartgrove, Jonathan. New Monasticism: What It Has to Say to Today's Church. 2008. 160p. pap. 15.99 *(978-1-58743-224-8(2))* Brazos Pr.

Withrow, Lisa R. Claiming New Life: A Church for the Future: A Practical Process Ecclesiology. 2008. 24.99 *(978-0-8272-0511-6(2))* Chalice Pr.

Woods, C. Jeff & Woods, Charles Jeffrey. On the Move: Adding Strength, Speed, & Balance to Your Congregation. 2009. 19.99 *(978-0-8272-2728-6(0))* Chalice Pr.

Yehoshua, Avram. The Lifting of the Veil: Acts 15:20-21. 2009. 268p. 22.78 *(978-1-4251-2328-4(7))* Trafford Publishing.

Zizioulas, John & McPartlan, Paul. Communion & Otherness: Further Studies in Personhood & the Church. 2007. (ENG.). 330p. 150.00 *(978-0-567-03147-1(0)*, T&T Clark Int'l) Continuum International Publishing Group, Ltd. GBR. Dist: National Bk. Network.

Zizioulas, John & Zizioulas. Communion & Otherness: Further Studies in Personhood & the Church. 2007. (ENG.). 330p. 55.00 *(978-0-567-03148-8(9)*, T&T Clark Int'l) Continuum International Publishing Group, Ltd. GBR. Dist: National Bk. Network.

CHURCH—AUTHORITY

see also Freedom of Speech in the Church

Anglican/Roman Catholic International Commission & Catholic Truth Society of Canada Staff. The Gift of Authority: An Agreed Statement by the Anglican-Roman Catholic International Commission (ARCIC) 48p. pap. 6.95 *(978-1-55126-246-8(0)*, 1550) Anglican Bk. Ctr. CAN. Dist: Forward Movement Pubns.

Arthur, Gordon. Law Liberty & Church: Authority & Justice in the Major Churches in England. 2006. (Ashgate New Critical Thinking in Religion, Theology, & Biblical Studies). 222p. 99.95 *(978-0-7546-5437-7(0))* Ashgate Publishing Co.

Avis, Paul. Beyond the Reformation? Authority, Primacy & Unity in the Conciliar Tradition. 2008. (ENG.). 256p. 49.95 *(978-0-567-03357-4(0)*, T&T Clark Int'l) Continuum International Publishing Group, Ltd. GBR. Dist: National Bk. Network.

Boardman, George Dana. The Church: The Divine Ideal. 2008. 234p. pap. 14.99 *(978-0-7684-2659-5(6))* Destiny Image Pubs.

Cahoy, William John. In the Name of the Church: Vocation & Authorization of Lay Ecclesial Ministry. 2012. ***(978-0-8146-3423-3(0))*** Liturgical Pr.

Christo, Gus George. Bishops as Successors to the Apostles According to John Chrysostom: Ecclesiastical Authority in the Early Church. 2008. 172p. 99.95 *(978-0-7734-4977-0(9))* Mellen, Edwin Pr., The.

de Kroon, Marijn. We Believe in God & in Christ. Not in the Church: The Influence of Wessel Gansfort on Martin Bucer. 2009. (Princeton Theological Seminary Studies in Reformed Theology & History Ser.). (ENG.). 128p. pap. 30.00 *(978-0-664-23293-1(0))* Westminster John Knox Pr.

Hanna, Tony. With Respect: Authority in the Catholic Church. 2008. (ENG.). 95p. pap. 19.95 *(978-1-85607-609-8(1))* Columba Pr. IRL. Dist: Dufour Editions, Inc.

Lacey, Michael J. & Oakley, Francis. The Crisis of Authority in Catholic Modernity, 1 vol. 2011. (ENG., Illus.). 392p. pap. 35.00 *(978-0-19-977878-2(7))* Oxford Univ. Pr., Inc.

McKenzie, John L. Authority in the Church. 2009. (John L. Mckenzie Reprint Ser.). 194p. pap. 22.00 *(978-1-60608-148-8(9)*, Wipf and Stock) Wipf & Stock Pubs.

Meckley, Philip. Conscience, Moral Discernment, & Magisterial Moral Decision Making. 2010. 224p. pap. *(978-3-8383-3737-1(9))* Lambert Academic Publishing.

Miller, Monica Migliorino. Sexuality & Authority in the Catholic Church. 2007. 320p. per. 28.00 *(978-1-58966-128-8(1))* Univ. of Scranton Pr.

Oelrich, Anthony. A Church Fully Engaged: Yves Congar's Vision of Ecclesial Authority. 2011. E-Book ***(978-0-8146-8042-1(9))*** Liturgical Pr.

Rankin, David. Tertullian & the Church. 2007. (ENG.). 248p. pap. 51.00 *(978-0-521-04400-4(6))* Cambridge Univ. Pr.

Sotinel, Claire. Church & Society in Late Antique Italy & Beyond: Convergences Tensions & Negotiations. 2010. (Variorum Collected Studies). (FRE & ENG., Illus.). 340p. 165.00 *(978-1-4094-0022-6(0))* Ashgate Publishing Co.

WordAlone Network, compiled by. By What Authority? Confronting Churches Who No Longer Believe their Own Message. 2008. (Illus.). 270p. pap. 14.95 *(978-0-9801835-0-4(2))* Hoffman Hse. Pr.

CHURCH—BIBLICAL TEACHING

Abingdon Press, ed. What's in the Bible about Church? 2009. (Why Is That in the Bible & Why Should I Care? Ser.). 68p. pap. 8.00 *(978-0-687-65294-5(4))* Abingdon Pr.

Ali, Hull, ed. The Church in the Power of the Spirit: Keswick Yearbook. 2006. (ENG., Illus.). 240p. per. 12.99 *(978-1-85078-720-4(4))* Authentic Media.

Anderson, Larry James. The Great Commission Revealed. 2008. 104p. pap. 12.49 *(978-1-4389-0909-7(8))* AuthorHouse.

Arment, Ben. Church in the Making: What Makes or Breaks a New Church Before It Starts. 2010. (ENG.). 208p. 17.99 *(978-0-8054-6473-3(5)*, B&H Bks.) B&H Publishing Group.

Ashmore, Ray. All things to all Men. 2010. 134p. pap. 15.95 *(978-0-557-59344-6(1))* Lulu Enterprises Inc.

Boardman, George Dana. The Church: The Divine Ideal. 2008. 234p. pap. 14.99 *(978-0-7684-2659-5(6))* Destiny Image Pubs.

Butticaz, Simon David. L'identité de L'église Dans les Actes des Apôtres: De la Restauration D'Israël à la Conquête Universelle. 2010. (Beihefte zur Zeitschrift für die neutestamentliche Wissenschaft und die Kunde der älteren Kirche Ser.). (FRE.). XXII, 556p. 182.00 ***(978-3-11-022953-0(6))*** De Gruyter, Walter Inc.

Carroll, B. Ecclesia the Church. 2006. 180p. per. 21.00 *(978-1-57978-325-9(2))* Baptist Standard Bearer, Inc.

Couch, Mal, ed. A Biblical Theology of the Church. 2006. 336p. pap. 22.99 *(978-0-8254-2411-3(9))* Kregel Pubns.

Dant, James & Dant, James C. How Does the Church Decide? 2009. pap. *(978-0-9821806-6-2(7))* NextSunday Resources.

Delotavo, Alan J. Contemporary Evangelicalism & the Restoration of the Prototypal Church. 2007. 228p. pap. 25.00 *(978-1-55635-395-6(2))* Wipf & Stock Pubs.

Dever, Mark. What Is a Healthy Church? 2007. (IXMarks Ser.). 128p. 12.99 *(978-1-58134-937-5(8))* Crossway.

Flew, R. Newton. Jesus & His Church. 2009. 192p. pap. 22.00 *(978-1-60608-722-0(3)*, Wipf and Stock) Wipf & Stock Pubs.

Friesen, John & Friesen, Virginia. What's Your Church Like? 2007. 264p. per. 15.99 *(978-1-60266-607-8(5))* Xulon Pr., Inc.

Getz, Gene A. The Measure of a Healthy Church: How God Defines Greatness in a Church. 2007. (ENG.). 224p. per. 14.99 *(978-0-8024-5124-8(1))* Moody Pubs.

Grant, Hector J. What Is the Church? Occasional & Seasonal Sermons for the Busy Pastor. 2007. 196p. per. 15.95 *(978-1-4327-0883-2(X))* Outskirts Pr., Inc.

Griswold, Alexander Viet. Christs Warning to the Churches A Sermon. 2006. pap. 15.95 *(978-1-4286-6202-5(2))* Kessinger Publishing, LLC.

Gulley, Philip. If the Church Were Christian: Rediscovering the Values of Jesus. 2010. (ENG.). 224p. 23.99 *(978-0-06-169876-7(8)*, HarperOne) HarperCollins Pubs.

Heukelum, Richard Van. Priority Mail: The Seven Churches of Revelation. 2007. (Illus.). 70p. pap. *(978-0-87227-523-2(X))* Regular Baptist Pr.

Hume, Douglas A. The Early Christian Community: A Narrative Analysis of Acts 2:41-47 & 4:32-35. 2011. (Wissenschaftliche Untersuchungen zum Neuen Testament, 2 / No. 298 Ser.). 187p. pap. 97.50 *(978-3-16-150729-8(0))* Mohr Siebeck GmbH & Co. KG DEU. Dist: Coronet Bks.

Jarrard, Dan. Behavior in the House of God. 2009. pap. 6.95 *(978-1-61623-848-3(8))* Independent Pub.

Johns, Terry. Truth or Tradition. 2009. 136p. pap. 14.99 *(978-1-60791-270-5(8))* Xulon Pr., Inc.

Johnson, Ali. Biography of the Bride: The Divine Union between Christ & His Church. 2009. 72p. pap. 12.95 *(978-1-4389-7498-9(1))* AuthorHouse.

Johnson, Andy & Brower, K. E. Holiness & Ecclesiology in the New Testament. Brower, Kent E. & Johnson, Andy, eds. 2007. 385p. per. 35.00 *(978-0-8028-4560-3(6))* Eerdmans, William B. Publishing Co.

Keller, Matt. The up the Middle Church: ... playing the game of ministry one yard at a Time... 2008. 204p. 24.99 *(978-1-4389-3573-7(0))*; pap. 19.99 *(978-1-4389-3574-4(9))* AuthorHouse.

Kendagor, Solomon K. Every Tongue & Nation: Biblical Perspective on Cultural Diversity in the Church Today. 2007. 116p. pap. 10.95 *(978-1-4327-0154-3(1))* Outskirts Pr., Inc.

Kryskow, Faytene. Marked: A Generation of Dread Champions Rising to Shift Nations. 2009. pap. 17.99 *(978-0-7684-2819-3(X))* Destiny Image Pubs.

Kuen, Alfred. Por Que la Iglesia? Why the Church. (SPA.). *(978-84-7645-419-0(8),* 223529) Clie, Editorial.

Lai Meng, Wan. Israel: A Light unto the Nations. 2009. (Illus.). 392p. pap. 17.99 *(978-1-4490-1253-3(1))* AuthorHouse.

Lalli, Nicholas T. New Testament Church & the Function of its Ministries. 58p. pap. 10.00 *(978-1-930989-04-7(0))* T.K.M. Pubns.

Lee, Mike. Release from Captivity. 2009. 264p. 24.99 *(978-1-4389-3811-0(X))*; pap. 16.50 *(978-1-4389-3810-3(1))* AuthorHouse.

Lee, Witness. Three Aspects of the Church: The Organization of the Church (Book 3) 2007. per. 9.00 *(978-0-7363-3475-4(0))* Living Stream Ministry.

—Three Crucial Matters for the Increase & Building of the Church: Begetting, Nourishing, & Teaching. 2007. per. 10.75 *(978-0-7363-3326-9(6))* Living Stream Ministry.

Martin, Isaac D. The Mystery of Christ & the Church. 2007. 79p. (YA). (gr. 11). pap. 3.95 *(978-0-7399-2389-4(7))* Rod & Staff Pubs., Inc.

Meacham, John & Ackelson, Lon. Is Your Church Heavenly? A Question from Christ for Every Christian. 2009. 216p. pap. 16.95 *(978-1-934363-34-8(0))* Zoe Life Publishing.

Neil M. Phelan, Jr. The Support of God's Ministry: Ordained of God. 2009. 204p. pap. 17.49 *(978-1-4389-3251-4(0))* AuthorHouse.

Paxton, W. Apostolic Church Being an Inquiry into T. 2006. 352p. per. 34.00 *(978-1-57978-642-7(1))* Baptist Standard Bearer, Inc.

Payne, J. L. Christian Theology of the New Testament Church: ¿A New Testament Church Ministry¿s Perspective of the Apostle Doctrines¿. 2007. (Illus.). 588p. per. 19.95 *(978-0-9800202-1-2(2))* Church Hse. Pub.

Pugliese, Ritchie. The Fourth Wave of the Holy Spirit: The Bravery Anointing to Do the Incredible & Conquer the Impossible, 1 vol. 2010. 92p. pap. 19.95 *(978-1-4489-4408-8(2))* PublishAmerica, Inc.

Quinn, Kay. How Much Does God Co$T? 2009. 120p. 21.49 *(978-1-4490-3998-1(7))*; pap. 14.95 *(978-1-4490-3997-4(9))* AuthorHouse.

Rast, Jeff. Free His People! Pursuing a More Biblical View of the People of God. 2008. 176p. pap. 12.45 *(978-1-4389-1721-4(X))* AuthorHouse.

Robertson, O. Palmer. God's People in the Wilderness: The Church in Hebrews. 2009. (ENG.). 160p. 17.99 *(978-1-84550-477-9(1),* Mentor) Christian Focus Pubns. GBR. Dist: STL Distribution North America.

Samra, James G. & Samra. Being Conformed to Christ in Community: A Study of Maturity, Maturation & the Local Church in the Undisputed Pauline Epistles. 2006. (Library of New Testament Studies: Vol. 320). (ENG.). 280p. 140.00 *(978-0-567-04354-2(1),* T&T Clark Int'l) Continuum International Publishing Group, Ltd. GBR. Dist: National Bk. Network.

Scales, LaFayette. What Is the Church Coming To. 2007. per. 0.01 net. *(978-1-60402-297-1(3))* Independent Pub.

Schweizer, Eduard. Church Order in the New Testament. 2006. 240p. pap. 25.00 *(978-1-59752-810-8(2),* Wipf and Stock) Wipf & Stock Pubs.

Scott, Johnny & Christ In Youth Staff. Speak: A 9-Week Small Group Collision - Obeying the Call. 2010. (Rock Your Face off Jr. High Resource Ser.). (ENG.). 128p. 14.99 *(978-0-7847-2406-4(7))* Standard Publishing.

Shaw, M. Thomas. Conversations with Scripture & with Each Other: Spiritual Formation for Lay Leaders. 2008. (ENG.). 132p. pap. 16.95 *(978-0-7425-6279-0(4))* Rowman & Littlefield Publishers, Inc.

Sheffield, Frederick R. Things They Don't Tell You Before Becoming a Christian. 2008. 228p. pap. 14.99 *(978-1-60477-654-6(4))* Xulon Pr., Inc.

Sherman, Paul R. Many Small Make A Great: A Study of the Church, the Body of Christ, as seen in the Tabernacle. 2009. 213p. 24.95 *(978-1-57736-417-7(1))* Providence Hse Pubs.

Smith, Frederick George. The Last Reformation. 2008. 180p. 25.99 *(978-0-554-24605-5(8))* 2008. 180p. 22.99 *(978-0-554-33908-5(0))* 2006. (ENG.). 160p. pap. 19.99 *(978-1-4264-6917-6(9))* 2006. (ENG.). 178p. pap. 21.99 *(978-1-4264-6999-2(3))* BiblioBazaar.

Sorge, Bob. It's Not Business, It's Personal. 2009. (Illus.). 87p. pap. 9.00 *(978-0-9749664-6-5(0))* Oasis Hse.

Stibbs, Alan. Such a Great Salvation: The Collected Essays of Alan Stibbs. Atherstone, Andrew, ed. 2008. (ENG., Illus.). 320p. pap. 19.99 *(978-1-84550-423-6(2),* Mentor) Christian Focus Pubns. GBR. Dist: STL Distribution North America.

Stinsen, Michael. Father Make Them One: A Prayer of Jesus. 2010. (ENG.). 176p. pap. 11.95 *(978-0-615-37256-3(2))* One Body Pr.

Stuart, C.E. Simple Papers on the Church of God. 2007. 172p. per. *(978-1-4067-8920-1(8),* Pierides Pr.) Read Bks.

Sunday Asylum, DVD + Book: Being the Church in Occupied Territory. 2010. (ENG.). pap. 39.99 *(978-0-8341-2596-4(X),* 9780834125964) Beacon Hill Pr. of Kansas City.

Tavo, Felise & Tavo, F. Woman, Mother & Bride: An Exegetical Investigation into the 'Ecclesial' Notions of the Apocalypse. 2007. (Biblical Tools & Studies). (ENG.). 420p. (C). 114.00 *(978-90-429-1814-6(4))* Peeters Pubs. & Booksellers BEL. Dist: Brown, David Bk. Co., The.

Terry, Thomas C. Army of the Lord. 2009. pap. 10.99 *(978-1-60791-247-7(3))* Xulon Pr., Inc.

Thompson, Richard P. Keeping the Church in Its Place: The Church as Narrative Character in Acts. 2006. (ENG.). 320p. pap. 34.95 *(978-0-567-02645-3(0),* T&T Clark Int'l) Continuum International Publishing Group, Ltd. GBR. Dist: National Bk. Network.

—Keeping the Church in Its Place: The Church as Narrative Character in the Book of Acts. 2006. (ENG.). 320p. 110.00 *(978-0-567-02654-5(X),* T&T Clark Int'l) Continuum International Publishing Group, Ltd. GBR. Dist: National Bk. Network.

Twelftree. People of the Spirit. 2009. xvii, 269p. pap. *(978-0-281-05536-4(X))* Baker Academic.

Twelftree, Graham H. People of the Spirit: Exploring Luke's View of the Church, 1 vol. 2009. 304p. (C). pap. 25.00 *(978-0-8010-3880-8(4))* Baker Academic.

Viola, Frank. Finding Organic Church: A Comprehensive Guide to Starting & Sustaining Authentic Christian Communities, 1 vol. 2009. (ENG.). 320p. pap. 14.99 *(978-1-4347-6866-7(X))* Cook, David C.

—From Eternity to Here: Rediscovering the Ageless Purpose of God, 1 vol. 2009. (ENG.). 320p. pap. 14.99 *(978-1-4347-6870-4(8))* Cook, David C.

—Reimagining Church: Pursuing the Dream of Organic Christianity. 2008. (ENG.). 320p. pap. 14.99 *(978-1-4347-6875-9(9))* Cook, David C.

Viola, Frank & Barna, George. Pagan Christianity? Exploring the Roots of Our Church Practices. (ENG.). 336p. 2012. pap. 14.99 ***(978-1-4143-6455-1(5))*** 2008. 17.99 *(978-1-4143-1485-3(X))* Tyndale Hse. Pubs. (BarnaBks.).

Vischer, Lukas, et al. Unity of the Church in the New Testament & Today. Crouch, James E., tr. from GER. 2010. 296p. pap. 40.00 *(978-0-8028-6376-8(0))* Eerdmans, William B. Publishing Co.

Vlach, Michael J. The Church as a Replacement of Israel: An Analysis of Supersessionism. 2009. (Edition Israelogie Ser.). 222p. 43.95 *(978-3-631-58603-7(5))* Lang, Peter GmbH, Europaischer Verlag der Wissenschaften DEU. Dist: Lang, Peter.

Walker, Kevin D. Different Colored Boats: Book 1, 1 vol. 2009. 175p. pap. 19.95 *(978-1-60749-635-9(6))* PublishAmerica, Inc.

Warren, Kay & Holladay, Tom. The Church: 11 Core Truths to Build Your Life On, 1 vol. 2008. (Foundations Ser.). (ENG.). 80p. pap. 7.99 *(978-0-310-27692-0(6))* Zondervan.

Witmer, Kenneth. The Church — "My Delight Is in Her" A Study of the Doctrine of the Church. 2007. 397p. (YA). (gr. 11). 12.30 *(978-0-7399-2360-3(9))* Rod & Staff Pubs., Inc.

Wright, Gary Douglas. Worship Awakening: An Urgent Message for the Dying American Church. 2007. 467p. per. 18.99 *(978-1-57921-899-7(7))* WinePress Publishing.

Wright, William Killen. Eternal Life: The Doctrine of Eternal Life Examined. 2009. 215p. pap. 15.95 *(978-1-4327-2393-4(6))* Outskirts Pr., Inc.

CHURCH—FOUNDATION

see also Christianity—Origin; Pentecost; Popes—Primacy

Del Vecchio, Daniel. Piedras Fundamentales de Fe Cristiana: Foundation of the Christian Faith. (SPA.). 160p. *(978-84-7228-525-5(1),* 363500) Clie, Editorial.

Eristhee, Thomas. The Church Revealed. 2007. 128p. per. *(978-1-55452-157-9(2))* Essence Publishing.

Hession, Patrick J. Reconciliation, Healing, & Restoration of the Church. 2008. 240p. pap. 15.50 *(978-0-615-20265-5(9))* Noisseh Publishing.

CHURCH—HISTORY OF DOCTRINES

Abraham, Martin. Evangelium und Kirchengestalt: Reformatorisches Kirchenverständnis heute. (Theologische Bibliothek Töpelmann Ser.).Tr. of Gospel & the Shape of the Church. A Reformational Understanding of the Church Today. (GER.). XV, 601p. 300.00 ***(978-3-11-181861-0(6))***; 2007. 182.00 *(978-3-11-019444-9(9))* De Gruyter, Walter Inc.

Alexander, David C. The Emergence of Augustine's Early Ecclesiology (386-391) 2008. (Patristic Studies). (C). 91.95 *(978-1-4331-0103-8(3))* Lang, Peter Publishing, Inc.

Anderson, Ray S. An Emergent Theology for Emerging Churches. 2006. (ENG., Illus.). 236p. per. 18.00 *(978-0-8308-3391-7(9),* IVP Bks.) InterVarsity Pr.

Becker, Judith. Gemeindeordnung und Kirchenzucht: Johannes a Lascos Kirchenordnung für London (1555) und die reformierte Konfessionsbildung. 2007. (Studies in Medieval & Reformation Traditions: History, Culture, Religion, Ideas). 576p. *(978-90-04-15784-2(0))* BRILL.

Bennett, Richard. School of the Prophet. 2010. 36p. 21.99 *(978-1-59038-996-6(4))* Deseret Bk. Co.

Benson, Pius. The Church in the Theological Writings of Avery Dulles: Impulses for African Ecclesiology. (European University Studies: Vol. 852). 341p. pap. 68.95 *(978-3-631-56492-9(9))* Lang, Peter GmbH, Europaischer Verlag der Wissenschaften DEU. Dist: Lang, Peter Publishing, Inc.

Boguslawski O.P., RevStephen & Fastiggi, Robert, eds. Called to Holiness & Communion: Vatican II on the Church. 2009. 300p. pap. 25.00 *(978-1-58966-158-5(3))* Univ. of Scranton Pr.

Bollinger, Dennis E. First-Generation Anabaptist Ecclesiology, 1525-1561: A study of Swiss, German, & Dutch Sources. 2009. (Illus.). 296p. 109.95 *(978-0-7734-4748-6(2))* Mellen, Edwin Pr., The.

Burgaleta, Claudio M. Manual de la Eclesiología para Los Católicos de Hoy. 2012. (SPA.). ***(978-0-7648-2038-0(9))*** Liguori Pubns.

Carroll, B. Ecclesia the Church. 2006. 180p. per. 21.00 *(978-1-57978-325-9(2))* Baptist Standard Bearer, Inc.

Chan, Simon. Liturgical Theology: The Church as Worshiping Community. 2006. (ENG.). 208p. per. 25.00 *(978-0-8308-2763-3(3),* IVP Acad.) InterVarsity Pr.

Cheatham, Richard C. The God Makers. 2009. 164p. pap. 13.00 *(978-1-4389-9393-5(5))* AuthorHouse.

Clark, Katherine. The Orthodox Church. 2009. (Simple Guides). (ENG., Illus.). 144p. pap. 10.95 *(978-1-85733-487-6(6),* Simple Guides) Kuperard Pubs. GBR. Dist: Random Hse., Inc.

Elizondo, Virgilio. Beyond Borders: Writings of Virgilio Elizondo & Friends. Matovina, Timothy, ed. 2009. 320p. pap. 37.00 *(978-1-60608-670-4(7),* Wipf and Stock) Wipf & Stock Pubs.

Ellingson, Stephen. The Megachurch & the Mainline: Remaking Religious Tradition in the Twenty-First Century. 2007. 256p. 52.50 *(978-0-226-20489-5(8))*; per. 22.50 *(978-0-226-20490-1(1))* Univ. of Chicago Pr.

Elstub, Colin. Contradiction & Controversy in the Bible. 2008. 163p. pap. 13.95 *(978-1-4092-3661-0(7))* Lulu Enterprises Inc.

Fehring, Richard J. & Notare, Theresa. Human Fertility: Where Faith & Science Meet: Proceedings of an Interdisciplinary Conference, August 11 & 12, 2006, Washington, DC. 2008. (C). pap. *(978-0-87462-732-9(X))* Marquette Univ. Pr.

Gadenz, Pablo T. Called from the Jews & from the Gentiles: Pauline Ecclesiology in Romans 9-11. 2009. (Wissenschaftliche Untersuchungen zum Neuen Testament Ser.). (Illus.). XI, 393p. pap. 157.50 *(978-3-16-150091-6(1))* Mohr Siebeck GmbH & Co. KG DEU. Dist: Coronet Bks.

Grimm, Veronika. From Feasting to Fasting: The Evolution of a Sin. 2010. (ENG.). 304p. pap. 39.95 *(978-0-415-58904-8(5))* Routledge.

Hanley, P. J. Israel Awakening: Why the Church Needs to Wake up Concerning Israel. 2008. 226p. per. 14.99 *(978-1-60247-889-3(9))* Tate Publishing & Enterprises, LLC.

Harms, Frederik Av. In God's Custody: The Church, a History of Divine Protection: A Study of John Calvin's Ecclesiology based on his Commentary on the Minor Prophets. 2010. (Reformed Historical Theology Ser.). (GER & ENG.). 248p. (C). 108.00 *(978-3-525-56922-1(X))* Vandenhoeck & Ruprecht GmbH & Co. KG DEU. Dist: ISD.

Hesse, O. & van Oort, J., eds. Christentum und Politik in der Alten Kirche. 2009. (Patristic Studies). (GER.). 154p. (C). pap. 55.00 *(978-90-429-2165-8(X))* Peeters Pubs. & Booksellers BEL. Dist: Brown, David Bk. Co., The.

Horst, Alicia, et al, eds. Missio Dei #14 English: Bike Movement. 2007. (SPA., Illus.). 21p. 3.95 *(978-1-933845-08-1(2),* Mission Focus) Mennonite Mission Network.

Izbicki, Thomas M. Reform, Ecclesiology, & the Christian Life in the Late Middle Ages. 2008. (Variorum Collected Studies). 286p. 144.95 *(978-0-7546-5948-8(8))* Ashgate Publishing Co.

Janz, Denis R. Luther & Late Medieval Thomism: A Study in Theological Anthropology. 2009. (ENG.). 200p. (C). pap. 38.95 *(978-1-55458-235-8(0))* Wilfrid Laurier Univ. Pr. CAN. Dist: Univ. of Toronto Pr.

Jenson, Matt & Wilhite, David. Church. 2010. (Guides for the Perplexed Ser.). (ENG.). 264p. 24.95 *(978-0-567-03337-6(6))*; 80.00 *(978-0-567-03336-9(8))* Continuum International Publishing Group, Ltd. GBR. (T&T Clark Int'l). Dist: National Bk. Network.

Jones, Tony. The Teaching of the Twelve: Believing & Practicing the Primitive Christianity of the Ancient Didache Community. 2009. (ENG.). 128p. (gr. 13). pap. 14.99 *(978-1-55725-590-7(3))* Paraclete Pr., Inc.

La Due, William J. The Trinity Guide to the Christian Church. 2006. (ENG.). 176p. pap. 29.95 *(978-0-8264-1950-7(X))* Continuum International Publishing Group, Ltd. GBR. Dist: National Bk. Network.

Malesic, Jonathan. Secret Faith in the Public Square: An Argument for the Concealment of Christian Identity. 2009. 256p. (C). pap. 28.00 *(978-1-58743-226-2(9))* Brazos Pr.

Malone, George K. The True Church: A Study in the Apologetics of Orestes Augustus Brownson. 2011. 122p. 39.95 ***(978-1-258-06187-6(2))*** Literary Licensing, LLC.

Markschies, Christoph. Origenes und Sein Erbe: Gesammelte Studien. 2007. (Texte und Untersuchungen zur Geschichte der altchristlichen Literatur Ser.). (GER.). X, 283p. 140.00 *(978-3-11-019278-0(0))* De Gruyter, Walter Inc.

McCarroll, Thomas. Secrets of the Cults. 2009. 206p. 25.50 *(978-1-60693-958-1(0),* Eloquent Bks.) AEG Literary Publishing Services, Inc.

Moore, Marvin. Challenge to the Remnant. 2008. pap. 16.99 *(978-0-8163-2273-2(2))* Pacific Pr. Publishing Assn.

Muther, Urs-Ullrich. Paulinische Ökonomie: Der Effizienzbegriff in 1. Korinther 12 und seine Bedeutung für die Gemeindekonzeption. 2010. (Religion in der Öffentlichkeit Ser.). (GER.). 386p. 90.95 *(978-3-631-60941-5(8))* Lang, Peter GmbH, Europaischer Verlag der Wissenschaften DEU. Dist: Lang, Peter.

Nichols, Aidan. Theology in the Russian Diaspora: Church, Fathers, Eucharist in Nikolai Afanas'ev (1893-1966) 2008. (ENG.). 312p. pap. 42.00 *(978-0-521-09147-3(0))* Cambridge Univ. Pr.

Owens, L. Roger. The Shape of Participation: A Theology of Church Practices. 2010. 204p. pap. 22.00 *(978-1-60608-519-6(0),* Cascade Bks.) Wipf & Stock Pubs.

Preus, Herman Amberg. The Communion of Saints: A Study of the Origin & Development of Luther's Doctrine of the Church. 184p. 2008. 37.95 *(978-1-4367-1384-9(6))* 2007. (ENG.). per. 22.95 *(978-1-4325-8149-7(X))* Kessinger Publishing, LLC.

—The Communion of Saints: A Study of the Origin & Development of Luther's Doctrine of the Church. 2008. 172p. pap. 15.00 *(978-1-60608-309-3(0),* Wipf and Stock) Wipf & Stock Pubs.

Ratzinger, Joseph, et al. Gottes Projekt: Nachdenken über Schöpfung und Kirche. 2009. (GER.). 140p. *(978-3-7917-2174-3(7))* Pustet, Friedrich GmbH & Co. KG.

Schroder, Tilman Matthias. Naturwissenschaften und Protestantismus im Deutschen Kaiserreich: Die Versammlungen der Gesellschaft Deutscher Naturforscher und Arzte und ihre Bedeutung für die Evangelische Theologie. 2008. (Contubernium. Tubinger Beitrage zur Universitats- und Wissenschaftsgeschichte Ser.). (GER., Illus.). 561p. (C). 135.00 *(978-3-515-09222-7(6))* Steiner, Franz Verlag Wiesbaden GmbH DEU. Dist: Brown, David Bk. Co., The.

Stone, Bryan. A Reader in Ecclesiology. 2012. (Ashgate Contemporary Ecclesiology Ser.). 256p. 29.95 ***(978-1-4094-2857-2(5))***; 296p. 99.95 ***(978-1-4094-2855-8(9))***; 296p. pap. 29.95 ***(978-1-4094-2856-5(7))*** Ashgate Publishing Co.

Stout, Tracey Mark. A Fellowship of Baptism: Karl Barth's Ecclesiology in Light of His Understanding of Baptism. 2010. (Princeton Theological Monographs). 208p. pap. 23.00 *(978-1-60608-995-8(1),* Pickwick Pubns.) Wipf & Stock Pubs.

Swedenborg, Emanuel. The New Jerusalem & Its Heavenly Doctrine. 2007. Orig. Title: De Nova Hierosolyma et Ejus Doctrina Coelesti. 140p. per. 14.99 *(978-1-60459-094-4(7))* Wilder Pubns. Ltd.

Thiessen, Gesa E. Apostolic & Prophetic. 2012. (ENG.). 206p. (C). pap. 39.00 ***(978-0-227-68025-4(1))*** Clarke, James Co., Ltd. GBR. Dist: Brown, David Bk. Co., The.

Thomasset, Alain. L'ecclésiologie de John Henry Newman Anglican (1816-1845) 2006. (Bibliotheca Ephemeridum Theologicarum Lovaniensium Ser.). (FRE & ENG.). 748p. (C). pap. 116.00 *(978-90-429-1742-2(5))* Peeters Pubs. & Booksellers BEL. Dist: Brown, David Bk. Co., The.

Vickers, Douglas. When God Converts a Sinner: Confessional Perspectives on Justification & the Christian Life. 2008. 172p. pap. 20.00 *(978-1-55635-982-8(9))* Wipf & Stock Pubs.

Vlach, Michael J. The Church as a Replacement of Israel: An Analysis of Supersessionism. 2009. (Edition Israelogie Ser.). 222p. 43.95 *(978-3-631-58603-7(5))* Lang, Peter GmbH, Europaischer Verlag der Wissenschaften DEU. Dist: Lang, Peter.

Walker, Neville Earl. Making Wise the Simple: Behaviors, Attitudes & Principles of the Body of Christ. 2007. 456p. per. 29.95 *(978-1-4120-9616-4(2))* Trafford Publishing.

Wasyliw, Patricia Healy. Martyrdom, Murder & Magic: Child Saints & Their Cults. 2007. 212p. (C). 67.95 *(978-0-8204-2764-5(0))* Lang, Peter Publishing, Inc.

Watts, Malcom H. What Is a Reformed Church? 2011. (ENG.). pap. 12.00 ***(978-1-60178-157-4(1))*** Reformation Heritage Bks.

Yarnell, Malcolm B. The Formation of Christian Doctrine. 2007. (ENG.). 192p. pap. 19.99 *(978-0-8054-4046-1(1),* B&H Academic) B&H Publishing Group.

Yoder, John Howard. Christian Attitudes to War, Peace, & Revolution, 1 vol. Koontz, Theodore J. & Alexis-Baker, Andy, eds. 2009. 472p. pap. 36.00 *(978-1-58743-231-6(5))* Brazos Pr.

Zoccali, Christopher. Whom God Has Called. 2010. 236p. pap. 26.00 *(978-1-60899-517-2(8),* Pickwick Pubns.) Wipf & Stock Pubs.

CHURCH—INFALLIBILITY

see also Catholic Church—Infallibility; Church—Teaching Office; Popes—Infallibility

Powell, Mark E. Papal Infallibility: A Protestant Evaluation of an Ecumenical Issue. 2009. 238p. pap. 40.00 *(978-0-8028-6284-6(5))* Eerdmans, William B. Publishing Co.

CHURCH—MARKS

see also Church—Unity

Dever, Mark. What Is a Healthy Church? 2007. (IXMarks Ser.). 128p. 12.99 *(978-1-58134-937-5(8))* Crossway.

Ehrich, Tom. Church Wellness: A Best Practices Guide to Nurturing Healthy Congregations. 2008. 160p. pap. 20.00 *(978-0-89869-597-7(X))* Church Publishing, Inc.

Grosshans, Hans-Peter & Sinaga, Martin L., eds. Like Living Stones: Lutheran Reflections on the One Holy, Catholic & Apostolic Church. 2011. 204p. pap. 15.00 *(978-1-932688-60-3(9))* Kirk Hse. Pubs.

Intervarsity Press. We Believe in One Holy Catholic & Apostolic Church, 1 vol. Di Berardino, Angelo, ed. 2010. (Ancient Christian Doctrine Ser.: Volume 5). (ENG.). 368p. 50.00 *(978-0-8308-2535-6(5),* IVP Acad.) InterVarsity Pr.

Stinsen, Michael. Father Make Them One: A Prayer of Jesus. 2010. (ENG.). 176p. pap. 11.95 *(978-0-615-37256-3(2))* One Body Pr.

Thabiti, Anyibwile & Anyabwile, Thabiti M. What Is a Healthy Church Member? 2008. (IXMarks Ser.). 128p. 12.99 *(978-1-4335-0212-5(7))* Crossway.

CHURCH—MISSION

see Mission of the Church

CHURCH—REFORM

see Church Renewal

CHURCH—STUDY AND TEACHING

Bishop, Mary Ann. Servants of the Most High God. 2010. 208p. pap. 17.99 *(978-1-60957-516-8(4))* Xulon Pr., Inc.

Cogdill, Roy E. The New Testament: Book by Book. 2007. 204p. pap. 16.95 *(978-1-58427-218-2(2))* Guardian of Truth Foundation.

Isenhower, Valerie K. & Todd, Judith A. Listen for God's Leading: A Workbook for Corporate Spiritual Discernment. 2009. 128p. pap. 15.00 *(978-0-8358-9985-7(3))* Upper Room Bks.

Meyers, Pamela. The Simplicity of the Addictive Mind. 2008. 64p. per. 9.99 *(978-1-60477-080-3(5))* Xulon Pr., Inc.

CHURCH—TEACHING OFFICE

see also Catechetics; Censorship; Christian Education; Church and Education; Missions; Prohibited Books; Theological Seminaries

Meckley, Philip. Conscience, Moral Discernment, & Magisterial Moral Decision Making. 2010. 224p. pap. (978-3-8383-3737-1(9)) Lambert Academic Publishing.

CHURCH—UNITY

Here are entered works on unity as one of the "marks" of the church. Works on prospective and actual mergers within and across denominational lines are entered under Christian Union. Works on a movement generally dated from the Edinburg Missionary Conference of 1910 to the formation of the World Council of Churches in 1948 for the purpose of church cooperation and unity are entered under Ecumenical Movement. Works on religious activites planned and conducted cooperatively by two or more Christian sects are entered under Interdenominational Cooperation.

Anselm, et al. Anselm of Havelberg, Anticimenon: On the Unity of the Faith & the Controversies with the Greeks. 2010. (978-0-87907-106-6(0)) Cistercian Pubns., Inc.

Armstrong, John H. Your Church Is Too Small: Why Unity in Christ's Mission Is Vital to the Future of the Church, 1 vol. 2010. (ENG.). 208p. pap. 19.99 (978-0-310-32114-9(X)) Zondervan.

Beozzo Oscar Staff. 2001/3: The Ecumenical Constitution of Churches Concilium June. 2011. pap. **(978-0-334-03064-5(1)**, SCM Pr.) Hymns Ancient & Modern Ltd.

Brigham, Erin. Sustaining the Hope for Unity: Ecumenical Dialogue in a Postmodern World. 2012. **(978-0-8146-8022-3(4))** Liturgical Pr.

Carroll, Richard C. Is Christ Divided? Approaching Our Conflicts in Christ. 2008. 288p. pap. 14.95 (978-1-57921-924-6(1)) WinePress Publishing.

Commins, Gary. Becoming Bridges: The Spirit & Practice of Diversity. 2007. (ENG., Illus.). 160p. per. 14.95 (978-1-56101-294-7(7)) Cowley Pubns.

Corbitt, Danny. Missing More Than Music: When Disputable Matters Eclipse Worship & Unity. 2008. 184p. pap. 17.99 (978-1-4343-4359-8(6)) AuthorHouse.

Crewdson, Robert Henry. Church Unity: And the Corinthian Correspondence. 2008. 96p. pap. 12.95 (978-0-9820172-1-0(9)) Mariner Publishing.

Cyprian of Carthage. On the Church: Select Letters, Bk.33. 2007. (ENG.). 250p. pap. 20.00 (978-0-88141-313-7(5)) St. Vladimir's Seminary Pr.

—On the Church: Select Treatises, Bk.32. 2007. (St. Vladimir's Seminary Press "Popular Patristics" Ser.: No. 32). (ENG.). 188p. pap. 16.00 (978-0-88141-312-0(7)) St. Vladimir's Seminary Pr.

Evans. Reception of the Faith - P. 240p. 23.00 (978-0-281-05092-5(9)) SPCK Publishing GBR. Dist: Pilgrim Pr., The/United Church Pr.

Grosshans, Hans-Peter, ed. One Holy, Catholic, & Apostolic Church: Some Lutheran & Ecumenical Perspectives. 2009. 192p. pap. 15.00 (978-1-932688-40-5(4), Lutheran Univ. Pr.) Kirk Hse. Pubs.

Harmon, Steven R. Ecumenism Means You, Too: Ordinary Christians & the Quest for Christian Unity. annot. ed. 2010. 132p. pap. 16.00 (978-1-60608-865-4(3)) Wipf & Stock Pubs.

Hellerman, Joseph H., et al. When the Church Was a Family: Recapturing Jesus' Vision for Authentic Christian Community, 1 vol. 2009. (ENG.). 240p. pap. 19.99 (978-0-8054-4779-8(2), B&H Academic) B&H Publishing Group.

Hogan, Linda & Thiessen, Gesa Elsbeth. Ecumenical Ecclesiology: Unity, Diversity & Otherness in a Fragmented World. Thiessen, Gesa Elsbeth, ed. 2011. (Ecclesiological Investigations Ser.). (ENG.). 260p. pap. 44.95 (978-0-567-61834-4(X), T&T Clark Int'l) Continuum International Publishing Group, Ltd. GBR. Dist: National Bk. Network.

Howard, Ken. Paradoxy: Creating Christian Community Beyond Us & Them. 2010. (978-1-55725-803-8(1)) Paraclete Pr., Inc.

Imbler, John M. & Tabbernee, William. A Passion for Christian Unity: Essays in Honor of William Tabbernee. 2009. 24.99 (978-0-8272-3010-1(9)) Chalice Pr.

Johnson, Ian. Our Oneness in Christ. 2006. (ENG.). 204p. per. 24.95 (978-1-4241-6035-8(9)) PublishAmerica, Inc.

Koivisto, Rex A. One Lord, One Faith, Second Edition: A Theology for Cross-Denominational Renewal. 2008. 428p. pap. 40.00 (978-1-55635-947-7(0), Wipf and Stock) Wipf & Stock Pubs.

Lubich, Chiara. Living Dialogue: Steps on the Way to Communion among Christians. 2009. (ENG.). 88p. pap. 9.95 (978-1-56548-326-2(X)) New City Pr.

Luz, Ulrich, et al. Ökumene im Neuen Testament und heute. 2009. (GER.). 339p. (C). pap. 48.00 (978-3-525-56355-7(6)) Vandenhoeck & Ruprecht GmbH & Co. KG DEU. Dist: ISD.

Maassen, Thorsten. Das Ökumeneverständnis Joseph Ratzingers. 2011. (Kirche, Konfession, Religion Ser.). (GER.). 407p. (C). 74.00 (978-3-89971-798-3(8)) Vandenhoeck & Ruprecht GmbH & Co. KG DEU. Dist: ISD.

Maoz, Baruch. Come Let Us Reason Together. 2009. 214p. pap. 19.99 (978-0-9820731-7-9(8)) Audubon Pr. & Christian Bk. Service.

McCoy, Jim. The Christian's Unity with Christ. 2007. 232p. (ENG.). 24.99 (978-1-60266-851-5(5)); per. 14.99 (978-1-60266-850-8(7)) Xulon Pr., Inc.

Schlosser, J., ed. Paul et l'unite des Chretiens. 2010. (Colloquium Oecumenicum Paulinum Ser.). (FRE.). 251p. (C). pap. 67.00 (978-90-429-2312-6(1)) Peeters Pubs. & Booksellers BEL. Dist: Brown, David Bk. Co., The.

Smolarski, Dennis Chester. Eucharist & American Culture: Liturgy, Unity, & Individualism. 2010. 112p. pap. 12.95 (978-0-8091-4670-3(3)) Paulist Pr.

Stinsen, Michael. Father Make Them One: A Prayer of Jesus. 2010. (ENG.). 176p. pap. 11.95 (978-0-615-37256-3(2)) One Body Pr.

Thomas, Norman E. Missions & Unity: Lessons from History, 1792Ntilde;2010. 2010. (American Society of Missiology Ser.). 346p. pap. 39.00 (978-1-60899-602-5(6), Cascade Bks.) Wipf & Stock Pubs.

van Beek, Huibert, ed. Revisioning Christian Unity. 2009. (Studies in Global Christianity Ser.). 320p. pap. 35.00 (978-1-60899-109-9(1), Wipf and Stock) Wipf & Stock Pubs.

Vischer, Lukas, et al. Unity of the Church in the New Testament & Today. Crouch, James E., tr. from GER. 2010. 296p. pap. 40.00 (978-0-8028-6376-8(0)) Eerdmans, William B. Publishing Co.

Walsh, Albert J. D., ed. United & Uniting: An Ecumenical Ecclesiology for a Church in Crisis. 2011. 122p. pap. 15.00 **(978-1-61097-197-3(3)**, Wipf and Stock) Wipf & Stock Pubs.

Wedler, Esther-Maria. Splendor caritatis: Ein ökumenisches Gespräch mit Hans Urs von Balthasar zur Theologie in der Moderne. Erfurter Theologische Studien. 2009. (GER.), xlvii, 338p. pap. (978-3-429-02912-8(0)) Echter Wuerzburg.

Westhelle, Vitor. The Church Event: Call & Challenge of a Church Protestant. 2009. 192p. (C). pap. 20.00 (978-0-8006-6332-2(2), Fortress Pr.) Augsburg Fortress, Pubs.

CHURCH, APOSTOLIC

see Church History—Primitive and Early Church, ca. 30-600

CHURCH ADMINISTRATION

see Church Management

CHURCH ADMINISTRATION, INDIGENOUS

see Indigenous Church Administration

CHURCH AND COLLEGE

Here are entered works on the influence of religious denominations and sects on colleges. Works on colleges supported and-or administered by a religious denomination or sect are entered under Church Colleges.

see also Universities and Colleges—Religion

AEHE Staff, et al. Christian Faith & Scholarship: An Exploration of Contemporary Developments. 2007. (J-B ASHE Higher Education Report Series (AEHE) Ser.: 120). (ENG.). 144p. pap. 29.00 (978-0-470-22889-0(X), Jossey-Bass) Wiley, John & Sons, Inc.

Arthur, James, et al. Education, Politics & Religion: Reconciling the Civic & the Sacred in Education. 2010. (ENG., Illus.). 176p. (C). pap. 39.95 (978-0-415-56549-3(9)) Routledge.

—Education Politics & Religion Arthur: Reconciling the Civil & the Sacred in Education. 2010. (ENG., Illus.). 176p. (C). 120.00 (978-0-415-56548-6(0), Routledge) Taylor & Francis Group GBR. Dist: Taylor & Francis Group.

Beers, Stephen Thomas. The Soul of a Christian University: A Field Guide for Educators. 2008. (Illus.). 208p. pap. 18.95 (978-0-89112-520-4(5), ACU Pr.) Abilene Christian Univ. Pr.

Effinger, George A. The Nick of Time. Cover, Arthur B., ed. Date not set. pap. (978-1-893475-22-9(0)) Alexander Publishing, Inc.

Howard, Thomas Albert. Protestant Theology & the Making of the Modern German University. 2009. (ENG.). 496p. pap. 55.00 (978-0-19-955447-8(1)) Oxford Univ. Pr., Inc.

Jacobsen, Douglas G. & Jacobsen, Rhonda Hustedt. Religion Matters: Higher Education for the 21st Century. 2012. (ENG.). 240p. 29.95 **(978-0-19-984473-9(9))** Oxford Univ. Pr., Inc.

Jeffrey, David L. The Bible & the University, 1 vol. Jeffrey, David Lyle et al, eds. 2007. (Scripture & Hermeneutics Ser.). (ENG.). 352p. (gr. 13). pap. 34.99 (978-0-310-23418-0(2)) Zondervan.

Magolda, Peter & Gross, Kelsey Ebben. It's All about Jesus! Faith as an Oppositional Collegiate Subculture. 2009. 368p. 75.00 (978-1-57922-354-0(0)); pap. 32.50 (978-1-57922-355-7(9)) Stylus Publishing, LLC.

Meyer, Albert J. Realizing Our Intentions: A Guide for Churches & Colleges with Distinctive Missions. 2009. 28.99 (978-0-89112-539-6(6)); pap. 19.99 (978-0-89112-537-2(X)) Abilene Christian Univ. Pr. (ACU Pr.).

Tewksbury, Donald George. The Founding of American Colleges & Universities Before the Civil War. 2011. 270p. pap. 14.95 **(978-1-61427-112-3(7))** Martino Publishing.

Tewksbury, Donald George. The Founding of American Colleges & Universities Before the Civil War: With Particular Reference to the Religious Influences Bearing upon the College Movement. 2010. (978-1-57898-879-2(9)) Martino Publishing.

Tyler, W. S. Prayer for Colleges, a Premium Essay. 2006. 220p. per. 20.99 (978-1-4255-1800-4(1)) MPublishing.

Yancey, George. Compromising Scholarship: Religious & Political Bias in American Higher Education. 2011. (ENG., Illus.). 250p. 34.95 (978-1-60258-268-2(8)) Baylor Univ. Pr.

CHURCH AND EDUCATION

Here are entered general works on the relation of the church to education. Works on instruction in the Christian religion in churches, schools, and homes are entered under Christian Education. Works on religious or secular instruction provided by a particular denomination are entered under the name of the denomination with the subdivision Education, e.g. Catholic Church—Education.

see also Church Schools; Missions—Educational Work; Religion in the Public Schools

Adams, Herbert B. The Church & Popular Education. (Johns Hopkins University Studies in the Social Sciences, Thirtieth Ser.: 8-9). reprint ed. 37.50 (978-0-404-61132-3(X)) AMS Pr., Inc.

Alexis, Jonas. In the Name of Education. 2007. (ENG.). 412p. per. 21.99 (978-1-60034-760-3(6)) Xulon Pr., Inc.

Avison, Margaret. A Kind of Perseverance. 2010. (ENG., Illus.). 56p. pap. 12.95 (978-0-88984-326-4(0)) Porcupine's Quill, Inc. CAN. Dist: Univ. of Toronto Pr.

Barr, Colin. The European Culture Wars in Ireland: The Callan Schools Affair, 1868-81. 2011. (ENG.). 320p. 89.95 (978-1-906359-53-9(9)) Univ. College Dublin Pr. IRL. Dist: Dufour Editions, Inc.

A Biblical Foundation for Early Childhood Education, 5 manuals, Set. Incl. Manual 1. Nizza, Barbara, ed. & compiled by. 250p. tchr. ed., spiral bd. (978-1-888191-00-4(7)); Manual 2. Knowing God Our Father. Early Childhood Education Center Staff. 138p. tchr. ed., spiral bd. (978-1-888191-01-1(5)); Manual 3. Knowing Jesus, God with Us. Early Childhood Education Center Staff. 218p. tchr. ed., spiral bd. (978-1-888191-02-8(3)); Manual 4. Knowing Jesus, Because of the Holy Spirit. Early Childhood Education Center Staff. 118p. spiral bd. (978-1-888191-03-5(1)); Manual 5. Training in Righteousness. Early Childhood Education Center Staff, contrib. by. 26p. pap. (978-1-888191-04-2(X)); 1996. (978-1-888191-08-0(2)) Univ. of the Nations.

Bowyer, Phil. Express Community Through Schools: Taking Social Action Beyond the Classroom. 2007. (ENG.). 80p. 15.99 (978-1-85078-750-1(6)) Authentic Media.

Brumberg, Stephan. Common Schools, Uncommon Faiths: Religious Conflict & the Shaping of American Education. 2007. (ENG.). 320p. 40.00 (978-0-300-11511-6(3)) Yale Univ. Pr.

Cairns, Jo. Faith Schools & Society: Civilising the Debate. 2009. (ENG.). 284p. 140.00 (978-1-84706-229-1(6)) Continuum International Publishing Group, Ltd. GBR. Dist: National Bk. Network.

Cairns, Jo. Faith Schools & Society: Civilizing the Debate. 2011. (ENG.). 284p. pap. 49.95 **(978-1-4411-9790-0(7))** Continuum International Publishing Group, Ltd. GBR. Dist: National Bk. Network.

Carper, James C. & Hunt, Thomas C. The Dissenting Tradition in American Education. 304p. (C). pap. 32.95 (978-0-8204-7920-0(9)) Lang, Peter Publishing, Inc.

Carper, James C. & Hunt, Thomas C., eds. The Praeger Handbook of Religion & Education in the United States, 2 vols. 2009. 624p. 150.00 (978-0-275-99227-9(6), C9227, Praeger Pubs.) Greenwood Publishing Group, Inc.

Clarke, Fred. Church, Community & State in Relation to Education (RLE Edu C) Towards a Theory of School Organization. 2012. (Routledge Library Editions: Education Ser.). (ENG.). 248p. 115.00 (978-0-415-67539-0(1)) Routledge.

Cline, Cecil. Sunrise over Appalachi. 2006. 232p. per. 15.95 (978-1-59858-205-5(4)) Dog Ear Publishing, LLC.

Culver, Raymond B. Horace Mann & Religion in the Massachusetts Public Schools. 2009. 314p. 45.95 (978-1-104-84130-0(4)) 2007. (ENG.). 312p. per. 30.95 (978-0-548-44165-7(0)) Kessinger Publishing, LLC.

Curran, Francis Xavier. The Churches & the Schools: American Protestantism & Popular Elementary Education. 2011. 160p. 41.95 **(978-1-258-08100-3(8))** Literary Licensing, LLC.

Dekker, Diane. Two Trees of Knowledge: A Biblical Case for the Separation of School & State. 2009. 324p. pap. 19.99 (978-1-4141-1301-2(3)) Pleasant Word.

Durst, R. Lewis. The Wisdom of Fools: The Official Religion of America's Public Schools. 2011. pap. 10.99 (978-1-61739-848-3(9)) Tate Publishing & Enterprises, LLC.

Fenzel, L. Mickey. Improving Urban Middle Schools: Lessons from the Nativity Schools. 2009. 144p. 59.50 (978-0-7914-9349-6(0)) State Univ. of New York Pr.

Fenzel, L. Mickey & Fenzel, L. Improving Urban Middle Schools: Lessons from the Nativity Schools. 2009. 144p. pap. 19.95 (978-0-7914-9350-2(4)) State Univ. of New York Pr.

Fisher, Samuel Ware. An Wisdom the Strength of True Manhood a Discourse Delivered at Salem, Mass , Nov 13, 1866, in Behalf of the Society for the Promotion of Collegiate. 2011. 34p. pap. 11.99 **(978-1-4181-9456-7(5))** MPublishing.

Glenn, Charles L. American Indian/First Nations Schooling: From the Colonial Period to the Present. 2011. (ENG.). 248p. 85.00 (978-0-230-11420-3(2)) Palgrave Macmillan.

Grenham, Thomas, ed. Who Do You Say I Am? Opportunies & Challenges for Pastoral Ministry. 2009. (ENG.). 128p. pap. 22.95 (978-1-84730-173-4(8)) Veritas Pubns. IRL. Dist: Dufour Editions, Inc.

Hatfield, Tyrel & Hatfield, Justin. Christian Academy, 1. Hatfield, Lisa & Hatfield, Kari, eds. 2007. (Illus.). 130p. cd-rom 99.00 (978-0-9766703-3-9(X)) Little Acorn LLC.

Hauerwas, Stanley M. The State of the University: Academic Knowledges & the Knowledge of God. 2007. (Illuminations: Theory & Religion Ser.). (ENG.). 232p. 110.95 (978-1-4051-6247-0(3)); pap. 44.95 (978-1-4051-6248-7(1)) Wiley, John & Sons, Inc. (Wiley-Blackwell).

Hooper, A. Duane. Christian School Teacher: Ministry of Caring for Kids. 2008. 284p. pap. 16.99 (978-1-60791-138-8(8)) Xulon Pr., Inc.

Hughes, Brian W. Saving Wisdom: Theology in the Christian University. 2011. 370p. pap. 41.00 (978-1-60608-958-3(7), Pickwick Pubns.) Wipf & Stock Pubs.

La Iglesia (The Church) Quarter 3, Level 3. (Caminando con Jesus (Walking with Jesus) Series A). (SPA.). tchr. ed. 2.50 (978-0-570-05145-9(2), 16-3803) Concordia Publishing Hse.

Jacobsen, Douglas & Jacobsen, Rhonda, eds. The American University in a Postsecular Age. 2008. (ENG., Illus.). 288p. 35.00 (978-0-19-532344-3(0)) Oxford Univ. Pr., Inc.

Justice, Benjamin. The War That Wasn't: Religious Conflict & Compromise in the Common Schools of New York State, 1865-1900. 2009. (Illus.). 285p. pap. 29.95 (978-0-7914-6212-6(9), Suny Pr.) State Univ. of New York Pr.

MacMullen, Ian. Faith in Schools? Autonomy, Citizenship, & Religious Education in the Liberal State. 2007. (ENG.), 240p. (C). 42.00 (978-0-691-13091-0(4)) Princeton Univ. Pr.

Maeba, Lawrence NuBari. The and Rebirth of a Broken Destiny. 2011. 324p. pap. 18.99 **(978-1-61379-286-5(7))** Xulon Pr., Inc.

Marder, John. You're God's Gift to Teachers: Passages of Biblical Encouragement for Teachers. 2008. 184p. pap. 13.95 (978-1-4327-3699-6(X)) Outskirts Pr., Inc.

Martin, Glenn W. Out of the Darkness of Academics into the Light of Jesus Christ-2009. 212p. 29.99 (978-1-4389-8309-7(3)) AuthorHouse.

Meyer-Blanck, Michael & Schmidt, Sebastian. Religion, Rationalität und Bildung. 2009. (Illus.). 249p. (978-3-89913-680-7(2)) Dietrich, Dr. Hans-Jurgen, Ergon Verlag.

Monroe Kullberg, Kelly, ed. Finding God at Harvard: Spiritual Journeys of Thinking Christians. 2007. (Veritas Bks.). (ENG., Illus.). 375p. per. 18.00 (978-0-8308-3433-4(8), IVP Bks.) InterVarsity Pr.

Murphy, James. Church, State & Schools. 2007. 176p. 200.00 (978-0-415-43269-6(3)) Routledge.

O'Lalor, Peter. Alexander Hamilton & the Duty & Obligation of Government. 2009. 248p. pap. (978-3-639-12440-8(5)) VDM Verlag Dr. Mueller e.K.

Slaughter, Micheal. Unlearning Church. 2008. 129p. pap. 18.00 (978-0-687-64708-8(8)) Abingdon Pr.

Smith, John E. Victorian Class Conflict? Schoolteaching & the Parson, Priest & Minister, 1837-1902. 2009. (ENG.). 233p. 70.00 (978-1-84519-295-2(8)) Sussex Academic Pr. GBR. Dist: International Specialized Bk. Services.

Sommerville, C. John. Religious Ideas for Secular Universities. 2009. (ENG.). 208p. pap. 18.00 (978-0-8028-6442-0(2)) Eerdmans, William B. Publishing Co.

Stambach, Amy. Faith in Schools: Religion, Education, & American Evangelicals in East Africa. 2009. (ENG.). 248p. 65.00 (978-0-8047-6850-4(1)); pap. 24.95 (978-0-8047-6851-1(X)) Stanford Univ. Pr.

Stern, Julian & Stern. Schools & Religions: Imagining the Real. 2007. (Continuum Studies in Research in Education Ser.). (ENG.). 224p. 150.00 (978-0-8264-8504-5(9)) Continuum International Publishing Group, Ltd. GBR. Dist: National Bk. Network.

Strasser, Mark. Religion Education & the State: An Unprincipled Doctrine in Search of Moorings. 2011. (Law, Justice & Power Ser.). 214p. 109.95 **(978-1-4094-3644-7(6))** Ashgate Publishing Co.

Szews, George R. Catholic & College Bound: 5 Challenges & 5 Opportunities. 2008. (Illus.). 64p. pap. 5.95 (978-0-87946-361-8(9)) ACTA Pubns.

Torok, Robyn. Schooling in the Name of God: Teachers' Perspectives. 2011. 420p. pap. **(978-3-8454-1952-7(0))** Lambert Academic Publishing.

Tuttle, Joseph F. An Address in Behalf of the Society for the Promotion of Collegiate & Theological Education at the West Delivered at Its Tenth Anniversary, in Worc. 2011. 22p. pap. 11.99 **(978-1-4181-9099-6(3))** MPublishing.

Vander Broek, Lyle D. Breaking Barriers: 1 Corinthians & Christian Community. 2007. 176p. pap. 20.00 (978-1-55635-557-8(2)) Wipf & Stock Pubs.

Watson, Keith & Ozanne, William, eds. Education & Religion. 2012. (ENG., Illus.). 160p. 125.00 **(978-0-415-69352-3(7))** Routledge.

Watzke, John/Louis, ed. Beyond Alternative Teacher Education: Integrating Teaching, Community, Spirituality & Leadership. 2007. 276p. per. 17.99 (978-0-9788793-1-0(7)); (Illus.). lib. bdg. 27.00 (978-0-9788793-0-3(9)) Alliance for Catholic Education Pr.

Weaver, Cornelius P. Jesus Goes to College. 2011. pap. 10.99 **(978-1-61663-930-3(X))** Tate Publishing & Enterprises, LLC.

Williams, Angela. Christian Spirituality Manifested in African American Students: Christian Spirituality Impacts the Academic Attitudes & Behaviors of African American Students. 2008. 108p. pap. (978-3-639-09078-9(0)) VDM Verlag Dr. Mueller e.K.

Zieman, Katherine. Singing the New Song: Literacy & Liturgy in Late Medieval England. 2008. (Middle Ages Ser.). (Illus.). 312p. (C). 59.95 (978-0-8122-4051-1(0)) Univ. of Pennsylvania Pr.

CHURCH AND EDUCATION—AFRICA

Kondolo, Kapembwa. The Spread of the African Independent Churches. 2011. 96p. pap. **(978-3-8433-8818-4(0))** Lambert Academic Publishing.

CHURCH AND EDUCATION—GREAT BRITAIN

Hilliard, F. H. & Desmond Y.T. Lee, eds. Christianity in Education (RLE Edu C) The Hibbert Lectures 1965. 2012. (Routledge Library Editions: Education Ser.). (ENG.). 112p. 100.00 **(978-0-415-67545-1(6))** Routledge.

CHURCH AND HOMOSEXUALITY

see also Homosexuality—Religious Aspects—Christianity

Bligen, James. Black Sheep Secret: The Homosexual Spirit Exposed. 2008. 84p. pap. 12.95 (978-1-4343-5160-9(2)) AuthorHouse.

CHURCH AND INTERNATIONAL AFFAIRS

see Christianity and International Affairs

CHURCH AND INTERNATIONAL ORGANIZATION

Araujo, Robert John & Lucal, John A. Papal Diplomacy & the Quest for Peace. 2010. (978-0-916101-64-0(9)) St. Joseph's Univ. Pr.

Darnell, Betty J. The Preacher Woman. 2011. 106p. pap. 11.99 ***(978-1-61379-003-8(1))*** Xulon Pr., Inc.

Fimister, Alan. Robert Schuman: Neo Scholastic Humanism & the Re-Unification of Europe. 2008. 278p. 55.95 *(978-90-5201-439-5(6))* PIE - Peter Lang BEL. Dist: Lang, Peter.

Melnyk, Roman/A. Vatican Diplomacy at the United Nations: A History of Catholic Global Engagement. 2009. vi, 269p. *(978-0-7734-3881-1(5))* Mellen, Edwin Pr., The.

CHURCH AND LABOR

see also Christianity and Economics; Church and Social Problems

George, Henry. The Condition of Labor. 2009. 86p. pap. *(978-1-151-37152-2(1))* Books LLC.

—Condition of Labor an Open Letter to Pop. 2006. pap. 18.95 *(978-1-59605-987-0(7),* Cosimo Classics) Cosimo, Inc.

Herrlinger, Page. Working Souls: Russian Orthodoxy & Factory Labor in St. Petersburg, 1881-1917. 2007. (Allan K. Wildman Group Historical Ser.). (ENG., Illus.). 308p. pap. 29.95 *(978-0-89357-339-3(6))* Slavica Pubs.

Prouty, Marco G. César Chávez, the Catholic Bishops, & the Farmworkers' Struggle for Social Justice, Prouty, Marco G. 2008. (ENG., Illus.). 208p. pap. 19.95 *(978-0-8165-2731-1(8))* Univ. of Arizona Pr.

—Cesar Chavez, the Catholic Bishops, & the Farmworkers' Struggle for Social Justice. 2006. (ENG., Illus.). 208p. 40.00 *(978-0-8165-2555-3(2))* Univ. of Arizona Pr.

Sorg, Rembert. Holy Work: Towards A Benedictine Theology of Manual Labor. 2011. 122p. 39.95 ***(978-1-258-02812-1(3))*** Literary Licensing, LLC.

—Towards a Benedictine Theology of Manual Labor. 2011. 126p. 40.95 ***(978-1-258-05845-6(6))*** Literary Licensing, LLC.

CHURCH AND RACE RELATIONS

see Race Relations—Religious Aspects—Christianity

CHURCH AND SLAVERY

see Slavery and the Church

CHURCH AND SOCIAL PROBLEMS

Here are entered works on the efforts of the church to deal with social problems. Works on the sociology of Christian denominations and general Christian social theory are entered under Sociology, Christian. Works on religious sociology in general are entered under Religion and Sociology.

see also Christian Socialism; Christian Sociology; Christianity and International Affairs; Church and International Organization; Church and Labor; Church Charities

Allen, Richard. The View from Murney Tower Vol. 1: Salem Bland, the Late-Victorian Controversies, & the Search for a New Christianity. 2008. (Illus.). 496p. *(978-0-8020-9748-4(0))* Univ. of Toronto Pr.

Benson, Ezra Taft. The American Heritage of Freedom: A Plan of God. 2011. 26p. 35.95 ***(978-1-258-09868-1(7))*** Literary Licensing, LLC.

Bossung-Winkler, Monika. Gottes Geist im Armenviertel: Protestantische Pfingstbewegung und Katholische Charismatische Erneuerung in Ecuador. (Europaische Hochschulschriften Ser.: Vol. 747). (GER., Illus.). 302p. 39.95 *(978-3-631-39545-5(0))* Lang, Peter Publishing, Inc.

Bowyer, Phil. Express Community Through Schools: Taking Social Action Beyond the Classroom. 2007. (ENG.). 80p. 15.99 *(978-1-85078-750-1(6))* Authentic Media.

Brown Spencer, Elaine A. Private Pain in Public Pews. 2010. 140p. 28.95 *(978-1-4497-0617-3(7))*; pap. 11.95 *(978-1-4497-0616-6(9))* Author Solutions, Inc. (WestBow Pr.).

Budde, Michael L. The Borders of Baptism: Identities, Allegiances, & the Church. 2011. (Theopolitical Visions: Ser.). 204p. pap. 22.00 ***(978-1-61097-135-5(3),*** Cascade Bks.) Wipf & Stock Pubs.

Burr, Elizabeth Geraldine & Smith, David Whitten. Understanding World Religions: A Road Map for Justice & Peace. 2007. (ENG., Illus.). 444p. 85.00 *(978-0-7425-5054-4(0))*; pap. 39.95 *(978-0-7425-5055-1(9))* Rowman & Littlefield Publishers, Inc.

Campbell, Will D. Writings on Reconciliation & Resistance. Goode, Richard C., ed. 2010. 237p. pap. 28.00 *(978-1-60608-128-0(4))* Cascade Bks.

Cannon, Mae Elise. Social Justice Handbook: Small Steps for a Better World. 2009. (BridgeLeader Partnership Ser.). (ENG.). 304p. pap. 20.00 *(978-0-8308-3715-1(9),* IVP Bks.) InterVarsity Pr.

Clements, Keith. Learning to Speak: The Church's Voice in Public Affairs. 2011. 254p. pap. 28.00 ***(978-1-61097-369-4(0),*** Wipf and Stock) Wipf & Stock Pubs.

Clouse, Robert G., et al, eds. The Cross & the Flag. 2007. 260p. pap. 29.00 *(978-1-55635-431-1(2))* Wipf & Stock Pubs.

Copeland, Warren R. Doing Justice in Our Cities: Lessons in Public Policy from America's Heartland. 2009. (ENG.). 176p. pap. 20.00 *(978-0-664-23229-0(9))* Westminster John Knox Pr.

Cox, Meg. Cynicism & Hope: Reclaiming Discipleship in a Postdemocratic Society. 2008. 136p. pap. 17.00 *(978-1-60608-214-0(0),* Cascade Bks.) Wipf & Stock Pubs.

Crane, Wesley L. Silly Flies: How to Get Caught in the System. 2009. 292p. 27.99 *(978-1-4343-3779-5(0))*; pap. 16.99 *(978-1-4343-3778-8(2))* AuthorHouse.

Davis, Jerome. Religion in Action. 2011. 332p. 50.95 ***(978-1-258-07338-1(2))*** Literary Licensing, LLC.

Dingle, Pastor Alfred A. The Church Held Hostage: The Plight of the Small Local Church. 2010. 88p. pap. 12.95 *(978-1-4269-3234-2(0))* Trafford Publishing.

Dommen, Edward & Bratt, James D., eds. John Calvin Rediscovered: The Impact of His Social & Economic Thought. 2007. (Princeton Theological Seminary Studies in Reformed Theology & History Ser.). (ENG.). 161p. per. 30.00 *(978-0-664-23227-6(2))* Westminster John Knox Pr.

Duckworth, Jenny & Duckworth, Justin. Against the Tide, Towards the Kingdom. 2011. (New Monastic Library: Resources for Radical Discipleship Ser.). 130p. pap. 16.00 ***(978-1-60899-867-8(3),*** Cascade Bks.) Wipf & Stock Pubs.

Dudley, Jonathan. Broken Words: The Abuse of Science & Faith in American Politics. 2011. (ENG.). 208p. 21.99 *(978-0-385-52526-8(5),* Doubleday Religion) Doubleday Religious Publishing Group, The.

Duncan, Malcolm. Kingdom Come: The Local Church as a Catalyst for Social Change. 1 vol. 2008. 352p. pap. 14.99 *(978-0-8254-6151-4(0),* Monarch Bks.) Lion Hudson PLC GBR. Dist: Kregel Pubns.

Duncan, Malcolm & Duncan. Building a Better World: Faith at Work for Change in Society. 2006. (ENG.). 184p. 19.95 *(978-0-8264-9152-7(9))* Continuum International Publishing Group, Ltd. GBR. Dist: National Bk. Network.

Easley, Roxanne. The Emancipation of the Serfs in Russia: Peace Arbitrators & the Development of Civil Society. 2008. (BASEES/Routledge Series on Russian & East European Studies). (ENG., Illus.). 240p. (C). 160.00 *(978-0-415-77639-4(2))* Routledge.

Edwards, Korie L. Living the Dream: The Power of Race in Interracial Churches. 2008. (ENG.). 240p. 29.95 *(978-0-19-531424-3(7))* Oxford Univ. Pr., Inc.

Elisha, Omri. Moral Ambition: Mobilization & Social Outreach in Evangelical Megachurches. 2011. (Anthropology of Christianity Ser.). (ENG.). 251p. 60.00 *(978-0-520-26750-3(8))*; pap. 24.95 *(978-0-520-26751-0(6))* Univ. of California Pr.

Forrester, Duncan B. Forrester on Christian Ethics: Collected Writings on Christianity India & the Social Order. 2010. (Ashgate Contemporary Thinkers on Religion: Collected Works Ser.). 536p. 144.95 *(978-0-7546-6438-3(4))* Ashgate Publishing Co.

Gaines Jr, Pastor Jake & Gaines Jr., Pastor Jake. Staring down the Barrel of My Faith. 2010. 132p. pap. 12.95 *(978-0-9826490-0-8(2))* ASA Publishing Co.

Gautier, Theophile. The Wife of King Candaules. 2007. (ENG.). 122p. 35.95 *(978-0-548-07209-7(4))* Kessinger Publishing, LLC.

Gladden, Washington. The Church & Modern Life. 2008. 140p. 24.99 *(978-0-554-24347-4(4))*; 21.99 *(978-0-554-33650-3(2))* BiblioBazaar.

—The Church & Modern Life. 2009. 92p. pap. *(978-0-217-38020-1(4))* Books LLC.

—The Church & Modern Life. 2007. 116p. per. *(978-1-4065-4494-7(9))* Dodo Pr.

—The Church & Modern Life. 2008. 230p. 41.95 *(978-0-548-92061-9(3))* 2007. (ENG.). 232p. per. 26.95 *(978-0-548-59781-1(2))* Kessinger Publishing, LLC.

Glancy, Jennifer A. Slavery as Moral Problem: In the Early Church & Today. 2011. (Facets Ser.). 96p. pap. 9.99 *(978-0-8006-9670-2(0),* Fortress Pr.) Augsburg Fortress, Pubs.

—Slavery in Early Christianity. 2006. 216p. per. 23.00 *(978-0-8006-3789-7(5),* Fortress Pr.) Augsburg Fortress, Pubs.

Hall, Jyl, et al, eds. A Guide to Acting on AIDS: Understanding the Global AIDS Pandemic & Responding through Faith in Action. 2006. (ENG., Illus.). 90p. per. 9.99 *(978-1-932805-80-2(X))* Authentic Media.

Hall, Tony. Changing the Face of Hunger, 0 vols. 2007. 224p. per. 14.99 *(978-0-8499-1869-8(3))* Nelson, Thomas Inc.

Harlow, S. Ralph. Thoughts for Times Like These. 2011. 190p. 42.95 ***(978-1-258-07436-4(2))*** Literary Licensing, LLC.

Hayworth, Miguel. The Deception of Love Evangelism. 2007. 68p. pap. 14.95 *(978-1-84753-502-3(X))* Lulu Enterprises Inc.

Hedda, Jennifer. His Kingdom Come: Orthodox Pastorship & Social Activism in Revolutionary Russia. 2007. 307p. 43.00 *(978-0-87580-382-1(2))* Northern Illinois Univ. Pr.

Hedda, Jennifer. His kingdom Come: Orthodox pastorship & social activism in revolutionary Russia. 2011. (ENG.). 382p. pap. 24.00 ***(978-0-87580-664-8(3))*** Northern Illinois Univ. Pr.

Hugen, Beryl & Scales, T. Laine, eds. Christianity & Social Work: Readings on the Integration of Christian Faith & Social Work Practice. 3rd ed. 2008. (ENG.). 424p. pap. 32.95 *(978-0-9715318-2-6(X))* North American Assn. of Christians in Social Work.

Idestrscaron;m, Jonas, ed. For the Sake of the World. 2009. (Church of Sweden Research Ser.). 156p. pap. 18.00 *(978-1-60899-108-2(3),* Pickwick Pubns.) Wipf & Stock Pubs.

Inch, Morris. Why Take the Church Seriously? 2006. 140p. pap. 24.95 *(978-1-4241-1985-1(5))* PublishAmerica, Inc.

Jeynes, William & Martinez, Enedina. Christianity, Education & Modern Society. 2007. *(978-1-59311-737-5(X))*; (ENG.). 312p. (C). per. *(978-1-59311-736-8(1))* Information Age Publishing, Inc.

Johnson, Paul G. Evidence of Hope: Grace & Truth in Social Issues. 2008. 140p. pap. 17.00 *(978-1-55635-493-9(2))* Wipf & Stock Pubs.

Jones, Dwayne A. Thinking with the Wrong Head. 2009. 100p. pap. 14.95 *(978-1-4120-0676-7(7))* Trafford Publishing.

Joseph, Ruben. Why Are the Young People Leaving the Church: What We Need to Do to Keep Them In. 2011. 102p. 24.99 ***(978-1-4653-4380-2(6))***; pap. 15.99 ***(978-1-4653-4379-6(2))*** Xlibris Corp.

Kasomo, Rt. Rev. Daniel W. The Relevance of Catholic Social Teaching Today. 2011. 452p. pap. ***(978-3-8443-8690-5(4))*** Lambert Academic Publishing.

Kauffman, J. Timothy. Reconnecting the Church. 2010. 234p. pap. 19.99 *(978-1-4500-8718-6(3))* Xlibris Corp.

Kershner, Howard E. God, Gold & Government: The Interrelationship of Christianity, Freedom, Self-Government & Economic Well Being. 2011. 144p. 40.95 ***(978-1-258-00414-9(3))*** Literary Licensing, LLC.

Kowalewski, Wojciech. Transforming Mission in Post-Communist Context. 2009. 296p. pap. *(978-3-639-12422-4(7))* VDM Verlag Dr. Mueller e.K.

Kuyper, Abraham Jr. & Kuyper, Abraham. The Problem of Poverty. 2011. 94p. ***(978-0-932914-87-3(X))*** Dordt College Pr.

Kwan, Enoch. Towards a 4-Ships Driven Culture - Revitalizing a Small Urban Church. 2009. 236p. pap. *(978-3-639-20698-2(3))* VDM Verlag Dr. Mueller e.K.

Leech, Kenneth. The Sky Is Red: Discerning the Signs of the Times. 2nd ed. 296p. pap. 26.00 *(978-0-232-52499-4(8))* Abingdon Pr.

Leffel, Gregory P. Faith Seeking Action: Mission, Social Movements, & the Church in Motion. 2007. (Intercultural Studies). (ENG.). 316p. per. 47.00 *(978-0-8108-5803-9(7))* Scarecrow Pr., Inc.

Lewis, Albert D., Jr. The Great Spiritual War, 7 vols., Set. Incl. Vol. 1. Great Spiritual War: What Is It? 64p. pap. 4.99 *(978-0-9633356-1-6(8))*; Vol. 2. Great Spiritual War: Our Real Foe(s) - Who Are They? 30p. pap. 2.99 *(978-0-9633356-2-3(6))*; Vol. 3. Great Spiritual War: Idol Worship. 26p. pap. 2.99 *(978-0-9633356-3-0(4))*; Vol. 5. Great Spiritual War: The Great Tribulation. 30p. pap. 2.99 *(978-0-9633356-5-4(0))*; Vol. 6. Great Spiritual War: Suicide; Forgiveness; Repentance: The Weapons of Our Warfare & a Letter to the President. 38p. pap. 4.99 *(978-0-9633356-6-1(9))*; Vol. 7. Great Spiritual War: My Personal Testimony. 106p. pap. 8.99 *(978-0-9633356-7-8(7))*; Vol. 4. AIDS & Abortion. 60p. pap. 6.99 *(978-0-9633356-4-7(2))*; (Illus.). 1997. Set pap. 33.99 *(978-0-9633356-9-2(3))* Harvest Time International, Inc.

Liacopulos, George P. Church & Society: Orthodox Christian Perspectives, Past Experiences, & Modern Challenges. 2007. *(978-0-9774610-6-8(8))*; pap. *(978-0-9774610-5-9(X))* Somerset Hall Pr.

Little, Jeri. Merchant to Romania: Business as Missions in Post-Communist Eastern Europe. 2009. (Life Stories Ser.). (Illus.). 224p. pap. *(978-1-84625-171-9(0))* DayOne Pubns.

Livermore, David. What Can I Do? Making a Global Difference Right Where You Are, 1 vol. 2011. (ENG.). 208p. pap. 14.99 *(978-0-310-32596-3(X))* Zondervan.

Logan, Samuel T., Jr., ed. Confronting Kingdom Challenges: A Call to Global Christians to Carry the Burden Together. 2007. (Illus.). 256p. pap. 15.99 *(978-1-58134-863-7(0))* Crossway.

MacColl, Allan W. Land, Faith & the Crofting Community: Christianity & Social Criticism in the Highlands of Scotland 1843-1893. 2006. (Scottish Historical Review Monographs: No. 14). (ENG.). 320p. (gr. 17). 113.00 *(978-0-7486-2382-2(5))* Edinburgh Univ. Pr. GBR. Dist: Columbia Univ. Pr.

MacFarland, Charles S. The Christian Ministry & the Social Order. 2009. 142p. pap. *(978-1-4588-6807-7(9))* Books LLC.

Mack, Burton L. Myth & the Christian Nation: A Social Theory of Religion. 2008. (Religion in Culture: Studies in Social Contest & Construction Ser.). (ENG.). 304p. (C). 99.95 *(978-1-84553-372-4(0))*; pap. 34.95 *(978-1-84553-373-1(9))* Equinox Publishing Ltd. GBR. Dist: ISD.

Maggay, Melba Padilla. Transforming Society. 2011. 114p. pap. 14.00 *(978-1-61097-040-2(3),* Wipf and Stock) Wipf & Stock Pubs.

Martin, Isaac D. The Christian's Social Responsibility. 2010. 87p. pap. 3.85 *(978-0-7399-2421-1(4))* Rod & Staff Pubs., Inc.

Mattson, A. D. Christian Social Consciousness: An Introduction to Christian Sociology. 2011. 280p. 47.95 ***(978-1-258-04954-6(6))*** Literary Licensing, LLC.

Maye, Brian. The Search for Justice: Trocaire: A History. 2010. (ENG., Illus.). 376p. pap. 24.95 *(978-1-84730-167-3(3))* Veritas Pubns. IRL. Dist: Dufour Editions, Inc.

McLaren, Brian D. Everything Must Change: Jesus, Global Crises, & a Revolution of Hope, 0 vols. 2009. 336p. pap. 14.99 *(978-1-4002-8029-2(X))* Nelson, Thomas Inc.

Messer, Mary Burt. The Science of Society: The Identity of Each As Godlike Embracing All. 2011. 248p. 46.95 ***(978-1-258-07348-0(X))*** Literary Licensing, LLC.

Meylahn, Johann-Albrecht. The Church in the Postmodern Global Village. 2010. 256p. pap. *(978-3-8383-3894-1(4))* Lambert Academic Publishing.

Mitchell, Apostle Duane. What's Wrong with the Church? Noticed the Problems & Addressing the Issues to Destroy the Yokes of Bondage. 2009. 65p. pap. 24.95 *(978-1-4327-4413-7(5))* Outskirts Pr., Inc.

Moberg, David O. The Great Reversal: Reconciling Evangelism & Social Concern. 2007. 228p. pap. 25.00 *(978-1-55635-124-2(0))* Wipf & Stock Pubs.

Moore, Shayne. Global Soccer Mom: Changing the World Is Easier Than You Think, 1 vol. 2011. (ENG.). 224p. pap. 14.99 *(978-0-310-32558-1(7))* Zondervan.

Murphy, Isaac. In Season, Out of Season. 2009. 144p. pap. *(978-3-639-17317-8(1))* VDM Verlag Dr. Mueller e.K.

Murray, Alexander. Suicide in the Middle Ages Vol. 1: The Violent Against Themselves. 2009. (ENG., Illus.). 510p. pap. 55.00 *(978-0-19-955311-2(4))* Oxford Univ. Pr., Inc.

Nemutanzhela, Sydney. The Traumatic Experience of Teenage Pregnancies by Married Men. 2009. 108p. pap. *(978-3-639-11161-3(3))* VDM Verlag Dr. Mueller e.K.

Nolan, Albert. Hope in an Age of Despair. Muyebe, Stan, ed. 2009. 192p. pap 18.00 *(978-1-57075-835-5(2))* Orbis Bks.

Parfrey, Adam & Wyllie, Timothy R., eds. Love, Sex, Fear, Death: The Untold Story of the Process Church of the Final Judgment Special Limited Edition. 2009. 380p. 93.00 *(978-1-932595-38-3(4))* Feral Hse.

Parker, Kathleen. Sacred Service in Civic Space. 2007. 368p. pap. 18.00 *(978-0-9795589-0-0(5))* Meadville Lombard Theological Schl. Pr.

Professor. Dalit Theology in the Twenty-First Century: Discordant Voices, Discerning Pathways. Clarke, Sathianathan & Deenabandhu, Manchala, eds. 2010. (ENG.). 320p. 50.00 *(978-0-19-806691-0(0))* Oxford Univ. Pr., Inc.

Rendle, Gilbert R. Journey in the Wilderness: New Life for Mainline Churches. 2010. 176p. pap. 16.00 *(978-1-4267-1065-0(8))* Abingdon Pr.

Rigby, Cynthia. Promotion of Social Righteousness. 2010. (ENG.). pap. 16.95 *(978-1-57153-064-6(9),* Witherspoon Pr.) Curriculum Publishing, Presbyterian Church (U. S. A.).

Rigney, Donna. Abused by the Church: From Victim to Victor. 2009. 236p. pap. 15.99 *(978-1-61579-445-4(X))* Xulon Pr., Inc.

Roberts, Howard. Approaching The Third Millennium United Methodist. 6.00 *(978-0-687-82117-4(7))* Abingdon Pr.

Rodgers, Felecia. Is Christ Divided? A Biblical View of the Local Church-para Church Anomaly. 2011. 164p. 30.95 ***(978-1-4497-1739-1(X))***; pap. 13.95 ***(978-1-4497-1737-7(3))*** Author Solutions, Inc. (WestBow Pr.).

Rogerson, J. W. According to the Scriptures? The Challenge of Using the Bible in Social, Moral & Political Questions. 2007. (Biblical Challenges in the Contemporary World Ser.). (ENG.). 192p. (C). 99.95 *(978-1-84553-127-0(2))*; per. 29.95 *(978-1-84553-128-7(0))* Equinox Publishing Ltd. GBR. Dist: ISD.

Sahayadoss, Santhosh J. Martin Luther on Social & Political Issues: His Relevance for Church & Society in India. 2006. 250p. pap. *(978-0-8204-8720-5(1))*; pap. *(978-3-631-55679-5(9))* Lang, Peter AG.

Schneider, Athanasius. Dominus Est - It Is the Lord: Reflections of a Bishop of Central Asia on Holy Communion. 2009. 63p. pap. 8.00 *(978-0-9778846-1-2(9))* Newman Hse.

Schori, Katharine Jefferts. The Heartbeat of God: Finding the Sacred in the Middle of Everything. 2010. 192p. 21.99 *(978-1-59473-292-8(2))* SkyLight Paths Publishing.

Sheppard, Carroll Anne & Dilliplane, Nancy Burton. Congregational Connections: Uniting Six Generations in the Church. 2011. 138p. 29.99 ***(978-1-4653-4447-2(0))***; pap. 19.99 ***(978-1-4653-4446-5(2))*** Xlibris Corp.

Shooter, Susan. How Survivors of Abuse Relate to God the Authentic Spirituality of the Annihilated Soul. 2012. (Explorations in Practical, Pastoral & Empirical Theology Ser.). 196p. 99.95 ***(978-1-4094-4126-7(1))*** Ashgate Publishing Co.

Sider, Ronald J. I Am Not a Social Activist: The Prism Essays. 2007. pap. 16.99 *(978-0-8361-9396-1(2))* Herald Pr.

Simarro, Juan. Cristianos Ante la Pobreza: A Christian Approach to Poverty. (SPA.). *(978-84-7645-396-4(5),* 223515) Clie, Editorial.

Snyder, John. These Sheep Bite. 2006. per. 18.95 *(978-0-9764256-1-8(0))* Appleseed Pr.

Stelzle, Charles. The Social Application of Religion. 2009. 144p. 21.99 *(978-0-554-40143-0(6))*; pap. 20.75 *(978-0-554-40140-9(1))* BiblioBazaar.

—The Social Application of Religion. 2009. 64p. pap. 14.14 *(978-1-4589-9939-9(4))* General Bks. LLC.

—The Social Application of Religion. 2008. 139p. pap. 12.00 *(978-1-60608-136-5(5),* Wipf and Stock) Wipf & Stock Pubs.

Stelzle, Charles, et al. The Social Application of Religion: the Merrick Lectures For 1907-08. 2007. (ENG.). 144p. per. 20.95 *(978-1-4304-4291-2(3))* Kessinger Publishing, LLC.

Stetson, Chuck, ed. Creating the Better Hour: Lessons from William Wilberforce. 2007. 349p. per. 24.95 *(978-0-9796462-1-8(9))* Stroud & Hall Publishing.

Sullivan, Susan Crawford. Living Faith: Everyday Religion & Mothers in Poverty. 2012. (Morality & Society Ser.). 288p. 78.00 *(978-0-226-78160-0(7))*; pap 26.00 ***(978-0-226-78161-7(5))*** Univ. of Chicago Pr.

Susin, Luiz Carlos, et al, eds. Different World Is Possible. 2011. 140p. pap. ***(978-0-334-03081-2(1),*** SCM Pr.) Hymns Ancient & Modern Ltd.

Vonruhland. Louder Than Words. 160p. 12.95 *(978-0-281-04931-8(9))* International Publishers Marketing.

Washington Gladden. The Church & Modern Life. 2007. (ENG.). 126p. pap. 13.99 *(978-1-4264-6032-6(5))*; 138p. pap. 19.99 *(978-1-4264-6398-3(7))* BiblioBazaar.

Widjaja, Paulus Sugeng. Character Formation & Social Transformation. 2010. 268p. pap. *(978-3-639-25963-6(7))* VDM Verlag Dr. Mueller e.K.

Wilke, Richard B. The Tie That Binds: Connecting with God, the Church, & the World. 2008. 167p. per. 16.00 *(978-0-687-65208-2(1))* Abingdon Pr.

Wilkinson, Michael & Studebaker, Steven M., eds. A Liberating Spirit: Pentecostals & Social Action in North America. 2010. (Pentecostals, Peacemaking, & Social Justice Ser.). 288p. pap. 32.00 *(978-1-60899-283-6(7),* Pickwick Pubns.) Wipf & Stock Pubs.

Wilson, C. Frederick. All They Want Is Your Money. 2009. 226p. pap. 14.99 *(978-1-890900-51-9(6))* Insight Publishing Group.

Wolseth, Jon. Jesus & the Gang: Youth Violence & Christianity in Urban Honduras. 2011. (ENG., Illus.). 176p. pap. 24.95 *(978-0-8165-2908-7(6))* Univ. of Arizona Pr.

Wyller, Trygve, ed. Heterotopic Citizen: New research on religious work for the disadvantaged. Research in Contemporary Religion 4. 2009. (Research in Contemporary Religion Ser.). (ENG., Illus.). 235p. (C). 77.00 *(978-3-525-60438-0(6))* Vandenhoeck & Ruprecht GmbH & Co. KG DEU. Dist: ISD.

Wyllie, Timothy R. & Parfrey, Adam, eds. Love, Sex, Fear, Death: The Inside Story of the Process Church of the Final Judgment. 2009. (ENG., Illus.). 304p. pap. 24.95 *(978-1-932595-37-6(6))* Feral Hse.

Yankoski, Mike & Yankoski, Danae. Zealous Love: A Practical Guide to Social Justice, 1 vol. 2009. (ENG.). 240p. pap. 16.99 *(978-0-310-29076-6(7))* Zondervan.

C

Zigon, Jarrett. HIV Is God's Blessing: Rehabilitating Morality in Neoliberal Russia. 2010. (ENG.). 272p. 60.00 (978-0-520-26762-6(1)); pap. 24.95 (978-0-520-26764-0(8)) Univ. of California Pr.

CHURCH AND SOCIAL PROBLEMS—CATHOLIC CHURCH

see also Catholic Action; Christian Democracy; Socialism and Catholic Church

Brady, Bernard V. Essential Catholic Social Thought. 2008. 294p. pap. 26.00 (978-1-57075-756-3(9)) Orbis Bks.

Butler, Sheila. Roman Catholicism: Ethics. 2nd ed. 2009. 152p. pap. 36.50 (978-0-340-98657-8(3)) Hodder Education GBR. Dist: Trans-Atlantic Pubns., Inc.

—Roman Catholicism - Ethics. 2009. (Illus.). 64p. pap. 20.00 (978-0-340-98717-9(0)) Hodder Education GBR. Dist: Trans-Atlantic Pubns., Inc.

Cadorette, Curt. Catholicism in Social & Historical Contexts: An Introduction. 2010. 288p. pap. 20.00 (978-1-57075-872-0(7)) Orbis Bks.

Carroll, John J. Engaging Society: The Sociologist in a War Zone. 2007. (Illus.). 330p. (C). 62.00 (978-971-550-505-5(8)) Univ. of Hawaii Pr.

Cullen. Catholic Social Justice: Theological & Practical Explorations. Hoose, Bernard & Mannion, Gerard, eds. 2007. (ENG.). 272p. 41.95 (978-0-567-04542-3(0)) Continuum International Publishing Group, Ltd. GBR. Dist: National Bk. Network.

Duffy, Michael. Catholic Social Thought & the Promotion of Justice. 2008. 204p. pap. (978-3-639-03766-1(9)) VDM Verlag Dr. Mueller e.K.

Dulles, Avery Robert. Church & Society: The Laurence J. Mcginley Lectures, 1988-2007. 3rd ed. 2008. (ENG.). 546p. 45.00 (978-0-8232-2862-1(2)) Fordham Univ. Pr.

Evans, Bernard F. Lazarus at the Table: Catholic & Social Justice. 2006. (Michael Glazier Bks.). 125p. per. 15.95 (978-0-8146-5114-8(3)) Liturgical Pr.

Gottlieb, Laurence. The Catholic Church & Economic Growth in Quebec from 1919 to 1929. 2007. (Illus.). 147p. (978-0-7734-5321-0(0)) Mellen, Edwin Pr., The.

Hudale, Martin. The Matrix of Mysticism: An in-depth ExposT Of. 2008. 476p. pap. 24.99 (978-1-60647-657-4(2)) Xulon Pr., Inc.

Ike, Roberto Marie. Advocacy Coalition & Welfare Policy: Analyzing Coalition Consensus. 2007. (ENG., Illus.). 220p. per. 38.99 (978-0-7618-3479-3(6)) Univ. Pr. of America, Inc.

Ilo, Stan Chu. The Church & Development in Africa: Aid & Development from the Perspective of Catholic Social Ethics. 2011. (African Christian Studies). 342p. pap. 38.00 **(978-1-60899-779-4(0)**, Pickwick Pubns.) Wipf & Stock Pubs.

International Jesuit Network Development Staff. The Development of Peoples: Challenges for Today & Tomorrow. 2007. (ENG.). 220p. per. 29.95 (978-1-85607-574-9(5)) Columba Pr. IRL. Dist: Dufour Editions, Inc.

John Paul II, pseud. On Social Concern: Solicitudo Rei Socialis. 112p. pap. 4.50 (978-0-8198-6923-4(6), 332-317) Pauline Bks. & Media.

Kehoe, S. Karly. Creating a Scottish Church: Catholicism, Gender & Ethnicity in Nineteenth-Century Scotland. 2010. (ENG., Illus.). 208p. 89.95 (978-0-7190-8078-4(9)) Manchester Univ. Pr. GBR. Dist: Macmillan.

Korgen, Jeffry Odell. Solidarity Will Transform the World: Stories of Hope from Catholic Relief Services. 2007. (Illus.). 161p. per. 16.00 (978-1-57075-744-0(5)) Orbis Bks.

Lezcano, Reynier. Beggars No More. 2007. 92p. pap. 11.50 (978-0-615-13578-6(1)) SMARTdollar Pr.

Massaro, Thomas. Living Justice: Catholic Social Teaching in Action. 2nd ed. 2011. (ENG.). 210p. pap. 21.95 (978-1-4422-1013-4(3)) Rowman & Littlefield Publishers, Inc.

Maurin, Peter. Easy Essays. 2010. (Catholic Worker Reprint Ser.). 236p. pap. 26.00 (978-1-60899-062-7(1), Wipf and Stock) Wipf & Stock Pubs.

McClory, Robert. Radical Disciple: Father Pfleger, St. Sabina Church, & the Fight for Social Justice. 2010. (ENG., Illus.). 240p. 24.95 (978-1-56976-528-9(6), Hill, Lawrence Bks.) Chicago Review Pr., Inc.

McDonagh, Enda. Immersed in Mystery: En Route to Theology. 2008. (ENG.). 232p. pap. 16.95 (978-1-85390-969-6(6)) Veritas Pubns. IRL. Dist: Dufour Editions, Inc.

Mulligan, Suzanne. Confronting the Challenge: Poverty, Gender, & HIV in South Africa. 2010. 209p. pap. 51.95 (978-3-03911-938-7(9)) Lang, Peter AG GBR. Dist: Lang, Peter.

O'Hanlon, Gerry. Theology in the Irish Public Square. 2010. (ENG.). 231p. pap. 27.95 (978-1-85607-685-2(7)) Columba Pr. IRL. Dist: Dufour Editions, Inc.

Pogorelc, Anthony & D'Antonio, William. Voices of the Faithful: Loyal Catholics Striving for Change. 2007. (Boston College Church in the 21st Century Ser.). (ENG.). 272p. pap. 24.95 (978-0-8245-2460-9(8), Herder & Herder) Crossroad Publishing Co., The.

Schmitt, Carl, et al. Vital Realities: The Necessity of Politics, the Russian Revolution & the Drift of Democracy. 2011. 280p. 47.95 **(978-1-258-06195-1(3))** Literary Licensing, LLC.

Seebold, Andrew L. Social Moral Reconstruction According to the Writings & Works of William Joseph Chaminade, 1761-1850. 2011. 196p. 42.95 **(978-1-258-04255-4(X))** Literary Licensing, LLC.

Snyder, Larry. Think & Act Anew: How Poverty in America Affects Us All & What We Can Do about It. 2011. 144p. pap. 16.00 (978-1-57075-904-8(9)) Orbis Bks.

Somerville, Henry. Studies in the Catholic Social Movement. 2011. (ENG., Illus.). 128p. pap. 20.95 (978-1-932528-18-3(0)) IHS Pr.

Stanford, Peter. Opening Up: Speaking Out in the Church. 192p. (978-0-232-52624-0(9)) Darton, Longman & Todd, Ltd.

Williams, Thomas D. The World as It Could Be: Catholic Social Thought for a New Generation. 2011. (ENG.). 240p. pap. 24.95 (978-0-8245-2666-5(X)) Crossroad Publishing Co., The.

CHURCH AND SOCIAL PROBLEMS—CHURCH OF ENGLAND

Spencer, Stephen. William Temple: A Calling to Prophecy. 132p. 12.00 (978-0-281-05437-4(1)) SPCK Publishing GBR. Dist: Pilgrim Pr., The/United Church Pr.

CHURCH AND SOCIAL PROBLEMS—MENNONITES

Loewen, Wendell J. Beyond Me: Grounding Youth Ministry in God's Story. 2008. pap. (978-0-8361-9403-6(9)) Faith & Life Pr.

CHURCH AND SOCIAL PROBLEMS—METHODIST CHURCH

The Book of Discipline & the Book of Resolutions 2009-2012 CD-ROM. 2009. cd-rom 20.00 (978-0-687-64749-1(5)) Abingdon Pr.

The Book of Resolutions of the United Methodist Church 2008. 2009. pap. 18.00 (978-0-687-64821-4(1)) Abingdon Pr.

Guidelines for Leading Your Congregation 2009-2012 - Church & Society: Advocating for Peace & Justice. 2008. 2.95 (978-0-687-64752-1(5)) Abingdon Pr.

Lavender, Wayne. Counting Ants While the Elephants March By: Thoughts on Church & State, Poverty & Terrorism, War & Peace. 2nd ed. 2007. per. (978-0-9794656-4-2(8)) Ithaca Publishing, Inc.

Lavender, Wayne Lavender. Counting Ants While the Elephants March By: Thoughts on Church & State, Poverty & Terrorism, War & Peace. 2007. (978-0-9794656-3-5(X)) Ithaca Publishing, Inc.

Mason, Howard & Christie, Neal. Justice in Everyday Life: A Study of the United Methodist Social Principles. 2007. 36p. pap. 6.00 (978-0-88177-491-7(X)) Discipleship Resources.

CHURCH AND SOCIAL PROBLEMS—STUDY AND TEACHING

Morehouse Publishing Staff. The Episcopal Handbook. 2008. (Illus.). 256p. pap. 15.00 (978-0-8192-2329-6(8), Morehouse Publishing) Church Publishing, Inc.

CHURCH AND SOCIAL PROBLEMS—AFRICA

Agina, Harry N. The Invasion of the Funky Pastors: Church Business at War with African Culture. 2010. 140p. 26.95 (978-1-4490-8120-1(7)); pap. 16.95 (978-1-4490-8119-5(3)) AuthorHouse.

Byamugisha, Gideon B. ISG 44: Church Communities Confronting HIV/AIDS. 2010. 128p. pap. **(978-0-281-06239-3(0))** SPCK Publishing.

Carpenter, Joel A. Walking Together: Christian Thinking & Public Life in South Africa. 2012. (ENG.). 416p. pap. 28.99 **(978-0-89112-315-6(6))** Abilene Christian Univ. Pr.

Ilo, Stan Chu. The Church & Development in Africa: Aid & Development from the Perspective of Catholic Social Ethics. 2011. (African Christian Studies). 342p. pap. 38.00 **(978-1-60899-779-4(0)**, Pickwick Pubns.) Wipf & Stock Pubs.

Ilo, Stan Chu, et al, eds. The Church as Salt & Light: Path to an African Ecclesiology of Abundant Life. 2011. (African Christian Studies). 192p. pap. 22.00 **(978-1-61097-100-3(0)**, Pickwick Pubns.) Wipf & Stock Pubs.

—The Church in Africa as Salt & Light: Path to an African Ecclesiology of Abundant Life. 2012. (ENG.). 192p. (C). pap. 35.00 **(978-0-227-68008-7(1))** Clarke, James Co., Ltd. GBR. Dist: Brown, David Bk. Co., The.

Jones, Sarah Rowland, compiled by. Faith in Action: Njongonkulu Ndungane Archbishop for the church & the World. 2011. 256p. pap. 27.95 (978-0-7963-0763-7(6)) NB Pubs. Ltd. ZAF. Dist: International Publishers Marketing.

Kabati, Jean-Daniel. The Role of Churches in Rebuilding Community Relations. 2010. 164p. pap. (978-3-8383-5871-0(6)) Lambert Academic Publishing.

Langa, Clement. A Good Slave: Dwelling in the Subtleties of Bondage. 2010. 104p. pap. (978-1-84748-667-7(3)) Athena Pr.

Mulligan, Suzanne. Confronting the Challenge: Poverty, Gender, & HIV in South Africa. 2010. 209p. pap. 51.95 (978-3-03911-938-7(9)) Lang, Peter AG GBR. Dist: Lang, Peter.

Paris, Peter J. Religion & Poverty: Pan-African Perspectives. 2009. (ENG., Illus.). 384p. 94.95 (978-0-8223-4356-1(8)); pap. 26.95 (978-0-8223-4378-3(9)) Duke Univ. Pr.

CHURCH AND SOCIAL PROBLEMS—FRANCE

Martin, Jr. Benjamin & Martin, Benjamin, Jr., Benjamin. Count Albert de Mun: Paladin of the Third Republic. 2011. (ENG.). 386p. pap. 50.00 (978-0-8078-9721-8(3)) Univ. of North Carolina Pr.

CHURCH AND SOCIAL PROBLEMS—GREAT BRITAIN

Cairns, Earle Edwin. Saints & Society: The Social Impact of Eighteenth Century English Revivals & Its Contemporary Relevance. 2011. 192p. 42.95 **(978-1-258-08090-7(7))** Literary Licensing, LLC.

Church of England, Commission on Urban Priority Areas Staff, contrib. by. Faith in the City: A Call for Action by Church & Nation. 2012. (Illus.). xvi, 398p. pap. **(978-0-7151-3709-3(3))** Church Hse. Publishing.

Inglis, Kenneth S. Churches & the Working Classes in Victorian England. 2006. 368p. 190.00 (978-0-415-41283-4(8)) Routledge.

Isaac, Les. Street Pastors. 2009. (ENG.). 224p. pap. 11.99 (978-1-84291-419-9(7)) Cook, David C.

Morgan, D. Densil. Span of the Cross: Christian Religion & Society in Wales, 1914-2000. 2nd ed. 2011. (ENG., Illus.). 310p. pap. 40.00 (978-0-7083-2397-7(9)) Univ. of Wales Pr. GBR. Dist: Chicago Distribution Ctr.

Pereiro, James. 'Ethos' & the Oxford Movement: At the Heart of Tractarianism. 2008. (ENG.). 320p. 150.00 (978-0-19-923029-7(3)) Oxford Univ. Pr., Inc.

Power, Maria. From Ecumenism to Community Relations: Inter-Church Relationships in Northern Ireland 1980-1999. 2007. 262p. (C). 75.00 (978-0-7165-3379-5(0)); pap. 32.50 (978-0-7165-3380-1(4)) Irish Academic Pr. IRL. Dist: International Specialized Bk. Services.

Prochaska, Frank. Christianity & Social Service in Modern Britain: The Disinherited Spirit. 2008. (ENG., Illus.). 228p. 45.00 (978-0-19-953979-6(0)) Oxford Univ. Pr., Inc.

Soloway, R.A. Prelates & People: Ecclesiastical Social Thought in England, 1783-1852. 2006. 464p. 180.00 (978-0-415-41298-8(6)) Routledge.

Stubbs, Charles. Charles Kingsley & the Christian Social Movement. 2007. (ENG.). 198p. 39.95 (978-0-548-05091-0(0)) Kessinger Publishing, LLC.

Ziemann, Benjamin. Katholische Kirche und Sozialwissenschaften 1945-1975. 2007. (Kritische Studien Zur Geschichtswissenschaft Ser.). (GER.). 396p. (C). pap. 63.00 (978-3-525-35156-7(9)) Vandenhoeck & Ruprecht GmbH & Co. KG DEU. Dist: ISD.

CHURCH AND SOCIAL PROBLEMS—PHILIPPINES

Carroll, John J. Engaging Society: The Sociologist in a War Zone. 2007. (Illus.). 330p. (C). 62.00 (978-971-550-505-5(8)) Univ. of Hawaii Pr.

CHURCH AND SOCIAL PROBLEMS—UNITED STATES

ABW Staff. ABW (A Better World), 3 vols. Incl. Vol. 1. Back to the Future. 162p. per. 10.00 (978-0-9641885-1-8(1)); Vol. 2. Is it Time to Break Away from the United Methodist Church? 18p. per. 5.00 (978-0-9641885-2-5(X)); Vol. 3. Law of One. 114p. per. 7.00 (978-0-9641885-3-2(8)); 1996. (978-0-9641885-0-1(3)) A B W.

Altrock, Craig. The Shaping of God's People: One Story of How God Is Shaping the North American Church Through Short-Term Missions. 2007. 80p. pap. 11.95 (978-0-615-16895-1(7)) Altrock, Craig.

Baker, Sharon L. & Hardin, Michael. Peace Be with You: Christ's Benediction amid Violent Empires. 2010. (978-1-931038-73-7(2)) Cascadia Publishing Hse., LLC.

Bradley, Anthony B., ed. Keep Your Head Up: America's New Black Christian Leaders, Social Consciousness, & the Cosby Conversation. 2012. 224p. pap. 15.99 (978-1-4335-0673-4(4)) Crossway.

Campolo, Tony. Is Jesus a Democrat or a Republican?, 0 vols. 2009. 208p. pap. 11.99 (978-0-8499-2927-4(X)) Nelson, Thomas Inc.

Carlson, Paul R. The Empty Pew: Why Americans are Abandoning the Churches. 2009. 307p. pap. 19.95 (978-1-4327-4083-2(0)) Outskirts Pr., Inc.

Carney, William H. How Would Jesus Vote? A Biblical Perspective on Today's Hot Political Issues. 2006. (ENG.). 80p. pap. 6.99 (978-1-59979-077-0(7), Creation Hse.) Charisma Media.

Carter, Jimmy. Our Endangered Values: America's Moral Crisis. 2006. (ENG.). 224p. pap. 15.00 (978-0-7432-8501-8(8)) Simon & Schuster.

Cleveland, Odell & Wineburg, Robert. Pracademics & Community Change: A True Story of Nonprofit Development & Social Entrepreneurship During Welfare Reform. 2010. (Illus.). xii, 196p. pap. 29.95 (978-1-933478-98-2(5)) Lyceum Bks., Inc.

Coleman, Monica A. The Dinah Project: A Handbook for Congregational Response to Sexual Violence. 2010. 192p. pap. 22.00 (978-1-60899-437-3(6), Wipf and Stock) Wipf & Stock Pubs.

Daly, Lew. God & the Welfare State. 2006. (Boston Review Bks.). (ENG.). 136p. (gr. 17). 14.95 (978-0-262-04236-9(3)) MIT Pr.

Djupe, Paul A. & Olson, Laura R. Religious Interests in Community Conflict: Beyond the Culture Wars. 2007. (Illus.). 353p. per. 39.95 (978-1-932792-51-5(1)) Baylor Univ. Pr.

Dorsett, Terry W. Developing Leadership Teams in the Bivocational Church. 2010. 160p. pap. 19.95 (978-1-61507-252-1(7)) Cross Bks. Publishing.

Drayton, Tony Ferdinand. Transformation & the Church: A Push toward Acceptance within the HIV/AIDS Pandemic. 2008. 176p. per. 19.95 (978-0-9787394-9-2(3)) Protective Hands Communications.

Evans, Bernard F. Lazarus at the Table: Catholic & Social Justice. 2006. (Michael Glazier Bks.). 125p. per. 15.95 (978-0-8146-5114-8(3)) Liturgical Pr.

Fusco, Daniel. Ahead of the Curve: Preparing the Church for Post-Postmodernism. 2011. pap. 9.99 (978-1-61739-441-6(6)) Tate Publishing & Enterprises, LLC.

Gill, Steve. Changing the Method of Change. 2009. 280p. pap. 16.99 (978-1-60791-431-0(X)) Xulon Pr., Inc.

Guidelines for Leading Your Congregation 2009-2012 - Church & Society: Advocating for Peace & Justice. 2008. 2.95 (978-0-687-64752-1(5)) Abingdon Pr.

Harper, Nile. Journeys into Justice. 2009. 368p. pap. 18.95 (978-1-935098-14-0(4)) Hillcrest Publishing Group, Inc.

Hartley, Benjamin L. Evangelicals at a Crossroads: Revivalism & Social Reform in Boston, 1860-1910. 2011. (Revisiting New England Ser.). (Illus.). 304p. (C). 85.00 (978-1-58465-928-0(9)); (ENG., pap. 39.95 (978-1-58465-929-7(7)) Univ. Pr. of New England. (University of New Hampshire Press).

Ike, Roberto Marie. Advocacy Coalition & Welfare Policy: Analyzing Coalition Consensus. 2007. (ENG., Illus.). 220p. per. 38.99 (978-0-7618-3479-3(6)) Univ. Pr. of America, Inc.

Jonasen, Marvin R. Why Have All the People Gone: The State of the Christian Church in America, 1 vol. 2009. 195p. pap. 19.95 (978-1-4489-9181-5(1)) PublishAmerica, Inc.

Jones, Margaret Wandel. Not of My Making: Bullying, Scapegoating & Misconduct in Churches. 2008. 412p. pap. 19.95 (978-0-9801491-0-4(X)) Pluck Pr.

Lockhart, Earline. A Prophetic Word to the Church & Our Nation. 2008. 124p. pap. 10.95 (978-0-7414-4716-6(9)) Infinity Publishing.

Manning, Gwennette. Killings in the Hous (Church) 2008. pap. 13.00 (978-0-8059-8090-5(3)) Dorrance Publishing Co., Inc.

Maurin, Peter. Easy Essays. 2010. (Catholic Worker Reprint Ser.). 236p. pap. 26.00 (978-1-60899-062-7(1), Wipf and Stock) Wipf & Stock Pubs.

Peters, Rebecca Todd & Hinson-Hasty, Elizabeth, eds. To Do Justice: A Guide for Progressive Christians. 2008. (ENG.). 164p. pap. 20.00 (978-0-664-23282-5(5)) Westminster John Knox Pr.

Rauschenbusch, Walter. Christianity & the Social Crisis. 2010. 456p. pap. 36.75 (978-1-177-14428-5(X)) 2010. (ENG.). 454p. pap. 36.75 (978-1-176-54748-3(8)) 2010. 454p. pap. 36.75 (978-1-144-20681-7(2)) 2010. 448p. pap. 36.75 (978-1-144-15600-6(9)) 2010. 450p. pap. 36.75 (978-1-142-59716-0(4)) 2010. 456p. pap. 36.75 (978-1-142-16281-8(8)) 2009. 448p. 34.99 (978-1-113-65336-9(1)) 2009. 448p. 34.99 (978-1-113-65330-7(2)) 2009. 448p. 41.99 (978-1-113-65332-1(9)) 2009. 448p. pap. 36.75 (978-1-113-65335-2(3)) 2009. 448p. pap. 35.75 (978-1-113-65333-8(7)) 2009. 448p. pap. 35.75 (978-1-113-65326-0(4)) 2009. 448p. pap. 36.75 (978-1-113-65328-4(0)) 2009. (ENG.). 446p. pap. 28.99 (978-1-113-65331-4(0), BiblioLife) 2009. (ENG.). 446p. pap. 26.99 (978-1-113-65329-1(9), BiblioLife) 2009. (ENG.). 446p. pap. 28.99 (978-1-113-65324-6(8), BiblioLife) BiblioBazaar.

—Christianity & the Social Crisis. 2009. 256p. pap. (978-1-4590-4241-4(7)) Books LLC.

—Christianity & the Social Crisis. 2007. (ENG.). 444p. 51.95 (978-0-548-15529-5(1)); pap. 36.95 (978-1-4304-4960-7(8)) Kessinger Publishing, LLC.

—Christianity & the Social Crisis. 2007. pap. **(978-1-4067-5864-1(7))** Read Bks.

Rauschenbusch, Walter. Christianity & the Social Crisis in the 21st Century: The Classic That Woke up the Church. 2008. 400p. pap. 14.95 (978-0-06-149726-1(6), HarperOne) HarperCollins Pubs.

Schuyler, Joseph B. Northern Parish: A Sociological & Pastoral Study. 2011. 404p. 54.95 **(978-1-258-08913-9(0))** Literary Licensing, LLC.

Snyder, Larry. Think & Act Anew: How Poverty in America Affects Us All & What We Can Do about It. 2011. 144p. pap. 16.00 (978-1-57075-904-8(9)) Orbis Bks.

Solomon, Lewis D. In God We Trust? Faith-Based Organizations & the Quest to Solve America's Social Ills. 2007. (Religion, Politics, & Society in the Millennium Ser.). (ENG.). 304p. per. 36.99 (978-0-7391-2420-8(X)) Lexington Bks.

Stafford, Tim. Shaking the System: What I Learned from the Great American Reform Movements. 2007. (ENG., Illus.). 176p. 17.00 (978-0-8308-3436-5(2), IVP Bks.) InterVarsity Pr.

Vera Mendez, Juan Antonio. Palabra con filo Liberador: De la conciencia solidaria a la transformacion Social. 2009. (SPA., Illus.). 142p. 15.00 (978-1-61505-022-2(1)) Publicaciones Gaviota.

Watt, Alan J. Farm Workers & the Churches: The Movement in California & Texas. 2010. (Fronteras Series, sponsored by Texas A&M International University Ser.). (ENG., Illus.). 264p. 48.00 (978-1-60344-174-2(3)); pap. 24.00 (978-1-60344-193-3(X)) Texas A&M Univ. Pr.

CHURCH AND SOCIETY

see Church and the World

CHURCH AND STATE

see also Anti-Clericalism; Asylum, Right Of; Christianity and Politics; Church and Education; Church and International Organization; Church Polity; Church Property; Ecclesiastical Law; Free Churches; Freedom of Religion; Government, Resistance to; Investiture; Liberty of Conscience; Patronage, Ecclesiastical; Popes—Temporal Power; Religion and State; Religion in the Public Schools; Secularization; Taxation, Exemption From

Adams, William. Christianity & Civil Government: a Discourse Delivered on Sabbath. 2007. (ENG.). 52p. per. 16.95 (978-1-4304-4982-9(9)) Kessinger Publishing, LLC.

Aguilar, Mario. Contemplating God Changing the World. 2009. 192p. pap. 18.00 (978-1-59627-108-1(6), Seabury Bks.) Church Publishing, Inc.

Bailey, Betty Jane & Bailey, Martin J. Who Are the Christians in the Middle East? Second Edition. 2nd ed. 2010. 243p. pap. 20.00 (978-0-8028-6595-3(X)) Eerdmans, William B. Publishing Co.

Baker, Hunter. The End of Secularism. 2009. 224p. pap. 17.99 (978-1-4335-0654-3(8)) Crossway.

Barth, Karl. Church & State - S. & H. 6.00 (978-0-687-82167-9(3)) Abingdon Pr.

—Community, State & Church. 2008. 26.75 (978-0-8446-1058-0(5)) Smith, Peter Pub., Inc.

Bautista, Julius. Christianity & the State in Asia: Complicity & Conflict. Gee, Francis Lim Khek, ed. 2009. (ENG., Illus.). 240p. 145.00 (978-0-415-48069-7(8)) Routledge.

Bautista, Julius & Khek Gee Lim, Francis, eds. Christianity & the State in Asia: Complicity & Conflict. 2012. (ENG., Illus.). 240p. (C). pap. 42.95 **(978-0-415-62742-9(7))** Routledge.

Beckwith, Francis J. Politics for Christians: Statecraft as Soulcraft. 2010. (Christian Worldview Integration Ser.). (ENG.). 175p. pap. 18.00 (978-0-8308-2814-2(1), IVP Acad.) InterVarsity Pr.

Bendel, Rainer & Spannenberger, Norbert. Kirchen Als Integrationsfaktor Für Die Migranten Im Südosten der Habsburgermonarchie Im 18. Jahrhundert. 2010. (GER & ENG., Illus.). 323p. pap. (978-3-643-10045-0(0)) Lit Verlag.

Betances, Emelio. The Catholic Church & Power Politics in Latin America: The Dominican Case in Comparative Perspective. 2007. (Critical Currents in Latin American Perspective Ser.). (ENG., Illus.). 292p. 89.00

(978-0-7425-5504-4(6)); per. 37.95 *(978-0-7425-5505-1(4))* Rowman & Littlefield Publishers, Inc.

Blancarte, Roberto. Los Retos de la Laicidad y la Secularización en el Mundo Contemporáneo. 2008. (Estudios Sociológicos Ser.). (SPA.). 493p. pap. 81.99 *(978-968-12-1345-9(9))* El Colegio de México, A.C., Biblioteca Miguel Cosío Villegas MEX. Dist: Fondo de Cultura Economica USA.

Boureau, Alain. La Religion de L'État: La Construction de la République étatique Dans le Discours Théologique de L'Occident Médiéval, 1250-1350. 2006. (FRE.). 356p. (C). pap. 50.00 ***(978-2-251-38080-3(9))*** Societe d'edition Les Belles lettres FRA. Dist: ISD.

Brann, Eva. Homage to Americans: Mile-High Meditations, Close Readings, & Time-Spanning Speculations. 2010. (ENG.). 260p. pap. 19.95 *(978-1-58988-062-7(5))* Dry, Paul Bks., Inc.

Bretherton, Luke. Christianity & Contemporary Politics: The Conditions & Possibilites of Faithful Witness. 2010. (ENG.). 272p. 99.95 *(978-1-4051-9968-1(7))*; pap. 42.95 *(978-1-4051-9969-8(5))* Wiley, John & Sons, Inc. (Wiley-Blackwell).

Brownson's Quarterly Review, Set, Vols. 1-29. Orig. Title: Boston Quarterly Review. reprint ed. lib. bdg. 1305.00 *(978-0-404-19506-9(7))* AMS Pr., Inc.

Brownson's Quarterly Review. 2009. Orig. Title: Boston Quarterly Review. 376p. pap. *(978-0-217-69336-3(9))*; 414p. pap. *(978-0-217-69326-4(1))*; 232p. pap. *(978-0-217-91340-9(7))*; 460p. pap. *(978-0-217-18278-2(X))*; 266p. pap. *(978-0-217-73184-3(8))*; 272p. pap. *(978-1-4590-5139-3(4))* Books LLC.

Brownson's Quarterly Review. 2009. Orig. Title: Boston Quarterly Review. 446p. pap. 31.26 *(978-0-217-73176-8(7))* General Bks. LLC.

Cane, Peter, et al, eds. Law & Religion in Theoretical & Historical Context. 2011. (ENG.). 338p. pap. 65.00 ***(978-1-107-40237-9(9))*** Cambridge Univ. Pr.

Cane, Peter, et al. Law & Religion in Theoretical & Historical Context. Cane, Peter et al, eds. 2008. (ENG.). 336p. 105.00 *(978-0-521-42590-2(5))* Cambridge Univ. Pr.

Castro, Fidel & Betto, Frei. Fidel y la Religion: Conversaciones con Frei Betto Sobre el Marxismo y la Teologia de la Liberacion. 2006. (Ocean Sur Ser.). (SPA & ENG.). 324p. pap. 19.95 *(978-1-920888-77-0(2))* Ocean Pr. AUS. Dist: Consortium Bk. Sales & Distribution.

Cavanaugh, William T. Migrations of the Holy: God, State, & the Political Meaning of the Church. 2011. pap. 18.00 *(978-0-8028-6609-7(3))* Eerdmans, William B. Publishing Co.

Cavarnos, Constantine & Patapios. The Cumenical Patriarchate & the Question of Greek-Turkish Relations Through the Centuries. 2010. (Illus.). 104p. ***(978-0-911165-89-0(4))*** Ctr. for Traditionalist Orthodox Studies.

Colson, Charles W. & Colson, Charles. God & Government: An Insider's View on the Boundaries Between Faith & Politics. 1 vol. rev. ed. 2007. (ENG.). 448p. pap. 14.99 *(978-0-310-27764-4(7))* Zondervan.

Crowell, John. Republics; 2006. 244p. per. 20.99 *(978-1-4255-2089-2(8))* MPublishing.

Dante Alighieri. The de Monarchia of Dante Alighieri. 2009. 166p. pap. *(978-0-217-75413-2(9))*; 134p. pap. *(978-0-217-75411-8(2))* Books LLC.

—The de Monarchia of Dante Alighieri. 2009. 146p. pap. 19.99 *(978-1-4588-6927-2(X))* General Bks. LLC.

Dekker, Diane. Two Trees of Knowledge: A Biblical Case for the Separation of School & State. 2009. 324p. pap. 19.99 *(978-1-4141-1301-2(3))* Pleasant Word.

Dempsey, Michael James. Separation of Church & State in the Works of Félicité Lamennais & Orestes Brownson: French & American Theories Compared. 2009. iii, 222p. *(978-0-7734-4794-3(6))* Mellen, Edwin Pr., The.

Durland, William. God or Nations: Radical Theology for the Religious Peace Movement. 2010. (Catholic Worker Reprint Ser.). 332p. (Orig.). pap. 36.00 *(978-1-60899-055-9(9))*, Wipf and Stock) Wipf & Stock Pubs.

Emilianides & Emilianides, Achilles C. Religion & Law in Cyprus. 2011. 250p. pap. ***(978-90-411-3438-7(7))*** Kluwer Law International.

Finney, Jerald. Seperation of Church & State: God's Churches - Spiritual or Legal Entities? 2009. 108p. pap. 11.99 *(978-1-60791-341-2(0))* Xulon Pr., Inc.

Force, JoBeth. When to Fight & When to Run. 2007. pap. 18.95 net. *(978-0-939925-20-9(6))* R. C. Law & Co., Inc.

Gandal, Keith. Class Representation in Modern Fiction & Film. annot. ed. 2007. (ENG.). 240p. 95.00 *(978-1-4039-7792-2(5))* Palgrave Macmillan.

Garcia, Joaquin F. The Natural Law: Foundation of Morality. 2011. 26p. 35.95 ***(978-1-258-04068-0(9))*** Literary Licensing, LLC.

Garcia, Mary. The Sufferings, Assassinations, & Martyrdom of the Missionary CHurch in Olancho, Hondouras (1963-1982) The History of a Church That Lived Its Commitment to the Poor. Whelan, Winifred, tr. from SPA. 2011. (Illus.). 360p. 139.95 ***(978-0-7734-3952-8(8))*** Mellen, Edwin Pr., The.

Garnett, George. Marsilius of Padua & 'the Truth of History' 2006. (ENG.). 240p. 110.00 *(978-0-19-929156-4(X))* Oxford Univ. Pr., Inc.

Gillespie, Katherine. Katherine Chidley. 2009. (Early Modern Englishwoman: A Facsimile Library of Essential Works - Printed Writings, 1641-1700: Ser. II, Part Four Ser.). 142p. 89.95 *(978-0-7546-6231-0(4))* Ashgate Publishing Co.

Gladstone, William E. The State in Its Relations with the Church. 2008. 334p. 45.95 *(978-1-4365-2925-9(5))* 2007. (ENG.). 336p. per. 30.95 *(978-0-548-73252-6(3))* Kessinger Publishing, LLC.

Hawkins, Merlyn P., ed. Henry David Thoreau on the Power of Simplicity: The Seer of Walden Weighs in on Work, Money, Success — and the Joy of Living with Less. 2010. 64p. pap. 8.95 *(978-0-9788806-3-7(3)*, Simple Samplers) Akoba Communications LLC.

Herndon, Jeffrey C. Eric Voegelin & the Problem of Christian Political Order. 2007. (Eric Voegelin Institute Series in Political Philosophy). (ENG.). 208p. (C). 39.95 *(978-0-8262-1737-0(0))* Univ. of Missouri Pr.

Hunter, Ian. The Secularisation of the Confessional State: The Political Thought of Christian Thomasius. 2011. (Ideas in Context Ser.). (ENG.). 233p. pap. 48.00 *(978-0-521-20083-7(0))* Cambridge Univ. Pr.

Idestrscaron;m, Jonas, ed. For the Sake of the World. 2009. (Church of Sweden Research Ser.). 156p. pap. 18.00 *(978-1-60899-108-2(3)*, Pickwick Pubns.) Wipf & Stock Pubs.

Iskander, Elizabeth. Sectarian Conflict in Egypt: Coptic Media, Identity & Representation. 2012. (Routledge Studies in Middle Eastern Politics Ser.). (ENG.). 240p. (C). 135.00 ***(978-0-415-69578-7(3))*** Routledge.

Joireman, Sandra, ed. Church, State, & Citizen: Christian Approaches to Political Engagement. 2009. (ENG.). 200p. pap. 24.95 *(978-0-19-537845-0(8))* Oxford Univ. Pr., Inc.

Joireman, Sandra Fullerton, ed. Church, State, & Citizen: Christian Approaches to Political Engagement. 2009. (ENG.). 200p. 99.00 *(978-0-19-537846-7(6))* Oxford Univ. Pr., Inc.

Kearsley, Roy. Church, Community & Power. 2009. 260p. 114.95 *(978-0-7546-6345-4(0))* Ashgate Publishing Co.

Keating, John Craig William. A Protestant Church in Communist China: Moore Memorial Church Shanghai, 1949-1989. 2012. (ENG.). 330p. 85.00 ***(978-1-61146-090-2(5))*** Lehigh Univ. Pr.

Kempen, Bernhard & Naumann, Kolja, eds. Demokratie und Religion: Tagungsband Zum Kolloquium der Wissenschaftlichen Arbeitsgruppe Für Weltkirchliche Aufgaben der Deutschen Bischofskonferenz und der Demokratie Stiftung an der Universität Zu Köln Am 23. 11. 2009 in Köln. 2011. (Kölner Schriften zu Recht und Staat Ser.). (GER.). 142p. 41.95 ***(978-3-631-62055-7(1))*** Lang, Peter GmbH, Europaischer Verlag der Wissenschaften DEU. Dist: Lang, Peter.

Larson, Ron. Hidden Fields: A Guide for Workplace Christian Fellowship Groups. 2007. pap. 9.00 *(978-0-8059-7454-6(7))* Dorrance Publishing Co., Inc.

Laski, Harold J. Studies in the Problem of Sovereignty. 2008. 304p. *(978-1-4437-2453-1(X))* 2006. (ENG.). 300p. per. *(978-1-4067-2921-4(3))* Read Bks. (Hesperides Pr.).

Lett, Gabe. Let's Get Together: Building Community in the Church. 2008. (Illus.). 160p. per. 12.99 *(978-1-60247-893-0(7))* Tate Publishing & Enterprises, LLC.

Long, Michael G. & Long, Michael G. God & Country? Diverse Perspectives on Christianity & Patriotism. Sadd, Tracy Wenger, ed. 2007. (ENG.). 304p. 89.00 *(978-1-4039-7300-9(8))* Palgrave Macmillan.

MacKenzie, Geoffrey Shisumu & Njonje, Billy. Church & Land. 2011. 104p. pap. ***(978-3-8443-8978-4(4))*** Lambert Academic Publishing.

Marcoccio, Robert. Establishing Federal Referendum. 2011. 58p. pap. 12.00 ***(978-1-257-37326-0(9))*** Lulu Enterprises Inc.

Mars-Proietti, Laura, ed. Religion & Law in America: An Encyclopedic Dictionary. 2nd ed. 2008. 600p. 135.00 *(978-1-59237-298-0(8))* Grey Hse. Publishing.

Mastnak, Tomaz, ed. Hobbes's Behemoth: Religion & Democracy. 2009. (ENG.). 250p. 80.00 *(978-1-84540-175-7(1))* Imprint Academic GBR. Dist: Ingram Pub. Services.

—Hobbes's Behemoth: Religion & Dremocracy. 2009. (ENG.). 350p. pap. 34.90 *(978-1-84540-176-4(X))* Imprint Academic GBR. Dist: Ingram Pub. Services.

Mbandi, Paul. A Theology of the Unity of the Church in a Multi-Ethnic Context. 2010. 204p. pap. *(978-3-639-18113-5(1))* VDM Verlag Dr. Mueller e.K.

McGahern, Una. Christian Palestinians in the Israeli State. 2011. (Durham Modern Middle East & Islamic World Ser.). (ENG., Illus.). 216p. (C). 140.00 *(978-0-415-60571-7(7))* Routledge.

Meier, Heinrich. The Lesson of Carl Schmitt: Four Chapters on the Distinction between Political Theology & Political Philosophy, Expanded Edition. Brainard, Marcus & Berman, Robert, trs. from GER. 2011. (Illus.). 240p. pap. 25.00 *(978-0-226-51886-2(8))* Univ. of Chicago Pr.

Miller, Keith Graber, ed. Prophetic Peacemaking: Selected Writings of J. R. Burkholder. 2010. 440p. pap. 27.99 *(978-0-8361-9523-1(X))* Herald Pr.

Miroshnikova, Elena. The Cooperation Model in State-Church Relations. 2011. 156p. pap. ***(978-3-8433-8998-3(5))*** Lambert Academic Publishing.

Morrison, Alan. Within These Walls: Control. 2011. 116p. 22.95 ***(978-1-4620-5698-9(9))***; pap. 12.95 ***(978-1-4620-5696-5(2))*** iUniverse, Inc.

Morrison, Clinton D. The Powers That Be. 2009. (Studies in Biblical Theology, First Ser.). 144p. pap. 18.00 *(978-1-60899-025-2(7)*, Wipf and Stock) Wipf & Stock Pubs.

Motha, Stewart, ed. Democracy's Empire: Sovereignty, Law, & Violence. 2007. (Journal of Law & Society Special Issues Ser.: 1). (ENG.). 160p. per. 39.95 *(978-1-4051-6313-2(5)*, Wiley-Blackwell) Wiley, John & Sons, Inc.

Murray, A. Victor. The State & the Church in a Free Society. 2008. (ENG.). 212p. pap. 32.99 *(978-0-521-08169-6(6))* Cambridge Univ. Pr.

Murvar, Vatro. Russian Social Monism & American Social Pluralism. 2011. 144p. 40.95 ***(978-1-258-03706-2(8))*** Literary Licensing, LLC.

Najar, Monica. Evangelizing the South: A Social History of Church & State in Early America. 2008. (ENG.). 256p. 60.00 *(978-0-19-530900-3(6))* Oxford Univ. Pr., Inc.

Novak, David. In Defense of Religious Liberty. 2009. (American Ideals & Institutions Ser.). (ENG.). 250p. (C). 28.00 *(978-1-933859-75-0(X))*; pap. 18.00 *(978-1-933859-76-7(8))* ISI Bks.

O'Mahony, Anthony, ed. Christianity & Jerusalem. 2010. 340p. pap. *(978-0-85244-646-1(2))* Gracewing, Ltd.

Oser, Lee. The Return of Christian Humanism: Chesterton, Eliot, Tolkien, & the Romance of History. 2007. (ENG.). 208p. (C). 39.95 *(978-0-8262-1775-2(3))* Univ. of Missouri Pr.

Pecknold, C. C. Christianity & Politics. 2010. (Cascade Companions Ser.). 196p. pap. 23.00 *(978-1-55635-242-3(5)*, Cascade Bks.) Wipf & Stock Pubs.

Pennings, Ray. Church & Caesar: A Legal Primer for Church Office-bearers. 2008. 66p. per. 7.00 *(978-1-60178-039-3(7))* Reformation Heritage Bks.

Redekop, John H. Politics under God. 2007. 223p. per. 11.99 *(978-0-8361-9355-8(5))* Herald Pr.

Reformed Presbytery. Act Declaration & Testimony: For the Whole of our Covenanted Reformation as Attained to & Established in Britain & Ireland; Particularly Betwixt the Years 1638 & 1649 Inclusive. 2007. (ENG.). 254p. pap. 21.99 *(978-1-4264-8427-8(5))*; 282p. pap. 23.99 *(978-1-4264-8485-8(2))* BiblioBazaar.

Riddell, Elder Donnie L. Dare to Go Against the Grain of the Porcupines: (Church Traditions & State Interpretations) 2008. 108p. pap. 16.95 *(978-1-60672-902-1(0))* PublishAmerica, Inc.

Robert, Morritt. Causes & Consequences: Decline & Fall of Empires, Church & State. 2011. 244p. pap. ***(978-3-639-33770-9(0))*** VDM Verlag Dr. Mueller e.K.

Rodopoulos, Panteleimon. An Overview of Orthodox Canon Law. Dragas, George, ed. 2007. 320p. pap. 18.95 *(978-1-933275-15-4(4)*, Orthodox Research Institute) Cocheco Falls Publishing.

Rommen, Heinrich A. The State in Catholic Thought: A Treatise in Political Philosophy. 2nd ed. 2007. 780p. 65.00 *(978-1-934182-21-5(4)*, 978-1-934182-21-5) Alethes Pr.

Salvatore, Armando. The Public Sphere: Liberal Modernity, Catholicism, Islam. (Culture & Religion in International Relations Ser.). (ENG.). 304p. 2010. pap. 31.00 *(978-0-230-62231-9(3))* 2007. 89.00 *(978-1-4039-7473-0(X))* Palgrave Macmillan.

Santos, Gabriel A. Redeeming the Broken Body: Church & State after Disaster. 2008. (Theopolitical Visions Ser.). 326p. pap. 36.00 *(978-1-55635-725-1(7)*, Cascade Bks.) Wipf & Stock Pubs.

Schinkel, Dirk. Die Himmlische Burgerschaft: Untersuchungen zu Einem Urchristlichen Sprachmotiv Im Spannungsfeld Von Religioser Integration und Abgrenzung Im 1.und. 2007. (Forschungen Zur Religion und Literatur des Alten & Neuen Testament Ser.). (GER.). 224p. (C). 98.00 *(978-3-525-53084-9(6))* Vandenhoeck & Ruprecht GmbH & Co. KG DEU. Dist: ISD.

Shahan, Michael, ed. A Report from the Front Lines: Conversations on Public Theology. A Festschrift in Honor of Robert Benne. 2008. 184p. pap. 30.00 *(978-0-8028-4863-5(X))* Eerdmans, William B. Publishing Co.

Simut, Corneliu S. A Critical Study of Hans Kung's Ecclesiology: From Traditionalism to Modernism. 2008. (ENG.). 208p. 84.00 *(978-0-230-60540-4(0))* Palgrave Macmillan.

Skillen, James & Skillen, James W. Prospects & Ambiguities of Globalization: Critical Assessments at a Time of Growing Turmoil. 2009. (ENG.). 150p. 68.50 *(978-0-7391-2669-1(5))*; pap. 28.50 *(978-0-7391-2670-7(9))* Lexington Bks.

Stephens, W. R. W. Saint Chrysostom His Life & Times. 2007. (ENG.). 488p. 53.95 *(978-0-548-03619-8(5))* Kessinger Publishing, LLC.

Sullivan-Gonzalez D. Piety, Power, & Politics: Religion & Nation Formation in Guatemala 1821-1871. 2008. (Pitt Latin American Studies). (ENG.). 200p. (C). pap. 24.95 *(978-0-8229-6022-5(2))* Univ. of Pittsburgh Pr.

Sünner, Stephan. Staatsgesetz vor Religionsgebot? Eine Analyse mit Bezug zum englischen Recht und zur Rechtsprechung des EGMR. 2010. (Schriften zum Staatskirchenrecht Ser.). (GER.). 316p. 83.95 *(978-3-631-59835-1(1))* Lang, Peter GmbH, Europaischer Verlag der Wissenschaften DEU. Dist: Lang, Peter.

Taylor, Isaac. Spiritual Despotism. 2009. 220p. pap. *(978-0-217-55993-5(X))*; 222p. pap. *(978-0-217-32151-8(8))* Books LLC.

—Spiritual Despotism. 2009. 222p. pap. 20.77 *(978-0-217-55997-3(2))* General Bks. LLC.

—Spiritual Despotism. 2007. (ENG.). 512p. 55.95 *(978-0-548-08236-2(7))*; 502p. 53.95 *(978-0-548-17027-4(4))*; 504p. per. 38.95 *(978-1-4304-6787-8(8))* Kessinger Publishing, LLC.

Tellenbach, Gerd. Church, State & Christian Society at the Time of the Investiture Contest. 2008. 228p. pap. 22.00 *(978-1-59740-488-4(8))* ACLS Humanities E-Book.

Thomasius, Christian. Essays on the Church, State, & Politics. 2007. (Natural Law & Enlightenment Classics Ser.). (ENG.). 327p. (C). (gr. 12). pap. 14.50 *(978-0-86597-499-9(3))* Liberty Fund, Inc.

—Essays on the Church, State, & Politics. 2007. (Natural Law & Enlightenment Classics Ser.). (ENG.). 327p. (C). (gr. 12). 24.00 *(978-0-86597-498-2(5))* Liberty Fund, Inc.

Thorndike, Herbert. The Theological Works of Herbert Thorndike V4. 2007. (ENG.). 486p. 53.95 *(978-0-548-15478-6(3))*; 488p. per. 38.95 *(978-1-4304-4902-7(0))* Kessinger Publishing, LLC.

Trainor, Brian. Christ, Society & the State. 2012. (ENG.). 614p. (C). pap. 40.50 *(978-1-921511-58-5(3))* ATF Pr. AUS. Dist: Brown, David Bk. Co., The.

Tsuruoka, Yoshio & ter Haar, Gerrie, eds. Religion & Society: An Agenda for the 21st Century. 2007. (International Studies in Religion & Society). 306p. pap. *(978-90-04-16123-8(6))* BRILL.

Valentine, Scott R. Barefoot & Pregnant: The Socialization of the Educated Korean Woman. 2007. per. 19.95 *(978-0-9704006-3-5(2))* Bound & Determined Pubs.

Van Dyke, Joseph Smith. Popery, the Foe of the Church, & of the Republic by Joseph S Van Dyke. 2006. 336p. per. 23.99 *(978-1-4255-3359-5(0))* MPublishing.

VanDrunen, David. Natural Law & the Two Kingdoms: A Study in the Development of Reformed Social Thought. 2009. 480p. pap. 35.00 *(978-0-8028-6443-7(0))* Eerdmans, William B. Publishing Co.

Vidler, Alec R. Orb & the Cross A Normative Study in. 2007. 180p. per. *(978-1-4067-8881-5(3)*, Pomona Pr.) Read Bks.

Vumuka-ku-Nanga, Cesar. Politische Theologie in Afrika: Das Dogmatisch-Politische Denken des hl Ambrosius von Mailand als Modell für die Beziehung Zwischen Staat und Kirche im Modernen Afrika. (Europaische Hochschulschriften Ser.: Vol. 744). (GER.). 410p. 53.95 *(978-3-631-39208-9(7))* Lang, Peter Publishing, Inc.

Wampler, Dee. One Nation under God: A Trial Lawyer Exposes the Myth of the Separation Between Church & State. 2008. (Illus.). 24.99 *(978-1-58169-284-6(6)*, Evergreen Pr.) Genesis Communications, Inc.

Williams, George H. The Norman Anonymous of 1100 A. D. Toward the Identification & Evaluation of the So-Called Anonymous of York. 2009. 249p. pap. 21.00 *(978-1-60608-374-1(0)*, Wipf and Stock) Wipf & Stock Pubs.

Williams, Roger. The Bloudy Tenent of Persecution. 2009. 358p. pap. *(978-0-217-88879-0(8))* Books LLC.

Wright, George. Religion, Politics & Thomas Hobbes. 2010. (International Archives of the History of Ideas / archives internationales d'histoire des Idées Ser.). (Illus.). xiv, 357p. pap. 249.00 *(978-90-481-7132-3(6)*, 9048171326) Springer.

Wright, Nigel Goring. Disavowing Constantine: Mission, Church & the Social Order in the Theologies of John Howard Yoder & Jurgen Moltmann. 2007. (Paternoster Theological Monographs Ser.). 286p. pap. 32.00 *(978-1-59752-793-4(9)*, Wipf and Stock) Wipf & Stock Pubs.

CHURCH AND STATE—CATHOLIC CHURCH

Bellarmine, Robert. Writings on Temporal & Spiritual Authority: On the Laity & on the Temporal Power of the Pope. Tutino, Stefania, ed. 2012. (Natural Law Cloth Ser.). (ENG.). 500p. (C). (gr. 12). 24.00 *(978-0-86597-716-7(X))* Liberty Fund, Inc.

Clarke, Peter D. & Duggan, Anne J., eds. Pope Alexander III(1159-81) The Art of Survival. 2012. (Church, Faith & Culture in the Medieval West Ser.). (Illus.). 400p. 134.95 ***(978-0-7546-6288-4(8))*** Ashgate Publishing Co.

Donnangelo Ii, John. Yearning to Be Free. 2008. 108p. pap. *(978-3-639-06924-2(2))* VDM Verlag Dr. Mueller e.K.

Gerhart, Eugene C. & Bacon, Francis. American Liberty & Natural Law. 2011. 224p. 44.95 ***(978-1-258-01252-6(9))*** Literary Licensing, LLC.

Goerner, Edward A. Peter & Caesar: The Catholic Church & Political Authority. 2012. (ENG.). 282p. (C). pap. 25.00 *(978-1-58731-626-5(9))* St. Augustine's Pr., Inc.

Höpfl, Harro. Jesuit Political Thought: The Society of Jesus & the State, C. 1540-1630. 2008. (Ideas in Context Ser.). (ENG.). 428p. pap. 55.00 *(978-0-521-06675-4(1))* Cambridge Univ. Pr.

Lehmann, Leo H. Behind the Dictators: A Factual Analysis of the Relationship of Nazi-Fascism & Roman Catholicism. 2011. 110p. 39.95 ***(978-1-258-01765-1(2))*** Literary Licensing, LLC.

Mazgaj, Marian S. Church & State in Communist Poland: A History, 1944-1989. 2010. (ENG., Illus.). 203p. pap. 55.00 *(978-0-7864-5904-9(2))* McFarland & Co., Inc. Pubs.

Pell, George. God & Caesar: Selected Essays on Religion, Politics, & Society. Casey, M. A., ed. 2007. 189p. per. 29.95 *(978-0-8132-1503-7(X))* Catholic Univ. of America Pr.

Reinhardt, Kurt F. The Commonwealth of Nations & the Papacy. 2011. 30p. 35.95 ***(978-1-258-04704-7(7))*** Literary Licensing, LLC.

Schaefer, Bernd. The East German State & the Catholic Church, 1945-1989. 2010. (SGH Ser.). 324p. 90.00 *(978-1-84545-737-2(4))* Berghahn Bks., Inc.

Schindler, Jeanne Heffernan. Christianity & Civil Society: Catholic & Neo-Calvinist Perspectives. 2008. (ENG.). 214p. 68.50 *(978-0-7391-0884-0(0))* Lexington Bks.

Serrano, Sol. Qué Hacer con Dios en la República? Política y Secularización en Chile (1845-1885) 2008. (Historia Ser.). (SPA.). 375p. pap. *(978-956-289-064-9(3))* Fondo de Cultura Economica.

Walsh, Pat. The Curious Case of the Mayo Librarian. 2009. (ENG., Illus.). 223p. pap. 19.95 *(978-1-85635-615-2(9))* Mercier Pr., Ltd., The IRL. Dist: Dufour Editions, Inc.

Wilson, Art. And So Help Us God! for Every American Who Still Wants His Liberties. 2011. 64p. 36.95 ***(978-1-258-02044-6(0))*** Literary Licensing, LLC.

CHURCH AND STATE—CHURCH OF ENGLAND

see Church and State—Great Britain

CHURCH AND STATE—HISTORY

Baudry. A Warrior Bishop of the Twelfth Century: The Deeds of Albero of Trier. Pavlac, Brian A., tr. from LAT. 2008. (Mediaeval Sources in Translation Ser.). (ENG.). pap. 15.95 *(978-0-88844-294-9(7))* Pontifical Institute of Mediaeval Studies, Dept. of Pubns. CAN. Dist: Univ. of Toronto Pr.

Besier, Gerhard. Religion, State & Society in the Transformations of the Twentieth Century: Modernization, Innovation & Decline. 2008. (ENG.). 360p. pap. 59.95 *(978-3-8258-0980-5(3))* Lit Verlag DEU. Dist: Transaction Pubs.

Boyd, William Kenneth. The Ecclesiastical Edicts of the Theodosian Code. 2009. 124p. 28.99 *(978-1-115-72835-5(0))* 2009. 124p. pap. 19.75 *(978-1-115-72837-9(7))* 2009. 124p. pap. 19.75 *(978-1-115-72838-6(5))* 2008. 128p. 21.99 *(978-0-559-42897-5(9))* 2008. 128p. pap. 19.75 *(978-0-559-42896-8(0))* BiblioBazaar.

—The Ecclesiastical Edicts of the Theodosian Code. 2007. (ENG.). 120p. 34.95 *(978-0-548-16048-0(1))*; 124p. per. 19.95 *(978-1-4304-5610-0(8))* Kessinger Publishing, LLC.

C

Brooke, Zachary N. The English Church & the Papacy, from the Conquest to the Reign of John. reprint ed. 42.00 (978-0-404-18756-9(0)) AMS Pr., Inc.
Carey, Hilary M. & Gascoigne, John. Church & State in Old & New Worlds. 2011. xi, 341p. (978-90-04-19200-3(X)) BRILL.
Eckhardt, Carl Conrad. The Papacy & World Affairs. 2011. 324p. 50.95 (978-1-258-05089-4(7)) Literary Licensing, LLC.
Fernández-Armesto, Felipe. 1492: The Year the World Began. 2010. (ENG.). 336p. pap. 14.99 (978-0-06-113228-5(4), HarperOne) HarperCollins Pubs.
Ferrari, Silvio & Cristofori, Rinaldo, eds. Law & Religion in the 21st Century: Relations Between States & Religious Communities. 2010. (Cultural Diversity & Law Ser.). 406p. 124.95 (978-1-4094-1143-7(5)) Ashgate Publishing Co.
Floyd, Richard D. Church, Chapel & Party: Religious Dissent & Political Modernization in Nineteenth-Century England. 2008. (Studies in Modern History Ser.). (ENG., Illus.). 264p. 89.00 (978-0-230-52540-5(7)) Palgrave Macmillan.
Frame, Tom & Treloar, Geoffrey R., eds. Agendas for Australian Anglicanism: Essays in Honour of Bruce Kaye. 2007. (ENG.). 305p. (C). per. 20.00 (978-1-920691-66-0(9)) ATF Pr. AUS. Dist: Brown, David Bk. Co., The.
Gavin, Frank. Seven Centuries of the Problem of Church & State. 2007. (ENG.). 140p. per. (978-1-4067-6941-8(X)) Read Bks.
Harrold, Philip. A Place Somewhat Apart: The Private Worlds of a Late Nineteenth-Century Public University. 2006. (Princeton Theological Monographs). 254p. pap. 26.00 (978-1-59752-619-7(3), Pickwick Pubns.) Wipf & Stock Pubs.
Henley, Grant. Cultural Confessionalism: Literary Resistance & the Bekennende Kirche. 2007. (Studies in Modern German Literature Ser.: Vol. 102). 200p. (C). pap. 53.95 (978-0-8204-7224-9(7)); 49.95 (978-3-03910-298-3(2)) Lang, Peter Publishing, Inc.
Indiana Conference, UMC. 2011 Official Journal of the Indiana Annual Conference. 2011. 596p. pap. 29.63 (978-1-4670-6099-8(2)) AuthorHouse.
James, Sydney V. John Clarke & His Legacies. 2008. pap. 23.95 (978-0-271-02815-6(7)) Pennsylvania State Univ. Pr.
Knight, Frances. Church in the Nineteenth Century. 2008. (I. B. Tauris History of the Christian Church Ser.). (ENG.). 256p. 42.00 (978-1-85043-899-1(4)) I. B. Tauris & Co., Ltd. GBR. Dist: Macmillan.
Kostroun, Daniella. Feminism, Absolutism, & Jansenism: Louis XIV & the Port Royal Nuns. 2011. (ENG.). 280p. 90.00 (978-1-107-00045-2(9)) Cambridge Univ. Pr.
Larson, Mark J. Calvin's Doctrine of the State: A Reformed Doctrine & Its American Trajectory, the Revolutionary War, & the Founding of the Republic. 2009. 148p. pap. 18.00 (978-1-60608-073-3(3)) Wipf & Stock Pubs.
Lemke-Paetznick, Klaus. Kirche in Revolutionärer Zeit: Die Staatskirche in Schleswig und Holstein, 1789-1851. 2012. (Arbeiten zur Kirchengeschichte Ser.). (GER.). X, 766p. (gr. 17). 210.00 (978-3-11-026415-9(3)) De Gruyter, Walter Inc.
McIntire, C. T. England Against the Papacy 1858-1861: Tories, Liberals & the Overthrow of Papal Temporal Power During the Italian Risorgimento. 2008. (ENG., Illus.). 264p. pap. 37.99 (978-0-521-09040-7(7)) Cambridge Univ. Pr.
Monsma, Stephen V. & Soper, J. Christopher. The Challenge of Pluralism: Church & State in Five Democracies. 2nd ed. 2008. (ENG.). 278p. 80.00 (978-0-7425-5416-0(3)); pap. 29.95 (978-0-7425-5417-7(1)) Rowman & Littlefield Publishers, Inc.
Parry, Ken, ed. The Blackwell Companion to Eastern Christianity. (Wiley-Blackwell Companions to Religion Ser.: 31). (ENG., Illus.). 528p. 2010. pap. 49.95 (978-1-4443-3361-9(5)) 2007. 188.95 (978-0-631-23423-4(3)) Wiley, John & Sons, Inc. (Wiley-Blackwell).
Petrie, George. Church & State in Early Maryland. 2009. (ENG.). 63p. pap. 16.75 (978-1-117-02565-0(9)); (ENG.). 63p. pap. 16.99 (978-1-117-02566-7(7), BiblioLife); 52p. pap. 16.75 (978-1-110-21938-4(5)); (ENG.). 51p. pap. 18.99 (978-1-110-21933-9(4), BiblioLife); (ENG.). 51p. pap. 16.99 (978-1-110-21932-2(6), BiblioLife) BiblioBazaar.
—Church & State in Early Maryland. 52p. 2010. 25.56 (978-1-169-20680-9(8)) 2010. 31.95 (978-1-161-86036-8(3)) 2009. pap. 16.95 (978-1-104-01221-2(9)) Kessinger Publishing, LLC.
Pritchard, Arnold. Catholic Loyalism in Elizabethan England. 2011. (ENG.). 256p. pap. 40.00 (978-0-8078-9755-3(8)) Univ. of North Carolina Pr.
Rose, Jacqueline. Godly Kingship in Restoration England: The Politics of the Royal Supremacy, 1660-1688. 2011. (Cambridge Studies in Early Modern British History Ser.). (ENG., Illus.). 336p. 99.00 (978-1-107-01142-7(6)) Cambridge Univ. Pr.
Schlachta, Astrid von. Gefahr oder Segen? Die Täufer in der politischen Kommunikation. 2009. (Schriften zur politischen Kommunikation Ser.). (GER.). 484p. (C). 84.00 (978-3-89971-758-7(9)) Vandenhoeck & Ruprecht GmbH & Co. KG DEU. Dist: ISD.
Scholder, Klaus. A Requiem for Hitler: And Other new Perspectives on the German Church Struggle. 2008. 216p. pap. 24.00 (978-1-60608-169-3(1), Wipf and Stock) Wipf & Stock Pubs.
Sekulow, Jay. Witnessing Their Faith: Religious Influence on Supreme Court Justices & Their Opinions. 2007. (ENG.). 368p. pap. 22.95 (978-0-7425-5065-0(6)) Rowman & Littlefield Publishers, Inc.
Shipp, Glover. In God We Trust ... or Do We? Our Nation Built on a Christian Foundation. 2011. 178p. pap. 20.00 (978-1-61097-430-1(1), Resource Pubns.) Wipf & Stock Pubs.
Smith, H. F. Russell. The Theory of Religious Liberty in the Reigns of Charles II & James II. 2007. (ENG.). 150p. 36.95 (978-0-548-04757-6(X)) Kessinger Publishing, LLC.
Tutino, Stefania. Law & Conscience: Catholicism in Early Modern England 1570-1625. 2007. (Catholic Christendom, 1300-1700 Ser.). 268p. 124.95 (978-0-7546-5771-2(X)) Ashgate Publishing Co.
Ullmann, Walter. The Growth of Papal Government in the Middle Ages. 2009. 524p. 166.00 (978-0-415-55575-3(2)) Routledge.
—The Growth of Papal Government in the Middle Ages: A study in the ideological relation of clerical to lay Power. 2008. 528p. pap. 52.00 (978-1-59740-489-1(6)) ACLS Humanities E-Book.
Vinas, Jaime. La Biblia - Guía de Comprension. 2008. 364p. pap. 17.99 (978-1-4259-6612-6(8)) AuthorHouse.
Wolf, Hubert & Kronenberg, Kenneth. Pope & Devil: The Vatican's Archives & the Third Reich. 2012. Orig. Title: Papst und Teufel: Die Archive des Vatikan und das Dritte Reich. (ENG., Illus.). 336p. pap. 19.95 (978-0-674-06426-3(7), Belknap Pr.) Harvard Univ. Pr.

CHURCH AND STATE—AFRICA

Adeola, Moses O. The Origin of Christianity. 2009. 140p. 22.50 (978-1-60860-186-8(2), Strategic Bk. Publishing) AEG Literary Publishing Services, Inc.
Dube, Jimmy G. A Socio-Political Agenda for the Twenty-First Century Zimbabwean Church: Empowering the Excluded. 2006. 220p. (978-0-7734-5577-1(9)) Mellen, Edwin Pr., The.
Gifford, Paul. Christianity, Politics, & Public Life in Kenya. 2009. (Columbia/Hurst Ser.). (ENG.). 276p. (gr. 17). 90.00 (978-0-231-15442-0(9)) Columbia Univ. Pr.
Musya, Justus K. Inculturating the Eucharist in Afric. 2011. 96p. pap. (978-3-8443-1847-0(X)) Lambert Academic Publishing.
Njagi, Catherine Wambui. Homosexuality Debate in Africa Today. 2011. 140p. pap. (978-3-8433-6132-3(0)) Lambert Academic Publishing.
Patterson, Amy S. The Church & AIDS in Africa: The Politics of Ambiguity. 2010. 200p. 58.50 (978-1-935049-04-3(6)) FirstForumPress.
Smith, R. Drew. Freedom's Distant Shores: American Protestants & Post-Colonial Alliances with Africa. annot. ed. 2006. 325p. per. 34.95 (978-1-932792-37-9(6)) Baylor Univ. Pr.
Twesigye, Emmanuel K. Religion, Politics & Cults in East Africa: God's Warriors & Saints. 2010. (Bible & Theology in Africa Ser.). 280p. (C). 78.95 (978-1-4331-0995-9(6)); pap. 39.95 (978-1-4331-1112-9(8)) Lang, Peter Publishing, Inc.

CHURCH AND STATE—AUSTRALIA

Frame, Tom. Anglicans in Australia. 2007. (ENG.). 304p. pap. 35.95 (978-0-86840-830-9(1), UNSW Press) NewSouth Publishing AUS. Dist: Independent Pubs. Group.
—Church & State: Australia's Imaginary Wall. 2006. (ENG.). 96p. (Orig.). pap. 15.95 (978-0-86840-916-0(2), UNSW Press) NewSouth Publishing AUS. Dist: Independent Pubs. Group.
Frame, Tom & Treloar, Geoffrey R., eds. Agendas for Australian Anglicanism: Essays in Honour of Bruce Kaye. 2007. (ENG.). 305p. (C). per. 20.00 (978-1-920691-66-0(9)) ATF Pr. AUS. Dist: Brown, David Bk. Co., The.

CHURCH AND STATE—CANADA

Norman, E. R. The Conscience of the State in North America. 2009. (ENG.). 212p. pap. 31.99 (978-0-521-10775-4(X)) Cambridge Univ. Pr.
Ogilvie, M. H. Religious Institutions & the Law in Canada. 3rd ed. 2010. (Essentials of Canadian Law Ser.). 453p. pap. (978-1-55221-185-4(1)) Irwin Law, Inc.
Riddell, Walter A. Rise of Ecclesiastical Control in Quebec. (Columbia University, Studies in the Social Sciences: No. 174). reprint ed. 22.50 (978-0-404-51174-6(0)) AMS Pr., Inc.

CHURCH AND STATE—EUROPE

Alexander, Stella. Church & State in Yugoslavia Since 1945. 2008. (Cambridge Russian, Soviet & Post-Soviet Studies). (ENG.). 376p. pap. 51.00 (978-0-521-08922-7(0)) Cambridge Univ. Pr.
Allen, J. W. A History of Political Thought in the 16th Century. 2010. (ENG.). 560p. 166.00 (978-0-415-55551-7(5)) Routledge.
Aoun, M., ed. Les statuts personnels en droit Compare: Evolutions recentes et implications Pratiques. 2009. (Law & Religion Studies). (FRE.). 336p. (C). pap. 80.00 (978-90-429-2087-3(4)) Peeters Pubs. & Booksellers BEL. Dist: Brown, David Bk. Co., The.
Basdevant-Gaudemet, B., ed. L' administration des cultes dans les pays de l'Union Europeenne. 2008. (Law & Religion Studies). (FRE.). 278p. (C). pap. 72.00 (978-90-429-2017-0(3)) Peeters Pubs. & Booksellers BEL. Dist: Brown, David Bk. Co., The.
Besier, Gerhard. Religion, State & Society in the Transformations of the Twentieth Century: Modernization, Innovation & Decline. 2008. (ENG.). 360p. pap. 59.95 (978-3-8258-0980-5(3)) Lit Verlag DEU. Dist: Transaction Pubs.
Bobic, Pavlina. War & Faith: The Catholic Church in Slovenia, 1914-1918. 2012. (Illus.). xviii, 261p. (978-90-04-20219-1(6)) BRILL.
Boyd, William Kenneth. The Ecclesiastical Edicts of the Theodosian Code. 2009. 124p. 28.99 (978-1-115-72835-5(0)) 2009. 124p. pap. 19.75 (978-1-115-72838-6(5)) 2009. 124p. pap. 19.75 (978-1-115-72837-9(7)) 2008. 128p. 21.99 (978-0-559-42897-5(9)) 2008. 128p. pap. 19.75 (978-0-559-42896-8(0)) BiblioBazaar.
—The Ecclesiastical Edicts of the Theodosian Code. 2007. (ENG.). 120p. 34.95 (978-0-548-16048-0(1)); 124p. per. 19.95 (978-1-4304-5610-0(8)) Kessinger Publishing, LLC.
Brodman, James. Charity & Religion in Medieval Europe. 2009. 328p. 59.95 (978-0-8132-1580-8(3)) Catholic Univ. of America Pr.
Burnell, Joel. Poetry, Providence, & Patriotism. 2009. (Princeton Theological Monographs). 320p. pap. 35.00 (978-1-60608-042-9(3), Pickwick Pubns.) Wipf & Stock Pubs.
Butterwick, Richard. The Polish Revolution & the Catholic Church, 1788-1792: A Political History. 2012. (ENG., Illus.). 384p. 125.00 (978-0-19-925033-2(2)) Oxford Univ. Pr., Inc.
Cram101 Textbook Reviews. Outlines & Highlights for the Crisis of Church & State: 1050-1300 by Tierney. 2011. 128p. pap. 28.95 (978-1-61812-844-7(2)) Cram101 Inc.
Emilianides, Achilles, ed. Religious Freedom in the European Union: The Application of the European Convention on Religious Freedom in the European Union: the Application of the European Convention on Human Rights in the European Union. Proceedings of the 19th Meeting of the European Consortium for Church & State Researc. 2011. (ENG & FRE.). 418p. (C). pap. 78.00 (978-90-429-2243-3(5)) Peeters Pubs. & Booksellers BEL. Dist: Brown, David Bk. Co., The.
Friedner, Lars. Churches & Other Religious Organisations as Legal Persons. Friedner, L., ed. 2007. (ENG & FRE.). 228p. (C). pap. 66.00 (978-90-429-1858-0(6)) Peeters Pubs. & Booksellers BEL. Dist: Brown, David Bk. Co., The.
Gjuzelev, Vassil & Petkov, Kiril, eds. State & Church: Studies in Medieval Bulgaria & Byzantium. 2011. (ENG., Illus.). 300p. (C). 39.95 (978-954-92571-2-0(6)) American Research Ctr. in Sofia.
Gottsmann, Andreas. Rom und die nationalen Katholizismen in der Donaumonarchie: Romischer Universalismus, habsburgische Reichspolitik und nationale Identitaten 1878-1914. 2010. (Publikationen des Historischen Instituts beim Osterreichischen Kulturforum in Rom, II. Abteilung, Quellen, 1. Reihe, Band 10 Ser.). (GER.). 408p. (C). pap. 110.00 (978-3-7001-6596-5(X)) Austrian Academy of Sciences Press AUT. Dist: Brown, David Bk. Co., The.
Körntgen, Ludger. Patterns of Episcopal Power / Strukturen Bischöflicher Herrschaftsgewalt Im Westlichen Europa des 10. und 11. Jahrhunderts: Bishops in Tenth & Eleventh Century Western Europe. 2011. (Prinz-Albert-Forschungen Ser.). (GER & ENG.). 226p. 126.00 (978-3-11-026202-5(9)) De Gruyter, Walter Inc.
Körntgen, Ludger & Waßenhoven, Dominik, eds. Patterns of Episcopal Power / Strukturen Bischöflicher Herrschaftsgewalt Im Westlichen Europa des 10. und 11. Jahrhunderts: Bishops in Tenth & Eleventh Century Western Europe. 2011. (Prinz-Albert-Forschungen Ser.). (ENG & GER., Illus.). 226p. 196.00 (978-3-11-916600-3(6)) De Gruyter, Walter Inc.
Maquet, Julien. 'Faire justice' dans le diocese de Liege au Moyen Age (VIII-XII Siecles) Essai de droit judiciaire Reconstitue. 2009. (BIBLIOTHeQUE de la FACULTe de PHILOSOPHIE et LETTRES de L'UNIVERSITe de LIeGE Ser.). (FRE., Illus.). 832p. (C). pap. 130.00 (978-2-87019-290-0(8)) Droz, Librairie CHE. Dist: Brown, David Bk. Co., The.
Margallo Bazago, Francisco & Margallo, Francisco. Cristianismo y Secularidad: Manual de Nueva Teología Política Europea. 2007. (Colección Diáspora Ser.). (SPA.). 215p. (978-84-8456-835-3(0)) Tirant lo Blanch.
Mayr-Harting, Henry. Religion & Society in the Medieval West: 600 - 1200 - Selected Papers. 2010. (Variorum Collected Studies). (Illus.). 340p. 165.00 (978-0-7546-6898-5(3)) Ashgate Publishing Co.
McCrea, Ronan. Religion & the Public Order of the European Union. 2010. (ENG.). 304p. 110.00 (978-0-19-959535-8(6)) Oxford Univ. Pr., Inc.
Nemec, Ludvik. Church & State in Czechoslovaki: Historical, Juridically & Theologically Documented. 2011. 608p. 64.95 (978-1-258-07256-8(4)) Literary Licensing, LLC.
Nowakowska, Natalia. Church State & Dynasty in Renaissance Poland: The Careet of Cardinal-Prince Fryderyk Jagiellon (1468-1503) 2007. (Catholic Christendom, 1300-1700 Ser.). (Illus.). 242p. 124.95 (978-0-7546-5644-9(6)) Ashgate Publishing Co.
Oakley, Francis. Empty Bottles of Gentilism: Kingship & the Divine in Late Antiquity & the Early Middle Ages (To 1050) 2010. (Emergence of Western Political Thought in the Latin Middle Ages Ser.). (ENG., Illus.). 320p. 38.00 (978-0-300-15538-9(7)) Yale Univ. Pr.
Oakley, Francis. The Mortgage of the Past: Reshaping the Ancient Political Inheritance (1050-1300) 2012. (Emergence of Western Political Thought in the Latin Middle Ages Ser.). (ENG.). 320p. 55.00 (978-0-300-17633-9(3)) Yale Univ. Pr.
Pease, Neal. Rome's Most Faithful Daughter: The Catholic Church & Independent Poland, 1914-1939. 2009. (Polish & Polish American Studies). (ENG.). 312p. pap. 26.95 (978-0-8214-1856-7(4)); (Illus.). 49.95 (978-0-8214-1855-0(6)) Ohio Univ. Pr.
Puza, Richard & Doe, Norman. Religion & Law in Dialogue: Convenantal & Non-convenantal Cooperation between State & Religion in Europe. Proceedings of the Conference Tubingen 18-21 November 2004 - Actes du Colloque Tubingen 18-21 Novembre 2004. Doe, N. & Puza, R., eds. 2006. (ENG & FRE.). 298p. (C). pap. 66.00 (978-90-429-1705-7(9)) Peeters Pubs. & Booksellers BEL. Dist: Brown, David Bk. Co., The.
Robbins, Keith, ed. Political & Legal Perspectives. 2011. (Dynamics of Religious Reform in Northern Europe, 1780ndash;1920 Ser.). 248p. 89.50 (978-90-5867-825-6(3)) Leuven Univ. Pr. BEL. Dist: Cornell Univ. Pr.
Romocea, Cristian. Church & State: Religious Nationalism & State Identification in Post-Communist Romania. 2011. (ENG.). 272p. 120.00 (978-1-4411-6857-3(5)) Continuum International Publishing Group, Ltd. GBR. Dist: National Bk. Network.
Safley, Thomas Max. A Companion to Multiconfessionalism in the Early Modern World. 2011. (Illus.). XII, 500p. (978-90-04-20697-7(3)) BRILL.
Schulze Wessel, Martin. Nationalisierung der Religion und Sakralisierung der Nation Im östlichen Europa. 2006. (Forschungen zur Geschichte und Kultur des Ostlichen Mitteleuropa (FGKOM) Ser.). (GER & ENG., Illus.). 272p. (C). 60.00 (978-3-515-08665-3(X)) Steiner, Franz Verlag Wiesbaden GmbH DEU. Dist: Brown, David Bk. Co., The.
Stan, Lavinia & Turcescu, Lucian. Church, State, & Democracy in Expanding Europe. 1 vol. 2011. (Religion & Global Politics Ser.). (ENG.). 304p. 65.00 (978-0-19-533710-5(7)) Oxford Univ. Pr., Inc.
Trio, Paul & de Smet, Marjan, eds. Use & Abuse of Sacred Places in Late Medieval Towns. 2006. (Mediaevalia Lovaniensia, Series I: Vol. 38). (Illus.). 264p. per. 43.95 (978-90-5867-519-4(X)) Leuven Univ. Pr. BEL. Dist: Cornell Univ. Pr.
Tsatsov, Boris, ed. Chronicle of the Bulgarian Orthodox Church: Volume 1. History & Personalities. 2010. 580p. 250.00 (978-954-463-124-6(0)) Bulgarian Bestseller - National Museum of Bulgarian Books & Polygraphy BGR. Dist: Coronet Bks.
Urbanczyk, Przemyslaw. Herrschaft und Politik im Fruhen Mittelalter. (GER., Illus.). 295p. pap. 62.95 (978-3-631-53725-1(5)) Lang, Peter GmbH, Europaischer Verlag der Wissenschaften DEU. Dist: Lang, Peter Publishing, Inc.
Wanner, Catherine. Communities of the Converted: Ukrainians & Global Evangelism. 2007. (Culture & Society after Socialism Ser.). (Illus.). 304p. 80.50 (978-0-8014-4592-7(2)); 305p. per. 26.95 (978-0-8014-7402-6(7)) Cornell Univ. Pr.
Winship, Michael P. Godly Republicanism: Puritans, Pilgrims, & a City on a Hill. 2012. (ENG.). 350p. 49.95 (978-0-674-06385-3(6)) Harvard Univ. Pr.

CHURCH AND STATE—FRANCE

see also Gallicanism

Bencheikh, Soheib. Marianne et le Prophète: L'islam Dans la France Laïque. (FRE.). 281p. (978-2-246-53871-4(8)) Grasset et Fasquello.
Brown, Frederick. For the Soul of France: Culture Wars in the Age of Dreyfus. 2011. (ENG., Illus.). 336p. pap. 16.00 (978-0-307-27921-7(9), Anchor) Knopf Doubleday Publishing Group.
Bulman, Jan K. The Court Book of Mende & the Secular Lordship of the Bishop: Recollecting the Past in Thirteenth-Century Gévaudan. 2008. (ENG., Illus.). 176p. (978-0-8020-9337-0(X)) Univ. of Toronto Pr.
Constable, Giles. Three Treatises from Bec on the Nature of Monastic Life. Smith, Bernard S., tr. from LAT. 2008. (Medieval Academy Bks.). (ENG., Illus.). 208p. (978-0-8020-9260-1(8)) Univ. of Toronto Pr.
de Jong, Mayke. The Penitential State: Authority & Atonement in the Age of Louis the Pious, 814-840. (ENG.). 340p. 2011. pap. 43.00 (978-0-521-20520-7(4)) 2009. (Illus.). 103.99 (978-0-521-88152-4(8)) Cambridge Univ. Pr.
Deguignet, Jean-Marie. Memoirs of a Breton Peasant. Asher, Linda, tr. from FRE. 2011. (ENG., Illus.). 432p. pap. 19.95 (978-1-60980-346-9(9)) Seven Stories Pr.
Gaposchkin, M. Cecilia. The Making of Saint Louis: Kingship, Sanctity, & Crusade in the Later Middle Ages. 2010. (Illus.). 352p. pap. 29.95 (978-0-8014-7625-9(9)) Cornell Univ. Pr.
—The Making of Saint Louis: Kingshnp, Sanctity, & Crusade in the Later Middle Ages. 2008. (Illus.). 331p. 47.50 (978-0-8014-4550-7(7)) Cornell Univ. Pr.
Gibson, W. The Abbe de Lamennais & the Liberal Catholic Movement in France. 2007. (ENG.). 350p. 46.95 (978-0-548-15850-0(9)); pap. 31.95 (978-1-4304-5354-3(0)) Kessinger Publishing, LLC.
Jolicoeur, Nicolas. La politique française envers les états pontificaux sous la monachrie de Juillet et la Seconde République (1830-1851) 2008. (Diplomatie et Histoire Ser.). (FRE., Illus.). 394p. pap. 46.95 (978-90-5201-388-6(8)) PIE - Peter Lang BEL. Dist: Lang, Peter.
Kaplan, Zvi Jonathan. Between the Devil & the Deep Blue Sea? French Jewry & the Problem of Church & State. 2009. (978-1-930675-61-2(5)) Brown Judaic Studies.
Kostroun, Daniella. Feminism, Absolutism, & Jansenism: Louis XIV & the Port Royal Nuns. 2011. (ENG.). 280p. 90.00 (978-1-107-00045-2(9)) Cambridge Univ. Pr.
Mitchell, Allan. Victors & Vanquished: The German Influence on Army & Church in France After 1870. 2011. (ENG.). 183p. pap. 30.00 (978-0-8078-9729-4(9)) Univ. of North Carolina Pr.
Ravitch, Norman. Sword & Mitre: Government & episcopate in France & England in the age of Aristocracy. (Studies in European History Ser.). (ENG.). 246p. 210.00 (978-3-11-210727-0(6)); 135.00 (978-3-11-100221-7(7)) De Gruyter, Mouton DEU. Dist: de Gruyter, Walter GmbH & Co. KG.
Shusterman, Noah. Religion & the Politics of Time: Holidays in France from Louis XIV Through Napoleon. 2010. (ENG.). 74.95 (978-0-8132-1725-3(3)) Catholic Univ. of America Pr.
Tziampiris, Aristotle. Faith & Reason of State: Lessons from Early Modern Europe & Cardinal Richelieu. 2009. (European Political, Economic, & Security Issues Ser.). 79.00 (978-1-60741-949-5(1)) Nova Science Pubs., Inc.
Walsh, Henry H. Concordat of 1801. (Columbia University, Studies in the Social Sciences: No. 387). reprint ed. 31.50 (978-0-404-51387-0(5)) AMS Pr., Inc.
Wright, Anthony. The Divisions of French Catholicism, 1629-1645: The Parting of the Ways. 2011. (Catholic Christendom, 1300-1700 Ser.). 226p. 124.95 (978-1-4094-2084-2(1)) Ashgate Publishing Co.

CHURCH AND STATE—GERMANY

Bonney, Richard. Confronting the Nazi War on Christianity: The Kulturkampf Newsletters, 1936-1939. 2009. (Illus.). 588p. 86.95 (978-3-03911-904-2(4)) Lang, Peter AG GBR. Dist: Lang, Peter.

Borutta, Manuel. Antikatholizismus: Deutschland und Italien im Zeitalter der europäischen Kulturkämpfe. 2010. (Burgertum Neue Folge Ser.). (GER.). 488p. (C). 84.00 *(978-3-525-36849-7(6))* Vandenhoeck & Ruprecht GmbH & Co. KG DEU. Dist: ISD.

Bulisch, Jens. Evangelische Presse in der DDR: "die Zeichen der Zeit" 2006. (Arbeiten Zur Kirchlichen Zeitgeschichte Ser.). (GER., Illus.). 496p. (C). 116.00 *(978-3-525-55744-0(2))* Vandenhoeck & Ruprecht GmbH & Co. KG DEU. Dist: ISD.

Cochrane, Arthur C. The Church's Confession under Hitler. 2011. 316p. 50.95 *(978-1-258-04470-1(6))* Literary Licensing, LLC.

Czermak, Gerhard. Religions- und Weltanschauungsrecht: Eine Einführung. 2007. (Springer-Lehrbuch Ser.). 327p. pap. 39.95 *(978-3-540-72048-5(0))* Springer.

Gailus, Manfred. Kirchliche Amtshilfe: Die Kirche und die Judenverfolgung im »Dritten Reich«. 2008. (GER., Illus.). 223p. (C). pap. 27.00 *(978-3-525-55340-4(4))* Vandenhoeck & Ruprecht GmbH & Co. KG DEU. Dist: ISD.

Godman, Peter. Hitler & the Vatican: Inside the Secret Archives That Reveal the New Story of the Nazis & the Church. 2007. (ENG.). 352p. pap. 20.95 *(978-0-7432-4598-2(9)*, Free Pr.) Free Pr.

Henley, Grant. Cultural Confessionalism: Literary Resistance & the Bekennende Kirche. 2007. (Studies in Modern German Literature Ser.: Vol. 102). 200p. (C). pap. 53.95 *(978-0-8204-7224-9(7))*; 49.95 *(978-3-03910-298-3(2))* Lang, Peter Publishing, Inc.

Heschel, S. Aryan Jesus - Christian Theologians & the Bible in Nazi German. 2010. (ENG., Illus.). 360p. (C). pap. 24.95 *(978-0-691-14805-2(8))* Princeton Univ. Pr.

Kämper, Heidrun, et al, eds. 1968: Eine sprachwissenschaftliche Zwischenbilanz. 2012. (Sprache und Wissen Ser.).Tr. of 1968. A Linguistic Interim Status Report. (GER., Illus.). 374p. (gr. 17). E-Book 210.00 *(978-3-11-219184-2(6))* De Gruyter, Walter Inc.

Könemann, Sandra. Das Staatskirchenrecht in der Wissenschaftlichen Diskussion der Weimarer Zeit. 2011. (Schriften zum Staatskirchenrecht Ser.). (GER.). 482p. 118.95 *(978-3-631-60178-5(6))* Lang, Peter GmbH, Europaischer Verlag der Wissenschaften DEU. Dist: Lang, Peter.

Kraft, Friedhelm. Religionsdidaktik Zwischen Kreuz und Hakenkreuz: Versuche Zur Bestimmung Von Aufgaben, Zielen und Inhalten des Evangelischen Religionsunterrichts, Dargestellt an Den Richtlinienentwürfen Zwischen 1933 und 1939. (Arbeiten zur Praktischen Theologie Ser.). (GER., Illus.). XXI, 282p. 224.00 *(978-3-11-175603-5(3))* De Gruyter, Walter Inc.

Lemke-Paetznick, Klaus. Kirche in Revolutionärer Zeit: Die Staatskirche in Schleswig und Holstein, 1789-1851. 2012. (Arbeiten zur Kirchengeschichte Ser.). (GER.). X, 766p. (gr. 17). 210.00 *(978-3-11-026415-9(3))* De Gruyter, Walter Inc.

Lutzer, Erwin W. When a Nation Forgets God: 7 Lessons We Must Learn from Nazi Germany, 1 vol. 2009. (ENG.). 160p. pap. 8.99 *(978-0-8024-4656-5(6))* Moody Pubs.

Metzner, Carolin. Johann Caspar Bluntschli: Leben, Zeitgeschehen und Kirchenpolitik. 2009. (Schriften zum Staatskirchenrecht Ser.). (GER.). 174p. 60.95 *(978-3-631-59679-1(0))* Lang, Peter GmbH, Europaischer Verlag der Wissenschaften DEU. Dist: Lang, Peter.

Moses, John Anthony. The Reluctant Revolutionary: Dietrich Bonhoeffer's Collision with Prusso-German History. 2009. 320p. 90.00 *(978-1-84545-531-6(2))* Berghahn Bks., Inc.

Ninness, Richard. Between Opposition & Collaboration: Nobles, Bishops, & the German Reformations in the Prince-Bishopric of Bamberg, 1555¿1619. 2011. (Studies in Central European Histories Ser.). (Illus.). 240p. *(978-90-04-20154-5(8))* BRILL.

Onnasch, Martin. Um kirchliche Macht und geistliche Vollmacht: Ein Beitrag zur Geschichte des Kirchenkampfes in der Kirchenprovinz Sachsen 1932-1945. 2010. (Greifswalder theologische Forschungen Ser.). (GER.). 506p. 115.95 *(978-3-631-59278-6(7))* Lang, Peter GmbH, Europaischer Verlag der Wissenschaften DEU. Dist: Lang, Peter.

Probst, Christopher J. Demonizing the Jews: Luther & the Protestant Church in Nazi Germany. 2012. (ENG., Illus.). 270p. 70.00 *(978-0-253-00098-9(X)*, 025300098X); pap. 25.00 *(978-0-253-00100-9(5)*, 0253001005) Indiana Univ. Pr.

Robbers. Religion in Germany. 2010. 382p. pap. *(978-90-411-3352-6(6))* Kluwer Law International.

Schaefer, Bernd. The East German State & the Catholic Church, 1945-1989. 2010. (SGH Ser.). 324p. 90.00 *(978-1-84545-737-2(4))* Berghahn Bks., Inc.

Schneider, Thomas Martin. Gegen den Zeitgeist: Der Weg zur VELKD als lutherischer Bekenntniskirche. Arbeiten zur Kirchlichen Zeitgeschichte. 2008. (Arbeiten Zur Kirchlichen Zeitgeschichte Ser.). (GER.). 314p. (C). 89.00 *(978-3-525-55749-5(3))* Vandenhoeck & Ruprecht GmbH & Co. KG DEU. Dist: ISD.

Scholder, Klaus. A Requiem for Hitler: And Other new Perspectives on the German Church Struggle. 2008. 216p. pap. 24.00 *(978-1-60608-169-3(1)*, Wipf and Stock) Wipf & Stock Pubs.

Schulze Pellengahr Freiherr von Freusberg-Steinhorst, Christian. Das Verbot der politischen Betätigung für Geistliche nach katholischem und evangelischem Kirchenrecht sowie im geltenden Staatskirchenrecht: Unter Berücksichtigung der Staaten- und Verfassungsgeschichte Deutschlands Und Österreichs. 2009. (Schriften zum Staatskirchenrecht Ser.). (GER.). 310p. 80.95 *(978-3-631-58914-4(X))* Lang, Peter GmbH, Europaischer Verlag der Wissenschaften DEU. Dist: Lang, Peter.

Spicer, Kevin P. Hitler's Priests: Catholic Clergy & National Socialism. 2008. (Illus.). 385p. 34.95 *(978-0-87580-384-5(9))* Northern Illinois Univ. Pr.

Thomas, Andrew L. A House Divided: Wittelsbach Confessional Court Cultures in the Holy Roman Empire, C. 1550-1650. 2010. (Illus.). 404p. *(978-90-04-18356-8(6))* BRILL.

Wolf, Hubert & Kronenberg, Kenneth. Pope & Devil: The Vatican's Archives & the Third Reich. 2012. Orig. Title: Papst und Teufel: Die Archive des Vatikan und das Dritte Reich. (ENG., Illus.). 336p. pap. 19.95 *(978-0-674-06426-3(7)*, Belknap Pr.) Harvard Univ. Pr.

Zocher, Peter. Edo Osterloh - Vom Theologen zum christlichen Politiker: Eine Fallstudie zum Verhältnis von Theologie und Politik im 20. Jahrhundert. 2007. (Arbeiten Zur Kirchlichen Zeitgeschichte Ser.). (GER., Illus.). 728p. (C). 144.00 *(978-3-525-55750-1(7))* Vandenhoeck & Ruprecht GmbH & Co. KG DEU. Dist: ISD.

CHURCH AND STATE—GERMANY—BAVARIA

Higby, Chester P. Religious Policy of the Bavarian Government During the Napoleonic Period. (Columbia University, Studies in the Social Sciences: No. 196). reprint ed. 42.50 *(978-0-404-51196-8(1))* AMS Pr., Inc.

CHURCH AND STATE—GREAT BRITAIN

Here are entered works dealing not only with church and state in England, Scotland and Ireland, or in any two of them, but also works dealing with England alone.

see also Puritans

Ambler, R. W., ed. Lincolnshire Parish Correspondence of John Kaye, Bishop of Lincoln 1827-53. 2006. (Publications of the Lincoln Record Society Ser.: Volume 94). (Illus.). 560p. 50.00 *(978-0-901503-79-4(7))* Lincoln Record Society GBR. Dist: Boydell & Brewer, Inc.

Arnold, Selwyn E. From Skepticism to Hope. 2010. 232p. pap. 15.99 *(978-1-60957-186-3(X))* Xulon Pr., Inc.

Barker, Ernest. Oliver Cromwell & the English People. 2012. (ENG.). 108p. pap. 24.00 *(978-1-107-66071-7(8))* Cambridge Univ. Pr.

Bourdin, Bernard. The Theological-Political Origins of the Modern State: The Controversy Between James I of England & Cardinal Bellarmine. Pickford, Susan, tr. from FRE. 2010. (ENG.). 296p. 59.95 *(978-0-8132-1791-8(1))* Catholic Univ. of America Pr.

Breed, William Pratt. Jenny Geddes, or, Presbyterianism & Its Great Conflict with Despotism by the Rev W P Breed, D D. 2006. 484p. per. 29.99 *(978-1-4255-5392-0(3))* MPublishing.

Brooke, Zachary N. The English Church & the Papacy, from the Conquest to the Reign of John. reprint ed. 42.00 *(978-0-404-18756-9(0))* AMS Pr., Inc.

Capp, Bernard. England's Culture Wars: Puritan Reformation & its Enemies in the Interregnum, 1649-1660. 2012. (ENG.). 320p. 125.00 *(978-0-19-964178-9(1))* Oxford Univ. Pr., Inc.

Chalmers, Thomas. On the Use & Abuse of Literary & Ecclesiastical Endowments. 2011. (Cambridge Library Collection - History Ser.). (ENG.). 200p. pap. 19.99 *(978-1-108-03667-2(8))* Cambridge Univ. Pr.

Child, Gilbert W. Church & State under the Tudors. 2010. 482p. pap. 37.75 *(978-1-178-43880-2(5))* BiblioBazaar.

Ellens, J. P. Religious Routes to Gladstonian Liberalism. 2008. pap. 29.95 *(978-0-271-02843-9(2))* Pennsylvania State Univ. Pr.

Fletcher, Catherine. The Divorce of Henry VIII: The Untold Story from Inside the Vatican. 2012. (ENG.). 288p. 28.00 *(978-0-230-34151-7(9))* Palgrave Macmillan.

Floyd, Richard D. Church, Chapel & Party: Religious Dissent & Political Modernization in Nineteenth-Century England. 2008. (Studies in Modern History Ser.). (ENG., Illus.). 264p. 89.00 *(978-0-230-52540-5(7))* Palgrave Macmillan.

Ha, Polly. English Presbyterianism, 1590-1640. 2010. (ENG., Illus.). 320p. 65.00 *(978-0-8047-5987-8(1))* Stanford Univ. Pr.

Haile, Martin. Life of Reginald Pole. 2009. (ENG.). 585p. 44.99 *(978-1-117-39372-8(0))*; pap. 43.75 *(978-1-117-39373-5(9))* BiblioBazaar.

—Life of Reginald Pole. 2007. (ENG.). 570p. 58.95 *(978-0-548-15125-9(3))*; 572p. per. 43.95 *(978-1-4304-4470-1(3))* Kessinger Publishing, LLC.

Henderson, G. D. Religious Life in Seventeenth-Century Scotland. 2011. (ENG.). 320p. pap. 24.99 *(978-0-521-24877-8(9))* Cambridge Univ. Pr.

Hill, Mark. Ecclesiastical Law. 3rd ed. 2008. (ENG.). 800p. 280.50 *(978-0-19-921712-0(2))* Oxford Univ. Pr., Inc.

Knight, Frances. Church in the Nineteenth Century. 2008. (I. B. Tauris History of the Christian Church Ser.). (ENG.). 256p. 42.00 *(978-1-85043-899-1(4))* I. B. Tauris & Co., Ltd. GBR. Dist: Macmillan.

Krugler, John D. English & Catholic: The Lords Baltimore in the Seventeenth Century. 2008. (Johns Hopkins University Studies in Historical & Political Science Ser.: 122). (ENG., Illus.). 336p. (gr. 17). pap. 27.00 *(978-0-8018-9083-3(7))* Johns Hopkins Univ. Pr.

Lahey, Stephen E. Philosophy & Politics in the Thought of John Wyclif. 2008. (Cambridge Studies in Medieval Life & Thought). (ENG.). 252p. pap. 37.99 *(978-0-521-05846-9(5))* Cambridge Univ. Pr.

Larking, Lambert B., ed. Proceedings Principally in the County of Kent, in Connection with the Parliaments Called in 1640, & Especially with the Committee of Religion Appointed in That Year. (Camden Society, London, Publications, First Ser.: No. 80a). reprint ed. 70.00 *(978-0-404-50180-8(X))* AMS Pr., Inc.

Leland, John, et al. De Viris Illustribus: Of Famous Men. 2010. (Studies & Texts). (LAT & ENG.). 498p. 95.00 *(978-0-88844-170-6(3))* Pontifical Institute of Mediaeval Studies, Dept. of Pubns. CAN. Dist: Univ. of Toronto Pr.

Mayer, Thomas F. Reginald Pole: Prince & Prophet. 2007. (ENG.). 488p. pap. 61.00 *(978-0-521-03869-0(3))* Cambridge Univ. Pr.

Mayer, Thomas F. & Walters, Courtney B. The Correspondence of Reginald Pole - A Biographical Companion Vol. 4: The British Isles. Gordon, Bruce et al, eds. 2008. (St Andrews Studies in Reformation History: Vol. 4). (LAT & ENG.). 656p. 165.00 *(978-0-7546-0329-0(6))* Ashgate Publishing Co.

Morris, Robert & Morris, R. M., eds. Church & State in 21st Century Britain: The Future of Church Establishment. 2009. (ENG., Illus.). 320p. 100.00 *(978-0-230-55511-2(X))* Palgrave Macmillan.

Neuheiser, Jö, et al. Krone, Kirche und Verfassung: Konservatismus in den englischen Unterschichten 1815 - 1867. 2010. (Kritische Studien Zur Geschichtswissenschaft Ser.). (GER.). 349p. (C). 77.00 *(978-3-525-37009-4(1))* Vandenhoeck & Ruprecht GmbH & Co. KG DEU. Dist: ISD.

Partington, Andrew. Church & State: The Contribution of the Church of England Bishops to the House of Lords During the Thatcher Years. 2006. (Studies in Christian History & Thought Ser.). (Illus.). 336p. pap. 34.00 *(978-1-59752-834-4(X)*, Wipf and Stock) Wipf & Stock Pubs.

Pereiro, James. 'Ethos' & the Oxford Movement: At the Heart of Tractarianism. 2008. (ENG.). 320p. 150.00 *(978-0-19-923029-7(3))* Oxford Univ. Pr., Inc.

Ravitch, Norman. Sword & Mitre: Government & episcopate in France & England in the age of Aristocracy. (Studies in European History Ser.). (ENG.). 246p. 210.00 *(978-3-11-210727-0(6))*; 135.00 *(978-3-11-100221-7(7))* De Gruyter, Mouton DEU. Dist: de Gruyter, Walter GmbH & Co. KG.

Rees, Wyn, et al. British Foreign Policy & the Anglican Church: Christian Engagement with the Contemporary World. 2008. (Illus.). 172p. pap. 39.95 *(978-0-7546-6037-8(0))* Ashgate Publishing Co.

Rose, Jacqueline. Godly Kingship in Restoration England: The Politics of the Royal Supremacy, 1660-1688. 2011. (Cambridge Studies in Early Modern British History Ser.). (ENG., Illus.). 336p. 99.00 *(978-1-107-01142-7(6))* Cambridge Univ. Pr.

Ross, Wyn. British Foreign Policy & the Anglican Church: Christian Engagement with the Contemporary World. Blewett, Timothy & Hyde-Price, Adrian, eds. 2008. (Illus.). 172p. 99.95 *(978-0-7546-6035-4(4))* Ashgate Publishing Co.

Serrano, Sol. Qué Hacer con Dios en la República? Política y Secularización en Chile (1845-1885) 2008. (Historia Ser.). (SPA.). 375p. pap. *(978-956-289-064-9(3))* Fondo de Cultura Economica.

Smith, H. F. Russell. The Theory of Religious Liberty in the Reigns of Charles II & James II. 2007. (ENG.). 150p. 36.95 *(978-0-548-04757-6(X))* Kessinger Publishing, LLC.

Sneddon, Andrew. Witchcraft & Whigs: The Life of Bishop Francis Hutchinson, 1660-1739. 2008. (ENG., Illus.). 232p. 84.00 *(978-0-7190-7612-1(9))* Manchester Univ. Pr. GBR. Dist: Macmillan.

Steel, D. J. National Index of Parish Registers. (Illus.).;p. *(978-1-85951-086-5(8))* Bow Historical Bks.

Tutino, Stefania. Law & Conscience: Catholicism in Early Modern England 1570-1625. 2007. (Catholic Christendom, 1300-1700 Ser.). 268p. 124.95 *(978-0-7546-5771-2(X))* Ashgate Publishing Co.

Uno, Ikpe. Answer to A Fathers Call. 2009. 131p. pap. 25.50 *(978-1-4092-7492-6(6))* Lulu Enterprises Inc.

Walker, Peter. James II & the Three Questions: Religious Toleration & the Landed Classes, 1687-1688. 2010. 337p. pap. 72.95 *(978-3-03911-927-1(3))* Lang, Peter AG GBR. Dist: Lang, Peter.

Williams, Glanmor, et al. Welsh Church from Reformation to Disestablishment, 1603-1920. 2007. (University of Wales - Bangor History of Religion Ser.). (Illus.). 384p. 74.95 *(978-0-7083-1877-5(0))* Univ. of Wales Pr. GBR. Dist: Chicago Distribution Ctr.

Womersley, David. Divinity & State. 2010. (ENG., Illus.). 400p. 110.00 *(978-0-19-925564-1(4))* Oxford Univ. Pr., Inc.

Wood-Legh, K. L. Studies in Church Life in England under Edward III. 2010. 200p. pap. 19.99 *(978-1-108-01012-2(1))* Cambridge Univ. Pr.

Worden, Blair. God's Instruments: Political Conduct in the England of Oliver Cromwell. 2012. (ENG.). 496p. 65.00 *(978-0-19-957049-2(3))* Oxford Univ. Pr., Inc.

Wright, Luke Savin Herrick. Samuel Taylor Coleridge & the Anglican Church. 2010. (ENG.). 312p. pap. 35.00 *(978-0-268-04418-3(X))* Univ. of Notre Dame Pr.

CHURCH AND STATE—GREECE

Frazee, Charles A. The Orthodox Church & Independent Greece, 1821-1852. 2009. (ENG.). 232p. pap. 36.99 *(978-0-521-11589-6(2))* Cambridge Univ. Pr.

CHURCH AND STATE—HOLY ROMAN EMPIRE

Boyd, William Kenneth. The Ecclesiastical Edicts of the Theodosian Code. 2009. 124p. 28.99 *(978-1-115-72835-5(0))* 2009. 124p. pap. 19.75 *(978-1-115-72838-6(5))* 2009. 124p. pap. 19.75 *(978-1-115-72837-9(7))* 2008. 128p. 21.99 *(978-0-559-42897-5(9))* 2008. 128p. pap. 19.75 *(978-0-559-42896-8(0))* BiblioBazaar.

—The Ecclesiastical Edicts of the Theodosian Code. 2007. (ENG.). 120p. 34.95 *(978-0-548-16048-0(1))*; 124p. per. 19.95 *(978-1-4304-5610-0(8))* Kessinger Publishing, LLC.

Ullmann, Walter. Medieval Papalism. 2009. 252p. 122.00 *(978-0-415-55576-0(0))* Routledge.

CHURCH AND STATE—INDIA

Presler, Franklin A. Religion under Bureaucracy: Policy & Administration for Hindu Temples in South India. 2008. (Cambridge South Asian Studies). (ENG.). 192p. pap. 28.99 *(978-0-521-05367-9(6))* Cambridge Univ. Pr.

CHURCH AND STATE—IRELAND

Butler, David. South Tipperary 1570-1841: Religion, Land & Rivalry. 2008. (Illus.). 336p. pap. 39.95 *(978-1-84682-091-5(X))* Four Courts Pr. IRL. Dist: International Specialized Bk. Services.

Clarke, Desmond M. Church & State: Essays in Political Philosophy. 275p. *(978-0-902561-29-8(4))*; pap. *(978-0-902561-30-4(8))* Cork Univ. Pr.

Fauske, Christopher. A Political Biography of William King, 1 vol. 2011. (Eighteenth-Century Political Biographies Ser.). (ENG.). 256p. 99.00 *(978-1-84893-010-0(0))* Pickering & Chatto Pubs., Ltd. GBR. Dist: Ashgate Publishing Co.

Moffitt, Miriam. The Society for Irish Church Missions to the Roman Catholics, 1849-1950. 2011. (ENG., Illus.). 320p. 95.00 *(978-0-7190-7879-8(2))* Manchester Univ. Pr. GBR. Dist: Macmillan.

Murray, Donal. Let Love Speak: Reflections on Renewal in the Irish Church. 2011. (ENG.). 176p. pap. 21.95 *(978-1-84730-268-7(8))* Veritas Pubns. IRL. Dist: Dufour Editions, Inc.

Scholes, Andrew. The Church of Ireland & the Third Home Rule Bill. 2010. 180p. 69.95 *(978-0-7165-3052-7(X))* Irish Academic Pr. IRL. Dist: International Specialized Bk. Services.

Sneddon, Andrew. Witchcraft & Whigs: The Life of Bishop Francis Hutchinson, 1660-1739. 2008. (ENG., Illus.). 232p. 84.00 *(978-0-7190-7612-1(9))* Manchester Univ. Pr. GBR. Dist: Macmillan.

Ugba, Abel. Shades of Belonging: African Pentecostals in Twenty-First Century Ireland. 2008. (Illus.). xii, 284p. *(978-1-59221-658-1(7))*; 302p. pap. *(978-1-59221-659-8(5))* Africa World Pr.

Walsh, Pat. The Curious Case of the Mayo Librarian. 2009. (ENG., Illus.). 223p. pap. 19.95 *(978-1-85635-615-2(9))* Mercier Pr., Ltd., The IRL. Dist: Dufour Editions, Inc.

CHURCH AND STATE—ITALY

Borutta, Manuel. Antikatholizismus: Deutschland und Italien im Zeitalter der europäischen Kulturkämpfe. 2010. (Burgertum Neue Folge Ser.). (GER.). 488p. (C). 84.00 *(978-3-525-36849-7(6))* Vandenhoeck & Ruprecht GmbH & Co. KG DEU. Dist: ISD.

Dante Alighieri. Dante Alighieri: On World Government (de Monarchia) Schneider, Herbert W., tr. 2008. (ENG.). 59p. (C). pap. 15.00 *(978-1-933859-67-5(9)*, Griffon Hse.) ISI Bks.

Halperin, S. William. Italy & the Vatican at War: A Study of Their Relations from the Outbreak of the Franco-Prussian War to the Death of Pius IX. 2011. 500p. 58.95 *(978-1-258-03417-7(4))* Literary Licensing, LLC.

McIntire, C. T. England Against the Papacy 1858-1861: Tories, Liberals & the Overthrow of Papal Temporal Power During the Italian Risorgimento. 2008. (ENG., Illus.). 264p. pap. 37.99 *(978-0-521-09040-7(7))* Cambridge Univ. Pr.

Shaw, Prue, ed. Dante's Monarchia. 2006. (Scholarly Digital Editions Ser.). cd-rom 90.00 *(978-1-904628-08-8(7))* Scholarly Digital Editions GBR. Dist: Boydell & Brewer, Inc.

Sotinel, Claire. Church & Society in Late Antique Italy & Beyond: Convergences Tensions & Negotiations. 2010. (Variorum Collected Studies). (FRE & ENG., Illus.). 340p. 165.00 *(978-1-4094-0022-6(0))* Ashgate Publishing Co.

Weber, Christoph. Episcopus et Princeps: Italienische Bischöfe als Fürsten, Grafen und Barone vom 17. bis zum 20. Jahrhundert. 2010. (Beiträge zur Kirchen- und Kulturgeschichte Ser.). (GER.). 218p. 64.95 *(978-3-631-60242-3(1))* Lang, Peter GmbH, Europaischer Verlag der Wissenschaften DEU. Dist: Lang, Peter.

CHURCH AND STATE—LATIN AMERICA

Williams, Philip. The Catholic Church & Politics in Nicaragua & Costa Rica. 2009. (Pitt Latin American Studies). (ENG.). 244p. pap. 25.95 *(978-0-8229-8370-5(2))* Univ. of Pittsburgh Pr.

CHURCH AND STATE—MEXICO

Bailey, David C. Viva Cristo Rey! The Cristero Rebellion & the Church-State Conflict in Mexico. 2011. (ENG., Illus.). 360p. pap. 30.00 *(978-0-292-73964-2(8))* Univ. of Texas Pr.

Bazant, Jan. Alienation of Church Wealth in Mexico: Social & Economic Aspects of the Liberal Revolution, 1856-1875. 2008. (Cambridge Latin American Studies). (ENG., Illus.). 352p. pap. 46.00 *(978-0-521-08868-8(2))* Cambridge Univ. Pr.

Costeloe, Michael P. Church Wealth in Mexico: A Study of the 'Juzgado de Capellanias' in the Archbishopric of Mexico 1800-1856. 2008. (Cambridge Latin American Studies). (ENG.). 156p. pap. 33.99 *(978-0-521-08347-8(8))* Cambridge Univ. Pr.

Dormady, Jason H. Primitive Revolution: Restorationist Religion & the Idea of the Mexican Revolution, 1940-1968. 2011. (ENG., Illus.). 216p. pap. 28.95 *(978-0-8263-4951-4(X))* Univ. of New Mexico Pr.

Meyer, Jean A. The Cristero Rebellion: The Mexican People Between Church & State, 1926-1929. 2008. (Cambridge Latin American Studies). (ENG.). 275p. pap. 37.99 *(978-0-521-10205-6(7))* Cambridge Univ. Pr.

Murphy, James. The Martyrdom of Saint Toribio Romo: Patron of Immigrants. 2007. 46p. pap. 5.95 *(978-0-7648-1666-5(7))* Liguori Pubns.

Palacios, Joseph M. & Palacios, Joseph Martin. The Catholic Social Imagination: Activism & the Just Society in Mexico & the United States. 2007. (Morality & Society Ser.). (Illus.). 320p. (ENG.). 70.00 *(978-0-226-64500-1(2))*; per. 30.00 *(978-0-226-64501-8(0))* Univ. of Chicago Pr.

CHURCH AND STATE—NORWAY

Robertson, Edwin H. Bishop of the Resistance: The Life of Eivind Berggrav. 224p. pap. 19.95 *(978-1-871828-57-3(0))* Handsel Pr., Ltd. GBR. Dist: Continuum International Publishing Group, Inc.

CHURCH AND STATE—PHILIPPINES

Carroll, John J. Engaging Society: The Sociologist in a War Zone. 2007. (Illus.). 330p. (C). 62.00 (978-971-550-505-5(8)) Univ. of Hawaii Pr.

Moreno, Antonio F. Church, State, & Civil Society in Postauthoritarian Philippines: Narratives of Engaged Citizenship. 2008. 372p. (C). pap. 39.00 (978-971-550-494-2(9)) Univ. of Hawaii Pr.

CHURCH AND STATE—ROME

Amerman, Pastor Pete. Fired Up! The Church in the Book of Acts. 2008. 305p. pap. 29.95 (978-1-4241-7576-5(3)) PublishAmerica, Inc.

Cook, John Granger. Roman Attitudes Toward the Christians: From Claudius to Hadrian. 2010. (Illus.). 378p. 197.50 (978-3-16-150553-9(0)) Mohr Siebeck GmbH & Co. KG DEU. Dist: Coronet Bks.

Crossan, John Dominic. God & Empire: Jesus Against Rome, Then & Now. 2007. (ENG.). 256p. 22.95 (978-0-06-084323-6(3), HarperOne) HarperCollins Pubs.

Elm, Susanna. Sons of Hellenism, Fathers of the Church: Emperor Julian, Gregory of Nazianzus, & the Vision of Rome. 2012. (Transformation of the Classical Heritage Ser.). (ENG.). 558p. 75.00 (978-0-520-26930-9(6)) Univ. of California Pr.

Girardet, Klaus M. Kaisertum, Religionspolitik und das Recht Von Staat und Kirche in der Spätantike. 2009. (GER., Illus.). 533p. (978-3-7749-3469-6(X)) Habelt GmbH, Dr. Rudolf.

Girardet, Klaus Martin. Der Kaiser und sein Gott: Das Christentum im Denken und in der Religionspolitik Konstantins des Großen. 2010. (Millennium-Studien / Millennium Studies). (GER., Illus.). IX, 213p. 98.00 (978-3-11-022788-8(6)) De Gruyter, Walter Inc.

Setton, Kenneth M. Christian Attitudes Towards the Emperor in the Fourth Century. (Columbia University, Studies in the Social Sciences: No. 482). reprint ed. 26.00 (978-0-404-51482-2(0)) AMS Pr., Inc.

CHURCH AND STATE—RUSSIA (FEDERATION)

Curanovic, Alicja. The Religious Factor in Russia's Foreign Policy. 2012. (Routledge Contemporary Russia & Eastern Europe Ser.). (ENG., Illus.). 368p. (C). 160.00 (978-0-415-68831-4(0)) Routledge.

—The Religious Factor in Russia's Foreign Policy: Keeping God on Our Side. 2012. 256p. E-Book (978-0-203-13327-9(7)) Routledge.

Geffert, Bryn. Eastern Orthodox & Anglicans: Diplomacy, Theology, & the Politics of Interwar Ecumenism. 2009. (ENG., Illus.). 560p. 60.00 (978-0-268-02975-3(X)) Univ. of Notre Dame Pr.

Gruber, Isaiah. Orthodox Russia in Crisis: Church & Nation in the Time of Troubles. 2012. (ENG., Illus.). 300p. 48.00 (978-0-87580-446-0(2)); (978-1-60909-049-4(7)) Northern Illinois Univ. Pr.

Hedda, Jennifer. His kingdom Come: Orthodox pastorship & social activism in revolutionary Russia. 2011. (ENG.). 382p. pap. 24.00 (978-0-87580-664-8(3)) Northern Illinois Univ. Pr.

Ligarides, Paisius. History of the Condemnation of the Patriarch Nicon: By a Plenary Council of the Orthodox Catholic Eastern Church Held at Moscow A. D. 1666-1667. Palmer, William, tr. 2010. (Cambridge Library Collection - History Ser.). (ENG.). 630p. pap. 43.00 (978-1-108-01488-5(7)) Cambridge Univ. Pr.

Lukasevicius, Arturas. Aleksandr Men''s Approach to the World's Religions. 2009. 212p. pap. (978-3-639-17059-7(8)) VDM Verlag Dr. Mueller e.K.

Manchester, Laurie. Holy Fathers, Secular Sons: Clergy, Intelligentsia, & the Modern Self in Revolutionary Russia. 2011. (ENG., Illus.). 302p. pap. 24.00 (978-0-87580-665-5(1)) Northern Illinois Univ. Pr.

Marsh, Christopher. Religion & the State in Russia & China: Suppression, Survival, & Revival. 2011. (ENG.). 288p. 120.00 (978-1-4411-0229-4(9)); pap. 29.95 (978-1-4411-1247-7(2)) Continuum International Publishing Group, Ltd. GBR. Dist: National Bk. Network.

Palmer, William, ed. Testimonies Concerning the Patriarch Nicon, the Tsar, & the Boyars, from the Travels of the Patriarch Macarius of Antioch. 2010. (Cambridge Library Collection - History Ser.). (ENG.). 640p. pap. 43.00 (978-1-108-01487-8(9)) Cambridge Univ. Pr.

Palmer, William, tr. The Replies of the Humble Nicon, by the Mercy of God Patriarch, Against the Questions of the Boyar Simeon Streshneff: And the Answers of the Metropolitan of Gaza Paisius Ligarides. 2010. (Cambridge Library Collection - History Ser.). (ENG.). 720p. pap. 48.00 (978-1-108-01455-7(0)) Cambridge Univ. Pr.

Petrenko, Vitali. The Development of Authority Within the Russian Orthodox Church: A Theological & Historical Inquiry. 2011. (ENG.). 310p. pap. 65.95 (978-3-03911-372-9(0)) Lang, Peter AG GBR. Dist: Lang, Peter.

Richters, Katja. The Post-Soviet Russian Orthodox Church: Politics, Culture & Greater Russia. 2012. (Routledge Contemporary Russia & Eastern Europe Ser.). (ENG., Illus.). 224p. (C). 140.00 (978-0-415-66933-7(2)) Routledge.

Romanoff, H. Sketches of the Rites & Customs of the Greco Russian Church. 2007. (ENG.). 446p. 51.95 (978-0-548-05243-3(3)) Kessinger Publishing, LLC.

Russian Society & the Orthodox Church: Religion in Russia after Communism. 2009. 264p. pap. 39.95 (978-0-415-54616-4(8)) Routledge.

Unregistered Religious Groups in Russia: Hearing Before the Commission on Security & Cooperation in Europe, One Hundred Ninth Congress, First Session, April 14, 2005. 2007. iii, 74p. (978-0-16-077910-7(3), 552-070-35347-0) United States Government Printing Office.

Young, Glennys. Power & the Sacred in Revolutionary Russia. 2008. (Illus.). xiv, 307p. pap. 28.95 (978-0-271-02837-8(8)) Pennsylvania State Univ. Pr.

Zhakevich, Valery. Evangelism & Church Planting in Russi. 2009. 188p. pap. (978-3-639-13838-2(4)) VDM Verlag Dr. Mueller e.K.

CHURCH AND STATE—SPAIN

Eastman, Scott. Preaching Spanish Nationalism across the Hispanic Atlantic, 1759-1823. 2012. 264p. 42.50 (978-0-8071-3957-8(2)) Louisiana State Univ. Pr.

Fernández del Riesgo, Manuel. Secularismo o Secularidad? El Conflicto Entre el Poder Político y el Poder Religiosos. 2010. (SPA.). 266p. (978-84-288-2230-5(1)) Promoción Popular Cristiana.

Lineham, Peter. Historical Memory & Clerical Activity in Medieval Spain & Portugal. 2012. (Variorum Collected Studies). 340p. 165.00 (978-1-4094-5110-5(0)) Ashgate Publishing Co.

López Camps, Jordi & López Camps, Jordi. Asuntos Religiosos: Una Propuesta de Política Pública. 2010. (SPA.). 359p. (978-84-288-2217-6(4)) Promoción Popular Cristiana.

Luxenberg, Alisa. The Galerie Espagnole & the Museo Nacional 1835-1853: Saving Spanish Art, or the Politics of Patrimony. 2008. (Illus.). 300p. 124.95 (978-0-7546-6190-0(3)) Ashgate Publishing Co.

Magnier, Grace. Pedro de Valencia & the Catholic Apologists of the Expulsion of the Moriscos: Visions of Christianity & Kingship. 2010. (Illus.). 436p. (978-90-04-18288-2(8)) BRILL.

Moral Roncal, Antonio M. & Moral Roncal, Antonio Manuel. La Cuestión Religiosa en la Segunda República Española: Iglesia y Carlismo. 2009. (SPA., Illus.). 263p. (978-84-9742-905-4(2)) Biblioteca Nueva, Editorial, S.L.

Motilla, Agustin. La Administración Española en Materia Religiosa (1808-1977) 2009. (SPA.). x, 207p. (978-84-9836-619-8(4)) Comares, Editorial SL.

Pardo Prieto, Paulino César & Prieto, Paulino César Pardo. Laicidad y Acuerdos Del Estado con Confesiones Religiosas. 2008. (SPA.). 478p. (978-84-9876-003-3(8)) Tirant lo Blanch.

Perrone, Sean T. Charles V & the Castilian Assembly of the Clergy: Negotiations for the Ecclesiastical Subsidy. 2008. (Illus.). 288p. (C). (978-90-04-17116-9(9)) BRILL.

Pilo, Rafaella & Nithard, Juan Everardo. Juan Everardo Nithard y Sus "Causas No Causas" Razones y Pretextos para el Fin de una Valimiento. 2010. (Silex Universidad Ser.). (SPA.). 285p. (978-84-7737-288-2(8)) Silex, Ediciones.

Pinedo, Isidoro, et al. Aspectos de la Política Religiosa en el Siglo XVIII: Estudios en Homenaje a Isidoro Pinedo Iparraguirre, S.J. 2010. (Historia/Universidad de Alicante Ser.). (SPA.). 280p. (978-84-9717-133-5(0)) Universidad de Alicante.

Shiels, W. Eugene. King & Church: The Rise & Fall of the Patronato Real. 2011. 412p. 54.95 (978-1-258-08339-7(6)) Literary Licensing, LLC.

CHURCH AND STATE—SOUTH AFRICA

Jones, Sarah Rowland, compiled by. Faith in Action: Njongonkulu Ndungane Archbishop for the church & the World. 2011. 256p. pap. 27.95 (978-0-7963-0763-7(6)) NB Pubs. Ltd. ZAF. Dist: International Publishers Marketing.

Noonan, Patrick. They're Burning the Churches. 2011. (ENG.). 288p. pap. 20.95 (978-1-77009-986-9(7)) Jacana Media ZAF. Dist: Independent Pubs. Group.

Peclard, et al. Swiss Churches, Apartheid & South Africa. 2011. 400p. pap. 49.95 (978-3-8258-9796-3(6)) Lit Verlag DEU. Dist: Transaction Pubs.

CHURCH AND STATE—SOVIET UNION

Braun, Leopold. In Lubianka's Shadow: The Memoirs of an American Priest in Stalin's Moscow, 1934-1945. Hamburg, G. M., ed. 2006. (Illus.). 456p. 35.00 (978-0-268-02199-3(6)) Univ. of Notre Dame Pr.

Froese, Paul. The Plot to Kill God: Findings from the Soviet Experiment in Secularization. 2008. (Illus.). 264p. 55.00 (978-0-520-25528-9(3)); pap. 26.95 (978-0-520-25529-6(1)) Univ. of California Pr.

Hedda, Jennifer. His Kingdom Come: Orthodox Pastorship & Social Activism in Revolutionary Russia. 2007. 307p. 43.00 (978-0-87580-382-1(2)) Northern Illinois Univ. Pr.

Manchester, Laurie. Holy Fathers, Secular Sons: Clergy, Intelligentsia, & the Modern Self in Revolutionary Russia. 2008. (Illus.). 302p. 43.00 (978-0-87580-380-7(6)) Northern Illinois Univ. Pr.

Pliguzov, Andrei. Documentary Sources for the History of the Rus' Metropolitanate. 2007. (Harvard Series in Ukrainian Studies). (Illus.). 880p. 64.95 (978-1-932650-02-0(4)) Harvard Univ. Pr.

CHURCH AND STATE—SWITZERLAND

Altermatt, Urs. Konfession, Nation und Rom: Essays zur Kulturgeschichte der Schweiz im 19. und 20. Jahrhundert. 2009. (GER.). 442p. (978-3-7193-1457-6(X)) Huber & Co., AG, Verlag.

CHURCH AND STATE—UNITED STATES

Adamson, Barry. Freedom of Religion, the First Amendment & the Supreme Court: How the Court Flunked History. 2007. (ENG.). 424p. pap. 25.95 (978-1-58980-520-0(8)) Pelican Publishing Co., Inc.

Allen, Brooke. Moral Minority: Our Skeptical Founding Fathers. (ENG.). 256p. 2007. per. 14.95 (978-1-56663-751-0(1)) 2006. 24.95 (978-1-56663-675-9(2)) Dee, Ivan R. Pub.

Anderson, Elder Richard C. After the Call: The Life of the Minister. 2011. 98p. pap. 15.99 (978-1-4628-6033-3(8)) Xlibris Corp.

Balmer, Randall H. God in the White House: A History - How Faith Shaped the Presidency from John F. Kennedy to George W. Bush. 2009. (ENG.). 256p. pap. 14.99 (978-0-06-087258-8(6), HarperOne) HarperCollins Pubs.

Berg, Thomas C., ed. The First Amendment: the Free Exercise of Religion Clause: Its Constitutional History & the Contemporary Debate. 2008. (Bill of Rights Ser.). (ENG.). 1p. per. 19.98 (978-1-59102-518-4(4)) Prometheus Bks., Pubs.

Bezanson, Randall P. How Free Can Religion Be? 2010. (ENG.). 296p. pap. 20.00 (978-0-252-07699-2(0)) Univ. of Illinois Pr.

Bothwell, Cecil. The Prince of War: Billy Graham's Crusade for a Wholly Christian Empire. 2007. 216p. 2nd rev. ed. (J). per. 16.00 (978-0-9700125-7-9(8)) 3rd rev. ed. (ENG.). lib. bdg. 24.00 (978-0-9700125-8-6(6)) Brave Ulysses Bks.

Bourne, Richard. Seek the Peace of the City: Christian Political Criticism as Public, Realistic & Transformative. 2010. (978-0-227-17284-1(1)) Clarke, James Co., Ltd.

Bowlby, David Dean. The Garden & the Wilderness: Church & State in America to 1789. 2011. (ENG.). 212p. 65.00 (978-0-7391-6874-5(6)) Lexington Bks.

Brownstein, Alan, ed. The Establishment of Religion Clause: The First Amendment, Its Constitutional History & the Contemporary Debate. 2008. (Bill of Rights Ser.). (ENG.). 1p. per. 19.98 (978-1-59102-517-7(6)) Prometheus Bks., Pubs.

Camp, Kathryn Page. In God We Trust: How the Supreme Court's First Amendment Decisions Affect Organized Religion. 2006. 210p. per. (978-1-932902-60-0(0)) FaithWalk Publishing.

Canipe, Lee. A Baptist Democracy: Separating God & Caesar in the Land of the Free. 2011. (Illus.). 192p. pap. 27.00 (978-0-88146-239-5(X)) Mercer Univ. Pr.

Carper, James C. & Hunt, Thomas C., eds. The Praeger Handbook of Religion & Education in the United States, 2 vols. 2009. 624p. 150.00 (978-0-275-99227-9(6), C9227, Praeger Pubs.) Greenwood Publishing Group, Inc.

Carter, Jimmy. Our Endangered Values: America's Moral Crisis. 2006. (ENG.). 224p. pap. 15.00 (978-0-7432-8501-8(8)) Simon & Schuster.

Chaput, Charles J. Render unto Caesar: Serving the Nation by Living Our Catholic Beliefs in Political Life. 2009. (ENG.). 272p. pap. 14.00 (978-0-385-52229-8(0), Image) Doubleday Religious Publishing Group, The.

—Render unto Caesar: Serving the Nation by Living Our Catholic Beliefs in Political Life. 2008. (ENG.). 272p. 21.95 (978-0-385-52228-1(2)) Knopf Doubleday Publishing Group.

Church, Forrest. So Help Me God: The Founding Fathers & the First Great Battle over Church & State. 2008. (ENG.). 540p. pap. 27.95 (978-0-15-603487-6(5), Mariner Bks.) Houghton Mifflin Harcourt Trade & Reference Pubs.

Church, Forrest, ed. The Separation of Church & State: Writings on a Fundamental Freedom by America's Founders. 2011. (ENG.). 176p. pap. 14.00 (978-0-8070-7747-4(0)) Beacon Pr.

Claiborne, Shane & Haw, Chris. Jesus for President: Politics for Ordinary Radicals, 1 vol. 2008. (ENG., Illus.). 176p. pap. 16.99 (978-0-310-27842-9(2)) Zondervan.

Cobb, Sanford H. The Rise of Religious Liberty in America: a History. 2007. pap. 43.95 (978-1-4304-5254-6(4)) Kessinger Publishing, LLC.

Collins, Christopher. Homeland Mythology: Biblical Narratives in American Culture. 2007. (ENG.). 264p. 29.95 (978-0-271-02993-1(5)) Pennsylvania State Univ. Pr.

Colwell, Stephen. The Position of Christianity in the United States, in Its Relations with Our Political Institutions,and Specially with Reference to Religious Instruct. 2006. 180p. per. 18.99 (978-1-4255-1393-1(X)) MPublishing.

Craig, Peter Stebbins, ed. Colonial Records of the Swedish Churches in Pennsylvania Vol. 4: From Lidman to Näsman. 2008. (Illus.). 406p. lib. bdg. 25.00 (978-0-9762501-4-2(4)) Swedish Colonial Society.

Crimm, Nina J. & Winer, Laurence H. Politics, Taxes, & the Pulpit: Provocative First Amendment Conflicts, 1 vol. 2010. (ENG., Illus.). 416p. 75.00 (978-0-19-538805-3(4)) Oxford Univ. Pr., Inc.

Daly, Lew. God's Economy: Faith-Based Initiatives & the Caring State. 2009. (ENG.). 344p. 37.50 (978-0-226-13483-3(0)) Univ. of Chicago Pr.

Davis, Derek. The Oxford Handbook of Church & State in the United States. 2010. (Oxford Handbooks Ser.). (ENG., Illus.). 592p. 150.00 (978-0-19-532624-6(5)) Oxford Univ. Pr., Inc.

Dierenfield, Bruce J. The Battle over School Prayer: How Engel V. Vitale Changed America. 2007. (Landmark Law Cases & American Society Ser.). 263p. 35.00 (978-0-7006-1525-4(3)); per. 15.95 (978-0-7006-1526-1(1)) Univ. Pr. of Kansas.

Doerr, Edd. Here I Stand. 2006. per. 12.00 (978-0-9785704-1-5(3), 061110) Potts Publishing.

Drakeman, Donald L. Church, State, & Original Intent. 2009. (ENG.). 382p. 93.00 (978-0-521-11918-4(9)); 297p. pap. 29.99 (978-0-521-13452-1(8)) Cambridge Univ. Pr.

Dreisbach, Daniel, et al, eds. The Forgotten Founders on Religion & Public Life. 2009. (ENG.). 352p. pap. 28.00 (978-0-268-02602-8(5)) Univ. of Notre Dame Pr.

Dreisbach, Daniel L. & Hall, Mark David, eds. Sacred Rights of Conscience: Selected Readings on Religious Liberty & Church-State Relations in the American Founding. 2009. (ENG.). 712p. (C). (gr. 12). 30.00 (978-0-86597-714-3(3)) Liberty Fund, Inc.

Duncan, Ann W. & Jones, Steven L. Church-State Issues in America Today: Religious Convictions & Practices in Public Life, 3 vols. 2007. (Praeger Perspectives Ser.). (978-0-275-99368-9(X), Praeger Pubs.) Greenwood Publishing Group, Inc.

Duncan, Ann W. & Jones, Steven L., eds. Church-State Issues in America Today: Religion & Government. 2007. (Praeger Perspectives Ser.). 840p. 300.00 (978-0-275-99367-2(1), C9367, Praeger Pubs.) Greenwood Publishing Group, Inc.

Dunn, Charles W. The Future of Religion in American Politics. Dunn, Charles W., ed. 2009. (ENG., Illus.). 288p. 30.00 (978-0-8131-2516-9(2)) Univ. Pr. of Kentucky.

Dworkin, Ronald. Is Democracy Possible Here? Principles for a New Political Debate. 2008. (ENG.). 192p. pap. 17.95 (978-0-691-13872-5(9)) 2006. 177p. 22.95 (978-0-691-12653-1(4)) Princeton Univ. Pr.

Dykstra, David. Yearning to Breathe Free? Thoughts on Im. 2006. pap. 15.99 (978-1-59925-084-7(5)) Solid Ground Christian Bks.

Eckenrode, Hamilton J. Separation of Church & State in Virginia. 164p. reprint ed. lib. bdg. 88.00 (978-0-7222-4638-2(2)) Library Reprints, Inc.

Edgar, Bob. Middle Church: Reclaiming the Moral Values of the Faithful Majority from the Religious Right. 2007. (ENG.). 272p. pap. 15.00 (978-0-7432-8950-4(1)) Simon & Schuster.

Eisgruber, Christopher L. & Sager, Lawrence G. Religious Freedom & the Constitution. 2010. 352p. pap. 18.95 (978-0-674-04582-8(3)) Harvard Univ. Pr.

Faircloth, Sean. Attack of the Theocrats! How the Religious Right Harms Us All, & What We Can Do about It. 2012. pap. (978-0-9844932-5-8(5)); 168p. 21.95 (978-0-9844932-4-1(7)) Pitchstone LLC.

Faith-Based Initiatives: Recommendations of the President's Advisory Council on Faith-Based & Community Partnerships & Other Current Issues: Hearing Before the Subcommittee on the Constitution, Civil Rights, & Civil Liberties of the Committee on the Judiciary, House of Representatives, One Hundred Eleventh Congress, Second Session, November 18, 2010. 2011. (Illus.). iv, 245p. (978-0-16-088327-9(X), 552-070-42632-9) United States Government Printing Office.

Federer, William J. Endangered Speeches - How the Aclu, Irs & Lbj Threaten Extinction of Free Speech. 2008. 244p. pap. 19.99 (978-0-9778085-8-8(0)) Amerisearch, Inc.

Finley, Martha. Elsie & Her Namesakes. 2008. 310p. 45.95 (978-0-548-92864-6(9)) 2007. (ENG.). 312p. per. 30.95 (978-0-548-57075-3(2)) Kessinger Publishing, LLC.

—Elsie & Her Namesakes. (Elsie Dinsmore Collection: No. 28). reprint ed. 14.00 (978-1-889128-28-3(7)) Mantle Ministries.

Finney, Jerald. God Betrayed: Separation of Church & State: the Biblical Principles & the American Application. 2008. 496p. pap. 23.99 (978-1-60647-541-6(X)) Xulon Pr., Inc.

Flowers, Ronald B., et al. Religious Freedom & the Supreme Court. 6th ed. 2009. (ENG.). 1200p. (C). pap. 69.95 (978-1-60258-160-9(6)) Baylor Univ. Pr.

Fritz, John & Slaughter, Gayle E. A Still Small Voice: The Vatican City State, the United States of America, & Israel in Bible Prophecy, 31 vols. 2007. 656p. per. 89.00 (978-0-9789470-0-2(2), 978-0-9789470-0-2) SkybridgePress.com.

Fuqua, Charles R. God's Law: The Only Political Solution: A Prophecy of the Downfall of the United States or a Blueprint for National Prosperity. 2011. (978-1-58982-838-4(0)) American Bk. Publishing Group.

Goldberg, Steven. Bleached Faith: The Tragic Cost When Religion Is Forced into the Public Square. 2008. (ENG.). 176p. 24.95 (978-0-8047-5861-1(1)) Stanford Univ. Pr.

Goldford, Dennis J. The Constitution of Religious Freedom: God, Politics, & the First Amendment. 2012. (ENG.). 270p. 44.95 (978-1-60258-419-8(2)) Baylor Univ. Pr.

Grasso Jr., Peter. In God We Betrayed. 2006. (ENG.). 21.99 (978-1-60034-565-4(4)); pap. 13.99 (978-1-60034-564-7(6)) Xulon Pr., Inc.

Green, Steven K. The Bible, the School, & the Constitution: The Clash that Shaped Modern Church-State Doctrine, 1 vol. 2012. (ENG., Illus.). 336p. 29.95 (978-0-19-982790-9(7)) Oxford Univ. Pr., Inc.

—The Bible, the School, & the Constitution: The Clash That Shaped Modern Church-State Doctrine. 2012. (Illus.). viii, 294p. E-Book (978-0-19-982791-6(5)) Oxford Univ. Pr., Inc.

Green, Steven K. The Second Disestablishment: Church & State in Nineteenth-Century America. 2010. (ENG.). 472p. 39.95 (978-0-19-539967-7(6)) Oxford Univ. Pr., Inc.

Greenawalt, Kent. Religion & the Constitution: Establishment & Fairness, 2 vols., Vol. 2. 2008. (ENG.). 568p. (C). 45.00 (978-0-691-12583-1(X)) Princeton Univ. Pr.

—Religion & the Constitution Vol. 1: Free Exercise & Fairness. (ENG.). 480p. (C). 2009. pap. 29.95 (978-0-691-14113-8(4)) 2006. 45.00 (978-0-691-12582-4(1)) Princeton Univ. Pr.

—Religion & the Constitution Vol. 2: Establishment & Fairness. 2009. (ENG.). 568p. (C). pap. 29.95 (978-0-691-14114-5(2)) Princeton Univ. Pr.

Gregg, Gary L., II & Hall, Mark David. America's Forgotten Founders, second Edition. 2nd ed. 2011. (ENG.). pap. 18.00 (978-1-61017-023-9(7)) ISI Bks.

Griffin, Leslie C. Griffin's Law & Religion, Cases & Materials, 2d. 2nd rev. ed. 2010. (University Casebook Ser.). 833p. 177.00 (978-1-59941-648-9(4), Foundation Pr.) West.

—Law & Religion: Cases & Materials. 2006. (University Casebook Ser.). 715p. 146.00 (978-1-59941-083-8(4), Foundation Pr.) West.

—Law & Religion: Cases in Context. 2010. (Illus.). xxi, 328p. (978-1-59941-649-6(2)) Kluwer Law International.

—Law & Religion, Cases & Materials, 2008 Supplement. 2008. (University Casebook Ser.). 116p. pap. 17.00 (978-1-59941-581-9(X), Foundation Pr.) West.

—Law & Religion, Cases & Materials, 2009 Supplement. 2009. (University Casebook Ser.). 215p. pap. 26.00 (978-1-59941-685-4(9), Foundation Pr.) West.

Griffin, Miriam. Law & Religion: Cases & Context. 2010. pap. 43.00 (978-0-7355-7819-7(2)) Wolters Kluwer Law & Business.

Gunn, T. Jeremy & Witte, John. No Establishment of Religion: America's Original Contribution to Religious Liberty. 2012. (ENG.). 424p. pap. 35.00 ***(978-0-19-986039-5(4))*** Oxford Univ. Pr., Inc.

Gunn, T. Jeremy & Witte, John, eds. No Establishment of Religion: America's Original Contribution to Religious Liberty. 2012. (ENG.). 424p. 99.00 ***(978-0-19-986037-1(8))*** Oxford Univ. Pr., Inc.

Hammar, Richard R. Pastor, Church & Law Volume 3: Employment Law (4th Edition), 3. Llautaud, Marian, ed. 4th ed. 2007. per. 24.95 *(978-0-917463-35-8(8))* Christianity Today International.

Harris, Sam. Letter to a Christian Nation. 2008. (Vintage Ser.). (ENG.). 144p. pap. 12.95 *(978-0-307-27877-7(8)*, Vintage) Knopf Doubleday Publishing Group.

Harrold, Philip. A Place Somewhat Apart: The Private Worlds of a Late Nineteenth-Century Public University. 2006. (Princeton Theological Monographs). 254p. pap. 26.00 *(978-1-59752-619-7(3)*, Pickwick Pubns.) Wipf & Stock Pubs.

Hart, Benjamin. Faith & Freedom: Recovering America's Christian Heritage. 2010. 384p. pap. 14.95 *(978-0-915463-94-7(6))* Jameson Bks., Inc.

Hart, Darryl G. A Secular Faith: Why Christianity Favors the Separation of Church & State. 2006. (ENG.). 288p. 26.95 *(978-1-56663-576-9(4))* Dee, Ivan R. Pub.

Heck, Gene W. God, Governance, & Economic Man: The Lessons of the Founders as Derived from Economic History. 2009. (ENG.). 326p. 41.99 *(978-0-7618-4816-5(9))* Univ. Pr. of America, Inc.

—God, Governance, & "Economic Man" The Lessons of the Founders As Derived from Economic History. 2009. xxiii, 302p. *(978-0-7618-4817-2(7))* Univ. Pr. of America, Inc.

Hedges, Chris. American Fascists: The Christian Right & the War on America. 2008. (ENG.). 304p. pap. 14.00 *(978-0-7432-8446-2(1)*, Free Pr.) Free Pr.

Hewitt, Hugh. GOP 5. 0: Republican Renewal under President Obama: Rules for Rebuilding the Conservative Majority in 2010 And 2012. 2009. 27.99 *(978-1-60791-155-5(8))* Xulon Pr., Inc.

Holscher, Kathleen A. Religious Lessons: Catholic Sisters & the Captured Schools Crisis in New Mexico. 2012. (ENG., Illus.). 304p. 55.00 ***(978-0-19-978173-7(7))*** Oxford Univ. Pr., Inc.

Howard, John A. Christianity: Lifeblood of America's Free Society (1620-1945) 2011. 140p. 28.95 ***(978-1-61507-859-2(2))***; pap. 11.95 ***(978-1-61507-858-5(4))*** Cross Bks. Publishing.

Hunt, Thomas C. & Carper, James C., eds. The Praeger Handbook of Faith-Based Schools in the United States, K-12, 2 vols. 2012. 570p. 173.00 ***(978-0-313-39139-2(4)***, A3191C) Greenwood Publishing Group, Inc.

Hutson, James H. Church & State in America: The First Two Centuries. 2007. (Cambridge Essential Histories Ser.). (ENG.). 222p. per. 23.99 *(978-0-521-68343-2(2))*; 220p. 73.99 *(978-0-521-86493-0(3))* Cambridge Univ. Pr.

Irons, Peter. God on Trial: Landmark Cases from America's Religious Battlefields. 2008. (ENG.). 384p. (gr. 12-18). 16.00 *(978-0-14-311375-1(5)*, Penguin (Non-Classics)) Penguin Group (USA) Inc.

Jackson, Harry R., Jr. The Truth in Black & White: A New Look at the Shifting Landscape of Race, Religion, & Politics in America Today. 2008. (ENG.). 256p. pap. 14.99 *(978-1-59979-268-2(0)*, Frontline) Charisma Media.

Jeffers, David. Understanding Evangelicals. 2006. pap. 13.99 *(978-1-60034-487-9(9))* Xulon Pr., Inc.

Jelen, Ted G. To Serve God & Mammon: Church-State Relations in American Politics. 2nd rev. ed. 2010. (Religion & Politics Ser.). (ENG.). 208p. (C). pap. 26.95 *(978-1-58901-637-8(8))* Georgetown Univ. Pr.

Johnson, Alvin W. & Yost, Frank H. Separation of Church & State in the United States. 2009. (ENG.). 287p. pap. 50.00 *(978-0-8166-5965-4(6))* Univ. of Minnesota Pr.

Johnson, Douglas F. Freedom of Religion: Locke V. Davey & State Blaine Amendments. 2010. (Law & Society Ser.). 230p. 65.00 *(978-1-59332-432-2(4))* LFB Scholarly Publishing LLC.

Justice, Benjamin. The War That Wasn't: Religious Conflict & Compromise in the Common Schools of New York State, 1865-1900. 2009. (Illus.). 285p. pap. 29.95 *(978-0-7914-6212-6(9)*, Suny Pr.) State Univ. of New York Pr.

Kemeny, P. C., ed. Church, State & Public Justice: Five Views. 2007. (Spectrum Multiview Book Ser.). (ENG.). 254p. per. 19.00 *(978-0-8308-2796-1(X)*, IVP Acad.) InterVarsity Pr.

Kuo, David. Tempting Faith: An Inside Story of Political Seduction. 2007. (ENG.). 320p. pap. 19.99 *(978-0-7432-8713-5(4)*, Free Pr.) Free Pr.

Kurland, Philip. Religion & the Law: Of Church & State & the Supreme Court. 2009. (ENG.). 127p. pap. 24.95 *(978-0-202-36304-2(X))* Aldine Transaction.

Lane, Frederick S. The Court & the Cross: The Religious Right's Crusade to Reshape the Supreme Court, 1 vol. 2009. (ENG.). 288p. pap. 19.00 *(978-0-8070-4425-4(3))* Beacon Pr.

Lauer, Paul E. Church & State in New England. (Johns Hopkins University. Studies in the Social Sciences, Thirtieth Ser.: 2-3). reprint ed. 29.50 *(978-0-404-61072-2(2))* AMS Pr., Inc.

Lawson, Richard B. A Home for the Nations. 2006. (ENG.). 248p. per. 17.99 *(978-1-4141-0670-0(X))* Pleasant Word.

Laycock, Douglas. Religious Liberty. 2010. 888p. pap. 35.00 *(978-0-8028-6465-9(1))* Eerdmans, William B. Publishing Co.

Ledewitz, Bruce. American Religious Democracy: Coming to Terms with the End of Secular Politics, 1 vol. annot. ed. 2007. 264p. 49.95 *(978-0-275-99460-0(0)*, C9460, Praeger Pubs.) Greenwood Publishing Group, Inc.

—Church, State, & the Crisis in American Secularism. 2011. (ENG., Illus.). 312p. 29.95 *(978-0-253-35634-5(2)*, 0253356342) Indiana Univ. Pr.

Lillback, Peter A. The Separation of Church & State: Does the Separation of Church & State Mean the Separation of God & Government? 2006. spiral bd. 11.95 *(978-0-9786052-2-3(5))* Providence Forum Pr.

—Wall of Misconception: Does the Separation of Church & State Mean the Separation of God & Government? 2008. (ENG., Illus.). 207p. 19.95 *(978-0-9786052-3-0(3))* ISI Bks.

Linker, Damon. The Theocons: Secular America under Siege. 2007. (ENG.). 304p. pap. 14.95 *(978-1-4000-9685-5(5)*, Anchor) Knopf Doubleday Publishing Group.

Lugo, Luis E., ed. Religion, Public Life, & the American Polity. 320p. 26.50 *(978-1-57233-261-4(1))* Univ. of Tennessee Pr.

Luker, Kristin. Salsa Dancing into the Social Sciences: Research in an Age of Info-Glut. 2010. (Illus.). 336p. pap. 18.95 *(978-0-674-04821-8(0))* Harvard Univ. Pr.

Lutzer, Erwin W. Is God on America's Side? The Surprising Answer & How It Affects Our Future. 2009. (ENG.). 112p. pap. 6.99 *(978-0-8024-8952-4(4))* Moody Pubs.

MacDonald, G. Jeffrey. Thieves in the Temple: The Christian Church & the Selling of the American Soul. 2010. (ENG.). 256p. (gr. 9). 25.95 *(978-0-465-00932-9(8))* Basic Bks.

Mansfield, Stephen. Ten Tortured Words: How the Founding Fathers Tried to Protect Religion in America ... & What's Happened Since. 2010. 246p. 26.00 *(978-1-4379-7332-7(9))* DIANE Publishing Co.

—Ten Tortured Words: How the Founding Fathers Tried to Protect Religion in America ... & What's Happened Since, 0 vols. annot. ed. 2007. 272p. 25.99 *(978-1-59555-084-2(4))* Nelson, Thomas Inc.

Mayer, Frederick E. The Religious Bodies of America. 4th ed. 616p. 26.99 *(978-0-7586-0231-2(6))* Concordia Publishing Hse.

McConnell, Michael W., et al. Religion & the Constitution. 3rd ed. 2011. xxiii, 845p. ***(978-0-7355-0983-2(2))*** Kluwer Law International.

—Religion & the Constitution. 2nd ed. 2006. xxi, 778p. 148.00 *(978-0-7355-6137-3(0))* 3rd ed. 2011. ***(978-0-7355-0718-0(X))*** Wolters Kluwer Law & Business. (Aspen Pubs.).

Mead, Sidney E. The Lively Experiment: The Shaping of Christianity in America. 2007. 240p. pap. 26.00 *(978-1-55635-276-8(X)*, Wipf and Stock) Wipf & Stock Pubs.

Merriman, Scott A. Religion & the Law in America: An Encyclopedia of Personal Belief & Public Policy, 2 vols., Set. 2007. (Illus.). 722p. 195.00 *(978-1-85109-863-7(1)*, AMRELA1C) ABC-CLIO, LLC.

Meyers, Robin. Why the Christian Right Is Wrong: A Minister's Manifesto for Taking Back Your Faith, Your Flag, Your Future. 2008. (ENG.). 224p. pap. 14.95 *(978-0-470-18463-9(9)*, Jossey-Bass) Wiley, John & Sons, Inc.

Moehlman, Conrad Henry, compiled by. The American Constitutions & Religion: Religious References in the Charters of the Thirteen Colonies & the Constitutions of the Forty-Eight States: A Source Book on Church & State in the United States. 2007. 75.00 *(978-1-58477-736-6(2))* Lawbook Exchange, Ltd., The.

Muñoz, Vincent Phillip. God & the Founders: Madison, Washington, & Jefferson. 2009. (ENG., Illus.). 252p. 92.00 *(978-0-521-51515-3(7))*; pap. 26.99 *(978-0-521-73579-7(3))* Cambridge Univ. Pr.

Murray, Bruce T. Religious Liberty in America: The First Amendment in Historical & Contemporary Perspective. 2008. 208p. pap. 19.95 net. *(978-1-55849-637-8(8))*; 213p. per. 80.00 net. *(978-1-55849-638-5(6))* Univ. of Massachusetts Pr.

Murray, William J. The Pledge: One Nation under God. annot. ed. 2007. 192p. per. 14.99 *(978-0-89957-035-8(6))* AMG Pubs.

National Convention To Secure The Religi. Proceedings of the National Convention to Secure the Religious Amendment of the Constitution of the United States eld in New York, Feb 26 And 27. 2011. 96p. pap. 14.99 ***(978-1-4255-0499-1(X))*** MPublishing.

Newcomb, Steven T. Pagans in the Promised Land: Decoding the Doctrine of Christian Discovery. 2008. (ENG.). 216p. pap. 19.95 *(978-1-55591-642-8(2))* Fulcrum Publishing.

Nicolay, Polly. We the People, Taking America Back. 2008. 248p. (ENG.). 24.99 *(978-1-60477-019-3(8))*; per. 14.99 *(978-1-60477-018-6(X))* Xulon Pr., Inc.

Nielsen, Niels C. God in the Obama Era: Presidents' Religion & Ethics from George Washington to Barack Obama. 2009. (ENG.). 404p. pap. 24.95 *(978-1-60037-646-7(0))* Morgan James Publishing.

Noonan, John T. & Gaffney, Edward McGlynn, Jr. Religious Freedom: History, Cases & Other Materials on the Interaction of Religion & Government. 3rd rev. ed. 2011. 1552p. 171.00 *(978-1-59941-243-6(8))* West Publishing Co., College & Schl. Div.

Norman, E. R. The Conscience of the State in North America. 2009. (ENG.). 212p. pap. 31.99 *(978-0-521-10775-4(X))* Cambridge Univ. Pr.

Nuttall, Clay. The Coming Conflict: The Separation of Church & State. 2011. 166p. pap. 13.99 ***(978-1-937129-07-1(1))*** Faithful Life Pubs.

O'Leary, Brad. America's War on Christianity. 2010. pap. 12.95 *(978-1-935071-24-2(6))* WND Bks, Inc.

Olsen, Glenn W. On the Road to Emmaus: The Catholic Dialogue with America & Modernity. 2012. (ENG.). 320p. 69.95 ***(978-0-8132-1954-7(X))*** Catholic Univ. of America Pr.

Owens, Michael Leo. God & Government in the Ghetto: The Politics of Church-State Collaboration in Black America. 2007. (Morality & Society Ser.). (Illus.). 304p. 60.00 *(978-0-226-64206-2(2))*; per. 25.00 *(978-0-226-64207-9(0))* Univ. of Chicago Pr.

Painter, Lou. The State versus Jesus Christ. 2007. per. 19.95 *(978-0-9791174-0-4(2))* Canaan Pr.

Palacios, Joseph M. & Palacios, Joseph Martin. The Catholic Social Imagination: Activism & the Just Society in Mexico & the United States. 2007. (Morality & Society Ser.). (Illus.). 320p. (ENG.). 70.00 *(978-0-226-64500-1(2))*; per. 30.00 *(978-0-226-64501-8(0))* Univ. of Chicago Pr.

Pally, Marcia. America's New Evangelicals: Expanding the Vision of the Common Good. 2011. 256p. pap. 20.00 ***(978-0-8028-6640-0(9))*** Eerdmans, William B. Publishing Co.

Petrie, George. Church & State in Early Maryland. 2009. (ENG.). 63p. pap. 16.75 *(978-1-117-02565-0(9))*; (ENG.). 63p. pap. 16.99 *(978-1-117-02566-7(7)*, BiblioLife); 52p. pap. 16.75 *(978-1-110-21938-4(5))*; (ENG.). 51p. pap. 18.99 *(978-1-110-21933-9(4)*, BiblioLife); (ENG.). 51p. pap. 16.99 *(978-1-110-21932-2(6)*, BiblioLife) BiblioBazaar.

—Church & State in Early Maryland. 52p. 2010. 25.56 *(978-1-169-20680-9(8))* 2010. 31.95 *(978-1-161-86036-8(3))* 2009. pap. 16.95 *(978-1-104-01221-2(9))* Kessinger Publishing, LLC.

Porterfield, Amanda. Conceived in Doubt: Religion & Politics in the New American Nation. 2012. (American Beginnings, 1500-1900 Ser.). (ENG.). 264p. 40.00 ***(978-0-226-67512-1(2))*** Univ. of Chicago Pr.

Ragosta, John A. Wellspring of Liberty: How Virginia's Religious Dissenters Helped Win the American Revolution & Secured Religious Liberty, 1 vol. 2010. (ENG., Illus.). 272p. 34.95 *(978-0-19-538806-0(2))* Oxford Univ. Pr., Inc.

Raley, Ivan. Just a Moment. 2011. 108p. 24.99 ***(978-1-4628-6989-3(0))***; pap. 15.99 ***(978-1-4628-6988-6(2))*** Xlibris Corp.

Ramazani, R. K., et al. Religion, State, & Society: Jefferson's Wall of Separation in Comparative Perspective. 2008. (ENG.). 252p. 100.00 *(978-0-230-61230-3(X))* Palgrave Macmillan.

Rasor, Paul B. & Bond, Richard E., eds. From Jamestown to Jefferson: The Evolution of Religious Freedom in Virginia. 2011. (ENG., Illus.). 216p. (gr. 17). 40.00 *(978-0-8139-3108-1(8))* Univ. Pr. of Virginia.

Ravitch, Frank S. Law & Religion, a Reader: Cases, Concepts, & Theory. 2nd ed. 2008. xix, 962p. *(978-0-314-18045-2(1))* West Publishing Co., College & Schl. Div.

—Masters of Illusion: The Supreme Court & the Religion Clauses. annot. ed. 2007. (ENG.). 288p. 50.00 *(978-0-8147-7585-1(3))* New York Univ. Pr.

Richardson, James. Saints under Siege: The Texas State Raid on the Fundamentalist Latter Day Saints. Wright, Stuart, ed. 2011. (ENG., Illus.). 281p. 80.00 ***(978-0-8147-9528-6(5))***; pap. 25.00 ***(978-0-8147-9529-3(3))*** New York Univ. Pr.

Rosenkötter, Maren. Die Establishment Clause der U. S. Verfassung und staatliche Unterstützung religiöser Privatschulen. 2011. (Schriften zum Staatskirchenrecht Ser.). (GER.). 176p. 60.95 *(978-3-631-61041-1(6))* Lang, Peter GmbH, Europaischer Verlag der Wissenschaften DEU. Dist: Lang, Peter.

Ross, Tara & Smith, Joseph C., Jr. Under God: George Washington & the Question of Church & State. 2009. (ENG.). 344p. pap. 15.95 *(978-0-9770722-1-7(5))* Colonial Pr., L.P.

Ross, Tara, et al. Under God: George Washington & the Question of Church & State. 2008. (ENG.). 320p. 24.95 *(978-1-890626-73-0(2)*, Vigilante, Richard Bks.

Rudin, Rabbi James. The Baptizing of America: The Religious Right's Plans for the Rest of Us. 2006. (ENG.). 336p. per. 16.95 *(978-1-56025-893-3(4))* Basic Bks.

Sandoz. The Sacred Rights of Conscience: Selected Readings on Religious Liberty & Church-State Relations in the American Founding. Dreisbach, Daniel & Hall, Mark David, eds. 2010. (ENG.). 712p. (C). (gr. 12). pap. 14.50 *(978-0-86597-715-0(1))* Liberty Fund, Inc.

Sekulow, Jay. Witnessing Their Faith: Religious Influence on Supreme Court Justices & Their Opinions. 2007. (ENG.). 368p. pap. 22.95 *(978-0-7425-5065-0(6))* Rowman & Littlefield Publishers, Inc.

Sharlet, Jeff. The Family: The Secret Fundamentalism at the Heart of American Power. 2009. 464p. pap. 15.99 *(978-0-06-056005-8(3)*, HarperPerennial) 2008. (ENG.). 352p. 25.95 *(978-0-06-055979-3(9))* HarperCollins Pubs.

Shiffrin, Steven H. The Religious Left & Church-State Relations. 2009. (ENG.). 256p. (C). 37.50 *(978-0-691-14144-2(4))* Princeton Univ. Pr.

Shipp, Glover. In God We Trust ... or Do We? Our Nation Built on a Christian Foundation. 2011. 178p. pap. 20.00 ***(978-1-61097-430-1(1)***, Resource Pubns.) Wipf & Stock Pubs.

Solomon, Stephen D. Ellery's Protest: How One Young Man Defied Tradition & Sparked the Battle over School Prayer. 2009. (ENG., Illus.). 440p. pap. 25.95 *(978-0-472-03345-4(X))* Univ. of Michigan Pr.

Stephens, Randall J. & Giberson, Karl W. The Anointed: Evangelical Truth in a Secular Age. 2011. (ENG., Illus.). 384p. 29.95 *(978-0-674-04818-8(0)*, Belknap Pr.) Harvard Univ. Pr.

Stevenson, Tyler Wigg. Brand Jesus: Christianity in a Consumerist Age. 2007. 256p. per. 16.00 *(978-1-59627-049-7(7))* Church Publishing, Inc.

Stringer, Phil. 50 Demonstrations of America's Christian Heritage. 2006. per. 5.00 *(978-1-60208-016-4(X))* FBC Pubns. & Printing.

Strong, William. Two Lectures upon the Relations of Civil Law to Church Polity, Discipline, & Property. 2006. 148p. per. 16.99 *(978-1-4255-1085-5(X))* MPublishing.

Sullivan, W. F. Prison Religion: Faith-Based Reform & the Constitution. 2009. (ENG.). 320p. (C). 49.95 *(978-0-691-13359-1(X))* Princeton Univ. Pr.

Sullivan, Winnifred. Prison Religion - Faith-Based Reform & the Constitution. 2011. (ENG.). 320p. (C). pap. 24.95 ***(978-0-691-15253-0(5))*** Princeton Univ. Pr.

Surratt, Geoff, et al. A Multi-Site Church Roadtrip: , 1 vol. 2009. (Leadership Network Innovation Ser.). (ENG.). 256p. (C). pap. 18.99 *(978-0-310-29394-1(4))* Zondervan.

Terrar, Edward. Social, Economic & Religious Beliefs among Maryland Catholic Laboring People During the Period of the English Civil War, 1639-1660. 2nd ed. 2008. (Illus.). 480p. pap. 9.95 net. *(978-0-9764168-5-2(9))* CWPublisher.

Terrar, Edward Toby. Liberation Theology along the Potomac: Labor's Golden Rule in Early American Catholicism. 2011. (Illus.). 220p. pap. 19.00 *(978-0-9764168-4-5(0))* CWPublisher.

Third Way Allegiance: Christian Witness in the Shadow of Religious Empire. 2011. 124p. pap. 12.95 *(978-1-931038-82-9(1))* Cascadia Publishing Hse., LLC.

Tipton, Steven M. Public Pulpits: Methodists & Mainline Churches in the Moral Argument of Public Life. 2008. 496p. 37.50 *(978-0-226-80474-3(7))* Univ. of Chicago Pr.

Tucker, Rev. R. E. A Visitation from Jesus: Orders from Headquarters' 2011. 358p. 29.99 ***(978-1-4653-4641-4(4))***; pap. 19.99 ***(978-1-4653-4640-7(6))*** Xlibris Corp.

Upchurch, Thomas Adams. Christian Nation? The United States in Popular Perception & Historical Reality, 1 vol. 2010. 198p. 44.95 *(978-0-313-38642-8(0)*, A3081C, Praeger Pubs.) Greenwood Publishing Group, Inc.

Urey, Winston M. Visiting Spirits! 2008. 212p. pap. 24.95 *(978-1-60672-874-1(1))* PublishAmerica, Inc.

Valletta, Thomas R. Great American Documents for LDS Families. 2011. 45.99 *(978-1-60641-952-6(8))* Deseret Bk. Co.

Viteritti, Joseph P. The Last Freedom: Religion from the Public School to the Public Square. 2007. (ENG.). 294p. (C). 27.95 *(978-0-691-13011-8(6))* Princeton Univ. Pr.

Walker, J. Brent. Church-State Matters: Fighting for Religious Liberty in Our Nation's Capital. 2008. (Illus.). 260p. 28.00 *(978-0-88146-115-2(6))* Mercer Univ. Pr.

Wallis, Jim. The Great Awakening: Reviving Faith & Politics in a Post-Religious Right America. 2008. 352p. 25.95 *(978-0-06-055829-1(6)*, HarperOne) HarperCollins Pubs.

—The Great Awakening: Seven Ways to Change the World. Lt. ed. 2008. 560p. per. 25.95 *(978-0-06-136407-5(X)*, HarperLuxe) HarperCollins Pubs.

Weeks, Stephen B. Church & State in North Carolina. (Johns Hopkins University. Studies in the Social Sciences, Thirtieth Ser.: 6). reprint ed. 37.50 *(978-0-404-61082-1(X))* AMS Pr., Inc.

West, Ellis. The Religion Clauses of the First Amendment: Guarantees of State's Rights? 2011. (ENG.). 250p. 70.00 *(978-0-7391-4677-4(7))* Lexington Bks.

West, Ellis McKinney. The Religion Clauses of the First Amendment: Guarantees of States' Rights? 2010. *(978-0-7391-4679-8(3))* Lexington Bks.

Wexler, Jay. Holy Hullabaloos: A Road Trip to the Battlegrounds of the Church/State Wars. 2009. (ENG.). 288p. pap. 20.00 *(978-0-8070-0044-1(2))*; xvii, 251p. pap. *(978-0-8070-0041-0(8))* Beacon Pr.

White, Mel. Holy Terror: Lies the Christian Right Tells Us to Deny Gay Equality. 2012. (ENG.). 350p. pap. 15.95 *(978-1-936833-09-2(3))* Magnus Bks.

White, Robert. Awake America! A Nation under Seige. 2008. (ENG.). 224p. pap. 13.99 *(978-1-59979-370-2(9)*, Creation Hse.) Charisma Media.

Williams, J. Samuel. Exilic Existence: Contributions of Black Churches in Prince Edward County, Virginia During the Modern Civil Rights Movement. 2011. 108p. pap. 14.99 ***(978-1-4670-3696-2(X))*** AuthorHouse.

Wills, Garry. Under God: Religion & American Politics. 2007. (ENG.). 448p. pap. 16.00 *(978-1-4165-4335-0(X))* Simon & Schuster.

Wilsey, John D. One Nation under God? An Evangelical Critique of Christian America. 2011. 226p. pap. 25.00 ***(978-1-60899-792-3(8)***, Pickwick Pubns.) Wipf & Stock Pubs.

Winship, Michael P. Godly Republicanism: Puritans, Pilgrims, & a City on a Hill. 2012. (ENG.). 350p. 49.95 ***(978-0-674-06385-3(6))*** Harvard Univ. Pr.

Winters, Michael Sean. God's Right Hand: How Jerry Falwell Made God a Republican & Baptized the American Right. 2012. (ENG.). 384p. 28.99 ***(978-0-06-197067-2(0)***, HarperOne) HarperCollins Pubs.

Witte, Jr., John, John & Nichols, Joel A. Religion & the American Constitutional Experiment: Essential Rights & Liberties. 3rd ed. 2010. (ENG.). 384p. (C). pap. 42.00 *(978-0-8133-4475-1(1))* Westview Pr.

Woodyard, David. The Church in the Time of Empire. 2011. (ENG.). 167p. pap. 16.95 ***(978-1-84694-595-3(X))*** O Bks., John Hunt.

Wright, Jonathan A. Separation of Church & State, 1 vol. 2010. (Historical Guides to Controversial Issues in America Ser.). 157p. 55.00 *(978-0-313-34769-6(7)*, GR4769) Greenwood Publishing Group, Inc.

Wright, Stuart A. & Richardson, James T. Saints under Siege: The Texas State Raid on the Fundamentalist Latter Day Saints. 2011. (Illus.). 304p. E-Book ***(978-0-8147-9530-9(7))*** New York Univ. Pr.

York, Tripp. Living on Hope While Living in Babylon: The Christian Anarchists of the 20th Century. 2009. 138p. pap. 17.00 *(978-1-55635-685-8(4)*, Wipf and Stock) Wipf & Stock Pubs.

Zabel, Orville H. God & Caesar in Nebraska A Study of Th. 2006. pap. 24.95 *(978-1-4286-6080-9(1))* Kessinger Publishing, LLC.

Zollman, Carl. American Civil Church Law. (Columbia University, Studies in the Social Sciences: No. 181). reprint ed. 39.50 *(978-0-404-51181-4(3))* AMS Pr., Inc.

Zollmann, Carl. American Civil Church Law. 2008. 488p. 53.95 *(978-1-4370-0710-7(4))*; pap. 38.95 *(978-1-4367-6527-5(7))* Kessinger Publishing, LLC.

—American Civil Church Law. 2008. 473p. 110.00 *(978-1-58477-882-0(2))* Lawbook Exchange, Ltd., The.

Zott, Lynn, ed. Church & State. 2011. (Opposing Viewpoints Ser.). (Illus.). 240p. (ENG.). pap. 27.50 (978-0-7377-5433-9(8), Greenhaven Pr., Inc.); (YA). (gr. 9-12). 39.70 (978-0-7377-5432-2(X)) Cengage Gale.

CHURCH AND THE WORLD

Here are entered works on the position and responsibilities of the Christian church in secular society.

see also Christian Sociology; Christianity and Economics; Christianity and International Affairs; Christianity and Politics; Church and Social Problems; History (Theology); Kingdom of God

Amankwah, John M. Dialogue: The Church & the Voice of the Other. 383p. pap. 82.95 (978-3-631-55940-6(2)); 2007. pap. 82.95 (978-0-8204-8762-5(7)) Lang, Peter Publishing, Inc.

Armstrong, Dave. Christian Worldview vs. Postmodernism. 2007. 224p. per. 16.95 (978-1-4303-2112-5(1)) Lulu Enterprises Inc.

Atherton, John. Public Theology for Changing Times. 176p. 22.00 (978-0-281-05209-7(3)) SPCK Publishing GBR. Dist: Pilgrim Pr., The/United Church Pr.

Barber, John J. My Almost for His Highest. 2010. 148p. pap. 18.00 (978-1-61097-632-2(8), Wipf and Stock) Wipf & Stock Pubs.

Bernardi, Peter J., ed. Maurice Blondel, Social Catholicism, & Action Francaise: The Clash over the Church's Role in Society During the Modernist Era. 2008. 320p. 79.95 (978-0-8132-1542-6(0)) Catholic Univ. of America Pr.

Boice, James Montgomery. Renewing Your Mind in a Mindless World: Learning to Think & Act Biblically, 1 vol. 2009. 144p. pap. 10.99 (978-0-8254-2572-1(7)) Kregel Pubns.

Budde, Michael L. The Borders of Baptism: Identities, Allegiances, & the Church. 2011. (Theopolitical Visions: Ser.). 204p. pap. 22.00 **(978-1-61097-135-5(3)**, Cascade Bks.) Wipf & Stock Pubs.

Buxton, Graham. Celebrating Life: Beyond the Sacred-Secular Divide. 2007. (ENG., Illus.). 220p. pap. 19.99 (978-1-84227-507-8(0), Paternoster) Authentic Media.

Byrd, Terriel. I Shall Not Be Moved: Racial Separation in Christian Worship. 2007. (ENG.). 96p. per. 25.50 (978-0-7618-3715-2(9)) Univ. Pr. of America, Inc.

Byrne, Georgina A. Modern Spiritualism & the Church of England, 1850-1939. 2010. (Studies in Modern British Religious History Ser.: Volume 25). 268p. 95.00 (978-1-84383-589-9(4), Boydell Press) Boydell & Brewer, Ltd. GBR. Dist: Boydell & Brewer, Inc.

Clarke, Fred. Church, Community & State in Relation to Education (RLE Edu C) Towards a Theory of School Organization. 2012. (Routledge Library Editions: Education Ser.). (ENG.). 248p. 115.00 (978-0-415-67539-0(1)) Routledge.

Clayton, Philip. Transforming Christian Theology: For Church & Society. 2009. 144p. (C). pap. 16.00 (978-0-8006-9699-3(9), Fortress Pr.) Augsburg Fortress, Pubs.

Connor, Timothy G. The Kenotic Trajectory of the Church in Donald MacKinnon's Theology: From Galilee to Jerusalem to Galilee. 2011. (T&T Clark Studies in Systematic Theology Ser.). (ENG.). 256p. 120.00 (978-0-567-11449-5(X), T&T Clark Int'l) Continuum International Publishing Group, Ltd. GBR. Dist: National Bk. Network.

Conyers, A. J. The Listening Heart: Vocation & the Crisis of Modern Culture. 2009. (ENG.). 232p. pap. 29.95 (978-1-60258-183-8(5)) Baylor Univ. Pr.

Doerksen, Paul G. & Koop, Karl, eds. The Church Made Strange for the Nations: Essays in Ecclesiology & Political Theology. 2011. (Princeton Theological Monographs). 204p. pap. 22.00 **(978-1-60899-398-7(1)**, Pickwick Pubns.) Wipf & Stock Pubs.

Douglas, Mark. Believing Aloud: Reflections on Being Religious in the Public Square. 2010. 198p. pap. 23.00 (978-1-60899-247-8(0), Cascade Bks.) Wipf & Stock Pubs.

Draper, Brian. Searching 4 Faith. 2007. (Questions of Faith Ser.). (Illus.). 156p. pap. 14.95 (978-1-59856-137-1(5)) Hendrickson Pubs. Marketing, LLC.

Ferguson, Dave, et al. The Big Idea: Focus the Message — Multiply the Impact, 1 vol. 2007. (Leadership Network Innovation Ser.). (ENG., Illus.). 208p. pap. 18.99 (978-0-310-27241-0(6)) Zondervan.

Fontana, David. Is Christianity Good for You? 2011. (ENG.). 252p. pap. 22.95 (978-1-84694-441-3(4)) Hunt, John Publishing Ltd. GBR. Dist: National Bk. Network.

Fosdick, Harry Emerson. Jesus' Ethical Message Confronts the World. 2011. 16p. pap. 35.95 **(978-1-258-02540-3(X))** Literary Licensing, LLC.

Furlong, Andy. C of E: The State It's in. 2nd ed. 2006. xiv, 418p. pap. (978-0-281-05845-7(8)) SPCK Publishing.

Garber, Steven. The Fabric of Faithfulness: Weaving Together Belief & Behavior. 2nd annot. ed. 2007. (ENG.). 222p. per. 16.00 (978-0-8308-3319-1(6), IVP Bks.) InterVarsity Pr.

Gascoigne, Robert. The Church & Secularity: Two Stories of Liberal Society. 2009. (Moral Traditions Ser.). (ENG.). 192p. pap. 26.95 (978-1-58901-490-9(1)) Georgetown Univ. Pr.

Greenhill, William. Stop Loving the World. Collier, Jay T., ed. & pref. by. 2011. 88p. pap. (978-1-60178-118-5(0)) Reformation Heritage Bks.

Gulley, Philip. Christians Awake. 2008. 120p. pap. 37.49 (978-1-4389-1177-9(7)) AuthorHouse.

Hansen, Collin, et al. Where Faith & Culture Meet Participant's Guide, 1 vol. 2007. (Intersect / Culture Ser.). (ENG.). 96p. (gr. 13). pap. 9.99 (978-0-310-28096-5(6)) Zondervan.

Herring. Introduction to the History of Christian. 2006. 288p. pap. (978-0-8264-6738-6(5)) Continuum International Publishing Group, Ltd.

Herring, George. Introduction to the History of Christianity: From the Early Church to the Enlightenment. 2006. (ENG., Illus.). 288p. 49.95 (978-0-8264-6737-9(7), Burns & Oates) Continuum International Publishing Group, Ltd. GBR. Dist: National Bk. Network.

Hughes, Ray H. Church of God Distinctives. 2007. 128p. per. 8.99 (978-87-14-81928-6(7)) Pathway Pr.

Hunter, James Davison. To Change the World: The Irony, Tragedy, & Possibility of Christianity in the Late Modern World, 1 vol. 2010. (ENG., Illus.). 368p. 27.95 (978-0-19-973080-3(6)) Oxford Univ. Pr., Inc.

Idestrscaron;m, Jonas, ed. For the Sake of the World. 2009. (Church of Sweden Research Ser.). 156p. pap. 18.00 (978-1-60899-108-2(3), Pickwick Pubns.) Wipf & Stock Pubs.

Jahn, Curtis A., ed. Here We Stand: A Confessional Christian Study of Worldviews. 2010. 360p. pap. (978-0-8100-2229-4(X)) Northwestern Publishing Hse.

Jewett, Robert, et al, eds. The Bible & the American Future. 2009. 306p. pap. 34.00 (978-1-60608-993-4(5), Cascade Bks.) Wipf & Stock Pubs.

Kasomo, Rt. Rev. Daniel W. The Relevance of Catholic Social Teaching Today. 2011. 452p. pap. **(978-3-8443-8690-5(4))** Lambert Academic Publishing.

Kauffman, J. Timothy. Reconnecting the Church. 2010. 234p. pap. 19.99 (978-1-4500-8718-6(3)) Xlibris Corp.

Kavanaugh, John F. Following Christ in a Consumer Society: The Spirituality of Cultural Resistance. 25th ed. 2006. (ENG.). 240p. (Orig.). per. 20.00 (978-1-57075-666-5(X)) Orbis Bks.

Keown, Mark J. What GodOs up to on Planet Earth? A No-Strings-Attached Explanation of the Christian Message. 2011. 160p. pap. 18.00 **(978-1-61097-132-4(9)**, Wipf and Stock) Wipf & Stock Pubs.

Kettle, David J. Western Culture in Gospel Context: Towards the Conversion of the West: Theological Bearings for Mission & Spirituality. 2011. 396p. pap. 44.00 **(978-1-61097-184-3(1)**, Cascade Bks.) Wipf & Stock Pubs.

Knighton, Ben, ed. Religion & Politics in Kenya: Essays in Honor of a Meddlesome Priest. 2009. (ENG., Illus.). 316p. 95.00 (978-0-230-61487-1(6)) Palgrave Macmillan.

König, Andrea, ed. Christliche Existenz in einer überwiegend nicht-christlichen Umgebung: Situationsbeschreibung, Initiativen und Perspektiven für die Zukunft. 2008. (Glaube und Denken. Jahrbuch der Karl-Heim-Gesellschaft Ser.). (GER & ENG., Illus.). 420p. pap. 99.95 (978-3-631-58300-5(1)) Lang, Peter GmbH, Europaischer Verlag der Wissenschaften DEU. Dist: Lang, Peter.

Lee, Mikyung. Public Dialogue Between Church & Others. 2009. 296p. pap. (978-3-639-11217-7(2)) VDM Verlag Dr. Mueller e.K.

Leech, Kenneth. The Sky Is Red: Discerning the Signs of the Times. 2nd ed. 296p. pap. 26.00 (978-0-232-52499-4(8)) Abingdon Pr.

Leedy, Randy. Love Not the World: Winning the War Against Worldliness. 2012. **(978-1-60682-041-4(9))** BJU Pr.

Lynch, Dan. God's Kingdom of Righteousness. 2007. per. 10.00 (978-1-59712-115-6(0)) Catawba Publishing Co.

Madges, William, ed. Vatican II: Forty Years Later. 2011. 400p. pap. 48.00 **(978-1-61097-739-5(4)**, Wipf and Stock) Wipf & Stock Pubs.

Maggay, Melba Padilla. Transforming Society. v, 108p. (978-971-8743-05-8(7)) Institute for Studies in Asian Church and Culture.

—Transforming Society. 2011. 114p. pap. 14.00 (978-1-61097-040-2(3), Wipf and Stock) Wipf & Stock Pubs.

Mahaney, C. J. Worldliness: Resisting the Seduction of a Fallen World. 2008. 191p. pap. (978-1-4335-0486-0(3)) Crossway.

Mahaney, C. J., ed. Worldliness: Resisting the Seduction of a Fallen World. 2008. 192p. 12.99 (978-1-4335-0280-4(1)) Crossway.

Martin, David. The Future of Christianity: Reflections on Violence & Democracy Religion & Secularisation. 2010. (Illus.). 240p. 99.95 (978-1-4094-0658-7(X)); pap. 29.95 (978-1-4094-0669-3(5)) Ashgate Publishing Co.

Maryniak, Irena. Offence: the Christian Case. 2009. (ENG., Illus.). 112p. 20.00 (978-1-906497-04-0(4)) Seagull Bks. GBR. Dist: Chicago Distribution Ctr.

McBride, Jennifer M. The Church for the World: A Theology of Public Witness, 1 vol. 2011. (ENG.). 352p. 74.00 **(978-0-19-975568-4(X))** Oxford Univ. Pr., Inc.

McThenia, Andrew W. & McThenia, Andrew W., Jr., eds. Radical Christian & Exemplary Lawyer: Honoring William Stringfellow. 2007. 192p. (Orig.). pap. 22.00 (978-1-55635-122-8(4), Wipf and Stock) Wipf & Stock Pubs.

Moffitt, Bob. If Jesus Were Mayor: How Your Local Church Can Transform Your Community, 1 vol. 2006. (Illus.). 392p. pap. 15.99 (978-0-8254-6129-3(4), Monarch Bks.) Lion Hudson PLC GBR. Dist: Kregel Pubns.

O'Halloran, James. Observe the Rustling Leaves: The Church & World of the Future. 2008. (ENG., Illus.). 64p. pap. 14.95 (978-1-85607-576-3(1)) Columba Pr. IRL. Dist: Dufour Editions, Inc.

O'Hanlon, Gerry. Theology in the Irish Public Square. 2010. (ENG.). 231p. pap. 27.95 (978-1-85607-685-2(7)) Columba Pr. IRL. Dist: Dufour Editions, Inc.

Percy, Martyn. The Ecclesial Cancopy: Faith Hope & Charity. 2012. (Explorations in Practical, Pastoral & Empirical Theology Ser.). 232p. 99.95 **(978-1-4094-4119-9(9))** Ashgate Publishing Co.

—The Ecclesial Canopy: Faith Hope & Charity. 2012. (Explorations in Practical, Pastoral & Empirical Theology Ser.). 232p. pap. 39.95 **(978-1-4094-4120-5(2))** Ashgate Publishing Co.

Phillips, L. Edward & Vaughan, Billy, eds. Courage to Bear Witness: Essays in Honor of Gene L. Davenport. 2009. 170p. pap. 20.00 (978-1-60608-536-3(0), Pickwick Pubns.) Wipf & Stock Pubs.

Rhonheimer, Martin. Changing the World: The Timeliness of Opus Dei. 2009. 138p. 14.95 (978-1-59417-068-3(1)) Scepter Pubs., Inc.

Robinson, Martin. Metavista: Bible, Church & Mission in an Age of Imagination. 2008. (Faith in an Emerging Culture Ser.). (ENG., Illus.). 256p. pap. 23.99 (978-1-84227-506-1(2), Paternoster) Authentic Media.

Rückle, Joachim. Seelsorge der Gemeinde: Voraussetzungen und Möglichkeiten ehrenamtlicher Seelsorge im Kontext von Kirche und Gesellschaft. 2010. (GER.). 358p. 86.95 (978-3-631-59833-7(5)) Lang, Peter GmbH, Europaischer Verlag der Wissenschaften DEU. Dist: Lang, Peter.

Rutledge, Fleming. Condemned into Redemption: The Meaning of the Crucifixion of Jesus for Today's World. (978-0-8028-3890-2(1)) Eerdmans, William B. Publishing Co.

Schillebeeckx, Edward. God the Future of Man: Schillebeeckx Collected Works 3. 2013. (ENG.). 160p. 110.00 **(978-0-567-45031-9(7)**, T&T Clark Int'l) Continuum International Publishing Group, Ltd. GBR. Dist: National Bk. Network.

—World & Church: Schillebeeckx Collected Works 4. 2013. (ENG.). 272p. 110.00 **(978-0-567-05422-7(5)**, T&T Clark Int'l) Continuum International Publishing Group, Ltd. GBR. Dist: National Bk. Network.

Sutton, Jerry. A Matter of Conviction: A History of Southern Baptist Engagement with the Culture. 2008. (ENG., Illus.). 532p. 24.99 (978-0-8054-4755-2(5), B&H Bks.) B&H Publishing Group.

Third Way Allegiance: Christian Witness in the Shadow of Religious Empire. 2011. 124p. pap. 12.95 (978-1-931038-82-9(1)) Cascadia Publishing Hse., LLC.

Trumper, Tim J. R. Preaching & Politics: Engagement without Compromise. 2009. 118p. pap. 15.00 (978-1-60608-008-5(3), Wipf and Stock) Wipf & Stock Pubs.

Tucker, Graham. Restoring the Vision: The Kingdom of God, the Church of the Future. 95p. pap. 10.95 (978-1-55126-216-1(9), 1510) Anglican Bk. Ctr. CAN. Dist: Forward Movement Pubns.

Ward, Graham. The Politics of Discipleship: Becoming Postmaterial Citizens. 2009. (Church & Postmodern Culture Ser.). 304p. (C). pap. 25.00 (978-0-8010-3158-8(3)) Baker Academic.

Webster, Alan. Reaching for Reality. 176p. 16.00 (978-0-281-05438-1(X)) SPCK Publishing GBR. Dist: Pilgrim Pr., The/United Church Pr.

Whitworth. Prepare for Exile. 2009. xx, 156p. pap. 19.95 (978-0-281-06003-0(7)) SPCK Publishing GBR. Dist: Westminster John Knox Pr.

Wilson, Jonathan R. Living Faithfully in a Fragmented World, Second Edition. 2nd rev. ed. 2011. (ENG.). 102p. pap. 31.25 (978-0-7188-9241-8(0)) Lutterworth Pr., The GBR. Dist: Printondemand-worldwide.com.

—Living Faithfully in a Fragmented World, Second Edition. 2nd ed. 2009. (New Monastic Library: Resources for Radical Discipleship Ser.). 102p. pap. 14.00 (978-1-55635-898-2(9), Cascade Bks.) Wipf & Stock Pubs.

Wright, Nigel Goring. Disavowing Constantine: Mission, Church & the Social Order in the Theologies of John Howard Yoder & Jurgen Moltmann. 2007. (Paternoster Theological Monographs: Ser.). 286p. pap. 32.00 (978-1-59752-793-4(9), Wipf and Stock) Wipf & Stock Pubs.

Wynne, Gordon. Broken Trust & How to Restore It. 2010. 64p. pap. (978-1-904884-30-9(X)) Church of Ireland Publishing.

Yallop, David. The Power & the Glory: Inside the Dark Heart of Pope John Paul II's Vatican. 2009. (ENG.). 560p. pap. 18.00 (978-0-465-01542-9(5)) Basic Bks.

Zahnd, Brian. Beauty Will Save the World: Rediscovering the Allure & Mystery of Christianity. 2012. xviii, 234p. E-Book **(978-1-61638-641-2(X))**; (ENG.). 256p. pap. 15.99 **(978-1-61638-585-9(5))** Charisma Media. (Charisma Hse.).

CHURCH ANTIQUITIES

see Christian Antiquities

CHURCH ARCHITECTURE

see also Abbeys; Architecture, Gothic; Basilicas; Cathedrals; Chapels; Church Decoration and Ornament; Cistercian Architecture; Vaults

Adler, Gerald. Robert Maguire & Keith Murray. 2012. (Twentieth-Century Architects Ser.). (ENG., Illus.). 160p. (C). pap. 40.00 (978-1-85946-165-5(4)) English Heritage GBR. Dist: Brown, David Bk. Co., The.

Akinsha, Konstantin, et al. The Holy Place: Architecture, Ideology, & History in Russia. 2007. (ENG., Illus.). 224p. 38.00 (978-0-300-11027-2(8)) Yale Univ. Pr.

Bailey, Gauvin. Andean Hybrid Baroque: Convergent Cultures in the Churches of Colonial Peru. 2010. (History Lang & Cult Spanish Portuguese Ser.). (ENG., Illus.). 1016p. 75.00 (978-0-268-02222-8(4)) Univ. of Notre Dame Pr.

Beaumont, Susan. Inside the Large Congregation. 2011. **(978-1-56699-419-4(5))** Alban Institute, Inc.

Bell, Gertrude Lowthian. Churches & Monasteries of the Tûr 'Abdîn & Neighbouring Districts. 2010. 94.88 (978-1-61719-509-9(X)) Gorgias Pr., LLC.

Bess, Philip. Till We Have Built Jerusalem: Architecture, Urbanism, & the Sacred. 2006. (Illus.). 325p. 28.00 (978-1-932236-96-5(1)); per. 18.00 (978-1-932236-97-2(X)) ISI Bks.

Block, Elaine C. & Billiet, F., eds. Lexicon of Medieval Choir Stalls. 2011. (Profane Arts of the Middle Ages Ser.). (ENG.). 225p. (C). 103.00 (978-2-503-51512-0(6)) Brepols Pubs. BEL. Dist: Brown, David Bk. Co., The.

Cadena, Richard. Lighting Design for Modern Houses of Worship. 2008. (ENG.). 160p. pap. 34.95 (978-0-9798107-1-8(X), 097981071X) Timeless Communications.

Christ-Janer, Albert & Foley, Mary Mix. Modern Church Architecture: A Guide to the Form & Spirit of Twentieth Century Religious Buildings. 2011. 340p. 51.95 **(978-1-258-10383-5(4))** Literary Licensing, LLC.

Costen, M. D. & Oakes, Catherine. Romanesque Churches of the Loire & Western France. (Illus.). 194p. 35.00 (978-0-7524-1444-7(5)) History Pr. Ltd.,The GBR. Dist: Trafalgar Square Publishing.

Edwards, Nancy. He BArchaeology of the Early Medieval Celtic Churches. 2009. (Society for medieval archaeology Monographs). (ENG., Illus.). 424p. (C). 95.00 (978-1-906540-61-6(6)) Maney Publishing GBR. Dist: Brown, David Bk. Co., The.

Geva, Anat. Frank Lloyd WrightS Sacred Architecture. 2011. (ENG., Illus.). 304p. (C). 70.00 (978-0-415-77508-3(6)) Routledge.

Grumeza, Ion. This Old Church: The Indispensable Guide for Restoring Church Buildings. 2010. 144p. pap. 18.00 (978-1-60899-180-8(6), Resource Pubns.) Wipf & Stock Pubs.

Halajian, John. Armenian Church Architecture: From Dormancy to Revival. 2006. (Illus.). 214p. per. 16.95 (978-1-59886-090-0(9)) Tate Publishing & Enterprises, LLC.

Hayman, Richard. Church Misericords & Bench Ends. 2009. (Shire Library). (ENG., Illus.). 64p. pap. 12.95 (978-0-7478-0744-5(2)) Shire Pubns., Ltd. GBR. Dist: Random Hse., Inc.

Hesperides. Colonial Churches. 2007. 392p. per. (978-1-4067-5944-0(9), Hesperides Pr.) Read Bks.

Kenaan-Kedar, Nurith. Ha-Madonah Shel Siah Ha-Tsabar: Masoret Ve-Hidush Ba-Tsiyur Ha-Notsri Ba-Arets Ba-Meot Ha-19 Veha-20: Kenesiyat Ha-Bikur Be-En-Kerem U-Khenesiyat Ba-Besorah Be-Natsrat. 2009. (HEB., Illus.). 158p. (978-965-217-300-3(2)) Yad Izhak Ben-Zvi.

Kieckhefer, Richard. Theology in Stone: Church Architecture from Byzantium to Berkeley. 2008. (ENG., Illus.). 384p. pap. 21.95 (978-0-19-534056-3(6)) Oxford Univ. Pr., Inc.

Lowrie, Walter. Art in the Early Church. 2007. (ENG.). 436p. per. (978-1-4067-5291-5(6)) Read Bks.

—Christian Art & Archaeology Being A Ha. 2006. pap. 37.95 (978-1-4286-3923-2(3)) Kessinger Publishing, LLC.

McAlpine, William R. Sacred Space for the Missional Church: Engaging Culture through the Built Environment. 2011. 222p. pap. 24.00 (978-1-60899-468-7(6), Wipf and Stock) Wipf & Stock Pubs.

Moffatt, Laura & Heathcote, Edwin. Contemporary Church Architecture. 2007. (ENG., Illus.). 240p. 90.00 (978-0-470-03156-8(5), Wiley) Wiley, John & Sons, Inc.

Nixon, Lucia. Making a Landscape Sacred: Outlying Churches & Icon Stands in Sphakia, Southwestern Crete. 2006. (ENG., Illus.). 184p. (C). per. 56.00 (978-1-84217-206-3(9)) Oxbow Bks., Ltd. GBR. Dist: Brown, David Bk. Co., The.

Pereira, Paulo. Convent of Christ, Tomar. 2010. (ENG., Illus.). 128p. pap. 29.95 (978-1-85759-383-9(9)) Scala, Editions FRA. Dist: National Bk. Network.

Phillipson, David W. Ancient Churches of Ethiopia. 2009. (ENG., Illus.). 288p. 65.00 (978-0-300-14156-6(4)) Yale Univ. Pr.

Plontke-Lüning, Annegret. Frühchristliche Architektur in Kaukasien: Die Entwicklung des Christlichen Sakralbaus in Lazika, Iberien, Armenien, Albanien und Den Grenzregionen Vom 4. Bis Zum 7. Jh. 2007. (VERoFFENTLICHUNGEN ZUR BYZANZFORSCHUNG Ser.). (GER., Illus.). 412p. (C). pap. 132.00 (978-3-7001-3682-8(X)) Austrian Academy of Sciences Press AUT. Dist: Brown, David Bk. Co., The.

Porter, Arthur Kingsley. Lombard Architecture. 2010. 534p. pap. (978-1-153-01030-6(5)) 2010. 580p. pap. (978-1-153-01028-3(3)) 2009. 402p. pap. (978-1-150-56994-4(8)) Books LLC.

—Lombard Architecture. 2009. 646p. pap. 38.41 (978-0-217-84354-6(9)) General Bks. LLC.

Ramsay, William Mitchell & Bell, Gertrude Lowthian. The Thousand & One Churches. Jackson, Mark P. C. & Ousterhout, Robert G., eds. 2008. (Illus.). 618p. (C). 49.95 (978-1-934536-05-6(9), Univ. of Pennsylvania Museum of Archaeology & Anthropology) Univ. Museum Pubns.

Ramzy, Nelly. Coptic Architecture. 2011. 188p. pap. **(978-3-8443-2651-2(0))** Lambert Academic Publishing.

Redol, Pedro & Silva, Jose Custfidio Vieira da. The Monastery of Batalha. 2007. (ENG., Illus.). 128p. pap. 29.95 (978-1-85759-382-2(0)) Scala, Editions FRA. Dist: National Bk. Network.

Remery, Michel. Mystery & Matter: On the Relationship Between Liturgy & Architecture in the Thought of Dom Hans Van der Laan OSB (1904-1991) 2011. 668p. (978-90-04-18296-7(9)) BRILL.

Roffey, Simon. The Medieval Chantry Chapel: An Archaeology. 2007. (Studies in the History of Medieval Religion Ser.: Volume 34). (Illus.). 206p. 90.00 (978-1-84383-334-5(4), Boydell Press) Boydell & Brewer, Ltd. GBR. Dist: Boydell & Brewer, Inc.

Rose, M. Ugly as Sin. 2009. (Illus.). 256p. pap. 18.95 (978-1-933184-44-9(2)) Sophia Institute Pr.

Rose, Michael S. Ugly as Sin. 2009. (Forthright Edition Ser.). (Illus.). 256p. pap. 18.95 (978-1-928832-36-2(9)) Sophia Institute Pr.

Seeliger, Hans Reinhard & Krumeich, Kirsten. Archäologie der Antiken Bischofssitze. 2007. (Sprachen und Kulturen des Christlichen Orients Ser.). (GER., Illus.). 176p. (C). 84.00 (978-3-89500-501-5(0)) Reichert, Ludwig Dr. DEU. Dist: Brown, David Bk. Co., The.

Sharpe, Geoffrey R. & Sharpe, Geoff. Historic English Churches: A Guide to Their Construction, Design & Features. 2011. (ENG., Illus.). 288p. 85.00 (978-1-84885-807-7(8)) I. B. Tauris & Co., Ltd. GBR. Dist: Macmillan.

Sorries, Reiner. Christliche Archaologie Compact. 2011. (GER., Illus.). 502p. (C). 168.00 **(978-3-89500-792-7(7))** Reichert, Ludwig Dr. DEU. Dist: Brown, David Bk. Co., The.

Spero, David, et al. Churches, 1 vol. Spero, David, ed. 2008. (ENG., Illus.). 144p. 45.00 (978-3-86521-308-2(1)) Steidl, Gerhard Druckerei und Verlag DEU. Dist: Innovative Logistics.

Stemp, Richard. The Secret Language of Churches & Cathedrals: Decoding the Sacred Symbolism of Christianity's Holy Buildings. 2010. (ENG., Illus.). 224p. 35.00 *(978-1-84483-916-2(8))* Duncan Baird Pubs. GBR. Dist: Sterling Publishing Co., Inc.

Sweetman, John J. The Unleashed Church. 2007. pap. 14.95 *(978-1-929451-22-7(9))* Preparing the Way Pubs.

Thibodeau, Timothy M., ed. The Rationale Divinorum Officiorum of William Durand of Mende Bk. 1: A New Translation of the Prologue. (Records of Western Civilization Ser.). (ENG.). 168p. (gr. 17). 2010. pap. 18.50 *(978-0-231-14181-9(5))* 2007. (Illus.). 40.00 *(978-0-231-14180-2(7))* Columbia Univ. Pr.

Torgerson, Mark A. An Architecture of Immanence: Architecture for Worship & Ministry Today. 2007. (Calvin Institute of Christian Worship Liturgical Studies). (Illus.). 312p. per. 24.00 *(978-0-8028-3209-2(1))* Eerdmans, William B. Publishing Co.

Van Millingen, Alexander. Byzantine Churches in Constantinople. 2008. 484p. *(978-1-4437-2475-3(0))* 2006. (ENG.). 480p. per. *(978-1-4067-3141-5(2))* Read Bks. (Hesperides Pr.).

Wilkinson, John. From Synagogue to Church: The Traditional Design. 2010. (ENG.). 304p. pap. 39.95 ***(978-0-415-59265-9(8))*** Routledge.

CHURCH ARCHITECTURE—DESIGNS AND PLANS

Jones, Douglas R. Sound of Worship: A Handbook of Acoustics & Sound System Design for the Church. 2010. (ENG., Illus.). 316p. pap. 49.95 *(978-0-240-81339-4(1)*, Focal Pr.) Elsevier Science & Technology Bks.

McCandless, Erich P. The Pattern of Church Planting. 2010. 94p. pap. 9.99 *(978-0-9845208-2-4(1))* Faithful Life Pubs.

McNamara, Denis. How to Read Churches: A Crash Course in Ecclesiastical Architecture. 2011. (Illus.). 256p. pap. 17.95 *(978-0-8478-3598-0(7))* Rizzoli International Pubns., Inc.

Nicholson, Gary. Building Momentum. 2010. (Illus.). 224p. *(978-1-4158-6883-6(2))* LifeWay Christian Resources.

Pocock, W. F. W. F. Pocock: Designs for Churches & Chapels. 2010. (ENG., Illus.). 120p. (C). 79.95 *(978-1-904965-29-9(6))* Spire Bks. Ltd. GBR. Dist: Brown, David Bk. Co., The.

Valleriano, Anthony J. Dedication: The Work of William P. Ginther, Ecclesiastical Architect. 2011. (Sacred Landmarks Ser.). 39.00 *(978-1-60635-103-1(6))* Kent State Univ. Pr.

Waltman, Larry. Church Planting with Paul: 7 Ancient Concepts, 7 Successful Marketing Techniques to Use for Church Planting Today. 2010. 92p. pap. 11.95 *(978-1-4401-9192-3(1))* iUniverse, Inc.

CHURCH ARCHITECTURE—DETAILS

Block, Elaine C. Corpus of Medieval Misericords: Belgium & the Netherlands. 2010. (Corpus of Medieval Misericords Ser.). (ENG., Illus.). 231p. (C). 196.00 *(978-2-503-51600-4(9))* Brepols Pubs. BEL. Dist: ISD.

Evans, E. p. & Evans, E. P. Animal Symbolism in Ecclesiastical Architecture. 2010. 390p. 48.95 *(978-1-161-38110-8(4))* Kessinger Publishing, LLC.

Gardner, Samuel. Gothic Sculpture. 2011. (ENG.). 188p. pap. 26.99 *(978-0-521-13155-1(3))* Cambridge Univ. Pr.

McNamara, Denis. How to Read Churches: A Crash Course in Ecclesiastical Architecture. 2011. (Illus.). 256p. pap. 17.95 *(978-0-8478-3598-0(7))* Rizzoli International Pubns., Inc.

CHURCH ARCHITECTURE—HISTORY

Ball, Philip. Universe of Stone: A Biography of Chartres Cathedral. 2008. (ENG.). 336p. 27.95 *(978-0-06-115429-4(6))* HarperCollins Pubs.

Brenk, Beat. The Apse, the Image & the Icon: An Historical Perspective of the Apse As a Space for Images. 2010. (Spatantike-Fruhes Christentum-Byzanz Ser.). (ENG., Illus.). 220p. (C). 50.00 *(978-3-89500-703-3(X))* Reichert, Ludwig Dr. DEU. Dist: Brown, David Bk. Co., The.

Hart, Stephen. Flint Flushwork: A Medieval Masonry Art. 2008. (Illus.). 199p. 50.00 *(978-1-84383-369-7(7)*, Boydell Press) Boydell & Brewer, Ltd. GBR. Dist: Boydell & Brewer, Inc.

Jenkins, Ian & Stancliffe, David. The Lion Companion to Church Architecture. 2009. (ENG., Illus.). 288p. 39.95 *(978-0-7459-5190-4(2))* Lion Hudson PLC GBR. Dist: Independent Pubs. Group.

Kilde, Jeanne Halgren. Sacred Power, Sacred Space: An Introduction to Christian Architecture & Worship. 2008. (ENG., Illus.). 224p. pap. 25.00 *(978-0-19-533606-1(2))* Oxford Univ. Pr., Inc.

McNamara, Denis. How to Read Churches: A Crash Course in Ecclesiastical Architecture. 2011. (Illus.). 256p. pap. 17.95 *(978-0-8478-3598-0(7))* Rizzoli International Pubns., Inc.

Minnis, John & Mitchell, Trevor. Religion & Place in Leeds. 2007. (Informed Conservation Ser.). (ENG., Illus.). 80p. pap. 16.00 *(978-1-905624-48-5(4))* English Heritage GBR. Dist: Brown, David Bk. Co., The.

Prentice, Sartell. The Voices of the Cathedral: Tales in Stone & Legends in Glass. 2007. (ENG.). 390p. 48.95 *(978-0-548-03678-5(0))* Kessinger Publishing, LLC.

Sundt, Richard. Whare Karakia: Maori Church Building, Decoration & Ritual in Aotearoa New Zealand, 1834-1863. 2010. (ENG., Illus.). 240p. 49.95 *(978-1-86940-456-7(4))* Auckland Univ. Pr. NZL. Dist: Independent Pubs. Group.

Webster, Christopher. R. D. Chantrell (1793-1872) & the Architecture of a Lost Generation. 2010. (ENG., Illus.). 347p. (C). 60.00 *(978-1-904965-22-0(9))* Spire Bks. Ltd. GBR. Dist: Brown, David Bk. Co., The.

Webster, Christopher, ed. Episodes in the Gothic Revival: Six church Architects. 2011. (ENG., Illus.). 240p. (C). 70.00 ***(978-1-904965-34-3(2))*** Spire Bks. Ltd. GBR. Dist: Brown, David Bk. Co., The.

CHURCH ARCHITECTURE—AUSTRALIA

Giurgola, Romaldo. Luminous Simplicity: The Architecture & Art of St. Patrick's Cathedral, Parramatta. rev. ed. 2006. (Illus.). 192p. (C). 99.00 *(978-1-876832-83-4(5))* Macmillan Art Publishing AUS. Dist: Brown, David Bk. Co., The.

CHURCH ARCHITECTURE—CANADA

Richardson, Peter & Richardson, Douglas. Canadian Churches: An Architectural History. 2007. (ENG., Illus.). 440p. 85.00 *(978-1-55407-239-2(5))* Firefly Bks., Ltd.

Saint-Amour, Suzanne. René Richer, 1887-1963, Architecte Maskoutain: Oublier Ne Puis. 2008. (FRE., Illus.). 276p. *(978-2-89634-029-3(7))* GID, Editions.

CHURCH ARCHITECTURE—EUROPE

Andas, Margrete Syrstad, et al, eds. The Medieval Cathedral of Trondheim: Architectural & Ritual Constructions in Their European Context. 2007. (Ritus et Artes Ser.). (GER & ENG., Illus.). 375p. (C). 102.00 *(978-2-503-52301-9(3))* Brepols Pubs. BEL. Dist: ISD.

Ball, Philip. Universe of Stone: A Biography of Chartres Cathedral. 2008. (ENG.). 336p. 27.95 *(978-0-06-115429-4(6))* HarperCollins Pubs.

Bangs, Herbert. The Return of Sacred Architecture: The Golden Ratio & the End of Modernism. 2006. (ENG., Illus.). 1p. per. 24.95 *(978-1-59477-132-3(4))* Inner Traditions International, Ltd.

Binding, Gunther. Antike Saulen ALS Spolien in Fruh- Und Hochmittelalterlichen Kirchen und Pfalzen - Materialspolie Oder Bedeutungs-Trager? 2007. (Sitzungsberichte der Wissenschaftlichen Gesellschaft an der Johann Wolfgang Goethe-Universitat Ser.). (ENG.). 49p. (C). pap. 30.00 *(978-3-515-08999-9(3))* Steiner, Franz Verlag Wiesbaden GmbH DEU. Dist: Brown, David Bk. Co., The.

Brenk, Beat. Christianization of the Late Roman World: Cities, Churches, Synagogues, Palaces, Private Houses & Monasteries in the Early Christian Period. 2013. (ENG., Illus.). 620p. (C). 300.00 *(978-1-899828-72-2(9))* Pindar Pr. GBR. Dist: Brown, David Bk. Co., The.

Bulzan, Ovidiu. Church Architecture & Baptist Missions in Transylvania, 1871 -1918. 2010. 180p. pap. *(978-3-8383-1351-1(8))* Lambert Academic Publishing.

Buxton, David. The Wooden Churches of Eastern Europe: An Introductory Survey. 2008. (ENG., Illus.). 416p. pap. 53.00 *(978-0-521-09054-4(7))* Cambridge Univ. Pr.

Conant, Kenneth John. Benedictine Contributions to Church Architecture. 2011. 80p. 37.95 ***(978-1-258-00203-9(5))*** Literary Licensing, LLC.

Connah, Roger. Grace & Architecture. 2008. 192p. pap. 26.00 *(978-951-682-502-4(8))* Rakennustieto oy FIN. Dist: Independent Pubs. Group.

De Jonge, K., et al. Gotiek in het hertogdom Brabant. 2009. (DUT.). 272p. (C). pap. 32.00 *(978-90-429-2275-4(3))* Peeters Pubs. & Booksellers BEL. Dist: Brown, David Bk. Co., The.

Fawcett, Richard. The Architecture of the Scottish Medieval Church, 1100-1560. 2011. (Paul Mellon Centre for Studies in Britis Ser.). (Illus.). 432p. 100.00 *(978-0-300-17049-8(1))* Yale Univ. Pr.

Gurrieri, Francesco & Manetti, Renzo. Dieci Secoli per la Basilica Di San Miniato Al Monte. 2007. (ITA., Illus.). 173p. (C). 46.00 *(978-88-596-0236-1(X))* Edizioni Polistampa ITA. Dist: Brown, David Bk. Co., The.

Jetsonen, Jari & Jetsonen, Sirkkaliisa. Sacral Space: Modern Finnish Churches. 2008. (ENG.). 144p. pap. 69.00 *(978-951-682-731-8(4))* Rakennustieto oy FIN. Dist: Independent Pubs. Group.

Khroushkova, Liudmila. Les Monuments Chretiens de la Cote Orientale de la Mer Noire: Abkhazie: IVe-XIVe Siecles. 2007. (Bibliothèque de l'Antiquité Tardive Ser.). (Illus.). 340p. pap. 139.00 *(978-2-503-52387-3(0))* Brepols Pubs. BEL. Dist: Brown, David Bk. Co., The.

McKasey, John. Ancient Chapels & Churches in Wales. 2007. (ENG., Illus.). 72p. pap. 11.95 *(978-0-86243-665-0(6)*, Virago Press) Y Lolfa GBR. Dist: Dufour Editions, Inc.

Opacic, Z. The Year 1300 & the Creation of the New European Architecture. Gajewski, Alexandrea, ed. 2008. (Architectura Medii Aev Ser.). (ENG.). 235p. (C). pap. 123.00 *(978-2-503-52286-9(6))* Brepols Pubs. BEL. Dist: ISD.

Spicer, Andrew & Thofner, Margit. Lutheran Churches in Early Modern Europe. 2012. (Illus.). 476p. 134.95 ***(978-0-7546-6583-0(6))*** Ashgate Publishing Co.

CHURCH ARCHITECTURE—FRANCE

Bonde, Sheila. Fortress-Churches of Languedoc: Architecture, Religion & Conflict in the High Middle Ages. 2008. (ENG.). 292p. pap. 34.99 *(978-0-521-05202-3(5))* Cambridge Univ. Pr.

Bonnet, Philippe & Rioult, Jean-Jacques. Bretagne Gothique: L'architecture Religieuse. 2010. (FRE., Illus.). 485p. *(978-2-7084-0883-8(6))* Picard, A.et J. Editions.

Schnell + Schnell, ed. Ronchamp. 2008. (ENG.). 88p. 19.95 *(978-3-7954-2050-5(4)*, Art Stock Bks. Ltd/Csi) Continental Sales, Inc.

CHURCH ARCHITECTURE—GERMANY

Manso, Iris. Gott dem Erloser und den Gottesdiensten der Reformierten Gewidmet 1753: Die spatbarocke Evangelisch-Reformierte Kirche in Gottingen. 2009. (GER., Illus.). 248p. (C). pap. 68.00 *(978-3-525-28000-3(9))* Vandenhoeck & Ruprecht GmbH & Co. KG DEU. Dist: ISD.

Overesch, Manfred. Himmlisches Jerusalem in Hildesheim: St. Michael und das Geheimnis der sakralen Mathematik vor 1000 Jahren. 2009. (GER., Illus.). 332p. (C). 41.00 *(978-3-525-55004-5(9))* Vandenhoeck & Ruprecht GmbH & Co. KG DEU. Dist: ISD.

Verstegen, Ute. Ausgrabungen und Beuforschungen in St. Gereon zu Köln. 2006. (Kölner Forschungen Ser.). (Illus.). 1023p. 153.00 *(978-3-8053-3352-8(8))* Zabern, Philipp von Verlag, GmbH DEU. Dist: Brown, David Bk. Co., The.

Voigt, Wolfgang, et al, texts. Gottfried Böhm, 1 vol. 2007. (ENG., Illus.). 272p. 60.00 *(978-3-936314-19-9(5))* Jovis Verlag GmbH DEU. Dist: D.A.P./Distributed Art Pubs.

CHURCH ARCHITECTURE—GREAT BRITAIN

Barr, Andrew. Song of Praise: The Nations Favourite Churches. 2006. (ENG., Illus.). 128p. 24.95 *(978-0-7459-5220-8(8)*, Lion) Lion Hudson PLC GBR. Dist: Independent Pubs. Group.

Belcher, Margaret, ed. The Collected Letters of A. W. N. Pugin: Volume 4: 1849-1850. 2012. (Collected Letters of A. W. N. Pugin Ser.). (ENG., Illus.). 748p. 240.00 *(978-0-19-960784-6(2))* Oxford Univ. Pr., Inc.

Benham, William. Old St Paul's Cathedral. 2007. (Illus.). 128p. per. *(978-1-4065-4775-7(1))* Dodo Pr.

Betjeman, John & Surman, Richard. Betjeman's Best British Churches. 2011. (ENG., Illus.). 896p. 55.00 ***(978-0-00-741567-0(2))*** HarperCollins Pubs. Ltd. GBR. Dist: Independent Pubs. Group.

Billings, Robert William. Baronial & Ecclesiastical Antiquities of Scotland, The - 2008. (Illus.). 204p. pap. *(978-1-84530-057-9(2))*; 208p. pap. *(978-1-84530-055-5(6))*; 204p. pap. *(978-1-84530-056-2(4))* Grimsay Pr.

Bloxam, Holbeche Matthew. The Principles of Gothic Ecclesiastical Architecture, Elucidated by Question & Answer. 2007. 124p. (ENG.). 94.99 *(978-1-4280-7621-1(2))*; per. 88.99 *(978-1-4280-7619-8(0))* IndyPublish.com.

Cannon, Jon & Williamson, Beth, eds. The Medieval Art, Architecture & History of Bristol Cathedral: An Enigma Explored. 2011. (Bristol Studies in Medieval Cultures Ser.: Volume 2). (Illus.). 376p. 95.00 *(978-1-84383-680-3(7)*, Boydell Press) Boydell & Brewer, Ltd. GBR. Dist: Boydell & Brewer, Inc.

Child, Mark. Churches & Churchyards. 2008. (Shire Discovering Ser.). (ENG., Illus.). 264p. pap. 25.95 *(978-0-7478-0659-2(4))* Shire Pubns., Ltd. GBR. Dist: Random Hse., Inc.

Cox, J. Charles. English Church Fittings, Furniture & Accessories. 2008. 336p. per. *(978-1-905217-93-9(5))* Mills, Jeremy Publishing.

—The English Parish Church. 2008. 360p. pap. *(978-1-905217-95-3(1))* Mills, Jeremy Publishing.

Doll, Peter. After the Primitive Christians. 2009. 88.00 *(978-1-60724-388-5(1))* Gorgias Pr., LLC.

Fergusson, Peter. Canterbury Cathedral Priory in the Age of Becket. 2011. (ENG., Illus.). 288p. 85.00 *(978-0-300-17569-1(8))* Yale Univ. Pr.

Friedman, Terry. The Eighteenth-Century Church in Britain. 2011. (Paul Mellon Centre for Studies in Britis Ser.). (ENG., Illus.). 800p. 100.00 *(978-0-300-15908-0(0))* Yale Univ. Pr.

Gardner, Samuel. Gothic Sculpture. 2011. (ENG.). 188p. pap. 26.99 *(978-0-521-13155-1(3))* Cambridge Univ. Pr.

Hamilton Thompson, A. The Historical Growth of the English Parish Church. 2nd rev. ed. 2012. (ENG.). 156p. pap. 19.99 ***(978-1-107-60578-7(4))*** Cambridge Univ. Pr.

Harris, Brian L. Harris's Guide to Churches & Cathedrals: Discovering the Unique & Unusual in over 500 Churches & Cathedrals. 2007. (ENG., Illus.). 512p. 45.00 *(978-0-09-191251-2(2))* Random Hse. GBR. Dist: Independent Pubs. Group.

Hart, Stephen. Flint Flushwork: A Medieval Masonry Art. 2008. (Illus.). 199p. 50.00 *(978-1-84383-369-7(7)*, Boydell Press) Boydell & Brewer, Ltd. GBR. Dist: Boydell & Brewer, Inc.

Hatts, Leigh. London's 100 Best Churches. 2010. (ENG., Illus.). 224p. pap. 22.99 *(978-1-85311-944-6(X)*, Canterbury Pr. Norwich) Hymns Ancient & Modern Ltd GBR. Dist: Westminster John Knox Pr.

Henderson, George. Vision & Image in Early Christian England. 2011. (ENG.). 310p. pap. 39.99 *(978-0-521-18073-3(2))* Cambridge Univ. Pr.

Howard, F. English Church Woodwork. 2007. 436p. per. *(978-1-905217-65-6(X))* Mills, Jeremy Publishing.

—The Medieval Styles of the English Parish Church. 2007. 208p. per. *(978-1-905217-77-9(3))* Mills, Jeremy Publishing.

Hume, John R. 1000 Churches to Visit in Scotland. 2006. (ENG., Illus.). 480p. pap. 14.95 *(978-1-905267-00-2(2))* NMS Enterprises Ltd. - Publishing GBR. Dist: National Bk. Network.

Humphrey, Stephen & Morris, James. Churches & Cathedrals of London. 2nd ed. 2007. (ENG., Illus.). 160p. per. 24.95 *(978-1-84537-337-5(5))* New Holland Pubs., Ltd. GBR. Dist: National Bk. Network.

Jeffery, Paul. City Churches of Sir Christopher Wren. 2007. (ENG., Illus.). 408p. per. 39.95 *(978-1-84725-014-8(9)*, Hambledon Continuum) Continuum International Publishing Group, Ltd. GBR. Dist: National Bk. Network.

Kenyon, John R. & Williams, Diane. Cardiff: Architecture & Archaeology in the Medieval Diocese of Llandaff. 2006. (Illus.). 236p. (C). (British Archaeological Association (BAA) Conference Transaction Ser.). 45.00 *(978-1-904350-81-1(X))*; (British Archaeological Association Conference Transactions Ser.: Vol. 29). 104.00 *(978-1-904350-80-4(1))* Northern Universities Pr. GBR. Dist: Brown, David Bk. Co., The.

Kinross, John. Discovering the Smallest Churches in Scotland. 2011. (ENG., Illus.). 128p. pap. 23.95 *(978-0-7524-5880-9(9))* History Pr. Ltd., The GBR. Dist: Independent Pubs. Group.

Maude, Thomas. Guided by a Stone-Mason: Exploring the Cathedrals, Abbeys & Churches of Britain. 2011. (ENG., Illus.). 176p. pap. 17.00 *(978-1-84885-547-2(8)*, Tauris Parke Paperbacks) I. B. Tauris & Co., Ltd. GBR. Dist: Macmillan.

Mortlock, D. P. Guide to Suffolk Churches. 2009. (Popular Guide Ser.). (ENG., Illus.). 392p. pap. 64.00 *(978-0-7188-3076-2(8))* Lutherworth Pr., The GBR. Dist: Brown, David Bk. Co., The.

Pevsner, Nikolaus. Buildings of England, City of London, Churches. 2nd abr. ed. (Illus.). 160p. pap. 19.95 *(978-0-14-071100-4(7))* Penguin Bks., Ltd. GBR. Dist: Trafalgar Square Publishing.

Potter, John F. Patterns in Stonework: The Early Church in Britain & Ireland. 2009. (Illus.). 191p. (C). pap. 132.50 *(978-1-4073-0600-1(6))* British Archaeological Reports Ltd. GBR. Dist: Brown, David Bk. Co., The.

Pugin, A. W. N. Contrasts & True Principles of Pointed or Christian Architecture. 2012. (ENG., Illus.). 244p. (C). 90.00 ***(978-1-904965-37-4(7))*** Spire Bks. Ltd GBR. Dist: Brown, David Bk. Co., The.

Robinson, David. The Cistercians in Wales: Architecture & Archaeology 1130-1540. 2006. (Reports of the Research Committee of the Society of Antiquaries of London: No. 73). (Illus.). 424p. (C). 110.00 *(978-0-85431-285-6(4))* Society of Antiquaries of London GBR. Dist: Brown, David Bk. Co., The.

Rodwell, Warwick. Dorchester Abbey Oxfordshire: The Archaeology & Architecture of a Cathedral, Monastery & Parish Church. 2009. (ENG., Illus.). 256p. (C). 76.00 *(978-1-84217-388-6(X))* Oxbow Bks., Ltd. GBR. Dist: Brown, David Bk. Co., The.

Rosewell, Roger. Medieval Monasteries. 2012. (Shire Library). (ENG., Illus.). 64p. pap. 12.95 ***(978-0-7478-1146-6(6))*** Shire Pubns., Ltd. GBR. Dist: Random Hse., Inc.

Sharpe, Geoffrey R. & Sharpe, Geoff. Historic English Churches: A Guide to Their Construction, Design & Features. 2011. (ENG., Illus.). 288p. pap. 25.00 *(978-1-84885-189-4(8))* I. B. Tauris & Co., Ltd. GBR. Dist: Macmillan.

Stanford, David. Suffolk Churches. 2006. (Illus.). 112p. 30.00 *(978-0-7112-2496-4(X))* Lincoln, Frances Ltd. GBR. Dist: Perseus-PGW.

Symondson, Anthony, et al. Sir Ninian Comper: An Introduction to His Life & Work, with Complete Gazetteer: With, of the Atmosphere of a Church. 2007. (Illus.). 336p. pap. *(978-1-904965-11-4(3))* Spire Bks. Ltd.

Thompson, A. Hamilton. The Ground Plan of the English Parish Church. 2011. (ENG.). 152p. pap. 19.99 *(978-1-107-40160-0(7))* Cambridge Univ. Pr.

Webster, Christopher. R. D. Chantrell (1793-1872) & the Architecture of a Lost Generation. 2010. (ENG., Illus.). 347p. (C). 60.00 *(978-1-904965-22-0(9))* Spire Bks. Ltd. GBR. Dist: Brown, David Bk. Co., The.

Webster, Christopher, ed. Episodes in the Gothic Revival: Six church Architects. 2011. (ENG., Illus.). 240p. (C). 70.00 ***(978-1-904965-34-3(2))*** Spire Bks. Ltd. GBR. Dist: Brown, David Bk. Co., The.

Yorke, Trevor. English Churches Explained. 2010. (England's Living History Ser.). (ENG., Illus.). 129p. pap. 21.95 *(978-1-84674-191-3(2))* Countryside Bks. GBR. Dist: Brown, David Bk. Co., The.

—Gravestones, Tombs & Memorials. 2010. (Britain's living History Ser.). (ENG., Illus.). 64p. (C). pap. 14.95 *(978-1-84674-202-6(1))* Countryside Bks. GBR. Dist: Brown, David Bk. Co., The.

CHURCH ARCHITECTURE—IRELAND

Crawford, John & Gillespie, Raymond, eds. St Patrick's Cathedral, Dublin: A History. 2009. (Illus.). 424p. 70.00 *(978-1-84682-044-1(8))* Four Courts Pr. IRL. Dist: International Specialized Bk. Services.

Grimes, Brendan. Majestic Shrines & Graceful Sanctuaries: The Church Architecture of Patrick Byrne 1783-1864. 2009. (Illus.). 197p. 65.00 *(978-0-7165-3073-2(2))* Irish Academic Pr. IRL. Dist: International Specialized Bk. Services.

Ó'Carragáin, Tomás. Churches in Early Medieval Ireland: Architecture, Ritual & Memory. 2011. (Paul Mellon Centre for Studies in Britis Ser.). (Illus.). 400p. 100.00 *(978-0-300-15444-3(5))* Yale Univ. Pr.

Potter, John F. Patterns in Stonework: The Early Church in Britain & Ireland. 2009. (Illus.). 191p. (C). pap. 132.50 *(978-1-4073-0600-1(6))* British Archaeological Reports Ltd. GBR. Dist: Brown, David Bk. Co., The.

Usher, Robin. Protestant Dublin, 1660-1760: Architecture & Iconography. 2012. (Early Modern History: Society & Culture Ser.). (ENG., Illus.). 264p. 85.00 ***(978-0-230-22389-9(3))*** Palgrave Macmillan.

CHURCH ARCHITECTURE—ITALY

Brogiolo, Gian Pietro & Ibsen, M., eds. Corpus Architecturae Religiosae Europeae (saec. IV-X), vol. II. I. 2011. (Corpus Architecturae Religiosae Europeae Ser.). (ENG.). 325p. (C). pap. 114.00 ***(978-953-6002-46-7(9))*** Brepols Pubs. BEL. Dist: Brown, David Bk. Co., The.

Carella, Silvio. Architecture religieuse haut-médievale en Italie Meridionale: Le diocese de Benevent. 2011. (Bibliotheque de l'antiquite Tardive Ser.). (FRE., Illus.). 255p. (C). pap. 94.00 *(978-2-503-53388-9(4))* Brepols Pubs. BEL. Dist: Brown, David Bk. Co., The.

Cerretelli, Claudio, et al. Il Duomo Di Prato. 2009. (ITA., Illus.). 279p. *(978-88-6087-259-3(6))* Le Lettere.

Claussen, Peter Cornelius, et al. Die Kirchen der Stadt Rom im Mittelalter 1050-1300, G-L. Band 3: S. Giacomo alla Lungara bis S. Lucia della Tinta. 2010. (Forschungen zur Kunstgeschichte und christlichen Archaologie Ser.). (GER., Illus.). 591p. (C). 210.00 *(978-3-515-09410-8(5))* Steiner, Franz Verlag Wiesbaden GmbH DEU. Dist: Brown, David Bk. Co., The.

Erwee, Michael. The Churches of Rome, 1527-1870. 2012. (ENG., Illus.). 520p. (C). 300.00 *(978-1-904597-28-5(9))* Pindar Pr. GBR. Dist: Brown, David Bk. Co., The.

Frothingham, A. L. Introduction of Gothic Architecture into Italy by the French Cistercian Monks. 2009. pap. 25.12 *(978-1-60724-496-7(9))* Gorgias Pr., LLC.

—Notes on Roman Artists of the Middle Ages. 2009. pap. 21.52 *(978-1-60724-493-6(4))* Gorgias Pr., LLC.

C

Frugoni, Chiara & Armandi Barbolini, Marina. The Cathedral of Modena, 3 vols. 2009. (ITA & ENG., Illus.). 1340p. 1160.00 *(978-88-7686-982-2(4))* Panini Franco Cosimo ITA. Dist: Antique Collectors' Club.

Goodson, Caroline J. The Rome of Pope Paschal I: Papal Power, Urban Renovation, Church Rebuilding & Relic Translation, 817-824. 2010. (Cambridge Studies in Medieval Life & Thought: Fourth Ser.). (ENG., Illus.). 408p. 99.00 *(978-0-521-76819-1(5))* Cambridge Univ. Pr.

Hickson, Sally Anne. Women Art & Architectural Patronage in Renaissance Mantua: Matrons Mystics & Monasteries. 2012. (Women & Gender in the Early Modern World Ser.). (Illus.). 204p. 104.95 ***(978-1-4094-2752-0(8))*** Ashgate Publishing Co.

Howard, Deborah & Moretti, Laura. Sound & Space in Renaissance Venice: Architecture, Music, Acoustics. 2010. (Illus.). 256p. 55.00 *(978-0-300-14874-9(7))* Yale Univ. Pr.

Martellini, Patrizia Angiolini, ed. The Basilica of San Vitale in Ravenna, 2 vols. 2008. (ITA & ENG., Illus.). 670p. 825.00 *(978-88-7686-806-1(2))* Panini Franco Cosimo ITA. Dist: Antique Collectors' Club.

Tronzo, William, ed. St. Peter's in the Vatican. 2008. (ENG., Illus.). 336p. (C). pap. 52.99 *(978-0-521-73210-9(7))* Cambridge Univ. Pr.

Zervas, Diane Finiello, et al. Orsanmichele in Florence, 2 vols. 2009. (ENG & ITA., Illus.). 1196p. 980.00 *(978-88-7686-775-0(9))* Panini Franco Cosimo ITA. Dist: Antique Collectors' Club.

CHURCH ARCHITECTURE—MEXICO

Connaughton, Brian F. & Lira González, Andrés. Las Fuentes Eclesiásticas para la Historia Social de México. 2009. (Otras Publicaciones Ser.). (SPA., Illus.). 420p. pap. 19.99 *(978-970-620-833-0(X))* El Colegio de México, A.C., Biblioteca Miguel Cosio Villegas MEX. Dist: Fondo de Cultura Economica USA.

Wake, Eleanor. Framing the Sacred: The Indian Churches of Early Colonial Mexico. 2010. (ENG.). 368p. (C). 65.00 *(978-0-8061-4033-9(X))* Univ. of Oklahoma Pr.

CHURCH ARCHITECTURE—PALESTINE

Milson, David. Art & Architecture of the Synagogue in Late Antique Palestine: In the Shadow of the Church. 2006. (Ancient Judaism & Early Christianity Ser.). (Illus.). 579p. *(978-90-04-15186-4(9))* BRILL.

Pringle, Denys. The City of Jerusalem, 4 vols. 2007. (Churches of the Crusader Kingdom of Jerusalem Ser.). (ENG., Illus.). 532p. 250.00 *(978-0-521-39038-5(9))* Cambridge Univ. Pr.

CHURCH ARCHITECTURE—SPAIN

Frischauer, A. S. Altspanischer Kirchenbau. (GER.). X, 100p. 224.00 ***(978-3-11-179034-3(7))*** De Gruyter, Walter Inc.

Frischauer, Alma Stefanie. Altspanischer Kirchenbau. (Studien zur spätantiken Kunstgeschichte Ser.). (GER.). IX, 98p. 210.00 ***(978-3-11-216115-9(7))***; 135.00 ***(978-3-11-102625-1(6))*** De Gruyter, Walter Inc.

King, Georgiana Goddard. The Way of Saint James, Volume I, 3 vols., I. 2008. (Illus.). 484p. pap. *(978-0-9790909-2-9(X))* Pilgrims Process, Inc.

—The Way of Saint James, Volume II. 2008. (Illus.). 532p. pap. 38.95 *(978-0-9790909-3-6(8))* Pilgrims Process, Inc.

—The Way of Saint James, Volume III. 2008. (Illus.). 726p. pap. 45.98 *(978-0-9790909-4-3(6))* Pilgrims Process, Inc.

Konemann Staff. Spanish Abbeys. Date not set. (Illus.). 250p. 19.95 *(978-3-8290-4076-1(8)*, 521510) Konemann.

Krieger, Peter & San Martín, Iván. Sacralización, Culto y Religiosidad en la Arquitectura Latinoamericana. 2009. (SPA., Illus.). xiii, 185p. *(978-607-02-0850-8(1))* Universidad Nacional Autónoma de México.

Puig, Jordi & Pla Boada, Ricard. Gaudi in the Cathedral of Mallorca, 1 vol. Vivas, Pere, ed. 2008. (ENG., Illus.). 144p. pap. 16.95 *(978-84-8478-148-6(8))* Triangle Postals, S.L. ESP. Dist: Innovative Logistics.

Vivas Ortiz, Pere. The Basilica of the Sagrada Familia, 1 vol. 2011. (ENG.). 240p. pap. 16.95 *(978-84-8478-511-8(4))* Triangle Postals, S.L. ESP. Dist: Innovative Logistics.

CHURCH ARCHITECTURE—UNITED STATES

Boosel, Brian D., et al. The Saint Vincent Basilica, Latrobe, Pennsylvania: One Hundred Years Opatka-Metzgar, Kimberley A., ed. 2006. (Illus.). 344p. per. 59.99 *(978-0-9708216-8-3(9))* St. Vincent Archabbey Pubns.

Cole, Dorothy B. God's Gift. 2008. 108p. pap. 11.99 *(978-1-60647-931-5(8))* Xulon Pr., Inc.

Collum, Maria O. & Krueger, Barbara E. Detroit's Historic Places of Worship. 2012. ***(978-0-8143-3424-9(5))***; E-Book ***(978-0-8143-3811-7(9))*** Wayne State Univ. Pr.

Covey, Frances Alden. The Earl Covey Story: A Master Builder in the Adirondacks Who Made Buildings as Beautiful as Nature Herself. rev. ed. 2010. 178p. pap. 20.00 *(978-0-615-34671-7(5))* Hoffer, Terry.

Crosbie, Michael J. Houses of God: Religious Architecture for a New Millennium, Vol. 3. 2006. (ENG., Illus.). 192p. 65.00 *(978-1-920744-97-7(5))* Images Publishing Group AUS. Dist: National Bk. Network.

Domes & Spires. 2008. 128p. 29.99 *(978-0-9796044-2-3(7))* Tribune-Democrat, The.

Herman, Barry K., et al. Cleveland's Vanishing Sacred Architecture. 2010. (Images of America Ser.). (ENG., Illus.). 128p. pap. 21.99 *(978-0-7385-8442-3(8))* Arcadia Publishing.

Jaimes, Rene S. The Roman Catholic Churches of Manhattan: Their History, Architecture & Decoration. 2007. (Illus.). 268p. 50.00 *(978-0-615-15726-9(2))* Jaimes, Rene Assocs., Publishing Consultants.

Kitt, Phyllis Pittman. God's Country: Historic Churches & Chapels of the Genesee Valley. 2009. 39.95 *(978-1-933360-37-9(2))* Rochester Institute of Technology, Cary Graphic Arts Pr.

Lemon, Mark. The Illustrated Alamo 1836: A Photographic Journey. 2008. (ENG., Illus.). 176p. 49.95 *(978-1-933337-18-0(4))* State Hse. Pr.

Lucero, Thomas L. & Steele, Thomas J. Religious Architecture in Hispano New Mexico. 2009. pap. 15.95 *(978-1-890689-40-7(8)*, Rio Grande Bks.) LPD Pr.

Mavromatis, Kally. Akron Churches: Early Architecture. 2008. (Images of America Ser.). (ENG., Illus.). 128p. pap. 19.99 *(978-0-7385-5202-6(X))* Arcadia Publishing.

Morgan, William. American Country Churches. 2006. (ENG., Illus.). 240p. 19.98 *(978-0-8109-8254-3(4))* Abrams.

Nicholson, Gary. Building Momentum. 2010. (Illus.). 224p. *(978-1-4158-6883-6(2))* LifeWay Christian Resources.

Nolan, Charles E. Splendors of Faith: New Orleans Catholic Churches, 1727-1930. 2010. (Illus.). 144p. 39.95 *(978-0-8071-3682-9(4))* Louisiana State Univ. Pr.

Pace, Sherry. Historic Churches of Mississippi. 2007. (ENG., Illus.). 178p. 40.00 *(978-1-57806-940-8(8))* Univ. Pr. of Mississippi.

Piguet-Panayatova, Dora. The Georgian Churches of Oski & Iskhani: Architecture & Ornament. 2013. (ENG., Illus.). 260p. (C). 240.00 *(978-1-899828-91-3(5))* Pindar Pr. GBR. Dist: Brown, David Bk. Co., The.

Valleriano, Anthony J. Dedication: The Work of William P. Ginther, Ecclesiastical Architect. 2011. (Sacred Landmarks Ser.). 39.00 *(978-1-60635-103-1(6))* Kent State Univ. Pr.

Wilkins, David G., ed. A Reflection of Faith: Saint Paul Cathedral, 1906-2006. 2007. (Illus.). 108p. per. 40.00 *(978-0-615-15404-6(2))* St. Paul Cathedral.

CHURCH ATTENDANCE

see also Public Worship

Bickel, Bruce & Jantz, Stan. Bruce & Stan's Pocket Guide to Going to Church: A User-Friendly Approach. Date not set. 120p. 6.99 *(978-0-7369-0247-2(3))* Harvest Hse. Pubs.

Cooper, Scott. I Don't Want to Go to Church! Practical Ways to Deal with Kids & Religion, Whether You're Religious or Not. 2006. 108p. per. 12.95 *(978-0-8091-4398-6(4)*, 4398-4) Paulist Pr.

Cruchley-Jones, Peter, ed. God at Ground Level: Reappraising Church Decline in the UK Through the Experience of Grass Roots Communities & Situations. 2007. 132p. pap. 32.95 *(978-3-631-57494-2(0))* Lang, Peter Publishing, Inc.

Dabrowski, Duane W. The Motivated Christian: in Search of the Right Church. 2007. 140p. per. 24.95 *(978-1-4241-7919-0(X))* PublishAmerica, Inc.

Duin, Julia. Quitting Church: Why the Faithful Are Fleeing & What to Do about It. 2008. *(978-0-8010-1322-5(4))* Baker Bks.

—Quitting Church: Why the Faithful are Fleeing & What to Do about It, 1 vol. 2009. 192p. pap. 12.99 *(978-0-8010-7227-7(1))* Baker Bks.

Gill, Robin. Myth of the Empty Church. 20.00 *(978-0-687-85835-4(6))* Abingdon Pr.

Hays, Edward. Letters to Exodus Christians: Comfort & Hope for Those Who Have Trouble Going to Church. 2008. 128p. pap. 11.95 *(978-0-939516-82-7(9)*, Forest of Peace Publishing) Ave Maria Pr.

Jones, Ian. The Local Church & Generational Change in Birmingham, 1945-2000. 2012. (Royal Historical Society Studies in History New Ser.: Volume 84). (Illus.). 208p. 80.00 ***(978-0-86193-317-4(6))*** Royal Historical Society GBR. Dist: Boydell & Brewer, Inc.

Justice, William G. Seven Deadly Sins of Dying Churches. 2009. 128p. pap. 13.95 *(978-1-4401-4628-2(4))* iUniverse, Inc.

Latkovich, Sallie. When Your Adult Children Don't Go to Mass. 2011. 24p. pap. 1.50 ***(978-0-7648-1990-2(9))*** Liguori Pubns.

Mast, Gerald J. Go to Church, Change the World: Christian Community As Calling. 2011. pap. ***(978-0-8361-9564-4(7))*** Herald Pr.

McIntosh, Gary L. Beyond the First Visit: The Complete Guide to Connecting Guests to Your Church. 2006. (Illus.). 192p. pap. 15.99 *(978-0-8010-9184-1(5))* Baker Bks.

McLarty, John. I Love It! Why I Highly Recommend God. 2010. *(978-0-8280-2379-5(4))* Review & Herald Publishing Assn.

Murrow, David. Why Men Hate Going to Church. 2011. 256p. pap. 15.99 *(978-0-7852-3215-5(X))* Nelson, Thomas Inc.

Noll, Mark A. What Ever Happened to Christian Canada. 2007. (ENG.). 60p. per. *(978-1-57383-405-6(X)*, Regent College Publishing) Regent College Publishing.

Pritchard. How to Go to Church. 2009. (Illus.). viii, 120p. pap. *(978-0-281-05810-5(5))* SPCK Publishing.

Saunders, Stan. Permission Granted: Liberation & Motivation for Spectator Churchgoers. 2011. pap. 10.99 *(978-1-61739-931-2(0))* Tate Publishing & Enterprises, LLC.

Sawler, David. Before They Say Goodbye. 2011. 256p. pap. ***(978-1-77069-293-0(2))*** Word Alive Pr.

Schroeder, Gordon H. The New Member's Guide. rev. ed. 16p. 4.00 *(978-0-8170-1436-0(5))* Judson Pr.

Standish, Colin D. & Standish, Russell R. Why Members Leave the Seventh-day Adventist Church. 2007. (ENG.). 256p. per. 15.95 *(978-0-923309-70-1(5))* Hartland Pubns.

Thiel, Jr. Eternity in Twelve Chapters. 2008. 168p. pap. 15.99 *(978-1-60647-310-8(7))* Xulon Pr., Inc.

Walser, Ron. The Bible Fix: Fixing God's Word to Match the Wisdom of Modern Man. 2010. 100p. pap. 11.95 *(978-1-4497-0337-0(2)*, WestBow Pr.) Author Solutions, Inc.

Woolever, Cynthia & Bruce, Deborah. A Field Guide to U. S. Congregations: Who's Going Where & Why. 2nd ed. 2010. (ENG., Illus.). 144p. pap. 20.00 *(978-0-664-23514-7(X))* Westminster John Knox Pr.

Yates, George L. Reaching the Summit. 2012. pap. ***(978-1-55452-825-7(9))*** Essence Publishing.

CHURCH BELLS

see Bells

CHURCH BENEFICES

see Benefices, Ecclesiastical

CHURCH BIOGRAPHY

see Christian Biography

CHURCH BUILDINGS

see also Baptisteries; Cathedrals; Cave Churches; Chapels; Church Architecture also names of individual churches.

Adler, Gerald. Robert Maguire & Keith Murray. 2012. (Twentieth-Century Architects Ser.). (ENG., Illus.). 160p. (C). pap. 40.00 *(978-1-85946-165-5(4))* English Heritage GBR. Dist: Brown, David Bk. Co., The.

Benes, Peter. Meetinghouses of Early New England. 2012. (ENG., Illus.). 512p. 49.95 ***(978-1-55849-910-2(5))*** Univ. of Massachusetts Pr.

Block, Elaine C. & Billiet, F., eds. Lexicon of Medieval Choir Stalls. 2011. (Profane Arts of the Middle Ages Ser.). (ENG.). 225p. (C). 103.00 *(978-2-503-51512-0(6))* Brepols Pubs. BEL. Dist: Brown, David Bk. Co., The.

Caver, Howard. Unhandcuffing God II. 2007. 88p. per. 12.99 *(978-0-9800663-0-2(1))* IFG Group.

Cirillo, Ettore & Martellotta, Francesco. Worship, Acoustics, & Architecture. 2007. (Illus.). 210p. per. 69.00 *(978-0-906522-44-8(7))* Multi Science Publishing Co., Ltd. GBR. Dist: Independent Pubs. Group.

Cittadino, Faye & Cittadino, Frank. Clinton & the Town of Kirkland. 2012. (Images of America Ser.). (ENG., Illus.). 128p. pap. 21.99 ***(978-0-7385-7680-0(8))*** Arcadia Publishing.

Curtin, Ralph D. Sharing Your Church Building. 2006. 186p. pap. 22.00 *(978-1-59752-916-7(8)*, Wipf and Stock) Wipf & Stock Pubs.

Drake, Terrance S. Temple Worship Simplified. 2009. pap. 8.99 *(978-1-59955-332-0(5))* Cedar Fort, Inc./CFI Distribution.

Dyas, Dee, ed. The English Parish Church through the Centuries: Daily Life & Spirituality, Art & Architecture, Literature & Music. 2010. (ENG., Illus.). (C). 29.95 *(978-0-9550673-2-7(4))* Christianity and Culture Project GBR. Dist: Brown, David Bk. Co., The.

Edwards, Nancy. He BArchaeology of the Early Medieval Celtic Churches. 2009. (Society for medieval archaeology Monographs). (ENG., Illus.). 424p. (C). 95.00 *(978-1-906540-61-6(6))* Maney Publishing GBR. Dist: Brown, David Bk. Co., The.

Elisha, Omri. Moral Ambition: Mobilization & Social Outreach in Evangelical Megachurches. 2011. (Anthropology of Christianity Ser.). (ENG.). 251p. 60.00 *(978-0-520-26750-3(8))*; pap. 24.95 *(978-0-520-26751-0(6))* Univ. of California Pr.

Finding, John E. Louisville's Crescent Hill. 2012. (Images of America Ser.). (ENG., Illus.). 128p. pap. 21.99 ***(978-0-7385-9215-2(3))*** Arcadia Publishing.

Finger, Reta Halteman. Roman House Churches for Today: A Practical Guide for Small Groups. 2nd ed. 2007. 207p. per. 15.00 *(978-0-8028-0764-9(X))* Eerdmans, William B. Publishing Co.

GuideOne Center for Risk Management Staff, contrib. by. The Missing Ministry: Safety, Risk Management, & Protecting Your Church. 2008. 192p. pap. 17.99 *(978-0-7644-3679-6(1))* Group Publishing, Inc.

Healy, James E. Building a New Church: A Process Manual for Pastors & Lay Leaders. 2009. pap. 18.95 *(978-0-8146-3269-7(6))* Liturgical Pr.

Lerner Jaccarino, Pamela, ed. Honor: Uriah P. Levy Center & Jewish Chapel. 2008. (ENG., Illus.). 148p. 49.95 *(978-0-9764713-9-4(6))* Sandow Media.

Lukings, Tim. Fruit Loose & Fancy Tree. 2009. 188p. pap. 14.99 *(978-1-60791-600-0(2))* Xulon Pr., Inc.

Luo, Zhewen & Chai, Fushan. Zhonghua Ming Si Da Guan. 2008. (Illus.). xii, 420p. *(978-7-111-23793-8(5))* China Machine-Building Industry Pr.

Marín, Eva. Converted Churches. 2008. (DUT, FRE & ENG., Illus.). 216p. *(978-90-76886-44-2(X))* Tectum B.V.B.A.

McAlpine, William R. Sacred Space for the Missional Church: Engaging Culture through the Built Environment. 2011. 222p. pap. 24.00 *(978-1-60899-468-7(6)*, Wipf and Stock) Wipf & Stock Pubs.

Paulson, Steve, et al. Church Signs Across America. 2009. (ENG., Illus.). 176p. (gr. 12-18). 14.95 *(978-1-59020-216-6(3))* Overlook Pr., The.

Pringle, Denys. The Churches of the Crusader Kingdom of Jerusalem: A Corpus: Volume 1, A-K (excluding Acre & Jerusalem) 2008. (Churches of the Crusader Kingdom of Jerusalem Ser.). (ENG., Illus.). 360p. pap. 48.00 *(978-0-521-07295-3(6))* Cambridge Univ. Pr.

—The Churches of the Crusader Kingdom of Jerusalem: A Corpus: Volume 2, L-Z (excluding Tyre) 2009. (Churches of the Crusader Kingdom of Jerusalem Ser.). (ENG., Illus.). 484p. pap. 58.00 *(978-0-521-10983-3(3))* Cambridge Univ. Pr.

—The Churches of the Crusader Kingdom of Jerusalem: Volume 3, the City of Jerusalem: A Corpus. 2010. (Churches of the Crusader Kingdom of Jerusalem Ser.). (ENG.). 534p. pap. 65.00 *(978-0-521-17283-7(7))* Cambridge Univ. Pr.

—A Corpus Vol. 1-3: The Cities of Acre & Tyre with Addenda & Corrigenda, 4 vols. 2009. (Churches of the Crusader Kingdom of Jerusalem Ser.). (ENG., Illus.). 340p. 205.00 *(978-0-521-85148-0(3))* Cambridge Univ. Pr.

Rose, M. Ugly as Sin. 2009. (Illus.). 256p. pap. 18.95 *(978-1-933184-44-9(2))* Sophia Institute Pr.

Rose, Michael S. Ugly as Sin. 2009. (Forthright Edition Ser.). (Illus.). 256p. pap. 18.95 *(978-1-928832-36-2(9))* Sophia Institute Pr.

The Seven Churches. 36p. (Orig.). pap. 0.95 *(978-0-937408-20-9(4))* GMI Pubns.

Stavtsov, Boris Sergeevich & Rakhmanov, Nikolai Nikolaevich. Riazan: Istoriia, Kultura, Pravoslavie. 2008. (Illus.). 191p. *(978-5-900384-12-2(8))* Delo, Izdatel'stvo.

Sundt, Richard. Whare Karakia: Maori Church Building, Decoration & Ritual in Aotearoa New Zealand, 1834-1863. 2010. (ENG., Illus.). 240p. 49.95 *(978-1-86940-456-7(4))* Auckland Univ. Pr. NZL. Dist: Independent Pubs. Group.

Trebilco, Paul. The Early Christians in Ephesus from Paul to Ignatius. 2007. 826p. per. 85.00 *(978-0-8028-0769-4(0))* Eerdmans, William B. Publishing Co.

Tye, Karen. Christian Education in the Small Membership Church. 2008. (Ministry in the Small Membership Church Ser.). 110p. pap. 15.00 *(978-0-687-65099-6(2))* Abingdon Pr.

Wallace, Robin Knowles. Worshiping in the Small Membership Church. 2008. (Ministry in the Small Membership Church Ser.). 118p. per. 13.00 *(978-0-687-65101-6(8))* Abingdon Pr.

White, Richard C. Building for Ministry: The Book That Will Save Your Church 1,000's of Dollars. 2008. 116p. pap. 18.50 *(978-1-4389-0999-8(3))* AuthorHouse.

Wilkinson, John. From Synagogue to Church: The Traditional Design. 2010. (ENG.). 304p. pap. 39.95 ***(978-0-415-59265-9(8))*** Routledge.

Wooding, Jonathan. The Churches & Chapels of Wales. Yates, Nigel, ed. 2011. (ENG., Illus.). 228p. pap. 25.00 *(978-0-7083-2118-8(6))* Univ. of Wales Pr. GBR. Dist: Chicago Distribution Ctr.

Zdero, Rad. Nexus: The World House Church Movement Reader. 2007. *(978-0-87808-374-9(X))* Carey, William Library Pubs.

CHURCH BUILDINGS—MAINTENANCE AND REPAIR

see Church Maintenance and Repair

CHURCH BUILDINGS—AFRICA

Adams, William Y. The Churches of Nobadia, 2 vols. 2009. (Bar S Ser.). (ENG., Illus.). 292p. (C). pap. 177.50 *(978-1-4073-0536-3(0))* British Archaeological Reports Ltd. GBR. Dist: Brown, David Bk. Co., The.

Burton, Michael C. Deep Roots: The African/Black Contribution to Christianity. 2008. 124p. pap. 10.95 *(978-1-4401-0323-0(2))* iUniverse, Inc.

Mercier, Jacques & Lepage, Claude. Lalibela: Christian Art of Ethiopia, the Monolithic Churches & Their Treasures. 2012. (ENG., Illus.). 320p. (C). 60.00 *(978-1-907372-19-3(9))* Holberton, Paul Publishing GBR. Dist: Univ. of Washington Pr.

Phillipson, David W. Ancient Churches of Ethiopia. 2009. (ENG., Illus.). 288p. 65.00 *(978-0-300-14156-6(4))* Yale Univ. Pr.

Sears, Gareth. Late Roman African Urbanism: Continuity & Transformation in the City. 2007. (Bar S Ser.). (ENG., Illus.). 171p. (C). pap. 87.50 *(978-1-4073-0131-0(4))* British Archaeological Reports Ltd. GBR. Dist: Brown, David Bk. Co., The.

CHURCH BUILDINGS—ASIA

Pratsch, Thomas, ed. Konflikt und Bewältigung: Die Zerstörung der Grabeskirche Zu Jerusalem Im Jahre 1009. 2011. (Millennium-Studien / Millennium Studies). (GER., Illus.). XIII, 373p. 140.00 ***(978-3-11-025351-1(8))*** De Gruyter, Walter Inc.

Vigo, Graziella, photos by. Armenia: The Holy Land - The Cradle of Christianity. 2010. (ARM, RUS, ITA, FRE & ENG., Illus.). 240p. 85.00 *(978-88-572-0410-9(3))* Skira Editore ITA. Dist: Random Hse., Inc.

CHURCH BUILDINGS—CANADA

Richardson, Peter & Richardson, Douglas. Canadian Churches: An Architectural History. 2007. (ENG., Illus.). 440p. 85.00 *(978-1-55407-239-2(5))* Firefly Bks., Ltd.

CHURCH BUILDINGS—EGYPT

Gabra, Gawdat & Van Loon, Gertrud J. M. The Churches of Egypt: From the Journey of the Holy Family to the Present Day. Ludwig, Carolyn, ed. 2007. (ENG., Illus.). 368p. 59.95 *(978-977-416-106-3(8))* American Univ. in Cairo Pr. EGY. Dist: Oxford Univ. Pr., Inc.

CHURCH BUILDINGS—EUROPE

Coster, Will & Spicer, Andrew, eds. Sacred Space in Early Modern Europe. 2011. (ENG.). 364p. pap. 45.00 *(978-0-521-20319-7(8))* Cambridge Univ. Pr.

Hayes, Dawn Marie. Body & Sacred Place in Medieval Europe, 1100-1389. 2009. 39.95 *(978-0-415-80352-6(7))* Routledge.

Jenkins, D. 'Holy, Holier, Holiest' The Sacred Topography of the Early Medieval Church. 2010. (Studia Traditionis Theologiae Ser.). (ENG.). 216p. (C). pap. 102.00 *(978-2-503-53316-2(7))* Brepols Pubs. BEL. Dist: ISD.

Jetsonen, Jari & Jetsonen, Sirkkaliisa. Sacral Space: Modern Finnish Churches. 2008. (ENG.). 144p. pap. 69.00 *(978-951-682-731-8(4))* Rakennustieto oy FIN. Dist: Independent Pubs. Group.

Juckes, Tim. St. Elizabeth's in Kosice: Town, Court & Church Building in Late Medieval Hungary. 2012. (Architectura Medii Aevi Ser.). (ENG., Illus.). 320p. (C). pap. 123.00 *(978-2-503-53109-0(1))* Brepols Pubs. BEL. Dist: ISD.

Makrides, Vasilios. Hellenic Temples & Christian Churches: A Concise History of the Religious Cultures of Greece from Antiquity to the Present. 2009. (ENG., Illus.). 360p. 48.00 *(978-0-8147-9568-2(4))* New York Univ. Pr.

McKasey, John. Ancient Chapels & Churches in Wales. 2007. (ENG., Illus.). 72p. pap. 11.95 *(978-0-86243-665-0(6)*, Virago Press) Y Lolfa GBR. Dist: Dufour Editions, Inc.

McNeill, Tom. Faith, Pride & Works: Medieval Church Building. 2006. (ENG., Illus.). 272p. per. 39.95 *(978-0-7524-3643-2(0))* History Pr. Ltd.,The GBR. Dist: Independent Pubs. Group.

Paces, Cynthia. Prague Panoramas: National Memory & Sacred Space in the Twentieth Century. 2009. (Pitt Russian East European Ser.). (ENG.). 352p. (C). pap. 27.95 *(978-0-8229-6035-5(4))*; (Illus.). 65.00 *(978-0-8229-4375-4(1))* Univ. of Pittsburgh Pr.

Puig, Jordi & Pla Boada, Ricard. Gaudi in the Cathedral of Mallorca, 1 vol. Vivas, Pere, ed. 2008. (ENG., Illus.). 144p. pap. 16.95 *(978-84-8478-148-6(8))* Triangle Postals, S.L. ESP. Dist: Innovative Logistics.

Puzovic, Predrag. Srpska Patrijarsija: Istorija Srpske Pravoslavne Crkve. 2009. (Illus.). 632p. *(978-86-83903-35-1(4))* Pravoslavna rec, Izdavacko preduzece.

Spicer, Andrew. Calvinist Churches in Early Modern Europe. 2008. (Studies in Early Modern European History Ser.). (ENG., Illus.). 304p. 89.00 *(978-0-7190-5487-7(7))* Manchester Univ. Pr. GBR. Dist: Macmillan.

Trio, Paul & de Smet, Marjan, eds. Use & Abuse of Sacred Places in Late Medieval Towns. 2006. (Mediaevalia Lovaniensia, Series I: Vol. 38). (Illus.). 264p. per. 43.95 *(978-90-5867-519-4(X))* Leuven Univ. Pr. BEL. Dist: Cornell Univ. Pr.

Yates, Nigel. Liturgical Space: Christian Worship & Church Buildings in Western Europe 1500-2000. 2008. (Liturgy, Worship & Society Ser.). (Illus.). 212p. 99.95 *(978-0-7546-5795-8(7))*; pap. 39.95 *(978-0-7546-5797-2(3))* Ashgate Publishing Co.

CHURCH BUILDINGS—FRANCE

Dufour, Jean. Le chartrier de la collegiale de Saint-Martin de Champeaux. 2009. (Hautes Etudes medievales et Modernes Ser.). (FRE., Illus.). 448p. (C). pap. 119.00 *(978-2-600-01348-2(2))* Droz, Librairie CHE. Dist: Brown, David Bk. Co., The.

Maxwell, Robert A. The Art of Medieval Urbanism: Parthenay in Romanesque Aquitaine. 2008. (ENG., Illus.). 360p. 90.00 *(978-0-271-02956-6(0))* Pennsylvania State Univ. Pr.

CHURCH BUILDINGS—GERMANY

Kappel, Kai. Dachau Concentration Camp Memorial Site: Religious Memorials. 2010. (ENG.). 96p. pap. 10.00 *(978-3-422-02238-6(4))* Deutscher Kunstverlag GmbH DEU. Dist: Independent Pubs. Group.

Overesch, Manfred. Himmlisches Jerusalem in Hildesheim: St. Michael und das Geheimnis der sakralen Mathematik vor 1000 Jahren. 2009. (GER., Illus.). 332p. (C). 41.00 *(978-3-525-55004-5(9))* Vandenhoeck & Ruprecht GmbH & Co. KG DEU. Dist: ISD.

Verstegen, Ute. Ausgrabungen und Bauforschungen in St. Gereon zu Köln. 2006. (Kölner Forschungen Ser.). (Illus.). 1023p. 153.00 *(978-3-8053-3352-8(8))* Zabern, Philipp von Verlag, GmbH DEU. Dist: Brown, David Bk. Co., The.

CHURCH BUILDINGS—GREAT BRITAIN

AA Publishing. Exploring Britain's Churches & Chapels: Inspirational Journeys of Discovery. 2011. (ENG., Illus.). 256p. 39.95 ***(978-0-7495-7074-3(1))*** Automobile Assn. GBR. Dist: Independent Pubs. Group.

Adams, Paul, et al. Shadows in the Nave: A Guide to the Haunted Church of England. 2011. (ENG., Illus.). 160p. pap. 24.95 ***(978-0-7524-5920-2(1))*** History Pr. Ltd.,The GBR. Dist: Independent Pubs. Group.

Allen, J. R. L. Building a Victorian Country Church: An Historical Archaeology of St. Mary the Virgin, Stratfield Mortimer, Berkshire. 2007. (Bar Ser.). (Illus.). 140p. (C). 77.50 *(978-1-4073-0262-1(0))* British Archaeological Reports Ltd. GBR. Dist: Brown, David Bk. Co., The.

—Late Churches & Chapels in Berkshire: A Geological Perspective from the Late Eighteenth Century to the First World War. 2007. (Bar S Ser.). (Illus.). 162p. (C). 90.00 *(978-1-4073-0037-5(7))* British Archaeological Reports Ltd. GBR. Dist: Brown, David Bk. Co., The.

Andrews, William. Curious Church Gleanings. 2009. 290p. 30.99 *(978-1-113-67489-C(X))*; 290p. pap. 28.75 *(978-1-113-67486-9(5))*; 290p. pap. 27.75 *(978-1-113-67485-2(7))*; 292p. 24.99 *(978-1-103-19224-3(8))*; 292p. pap. 18.99 *(978-1-103-19223-6(X))* BiblioBazaar.

—Curious Church Gleanings. 2010. 108p. pap. *(978-1-152-01600-2(8))* Books LLC.

—Curious Church Gleanings. 2008. 296p. pap. *(978-1-4097-1180-3(3))* Read Bks.

Andrews, William, ed. Curious Church Gleanings. 2007. (ENG.). 300p. 43.95 *(978-0-548-08700-8(8))* Kessinger Publishing, LLC.

Barr, Andrew. Song of Praise: The Nations Favourite Churches. 2006. (ENG., Illus.). 128p. 24.95 *(978-0-7459-5220-8(8))*, Lion) Lion Hudson PLC GBR. Dist: Independent Pubs. Group.

Berg, Mary & Jones, Howard. Norman Churches in the Canterbury Diocese. 2009. (ENG., Illus.). 208p. pap. 39.95 *(978-0-7524-4776-6(9))* History Pr. Ltd.,The GBR. Dist: Independent Pubs. Group.

Betjeman, John & Surman, Richard. Betjeman's Best British Churches. 2011. (ENG., Illus.). 896p. 55.00 ***(978-0-00-741567-0(2))*** HarperCollins Pubs. Ltd. GBR. Dist: Independent Pubs. Group.

Billett, Michael. English Thatched Churches. (ENG., Illus.). 256p. 2009. pap. 19.95 *(978-0-7090-8907-0(4))* 2007. 60.00 ***(978-0-7090-7985-9(0))*** Hale, Robert Ltd. GBR. Dist: Independent Pubs. Group.

Butler, Lawrence, ed. The Yorkshire Church Notes of Sir Stephen Glynne (1825-1874) 2007. (Yorkshire Archaeological Soc Record Ser.: Volume 159). (Illus.). 560p. 50.00 *(978-1-903564-80-6(8))* Yorkshire Archaeological Society GBR. Dist: Boydell & Brewer, Inc.

Caponigro, Paul, photos by. Stone Churches of Ireland. 2007. pap. 24.95 *(978-1-888899-39-9(5))*; 100.00 ***(978-1-888899-40-5(9))*** Lodima Pr.

Carroll, Lewis, pseud. The New Belfry of Christ Church, Oxford. reprint ed. lib. bdg. 98.00 *(978-0-7426-2275-3(4))* Classic Bks.

Cole, R. E. G., ed. Lincolnshire Church Notes Made by Gervase Holles, AD 1634-1642. 2010. (Publications of the Lincoln Record Society Ser.: Volume 1). (LAT & ENG., Illus.). 297p. 45.00 *(978-0-901503-90-9(8))* Lincoln Record Society GBR. Dist: Boydell & Brewer, Inc.

Hamilton Thompson, A. The Historical Growth of the English Parish Church. 2nd rev. ed. 2012. (ENG.). 156p. pap. 19.99 ***(978-1-107-60578-7(4))*** Cambridge Univ. Pr.

Harris, Brian L. Harris's Guide to Churches & Cathedrals: Discovering the Unique & Unusual in over 500 Churches & Cathedrals. 2007. (ENG., Illus.). 512p. 45.00 *(978-0-09-191251-2(2))* Random Hse. GBR. Dist: Independent Pubs. Group.

Hart, Stephen. Medieval Church Window Tracery in England. 2010. (Illus.). 184p. 80.00 *(978-1-84383-533-2(9)*, Boydell Press) Boydell & Brewer, Ltd. GBR. Dist: Boydell & Brewer, Inc.

Horsler, Val. Shakespeare's Church. 2010. (ENG., Illus.). 160p. 40.00 *(978-1-906507-33-6(3)*, Third Millenium Pub Ltd) Antique Collectors' Club GBR. Dist: National Bk. Network.

Hume, John R. 1000 Churches to Visit in Scotland. 2006. (ENG., Illus.). 480p. pap. 14.95 *(978-1-905267-00-2(2))* NMS Enterprises Ltd. - Publishing GBR. Dist: National Bk. Network.

Humphrey, Stephen & Morris, James. Churches & Cathedrals of London. 2nd ed. 2007. (ENG., Illus.). 160p. per. 24.95 *(978-1-84537-337-5(5))* New Holland Pubs., Ltd. GBR. Dist: National Bk. Network.

Jeffery, Paul. City Churches of Sir Christopher Wren. 2007. (ENG., Illus.). 408p. per. 39.95 *(978-1-84725-014-8(9)*, Hambledon Continuum) Continuum International Publishing Group, Ltd. GBR. Dist: National Bk. Network.

Johnson, Walter. Byways in British Archaeology. 2011. (ENG.). 542p. pap. 39.99 ***(978-0-521-22877-0(8))*** Cambridge Univ. Pr.

Kinross, John. Discovering the Smallest Churches in Scotland. 2011. (ENG., Illus.). 128p. pap. 23.95 *(978-0-7524-5880-9(9))* History Pr. Ltd.,The GBR. Dist: Independent Pubs. Group.

Leonard, John. London's Parish Churches. 2011. (ENG., Illus.). 352p. (C). 80.00 ***(978-1-904965-33-6(4))*** Spire Bks. Ltd. GBR. Dist: Brown, David Bk. Co., The.

Martin, Christopher. A Glimpse of Heaven: Catholic Churches of England & Wales. 2010. (ENG., Illus.). 224p. (C). pap. 40.00 *(978-1-905624-62-1(X))* English Heritage GBR. Dist: Brown, David Bk. Co., The.

Maude, Thomas. Guided by a Stone-Mason: Exploring the Cathedrals, Abbeys & Churches of Britain. 2011. (ENG., Illus.). 176p. pap. 17.00 *(978-1-84885-547-2(8)*, Tauris Parke Paperbacks) I. B. Tauris & Co., Ltd. GBR. Dist: Macmillan.

Miles, Adrian, et al. Burial at the Site of the Parish Church of St Benet Sherehog Before & after the Great Fire: Excavations at 1 Poultry, City of London. 2008. (MoLAS Monograph Ser.). (Illus.). 112p. (C). 26.00 *(978-1-901992-75-5(6))* Museum of London Archaeology Service GBR. Dist: Brown, David Bk. Co., The.

Millar, Stephen. London's City Churches. (ENG., Illus.). 2011. 224p. pap. 14.95 ***(978-1-902910-41-3(9))*** 2006. 200p. pap. 13.95 *(978-1-902910-24-6(9))* Metro Pubns. GBR. Dist: Independent Pubs. Group.

Mortlock, D. P. Guide to Suffolk Churches. 2009. (Popular Guide Ser.). (ENG., Illus.). 392p. pap. 64.00 *(978-0-7188-3076-2(8))* Lutherworth Pr., The GBR. Dist: Brown, David Bk. Co., The.

Mortlock, D. P. & Roberts, C. V. The Guide to Norfolk Churches. 2nd ed. 2007. (Popular Guide Ser.). (ENG., Illus.). 392p. pap. 58.00 *(978-0-7188-3064-9(4))* Lutherworth Pr., The GBR. Dist: Brown, David Bk. Co., The.

O'Brien, Caimin & Williams, Mary Ann. Stories from a Sacred Landscape: Croghan Hill to Clonmacnoise. 2006. (ENG., Illus.). 244p. 63.95 *(978-1-85635-489-9(X))* Mercier Pr., Ltd., The IRL. Dist: Dufour Editions, Inc.

O'Donoghue, Rod E. L. Medieval Stained Glass in Suffolk Churches: Let the Stained Glass Speak. 2009. (Illus.). 280p. pap. 67.99 *(978-1-4389-8955-6(5))* AuthorHouse.

Pevsner, Nikolaus. Buildings of England, City of London, Churches. 2nd abr. ed. (Illus.). 160p. pap. 19.95 *(978-0-14-071100-4(7))* Penguin Bks., Ltd. GBR. Dist: Trafalgar Square Publishing.

Reeve, Matthew M. Thirteenth-Century Wall Painting of Salisbury Cathedral: Art, Liturgy, & Reform. 2008. (Illus.). 230p. 80.00 *(978-1-84383-331-4(X)*, Boydell Press) Boydell & Brewer, Ltd. GBR. Dist: Boydell & Brewer, Inc.

Rock, Hugh. Church Clocks. 2009. (Shire Library). (ENG., Illus.). 64p. pap. 12.95 *(978-0-7478-0687-5(X))* Shire Pubns., Ltd. GBR. Dist: Random Hse., Inc.

Sharpe, Geoffrey R. & Sharpe, Geoff. Historic English Churches: A Guide to Their Construction, Design & Features. 2011. (ENG., Illus.). 288p. 85.00 *(978-1-84885-807-7(6))*; pap. 25.00 *(978-1-84885-189-4(8))* I. B. Tauris & Co., Ltd. GBR. Dist: Macmillan.

Surman, Richard. Dog Collar: Inspiring Stories of Clergy & Their Dogs. 2007. (ENG., Illus.). 96p. 19.95 *(978-0-00-724164-4(X))* HarperCollins Pubs. Ltd. GBR. Dist: Independent Pubs. Group.

Tatton-Brown, Tim & Crook, John. The English Church. 2006. (ENG., Illus.). 240p. 60.00 *(978-1-84330-965-9(3))* New Holland Pubs., Ltd. GBR. Dist: National Bk. Network.

Wood-Legh, K. L. Perpetual Chantries in Britain. 2008. (ENG.). 376p. pap. 48.00 *(978-0-521-08957-9(3))* Cambridge Univ. Pr.

Yelton, Michael & Salmon, John. Anglican Church-Building in London 1915-1945. 2007. (Illus.). 250p. (C). *(978-1-904965-14-5(8))* Spire Bks. Ltd.

CHURCH BUILDINGS—ITALY

Guido, Sante & Mantella, Guiseppe, eds. Storie di Restauri Nella Chiesa Conventuale di San Giovanni Battista a la Valletta. 2008. (ITA., Illus.). 492p. (C). 285.00 *(978-99932-7-202-1(7))* Midsea Bks. Ltd. MLT. Dist: Brown, David Bk. Co., The.

Howard, Deborah & Moretti, Laura. Sound & Space in Renaissance Venice: Architecture, Music, Acoustics. 2010. (Illus.). 256p. 55.00 *(978-0-300-14874-9(7))* Yale Univ. Pr.

Tylenda, Joseph N. The Pilgrim's Guide to Rome's Principal Churches. 2010. (Illus.). xvi, 425p. *(978-1-892331-78-6(0))* Angelus Pr.

Valandro, Marie-Laure. Letters from Florence: Observations on the Inner Art of Travel. 2010. (Illus.). 174p. pap. 20.00 *(978-1-58420-082-6(0)*, Lindisfarne Bks.) SteinerBooks, Inc.

Vichi, Marco. Pellegrinaggio in Città: Uno Scrittore Racconta il Suo Viaggio Nell'anima Di Firenze. 2010. (non Guide Ser.). (ITA.). 176p. (C). pap. 20.00 *(978-88-564-0107-3(X))* Polistampa ITA. Dist: Brown, David Bk. Co., The.

CHURCH BUILDINGS—MEXICO

Giffords, Gloria Fraser. Sanctuaries of Earth, Stone, & Light: The Churches of Northern New Spain, 1530-1821. 2007. (Southwest Center Ser.). (ENG., Illus.). 480p. 75.00 *(978-0-8165-2589-8(7))* Univ. of Arizona Pr.

CHURCH BUILDINGS—PALESTINE

McCormick, Michael. Charlemagne's Survey of the Holy Land: Wealth, Personnel, & Buildings of a Mediterranean Church Between Antiquity & the Middle Ages. 2011. (Dumbarton Oaks Medieval Humanities Ser.). (ENG., Illus.). 310p. 39.95 *(978-0-88402-363-0(X))* Dumbarton Oaks.

CHURCH BUILDINGS—ROMANIA

Botár, István, Kövek, Falak, Templomok: Régészeti Kutatások Csík Középkori Templomaiban 2002-2007 Között. 2009. (HUN., Illus.). 110p. *(978-973-665-284-4(X))* Pallas-Akademia.

CHURCH BUILDINGS—TURKEY

Darnault, Sezim Sezer. Latin Catholic Buildings in Istanbul. 2010. 111.20 *(978-1-61719-127-5(2))* Gorgias Pr., LLC.

Yerasimos, Stephane. Constantinople: Istanbul's Historical Heritage. 2008. (Art & Architecture Ser.). (Illus.). 400p. pap. 24.95 *(978-0-8416-0062-1(7))* American Map Corp.

CHURCH BUILDINGS—UNITED STATES

Andrews, Raymond Patterson. Simple Times, Simple Faith. 2007. 162p. pap. 10.00 *(978-0-9789908-2-4(X))* Ketch Publishing.

Benson, James E. Brockton Revisited. 2012. (Images of America Ser.). (ENG., Illus.). 128p. pap. 21.99 ***(978-0-7385-7668-8(9))*** Arcadia Publishing.

Bullard, Duane. Tippah County. 2012. (Images of America Ser.). (ENG., Illus.). 128p. pap. 21.99 ***(978-0-7385-8784-4(2))*** Arcadia Publishing.

Cawthon, Richard J. Lost Churches of Mississippi. 2010. (ENG., Illus.). 240p. 35.00 *(978-1-60473-436-2(1))* Univ. Pr. of Mississippi.

Collum, Maria O. & Krueger, Barbara E. Detroit's Historic Places of Worship. 2012. ***(978-0-8143-3424-9(5))***; E-Book ***(978-0-8143-3811-7(9))*** Wayne State Univ. Pr.

Colonial Churches: A Series of Sketches of Churches in the Original Colony of Virginia. 2007. (ENG.). 386p. 48.95 *(978-0-548-04656-2(5))* Kessinger Publishing, LLC.

Couch, S. Jason. Elkin. 2012. (Images of America Ser.). (ENG., Illus.). 128p. pap. 21.99 ***(978-0-7385-9210-7(2))*** Arcadia Publishing.

Currin, Beverly Madison. The Search for the Lost Rectors: Reflections on the History of Old Christ Church & Pensacola in the Nineteenth Century. 2009. (Illus.). 123p. pap. *(978-0-9798292-2-2(4))* Univ. of West Florida Foundation, Inc.

de Socarras, Christine & The Nockamixon Historical Society. Nockamixon Township. 2012. (Images of America Ser.). (ENG., Illus.). 128p. pap. 21.99 ***(978-0-7385-7392-2(2))*** Arcadia Publishing.

First, Debra. Founded in Faith: Cleveland's Lost Catholic Legacy. 2010. (Illus.). 144p. pap. 19.95 *(978-0-936760-28-5(1))* Cleveland Landmarks Pr., Inc.

Gallery, John Andrew. Sacred Sites of Center City: A Guide to Philadelphia's Historic Churches, Synagogues, & Meetinghouses. 2008. (ENG., Illus.). 28p. pap. 9.95 *(978-1-58988-042-9(0))* Dry, Paul Bks., Inc.

Giffords, Gloria Fraser. Sanctuaries of Earth, Stone, & Light: The Churches of Northern New Spain, 1530-1821. 2007. (Southwest Center Ser.). (ENG., Illus.). 480p. 75.00 *(978-0-8165-2589-8(7))* Univ. of Arizona Pr.

Greenagel, Frank L. A Guide to the Historic Churches of Somerset County, New Jersey. 2006. pap. 24.99 *(978-1-59629-202-4(4))* History Pr., The.

Hamedy, Jim & Hamedy, Jane Diggins. Historic Churches, Synagogues & Spiritual Places of Eastern Maine. 2011. (Illus.). 160p. pap. 19.99 ***(978-1-59629-409-7(4))*** History Pr., The.

Hesperides. Bruton Parish Church. 2007. 212p. per. *(978-1-4067-5624-1(5)*, Hesperides Pr.) Read Bks.

Kearney, Milo & Galan, Francis. San Antonio's Churches. 2012. (Images of America Ser.). (ENG., Illus.). 128p. pap. 21.99 ***(978-0-7385-8536-9(X))*** Arcadia Publishing.

Kerns, Linda C. Faith of Our Fathers: The Churches of Missouri. 2007. *(978-1-57864-457-5(7))* Donning Co. Pubs.

Krentz, Roger F. St. John the Baptist Catholic Church Princeton, Wisconsin. 2010. 112p. pap. 47.96 *(978-0-557-40886-3(5))* Lulu Enterprises Inc.

Krol, Laura V. Deming. 2012. (Images of America Ser.). (ENG., Illus.). 128p. pap. 21.99 ***(978-0-7385-8537-6(8))*** Arcadia Publishing.

Lancaster, Robert A., Jr. Historic Virginia Homes & Churches. (Illus.). 527p. reprint ed. lib. bdg. 98.00 *(978-0-7222-4661-0(7))* Library Reprints, Inc.

LaVor, Marty. The Basilica of the Assumption. 2007. per. 34.95 *(978-0-9632680-4-4(X))* LaVor Group.

Lennon, Nancy. St. Ignatius Parish, Chicago: The First Century. 2007. *(978-1-57864-462-9(3))* Donning Co. Pubs.

LeSieur, Cevan. The Avenues. 2012. (Images of America Ser.). (ENG., Illus.). 128p. pap. 21.99 ***(978-0-7385-8535-2(1))*** Arcadia Publishing.

Levitt, Ellen. The Lost Synagogues of Brooklyn: The Stories Behind How & Why Many Brooklyn Synagogues, Now Old Ex-Shuls, Were Converted to Other Uses, Primarily As Christian Churches. 2009. (Illus.). 196p. pap. 26.00 *(978-1-886223-39-4(4))* Avotaynu, Inc.

Longo, Stephanie. Dunmore. 2012. (Images of America Ser.). (ENG., Illus.). 128p. pap. 21.99 ***(978-0-7385-9228-2(5))*** Arcadia Publishing.

Meek, A. J., photos by. Sacred Light: Holy Places in Louisiana. 2010. (ENG.). 112p. 35.00 *(978-1-60473-741-7(7))* Univ. Pr. of Mississippi.

Miller, David. American Churches. 2008. (Illus.). 255p. 29.99 *(978-0-7858-2220-2(8)*, Chartwell) Book Sales, Inc.

Monadnock Historical Societies Forum, compiled by. Sacred & Secular: Historic Churches & Meetinghouses of the Monadnock Region, 1750-1850. 2006. 10.00 *(978-0-9724478-6-7(5))* Historical Society of Cheshire Cty.

Nolan, Charles E. Splendors of Faith: New Orleans Catholic Churches, 1727-1930. 2010. (Illus.). 144p. 39.95 *(978-0-8071-3682-9(4))* Louisiana State Univ. Pr.

Pace, Sherry. Historic Churches of Mississippi. 2007. (ENG., Illus.). 178p. 40.00 *(978-1-57806-940-8(8))* Univ. Pr. of Mississippi.

Partridge, Nancy Fleming. Around Shabbona. 2012. (Images of America Ser.). (ENG., Illus.). 128p. pap. 21.99 ***(978-0-7385-8867-4(9))*** Arcadia Publishing.

The Philadelphia Church. 27p. (Orig.). pap. 0.95 *(978-0-937408-19-3(0))* GMI Pubns.

Preisler, Julian H. Historic Synagogues of Philadelphia & the Delaware Valley. 2008. 19.99 *(978-1-59629-572-8(4))* History Pr., The.

Prevas, Nicholas M. House of God... Gateway to Heaven: A Centennial History of the Greek Orthodox Cathedral of the Annunciation. 2007. (Illus.). 460p. 60.00 *(978-0-9790235-0-7(5))* Greek Orthodox Cathedral of the Annunciation.

Reiner, Donna J. & Kitson, Jennifer. Phoenixrsquo;s Greater Coronado Neighborhood. 2012. (Images of America Ser.). (ENG., Illus.). 128p. pap. 21.99 ***(978-0-7385-8533-8(5))*** Arcadia Publishing.

Rines, Edward F. Old Historic Churches of America: Their Romantic History & Their Traditions. (Illus.). 373p. reprint ed. lib. bdg. 98.00 *(978-0-7222-0501-3(5))* Library Reprints, Inc.

Sokol, David M. The Noble Room: The Inspired Conception & Tumultuous Creation of Frank Lloyd Wright's Unity Temple. 100th ed. 2008. (Illus.). 181p. 22.95 *(978-0-9789270-3-5(6))* Top Five Bks.

Spence, Roy M. The Amazing Faith of Texas: Common Ground on Higher Ground. 2006. (ENG., Illus.). 160p. 29.95 *(978-0-292-72176-0(5)*, Idea City Pre) GSD&M.

Stebbins Craig, Peter, ed. Colonial Records of the Swedish Churches in Pennsylvania: The Sandel Years, 1702-1719, Vol. 3. 2007. (ENG., Illus.). 320p. lib. bdg. 25.00 *(978-0-9762501-3-5(6))* Swedish Colonial Society.

Taylor, David L. Murder in the House of God! The Curious, Morbid Tale of John W. Beavers. 2008. 84p. pap. 10.00 *(978-0-9639880-3-4(4))* TaylorMade Write.

Taylor, John. Catholics along the Rio Grande. 2011. (Images of America Ser.). (ENG., Illus.). 128p. pap. 21.99 *(978-0-7385-7975-7(0))* Arcadia Publishing.

Tseng, Timothy & Chuck, James. The 2008 Report: Bay Area Chinese Churches Research Project, Phase II. 2009. 276p. pap. 20.00 *(978-0-578-01248-3(0))* ISAAC.

Wainwright, Paul, photos by. A Space for Faith: The Colonial Meetinghouses of New England. 2010. (Illus.). 128p. 35.00 *(978-0-9817898-5-9(4)*, Jetty Hse.) Randall, Peter E. Pub.

Wickersheim, Laurel Michele & LeBaron, Rawlene Briar. Colorado on the Eve of Statehood: An Edited Business Directory of the Pioneers Who Built the Centennial State. 2008. (Illus.). iv, 246p. *(978-0-7884-7314-2(X))* Heritage Bks.

William, Ecenbarger & Susan, Ecenbarger. Glory By The Wayside. 2008. 88p. 29.95 *(978-0-9776139-0-8(9))* Passage Pr., Inc.

Wood, Kenneth J. Marshfield. 2012. (Images of America Ser.). (ENG., Illus.). 128p. pap. 21.99 ***(978-0-7385-8872-8(5))*** Arcadia Publishing.

Worthington, Anne Pepper, ed. Sketches of Original Free Will Baptist Churches: Trinity of Memories, Past, Present, Future. 2007. (Illus.). pap. 5.00 *(978-1-880994-89-4(5))* Mount Olive College Pr.

CHURCH BUILDINGS IN ART

Dubowitz, Dan. Wastelands. 2010. (ENG., Illus.). 176p. 55.00 ***(978-1-904587-83-5(6))*** Lewis, Dewi Publishing GBR. Dist: Consortium Bk. Sales & Distribution.

Hedges, Andrew H., et al. Through the Lens: The Original 1907 Church History Photographs of George Edward Anderson. 2010. 49.99 *(978-1-60641-236-7(1))* Deseret Bk. Co.

Hoskin, Kathy, photos by. The old Church. 2007. (Illus.). 20p. spiral bd. 25.00 *(978-0-615-20528-1(3))* Hoskin, Kathy.

Milugina, E. G. Doroga K Khramu. 2010. (RUS., Illus.). 265p. *(978-5-7793-2021-4(7))* Belyj Gorod.

Vanhaelen, Angela. The Wake of Iconoclasm: Painting the Church in the Dutch Republic. 2012. (ENG.). 240p. ***(978-0-271-05061-4(6))*** Pennsylvania State Univ. Pr.

C

Worthington, Anne Pepper, ed. Sketches of Original Free Will Baptist Churches: Trinity of Memories, Past, Present, Future. 2007. (Illus.). pap. 5.00 *(978-1-880994-89-4(5))* Mount Olive College Pr.

CHURCH BULLETINS

Ellie Claire Staff. Great Is Thy Faithfulness. 2010. (ENG.). 160p. 14.99 *(978-1-935416-81-4(2))* Ellie Claire & Summerside Pr.

Father's Day - Set an Example. l.t. ed. 2007. 5.25 *(978-0-687-08205-6(6))* Abingdon Pr.

Glory to God. 4.50 *(978-0-687-02287-8(8))*; 4.50 *(978-0-687-02317-2(3))*; 4.50 *(978-0-687-02327-1(0))* Abingdon Pr.

Homecoming. 4.50 *(978-0-687-06549-3(6))*; 4.50 *(978-0-687-05192-2(4))*; 5.00 *(978-0-687-05272-1(6))* Abingdon Pr.

Ideals Publications Inc. Staff, creator. Silent Night. 2006. (Pageant of Lights Book Ser.). (ENG., Illus.). 16p. (J). (gr. -1-k). bds. 12.99 *(978-0-8249-6680-5(5),* Candy Cane Pr.) Ideals Pubns.

It Is Well. l.t. ed. 5.00 *(978-0-687-06673-5(5))* Abingdon Pr.

Joy to the World Nativity: Regular. 4.50 *(978-0-687-00641-0(4))* Abingdon Pr.

Love. 2009. (ENG., Illus.). pap. 14.95 *(978-0-615-27188-0(X))* RoyalMan Expressions.

Nativity. 4.50 *(978-0-687-02377-6(7))*; 4.50 *(978-0-687-02485-8(4))*; 4.50 *(978-0-687-02495-7(1))*; 5.00 *(978-0-687-02507-7(9))* Abingdon Pr.

Praise the Lord. 2.00 *(978-0-687-06566-0(6))* Abingdon Pr.

Silent Night. 5.00 *(978-0-687-02309-7(2))* Abingdon Pr.

CHURCH CALENDAR

see also Church History—Chronology; Church Year; Fasts and Feasts; Saints—Calendar

Arbogast, Joan Marie. Feast Days & Holidays. 2012. (ENG.). 160p. spiral bd. 19.95 ***(978-0-8198-2707-4(X))*** Pauline Bks. & Media.

Calendar Unit. (Illus.). 12.95 *(978-0-88396-649-5(2),* Blue Mountain Pr.) Blue Mountain Arts Inc.

Klews, Michael E. Die Herleitung der Osterformeln von Gauß, Butcher & Jones, Meeus sowie Knuth aus dem computus Paschalis: Ein Beitrag zum mathematischen Verständnis des Julianischen und Gregorianischen Lunisolarkalenders. 2008. (GER.). 206p. pap. *(978-3-8325-1923-0(8))* Logos Verlag Berlin.

Kovacs, Charles. The Spiritual Background to Christian Festivals. 2007. 77p. per. *(978-0-86315-601-4(0))* Floris Bks.

Mosshammer, Alden A. The Easter Computus & the Origins of the Christian Era. 2008. (Oxford Early Christian Studies). (ENG., Illus.). 432p. 150.00 *(978-0-19-954312-0(7))* Oxford Univ. Pr., Inc.

Shusterman, Noah. Religion & the Politics of Time: Holidays in France from Louis XIV Through Napoleon. 2010. (ENG.). 74.95 *(978-0-8132-1725-3(3))* Catholic Univ. of America Pr.

Taylor, Roger. Celebrating Christ's Victory. 2009. 144p. pap. 16.95 *(978-0-281-05979-9(9))* SPCK Publishing GBR. Dist: Westminster John Knox Pr.

Tobin, Greg. Holy Holidays! The Catholic Origins of Celebration. 2011. (ENG.). 256p. pap. 16.00 *(978-0-230-10487-7(8))* Palgrave Macmillan.

Viscuso, Patrick. A Quest for Reform of the Orthodox Church: The 1923 Pan-Orthodox Congress: An Analysis & Translation of Its Acts & Decisions. 2007. *(978-1-932401-09-7(1))* InterOrthodox Pr.

Ward, Benedicta. A True Easter: The Synod of Whitby 664 AD. 2008. 22p. pap. *(978-0-7283-0170-2(9))* SLG Pr.

Warntjes, Immo. The Munich Computus - Text & Translation: Irish computistics between Isidore of Seville & the Venerable Bede & its reception in Carolingian Times. 2010. (Sudhoffs Archiv - Beihefte Ser.). (LAT & ENG., Illus.). 402p. (C). 134.00 *(978-3-515-09701-7(5))* Steiner, Franz Verlag Wiesbaden GmbH DEU. Dist: Brown, David Bk. Co., The.

CHURCH CAMPS

Fergeson, Nancy. Training Staff to Be Spiritual Leaders: Activities & Resources for Christian Camps. 2008. (Illus.). 123p. pap. 19.95 *(978-1-58518-665-5(1),* Healthy Learning) Coaches Choice.

Holliday, John F. & Holliday, Richard D. Muskoka Miracles: 80th Anniversary. 2010. 288p. pap. 20.95 *(978-1-4502-5224-9(9))* iUniverse, Inc.

Loughmiller, Lynn & Loughmiller, Campbell. Let's Go Camping: Camping & Christian Growth. 2011. 46p. 35.95 ***(978-1-258-07968-0(2))*** Literary Licensing, LLC.

Mattson, Lloyd & Graendorf, Werner. Introduction to Christian Camping. rev. ed. (Illus.). (C). reprint ed. pap. 7.95 *(978-0-942684-07-0(9))* Wordshed.

CHURCH CHARITIES

see also subdivision Charities under names of religions, religious denominations, etc., e.g. Catholic Church—Charities

Abue, Peter. Participation & Social Learning in Church-Based Organizations - a Third Approach to Poverty Eradication in Developing Countries. 2007. 276p. per. *(978-3-8364-2729-6(X))* VDM Verlag Dr. Mueller e.K.

Atkins, Jimmy Arthur. Serving Communities in Need. 2011. 112p. pap. ***(978-3-8443-9931-8(3))*** Lambert Academic Publishing.

Boddie, Stephanie C. & Cnaan, Ram A. Faith-Based Social Services: Measures, Assessments, & Effectiveness. 2007. (ENG., Illus.). 322p. 175.00 *(978-0-7890-3523-3(5))*; per. 56.95 *(978-0-7890-3524-0(3))* Routledge.

Chastel, Tiennne Louis. The Charity of the Primitive Churches. 2006. 364p. per. 26.99 *(978-1-4255-3787-6(1))* MPublishing.

Cnaan, Ram A. The Other Philadelphia Story: How Local Congregations Support Quality of Life in Urban America. 2006. (City in the Twenty-First Century Ser.). (Illus.). 352p. (C). 69.95 *(978-0-8122-3949-2(0))* Univ. of Pennsylvania Pr.

Colon-Molfulleda, Wanda. Charitable Choice & Faith-Based Organizations. 2010. 132p. pap. *(978-3-639-20452-0(2))* VDM Verlag Dr. Mueller e.K.

Daly, Lew. God's Economy: Faith-Based Initiatives & the Caring State. 2009. (ENG.). 344p. 37.50 *(978-0-226-13483-3(0))* Univ. of Chicago Pr.

Dinham, Adam. Faith, Public Policy & Civil Society: Problems, Policies, Controversies. 2009. (ENG., Illus.). 304p. 95.00 *(978-0-230-57330-7(4))* Palgrave Macmillan.

Elliott, Barbara J. Street Saints: Renewing America's Cities. 2006. (Illus.). 320p. per. 16.95 *(978-1-59947-107-5(8))* Templeton Pr.

Fadica, ed. The Catholic Funding Guide: A Directory of Resources for Catholic Activities. 6th ed. 2009. (ENG.). 568p. pap. 150.00 *(978-1-891646-06-5(0))* Foundations & Donors Interested in Catholic Activities, Inc.

FADICA, Inc. Staff. The Catholic Funding Guide: A Directory of Resources for Catholic Activities. 2007. 530p. per. 110.00 *(978-1-891646-05-8(2))* Foundations & Donors Interested in Catholic Activities, Inc.

Habib, Adam & Maharaj, Brij, eds. Giving & Solidarity: Resource Flows for Poverty Alleviation in South Africa. 2008. (ENG., Illus.). 332p. pap. 27.95 *(978-0-7969-2201-4(2))* Human Sciences Research Council ZAF. Dist: Independent Pubs. Group.

Jellinek, Paul. Promise to Mary: A Story of Faith in Action. 2008. (ENG.). 304p. pap. 30.00 *(978-0-470-29268-6(7),* Jossey-Bass) Wiley, John & Sons, Inc.

Kennedy, Sheila Suess & Bielefeld, Wolfgang. Charitable Choice at Work: Evaluating Faith-Based Job Programs in the States. 2006. (Public Management & Change Ser.). (ENG.). 248p. 44.95 *(978-1-58901-131-1(7))*; per. 19.95 *(978-1-58901-132-8(5))* Georgetown Univ. Pr.

Korgen, Jeffry Odell. Solidarity Will Transform the World: Stories of Hope from Catholic Relief Services. 2007. (Illus.). 161p. per. 16.00 *(978-1-57075-744-0(5))* Orbis Bks.

Lake, S. The Church & the sick in Latin West (4th-8th Centuries). 2011. (Beiträge zur Altertumskunde Ser.). (ENG.). 400p. 117.00 *(978-3-11-019507-1(0))* De Gruyter, Walter Inc.

Mettey, Wendell E. What God Desires: The Story of the Center of Humanitarian Aid & Disaster Relief. 2008. (Illus.). xi, 116p. *(978-1-57736-410-8(4))* Providence Hse Pubs.

Monsma, Stephen V. & Soper, J. Christopher. Faith, Hope, & Jobs: Welfare-to-Work in Los Angeles. 2006. (Religion & Politics Ser.). (ENG., Illus.). 224p. 44.95 *(978-1-58901-111-3(2))*; per. 19.95 *(978-1-58901-110-6(4))* Georgetown Univ. Pr.

Pierson, Arthur T. Forward Movements of the Last Half Century. 2009. (ENG.). 431p. 41.99 *(978-1-117-27721-9(6))*; 432p. pap. 34.75 *(978-1-117-27722-6(4))*; (ENG.). 431p. pap. 26.99 *(978-1-117-27723-3(2),* BiblioLife) BiblioBazaar.

Prochaska, Frank. Christianity & Social Service in Modern Britain: The Disinherited Spirit. 2008. (ENG., Illus.). 228p. 45.00 *(978-0-19-953979-6(0))* Oxford Univ. Pr., Inc.

Scheitle, Christopher P. Beyond the Congregation: The World of Christian Nonprofits. 2010. (ENG., Illus.). 256p. 99.00 *(978-0-19-973352-1(X))*; pap. 24.95 *(978-0-19-973351-4(1))* Oxford Univ. Pr., Inc.

Schneider, Bernhard, ed. Konfessionelle Armutsdiskurse und Armenfürsorgepraktiken im langen 19. Jahrhundert. 2010. (Inklusion/Exklusion. Studien zu Fremdheit und Armut von der Antike bis zur Gegenwart Ser.). (GER.). 334p. 79.95 *(978-3-631-60199-0(9))* Lang, Peter GmbH, Europaischer Verlag der Wissenschaften DEU. Dist: Lang, Peter.

Solomon, Lewis D. In God We Trust? Faith-Based Organizations & the Quest to Solve America's Social Ills. 2007. (Religion, Politics, & Society in the Millennium Ser.). (ENG.). 304p. per. 36.99 *(978-0-7391-2420-8(X))* Lexington Bks.

Strom, Kay Marshall. Harvest of Hope: Stories of Life-Changing Gifts. 2007. (ENG., Illus.). 200p. per. 15.00 *(978-0-8308-3442-6(7),* IVP Bks.) InterVarsity Pr.

Weaver, John. A Flame on the Front Line: Journey from America to Afghanistan. 2009. 160p. pap. 14.99 *(978-1-61579-166-8(3))* Xulon Pr., Inc.

CHURCH CHRONOLOGY

see Church History—Chronology

CHURCH COLLEGES

Here are entered works on colleges supported and-or administered by a religious denomination or sect. Works on the influence of religious denominations and sects on colleges are entered under Church and College.

Arthur. Faith & Secularisation in Religious Colleges & Universities. 2006. (ENG.). 192p. (C). 168.95 *(978-0-415-35940-5(6))* Routledge.

Bays, Daniel & Widmer, Ellen. China's Christian Colleges: Cross-Cultural Connections, 1900-1950. 2009. (ENG., Illus.). 432p. 65.00 *(978-0-8047-5948-9(0))*; pap. 24.95 *(978-0-8047-5949-6(9))* Stanford Univ. Pr.

Cossa, Jost. African Renaissance & Higher Education: A View Through the Lenses of Christian Higher Education. 2008. 88p. pap. *(978-3-639-08733-8(X))* VDM Verlag Dr. Mueller e.K.

Dockery, David S. Renewing Minds: Serving Church & Society Through Christian Higher Education, Revised & Updated. 2008. (ENG.). 240p. pap. 19.99 *(978-0-8054-4788-0(1),* B&H Academic) B&H Publishing Group.

Downey, Deane E. D. & Porter, Stanley E., eds. Christian Worldview & the Academic Disciplines: Crossing the Academy. 2009. (McMaster Divinity College Press General Ser.). 542p. pap. 53.00 *(978-1-60608-529-5(8),* Pickwick Pubns.) Wipf & Stock Pubs.

Feng, Jin. The Making of a Family Saga: Ginling College. 2009. 304p. 80.00 *(978-1-4384-2913-7(4))* State Univ. of New York Pr.

Gardner, Lynn. Ozark Christian College. 360p. 19.99 *(978-0-89900-590-4(X))* College Pr. Publishing Co., Inc.

Hankins, Barry G. & Schmeltekopf, Donald D., eds. The Baylor Project: Taking Christian Higher Education to the Next Level. 2007. 352p. 30.00 *(978-1-58731-062-1(7))* St. Augustine's Pr., Inc.

Kaye, Elaine. For the Work of Ministry: A History of Northern College & it's Predecessors. (Illus.). 304p. *(978-0-567-08659-4(3),* Burns & Oates) Continuum International Publishing Group, Ltd.

Lantinga, Nick. Christian Higher Education in the Global Context: Implications for Curriculum, Pedagogy, & Administration: Proceedings of the International Conference, International Association for the Promotion of Christian Higher Education, 15-19 November 2006, Granada, Nicaragua. 2008. 385p. pap. *(978-0-932914-78-1(0))* Dordt College Pr.

Meyer, Albert J. Realizing Our Intentions: A Guide for Churches & Colleges with Distinctive Missions. 2009. 28.99 *(978-0-89112-539-6(6))*; pap. 19.99 *(978-0-89112-537-2(X))* Abilene Christian Univ. Pr. (ACU Pr.).

Morgan, Ron & Toms Smedley, Cynthia, eds. Transformations at the Edge of the World: Forming Globally Engaged Christians through the Study Abroad Experience. 2010. 304p. pap. 25.00 *(978-0-89112-047-6(5),* ACU Pr.) Abilene Christian Univ. Pr.

Saggio, Joseph J. & Dempsey, Jim. American Indian College: A Witness to the Tribes: A Compilation of Works & Essays in Honor of the First Fifty Years of American Indian College of the Assemblies of God in Phoenix, Arizona, 1957-2007. 2008. (Illus.). xiv, 433p. pap. *(978-1-60585-167-9(1))* Gospel Publishing Hse.

Schuman, Samuel. Seeing the Light: Religious Colleges in Twenty-First-Century America. 2009. (ENG.). 336p. (gr. 17). 50.00 *(978-0-8018-9372-8(0))* Johns Hopkins Univ. Pr.

Schutte, Kelli. Academic Women at Work & at Home. 2008. 144p. pap. *(978-3-639-08611-9(2))* VDM Verlag Dr. Mueller e.K.

Wang, Dong. Managing God's Higher Learning: U. S. -China Cultural Encounter & Canton Christian College (Lingnan University), 1888-1952. Wang, Dong, ed. 2007. (ENG., Illus.). 226p. pap. 36.99 *(978-0-7391-1936-5(2))* Lexington Bks.

—Managing Gods Higher Learning: U. S. -China Cultural Encounter & Canton Christian College (Lingnan University), 1888-1952. Wang, Dong, ed. 2007. (ENG., Illus.). 226p. 89.50 *(978-0-7391-1935-8(4))* Lexington Bks.

Ward, Roger & Gushee, David P., eds. The Scholarly Vocation & the Baptist Academy: Essays on the Future of Baptist Higher Education. 2008. 304p. pap. 30.00 *(978-0-88146-104-6(0))* Mercer Univ. Pr.

Wright, Michael & Arthur, James. Leadership in Christian Higher Education. 2010. (ENG.). 250p. pap. 34.90 *(978-1-84540-189-4(1))* Imprint Academic GBR. Dist: Ingram Pub. Services.

Yancey, George A. Neither Jew nor Gentile: Exploring Issues of Racial Diversity on Protestant College Campuses. 2010. (ENG., Illus.). 224p. 29.95 *(978-0-19-973543-3(3))* Oxford Univ. Pr., Inc.

CHURCH COMMITTEES

see also Parish Councils

Addington, T. J. High-Impact Church Boards: How to Develop Healthy, Intentional, & Empowered Church Leaders. 2010. (LifeChange Ser.). 224p. pap. 14.99 *(978-1-60006-674-0(7))* NavPress Publishing Group.

Birnler, Richard & Bickel, Kurt. Till We Meet Again: Ten Strategies for Effective Church Meetings. 2007. (ENG., Illus.). 64p. pap. 12.95 *(978-0-9798057-0-7(8))* Strobickan Publishing LLC.

Guidelines for Leading Your Congregation 2009-2012 - Church Council: Connecting Vision & Ministry in Your Church. 2008. 2.95 *(978-0-687-64791-0(6))* Abingdon Pr.

Hotchkiss, Dan. Governance & Ministry: Rethinking Board Leadership. 2009. *(978-1-56699-370-8(9))* Alban Institute, Inc.

LifeWay Christian Resources Staff, contrib. by. Pastor Search Committee Handbook. 2007. 42p. pap. 14.95 *(978-1-4158-5214-9(6))* LifeWay Christian Resources.

Spradling, Robert K. & Wiersbe, Warren W. The Lost Shepherd: Finding & Keeping the Right Pastor. 2008. (ENG., Illus.). 112p. per. 9.99 *(978-1-57293-236-4(8))* Discovery Hse. Pubs.

Turner, Paul & Prendergast, Michael. Guide for Liturgy Committees. 2009. (Illus.). ix, 95p. pap. *(978-1-56854-799-2(4))* Liturgy Training Pubns.

Vonhof, John. The Pastoral Search Journey: A Guide to Finding Your Next Pastor. 2010. *(978-1-56699-402-6(0))* Alban Institute, Inc.

CHURCH CONFLICTS

see Church Controversies

CHURCH CONTROVERSIES

Beasley, Robert. Set Me Free! Understanding Our Traditions in the Light of Grace. 208p. 11.95 *(978-0-9714289-9-7(9),* Leafwood Pubs.) Abilene Christian Univ. Pr.

Bisagno, John R. Inside Information: Resolving Controversies in Baptist Churches Worship Wars, Calvinism, Elder Rule. 2010. 128p. 28.95 *(978-1-61507-263-7(2))*; pap. 11.95 *(978-1-61507-262-0(4))* Cross Bks. Publishing.

Bixby, Douglas J. Challenging the Church Monster: From Conflict to Community. 2007. 126p. pap. 16.00 *(978-1-55635-628-5(5),* Wipf and Stock) Wipf & Stock Pubs.

Blue, Brenda. Where Are You At? Overcoming Church Conflicts & More. 2010. 108p. 28.95 *(978-1-61507-197-5(0))*; pap. 11.95 *(978-1-61507-196-8(2))* Cross Bks. Publishing.

Brubaker, David. Promise & Peril: Understanding & Managing Change & Conflict in Congregations. 2009. *(978-1-56699-382-1(2))* Alban Institute, Inc.

Bullard, George W., Jr. Every Congregation Needs a Little Conflict. 2008. (Columbia Partnership Leadership Ser.). 164p. pap. 19.99 *(978-0-8272-0819-3(7))* Chalice Pr.

Burleson, Wade. Hardball Religion: Fundamentalism's Fury at the International Mission Board of the Southern Baptist Convention, 2006-2008. 2009. pap. *(978-1-57312-527-7(X))* Smyth & Helwys Publishing, Inc.

Carroll, Richard C. Is Christ Divided? Approaching Our Conflicts in Christ. 2008. 288p. pap. 14.95 *(978-1-57921-924-6(1))* WinePress Publishing.

Cavanagh, Lorraine. By One Spirit: Reconciliation & Renewal in Anglican Life. 2009. 285p. pap. 54.95 *(978-3-03911-389-7(5))* Lang, Peter AG GBR. Dist: Lang, Peter.

Christman, Robert J. Doctrinal Controversy & Lay Religiosity in Late Reformation Germany: The Case of Mansfeld. 2011. (ENG.). XII, 304p. ***(978-90-04-21565-8(4))*** BRILL.

Clowes, John. Pure Evangelical Religion Restored or Charity, Faith & Good Works Reunited. 2007. (ENG.). 118p. 34.95 *(978-0-548-03046-2(4))* Kessinger Publishing, LLC.

Cunningham, Sarah Raymond & Cunningham, Sarah. Dear Church: Letters from a Disillusioned Generation, 1 vol. 2006. (ENG.). 224p. pap. 12.99 *(978-0-310-26958-8(X))* Zondervan.

Engelsma, David J., et al. Always Reforming: Continuation of the Sixteenth-Century Reformation. Engelsma, David J., ed. Hoeksema, Homer C., tr. 2009. (ENG.). 318p. pap. 16.95 *(978-0-916206-99-4(8))* Reformed Free Publishing Assn.

Fox, Matthew. The Pope's War: Why Ratzinger's Secret Crusade Has Imperiled the Church & How It Can Be Saved. 2011. (ENG.). 304p. 22.95 *(978-1-4027-8629-7(8))* Sterling Publishing Co., Inc.

Gench, Frances Taylor. Faithful Disagreement: Wrestling with Scripture in the Midst of Church Conflict. 2009. (ENG.). 176p. pap. 17.00 *(978-0-664-23338-9(4))* Westminster John Knox Pr.

Gribben, Crawford. God's Irishmen: Theological Debates in Cromwellian Ireland. 2007. (Oxford Studies in Historical Theology Ser.). (ENG.). 304p. 85.00 *(978-0-19-532531-7(1))* Oxford Univ. Pr., Inc.

Hawkins, Ralph K. A Heritage in Crisis: Where We've Been, Where We Are, & Where We're Going in the Churches of Christ. 2008. (ENG.). 160p. pap. 28.50 *(978-0-7618-4080-0(X))* Univ. Pr. of America, Inc.

James, Nancy C. The Developing Schism Within the Episcopal Church, 1960-2010: Social Justice, Ordination of Women, Charismatics, Homosexuality, Extra- Territorial Bishops, Etc. 2010. (Illus.). viii, 259p. 109.95 *(978-0-7734-1397-9(9))* Mellen, Edwin Pr., The.

Jerry M. Williams. Spiritual Resolution: A Biblical Perspective on Handling & Resolving Organizational Conflict in the Local Church. 2009. 140p. pap. 11.99 *(978-1-4389-5405-9(0))* AuthorHouse.

Kaatz, Kevin W. Early Controversies & the Growth of Christianity, 1 vol. 2012. (Praeger Series on the Ancient World Ser.). (Illus.). 163p. 47.00 *(978-0-313-38359-5(6),* A2852C, Praeger Pubs.) Greenwood Publishing Group, Inc.

Kaye, Bruce N. Conflict & the Practice of Christian Faith. 2011. (ENG.). 192p. pap. 36.25 *(978-0-7188-9243-2(7))* Lutherworth Pr., The GBR. Dist: Printondemand-worldwide.com.

Kell, Carl L. Against the Wind: The Moderate Voice in Baptist Life. 2009. (ENG.). 36.95 *(978-1-57233-674-2(9))* Univ. of Tennessee Pr.

Kell, Carl L., ed. Exiled: Voices of the Southern Baptist Convention Holy War. 2007. (Illus.). 240p. per. 22.50 *(978-1-57233-590-5(4))* Univ. of Tennessee Pr.

King, Michael A., ed. Stumbling Toward a Genuine Conversation on Homosexuality. 2007. (Living Issues Discussion Ser.: 4). 312p. pap. 22.95 *(978-1-931038-47-8(3))* Cascadia Publishing Hse., LLC.

Milton, Michael A. Hit by Friendly Fire: What to Do When Christians Hurt You. 2008. (Faith for Living: Ser.). 24p. pap. 2.50 *(978-1-55635-928-6(4),* Wipf and Stock) Wipf & Stock Pubs.

Nordenbrock, William A. Beyond Accompaniment: Guiding a Fractured Community to Wholeness. 2011. 19.95 *(978-0-8146-3307-6(2))*; E-Book *(978-0-8146-3938-2(0))* Liturgical Pr.

Osterhaus, James P., et al. Thriving Through Ministry Conflict: A Parable on How Resistance Can Be Your Ally, 1 vol. 2009. (ENG.). 160p. pap. 16.99 *(978-0-310-32466-9(1))* Zondervan.

Palladini, Fiammetta. Die Berliner Hugenotten und der Fall Barbeyrac: Orthodoxe und 'Sozinianer' im Refuge (1685-1720) 2011. (GER., Illus.). ***(978-90-04-20947-3(6))*** BRILL.

Poirier, Alfred. The Peacemaking Pastor: A Biblical Guide to Resolving Church Conflict. 2006. (Illus.). 320p. pap. 18.99 *(978-0-8010-6589-7(5))* Baker Bks.

Powell, Jake. Dark Secrets Your Pastor Won't Reveal. 2010. pap. 14.95 *(978-0-578-05580-0(5))* Dark Secret Publishing LLC.

Saunders, Joseph. The Church in the Age of Hip Hop. 2009. 134p. pap. 18.81 *(978-0-578-01448-7(3))* Desktop Prepress Services.

Sawyer, David. Hope in Conflict: Discovering Wisdom in Congregational Turmoil. 2007. *(978-0-8298-1758-4(1))* Pilgrim Pr., The/United Church Pr.

Schlabach, Gerald W. Unlearning Protestantism: Sustaining Christian Community in an Unstable Age. 2010. 272p. pap. 30.00 *(978-1-58743-111-1(4))* Brazos Pr.

Sparkman, G. Temp. Saying No to Power: FOOTNOTE to 1980s SOUTHERN BAPTIST TUMULT. 2008. 220p. pap. 21.95 *(978-1-4357-0666-8(8))* Lulu Enterprises Inc.

Spencer, Cleon E. An Experiential View of Conflict in the Local Church: Focusing on Smaller & Medium-Sized Protestant Churches. 2009. 50p. pap. *(978-1-926585-44-4(5), CCB Publishing)* CCB Publishing.
Steinke, Peter L. Healthy Congregations: A Systems Approach. 2nd ed. 2006. (Illus.). xv, 125p. *(978-1-56699-330-2(X))* Alban Institute, Inc.
—How Your Church Family Works: Understanding Congregations As Emotional Systems. 2006. xx, 146p. *(978-1-56699-329-6(6))* Alban Institute, Inc.
Strauch, Alexander. If You Bite & Devour One Another: Biblical Principles for Handling Conflict. 2011. (ENG.). 192p. pap. 13.99 *(978-0-936083-31-5(X))* Lewis & Roth Pubs.
Udis-Kessler, Amanda. Queer Inclusion in the United Methodist Church. 2008. (New Approaches in Sociology Ser.). (ENG., Illus.). 268p. 125.00 *(978-0-415-96249-0(8))* Routledge.
What Is a Southern Baptist? Key Denominational Distinctives. 2008. 28p. pap. 5.00 *(978-0-9776250-1-7(X))* Mount Pisgah Publishing Co.

CHURCH COSTUME
see Church Vestments

CHURCH COUNCILS
see Councils and Synods

CHURCH COURTS
see Ecclesiastical Courts

CHURCH DECORATION AND ORNAMENT
see also Altarpieces; Altars; Choir Stalls; Christian Art and Symbolism; Church Furniture; Flower Arrangement in Churches; Fonts; Glass Painting and Staining; Mosaics; Mural Painting and Decoration

Anderson, M. D. Animal Carvings in British Churches. 2011. (ENG.). 110p. pap. 19.99 *(978-0-521-15205-8(0))* Cambridge Univ. Pr.
Aquilina, Mike. Signs & Mysteries: Revealing ancient christian Symbols. 2008. per. 15.95 *(978-1-59276-450-1(9))* Our Sunday Visitor, Publishing Div.
Barré, François, et al. David Tremlett, Architecte de Lumière: Les Vitraux Contemporains de Villenauxe-La-Grande. 2010. (FRE & ENG., Illus.). 96p. *(978-2-914528-98-6(1))* Lieux Dits Etude Et Mise En Valeur Du Patrimoine.
Barton, Paulette E. Mercy & the Misericord in Late Medieval England: Cathedral Theology & Architecture. 2009. (Illus.). 272p. 109.95 *(978-0-7734-4841-4(1))* Mellen, Edwin Pr., The.
Blacklock, Judith. Church Flowers. 2009. (ENG.). 416p. 65.00 *(978-0-9552391-6-8(8),* Falcon Guides) Globe Pequot Pr., The.
Bourdua, Louise. The Franciscans & Art Patronage in Late Medieval Italy. 2011. (ENG., Illus.). 256p. (C). pap. 36.99 *(978-0-521-28128-7(8))* Cambridge Univ. Pr.
Bünker, Michael & Binski, Paul. Peterborough Cathedral: Five Years after 22 November 2001. 2006. (ENG., Illus.). 128p. 50.00 ***(978-1-903470-55-8(2))*** Holberton, Paul Publishing GBR. Dist: Casemate Pubs. & Bk. Distributors, LLC.
Camille, Michael. The Gargoyles of Notre-Dame: Medievalism & the Monsters of Modernity. 2009. (Illus.). 464p. 49.00 *(978-0-226-09245-4(3))* Univ. of Chicago Pr.
Cerretelli, Claudio, et al. Il Duomo Di Prato. 2009. (ITA., Illus.). 279p. *(978-88-6087-259-3(6))* Le Lettere.
Christ-Janer, Albert & Foley, Mary Mix. Modern Church Architecture: A Guide to the Form & Spirit of Twentieth Century Religious Buildings. 2011. 340p. 51.95 ***(978-1-258-10383-5(4))*** Literary Licensing, LLC.
Claussen, Peter Cornelius, et al. Die Kirchen der Stadt Rom im Mittelalter 1050-1300, G-L. Band 3: S. Giacomo alla Lungara bis S. Lucia della Tinta. 2010. (Forschungen zur Kunstgeschichte und christlichen Archaologie Ser.). (GER., Illus.). 591p. (C). 210.00 *(978-3-515-09410-8(5))* Steiner, Franz Verlag Wiesbaden GmbH DEU. Dist: Brown, David Bk. Co., The.
Cowen, Painton. English Stained Glass. 2008. (ENG., Illus.). 128p. 29.95 *(978-0-500-23846-2(4))* Thames & Hudson.
Cutler, Anthony. Refiguring the Face of God: The Daphni Pantokrator. 2011. (Studies in the Visual Cultures of the Middle Ages Ser.). (ENG., Illus.). 250p. (C). pap. 102.00 *(978-2-503-52766-6(3))* Brepols Pubs. BEL. Dist: Brown, David Bk. Co., The.
De Giorgio, Cynthia. The Conventual Church of the Knights of Malta. Splendour, history & art of St John's Co-Cathedral, Valletta. 2010. (ENG., Illus.). 144p. (C). 110.00 *(978-99932-7-291-5(4))* Midsea Bks. Ltd. MLT. Dist: Brown, David Bk. Co., The.
Eck, Xander van & Van Eck, Xander. Clandestine Splendor: Paintings for the Catholic Church in the Dutch Republic. 2008. (ENG., Illus.). 368p. 100.00 *(978-90-400-8468-3(8))* Waanders B.V., Uitgeverij NLD. Dist: National Bk. Network.
Faleer, Robert A. Church Woodwork in the British Isles, 1100-1535: An Annotated Bibliography. 2009. (ENG., Illus.). 472p. (gr. 17). 110.00 *(978-0-8108-6739-0(7))* Scarecrow Pr., Inc.
Fontana, Bernard L. A Gift of Angels: The Art of Mission San Xavier del Bac. 2010. (Southwest Center Ser.). (ENG., Illus.). 376p. 75.00 *(978-0-8165-2840-0(3))* Univ. of Arizona Pr.
Frugoni, Chiara & Armandi Barbolini, Marina. The Cathedral of Modena, 3 vols. 2009. (ITA & ENG., Illus.). 1340p. 1160.00 *(978-88-7686-982-2(4))* Panini Franco Cosimo ITA. Dist: Antique Collectors' Club.
Garton, John. Grace & Grandeur: The Portraiture of Paolo Veronese. 2008. (Studies in Medieval & Early Renaissance Art History Ser.). (Illus.). 268p. 160.00 *(978-1-905375-23-3(9))* Miller, Harvey Pubs. GBR. Dist: Brown, David Bk. Co., The.
Hammond, Jay M. & Ginther, James R., eds. The Virtual Basilica of Saint Francis of Assisi: An Interactive, Explorable Environment with Integrated Text. 2006. cd-rom 49.95 *(978-0-9791418-0-5(X))* Institute of Digital Theology.
Howard, F. English Church Woodwork. 2007. 436p. per. *(978-1-905217-65-6(X))* Mills, Jeremy Publishing.
Huerta, Pedro Luis. Maestros Del Románico en el Camino de Santiago. 2010. (SPA., Illus.). 239p. *(978-84-89483-71-2(X))* Fundacion Santa Maria La Real, Centro de Estudios del Romanico.
Kauffmann, Jean. Lutte avec l Ange. pap. 18.95 *(978-2-07-042016-2(7))* Gallimard, Editions FRA. Dist: Distribooks, Inc.
Mancuso, Anthony Joseph & Thomas, Caroline M. Envisioning Environment: Enhancing the Liturgical Experience. 2011. pap. *(978-0-89390-695-5(6))* Resource Pubns., Inc.
Martellini, Patrizia Angiolini, ed. The Basilica of San Vitale in Ravenna, 2 vols. 2008. (ITA & ENG., Illus.). 670p. 825.00 *(978-88-7686-806-1(2))* Panini Franco Cosimo ITA. Dist: Antique Collectors' Club.
Mazza, Antonino & Zuffetti, Zaira. Il Miracolo Dell'Incoronata: Un Capolavoro Visto Da Vicino. 2010. (ITA., Illus.). 207p. *(978-88-7827-191-3(8))* Bolis.
Micklethwaite, J. T. The Ornaments of the Rubric. 2010. pap. 25.60 *(978-1-61719-387-3(9))*; pap. 25.60 *(978-1-61719-384-2(4))* Gorgias Pr., LLC.
Milby, Th And Kathleen & Danson, Lex. Native & Garden Plants for the Church Altar. 2009. 124p. pap. 36.99 *(978-1-4389-0798-7(2))* AuthorHouse.
Moss, Rachel. Romanesque Chevron Ornament: The Language of British, Norman & Irish Sculpture in the Twelfth Century. 2009. (Bar S Ser.). (ENG., Illus.). 137p. (C). pap. 82.50 *(978-1-4073-0391-8(0))* British Archaeological Reports Ltd. GBR. Dist: Brown, David Bk. Co., The.
Nenci, Cinzia, et al. The Cathedral of Pisa, 3 vols. Peroni, Adriano, ed. 2008. (ENG., Illus.). 1634p. 1280.00 *(978-88-7686-614-2(0))* Panini Franco Cosimo ITA. Dist: Antique Collectors' Club.
Nolan, Charles E. Splendors of Faith: New Orleans Catholic Churches, 1727-1930. 2010. (Illus.). 144p. 39.95 *(978-0-8071-3682-9(4))* Louisiana State Univ. Pr.
Orenduff, Lai-Kent Chew. The Transformation of Catholic Religious Art in the Twentieth Century: Father Marie-Alain Couturier & the Church at Assy, France. 2008. (Illus.). 212p. 109.95 *(978-0-7734-4985-5(X))* Mellen, Edwin Pr., The.
Paolucci, Antonio. The Tempio Malatestiano in Rimini, 2 vols. Settis, Salvatore, ed. 2011. (ITA & ENG., Illus.). 608p. 815.00 *(978-88-248-0353-3(9))* Panini Franco Cosimo ITA. Dist: National Bk. Network.
Parkstone Press Staff. Apocalypse. 2012. (Mega Square Ser.). (ENG., Illus.). 256p. 12.95 ***(978-1-906981-46-4(9))*** Parkstone Pr. USA, Ltd.
Paul, Benjamin. Nuns & Reform Art in Early Modern Venice: The Architecture of Santi Cosma E Damiano & Its Decoration from Tintoretto to Tiepolo. 2012. (Illus.). 344p. 124.95 ***(978-1-4094-1186-4(9))*** Ashgate Publishing Co.
Prentice, Sartell. The Voices of the Cathedral: Tales in Stone & Legends in Glass. 2007. (ENG.). 390p. 48.95 *(978-0-548-03678-5(0))* Kessinger Publishing, LLC.
Richardson, Peter & Richardson, Douglas. Canadian Churches: An Architectural History. 2007. (ENG., Illus.). 440p. 85.00 *(978-1-55407-239-2(5))* Firefly Bks., Ltd.
Rosewell, Roger. Medieval Wall Paintings in English & Welsh Churches. 2011. (Illus.). 350p. pap. 34.95 *(978-1-84383-484-7(7),* Boydell Press) Boydell & Brewer, Ltd. GBR. Dist: Boydell & Brewer, Inc.
Sundell, Michael G. Mosaics in the Eternal City. 2007. *(978-0-86698-376-1(7))* Arizona State Univ., Arizona Ctr. for Medieval & Renaissance Studies.
Viollet-le-Duc, Eugene-Emmanuel & Ouradou, Maurice. Designs & Ornaments from the Chapels of Notre Dame. 2011. (Dover Pictorial Archive Ser.). (ENG., Illus.). 80p. pap. 16.95 *(978-0-486-47538-7(7))* Dover Pubns., Inc.
Zervas, Diane Finiello, et al. Orsanmichele in Florence, 2 vols. 2009. (ENG & ITA., Illus.). 1196p. 980.00 *(978-88-7686-775-0(9))* Panini Franco Cosimo ITA. Dist: Antique Collectors' Club.

CHURCH DISCIPLINE
see also Absolution; Asceticism; Celibacy; Church Orders, Ancient; Confession; Ecclesiastical Courts; Indulgences; Penance; Purgatory; Visitations, Ecclesiastical
also subdivision Discipline under names of religions, religious denominations, etc., e.g. Catholic Church—Discipline

Bargerhuff, Eric J. Love that Rescues: God's Fatherly Love in the Practice of Church Discipline. 2010. 224p. pap. 25.00 *(978-1-60608-561-5(1),* Wipf and Stock) Wipf & Stock Pubs.
Bunsen, Christian C. J. Hippolytus & His Age V3: Or the Doctrine & Practice of the Church of Rome under Commodus & Alexander Severus; & Ancient & Modern Christianit. 2007. 428p. 51.95 *(978-0-548-25953-5(4))*; (ENG.). 432p. per. 36.95 *(978-1-4326-6335-3(6))* Kessinger Publishing, LLC.
Bunsen, Christian Charles Josias. Hippolytus & His Age V1: Or the Beginnings & Prospects of Christianity. 2007. 568p. 58.95 *(978-0-548-56115-7(X))*; (ENG.). per. 43.95 *(978-0-548-51242-5(6))* Kessinger Publishing, LLC.
Cooper, Kate & Gregory, Jeremy, eds. Discipline & Diversity: Papers Read at the 2005 Summer Meeting & the 2006 Winter Meeting of the Ecclesiastical History Society. 2007. (Studies in Church History Ser.: Volume 43). 448p. 80.00 *(978-0-9546809-3-0(6))* Ecclesiastical History Society GBR. Dist: Boydell & Brewer, Inc.
Craun, Edwin D. Ethics & Power in Medieval English Reformist Writing. 2010. (Cambridge Studies in Medieval Literature Ser.). (ENG.). 232p. 85.00 *(978-0-521-19932-2(8))* Cambridge Univ. Pr.
Cyprian of Carthage. On the Church: Select Letters, Bk.33. 2007. (ENG.). 250p. pap. 20.00 *(978-0-88141-313-7(5))* St. Vladimir's Seminary Pr.
—On the Church: Select Treatises, Bk.32. 2007. (St. Vladimir's Seminary Press "Popular Patristics" Ser.: No. 32). (ENG.). 188p. pap. 16.00 *(978-0-88141-312-0(7))* St. Vladimir's Seminary Pr.
Guidelines for Leading Your Congregation 2009-2012 - Adult Ministries: Ministries that Help Adults Love God & Neighbor. 2008. 2.95 *(978-0-687-64682-1(0))* Abingdon Pr.
Guidelines for Leading Your Congregation 2009-2012 - Children's Ministries: Ministries that Help Children Grow in Faith. 2008. 2.95 *(978-0-687-64951-8(X))* Abingdon Pr.
Guidelines for Leading Your Congregation 2009-2012 - Christian Education: Planning for Lifelong Faith Formation. 2008. 2.95 *(978-0-687-64941-9(2))* Abingdon Pr.
Guidelines for Leading Your Congregation 2009-2012 - Church & Society: Advocating for Peace & Justice. 2008. 2.95 *(978-0-687-64752-1(5))* Abingdon Pr.
Guidelines for Leading Your Congregation 2009-2012 - Church Council: Connecting Vision & Ministry in Your Church. 2008. 2.95 *(978-0-687-64791-0(6))* Abingdon Pr.
Guidelines for Leading Your Congregation 2009-2012 - Church Historians: Remembering the Past & Inspiring the Future. 2008. 2.95 *(978-0-687-64851-1(3))* Abingdon Pr.
Guidelines for Leading Your Congregation 2009-2012 - Committee on Lay Leadership: Identifying, Equipping, & Deploying Spiritual Leaders for the Mission of the Church. 2008. 2.95 *(978-0-687-64771-2(1))* Abingdon Pr.
Guidelines for Leading Your Congregation 2009-2012 - Evangelism: Sharing the Good News. 2008. 2.95 *(978-0-687-64921-1(8))* Abingdon Pr.
Guidelines for Leading Your Congregation 2009-2012 - Family Ministries: Helping Families Become Centers of Faith Formation. 2008. 2.95 *(978-0-687-64702-6(9))* Abingdon Pr.
Guidelines for Leading Your Congregation 2009-2012 - Finance: Funding Ministries that Nurture Persons in Their Faith. 2008. 2.95 *(978-0-687-64891-7(2))* Abingdon Pr.
Guidelines for Leading Your Congregation 2009-2012 - Lay Leader/Lay Member: Connecting Your Congregation & Your Annual Conference. 2008. 2.95 *(978-0-687-64811-5(4))* Abingdon Pr.
Guidelines for Leading Your Congregation 2009-2012 - Men's Ministries: Ministry to & through Men. 2008. 2.95 *(978-0-687-64732-3(0))* Abingdon Pr.
Guidelines for Leading Your Congregation 2009-2012 - Mission: Reaching the World. 2008. 2.95 *(978-0-687-64931-0(5))* Abingdon Pr.
Guidelines for Leading Your Congregation 2009-2012 - Pastor: Providing Spiritual Leadership for the Church in Mission. 2008. 2.95 *(978-0-687-64801-6(7))* Abingdon Pr.
Guidelines for Leading Your Congregation 2009-2012 - Pastor-Parish Relations: Connecting the Pastor, Staff, & Congregation. 2008. 2.95 *(978-0-687-64781-1(9))* Abingdon Pr.
Guidelines for Leading Your Congregation 2009-2012 - Small Group Ministries: Where Two or Three Are Gathered ... 2008. 2.95 *(978-0-687-64841-2(6))* Abingdon Pr.
Guidelines for Leading Your Congregation 2009-2012 - Small Membership Church: Serving with Significance in Your Context. 2008. 2.95 *(978-0-687-64952-5(8))* Abingdon Pr.
Guidelines for Leading Your Congregation 2009-2012 - Stewardship: Yes, It's about Money, but a whole Lot More — Using God's Resources Responsibly. 2008. 2.95 *(978-0-687-64911-2(0))* Abingdon Pr.
Guidelines for Leading Your Congregation 2009-2012 - Trustees: Managing the Property, Equipment, & Investments God Has Entrusted to our Ministry. 2008. 2.95 *(978-0-687-64881-8(5))* Abingdon Pr.
Guidelines for Leading Your Congregation 2009-2012 - Worship: The Gifts of God from the People of God. 2008. 2.95 *(978-0-687-64901-3(3))* Abingdon Pr.
Guidelines for Leading Your Congregation 2009-2012 - Youth Ministries: Ministries for, by, & with Youth. 2008. 2.95 *(978-0-687-64692-0(8))* Abingdon Pr.
Jackson, John. God-Size Your Church: Beyond Growth for Growth's Sake. 2008. 184p. pap. 20.00 *(978-0-687-64909-9(9))* Abingdon Pr.
The Jubilee Gospel: The Jubilee, Spirit & the Church. 2008. (ENG.). 140p. 11.99 *(978-1-86024-703-3(2))* Authentic Media.
Laney, J. Carl. A Guide to Church Discipline: God's Loving Plan for Restoring Believers to Fellowship with Himself & with the Body of Christ. 2010. 176p pap. 20.00 *(978-1-60899-452-6(X),* Wipf and Stock) Wipf & Stock Pubs.
Lee, Mike. Release from Captivity. 2009. 264p. 24.99 *(978-1-4389-3811-0(X))*; pap. 16.50 *(978-1-4389-3810-3(1))* AuthorHouse.
Leeman, Jonathan. The Church & the Surprising Offense of God's Love: Reintroducing the Doctrines of Church Membership & Discipline. 2010. (IX Marks Ser.). 384p. pap. 19.99 *(978-1-4335-0905-6(9))* Crossway.
Meadows, James L. A Study of Church Discipline. pap. 5.50 *(978-0-89098-382-9(8))* Twentieth Century Christian Bks.
Mell, P. Corrective Church Discipline with A Deve. 2006. 152p. per. 19.00 *(978-1-57978-640-3(5))* Baptist Standard Bearer, Inc.
Methodist Episcopal Church. Doctrines & Discipline of the Methodist Episcopal Church. 2006. 236p. per. 20.99 *(978-1-4255-2002-1(2))* MPublishing.
—The Doctrines & Discipline of the Methodist Episcopal Church 1860 with an Appendix. 2006. 328p. per. 23.99 *(978-1-4255-3247-5(0))* MPublishing.
—The Doctrines & Discipline of the Methodist Episcopal Church, 1868 with an Appendix. 2006. 380p. per. 26.99 *(978-1-4255-4014-2(7))* MPublishing.
—The Doctrines & Discipline of the Methodist Episcopal Church 1876: With an Appendix. 2006. 432p. per. 26.99 *(978-1-4255-4657-1(9))* MPublishing.
—Doctrines & Discipline of the Methodist Episcopal Church with an Appendix. 2006. 340p. per. 23.99 *(978-1-4255-3447-9(3))* MPublishing.
Methodist Episcopal Church, South. The Doctrines & Discipline of the Methodist Episcopal Church South. 2006. 276p. per. 23.99 *(978-1-4255-2452-4(4))* MPublishing.
Richardson, Wyman Lewis. Walking Together: A Congregational Reflection on Biblical Church Discipline. 2007. (Illus.). 114p. pap. 14.00 *(978-1-55635-115-0(1))*; (Illus.). 114p. pap., wbk. ed. 14.00 *(978-1-55635-114-3(3))*; 134p. pap. 17.00 *(978-1-55635-112-9(7))* Wipf & Stock Pubs. (Wipf and Stock).
Schweizer, Eduard. Church Order in the New Testament. 2006. 240p. pap. 25.00 *(978-1-59752-810-8(2),* Wipf and Stock) Wipf & Stock Pubs.
Williamson, John. Sin in the Assembly: A Guide for Local Baptist Church Discipline. 2007. 64p. per. 16.95 *(978-1-60441-178-2(3))* PublishAmerica, Inc.

CHURCH DISPUTES
see Church Controversies

CHURCH ENTERTAINMENTS

Cosby, Brian H. Giving up Gimmicks: Reclaiming Youth Ministry from an Entertainment Culture. 2012. pap. ***(978-1-59638-394-4(1))*** P & R Publishing.
Jones, Barbara C. Easy Church Suppers. 2007. 288p. per. 16.95 *(978-1-931294-71-3(2))* Cookbook Resources, LLC.
Larsen, Linda Johnson. Church Potluck Slow Cooker: Homestyle Recipes for Family & Community Celebrations. 2008. (ENG.). 224p. pap. 15.95 *(978-1-59869-774-2(9))* Adams Media Corp.

CHURCH ETIQUETTE

Ashmore, Ray. All things to all Men. 2010. 134p. pap. 15.95 *(978-0-557-59344-6(1))* Lulu Enterprises Inc.
Harps-Morrow, Verna. Minding Our Manners in Church. 2008. 40p. pap. 16.95 *(978-1-4327-3253-0(6))* Outskirts Pr., Inc.
Hawkins, James Barney. Episcopal Etiquette & Ethics: Living the Craft of Priesthood in the Episcopal Church. 2012. 128p. pap. 18.00 *(978-0-8192-2406-4(5))* Church Publishing, Inc.
Masters, Henry L. Makin' Room in the Inn: Christmas Hospitality Through an African American Experience. 2010. 64p. 7.00 *(978-1-4267-0371-3(6))* Abingdon Pr.
Matlins, Stuart M. & Magida, Arthur J., eds. How to Be a Perfect Stranger: The Essential Religious Etiquette Handbook. 5th ed. 2010. 432p. pap. 19.99 *(978-1-59473-294-2(9))* SkyLight Paths Publishing.
Moore, June Hines. Manners Made Easy for the Family: 365 Timeless Etiquette Tips for Every Occasion. 2008. (ENG.). 400p. 14.99 *(978-0-8054-4741-5(5),* B&H Bks.) B&H Publishing Group.
Muller, Gladys Blanchard & Bennett, Dorothy Blanchard. I Seen Him When He Done It: A Handbook on Christian Etiquette. 2011. 72p. 36.95 ***(978-1-258-08282-6(9))*** Literary Licensing, LLC.
Smith, Bishop Alton A. Order in the Church: [Proper Church Etiquette & Protocol]. 2011. 68p. pap. 9.99 ***(978-1-4567-6936-9(7))*** AuthorHouse.
Togni, P. Louis & Audo, Thomas. Instructions for Ministers of the Church. 2010. (SYR.). 114.20 *(978-1-61143-345-6(2))* Gorgias Pr., LLC.
Williams, Linda J. Church Etiquette: A Handbook for Manners & Appropriate Behavior in Church. 2009. 80p. pap. 12.99 *(978-1-4389-3340-5(1))* AuthorHouse.

CHURCH FACILITIES

Dammarell, John L. Churches Without Walls: The Mandate of Isaiah 58. 2008. 112p. pap. 10.99 *(978-1-60477-967-7(5))* Xulon Pr., Inc.
Healy, James E. Building a New Church: A Process Manual for Pastors & Lay Leaders. 2009. pap. 18.95 *(978-0-8146-3269-7(6))* Liturgical Pr.
Vila, Samuel. Pulpito Cristiano: Christian Pulpit. (SPA.). 248p. *(978-84-7228-040-3(3),* 220731) Clie, Editorial.

CHURCH FATHERS
see Fathers of the Church

CHURCH FESTIVALS
see Fasts and Feasts

CHURCH FIGHTS
see Church Controversies

CHURCH FINANCE
Here are entered works on the solicitation and administration of church funds. Works on the duty of the individual Christian to contribute time, talents, and material possessions in the service of God are entered under Christian Stewardship. Works on the duty of the individual Christian to contribute financially to the church are entered under Christian Giving.
see also Benefices, Ecclesiastical; Christian Giving; Christian Stewardship; Church Charities; Church Property; Churchwardens' Accounts; Clergy—Salaries, Pensions, Etc.; Tithes
also subdivision Finance under Church denominations and under special topics, e.g. Church of England—Finance

Abingdon. Ready-to-Go Fundraisers 75 Ways to Fund Your Ministry. 2007. (Illus.). 114p. 19.00 *(978-0-687-33507-7(8))* Abingdon Pr.
Annual Report of the Committee on Finance. 0.25 *(978-0-687-25117-9(6))* Abingdon Pr.
Annual Report of the Committee on Finance 2001-2004. 1.25 *(978-0-687-09767-8(3))*; 6.00 *(978-0-687-09692-3(8))* Abingdon Pr.

C

Barnes, Aston A. Church Financing: Yesterday, Today, & Tomorrow: A Funding Solution for Seventh-Day Adventism. 2010. 110p. pap. 11.95 *(978-1-57258-615-4(X))* TEACH Services, Inc.

Bauer, Gerald W. Congregational Endowment Funds: Empowering the Vision of God's Coming Kingdom. pap. 7.50 *(978-1-56699-161-2(7))* Alban Institute, Inc.

Byfield, Richard & Shaw, James P. Your Money & Your Church. 2011. 236p. 46.95 **(978-1-258-10211-1(0))** Literary Licensing, LLC.

Clark, M. Douglas. Risk Control for Churches. (Illus.). ring bd. 39.50 *(978-0-88061-007-0(7))* International Loss Control Institute, Inc.

Clark, Wayne B. Beyond Fundraising: A Complete Guide to Congregational Stewardship. 2007. pap. 20.00 *(978-1-55896-523-2(8))* Unitarian Universalist Assn.

Durran, Maggie. Making the Most of Your Church's Money: A Practical Guide. 2011. (ENG.). 128p. pap. 17.99 *(978-1-84825-039-0(8))*, Canterbury Pr. Norwich) Hymns Ancient & Modern Ltd GBR. Dist: Westminster John Knox Pr.

Easum, William M. & Tenny-Brittian, William. Ministry in Hard Times. 2010. 118p. pap. 12.00 *(978-1-4267-0842-8(4))* Abingdon Pr.

Elishaphat, Apostle. In a World of Darkness, Let There Be Light! 220p. 2011. 26.20 *(978-1-4520-8001-7(1))* 2011. pap. 18.99 *(978-1-4520-8000-0(3))* 2008. 37.99 *(978-1-4389-1498-5(9))* 2008. pap. 35.99 *(978-1-4389-1497-8(0))* AuthorHouse.

Five Fold Ministries Church & Tax Guide. 2006. per. *(978-0-9787128-2-2(X))* Palm Tree Pubns.

Garrison, Becky. Starting from Zero with $0: Building Mission-Shaped Ministries on a Shoestring. 2010. xiv, 154p. **(978-1-59627-141-8(8))**; E-Book **(978-1-59627-142-5(6))** Church Publishing, Inc. (Seabury Bks.).

Grissen, Lillian V. Firstfruits: Managing the Master's Money. tchr. ed. 13.25 *(978-1-56212-020-7(4)*, 151405); 2nd ed. pap. 8.25 *(978-1-56212-019-1(0)*, 151400) Faith Alive Christian Resources.

Guidelines 2001-2004 Church Treasurer/Finance. 2.50 *(978-0-687-03570-0(8))* Abingdon Pr.

Guidelines for Leading Your Congregation 2009-2012 - Finance: Funding Ministries that Nurture Persons in Their Faith. 2008. 2.95 *(978-0-687-64891-7(2))* Abingdon Pr.

Guidelines for Leading Your Congregation 2009-2012 - Stewardship: Yes, It's about Money, but a whole Lot More — Using God's Resources Responsibly. 2008. 2.95 *(978-0-687-64911-2(0))* Abingdon Pr.

Hammar, Richard. Church & Clergy Tax Guide: 2007 Edition. 2007. per. 29.95 *(978-0-917463-32-7(3))* Christianity Today International.

—The 2008 Church & Clergy Tax Guide. Liautaud, Marian, ed. 2007. cd-rom 29095.00 *(978-0-917463-41-9(2))* Christianity Today International.

Hammar, Richard R. The 2008 Compensation Handbook. 2007. per. 29.95 *(978-0-917463-36-5(6))* Christianity Today International.

Handbook on Local Church Financial Record System. 6.95 *(978-0-687-22525-5(6))* Abingdon Pr.

Hudnut-Beumler, James. In Pursuit of the Almighty's Dollar: A History of Money & American Protestantism. 2007. (ENG., Illus.). 288p. 34.95 *(978-0-8078-3079-6(8))* Univ. of North Carolina Pr.

Jamieson, Philip D. & Jamieson, Janet T. Ministry & Money: A Practical Guide for Pastors. 2009. (ENG., Illus.). 216p. pap. 20.00 *(978-0-664-23198-9(5))* Westminster John Knox Pr.

Johnson, Douglas W. Finance in Your Church. 9.00 *(978-0-687-12987-4(7))* Abingdon Pr.

Kennedy, Neil. God's Currency: Living under an Open Heaven. 2007. per. *(978-0-9777039-6-8(7))* Andrews, Michael S. Publishing, LLC.

Kioulachoglou, Anastasios. Tithing, Giving & the New Testament. 2008. 104p. pap. 10.99 *(978-1-60791-114-2(0))* Xulon Pr., Inc.

Liautaud, Marian, ed. The 2008 Church & Clergy Tax Guide. 2007. per. 29.95 *(978-0-917463-37-2(4))* Christianity Today International.

Mallonee, David. Foolproof Finances. 167p. pap. 14.97 incl. audio *(978-1-883906-11-5(3))* Kingdom Productions.

Malphurs, Aubrey & Stroope, Steve. Money Matters in Church: A Practical Guide for Leaders. 2007. (Illus.). 224p. pap. 16.99 *(978-0-8010-6627-6(1))* Baker Bks.

Martin, Francis P. The Kingdom's Economy: A Guide to Proper Giving. 2011. pap. 12.99 *(978-1-61739-550-5(1))* Tate Publishing & Enterprises, LLC.

Mead, Loren B. Endowed Congregations: Pros & Cons. pap. 8.00 *(978-1-56699-105-6(6)*, OD92) Alban Institute, Inc.

Morton, Scott. Funding Your Ministry. 2007. (Discipleship Journal Bible Study Ser.). (ENG.). 264p. pap. 19.99 *(978-0-9729023-7-3(6))* NavPress Publishing Group.

—Funding Your Ministry - Spanish Version. 2007. (Design for Discipleship Ser.). (ENG.). 234p. pap. 19.99 *(978-0-9729023-5-9(X))* NavPress Publishing Group.

Morton, Scott & Navigators Staff. Raising Personal Support: A Step-by-Step Guide to Fulfilling Your Personal Calling. 2007. (Hollywood Nobody Ser.). (ENG.). 96p. spiral bd. 14.99 *(978-1-60006-343-5(8))* NavPress Publishing Group.

Nuffer, Bruce. The Church Treasurer's Manual: A Practical Guide for Managing Church Finances. 2nd ed. 2008. (ENG.). 160p. pap. 49.99 *(978-0-8341-2383-0(5)*, 9780834123830) Beacon Hill Pr. of Kansas City.

Pillado, Francisco. Los Bienes de Dios: God's Property-Should We Tithe? (SPA.). 144p. *(978-84-7228-357-2(7)*, 220111) Clie, Editorial.

Robertson, C. K. Transforming Stewardship. Lemler James, ed. 2009. (Transformations Ser.). 176p. pap. 16.00 *(978-0-89869-607-3(0))* Church Publishing, Inc.

Ronsvalle, John & Ronsvalle, Sylvia. The State of Church Giving Through 2005: Abolition of the Institutional Enslavement of Overseas Missions. 2007. 168p. pap. 30.00 *(978-0-9679633-7-2(0))* Empty Tomb, Inc.

Ronsvalle, John L. & Ronsvalle, Sylvia. The State of Church Giving Through 2009: Jesus Christ, the Church in the U. S. , & the 16 No-Progress-in-Child Deaths Nations, 10 Being 84% Christian. 21st ed. 2011. (Illus.). 207p. pap. 36.00 **(978-0-9843665-1-4(2))** Empty Tomb, Inc.

Russell, Cindy. Scriptural Truths about Tithes. 2006. 172p. per. 20.00 *(978-1-59858-191-1(0))* Dog Ear Publishing, LLC.

Shiplett, Gary R. A New Paradigm for Funding Ministry: How to Grow Giving in the Church, 1 vol. 2009. 132p. pap. 19.95 *(978-1-60703-136-9(1))* PublishAmerica, Inc.

Skjegstad, Joy. Winning Grants to Strengthen Your Ministry. 2007. *(978-1-56699-341-8(5))* Alban Institute, Inc.

Thompson, Linda J. Kingdom Building: A Labor of Love Journey. 2008. 73p. pap. 8.95 *(978-0-7414-4655-8(3))* Infinity Publishing.

Uvog, James. Once upon Internal Control: A tale of good & bad ways to implement internal controls in a local Church. 2008. 16p. 5.00 *(978-0-9774361-4-9(4))* Riverstone Finance Pr.

Vroom, Wim. Financing Cathedral Building in the Middle Ages: The Generosity of the Faithful. 2010. (ENG., Illus.). 734p. *(978-90-8964-035-2(5))* Amsterdam Univ. Pr.

Walley, Kenneth. Wealth Deployment in the Church. 2007. 108p. per. 10.99 *(978-1-60266-824-9(8))* Xulon Pr., Inc.

2009-2012 United Methodist Church Financial Records Handbook. 2009. 12.00 *(978-0-687-65573-1(0))* Abingdon Pr.

CHURCH FINANCE—EARLY CHURCH, CA. 30-600

Nickle, Keith F. The Collection: A Study in Paul's Strategy. 2009. 176p. pap. 20.00 *(978-1-60608-690-2(1))*, Wipf and Stock) Wipf & Stock Pubs.

Yasin, Ann Marie. Saints & Church Spaces in the Late Antique Mediterranean: Architecture, Cult, & Community. 2009. (Greek Culture in the Roman World Ser.). (ENG., Illus.). 360p. 107.00 *(978-0-521-76783-5(0))* Cambridge Univ. Pr.

CHURCH FLOWER ARRANGEMENT

see Flower Arrangement in Churches

CHURCH FURNITURE

see also Altarpieces; Altars; Choir Stalls; Fonts

Cox, J. Charles. English Church Fittings, Furniture & Accessories. 2008. 336p. per. *(978-1-905217-93-9(5))* Mills, Jeremy Publishing.

Cox, John Charles & Harvey, Alfred. English Church Furniture. 2008. 510p. 55.95 *(978-1-4366-6781-4(X))*; 512p. pap. 40.95 *(978-0-548-85728-1(8))* Kessinger Publishing, LLC.

Roe, Fred. Ancient Church Chests & Chairs. 2007. 144p. per. *(978-1-905217-80-9(3))* Mills, Jeremy Publishing.

Sadlowski, Erwin L. Sacred Furnishings of Churches. 2006. pap. 22.95 *(978-1-4286-5608-6(1))* Kessinger Publishing, LLC.

CHURCH GARDENS

Johnson, Norris Brock. Tenryuji: Life & Spirit of a Kyoto Garden. 2012. (ENG., Illus.). 368p. 39.95 **(978-1-61172-004-4(4))** Stone Bridge Pr.

CHURCH-GOING

see Church Attendance

CHURCH GOVERNMENT

see Church Polity

CHURCH GROUP WORK

see also Church Meetings; Prayer Groups

Addington, T. J. Leading from the Sandbox: How to Develop, Empower, & Release High-Impact Ministry Teams. 2010. (Becoming a Woman Of ... Ser.). 208p. pap. 14.99 *(978-1-60006-675-7(5))* NavPress Publishing Group.

Atkins, Jimmy Arthur. Serving Communities in Need. 2011. 112p. pap. **(978-3-8443-9931-8(3))** Lambert Academic Publishing.

Atkinson, John & Easum, Bill. Go Big with Small Groups: Eleven Steps to an Explosive Small Group Ministry. 2007. (Illus.). 122p. per. 16.00 *(978-0-687-49135-3(5))* Abingdon Pr.

Ballard, M. Russell. Counseling with Our Councils, Rev. Ed: Learning to Minister Together in the Church & in the Family. 2012. 26.99 **(978-1-60907-047-2(X))** Deseret Bk. Co.

The Bible in 90 Days: Whole-Church Challenge - Session 10 with Jack Modesett, 1 vol. 2009. 4.99 *(978-0-310-94835-3(5))*; 2.99 *(978-0-310-94836-0(3))*; 2.99 *(978-0-310-94834-6(7))* Zondervan.

The Bible in 90 Days: Whole-Church Challenge - Session 10 with John Walton, 1 vol. 2009. 2.99 *(978-0-310-94314-3(0))*; 2.99 *(978-0-310-94345-7(0))*; 4.99 *(978-0-310-94344-0(2))* Zondervan.

The Bible in 90 Days: Whole-Church Challenge - Session 11 with Jack Modesett, 1 vol. 2009. 2.99 *(978-0-310-94839-1(8))*; 4.99 *(978-0-310-94838-4(X))*; 2.99 *(978-0-310-94837-7(1))* Zondervan.

The Bible in 90 Days: Whole-Church Challenge - Session 11 with Mark Strauss, 1 vol. 2009. 2.99 *(978-0-310-94315-0(9))*; 4.99 *(978-0-310-94346-4(9))*; 2.99 *(978-0-310-94347-1(7))* Zondervan.

The Bible in 90 Days: Whole-Church Challenge - Session 12 with Jack Modesett, 1 vol. 2009. 2.99 *(978-0-310-94840-7(1))*; 2.99 *(978-0-310-94842-1(8))*; 4.99 *(978-0-310-94841-4(X))* Zondervan.

The Bible in 90 Days: Whole-Church Challenge - Session 12 with Mark Strauss, 1 vol. 2009. 4.99 *(978-0-310-94348-8(5))*; 2.99 *(978-0-310-94349-5(3))*; 2.99 *(978-0-310-94316-7(7))* Zondervan.

The Bible in 90 Days: Whole-Church Challenge - Session 13 with Jack Modesett, 1 vol. 2009. 2.99 *(978-0-310-94843-8(6))*; 2.99 *(978-0-310-94845-2(2))*; 4.99 *(978-0-310-94844-5(4))* Zondervan.

The Bible in 90 Days: Whole-Church Challenge - Session 13 with Mark Strauss, 1 vol. 2009. 2.99 *(978-0-310-94317-4(5))*; 4.99 *(978-0-310-94350-1(7))*; (ENG.). 2.99 *(978-0-310-94351-8(5))* Zondervan.

The Bible in 90 Days: Whole-Church Challenge - Session 14 with Jack Modesett, 1 vol. 2009. 2.99 *(978-0-310-94854-4(1))*; (ENG.). 4.99 *(978-0-310-94326-6(4))*; (ENG.). 2.99 *(978-0-310-94855-1(X))* Zondervan.

The Bible in 90 Days: Whole-Church Challenge - Session 14 with Mark Strauss, 1 vol. 2009. 2.99 *(978-0-310-94305-1(1))*; (ENG.). 4.99 *(978-0-310-94853-7(3))*; (ENG.). 2.99 *(978-0-310-94327-3(2))* Zondervan.

The Bible in 90 Days: Whole-Church Challenge - Session 2 with Jack Modesett, 1 vol. 2009. (ENG.). 2.99 *(978-0-310-94812-4(6))*; 2.99 *(978-0-310-94810-0(X))*; (ENG.). 4.99 *(978-0-310-94811-7(8))* Zondervan.

The Bible in 90 Days: Whole-Church Challenge - Session 2 with John Walton, 1 vol. 2009. 2.99 *(978-0-310-94306-8(X))*; (ENG.). 2.99 *(978-0-310-94329-7(9))*; (ENG.). 4.99 *(978-0-310-94328-0(0))* Zondervan.

The Bible in 90 Days: Whole-Church Challenge - Session 3 with Jack Modesett, 1 vol. 2009. 2.99 *(978-0-310-94813-1(4))*; (ENG.). 2.99 *(978-0-310-94815-5(0))*; (ENG.). 4.99 *(978-0-310-94814-8(2))* Zondervan.

The Bible in 90 Days: Whole-Church Challenge - Session 3 with John Walton, 1 vol. 2009. (ENG.). 4.99 *(978-0-310-94330-3(2))*; 2.99 *(978-0-310-94307-5(8))*; (ENG.). 2.99 *(978-0-310-94331-0(0))* Zondervan.

The Bible in 90 Days: Whole-Church Challenge - Session 4 with Jack Modesett, 1 vol. 2009. 2.99 *(978-0-310-94816-2(9))*; (ENG.). 2.99 *(978-0-310-94818-6(5))*; (ENG.). 4.99 *(978-0-310-94817-9(7))* Zondervan.

The Bible in 90 Days: Whole-Church Challenge - Session 4 with John Walton, 1 vol. 2009. (ENG.). 2.99 *(978-0-310-94333-4(7))*; 2.99 *(978-0-310-94308-2(6))*; (ENG.). 4.99 *(978-0-310-94332-7(9))* Zondervan.

The Bible in 90 Days: Whole-Church Challenge - Session 5 with Jack Modesett, 1 vol. 2009. (ENG.). 4.99 *(978-0-310-94820-9(7))*; (ENG.). 2.99 *(978-0-310-94821-6(5))*; 2.99 *(978-0-310-94819-3(3))* Zondervan.

The Bible in 90 Days: Whole-Church Challenge - Session 5 with John Walton, 1 vol. 2009. 2.99 *(978-0-310-94309-9(4))*; (ENG.). 4.99 *(978-0-310-94334-1(5))*; (ENG.). 2.99 *(978-0-310-94335-8(3))* Zondervan.

The Bible in 90 Days: Whole-Church Challenge - Session 6 with Jack Modesett, 1 vol. 2009. 2.99 *(978-0-310-94822-3(3))*; (ENG.). 2.99 *(978-0-310-94824-7(X))*; (ENG.). 4.99 *(978-0-310-94823-0(1))* Zondervan.

The Bible in 90 Days: Whole-Church Challenge - Session 6 with John Walton, 1 vol. 2009. (ENG.). 2.99 *(978-0-310-94337-2(X))*; (ENG.). 4.99 *(978-0-310-94336-5(1))*; 2.99 *(978-0-310-94310-5(8))* Zondervan.

The Bible in 90 Days: Whole-Church Challenge - Session 7 with Jack Modesett, 1 vol. 2009. (ENG.). 4.99 *(978-0-310-94826-1(6))*; 2.99 *(978-0-310-94825-4(8))*; (ENG.). 2.99 *(978-0-310-94827-8(4))* Zondervan.

The Bible in 90 Days: Whole-Church Challenge - Session 7 with John Walton, 1 vol. 2009. (ENG.). 2.99 *(978-0-310-94339-6(6))*; (ENG.). 4.99 *(978-0-310-94338-9(8))*; 2.99 *(978-0-310-94311-2(6))* Zondervan.

The Bible in 90 Days: Whole-Church Challenge - Session 8 with Jack Modesett, 1 vol. 2009. 2.99 *(978-0-310-94828-5(2))*; (ENG.). 2.99 *(978-0-310-94830-8(4))*; (ENG.). 4.99 *(978-0-310-94829-2(0))* Zondervan.

The Bible in 90 Days: Whole-Church Challenge - Session 8 with John Walton, 1 vol. 2009. (ENG.). 4.99 *(978-0-310-94340-2(X))*; (ENG.). 2.99 *(978-0-310-94341-9(8))*; 2.99 *(978-0-310-94312-9(4))* Zondervan.

The Bible in 90 Days: Whole-Church Challenge - Session 9 with Jack Modesett, 1 vol. 2009. 2.99 *(978-0-310-94831-5(2))*; (ENG.). 4.99 *(978-0-310-94832-2(0))*; (ENG.). 2.99 *(978-0-310-94833-9(9))* Zondervan.

The Bible in 90 Days: Whole-Church Challenge - Session 9 with John Walton, 1 vol. 2009. 4.99 *(978-0-310-94342-6(6))* Zondervan.

Bielo, James. Words upon the Word: An Ethnography of Evangelical Group Bible Study. 2009. (ENG.). 208p. 70.00 *(978-0-8147-9121-9(2))*; pap. 21.00 *(978-0-8147-9122-6(0))* New York Univ. Pr.

Boren, M. Scott. How Do We Get There from Here? Navigating the Transformation to Holistic Small Groups. 2007. (Illus.). 370p. per. 21.50 *(978-0-9788779-1-0(8))* Touch Pubns.

Boren, Scott. The Relational Way: From Small Group Structures to Holistic Life Connections. 2007. (Illus.). 276p. per. 21.50 *(978-0-9788779-0-3(X))* Touch Pubns.

Briars, Steve and Mandy. Homegroups: The EverythingYouNeedToKnowGuide. 2007. (ENG.). 171p. pap. 11.99 *(978-1-934068-07-6(1))* Authentic Media.

Brixey, Kimberly. The Essence of Leading Prolific Small Group Meetings: Leadership Package. 2007. 144p. per. 79.95 incl. DVD *(978-0-9793020-4-6(8))* R4C Ranch Productions.

Bushman, Tony & Hamilton-Holway, Bill. Gatherings: Small Group Ministry for Men. 2006. vii, 56p. pap. 10.00 *(978-1-55896-514-0(9)*, Skinner Hse. Bks.) Unitarian Universalist Assn.

Certain, Robert G. The Spiritual Quest: Christian Spiritual Direction in 12 Simple Steps. 2008. (Illus.). iii, 113p. pap. *(978-0-88280-160-5(0))* ETC Pubns.

City on a Hill Productions. Storm: Tough Questions about the Christian Faith Kit. 2007. 99.99 *(978-0-7847-1998-5(5))* Standard Publishing.

Collison, Brooke B. Know & Be Known: Small Groups That Nourish & Connect. 2007. *(978-1-56699-335-7(0))* Alban Institute, Inc.

Comiskey, Joel. How to Lead a Great Small Group Meeting: ... So People Want to Come Back. 2010. (Illus.). 137p. pap. 16.99 *(978-0-9825352-2-6(8))* Touch Pubns.

Conder, Tim & Rhodes, Daniel. Free for All: Rediscovering the Bible in Community. 2009. (Emersion). (Illus.). 256p. pap. 16.99 *(978-0-8010-7147-8(X))* Baker Bks.

Cooper, Ted. The Bible in 90 Days - Whole-Church Challenge: 14 Sessions, 1 vol. 2009. (ENG.). 160p. pap., instr.'s gde. ed. 9.99 *(978-0-310-94184-2(9))* Zondervan.

Craghan, John F., et al. The Word into Life: Year A: A Guide for Group Reflection on the Sunday Scripture. 2007. 176p. per. 9.95 *(978-0-7648-1626-0(8))* Liguori Pubns.

Crawford, Linda, et al. Group's Dinner & a Movie: G-Rated: Friendship, Faith, & Fun for All Ages. Rozum, Ann Marie, ed. 2007. (Illus.). 92p. per. 19.99 *(978-0-7644-3661-1(9))* Group Publishing, Inc.

Dantzer, Judy Elliott. The Big Book of Family Gatherings: For Parish Faith Formation. 2007. (Big Book Of Ser.). (Illus.). 212p. per. 24.95 *(978-1-59276-266-8(2))* Our Sunday Visitor, Publishing Div.

Decker, John & Decker, Sonja. Holy Spirit Empowered Small Groups: Shaping, Equipping, & Releasing Spirit-Formed Believers. 2006. (ENG.). 160p. pap. 12.99 *(978-1-59979-083-1(1)*, Creation Hse.) Charisma Media.

Dennis, Marie. Diversity of Vocations. 2008. (Catholic Spirituality for Adults Ser.). 142p. per. 14.00 *(978-1-57075-716-7(X))* Orbis Bks.

Diede, Brian, et al. Group's Dinner & a Movie: Adrenaline Rush: Flix for Guys. Rozum, Ann Marie, ed. 2007. (Illus.). 108p. per. 19.99 *(978-0-7644-3710-6(0))* Group Publishing, Inc.

Earley, Dave & Dempsey, Rod. The Pocket Guide to Leading a Small Group: 52 Ways to Help You & Your Small Group Grow. 2007. 263p. per. 9.95 *(978-0-9788779-2-7(6))* Touch Pubns.

Egli, Jim. Upward, Inward, Outward, Forward: Improving the 4 Dynamics of Your Small Group. 3rd ed. 2007. 71p. pap. 11.25 *(978-0-9788779-4-1(2))* Touch Pubns.

Fendall, Lon, et al. Practicing Discernment Together: Finding God's Way Forward in Decision Making. 2007. 145p. pap. 16.00 *(978-1-59498-009-1(8))* Barclay Pr., Inc.

Fryling, Alice. Seeking God Together: An Introduction to Group Spiritual Direction, 1 vol. 2008. (ENG.). 152p. pap. 15.00 *(978-0-8308-3524-9(5)*, IVP Bks.) InterVarsity Pr.

Gay Reese. Unbinding Your Heart: 40 Days of Prayer & Faith Sharing. 2008. (Real Life Evangelism Ser.). (Illus.). 162p. per. 19.99 *(978-0-8272-3805-3(3))* Chalice Pr.

Glenn, Mike & Broadman and Holman Publishers Staff. In Real Time: Authentic Young Adult Ministry As It Happens. 2009. (ENG.). 192p. pap. 12.99 *(978-0-8054-4694-4(X)*, B&H Bks.) B&H Publishing Group.

Greggo, Stephen P. Trekking Toward Wholeness: A Resource for Care Group Leaders. 2008. (ENG.). 293p. pap. 23.00 *(978-0-8308-2824-1(9)*, IVP Acad.) InterVarsity Pr.

Grubb, Norman. Touching the Invisible. 2007. (ENG.). 95p. mass mkt. 5.99 *(978-0-87508-975-1(5))* CLC Pubns.

Guidelines for Leading Your Congregation 2009-2012 - Small Group Ministries: Where Two or Three Are Gathered ... 2008. 2.95 *(978-0-687-64841-2(6))* Abingdon Pr.

Guidelines for Leading Your Congregation 2009-2012 - Small Membership Church: Serving with Significance in Your Context. 2008. 2.95 *(978-0-687-64952-5(8))* Abingdon Pr.

Henry, Barbara. Making Disciples in Your Community: Coming Together to Grow in Christ. 2009. (Following God Discipleship Ser.). (ENG.). 176p. (gr. 11). pap. 14.99 *(978-0-89957-346-5(0))* AMG Pubs.

Hill, Harriet S. & Hill, Margaret. Translating the Bible into Action: How the Bible Can Be Relevant in All Languages & Cultures. 2008. (Illus.). 320p. pap. *(978-1-903689-53-0(8))* Piquant Editions Ltd.

Holladay, Tom, et al. The Bible: 11 Core Truths to Build Your Life On, 1 vol. 2008. (Foundations Ser.). (ENG., Illus.). 80p. (gr. 13). pap. 6.99 *(978-0-310-27670-8(5))* Zondervan.

—Holy Spirit: Small Group Study, 1 vol. 2008. (Foundations Ser.). (ENG., Illus.). 80p. pap. 6.99 *(978-0-310-27676-0(4))* Zondervan.

Hybels, Bill, et al. Romans 8: Inseparable, 1 vol. 2009. (New Community Bible Study Ser.). (ENG.). 96p. pap. 7.99 *(978-0-310-28059-0(1))* Zondervan.

Johnson, Jan. Storm Leader's Guide. 2007. per. 6.99 *(978-0-7847-1999-2(3))* Standard Publishing.

Johnson, Kurt W. Successful Small Groups: From Theory to Service. 2011. *(978-0-8280-2561-4(4))* Review & Herald Publishing Assn.

Kirk, J. Alex, et al. Small Group Leaders' Handbook: Developing Transformational Communities. 2009. (ENG.). 180p. pap. 16.00 *(978-0-8308-2112-9(0)*, IVP Conn.) InterVarsity Pr.

Laster, John E. Gaining Traction: Filed Guide for Leadership Teams. 2007. (Illus.). 166p. per. 16.99 *(978-0-8272-1253-4(4))* Chalice Pr.

Latini, Theresa F. The Church & the Crisis of Community: A Practical Theology of Small Group Ministry. 2011. 248p. pap. 29.00 *(978-0-8028-6586-1(0))* Eerdmans, William B. Publishing Co.

Lentz, Dan. Let's Get Started! How to Begin Your Small Groups Ministry. 2007. (Small Group Help Guides). (Illus.). 96p. per. 8.99 *(978-0-7847-2073-8(6))* Standard Publishing.

MacDowell, Katherine. Sacred Groves: Creating & Sustaining Neopagan Covens. 2009. 148p. pap. 16.99 *(978-0-557-08864-5(X))* Lulu Enterprises Inc.

McPherson, Miles. DO Something! Participant's Guide: Make Your Life Count, 1 vol. 2009. (ENG.). 80p. pap. 9.99 *(978-0-8010-7249-9(2))* Baker Bks.

—DO Something! Small Group Leader's Kit: Make Your Life Count, 1 vol. 2009. (ENG.). 49.99 *(978-0-8010-7250-5(6))* Baker Bks.

Mead, Loren B. & Alban, Billie. Creating the Future Together: Large Group Methods for Faith Communities. 2008. *(978-1-56699-364-7(4))* Alban Institute, Inc.

Mews, Sally L. Catholics Continuing the Journey: A Faith-Sharing Program for Small Groups. 2006. (Illus.). 31p. pap. 5.95 *(978-0-7648-1503-4(2))* Liguori Pubns.

Miller, Tara & Peppers, Jenn. Finding the Flow: A Guide for Leading Small Groups & Gatherings. 2008. (ENG.). 240p. pap. 17.00 *(978-0-8308-1094-9(3)*, IVP Conn.) InterVarsity Pr.

Mitchell, Joyce A. Teams Work: A No-Nonsense Approach for Achieving More Together. 2008. (ENG., Illus.). 160p. pap. 12.99 *(978-1-59669-211-4(1))* New Hope Pubs.

Murren, Doug. Neutralizing Fear in Your Congregation. pap. 14.00 *(978-0-687-04372-9(7))* Abingdon Pr.

Neighbour, Ralph W., Jr. Christ's Basic Bodies: Embracing God's Presence, Power, & Purposes in True Biblical Community. 2008. (Illus.). 254p. pap. 21.50 *(978-0-9788779-8-9(5))* Touch Pubns.

Neighbour, Randall G. The Naked Truth about Small Group Ministry: When It Won't Work & What to Do about It. 2009. (Illus.). 255p. pap. 20.99 *(978-0-9788779-6-5(9))* Touch Pubns.

Nielson, Kathleen Buswell. Proverbs: The Ways of Wisdom. 2007. (Living Word Bible Studies). 182p. spiral bd. 12.99 *(978-1-59638-081-3(0))* P & R Publishing.

O'Halloran, James. The Brendan Book of Prayer for Small Groups. 2008. (ENG.). 144p. pap. 18.95 *(978-1-85607-626-5(1))* Columba Pr. IRL. Dist: Dufour Editions, Inc.

—Three Dancers One Dance: Vision & Practicalities of Small Christian Communities & Groups. 2010. (ENG.). 69p. pap. 14.95 *(978-1-85607-653-1(9))* Columba Pr. IRL. Dist: Dufour Editions, Inc.

Oladimeji, Seyi. Growing Your Church from Within: Building A Dynamic Home-Fellowship System. 2011. (Illus.). 116p. pap. 15.65 *(978-1-4567-8535-2(4))* AuthorHouse.

Osborne, Larry. Sticky Church, 1 vol. 2008. (Leadership Network Innovation Ser.). (ENG., Illus.). 208p. pap. 18.99 *(978-0-310-28508-3(9))* Zondervan.

Pettit, Paul. Foundations of Spiritual Formation: A Community Approach to Becoming Like Christ. Pettit, Paul, ed. 2008. 320p. pap. 22.99 *(978-0-8254-3469-3(6))* Kregel Pubns.

Powell, Kara. The Christian Life. Powell, Kara, ed. 2009. (Uncommon Ser.). (ENG., Illus.). 192p. (J). pap. 14.99 *(978-0-8307-4642-2(0))* Gospel Light Pubns.

Robinson, Christine C. & Hawkins, Alicia. Soul to Soul: Fourteen Gatherings for Reflection & Sharing. 2011. E-Book ***(978-1-55896-652-9(8))***; (ENG.). 1p. pap. 14.00 ***(978-1-55896-649-9(8))*** Unitarian Universalist Assn. (Skinner Hse. Bks.).

Robinson, Christine C., et al. Heart to Heart: Fourteen Gatherings for Reflection & Sharing. 2009. (ENG.). 1p. pap. 14.00 *(978-1-55896-550-8(5)*, Skinner Hse. Bks.) Unitarian Universalist Assn.

Satrape, Ron. Retooling the Church: Finding Your Place in Ministry. 2007. 204p. per. 15.99 *(978-0-7684-2438-6(0))* Destiny Image Pubs.

Schnase, Robert. Cultivating Fruitfulness: Five Weeks of Prayer & Practice for Congregations. 2008. 94p. pap. 7.00 *(978-0-687-65433-8(5))* Abingdon Pr.

Searcy, Nelson & Thomas, Kerrick. Activate: An Entirely New Approach to Small Groups. 2008. (ENG., Illus.). 224p. pap. 14.99 *(978-0-8307-4566-1(1))* Gospel Light Pubns.

Shepherd, Sheri Rose. His Princess Retreat Weekend. 2007. (ENG., Illus.). 192p. per. 11.99 *(978-1-934384-10-7(0))* Treasure Publishing.

Sikora, Pat J. Why Didn't You Warn Me? How to Deal with Challenging Group Members. 2007. (Small Group Help Guides). (Illus.). 96p. per. 8.99 *(978-0-7847-2075-2(4))* Standard Publishing.

Stevens, Woodie J. & Sailors, J. D. Every Paul Needs a Timothy: Blessings for Teachers & Small-Group Leaders. 2009. (ENG.). 64p. pap. 4.99 *(978-0-8341-2476-9(9)*, 9780834124769) Beacon Hill Pr. of Kansas City.

Stewart, Teena. Successful Small Groups: From Concept to Practice. 2007. (ENG., Illus.). 192p. per. 15.99 *(978-0-8341-2337-3(1)*, 083-412-3371) Beacon Hill Pr. of Kansas City.

Tripp, Paul David. A Quest for More Small Group & Disscusion Guide: Living for Something Bigger Than You. Breece, Michael, ed. ldr.'s ed. 2008. (ENG.). 168p. per. 8.99 *(978-0-9785567-8-5(X))* New Growth Pr.

Watson, Gayle Turner. Guide for Covenant Discipleship Groups. 2011. 80p. pap. 11.00 ***(978-1-61097-396-0(8)***, Wipf and Stock) Wipf & Stock Pubs.

Wieman, Roxanne, ed. Group's Emergency Response Handbook: For Small Group Leaders. 2006. (Illus.). 160p. per. 14.99 *(978-0-7644-3181-4(1))* Group Publishing, Inc.

Wink, Walter. Transforming Bible Study. 2009. 176p. pap. 20.00 *(978-1-60608-665-0(0)*, Wipf and Stock) Wipf & Stock Pubs.

Zondervan Publishing Staff. The Bible in 90 Days: Whole-Church Challenge Leader's Pack, 1 vol. 2009. (ENG.). pap. 54.99 *(978-0-310-94185-9(7))* Zondervan.

CHURCH GROUP WORK WITH YOUTH

Baker, Dori Grinenko & Mercer, Joyce A. Lives to Offer: Accompanying Youth on Their Vocational Quests. 2007. (Youth Ministry Alternatives Ser.). 191p. per. *(978-0-8298-1726-3(3))* Pilgrim Pr., The/United Church Pr.

Baker, Jenny. Heart Soul Mind Strength: 50 Creative Worship Ideas for Youth Groups, 1 vol. 2009. 200p. pap. 14.99 *(978-0-8254-6302-0(5)*, Monarch Bks.) Lion Hudson PLC GBR. Dist: Kregel Pubns.

Baughman, Michael. Worship Feast Advent & Christmas: Worship Experiences to Celebrate the Season. Youngman, Jennifer, ed. 2008. 48p. pap. 20.00 *(978-0-687-46542-2(7))* Abingdon Pr.

Bowen, John P. Growing up Christian: Why Young People Stay in Church, Leave Church, & (Sometimes) Come Back to Church. 2010. *(978-1-57383-431-5(9))* Regent College Publishing.

Burns, Jim. Dramas, Skits & Sketches. 2009. (Uncommon Ser.). (ENG.). 224p. (J). (gr. 6-12). 34.99 *(978-0-8307-4791-7(5))* Gospel Light Pubns.

—The Life of Jesus. 2009. (Uncommon Ser.). (ENG.). 208p. (J). (gr. 9-12). pap. 14.99 *(978-0-8307-4726-9(5))* Gospel Light Pubns.

Caro, Stephanie. 99 Thoughts for Smaller Church Youth Workers: Doing More with Less. 2011. pap. *(978-0-7644-6606-9(2))* Group Publishing, Inc.

Chromey, Rick & Caro, Stephanie. Thriving Youth Ministry in Smaller Churches: Secrets for Cultivating a Dynamic Youth Ministry. 2009. pap. *(978-0-7644-4051-9(9))* Group Publishing, Inc.

Crabtree, Jack. Better Safe Than Sued, 1 vol. 2008. (ENG.). 208p. pap. 16.99 *(978-0-310-28261-7(6))* Zondervan.

Davis, Jimmie L. Girls' Ministry Idea Book. 2009. 125p. pap. 14.95 *(978-1-4158-6729-7(1))* LifeWay Christian Resources.

Durso, Chris. Misfit: Dealing with Our God-Given Discomfort, 1 vol. 2011. (ENG.). 144p. pap. 9.99 *(978-0-310-67117-6(5))* Zondervan.

Edie, Fred P. Book, Bath, Table, & Time: Christian Worship as Source & Resource for Youth Ministry. 2007. (Youth Ministry Alternatives Ser.). 258p. per. *(978-0-8298-1744-7(1))* Pilgrim Pr., The/United Church Pr.

Ferguson, Tim. Not the Same Old, Done-It-Before Youth Meetings. 2007. 376p. 31.99 *(978-1-60266-006-9(9))*; per. 19.99 *(978-1-60266-005-2(0))* Xulon Pr., Inc.

Folmsbee, Chris. A New Kind of Youth Ministry, 1 vol. 2006. (ENG., Illus.). 160p. (gr. 13). pap. 15.99 *(978-0-310-26989-2(X))* Zondervan.

—Story, Signs, & Sacred Rhythms: A Narrative Approach to Youth Ministry, 1 vol. 2010. (ENG.). 192p. 14.99 *(978-0-310-29199-2(2))* Zondervan.

Franklin, Paul. Cool Beans. 2010. 70p. pap. 16.95 *(978-1-4452-4889-9(1))* Lulu Enterprises Inc.

Gundry, Stanley N. & Yaconelli, Mike. Getting Fired for the Glory of God, 1 vol. 2008. (ENG.). 144p. 16.99 *(978-0-310-28358-4(2))* Zondervan.

Hawkins, Tim. Disciples Who Will Last: How to Develop an Effective Youth Ministry with Lasting Impact. 2010. 212p. pap. *(978-1-906334-62-8(5))* Good Bk. Co.

Heflin, Houston. Youth Pastor: The Theology & Practice of Youth Ministry. 2009. 160p. pap. 16.00 *(978-0-687-65054-5(2))* Abingdon Pr.

Kageler, Len. The Volunteer's Field Guide to Youth Ministry: Practical Ways to Make a Permanent Difference in Teenagers. 2011. pap. *(978-0-7644-4682-5(7))* Group Publishing, Inc.

—The Youth Ministry Survival Guide: How to Thrive & Last for the Long Haul, 1 vol. 2008. (ENG., Illus.). 208p. (gr. 13). pap. 14.99 *(978-0-310-27663-0(2))* Zondervan.

Kirk, Brian T. & Thorne, Jacob. Missional Youth Ministry: Moving from Gathering Teenagers to Scattering Disciples, 1 vol. 2011. (ENG.). 256p. pap. 16.99 *(978-0-310-57884-0(1))* Zondervan.

Lawrence, Joy-Elizabeth, et al. Scary, Gross & Weird Stories from the Bible: Bloody Tent Pegs, Disembodied Fingers, & Suicidal Pigs... the Truths Buried in the Bizarre. Holburn, Kate S., ed. 2007. (Illus.). 133p. (J). (gr. 3-7). per. 19.99 *(978-0-7644-3699-7(8))* Group Publishing, Inc.

Linhart, Terry. High School Talksheets, 1 vol. 2008. (TalkSheets Ser.). (ENG.). 112p. pap. 16.99 *(978-0-310-28552-6(6))* Zondervan.

—Middle School Talksheets: 50 Ready-to-Use Discussions on the Life of Christ, 1 vol. 2008. (TalkSheets Ser.). (ENG.). 112p. pap. 16.99 *(978-0-310-28553-3(4))* Zondervan.

Lynn, David. High School: 50 Ready-to-Use New Testament Discussions, 1 vol. 2009. (TalkSheets Ser.). (ENG.). 128p. pap. 14.99 *(978-0-310-66871-8(9))* Zondervan.

—Middle School Talksheets, 1 vol. 2009. (TalkSheets Ser.). (ENG.). 128p. pap. 14.99 *(978-0-310-66872-5(7))* Zondervan.

Lynn, David & Davis, Rick. 52 Discussions to Confirm the Faith of Your Teenagers, 1 vol. 2009. (TalkSheets Ser.). (ENG.). 128p. pap. 14.99 *(978-0-310-66873-2(5))* Zondervan.

Lyons, Gabe & Fermi Project Staff. UnChristian: Change the Perception. 2009. (Society Room Ser.). 70.00 *(978-0-8010-0317-2(2))* Baker Bks.

McAdoo, Jennifer, et al. Journeys of the Spirit: Planning & Leading Mission Trips with Youth. 2010. pap. 15.00 ***(978-1-55896-572-0(6))*** Unitarian Universalist Assn.

McKee, Jonathan. Getting Students to Show Up: Practical Ideas for Any Outreach Event - from 10 To 10,000, 1 vol. 2007. (ENG.). 144p. (gr. 13). pap. 12.99 *(978-0-310-27216-8(5))* Zondervan.

Millspaugh, Sarah Gibb, et al. Coming of Age Handbook for Congregations. 2009. (Illus.). xii, 257p. 30.00 ***(978-1-55896-540-9(8))*** Unitarian Universalist Assn.

Mitchell, Alison. FAQs: Biblical Answers to Youth & Children's Leaders' Questions. 2010. (Illus.). 160p. pap. *(978-1-905564-45-3(7))* Good Bk. Co.

Mitchell, Claudia & Goad, Kim. For Planning Events, Retreats, & Small Groups. ldr.'s ed. 2009. (One Girl Ser.). (ENG.). 144p. (YA). pap. 19.99 *(978-0-7847-2231-2(5))* Standard Publishing.

Moser, Ken. Changing the World 2: Creative Christian Ideas for Youth Groups. 2010. 130p. pap. *(978-1-906334-25-3(0))* Good Bk. Co.

Nelson, Carl Ellis. Growing up Christian: A Congregational Strategy for Nurturing Disciples. 2008. pap. 16.00 *(978-1-57312-523-9(7))* Smyth & Helwys Publishing, Inc.

Penner, Marv. Building & Mobilizing Teams. 2009. (Youth Ministry in the Trenches Ser.). (ENG.). 144p. (YA). pap. 12.99 *(978-0-7847-2316-6(8))* Standard Publishing.

Powell, Kara. Friends & Peer Pressure. 2009. (Uncommon Ser.). (ENG.). 192p. (J). (gr. 6-8). 14.99 *(978-0-8307-4790-0(7))* Gospel Light Pubns.

Powell, Kara, ed. The Life of Jesus. 2009. (Uncommon Ser.). (ENG.). 192p. (J). pap. 14.99 *(978-0-8307-4643-9(9))* Gospel Light Pubns.

Powell, Kara Eckmann. The Armor of God. 2011. pap. ***(978-0-8307-5899-9(2))*** Gospel Light Pubns.

Provencher, Maureen P. Never Too Young to Lead: Developing Leadership in Young Adolescents. 2006. 96p. per. 24.25 *(978-0-88489-873-3(3))* St. Mary's Pr.

Sandler, Lauren. Righteous: Dispatches from the Evangelical Youth Movement. 2007. (ENG., Illus.). 272p. (gr. 12-18). 15.00 *(978-0-14-311237-2(6)*, Penguin (Non-Classics)) Penguin Group (USA) Inc.

Schulenburg, Brian. When I: 500 Sentence-Finishers to Get Your Students Talking, 1 vol. 2008. (Quick Questions Ser.). (ENG.). 144p. pap. 10.99 *(978-0-310-28327-0(2))* Zondervan.

Singer-Towns, Brian. Biblical Literacy Made Easy: A Practical Guide for Catechists, Teachers, & Youth Ministers. 2008. (Illus.). 69p. pap. 7.25 *(978-0-88489-956-3(X))* St. Mary's Pr.

SkillAbilities for Youth Ministries. 72.00 *(978-0-687-07785-4(0))* Abingdon Pr.

Taylor, Adam. Mobilizing Hope: Faith-Inspired Activism for a Post-Civil Rights Generation. 2010. (ENG.). 238p. pap. 18.00 *(978-0-8308-3837-0(6)*, IVP Bks.) InterVarsity Pr.

Theisen, Michael. FaithSharing for Teens: 25 Experiences That Connect Faith & Life. 2007. (Illus.). 111p. per. 22.00 *(978-0-88489-946-4(2))* St. Mary's Pr.

Young, Julie. The Cyo in Indianapolis & Central Indiana. 2011. 160p. pap. 19.99 ***(978-1-60949-206-9(4))*** History Pr., The.

CHURCH GROWTH

Anyang, John. Our Dying Churches & the Missing Link. 2011. 152p. 25.00 *(978-1-4269-5021-6(7))*; pap. 15.00 *(978-1-4269-5020-9(9))* Trafford Publishing.

Archbishop's Council on Mission and Foreign Affairs. Mission-Shaped Church: Church Planting & Fresh Expressions in A Changing Context. 2nd ed. 2010. 192p. pap. 20.00 *(978-1-59627-126-5(4)*, Seabury Bks.) Church Publishing, Inc.

Arment, Ben. Church in the Making: What Makes or Breaks a New Church Before It Starts. 2010. (ENG.). 208p. 17.99 *(978-0-8054-6473-3(5)*, B&H Bks.) B&H Publishing Group.

Arview, Tim. Firefall Restoring Power to the Body of Christ. 2011. 38p. pap. 16.95 ***(978-1-4560-7067-0(3))*** PublishAmerica, Inc.

Ballard, M. Russell. Counseling with Our Councils, Rev. Ed: Learning to Minister Together in the Church & in the Family. 2012. 26.99 ***(978-1-60907-047-2(X))*** Deseret Bk. Co.

Bass, Diana Butler. Christianity for the Rest of Us: How the Neighborhood Church Is Transforming the Faith. 2007. (ENG.). 336p. pap. 14.99 *(978-0-06-085949-7(0)*, HarperOne) HarperCollins Pubs.

Bell, Michale. Constant Contact. 2009. pap. 12.95 *(978-1-61534-466-1(X))* Independent Pub.

Belote, Thom. The Growing Church: Insights from Unitarian Universalist Ministers. 2010. pap. 12.00 *(978-1-55896-559-1(9)*, Skinner Hse. Bks.) Unitarian Universalist Assn.

Benesh, Sean. Metrospiritual: The Geography of Church Planting. 2011. 190p. pap. 22.00 *(978-1-60899-943-9(2)*, Resource Pubns.) Wipf & Stock Pubs.

Bickers, Dennis W. Intentional Ministry in a Not-So-Mega Church: Becoming a Missional Community. 2009. (ENG.). 160p. pap. 13.99 *(978-0-8341-2434-9(3)*, 9780834124349) Beacon Hill Pr. of Kansas City.

Böhlemann, Peter. Wie die Kirche wachsen kann und was sie davon abhält. 2009. (GER., Illus.). 139p. (C). pap. 22.00 *(978-3-525-60424-3(6))* Vandenhoeck & Ruprecht GmbH & Co. KG DEU. Dist: ISD.

Borden, Paul. Direct Hit: Aiming Real Leaders at the Mission Field. 2006. (Convergence eBook Ser.). 159p. per. 20.00 *(978-0-687-33194-9(3))* Abingdon Pr.

Boshart, David W. Becoming Missional: Denominations & New Church Development in Complex Social Contexts. 2010. 182p. pap. 21.00 *(978-1-60899-698-8(0)*, Wipf and Stock) Wipf & Stock Pubs.

Bowers, Laurene Beth. Designing Contemporary Congregations: Strategies to Attract Those under Fifty. 2008. 128p. pap. 14.00 *(978-0-8298-1789-8(1))* Pilgrim Pr., The/United Church Pr.

Bridges, Leander. Building the Black Church: 7 Curses Facing the Black Church. 2010. pap. 9.99 *(978-1-61663-310-3(7))* Tate Publishing & Enterprises, LLC.

Browning, David. Deliberate Simplicity, 1 vol. 2009. (Leadership Network Innovation Ser.). (ENG.). 208p. pap. 18.99 *(978-0-310-28567-0(4))* Zondervan.

Bunn, Tim W. God's Plan for Church Planting. 2006. pap. 0.00 *(978-0-9769622-6-7(8))* IMD Pr.

—God's Plan for Church Planting - Hindi. 2007. per. 14.95 *(978-0-9788201-0-7(X))* IMD Pr.

—God's Plan for Church Planting - Spanish: Church Planting Manual Using God's Timeless, Supra-Cultural Principles. 2007. per. 7.95 *(978-0-9788201-4-5(2))* IMD Pr.

—God's Plan for Church Planting - Telugu. 2007. per. 14.95 *(978-0-9788201-1-4(8))* IMD Pr.

—God's Plan for Church Planting, Revised Edition: Church Planting Manual Using God's Timeless, Supra-Cultural Principles. rev. ed. 2007. per. 0.00 *(978-0-9788201-5-2(0))* IMD Pr.

Callahan, Kennon L. The Twelve Keys: An Approach for Grassroots, Key Leaders, & Pastors Together. 2nd ldr.'s ed. 2010. (ENG., Illus.). 224p. 22.95 *(978-0-470-55928-4(4)*, Jossey-Bass) Wiley, John & Sons, Inc.

—The Twelve Keys Bible Study. 2010. (ENG., Illus.). 96p. pap. 12.95 *(978-0-470-55916-1(0)*, Jossey-Bass) Wiley, John & Sons, Inc.

Cao, Nanlai. Constructing China's Jerusalem: Christians, Power, & Place in Contemporary Wenzhou. 2010. (Contemporary Issues in Asia & Pacific Ser.). (ENG., Illus.). 232p. 55.00 *(978-0-8047-7080-4(8))*; pap. 21.95 *(978-0-8047-7360-7(2))* Stanford Univ. Pr.

Capers Jr., William T. Hit the Ground Running in Your Ministry: Fundamental Principles for Ministry Growth. 2011. 158p. pap. 24.95 ***(978-1-4560-8349-6(X))*** PublishAmerica, Inc.

Carter, Gary W. The Small Town Mega Church. 2010. 226p. pap. *(978-1-926676-90-6(4))* Word Alive Pr.

Catt, Michael. Prepare for Rain: The Story of a Church That Believed God for the Impossible. 2007. (ENG., Illus.). 183p. pap. 12.99 *(978-0-87508-977-5(1))* CLC Pubns.

Comiskey, Joel. The Church That Multiplies: Growing a Healthy Cell Church in North America. 2007. (ENG., Illus.). 183p. per. 14.95 *(978-0-9790679-3-8(6)*, CCS Publishing) CCS Pubs.

—Plantando Iglesias Que Se Reproducen. 2010. 208p. pap. 14.95 *(978-0-9843110-5-7(X)*, CCS Publishing) CCS Pubs.

—Planting Churches that Reproduce: Starting a Network of Simple Churches. 2008. (ENG.). 205p. pap. 15.95 *(978-0-9790679-6-9(0)*, CCS Publishing) CCS Pubs.

Cootsona, Gregory S. The Church of the Last Stop: The Story of Bidwell Presbyterian Church. 2007. (Illus.). 28p. 1.00 *(978-0-664-50295-9(4))* Geneva Pr.

Dale, Robert D. Cultivating Perennial Churches: Your Guide to Long-Term Growth. 2008. xii, 148p. 19.99 *(978-0-8272-0512-3(0))* Chalice Pr.

Dinkler, Fred. Diary of a Mountain Preacher. 94p. 6.95 *(978-1-56794-237-8(7))* Star Bible & Tract Corp.

Dodoo, Robert Albert. Church Planting. 2008. (ENG.). 226p. 20.99 *(978-9988-596-01-9(4))* Parchment Hse. GHA. Dist: STL Distribution North America.

Easum, William. Preaching for Church Transformation. 2010. 128p. pap. 13.00 *(978-1-4267-1062-9(3))* Abingdon Pr.

Eby, David. Power Preaching for Church Growth: Revised updated Version. 2009. (ENG.). 256p. 17.99 *(978-1-84550-434-2(8)*, Mentor) Christian Focus Pubns. GBR. Dist: STL Distribution North America.

Edwards, Gene. How to Start a House Church from Scratch. 2007. per. 8.95 *(978-0-9778033-7-8(6))* Seedsowers, The.

—Why So Many House Churches Fail & What to do about It. 2007. per. 7.95 *(978-0-9778033-8-5(4))* Seedsowers, The.

Eshleman, J. David. Now Go Forward: Reaching Out to Grow Your Congregation. 2009. pap. 19.99 *(978-0-8361-9445-6(4))* Herald Pr.

Evangelism & Church Growth Reference Library, 21 bks., Set. E-Book 29.99 incl. cd-rom *(978-0-8307-2520-5(2)*, Gospel Light) Gospel Light Pubns.

Gallagher, Carol J. Reweaving the Sacred: A Practical Guide to Change & Growth for Challenged Congregations. 2008. 144p. pap. 16.00 *(978-0-89869-588-5(0))* Church Publishing, Inc.

Galloway, Dale E. & Bird, Warren. Innovative Transitions: How Change Can Take Your Church to the Next Level. 2007. (ENG.). 160p. per. 14.99 *(978-0-8341-2339-7(8)*, 083-412-3398) Beacon Hill Pr. of Kansas City.

Garrison, Becky. Ancient Future Disciples: Meeting Jesus in Mission-Shaped Ministries. 2011. E-Book ***(978-1-59627-232-3(5)***, Seabury Bks.) Church Publishing, Inc.

—Starting from Zero with $0: Building Mission-Shaped Ministries on a Shoestring. 2010. xiv, 154p. ***(978-1-59627-141-8(8))***; E-Book ***(978-1-59627-142-5(6))*** Church Publishing, Inc. (Seabury Bks.).

Gay, Doug. Remixing the Church: Towards an Emerging Ecclesiology. 2011. 224p. pap. 30.00 *(978-0-334-04396-5(4)*, SCM Pr.) Hymns Ancient & Modern Ltd GBR. Dist: Westminster John Knox Pr.

Gibbs, Eddie & Cohick, Lynn. ChurchMorph: How Megatrends Are Reshaping Christian Communities, 1 vol. 2009. (Allelon Missional Ser.). (Illus.). 224p. (C). pap. 20.00 *(978-0-8010-3762-7(X))* Baker Academic.

Gifford, Mary Louise. The Turnaround Church: Inspiration & Tools for Life-Sustaining Change. 2009. *(978-1-56699-393-7(8))* Alban Institute, Inc.

Global Pathway: A Pastor's Guide to Building a Great Commission Church. 2006. *(978-0-9786792-0-0(2))* Calvary International.

God's Plan for Church Planting - Punjabi. 2007. per. 14.95 *(978-0-9788201-2-1(6))* IMD Pr.

Goodhew, David. Church Growth in Britain, 1980-2010: Vitality of Contemporary Christianity. 2012. (Ashgate Contemporary Ecclesiology Ser.). 240p. 99.95 ***(978-1-4094-2577-9(0))*** Ashgate Publishing Co.

Goodhew, David, ed. Church Growth in Britain, 1980-2010: Vitality of Contemporary Christianity. 2012. (Ashgate Contemporary Ecclesiology Ser.). 240p. pap. 34.95 ***(978-1-4094-2576-2(2))*** Ashgate Publishing Co.

Goodpaster, Larry M. There's Power in the Connection: Building a Network of Dynamic Congregations. 2008. 146p. pap. 16.00 *(978-0-687-64979-2(X))* Abingdon Pr.

Gorini, Frederick D. Truth Be Told: A Sequel to the Unkonwn God. 2008. 248p. pap. 15.99 *(978-1-60791-139-5(6))* Xulon Pr., Inc.

Green, Hollis. Titanic Lessons. 2007. 120p. per. 14.95 *(978-0-9796019-6-5(7))* Global Education Advance.

Greenway, Jeffrey E. Make Room to Grow: Transform the Church Without Killing the Congregation. 2007. 72p. per. 10.00 *(978-0-687-49155-1(X))* Abingdon Pr.

Griffith, Jim & Easum, Bill. Ten Most Common Mistakes Made by New Church Starts. 2008. 122p. pap. 19.99 *(978-0-8272-3647-9(6))* Chalice Pr.

Guidelines for Leading Your Congregation 2009-2012 - Evangelism: Sharing the Good News. 2008. 2.95 *(978-0-687-64921-1(8))* Abingdon Pr.

Guidry, Dustin. Turning the Ship. 2009. 164p. 22.99 *(978-1-60791-263-7(5))*; pap. 14.99 *(978-1-60791-262-0(7))* Xulon Pr., Inc.

Haggard, Ted. Dog Training, Fly Fishing, & Sharing Christ in the 21st Century: Empowering Your Church to Build Community Through Shared Interests, 0 vols. 2008. (Illus.). 224p. pap. 14.99 *(978-0-8499-2897-0(4))* Nelson, Thomas Inc.

Hamilton, Adam. Selling Swimsuits in the Arcti. 2006. 72p. pap. 9.50 *(978-0-687-46530-9(3))* Abingdon Pr.

—Selling Swimsuits in the Arctic: Seven Simple Keys to Growing Churches. ldr.'s ed. 2006. (Illus.). 99.00 incl. cd-rom *(978-0-687-33393-6(8))* Abingdon Pr.

Hammer, Randy. 52 Ways to Ignite Your Congregation — Practical Hospitality. 2009. *(978-0-8298-1825-3(1))* Pilgrim Pr., The/United Church Pr.

Harding, Kevass J. Can These Bones Live? Bringing New Life to a Dying Church. 2007. 90p. per. 14.00 *(978-0-687-33557-2(4))* Abingdon Pr.

Harmon Sr., E. Ken. Growing God's Kingdom. 2008. 124p. pap. 10.99 *(978-1-60477-972-1(1))* Xulon Pr., Inc.

Harrison, Rodney, et al. Spin-off Churches: How One Church Successfully Plants Another. 2008. (ENG.). 336p. (C). pap. 24.99 *(978-0-8054-4685-2(0)*, B&H Academic) B&H Publishing Group.

Hawkins, Clevester. Scratch Where They Itch: A Model for Enhancing Christian Ministry Participation. 2011. 181p. pap. 14.95 *(978-1-4327-5265-1(0))* Outskirts Pr., Inc.

Hemphill, Ken & Hemphill, Paula. Splash: Show People Love & Share Him. 2011. pap. 4.99 ***(978-1-4276-5246-1(5))*** Aardvark Global Publishing.

Heward-Mills, Dag. The Mega Church: How to Make Your Church Grow. 2007. (ENG.). 224p. pap. 10.99 *(978-9988-596-48-4(0))* Parchment Hse. GHA. Dist: STL Distribution North America.

Hirsch, Alan & Catchim, Tim. The Permanent Revolution: Apostolic Imagination & Practice for the 21st Century Church. 2012. (Jossey-Bass Leadership Network Ser.: 57). (ENG., Illus.). 368p. 24.95 ***(978-0-470-90774-0(6)***, Jossey-Bass) Wiley, John & Sons, Inc.

Holmes, Greg. If He Builds It, They Will Come: The Secret to True Church Growth. 2007. 254p. per. 15.99 *(978-0-7684-2508-6(5))* Destiny Image Pubs.

Hooker, Morna D. Holiness & Mission: Learning from the Early Church about Mission in City Contexts. 2010. (ENG.). viii, 124p. pap. 30.00 *(978-0-334-04381-2(6)*, SCM Pr.) Hymns Ancient & Modern Ltd GBR. Dist: Westminster John Knox Pr.

Hornsby, Billy. The Attractional Church: Growth Through a Refreshing, Relational, & Relevant Church Experience. 2011. (ENG.). 208p. 19.99 *(978-0-446-57214-9(4))* FaithWords.

Hull, Bill. The Disciple-Making Pastor: Leading Others on the Journey of Faith. rev. ed. 2007. (Illus.). 320p. (gr. 13). pap. 22.00 *(978-0-8010-6622-1(0))* Baker Bks.

Hunter, George G. The Apostolic Congregation: Church Growth Reconceived for a New Generation. 2009. 160p. pap. 16.00 *(978-1-4267-0211-2(6))* Abingdon Pr.

Hyde, Daniel R. & Lems, Shane, eds. Planting, Watering, Growing: Planting Confessionally Reformed Churches in the 21st Century. 2011. pap. *(978-1-60178-126-0(1))* Reformation Heritage Bks.

Ingebretson, Ben, et al. Multiplication Moves: A Field Guide for Churches Planting Churches. 2012. ***(978-1-59255-726-4(0))*** Faith Alive Christian Resources.

Ivan & Peterson, Donelda. Tears & Triumphs: Fifty Years of Overseas Ministry. 2009. pap. 17.99 *(978-1-60791-737-3(8))* Xulon Pr., Inc.

Jackson, John. God-Size Your Church: Beyond Growth for Growth's Sake. 2008. 184p. pap. 20.00 *(978-0-687-64909-9(9))* Abingdon Pr.

—Pastorprenuer. 2009. 176p. pap. 17.00 *(978-0-687-65842-8(X))* Abingdon Pr.

Josiah (1 Kgs 13:2). Self-Interest Is Destroying the Gospel & the Church Today. 2011. 98p. pap. 12.10 ***(978-1-4567-7647-3(9))*** AuthorHouse.

Keller, Matt. The up the Middle Church: ... playing the game of ministry one yard at a Time... 2008. 204p. 24.99 *(978-1-4389-3573-7(0))*; pap. 19.99 *(978-1-4389-3574-4(9))* AuthorHouse.

Kim, Paul K. S. & Martin, Joyce Sweeney. Team Jesus: Planting Churches the Master's Way. 2009. 132p. pap. 14.99 *(978-1-61579-091-3(8))* Xulon Pr., Inc.

Lewis, Alvin. Orinoco! God at Work in Venezuela. pap. 19.99 *(978-1-59781-007-4(X))* Xulon Pr., Inc.

Lindsay, Ross. Building a Church to Last. 2011. 232p. 25.99 ***(978-1-61379-324-4(3))***; pap. 15.99 ***(978-1-61379-323-7(5))*** Xulon Pr., Inc.

Lukings, Tim. Fruit Loose & Fancy Tree. 2009. 188p. pap. 14.99 *(978-1-60791-600-0(2))* Xulon Pr., Inc.

Mackenzie, Geoffrey Shisumu & MacKenzie, Geoffrey Shisumu. Multicultural Church Planting. 2011. 96p. pap. ***(978-3-8443-2827-1(0))*** Lambert Academic Publishing.

MacMaster, Richard K. Mennonite & Brethren in Christ Churches of New York City. 32.00 *(978-1-894710-70-1(3))* Pandora Pr. CAN. Dist: Herald Pr.

Mastin, Jim. A Radical Plan to Grow Smaller Plateaued Churches. 2007. 73p. pap. 9.95 *(978-0-7414-3833-1(X))* Infinity Publishing.

McConnell, William T. Renew Your Congregation: Healing the Sick, Raising the Dead. 2007. (Columbia Partnership Leadership Ser.). 135p. per. 19.99 *(978-0-8272-3255-6(1))* Chalice Pr.

McDonald, Glenn. The Disciple Making Church: From Dry Bones to Spiritual Vitality. rev. ed. 2007. 268p. per. *(978-1-932902-67-9(8))* FaithWalk Publishing.

McIntosh, Gary L. Beyond the First Visit: The Complete Guide to Connecting Guests to Your Church. 2006. (Illus.). 192p. pap. 15.99 *(978-0-8010-9184-1(5))* Baker Bks.

—Taking Your Church to the Next Level: What Got You Here Won't Get You There, 1 vol. 2009. 224p. pap. 16.99 *(978-0-8010-9198-8(5))* Baker Bks.

McKinley, Mike. Church Planting Is for Wimps: How God Uses Messed-Up People to Plant Ordinary Churches That Do Extraordinary Things. 2010. (IXMarks Ser.). 128p. pap. 10.99 *(978-1-4335-1497-5(4))* Crossway.

McMullen, Shawn A. Releasing the Power of the Smaller Church. 2007. (Escn Ser.). (ENG.). 160p. pap. 14.99 *(978-0-7847-2146-9(7))* Standard Publishing.

Miller, James F. Go Build a Church! Spiritual Administration for Growth. 2007. (Illus.). 221p. per. 14.99 *(978-1-57921-881-2(4))* WinePress Publishing.

—Go Grow Your Church! Spiritual Leadership for African American Congregations. 2008. (Illus.). 176p. *(978-0-8298-1801-7(4))* Pilgrim Pr., The/United Church Pr.

Miller, Robert D. A Legacy of Church Planting: Passing Truth from One Generation to the Next. 2009. 260p. pap. 16.99 *(978-1-61507-032-9(X))* Cross Bks. Publishing.

Milne, Bruce. Acts: Witness to Him. 2010. (Focus on the Bible Ser.). (ENG.). 544p. 19.99 *(978-1-84550-507-3(7))* Christian Focus Pubns. GBR. Dist: STL Distribution North America.

Mittelberg, Mark. Becoming a Contagious Church: Increasing Your Church's Evangelistic Temperature, 1 vol. rev. ed. 2007. (ENG.). 224p. pap. 14.99 *(978-0-310-27919-8(4))* Zondervan.

Monaco, Cary J. Planting Churches in America: That They Might Be Saved. 2007. per. *(978-1-60208-042-3(9))* FBC Pubns. & Printing.

Moore, Ralph. How to Multiply Your Church: The Most Effective Way to Grow God's Kingdom. 2009. (ENG.). 256p. pap. 14.99 *(978-0-8307-5133-4(5))* Gospel Light Pubns.

Morgan, Tony & Broadman and Holman Publishers Staff. Killing Cockroaches: And Other Scattered Musings on Leadership, 1 vol. 2009. (ENG., Illus.). 256p. pap. 16.99 *(978-0-8054-4785-9(7)*, B&H Bks.) B&H Publishing Group.

Nees, Tom. Best Practices of Growing Churches: Profiles & Conversations with Ministry Leaders. 2006. (Voices Ser.). (ENG.). 160p. per. 14.99 *(978-0-8341-2304-5(5)*, 083-412-3045) Beacon Hill Pr. of Kansas City.

Neighbour, Ralph W., Jr. Christ's Basic Bodies: Embracing God's Presence, Power, & Purposes in True Biblical Community. 2008. (Illus.). 254p. pap. 21.50 *(978-0-9788779-8-9(5))* Touch Pubns.

Nelson, Gary Vincent, et al. Going Global: A Congregation's Introduction to Mission Beyond Our Borders. 2011. pap. *(978-0-8272-1257-2(7))* Chalice Pr.

Nkrumah, Kingsley & Nkrumah, Trish. Exposing the Spirit of Deception: A Letter to the Church. 2011. 60p. pap. 9.95 ***(978-1-4502-8211-6(3))*** iUniverse, Inc.

Obwoge, Hezekiah. Church & Development. 2010. 224p. pap. *(978-3-8383-5157-5(6))* Lambert Academic Publishing.

Odukoya, Adebola T. Wolves in the Church. 2008. 178p. pap. 17.49 *(978-0-557-03036-1(6))* Lulu Enterprises Inc.

Oladimeji, Seyi. Growing Your Church from Within: Building A Dynamic Home-Fellowship System. 2011. (Illus.). 116p. pap. 15.66 ***(978-1-4567-8535-2(4))*** AuthorHouse.

Osborne, Larry. Sticky Church, 1 vol. 2008. (Leadership Network Innovation Ser.). (ENG., Illus.). 208p. pap. 18.99 *(978-0-310-28508-3(9))* Zondervan.

Otto, Martin. Church on the Oceans: A Missionary Vision for the 21st Century. 2007. (Illus.). 132p. pap. *(978-1-903689-49-3(X))* Piquant Editions Ltd.

Page, Frank & Perry, John. The Incredible Shrinking Church. 2008. (ENG.). 160p. per. 14.99 *(978-0-8054-4661-6(3)*, B&H Bks.) B&H Publishing Group.

Paterson, Ross. The Antioch Factor. 256p. *(978-1-85240-284-6(9))* Sovereign World, Ltd.

Patrick, Darrin. Church Planting: The Man, the Message, the Mission. 2010. (Re:Lit Ser.). 240p. pap. 15.99 *(978-1-4335-1576-7(8))* Crossway.

Payne, J. D. Discovering Church Planting: An Introduction to the Whats, Whys, & Hows of Global Church Planting. 2009. (ENG.). 492p. pap. 22.99 *(978-1-60657-029-6(3)*, Paternoster) Authentic Media.

Pedrini, Alirio J. Programar el Crecimiento de los Grupos Carismaticos. 112p. 4.95 *(978-958-607-860-3(4))* Sociedad de San Pablo ESP. Dist: St Pauls/Alba Hse. Pubs.

Picardo, Rosario. How I Unsuccessfully Planted a Church. 2011. 68p. 18.00 ***(978-1-60947-023-4(0))*** Emeth Pr.

Pocock, Michael & Henriques, Joseph. Cultural Change & Your Church: Helping Your Church Thrive in a Diverse Society. 2007. 240p. pap. 26.00 *(978-1-55635-225-6(5)*, Wipf and Stock) Wipf & Stock Pubs.

Pollard, Neal. Rise up & Build. 2007. *(978-0-929540-62-7(X))* Publishing Designs, Inc.

Putman, Jim. Church Is a Team Sport: A Championship Strategy for Doing Ministry Together. 2009. pap. 15.99 *(978-0-8010-7208-6(5))* Baker Bks.

Rainer, Thom S. Breakout Churches: Discover How to Make the Leap, 1 vol. 2009. (ENG.). 272p. pap. 16.99 *(978-0-310-29347-7(2))* Zondervan.

Rainer, Thom S. & Geiger, Eric. Simple Church: Returning to God's Process for Making Disciples. 2011. (ENG.). 296p. pap. 14.99 *(978-0-8054-4799-6(7))* B&H Publishing Group.

Rainer, Thom S., et al. Vibrant Church: Becoming a Healthy Church in the 21st Century. 2008. 160p. pap. 7.95 *(978-1-4158-6541-5(8))* LifeWay Christian Resources.

Rankin, L. Letting Go of the Pews. 2006. pap. 9.99 *(978-1-60034-509-8(3))* Xulon Pr., Inc.

Rasbeary, James. From One Church Planter to Another: Helps for the Pioneer Church Planter. 2008. 108p. per. *(978-0-9800096-8-2(5))* Calvary Publishing.

Reeves, D. Avanzando: Estrategias Modernas De: Always Advancing: Church Growth. (SPA.). *(978-84-7645-293-6(4)*, 223361) Clie, Editorial.

Reid, Gregory R. Trojan Church. 2008. 208p. pap. 15.99 *(978-1-60647-733-5(1))* Xulon Pr., Inc.

Rhodes, Dale. How to Plant a Church the Easy Way (No Such Thing) 2010. 60p. pap. 8.50 *(978-0-557-58441-3(8))* Lulu Enterprises Inc.

Ripley, David. Help! I Want My Church to Grow: 31 Myth-Busting Ideas to Make Your Church the Place to Be. 2008. 89p. pap. 12.99 *(978-0-8280-2039-8(6))* Review & Herald Publishing Assn.

Roberts, Bob, Jr. The Multiplying Church: The New Math for Starting New Churches, 1 vol. 2008. (ENG., Illus.). 192p. (gr. 13). 19.99 *(978-0-310-27716-3(7))* Zondervan.

Rouse, Rick & Van Gelder, Craig. A Field Guide for the Missional Congregation: Embarking on a Journey of Transformation. 2008. (Illus.). 152p. pap. 14.99 *(978-0-8066-8044-6(X))* Augsburg Fortress, Pubs.

Saarinen, Martin F. The Life Cycle of a Congregation. pap. 7.95 *(978-1-56699-189-6(7)*, OD124) Alban Institute, Inc.

Savage, Sarah, et al. The Human Face of Church: A Social Psychology & Pastoral Theology Resource for Pioneer & Traditional Ministry. 2007. (Illus.). 333p. per. 29.99 *(978-1-85311-812-8(5))* Canterbury Pr.

Scheidler, Bill. Growing Strong Churches. 300p. pap. 16.99 *(978-1-59383-024-3(6))* City Christian Publishing.

Schnase, Robert. Passionate Worship. 2008. 32p. pap. 7.00 *(978-1-4267-0002-6(4))* Abingdon Pr.

Schuller, Robert H. Su Iglesia Tiene Posibilidades: Your Church Has Real Possibilities. (SPA.). 224p. *(978-84-7228-239-1(2)*, 220854) Clie, Editorial.

Scott, Marvin. 25 Reasons Why Small Churches Arent Grow. 2006. pap. 14.99 *(978-1-60034-700-9(2))* Xulon Pr., Inc.

Searcy, Nelson & Henson, Jennifer Dykes. Ignite: How to Spark Immediate Growth in Your Church, 1 vol. 2009. 160p. pap. 14.99 *(978-0-8010-7216-1(6))* Baker Bks.

Searcy, Nelson & Thomas, Kerrick. Launch: Starting a New Church from Scratch. 2007. (ENG., Illus.). 224p. per. 14.99 *(978-0-8307-4310-0(3))* Gospel Light Pubns.

Seay, Chris & McLaren, Brian D. The Dust off Their Feet: Lessons from the First Church, 0 vols. 2006. (Voice Ser.). (Illus.). 224p. pap. 9.99 *(978-0-529-12346-6(0))* Nelson, Thomas Inc.

Shenk, Wilbert R., ed. Exploring Church Growth. 2010. 320p. pap. 35.00 *(978-1-60899-872-2(X)*, Wipf and Stock) Wipf & Stock Pubs.

Spellers, Stephanie. Radical Welcome: Embracing God, the Other, & the Spirit of Transformation. 2006. 175p. per. 18.00 *(978-0-89869-520-5(1))* Church Publishing, Inc.

Spitzer, Lee B. Making Friends, Making Disciples: Growing Your Church through Authentic Relationships. 2010. 160p. pap. 16.00 *(978-0-8170-1645-6(7))* Judson Pr.

Stetzer, Ed & Bird, Warren. Viral Churches: Helping Church Planters Become Movement Makers. 2010. (Jossey-Bass Leadership Network Ser.: 50). (ENG., Illus.). 256p. 24.95 *(978-0-470-55045-8(7)*, Jossey-Bass) Wiley, John & Sons, Inc.

Stetzer, Ed & Dodson, Mike. Comeback Churches: How 300 Churches Turned Around & Yours Can Too. 2007. (ENG., Illus.). 224p. 17.99 *(978-0-8054-4536-7(6)*, B&H Bks.) B&H Publishing Group.

Stevens, Sr. Your Church Can Be Healthy Too: Not Size, but Substance. 2009. 68p. pap. 12.00 *(978-1-4389-9403-1(6))* AuthorHouse.

Stevenson, Phil. 5 Things Anyone Can Do to Help Their Church Grow. 2007. (You Can! Ser.). 95p. per. 7.99 *(978-0-89827-366-3(8))* Wesleyan Publishing Hse.

Stewart, Carlyle Fielding, III, ed. Growing the African American Church. 2006. 177p. per. 21.00 *(978-0-687-49839-0(2))* Abingdon Pr.

Strange, Mack & Norfleet, Douglas N. Jesus @ the Wildhorse: How to Connect with Everyday People on Christmas Eve. 2008. *(978-1-59186-700-5(2))* Common Thread Media, LLC.

Surratt, Geoff. Ten Stupid Things That Keep Churches from Growing: How Leaders Can Overcome Costly Mistakes, 1 vol. 2009. (ENG.). 208p. 18.99 *(978-0-310-28530-4(5))* Zondervan.

Tangen, Karl Inge. Ecclesial Identification beyond Late Modern Individualism? A Case Study of Life Strategies in Growing Late Modern Churches. 2012. (Global Pentecostal & Charismatic Studies). (ENG.). ***(978-90-04-20617-5(5))*** BRILL.

Tenny-Brittian, J. Kristina. Top 10 Ways to Defuse Your Congregational Time Bomb. 2008. xii, 159p. *(978-0-8298-1804-8(9))* Pilgrim Pr., The/United Church Pr.

Tippett, A. R. Iglecrecimiento y la Palabra de Dios: Church Growth & God's Word. (SPA.). 112p. *(978-84-7228-422-7(0)*, 220480) Clie, Editorial.

Towns, Elmer L. & Henderson, Daniel. The Church That Prays Together: Inside the Prayer Life of 10 Dynamic Churches. 2008. (Hollywood Nobody Ser.). 144p. pap. 9.99 *(978-1-60006-348-0(9))* NavPress Publishing Group.

Vernon, Henry. Steps for Starting New Churches: A Manual for Starting New Churches & Redeveloping Old Ones. 2011. 190p. 29.99 ***(978-1-4568-8690-5(8))***; pap. 19.99 ***(978-1-4568-8689-9(4))*** Xlibris Corp.

Virgo, Terry. Does the Future Have a Church? 2011. 142p. pap. 8.99 ***(978-0-9814803-4-3(9))*** Newfrontiers USA.

Wagner, C. Peter. Church Planting for a Greater Harvest: A Comprehensive Guide. 2010. (ENG.). 156p. pap. 18.00 *(978-1-60899-441-0(4)*, Wipf and Stock) Wipf & Stock Pubs.

—Como Ser Libre del Espiritu Religioso, 1 vol. 2007. (SPA.). 160p. per. 7.99 *(978-987-557-111-2(3))* Vida Pubs.

—Strategies for Church Growth: Tools for Effective Mission & Evangelism. 2010. 216p. pap. 24.00 *(978-1-60899-381-9(7)*, Wipf and Stock) Wipf & Stock Pubs.

—Su Iglesia Puede Crecer: Your Church Can Grow. (SPA.). 224p. *(978-84-7228-494-4(8)*, 220853) Clie, Editorial.

Waltz, Mark & Waltz, Mark L. How to Wow Your Church Guests: 101 Ways to Make a Meaningful First Impression. 2011. pap. ***(978-0-7644-6991-6(6)***, Group) Group Publishing, Inc.

Warren, Rick. The Purpose-Driven Church: Growth Without Compromising Your Message & Mission, 1 vol. 2010. 416p. 21.99 *(978-0-310-25894-0(4))* 2008. 400p. pap. 4.99 *(978-0-310-28590-8(9))* Zondervan.

Webster, Douglas D. Selling Jesus. 2009. 166p. pap. 19.00 *(978-1-60608-887-6(4)*, Wipf and Stock) Wipf & Stock Pubs.

Weeks, Louis. All for God's Glory: Redeeming Church Scutwork. 2008. *(978-1-56699-379-1(2))* Alban Institute, Inc.

Wilhoit, James C. Spiritual Formation As If the Church Mattered: Growing in Christ Through Community. 2008. (Illus.). 240p. (C). pap. 22.99 *(978-0-8010-2776-5(4))* Baker Academic.

Wilson, Mark O. Filled up, Poured Out: How God's Spirit Can Revive Your Passion & Purpose. 2012. ***(978-0-89827-527-8(X))*** Wesleyan Publishing Hse.

Young, Robert A. How to Lead a Church to Reach People & Grow. 2009. 218p. pap. 17.99 *(978-1-60791-857-8(9))* Xulon Pr., Inc.

Zigarelli, Michael & Babbes, George. The Minister's MBA: Essential Business Tools for Maximum Ministry Success. 2006. (ENG., Illus.). 128p. pap. 14.99 *(978-0-8054-4393-6(2)*, Holman Reference) B&H Publishing Group.

CHURCH HISTORY

Here are entered works on the institutional history of the church. Works on the Christian religion including its origin, belief, practices and influences treated collectively are entered under Christianity.

see also Christian Sects; Christianity; Ecclesiastical Geography; Protestantism; Sisterhoods

also headings beginning with the word Christian; names of denominations, sects, churches, councils, etc.; and subdivision Church History under names of countries, cities, etc.

Adair, James R. Introducing Christianity. 2008. (World Religions Ser.). (Illus.). 498p. 130.00 *(978-0-415-77211-2(7)*, 0415772117); 512p. pap. 36.95 *(978-0-415-77212-9(5)*, 0415772125) Routledge.

Ageira, Benedicta Leonilla. Through the Eyes of Mary Magdalene. 2009. 112p. pap. 11.95 *(978-0-9825255-1-7(6)*, Epigraph Bks.) Monkfish Bk. Publishing Co.

Albala, Ken & Eden, Trudy, eds. Food & Faith in Christian Culture. 2011. (Arts & Traditions of the Table: Perspectives on Culinary History Ser.). (ENG., Illus.). 280p. (gr. 17). pap. 26.50 ***(978-0-231-14997-6(2))*** Columbia Univ. Pr.

Alberigo, G., ed. Geschichte des Zweiten Vatikanischen Konzils, Band V. ein Konzil des Ubergangs. September - Dezember 1965: Deutsche Ausgabe herausgegeben von G. Wassilowsky. 2007. (Geschichte des Zweiten Vatikanischen Konzils Ser.). (GER.). 738p. (C). 112.00 *(978-90-429-1862-7(4))* Peeters Pubs. & Booksellers BEL. Dist: Brown, David Bk. Co., The.

Andrea C. Paterson. Three Monotheistic Faiths - Judaism, Christianity, Islam: An Analysis & Brief History. 2009. 216p. 25.99 *(978-1-4343-9246-6(5))*; pap. 14.95 *(978-1-4343-6890-4(4))* AuthorHouse.

Andrews, Handel. The Church's One Foundation: Church & Bible Themes. 2011. 328p. 29.99 ***(978-1-4628-6966-4(1))***; pap. 19.99 ***(978-1-4628-6965-7(3))*** Xlibris Corp.

Anselm, et al. Anselm of Havelberg, Anticimenon: On the Unity of the Faith & the Controversies with the Greeks. 2010. *(978-0-87907-106-6(0))* Cistercian Pubns., Inc.

Antonsson, Haki Thor. St. Magns of Orkney: A Scandinavian Martyr-Cult in Context. 2007. (Northern World Ser.: 29). (Illus.). 269p. *(978-90-04-15580-0(5))* BRILL.

Armogathe, Jean Robert, et al. Histoire Générale du Christianisme, 2 vols. 2010. (FRE., Illus.). *(978-2-286-07293-3(0))*; *(978-2-13-052292-8(0))* Penguin Group (USA) Inc. (Puffin).

Asensi, Francisco. Sombras Sobre el Vaticano (Shadows in the Vatican) (SPA.). 256p. 18.50 *(978-84-01-32749-0(0))* Plaza & Janes Editories, S.A. ESP. Dist: Astran, Inc.

Ashanin, Charles B. Essays on Orthodox Christianity & Church History. rev. ed. 2006. per. 17.95 *(978-1-933275-08-6(1)*, Orthodox Research Institute) Cocheco Falls Publishing.

Atkins, Gaius Glenn. Pilgrims of the Lonely Road. 2007. (ENG.). 344p. 46.95 *(978-0-548-08783-1(0))* Kessinger Publishing, LLC.

Ayer, Joseph C. Sourcebook of Ancient Church History. reprint ed. lib. bdg. 64.50 *(978-0-404-00436-1(9))* AMS Pr., Inc.

Babinsky, Joseph. I Thought I Killed Jesus. 2008. 116p. pap. 14.95 *(978-1-4116-9847-5(9))* Lulu Enterprises Inc.

Bäck, Sven-Olav & Holmen, Tom. Institutions of the Emerging Church. 2013. (Library of New Testament Studies, the Ser.). (ENG.). 256p. 130.00 *(978-0-567-03074-0(1)*, T&T Clark Int'l) Continuum International Publishing Group, Ltd. GBR. Dist: National Bk. Network.

Backhouse, Stephen. The Compact Guide to Christian History. 2011. (Compact Encyclopedia Ser.) (ENG., Illus.). 208p. pap. 14.95 *(978-0-7459-5506-3(1))* Lion Hudson PLC GBR. Dist: Independent Pubs. Group.

Bainton, Roland H. Christian Attitudes Toward War & Peace: A Historical Survey & Critical Re-Evaluation. 2008. (Roland Bainton Reprints Ser.). (Illus.). 300p. pap. 33.00 *(978-1-55635-788-6(5))* Wipf & Stock Pubs.

Baker, Derek. Schism, Heresy & Religious Protest. 2008. (Studies in Church History Ser.). (ENG.). 424p. pap. 53.00 *(978-0-521-10178-3(6))* Cambridge Univ. Pr.

Bandas, Rudolph G. Christ the Way: The Commandments of God & Precepts of the Church. 2011. 172p. 42.95 ***(978-1-258-01673-9(7))*** Literary Licensing, LLC.

Bar Hebraeus, Gregory. Ecclesiastical History of Bar Hebraeus. 2010. (SYR.). pap. 69.76 *(978-1-61719-916-5(8))* Gorgias Pr., LLC.

Bardill, Jonathan. Constantine, Divine Emperor of the Christian Golden Age. 2011. (ENG., Illus.). 461p. 99.00 *(978-0-521-76423-0(8))* Cambridge Univ. Pr.

Barker, James L. The Divine Church V2: Down Through Change, Apostasy, Therefrom, & Restoration. 2011. 202p. 44.95 ***(978-1-258-00721-8(5))*** Literary Licensing, LLC.

Barnum, Thaddeus. Never Silent: How Third World Missionaries are Bringing the Gospel to the US. Bubeck, Craig, ed. 2008. 380p. 24.99 *(978-0-615-20694-3(8))* Eleison Publishing.

Barrow, Simon, ed. Fear or Freedom? 2008. 152p. pap. *(978-1-905565-14-6(3))* Shoving Leopard Productions.

Bass, Diana Butler. A People's History of Christianity: The Other Side of the Story. 2010. (ENG.). 368p. pap. 14.99 *(978-0-06-144871-3(0)*, HarperOne) HarperCollins Pubs.

—People's History of Christianity: The Other Side of the Story. 2009. 368p. 25.99 *(978-0-06-144870-6(2)*, HarperOne) HarperCollins Pubs.

Basse, Michael. Von den Reformkonzilien bis zum Vorabend der Reformation. 2008. (Kirchengeschichte in Einzeldarstellungen Ser.). (GER.). 224p. (C). 55.00 *(978-3-374-02494-0(7))* Evangelische Verlagsanstalt GmbH DEU. Dist: Brown, David Bk. Co., The.

Baudry. A Warrior Bishop of the Twelfth Century: The Deeds of Albero of Trier. Pavlac, Brian A., tr. from LAT. 2008. (Mediaeval Sources in Translation Ser.). (ENG.). pap. 15.95 *(978-0-88844-294-9(7))* Pontifical Institute of Mediaeval Studies, Dept. of Pubns. CAN. Dist: Univ. of Toronto Pr.

Bede. The Ecclesiastical History of the English People. 2007. *(978-1-904799-15-3(9))* Tiger of the Stripe.

Bede, Adam. The Ecclesiastical History of the English People: The Greater Chronicle - Bede's Letter to Egbert. McClure, Judith & Collins, Roger, eds. Colgrave, Bertram, tr. from LAT. 2009. (Oxford World's Classics Ser.). (ENG., Illus.). 496p. 13.95 *(978-0-19-953723-5(2))* Oxford Univ. Pr., Inc.

Bedouelle, Guy. An Illustrated History of the Church: The Great Challenges. 2007. (Illus.). 271p. 90.00 *(978-1-56854-516-5(9))* Liturgy Training Pubns.

Belayche, N. & Mimouni, S., eds. Entre lignes de partage et territoires de Passage: Les identites religieuses dans les mondes grec et romain. Paganismes, judaismes, Christianismes. 2009. (Collection de la Revue des Etudes Juives Ser.). (FRE & ENG.). 502p. (C). pap. 109.00 *(978-90-429-2130-5(7))* Peeters Pubs. & Booksellers BEL. Dist: Brown, David Bk. Co., The.

Bell, Rob. The Love Wins Companion: A Study Guide for Those Who Want to Go Deeper. VanderVeen, David, ed. 2011. (ENG.). 160p. pap. 13.99 ***(978-0-06-212280-3(0)***, HarperOne) HarperCollins Pubs.

Bellitto, Christopher M. Church History 101: A Concise Overview. 2008. (Illus.). 141p. per. 14.95 *(978-0-7648-1603-1(9))* Liguori Pubns.

Bentley Hart, David. The Story of Christianity. 2012. (ENG., Illus.). 256p. 29.95 ***(978-1-84724-845-9(4))*** Quercus GBR. Dist: Independent Pubs. Group.

Bertram, Robert W., et al. A Time for Confessing. Hoy, Michael, ed. 2008. (Lutheran Quarterly Bks.). 220p. pap. 30.00 *(978-0-8028-2461-5(7))* Eerdmans, William B. Publishing Co.

Bevan, Wilson Lloyd. Church History: Mediaeval & Modern. 2007. (ENG.). 354p. 46.95 *(978-0-548-04119-2(9))* Kessinger Publishing, LLC.

Bienert, Wolfgang A. & Bienert, Wolfgang. Kirchengeschichte in ökumenischer Verantwortung: Ausgewählte Studien. Gemeinhardt, Peter & Pinggera, Karl, eds. 2009. (Kirche, Konfession, Religion Ser.). (GER., Illus.). 415p. (C). 74.00 *(978-3-89971-753-2(8))* Vandenhoeck & Ruprecht GmbH & Co. KG DEU. Dist: ISD.

Bingham, Jane. Christianity. 2007. (Atlas of World Faiths/Arcturus Ser.). (Illus.). 48p. (YA). (gr. 7-12). lib. bdg. 32.80 *(978-1-59920-054-5(6))* Black Rabbit Bks.

Bird, Michael F. & Crossley, James G. How Did Christianity Begin? A Believer & Non-Believer Examine the Evidence. 2008. 224p. pap. 19.95 *(978-1-59856-341-2(6))* Hendrickson Pubs. Marketing, LLC.

Blackburn, W. M. History of the Christian Church from Its. 2006. pap. 51.95 *(978-1-4286-4459-5(8))* Kessinger Publishing, LLC.

Blumhofer. People of Faith: A History of Western Christianity a History of Western Christianity. 2010. (ENG.). 272p. 69.95 *(978-1-4051-3248-0(5))*; pap. 26.95 *(978-1-4051-3249-7(3))* Wiley, John & Sons, Inc. (Wiley-Blackwell).

Bobrinskoy, Boris. The Mystery of the Church: Course in Orthodox Dogmatic Theology. 2012. ***(978-0-88141-388-5(7))*** St. Vladimir's Seminary Pr.

Bowman, Hamilton B. Hey, It's Only A Story: A Layman's Search for Understanding of Early Christianity. 2011. 48p. pap. 9.95 ***(978-1-4497-2645-4(3)***, WestBow Pr.) Author Solutions, Inc.

Boyce, James John. Carmelite Liturgy & Spiritual Identity: The Choir Books of Krakow. 2009. (Medieval Church Studies). (ENG, FRE & LAT., Illus.). 524p. (C). 152.00 *(978-2-503-51714-8(5))* Brepols Pubs. BEL. Dist: ISD.

Bracelis, Reineiro. Historias sin Final: A Story with No End. (SPA.). *(978-84-7645-311-7(6)*, 223437) Clie, Editorial.

Brandmuller, Walter. Light & Shadows: Defending Church History amid Faith, Facts & Legends. 2009. 160p. pap. 16.95 *(978-1-58617-273-2(5))* Ignatius Pr.

Brent, Allen. A Political History of Early Christianity. 2009. (ENG.). 344p. 44.95 *(978-0-567-03175-4(6))*; 140.00 *(978-0-567-03174-7(8))* Continuum International Publishing Group, Ltd. GBR. (T&T Clark Int'l). Dist: National Bk. Network.

Brooks, John P. The Divine Church. 2011. 296p. 48.95 ***(978-1-258-04584-5(2))*** Literary Licensing, LLC.

Brown, Callum G. & Snape, Michael. Secularisation in the Christian World. 2010. (Illus.). 248p. 89.95 *(978-0-7546-6131-3(8))* Ashgate Publishing Co.

Brown, Stewart J. & Tackett, Timothy, eds. Enlightenment, Reawakening & Revolution 1660-1815. 2007. (Cambridge History of Christianity Ser.: Vol. 7). (ENG., Illus.). 694p. 242.00 *(978-0-521-81605-2(X))* Cambridge Univ. Pr.

Brownson's Quarterly Review, Set, Vols. 1-29. Orig. Title: Boston Quarterly Review. reprint ed. lib. bdg. 1305.00 *(978-0-404-19506-9(7))* AMS Pr., Inc.

Brownson's Quarterly Review. 2009. Orig. Title: Boston Quarterly Review. 376p. pap. *(978-0-217-69336-3(9))*; 414p. pap. *(978-0-217-69326-4(1))*; 232p. pap. *(978-0-217-91340-9(7))*; 266p. pap. *(978-0-217-73184-3(8))*; 460p. pap. *(978-0-217-18278-2(X))*; 272p. pap. *(978-1-4590-5139-3(4))* Books LLC.

Brownson's Quarterly Review. 2009. Orig. Title: Boston Quarterly Review. 446p. pap. 31.26 *(978-0-217-73176-8(7))* General Bks. LLC.

Brubaker, Leslie. Inventing Byzantine Iconoclasm. Wood, Ian, ed. 2012. (Illus.). 160p. pap. 27.95 *(978-1-85399-750-1(1))* Duckworth Publishers GBR. Dist: International Publishers Marketing.

Brumback, Robert H. History of the Church Through the Ages: From the Apostolic Age, Through the Apostasies, the Dark Ages, the Reformation, & the Restoration. 2007. 428p. pap. 47.00 *(978-1-55635-196-9(8)*, Wipf and Stock) Wipf & Stock Pubs.

Burgess, Pablo. Veinte Siglos del Cristianismo: Twenty Centuries of Christianity. (SPA.). *(978-84-7645-081-9(8)*, 223143) Clie, Editorial.

Butcher, John Beverley. Sacred Partnership: Jesus & Mary Magdelene. 2011. 350p. pap. 22.95 ***(978-1-937002-04-6(7))*** Apocryphile Pr.

Butler, Jennifer S. Born Again: The Christian Right Globalized. 2006. (ENG.). 224p. 84.00 *(978-0-7453-2243-8(3))* Pluto Pr. GBR. Dist: Macmillan.

Byers, James. The Apostle John: A Blessed Life. 2008. (ENG.). 128p. pap. 10.00 *(978-0-9800285-2-2(3))* O'More Publishing.

Campbell, R. K. Prophetic History of Christendom. 7.95 *(978-0-88172-012-9(7))* Believers Bookshelf, Inc.

Canfield, K. Los Siete Secretos de los Padres Eficaces.Tr. of Seven Secrets of Effective Fatherhood. (SPA.). 260p. pap. 8.99 *(978-1-56063-940-4(7)*, 497674) Editorial Unilit.

Carrier, Richard. Not the Impossible Faith. 2009. 454p. pap. 28.96 *(978-0-557-04464-1(2))* Lulu Enterprises Inc.

Carus, Paul. The Pleroma: An Essay on the Origin of Christianity. 2007. (ENG.). 184p. per. 15.50 *(978-1-60206-360-0(5))* Cosimo, Inc.

Castelli, Elizabeth A. Martyrdom & Memory: Early Christian Culture Making. 2007. (Gender, Theory, & Religion Ser.). (ENG., Illus.). 360p. (gr. 17). pap. 27.00 *(978-0-231-12987-9(4))* Columbia Univ. Pr.

Catherwood, Christopher. Church History: A Crash Course for the Curious. 2007. 224p. pap. 12.99 *(978-1-58134-841-5(X))* Crossway.

Cheikho, Louis. Christianity & Christian Literature in Arabia before Islam. 2006. (Christianity in the Islamic World Ser.: 3). 556p. 109.00 *(978-1-59333-547-2(4))* Gorgias Pr., LLC.

Cheshire, Michael. How to Knock over A 7-Eleven: And Other Ministry Training. 2011. 172p. pap. 13.95 ***(978-1-4497-2737-6(9)***, WestBow Pr.) Author Solutions, Inc.

Christianson, Gerald & Bond, H. Lawrence. Church Reform & the Theological Task in Nicholas of Cusa & His Age. 2011. (Variorum Collected Studies Ser.). (Illus.). 362p. 134.95 ***(978-1-4094-2960-9(1))*** Ashgate Publishing Co.

Christianson, Gerald, et al. The Church, the Councils, & Reform: The Legacy of the Fifteenth Century. 2008. 352p. (C). 79.95 *(978-0-8132-1527-3(7))* Catholic Univ. of America Pr.

Clara A. Urann, Mary P. Pringle and. The Celebration of Christmas in Europe & America: Yuletide Traditions from Many Lands. 2009. 100p. pap. 11.95 *(978-0-557-00051-7(3))* Lulu Enterprises Inc.

Clatworthy, Jonathan. Liberal Faith in a Divided Church. 2008. (ENG.). 320p. pap. 29.95 *(978-1-84694-116-0(4))* Hunt, John Publishing Ltd. GBR. Dist: National Bk. Network.

Clayton, Paul B. The Christology of Theodoret of Cyrus: Antiochene Christology from the Council of Ephesus (431) to the Council of Chalcedon (451) 2007. (Oxford Early Christian Studies). (ENG.). 368p. 175.00 *(978-0-19-814398-7(2))* Oxford Univ. Pr., Inc.

Clouse, Robert G. The Church from Age to Age: A History from Galilee to Global Christianity. 2011. 1048p. pap. 36.99 *(978-0-7586-2646-2(0))* Concordia Publishing Hse.

Coldiron, Jim. Expository Messages in the Epistle of 1 John. 2010. 112p. pap. 11.95 *(978-1-61507-169-2(5))* Cross Bks. Publishing.

Collard, Jared J. Papered Over: Exploring the New Testament's Inconsistencies & Contradictions. 2010. 254p. pap. 14.95 *(978-1-60860-890-4(5)*, Eloquent Bks.) AEG Literary Publishing Services, Inc.

Comby, Jean. How to Read Church History, Vol. 1. Bowden, J., tr. from FRE. 2011. (Illus.). 128p. ***(978-0-334-02050-9(6)***, SCM Pr.) Hymns Ancient & Modern Ltd.

Comfort, Carol Personette, compiled by. St. Mark's Episcopal Cemetery, Orange, Essex County, New Jersey: History of the Cemetery, Expanded List of Interments, & Early History of St. Mark's Church. 2010. (Illus.). 291p. ***(978-0-7884-4770-9(X))*** Heritage Bks.

Conner, Kenneth E. They Captured the Spirit. 2007. 220p. per. 12.95 *(978-1-60364-001-5(0)*, Honey Locust Pr.) Wolfmont, LLC.

Cook, Tony. The Routledge Companion to Christian History. 2007. (Routledge Companions to History Ser.). (Illus.). 384p. 30.95 *(978-0-415-38363-9(3))*; 120.00 *(978-0-415-38362-2(5))* Routledge.

Cook, William R. Lives of Great Christians. 2007. per. 34.95 *(978-1-59803-331-1(X))* Teaching Co., LLC, The.

Cooper, Kate & Gregory, Jeremy, eds. Elite & Popular Religion. 2006. (Studies in Church History Ser.: Volume 42). (Illus.). 456p. 80.00 *(978-0-9546809-2-3(8))* Ecclesiastical History Society GBR. Dist: Boydell & Brewer, Inc.

—Revival & Resurgence in Christian History: Papers Read at the 2006 Summer Meeting & the 2007 Winter Meeting of the Ecclesiastical History Society. 2008. (Studies in Church History Ser.: Volume 44). (Illus.). 420p. 80.00 *(978-0-9546809-4-7(4))* Ecclesiastical History Society GBR. Dist: Boydell & Brewer, Inc.

Coxe, A. Cleveland. Institutes of Christian History: an Introduction to Historic Reading And. 2007. (ENG.). 340p. per. 30.95 *(978-1-4304-4544-9(0))* Kessinger Publishing, LLC.

Cram101 Textbook Reviews. Outlines & Highlights for the European Reformations by Carter Lindberg, Isbn: 9781557865755. 2010. 114p. pap. 28.95 *(978-1-61698-205-8(5))* Cram101 Inc.

Cram101 Textbook Reviews Staff. Outlines & Highlights for a Concise History of Christianity by R Dean Peterson, Isbn: 9780495130307. 2009. 98p. pap. 27.95 *(978-1-4288-9288-0(5))* Cram101 Inc.

Crawford, Jeffrey. Objective Truth & the Church in a Postmodern World. 2008. 159p. pap. 24.95 *(978-1-60672-687-7(0))* PublishAmerica, Inc.

Cresswell, Peter. Jesus the Terrorist. 2010. (ENG., Illus.). 440p. pap. 29.95 *(978-1-84694-274-7(8))* Hunt, John Publishing Ltd. GBR. Dist: National Bk. Network.

Crick, Julia, ed. Charters of St Albans. 2008. (Anglo-Saxon Charters Ser.). (ENG., Illus.). 240p. 99.00 *(978-0-19-726396-9(8))* Oxford Univ. Pr., Inc.

Cross, Anthony R., ed. Ecumenism & History: Studies in Honor of John H. Y. Briggs. 2007. (Studies in Christian History & Thought: Ser.). 391p. pap. 39.00 *(978-1-59752-761-3(0)*, Wipf and Stock) Wipf & Stock Pubs.

Crossan, John Dominic & Crossan, John D. God & Empire: Jesus Against Rome, Then & Now. 2008. (ENG.). 272p. pap. 13.99 *(978-0-06-085831-5(1)*, HarperOne) HarperCollins Pubs.

Cummins, D. & Cummins, D. Duane. The Disciples: A Struggle for Reformation. 2009. 384p. 59.99 *(978-0-8272-0636-6(4))*; pap. 37.99 *(978-0-8272-0637-3(2))* Chalice Pr.

Cupitt, Don. New Great Story. 2010. 120p. pap. 19.00 *(978-1-59815-026-1(X))* Polebridge Pr.

Curbelo, Nestor. The History of the Mormons in Argentina. Jennings, Erin, tr. from SPA. 2008. lib. bdg. 70.00 *(978-1-58958-116-6(4))*; pap. 24.95 *(978-1-58958-052-7(4))*; 300p. 24.95 *(978-1-58958-059-6(1))* Kofford, Greg Books, Inc.

—The History of the Mormons in Argentina. ltd. collector's ed. 2009. 159.95 *(978-1-58958-051-0(6))* Kofford, Greg Books, Inc.

—The History of the Mormons in Argentina. Jennings, Erin, tr. ltd. collector's ed. 2008. 300p. 159.95 *(978-1-58958-058-9(3))* Kofford, Greg Books, Inc.

Cushing, Kathleen G. & Brasington, Bruce C., eds. Bishops, Texts & the Use of Canon Law Around 1100: Essays in Honour of Martin Brett. 2008. (Church, Faith & Culture in the Medieval West Ser.). (Illus.). 242p. 124.95 *(978-0-7546-6015-6(X))* Ashgate Publishing Co.

Daniel, W. Harrison. Historical Atlas of the Methodist Movement. 2009. 144p. 21.00 *(978-0-687-65651-6(6))* Abingdon Pr.

Davies, Philip R. Tribute to Geza Vermes: Essays on Jewish & Christian Literature & History. White, Richard T., ed. 2009. (Library of Hebrew Bible/Old Testament Studies, the Ser.). (ENG.). 406p. 65.00 *(978-0-567-19151-9(6)*, T&T Clark) Continuum International Publishing Group, Ltd. GBR. Dist: National Bk. Network.

Dawson, Christopher. The Dividing of Christendom. 2009. 260p. pap. 16.95 *(978-1-58617-238-1(7))* Ignatius Pr.

Day, Duane L. God's Establishment: What Happened? 2011. pap. 12.99 ***(978-1-61346-098-6(8))*** Tate Publishing & Enterprises, LLC.

De Cesarea, Eusebio. Historia Eclesiastica: History of the Christian Church, 2 bks., Tomo II. (SPA.). *(978-84-7645-354-4(X)*, 223457) Clie, Editorial.

De Giorgio, Cynthia. St. John's Co-Cathedral, Valletta. 2007. (ENG.). 56p. (C). pap. 9.95 *(978-99932-7-171-0(3))* Midsea Bks. Ltd. MLT. Dist: Brown, David Bk. Co., The.

De Schweinitz, E. The Moravian Manual; Containing an Account of the Protestant Church of the Moravian United Brethren, or Unitas Fratrum by E de Schweinitz Publis. 2006. 188p. per. 18.99 *(978-1-4255-1516-4(9))* MPublishing.

Detroit (Mich.) First Congregational chu. Quarter Centennial Twenty-Fifth Anniversary of the Organization of the First Congregational Church of Detroit, Michigan December 8th, 9th And. 2006. 160p. per. 18.99 *(978-1-4255-1187-6(2))* MPublishing.

Dickson, John. A Spectator's Guide to Jesus: An Introduction to the Man from Nazareth. 2008. (ENG.). 176p. pap. 12.95 *(978-0-7459-5307-6(7))* Lion Hudson PLC GBR. Dist: Independent Pubs. Group.

Doles, Jeff. Miracles & Manifestations of the Holy Spirit in the History of the Church. 2007. 280p. pap. 24.95 *(978-0-9744748-9-2(4))* Walking Barefoot Ministries.

Dorsett, Terry W. Developing Leadership Teams in the Bivocational Church. 2010. 160p. pap. 19.95 *(978-1-61507-252-1(7))* Cross Bks. Publishing.

Dryer, George H. History of the Christian Church. 2009. 622p. pap. 44.75 *(978-1-115-78335-4(1))*; 746p. pap. 51.75 *(978-1-115-78329-3(7))* BiblioBazaar.

Dudley, Dean. History of the First Council of Nice. 2009. 124p. 24.99 *(978-1-110-47275-8(7))*; pap. 19.75 *(978-1-110-47272-7(2))* BiblioBazaar.

—History of the First Council of Nice. 2009. 84p. pap. *(978-1-151-65942-2(8))* Books LLC.

Dunn, James D. G. Beginning from Jerusalem Vol. 1. 2008. (Illus.). 1392p. 80.00 *(978-0-8028-3932-9(0))* Eerdmans, William B. Publishing Co.

Dunn, Roger & Dunn, Marilyn. The Christianization of the Anglo-Saxons C,597-C700: Discources of Life, Death & after Life. 2009. (ENG., Illus.). 288p. 120.00 *(978-1-84725-189-3(7))* Continuum International Publishing Group, Ltd. GBR. Dist: National Bk. Network.

Duquesne, Jacques & Lebrette, Francois. The History of the Church through 100 Masterpieces. Borges, M. Cristina, tr. from FRE. 2011. (Illus.). 225p. pap. 29.95 *(978-0-8207-0437-1(7))* Duquesne Univ. Pr.

Duren, Marty & Wright, Todd. Journeys: Transitioning Churches to Relevance. 2008. 192p. per. 14.99 *(978-0-9798053-1-8(7))* Missional Pr.

Eby, James R. World Impacting Churches: 10 Essential Characteristics for Changing the World & Finishing the Great Commission. 2007. 259p. per. 14.99 *(978-1-60247-353-9(6))* Tate Publishing & Enterprises, LLC.

Ekelund, Robert B., Jr., et al. The Marketplace of Christianity. 2008. (ENG., Illus.). 368p. (gr. 17). pap. 15.95 *(978-0-262-55071-0(7))* MIT Pr.

Ekonomou, Andrew. Byzantine Rome & the Greek Popes: Eastern Influences on Rome & the Papacy from Gregory the Great to Zacharias, A. D. 590-752. 2009. (Roman Studies: Interdisciplinary Approaches Ser.). (ENG.). 302p. pap. 34.99 *(978-0-7391-1978-5(8))* Lexington Bks.

Ekonomou, Andrew J. Byzantine Rome & the Greek Popes: Eastern Influences on Rome & the Papacy from Gregory the Great to Zacharias, A. D. 590-752. 2007. (Roman Studies: Interdisciplinary Approaches Ser.). (ENG.). 358p. 73.50 *(978-0-7391-1977-8(X))* Lexington Bks.

El Shaddai, Queen Juliet. It Is Finished Church: Tetelestai, Paid in Full! 2010. 248p. 31.95 *(978-1-4327-5771-7(7))*; (ENG.). pap. 19.95 *(978-1-4327-5174-6(3))* Outskirts Pr., Inc.

Eldeiry, Subhi. The Great Flood Survivors - the End Is Coming. 2009. 152p. pap. 35.00 *(978-0-9664057-1-2(4))* Eldeiry, Subhi.

Endsjo, Dag Oistein. Greek Resurrection Beliefs & the Success of Christianity. 2009. (ENG.). 284p. 100.00 *(978-0-230-61729-2(8))* Palgrave Macmillan.

Engammare, Max & Maag, Karin. On Time, Punctuality, & Discipline in Early Modern Calvinism. 2009. (ENG., Illus.). 286p. 93.00 *(978-0-521-76997-6(3))* Cambridge Univ. Pr. GBR. Dist: Cambridge Univ. Pr.

Engelke, Matthew Eric. A Problem of Presence: Beyond Scripture in an African Church. 2007. (Anthropology of Christianity Ser.). (Illus.). 296p. 60.00 *(978-0-520-24903-5(8))*; 304p. per. 26.95 *(978-0-520-24904-2(6))* Univ. of California Pr.

Eriks, Garrett, et al. The Sixteenth-Century Reformation of the Church. Engelsma, David, ed. 2007. (ENG.). 208p. pap. 1[illegible].95 *(978-0-916206-95-6(5))* Reformed Free Publishing Assn.

Falwell, Jonathan. Innovatechurch: Innovative Leadership for the Next Generation Church. 2008. (ENG.). 288p. pap. 14.99 *(978-0-8054-4826-9(8)*, B&H Bks.) B&H Publishing Group.

Fassler, Margot E. The Virgin of Chartres: Making History Through Liturgy & the Arts. 2010. (Illus.). 632p. 55.00 *(978-0-300-11088-3(X))* Yale Univ. Pr.

Feliz, Guido. Corrientes Neo-Teologicas: Neo-Theological Trends. (SPA.). 296p. *(978-84-7228-351-0(8)*, 220190) Clie, Editorial.

Ferguson, Everett. The New Testament Church. 2008. 96p. pap. 7.95 *(978-0-89112-523-5(X))* Abilene Christian Univ. Pr.

Ferguson, Richard. A Real-Life Christian Spiritual Journey. 2011. 312p. 31.95 ***(978-1-4620-1674-7(X))***; pap. 21.95 ***(978-1-4620-1672-3(3))*** iUniverse, Inc.

Ferngren, Gary B. Medicine & Health Care in Early Christianity. 2009. (ENG.). 264p. (gr. 17). 37.00 *(978-0-8018-9142-7(6))* Johns Hopkins Univ. Pr.

Ffoulkes, Edmund S. Christendoms Divisions Being A Philosoph. 2006. pap. 28.95 *(978-1-4286-4265-2(X))* Kessinger Publishing, LLC.

Fiedler, Klaus. The Gospel Takes Roots on Kilimanjaro. 2006. 84p. pap. *(978-99908-76-08-6(8))* Fountain Pubs. Ltd. UGA. Dist: Michigan State Univ. Pr.

Field, John. Kingdom, Power & Glory: Historical Guide to Westminster Abbey. 2009. (ENG., Illus.). 162p. pap. 25.00 *(978-0-907383-71-0(8)*, Third Millenium Pub Ltd) Antique Collectors' Club GBR. Dist: National Bk. Network.

Field, Walter. Stones of the Temple or Lessons from the Fabric & Furniture of the Church. 2007. (ENG.). 328p. 45.95 *(978-0-548-04277-9(2))* Kessinger Publishing, LLC.

Fisk, Basil C. Understanding Christian History. 2010. (Illus.). 392p. pap. *(978-0-7552-1262-0(2))* Authors OnLine, Ltd.

Fletcher, Alan John. Late Medieval Popular Preaching in Britain & Ireland: Texts, Studies, & Interpretations. 2010. (Sermo Ser.). (ENG, ENM & LAT., Illus.). 339p. (C). 131.00 *(978-2-503-52391-0(9))* Brepols Pubs. BEL. Dist: ISD.

Fletcher, Juan. Historia Compendiada Iglesia: History of the Christian Church. (SPA.). 584p. *(978-84-7228-947-5(8)*, 223043) Clie, Editorial.

Flores, José. Del Eden a Egipto: From Eden to Egypt. (SPA.). 192p. *(978-84-7228-927-7(3)*, 223006) Clie, Editorial.

Foakes-Jackson, F. J. & Jennings, A. C. The History of the Christian Church. 2010. pap. 90.64 *(978-1-61719-347-7(X))* Gorgias Pr., LLC.

Foster, John. Church History, Vol. 2. (Illus.). 216p. 13.00 (978-0-281-02789-7(7)) SPCK Publishing GBR. Dist: Pilgrim Pr., The/United Church Pr.

Fowler, Hank. The Whole Armor of God-Volume I -Foundations of Christianity: Separating Truth from Custom, Tradition & Counterfeit. 2008. 254p. pap. 20.00 (978-0-8059-7801-8(1)) Dorrance Publishing Co., Inc.

Foxe, John. Acts & Monuments, 8 vols. Cattley, S. R. & Townsend, George, eds. reprint ed. 895.00 (978-0-404-02590-8(0)) AMS Pr., Inc.

—Foxe's Book of Martyrs. Berry, W., ed. 2007. (ENG.). 428p. per. 18.95 (978-1-933993-57-7(X)) Apocryphile Pr.

—Foxe's Book of Martyrs. 2011. 526p. pap. 40.75 (978-1-246-21743-8(0)) BiblioBazaar.

—Foxe's Book of Martyrs. 2011. 412p. pap. 12.99 (978-1-4209-4284-2(0)) Digireads.com.

—Foxe's Book of Martyrs. 2010. 444p. 41.56 (978-1-169-34385-6(6)); pap. 29.56 (978-1-162-66348-7(0)) Kessinger Publishing, LLC.

—Foxe's Book of Martyrs. Berry, William Grinton, ed. 2010. 444p. 41.56 (978-1-166-67098-6(8)); pap. 29.56 (978-1-166-61944-2(3)) Kessinger Publishing, LLC.

—Foxe's Book of Martyrs. 2010. 444p. 51.95 (978-1-161-43213-8(2)) Kessinger Publishing, LLC.

—Foxe's Book of Martyrs. Berry, William Grinton, ed. 2009. 444p. 51.95 (978-1-120-38638-0(1)); pap. 36.95 (978-1-120-28290-3(X)) Kessinger Publishing, LLC.

—Foxe's Book of Martyrs. 2011. 434p. pap. 19.99 (978-1-61720-224-7(X)) Wilder Pubns., Ltd.

—Foxe's Book of Martyrs: A History of the Lives, Sufferings, & Triumphant Deaths of the Early Christian & the Protestant Martyrs. 2010. (Illus.). 288p. pap. 14.95 (978-0-9824881-8-8(1)) Lighthouse Trails Publishing Co.

—Foxe's Christian Martyrs. 2010. (Abridged Christian Classics Ser.). (ENG.). 192p. pap. 2.99 (978-1-60260-857-3(1), Barbour Bks.) Barbour Publishing, Inc.

—Fox's Book of Martyrs. 2008. (ENG.). 432p. per. 35.75 (978-1-4375-2248-8(3)); 384p. per. 32.75 (978-1-4375-2073-6(1)); 334p. per. 31.75 (978-1-4375-2242-6(4)); 300p. per. 28.75 (978-1-4375-2067-5(7)) BiblioBazaar.

—Fox's Book of Martyrs. 2009. 442p. pap. (978-0-217-93915-7(5)) Books LLC.

—Fox's Book of Martyrs. 2009. 608p. pap. 18.45 (978-1-4385-1079-8(9), Book Jungle) Standard Pubns., Inc.

—Fox's Book of Martyrs. 2009. 436p. pap. 10.29 (978-1-60459-716-5(X)) Wilder Pubns., Ltd.

Fredriksen, Paula. Augustine & the Jews: A Christian Defense of Jews & Judaism. 2010. 528p. pap. 20.00 (978-0-300-16628-6(1)) Yale Univ. Pr.

Freeburn, Ryan P. Hugh of Amiens & the Twelfth-Century Renaissance. 2011. (Church, Faith & Culture in the Medieval West Ser.). 290p. 119.95 (978-1-4094-2734-6(X)) Ashgate Publishing Co.

Freeman, Charles. A. D. 381: Heretics, Pagans, & the Dawn of the Monotheistic State. 2009. (ENG.). 256p. (gr. 12). 27.95 (978-1-59020-171-8(X)) Overlook Pr., The.

Friend, Andrew. A Bell Curve: The Rise & Decline of Traditional Religion. 2011. 408p. pap. 19.99 (978-1-4567-5803-5(9)) AuthorHouse.

Gaddy, Carolyn Caldwell & Surratt, Jerry L. The History of Wingate Baptist Church: 1810-2008. 2009. 384p. 40.00 (978-1-934936-24-5(3)) Righter Publishing Co., Inc.

Gardner, Lawrence. The Magadalene Legacy: The Jesus & Mary Bloodline Conspiracy. 2007. (Illus.). 395p. pap. 18.95 (978-1-57863-403-3(2), Weiser Bks.) Red Wheel/Weiser.

Garretson, Arthur Samuel. Primitive Christianity & Early Criticisms: a Work of Negation. 2007. pap. 30.95 (978-1-4304-4961-4(6)) Kessinger Publishing, LLC.

Ghosh, Kantik & Gillespie, Vincent, eds. After Arundel: Religious Writing in Fifteenth-century England. 2012. (Medieval Church Studies). (ENG, FRE & LAT., Illus.). 657p. (C). 196.00 (978-2-503-53402-2(3)) Brepols Pubs. BEL. Dist: ISD.

Gieseler, Johann Karl Ludwig. A Text-Book of Church History. 2006. 592p. per. 32.99 (978-1-4255-6380-6(5)) MPublishing.

Girardet, Klaus Martin. Der Kaiser und sein Gott: Das Christentum im Denken und in der Religionspolitik Konstantins des Großen. 2010. (Millennium-Studien / Millennium Studies). (GER., Illus.). IX, 213p. 98.00 (978-3-11-022788-8(6)) De Gruyter, Walter Inc.

Glen, Marie & glen, marie. As It Was in the Beginning. 2009. 82p. pap. 14.95 (978-0-615-23587-5(5)) Inner-monastery.com.

Godfrey, Jim. Six of the most asked questions in Christendom. 2007. pap. 8.95 (978-0-533-15317-6(4)) Vantage Pr., Inc.

Golightly Marshall, Brian Leonard. Great Pyramid CODE Discovered Prophecy Revealed by Moon Lunation's & Solar Eclipse. 2008. 512p. pap. 46.95 (978-1-4092-2014-5(1)) Lulu Enterprises Inc.

González, Justo L. The Story of Christianity Vol. 1: The Early Church to the Dawn of the Reformation. 2010. (ENG., Illus.). 448p. pap. 25.99 (978-0-06-185588-7(X), HarperOne) HarperCollins Pubs.

—The Story of Christianity Vol. 2: The Reformation to the Present Day. 2nd ed. 2010. (ENG.). 432p. pap. 25.99 (978-0-06-185589-4(8), HarperOne) HarperCollins Pubs.

Gordon, Patricia. Transitions & Memories. 2007. 113p. per. 10.99 (978-1-59886-755-8(5)) Tate Publishing & Enterprises, LLC.

Gordon, Robert. 7 Things to Keep in Mind When Looking for a Church. 2011. 58p. pap. 16.95 (978-1-4626-3784-3(1)) PublishAmerica, Inc.

Graffin, René. Revue de L'orient ChréTien (1896-1946) 2010. (FRE.). 3800.00 (978-1-60724-760-9(7)); 3800.00 (978-1-60724-759-3(3)); 3800.00 (978-1-60724-750-0(X)); 3800.00 (978-1-60724-749-4(6)) Gorgias Pr., LLC.

Graffin, René, ed. Revue de L'orient ChréTien (1896-1946) 2010. (FRE.). 3800.00 (978-1-60724-753-1(4)); 3800.00 (978-1-60724-757-9(7)); 3800.00 (978-1-60724-754-8(2)); 3800.00 (978-1-60724-769-2(0)); 3800.00 (978-1-60724-755-5(0)); 3800.00 (978-1-60724-748-7(8)); 3800.00 (978-1-60724-743-2(7)); 3800.00 (978-1-60724-740-1(2)); 3800.00 (978-1-60724-756-2(9)); 3800.00 (978-1-60724-751-7(8)); 3800.00 (978-1-60724-768-5(2)); 3800.00 (978-1-60724-742-5(9)); 3800.00 (978-1-60724-746-3(1)); 3800.00 (978-1-60724-762-3(3)); 3800.00 (978-1-60724-744-9(5)); 3800.00 (978-1-60724-745-6(3)); 3800.00 (978-1-60724-761-6(5)); 3800.00 (978-1-60724-765-4(8)); 3800.00 (978-1-60724-767-8(4)); 3800.00 (978-1-60724-747-0(X)); 3800.00 (978-1-60724-752-4(6)); 3800.00 (978-1-60724-758-6(5)); 3800.00 (978-1-60724-763-0(1)); 3800.00 (978-1-60724-764-7(X)); 3800.00 (978-1-60724-766-1(6)) Gorgias Pr., LLC.

Green, Michael. Asian Tigers for Christ: The Dynamic Growth of the Church in South East Asia. 128p. 12.00 (978-0-281-05369-8(3)) SPCK Publishing GBR. Dist: Pilgrim Pr., The/United Church Pr.

Greider, John C. The English Bible Translations & History. 2007. 316p. (ENG.). 29.99 (978-1-4257-8123-1(3)); per. 19.99 (978-1-4257-8103-3(9)) Xlibris Corp.

Gretsch, Mechthild. Aelfric & the Cult of Saints in Late Anglo-Saxon England. 2009. (Cambridge Studies in Anglo-Saxon England Ser.). (ENG.). 276p. pap. 38.00 (978-0-521-09307-1(4)) Cambridge Univ. Pr.

Griffith, Brian. Different Visions of Love. 2008. 512p. per. 17.95 (978-1-4327-1759-9(6)) Outskirts Pr., Inc.

Guignebert, Charles Alfred Honore. Ancient, Medieval, & Modern Christianity: The Evolution of A Religion. 2011. 542p. 62.95 (978-1-258-01389-9(4)) Literary Licensing, LLC.

Guirguis, Magdi & van Doorn-Harder, Nelly. The Emergence of the Modern Coptic Papacy: The Popes of Egypt: A History of the Coptic Church & Its Patriarchs, Volume 3. 2011. (ENG., Illus.). 256p. 29.95 (978-977-416-103-2(3)) American Univ. in Cairo Pr. EGY. Dist: Oxford Univ. Pr., Inc.

Haddad, Robert M. The Case for Christianity: St Justin Martyr's Arguments for Religious Liberty. 2010. (ENG.). 210p. pap. 14.95 (978-1-58979-575-4(X)) Taylor Trade Publishing.

Haight, Roger & Haight. Christian Community in History, Volume 3: Ecclesial Existence, 3 vols., Vol. 3. 2008. (ENG.). 320p. 39.95 (978-0-8264-2947-6(5)) Continuum International Publishing Group, Ltd. GBR. Dist: National Bk. Network.

Halahawi, Shalomim Y. The Way! the Prophetic Messianic Voice to the Path of the Edenic Kingdom Redemption. 2007. 466p. pap. 34.96 (978-1-4303-0816-4(8)) Lulu Enterprises Inc.

Hall, Lindsey, et al. Christian Doctrine. 2010. (SCM Readers Ser.). (ENG.). 576p. (C). pap. 50.00 (978-0-334-04345-4(X), SCM Pr.) Hymns Ancient & Modern Ltd GBR. Dist: Westminster John Knox Pr.

Hankins, Barry. Jesus & Gin: Evangelicalism, the Roaring Twenties & Today's Culture Wars. 2010. (ENG.). 256p. 26.00 (978-0-230-61419-2(1)) Palgrave Macmillan.

Hannah, John D. Church History Vol. 3: The Triumph of the Church, A. D. 500-1500. 2007. (Kregel Pictorial Guide to Church History Ser.). (Illus.). 32p. pap. 9.99 (978-0-8254-2784-8(3)) Kregel Pubns.

Hardiman, David, ed. Healing Bodies, Saving Souls: Medical Missions in Asia & Africa. 2006. (Clio Medica/The Wellcome Institute Series in the History of Medicine: 94). (Illus.). 354p. 94.00 (978-90-420-2106-8(3)) Rodopi.

Harmening, William. Forgiving Judas: Manifesto for a New Christianity. 2007. 192p. per. 16.95 (978-0-595-44162-4(9)) iUniverse, Inc.

Harmon, Lee. Revelation. 2010. 346p. pap. 16.95 (978-1-936183-62-3(5)) Hillcrest Publishing Group, Inc.

Harnack, Adolf. The Expansion of Christianity in the First Three Centuries. 2009. 500p. pap. 37.75 (978-1-115-70723-7(X)); 33.99 (978-1-115-70720-6(5)); pap. 29.99 (978-1-115-70722-0(1)) BiblioBazaar.

—The Expansion of Christianity in the First Three Centuries. Moffatt, James, tr. 2008. 576p. 58.95 (978-1-4365-4852-6(7)) 2007. (ENG.). 580p. per. 43.95 (978-0-548-72303-6(6)) Kessinger Publishing, LLC.

Harris, J. Rendel. Hermas in Arcadia & Other Essays. 2007. 87p. pap. 14.00 (978-1-55635-061-0(9), Wipf and Stock) Wipf & Stock Pubs.

Hart, David Bentley. The Story of Christianity: An Illustrated History of 2000 Years of the Christian Faith. 2008. (Illus.). 255p. (978-1-84724-140-5(9)) Quercus.

—The Story of Christianity: An Illustrated History of 2000 Years of the Christian Faith. 2012. (ENG., Illus.). 256p. 22.95 (978-0-85738-342-6(6)) Quercus GBR. Dist: Independent Pubs. Group.

Harwood, William. God, Jesus, & the Bible: The Origin & Evolution of Religion. 2009. 458p. 40.00 (978-1-935444-28-2(X)) World Audience Pubs.

Harwood, William, et al. God, Jesus, & the Bible. 2009. 458p. pap. 28.00 (978-1-935444-84-8(0)) World Audience Pubs.

Hatch, Edwin. The Growth of Church Institutions. 2008. 244p. 41.95 (978-1-4365-5717-7(8)) 2007. (ENG.). 248p. per. 26.95 (978-0-548-75773-4(9)) Kessinger Publishing, LLC.

Hauerwas, Stanley M., narrated by. Heresies & How to Avoid Them: Why It Matters What Christians Believe. 2007. 148p. per. 16.95 (978-1-59856-013-8(1)) Hendrickson Pubs. Marketing, LLC.

Hayes, Victor. Eliminating Church Fights with by-Laws: Quick Wisdom for Church Leadership. 2008. 94p. pap. 9.96 (978-0-557-02464-3(1)) Lulu Enterprises Inc.

Hazen, Mark E. Addressing the Needs of the Poor: A Church Mobilization Guide. 2011. 144p. 28.95 (978-1-4627-0616-7(9)); pap. 11.95 (978-1-4627-0615-0(0)) Cross Bks. Publishing.

Heales, Alfred. The History & Law of Church Seats, or Pews. 2010. 256p. pap. (978-1-152-94652-1(8)) Books LLC.

Heath, Gordon L. Doing Church History: A User-Friendly Introduction to Researching the History of Christianity. 2008. 108p. pap. (978-1-894667-90-6(5)) Clements Publishing.

Hemphill, Ken & James, Mike. V. E. L. C. R. O. Church. 2012. (ENG.). 88p. pap. 8.99 (978-0-578-09507-3(6)) Auxano Pr.

Henderson, Robert Thornton & Henderson, Robert T. Enchanted Community: Journey into the Mystery of the Church. 2006. 240p. pap. 25.00 (978-1-59752-665-4(7), Wipf and Stock) Wipf & Stock Pubs.

Hendrix, Scott H. Early Protestant Spirituality. 2009. (Classics of Western Spirituality Ser.). 368p. 39.95 (978-0-8091-0566-3(7)); pap. 29.95 (978-0-8091-4211-8(2)) Paulist Pr.

Herring. Introduction to the History of Christian. 2006. 288p. pap. (978-0-8264-6738-6(5)) Continuum International Publishing Group, Ltd.

Herring, George. Introduction to the History of Christianity. 2006. (ENG., Illus.). 350p. 75.00 (978-0-8147-3699-9(8)); pap. 24.00 (978-0-8147-3700-2(5)) New York Univ. Pr.

—Introduction to the History of Christianity: From the Early Church to the Enlightenment. 2006. (ENG., Illus.). 288p. 49.95 (978-0-8264-6737-9(7), Burns & Oates) Continuum International Publishing Group, Ltd. GBR. Dist: National Bk. Network.

—Modern Christianity: An Introductory History. 2016. (ENG.). 352p. 29.95 (978-1-84706-001-3(3)); 95.00 (978-1-84706-000-6(5)) Continuum International Publishing Group, Ltd. GBR. Dist: National Bk. Network.

Hesperides. Colonial Churches. 2007. 392p. per. (978-1-4067-5944-0(9), Hesperides Pr.) Read Bks.

Heyman, George. The Power of Sacrifice: Roman & Christian Discourses in Conflict. 2007. (Illus.). 256p. 74.95 (978-0-8132-1489-4(0)) Catholic Univ. of America Pr.

Heyndrikx, Marcel. Towards Another Future: On the Christian Faith & Its Shape Between Yesterday & Tomorrow. 2006. (Louvain Theological & Pastoral Monographs: Vol. 34). (ENG.). x, 358p. (C). pap. 42.00 (978-90-429-1774-3(1)) Peeters Pubs. & Booksellers BEL. Dist: Brown, David Bk. Co., The.

Hill, Jonathan. History of Christianity, 1 vol. 2007. (ENG., Illus.). 560p. instr.'s hndbk. ed. 39.99 (978-0-310-26270-1(4)) Zondervan.

Hillerbrand, Hans J. The Division of Christendom: Christianity in the Sixteenth Century. 2007. (ENG.). 504p. per. 50.00 (978-0-664-22402-8(4)) Westminster John Knox Pr.

Holding, James. The Impossible Faith. 2007. 112p. per. 10.99 (978-1-60266-084-7(0)) Xulon Pr., Inc.

Holland, Tom. The Forge of Christendom: The End of Days & the Epic Rise of the West. 2010. (ENG., Illus.). 512p. pap. 19.95 (978-0-307-27870-8(0), Anchor) Knopf Doubleday Publishing Group.

Hollandbeck, Beverly. Christian Chronicles: Bargersville First Christian. 2008. 640p. pap. 33.49 (978-1-4343-9250-3(3)) AuthorHouse.

Holmes, John S. How to Make the Scriptures Have No Effect: False Doctrines in the Church Today. 2008. 54p. pap. 16.95 (978-1-60441-402-8(2)) PublishAmerica, Inc.

Hood, R. Serpent Handling Christians. 2008. (Illus.). 328p. (C). 60.00 (978-0-520-23147-4(3)) Univ. of California Pr.

Howard, Brian Arundell of Wardour. Judah Scepter: A Historical & Religious Perspective. 2010. 204p. (ENG.). 27.95 (978-1-4502-3978-3(1)); pap. 17.95 (978-1-4502-3976-9(5)) iUniverse, Inc.

Hsia, R. Po-chia, ed. Reform & Explansion 1500-1660. 2007. (Cambridge History of Christianity Ser.: Vol. 6). (ENG., Illus.). 772p. (C). 237.00 (978-0-521-81162-0(7)) Cambridge Univ. Pr.

Hughes, Marilynn. Near Death & Out-of-Body Experiences (Auspicious Births & Deaths) Of the Prophets, Saints, Mystics & Sages in World Religions. 2007. 210p. pap. 14.95 (978-1-4116-1916-6(1)) Lulu Enterprises Inc.

Hughes, Robert Don & Lee-Thorp, Karen. History: Think for Yourself about What Shaped the Church. 2008. (TH1NK Reference Collection). (ENG.). 288p. (YA). pap. 12.99 (978-1-60006-137-0(0), Th1nk Bks.) NavPress Publishing Group.

Huller, Stephan. The Real Messiah: The Throne of St. Mark & the True Origins of Christianity. 2009. (ENG.). 288p. 24.95 (978-1-906787-12-7(3), Watkins Publishing) Duncan Baird Pubs. GBR. Dist: Sterling Publishing Co., Inc.

Hunt, John. Concise Church History. 2007. (AMG Concise Ser.). (ENG.). 400p. 17.99 (978-0-89957-696-1(6)) AMG Pubs.

Hutton, J. E. A History of the Moravian Church. 2008. 452p. 32.99 (978-0-554-21484-9(9)); 30.99 (978-0-554-30787-9(1)) BiblioBazaar.

—The History of the Moravian Church. 2010. 380p. 39.16 (978-1-169-33259-1(5)); pap. 27.16 (978-1-162-66638-9(2)) Kessinger Publishing, LLC.

Hutton, J. e. & Hutton, J. E. The History of the Moravian Church. 2010. 380p. 48.95 (978-1-161-43503-0(4)) Kessinger Publishing, LLC.

Hutton, J. E. (Joseph Edmund), creator. A History of the Moravian Church. 2010. 524p. pap. 40.75 (978-1-172-08689-4(3)) BiblioBazaar.

Hutton, Joseph Edmund. A History of the Moravian Church. 2010. (Illus.). 286p. pap. 36.46 (978-1-153-58350-3(X)) General Bks. LLC.

Hutton, William Holden. The Church of the Sixth Century: Six Chapters In Ecclesiastical History. 2006. (ENG.). 344p. per. 31.95 (978-1-4286-4141-9(6)) Kessinger Publishing, LLC.

Hylson-Smith, Kenneth. To the Ends of the Earth: The Globalization of Christianity. 2007. (ENG.). 240p. per. 23.99 (978-1-84227-475-0(9), Paternoster) Authentic Media.

Iams, F. Before the FootLights. 2006. 276p. per. 29.00 (978-1-57978-634-2(0)) Baptist Standard Bearer, Inc.

Ironside, Henry A. De Malaquias a Mateo: Four Hundred Years of Silence. (SPA.). (978-84-7645-421-3(X), 223436) Clie, Editorial.

Isbouts, Jean-Pierre. Young Jesus: Restoring the "Lost Years" of a Social Activist & Religious Dissident. 2008. (ENG., Illus.). 336p. 24.95 (978-1-4027-5713-6(1)) Sterling Publishing Co., Inc.

Ivanovic, Filip. Symbol & Icon: Dionysius the Areopagite & the Iconoclastic Crisis. 2010. 116p. pap. 14.00 (978-1-60899-335-2(3), Pickwick Pubns.) Wipf & Stock Pubs.

J. E. Hutton, M. A. A History of the Moravian Church. I.t ed. 2007. (ENG.). 482p. pap. 30.99 (978-1-4264-0226-5(0)) BiblioBazaar.

Jacobsen, Douglas. The World's Christians: Who They Are, Where They Are, & How They Got There. 2011. (ENG., Illus.). 416p. 94.95 (978-1-4051-8889-0(8), Wiley-Blackwell) Wiley, John & Sons, Inc.

Jean-Marie, Vivaldi. Kierkegaard: History & Eternal Happiness. 2008. (ENG.). 142p. pap. 29.50 (978-0-7618-4145-6(8)) Univ. Pr. of America, Inc.

Jenkins, Allan K. & Preston, Patrick. Biblical Scholarship & the Church: A Sixteenth Century Crisis of Authority. 2007. (Ashgate New Critical Thinking in Religion, Theology, & Biblical Studies). 340p. 124.95 (978-0-7546-3703-5(4)) Ashgate Publishing Co.

Jenkins, John P. The Lost History of Christianity: The Thousand-Year Golden Age of the Church in the Middle East, Africa, & Asia — And How It Died. 2008. (ENG.). 336p. 26.95 (978-0-06-147280-0(8), HarperOne) HarperCollins Pubs.

Jijawi, Dionisios & Ibrahim, Gregorios, trs. Lamp of the Sanctuary by Mar Gregorios Yohanna Bar Ebroyo Maphryono D-Madnho. 2009. (ARA.). 186.00 (978-1-60724-260-4(5)) Gorgias Pr., LLC.

Johnson, Donald & Johnson, Jean. Universal Religions in World History: Buddhism, Christianity, & Islam. 2007. (ENG., Illus.). 240p. (C). pap. 35.67 (978-0-07-295428-9(0), 0072954280) McGraw-Hill Cos., The.

Joiner, Don. Antebellum Churches in Georgia. 2007. 191p. pap. 18.95 (978-1-4357-0245-5(X)) Lulu Enterprises Inc.

Jones, Timothy Paul. Christian History Made Easy. 2009. (PowerPoint Presentations Ser.). (ENG.). cd-rom 39.99 (978-1-59636-341-0(X)); (Illus.). 224p. pap. 14.99 (978-1-59636-328-1(2)) Rose Publishing.

Jones, W. Eclectic Almanac for the Faith. 2006. 440p. pap. 19.00 (978-0-8358-9849-2(0)) Upper Room Bks.

Jongeneel, Jan A. B. Jesus Christ in World History: His Presence & Representation in Cyclical & Linear Settings. 2009. (IC - Studien zur interkulturellen Geschichte des Christentums. Etudes d'histoire interculturelle de christianisme. Studies in the Intercultural History of Christianity Ser.). 472p. 112.95 (978-3-631-59688-3(X)) Lang, Peter GmbH, Europaischer Verlag der Wissenschaften DEU. Dist: Lang, Peter.

Joyner, Rick. Church History: The First Century. 2009. 216p. mass mkt. 11.99 (978-1-60708-285-9(3)) MorningStar Pubns., Inc.

Jung, Martin H. & H Jung, Martin. Kirchengeschichte. 2010. (Grundwissen Christentum Ser.). (GER.). 300p. (C). pap. 38.00 (978-3-525-56851-4(7)) Vandenhoeck & Ruprecht GmbH & Co. KG DEU. Dist: ISD.

Karant-Nunn, Susan C. The Reformation of Feeling: Shaping the Religious Emotions in Early Modern Germany. 2010. (ENG.). 336p. 74.00 (978-0-19-539973-8(0)) Oxford Univ. Pr., Inc.

Kasomo, Rt. Rev. Daniel W. History of Christianity in Africa Made Simple. 2011. 332p. pap. (978-3-8454-0626-8(7)) Lambert Academic Publishing.

—The Relevance of Catholic Social Teaching Today. 2011. 452p. pap. (978-3-8443-8690-5(4)) Lambert Academic Publishing.

Kastning, Wieland. Morgenröte Künftigen Lebens: Das Reformatorische Evangelium Als Neubestimmung der Geschichte: Untersuchungen Zu Martin Luthers Geschichts- und Wirklichkeitsverständnis. 2008. (Forschungen Zur Systematischen und Okumenischen Theologie Ser.). (GER.). 458p. (C). 111.00 (978-3-525-56345-8(0)) Vandenhoeck & Ruprecht GmbH & Co. KG DEU. Dist: ISD.

Kaufmann, Thomas. Türckenbüchlein: Zur Christlichen Wahrnehmung "Türkischer Religion" in Spätmittelalter und Reformation. 2008. (Forschungen Zur Kirchen- und Dogmengeschichte Ser.). (GER., Illus.). 299p. (C). 84.00 (978-3-525-55222-3(X)) Vandenhoeck & Ruprecht GmbH & Co. KG DEU. Dist: ISD.

Kaye, Bruce N. Conflict & the Practice of Christian Faith. 2009. 192p. pap. 22.00 (978-1-55635-970-5(5), Cascade Bks.) Wipf & Stock Pubs.

Keen, Ralph. Christian Tradition. 2008. (ENG.). 400p. pap. 64.95 (978-0-7425-6089-5(9)) Rowman & Littlefield Publishers, Inc.

Kennedy, Philip. Christianity: An Introduction. 2011. (I. B. Tauris Introductions to Religion Ser.). (ENG., Illus.). 288p. 85.00 (978-1-84885-382-9(3)); pap. 25.00 (978-1-84885-383-6(1)) I. B. Tauris & Co., Ltd. GBR. Dist: Macmillan.

Ketcherside, Carl W. Which Church? pap. 0.99 (978-0-87377-063-7(3)) GAM Pubns.

Kip, William Ingraham. The Early Conflicts of Christianity. 2007. (ENG.). 288p. 43.95 (978-0-548-15546-2(1)); pap. 28.95 (978-1-4304-4985-0(3)) Kessinger Publishing, LLC.

Kisker, Scott Thomas. Foundation for Revival: Anthony Horneck, the Religious Societies, & the Construction of an Anglican Pietism. 2007. (Revitalization:

Explorations in World Christian Movements Ser.). (ENG., Illus.). 268p. per. 64.00 *(978-0-8108-5799-5(5))* Scarecrow Pr., Inc.

Kleinberg, Aviad M. Flesh Made Word: Saints' Stories & the Western Imagination. Todd, Jane Marie, tr. from FRE. 2008. 352p. 29.95 *(978-0-674-02647-6(0)*, Belknap Pr.) Harvard Univ. Pr.

Knowles, Dom David. The Historian & Character: And Other Essays. 2008. (ENG.). 424p. pap. 53.00 *(978-0-521-08841-1(0))* Cambridge Univ. Pr.

Kömtgen, Ludger & Waßenhoven, Dominik, eds. Patterns of Episcopal Power / Strukturen Bischöflicher Herrschaftsgewalt Im Westlichen Europa des 10. und 11. Jahrhunderts: Bishops in Tenth & Eleventh Century Western Europe. 2011. (Prinz-Albert-Forschungen Ser.). (ENG & GER., Illus.). 226p. 196.00 ***(978-3-11-916600-3(6))*** De Gruyter, Walter Inc.

Kotker, Norman. Jesus & the Holy Land. 2011. (ENG., Illus.). 224p. pap. 11.95 *(978-1-59687-351-3(5))* IBks., Inc.

Kravchenko, Iryna. The Role of Bishops in Icelandic Society Political & Social Aspects of Activities. 2009. 92p. pap. *(978-3-639-10688-6(1))* VDM Verlag Dr. Mueller e.K.

Laamann, Lars P. Christian Heretics in Late Imperial China: Christian Inculturation & State Control, 1720-1850. 2007. (Routledge Studies in the Modern History of Asia: Vol. 40). (Illus.). 204p. 160.00 *(978-0-415-29779-0(6))* Routledge.

Laato, Antii & Lindqvist, Pekka, eds. Encounters of the Children of Abraham from Ancient to Modern Times. 2010. (Studies on the Children of Abraham Ser.). x, 330p. *(978-90-04-18728-3(6))* BRILL.

Lacueva, Francisco. La Iglesia: Cuerpo de Cristo Church: The Body of Christ, 1 vol. 2008. (SPA.). 352p. pap. 10.99 *(978-84-7228-091-5(8)*, 220240) Clie, Editorial ESP. Dist: Zondervan.

Lacy, G. H. Breve Historia Del Cristianismo: A Concise History of the Christian. (SPA.). *(978-84-7645-274-5(8)*, 223325) Clie, Editorial.

LaFont, Ghislain. A Theological Journey: Christian Faith & Human Salvation. Burkhard, John J., tr. from FRE. 2007. (Michael Glazier Bks.). 151p. per. 15.95 *(978-0-8146-5213-8(1))* Liturgical Pr.

Lagarde, Paul de. Collected Works. 2010. (GRE & LAT.). 265.92 *(978-1-61719-028-5(4))*; 265.92 *(978-1-61719-026-1(8))*; 265.92 *(978-1-61719-027-8(6))* Gorgias Pr., LLC.

Landon, William. Leviathan: The relation between organized religion & Christianity. 2007. 256p. per. 19.95 *(978-0-595-44582-0(9))* iUniverse, Inc.

Lasker, Daniel. Jewish Philosophical Polemics Against Christianity in the Middle Ages: With a New Introduction. 2nd ed. 2007. 318p. pap. 29.95 *(978-1-904113-51-5(6))* Littman Library of Jewish Civilization, The GBR. Dist: International Specialized Bk. Services.

Laufhütte, Hartmut & Titzmann, Michael, eds. Heterodoxie in der Frühen Neuzeit. (Frahe Neuzeit Ser.). (GER., Illus.). VI, 492p. 344.00 ***(978-3-11-183983-7(4))*** De Gruyter, Walter Inc.

Law, William. Three Letters to the Bishop of Bangor. 2008. 614p. 59.95 *(978-1-4365-4958-5(2))* 2007. (ENG.). 616p. per. 44.95 *(978-0-548-69933-1(X))* Kessinger Publishing, LLC.

Lawrence, Bert. A Skeptic in the Bible Belt. 2008. 138p. pap. 24.95 *(978-1-60441-506-3(1))* PublishAmerica, Inc.

Lazarus, William P. & Sullivan, Mark. Comparative Religion for Dummies. 2008. (ENG., Illus.). 366p. pap. 19.99 *(978-0-470-23065-7(7)*, For Dummies) Wiley, John & Sons, Inc.

Lea, Henry C. Studies in Church History. 2010. 514p. pap. 39.75 *(978-1-147-12626-6(7))* BiblioBazaar.

Lea, Henry Charles. Studies in Church History: the Rise of the Temporal Power; Benefit. 2007. (ENG.). 520p. per. 40.95 *(978-1-4304-4624-8(2))* Kessinger Publishing, LLC.

Leadingham, Everett. Mosaic of Faith: Piecing Together Our Christian Story. 2007. 7.99 *(978-0-8341-2285-7(5))*; pap. 7.50 *(978-0-8341-2286-4(3))* Nazarene Publishing Hse.

Leafe, G. Harry. The Way We Are. 2011. 112p. pap. 9.95 ***(978-0-7375-0168-1(5))*** Biblical Studies Pr.

Letham, Robert. The Westminster Assembly: Reading Its Theology in Historical Context. 2009. pap. *(978-0-87552-612-6(8))* P & R Publishing.

Leyser, Conrad & Smith, Lesley. Motherhood Religion & Society in Medieval Europe 400-1400. 2011. (Church, Faith & Culture in the Medieval West Ser.). (Illus.). 388p. 134.95 ***(978-1-4094-3145-9(2))*** Ashgate Publishing Co.

Liderbach, Daniel. Roman Catholic Belief Seeking Understanding. 2011. 88p. pap. 19.95 ***(978-1-4560-8310-6(4))*** PublishAmerica, Inc.

Lightfoot, J. B. Historical Essays. 2008. 268p. pap. *(978-1-4097-0454-6(8))* Read Bks.

Lindberg, Carter. The European Reformations. 2nd ed. 2009. (ENG., Illus.). 472p. 110.95 *(978-1-4051-8068-9(4))*; pap. 56.95 *(978-1-4051-8067-2(6))* Wiley, John & Sons, Inc. (Wiley-Blackwell).

Lindenfeld, David F. & Richardson, Miles, eds. Beyond Conversion & Syncretism: Indigenous Encounters with Missionary Christianity, 1800-2000. 2011. (ENG.). 328p. 95.00 ***(978-0-85745-217-7(7))*** Berghahn Bks., Inc.

Littell, Franklin H. Carta's Illustrated Histoty of Christianity. 2006. 440p. pap. 29.95 *(978-965-220-666-4(0))* Carta, The Israel Map & Publishing Co., Ltd. ISR. Dist: Eisenbrauns, Inc.

Little Boy Blue. The African American Church: A Sociological History. 2009. 144p. pap. 11.99 *(978-1-4389-5526-1(X))* AuthorHouse.

Loane, Marcus L. Let God Arise: Landmarks in Church History. 2008. (ENG., Illus.). 128p. 10.99 *(978-1-84550-380-2(5))* Christian Focus Pubns. GBR. Dist: STL Distribution North America.

Loewen, Harry. Through Fire & Water: An Overview of Mennonite History. 2010. (ENG.). 350p. (YA). pap. 16.99 *(978-0-8361-9506-4(X))* Herald Pr.

Logos. Christian History Library in Libronix. 2007. cd-rom 129.95 *(978-0-912498-55-3(2))* Foundation for American Christian Education.

Louth, Andrew. Patrology: The Eastern Fathers from the Council of Chalcedon to John of Damascus. Di Berardino, Angelo, ed. Walford, Adrian, tr. 2nd ed. 2008. (ENG.). 736p. pap. 105.00 *(978-0-227-17264-3(7))* Clarke, James Co., Ltd. GBR. Dist: Brown, David Bk. Co., The.

Lugioyo, Brian. Martin Bucer's Doctrine of Justification: Reformation Theology & Early Modern Irenicism, 1 vol. 2010. (Oxford Studies in Historical Theology Ser.). (ENG.). 320p. 74.00 *(978-0-19-538736-0(8))* Oxford Univ. Pr., Inc.

Lukaszewski, Michael. From the Top Down. 2010. 155p. pap. 14.99 *(978-0-557-50198-4(9))* Lulu Enterprises Inc.

MacCulloch, Diarmaid. Christianity: The First Three Thousand Years. (ENG.). (gr. 12). 2011. 1216p. 25.00 *(978-0-14-311869-5(2)*, Penguin (Non-Classics)) 2010. (Illus.). 1184p. 45.00 *(978-0-670-02126-0(1)*, Viking Adult) Penguin Group (USA) Inc.

Macdonald, James. Beyond Belief: Two Thousand Years of Bad Faith in the Christian Church. 2011. 512p. 74.95 *(978-0-86372-346-9(2))* Garnet Publishing, Ltd. GBR. Dist: International Publishers Marketing.

Maffly-Kipp, Laurie F. & Neilson, Reid L., eds. Proclamation to the People: Nineteenth-Century Mormonism & the Pacific Basin Frontier. 2008. (ENG.). 342p. (gr. 15). 29.95 *(978-0-87480-918-3(5))* Univ. of Utah Pr.

Mannion. Comparative Ecclesiology: Critical Investigations. 2008. (Ecclesiological Investigations Ser.). (ENG.). 240p. 130.00 *(978-0-567-03241-6(8)*, T&T Clark Int'l) Continuum International Publishing Group, Ltd. GBR. Dist: National Bk. Network.

—The Routledge Companion to the Christian Church. 2010. (Routledge Companions Ser.). (ENG.). 704p. (C). pap. 50.00 *(978-0-415-56768-8(8))* Routledge.

Mannion, Gerard & Mudge, Lewis S., eds. The Routledge Companion to the Christian Church. 2008. (Routledge Companions Ser.). (ENG.). 704p. (C). 200.00 *(978-0-415-37420-0(0)*, 0415374200) Routledge.

Marie, Sr. Rosena. The Mystery & Destiny of the Church. 2008. pap. 17.95 *(978-1-933184-35-7(3))* Sophia Institute Pr.

Martinez, Emilio. Recuerdos de Antano: Memories of the Spanish Inquisition. (SPA., Illus.). 432p. *(978-84-7228-317-6(8)*, 220751) Clie, Editorial.

Marty, Martin E. The Christian Story. 2007. (Illus.). 47p. per. 14.99 *(978-1-56364-624-9(2))* Vision Video.

—The Christian World. 2009. (Modern Library Chronicles Ser.: Vol. 29). (ENG., Illus.). 288p. pap. 16.00 *(978-0-8129-7677-9(0)*, Modern Library) Random House Publishing Group.

Mason, Shane. The Ever Advancing Kingdom. 2007. 144p. per. 13.99 *(978-1-60477-031-5(7))* Xulon Pr., Inc.

Matkin, J. Michael. Early Christianity. 2008. (Complete Idiot's Guide Ser.). (ENG., Illus.). 320p. (gr. 12-18). 18.95 *(978-1-59257-756-9(3)*, Alpha Bks.) Penguin Group (USA) Inc.

Mavrakos, Pastor Tony. The Church Needs a Wake up Call: It's time for the church to come out of the Closet. 2011. 248p. pap. 24.95 ***(978-1-4626-2985-5(7))*** PublishAmerica, Inc.

McBride, Alfred. Story of the Church. 2009. 224p. pap. 16.95 *(978-0-86716-876-1(5))* Franciscan Media.

McBride, Calvin. Walking into A New Spirituality: Chronicling the Life, Ministry, & Contributions of Elder Robert E. Hart, B. D. , LL. B. , D. D. , to the CME Church & COGIC: with Some Additional COGIC History. 2007. 216p. per. 17.95 *(978-0-595-46257-5(X))* iUniverse, Inc.

McDonald, James. Beyond Belief: Two Thousand Years of Bad Faith in the Christian Church. 2011. 512p. pap. 34.95 *(978-0-86372-345-2(4)*, Ithaca Pr.) Garnet Publishing, Ltd. GBR. Dist: International Publishers Marketing.

McDonald, Lee Martin, et al. From Biblical Criticism to Biblical Faith: Essays in Honor of Lee Martin Mcdonald. 2007. 450p. 45.00 *(978-0-88146-052-0(4))* Mercer Univ. Pr.

Mcgee, Jerry E. Roberdell: A village of Grace. 2009. *(978-1-61623-402-7(4))* Independent Pub.

McGiffert, Arthur Cushman. A History of Christianity in the Apostolic Age. 2009. 696p. 39.99 *(978-1-116-51043-0(X))*; 46.99 *(978-1-116-51042-3(1))*; pap. 47.75 *(978-1-116-51045-4(6))*; pap. 48.75 *(978-1-116-51044-7(8))*; pap. 47.75 *(978-1-115-78317-0(3))* BiblioBazaar.

—A History of Christianity in the Apostolic Age. 2009. 438p. pap. *(978-0-217-67099-9(7))*; 404p. pap. *(978-0-217-15976-0(1))* Books LLC.

McNamer, Elizabeth & Pixner, Bargil. Jesus & First-Century Christianity in Jerusalem. 2008. (Illus.). 112p. pap. 19.95 *(978-0-8091-4523-2(5))* Paulist Pr.

Mehr, Bethany. The Hoax: Satan's Grand Deception, 1 vol. 2009. 173p. pap. 24.95 *(978-1-60836-563-0(8))* PublishAmerica, Inc.

Meister, Chad & Stump, James. Christian Thought. 2010. (ENG., Illus.). 552p. (C). 125.00 *(978-0-415-44006-6(8))* Routledge.

Menconi, Peter. The Intergenerational Church: Understanding Congregations from WWII to Www. com. 2008. 215p. pap. *(978-0-615-18916-1(4))* Mount Sage Publishing.

Meyers, Robin. The Underground Church: Reclaiming the Subversive Way of Jesus. 2012. (ENG.). 288p. 24.95 ***(978-1-118-06159-6(4)***, Jossey-Bass) Wiley, John & Sons, Inc.

Milkias, Paulos. Dictionary of Ethiopian Christianity. 2010. (ENG.). 410p. pap. 48.50 *(978-0-7618-5246-9(8))* Univ. Pr. of America, Inc.

Miller, Nicholas P. The Religious Roots of the First Amendment: Dissenting Protestantism & the Separation of Church & State. 2012. (ENG.). 272p. 35.00 ***(978-0-19-985836-1(5))*** Oxford Univ. Pr., Inc.

Milne, Bruce. Acts: Witness to Him. 2010. (Focus on the Bible Ser.). (ENG.). 544p. 19.99 *(978-1-84550-507-3(7))* Christian Focus Pubns. GBR. Dist: STL Distribution North America.

Moltmann, Jurgen. Sun of Righteousness, Arise! God's Future for Humanity & the Earth. 2010. 256p. (C). pap. 25.00 *(978-0-8006-9658-0(1)*, Fortress Pr.) Augsburg Fortress, Pubs.

Monagle, C. Christological Nihilism in the Twelfth Century: The Contested Reception of Peter Lombard's Senteniae. 2011. (Europa Sacra Ser.). (ENG.). 240p. (C). 87.00 *(978-2-503-52795-6(7))* Brepols Pubs. BEL. Dist: Brown, David Bk. Co., The.

Montgomery, Robert. The Spread of Religions: A Social Scientific Theory Based on the Spread of Buddhism, Christianity & Islam. 2007. 372p. per. 20.00 *(978-1-59899-086-7(1))* Long Dash Publishing.

Moorman, John R. H. Church Life in England in the Thirteenth Century. 2010. (Cambridge Library Collection - History Ser.). (ENG., Illus.). 486p. pap. 35.99 *(978-1-108-01018-4(0))* Cambridge Univ. Pr.

Morgan, D. Densil. Span of the Cross: Christian Religion & Society in Wales, 1914-2000. 2nd ed. 2011. (ENG., Illus.). 310p. pap. 40.00 *(978-0-7083-2397-7(9))* Univ. of Wales Pr. GBR. Dist: Chicago Distribution Ctr.

Mullin, Robert Bruce. A Short World History of Christianity. 2008. (ENG.). 312p. pap. 30.00 *(978-0-664-22686-2(8))* Westminster John Knox Pr.

Muntazir, Patrick. Peace Without Domination: Life not Death. 2009. (ENG., Illus.). 296p. mass mkt. 24.95 *(978-0-9741699-1-0(9))* Finimex Publishing.

Murphy, Joseph. Wheels of Truth. 2010. 98p. pap. 8.95 *(978-1-57898-914-0(0))* Martino Publishing.

Nagell, Edward. Destiny: Volume Three: Christianity, the Do-It-Yourself Religion. 2006. 269p. pap. 15.95 *(978-0-7414-3694-8(9))* Infinity Publishing.

Ncozana, Silas S. The Spirit Dimension in African Christianity: A Pastoral Study among the Tumbuka People of Northern Malawi. 2006. (Illus.). 207p. pap. 29.95 *(978-99908-81-03-5(0))* Kachere Series, Bks. on Religion, Theology & Society in Malawi MWI. Dist: Michigan State Univ. Pr.

Neander, Johann A. General History of the Christian Religion & Church, 9 vols., Set. Torrey, Joseph, tr. from GER. rev. ed. reprint ed. lib. bdg. 495.00 *(978-0-404-09590-1(9))* AMS Pr., Inc.

Newman, Barbara, ed. The Collected Saints' Lives of Thomas of Cantimpre: Christina the Astonishing, Lutgard of Aywieres, Margaret of Ypres, & Abbot John of Cantimpre. King, Margot H., tr. from LAT. 2008. (Medieval Women Texts & Contexts Ser.). (ENG & LAT., Illus.). 324p. (C). 102.00 *(978-2-503-52078-0(2))* Brepols Pubs. BEL. Dist: ISD.

Newman, Louis I. Jewish Influence on Christian Reform Movements. (Columbia University, Oriental Studies: No. 23). reprint ed. 45.00 *(978-0-404-50513-4(9))* AMS Pr., Inc.

Nicholas, Tracy. The Fenders vs Xspellers the Beginning. 2009. 172p. pap. 13.63 *(978-0-557-14644-4(5))* Lulu Enterprises Inc.

Nichols, Stephen J. The Reformation: How a Monk & a Mallet Changed the World. 2007. (Illus.). 160p. pap. 13.99 *(978-1-58134-829-3(0))* Crossway.

Noel, Gerard. The Renaissance Popes: Statesmen, Warriors & the Great Borgia Myth. 2006. (ENG., Illus.). 320p. 27.95 *(978-0-7867-1841-2(2))* Basic Bks.

Noll, Mark A. Turning Points: Decisive Moments in the History of Christianity. 2nd ed. 2007. (Illus.). 352p. (C). reprint ed. pap. 21.99 *(978-0-8010-6211-7(X))* Baker Academic.

O'Donnell, Kevin. The Christian History. 2009. (ENG., Illus.). 224p. pap. 9.95 *(978-0-7459-5287-1(9))* Lion Hudson PLC GBR. Dist: Independent Pubs. Group.

Olson, Roger E. God in Dispute: Conversations among Great Christian Thinkers, 1 vol. 2009. 304p. (C). pap. 26.00 *(978-0-8010-3639-2(9))* Baker Academic.

Ordericus Vitalis Staff. Ecclesiastical History of England & Normandy, 4 Vols, Set. Forrester, T., tr. (Bohn's Antiquarian Library). reprint ed. 185.00 *(978-0-404-50040-5(4))* AMS Pr., Inc.

Orsuto, Donna & Orsuto. Holiness. 2007. (New Century Theology Ser.). (ENG., Illus.). 224p. 34.95 *(978-0-8264-5398-3(8))* Continuum International Publishing Group, Ltd. GBR. Dist: National Bk. Network.

Osei-Bonsu, Robert. The Nature of the Church & Ministry. 2010. 232p. pap. *(978-3-639-26605-4(6))* VDM Verlag Dr. Mueller e.K.

Packer, James S. Saints, Sinners, & Christian History: The Contradictions of the Christian Past. 2008. 230p. pap. 16.99 *(978-1-59955-137-1(3))* Cedar Fort, Inc./CFI Distribution.

Painter, John. The Quest for the Messiah: The History, Literature & Theology of the Johannine Community. 2nd ed. 490p. pap. *(978-0-567-29246-9(0)*, Burns & Oates) Continuum International Publishing Group, Ltd.

Palmer, William. A Compendiolus Ecclesiastical History from the Earliest Period to the Present Time. 2007. 244p. 41.95 *(978-0-548-05704-9(4))* Kessinger Publishing, LLC.

Papadogiannakis, Yannis. Christianity & Hellenism in the Fifth-Century Greek East: Theodoret's Apologetics Against the Greeks in Context. 2012. (Hellenic Studies Ser.). (ENG., Illus.). 200p. pap. 19.95 *(978-0-674-06067-8(9))* Harvard Univ., Ctr. for Hellenic Studies.

Parfrey, Adam & Wyllie, Timothy R., eds. Love, Sex, Fear, Death: The Untold Story of the Process Church of the Final Judgment Special Limited Edition. 2009. 380p. 93.00 *(978-1-932595-38-3(4))* Feral Hse.

Parigi, Paolo. The Rationalization of Miracles: How the Catholic Church Created Modern Sainthood. 2012. (ENG., Illus.). 232p. (C). 99.00 ***(978-1-107-01368-1(2))*** Cambridge Univ. Pr.

Paris, Andreas. Planet of Gold. 2008. 364p. pap. 18.95 *(978-1-60693-455-5(4)*, Eloquent Bks.) AEG Literary Publishing Services, Inc.

Parker. Annals of the Christian Church in Familiar Conversations for Young. 2007. (ENG.). 348p. per. 31.95 *(978-1-4304-4602-6(1))* Kessinger Publishing, LLC.

Pattengale, Jerry A. A Brief Guide to Objective Inquiry. 2007. (Illus.). v, 58p. pap. *(978-1-931283-20-5(6))* Triangle Publishing Co.

Patton-Bronson, Cheryl. One Day... This Day! 2007. 288p. per. 19.95 *(978-0-615-14908-0(1))* 4 Your Spirit Productions.

Pavlantos, Stephanie. The Few, the Humble, the Church. 2008. 140p. pap. 13.99 *(978-1-60647-265-1(8))* Xulon Pr., Inc.

Pfatteicher, Philip H. New Book of Festivals & Commemorations: A Proposed Common Calendar of Saints. 2008. 718p. (C). 50.00 *(978-0-8006-2128-5(X)*, Fortress Pr.) Augsburg Fortress, Pubs.

Phipps, William E. Supernaturalism in Christianity: Its Growth & Cure. 2008. 372p. 50.00 *(978-0-88146-093-3(1))* 2007. 356p. pap. 23.00 *(978-0-88146-094-0(X))* Mercer Univ. Pr.

Ping, Bob. Changing of the Gods: The Future of Judeo-Christian-Islamic Religion in a Postmodern World. 2010. 628p. pap. 23.49 *(978-1-4490-8709-8(4))* AuthorHouse.

Popkin, Richard H. Disputing Christianity: The 400-Year-Old Debate over Rabbi Isaac Ben Abraham Troki's Classic Arguments. 2007. (ENG.). 300p. 49.98 *(978-1-59102-384-5(X)*, Humanity Bks.) Prometheus Bks., Pubs.

Prince Michael of Albany & Salhab, Walid Amine. The Knights Templar of the Middle East: The Hidden History of the Islamic Origins of Freemasonry. 2006. (ENG.). 1p. 24.95 *(978-1-57863-346-3(X))* Red Wheel/Weiser.

Printy, Michael, et al, eds. Politics & Reformations: Histories & Reformations: Essays in Honour of Thomas A. Brady, Jr. 2007. (Studies in Medieval & Reformation Traditions: History, Culture, Religion, Ideas). (Illus.). 471p. *(978-90-04-16172-6(4))* BRILL.

Publishing, Rose. Rose Book of Bible & Christian History Time Lines: More Than 6000 Years at a Glance. 2006. (ENG., Illus.). 31p. 29.99 *(978-1-59636-084-6(4))* Rose Publishing.

Purves, George T., ed. The Apostolic Age. abr. ed. 2011. (Series: Religion & Spirituality Ser.). 95.00 *(978-1-59033-422-5(1))* Nova Science Pubs., Inc.

Rae, Murray & Rae. History & Hermeneutics. 2006. (ENG.). 176p. 60.00 *(978-0-567-08092-9(7)*, T&T Clark Int'l) Continuum International Publishing Group, Ltd. GBR. Dist: National Bk. Network.

Rancour-Laferriere, Daniel. The Sign of the Cross: From Golgotha to Genocide. 2011. (ENG.). 313p. 39.95 *(978-1-4128-1133-0(3))* Transaction Pubs.

Redpath, Irene M. St James the Less, Penicuik 1882 - 1982. 2009. 84p. pap. 12.95 *(978-1-4452-3245-4(6))* Lulu Enterprises Inc.

Reimer, James A. Christians & War: A History of Practices & Teachings. 2010. (Facets Ser.). 208p. pap. 9.99 *(978-0-8006-3819-1(0))* Augsburg Fortress, Pubs.

Religion & Folklore, Set. 2008. (ENG.). 432p. (C). 240.00 *(978-0-415-46345-4(9))* Routledge.

Rhodes, Ron. Halloween: What You Need to Know. 2008. (Quick Reference Guides). 16p. 4.99 *(978-0-7369-2179-4(6))* Harvest Hse. Pubs.

Ribak, Eliya. Religious Communities in Byzantine Palestina: The Relationship Between Judaism, Christianity & Islam AD 400-700. 2007. (Bar S Ser.). (Illus.). viii, 234p. (C). pap. 90.00 *(978-1-4073-0080-1(6))* British Archaeological Reports Ltd. GBR. Dist: Brown, David Bk. Co., The.

Rickards Mozley, John. The Divine Aspect of History: Volume 2. 2011. (ENG.). 520p. pap. 48.00 ***(978-1-107-60518-3(0))*** Cambridge Univ. Pr.

Robertson, C. K. A Dangerous Dozen: Twelve Christians Who Threatened the Status Quo but Taught Us to Live Like Jesus. 2011. 160p. pap. 16.99 *(978-1-59473-298-0(1))* SkyLight Paths Publishing.

Roldanus, Johannes. The Church in the Age of Constantine: The Theological Challenges. annot. ed. 2006. (Illus.). (ENG.). 256p. (C). 115.00 *(978-0-415-40903-2(9))*; 227p. per. 35.95 *(978-0-415-40904-9(7))* Routledge.

Rowland, Christopher. Christian Origins. 2nd ed. 480p. 32.00 *(978-0-281-05366-7(9))* SPCK Publishing GBR. Dist: Pilgrim Pr., The/United Church Pr.

Rupp, Gordon. Patterns of Reformation. 2009. 460p. pap. 55.00 *(978-1-60608-729-9(0)*, Wipf and Stock) Wipf & Stock Pubs.

Samuel Simon. The Church of the Redeemer, As Developed Within the General Synod of the Lutheran Church in America with a Historic Outline from the Apostolic Age T. 2006. 288p. per. 23.99 *(978-1-4255-2650-4(0))* MPublishing.

Sandwell, Isabella. Religious Identity in Late Antiquity: Greeks, Jews & Christians in Antioch. (Greek Culture in the Roman World Ser.). (ENG.). 2011. 324p. pap. 60.00 *(978-0-521-29691-5(9))* 2007. 322p. 124.00 *(978-0-521-87915-6(9))* Cambridge Univ. Pr.

Schaff, Philip. History of the Apostolic Church; with a General Introduction to Church History, by Philip Schaff Tr by Edward D Yeomans. 2006. 708p. per. 38.99 *(978-1-4255-6882-5(3))* MPublishing.

—History of the Christian Church. 2009. 814p. 42.99 *(978-1-113-20160-7(6))*; pap. 54.75 *(978-1-113-20159-1(2))* BiblioBazaar.

—History of the Christian Church. 2009. 498p. pap. *(978-0-217-00523-4(3))*; 706p. pap. *(978-0-217-00548-7(9))*; 698p. pap. *(978-0-217-22419-2(9))*; 692p. pap. *(978-0-217-22421-5(0))*; 696p. pap. *(978-0-217-00537-1(3))* Books LLC.

Scher, Addai. The School of Nisibis. 2010. (ARA.). pap. 24.40 *(978-1-61719-605-8(3))* Gorgias Pr., LLC.

Schorsch, J. Swimming the Christian Atlantic: Judeoconversos, Afroiberians & Amerindians in the Seventeenth Century, 2 vols. 2008. (Atlantic World Ser.). (Illus.). 592p. *(978-90-04-17040-7(5))* BRILL.

Schorsch, Jonathan. Swimming the Christian Atlantic: Judeoconversos, Afroiberians & Amerindians in the Seventeenth Century. 2009. 282p. (978-90-04-17252-4(1)) BRILL.

Schultz, Doug & Esau, Ken. Let's Face It! A Group Study in the Nature of the Church. 81p. pap. 3.95 (978-0-921788-52-2(5)) Kindred Productions.

Scott, Otto. The Great Christian Revolution. Date not set. reprint ed. pap. (978-1-887690-04-1(2)) Reformer, The.

Severson, Eric R. The Least of These: Selected Readings in Christian History. 2007. 282p. pap. 31.00 (978-1-55635-106-8(2), Cascade Bks.) Wipf & Stock Pubs.

Shafi, Joseph. Unmasking Muhamad's Life. 2008. 272p. pap. 16.99 (978-1-60266-888-1(4)) Xulon Pr., Inc.

Sheldon, Henry C. History of the Christian Church. 2009. 452p. 41.99 (978-1-117-33892-7(4)); 458p. 42.99 (978-1-117-31843-1(5)); (ENG.). 456p. pap. 35.75 (978-1-117-31844-8(3)); (ENG.). 450p. pap. 35.75 (978-1-117-33893-4(2)) BiblioBazaar.

Sheldon, Rose Mary & Voskullen, Thijs. Operation Messiah. 2008. (Illus.). 284p. 79.95 (978-0-85303-701-9(9)); pap. 32.95 (978-0-85303-702-6(7)) Valentine Mitchell Pubs. GBR. Dist: International Specialized Bk. Services.

Sheldrake, Philip. A Brief History of Spirituality. 2007. (Blackwell Brief Histories of Religion Ser.). (ENG., Illus.). 272p. 99.95 (978-1-4051-1770-8(2), Wiley-Blackwell) Wiley, John & Sons, Inc.

Shelley, Bruce L. Church History in Plain Language: Third Edition, 0 vols. 3rd ed. 2008. 560p. pap. 29.99 (978-0-7180-2553-3(9)) Nelson, Thomas Inc.

Shenk, Wilbert R., ed. Enlarging the Story: Perspectives on Writing World Christian History. 2011. 160p. pap. 18.00 (978-1-61097-624-4(X), Wipf and Stock) Wipf & Stock Pubs.

Sheppard, Carroll Anne & Dilliplane, Nancy Burton. Congregational Connections: Uniting Six Generations in the Church. 2011. 138p. 29.99 (978-1-4653-4447-2(0)); pap. 19.99 (978-1-4653-4446-5(2)) Xlibris Corp.

Shipton, Warren Arthur. The Golden River: That Flows through Time. 2010. 332p. pap. 17.95 (978-1-60594-513-2(7), Llumina Pr.) Aeon Publishing Inc.

Shubin, Daniel H. Heavenly Relationships. 2008. 239p. pap. 16.99 (978-0-557-02371-4(8)) Lulu Enterprises Inc.

Siemens, James. The Christology of Theodore of Tarsus. 2010. (Studia Traditionis Theologiae Ser.). (ENG.). 211p. (C). pap. 102.00 (978-2-503-53385-8(X)) Brepols Pubs. BEL. Dist: ISD.

Siniossoglou, Niketas. Plato & Theodoret: The Christian Appropriation of Platonic Philosophy & the Hellenic Intellectual Resistance. 2011. (Cambridge Classical Studies). (ENG.). 280p. pap. 36.99 (978-0-521-30065-0(7)) Cambridge Univ. Pr.

Skelton, Colin. Spiritual Circles. 2010. 80p. pap. (978-3-8383-4080-7(9)) Lambert Academic Publishing.

Slack, S. B. Early Christianity: Religions Ancient & Modern 1914. 2007. (ENG.). 108p. 34.95 (978-0-548-05561-8(0)) Kessinger Publishing, LLC.

Smith, Don M. With Total Abandon: The Discipleship Journey. 2007. 169p. per. 12.99 (978-1-59886-580-6(3)) Tate Publishing & Enterprises, LLC.

Smith, Hampton. The Spirit & the Bride: A History of St. Clement's Episcopal Church, St. Paul, Minnesota. 1895 - 1995. 2007. pap. (978-0-9792833-0-7(2)) St. Clement's Episcopal Church.

Smith, Hampton Smith. The Spirit & the Bride: A History of St. Clement's Episcopal Church, 1893-1996. 2007. (978-0-9792833-1-4(0)) St. Clement's Episcopal Church.

Smith, John. The Third Watch. 2010. 496p. 36.99 (978-1-60957-669-1(1)); pap. 24.99 (978-1-60957-668-4(3)) Xulon Pr., Inc.

Smith, Joseph Fielding. Essentials in Church History: A History of the Church of Jesus Christ of Latter Day Saints from the Birth of Joseph Smith to the Present Time 1922. 2007. (ENG.). 702p. 65.95 (978-0-548-04871-9(1)) Kessinger Publishing, LLC.

Smith, Oswald J. De Muerte a Vida: From Death to Life. (SPA.). (978-84-7645-037-6(0), 223108) Clie, Editorial.

Solange Lefebvre Staff. Concilium 2007/5: Ages of Life & Christian Experience. 2010. 125p. pap. (978-0-334-03096-6(X), SCM Pr.) Hymns Ancient & Modern Ltd.

Spiteri, Laurence John. At Your Fingertips: A History of the Roman Catholic Church until the Council of Trent. 2008. (978-0-8189-1273-3(1), St. Pauls) St Pauls/Alba Hse. Pubs.

Springer, Michael S. Restoring Christ's Church: John a Lasco & Hte Forma AC Ratio. 2007. (St Andrews Studies in Reformation History Ser.). (Illus.). 198p. 114.95 (978-0-7546-5601-2(2)) Ashgate Publishing Co.

Stanley, Arthur Penrhyn. Lectures on the History of the Eastern C. 2006. pap. 40.95 (978-1-4286-5167-8(5)) Kessinger Publishing, LLC.

—Lectures on the History of the Eastern Church, with an Introduction on the Study of Ecclesiastical History, by Arthur Penrhyn Stanley. 2006. 556p. per. 32.99 (978-1-4255-6128-4(4)) MPublishing.

Stark, Rodney. The Triumph of Christianity: How the Jesus Movement Became the World's Largest Religion. 2012. (ENG.). 272p. pap. 14.99 (978-0-06-200769-8(6), HarperOne) HarperCollins Pubs.

Stayer, James M. & Roth, John D., eds. A Companion to Anabaptism & Spiritualism, 1521-1700. 2006. (Brill's Companions to the Christian Tradition Ser.: Vol. 6). (Illus.). 574p. (978-90-04-15402-5(7)) BRILL.

Stevens, Tim. Pop Goes the Church: Should the Church Engage Pop Culture? 2008. (Illus.). 256p. pap. 16.95 (978-0-9790174-9-0(1)) Power Publishing.

Stevenson, Wayne. New Eusebius. 2nd ed. 432p. 25.00 (978-0-281-04268-5(3)) SPCK Publishing GBR. Dist: Pilgrim Pr., The/United Church Pr.

Stewart, Charles. A Search for Original Christianity. 2006. (ENG.). 200p. per. 24.95 (978-1-4241-3555-4(9)) PublishAmerica, Inc.

Sykes, Norman. Man as Churchman. 2009. (ENG.). 216p. pap. 28.99 (978-0-521-13583-2(4)) Cambridge Univ. Pr.

Tabor, James D. The Jesus Dynasty: The Hidden History of Jesus, His Royal Family, & the Birth of Christianity. 2007. (ENG., Illus.). 400p. pap. 16.00 (978-0-7432-8724-1(X)) Simon & Schuster.

Tanner, Norman. The Church in Council: Conciliar Movements, Religious Practice & the Papacy from Nicea to Vatican II. 2011. (International Library of Historical Studies). (ENG., Illus.). 272p. 92.00 (978-1-84885-513-7(3)) I. B. Tauris & Co., Ltd. GBR. Dist: Macmillan.

Taylor, Robert. The Diegesis. 2009. 384p. pap. (978-1-4589-1409-5(7)) Books LLC.

The Temple. 7.00 (978-0-8309-0815-8(3)) Herald Publishing Hse.

Teneriello, Andrew Michael. Blinded by the Devil. 2008. 212p. pap. 14.99 (978-1-60647-584-3(3)) Xulon Pr., Inc.

Teresa Okuru Staff. Concilium 2005/5: African Christianities. 2010. 141p. pap. (978-0-334-03086-7(2), SCM Pr.) Hymns Ancient & Modern Ltd.

Tessera, Miriam Rita. Orientalis Ecclesia: Papato, Chiesa e Regno Latino Di Gerusalemme (1099-1187) 2010. (ITA., Illus.). 660p. (978-88-343-1849-2(8)) Vita e Pensiero.

Thompson, Augustine Op. Revival Preachers & Politics in Thirteenth Century Italy: The Great Devotion Of 1233. 2010. 258p. pap. 28.00 (978-1-60899-494-6(5), Wipf and Stock) Wipf & Stock Pubs.

Thompson, Peter J. The Christian Story: Past, Present & Future. 2009. 152p. 22.49 (978-1-4490-2340-9(1)); pap. 11.99 (978-1-4490-2341-6(X)) AuthorHouse.

Thomson, John Mansfield, ed. Farewell Colonialism: The New Zealand International Exhibition Christchurch, 1906-07. (Illus.). 170p. (978-0-86469-318-1(4)) Dunmore Publishing, Ltd.

Thomson, Neil. New Movements AD 1500-1800. 12.95 (978-0-281-02930-3(X)) International Publishers Marketing.

Thornton, Norman. Searching for Christianity. 2011. (ENG.). 258p. pap. 27.18 (978-1-906791-72-8(4)) Arena Bks. GBR. Dist: Lightning Source UK, Ltd.

Tickle, Phyllis. The Great Emergence: How Christianity Is Changing & Why. 2008. (Mersion: Emergent Village Resources for Communities of Faith Ser.). (Illus.). 176p. 17.99 (978-0-8010-1313-3(5)) Baker Bks.

Tomkins, Stephen. A Short History of Christianity. 2006. 256p. per. 15.00 (978-0-8028-3382-2(9)) Eerdmans, William B. Publishing Co.

Trickler, C. Jack. A Layman's Guide To: Why Are There So Many Christian Denominations? 2010. 292p. pap. 15.49 (978-1-4490-4576-0(6)) AuthorHouse.

Troeltsch, Ernst. Funf Vortrage Zu Religion und Geschichtsphilosophie Fur England und Schottland. der Historismus und Seine Uberwindung (1924)/Christian Thought. Its History & Application (1923) 2006. (GER & ENG., Illus.). XVI, 268p. 189.00 (978-3-11-018232-3(7)) De Gruyter, Walter Inc.

Tucker, Ruth A. Parade of Faith: A Biographical History of the Christian Church, 1 vol. 2011. (ENG.). 448p. pap. 39.99 (978-0-310-20638-5(3)) Zondervan.

Tutson, A. James & SaRa Djehuty, Yahdah. From Death to Life: Before Judaism, Christianity or Islam There Was God... So Who Were You? 2010. 40p. pap. 10.00 (978-0-557-27898-5(8)) Lulu Enterprises Inc.

Udoh, Fabian E. & Sanders, E. P. Redefining First-Century Jewish & Christian Identities: Essays in Honor of Ed Parish Sanders. Udoh, Fabian E., ed. 2008. (ND Christianity & Judaism Anitqui Ser.). (ENG.). 440p. 60.00 (978-0-268-04453-4(8)) Univ. of Notre Dame Pr.

Usener, Hermann. Religionsgeschichtliche Untersuchungen. 2010. 468p. pap. 37.75 (978-1-143-14587-2(9)) BiblioBazaar.

van Dijkhuizen, J. F. & Todd, R., eds. The Reformation Unsettled: British Literature & the Question of Religious Identity, 1560 - 1660. 2009. (Proteus Ser.). (ENG., Illus.). 246p. (C). 102.00 (978-2-503-52624-9(1)) Brepols Pubs. BEL. Dist: ISD.

Van Dijkhuizen, Jan Frans & Enenkel, Karl A. E., eds. The Sense of Suffering: Constructions of Physical Pain in Early Modern Culture. 2008. (Intersections Ser.). 528p. (978-90-04-17247-0(5)) BRILL.

Van Hagen, John. Rescuing Religion: How Faith Can Survive Its Encounter with Science. 2012. (ENG.). 288p. pap. 25.00 (978-1-59815-037-7(5)) Polebridge Pr.

Van Kirk, Agnes E. The Church, Her Purpose: The Extension of the Incarnation. 2011. 84p. 37.95 (978-1-258-04771-9(3)) Literary Licensing, LLC.

Velez, Thomas. Antichrist invades Earth: Our Future. 2006. 136p. pap. 13.99 (978-1-59755-048-2(5), Advantage Inspirational) Advantage Bks.

Vermes, Geza. The Story of the Scrolls: The Miraculous Discovery & True Significance of the Dead Sea Scrolls. 2010. (ENG.). 272p. pap. 17.00 (978-0-14-104615-0(5), Penguin Global) Penguin Group (USA) Inc.

Veyne, Paul. When Our World Became Christian. 2010. (ENG.). 240p. pap. 24.95 (978-0-7456-4499-8(6)) Polity Pr. GBR. Dist: Wiley, John & Sons, Inc.

—When Our World Became Christian, 312-394. 2010. (ENG.). 240p. 69.95 (978-0-7456-4498-1(8)) Polity Pr. GBR. Dist: Wiley, John & Sons, Inc.

Viccone, Anthony. The Last Days of Jesus. 2006. 9.00 (978-0-8059-8267-1(1)) Dorrance Publishing Co., Inc.

Volney, Constantin-Fran§Ois. The Ruins. 2010. 420p. pap. 24.95 (978-0-557-01441-5(7)) Lulu Enterprises Inc.

Walker, Williston. A History of the Christian Church. 2009. 676p. pap. (978-0-217-77031-6(2)); 614p. pap. (978-0-217-66812-5(7)) Books LLC.

—A History of the Christian Church. 2010. pap. 92.32 (978-1-61719-344-6(5)) Gorgias Pr., LLC.

—A History of the Christian Church. 2008. 650p. 63.95 (978-1-4365-7352-8(1)) 2007. (ENG.). 652p. per. 48.95 (978-0-548-75504-4(3)) Kessinger Publishing, LLC.

Wandel, Lee Palmer. The Reformation: Towards a New History. 2011. (ENG., Illus.). 284p. (C). 90.00 (978-0-521-88949-0(9)); pap. 26.99 (978-0-521-71797-7(3)) Cambridge Univ. Pr.

Ward, Keith. Re-Thinking Christianity. 2007. (ENG.). 256p. pap. 29.95 (978-1-85168-506-6(5)) Oneworld Pubns. GBR. Dist: National Bk. Network.

Waring, Diana, ed. Romans, Reformers, Revolutionaries: A Biblical World History Curriculum Resurrection to Revolution AD 30-AD 1799. 2008. (Illus.). 351p. (J). pap. 29.99 (978-1-60092-171-1(X)) Answers in Genesis Ministries.

—Romans, Reformers, Revolutionaries: Resurrection to Revolution AD 30-AD 1799. 2008. (History Revealed Ser.). (J). pap. 8.99 (978-1-60092-177-3(9)); (Illus.). 39.99 (978-1-60092-169-8(8)) Answers in Genesis Ministries.

Waschbü, et al. Alter Melanchthon: Muster theologischer Autoritätsstiftung bei Matthias Flacius Illyricus. Forschungen zur Kirchen- und Dogmengeschichte 96. 2008. (Forschungen Zur Kirchen- und Dogmengeschichte Ser.). (GER.). 208p. (C). 63.00 (978-3-525-55300-8(5)) Vandenhoeck & Ruprecht GmbH & Co. KG DEU. Dist: ISD.

Waterfield, Robin. Christians in Persia (Rle Iran A) 2011. (Routledge Library Editions Ser.). (ENG.). 208p. 115.00 (978-0-415-61048-3(6)) Routledge.

Waters, C. Virgins & Scholars a Fifteen-Century Compilation of the Lives of John the Baptist, John. 2008. (Medieval Women: Texts & Contexts Ser.). (ENG & ENM., Illus.). 494p. (C). 152.00 (978-2-503-51452-9(9)) Brepols Pubs. BEL. Dist: ISD.

Welch, P., ed. Church & Settler in Colonial Zimbabwe: A Study in the History of the Anglican Diocese of Mashonaland/Southern Rhodesia, 1890-1925. 2008. (Studies of Religion in Africa Ser.). (Illus.). 250p. (C). (978-90-04-16746-9(3)) BRILL.

Weston, John. Patmos Speaks Today. 2007. 88p. per. (978-0-901860-66-8(2)) Scripture Truth Pubns.

Whately, Elizabeth Jane. Plymouth Brethrenism. 2010. 128p. pap. 26.95 (978-1-4460-0031-1(1)) Audubon Pr. & Christian Bk. Service.

White, Cynthia. The Emergence of Christianity, 1 vol. 2007. (Greenwood Guides to Historic Events of the Ancient World). (Illus.). 248p. 45.00 (978-0-313-32799-5(8), GR2799, Greenwood Pr.) Greenwood Publishing Group, Inc.

Wilken, Robert L. The Myth of Christian Beginnings. 2009. 232p. pap. 26.00 (978-1-60608-693-3(6), Wipf and Stock) Wipf & Stock Pubs.

Wilken, Robert Louis. The First Thousand Years. 2012. (ENG.). 416p. 35.00 (978-0-300-11884-1(8)) Yale Univ. Pr.

Wilkins, David G., ed. A Reflection of Faith: Saint Paul Cathedral, 1906-2006. 2007. (Illus.). 198p. per. 40.00 (978-0-615-15404-6(2)) St. Paul Cathedral.

Winn, Robert E. Eusebius of Emesa: Church & Theology in the Mid-Fourth Century. 2011. 304p. 69.95 (978-0-8132-1876-2(4)) Catholic Univ. of America Pr.

Wright, Jonathan. Heretics: The Creation of Christianity from the Gnostics to the Modern Church. 2011. (ENG., Illus.). 352p. 28.00 (978-0-15-101387-6(X)) Houghton Mifflin Harcourt Trade & Reference Pubs.

Wyllie, Timothy R. & Parfrey, Adam, eds. Love, Sex, Fear, Death: The Inside Story of the Process Church of the Final Judgment. 2009. (ENG., Illus.). 304p. pap. 24.95 (978-1-932595-37-6(6)) Feral Hse.

Yonge, Charlotte M. The Chosen People: A Compendium of Sacred & Church History for School-Children. by the Author of the Heir of Redelyffe. 2006. 200p. (gr. 4-7). per. 18.99 (978-1-4255-1633-8(5)) MPublishing.

Young, Samuel. God's Unfailing Faithfulness: The Life of Charles S. Jenkins. 2011. 86p. 38.95 (978-1-258-07661-0(6)) Literary Licensing, LLC.

Zahl, Paul F.M. 2000 Years of Amazing Grace: The Story & Meaning of the Christian Faith. 2006. (ENG.). 480p. 26.95 (978-0-7425-5276-0(4)) Rowman & Littlefield Publishers, Inc.

Zomber, Michael. Jesus & the Samurai: The Shining Religion & the Samurai. 2009. 48p. pap. 9.95 (978-1-4401-7684-5(1)) iUniverse, Inc.

1st Evangelical Lutheran Church. Through These Doors & Beyond. 2011. 96p. pap. 9.99 (978-1-4634-5985-7(8)) AuthorHouse.

CHURCH HISTORY—CHRONOLOGY

see also Church Calendar

Bigelow, Christopher Kimball. The Timechart History of Mormonism: From Premortality to the Present. 2007. (Illus.). 31p. 17.99 (978-1-903025-40-6(0)) Worth Pr. Ltd. GBR. Dist: Book Sales, Inc.

Dowley, Tim. The Christians: An Illustrated History. 2008. (ENG., Illus.). 176p. 24.95 (978-0-7459-5225-3(9)) Lion Hudson PLC GBR. Dist: Independent Pubs. Group.

"God's Friend". A Christian Chronology of History: A Time Line of Human History from a Christian Prospective. 2011. 172p. pap. 13.96 (978-1-4269-5603-4(7)) Trafford Publishing.

Mosshammer, Alden A. The Easter Computus & the Origins of the Christian Era. 2008. (Oxford Early Christian Studies). (ENG., Illus.). 432p. 150.00 (978-0-19-954312-0(7)) Oxford Univ. Pr., Inc.

Summon, Parminder Singh. Summon's Compendium of Days: An Essential Digest of Daily History, Biography, Philosophy, Customs & Traditions, Curiosities of Human Nature, & Learned Discourse Designed to Inspire & Entertain. 2007. (Illus.). 408p. per. 29.00 (978-1-59627-057-2(8), Seabury Bks.) Church Publishing, Inc.

CHURCH HISTORY—DICTIONARIES

Benedetto, Robert, ed. The New Westminster Dictionary of Church History: The Early, Medieval, & Reformation Eras. 2008. (ENG.). 768p. 60.00 (978-0-664-22416-5(4)) Westminster John Knox Pr.

Benedetto, Robert & McKim. Historical Dictionary of the Reformed Churches. 2nd ed. 2009. (Historical Dictionaries of Religions, Philosophies, & Movements Ser.). (ENG.). 790p. 158.00 (978-0-8108-5807-7(X)) Scarecrow Pr., Inc.

Bowman, Carl W. & Durnbaugh, Donald F., eds. The Brethren Encyclopedia, Vol. 4. (978-0-936693-04-0(5)) Brethren Encyclopedia, Inc.

Brackney, William H. Historical Dictionary of Radical Christianity. 2012. (Historical Dictionaries of Religions, Philosophies, & Movements Ser.). (ENG.). 368p. 100.00 (978-0-8108-7179-3(3)) Scarecrow Pr., Inc.

Braun, Hannelore & Grunzinger, Gertraud. Personenlexikon zum deutschen Protestantismus 1919 -1949. 2006. (Arbeiten zur Kirchlichen Zcitgcsehichte - Ser.: Vol. 12). (GER.). 293p. (C). 59.00 (978-3-525-55761-7(2)) Vandenhoeck & Ruprecht GmbH & Co. KG DEU. Dist: ISD.

Collinge, William J. Historical Dictionary of Catholicism. 2nd ed. 2012. E-Book (978-0-8108-7979-9(4)); (ENG.). 622p. 95.00 (978-0-8108-5755-1(2)) Scarecrow Pr., Inc.

Feldmeth, Nathan P. Pocket Dictionary of Church History. 2008. (IVP Pocket Reference Ser.). (ENG.). 151p. pap. 8.00 (978-0-8308-2703-9(X), IVP Acad.) InterVarsity Pr.

Gabra, Gawdat. Historical Dictionary of the Coptic Church. 2008. (Historical Dictionaries of Religions, Philosophies, & Movements Ser.). (ENG.). 360p. 99.00 (978-0-8108-6097-1(X)) Scarecrow Pr., Inc.

Kaufhold, Hubert, ed. Kleines Lexikon des Christlichen Orients. 2nd ed. 2007. (GER., Illus.). 655p. 102.00 (978-3-447-05382-2(8)) Harrassowitz, Otto Verlag DEU. Dist: ISD.

Livingstone, E. A., ed. The Concise Oxford Dictionary of the Christian Church. 2nd rev. ed. 2006. (Oxford Paperback Reference Ser.). (ENG.). 672p. per. 21.95 (978-0-19-861442-5(X)) Oxford Univ. Pr., Inc.

McClintock, John & Strong, James. Cyclopaedia of Biblical, Theological, & Ecclesiastical Literature: Cyclopedia of Biblical Literature, Vol. 1 10. 250.00 (978-0-405-00020-1(0), 11917) Ayer Co. Pubs., Inc.

Reeve, W. Paul & Parshall, Ardis E. Mormonism: A Historical Encyclopedia. 2010. (Illus.). xxviii, 449p. E-Book (978-1-59884-108-4(4)) ABC-CLIO, LLC.

Reeve, W. Paul & Parshall, Ardis E., eds. Mormonism: A Historical Encyclopedia, 1 vol. 2010. (Illus.). 449p. 85.00 (978-1-59884-107-7(6), MORMON1C) ABC-CLIO, LLC.

Vila, Samuel. Enciclopedia de Historia de la Iglesia: Encyclopedia of Church History. (SPA., Illus.). 696p. (978-84-7228-447-0(6), 220360) Clie, Editorial.

CHURCH HISTORY—HISTORIOGRAPHY

Braun, Willi. It's Just Another Story: The Politics of Remembering the Earliest Christians. 2012. (Religion in culture: studies in social contest & Construction Ser.). (ENG.). 160p. (C). pap. 28.95 (978-1-84553-009-9(8)); 85.00 (978-1-84553-008-2(X)) Equinox Publishing Ltd. GBR. Dist: ISD.

Bremmer, Jan N. The Rise of Christianity Through the Eyes of Gibbon, Harnack & Rodney Stark: A Valedictory Lecture on the Occasion of His Retirement from the Chair of Religious Studies, in the Faculty of Theology & Religious Studies. 2nd ed. 2010. (ENG.). 87p. (C). pap. 20.00 (978-90-77922-70-5(9)) Barkhuis Publishing NLD. Dist: Brown, David Bk. Co., The.

Chadwick, Owen. Catholicism & History: The Opening of the Vatican Archives. 2009. (ENG.). 184p. pap. 31.99 (978-0-521-09330-9(9)) Cambridge Univ. Pr.

D'Elia, Donald J. & Foley, Patrick, eds. The Catholic As Historian. 2006. 256p. pap. 24.95 (978-1-932589-27-6(9)) Ave Maria Univ.

Dipple, Geoffrey Luke. "Just As in the Time of the Apostles" Uses of History in the Radical Reformation. 30.00 (978-1-894710-58-9(4)) Pandora Pr. CAN. Dist: Herald Pr.

Guidelines 2001-2004 Church Historian. 2.50 (978-0-687-03551-9(1)) Abingdon Pr.

Guidelines for Leading Your Congregation 2009-2012 - Church Historians: Remembering the Past & Inspiring the Future. 2008. 2.95 (978-0-687-64851-1(3)) Abingdon Pr.

Harris, Matthew Edward. The Notion of Papal Monarchy in the Thirteenth Century: The Idea of Paradigm in Church History. 2011. 160p. 109.95 (978-0-7734-1441-9(X)) Mellen, Edwin Pr., The.

Heath, Gordon L. Doing Church History: A User-Friendly Introduction to Researching the History of Christianity. 2008. 108p. pap. (978-1-894667-90-6(5)) Clements Publishing.

Kaldellis, Anthony. The Christian Parthenon: Classicism & Pilgrimage in Byzantine Athens. 2009. (ENG., Illus.). 268p. 107.00 (978-0-521-88228-6(1)) Cambridge Univ. Pr.

Van Liere, Katherine, et al, eds. Sacred History: Uses of the Christian Past in the Renaissance World. 2012. (ENG., Illus.). 320p. 125.00 (978-0-19-959479-5(1)) Oxford Univ. Pr., Inc.

Verdoner, Marie. Narrated Reality: The Historia Ecclesiastica of Eusebius of Caesarea. 2011. (Early Christianity in the Context of Antiquity Ser.). (Illus.). 216p. 66.95 (978-3-631-60588-2(9)) Lang, Peter GmbH, Europaischer Verlag der Wissenschaften DEU. Dist: Lang, Peter.

CHURCH HISTORY—JUVENILE LITERATURE

Yonge, Charlotte Mary. The Chosen People: A Compendium of Sacred & Church History for School-Children. 2009. 202p. (gr. 4-7). 28.99 (978-1-116-77830-4(0)); 32.99 (978-1-116-77829-8(7)); pap. 23.75 (978-1-116-77832-8(7)); pap. 24.75 (978-1-116-77831-1(9)) BiblioBazaar.

CHURCH HISTORY—OUTLINES, SYLLABI, ETC.

Cram101 Textbook Reviews & Cram101 Textbook Reviews. Outlines & Highlights for the European Reformations by Carter Lindberg, Isbn: 9781405180672 1405180676. 2011. 352p. pap. 33.95 ***(978-1-61490-218-8(6))*** Cram101 Inc.

Cram101 Textbook Reviews Staff. Outlines & Highlights for the European Reformations by Carter Lindberg, Isbn: 9781557865755. 2009. 100p. pap. 27.95 *(978-1-4288-9268-2(0))* Cram101 Inc.

Kuipers, Ken. A. D. A Study of Church History. (Crossroads Ser.). 133p. tchr. ed. 16.25 *(978-0-930265-45-8(9)*, 120015) Faith Alive Christian Resources.

CHURCH HISTORY—PHILOSOPHY

Pitre, Roy. Where Is the Fire of the Book of Acts? 2007. pap. 16.99 *(978-1-60266-034-2(4))* Xulon Pr., Inc.

Schultenover, David G. The Reception of Pragmatism in France & the Rise of Roman Catholic Modernism, 1890-1914. 2009. 264p. 74.95 *(978-0-8132-1572-3(2))* Catholic Univ. of America Pr.

Vincelette, Alan Roy. Recent Catholic Philosophy: The Nineteenth Century. 2008. pap. *(978-0-87462-756-5(7))* Marquette Univ. Pr.

CHURCH HISTORY—SOURCES

see also Christian Literature, Early

Beresford, Andrew M. The Legends of the Holy Harlots: Thaïs & Pelagia in Medieval Spanish Literature. 2007. (Monografías A Ser.: Volume 238). 174p. 90.00 *(978-1-85566-144-8(6)*, Tamesis Bks.) Boydell & Brewer, Ltd. GBR. Dist: Boydell & Brewer, Inc.

Bettenson, Henry & Maunder, Chris. The Documents of the Christian Church. 4th ed. 2011. (ENG.). 528p. pap. 29.95 *(978-0-19-956898-7(7))* Oxford Univ. Pr., Inc.

Caraccioli, Louis-Antoine. Interesting Letters of Pope Clement Xiv, Ganganelli V1: To Which Are Prefixed Anecdotes of His Life (1781) Lottin Le Jeune, tr. 2008. 318p. 45.95 *(978-1-4365-2683-8(3))* 2007. 320p. per. 30.95 *(978-0-548-71520-8(3))* Kessinger Publishing, LLC.

Clement, Pope. Interesting Letters of Pope Clement Xiv, Ganganelli V1: To Which Are Prefixed, Anecdotes of His Life (1777) 2008. 352p. 46.95 *(978-1-4366-5364-0(9))*; pap. 31.95 *(978-0-548-88958-9(9))* Kessinger Publishing, LLC.

—Interesting Letters of Pope Clement Xiv, Ganganelli V2: To Which Are Prefixed, Anecdotes of His Life (1777) 2008. 276p. 42.95 *(978-1-4366-4055-8(5))*; pap. 27.95 *(978-0-548-86867-6(0))* Kessinger Publishing, LLC.

Drobner, Hubertus R. The Fathers of the Church: A Comprehensive Introduction. Schatzmann, Siegfried S., tr. from GER. 2007. 632p. 44.95 *(978-1-56563-331-5(8))* Hendrickson Pubs. Marketing, LLC.

Everett, Isaac. The Emergent Psalter. 2009. 288p. pap. 25.00 *(978-0-89869-617-2(8))* Church Publishing, Inc.

Lamy, Thomas Josephus. Concilium Seleuciae et Ctesiphonti Habitum Anno 410. 2010. (SYR & LAT.). pap. 25.12 *(978-1-61143-611-2(7))* Gorgias Pr., LLC.

Land, Jan Pieter Nicolaas, ed. Anecdota Syriaca. 2010. (LAT.). 523.04 *(978-1-60724-875-0(1))* Gorgias Pr., LLC.

Minns, Denis & Parvis, Paul, eds. Justin, Philosopher & Martyr: Apologies. 2009. (Oxford Early Christian Texts). (ENG.). 384p. 170.00 *(978-0-19-954250-5(3))* Oxford Univ. Pr., Inc.

Nichols, Stephen J. Pages from Church History: A Guided Tour of Christian Classics. 2006. (Illus.). 329p. per. 15.99 *(978-0-87552-636-2(5))* P & R Publishing.

Spaulding, John G., ed. Pulpit Publications, 1660-1782, 6 vols., Set. Incl. Vol. 1. lib. bdg. *(978-0-88354-126-5(2))*; Vol. 2. lib. bdg. *(978-0-88354-127-2(0))*; Vol. 3. lib. bdg. *(978-0-88354-128-9(9))*; Vol. 4. lib. bdg. *(978-0-88354-129-6(7))*; Vol. 5. lib. bdg. *(978-0-88354-130-2(0))*; Vol. 6. lib. bdg. *(978-0-88354-131-9(9))*; 1996. Set lib. bdg. 400.00 *(978-0-88354-149-4(1))* Ross Publishing Incorporated.

Van Liere, Katherine, et al, eds. Sacred History: Uses of the Christian Past in the Renaissance World. 2012. (ENG., Illus.). 320p. 125.00 ***(978-0-19-959479-5(1))*** Oxford Univ. Pr., Inc.

Weaver, C. Douglas, et al, eds. Exploring Christian Heritage: A Reader in History & Theology. 2012. (ENG.). 350p. pap. 59.95 ***(978-1-60258-415-0(X))*** Baylor Univ. Pr.

Williams, D. H., ed. Tradition, Scripture, & Interpretation: A Sourcebook of the Ancient Church. 2006. (Evangelical Ressourcement Ser.). 192p. (C). pap. 22.00 *(978-0-8010-3164-9(8))* Baker Academic.

CHURCH HISTORY—PRIMITIVE AND EARLY CHURCH, CA. 30-600

see also Alexandrian School, Christian; Apologetics—Early Church, ca. 30-600; Apostles; Apostolic Fathers; Catacombs; Church Orders, Ancient; Ebionism; Fathers of the Church; Heresies and Heretics—Early Church, ca. 30-600; Monasticism and Religious Orders—Early Church, ca. 30-600; Montanism; Neoplatonism; Theology, Doctrinal—History—Early Church, ca. 30-600

Aageson, James W. Paul, the Pastoral Epistles, & the Early Church. Porter, Stanley E., ed. 2008. (Library of Pauline Studies). 235p. per. *(978-1-59856-041-1(7))* Hendrickson Pubs. Marketing, LLC.

Abbott, Daniel H. Revolutionary Strategies in Early Christianity: 4th Generation Warfare (4GW) Against the Roman Empire, & the Counterinsurgency (COIN) Campaign to Sa. 2008. 48p. pap. 19.16 *(978-1-934840-36-8(X))* Nimble Bks. LLC.

Aguirre Monasterio, Rafael. Del Movimiento de Jesús a la Iglesia Cristiana: Ensayo de Exégesis Sociológica Del Cristianismo Primitivo. 2009. (Ágora Ser.: Vol. 4). (SPA.). 243p. *(978-84-8169-927-2(6))* Verbo Divino, Editorial.

Aland, Barbara. Was ist Gnosis? Studien zum frühen Christentum, zu Marcion und zur kaiserzeitlichen Philosophie. 2009. 434p. 235.00 *(978-3-16-149967-8(0))* Mohr Siebeck GmbH & Co. KG DEU. Dist: Coronet Bks.

Alikin, Valeriy A. The Earliest History of the Christian Gathering: Origin, Development, & Content of the Christian Gathering in the First to Third Centuries. 2010. (Illus.). 342p. *(978-90-04-18309-4(4))* BRILL.

Amidon, Philip R., tr. from GEC. Philostorgius: Church History. 2007. (SBL: Writings from the Greco-Roman World). 284p. *(978-90-04-14671-6(7))* BRILL.

—Philostorgius: Church History. 2007. 312p. per. 34.95 *(978-1-58983-215-2(9))* Society of Biblical Literature.

Apostle D M Lake. Who Is Jesus Christ. 2008. 108p. pap. *(978-0-9549243-8-6(X))* Esteemworld Pubns.

Aquilina, Mike. Companion Guide to Pope Benedict's The Fathers. 2008. 95p. pap. *(978-1-59276-542-3(4))* Our Sunday Visitor, Publishing Div.

Ashwin-Siejkowski, Piotr & Ashwin-Siejkowski. Clement of Alexandria: A Project of Christian Perfection. Ashwin-Siejkowski, Piotr, tr. 2008. (ENG.). 272p. 130.00 *(978-0-567-03287-4(6)*, T&T Clark Int'l) Continuum International Publishing Group, Ltd. GBR. Dist: National Bk. Network.

Augustine, Saint. The Manichean Debate. 2006. 424p. 44.00 *(978-1-56548-247-0(6))* New City Pr.

Ayer, Joseph C. Sourcebook of Ancient Church History. reprint ed. lib. bdg. 64.50 *(978-0-404-00436-1(9))* AMS Pr., Inc.

Baker-Brian, Nicholas John. Manichaeism in the Later Roman Empire: A Study of Augustine's Contra Adimantum. 2009. 392p. 119.95 *(978-0-7734-4755-4(5))* Mellen, Edwin Pr., The.

Balch, David L. & Lamoreaux, Jason T., eds. Finding A Woman's Place: Essays in Honor of Carolyn Osiek. 2010. (Princeton Theological Monographs). (Illus.). 406p. pap. 45.00 *(978-1-60608-989-7(7)*, Pickwick Pubns.) Wipf & Stock Pubs.

Barcelo, Pedro, ed. Religiöser Fundamentalismus in der römischen Kaiserzeit. 2010. (Potsdamer Altertumswissenschaftliche Beitrage (PAwB) Ser.). (GER., Illus.). 250p. (C). pap. 80.00 *(978-3-515-09444-3(X))* Steiner, Franz Verlag Wiesbaden GmbH DEU. Dist: Brown, David Bk. Co., The.

Barnes, Julian & Barnes, Timothy. Constantine: Dynasty, Religion & Power in the Later Roman Empire. 2011. (Blackwell Ancient Lives Ser.: 16). (ENG., Illus.). 288p. 128.95 *(978-1-4051-1727-2(3)*, Wiley-Blackwell) Wiley, John & Sons, Inc.

Barnes, Timothy D. Early Christian Hagiography & Roman History. 2010. 437p. pap. 57.50 *(978-3-16-150226-2(4))* Mohr Siebeck GmbH & Co. KG DEU. Dist: Coronet Bks.

Baur, Ferdinand C. Apollonius von Tyana und Christus. 2009. 227p. pap. 20.00 *(978-1-60608-511-0(5)*, Wipf and Stock) Wipf & Stock Pubs.

Beaton, Richard. Isaiah's Christ in Matthew's Gospel. 2007. (Society for New Testament Studies Monograph Ser.). (ENG.). 260p. pap. 55.00 *(978-0-521-03610-8(0))* Cambridge Univ. Pr.

Beeley, Christopher A. The Unity of Christ: Continuity & Conflict in Patristic Tradition. 2012. (ENG.). 400p. 50.00 ***(978-0-300-17862-3(X))*** Yale Univ. Pr.

Benedict XV , pseud. The Fathers. 2008. 192p. per. 14.95 *(978-1-59276-440-2(1))* Our Sunday Visitor, Publishing Div.

—Great Christian Thinkers: From the Early Church through the Middle Ages. 2011. 328p. pap. 16.99 *(978-0-8006-9851-5(7)*, Fortress Pr.) Augsburg Fortress, Pubs.

—Study Guide for the Fathers. 2008. 60p. pap. 4.95 *(978-1-59276-448-8(7))* Our Sunday Visitor, Publishing Div.

Bigg, Charles. The Church's Task under the Roman Empire. 2009. 74p. pap. *(978-0-217-88759-5(7))*; (Illus.). pap. *(978-1-4588-7153-4(3))* Books LLC.

Bishop of Caesarea, Eusebius. History of the Martyrs in Palestine: Discovered in a very Antient Syriac Manuscript. 2008. 163p. pap. 19.50 *(978-0-557-00829-2(8))* Lulu Enterprises Inc.

Bowes, Kimberley. Private Worship, Public Values, & Religious Change in Late Antiquity. 2008. (ENG., Illus.). 376p. 102.99 *(978-0-521-88593-5(0))* Cambridge Univ. Pr.

Bradshaw, Paul, ed. Essays in Early Eastern Initiation. 2009. 88.00 *(978-1-60724-363-2(6))* Gorgias Pr., LLC.

Bradshaw, Paul F. & Johnson, Maxwell E. The Origins of Feasts, Fasts, & Seasons in Early Christianity. 2011. xvi, 222p. pap. 29.95 *(978-0-8146-6244-1(7))* Liturgical Pr.

Brakke, David. The Gnostics: Myth, Ritual, & Diversity in Early Christianity. 2011. (ENG.). 180p. 29.95 *(978-0-674-04684-9(6))* Harvard Univ. Pr.

Brakke, David, et al, eds. Beyond Reception: Mutual Influences Between Antique Religion Judaism, & Early Christianity, Vol. 1. 2006. (Eary Christianity in the Context of Antiquity Ser.: Vol. 1). 245p. pap. *(978-3-631-55583-5(0))*; pap. *(978-0-8204-8705-2(8))* Lang, Peter AG.

Brandon, S. G. F. The Fall of Jerusalem & the Christian Church. 2010. 314p. pap. 36.00 *(978-1-60899-747-3(2)*, Wipf and Stock) Wipf & Stock Pubs.

Bray, Gerald. Creeds, Councils & Christ: Did the early Christians misrepresent Jesus? 2009. (ENG.). 224p. 20.00 *(978-1-84550-513-4(1)*, Mentor) Christian Focus Pubns. GBR. Dist: STL Distribution North America.

Bremmer, Jan N. The Rise of Christianity Through the Eyes of Gibbon, Harnack & Rodney Stark: A Valedictory Lecture on the Occasion of His Retirement from the Chair of Religious Studies, in the Faculty of Theology & Religious Studies. 2nd ed. 2010. (ENG.). 87p. (C). pap. 20.00 ***(978-90-77922-70-5(9))*** Barkhuis Publishing NLD. Dist: Brown, David Bk. Co., The.

Brent, Allen. Ignatius of Antioch: A Martyr Bishop & the origin of Episcopacy. 2009. (ENG.). 192p. 39.95 *(978-0-567-22264-0(0)*, T&T Clark Int'l) Continuum International Publishing Group, Ltd. GBR. Dist: National Bk. Network.

Brent, Allen & Brent. Ignatius of Antioch: A Martyr Bishop & the Origin of Episcopacy. 2007. (ENG.). 192p. 130.00 *(978-0-567-03200-3(0)*, T&T Clark Int'l) Continuum International Publishing Group, Ltd. GBR. Dist: National Bk. Network.

Bright, William. Age of the Fathers, 2 vols. reprint ed. 115.00 *(978-0-404-01077-5(6)*, AMS Pr., Inc.

Broadhead, Edwin K. Jewish Ways of Following Jesus: Redrawing the Religious Map of Antiquity. 2010. (Wissenschaftliche Untersuchungen zum Neuen Testament, No. 266 Ser.). (Illus.). 459p. 257.50 *(978-3-16-150304-7(X))* Mohr Siebeck GmbH & Co. KG DEU. Dist: Coronet Bks.

Brodd, Jeffrey & Reed, Jonathan L. Rome & Religion: A Cross-Disciplinary Dialogue on the Imperial Cult. 2011. ***(978-1-58983-613-6(8))***; ***(978-1-58983-612-9(X))*** Society of Biblical Literature.

Brown, Alan. The Life of Wisdom: An Introduction to Classical Philosophy & Early Christianity. 2013. (ENG.). 200p. 72.50 *(978-1-84511-007-9(2))*; (Illus.). pap. 24.95 *(978-1-84511-008-6(0))* I. B. Tauris & Co., Ltd. GBR. Dist: Macmillan.

Brown, Peter. The Body & Society: Men, Women, & Sexual Renunciation in Early Christianity. 20th anniv. ed. 2008. (Columbia Classics in Religion Ser.). (ENG., Illus.). 568p. (gr. 17). 79.50 *(978-0-231-14406-3(7))* Columbia Univ. Pr.

—The Body & Society: Men, Women, & Sexual Renunciation in Early Christianity; Twentieth Anniversary Edition with a New Introduction. 20th anniv. ed. 2008. (Columbia Classics in Religion Ser.). (ENG., Illus.). 568p. (gr. 17). pap. 27.50 *(978-0-231-14407-0(5)*, Columbia Univ. Pr.

Brown, Peter. Through the Eyes of a Needle. 2012. (ENG.). 806p. 39.95 ***(978-0-691-15290-5(X))*** Princeton Univ. Pr.

Buitenwerf, Rieuward & Hollander, Harm. W., eds. Jesus, Paul, & Early Christianity: Studies in Honour of Henk Jan de Jonge. 2008. (Novum Testamentum Supplements Ser.). 480p. (C). *(978-90-04-17033-9(2))* BRILL.

Burnazhnov, D., et al, eds. Bibel, Byzanz und Christlicher Orient: Festschrift fur Stephen Gero zum 65. Geburtstag. 2011. (Orientalia Lovaniensia Analecta Ser.). (ENG & GER., Illus.). 683p. (C). 140.00 *(978-90-429-2177-1(3))* Peeters Pubs. & Booksellers BEL. Dist: Brown, David Bk. Co., The.

Burgess, Richard. The Lectures on the Insufficiency of Unrevealed Religion, & On. 2007. (ENG.). 352p. per. 31.95 *(978-1-4304-4329-2(4))* Kessinger Publishing, LLC.

Burkitt, F. C, et al. Early & Later Jewish Influence on Christianity: Essays on Hebrew Influence on Religion, Language & Literature. 2007. (Analecta Gorgiana Ser.: 38). per. 29.00 *(978-1-59333-692-9(6))* Gorgias Pr., LLC.

Burns And Oates Staff. Origins of the Cult of the Virgin Mary. Maunder, Chris, ed. 2008. (ENG., Illus.). 224p. 39.95 *(978-0-86012-456-6(8)*, Burns & Oates) Continuum International Publishing Group, Ltd. GBR. Dist: National Bk. Network.

Burrus, Virginia, ed. Late Ancient Christianity. 2010. 320p. (C). pap. 24.00 *(978-0-8006-9720-4(0)*, Fortress Pr.) Augsburg Fortress, Pubs.

Calhoun, Robert L. Scripture, Creed, Theology: Lectures on the History of Christian Doctrine in the First Centuries. Lindbeck, George, ed. 2010. 508p. pap. 55.00 *(978-1-55635-494-6(0)*, Cascade Bks.) Wipf & Stock Pubs.

Cameron, Alan. The Last Pagans of Rome, 1 vol. 2010. (ENG., Illus.). 912p. 85.00 *(978-0-19-974727-6(X))* Oxford Univ. Pr., Inc.

Cameron, Averil & Hoyland, Robert. Doctrine & Debate in the East Christian World 300-1500. 2011. (Worlds of Eastern Christianity, 300ndash;1500 Ser.). 470p. 190.00 ***(978-1-4094-0034-9(4))*** Ashgate Publishing Co.

Caner, Daniel, ed. History & Hagiography from the Late-Antique Sinai. 2010. (ENG., Illus.). 256p. pap. 40.00 *(978-1-84631-216-8(7))* Liverpool Univ. Pr. GBR. Dist: Chicago Distribution Ctr.

Capes, David B., et al, eds. Israel's God & Rebecca's Children: Christology & Community in Early Judaism & Christianity: Essays in Honor of Larry W. Hurtado & Alan F. Segal. 2007. (Illus.). 510p. 79.95 *(978-1-60258-026-8(X))* Baylor Univ. Pr.

Carrington, Philip. The Early Christian Church: Volume 1, the First Christian Church. 2010. (ENG., Illus.). 575p. pap. 32.99 *(978-0-521-16641-6(1))* Cambridge Univ. Pr.

Carrington, Phillip. The Early Christian Church: Volume 2, the Second Christian Century. 2010. (ENG., Illus.). 567p. pap. 32.99 *(978-0-521-15738-4(2))* Cambridge Univ. Pr.

Chastel, Ttienne Louis. The Charity of the Primitive Churches. 2006. 364p. per. 26.99 *(978-1-4255-3787-6(1))* MPublishing.

Clark, Jonas. Effective Ministries & Believers: Introducing Apostolic Ministry & What It Means to You. 2008. 315p. per. 14.99 *(978-1-886885-25-7(7))* Spirit of Life.

Cobb, L. Stephanie. Dying to Be Men: Gender & Language in Early Christian Martyr Texts. 2008. (Gender, Theory, & Religion Ser.). (ENG.). 224p. (gr. 17). 55.00 *(978-0-231-14498-8(9))* Columbia Univ. Pr.

Cole, Lawrence Thomas. The Basis of Eary Christian Theism. 2008. 56p. pap. *(978-1-4099-5127-8(8))* Dodo Pr.

Coleman, Christopher B. Constantine the Great & Christianity. (Columbia University, Studies in the Social Sciences: No. 146). reprint ed. 37.50 *(978-0-404-51146-3(5))* AMS Pr., Inc.

Collins, John J. & Evans, Craig A., eds. Christian Beginnings & the Dead Sea Scrolls. 2006. (Acadia Studies in Bible & Theology Ser.). 144p. (C). pap. 18.00 *(978-0-8010-2837-3(X))* Baker Academic.

Cooper, Basil Henry. Free Church of Ancient Christendom & I. 2006. pap. 34.95 *(978-1-4286-4125-9(4))* Kessinger Publishing, LLC.

Corley, Kathleen E. Maranatha: Women's Funerary Rituals & Christian Origins 2010. 280p. (C). 35.00 *(978-0-8006-6236-3(9)*, Fortress Pr.) Augsburg Fortress, Pubs.

Creeds Councils & Controversies-Spck. 30.00 *(978-0-687-85177-5(7))* Abingdon Pr.

Crook, Zeba & Harland, Philip, eds. Identity & Interaction in the Ancient Mediterranean: Jews, Christians & Others. Essays in Honour of Stephen G. Wilson. 2007. (Illus.). 312p. *(978-1-906055-17-2(3))* Sheffield Phoenix Pr.

Crossley, James G. Why Christianity Happened: A Sociohistorical Account of Christian Origins (26-50 CE) 2006. (ENG.). 232p. per. 30.00 *(978-0-664-23094-4(6))* Westminster John Knox Pr.

Crowell, John. Republics; 2006. 244p. per. 20.99 *(978-1-4255-2089-2(8))* MPublishing.

Cruttwell, Charles Thomas. Saxon Church & the Norman Conquest. 2006. pap. 28.95 *(978-1-4286-3881-5(4))* Kessinger Publishing, LLC.

Cureton, William, ed. History of Martyrs in Palestine, by Eusebius, Bishop of Caesarea. 2010. 99.68 *(978-1-60724-898-9(0))* Gorgias Pr., LLC.

Cureton, William, intro. The Third Part of the Ecclesiastical History of John, Bishop of Ephesus. 2010. (SYR.). 132.32 *(978-1-60724-900-9(6))* Gorgias Pr., LLC.

Dalrymple, William. From the Holy Mountain. 2012. (Vintage Ser.). (ENG., Illus.). 512p. pap. 16.95 ***(978-0-307-94889-2(7)***, Vintage) Knopf Doubleday Publishing Group.

Daniel-Hughes, Carly. The Salvation of the Flesh in Tertullian of Carthage: Dressing for the Resurrection. 2011. (ENG., Illus.). 192p. 85.00 *(978-0-230-11773-0(2))* Palgrave Macmillan.

Daniélou, Jean. Origen. Mitchell, Walter, tr. (Orthodoxies & Heresies in the Early Church Ser.). reprint ed. 36.00 *(978-0-404-62381-4(6))* AMS Pr., Inc.

Daunton-Fear, Andrew. Healing in the Early Church. 2009. (Studies in Christian History & Thought: Ser.). 210p. pap. 23.00 *(978-1-60608-874-6(2)*, Wipf and Stock) Wipf & Stock Pubs.

Davies, Russell P. The Doubting Thomas Today. 2011. 352p. 51.95 ***(978-1-258-07640-5(3))*** Literary Licensing, LLC.

De Halleux, Andre. Philoxene de Mabbog: Sa Vie, Ses Ecrits, Sa Theologie. (Orthodoxies & Heresies in the Early Church Ser.). reprint ed. 64.50 *(978-0-404-62387-6(5))* AMS Pr., Inc.

De Labriolle, Piere C. La Crise Montaniste: Bibliotheque de la Fondation Thiers, fasc. XXXI. (Orthodoxies & Heresies in the Early Church Ser.). reprint ed. 57.50 *(978-0-404-62389-0(1))* AMS Pr., Inc.

De Pressense, E. Christian Life & Practice in the Early. 2006. pap. 42.95 *(978-1-4286-4667-4(1))* Kessinger Publishing, LLC.

Decret, François. Early Christianity in North Africa. 2011. (ENG.). 240p. pap. 38.00 *(978-0-227-17356-5(2))* Clarke, James Co., Ltd. GBR. Dist: Brown, David Bk. Co., The.

—Early Christianity in North Africa. Smither, Edward L., tr. 2009. 240p. pap. 26 00 *(978-1-55635-692-6(7)*, Cascade Bks.) Wipf & Stock Pubs.

Dein, Simon. Lubavitcher Messianism: What Really Happens When Prophecy Fails? 2011. (Continuum Studies in Jewish Thought Ser.). (ENG., Illus.). 192p. 120.00 *(978-1-4411-1223-1(5))* Continuum International Publishing Group, Ltd. GBR. Dist: National Bk. Network.

Delotavo, Alan J. Contemporary Evangelicalism & the Restoration of the Prototypal Church. 2007. 228p. pap. 25.00 *(978-1-55635-395-6(2))* Wipf & Stock Pubs.

Demacopoulos, George E. Five Models of Spiritual Direction in the Early Church. 2006. 256p. per. 30.00 *(978-0-268-02590-8(8))* Univ. of Notre Dame Pr.

Di Pardo, Armando. Tratado de Historia Eclesiastica: Church History - First Centuries. (SPA.). *(978-84-399-7100-9(1)*, 220461) Clie, Editorial.

Di Santo, Emanuele. L'apologetica Dell'Ambrosiaster: Cristiani, Pagani e Giudei Nella Roma Tardoantica. 2008. (ITA.). 607p. *(978-88-7961-121-3(6))* Ist. Patristico Augustinianum.

Digeser, Elizabeth Depalma. A Threat to Public Piety: Christians, Platonists, & the Great Persecution. 2012. (ENG.). 240p. 45.00 *(978-0-8014-4181-3(1))* Cornell Univ. Pr.

Dijkstra, J. H. F. Philae & the End of Ancient Egyptian Religion: A Regional Study of Religious Transformation (298-642 CE) 2008. (Orientalia Lovaniensia Analecta Ser.). (EGY., Illus.). 466p. (C). 124.00 *(978-90-429-2031-6(9))* Peeters Pubs. & Booksellers BEL. Dist: Brown, David Bk. Co., The.

Dipple, Geoffrey Luke. "Just As in the Time of the Apostles" Uses of History in the Radical Reformation. 30.00 *(978-1-894710-58-9(4))* Pandora Pr. CAN. Dist: Herald Pr.

Dodds, E. R. Païens et Chrétiens Dans un âge D'angoisse: Aspects de L'expérience Religieuse de Marc Aurèle à Constantin. 2nd ed. 2010. (FRE.). 174p. (C). pap. 38.00 ***(978-2-251-42040-0(1))*** Societe d'edition Les Belles lettres FRA. Dist: ISD.

Douglass, Scot, et al, eds. Gregory of Nyssa: Contra Eunomium II. 2007. (Supplements to Vigiliae Christianae Ser.). (ENG, FRE & GER.). 553p. *(978-90-04-15518-3(X))* BRILL.

Draguet, Rene, ed. Julien d'Halicarnasse et Sa Controverse avec Severe d'Antioch sur l'Incorruptibilite du Corps du Christ. (Orthodoxies & Heresies in the Early Church Ser.). reprint ed. 45.00 *(978-0-404-62382-1(4))* AMS Pr., Inc.

Driver, Lisa D. Maugans. Christ at the Center: The Early Christian Era. 2009. (Westminster History of Christian Thought Ser.). (ENG.). 248p. pap. 30.00 *(978-0-664-22897-2(6))* Westminster John Knox Pr.

Drobner, Hubertus R. The Fathers of the Church: A Comprehensive Introduction. Schatzmann, Siegfried S., tr. from GER. 2007. 632p. 44.95 *(978-1-56563-331-5(8))* Hendrickson Pubs. Marketing, LLC.

Duncan, William Cocil. History of the Early Baptists: From the Beginning of the Gospel to the Rise of Affusion As Baptism, & of infant Baptism, 28 A. D. -250 A. D. with An. 2006. 280p. per. 23.99 *(978-1-4255-2547-7(4))* MPublishing.

Dungan, David L. Constantine's Bible: Politics & the Making of the New Testament. 2006. 236p. per. 18.00 (978-0-8006-3790-3(9), Fortress Pr.) Augsburg Fortress, Pubs.

Duriez, Colin. Ad 33: The Year That Changed the World. 2008. (ENG., Illus.). 288p. pap. 22.95 (978-0-7509-3976-8(1)) History Pr. Ltd., The GBR. Dist: Independent Pubs. Group.

Dyas, Dee, ed. The English Parish Church through the Centuries: Daily Life & Spirituality, Art & Architecture, Literature & Music. 2010. (ENG., Illus.). (C). 29.95 (978-0-9550673-2-7(4)) Christianity and Culture Project GBR. Dist: Brown, David Bk. Co., The.

Eckhardt, John. Ordinary People Extraordinary Power: Be Activated to Heal, Deliver, Prophesy, Preach, & Demonstrate God's Kingdom. 2010. (ENG.). 224p. pap. 14.99 (978-1-61638-166-0(3), Charisma Hse.) Charisma Media.

Edmundson, George. The Church in Rome in the First Century. 2009. 312p. 36.99 (978-1-113-65579-0(8)); 312p. 32.99 (978-1-113-65577-6(1)); 312p. pap. 28.75 (978-1-113-65574-5(7)); 312p. pap. 29.75 (978-1-113-65576-9(3)); (ENG.). 311p. pap. 24.99 (978-1-113-65572-1(0), BiblioLife) BiblioBazaar.

—The Church in Rome in the First Century. 2009. 276p. pap. (978-0-217-57542-3(0)) Books LLC.

—The Church in Rome in the First Century: An Examination of Various Controverted Questions Relating to its History, Chronology, Literature & Traditions. 2008. 296p. pap. 25.00 (978-1-55635-846-3(6), Wipf and Stock) Wipf & Stock Pubs.

Edwards, Mark. Catholicity & Heresy in the Early Church. 2009. 208p. 99.95 (978-0-7546-6291-4(8)); pap. 29.95 (978-0-7546-6297-6(7)) Ashgate Publishing Co.

Ehrensperger, Kathy. Paul & the Dynamics of Power: Communication & Interaction in the Early Christ-Movement. (Library of New Testament Studies, the Ser.). (ENG.). 2009. 256p. 39.95 (978-0-567-61494-0(8)) 2007. 250p. 140.00 (978-0-567-04374-0(6)) Continuum International Publishing Group, Ltd. GBR. (T&T Clark Int'l). Dist: National Bk. Network.

Ekelund, Robert B., Jr. & Tollison, Robert D. Economic Origins of Roman Christianity. 2011. (ENG., Illus.). 288p. 45.00 (978-0-226-20002-6(7)) Univ. of Chicago Pr.

Elm, Susanna. Sons of Hellenism, Fathers of the Church: Emperor Julian, Gregory of Nazianzus, & the Vision of Rome. 2012. (Transformation of the Classical Heritage Ser.). (ENG.). 558p. 75.00 (978-0-520-26930-9(6)) Univ. of California Pr.

Engberg, Jakob. Impulsore Chresto: Opposition to Christianity in the Roman Empire c. 50-250 AD. 2007. 349p. pap. 68.95 (978-3-631-56778-4(2)) Lang, Peter GmbH, Europaischer Verlag der Wissenschaften DEU. Dist: Lang, Peter Publishing, Inc.

Ennodius, Magnus Felix & Gioanni, Stéphane. Lettres. 2010. (Collection des universites de France Serie Latine Ser.). (LAT & FRE.). 207p. (C). pap. 68.00 (978-2-251-01456-2(3)) Societe d'edition Les Belles lettres FRA. Dist: ISD.

Eno, S. S., Robert B. The Rise of the Papacy. 2008. 184p. pap. 21.00 (978-1-60608-170-9(5), Wipf and Stock) Wipf & Stock Pubs.

Ermatinger, James W. Daily Life in the New Testament. 2008. (Greenwood Press Daily Life Through History Ser.). (Illus.). 184p. 49.95 (978-0-313-34175-5(3), GR4175, Greenwood Pr.) Greenwood Publishing Group, Inc.

Eusebius Pamphilus. The Ecclesiastical History of Eusebius Pamphilus. C. F. Cruse & S. E. Parker, trs. 2011. 472p. pap. 9.95 (978-1-60386-398-8(2), Watchmaker Publishing) Wexford College Pr.

—Eusebius' Ecclesiastical History. C. F. Cruse, tr. 2011. 472p. pap. 9.88 (978-1-60386-408-4(3), Merchant Bks.) Rough Draft Printing.

Evagrius, Scholasticus. The Ecclesiastical History of Evagrius: A History of the Church from Ad 431 to Ad 594. 2008. (978-1-889758-88-6(4), Evolution Publishing & Manufacturing) Arx Publishing.

Evans, Craig A. The World of Jesus & the Early Church: Identity & Interpretation in Early Communities of Faith. 2011. (Illus.). 260p. 29.95 (978-1-59856-825-7(6)) Hendrickson Pubs. Marketing, LLC.

Ferngren, Gary B. Medicine & Health Care in Early Christianity. 2009. (ENG.). 264p. (gr. 17). 37.00 (978-0-8018-9142-7(6)) Johns Hopkins Univ. Pr.

Fisher, Norman A. The Genesis & Growth of the Apostolic Church: An Analysis of the Acts of the Apostles. 2011. 232p. pap. 17.95 (978-1-61507-732-8(4)) Cross Bks. Publishing.

Flesher, Paul V. M. & Chilton, Bruce. The Targums: A Critical Introduction. 2011. (ENG., Illus.). 575p. pap. 69.95 (978-1-60258-382-5(X)) Baylor Univ. Pr.

Fortescue, Adrian. Early Papacy. 2008. 130p. pap. 12.95 (978-1-58617-176-6(3)) Ignatius Pr.

Foster, Paul, ed. Early Christian Thinkers: The Lives & Legacies of Twelve Key Figures. 2011. (ENG.). 204p. pap. 23.00 (978-0-8308-3937-7(2), IVP Acad.) InterVarsity Pr.

Foster, Russell J. Early Christian Thinkers: The Lives & Legacies of Twelve Key Figures. Foster, Paul, ed. 2010. (Illus.). 224p. pap. (978-0-281-06098-6(3)) SPCK Publishing.

—First Advance AD 29-500. 2nd ed. (Illus.). 208p. 12.00 (978-0-281-04561-7(5)) SPCK Publishing GBR. Dist: Pilgrim Pr., The/United Church Pr.

Freeman, Charles. A New History of Early Christianity. 2011. (Illus.). 400p. pap. 23.00 (978-0-300-17083-2(1)) Yale Univ. Pr.

Frend, W. H. C. & Stevenson, J., eds. Creeds, Councils & Controversies: Documents Illustrating the History of the Church, AD 337-461. 2012. 504p. (C). pap. 45.00 (978-0-8010-3970-6(3)) Baker Academic.

—A New Eusebius: Documents Illustrating the History of the Church to AD 337. 2012. 504p. (C). pap. 45.00 (978-0-8010-3971-3(1)) Baker Academic.

Frend, William. Rise of the Monophysite Movement. 2008. (ENG.). 424p. pap. 53.00 (978-0-227-17241-4(8)) Clarke, James Co., Ltd. GBR. Dist: Brown, David Bk. Co., The.

Freyne, Sean, et al. A Wandering Galilean: Essays in Honour of Sean Freyne. 2008. (978-90-04-17355-2(2)) BRILL.

Fuhrer, Therese. Die Christlich-Philosophischen Diskurse der Spatantike: Texte, Personen, Institutionen. 2008. (Philosophie der Antike Ser.). (ENG.). 438p. (C). 98.00 (978-3-515-09083-4(5)) Steiner, Franz Verlag Wiesbaden GmbH DEU. Dist: Brown, David Bk. Co., The.

Girardet, Klaus M. Kaisertum, Religionspolitik und das Recht Von Staat und Kirche in der Spätantike. 2009. (GER., Illus.). 533p. (978-3-7749-3469-6(X)) Habelt GmbH, Dr. Rudolf.

Glover, T. R. The Influence of Christ in the Ancient World. 2012. (ENG.). 130p. pap. 39.99 (978-1-107-67021-1(7)) Cambridge Univ. Pr.

—The Influence of Christ in the Ancient World. 2007. (ENG.). 130p. 35.95 (978-0-548-01538-4(4)) Kessinger Publishing, LLC.

Glover, T. R. The World of the New Testament. 2012. (ENG.). 202p. pap. 24.00 (978-1-107-65640-6(0)) Cambridge Univ. Pr.

Goettmann, Alphonse & Goettmann, Rachel. The Spiritual Wisdom & Practices of Early Christianity. Nottingham, Theodore J., tr. from FRE. rev. ed. 2006. Orig. Title: Sagesse et Pratiques du Christianisme. 144p. per. 13.95 (978-1-933275-09-3(X), Orthodox Research Institute) Cocheco Falls Publishing.

González, Justo L. & González, Catherine Gunsalus. Heretics for Armchair Theologians. 2008. (Armchair Ser.). (ENG., Illus.). 200p. pap. 17.00 (978-0-664-23205-4(1)) Westminster John Knox Pr.

Goodwin, Bennie. Acts: Luke's Portrait of the Early Christian Church. 2010. 108p. pap. 7.95 (978-1-932715-54-5(1)) UMI (Urban Ministries, Inc.).

Grabner-Haider, Anton & Maier, Johann. Kulturgeschichte des frühen Christentums: Von 100 bis 500 n.Chr. 2008. (GER.). 232p. (C). 54.00 (978-3-525-54003-9(5)) Vandenhoeck & Ruprecht GmbH & Co. KG DEU. Dist: ISD.

Graf, Friedrich Wilhelm & Wiegandt, Klaus. Die Anfänge des Christentums. 2009. (GER., Illus.). 505p. pap. (978-3-596-18277-0(8)) Fischer Taschenbuch Verlag.

Grant, Robert M. The Sword & the Cross. 2009. 144p. pap. 18.00 (978-1-60608-317-8(1), Wipf and Stock) Wipf & Stock Pubs.

Gray, Patrick T. R., ed. Leontius of Jerusalem: Against the Monophysites: Testimonies of the Saints & Aporiae. 2006. (Oxford Early Christian Texts). (ENG & GEC.). 256p. 125.00 (978-0-19-926644-9(1)) Oxford Univ. Pr., Inc.

Greatrex, Geoffrey, ed. The Chronicle of Pseudo-Zachariah Rhetor: Religion & War in Late Antiquity. Horn, Cornelia B. & Phenix, Robert R., trs. 2011. (Liverpool University Press - Translated Texts for Historians Ser.). (ENG.). 416p. pap. 36.95 (978-1-84631-494-0(1)) Liverpool Univ. Pr. GBR. Dist: Chicago Distribution Ctr.

Greatrex, Geoffrey, et al, trs. The Chronicle of Pseudo-Zachariah Rhetor: Church & War in Late Antiquity. 2011. (Liverpool University Press - Translated Texts for Historians Ser.). (ENG.). 562p. 120.00 (978-1-84631-493-3(3)) Liverpool Univ. Pr. GBR. Dist: Chicago Distribution Ctr.

Green, Ken & Green, Bernard. Christianity in Ancient Rome: The First Three Centuries. 2010. (ENG.). 272p. 29.95 (978-0-567-03250-8(7), T&T Clark Int'l) Continuum International Publishing Group, Ltd. GBR. Dist: National Bk. Network.

Greenslade, Stanley L. Schism in the Early Church: Edward Cadbury Lectures, 1949-50. (Orthodoxies & Heresies in the Early Church Ser.). reprint ed. 28.50 (978-0-404-62384-5(0)) AMS Pr., Inc.

Greer, Rowan A. The Fear of Freedom. 2008. 228p. per. 24.95 (978-0-271-02799-9(1)) Pennsylvania State Univ. Pr.

Grillmeier, SJ, Alois, Alois, et al. Christ in Christian Tradition: Volume 2 Part 3: The Churches of Jerusalem & Antioch. 2012. (ENG.). 664p. 350.00 (978-0-19-921288-0(0)) Oxford Univ. Pr., Inc.

Gryson, R. Scientiam Salutis: Quarante annees de recherches sur l'Antiquite Chretienne. 2008. (Bibliotheca Ephemeridum Theologicarum Lovaniensium Ser.). (FRE.). 879p. (C). pap. 128.00 (978-90-429-1904-4(3)) Peeters Pubs. & Booksellers BEL. Dist: Brown, David Bk. Co., The.

Gumerlock, Francis X. Fulgentius of Ruspe on the Saving Will of God: The Development of a Sixth-Century African Bishop's Interpretation of 1 Timothy 2:4 During the Semi-Pelagian Controversy. 2009. 256p. 109.95 (978-0-7734-4935-0(3)) Mellen, Edwin Pr., The.

Guy, Laurie. Introducing Early Christianity: A Topical Survey of Its Life, Beliefs & Practices. 2011. (ENG.). 310p. pap. 24.00 (978-0-8308-3942-1(9), IVP Acad.) InterVarsity Pr.

Haar Romeny, R. B. ter. Religious Origins of Nations? The Christian Communities of the Middle East. 2009. 384p. (978-90-04-17375-0(7)) BRILL.

Hahn, Johannes, et al. From Temple to Church: Destruction & Renewal of Local Cultic Topography in Late Antiquity. 2008. (Religions in the Graeco-Roman World Ser.: Vol. 163). (GER & ENG., Illus.). xi, 378p. (C). (978-90-04-13141-5(8)) BRILL.

Hainthaler, Theresia. Christliche Araber Vor Dem Islam: Verbreitung und Konfessionelle Zugehorigkeit. eine Hinfuhrung. 2007. (Eastern Christian Studies Ser.). (ENG., Illus.). 188p. (C). pap. 65.00 (978-90-429-1917-4(5)) Peeters Pubs. & Booksellers BEL. Dist: Brown, David Bk. Co., The.

Hall, Stuart G. Doctrine & Practice in the Early Church, 2nd Edition. 2011. 272p. pap. 30.00 (978-1-61097-051-8(9), Cascade Bks.) Wipf & Stock Pubs.

Hamlin, Ann Elizabeth. The Archaeology of Early Christianity in the North of Ireland. Kerr, Thomas R., ed. 2008. (Bar Ser.). (Illus.). 424p. (C). 137.50 (978-1-4073-0285-0(X)) British Archaeological Reports Ltd. GBR. Dist: Brown, David Bk. Co., The.

Hammerling, Roy. The Lord's Prayer in the Early Church: The Pearl of Great Price. 2010. (ENG.). 208p. 84.00 (978-0-230-10589-8(0)) Palgrave Macmillan.

Hanson, Kenneth. Blood Kin of Jesus: James & the Lost Jewish Church. 2009. (ENG., Illus.). 248p. pap. 20.00 (978-1-57178-224-3(9)) Council Oak Bks.

Hardy, Ernest George. Christianity & the Roman Government: a Study in Imperial. 2007. pap. 24.95 (978-1-4304-4974-4(8)) Kessinger Publishing, LLC.

Harland, Philip A. Dynamics of Identity in the World of the Early Christians. 2009. (ENG., Illus.). 256p. 110.00 (978-0-567-61328-8(3)); pap. 34.95 (978-0-567-11146-3(6)) Continuum International Publishing Group, Ltd. GBR. (T&T Clark Int'l). Dist: National Bk. Network.

Harmless, William, ed. Augustine in His Own Words. 2010. 496p. (C). pap. 34.95 (978-0-8132-1743-7(1)) Catholic Univ. of America Pr.

Hart, David Bentley. Atheist Delusions: The Christian Revolution & Its Fashionable Enemies. 2010. (ENG.). 272p. pap. 17.00 (978-0-300-16429-9(7)) Yale Univ. Pr.

Hartog, Paul, ed. The Contemporary Church & the Early Church: Case Studies in Ressourcement. 2010. (Evangelical Theological Society Monograph Ser.). 262p. pap. 29.00 (978-1-60608-899-9(8), Pickwick Pubns.) Wipf & Stock Pubs.

Harvey, Susan Ashbrook & Hunter, David G. The Oxford Handbook of Early Christian Studies. 2010. (ENG., Illus.). 1148p. pap. 55.00 (978-0-19-959652-2(2)) Oxford Univ. Pr., Inc.

—The Oxford Handbook of Early Christian Studies. Harvey, Susan Ashbrook & Hunter, David, eds. 2008. (Oxford Handbooks Ser.). (ENG., Illus.). 800p. 165.00 (978-0-19-927156-6(9)) Oxford Univ. Pr., Inc.

Hauben, Hans & Nuffelen, Peter Van. Studies on the Melitian Schism in Egypt (304-335 A. D.) 2012. (Variorum Collected Studies). 280p. 154.95 (978-1-4094-3942-4(9)) Ashgate Publishing Co.

Hausammann, Susi. Von Gott Reden, Heisst, in Bildern Reden: Mythologien und Begriffliche Spekulationen Im Frühchristlichen und Byzantinischen Weltbild und Die Botschaft des Fünften Ökumenischen Konzils Von 553. 2007. (GER.). 133p. (C). 47.00 (978-3-89971-349-7(4)) Vandenhoeck & Ruprecht GmbH & Co. KG DEU. Dist: ISD.

Hay, Alex Rattray. The New Testament Order for Church & Missionary. 2010. 542p. pap. 45.00 (978-1-60899-934-7(3), Wipf and Stock) Wipf & Stock Pubs.

Hengel, Martin. Earliest Christianity. 2012. 244p. pap. (978-0-334-00346-5(6), SCM Pr.) Hymns Ancient & Modern Ltd.

Hengel, Martin. Property & Riches in the Early Church. Bowden, John, tr. Date not set. viii, 96p. pap. 12.00 (978-1-888961-03-4(1), 1031) Sigler Pr.

Hengel, Martin & Bowden, John. Property & Riches in the Early Church: Aspects of a Social History of Early Christianity. 2012. viii, 96p. pap. (978-0-334-01329-7(1), SCM Pr.) Hymns Ancient & Modern Ltd.

Herrero de Jáuregui, Miguel. Helicon to Sion: Orpheus & Christianity in Late Antiquity. 2010. (Sozomena Ser.). (ENG.). XIII, 442p. 123.00 (978-3-11-020633-3(1)) De Gruyter, Walter Inc.

Herron, Thomas J. Clement & the Early Church of Rome: On the dating of Clement's First Epistle to the Corinthians. 2010. 136p. pap. 12.00 (978-1-931018-47-0(2)) Emmaus Road Publishing.

Hesse, O. & van Oort, J., eds. Christentum und Politik in der Alten Kirche. 2009. (Patristic Studies). (GER.). 154p. (C). pap. 55.00 (978-90-429-2165-8(X)) Peeters Pubs. & Booksellers BEL. Dist: Brown, David Bk. Co., The.

Hill, C. E. Who Chose the Gospels? Probing the Great Gospel Conspiracy. (ENG., Illus.). 2012. 320p. pap. 16.95 (978-0-19-964029-4(7)) 2010. 240p. 27.95 (978-0-19-955123-1(5)) Oxford Univ. Pr., Inc.

Hirsch-Luipold, Rainer, et al. Religiöse Philosophie und philosophische Religion der frühen Kaiserzeit: Literaturgeschichtliche Perspektiven. Ratio Religionis Studien I. 2009. (GER.). 418p. pap. 125.00 (978-3-16-149593-9(4)) Mohr Siebeck GmbH & Co. KG DEU. Dist: Eisenbrauns, Inc.

Hobar, Linda Lacour. The Mystery of History: The Early Church & the Middle Ages. 2007. (Mystery of History Ser.). (Illus.). 715p. per. 49.95 (978-1-892427-06-9(0)) Bright Ideas! Educational Resources.

Holman, Susan R., ed. Wealth & Poverty in Early Church & Society. 2008. (Holy Cross Studies in Patristic Theology & History Ser.). (Illus.). 320p. (C). pap. 35.00 (978-0-8010-3549-4(X)) Baker Academic.

Holzapfel, Richard Neitzel & Wayment, Thomas A. The Life & Teachings of the New Testament Apostles: From the Day of Pentecost to the Apocalypse. 2010. x, 358p. 34.99 (978-1-60641-824-6(6)) Deseret Bk. Co.

Horsley, Richard, ed. Christian Origins. 2010. (People's History to Christianity Ser.). 320p. (C). pap. 24.00 (978-0-8006-9719-8(7), Fortress Pr.) Augsburg Fortress, Pubs.

Horst, Pieter Willem van der. Jews & Christians in Their Graeco-Roman Context: Selected Essays on Early Judaism, Samaritanism, Hellenism, & Christianity. 2006. (Wissenschaftliche Untersuchungen Zum Neuen Testament Ser.: Vol. 196). 362p. 175.00 (978-3-16-148851-1(2)) Mohr Siebeck GmbH & Co. KG DEU. Dist: Coronet Bks.

Hort, Fenton John. Judaistic Christianity. 2007. (ENG.). 240p. 41.95 (978-0-548-08097-9(6)) Kessinger Publishing, LLC.

Hort, Fenton John Anthony. The Christian Ecclesia: A Course of Lectures on the Early History & Early Conceptions of the Ecclesia, & Four Sermons. 2010. (Cambridge Library Collection - Religion Ser.). (ENG.). 324p. pap. 24.99 (978-1-108-00755-9(4)) Cambridge Univ. Pr.

Houlden, Leslie, et al. Decoding Early Christianity: Truth & Legend in the Early Church, 1 vol. 2007. 160p. 49.95 (978-1-84645-018-1(7), GWP018) Greenwood Publishing Group, Inc.

Humm, Alan. Psychology of Prophecy in Early Christianity. 2009. 112.76 (978-1-60724-618-3(X)) Gorgias Pr., LLC.

Husbands, Mark & Greenman, Jeffrey P., eds. Ancient Faith for the Church's Future. 2008. (ENG.). 272p. pap. 24.00 (978-0-8308-2881-4(8), IVP Acad.) InterVarsity Pr.

Huttman, Maude A. Establishment of Christianity & the Proscription of Paganism. (Columbia University, Studies in the Social Sciences: No. 147). reprint ed. 37.50 (978-0-404-51147-0(3)) AMS Pr., Inc.

Hyde, Walter Woodburn. Paganism to Christianity in the Roman Empire. 2011. 304p. 48.95 (978-1-258-03900-4(1)) Literary Licensing, LLC.

—Paganism to Christianity in the Roman Empire. 2008. 296p. pap. 25.00 (978-1-60608-349-9(X)) Wipf & Stock Pubs.

Inglebert, Hervé, et al. Le Problème de la Christianisation du Monde Antique. 2010. (FRE & ENG., Illus.). 415p. (978-2-7084-0872-2(0)) Picard, A.et J. Editions.

Jacobs, Andrew S. Christ Circumcised: A Study in Early Christian History & Difference. 2012. (Divinations: Rereading Late Ancient Religion Ser.). 320p. (C). 75.00 (978-0-8122-4397-0(8)) Univ. of Pennsylvania Pr.

Jacobsen, Anders-Christian, ed. Religion & Normativity Vol. 1: The Discursive Struggle over Religious Texts in Antiquity, 3 vols. 2009. (ENG., Illus.). 207p. (C). 42.00 (978-87-7934-427-3(5)) Aarhus Universitetsforlag DNK. Dist: ISD.

Jacobsen, Anders-Christian & Ulrich, Jorg, eds. Three Greek Apologists Drei Griechische Apologeten: Origen, Eusebius, & Athanasius Origenes, Eusebius und Athanasius. 2007. (Early Christianity in the Context of Antiquity Ser.: Vol. 3). 214p. pap. (978-3-631-56833-0(9)) Lang, Peter AG.

Janssen, Martina, et al, eds. Fruhes Christentum und Religionsgeschichtliche Schule: Festschrift zum 65. Geburtstag von Gerd Ludemann. 2011. (Novum Testamentum et Orbis Antiquus/Studien zur Umwelt des Neuen Testaments (NTOA/StUNT) Ser.). (GER.). 218p. (C). 95.00 (978-3-525-53977-4(0)) Vandenhoeck & Ruprecht GmbH & Co. KG DEU. Dist: ISD.

Jeffery, Peter. Moving Out: With the Christian Faith. 2007. 126p. per. (978-0-85234-609-9(3)) Evangelical Pr.

Jenkins, John Philip. Jesus Wars: How Four Patriarchs, Three Queens, & Two Emperors Decided What Christians Would Believe for the Next 1,500 Years. (ENG.). 2011. 288p. pap. 15.99 (978-0-06-176893-4(6)) 2010. 352p. 26.99 (978-0-06-176894-1(4)) HarperCollins Pubs. (HarperOne).

—The Lost History of Christianity: The Thousand-Year Golden Age of the Church in the Middle East, Africa, & Asia — And How It Died. 2009. (ENG.). 304p. pap. 15.99 (978-0-06-147281-7(6), HarperOne) HarperCollins Pubs.

Johnson, Maxwell. Liturgy in Early Christian Egypt. 2009. 88.00 (978-1-60724-384-7(9)) Gorgias Pr., LLC.

Jones, A. H. M. Constantine & the Conversion of Europe. 2007. 284p. per. (978-1-4067-6011-8(0)) Read Bks.

Jossa, Giorgio. Jews or Christians? The Followers of Jesus in Search of Their Own Identity. Roger, Molly, tr. from ITA. (Wissenschaftliche Untersuchungen Zum Neuen Testament Ser.: 202). 175p. 105.00 (978-3-16-149192-4(0)) Mohr Siebeck GmbH & Co. KG DEU. Dist: Eisenbrauns, Inc.

Judge, E. A. & Scholer, David M. Social Distinctives of the Christians in the First Century: Pivotal Essays. 2008. 232p. pap. (978-1-56563-880-8(8)) Hendrickson Pubs. Marketing, LLC.

Kaatz, Kevin W. Early Controversies & the Growth of Christianity, 1 vol. 2012. (Praeger Series on the Ancient World Ser.). (Illus.). 163p. 47.00 (978-0-313-38359-5(6), A2852C, Praeger Pubs.) Greenwood Publishing Group, Inc.

Kahlos, Maijastina. Forbearance & Compulsion: The Rhetoric of Religious Tolerance & Intolerance in Late Antiquity. 2009. 204p. 130.00 (978-0-7156-3698-5(7)) Duckworth Publishers GBR. Dist: International Publishers Marketing.

Kalantzis, George & Tooley, Andrew. Evangelicals & the Early Church: Recovery, Reform, Renewal. 2011. (Wheaton Center for Early Christian Studies). (ENG.). 288p. pap. 32.00 (978-1-61097-459-2(X), Cascade Bks.) Wipf & Stock Pubs.

Kasomo, Daniel W. In-Depth Study of the Catholic Church. 2011. 188p. pap. (978-3-8443-1217-1(X)) Lambert Academic Publishing.

Kelly, J. N. D. & Kelly. Early Christian Creeds. 3rd rev. ed. 2006. (ENG.). 460p. 65.00 (978-0-8264-9216-6(9)) Continuum International Publishing Group, Ltd. GBR. Dist: National Bk. Network.

Kesich, Veselin. Formation & Struggles the Church AD 33-450 Part I: The Birth of the Church AD 33-200, 6 vols., Vol 1. 2007. (Illus.). 209p. pap. 20.00 (978-0-88141-319-9(4)) St. Vladimir's Seminary Pr.

Kidd, B. J. The Roman Primacy to A. D. 461. 2010. 160p. pap. 18.00 (978-1-60899-722-0(7), Wipf and Stock) Wipf & Stock Pubs.

Killen, W. D. The Ancient Church: Its History, Doctrine, Worship, & Constitution. 2007. 624p. per. (978-1-4065-1919-8(7)) Dodo Pr.

Killen, William Dool. The Ancient Church: Its History, Doctrine, Worship & Constitution. 2007. 610p. pap. 31.99 (978-1-4346-0237-4(0)); (ENG.). 684p. pap. 34.99 (978-1-4346-0311-1(3)) BiblioBazaar.

Kinkel, R. John. Cinderella Church. 2008. 216p. pap. 17.95 (978-0-595-52348-1(X)) iUniverse, Inc.

Knight, Jonathan. Christian Origins. 2008. (ENG.). 472p. 39.95 (978-0-567-03351-2(1), T&T Clark Int'l) Continuum International Publishing Group, Ltd. GBR. Dist: National Bk. Network.

Knox, Wilfred Lawrence. St Paul & the Church of Jerusalem. 2010. (Cambridge Library Collection - Religion Ser.). 430p. pap. 32.99 (978-1-108-01620-9(0)) Cambridge Univ. Pr.

Koch, Dietrich-Alex & Horn, Friedrich Wilhelm. Hellenistisches Christentum: Schriftverstandnis, Ekklesiologie, Geschichte. 2008. (Novum Testamentum et

Orbis Antiquus/Stud en zur Umwelt des Neuen Testaments (NTOA/StUNT) Ser.). (GER., Illus.). 378p. (C). 137.00 *(978-3-525-54001-5(9))* Vandenhoeck & Ruprecht GmbH & Co. KG DEU. Dist: ISD.

Kostenberger, Andreas J. & Kruger, Michael J. The Heresy of Orthodoxy: How Contemporary Culture's Fascination with Diversity Has Reshaped Our Understanding of Early Christianity. 2010. 256p. pap. 17.99 *(978-1-4335-0143-2(0))* Crossway.

Köstenberger, Andreas J. & Kruger, Michael J. The Heresy of Orthodoxy: How Contemporary Culture's Fascination with Diversity Has Reshaped Our Understanding of Early Christianity. 2010. *(978-1-4335-1813-3(9))* Crossway.

Kuhn, Alvin. Shadow of tne Third Century: A Revaluation of Christianity. 2007. 664p. 36.99 *(978-1-59986-725-0(7))* Filiquarian Publishing, LLC.

Kuhn, Alvin Boyd. Shadow of the Third Century: A Revaluation of Christianity. 2007. pap. 29.99 *(978-1-59986-838-7(5)*, FQ Classics) Filiquarian Publishing, LLC.

Laan, Ray Vander & Sorenson, Amanda. Early Church, 1 vol., Vol. 5. exp. rev. ed. 2008. (Faith Lessons Ser.). (ENG.). 192p. pap. 9.99 *(978-0-310-27971-6(2))* Zondervan.

Lamson, Alvan. The Church of the First Three Centuries: Or, Notices of the Lives & Opinions of the Early Fathers, with Special Reference to the Doctrine of the Tri. 2006. 424p. per. 26.99 *(978-1-4255-4639-7(0))* MPublishing.

—The Church of the First Three Centuries - with Special Reference to the Doctrine of the Trinity. 2007. 424p. 29.95 *(978-1-933998-86-2(5)*, Merchant Bks.) Rough Draft Printing.

—Church of the First Three Centuries or N. 2006. pap. 38.95 *(978-1-4286-3572-2(6))* Kessinger Publishing, LLC.

Lamy, Thomas Josephus. Concilium Seleuciae et Ctesiphont Habitum Anno 410. 2010. (SYR & LAT.). pap. 25.12 *(978-1-61143-611-2(7))* Gorgias Pr., LLC.

Leemans, Johan, et al, eds. Episcopal Elections in Late Antiquity. 2011. (Arbeiten zur Kirchengeschichte Ser.). XII, 606p. (ENG., Illus.). E-Book 280.00 ***(978-3-11-026861-4(2))***; (FRE, GER & ENG.). 182.00 ***(978-3-11-026855-3(8))*** De Gruyter, Walter Inc.

Leithart, Peter J. Defending Constantine: The Twilight of an Empire & the Dawn of Christendom. 2010. (ENG.). 373p. pap. 27.00 *(978-0-8308-2722-0(6)*, IVP Acad.) InterVarsity Pr.

Lenski, Noel, ed. The Cambridge Companion to the Age of Constantine. 2nd rev. ed. (Cambridge Companions to the Ancient World Ser.). (ENG., Illus.). (C). 2012. 550p. pap. 39.99 ***(978-1-107-60110-9(X))*** 2011. 492p. 99.00 ***(978-1-107-01340-7(2))*** Cambridge Univ. Pr.

Lenski, Noel & Cain, Andrew. The Power of Religion in Late Antiquity: Selected Papers from the Seventh Biennial Shifting Frontiers in Late Antiquity Conference. 2009. (Illus.). 486p. 134.95 *(978-0-7546-6725-4(1))* Ashgate Publishing Co.

Levieils, Xavier. Contra Christianos: La Critique Sociale et Religieuse du Christianisme des Origenes Au Concile de Nicee (45-325) 2007. (Beihefte Zur Zeitschrift Für Die Neutestamentliche Wissenschaft und Die Kunde der älteren Kirche Ser.). (FRE.). XIII, 548p. 196.00 *(978-3-11-019554-5(2))* De Gruyter, Walter Inc.

Liebeschuetz, J. H. W. G. Ambrose & John Chrysostom: Clerics between Desert & Empire. 2011. (ENG.). 320p. 110.00 *(978-0-19-959664-5(6))* Oxford Univ. Pr., Inc.

Lightfoot, Joseph B. Dissertations on the Apostolic Age. 2008. 444p. pap. 38.00 *(978-1-60608-356-7(2))* Wipf & Stock Pubs.

Lindsay, Thomas M. The Church & Ministry in the Early Centuries. 2007. (ENG.). 420p. 49.95 *(978-0-548-09636-9(8))* Kessinger Publishing, LLC.

—The Church & the Ministry in the Early Centuries. 2008. 398p. pap. 34.00 *(978-1-55635-847-0(4)*, Wipf and Stock) Wipf & Stock Pubs.

Loehr, Winrich A., et al, eds. Constantine to c.600. 2007. (Cambridge History of Christianity Ser.: Vol. 2). (ENG., Illus.). 784p. (C). 230.00 *(978-0-521-81244-3(5))* Cambridge Univ. Pr.

Longenecker, Bruce. Remember the Poor: Paul, Poverty, & the Greco-Roman World. 2010. 284p. pap. 25.00 *(978-0-8028-6373-7(6))* Eerdmans, William B. Publishing Co.

Loomis, Louise Ropes, tr. The Book of the Popes (Liber Pontificalis) To the Pontificate of Gregory I. 2006. (Christian Roman Empire Ser.: No. 3). 204p. pap. 19.95 *(978-1-889758-86-2(8)*, Evolution Publishing & Manufacturing) Arx Publishing.

Lössl, Josef. The Early Church: History & Memory. 2010. (ENG., Illus.). 256p. 29.95 *(978-0-567-16561-9(2))*; 130.00 *(978-0-567-46464-4(4))* Continuum International Publishing Group, Ltd. GBR. (T&T Clark Int'l). Dist: National Bk. Network.

Lowrie, Walter. Art in the Early Church. 2007. (ENG.). 436p. per. *(978-1-4067-5291-5(6))* Read Bks.

—Christian Art & Archaeology Being A Ha. 2006. pap. 37.95 *(978-1-4286-3923-2(3))* Kessinger Publishing, LLC.

Ludemann, Gerd. Das Urchristentum: Eine Kritische Bilanz Seiner Erforschung. (Arbeiten zur Religion und Geschichte des Urchristentums Ser.: Vol. 12). (GER.). 167p. 26.95 *(978-3-631-39211-9(7))* Lang, Peter Publishing, Inc.

Luomanen, Petri & Pyysiäinen, Ilkka, eds. Explaining Christian Origins & Early Judaism: Contributions from Cognitive & Social Science. 2007. (Biblical Interpretation Ser.). (Illus.). 312p. *(978-90-04-16329-4(8))* BRILL.

Lyda, Hap C. S. History of Biblical Christianity: An Introductory Study of Beginning Christianity & the New Testament. 2006. *(978-0-9630629-6-3(4))* 21st Century Pr.

Lynch, Joseph H. Early Christianity: A Brief History. 2009. (ENG., Illus.). 288p. (C). 64.95 *(978-0-19-513855-9(4))*; pap. 34.95 *(978-0-19-513803-0(1))* Oxford Univ. Pr., Inc.

Maasri, Zeina. Off the Wall: Political Posters of the Lebanese Civil War. 2008. (ENG., Illus.). 208p. 31.00 *(978-1-84511-951-5(7))* I. B. Tauris & Co., Ltd. GBR. Dist: Macmillan.

MacMullen, R. The Second Church: Popular Christianity A. D. 200-400. 2009. (SBL: Writings from the Greco-Roman World). 222p. *(978-90-04-16919-7(9))* BRILL.

MacMullen, Ramsay. The Second Church: Popular Christianity A.D. 200-400. 2009. pap. 24.95 *(978-1-58983-403-3(8))* Society of Biblical Literature.

—Voting about God in Early Church Councils. 2006. (ENG., Illus.). 192p. 32.00 *(978-0-300-11596-3(2))* Yale Univ. Pr.

Marjanen, Antti & Luomanen, Petri. A Companion to Second-Century Christian "Heretics" 2008. pap. *(978-90-04-17038-4(3))* BRILL.

Markus, R. A. Signs & Meanings: World & Text in Ancient Christianity, 2nd Edition. 2011. 158p. pap. 18.00 ***(978-1-61097-400-4(X)***, Wipf and Stock) Wipf & Stock Pubs.

Martens, Peter W. Origen & Scripture: The Contours of the Exegetical Life. 2012. (Oxford Early Christian Studies). (ENG.). 352p. 125.00 ***(978-0-19-963955-7(8))*** Oxford Univ. Pr., Inc.

Martin, Edward James. The Emperor Julian: an Essay on His Relations with the Christian. 2007. (ENG.). 128p. per. 20.95 *(978-1-4304-4338-4(3))* Kessinger Publishing, LLC.

Martin, Jochen. Der Weg zur Ewigkeit führt über Rom: Die Frühgeschichte des Papsttums und die Darstellung der neutestamentlichen Heilsgeschichte im Triumphbogenmosaik von Santa Maria Maggiore in Rom. 2010. (GER., Illus.). 184p. (C). 59.00 *(978-3-515-09386-6(9))* Steiner, Franz Verlag Wiesbaden GmbH DEU. Dist: Brown, David Bk. Co., The.

Mason, Steve & Helfield, Michael W. Josephus, Judea, & Christian Origins: Methods & Categories. 2009. 450p. pap. *(978-1-59856-254-5(1))* Hendrickson Pubs. Marketing, LLC.

Mathisen. People, Personal Expression & Social Relations in Late Antiquity: Text from Gaul & Western Europe, Vol. 1. (Illus.). (C). *(978-0-472-10771-1(2))* Univ. of Michigan Pr.

—People, Personal Expression & Social Relations in Late Antiquity: Texts from Gaul & Western Europe, Vol. 2. (Illus.). (C). *(978-0-472-10772-8(0))* Univ. of Michigan Pr.

Matthews, Shelly. Perfect Martyr: The Stoning of Stephen & the Construction of Christian Identity. (ENG.). 2012. 240p. pap. 24.95 ***(978-0-19-992465-3(1))*** 2010. 224p. 65.00 *(978-0-19-539332-3(5))* Oxford Univ. Pr., Inc.

Maxwell, Jaclyn L. Christianization & Communication in Late Antiquity: John Chrysostom & His Congregation in Antioch. 2006. (ENG.). 210p. 101.00 *(978-0-521-86040-6(7))* Cambridge Univ. Pr.

Maxwell, Jaclyn L. & Maxwell, Jaclyn LaRae. Christianization & Communication in Late Antiquity: John Chrysostom & His Congregation in Antioch. 2009. (ENG.). 212p. pap. 35.00 *(978-0-521-11771-5(2))* Cambridge Univ. Pr.

McEimie, Stewart. Retorno a la Iglesia Primitiva: Search for the Early Church. (SPA.). 208p. *(978-84-7228-733-4(5)*, 220775) Clie, Editorial.

McGrath, James F. The Only True God: Early Christian Monotheism in Its Jewish Context. 2009. (ENG.). 168p. 42.00 *(978-0-252-03418-3(X))* Univ. of Illinois Pr.

McGuckin, John Anthony. The Ascent of Christian Law: Patristic & Byzantine Formulations of a New Civilization. 2012. ***(978-0-88141-403-5(4))*** St. Vladimir's Seminary Pr.

McLynn, Neil. Christian politics & religious culture in late Antiquity. 2009. (Variorum Collected Studies). (Illus.). 334p. 154.95 *(978-0-7546-5992-1(5))* Ashgate Publishing Co.

McSherry, James. Outreach & Renewal: A First-Millennium Legacy for the Third-Millennium Church. 2011. x, 276p. pap. 34.95 *(978-0-87907-236-0(9))*; E-Book *(978-0-87907-798-3(0))* Cistercian Pubns., Inc.

Menze, Volker L. Justinian & the Making of the Syrian Orthodox Church. 2008. (Oxford Early Christian Studies). (ENG.). 336p. 125.00 *(978-0-19-953487-6(X))* Oxford Univ. Pr., Inc.

Meredith-Lobay, Megan. A Contextual Landscape Study of the Early Christian Churches of Argyll. 2009. (ENG., Illus.). 170p. (C). pap. 90.00 *(978-1-4073-0443-4(7))* British Archaeological Reports Ltd. GBR. Dist: Brown, David Bk Co., The.

Merivale, Charles. The Conversion of the Roman Empire; the Boyle Lectures for the Year 1864, Delivered at the Chapel Royal, Whitehall, by Charles Merivale. 2006. 276p. per. 23.99 *(978-1-4255-2500-2(8))* MPublishing.

Meyer, Ben F. The Early Christians: Their World Mission & Self-Discovery. 2009. 245p. pap. 27.00 *(978-1-60608-370-3(8)*, Wipf and Stock) Wipf & Stock Pubs.

Milman, Henry H. History of Christianity from the Birth of Christ to the Abolition of Paganism in the Roman Empire, 3 vols. rev. ed. reprint ed. 210.00 *(978-0-404-04350-6(X))* AMS Pr., Inc.

Mingana, Alphonse. The Early Spread of Christianity in Central Asia & the Far East. 2010. pap. 25.12 *(978-1-61719-589-1(8))* Gorgias Pr., LLC.

Mitchell, S. & Van Nuffelen, P., eds. Monotheism between Pagans & Christians in Late Antiquity. 2010. (Interdisciplinary Studies in Ancient Culture & Religion Ser.). (ENG.). 225p. (C). pap. 70.00 *(978-90-429-2242-6(7))* Peeters Pubs. & Booksellers BEL. Dist: Brown, David Bk. Co., The.

Moel, Dennis. The Shadow of the Temple: Jerusalem in Jesus' Day. 2008. (Illus.). 212p. pap. 16.99 *(978-1-60477-635-5(8))* Xulon Pr., Inc.

Moss, Candida R. Ancient Christian Martyrdom: Diverse Practices, Theologies, & Traditions. 2012. (Anchor Yale Bible Reference Library). (ENG.). 272p. 40.00 ***(978-0-300-15465-8(8))*** Yale Univ. Pr.

Nasrallah, Laura, et al. Prejudice & Christian Beginnings: Investigating Race, Gender, & Ethnicity in Early Christian Studies. Schussler-Fiorenza, Elisabeth, ed. 2009. 288p. (C). pap. 26.00 *(978-0-8006-6340-7(3)*, Fortress Pr.) Augsburg Fortress, Pubs.

Nasrallah, Laura Salah. Christian Responses to Roman Art & Architecture: The Second-Century Church amid the Spaces of Empire. (ENG., Illus.). (C). 2011. 352p. pap. 39.99 ***(978-1-107-64499-1(2))*** 2010. 350p. 99.00 *(978-0-521-76652-4(4))* Cambridge Univ. Pr.

Neander, Augustus. The History of the Christian Religion & Church During the First Three Centuries. Rose, Henry, tr. 2007. (ENG.). 116p. per. 12.75 *(978-1-60206-331-0(1))* Cosimo, Inc.

—History of the Planting & Training of the Christian Church by the Apostles, 2 vols. Ryland, J. E., tr. reprint ed. 250.00 *(978-0-7222-2141-9(X))* Library Reprints, Inc.

Neander, Augustus & Ryland, J. E. History of the Planting & Training of the Christian Church by the Apostles. 2009. 556p. pap. 41.75 *(978-1-116-51027-0(8))*; pap. 42.75 *(978-1-116-51026-3(X))*; 37.99 *(978-1-116-51025-6(1))*; 44.99 *(978-1-116-51024-9(3))* BiblioBazaar.

Newman, John Henry. The Church of the Fathers. 2007. (ENG.). 324p. 45.95 *(978-0-548-18245-1(0))*; per. 30.95 *(978-1-4304-8405-9(5))* Kessinger Publishing, LLC.

—Historical Sketches: The Turks in Their Relation to Europe; Marcus Tullius Cicero; Apollonius of Tyana; Primitive Christianity. 2007. (ENG.). 372p. pap. 25.99 *(978-1-4346-4537-1(1))*; 414p. pap. 28.99 *(978-1-4346-4538-8(X))* BiblioBazaar.

—Historical Sketches V1. 2008. 468p. 52.95 *(978-1-4365-6975-0(3))* 2007. 472p. per. 37.95 *(978-0-548-75480-1(2))* Kessinger Publishing, LLC.

Odahl, Charles M. Constantine & the Christian Empire. 2nd rev. ed. 2010. (Roman Imperial Biographies Ser.). (ENG., Illus.). 434p. 123.00 *(978-0-415-57534-8(6))* Routledge.

Oegema, Gerbern S. & Charlesworth, James H., eds. The Pseudepigrapha & Christian Origins: Essays from the Studiorum Novi Testamenti Societas. 2011. (ENG.). 312p. pap. 49.95 ***(978-0-567-43054-0(5)***, T&T Clark Int'l) Continuum International Publishing Group, Ltd. GBR. Dist: National Bk. Network.

Oegema, Gerbern S. & Oegema. Pseudepigrapha & Christian Origins: Essays from the Studiorum Novi Testamenti Societas. Charlesworth, James H., ed. 2008. (Jewish & Christian Text Ser.). (ENG.). 312p. 140.00 *(978-0-567-02719-1(8)*, T&T Clark Int'l) Continuum International Publishing Group, Ltd. GBR. Dist: National Bk. Network.

Orosius. Orosius: Seven Books of History Against the Pagans. Fear, A. T., ed. 2010. (Liverpool University Press - Translated Texts for Historians Ser.). (ENG.). 456p. pap. 39.95 *(978-1-84631-239-7(6))* Liverpool Univ. Pr. GBR. Dist: Chicago Distribution Ctr.

Orosius, Paulus. Orosius: Seven Books of History Against the Pagans. Fear, A. T., ed. 2010. (Liverpool University Press - Translated Texts for Historians Ser.). (ENG.). 456p. 95.00 *(978-1-84631-473-5(9))* Liverpool Univ. Pr. GBR. Dist: Chicago Distribution Ctr.

Paget, James Carleton. Jews, Christians & Jewish Christians in Antiquity. 2010. (Illus.). 543p. 257.50 *(978-3-16-150312-2(0))* Mohr Siebeck GmbH & Co. KG DEU. Dist: Coronet Bks.

Pagoulatos, Gerasimos P. Tracing the Bridegroom in Dura: The Bridal Initiation Service of the Dura-Europos Christian Baptistery as Early Evidence of the Use of Images in Christian & Byzantine Worship. 2007. per. 47.00 *(978-1-59333-738-4(8))* Gorgias Pr., LLC.

Patsavos, Elias I. A Noble Task: Entry into the Clergy in the First Five Centuries. 2007. (C). pap. *(978-1-885652-97-3(6))* Holy Cross Orthodox Pr.

Patten, Priscilla & Patten, Rebecca. The World of the Early Church: A Companion to the New Testament. 2008. 276p. pap. 30.00 *(978-1-55635-860-9(1))* Wipf & Stock Pubs.

Payne Smith, Robert, intro. The Third Part of the Ecclesiastical History of John, Bishop of Ephesus. 2010. 142.64 *(978-1-60724-961-0(8))* Gorgias Pr., LLC.

Percival, Henry R. & Wace, Henry. The Seven Ecumenical Councils of the Undivided Church: Their Canons & Dogmatic Decrees Together with the Canons of All the Local synods Which Have. Schaff, Philip, ed. 2011. 926p. pap. ***(978-1-84902-364-1(6))*** Benediction Classics.

Perkins, Judith. Roman Imperial Identities in the Early Christian Era. 2010. 214p. pap. 39.95 *(978-0-415-59488-2(X))* Routledge.

Pfleiderer, Otto. Primitive Christianity V4: Its Writings & Teachings in Their Historical. Montgomery, W., tr. 2007. pap. 42.95 *(978-1-4304-4975-1(6))* Kessinger Publishing, LLC.

Porter, Stanley, et al, eds. Journal of Greco-Roman Christianity & Judaism. 2007. 248p. *(978-1-905048-58-8(0))* Sheffield Phoenix Pr.

Porter, Stanley E. Journal of Greco-Roman Christianity & Judaism. 2008. 236p. *(978-1-906055-28-8(9))* Sheffield Phoenix Pr.

Porter, Stanley E., et al, eds. Journal of Greco-Roman Christianity & Judaism. 2010. 244p. *(978-1-906055-83-7(1))* Sheffield Phoenix Pr.

Puller, F. W. The Primitive Saints & the See of Rome. 2007. (ENG.). 464p. 52.95 *(978-0-548-08386-4(X))* Kessinger Publishing, LLC.

Raisanen, Heikki. The Rise of Christian Beliefs: The Thought World of Early Christians. 2009. 432p. (C). pap. 39.00 *(978-0-8006-6266-0(0)*, Fortress Pr.) Augsburg Fortress, Pubs.

Rammelt, Claudia. Ibas von Edessa: Rekonstruktion einer Biographie und dogmatischen Position zwischen den Fronten. 2008. (Arbeiten zur Kirchengeschichte Ser.).Tr. of Ibas of Edessa. Reconstruction of a Biography & Dogmatic Position between the Fronts. (GER.). X, 344p. 147.00 *(978-3-11-020218-2(2))*; 224.00 ***(978-3-11-916661-4(8))*** De Gruyter, Walter Inc.

Rankin, David. From Clement to Origen: The Social & Historical Context of the Church Fathers. 2006. 182p. 99.95 *(978-0-7546-5716-3(7))* Ashgate Publishing Co.

Rasimus, Tuomas, et al, eds. Stoicism in Early Christianity. 2010. (C). pap. 40.00 *(978-0-8010-3951-5(7))* Baker Academic.

Rasimus, Tuomas, et al. Stoicism in Early Christianity. 2010. *(978-1-59856-445-7(5))* Hendrickson Pubs. Marketing, LLC.

Ratti, S., ed. Antiquus Error: Les ultimes feux de la resistance Paienne. 2010. (Bibliotheque de l'antiquite Tardive Ser.). (FRE.). 328p. (C). pap. 58.00 *(978-2-503-53261-5(6))* Brepols Pubs. BEL. Dist: Brown, David Bk. Co., The.

Redford, Douglas. The New Testament Church Vol. 2: Acts - Revelation. 2007. (Standard Reference Library NT Ser.). 304p. 19.99 *(978-0-7847-1901-5(2))* Standard Publishing.

Rees, Elizabeth. Paul & Phoebe: Early Christianity on the Peloponnese. 2011. (Illus.). 192p. 30.00 ***(978-1-4456-0109-0(5))*** Amberley Publishing GBR. Dist: Casemate Pubs. & Bk. Distributors, LLC.

Renan, Ernest. Lectures on the Influence of the Institutions: Thought & Culture in Rome, on Christianity & the Development of the Catholic Church. Beard, Charles, tr. 2006. (Hibbert Lectures). 222p. pap. 24.00 *(978-1-59752-706-4(8)*, Wipf and Stock) Wipf & Stock Pubs.

Ricciotti, Giuseppe. Julian the Apostate. Costelloe, M. Joseph, tr. 2007. (ENG.). 292p. 43.95 *(978-0-548-08098-6(4))* Kessinger Publishing, LLC.

Richards, Carol. Columbanus: Poet, Preacher, Statesman, Saint. 2010. (ENG., Illus.). 128p. pap. 29.90 *(978-1-84540-190-0(5))* Imprint Academic GBR. Dist: Ingram Pub. Services.

Richardson, Marianna. Alfred Edersheim: Prophecies Fulfilled. 2008. pap. 14.99 *(978-1-59955-112-8(8))* Cedar Fort, Inc./CFI Distribution.

Riddle, Donald W. The Martyrs: A Study in Social Control. 2011. 242p. 46.95 ***(978-1-258-05108-2(7))*** Literary Licensing, LLC.

Rizzi, Marco. Hadrian & the Christians. 2010. (Millennium-Studien / Millennium Studies).Tr. of Hadrian & the Christians. (ITA & ENG., Illus.). 186p. 98.00 *(978-3-11-022470-2(4))* De Gruyter, Walter Inc.

Rizzi, Marco, ed. Hadrian & the Christians. 2011. (Millennium-Studien / Millennium Studies).Tr. of Hadrian & the Christians. (ENG & ITA., Illus.). VI, 186p. 154.00 ***(978-3-11-916286-9(8))*** De Gruyter, Walter Inc.

Royalty, Robert M. The Origin of Heresy. 2012. (Routledge Studies in Religion Ser.). (ENG.). 272p. (C). 125.00 ***(978-0-415-53694-3(4))*** Routledge.

Rüpke, Jörg. Gruppenreligionen im römischen Reich: Sozialformen, Grenzziehungen und Leistungen. 2007. (Studies & Texts in Antiquity & Christianity Ser.: Vol. 43). 212p. (C). pap. 75.00 *(978-3-16-149128-3(9))* Mohr Siebeck GmbH & Co. KG DEU. Dist: Eisenbrauns, Inc.

Russell, Peter J. Heterodoxy Within Second-Temple Judaism & Sectarian Diversity Within the Early Church: A Correlative Study. 2008. 482p. *(978-0-7734-4938-1(8))* Mellen, Edwin Pr., The.

Rutgers, L. V. Making Myths: Jews in Early Christian Identity Formation. 2009. (ENG.). 159p. (C). pap. 32.00 *(978-90-429-2240-2(0))* Peeters Pubs. & Booksellers BEL. Dist: Brown, David Bk. Co., The.

Samellas, Antigone. Alienation: The Experience of the Eastern Mediterranean, 50-600 A. D. 2010. 556p. pap. *(978-3-03911-789-5(0))* Lang, Peter.

Sandnes, Karl Olav & Sandnes. The Challenge of Homer: School, Pagan Poets & Early Christianity. 2009. (Library of New Testament Studies, the Ser.). (ENG.) 336p. 150.00 *(978-0-567-42664-2(5)*, T&T Clark Int'l) Continuum International Publishing Group, Ltd. GBR. Dist: National Bk. Network.

Sarris, Peter, et al. An Age of Saints? Power, Conflict, & Dissent in Early Medieval Christianity. 2011. 256p. *(978-90-04-20660-1(4))* BRILL.

Schilling, A. M. Die Anbetung der Magier und die Taufe der Sasaniden: Zur Geistesgeschichte des iranischen Christentums in der Spatantike. 2008. (Corpus Scriptorum Christianorum Orientalium Ser.). (GER.). 376p. (C). pap. 124.00 *(978-90-429-1815-3(2))* Peeters Pubs. & Booksellers BEL. Dist: Brown, David Bk. Co., The.

Scholasticus, Socrates. The Ecclesiastical History. 2007. (ENG.). 308p. per. 19.99 *(978-1-59547-906-8(6))* NuVision Pubns., LLC.

Schott, Jeremy. Christianity, Empire, & the Making of Religion in Late Antiquity. 2008. (Divinations: Rereading Late Ancient Religion Ser.). 272p. (C). 65.00 *(978-0-8122-4092-4(8))* Univ. of Pennsylvania Pr.

Schroter, Jens. Von Jesus zum Neuen Testament. 2007. (Wissenschaftliche Untersuchungen Zum Neuen Testament Ser.: 204). 441p. (C). 157.50 *(978-3-16-149231-0(5))* Mohr Siebeck GmbH & Co. KG DEU. Dist: Coronet Bks.

Segal, Alan F. Two Powers in Heaven: Early Rabbinic Reports about Christianity & Gnosticism. 2012. (ENG.). 339p. pap. 39.95 ***(978-1-60258-549-2(0))*** Baylor Univ. Pr.

Sellew, Philip & Smith, James D., eds. The Fabric of Early Christianity: Reflections in Honor of Helmut Koester by Fifty Years of Harvard Students. 2006. (Illus.). 168p. pap. 20.00 *(978-1-59752-974-7(5)*, Pickwick Pubns.) Wipf & Stock Pubs.

Shahid, Irfan & Shahid, I. Byzantium & the Arabs in the Sixth Century, Volume 2 Part 2. 2010. (Dumbarton Oaks Other Titles in Byzantine Studies). (Illus.). 480p. 50.00 *(978-0-88402-347-0(8))* Dumbarton Oaks.

Shaw, Brent D. Sacred Violence: African Christians & Sectarian Hatred in the Age of Augustine. 2011. (ENG., Illus.). 930p. 160.00 *(978-0-521-19605-5(1))*; pap. 65.00 *(978-0-521-12725-7(4))* Cambridge Univ. Pr.

Sisebut. King Sisebut & the Culture of Visigothic Spain, with Translations of the Lives of Saint Desiderius of Vienne & Saint Masona of Mérida: Vita Vel Passio

Sancti Desiderii a Sisebuto Rege Composita & Vita Sancti Masonae Emeretensis. Martyn, John R. C., tr. from LAT. & intro. by. 2008. (LAT & ENG.). 248p. 109.95 *(978-0-7734-5033-2(5))* Mellen, Edwin Pr., The.

Skarsaune, Oskar. In the Shadow of the Temple: Jewish Influences on Early Christianity. 2008. (ENG.). 455p. pap. 28.00 *(978-0-8308-2844-9(3)*, IVP Acad.) InterVarsity Pr.

Smith, James. Black Saints, Mystics & Holy Folk: The Ancient African Liturgical Church - Volume 1. 2007. 456p. per. 20.95 *(978-1-60145-088-3(5))* Booklocker.com, Inc.

Sommer, Carl. We Look for a Kingdom: The Everyday Lives of the Early Christians. 2007. (Illus.). 422p. pap. 19.95 *(978-1-58617-079-0(1))* Ignatius Pr.

Sotinel, Claire. Church & Society in Late Antique Italy & Beyond: Convergences Tensions & Negotiations. 2010. (Variorum Collected Studies). (FRE & ENG., Illus.). 340p. 165.00 *(978-1-4094-0022-6(0))* Ashgate Publishing Co.

Stanton, Graham N. & Stroumsa, Guy G., eds. Tolerance & Intolerance in Early Judaism & Christianity. 2008. (ENG.). 388p. pap. 46.00 *(978-0-521-05057-9(X))* Cambridge Univ. Pr.

Stapert, Calvin R. A New Song for an Old World: Musical Thought in the Early Church. 2006. (Calvin Institute of Christian Worship Liturgical Studies). (Illus.). 232p. per. 18.00 *(978-0-8028-3219-1(9))* Eerdmans, William B. Publishing Co.

Stark, Rodney. Cities of God: The Real Story of How Christianity Became an Urban Movement & Conquered Rome. 2007. (ENG., Illus.). 288p. pap. 13.95 *(978-0-06-134988-1(7)*, HarperOne) HarperCollins Pubs.

Stauffer, Ethelbert. Christ & the Caesars. 2008. 293p. pap. 32.00 *(978-1-55635-818-0(0)*, Wipf and Stock) Wipf & Stock Pubs.

Stephenson, Paul. Constantine: Roman Emperor, Christian Victor. 2010. (ENG.). 352p. (gr. 12). 30.00 *(978-1-59020-324-8(0))* Overlook Pr., The.

Stewart-Sykes, Alistair & Newman, Judith. Early Jewish Liturgy. 2009. 88.00 *(978-1-60724-400-4(4))* Gorgias Pr., LLC.

Stouck, Mary-Ann, ed. A Short Reader of Medieval Saints. (Readings in Medieval Civilizations & Cultures Ser.). (ENG., Illus.). 200p. 2009. *(978-1-4426-0131-4(0))* 2008. pap. *(978-1-4426-0094-2(2))* Univ. of Toronto Pr.

Stroumsa, Guy G. The End of Sacrifice: Religious Transformations in Late Antiquity. Emanuel, Susan, tr. from FRE. 2009. (ENG.). 160p. 32.00 *(978-0-226-77738-2(3))* Univ. of Chicago Pr.

Symes, Kenneth G. Jews, Gentiles & the Church Age. 2008. 88p. per. 9.99 *(978-1-60477-540-2(8))* Xulon Pr., Inc.

Taylor, John W. The Coming of the Saints: Imaginations & Studies in Early Church History & Tradition. 276p. 2010. 34.36 *(978-1-163-43592-2(9))* 2007. (ENG.). 42.95 *(978-0-548-12893-0(6))* Kessinger Publishing, LLC.

—Coming of the Saints Imaginations & St. 2006. pap. 27.95 *(978-1-4286-3918-8(7))* Kessinger Publishing, LLC.

Taylor, William. Partnership: Philippians: Concise, Portable Spiritual Food. 2007. (ENG.). 192p. per. 10.99 *(978-1-84550-231-7(0))* Christian Focus Pubns. GBR. Dist: STL Distribution North America.

Tellbe, Mikael. Christ-Believers in Ephesus: A Textual Analysis of Early Christian Identity Formation in a Local Perspective. 2009. (Wissenschaftliche Untersuchungen zum Neuen Testament Ser.). (Illus.). 361p. 177.50 *(978-3-16-150048-0(2))* Mohr Siebeck GmbH & Co. KG DEU. Dist: Coronet Bks.

Theissen, Gerd. Von Jesus zur urchristlichen Zeichenwelt: Neutestamentliche Grenzgänge im Dialog. 2011. (Novum Testamentum et Orbis Antiquus/Studien zur Umwelt des Neuen Testaments (NTOA/StUNT) Ser.). (GER.). 237p. (C). 81.00 *(978-3-525-55023-6(5))* Vandenhoeck & Ruprecht GmbH & Co. KG DEU. Dist: ISD.

Theodore, James. Cultivating the Cook's Garden: The Classic Guide to Organic Gourmet Gardening. 2010. 200p. pap. 18.00 *(978-1-57178-223-6(0))* Council Oak Bks.

Theodoret & Evagrius, Scholasticus. A History of the Church from AD 322 to the Death of Theodore Of. 2007. (ENG.). 496p. per. 38.95 *(978-1-4304-4399-5(5))* Kessinger Publishing, LLC.

Theron, Daniel J. Evidence of Tradition: Selected Source Material for the Study of the History of the Early Church, the New Testament Books, & the New Testament Canon. 2009. 149p. pap. 13.00 *(978-1-60608-588-2(3)*, Wipf and Stock) Wipf & Stock Pubs.

Thier, Sebastian. Kirche bei Pelagius. (Patristische Texte und Studien Ser.). (GER.). IX, 358p. 344.00 ***(978-3-11-175196-2(1))*** De Gruyter, Walter Inc.

Thiessen, Gesa E. Apostolic & Prophetic. 2012. (ENG.). 206p. (C). pap. 39.00 ***(978-0-227-68025-4(1))*** Clarke, James Co., Ltd. GBR. Dist: Brown, David Bk. Co., The.

Thompson, Jay E. A Tale of Five Cities: A History of the Five Patriarchal Cities of the Early Church. 2009. 168p. pap. 19.00 *(978-1-60608-704-6(5)*, Wipf and Stock) Wipf & Stock Pubs.

Tollinton, R. B. Clement of Alexandria. 2010. pap. 121.04 *(978-1-61719-658-4(4))*; pap. 121.04 *(978-1-61719-659-1(2))* Gorgias Pr., LLC.

Tomasino, Anthony J. The World of Jesus. 2011. (Putting the Bible in Its Place Ser.). 174p. pap. 20.00 ***(978-1-60899-137-2(7)***, Wipf and Stock) Wipf & Stock Pubs.

Trebilco, Paul. Self-designations & Group Identity in the New Testament. 2011. (ENG., Illus.). 392p. 99.00 ***(978-1-107-01299-8(6))*** Cambridge Univ. Pr.

Trompf, G. W. Early Christian Historiography: Narratives of Retribution. 2007. (ENG.). 382p. (C). pap. 39.95 *(978-1-84553-186-1(4))* Equinox Publishing Ltd. GBR. Dist: ISD.

Tucker, T. G. Life in the Roman World of Nero & St. Paul. 2007. 256p. pap. 21.99 *(978-1-4264-6436-2(3))* 2006. (ENG.). 284p. pap. 23.99 *(978-1-4264-6510-9(6))* BiblioBazaar.

Tyrwhitt, Richard. The Art Teaching of the Primitive Church with an Index of Subjects, Historical & Emblematic. 2007. (ENG.). 394p. 49.95 *(978-0-548-05256-3(5))* Kessinger Publishing, LLC.

Tzamalikos, Panayiotis. A Newly Discovered Greek Father: Cassian the Sabaite eclipsed by John Cassian of Marseilles. 2012. (Vigiliae Christianae Supplements Ser.). (ENG & GEC.). ***(978-90-04-22441-4(6))*** BRILL.

—The Real Cassian Revisited: Monastic Life, Greek Paideia, & Origenism in the Sixth Century. 2012. (Vigiliae Christianae Supplements Ser.). (ENG.). ***(978-90-04-22440-7(8))*** BRILL.

Van Dam, Raymond. The Roman Revolution of Constantine. (ENG.). 458p. 2009. (C). pap. 30.99 *(978-0-521-13301-2(7))* 2007. (Illus.). 87.00 *(978-0-521-88209-5(5))* Cambridge Univ. Pr.

van Oort, J. & Wyrwa, D., eds. Autobiographie und Hagiographie in der christlichen Antike. 2009. (Patristic Studies). (GER.). 129p. (C). pap. 53.00 *(978-90-429-2212-9(5))* Peeters Pubs. & Booksellers BEL. Dist: Brown, David Bk. Co., The.

Vaschalde, Arthur. Three Letters of Philoxenus, Bishop of Mabbôgh (485-519) 2011. (SYR.). pap. 42.40 *(978-1-61143-890-1(X))*; pap. 42.40 *(978-1-61143-855-0(1))* Gorgias Pr., LLC.

Vaughan, Robert. The Causes of the Corruption of Christianity. 2009. 200p. pap. 19.99 *(978-1-4589-1222-0(1))* General Bks. LLC.

Vinzent, Markus. Der Ursprung des Apostolikums Im Urteil der Kritischen Forschung. 2006. (Forschungen Zur Kirchen- und Dogmengeschichte Ser.). (GER.). 480p. (C). 114.00 *(978-3-525-55197-4(5))* Vandenhoeck & Ruprecht GmbH & Co. KG DEU. Dist: ISD.

Viola, Frank. Reimagining Church: Pursuing the Dream of Organic Christianity. 2008. (ENG.). 320p. pap. 14.99 *(978-1-4347-6875-9(9))* Cook, David C.

von Gemunden, Petra. Affekt und Glaube: Studien zur Historischen Psychologie des Frühjudentums und Urchristentums. Novum Testamentum et Orbis Antiquus / Studien zur Umwelt des Neuen Testaments 73. 2009. (Novum Testamentum et Orbis Antiquus/Studien zur Umwelt des Neuen Testaments (NTOA/StUNT) Ser.). (GER., Illus.). 389p. (C). 110.00 *(978-3-525-53385-7(3))* Vandenhoeck & Ruprecht GmbH & Co. KG DEU. Dist: ISD.

Waddington, George. A History of the Church from the Earliest Ages to the Reformation. 2009. 404p. pap. *(978-0-217-77134-4(3))*; 366p. pap. *(978-1-4432-8683-1(4))* Books LLC.

—A History of the Church from the Earliest Ages to the Reformation. 2009. 448p. pap. 26.81 *(978-1-4590-1146-5(5))* General Bks. LLC.

Walker, Peter. In the Steps of Paul, 1 vol. 2008. (ENG.). 224p. 19.99 *(978-0-310-29065-0(1))* Zondervan.

Walters, Patricia & Tobin, Thomas H. From Judaism to Christianity: Tradition & Transition: A Festschrift for Thomas H. Tobin, S.J., on the Occasion of His Sixty-Fifth Birthday. 2010. *(978-90-04-18769-6(3))* BRILL.

Watson, Francis. Paul, Judaism, & the Gentiles: Beyond the New Perspective. 2007. 400p. per. 32.00 *(978-0-8028-4020-2(5))* Eerdmans, William B. Publishing Co.

Werline, Rodney Alan. Experientia: Inquiry into Religious Experience in Early Judaism & Christianity. Flannery, Frances & Shantz, Colleen, eds. 2008. (SBL - Symposium Ser.). 272p. *(978-90-04-16911-1(3))* BRILL.

Werline, Rodney Alan, et al. Experientia: Sites for Inquiry for Religious Experience in Early Judaism & Christianity. 2008. 272p. pap. 32.95 *(978-1-58983-368-5(6))* Society of Biblical Literature.

Wessel, Susan. Leo the Great & the Spiritual Rebuilding of a Universal Rome. 2008. (Illus.). 436p. *(978-90-04-17052-0(9))* BRILL.

Wheatley, Alan B. Patronage in Early Christianity: Its Use & Transformation from Jesus to Paul of Samosata. 2011. (Princeton Theological Monographs). 212p. pap. 23.00 ***(978-1-59752-587-9(1)***, Pickwick Pubns.) Wipf & Stock Pubs.

Williams, A. N. The Divine Sense: The Intellect in Patristic Theology. 2009. (ENG.). 268p. pap. 29.00 *(978-0-521-12689-2(4))* Cambridge Univ. Pr.

Williams, Cassandra Carkuff. Learning the Way: Reclaiming Wisdom from the Earliest Christian Communities. 2009. *(978-1-56699-385-2(7))* Alban Institute, Inc.

Williams, D. H., ed. Tradition, Scripture, & Interpretation: A Sourcebook of the Ancient Church. 2006. (Evangelical Ressourcement Ser.). 192p. (C). pap. 22.00 *(978-0-8010-3164-9(8))* Baker Academic.

Wineland, John D. & Wineland, John, eds. The Light of Discovery: Studies in Honor of Edwin M. Yamauchi. 2007. (Evangelical Theological Society Monograph Ser.). (Illus.). 338p. pap. 32.00 *(978-1-55635-045-0(7)*, Pickwick Pubns.) Wipf & Stock Pubs.

Witetschek, S. Ephesische Enthullungen 1: Fruhe Christen in einer antiken Grosstadt. Zugleich ein Beitrag zur Frage nach den Kontexten der Johannesapokalypse. 2008. (Biblical Tools & Studies). (GER.). 526p. (C). 111.00 *(978-90-429-2108-5(0))* Peeters Pubs. & Booksellers BEL. Dist: Brown, David Bk. Co., The.

Woolley, Reginald. The Liturgy of the Primitive Church. 2007. (ENG.). 190p. 37.95 *(978-0-548-05260-0(3))* Kessinger Publishing, LLC.

Worth, Roland H., Jr. Shapers of Early Christianity: 52 Biographies, A. D. 100-400. 2007. (ENG., Illus.). 201p. 75.00 *(978-0-7864-2923-3(2))* McFarland & Co., Inc. Pubs.

Worth, Roland H. Shapers of Early Christianity: 52 Biographies, A. D. 100-400. alt. ed. 2012. (ENG.). 201p. pap. 25.00 ***(978-0-7864-6942-0(0))*** McFarland & Co., Inc. Pubs.

Young, Robin Darling & Aune, David E., eds. Reading Religions in the Ancient World: Essays Presented to Robert Mcqueen Grant on His 90th Birthday. 2007. (Novum Testamentum Supplements Ser.). (Illus.). 305p. *(978-90-04-16196-2(1))* BRILL.

ZHdanovych, Olesia. Arianstvo V Epokhu Konstantyna Velykoho. 2009. (UKR.). 219p. *(978-966-02-5122-9(X))* National Academy of Sciences of Ukraine.

CHURCH HISTORY—MIDDLE AGES, 600-1500

see also Albigenses; Apologetics—Middle Ages, 600-1500; Crusades; Monasticism and Religious Orders—Middle Ages, 600-1500; Mysticism—Middle Ages, 600-1500; Papacy; Patarines; Popes—Temporal Power; Reformation—Early Movements; Schism, The Great Western, 1378-1417; Waldenses

Akhlat, Solomon of. The Book of the Bee. 2006. 78.00 *(978-1-59333-402-4(8))* Gorgias Pr., LLC.

Allies, Mary H. Three Catholic Reformers of the Fifteenth Century. 2010. (Illus.). 90p. pap. 14.84 *(978-1-154-87131-9(2))* General Bks. LLC.

Ames, Christine Caldwell. Righteous Persecution: Inquisition, Dominicans, & Christianity in the Middle Ages. 2008. (Middle Ages Ser.). 320p. (C). 59.95 *(978-0-8122-4133-4(9))* Univ. of Pennsylvania Pr.

Angelov, Dimiter G. Church & Society in Late Byzantium. 2009. 20.00 *(978-1-58044-143-8(2))*; 40.00 *(978-1-58044-142-1(4))* Medieval Institute Pubns.

Asbridge, Thomas. The Crusades: The Authoritative History of the War for the Holy Land. 2011. (ENG.). 384p. pap. 19.99 *(978-0-06-078729-5(5)*, Ecco) HarperCollins Pubs.

Auffarth, Christoph & Kerth, Sonja. Glaubensstreit und Gelächter: Reformation und Lachkultur im Mittelalter und in der Frühen Neuzeit. 2008. (GER., Illus.). viii, 217p. *(978-3-8258-1212-6(X))* Lit Verlag.

Bakos, Gergely Tibor. On Faith, Rationality, & the Other in the Late Middle Ages: A Study of Nicholas of Cusa's Manuductive Approach to Islam. 2010. (Princeton Theological Monographs). 360p. pap. 40.00 *(978-1-60608-342-0(2)*, Pickwick Pubns.) Wipf & Stock Pubs.

Barrow, Julia, ed. English Episcopal Acta 35, Hereford 1234-1275. 2010. (English Episcopal Acta Ser.). (ENG & LAT., Illus.). 280p. 99.00 *(978-0-19-726453-9(0))* Oxford Univ. Pr., Inc.

Barton, Simon & Linehan, Peter, eds. Cross, Crescent & Conversion: Studies on Medieval Spain & Christendom in Memory of Richard Fletcher. 2007. (Medieval Mediterranean Ser.). (Illus.). 362p. *(978-90-04-16343-0(3))* BRILL.

Bede. Ecclesiastical History of the English People. Gray, G., ed. 2008. 428p. pap. *(978-1-904799-31-3(0))* Tiger of the Stripe.

Beer, Max. Social Struggles in the Middle Ages (Routledge Revivals) 2010. (Routledge Revivals Ser.). (ENG.). 220p. 95.00 *(978-0-415-59975-7(X))* Routledge.

Benedict XVI, pseud. Great Christian Thinkers: From the Early Church through the Middle Ages. 2011. 328p. pap. 16.99 *(978-0-8006-9851-5(7)*, Fortress Pr.) Augsburg Fortress, Pubs.

Blumenthal, Uta-Renate, et al, eds. Canon Law, Religion, & Politics: Liber Amicorum Robert Somerville. 2012. (ENG.). 344p. 69.95 ***(978-0-8132-1975-2(2))*** Catholic Univ. of America Pr.

Bornstein, Daniel, ed. Medieval Christianity. 2010. 320p. (C). pap. 24.00 *(978-0-8006-9722-8(7)*, Fortress Pr.) Augsburg Fortress, Pubs.

Boureau, Alain. La Religion de L'État: La Construction de la République étatique Dans le Discours Théologique de L'Occident Médiéval, 1250-1350. 2006. (FRE.). 356p. (C). pap. 50.00 ***(978-2-251-38080-3(9))*** Societe d'edition Les Belles lettres FRA. Dist: ISD.

Brooke, C. N. L., et al, eds. Church & Government in the Middle Ages: Essays presented to C. R. Cheney on his 70th Birthday & Edited by C. N. L. Brooke, D. E. Luscombe, G. H. Martin & Dorothy Owen. 2008. (ENG.). 336p. pap. 46.00 *(978-0-521-08929-6(8))* Cambridge Univ. Pr.

Brooke, Zachary N. The English Church & the Papacy, from the Conquest to the Reign of John. reprint ed. 42.00 *(978-0-404-18756-9(0))* AMS Pr., Inc.

Brown, George Hardin & Voigts, Linda Ehrsam. The Study of Medieval Manuscripts of England: Festschrift in Honor of Richard W. Pfaff. 2010. (Illus.). ix, 438p. *(978-0-86698-432-4(1))* MRTS.

Brown, George Hardin, et al. The Study of Medieval Manuscripts of England: Festschrift in Honor of Richard W. Pfaff. 2010. (Illus.). ix, 438p. ***(978-2-503-53383-4(3))*** ACMRS.

Brown, Virginia. Beneventan Discoveries: Collected Manuscript Catalogues, 1978¿2008. 2012. (Studies & Texts: 179). (ENG & LAT.). 300p. 90.00 ***(978-0-88844-179-9(7))*** Pontifical Institute of Mediaeval Studies, Dept. of Pubns. CAN. Dist: Univ. of Toronto Pr.

Burman, Thomas E. Reading the Qur'an in Latin Christendom, 1140-1560. 2009. (Material Texts). (Illus.). 328p. (C). pap. 24.95 *(978-0-8122-2062-9(5))* Univ. of Pennsylvania Pr.

Bynum, Caroline Walker. Christian Materiality: An Essay on Religion in Late Medieval Europe. 2011. (ENG., Illus.). 440p. (gr. 17). 32.95 *(978-1-935408-10-9(0))* Zone Bks.

Caciola, Nancy. Discerning Spirits: Divine & Demonic Possession in the Middle Ages. 2006. (Conjunctions of Religion & Power in the Medieval Past Ser.). (Illus.). 327p. per. 23.95 *(978-0-8014-7334-0(9)*, Comstock Publishing Assocs.) Cornell Univ. Pr.

Cameron, Averil & Hoyland, Robert. Doctrine & Debate in the East Christian World 300-1500. 2011. (Worlds of Eastern Christianity, 300ndash;1500 Ser.). 470p. 190.00 ***(978-1-4094-0034-9(4))*** Ashgate Publishing Co.

Coulton, G. G. Ten Medieval Studies: With Four Appendices. 2010. (Cambridge Library Collection - History Ser.). (ENG.). 318p. pap. 24.99 *(978-1-108-01065-8(2))* Cambridge Univ. Pr.

Craig, Leigh Ann. Wandering Women & Holy Matrons: Women As Pilgrims in the Later Middle Ages. 2009. *(978-90-04-17426-9(5))* BRILL.

Cram101 Textbook Reviews. Outlines & Highlights for the Crisis of Church & State: 1050-1300 by Tierney. 2011. 128p. pap. 28.95 ***(978-1-61812-844-7(2))*** Cram101 Inc.

Cram101 Textbook Reviews Staff. Outlines & Highlights for Medieval Christianity: A Peoples History of Christianity, Vol. 4 by Daniel E. Bornstein (Editor), ISBN. 2009. 58p. pap. 26.95 *(978-1-4288-9291-0(5))* Cram101 Inc.

—Outlines & Highlights for the European Reformations by Carter Lindberg, Isbn: 9781557865755. 2009. 100p. pap. 27.95 *(978-1-4288-9268-2(0))* Cram101 Inc.

Cruttwell, Charles Thomas. Saxon Church & the Norman Conquest. 2006. pap. 28.95 *(978-1-4286-3881-5(4))* Kessinger Publishing, LLC.

Currie, Stephen. Miracles, Saints, & Pagan Superstition: The Medieval Mind. 2006. (Lucent Library of Historical Eras). (ENG., Illus.). 104p. (gr. 5-9). lib. bdg. 33.45 *(978-1-59018-861-3(6)*, Lucent Bks.) Cengage Gale.

Daniel, E. Randolph. Abbot Joachim of Fiore & Joachimism: Selected Articles. 2011. (Variorum Collected Studies). (Illus.). 374p. 154.95 *(978-1-4094-2401-7(4))* Ashgate Publishing Co.

Davis, Michael R. Henry of Blois: Prince Bishop of the Twelfth Century Renaissance. 2009. 630p. pap. 39.95 *(978-1-60749-753-0(0))* PublishAmerica, Inc.

D'Aygalliers, A. Wautier. The Church in the 14th Century. 2010. 16p. pap. 10.36 ***(978-1-163-01579-7(2))*** 2006. pap. 12.95 *(978-1-4286-8238-2(4))* Kessinger Publishing, LLC.

Deane, Jennifer. A History of Medieval Heresy & Inquisition. 2011. (Critical Issues in World & International History Ser.). (ENG.). 328p. 84.00 *(978-0-7425-5575-4(5))*; pap. 95.00 *(978-0-7425-5576-1(3))* Rowman & Littlefield Publishers, Inc.

Deane, Jennifer Kolpacoff. A History of Medieval Heresy & Inquisition. 2011. *(978-0-7425-6811-2(3))* Rowman & Littlefield Publishers, Inc.

Decker, Rainer. Witchcraft & the Papacy: An Account Drawing on the Formerly Secret Records of the Roman Inquisition. Midelfort, H. C. Erik, tr. 2010. (Studies in Early Modern German History Ser.). (ENG., Illus.). 280p. (C). (gr. 13-17). pap. 22.50 *(978-0-8139-2748-0(X))* Univ. Pr. of Virginia.

Drossbach, Gisela & Schmidt, Hans-Joachim, eds. Zentrum und Netzwerk: Kirchliche Kommunikationen und Raumstrukturen im Mittelalter. 2008. (Scrinium Friburgense Ser.).Tr. of Centre & Network. (GER.). 396p. 147.00 *(978-3-11-019660-3(3))* De Gruyter, Walter Inc.

Dvornik, Francis. The Idea of Apostolicity in Byzantium & the Legend of Apostle Andrew. 2011. 352p. 51.95 ***(978-1-258-08369-4(8))*** Literary Licensing, LLC.

Ekelund, Robert B., Jr. & Tollison, Robert D. Economic Origins of Roman Christianity. 2011. (ENG., Illus.). 288p. 45.00 *(978-0-226-20002-6(7))* Univ. of Chicago Pr.

Eldevik, John. Episcopal Power & Ecclesiastical Reform in the German Empire: Tithes, Lordship & Community, 950#x2013;1150. 2012. (Cambridge Studies in Medieval Life & Thought: Fourth Ser.: 86). (ENG., Illus.). 320p. 99.00 ***(978-0-521-19346-7(X))*** Cambridge Univ. Pr.

Evans, G. R. The Church in the Early Middle Ages. annot. ed. 2007. (I. B. Tauris History of the Christian Church Ser.). (ENG., Illus.). 256p. 47.00 *(978-1-84511-150-2(8))* I. B. Tauris & Co., Ltd. GBR. Dist: Macmillan.

Field, Sean L. The Beguine, the Angel, & the Inquisitor: The Trials of Marguerite Porete & Guiard of Cressonessart. 2012. (ENG.). 416p. pap. 40.00 ***(978-0-268-02892-3(3))*** Univ. of Notre Dame Pr.

Finucane, Ronald C. Contested Canonizations: The Last Medieval Saints, 1482-1523. 2011. 288p. 64.95 ***(978-0-8132-1875-5(6))*** Catholic Univ. of America Pr.

Fischer, Andreas. Kardinale Im Konklave: Die Lange Sedisvakanz der Jahre 1268 Bis 1271. 2008. (Bibliothek des Deutschen Historischen Instituts in ROM Ser.). (GER.). X, 533p. *(978-3-484-82118-7(3))* Verlag Max Niemeyer.

Fliegel, Stephen N. Resplendent Faith: Liturgical Treasuries of the Middle Ages. 2009. (Illus.). 96p. 19.95 *(978-0-87338-979-2(4))* Kent State Univ. Pr.

Fullerton, Georgiana. The Life of St Frances of Rome & Others. 2008. 240p. 24.99 *(978-0-554-32075-5(4))*; 27.99 *(978-0-554-22772-6(X))* BiblioBazaar.

—The Life of St Frances of Rome & Others. 2007. (ENG.). 200p. per. *(978-1-4065-8120-1(8))* Dodo Pr.

—The Life of St Frances of Rome & Others. 2010. 178p. pap. 18.36 *(978-1-162-70004-5(1))*; 30.36 ***(978-1-169-27708-3(X))***; 37.95 *(978-1-161-46869-4(2))* Kessinger Publishing, LLC.

—The Life of St Frances of Rome, & Others. 2010. 138p. pap. 22.72 *(978-1-153-70936-1(8))* General Bks. LLC.

Gosselin, Jean Edme Auguste. The Power of the Pope During the Middle Ages; 2006. 384p. per. 26.99 *(978-1-4255-4055-5(4))* MPublishing.

Grenzmann, Ludger, et al, eds. Wechselseitige Wahrnehmung der Religionen im Spätmittelalter und in der Frahen Neuzeit: I. Konzeptionelle Grundfragen und Fallstudien (Heiden, Barbaren, Juden) 2009. (Abhandlungen der Akademie der Wissenschaften zu Göttingen. Neue Folge Ser.).Tr. of Mutual Perceptions of Religions in the Late Middle Ages & the Early Modern Age. (GER.). X, 281p. 168.00 ***(978-3-11-173317-3(3))*** De Gruyter, Walter Inc.

Grenzmann, Ludger, et al, eds. Wechselseitige Wahrnehmung der Religionen im Spätmittelalter und in der Frühen Neuzeit: I. Konzeptionelle Grundfragen und Fallstudien (Heiden, Barbaren, Juden) 2009. (Abhandlungen der Akademie der Wissenschaften zu Göttingen. Neue Folge Ser.).Tr. of Mutual Perceptions of Religions in the Late Middle Ages & the Early Modern Age. (GER., Illus.). X, 281p. 112.00 *(978-3-11-021352-2(4))* De Gruyter, Walter Inc.

Gunn, Vicky A. & Gunn, Vicky. Bede's Historiae: Genre, Rhetoric & the Construction of the Anglo-Saxon Church History. 2009. 256p. 90.00

(978-1-84383-465-6(0), Boydell Press) Boydell & Brewer, Ltd. GBR. Dist: Boydell & Brewer, Inc.

Haar Romeny, R. B. ter. Religious Origins of Nations? The Christian Communities of the Middle East. 2009. 384p. (978-90-04-17375-0(7)) BRILL.

Halverson, James L. Contesting Christendom: Readings in Medieval Religion & Culture. 2007. (ENG.). 254p. 85.00 (978-0-7425-5471-9(5)); per. 29.95 (978-0-7425-5472-6(4)) Rowman & Littlefield Publishers, Inc.

Hannah, John & Hannah, John D. Church History: The Reformation of the Church (The Early Modern Period) - A. D. 1500-1650, 1 vol. 2009. (Kregel Pictorial Guide Ser.). 32p. pap. 9.99 (978-0-8254-2785-5(1)) Kregel Pubns.

Harper-Bill, Christopher. English Episcopal Acta, Volume 40: Norwich 1266-1288. 2012. (English Episcopal Acta Ser.). (ENG & LAT., Illus.). 278p. 99.00 **(978-0-19-726516-1(2))** Oxford Univ. Pr., Inc.

—English Episcopal Acta, Volume 41: Norwich 1289-1299. 2012. (English Episcopal Acta Ser.). (ENG & LAT., Illus.). 194p. 85.00 **(978-0-19-726517-8(0))** Oxford Univ. Pr., Inc.

Harris, Stephen, et al. Misconceptions about the Middle Ages. Grigsby, Bryon L., ed. 2007. (Routledge Studies in Medieval Religion & Culture Ser.). 320p. 141.00 (978-0-415-77053-8(X)) Routledge.

Healy, Patrick. The Chronicle of Hugh of Flavigny: Reform & the Investiture Contest in the Late-Eleventh Century. 2006. (Church, Faith, & Culture in the Medieval West Ser.). (Illus.). 274p. 140.00 (978-0-7546-5526-8(1)) Ashgate Publishing Co.

Higham, N. J. Re-Reading Bede: The Ecclesiastical History in Context. 2006. (ENG., Illus.). 296p. (C). per. 40.95 (978-0-415-35368-7(8)) Routledge.

—(Re-)Reading Bede: The Ecclesiastical History in Context. 2006. (Illus.). 279p. 140.00 (978-0-415-35367-0(X)) Routledge.

Hobar, Linda Lacour. The Mystery of History: The Early Church & the Middle Ages. 2007. (Mystery of History Ser.). (Illus.). 715p. per. 49.95 (978-1-892427-06-9(0)) Bright Ideas! Educational Resources.

Horie, Ruth. Perceptions of Ecclesia: Church & Soul in Medieval Dedication Sermons. 2006. (Sermo Ser.). (ENG & LAT.). 247p. (C). 65.00 (978-2-503-52059-9(6)) Brepols Pubs. BEL. Dist: ISD.

Hornby, Emma. Medieval Liturgical Chant & Patristic Exegesis: Words & Music in the Second-Mode Tracts. 2009. (Studies in Medieval & Renaissance Music Ser.: Volume 9). (Illus.). 344p. 95.00 (978-1-84383-471-7(5), Boydell Press) Boydell & Brewer, Ltd. GBR. Dist: Boydell & Brewer, Inc.

Howorth, Henry Hoyle. Golden Days of the Early English Church from the Arrival of Theodore to the Death of Bede, 3 vols. reprint ed. 75.00 (978-0-404-09470-6(8)) AMS Pr., Inc.

Jamroziak, E. & Burton, J. E., eds. Religious & Laity in Western Europe, 1000-1400: Interaction, Negotiation, & Power. 2007. (Europa Sacra Ser.). (ENG., Illus.). 399p. (C). 131.00 (978-2-503-52067-4(7)) Brepols Pubs. BEL. Dist: ISD.

Janz, Denis R. Luther & Late Medieval Thomism: A Study in Theological Anthropology. 2009. (ENG.). 200p. (C). pap. 38.95 (978-1-55458-235-8(0)) Wilfrid Laurier Univ. Pr. CAN. Dist: Univ. of Toronto Pr.

Johrendt, Jochen. Die Diener des Apostelfürsten: Das Kapitel von St. Peter im Vatikan (11.-13. Jahrhundert) 2011. (Bibliothek des Deutschen Historischen Instituts in Rom Ser.). (GER.). X, 564p. 112.00 **(978-3-11-023407-7(6))** De Gruyter, Walter Inc.

Johrendt, Jochen & Müller, Harald, eds. Römisches Zentrum und kirchliche Peripherie: Das universale Papsttum als Bezugspunkt der Kirchen von den Reformpäpsten bis zu Innozenz III. 2008. (Abhandlungen der Akademie der Wissenschaften zu Göttingen. Neue Folge Ser.). (GER., Illus.). X, 356p. 91.00 (978-3-11-020223-6(9)) De Gruyter, Walter Inc.

Keller, David G. R. Desert Banquet: A Year of Wisdom from the Desert Mothers & Fathers. 2011. E-Book **(978-0-8146-3388-5(9))** Liturgical Pr.

Kerby-Fulton, Kathryn. Books under Suspicion: Censorship & tolerance of Revelatory Writing in Late Medieval England. 2011. (ENG., Illus.). 616p. pap. 35.00 **(978-0-268-03323-1(4))** Univ. of Notre Dame Pr.

Körntgen, Ludger. Patterns of Episcopal Power / Strukturen Bischöflicher Herrschaftsgewalt Im Westlichen Europa des 10. und 11. Jahrhunderts: Bishops in Tenth & Eleventh Century Western Europe. 2011. (Prinz-Albert-Forschungen Ser.). (GER & ENG.). 226p. 126.00 **(978-3-11-026202-5(9))** De Gruyter, Walter Inc.

Kullmann, Dorothea. The Church & Vernacular Literature in Medieval France. 2009. (Studies & Texts). (FRE & ENG., Illus.). vi, 296p. 75.00 (978-0-88844-165-2(7)) Pontifical Institute of Mediaeval Studies, Dept. of Pubns. CAN. Dist: Univ. of Toronto Pr.

Levy, Ian Christopher. Holy Scripture & the Quest for Authority at the End of the Middle Ages. 2012. (ND Reading the Scriptures Ser.). (ENG.). 352p. pap. 38.00 **(978-0-268-03414-6(1))** Univ. of Notre Dame Pr.

Lineham, Peter. Historical Memory & Clerical Activity in Medieval Spain & Portugal. 2012. (Variorum Collected Studies). 340p. 165.00 **(978-1-4094-5110-5(0))** Ashgate Publishing Co.

Logan, F. Donald. A History of the Church in the Middle Ages. 2nd rev. ed. 2012. (ENG., Illus.). 360p. (C). 130.00 (978-0-415-66993-1(6)); pap. 37.95 (978-0-415-66994-8(4)) Routledge.

Loud, G. A. The Latin Church in Norman Italy. 2011. (ENG., Illus.). 595p. pap. 70.00 (978-0-521-18148-8(8)) Cambridge Univ. Pr.

Louth, Andrew. Greek East & Latin West: The Church AD 681-1071, 6 vols., Vol.2. 2007. (Illus.). 384p. pap. 28.00 (978-0-88141-320-5(8)) St. Vladimir's Seminary Pr.

Maccoull, Leslie S. B. Documenting Christianity in Egypt: Sixth to Fourteenth Centuries. 2011. (Variorum Collected Studies). (Illus.). 350p. 149.95 **(978-1-4094-2788-9(9))** Ashgate Publishing Co.

MacGregor, Kirk R. A Comparative Study of Adjustments to Social Catastrophes in Christianity & Buddhism: The Black Death in Europe & the Kamakura Takeover in Japan As Causes of Religious Reform. 2011. 400p. 129.95 **(978-0-7734-1549-2(1))** Mellen, Edwin Pr., The.

Maitland, Samuel Roffey. The Dark Ages: Essays Illustrating the State of Religion & Literature in the Ninth, Tenth, Eleventh & Twelfth Centuries. 2007. (ENG.). 536p. 57.95 (978-0-548-05223-5(9)) Kessinger Publishing, LLC.

Mann, Horace K. The Lives of the Popes in the Early Middle Ages. 2007. 448p. (ENG.). 39.95 (978-1-4344-8731-5(8)); per. 22.95 (978-1-4344-8730-8(X)) Wildside Pr., LLC.

Mann, Horace Kinder. The Lives of the Popes in the Early Middle Ages. 2008. 520p. 32.99 (978-0-559-58788-7(0)); pap. 38.75 (978-0-559-58785-6(6)) BiblioBazaar.

—The Lives of the Popes in the Early Middle Ages. 2009. 202p. pap. (978-1-151-10443-4(4)) Books LLC.

—The Lives of the Popes in the Early Middle Ages. 2009. 280p. pap. 22.54 (978-1-151-28536-2(6)); 268p. pap. 22.35 (978-1-150-62650-0(X)); 318p. pap. 24.21 (978-1-4589-2337-5(3)) General Bks. LLC.

Manning, Bernard Lord. The People's Faith in the Time of Wyclif. 2008. 208p. 39.95 (978-1-4365-1218-3(2)) 2007. (ENG.). 212p. per. 24.95 (978-0-548-71494-2(0)) Kessinger Publishing, LLC.

—The People's Faith in the Time of Wyclif. 2006. (978-1-57898-568-5(4)) Martino Publishing.

Mayr-Harting, Henry. Religion & Society in the Medieval West: 600 - 1200 - Selected Papers. 2010. (Variorum Collected Studies). (Illus.). 340p. 165.00 (978-0-7546-6898-5(3)) Ashgate Publishing Co.

McAvoy, Liz Herbert, ed. The Anchoritic Traditions of Medieval Europe. 2010. 256p. 90.00 (978-1-84383-520-2(7), Boydell Press) Boydell & Brewer, Ltd. GBR. Dist: Boydell & Brewer, Inc.

McAvoy, Liz Herbert & Hughes-Edwards, Mari, eds. Anchorites, Wombs & Tombs: Intersections of Gender & Enclosure in the Middle Ages. 2010. (University of Wales Press - Religion & Culture in the Middle Ages Ser.). (ENG.). 256p. pap. 35.00 (978-0-7083-2200-0(X)) Univ. of Wales Pr. GBR. Dist: Chicago Distribution Ctr.

McSherry, James. Outreach & Renewal: A First-Millennium Legacy for the Third-Millennium Church. 2011. x, 276p. pap. 34.95 (978-0-87907-236-0(9)); E-Book (978-0-87907-798-3(0)) Cistercian Pubns., Inc.

Meredith-Lobay, Megan. A Contextual Landscape Study of the Early Christian Churches of Argyll. 2009. (ENG., Illus.). 170p. (C). pap. 90.00 (978-1-4073-0443-4(7)) British Archaeological Reports Ltd. GBR. Dist: Brown, David Bk. Co., The.

Müller-Wille, Michael. Slawenmission in Mitteleuropa. 2006. (Abhandlungen der Geistes- und Sozialwissenschaftlichen Klasse (AM-GS) Ser.). (GER., Illus.). 29p. (C). 12.00 (978-3-515-08864-0(4)) Steiner, Franz Verlag Wiesbaden GmbH DEU. Dist: Brown, David Bk. Co., The.

Nicol, Donald M. Church & Society in Byzantium. 2008. (ENG.). 176p. pap. 38.99 (978-0-521-07167-3(4)) Cambridge Univ. Pr.

Noble, Thomas F. X. & Smith, Julia M. H., eds. Early Medieval Christianities, C. 600-C. 1100, Vol. 3. 2008. (Cambridge History of Christianity Ser.). (ENG., Illus.). 880p. 185.00 (978-0-521-81775-2(7)) Cambridge Univ. Pr.

Noble, Thomas F. X. & Van Engen, John, eds. European Transformations: The Long Twelfth Century. 2012. (ND Conf Medieval Studies). (ENG., Illus.). 520p. pap. 65.00 **(978-0-268-03610-2(1))** Univ. of Notre Dame Pr.

Novalija, Alen. Bede S Ecclesiastical History. 2008. 60p. pap. (978-3-639-07074-3(7)) VDM Verlag Dr. Mueller e.K.

O Croinin, Daibhi & Warntjes, D., eds. The Easter Controversy of Late Antiquity & the Early Middle Ages. Its Manuscripts, Texts & Tables. Proceedings of the 2nd International Conference on the Science of Computus, Galway, 18-20 July 2008. 2011. (Studia Traditionis Theologiae Ser.). (ENG.). 400p. (C). pap. 95.00 **(978-2-503-53668-2(9))** Brepols Pubs. BEL. Dist: Brown, David Bk. Co., The.

O'Mara, V. & Rivers, K., eds. Preaching the Memory of Virtue & Vice: Memory, Images, & Preaching in the Late Middle Ages. 2010. (Sermo Ser.). (ENG., Illus.). 377p. (C). 123.00 (978-2-503-51525-0(8)) Brepols Pubs. BEL. Dist: ISD.

Ott, John S. & Jones, Anna Trumbore, eds. The Bishop Reformed: Studies on Episcopal Power & Culture in the Central Middle Ages. 2007. (Church, Faith & Culture in the Medieval West Ser.). (Illus.). 296p. 124.95 (978-0-7546-5765-1(5)) Ashgate Publishing Co.

Pius, II. Commentaries Books, 2 vols., Volume 2. Meserve, Margaret & Simonetta, Marcello, eds. 2007. (I Tatti Renaissance Library: 29). (LAT & ENG., Illus.). 416p. 29.95 (978-0-674-02489-2(3)) Harvard Univ. Pr.

Pratsch, Thomas, ed. Konflikt und Bewältigung: Die Zerstörung der Grabeskirche Zu Jerusalem Im Jahre 1009. 2011. (Millennium-Studien / Millennium Studies). (GER., Illus.). XIII, 373p. 140.00 **(978-3-11-025351-1(8))** De Gruyter, Walter Inc.

Prudlo, Donald. The Origin, Development, & Refinement of Medieval Religious Mendicancies. 2011. 530p. (978-90-04-18180-9(6)) BRILL.

Riley-Smith, Jonathan. The First Crusade & the Idea of Crusading. 2009. (Middle Ages Ser.). (Illus.). 232p. (C). pap. 24.95 (978-0-8122-2076-6(5)) Univ. of Pennsylvania Pr.

Riley-Smith, Jonathan Simon Christopher. The First Crusade & the Idea of Crusading. (Illus.). 240p. pap. (978-0-485-12094-3(1)) Continuum International Publishing Group, Ltd.

Russell, Eugenia. St. Demetrius of Thessalonica: Cult & Devotion in the Middle Ages. 2010. (ENG.). 213p. pap. 51.95 (978-3-0343-0181-7(2)) Lang, Peter AG GBR. Dist: Lang, Peter.

Sarris, Peter, et al. An Age of Saints? Power, Conflict, & Dissent in Early Medieval Christianity. 2011. 256p. (978-90-04-20660-1(4)) BRILL.

Sayers, Jane E. Papal Government & England during the Pontificate of Honorius III (1216-1227) 2008. (Cambridge Studies in Medieval Life & Thought: Third Ser.). (ENG.). 312p. pap. 42.00 (978-0-521-07331-8(6)) Cambridge Univ. Pr.

Schabel, Christopher, ed. Theological Quodlibeta in the Middle Ages: The Fourteenth Century. 2007. (Brill's Companions to the Christian Tradition Ser.). 791p. (978-90-04-16285-4(7)) BRILL.

—Theological Quodlibeta in the Middle Ages: The Thirteenth Century. 2006. (Brill's Companions to the Christian Tradition Ser.: Vol. 1). 480p. (978-90-04-12333-5(4)) BRILL.

Schreiner, Susan. Are You Alone Wise? The Search for Certainty in the Early Modern Era. 2010. (Oxford Studies in Historical Theology Ser.). (ENG.). 352p. 74.00 (978-0-19-531342-0(9)) Oxford Univ. Pr., Inc.

Setback & Recovery Ad 500-1500 Church History 2- 6.50 (978-0-687-86215-3(9)) Abingdon Pr.

Shinners, John, ed. Medieval Popular Religion, 1000-1500: A Reader. 2nd ed. 2006. (Readings in Medieval Civilizations & Cultures Ser.). (ENG., Illus.). 545p. pap. (978-1-4426-0106-2(X)) Univ. of Toronto Pr.

Shogimen, Takashi. Ockham & Political Discourse in the Late Middle Ages. 2007. (Cambridge Studies in Medieval Life & Thought). (ENG.). 322p. 116.00 (978-0-521-84581-6(5)) Cambridge Univ. Pr.

Soames, Henry. The Latin Church During Anglo Saxon Times. 2007. (ENG.). 528p. 55.95 (978-0-548-04761-3(8)) Kessinger Publishing, LLC.

Somerville, Robert. Pope Urban II's Council of Piacenza. 2011. (ENG.). 208p. 110.00 (978-0-19-925853-8(7)) Oxford Univ. Pr., Inc.

Stansbury, Ronald J., ed. A Companion to Pastoral Care in the Late Middle Ages (1200-1500) (Illus.). 428p. (978-90-04-18353-7(1)) BRILL.

Stouck, Mary-Ann, ed. A Short Reader of Medieval Saints. (Readings in Medieval Civilizations & Cultures Ser.). (ENG., Illus.). 200p. 2009. (978-1-4426-0131-4(0)) 2008. pap. (978-1-4426-0094-2(2)) Univ. of Toronto Pr.

Sumption, Jonathan. Pilgrimage. 2006. (Illus.). 391p. reprint ed. pap. 20.00 (978-1-4223-5345-5(1)) DIANE Publishing Co.

Tanner, Norman P. The Church in the Later Middle Ages. 2008. (I. B. Tauris History of the Christian Church Ser.). (ENG., Illus.). 256p. 42.00 (978-1-84511-438-1(8)) I. B. Tauris & Co., Ltd. GBR. Dist: Macmillan.

Ullmann, Walter. The Growth of Papal Government in the Middle Ages. 2009. 524p. 166.00 (978-0-415-55575-3(2)) Routledge.

Urbanczyk, Przemyslaw. Herrschaft und Politik im Fruhen Mittelalter. (GER., Illus.). 295p. pap. 62.95 (978-3-631-53725-1(5)) Lang, Peter GmbH, Europaischer Verlag der Wissenschaften DEU. Dist: Lang, Peter Publishing, Inc.

Van Dussen, Michael. From England to Bohemia: Heresy & Communication in the Later Middle Ages. 2012. (Cambridge Studies in Medieval Literature Ser.). (ENG., Illus.). 232p. 85.00 **(978-1-107-01679-8(7))** Cambridge Univ. Pr.

Van Rhijn, Carine. Shepherds of the Lord: Priests & Episcopal Statutes in the Carolingian Period. 2007. (Cultural Encounters in Late Antiquity & the Middle Ages Ser.: Vol. 6). (ENG.). 246p. (C). 102.00 (978-2-503-52319-4(6)) Brepols Pubs. BEL. Dist: ISD.

Vegvar, Carol Neuman De & Ó Carragáin, Eamonn. Roma Felix-Formation & Relections of Medieval Rome. 2008. (Church, Faith & Culture in the Medieval West Ser.). (Illus.). 368p. 134.95 (978-0-7546-6096-5(6)) Ashgate Publishing Co.

Verbist, P. Duelling with the Past: Medieval Authors & the Problem of the Christian Era (C. 990 - 1135) 2010. (Studies in the Early Middle Ages Ser.). (ENG., Illus.). 366p. (C). 123.00 (978-2-503-52073-5(1)) Brepols Pubs. BEL. Dist: ISD.

Vlasto, A. P. The Entry of the Slavs into Christendom: An Introduction to the Medieval History of the Slavs. 2009. (ENG.). 448p. pap. 46.00 (978-0-521-10758-7(X)) Cambridge Univ. Pr.

Waddington, George. A History of the Church from the Earliest Ages to the Reformation. 2009. 404p. pap. (978-0-217-77134-4(3)); 366p. pap. (978-1-4432-8683-1(4)) Books LLC.

—A History of the Church from the Earliest Ages to the Reformation. 2009. 448p. pap. 26.81 (978-1-4590-1146-5(5)) General Bks. LLC.

Walter, Philippe. Christianity: The Origins of a Pagan Religion. Graham, Jon E., tr. from FRE. 2006. (ENG., Illus.). 1p. per. 16.95 (978-1-59477-096-8(4)) Inner Traditions International, Ltd.

Whalen, Brett Edward. Dominion of God: Christendom & Apocalypse in the Middle Ages. 2009. (Illus.). 336p. 31.50 (978-0-674-03629-1(8)) Harvard Univ. Pr.

Wood, Susan. The Proprietary Church in the Medieval West. 2009. (ENG., Illus.). 1020p. pap. 85.00 (978-0-19-955263-4(0)) Oxford Univ. Pr., Inc.

Wright, J. Robert. A Companion to Bede. 2008. (Illus.). 144p. 25.00 (978-0-8028-6309-6(4)) Eerdmans, William B. Publishing Co.

CHURCH HISTORY—MIDDLE AGES, 600-1500—HISTORIOGRAPHY

Harrison, Kenneth. The Framework of Anglo-Saxon History: To A. D. 900. 2010. (ENG.). 184p. pap. 19.99 (978-0-521-14392-9(6)) Cambridge Univ. Pr.

Rowley, Sharon M. The Old English Version of Bede's Historia Ecclesiastica. 2011. (Anglo-Saxon Studies: Volume 16). (ANG & ENG., Illus.). 270p. 99.00 (978-1-84384-273-6(4), D. S. Brewer) Boydell & Brewer, Ltd. GBR. Dist: Boydell & Brewer, Inc.

CHURCH HISTORY—REFORMATION, 1517-1648

see Reformation

CHURCH HISTORY—MODERN PERIOD, 1500-

see also Counter-Reformation; Evangelical Revival; Missions—History; Protestantism—History; Reformation; Sects

Alfani, Guido & Gourdon, Vincent, eds. Spiritual Kinship in Europe, 1500-1900. 2012. (ENG., Illus.). 336p. 85.00 **(978-0-230-36221-5(4))** Palgrave Macmillan.

Blunt, John Henry. A Key to the Knowledge of Church History. 2009. 174p. 26.99 (978-1-110-68147-1(X)) 2009. 174p. pap. 21.75 (978-1-110-68145-7(3)) 2008. (ENG.). 132p. per. 19.75 (978-1-4375-2032-3(4)) 2008. (ENG.). 146p. per. 21.75 (978-1-4375-2207-5(6)) BiblioBazaar.

Bossuet, Jacques B. History of the Variations of the Protestant Churches, 2 vols., Set. reprint ed. 75.00 (978-0-404-19872-5(4)) AMS Pr., Inc.

Dupre, Louis. Religion & the Rise of Modern Culture. 2008. (Erasmus Institute Bks.). (ENG.). 128p. pap. 25.00 (978-0-268-02594-6(0)) Univ. of Notre Dame Pr.

Ekelund, Robert B., Jr., et al. The Marketplace of Christianity. 2006. (ENG., Illus.). 368p. (gr. 17). 31.95 (978-0-262-05082-1(X)) MIT Pr.

Finucane, Ronald C. Contested Canonizations: The Last Medieval Saints, 1482-1523. 2011. 288p. 64.95 **(978-0-8132-1875-5(6))** Catholic Univ. of America Pr.

Jurgens, Henning P. & Weller, Thomas, eds. Religion und Mobilität: Zum Verhältnis von raumbezogener Mobilität und religiöser Identitätsbildung im frühneuzeitlichen Europa. 2010. (Veröffentlichungen des Instituts fur Europaische Geschichte Mainz - Beihefte Abendländische Religionsgeschichte Ser.). (GER., Illus.). 425p. (C). 90.00 (978-3-525-10094-3(9)) Vandenhoeck & Ruprecht GmbH & Co. KG DEU. Dist: ISD.

Lupieri, Edmondo, et al. In the Name of God: Christian Identities Outside Europe. 2011. pap. 16.00 **(978-0-8028-4017-2(5))** Eerdmans, William B. Publishing Co.

Morris, Jeremy. The Church in the Modern Age. annot. ed. 2007. (I. B. Tauris History of the Christian Church Ser.). (ENG.). 256p. 47.00 (978-1-84511-317-9(9)) I. B. Tauris & Co., Ltd. GBR. Dist: Macmillan.

Norwood, Frederick A. The Development of Modern Christianity Since 1500. 2011. 258p. 47.95 **(978-1-258-08185-0(7))** Literary Licensing, LLC.

Numbers, Ronald L. Science & Christianity in Pulpit & Pew. 2007. (ENG., Illus.). 224p. per. 24.99 (978-0-19-532038-1(7)) Oxford Univ. Pr., Inc.

O'Connor, Elizabeth. Servant Leaders, Servant Structures. Devers, Dorothy, ed. (Illus.). 96p. (Orig.). pap. 9.95 (978-1-929717-01-0(2)) Potter's Hse. Bookservice.

Porterfield, Amanda & Ruether, David. Modern Christianity to 1900. 2010. 320p (C). pap. 24.00 (978-0-8006-9724-2(3), Fortress Pr.) Augsburg Fortress, Pubs.

Rogers, Francis M. The Quest for Eastern Christians: Travels & Rumor in the Age of Discovery. 2009. (ENG.). 240p. pap. 50.00 (978-0-8166-5861-9(7)) Univ. of Minnesota Pr.

Safley, Thomas Max. A Companion to Multiconfessionalism in the Early Modern World. 2011. (Illus.). XII, 500p. **(978-90-04-20697-7(3))** BRILL.

Schreiner, Susan. Are You Alone Wise? The Search for Certainty in the Early Modern Era. 2010. (Oxford Studies in Historical Theology Ser.). (ENG.). 352p. 74.00 (978-0-19-531342-0(9)) Oxford Univ. Pr., Inc.

Trueman, Carl R. Reformation: Yesterday, Today & Tomorrow. 100p. 8.99 (978-1-85049-175-0(5)) Bryntirion Pr. GBR. Dist: Spring Arbor Distributors, Inc.

CHURCH HISTORY—18TH CENTURY

see also Evangelical Revival

Callahan, William J. & Higgs, David. Church & Society in Catholic Europe of the Eighteenth Century. 2008. (ENG.). 180p. pap. 31.99 (978-0-521-09077-3(6)) Cambridge Univ. Pr.

Cordes, Harm. Hilaria Evangelica Academica: Das Reformationsjubiläum Von 1717 an Den Deutschen Lutherischen Universitäten. 2006. (Forschungen Zur Kirchen- und Dogmengeschichte Ser.). (GER.). 361p. (C). 78.00 (978-3-525-55198-1(3)) Vandenhoeck & Ruprecht GmbH & Co. KG DEU. Dist: ISD.

Duncan, Kathryn. Religion in the Age of Reason: A Transatlantic Study of the Long Eighteenth Century. 2006. (AMS Studies in the Eighteenth Century: No. 53). (978-0-404-64853-4(3)) AMS Pr., Inc.

Hagenbach, K. R. (Karl Rudolf). German Rationalism, in Its Rise, Progress, & Decline, in Relation to Theologians, Scholars, Poets, Philosophers, & the People: A Contribution to T. 2006. 436p. per. 26.99 (978-1-4255-4744-8(3)) MPublishing.

James, Nancy Carol. The Conflict over the Heresy of Pure Love in Seventeenth-Century France: The Tumult over the Mysticism of Madame Guyon. 2008. 224p. 109.95 (978-0-7734-5009-7(2)) Mellen, Edwin Pr., The.

Shaw, Ian. Church & Empire: 1789-1914. 2007. (Baker History of the Church Ser.). 400p. 29.99 (978-0-8010-1279-2(1)) Baker Bks.

Smith, Leonard S. Religion & the Rise of History: Martin Luther & the Cultural Revolution in Germany, 1760-1810. 2009. 306p. pap. 33.00 (978-1-55635-830-2(X), Cascade Bks.) Wipf & Stock Pubs.

CHURCH HISTORY—19TH CENTURY

Baird, Robert. The Christian Retrospect & Register. 2009. 300p. pap. 21.42 (978-1-4588-6822-0(2)) General Bks. LLC.

—The Christian Retrospect & Register. 2006. 448p. per. 26.99 (978-1-4255-4940-4(3)) MPublishing.

Beecher, Henry, abr. New Star Papers. 2009. (Amer Philosophy, Religion Ser.). (ENG.). 412p. pap. 25.95 (978-1-4290-1982-8(4)) Applewood Bks.

Beecher, Henry Ward. Star Papers. 2009. (Amer Philosophy, Religion Ser.). (ENG.). 364p. pap. 22.95 (978-1-4290-1904-0(2)) Applewood Bks.

Blanco, John D. Frontier Constitutions: Christianity & Colonial Empire in the Nineteenth-Century Philippines. 2009. (Asia Pacific Modern Ser.). (ENG., Illus.). 390p. 49.95 (978-0-520-25519-7(4)) Univ. of California Pr.

Brunton, Lauder. Truth & Delusion. 2006. pap. 15.95 (978-1-4286-3914-0(4)) Kessinger Publishing, LLC.

Burroughs, P. E. The Spiritual Conquest of the Second Frontier. 2007. (ENG.). 246p. 41.95 (978-0-548-07147-2(0)) Kessinger Publishing, LLC.

Drummond, Henry. The New Evangelism & Other Papers. 2007. (ENG.). 216p. 39.95 (978-0-548-17583-5(7)); 220p. per. 24.95 (978-1-4304-7512-5(9)) Kessinger Publishing, LLC.

—The New Evangelism & Other Papers. 2008. 92p. per. 14.99 (978-1-60459-183-5(8)) Wilder Pubns., Ltd.

Drummond, Henry. The Program of Christianity. 2011. 40p. pap. 7.99 **(978-1-61203-222-1(2))** Bottom of the Hill Publishing.

—The Program of Christianity. 2008. 48p. per. 7.99 (978-1-60459-174-3(9)) Wilder Pubns., Ltd.

Edward Caldwell Moore. An Outline of the History of Christian Thought since Kant. l.t. ed. 2007. 262p. pap. 23.99 (978-1-4264-8971-6(4)) BiblioBazaar.

Hagenbach, K. R. (Karl Rudolf). German Rationalism, in Its Rise, Progress, & Decline, in Relation to Theologians, Scholars, Poets, Philosophers, & the People: A Contribution to T. 2006. 436p. per. 26.99 (978-1-4255-4744-8(3)) MPublishing.

Kildani, Hanna Said. Modern Christianity in the Holy Land: Development of the Structure of Churches & the Growth Of...: Translated by George Musleh. 2010. xviii, 719p. (978-1-4490-5286-7(X)) AuthorHouse.

Kildani, Rev. Hanna. Modern Christianity in the Holy Land: Development of the Structure of Churches & the Growth of Christian Institutions in Jordan & Palestine. 2010. 740p. (ENG.). 46.99 (978-1-4490-5285-0(1)); pap. 33.49 (978-1-4490-5284-3(3)) AuthorHouse.

Larsen, Timothy. Friends of Religious Equality: Nonconformist Politics in Mid-Victorian England. 2008. (Studies in Christian History & Thought Ser.). 320p. pap. 38.00 (978-1-55635-663-6(3)) Wipf & Stock Pubs.

Macleod, Norman. Parish Papers. 2006. 340p. per. 23.99 (978-1-4255-3414-1(7)) MPublishing.

Macloed, Norman. Parish Papers. 2007. 222p. pap. 20.99 (978-1-4264-6193-4(3)) 2006. (ENG.). 248p. pap. 22.99 (978-1-4264-6248-1(4)) BiblioBazaar.

Moore, Edward Caldwel. Outline of the History of Christian Thou. 2006. pap. 27.95 (978-1-4286-4186-0(6)) Kessinger Publishing, LLC.

Pierson, Arthur T. Forward Movements of the Last Half Century. 2009. (ENG.). 431p. 41.99 (978-1-117-27721-9(6)); 432p. pap. 34.75 (978-1-117-27722-6(4)); (ENG.). 431p. pap. 26.99 (978-1-117-27723-3(2), BiblioLife) BiblioBazaar.

Shaw, Ian. Church & Empire: 1789-1914. 2007. (Baker History of the Church Ser.). 400p. 29.99 (978-0-8010-1279-2(1)) Baker Bks.

Snell, K.D.M. Church & Chapel. 96p. pap. (978-0-7185-2038-0(6), Burns & Oates) Continuum International Publishing Group, Ltd.

CHURCH HISTORY—20TH CENTURY

Bradley, Mark. Iran & Christianity: Historical Identity & Present Relevance. 2011. (ENG., Illus.). 210p. pap. 44.95 **(978-1-4411-1167-8(0))** Continuum International Publishing Group, Ltd. GBR. Dist: National Bk. Network.

Burroughs, P. E. The Spiritual Conquest of the Second Frontier. 2007. (ENG.). 246p. 41.95 (978-0-548-07147-2(0)) Kessinger Publishing, LLC.

Chiniquy, Charles. Forty Years in the Church of Christ. 2008. 504p. 32.99 (978-0-559-72353-7(9)); pap. 38.75 (978-0-559-72350-6(4)) BiblioBazaar.

Church & Ideology: 1914-1945. 2007. (Baker History of the Church Ser.). 400p. 29.99 (978-0-8010-1280-8(5)) Baker Bks.

Dosendrode, S. & Dosenrode-Lynge, Sören Zibrandt von. Christianity & Resistance in the 20th Century: From Kaj Munk & Dietrich Bonhoeffer to Desmond Tutu. 2008. (International Studies in Religion & Society). 265p. (C). (978-90-04-17126-8(6)) BRILL.

Gellman, Erik S. & Roll, Jarod. The Gospel of the Working Class: Labor's Southern Prophets in New Deal America. 2011. (Working Class in American History Ser.). (Illus.). 232p. pap. 30.00 **(978-0-252-07840-8(3))** Univ. of Illinois Pr.

Grams, Rocky. In Awe in Argentina. 2006. (ENG.). 256p. pap. 13.99 (978-1-59979-022-0(X), Creation Hse.) Charisma Media.

Hawkins, Billy. Abnormality in the Church. Date not set. 100p. pap. (978-0-9702305-0-8(8)) Sadiki Publishing.

Hedda, Jennifer. His Kingdom Come: Orthodox Pastorship & Social Activism in Revolutionary Russia. 2007. 307p. 43.00 (978-0-87580-382-1(2)) Northern Illinois Univ. Pr.

Heineke, H. A. All Preachers Are Hypocrites. 2010. 200p. pap. 14.95 (978-1-58850-151-6(5)) Veloce Enterprises, Inc.

Koschorke, Klaus, ed. Falling Walls: The Year 1989/90 as a Turning Point in the History of World Christianity / Einsturzende Mauern: das Jahr 1989/90 als Epochenjahr in der Geschichte des Weltchristentums. 2009. (Studien zur Aussereuropaischen Christentumsgeschichte (Asien Ser.). (ENG & GER.). 451p. (C). pap. 81.00 (978-3-447-05995-4(8)) Harrassowitz, Otto Verlag DEU. Dist: ISD.

Lannoye, Most Rev. Leland J. Ante Annum MCMLXIII, 1 vol. 2010. 48p. pap. 16.95 (978-1-4489-5853-5(9)) PublishAmerica, Inc.

Leimdorfer, Karen. Cultural Imperialism or Cultural Encounters. 2008. 212p. pap. (978-3-8364-3667-0(1)) VDM Verlag Dr. Mueller e.K.

McLeod, Hugh. The Religious Crisis of The 1960s. (ENG.). 2010. 304p. pap. 39.95 (978-0-19-958202-0(5)) 2008. 288p. 110.00 (978-0-19-929825-9(4)) Oxford Univ. Pr., Inc.

Mondragon, Carlos. Like Leaven Dough: Protestant Social Thought in Latin America, 1920-1950. 2010. (ENG.). 186p. 60.00 (978-1-61147-056-7(0)) Fairleigh Dickinson Univ. Pr.

Muncy, Eloise & Williams, John. Making History: Ray Muncy in His Time. 357p. 18.00 (978-0-9714289-5-9(6), Leafwood Pubs.) Abilene Christian Univ. Pr.

Murray, Stuart. Church after Christendom. 2006. (After Christendom Ser.). (ENG.). 192p. per. 19.99 (978-1-84227-292-3(6)) Authentic Media.

Rebuilding the Tower of Babel: The Dark side of Rick Warren's Purpose Driven Church. 2007. pap. (978-0-9768167-1-3(7)) Cutting Edge Ministries.

Sanneh, Lamin. Disciples of All Nations: Pillars of World Christianity. 2007. (Oxford Studies in World Christianity Ser.). (ENG., Illus.). 368p. per. 19.95 (978-0-19-518961-2(2)) Oxford Univ. Pr., Inc.

Shaw, Ian. Church & Empire: 1789-1914. 2007. (Baker History of the Church Ser.). 400p. 29.99 (978-0-8010-1279-2(1)) Baker Bks.

Smith, Kevin John. The Origins, Nature, & Significance of the Jesus Movement as a Revitalization Movement. 2011. 512p. pap. 48.00 **(978-1-60947-019-7(2))** Emeth Pr.

Soskice, Janet Martin. The Sisters of Sinai: How Two Lady Adventurers Discovered the Hidden Gospels. 2010. (Vintage Ser.). (ENG., Illus.). 336p. pap. 16.95 (978-1-4000-3474-1(4), Vintage) Knopf Doubleday Publishing Group.

White, James F. Christian Worship in North America: A Retrospective, 1955-1995. 2007. (Illus.). 328p. pap. 36.00 (978-1-55635-651-3(X)) Wipf & Stock Pubs.

A World Church: 1945-2005. 2008. (Baker History of the Church Ser.). 400p. 29.99 (978-0-8010-1281-5(3)) Baker Bks.

CHURCH HISTORY—21ST CENTURY

Adeney, Miriam. Kingdom Without Borders: The Untold Story of Global Christianity, 1 vol. 2009. (ENG.). 295p. pap. 18.00 (978-0-8308-3849-3(X), IVP Bks.) InterVarsity Pr.

Butler Tom & Butler, Tom. Religion & Public Life: Tom Butler's Thoughts for the Day. 2012. (ENG.). 216p. pap. 22.95 (978-1-4411-0177-8(2)) Continuum International Publishing Group, Ltd. GBR. Dist: National Bk. Network.

Clay, Jr. Creative Thinking for the 21st Century. 2011. 160p. pap. 24.95 **(978-1-4626-0638-2(5))** PublishAmerica, Inc.

Coleson, Joseph, ed. The Church Jesus Builds: A Dialogue on the Church in the 21st Century. 2006. (Wesleyan Theological Perspectives Ser.). 205p. per. 14.99 (978-0-89827-349-6(8)) Wesleyan Publishing Hse.

Francis, Leslie J., et al. Gone for Good? Church-Leaving & Returning in the Twenty-First Century. 2008. (Illus.). 360p. pap. (978-0-7162-0633-0(1)) Epworth Pr., The.

Lee, Connita. A Voice to Be Heard: Reaching Youth & Keeping Them Reached in the 21st Century. 2009. 160p. pap. 17.99 (978-1-4389-7925-0(8)) AuthorHouse.

MacDonald, Gordon. Who Stole My Church: What to Do When the Church You Love Tries to Enter the 21st Century, 0 vols. 2010. 272p. pap. 15.99 (978-0-7852-3049-6(1)) Nelson, Thomas Inc.

Meylahn, Johann-Albrecht. The Church in the Postmodern Global Village. 2010. 256p. pap. (978-3-8383-3894-1(4)) Lambert Academic Publishing.

Murphy, Francesca Aran & Asprey, Chris. Ecumenism Today: The Universal Church in the 21St Century. 2008. 238p. 99.95 (978-0-7546-5961-7(5)) Ashgate Publishing Co.

Murray, Stuart. Church after Christendom. 2006. (After Christendom Ser.). (ENG.). 192p. per. 19.99 (978-1-84227-292-3(6)) Authentic Media.

Partee, Milton. Discipleship Dynamics. 2009. 88p. pap. 14.95 (978-1-4489-2579-7(7)) PublishAmerica, Inc.

Pfeifer, Mark. Alignment: A Blueprint for the 21st Century Church. 2008. 382p. pap. 15.00 (978-0-9788765-1-7(2)) Soma.

Sanneh, Lamin. Disciples of All Nations: Pillars of World Christianity. 2007. (Oxford Studies in World Christianity Ser.). (ENG., Illus.). 368p. per. 19.95 (978-0-19-518961-2(2)) Oxford Univ. Pr., Inc.

Smith, Hamilton. Short Papers on the Church. 2008. 96p. per. (978-0-901860-80-4(8)) Scripture Truth Pubns.

Wilson, Douglas. Heaven Misplaced: Christ's Kingdom on Earth. 2008. (ENG.). 19.00 (978-1-59128-051-4(6)) Canon Pr.

Woolverton, Gary H. Church Ministry by Design: Designing Effective Ministry for Tomorrow's Church. 2011. pap. 29.99 **(978-1-61777-413-3(8))** Tate Publishing & Enterprises, LLC.

A World Church: 1945-2005. 2008. (Baker History of the Church Ser.). 400p. 29.99 (978-0-8010-1281-5(3)) Baker Bks.

CHURCH LANDS

Cambi Schmitter, Luciana. Carte Della Badia Di Marturi: Nell'Archivio Di Stato Di Firenze (971-1199) 2009. (LAT & ITA.). 396p. (978-88-596-0522-5(9)) Polistampa.

Giaimo, Michael S. & Lucero, Lora A. The RLUIPA Reader: Religious Land Uses, Zoning, & the Courts. 2009. (ENG.). 250p. pap. 79.95 (978-1-60442-358-7(7)) American Bar Assn.

Górecki, Piotr. A Local Society in Transition: The Henryków Book & Related Documents. 2007. (Studies & Texts). (ENG.). 296p. 74.95 (978-0-88844-155-3(X)) Pontifical Institute of Mediaeval Studies, Dept. of Pubns. CAN. Dist: Univ. of Toronto Pr.

Hey, David, et al. A Monastic Community in Local Society: The Beauchief Abbey Cartulary. 2012. (Camden Fifth Ser.). (Illus.). viii, 304p. 80.00 **(978-1-107-01646-0(0))** Cambridge Univ. Pr.

Lyons, Barry J. Remembering the Hacienda: Religion, Authority, & Social Change in Highland Ecuador. 2006. (Joe R. & Teresa Lozano Long Series in Latin American & Latin Art & Culture). (ENG., Illus.). 362p. mass mkt. 24.95 (978-0-292-71439-7(4)) Univ. of Texas Pr.

MacKenzie, Geoffrey Shisumu & Njonje, Billy. Church & Land. 2011. 104p. pap. **(978-3-8443-8978-4(4))** Lambert Academic Publishing.

Stacy, N. E., ed. Charters & Custumals of Shaftesbury Abbey, 1089-1216. 2006. (Records of Social & Economic History, New Ser.). (Illus.). 266p. 140.00 (978-0-19-726375-4(5)) Oxford Univ. Pr., Inc.

CHURCH LATIN

see Latin Language—Church Latin

CHURCH LAW

see Ecclesiastical Law

CHURCH LEADERSHIP

see Christian Leadership

CHURCH LIBRARIES

Bednarczyk, Jan. Ewangelizacyjna Rola Bibliotek Parafialnych W Archidiecezji Krakowskiej. 2007. (POL., Illus.). 565p. (978-83-7438-146-8(9)) Papieska Akademia Teologiczna, Wydawnictwo Naukowe.

Deitrick, Bernard E. A Basic Book List for Church Libraries. 6th rev. ed. pap. (978-0-915324-46-0(6)) Church & Synagogue Library Assn., Inc.

CHURCH MAINTENANCE AND REPAIR

Grumeza, Ion. This Old Church: The Indispensable Guide for Restoring Church Buildings. 2010. 144p. pap. 18.00 (978-1-60899-180-8(6), Resource Pubns.) Wipf & Stock Pubs.

Hitchman, Valerie. Omnia Bene or Ruinosa? 2009. 320p. pap. (978-3-639-17813-5(0)) VDM Verlag Dr. Mueller e.K.

CHURCH MANAGEMENT

see also Advertising—Churches; Church Controversies; Church Finance; Parish Councils

Abade, Samuel. Re-Orienting Leadership in Afric. 2011. 68p. pap. **(978-3-8443-2081-7(4))** Lambert Academic Publishing.

Abingdon. Middle Elementary. (Illus.). 6.75 (978-0-687-05646-0(2)) Abingdon Pr.

—Older Elementary. (Illus.). 6.75 (978-0-687-05647-7(0)) Abingdon Pr.

Abingdon Gde Funding Ministry: Macintosh Software, Vol. 4. 24.95 (978-0-687-05736-8(1)) Abingdon Pr.

Abingdon Gde to Funding Ministry: Windows Software, Vol. 4. 24.95 (978-0-687-05806-8(6)) Abingdon Pr.

Adams, Jay Edward. Preaching That Persuades. 2007. (Ministry Monographs for Modern Times Ser.). 60p. per. 11.55 (978-1-889032-55-9(7)) Timeless Texts, Inc.

Aguilar, Ron. Keeping Your Church Safe: No Subtitle. 2008. 148p. pap. 13.99 (978-1-60647-332-0(8)) Xulon Pr., Inc.

Anderson, Charlie. Where Have All the Men Gone. 2011. 92p. pap. 15.99 **(978-1-4568-4019-8(3))** Xlibris Corp.

Anderson, Ray S. Minding GodÕs Business. 2008. (Ray S. Anderson Collection Ser.). 164p. pap. 19.00 (978-1-60608-219-5(1), Wipf and Stock) Wipf & Stock Pubs.

Annual Report of Trustees. 6.00 (978-0-687-09694-7(4)); 0.25 (978-0-687-25197-1(4)) Abingdon Pr.

Annual Report of Trustees 2001-2004. 1.25 (978-0-687-09768-5(1)) Abingdon Pr.

Arbuckle, Gerald. Grieving for Change. (Illus.). 160p. pap. (978-0-225-66638-0(3), Burns & Oates) Continuum International Publishing Group, Ltd.

Arch-Bishop D.A. Miller D.D. Are You Ready to Be a Deacon in the Church. 2011. 96p. pap. 19.95 **(978-1-4626-2910-7(5))** PublishAmerica, Inc.

Arment, Ben. Church in the Making: What Makes or Breaks a New Church Before It Starts. 2010. (ENG.). 208p. 17.99 (978-0-8054-6473-3(5), B&H Bks.) B&H Publishing Group.

Bacher, Robert & Cooper-White, Michael. Church Administration: Programs/Process/Purpose. 2007. (Illus.). 352p. 26.00 (978-0-8006-3742-2(9), Fortress Pr.) Augsburg Fortress, Pubs.

Baker, Chris. The Hybrid Church in the City: Third Space Thinking. 2007. 174p. 99.95 (978-0-7546-5513-8(X)) Ashgate Publishing Co.

Bangs, John C. The Mother Church: A Church Leader's Guide to Birthing & Nurturing Thriving New Congregations. 2010. 192p. (ENG.). 26.95 (978-1-4502-2099-6(1)); pap. 16.95 (978-1-4502-2100-9(9)) iUniverse, Inc.

Barnett, Barry W. The Cure for the Dysfunctional Church: Becoming What We Were Created to Be. 2009. pap. 14.99 (978-1-60799-333-9(3)) Tate Publishing & Enterprises, LLC.

Beck, James P., Jr. & Silverberg, Neil. Not Many Fathers. 2007. (ENG.). per. 12.99 (978-1-60037-222-3(8)) Morgan James Publishing.

Berkley, James D., ed. Leadership Handbook of Management & Administration. rev. ed. 2008. 560p. pap. 24.99 (978-0-8010-6814-0(2)) Baker Bks.

Bernier, Ronald L. Principles & Practice of Pastoral Ministry. 2009. 412p. pap. 24.00 (978-1-61529-000-0(1)) Vision Publishing.

Bixby, Douglas J. Challenging the Church Monster: From Conflict to Community. 2007. 126p. pap. 16.00 (978-1-55635-628-5(5), Wipf and Stock) Wipf & Stock Pubs.

—The Honest to God Church: A Pathway to God's Grace. 2007. (978-1-56699-344-9(X)) Alban Institute, Inc.

Boardman, Henry Augustus. 2 Discourses on the Common Objections to the Doctrin of Election. 2009. 89p. pap. 9.99 (978-1-879737-64-8(7)) Calvary Pr.

Brennan, Patrick J. The Mission Driven Parish. 2007. (Illus.). 159p. per. 20.00 (978-1-57075-692-4(9)) Orbis Bks.

Busby, Dan. Tax & Financial Guide 2010, 1 vol. 2010. (ENG.). 224p. pap. 15.99 (978-0-310-32783-7(0)) Zondervan.

Byassee, Jason. The Gifts of the Small Church. 2010. 114p. pap. 15.00 (978-0-687-46659-7(8)) Abingdon Pr.

Calheiros, Izes. Dressed for Ministry: No Subtitle. 2008. 180p. pap. 13.99 (978-1-60647-553-9(3)) Xulon Pr., Inc.

Callahan, Kennon L. The Twelve Keys: An Approach for Grassroots, Key Leaders, & Pastors Together. 2nd ldr.'s ed. 2010. (ENG., Illus.). 224p. 22.95 (978-0-470-55928-4(4), Jossey-Bass) Wiley, John & Sons, Inc.

—The Twelve Keys Bible Study. 2010. (ENG., Illus.). 96p. pap. 12.95 (978-0-470-55916-1(0), Jossey-Bass) Wiley, John & Sons, Inc.

Campbell, Bill. The Magnificent Church. 2006. pap. 14.99 (978-1-60034-713-9(4)) Xulon Pr., Inc.

Caro, Stephanie. 99 Thoughts for Smaller Church Youth Workers: Doing More with Less. 2011. pap. (978-0-7644-6606-9(2)) Group Publishing, Inc.

Carroll, David & Franks, Tony. From Your Heart to Theirs: Delivering an Effective Sermon. 2008. 26p. pap. 6.00 (978-0-88177-536-5(3)) Discipleship Resources.

—From Your Heart to Theirs Instructor's Guide: Delivering an Effective Sermon. 2008. 36p. pap. 8.00 (978-0-88177-535-8(5)) Discipleship Resources.

Carroll, Jackson W., et al, eds. Handbook for Congregational Studies. 192p. (Orig.). 21.00 (978-0-687-16562-9(8)) Abingdon Pr.

Carson, Dana. The Doors of the Church Are Closed. 2008. 164p. pap. 13.99 (978-1-60477-947-9(0)) Xulon Pr., Inc.

Catt, Steven R. When Do I Cry Wolf? 2009. 120p. pap. 11.99 (978-1-60791-194-4(9)) Xulon Pr., Inc.

Chevreau, Guy. Vital Signs of a Healthy Church: A Diagnostic. 2007. 127p. pap. (978-1-905991-01-3(0)) New Wine Pr.

Christie, Les. Awaken Your Creativity: Hearing Yes in the Midst of a Multitude of No's, 1 vol. 2009. (ENG.). 160p. pap. 12.99 (978-0-310-28778-0(2)) Zondervan.

Chromey, Rick. Energizing Children's Ministry in the Smaller Church. 2008. (Escn Ser.). (ENG.). 176p. (J). pap. 17.99 (978-0-7847-2192-6(0)) Standard Publishing.

Chromey, Rick & Caro, Stephanie. Thriving Youth Ministry in Smaller Churches: Secrets for Cultivating a Dynamic Youth Ministry. 2009. pap. (978-0-7644-4051-9(9)) Group Publishing, Inc.

Church in a Field of Flowers. 5.00 (978-0-687-08080-9(0)) Abingdon Pr.

Church Programs for All Seasons. 3.95 (978-0-687-08270-4(6)) Abingdon Pr.

Clark, M. Douglas. Risk Control for Churches. (Illus.). ring bd. 39.50 (978-0-88061-007-0(7)) International Loss Control Institute, Inc.

Comiskey, Joel. Plantando Iglesias Que Se Reproducen. 2010. 208p. pap. 14.95 (978-0-9843110-5-7(X), CCS Publishing) CCS Pubs.

—Planting Churches that Reproduce: Starting a Network of Simple Churches. 2008. (ENG.). 205p. pap. 15.95 (978-0-9790679-6-9(0), CCS Publishing) CCS Pubs.

Conner, Mark. 7 Strategic Changes Every Church Must Make. 2006. 192p. 15.99 (978-1-59383-051-9(3)) City Christian Publishing.

Cooke, Graham & Goodell, Gary. Permission Is Granted to Do Church Differently in the 21st Century. 2006. pap. 14.99 (978-0-7684-2380-8(5)) Destiny Image Pubs.

Crandall, Ronald K. Turnaround & Beyond: A Hopeful Future for the Small Membership Church. 2008. 180p. pap. 20.00 (978-0-687-64699-9(5)) Abingdon Pr.

Crossley, Gareth. Growing Leaders in the Church: A Leadership Development Resource. 2007. (Illus.). 302p. per. (978-0-85234-553-5(4)) Evangelical Pr.

Curtin, Ralph D. Sharing Your Church Building. 2006. 186p. pap. 22.00 (978-1-59752-916-7(8), Wipf and Stock) Wipf & Stock Pubs.

Dale, Tony, et al. The Rabbit & the Elephant: Why Small Is the New Big for Today's Church. 2009. (ENG.). 256p. 17.99 (978-1-4143-2553-8(3), BarnaBks.) Tyndale Hse. Pubs.

Daman, Glenn & Daman, Glenn C. Developing Leaders for the Small Church: A Guide for Spiritual Transformation for the Church Board, 1 vol. 2009. 304p. pap. 19.99 (978-0-8254-2455-7(0)) Kregel Pubns.

Destinations: Mapping Your Congregation's Journey. 2007. 9.95 (978-0-9795847-0-1(1)) Cooperative Baptist Fellowship.

Dick, Dan R. & Dick, Barbara A. Equipped for Every Good Work: Building a Gifts-Based Church. 2011. 166p. pap. 19.00 **(978-1-61097-240-6(6)**, Wipf and Stock) Wipf & Stock Pubs.

Dillon, Lou. Center Stage for Churches. 2006. 16.00 (978-0-8059-9199-4(9)) Dorrance Publishing Co., Inc.

Dixon, Ameka K. Fed up with Church Mess. 2008. 64p. pap. 16.95 (978-1-60474-927-4(X)) PublishAmerica, Inc.

Dock, Albert W. Keeping Members in the Church. 2008. 112p. pap. 10.99 (978-1-60647-042-8(6)) Xulon Pr., Inc.

Donnellan, M. L. & Naumann, M. Div. The Complete Guide to Church Management. 266p. 2015. 33.99 **(978-1-61379-756-3(7))** 2011. pap. 18.99 **(978-1-61379-755-6(9))** Xulon Pr., Inc.

Dowdy, Naomi. Commissioning: The Process, Protocol, & Importance of Commissioning Modern-Day Apostles. 2006. pap. 10.00 (978-1-934201-03-9(0)); (SPA.). pap. 10.00 (978-1-934201-04-6(9)) Dowdy, Naomi Pubns.

Drayton, Evelyn Murray. Watermelon Faith. 2008. 128p. pap. 14.99 *(978-1-60791-029-9(2))* Xulon Pr., Inc.
Drummond, Sarah B. Holy Clarity: The Practice of Planning & Evaluation. 2009. *(978-1-56699-387-6(3))* Alban Institute, Inc.
Duffy, Eugene, ed. Parishes in Transition. 2011. (ENG., Illus.). 240p. pap. 26.95 *(978-1-85607-706-4(3))* Columba Pr. IRL. Dist: Dufour Editions, Inc.
Duncan, Graham. Partnership in Mission: A Critical Historical Evaluation of the Relationship between 'older' & younger' Churches with Special Reference to the Church of Scotland. 2008. 284p. pap. *(978-3-639-08865-6(4))* VDM Verlag Dr. Mueller e.K.
Edwards, Gene. Problems & Solutions in House Churches. 2007. per. 9.95 *(978-0-9778033-5-4(X))* Seedsowers, The.
—Why So Many House Churches Fail & What to do about It. 2007. per. 7.95 *(978-0-9778033-8-5(4))* Seedsowers, The.
Epperly, Bruce Gordon & Hollinger, Daryl. From a Mustard Seed: Enlivening Worship & Music in the Small Church. 2010. *(978-1-56699-406-4(3))* Alban Institute, Inc.
Erlandson, Greg. En la Cabina de Votacion: Una Guia Catolica. Estenger, Vilma G., tr. 2008. 1p. 14.95 *(978-1-59276-347-4(2))* Our Sunday Visitor, Publishing Div.
Evans, Roderick L. Faith for the Journey (Volume II) Daily Inspiration for Christian Living. 2009. (ENG.). 30p. pap. 9.95 *(978-1-60141-103-7(0)*, 368295) Kingdom Builders Publishing.
—For the Perfecting of the Saints: Exploring the Ministries of the Pastor & of the Teacher. 2006. 122p. pap. 12.95 *(978-1-60141-102-0(2)*, 367426) Kingdom Builders Publishing.
Everett, Isaac. The Emergent Psalter. 2009. 288p. pap. 25.00 *(978-0-89869-617-2(8))* Church Publishing, Inc.
Exley, Richard & Exley, Don. Pastoral Ministry-Student Manual. McGhee, Quentin, ed. 2nd ed. 2011. (Illus.). 204p. stu. ed., spiral bd. 25.00 *(978-1-931984-49-2(2)*, 4431-E0) Faith & Action Team.
Flodquist, Paul. Avoiding a Small Church Mentality. 2010. 34p. pap. 5.00 *(978-1-60899-430-4(9)*, Resource Pubns.) Wipf & Stock Pubs.
Fowler, Larry. Rock Solid Volunteers: Keep Your Ministry Team Engaged. 2012. (ENG.). 176p. pap. 12.99 ***(978-0-8307-6437-2(2))*** Gospel Light Pubns.
Fryar, Jane L. Trust & Teams. (Christian Leadership Ser.). 124p. 9.99 *(978-0-570-06772-6(3))* Concordia Publishing Hse.
Fusco, Daniel. Ahead of the Curve: Preparing the Church for Post-Postmodernism. 2011. pap. 9.99 *(978-1-61739-441-6(6))* Tate Publishing & Enterprises, LLC.
Gangel, Kenneth O. Coaching Ministry Teams: Leadership & Management in Christian Organizations. 2006. 232p. pap. 26.00 *(978-1-59752-657-9(6)*, Wipf and Stock) Wipf & Stock Pubs.
—Surviving Toxic Leaders: How to Work for Flawed People in Churches, Schools, & Christian Organizations. 2007. 106p. pap. 13.00 *(978-1-55635-090-0(2))* Wipf & Stock Pubs.
Graham, Rose. The Church Administrative Assistant's Handbook: A Practical Guide to Maximize the Ministry of the Pastor & Staff. 2007. (ENG.). 176p. ring bd. 69.99 *(978-0-8341-2334-2(7)*, 083-412-3347) Beacon Hill Pr. of Kansas City.
Grapes & Bread. 4.50 *(978-0-687-09822-4(X))* Abingdon Pr.
Grate, Gene. The Church Administration Kit: Resources for Daily Operations. 2008. (ENG.). 160p. pap. 49.99 *(978-0-8341-2386-1(X)*, 9780834123861) Beacon Hill Pr. of Kansas City.
Graves, Stan. Run for Cover! 2007. 128p. per. 19.95 *(978-1-4241-8880-2(6))* PublishAmerica, Inc.
Green, Hollis. Titanic Lessons. 2007. 120p. per. 14.95 *(978-0-9796019-6-5(7))* Global Education Advance.
—Why Churches Die. 2007. (ENG.). 228p. per. 14.95 *(978-0-9796019-0-3(8))* Global Education Advance.
Greenwood, Robin. Ministry Team Handbook. (Illus.). 112p. 12.00 *(978-0-281-05279-0(4))* SPCK Publishing GBR. Dist: Pilgrim Pr., The/United Church Pr.
Grey, Mary. New Day for Preaching. rev. ed. 128p. 15.00 *(978-0-281-04967-7(X))* SPCK Publishing GBR. Dist: Pilgrim Pr., The/United Church Pr.
Griffin, Mark L. Pastor, CEO. 2010. 100p. pap. 10.99 *(978-1-60957-783-4(3))* Xulon Pr., Inc.
Grumeza, Ion. This Old Church: The Indispensable Guide for Restoring Church Buildings. 2010. 144p. pap. 18.00 *(978-1-60899-180-8(6)*, Resource Pubns.) Wipf & Stock Pubs.
Guidelines for Leading Your Church 1997-2000. 25.00 *(978-0-687-06931-6(9))* Abingdon Pr.
Guidelines for Leading Your Congregation 2009-2012 - Adult Ministries: Ministries that Help Adults Love God & Neighbor. 2008. 2.95 *(978-0-687-64682-1(0))* Abingdon Pr.
Guidelines for Leading Your Congregation 2009-2012 - Pastor-Parish Relations: Connecting the Pastor, Staff, & Congregation. 2008. 2.95 *(978-0-687-64781-1(9))* Abingdon Pr.
Guidelines for Leading Your Congregation 2009-2012 - Trustees: Managing the Property, Equipment, & Investments God Has Entrusted to our Ministry. 2008. 2.95 *(978-0-687-64861-8(5))* Abingdon Pr.
Guidelines for Leading Your Congregation 2009-2012 CD-ROM. 2008. 59.00 *(978-0-687-49059-2(6))* Abingdon Pr.
Guidelines Managing Your Churchs Assets. 1.00 *(978-0-687-01937-3(0))* Abingdon Pr.
Guidelines Organizing the Work of the Church. 1.00 *(978-0-687-01936-6(2))* Abingdon Pr.
GuideOne Center for Risk Management Staff, contrib. by. The Missing Ministry: Safety, Risk Management, & Protecting Your Church. 2008. 192p. pap. 17.99 *(978-0-7644-3679-6(1))* Group Publishing, Inc.
Guise, Marty. Seeing from the Summit: The Journey to an Effective Church. 2010. 158p. pap. 18.00 *(978-1-60899-932-3(7)*, Resource Pubns.) Wipf & Stock Pubs.
Gutierrez, Marin. Como Organizar una Iglesia: Administration for the Church. (SPA.). *(978-84-7645-375-9(2)*, 223503) Clie, Editorial.
Harcum, E. Rae. Saving Our Church: Five Systemic Diseases Pose a Vital Mission for the Organized Church. 2009. (ENG.). 150p. pap. 27.99 *(978-0-7618-4698-7(0))* Hamilton Bks.
Hargrave, Cpa. Weeds in the Garden. 2009. 180p. pap. 18.00 *(978-0-9705433-9-4(5))* National Assn. of Church Business Administration/NACBA Pr.
Harney, Kevin. Leadership from the Inside Out: Examining the Inner Life of a Healthy Church Leader, 1 vol. 2007. (Leadership Network Innovation Ser.). (ENG., Illus.). 208p. (gr. 13). pap. 18.99 *(978-0-310-25943-5(6))* Zondervan.
Harrison, Rodney, et al. Spin-off Churches: How One Church Successfully Plants Another. 2008. (ENG.). 336p. (C). pap. 24.99 *(978-0-8054-4685-2(0)*, B&H Academic) B&H Publishing Group.
Hart, Dirk. Charting a Course for Your Church. (Healthy Church Ser.). 2.95 *(978-1-56212-256-0(8)*, 216776) Faith Alive Christian Resources.
—New Designs for Ministry Structure. (Healthy Church Ser.). 2.95 *(978-1-56212-200-3(2)*, 216774) Faith Alive Christian Resources.
Hawkins, Clevester. Scratch Where They Itch: A Model for Enhancing Christian Ministry Participation. 2011. 181p. pap. 14.95 *(978-1-4327-5265-1(0))* Outskirts Pr., Inc.
Hays, Rita B. The Children's Minister. 2008. 127p. per. 13.00 *(978-0-88177-527-3(4))* Discipleship Resources.
Heales, Alfred. The History & Law of Church Seats, or Pews. 2010. 256p. pap. *(978-1-152-94652-1(8))* Books LLC.
Heckman, Garth. Surrender: 14 Event-Driven Student Ministry Outlines. 2009. (On the Altar Ser.). (ENG.). 128p. (YA). pap. 16.99 *(978-0-7847-2242-8(0))* Standard Publishing.
Hendricks, Kathy. Parish Life Coordinators: Profile of an Emerging Ministry. 2009. pap. 11.95 *(978-0-8294-2648-9(5))* Loyola Pr.
Herbster, Carl & Howerton, Kenneth. Pastor & Deacons: Servants Working Together. 2006. 190p. per. 9.99 *(978-1-932307-57-3(5)*, Ambassador-Emerald, International) Emerald Hse. Group, Inc.
Heward-Mills, Dag. Church Administration & Management. 2011. 544p. pap. 34.95 *(978-1-4497-1253-2(3)*, WestBow Pr.) Author Solutions, Inc.
—Church Administration & Management. 2011. 554p. pap. 27.99 *(978-1-61215-749-8(1))* Xulon Pr., Inc.
Hey Preacher, Who Made You God? 2006. pap. 10.99 *(978-1-60034-186-1(1))* Xulon Pr., Inc.
Holley, Jim. When the Vision Is Bigger Than the Budget. 2008. 84p. pap. 17.95 *(978-1-58942-469-2(7))* R.H. Boyd Publishing Corp.
Hotchkiss, Dan. Governance & Ministry: Rethinking Board Leadership. 2009. *(978-1-56699-370-8(9))* Alban Institute, Inc.
Howerton, Rick. Destination: Small-Group Ministry Manual. 2007. pap. 12.99 *(978-1-57494-352-8(9)*, Serendipity Hse.) LifeWay Christian Resources.
Hoyt, William R. Effectiveness by the Numbers: Counting What Counts in the Church. 2007. 124p. pap. 22.00 *(978-0-687-64175-8(6))* Abingdon Pr.
Huston, Larry. The Breath of Life in Spirit - Soul - Body. 2008. 332p. pap. 18.99 *(978-1-60647-847-9(8))* Xulon Pr., Inc.
Interim Change of Appointment Within Conference Ac/Es. 0.25 *(978-0-687-25187-2(7))* Abingdon Pr.
Interim Process. 2.00 *(978-0-687-82351-2(X))* Abingdon Pr.
Iorg, Jeff. The Painful Side of Leadership: Moving Forward Even When It Hurts. 2009. (ENG.). 288p. pap. 14.99 *(978-0-8054-4870-2(5)*, B&H Bks.) B&H Publishing Group.
Iverson, Dick. Guarding the Local Church: Identifying False Ministries. 96p. pap. 11.99 *(978-1-59383-022-9(X))* City Christian Publishing.
Jarema, William J. A Survival Guide for Church Ministers. 2011. (Illus.). 208p. pap. 19.95 *(978-0-8091-4721-2(1))* Paulist Pr.
Jenkins, Woody. The Role of the Pastor in a Dying Congregation. 2011. pap. *(978-1-57312-571-0(7))* Smyth & Helwys Publishing, Inc.
(Jim)Wilcox, J. W. How to Do Church. 2011. 188p. pap. 14.99 *(978-1-61215-495-4(6))* Xulon Pr., Inc.
Jinadu, Philip & Lawrence, David. Winning Ways: How to Create a Culture of Outreach in Your Church. 2007. (ENG., Illus.). 192p. per. 14.99 *(978-1-85078-738-9(7))* Authentic Media.
Johnson, Abigail. Shaping Spiritual Leaders: Supervision & Formation in Congregations. 2007. *(978-1-56699-350-0(4))* Alban Institute, Inc.
Judicial Council Umc, compiled by. Decisions of the Judicial Council 906-1110. 2010. 436p. 39.00 *(978-1-4267-1171-8(9))* Abingdon Pr.
Keller, Matt. The up the Middle Church: ... playing the game of ministry one yard at a Time... 2008. 204p. 24.99 *(978-1-4389-3573-7(0))*; pap. 19.99 *(978-1-4389-3574-4(9))* AuthorHouse.
Kemp, Bill. David's Harp: Returning Harmony to Conflicted Congregations. 2008. (Illus.). 110p. pap. 9.00 *(978-0-88177-530-3(4))* Discipleship Resources.
—Jesus' New Command: Rediscovering the Joy of Fellowship. 2008. 96p. pap. 9.00 *(978-0-88177-532-7(0))* Discipleship Resources.
Kirkland, James. Elders & Deacons & Saints, Oh My! Defining Biblical Roles, Structure & Organization for a Team Ministry that Achieves the Fivefold Purpose of T. 2011. 200p. 33.95 ***(978-1-61507-824-0(X))***; pap. 17.95 ***(978-1-61507-823-3(1))*** Cross Bks. Publishing.
Kujawa-Holbrook, Sheryl A. & Thompsett, Fredrica Harris. Born of Water, Born of Spirit: Supporting the Ministry of the Baptized in Small Congregations. 2010. *(978-1-56699-400-2(4))* Alban Institute, Inc.
Kunjufu, Jawanza. Developing Strong Black Male Ministries. 2006. (ENG., Illus.). 180p. pap. 14.95 *(978-0-9749000-9-4(5))* African American Images.
Langford, Andy, et al. Beginnings - Longing to Belong Participant's Companion: Around the Fire. 2008. (Beginnings Ser.). (Illus.). 184p. per. 10.50 *(978-0-687-65012-5(7))* Abingdon Pr.
Leadership Network Innovation Series Bundle, ZCS. 2008. (Leadership Network Innovation Ser.). pap., pap., pap. 84.95 *(978-0-310-68050-5(6))* Zondervan.
Lee, Witness. The Administration of the Church & the Ministry of the Word. 2007. 195p. per. 9.00 *(978-0-7363-3243-9(X))* Living Stream Ministry.
—Three Aspects of the Church: The Organization of the Church (Book 3) 2007. per. 9.00 *(978-0-7363-3475-4(0))* Living Stream Ministry.
—Three Crucial Matters for the Increase & Building of the Church: Begetting, Nourishing, & Teaching. 2007. per. 10.75 *(978-0-7363-3325-9(6))* Living Stream Ministry.
Little, Steve. Leading God's Way. 2010. 100p. pap. 11.99 *(978-1-61507-083-1(4))* Cross Bks. Publishing.
Locker, Denise. The Volunteer Book: A Guide for Churches & Nonprofits. 2010. (ENG.). 160p. pap. 13.99 *(978-0-8341-2494-3(7)*, 9780834124943) Beacon Hill Pr. of Kansas City.
The Lord Has Done Great Things. 5.00 *(978-0-687-06358-1(2))*; 4.50 *(978-0-687-06338-3(8))* Abingdon Pr.
Louden, G H. Is There a Leadership Crisis in the Church? 2006. (Illus.). 107p. per. 15.95 *(978-1-60002-232-6(4)*, 4213) Mountain Valley Publishing, LLC.
Lupton, Robert D. Toxic Charity: How Churches & Charities Hurt Those They Help (And How to Reverse It) 2011. (ENG.). 208p. 22.99 *(978-0-06-207620-5(5)*, HarperOne) HarperCollins Pubs.
MacDonald, G. Jeffrey. Thieves in the Temple: The Christian Church & the Selling of the American Soul. 2010. (ENG.). 256p. (gr. 9). 25.95 *(978-0-465-00932-9(8))* Basic Bks.
Mack, Michael. I'm a Leader ... Now What? How to Guide an Effective Small Group. 2007. (Small Group Help Guides). (Illus.). 96p. per. 8.99 *(978-0-7847-2076-9(2))* Standard Publishing.
Mackenzie, Geoffrey Shisumu, et al. Church Splits. 2011. 76p. pap. ***(978-3-8443-3337-4(1))*** Lambert Academic Publishing.
Malphurs, Aubrey. Planeamiento Estrategico: Un Nuevo Modelo para la Iglesia y los Lideres, 1 vol. 2006. (SPA., Illus.). 304p. (gr. 11). pap. 9.99 *(978-987-557-114-3(8))* Peniel, Editorial ARG. Dist: Zondervan.
Martinez, Juan. Caminando Entre el Pueblo. 2008. 144p. pap. 18.00 *(978-0-687-49276-3(9))* Abingdon Pr.
May, David. Call to Arms Out of the Pews & into T. 2007. 264p. pap. 11.95 *(978-1-4327-0298-4(X))* Outskirts Pr., Inc.
McBride, Deacon Calvin S. Frank Avant vs. C H Mason: Mason & the Holy Ghost on Trial. 2009. 288p. pap. 20.95 *(978-1-4401-4310-6(2))* iUniverse, Inc.
McFadden, Linda & Wiehe, Philip. More Dumb Things Churches Do & New Strategies for Avoiding Them. 2009. 160p. pap. 16.00 *(978-0-8192-2258-9(5)*, Morehouse Publishing) Church Publishing, Inc.
McGhee, Quentin. Pastoral Ministry-Teachers Guide. Moeckl, Trudy, ed. 2011. pap., tchr. ed. 10.00 *(978-1-931984-48-5(4)*, 4431-31E1) Faith & Action Team.
McGlone, Lee. The Minister's Manual. 2009th ed. 2008. (Minister's Manual Ser.: 10). (ENG.). 432p. pap. 19.95 *(978-0-470-22942-2(X)*, Jossey-Bass) Wiley, John & Sons, Inc.
McIntosh, Gary L. One Size Doesn't Fit All: Bringing Out the Best in Any Size Church. 2007. (Illus.). 176p. (gr. 13-18). reprint ed. pap. 16.99 *(978-0-8007-5699-4(1))* Revell.
Mellado, Jim. How to Change Your Church (Without Killing It), 0 vols. 2008. 384p. pap. 21.99 *(978-0-7852-9691-1(3))* Nelson, Thomas Inc.
Michell, Neal O. Beyond Business as Usual: Vestry Leadership Development. 2007. 144p. per. 15.00 *(978-0-89869-569-4(4))* Church Publishing, Inc.
Miller, Bruce B. Your Church in Rhythm: The Forgotten Dimensions of Seasons & Cycles. 2011. (Jossey-Bass Leadership Network Ser.: 52). (ENG., Illus.). 224p. 24.95 *(978-0-470-59887-0(5)*, Jossey-Bass) Wiley, John & Sons, Inc.
Miller, Craig Kennet. 7 Myths of the United Methodist Church. 2008. (Illus.). 188p. pap. 14.00 *(978-0-88177-529-7(0))* Discipleship Resources.
Miller, James F. Go Build a Church! Spiritual Administration for Growth. 2007. (Illus.). 221p. per. 14.99 *(978-1-57921-881-2(4))* WinePress Publishing.
Miller, Wayne A. The Growing of Christianity: A Different Perspective. 2008. 153p. pap. 24.95 *(978-1-60610-403-3(9))* PublishAmerica, Inc.
Morgan, Tony & Broadman and Holman Publishers Staff. Killing Cockroaches: And Other Scattered Musings on Leadership, 1 vol. 2009. (ENG., Illus.). 256p. pap. 16.99 *(978-0-8054-4785-9(7)*, B&H Bks.) B&H Publishing Group.
Morisy, Ann. Bothered & Bewildered: Enacting Hope in Troubled Times. 2009. (ENG., Illus.). 144p. 29.95 *(978-1-84706-480-6(9))* Continuum International Publishing Group, Ltd. GBR. Dist: National Bk. Network.
Morton, Scott & Navigators Staff. Raising Personal Support: A Step-by-Step Guide to Fulfilling Your Personal Calling. 2007. (Hollywood Nobody Ser.). (ENG.). 96p. spiral bd. 14.99 *(978-1-60006-343-5(8))* NavPress Publishing Group.
Murray, Stuart. Planting Churches in the 21st Century: A Guide for Those Who Want Fresh Perspectives & New Ideas for Creating Congregations: A Framework for Practitioners. 2010. (ENG.). 280p. pap. 19.99 *(978-0-8361-9424-1(1))* Herald Pr.
Mushishi, Clifford. Church Administration: A Devotional & Motivational Guide. 2010. 242p. pap. 27.00 *(978-1-60899-281-2(0)*, Resource Pubns.) Wipf & Stock Pubs.
Neil M. Phelan, Jr. The Support of God's Ministry: Ordained of God. 2009. 204p. pap. 17.49 *(978-1-4389-3251-4(0))* AuthorHouse.
Nelson, Alan E. Me to We: A Pastor's Discovery of the Power of Partnership. 2007. (Illus.). 207p. per. 19.99 *(978-0-7644-3486-0(1))* Group Publishing, Inc.
Nichols, Bishop Robert. This Business: The Office of the Deacon. 2010. 108p. (ENG.). 21.49 *(978-1-4520-1700-6(X))*; pap. 14.99 *(978-1-4520-1699-3(2))* AuthorHouse.
O'Brien, Brandon J. The Strategically Small Church: Intimate, Nimble, Authentic, & Effective, 1 vol. 2010. (ENG.). 160p. pap. 15.99 *(978-0-7642-0783-9(0))* Bethany Hse. Pubs.
O'Dell, Shannon. Transforming Church in Rural America: Breaking all the Rurals. 2009. 176p. pap. 12.99 *(978-0-89221-694-9(8)*, New Leaf Pr.) New Leaf Pr. Inc.
Odukoya, Adebola T. Wolves in the Church. 2008. 178p. pap. 17.49 *(978-0-557-03036-1(6))* Lulu Enterprises Inc.
Ogne, Steve & Roehl, Tim. TransforMissional Coaching: Empowering Leaders in a Changing Ministry World. 2008. (ENG.). 304p. 19.99 *(978-0-8054-4781-1(4)*, B&H Bks.) B&H Publishing Group.
Oladimeji, Seyi. Church Adminisration & Management. 2011. 124p. pap. 15.66 ***(978-1-4567-8513-0(3))*** AuthorHouse.
Oliver, Juan. Ripe Fields: The Promise & Challenge of Latino Ministry. 2009. 160p. pap. 20.00 *(978-0-89869-611-0(9))* Church Publishing, Inc.
Olsen, Charles M. The Wisdom of the Seasons: How the Church Year Helps Us Understand Our Congregational Stories. 2009. *(978-1-56699-396-8(2))* Alban Institute, Inc.
Owsley, D. Thomas. The Perfect Pastor? 2007. 428p. per. 21.99 *(978-1-60266-656-6(3))* Xulon Pr., Inc.
Page, Frank & Perry, John. The Incredible Shrinking Church. 2008. (ENG.). 160p. per. 14.99 *(978-0-8054-4661-6(3)*, B&H Bks.) B&H Publishing Group.
Parker, Mary, ed. Safe Place: Guidelines for Creating an Abuse-Free Environment in Local Church Ministry. 2009. 175p. pap. 24.99 *(978-1-60066-236-2(6))* WingSpread Publishers.
Payne, J. D. Missional House Churches: Reaching Our Communities with the Gospel. 2008. (ENG.). 207p. pap. 16.99 *(978-1-934068-25-0(X)*, Paternoster) Authentic Media.
Payne, Patricia Ann. The Deceit of the Church. 2008. 80p. pap. 9.99 *(978-1-60477-500-6(9))* Xulon Pr., Inc.
Pearson, John. Mastering the Management Buckets: 20 Critical Competencies for Leading Your Business or Nonprofit. 2008. (ENG., Illus.). 288p. 19.99 *(978-0-8307-4594-4(7))* Gospel Light Pubns.
Penner, Marv. Building & Mobilizing Teams. 2009. (Youth Ministry in the Trenches Ser.). (ENG.). 144p. (YA). pap. 12.99 *(978-0-7847-2316-6(8))* Standard Publishing.
Peri, Paul F. Catholic Parish Administration: A Handbook. 2012. viii, 72p. ***(978-1-61643-092-4(3))***; 80p. pap. 9.95 ***(978-0-8091-4752-6(1))*** Paulist Pr.
Philpott, Kent. How to Care for Your Pastor: A Guide for Small Churches. 2007. 122p. pap. *(978-0-85234-666-2(2))* Evangelical Pr.
Pickard, Stephen. Theological Foundations for Collaborative Ministry: One of Another. 2009. (Explorations in Practical, Pastoral & Empirical Theology Ser.). 266p. pap. 34.95 *(978-0-7546-6835-0(5))* Ashgate Publishing Co.
—Theological Foundations for Collaborative Ministry: One of Another. 2009. (Explorations in Practical, Pastoral & Empirical Theology Ser.). 266p. 114.95 *(978-0-7546-6829-9(0))* Ashgate Publishing Co.
Pickett, William L. A Concise Guide to Pastoral Planning. 2007. (Concise Guide Ser.). (Illus.). 254p. per. 16.95 *(978-1-59471-135-0(6))* Ave Maria Pr.
Porcher, Philip G., Jr. What You Can Expect from an Interim Pastor & an Interim Consultant. pap. 6.75 *(978-1-56699-101-8(3)*, OD71) Alban Institute, Inc.
Powers, Bruce P., ed. Church Administration Handbook. 3rd ed. 2008. (ENG., Illus.). 352p. pap. 29.99 *(978-0-8054-4490-2(4)*, B&H Academic) B&H Publishing Group.
Rainey, Joel. Planting Churches in the Real World. 2008. 158p. per. 14.99 *(978-0-9798053-2-5(5))* Missional Pr.
Rasbeary, James. From One Church Planter to Another: Helps for the Pioneer Church Planter. 2008. 108p. per. *(978-0-9800096-8-2(5))* Calvary Publishing
ReConnecting Worship DVD. 30.00 *(978-0-687-06313-0(2))* Abingdon Pr.
ReConnecting Worship VHS. 30.00 *(978-0-687-05763-4(9))* Abingdon Pr.
Rendle, Gilbert R. & Beaumont, Susan K. When Moses Meets Aaron: Staffing & Supervision in Large Congregations. 2007. *(978-1-56699-351-7(2))* Alban Institute, Inc.
Riddle, Mark. Inside the Mind of Youth Pastors: A Church Leader's Guide to Staffing & Leading Youth Pastors, 1 vol. 2008. (ENG.). 192p. pap. 16.99 *(978-0-310-28365-2(5))* Zondervan.
Riggins, Mary Beth. Saving Our Singles - 101 Ways the Church Can Reach the Single Parent. 2008. 96p. pap. 10.95 *(978-0-9816172-5-1(5))* Westview Publishing Co., Inc.
Risley, Jean F. A Place Where Everybody Matters: Life & Ministry in A Small Church. 2010. (House of Prisca & Aquila Ser.). 152p. pap. 17.00 *(978-1-60899-306-2(X)*, Wipf and Stock) Wipf & Stock Pubs.
Rudowski, Peter. Connecting the Dots. 2009. 328p. 29.99 *(978-1-4415-2284-9(0))*; pap. 19.99 *(978-1-4415-2283-2(2))* Xlibris Corp.
Ryals, Jimmy. Biblical World Ministry Park, Inc: Enter A New World of Ministry. 2009. 80p. pap. 14.95 *(978-1-4327-1232-7(2))* Outskirts Pr., Inc.

C

Sattem, Jan. A Task Analysis of the Reformed North American Pastor. 2009. 132p. pap. *(978-3-639-08632-4(5))* VDM Verlag Dr. Mueller e.K.
Sawyer, David. Hope in Conflict: Discovering Wisdom in Congregational Turmoil. 2007. *(978-0-8298-1758-4(1))* Pilgrim Pr., The/United Church Pr.
Schnase, Robert C. Five Practices of Fruitful Congregations Bookmark (Package Of 25) 2008. ring bd. 4.00 *(978-0-687-65793-3(8))* Abingdon Pr.
Shupe, Bob G. The Little Brown Church in the Vale ... When Did the Lights Go Out? 2008. pap. 13.95 *(978-1-60494-137-1(5))* Wheatmark.
Simpson, Ray & Lee, Brent Lyons. Emerging Downunder. 2008. (ENG.). 236p. (C). pap. 10.00 *(978-1-920691-91-2(X))* ATF Pr. AUS. Dist: Brown, David Bk. Co., The.
Smith, Daniel P. & Sellon, Mary K. Pathway to Renewal: Practical Steps for Congregations. 2008. *(978-1-56699-371-5(7))* Alban Institute, Inc.
Southern, Jewel. Taste & See. 2008. 59p. pap. 16.95 *(978-1-60474-103-2(1))* PublishAmerica, Inc.
Sports Spots, No. 1458. (Illus.). 48p. 5.95 *(978-1-878259-13-4(X))* Neibauer Pr.
Stanley, Terry. Home Church. 2007. 227p. pap. 14.95 *(978-0-615-17108-1(7))* New Testament Church Life Publishing.
—The Way Church Was Meant to Be A Roadmap for the Worldwide Exodus Out of Traditional Church. 2007. 227p. pap. 14.95 *(978-0-615-16831-9(0))* New Testament Church Life Publishing.
Stevenson, Phil. 5 Things Anyone Can Do to Help Start a Church. 2008. 96p. pap. 7.99 *(978-0-89827-382-3(X))* Wesleyan Publishing Hse.
Stewart, Rodney D. Church Vipers. 2006. 132p. per. 15.00 *(978-1-4251-0286-9(7))* Trafford Publishing.
Stoltzfus, Tony. Peer Coach Training Facilitator's Guide. 2007. (ENG., Illus.). 84p. spiral bd. 24.99 *(978-0-9794163-1-6(0))* Coach22 Bookstore LLC.
—Peer Coach Training Workbook. 2007. (ENG., Illus.). 80p. spiral bd. 12.99 *(978-0-9794163-0-9(2))* Coach22 Bookstore LLC.
Surratt, Geoff, et al. A Multi-Site Church Roadtrip: , 1 vol. 2009. (Leadership Network Innovation Ser.). (ENG.). 256p. (C). pap. 18.99 *(978-0-310-29394-1(4))* Zondervan.
Swanson, Eric & Rusaw, Rick. The Externally Focused Quest: Becoming the Best Church for the Community. 2010. (Jossey-Bass Leadership Network Ser.: 44). (ENG., Illus.). 272p. 24.95 *(978-0-470-50078-1(6),* Jossey-Bass) Wiley, John & Sons, Inc.
Sweet, Leonard, ed. The Church of the Perfect Storm. 2008. 187p. per. 17.00 *(978-0-687-65089-7(5))* Abingdon Pr.
Sweetser, Thomas P. Keeping the Covenant: Taking Parish to the Next Level. 2007. (ENG., Illus.). 288p. pap. 19.95 *(978-0-8245-2466-1(7))* Crossroad Publishing Co., The.
Taylor, William. Partnership: Philippians: Concise, Portable Spiritual Food. 2007. (ENG.). 192p. per. 10.99 *(978-1-84550-231-7(0))* Christian Focus Pubns. GBR. Dist: STL Distribution North America.
The Hopper Staff. In the Eye of the Storm. 2008. 148p. pap. 24.95 *(978-1-60474-937-3(7))* PublishAmerica, Inc.
Thompson, Murray. Christianity's New Model for Ministry: The Multi-denominational Church. 2007. pap. 14.00 *(978-0-8059-8439-2(9))* Dorrance Publishing Co., Inc.
Thompson, Sue. Ministry of Administrative Assistants. Hamilton, Adam, ed. 2008. (Crmg Ser.). (Illus.). 60p. pap. 9.00 *(978-0-687-64709-5(6))* Abingdon Pr.
Toler, Stan. Stan Toler's Practical Guide to Hiring Staff: How to Recruit & Retain an Effective Ministry Team. 2009. *(978-0-89827-384-7(6))* Wesleyan Publishing Hse.
Tully, Kevin. Stop Changing Youth Ministers! Ways to Increase Youth Ministers' Stability & Effectiveness in the Local Church. 2008. 276p. pap. *(978-3-639-09248-6(1))* VDM Verlag Dr. Mueller e.K.
Tyson, John. Administration in the Small Me. 2007. 112p. pap. 15.00 *(978-0-687-64643-2(X))* Abingdon Pr.
Van Gelder, Craig. The Ministry of the Missional Church: A Community Led by the Spirit. 2007. (Illus.). 208p. pap. 16.99 *(978-0-8010-9139-1(X))* Baker Bks.
van Harmelen, Rachel Boehm. Discover Your Church: And Why You Need Each Other. (Discover Series for Junior High Ser.). tchr. ed. 9.50 *(978-1-56212-411-3(0),* 120505) Faith Alive Christian Resources.
Vincentian Center for Church and Society Staff. Concise Guide to Catholic Church Management. 2010. (Illus.). 256p. pap. 18.95 *(978-1-59471-227-2(1))* Ave Maria Pr.
The Vital Church. ldr.'s ed. 2.00 incl. audio *(978-0-687-76225-5(1))* Abingdon Pr.
Walk with Me: A Model for Youth Ministry. pap. 24.50 incl. VHS *(978-1-56212-457-1(9),* 138900) Faith Alive Christian Resources.
Webb Rel. D., Larry E. Healthy Church Dna(R) 2008. 212p. 27.95 *(978-0-595-50680-4(1));* pap. 17.95 *(978-0-595-48512-3(X))* iUniverse, Inc.
Weber, Charles. A Little Guidebook for the Servant-Leader. 2008. 64p. pap. 10.95 *(978-1-4327-2700-0(1))* Outskirts Pr., Inc.
Webster, Douglas D. Selling Jesus. 2009. 166p. pap. 19.00 *(978-1-60608-887-6(4),* Wipf and Stock) Wipf & Stock Pubs.
Wehner, Mary. A Heart for Your Church. 2007. 60p. per. 16.95 *(978-1-4241-8004-2(X))* PublishAmerica, Inc.
Welch, Robert H. Church Administration: Creating Efficiency for Effective Ministry. 2nd ed. 2011. (ENG.). 416p. pap. 29.99 *(978-1-4336-7377-1(0),* B&H Academic) B&H Publishing Group.
Welch, Tim. Technology Tools for Your Ministry: No Mousing Around! 2008. (Illus.). 120p. pap. 16.95 *(978-1-58595-676-0(7))* Twenty-Third Pubns./Bayard.
White, Richard C. Building for Ministry: The Book That Will Save Your Church 1,000's of Dollars. 2008. 116p. pap. 18.50 *(978-1-4389-0999-8(3))* AuthorHouse.
Williams, Gene. Out of the Pulpit, into the Pew: A Pastor's Guide to Meaningful Service after Retirement. 2007. (ENG.). 128p. per. 11.99 *(978-0-8341-2322-9(3),* 0834123223) Beacon Hill Pr. of Kansas City.
Williams, Janet Y. God's Business [Kingdom-Building] Manager: A Letters & Forms Reference Guide for Kingdom-Minded Church Administrators. 19.95 incl. audio compact disk *(978-0-9761024-1-0(2))* Williams, Janet Y.
Williams, Joseph. Our Pentecostal Birthright. 2010. (ENG.). 136p. pap. 12.95 *(978-1-60530-138-9(8),* iTouch Pubs.) Higher Standard Enterprises, Inc.
Williamson, John. Sin in the Assembly: A Guide for Local Baptist Church Discipline. 2007. 64p. per. 16.95 *(978-1-60441-178-2(3))* PublishAmerica, Inc.
Wimberly, John W. The Business of the Church: The Uncomfortable Truth That Faithful Ministry Requires Effective Management. 2010. x, 164p. *(978-1-56699-404-0(7))* Alban Institute, Inc.
Winders, Barry. Finding the Missional Path. 2007. 144p. per. 13.99 *(978-1-60266-817-1(5))* Xulon Pr., Inc.
Wolcott, Theresa Hunt. 500 Ways to Help Your Church: The Minister's Social Helper. 2007. (ENG.). 364p. 46.95 *(978-0-548-02920-6(2))* Kessinger Publishing, LLC.
Wrenn, Bud. Innovative Planning: Your Church in 4-D. 2008. 144p. pap. 24.99 *(978-0-8272-1650-1(5))* Chalice Pr.
Wright, Alan. Spiritual Dimensions of Team. 2010. (Columbia Partnership Ser.). 144p. pap. 16.99 *(978-0-8272-3471-0(6))* Chalice Pr.
Zech, Charles. Best Practices in Catholic Church Ministry Performance Management. 2010. (ENG.). 130p. 57.99 *(978-0-7391-4523-4(1))* Lexington Bks.
2009-2012 United Methodist Church Financial Records Handbook. 2009. 12.00 *(978-0-687-65573-1(0))* Abingdon Pr.
2009-2012 United Methodist Membership Records Manual. 2009. 12.00 *(978-0-687-65563-2(3))* Abingdon Pr.

CHURCH MANAGEMENT—LAW AND LEGISLATION

Decisions Judicial Counseling from Year 1940-1968 #1-255. 10.00 *(978-0-687-10405-5(X))* Abingdon Pr.
Finney, Jerald. Separation of Church & State: God's Churches: Spiritual or Legal Entities? 2009. 108p. pap. 8.95 *(978-0-9816226-3-7(1))* Kerygma Publishing Co.
Rademacher, William J., et al. Understanding Today's Catholic Parish. 2007. 174p. per. 19.95 *(978-1-58595-630-2(9))* Twenty-Third Pubns./Bayard.

CHURCH MANAGEMENT, INDIGENOUS

see Indigenous Church Administration

CHURCH MEETINGS

Bimler, Richard & Bickel, Kurt. Till We Meet Again: Ten Strategies for Effective Church Meetings. 2007. (ENG., Illus.). 64p. pap. 12.95 *(978-0-9798057-0-7(8))* Strobickan Publishing LLC.
Bloomfield, Arthur E. & Bloomfield, Shirley. 100+ Games, Quizzes, & Icebreakers, 1 vol. 2009. (Illus.). 224p. pap. 14.99 *(978-0-8254-6287-0(8),* Monarch Bks.) Lion Hudson PLC GBR. Dist: Kregel Pubns.
Davis, Cyprian, et al. The Journal of the Black Catholic Theological Symposium, Volume 1. Flint-Hamilton, Kimberly, ed. 2007. 125p. pr. 29.99 *(978-0-9789635-6-9(3))* Fortuity Pr., LLC.
Kemp, Bill. David's Harp: Returning Harmony to Conflicted Congregations. 2008. (Illus.). 110p. pap. 9.00 *(978-0-88177-530-3(4))* Discipleship Resources.
—Jesus' New Command: Rediscovering the Joy of Fellowship. 2008. 96p. pap. 9.00 *(978-0-88177-532-7(0))* Discipleship Resources.
Korean Class Meeting 2010. 2009. 11.00 *(978-0-687-65753-7(9),* Cokesbury) Abingdon Pr.
Langford, Andy, et al. Beginnings: Longing to Belong. 2008. 88p. pap. 18.00 *(978-0-687-33576-3(0))* Abingdon Pr.
—Beginnings - Longing to Belong Participant's Companion: Around the Fire. 2008. (Beginnings Ser.). (Illus.). 184p. per. 10.50 *(978-0-687-65012-5(7))* Abingdon Pr.
—Beginnings - Longing to Belong Small Group Leader's Guide. 2008. (Beginnings Ser.). 51p. pap., instr.'s gde. ed. 9.00 *(978-0-687-33596-1(5));* 72p. per., instr.'s gde. ed. 12.00 *(978-0-687-33586-2(8))* Abingdon Pr.
Minutes of the Charge/Church Conference 1997-2000. 0.25 *(978-0-687-25105-6(2))* Abingdon Pr.
Minutes of the Charge/Church Conference 2001-2004. 6.00 *(978-0-687-09691-6(X));* 1.25 *(978-0-687-09759-3(2))* Abingdon Pr.
Powell, Kara. Essential Leadership: Ministry Team Meetings That Work, 1 vol. 2009. (ENG., Illus.). 128p. pap., instr.'s gde. ed. 9.99 *(978-0-310-66934-0(0))* Zondervan.
—Ministry Team Meetings That Work, 1 vol. ldr.'s ed. 2009. (ENG.). 144p. pap. 14.99 *(978-0-310-66933-3(2))* Zondervan.
Rogers. Building a House for All God's Children: Diversity Leadership in the Church. 2008. 162p. pap. 14.00 *(978-0-687-64999-0(4))* Abingdon Pr.
Schnase, Robert C. Five Practices of Fruitful Congregations Bookmark (Package Of 25) 2008. ring bd. 4.00 *(978-0-687-65793-3(8))* Abingdon Pr.
Stanley, Terry. Home Church. 2007. 227p. pap. 14.95 *(978-0-615-17108-1(7))* New Testament Church Life Publishing.
—The Way Church Was Meant to Be A Roadmap for the Worldwide Exodus Out of Traditional Church. 2007. 227p. pap. 14.95 *(978-0-615-16831-9(0))* New Testament Church Life Publishing.

CHURCH MEMBERSHIP

see also Baptism; Church Discipline; Confirmation; Lord's Supper

Aird, Polly. Mormon Convert, Mormon Defector: A Scottish Immigrant in the American West, 1848-1861. 2009. (ENG.). 320p. (C). 39.95 *(978-0-87062-369-1(9),* Clark, Arthur H. Co., The) Univ. of Oklahoma Pr.
Arant, Charles. Rooted in Faith: Preparation for Church Membership. 2010. (Illus.). 64p. pap. ***(978-0-7586-1637-1(6))*** Concordia Publishing Hse.
Bass, Diana Butler. Christianity for the Rest of Us: How the Neighborhood Church Is Transforming the Faith. 2007. (ENG.). 336p. pap. 14.99 *(978-0-06-085949-7(0),* HarperOne) HarperCollins Pubs.
Bennett, Jana Marguerite & Nussbaum, Melissa Musick. Free to Leave, Free to Stay: Fruits of the Spirit & Church Choice. 2009. 114p. pap. 15.00 *(978-1-55635-899-9(7))* Cascade Bks.
Benton, John. Why Join a Small Church. 2008. (ENG.). 7.99 *(978-1-84550-407-6(0))* Christian Focus Pubns. GBR. Dist: STL Distribution North America.
Bornstein, Kate. A Queer & Pleasant Danger: The True Story of a Nice Jewish Boy Who Joins the Church of Scientology & Leaves Twelve Years Later to Become the Lovely Lady She Is Today. 2012. (ENG.). 280p. 24.95 ***(978-0-8070-0165-3(1))*** Beacon Pr.
Briggs, Carolyn S. Higher Ground: A Memoir of Salvation Found & Lost. 2011. (ENG.). 320p. pap. 16.95 ***(978-1-4422-1438-5(4))*** Rowman & Littlefield Publishers, Inc.
Detroit (Mich.) First Presbyterian Churc. Articles of Faith & Covenant of the First Presbyterian Church, of the City of Detroit Revised & Printed, February 1850. 2011. 26p. pap. 11.99 ***(978-1-4181-9234-1(1))*** MPublishing.
Downey, Paul W. More Than Spectators: Fulfilling Your Role in the Local Church. 2007. 251p. per. *(978-1-59166-732-2(1))* BJU Pr.
Drury, Amanda. Becoming a Member of the Church. 2007. (D Ser.). (Illus.). 64p. per. 7.99 *(978-0-89827-370-0(6))* Wesleyan Publishing Hse.
Duin, Julia. Quitting Church: Why the Faithful Are Fleeing & What to Do about It. 2008. *(978-0-8010-1322-5(4))* Baker Bks.
—Quitting Church: Why the Faithful are Fleeing & What to Do about It, 1 vol. 2009. 192p. pap. 12.99 *(978-0-8010-7227-7(1))* Baker Bks.
Frack, Kevin C. The Foundation of Our Faith: Preparation for membership in the Moravian Church. Interprovincial Board of Communication of The Moravian Church, ed. 2007. 166p. per. 14.95 *(978-1-878422-65-1(0))* Interprovincial Board of Communication.
Green, John C. The Faith Factor: How Religion Influences American Elections. 2010. (Illus.). 242p. pap. 21.95 *(978-1-59797-430-1(7))* Potomac Bks., Inc.
Guidelines for Leading Your Congregation 2009-2012 - Small Membership Church: Serving with Significance in Your Context. 2008. 2.95 *(978-0-687-64952-5(8))* Abingdon Pr.
Halter, Hugh & Smay, Matt. The Tangible Kingdom: Creating Incarnational Community. 2008. (Jossey-Bass Leadership Network Ser.: 25). (ENG., Illus.). 224p. 24.95 *(978-0-470-18897-2(9),* Jossey-Bass) Wiley, John & Sons, Inc.
Hampson, Michael. Last Rites: The End of the Church of England. 2006. (ENG.). 208p. per. 24.95 *(978-1-86207-891-8(2))* Granta Bks. GBR. Dist: Independent Pubs. Group.
James, Bill. Baptism & Church Membership. 2006. 27p. pap. *(978-0-9527913-3-1(1))* Reformation Today Trust.
Jamieson, Alan. A Churchless Faith: Faith Journeys Beyond the Churches. 208p. 16.00 *(978-0-281-05465-7(7))* SPCK Publishing GBR. Dist: Pilgrim Pr., The/United Church Pr.
Jenkins, Philip. The Next Christendom: The Coming of Global Christianity, 1 vol. 3rd ed. 2011. (ENG., Illus.). 400p. pap. 15.95 *(978-0-19-976746-5(7))* Oxford Univ. Pr., Inc.
Jost, Beat. The Workers of the Eleventh Hour. 2007. pap. *(978-0-87808-521-7(1))* Carey, William Library Pubs.
Leeman, Jonathan. The Church & the Surprising Offense of God's Love: Reintroducing the Doctrines of Church Membership & Discipline. 2010. (IX Marks Ser.). 384p. pap. 19.99 *(978-1-4335-0905-6(9))* Crossway.
Mack, Wayne A. & Swavely, Dave. Life in the Father's House: A Member's Guide to the Local Church. 2nd rev. ed. 2006. 277p. (Orig.). per. 12.99 *(978-1-59638-034-9(9))* P & R Publishing.
Masters, Peter. Church Membership in the Bible. 2008. 61p. pap. *(978-1-870855-64-8(7))* Wakeman Trust, The.
Nixon, Debi & HAMILTON, Adam. Catch a New Life: Connect with a Church. 2009. (GoFish Ser.). 144p. pap. 10.00 *(978-0-687-65674-5(5))* Abingdon Pr.
Parks, Lewis. Preaching in the Small Members. 2009. (Small Membership Church Ser.). 112p. pap. 14.00 *(978-0-687-64584-8(0))* Abingdon Pr.
Pratt, Richard L., Jr. Why Do We Baptize Our Children? (Profession of Faith, Baptism, Church Membership Ser.). 16.99 *(978-1-930773-09-7(9),* 155315) Third Millennium Ministries.
Rollo-Koster, Joelle. The People of Curialavignon: A Critical Edition of the Liber Divisionis & the Matriculae of Notre Dame la Majonr. 2009. (Illus.). 468p. 129.95 *(978-0-7734-4680-9(X))* Mellen, Edwin Pr., The.
Sanders, Brian. Life after Church: God's Call to Disillusioned Christians. 2007. (ENG.). 191p. pap. 15.00 *(978-0-8308-3606-2(3),* IVP Bks.) InterVarsity Pr.
Searcy, Nelson & Henson, Jennifer Dykes. Fusion: Turning First-Time Guests into Fully-Engaged Members of Your Church. 2008. (ENG., Illus.). 192p. per. 14.99 *(978-0-8307-4531-9(9))* Gospel Light Pubns.
Sittser, Gerald L. Love One Another: Becoming the Church Jesus Longs For. 2008. (ENG.). 189p. pap. 15.00 *(978-0-8308-3449-5(4),* IVP Bks.) InterVarsity Pr.
Streib, Heinz, et al. Deconversion: Qualitative & Quantitative Results from Cross-Cultural Research in Germany & the United States of America. 2009. (Research in Contemporary Religion Ser.). (ENG., Illus.). 259p. (C). 87.00 *(978-3-525-60439-7(4))* Vandenhoeck & Ruprecht GmbH & Co. KG DEU. Dist: ISD.
Suggs, George G. Washing the Disciples' Feet: Vignettes of White Oak Original Free Will Baptist Church of Bladenboro, North Carolina. 2011. 116p. pap. 12.95 ***(978-1-4620-4124-4(8))*** iUniverse, Inc.
Turner, Timothy. Welcoming the Baptized. 2009. 88.00 *(978-1-60724-385-4(7))* Gorgias Pr., LLC.
Walther, C. F. W. For the Life of the Church: A Practical Edition of Pastor Walther's Prayers & Addresses. Schaum, Charles P., ed. 2011. 220p. pap. 19.99 ***(978-0-7586-3139-8(1))*** Concordia Publishing Hse.
Woolever, Cynthia & Bruce, Deborah. A Field Guide to U. S. Congregations: Who's Going Where & Why. 2nd ed. 2010. (ENG., Illus.). 144p. pap. 20.00 *(978-0-664-23514-7(X))* Westminster John Knox Pr.
Yates, George L. Reaching the Summit. 2012. pap. ***(978-1-55452-825-7(9))*** Essence Publishing.
2009-2012 United Methodist Membership Records Manual. 2009. 12.00 *(978-0-687-65563-2(3))* Abingdon Pr.

CHURCH MISSIONARY SOCIETY

Middleton, Angela. Te Puna - a New Zealand Mission Station: Historical Archaeology in New Zealand. 2008. (Contributions to Global Historical Archaeology Ser.). (Illus.). 257p. 119.00 *(978-0-387-77620-0(6))* Springer.
—Te Puna - A New Zealand Mission Station: Historical Archaeology in New Zealand. 2010. (Contributions to Global Historical Archaeology Ser.). (Illus.). xv, 276p. pap. 119.00 *(978-1-4419-2659-3(3),* 1441926593) Springer.
Oyemakinde, Wale, ed. Introduction to Church Missionary Society Manuscripts. 160p. pap. 27.95 *(978-978-31178-4-6(X))* College Pr. Pubs. NGA. Dist: Michigan State Univ. Pr.

CHURCH MUSIC

Here are entered works on church music and on sacred vocal music in general. Sacred vocal compositions are entered under the heading Sacred Vocal Music and headings referred to under that heading.

see also Carillons; Chapels (Music); Choirs (Music); Choral Music; Chorale; Christmas Music; Easter Music; Funeral Music; Hymns; Lenten Music; Mary, Blessed Virgin, Saint—Songs and Music; Mass (Music); Music in Churches; Oratorio; Organ Music; Psalmody; Sequences (Liturgy); Wedding Music

Abbington, James. Readings in African American Church Music & Worship. 2009. (ENG.). 602p. pap. 36.95 *(978-1-57999-767-0(8))* G I A Pubns., Inc.
Abbington, James, et al. A Primer for the Visiting Organist. Moleck, Fred, ed. 2007. 89p. per. 14.95 *(978-1-57999-635-2(3),* G-6814) G I A Pubns., Inc.
Abingdon Press, creator. Choir Director's Organizer. 2007. (Illus.). 99p. spiral bd. 15.00 *(978-0-687-64251-9(5))* Abingdon Pr.
Acker, Mark. The Passion-Driven Youth Choir. annot. ed. 2007. 138p. per. 12.00 *(978-0-687-49224-4(6))* Abingdon Pr.
Alexander, Peter. Writing & Performing Christian Music: God's Plan & Purpose for the Church. 2007. 156p. pap. 16.95 *(978-0-939067-77-0(3))* Alexander Publishing.
Alfred Publishing, creator. Christmas Carols from Around the World: A Celebration of International Carols & Regional Traditions. 2007. (ENG., Illus.). 112p. per. 14.95 *(978-0-7390-4899-3(6))* Alfred Publishing Co., Inc.
Alfred Publishing Staff. Exalted: 10 Christian Worship Favorites. 2011. (Sacred Performer Collections). (ENG.). 48p. pap. 14.99 ***(978-0-7390-8390-1(2))*** Alfred Publishing Co., Inc.
—Getty & Townend Praise Classics: The Songs of Keith Getty, Kristyn Getty & Stuart Townend. 2011. (Sacred Performer Collections). (ENG.). 52p. pap. 14.99 ***(978-0-7390-8353-6(8))*** Alfred Publishing Co., Inc.
—How Can We Keep from Singing? Songs by Getty, Townend, Tomlin, & Redman (Songbook) 2011. 112p. pap. 8.99 ***(978-0-7390-8277-5(5))*** Alfred Publishing Co., Inc.
—Hymns for Today: 12 Contemporary Arrangements of Traditional Hymns. 2009. (Sacred Performer Collections). (ENG.). 40p. pap. 12.99 *(978-0-7390-6089-6(9))* Alfred Publishing Co., Inc.
—Living Praise Instrumental Collection: B-flat Instruments (Trumpet, Clarinet, Tenor Saxophone), Book & CD. 2009. (ENG.). 24p. pap. 12.95 *(978-0-7390-6361-3(8))* Alfred Publishing Co., Inc.
—Living Praise Instrumental Collection: C Instruments (Flute, Oboe, Violin, Mallet Percussion) , Book & CD. 2009. (ENG.). 24p. pap. 12.95 *(978-0-7390-6360-6(X))* Alfred Publishing Co., Inc.
—Living Praise Instrumental Collection: E-flat Instruments (Alto Saxophone, Baritone Saxophone), Book & CD. 2009. (ENG.). 24p. pap. 12.95 *(978-0-7390-6362-0(6))* Alfred Publishing Co., Inc.
—Living Praise Instrumental Collection: Piano Acc. , Book & CD. 2009. (ENG.). 52p. pap. 14.95 *(978-0-7390-6363-7(4))* Alfred Publishing Co., Inc.
—The Prayer: 15 Celebrated Inspirational Solos for Medium Voice, Book & CD. 2009. (ENG.). 108p. pap. 34.95 *(978-0-7390-6507-5(6))* Alfred Publishing Co., Inc.
—Sunday Morning Organist: Best of the Saint Cecilia Series. 2009. (Alfred's Classic Editions Ser.). (ENG.). 148p. pap. 19.95 *(978-0-7390-6529-7(7))* Alfred Publishing Co., Inc.
—Sunday Morning Organist: Introductions for Hymns & Carols. 2009. (Alfred's Classic Editions Ser.). (ENG.). 96p. pap. 14.95 *(978-0-7390-6528-0(9))* Alfred Publishing Co., Inc.
—Sunday Morning Organist Vol. 3: Hymn Accompaniments & Reharmonizations. 2009. (Alfred's Classic Editions Ser.). (ENG.). 72p. pap. 12.95 *(978-0-7390-6527-3(0))* Alfred Publishing Co., Inc.
—Sunday Morning Organist, Vol 1: Solos for Christmas. 2009. (Alfred's Classic Editions Ser.). (ENG.). 120p. pap. 17.95 *(978-0-7390-6208-1(5))* Alfred Publishing Co., Inc.

—Sunday Morning Organist, Vol 2: Solos for Special Sundays. 2009. (Alfred's Classic Editions Ser.). (ENG.). 128p. pap. 17.95 *(978-0-7390-6209-8(3))* Alfred Publishing Co., Inc.
Allen, Dennis, et al, contrib. by. Jesus Christ, Forever, Amen: An Easter Presentation of 5 Songs in Unison/2-Part. 2010. (ENG.). 44p. pap. 5.99 *(978-0-8341-7847-2(8)*, 9780834178472) Lillenas Publishing Co.
Allen, Dennis & Allen, Nan. O Holy Night. 49.95 *(978-0-7673-1210-3(4))* LifeWay Christian Resources.
Allen, Dennis and Nan. Thanks Be to God. pap. 1.45 *(978-0-8341-9491-5(0))* Lillenas Publishing Co.
Anders, Roger D. Thirty-Seven Songs & Choruses: For Sunday School, Vacation Bible School, or Special Children Services. 2010. pap. 8.99 *(978-1-60799-589-0(1))* Tate Publishing & Enterprises, LLC.
Andrews, Carroll. Organ Classics: For Weddings & Worship Services. pap. 12.99 *(978-0-8341-9693-3(X))* Lillenas Publishing Co.
Andrews, Pam & Gambill, Luke, creators. It's a Wonder-Full Life: A Musical about the Best Gift at Christmas... Jesus. 2008. 10.98 *(978-5-557-40585-0(2)*, Brentwood-Benson Music Publishing, Inc.) Brentwood Music, Inc.
Angotti, John. Rise up My People. pap. *(978-1-58459-067-5(X)*, 7360) World Library Pubns.
The Ash Grove Online Handbell Piece. 5.00 *(978-0-687-07352-8(9))* Abingdon Pr.
Atkins, Ivor A. The Early Occupants of the Office of Organist & Master of the Choristers of the Cathedral Church of Christ & the Blessed Virgin Mary, Worcester. reprint ed. 39.50 *(978-0-404-12855-5(6))* AMS Pr., Inc.
Audio Adrenaline, et al, contrib. by. Live from Hawaii: the Farewell Concert. 2007. 17.99 *(978-5-557-62912-9(6))* ForeFront Records.
Austell, Robert. Biblical Worship through Music. 2009. (ENG.). 328p. pap. 16.96 *(978-0-557-04739-0(0))* Lulu Enterprises Inc.
Barker, Lorna. Vocal Descants: For 101 Noteworthy Hymns. 2010. 128p. spiral bd. 18.00 *(978-0-89869-549-3(6))* Church Publishing, Inc.
Bathe, William. A Briefe Introduction to the Skill of Song [Facsimile of Edition Printed by Thomas Este, Circa 1587]. 2008. (Illus.). 52p. pap. *(978-1-904331-70-4(X))* Travis & Emery Music Bookshop.
Bell, John. What Would Jesus Sing? Experimentation & Tradition in Church Music. Haskel, Marilyn L., ed. 2007. 192p. per. 18.00 *(978-0-89869-563-2(5))* Church Publishing, Inc.
Bennett, Jeff. O Night Divine! Celebrating the Birth of Christ. 2009. (ENG.). 48p. pap. 15.99 *(978-0-8341-7744-4(7)*, 9780834177444) Lillenas Publishing Co.
Bennett, Jeff. Our God Is Holy! Contemporary Songs & Timeless Hymns. 2011. (ENG.). 64p. pap. 15.99 ***(978-0-8341-7881-6(8)***, 9780834178816) Lillenas Publishing Co.
Berry, Cindy. Hallelujah! 45.00 *(978-0-7673-1232-5(5))* LifeWay Christian Resources.
The Best of Tom Fettke for Women's Voices, Volume 1. 2011. (ENG.). 108p. pap. 8.99 *(978-0-8341-7897-7(4)*, 9780834178977) Lillenas Publishing Co.
Blanton, Gail, et al. Scripts of Hope & Restoration. 2006. (ENG.). 56p. pap. 19.99 *(978-0-8341-7537-2(1)*, 0834175371) Lillenas Publishing Co.
Bober, Melody. A Call to Prayer: 10 Arrangements of Hymns That Speak to the Heart. 2008. (Sacred Performer Collections Ser.). (ENG.). 44p. pap. 12.95 *(978-0-7390-5310-2(8))* Alfred Publishing Co., Inc.
Boersma, Susan Bentall. The Yearning: Satb. 2011. 10p. pap. 1.95 ***(978-1-4291-2590-1(X))*** Lorenz Corp., The.
Boesiger, R. Kevin. Shout to God with Thanksgiving: SATB with Opt. Brass & Percussion. 2011. 16p. pap. 1.95 ***(978-1-4291-2561-1(6))*** Lorenz Corp., The.
—This Is Love: (A Communion Anthem), SATB. 2011. 8p. pap. 1.85 ***(978-1-4291-2214-6(5))*** Lorenz Corp., The.
Bone, David L. & Scifres, Mary J. The United Methodist Music & Worship Planner 2008-2009. 2008. pap. 21.00 *(978-0-687-64546-6(8))* Abingdon Pr.
—The United Methodist Music & Worship Planner 2010-2011. 2010. spiral bd. 22.00 *(978-1-4267-0648-6(0))* Abingdon Pr.
Braman, Barry. Dp Remember My Love. 1.05 *(978-0-7673-0307-1(5))* LifeWay Christian Resources.
Brentwood-Benson Music Publishing Staff, creator. CCM Hits 2006. 2007. (ENG.). 184p. per. 24.99 *(978-1-59802-081-6(1)*, 1598020811) Brentwood Music, Inc.
A Bright Flame Before Me Anthem. 1.25 *(978-0-687-02812-2(4))* Abingdon Pr.
Brown, Frank Burch. Inclusive yet Discerning: Navigating Worship Artfully. 2009. (Illus.). 176p. pap. 20.00 *(978-0-8028-6256-3(X))* Eerdmans, William B. Publishing Co.
Browning, Patricia. The Scripture Sings: Devotions Based on Scriptures about Music. 2011. 156p. 30.95 ***(978-1-61507-765-6(0))***; pap. 13.95 ***(978-1-61507-764-9(2))*** Cross Bks. Publishing.
Burde, Ines. Die venezianische Kirchenmusik von Baldassare Galuppi. 2008. 186p. pap. 56.95 *(978-3-631-57920-6(9))* Lang, Peter GmbH, Europaischer Verlag der Wissenschaften DEU. Dist: Lang, Peter.
Burns, Jeffrey. The Music of Psalms, Proverbs & Job in the Hebrew Bible: A Revised Theory of Musical Accents in the Hebrew Bible with a DVD of Musically Reconstructed Psalms, Proverbs & Job, sung by Computer Speech Synthesis. 2011. (Jüdische Musik Ser.). (ENG., Illus.). 169p. (C). 102.00 *(978-3-447-06191-9(X))* Harrassowitz, Otto Verlag DEU. Dist: ISD.
Burrows, Mark, contrib. by. Asante Sana, Yesu (Thank You, Jesus) SATB or SAB & Solo a Capella with Opt. Percussion. 2011. 8p. pap. 1.85 ***(978-1-4291-2545-1(4))*** Lorenz Corp., The.
Bushn, Eliza. Finding God's Majesty in the Mundane: Devotionals for the Common Man. 2011. 140p. pap. 47.95 ***(978-1-61507-805-9(3))*** Cross Bks. Publishing.
Caltagirone, Carmen L. Amistad Como Sacramento. (SPA.). 112p. 5.95 *(978-980-350-117-4(8))* Sociedad de San Pablo COL. Dist: St Pauls/Alba Hse. Pubs.
Carver, Anthony F. Cori Spezzati: Volume 1, the Development of Sacred Polychoral Music to the Time of Schutz, 2 vols. 2009. (ENG., Illus.). 300p. pap. 38.99 *(978-0-521-10632-0(X))* Cambridge Univ. Pr.
Carver, Anthony F., ed. Cori Spezzati: Volume 2: An Anthology of Sacred Polychoral Music, 2 vols. 2009. (ENG., Illus.). 172p. pap. 26.99 *(978-0-521-10635-1(4))* Cambridge Univ. Pr.
Casting Crowns. Best of Casting Crowns: Easy Guitar with Notes & Tab. 2010. (ENG.). 56p. pap. 12.99 *(978-1-4234-8273-4(5)*, 1423482735) Leonard, Hal Corp.
Caudill, Susan. Christmas for Organ: Classics & Carols. pap. 12.99 *(978-0-8341-9825-8(8))* Lillenas Publishing Co.
—Resounding Praise: Artistic Settings of Hymns & Classics. 2009. (ENG.). 56p. pap. 16.99 *(978-0-8341-7707-9(2)*, 9780834177079) Lillenas Publishing Co.
Celebrating the Eucharist: Music Planner. 144p. spiral bd. 19.95 *(978-0-8146-2719-8(6)*, Liturgical Pr. Bks.) Liturgical Pr.
Cherry, Constance M., et al. Selecting Worship Songs: A Guide for Leaders. 2011. (Illus.). 64p. ***(978-1-931283-42-7(7))*** Triangle Publishing.
Childrens Choir. 4.98 *(978-0-7673-6228-3(4))*; 2.95 *(978-0-7673-6200-9(4))* LifeWay Christian Resources.
Children's Choir. *(978-0-7673-8478-0(4))* LifeWay Christian Resources.
Choplin, Pepper, et al. Classic Hymns We Love: Your Favorite Composers Share a Few of Their Favorites. 2011. 68p. pap. 18.00 ***(978-1-4291-2367-9(2))*** Lorenz Corp., The.
Choplin, Pepper. Come, Emmanuel! SATB with Opt. Orchestra. 2011. 11p. pap. 1.95 ***(978-1-4291-2592-5(6))*** Lorenz Corp., The.
—How Long? SATB a Capella. 2011. 8p. pap. 1.85 ***(978-1-4291-2591-8(8))*** Lorenz Corp., The.
—I Bring a Heart of Thanks: Satb. 2011. 16p. pap. 1.95 ***(978-1-4291-2575-8(6))*** Lorenz Corp., The.
—Open Prayer: Satb. 2011. 8p. pap. 1.85 ***(978-1-4291-2493-5(8))*** Lorenz Corp., The.
—A Servant in Your Heavenly House: Satb. 2011. 12p. pap. 1.95 ***(978-1-4291-2509-3(8))*** Lorenz Corp., The.
—Sweet Harmony. 2011. 11p. pap. 1.95 ***(978-1-4291-2358-7(3))*** Lorenz Corp., The.
Christmas Mosaic: A Festival of Carols for Any Choir. 2009. (ENG.). 104p. pap. 6.99 *(978-0-8341-7694-2(7)*, 9780834176942) Lillenas Publishing Co.
The Christmas Story: In Carols & Poetry. 2009. (ENG.). 80p. pap. 7.99 *(978-0-8341-7697-3(1)*, 9780834176973) Lillenas Publishing Co.
The Church - Starfish. pap. 13.95 *(978-0-89524-405-5(5))* Cherry Lane Music Co.
Church Publishing Staff. Music by Heart: Paperless Songs for Evening Worship. 2008. 176p. spiral bd. 27.00 *(978-0-89869-590-8(2))* Church Publishing, Inc.
Clark, Dave. We Hold These Truths: A Patriotic Celebration of Faith. 2010. (ENG.). 48p. pap. 4.99 *(978-0-8341-7782-6(X)*, 9780834177826) Lillenas Publishing Co.
—Worship Where You're Planted: A Primer for the Local Church Worship Leader. 2010. (ENG.). 160p. pap. 14.99 *(978-0-8341-2555-1(2)*, 9780834125551) Beacon Hill Pr. of Kansas City.
Clark Jr., Paul B. Tune My Heart to Sing Thy Grace: Worship Renewal through Congregational Singing. 2010. 184p. pap. 13.95 *(978-1-61507-204-0(7))* Cross Bks. Publishing.
Clarke, Martin. Music & Theology in Nineteenth-Century Britain. 2012. (Music in Nineteenth-Century Britain Ser.). (Illus.). 280p. 114.95 ***(978-1-4094-0989-2(9))*** Ashgate Publishing Co.
Cloninger, Claire, narrated by. Unspeakable Joy: A Christmas Musical; SATB. 2007. 139p. pap. 8.95 *(978-5-557-77134-4(4)*, Word Music) Word Entertainment.
Coleman, Gerald Patrick. How Can I Keep from Singing? Conversations in Renewal for the Church's Musicians. 73p. pap. 9.95 *(978-0-570-01342-6(9)*, 99-1337) Concordia Publishing Hse.
Cometti, Pedro. Amar No Es Tan Facil. (SPA.). 96p. 3.95 *(978-958-607-466-7(8))* Sociedad de San Pablo COL. Dist: St Pauls/Alba Hse. Pubs.
Corbitt, J. Nathan. The Sound of the Harvest: Music's Mission in Church & Culture. pap. 18.99 *(978-1-900507-88-2(9))* Solway GBR. Dist: O. M. Literature.
Cottrell, Travis, contrib. by & creator. Glorious Day: A Modern Worship Choir Collection. 2008. audio compact disk 10.00 *(978-5-557-42394-6(X)*, Brentwood-Benson Music Publishing, Inc.) Brentwood Music, Inc.
Crowder, Band, David. David Crowder*Band - Church Music. 2009. (ENG.). 128p. pap. 17.99 *(978-1-4234-3599-5(8)*, 1423485998) Leonard, Hal Corp.
Curnow, James, ed. Concert Collection: FlexScore Series - Bb Soprano Saxophone & Bb Tenor Saxophone. 2007. 28p. pap. 5.95 *(978-90-431-2685-4(3)*, 9043126853) Leonard, Hal Corp.
—Concert Collection: FlexScore Series - Bb Trumpet, Bb Euphonium & Bb Bass TC. 2007. (ENG.). 28p. pap. 5.95 *(978-90-431-2686-1(1)*, 9043126861) Leonard, Hal Corp.
—Concert Collection: FlexScore Series - C Instruments BC. 2007. (ENG.). 28p. pap. 5.95 *(978-90-431-2688-5(8)*, 9043126888) Leonard, Hal Corp.
—Concert Collection: FlexScore Series - C Instruments TC. 2007. (ENG.). 28p. pap. 5.95 *(978-90-431-2682-3(9)*, 9043126829) Leonard, Hal Corp.
—Concert Collection: FlexScore Series - Clarinet. 2007. (ENG.). 28p. pap. 5.95 *(978-90-431-2683-0(7)*, 9043126837) Leonard, Hal Corp.
—Concert Collection: FlexScore Series - Eb Instruments. 2007. (ENG.). 28p. pap. 5.95 *(978-90-431-2684-7(5)*, 9043126845) Leonard, Hal Corp.
—Concert Collection: FlexScore Series - French Horn. 2007. 28p. pap. 5.95 *(978-90-431-2687-8(X)*, 904312687X) Leonard, Hal Corp.
—Concert Collection: FlexScore Series - Mallet Percussion Specialist & Violin 2007. (ENG.). 28p. pap. 5.95 *(978-90-431-2691-5(8)*, 9043126918) Leonard, Hal Corp.
—Concert Collection: FlexScore Series - Percussion. 2007. (ENG.). 28p. pap. 5.95 *(978-90-431-2692-2(6)*, 9043126926) Leonard, Hal Corp.
Darnall, Beverly. Messiah True & Faithful. 50.00 *(978-0-7673-0731-4(3))* LifeWay Christian Resources.
David, Jonathan. Together Let Us Sweetly Live: The Singing & Praying Bands. 2007. (Music in American Life Ser.). (Illus.). 264p. 83.00 *(978-0-252-03170-0(9))*; pap. 28.00 *(978-0-252-07419-6(X))* Univ. of Illinois Pr.
Davis, B. J., et al, contrib. by. Made Me Glad: A Choral Collection of Songs from Hillsong Church. 2008. 127p. pap. 8.95 *(978-5-557-38649-4(1))* Point of Grace Entertainment Group.
—Still Amazed Live at Southeast Christian Church: Satb. 2007. 134p. pap. 7.95 *(978-5-557-61410-8(9)*, Brentwood-Benson Music Publishing, Inc.) Brentwood Music, Inc.
Daw, Carl P., Jr. & Pavlechko, Thomas. Liturgical Music for the Revised Common Lectionary Year A. 2007. (Illus.). 176p. per. 30.00 *(978-0-89869-556-4(2))* Church Publishing, Inc.
—Liturgical Music for the Revised Common Lectionary, Year B. 2008. 176p. pap. 30.00 *(978-0-89869-589-2(9))* Church Publishing, Inc.
Diaz, Jonny & Diaz, Gwendolyn. More Beautiful You: A Study in True Beauty. 2010. (ENG.). 176p. (YA). pap. 13.99 *(978-1-60683-027-7(9))* Harrison House Pubs.
Dickinson, Edward. Music in the History of the Western Church. 2009. 236p. pap. *(978-0-217-23890-8(4))* Books LLC.
Digital Praise Inc. Guitar Praise Expansion Pack 1, 0 vols. 2009. cd-rom 19.99 *(978-1-4003-1569-7(7))* Nelson, Thomas Inc.
Doukhan, Lilianne. In Tune with God: The Challenge of Music in Worship. 2010. 301p. 24.99 *(978-0-8127-0500-3(9))* Autumn Hse. Publishing Co.
Drennan, Patti. The Day of Resurrection. 2009. cd-rom 35.00 *(978-1-4234-8715-9(X)*, 142348715X) Shawnee Pr., Inc.
Drummond, Fred. All That Jazz: Learning to Hear the Kingdom Tune in a New Setting. 2007. (ENG.). 224p. per. 20.99 *(978-1-85078-733-4(6))* Authentic Media.
Duncan-Jones, A. S. Church Music. 2009. (ENG.). 110p. 28.99 *(978-1-117-29716-3(0))*; pap. 19.75 *(978-1-117-29717-0(9))* BiblioBazaar.
Edel Staff. A Concert of Angels: Music from J. S. Bach to Gustav Mahler. 2006. (ENG.). 14.95 incl. lp *(978-3-937406-58-9(1))* Edel Classica Gmbh.
Edwards, Dan R. Peals of Praise: 3 or 5 Octaves, Level 2+ 2011. 8p. pap. 4.50 ***(978-1-4291-2329-7(X))*** Lorenz Corp., The.
Eichenberger, Jim. Tuning into God the Beatles 1. 2007. (Tuning into God Ser.). 48p. pap. 7.99 *(978-0-7847-1994-7(2))* Standard Publishing.
English Sacred Lyrics. 2009. 328p. pap. *(978-0-217-71583-6(4,)*; pap. *(978-0-217-71580-5(X))* Books LLC.
Epperly, Bruce Gordon & Hollinger, Daryl. From a Mustard Seed: Enlivening Worship & Music in the Small Church. 2010. *(978-1-56699-406-4(3))* Alban Institute, Inc.
Erler, Mary, ed. Ecclesiastical London. 2008. (Records of Early English Drama Ser.). (ENG.). 504p. *(978-0-8020-9858-0(4))* Univ. of Toronto Pr.
Evans, Roderick L. The Fine Arts of Christian Service: Biblical Insights for Fruitful Christian Service. 2009. (ENG.). pap. 11.95 *(978-1-60141-108-2(1)*, 562644) Kingdom Builders Publishing.
Everett, Isaac. The Emergent Psalter. 2009. 288p. pap. 25.00 *(978-0-89869-617-2(8))* Church Publishing, Inc.
Ferguson, Everett. A Cappella Music in the Public Worship of the Church. rev. ed. 112p. pap. 6.95 *(978-1-56794-217-0(2)*, C-2575) Star Bible & Tract Corp.
Ferris, William. Be with Me Lord. pap. *(978-1-58459-052-1(1)*, 3530) World Library Pubns.
Fettke, Tom, et al. An Evening in December: Orchestration. 2008. (ENG.). 624p pap. 350.00 *(978-0-7390-5472-7(4))* Alfred Publishing Co., Inc.
—An Evening in December: SATB Choral Score, Choral Score. 2008. (ENG.). 104p. pap. 8.95 *(978-0-7390-5468-0(6))* Alfred Publishing Co., Inc.
Fettke, Tom, contrib. by. God Exalted Him. pap. 1.35 *(978-0-8341-9702-2(2))* Lillenas Publishing Co.
Filippi, D. Selva Armonica: La Musica Spirituale e Roma tra Cinque e Seicento. 2008. (Speculum Musicae Ser.). (ITA.). 484p. (C). 174.00 *(978-2-503-52778-9(7))* Brepols Pubs. BEL. Dist: Brown, David Bk. Co., The.
Fitts, Elizabeth Crouch. The New Music Review & Church Music Review, 1901-1935, 6 vols. 2008. (Répertoire International de la Presse Musicale Ser.). xxxiv, 2216p. *(978-1-59662-057-5(9))*; *(978-1-59662-058-2(7))*; *(978-1-59662-059-9(5))*; *(978-1-59662-055-1(2))*; *(978-1-59662-053-7(6))*; *(978-1-59662-054-4(4))*; *(978-1-59662-056-8(0))* RIPM Consortium Ltd., The.
Foley, Edward. Foundations of Christian Music. 2009. 88.00 *(978-1-60724-375-5(X))* Gorgias Pr., LLC.
Frandsen, Mary E. Crossing Confessional Boundaries: The Patronage of Italian Sacred Music in Seventeenth-Century Dresden, 1 vol. 2011. (ENG., Illus.). 530p. pap. 35.00 ***(978-0-19-986249-8(4))*** Oxford Univ. Pr., Inc.
Franklin, Kirk. The Kirk Franklin Collection. 2011. (ENG.). 130p. pap. 17.99 ***(978-1-61780-463-2(0)***, 1617804630) Leonard, Hal Corp.
Friedmann, Jonathan L., compiled by. The Value of Sacred Music: An Anthology of Essential Writings, 1801-1918. 2008. (ENG.). 186p. pap. 45.00 *(978-0-7864-4201-0(8))* McFarland & Co., Inc. Pubs.
Fry, Steve. Let It Be Said of Us: SATB with Opt. Percussion & Digital Strings. 2011. 12p. pap. 2.10 ***(978-1-4291-2422-5(9))*** Lorenz Corp., The.
—Let It Be Said of Us: TTBB with Opt. Percussion & Digital Strings. 2011. 12p. pap. 2.10 ***(978-1-4291-2423-2(7))*** Lorenz Corp., The.
Gabriel, Charles H. That Will Be Glory. *(978-0-8054-5948-7(0))* B&H Publishing Group.
Gaines, David S. Keys for Kids: Hymn Arrangements for Performance & Worship. 2011. (ENG.). 32p. pap. 19.99 ***(978-0-8341-8132-8(0)***, 9780834181328) Lillenas Publishing Co.
Gastoue, Amedee. Musique et Liturgie: Le Graduel et l'Antiphonaire Romains; Histoire et Description. (FRE.). reprint ed. 45.00 *(978-0-404-56608-1(1))* AMS Pr., Inc.
Gatens, William J. Victorian Cathedral Music in Theory & Practice. 2009. (ENG.). 240p. pap. 34.99 *(978-0-521-10483-8(1))* Cambridge Univ. Pr.
Gerou, Tom, contrib. by. Popular Praise: 5 Finger: 10 Timeless Christian Worship Songs: Elementary Piano Solos with Optional Duet Accompaniments. 2010. (Popular Praise Ser.). (ENG.). 40p. pap. 8.99 *(978-0-7390-6989-9(6))* Alfred Publishing Co., Inc.
Gerou, Tom & Labenske, Victor. Play Praise — Most Requested: 9 Piano Arrangements of Contemporary Worship Songs. 2008. (Play Praise Ser.). (ENG.). 32p. pap. 9.99 *(978-0-7390-4909-9(7))*; pap. 9.95 *(978-0-7390-4910-5(0))* Alfred Publishing Co., Inc.
Giles, Gordon. O Clap Your Hands: A Musical Tour of Sacred Choral Works. 2008. 150p. 26.95 incl. audio compact disk *(978-1-55725-567-9(9))* Paraclete Pr., Inc.
Gittli, Geoff. Tuning into God Eagles - The Very Best Of. 2007. (Tuning into God Ser.). 48p. pap. 7.99 *(978-0-7847-1997-8(7))* Standard Publishing.
Gordon, Randy. Tuning into God 50 Number Ones. 2007. (Tuning into God Ser.). 48p. pap. 7.99 *(978-0-7847-1995-4(0))* Standard Publishing.
Gordon, T. David. Why Johnny Can't Sing Hymns: How Pop Culture Rewrote the Hymnal. 2010. pap. *(978-1-59638-195-7(7))* P & R Publishing.
Grace Baptist Church Music Ministry. Amazing Grace. 2007. *(978-1-60208-047-8(X))* FBC Pubns. & Printing.
Grant, Natalie. The Natalie Grant Collection. 2010. (ENG.). 104p. pap. 17.99 *(978-1-4234-9018-0(5)*, 1423490185) Leonard, Hal Corp.
Green, Barton. Between the Lines & Spaces: Christian Artists Share the Stories Behind Their Songs. 2006. (Power of Christian Music Ser.). (Illus.). 224p. 14.99 *(978-0-7847-1656-4(0))* Standard Publishing.
Gregori, Josep Ma & Cabot i Sagrera, Neus. Fons Del Museu-Arxiu de Santa Maria de Mataró. 2010. (CAT., Illus.). iv, 362p. *(978-84-490-2625-6(3))*; *(978-84-393-8267-6(7))* Generalitat de Catalunya.
Griffin, Robert W. Yona: A Chamber Opera. 2011. 280p. ring bd. ***(978-1-889314-04-4(8))*** Beinn Ard Publishing.
Grutschnig-Kieser, Konstanze. Der "Geistliche Würtz= Kräuter= und Blumen=Garten" des Christoph Schütz: Ein Radikalpietistisches "UNIVERSAL-Gesang=Buch" 2006. (Arbeiten Zur Geschichte des Pietismus Ser.). (GER., Illus.). 346p. (C). 74.00 *(978-3-525-55835-5(X))* Vandenhoeck & Ruprecht GmbH & Co. KG DEU. Dist: ISD.
Hö, et al. Die Rezeption der Kirchenmusik Anton Bruckners: Genese, Tradition und Instrumentalisierung des Vergleichs mit Giovanni Pierluigi da Palestrina. 2011. (Abhandlungen zur Musikgeschichte Ser.). (GER., Illus.). 421p. (C). 74.00 *(978-3-89971-601-6(9))* Vandenhoeck & Ruprecht GmbH & Co. KG DEU. Dist: ISD.
Hal Leonard Corp. Modern Worship: Drum Play-along Volume 27. 2011. (ENG.). 48p. pap. 12.99 incl. audio compact disk ***(978-1-61780-433-5(9)***, 1617804339) Leonard, Hal Corp.
—Music of the Masters for the Master. 2011. (ENG.). 68p. pap. 19.99 ***(978-1-4584-2098-5(1)***, 1458420981, Flammer, Harold Music) Shawnee Pr., Inc.
—Piano Praise for 2: Duets for 4-Hands, 1-Piano. 2010. (ENG.). 80p. pap. 18.99 *(978-0-8341-7871-7(0)*, 0834178710) Lillenas Publishing Co.
—Top Worship Songs. 2011. (ENG.). 64p. pap. 10.99 ***(978-1-61780-558-5(0)***, 1617805580) Leonard, Hal Corp.
—Worship Songs for Ukulele. 2011. (ENG.). 64p. pap. 12.99 ***(978-1-4584-1528-8(7)***, 1458415287) Leonard, Hal Corp.
—WOW Hits 2011 Songbook: 30 of Today's Top Christian Artists & Hits. 2011. (ENG.). 238p. pap. 32.95 ***(978-1-4584-1884-5(7)***, 1458418847) Leonard, Hal Corp.
Hal Leonard Corp., creator. Grace Notes: Songs of God's Amazing Grace. 2009. (ENG.). 40p. pap. 15.99 *(978-0-8341-7705-5(6)*, 9780834177055) Lillenas Publishing Co.
—Shabbat Anthology Vol. V. 2011. (ENG.). 130p. pap. 34.95 incl. audio compact disk *(978-0-8074-1143-8(4)*, 0807411434) Transcontinental Music Pubns.
—Solos for the Sanctuary - Spirituals: Mid-Intermediate Level. 2011. (ENG.). 24p. pap. 7.99 *(978-1-61780-651-3(X)*, 161780651X) Willis Music Co.
—Today's Worship Hits. 2011. (ENG.). 210p. pap. 17.99 ***(978-1-4584-0537-1(0)***, 1458405370) Leonard, Hal Corp.
—Worship Favorites: Instrumental Play-along for Cello. 2011. (ENG.). 16p. pap. 12.99 incl. audio compact disk ***(978-1-4234-9938-1(7)***, 1423499387) Leonard, Hal Corp.
—Worship Favorites: Instrumental Play-along for Horn. 2011. (ENG.). 16p. pap. 12.99 incl. audio compact disk ***(978-1-4234-9934-3(4)***, 1423499344) Leonard, Hal Corp.
—Worship Favorites: Instrumental Play-along for Tenor Sax. 2011. (ENG.). 16p. pap. 12.99 incl. audio compact disk ***(978-1-4234-9932-9(8)***, 1423499328) Leonard, Hal Corp.

—Worship Favorites: Instrumental Play-along for Trombone. 2011. (ENG.). 16p. pap. 12.99 incl. audio compact disk ***(978-1-4234-9935-0(2)***, 1423499352) Leonard, Hal Corp.
—Worship Favorites: Instrumental Play-along for Trumpet. 2011. (ENG.). 16p. pap. 12.99 incl. audio compact disk ***(978-1-4234-9933-6(6)***, 1423499336) Leonard, Hal Corp.
—Worship Favorites: Instrumental Play-along for Viola. 2011. (ENG.). 16p. pap. 12.99 incl. audio compact disk ***(978-1-4234-9937-4(9)***, 1423499379) Leonard, Hal Corp.
—Worship Favorites: Instrumental Play-along for Violin. 2011. (ENG.). 16p. pap. 12.99 incl. audio compact disk ***(978-1-4234-9936-7(0)***, 1423499360) Leonard, Hal Corp.
Hal Leonard Corporation Staff. Simply Beautiful. 2011. (ENG.). 56p. pap. 16.95 *(978-1-61774-116-6(7)*, 1617741167) Shawnee Pr., Inc.
Hal Leonard Corporation Staff, creator. Baching Around the Christmas Tree: Flute. 2008. (ENG.). 24p. pap. 10.95 incl. audio compact disk *(978-1-60378-044-5(0)*, 1603780440) Cherry Lane Music Co.
—Christian Pop/Rock Favorites. 2009. (ENG.). 80p. pap. 12.99 *(978-1-4234-8770-8(2)*, 1423487702) Leonard, Hal Corp.
—Classic Hymns for Violin & Piano: Advanced Solos for the Church Violinist. 2009. (ENG.). 32p. pap. 19.99 *(978-0-8341-7709-3(9)*, 9780834177093) Lillenas Publishing Co.
—Guitars for Christmas: 20 Christmas Carols for One or Two Guitars. 2007. 32p. pap. 17.95 incl. audio compact disk *(978-1-902455-75-4(4)*, 1902455754) Schott Music Corp.
—Joy to the World - Bass Edition: Worship Band Play-along Volume 5. 2009. (ENG.). 48p. pap. 12.99 incl. audio compact disk *(978-1-4234-7085-4(0)*, 1423470850) Leonard, Hal Corp.
—Joy to the World - Drum Edition: Worship Band Play-along Volume 5. 2009. (ENG.). 40p. pap. 12.99 incl. audio compact disk *(978-1-4234-7086-1(9)*, 1423470869) Leonard, Hal Corp.
—Joy to the World - Guitar Edition: Worship Band Play-along Volume 5. 2009. (ENG.). 48p. pap. 12.99 incl. audio compact disk *(978-1-4234-7084-7(2)*, 1423470842) Leonard, Hal Corp.
—Joy to the World - Keyboard Edition: Worship Band Play-along Volume 5. 2009. (ENG.). 56p. pap. 12.99 incl. audio compact disk *(978-1-4234-7083-0(4)*, 1423470834) Leonard, Hal Corp.
—Joy to the World - Vocal Edition: Worship Band Play-along Volume 5. 2009. (ENG.). 40p. pap. 12.99 incl. audio compact disk *(978-1-4234-7082-3(6)*, 1423470826) Leonard, Hal Corp.
—More of the Best Praise & Worship Songs Ever. 2009. (ENG.). 304p. pap. 19.99 *(978-1-4234-6074-9(X)*, 142346074X) Leonard, Hal Corp.
—My First Hymn Book. 2009. (ENG.). 24p. pap. 7.99 *(978-1-4234-7403-6(1)*, 1423474031) Leonard, Hal Corp.
—Sacred Songs & Arias for Baritone/Bass: The Ultimate Collection. 2008. (ENG.). 8p. cd-rom 19.95 *(978-1-4234-3944-8(9)*, 1423439449) Leonard, Hal Corp.
—Sacred Songs & Arias for Mezzo-Soprano/Alto: The Ultimate Collection. 2008. (ENG.). 8p. cd-rom 19.95 *(978-1-4234-3942-4(2)*, 1423439422) Leonard, Hal Corp.
—Solos for Celebrations - Volume 1: 24 Songs for Special Church Occasions. 2010. (ENG.). 96p. pap. 14.99 *(978-1-4234-7383-1(3)*, 1423473833) Leonard, Hal Corp.
—Solos for Celebrations - Volume 2: 24 Songs for Special Church Occasions, 1 vol. 2010. (ENG.). 96p. pap. 14.99 *(978-1-4234-7384-8(1)*, 1423473841) Leonard, Hal Corp.
—Top Christian Hits of '08-'09. 2009. (ENG.). 144p. pap. 14.99 *(978-1-4234-6707-6(8)*, 1423467078) Leonard, Hal Corp.
—The Ultimate Christian Wedding Music Kit. 2008. (ENG.). 104p. pap. 24.95 incl. audio compact disk *(978-1-59235-251-7(0)*, 1592352510) Shawnee Pr., Inc.
Hall, Stephanie, ed. America's Newest Worship Favorites: 10 Top Songs of the Church. 2009. 131p. pap. 7.99 *(978-1-4234-8907-8(1))* Leonard, Hal Corp.
Ham, Marilynn. Standing on the Promises: Hymns of Faith & Songs of Assurance. 2010. (ENG.). 48p. pap. 16.99 *(978-0-8341-7873-1(7)*, 9780834178731) Lillenas Publishing Co.
Ham, Marilynn & Varner, Kenneth D. Glory & Majesty: Powerful Duets for Piano & Organ. 2006. (ENG.). 104p. pap. 18.99 *(978-0-8341-7523-5(1)*, 083-417-5231) Lillenas Publishing Co.
Hamlin, Carolyn. Was I Faithful? SAB with Opt. Orchestra. 2011. 11p. pap. 1.95 ***(978-1-4291-2488-1(1))*** Lorenz Corp., The.
—Was I Faithful? SATB with Opt. Orchestra. 2011. 11p. pap. 1.95 ***(978-1-4291-2487-4(3))*** Lorenz Corp., The.
Hankeln, Roman. Offertory & its Verses: Research, Past, Present & Future. 2007. (Illus.). 180p. 62.00 incl. cd-rom *(978-82-519-2204-3(6))* Tapir Forlag NOR. Dist: International Specialized Bk. Services.
Harris, Jacob. The Dos & Don'ts of Music Ministry & More. 2009. 141p. pap. 16.95 *(978-1-4327-4458-8(5))* Outskirts Pr., Inc.
Harvey, Susan Ashbrook. Song & Memory: Biblical Women in Syriac Tradition. 2010. *(978-0-87462-590-5(4))* Marquette Univ. Pr.
Hascher-Burger, Ulrike. Singen Fur die Seligkeit: Studien Zu Einer Liedersammlung der Devotio Moderna: Zwolle, Historisch Centrum Overijssel, Coll. Emmanuelshuizen, Cat. VI. Edition und Faksimile. 2007. (Brill's Series in Church History Ser.). (Illus.). 337p. *(978-90-04-16151-1(1))* BRILL.
Hastings, Thomas. Dissertation on Musical Taste. 2009. 148p. pap. *(978-0-217-46461-1(0))*; 150p. pap. *(978-0-217-92537-2(5))* Books LLC.
Hayes, Mark, contrib. by. What a Friend: SATB & Soloist with Opt. Instrumental Ensemble. 2011. 15p. pap. 1.95 ***(978-1-4291-2484-3(9))*** Lorenz Corp., The.
—Zion's Walls: SAB with 4-Hand Piano or Opt. 2-Hand Piano. 2011. 15p. pap. 1.95 ***(978-1-4291-2547-5(0))*** Lorenz Corp., The.
—Zion's Walls: SATB with 4-Hand Piano or Opt. 2-Hand Piano. 2011. 15p. pap. 1.95 ***(978-1-4291-2546-8(2))*** Lorenz Corp., The.
—Zion's Walls: SSA with 4-Hand Piano or Opt. 2-Hand Piano. 2011. 15p. pap. 1.95 ***(978-1-4291-2548-2(9))*** Lorenz Corp., The.
Heaven: Songs for the Soul-Winning Church. 2007. (ENG.). 104p. pap. 7.99 *(978-0-8341-7597-6(5)*, 0834175975) Lillenas Publishing Co.
Helman, Michael. Shall We Gather at the River: 3, 4 or 5 Octaves with Opt. Handchimes (3, 4 or 5 Octaves), Level 3. 2011. 8p. pap. 4.50 ***(978-1-4291-2337-2(0))*** Lorenz Corp., The.
Henley, Darren. Lost Souls Against the World. 2011. 156p. 29.99 ***(978-1-4568-8009-5(8))***; pap. 19.99 ***(978-1-4568-8008-8(X))*** Xlibris Corp.
Hess, Debbie. Chord Progressions for Open Worship. 2007. 27p. 20.00 *(978-0-9798491-3-8(6))* Gospel Piano Resource.
Highben, Zebulon & Langlois, Kristina, eds. With a Voice of Singing: Essays on Children, Choirs, & Music in the Church. 2007. (Illus.). 184p. pap. 16.00 *(978-1-933794-03-7(8))* Kirk Hse. Pubs.
Higher Ground: Inspirational Gospel Songs of Hope, Assurance & Celebration. 2008. (ENG.). 136p. pap. 7.99 *(978-0-8341-7662-1(9)*, 9780834176621) Lillenas Publishing Co.
Hiley, David. Gregorian Chant. 2009. (Cambridge Introductions to Music Ser.). (ENG., Illus.). 270p. (C). 80.00 *(978-0-521-87020-7(8))*; pap. 27.99 *(978-0-521-69035-5(8))* Cambridge Univ. Pr.
Hogan, Ed. Creative Hymns for Brass Quartet Vol. 1: Traditional Hymns with a Popular Twist. 2010. (ENG.). 36p. pap. 59.99 *(978-0-8341-7825-0(7)*, 9780834178250) Lillenas Publishing Co.

—Meditative Solos for Alto Saxophone: Creative Solos for the Church Musician. 2008. (ENG.). 32p. pap. 19.99 *(978-0-8341-7715-4(3)*, 9780834177154) Lillenas Publishing Co.
—Meditative Solos for Clarinet: Creative Solos for the Church Musician. 2008. (ENG.). 32p. pap. 19.99 *(978-0-8341-7714-7(5)*, 9780834177147) Lillenas Publishing Co.
—Meditative Solos for Flute: Creative Solos for the Church Musician. 2008. (ENG.). 32p. pap. 19.99 *(978-0-8341-7712-3(9)*, 9780834177123) Lillenas Publishing Co.
—Meditative Solos for Trumpet: Creative Solos for the Church Musician. 2008. (ENG.). 32p. pap. 19.99 *(978-0-8341-7711-6(0)*, 9780834177116) Lillenas Publishing Co.
—Meditative Solos for Violin: Creative Solos for the Church Musician. 2008. (ENG.). 32p. pap. 19.99 incl. audio compact disk *(978-0-8341-7718-5(8)*, 0834177188) Lillenas Publishing Co.
Hooray for Baby Jesus! A Musical for Preschoolers Celebrating the Gift of Our Savior. 2011. (ENG.). 32p. pap. 19.99 ***(978-0-8341-7905-9(9)***, 9780834179059) Lillenas Publishing Co.
Hopson, Hal H., ed. The Psalter, Choral Edition: Psalms & Canticles for Singing. 2011. (ENG.). 136p. pap. 20.00 *(978-0-664-23704-2(5))* Westminster John Knox Pr.
Hospenthal, Cristina. Tropen zum Ordinarium missae in St. Gallen: Untersuchungen zu den Beständen in den Handschriften St. Gallen, Stiftsbibliothek 381, 484, 376, 378, 380 Und 382. 2010. (Publikationen der Schweizerischen Musikforschenden Gesellschaft Serie II Publicatons de la Société Suisse de Musicologie Série II Ser.). (GER.). 231p. pap. *(978-3-03911-673-7(8))* Lang, Peter.
How We Thank You: Modern Music in the Ancient Sanctuary. 2008. (ENG.). 136p. pap. 29.99 *(978-0-8341-7684-3(X)*, 9780834176843) Lillenas Publishing Co.
Hsieh, Fang-Lan. A History of Chinese Christian Hymnody: From Its Missionary Origins to Contemporary Indigenous Productions. 2010. (Illus.). xv, 269p. *(978-0-7734-3816-3(5))* Mellen, Edwin Pr., The.
Hughes, Edwin Holt, et al. Worship in Music. 2011. 206p. 44.95 ***(978-1-258-06094-7(9))*** Literary Licensing, LLC.
Hughes, Tim. Here I Am to Worship: 2 or 3 Octaves (Handbells or Handchimes), Level 2+ 2011. 7p. pap. 4.95 ***(978-1-4291-2377-8(X))*** Lorenz Corp., The.
Husmann, Heinrich. Die Melodien der Jakobitischen Kirche. 2010. 230p. 10.36 *(978-1-60724-731-9(3))* 2010. 282p. 10.36 ***(978-1-60724-730-2(5))*** 2008. (Gorgias Liturgical Studies: 2). (GER & SYR.). 105.00 *(978-1-59333-801-5(5))* Gorgias Pr., LLC.
Hymns to Millennium, Vol. 32. *(978-0-404-60932-0(5))* AMS Pr., Inc.
Hyzer, Matt. Hymns for the Spirit: 10 Contemporary Arrangements for Worship. 2009. (Sacred Performer Collections). (ENG.). 40p. pap. 12.95 *(978-0-7390-6090-2(2))* Alfred Publishing Co., Inc.
I Praise You, Lord Anthem. 1.50 *(978-0-687-04467-2(7))* Abingdon Pr.
Ibrahim, Gregorios. Syrian Orthodox Music. 2009. (ARA, SYR & ENG.). 100.00 *(978-1-60724-264-2(8))* Gorgias Pr., LLC.
Idle, Steve. Tuning into God Forty Licks. 2007. (Tuning into God Ser.). 48p. pap. 7.99 *(978-0-7847-1996-1(9))* Standard Publishing.
Ikerman. Blessings for Church Occasion. 2.95 *(978-0-687-03624-0(0))* Abingdon Pr.
It's Easter! An Easy-to-sing, Easy-to-stage Kids Musical about God's Love & Grace. 2011. (ENG.). 24p. pap. 5.99 ***(978-0-8341-8120-5(7)***, 9780834181205) Lillenas Publishing Co.
Jackson, Gabriel. Let Us All Rejoice in the Lord. 2009. (ENG.). 8p. pap. 2.35 *(978-0-19-336575-9(8))* Oxford Univ. Pr., Inc.
Jackson, George Pullen. The Story of the Sacred Harp, 1844-1944. 2010. (ENG., Illus.). 56p. lib. bdg. 22.50 *(978-0-8265-1018-1(3))* Vanderbilt Univ. Pr.
Jason, Pamela. 101 Church Signs: (God's Best Ad Men) 2010. 48p. pap. 9.95 *(978-1-4502-5754-1(2))* iUniverse, Inc.
Jesus Is Alive! An Easter Worship Service Package. 2011. (ENG.). 60p. pap. 4.99 ***(978-0-8341-8137-3(1)***, 9780834181373) Lillenas Publishing Co.
John Bell-Editor Staff. Hymns of Glory, Songs of Praise-Full Music. 2009. 56.00 *(978-1-85311-900-2(8))* Hymns Ancient & Modern Ltd GBR. Dist: Church Publishing, Inc.
Johnson, Aubrey. Music Matters: In the Lord's Church. pap. 7.99 *(978-0-89098-141-2(8))* Twentieth Century Christian Bks.
Johnson, Victor C. Be Still & Know: SATB Divisi. 2011. 7p. pap. 1.85 ***(978-1-4291-2536-9(5))*** Lorenz Corp., The.
Jones, Douglas R. Sound of Worship: A Handbook of Acoustics & Sound System Design for the Church. 2010. (ENG., Illus.). 316p. pap. 49.95 *(978-0-240-81339-4(1)*, Focal Pr.) Elsevier Science & Technology Bks.
Jones, Paul S. What Is Worship Music? 2010. pap. *(978-1-59638-198-8(1))* P & R Publishing.
Joseph M. Martin. Whispers of the Passion. 2010. (ENG.). 68p. pap. 8.95 *(978-1-4234-9977-0(8)*, 1423499778, Flammer, Harold Music) Shawnee Pr., Inc.
Keats, Ezra Jack, illus. The Little Drummer Boy. 2007. (ENG.). 32p. (J). (gr. -1-18). bds. 6.99 *(978-0-670-06282-9(0)*, Viking Juvenile) Penguin Group (USA) Inc.
Keeston, David R. Grace Notes: Theme & Variations. 2009. 141p. pap. 21.50 *(978-1-4452-1558-7(6))* Lulu Enterprises Inc.
Kidula, Jean Ngoya. Music in Kenyan Christianity: Logooli Religious Song. 2012. (Ethnomusicology Multimedia Ser.). (ENG.). 248p. pap. 30.00 ***(978-0-253-00668-4(6)***, 0253006686); (Illus.). 85.00 ***(978-0-253-00667-7(8)***, 0253006678) Indiana Univ. Pr.
Kimbrough, S. T., ed. Music & Mission: Toward a Theology of Practice of Global Song. 2006. 200p. pap. *(978-1-933663-08-1(1)*, GBGMusik) General Board of Global Ministries, The United Methodist Church.
King, Roberta & Kidula, Jean Ngoya. Music in the Life of the African Church. 2008. (Illus.). 165p. pap. 29.95 *(978-1-60258-022-0(7))* Baylor Univ. Pr.
Kirkman, Andrew. Sacred & Liturgical Renaissance Music. 2012. (Library of Essays on Renaissance Music Ser.). 500p. 300.00 ***(978-0-7546-2940-5(6))*** Ashgate Publishing Co.
Knighton, Tess & Torrente, Alvaro, eds. Devotional Music in the Iberian World, 1450-1800: The Villancico & Related Genres. 2007. (Illus.). 490p. 144.95 *(978-0-7546-5841-2(4))* Ashgate Publishing Co.
Kraeuter, Tom. The Worship Leader's Handbook: Practical Answers to Tough Questions. rev. ed. 2007. (ENG.). 191p. per. *(978-1-932096-42-2(6))* Emerald Bks.
Kroeker, Charlotte Yvonne. The Sounds of Our Offerings: Achieving Excellence in Church Music. 2011. ***(978-1-56699-395-1(4))*** Alban Institute, Inc.
Krug, Jason W. Faith, Hope, & Love: 3, 4, 5 or 6 Octaves with Opt. Handchimes (2 Octaves), Level 2. 2011. 11p. pap. 4.95 ***(978-1-4291-2328-0(1))*** Lorenz Corp., The.
Kutless. Kutless - It Is Well, 1 vol. 2009. (ENG.). 80p. pap. 16.99 *(978-1-4234-8918-4(7)*, 1423489187) Leonard, Hal Corp.
Labenske, Victor. Heaven's Song: Hymns of Eternal Promise. 2009. (ENG.). 64p. pap. 16.99 *(978-0-8341-7703-1(X)*, 9780834177031) Lillenas Publishing Co.
Labenske, Victor, contrib. by. Sunday Morning Companion: 33 of the Greatest Hymns of All Time: Intermediate to Late Intermediate Piano. 2007. (Alfred's Sacred Performer Collections). (ENG.). 128p. pap. 24.95 *(978-0-7390-4855-9(4))* Alfred Publishing Co., Inc.
Lane, Tom. The Worship Band Book: Training & Empowering Your Worship Band. 2012. (ENG., Illus.). 160p. spiral bd. 16.99 ***(978-1-4584-1817-3(0)***, 1458418170) Leonard, Hal Corp.

Lantz, David Iii & Bentall Boersma, Susan. Come, Holy Spirit, Come! 2009. cd-rom 30.00 *(978-1-4234-8712-8(5)*, 1423487125) Shawnee Pr., Inc.
Laporta, Jose. Comunicacion Musical Evangelica: Christian Music Manual. (SPA.). *(978-84-7645-025-3(7)*, 223103) Clie, Editorial.
Larson, Lloyd. Ashes to Fire: the Piano Project: Hymns & Worship Songs for Ash Wednesday through Pentecost. 2011. (ENG.). 64p. pap. 19.99 ***(978-0-8341-7878-6(8)***, 9780834178786) Lillenas Publishing Co.
—Forever Exalted! Contemporary Medleys of Praise. 2007. (ENG.). 64p. pap. 16.99 *(978-0-8341-7609-6(2)*, 0834176092) Lillenas Publishing Co.
—Light a Candle in the Night: Unison or Two-Part Any Combination with Opt. Congregation & Narration. 2011. 12p. pap. 1.95 ***(978-1-4291-2554-3(3))*** Lorenz Corp., The.
—You Are My God! SATB Divisi with Opt. Brass & Percussion. 2011. 12p. pap. 1.95 ***(978-1-4291-2588-8(8))*** Lorenz Corp., The.
Leaver, Robin A. The Theological Character of Music in Worship. Schalk, Carl, ed. 32p. reprint ed. pap. 2.75 *(978-0-570-01339-6(9)*, 99-1296) Concordia Publishing Hse.
Leeson, Jane Eliza. Savior, Teach Me: SATB or SAB with Opt. Solo & Rhythm. 2011. 11p. pap. 1.95 ***(978-1-4291-2557-4(8))*** Lorenz Corp., The.
Lifetime Media Staff, ed. The Sermon Notebook. 2010. (ENG.). 120p. 9.95 *(978-0-9816368-7-0(X))* LifeTime Media, Inc.
Lim, Swee Hong. Giving Voice to Asian Christians. 2008. 344p. pap. *(978-3-639-06074-4(1))* VDM Verlag Dr. Mueller e.K.
Linner, Maria Margarete. Lied und Singen in der konfessionellen Jugendbewegung des frühen 20. Jahrhunderts. 2009. (Beiträge zur Geschichte der Musikpädagogik Ser.). (GER.). 210p. 50.95 *(978-3-631-59148-2(9))* Lang, Peter GmbH, Europäischer Verlag der Wissenschaften DEU. Dist: Lang, Peter.
Lister, Mosie. Is Your Name Written There? (Mountaintop Ser.). 8p. pap. 1.45 *(978-0-8341-9170-9(9))* Lillenas Publishing Co.
Lord Be Glorified (Keyboard/Vocal Edition) Companion Hymnal for Blended Worship. Date not set. 224p. *(978-1-57992-051-7(9))* Oregon Catholic Pr.
Lorenz Publishing, creator. The Church Pianist's Library, Volume 9. 2011. 98p. pap. 19.95 ***(978-1-4291-2173-6(4))*** Lorenz Corp., The.
—Easy Organ Library, Volume 50. 2011. 98p. spiral bd. 19.95 ***(978-1-4291-2171-2(8))*** Lorenz Corp., The.
—The Organist's Library. 2011. (Organist's Library). 98p. pap. 19.95 *(978-1-4291-2163-7(7))* Lorenz Corp., The.
Lorenz Publishing, creator. The Organist's Library, Volume 50. 2011. 98p. pap. 19.95 ***(978-1-4291-2172-9(6))*** Lorenz Corp., The.
Lowry, Robert. Shall We Gather. *(978-0-8054-5963-0(4))* B&H Publishing Group.
Mannaerts, P. Beghinae in cantu Instructae: Musical patrimony from Flemish beguinages (Middle Ages - Late 18th C.) 2010. (Epitome Musical Ser.). (ENG & LAT., Illus.). 296p. (C). pap. 80.00 ***(978-2-503-53015-4(X))*** Brepols Pubs. BEL. Dist: ISD.
Marini, Stephen A. Sacred Song in America: Religion, Music, & Public Culture. 2010. (Public Expression Religion America Ser.). (Illus.). 416p. pap. 30.00 *(978-0-252-07803-3(9))* Univ. of Illinois Pr.
Marlatt, David. Songs for Worship & Celebration, Vol 1. 2010. pap. 10.00 *(978-1-55472-946-3(7))* Alfred Publishing Co., Inc.
Marshall, Jane M., et al. Family of God. 2008. pap. 8.00 *(978-0-687-49089-9(8))* Abingdon Pr.
Martin, Joseph M. The Lenten Sketches. 2009. (ENG.). 72p. pap. 8.95 *(978-1-4234-8820-0(2)*, 1423488202) Shawnee Pr., Inc.
—We Are Made for Praise. 2009. cd-rom 60.00 *(978-1-4234-8682-4(X)*, 142348682X) Shawnee Pr., Inc.
Martin, Pamela. Echo Christmas Joy: SAB with Opt. Orchestra or Instrumental Ensemble. 2011. 11p. pap. 1.95 ***(978-1-4291-2480-5(6))*** Lorenz Corp., The.
—The Time for Turning: Sab. 2011. 8p. pap. 1.85 ***(978-1-4291-2538-3(1))*** Lorenz Corp., The.
—The Time for Turning: Ssa. 2011. 8p. pap. 1.85 ***(978-1-4291-2537-6(3))*** Lorenz Corp., The.
McDonald, Mary. His Grace Will Lead Us Through: SATB with Opt. Orchestra. 2011. 11p. pap. 1.95 ***(978-1-4291-2404-1(0))*** Lorenz Corp., The.
—His Grace Will Lead Us Through: TTBB with Opt. Orchestra. 2011. 11p. pap. 1.95 ***(978-1-4291-2405-8(9))*** Lorenz Corp., The.
—How Excellent Are Your Ways: SAB with Opt. Brass & Rhythm. 2011. 12p. pap. 1.95 ***(978-1-4291-2380-8(X))*** Lorenz Corp., The.
—How Excellent Are Your Ways: SATB with Opt. Brass & Rhythm. 2011. 12p. pap. 1.95 ***(978-1-4291-2379-2(6))*** Lorenz Corp., The.
McGuire, Jan. The Voice of God: SATB with Opt. Cello. 2011. 11p. pap. 1.95 ***(978-1-4291-2586-4(1))*** Lorenz Corp., The.
Medley, Mark. Because He's Worthy. 2008. (ENG.). per. 24.95 *(978-1-60037-095-3(0))* Morgan James Publishing.
Mellers, Wilfrid. Bach & the Dance of God. 336p. 2009. *(978-1-904331-87-2(4))* 2007. (ENG.). per. *(978-1-904331-21-6(1))* Travis & Emery Music Bookshop.
Metcalf, Frank J. American Writers & Compilers of Sacred Music. 2007. (ENG.). 424p. per. *(978-1-4067-5144-4(8))* Read Bks.
Miller, Joseph. Singer & Songs of the Church. reprint ed. lib. bdg. 75.00 *(978-0-7812-0770-6(3))* Reprint Services Co.
Monks of New Skete Staff. Annunciation of the Theotokos: Choral Chants. Mancuso, Laurence, tr. from GRE. Date not set. (Liturgical Music Series I: Vol. 12). 35p. pap. 15.00 *(978-0-935129-33-5(2))* Monks of New Skete.
Monks of the Abbey of St. Peter of Solesmes Staff. Liber Cantualis: Latin Chants for the Ordinary of the Mass. (LAT.). 120p. (C). 14.95 *(978-2-85274-040-2(0)*, 3009) Abbey of St. Peter of Solesmes, The FRA. Dist: Paraclete Pr., Inc.
Morning Has Broken. 4.50 *(978-0-687-09479-0(8))* Abingdon Pr.
Muchimba, Felix. Liberating the African Soul: Comparing African & Western Christian Music & Worship Styles. 2008. (ENG.). 156p. per. 14.99 *(978-1-934068-42-7(X))* Authentic Media.
Music Leader. 3.95 *(978-0-7673-6144-6(X))* LifeWay Christian Resources.
Music Makers Pak. 54.95 *(978-0-7673-6116-3(4))* LifeWay Christian Resources.
Music Makers Spring 2000. *(978-0-7673-8463-6(6))* LifeWay Christian Resources.
Music Makers Summer 2000. *(978-0-7673-8474-2(1))* LifeWay Christian Resources.
Music Time Activity. 4.98 *(978-0-7673-6186-6(5))* LifeWay Christian Resources.
Music Time Pak. 54.95 *(978-0-7673-6172-9(5))* LifeWay Christian Resources.
The New Oxford Easy Anthem Book. 2006. 256p. spiral bd. 26.95 *(978-0-19-335578-1(7))* Oxford Univ. Pr., Inc.
A Night of Hope: A Christmas Worship Celebration. 2009. (ENG.). 160p. pap. 8.99 *(978-0-8341-7696-6(3)*, 9780834176966) Allegis Pubns.
Not Just a Story: An Easter Musical for Unison/2-Part Choir. 2011. (ENG.). 44p. pap. 5.99 ***(978-0-8341-8136-6(3)***, 9780834181366) Lillenas Publishing Co.
Ogasapian, John. Church Music in America, 1620-2000. 2007. 284p. 49.95 *(978-0-88146-026-1(5))* Mercer Univ. Pr.
Okun, Milton, ed. Contemporary Christian Today. pap. 14.95 *(978-0-89524-793-3(3))* Cherry Lane Music Co.
Ol'Leka, Shitandi Wilson. Meaning in Music, Culture & Theology: An Analysis of Legio Maria Church Hymnody in Kenya. 2011. 216p. pap. ***(978-3-639-33094-6(3))*** VDM Verlag Dr. Mueller e.K.
One: Songs Celebrating God's Call to Holiness. 2007. (ENG.). 56p. pap. 4.99 *(978-0-8341-7586-0(X)*, 083417586X) Lillenas Publishing Co.
Open Windows. 1.55 *(978-0-7673-4716-7(1))* LifeWay Christian Resources.
Ostrem, E., et al. Medieval Ritual & Early Modern Music: The Devotional Practice of Lauda Singing in Late-Renaissance Italy. 2008. (Ritus et Artes Ser.). (ENG

& ITA., Illus.). 348p. (C). 102.00 *(978-2-503-52066-7(9))* Brepols Pubs. BEL. Dist: ISD.

Owens, Jimmy, et al. The Country Favorites: How to Write & Select Songs for Worship. 2009. (ENG.). 174p. pap. 19.99 *(978-1-4234-3536-5(2),* 1423435362) Leonard, Hal Corp.

Page, Christopher. The Christian West & Its Singers: The First Thousand Years. 2010. (Illus.). 400p. 45.00 *(978-0-300-11257-3(2))* Yale Univ. Pr.

Panoyan, Kevork. Classification of Hymns of the Armenian Apostolic Church Vol. 1. 2009. (ARM., Illus.). 120p. pap. 25.00 *(978-0-9842573-1-7(4))* Drazark Pr.

Parachute Band, contrib. by. Roadmaps & Revelations. 2007. (Worshiptools Ser.). (Illus.). 46p. pap. 29.95 incl. audio compact disk *(978-5-557-57357-3(7))* Integrity Music, Inc.

Parks, Marty. O for a Dozen Tongues to Sing - Gospel Hymns: Six Ready-to-Sing Anthems for Two-part Mixed Voices. 2009. spiral bd. 29.95 *(978-1-4267-0016-3(4))* Abingdon Pr.

Parks, Marty & Bible, Ken, contrib. by. Songs for All Seasons: Choral Selections to Highlight Special Days. 2007. (ENG.). 152p. pap. 8.99 *(978-0-8341-7591-4(6),* 0834175916) Lillenas Publishing Co.

Passion. Passion - Awakening. 2010. (ENG.). 128p. pap. 16.99 *(978-1-935288-09-1(1),* 1935288091) Leonard, Hal Corp.

Pathway Press, creator. Church Hymnal. 2009. 410p. 8.99 *(978-1-59684-421-6(3))* Pathway Pr.

Patrick, Millar. The Story of the Church's Song. 2008. 196p. *(978-1-4437-3265-9(6))* 2007. 192p. per. *(978-1-4067-8859-4(7))* Read Bks. (Pomona Pr.).

Peace Literary House, compiled by. Praise to the Lord for Ever & Ever. 2007. (MUL.). 176p. per. *(978-1-55452-136-4(X))* Essence Publishing.

Pearce, Ted & Be'er Sheva, contrib. by. Hallelu et Adonai: Praise the Lord: Messianic Praise & Worship: Chords, Lyrics, & Melodies. 2008. (Illus.). 48p. pap. 16.98 *(978-5-557-36610-6(5))* Point of Grace Entertainment Group.

Pearsall, Robert. Let Your Light So Shine. 2009. pap., pap. 2.00 *(978-0-19-395388-8(9))* Oxford Univ. Pr., Inc.

Pethel, Stan, contrib. by. Strings of Praise: 12 Worship Arrangements for One or More String Players. 2008. (ENG.). 64p. pap. 14.95 *(978-1-59235-250-0(2),* 1592352502) Shawnee Pr., Inc.

Phillips, Christopher, et al, contrib. by. He Still Leads: Satb. 2008. audio compact disk 10.00 *(978-5-557-48398-8(5),* Brentwood-Benson Music Publishing, Inc.) Brentwood Music, Inc.

—He Still Leads: Satb. 2008. (ENG.). 215p. pap. 8.99 *(978-5-557-48401-5(9))* Brentwood-Benson Music Publishing.

Powell, Paul Richard & Eskew, Harry. Hymnology in the Service of the Church: Essays in Honor of Harry Eskew. 2008. (C). 30.00 *(978-0-944529-47-8(X))* Morning Star Music Pubs.

The Power of the Cross: A Musical Praising Christ, the Risen Lamb. 2007. (ENG.). 96p. pap. 6.99 *(978-0-8341-7593-8(2),* 0834175932) Lillenas Publishing Co.

Praise & Worship Hymnal. ring bd. 19.99 *(978-0-8341-9641-4(7))* Lillenas Publishing Co.

Prentice, David A. Loaves & Fishes Worship Team Training: Transforming Small Church Resources into Quality Music Ministry. 2007. 76p. per. 16.95 *(978-1-4241-7765-3(0))* PublishAmerica, Inc.

Quantz, Johann Joachim. Johann Joachim Quantz: Pastorale in G Major. Goebel, Reinhard, ed. 2011. pap. 15.00 net. *(978-0-89579-703-2(8))* A-R Editions, Inc.

Raley, J. Michael & Loftis, Deborah Carlton, eds. Minds & Hearts in Praise of God: Hymns & Essays in Church Music in Honor of Hugh T. Mcelrath. 2007. (Illus.). 310p. per. 24.95 net. *(978-1-57736-307-1(8))* Providence Hse Pubs.

Reinke, Stephan Alexander & Reinke, Stephan A. Musik im Kasualgottesdienst: Funktion und Bedeutung am Beispiel von Trauung und Bestattung. 2010. (GER.). 291p. (C). pap. 41.00 *(978-3-525-60127-3(1))* Vandenhoeck & Ruprecht GmbH & Co. KG DEU. Dist: ISD.

Reynolds, William J. Dp God of Our Fathers. 1.05 *(978-0-7673-0251-7(6))* LifeWay Christian Resources.

Richardson, Paul Akers & Sharp, Timothy. Jubilate, Amen! A Festschrift in Honor of Donald Paul Hustad. 2010. (Illus.). xiii, 471p. *(978-1-57647-138-8(1))* Pendragon Pr.

Rio, Jamie & Buono, Chris. House of Worship Sound Reinforcement. 2nd ed. 2009. (ENG.). 256p. pap. 34.99 *(978-1-59863-613-0(8))* Course Technology.

Riverview Staff. Encounter. pap. Whitaker Hse.

Robertson, Barny. Tune My Heart for Praise: Enduring Hymns for Today's Church. 2008. (ENG.). 56p. pap. 16.99 *(978-0-8341-7520-4(7),* 083-417-5207) Lillenas Publishing Co.

Rogal, Samuel. Commentary, Notes, & Introductions to the 1858 Sabbath Hymn Book: The Musicalized Theology of Popular Belief Just Before the Civil War, 4 vols. 2009. 536p. 139.95 *(978-0-7734-4791-2(1))*; 460p. 129.95 *(978-0-7734-4795-0(4))* Mellen, Edwin Pr., The.

Rush-Arr., et al. Dp Your Love Lifted Me. 1.05 *(978-0-7673-0344-6(X))* LifeWay Christian Resources.

Sadoh, Godwin. Thomas Ekundayo Phillips: The Doyen of Nigerian Church Music. 2009. 200p. pap. 16.95 *(978-1-4401-1909-5(0))* iUniverse, Inc.

Sanga, Imani. Sounds of Muziki Wa Injili. 2010. 240p. pap. *(978-3-8383-6325-7(6))* Lambert Academic Publishing.

Schaefer, Edward. Evangélia Cantáta: A Notated Book of Gospels, 3 Volume Set (Black & White), 3 vols. 2007. 1003p. *(978-0-9801576-3-5(3))* Priory Pr.

—Evangélia Cantáta: A Notated Book of Gospels, 3 Volume Set (Color), 3. 2007. 1003p. *(978-0-9801576-7-3(6))* Priory Pr.

—Evangélia Cantáta: A Notated Book of Gospels, Year A (Black & White), 3 vols, Year A (Black and White) 2007. 341p. *(978-0-9801576-0-4(9))* Priory Pr.

—Evangélia Cantáta: A Notated Book of Gospels, Year A (Color), 3, Year A (Color) 2007. 341p. *(978-0-9801576-4-2(1))* Priory Pr.

—Evangélia Cantáta: A Notated Book of Gospels, Year B (Black & White), 3, Year B (Black and White) 2007. 317p. *(978-0-9801576-1-1(7))* Priory Pr.

—Evangélia Cantáta: A Notated Book of Gospels, Year B (Color), 3, Year B (Color) 2007. 317p. *(978-0-9801576-5-9(X))* Priory Pr.

—Evangélia Cantáta: A Notated Book of Gospels, Year C (Black & White), 3, Year C (Black and White) 2007. 345p. *(978-0-9801576-2-8(5))* Priory Pr.

—Evangélia Cantáta: A Notated Book of Gospels, Year C (Color), 3, Year C (Color) 2007. 345p. *(978-0-9801576-6-6(8))* Priory Pr.

—Evangélia Cantáta: A Notated Book of Gospels (BW) For Sundays, Solemnities, & Selected Feasts of the Lord & the Saints. 2007. 774p. *(978-0-9801576-9-7(2))* Priory Pr.

—Evangélia Cantáta: A Notated Book of Gospels (Color) For Sundays, Solemnities, & Selected Feasts of the Lord & the Saints. 2007. 774p. *(978-0-9801576-8-0(4))* Priory Pr.

Schelkes, Dorothea. Johann Martin Spieß (1691 - 1772) Ein kurpfälzischer Komponist im Dienst der reformierten Kirche. 2009. (Mannheimer Hochschulschriften Ser.). (GER.). 322p. 76.95 *(978-3-631-58622-8(1))* Lang, Peter GmbH, Europaischer Verlag der Wissenschaften DEU. Dist: Lang, Peter.

Schram, Ruth Elaine. When You Call: Satb. 2011. 8p. pap. 1.85 ***(978-1-4291-2491-1(1))*** Lorenz Corp., The.

Schreiner, Alexander. Sunday Morning Organist, Vol 6: Voluntaries (with Pedal) 2011. (Alfred's Classic Editions Ser.). (ENG.). 192p. pap. 24.99 ***(978-0-7390-8275-1(2))*** Alfred Publishing Co., Inc.

—Sunday Morning Organist, Vol 7: Voluntaries (without Pedal) 2011. (Alfred's Classic Editions Ser.). (ENG.). 184p. pap. 24.99 ***(978-0-7390-8276-8(0))*** Alfred Publishing Co., Inc.

Schubert, Myra. Just a Closer Walk: Gospel Favorites for the Journey of Faith. 2011. (ENG.). 48p. pap. 16.99 ***(978-0-8341-7918-9(0),*** 9780834179189) Lillenas Publishing Co.

Scism, Stanley Devoted. 2009. pap. 5.00 *(978-1-61584-696-2(4))* Independent Pub.

—Stanley Scism Songs. 2009. pap. 4.00 *(978-1-61584-694-8(8))* Independent Pub.

Service Music & Music from Taize. 10.00 incl. audio *(978-0-687-04916-5(4))* Abingdon Pr.

Shackley, Larry, contrib. by. Climbin' up the Mountain, Children: Satb. 2011. 12p. pap. 1.95 ***(978-1-4291-2555-0(1))*** Lorenz Corp., The.

—How Firm a Foundation: Satb. 2011. 8p. pap. 1.85 ***(978-1-4291-2587-1(X))*** Lorenz Corp., The.

Shackley, Larry, ed. Exaltation... Plugged & Unplugged, Level 2: Praise & Worship Duets for Piano & Digital Keyboard. 2011. 56p. pap. 21.95 ncl. audio compact disk *(978-1-4291-2096-8(7))* Lorenz Corp., The.

Shafferman, Jean Anne, contrib. by. Make Us Instruments of Your Peace: SATB or SAB. 2011. 8p. pap. 1.85 ***(978-1-4291-2589-5(6))*** Lorenz Corp., The.

Sirota, Victoria. Preaching to the Choir: Reclaiming the Role of Sacred Musician. 2006. 150p. per. 16.00 *(978-0-89869-528-1(7))* Church Publishing, Inc.

Slough, Rebecca & King, Shirley Sprunger, eds. Nurturing Spirit Through Song: The Life of Mary K. Oyer. 2007. (Illus.). 271p. per. 22.95 *(978-1-931038-42-3(2))* Cascadia Publishing Hse., LLC.

Smith, Bill. Holidays & Holy Days. 2010. 212p. 27.95 *(978-1-60844-569-1(0))*; pap. 14.99 *(978-1-60844-546-2(1))* Dog Ear Publishing, LLC.

Smith, J. Daniel, contrib. by. Creation: Satb. 2008. 119p. pap. 7.95 *(978-5-557-48309-4(8),* Brentwood-Benson Music Publishing, Inc.) Brentwood Music, Inc.

Smith, John Arthur. Music in Ancient Judaism & Early Christianity. 2011. (Illus.). 294p. 114.95 *(978-1-4094-0907-6(4))* Ashgate Publishing Co.

Smith, Karen & Snyder, David. O Holy Night: A Christmas Collection for Flute & Piano. 2009. (ENG.). 96p. pap. 19.99 incl. audio compact disk *(978-1-4234-8941-2(1),* 1423489411) Leonard, Hal Corp.

Smith, Randy. I Speak to You of Jesus Orchestration. 49.95 *(978-0-7673-0040-7(8))* LifeWay Christian Resources.

Smith, Scott McBride, ed. American Popular Piano - Christmas: Preparatory Level. 2008. (ENG.). 14p. pap. 5.95 *(978-1-897379-44-8(7),* 1897379447) Novus Via Music Group Inc. CAN. Dist: Leonard, Hal Corp.

Smith, William S. Joyful Noise: A Guide to Music in the Church for Pastors & Musicians. 2007. (Illus.). 306p. per. 24.95 *(978-1-57736-397-2(3))* Providence Hse Pubs.

Sohl, Joyce. God's Mission, God's Song (Korean Edition) Yoo, Yani, tr. from ENG. 2007. (KOR.). 142p. spiral bd. 10.95 *(978-1-933663-15-9(4),* WD/GBGM Bks.) General Board of Global Ministries, The United Methodist Church.

Songs God Sings to Me. 2006. pap. 13.99 *(978-1-60034-205-9(1))* Xulon Pr., Inc.

Sorenson, Heather. God Is: Ageless Hymns Reflecting the Nature of God. 2011. (ENG.). 52p. pap. 16.99 ***(978-0-8341-7917-2(2),*** 9780834179172) Lillenas Publishing Co.

—God of Heaven. 2009. cd-rom 60.00 *(978-1-4234-8679-4(X),* 142348679X) Shawnee Pr., Inc.

—How Sweet the Sound! Old Hymns Made New. 2009. (ENG.) 64p. pap. 16.99 *(978-0-8341-7704-8(8),* 9780834177048) Lillenas Publishing Co.

Sovereign Lord: A Musical Proclaiming the Risen, Conquering King. 2008. (ENG.). 112p. pap. 8.99 *(978-0-8341-7661-4(0),* 9780834176614) Allegis Pubns.

Steinhilber, Alexander. Die Musikhandschrift F. K. Mus. 76/II. Abt. der Fürst Thurn und Taxis Hofbibliothek Regensburg: Eine wenig beachtete Quelle zur Musik des frühprotestantischen Gottesdienstes. 2011. (Abhandlungen zur Musikgeschichte Ser.). (GER., Illus.). 600p. (C). 110.00 *(978-3-89971-638-2(8))* Vandenhoeck & Ruprecht GmbH & Co. KG DEU. Dist: ISD.

Sterling, Robert. Count the Cost. 195.00 *(978-0-7673-1194-6(9))* LifeWay Christian Resources.

—The Craft of Christian Songwriting. 2009. (ENG.). 200p. pap. 24.99 *(978-1-4234-6339-9(0),* 1423463390) Leonard, Hal Corp.

Stern, Max. Bible & Music: Influences of the Old Testament on Western Music. 2011. ***(978-1-60280-166-0(5))*** Ktav Publishing Hse., Inc.

Stubbings, George W. A Dictionary of Church Music. *(978-0-8022-1667-0(6))* Philosophical Library, Inc.

Swain, Joseph P. The A to Z of Sacred Music. 2010. (A to Z Guide Ser.). (ENG.). 336p. pap. 34.45 *(978-0-8108-7621-7(3))* Scarecrow Pr., Inc.

Swain, Joseph Peter. Historical Dictionary of Sacred Music. 2006. (Historical Dictionaries Ser.). (ENG., Illus.). 336p. 87.00 *(978-0-8108-5530-4(5))* Scarecrow Pr., Inc.

Szö, et al. Kirchenlieder zwischen Pest und Stadtbrand: Das Kronstädter Kantional I.F. 78 aus dem 17. Jahrhundert. 2009. (GER., Illus.). xii, 437p. *(978-3-412-20239-2(8))* Bohlau Verlag Gmbh & Cie.

Temperley, Nicholas. Studies in English Church Music, 1550-1900. 2009. (Variorum Collected Studies). (Illus.). 368p. 170.00 *(978-0-7546-5998-3(4))* Ashgate Publishing Co.

Temperley, Nicholas & Banfield, Stephen 0, eds. Music & the Wesleys. 2010. (ENG., Illus.). 296p. 80.00 *(978-0-252-03581-4(X))*; pap. 25.00 *(978-0-252-07767-8(9))* Univ. of Illinois Pr.

Tenth Avenue North. Tenth Avenue North - over & Underneath. 2010. (ENG.). 80p. pap. 16.99 *(978-1-4234-9016-6(9),* 1423490169) Leonard, Hal Corp.

Terry, Ph.D., Lindsay. The Sacrifice of Praise: Stories Behind the Greatest Praise & Worship Songs of All Time, 0 vols. 2010. 240p. pap. 14.99 *(978-0-7852-9795-6(2))* Nelson, Thomas Inc.

The Committee O, Research. Church Music & Musical Life in Pennsyl. 2006. pap. 26.95 *(978-1-4286-5487-7(9))* Kessinger Publishing, LLC.

The Theology of the Faith We Sing. 10.00 incl. audio *(978-0-687-04956-1(3))* Abingdon Pr.

Thomas Nelson Publishing Staff. The Voice of Psalms Devotional, 0 vols. 2009. 288p. pap. 24.99 *(978-1-4185-4152-1(4))* Nelson, Thomas Inc.

Thompson, Nancy Eden. The Spirit & the Bride Say Come: Meditations from the Song of Solomon. 2009. 110p. pap. 14.95 *(978-1-4327-3635-4(3))* Outskirts Pr., Inc.

Tindal, Mardi & Middleton, Kate. Spirit of Singing. Date not set. 128p. pap. 6.95 *(978-0-929032-85-6(3))* Wood Lake Publishing, Inc. CAN. Dist: Westminster John Knox Pr.

Todd, Matthew. The Interface of the Percussive Arts, Religious Experience, & Sacred Association. 2008. 208p. pap. *(978-1-897373-20-0(1))* Word Alive Pr.

Tomlin, Chris, et al. How Can I Keep from Singing? SATB with Opt. Rhythm. 2011. 12p. pap. 2.10 ***(978-1-4291-2562-8(4))*** Lorenz Corp., The.

—How Great Is Our God: SATB or SAB with Opt. Rhythm. 2011. 12p. pap. 2.10 ***(978-1-4291-2392-1(3))*** Lorenz Corp., The.

Tornquist, Carol. Medleys for Blended Worship, Bk 1: 10 Contemporary Arrangements of Praise Songs with Hymns. 2010. (Sacred Performer Collections). (ENG.). 48p. pap. 14.99 *(978-0-7390-6960-8(8))* Alfred Publishing Co., Inc.

Tornquist, Carol. Pure & Simple Worship. 2011. (Pure & Simple Ser.). (ENG.). 80p. pap. 14.99 ***(978-0-7390-5954-8(8))*** Alfred Publishing Co., Inc.

Tornquist, Carol, contrib. by. Popular Praise: Big Note: 10 Timeless Christian Worship Songs: Late Elementary to Early Intermediate Piano Solos. 2010. (Popular Praise Ser.). (ENG.). 28p. pap. 8.99 *(978-0-7390-6990-5(X))* Alfred Publishing Co., Inc.

Tranchell, Peter. If Ye Would Hear the Angels Sing. 2009. 4p. pap. 2.50 *(978-0-19-395018-4(9))* Oxford Univ. Pr., Inc.

Tuned for Worship B Flat Tenor Sax. 8.00 *(978-0-687-03085-9(4))* Abingdon Pr.

Tuned for Worship Conductors Score. 20.00 *(978-0-687-03107-8(9))* Abingdon Pr.

Tuned for Worship Descant in B Flat. 8.00 *(978-0-687-03344-7(6))* Abingdon Pr.

Tuned for Worship Descant in C. 8.00 *(978-0-687-03298-3(9))* Abingdon Pr.

Tuned for Worship E Flat. 8.00 *(978-0-687-03132-0(X))* Abingdon Pr.

Turner, Jay. Dp Gods Gift of Grace. 12.00 *(978-0-7673-1266-0(X))* LifeWay Christian Resources.

Vigh, Jim. Improving Your Skills in Music Ministry. 2007. 124p. per. 11.99 *(978-1-60477-287-6(5))* Xulon Pr., Inc.

Visions of Worship, creator. To God Be the Glory. 2007. audio compact disk 19.99 *(978-5-557-53277-8(3))* Vision Video.

Wagner, Douglas E. Bless the Lord, O My Soul: SATB or Two-Part Mixed with Opt. Handbells or Handchimes (2 Oct.) 2011. 12p. pap. 1.95 ***(978-1-4291-2522-2(5))*** Lorenz Corp., The.

Wagner, Douglas E. Come, Creator Spirit. 2011. 7p. pap. 4.50 *(978-1-4291-2135-4(1))* Lorenz Corp., The.

Walk in the Land. pap. *(978-1-58459-054-5(8),* 3685) World Library Pubns.

Wallace, Peter. Connected: You & God in the Psalms. 2009. 208p. pap. 18.00 *(978-0-8192-2308-1(5),* Morehouse Publishing) Church Publishing, Inc.

Warner, Steven C. Prophets of Joy. pap. *(978-1-58459-051-4(3),* 7215) World Library Pubns.

Warner, Steven C. & Kirner, Karen Schneider. Psalms of the Notre Dame Folk Choir Songbook. 2008. 72p. pap. 14.95 *(978-1-58459-360-7(1))* World Library Pubns.

Whitbourn, James. In Tuneful Accord. (Illus.). 144p. 17.95 *(978-0-281-04825-0(8))* International Publishers Marketing.

White, Robert & Dunkley, Sally. Lamentations. 2009. 48p. 10.95 *(978-0-19-380491-3(3))* Oxford Univ. Pr., Inc.

Wilcox, Diana. Thank God in Advance: A Companion to the Album. 2011. pap. 16.99 ***(978-1-61777-561-1(4))*** Tate Publishing & Enterprises, LLC.

Williams, J. Paul, et al. One Rehearsal Wonders Vol. 3: Almost Instant Anthems for Any Occasion. 2009. (ENG.). 88p. pap. 7.95 *(978-1-4234-8817-0(2),* 1423488172) Shawnee Pr., Inc.

Williams, J. Paul & Barrett, Michael. The Lord Is Risen. 2009. cd-rom 60.00 *(978-1-4234-8729-6(X),* 142348729X) Shawnee Pr., Inc.

Williamson, Dave. Dp I Will Sing Forever. 12.00 *(978-0-7673-1280-6(5))* LifeWay Christian Resources.

Wilson Jr., Eli. Equipping the Church Choir for Ministry: A Resource for Church Music Leaders & Choir Members. 2008. 124p. pap. 10.99 *(978-1-4389-0351-4(0))* AuthorHouse.

Witvliet, John D. Sing a Solo. (So You've Been Asked to... Ser.). pap. 1.95 *(978-1-56212-216-4(9),* 410102) Faith Alive Christian Resources.

Wolaver, Bill, contrib. by. 17 Contemporary Worship Hits, Volume 1. 2007. 48p. per. 14.95 *(978-5-557-61412-2(5),* Brentwood-Benson Music Publishing, Inc.) Brentwood Music, Inc.

Wonder of Wonders: 10 Dynamic Arrangements for Senior Adult Choir. 2008. (ENG.). pap. 7.99 *(978-0-8341-7663-8(7),* 9780834176638) Lillenas Publishing Co.

Young Musicians. 2.95 *(978-0-7673-6047-0(8))*; 4.98 *(978-0-7673-6075-3(3))* LifeWay Christian Resources.

Young Musicians Pak. 54.95 *(978-0-7673-6061-6(3))* LifeWay Christian Resources.

Your Great Name: A Worship Event Lifting up the Name of Jesus. 2011. (ENG.). 144p. pap. 8.99 ***(978-0-8341-8134-2(7),*** 9780834181342) Lillenas Publishing Co.

Zager, Daniel, ed. Music & Theology: Essays in Honor of Robin A. Leaver. 2006. (ENG., Illus.). 296p. 116.00 *(978-0-8108-5414-7(7))* Scarecrow Pr., Inc.

Zsolt, Alex. Draw Me Nearer: Inspirational Hymn Settings for Solo Piano. 2010. (ENG.). 64p. pap. 16.99 *(978-0-8341-7749-9(8),* 0834177498) Lillenas Publishing Co.

CHURCH MUSIC—CATHOLIC CHURCH

see also Mass (Music)

Basile, Salvatore. Fifth Avenue Famous: The Extraordinary Story of Music at St. Patrick's Cathedral. 2010. (ENG., Illus.). 288p. 65.00 *(978-0-8232-3187-4(9))* Fordham Univ. Pr.

Baxter, James H. An Old St. Andrews Music Book. (Medieval Studies). reprint ed. 52.50 *(978-0-404-56525-1(5))* AMS Pr., Inc.

Bennett, Peter. Sacred Repertories in Paris under Louis XIII: Paris, Bibliothèque Nationale de France, Vma MS Rés. 571. 2009. (Royal Musical Association Monographs). (Illus.). 232p. 99.95 *(978-0-7546-6821-3(5))* Ashgate Publishing Co.

Collins, Paul, ed. Renewal & Resistance: Catholic Church Music from the 1850s to Vatican II. 2010. (ENG.). 283p. pap. 61.95 *(978-3-03911-381-1(X))* Lang, Peter AG GBR. Dist: Lang, Peter.

Cummings, Anthony M. The Lion's Ear: Pope Leo X, the Renaissance Papacy, & Music. 2012. (ENG.). 328p. (C). 75.00 ***(978-0-472-11791-8(2))*** Univ. of Michigan Pr.

Fassler, Margot E. Gothic Song: Victorine Sequences & Augustinian Reform in Twelfth-Century Paris. 2nd ed. 2011. (ENG., Illus.). 536p. pap. 55.00 *(978-0-268-02889-3(3))* Univ. of Notre Dame Pr.

Foley, Edward. A Lyrical Vision: The Music Documents of the US Bishops. 2009. 75p. pap. 9.95 *(978-0-8146-3279-6(3))* Liturgical Pr.

Gill, Gerald Dennis. Music in Catholic Liturgy: A Pastoral & Theological Companion to Sing to the Lord. 2009. 140p. 19.00 *(978-1-59525-028-5(X))* Hillenbrand Bks.

Harmon, Kathleen A. The Mystery We Celebrate, the Song We Sing: A Theology of Liturgical Music. 2008. 78p. pap. 29.95 *(978-0-8146-6190-1(4))* Liturgical Pr.

Johner, Dominic. The Chants of the Vatican Gradual. Monks Of St. John's Abbey, tr. 2011. 516p. 60.95 ***(978-1-258-04436-7(6))*** Literary Licensing, LLC.

Kelly, Thomas Forrest, ed. Plainsong in the Age of Polyphony. 2009. (Cambridge Studies in Performance Practice Ser.). (ENG., Illus.). 256p. pap. 36.99 *(978-0-521-10689-4(3))* Cambridge Univ. Pr.

Miller, Michael J. Musica Sacra: Music at Mass, a Liturgical & Pastoral Challenge: Papers from the Second Study Day on the Anniverary of Sacrosanctum Concilium, Vatican City, December 5, 2005. 2010. 181p. ***(978-1-58617-301-2(4))*** Ignatius Pr.

Monson, Craig A. Divas in the Convent: Nuns, Music, & Defiance in Seventeenth-Century Italy. 2012. (ENG., Illus.). 296p. pap. 25.00 ***(978-0-226-53519-7(3))*** Univ. of Chicago Pr.

Muir, T. E. Roman Catholic Church Music in England, 1791-1914: A Handmaid of the Liturgy? 2008. (Music in Nineteenth-Century Britain Ser.). (Illus.). 310p. 124.95 *(978-0-7546-6105-4(9))* Ashgate Publishing Co.

Rossini, C. Gregorian Symphony in Black & White: An Early Contribution to the National Celebration of A Golden Jubilee, 1903-1953. 2011. 48p. 35.95 ***(978-1-258-02140-5(4))*** Literary Licensing, LLC.

Rossini, Carlo. The Priests Chants & Recitatives at the Altar. 2011. 134p. 40.95 ***(978-1-258-05320-8(9))*** Literary Licensing, LLC.

Rumbold, Ian, et al, eds. Der Mensuralcodex St. Emmeram: Faksimile der Handschrift Clm 14274 der Bayerischen Staatsbibliothek Munchen, 2 vols. 2006. (Elementa Musicae Ser.). (GER & ENG., Illus.). 488p. (C). 439.00

(978-3-89500-506-0(1)) Reichert, Ludwig Dr. DEU. Dist: Brown, David Bk. Co., The.

Russell, Craig H. From Serra to Sancho: Music & Pageantry in the California Missions, 1 vol. (Currents in Latin American & Iberian Music Ser.). (ENG., Illus.). 480p. 2012. pap. 35.00 **(978-0-19-991616-0(0))** 2009. 65.00 (978-0-19-534327-4(1)) Oxford Univ. Pr., Inc.

Swain, Joseph Peter. Sacred Treasure: Understanding Catholic Liturgical Music. 2012. **(978-0-8146-6255-7(2))** Liturgical Pr.

Torres y Vargas, Canon Diego. Report on the Island & Diocese of Puerto Rico (1647) Vidal, Jaime R., tr. from SPA. 2010. (ENG., Illus.). 200p. pap. 25.00 (978-1-58966-189-9(3)) Univ. of Scranton Pr.

Turner, Paul & Kerr Breedlove, Jennifer. Guide for Music Ministers, Second Edition. 2010. (Liturgical Ministry Ser.). 112p. 6.95 (978-1-56854-916-3(4)) Liturgy Training Pubns.

Twomey, Vincent & Rutherford, Janet Elaine. Benedict XVI & Beauty in Sacred Music. 2011. (Illus.). 224p. **(978-1-84682-311-4(0))** Four Courts Pr. IRL. Dist: International Specialized Bk. Services.

USCCB Publishing, creator. Sing to the Lord: Music in Divine Worship. 2008. (Pastoral Liturgy Ser.). 80p. pap. 9.95 (978-1-60137-022-8(9)) United States Conference of Catholic Bishops.

Wright, Craig. Music & Ceremony at Notre Dame of Paris, 500-1550. 2008. (Cambridge Studies in Music Ser.). (ENG., Illus.). 420p. pap. 53.00 (978-0-521-08834-3(8)) Cambridge Univ. Pr.

CHURCH MUSIC—CHORUSES AND CHOIR BOOKS

see Choruses, Sacred; Sacred Vocal Music; Service Books (Music)

CHURCH MUSIC—CHURCH OF ENGLAND

85.00 Broude Brothers, Ltd.

Beeson, Trevor. In Tuneful Accord: The Church Musicians. 2009. 256p. pap. 29.99 (978-0-334-04193-1(7), SCM Pr.) Hymns Ancient & Modern Ltd GBR. Dist: Westminster John Knox Pr.

Burrows, Donald. Handel & the English Chapel Royal. 2008. (ENG., Illus.). 656p. pap. 85.00 (978-0-19-955096-8(4)) Oxford Univ. Pr., Inc.

Horton, Peter. Samuel Sebastian Wesley: A Life. 2010. (Oxford Studies in British Church Music Ser.). (ENG., Illus.). 400p. 55.00 (978-0-19-958268-6(8)) Oxford Univ. Pr., Inc.

Kim, Hyun-Ah. Humanism & the Reform of Sacred Music in Early Modern England: John Merbecke the Orator & the Booke of Common Praier Noted (1550) 2008. (St Andrews Studies in Reformation History Ser.). (Illus.). 274p. 124.95 (978-0-7546-6268-6(3)) Ashgate Publishing Co.

Muir, T. E. Roman Catholic Church Music in England, 1791-1914: A Handmaid of the Liturgy? 2008. (Music in Nineteenth-Century Britain Ser.). (Illus.). 310p. 124.95 (978-0-7546-6105-4(9)) Ashgate Publishing Co.

Quitslund, Beth. The Reformation in Rhyme: Sternhold, Hopkins & the English Metrical Psalter, 1547-1603. 2008. (Sternhold, Hopkins & the English Metrical Psalter, 1547ndash;1603 Ser.). 340p. 124.95 (978-0-7546-6326-3(4)) Ashgate Publishing Co.

CHURCH MUSIC—CHURCH OF JESUS CHRIST OF LATTER-DAY SAINTS

Black, Susan Easton, ed. The Best of the Frontier Guardian. 2009. (ENG., Illus.). 186p. pap. 19.95 (978-0-8425-2740-8(0), Brigham Young Univ. Studies) Brigham Young Univ.

Esplin, Scott C. & Holzapfel, Richard Neitzel, eds. The Voice of My Servants. 2010. (Illus.). 250p. 23.99 (978-0-8425-2773-6(7)) Brigham Young Univ.

Ferguson, Danyelle & Parsons, Lynn. (Dis)Abilities & the Gospel: How to Bring People with Special Needs Closer to Christ. 2011. pap. 16.90 (978-1-59955-820-2(3)) Cedar Fort, Inc./CFI Distribution.

Gibbons, Francis. Howard W. Hunter: Man of Thought & Independence, Prophet of God. 2011. 272p. pap. 24.99 (978-1-60641-943-4(9)) Deseret Bk. Co.

Graham, Patricia Kelsey. We Shall Make Music: Stories of the Primary Songs & How They Came to Be. 2007. (Illus.). 285p. per. 19.99 (978-0-88290-818-2(9)) Cedar Fort, Inc./CFI Distribution.

Hartley, William G. My Fellow Servants: Essays on the History of the Priesthood. 2010. (Illus.). 450p. pap. (978-0-8425-2767-5(2), Brigham Young Univ. Studies) Brigham Young Univ.

Kuehne, Raymond M. Henry Burkhardt & LDS Realpolitik in Communist East Germany. 2011. (ENG., Illus.). 248p. (gr. 13). pap. 26.95 **(978-1-60781-149-7(9))** Univ. of Utah Pr.

Minert, Roger P. In Harm's Way: East German Latter-day Saints in World War II. 2009. (Illus.). 559p. (978-0-8425-2746-0(X), Brigham Young Univ. Religious Studies Ctr.) Brigham Young Univ.

Moore, Richard G. Strange Roads & Forbidden Paths: Avoiding Apostasy in the Latter Days. 2008. pap. 13.99 (978-1-59955-211-8(6)) Cedar Fort, Inc./CFI Distribution.

Riddle, Lori. Choose to Believe, Live to Receive. 2008. pap. 8.99 (978-1-59955-177-7(2)) Cedar Fort, Inc./CFI Distribution.

Romney, Virginia Hatch & Cowan, Richard Olsen. The Colonia Juarez Temple: A Prophet's Inspiration. 2009. (Illus.). 240p. (978-0-8425-2727-9(3), Brigham Young Univ. Religious Studies Ctr.) Brigham Young Univ.

Sirrine, Carma B. Marriage Works-You Better Believe It: A Compilation of Real Experiences. 2009. pap. 9.99 (978-1-59955-196-8(9)) Cedar Fort, Inc./CFI Distribution.

Spencer, Thomas M. The Missouri Mormon Experience. 2010. (ENG., Illus.). 200p. (C). 34.95 (978-0-8262-1887-2(3)) Univ. of Missouri Pr.

Woolley, Tamara Leigh. Family Home Evening for Me: A Resource Manual. 2006. 199p. per. (978-0-88290-935-6(5)) Horizon Books.

Young, Brigham & Van Wagoner, Richard S. The Complete Discourses of Brigham Young. 2009. (978-1-56085-206-3(2), Smith Research Assocs.) Signature Bks., LLC.

CHURCH MUSIC—GREEK CHURCH

see Church Music—Orthodox Eastern Church

CHURCH MUSIC—HISTORY AND CRITICISM

see Church Music

CHURCH MUSIC—LUTHERAN CHURCH

see also Chorale

Hendrickson, Marion Lars. Musica Christi: A Lutheran Aesthetic, Vol. 244. 2006. (American University Studies: Vol. 244). (Illus.). 313p. 75.95 (978-0-8204-6346-9(9)) Lang, Peter Publishing, Inc.

Leaver, Robin A. Luther's Liturgical Music: Principles & Implications. 2007. (Lutheran Quarterly Books). (Illus.). 485p. per. 32.00 (978-0-8028-3221-4(0)) Eerdmans, William B. Publishing Co.

CHURCH MUSIC—MORAVIAN CHURCH

Steelman, Robert, ed. Catalog of the Lititz Congregation Collection. 2011. (ENG.). 499p. pap. 50.00 **(978-0-8078-6830-0(2))** Univ. of North Carolina Pr.

CHURCH MUSIC—ORTHODOX EASTERN CHURCH

Lambertsen, Isaac E., tr. from RUS. St. Job of Pochaev: Life, Service & Akathist Hymn. Date not set. 96p. pap. 5.00 (978-0-912927-79-4(6), X050) St. John of Kronstadt Pr., The.

Lind, Tore Tvarn. Past Is Always Present: The Revival of the Byzantine Musical Tradition at Mount Athos. 2011. (Europea: Ethnomusicologies & Modernities Ser.). (ENG., Illus.). 262p. (gr. 17). 85.00 **(978-0-8108-8147-1(0))** Scarecrow Pr., Inc.

—The Past Is Always Present: The Revival of the Byzantine Musical Tradition at Mount Athos. 2012. (Illus.). xx, 241p. E-Book **(978-0-8108-8148-8(9))** Scarecrow Pr., Inc.

Papachristopoulos, Ioannis. Beziehungen Zwischen Den Drei Subkategorien der Heirmologischen Gesänge-Hauptgattung in der Griechischen Kirchenmusik: Verdeutlicht Am Fall Eines Im Dritten Echos Vertonten und Durch das Analytische Notationssystem Transkribierten Dreifachen Melos' (Theotoke, I Elpis Panton Ton Christianon. en Nomo, Skia Kai Grammati) Aus Dem 18. und 19. Jahrhundert. 2011. (GER.). 152p. 41.95 **(978-3-631-62023-6(3))** Lang, Peter GmbH, Europaischer Verlag der Wissenschaften DEU. Dist: Lang, Peter.

Wanek, Nina-Maria. Nachbyzantinischer Liturgischer Gesang Im Wandel: Studien Zu Den Musikhandschriften des Supplementum Graecum der Österreichischen Nationalbibliothek. 2007. (VERoFFENTLICHUNGEN ZUR BYZANZFORSCHUNG Ser.). (GER., Illus.). 378p. (C). pap. 186.00 (978-3-7001-3543-2(2)) Austrian Academy of Sciences Press AUT. Dist: Brown, David Bk. Co., The.

Wolfram, Gerda & Wolfram, G., eds. Tradition & Innovation in Late- & Postbyzantine Liturgical Chant: Acta of the Congress Held at Hernen Castle, the Netherlands, in April 2005. 2008. (Eastern Christian Studies). (GER & ENG., Illus.). 381p. (C). pap. 95.00 (978-90-429-2015-6(7)) Peeters Pubs. & Booksellers BEL. Dist: Brown, David Bk. Co., The.

CHURCH MUSIC—PROTESTANT CHURCHES

Bauer, Siegfried, et al. Musik-Horizonte: Festschrift Für Siegfried Bauer. 2009. (GER., Illus.). 213p. (978-3-89912-131-5(7)) Strube Verlag - GmbH.

James, Nancy Carol. In Your Mercy, Lord, You Called Me: A Sung Prayer in the Christian Tradition. 2010. (Illus.). 104p. (978-0-7734-3630-5(8)) Mellen, Edwin Pr., The.

Jorritsma, Marie R. Sonic Spaces of the Karoo: The Sacred Music of a South African Coloured Community. 2011. (African Soundscapes Ser.). (Illus.). (ENG.). 224p. 59.50 (978-1-4399-0237-0(2)); 216p. E-Book (978-1-4399-0239-4(9)) Temple Univ. Pr.

Martens, Helen. Hutterite Songs. 30.00 (978-1-894710-24-4(X)) Pandora Pr. CAN. Dist: Herald Pr.

Mcintyre, Dean & Fosua, Safiyah. Hymns for the Revised Common L. 2008. 224p. pap. 16.00 (978-0-88177-546-4(0)) Upper Room Bks.

Pierce, Robert B. A Stable-Lamp Is Lighted: A Sung Prayer of the Christian Tradition. 2010. v, 42p. 39.95 (978-0-7734-3650-3(2)) Mellen, Edwin Pr., The.

Rogal, Samuel J. Once in Royal David's City: A Sung Prayer of the Christian Tradition. 2011. (Illus.). 76p. 99.95 **(978-0-7734-1527-0(0))** Mellen, Edwin Pr., The.

Willis, Jonathan P. Church Music & Protestantism in Post-Reformation England: Discourses, Sites & Identities. 2010. (St Andrews Studies in Reformation History Ser.). (Illus.). 314p. 124.95 (978-1-4094-0071-4(9)) Ashgate Publishing Co.

CHURCH MUSIC—SERVICE BOOKS

see Service Books (Music)

CHURCH OF CHRIST

Allen, C. Leonard & Swick, Danny. Participating in God's Life: Two Crossroads for Churches of Christ. 202p. pap. 15.95 (978-0-9700836-4-7(5), Leafwood Pubs.) Abilene Christian Univ. Pr.

Allen, Leonard, ed. Transforming of a Tradition: Churches of Christ in the New Millennium. 224p. pap. 14.95 (978-0-9700836-7-8(X), Leafwood Pubs.) Abilene Christian Univ. Pr.

Anderson, Brian & Whitwer, Glynnis. Small Group in a Box Volume #4: Welcome to Community. 2007. 75.00 (978-0-9798104-9-7(3)) Ampelon Publishing, LLC.

Clark, David L. Joseph Bates Noble: Polygamy & the Temple Lot Case. 2009. (ENG., Illus.). 224p. (gr. 13). 24.95 (978-0-87480-937-4(1)) Univ. of Utah Pr.

Clements, Phillip. Victory Vision: One World to Reach. One Way to Reach It. 2008. 144p. pap. 10.99 (978-0-9779535-2-3(1)) 21st Century Pr.

Corprew-Boyd, Angela L. Church Hurt: The Wounded Trying to Heal. 2008. (ENG.). 128p. 14.99 (978-1-59979-371-9(7), Creation Hse.) Charisma Media.

Douglas, Robert C. The Exercise of Informal Power within the Church of Christ: Black Civil Rights, Muted Justice, & Denominational Politics. 2008. 192p. 99.95 (978-0-7734-5012-7(2)) Mellen, Edwin Pr., The.

Dykes, J. Harvey. 2000 Years Ago the Church of Christ Was Established & Today... reprint ed. pap. 2.95 (978-1-56794-245-3(8), C-2032) Star Bible & Tract Corp.

Fewson, Michael. Will the Real Church Stand up. 2006. pap. 13.99 (978-1-60034-453-4(4)) Xulon Pr., Inc.

Gambill, Joe. The Church of Christ. 2007. pap. 9.95 (978-1-58427-200-7(7)) Guardian of Truth Foundation.

Glasgow, Kirk. Let's Get Together. 2007. 160p. pap. 12.95 (978-0-9779775-2-9(8)) Manna F.O.H Publishing.

Shittu, T. J. Flames of the End! The Revival Is Coming! 2010. pap. 9.99 (978-1-61566-477-1(7)) Tate Publishing & Enterprises, LLC.

Smith, Israel A. & Hancock, Pauline. Letters, Israel Smith & Pauline Hancock: Mistakes Should Not Fetter, in the Saints' Herald, January 17 1955. 2011. 54p. 36.95 **(978-1-258-10372-9(9))** Literary Licensing, LLC.

Turner, Mary Donovan. The God We Seek: Portraits of God in the Old Testament. 2010. 160p. pap. 19.99 (978-0-8272-1251-0(8)) Chalice Pr.

Umar, Pastor. Emergence of the Priests: God's End Time Army. 2011. 288p. pap. 20.38 **(978-1-4567-8588-8(5))** AuthorHouse.

Vargas, Gloria Pardo, tr. Conozca a la Iglesia de Cristo.Tr. of Introducing the Church of Christ. (SPA.). 219p. 4.95 (978-1-56794-179-1(6)) Star Bible & Tract Corp.

Waldrep, B. Dwain & Billingsley, Scott. Recovering the Margins of American Religious History: The Legacy of David Edwin Harrell, Jr. 2012. **(978-0-8173-8609-2(2))** Univ. of Alabama Pr.

Waldrep, B. Dwain & Billingsley, Scott, eds. Recovering the Margins of American Religious History: The Legacy of David Edwin Harrell Jr. 2012. (Religion & American Culture Ser.). (ENG.). 160p. pap. 22.95 **(978-0-8173-5708-5(4))** Univ. of Alabama Pr.

Woodroof, Tim. A Church That Flies: A New Call to Restoration in Churches of Christ. 224p. pap. 14.95 (978-0-9700836-1-6(0), Leafwood Pubs.) Abilene Christian Univ. Pr.

CHURCH OF CHRIST OF LATTER-DAY SAINTS

see Church of Jesus Christ of Latter-Day Saints

CHURCH OF ENGLAND

see also Dissenters, Religious—England

Anderson, Robert. The Buddha of Christendom. 2007. 344p. per. 21.95 (978-1-60206-204-7(8)) Cosimo, Inc.

Andrewes, Lancelot. A Pattern of Catechistical Doctrine, & Other Minor Works of Lancelot Andrewes, Sometime Lord Bishop of Winchester. 2008. 457p. pap. 38.00 (978-1-60608-123-5(3), Wipf and Stock) Wipf & Stock Pubs.

—Two Answers to Cardinal Perron, & Other Miscellaneous Works of Lancelot Andrewes. Bliss, James, ed. 2008. 590p. pap. 49.00 (978-1-55635-047-4(3), Wipf and Stock) Wipf & Stock Pubs.

Anglican Cycle of Prayer: 2003. 112p. pap. 2.95 (978-0-88028-243-7(6), 1722) Forward Movement Pubns.

Archbishop's Council on Mission and Foreign Affairs. Mission-Shaped Church: Church Planting & Fresh Expressions in A Changing Context. 2nd ed. 2010. 192p. pap. 20.00 (978-1-59627-126-5(4), Seabury Bks.) Church Publishing, Inc.

Arnold, Matthew. St. Paul & Protestantism: With an Introduction on Puritanism & the Church of England. (Collected Works of Matthew Arnold). reprint ed. lib. bdg. 98.00 (978-0-7426-2168-8(5)) Classic Bks.

—St Paul & Protestantism with an Essay. 2006. pap. 36.95 (978-1-4286-4188-4(2)) Kessinger Publishing, LLC.

Avis, Paul D. L. The Anglican Understanding of the Church: An Introduction. 104p. 10.00 (978-0-281-05282-0(4)) SPCK Publishing GBR. Dist: Pilgrim Pr., The/United Church Pr.

Bacon, Francis. Certain Considerations Touching the Better Pacification & Edification of the Church of England. reprint ed. lib. bdg. 98.00 (978-0-7426-2005-6(0)) Classic Bks.

—A Wise & Moderate Discourse, Concerning Church Affairs: As It Was Written, Long Since, by the Famous Author of Those Considerations, Which Seem to Have Some Reference to This. reprint ed. lib. bdg. 98.00 (978-0-7426-2022-3(0)) Classic Bks.

Balleine, G. R. A History of the Evangelical Party in the Church of England. 2007. (ENG.). 368p. 48.95 (978-0-548-10549-8(9)) Kessinger Publishing, LLC.

Barrow, Isaac. Theological Works of Isaac Barrow, 9 vols. Napier, Alexander, ed. reprint ed. lib. bdg. 215.00 (978-0-404-00670-9(1)) AMS Pr., Inc.

Becon, Thomas. The Early Works of Thomas Becon. Ayre, John, ed. 2007. 518p. 55.95 (978-0-548-03870-3(8)) Kessinger Publishing, LLC.

Best, Geoffrey. Temporal Pillars: Queen Anne's Bounty, the Ecclesiastical Commissioners, & the Church of England. 2010. (ENG.). 600p. pap. 39.99 (978-0-521-14303-5(9)) Cambridge Univ. Pr.

Beveridge, William. Complete Works, 12 vols. (Library of Anglo-Catholic Theology: No. 2). reprint ed. (978-0-404-52040-3(5)) AMS Pr., Inc.

Bicknell, E. J. A Theological Introduction to the Thirty-Nine Articles of the Church of England. Carpenter, H. J., ed. 3rd ed. 2008. 484p. pap. 53.00 (978-1-55635-682-7(X)) Wipf & Stock Pubs.

Black, Joseph, ed. The Martin Marprelate Tracts: A Modernized & Annotated Edition. 2008. (ENG., Illus.). 432p. 144.00 (978-0-521-87579-0(X)) Cambridge Univ. Pr.

Black, Joseph L., ed. The Martin Marprelate Tracts: A Modernized & Annotated Edition. 2011. (ENG., Illus.). 438p. pap. 55.00 (978-0-521-18864-7(4)) Cambridge Univ. Pr.

Briden, Timothy. Moore's Introduction to English Canon Law, Vol. 3. 3rd ed. (Illus.). 192p. pap. (978-0-264-67272-4(0)) Mowbray, A. R. & Co., Ltd. GBR. Dist: Continuum International Publishing Group, Inc.

Browne, Edward Harold. Exposition of the ThirtyNine Articles V1. 2006. pap. 38.95 (978-1-4286-3758-0(3)) Kessinger Publishing, LLC.

—Exposition of the ThirtyNine Articles V2. 2006. pap. 49.95 (978-1-4286-3759-7(1)) Kessinger Publishing, LLC.

Burnet, Gilbert. Exposition of the ThirtyNine Articles of. 2006. pap. 40.95 (978-1-4286-3999-7(3)) Kessinger Publishing, LLC.

Chapman, Mark, ed. Hope of Things to Come: Anglicanism & the Future. 2010. (Affirming Catholicism Ser.). (ENG.). 192p. 24.95 (978-0-567-58884-5(X)) Mowbray, A. R. & Co., Ltd. GBR. Dist: National Bk. Network.

Chapman, Mark, et al, eds. The Established Church: Past, Present & Future. 2011. (Affirming Catholicism Ser.). (ENG.). 224p. pap. 24.95 (978-0-567-35809-7(7), T&T Clark Int'l) Continuum International Publishing Group, Ltd. GBR. Dist: National Bk. Network.

Chartres, Caroline & Chartres. Why I Am Still an Anglican: Essays & Conversations. 2007. (ENG.). 176p. 27.95 (978-0-8264-8312-6(7)) Continuum International Publishing Group, Ltd. GBR. Dist: National Bk. Network.

Church of England, Commission on Urban Priority Areas Staff, contrib. by. Faith in the City: A Call for Action by Church & Nation. 2012. (Illus.). xvi, 398p. pap. **(978-0-7151-3709-3(3))** Church Hse. Publishing.

Coakley, Sarah & Ward, Frances. Fear & Friendship: Anglicans Engaging with Islam. Coakley, Sarah & Ward, Frances, eds. 2012. (ENG.). 224p. pap. 22.95 (978-1-4411-0149-5(7)) Continuum International Publishing Group, Ltd. GBR. Dist: National Bk. Network.

Cook, Christopher D. Love Thy Neighbor: An Exhibition Commemorating the Completion of the Episcopal Chapel of St. John the Divine. 2007. (ENG., Illus.). 28p. 3.00 (978-0-9788134-1-3(3)) Rare Book & Manuscript Library.

Coverdale, Miles & Coverdale, Miles, Jr. Remains of Myles Coverdale, Bishop of Exeter: Containing Prologues to the Translation of the Bible, Treatise on Death, Hope of the Faithful, Exhortation to the Carrying of Christ's Cross, Exposition upon the Twenty-Third Psalm, Confutation of the Treatise of John Standish, Defense of a Certain Poor Christian Man, Letters, Ghostly Psalms & Spiritual Songs. Pearson, George, ed. 2007. (Parker Society: Ser.). 641p. pap. 62.00 (978-1-55635-066-5(X), Wipf and Stock) Wipf & Stock Pubs.

Crakanthorp, Richard. Defensio Ecclesiae Anglicanae. (Library of Anglo-Catholic Theology: No. 6). reprint ed. 65.00 (978-0-404-52087-8(1)) AMS Pr., Inc.

Crick, Julia, ed. Charters of St Albans. 2008. (Anglo-Saxon Charters Ser.). (ENG., Illus.). 240p. 99.00 (978-0-19-726396-9(8)) Oxford Univ. Pr., Inc.

Dales, Douglas. Light to the Isles. 2010. (ENG.), 188p. pap. 42.50 (978-0-227-17341-1(4)) Clarke, James Co., Ltd. GBR. Dist: Brown, David Bk. Co., The.

Davie, Martin & Davie. Guide to the Church of England. 2008. (ENG., Illus.). 264p. 19.95 (978-1-906286-13-2(2)) Mowbray, A. R. & Co., Ltd. GBR. Dist: National Bk. Network.

Davies, Douglas & Rumble, Hannah. Natural Burial: Traditional - Secular Spiritualities & Funeral Innovation. 2012. (ENG., Illus.). 192p. 120.00 **(978-1-4411-2296-4(6))**; pap. 34.95 **(978-1-4411-5278-7(4))** Continuum International Publishing Group, Ltd. GBR. Dist: National Bk. Network.

Davis, Kortright. Cross & Crown in Barbados: Caribbean Political Religion in the Late 19th Century. 2011. 196p. pap. 22.00 (978-1-61097-061-7(6), Wipf and Stock) Wipf & Stock Pubs.

Dyas, Dee, ed. The English Parish Church through the Centuries: Daily Life & Spirituality, Art & Architecture, Literature & Music. 2010. (ENG., Illus.). (C). 29.95 (978-0-9550673-2-7(4)) Christianity and Culture Project GBR. Dist: Brown, David Bk. Co., The.

Edwards, David L. What Anglicans Believe: In the Twenty-First Century. rev. ed. 136p. pap. 2.95 (978-0-88028-170-6(7), 503) Forward Movement Pubns.

Ellens, J. P. Religious Routes to Gladstonian Liberalism. 2008. pap. 29.95 (978-0-271-02843-9(2)) Pennsylvania State Univ. Pr.

Ferguson, Paul. Great Is the Mystery of Faith: Exploring Faith Through the Words of Worship. 2011. 176p. pap. 19.99 (978-1-84825-055-0(X), Canterbury Pr. Norwich) Hymns Ancient & Modern Ltd GBR. Dist: Westminster John Knox Pr.

Fetzer, Margret. John Donne's Performances. 2011. (ENG.). 320p. 90.00 (978-0-7190-8344-0(3)) Manchester Univ. Pr. GBR. Dist: Macmillan.

Fitch, John. Anglican Eirenicon: The Concept of Churchmanship in the Quest for Christian Unity. 2009. (Illus.). 284p. pap. 38.00 (978-0-7188-9212-8(7)) Lutherworth Pr., The GBR. Dist: Brown, David Bk. Co., The.

Frame, Tom. Anglicans in Australia. 2007. (ENG.), 304p. pap. 35.95 (978-0-86840-830-9(1), UNSW Press) NewSouth Publishing AUS. Dist: Independent Pubs. Group.

Furlong, Andy. C of E: The State It's in. 2nd ed. 2006. xiv, 418p. pap. (978-0-281-05845-7(8)) SPCK Publishing.

Furlong, Monica, ed. Act of Synod — Act of Folly? 144p. 18.00 (978-0-334-02746-1(2)) Hymns Ancient & Modern Ltd GBR. Dist: Morehouse Publishing.

Gasquet, Francis Aid. Edward VI & the Book of Common Prayer. 2006. pap. 40.95 (978-1-4286-3992-8(6)) Kessinger Publishing, LLC.

Geffert, Bryn. Eastern Orthodox & Anglicans: Diplomacy, Theology, & the Politics of Interwar Ecumenism. 2009. (ENG., Illus.). 560p. 60.00 (978-0-268-02975-3(X)) Univ. of Notre Dame Pr.

Gibson, Tim. Church & Countryside: Insights from Rural Theology. 2010. (ENG.). xii, 140p. pap. 32.99 (978-0-334-04203-7(8), SCM Pr.) Hymns Ancient & Modern Ltd GBR. Dist: Westminster John Knox Pr.

Gill. Women & Church of England. 320p. 23.00 (978-0-281-04768-0(5)) SPCK Publishing GBR. Dist: Pilgrim Pr., The/United Church Pr.

Guinness, Michele. Chosen: An Autobiography, 1 vol. 2008. (Illus.). 384p. pap. 14.99 (978-0-8254-6283-2(5), Monarch Bks.) Lion Hudson PLC GBR. Dist: Kregel Pubns.

—Promised Land. 2nd ed. 255p. pap. 15.99 (978-0-340-70987-0(1), Coronet) Hodder General Publishing Div. GBR. Dist: Trafalgar Square Publishing.

Hall, Joseph. Works of Bishop Joseph Hall, 10 vols. Wynter, P., ed. reprint ed. 375.00 (978-0-404-03070-4(X)) AMS Pr., Inc.

Henson, Herbert Hensley. The Church of England. 2012. (ENG.). 298p. pap. 46.00 (978-1-107-61951-7(3)) Cambridge Univ. Pr.

Hooker, Richard. Works of Mr Richard Hooker V1 in Eight B. 2006. pap. 33.95 (978-1-4286-4372-7(9)) Kessinger Publishing, LLC.

—Works of Mr Richard Hooker V3 in Eight B. 2006. pap. 37.95 (978-1-4286-4374-1(5)) Kessinger Publishing, LLC.

Howe, John W. Our Anglican Heritage. 2007. 176p. pap. 21.00 (978-1-59752-946-4(X), Wipf and Stock) Wipf & Stock Pubs.

Jewel, John. An Apology of the Church of England. 2009. 226p. 28.99 (978-1-116-91775-8(0)); 226p. 32.99 (978-1-116-91774-1(2)); (ENG.). 225p. pap. 20.99 (978-1-116-91779-6(3), BiblioLife); (ENG.). 225p. pap. 22.99 (978-1-116-91778-9(5), BiblioLife); 226p. pap. 25.75 (978-1-116-91776-5(9)); 226p. pap. 24.75 (978-1-116-91777-2(7)) BiblioBazaar.

—The Apology of the Church of England. 2008. 128p. 24.99 (978-0-554-26125-6(1)) 2008. 128p. 21.99 (978-0-554-35428-6(4)) 2007. 112p. pap. 18.99 (978-1-4346-0482-8(9)) 2007. (ENG.). 124p. pap. 19.99 (978-1-4346-0515-3(9)) BiblioBazaar.

—The Apology of the Church of England. Morley, Henry, ed. Bacon, Lady Ann, tr. 2007. 100p. per. (978-1-4065-3473-3(0)) Dodo Pr.

Johnson, Eleanor & Clark, John, eds. Anglicans in Mission: A Transforming Journey: Report of MISSIO, the Mission Commission of the Anglican Communion, to the Anglican Consultative Council, Meeting in Edinburgh, Scotland, September 1999. 160p. 21.00 (978-0-281-05322-3(7)) SPCK Publishing GBR. Dist: Pilgrim Pr., The/United Church Pr.

Kandagor, Daniel Rotich. Women's Roles in the Anglican Church of Keny. 2010. 200p. pap. (978-3-639-26527-9(0)) VDM Verlag Dr. Mueller e.K.

Kerfoot, Donna. Caroline Fry: A Practical Theology of the Sacraments. 2010. 84p. pap. (978-3-8383-3501-8(5)) Lambert Academic Publishing.

Kollar, Rene Osb. A Foreign & Wicked Institution? The Campaign Against Convents in Victorian England. 2011. (ENG.). 318p. pap. 47.00 (978-0-227-67992-0(X)) Lutterworth Pr., The GBR. Dist: Brown, David Bk. Co., The.

Kroll, Richard, et al, eds. Philosophy, Science, & Religion in England 1640-1700. 2008. (ENG.). 304p. (C). pap. 42.00 (978-0-521-07585-5(8)) Cambridge Univ. Pr.

Lindsay, Ross. Out of Afric: The Breakaway Anglican Churches. 2011. 176p. 29.99 (978-1-61379-606-1(4)) Xulon Pr., Inc.

Llewellyn, Nigel. Funeral Monuments in Post-Reformation England. 2009. (ENG., Illus.). 500p. pap. 58.00 (978-0-521-10752-5(0)) Cambridge Univ. Pr.

Maiden, John. National Religion & the Prayer Book Controversy, 1927-1928. 2009. (Studies in Modern British Religious History Ser.: Volume 21). 226p. 90.00 (978-1-84383-521-9(5), Boydell Press) Boydell & Brewer, Ltd. GBR. Dist: Boydell & Brewer, Inc.

Maidment, Pete. Reconnecting with Confirmation. 2010. (ENG.). pap. 21.99 (978-0-7151-4208-0(9)) Church Hse. Publishing GBR. Dist: Westminster John Knox Pr.

McIlvaine, Charles Pettit. Righteousness by Faith: Nature & Means of Our Justification Before God. 2nd ed. 2007. 494p. pap. 42.00 (978-1-55635-708-4(7)) Wipf & Stock Pubs.

—Righteousness by Faith; or, the Nature & Means of Our Justification Before God; Illustrated by a Comparison of the Doctrine of the Oxford Tracts Wit. 2006. (Illus.). 500p. per. 29.99 (978-1-4255-5582-5(9)) MPublishing.

Meara, David. Pugin & Revival of Memorial Brasse. (Illus.). 192p. pap. (978-0-7201-2171-1(X), Burns & Oates) Continuum International Publishing Group, Ltd.

Moore, E.Garth. Moore's Introduction to English Canon Law, Vol. 3. 3rd ed. (Illus.). 192p. (978-0-264-67274-8(7)) Mowbray, A. R. & Co., Ltd. GBR. Dist: Continuum International Publishing Group, Inc.

Nelson, Louis P. The Beauty of Holiness: Anglicanism & Architecture in Colonial South Carolina. 2009. (Richard Hampton Jenrette Series in Architecture & the Decorative Arts Ser.). (ENG., Illus.). 516p. 52.95 (978-0-8078-3233-2(2)) Univ. of North Carolina Pr.

Newbolt, W. C. E. Consolidation. 2010. 81.92 (978-1-61719-561-7(8)); pap. 17.92 (978-1-61719-641-6(X)) Gorgias Pr., LLC.

Northeast, Peter & Falvey, Heather. Index of Wills of the Archdeaconry of Sudbury, 1439-1474: Index of Wills from the Register 'Baldwyne' 2010. (Suffolk Records Society Ser.). 252p. 60.00 (978-1-84383-593-6(2), Boydell Press) Boydell & Brewer, Ltd. GBR. Dist: Boydell & Brewer, Inc.

Northeast, Peter & Falvey, Heather, eds. Wills of the Archdeaconry of Sudbury, 1439-1474, 2 vols. 2010. (Suffolk Records Society Ser.: Volume 53). (Illus.). 620p. 60.00 (978-1-84383-532-5(0), Boydell Press) Boydell & Brewer, Ltd. GBR. Dist: Boydell & Brewer, Inc.

Paget, Francis. Introduction to the Fifth Book of Hooker. 2007. 344p. per. (978-1-4067-8884-6(3), Pomona Pr.) Read Bks.

Paley, William. The Miscellaneous Works of William Paley. 2009. 370p. pap. (978-0-217-09257-9(3)) Books LLC.

Quantin, Jean-Louis. The Church of England & Christian Antiquity: The Construction of a Confessional Identity in the 17th Century. 2009. (Oxford-Warburg Studies). (ENG.). 480p. 199.00 (978-0-19-955786-8(1)) Oxford Univ. Pr., Inc.

Quitslund, Beth. The Reformation in Rhyme: Sternhold, Hopkins & the English Metrical Psalter, 1547-1603. 2008. (Sternhold, Hopkins & the English Metrical Psalter, 1547ndash;1603 Ser.). 340p. 124.95 (978-0-7546-6326-3(4)) Ashgate Publishing Co.

Religious Tract and Book Society for Ireland, Dublin Staff. The Scripture Text Book. 2006. 288p. per. 23.99 (978-1-4255-2624-5(1)) MPublishing.

Replies to Essays & Reviews with a Preface by the Lord Bishop of Oxford: And Letters from the Radcliffe Observer & the Reader in Geology In. 2006. 448p. per. 26.99 (978-1-4255-4944-2(6)) MPublishing.

Ridley, Nicholas. The Works of Nicholas Ridley, D. D. Sometime Lord Bishop of London, Martyr 1555. Christmas, Henry, ed. 2008. (Parker Society Ser.). 544p. pap. 47.00 (978-1-60608-060-3(1)) Wipf & Stock Pubs.

Royle, Edward. Bishop Bickersteth's Visitation Returns for the Archdeaconry of Craven 1858. 2009. (Illus.). 336p. pap. (978-1-904497-26-4(8)) Borthwick Institute of Historical Research.

Simons, John, ed. The Challenge of Tradition: Responses to the Declaration of Anglican Essentials. 192p. pap. 12.95 (978-1-55126-163-8(4), 1410) Forward Movement Pubns.

Soloway, R.A. Prelates & People: Ecclesiastical Social Thought in England, 1783-1852. 2006. 464p. 180.00 (978-0-415-41298-8(6)) Routledge.

Stebbing, Nicholas & Taylor, Benjamin F., eds. Walter Frere. 2011. 224p. pap. 28.99 (978-1-85311-868-5(0), Canterbury Pr. Norwich) Hymns Ancient & Modern Ltd GBR. Dist: Westminster John Knox Pr.

Steven, James H. S. Worship in the Spirit: Charismatic Worship in the Church of England. 2007. (Studies in Evangelical History & Thought Ser.). 261p. pap. 27.00 (978-1-59752-789-7(0), Wipf and Stock) Wipf & Stock Pubs.

Taylor, Isaac. Ancient Christianity & the Doctrines O. 2006. pap. 43.95 (978-1-4286-4276-8(5)); pap. 42.95 (978-1-4286-4275-1(7)) Kessinger Publishing, LLC.

Taylor, Jeremy. Whole Works of the Right Rev Jeremy Tayl. 2006. (ENG.). pap. 37.95 (978-1-4286-4650-6(7)); (ENG.). pap. 40.95 (978-1-4286-4649-0(3)); (ENG.). pap. 40.95 (978-1-4286-4648-3(5)); (ENG.). pap. 42.95 (978-1-4286-4651-3(5)); pap. 34.95 (978-1-4286-4653-7(1)); (ENG.). pap. 45.95 (978-1-4286-4652-0(3)) Kessinger Publishing, LLC.

Thompson, David M., et al, eds. Protestant Nonconformist Texts Vol. 4: The Twentieth Century, 4 vols. 2007. (Protestant Nonconformist Texts Ser.). 432p. 144.95 (978-0-7546-4013-4(2)) Ashgate Publishing Co.

Thornton, Martin. Christian Proficiency. 2010. 216p. pap. 24.00 (978-1-60899-663-6(8), Wipf and Stock) Wipf & Stock Pubs.

Tinti, Francesca. Sustaining Belief: Astoral Care in Late Anglo-Saxon Diocese of Worcester. 2010. (Studies in Early Medieval Britain Ser.). (Illus.). 376p. 134.95 (978-0-7546-0902-5(2)) Ashgate Publishing Co.

Tonning, Judith E. & Wolfe, Brendan N. C. S. Lewis & the Church: Essays in Honour of Walter Hooper. 2011. (ENG.). 208p. 110.00 (978-0-567-04736-6(9), T&T Clark Int'l) Continuum International Publishing Group, Ltd. GBR. Dist: National Bk. Network.

Tovey, Phillip. The Theory & Practice of Extended Communion. 2009. (Liturgy, Worship & Society Ser.). (Illus.). 210p. 99.95 (978-0-7546-6684-4(0)) Ashgate Publishing Co.

Tucker, Louis Leonard. The Church of England & Religious Liberty at Pre-Revolutionary Yale: The William & Mary Quarterly V17, No. 3, July 1960. 2011. 20p. pap. 35.95 (978-1-258-02270-9(2)) Literary Licensing, LLC.

Turnbull, Richard & Turnbull. Anglican & Evangelical? 2007. (ENG.). 192p. 29.95 (978-0-8264-8164-1(7)) Continuum International Publishing Group, Ltd. GBR. Dist: National Bk. Network.

Tyndale, William. Doctrinal Treatises & Introductions to Different Portions of the Holy Scriptures. Walter, Henry, ed. 2008. 604p. 59.95 (978-0-548-94480-6(6)) 2007. (ENG.). 608p. per. 44.95 (978-0-548-60772-5(9)) Kessinger Publishing, LLC.

Underhill, Evelyn. Fragments from an Inner Life: The Notebooks of Evelyn Underhill. Greene, Dana, ed. 2011. 132p. pap. 16.00 (978-1-61097-143-0(4), Wipf and Stock) Wipf & Stock Pubs.

Wells And Coakley Staff, et al. Praying for England: Priestly Presence in Contemporary Culture. 2008. (ENG.). 208p. 27.95 (978-0-567-03230-0(2)) Continuum International Publishing Group, Ltd. GBR. Dist: National Bk. Network.

Wilson, D. D., Thomas. The Works of the Right Reverend Father in God, Thomas Wilson, D. D. , Lord Bishop of Sodor & Man. Vol. 5: Sacra Privata. - Supplement to Sacra Privata. Maxims of Piety & Morality. - Supplement to Maxims. 2008. 650p. pap. 47.00 (978-1-60608-138-9(1), Wipf and Stock) Wipf & Stock Pubs.

Wilson, Todd. John Henry Newman: Prayers, Poems, Meditations. 2007. pap. (978-0-281-05973-7(X)) SPCK Publishing.

CHURCH OF ENGLAND—BIOGRAPHY

see also Church of England—Clergy—Biography

Atherstone, Andrew. Heart of Faith: Following Christ in the Church of England. 2008. (ENG.). 180p. pap. 33.00 (978-0-7188-3072-4(5)) Lutterworth Pr., The GBR. Dist: Brown, David Bk. Co., The.

—Oxford's Protestant Spy: The Controversial Career of Charles Golightly. 2007. (Studies in Evangelical History & Thought Ser.). (Illus.). 362p. pap. 43.00 (978-1-55635-491-5(6)) Wipf & Stock Pubs.

Chandler, Andrew. The Church & Humanity: The Life & Work of George Bell, 1883-1958. 2012. 240p. 99.95 (978-1-4094-2557-1(6)); 99.95 (978-1-4094-2556-4(8)) Ashgate Publishing Co.

Chapman, Raymond. Law & Revelation: Richard Hooker & His Writings. 2009. 256p. pap. 28.99 (978-1-85311-991-0(1), Canterbury Pr. Norwich) Hymns Ancient & Modern Ltd GBR. Dist: Westminster John Knox Pr.

Daughrity, Dyron B. A Genuinely Human Existence: An Historical Investigation in the Conflicted Life of Bishop Stephen Neill up to the Termination of His Bishopric (1945) 2007. (American University Studies VII: Theology & Religion Ser.). (C). 77.95 (978-1-4331-0165-6(3)) Lang, Peter Publishing, Inc.

Hein, David. Geoffrey Fisher: Archbishop of Canterbury. 2008. (ENG.). 140p. pap. 38.00 (978-0-227-17295-7(7)) Clarke, James Co., Ltd. GBR. Dist: Brown, David Bk. Co., The.

—Geoffrey Fisher: Archbishop of Canterbury, 1945-1961. 2007. (Princeton Theological Monograph Ser.). 140p. pap. 17.00 (978-1-59752-824-5(2), Pickwick Pubns.) Wipf & Stock Pubs.

Le Neve, John. Fasti Ecclesiae Anglicanae, 1541-1857. (978-0-485-17126-6(0)) Bow Historical Bks.

Pawley, Margaret. Donald Coggan: Servant of Christ. 24.00 (978-0-687-85156-0(4)) Abingdon Pr.

Pfatteicher, Carl F. John Redford: Organist & Almoner of St. Paul's Cathedral in the Reign of Henry VIII. reprint ed. 32.50 (978-0-404-13089-6(7)) AMS Pr., Inc.

Plouviez, Charles, ed. Christopher Wordsworth: Six Letters from Greece. 2009. (ENG., Illus.). 41p. (C). pap. 16.95 (978-1-905739-26-4(5)) Archaeopress GBR. Dist: Brown, David Bk. Co., The.

Robinson, John. Somebody's Child: The Story of a Man Who Found Hope — and Took It Back to the Streets, 1 vol. 2007. (Illus.). 176p. pap. 11.99 (978-0-8254-6149-1(9), Monarch Bks.) Lion Hudson PLC GBR. Dist: Kregel Pubns.

Susan Wesley Mounted Picture. 10.95 (978-0-687-31336-5(8), Abingdon Pr.

Thorndike, Herbert. The Theological Works of Herbert Thorndike V4. 2007. (ENG.). 486p. 53.95 (978-0-548-15478-6(3)); 488p. per. 38.95 (978-1-4304-4902-7(0)) Kessinger Publishing, LLC.

Waite, Terry. Taken on Trust. 2010. (ENG., Illus.). 496p. pap. 16.95 (978-0-340-60969-9(9), Hodder & Stoughton) Hodder General Publishing Div. GBR. Dist: Independent Pubs. Group.

CHURCH OF ENGLAND—BISHOPS

Chandler, Andrew. The Church & Humanity: The Life & Work of George Bell, 1883-1958. 2012. 240p. 99.95 (978-1-4094-2557-1(6)); 99.95 (978-1-4094-2556-4(8)) Ashgate Publishing Co.

Daughrity, Dyron B. A Genuinely Human Existence: An Historical Investigation in the Conflicted Life of Bishop Stephen Neill up to the Termination of His Bishopric (1945) 2007. (American University Studies VII: Theology & Religion Ser.). (C). 77.95 (978-1-4331-0165-6(3)) Lang, Peter Publishing, Inc.

Davies, Douglas J. & Guest, Mathew. Bishops, Wives & Children: Spiritual Capital Across the Generations. 2007. (Illus.). 228p. 99.95 (978-0-7546-5485-8(0)) Ashgate Publishing Co.

Gibson, William. James II & the Trial of the Seven Bishops. 2009. (ENG.). 272p. 89.00 (978-0-230-20400-3(7)) Palgrave Macmillan.

Grundy, Malcolm. Leadership & Oversight::New Models for Episcopal Ministry. 2011. (ENG.). 256p. pap. 27.95 (978-1-4411-4401-0(3)) Mowbray, A. R. & Co., Ltd. GBR. Dist: National Bk. Network.

Hein, David. Geoffrey Fisher: Archbishop of Canterbury. 2008. (ENG.). 140p. pap. 38.00 (978-0-227-17295-7(7)) Clarke, James Co., Ltd. GBR. Dist: Brown, David Bk. Co., The.

—Geoffrey Fisher: Archbishop of Canterbury, 1945-1961. 2007. (Princeton Theological Monograph Ser.). 140p. pap. 17.00 (978-1-59752-824-5(2), Pickwick Pubns.) Wipf & Stock Pubs.

Partington, Andrew. Church & State: The Contribution of the Church of England Bishops to the House of Lords During the Thatcher Years. 2006. (Studies in Christian History & Thought Ser.). (Illus.). 336p. pap. 34.00 (978-1-59752-834-4(X), Wipf and Stock) Wipf & Stock Pubs.

Pawley, Margaret. Donald Coggan: Servant of Christ. 24.00 (978-0-687-85156-0(4)) Abingdon Pr.

Plouviez, Charles, ed. Christopher Wordsworth: Six Letters from Greece. 2009. (ENG., Illus.). 41p. (C). pap. 16.95 (978-1-905739-26-4(5)) Archaeopress GBR. Dist: Brown, David Bk. Co., The.

Rigney, James. Women as Bishops. 2008. (Affirming Catholicism Ser.). (ENG.). 216p. 24.95 (978-0-567-03224-9(8)) Mowbray, A. R. & Co., Ltd. GBR. Dist: National Bk. Network.

Russell, Matheson, ed. On Rowan Williams: Critical Essays. 2008. 262p. pap. 29.00 (978-1-55635-973-6(X), Cascade Bks.) Wipf & Stock Pubs.

Ryle, J. C. That Man of Granite with the Heart of a Child: Eric Russell. 2008. (Hisotry Makers Ser.). (ENG.). 256p. pap. 13.99 (978-1-84550-387-1(2)) Christian Focus Pubns. GBR. Dist: STL Distribution North America.

Shortt, Rupert. Rowan's Rule: The Biography of the Archbishop of Canterbury. 2009. 484p. 30.00 (978-0-8028-6461-1(9)) Eerdmans, William B. Publishing Co.

Sykes, Norman. Old Priest & New Presbyter. 2008. (ENG.). 276p. pap. 37.99 (978-0-521-07289-2(1)) Cambridge Univ. Pr.

Truax, Jean. Ralph D'Escures William of Corbeil & Theobald of Bec: Archbishops of Canterbury. 2012. (Archbishops of Canterbury Ser.). 256p. 99.95 (978-0-7546-6836-7(3)); pap. 49.95 (978-0-7546-6833-6(9)) Ashgate Publishing Co.

CHURCH OF ENGLAND—BOOK OF COMMON PRAYER

Alternative Service Book. 16.00 (978-0-687-85029-7(0)) Abingdon Pr.

Baker Publishing Group Staff. BCP 1662. enl. ed. 2006. (ENG.). 704p. lthr. 109.99 (978-0-521-69151-2(6)) Cambridge Univ. Pr.

—Book of Common Prayer. 2006. (ENG.). 704p. im. lthr. 150.00 (978-0-521-86957-7(9)); Vol. 1. lthr. 450.00 (978-0-521-68970-0(8)) Cambridge Univ. Pr.

—Book of Common Prayers, 1662. enl. ed. 2006. (ENG.). 704p. lthr. 94.99 (978-0-521-69117-8(6)) Cambridge Univ. Pr.

The Book of Common Prayer: Pew Size, Print style B. 800p. 16.95 (978-0-921846-59-8(2), 1022) Forward Movement Pubns.

Braddock, Andrew. The Role of the Book of Common Prayer in the Formation of Modern Anglican Church Identity: A Study of English Parochial Worship, 1750-1850. 2010. 340p. 119.95 (978-0-7734-1442-6(8)) Mellen, Edwin Pr., The.

Buchanan, Colin, intro. The Savoy Conference Revisited. 2009. 88.00 (978-1-60724-403-5(9)) Gorgias Pr., LLC.

Burnet, Gilbert. An Exposition of the Thirty-Nine Articles of the Church of England: By Gilbert, Bishop of Sarum. with an Appendix, Containing the Augsburg Confession, 2006. 640p. per. 34.99 (978-1-4255-6652-4(9)) MPublishing.

Cairncross, Henry, compiled by. Ritual Notes, Ninth Edition (1946) with an Appendix on the Ceremonial of the Revised Holy Week (1955) A Comprehensive Guide to the Rites & Ceremonies of the Book of Common Prayer of the English Church. 9th ed. 2007. Orig. Title: Ritual Notes. 405p. reprint ed. spiral bd. 25.00 (978-0-9777093-2-8(9)) Lancelot Andrewes Pr.

Church Of England. The Book of Common Prayer & Administration of the Sacraments. 2007. pap. 37.95 (978-1-4304-5187-7(4)) Kessinger Publishing, LLC.

—The Book of Common Prayer & Administration of the Sacraments. 2007. 658p. 63.95 (978-0-548-16762-5(1)); (ENG.). 660p. per. 48.95 (978-1-4304-6473-0(9)) Kessinger Publishing, LLC.

—The Book of Common Prayer & Administration of the Sacraments, & Other Rites & Ceremonies of the Church. 2007. 460p. 52.95 (978-0-548-15708-4(1)) Kessinger Publishing, LLC.

Church Publishing, creator. Burial Rites for Adults, Together with a Rite for the Burial of a Child: Enriching Our Worship 3. 2007. 104p. per. 16.00 (978-0-89869-539-7(2)) Church Publishing, Inc.

Cummings, Brian, ed. The Book of Common Prayer: The Texts of 1549, 1559, And 1662. 2011. (ENG., Illus.). 896p. 29.95 (978-0-19-920717-6(8)) Oxford Univ. Pr., Inc.

Dailey, Prudence. The Book of Common Prayer: Past, Present & Future: A 350th Anniversary Celebration. Dailey, Prudence, ed. 2011. (ENG., Illus.). 216p. pap. 19.95 (978-1-4411-2818-8(2)) Continuum International Publishing Group, Ltd. GBR. Dist: National Bk. Network.

Dalby, Mark. Anglican Missals & their Canons. 2009. 88.00 (978-1-60724-392-2(X)) Gorgias Pr., LLC.

Frere, W. H. The Liturgical Gospels. 2011. 56p. pap. 5.00 (978-1-61097-003-7(9), Wipf and Stock) Wipf & Stock Pubs.

—Some Principles of Liturgical Reform: A Contribution towards the Revision of the Book of Common Prayer. 2008. 221p. pap. 19.00 (978-1-60608-304-8(X), Wipf and Stock) Wipf & Stock Pubs.

Frere, Walter Howard. The Liturgical Gospels. 2010. 85.40 (978-1-61719-211-1(2)) Gorgias Pr., LLC.

Gleason, Edward S. Dying We Live. 188p. pap. 2.95 (978-1-56101-014-1(6), 1747) Forward Movement Pubns.

Hefling, Charles & Shattuck, Cynthia. The Book of Common Prayer: A Worldwide Survey. 2008. (ENG., Illus.). 640p. per. 30.00 (978-0-19-529762-1(8)) Oxford Univ. Pr., Inc.

Jeanes. Signs of God's Promise: Thomas Cranmer's Sacramental Theology & the Book of Common Prayer. 2008. (ENG., Illus.). 328p. 150.00 (978-0-567-03188-4(8), T&T Clark Int'l) Continuum International Publishing Group, Ltd. GBR. Dist: National Bk. Network.

Jeanes, Gordon P. Signs of God's Promise: Thomas Cranmer's Sacramental Theology & the Book of Common Prayer. 2008. (ENG., Illus.). 328p. 49.95 (978-0-567-03189-1(6), T&T Clark Int'l) Continuum International Publishing Group, Ltd. GBR. Dist: National Bk. Network.

Morison, Stanley. English Prayer Books: An Introduction to the Literature of Christian Public Worship. 2009. (ENG.). 268p. pap. 42.00 (978-0-521-14252-6(0)) Cambridge Univ. Pr.

Oxford, ed. The Book of Common Prayer 1928. 2007. (ENG.). 611p. 44.99 (978-0-19-528525-3(5)) Oxford Univ. Pr., Inc.

—The Book of Common Prayer 1979. 2008. (ENG.). 1056p. 19.99 (978-0-19-528775-2(4)) Oxford Univ. Pr., Inc.

—Book of Common Prayer 1979. 2009. (ENG.). 2544p. 75.00 (978-0-19-528839-1(4)) Oxford Univ. Pr., Inc.

—1979 Book of Common Prayer Gift Edition. 2008. (ENG.). 1056p. 29.99 (978-0-19-528777-6(0)) Oxford Univ. Pr., Inc.

C

—1979 Book of Common Prayer Personal Edition, 4 3/8 X 6. 2008. (ENG.). 1056p. 44.99 (978-0-19-528782-0(7)) Oxford Univ. Pr., Inc.

Rosendale, Timothy. Liturgy & Literature in the Making of Protestant England. (ENG.). 248p. 2011. pap. 39.99 (978-0-521-17398-8(1)) 2007. 104.00 (978-0-521-87774-9(1)) Cambridge Univ. Pr.

Schnitker, Thaddaeus A. The Church's Worship. 2009. 260p. pap. 29.00 (978-1-60899-114-3(8), Wipf and Stock) Wipf & Stock Pubs.

CHURCH OF ENGLAND—BOOK OF COMMON PRAYER—PSALTER

see also Psalters

Oxford, ed. The Book of Common Prayer 1979. 2008. (ENG.). 1056p. 34.99 (978-0-19-528789-9(4)) Oxford Univ. Pr., Inc.

—1979 Book of Common Prayer, Economy Green Leather. 2008. (ENG.). 1056p. 19.99 (978-0-19-528718-9(5)) Oxford Univ. Pr., Inc.

—1979 Book of Common Prayer, Gift Edition. 2008. (ENG.). 1056p. 29.99 (978-0-19-528779-0(7)) Oxford Univ. Pr., Inc.

—1979 Book of Common Prayer (RCL edition) & the New Revised Standard Version Bible with Apocrypha, genuine leather Black, 9634AP. 2007. (ENG.). 2544p. 100.00 (978-0-19-528841-4(6)) Oxford Univ. Pr., Inc.

—1979 Book of Common Prayer Reader's Edition Genuine Leather. 2008. (ENG.). 1056p. 64.99 (978-0-19-528793-6(2)) Oxford Univ. Pr., Inc.

1979 Book of Common Prayer Reader's Edition Burgandy Genuine Leather. 2008. 1056p. lthr. 64.99 (978-0-19-528794-3(0)) Oxford Univ. Pr., Inc.

CHURCH OF ENGLAND—CATECHISMS AND CREEDS

Sykes, Norman. William Wake: Archbishop of Canterbury ,1657-1757, 2 vols. 2008. (ENG., Illus.). 681p. (C). pap. 90.00 (978-0-521-74328-0(1)) Cambridge Univ. Pr.

CHURCH OF ENGLAND—CLERGY

see also Anglican Orders; Apostolic Succession; Episcopacy

Allred, Frank. Why I Love Jesus: A Personal Testimony. 2008. 88p. pap. (978-0-946462-73-5(9)) Grace Pubns. Trust.

Baxter, Richard. The Reformed Pastor. 2010. 330p. pap. 31.75 (978-1-149-06693-5(8)) BiblioBazaar.

—The Reformed Pastor. 2009. 208p. pap. (978-1-150-12820-2(8)) Books LLC.

—The Reformed Pastor. 2007. 340p. 46.95 (978-0-548-11393-6(9)) Kessinger Publishing, LLC.

Carretta, Vincent & Reese, Ty M., eds. The Life & Letters of Philip Quaque, the First African Anglican Missionary. 2010. (Race in the Atlantic World, 1700-1900 Ser.). (ENG., Illus.). 240p. 39.95 (978-0-8203-3319-9(0)) Univ. of Georgia Pr.

Clerical Profession. 5.00 (978-0-687-85140-9(8)) Abingdon Pr.

Hedley, Douglas & Hebblethwaite, Brian L., eds. The Human Person in God's World: Studies to Commemorate the Austin Farrer Centenary. 2006. 150p. (978-0-334-04110-8(4)); per. (978-0-334-04106-1(6)) Hymns Ancient & Modern Ltd.

Jasper, Ronald C. D., ed. Walter Howard Frere: His Correspondence on Liturgical Revision & Construction. 2011. 332p. pap. 39.00 (**978-1-61097-237-6(6)**, Wipf and Stock) Wipf & Stock Pubs.

Kingsley, Charles. Charles Kingsley, His Letters, & Memories of His Life. 2007. (ENG.). 444p. 35.00 (978-1-4344-9182-4(X)); (ENG.). 432p. 35.00 (978-1-4344-9181-7(1)); (ENG.). 444p. per. 19.95 (978-1-4344-9088-9(2)); 432p. per. 19.95 (978-1-4344-9087-2(4)) Wildside Pr., LLC.

Kingsley, Charles. Charles Kingsley, his Letters & Memories of his Life. Kingsley, Frances Eliza, ed. 2011. (Cambridge Library Collection - Literary Studies). (ENG.). 518p. pap. 37.99 (**978-1-108-03485-2(3)**; (Illus.). 522p. pap. 37.99 (**978-1-108-03484-5(5)**) Cambridge Univ. Pr.

Lewis-Anthony, Justin. If You Meet George Herbert on the Road, Kill Him: Radically Re-Thinking Priestly Ministry. 2009. (ENG.). 256p. 29.95 (978-1-906286-17-0(5)) Mowbray, A. R. & Co., Ltd. GBR. Dist: National Bk. Network.

May, Trevor. The Victorian Clergyman. 2008. (Shire Library). (ENG., Illus.). 40p. per. 11.95 (978-0-7478-0658-5(6)) Shire Pubns., Ltd. GBR. Dist: Random Hse., Inc.

Melinsky, M. A. Hugh. The Shape of the Ministry. 2012. xiii, 302p. pap. (**978-1-85311-047-4(7)**) Church Hse. Publishing.

Robbins, Mandy. Clergywomen in the Church of England: A Psychological Study. 2008. 248p. 109.95 (978-0-7734-4948-0(5)) Mellen, Edwin Pr., The.

Ruderman, David B. Connecting the Covenants: Judaism & the Search for Christian Identity in Eighteenth-Century England. 2007. (Jewish Culture & Contexts Ser.). 152p. (C). 59.95 (978-0-8122-4016-0(2)) Univ. of Pennsylvania Pr.

Talbot, C. H. Letters from the English Abbots to the Chapter at Citeaux, 1442-1521. (Camden Fourth Ser.: No. 4). 200p. 27.00 (978-0-901050-64-9(4)) Brown, David Bk. Co., The.

Thomson, Andrew. The Clergy of Winchester, England, 1615-1698: A Diocesan Ministry in Crisis. 2011. (Illus.). vii, 288p. (**978-0-7734-3822-4(X)**) Mellen, Edwin Pr., The.

Thomson, Andrew. The Clergy of Winchester, England 1615-1698: A Diocesan Ministry n CrisisThe Clergy of Winchester, England 1615-1698The Clergy of Winchester, England 1615-1698. 2011. (Illus.). 304p. 129.95 (978-0-7734-1580-5(7)) Mellen, Edwin Pr., The.

Trollope, Anthony. Clergymen of the Church of England. reprint ed. lib. bdg. 98.00 (978-0-7426-2453-5(6)) Classic Bks.

Turton, Douglas W. Clergy Burnout & Emotional Exhaustion: A Socio-Psychological Study of Job Stress & Job Satisfaction. 2010. xi, 288p. (978-0-7734-3648-0(0)) Mellen, Edwin Pr., The.

VanNerley, David. The Voice of the Stranger. 2009. 132p. pap. (978-3-639-12972-4(5)) VDM Verlag Dr. Mueller e.K.

Village, Andrew & Francis, Leslie J. The Mind of the Anglican Clergy: Assessing Attitudes & Beliefs in the Church of England. 2009. (Illus.). 228p. 109.95 (978-0-7734-4803-2(9)) Mellen, Edwin Pr., The.

White, Andrew. Faith under Fire: What the Middle East Conflict Has Taught Me about God, 1 vol. 2011. (Illus.). 160p. pap. 13.99 (978-1-85424-962-3(2), Monarch Bks.) Lion Hudson PLC GBR. Dist: Kregel Pubns.

CHURCH OF ENGLAND—CLERGY—BIOGRAPHY

Aitken, Jonathan. John Newton: From Disgrace to Amazing Grace. 2007. 400p. 21.99 (978-1-58134-848-4(7)) Crossway.

Beardsley, Christina. Unutterable Love: The Passionate Life & Preaching of F. W. Robertson. 2009. (ENG., Illus.). 424p. pap. 58.00 (978-0-7188-9210-4(0)) Lutherworth Pr., The GBR. Dist: Brown, David Bk. Co., The.

Beardsley, Eben Edwards. Life & Correspondence of Samuel Johnson, D D , Missionary of the Church of England in Connecticut, & First President of King's College, New York. 2006. 396p. per. 26.99 (978-1-4255-4262-7(X)) MPublishing.

Bonwicke, Ambrose. Life of Ambrose Bonwicke. Mayor, John E. B., ed. 2007. (ENG.). 280p. 42.95 (978-0-548-14061-1(8)) Kessinger Publishing, LLC.

—Life of Ambrose Bonwicke. 2006. pap. 27.95 (978-1-4286-5260-6(4)) Kessinger Publishing, LLC.

Butler, John R. The Red Dean of Canterbury: The Public & Private Faces of Hewlett Johnson. 2011. (ENG., Illus.). 352p. 29.95 (**978-1-85759-736-3(2)**) Scala, Editions FRA. Dist: National Bk. Network.

Chapman, Alister. Godly Ambition: John Stott & the Evangelical Movement, 1 vol. 2011. (ENG.). 240p. 55.00 (**978-0-19-977397-8(1)**) Oxford Univ. Pr., Inc.

Church, Mary C. Life & Letters of Dean Church. 2009. 382p. 33.99 (978-1-113-59607-9(4)); pap. 33.75 (978-1-113-60868-0(4)); pap. 20.99 (978-1-113-59606-2(6)) BiblioBazaar.

—Life & Letters of Dean Church. 2009. 166p. pap. (978-0-217-01093-1(8)) Books LLC.

Church, Mary C., ed. Life & Letters of Dean Church. 2007. (ENG.). 384p. 48.95 (978-0-548-09049-7(1)) Kessinger Publishing, LLC.

Greaves, John Neville. Faith & Works: An Experience of God in Ministry. 2007. (Illus.). 148p. per. (978-1-84401-998-4(5)) Athena Pr.

Green, Dudley. Patrick Bronte: Father of Genius. 2009. (ENG., Illus.). 284p. 34.95 (978-1-84588-625-7(9)) History Pr. Ltd., The GBR. Dist: Independent Pubs. Group.

—Patrick Brontë: Father of Genius. 2010. (ENG., Illus.). 384p. pap. 24.95 (978-0-7524-5445-0(5)) History Pr. Ltd., The GBR. Dist: Independent Pubs. Group.

Haslam, William. From Death into Life Twenty Years of My. 2007. pap. (978-1-4068-1390-6(7)) Echo Library.

Haydon, Colin. John Henry Williams (1747-1829) - Political Clergyman: War, the French Revolution, & the Church of England. 2007. (Studies in Modern British Religious History Ser.: Volume 16). (Illus.). 192p. 90.00 (978-1-84383-330-7(1), Boydell Press) Boydell & Brewer, Ltd. GBR. Dist: Boydell & Brewer, Inc.

Kinsolving, Kathleen. Gadfly: The Life & Times of les Kinsolving-White House Watchdog. 2010. 384p. 25.95 (978-1-935071-80-8(7)) WND Bks, Inc.

Knox, Francesca Bugliani. The Eye of the Eagle: John Donne & the Legacy of Ignatius Loyola. 2011. (Illus.). 356p. pap. 75.95 (978-3-0343-0225-8(8)) Lang, Peter AG GBR. Dist: Lang, Peter.

The Life of the Rev. Rowland Hill, A. M. 2010. pap. 18.88 (978-1-61143-163-6(8)) Gorgias Pr., LLC.

Murray, J. Todd, ed. Beyond Amazing Grace: Timeless Pastoral Wisdom from the Letters, Sermons & Hymns of John Newton. 2007. (Illus.). 282p. per. (978-0-85234-653-2(0)) Evangelical Pr.

Newton, John. The Amazing Works of John Newton. 2009. (Pure Gold Classics Ser.). (Illus.). 368p. pap. 14.99 incl. audio compact disk (978-0-88270-809-6(0)) Bridge-Logos Foundation.

Nourse, John. A Love of High Places. 2007. pap. 17.95 (978-988-99937-1-9(6)) Inkstone Bks.

Phillips, Patrick. Life Is Meant to be a Challenge. 2006. (Illus.). 68p. pap. (978-1-84401-842-0(3)) Athena Pr.

Piper, John. The Roots of Endurance: Invincible Perseverance in the Lives of John Newton, Charles Simeon, & William Wilberforce. 2nd ed. 2006. (Swans Are Not Silent Ser.: Vol. 3). 176p. pap. 14.99 (978-1-58134-814-9(2)) Crossway.

Polkinghorne, John. From Physicist to Priest: An Autobiography. 2008. (Illus.). 208p. pap. 23.00 (978-1-55635-910-1(1)) Wipf & Stock Pubs.

Ransome, Joyce. The Web of Friendship: Nicholas Ferrar & Little Gidding. 2011. (ENG., Illus.). 291p. pap. 53.00 (978-0-227-17348-0(1)) Clarke, James Co., Ltd. GBR. Dist: Brown, David Bk. Co., The.

Robinson, Charles Henry & Robinson, Forbes. Letters to His Friends. 2009. (ENG.). 225p. 32.99 (978-1-117-61960-6(5)); pap. 24.75 (978-1-117-61961-3(3)) BiblioBazaar.

—Letters to his Friends. 2009. (ENG.). 225p. pap. 20.99 (978-1-117-61962-0(1), BiblioLife) BiblioBazaar.

Robinson, Forbes. Letters to His Friends. 2010. 222p. pap. 24.75 (978-1-143-37148-6(8)) 2009. 224p. 28.99 (978-1-110-86715-8(8)) 2009. 224p. pap. 24.75 (978-1-110-86713-4(1)) 2009. 160p. 22.99 (978-0-559-07023-5(3)) 2009. 160p. 25.99 (978-0-559-07009-9(8)) 2009. 160p. pap. 20.75 (978-0-559-07019-8(5)) 2009. 160p. pap. 21.75 (978-0-559-07012-9(8)) BiblioBazaar.

—Letters to His Friends. 2009. 100p. pap. (978-1-151-53263-3(0)) Books LLC.

—Letters to His Friends. Robinson, Charles, ed. 2009. 156p. pap. (978-1-4099-7452-9(9)) Dodo Pr.

—Letters to His Friends. 2010. (Illus.). 92p. pap. 20.00 (978-1-153-75517-7(3)) General Bks. LLC.

—Letters to His Friends. Robinson, Charles, ed. 212p. 2010. 31.96 (**978-1-165-56076-9(3)**) 2010. pap. 19.96 (**978-1-165-53605-4(6)**) 2009. 39.95 (978-1-104-27615-7(1)) 2009. pap. 24.95 (978-1-104-25144-4(2)) Kessinger Publishing, LLC.

Robinson, Forbes. Letters to his Friends. 2009. (ENG.). 223p. pap. 20.99 (978-1-110-86709-7(3), BiblioLife) BiblioBazaar.

Ryle, J. C. That Man of Granite with the Heart of a Child: Eric Russell. 2008. (Hisotry Makers Ser.). (ENG.). 256p. pap. 13.99 (978-1-84550-387-1(2)) Christian Focus Pubns. GBR. Dist: STL Distribution North America.

Schofield, Nicholas. William Lockhart. 2011. (Illus.). 212p. pap. (**978-0-85244-753-6(1)**) Gracewing, Ltd.

Shortt, Rupert. Rowan's Rule: The Biography of the Archbishop of Canterbury. 2009. 484p. 30.00 (978-0-8028-6461-1(9)) Eerdmans, William B. Publishing Co.

Smith, Sydney. The Works of the Rev Sydney Smith. 2009. 324p. pap. (978-0-217-96528-6(8)); 156p. pap. (978-0-217-28790-6(5)) Books LLC.

—The Works of the Rev Sydney Smith. 2009. 302p. pap. 24.39 (978-1-4589-8660-3(8)) General Bks. LLC.

—The Works of the Rev Sydney Smith. 2006. 488p. per. 29.99 (978-1-4255-5385-2(0)) MPublishing.

Steer, Roger. Basic Christian: The Inside Story of John Stott. 2010. (ENG.). 288p. pap. 19.00 (978-0-8308-3846-2(5), IVP Bks.) InterVarsity Pr.

Stephens, W. R. W. Life & Letters of Walter Farquhar Hook. 2006. pap. 45.95 (978-1-4286-5430-3(5)) Kessinger Publishing, LLC.

Strom, Kay Marshall. Once Blind: The Life of John Newton. 2008. (ENG.). 256p. per. 14.99 (978-1-934068-27-4(6)) Authentic Media.

Thomas Nelson Publishing Staff. The Bishop of Rwanda, 0 vols. 2008. 256p. pap. 14.99 (978-1-59555-237-2(5)) Nelson, Thomas Inc.

Townsend, Mark. The Path of the Blue Raven. 2009. (ENG.). 240p. pap. 24.95 (978-1-84694-238-9(1)) Hunt, John Publishing Ltd. GBR. Dist: National Bk. Network.

Urquhart. Faith for the Future. 203p. pap. (978-0-340-32262-8(4), Hodder & Stoughton) Hodder General Publishing Div.

Walters, S. M. & Stow, E. A. Darwin's Mentor: John Stevens Henslow, 1796-1861. 2009. (Illus.). 368p. pap. 38.99 (978-0-521-11799-9(2)) Cambridge Univ. Pr.

William Haslam. From Death to Life: Or twenty years of my Ministry. I.t. ed. 2007. (ENG.). 282p. pap. 23.99 (978-1-4264-8178-9(0)) BiblioBazaar.

Wright, Christopher J. H., ed. Portraits of a Radical Disciple: Recollections of John Stott's Life & Ministry. 2011. (ENG.). 242p. pap. 16.00 (**978-0-8308-3810-3(4)**, IVP Bks.) InterVarsity Pr.

CHURCH OF ENGLAND—CONSTITUTION

see Church of England—Government

CHURCH OF ENGLAND—DIRECTORIES

Cosin, John. The Works of the Right Reverend Father in God, John Cosin, Lord Bishop of Durham. vol. IV: Miscellaneous Works. 2008. 544p. pap. 41.00 (978-1-60608-139-6(X), Wipf and Stock) Wipf & Stock Pubs.

CHURCH OF ENGLAND—DOCTRINES

Ball, Peter. Anglican Spiritual Direction. 2nd ed. 2007. (Spiritual Directors International Book Ser.). 144p. per. 22.00 (978-0-8192-2254-1(2)) Church Publishing, Inc.

Barry, Alfred, ed. Masters in English Theology: Being the King's College Lectures For. 2007. (ENG.). 268p. per. 27.95 (978-1-4304-4677-4(3)) Kessinger Publishing, LLC.

Becon, Thomas. The Catechism of Thomas Becon. 2009. 58p. pap. (978-1-151-68972-6(6)) Books LLC.

Bingham, Joseph. Works of the Reverend Joseph Bingham V3. 2006. pap. 45.95 (978-1-4286-5108-1(X)) Kessinger Publishing, LLC.

—Works of the Reverend Joseph Bingham V7. 2006. pap. 37.95 (978-1-4286-5107-4(1)) Kessinger Publishing, LLC.

Brendlinger, Irv A. Social Justice Through the Eyes of Wesley: John Wesley's Theological Challenge to Slavery. 2006. xvii, 271p. pap. 24.99 (978-1-894400-23-7(2)) Sola Scriptura.

Crimmins, James E., et al. Church-of-Englandism & its Catechism Examined. 2011. (ENG.). 688p. 160.00 (978-0-19-959025-4(7)) Oxford Univ. Pr., Inc.

Dormor, Duncan. An Acceptable Sacrifice. 2007. pap. (978-0-281-05851-8(2)) SPCK Publishing.

Durand, William, et al. The Clergy & Their Vestments Bks. 2-3: A New Translation of the Rationale Divinorum Officiorum. Thibodeau, Timothy M., tr. from LAT. & intro. by. 2009. (Illus.). 262p. pap. 35.00 (978-1-58966-191-2(5)) Univ. of Scranton Pr.

Foulkes, Richard. Church & Stage in Victorian England. 2006. (ENG.). 280p. pap. 60.00 (978-0-521-03437-1(X)) Cambridge Univ. Pr.

Goode, William. A Vindication of the Doctrine of the Church of England on the Validity of the Orders of the Scotch & Foreign Non-Episcopal Churches: In Three Pamphl. 2006. 148p. per. 16.99 (978-1-4255-1065-7(5)) MPublishing.

Jewel, John. The Works of John Jewel, Bishop of Salisbury. Ayre, John, ed. 2010. (Parker Society Ser.). 596p. pap. 50.00 (978-1-60608-064-1(4), Wipf and Stock) Wipf & Stock Pubs.

Law, William. The Works of the Reverend William Law V2. 2007. (ENG.). 196p. 37.95 (978-0-548-09168-5(4)) Kessinger Publishing, LLC.

—The Works of the Reverend William Law V5. 2007. (ENG.). 192p. 37.95 (978-0-548-09171-5(4)) Kessinger Publishing, LLC.

—The Works of the Reverend William Law V6. 2007. (ENG.). 268p. 42.95 (978-0-548-09172-2(2)) Kessinger Publishing, LLC.

—The Works of the Reverend William Law V7. 2007. (ENG.). 212p. 39.95 (978-0-548-09173-9(0)) Kessinger Publishing, LLC.

Lloyd, Trevor & Tovey, Phillip. Celebrating Forgiveness. 2009. 88.00 (978-1-60724-348-9(2)) Gorgias Pr., LLC.

Locke, Kenneth A. The Church in Anglian Theology: An Historical, Theological & Ecumenical Exploration. 2009. (Illus.). 232p. 99.95 (978-0-7546-6530-4(5)) Ashgate Publishing Co.

Maurice, Frederick Denison. The Kingdom of Christ. 2009. 506p. pap. (978-0-217-33230-9(7)) Books LLC.

Mburugu, Naftaly. The Crucified & Buried Church. 2011. 56p. pap. (**978-3-8443-2406-8(2)**) Lambert Academic Publishing.

McAdoo, H. R. The Mystery of the Eucharist in the Anglican Tradition. 2008. 218p. pap. 24.00 (978-1-60608-210-2(8), Wipf and Stock) Wipf & Stock Pubs.

More, Paul E. & Cross, Frank L., Jr., eds. Anglicanism: The Thought & Practice of the Church of England. 2009. (ENG.). 812p. pap. 64.00 (978-0-227-17290-2(6)) Clarke, James Co., Ltd. GBR. Dist: Brown, David Bk. Co., The.

Newman, John Henry C., ed. Apologia Pro Vita Sua & Six Sermons. 2007.Tr. of Apologia Pro Vita Sua. (ENG.). 312p. per. (978-1-4065-4966-9(5)) Dodo Pr.

—Apologia Pro Vita Sua & Six Sermons. 2007.Tr. of Apologia Pro Vita Sua. (ENG.). pap. (978-1-4068-3519-9(6)) Echo Library.

Newman, John Henry C. & Turner, Frank M. Apologia Pro Vita Sua & Six Sermons. 2012.Tr. of Apologia Pro Vita Sua. (ENG., Illus.). 528p. pap. 30.00 (978-0-300-17786-2(0)) Yale Univ. Pr.

Newman, John Henry C. & Turner, Frank M., eds. Apologia Pro Vita Sua & Six Sermons. 2008.Tr. of Apologia Pro Vita Sua. 528p. 55.00 (978-0-300-11507-9(5)) Yale Univ. Pr.

Newton, John. The Amazing Works of John Newton. 2009. (Pure Gold Classics Ser.). (Illus.). 368p. pap. 14.99 incl. audio compact disk (978-0-88270-809-6(0)) Bridge-Logos Foundation.

O'Donovan, Oliver. On the Thirty-Nine Articles: A Conversation with Tudor Christianity. 2011. 180p. pap. 30.00 (**978-0-334-04398-0(0)**, SCM Pr.) Hymns Ancient & Modern Ltd GBR. Dist: Westminster John Knox Pr.

Packer, J. I. & Beckwith, Roger T. The Thirty-Nine Articles: Their Place & Use Today. 2007. (ENG.). 104p. per. (978-1-57383-413-1(0), Regent College Publishing) Regent College Publishing.

Perham. Revised Common Lection (Green), 20, Pack. rev. ed. (Illus.). 980p. (978-0-264-67473-5(1), Morehouse Publishing) Church Publishing, Inc.

Pickard, Stephen. In Between God: Theology, Community, & Discipleship. 2012. (ENG.). (C). pap. 29.95 (**978-1-921817-10-6(0)**) ATF Pr. AUS. Dist: Brown, David Bk. Co., The.

Poole, Eve. The Church on Capitalism: Theology & the Market. 2010. (ENG., Illus.). 240p. 100.00 (978-0-230-27516-4(8)) Palgrave Macmillan.

Rees, Wyn, et al. British Foreign Policy & the Anglican Church: Christian Engagement with the Contemporary World. 2008. (Illus.). 172p. pap. 39.95 (978-0-7546-6037-8(0)) Ashgate Publishing Co.

Rogers, Thomas. The Catholic Doctrine of the Church of England. 2009. 402p. 41.99 (978-1-117-16122-8(6)); (ENG.). 401p. pap. 33.75 (978-1-117-16123-5(4)) BiblioBazaar.

Ross, Wyn. British Foreign Policy & the Anglican Church: Christian Engagement with the Contemporary World. Blewett, Timothy & Hyde-Price, Adrian, eds. 2008. (Illus.). 172p. 99.95 (978-0-7546-6035-4(4)) Ashgate Publishing Co.

Smith, James. The Eucharistic Doctrine of the Later Nonjurors. 2009. 88.00 (978-1-60724-396-0(2)) Gorgias Pr., LLC.

Staley, Vernon. The Catholic Religion: A Manual of Instruction for Members of the Anglican Communion. 2007. (Illus.). 424p. pap. 47.00 (978-1-55635-468-7(1), Wipf and Stock) Wipf & Stock Pubs.

Thomasset, Alain. L'ecclésiologie de John Henry Newman Anglican (1816-1845) 2006. (Bibliotheca Ephemeridum Theologicarum Lovaniensium Ser.). (FRE & ENG.). 748p. (C). pap. 116.00 (978-90-429-1742-2(3)) Peeters Pubs. & Booksellers BEL. Dist: Brown, David Bk. Co., The.

Throness, Laurie. A Protestant Purgatory: Theological Origins of the Penitentiary ACT, 1779. 2008. 390p. 134.95 (978-0-7546-6392-8(2)) Ashgate Publishing Co.

Village, Andrew & Francis, Leslie J. The Mind of the Anglican Clergy: Assessing Attitudes & Beliefs in the Church of England. 2009. (Illus.). 228p. 109.95 (978-0-7734-4803-2(9)) Mellen, Edwin Pr., The.

Williams, Charles & Underhill, Evelyn, , Evelyn. The Letters of Evelyn Underhill. 2009. 318p. pap. 55.50 (978-1-4092-0922-5(9)) Lulu Enterprises Inc.

CHURCH OF ENGLAND—GOVERNMENT

Briden, Timothy & MacMorran, Kenneth. A Churchwardens & Parochial Church Councillors. 14th rev. ed. 2010. (ENG., Illus.). 208p. instr.'s hndbk. ed. 16.95 (978-1-4411-5474-3(4)) Mowbray, A. R. & Co., Ltd. GBR. Dist: National Bk. Network.

Ditchfield, Peter Hampson. The Parish Clerk. 2008. 332p. 28.99 (978-0-554-33922-1(6)) 2008. 332p. 29.99 (978-0-554-24619-2(8)) 2007. (ENG.). 298p. pap. 21.99 (978-1-4264-6930-5(6)) 2007. (ENG.). 330p. pap. 24.99 (978-1-4264-7012-7(6)) BiblioBazaar.

—The Parish Clerk. 2009. 260p. pap. (978-0-217-39545-8(7)) Books LLC.

—The Parish Clerk. 2008. (Illus.). 308p. per. (978-1-4065-8754-8(0)) Dodo Pr.

—The Parish Clerk. 2007. (ENG.). 200p. per. (978-1-4068-6147-1(2)) Echo Library.
—The Parish Clerk. 2007. (ENG.). 416p. per. 34.95 (978-0-548-65388-3(7)) Kessinger Publishing, LLC.
Hampson, Michael. Last Rites: The End of the Church of England. 2006. (ENG.). 208p. per. 24.95 (978-1-86207-891-8(2)) Granta Bks. GBR. Dist: Independent Pubs. Group.
Hill, Mark. Ecclesiastical Law. 3rd ed. 2008. (ENG.). 800p. 280.50 (978-0-19-921712-0(2)) Oxford Univ. Pr., Inc.
Hooker, Richard. Of the Laws of Ecclesiastical Polity. 2009. 192p. 22.99 (978-1-103-56704-1(7)); pap. 16.99 (978-1-103-56702-7(0)) BiblioBazaar.
Johnson, John. Collection of the Laws & Canons of the Church of England: Theological Works, 4 vols. (Library of Anglo-Catholic Theology: No. 10). reprint ed. 115.00 (978-0-404-52110-3(X)) AMS Pr., Inc.
Overall, John. Convocation Book of Sixteen Six. (Library of Anglo-Catholic Theology: No. 15). reprint ed. 27.50 (978-0-404-52107-3(X)) AMS Pr., Inc.
Pitchford. Abc for the Pcc 5th Ed (p) 5th rev. ed. 2008. (ENG.). 228p. pap. 24.95 (978-1-906286-07-1(8)) Mowbray, A. R. & Co., Ltd. GBR. Dist: National Bk. Network.
Ramsey, Arthur Michael, ed. Lambeth Essays on Ministry: Essays Written for the Lambeth Conference 1968. 2010. 104p. pap. 13.00 (978-1-60899-798-5(7), Wipf and Stock) Wipf & Stock Pubs.

CHURCH OF ENGLAND—HISTORY

Abbey, Charles. English Church in the Eighteenth Century. 2006. pap. (978-1-4068-0610-6(2)) Echo Library.
Abbey, Charles J. The English Church in the Eighteenth Century. 2009. 636p. 38.99 (978-0-559-05310-8(X)); 34.99 (978-0-559-05324-5(X)); pap. 44.75 (978-0-559-05322-1(3)); pap. 45.75 (978-0-559-05314-6(2)) BiblioBazaar.
—The English Church in the Eighteenth Century. 2010. (Illus.). 426p. pap. 49.46 (978-1-153-70141-9(3)) General Bks. LLC.
Abbey, Charles John. The English Church in the Eighteenth Century. 2012. 516p. pap. 39.75 (978-1-276-93842-6(X)) 2010. 598p. pap. 44.75 (978-1-147-14773-5(6)) BiblioBazaar.
—The English Church in the Eighteenth Century. 2010. 424p. pap. (978-1-152-05515-5(1)) 2009. 524p. pap. (978-0-217-79687-3(7)) Books LLC.
—The English Church in the Eighteenth Century. 2010. 416p. pap. 22.72 (978-1-152-05518-6(6)) General Bks. LLC.
Abbey, Charles John & Overton, John Henry. The English Church in the Eighteenth Century. 2010. (ENG.). 594p. pap. 44.75 (978-1-177-04057-0(3)); 546p. pap. 41.75 (978-1-177-83475-9(8)) BiblioBazaar.
Anderson, James S. M. History of the Church of England V1. 2006. pap. 43.95 (978-1-4286-4435-9(0)) Kessinger Publishing, LLC.
—History of the Church of England V2 in T. 2006. pap. 44.95 (978-1-4286-4436-6(9)) Kessinger Publishing, LLC.
—History of the Church of England V3 in T. 2006. pap. 49.95 (978-1-4286-4437-3(7)) Kessinger Publishing, LLC.
Appleby, David. Black Bartholomew's Day: Preaching, Polemic & Restoration Nonconformity. 2008. (Politics, Culture & Society in Early Modern Britain Ser.). (ENG.). 272p. 89.00 (978-0-7190-7561-2(0)) Manchester Univ. Pr. GBR. Dist: Macmillan.
Barrett, C. K. Barchester. (Illus.). 499p. 51.00 (978-0-281-04667-6(0)) SPCK Publishing GBR. Dist: Pilgrim Pr., The/United Church Pr.
Beasley, Nicholas M. Christian Ritual & the Creation of British Slave Societies, 1650-1780. 2009. (Race in the Atlantic World, 1700-1900 Ser.). (ENG., Illus.). 240p. lib. bdg. 44.95 (978-0-8203-3339-7(5)) Univ. of Georgia Pr.
Bernard, E. R. The Church of England & the Church of Sweden. 2010. pap. 22.00 (978-1-61719-383-5(6)); pap. 22.00 (978-1-61719-386-6(0)) Gorgias Pr., LLC.
Biddle, Martin & Birthe Kjolbye-Biddle, Magister. St Albans Cathedral & Abbey. 2009. (ENG., Illus.). 128p. pap. 35.00 (978-1-85759-554-3(8)) Scala, Editions FRA. Dist: National Bk. Network.
Black, Vicki K. Welcome to Anglican Spiritual Traditions. 2010. (Welcome to the Episcopal Church Ser.). 144p. pap. 14.00 (978-0-8192-2368-5(9), Morehouse Publishing) Church Publishing, Inc.
Blackmore, Henrietta, ed. The Beginning of Women's Ministry: The Revival of the Deaconess in the Nineteenth-Century Church of England. 2007. (Church of England Record Society Ser.: Volume 14). (Illus.). 204p. 90.00 (978-1-84383-308-6(5), Boydell Press) Boydell & Brewer, Ltd. GBR. Dist: Boydell & Brewer, Inc.
Blaxland, Bruce. Struggle with Puritanism. 2006. pap. 26.95 (978-1-4286-3657-6(9)) Kessinger Publishing, LLC.
Blunt, John Henry. The Reformation of the Church of England. 2009. 510p. pap. (978-0-217-64006-0(0)) Books LLC.
Bowden, Martha F. Yorick's Congregation: The Church of England in the Time of Laurence Sterne. 2007. (Illus.). (C). (978-0-87413-955-6(4)) Univ. of Delaware Pr.
Brendlinger, Irv A. Social Justice Through the Eyes of Wesley: John Wesley's Theological Challenge to Slavery. 2006. xvii, 271p. 24.99 (978-1-894400-23-7(2)) Sola Scriptura.
Broad, John, ed. Bishop Wake's Summary of Visitation Returns from the Diocese of Lincoln 1705-15, Part 1: Lincolnshire. 2012. (ENG.). 420p. 160.00 (978-0-19-726518-5(9)) Oxford Univ. Pr., Inc.
—Bishop Wake's Summary of Visitation Returns from the Diocese of Lincoln 1706-15, Part 2: Huntingdonshire, Hertfordshire (part), Bedfordshire, Leicestershire, Buckinghamshire. 2012. (Records of Social & Economic History, New Ser.). (ENG.). 520p. 175.00 (978-0-19-726519-2(7)) Oxford Univ. Pr., Inc.
Cartwright, Thomas. Diary of Dr. Thomas Cartwright, Bishop of Chester 1686-1687. (Camden Society, London, Publications, First Ser.: No. 22). reprint ed. 32.00 (978-0-404-50122-8(2)) AMS Pr., Inc.
Chandler, Andrew. The Church of England in the Twentieth Century: The Church Commissioners & the Politics of Reform, 1948-1998. 2009. 578p. pap. 45.00 (978-1-84383-501-1(0), Boydell Press) Boydell & Brewer, Ltd. GBR. Dist: Boydell & Brewer, Inc.
The Church Establishment of England. 2010. pap. 18.88 (978-1-61143-170-4(0)) Gorgias Pr., LLC.
Cragg, G. R. From Puritanism to the Age of Reason: A Study of Changes in Religious Thought within the Church of England 1660 To 1700. 2008. (ENG.). 260p. pap. 37.99 (978-0-521-08160-3(2)) Cambridge Univ. Pr.
Crumb, Lawrence N. The Oxford Movement & Its Leaders: A Bibliography of Secondary & Lesser Primary Sources. 2nd ed. 2009. (ATLA Bibliography Ser.). (ENG.). 936p. 195.00 (978-0-8108-6193-0(3)) Scarecrow Pr., Inc.
Davie, Donald. A Gathered Church (Routledge Revivals) The Literature of the English Dissenting Interest, 1700-1930. 2011. (Routledge Revivals Ser.). (ENG.). 170p. 110.00 (978-0-415-50033-3(8)) Routledge.
Elliott, Kenneth Ray. Anglican Church Policy, Eighteenth Century Conflict, & the American Episcopate. 2011. 227p. (978-1-4331-1431-1(3)) Lang, Peter GmbH, Europaischer Verlag der Wissenschaften.
Fti, Brother Anthony Josemaria. The Blessed Virgin Mary in England: Vol. II. 2009. 464p. pap. 34.95 (978-0-595-50671-2(2)) iUniverse, Inc.
Gerard, W. B. Divine Rhetoric: Essays on the Sermons of Laurence Sterne. 2010. (ENG.). 62.50 (978-1-61149-121-0(5)) Univ. of Delaware Pr.
Gerard, William Blake, intro. Divine Rhetoric: Essays on the Sermons of Laurence Sterne. 2010. (Illus.). 284p. 62.50 (978-0-87413-063-8(8)) Univ. of Delaware Pr.
Gore, Charles. Essays in Aid of the Reform of the Church. 2008. 388p. pap. 33.95 (978-1-4368-3790-3(1)) Kessinger Publishing, LLC.
Gore, Charles, ed. Essays in Aid of the Reform of the Church. 2008. 392p. pap. 33.00 (978-1-60608-120-4(9)) Wipf & Stock Pubs.
Grimmett, Richard F. St John's Church, Lafayette Square: The History & Heritage of the Church of the Presidents, Washington, DC. 2009. (ENG., Illus.). 360p. pap. 18.95 (978-1-934248-53-9(3)) Mill City Pr., Inc.
Groves, Phil, ed. The Anglican Communion & Homosexuality: The official study guide to enable listening & dialogue. 2008. 288p. pap. (978-0-281-05963-8(2)) SPCK Publishing.
Gunstone, John. Lift High the Cross: Anglo-Catholicism in the Congress Years. 2010. (ENG., Illus.). 384p. pap. 35.00 (978-1-85311-817-3(6), Canterbury Pr. Norwich) Hymns Ancient & Modern Ltd GBR. Dist: Westminster John Knox Pr.
Hampton, Stephen William Peter. Anti-Arminians: The Anglican Reformed Tradition from Charles II to George I. 2008. (Oxford Theological Monographs). (ENG.). 304p. 240.00 (978-0-19-953336-7(9)) Oxford Univ. Pr., Inc.
Haugaard, William P. Elizabeth & the English Reformation: The Struggles for a Stable Settlement of Religion. 2008. (ENG.). 412p. pap. 53.00 (978-0-521-08551-9(9)) Cambridge Univ. Pr.
Haydon, Colin. John Henry Williams (1747-1829) - Political Clergyman: War, the French Revolution, & the Church of England. 2007. (Studies in Modern British Religious History Ser.: Volume 16). (Illus.). 192p. 90.00 (978-1-84383-330-7(1), Boydell Press) Boydell & Brewer, Ltd. GBR. Dist: Boydell & Brewer, Inc.
Hebb, Ross N. Samuel Seabury & Charles Inglis: Two Bishops, Two Churches. 2010. 43.50 (978-0-8386-4257-3(8)); (ENG.). 164p. 43.50 (978-1-61147-432-9(9)) Fairleigh Dickinson Univ. Pr.
Higgs, Owen & Howe, Anthony. In This Sign Conquer: A History of the Society of the Holy Cross (Societas Sanctae Crucis) 1855-2005. Houlding, David, ed. 2006. (ENG., Illus.). 232p. 35.95 (978-0-8264-9186-2(3)) Continuum International Publishing Group, Ltd. GBR. Dist: National Bk. Network.
Hubert C. Corlette. Bell's Cathedrals: Chichester: Short History & Description of Its Fabric with An. l.t. ed. 2007. (ENG.). 144p. pap. 19.99 (978-1-4264-7000-4(2)) BiblioBazaar.
Hutton, William Holden. The English Church: From the Accession of Charles I to the Death of Anne 1625-1714. 2006. pap. 33.95 (978-1-4286-5115-9(2)) Kessinger Publishing, LLC.
—English Church from the Accession of Charles First to the Death of Anne, 1625-1714. (History of the English Church Ser.: No. 6). reprint ed. 62.50 (978-0-404-50756-5(5)) AMS Pr., Inc.
Jacob. Making of Anglican Church Worldwde. (Illus.). 352p. 29.00 (978-0-281-05043-7(0)) SPCK Publishing GBR. Dist: Pilgrim Pr., The/United Church Pr.
Kaye, Bruce. An Introduction to World Anglicanism. 2008. (Introduction to Religion Ser.). (ENG., Illus.). 288p. pap. 30.00 (978-0-521-61866-3(5)) Cambridge Univ. Pr.
Klose, Josef. Die Urkunden Abt Hermanns Von Niederaltaich (1242-1273) 2010. (GER., Illus.). 84p. (978-3-406-10413-8(4)) Beck, F. A.
Knight, Frances. Church in the Nineteenth Century. 2008. (I. B. Tauris History of the Christian Church Ser.). (ENG.). 256p. 42.00 (978-1-85043-899-1(4)) I. B. Tauris & Co., Ltd. GBR. Dist: Macmillan.
Kollar, Rene. A Foreign & Wicked Institution? The Campaign Against Convents in Victorian England. 2011. 318p. pap. 35.00 (978-1-60608-336-9(8), Pickwick Pubns.) Wipf & Stock Pubs.
Lee, Robert. The Church of England & the Durham Coalfield, 1810-1926: Clergymen, Capitalists & Colliers. 2007. (Regions & Regionalism in History Ser.: Volume 8). (Illus.). 354p. 90.00 (978-1-84383-347-5(6), Boydell Press) Boydell & Brewer, Ltd. GBR. Dist: Boydell & Brewer, Inc.
Mason, A. J. The Church of England & Episcopacy. 2012. (ENG.). 576p. pap. 63.00 (978-1-107-67345-8(3)) Cambridge Univ. Pr.
May, Trevor. The Victorian Clergyman. 2008. (Shire Library). (ENG., Illus.). 40p. per. 11.95 (978-0-7478-0658-5(6)) Shire Pubns., Ltd. GBR. Dist: Random Hse., Inc.
Moorhouse, Geoffrey. The Last Divine Office: Henry VIII & the Dissolution of the Monasteries. 2009. (ENG.). 304p. 24.95 (978-1-933346-18-2(3)) BlueBridge.
Morey, Dom Adrian & Brooke, C. N. L. Gilbert Foliot & His Letters. 2008. (Cambridge Studies in Medieval Life & Thought: New Ser.). (ENG.). 636p. pap. 48.00 (978-0-521-07288-5(3)) Cambridge Univ. Pr.
Newman, John Henry. Historical Sketches - Rise & Progress of Universities - Northmen & Normans in England & Ireland - Medieval Oxford - Convocation of Cant. 2007. 436p. per. (978-1-4086-0367-3(5)) Read Bks.
—Historical Sketches V3. 2008. 434p. 51.95 (978-1-4365-6822-7(6)) 2007. (ENG.). 436p. per. 36.95 (978-0-548-75669-0(4)) Kessinger Publishing, LLC.
—John Henry Newman: Selected Writings To 1845. Radcliffe, Albert, ed. 2006. (Fyfield Bks.). (ENG.). 206p. per. 19.95 (978-1-85754-545-6(1)) Carcanet Pr., Ltd. GBR. Dist: Independent Pubs. Group.
Oxford, ed. The Book of Common Prayer 1979. 2008. (ENG.). 1056p. 19.99 (978-0-19-528776-9(2)) Oxford Univ. Pr., Inc.
Payne, Reider. Ecclesiastical Patronage in England, 1770-1801: A Study of Four Family & Political Networks. 2010. 372p. 119.95 (978-0-7734-3789-0(4)) Mellen, Edwin Pr., The.
Pinnock, W. H. The Law of the Rubric & the Transition Period of the Church of England. 2007. (ENG.). 118p. 34.95 (978-0-548-04693-7(X)) Kessinger Publishing, LLC.
Prickett, Stephen. Romanticism & Religion: The Tradition of Coleridge & Wordsworth in the Victorian Church. 2008. (ENG.). 304p. pap. 42.00 (978-0-521-10217-9(0)) Cambridge Univ. Pr.
Purvis, J. S. Tudor Parish Documents of the Diocese of York: A Selection with Introduction & Notes. 2008. (ENG.). 268p. pap. 37.99 (978-0-521-08102-3(5)) Cambridge Univ. Pr.
Sampson, H. Grant. The Anglican tradition in eighteenth-century Verse. (De Proprietatibus Litterarum. Series Practica Ser.). (ENG.). 378p. 210.00 (978-3-11-198328-8(5)); 142.00 (978-3-11-099202-1(7)) De Gruyter, Mouton DEU. Dist: de Gruyter, Walter GmbH & Co. KG.
Schofield, Nicholas. William Lockhart. 2011. (Illus.). 212p. pap. (978-0-85244-753-6(1)) Gracewing, Ltd.
Short, Edward. Newman & His Contemporaries. 2011. 544p. 110.00 (978-0-567-02688-0(4)); (ENG.). pap. 32.95 (978-0-567-02689-7(2)) Continuum International Publishing Group, Ltd. GBR. (T&T Clark Int'l). Dist: National Bk. Network.
Starkie, Andrew. The Church of England & the Bangorian Controversy, 1716-1721. 2007. (Studies in Modern British Religious History Ser.: Volume 14). (Illus.). 272p. 90.00 (978-1-84383-288-1(7), Boydell Press) Boydell & Brewer, Ltd. GBR. Dist: Boydell & Brewer, Inc.
Stewart, Carol. The Eighteenth-Century Novel & the Secularisation of Ethics. 2010. 228p. 99.95 (978-0-7546-6348-5(5)) Ashgate Publishing Co.
Sutherland, Martin. Peace, Toleration & Decay: The Ecclesiology of Later Stuart Dissent. 2007. (Studies in Christian History & Thought: Ser.). 246p. pap. 26.00 (978-1-59752-791-0(2), Wipf and Stock) Wipf & Stock Pubs.
Tatham, G. B. Dr John Walker & the Sufferings of the Clergy. 2009. (ENG.). 440p. pap. 55.00 (978-0-521-10138-7(7)) Cambridge Univ. Pr.
Thomson, Andrew. The Clergy of Winchester, England, 1615-1698: A Diocesan Ministry in Crisis. 2011. (Illus.). vii, 288p. (978-0-7734-3822-4(X)) Mellen, Edwin Pr., The.
Thomson, Andrew. The Clergy of Winchester, England 1615-1698: A Diocesan Ministry n CrisisThe Clergy of Winchester, England 1615-1698The Clergy of Winchester, England 1615-1698. 2011. (Illus.). 304p. 129.95 (978-0-7734-1580-5(7)) Mellen, Edwin Pr., The.
Van Kirk, Agnes E. The Church, Her Purpose: The Extension of the Incarnation. 2011. 84p. 37.95 (978-1-258-04771-9(3)) Literary Licensing, LLC.
Wakeman, Henry Offley. An Introduction to the History of the Church of England From the Earliest Times to the Present Day. 2007. (ENG.). 526p. 55.95 (978-0-548-23779-3(4)); 528p. per. 40.95 (978-1-4326-3899-3(8)) Kessinger Publishing, LLC.
Walsh, John & Taylor, Stephen, eds. The Papers of the Elland Society, 1769-1828. 2013. (Church of England Record Society Ser.). 430p. 115.00 (978-1-84383-444-1(8), Boydell Press) Boydell & Brewer, Ltd. GBR. Dist: Boydell & Brewer, Inc.
Ware, Sedley L. The Elizabethan Parish in Its Ecclesiastical & Financial Aspects. (Johns Hopkins University. Studies in the Social Sciences, Thirtieth Ser.: 7-8). reprint ed. 39.50 (978-0-404-61177-4(X)) AMS Pr., Inc.
Warre-Cornish, Francis. English Church in the Nineteenth Century, 2 vols. (History of the English Church Ser.: No. 8). reprint ed. 125.00 (978-0-404-50760-2(3)) AMS Pr., Inc.
Watson, Edward William. The Church of England. 2009. 258p. 34.99 (978-1-117-35993-9(X)) BiblioBazaar.
Witsell, William Postell. Our Church: One Through the Ages. 2007. (ENG.). 172p. 37.95 (978-0-548-06492-4(X)) Kessinger Publishing, LLC.
Worall, D. Making of the Modern Church. 2nd ed. 352p. 23.00 (978-0-281-04704-8(9)) SPCK Publishing GBR. Dist: Pilgrim Pr., The/United Church Pr.

CHURCH OF ENGLAND—HYMNS

Canterbury Press Staff, compiled by. Common Praise: The Definitive Hymn Book for the Christian Year. 1440p. 35.00 (978-1-85311-264-5(X)) Norwich Bks. & Music GBR. Dist: Morehouse Publishing.
Hymns Ancient & Modern for Use in the Services of the Church. 2006. 452p. per 29.99 (978-1-4255-4996-1(9)) MPublishing.

CHURCH OF ENGLAND—LITURGY

see also Church of England—Book of Common Prayer

Algarate, Pablo. La Iglesia Celebra a Jesucristo.Tr. of Church Celebrates Jesus Christ. (SPA.). 254p. pap. 9.95 (978-950-861-135-2(9)) Sociedad de San Pablo ARG. Dist: St Pauls/Alba Hse. Pubs.
Andrew Burnham Staff. Heaven & Earth in Little Space: The Re-Enchantment of Liturgy. 2010. (ENG., Illus.). 224p. pap. 30.00 (978-1-84825-005-5(3), Canterbury Pr. Norwich) Hymns Ancient & Modern Ltd GBR. Dist: Westminster John Knox Pr.
Augustine, Saint. Treasures of the English Church. 2008. (Illus.). 160p. pap. 40.00 (978-1-903470-74-9(9)) Holberton, Paul Publishing GBR. Dist: Casemate Pubs. & Bk. Distributors, LLC.
Barbee, C. Frederick & Zahl, Paul F. M., compiled by. The Collects of Thomas Cranmer. 2006. 119p. per. 12.00 (978-0-8028-1759-4(9)) Eerdmans, William B. Publishing Co.
Baxter, Philip. Sarum Use: The Ancient Customs of Salisbury. 2008. (ENG., Illus.). 118p. (C). pap. (978-1-904965-18-3(0)) Spire Bks. Ltd.
Blunt, John Henry. Annotated Book of Common Prayer Being an. 2006. pap. 52.95 (978-1-4286-3633-0(1)) Kessinger Publishing, LLC.
The Book of Alternative Services: Pew Edition. 928p. 17.95 (978-0-919891-27-2(6), 1293) Forward Movement Pubns.
Bradshaw, Paul F., ed. Companion to Common Worship, 2 vols. (Illus.). 288p. 29.00 (978-0-281-05266-0(2)) SPCK Publishing GBR. Dist: Pilgrim Pr., The/United Church Pr.
Buchanan. Anglican Liturgy in Changing Times. 2009. xxvi, 198p. pap. (978-0-281-06026-9(6)) SPCK Publishing.
Buchanan, Colin, ed. The Bishop in Liturgy. 2009. 88.00 (978-1-60724-361-8(X)) Gorgias Pr., LLC.
—Liturgies of the Spanish & Portuguese Reformed Episcopal Churches. 2009. 88.00 (978-1-60724-352-6(0)) Gorgias Pr., LLC.
Buchanan, Colin, intro. The Savoy Conference Revisited. 2009. 88.00 (978-1-60724-403-5(9)) Gorgias Pr., LLC.
Church Of England. The Book of Common Prayer & Administration of the Sacraments. 2007. pap. 37.95 (978-1-4304-5187-7(4)) Kessinger Publishing, LLC.
—The Book of Common Prayer & Administration of the Sacraments. 2007. 658p. 63.95 (978-0-548-16762-5(1)); (ENG.). 660p. per. 48.95 (978-1-4304-6473-0(9)) Kessinger Publishing, LLC.
—The Book of Common Prayer & Administration of the Sacraments, & Other Rites & Ceremonies of the Church. 2007. 460p. 52.95 (978-0-548-15708-4(1)) Kessinger Publishing, LLC.
Companion to the Alternative Service Book. 4.00 (978-0-687-85151-5(3)) Abingdon Pr.
Dalby, Mark. Anglican Missals & their Canons. 2009. 88.00 (978-1-60724-392-2(X)) Gorgias Pr., LLC.
Development of the Anglican Liturgy 1662-1980. 5.00 (978-0-687-85226-0(9)) Abingdon Pr.
Freeman, Philip. Principles of Divine Service V1. 2006. pap. 36.95 (978-1-4286-4471-7(7)) Kessinger Publishing, LLC.
—Principles of Divine Service V2. 2006. pap. 51.95 (978-1-4286-4472-4(5)) Kessinger Publishing, LLC.
Giles, Richard. Times & Seasons: Creating Transformative Worship Throughout the Year. 2008. 192p. pap. 30.00 (978-0-89869-613-4(5)) Church Publishing, Inc.
Gleason, Edward S. Dying We Live. 188p. pap. 2.95 (978-1-56101-014-1(6), 1747) Forward Movement Pubns.
Gray-Reeves, Mary & Perham, Michael. The Hospitality of God: Emerging Worship for a Missional Church. 2011. pap. (978-1-59627-140-1(X), Seabury Bks.) Church Publishing, Inc.
Hebblethwaite, David. Liturgical Revision in the Church of England 1984-2004. 2009. 88.00 (978-1-60724-406-6(3)) Gorgias Pr., LLC.
Houlden, Leslie & Rogerson, John, eds. Common Worship Lectionary: A Scripture Commentary (Year B) 296p. 32.00 (978-0-281-05326-1(X)) SPCK Publishing GBR. Dist: Pilgrim Pr., The/United Church Pr.
Hughes, Alex. Public Worship & Communion by Extension. 2009. 88.00 (978-1-60724-402-8(0)) Gorgias Pr., LLC.
James, Paul. Liturgical Presidency. 2009. 88.00 (978-1-60724-376-2(8)) Gorgias Pr., LLC.
Jan Brind Staff. Baptism, Confirmation & Liturgiesfor the Journey. 2010. (Creative Ideas for Pastoral Liturgy Ser.). (ENG., Illus.). 224p. pap. 30.99 (978-1-85311-950-7(4), Canterbury Pr. Norwich) Hymns Ancient & Modern Ltd GBR. Dist: Westminster John Knox Pr.
Jeanes. Signs of God's Promise: Thomas Cranmer's Sacramental Theology & the Book of Common Prayer. 2008. (ENG., Illus.). 328p. 150.00 (978-0-567-03188-4(8), T&T Clark Int'l) Continuum International Publishing Group, Ltd. GBR. Dist: National Bk. Network.
Jeanes, Gordon. The Origins of the Roman Rite. 2009. 88.00 (978-1-60724-357-1(1)); 88.00 (978-1-60724-358-8(X)) Gorgias Pr., LLC.

Jeanes, Gordon P. Signs of God's Promise: Thomas Cranmer's Sacramental Theology & the Book of Common Prayer. 2008. (ENG., Illus.). 328p. 49.95 *(978-0-567-03189-1(6),* T&T Clark Int'l) Continuum International Publishing Group, Ltd. GBR. Dist: National Bk. Network.

Joyce CSF Staff & Colin SSF Staff. The Daily Office SSF. rev. ed. 2010. (ENG.). 710p. 29.95 *(978-1-906286-15-6(9))* Mowbray, A. R. & Co., Ltd. GBR. Dist: National Bk. Network.

Ketley, Joseph, ed. Two Liturgies, A. D. 1549 & A. D. 1552: With other documents set forth by authority in the reign of King Edward VI. 2007. (Parker Society: Ser.). 607p. pap. 45.00 *(978-1-55635-064-1(3),* Wipf and Stock) Wipf & Stock Pubs.

Liturgical Commission of the Church of England Staff. Words for Worship: Classic Anglican Prayers. 2012. (ENG.). 96p. pap. 14.99 *(978-0-7151-2190-0(1))* Church Hse. Publishing GBR. Dist: Westminster John Knox Pr.

Lloyd, Trevor & Tovey, Phillip. Celebrating Forgiveness. 2009. 88.00 *(978-1-60724-348-9(2))* Gorgias Pr., LLC.

Micklethwaite, J. T. The Ornaments of the Rubric. 2010. pap. 25.60 *(978-1-61719-384-2(4))*; pap. 25.60 *(978-1-61719-387-3(9))* Gorgias Pr., LLC.

Oxford, ed. Book of Common Prayer 1979. 2009. (ENG.). 2544p. 75.00 *(978-0-19-528839-1(4))* Oxford Univ. Pr., Inc.

Parker, James, ed. The Second Prayer-Book of Edward VI, Issued 1552. 2006. 182p. pap. 21.00 *(978-1-55635-051-1(1),* Wipf and Stock) Wipf & Stock Pubs.

Perham, Michael. New Handbook of Pastoral Liturgy. 272p. 25.00 *(978-0-281-05252-3(2))* SPCK Publishing GBR. Dist: Pilgrim Pr., The/United Church Pr.

Peters, Bosco. The Anglican Eucharist in New Zealand 1814-1989. 2009. 88.00 *(978-1-60724-374-8(1))* Gorgias Pr., LLC.

Slee, Nicola. Seeking the Risen Christ. 2011. 188p. pap. ***(978-0-281-06256-0(0))*** SPCK Publishing.

Staley, Vernon. Hierurgia Anglicana, Part 1: Documents & Extracts Illustrative of the Ceremonial of the Anglican Church after the Reformation. 2008. 332p. pap. 27.00 *(978-1-60608-359-8(7),* Wipf and Stock) Wipf & Stock Pubs.

—Hierurgia Anglicana, Part 2: Documents & Extracts Illustrative of the Ceremonial of the Anglican Church after the Reformation. 2008. 356p. pap. 35.00 *(978-1-60608-360-4(0),* Wipf and Stock) Wipf & Stock Pubs.

Stancliffe, David & Stancliffe. The Pilgrim Prayerbook. 2nd ed. 2007. (ENG.). 288p. 27.95 *(978-0-8264-8360-7(7))* Continuum International Publishing Group, Ltd. GBR. Dist: National Bk. Network.

Thomas, Talley, ed. A Kingdom of Priests. 2009. 88.00 *(978-1-60724-360-1(1))* Gorgias Pr., LLC.

Toy, John, ed. English Saints in the Medieval Liturgies of Scandinavian Churches. 2009. (Henry Bradshaw Society Subsidia Ser.: Volume 6). (Illus.). 250p. 90.00 *(978-1-870252-46-1(2))* Bradshaw, Henry Society GBR. Dist: Boydell & Brewer, Inc.

Wyatt, E. G. F. The Burial Service. 2010. 83.00 *(978-1-61719-209-8(0))* Gorgias Pr., LLC.

CHURCH OF ENGLAND—MARRIAGE

see Marriage—Religious Aspects—Church of England

CHURCH OF ENGLAND—MISSIONS

Daughrity, Dyron B. A Genuinely Human Existence: An Historical Investigation in the Conflicted Life of Bishop Stephen Neill up to the Termination of His Bishopric (1945) 2007. (American University Studies VII: Theology & Religion Ser.). (C). 77.95 *(978-1-4331-0165-6(3))* Lang, Peter Publishing, Inc.

Feild, Edward. Extracts from a Journal of a Voyage of Visitation in the 'Hawk,' 1859. 2007. 48p. per. *(978-1-4065-1698-2(8))* Dodo Pr.

Myers, James P. The Ordeal of Thomas Barton: Anglican Missionary in the Pennsylvania Backcountry, 1755-1780. 2010. 52.50 *(978-0-9821313-4-3(8))* Lehigh Univ. Pr.

Myers, James P., Jr. The Ordeal of Thomas Barton: Anglican Missionary in the Pennsylvania Backcountry, 1755-1780. 2010. (ENG.). 278p. 52.50 *(978-1-61146-063-6(8))* Lehigh Univ. Pr.

Selwyn, George Augustus. New Zealand. 2010. (Cambridge Library Collection - Religion Ser.). (Illus.). 418p. pap. 37.99 *(978-1-108-01826-5(2))* Cambridge Univ. Pr.

Tengatenga, James. The UMCA in Malawi. 446p. pap. *(978-99908-87-65-5(9))* Michigan State Univ. Pr.

Wild-Wood, Emma & Ward, Kevin. The East African Revival: History & Legacies. 2012. (Illus.). 252p. 99.95 ***(978-1-4094-2674-5(2))*** Ashgate Publishing Co.

CHURCH OF ENGLAND—PASTORAL THEOLOGY

see Pastoral Theology—Anglican Communion

CHURCH OF ENGLAND—PRAYERS AND DEVOTIONS

Anglican Church of Canada Staff. Common Praise: Music Edition: Anglican Church of Canada. l.t. ed. 1000p. 27.95 *(978-1-55126-283-3(5),* 1533) Forward Movement Pubns.

Barclay, William. Prayers for the Christian Year. 2012. 175p. pap. ***(978-0-334-01287-0(2),*** SCM Pr.) Hymns Ancient & Modern Ltd.

Church Literature Associa Staff. The English Office Book. 2006. 368p. 29.99 *(978-1-85311-698-8(X))* Norwich Bks. & Music GBR. Dist: Westminster John Knox Pr.

Cosin, John. Complete Works of John Cosin, 5 vols. (Library of Anglo-Catholic Theology: No. 5). reprint ed. *(978-0-404-52080-9(4))* AMS Pr., Inc.

Oxenden, Ashton. The Earnest Communicant. 2009. 48p. *(978-1-60178-069-0(9))* Reformation Heritage Bks.

Parker, James, ed. The Second Prayer-Book of Edward VI, Issued 1552. 2006. 182p. pap. 21.00 *(978-1-55635-051-1(1),* Wipf and Stock) Wipf & Stock Pubs.

Stancliffe, David & Stancliffe. The Pilgrim Prayerbook. 2nd ed. 2007. (ENG.). 288p. 27.95 *(978-0-8264-8360-7(7))* Continuum International Publishing Group, Ltd. GBR. Dist: National Bk. Network.

Van de Weyer, Robert. First English Prayer Book: The First Worship Edition Since the Original Publication in 1549. 2008. (ENG.). 160p. 19.95 *(978-1-84694-130-6(X))* Hunt, John Publishing Ltd. GBR. Dist: National Bk. Network.

CHURCH OF ENGLAND—RELATIONS

Aveling, J. C., et al. Rome & the Anglicans: Historical & Doctrinal Aspects of Anglican-Roman Catholic Relations. Haase, Wolfgang, ed. (ENG.). IV, 301p. 225.00 ***(978-3-11-176503-7(2))*** De Gruyter, Walter Inc.

Hill, Christopher. Anglicans & Roman Catholics Search for Unity. vii, 344p. *(978-0-281-04745-1(6))* SPCK Publishing.

Spoer, Hans H. Aid for Churchmen, Episcopal & Orthodox. reprint ed. 32.50 *(978-0-404-06197-5(4))* AMS Pr., Inc.

Sykes, Norman. Old Priest & New Presbyter. 2008. (ENG.). 276p. pap. 37.99 *(978-0-521-07289-2(1))* Cambridge Univ. Pr.

Yelton, Michael. Anglican Papalism: A History: 1900-1960. 2008. (Illus.). 266p. pap. 39.99 *(978-1-85311-861-6(3))* Canterbury Pr.

CHURCH OF ENGLAND—SERMONS

Andrewes, Lancelot. Ninety-Six Sermons by the Right Honourable & Reverend Father in God, Lancelot Andrewes, Sometime Lord Bishop of Winchester, Vol. IV. 2008. 425p. pap. 36.00 *(978-1-60608-122-8(5),* Wipf and Stock) Wipf & Stock Pubs.

—Ninety-Six Sermons by the Right Honourable & Reverend Father in God, Lancelot Andrewes, Sometime Lord Bishop of Winchester, Vol. V. 2008. 592p. pap. 50.00 *(978-1-60608-121-1(7),* Wipf and Stock) Wipf & Stock Pubs.

Arber, Edward. Seven Sermons Before Edward VI. 2006. 212p. per. *(978-1-4067-0789-2(9),* Hesperides Pr.) Read Bks.

Arnold, Thomas. Christian Life Its Hopes Its Fears & I. 2006. pap. 38.95 *(978-1-4286-3910-2(1))* Kessinger Publishing, LLC.

Attard SDB, Fabio. Conscience & the 'Parochial & Plain Sermons' of John Henry Newman. 2008. (ENG.). 266p. (C). pap. 19.95 *(978-99932-7-190-1(X))* Midsea Bks. Ltd. MLT. Dist: Brown, David Bk. Co., The.

The British Reformers. Writing of the Rev. Thomas Becon, Chaplain to Archbishop Cranmer, & Prebendary of Canterbury. 2010. pap. 18.16 *(978-1-61143-191-9(3))* Gorgias Pr., LLC.

Church of England. Book of Homilies. Griffiths, John, ed. 2008. 716p. pap. *(978-1-57383-391-2(6))* Regent College Publishing.

Church, R. W. Cathedral & University Sermons. 2007. (ENG.). 328p. 45.95 *(978-0-548-10603-7(7))* Kessinger Publishing, LLC.

Churchill, Charles. The Works of C. Churchill V1. 2006. pap. 26.95 *(978-1-4286-5887-5(4))* Kessinger Publishing, LLC.

—The Works of C. Churchill V2. 2006. pap. 26.95 *(978-1-4286-5888-2(2))* Kessinger Publishing, LLC.

—The Works of C. Churchill V3. 2006. pap. 26.95 *(978-1-4286-5889-9(0))* Kessinger Publishing, LLC.

—The Works of C. Churchill V4. 2006. pap. 26.95 *(978-1-4286-5890-5(4))* Kessinger Publishing, LLC.

Donne, John. On Death. 2008. (On Ser.). (ENG.). 112p. pap. 13.95 *(978-1-84391-600-0(2))* Hesperus Pr. GBR. Dist: Independent Pubs. Group.

—A Sermon of Commemoration of the Lady Danvers, Late Wife of Sr. John Danvers. 2006. (Funeral Sermons for Women (1601-1630) Ser.). *(978-0-8201-1554-2(1))* Scholars' Facsimiles & Reprints.

Farrar, Adam Storey. Science in Theology Sermons Preached in St Marys, Oxford, Before the University by Adam S Farrar. 2006. 252p. per. 23.99 *(978-1-4255-2203-2(3))* MPublishing.

Farrar, F. W. Truths to Live By. 2007. (ENG.). 382p. 48.95 *(978-0-548-02329-7(8))* Kessinger Publishing, LLC.

Heber, Reginald. Sermons Preached in India. 2011. (Cambridge Library Collection - Religion Ser.). (ENG.). 350p. pap. 28.99 *(978-1-108-09333-0(7))* Cambridge Univ. Pr.

Ingram, Arthur Foley Winnington. The after-Glow of a Great Reign. 2007. 48p. per. *(978-1-4065-3952-3(X))* Dodo Pr.

James, Eric & James. The Trumpet Shall Sound. 2006. (ENG.). 160p. 19.95 *(978-0-8264-9359-0(9))* Continuum International Publishing Group, Ltd. GBR. Dist: National Bk. Network.

Keble, John. Sermons for the Christian Year. 2009. 276p. pap. *(978-1-4588-4765-2(9))*; 322p. pap. *(978-1-4588-4764-5(0))*; 236p. pap. *(978-0-217-99505-4(5))*; 284p. pap. *(978-0-217-99501-6(2))* Books LLC.

—Sermons for the Christian Year. 2008. 508p. 55.95 *(978-1-4365-4565-5(X))* 2007. (ENG.). 512p. per. 40.95 *(978-0-548-74265-5(0))* Kessinger Publishing, LLC.

—Sermons for the Christian Year. 2008. 524p. pap. *(978-1-4097-0754-7(7))* Read Bks.

Kingsley, Charles. All Saints' Day & Other Sermons. 2007. 268p. per. *(978-1-4065-2854-1(4))* Dodo Pr.

—Discipline & Other Sermons. 2008. 148p. pap. 7.99 *(978-1-60450-332-6(7))* Arc Manor.

—Discipline & Other Sermons. 2008. 176p. 25.99 *(978-0-554-23003-0(8))* 2008. 176p. 22.99 *(978-0-554-32306-0(0))* 2007. (ENG.). 156p. pap. 19.99 *(978-1-4264-3505-8(3))* 2007. 172p. pap. 21.99 *(978-1-4264-3540-9(1))* BiblioBazaar.

—Discipline & Other Sermons. 2007. 144p. per. *(978-1-4065-2860-2(9))* Dodo Pr.

—The Good News of God. 2009. 204p. pap. 9.99 *(978-1-60450-624-2(5),* Serenity Pubs.) Arc Manor.

—The Good News of God. 2008. 260p. 28.99 *(978-0-554-23141-9(7))*; 25.99 *(978-0-554-32444-9(X))* BiblioBazaar.

—The Good News of God. 2007. 216p. per. *(978-1-4065-2863-3(3))* Dodo Pr.

—The Gospel of the Pentateuch: A Set of Parish Sermons. 2007. 140p. per. *(978-1-4065-2864-0(1))* Dodo Pr.

—Sermons for the Times. 2008. 232p. 27.99 *(978-0-554-23667-4(2))* 2008. 232p. 24.99 *(978-0-554-32970-3(0))* 2007. (ENG.). 210p. pap. 20.99 *(978-1-4264-4857-7(0))* 2007. (ENG.). 230p. pap. 22.99 *(978-1-4264-4900-0(3))* BiblioBazaar.

—Sermons for the Times. 2007. 188p. per. *(978-1-4065-2877-0(3))* Dodo Pr.

—True Words for Brave Men. 2009. 260p. 24.99 *(978-1-103-54260-4(5))* 2009. 260p. pap. 18.99 *(978-1-103-54257-4(5))* 2008. 220p. 24.99 *(978-0-554-36897-9(8))* 2008. 220p. 27.99 *(978-0-554-27594-9(5))* 2007. 198p. pap. 19.99 *(978-1-4346-3554-9(6))* 2007. (ENG.). 216p. pap. 22.99 *(978-1-4346-3555-6(4))* BiblioBazaar.

—True Words for Brave Men. 2007. 180p. per. *(978-1-4065-2882-4(X))* Dodo Pr.

—Twenty-Five Village Sermons. 2009. 280p. 24.99 *(978-1-103-68525-7(2))* 2009. 280p. pap. 18.99 *(978-1-103-68524-0(4))* 2009. 280p. 24.99 *(978-1-103-26550-3(4))* 2009. 280p. pap. 18.99 *(978-1-103-26546-6(6))* 2009. 280p. 24.99 *(978-1-103-08946-8(3))* 2009. 280p. pap. 18.99 *(978-1-103-08943-7(9))* 2008. 192p. 25.99 *(978-0-554-28277-0(1))* 2008. 192p. 22.99 *(978-0-554-37580-9(X))* 2007. (ENG.). 172p. pap. 19.99 *(978-1-4346-5047-4(2))* 2007. (ENG.). 190p. pap. 21.99 *(978-1-4346-5048-1(0))* BiblioBazaar.

—Twenty-Five Village Sermons. 2007. 156p. per. *(978-1-4065-2883-1(8))* Dodo Pr.

Lams, Victor J. Newman's Visionary Georgic: A Reading of Parochial Sermons. 2006. xxiii, 143p. (C). 62.95 *(978-0-8204-6377-3(9))* Lang, Peter Publishing, Inc.

Latimer, Hugh. Sermons on the Card & Other Discourses. 2007. (ENG.). 84p. per. *(978-1-4065-3577-8(X))* Dodo Pr.

—Sermons on the Card & Other Discourses. 2007. 96p. per. *(978-1-4068-1517-7(9))* Echo Library.

Lloyd-Jones, D. Martyn. Studies in the Sermon on the Mount [Two. 2011. 656p. pap. 18.50 ***(978-1-61427-116-1(X))*** Martino Publishing.

Mackay H.F.B. Staff. Assistants at the Passion. 2007. 192p. per. *(978-1-4067-8833-4(3),* Pomona Pr.) Read Bks.

McCullough, Peter. Sermons at Court: Politics & Religion in Elizabethan & Jacobean Preaching. 2011. (Cambridge Studies in Early Modern British History Ser.). (ENG., Illus.). 256p. pap. 37.99 *(978-0-521-02205-7(3))* Cambridge Univ. Pr.

McGrath, Francis J. & Murray, Dom Placid. John Henry Newman Sermons 1824-1843: Volume III: Sermons & Lectures for Saint's Days & Holy Days & General Theology. 2010. (John Henry Newman Sermons Ser.). (ENG.). 528p. 199.99 *(978-0-19-920090-0(4))* Oxford Univ. Pr., Inc.

Melvill, Henry. Lectures on Practical Subjects, Delivered at St Margaret's Lothbury, by the Rev Henry Melvill. 2006. 408p. per. 26.99 *(978-1-4255-4361-7(8))* MPublishing.

Millington, Thomas Street. Words to Win Souls: Twelve Sermons, Preached A. D. 1620-1650, by Eminent Divines of the Church of England. 2006. 328p. per. 23.99 *(978-1-4255-3339-7(6))* MPublishing.

Newman, John Henry. Sermons Bearing on Subjects of the Day. 2007. (ENG.). 452p. 52.95 *(978-0-548-09967-4(7))* Kessinger Publishing, LLC.

Percival, John. Sermons at Rugby. 216p. 2008. 39.95 *(978-1-4365-8018-2(8))* 2007. (ENG.). per. 24.95 *(978-0-548-79858-4(3))* Kessinger Publishing, LLC.

Ramsey, Arthur Michael. Freedom, Faith, & the Future. 2010. 48p. pap. 7.00 *(978-1-60899-820-3(7),* Wipf and Stock) Wipf & Stock Pubs.

Robertson, Frederick W. Sermons Preached at Brighton: Third Series. 2007. (ENG.). 228p. pap. 20.99 *(978-1-4346-0215-2(X))*; 252p. pap. 23.99 *(978-1-4346-0289-3(3))* BiblioBazaar.

—Sermons Preached at Trinity Chapel, Brighton, by Rev Frederick W Robertson. 2006. 712p. per. 38.99 *(978-1-4255-6889-4(0))* MPublishing.

Romaine, W. Jepthahs Vow Fulfilled & His Daughter. 2006. pap. 15.95 *(978-1-4286-5806-6(8))* Kessinger Publishing, LLC.

Ryle, J. C. Heading for Heaven. 2009. 127p. *(978-0-85234-710-2(3))* Evangelical Pr.

Sandys, Edwin. The Sermons of Edwin Sandys, D. D., Successively Bishop of Worcester & London, & Archbishop of York: To Which Are Added Some Miscellaneous Pieces by the Same Author. Ayre, John, ed. 2007. (Parker Society: Ser.). 504p. pap. 48.00 *(978-1-55635-046-7(5),* Wipf and Stock) Wipf & Stock Pubs.

South, Robert. Sermons Preached upon Several Occasions, by Robert South. 2006. 536p. per. 29.99 *(978-1-4255-5990-8(5))* MPublishing.

—Sermons Preached upon Various Occasions, 8 vols., Set. reprint ed. 410.00 *(978-0-404-06180-7(X))* AMS Pr., Inc.

Sterne, Laurence. The Sermons of Mr. Yorick. reprint ed. lib. bdg. 196.00 *(978-0-7426-2067-4(0))* Classic Bks.

—The Sermons of Mr. Yorick, Vol. 1. 2007. 400p. 49.95 *(978-0-548-34898-7(7))*; per. 34.95 *(978-0-548-29127-6(6))* Kessinger Publishing, LLC.

Trench, Richard Chenev. Sermons Preached in Westminster Abbey. 2006. pap. 33.95 *(978-1-4286-3994-2(2))* Kessinger Publishing, LLC.

Westcott, Brooke Foss. The Christian Life, Manifold & One: Six Sermons Preached In. 2007. (ENG.). 84p. pap. 17.95 *(978-1-4304-4583-8(1))* Kessinger Publishing, LLC.

Whitefield, George. George Whitefield Daily Readings. 2010. (ENG.). 384p. im. lthr. 19.99 *(978-1-84550-580-6(8),* Christian Heritage) Christian Focus Pubns. GBR. Dist: STL Distribution North America.

CHURCH OF ENGLAND—SCOTLAND

see Episcopal Church in Scotland

CHURCH OF ENGLAND—UNITED STATES

Anderson, James S. M. History of the Church of England V1. 2006. pap. 43.95 *(978-1-4286-4435-9(0))* Kessinger Publishing, LLC.

—History of the Church of England V2 in T. 2006. pap. 44.95 *(978-1-4286-4436-6(9))* Kessinger Publishing, LLC.

—History of the Church of England V3 in T. 2006. pap. 49.95 *(978-1-4286-4437-3(7))* Kessinger Publishing, LLC.

Bell, James. A War of Religion: Dissenters, Anglicans & the American Revolution. 2008. (Studies in Modern History Ser.). (ENG., Illus.). 352p. 95.00 *(978-0-230-54297-6(2))* Palgrave Macmillan.

Brydon, George MacLaren. Religious Life of Virginia in the Seventeenth Century: The Faith of Our Fathers. 2011. 68p. 36.95 ***(978-1-258-03510-5(3))*** Literary Licensing, LLC.

Cain, Robert J. & Poff, Jan-Michael, eds. The Church of England in North Carolina: Documents, 1742-1763, Vol. 11. 2007. (Illus.). 643p. 55.00 *(978-0-86526-322-2(1))* North Carolina Office of Archives & History.

Cross, Arthur Lyon. The Anglican Episcopate & the American Colonies. 2009. (ENG.). 379p. 38.99 *(978-1-117-13190-0(4))* BiblioBazaar.

—The Anglican Episcopate & the American Colonies. 2009. (Illus.). 272p. pap. 23.46 *(978-1-150-29142-5(7))* General Bks. LLC.

—The Anglican Episcopate & the American Colonies. 2007. (ENG.). 384p. 48.95 *(978-0-548-12420-8(5))* Kessinger Publishing, LLC.

—The Anglican Episcopate & the American Colonies. (Harvard Historical Studies). 368p. reprint ed. 98.00 *(978-0-7222-6593-2(X))*; 98.00 *(978-0-7222-7281-7(2))* Library Reprints, Inc.

Eckenrode, Hamilton J. Separation of Church & State in Virginia. 164p. reprint ed. lib. bdg. 88.00 *(978-0-7222-4638-2(2))* Library Reprints, Inc.

Grimmett, Richard F. St John's Church, Lafayette Square: The History & Heritage of the Church of the Presidents, Washington, DC. 2009. (ENG., Illus.). 360p. pap. 18.95 *(978-1-934248-53-9(3))* Mill City Pr., Inc.

Hawks, Francis L. Documentary History of the Protestant Episcopal Church in the United States of America. 2006. 364p. per. 26.99 *(978-1-4255-3794-4(4))*; 332p. per. 23.99 *(978-1-4255-3378-6(7))* MPublishing.

Perry, William S. Historical Collections Relating to the American Colonial Church, 5 pts. in 4 vols. reprint ed. 375.00 *(978-0-404-05070-2(0))* AMS Pr., Inc.

Sellar, Robert. The Tragedy of Quebec. 2009. (ENG.). 321p. 36.99 *(978-1-117-32395-4(1))*; pap. 29.75 *(978-1-117-32396-1(X))*; pap. 23.99 *(978-1-117-32397-8(8),* BiblioLife) BiblioBazaar.

CHURCH OF GOD

Here are entered works on the various religious bodies using the words Church of God in their name.

Aghedo, Zaragrace. My Call: The Prophetic Vision. 2009. 240p. 25.99 *(978-1-60791-651-2(7))*; pap. 15.99 *(978-1-60791-650-5(9))* Xulon Pr., Inc.

Allison, Joseph D., ed. Basics for Belief. 2nd ed. 2008. 128p. pap. 12.95 *(978-1-59317-318-0(0))* Warner Pr. Pubs.

Barton, Cheryl. River of Delights: International Testimonies of God's Abundant Blessings. 2009. (Illus.). 96p. pap. *(978-1-59317-372-2(5))* Warner Pr. Pubs.

Byers, A. L. Two Hundred Genuine Instances of Divine Healing: The Doctrine Explained. 2007. 20.00 *(978-1-60416-063-5(2))*; per. 13.00 *(978-1-60416-062-8(4))* Reformation Pubs.

Callen, Barry, compiled by. Following Our Lord: Understanding the Beliefs & Practices of the Church of God Movement (Anderson) 2008. 204p. pap. 14.95 *(978-1-59317-342-5(3))* Warner Pr. Pubs.

Callen, Barry L. The Church That God Intends: Reconsidering the Reformation Heritage of the Church of God Movement (Anderson) 2009. *(978-0-9797935-7-8(2))* Emeth Pr.

—A Pilgrim's Progress: The Autobiography of Barry L. Callen. 2008. 440p. *(978-0-9797935-2-3(1))* Emeth Pr.

Cassady, David. Unconditional Eternal Security. 2008. 88p. pap. 9.99 *(978-1-60647-624-6(6))* Xulon Pr., Inc.

Crose, Lester A., et al, contrib. by. Into All the World: A Century of Church of God Missions. 2009. (Illus.). 488p. 45.00 *(978-1-59317-371-5(7))* Warner Pr. Pubs.

Flurry, Stephen. Raising the Ruins: The Fight to Revive the Legacy of Herbert W. Armstrong. 2006. (Illus.). 415p. 19.95 *(978-0-9745507-1-8(X))* Philadelphia Church of God.

Gospel Trumpet Company, compiled by. Select Camp-Meeting Sermons. 2007. per. 13.00 *(978-1-60416-012-3(8))* Reformation Pubs.

Hall, Connor B. & Hall, Jimi, eds. Hymns of the Spirit: Shape Note Edition. 2009. (Illus.). 511p. 9.99 *(978-1-59684-425-4(6))*; (ENG., 9.99 *(978-1-59684-424-7(8))* Pathway Pr.

Hughes, Ray H. Classic Pentecostal Sermon Library. 2011. pap. ***(978-1-59684-561-9(9))***; pap. ***(978-1-59684-563-3(5))***; pap. ***(978-1-59684-565-7(1))***; pap. ***(978-1-59684-567-1(8))***; pap. ***(978-1-59684-559-6(5))***; pap. ***(978-1-59684-558-9(9))*** Pathway Pr.

Johnson, Otis L. Standards of the Church: Christian Dress. 2007. pap. 13.00 *(978-1-60416-067-3(5))* Reformation Pubs.

Kelly, William. Lectures on the Church of God. 2007. 244p. (ENG.). *(978-0-901860-55-2(7))*; per. *(978-0-901860-50-7(6))* Scripture Truth Pubns.

Kurrle, Norberto. A History of the Church of God in Paraguay. 2009. 288p. pap. *(978-3-639-12499-6(5))* VDM Verlag Dr. Mueller e.K.

Martin, Earl L. This We Believe... This We Proclaim. 2007. 20.00 *(978-1-60416-054-3(3))*; per. 10.00 *(978-1-60416-005-5(5))*; per. 10.00 *(978-1-60416-053-6(5))* Reformation Pubs.

McBride, Calvin. Walking into A New Spirituality: Chronicling the Life, Ministry, & Contributions of Elder Robert E. Hart, B. D., LL. B., D. D., to the CME Church & COGIC: with Some Additional COGIC History. 2007. 216p. per. 17.95 *(978-0-595-46257-5(X))* iUniverse, Inc.

Nachtigall, Patrick. Mosaic: A Journey Across the Church of God. 2010. (ENG.). 287p. pap. 19.95 *(978-1-59317-513-9(2))* Warner Pr. Pubs.

Naylor, C. W. The Teachings of D. S. Warner & His Associates: A Survey & Analysis. 2007. per. 13.00 *(978-1-60416-064-2(0))* Reformation Pubs.

Oglesby, E. Hammond. Pressing Toward the Mark: Christian Ethics for the Black Church Today. 2007. 158p. pap. 18.00 *(978-1-55635-154-9(2))*, Wipf and Stock) Wipf & Stock Pubs.

The Pentecostal Deacon: Empowered to Serve: 2nd Edition. 2007. (ENG.). pap. 15.95 *(978-0-9774687-1-3(2))* We Believe In You Pubs.

Riggle, H. M. The Cream of My Life's Work: Sermons for Every Occasion. 2007. 20.00 *(978-1-60416-072-7(1))*; pap. 13.00 *(978-1-60416-071-0(3))* Reformation Pubs.

Stephens, Michael S. Who Healeth All Thy Diseases: Health, Healing, & Holiness in the Church of God Reformation Movement. 2008. (Pentecostal & Charismatic Studies). (ENG.). 248p. pap. 60.00 *(978-0-8108-5840-4(1))* Scarecrow Pr., Inc.

Strege, Merle D., rev. The Quest for Holiness & Unity. 2nd exp. ed. 2009. (Illus.). 530p. pap. 24.95 *(978-1-59317-373-9(3))* Warner Pr. Pubs.

Susag, S. O. Personal Experiences of S. O. Susag. 2007. 152p. pap. 19.99 *(978-1-4264-3413-6(8))* BiblioBazaar.

—Personal Experiences of SO Susag. 2006. pap. 14.95 *(978-1-59605-757-9(2)*, Cosimo Classics) Cosimo, Inc.

Ukah, Asonzeh F. K. A New Paradigm of Pentecostal Power: A Study of the Redeemed Christian Church of God in Nigeria. 2008. (Illus.). xxiv, 410p. *(978-1-59221-620-8(X))*; pap. *(978-1-59221-621-5(8))* Africa World Pr.

Warner, D. S. How the Trumpet Sounded: The Church of God. 2007. pap. 13.00 *(978-1-60416-068-0(3))* Reformation Pubs.

Williams, Steven V., compiled by. Sermon Outlines of F. G. Smith. 2007. One. 20.00 *(978-1-60416-040-6(3))*One. per. 13.00 *(978-1-60416-037-6(3))*Three. 20.00 *(978-1-60416-042-0(X))*Three. per. 13.00 *(978-1-60416-039-0(X))*Two. per. 13.00 *(978-1-60416-038-3(1))* Reformation Pubs.

CHURCH OF IRELAND

Acheson, Alan. Why the Whistle Went: A Memoir. 2009. (ENG.). 224p. pap. 29.95 *(978-1-85607-636-4(9))* Columba Pr. IRL. Dist: Dufour Editions, Inc.

Brannigan, Andrew. Church of Ireland: Origins, History & Present Day Practice. 2010. (Illus.). 85p. pap. *(978-1-904884-32-3(6))* Church of Ireland Publishing.

Church of Ireland. BCP - Holy Communion. l.t. ltd. ed. 2006. (ENG.). 170p. 189.95 *(978-1-85607-545-9(1))* Columba Pr. IRL. Dist: Dufour Editions, Inc.

Cook, Daniel. Cook: The Lives of Jonathan Swift, 3 vols. 2011. *(978-0-415-59136-2(8))*; *(978-0-415-59137-9(6))*; *(978-0-415-59135-5(X))* Routledge.

Cook, Daniel, ed. Cook Set: The Lives of Jonathan Swift, 3 vols. 2011. (ENG.). 1669p. (C). 795.00 *(978-0-415-59134-8(1))* Routledge.

Crooks, D. W. T., et al. Clergy of Clogher: Biographical Succession Lists. 2006. (ENG., Illus.). 303p. *(978-1-903688-62-5(0))* Ulster Historical Foundation GBR. Dist: Independent Pubs. Group.

Fauske, Christopher. A Political Biography of William King, 1 vol. 2011. (Eighteenth-Century Political Biographies Ser.). (ENG.). 256p. 99.00 *(978-1-84893-010-0(0))* Pickering & Chatto Pubs., Ltd. GBR. Dist: Ashgate Publishing Co.

Hayden, Mark. Changing Collars. 2008. (ENG.). 96p. per. 22.95 *(978-1-85607-572-5(9))* Columba Pr. IRL. Dist: Dufour Editions, Inc.

Kelly, Ann Cline. Jonathan Swift & Popular Culture: Myth, Media, & the Man. 2008. (ENG., Illus.). 256p. pap. 32.00 *(978-0-230-60234-2(7))* Palgrave Macmillan.

Kennerley, Ginnie. Embracing Women: Making History in the Church of Ireland. 2009. (ENG., Illus.). 180p. pap. 24.95 *(978-1-85607-625-8(3))* Columba Pr. IRL. Dist: Dufour Editions, Inc.

McCafferty, John. The Reconstruction of the Church of Ireland: Bishop Bramhall & the Laudian Reforms, 1633-1641. (Cambridge Studies in Early Modern British History Ser.). (ENG.). 288p. 2011. pap. 36.99 *(978-0-521-18146-4(1))* 2007. (Illus.). 132.00 *(978-0-521-64318-4(X))* Cambridge Univ. Pr.

Moffitt, Miriam. The Society for Irish Church Missions to the Roman Catholics, 1849-1950. 2011. (ENG., Illus.). 320p. 95.00 *(978-0-7190-7879-8(2))* Manchester Univ. Pr. GBR. Dist: Macmillan.

Morrissey, Thomas. Where Two Traditions Meet: John Sullivan SJ 1861 - 1933. 2009. (ENG.). 128p. pap. 22.95 *(978-1-85607-644-9(X))* Columba Pr. IRL. Dist: Dufour Editions, Inc.

Morrissey, Thomas J. Edward J. Byrne, 1872-1941: The Forgotten Archbishop of Dublin. 2011. (ENG., Illus.). 312p. 35.95 *(978-1-85607-703-3(9))* Columba Pr. IRL. Dist: Dufour Editions, Inc.

Ó Corráin, Daithí. Rendering to God & Caesar: The Irish Churches & the Two States in Ireland, 1949-73. 2008. (ENG., Illus.). 288p. pap. 28.00 *(978-0-7190-7347-2(2))* Manchester Univ. Pr. GBR. Dist: Macmillan.

Salmon, George. Gnosticism & Agnosticism & Other Sermons. 2007. (ENG.). 382p. 48.95 *(978-0-548-03576-4(8))* Kessinger Publishing, LLC.

—Gnosticism & Agnosticism & Other Sermons 1887. 2007. (ENG.). 382p. 48.95 *(978-0-548-05594-6(7))* Kessinger Publishing, LLC.

Scholes, Andrew. The Church of Ireland & the Third Home Rule Bill. 2010. 180p. 69.95 *(978-0-7165-3052-7(X))* Irish Academic Pr. IRL. Dist: International Specialized Bk. Services.

Semple, Pat. The Rector Who Wouldn't Pray for Rain: A Memoir. 2008. (ENG.). 224p. per. 24.95 *(978-1-85635-560-5(8))* Mercier Pr., Ltd., The IRL. Dist: Dufour Editions, Inc.

Stephen, Leslie. Swift. 2011. (Cambridge Library Collection - English Men of Letters Ser.). (ENG.). 228p. pap. 22.99 ***(978-1-108-03449-4(7))*** Cambridge Univ. Pr.

Stubblefield, R. Jay & Degategno, Paul J. Critical Companion to Jonathan Swift: A Literary Reference to His Life & Work. 2006. (Critical Companion Ser.). (Illus.). 480p. (C). (gr. 9). 75.00 *(978-0-8160-5093-2(7))* Facts On File, Inc.

Warre-Cornish, Francis. English Church in the Nineteenth Century, 2 vols. (History of the English Church Ser.: No. 8). reprint ed. 125.00 *(978-0-404-50760-2(3))* AMS Pr., Inc.

CHURCH OF JESUS CHRIST OF LATTER-DAY SAINTS

see also Reorganized Church of Jesus Christ of Latter-Day Saints

Aird, Polly, et al, eds. Playing with Shadows: Voices of Dissent in the Mormon West. 2011. (Kingdom in the West Ser.). (ENG., Illus.). 496p. 45.00 *(978-0-87062-380-6(X)*, Clark, Arthur H. Co., The) Univ. of Oklahoma Pr.

Aird, Polly, et al. Playing with Shadows: Voices of Dissent in the Mormon West. 2011. ***(978-0-87062-403-2(2)***, Clark, Arthur H. Co., The) Univ. of Oklahoma Pr.

Akenson, Donald Harman. Some Family: The Mormons & How Humanity Keeps Track of Itself. (Illus.). 2010. 349p. pap. *(978-0-7735-3727-9(9))* 2007. (ENG., 360p. *(978-0-7735-3295-3(1))* McGill-Queen's Univ. Pr.

Alder, Shannon L. 300 Questions for a More Vibrant Marriage. 2011. pap. 11.99 *(978-0-88290-976-9(2))* Cedar Fort, Inc./CFI Distribution.

Alexander, Thomas G. Brigham Young, the Quorum of the Twelve, & the Latter-Day Saint Investigation of the Mountain Meadows Massacre: Arrington Lecture No. Twelve. 2007. (Arrington Lecture Ser.). (ENG.). 48p. (gr. 13). pap. 7.95 *(978-0-87421-687-5(7)*, Utah State Univ. Pr.) Univ. Pr. of Colorado.

Allen, James. Men with a Mission Reprint. 2009. 480p. pap. 27.95 *(978-1-59038-998-0(0))* Deseret Bk. Co.

Allen, Richard J. Essential Gospel Teachings: Insights & Answers for Your Gospel Study. 2009. 449p. *(978-1-59811-941-1(9))* Covenant Communications.

Allen, Richard J. Unlocking the New Testament: A Side-By-Side Commentary. 2010. (Illus.). viii, 404p. ***(978-1-60861-119-5(1))*** Covenant Communications, Inc.

Anderson, Devery S., ed. The Development of LDS Temple Worship, 1846-2000: A Documentary History. 2010. 600p. 49.95 *(978-1-56085-211-7(9))* Signature Bks., LLC.

Andrus, Hyrum Leslie & Andrus, Helen Mae. Personal Glimpses of the Prophet Joseph Smith. 2009. 198p. pap. *(978-1-59811-760-8(2))* Covenant Communications, Inc.

Ankerberg, John, et al. The Facts on the Mormon Church. 2009. (Facts on Ser.). 96p. pap. 5.99 *(978-0-7369-2216-6(4))* Harvest Hse. Pubs.

Arnold, Marilyn. From the Heart: Charity in the Book of Mormon. 2011. pap. 13.99 *(978-1-59955-485-3(2))* Cedar Fort, Inc./CFI Distribution.

Arrington, Leonard J. Brigham Young: American Moses. 2012. (Vintage Ser.). (ENG., Illus.). 560p. pap. 17.95 ***(978-0-345-80321-4(3)***, Vintage) Knopf Doubleday Publishing Group.

Arrington, Leonard J., et al. Mothers of the Prophets. 3rd ed. 2009. (Illus.). 304p. 21.95 *(979-1-60641-044-8(X))* Deseret Bk. Co.

—Reflections of a Mormon Historian: Leonard J. Arrington on the New Mormon History. 2006. (ENG.). 368p. (C). 36.95 *(978-0-87062-348-6(6)*, Clark, Arthur H. Co., The) Univ. of Oklahoma Pr.

Ashton, Joyce & Ashton, Dennis. But If Not: When Bad Things Threaten to Destroy Good People. 2008. 14.99 *(978-1-59955-166-1(7))* Cedar Fort, Inc./CFI Distribution.

Atherton, Lionel. A Short Encounter with the Latter-Day Saints. 2010. (Illus.). 124p. pap. 10.99 *(978-1-4490-9146-0(6))* AuthorHouse.

Awake, Arise, & Come unto Christ, Talks from the 2008 Byu Women's Conference. 2009. 240p. pap. 22.95 *(978-1-60641-039-4(3))* Deseret Bk. Co.

Baadsgaard, Janene Wolsey. Healing from Abuse: How the Atonement of Jesus Christ Can Heal Broken Lives & Broken Hearts. 2007. pap. 16.95 *(978-1-59038-714-6(7))* Deseret Bk. Co.

Baker, Maureen. Choices & Constraints in Family Life. (Themes in Canadian Sociology Ser.). (ENG., Illus.). 2007. 216p. pap. 45.00 *(978-0-19-542105-7(1))* 2nd ed. 2010. 264p. 39.95 *(978-0-19-543159-9(6))* Oxford Univ. Pr., Inc.

Ballard, M. Russell. Counseling with Our Councils, Rev. Ed: Learning to Minister Together in the Church & in the Family. 2012. 26.99 ***(978-1-60907-047-2(X))*** Deseret Bk. Co.

Ballard, M. Russell. Daughters of God. 2009. (Illus.). xiii, 65p. 13.99 *(978-1-60641-043-1(1))* Deseret Bk. Co.

Barkdull, Larry. Priesthood Power: Blessing the Sick & Afflicted. 2008. xi, 95p. *(978-1-59811-641-0(X))* Covenant Communications.

Barker, Dan. Mormon History 101. 2011. 192p. pap. 13.99 *(978-1-59955-798-4(3))* Cedar Fort, Inc./CFI Distribution.

—Unique Stories from LDS History. 2010. pap. 12.99 *(978-1-59955-349-8(X))* Cedar Fort, Inc./CFI Distribution.

Barker, Shane R. Stepping up, Taking Charge, & Leading the Way. 2011. pap. 11.99 *(978-1-59955-503-4(4)*, Bonneville Bks.) Cedar Fort, Inc./CFI Distribution.

Baron, Ross. Social Ethics of the Church of Jesus Christ of Latter-Day Saints. 2008. 248p. pap. *(978-3-639-04825-4(3))* VDM Verlag Dr. Mueller e.K.

Barrett, Robert, illus. Prophets of the Lord (Updated) Individual Portraits & Biographical Sketches of the Sixteen Presidents of the Church. 2010. 16p. pap. 17.99 *(978-1-60641-188-9(8))* Deseret Bk. Co.

Bassett, Doug, compiled by. Doctrinal Insights to the Book of Mormon. 2007. 326p. pap. 24.99 *(978-1-59955-051-0(2))* Cedar Fort, Inc./CFI Distribution.

Bassett, K. Douglas, compiled by. Doctrinal Insights to the Book of Mormon: Volume 3: Helaman Through Moroni. 2008. 231p. pap. 24.99 *(978-1-59955-056-5(3))* Cedar Fort, Inc./CFI Distribution.

—Doctrinal Insights to the Book of Mormon Volume Two: Jacob Through Alma. 2007. 273p. per. 24.99 *(978-1-59955-055-8(5))* Cedar Fort, Inc./CFI Distribution.

Baugh, Alexander L. & Black, Susan Easton, eds. Banner of the Gospel: Wilford Woodruff. 2010. (Illus.). 385p. 24.99 *(978-0-8425-2776-7(1))* Brigham Young Univ.

Beck, Glenn. An Unlikely Mormon: The Conversion Story of Glenn Beck. 2008. 19.95 *(978-1-59038-943-0(3))* Deseret Bk. Co.

Beckham, Raymond E. How to Help Your Missionary: A Guide for Parents of Missionaries, Including Messages of Inspiration & Encouragement. 2006. 320p. per. 10.99 *(978-1-55517-966-3(5))* Cedar Fort, Inc./CFI Distribution.

Bennett, Bob. Leap of Faith. 2009. 336p. 29.95 *(978-1-60641-053-0(9))* Deseret Bk. Co.

Bennett, Richard. School of the Prophet. 2010. 36p. 21.99 *(978-1-59038-996-6(4))* Deseret Bk. Co.

Benson, Brett D. Always Remember Him: Jesus Christ, the Way, the Truth, & the Eternal Life of Man. 2010. pap. 17.99 *(978-1-59955-300-9(7))* Cedar Fort, Inc./CFI Distribution.

Benson, Ezra Taft. The American Heritage of Freedom: A Plan of God. 2011. 26p. 35.95 ***(978-1-258-09868-1(7))*** Literary Licensing, LLC.

Bergera, Gary James. Statements of the LDS First Presidency: A Topical Compendium. 2007. 539p. pap. 34.95 *(978-1-56085-195-0(3))* Signature Bks., LLC.

Berrett, William E. Teachings of the Book of Mormon. 2011. 134p. 40.95 ***(978-1-258-04184-7(7))*** Literary Licensing, LLC.

Berrett, William E. & Burton, Alma P. Readings in L D S Church History V1: From Original Manuscripts. 2011. 590p. 63.95 ***(978-1-258-03641-6(X))*** Literary Licensing, LLC.

—Readings in L D S Church History V2: From Original Manuscripts. 2011. 650p. 68.95 ***(978-1-258-03653-9(3))*** Literary Licensing, LLC.

—Readings in L D S Church History V3: From Original Manuscripts. 2011. 582p. 63.95 ***(978-1-258-03654-6(1))*** Literary Licensing, LLC.

Bigelow, Christopher Kimball. Temples of the Church of Jesus Christ of Latter-Day Saints. 2009. (ENG.). 224p. 34.95 *(978-1-59223-990-0(0)*, Thunder Bay Pr.) Advantage Pubs. Group.

—The Timechart History of Mormonism: From Premortality to the Present. 2007. (Illus.). 31p. 17.99 *(978-1-903025-40-6(0))* Worth Pr. Ltd. GBR. Dist: Book Sales, Inc.

Bigelow, Christopher Kimball & Langford, Jonathan. The Latter-Day Saints Family Encyclopedia. 2010. (ENG.). 400p. 34.95 *(978-1-60710-111-6(4)*, Thunder Bay Pr.) Advantage Pubs. Group.

Bird, Randall. Adam-Ondi-Ahman & the Last Days. 2011. 96p. pap. 8.99 ***(978-1-59955-937-7(4))*** Cedar Fort, Inc./CFI Distribution.

Bitton, Davis & Alexander, Thomas G. The A to Z of Mormonism. 110th ed. 2009. (A to Z Guide Ser.: No. 110). (ENG.). 358p. pap. 34.45 *(978-0-8108-6897-7(0))* Scarecrow Pr., Inc.

Black, Susan Easton, ed. The St. Louis Luminary. 2010. (ENG., Illus.). 192p. 21.95 *(978-0-8425-2752-1(4)*, Brigham Young Univ. Studies) Brigham Young Univ.

Black, Susan Easton, et al. Legacy of Sacrifice: Missionaries to Scandinavia, 1972 - 1894. 2007. (Illus.). 512p. 34.95 *(978-0-8425-2668-5(4)*, Brigham Young Univ. Religious Studies Ctr.) Brigham Young Univ.

Blacoe, William Victor. Understanding the New Testament: 1 & 2 Timothy, Titus & Philemon. 2011. 256p. pap. 19.99 *(978-1-59955-900-1(5))* Cedar Fort, Inc./CFI Distribution.

Boice, Trina. Great Ideas for Primary Activity Days. 2007. (Illus.). 121p. per. 12.95 *(978-1-932898-69-9(7))* Spring Creek Bk. Co.

—The Ready Resource for Relief Society, Vol. 5. 2009. 160p. pap. 12.99 *(978-1-59955-376-4(7))* Cedar Fort, Inc./CFI Distribution.

Boice, Trina. 2012 Ready Resource for Relief Society. 2011. pap. ***(978-1-59955-930-8(7))*** Cedar Fort, Inc./CFI Distribution.

Bowman, Matthew. The Mormon People: The Making of an American Faith. 2012. (ENG.). 352p. 26.00 ***(978-0-679-64490-3(3)***, Random House) Random House Publishing Group.

Boyack, Merrilee. Standing up in a Sit-down World: Service, Leadership, & Involvement. 2012. pap. 14.99 ***(978-1-60907-057-1(7))*** Deseret Bk. Co.

Boyack, Merrilee Browne. In Trying Times, Just Keep Trying! 2010. x, 148p. *(978-1-60641-597-9(2))* Deseret Bk. Co.

Broderick, Carlf. The Uses of Adversity. 2008. 64p. 10.95 *(978-1-59038-851-8(6))* Deseret Bk. Co.

Brown, Dennis K. Evidences of the True Church. 2008. 154p. pap. 13.98 *(978-0-88290-712-3(3))* Cedar Fort, Inc./CFI Distribution.

Brown, Matthew B. Exploring the Connection Between Mormons & Masons. 2009. 211p. *(978-1-59811-893-3(5)*, North Winds Pr) Covenant Communications, Inc.

—A Pillar of Light: The History & Message of the First Vision. 2009. (Illus.). xii, 268p. *(978-1-59811-795-0(5)*, Deboisillo) Covenant Communications, Inc.

Brown, Rodney J. Mormons & Science. 2008. (Setting the Record Straight Ser.) (Illus.). 69p. pap. 9.95 *(978-1-932597-45-5(X))* Millennial Pr., Inc.

Brown, Samuel Morris. In Heaven as It Is on Earth: Joseph Smith & the Early Mormon Conquest of Death, 1 vol. 2012. (ENG., Illus.). 408p. 34.95 ***(978-0-19-979357-0(3))*** Oxford Univ. Pr., Inc.

Burbidge, Clark. Life on the Narrow Path. 2011. 144p. pap. 10.99 *(978-1-59955-457-0(7)*, Bonneville Bks.) Cedar Fort, Inc./CFI Distribution.

Bushman, Claudia L. Contemporary Mormonism: Latter-Day Saints in Modern America. 2008. (ENG.). 256p. per. 27.95 *(978-0-7425-6238-7(7))* Rowman & Littlefield Publishers, Inc.

Bushman, Claudia Lauper. Building the Kingdom: A History of Mormons in America. 2009. (ENG.). 123p. pap. 10.00 *(978-1-4379-6516-2(4))* DIANE Publishing Co.

Bushman, Richard Lyman. Mormonism. 2008. (Very Short Introductions Ser.). (ENG., Illus.). 144p. pap. 11.95 *(978-0-19-531030-6(6))* Oxford Univ. Pr., Inc.

Byetheway, John. Supersonic Saints. 2007. 192p. 19.95 *(978-1-59038-747-4(3))* Deseret Bk. Co.

Bytheway, John. Fishing: Observations of a Reel Man. 2010. (Illus.). 170p. *(978-1-60641-634-1(0))* Deseret Bk. Co.

—How to Be an Extra Ordinary Missionary. 2010. 64p. pap. 7.99 *(978-1-60641-772-0(X))* Deseret Bk. Co.

—How to Be Totally Miserable: A Self-Hinder Book. 2007. (Illus.). 81p. per. 5.95 *(978-1-59038-743-6(0)*, Shadow Mountain) Deseret Bk. Co.

—Of Pigs, Pearls, & Prodigals: A Fresh Look at the Parables of Jesus. 2010. 224p. 19.99 *(978-1-59038-808-2(9))* Deseret Bk. Co.

—Sports: Life Lessons from Court, Field, & Gridiron. 2009. (Illus.). vii, 183p. 18.95 *(978-1-60641-092-9(X))* Deseret Bk. Co.

—Supersonic Saints 2: More Thrilling Stories from LDS Pilots. 2008. 256p. 21.95 *(978-1-59038-911-9(5))* Deseret Bk. Co.

BYU Religious Studies Center. The 2008 Brigham Young University Religious Education Student Symposium. 2008. (Illus.). 184p. pap. *(978-0-8425-2718-7(4)*, Brigham Young Univ. Religious Studies Ctr.) Brigham Young Univ.

Caldwell, C. M. Power from on High. 2008. 263p. *(978-1-59811-659-5(2))* Covenant Communications.

Campbell, Beverl. You Don't Need to Slay My Dragons, Just Take Out the Trash. 2008. 176p. 18.95 *(978-1-59038-862-4(3))* Deseret Bk. Co.

Cannon, Hugh J. To the Peripheries of Mormondom: The Apostolic Around-the-World Journey of David O Mckay, 1920-1921. Neilson, Reid L., ed. 2011. (ENG., Illus.). 350p. 29.95 *(978-1-60781-010-0(7))* Univ. of Utah Pr

Cannon, Joe, ed. Why I'm a Mormon. 2012. (Illus.). vii, 360p. pap. 19.99 *(978-1-60908-739-5(9))* Deseret Bk. Co.

Cardon, Joseph E. & Bennion, Samuel O., eds. Testimonies of the Divinity of the Church of Jesus Christ of Latter-Day Saints. 2011. 312p. 50.95 ***(978-1-258-04212-7(6))*** Literary Licensing, LLC.

Carling, Matthew. Dry Council Sunday. 2010. (ENG.). 81p. pap. 10.95 *(978-0-557-34076-7(4))* Lulu Enterprises Inc.

Carroll, Jason S., et al, contrib. by. Successful Marriages & Families. 2011. (Illus.). 360p. (C). ***(978-0-8425-2803-0(2)***, Brigham Young Univ. Studies) Brigham Young Univ.

Carver, Timothy L. That's Faith! 2009. 102p. pap. 8.99 *(978-1-59955-237-8(X))* Cedar Fort, Inc./CFI Distribution.

Chase, Alice K., ed. The Best from Brigham Young: Statements from His Sermons on Religion, Education & Community Building. 2011. 50p. 35.95 ***(978-1-258-00585-6(9))*** Literary Licensing, LLC.

Choose Ye This Day to Serve the Lord: Talks from the 2010 BYU Women's Conference. 2011. 224p. 22.99 *(978-1-60641-932-8(3))* Deseret Bk. Co.

Christensen, Rachelle J. Lost Children: Coping with Miscarriage. 2010. (Illus.). xix, 75p. pap. 9.99 *(978-1-59955-248-4(5))* Cedar Fort, Inc./CFI Distribution.

Christensen, Reg. Fear Not: Messages of Hope, Healing, & Peace in the Book of Revelation. 2010. xii, 264p. ***(978-1-59811-995-4(8))*** Covenant Communications.

Christianson, Jack R. & Bassett, K. Douglas. Life Lessons from the Book of Mormon. 2007. 245p. per. 16.99 *(978-1-59955-079-4(2))* Cedar Fort, Inc./CFI Distribution.

Christianson, Jack R., et al. Where Can I Turn for Peace? 2009. (Illus.). 102p. *(978-1-59811-863-6(3))* Covenant Communications.

Clark, David L. Joseph Bates Noble: Polygamy & the Temple Lot Case. 2009. (ENG., Illus.). 224p. (gr. 13). 24.95 *(978-0-87480-937-4(1))* Univ. of Utah Pr.

Clark, John A. Gleanings by the Way. 2008. 354p. 46.95 *(978-0-548-93331-2(6))* 2007. (ENG.). 356p. per. 31.95 *(978-0-548-59097-3(4))* Kessinger Publishing, LLC.

Clark Jr., J. Reuben. On the Way to Immortality & Eternal Life. 2011. 482p. 58.95 ***(978-1-258-03447-4(6))*** Literary Licensing, LLC.

Clark, Kim. Armor: Divine Protection in a Darkening World. 2007. 320p. 21.95 *(978-1-59038-756-6(2))* Deseret Bk. Co.

Cole, Rosemarie. A Call to War Against the Enemies of Our Faith. 2007. 116p. per. 10.99 *(978-1-60477-398-9(7))* Xulon Pr., Inc.

Collier, Mardi. What Do I Know about My God? 2006. 123p. per. *(978-1-59166-681-3(3))* BJU Pr.

Collingridge, Dave. Light, Truth & Secular Knowledge: God's Hand in Modern Science. 2008. pap. 12.99 *(978-1-59955-082-4(2))* Cedar Fort, Inc./CFI Distribution.

Cook, Gene R. Searching the Scriptures. 2007. 240p. pap. 17.99 *(978-1-59038-566-1(7))* Deseret Bk. Co.

—Teaching by the Spirit. 2011. 232p. pap. 17.99 *(978-1-60641-958-8(7))* Deseret Bk. Co.

C

Cowan, Richard O. & Manscill, Craig K. The A to Z of the Doctrine & Covenants & Church History. 2008. (Illus.). 334p. pap. 24.95 (978-1-59992-119-8(7)) Leatherwood Pr.

Cramer, Paul. A Mormon on the Road to Emmaus. 2008. 260p. per. 15.99 (978-1-60477-686-7(2)) Xulon Pr., Inc.

Cramer, Steven A. Reaching Higher: Twenty-Five Ways to Feel Better about Yourself. 2008. pap. 12.99 (978-1-59955-122-7(5)) Cedar Fort, Inc./CFI Distribution.

Crane, Steven A. & Crane, Charles A. Ashamed of Joseph: Mormon Foundations Crumble. 2011. 186p. pap. 21.00 (978-1-61097-219-2(8), Resource Pubns.) Wipf & Stock Pubs.

Crowther, Duane S. The Godhead: New Scriptural Insights on the Father, the Son, & the Holy Ghost. 2007. 408p. per. 26.99 (978-0-88290-828-1(6)) Cedar Fort, Inc./CFI Distribution.

—They Walked with God: Intimate Biographies of Patriarchs from the Book of Genesis. 2009. pap. 17.99 (978-0-88290-968-4(1)) Cedar Fort, Inc./CFI Distribution.

Curbelo, Nestor. The History of the Mormons in Argentina. Jennings, Erin, tr. from SPA. 2008. lib. bdg. 70.00 (978-1-58958-116-6(4)); pap. 24.95 (978-1-58958-052-7(4)); 300p. 24.95 (978-1-58958-059-6(1)) Kofford, Greg Books, Inc.

—The History of the Mormons in Argentina. ltd. collector's ed. 2009. 159.95 (978-1-58958-051-0(6)) Kofford, Greg Books, Inc.

—The History of the Mormons in Argentina. Jennings, Erin, tr. ltd. collector's ed. 2008. 300p. 159.95 (978-1-58958-058-9(3)) Kofford, Greg Books, Inc.

Dalton, Elaine S. A Return to Virtue. 2011. (Illus.). xviii, 141p. (YA). 22.99 (**978-1-60908-924-5(3)**) Deseret Bk. Co.

Dana, Bruce. Prophetic Teachings on Death, Angels, & Heavenly Manifestations. 2011. 160p. pap. 12.99 (978-1-59955-491-4(7), Bonneville Bks.) Cedar Fort, Inc./CFI Distribution.

Dana, Bruce E. The Apostleship: From the Original Twelve to the Latter-Day Apostles. 2006. (Illus.). xiii, 203p. pap. 14.99 (978-1-55517-899-4(5)) Cedar Fort, Inc./CFI Distribution.

Dastrup, Boyd L. Plowmen: A Brief History of the Mormon Church in Oklahoma, 1855-2000. 2007. (978-1-58982-408-9(3)) American Bk. Publishing Group.

Davidson, Karen Lynn. Our Latter-Day Hymns: The Stories & the Messages. 2009. 29.95 (978-1-60641-068-4(7)) Deseret Bk. Co.

Davidson, Ruth. Out of the Ashes. 2007. 14.95 (978-0-9795690-0-5(1)) Gatehouse Media.

Davies, Douglas J. Jesus, Satan & Joseph Smith. 2010. 292p. 99.95 (978-1-4094-0649-5(0)); pap. 29.95 (978-1-4094-0670-9(9)) Ashgate Publishing Co.

Davis, Carmen. I'm a Mormon, Now What? 2010. 128p. pap. 9.99 (978-1-59955-470-9(4)) Cedar Fort, Inc./CFI Distribution.

Davis, Lisa. The Sins of Brother Curtis: A Story of Betrayal, Conviction, & the Mormon Church. 2011. (ENG., Illus.). 368p. 27.00 (978-1-4165-9103-0(6), Scribner) Scribner.

Daynes, Kathryn M. More Wives Than One: Transformation of the Mormon Marriage System, 1840-1910. 2008. (ENG., Illus.). 328p. pap. 26.00 (978-0-252-07560-5(9)) Univ. of Illinois Pr.

Daynes, Kerstin. Infertility: Help, Hope, & Healing. 2010. pap. 13.99 (978-1-59955-296-5(5)) Cedar Fort, Inc./CFI Distribution.

Deborah, Rowley. Before They Turn Twelve. 2007. 128p. pap. 9.95 (978-1-59038-847-1(X)) Deseret Bk. Co.

Dennis, Ronald D., ed. Zion's Trumpet. 2010. 480p. 25.99 (978-0-8425-2782-8(6)) Vol. 3. 2012. (**978-0-8425-2808-5(3)**) Brigham Young Univ. (Brigham Young Univ. Religious Studies Ctr.).

Deseret Book. By Small & Simple Things: Talks from the 2011 BYU Women's Conference. 2012. 24.99 (**978-1-60908-898-9(0)**) Deseret Bk. Co.

Dew, Sheri L. & Pearce, Virginia H. The Beginning of Better Days: Divine Instruction to Women from the Prophet Joseph Smith. 2012. (**978-1-60641-851-2(3)**) Deseret Bk. Co.

Dewey, Simon. My Redeemer Lives: Remembering His Atonement & Resurrection. 2009. (Illus.). 89p. (978-1-59811-789-9(0)) Covenant Communications.

DiGirolamo, Vincent. Grace Divine. 2008. 100p. pap. 10.99 (978-0-9786815-6-2(8)); (ENG., Illus.). 296p. (978-0-9786815-7-9(6)) Celestine Publishing, LLC.

—Principles with Promise: For members of the Church of Jesus Christ of Latter Day Saints. 2007. 880p. 79.00 (978-0-9786815-0-0(9)) Celestine Publishing, LLC.

—Principles with Promise: For Members of the Church of Jesus Christ of Latter-day Saints. 2008. 769p. pap. 39.95 (978-0-9786815-5-5(X)) Celestine Publishing, LLC.

—Principles with Promise: Study Companion for the Book of Mormon: Another Testament of Jesus Christ. 2008. 296p. pap. 32.99 (978-0-9786815-2-4(5)) Celestine Publishing, LLC.

Dinger, John S. The Nauvoo City & High Council Minutes. 2011. (**978-1-56085-214-8(3)**) Signature Bks., LLC.

Dobberfuhl, Douglas. Overcoming Addiction: A Twelve-Step Companion Guide. 2011. 141p. pap. 16.95 (978-1-935217-93-0(3), Walnut Springs Press) Leatherwood Pr.

Dorius, Guy L., et al, eds. Regional Studies in Latter-day Saint Church History: Ohio & Upper Canada. 2006. (Studies in Latter-Day Saint History: 6). (Illus.). 218p. pap. 14.95 (978-0-8425-2653-1(6), Brigham Young Univ. Religious Studies Ctr.) Brigham Young Univ.

Draughon, Wallace R. History of the Church of Jesus Christ of Latter-Day Saints in North Carolina. (Illus.). 320p. reprint ed. lib. bdg. 18.95 (978-1-881851-01-1(X)) Genealogy Publishing Service.

Eaton, Robert. Extremes: How to Keep Your Virtues from Becoming Vices. 2008. (Illus.). 272p. pap. 17.95 (978-1-59038-957-7(3)) Deseret Bk. Co.

Eaton, Robert I. & Beecher, Mark. Becoming a Great Gospel Teacher: Bringing the Gospel Classroom to Life. 2007. xi, 185p. (978-1-59811-255-9(4)) Covenant Communications.

Elijah's Power: Early Mormon Mysticism & America's Ancient Wisdoms. 2007. 114p. per. 12.95 (978-0-929582-03-0(9)) Concord Pr. International.

England, Eugene. Why the Church Is as True as the Gospel. 2007. (ENG.). 172p. per. 15.95 (978-0-85051-401-7(1), Mormon Arts & Letters) Luso-Brazilian Bks.

Errand of Angels: In Honor & Praise of Mothers. 2007. (Illus.). (978-1-59811-341-9(0)) Covenant Communications.

Evans, Joe. Encompassing Charity. 2010. pap. 12.99 (978-1-59955-311-5(2)) Cedar Fort, Inc./CFI Distribution.

Evenson, William & Jeffery, Duane, eds. Mormonism & Evolution: The Authoritative LDS Statements. ltd. collector's ed. 2007. 159.95 (978-1-58958-097-8(4)) Kofford, Greg Books, Inc.

Eyre, Linda & Pothier, Shawni Eyre. A Mother's Book of Secrets. 2009. xiv, 154p. (978-1-60641-070-7(9)) Deseret Bk. Co.

Families. (Early Intervention Levels Ser.). 32.22 (978-0-7362-1050-8(4)); 5.37 (978-0-7362-0957-1(3)) Hampton-Brown Bks.

Faulconer, James E. Faith, Philosophy, Scripture. 2010. 268p. pap. (978-0-8425-2778-1(8), Maxwell, Neal A. Institute for Religious Scholarship) Brigham Young Univ.

Ferrell, James. The Holy Secret. 2008. 224p. 24.99 (978-1-59038-718-4(X)) Deseret Bk. Co.

Ferrell, James L. Falling to Heaven: The Surprising Path to Happiness. 2012. 24.99 (**978-1-60908-900-9(6)**) Deseret Bk. Co.

—The Hidden Christ: Beneath the Surface of the Old Testament. 2012. pap. 24.99 (**978-1-60908-915-3(4)**) 2009. 29.95 (978-1-59038-477-0(6)) Deseret Bk. Co.

Flake, Lawrence R. Twelve Sons of Britain: General Authorities of the Church of Jesus Christ of Latter-Day Saints Who Were Born in England. 2008. pap. 7.99 (978-1-59955-136-4(5)) Cedar Fort, Inc./CFI Distribution.

Fletcher, Allen J. A Scriptural Discussion of Light. 2007. 265p. per. 14.99 (978-1-59955-032-9(6)) Cedar Fort, Inc./CFI Distribution.

Flynn, DeAnne. The Time-Starved Family. 2008. 160p. pap. 17.95 (978-1-60641-071-4(7)) Deseret Bk. Co.

Freeman, Emily. The Woman at the Well. 2008. 48p. 19.95 (978-1-59038-967-6(0), Shadow Mountain) Deseret Bk. Co.

Freeman, Robert C., ed. Nineteenth-Century Saints at War. 2007. pap. 14.95 (978-0-8425-2694-4(3), Brigham Young Univ. Religious Studies Ctr.) Brigham Young Univ.

Freeman, Robert C., et al, eds. Regional Studies in Latter-day Saint Church History: British Isles, 7. 2007. (Studies in Latter-Day Saint History). (Illus.). 240p. pap. (978-0-8425-2672-2(2), Brigham Young Univ. Religious Studies Ctr.) Brigham Young Univ.

Freeman, Robert C. & Felt, Jon A. German Saints at War. 2008. 29.99 (978-1-59955-224-8(8)) Cedar Fort, Inc./CFI Distribution.

Gashler, S. Ted. Opening the Seventh Seal. 2009. pap. 15.99 (978-1-59955-265-1(5)) Cedar Fort, Inc./CFI Distribution.

Gaskill, Alonzo, ed. The Doctrine & Covenants: Revelations in Context: The 37th Annual Sidney B. Sperry Symposium. 2008. 242p. 24.95 (978-1-60641-015-8(6)) Deseret Bk. Co.

Gaskill, Alonzo L. Odds Are, You're Going to Be Exalted! Evidence That the Plan of Salvation Works. 2008. 159p. 21.95 (978-1-59038-918-8(2)) Deseret Bk. Co.

Gentry, Leland Homer & Compton, Todd M. Fire & Sword: A History of the Latter-Day Saints in Northern Missouri, 1836-39. 2011. (ENG.). 635p. 36.95 (978-1-58958-120-3(2)) Kofford, Greg Books, Inc.

Gibbons, Francis. David O. Mckay: Apostle to the World, Prophet of God. 2009. 464p. pap. 25.99 (978-1-60641-215-2(9)) Deseret Bk. Co.

—George Albert Smith: Kind & Caring Christian, Prophet of God. 2009. 400p. pap. 25.99 (978-1-60641-214-5(0)) Deseret Bk. Co.

—Harold B. Lee: Man of Vision, Prophet of God. 2009. 544p. pap. 25.99 (978-1-60641-217-6(5)) Deseret Bk. Co.

—Heber J. Grant: Man of Steel, Prophet of God. 2009. 252p. pap. 25.99 (978-1-60641-213-8(2)) Deseret Bk. Co.

—John Taylor: Philosopher, Prohet of God. 2009. 320p. pap. 25.99 (978-1-60641-209-1(4)) Deseret Bk. Co.

—Joseph F. Smith: Patriarch & Preacher. Prophet of God. 2009. 352p. pap. 25.99 (978-1-60641-212-1(4)) Deseret Bk. Co.

—Joseph Fielding Smith: Gospel Scholar, Prophet of God. 2009. 544p. pap. 25.99 (978-1-60641-216-9(7)) Deseret Bk. Co.

—Joseph Smith: Martyr, Prophet of God. 2009. 392p. pap. 25.99 (978-1-60641-207-7(8)) Deseret Bk. Co.

—Lorenzo Snow: Spiritual Giant, Prophet of God. 2009. 256p. pap. 25.99 (978-1-60641-211-4(6)) Deseret Bk. Co.

—Spencer W. Kimball: Resolute Disciple, Prophet of God. 2009. 336p. pap. 25.99 (978-1-60641-218-3(3)) Deseret Bk. Co.

—Wilford Woodruff: Wondrous Worker, Prophet of God. 2009. 416p. pap. 25.99 (978-1-60641-210-7(8)) Deseret Bk. Co.

Gibbons, Ted. Be Not Afraid. 2009. pap. 12.99 (978-1-59955-274-3(4)) Cedar Fort, Inc./CFI Distribution.

Givens, Terryl L. & Grow, Matthew J. Parley P. Pratt: The Apostle Paul of Mormonism, 1 vol. 2011. (ENG., Illus.). 512p. 34.95 (978-0-19-537573-2(4)) Oxford Univ. Pr., Inc.

Godfrey, Matthew C. Religion, Politics, & Sugar: The Mormon Church, the Federal Government, & the Utah-Idaho Sugar Company, 1907-1921. 2007. (Illus.). 226p. 34.95 (978-0-87421-658-5(3), Utah State Univ. Pr.) Univ. Pr. of Colorado.

Gordon, Sarah Barringer. In-Laws & Outlaws: Lessons in Research & Friendship & a Report from the Archives. 2007. (Arrington Lecture Ser.). (ENG., Illus.). 37p. (gr. 13). pap. 7.95 (978-0-87421-682-0(6), Utah State Univ. Pr.) Univ. Pr. of Colorado.

Green, Steven D. The Tribe of Ephraim: Covenant & Bloodline. 2007. pap. 16.99 (978-0-88290-822-9(7)) Cedar Fort, Inc./CFI Distribution.

Groberg, John H. Anytime, Anywhere. 2006. (Illus.). vi, 218p. 19.95 (978-1-59038-643-9(4)) Deseret Bk. Co.

Gunnison, J. W. (John Williams). The Mormons, or, Latter-Day Saints, in the Valley of the Great Salt Lake; a History of Their Rise & Progress, Peculiar Doctrines, Present Condition. 2006. 180p. per. 18.99 (978-1-4255-1401-3(4)) MPublishing.

Gunnison, John Williams. The Mormons, Or, Latter-Day Saints. 2009. (Amer Philosophy, Religion Ser.). (ENG.). 196p. pap. 14.95 (978-1-4290-1931-6(X)) Applewood Bks.

Guymon, Shannon. Child of Many Colors: Stories of Transracial Adoption. 2010. pap. 9.99 (978-1-59955-325-2(2)) Cedar Fort, Inc./CFI Distribution.

Hafen, Bruce. Broken Heart. 2008. 320p. pap. 15.95 (978-1-59038-885-3(2)) Deseret Bk. Co.

—A Disciple's Life: The Biography of Neal A. Maxwell. 2010. 656p. pap. 34.99 (978-1-60641-250-3(7)) Deseret Bk. Co.

Hafen, Bruce C. Spiritually Anchored in Unsettled Times. 2009. (Illus.). xi, 132p. 17.95 (978-1-60641-069-1(5)) Deseret Bk. Co.

Hales, Robert D. Return with Light & Honor: Four Phases of Our Mortal Journey Home. 2010. 27.99 (978-1-57008-769-1(5)) Deseret Bk. Co.

Hammari, Kimiko. I Know My Savior Lives. 2009. 160p. pap. 14.99 (978-1-59955-369-6(4)) Cedar Fort, Inc./CFI Distribution.

Hammond, John J. Volume 1 Family & Mormon Church Roots: Colonial Period To 1820. 2011. 478p. pap. 23.99 (**978-1-4628-7364-7(2)**) Xlibris Corp.

—Volume II the Creation of Mormonism: Joseph smith jr. in The 1820s. 2011. 412p. pap. 23.99 (**978-1-4628-7851-2(2)**) Xlibris Corp.

Hansen, Gerald E. & Brinkerhoff, Val. Sacred Walls: Learning from Temple Symbols. 2009. (Illus.). ix, 86p. (978-1-59811-772-1(6), North Winds Pr) Covenant Communications, Inc.

Hansen, Pamela. Finding the Angel Within. 2008. 176p. pap. 14.95 (978-1-59038-865-5(8)) Deseret Bk. Co.

Hansen, Vaughn E. Israel's Lost 10 Tribes: Migrations to Britain & USA. 2011. (**978-1-59955-951-3(X)**) Cedar Fort, Inc./CFI Distribution.

Hardy, B. Carmon. The Works of Abraham: Mormon Polygamy: Sources on Its Origin, Thought, & Practice. 2007. (978-0-87062-352-3(4), Clark, Arthur H. Co., The) Univ. of Oklahoma Pr.

Hardy, B. Carmon, ed. Doing the Works of Abraham: Mormon Polygamy, Its Origins, Practice, & Demise. 2007. (Kingdom in the West Ser.). (ENG., Illus.). 448p. (C). 39.95 (978-0-87062-344-8(3), Clark, Arthur H. Co., The) Univ. of Oklahoma Pr.

Harper, Steven C. The Word of Wisdom. 2008. (Setting the Record Straight Ser.). (Illus.). 99p. per. 9.95 (978-1-932597-43-1(3)) Millennial Pr., Inc.

Harrell, Charles R. This Is My Doctrine: The Development of Mormon Theology. 2011. (ENG.). 596p. 34.95 (978-1-58958-103-6(2)) Kofford, Greg Books, Inc.

Harris, Philip H. The Voyage. 2011. 192p. 29.99 (**978-1-4568-4735-7(X)**); pap. 19.99 (**978-1-4568-4734-0(1)**) Xlibris Corp.

Harrison, Mark. Hiking Boots & Gospel Truths: Building Testimonies in the Outdoors. 2009. pap. 8.99 (978-1-59955-282-8(5)) Cedar Fort, Inc./CFI Distribution.

Hartley, Taylor. The Advocate: An LDS Perspective on the Morality of Criminal Defense. 2011. 192p. pap. 14.99 (978-1-59955-799-1(1)) Cedar Fort, Inc./CFI Distribution.

Hedges, Andrew H. & Holzapfel, Richard Neitzel, eds. Within These Prison Walls: Lorenzo Snow's Record Book 1886 - 1897. 2010. (Illus.). 216p. 21.99 (978-0-8425-2762-0(1), Brigham Young Univ. Religious Studies Ctr.) Brigham Young Univ.

Hedges, Andrew H., et al. Through the Lens: The Original 1907 Church History Photographs of George Edward Anderson. 2010. 49.99 (978-1-60641-236-7(1)) Deseret Bk. Co.

Hilton, John, 3rd. Please Pass the Scriptures. 2007. 208p. (YA). pap. 15.95 (978-1-59038-790-0(2)) Deseret Bk. Co.

Hilton, John & Sweat, Anthony. Why? Powerful Answers & Practical Reasons for Living LDS Standards. 2009. (978-1-60641-040-0(7)) Deseret Bk. Co.

Hinckley, Gordon. In the Arms of His Love: 2007 Mother's Day Booklet. 2007. 16p. pap. 2.49 (978-1-59038-705-4(8)) Deseret Bk. Co.

Hinckley, Kevin. Promptings or Me? 2011. pap. 11.99 (978-1-59955-490-7(9), Bonneville Bks.) Cedar Fort, Inc./CFI Distribution.

Hoffmann, John P. Japanese Saints: Mormons in the Land of the Rising Sun. 2007. (ENG., Illus.). 244p. 73.50 (978-0-7391-1689-0(4)) Lexington Bks.

Holland, Jeffrey R. Broken Things to Mend. 2008. viii, 230p. 24.95 (978-1-60641-024-0(5)) Deseret Bk. Co.

—Created for Greater Things. 2011. 15.99 (978-1-60641-940-3(4)) Deseret Bk. Co.

Holzapfel, Richard. He Will Give You Rest. 2010. 32p. 18.99 (978-1-60641-667-9(7)) Deseret Bk. Co.

—Making Sense of the NT. 2010. 544p. 34.99 (978-1-60641-668-6(5)) Deseret Bk. Co.

HOlzapfel, Richard Neitzel & Jackson, Kent P., eds. Joseph Smith, the Prophet & Seer. 2010. (Illus.). 524p. 29.99 (978-0-8425-2753-8(2), Brigham Young Univ. Religious Studies Ctr.) Brigham Young Univ.

Holzapfel, Richard Neitzel, et al. Jesus Christ & the World of the New Testament: An Illustrated Reference for Latter-day Saints. 2006. 39.95 (978-1-59038-442-8(3)) Deseret Bk. Co.

Hopkins, Richard R. How Greek Philosophy Corrupted the Christian Concept of God. 2009. 466p. pap. 27.99 (978-0-88290-782-6(4)) Cedar Fort, Inc./CFI Distribution.

Horne, Dennis B. Faith to Heal & Be Healed: Insights Drawn from Inspirational Accounts of Faith, Blessing the Sick, & Healings. 2009. pap. 15.99 (978-1-59955-253-8(1)) Cedar Fort, Inc./CFI Distribution.

Howick, E. Keith. A Concise History of Kirtland. 2007. (Concise History of the Early Church Ser.). (ENG., Illus.). 80p. per. 6.95 (978-1-886249-16-5(4)) WindRiver Publishing, Inc.

—A Concise History of Nauvoo. 2006. (Concise History of the Early Church Ser.). (ENG., Illus.). 84p. per. 6.95 (978-1-886249-34-9(2)) WindRiver Publishing, Inc.

—A Concise History of Palmyra. 2007. (Concise History of the Early Church Ser.). (ENG., Illus.). 64p. per. 6.95 (978-1-886249-15-8(6)) WindRiver Publishing, Inc.

—A Concise History of the Early Church, 4. 2007. per. 27.80 (978-1-886249-11-0(3)) WindRiver Publishing, Inc.

—A Concise History of Zion. 2007. (Concise History of the Early Church Ser.). (ENG., Illus.). 80p. per. 6.95 (978-1-886249-17-2(2)) WindRiver Publishing, Inc.

—Polygamy: The Mormon Enigma. 2008. (ENG., Illus.). 216p. 14.95 (978-1-886249-19-6(9)) WindRiver Publishing, Inc.

—Unique Evidences of the Restoration. 2008. (ENG.). 224p. per. 12.95 (978-1-886249-35-6(0)) WindRiver Publishing, Inc.

Huntsman, Eric D. God So Loved the World: The Final Days of the Savior's Life. 2011. 112p. 21.99 (978-1-60641-975-5(7)) Deseret Bk. Co.

In the Strength of the Lord: Talks from the 2009 BYU Women's Conference. 2010. (978-1-60641-228-2(0)) Deseret Bk. Co.

Irvine, Rebecca. Adventures with the Word of God: Making Scripture Study Exciting for the Entire Family. 2008. pap. 12.99 (978-0-88290-845-8(6)) Cedar Fort, Inc./CFI Distribution.

Jackson, Kent J. The King James Bible & the Restoration. 2011. (Illus.). 304p. (**978-0-8425-2802-3(4)**, Brigham Young Univ. Religious Studies Ctr.) Brigham Young Univ.

Jacob, Carl H. While of These Emblems. 2011. 204p. 44.95 (**978-1-258-08390-8(6)**) Literary Licensing, LLC.

Janae Thorne-Bird. Heart Wide Open: A True Story by Janae Thorne-Bird. 2010. 224p. pap. 18.95 (978-1-4401-8576-2(X)) iUniverse, Inc.

Jensen, R. Devan. God's Greatest Gifts. 2010. pap. 8.99 (978-1-59955-333-7(3)) Cedar Fort, Inc./CFI Distribution.

Jensen, Robin Scott, ed. The Joseph Smith Papers: Revelations & Translations. 2011. 770p. 69.95 (978-1-60641-942-7(0)) Deseret Bk. Co.

Jenson, Andrew, ed. Church Chronology: A Record of Important Events Pertaining to the History of the Church of Jesus Christ of Latter Day Saints. 2007. (ENG.). 538p. 57.95 (978-0-548-04882-5(7)) Kessinger Publishing, LLC.

Jessee, Dean C., et al, eds. The Joseph Smith Papers Vol. 1: Journals, 1832-1839. 2008. 512p. 49.95 (978-1-57008-849-0(7)) Deseret Bk. Co.

Jessop, Flora & Brown, Paul T. Church of Lies. (ENG.). 328p. 2010. pap. 14.95 (978-0-470-56546-9(2)) 2009. (Illus.). 25.95 (978-0-7879-9462-4(6)) Wiley, John & Sons, Inc. (Jossey-Bass).

Johnson, Jane. I Am A Mother. 2010. 144p. pap. 15.99 (978-1-60641-599-3(9)) Deseret Bk. Co.

Johnson, Jane Clayson. I Am a Mother. 2007. xviii, 138p. 15.95 (978-1-59038-717-7(1)) Deseret Bk. Co.

Johnson, Janiece Lyn. Give It All up & Follow Your Lord: Mormon Female Religisity, 1831 - 1843. 2008. (Illus.). pap. (978-0-8425-2711-8(7), Brigham Young Univ. Pr.) Brigham Young Univ.

Joslin, Connie R. The End of Times. 2008. pap. 14.99 (978-0-88290-836-6(7)) Cedar Fort, Inc./CFI Distribution.

Judd, Daniel K. The Fortunate Fall: Understanding the Blessings & Burdens of Adversity. 2011. 208p. 23.99 (978-1-60641-843-7(2)) Deseret Bk. Co.

Judd, Frank F. & Stratheam, Gaye. How the New Testament Came to Be: 35th Annual Sidney B. Sperry Symposium. 2006. 432p. 24.95 (978-1-59038-627-9(2)) Deseret Bk. Co.

—Sperry Syposium Classics: The New Testament. 2006. 464p. 24.95 (978-1-59038-628-6(0)) Deseret Bk. Co.

Judd, Mary Grant. Jedediah M Grant: Pioneer, Statesman. 2011. 158p. 41.95 (**978-1-258-07415-9(X)**) Literary Licensing, LLC.

Kacher, Larry. Behold I Am A Disciple of Jesus Christ. 2007. 100p. pap. 12.95 (978-1-4327-0110-9(X)) Outskirts Pr., Inc.

Kapp, Ardeth G. Doing What We Came to Do: Living a Life of Love. 2011. 15.99 (978-1-60908-743-2(7)) Deseret Bk. Co.

Kelly, Brian & Kelly, Petrea, compiled by. Illustrated History of the Church. 2008. (Illus.). 617p. (**978-1-59811-669-4(X)**) Covenant Communications.

Kimball, Edward L. Father of a Prophet. 2011. (Illus.). pap. (978-0-8425-2795-8(8), Brigham Young Univ. Studies) Brigham Young Univ.

—Spencer W. Kimball. 2006. 438p. 23.00 (978-1-59038-701-6(5)) Desert Bks.

Kimball, Linda Hoffman. Enriching Ideas: Strengthening Your Sisters through the New Enrichment Program. 2006. per. 10.99 *(978-1-55517-965-6(7))* Cedar Fort, Inc./CFI Distribution.

Kimball, Spencer W., et al. A Prophet's Voice: Inspiring Quotes from Spencer W. Kimball. 2007. 180p. *(978-1-59811-307-5(0))* Covenant Communications.

Kimball, Stanley B. Villages on Wheels: A Social History of the Gathering to Zion. 2011. (ENG.). 354p. pap. 24.95 ***(978-1-58958-119-7(9))*** Kofford, Greg Books, Inc.

King, Larry. The Kings of the Kingdom: The Life of Thomas Rice King & his Family. 2008. 35.00 *(978-0-8425-2710-1(9)*, Brigham Young Univ. Pr.) Brigham Young Univ.

Kinney, Brandon. Mormon War: Zion & the Missouri Extermination Order of 1838. 2011. (Illus.). 288p. 23.00 *(978-1-59416-130-8(5))* Westholme Publishing.

Kirkpatrick, Diane. 52 Weeks of Family Night 2: Scripture Study Edition. 2009. *(978-1-60641-198-8(5))* Deseret Bk. Co.

Koralewski, Brian. Doctrinal Quotes volume I. 2010. 397p. pap. 20.79 *(978-0-557-48100-2(7))* Lulu Enterprises Inc.

—Doctrinal Quotes volume II. 2010. 293p. pap. 16.63 *(978-0-557-52764-9(3))* Lulu Enterprises Inc.

Kuehne, Raymond. Mormons as Citizens of A Communist State: A Documentary History of the Church of Jesus Christ of Latter-day Saints in East Germany, 1945-1990. 2010. (ENG., Illus.). 470p. (gr. 13). pap. 39.95 *(978-0-87480-993-0(2))* Univ. of Utah Pr.

Larry D. Thomas Sr. My People Perish for the Lack of Knowledge: Study to Shew Thyself Approved unto God. 2009. 64p. pap. 9.95 *(978-1-4401-7850-4(X))* iUniverse, Inc.

Larsen, David. How to Remember Everything in the Doctrine & Covenants. 2008. 112p. pap. 10.99 *(978-1-59955-239-2(6))* Cedar Fort, Inc./CFI Distribution.

Larsen, David R. How to Remember Everything in the New Testament & General Conference. 2006. 205p. per. 14.99 *(978-1-55517-997-7(5))* Cedar Fort, Inc./CFI Distribution.

Larsen, Dean L. Mormon Temples. 2008. (Setting the Record Straight Ser.). (Illus.). 81p. per. 9.95 *(978-1-932597-42-4(5))* Millennial Pr., Inc.

The Latter-day Sacrament Speaker's Resource Guide. 2008. 350p. pap. 19.95 *(978-1-59992-092-4(1))* Leatherwood Pr.

Lauritsen, Ed. Mormons under the Microscope. 2010. pap. 15.99 *(978-1-59955-397-9(X))* Cedar Fort, Inc./CFI Distribution.

Leavitt, Dennis H. & Christensen, Richard O. Scripture Study for Latter-Day Saint Families: The Old Testament. 2009. 21.99 *(978-1-60641-141-4(1))* Deseret Bk. Co.

Ledwith, Stuart. John the Baptist; As His Soul Remembers. 2007. 164p. per. 14.95 *(978-0-9627250-1-2(3))* Soul Works International.

Lee, Robert E. I'm Home, Now What? Twenty Missionary Habits to Have a Successful Life. 2008. pap. 8.99 *(978-1-59955-214-9(0))* Cedar Fort, Inc./CFI Distribution.

Lindholm, Philip. Latter-Day Dissent: At the Crossroads of Intellectual Inquiry & Ecclesiastical Authority. Lindholm, Philip, ed. 2011. 272p. 24.95 *(978-1-58958-128-9(8))* Kofford, Greg Books, Inc.

Lingle, Wilbur & Delancy, Robert. 25 Important Questions for Mormons. 2007. (ENG.). 46p. 3.99 *(978-0-87508-539-5(3))* CLC Pubns.

Lisonbee, Dan A. & Lisonbee, Janet. Far West, Missouri: "It Shall Be Called Most Holy" 2010. (Illus.). viii, 186p. 13.99 *(978-1-59955-334-4(1))* Cedar Fort, Inc./CFI Distribution.

Littlefield, Lyman O. The Mormon Martyrs: A Sketch of the Lives & a Full Account of the Martyrdom of the Joseph & Hyrum Smith. 2007. (ENG.). 126p. 35.95 *(978-0-548-04881-8(9))* Kessinger Publishing, LLC.

Lund, Gerald. Hearing the Voice of the Lord. 2007. 448p. 26.99 *(978-1-59038-893-8(3))* Deseret Bk. Co.

Lund, Gerald N. Divine Signatures: The Confirming Hand of God. 2011. audio compact disk 49.99 *(978-1-60641-930-4(7))* 2010. 25.99 *(978-1-60641-927-4(7))* Deseret Bk. Co.

Lyman, Edward Leo. Amasa Mason Lyman, Mormon Apostle & Apostate: A Study in Dedication. 2009. (ENG., Illus.). 666p. 39.95 *(978-0-87480-940-4(1))* Univ. of Utah Pr.

Maffly-Kipp, Laurie F. & Neilson, Reid L., eds. Proclamation to the People: Nineteenth-Century Mormonism & the Pacific Basin Frontier. 2008. (ENG.). 342p. (gr. 15). 29.95 *(978-0-87480-918-3(5))* Univ. of Utah Pr.

Malava, Jenni Rose. Mormons: Tall Tales & Truths. 2011. *(978-1-58982-783-7(X))* American Bk. Publishing Group.

Mangus, Jade Chris. Healing Secrets: Self-Medicating Our Most Important Relationships. 2010. pap. 9.99 *(978-1-59955-318-4(X))* Cedar Fort, Inc./CFI Distribution.

Manning, Jill. What's the Big Deal about Pornography? 2008. 176p. pap. 12.95 *(978-1-59038-853-2(4)*, Shadow Mountain) Deseret Bk. Co.

Manscill, Craig K., et al. The Presidents of the Church. 2008. 29.99 *(978-1-59955-163-0(2))* Cedar Fort, Inc./CFI Distribution.

Mansell, Bill. Yikes! I Have to Talk in Church: How to Prepare & Deliver a Great Sacrament Meeting Talk. 2011. (ENG., Illus.). 184p. pap. 14.95 ***(978-0-9836540-0-1(X))*** MindPerk.

Marquardt, H. Michael, compiled by. Early Patriarchal Blessings of the Church of Jesus Christ of Latter-Day Saints. 2007. 447p. *(978-1-56085-202-5(X)*, Smith Research Assocs.) Signature Bks., LLC.

Mason, Patrick Q. The Mormon Menace: Violence & Anti-Mormonism in the Postbellum South, 1 vol. 2011. (ENG., Illus.). 288p. 29.95 *(978-0-19-974002-4(X))* Oxford Univ. Pr., Inc.

Maxwell, Neal. The Neal A. Maxwell Quote Book, ILLUS Editon. 2009. 448p. 49.99 *(978-1-60641-026-4(1))* Deseret Bk. Co.

—Not My Will, but Thine. 2008. 192p. pap. 12.95 *(978-1-59038-875-4(5))* Deseret Bk. Co.

Maxwell, Neal A. The Promise of Discipleship. 2010. 160p. pap. 13.99 *(978-1-60641-645-7(6))* Deseret Bk. Co.

McConkie, Clay. The Drama & Majesty of the Second Coming. 2010. pap. 12.99 *(978-1-59955-279-8(5))* Cedar Fort, Inc./CFI Distribution.

—The Final Countdown: The Seven Final Events Before the Second Coming. 2007. 103p. per. 10.99 *(978-1-59955-017-6(2))* Cedar Fort, Inc./CFI Distribution.

McConkie, Clay & McConkie, John, illus. A Man Named Peleg: An Exploration into the Days of Peleg. 2007. 139p. per. 13.99 *(978-1-59955-024-4(5))* Cedar Fort, Inc./CFI Distribution.

McElveen, Floyd C. Mormones, Sus Doctrinas y Sus Errores: Will the Saints Go Marching in? (SPA.). 200p. *(978-84-7228-519-4(7)*, 220608) Clie, Editorial.

McInelly, Brett C. Men & the Art of Marriage Maintenance. 2006. (Illus.). 134p. per. 10.99 *(978-0-88290-807-6(3))* Cedar Fort, Inc./CFI Distribution.

McLachlan, James M. & Ericson, Loyd, eds. Discourses in Mormon Theology: Philosophical & Theological Possibilities. 2007. pap. 24.95 *(978-1-58958-104-3(0))* Kofford, Greg Books, Inc.

McLellin, William E. The William E. Mclellin Papers, 1854-1880. Passey, Samuel & Larson, Stan, eds. 2007. (Illus.). 637p. 39.95 *(978-1-56085-144-8(9))* Signature Bks., LLC.

McPheters, Mike. Agent Bishop. 2009. pap. 17.99 *(978-1-59955-317-7(1))* Cedar Fort, Inc./CFI Distribution.

McPhie, Leslie Harston, illus. My First Story of the Latter-Day Prophets. 2010. *(978-1-60641-155-1(1))* Deseret Bk. Co.

Mendenhall, Mark, et al, eds. Joseph & Hyrum — -Leading as One. 2010. (Illus.). 261p. 21.99 *(978-0-8425-2754-5(0)*, Brigham Young Univ. Religious Studies Ctr.) Brigham Young Univ.

Millet, Robert. Beyond the Shadows of Doubt: Building a Testamony That Will Get You through Anything. 2008. 192p. pap. 16.95 *(978-1-59038-919-5(0))* Deseret Bk. Co.

—Grace Works. 2007. 176p. pap. 13.95 *(978-1-59038-760-3(0))* Deseret Bk. Co.

Millet, Robert L. Coming to Know Christ. 2012. 18.99 ***(978-1-60907-013-7(5))*** Deseret Bk. Co.

—Lehi's Dream. 2011. 80p. 24.99 ***(978-1-60641-225-1(6))*** Deseret Bk. Co.

—Making Sense of the Book of Revelation. 2011. 160p. pap. 18.99 *(978-1-60641-944-1(7))* Deseret Bk. Co.

—Men of Valor: The Powerful Impact of a Righteous Man. 2007. vii, 145p. *(978-1-59038-711-5(2))* Deseret Bk. Co.

—Modern Mormonism: Myths & Realities. 2011. 160p. pap. 14.95 *(978-1-58958-127-2(X))* Kofford, Greg Books, Inc.

—Talking with God: Divine Conversations That Transform Daily Life. 2010. 19.99 *(978-1-60641-654-9(5))* Deseret Bk. Co.

—The Vision of Mormonism: Pressing the Boundaries of Christianity. 2007. (Visions of Reality Ser.). (ENG.). 400p. pap. 19.95 *(978-1-55778-868-9(5))* Paragon Hse. Pubs.

—What Happened to the Cross? Distinctive Teachings of the Restoration. 2007. 21.95 *(978-1-59038-789-4(9))* Deseret Bk. Co.

Millet, Robert L., ed. No Weapon Shall Prosper. 2011. (Illus.). 480p. 27.99 *(978-0-8425-2794-1(X)*, Brigham Young Univ. Religious Studies Ctr.) Brigham Young Univ.

Millet, Robert L. & Johnson, Gregory C. V. Bridging the Divide: The Continuing Conversation Between a Mormon & an Evangelical. 2007. (ENG.). 240p. per. 14.95 *(978-0-9766843-6-7(5))* Monkfish Bk. Publishing Co

Millet, Robert L. & McDermott, Gerald R. Evangelicals & Mormons: Exploring the Boundaries. 2010. ***(978-1-57383-449-0(1))*** Regent College Publishing.

Millet, Robert L., et al. Latter-day Doctrines: An Essential Reference. 2011. 23.99 net. *(978-1-60908-059-4(9))* Deseret Bk. Co.

Millet, Robert. Men of Influence: The Potential of the Priesthood to Lift the World. 2009. 144p. 18.95 *(978-1-60641-095-0(4))* Deseret Bk. Co.

Minert, Roger P. Under the Gun. 2011. (Illus.). 430p. 29.99 *(978-0-8425-2798-9(2)*, Brigham Young Univ. Religious Studies Ctr.) Brigham Young Univ.

Monson, Thomas S. Teachings of Thomas S. Monson. 2011. (C). 34.99 ***(978-1-60908-890-3(5))*** Deseret Bk. Co.

Moon, Shawn D. My Roof, My Rules: A Young Adult Guide to Making Smart Decisions. 2009. pap. 14.99 *(978-1-59955-260-6(4))* Cedar Fort, Inc./CFI Distribution.

Moore, Richard G. Know Your Religions, Volume 2: A Comparative Look at Mormonism & the Community of Christ. 2009. (Know Your Religions Ser.). (Illus.). 242p. pap. 14.95 *(978-1-932597-67-7(0))* Millennial Pr., Inc.

Mortensen, Joann Follett. The Man Behind the Discourse: A Biography of King Follett. 2011. 632p. pap. ***(978-1-58958-036-7(2))*** Kofford, Greg Books, Inc.

Mosser, Carl & Sherlock, Richard, eds. The Mormon World. 2012. (Routledge Worlds Ser.). (ENG.). 632p. (C). 240.00 *(978-0-415-61481-8(3))* Routledge.

Mueller, Warren M. Truth Seeker: Straight Talk from the Bible. 2007. (ENG.). 236p. 19.95 *(978-1-58982-402-7(4)*, Millennial Mind Publishing) American Bk. Publishing Group.

Mullins, Larry. Bodyguard to the Prophets. 2010. pap. 10.99 *(978-1-59955-336-8(8))* Cedar Fort, Inc./CFI Distribution.

Murphy, Nancy. Whisperings of the Spirit. 2008. 160p. 16.95 *(978-1-59038-869-3(0))* Deseret Bk. Co.

Musser, Donald W. & Paulsen, David L., eds. Mormonism in Dialogue with Contemporary Christian Theologies. 2008. 562p. 50.00 *(978-0-88146-083-4(4))* Mercer Univ. Pr.

Nadauld, Stephen. Why God Lets Us Choose: How Agency Explains the Way Life Works. 2009. 256p. 23.95 *(978-1-60641-030-1(X))* Deseret Bk. Co.

Neilson, Reid L., ed. Global Mormonism in the Twenty-first Century. 2008. 342p. 32.95 *(978-0-8425-2696-8(X)*, Brigham Young Univ. Religious Studies Ctr.) Brigham Young Univ.

Neilson, Reid L., et al, eds. Regional Studies in Latter-day Saint Church History: The Pacific Isles, 8 Volumes, Vol. 8. 2008. (Illus.). 224p. pap. 14.95 *(978-0-615-20037-8(0))* Religious Studies Center.

Neilson, Reid Larkin. Exhibiting Mormonism: The Latter-Day Saints & the 1893 Chicago World's Fair. 2011. (Religion in America Ser.). (ENG., Illus.). 240p. 29.95 *(978-0-19-538403-1(2))* Oxford Univ. Pr., Inc.

Nelson, Kim. Getting Past If Only. 2010. 36p. pap. 14.99 *(978-1-60641-664-8(2))* Deseret Bk. Co.

Nelson, Kim A. If God Loves Me, Why This? Finding Peace in God's Plan for Us. 2007. 160p. 14.95 *(978-1-59038-715-3(5))* Deseret Bk. Co.

Nelson, Russell M. Wise Men & Women Still Adore Him. 2010. 12p. pap. ***(978-1-60641-835-2(1)***, Wiley-Blackwell) Deseret Bk. Co.

Nelson, Russell Marion. Hope in Our Hearts. 2009. *(978-1-60641-201-5(9))* Deseret Bk. Co.

Nelson, Wendy Watson. Change Your Questions, Change Your Life. 2009. *(978-1-59038-598-2(5))* Deseret Bk. Co.

—Purity & Passion: Spiritual Truths about Intimacy That Will Strengthen Your Marriage. 2009. (Illus.). 193p. *(978-1-59038-410-7(5))* Deseret Bk. Co.

Neville, Dan. Scientific Discoveries That Build Testimonies & Strengthen Faith. 2009. pap. 16.99 *(978-0-88290-965-3(7))* Cedar Fort, Inc./CFI Distribution.

Newell, Lloyd, ed. Let Him Ask of God: Daily Wisdom from the Life & Teachings of Joseph Smith. 2008. (Illus.). 400p. 15.95 *(978-1-60641-001-1(6))* Deseret Bk. Co.

Newell, Lloyd D. Come, Listen to a Prophet's Voice: Daily Counsel & Inspiration from Latter-day Prophets. 2006. 411p. 14.95 *(978-1-59038-621-7(3))* Deseret Bk. Co.

Newell, Lloyd D. Virtue & the Abundant Life. 2012. xv, 341p. pap ***(978-1-60908-064-8(5))*** Deseret Bk. Co.

Newell, Lloyd D. & Staheli, Don H. The Healer's Art: Faith & the Healing Power of Jesus Christ. 2007. 16.95 *(978-1-59038-829-7(1))* Deseret Bk. Co.

Newton, Marjorie. Tiki & Temple: The Mormon Mission in New Zealand, 1854¿1958. 2012. (ENG.). 354p. pap. 29.95 ***(978-1-58958-121-0(0))*** Kofford, Greg Books, Inc.

Nibley, Hugh. Eloquent Witness: Nibley on Himself, Others, & the Temple. 2008. 39.95 *(978-1-60641-003-5(2))* Deseret Bk. Co.

Nibley, Hugh, et al. One Eternal Round. 2010. *(978-1-60641-237-4(X))* Deseret Bk. Co.

Nowak, Jennifer. Families. 2006. (Rosen Real Readers Big Bookstm Ser.). (ENG.). 8p. (gr. k-1). 29.95 *(978-1-4042-6212-6(1))* Rosen Publishing Group, Inc., The.

Nuttall, L. John. In the President's Office: The Diaries of L. John Nuttall, 1879-1892. Rogers, Jedediah S., ed. 2007. (Significant Mormon Diaries). 511p. *(978-1-56085-196-7(1))* Signature Bks., LLC.

Oaks, Kristen. A Single Voice. 2008. 224p. pap. 17.95 *(978-1-59038-859-4(3))* Deseret Bk. Co.

Ogden, D. Kelly & Skinner, Andrew C. Verse by Verse, Acts Through Revelation. 2006. (Illus.). ix, 422p. 24.99 *(978-1-59038-590-6(X))* Deseret Bk. Co.

—Verse by Verse, the Four Gospels. 2006. (Illus.). viii, 856p. *(978-1-59038-583-8(7))* Deseret Bk. Co.

Olsen, Andrew D. The Price We Paid: The Extraordinary Story of the Willie & Martin Handcart Pioneers. 2006. (Illus.). 480p. 23.95 *(978-1-59038-624-8(8))* Deseret Bk. Co.

Olson, Camille Fronk. Giver of Life: Lessons from Eve. 2010. 14p. *(978-1-60641-764-5(9))* Deseret Bk. Co.

Organized for A Mission: A Guide for Parents & Missionaries. 2008. (Illus.). 225p. pap. 9.45 *(978-0-9788579-3-6(3))* Ricks, Marie.

Ostler, Blake T. Exploring Mormon Thought: The Attributes of God. 2008. 536p. lthr. 159.95 *(978-1-58958-002-2(8))* Kofford, Greg Books, Inc.

Ostling, Richard & Ostling, Joan K. Mormon America: The Power & the Promise. rev. ed. 2007. (ENG., Illus.). 496p. pap. 17.99 *(978-0-06-143295-8(4)*, HarperOne) HarperCollins Pubs.

Oswald, Lowell K. & Waterbury, John. Becometh As a Child: A Guide to Healing Emotionally, Growing Spiritually, & Experiencing a Change of Heart. 2009. 14.99 *(978-1-59955-331-3(7))* Cedar Fort, Inc./CFI Distribution.

Otten, L. G. & Caldwell, C. M. Sacred Truths of the Book of Mormon, 2 vols. 2007. (Illus.). *(978-1-59811-082-1(9))*; *(978-1-59811-083-8(7))* Covenant Communications.

Packer, Boyd K. The Earth Shall Teach Thee. 2011. (Illus.). 200p. ***(978-0-8425-2806-1(7)***, Brigham Young Univ. Religious Studies Ctr.) Brigham Young Univ.

—The Holy Temple. 2007. 39.95 *(978-1-59038-801-3(1))* Deseret Bk. Co.

—Let Not Your heart Be Troubled. 2010. 320p. pap. 17.99 *(978-1-60641-822-2(X))* Deseret Bk. Co.

—Mine Errand from the Lord: Quotations & Teachings from Boyd K. Packer. 2008. (Illus.). xxiii, 632p. 34.95 *(978-1-60641-023-3(7))* Deseret Bk. Co.

—That All May Be Edified: Blueprints for Building Spirituality. 2006. 368p. pap. 16.95 *(978-1-59038-666-8(3))* Deseret Bk. Co.

Packer, Rand H. A Lion & a Lamb: The true story of a young couple's 24-year mission to return the LDS church to its Birthplace. 2007. 194p. pap. 14.95 *(978-1-932898-73-6(5))* Spring Creek Bk. Co.

Packham, E. Richard. Enabled by the Power of Christ. 2008. pap. 12.99 *(978-1-59955-227-9(2))* Cedar Fort, Inc./CFI Distribution.

Page, Kenneth M. A Father's Blessing: The Power & Privilege of the Priesthood. 2008. vii, 119p. *(978-1-59811-650-2(9))* Covenant Communications.

Palmer, Alison. Sharing Through Primary Songs: I'll Follow Him in Faith. 2006. cd-rom 9.99 *(978-0-88290-815-1(4)*, Cedar Fort, Inc.) Cedar Fort, Inc./CFI Distribution.

Parry. Understanding the Signs of the Times. 2008. 576p. pap. 21.95 *(978-1-59038-999-7(9))* Deseret Bk. Co.

Parry, Donald & Parry, Jay A. Symbols & Shadows: Unlocking a Deeper Understanding of the Atonement. 2009. 29.95 *(978-1-60641-129-2(2))* Deseret Bk. Co.

Parry, Edwin F. Sketches of Missionary Life. 2007. (ENG.). 144p. 35.95 *(978-0-548-08684-1(2))* Kessinger Publishing, LLC.

Parry, Edwin F., ed. Joseph Smith's Teachings: A Classified Arrangement of the Doctrinal Sermons & Writings of the Great Mormon Latter Day Prophet. 2007. (ENG.). 192p. 37.95 *(978-0-548-04879-5(7))* Kessinger Publishing, LLC.

Parry, Jay. Vital Signs, 13 Prophetic Clues You Can't Afford to Miss. 2009. 176p. 19.95 *(978-1-60641-147-6(0))* Deseret Bk. Co.

Parry, Jay & Parry, Donald. Understanding the BK of Revelation. 2007. 368p. pap. 16.95 *(978-1-59038-762-7(7))* Deseret Bk. Co.

Parry, Jay A. Understanding the Parables of Jesus Christ. 2010. 320p. pap. 18.99 *(978-1-60641-900-7(5))* Deseret Bk. Co.

Parry, Jay A. & Parry, Donald W. Understanding the Parables of Jesus Christ. 2006. 320p. 21.95 *(978-1-59038-626-2(4))* Deseret Bk. Co.

Pearce, Virginia Hinckley. Through His Eyes: Rethinking what you Believe About Yourself. 2011. 160p. 19.99 *(978-1-60641-242-8(6))* Deseret Bk. Co.

Pearson, Carol Lynn. No More Goodbyes: Circling the Wagons Around Our Gay Loved Ones. annot. ed. 2007. 288p. per. 14.95 *(978-0-9638852-4-1(3))* Pivot Point Bks.

Perry, L. Tom. Family Ties: A Message for Fathers. 2011. 15.99 *(978-1-60908-768-5(2))* Deseret Bk. Co.

Peterson, H. Donl. Moroni: Ancient Prophet, Modern Messenger. 2008. 211p. pap. 14.99 *(978-1-59955-141-8(1))* Cedar Fort, Inc./CFI Distribution.

Peterson, Janet & Gaunt, LaRene. Faith, Hope, & Charity: Inspiration from the Lives of General Relief Society Presidents. 2008. 313p. *(978-1-59811-520-8(0)*, Debolsillo) Covenant Communications, Inc.

Pinegar, Ed J. & Allen, Richard J. Rejoice in Christ: Daily Inspiration from the Book of Mormon. 2007. vi, 393p. pap. *(978-1-59811-454-6(9))* Covenant Communications.

A Plea for Polygamy: Church of Jesus Christ of Latter Day Saints. 2007. (ENG.). 266p. 42.95 *(978-0-548-05343-0(X))* Kessinger Publishing, LLC.

Poelman, Anne Os. The Simeon Solution. 2008. 160p. pap. 14.95 *(978-1-59038-888-4(7))* Deseret Bk. Co.

Pratt, Parley P. The Autobiography of Parley P. Pratt. 2007. im. lthr. 29.95 *(978-1-59038-817-4(8))* Deseret Bk. Co.

—Spirituality: The Key to the Science of Theology. 2008. pap. 12.99 *(978-1-59955-116-6(0))* Cedar Fort, Inc./CFI Distribution.

Price, Lynn F. One in Thine Hand: The Stick of Judah & the Stick of Joseph. 2007. 365p. per. 21.99 *(978-0-88290-816-8(2))* Cedar Fort, Inc./CFI Distribution.

Rasmussen, Vicki Lynn. Head Start with the Book of Mormon: Using the Scriptures to Teach Children Reading & Writing Skills. 2007. 129p. per. 12.99 *(978-1-59955-067-1(9))* Cedar Fort, Inc./CFI Distribution.

Read, David. The Inspired Constitution: Answers to the Big Questions- What Every Latter-Day Saint Should. 2011. 400p. pap. 21.99 *(978-1-60641-945-8(5))* Deseret Bk. Co.

Read, Teena. The ABC's of Being LDS: Living the "Mormon" Lifestyle. 2008. pap. 12.99 *(978-1-59955-220-0(5))* Cedar Fort, Inc./CFI Distribution.

Rees, Robert A. Why I Stay: The Challenges of Discipleship for Contemporary Mormons. 2011. ***(978-1-56085-213-1(5))*** Signature Bks., LLC.

Reeve, W. Paul & Parshall, Ardis E. Mormonism: A Historical Encyclopedia. 2010. (Illus.). xxviii, 449p. E-Book *(978-1-59884-108-4(4))* ABC-CLIO, LLC.

Reeve, W. Paul & Parshall, Ardis E., eds. Mormonism: A Historical Encyclopedia, 1 vol. 2010. (Illus.). 449p. 85.00 *(978-1-59884-107-7(6)*, MORMON1C) ABC-CLIO, LLC.

Reiser, A. Hamer & Merkley, Marion G. What It Means to Be a Latter-Day Saint. 2011. 150p. 40.95 ***(978-1-258-05870-8(7))*** Literary Licensing, LLC.

Rhodes, Michael D. & Moody, J. Ward, eds. Converging Paths to Truth. 2011. (Illus.). 176p. 19.99 *(978-0-8425-2786-6(9)*, Brigham Young Univ. Religious Studies Ctr.) Brigham Young Univ.

Rich, Wendell O. Distinctive Teachings of the Restoration. 2011. 224p. 44.95 ***(978-1-258-10281-4(1))*** Literary Licensing, LLC.

Richardson, Marianna. Alfred Edersheim: Prophecies Fulfilled. 2008. pap. 14.99 *(978-1-59955-112-8(8))* Cedar Fort, Inc./CFI Distribution.

Ridges, David J. Jeremiah Made Easier. 2010. 208p. pap. 19.99 *(978-1-59955-400-6(3))* Cedar Fort, Inc./CFI Distribution.

—Our Savior, Jesus Christ: His Life & Mission to Cleanse & Heal. 2008. 26.99 *(978-1-59955-172-2(1))* Cedar Fort, Inc./CFI Distribution.

—The Pearl of Great Price Made Easier. 2009. pap. 18.99 *(978-1-59955-344-3(9))* Cedar Fort, Inc./CFI Distribution.

—Your Study of Isaiah Made Easier: In the Bible & Book of Mormon. 2nd ed. 2009. (Gospel Studies). 276p. pap. 17.99 *(978-1-59955-388-7(0))* Cedar Fort, Inc./CFI Distribution.

C

—65 Signs of the Times: Leading up to the Second Coming. 2009. pap. 14.99 *(978-1-59955-366-5(X))* Cedar Fort, Inc./CFI Distribution.
Rife, Richard C. The Divine Virtues: 14 Values to Live By. 2010. pap. 12.99 *(978-1-59955-390-0(2))* Cedar Fort, Inc./CFI Distribution.
Rise to the Divinity Within You: Talks from the 2006 BYU Women's Conference. 2007. vii, 260p. *(978-1-59038-712-2(0))* Deseret Bk. Co.
Riskas, Thomas. Deconstructing Mormonism: An Analysis & Assessment of the Mormon Faith. 2011. 784p. mass mkt. 29.95 *(978-1-57884-007-6(4))* American Atheist Pr.
Robbins, Bill. The Latter Days at the Time of the End. 2008. 230p. pap. 16.95 *(978-0-7414-4476-9(3))* Infinity Publishing.
Robbins, Edward E. & Robbins, Flora J. Moonshiner Goes West. 2011. *(978-1-58982-806-3(2),* Millennial Mind Publishing) American Bk. Publishing Group.
Robertson, Judy. Out of Mormonism: A Woman's True Story. rev. ed. 2011. pap. 14.99 *(978-0-7642-0901-7(9))* Bethany Hse. Pubs.
Robinson, Jodi Marie. Women of Virtue. 2009. pap. 12.99 *(978-1-59955-255-2(8))* Cedar Fort, Inc./CFI Distribution.
Robison, Dustin. Money after the Mission. 2009. pap. 12.99 *(978-1-59955-232-3(9))* Cedar Fort, Inc./CFI Distribution.
Romney, Park. The Apostasy of a High Priest: The Sociology of an American Cult. 2011. pap. 13.95 ***(978-0-7414-6294-7(X))*** Infinity Publishing.
Rose Publishing Staff. Mormanism: Key Beliefs, Practices, & History. 2006. 12p. 3.99 *(978-1-59636-117-1(4))* Rose Publishing.
Rose, Tom G. Proof: How to Know the Book of Mormon Is True. 2011. 144p. pap. 9.99 ***(978-1-59955-889-9(0))*** Cedar Fort, Inc./CFI Distribution.
Rowley, Derek G. By Man Least Understood: Repentance, Agency, Restoration, Atonement & the Everlasting Covenant. 2007. 131p. per. 12.99 *(978-1-55517-940-3(1))* Cedar Fort, Inc./CFI Distribution.
Scantlebury, Michael. I Will Build My Church - Jesus Christ. 2010. 388p. pap. *(978-1-926676-80-7(7))* Word Alive Pr.
Scott, Joe. God Is Chicago: A Missionary's Journal. 2010. pap. 9.99 *(978-1-61566-011-7(9))* Tate Publishing & Enterprises, LLC.
Scott, Latayne C. & Scott, Latayne. The Mormon Mirage: A Former Member Looks at the Mormon Church Today, 1 vol. 3rd ed. 2009. (ENG.). 272p. pap. 16.99 *(978-0-310-29153-4(4))* Zondervan.
Setzer, Lee Ann. I'll Follow Him in Faith, Vol. 7. 2006. (Tiny Talks Ser.). (Illus.). 76p. (J). per. 7.99 *(978-1-55517-922-9(3))* Cedar Fort, Inc./CFI Distribution.
Shaffer, Kimberly S. The Ready Resource for Relief Society: Joseph Smith. 2008. 154p. pap. 12.99 *(978-1-59955-258-3(2))* Cedar Fort, Inc./CFI Distribution.
Shaffer, Kimberly S., compiled by. The Ready Resource for Relief Society, Volume Two: Teachings of Presidents of the Church: Spencer W Kimball. 2006. 142p. per. 11.99 *(978-1-55517-981-6(9),* Cedar Fort, Inc.) Cedar Fort, Inc./CFI Distribution.
Shields, Mark A. Gospel Symbols: Finding the Creator in Creation. 2010. pap. 12.99 *(978-1-59955-269-9(8))* Cedar Fort, Inc./CFI Distribution.
—Your Endowment. 2009. 144p. pap. 11.99 *(978-1-59955-287-3(6))* Cedar Fort, Inc./CFI Distribution.
Shuster, Eric. Catholic Roots, Mormon Harvest. 2009. pap. 17.99 *(978-1-59955-257-6(4))* Cedar Fort, Inc./CFI Distribution.
Shuster, Eric & Sale, Charles. The Biblical Roots of Mormonism. 2010. 288p. pap. 17.99 *(978-1-59955-406-8(2))* Cedar Fort, Inc./CFI Distribution.
Skinner, Andrew. A Bible Fit for the Restoration: The Epic Struggle that Brought Us the King James Version. 2011. 128p. pap. 9.99 ***(978-1-59955-908-7(0))*** Cedar Fort, Inc./CFI Distribution.
Skinner, Andrew C. Bountiful Harvest. Davis, D., ed. 2012. (ENG., Illus.). 482p. 39.95 ***(978-0-8425-2804-7(0))*** Brigham Young Univ.
Skinner, Andrew C. & Strathearn, Gaye, eds. Third Nephi: An Incomparable Scripture. 2011. (C). 34.99 ***(978-1-60908-907-8(3))*** Deseret Bk. Co.
Skinner, Andrew C., et al. Parables of Redemption: The Restored Doctrine of the Atonement as Taught in the Parables of Jesus Christ. 2007. 104p. per. 9.99 *(978-0-88290-834-2(0))* Cedar Fort, Inc./CFI Distribution.
Smith, David E. Mormons & Evangelicals: Reasons for Faith. 2009. *(978-1-60724-027-3(0))* Gorgias Pr., LLC.
Smith, Joseph. The Doctrine & Covenants of the Church of Jesus Christ of Latter-Day Saints. 2009. (Amer Philosophy, Religion Ser.). (ENG.). 548p. pap. 31.95 *(978-1-4290-1796-1(1))* Applewood Bks.
—El Libro de Mormon. Trejo, Meliton G. & Stewart, James Z., trs. 2008. 532p. pap. 24.95 *(978-1-60135-658-7(6))* AMWAAW LLC.
—Parallel Book of Mormon: The 1830, 1837, & 1840 Editions. 2008. *(978-1-56085-203-2(8),* Smith Research Assocs.) Signature Bks., LLC.
—The Parallel Doctrine & Covenants: The 1832-1833, 1833, & 1835 Editions of Joseph Smith's Revelations. 2009. *(978-1-56085-205-6(4),* Smith Research Assocs.) Signature Bks., LLC.
Smith, Joseph & Redd, Sterling H. Topical Quotes of the Prophet Joseph Smith. 2007. pap. 21.99 *(978-0-88290-830-4(8))* Cedar Fort, Inc./CFI Distribution.
Smith, Joseph, et al. Manuscript Revelation Books. 2011. (Illus.). xiii, 529p. 79.95 *(978-1-60641-909-0(9))* Deseret Bk. Co.
—Revelations & Translations. 2009. (Joseph Smith Papers: Vol. 1). 99.95 *(978-1-57008-850-6(0),* Bookcraft, Inc.) Deseret Bk. Co.
Smith, Joseph Fielding. Essentials in Church History: A History of the Church of Jesus Christ of Latter Day Saints from the Birth of Joseph Smith to the Present Time 1922. 2007. (ENG.). 702p. 65.95 *(978-0-548-04871-9(1))* Kessinger Publishing, LLC.
Spears, Dale. Secrets of the Prophets. 2009. pap. 12.99 *(978-1-59955-283-5(3))* Cedar Fort, Inc./CFI Distribution.
Sperry, Kip. A Guide to Mormon Family History Sources. 2007. (Illus.). 231p. per. 16.95 *(978-1-59331-301-2(2))* Turner Publishing Co.
Spiritual Matters: Wisdom & Inspiration from the BK of Mormon. 2008. 168p. pap. 11.95 *(978-1-59992-080-1(8))* Leatherwood Pr.
Staheli, Don H. & Newell, Lloyd D. The Healer's Art: Reflections on the Healing Power of Jesus Christ. 2006. (Illus.). xvi, 109p. 16.95 *(978-1-59038-620-0(5))* Deseret Bk. Co.
Stainback, Lily. Teaching Christ-Like Virtues in the Home. 2008. pap. 12.99 *(978-0-88290-844-1(8))* Cedar Fort, Inc./CFI Distribution.
Staker, Mark Lyman. Hearken, O Ye People: The Historical Setting of Joseph Smith's Ohio Revelations. 2008. 34.95 *(978-1-58958-113-5(X))* Kofford, Greg Books, Inc.
Stansfield, Anita. Of Infinite Worth. 2007. 25p. *(978-1-59811-344-0(5))* Covenant Communications.
Stenhouse, Fanny. Expose of Polygamy: A Lady's Life among the Mormons. DeSimone, Linda Wilcox, ed. 2008. (Life Writings of Frontier Women Ser.). (ENG., Illus.). 200p. 29.95 *(978-0-87421-713-1(X),* Utah State Univ. Pr.) Univ. Pr. of Colorado.
Stephan, Eric G. & Pace, R. Wayne. To Lead as Jesus Led. 2006. 105p. per. 11.99 *(978-1-55517-993-9(2))* Cedar Fort, Inc./CFI Distribution.
Stevens, Grant L. & Stevens, Richard. Remembering Kirtland. 2008. (Illus.). 111p. *(978-1-59811-583-3(9))* Covenant Communications.
Stewart, Chris. Missionary Miracles: Stories & Letters from the Field. 2008. pap. 12.95 *(978-1-59038-749-8(X))* Deseret Bk. Co.
—Redefining Joy in the Last Days. 2009. 64p. 9.95 *(978-1-60641-035-6(0))* Deseret Bk. Co.
Stewart, David Grant, Jr. The Law of the Harvest: Practical Principles of Effective Missionary Work, 0. 2007. 460p. per. 19.95 *(978-0-9795121-0-0(7))* Cumorah Foundation.
Stitt, David. Resisting Temptation. 2007. pap. 10.99 *(978-1-59955-080-0(6))* Cedar Fort, Inc./CFI Distribution.
Sullivan, Marlene Bateman. Brigham's Boys. 2009. pap. 13.99 *(978-1-59955-124-1(1))* Cedar Fort, Inc./CFI Distribution.
Sweat, Anthony. I'm Not Perfect, Can I Still Go to Heaven? Finding Hope for the Celestial Kingdom Through the Atonement of Christ. 2010. *(978-1-60641-231-2(0))* Deseret Bk. Co.
—Mormons: An Open Book. 2012. pap. 16.99 *(978-1-60908-811-8(5),* Ensign Peak) Deseret Bk. Co.
Swinton, Heidi. To the Rescue: The Biography of Thomas S. Monson. 2010. 608p. 34.99 *(978-1-60641-898-7(X))* Deseret Bk. Co.
Swinton, Heidi S. Al Rescate: La Biografia de Thomas S. Monson. 2012. (SPA.). 22.99 ***(978-1-60907-001-4(1))*** Deseret Bk. Co.
Syed, Hasanat Ahmad. The Second Coming of Jesus Christ. 2009. 132p. pap. 13.95 *(978-1-4401-3210-0(0))* iUniverse, Inc.
Tanner, John S. Notes from an Amateur. 2011. (Illus.). 144p. 24.99 ***(978-0-8425-2801-6(6),*** Brigham Young Univ. Religious Studies Ctr.) Brigham Young Univ.
Taylor, Gary G. RX for Emotional Headaches. 2007. pap. 12.99 *(978-1-59955-066-4(0))* Cedar Fort, Inc./CFI Distribution.
Taysom, Stephen C. Dimensions of Faith: A Mormon Studies Reader. 2011. ***(978-1-56085-212-4(7))*** Signature Bks., LLC.
Taysom, Stephen C. Shakers, Mormons, & Religious Worlds: Conflicting Visions, Contested Boundaries. 2010. (Religion in North America Ser.). (ENG.). 280p. 34.95 *(978-0-253-35540-9(0),* 0253355400) Indiana Univ. Pr.
TICE. Inside the Mormon Mind: The Social Psychology of Mormonism ASHFORD UNIVERSITY. 2009. (ENG.). (C). pap. 23.60 *(978-0-558-09781-3(2))* Pearson Learning Solutions.
Tietjen, Gail Jennings. How to Survive Your Child's Mission: A Parent's Perspective. 2009. pap. 8.99 *(978-1-59955-295-8(7))* Cedar Fort, Inc./CFI Distribution.
Tingey, Earl. Old Testament Prophecies of Jesus Christ. 2012. xi, 164p. (C). pap. 19.99 ***(978-1-60908-894-1(8))*** Deseret Bk. Co.
Top, Brent. When You Can't Do It Alone. 2008. 160p. 17.95 *(978-1-59038-958-4(1))* Deseret Bk. Co.
Top, Brent L. What's on the Other Side? What the Gospel Teaches Us about the Spirit World. 2012. 15.99 ***(978-1-60907-046-5(1))*** Deseret Bk. Co.
Topping, Gary. Leonard J. Arrington: A Historian's Life. 2008. (ENG., Illus.). 256p. (C). 39.95 *(978-0-87062-363-9(X),* Clark, Arthur H. Co., The) Univ. of Oklahoma Pr.
Toscano, Paul James. The Sacrament of Doubt. 2007. 168p. 21.95 *(978-1-56085-146-2(5))* Signature Bks., LLC.
Trepanier, Lee & Newswander, Lynita K. LDS in the USA: Mormonism & the Making of American Culture. 2012. (ENG.). 176p. pap. 24.95 ***(978-1-60258-327-6(7))*** Baylor Univ. Pr.
Turley, Richard E., Jr. & Harper, Steven C., eds. Preserving the History of the Latter-day Saints. 2010. (Illus.). 288p. 21.99 *(978-0-8425-2777-4(X))* Brigham Young Univ.
Uchtdorf, Dieter F. Your Happily Ever After. 2011. (Illus.). 64p. 14.99 ***(978-1-60641-652-5(9))*** Deseret Bk. Co.
Ulrich, Wendy. Forgiving Ourselves. 2008. 272p. pap. 16.95 *(978-1-59038-857-0(7))* Deseret Bk. Co.
—Weakness Is Not Sin: The Liberating Distinction That Awakens Our Strengths. 2009. 15.95 *(978-1-60641-139-1(X))* Deseret Bk. Co.
Urick, Steve. The Church in the Coming Great Tribulation: A Biblical Defense of the Posttribulational Rapture & the Second Coming of Jesus Christ. 2009. 116p. pap. 13.99 *(978-1-4389-4021-2(1))* AuthorHouse.
Ustach, Janene E. Walking into a Hug. 2009. pap. 11.99 *(978-1-59955-225-5(6))* Cedar Fort, Inc./CFI Distribution.
Van Dyke, Katie. Unlikely Truths of Motherhood. 2009. 9.99 *(978-1-59955-289-7(2))* Cedar Fort, Inc./CFI Distribution.
Vandagriff, David P. I Need Thee Every Hour: Applying the Atonement in Everyday Life. 2010. 180p. *(978-1-59811-910-7(9))* Covenant Communications.
Vandagriff, G. G., et al. Deliverance from Depression: Finding Hope & Healing Through the Atonement of Christ. 2008. 100p. *(978-1-59811-648-9(7),* Debolsillo) Covenant Communications, Inc.
Vermeeren, Douglas J. Testimony: Carefully Obtained & Carefully Maintained. 2006. 66p. per. 7.99 *(978-1-55517-996-0(7))* Cedar Fort, Inc./CFI Distribution.
Walker, Kyle R. The Joseph Sr. & Lucy Mack Smith Family: A Family Process Analysis of a Nineteenth Century Household. 2008. (Illus.). *(978-0-8425-2714-9(1),* Brigham Young Univ. Pr.) Brigham Young Univ.
Walker, Ronald W., et al. Mormon History. 2010. (ENG.). 296p. pap. 25.00 *(978-0-252-07773-9(3))* Univ. of Illinois Pr.
Walton, Rick. Much Ado about Mormons. 2011. (Illus.). 221p. ***(978-1-60861-076-1(4))*** Covenant Communications.
Wayment, Thomas A. The Greatest Teacher. 2008. *(978-1-59038-956-0(5))* Deseret Bk. Co.
—To Teach As Jesus Taught: 11 Attributes of a Master Teacher. 2009. pap. 12.99 *(978-1-59955-285-9(X))* Cedar Fort, Inc./CFI Distribution.
Welch, John W. & Parry, Donald W., eds. Tree of Life: From Eden to Eternity. 2011. 23.99 *(978-1-60908-674-9(0))* Deseret Bk. Co.
Weston, Joseph Harry. Mormons Are Different! 2011. 228p. 46.95 ***(978-1-258-07783-2(8))*** Literary Licensing, LLC.
White, James. Letters to a Mormon Elder. 2007. 308p. per. 20.00 *(978-1-59925-119-6(1))* Solid Ground Christian Bks.
White, James R. Is the Mormon My Brother? 2008. 268p. pap. 20.00 *(978-1-59925-120-2(5))* Solid Ground Christian Bks.
Whitefield, Jim. The Mormon Delusion: The Secret Truth Withheld from 13 Million Mormons, 3 vols., Vol. 2. 2009. 423p. (Illus.). 54.50 *(978-1-4092-8072-9(1));* pap. 34.95 *(978-1-4092-7885-6(9))* Lulu Enterprises Inc.
Whiting, Camille Call. For They Shall Be Comforted: Grieving the Loss of a Child. 2009. 100p. pap. *(978-1-59811-724-0(6),* Debolsillo) Covenant Communications, Inc.
Whittaker, David J., ed. Colonel Thomas L. Kane & the Mormons, 1846-1883. 2010. (ENG., Illus.). 224p. pap. 19.95 *(978-0-8425-2756-9(7),* Brigham Young Univ. Studies) Brigham Young Univ.
Whittaker, David J. & Garr, Arnold K., eds. A Firm Foundation. 2011. (Illus.). 760p. 29.99 *(978-0-8425-2785-9(0),* Brigham Young Univ. Religious Studies Ctr.) Brigham Young Univ.
Widtsoe, Osborne J. P. What Jesus Taught: A Mormon Perspective. 2007. (ENG.). 338p. 46.95 *(978-0-548-04866-5(5))* Kessinger Publishing, LLC.
Wilcox. Who Shall Be Able To Stand? Finding Personal Meaningin the Book of Revelation. 2011. 352p. 19.99 *(978-1-60908-700-5(3))* Deseret Bk. Co.
Wilcox, Brad. The Continuous Atonement. 2009. 224p. 21.95 *(978-1-60641-037-0(7))* Deseret Bk. Co.
Wilcox, S. Michael. Of These Emblems. 2010. ix, 102p. ***(978-1-59811-706-6(8))*** Covenant Communications.
—Sunset: On the Passing of Those We Love. 2011. 135p. 16.99 *(978-1-60908-834-7(4))* Deseret Bk. Co.
—Walking on Water & Other Classic Talks. 2011. 245p. (C). 22.99 *(978-1-60908-362-5(8))* Deseret Bk. Co.
—What the Scriptures Teach Us about Adversity. 2010. 19.99 *(978-1-60641-811-6(4))* Deseret Bk. Co.
—What the Scriptures Teach Us about Raising a Child. 2009. 18.95 *(978-1-60641-130-8(6))* Deseret Bk. Co.
Wilde, Bradley R. The Liahona Principle: Finding Direction in the Word of God. 2006. 120p. per. 9.99 *(978-1-55517-932-8(0))* Cedar Fort, Inc./CFI Distribution.
Wille, Gregory R. Now, What Do You Believe? 2008. 109p. pap. 10.99 *(978-0-88290-840-3(5))* Cedar Fort, Inc./CFI Distribution.
Willes, Laura F. Christmas with the Prophets. 2010. 21.99 *(978-1-60641-828-4(9))* Deseret Bk. Co.
Winder, Michael Kent. Presidents & Prophets: The Story of America's Presidents & the LDS Church. 2007. (Illus.). 428p. *(978-1-59811-452-2(2))* Covenant Communications.
Woodger, Mary Jane, ed. John Taylor: Champion of Liberty. 2009. (Illus.). 384p. *(978-0-8425-2736-1(2),* Brigham Young Univ. Religious Studies Ctr.) Brigham Young Univ.
Woodger, Mary Jane, et al, eds. Latter-Day Saint Courtship Patterns. 2007. (Studies in Religion & the Social Order). (ENG., Illus.). 242p. per. 40.99 *(978-0-7618-3854-8(6))* Univ. Pr. of America, Inc.
Wright, Randal A. Achieving Your Life Mission. 2009. pap. 14.99 *(978-1-59955-348-1(1))* Cedar Fort, Inc./CFI Distribution.
Zollinger, Ronald R. Mere Mormonism: Defense of Mormon Theology. 2009. 17.99 *(978-1-59955-264-4(7))* Cedar Fort, Inc./CFI Distribution.
The 2007 BYU Religious Education Student Symposium. 2007. 200p. pap. 10.95 *(978-0-8425-2685-2(4),* Brigham Young Univ. Religious Studies Ctr.) Brigham Young Univ.

CHURCH OF SCOTLAND

see also Covenanters; Presbyterian Church; Presbyterianism

Blyth, James G. S. One Man's Pilgrimage. 2010. 208p. pap. 17.69 *(978-1-4251-7029-5(3))* Trafford Publishing.
Bonar, Andrew A. The Biography of Robert Murray M'Cheyne. 2008. 220p. 24.99 *(978-0-554-34548-2(X))* 2008. 220p. 27.99 *(978-0-554-25245-2(7))* 2007. (ENG.). 190p. pap. 19.99 *(978-1-4264-8542-8(5))* 2007. 216p. pap. 22.99 *(978-1-4264-8599-2(9))* BiblioBazaar.
Bonar, Horatius. Christ Is All: The Piety of Horatius Bonar. 2008. (Illus.). per. *(978-1-60178-033-1(8))* Reformation Heritage Bks.
Bruce, Alexander Hugh. An Historical Account of the Rise & Development of Presbyterianism in Scotland. 2011. (ENG.). 180p. pap. 19.99 *(978-1-107-40193-8(3))* Cambridge Univ. Pr.
Calderwood, David. The True History of the Church of Scotland: From the Beginnings of the Reform to the End of the Reign of King James VI, 8 vols. Thomson, Thomas, ed. reprint ed. *(978-0-404-19894-7(5))* AMS Pr., Inc.
Carlyle, Alexander. Autobiography of the Rev Dr Alexander Carlyle, Minister of Inveresk; Containing Memorials of the Men & Events of His Time. 2006. 480p. per. 29.99 *(978-1-4255-5342-5(7))* MPublishing.
Carson, Alexander. Reply to Mr Browns Vindication of the Pr. 2006. 456p. per. 42.00 *(978-1-57978-845-2(9))* Baptist Standard Bearer, Inc.
Donaldson. The Scottish Reformation. 2008. (ENG.). 252p. pap. 34.99 *(978-0-521-07284-7(0))* Cambridge Univ. Pr.
Donaldson, David. The Scottish Parish System - Seen As Incarnational. 2009. 108p. pap. *(978-3-639-16623-1(X))* VDM Verlag Dr. Mueller e.K.
Duncan, Graham. Partnership in Mission: A Critical Historical Evaluation of the Relationship between 'older' & younger' Churches with Special Reference to the Church of Scotland. 2008. 284p. pap. *(978-3-639-08865-6(4))* VDM Verlag Dr. Mueller e.K.
Fisher, James. The Westminster Assembly's Shorter Catechism Explained, by Way of Question & Answer. 2006. 484p. per. 29.99 *(978-1-4255-5384-5(2))* MPublishing.
Hardage, Jeanette. Mary Slessor - Everybody's Mother: The Era & Impact of a Victorian Missionary. 2010. (ENG., Illus.). 369p. pap. 43.00 *(978-0-7188-9185-5(6))* Lutterworth Pr., The GBR. Dist: Brown, David Bk. Co., The.
—Mary Slessor-Everybody's Mother: The Era & Impact of a Victorian Missionary. 2008. (Illus.). 382p. pap. 39.00 *(978-1-55635-601-8(3))* Wipf & Stock Pubs.
Hetherington, William Maxwell. History of the Church of Scotland from the Introduction of Christianity to the Period of the Disruption In 1843. 2006. 508p. per. 29.99 *(978-1-4255-5643-3(4))* MPublishing.
Keddie, John. George Smeaton: Victorian Theologian & Biblical Scholar. 2007. (Illus.). 214p. per. *(978-0-85234-636-5(0))* Evangelical Pr.
Knox, John. The Liturgy of John Knox: Received by the Church of Scotland in 1564. 2008. 248p. pap. 21.00 *(978-1-60608-305-5(8))* Wipf & Stock Pubs.
Livingstone, W. P. Mary Slessor of Calabar: Pioneer Missionary. 2007. (ENG.). 400p. pap. 25.99 *(978-1-4264-3290-3(9));* 430p. pap. 28.99 *(978-1-4264-3345-0(X))* BiblioBazaar.
Mccallum, John. Reforming the Scottish Parish: The Reformation in Fife, 1560-1640. 2010. (St Andrews Studies in Reformation History Ser.). (Illus.). 286p. 124.95 *(978-0-7546-6910-4(6))* Ashgate Publishing Co.
McKay, Johnston. The Kirk & the Kingdom. 2011. (ENG.). 144p. (gr. 17). 75.00 ***(978-0-7486-4473-5(3))*** Edinburgh Univ. Pr. GBR. Dist: Columbia Univ. Pr.
Melville, James. Diary of Mr. James Melville, 1556-1601. (Bannatyne Club, Edinburgh Publications: No. 34). reprint ed. 32.50 *(978-0-404-52740-2(X))* AMS Pr., Inc.
Office for Worship & Doctrine, compiled by. Pray Now: Daily Devotions for the Year 2008. 2007. (Illus.). 88p. pap. *(978-0-86153-386-2(0))* Saint Andrew Pr., Ltd.
Paterson, Alexander Smith. The A Concise System of Theology: Being the Shorter Catechism Of. 2007. (ENG.). 468p. per. 37.95 *(978-1-4304-4692-7(7))* Kessinger Publishing, LLC.
Paton, David. The Clergy & the Clearances: The Church & the Highland Crisis 1790-1850. 2006. (ENG., Illus.). 251p. (C). pap. 36.95 *(978-0-85976-626-5(8),* Donald, John) Birlinn, Ltd. GBR. Dist: Independent Pubs. Group.
Prime, Derek. Travel with Robert Murray Mocheyne. Edwards, Brian H., ed. 2007. (Day One Travel Guides). (Illus.). 128p. per. 15.00 *(978-1-84625-057-6(9))* DayOne Pubns. GBR. Dist: STL Distribution North America.
Rankin, James. A Handbook of the Church of Scotland. 2010. 212p. pap. 28.95 *(978-1-4455-5429-7(1))* Barclay Pr., Inc.
Reformed Presbytery Staff. The Auchensaugh Renovation of the National Covenant & Solemn League & Covenant: With the Acknowledgment of Sins & Engagement to Duties, as They Were Renewed at Auchensaugh, near Douglas, July 24, 1712. (Compared with the Editions of Paisley, 1820, & Belfast, 1835.) Also, the Renovation of These Public Federal Deeds Ordained at Philadelphia, October 8, 1880, by the Reformed Presbytery, with Accommodation of the Original Covenants, in Both Transactions, to Their Times and. 2007. (ENG.). 144p. pap. 18.99 *(978-1-4264-6036-4(8));* 158p. pap. 21.99 *(978-1-4264-6107-1(0))* BiblioBazaar.
Religious Tract and Book Society for Ireland, Dublin Staff. The Scripture Text Book. 2006. 288p. per. 23.99 *(978-1-4255-2624-5(1))* MPublishing.
Robertson, David. Awakening: The Life & Ministry of Robert Murray Mccheyne. 2nd ed. 2010. (ENG., Illus.). 352p. 15.99 *(978-1-84550-542-4(5))* Christian Focus Pubns. GBR. Dist: STL Distribution North America.
Rodger, Lord & Rodger, Alan. The Courts, the Church & the Constitution: Aspects of the Disruption of 1843. 2009. (ENG., Illus.). 160p. (gr. 17). pap. 55.00 *(978-0-7486-3754-6(0))* Edinburgh Univ. Pr. GBR. Dist: Columbia Univ. Pr.

Rothes, John L. Relation of Proceedings Concerning the Affairs of the Kirk of Scotland. (Bannatyne Club, Edinburgh Publications: No. 37). reprint ed. 38.50 *(978-0-404-52743-3(4))* AMS Pr., Inc.

Smith, George. The Life of Alexander Duff, D. D., LL. D: In Two Volumes, with Portraits by Jeens. 2010. (Cambridge Library Collection - Religion Ser.). (ENG.). 572p. pap. 39.99 *(978-1-108-00830-3(5))*; (Illus.). 496p. pap. 35.99 *(978-1-108-00829-7(1))* Cambridge Univ. Pr.

—The Life of Alexander Duff, D. D., LL. D: Volume SET: In Two Volumes, with Portraits by Jeens. 2010. (Cambridge Library Collection - Religion Ser.). (ENG.). 1064p. pap. 75.00 *(978-1-108-00831-0(3))* Cambridge Univ. Pr.

Stanley, Arthur Penrhyn. Lectures on the History of the Church of Scotland, Delivered in Edinburgh in 1872 by Arthur Penrhyn Stanley, D D. 2006. 240p. per. 20.99 *(978-1-4255-2062-5(6))* MPublishing.

Sykes, Norman. Old Priest & New Presbyter. 2008. (ENG.). 276p. pap. 37.99 *(978-0-521-07289-2(1))* Cambridge Univ. Pr.

Thomson, Thomas. Acts & Proceedings of the General Assemblies of the Kirk of Scotland. 2010. (Illus.). 250p. pap. 22.72 *(978-1-153-91790-2(4))* General Bks. LLC.

VanDoodewaard, William. The Marrow Controversy & Seceder Tradition: Atonement, Saving Faith, & the Gospel Offer in Scotland (1718¿1799) 2011. 336p. pap. 25.00 ***(978-1-60178-149-9(0))*** Reformation Heritage Bks.

Vayahiy Press. The Scottish Psalter: Including Scripture Paraphrases & Hymns. Cardwell, Jon, ed. 2010. (ENG.). 146p. pap. 19.95 *(978-1-4538-5624-6(2))* CreateSpace.

Whytock, Jack C. "An Educated Clergy" Scottish Theological Education & Training in the Kirk & Secession, 1560-1850. 2007. (Studies in Christian History & Thought Ser.). 458p. pap. 44.99 *(978-1-84227-512-2(7))* Authentic Media.

—Continental Calvinian Influences on the Scottish Reformation: The First Book of Discipline (1560) 2009. (Illus.). 160p. 99.95 *(978-0-7734-4751-6(2))* Mellen, Edwin Pr., The.

Wodrow, Robert. Collections upon the Lives of the Reformers & Most Eminent Ministers of the Church of Scotland, 2 vols. in 3 pts. (Maitland Club, Glasgow Publications: No. 32). reprint ed. 105.00 *(978-0-404-52993-2(3))* AMS Pr., Inc.

—Collections upon the Lives of the Reformers & Most Eminent Ministers of the Church of Scotland. 2010. 390p. pap. 33.75 *(978-1-148-54786-2(X))* BiblioBazaar.

—Collections upon the Lives of the Reformers & Most Eminent Ministers of the Church of Scotland. 2009. 308p. pap. *(978-1-150-33967-7(5))* Books LLC.

—Collections upon the Lives of the Reformers & Most Eminent Ministers of the Church of Scotland. 2010. 248p. pap. 23.37 *(978-1-154-40340-4(8))* General Bks. LLC.

—The History of the Sufferings of the Church of Scotland: Volume 3. 2008. 524p. 65.00 *(978-1-59925-184-4(1))* Solid Ground Christian Bks.

—The History of the Sufferings of the Church of Scotland: Volume 4. 2008. 576p. 65.00 *(978-1-59925-185-1(X))* Solid Ground Christian Bks.

—The History of the Sufferings of the Church of Scotland: Volume One. 2008. 524p. 65.00 *(978-1-59925-182-0(5))* Solid Ground Christian Bks.

—The History of the Sufferings of the Church of Scotland: Volume Two. 2008. 516p. 65.00 *(978-1-59925-183-7(3))* Solid Ground Christian Bks.

CHURCH OF SCOTLAND—SERMONS

Boston, Thomas. The Crook in the Lot. 2009. 128p. pap. *(978-0-217-84690-5(4))* Books LLC.

—The Crook in the Lot. 2007. 80p. per. 8.25 *(978-1-58960-123-9(8))* Sovereign Grace Pubs., Inc.

Durham, James. Christ Crucified: The Marrow of the Gospel in 72 Sermons on Isaiah 53. Coldwell, Christopher, ed. & pref. by. Carstairs, John, pref. 2nd ed. 2007. 703p. 45.00 *(978-0-941075-46-6(X))* Naphtali Pr.

Gray, Andrew. Loving Christ & Fleeing Temptation: Select Sermons of Andrew Gray. Beeke, Joel R. & Van Wyck, Kelly, eds. 2007. *(978-1-60178-018-8(4))* Reformation Heritage Bks.

Leaver, Robin & Spinks. A Communion Sunday in Scotland Ca. 1780: Liturgies & Sermons. 13th ed. 2009. (Drew University Studies in Liturgy Ser.). (ENG.). 180p. 63.00 *(978-0-8108-6980-6(2))* Scarecrow Pr., Inc.

M'Cheyne, Robert, et al, contrib. by. Precious Seed: Discourses by Scottish Worthies. 2007. 440p. per. 30.00 *(978-1-59925-097-7(7))* Solid Ground Christian Bks.

Robertson, Alexander. Venetian Sermons Drawn from the History, Art & Customs of Venice. 2007. (ENG.). 464p. 52.95 *(978-0-548-03318-0(9))* Kessinger Publishing, LLC.

CHURCH OF SOUTH INDIA

Newbigin, Lesslie. The Reunion of the Church, Revised Edition: A Defence of the South India Scheme. 2011. 220p. pap. 25.00 ***(978-1-61097-512-4(X)***, Wipf and Stock) Wipf & Stock Pubs.

Stults, Donald Le Roy. Grasping Truth & Reality: Lesslie Newbigin's Theology of Mission to the Western World. 2008. 308p. pap. 34.00 *(978-1-55635-723-7(0)*, Wipf and Stock) Wipf & Stock Pubs.

CHURCH OF THE BRETHREN

Bowman, Carl Desportes. Portrait of a People: The Church of the Brethren At 300. 2008. (ENG.). 146p. pap. 15.95 *(978-0-87178-085-0(2))* Brethren Pr.

Bowman, Carl W. & Durnbaugh, Donald F., eds. The Brethren Encyclopedia, Vol. 4. *(978-0-936693-04-0(5))* Brethren Encyclopedia, Inc.

Bucher, Christina, et al. The Witness of the Hebrew Bible for a New Testament Church. 2010. pap. *(978-0-87178-145-1(X))* Brethren Pr.

Denis, Seachrist. Snow Hill. 2011. (Illus.). 288p. 45.00 *(978-1-60635-065-2(X))* Kent State Univ. Pr.

Dickson, Neil, et al. The Growth of the Brethren Movement: National & International Experiences: Essays in Honour of Harold H. Rowdon. 2006. (Illus.). xiv, 271p. 33.99 *(978-1-84227-427-9(9))*, Paternoster) Authentic Media.

Dickson, Neil T. R., et al, eds. The Growth of the Brethren Movement: National & International Experiences: Essays in Honor of Harold H. Rowdon. 2006. (Studies in Evangelical History & Thought Ser.). 296p. pap. 30.00 *(978-1-55635-117-4(8)*, Wipf and Stock) Wipf & Stock Pubs.

Flory, John S. Literary Activity of the German Baptist Brethren in the Eighteenth Century. 2007. (ENG.). 348p. 46.95 *(978-0-548-04297-7(7))* Kessinger Publishing, LLC.

Fresh from the Word: Devotions for the 300th Anniversary of the Brethren. 2007. 539p. 20.00 *(978-0-87178-079-9(8))* Brethren Pr.

Gibbons, Phebe Earle. Pennsylvania Dutch & Other Essays. 2007. (ENG.). 320p. 45.95 *(978-0-548-09287-3(7))* Kessinger Publishing, LLC.

Gillin, John Lewis. The Dunkers: A Sociological Interpretation. 2009. 244p. 28.99 *(978-1-115-51811-6(9))*; 32.99 *(978-1-115-51810-9(0))*; pap. 26.75 *(978-1-115-51812-3(7))*; pap. 25.75 *(978-1-115-51813-0(5))*; 23.99 *(978-1-103-10346-1(6))*; 23.99 *(978-1-103-10855-8(7))*; pap. 17.99 *(978-1-103-10852-7(2))*; pap. 17.99 *(978-1-103-10343-0(1))* BiblioBazaar.

Holsinger, H. R. History of the Tunkers & the Brethren Church. 2007. (Illus.). 826p. pap. 25.00 net. *(978-1-60121-000-5(0))* Graphe Pr.

Kline, John. Life & Labors of Elder John Kline, the Martyr Missionary. 2009. 536p. 32.99 *(978-0-559-09300-5(4))*; 35.99 *(978-0-559-09288-6(1))*; pap. 39.75 *(978-0-559-09297-8(0))*; pap. 40.75 *(978-0-559-09292-3(X))* BiblioBazaar.

Kovac, Jeffrey. Refusing War, Affirming Peace: A History of Civilian Public Service Camp #21 at Cascade Locks. 2009. (ENG., Illus.). 192p. pap. 21.95 *(978-0-87071-575-4(5))* Oregon State Univ. Pr.

Lehman, James H. The Old Brethren: People of Wisdom & Simplicity Speak to Our Time. 2nd ed. 2008. (ENG.). 263p. pap. 18.95 *(978-0-87178-089-8(5))* Brethren Pr.

Longacre, James C. Like Those Who Dream: Sermons for Salford Mennonite Church & Beyond. 2009. 200p. pap. 18.95 *(978-1-931038-51-5(1))* Cascadia Publishing Hse., LLC.

Longenecker, Stephen L. & Bach, Jeff. Lines, Places, & Heritage: Essays Commemorating the 300th Anniversary of the Church of the Brethren. 2008. xviii, 263p. *(978-0-89725-841-8(X)*, Penobscot Pr.) Picton Pr.

Meier, Marcus. Die Schwarzenauer Neutäufer: Genese einer Gemeindebildung zwischen Pietismus und Täufertum. Arbeiten zur Geschichte des Pietismus. 2008. (Arbeiten Zur Geschichte des Pietismus Ser.). (GER.). 304p. (C). 74.00 *(978-3-525-55834-8(1))* Vandenhoeck & Ruprecht GmbH & Co. KG DEU. Dist: ISD.

Ramirez, Frank. Brethren Brush with Greatness: 32 Stories. 2008. (ENG., Illus.). 149p. pap. 15.95 *(978-0-87178-095-9(X))* Brethren Pr.

's Secretary Office, compiled by. Manual of Doctrine & Government of the Brethren in Christ Church: 2006 Edition. 2006. per. 6.99 *(978-1-928915-93-5(0))* Evangel Publishing Hse.

Shuff, Roger N. Searching for the True Church: Brethren & Evangelicals in Mid-Twentieth-Century England. 2007. (Studies in Evangelical History & Thought Ser.). (Illus.). 323p. pap. 32.00 *(978-1-59752-794-1(7)*, Wipf and Stock) Wipf & Stock Pubs.

Stevens, Alec. E. J. Pace: Christian Cartoonist. 2007. (Illus.). 250p. pap. 19.95 *(978-0-9778214-1-9(2))* Calvary Comics.

Stoffer, Dale R. A Gleam of Shining Hope: The Story of Theological Education & Christian Witness at Ashland Theological Seminary (1906-2006) & Ashland College/University (1878-2006) 2007. (Illus.). xii, 460p. *(978-0-9793775-0-1(1))* Ashland Theological Seminary.

Wheeler, Charles Gidley. A Good Boy Tomorrow: Memoirs of A Fundamentalist Upbringing. 2007. 128p. per. 13.95 *(978-0-595-43685-9(4))* iUniverse, Inc.

Winger, Otho. History of the Church of the Brethren in Indiana. (Illus.). 479p. reprint ed. lib. bdg. 98.00 *(978-0-7222-0845-8(6))* Library Reprints, Inc.

CHURCH OF THE LIVING GOD, THE PILLAR AND GROUND OF THE TRUTH

Lopez De Maya, E. La Iglesia Del Dios Vivo: The Church of the Living God. (SPA.). 112p. *(978-84-7228-720-4(3)*, 360300) Clie, Editorial.

CHURCH OF THE NEW JERUSALEM

see New Jerusalem Church

CHURCH OF THE PROVINCE OF SOUTH AFRICA

Allen, John. Desmond Tutu: Rabble-Rouser for Peace - The Authorized Biography. 2008. (ENG.). 496p. pap. 16.95 *(978-1-55652-798-2(5)*, Hill, Lawrence Bks.) Chicago Review Pr., Inc.

Jones, Sarah Rowland, compiled by. Faith in Action: Njongonkulu Ndungane Archbishop for the church & the World. 2011. 256p. pap. 27.95 *(978-0-7963-0763-7(6))* NB Pubs. Ltd. ZAF. Dist: International Publishers Marketing.

CHURCH OFFICERS

see also Church Secretaries; Church Ushers; Deacons; Elders (Church Officers)

Addington, T. J. High-Impact Church Boards: How to Develop Healthy, Intentional, & Empowered Church Leaders. 2010. (LifeChange Ser.). 224p. pap. 14.99 *(978-1-60006-674-0(7))* NavPress Publishing Group.

Asquith, Glenn H. The Work of the Church Officer. 2009. 116p. pap. 10.00 *(978-0-8170-1639-5(2))* Judson Pr.

Bell, Buddy. Greeting 101: Easy Steps to Greeting in the Local Church. 2007. (Illus.). 110p. (gr. k-12). per. 6.99 *(978-1-57794-887-2(4))* Harrison House Pubs.

Cobble, James F., Jr. & Hammar, Richard R. The 2007 Compensation Handbook for Church Staff. 2006. per. 29.95 *(978-0-917463-29-7(3))* Christianity Today International.

Harris, Jacob. The Dos & Don'ts of Music Ministry & More. 2009. 141p. pap. 16.95 *(978-1-4327-4458-8(5))* Outskirts Pr., Inc.

Hart, Dirk. Staffing the Established Church. (Healthy Church Ser.). 2.95 *(978-1-56212-715-2(2)*, 216773) Faith Alive Christian Resources.

Hartshorn, Leon R., compiled by. Outstanding Stories by Past General Authorities. 2007. 160p. pap. 13.95 *(978-1-932898-58-3(1))* Spring Creek Bk. Co.

Hartung, Bruce. Holding up the Prophet's Hand: Supporting Church Workers. 2011. 318p. pap. 12.99 ***(978-0-7586-0548-1(X))*** Concordia Publishing Hse.

Harvey, Christopher Howell. Until My Blindfold Comes Off. 2008. 196p. 22.99 *(978-1-60791-144-9(2))* Xulon Pr., Inc.

Heavner, Betsey. Job Descriptions & Leadership Training in the United Methodist Church: A Leader Development Guide. 2009. 98p. pap. 20.00 *(978-0-88177-548-8(7))* Discipleship Resources.

Hotchkiss, Dan. Governance & Ministry: Rethinking Board Leadership. 2009. *(978-1-56699-370-8(9))* Alban Institute, Inc.

Jarema, William J. A Survival Guide for Church Ministers. 2011. (Illus.). 208p. pap. 19.95 *(978-0-8091-4721-2(1))* Paulist Pr.

Johnson, Earl S., Jr., Earl S. Selected to Serve, Second Edition: A Guide for Church Leaders. 2012. (ENG.). 200p. pap. 20.00 ***(978-0-664-50317-8(9))*** Geneva Pr.

Johnson, Alan. Encounters at the Counter: What Congregations Can Learn about Hospitality from Business. 2009. xvi, 143p. *(978-0-8298-1817-8(0))* Pilgrim Pr., The/United Church Pr.

Kessler, Martin. Johann Gottfried Herder: Der Theologe Unter Den Klassikern: Das Amt des Generalsuperintendenten Von Sachsen-Weimar, 2 vols. 2007. (Arbeiten zur Kirchengeschichte Ser.). (GER.). LIV, 1130p. 280.00 *(978-3-11-019152-3(0))* De Gruyter, Walter Inc.

Miller, Tim E. 30x60x100: A Manual for Making Disciples & Developing Discipleship Curriculum. 2008. 150p. per. *(978-0-9788201-6-9(9))* IMD Pr.

Ryan, G. Thomas & Laughlin, Corinna. The Sacristy Manual, Second Edition. 2011. 272p. pap. 29.95 ***(978-1-61671-042-2(X))*** Liturgy Training Pubns.

CHURCH ORDERS, ANCIENT

see also Canon Law; Church History—Primitive and Early Church, ca. 30-600; Liturgies, Early Christian; Theology, Doctrinal—History—Early Church, ca. 30-600

Bradshaw, Paul & Bebawi, Carol, eds. The Canons of Hippolytus. 2009. 88.00 *(978-1-60724-347-2(4))* Gorgias Pr., LLC.

Brent, Allen. Ignatius of Antioch: A Martyr Bishop & the origin of Episcopacy. 2009. (ENG.). 192p. 39.95 *(978-0-567-22264-0(0)*, T&T Clark Int'l) Continuum International Publishing Group, Ltd. GBR. Dist: National Bk. Network.

Cooper, James & MacLean, Arthur John. The Testament of Our Lord: Translated into English Form the Syriac with Introduction & Notes. 2008. 287p. pap. 25.00 *(978-1-60608-350-5(3))* Wipf & Stock Pubs.

Cuming, Geoffrey. Hippolytus: A Text for Students. 2009. 88.00 *(978-1-60724-354-0(4))* Gorgias Pr., LLC.

Gibson, Margaret Dunlop, ed. The Didascalia Apostolorum in Syriac: Edited from a Mesopotamian Manuscript with Various Readings & Collations of Other MSS. 2011. (Cambridge Library Collection - Religion Ser.). (SYR.). 254p. pap. 23.99 *(978-1-108-01896-8(3))* Cambridge Univ. Pr.

Gibson, Margaret Dunlop, tr. The Didascalia Apostolorum in English. 2011. (Cambridge Library Collection - Religion Ser.). (ENG.). 138p. pap. 19.99 *(978-1-108-01897-5(1))* Cambridge Univ. Pr.

Harnack, Adolf von. Sources of the Apostolic Canon: With a Treatise on the Origin of the Readership & Other Lower Orders. 2008. 235p. pap. 20.00 *(978-1-60608-280-5(9)*, Wipf and Stock) Wipf & Stock Pubs.

Sperry-White, Grant, notes. The Testamentum Domini. 2009. 88.00 *(978-1-60724-373-1(3))* Gorgias Pr., LLC.

Stewart-Sykes, Alistair. The Didascalia Apostolorum: An English Version with Introduction & Annotation. 2009. (Studia Traditionis Theologiae. Explorations in Early & Medieval Theology Ser.). (EGY & ENG.). 296p. (C). pap. 102.00 *(978-2-503-52993-6(3))* Brepols Pubs. BEL. Dist: ISD.

CHURCH ORNAMENT

see Church Decoration and Ornament

CHURCH PLATE

Augustine, Saint. Treasures of the English Church. 2008. (Illus.). 160p. pap. 40.00 ***(978-1-903470-74-9(9))*** Holberton, Paul Publishing GBR. Dist: Casemate Pubs. & Bk. Distributors, LLC.

CHURCH POLITY

see also Cardinals; Church and State; Church Discipline; Church Finance; Church Membership; Church Officers; Church Orders, Ancient; Church Property; Clergy; Congregationalism; Covenants (Church Polity); Dioceses; Ecclesiastical Law; Episcopacy; Indigenous Church Administration; Institutionalism (Religion); Investiture; Laity; Methodism; Patronage, Ecclesiastical; Presbyterianism; Puritans

also subdivision Government under church denominations, e.g. Church of England—Government

Alexander, Joseph Addison. Essays on the Primitive Church Offices. 2006. 192p. per. 18.99 *(978-1-4255-1574-4(6))* MPublishing.

Bannerman, James. The Church of Christ: Volume One. 2009. 498p. pap. 40.00 *(978-1-59925-227-8(9))* Solid Ground Christian Bks.

—The Church of Christ: Volume Two. 2009. 478p. pap. 35.00 *(978-1-59925-228-5(7))* Solid Ground Christian Bks.

Carson, Alexander. Ecclesiastical Polity of the New Testame. 2006. 596p. per. 53.00 *(978-1-57978-847-6(5))* Baptist Standard Bearer, Inc.

Clark, Catherine H. Annual Church Review Procedure: The Church's Ministry & the Minister. pap. 12.00 *(978-1-56699-060-8(2))* Alban Institute, Inc.

Coffey, John & Lim, Paul C. H., eds. The Cambridge Companion to Puritanism. 2008. (Cambridge Companions to Religion Ser.). (ENG.). 400p. (C). pap. 30.99 *(978-0-521-67800-1(5))* Cambridge Univ. Pr.

Coffey, John & Lim, Paul Chang-Ha. The Cambridge Companion to Puritanism. Coffey, John & Lim, Paul C. H., eds. 2008. (Cambridge Companions to Religion Ser.). (ENG.). 400p. (C). 89.00 *(978-0-521-86088-8(1))* Cambridge Univ. Pr.

Confalonieri, Luca Badini. Democracy in the Christian Church: An Historical, Theological & Political Case. 2012. (ENG.). 304p. 120.00 ***(978-0-567-44952-8(1)***, T&T Clark Int'l) Continuum International Publishing Group, Ltd. GBR. Dist: National Bk. Network.

Connolly, R. Hugh, ed. Didascalia Apostolorum: The Syriac Version Translated & Accompanied by the Verona Latin Fragments. 2010. (Ancient Texts & Translations Ser.). 386p. pap. 45.00 *(978-1-55635-669-8(2)*, Wipf and Stock) Wipf & Stock Pubs.

Crowell, William. The Church Member's Manual, of Ecclesiastical Principles, Doctrine, & Discipline: Presenting A Systematic View of the Structure, Polity, Doctrines, 2006. 288p. per. 23.99 *(978-1-4255-2600-9(4))* MPublishing.

Dagg, John. Treatise on Church Order. 2006. 328p. per. 33.00 *(978-1-57978-498-0(4))* Baptist Standard Bearer, Inc.

De Schweinitz, E. The Moravian Manual; Containing an Account of the Protestant Church of the Moravian United Brethren, or Unitas Fratrum by E de Schweinitz Publis. 2006. 188p. per. 18.99 *(978-1-4255-1516-4(9))* MPublishing.

Ellis, Jimmie A., III. The Anointing of Government in the Local Church. 2007. (ENG.). 76p. per. 11.99 *(978-1-59755-111-3(2)*, 7016, Advantage Inspirational) Advantage Bks.

Essays on the Primitive Church Offices Reprinted by Permission from the Princeton Review, with Corrections & Additions by the Same Writer. 2006. 192p. per. 18.99 *(978-1-4255-1551-5(7))* MPublishing.

Frank, Thomas Edward. Polity, Practice & Mission of the United Methodist Church Korean Edition. 2008. 288p. pap. 15.00 *(978-0-687-64280-9(9))* Abingdon Pr.

Gibson, Margaret Dunlop, ed. The Didascalia Apostolorum in Syriac: Edited from a Mesopotamian Manuscript with Various Readings & Collations of Other MSS. 2011. (Cambridge Library Collection - Religion Ser.). (SYR.). 254p. pap. 23.99 *(978-1-108-01896-8(3))* Cambridge Univ. Pr.

Gibson, Margaret Dunlop, tr. The Didascalia Apostolorum in English. 2011. (Cambridge Library Collection - Religion Ser.). (ENG.). 138p. pap. 19.99 *(978-1-108-01897-5(1))* Cambridge Univ. Pr.

Gillespie, Katherine. Katherine Chidley. 2009. (Early Modern Englishwoman: A Facsimile Library of Essential Works - Printed Writings, 1641-1700: Ser. II, Part Four Ser.). 142p. 89.95 *(978-0-7546-5231-0(4))* Ashgate Publishing Co.

Guidelines for Leading Your Congregation 2009-2012 - Church Council: Connecting Vision & Ministry in Your Church. 2008. 2.95 *(978-0-687-64791-0(6))* Abingdon Pr.

Harnack, Adolf von. Sources of the Apostolic Canon: With a Treatise on the Origin of the Readership & Other Lower Orders. 2008. 235p. pap. 20.00 *(978-1-60608-280-5(9)*, Wipf and Stock) Wipf & Stock Pubs.

Hay, Alex Rattray. The New Testament Order for Church & Missionary. 2010. 542p. pap. 45.00 *(978-1-60899-934-7(3)*, Wipf and Stock) Wipf & Stock Pubs.

Hellerman, Joseph H., et al. When the Church Was a Family: Recapturing Jesus' Vision for Authentic Christian Community, 1 vol. 2009. (ENG.). 240p. pap. 19.99 *(978-0-8054-4779-8(2)*, B&H Academic) B&H Publishing Group.

Hooker, Richard. Of the Laws of Ecclesiastical Polity. 2009. 192p. 22.99 *(978-1-103-56704-1(7))*; pap. 16.99 *(978-1-103-56702-7(0))* BiblioBazaar.

—Works of Mr Richard Hooker V1 in Eight B. 2006. pap. 33.95 *(978-1-4286-4372-7(9))* Kessinger Publishing, LLC.

—Works of Mr Richard Hooker V3 in Eight B. 2006. pap. 37.95 *(978-1-4286-4374-1(5))* Kessinger Publishing, LLC.

Hotchkiss, Dan. Governance & Ministry: Rethinking Board Leadership. 2009. *(978-1-56699-370-8(9))* Alban Institute, Inc.

Jacob, George Andrew. The Ecclesiastical Polity of the New Testament a Study for the Present Crisis in the Church of England. 2006. 436p. per. 26.99 *(978-1-4255-4788-2(5))* MPublishing.

Lightfoot, J. b. & Lightfoot, J. B. The Christian Ministry. 2010. 150p. 28.99 *(978-1-140-08151-7(9))*; pap. 21.75 *(978-1-140-08152-4(7))* BiblioBazaar.

Lucas, Sean Michael. What is Church Government? 2009. pap. *(978-1-59638-150-6(7))* P & R Publishing.

Mannion, Gerard & Borght, Eddy van der, eds. John Calvin's Ecclesiology: Ecumenical Perspectives. 2011. (Ecclesiological Investigations Ser.). (ENG.). 254p. 120.00 *(978-0-567-08102-5(8)*, T&T Clark Int'l) Continuum International Publishing Group, Ltd. GBR. Dist: National Bk. Network.

McCleary, Paul F. Structure, Governance & the United Methodist Church. 2011. 90p. 24.99 ***(978-1-4653-6197-4(9))***; pap. 15.99 ***(978-1-4653-6196-7(0))*** Xlibris Corp.

Morris, Thomas Asbury. A Discourse on Methodist Church Polity. 2008. 100p. pap. 18.95 *(978-1-4367-2577-4(1))* Kessinger Publishing, LLC.

Oswald, Roy M. Power Analysis of a Congregation. pap. 6.25 *(978-1-56699-008-0(4))* Alban Institute, Inc.

C

—Running Through the Thistles: Terminating a Ministerial Relationship with a Parish. pap. 7.25 *(978-1-56699-004-2(1))* Alban Institute, Inc.

Overall, John. Convocation Book of Sixteen Six. (Library of Anglo-Catholic Theology: No. 15). reprint ed. 27.50 *(978-0-404-52107-3(X))* AMS Pr., Inc.

Paget, Francis. An Introduction to the Fifth Book of Hooker's Treatise of the Laws of Ecclesiastical Polity. 2009. 200p. pap. 18.22 *(978-1-150-42904-0(6))* General Bks. LLC.

—An Introduction to the Fifth Book of Hooker's Treatise of the Laws of Ecclesiastical Polity. 2007. (ENG.). 280p. 42.95 *(978-0-548-33840-7(X))*; per. 27.95 *(978-1-4326-9762-4(5))* Kessinger Publishing, LLC.

Palmer, William. A Treatise on the Church of Christ, Volume 1: Designed Chiefly for the Use of Students in Theology. 2nd ed. 2008. 1198p. pap. 102.00 *(978-1-55635-048-1(1))* Wipf & Stock Pubs.

Reynolds, J. Church Polity or the Kingdom of Christ I. 2006. 264p. per. 28.00 *(978-1-57978-519-2(0))* Baptist Standard Bearer, Inc.

Steckel, Clyde J. New Ecclesiology & Polity: The United Church of Christ. 2009. *(978-0-8298-1857-4(X))* Pilgrim Pr., The/United Church Pr.

Taylor, Isaac. Spiritual Despotism. 2009. 222p. pap. *(978-0-217-32151-8(8))*; 220p. pap. *(978-0-217-55993-5(X))* Books LLC.

—Spiritual Despotism. 2009. 222p. pap. 20.77 *(978-0-217-55997-3(2))* General Bks. LLC.

—Spiritual Despotism. 2007. (ENG.). 512p. 55.95 *(978-0-548-08236-2(7))*; 502p. 53.95 *(978-0-548-17027-4(4))*; 504p. per. 38.95 *(978-1-4304-6787-8(8))* Kessinger Publishing, LLC.

Victa III, Francisco. A Kingdom Is Not a Democracy. 2006. pap. 13.99 *(978-1-60034-428-2(3))* Xulon Pr., Inc.

Vnuk, Richard J. Tested in the Fire of Hell. 2010. 208p. 29.99 *(978-1-4500-4784-5(X))*; pap. 19.99 *(978-1-4500-4783-8(1))* Xlibris Corp.

Waters, Guy Prentiss. How Jesus Runs the Church. 2011. pap. ***(978-1-59638-252-7(X))*** P & R Publishing.

Zimmer, Donald E. Leadership & Listening: Spiritual Foundations for Church Governance. 2011. ***(978-1-56699-414-9(4))*** Alban Institute, Inc.

CHURCH PROPERTY

see also Benefices, Ecclesiastical; Church Lands; Convents; Monasteries; Patronage, Ecclesiastical; Privileges and Immunities, Ecclesiastical; Secularization

Bascom, H. B. (Henry Bidleman). complain. The Methodist Church Property Case Report of the Suit of Henry B Bascom, & Others, vs. George Lane, & Others, Heard Before the Hon Judges Nelso. 2006. 380p. per. 26.99 *(978-1-4255-3952-8(1))* MPublishing.

Bazant, Jan. Alienation of Church Wealth in Mexico: Social & Economic Aspects of the Liberal Revolution, 1856-1875. 2008. (Cambridge Latin American Studies). (ENG., Illus.). 352p. pap. 46.00 *(978-0-521-08868-8(2))* Cambridge Univ. Pr.

Brooks, Erastus. Brooksiana; or, the Controversy Between Senator Brooks & Archbishop Hughes: Growing Out of the Recently Enacted Church Property Bill / with an Int. 2006. 220p. per. 20.99 *(978-1-4255-1824-0(9))* MPublishing.

Krall, Johannes. Kirchenvermögen - Nachhaltigkeit - Wirtschaftsethik: Rechtliche Gestaltungsmöglichkeiten bei der Verwaltung von Kirchenvermögen unter nachhaltigen und Wirtschaftsethischen Überlegungen. 2008. (Wissenschaft und Religion. Veröffentlichungen des Internationalen Forschungszentrums für Grundfragen der Wissenschaften Salzburg Ser.). (GRE.). 322p. 83.95 *(978-3-631-59122-2(5))* Lang, Peter GmbH, Europäischer Verlag der Wissenschaften DEU. Dist: Lang, Peter.

Ocker, Christopher. Church Robbers & Reformers in Germany, 1525-1547: Confiscation & Religious Purpose in the Holy Roman Empire. 2006. (Studies in Medieval & Reformation Traditions: History, Culture, Religion, Ideas: Vol. 114). (Illus.). 338p. *(978-90-04-15206-9(7))* BRILL.

Putnam, James O. Speech of James O Putnam, of Buffalo, on the Bill, Providing for the Vesting of the Title of Church Property in Lay Trustees, Delivered in the Senate. 2011. 18p. pap. 11.99 ***(978-1-4181-8961-7(8))*** MPublishing.

Renken, John Anthony. Church Property: A Commentary on Canon Law Governing Temporal Goods in the United States & Canada. 2009. *(978-0-8189-1297-9(9))* St Pauls.

Rosenwein, Barbara H. To Be the Neighbor of Saint Peter: The Social Meaning of Cluny's Property, 909-1049. 2006. (Illus.). 280p. pap. 27.95 *(978-0-8014-7345-6(4))*, Comstock Publishing Assocs.) Cornell Univ. Pr.

Wood, Susan. The Proprietary Church in the Medieval West. 2009. (ENG., Illus.). 1020p. pap. 85.00 *(978-0-19-955263-4(0))* Oxford Univ. Pr., Inc.

CHURCH PROPERTY—TAXATION

see also Taxation, Exemption From

Ellens, J. P. Religious Routes to Gladstonian Liberalism. 2008. pap. 29.95 *(978-0-271-02843-9(2))* Pennsylvania State Univ. Pr.

CHURCH PROTOCOL

see Church Etiquette

CHURCH RECORDS AND REGISTERS

see Church Statistics; Registers of Births, etc.

CHURCH REFORM

see Church Renewal

CHURCH RENEWAL

see also Counter-Reformation, Mission of the Church; Reformation—Early Movements

Abraham, Martin. Evangelium und Kirchengestalt: Reformatorisches Kirchenverständnis heute. (Theologische Bibliothek Töpelmann Ser.).Tr. of Gospel & the Shape of the Church. A Reformational Understanding of the Church Today. (GER.). XV, 601p. 300.00 ***(978-3-11-181861-0(6))***; 2007. 182.00 *(978-3-11-019444-9(9))* De Gruyter, Walter Inc.

Adams, Wes & Hughey, Rhonda. Revival: Its Present Relevance & Coming Role at the End of the Age. annot. ed. 2010. (ENG.). 246p. pap. 15.99 *(978-0-9826018-4-6(0))* Casis Hse.

Ahn, C. En Medio del Fuego.Tr. of Into the Fire. 9.99 *(978-0-7899-0615-1(5)*, 497763) Editorial Unilit.

Alexander, Charles. There Must Be Another Way. 2006. pap. *(978-1-55452-064-0(9))* Essence Publishing.

Anderson, Neil T. Extreme Church Makeover. 2010. (ENG.). 288p. pap. 15.99 *(978-0-8307-3759-8(6)*, Regal Bks.) Gospel Light Pubns.

Andrews, Reg. Timber: A Call to Personal & Corporate Renewal. 2007. 176p. per. *(978-1-55452-224-8(2))* Essence Publishing.

Anyang, John. Our Dying Churches & the Missing Link. 2011. 152p. 25.00 *(978-1-4269-5021-6(7))*; pap. 15.00 *(978-1-4269-5020-9(9))* Trafford Publishing.

Baars, Conrad W., et al. I Will Give Them a New Heart: Reflections on the Priesthood & the Renewal of the Church. 2007. *(978-0-8189-1245-0(6)*, St. Pauls) St Pauls/Alba Hse. Pubs.

Baker, Allen M. Seeking a Revival Culture. 2009. 174p. pap. 20.00 *(978-1-60608-524-0(7)*, Resource Pubns.) Wipf & Stock Pubs.

Barber, John J. My Almost for His Highest. 2010. 148p. pap. 18.00 *(978-1-60899-632-2(8)*, Wipf and Stock) Wipf & Stock Pubs.

Barrow, Simon, ed. Fear or Freedom? 2008. 152p. pap. *(978-1-905565-14-6(3))* Shoving Leopard Productions.

Bass, Diana Butler. Christianity for the Rest of Us: How the Neighborhood Church Is Transforming the Faith. 2007. (ENG.). 336p. pap. 14.99 *(978-0-06-085949-7(0)*, HarperOne) HarperCollins Pubs.

Beach, Nancy & Groeschel, Craig. It: How Churches & Leaders Can Get It & Keep It: How Churches & Leaders Can Get It & Keep It, 1 vol. 2008. (ENG.). 160p. 18.99 *(978-0-310-28682-0(4))* Zondervan.

Bergquist, Linda & Karr, Allan. Church Turned Inside Out: A Guide for Designers, Refiners, & Re-Aligners. 2009. (Jossey-Bass Leadership Network Ser.: 34). (ENG., Illus.). 240p. 24.95 *(978-0-470-38317-9(8)*, Jossey-Bass) Wiley, John & Sons, Inc.

Beyond the Emerging Church: The End & the Beginning of a Movement. 2007. per. 17.99 *(978-0-9672944-2-1(8))* Damah Media.

Borden, Paul. Direct Hit: Aiming Real Leaders at the Mission Field. 2006. (Convergence eBook Ser.). 159p. per. 20.00 *(978-0-687-33194-9(3))* Abingdon Pr.

Broadman and Holman Publishers Staff & Broadman and Holman. Evangelicals Engaging Emergent: A Discussion of the Emergent Church Movement, 1 vol. Henard, William & Greenway, Adam, eds. 2009. (ENG.). 352p. pap. 24.99 *(978-0-8054-4739-2(3)*, B&H Academic) B&H Publishing Group.

Brown, Stewart J. & Nockles, Peter B., eds. The Oxford Movement: Europe & the Wider World 1830#x2013;1930. 2012. (ENG.). 288p. 99.00 ***(978-1-107-01644-6(4))*** Cambridge Univ. Pr.

Bruce, Tricia Colleen. Faithful Revolution: How Voice of the Faithful Is Changing the Church. 2011. (ENG., Illus.). 240p. 49.95 *(978-0-19-538584-7(5))* Oxford Univ. Pr., Inc.

Burns, M. P. Orthodoxy: Pushing at the Boundaries of Faith. 2009. 181p. pap. 16.95 *(978-1-4092-7224-3(9))* Lulu Enterprises Inc.

Burrier, Doug. Here to There. 2008. 164p. 21.99 *(978-1-60477-751-2(6))*; pap. 13.99 *(978-1-60477-750-5(8))* Xulon Pr., Inc.

Bush, Peter George. In Dying We Are Born: The Challenge & the Hope for Congregations. 2007. *(978-1-56699-357-9(1))* Alban Institute, Inc.

Callahan, Kennon L. Twelve Keys to an Effective Church: Strong, Healthy Congregations Living in the Grace of God. 2nd ed. 2010. (ENG., Illus.). 288p. 22.95 *(978-0-470-55929-1(2)*, Jossey-Bass) Wiley, John & Sons, Inc.

Cameron, Helen. Resourcing Mission: Practical Theology for Changing Churches. 2010. (ENG.). 192p. pap. 25.00 *(978-0-334-04146-7(5)*, SCM Pr.) Hymns Ancient & Modern Ltd GBR. Dist: Westminster John Knox Pr.

Clark, R. Scott. Recovering the Reformed Confession: Our Theology, Piety, & Practice. 2008. pap. *(978-1-59638-110-0(8))* P & R Publishing.

Cole, Neil. Church 3. 0: Upgrades for the Future of the Church. 2010. (Jossey-Bass Leadership Network Ser.: 49). (ENG., Illus.). 304p. 24.95 *(978-0-470-52945-4(8)*, Jossey-Bass) Wiley, John & Sons, Inc.

Cootsona, Gregory S. The Church of the Last Stop: The Story of Bidwell Presbyterian Church. 2007. (Illus.). 28p. 1.00 *(978-0-664-50295-9(4))* Geneva Pr.

Countryman, Louis William. Calling on the Spirit in Unsettling Times. 2012. E-Book ***(978-0-8192-2771-3(4)***, Morehouse Publishing) Church Publishing, Inc.

Craun, Edwin D. Ethics & Power in Medieval English Reformist Writing. 2010. (Cambridge Studies in Medieval Literature Ser.). (ENG.). 232p. 85.00 *(978-0-521-19932-2(8))* Cambridge Univ. Pr.

Croft, Steven, ed. Mission-Shaped Questions: Defining Issues for Today's Church. 2010. (Illus.). 240p. pap. 22.00 *(978-1-59627-127-2(2)*, Seabury Bks.) Church Publishing, Inc.

Cullinane, Peter J. In-Between God. 2011. (ENG.). 153p. (C). pap. 24.00 ***(978-1-921817-32-8(1))*** ATF Pr. AUS. Dist: Brown, David Bk. Co., The.

Dally, John Addison. Choosing the Kingdom: Missional Preaching for the Household of God. 2007. *(978-1-56699-359-3(8))* Alban Institute, Inc.

Davies, Mervyn & Dodds, Graham. Leadership in the Church for a People of Hope. 2011. (ENG., Illus.). 200p. 110.00 *(978-0-567-38621-2(X))*; pap. 32.95 *(978-0-567-01407-8(X))* Continuum International Publishing Group, Ltd. GBR. (T&T Clark Int'l). Dist: National Bk. Network.

Dick, Dan. A New Kind of Church: A Systems Approach. 2006. (Illus.). 101p. per. 13.00 *(978-0-88177-484-9(7))* Discipleship Resources.

Dixit, Rajkumar. Branded Faith. 2010. (Illus.). 180p. pap. 21.00 *(978-1-60899-559-2(3)*, Wipf and Stock) Wipf & Stock Pubs.

Do-Nguyen, Mariette. Process of Healing the the World, Vol. IX. 2007. (Mysteries of God Revealed to Man Ser.: IX). per. 55.00 *(978-0-9652169-8-2(5)*, ID0010) Kingdom of Heaven - World Divine Government.

—Seventh Angel Belew A Trumpet, Vol. X. 2007. (Mysteries of God Revealed to Man Ser.: X). per. 55.00 *(978-0-9715329-0-8(7)*, ID0011) Kingdom of Heaven - World Divine Government.

Dragt, Gordon R. One Foot Planted in the Center, the Other Dangling off the Edge: How Intentional Leadership Can Transform Your Church. 2009. (ENG.). 192p. pap. 19.95 *(978-1-58982-494-2(6)*, Millennial Mind Publishing) American Bk. Publishing Group.

Drane, John. After Mcdonaldization: Mission, Ministry, & Christian Discipleship in an Age of Uncertainty. 2008. (Illus.). 192p. (C). pap. 23.00 *(978-0-8010-3611-8(9))* Baker Academic.

—Do Christians Know How to Be Spiritual. 240p. *(978-0-232-52632-5(X))* Darton, Longman & Todd, Ltd.

Easum, William M. A Second Resurrection: Leading Your Congregation to New Life. 2007. 160p. pap. 16.00 *(978-0-687-64653-1(7))* Abingdon Pr.

Edwards, Joel. An Agenda for Change, 1 vol. 2008. (ENG.). 144p. pap. 12.99 *(978-0-310-28371-3(X))* Zondervan.

—An Agenda for Change: A Global Call for Spiritual & Social Transformation, 1 vol. 2008. (ENG., Illus.). 144p. (gr. 13). 14.99 *(978-0-310-28400-0(7))* Zondervan.

Edwards, Judson. Making the Good News Good Again: Recovering the Wonder of the Gospel. 2009. pap. *(978-1-57312-529-1(6))* Smyth & Helwys Publishing, Inc.

Ekblad, Bob. A New Christian Manifesto: Pledging Allegiance to the Kingdom of God. 2008. (ENG.). 184p. pap. 20.00 *(978-0-664-23231-3(0))* Westminster John Knox Pr.

Elbert, Paul, ed. Faces of Renewal: Studies in Honor of Stanley M. Horton. 2007. 320p. pap. 35.00 *(978-1-55635-250-8(6)*, Wipf and Stock) Wipf & Stock Pubs.

Ellingson, Stephen. The Megachurch & the Mainline: Remaking Religious Tradition in the Twenty-First Century. 2007. 256p. 52.50 *(978-0-226-20489-5(8))*; per. 22.50 *(978-0-226-20490-1(1))* Univ. of Chicago Pr.

Evans, Roderick L. The Apostolic Revolution: Examining the Apostolic Restoration & Reformation. 2011. 82p. pap. 11.95 *(978-1-60141-104-4(9)*, 374353) Kingdom Builders Publishing.

—Faith for the Journey (Volume III) Daily Reflections for Christian Living. 2009. (ENG.). 30p. pap. 9.95 *(978-1-60141-105-1(7)*, 374382) Kingdom Builders Publishing.

Ford, David. Growing the Church. 2008. 112p. per. 10.99 *(978-1-60477-524-2(6))* Xulon Pr., Inc.

Ford, Kevin G. Transforming Church: Bringing Out the Good to Get to Great. 2008. (ENG.). 288p. pap. 14.99 *(978-1-4347-6704-2(3))* Cook, David C.

Gallagher, Carol J. Reweaving the Sacred: A Practical Guide to Change & Growth for Challenged Congregations. 2008. 144p. pap. 16.00 *(978-0-89869-588-5(0))* Church Publishing, Inc.

Galloway, Dale E. & Bird, Warren. Innovative Transitions: How Change Can Take Your Church to the Next Level. 2007. (ENG.). 160p. per. 14.99 *(978-0-8341-2339-7(8)*, 083-412-3398) Beacon Hill Pr. of Kansas City.

Gerald, Kevin. By Design or Default: Creating a Church Culture That Works, 0 vols. 2007. (Illus.). 160p. per. 12.99 *(978-1-59951-030-9(8))* Nelson, Thomas Inc.

Gibbs, Eddie & Cohick, Lynn. ChurchMorph: How Megatrends Are Reshaping Christian Communities, 1 vol. 2009. (Allelon Missional Ser.). (Illus.). 224p. (C). pap. 20.00 *(978-0-8010-3762-7(X))* Baker Academic.

Gifford, Mary Louise. The Turnaround Church: Inspiration & Tools for Life-Sustaining Change. 2009. *(978-1-56699-393-7(8))* Alban Institute, Inc.

Goodpaster, Larry M. There's Power in the Connection: Building a Network of Dynamic Congregations. 2008. 146p. pap. 16.00 *(978-0-687-64979-2(X))* Abingdon Pr.

Gordon, A. J., et al. How Christ Came to Church: The Pastor's Dream A Spiritual Autobiography. l.t. ed. 2011. pap. 17.99 *(978-1-59415-394-5(9))* Cengage Gale.

Gore, Charles. Essays in Aid of the Reform of the Church. 2008. 388p. pap. 33.95 *(978-1-4368-3790-3(1))* Kessinger Publishing, LLC.

Gore, Charles, ed. Essays in Aid of the Reform of the Church. 2008. 392p. pap. 33.00 *(978-1-60608-120-4(9))* Wipf & Stock Pubs.

Greenwood, Robin. Transforming Church: Liberating Structures for Ministry. 160p. 14.00 *(978-0-281-05208-0(5))* SPCK Publishing GBR. Dist: Pilgrim Pr., The/United Church Pr.

Grenz, Linda L. Transforming Disciples. 2008. (Transformations Ser.). 192p. pap. 16.00 *(978-0-89869-598-4(8))* Church Publishing, Inc.

Hagey, Douglas. In Search of the Church. 2007. 212p. (ENG.). 24.99 *(978-1-60477-144-2(5))*; per. 14.99 *(978-1-60477-143-5(7))* Xulon Pr., Inc.

Halter, Hugh & Smay, Matt. The Tangible Kingdom: Creating Incarnational Community. 2008. (Jossey-Bass Leadership Network Ser.: 25). (ENG., Illus.). 224p. 24.95 *(978-0-470-18897-2(9)*, Jossey-Bass) Wiley, John & Sons, Inc.

—The Tangible Kingdom Primer: An eight-week guide to incarnational Community. 2009. (Illus.). 228p. spiral bd. 14.99 *(978-0-9823233-0-4(1))* Church Resource Ministries.

Hamm, Richard L. Recreating the Church: Leadership for the Postmodern Age. 2007. (Columbia Partnership Leadership Ser.). (Illus.). 130p. per. 19.99 *(978-0-8272-3253-2(5))* Chalice Pr.

Hampson, Michael. Last Rites: The End of the Church of England. 2006. (ENG.). 208p. per. 24.95 *(978-1-86207-891-8(2))* Granta Bks. GBR. Dist: Independent Pubs. Group.

Hamstra, Sam & Hamstra, Sam, Jr. Principled Worship: Biblical Guidelines for Emerging Liturgies. 2006. 142p. pap. 18.00 *(978-1-59752-523-7(5)*, Wipf and Stock) Wipf & Stock Pubs.

Handley, Larry. Salt Without Savour. 2007. 193p. pap. 24.95 *(978-1-4241-6394-6(3))* PublishAmerica, Inc.

Harding, Kevass J. Can These Bones Live? Bringing New Life to a Dying Church. 2007. 90p. per. 14.00 *(978-0-687-33557-2(4))* Abingdon Pr.

Heath, Elaine A. & Kisker, Scott T. Longing for Spring. 2011. (ENG.). 116p. pap. 31.25 *(978-0-7188-9242-5(9))* Lutterworth Pr., The GBR. Dist: Printondemand-worldwide.com.

—Longing for Spring. 2009. (New Monastic Library: Resources for Radical Discipleship Ser.). 118p. pap. 17.00 *(978-1-55635-519-6(X)*, Cascade Bks.) Wipf & Stock Pubs.

Hill, Robert Allan. Renewal: Thought Word & Deed. 2009. (ENG.). 162p. pap. 27.99 *(978-0-7618-4691-8(3))* Hamilton Bks.

Hurley, Michael. Parish Cell Communities as Agents of Renewal in the Catholic Church in Ireland: A Sociological Analysis. 2011. (ENG.). 516p. 149.95 ***(978-0-7734-2558-3(6))*** Mellen, Edwin Pr., The.

Husbands, Mark & Greenman, Jeffrey P., eds. Ancient Faith for the Church's Future. 2008. (ENG.). 272p. pap. 24.00 *(978-0-8308-2881-4(8)*, IVP Acad.) InterVarsity Pr.

James, John. Dry Bones Can Live: How to be Part of a Healthy Church. 2010. (ENG.). 209p. pap. 24.95 *(978-1-84694-282-2(9))* Hunt, John Publishing Ltd. GBR. Dist: National Bk. Network.

Janssen, Brian V. Cursillo. 2009. 280p. pap. 31.00 *(978-1-60608-775-6(4)*, Resource Pubns.) Wipf & Stock Pubs.

Jinkins, Michael. The Church Transforming: What's Next for the Reformed Project? 2012. (ENG.). 144p. pap. 17.00 ***(978-0-664-23843-8(2))*** Westminster John Knox Pr.

Jones, Toby. The Way of Jesus: Re-Forming Spiritual Communities in a Post-Church Age. 2010. 154p. pap. 18.00 *(978-1-60899-152-5(0)*, Resource Pubns.) Wipf & Stock Pubs.

Joyner, Rick. The Apostolic Ministry. 2006. (ENG.). 203p. mass mkt. 9.99 *(978-1-929371-99-0(3))* MorningStar Pubns., Inc.

Kalaga, Wojciech & Kubisz, Marzena, eds. A Culture of Recycling / Recycling Culture? 2011. (Literary & Cultural Theory Ser.). 180p. 53.95 ***(978-3-631-60163-1(8))*** Lang, Peter GmbH, Europäischer Verlag der Wissenschaften DEU. Dist: Lang, Peter.

Kelly, John P. & Costa, Paul. End Time Warriors. 2006. per. *(978-0-9787128-0-8(3))* Palm Tree Pubns.

Kemp, Bill. Peter's Boat: Renewing the Vitality of Burned-Out Church Workers. 2007. 104p. per. *(978-0-88177-499-3(5))* Discipleship Resources.

—Sauls Armor. 2007. 96p. pap. 6.00 *(978-0-88177-518-1(5))* Discipleship Resources.

Kimball, Dan. They Like Jesus but Not the Church: Insights from Emerging Generations, 1 vol. 2007. (ENG., Illus.). 208p. pap. 18.99 *(978-0-310-24590-2(7))* Zondervan.

—They Like Jesus but Not the Church: Responding to Culture's Objections to Christianity. 2008. (ENG.). (gr. 13). pap., pap. 52.99 *(978-0-310-27787-3(6))* Zondervan.

Kisker, Scott. Mainline or Methodist? Rediscovering Our Evangelistic Mission. 2008. 128p. pap. 13.00 *(978-0-88177-541-9(X))* Upper Room Bks.

Koivisto, Rex A. One Lord, One Faith, Second Edition: A Theology for Cross-Denominational Renewal. 2008. 428p. pap. 40.00 *(978-1-55635-947-7(0)*, Wipf and Stock) Wipf & Stock Pubs.

Lakeland, Paul & Lakeland. Catholicism at the Crossroads: How the Laity Can Save the Church. 2007. (ENG.). 176p. pap. 22.95 *(978-0-8264-2810-3(X))* Continuum International Publishing Group, Ltd. GBR. Dist: National Bk. Network.

Laubach, David C. 12 Steps to Congregational Transformation: A Practical Guide for Leaders. 2006. (Illus.). 143p. per. 12.00 *(978-0-8170-1502-2(7))* Judson Pr.

Lemler, James. Transforming Congregations. 2008. (Transformations Ser.). 192p. pap. 16.00 *(978-0-89869-584-7(8))* Church Publishing, Inc.

Long, Eddie. Este Es su Momento: Reclame su Territorio para el Reino. 2007. (SPA.). 191p. per. 10.99 *(978-0-88368-791-8(7))* Whitaker Hse.

Luecke, David S. Builder Ministry in the Twenty-First Century. 2010. pap. 19.99 *(978-0-7586-1669-2(4))* Concordia Publishing Hse.

Lynch, Don. The Spirit & Power of Elijah: Prophetic Parallels of the Ancient Prophets & Leaders of Today. 2007. 188p. per. 15.99 *(978-0-7684-2590-1(5))* Destiny Image Pubs.

MacDonald, Gordon. Who Stole My Church: What to Do When the Church You Love Tries to Enter the 21st Century, 0 vols. 2010. 272p. pap. 15.99 *(978-0-7852-3049-6(1))* Nelson, Thomas Inc.

MacGregor, Kirk R. A Comparative Study of Adjustments to Social Catastrophes in Christianity & Buddhism: The Black Death in Europe & the Kamakura Takeover in Japan As Causes of Religious Reform. 2011. 400p. 129.95 ***(978-0-7734-1549-2(1))*** Mellen, Edwin Pr., The.

Maldonado, Guillermo. The New Wine Generation. 3rd ed. 2007. 195p. per. 13.99 *(978-1-59272-039-2(0))* GM Ministries.

Malick, Faisal. More Glory: Open Your Heart to All of God. 2011. 240p. pap. 16.99 (978-0-7684-3089-9(5)) Destiny Image Pubs.

Martin, Glen. Power House: A Step-by-Step Guide to Building A Church That Prays. 2010. 276p. pap. 17.99 (978-1-61507-069-5(9)) Cross Bks. Publishing.

Martin, Martin Michael & Martin, Dennis Michael. Spiritual Poetic Meditations. 2009. 80p. pap. 10.99 (978-1-61579-094-4(2)) Xulon Pr., Inc.

Mather, Paul, et al. Missional Communities: The Rise of the Post-Congregational Church. 2011. (Jossey-Bass Leadership Network Ser.: 55). (ENG.). 192p. 24.95 (978-0-470-63345-8(X), Jossey-Bass) Wiley, John & Sons, Inc.

Matthey, Jacques. Come Holy Spirit, Heal & Reconcile: Report of the WCC Conference on World Mission & Evangelism, Athens, Greece, May 2005. 2008. 360p. pap. 35.00 incl. cd-rom (978-2-8254-1497-2(2)) World Council of Churches/Conseil Oecumenique des Eglises CHE. Dist: International Specialized Bk. Services.

McClure, Joshua A. Can These Bones Live? The Miraculous story of what can happen to a church that follows God's Vision. 2006. 250p. 14.95 (978-1-59886-472-4(6)) Tate Publishing & Enterprises, LLC.

McConnell, William T. Renew Your Congregation: Healing the Sick, Raising the Dead. 2007. (Columbia Partnership Leadership Ser.). 135p. per. 19.99 (978-0-8272-3255-6(1)) Chalice Pr.

McDermott, Patti D. Wake up My Children: Wake up God's Slumbering Bride. 2009. 344p. pap. 18.99 (978-1-61579-590-1(1)) Xulon Pr., Inc.

McDonald, Glenn. The Disciple Making Church: From Dry Bones to Spiritual Vitality. rev. ed. 2007. 268p. per. (978-1-932902-67-9(8)) FaithWalk Publishing.

McIntosh, Gary L. Taking Your Church to the Next Level: What Got You Here Won't Get You There, 1 vol. 2009. 224p. pap. 16.99 (978-0-8010-9198-8(5)) Baker Bks.

McNeal, Reggie. The Present Future: Six Tough Questions for the Church. 2006. (Jossey-Bass Leadership Network Ser.). (ENG.). 48p. pap. 9.95 (978-0-7879-9170-8(8), Jossey-Bass) Wiley, John & Sons, Inc.

McNeal, Reggie & McNeal. Missional Renaissance: Changing the Scorecard for the Church. 2009. (Jossey-Bass Leadership Network Ser.: 28). (ENG.). 224p. 24.95 (978-0-470-24344-2(9), Jossey-Bass) Wiley, John & Sons, Inc.

—The Present Future: Six Tough Questions for the Church. 2009. (Jossey-Bass Leadership Network Ser.: 42). (ENG.). 176p. pap. 16.95 (978-0-470-45315-5(X), Jossey-Bass) Wiley, John & Sons, Inc.

Metzler, Karin. Eustathios von Thessalonike und das Monchtum: Untersuchungen und Kommentar Zur Schrift de Emendanda Vita Monachica. 2006. (Supplementa Byzantina Ser.). (GER.). XIII, 624p. 196.00 (978-3-11-018905-6(4)) De Gruyter, Walter Inc.

Metzler, Karin, ed. Eustathii Thessalonicensis de Emendanda Vita Monachica. 2006. (Corpus Fontium Historiae Byzantinae Ser.). (GER.). VIII, 326p. 154.00 (978-3-11-018904-9(6)) De Gruyter, Walter Inc.

Möller, Christian. Kirche, Die Bei Trost Ist: Plädoyer Für eine Seelsorgliche Kirche. 2007. (GER.). 205p. (C). pap. 27.00 (978-3-525-60419-9(X)) Vandenhoeck & Ruprecht GmbH & Co. KG DEU. Dist: ISD.

Moss, Claudette. Washed White & the Seven Spirits of God. 2009. 244p. 25.99 (978-1-60791-484-6(0)); pap. 15.99 (978-1-60791-483-9(2)) Xulon Pr., Inc.

Mosser, David N., ed. Transitions: Leading Churches through Change. 2011. (ENG.). 256p. pap. 20.00 (978-0-664-23543-7(3)) Westminster John Knox Pr.

Murchison, William. Mortal Follies: Episcopalians & the Decline of Mainstream Christianity. 2009. (ENG.). 288p. 25.95 (978-1-59403-230-1(0)) Encounter Bks.

Nathan, Rich & Wilson, Ken. Empowered Evangelicals. 276p. pap. 11.99 (978-0-8307-3416-0(3), Regal Bks.) Gospel Light Pubns.

Neighbour, Ralph W., Jr. Christ's Basic Bodies: Embracing God's Presence, Power, & Purposes in True Biblical Community. 2008. (Illus.). 254p. pap. 21.50 (978-0-9788779-8-9(5)) Touch Pubns.

Nelson, Alan E. Me to We: A Pastor's Discovery of the Power of Partnership. 2007. (Illus.). 207p. per. 19.99 (978-0-7644-3486-0(1)) Group Publishing, Inc.

Nelson, Gary V. Borderland Churches: A Congregation's Introduction to Missional Living. 2008. 192p. pap. 19.99 (978-0-8272-0238-2(5)) Chalice Pr.

Nicholas of Cusa & Nicholas of Cusa. Writings on Church & Reform. Izbicki, Thomas M., tr. from LAT. 2008. (I Tatti Renaissance Library: 33). (LAT.). 688p. 29.95 (978-0-674-02524-0(5)) Harvard Univ. Pr.

Nixon, Paul. I Refuse to Lead a Dying Church! 2007. 122p. per. (978-0-8298-1759-1(X)) Pilgrim Pr., The/United Church Pr.

Ojara, Pius. New Birth. 2009. 196p. pap. 23.00 (978-1-60608-647-6(2), Wipf and Stock) Wipf & Stock Pubs.

O'Malley, Steven J., ed. World Revitalization Movements. 2011. pap. 35.00 (978-1-60947-018-0(4)) Emeth Pr.

Piazza, Michael & Trimble, Cameron. Liberating Hope: Daring to Renew the Mainline Church. 2011. (978-0-8298-1886-4(3)) Pilgrim Pr., The/United Church Pr.

Pogorelc, Anthony & D'Antonio, William. Voices of the Faithful: Loyal Catholics Striving for Change. 2007. (Boston College Church in the 21st Century Ser.). (ENG.). 272p. pap. 24.95 (978-0-8245-2460-9(8), Herder & Herder) Crossroad Publishing Co., The.

Powell, Brad. Change Your Church for Good: The Art of Sacred Cow Tipping, 0 vols. 2007. 320p. 16.99 (978-0-8499-1875-9(8)) Nelson, Thomas Inc.

Pugh, Jeffrey. Fantasyland Faith- the Redemptive Role of Ethical Lectors Within Neurotic Church Systems. 2007. pap. (978-3-8364-2896-5(2)) VDM Verlag Dr. Mueller e.K.

Ravenhill, Leonard. Revival God's Way: A Message for the Church. 2006. 160p. reprint ed. pap. 12.99 (978-0-7642-0302-2(9)) Bethany Hse. Pubs.

Reeder, Harry L. & Reeder, Harry L., III. From Embers to a Flame: How God Can Revitalize Your Church. 2008. 234p. per. (978-1-59638-071-4(3)) P & R Publishing.

Reid, Gregory R. Trojan Church. 2008. 208p. pap. 15.99 (978-1-60647-733-5(1)) Xulon Pr., Inc.

Rennie, K. Law & Practice in the Age of Reform: The Legatine Work of Hugh of Die (1073-1106) 2010. (Medieval Church Studies). (ENG., Illus.). 246p. (C). 102.00 (978-2-503-53190-8(3)) Brepols Pubs. BEL. Dist: ISD.

Robinson, Anthony B. Changing the Conversation: A Third Way for Congregations. 2008. 208p. pap. 18.00 (978-0-8028-0759-5(3)) Eerdmans, William B. Publishing Co.

Rollins, Peter. How (Not) to Speak of God. 2006. (ENG., Illus.). 144p. (gr. 13). pap. 19.99 (978-1-55725-505-1(9)) Paraclete Pr., Inc.

Rouse, Rick & Van Gelder, Craig. A Field Guide for the Missional Congregation: Embarking on a Journey of Transformation. 2008. (Illus.). 152p. pap. 14.99 (978-0-8066-8044-6(X)) Augsburg Fortress, Pubs.

Rowdon, Harold, ed. 10 Changing Churches. 2006. (ENG.). pap. 10.99 (978-0-900128-21-9(6), Paternoster) Authentic Media.

Ruffle, Douglas W. Roadmap to Renewal: Rediscovering the Church's Mission. 2009. 94p. pap. 9.95 (978-1-933663-39-5(1), GBGM Bks.) General Board of Global Ministries, The United Methodist Church.

Sadler, Paul Hobson. 52 Ways to Ignite Your Congregation — Worship. 2011. (978-0-8298-1878-9(2)) Pilgrim Pr., The/United Church Pr.

Sandford, R. Loren. The Prophetic Church: Wielding the Power to Change the World. 2009. 224p. pap. 17.00 (978-0-8007-9462-0(1)) Chosen Bks.

Sanguin, Bruce. The Emerging Church: A Model for Change & a Map for Renewal. 2008. (ENG., Illus.). 224p. pap. 24.95 (978-1-55145-566-2(8), Copperhouse) Wood Lake Publishing, Inc. CAN. Dist: Westminster John Knox Pr.

Savage, Sarah, et al. The Human Face of Church: A Social Psychology & Pastoral Theology Resource for Pioneer & Traditional Ministry. 2007. (Illus.). 333p. per. 29.99 (978-1-85311-812-8(5)) Canterbury Pr.

Schieler, Robert D. Revive Your Mainline Congregation: Prescriptions for Vital Church Life. 2010. 154p. pap. 18.00 (978-1-60899-228-7(4), Wipf and Stock) Wipf & Stock Pubs.

Schnase, Robert. Five Practices of Fruitful Congregations. 2007. 144p. per. 18.00 (978-0-687-64540-4(9)) Abingdon Pr.

—Radical Hospitality. 2008. 31p. pap. 7.00 (978-0-687-65423-9(8)) Abingdon Pr.

Schnase, Robert C. Five Practices of Fruitful Congregations (Korean Version) Kim, Hyo Shik Rev, tr. 2010. 144p. mass mkt. 18.00 (978-1-4267-0054-5(7)) Abingdon Pr.

Scott, Katherine Tyler. Transforming Leadership. 2010. (Transformations Ser.). 144p. pap. 16.00 (978-0-89869-599-1(6)) Church Publishing, Inc.

Short, L. Faye & Kiser, Kathryn D. Reclaiming the Wesleyan Social Witness: Offering Christ. 2008. 214p. pap. 18.95 (978-1-57736-409-2(0)) Providence Hse Pubs.

Smith, Daniel P. & Sellon, Mary K. Pathway to Renewal: Practical Steps for Congregations. 2008. (978-1-56699-371-5(7)) Alban Institute, Inc.

Smith Jr., Ron. Churches Gone Wild: Exposing the Church to the Vision of God, so the Church Will Quit Exposing Itself to the World! 2011. 192p. 30.95 (978-1-61507-714-4(6)); pap. 13.95 (978-1-61507-715-1(4)) Cross Bks. Publishing.

Smith, Luther E. Jr., et al. Intimacy & Mission: Intentional Community as Crucible for Radical Discipleship. 2007. 188p. pap. 22.00 (978-1-55635-537-0(8), Wipf and Stock) Wipf & Stock Pubs.

Snyder, Howard A. Yes in Christ: Wesleyan Reflections on Gospel, Mission & Culture. 2011. (978-1-894667-99-9(9), Clements Academic) Clements Publishing.

Snyder, Howard A. & Runyan, Daniel V. Decoding the Church: Mapping the DNA of Christ's Body. 2011. 208p. pap. 23.00 (978-1-61097-710-4(6), Wipf and Stock) Wipf & Stock Pubs.

Snyder, James L., compiled by. Rut, Rot or Revival: The Problem of Change & Breaking Out of the Status Quo. 2006. 163p. pap. 12.99 (978-1-60066-048-1(7)) WingSpread Publishers.

Spencer, Aída Besançon, et al. Global Voices on Biblical Equality: Women & Men Ministering Together in the Church. 2008. (House of Prisca & Aquila Ser.). 264p. pap. 29.00 (978-1-55635-055-9(4)) Wipf & Stock Pubs.

Spong, John Shelby. Jesus for the Non-Religious: Seeking the Divine Christ in the Heart of the Human Jesus. 2007. 336p. 24.95 (978-0-06-076207-0(1), HarperOne) HarperCollins Pubs.

Stackhouse, Reginald. Alive Again: Recession & Recovery in the Churches. 144p. pap. 13.95 (978-1-55126-257-4(6), 1532) Anglican Bk. Ctr. CAN. Dist: Forward Movement Pubns.

Stearns, Robert. Prepare the Way (or Get Out of the Way!) 12 Issues That Will Make or Break the Church. 2007. 285p. per. 15.99 (978-0-7684-2601-4(4)) Destiny Image Pubs.

Steinke, Peter L. A Door Set Open: Grounding Change in Mission & Hope. 2010. (978-1-56699-403-3(9)) Alban Institute, Inc.

Stetzer, Ed, et al. 11 Innovations in the Local Church: How Today's Leaders Can Learn, Discern & Move into the Future. 2007. (ENG., Illus.). 256p. per. 14.99 (978-0-8307-4378-0(2)) Gospel Light Pubns.

Stewart, Carlyle Fielding, III, ed. Growing the African American Church. 2006. 177p. per. 21.00 (978-0-687-49839-0(2)) Abingdon Pr.

Stockstill, Larry. The Remnant: Restoring Integrity to American Ministry. 2008. (ENG.). 208p. pap. 10.99 (978-1-59979-454-9(3), Charisma Hse.) Charisma Media.

Sweet, Leonard. So Beautiful: Divine Design for Life & the Church. 2009. (ENG.). 304p. pap. 16.99 (978-1-4347-9979-1(4)) Cook, David C.

Swindoll, Charles R. The Church Awakening: An Urgent Call for Renewal. 2010. (ENG.). 304p. 23.99 (978-0-446-55653-8(X)) FaithWords.

Tenny-Brittian, J. Kristina. Top 10 Ways to Defuse Your Congregational Time Bomb. 2008. xii, 159p. (978-0-8298-1804-8(9)) Pilgrim Pr., The/United Church Pr.

Thompson, Beverly & Thompson, George B. Grace for the Journey: Practices & Possibilities for In-Between Times. 2011. (978-1-56699-420-0(9)) Alban Institute, Inc.

Thorpe, Jacqulyln, ed. God Delivers Me: A Model from Strengthening the Black Church for the 21st Century. 2008. 250p. 16.00 (978-0-687-64889-4(0)) Abingdon Pr.

Tracy, Denise D. Healing the Congregation: A Resource. pap. 10.00 (978-1-56699-160-5(9)) Alban Institute, Inc.

Tucker, Graham. Restoring the Vision: The Kingdom of God, the Church of the Future. 95p. pap. 10.95 (978-1-55126-216-1(9), 1510) Anglican Bk. Ctr. CAN. Dist: Forward Movement Pubns.

Van Eijnatten, Joris & Yates, Paula, eds. The Churches. 2011. (Dynamics of Religious Reform in Northern Europe, 1780ndash;1920 Ser.). 288p. 89.50 (978-90-5867-826-3(1)) Leuven Univ. Pr. BEL. Dist: Cornell Univ. Pr.

Vickers, Jason E. Minding the Good Ground: A Theology for Church Renewal. 2011. (ENG.). 151p. pap. 24.95 (978-1-60258-360-3(9)) Baylor Univ. Pr.

Vila, Samuel. Se Renueva la Iglesia: Is the Catholic Church Renewing? (SPA.). (978-84-7645-231-8(4), 223271) Clie, Editorial.

Viola, Frank. Finding Organic Church: A Comprehensive Guide to Starting & Sustaining Authentic Christian Communities, 1 vol. 2009. (ENG.). 320p. pap. 14.99 (978-1-4347-6866-7(X)) Cook, David C.

—From Eternity to Here: Rediscovering the Ageless Purpose of God, 1 vol. 2009. (ENG.). 320p. pap. 14.99 (978-1-4347-6870-4(8)) Cook, David C.

—Reimagining Church: Pursuing the Dream of Organic Christianity. 2008. (ENG.). 320p. pap. 14.99 (978-1-4347-6875-9(9)) Cook, David C.

Viola, Frank & Barna, George. Pagan Christianity? Exploring the Roots of Our Church Practices. (ENG.). 336p. 2012. pap. 14.99 (978-1-4143-6455-1(5)) 2008. 17.99 (978-1-4143-1485-3(X)) Tyndale Hse. Pubs. (BarnaBks.).

Wagner, C. Peter. Como Ser Libre del Espiritu Religioso, 1 vol. 2007. (SPA.). 160p. per. 7.99 (978-987-557-111-2(3)) Vida Pubs.

Waking to God's Dream. 15.00 (978-0-687-00564-2(7)) Abingdon Pr.

Wardle, Terry. Untamed Christian, Unleashed Church: The Extravagance of the Holy Spirit in Life & Ministry. 2010. 192p. pap. 14.99 (978-0-89112-637-9(6), Leafwood Pubs.) Abilene Christian Univ. Pr.

Warford, Malcolm L. Becoming a New Church. 2009. 158p. pap. 18.00 (978-1-55635-517-2(3), Wipf and Stock) Wipf & Stock Pubs.

Watson, David. I Believe in the Church. (Illus.). 432p. pap. 15.95 (978-0-340-74554-0(1), Coronet) Hodder General Publishing Div. GBR. Dist: Trafalgar Square Publishing.

Webster, Alan. Reaching for Reality. 176p. 16.00 (978-0-281-05438-1(X)) SPCK Publishing GBR. Dist: Pilgrim Pr., The/United Church Pr.

Whitcomb, Norman K. Myopic Man: Can a United Church Prevent the Collapse of the American Empire? 2010. 236p. (ENG.). 28.95 (978-1-4502-2624-0(8)); pap. 18.95 (978-1-4502-2622-6(1)) iUniverse, Inc.

Whitesel, Bob. Preparing for Change Reaction: How to Introduce Change in Your Church. 2008. (Illus.). 222p. per. (978-0-89827-364-9(1)) Wesleyan Publishing Hse.

Whiting, Robert. The Reformation of the English Parish Church. 2010. (ENG., Illus.). 318p. 104.00 (978-0-521-76286-1(3)) Cambridge Univ. Pr.

Whitsitt, Landon. Open Source Church: Making Room for the Wisdom of All. 2011. (978-1-56699-412-5(8)) Alban Institute, Inc.

Willert, Trine Stauning & Molokotos-Liederman, Lina. Innovation in the Christian Orthodox Tradition? the Question of Change in Greek Orthodox Thought & Practice. 2012. (Illus.). 256p. 99.95 (978-1-4094-2077-4(9)) Ashgate Publishing Co.

Wilson, Mark O. Filled up, Poured Out: How God's Spirit Can Revive Your Passion & Purpose. 2012. (978-0-89827-527-8(X)) Wesleyan Publishing Hse.

Young, David S. Springs of Living Water: Christ-Centered Church Renewal. 2008. (Illus.). 387p. pap. 16.99 (978-0-8361-9411-1(X)) Herald Pr.

CHURCH RENEWAL—CATHOLIC CHURCH

Basse, Michael. Von den Reformkonzilien bis zum Vorabend der Reformation. 2008. (Kirchengeschichte in Einzeldarstellungen Ser.). (GER.). 224p. (C). 55.00 (978-3-374-02494-0(7)) Evangelische Verlagsanstalt GmbH DEU. Dist: Brown, David Bk. Co., The.

Baudry. A Warrior Bishop of the Twelfth Century: The Deeds of Albero of Trier. Pavlac, Brian A., tr. from LAT. 2008. (Mediaeval Sources in Translation Ser.). (ENG.). pap. 15.95 (978-0-88844-294-9(7)) Pontifical Institute of Mediaeval Studies, Dept. of Pubns. CAN. Dist: Univ. of Toronto Pr.

Bowen, John P., ed. The Missionary Letters of Vincent Donovan: 1957-1973. 2010. (Illus.). 252p. pap. 28.00 (978-1-60899-117-4(2), Pickwick Pubns.) Wipf & Stock Pubs.

Christianson, Gerald & Bond, H. Lawrence. Church Reform & the Theological Task in Nicholas of Cusa & His Age. 2011. (Variorum Collected Studies Ser.). (Illus.). 362p. 134.95 (978-1-4094-2960-9(1)) Ashgate Publishing Co.

Congar, Yves. True & False Reform in the Church. 2011. 39.95 (978-0-8146-5693-8(5)); E-Book (978-0-8146-8009-4(7)) Liturgical Pr.

Crosby, Michael H. Repair My House: Becoming a Kindom Catholic. 2012. (ENG.). 192p. pap. 22.00 (978-1-57075-953-6(7)) Orbis Bks.

Duffy, Eugene, ed. Parishes in Transition. 2011. (ENG., Illus.). 240p. pap. 26.95 (978-1-85607-706-4(3)) Columba Pr. IRL. Dist: Dufour Editions, Inc.

Griffith, Colleen M., ed. Prophetic Witness: Catholic Women's Strategies for Reform. 2009. (ENG.). 296p. pap. 39.95 (978-0-8245-2526-2(4)) Crossroad Publishing Co., The.

Grudzen, Gerald & Raymaker, John. Steps Toward Vatican III: Catholics Pathfinding a Global Spirituality with Islam & Buddhism. 3rd ed. 2008. (ENG.). 222p. pap. 38.99 (978-0-7618-4051-0(6)) Univ. Pr. of America, Inc.

Haverkamp, Paul. Rückkehr Zu Den Jesuanischen Quellen: Momentaufnahmen Zur Katholischen Kirche Am Beginn des 3. Jahrtausends. 2008. (GER.). 239p. (978-3-86557-175-5(1)) Nora Verlagsgemeinschaft Dyck and Westerheide.

Hayes, Michael A., ed. New Religious Movements in the Catholic Church. 2006. (ENG.). 192p. 19.95 (978-0-8264-9357-6(2)) Continuum International Publishing Group, Ltd. GBR. Dist: National Bk. Network.

Hill, Brennan. The Ongoing Renewal of Catholicism. 2008. pap. 35.00 (978-0-88489-954-9(3)) St. Mary's Pr.

Kennedy, Kerry. Being Catholic Now: Prominent Americans Talk about Change in the Church & the Quest for Meaning. 2009. (ENG., Illus.). 288p. pap. 15.00 (978-0-307-34685-8(4), Three Rivers Pr.) Crown Publishing Group.

Kronenberger, Donald Louis. Reinventing the Catholic Church: Why It Must Be Done & How to Do It. 2007. (ENG.). 192p. per. 15.95 (978-1-58736-833-2(1)) Wheatmark.

Larkin, Brian. The Very Nature of God: Baroque Catholicism & Religious Reform in Bourbon Mexico City. 2010. (ENG., Illus.). 326p. (C). pap. 27.95 (978-0-8263-4834-0(3)) Univ. of New Mexico Pr.

McDannell, Colleen. The Spirit of Vatican II: A History of Catholic Reform in America. 2011. (ENG.). 304p. (gr. 9). 26.99 (978-0-465-04480-1(8)) Basic Bks.

Mixson, James D. Poverty's Proprietors: Ownership & Mortal Sin at the Origins of the Observant Movement. 2009. (978-90-04-17405-4(2)) BRILL.

Newman, John Henry, et al. Newman's Second Spring: And the Evangelization of Modern Culture. 2009. pap. (978-1-933184-52-4(3)) Sophia Institute Pr.

Orsy, Ladislas. Receiving the Council. 2009. 176p. pap. 29.95 (978-0-8146-5377-7(4), Liturgical Pr. Bks.) Liturgical Pr.

Pable, Martin. Reclaim the Fire: A Parish Guide to Evangelization. 2009. (Illus.). 168p. pap. 12.95 (978-0-87946-395-3(3)) ACTA Pubns.

Petot, Patrick. Alain de Solminihac (1593-1659), Prélat Réformateur: De L'abbaye de Chancelade à L'évêché de Cahors, 2 vols. 2009. (Bibliotheca Victorina Ser.). (FRE & ENG., Illus.). 1091p. (C). 203.00 (978-2-503-53278-3(0)) Brepols Pubs. BEL. Dist: ISD.

Piderit, John J. & Morey, Melanie. Renewing Parish Culture: Building for a Catholic Future. 2008. (ENG.). 256p. pap. 32.95 (978-0-7425-5904-2(1)) Rowman & Littlefield Publishers, Inc.

Piderit/Morey. Renewing Catholic in Parishes: Cb. 2008. (ENG.). 256p. 85.00 (978-0-7425-5903-5(3)) Rowman & Littlefield Publishers, Inc.

Schreck, Alan. Rebuild My Church: God's Plan for Authentic Catholic Renewal. 2010. 272p. pap., pap. 19.99 (978-0-86716-947-8(8), Servant Bks.) Franciscan Media.

Seasoltz, R. Kevin. A Virtuous Church: Catholic Theology, Ethics, & Liturgy for the 21st Century. 2012. (ENG.). 288p. pap. 38.00 (978-1-57075-973-4(1)) Orbis Bks.

Stolarski, Piotr. Friars on the Frontier: Catholic Renewal & the Dominican Order in Southeastern Poland, 1594-1648. 2010. (Catholic Christendom, 1300-1700 Ser.). (Illus.). 282p. 124.95 (978-1-4094-0595-5(8)) Ashgate Publishing Co.

Swidler, Leonard. Making the Church Our Own: How We Can Reform the Catholic Church from the Ground Up. Swidler, Leonard, ed. 2007. (ENG.). 176p. pap. 14.95 (978-1-58051-215-2(1), Sheed & Ward) Rowman & Littlefield Publishers, Inc.

CHURCH SCHOOLS

see also Vacation Schools, Religious

also subdivision Education under names of religious denominations, e.g. Lutheran Church—Education

Abrams, Paula. Cross Purposes: Pierce V. Society of Sisters & the Struggle over Compulsory Public Education. 2009. (ENG., Illus.). 296p. (C). 70.00 (978-0-472-11700-0(9)) Univ. of Michigan Pr.

Akins, Harold Deane Thomason. Founded on the Rock, Jesus Christ: Autobiography of the Co-Founder & History of the Renowned Savannah Christian Preparatory School. 2007. (Illus.). 200p. pap. (978-0-9724224-5-1(5)) Bonaventure Bks.

Austin, Sandy J. Crisis Manual for Christian Schools & Youth Workers: How to Prepare for & Handle Tragedy. 2006. (ENG.). 192p. per. 14.99 (978-0-8341-2310-6(X), 083-412-310X) Beacon Hill Pr. of Kansas City.

Barrera-Osorio, Felipe, et al, eds. Emerging Evidence on Vouchers & Faith-Based Providers in Education: Case Studies from Africa, Latin America, & Asia. 2009. (Directions in Development Ser.). (ENG., Illus.). 208p. pap. 25.00 (978-0-8213-7976-9(3), 9780821379769) World Bank Pubns.

Bays, Patricia. Eucharist. (Anglican Learning Centres Ser.). pap. 15.95 (978-1-55126-330-4(0), 1672) Forward Movement Pubns.

Bergt, Carolyn S., et al. Concordia Curriculum Guide, 8 vols. 2007. 31.99 (978-0-7586-1439-1(X)); 31.99 (978-0-7586-1441-4(1)); 29.99 (978-0-7586-1431-5(4)); 29.99 (978-0-7586-1429-2(2)); 30.99 (978-0-7586-1435-3(7)); 30.99 (978-0-7586-1437-7(3)); 29.99 (978-0-7586-1427-8(6)); 30.99 (978-0-7586-1433-9(0)) Concordia Publishing Hse.

Cairns, Jo. Faith Schools & Society: Civilising the Debate. 2009. (ENG.). 284p. 140.00 (978-1-84706-229-1(6)) Continuum International Publishing Group, Ltd. GBR. Dist: National Bk. Network.

Cairns, Jo. Faith Schools & Society: Civilising the Debate. 2011. (ENG.). 284p. pap. 49.95 **(978-1-4411-9790-0(7))** Continuum International Publishing Group, Ltd. GBR. Dist: National Bk. Network.

Coley, Kenneth S. Navigating the Storms: Leading Christian Schools with Character & Conviction. 2010. pap. (978-1-58331-351-0(6)) Assn. of Christian Schls. International.

Deuink, James W. & Carruthers, Brian A. Management Principles for Christian Schools. 2nd ed. 2008. ix, 458p. (978-1-59166-803-9(4)) BJU Pr.

Engebretson, Kath, et al, eds. International Handbook of Inter-religious Education, 2 vols. 2010. (International Handbooks of Religion & Education Ser.). (ENG., Illus.). xv, 1185p. 699.00 (978-1-4020-9273-2(3), 1402092733) Springer.

General Record Book for the Church School & Small Group Ministry 2005-2008. 5.00 incl. cd-rom (978-0-687-05544-9(X)) Abingdon Pr.

Green, Janet. How to Turn Your Talent into a Business. 2011. (Illus.). 142p. pap. 18.95 net. **(978-1-934194-98-0(0))** Olmstead Publishing LLC.

Hunt, Thomas C. & Carper, James C., eds. The Praeger Handbook of Faith-Based Schools in the United States, K-12, 2 vols. 2012. 570p. 173.00 **(978-0-313-39139-2(4)**, A3131C) Greenwood Publishing Group, Inc.

Huntington, John T. Our Schools & Colleges by Rev John T Huntington. 2011. 36p. pap. 11.99 **(978-1-4181-9505-2(7))** MPublishing.

Ji, Chang-Ho C. Religiosity, Cultural Capital, & Parochial Schooling Psychological Empirical Research. 2010. (978-1-60752-381-9(7)); pap. (978-1-60752-380-2(9)) Information Age Publishing, Inc.

Johnson, Helen, ed. Reflecting on Faith Schools: A Contemporary Project & Practice in a Multi-Cultural Society. 2008. 240p. pap. 39.95 (978-0-415-46381-2(5)) 2006. (ENG., Illus.). 136p. 130.00 (978-0-415-40046-6(5)) Routledge.

Jones, Steven L. Religious Schooling in America: Private Education & Public Life, 1 vol. 2008. 208p. 49.95 (978-0-313-35189-1(9), C35189, Praeger Pubs.) Greenwood Publishing Group, Inc.

Lee, HeeKap. Faith-Based Education That Constructs. 2010. 324p. pap. 36.00 (978-1-60608-674-2(X), Wipf and Stock) Wipf & Stock Pubs.

MacMullen, Ian. Faith in Schools? Autonomy, Citizenship, & Religious Education in the Liberal State. 2007. (ENG.). 240p. (C). 42.00 (978-0-691-13091-0(4)) Princeton Univ. Pr.

Peppard, Doris. Teaching Tips. 2008. 219p. pap. 12.95 (978-0-929291-84-0(0)) Gospel Projects Pr.

Sengupta, Parna. Pedagogy for Religion: Missionary Education & the Fashioning of Hindus & Muslims in Bengal. 2011. (ENG.). 216p. 65.00 **(978-0-520-26829-6(6))** Univ. of California Pr.

—Pedagogy for Religion: Missionary Education & the Self-Fashioning of Hindus & Muslims in Bengal. 2011. (ENG.). 216p. pap. 26.95 **(978-0-520-26831-9(8))** Univ. of California Pr.

Southern, Louise. Disunited Kingdom. 2009. xvi, 180p. pap. 26.50 (978-1-906837-05-1(8)) Civitas:Institute for the Study of Civil Society GBR. Dist: Coronet Bks.

Strasser, Mark. Religion Education & the State: An Unprincipled Doctrine in Search of Moorings. 2011. (Law, Justice & Power Ser.). 214p. 109.95 **(978-1-4094-3644-7(6))** Ashgate Publishing Co.

Weinberg, Lawrence D. Religious Charter Schools: Legalities & Practicalities. 2007. (ENG.). 188p. (C). (978-1-59311-759-7(0)); per. (978-1-59311-758-0(2)) Information Age Publishing, Inc.

CHURCH SECRETARIES

Selles, Johanna M. The World Student Christian Federation, 1895Ð1925: Motives, Methods, & Influential Women. 2011. 312p. pap. 34.00 (978-1-60899-508-0(9), Pickwick Pubns.) Wipf & Stock Pubs.

Thompson, Sue. Ministry of Administrative Assistants. Hamilton, Adam, ed. 2008. (Cmg Ser.). (Illus.). 60p. pap. 9.00 (978-0-687-64709-5(6)) Abingdon Pr.

CHURCH SETTLEMENTS

see Social Settlements

CHURCH SLAVIC LANGUAGE

Bennett, Brian. Religion & Language in Post-Soviet Russia. 2011. (Routledge Contemporary Russia & Eastern Europe Ser.). (ENG., Illus.). 200p. (C). 145.00 (978-0-415-78063-6(2)) Routledge.

Le Feuvre, C. Le vieux Slave. 2009. (langues du Monde Ser.). (FRE.). 242p. (C). pap. 41.00 (978-90-429-2281-5(8)) Peeters Pubs. & Booksellers BEL. Dist: Brown, David Bk. Co., The.

Lunt, Horace Gray. Old Church Slavonic Grammar. 4th ed. (GER.). XIII, 143p. 210.00 **(978-3-11-216566-9(7))**; 135.00 **(978-3-11-119193-5(1))** De Gruyter, Mouton DEU. Dist: de Gruyter, Walter GmbH & Co. KG.

—Old church Slavonic Grammar. 5th ed. (ENG.). XIII, 143p. 210.00 **(978-3-11-218510-0(2))**; 135.00 **(978-3-11-119192-8(3))** De Gruyter, Mouton DEU. Dist: de Gruyter, Walter GmbH & Co. KG.

TSeitlin, R. M., et al. Staroslavianskii Slovar (Po Rukopisiam X-XI Vekov) (CZE, GRE, RUS & CHU.). 842p. (978-5-200-01113-1(2)) Russkij jazyk.

CHURCH SLAVIC LANGUAGE—BULGARIAN RECENSION

Jovceva, Marija, et al, eds. Berlinski Sbornik: Ein kirchenslavisches Denkmal mittelbulgarischer Redaktion des beginnenden 14. Jahrhunderts ergänzt aus weiteren handschriftlichen Quellen. 2006. (Schriften der Balkan-Kommission Ser.). (GER.). 456p. (C). pap. 126.00 (978-3-7001-3578-4(5)) Austrian Academy of Sciences Press AUT. Dist: Brown, David Bk. Co., The.

CHURCH SLAVIC LITERATURE

Franklin, Simon. Sermons & Rhetoric of Kievan Rus', 5. 2011. (Harvard Library of Early Ukrainian Literature Ser.). (ENG., Illus.). 326p. pap. 29.95 (978-1-932650-08-2(3)) Harvard Ukrainian Research Institute.

Smith, T. Allan. The Volokolamsk Paterikon: A Window on a Muscovite Monastery. 2008. (Studies & Texts). (ENG.). 74.95 (978-0-88844-160-7(6)) Pontifical Institute of Mediaeval Studies, Dept. of Pubns. CAN. Dist: Univ. of Toronto Pr.

CHURCH SOCIABLES

see Church Entertainments

CHURCH STAFF

see Church Officers

CHURCH STATISTICS

see also Church Work—Forms; Ecclesiastical Geography

American-French Genealogical Society Staff. Baptisms of Blessed Sacrament Catholic Church, Fall River, MA (1892 - 1995) 2007. 378p. spiral bd. 45.00 (978-1-60305-018-0(3)) American French Genealogical Society.

Anglen, Lavone Johnson. University United Methodist Church, Kansas City, Kansas, Records, 1919-2009, Members, Baptisms, Marriages, Deaths, Ministers. 2009. pap. 26.00 (978-0-7884-5020-4(4)) Heritage Bks.

Anglen, Lavone Johnson, compiled by. University United Methodist Church, Kansas City, Kansas: Records, 1919-2009: Members, Baptisms, Marriages, Deaths, Ministers. 2009. (Illus.). **(978-0-7884-8249-6(1))** Heritage Bks.

Bigart, Robert J., ed. Crossroad of Cultures: Sacramental Records at St. John the Baptist Catholic Church, Frenchtown, Montana, 1866-1899. Scott, Anita O. & Scott, James M., trs. from LAT. 2009. (Illus.). 240p. pap. 12.95 (978-1-934594-05-6(9)) Salish Kootenia College Pr.

Black, Lois. Danforth & North Broadview United Churches, Toronto (Formerly Methodist & Presbyterian): Baptisms, 1891-1925, Marriages, 1909-1925, Burials, 1909-1925: Fonds 1604 North Broadview Presbyterian Church, Fonds 1602 Danforth Methodist Church. 2010. (Illus.). viii, 133p. pap. **(978-0-7779-0423-7(3))** Ontario Genealogical Society.

—Queen Street United Church (Formerly Methodist), Queen Street at Euclid Avenue, Toronto, Ontario: Baptisms, 1867-1916: Marriages, 1868-1925: Burials, 1912-1921: Fonds 1295, 3425, 3457: A Genealogical Reference Listing. 2008. (Places of Worship Vital Statistics Ser.). xi, 377p. **(978-0-7779-0417-6(9))** Ontario Genealogical Society.

—Westennial United Church (Formerly Methodist), Toronto, Ontario: Baptisms, 1900-1925: Marriages, 1896-1925: Burials, 1900-1925: Fonds 2519, Including Fonds 2518 Wesley United Church, Fonds 1795 Grace-Carman United Church. 2009. (Illus.). **(978-0-7779-0419-0(5))** Ontario Genealogical Society.

Bray, Gerald, ed. Introduction. 2011. (Records of Convocation Ser.: Volume 19). 554p. 130.00 (978-1-84383-242-3(9), Boydell Press) Boydell & Brewer, Ltd. GBR. Dist: Boydell & Brewer, Inc.

Church, Diana. Zion in the Fields. 2009. (Illus.). 96p. pap. 24.00 (978-0-615-25570-5(1)) D-K Pubns.

Deeben, John Paul. Parish Records of Zion's Evangelical Lutheran Church, Trevorton, Northumberland County: Births, Marriages, & Deaths/Burials, 1859-1939. 2009. 117p. (978-1-55856-511-1(6)) Closson Pr.

Dobson, David. Searching for Scotch-Irish Roots in Scottish Records, 1600-1750. 2007. (Illus.). xii, 107p. pap. 19.50 (978-0-8063-5317-3(1)) Clearfield Co.

Dupuis, Kateri (Teri) & Cayen, Don. St Louis Catholic Parish, Fond du Lac, Wisconsin: Repertoire of Baptisms, Marriages & Burials, 1850-1920. 2010. (Illus.). 244p. pap. 25.00 (978-0-8063-5478-1(X)) Clearfield Co.

Fogle, Patricia A. Frederick County, Maryland, Church & Cemetery Records, Volume 4. 2008. 260p. per. 24.00 (978-1-58549-639-6(1)) Heritage Bks.

Gailus, Manfred. Kirchliche Amtshilfe: Die Kirche und die Judenverfolgung im »Dritten Reich«. 2008. (GER., Illus.). 223p. (C). pap. 27.00 (978-3-525-55340-4(4)) Vandenhoeck & Ruprecht GmbH & Co. KG DEU. Dist: ISD.

Gandy, Michael. Family History Cultures & Faiths: How Your Ancestors Lived & Worshipped. 2007. (Illus.). 256p. pap. 8.00 (978-1-905615-11-7(6)) National Archives (PRO), The GBR. Dist: International Publishers Marketing.

General Record Book for the Church School & Small Group Ministry 2005-2008. 5.00 incl. cd-rom (978-0-687-05544-9(X)) Abingdon Pr.

Haile, John J., Jr., compiled by. Saint Edward's Roman Catholic Cemetery - Coal Township, Northumberland County, Pennsylvania: Record of Interments 1870-2005. 2006. (Illus.). 856p. lib. bdg. (978-0-9711236-2-5(4)) Firenze Pr.

Hansen, Kevan M. Map Guide to German Parish Registers - Kingdom of Bavaria I - Regierungsbezirk Unterfranken. 2007. lib. bdg. 65.00 (978-1-933194-17-2(0)); per. 34.95 (978-1-933194-16-5(2), FR0027) Family Roots Publishing Co.

—Map Guide to German Parish Registers - Kingdom of Bavaria II - Regierungsbezirk Oberfranken. 2007. lib. bdg. 65.00 (978-1-933194-19-6(7)); per. 34.95 (978-1-933194-18-9(9)) Family Roots Publishing Co.

—Map Guide to German Parish Registers - Kingdom of Bavaria III - Regierungsbezirk Mittelfranken. 2007. lib. bdg. 65.00 (978-1-933194-21-9(9)); per. 34.95 (978-1-933194-20-2(0)) Family Roots Publishing Co.

—Map Guide to German Parish Registers - Kingdom of Bavaria IV - Regierungsbezirk Oberpfalz. 2007. lib. bdg. 65.00 (978-1-933194-24-0(3)); per. 34.95 (978-1-933194-23-3(5)) Family Roots Publishing Co.

—Map Guide to German Parish Registers - Kingdom of Bavaria V - Regierungsbezirk Schwaben. 2007. lib. bdg. 65.00 (978-1-933194-26-4(X)); per. 34.95 (978-1-933194-25-7(1)) Family Roots Publishing Co.

—Map Guide to German Parish Registers - Kingdom of Prussia - Province of Rhineland I - Regierungsbezirk Aachen & Duesseldorf. 2007. 65.00 net. (978-1-933194-11-0(1)); per. 34.95 net. (978-1-933194-10-3(3)) Family Roots Publishing Co.

—Map Guide to German Parish Registers - Kingdom of Prussia - Province of Rhineland II - Regierungsbezirks Köln & Koblenz. 2007. 65.00 net. (978-1-933194-13-4(8)); per. 34.95 net. (978-1-933194-12-7(X)) Family Roots Publishing Co.

—Map Guide to German Parish Registers - Kingdom of Prussia - Province of Rhineland III - Regierungsbezirk Trier & Kingdom of Bavaria - Palatinate (Pfalz) 2007. 65.00 net. (978-1-933194-15-8(4)); per. 34.95 net. (978-1-933194-14-1(6)) Family Roots Publishing Co.

—Map Guide to German Parish Registers - Kingdom of Prussia - Province of Westphalia I. 2011. 65.00 (978-1-933194-76-9(6)); pap. 34.95 (978-1-933194-75-2(8)) Family Roots Publishing Co.

—Map Guide to German Parish Registers - Kingdom of Prussia - Province of Westphalia II. 2011. 65.00 (978-1-933194-78-3(2)); pap. 34.95 (978-1-933194-77-6(4)) Family Roots Publishing Co.

Hoyt, William R. Effectiveness by the Numbers: Counting What Counts in the Church. 2007. 124p. pap. 22.00 (978-0-687-64175-8(6)) Abingdon Pr.

Huffman, Dennis, et al. Queen Street United Church Marriages, 1896-1945: City of Kingston, Frontenac County, Ontario. 2009. **(978-0-7779-2684-0(9))** Ontario Genealogical Society.

Jones, Patricia Dewey. Early Records of the Episcopal Church in Southwestern Idaho, 1867-1916: Silver City & Delamar. 2006. (978-0-9788882-0-6(0)) Boise State Univ.Albertsons Library.

Kelly, Arthur C. M. Vital Records of Cold Spring Methodist Church, Putnam County, NY 1863-1893: Baptisms 1864-1893, Marriages 1865-1893, Members 1825-1914. 2007. 36p. pap. 11.00 (978-1-56012-297-5(8)) Kinship.

—Vital Records of Freedom Plains Presbyterian Church, Lagrangeville, NY, Dutchess County, 1827-1900: Baptisms 1838-1890, Marriages 1838-1897, Deaths 1838-1890, Members 1827-1900. 2007. 91p. pap. 20.00 (978-1-56012-294-4(3)) Kinship.

—Vital Records of Presbyterian Church, Pleasant Valley, NY, Dutchess County, 1793-1947: Baptisms-1793-1830; 1869-1947, Marriages 1793-1947. 2007. 147p. pap. 34.00 (978-1-56012-292-0(7)) Kinship.

—Vital Records of Second Baptist Church, Philipstown, Cold Spring, Putnam County, NY 1808-1853: Marriages 1828-1853, Members 1808-1827. 2007. 11p. pap. 7.00 (978-1-56012-298-2(6)) Kinship.

Kotre, John. The View from the Border: Why Catholics Leave the Church & Why They Stay. 2009. (ENG., Illus.). 283p. pap. 24.95 (978-0-202-36307-3(4)) Aldine Transaction.

Middleton-Stewart, Judith, ed. Records of the Churchwardens of Mildenhall: Collections (1446-1454) & Accounts (1503-1553) 2011. (Suffolk Records Society Ser.: Volume 54). (Illus.). 318p. 60.00 (978-0-85115-578-4(2), Boydell Press) Boydell & Brewer, Ltd. GBR. Dist: Boydell & Brewer, Inc.

Murray, Sonia, compiled by. The First Parish Register of Belize, 1794-1810, & the First Four Censuses, 1816-1826. 2010. 292p. pap. 29.50 (978-0-8063-5482-8(8)) Clearfield Co.

Neininger, Falko. Brandenburgische Kirchenbuchduplikate 1794-1874: Ein Verzeichnis der Überlieferung im Brandenburgischen Landeshauptarchiv. 2008. (Quellen, Findbücher und Inventare des Brandenburgischen Landeshauptarchivs Ser.). 266p. pap. 65.95 (978-3-631-58057-8(6)) Lang, Peter GmbH, Europaischer Verlag der Wissenschaften DEU. Dist: Lang, Peter.

Ni Mhurchadha, Maighread, ed. The Vestry Records of the United Parishes of Finglas, St Margaret's Artane & the Ward: 1657-1758. 2007. (Illus.). 240p. 74.50 (978-1-84682-052-6(9)) Four Courts Pr. IRL. Dist: International Specialized Bk. Services.

Ontario Genealogical Society, Halton-Peel Branch Staff & Ontario Genealogical Society, Toronto Branch Staff, contrib. by. Davisville & Eglinton Communities, Toronto United Churches (Formerly Congregational, Methodist & Presbyterian) Baptisms, 1834-1925, Marriages, 1837-1925, Burials, 1936-1925. 2010. (Illus.). x, 186p. pap. **(978-0-7779-0428-2(4))** Ontario Genealogical Society.

—New Credit Indian Mission & Cooksville United Church (Formerly Methodist), Peel County, Ontario: Baptisms, 1802-1922, Marriages, 1836-1925, Burials, 1868-1922: Fonds 1434, New Credit Indian Mission, Port Credit, Fonds 1362, Cooksville Methodist Circuit, Fonds 1606, Clarkson Community Church. 2007. (Places of Worship Vital Statistics Ser.). **(978-0-7779-2746-5(2))** Ontario Genealogical Society.

Ontario Genealogical Society, Oxford County Branch Staff, contrib. by. Cemetery Transcription of African Methodist Episcopal Cemetery: Concession VIII, Lot 12, South Norwich Township, Now Known As 732695 Pick Line, Norwich Township. 2008. (Illus.). 7p. pap. **(978-0-7779-3520-0(1))** Ontario Genealogical Society.

—Cemetery Transcription of Pine Street Burying Ground (Also Known As the Friend's Cemetery) Concession IX, Lot 13, South Norwich Township, Now Known As 356 Main Street W, Otterville, Norwich Township. 2008. (Illus.). 17p. pap. **(978-0-7779-3519-4(8))** Ontario Genealogical Society.

—Cemetery Transcription of Rosanna Cemetery: Concession XI, Lot 18, South Norwich Township, Now Known As 145199 Potters Road, Norwich Township. 2008. (Illus.). 19p. pap. **(978-0-7779-3522-4(8))** Ontario Genealogical Society.

Pastor King: Martin Luther King, Jr. , as Spiritual Leader. 2011. pap. 19.00 (978-0-687-64496-4(8)) Abingdon Pr.

Peden, Henry C., Jr. A Closer Look at St. John¿s Parish Registers [Baltimore County, Maryland], 1701-1801. 2007. iii, 103p. pap. 15.00 (978-1-58549-843-7(2)) Heritage Bks.

Phillips, Willard. Death in Hollywood. 2012. (ENG.). 508p. pap. 17.99 **(978-1-4611-0632-6(X))** CreateSpace.

Price, Mitzi Fox. Friedens Church Register: Shenandoah County, Virginia; 1821-1874. 2008. (Illus.). 476p. pap. 45.00 (978-0-9802371-0-8(6)) Hottel Keller Memorial Inc.

Ranzan, David A. & Pardo, Janette Maria. The Asbury Methodist Episcopal Church Collection: Salisbury, Wicomico County, Maryland. 2009. 229p. pap. (978-1-55856-515-9(9)) Closson Pr.

Rudolph, Orion A., compiled by. Church Book: Evangelical Lutheran Hoffnungs Gemeinde, 1904-1944. 2008. (Illus.). 93p. (978-1-891193-68-2(6)) North Dakota State Univ. Libraries.

Savage, Ginette. Baptêmes de la Paroisse Saint-Jean-De-La-Croix, Montréal, 1900-1941. 2010. (FRE., Illus.). 706p. (978-2-923774-07-7(8)) Societe genealogique Canadienne-Francaise.

Stanford, Charlotte A. Commemorating the Dead in Late Medieval Strasbourg: The Cathedral Book of Benefactors, 1320-1520. 2011. (Church, Faith & Culture in the Medieval West Ser.). (Illus.). 348p. 124.95 **(978-1-4094-0136-0(7))** Ashgate Publishing Co.

Steel, D. J. National Index of Parish Registers. (Illus.).;p. (978-1-85951-086-5(8)) Bow Historical Bks.

Tharp, Jr. Standing Out of Sight: A History of Denominational Statistics in the Southern Baptist Convention 1882-2009. 2010. 160p. pap. 13.95 (978-1-61507-328-3(0)) Cross Bks. Publishing.

Todd, Margo, ed. The Perth Kirk Session Book, 1577-1590. 2012. (Scottish History Society 6th Ser.: Volume 2). (Illus.). 584p. 70.00 **(978-0-906245-31-6(1))** Scottish History Society GBR. Dist: Boydell & Brewer, Inc.

Venango County Historical Society Staff, contrib. by. VENANGO COUNTY, PENNSYLVANIA Cemetery Records & Early Church Histories. 2011. (Illus.). **(978-1-55856-542-5(6))** Closson Pr.

Wallace, W.J.R., ed. The Vestry Records of the Parish of St Bride, Dublin, 1662-1742. 2011. (Illus.). 352p. 70.00 (978-1-84682-285-8(8)) Four Courts Pr. IRL. Dist: International Specialized Bk. Services.

Woolever, Cynthia & Bruce, Deborah. A Field Guide to U. S. Congregations: Who's Going Where & Why. 2nd ed. 2010. (ENG., Illus.). 144p. pap. 20.00 (978-0-664-23514-7(X)) Westminster John Knox Pr.

Wright, F. Edward. Cumberland County, Pennsylvania, Church Records: 18th Century. 2008. 169p. per. 18.00 (978-1-58549-279-4(5)) Heritage Bks.

CHURCH TOWERS

see Towers

CHURCH UNITY

see Christian Union

CHURCH USHERS

Bell, Buddy. Ushering 101: Easy Steps to Ushering in the Local Church. 2007. (Illus.). 172p. (gr. k-12). per. 7.99 (978-1-57794-888-9(2)) Harrison House Pubs.

Degraw, Robert. The Church Usher: A Reference for Sanctuary, Greeting, Parking Lot, & Driving Ushers. 2010. pap. 14.95 (978-1-60799-252-3(3)) Tate Publishing & Enterprises, LLC.

2003 Guide for the Ushers' Auxiliary. (978-1-58942-120-2(5)) R.H. Boyd Publishing Corp.

CHURCH VACATION SCHOOLS

see Vacation Schools, Religious

CHURCH VESTMENTS

Dearmer, Percy. Linen Ornaments of the Church. 2010. pap. 19.24 (978-1-61719-835-9(8)); pap. 19.24 (978-1-61719-820-5(X)) Gorgias Pr., LLC.

Durand, William, et al. The Clergy & Their Vestments Bks. 2-3: A New Translation of the Rationale Divinorum Officiorum. Thibodeau, Timothy M., tr. from LAT. & intro. by. 2009. (Illus.). 262p. pap. 35.00 (978-1-58966-191-2(5)) Univ. of Scranton Pr.

Hattingh, Charl. Bridal Garment. 2007. 128p. per. 13.99 (978-1-60266-985-7(6)) Xulon Pr., Inc.

Karydis, Christos. The Orthodox Christian Sakkos: Ecclesiastical Garments Dating from the 15th to the 20th Centuries from the Holy Mountain of Athos. 2010. (Bar S Ser.). (ENG., Illus.). 410p. (C). pap. 157.50 (978-1-4073-0716-9(9)) British Archaeological Reports Ltd. GBR. Dist: Brown, David Bk. Co., The.

Sadlowski, Erwin L. Sacred Furnishings of Churches. 2006. pap. 22.95 (978-1-4286-5608-6(1)) Kessinger Publishing, LLC.

CHURCH WARDENS' ACCOUNTS

see Churchwardens' Accounts

CHURCH WORK

see also Christian Leadership; Church Entertainments; Church Group Work; City Churches; City Clergy; Deaconesses; Interdenominational Cooperation; Lay Ministry; Motion Pictures in Church Work; Pastoral Theology; Rural Churches; Suburban Churches; Visitations (Church Work); Women in Church Work

Abingdon Press. Rock-a-Bye Babies & Woddlers Ministry Guide: Teaching Faith in the Nursery. 2009. (Rock-a-Bye Ser.). 64p. 14.00 (978-0-687-65891-6(8)) Abingdon Pr.

Adams, Carl L. God's Dream Catcher. 2008. 260p. pap. 26.99 (978-1-60647-716-8(2)); pap. 16.99 (978-1-60647-715-1(3)) Xulon Pr., Inc.

Aeschliman, Gordon & Campolo, Tony. Everybody Wants to Change the World: Practical Ideas for Social Justice. 2006. (ENG.). 220p. per. 14.99 (978-0-8307-4283-7(2)) Gospel Light Pubns.

Albertini, Velmarie. Synergistic Collaborations: Pastoral Care & Church Social Work. 2010. (ENG.). 158p. pap. 24.99 *(978-0-7618-5430-2(4))* Univ. Pr. of America, Inc.

Allen, Roland. The Ministry of the Spirit: Selected Writings of Roland Allen. Paton, David M., ed. 2011. 240p. pap. 27.00 ***(978-1-61097-597-1(9)***, Wipf and Stock) Wipf & Stock Pubs.

Bailey, Keith M. Servants in Charge: A Training Manual for Elders & Deacons. 2007. 186p. pap. 11.99 *(978-1-60066-104-4(1))* WingSpread Publishers.

Bailey, Marcia. Choosing Partnership, Sharing Ministry: A Vision for New Spiritual Community. 2007. *(978-1-56699-343-2(1))* Alban Institute, Inc.

Baker, Kimball. Go to the Worker: America's Labor Apostles. 2010. pap. *(978-0-87462-749-7(4))* Marquette Univ. Pr.

Baldwin, Robert H. & Blom, Galen E. The Missing Church: The Power of Being the Body of Christ in the Family, Neighborhood & Workplace. 2010. pap. 27.99 *(978-1-60696-145-2(4))* Tate Publishing & Enterprises, LLC.

Banker, Sue. Mailbox Ministry: Greeting Cards That Share the Faith. 2009. 128p. 28.00 *(978-0-8192-2307-4(7)*, Morehouse Publishing) Church Publishing, Inc.

Bass, Diana Butler. Christianity for the Rest of Us: How the Neighborhood Church Is Transforming the Faith. 2007. (ENG.). 336p. pap. 14.99 *(978-0-06-085949-7(0)*, HarperOne) HarperCollins Pubs.

Beyond the Roll Book. 2006. 32p. 21.00 *(978-0-687-64140-6(3))* Abingdon Pr.

Bob, Moffitt. Si Jesus Fuiese Alcalde/If Jesus Were Mayor, 1 vol. 2009. (SPA.). 448p. pap. 14.99 *(978-987-557-231-7(4))* Vida Pubs.

Bos, A. David. Bound Together: A Theology for Ecumenical Community Ministry. 2010. 158p. pap. 18.00 *(978-1-60899-215-7(2)*, Wipf and Stock) Wipf & Stock Pubs.

Bouman, Stephen & Deffenbaugh, Ralston. They Are Us: Lutherans & Immigration. 2009. 160p. pap. 15.99 *(978-0-8066-5763-9(4)*, Augsburg Bks.) Augsburg Fortress, Pubs.

Bownas, Samuel. A Description of the Qualifications Necessary to a Gospel Minister. 2009. 62p. pap. *(978-1-151-34120-4(7))* Books LLC.

—A Description of the Qualifications Necessary to a Gospel Minister. 2008. 112p. 34.95 *(978-1-4368-8741-0(0))*; pap. 19.95 *(978-1-4367-2438-8(4))* Kessinger Publishing, LLC.

Bozeman, Hurdis. Lord, Why Not Me? 2007. per. *(978-1-59581-341-1(1)*, Brentwood Christian Pr.) Brentwood Communications Group.

Brendel, Doug. Why I Quit the Church. 2011. 248p. pap. 19.95 ***(978-0-557-86810-0(6))*** Lulu Enterprises Inc.

Bretherton, Luke. Christianity & Contemporary Politics: The Conditions & Possibilites of Faithful Witness. 2010. (ENG.). 272p. 99.95 *(978-1-4051-9968-1(7))*; pap. 42.95 *(978-1-4051-9969-8(5))* Wiley, John & Sons, Inc. (Wiley-Blackwell).

Broadwater, Donald A. God's Fire Starters. 2008. 244p. 25.99 *(978-1-60647-870-7(2))*; pap. 15.99 *(978-1-60647-869-1(9))* Xulon Pr., Inc.

Brown, Cheryl. M A F I A Ministry: A Crying Shame. 2011. 120p. pap. 12.95 ***(978-1-4620-0915-2(8))*** iUniverse, Inc.

Brunk, Truman H. That Amazing Junk-Man: The Agony & Ecstasy of a Pastor's Live. 2007. 216p. pap. 14.95 *(978-1-931038-44-7(9)*, DreamSeeker Bks.) Cascadia Publishing Hse., LLC.

Bunch, Randy. Offenses: Keeping the Church from Stumbling. 47p. (Orig.). pap. 3.95 *(978-0-940487-10-9(1))* Jubilee Pr.

Burns, C. E. The Zeal of Thine House Has Eaten Me Up! To the Church of the Living God with Love. 2010. 64p. pap. 9.95 *(978-1-4497-0508-4(1)*, WestBow Pr.) Author Solutions, Inc.

Cahalan, Kathleen A. Introducing the Practice of Ministry. 2010. 19.95 *(978-0-8146-3169-0(X))*; E-Book 9.95 *(978-0-8146-3928-3(3))* Liturgical Pr.

Cart, T. Michael. T R U T H in Ministry. 2008. 104p. pap. 12.95 *(978-1-934925-82-9(9)*, Strategic Bk. Publishing) AEG Literary Publishing Services, Inc.

Case, David. Releasing God's Life Through the Hearts of Men: Transforming a Broken Generation into Men & Women of God. 2008. (ENG.). 240p. pap. 13.99 *(978-1-59979-328-3(8)*, Creation Hse.) Charisma Media.

Chamness, Ben R. Notes to New Pastors. 2008. pap. 6.50 *(978-1-4267-0015-6(6))* Abingdon Pr.

Cole, Allan Hugh, Jr. Be Not Anxious: Pastoral Care of Disquieted Souls. 2008. 224p. pap. 20.00 *(978-0-8028-6310-2(8))* Eerdmans, William B. Publishing Co.

Coleman, Monica A. The Dinah Project: A Handbook for Congregational Response to Sexual Violence. 2010. 192p. pap. 22.00 *(978-1-60899-437-3(6)*, Wipf and Stock) Wipf & Stock Pubs.

Collins, Gary R. Christian Coaching: Helping Others Turn Potential into Reality. 2nd ed. 2009. (Walking with God Ser.). (ENG.). 416p. 27.99 *(978-1-60006-361-9(6))* NavPress Publishing Group.

Comiskey, Joel. Recoged la Cosech. 2011. 190p. pap. 12.95 ***(978-1-935789-02-4(3)***, CCS Publishing) CCS Pubs.

Conner, Benjamin T. Practicing Witness. 2011. 136p. pap. 16.00 *(978-0-8028-6611-0(5))* Eerdmans, William B. Publishing Co.

Cooke, Phil. Branding Faith: Why Some Churches & Non-Profits Make a Difference & Other's Don't. 2008. (ENG.). 224p. 17.99 *(978-0-8307-4563-0(7))* Gospel Light Pubns.

—Creative Christian Media. 2006. pap. 13.99 *(978-1-60034-600-2(6))* Xulon Pr., Inc.

Cooper, Terry D. & Randall, Robert L. Grace for the Injured Self: The Healing Approach of Heinz Kohut. 2011. 178p. pap. 20.00 *(978-1-60899-839-5(8)*, Pickwick Pubns.) Wipf & Stock Pubs.

Cordeiro, Wayne. Doing Church as a Team The Miracle of Teamwork & How It Transforms Churches. rev. ed. 2009. (ENG.). 232p. pap. 14.99 *(978-0-8307-3681-2(6))* Gospel Light Pubns.

Craycraft, Ron. It's Comeback Time. 2008. 148p. pap. 14.99 *(978-1-60647-971-1(7))* Xulon Pr., Inc.

Cress, James A. Common Sense Ministry Multiplied. 2010. pap. 11.99 *(978-0-8163-2411-8(5))* Pacific Pr. Publishing Assn.

Crocker, David W. The Samaritan Way: A Call to Lifestyle Compassion Ministry. 2008. (Columbia Partnership Leadership Ser.). 19.99 *(978-0-8272-3469-7(4))* Chalice Pr.

Crosby, Renee. Soup Kitchen for the Soul: What I didn't learn about God in church, I learned in a soup Kitchen! 2010. 148p. pap. 12.99 *(978-1-893729-79-7(6))* Energion Pubns.

Curran, Charles E. The Social Mission of the U. S. Catholic Church: A Theological Perspective. 2010. (Moral Traditions Ser.). (ENG.). 208p. pap. 29.95 *(978-1-58901-743-6(9))* Georgetown Univ. Pr.

Curran, Charles E. The Social Mission of the U.S. Catholic Church: A Theological Perspective. 2011. xi, 196p. ***(978-1-58901-717-7(X))*** Georgetown Univ. Pr.

Dadswell, David. Consultancy Skills for Mission & Ministry. 2011. 224p. pap. 35.00 ***(978-0-334-04373-7(5)***, SCM Pr.) Hymns Ancient & Modern Ltd GBR. Dist: Westminster John Knox Pr.

Davis, Tom. Red Letters: Living a Faith That Bleeds. 2007. (ENG.). 192p. per. 14.99 *(978-0-7814-4535-1(3))* Cook, David C.

DeGraw, Kathy. Time to Set the Captives Free: How to Start a Deliverance Ministry. 2011. 144p. 28.95 *(978-1-4497-1114-6(6))*; pap. 11.95 *(978-1-4497-1115-3(4))* Author Solutions, Inc. (WestBow Pr.).

DeKruyter, Arthur H. & Schultze, Quentin J. The Suburban Church: Practical Advice for Authentic Ministry. 2008. (ENG.). 148p. pap. 19.00 *(978-0-664-23294-8(9))* Westminster John Knox Pr.

Drescher, Elizabeth. Tweet If You Heart Jesus: Practicing Church in the Digital Reformation. 2011. E-Book *(978-0-8192-2452-1(9)*, Morehouse Publishing) Church Publishing, Inc.

Driver, Thomas L. 7 Keys to Effective Lay Ministry. 2012. 96p. pap. ***(978-1-55452-834-9(8))*** Essence Publishing.

D'Souza, Joseph & Rogers, Benedict. On The Side of the Angels: Justice, Human Rights, & Kingdom Mission. 2007. (ENG.). 216p. per. 14.99 *(978-1-932805-70-3(2))* Authentic Media.

Dunn, Heather, et al. Field Guide to Neighborhood Outreach. 2007. (Illus.). 143p. per. 9.99 *(978-0-7644-3589-8(2))* Group Publishing, Inc.

Dykstra, Craig & Bass, Dorothy C., eds. For Life Abundant: Practical Theology, Theological Education, & Christian Ministry. 2008. 372p. pap. 26.00 *(978-0-8028-3744-8(1))* Eerdmans, William B. Publishing Co.

Ebuziem, Cajetan E. Doing Ministry in the Igbo Context: Towards an Emerging Model & Method for the Church in Africa. 2010. (Bible & Theology in Africa Ser.). 288p. (C). 80.95 *(978-1-4331-1154-9(3))* Lang, Peter Publishing, Inc.

Edersheim, Alfred. Templo: Su Ministerio y Servicio En: Temple, First Ministry &... (SPA.). *(978-84-7645-388-9(4)*, 223483) Clie, Editorial.

Elisha, Omri. Moral Ambition: Mobilization & Social Outreach in Evangelical Megachurches. 2011. (Anthropology of Christianity Ser.). (ENG.). 251p. 60.00 *(978-0-520-26750-3(8))*; pap. 24.95 *(978-0-520-26751-0(6))* Univ. of California Pr.

Ellis, Wendy. The Hands of Time: A Passionate Look at Mentoring God's Way. 2010. 124p. 21.95 *(978-1-60976-281-0(9)*, Strategic Bk. Publishing) AEG Literary Publishing Services, Inc.

Ellison, Edna. Stronger Still: A Woman's Guide to Turning Your Hurt into Healing for Others. 2007. (ENG., Illus.). 224p. per. 14.99 *(978-1-59669-090-5(9))* New Hope Pubs.

Empowering Lay Volunteers. 2.00 incl. audio *(978-0-687-76228-6(6))* Abingdon Pr.

Epperly, Bruce Gordon & Epperly, Katherine Gould. Tending to the Holy: The Practice of the Presence of God in Ministry. 2009. *(978-1-56699-391-3(1))* Alban Institute, Inc.

Evans, Roderick L. The Believer's Guide to the Prophetic Ministry. 2008. 98p. pap. 16.95 *(978-1-60610-999-1(5))* PublishAmerica, Inc.

—He Gave Gifts unto Men: God's Plan for Ministry in the Kingdom. 2011. 50p. pap. 11.95 *(978-1-60141-003-0(4)*, 67041) Kingdom Builders Publishing.

Farabaugh, Timothy M. Lay Pastoral Care Giving. 2009. 154p. pap. 18.00 *(978-0-88177-554-9(1))* Upper Room Bks.

Fenimore, Brian. The Voice of the Lord Thunders. 2010. 202p. pap. 13.99 *(978-0-557-12359-9(3))* Lulu Enterprises Inc.

Fuder, John E. & Castellanos, Noel. A Heart for the Community: New Models for Urban & Suburban Ministry. 2012. (ENG.). 496p. pap. 29.99 ***(978-0-8024-0573-9(8))*** Moody Pubs.

Fulkerson, Mary McClintock. Places of Redemption: Theology for a Worldly Church. 2007. (ENG.). 266p. 75.00 *(978-0-19-929647-7(2))* Oxford Univ. Pr., Inc.

Gangel, Kenneth O. Coaching Ministry Teams: Leadership & Management in Christian Organizations. 2006. 232p. pap. 26.00 *(978-1-59752-657-9(6)*, Wipf and Stock) Wipf & Stock Pubs.

Gatta, Julia. The Nearness of God: Parish Ministry as Spiritual Practice. 2010. 160p. pap. 22.00 *(978-0-8192-2318-0(2)*, Morehouse Publishing) Church Publishing, Inc.

Gay Reese. Unbinding Your Church: Pastor's Guide: Steps & Sermons. 2008. (Real Life Evangelism Ser.). (Illus.). 129p. per. 19.99 *(978-0-8272-3806-0(1))* Chalice Pr.

Gordon, Wayne. Who Is My Neighbor? Lessons Learned from a Man Left for Dead. 2010. (ENG.). 192p. pap. 12.99 *(978-0-8307-5765-7(1))* Gospel Light Pubns.

Gould, Meredith. The Word Made Fresh: Communicating Church & Faith Today. 2008. 192p. pap. 22.00 *(978-0-8192-2285-5(2)*, Morehouse Publishing) Church Publishing, Inc.

Group Publishing, creator. Outreach Ministry in the 21st Century: The Encyclopedia of Practical Ideas. 2007. (Illus.). 224p. per. 24.99 *(978-0-7644-3437-2(3))* Group Publishing, Inc.

Guidelines 2001-2004 Mens Ministries. 2.50 *(978-0-687-03526-7(0))* Abingdon Pr.

Guidelines Organizing the Work of the Church. 1.00 *(978-0-687-01936-6(2))* Abingdon Pr.

Gula, Richard M. Just Ministry: Professional Ethics for Pastoral Ministers. 2010. 288p. pap. 19.95 *(978-0-8091-4631-4(2))* Paulist Pr.

Hamilton, Myrlene L. J. On the Road to Emmaus: A Travel Guide Through Grief. 2008. 160p. pap. 15.00 *(978-0-8170-1533-6(7))* Judson Pr.

Hannaford, Chuck. Picking up the Pieces Handbook: Creating a Dynamic Soul-Care Ministry in Your Church. 2009. 175p. pap. *(978-1-57494-344-3(8)*, Serendipity Hse.) LifeWay Christian Resources.

Harral, Stewart. Successful Letters for Churches: Tested Ways of Building Good Will by Mail. 2011. 246p. 46.95 ***(978-1-258-04090-1(5))*** Literary Licensing, LLC.

Hartung, Bruce. Holding up the Prophet's Hand: Supporting Church Workers. 2011. 318p. pap. 12.99 ***(978-0-7586-0548-1(X))*** Concordia Publishing Hse.

Harvey, Richard D. The Four Dimensions of the Ministry of Christ. 2008. 64p. pap. 9.99 *(978-1-60647-436-5(7))* Xulon Pr., Inc.

Hatmaker, Jennifer. Interrupted: An Adventure in Relearning the Essentials of Faith. 2009. (Experience the Life Ser.). (ENG.). 176p. pap. 12.99 *(978-1-60006-217-9(2))* NavPress Publishing Group.

Headley, Anthony J. Reframing Your Ministry: Balancing Professional Responsibilities & Personal Needs. 2007. 205p. per. 16.99 *(978-1-928915-97-3(3))* Evangel Publishing Hse.

Herb, Reese. Doing Good Well: Thirty Daily Meditations on Developing a Biblical & Focused Discipline of Good Works. 2007. 130p. spiral bd. 9.00 *(978-0-9797846-0-6(3))* New Commandment Men's Ministries.

Hernandez, Wil. Henri Nouwen & Soul Care: A Ministry of Integration. 2008. (Illus.). 128p. pap. 14.95 *(978-0-8091-4546-1(4))* Paulist Pr.

Heywood, David. Reimagining Ministry. 2011. 224p. pap. 32.99 *(978-0-334-04367-6(0)*, SCM Pr.) Hymns Ancient & Modern Ltd GBR. Dist: Westminster John Knox Pr.

Hibbert, Albert. Smith Wigglesworth: The Secret of His Power. 2009. 128p. pap. 9.99 *(978-1-57794-977-0(3))* Harrison House Pubs.

Hickey, Marilyn. Know Your Ministry. pap. 4.95 *(978-1-56441-012-2(9))* Hickey, Marilyn Ministries.

Hodges, Houston. The Lessons. 2010. 230p. pap. 19.70 *(978-0-557-22187-5(0))* Lulu Enterprises Inc.

Holsinger, James W. How to Develop Lay Ministry Within a Local Church: Enlarging Personal Faith Through Christian Leadership. 2010. iv, 117p. 99.95 *(978-0-7734-3593-3(X))* Mellen, Edwin Pr., The.

Holton, M. Jan. Building the Resilient Community: Lessons from the Lost Boys of Sudan. 2010. 186p. pap. 21.00 *(978-1-60899-245-4(4)*, Cascade Bks.) Wipf & Stock Pubs.

Hondagneu-Sotelo, Pierrette, ed. Religion & Social Justice for Immigrants. 2006. (ENG.). 256p. 68.00 *(978-0-8135-3908-9(0))*; per. 25.95 *(978-0-8135-3909-6(9))* Rutgers Univ. Pr.

Hryniuk, Michael. Theology, Disability, & Spiritual Transformation: Learning from the Communities of L'Arche. 2010. *(978-1-60497-694-6(2))* Cambria Pr.

Jeary, Tony. Purpose-Filled Presentations: How Any Christian Can Communicate More Effectively to Anybody, Anytime, Anywhere. 2009. (ENG.). 240p. pap. 14.99 *(978-0-7847-2314-2(1))* Standard Publishing.

Johnson-Gordon, Mary L. Tell My People the Unalterable, Inconvenient Truths. 2008. 216p. pap. 15.99 *(978-1-60647-969-8(5))* Xulon Pr., Inc.

Joiner, Donald W. & Wimberly, Norma. The Abingdon Guide to Funding Ministry Vol. 3: An Innovative Sourcebook for Pastors & Church Leaders. pap. 19.99 *(978-0-687-05737-5(X))* Abingdon Pr.

Kamese, Donald. Mission Possible. 2011. 152p. pap. 25.50 ***(978-1-4461-8143-0(X))*** Lulu Enterprises Inc.

Kasper, Walter Cardinal. A Celebration of Priestly Ministry: Challenge, Renewal, & Joy in the Catholic Priesthood. McNeil, Brian, tr. from GER. 2007. (ENG.). 192p. 19.95 *(978-0-8245-2467-8(5))* Crossroad Publishing Co., The.

Kemp, Bill. Peter's Boat: Renewing the Vitality of Burned-Out Church Workers. 2007. 104p. per. *(978-0-88177-499-3(5))* Discipleship Resources.

Kettler, Christian D. Reading Ray S. Anderson. 2010. (Ray S. Anderson Collection Ser.). (Illus.). 200p. pap. 23.00 *(978-1-60899-329-1(9)*, Pickwick Pubns.) Wipf & Stock Pubs.

Kibbey, Sue Nilson. Ultimately Responsible: When You're in Charge of Igniting a Ministry. 2006. (Illus.). 173p. 19.00 *(978-0-687-33492-6(6))* Abingdon Pr.

Knuth, Jane. Thrift Store Graces: Finding God's Gifts in the Midst of the Mess. 2012. (ENG.). 144p. pap. 13.95 ***(978-0-8294-3692-1(8))*** Loyola Pr.

Kok, James R. 90% of Helping Is Just Showing Up. 2nd ed. 2007. 128p. per. 11.95 *(978-1-59255-413-3(X))* Faith Alive Christian Resources.

Korgen, Jeffry Odell. My Lord & My God: Engaging Catholics in Social Ministry. 2007. 153p. per. 18.95 *(978-0-8091-4370-2(4)*, 4370-4) Paulist Pr.

Kownacki, Mary Lou. A Monk in the Inner City: The ABCs of a Spiritual Journey. 2008. 155p. pap. 18.00 *(978-1-57075-760-0(7))* Orbis Bks.

Kreider, Larry. Building Your Life on the Basic Truths of Christianity: Pretitle: Biblical Foundations for Your Life; Subtitle: Learning to Fellowship with God, What Is the Church?, Authority & Accountability, God's Perspective on Finances, Called to Minister, & the Great Commission. 2009. pap. 17.99 *(978-0-7684-2749-3(5))* Destiny Image Pubs.

Laizure, Rob, Sr. & Laizure, Lisa. Teamwork: What we as the Church should look Like. 2011. 142p. pap. 8.00 ***(978-0-9839929-3-6(2))*** Premier Graphics Publishing.

Lathrop, John P. Apostles, Prophets, Evangelists, Pastors, & Teachers Then & Now. 2008. 152p. pap. 13.99 *(978-1-60647-459-4(6))* Xulon Pr., Inc.

Learning & Leading in Ministry. 2008. pap. 10.99 *(978-1-56722-725-3(2))* Word Aflame Pr.

Lee, Inn Sook & Son, Timothy D., eds. Asian Americans & Christian Ministry. 2009. 338p. pap. 37.00 *(978-1-60608-546-2(8)*, Wipf and Stock) Wipf & Stock Pubs.

Lentz, Dan. Let's Get Started! How to Begin Your Small Groups Ministry. 2007. (Small Group Help Guides). (Illus.). 96p. per. 8.99 *(978-0-7847-2073-8(8))* Standard Publishing.

Lewis, Alvin. Orinoco! God at Work in Venezuela. pap. 19.99 *(978-1-59781-007-4(X))* Xulon Pr., Inc.

Lienhard, Joseph T. Ministry. 2011. 184p. pap. 21.00 ***(978-1-61097-648-0(7)***, Wipf and Stock) Wipf & Stock Pubs.

Life on Loan Church Experience Kit. 2007. 159.99 *(978-0-7847-2063-9(0))* Standard Publishing.

Luchon, Tim. Don't Muzzle the Ox. 2006. per. 7.00 *(978-1-60208-003-4(8))* FBC Pubns. & Printing.

Luebering, Carol. Wisdom for Everyday Life from the Book of Revelation. 2010. 144p. pap. 13.99 *(978-0-86716-905-8(2)*, Servant Bks.) Franciscan Media.

Lueking, F. Dean. The Grace of It All: Reflections on the Art of Ministry. 2006. xvi, 152p. *(978-1-56699-332-6(6))* Alban Institute, Inc.

Lwhorn, Shannon. Reaching the City for the King: God's Blueprint for Effective Outreach Ministry in the Inner City. 2009. pap. 12.99 *(978-1-61584-915-4(7))* Independent Pub.

Maddex, Mike. Musings of a Story Teller Wannabe. 2010. 211p. pap. 13.94 *(978-0-557-19742-2(2))* Lulu Enterprises Inc.

Maldonado, Guillermo. The Ministry of the Apostle: Discover the Truth about Apostolic Ministry. 2007. 186p. per. 13.99 *(978-1-59272-236-5(9))* GM Ministries.

Malphurs, Aubrey. A New Kind of Church: Understanding Models of Ministry for the 21st Century. 2007. (Illus.). 208p. pap. 15.99 *(978-0-8010-9189-6(6))* Baker Bks.

Markle, David. Next Steps to Ministry: Entering a Life in Christian Ministry. 2007. xiii, 253p. pap. *(978-1-59317-175-9(7))* Warner Pr. Pubs.

Marti, Gerardo. Hollywood Faith: Holiness, Prosperity, & Ambition in a Los Angeles Church. 2008. (ENG.). 288p. (C). pap. 25.95 *(978-0-8135-4349-9(5))*, Rutgers Univ. Pr.

Massey, Rhett Tyrone. To Live Again, a New Beginning. 2008. 300p. 28.99 *(978-1-60647-764-9(1))*; pap. 18.99 *(978-1-60647-763-2(3))* Xulon Pr., Inc.

McAlpin, Kathleen. Ministry That Transforms: A Contemplative Process of Theological Reflection. 2009. 160p. pap. 15.95 *(978-0-8146-3222-2(X))* Liturgical Pr.

McCormick, Deb. Making the Connection: A Reference Guide for Small Group Ministry Leaders. 2006. 24p. 8.95 *(978-0-9801644-1-1(9))* Teamed UP, LLC.

McCullen, Carl L. Church Worker's Manual, Vol. 1. Date not set. (Orig.). pap. *(978-1-887939-26-3(1)*, Go & Compel) VisionQuest Media Publishing Co.

McDuff, Mallory. Sacred Acts: How Chruches are Working to Protect Earth's Climate. 2012. (ENG., Illus.). 288p. pap. 17.95 ***(978-0-86571-700-8(1)***, 9780865717008) New Society Pubs., Ltd. CAN. Dist: Consortium Bk. Sales & Distribution.

McFarlane, Doreen M. Funerals with Today's Families in Mind: A Handbook for Pastors. 2008. 136p. per. *(978-0-8298-1786-7(7))* Pilgrim Pr., The/United Church Pr.

McIntosh, Gary L. Beyond the First Visit: The Complete Guide to Connecting Guests to Your Church. 2006. (Illus.). 192p. pap. 15.99 *(978-0-8010-9184-1(5))* Baker Bks.

McLaughlin, Tim & Navigators Staff. Pedaling Tandem for the Long Haul: On Managing Your Marriage. 2007. (Real Life Stuff for Couples Ser.). (ENG.). 160p. pap. 9.99 *(978-1-60006-163-9(X))* NavPress Publishing Group.

—Shooting the Rapids in a Wooden Canoe: On Navigating Transitions. 2007. (Real Life Stuff for Couples Ser.). (ENG.). 160p. pap. 9.99 *(978-1-60006-164-6(8))* NavPress Publishing Group.

McMahon, Christopher. Called Together: An Introduction to Ecclesiology. 2010. (ENG.). (C). pap. 23.95 *(978-1-59982-005-7(6))* St. Mary's Pr.

McMullen, Shawn A. Releasing the Power of the Smaller Church. 2007. (Escn Ser.). (ENG.). 160p. pap. 14.99 *(978-0-7847-2146-9(7))* Standard Publishing.

McQuilken, Robertson. The Five Smooth Stones: Essential Principles for Biblical Ministry. 2007. (ENG., Illus.). 240p. per. 14.99 *(978-0-8054-4518-3(8)*, B&H Bks.) B&H Publishing Group.

Meiners, Phyllis A. & Sanford, Greg A. National Directory of Church Philanthropy. (Illus.). 400p. pap. *(978-0-9633694-4-4(X))* CRC Publishing Co.-EagleRock Bks.

Melander, Rochelle. A Generous Presence: Spiritual Leadership & the Art of Coaching. 2006. xii, 370p. *(978-1-56699-325-8(3))* Alban Institute, Inc.

Merritt, Carol Howard. Reframing Hope: Vital Ministry in a New Generation. 2010. *(978-1-56699-394-4(6))* Alban Institute, Inc

Miles, Sara. Jesus Freak: Feeding Healing Raising the Dead. 2010. (ENG.). 192p. 21.95 *(978-0-470-48166-0(8)*, Jossey-Bass) Wiley, John & Sons, Inc.

Milhouse, Paul W. Enlisting & Developing Church Leaders. 2007. (ENG.). 108p. 34.95 *(978-0-548-06031-5(2))* Kessinger Publishing, LLC.

Miller, Bruce B. Your Church in Rhythm: The Forgotten Dimensions of Seasons & Cycles. 2011. (Jossey-Bass Leadership Network Ser.: 52). (ENG., Illus.). 224p. 24.95 *(978-0-470-59887-0(5),* Jossey-Bass) Wiley, John & Sons, Inc.

Miller D.D: Founder and Presiding Prelate, Arch-Bishop D. A. The Ministry of an Armourbearer: A Spiritual Approach, 1 vol. 2010. 52p. pap. 16.95 *(978-1-4489-9134-1(X))* PublishAmerica, Inc.

Miller, Linda J. & Hall, Chad W. Coaching for Christian Leaders: A Practical Guide. 2007. (Columbia Partnership Leadership Ser.). (Illus.). 148p. per. 19.99 *(978-0-8272-0507-9(4))* Chalice Pr.

Miller, Ricardo Sr. The Traveling Minister's Handbook: Keys to Developing A Successful Itinerant Ministry. 2011. 150p. pap. 19.99 ***(978-1-4568-8658-5(4))*** Xlibris Corp.

Miller, Robert S. Survival Handbook for Young Pastors: Keys to Overcoming Seven Imposing Battlefields of Pastoral Ministry. 2009. 216p. pap. 15.99 *(978-1-60647-977-3(6))* Xulon Pr., Inc.

Möller, Christian. Kirche, Die Be Trost Ist: Plädoyer Für eine Seelsorgliche Kirche. 2007. (GER.). 205p. (C). pap. 27.00 *(978-3-525-60419-9(X))* Vandenhoeck & Ruprecht GmbH & Co. KG DEU. Dist: ISD.

Moore, Steve. Who Is My Neighbor? Being a Good Samaritan in a Connected World. 2011. (LifeChange Ser.). (Illus.). 176p. 17.99 *(978-1-61521-723-6(1))* NavPress Publishing Group.

Morris, Leslie Takahashi, et al. The Arc of the Universe Is Long: Unitarian Universalists, Anti-Racism, & the Journey from Calgary. 2009. pap. 24.00 *(978-1-55896-548-5(3),* Skinner Hse. Bks.) Unitarian Universalist Assn.

Murphy, Doris. Learning Centers for First Reconciliation, First Eucharist, & the Whole Community. 2007. (Illus.). 91p. per. 14.95 *(978-1-58595-564-0(7))* Twenty-Third Pubns./Bayard.

Nance, Terry. God's Armorbearer: Running with Your Pastor's Vision. 2008. (God's Armorbearer Ser.). 166p. par. 14.99 *(978-0-7684-2611-3(1))* Destiny Image Pubs.

Nanko-Fernandez, Carmen. Theologizing en Espanglish: Context, Community, & Ministry. 2010. 208p. pap. 25.00 *(978-1-57075-864-5(6))* Orbis Bks.

Naylor, Beth & Seifert, Sheila. Sharing God: With Others. 2007. (Dsj Ser.). (Illus.). 112p. per. 16.99 *(978-0-7814-4443-9(8),* Nexgen) Cook, David C.

Nees, Tom. Best Practices of Growing Churches: Profiles & Conversations with Ministry Leaders. 2006. (Voices Ser.). (ENG.). 160p. per. 14.99 *(978-0-8341-2304-5(5),* 083-412-3045) Beacon Hill Pr. of Kansas City.

Nelson, John, ed. 101 Ideas to Transform the Local Church: A Modern Guide. 2011. (ENG.). 160p. pap. 22.99 *(978-1-84825-045-1(2),* Canterbury Pr. Norwich) Hymns Ancient & Modern Ltd GBR. Dist: Westminster John Knox Pr.

Newman, Lorie. A Cup of Cold Water in His Name: 60 Ways to Help the Needy. 2012. (ENG.). 320p. pap. 13.99 ***(978-1-57293-512-9(X))*** Discovery Hse. Pubs.

Nouwen, Henri J. M. The Way of the Heart: The Spirituality of the Desert Fathers & Mothers. 2009. (ENG.). 96p. pap. 10.99 *(978-0-06-066330-8(8),* HarperOne) HarperCollins Pubs.

Osei-Bonsu, Robert. The Nature of the Church & Ministry. 2010. 232p. pap. *(978-3-639-26605-4(6))* VDM Verlag Dr. Mueller e.K.

Pankau, Jason/ K. Omega Course Workbook: An Intensive 12 Session Journey Equipping You for a Lifetime of Discipleship! 2007. (Illus.). 249p. spiral bd. 29.95 *(978-0-9797141-0-6(9))* Life Spring Network.

Panos, Chris. God's Spy. Logos International Staff, ed. 5th ed. 270p. reprint ed. 15.95 *(978-0-910743-07-5(X));* pap. 6.95 *(978-0-910743-06-8(1));* pap. 5.95 *(978-0-910743-00-6(2))* Gold Bks. International, Inc.

Parker, Kathleen. Sacred Service in Civic Space. 2007. 368p. pap. 18.00 *(978-0-9795589-0-0(5))* Meadville Lombard Theological Schl. Pr.

Patterson, Deborah L. Health Ministries: A Primer for Clergy & Congregations. 2008. 127p. pap. 12.00 *(978-0-8298-1791-1(3))* Pilgrim Pr., The/United Church Pr.

Paul, Greg. The Twenty-Piece Shuffle: Why the Poor & Rich Need Each Other. 2008. (ENG.). 240p. pap. 14.99 *(978-1-4347-9942-5(5))* Cook, David C.

Pecknold, C. C. Christianity & Politics. 2010. (Cascade Companions Ser.). 196p. pap. 23.00 *(978-1-55635-242-3(5),* Cascade Bks.) Wipf & Stock Pubs.

Pembroke, Neil. Pastoral Care in Worship: Liturgy & Psychology in Dialogue. 2010. (ENG.). 208p. 32.95 *(978-0-567-33144-1(X));* 120.00 *(978-0-567-26265-3(0))* Continuum International Publishing Group, Ltd. GBR. (T&T Clark Int'l). Dist: National Bk. Network.

Penley, David. Cross-cultural Leadership. 2006. pap. 14.99 *(978-1-60034-590-6(5))* Xulon Pr., Inc.

Pennel, Joe E. The Gift of Presence: A Guide to Helping Those Who Suffer. 2009. 141p. 10.00 *(978-1-4267-0214-3(0))* Abingdon Pr.

Peters, Ronald E. Urban Ministry: An Introduction. 2007. (Illus.). 197p. per. 22.00 *(978-0-687-64225-0(6))* Abingdon Pr.

Petersen, Bruce L. Foundations of Pastoral Care. 2006. (ENG.). 320p. 44.99 *(978-0-8341-2305-2(3),* 083-412-3053) Beacon Hill Pr. of Kansas City.

A Poke in the Ribs. 2006. 176p. per. 10.95 *(978-0-938978-41-1(1))* Wycliffe Bible Translators.

Powell, Terry. Now That's a Good Question! How to Lead Quality Bible Discussions. 2007. (Small Group Help Guides). (Illus.). 96p. per. 8.99 *(978-0-7847-2074-5(6))* Standard Publishing.

Pozdol, Mary Beth. Doing the Works of Jesus. Date not set. (Character Ser.: Vol. 3). ring bd. 19.95 *(978-1-889723-17-4(7))* Family Harvest Church.

Pratt, Andrew. Practical Skills for Ministry. 2010. (SCM Studyguides Ser.). (ENG., Illus.). 192p. (C). pap. 32.99 *(978-0-334-04359-1(X),* SCM Pr.) Hymns Ancient & Modern Ltd GBR. Dist: Westminster John Knox Pr.

Presa, Neal D., ed. Insights from the Underside: An Intergenerational Conversation of Ministers. 2008. per. 17.00 *(978-1-56591-357-8(4),* Broadmind Pr.) Hollym International Corp.

Press Abingdon. Claim the Life - Journey. 2007. 80p. 18.75 *(978-0-687-64164-2(0))* Abingdon Pr.

—Claim the Life - Journey Semester. 2007. 80p. pap., stu. ed. 7.75 *(978-0-687-64174-1(8));* pap. 18.75 *(978-0-687-64234-2(5))* Abingdon Pr.

—Claim the Life - Promise. 2007. 80p. pap. 7.75 *(978-0-687-64194-9(2))* Abingdon Pr.

—Claim the Life - Promise Semester 2. ldr.'s ed. 2007. 80p. 18.75 *(978-0-687-64154-3(3))* Abingdon Pr.

—Claim the Life - Promise Semester 2 Student. 2007. 80p. pap. 7.75 *(978-0-687-64144-4(6))* Abingdon Pr.

—Claim the Life Journey 2007. 80p. pap., stu. ed. 7.75 *(978-0-687-64264-9(7))* Abingdon Pr.

—Claim the Life Promise Leaders. 2007. 80p. 18.75 *(978-0-687-64184-0(5))* Abingdon Pr.

Purves, Andrew. Crucifixion of Ministry: Surrendering Our Ambitions to the Service of Christ. 2007. (ENG.). 152p. pap. 15.00 *(978-0-8308-3439-6(7),* IVP Bks.) InterVarsity Pr.

Redding, Mary Lou. Where the World Meets to Pray: People & Stories of the Upper Room. 2009. 127p. pap. 20.00 *(978-0-8358-9991-8(8))* Upper Room Bks.

Richey, Russell E. Doctrine in Experience: A Methodist Theology of Church & Ministry. 2009. (Kingswood Ser.). (Illus.). 362p. pap. 49.00 *(978-1-4267-0010-1(5),* Kingswood Bks.) Abingdon Pr.

Richmond, Clarence Floyd. Audio, Video, & Media in the Ministry, 0 vols. Lawson, Michael, ed. 2010. (Nelson's Tech Guides). 176p. pap. 19.99 *(978-1-4185-4174-3(5))* Nelson, Thomas Inc.

Roberts, Barbara. Helping Those Who Hurt: A Handbook for Caring & Crisis. 2009. (Sword of Lyric Ser.). (ENG.). 208p. pap. 12.99 *(978-1-60006-382-4(9))* NavPress Publishing Group.

Robinson, Tyrone H. Show Yourself & Be Not Ashamed - a Call to the African American Male for Visibility. 2008. 72p. pap. *(978-3-639-00445-8(0))* VDM Verlag Dr. Mueller e.K.

Rogers, Glenn. Evangelizing Immigrants: Outreach & Ministry among Immigrants & their Children. 2006. per. 16.95 *(978-0-9774396-8-3(2))* Mission & Ministry Resources.

Sample, Tex. Blue Collar Resistance & the Politics of Jesus: Doing Ministry with Working Class Whites. 2006. 138p. per. 18.00 *(978-0-687-33502-2(7))* Abingdon Pr.

Sanders, Martin. The Power of Mentoring: Shaping People Who Will Shape the World. 2009. (ENG.). 205p. pap. 14.99 *(978-1-60066-235-5(8))* WingSpread Publishers.

Schipani, Daniel S. & Bueckert, Leah Dawn. Spiritual Caregiving in the Hospital: Windows to Chaplaincy Ministry. vii, 263p. 26.00 *(978-1-894710-65-7(7))* Pandora Pr. CAN. Dist: Herald Pr.

Schultze, George E. Strangers in a Foreign Land: The Organizing of Catholic Latinos in the United States. 2006. (ENG.). 188p. 55.99 *(978-0-7391-1745-3(9));* per. 26.50 *(978-0-7391-1746-0(7))* Lexington Bks.

Seaton, Wayne, ed. The Dallas Meeting. 2010. 284p. pap. 27.95 *(978-1-58427-279-3(1))* Guardian of Truth Foundation.

The Service of Women in the Church. (Touchpoint Ser.). 30p. pap. 2.99 *(978-0-570-09560-6(3),* 20-2504); 40p. pap., stu. ed. 2.99 *(978-0-570-09559-0(X),* 20-2503) Concordia Publishing Hse.

Shenk, Joanna. Widening the Circle: Experiments in Christian Discipleship. 2011. pap. ***(978-0-8361-9558-3(2))*** Herald Pr.

Sherman, Cecil E. To Be a Good & Faithful Servant: The Life & Work of a Minister. 2010. xvi, 188p. pap. *(978-1-57312-559-8(8))* Smyth & Helwys Publishing, Inc.

Simmank, Sarah. Challenges of Knowledge Management in Global Faith-Based NPOs: The Example of the World Alliance of YMCAs. 2008. 72p. pap. *(978-3-8364-7245-6(7))* VDM Verlag Dr. Mueller e.K.

Smith, Chuck. The Philosophy of Ministry of Calvary Chapel. rev. ed. 2009. (Illus.). 36p. pap. 3.99 *(978-1-934820-12-4(1))* Somebody Loves You Media Group.

Smith, Pamela R. Called along Side-Ministering in the Spirit of an Armorbearer: Understanding the Ministry of an Adjutant. 2008. (Illus.). 165p. per. 20.00 *(978-0-9752742-6-2(0))* Turning Point Pubns., LLC.

Standing, Roger. As a Fire by Burning: Mission As the Life of the Local Congregation. 2012. 224p. pap. 40.00 ***(978-0-334-04370-6(0),*** SCM Pr.) Hymns Ancient & Modern Ltd GBR. Dist: Westminster John Knox Pr.

Steele, Chris & Wetherholt, Jason. Life on Loan Student Ministry Edition. 2007. (YA). 39.99 *(978-0-7847-1884-1(9))* Standard Publishing.

Stella, Constance E. Wiring Your Church for Worship. Hamilton, Adam, ed. 2007. (Abingdon Press & the Church of the Resurrection Ministry Guides Ser.). 72p. per. 9.00 *(978-0-687-64281-6(7))* Abingdon Pr.

Stiller, Karen & Metzger, Willard. Going Missional. 2010. 184p. pap. *(978-1-77069-021-9(2))* Word Alive Pr.

Stokes, Virginia Cooper. The Journey of a Shepherd's Wife. 2010. pap. 12.99 *(978-1-61663-202-1(X))* Tate Publishing & Enterprises, LLC.

Stoltzfus, Tony. Coaching Questions: A Coach's Guide to Powerful Asking Skills. 2008. (Illus.). 100p. pap. 14.99 *(978-0-9794163-6-1(1))* Coach22 Bookstore LLC.

—Peer Coach Training Facilitator's Guide. 2007. (ENG., Illus.). 84p. spiral bd. 24.99 *(978-0-9794163-1-6(0))* Coach22 Bookstore LLC.

—Peer Coach Training Workbook. 2007. (ENG., Illus.). 80p. spiral bd. 12.99 *(978-0-9794163-0-9(2))* Coach22 Bookstore LLC.

Stone, Bryan P. & Wolfteich, Claire E. Sabbath in the City: Sustaining Urban Pastoral Excellence. 2008. (ENG.). 168p. pap. 20.00 *(978-0-664-23349-5(X))* Westminster John Knox Pr.

Stone, Charles. Five Ministry Killers & How to Defeat Them: Help for Frustrated Pastors — Including New Research from the Barna Group. 2011. 224p. pap. 15.99 *(978-0-7642-0854-6(3))* Bethany Hse. Pubs.

Stoter, David J. Spiritual Aspects of Health Care. 2008. 176p. pap. 19.00 *(978-1-55635-892-0(X),* Wipf and Stock) Wipf & Stock Pubs.

Styles, George. Ethical Pursuits. 2008. 60p. pap. 12.95 *(978-1-886057-10-4(9))* Warren Publishing, Inc.

Swan, Sandra S. The New Outreach: Doing Good the Better Way. 2010. (Illus.). 192p. pap. 24.00 *(978-0-89869-644-8(5))* Church Publishing, Inc.

Thompson, David W. A Stranger's Journey. 2007. 124p. per. 10.99 *(978-1-60477-471-9(1))* Xulon Pr., Inc.

Thompson, Linda J. Kingdom Building: A Labor of Love Journey. 2008. 73p. pap. 8.95 *(978-0-7414-4655-8(3))* Infinity Publishing.

Thompson, Melvin. The Mistress Called Ministry: Helping God's Leaders. 2011. 88p. pap. 9.95 ***(978-1-4327-7556-8(1))*** Outskirts Pr., Inc.

Thompson, R. Jan & Thompson, Roma Jo. Beyond Our Means: How the Brethren Service Center Dared to Embrace the World. 2009. pap. 18.95 *(978-0-87178-100-0(X))* Brethren Pr.

Threadgill, Shirley. The New Millennium Warrior, 1 vol. 2009. (ENG.). 63p. pap. 16.95 *(978-1-60749-588-8(0))* PublishAmerica, Inc.

Toler, Stan. The Community-Minded Church: Resources for Connecting with the World Outside Your Walls. 2009. (ENG.). 192p. ring bd. 49.99 *(978-0-8341-2277-2(4),* 9780834122772) Beacon Hill Pr. of Kansas City.

Torrey, R. A. Manual Del Obrero Cristiano: Christian Worker's Manual. (SPA.). 240p. *(978-84-7228-869-0(2),* 220568) Clie, Editorial.

—Personal Work Being Part One of How to W. 2006. pap. 22.95 *(978-1-4286-3773-3(7))* Kessinger Publishing, LLC.

Twentier, James A. En los Negocios de Mi Padre Me Es Necesario Estar: Avivamiento y Evangelismo • Pasión Por Dios • Compasión Por Los Perdidos. 2011. (SPA.). 372p. 35.09 ***(978-1-4269-8884-4(2))*** Trafford Publishing.

Tyson, John. Administration in the Small Me. 2007. 112p. pap. 15.00 *(978-0-687-64643-2(X))* Abingdon Pr.

VanSickle, Elizabeth. Crossing Jordan. 2008. 184p. pap. 10.95 *(978-0-557-00449-2(7))* Lulu Enterprises Inc.

Währisch-Oblau, Claudia. The Missionary Self-Perception of Pentecostal/Charismatic Church Leaders from the Global South in Europe: Bringing Back the Gospel. 2009. *(978-90-04-17508-2(3))* BRILL.

Waltz, Mark L. Lasting Impressions: From Visiting to Belonging. 2008. pap. *(978-0-7644-3747-2(X),* Group) Group Publishing, Inc.

Warren, Jeff. Live Forgiven. 2008. 200p. pap. 14.99 *(978-1-60647-486-0(3))* Xulon Pr., Inc.

Weaver, John. Outside-in: Theological Reflections on Life. 2006. (Regent's Study Guides). (Illus.). 248p. per. *(978-1-57312-472-0(9))* Smyth & Helwys Publishing, Inc.

Weaver, Sonia K. What Is Palestine-Israel? Answers to Common Questions. 2007. pap. 10.99 *(978-0-8361-9366-4(0))* Herald Pr.

Wells, Samuel & Owen, Marcia A. Living Without Enemies: Being Present in the Midst of Violence. 2011. (Resources for Reconciliation Ser.). (ENG.). 144p. pap. 15.00 *(978-0-8308-3456-3(7),* IVP Bks.) InterVarsity Pr.

Wiersbe, Warren W. On Being a Servant of God. rev. ed. 2007. 144p. pap. 13.99 *(978-0-8010-6819-5(3))* Baker Bks.

Wild-Wood, E. Migration & Christian Identity in Congo (DRC) 2008. (Studies of Religion in Africa Ser.). (Illus.). 250p. *(978-90-04-16464-2(2))* BRILL.

Wilke, Richard B. The Tie That Binds: Connecting with God, the Church, & the World. 2008. 167p. per. 16.00 *(978-0-687-65208-2(1))* Abingdon Pr.

Wilson, Catherine. The Politics of Latino Faith: Religion, Identity, & Urban Community. 2008. (ENG.). 320p. (C). 75.00 *(978-0-8147-9413-5(0));* pap. 25.00 *(978-0-8147-9414-2(9))* New York Univ. Pr.

Wilson, Len & Moore, Jason. The Wired Church 2. 0. 2008. (Illus.). 169p. pap. 19.00 *(978-0-687-64899-3(8))* Abingdon Pr.

Wolf, Christopher B. Giving Faith a Second Chance: Restarts, Mulligans & Do-Overs. 2007. 182p. per. *(978-1-932902-68-6(6))* FaithWalk Publishing.

Wood, Charles M., et al. Attentive to God: Thinking Theologically in Ministry. 2008. 138p. per. 16.00 *(978-0-687-65162-7(X))* Abingdon Pr.

Wright, Frank. Pastoral Care for Lay People. 2012. viii, 114p. pap. ***(978-0-334-02240-4(1),*** SCM Pr.) Hymns Ancient & Modern Ltd.

Wright, Gary Douglas. Worship Awakening: An Urgent Message for the Dying American Church. 2007. 467p. per. 18.99 *(978-1-57921-899-7(7))* WinePress Publishing.

Yusko, Pastor Albert. Hands-on Ministry. 2007. 128p. per. 11.95 *(978-1-934246-16-0(6))* Peppertree Pr., The.

CHURCH WORK—FORMS

General Record Book for the Church School Secretary-Treasurer. 6.50 *(978-0-687-08367-1(2))* Abingdon Pr.

Presbyterian Church in the U.S.A. Board. The Presbyterian Manual; Containing Forms for the Records of the Session, Presbytery, & Synod; & for the Judicial & Other Ecclesiastical Proceed. 2006. 152p. per. 18.99 *(978-1-4255-1157-9(0))* MPublishing.

Smith, D. Guide to Bishops' Registers. xvi, 286p. 27.00 *(978-0-901050-72-4(5))* Brown, David Bk. Co., The.

CHURCH WORK—VOCATIONAL GUIDANCE

see also Clergy—Appointment, Call and Election

Anyaogu, Okorie Chukwu. Manual on Adventist Pilot Project. 2011. 220p. pap. ***(978-3-8443-2233-0(7))*** Lambert Academic Publishing.

Chisam, Donna P. & Lincoln, John R. Architecture for Hiring: A design/build process to help in hiring Ministers. 2008. 132p. pap. 16.99 *(978-1-4389-1315-5(X))* AuthorHouse.

CHURCH WORK, RURAL

see Rural Churches

CHURCH WORK AS A PROFESSION

see Church Work—Vocational Guidance

CHURCH WORK WITH ADULTS

see Church Work; Church Work with Men; Church Work with Women

CHURCH WORK WITH ALCOHOLICS

Berry, Mae Elizabeth. Hope for Codependents. 2011. (ENG., Illus.). 102p. pap. 6.50 ***(978-0-615-39020-8(X))*** Mae Elizabeth Pubns.

Hammond, Adam. Alcohol in the Home: What Should the Church Do? 2010. 124p. pap. 11.95 *(978-1-61507-297-2(7))* Cross Bks. Publishing.

CHURCH WORK WITH CHILDREN

see also Church Camps

Adam, Gottfried, ed. Die Inhalte von Kinderbibeln. Kriterien ihrer Auswahl. 2008. (Arbeiten zur Religionspadagogik Ser.). (GER., Illus.). 365p. (C). 68.00 *(978-3-89971-489-0(X))* Vandenhoeck & Ruprecht GmbH & Co. KG DEU. Dist: ISD.

Almquist, Beth, et al. Growing in God's Love: Weekly Meeting Plans for Voyager Leaders. 2007. (J). 19.95 *(978-0-9743503-4-9(6))* Pioneer Clubs.

—Growing in God's Way: Weekly Meeting Plans for Voyager Leaders. 2007. (J). 19.95 *(978-0-9743503-3-2(8))* Pioneer Clubs.

Baker, H. A. Visions Beyond the Veil: Visions of Heaven, Angels, Satan, Hell, & the End of the Age. 2006. 190p. per. 9.99 *(978-0-88368-786-4(0))* Whitaker Hse.

Baker, Heidi, et al. Expecting Miracles: True Stories of God's Supernatural Power & How You Can Experience It. 2007. (Illus.). 208p. pap. 14.99 *(978-0-8007-9434-7(6))* Chosen Bks.

Barrick, Michael. Seven Days in Haiti. 2007. pap. 13.99 *(978-1-60034-982-9(X))* Xulon Pr., Inc.

Beckwith, Ivy. Formational Children's Ministry: Shaping Children Using Story, Ritual, & Relationship, 1 vol. 2010. (Mersion: Emergent Village Resources for Communities of Faith Ser.). (ENG.). 160p. pap. 15.99 *(978-0-8010-7187-4(9))* Baker Bks.

—The Ultimate Survival Guide for Children's Ministry Workers: Step-by-Step Helps to Make Your Job Easier & More Fulfilling. 2007. (ENG.). 144p. per. 6.99 *(978-0-8307-4366-7(9))* Gospel Light Pubns.

Blackwell, Jodi & Goldner, Jill. Zowie! 200+ Ministries Kids Can Do. 2008. (ENG., Illus.). 128p. pap. 12.99 *(978-1-59669-222-0(7))* New Hope Pubs.

Capps, Donald. Striking Out: The Religious Journey of Teenage Boys. 2011. 160p. pap. 18.00 ***(978-1-61097-300-7(3),*** Cascade Bks.) Wipf & Stock Pubs.

Champions Challenge Holiday Club Programme. 2007. 80p. pap. *(978-1-84427-270-9(2))* Scripture Union.

Childrens Choir. 4.98 *(978-0-7673-6228-3(4));* 2.95 *(978-0-7673-6200-9(4))* LifeWay Christian Resources.

Children's Choir. *(978-0-7673-8478-0(4))* LifeWay Christian Resources.

Chromey, Rick. Energizing Children's Ministry in the Smaller Church. 2008. (Escn Ser.). (ENG.). 176p. (J). pap. 17.99 *(978-0-7847-2192-6(0))* Standard Publishing.

Collins, Katy. Tell Me More about Your Life! Children's Ministry Curriculum. 2010. 72p. pap. 10.95 *(978-1-4401-7399-8(0))* iUniverse, Inc.

Comstock, Judy. Children's Ministry. Hamilton, Adam, ed. 2006. (Crmg Ser.: Vol. 1). (Illus.). 64p. per. 9.00 *(978-0-687-33413-1(6))* Abingdon Pr.

Couture, Pamela. Child Poverty: Love, Justice, & Social Responsibility. 2008. 235p. per. 29.99 *(978-0-8272-0509-3(0))* Chalice Pr.

Crosson-Tower, Cynthia. A Clergy Guide to Child Abuse & Neglect. 2006. 256p. per. *(978-0-8298-1595-5(3))* Pilgrim Pr., The/United Church Pr.

Csinos, David M. ChildrenÕs Ministry That Fits: Beyond One-Size-Fits-All Approaches to Nuturing ChildrenÕs Spirituality. 2011. 188p. pap. 22.00 *(978-1-61097-121-8(3),* Wipf and Stock) Wipf & Stock Pubs.

Daley, Sheela. Leave 'em Wanting More: Children's Ministry That Thrills as It Teaches. 2007. (Illus.). 271p. per. 20.99 *(978-1-60247-236-5(X))* Tate Publishing & Enterprises, LLC.

David C. Cook Publishing Company Staff. Active Bible Play, 1 vol. 2009. (Bible Funstuff Ser.). 112p. (J). pap. 19.99 *(978-1-4347-6725-7(6))* Cook, David C.

Davison, Jean. Connections of Hope. 2006. pap. 10.99 *(978-1-60034-779-5(7))* Xulon Pr., Inc.

Dingwall, Cindy. More Bible Times with Kids: 200+ Bible-Based Activities to Use with Children. 2006. (Illus.). 154p. per. 24.00 *(978-0-687-49230-5(0))* Abingdon Pr.

Dockray, Lydia. The G. O. D. Adventure. 2008. 142p. pap. 39.95 *(978-1-4092-1326-0(9))* Lulu Enterprises Inc.

Donnelly, John. A Twist of Faith: An American Christian's Quest to Help Orphans in Africa. 2012. (ENG.). 200p. 25.95 ***(978-0-8070-0132-5(5))*** Beacon Pr.

Downs, Lisa, et al, contrib. by. Group's Emergency Response Handbook for Children's Ministry. 2007. 156p. per. 14.99 (978-0-7644-3626-0(0)) Group Publishing, Inc.

Dykstra, Robert C., et al. Losers, Loners, & Rebels: The Spiritual Struggles of Boys. 2007. (ENG.). 204p. per. 20.00 (978-0-664-22961-0(1)) Westminster John Knox Pr.

Erickson, Al & Malloy, Patricia. Parents Arise! Grandparents Arise! Book. 2011. 212p. pap. 15.95 **(978-1-880292-39-6(4))** LangMarc Publishing.

Erickson, Alvin & Malloy, Patricia. Parents Arise! Grandparents Arise! Book 2 Ten Actions to Take to Safeguard Our Children. 2011. 230p. pap. 15.95 **(978-1-880292-40-2(8))** LangMarc Publishing.

Five Practices for Children. 2011. 130p. pap. 16.00 (978-1-4267-1642-3(7)) Abingdon Pr.

Fosarelli, Patricia D. ASAP: Ages, Stages, & Phases: From Infancy to Adolescence. 2006. 136p. per. 5.95 (978-0-7648-1501-0(6)) Liguori Pubns.

Garza, Ray. The Little Cross. 2010. (ENG.). 24p. (J). 9.95 (978-0-9795680-2-2(1)) Believers Publishing.

Geitz, Elizabeth Rankin. I Am That Child: Changing Hearts & Changing the World. 2012. E-Book **(978-0-8192-2779-9(X)**, Morehouse Publishing); 176p. pap. 18.00 **(978-0-8192-2778-2(1))** Church Publishing, Inc.

Group Publishing, compiled by. Large-As-Life Bible Adventures: 13 Amazing You-Are-There Bible Experiences. 2007. (Illus.). 79p. pap. 24.99 incl. audio compact disk (978-0-7644-3549-2(3)) Group Publishing, Inc.

Group Publishing, creator. Coloring Creations 2. 2007. (Illus.). 110p. per. 19.99 (978-0-7644-3506-5(X)) Group Publishing, Inc.

—Crafts: 110 Totally Awesome Crafts for All Ages. 2006. (Illus.). 127p. per. 17.99 (978-0-7644-3439-6(X), Group) Group Publishing, Inc.

—Devotions: 110 Eye-Popping, Jaw-Dropping Children's Messages. 2006. (Illus.). 128p. per. 17.99 (978-0-7644-3440-2(3)) Group Publishing, Inc.

—Games: 110 Out-of-This-World Games Kids Love. 2006. (Illus.). 126p. per. 17.99 (978-0-7644-3438-9(1)) Group Publishing, Inc.

Group Publishing Staff, contrib. by. The Quick Guide to Discipline for Children's Ministry: 101 Good Ideas for Bad Behavior. 2009. pap. (978-0-7644-4004-5(7)) Group Publishing, Inc.

Guide Editors, contrib. by. Sabbath Action Blast! 101 Ways to Celebrate God's Special Day. 2008. 96p. pap. 11.99 (978-0-8280-2368-9(9)) Review & Herald Publishing Assn.

Guidelines for Leading Your Congregation 2009-2012 - Children's Ministries: Ministries that Help Children Grow in Faith. 2008. 2.95 (978-0-687-64951-8(X)) Abingdon Pr.

Harder, Jeannette. Let the Children Come: Preparing Faith Communities to End Child Abuse & Neglect. 2010. 213p. pap. 12.99 (978-0-8361-9518-7(3)) Herald Pr.

Haugen, Gary A. & Hunter, Gregg. Terrify No More: Young Girls Held Captive & the Daring Undercover Operation to Win Their Freedom, 0 vols. 2010. 264p. pap. 14.99 (978-1-59555-980-7(9)) Nelson, Thomas Inc.

Haywood, Janice. Enduring Connections: Creating a Preschool & Children's Ministry. 2007. (Columbia Partnership Leadership Ser.). 170p. per. 19.99 (978-0-8272-0821-6(9)) Chalice Pr.

Heijst, Annelies van. Models of Charitable Care: Catholic Nuns & Children in Their Care in Amsterdam, 1852-2002. 2008. (Brill's Series in Church History: Vol. 33). (Illus.). 432p. (C). (978-90-04-16833-6(8)) BRILL.

Holmen, Mark & Texeira, David. Take It Home. 2007. (ENG.). 160p. 49.99 (978-0-8307-4457-2(6), Regal Bks.) Gospel Light Pubns.

Houser, Tina. Building Children's Ministry: A Practical Guide, 0 vols. 2008. (Illus.). 224p. per. 24.99 (978-1-4185-2681-8(9)) Nelson, Thomas Inc.

Hudson, Dale. Turbocharged! 100 Simple Secrets to Preschool Ministry. 2009. pap. (978-0-7644-4003-8(9)) Group Publishing, Inc.

Hudson, Dale & Werner, Scott A. Turbocharged! 100 Simple Secrets to Successful Children's Ministry. 2008. 240p. pap. 19.99 (978-0-7644-3690-1(2)) Group Publishing, Inc.

Jensen, Annie. A Heart for Africa: Rosemary Jensen & the Story of Rafiki. 2007. (Illus.). 80p. 13.99 (978-0-8254-3889-9(6)) Kregel Pubns.

Johnston, Kurt. Middle School Ministry Made Simple. 2008. (Ministry Made Simple Ser.). (ENG.). 192p. (YA). pap. 16.99 (978-0-7847-2233-6(1)) Standard Publishing.

Jutila, Craig, et al. Children's Ministry in the 21st Century. 2006. (Illus.). 205p. per. 24.99 (978-0-7644-3389-4(X)) Group Publishing, Inc.

Kee, Florence R. How to Reach the Children for Jesus. 2011. 60p. 36.95 **(978-1-258-08586-5(0))** Literary Licensing, LLC.

Keeley, Robert J. Helping Our Children Grow in Faith: How the Church Can Nurture the Spiritual Development of Kids. 2008. 160p. pap. 15.00 (978-0-8010-6829-4(0)) Baker Bks.

Kientz, Michael. Teach Them: 50 Fantastic Object Lessons for Children's Ministry. 2010. 162p. pap. 22.10 (978-0-557-17835-3(5)) Lulu Enterprises Inc.

Kilbourn, Phyllis. Shaping the Future: Girls & Our Destiny. 2008. pap. (978-0-87808-002-1(3)) Carey, William Library Pubs.

Lawson, Jean. Raising up Spiritual Champions Newsletters. 2007. (ENG., Illus.). 128p. (J). 49.99 (978-0-8307-4493-0(2)) Gospel Light Pubns.

Martin, W. C. Small Town, Big Miracle: How Love Came to the Least of These. 2007. (ENG., Illus.). 168p. pap. 13.99 (978-1-58997-443-2(3)) Tyndale Hse. Pubs.

McGhee, Quentin. Children's Ministry-Teachers Guide. Moeckl, Trudy, ed. 2011. (SPA.). spiral bd. 10.00 (978-1-931984-50-8(6), 4431-32E1) Faith & Action Team.

Melton, Joy Thornburg. Safe Sanctuaries: Reducing the Risk of Abuse in the Church for Children & Youth. 2008. 144p. pap. 25.00 (978-0-88177-543-3(6)) Upper Room Bks.

Moore, Mary Elizabeth & Wright, Almeda. Children, Youth, & Spirituality in a Troubling World. Moore-Keish, Martha L., ed. 2008. 288p. pap. 29.99 (978-0-8272-0513-0(9)) Chalice Pr.

Nash. Working with Dying Children & Their Families. 2011. (Illus.). xii, 178p. pap. **(978-0-281-06005-4(3))** SPCK Publishing.

Nelson, Carl Ellis. Growing up Christian: A Congregational Strategy for Nurturing Disciples. 2008. pap. 16.00 (978-1-57312-523-9(7)) Smyth & Helwys Publishing, Inc.

Olson, Diane & Friedrich, Laura Dean. Weaving A Just Future for Children. 2008. 160p. pap. 15.00 (978-0-88177-547-1(9)) Upper Room Bks.

Reiser, A. Hamer & Merkley, Marion G. What It Means to Be a Latter-Day Saint. 2011. 150p. 40.95 **(978-1-258-05870-8(7))** Literary Licensing, LLC.

Roehlkepartain, Jolene L. 101 Games That Keep Kids Coming: Get-to-Know-You-Games for Ages 3-12. 2008. (Illus.). 101p. per. 17.00 (978-0-687-65120-7(4)) Abingdon Pr.

—101 More Great Games for Kids: Active, Bible-Based Fun for Christian Education. 2007. (Illus.). per. 18.99 (978-0-687-33407-0(1)) Abingdon Pr.

Rorheim, Art. Art Rorheim, Mr. Awana: Over 60 Years of Impacting the World for Christ. 2011. (978-1-60265-028-2(4)) Grace Acres Pr.

—Mr. Awana: Sixty-plus Years of Changing the World for Christ. 2011. (ENG., Illus.). 288p. pap. 19.95 (978-1-60265-027-5(6)) Grace Acres Pr.

Schorr, Vernie & Haystead, Wes. Staffing Your ChildrenÕs Ministry. 2009. 112p. pap. 13.00 (978-1-60608-492-2(5), Wipf and Stock) Wipf & Stock Pubs.

Schultz, Joani, et al, contrib. by. The Humongous Book of Preschool Ideas. 2007. 224p. (J). (gr. 3-7). per. 29.99 (978-0-7644-3601-7(5)) Group Publishing, Inc.

Scripture Union Staff, contrib. by. Matchday Programme: Holiday Club Resource Material for 5 to 11 Year-Olds. 2007. 64p. pap. **(978-1-84427-333-1(4))** Scripture Union.

Seiden, Jerry & Halverstadt, Jonathan Scott. ADD, Christianity, & the Church: A Compassionate Healing Resource to Inform, Inspire, & Illuminate. 2008. 208p. pap. 12.95 (978-1-929753-22-2(5)) Spirit of Hope Publishing.

Service Squad VBS. 2008. pap. 5.99 (978-0-687-65163-4(8)) Abingdon Pr.

Snow, Patrick. Leading Preteens. 2008. (Growing Ministry Guide Ser.). (ENG.). (J). pap. 12.99 (978-0-7847-2180-3(7)) Standard Publishing.

Stacey W. Smith & Sandra L. Haner. Children of Faith: Sowing Seeds for Eternity. 2011. 256p. 29.99 **(978-1-4500-7214-4(3))**; pap. 19.99 **(978-1-4500-7213-7(5))** Xlibris Corp.

Stafford, Wess & Merrill, Dean. Just a Minute: In the Heart of a Child, One Moment... Can Last Forever. 2012. (ENG.). 224p. 19.99 **(978-0-8024-0472-5(3))** Moody Pubs.

Standard Publishing Staff. Awards & More! 2009. (Children's Ministry Helps Ser.). (ENG.). (J). cd-rom 19.99 (978-0-7847-2288-6(9)) Standard Publishing.

Standard Publishing Staff, creator. Life on Loan. 2007. (J). DVD, cd-rom 39.99 (978-0-7847-1907-7(1)) Standard Publishing.

Stonehouse, Catherine & May, Scottie. Listening to Children on the Spiritual Journey: Guidance for Those Who Teach & Nurture, 1 vol. 2010. (ENG., Illus.). 192p. (C). pap. 20.00 (978-0-8010-3236-3(9)) Baker Academic.

Stott, Roscoe Gilmore. How to Win Boys: A Book of Information & Inspiration for the Sunday School Worker. 2007. (ENG.). 180p. 37.95 (978-0-548-06210-4(2)) Kessinger Publishing, LLC.

Strom, Kay Marshall & Rickett, Michele. Forgotten Girls: Stories of Hope & Courage, 1 vol. 2009. (ENG.). 175p. pap. 16.00 (978-0-8308-3731-1(0), IVP Bks.) InterVarsity Pr.

Trotman. Developing a Model for a Child-Friendly Church. 2010. 288p. pap. (978-3-639-24740-4(X)) VDM Verlag Dr. Mueller e.K.

VanCleave, Janice Pratt. Hands-on Bible Explorations: 52 Fun Activities for Christian Learning. 2006. (ENG., Illus.). 144p. pap. 14.95 (978-0-471-47201-8(8), Wiley) Wiley, John & Sons, Inc.

Weber, Jason. Launching an Orphans Ministry in Your Church. 2007. (Illus.). 57p. pap. 9.99 (978-1-57229-983-4(4)) FamilyLife.

Wright, Josephine-Joy, ed. Celebrating Children: Equipping People Working with Children & Young People Living in Difficult Circumstances Around the World. 2006. (ENG., Illus.). 442p. per. 34.99 (978-1-84227-060-8(5), Paternoster) Authentic Media.

CHURCH WORK WITH CRIMINALS

see also Church Work with Juvenile Delinquents

Goode, W. Wilson, Sr., et al. Ministry with Prisoners & Families: The Way Forward. 2011. 192p. pap. 17.99 (978-0-8170-1664-7(3)) Judson Pr.

Hicks, U. S. Grip on the City: Liberating Harlem Heights. 2011. 280p. pap. 22.74 (978-1-4269-2309-8(0)) Trafford Publishing.

Houston, Kirk. The Church's Return Policy: Equipping the Church to Minister to Ex-Offenders. 2008. 96p. pap. 12.95 (978-1-4389-2965-1(X), AuthorHouse.

Johnson, Byron R. More God, Less Crime: How Religion & Faith-Based Approaches Reduce Crime & Foster Hope. 2011. (ENG.). 283p. 26.95 (978-1-59947-373-4(9)) Templeton Pr.

CHURCH WORK WITH DISASTER VICTIMS

Bagley, Robert E. Disaster Relief. 2009. (ENG.). 140p. pap. 14.99 (978-0-7644-3746-5(1)) Group Publishing, Inc.

Barnett, Michael N. & Stein, Janice Gross. Sacred Aid: Faith & Humanitarianism. 2012. (ENG.). 272p. 99.00 **(978-0-19-991602-3(0))**; pap. 29.95 **(978-0-19-991609-2(8))** Oxford Univ. Pr., Inc.

Brenner, Grant H., et al. Creating Spiritual & Psychological Resilience: Integrated Care in Disaster Re: Integrated Care in Disaster Re. 2009. (ENG., Illus.). 264p. (C). 125.00 (978-0-7890-3454-0(9)); pap. 41.95 (978-0-7890-3455-7(7)) Routledge.

Haueisen, Kathy & Flores, Carol. A Ready Hope: Effective Disaster Ministry for Congregations. 2009. (978-1-56699-386-9(5)) Alban Institute, Inc.

Johnson, Bob. I Saw God — in the Midst of Tragedy: A Chaplain's Experience at Ground Zero. 2008. (Illus.). 84p. pap. (978-0-9778439-1-6(2)) Johnson, Robert.

Ross, Robert R.N & Ross, Deanne E. B. Walking to New Orleans Ethics & the Concept of Participatory Design in Post-Disaster Reconstruction. 2008. (Illus.). 602p. pap. 59.00 (978-1-55635-224-9(7)) Wipf & Stock Pubs.

Swain, Storm. Trauma & Transformation at Ground Zero: A Pastoral Theology. 2011. (Illus.). 216p. (C). pap. 27.00 (978-0-8006-9805-8(3), Fortress Pr.) Augsburg Fortress, Pubs.

When All Plans Fail. 2008. 256p. pap. 15.00 (978-0-615-20937-1(8)) Mountain View Publishing.

CHURCH WORK WITH DIVORCED PEOPLE

Bosco, Antoinette. Growing in Faith When a Catholic Marriage Fails: For Divorced or Separated Catholics & Those Who Minister with Them. 2006. (Illus.). 125p. per. (978-1-933066-04-2(0), Resurrection Pr.) Catholic Bk. Publishing Corp.

Medina, Hector M. December Roses: Pastoral Reflections on Divorce. DuClos, Yolanda R. & Skarda, Pat, eds. 2011. 190p. pap. 22.00 (978-1-61097-073-0(X), Resource Pubns.) Wipf & Stock Pubs

Qualls, Charles. Divorce Ministry: A Guidebook. 2011. **(978-1-57312-588-8(1))** Smyth & Helwys Publishing, Inc.

CHURCH WORK WITH DRUG ADDICTS

Dunnington, Kent J. Addiction & Virtue: Beyond the Models of Disease & Choice. 2011. (Strategic Initiatives in Evangelical Theology Ser.). (ENG.). 199p. pap. 30.00 (978-0-8308-3901-8(1), IVP Acad.) InterVarsity Pr.

Hunt, Chad D. Addiction Deliverance Outreach: A Christ-Centered Recovery Program for Your Church. 2009. 364p. pap. 20.99 (978-1-61507-054-1(0)) Cross Bks. Publishing.

Lightsey, Dan. Grace Overcomers Addiction Ministry: Founded on the Finished Work of Jesus Christ. 2010. pap. 11.99 (978-1-61663-225-0(9)) Tate Publishing & Enterprises, LLC.

Marshall, John. Hope Reclaimed: A Plan & Hope for the Future. 2010. 144p. pap. 10.95 (978-1-4327-5566-9(8), Outskirts Pr., Inc.

—Hope Reclaimed: A plan & hope for the Future. 2010. 144p. 20.95 (978-1-4327-6302-2(4)) Outskirts Pr., Inc.

CHURCH WORK WITH EXCEPTIONAL CHILDREN

Richardson, Susan. Child by Child: Supporting Children with Learning Differences & Their Families. 2011. E-Book **(978-0-8192-2752-2(8)**, Morehouse Publishing) Church Publishing, Inc.

CHURCH WORK WITH FAMILIES

Albrecht, Elizabeth Soto. Family Violence: Reclaiming a Theology of Nonviolence. 2008. (Women from the Margins Ser.). 182p. pap. 20.00 (978-1-57075-757-0(7)) Orbis Bks.

Anderson, Ray S. Something Old/Something New: Marriage & Family Ministry in a Postmodern Culture. 2007. (Ray S. Anderson Collection Ser.). (Illus.). 242p. pap. 27.00 (978-1-55635-474-8(6), Wipf and Stock) Wipf & Stock Pubs.

Andrews, Arlene Bowers, et al. Send Me! the Story of Salkehatchie Summer Service. 2006. (Illus.). 336p. pap. 29.95 (978-1-57736-380-4(9)) Providence Hse Pubs.

Badiu, Mihail. A Strategy for Strengthening Romanian Seventh Day Adventist Families. 2009. 168p. pap. (978-3-639-17327-7(9)) VDM Verlag Dr. Mueller e.K.

Branson, Brenda. Violence among Us: Ministry to Families in Crisis. 2007. (Illus.). 150p. per. 16.00 (978-0-8170-1515-2(9)) Judson Pr.

Broadman and Holman. Perspectives on Family Ministry: Three Views, 1 vol. Jones, Timothy Paul, ed. 2009. (Perspectives Ser.). (ENG.). 208p. pap. 19.99 (978-0-8054-4845-0(4), B&H Academic) B&H Publishing Group.

—Perspectives on Your Child's Education: Four Views, 1 vol. Jones, Timothy Paul, ed. 2009. (ENG.). 144p. pap. 19.99 (978-0-8054-4844-3(6), B&H Academic) B&H Publishing Group.

Crosson-Tower, Cynthia. A Clergy Guide to Child Abuse & Neglect. 2006. 256p. per. (978-0-8298-1595-5(3)) Pilgrim Pr., The/United Church Pr.

Dankert, Judy, et al. Ministry Ideas for Celebrating Lent & Easter with Teens, Families, & Parishes. 2007. (Illus.). 108p. per. 26.25 (978-0-88489-871-9(7)) St. Mary's Pr.

Davison, Jean. Connections of Hope. 2006. pap. 10.99 (978-1-60034-779-5(7)) Xulon Pr., Inc.

Garland, Diana R. Family Ministry: A Comprehensive Guide. 2nd rev. ed. 2012. (ENG.). 640p. 50.00 **(978-0-8308-3971-1(2)**, IVP Acad.) InterVarsity Pr.

Group Publishing Staff, contrib. by. Sticky Faith: 52 Family Messages for Big Church. 2008. pap. (978-0-7644-3711-3(9), Group) Group Publishing, Inc.

Guidelines for Leading Your Congregation 2009-2012 - Family Ministries: Helping Families Become Centers of Faith Formation. 2008. 2.95 (978-0-687-64702-6(9)) Abingdon Pr.

Haynes, Brian. Shift: What It Takes to Finally Reach Families Today. 2009. pap. (978-0-7644-3898-1(0)) Group Publishing, Inc.

Hemrich-Skomer, Denise & Tyrtania, Joachim. Let the Children Come: A Family Guide to the Liturgy of the Word Cycle A. 2007. 64p. (J). per. 6.95 (978-0-9787087-1-9(7)) Bound by Grace Pr., LLC.

Joiner, Reggie. Orange Leader Handbook: A Think Orange Companion. 2010. (Illus.). 183p. E-Book (978-1-4347-0186-2(7)) Kingsway Pubns.

—The Think Orange: Imagine the Impact When Church & Family Collide... 2009. (ENG.). 272p. 21.99 (978-1-4347-6483-6(4)) Cook, David C.

Jones, Timothy Paul & Jones, Timothy P. Family Ministry Field Guide: How the Church Can Equip Parents to Make Disciples. 2011. (Illus.). 224p. (978-0-89827-457-8(5)) Wesleyan Publishing Hse.

Kettler, Christian D. & Speidell, Todd H., eds. Incarnational Ministry: The Presence of Christ in Church, Society, & Family. 2009. (Ray S. Anderson Collection Ser.). 348p. pap. 32.00 (978-1-60899-334-5(5)); pap. 22.00 (978-1-60899-139-6(3)) Wipf & Stock Pubs. (Wipf and Stock).

Nash. Working with Dying Children & Their Families. 2011. (Illus.). xii, 178p. pap. **(978-0-281-06005-4(3))** SPCK Publishing.

Nason-Clark, Nancy, et al, eds. Responding to Abuse in Christian Homes: A Challenge to Churches & their Leaders. 2011. (House of Prisca & Aquila Ser.). 262p. pap. 29.00 (978-1-61097-178-2(7), Wipf and Stock) Wipf & Stock Pubs.

Richardson, Susan. Child by Child: Supporting Children with Learning Differences & Their Families. 2011. E-Book **(978-0-8192-2752-2(8)**, Morehouse Publishing) Church Publishing, Inc.

Shook, Jill Suzanne, ed. Making Housing Happen: Faith-Based Affordable Housing Models. 2010. 286p. pap. 20.00 (978-1-60899-959-0(9), Wipf and Stock) Wipf & Stock Pubs.

Stevens, Wesley. Learning to Sing in a Strange Land: When a Loved One Goes to Prison. 2009. 210p. pap. 23.00 (978-1-59752-535-0(9), Resource Pubns.) Wipf & Stock Pubs.

Strommen, Merton P., et al. Passing on the Faith: A Radical Model for Youth & Family Ministry. 2nd ed. 2008. (Illus.). 397p. pap. 26.25 (978-0-88489-970-9(5)) St. Mary's Pr.

Tyrtania, Joachim & Hemrich-Skomer, Denise. Let the Children Come: A Family Guide to the Liturgy of the Word. 2006. 65p. (J). per. 6.95 (978-0-9787087-0-2(9)) Bound by Grace Pr., LLC.

CHURCH WORK WITH GAYS

Campbell, William P. Turning Controversy into Church Ministry: A Christlike Response to Homosexuality, 1 vol. 2010. (ENG.). 240p. pap. 18.99 (978-0-310-32132-3(8)) Zondervan.

Chambers, Alan. God's Grace & the Homosexual Next Door: Reaching the Heart of the Gay Men & Women in Your World. 2006. 282p. per. 13.99 (978-0-7369-1691-2(1)) Harvest Hse. Pubs.

—La Gracia de Dios y el Vecino Homosexual. 2007. (ENG & SPA.). 270p. 9.99 (978-1-59979-106-7(4), Casa Creacion) Charisma Media.

—Leaving Homosexuality: A Practical Guide for Men & Women Looking for a Way Out. 2009. 160p. pap. 11.99 (978-0-7369-2610-2(0)) Harvest Hse. Pubs.

Cole, Beverly. Voices from the Kingdom: All God's Children Have Keys. 2007. (ENG.). 188p. pap. 13.95 (978-0-9788522-0-7(6)) Kimimi Pubns.

Estwick, Daphne. Arms Out, Palms Open: Conflict, Reconciliation, & Gay Inclusion. 2012. 176p. pap. 20.00 **(978-0-8192-2758-4(7)**, Morehouse Publishing) Church Publishing, Inc.

Estwick, Daphne G. Arms Out, Palms Open: Conflict, Reconciliation, & Gay Inclusion. 2012. E-Book **(978-0-8192-2759-1(5)**, Morehouse Publishing) Church Publishing, Inc.

Godfrey, Donal. Gays & Grays: The Story of the Inclusion of the Gay Community at Most Holy Redeemer Catholic Parish in San Francisco. (ENG.). 208p. 2008. pap. 26.50 (978-0-7391-1938-9(9)) 2007. 78.99 (978-0-7391-1937-2(0)) Lexington Bks.

Kundtz, David & Schlager, Bernard S. Ministry among God's Queer Folk: LGBT Pastoral Care. 2007. (C). (978-0-8298-1706-5(9)) Pilgrim Pr., The/United Church Pr.

CHURCH WORK WITH HOMOSEXUALS

see Church Work with Gays

CHURCH WORK WITH JUVENILE DELINQUENTS

Boyle, Gregory. Tattoos on the Heart: The Power of Boundless Compassion. (ENG.). 240p. 2011. pap. 14.00 (978-1-4391-5315-4(9)) 2010. 25.00 (978-1-4391-5302-4(7)) Free Pr. (Free Pr.).

—Tatuajes en el Corazon: El Poder de la Compasión Sin Límite. Ochoa, Santiago, tr. 2010. (SPA & ENG.). 256p. pap. 16.00 (978-1-4391-6098-5(8), Free Pr.) Free Pr.

Brenneman, Robert. Homies & Hermanos: God & the Gangs in Central America, 1 vol. 2011. (ENG., Illus.). 312p. 99.00 (978-0-19-975384-0(9)); pap. 24.95 (978-0-19-975390-1(3)) Oxford Univ. Pr., Inc.

Evans, Troy, et al. The Edge of Redemption: A Story of Hope for Rescuing the Unreachable. 2011. **(978-0-89827-489-9(3))** Wesleyan Publishing Hse.

Fremon, Celeste. G-Dog & the Homeboys: Father Greg Boyle & the Gangs of East Los Angeles. rev. ed. 2008. (ENG.). 328p. pap. 21.95 (978-0-8263-4485-4(2)) Univ. of New Mexico Pr.

Stanley, Lee. Faith in the Land of Make Believe: What God Can Do... Even in Hollywood, 1 vol. 2011. (ENG.). 272p. 19.99 (978-0-310-32545-1(5)) Zondervan.

Wilkerson, David, et al. The Cross & the Switchblade. 45th ed. 2008. 240p. pap. 14.99 (978-0-8007-9446-0(X)) Chosen Bks.

CHURCH WORK WITH MEN

Clark, Ron. Freeing the Oppressed: A Call to Christians concerning Domestic Abuse. 2009. 172p. pap. 20.00 (978-1-60608-484-7(4), Cascade Bks.) Wipf & Stock Pubs.

Diede, Brian, et al. Group's Dinner & a Movie: Adrenaline Rush: Flix for Guys. Rozum, Ann Marie, ed. 2007. (Illus.). 108p. per. 19.99 (978-0-7644-3710-6(0)) Group Publishing, Inc.

C

Guidelines for Leading Your Congregation 2009-2012 - Men's Ministries: Ministry to & through Men. 2008. 2.95 *(978-0-687-64732-3(0))* Abingdon Pr.

Herb, Reese. Developing a Men's Team Ministry to Widows, Widowers & Single Parents. 2007. (Illus.). 29p. spiral bd. 7.00 *(978-0-9797846-2-0(X))* New Commandment Men's Ministries.

Morley, Patrick. Pastoring Men: What Works, What Doesn't, & Why It Matters Now More Than Ever. 2009. (ENG.). 256p. 19.99 *(978-0-8024-7553-4(1))* Moody Pubs.

Mosley, Jerard R. Can You See Me Now? Developing Men's Ministry in the Local Church through Fellowship, Mission & Evangelism. 2010. 68p. pap. 13.75 *(978-1-4520-3292-4(0))* AuthorHouse.

Muravchik, Stephanie. American Protestantism in the Age of Psychology. 2011. (ENG., Illus.). 224p. 90.00 *(978-1-107-01067-3(5))* Cambridge Univ. Pr.

Murrow, David. How Women Help Men Find God, 0 vols. 2008. (Illus.). 256p. pap. 14.99 *(978-0-7852-2632-1(X))* Nelson, Thomas Inc.

—Why Men Hate Going to Church. 2011. 256p. pap. 15.99 *(978-0-7852-3215-5(X))* Nelson, Thomas Inc.

Sonderman, Steve. How to Build a Life-Changing Men's Ministry: Practical Ideas & Insights for Your Church, 1 vol. rev. ed. 2010. (ENG.). 272p. reprint ed. pap. 18.00 *(978-0-7642-0748-8(2))* Bethany Hse. Pubs.

Stevenson, Michael A. No More Excuses: Creating a Culture in the Church That Reaches African-American Men. 2008. (ENG.). 128p. pap. 9.99 *(978-1-59979-391-7(1)*, Creation Hse.) Charisma Media.

Toler, Stan & Brechesisen, Jerry. The Complete Men's Ministries Kit: Everything You Need to Power up Your Program. 2007. (ENG.). 160p. ring bd. 89.99 *(978-0-8341-2336-6(3)*, 083-412-3363) Beacon Hill Pr. of Kansas City.

CHURCH WORK WITH MIGRANT LABOR

Watt, Alan J. Farm Workers & the Churches: The Movement in California & Texas. 2010. (Fronteras Series, sponsored by Texas A&M International University Ser.). (ENG., Illus.). 264p. 48.00 *(978-1-60344-174-2(3))*; pap. 24.00 *(978-1-60344-193-3(X))* Texas A&M Univ. Pr.

CHURCH WORK WITH MINORITIES

Alban Institute Action Research Team on Conflict Management. Pacific Asian American Ministry in a Time of Shifting Paradigms: The Example of Asian American Conflict Management. pap. 7.50 *(978-1-56699-163-6(3)*, OD117) Alban Institute, Inc.

Bowers, Laurene Beth. Becoming A Multicultural Church. 2010. 192p. pap. 22.00 *(978-1-60899-229-4(2)*, Wipf and Stock) Wipf & Stock Pubs.

Chinula, Donald M. Building King's Beloved Community. 2009. 128p. pap. 16.00 *(978-1-60899-143-3(1)*, Wipf and Stock) Wipf & Stock Pubs.

DeYmaz, Mark. Building a Healthy Multi-Ethnic Church: Mandate, Commitments & Practices of a Diverse Congregation. 2007. (Jossey-Bass Leadership Network Ser.: 22). (ENG.). 240p. 24.95 *(978-0-7879-9551-5(7)*, Jossey-Bass) Wiley, John & Sons, Inc.

DeYmaz, Mark & Li, Harry. Ethnic Blends: Mixing Diversity into Your Local Church, 1 vol. 2010. (Leadership Network Innovation Ser.). (ENG.). 240p. pap. 18.99 *(978-0-310-32123-1(9))* Zondervan.

Elizondo, Virgilio P. Charity. 2008. 144p. pap. 14.00 *(978-1-57075-720-4(8))* Orbis Bks.

Fernandez, Eleazar S. & Segovia, Fernando F., eds. A Dream Unfinished: Theological Reflections on America from the Margins. 2007. (Illus.). 302p. pap. 33.00 *(978-1-55635-441-0(X)*, Wipf and Stock) Wipf & Stock Pubs.

Garces-Foley, Kathleen. Crossing the Ethnic Divide: The Multiethnic Church on a Mission, 1 vol. 2011. (Aar Academy Ser.). 194p. pap. 24.95 *(978-0-19-979680-9(7))* Oxford Univ. Pr., Inc.

Hughes, Dewi Arwel. Ethnic Identity from the Margins: A Christian Perspective. 2011. *(978-0-87808-459-3(2))* Carey, William Library Pubs.

Martinez, Juan. Walk with the People: Latino Ministry in the United States. 2008. 148p. pap. 18.00 *(978-0-687-64719-4(3))* Abingdon Pr.

McIntosh, Gary & McMahan, Alan. Being the Church in a Multi-Ethnic Community: Why It Matters & How It Works. 2012. ***(978-0-89827-490-5(7))*** Wesleyan Publishing Hse.

Rogers, Glenn. Becoming A Multiethnic Church. 2007. pap. 16.95 *(978-0-9792072-1-1(5))* Mission & Ministry Resources.

—North American Cross-Cultural Church Planting. 2008. 256p. pap. 23.95 *(978-0-9792072-2-8(3))* Mission & Ministry Resources.

Shannahan, Chris. Voices from the Borderland: Re-Imagining Cross-Cultural Urban Theology in the Twenty-First Century. 2010. (Cross Cultural Theologies Ser.). (ENG., Illus.). 324p. (C). 120.00 *(978-1-84553-703-6(3))*; pap. 34.95 *(978-1-84553-704-3(1))* Equinox Publishing Ltd. GBR. Dist: ISD.

Slade, Peter. Open Friendship in a Closed Society: Mission Mississippi & a Theology of Friendship. 2009. (ENG., Illus.). 280p. 45.00 *(978-0-19-537262-5(X))* Oxford Univ. Pr., Inc.

Soerens, Matthew & Hwang, Jenny. Welcoming the Stranger: Justice, Compassion & Truth in the Immigration Debate, 1 vol. 2009. (ENG.). 240p. pap. 15.00 *(978-0-8308-3359-7(5)*, IVP Bks.) InterVarsity Pr.

Zwick, Mark & Zwick, Louise. Mercy Without Borders: The Catholic Worker & Immigration. 2010. 288p. pap. *(978-0-8091-4689-5(4))* Paulist Pr.

CHURCH WORK WITH NARCOTIC ADDICTS

see Church Work with Drug Addicts

CHURCH WORK WITH OLDER PEOPLE

Cress, Mark & Hobgood, Chris. Caring Directions: 50 Places Where God May be Calling You to Serve as a Community Chaplain. 2007. (ENG.). 144p. per. 14.99 *(978-0-9786039-2-2(3))* Lanphier Pr.

Gentzler, Richard H., Jr. Aging & Ministry in the 21st Century: An Inquiry Approach. 2008. 128p. pap. 13.00 *(978-0-88177-540-2(1))* Upper Room Bks.

Hanson, Amy. Baby Boomers & Beyond: Tapping the Ministry Talents & Passions of Adults Over 50. 2010. (Jossey-Bass Leadership Network Ser.: 45). (ENG.). 224p. 24.95 *(978-0-470-50079-8(4)*, Jossey-Bass) Wiley, John & Sons, Inc.

Hisbon, Janet Mitchell. Senior Spirit: An Outreach Ministry to Older Adults. 2009. *(978-0-8298-1827-7(8))* Pilgrim Pr., The/United Church Pr.

Hobgood, Chris. Community Chaplain Training Workbook. 2007. (ENG.). 84p. pap. 14.95 *(978-0-9786039-3-9(1))* Lanphier Pr.

Houston, James M. & Parker, Michael. A Vision for the Aging Church: Renewing Ministry for & by Seniors. 2011. (ENG.). 279p. pap. 24.00 ***(978-0-8308-3948-3(8)***, IVP Acad.) InterVarsity Pr.

Johnson, Richard P. Parish Ministry for Maturing Adults: Principles, Plans, & Bold Proposals. 2007. 119p. per. 12.95 *(978-1-58595-621-0(X))* Twenty-Third Pubns./Bayard.

MacKinlay, Elizabeth, ed. Ageing, Disability & Spirituality: Addressing the Challenge of Disability in Later Life. 2008. (ENG., Illus.). 272p. per. *(978-1-84310-584-8(5))* Kingsley, Jessica Ltd.

CHURCH WORK WITH PEOPLE WITH DISABILITIES

Broesterhuizen, Marcel. The Gospel Preached by the Deaf: Proceedings of a Conference about Deaf Liberation Theology held at the Faculty of Theology of the Catholic University of Leuven (Belgium), May 19 2003. Broesterhuizen, M., ed. 2007. (Annua Nuntia Lovaniensia Ser.). (ENG.). 123p. (C). pap. 71.00 *(978-90-429-1854-2(3))* Peeters Pubs. & Booksellers BEL. Dist: Brown, David Bk. Co., The.

Carter, Erik W. Including People with Disabilities in Faith Communities: A Guide for Service Providers, Families, & Congregations. 2007. (Illus.). 236p. per. 27.95 *(978-1-55766-743-4(8))* Brookes, Paul H. Publishing Co.

Chang, Raymond. Beyond the Magic Bullet: The Anti-Cancer Cocktail: A New Approach to Beating Cancer. 2011. (ENG.). 208p. pap. 16.95 *(978-0-7570-0232-8(3))* Square One Pubs.

Clark, Allen B., Jr. & Clark, Allen B. Wounded Soldier, Healing Warrior: A Personal Story of a Vietnam Veteran Who Lost His Legs but Found His Soul. rev. ed. 2007. (ENG., Illus.). 320p. 27.00 *(978-0-7603-3113-2(8))*, 0760331138, Zenith Pr.) MBI Publishing Co. LLC.

Conner, Benjamin T. Amplifying Our Witness: Practice-Centered Ministry with Adolescents & Adolescents with Developmental Disabilities. 2012. pap. ***(978-0-8028-6721-6(9))*** Eerdmans, William B. Publishing Co.

Cook, John G. A Compassionate Journey: Coming Alongside People with Disabilities or Chronic Illnesses. 2008. *(978-1-59255-399-0(0))* Faith Alive Christian Resources.

Davison, Jean. Connections of Hope. 2006. pap. 10.99 *(978-1-60034-779-5(7))* Xulon Pr., Inc.

Disability Advocacy among Religious Organizations: Histories & Reflections. 2006. (ENG.). 250p. (C). 124.00 *(978-0-7890-3289-8(9))* Routledge.

Disability Advocacy among Religious Organizations: Histories & Reflections. 2006. (ENG.). 250p. per. 50.50 *(978-0-7890-3290-4(2))* Routledge.

Frank, Dallas. Writing in the Margins: among People with Developmental Disabilities. 2009. 114p. pap. 9.70 *(978-0-557-22116-5(1))* Lulu Enterprises Inc.

Hauerwas, Stanley M., et al. Living Gently in a Violent World: The Prophetic Witness of Weakness. 2008. (Resources for Reconciliation Ser.). (ENG.). 117p. pap. 15.00 *(978-0-8308-3452-5(4)*, IVP Bks.) InterVarsity Pr.

Hisbon, Janet Mitchell. Senior Spirit: An Outreach Ministry to Older Adults. 2009. *(978-0-8298-1827-7(8))* Pilgrim Pr., The/United Church Pr.

Hubach, Stephanie O. Same Lake, Different Boat: Coming Alongside People Touched by Disability. 2006. (Illus.). 234p. per. 14.99 *(978-1-59638-051-6(9))* P & R Publishing.

Jacobs, Martha & Jacobs, Martha R. A Clergy Guide to End-Of-Life Issues. 2010. *(978-0-8298-1859-8(6))* Pilgrim Pr., The/United Church Pr.

Kroeger, Catherine Clark & Nason-Clark, Nancy. No Place for Abuse: Biblical & Practical Resources to Counteract Domestic Violence. rev. ed. 2010. (ENG.). 249p. pap. 17.00 *(978-0-8308-3838-7(4)*, IVP Bks.) InterVarsity Pr.

Liedke, Ulf. Beziehungsreiches Leben: Studien zu einer inklusiven theologischen Anthropologie für Menschen mit und ohne Behinderung. 2009. (Arbeiten zur Pastoraltheologie, Liturgik und Hymnologie Ser.). (GER., Illus.). 652p. (C). pap. 123.00 *(978-3-525-62410-4(7))* Vandenhoeck & Ruprecht GmbH & Co. KG DEU. Dist: ISD.

MacKinlay, Elizabeth, ed. Ageing, Disability & Spirituality: Addressing the Challenge of Disability in Later Life. 2008. (ENG., Illus.). 272p. per. *(978-1-84310-584-8(5))* Kingsley, Jessica Ltd.

Pinsky, Mark I. Amazing Gifts: Stories of Faith, Disability, & Inclusion. 2011. ***(978-1-56699-421-7(7))*** Alban Institute, Inc.

Preheim-Bartel, Dean A. & Neufeldt, Aldred H. Supportive Care in the Congregation: Providing a Congregational Network of Care for Persons with Significant Disabilities. 2011. pap. *(978-0-8361-9572-9(8))* Herald Pr.

Reimer, Kevin. Living L'Arche. 2009. 192p. 26.95 *(978-0-8146-3299-4(8)*, Liturgical Pr. Bks.) Liturgical Pr.

Reinders, Hans S. Paradox of Disability. 2010. viii, 183p. pap. 18.00 *(978-0-8028-6511-3(9))* Eerdmans, William B. Publishing Co.

Reynolds, Thomas E. Vulnerable Communion: A Theology of Disability & Hospitality. 2008. 256p. (C). pap. 25.00 *(978-1-58743-177-7(7))* Brazos Pr.

Rich, Cynthia Holder & Ross-Mockaitis, Martha. Learning Disabilities & the Church: Including All God's Kids in Your Education & Worship. 2006. 80p. pap. 12.95 *(978-1-59255-262-7(5))* Faith Alive Christian Resources.

Swinton, John & Swinton. Theology, Disability & the New Genetics: Why Science Needs the Church. Brock, Brian, ed. 2007. (ENG., Illus.). 264p. 155.00 *(978-0-567-04543-0(9)*, T&T Clark Int'l) Continuum International Publishing Group, Ltd. GBR. Dist: National Bk. Network.

—Theology, Disability & the New Genetics: Why Science Needs the Church. Brock, Brian, ed. 2007. (ENG., Illus.). 264p. 41.95 *(978-0-567-04558-4(7)*, T&T Clark Int'l) Continuum International Publishing Group, Ltd. GBR. Dist: National Bk. Network.

Webb-Mitchell, Brett. Dancing with Disabilities: Opening the Church to All GodÕs Children. 2008. 170p. pap. 20.00 *(978-1-60608-144-0(6)*, Wipf and Stock) Wipf & Stock Pubs.

—Unexpected Guests at GodÕs Banquet: Welcoming People with Disabilities into the Church. 2009. 204p. pap. 22.00 *(978-1-60608-559-2(X)*, Wipf and Stock) Wipf & Stock Pubs.

Yong, Amos. The Bible, Disability, & the Church: A New Vision of the People of God. 2011. 178p. pap. 20.00 *(978-0-8028-6608-0(5))* Eerdmans, William B. Publishing Co.

—Theology & Down Syndrome: Reimagining Disability in Late Modernity. 2007. (ENG.). 425p. per. 39.95 *(978-1-60258-006-0(5))* Baylor Univ. Pr.

CHURCH WORK WITH PEOPLE WITH MENTAL DISABILITIES

Berken, Kathleen C. Walking on a Rolling Deck: Life on the Ark. 2008. pap. 14.95 *(978-0-8146-1861-5(8))* Liturgical Pr.

Clarke, William. Enough Room for Joy: The Early Days of Jean Vanier's L'Arche. 2007. (ENG., Illus.). 144p. per. 14.95 *(978-1-933346-06-9(X))* BlueBridge.

Grainger, Roger. Prospero's Island: Navigating Pastoral Care. 2010. 164p. pap. 23.00 *(978-1-4269-2927-4(7))* Trafford Publishing.

Kobold, Claudia. Einander unbehindert Begegnen: Weggemeinschaft von Menschen mit und ohne Behinderung. 2008. (Europäische Hochschulschriften. Reihe 23: Theologie Ser.). 118p. pap. 35.95 *(978-3-631-56655-8(7))* Lang, Peter GmbH, Europaischer Verlag der Wissenschaften DEU. Dist: Lang, Peter.

Nolan, Steve. Spiritual Care at the End of Life. 2011. (ENG.). 160p. pap. ***(978-1-84905-199-6(2))*** Kingsley, Jessica Ltd.

Pattison. Pastoral Care & Liberation Theology. 288p. 22.00 *(978-0-281-05048-2(1))* SPCK Publishing GBR. Dist: Pilgrim Pr., The/United Church Pr.

Tada, Joni Eareckson. Special Needs Smart Pages: Advice, Answers & Articles about Teaching Children with Special Needs. 2009. (ENG.). 328p. (J). 49.99 *(978-0-8307-4719-1(2))* Gospel Light Pubns.

CHURCH WORK WITH PRISONERS

see also Religious Work with Prisoners

Bevis, James C. Making It on the Inside: (So You Can Make It on the Outside!) 2009. 138p. pap. 24.95 *(978-1-60672-124-7(0))* PublishAmerica, Inc.

Burke, Dennis. Doing Time: Finding Hope at San Quentin. 2008. 144p. per. 14.95 *(978-0-8091-4527-0(8))* Paulist Pr.

Davis, Rick. The Prison Sermons. 2007. 268p. per. 15.99 *(978-1-60266-056-4(5))* Xulon Pr., Inc.

Fisher, Adarrel. Confrontations. 2007. 272p. per. 15.99 *(978-1-60477-168-8(2))* Xulon Pr., Inc.

Goode, W. Wilson, Sr., et al. Ministry with Prisoners & Families: The Way Forward. 2011. 192p. pap. 17.99 *(978-0-8170-1664-7(3))* Judson Pr.

Hemenway, Joanne. Forget Them Not: A Holistic Guide to Prison Ministry. 2010. 184p. pap. 21.00 *(978-1-60899-320-8(5)*, Wipf and Stock) Wipf & Stock Pubs.

Johnson, Aaron & Rev. Aaron Johnson With Deb Cleveland. Man from Macedoni: My life of service, struggle, faith, & Hope. 2010. 272p. 35.95 *(978-1-4497-0030-0(6)*, WestBow Pr.) Author Solutions, Inc.

Langley, Wanda. Prison Ministry Made Easy. 2010. 32p. pap. 9.95 *(978-0-557-23857-6(9))* Lulu Enterprises Inc.

Maness, Michael Glenn. Queen of Prison Ministry: The Story of Gertha Rogers, First Woman to Minister on Texas Death Row. 2008. 200p. 27.95 *(978-1-4343-9144-5(2))*; pap. 22.95 *(978-1-4343-9143-8(4))* AuthorHouse.

Pickett, Carroll & Stowers, Carlton. Within These Walls: Memoirs of a Death House Chaplain. 2009. (ENG.). 256p. pap. 16.95 *(978-1-904132-74-5(X))* Vision Paperbacks GBR. Dist: Independent Pubs. Group.

Speer, John. Uncommon Community: One Congregation's Work with Prisoners. 2008. pap. 14.00 *(978-1-55896-538-6(6)*, Skinner Hse. Bks.) Unitarian Universalist Assn.

Spitale, Lennie. Help! My Loved One Is in Jail. What Do I Do Now? 2007. 63p. per. 3.95 *(978-1-879089-41-9(6))* Evangelism & Missions Information Service (EMIS).

Stevens, Wesley. Learning to Sing in a Strange Land: When a Loved One Goes to Prison. 2009. 210p. pap. 23.00 *(978-1-59752-535-0(9)*, Resource Pubns.) Wipf & Stock Pubs.

Wilbur, William H. Finding Freedom in Panama. pap. 12.95 *(978-1-883928-34-6(6))* Longwood Communications.

CHURCH WORK WITH PROBLEM CHILDREN

Downs, Lisa, et al, contrib. by. Group's Emergency Response Handbook for Children's Ministry. 2007. 156p. per. 14.99 *(978-0-7644-3626-0(0))* Group Publishing, Inc.

Stringer, Doug. Hope for a Fatherless Generation: Rebuilding our Foundations. 2009. pap. 16.99 *(978-0-7684-2822-3(X))* Destiny Image Pubs.

CHURCH WORK WITH REFUGEES

Lacey, Marilyn. This Flowing Toward Me: A Story of God Arriving in Strangers. 2009. 224p. pap. 16.95 *(978-1-59471-197-8(6))* Ave Maria Pr.

Leddy, Mary Jo. The Other Face of God: When the Stranger Calls Us Home. 2011. 160p. pap. 20.00 *(978-1-57075-910-9(3))* Orbis Bks.

Martin, James. This Our Exile: A Spiritual Journey with the Refugees of East Africa. 2011. (Illus.). 240p. pap. 18.00 *(978-1-57075-923-9(5))* Orbis Bks.

Mosley, Donald. Faith Beyond Borders: Doing Justice in a Dangerous World. 2010. 142p. pap. 15.00 *(978-1-4267-0789-6(4))* Abingdon Pr.

Schaap, James. Crossing Over: Stories of Asian Refugee Christians. 2006. 148p. per. 14.00 *(978-0-932914-67-5(5))* Dordt College Pr.

Smith, Gary N. They Come Back Singing: Finding God with the Refugees. 2008. (ENG., Illus.). 248p. per. 14.95 *(978-0-8294-2701-1(5))* Loyola Pr.

CHURCH WORK WITH SINGLE PEOPLE

Franck, Dennis. Reaching Single Adults: An Essential Guide for Ministry. 2007. 224p. pap. 17.00 *(978-0-8010-9190-2(X))* Baker Bks.

Single Adult Ministry Drive,in. *(978-0-7673-9417-8(8))* LifeWay Christian Resources.

CHURCH WORK WITH STUDENTS

Calhoun, Mike & Garland, Ric. Where Was God When? 2010. 120p. (YA). lib. bdg. 14.95 *(978-1-935475-10-1(X))* Word of Life Fellowship, Inc.

Franklin, Paul. New Ground: a primer in planting student Households. 2010. 42p. pap. 8.50 *(978-1-4457-3867-3(8))* Lulu Enterprises Inc.

Garber, Steven. The Fabric of Faithfulness: Weaving Together Belief & Behavior. 2nd annot. ed. 2007. (ENG.). 222p. per. 16.00 *(978-0-8308-3319-1(6)*, IVP Bks.) InterVarsity Pr.

Guidelines for Leading Your Congregation 2009-2012 - Higher Education & Campus Ministry: Connecting with Students in Schools, Colleges, & Campus Ministries. 2008. 2.95 *(978-0-687-64762-0(2))* Abingdon Pr.

Isbell, Roy S. Campus Ministry: How to Reach Your Campus for Christ. 2011. 144p. 22.50 ***(978-1-4634-1956-1(2))***; pap. 12.00 ***(978-1-4634-1957-8(0))*** AuthorHouse.

Kim, Rebecca. God's New Whiz Kids? Korean American Evangelicals on Campus. annot. ed. 2006. (ENG.). 192p. 45.00 *(978-0-8147-4790-2(6))* New York Univ. Pr.

Labelle, Jeffrey & Kendall, Daniel. Catholic Colleges in the 21st Century: A Road Map for Campus Ministry. 2011. 112p. pap. 9.95 *(978-0-8091-4733-5(5))* Paulist Pr.

Ma, Jaeson. The Blueprint: A Revolutionary Plan to Plant Missional Communities on Campus. 2007. (ENG.). 256p. per. 14.99 *(978-0-8307-4408-4(8))* Gospel Light Pubns.

MacLeod, A. Donald. C. Stacey Woods & the Evangelical Rediscovery of the University. 2007. (ENG., Illus.). 283p. per. 25.00 *(978-0-8308-3432-7(X)*, IVP Acad.) InterVarsity Pr.

McDowell, Josh & Bellis, David H. La Ultima Generacion de Cristianos. Valverde, Hubert, tr. 2007. (SPA.). 176p. pap. 9.50 *(978-0-311-46321-3(5)*, Editorial Mundo Hispano) Casa Bautista de Publicaciones.

Senn, William J. Taking the Cross of Christ to the Campus: A Manual for Church-Based Campus Ministry. 2008. (Illus.). xi, 195p. *(978-1-59166-810-7(7))* BJU Pr.

Shaw, Ryan. Waking the Giant: The Resurging Student Mission Movement. 2006. 208p. *(978-0-87808-372-5(3))* Carey, William Library Pubs.

Vandegriff, Steve. Campus Ministry, Third Ed. 2006. (C). per. *(978-1-60036-022-0(X))* Academx Publishing Services, Inc.

CHURCH WORK WITH THE AGED

see Church Work with Older People

CHURCH WORK WITH THE BABY BOOM GENERATION

Hanson, Amy. Baby Boomers & Beyond: Tapping the Ministry Talents & Passions of Adults Over 50. 2010. (Jossey-Bass Leadership Network Ser.: 45). (ENG.). 224p. 24.95 *(978-0-470-50079-8(4)*, Jossey-Bass) Wiley, John & Sons, Inc.

CHURCH WORK WITH THE BEREAVED

see also Funeral Service

Croft, Brian & Newton, Phil A. Conduct Gospel-Centered Funerals: Applying the Gospel at the Unique Challenges of Death. 2011. (Ministering the Master's Way Ser.). 106p. pap. ***(978-1-84625-266-2(0))*** DayOne Pubns.

Fowler, Gene. Ministry of Lament: Caring for the Bereaved. 2010. 160p. pap. 19.99 *(978-0-8272-2335-6(8))* Chalice Pr.

Goddard, Danny. Pastoral Care in Times of Death & Dying. 2009. (ENG.). 160p. pap. 13.99 *(978-0-8341-2436-3(X)*, 9780834124363) Beacon Hill Pr. of Kansas City.

Kelley, Melissa M. Grief: Contemporary Theory & the Practice of Ministry. 2010. 160p. (C). pap. 20.00 *(978-0-8006-9661-0(1)*, Fortress Pr.) Augsburg Fortress, Pubs.

Lampe, Karen. The Caring Congregation: How to Become One & Why it Matters. 2011. 112p. pap. 13.00 *(978-1-4267-2733-7(X))* Abingdon Pr.

Mayfield, James L. Amazing Grace in the Midst of Grief. 2011. 128p. pap. 16.00 ***(978-1-60899-944-6(0)***, Cascade Bks.) Wipf & Stock Pubs.

Nelson, Jan & Aaker, David. The Bereavement Ministry Program: A Comprehensive Guide for Churches. rev. ed. 2009. 288p. 49.95 *(978-1-59471-192-3(5))* Ave Maria Pr.

Smith, Harold Ivan. The Grief Care Kit: Bereavement Resources for Counselors & Recovery Group Leaders. 2008. (ENG.). 192p. pap. 49.99 *(978-0-8341-2382-3(7)*, 9780834123823) Beacon Hill Pr. of Kansas City.

Speck, Peter. Letting Go. 12.00 *(978-0-687-85670-1(1))* Abingdon Pr.

Tautges, Paul. Comfort Those Who Grieve: Ministering God's Grace in Times of Loss. 2009. (Ministering the Master's Way Ser.). 143p. pap. *(978-1-84625-155-9(9))* DayOne Pubns.

Townsend, Loren L. Suicide. 2006. (Pastoral Responses Ser.). (Illus.). 144p. per. 18.00 *(978-0-687-49297-8(1))* Abingdon Pr.

CHURCH WORK WITH THE HANDICAPPED

see Church Work With People With Disabilities

CHURCH WORK WITH THE HOMELESS

Christmas, Candy. On the Other Side: Life-Changing Stories from under the Bridge. 2010. 200p. pap. 14.99 *(978-0-89112-043-8(2),* Leafwood Pubs.) Abilene Christian Univ. Pr.

Ferguson, Bonnie. The Streets of Kingston. 2012. ***(978-1-55452-775-5(9))*** Essence Publishing.

Flowers, John & Vannoy, Karen. Not Just a One-Night Stand: Ministry with the Homeless. 2009. 128p. pap. 14.00 *(978-0-88177-557-0(6))* Discipleship Resources.

Garon, Henry. The Wanderers. 2009. 160p. pap. 16.00 *(978-1-57075-820-1(4))* Orbis Bks.

Gathje, Peter R. Sharing the Bread of Life: Hospitality & Resistance at the Open Door Community. anniv. ed. 2006. per. *(978-0-9715893-2-2(1))* Open Door Community.

Gittins, Anthony J. Where There's Hope There's Life: Womens Stories of Homelessness & Survival with Theological & Pastoral Reflections. annot. ed. 2006. 172p. per. 16.95 *(978-0-7648-1410-5(9),* Liguori/Triumph) Liguori Pubns.

Huff, Tim. Bent Hope: A Street Journal. 2008. *(978-1-894860-36-9(5))* Castle Quay Bks. Canada.

Mannis, Jedediah. Joseph Tuckerman & the Outdoor Church. 2009. (Princeton Theological Monographs). 242p. pap. 27.00 *(978-1-55635-551-6(3),* Pickwick Pubns.) Wipf & Stock Pubs.

McCaig, Wendy R. From the Sanctuary to the Streets. 2010. (Illus.). 180p. pap. 19.00 *(978-1-60899-089-4(3),* Cascade Bks.) Wipf & Stock Pubs.

Rhodes, David. Faith in Dark Places - P. 112p. 10.00 *(978-0-281-04986-8(6))* SPCK Publishing GBR. Dist: Pilgrim Pr., The/United Church Pr.

Saunders, Stanley P. & Campbell, Charles L. The Word on the Street: Performing the Scriptures in the Urban Context. 2006. (Illus.). 212p. pap. 24.00 *(978-1-59752-885-6(4),* Wipf and Stock) Wipf & Stock Pubs.

Still Living on Skid Row. 2007. 14.00 net. *(978-0-9786285-2-9(7))* Salierno, Kurt.

Wilson, Christopher. Radically Changed: 37 Real Life Inspirational Stories. 2010. 352p. pap. 17.99 *(978-1-4490-8146-1(0))* AuthorHouse.

CHURCH WORK WITH THE MENTALLY HANDICAPPED

see Church Work with People with Mental Disabilities

CHURCH WORK WITH THE MENTALLY ILL

Clinton, Tim, et al, eds. Caring for People God's Way: Personal & Emotional Issues, Addictions, Grief, & Trauma, 0 vols. 2009. 576p. pap. 22.99 *(978-0-7852-9775-8(8))* Nelson, Thomas Inc.

Foskett, John. Meaning in Madness. 12.00 *(978-0-687-85762-3(7))* Abingdon Pr.

Otwell, Patricia Anne. Guide to Ministering: To Alzheimer's Patients & Their Families. 2008. (ENG.). 296p. 79.95 *(978-0-7890-2902-7(2));* pap. 54.50 *(978-0-7890-2903-4(0))* Routledge.

Smith, H. Humanism V Creationism: Mental illness in the Church. 2008. 136p. pap. *(978-1-84747-600-5(7))* Chipmunkapublishing.

Speck, Peter. Letting Go. 12.00 *(978-0-687-85670-1(1))* Abingdon Pr.

Stanford, Matthew S. Grace for the Afflicted: A Clinical & Biblical Perspective on Mental Illness. 2008. (ENG., Illus.). 271p. pap. 19.99 *(978-1-934068-44-1(6),* Paternoster) Authentic Media.

CHURCH WORK WITH THE POOR

Baker, Heidi. Compelled by Love: How to Change the World Through the Simple Power of Love in Action. 2008. (ENG., Illus.). 176p. pap. 12.99 *(978-1-59979-351-1(2),* Charisma Hse.) Charisma Media.

Barker, Ash. Make Poverty Personal: Taking the Poor as Seriously as the Bible Does. 2009. (Mersion: Emergent Village Resources for Communities of Faith Ser.). 206p. pap. 16.00 *(978-0-8010-7189-8(5))* Baker Bks.

Barreto, Raimundo. Facing the Poor. 2009. 314p. pap. *(978-3-639-17703-9(7))* VDM Verlag Dr. Mueller e.K.

Bessenecker, Scott A. The New Friars: The Emerging Movement Serving the World's Poor. 2006. (ENG., Illus.). 199p. per. 16.00 *(978-0-8308-3601-7(2),* IVP Bks.) InterVarsity Pr.

Bessenecker, Scott A., ed. Living Mission: The Vision & Voices of New Friars. 2010. (ENG.). 176p. pap. 16.00 *(978-0-8308-3633-8(0),* IVP Bks.) InterVarsity Pr.

Closkey, Pilar Hogan & Hogan, John P., eds. Romero's Legacy: The Call to Peace & Justice. 2007. (Sheed & Ward Book Ser.). (ENG.). 144p. 54.00 *(978-0-7425-4821-3(X))* per. 19.95 *(978-0-7425-4822-0(8))* Rowman & Littlefield Publishers, Inc.

Corbett, Steve & Fikkert, Brian. When Helping Hurts: How to Alleviate Poverty Without Hurting the Poor ... & Yourself. (ENG.). 2012. 288p. pap. 14.99 ***(978-0-8024-5706-6(1))*** 2009. 232p. pap. 14.99 *(978-0-8024-5705-9(3))* Moody Pubs.

Couture, Pamela. Child Poverty: Love, Justice, & Social Responsibility. 2008. 235p. per. 29.99 *(978-0-8272-0509-3(0))* Chalice Pr.

Daly, Lew. God & the Welfare State. 2006. (Boston Review Bks.). (ENG.). 136p. (gr. 17). 14.95 *(978-0-262-04236-9(3))* MIT Pr.

Duckworth, Jenny & Duckworth, Justin. Against the Tide, Towards the Kingdom. 2011. (New Monastic Library: Resources for Radical Discipleship Ser.). 130p. pap. 16.00 ***(978-1-60899-867-8(3),*** Cascade Bks.) Wipf & Stock Pubs.

Ellis, Marc H. Peter Maurin. 2010. (Catholic Worker Reprint Ser.). (Illus.). 204p. pap. 23.00 *(978-1-60899-060-3(5),* Wipf and Stock) Wipf & Stock Pubs.

Flowers, John & Vannoy, Karen. Not Just a One-Night Stand: Ministry with the Homeless. 2009. 128p. pap. 14.00 *(978-0-88177-557-0(6))* Discipleship Resources.

Galloway. Sharing the Blessing: Overcoming Injustice & Poverty. 2008. 112p. pap. *(978-0-281-05949-2(7))* SPCK Publishing.

Garcia-Johnson, Oscar. The Mestizo/a Community of the Spirit: A Postmodern Latino/a Ecclesiology. 2008. (Princeton Theological Monographs). 174p. pap. 19.00 *(978-1-55635-719-0(2),* Pickwick Pubns.) Wipf & Stock Pubs.

Garon, Henry. The Wanderers. 2009. 160p. pap. 16.00 *(978-1-57075-820-1(4))* Orbis Bks.

Gonzalez-Balado, Jose Luis. Teresa of Calcutta: A Personal Memoir. 2007. (Illus.). 185p. per. 12.95 *(978-0-7648-1547-8(4))* Liguori Pubns.

Greer, Peter & Smith, Phil. The Poor Will Be Glad: Joining the Revolution to Lift the World Out of Poverty, 1 vol. 2009. (ENG.). 256p. 19.99 *(978-0-310-29359-0(6))* Zondervan.

Hefferan, Tara. Twinning Faith & Development: Catholic Parish Partnering in the US & Haiti. 2007. (Illus.). 256p. pap. 24.95 *(978-1-56549-236-3(6))* Stylus Publishing, LLC.

Heim, Joseph A. What the Taught Us: How Maryknoll Missioners Were Evangelized by the Poor. 2009. (Illus.). 128p. pap. 15.00 *(978-1-57075-818-8(2))* Orbis Bks.

Himmelgreen, David & Kedia, Satish, eds. Intersections of Faith & Development in Local & Global Contexts, Number 33. 2010. (NAPA Bulletin Ser.: 3). (ENG., Illus.). 200p. pap. 28.95 *(978-1-4443-3911-6(7),* Wiley-Blackwell) Wiley, John & Sons, Inc.

Hoefner, Lisa Jean. Creation Vacation. 2008. 108p. pap. *(978-3-639-01534-8(7))* VDM Verlag Dr. Mueller e.K.

Kammer, Fred. Faith. Works. Wonders: An Insider's Guide to Catholic Charities. 2009. 220p. pap. 24.00 *(978-1-60608-927-9(7),* Pickwick Pubns.) Wipf & Stock Pubs.

Knuth, Jane. Thrift Store Saints: Meeting Jesus 25 at a Time. 2010. (ENG.). 176p. pap. 13.95 *(978-0-8294-3301-2(5))* Loyola Pr.

Korgen, Jeffry Odell. Solidarity Will Transform the World: Stories of Hope from Catholic Relief Services. 2007. (Illus.). 161p. per. 16.00 *(978-1-57075-744-0(5))* Orbis Bks.

Kownacki, Mary Lou. A Monk in the Inner City: The ABCs of a Spiritual Journey. 2008. 155p. pap. 18.00 *(978-1-57075-760-0(7))* Orbis Bks.

Kuyper, Abraham Jr. & Kuyper, Abraham. The Problem of Poverty. 2011. 94p. ***(978-0-932914-87-3(X))*** Dordt College Pr.

Longenecker, Bruce. Remember the Poor: Paul, Poverty, & the Greco-Roman World. 2010. 284p. pap. 25.00 *(978-0-8028-6373-7(6))* Eerdmans, William B. Publishing Co.

Lupton, Robert D. Compassion, Justice & the Christian Life: Rethinking Ministry to the Poor. 2007. (ENG.). 144p. per. 11.99 *(978-0-8307-4379-7(0))* Gospel Light Pubns.

Mary Nelson. Empowerment: A Key Component of Christian Community Development. 2010. 112p. pap. 12.95 *(978-1-4401-8532-8(8))* iUniverse, Inc.

McAfee, Donald R. Called but it should be Called? 2010. (ENG.). pap. 19.95 *(978-1-58992-605-2(1),* Millennial Mind Publishing) American Bk. Publishing Group.

Mettey, Wendell E. What God Desires: The Story of the Center of Humanitarian Aid & Disaster Relief. 2008. (Illus.). xi, 116p. *(978-1-57736-410-8(4))* Providence Hse Pubs.

Miles, Sara. Take This Bread: A Radical Conversion. 2008. (ENG.). 320p. per. 15.00 *(978-0-345-49579-2(9),* Ballantine Bks.) Random House Publishing Group.

Milner, Rev. J. Allen. God's Special Provisions for the Poor. 2010. 153p. pap. 12.95 *(978-0-557-59439-9(1))* Lulu Enterprises Inc.

Mother Teresa of Calcutta & Kolodiejchuk, Brian. Mother Teresa: Come Be My Light. 2007. (ENG.). 416p. 24.00 *(978-0-385-52037-9(9),* Doubleday) Doubleday Religious Publishing Group, The.

Myers, Bryant. Walking with the Poor: Principles & Practices of Transformational Development. 2011. (Illus.). 416p. pap. 30.00 *(978-1-57075-939-0(1))* Orbis Bks.

Ndungane, Njongonkulu. World with a Human Face: A Voice from Africa. 2011. 160p. pap. 28.95 *(978-0-86486-614-1(3))* International Publishers Marketing.

Nelson, Toni. A Beggars Purse. 2010. pap. 10.99 *(978-1-61663-117-8(1))* Tate Publishing & Enterprises, LLC.

Poloma, Margaret & Hood, Ralph W., Jr. Blood & Fire: Godly Love in a Pentecostal Emerging Church. 2008. (ENG.). 304p. (C). 45.00 *(978-0-8147-6748-1(6))* New York Univ. Pr.

Prochaska, Frank. Christianity & Social Service in Modern Britain: The Disinherited Spirit. 2008. (ENG., Illus.). 228p. 45.00 *(978-0-19-953979-6(0))* Oxford Univ. Pr., Inc.

Radcliffe, Timothy, ed. Just One Year: A Global Treasury of Prayer & Worship. 2007. 288p. per. 20.00 *(978-1-57075-714-3(3))* Orbis Bks.

Raphael, Lutz & Uerlings, Herbert, eds. Zwischen Ausschluss und Solidarität: Modi der Inklusion/Exklusion von Fremden und Armen in Europa seit der Spätantike. 2008. (Inklusion/Exklusion. Studien zu Fremdheit und Armut von der Antike bis zur Gegenwart Ser.). (GER., Illus.). 570p. pap. 124.95 *(978-3-631-58204-6(8))* Lang, Peter GmbH, Europaischer Verlag der Wissenschaften DEU. Dist: Lang, Peter.

Simon, Arthur. The Rising of Bread for the World: An Outcry of Citizens Against Hunger. 2009. 176p. pap. 16.95 *(978-0-8091-4600-0(2))* Paulist Pr.

Stearns, Richard. The Hole in Our Gospel: What Does God Expect of Us? The Answer That Changed My Life & Might Just Change the World. l.t. ed. 2010. 416p. pap. 17.99 *(978-1-59415-323-5(X))* Cengage Gale.

—The Hole in Our Gospel: What God Expect of Us? The Answer That Changed My Life & Might Just Change the World, 0 vols. 2010. 352p. pap. 15.99 *(978-0-8499-4700-1(6))* Nelson, Thomas Inc.

Still Living on Skid Row. 2007. 14.00 net. *(978-0-9786285-2-9(7))* Salierno, Kurt.

Strom, Kay Marshall. Harvest of Hope: Stories of Life-Changing Gifts. 2007. (ENG., Illus.). 200p. per. 15.00 *(978-0-8308-3442-6(7),* IVP Bks.) InterVarsity Pr.

Sullivan, Susan Crawford. Living Faith: Everyday Religion & Mothers in Poverty. 2012. (Morality & Society Ser.). 288p. 78.00 *(978-0-226-78160-0(7));* pap. 26.00 ***(978-0-226-78161-7(5))*** Univ. of Chicago Pr.

Sung, Jung Mo. The Subject, Capitalism, & Religion: Horizons of Hope in Complex Societies. 2011. (New Approaches to Religion & Power Ser.). (ENG., Illus.). 208p. 85.00 *(978-0-230-11975-8(1))* Palgrave Macmillan.

Sutter, Arloa. The Invisible: Finding & Serving the Least of These. 2010. *(978-0-89827-456-1(7))* Wesleyan Publishing Hse.

Thacker, Justin. Micah's Challenge: The Church's Responsibility to the Global Poor. 2008. (ENG.). 214p. 19.99 *(978-1-84227-606-8(9),* Paternoster) Authentic Media.

Wingeier-Rayo, Philip D. Where Are the Poor? A Comparison of the Ecclesial Base Communities & PentecostalismNtilde;A Case Study in Cuernavaca, Mexico. 2011. (Princeton Theological Monographs). 174p. pap. 20.00 ***(978-1-60608-901-9(3),*** Pickwick Pubns.) Wipf & Stock Pubs.

CHURCH WORK WITH THE SICK

see also Pastoral Medicine

Barkdull, Larry. Priesthood Power: Blessing the Sick & Afflicted. 2008. xi, 95p. *(978-1-59811-641-0(X))* Covenant Communications.

Cortino, Becky. A Heart 4 Clowning: How to Establish a Hospital Clown or Creative Ministry Guide. 2007. 110p. spiral bd. 22.00 *(978-0-9799093-0-6(9))* Heart 4 Clowning Pr., A.

Cress, Mark & Hobgood, Chris. Caring Directions: 50 Places Where God May be Calling You to Serve as a Community Chaplain. 2007. (ENG.). 144p. per. 14.99 *(978-0-9786039-2-2(3))* Lanphier Pr.

DelBene, Ron. Into the Light: Ministering to the Sick & the Dying. Montgomery, Mary & Montgomery, Herb, eds. 2009. 144p. pap. 18.00 *(978-1-55635-171-6(2),* Wipf and Stock) Wipf & Stock Pubs.

Dudley. Manual for Ministry to Sick - P. 160p. 14.95 *(978-0-281-04903-5(3))* International Publishers Marketing.

Dunlap, Susan J. Caring Cultures: How Congregations Respond to the Sick. 2009. (ENG.). 260p. pap. 24.95 *(978-1-932792-87-4(2))* Baylor Univ. Pr.

Echema, Austin. Anointing of the Sick & the Healing Ministry: The Nigerian Pastoral Experience. 2006. 212p. (gr. 11). pap. 32.95 *(978-3-88939-831-4(6))* IKO Verlag fur Interkulturelle Kommunikation DEU. Dist: Transaction Pubs.

Gemignani, Michael C. Making Your Church a House of Healing. 2008. 144p. pap. 14.00 *(978-0-8170-1530-5(2))* Judson Pr.

Harris, Angelique. AIDS, Sexuality, & the Black Church: Making the Wounded Whole. 2010. (Martin Luther King, Jr. Memorial Studies in Religion, Culture, & Social Development Ser.). 198p. (C). 72.95 *(978-1-4331-0943-0(3))* Lang, Peter Publishing, Inc.

Hisbon, Janet Mitchell. Senior Spirit: An Outreach Ministry to Older Adults. 2009. *(978-0-8298-1827-7(8))* Pilgrim Pr., The/United Church Pr.

Hobgood, Chris. Community Chaplain Training Workbook. 2007. (ENG.). 84p. pap. 14.95 *(978-0-9786039-3-9(1))* Lanphier Pr.

Holst, Lawrence E., ed. Hospital Ministry: The Role of the Chaplain Today. 2006. 256p. pap. 26.00 *(978-1-59752-814-6(5),* Wipf and Stock) Wipf & Stock Pubs.

Ihewulezi, Cajetan. Hospital Preaching as Informed by Bedside Listening: A Homiletical Guide for Preachers, Pastors, & Chaplains in Hospital, Hospice, Prison, & Nursing Home Ministries. 2010. (ENG.). 94p. pap. 18.50 *(978-0-7618-5292-6(1))* Univ. Pr. of America, Inc.

Kö, et al. Ethik im Krankenhaus: Diakonie - Seelsorge - Medizin. 2007. (GER.). 238p. (C). pap. 35.00 *(978-3-525-62399-2(2))* Vandenhoeck & Ruprecht GmbH & Co. KG DEU. Dist: ISD.

Klaits, Frederick. Death in a Church of Life: Moral Passion During Botswana's Time of AIDS. 2010. (Anthropology of Christianity Ser.). (ENG., Illus.). 368p. pap. 25.95 *(978-0-520-25966-9(1))* Univ. of California Pr.

—Death in a Church of Life: Moral Passion During Botswana's Time of AIDS. 2010. (Anthropology of Christianity Ser.). (ENG., Illus.). 368p. 60.00 *(978-0-520-25965-2(3))* Univ. of California Pr.

Lampe, Karen. The Caring Congregation: How to Become One & Why it Matters 2011. 112p. pap. 13.00 *(978-1-4267-2733-7(X))* Abingdon Pr.

Lauterbach, William A. Prayers for the Sickroom. 32p. 2.25 *(978-0-7586-0254-1(5))* Concordia Publishing Hse.

Lehmann, Axel. Krankenhaus und EG-Beihilferecht: Die Vereinbarkeit des Krankenhausfinanzierungsrechts mit Art. 87 ff. EG-Vertrag. 2008. (Schriften zum Staatskirchenrecht Ser.). 240p. pap. 61.95 *(978-3-631-57685-4(4))* Lang, Peter GmbH, Europaischer Verlag der Wissenschaften DEU. Dist: Lang, Peter.

Makoski, Kyrill. Kirchliche Krankenhäuser und staatliche Finanzierung: Geschichte, Ausgestaltung, verfassungsrechtliche Anforderungen. 2010. (Schriften zum Staatskirchenrecht Ser.). (GER.). 428p. 101.95 *(978-3-631-59918-1(8))* Lang, Peter GmbH, Europaischer Verlag der Wissenschaften DEU. Dist: Lang, Peter.

McNamara, Jill Westberg. Health & Wellness: What Your Faith Community Can Do. 2006. 96p. per. *(978-0-8298-1740-9(9))* Pilgrim Pr., The/United Church Pr.

Moser, Ingrid Friesen. Body Talk: Speaking the Words of Health. 2007. pap. 12.00 *(978-0-8361-9370-1(9))* Herald Pr.

Musgrave, Beverly Anne & McGettigan, Neil J. Spiritual & Psychological Aspects of Illness: Dealing with Sickness, Loss, Dying, & Death. 2010. 368p. pap. 27.95 *(978-0-8091-4661-1(4))* Paulist Pr.

O'Connor, Brian P., et al. The Role of the Minister in Caring for the Dying Patient & the Bereaved. 19.95 *(978-0-405-12504-1(6))* Ayer Co. Pubs., Inc.

Patterson, Deborah L. The Healing Word: Preaching & Teaching Health Ministry. 2009. *(978-0-8298-1849-9(9))* Pilgrim Pr., The/United Church Pr.

Pennington, M. Basil. The Christ Chaplain: The Way to a Deeper, More Effective Hospital Ministry. 2007. (ENG.). 86p. pap. 50.50 *(978-0-7890-0901-2(3));* 116.00 *(978-0-7890-0647-9(2))* Routledge.

Phillips, Sarah Webb. Pastoral Prayers for the Hospital Visit. 2006. (Just in Time! Ser.). 80p. per. 12.00 *(978-0-687-49658-7(6))* Abingdon Pr.

Rose, Mboya. An Investigation into a Local Church's Response to Hiv in South Africa: Challenges That a Small Local Church Faces When Responding to Hiv in South Africa (1990S-2005) 2011. 84p. pap. ***(978-3-639-33177-6(X))*** VDM Verlag Dr. Mueller e.K.

Sanchez Torres, Beatriz Carranza. Seleccion de Oraciones para las Horas de Enfermedad. 2008. 80p. per. 6.00 *(978-0-8146-4262-7(4),* Buena Prensa Bks.) Liturgical Pr.

Smucker, Carol J. & Weinberg, Linda. Faith Community Nursing: Developing a Quality Practice. 2008. pap. *(978-1-55810-252-1(3))* American Nurses Publishing.

Spearman, Bonny V. Hospital Visitation Handbook for Ministers. 2007. mass mkt. 11.99 *(978-0-9796106-0-8(5))* Steward Publishing.

Street, A. D. But the Pain Is Still There: Guidelines & Testimonies for Hospital Visitors. 2009. 68p. pap. *(978-1-84748-561-8(8))* Athena Pr.

Sullivan, Jackie. Pastoral Care to Younger Adults in Long-Term Care. 2007. (ENG., Illus.). 220p. 135.00 *(978-0-7890-2941-6(3))* Routledge.

—Pastoral Care with Young & Midlife Adults in Long-Term Care. 2007. (ENG., Illus.). 220p. per. 31.95 *(978-0-7890-2942-3(1))* Routledge.

Tinsley, Sarah V. HEARTS TOUCHING HEARTS Nursing Home Ministry. 2008. 68p. pap. 14.95 *(978-1-4357-4601-5(5))* Lulu Enterprises Inc.

UNAIDS. A Faith-based Response to HIV in Southern Africa: The Choose to Care Inititative. 2006. (UNAIDS Publication). (ENG.). 75p. pap. 18.00 *(978-92-9173-546-4(9))* World Health Organization.

CHURCH WORK WITH WOMEN

Amadi-Azuogu, Adolphus Chinedu. Gender & Ministry in Early Christianity & the Church Today. 2007. (ENG.). 272p. per. 44.50 *(978-0-7618-3016-0(2))* Univ. Pr. of America, Inc.

Barr, Beth Allison. The Pastoral Care of Women in Late Medieval England. 2008. (Gender in the Middle Ages Ser.: Volume 3). (Illus.). 182p. 90.00 *(978-1-84383-373-4(5),* Boydell Press) Boydell & Brewer, Ltd. GBR. Dist: Boydell & Brewer, Inc.

Birkey, Verna. Women Connecting with Women: Equipping Women for Friend-to-Friend Support & Mentoring. 2007. (ENG.). 340p. per. 19.99 *(978-1-4141-0993-0(8))* Pleasant Word.

—Women Connecting with Women, Study Guide. 2007. (ENG.). 96p. per. 11.99 *(978-1-4141-0994-7(6))* Pleasant Word.

Brolsma, Jody. Devotions Galore: Warm-Ups, Wrap-Ups, & Prayers for Women's Groups. 2008. (Illus.). 112p. pap. 19.99 *(978-0-7644-3695-6(3))* Group Publishing, Inc.

Carman, Anita. Transforming for a Purpose: Fulfilling God's Mission as Daughters of the King. Wilkerson, Dana, ed. 2009. (ENG.). 208p. pap. 14.99 *(978-0-8024-5855-1(6))* Moody Pubs.

Clark, Ron. Freeing the Oppressed: A Call to Christians concerning Domestic Abuse. 2009. 172p. pap. 20.00 *(978-1-60608-484-7(4),* Cascade Bks.) Wipf & Stock Pubs.

Clinton, Tim & Langberg, Diane. The Quick-Reference Guide to Counseling Women. 2011. 320p. pap. 24.99 *(978-0-8010-7234-5(4))* Baker Bks.

Davis, Diana, et al. Deacon Wives: Fresh Ideas to Encourage Your Husband & the Church, 1 vol. 2009. (ENG.). 192p. pap. 12.99 *(978-0-8054-4823-8(3),* B&H Bks.) B&H Publishing Group.

Earls, Denvis. Daughters of God: Southern Baptist Women. 2006. 105p. pap. 16.95 *(978-1-4241-5252-0(6))* PublishAmerica, Inc.

Edwards, Sue, et al. Leading Women Who Wound: Strategies for an Effective Ministry, 1 vol. 2009. (ENG.). 192p. pap. 13.99 *(978-0-8024-8153-5(1))* Moody Pubs.

English, Margaret. Removing the Veil: Revealing God's Truth for Women. 2008. 224p. pap. 13.99 *(978-0-88270-465-4(6))* Bridge-Logos Foundation.

Hislop, Bev. Shepherding Women in Pain: Real Women, Real Issues & What You Need to Know to Truly Help, 1 vol. 2010. (ENG.). 384p. pap. 14.99 *(978-0-8024-7705-7(4))* Moody Pubs.

Hollies, Linda H. Sister, Save Yourself! Direct Talk about Domestic Violence. annot. ed. 2006. 127p. per. *(978-0-8298-1731-7(X))* Pilgrim Pr., The/United Church Pr.

Hunt, Susan. Spiritual Mothering: The Titus 2 Model for Women Mentoring Women. 2009. 208p. pap. 15.99 *(978-1-4335-0313-9(1))* Crossway.

Jackson, Jennifer. Young Women Activities. 2009. 112p. pap. 12.95 *(978-1-60641-185-8(3))* Deseret Bk. Co.

Martin, Jaye, et al. Women Leading Women: The Biblical Model for the Church 2009. (ENG.). 256p. 29.99 *(978-0-8054-4760-6(1),* B&H Academic) B&H Publishing Group.

C

Moore, Beth. A Woman's Heart: God's Dwelling Place. 2007. (Illus.). 222p. per. 14.95 (978-1-4158-5581-2(1)) LifeWay Christian Resources.

—A Woman's Heart Leader's Guide: God's Dwelling Place. 2007. 31p. pap. 6.95 (978-1-4158-5579-9(X)) LifeWay Christian Resources.

Nason-Clark, Nancy, et al, eds. Responding to Abuse in Christian Homes: A Challenge to Churches & their Leaders. 2011. (House of Prisca & Aquila Ser.). 262p. pap. 29.00 (978-1-61097-178-2(7), Wipf and Stock) Wipf & Stock Pubs.

Ney, Margarete. Orte gesellschaftlichen Lernens: Frauenhäuser in Luxemburg als Aufgabenfeld der katholischen Kirche. 2008. (Übergänge. Studien zur Evangelischen und Katholischen Theologie/Religionspädagogik Ser.). 214p. pap. 56.95 (978-3-631-56341-0(8)) Lang, Peter GmbH, Europaischer Verlag der Wissenschaften DEU. Dist: Lang, Peter.

Nielson, Kathleen Buswell. Proverbs: The Ways of Wisdom. 2007. (Living Word Bible Studies). 182p. spiral bd. 12.99 (978-1-59638-081-3(0)) P & R Publishing.

Parker, Janelle R. The Complete Women's Ministries Kit: Everything You Need to Run a Successful Program. 2006. (ENG.). 192p. ring bd. 99.99 (978-0-8341-2309-0(6), 083-412-3096) Beacon Hill Pr. of Kansas City.

Pattison. Pastoral Care & Liberation Theology. 288p. 22.00 (978-0-281-05048-2(1)) SPCK Publishing GBR. Dist: Pilgrim Pr., The/United Church Pr.

Rose, Monica. Survey of Women's Ministries. 2007. (C). per. (978-1-60036-123-4(4)) Academx Publishing Services, Inc.

Schweitzer, Carol L. Schnabl. The Stranger's Voice: Julia Kristeva's Relevance for a Pastoral Theology for Women Struggling with Depression. 2010. (Practical Theology Ser.). 228p. (C). 74.95 (978-1-4331-0884-6(4)) Lang, Peter Publishing, Inc.

Smith, James M. Ireland's Magdalen Laundries & the Nation's Architecture of Containment. 2007. (ENG., Illus.). 320p. per. 28.00 (978-0-268-04127-4(X)) Univ. of Notre Dame Pr.

Strom, Kay Marshall & Rickett, Michele. Forgotten Girls: Stories of Hope & Courage, 1 vol. 2009. (ENG.). 175p. pap. 16.00 (978-0-8308-3731-1(0), IVP Bks.) InterVarsity Pr.

Witt, Connie & Workman, Cathi. That Makes Two of Us: Lifestyle Mentoring for Women. 2008. pap. (978-0-7644-3828-8(X), Group) Group Publishing, Inc.

Wuellner, Jill. Icebreakers Galore! The Ultimate Game Guide for Girlfriends. 2007. (Illus.). 109p. per. 19.99 (978-0-7644-3625-3(2)) Group Publishing, Inc.

CHURCH WORK WITH YOUNG ADULTS

Case, Steven L. & Case, Steven. Help! I'm a Frustrated Youth Worker! A Practical Guide to Avoiding Burnout in Your Ministry, 1 vol. 2008. (ENG.). 144p. pap. 10.99 (978-0-310-27888-7(0)) Zondervan.

Fannin, B. Kathleen. Wonder & Other Life Skills: Spiritual Life Retreats for Young Adults Using the Creative Arts. 2007. (ENG., Illus.). 144p. (J). (gr. -1-12). per. 16.95 (978-1-56101-307-4(2)) Cowley Pubns.

Fishell, Randy. Ready 2 Go: 15 Heart-Changing Programs for Youth & Young Adults. 2008. (ENG., Illus.). 124p. pap. 15.99 (978-0-8127-0459-4(2)) Review & Herald Publishing Assn.

Gitome, Josephine. Pastoral Care in African Context. 2011. 100p. pap. **(978-3-8443-9467-2(2))** Lambert Academic Publishing.

Glenn, Mike & Broadman and Holman Publishers Staff. In Real Time: Authentic Young Adult Ministry As It Happens. 2009. (ENG.). 192p. pap. 12.99 (978-0-8054-4694-4(X), B&H Bks.) B&H Publishing Group.

Ham, Ken, et al. Already Gone: Why Your Kids Will Quit Church & What You Can Do to Stop It. 2009. (Illus.). 189p. (978-0-89051-529-7(8)) Master Bks.

Hancock, Jim. How to Volunteer Like a Pro: An Amateur's Guide for Working with Kids, 1 vol. 2008. (ENG.). 144p. 12.99 (978-0-310-28776-6(6)) Zondervan.

Iwanski, Sandra, et al. The Practical Guide to High School Campus Ministry. 2007. 102p. per. 26.25 (978-0-88489-963-1(2)) St. Mary's Pr.

Iwas, Alya. Adult Identity Formation Model in the Syriac Orthodox Church. 2011. 116p. pap. **(978-3-8433-6389-1(7))** Lambert Academic Publishing.

Kimball, Dan. They Like Jesus but Not the Church: Insights from Emerging Generations, 1 vol. 2007. (ENG., Illus.). 208p. pap. 18.99 (978-0-310-24590-2(7)) Zondervan.

—They Like Jesus but Not the Church: Responding to Culture's Objections to Christianity. 2008. (ENG.). (gr. 13). pap., pap. 52.99 (978-0-310-27787-3(6)) Zondervan.

Kinnaman, David & Lyons, Gabe. Unchristian: What a New Generation Really Thinks about Christianity ... & Why It Matters. 2012. pap. 14.99 **(978-0-8010-7271-0(9))** Baker Bks.

Kinnaman, David & Lyons, Gabe. UnChristian: What a New Generation Really Thinks about Christianity... & Why It Matters. 2007. (Illus.). 256p. 18.99 (978-0-8010-1300-3(3)); 255p. (978-0-8010-7066-2(X)) Baker Bks.

Kyncl, David, et al. Listening Inside Out: Conversations with Twentysomethings about Faith, Culture, & the Church. 2008. 128p. pap. 11.99 (978-0-8341-2369-4(X), 9780834123694) Beacon Hill Pr. of Kansas City.

Merritt, Carol Howard. Tribal Church: Ministering to the Missing Generation. 2007. (978-1-56699-347-0(4)) Alban Institute, Inc.

Muldoon, Tim. Seeds of Hope: Young Adults & the Catholic Church in the United States. 2008. 225p. per. 24.95 (978-0-8091-4514-0(6)) Paulist Pr.

Oestreicher, Mark & Rubin, Scott. Middle School Ministry: A Comprehensive Guide to Working with Early Adolescents. 2009. (ENG.). 256p. pap. 15.99 (978-0-310-28494-9(5)) Zondervan.

Riddle, Mark. Inside the Mind of Youth Pastors: A Church Leader's Guide to Staffing & Leading Youth Pastors, 1 vol. 2008. (ENG.). 192p. pap. 16.99 (978-0-310-28365-2(5)) Zondervan.

Riebock, Josh James. My Generation: A Real Journey of Change & Hope, 1 vol. 2009. 208p. pap. 14.99 (978-0-8010-7198-0(4)) Baker Bks.

Simmons, Brian. Wandering in the Wilderness: Changes & Challenges to Emerging Adults' Christian Faith. 2011. pap. 14.99 (978-0-89112-285-2(0), ACU Pr.) Abilene Christian Univ. Pr.

Stetzer, Ed, et al. Lost & Found: The Younger Unchurched & the Churches That Reach Them. 2009. (ENG.). 240p. 17.99 (978-0-8054-4878-8(0), B&H Bks.) B&H Publishing Group.

USCCB Publishing, creator. Sons & Daughters of the Light: A Pastoral Plan for Ministry with Young Adults. 2010. 62p. pap. (978-1-60137-090-7(3)) United States Conference of Catholic Bishops.

Van Pelt, Rich, et al. Youth Workers Guide to Helping Teenagers in Crisis, 1 vol. 2007. (ENG.). 304p. (gr. 13). pap. 14.99 (978-0-310-28249-5(7)) Zondervan.

Watkins, Ralph & Stephens, Benjamin. From Jay-Z to Jesus: Reaching & Teaching Young Adults in the Black Church. 2009. 128p. pap. 15.99 (978-0-8170-1545-9(0)) Judson Pr.

Whitesel, Bob. Inside the Organic Church: Learning from 12 Emerging Congregations. 2006. (Illus.). 154p. per. 18.00 (978-0-687-33116-1(1)) Abingdon Pr.

Wilder, Michael S. & Parker, Shane W. TransforMission: Making Disciples through Short-Term Missions, 1 vol. 2010. (ENG.). 256p. 19.99 (978-0-8054-4774-3(1), B&H Academic) B&H Publishing Group.

CHURCH WORK WITH YOUTH

see also Church Camps; Church Group Work with Youth; Church Work with Juvenile Delinquents

Abba, Joe-Barth C. Special Pastoral Formation for Youths in Africa in the 21st Century: The Nigerian Perspective. 2009. 408p. pap. 99.95 (978-3-631-58434-7(2)) Lang, Peter GmbH, Europaischer Verlag der Wissenschaften DEU. Dist: Lang, Peter.

Anderson, Neil T., et al. Busting Free: Helping Youth Discover Their True Identity in Christ. 2010. (ENG.). 176p. 19.99 (978-0-8307-4792-4(3)) Gospel Light Pubns.

Arrington, Marcus L. Young, Anointed & Empowered. 2011. 280p. pap. 16.99 (978-1-61215-368-1(2)) Xulon Pr., Inc.

Arthur, Sarah. The God-Hungry Imagination: The Art of Storytelling for Postmodern Youth Ministry. 2007. (Illus.). 207p. per. (978-0-8358-9919-2(5)) Upper Room Bks.

Arzola, Fernando, Jr. Toward a Prophetic Youth Ministry: Theory & Praxis in Urban Context. 2008. (ENG., Illus.). 186p. pap. 18.00 (978-0-8308-2802-9(8), IVP Acad.) InterVarsity Pr.

Baker, Tim. The Youth Worker Book of Hope, 1 vol. 2009. (ENG.). 176p. pap. 12.99 (978-0-310-28364-5(7)) Zondervan.

Balcomb, Marcey. Single-Digit Youth Groups 2: More Activities, Plus Mission Ideas. 2006. (Youth Groups Ser.). (Illus.). 112p. per. 16.00 (978-0-687-33421-6(7)) Abingdon Pr.

Barna, George. Como Transformar a los Ninos en Campeones Espirituales. 2006. (SPA & ENG.). 144p. 8.99 (978-1-59185-939-0(5), Casa Creacion) Charisma Media.

Binion, Nathaniel, et al. The Art of Youth Work. 2011. **(978-0-7577-4034-3(0))** Pentecostal Publishing Hse.

Black, George. In the Midst of the Congregation: Psalms for Worship, RCL Feasts & Holy Days:Accompanist. 16.95 (978-1-55126-299-4(1), 1669) Anglican Bk. Ctr. CAN. Dist: Forward Movement Pubns.

—In the Midst of the Congregation: Psalms for Worship, RCL Feasts & Holy Days:Cantor. 16.95 (978-1-55126-295-6(9), 1668) Anglican Bk. Ctr. CAN. Dist: Forward Movement Pubns.

—In the Midst of the Congregation: Psalms for Worship, RCL Year B:Accompanist. 16.95 (978-1-55126-297-0(5), 1663) Anglican Bk. Ctr. CAN. Dist: Forward Movement Pubns.

—In the Midst of the Congregation: Psalms for Worship, RCL Year B:Cantor. 16.95 (978-1-55126-293-2(2), 1662) Anglican Bk. Ctr. CAN. Dist: Forward Movement Pubns.

Bolden, Elder Clyde Nickerson. Bridging the Gulf: Understanding & Ministering to Hip-Hop Youth. 2008. 148p. pap. 24.95 (978-1-60610-607-5(4)) PublishAmerica, Inc.

Bomar, Chuck. College Ministry 101: A Guide to Working with 18-25 Year Olds, 1 vol. 2009. (ENG.). 256p. pap. 15.99 (978-0-310-28547-2(X)) Zondervan.

Brewster, Charisma. Youth Ministry in Action. 2011. 108p. pap. 15.00 **(978-1-4507-6488-9(6))** Abraham's Publishing Co.

Brown, Damon. Porn & Pong: How Grand Theft Auto, Tomb Raider & Other Sexy Games Changed Our Culture. 2008. (ENG., Illus.). 230p. pap. 15.00 (978-1-932595-36-9(8)) Feral Hse.

Brown, Richard. Youth 460 Worktext: Programs for Youth Ministry. 2007. (C). spiral bd. (978-1-60036-076-3(9)) Academx Publishing Services, Inc.

Buela, Carlos Miguel. Jovenes en el Tercer Milenio. 2007.Tr. of Youth in the Third Millennium. (SPA.). 442p. (YA). pap. 18.95 (978-1-933871-01-1(6)) IVE Pr.

Bundschuh, Rick. Reaching Unchurched Teens. 2009. (Youth Ministry in the Trenches Ser.). (ENG.). 144p. (YA). pap. 12.99 (978-0-7847-2315-9(X)) Standard Publishing.

Burns, Jim. Games & Icebreakers. 2008. (Uncommon Ser.). (ENG.). 208p. (J). 34.99 (978-0-8307-4635-4(8)) Gospel Light Pubns.

—Resisting Temptation. 2009. (Uncommon Ser.). (ENG.). 208p. (J). (gr. 9-12). 14.99 (978-0-8307-4789-4(3)) Gospel Light Pubns.

—Youth Ministry: Your Onramp to Launching an Extraordinary Youth Ministry. 2008. (Uncommon Ser.). (ENG.). 320p. (J). pap. 16.99 (978-0-8307-4683-5(8)) Gospel Light Pubns.

C. A. Smith, P. Kendall, et al. Youth Ministry in a Technological Age. 2011. 90p. 24.99 **(978-1-4628-9932-6(3))** Xlibris Corp.

C.A. Smith, P. Kendall, et al. Youth Ministry in a Technological Age. 2011. 90p. pap. 15.99 **(978-1-4628-9931-9(5))** Xlibris Corp.

Calhoun, Mike & Garland, Ric. Where Was God When? 2010. 120p. (YA). lib. bdg. 14.95 (978-1-935475-10-1(X)) Word of Life Fellowship, Inc.

Calhoun, Mike & Walker, Mel. Pushing the Limits: Unleashing the Potential of Student Ministry, 0 vols. 2006. 224p. 18.99 (978-0-8499-0349-6(1)) Nelson, Thomas Inc.

Camacho Garcia, Carlos. Changed: Real Lives in a Real World. 2009. (Illus.). 128p. pap. 1.99 (978-0-8163-9322-0(2)) Pacific Pr. Publishing Assn.

Capps, Donald. Striking Out: The Religious Journey of Teenage Boys. 2011. 160p. pap. 18.00 **(978-1-61097-300-7(3)**, Cascade Bks.) Wipf & Stock Pubs.

Carafano, Vinnie. Practical Ministry Training. 2008. (978-1-57658-470-5(4)) YWAM Publishing.

Case, Steve L. Caffeine & Cash. 2009. (978-0-8298-1845-1(6)) Pilgrim Pr., The/United Church Pr.

—Caffeine & Celebrations. 2009. (978-0-8298-1846-8(4)) Pilgrim Pr., The/United Church Pr.

—Caffeine & Chutzpah. 2009. (978-0-8298-1844-4(8)) Pilgrim Pr., The/United Church Pr.

—Caffeine & Courage. 2009. (978-0-8298-1843-7(X)) Pilgrim Pr., The/United Church Pr.

Christie, Les. Awaken Your Creativity: Hearing Yes in the Midst of a Multitude of No's, 1 vol. 2009. (ENG.). 160p. pap. 12.99 (978-0-310-28778-0(2)) Zondervan.

—Gimme Five: 565 More Ways to Get Your Students Talking, 1 vol. 2006. (Quick Questions Ser.). (ENG.). 160p. pap. 10.99 (978-0-310-27315-8(3)) Zondervan.

Clark, Chap, et al. Deep Justice in a Broken World: Helping Your Kids Serve Others & Right the Wrongs Around Them, 1 vol. 2007. (ENG., Illus.). 256p. pap. 18.99 (978-0-310-27377-6(3)) Zondervan.

—Deep Ministry in a Shallow World: Not-So-Secret Findings about Youth Ministry, 1 vol. 2006. (ENG., Illus.). 256p. pap. 18.99 (978-0-310-26707-2(2)) Zondervan.

Conner, Benjamin T. Amplifying Our Witness: Practice-Centered Ministry with Adolescents & Adolescents with Developmental Disabilities. 2012. pap. **(978-0-8028-6721-6(9))** Eerdmans, William B. Publishing Co.

Cosby, Brian H. Giving up Gimmicks: Reclaiming Youth Ministry from an Entertainment Culture. 2012. pap. **(978-1-59638-394-4(1))** P & R Publishing.

Craig, Alan & Chiodo, Suzie. The Living Rock: Between Me & a Hard Place. 2008. (978-1-55452-298-9(6)) Essence Publishing.

Davis, Diana. Fresh Ideas: 1,000 Ways to Grow a Thriving & Energetic Church. 2007. (ENG.). 224p. per. 12.99 (978-0-8054-4492-6(0), B&H Bks.) B&H Publishing Group.

Davis, Erin. Graffiti: Learning to See the Art in Ourselves. ldr.'s ed. 2008. (ENG., Illus.). 72p. pap. 9.99 (978-0-8024-4586-5(1)) Moody Pubs.

Davis, Rebecca & Marcel, Colleen. Storm Chasers: Seeking God's Will in the Storm. 2011. pap. 18.99 **(978-1-61346-108-2(9))** Tate Publishing & Enterprises, LLC.

Delgatto, Laurie. Scripture-Based Retreats for Teens Ages 10-19. Halbur, Virginia, ed. 2008. 137p. (YA). per. 26.25 (978-0-88489-937-2(3)) St. Mary's Pr.

Derr, Colleen. Explore. 2009. (Illus.). (978-0-89827-418-9(4)) Wesleyan Publishing Hse.

DeVries, Mark. Sustainable Youth Ministry: Why Most Youth Ministry Doesn't Last & What Your Church Can Do about It. 2008. (ENG., Illus.). 225p. pap. 16.00 (978-0-8308-3361-0(7), IVP Bks.) InterVarsity Pr.

DeVries, Mark & Dunn-Rankin, Jeff. The Indispensable Youth Pastor: How to Land, Love, & Lock in Your Youth Ministry Dream Job. 2011. pap. (978-0-7644-6610-6(0)) Group Publishing, Inc.

Donovan, Patrick J. Using the Remote to Channel Jesus: 50 Movie Clips for Ministry. 2009. (ENG.). 124p. (YA). pap. 26.25 (978-1-59982-011-8(0)) St. Mary's Pr.

Duckworth, Jenny & Duckworth, Justin. Against the Tide, Towards the Kingdom. 2011. (New Monastic Library: Resources for Radical Discipleship Ser.). 130p. pap. 16.00 **(978-1-60899-867-8(3)**, Cascade Bks.) Wipf & Stock Pubs.

Dudley, Roger L. The Complex Religion of Teens: A Lifetime of Research Reveals How Adolescents Relate to Spiritual Matters. 2007. (ENG.). 128p. pap. 14.99 (978-0-8280-2025-1(6)) Review & Herald Publishing Assn.

Eichenberger, Jim, ed. High School Teacher: Meeting God Face-to-Face, June, July, August. 2008. (Encounter Curriculum Ser.). (Illus.). 88p. pap. 6.49 (978-0-7847-5552-5(3)) Encounter Bks.

Endres, David J. American Crusade: Catholic Youth in the World Mission Movement from World War I Through Vatican II. 2010. (American Society of Missiology Monograph Ser.). 212p. pap. 23.00 (978-1-60899-071-9(0), Pickwick Pubns.) Wipf & Stock Pubs.

Fannin, B. Kathleen. Wonder & Other Life Skills: Spiritual Life Retreats for Young Adults Using the Creative Arts. 2007. (ENG., Illus.). 144p. (J). (gr. -1-12). per. 16.95 (978-1-56101-307-4(2)) Cowley Pubns.

Fatica, Justin. Hard as Nails: A Mission to Awaken Youth to the Power of God's Love. 2009. (ENG.). 208p. pap. 14.00 (978-0-385-52717-0(9), Image) Doubleday Religious Publishing Group, The.

Fields, Doug. Live Large. Be Different. Shine Bright. 2009. 148p. pap. 11.99 (978-0-7644-6319-8(5)) Group Publishing, Inc.

—Purpose Driven Youth Ministry: One Step Beyond. 2011. (ENG.). 416p. 19.99 (978-0-310-28307-2(8)) Zondervan.

—Youth Leader Training on the Go. 2006. (Illus.). 126p. pap. 29.99 incl. cd-rom, audio compact disk (978-0-7644-2821-0(7)) Group Publishing, Inc.

Fields, Doug & McGill, Matt. Small Group Start to Finish. 2006. 193p. pap. 49.00 incl. cd-rom (978-0-7644-6005-0(6)) Group Publishing, Inc.

Fields, Doug, et al. Speaking to Teenagers: How to Think about, Create, & Deliver Effective Messages, 1 vol. 2007. (ENG., Illus.). 256p. (gr. 13). pap. 18.99 (978-0-310-27376-9(5)) Zondervan.

Fireside Catholic Publishing, creator. Thematic Plans & Activities for Catholic Youth: A Guide for Catholic Youth Ministers. 2007. 47p. pap. 19.95 (978-1-55665-051-2(5)) Fireside Catholic Bibles.

Fishell, Randy. Ready 2 Go: 15 Heart-Changing Programs for Youth & Young Adults. 2008. (ENG., Illus.). 124p. pap. 15.99 (978-0-8127-0459-4(2)) Review & Herald Publishing Assn.

Franklin, Paul. New Ground: a primer in planting student Households. 2010. 42p. pap. 8.50 (978-1-4457-3867-3(8)) Lulu Enterprises Inc.

—1 Samuel: A Bible Study Guide for Youth Cells. 2010. 64p. pap. 21.50 (978-1-4461-5701-5(6)) Lulu Enterprises Inc.

Gane, Barry. Loving Them Back, Leading Them Home. 2009. 96p. pap. 14.99 (978-0-8280-2378-8(6)) Review & Herald Publishing Assn.

Gant, Jason. Youth Ministry. Hamilton, Adam, ed. 2008. (Crmg Ser.). (Illus.). 64p. pap. 9.00 (978-0-687-65039-2(9)) Abingdon Pr.

Geiger, Eric, et al. Simple Student Ministry: A Clear Process for Strategic Youth Discipleship, 1 vol. 2009. (ENG.). 232p. pap. 16.99 (978-0-8054-4794-1(6)) B&H Publishing Group.

Gerali, Steve. What Do I Do When Teenagers Deal with Death?, 1 vol. 2009. (What Do I Do When Ser.). (ENG.). 128p. pap. 6.99 (978-0-310-29193-0(3)) Zondervan.

—What Do I Do When Teenagers Encounter Bulling & Violence?, 1 vol. 2009. (What Do I Do When Ser.). (ENG.). 128p. pap. 6.99 (978-0-310-29194-7(1)) Zondervan.

Gerali, Steven. Teenagers Are Depressed & Contemplating Suicide?, 1 vol. 2009. (What Do I Do When Ser.). (ENG.). 128p. pap. 6.99 (978-0-310-29196-1(8)) Zondervan.

—What Do I Do When Teenagers Are Victims of Abuse?, 1 vol. 2009. (What Do I Do When Ser.). (ENG.). 128p. pap. 6.99 (978-0-310-29195-4(X)) Zondervan.

Glidewell, Roger. Growing Up: Youth Ministry Coming of Age. 2008. 148p. (C). pap. 14.99 (978-0-615-19753-1(1)) Global Youth Ministry.

Godfrey, Jay & Lutz, Alison. I'm Living the Faith: Youth Study. 2008. (YA). pap. 7.00 (978-1-933663-22-7(7), WD/GBGM Bks.) General Board of Global Ministries, The United Methodist Church.

Goebel, Jerry. The Deepest Longing of Young People: Loving Without Conditions. 2006. 133p. per. 16.75 (978-0-88489-935-8(7)) St. Mary's Pr.

Grieg, Phil & Brush, Sarah. Moving Images, Changing Lives: Exploring the Christian Life & Confirmation with Young People Through Film. 2011. (Illus.). 128p. pap. 39.99 (978-0-7151-4207-3(0)) Church Hse. Publishing GBR. Dist: Westminster John Knox Pr.

Griffin, Joshua. 99 Thoughts for Youth Workers: Random Insightful Tips for Anyone in Youth Ministry. 2009. 72p. pap. 4.99 (978-0-7644-6301-3(2)) Group Publishing, Inc.

Group Magazine. Best of Try This One: The Most Popular Ideas from the #1 Youth Ministry Resource. 2006. (Illus.). 120p. per. 17.99 (978-0-7644-3414-3(4)) Group Publishing, Inc.

Group Publishing, compiled by. Emergency Response Handbook for Youth Ministry. 2007. 147p. per. 14.99 (978-0-7644-3574-4(4), Group) Group Publishing, Inc.

Group Publishing, creator. Breathe: Devotions for the Youth Worker's Soul. 2006. (Illus.). 40p. 14.99 incl. audio compact disk (978-0-7644-3310-8(5)) Group Publishing, Inc.

—Crocodile Dock Bayou Bash Youth Leader Manual. 2009. (Crocodile Dock Ser.). (Illus.). 53p. pap. 14.99 (978-0-7644-3765-6(8)) Group Publishing, Inc.

Guide Editors, contrib. by. Sabbath Action Blast! 101 Ways to Celebrate God's Special Day. 2008. 96p. pap. 11.99 (978-0-8280-2368-9(9)) Review & Herald Publishing Assn.

Guidelines for Leading Your Congregation 2009-2012 - Scouting & Civic Youth-Serving Ministry: Building Effective Scouting Ministry in Your Church. 2008. 2.95 (978-0-687-64742-2(8)) Abingdon Pr.

Guidelines for Leading Your Congregation 2009-2012 - Youth Ministries: Ministries for, by, & with Youth. 2008. 2.95 (978-0-687-64692-0(8)) Abingdon Pr.

Hakowski, Maryann. Youth Retreats for Any Schedule. 2007. 166p. per. 25.25 (978-0-88489-934-1(9)) St. Mary's Pr.

Ham, Ken, et al. Already Gone: Why Your Kids Will Quit Church & What You Can Do to Stop It. 2009. (Illus.). 189p. (978-0-89051-529-7(8)) Master Bks.

Hancock, Jim & Powell, Kara. Good Sex 2. 0 Leader's Guide, 1 vol. rev. ed. 2008. (ENG.). 272p. pap. 17.99 (978-0-310-28271-6(3)) Zondervan.

Hancock, Jim & Powell, Kara E. Good Sex 2. 0 Curriculum Kit. 2008. (ENG.). 288p. pap., pap. 49.99 incl. DVD (978-0-310-28268-6(3)) Zondervan.

Hancock, Jim & Powell, Kara Eckmann. Good Sex 2.0: What (Almost) Nobody Will Tell You about Sex:A Student Journal, 1 vol. rev. ed. 2008. (ENG.). 176p. (YA). pap. 9.99 (978-0-310-28270-9(5)) Zondervan.

Hardesty-Crouch, Brian. Holy Things for Youth Ministry: 13 Practical Lessons. 2010. ix, 244p. **(978-0-8298-1853-6(7))** Pilgrim Pr., The/United Church Pr.

Hayes, Lisa. R A C K & Ruins. 2008. 168p. pap. 14.95 (978-0-9801357-8-7(8)) Tree of Life Publishing Hse.

Heckman, Garth. Surrender: 14 Event-Driven Student Ministry Outlines. 2009. (On the Altar Ser.). (ENG.). 128p. (YA). pap. 16.99 *(978-0-7847-2242-8(0))* Standard Publishing.
Heischman, Daniel R. Good Influence: Teaching the Wisdom of Adulthood. 2009. 160p. pap. 16.00 *(978-0-8192-2363-0(8),* Morehouse Publishing) Church Publishing, Inc.
Hoeksma, Liza. Soul Food for Youth Workers: 80 Reflections to Deepen Your Spiritual Life, 1 vol. 2009. 256p. pap. 12.99 *(978-0-8254-6303-7(3),* Monarch Bks.) Lion Hudson PLC GBR. Dist: Kregel Pubns.
Huggins, William Sydney. An Three Sermons to Young Men, Preached by Rev William S Huggins & a Funeral Discourse, by Rev Samuel Haskell with an Account of the Funeral. 2006. 152p. per. 16.99 *(978-1-4255-1134-0(1))* MPublishing.
Isaac, Les. Street Pastors. 2009. (ENG.). 224p. pap. 11.99 *(978-1-84291-419-9(7))* Cook, David C.
Iwanski, Sandra, et al. The Practical Guide to High School Campus Ministry. 2007. 102p. per. 26.25 *(978-0-88489-963-1(2))* St. Mary's Pr.
Jacober, Amy. The Pastor's Guide to Youth Ministry. 2006. 82p. per. 15.00 *(978-0-687-49579-5(2))* Abingdon Pr.
Jensen, Annie. A Heart for Africa: Rosemary Jensen & the Story of Rafiki. 2007. (Illus.). 80p. 13.99 *(978-0-8254-3889-9(6))* Kregel Pubns.
Johnston, Kurt & Rubin, Scott. Kurt & Scott's Junior High Adventure: Taking Your Ministry Beyond Duct Tape, Dodgeball & Double-Dog Dares. 2008. (Illus.). 77p. per. 17.99 *(978-0-7644-3739-7(9))* Group Publishing, Inc.
Kaethler, Andy Brubacher & Yoder, Bob. Youth Ministry at a Crossroads: Tending to the Faith Formation of Mennonite Youth. 2011. pap. ***(978-0-8361-9563-7(9))*** Herald Pr.
Kara Powell and Fuller's Center for Youth and Family Ministry, et al. Deep Justice Journeys: Moving Mission Trips to Missional Living, 1 vol. 2009. (ENG.). 32p. (YA). pap. 9.99 *(978-0-310-28773-5(1))* Zondervan.
Kendall, Peggy. Rewired: Youth Ministry in an Age of IM & Myspace. 2007. 128p. per. 12.00 *(978-0-8170-1513-8(2))* Judson Pr.
Kenerson, Ed. The Cheshire Teens Story. 2008. 124p. 19.99 *(978-1-60647-513-3(4));* pap. 11.99 *(978-1-60647-512-6(6))* Xulon Pr., Inc.
Kent, Julian C. & Julian, Kent. 101 Ideas for Making Disciples in Your Youth Group, 1 vol. 2008. (ENG.). 176p. pap. 18.99 *(978-0-310-27495-7(8))* Zondervan.
Kimball, Dan L., et al. Soul Shaper Sacred Space, 1 vol. 2008. (Soul Shaper Ser.). (ENG.). 176p. pap. 29.99 *(978-0-310-27111-6(8))* Zondervan.
King, Mike. Millennial Leap: Launching a Strategic, City Wide Youth Ministry Model for the 21st Century. Date not set. pap. 20.00 *(978-0-9678689-0-5(4))* KCYFC.
—Presence-Centered Youth Ministry: Guiding Students into Spiritual Formation. annot. ed. 2006. (ENG.). 192p. per. 16.00 *(978-0-8308-3383-2(8),* IVP Bks.) InterVarsity Pr.
Kinnaman, David & Lyons, Gabe. Unchristian: What a New Generation Really Thinks about Christianity ... & Why It Matters. 2012. pap. 14.99 ***(978-0-8010-7271-0(9))*** Baker Bks.
Kinnaman, David & Lyons, Gabe. UnChristian: What a New Generation Really Thinks about Christianity... & Why It Matters. 2007. (Illus.). 256p. 18.99 *(978-0-8010-1300-3(3));* 255p. *(978-0-8010-7066-2(X))* Baker Bks.
Kizinna, Doris E. Go Deep: Spiritual Practices for Youth Ministry. 2009. (ENG.). 256p. pap. 29.95 *(978-1-55145-575-4(7),* Copperhouse) Wood Lake Publishing, Inc. CAN. Dist: Westminster John Knox Pr.
Kopp, Scott M. Postmodernism & Youth Ministry: An Introduction. 2010. 112p. pap. 14.00 *(978-1-60899-352-9(3))* Wipf & Stock Pubs.
Korczak, Grzegorz M. Szkoa Jeuness-Lumière O. Daniela-Ange: Próba Syntezy Duchowosci. 2009. (POL.). 309p. *(978-83-7363-830-3(X))* Katolicki Uniwersytet Lubelski, Wydawnictwo.
Kunjufu, Jawanza. What Is the Role of Teens in Your Church? 2011. (ENG.). 140p. pap. 15.95 *(978-1-934155-49-3(7))* African American Images.
LaDue, Rick & Sponseller, Susan. Creative Events for Youth Ministry. 2009. 48p. pap. 13.00 *(978-0-557-06738-1(3))* Lulu Enterprises Inc.
Lasater, Ken. Home-Based Student Ministry: Leading a student ministry focused on the Family. 2008. pap. 14.00 *(978-1-933840-04-8(8))* Southern Baptists of Texas Convention.
Lawrence, Rick. Jesus-Centered Youth Ministry. 2007. (Illus.). 168p. pap. 19.99 *(978-0-7644-3504-1(3))* Group Publishing, Inc.
Leys, Lucas. El Ministerio Juvenil Efectivo, 1 vol. 2009. (Especialidades Juveniles Ser.). (SPA.). 208p. pap. 9.99 *(978-0-8297-5508-4(X))* Vida Pubs.
Lindsey, Brooklyn E. & Lindsey, Brooklyn. Opposite Day: Upside-Down Questions to Keep Students Talking & Listening, 1 vol. 2009. (ENG.). 176p. pap. 10.99 *(978-0-310-29278-4(6))* Zondervan.
Livingstone Corporation Staff. The Complete New Testament Resource for Youth Workers, Volume 1, 1 vol. 2009. (ENG.). 416p. pap. 29.99 *(978-0-310-27335-6(8))* Zondervan.
Loewen, Wendell J. Beyond Me: Grounding Youth Ministry in God's Story. 2008. pap. *(978-0-8361-9403-6(9))* Faith & Life Pr.
Losey, John. Youth Ministry Vol. 2: Using Intentional Activity to Grow the Whole Person, 1 vol. 2007. (ENG., Illus.). 144p. (gr. 13). pap., instr.'s hndbk. ed. 16.99 *(978-0-310-27096-6(0))* Zondervan.
Mack, Cassandra. Smart Moves That Successful Youth Workers Make. 2nd rev. expurg. ed. 2007. 220p. per. 17.95 *(978-0-595-47244-4(3),* Authors Choice Pr.) iUniverse, Inc.
Mahan, Brian J., et al. Awakening Youth Discipleship: Christian Resistance in a Consumer Culture. 2007. 138p. pap. 17.00 *(978-1-55635-136-5(4))* Wipf & Stock Pubs.
Matthaei, Sondra Higgins. Loving God, Loving Neighbor. 2008. 276p. 29.99 *(978-1-4257-8928-2(5));* pap. 19.99 *(978-1-4257-8882-7(3))* Xlibris Corp.
Mcevoy, Bruce. A Strategy & Model for Early Adolescent Ministry in a Church. 2009. 160p. pap. *(978-3-639-20701-9(7))* VDM Verlag Dr. Mueller e.K.
McKee, Jonathan. Connect: Real Relationships in a World of Isolation, 1 vol. 2009. (ENG.). 176p. pap. 14.99 *(978-0-310-28777-3(4))* Zondervan.
—10 Minute Talks, 1 vol. 2008. (ENG.). 288p. pap. 24.99 *(978-0-310-27494-0(X))* Zondervan.
McKinney, Denise. Mile Markers: A Path for Nurturing Adolescent Faith, 1 vol. 2009. (ENG.). 144p. pap. 14.99 *(978-0-310-29279-1(4))* Zondervan.
Melton, Joy Thornburg. Safe Sanctuaries: Reducing the Risk of Abuse in the Church for Children & Youth. 2008. 144p. pap. 25.00 *(978-0-88177-543-3(6))* Upper Room Bks.
Merritt, Carol Howard. Tribal Church: Ministering to the Missing Generation. 2007. *(978-1-56699-347-0(4))* Alban Institute, Inc.
Miller, Patricia A. & Miller, Keith R. Quick Scripture Reference for Counseling Youth. 2006. 256p. spiral bd. 12.99 *(978-0-8010-6608-5(5))* Baker Bks.
Moore, Joseph. When a Teen Chooses You: Practical Advice for Any Adult. 2012. (ENG.). 101p. pap. 6.99 ***(978-1-61636-241-6(3))*** Franciscan Media.
Moore, Mary Elizabeth & Wright, Almeda. Children, Youth, & Spirituality in a Troubling World. Moore-Keish, Martha L., ed. 2008. 288p. pap. 29.99 *(978-0-8272-0513-0(9))* Chalice Pr.
Morris, Tom. Someone Died Now What? A Youth Pastor's Survival Guide. 2010. 316p. 35.99 *(978-0-557-49557-3(1))* Lulu Enterprises Inc.
Mueller, Walt. The Space Between, 1 vol. 2009. (ENG.). 128p. pap. 9.99 *(978-0-310-28771-1(5))* Zondervan.
—Youth Culture 101, 1 vol. 2007. (ENG.). 480p. (gr. 13). pap. 19.99 *(978-0-310-27313-4(7))* Zondervan.
Myers, William R. Black & White Styles of Youth Ministry. 2009. 232p. pap. 26.00 *(978-1-60899-063-4(X),* Wipf and Stock) Wipf & Stock Pubs.
Noel, Bradley Truman. Pentecostal & Postmodern Hermeneutics: Comparisons & Contemporary Impact. 2010. 216p. pap. 24.00 *(978-1-60608-905-7(6),* Wipf and Stock) Wipf & Stock Pubs.
Oestreicher, Jeannie, et al. Imaginative Prayer for Youth Ministry: A Guide to Transforming Your Students' Spiritual Lives into Journey, Adventure, & Encounter, 1 vol. 2006. (ENG.). 160p. (gr. 13). pap. 14.99 *(978-0-310-27094-2(4))* Zondervan.
Oestreicher, Mark. Youth Ministry 3. 0: A Manifesto of Where We've Been, Where We Are & Where We Need to Go. 2008. (ENG.). 160p. 12.99 *(978-0-310-66866-4(2))* Zondervan.
Oestreicher, Mark & Rubin, Scott. Middle School Ministry: A Comprehensive Guide to Working with Early Adolescents. 2009. (ENG.). 256p. pap. 15.99 *(978-0-310-28494-9(5))* Zondervan.
Olsen, Peter Christian. Youth at Risk. 2010. 126p. pap. 16.00 *(978-1-60899-569-1(0),* Wipf and Stock) Wipf & Stock Pubs.
Outcalt, Todd. The $5 Youth Ministry: Low Cost Ideas for Effective Ministry. 2009. 120p. pap. 9.99 *(978-0-7644-6302-0(0))* Group Publishing, Inc.
Parolini, Steve, ed. On the Spot: No-Prep Devotions for Youth Ministry. 2007. 24p. pap. 5.99 *(978-0-7644-3675-8(9))* Group Publishing, Inc.
Pearson, Don & Santhouse, Paul. YOUthwork: Let God Use Your Influence. 2009. (ENG.). 192p. pap. 12.99 *(978-0-8024-0970-6(9))* Moody Pubs.
Powell, Kara. The Christian Life. Powell, Kara, ed. 2009. (Uncommon Ser.). (ENG., Illus.). 192p. (J). pap. 14.99 *(978-0-8307-4642-2(0))* Gospel Light Pubns.
—Essential Leadership: Ministry Team Meetings That Work, 1 vol. 2009. (ENG., Illus.). 128p. pap., instr.'s gde. ed. 9.99 *(978-0-310-66934-0(0))* Zondervan.
—Ministry Team Meetings That Work, 1 vol. ldr.'s ed. 2009. (ENG.). 144p. pap. 14.99 *(978-0-310-66933-3(2))* Zondervan.
Powell, Kara E. & Griffin, Brad M. Deep Justice Journeys Leader's Guide, 1 vol. 2009. (ENG.). 32p. pap. 14.99 *(978-0-310-28603-5(4))* Zondervan.
Prosperi, Whitney. Girls' Ministry 101: Ideas for Retreats, Small Groups, & Everyday Life with Teenage Girls, 1 vol. 2006. (ENG., Illus.). 160p. pap. 14.99 *(978-0-310-26747-8(1))* Zondervan.
Provencher, Maureen P. Never Too Young to Lead: Developing Leadership in Young Adolescents. 2006. 96p. per. 24.25 *(978-0-88489-873-3(3))* St. Mary's Pr.
Rahn, Dave & Linhart, Terry. Evangelism Remixed: Empowering Students for Courageous & Contagious Faith, 1 vol. 2009. (ENG.). 176p. pap. 16.99 *(978-0-310-29293-7(X))* Zondervan.
Rathbun, Russell E. D. NuChristian: Finding Faith in a New Generation. 2009. 192p. pap. 15.00 *(978-0-8170-1549-7(3))* Judson Pr.
Ray, Mark. Ready-to-Go Devotions for Mission & Service. 2008. 104p. 19.99 *(978-0-687-49217-6(3))* Abingdon Pr.
Rayburn, Jim. The Diaries of Jim Rayburn. 2008. (Illus.). 540p. *(978-0-9756577-7-9(0))* Whitecaps Media.
Regan, Patrick. Fighting Chance: Tackling Britain's Gang Culture. 2011. (ENG., Illus.). 224p. pap. 13.95 *(978-0-340-99632-4(3),* Hodder & Stoughton) Hodder General Publishing Div. GBR. Dist: Independent Pubs. Group.
Reid, Alvin L. Join the Movement: God Is Calling You to Change the World. 2007. 160p. pap. 10.99 *(978-0-8254-3652-9(4))* Kregel Pubns.
Rice, Wayne. Engaging Parents as Allies. 2009. (Youth Ministry in the Trenches Ser.). (ENG.). 144p. (YA). pap. 12.99 *(978-0-7847-2317-3(6))* Standard Publishing.
Riddle, Mark. The (Un) Official Church Staff Manual, 1 vol. 2009. (ENG.). 128p. pap. 5.99 *(978-0-310-28366-9(3))* Zondervan.
Riebock, Josh James. My Generation: A Real Journey of Change & Hope, 1 vol. 2009. 208p. pap. 14.99 *(978-0-8010-7198-0(4))* Baker Bks.
Rogers, Frank. Finding God in the Graffiti: Empowering Teenagers Through Stories. 2011. ***(978-0-8298-1802-4(2))*** Pilgrim Pr., The/United Church Pr.
Root, Andrew. Relationships Unfiltered: Help for Youth Workers, Volunteers, & Parents on Creating Authentic Relationships, 1 vol. 2009. (ENG.). 176p. pap. 14.99 *(978-0-310-66875-6(1))* Zondervan.
—Revisiting Relational Youth Ministry: From a Strategy of Influence to a Theology of Incarnation. 2007. (ENG.). 221p. pap. 17.00 *(978-0-8308-3488-4(5),* IVP Bks.) InterVarsity Pr.
Rounds, Dayle Gillespie, et al. Omg: A Youth Ministry Handbook. 2010. 163p. pap. 26.00 *(978-1-4267-0008-8(3))* Abingdon Pr.
Sawler, David. Before They Say Goodbye. 2011. 256p. pap. ***(978-1-77069-293-0(2))*** Word Alive Pr.
Saylor, Ann & Ragsdale, Susan. Ready-to-Go Service Projects: 140 Ways for Youth Groups to Lend a Hand. 2008. 191p. pap. 19.00 *(978-0-687-49227-5(0))* Abingdon Pr.
Schnase, Robert C. & Carty, Terry B. Five Practices of Fruitful Youth Ministry: A Youth Leader's Guide. 2009. 64p. pap. 7.00 *(978-0-687-65776-6(8))* Abingdon Pr.
Schulenburg, Brian. Choose Your Top 3: 500 Dynamic Discussion Starters to Get Your Teenagers Talking, 1 vol. 2006. (Quick Questions Ser.). (ENG., Illus.). 144p. pap. 10.99 *(978-0-310-26746-1(3))* Zondervan.
Schultz, Jason. Ready-to-Go Missions: 12 Complete Plans for Life-Changing Experiences. 2006. (Illus.). 112p. per. 17.00 *(978-0-687-49738-6(8))* Abingdon Pr.
Schwendeman, Jill. When Youth Lead: Intergenerational Social Justice Ministry. 2007. ix, 139p. pap. 15.00 *(978-1-55896-520-1(3))* Unitarian Universalist Assn.
Scott, Johnny & Christ In Youth Staff. Speak: A 9-Week Small Group Collision - Obeying the Call. 2010. (Rock Your Face off Jr. High Resource Ser.). (ENG.). 128p. 14.99 *(978-0-7847-2406-4(7))* Standard Publishing.
Semmel, Christina J. No Meeting Required: Strategies for Nongathered Ministry with Young People. 2007. 119p. per. 14.75 *(978-0-88489-928-0(4))* St. Mary's Pr.
Senn, William J. Taking the Cross of Christ to the Campus: A Manual for Church-Based Campus Ministry. 2008. (Illus.). xi, 195p. *(978-1-59166-810-7(7))* BJU Pr.
Senter, Mark H. III. When God Shows Up: A History of Protestant Youth Ministry in America, 1 vol. 2010. (ENG.). 384p. (C). pap. 28.00 *(978-0-8010-3590-6(2))* Baker Academic.
Service Learning in Congregations Youth. 15.00 *(978-0-687-00744-8(5))* Abingdon Pr.
Shafer, Barry & Novelli, Michael. Shaped by the Story: Helping Students Encounter God in a New Way, 1 vol. 2008. (ENG.). 176p. pap. 29.99 *(978-0-310-27366-0(8))* Zondervan.
Shepp, Victoria. Letting Go of the Chaos: Ideas for Addressing Ministry-Related Stress. 2007. 60p. per. 14.75 *(978-0-88489-953-2(5))* St. Mary's Pr.
Shoemaker, Tim. Dangerous Devotions for Guys: Dare to Live Your Faith. 2008. pap. *(978-0-7644-3734-2(8),* Group) Group Publishing, Inc.
Smith, R. LaMont. Are we There Yet. 2011. 220p. pap. 15.99 ***(978-1-61379-316-9(2))*** Xulon Pr., Inc.
Standard Publishing Staff, creator. High School Student: Meeting God Face-to-Face: June, July, August. 2008. (Encounter Curriculum Ser.). (Illus.). 55p. pap. 3.59 *(978-0-7847-5554-9(X))* Encounter Bks.
Steiner, Craig. Moving Forward by Looking Back, 1 vol. 2008. (ENG.). 288p. pap. 16.99 *(978-0-310-28250-1(0))* Zondervan.
Stoner, Marcia. Drama Queens (and Kings) Positive Ways for Tweens to Act Out. 2006. (Illus.). 64p. (J). (gr. 4-7). pap. 10.00 *(978-0-687-49699-0(3))* Abingdon Pr.
Strommen, Merton P., et al. Passing on the Faith: A Radical Model for Youth & Family Ministry. 2nd ed. 2008. (Illus.). 397p. pap. 26.25 *(978-0-88489-970-9(5))* St. Mary's Pr.
Tener, Bryan Patrick. Squeezed: Youth Ministry During Tough Economic Times. 2009. mass mkt. 5.00 *(978-1-4267-0261-7(2))* Abingdon Pr.
Thompson, Martin. Searching for the Perfect Youth Ministry. 2008. 104p. per. 9.99 *(978-1-60477-692-8(7))* Xulon Pr., Inc.
Tucker, Jason. The Whole Youth Worker: Advice on Professional, Personal, & Physical Wellness from the Trenches. 2009. pap. *(978-1-932690-81-1(6))* Loving Healing Pr., Inc.
Tucker, Jay. The Whole Youth Worker: Advice on Professional, Personal, & Physical Wellness from the Trenches, 2nd Ed. 2011. 174p. 29.95 ***(978-1-61599-041-2(0));*** pap. 18.95 ***(978-1-61599-078-8(X))*** Loving Healing Pr., Inc.
Turpin, Katherine. Branded: Adolescents Converting from Consumer Faith. 2006. (Youth Ministry Alternatives Ser.). *(978-0-8298-1738-6(7))* Pilgrim Pr., The/United Church Pr.
Van Pelt, Rich, et al. Youth Workers Guide to Helping Teenagers in Crisis, 1 vol. 2007. (ENG.). 304p. (gr. 13). pap. 14.99 *(978-0-310-28249-5(7))* Zondervan.
Vandegriff, Steve. Contemporary Youth Communication, YOUT 448. 2006. (C). per. *(978-1-60036-033-6(5))* Academx Publishing Services, Inc.
—Foundations of Youth Ministry. 2006. (C). per. *(978-1-60036-021-3(1))* Academx Publishing Services, Inc.
—Professional Orientation to Youth Ministry. 2006. (C). per. *(978-1-60036-023-7(8))* Academx Publishing Services, Inc.
Vandegriff, Steve & Vukich, Lee. Timeless Youth Ministry: A Handbook for Successfully Reaching Today's Youth. 2008. (ENG.). 464p. per. 24.99 *(978-0-8024-2944-5(0))* Moody Pubs.
Vankat, Jenni. Seasonal Retreats & Prayer Services for Young Adolescents. 2007. (Illus.). 140p. per. 26.25 *(978-0-88489-950-1(0))* St. Mary's Pr.
Veerman, Dave & Woods, Len V. If I Knew Then What I Know Now: Youth Workers Share Their Worst Failures & Best Advice, 1 vol. 2009. (ENG.). 192p. pap. 14.99 *(978-0-310-28602-8(6))* Zondervan.
Venable, Eric. A Tale of Two Youth Workers: A Youth Ministry Fable, 1 vol. 2009. (ENG.). 128p. 12.99 *(978-0-310-28524-3(0))* Zondervan.
Vukich, Lee. Discipleship in Youth Ministry. 3rd ed. 2006. (C). per. *(978-1-60036-020-6(3))* Academx Publishing Services, Inc.
Walker, Steven. How to Run Children's Clubs & Meetings: Practical Suggestions for People in Youth Ministry. 2007. 141p. pap. 13.00 *(978-1-84625-060-6(9))* DayOne Pubns. GBR. Dist: STL Distribution North America.
Ward-Jackson, Peter. Youthwork & the Mission of God: Frameworks for Relational Outreach. (Illus.). 160p. 16.00 *(978-0-281-05044-4(9))* SPCK Publishing GBR. Dist: Pilgrim Pr., The/United Church Pr.
Wardwell, Rodney W. Green: Youth Ministry Lessons I Learned the Hard Way. 2010. pap. 10.99 *(978-1-61566-104-6(2))* Tate Publishing & Enterprises, LLC.
Whitney, Susan B. Mobilizing Youth: Communists & Catholics in Interwar France. 2009. (ENG., Illus.). 336p. 89.95 *(978-0-8223-4595-4(1));* pap. 24.95 *(978-0-8223-4613-5(3))* Duke Univ. Pr.
Williams, Sue. World Beyond Tears: The Ongoing Story of Father Chris Riley. 2007. 304p. (Orig.). *(978-0-7322-8265-3(9))* HarperCollins Pubs. Australia.
Willis, Adam. Things I Failed to Learn in Seminary. 2009. 152p. pap. 19.99 *(978-0-9797358-6-8(6))* Creative Team Publishing.
Wilson McCarty, Maggie & McCarty, Robert J. Be a Champion of Youth: Standing with, by, & for Young People. 2007. 102p. per. 22.00 *(978-0-88489-939-6(X))* St. Mary's Pr.
Yaconelli, Mark. Downtime: Teaching Teens to Pray, 1 vol. 2008. (ENG.). 288p. 19.99 *(978-0-310-28362-1(0))* Zondervan.
Yaconelli, Mike & Christie, Les. When Church Kids Go Bad: How to Love & Work with Rude, Obnoxious, & Apathetic Students, 1 vol. 2008. (ENG.). 192p. pap. 16.99 *(978-0-310-27665-4(9))* Zondervan.
Youth for Christ International. Faith Journey. 2008. 160p. pap. 6.99 *(978-1-60006-314-5(4))* NavPress Publishing Group.
—Reaching Out: Making a Difference in Your World. 2008. 128p. pap. 6.99 *(978-1-60006-313-8(6))* NavPress Publishing Group.

CHURCH YEAR

Here are entered works on the Christian festivals with their cycles, as making up the Christian or church year. Works on the origin of festivals and fasts are entered under Fasts and Feasts. Works containing compendiums for finding these days are entered under Church Calendar.

see also Advent; Christmas; Church Year Sermons; Easter; Lent; Mary, Blessed Virgin, Saint—Feasts; Pentecost Festival

Allen, O. Wesley & Allen, O. Wesley, Jr. Preaching & Reading the Lectionary: A Three-Dimensional Approach to the Liturgical Year. 2007. (Illus.). 210p. pap. 34.99 incl. cd-rom *(978-0-8272-3006-4(0))* Chalice Pr.
Blythe, Ronald. Borderland: Continuity & Change in the Countryside, a Country Diary. 2007. (Wormingford Ser.). (Illus.). 416p. pap. 18.99 *(978-1-85311-851-7(6))* Canterbury Pr.
—Word from Wormingford: A Parish Year. 2007. (Wormingford Ser.). (Illus.). 244p. per. 16.99 *(978-1-85311-845-6(1))* Canterbury Pr.
Brehm, David. Celebrate the Sunday Readings: Cycle C. 258p. pap. 24.95 *(978-0-15-950608-0(5))* Harcourt Religion Pubs.
Brown, Raymond Edward & Donahue, John R. Christ in the Gospels of the Liturgical Year. Witherup, Ronald D., ed. 2008. 456p. pap. 29.95 *(978-0-8146-1860-8(X))* Liturgical Pr.
Carter, Kenneth H. Prayers & Liturgies of Confession & Assurance. 2009. (Just in Time Ser.). 102p. pap. 12.00 *(978-0-687-65489-5(0))* Abingdon Pr.
Case, Steve L. Caffeine & Celebrations. 2009. *(978-0-8298-1846-8(4))* Pilgrim Pr., The/United Church Pr.
Chelhot, Ignatius George V., pref. Calendar of the Church Year according to the Rite of the Syriac Church of Antioch. 2010. (ARA.). 98.48 *(978-1-61719-416-0(6))* Gorgias Pr., LLC.
Chlachula, Roxane Kadrlik & Shrader, Mary. Exploring Liturgical Seasons with Young Adolescents. 2008. (Illus.). 103p. pap. 29.50 *(978-0-88489-729-3(X))* St. Mary's Pr.
Connell, Martin. Eternity Today - On the Liturgical Year: On God & Time, Advent, Christmas, Epiphany, Candlemas. 2006. (ENG.). 256p. 80.00 *(978-0-8264-1870-8(8))* Continuum International Publishing Group, Ltd. GBR. Dist: National Bk. Network.
—Eternity Today - On the Liturgical Year: On God & Time, Advent, Christmas, Epiphany, Candlemas; Volume 1. 2006. (ENG.). 256p. pap. 39.95 *(978-0-8264-1871-5(6))* Continuum International Publishing Group, Ltd. GBR. Dist: National Bk. Network.
Connell, Martin & Connell. Eternity Today - On the Liturgical Year Vol. 2: Christmas, Epiphany, Advent, Cladlemas, Ordinary Time, the Communion of Saints. 2006. (ENG.). 256p. 80.00 *(978-0-8264-1872-2(4))* Continuum International Publishing Group, Ltd. GBR. Dist: National Bk. Network.
—Eternity Today - On the Liturgical Year Vol. 2: Sunday Lent, the Three Days, the Easter Season Ordinary Time. 2006. (ENG.). 256p. pap. 22.95 *(978-0-8264-1873-9(2))* Continuum International Publishing Group, Ltd. GBR. Dist: National Bk. Network.

C

Curtis, H. R. Ordering Our Days in His Peace: An Introduction to the Christian Church Year. 2009. (Illus.). 48p. 9.49 (978-0-7586-1549-7(3)) Concordia Publishing Hse.

Doherty, Catherine. Season of Mercy: Lent & Easter. 160p. pap. (978-0-921440-43-7(X)) Madonna Hse. Pubns.

Duck, Ruth C., ed. Flames of the Spirit: Resources for Worship. 2009. 124p. pap. 15.00 (978-1-60608-584-4(0), Wipf and Stock) Wipf & Stock Pubs.

Dudley-Smith, Timothy. High Days & Holy Days: Thirty Contemporary Hymns for Annual Occasions in the Life of the Local Church. Llewellyn, William, ed. 2007. 60p. pap. 15.99 (978-1-85311-819-7(2)) Canterbury Pr.

Ellsworth, Roger. Simon Peter: Encountering the Preacher at Pentecost. 2007. (Face2face With Ser.). 128p. pap. 9.00 (978-1-84625-092-7(7)) DayOne Pubns. GBR. Dist: STL Distribution North America.

Etter, Mark. Pentecost I. ldr.'s ed. (Church Year Bible Study Series A). pap. 5.50 (978-0-570-09447-0(X), 20-2565) Concordia Publishing Hse.

Giles, Richard. Times & Seasons: Creating Transformative Worship Throughout the Year. 2008. 192p. pap. 30.00 (978-0-89869-613-4(5)) Church Publishing, Inc.

Gilmore, Alec. Aid Matters. 160p. 17.00 (978-0-334-02717-1(9)) Hymns Ancient & Modern Ltd GBR. Dist: Morehouse Publishing.

Gooder, Paula. Everyday God: The spirit of ordinary Time. 2011. 144p. pap. 13.99 (**978-1-84825-116-8(5)**, Canterbury Pr. Norwich) Hymns Ancient & Modern Ltd GBR. Dist: Westminster John Knox Pr.

Greisen, Thomas A., et al. Living Liturgy: Spirituality, Celebration, & Catechesis for Sundays & Solemnities - Year A 2008. 2007. (Illus.). 320p. per. 16.95 (978-0-8146-2745-7(5), Liturgical Pr. Bks.) Liturgical Pr.

Gwynne, Walker. The Christian Year: Its Purpose & Its History. 2010. 166p. pap. 21.75 (978-1-141-53231-5(X)) 2009. 166p. pap. 21.75 (978-1-141-04769-7(1)) 2008. 182p. 22.99 (978-0-554-87227-8(7)) 2008. 182p. pap. 20.75 (978-0-554-87226-1(9)) 2008. 170p. 25.99 (978-0-554-87223-0(4)) 2008. 182p. pap. 21.75 (978-0-554-87224-7(2)) BiblioBazaar.

—The Christian Year: Its Purpose & Its History. 2010. 156p. 29.56 (978-1-163-21649-1(6)); pap. 17.56 (978-1-162-78118-1(1)) Kessinger Publishing, LLC.

Habel, Norman C. & Rhoads, David, eds. The Season of Creation: A Preaching Commentary. 2011. 248p. (C). pap. 29.00 (978-0-8006-9657-3(3), Fortress Pr.) Augsburg Fortress, Pubs.

Ireton, Kimberlee Conway. The Circle of Seasons: Meeting God in the Church Year. 2008. (ENG.). 139p. pap. 15.00 (978-0-8308-3625-3(X), IVP Bks.) InterVarsity Pr.

Lawrence, Emeric A. Each Month with Christ: Insights into the Liturgy of the Months. 2011. 124p. 40.95 (**978-1-258-02337-9(7)**) Literary Licensing, LLC.

Leckey, Dolores R. Grieving with Grace: A Woman's Perspective. 2008. (Called to Holiness). 112p. pap. 11.95 (978-0-86716-888-4(9)) Franciscan Media.

Merton, Thomas. Seasons of Celebration: Meditations on the Cycle of Liturgical Feasts. 2009. 224p. pap. 17.95 (978-1-59471-170-1(4)) Ave Maria Pr.

Newland, Mary Reed. The Year & Our Children: Catholic Family Celebrations for Every Season. 2007. 328p. per. 19.95 (978-1-933184-27-2(2)) Sophia Institute Pr.

Olsen, Charles M. The Wisdom of the Seasons: How the Church Year Helps Us Understand Our Congregational Stories. 2009. (978-1-56699-396-8(2)) Alban Institute, Inc.

Perham. Celebrate the Christian Story - P. 128p. 12.00 (978-0-281-05107-6(0)) SPCK Publishing GBR. Dist: Pilgrim Pr., The/United Church Pr.

Ratzinger, Joseph. Images of Hope: Meditations on Major Feasts. Rock, John & Harrison, Graham, trs. from GER. 2006. (Illus.). 109p. 14.95 (978-0-89870-964-3(4)) Ignatius Pr.

Raya, Joseph M. Christmas: Birth of Our Lord God & Saviour, Jesus Christ. 140p. (978-0-921440-45-1(6)) Madonna Hse. Pubns.

Rupp, Joyce. Out of the Ordinary: Prayers, Poems, & Reflections for Every Season. anniv. ed. 2011. 256p. pap. 16.95 (978-1-59471-220-3(4)) Ave Maria Pr.

Salzmann, Andrew & Narendran, Sabitha. Catholic & Loving It: Traditions for a New Generation. annot. ed. 2007. 178p. per. (978-0-86716-807-5(2)) Franciscan Media.

Schaeffler, Janet. Catechist's Companion: How to Celebrate the Liturgical Year. 2007. per. 17.95 (978-1-59276-391-7(X)) Our Sunday Visitor, Publishing Div.

—The Liturgical Year. 2007. (Catechist's Companion Ser.). (Illus.). 7p. pap. 2.95 (978-1-59276-189-0(5)) Our Sunday Visitor, Publishing Div.

Schmidt, Donald. Emerging Word. 2009. 151p. pap. 15.00 (978-0-578-03628-1(2)) Corona Publishing.

Schneider, M. Valerie. 26 Creative Celebrations for All Generations: Interactive Prayers, Gospel Reflections, & Activities for the Liturgical Year. 2008. pap. (978-1-58595-702-6(X)) Twenty-Third Pubns./Bayard.

Tirabassi, Maren C. & Eddy, Kathy Wonson. Gifts in Open Hands: More Resources for the Global Community. 2011. pap. (978-0-8298-1839-0(1)) Pilgrim Pr., The/United Church Pr.

Van Nieuwenhove, Rik & Faesen, Robert, eds. Late Medieval Mysticism of the Low Countries. 2008. (Classics of Western Spirituality Ser.). (Illus.). 432p. 39.95 (978-0-8091-0569-4(1)) Paulist Pr.

Waalkes, Scott. The Fullness of Time in a Flat World. 2009. (Theopolitical Visions Ser.). 384p. pap. 42.00 (978-1-55635-863-0(6), Cascade Bks.) Wipf & Stock Pubs.

Walking the Prophetic Journey. 2007. 20.00 (978-0-9793767-7-1(7)) SOFIA.

Waller, Gary Lee. Celebrations & Observances of the Church Year: Leading Meaningful Services from Advent to All Saints' Day. 2009. (ENG.). 192p. pap. 15.99 (978-0-8341-2433-2(5), 9780834124332) Beacon Hill Pr. of Kansas City.

Why Jesus for Me? 2010. pap. 15.95 (978-0-687-65801-5(2)) Abingdon Pr.

Wolkenhauer, Richard & Seto, Lester. Advent, Christmas, Epiphany. (Church Year Bible Study Series A). pap., stu. ed. 5.50 (978-0-570-09442-5(9), 20-2560) Concordia Publishing Hse.

Zaerr Brenneman, Diane. Words for Worship 2. 2009. pap. 24.99 (978-0-8361-9473-9(X)) Herald Pr.

Zimmerman, Joyce, ed. Living Liturgy for Extraordinary Ministers Year C 2010. 2009. 136p. pap. 6.95 (978-0-8146-3005-1(7), Liturgical Pr. Bks.) Liturgical Pr.

—Living Liturgy Year C 2010. 2009. 336p. pap. 16.95 (978-0-8146-2747-1(1), Liturgical Pr. Bks.) Liturgical Pr.

CHURCH YEAR—MEDITATIONS

Barren Earth to New Growth. 2007. per. 5.95 (978-0-9719921-8-4(5)) Tau Publishing.

Benedict. A Year with Pope Benedict XVI. 2010. lv, 367p. (**978-1-60137-125-6(X)**) United States Conference of Catholic Bishops.

Bergant, Dianne. The Word for Every Season: Reflections on the Lectionary Readings (Cycle A) 2010. 208p. pap. 19.95 (978-0-8091-4673-4(8)) Paulist Pr.

—The Word for Every Season: Reflections on the Lectionary Readings (Cycle B) 2008. (Illus.). 208p. pap. 16.95 (978-0-8091-4545-4(6)) Paulist Pr.

—The Word for Every Season: Reflections on the Lectionary Readings (Cycle C) 2009. 208p. pap. 16.95 (978-0-8091-4607-9(X)) Paulist Pr.

Black, Vicki K. Speaking to the Soul: Daily Readings for the Christian Year. Black, Vicki K., ed. 2009. 352p. pap. 24.00 (978-0-8192-2365-4(4), Morehouse Publishing) Church Publishing, Inc.

Bratton, Heidi. Homegrown Faith: For Catholic Families. 2010. (978-1-933271-41-5(8)) Circle Pr.

Bratton, Heidi. Homegrown Faith: Nurturing Your Catholic Family. 2011. (**978-1-61636-134-1(4)**, Servant Bks.) Franciscan Media.

Camille, Alice. 2010: A Book of Grace-Filled Days. 2009. (ENG.). 408p. pap. 11.95 (978-0-8294-2525-3(X)) Loyola Pr.

Christ, Jennifer. Journeying with Luke: Five Minute Preparation for Each Sunday Liturgy. 2006. (Illus.). 73p. per. 7.95 (978-0-8091-4411-2(5), 4411-5) Paulist Pr.

—Journeying with Matthew: Five Minute Preparation for each Sunday Liturgy. 2007. (Illus.). 80p. pap. 7.95 (978-0-8091-4477-8(8), 4477-8) Paulist Pr.

Craghan, John F. The Gospels of the Weekday Lectionary: Commentary & Reflections. 2010. 29.95 (978-0-8146-3338-0(2)); E-Book 19.95 (978-0-8146-3933-7(X)) Liturgical Pr.

Dant, Jim. The Truth Is Sensational Enough: Meditations for the Church Year. 2007. 124p. pap. 16.00 (978-0-88146-064-3(8)) Mercer Univ. Pr.

D'Avila-Latourrette, Victor-Antoine. Sacred Feasts: From a Monastery Kitchen. 2009. 208p. pap. 29.99 (978-0-7648-1862-2(7)) Liguori Pubns.

de Blas, Alonso. Barren Earth to New Growth. 2007. (978-0-9719921-9-1(3)) Tau Publishing.

Digiacomo, James. Sundays with Jesus: Reflections for the Year of Matthew. 2007. 111p. per. 7.95 (978-0-8091-4482-2(4), 4482-2) Paulist Pr.

Dunlap, Judith. Bringing Home the Gospel: A Weekly Journal for Catholic Parents. 2006. 128p. per. 10.95 (978-0-86716-782-5(3)) Franciscan Media.

—Bringing Home the Gospel: A Weekly Journal for Catholic Parents: The Year of Mark. 2008. 128p. pap. 10.95 (978-0-86716-781-8(5)) Franciscan Media.

—Bringing Home the Gospel: The Year of Matthew: A Weekly Journal for Catholic Parents. 2007. 126p. per. 10.95 (978-0-86716-780-1(7)) Franciscan Media.

Faley, Roland J. Reflections on the Weekday Lectionary Readings. 2010. 576p. pap. 39.95 (978-0-8091-4541-6(3)) Paulist Pr.

Fénelon, François & Helms, Hal McElwaine. The Complete Fenelon. Edmonson, Robert, ed. 2008. (Paraclete Giants Ser.). (ENG.). 310p. (gr. 13). pap. 24.95 (978-1-55725-607-2(1)) Paraclete Pr., Inc.

Fenelon, Marge. When's God Gonna Show Up? Daily Discoveries of the Divine. 2009. 176p. pap. (978-0-7648-1832-5(5), Liguori) Liguori Pubns.

Figueiredo, Anthony J. A Priest for All Liturgical Seasons: Changing Calendar, Unchanging Virtue. 2009. (978-0-8189-1298-6(7)) St Pauls/Alba Hse. Pubs.

France, Dorothy D. Bless Us, O God: Services & Prayers for Special Days. 2007. 116p. per. 9.99 (978-0-8272-0237-5(7)) Chalice Pr.

Franklin, Barbara Jean. Through Another Lens: Reflections on the Gospels, Year A. 2010. vi, 137p. pap. (978-0-7648-1908-7(9)) Liguori Pubns.

Franklin, Barbara Jean. Through Another Lens: Reflections on the Gospels, Year B. 2011. (**978-0-7648-1989-6(5)**) Liguori Pubns.

Fruehwirth, Gregory. Words for Silence: A Year of Contemplative Meditations. 2008. 208p. 21.95 (978-1-55725-601-0(2)) Paraclete Pr., Inc.

Giertz, Bo. To Live with Christ: Devotions. 2008. 20.49 (978-0-7586-1382-0(2)) Concordia Publishing Hse.

Gilbert, Abbot Hugh. Unfolding the Mystery. 2007. 172p. per. (978-0-85244-093-3(6)) Gracewing, Ltd.

Glenstal Book of Readings for the Seasons. 2008. 305p. im. lthr. 34.95 (978-0-8146-1876-9(6)) Liturgical Pr.

Goan, Sean & Hogan, Martin. Jesus Our Servant: Reflections on the Sunday Readings for Mark's Year. 2009. (ENG.). 147p. pap. 18.95 (978-1-85607-632-6(6)) Columba Pr. IRL. Dist: Dufour Editions, Inc.

Goebel, Bernardine. Meditations V1, Advent to Ash Wednesday: Adapted for the Use of the Friars Minor Capuchin. Bittle, Berchmans, tr. 2011. 530p. 60.95 (**978-1-258-03271-5(6)**) Literary Licensing, LLC.

—Meditations V2, Ash Wednesday to Holy Saturday: Adapted for the Use of the Friars Minor Capuchin. Bittle, Berchmans, tr. 2011. 260p. 47.95 (**978-1-258-03226-5(0)**) Literary Licensing, LLC.

—Meditations V5, Twelfth Sunday after Pentecost to Advent: Adapted for the Use of the Friars Minor Capuchin. Bittle, Berchmans, tr. 2011. 482p. 58.95 (**978-1-258-03228-9(7)**) Literary Licensing, LLC.

Gross, Bobby. Living the Christian Year: Time to Inhabit the Story of God. 2009. (ENG.). 334p. pap. 17.00 (978-0-8308-3520-1(2), IVP Bks.) InterVarsity Pr.

Guthrie, Suzanne E. Grace's Window: Entering the Seasons of Prayer. 2008. 168p. pap. 18.00 (978-0-8192-2325-8(5), Morehouse Publishing) Church Publishing, Inc.

Holyhead, Verna A. Welcoming the Word in Year A: Building on Rock. 2007. 248p. pap. 19.95 (978-0-8146-1832-5(4), Liturgical Pr. Bks.) Liturgical Pr.

—Welcoming the Word in Year B: Sowing the Seed. 2008. 240p. pap. 19.95 (978-0-8146-1833-2(2)) Liturgical Pr.

—Welcoming the Word in Year C: With Burning Hearts. 2006. 217p. per. 19.95 (978-0-8146-1834-9(0)) Liturgical Pr.

Job, Rueben. When You Pray: Daily Practices for Prayerful Living. 2009. 240p. 10.00 (978-1-4267-0266-2(3)) Abingdon Pr.

Kelly, Francis D. Through the Church Year: Reflections for Feasts & Seasons. 2009. 192p. pap. 13.95 (978-1-59471-174-9(7)) Ave Maria Pr.

Kent, Karen. On the Journey: A Resource Book for Catechists, Chaplains & All Who Pray with Young People. 2006. (ENG.). 108p. per. 23.95 (978-1-85607-530-5(3)) Columba Pr. IRL. Dist: Dufour Editions, Inc.

Knight, David. Immersed in Christ Invitation 3: Prophet. 2010. 4.95 (978-0-87029-433-4(4)) Abbey Pr.

—Immersed in Christ Promise 5. 2010. 1.95 (978-0-87029-438-9(5)) Abbey Pr.

—Immersed in Christ Reflections 5. 2010. 0.95 (978-0-87029-437-2(7)) Abbey Pr.

—Immersed in Christ Through Immersion in the Mass: Lectionary Reflections for Each Day of Lent 2011. 2011. 5.95 (978-0-87029-456-3(3)) Abbey Pr.

Knight, David M. Experiencing the Mass — Five Moments of Mystery: Daily Reflections for Lent 2011. 2010. 4.95 (978-0-87029-452-5(0)) Abbey Pr.

Knight, David M. Immersed in Christ: Faith Formation Series. 2009. (**978-0-87029-435-8(0)**) Abbey Pr.

Krenz, Leo M. Our Way to the Father V2: From the First Week of Lent to the Feast of Ascension. Husslein, Joseph, ed. 2011. 420p. 54.95 (**978-1-258-03527-3(8)**) Literary Licensing, LLC.

—Our Way to the Father V3: From the Pre-Pentecost Novena to the Thirteenth Week after Pentecost. Husslein, Joseph, ed. 2011. 544p. 62.95 (**978-1-258-03528-0(6)**) Literary Licensing, LLC.

Kurtz, Dennis. Youth Engaging Scripture: Diving into the Sunday Gospels. 2007. 376p. per. 18.95 (978-0-88489-912-9(8)) St. Mary's Pr.

Lawrence, Emeric A. The Week with Christ: Liturgy for the Apostolate. 2011. 340p. 51.95 (**978-1-258-10187-9(4)**) Literary Licensing, LLC.

McCutchan, Stephen P. Streams of Living Water: Lectionary Devotional for Cycle B. 2008. (978-0-7880-2549-5(X)) CSS Publishing Co.

—Water from the Rock: Lectionary Devotional for Cycle C. 2009. (978-0-7880-2626-3(7)) CSS Publishing Co.

—Water from the Well: Lectionary Devotional for Cycle A. 2007. 283p. per. (978-0-7880-2481-8(7)) CSS Publishing Co.

McGee, Margaret D. Sacred Attention: A Spiritual Practice for Finding God in the Moment. 2007. 176p. 19.99 (978-1-59473-232-4(9)) SkyLight Paths Publishing.

Nielson, Merritt J. Ashes to Fire Year B Devotional: Daily Reflections from Ash Wednesday to Pentecost. 2011. (ENG.). 192p. lthr. 19.99 (**978-0-8341-2762-3(8)**, 9780834127623) Beacon Hill Pr. of Kansas City.

Pfatteicher, Philip H. New Book of Festivals & Commemorations: A Proposed Common Calendar of Saints. 2008. 718p. (C). 50.00 (978-0-8006-2128-5(X), Fortress Pr.) Augsburg Fortress, Pubs.

Raab C.S.C., Ronald Patrick. The Unsheltered Heart: An at-Home Advent Retreat (Cycle B) 2011. 96p. 5.95 (**978-1-59471-284-5(0)**) Ave Maria Pr.

Raab, Ronald Patrick. The Unsheltered Heart: An at Home Advent Retreat, Cycle A. 2010. 64p. 5.95 (978-1-59471-254-8(9)) Ave Maria Pr.

Radcliffe, Timothy, ed. Just One Year: A Global Treasury of Prayer & Worship. 2007. 288p. per. 20.00 (978-1-57075-714-3(3)) Orbis Bks.

Ralph, Margaret Nutting. Breaking Open the Lectionary: Lectionary Readings in their Biblical Context for RCIA, Faith Sharing Groups & Lectors - Cycle A. 2007. 240p. pap. 19.95 (978-0-8091-4471-6(9), 4471-6) Paulist Pr.

Reid, Barbara E. Abiding Word: Sunday Reflections for Year B. 2011. 18.95 (978-0-8146-3312-0(9)) Liturgical Pr.

Rigsby, Sandy & Mason, Steve. Exploring the Sunday Lectionary: A Teenager's Guide to the Readings Cycle C. 2006. 191p. per. 19.95 (978-0-8091-9582-4(8), 4410-7) Paulist Pr.

Rupp, Joyce. God's Enduring Presence: Strength for the Spiritual Journey. 2008. 136p. pap. 12.95 (978-1-58595-720-0(8)) Twenty-Third Pubns./Bayard.

Schaper, Donna E. Calmly Plotting the Resurrection: Lenten Reflections for Individuals & Groups. 2008. 100p. (Orig.). pap. 14.00 (978-1-59752-020-1(9)) Wipf & Stock Pubs.

Schmidt, Richard H. A Gracious Rain: A Devotional Commentary on the Prayers of the Church Year. 2008. 208p. pap. 18.00 (978-0-8192-2326-5(3), Morehouse Publishing) Church Publishing, Inc.

Sheehan, Jill. Encouraging Words. 2006. (ENG., Illus.). 128p. pap. 13.95 (978-1-85390-957-3(2)) Veritas Pubns. IRL. Dist: Dufour Editions, Inc.

Sirois, Celia. Word of Life: Daily Scripture Companion. 2008. 566p. pap. (978-0-8198-8318-6(2)) Pauline Bks. & Media.

Snyder, Walter. Our Suffering Savior Daily Devotions. 2006. (Illus.). 57p. 2.29 (978-0-7586-1025-6(4)) Concordia Publishing Hse.

Steagald, Thomas R. Every Disciple's Journey: Following Jesus to a God-Focused Faith. 2007. (Real Life Stuff for Women Ser.). (ENG.). 192p. pap. 12.99 (978-1-57683-880-8(3)) NavPress Publishing Group.

Various Contributors. A Year in the New Testament: Meditations for Each Day of the Church Year. 2011. 400p. pap. 29.99 (978-0-7586-2590-8(1)) Concordia Publishing Hse.

Welborn, Amy. Prayerful Pauses: Finding God's Presence in Daily Life. 2011. 128p. pap. 12.95 (978-1-58595-782-8(8)) Twenty-Third Pubns./Bayard.

Witherington, Ben, III. The Living Legacy: The Soul in Paraphrase, the Heart in Pilgrimage. 2008. (Illus.). 312p. pap. 34.00 (978-1-55635-895-1(4)) Wipf & Stock Pubs.

Wright, N. T. Twelve Months of Sundays: Reflections on Bible Readings. 144p. 10.00 (978-0-281-05289-9(1)); 10.00 (978-0-281-05288-2(3)) SPCK Publishing GBR. Dist: Pilgrim Pr., The/United Church Pr.

CHURCH YEAR—PRAYERS AND DEVOTIONS

Arthur, Sarah. At the Still Point: A Literary Guide to Prayer in Ordinary Time. 2011. (ENG.). 200p. (gr. 13). pap. 16.99 (978-1-55725-785-7(X)) Paraclete Pr., Inc.

Barth, Karl & Barth, Karl. Fifty Prayers. Stassen, David Carl, tr. from GER. 2008. (ENG.). 63p. pap. 13.00 (978-0-664-23153-8(5)) Westminster John Knox Pr.

Boers, Arthur, et al, compiled by. Take Our Moments & Our Days: An Anabaptist Prayer Book Advent through Pentecost. 2010. 912p. 34.99 (978-0-8361-9449-4(7)) Herald Pr.

Doerr, Nan Lewis & Owens, Virginia Stem. Praying with Beads: Daily Prayers for the Christian Year. 2007. (Illus.). 87p. per. 12.00 (978-0-8028-2727-2(6)) Eerdmans, William B. Publishing Co.

France, Dorothy D. Bless Us, O God: Services & Prayers for Special Days. 2007. 116p. per. 9.99 (978-0-8272-0237-5(7)) Chalice Pr.

Gunning, Tom. The Little Book of Christian Rituals in the Home. 2008. (ENG.). 96p. pap. 13.95 (978-1-84730-023-2(5)) Veritas Pubns. IRL. Dist: Dufour Editions, Inc.

Killinger, John. God's People at Prayer: A Year of Prayers & Responses for Worship. 2006. 116p. per. 14.00 (978-0-687-33463-6(2)) Abingdon Pr.

Kwatera, Michael. Collegeville Prayer of the Faithful Years A, B, C. 2009. 480p. pap. 24.95 (978-0-8146-3282-6(3), Liturgical Pr. Bks.) Liturgical Pr.

Langford, Alec J. Communion Prayers for Holy Days & Holidays. 2007. 104p. per. 9.99 (978-0-8272-0508-6(2)) Chalice Pr.

McCann, Deborah. Lift up Your Hearts! 50 Blessings & Prayers for Parish Meetings & Ministries. 2007. 129p. per. 19.95 (978-1-58595-652-4(X)) Twenty-Third Pubns./Bayard.

Piper, Sophie. Prayers for All Seasons. 2011. (ENG., Illus.). 64p. (J). (gr. k-2). 9.99 (978-0-7459-6260-3(2)) Lion Hudson PLC GBR. Dist: Independent Pubs. Group.

Reinhart, Dietrich & Kwatera, Michael. To Thank & Bless: Prayers at Meals. 2nd ed. 2007. (Illus.). 96p. per. 7.95 (978-0-8146-3170-6(3)) Liturgical Pr.

Schnase, Robert C. Practicing Extravagant Generosity: Daily Readings on the Grace of Giving. 2011. 72p. pap. 10.00 (978-1-4267-2855-6(7)) Abingdon Pr.

Shakespeare, Steven. Prayers for an Inclusive Church. 2009. 208p. pap. 20.00 (978-0-89869-635-6(6)) Church Publishing, Inc.

Smith, Peter Andrew. All Things Are Ready: Communion Prayers for the Church Year & Pastoral Occasions. 2007. 92p. per. (978-0-7880-2487-0(6)) CSS Publishing Co.

Sparks, David. Pastoral Prayers to Share, Year A: Prayers of the People for Each Sunday of the Church Year. 2010. (ENG.). 256p. pap., E-Book 29.95 (978-1-55145-585-3(4)) Wood Lake Publishing, Inc. CAN. Dist: Westminster John Knox Pr.

Sparks, David. Pastoral Prayers to Share, Year B: Prayers of the People for Each Sunday of the Church Year, 2 vols. 2011. (ENG., Illus.). 270p. pap. 29.95 (**978-1-55145-592-1(7)**) Wood Lake Publishing, Inc. CAN. Dist: Westminster John Knox Pr.

Storey, William. A Book of Marian Prayers. 2011. (ENG.). 392p. 9.95 (978-0-8294-3574-0(3)) Loyola Pr.

CHURCH YEAR SERMONS

see also Advent Sermons; Christmas Sermons; Lenten Sermons

Abingdon Preaching. 32.00 incl. cd-rom (978-0-687-32889-5(6)); 21.00 (978-0-687-04494-8(4)) Abingdon Pr.

Abingdon Preaching Ann 96 Ed Win 35 Software. 29.95 (978-0-687-00124-8(2)) Abingdon Pr.

Abingdon Preaching Annual 1995 DOS 35. 29.95 (978-0-687-01441-5(7)) Abingdon Pr.

Abingdon Preaching Annual 1995 DOS 525. 29.95 (978-0-687-01442-2(5)) Abingdon Pr.

Abingdon Preaching Annual 1995 Wind 35. 29.95 (978-0-687-01443-9(3)) Abingdon Pr.

Abingdon Preaching Annual 1996 Software Edition. 29.95 (978-0-687-00123-1(4)) Abingdon Pr.

Abingdon Preaching Annual 1999 Windows Software. 31.95 (978-0-687-05425-1(7)) Abingdon Pr.

Abingdon Preaching Annual 96 Edit Dos Software. 29.95 (978-0-687-00122-4(6)) Abingdon Pr.

Abingdon Preaching Library Deluxe Upgrade Software. 200.00 (978-0-687-05682-8(9)) Abingdon Pr.

Alfaro, Juan. Homilias Sobre Los Evangelios de Domingos. 2011. (SPA.). 160p. pap. 16.95 (**978-0-8146-3359-5(5)**) Liturgical Pr.

Alfaro, Juan I. Homilias Sobre Los Evangelios de Domingos. 2011. (SPA.). ***(978-0-8146-3962-7(3))***; (SPA.). 16.95 *(978-0-8146-3358-8(7))*; E-Book *(978-0-8146-3947-4(X))* Liturgical Pr.
Allen, Ronald J., et al, eds. Preaching God's Transforming Justice: A Lectionary Commentary, Year B. 2011. (ENG.). 544p. 50.00 *(978-0-664-23454-6(2))* Westminster John Knox Pr.
Allen, Ronald J., et al, eds. Preaching God's Transforming Justice: A Lectionary Commentary, Year C. 2012. (ENG.). 544p. 50.00 ***(978-0-664-23455-3(0))*** Westminster John Knox Pr.
Allen, Ronald J. & Williamson, Clark M. Preaching the Old Testament: A Lectionary Commentary. annot. ed. 2007. (ENG.). 309p. 30.00 *(978-0-664-23068-5(7))* Westminster John Knox Pr.
Augustine, Saint. Responses to Miscellaneous Questions. Ramsey, Boniface, tr. 2008. (Works of Saint Augustine A Translation for the 21st Century Ser.). 296p. 44.00 *(978-1-56548-277-7(8))* New City Pr.
Bales, David O. To the Cross & Beyond. 2010. (Illus.). 136p. pap. 14.95 ***(978-0-7880-2634-8(8))*** CSS Publishing.
Brooks, Phillips. Sermons for the Principal Festivals & Fasts of the Church Year. 2009. 196p. pap. *(978-0-217-98811-7(3))* Books LLC.
—Sermons for the Principal Festivals & Fasts of the Church Year. Brooks, John Cotton, ed. 2007. (ENG.). 358p. 46.95 *(978-0-548-15716-9(2))*; pap. 31.95 *(978-1-4304-5196-9(3))* Kessinger Publishing, LLC.
Carter, William G. God in Present Tense: Cycle B Sermons for Pentecost 2, Based on the Gospel Text. 2011. ***(978-0-7880-2671-3(2))*** CSS Publishing Co.
Chilcott-Monk, Julien, ed. In the Name of the Father: Homilies for the Extraordinary Rite. 2010. (ENG.). 254p. pap. 26.99 *(978-1-84825-027-7(4)*, Canterbury Pr. Norwich) Hymns Ancient & Modern Ltd GBR. Dist: Westminster John Knox Pr.
Clarke, John W. The View from the Cross: Cycle B Sermons for Lent & Easter Based on the Gospel Texts. 2011. ***(978-0-7880-2664-5(X))*** CSS Publishing Co.
Craghan, John F., et al. The Word into Life: Year A: A Guide for Group Reflection on the Sunday Scripture. 2007. 176p. per. 9.95 *(978-0-7648-1626-0(8))* Liguori Pubns.
Css Publishing Company, compiled by. Sermons on the First Readings, Series III, Cycle C. 2009. (Illus.). 426p. pap. 37.95 *(978-0-7880-2619-5(4))* CSS Publishing.
—Sermons on the Gospel Readings, Series III, Cycle C. 2009. (Illus.). 408p. pap. 37.95 *(978-0-7880-2621-8(6))* CSS Publishing.
—Sermons on the Second Readings, Series III, Cycle C. 2009. (Illus.). 450p. pap. 37.95 *(978-0-7880-2620-1(8))* CSS Publishing.
Davis, David A. A Kingdom We Can Taste: Sermons for the Church Year. 2007. 82p. per. 16.00 *(978-0-8028-2747-0(0))* Eerdmans, William B. Publishing Co.
Deiss, Lucien. God's Word Is Our Joy: Advent, Christmas, Lent, Easter, Cycle A. Date not set. pap. 14.95 *(978-0-937690-27-7(9))* World Library Pubns.
—God's Word Is Our Joy: Advent, Christmas, Lent, Easter, Cycle B. Date not set. pap. 14.95 *(978-0-937690-29-1(5))* World Library Pubns.
—God's Word Is Our Joy: Advent, Christmas, Lent, Easter, Cycle C. Date not set. pap. 14.95 *(978-0-937690-31-4(7))* World Library Pubns.
—God's Word Is Our Joy: Sundays 2-34 of the Year, Cycle A. Date not set. pap. 17.95 *(978-0-937690-28-4(7))* World Library Pubns.
—God's Word Is Our Joy: Sundays 2-34 of the Year, Cycle C. Date not set. pap. 17.95 *(978-0-937690-32-1(5))* World Library Pubns.
DiGiacomo, James. Sundays with Jesus: Reflections for the Year of Mark. 2008. 112p. pap. 7.95 *(978-0-8091-4503-4(0))* Paulist Pr.
Elder, Robert J. Sermons on the Gospel Readings. 2008. 408p. pap. *(978-0-7880-2544-0(9))* CSS Publishing Co.
Everett, Tony. Show-and-Tell. 2010. (Illus.). 120p. pap. 14.95 ***(978-0-7880-2629-4(1))*** CSS Publishing.
Everett, Tony S., et al. Sermons on the First Readings: Series II, Cycle A. 2007. 410p. per. *(978-0-7880-2451-1(5))* CSS Publishing Co.
Fernandez, Tiburtius. Homilies for the Year C. 2006. (ENG.). 328p. per. 19.95 *(978-1-59526-629-3(1))* Aeon Publishing Inc.
Gribble, Richard. Sermons on the First Readings. 2008. *(978-0-7880-2542-6(2))* CSS Publishing Co.
GutiZcaron;rrez, Gustavo. Sharing the Word through the Liturgical Year. 2009. 304p. pap. 35.00 *(978-1-60608-544-8(1)*, Wipf and Stock) Wipf & Stock Pubs.
Hammer, Randy. The Shining Light: 26 Children Sermons with Activities. 2010. *(978-0-8298-1868-0(5))* Pilgrim Pr., The/United Church Pr.
—The Talking Stick: 40 Children's Sermons with Activities. 2007. (New Brown Bag Ser.). (Illus.). 110p. per. *(978-0-8298-1761-4(1))* Pilgrim Pr., The/United Church Pr.
Hasler, Richard A. Facing the Future with Hope: Sermons for Advent, Christmas, & Epiphany: Cycle B Gospel Texts. 2011. ***(978-0-7880-2644-7(5))*** CSS Publishing Co.
Ibsen, Harald & Ibsen, Joy M. Unafraid: Life Lessons: Sermons to Live by & Tales of Listeners Learning to Live Unafraid. 2009. 260p. pap. 29.00 *(978-1-60608-455-7(0)*, Wipf and Stock) Wipf & Stock Pubs.
Jarboe, Robert S. More Services for the Advent Wreath: Cycle C. 2006. (Illus.). 63p. pap. *(978-0-7880-2409-2(4))* CSS Publishing Co.
Keble, John. Sermons for the Christian Year. 2009. 322p. pap. *(978-1-4588-4764-5(0))*; 276p. pap. *(978-1-4588-4765-2(9))*; 284p. pap. *(978-0-217-99501-6(2))*; 236p. pap. *(978-0-217-99505-4(5))* Books LLC.
—Sermons for the Christian Year. 2008. 508p. 55.95 *(978-1-4365-4565-5(X))* 2007. (ENG.). 512p. per. 40.95 *(978-0-548-74265-5(0))* Kessinger Publishing, LLC.
—Sermons for the Christian Year. 2008. 524p. pap. *(978-1-4097-0754-7(7))* Read Bks.
Killen, James L. What Can We Believe? Reflections on the Second Readings for Cycle a Proper 23 Through Thanksgiving. 2010. ***(978-0-7880-2631-7(3))*** CSS Publishing Co.
Kinn, James W. Teach, Delight, Persuade: Scriptural Homilies for Years a, B, & C. 2009. vii, 368p. *(978-1-59525-026-1(3))* Hillenbrand Bks.
Letellier, Robert. Sunday & Feastday Sermons: Cycles a, B, & C. 2011. ***(978-0-8189-1331-0(2)***, St. Pauls) St Pauls/Alba Hse. Pubs.
Lightfoot, Michael. Sermons for the Orthodox Liturgical Year. 2006. 483p. pap. 22.00 *(978-0-913026-72-4(7))* St. Nectarios Pr.
Lindemann, Fred Herman. Advent & Epiphany: The Sermon & the Propers V1. 2011. 206p. 44.95 ***(978-1-258-01567-1(6))*** Literary Licensing, LLC.
—Pre-Lent to Pentecost: The Sermon & the Propers V2. 2011. 252p. 46.95 ***(978-1-258-01572-5(2))*** Literary Licensing, LLC.
—Trinity Season, First Half: The Sermon & the Propers V3. 2011. 212p. 44.95 ***(978-1-258-01573-2(0))*** Literary Licensing, LLC.
Luther, Martin. Through the Year with Martin Luther. 2007. 463p. 19.95 *(978-1-59856-123-4(5))* Hendrickson Pubs. Marketing, LLC.
—Through the Year with Martin Luther: A Selection of Sermons Celebrating the Feasts & Seasons of the Christian Year. 2007. 463p. 12.97 *(978-1-59856-148-7(0))* Hendrickson Pubs. Marketing, LLC.
Luther, Martin, et al. Luther's Works: Selected Sermons V. 2010. 49.99 *(978-0-7586-1387-5(3))* Concordia Publishing Hse.
McGuire, Brendan. Seeds for the Soul: Sunday Homilies for Cycle A. 2007. (ENG.). 144p. per. 19.95 *(978-1-85607-569-3(3))* Columba Pr. IRL. Dist: Dufour Editions, Inc.
Mengelle, Ervens. El Camino del Espiritu. 2007.Tr. of Path of the Spirit. (SPA.). 376p. pap. 19.95 *(978-1-933871-04-2(0))* IVE Pr.
Mengelle, Ervens Dario. Jesucristo, Misterio y Mysteria. 2009. (SPA.). 411p. 19.95 *(978-1-933871-09-7(1))* IVE Pr.
—El Padre y su Reino: Homilias Dominicales y Festivas para el ciclo A siguiendo el Catecismo de la Iglesia Catolica. 2007. (SPA.). 391p. pap. 19.95 *(978-1-933871-46-2(6))* IVE Pr.
Mosser. Abingdon Preaching. 24.00 *(978-0-687-34286-0(4))*; 32.00 incl. cd-rom *(978-0-687-07360-3(X))* Abingdon Pr.
Nan. Twelve Months of Sundays: Life Lessons from Spirit-Filled Teaching. 2008. 27.99 *(978-1-60647-616-1(5))*; pap. 17.99 *(978-1-60647-615-4(7))* Xulon Pr., Inc.
O'Loughlin, Thomas. Liturgical Resources for Matthew's Year: Sundays in Ordinary Time in Year A. 2007. (ENG.). 332p. pap. 26.95 *(978-1-85607-593-0(1))* Columba Pr. IRL. Dist: Dufour Editions, Inc.
Palamas, St. Gregory. Saving Work of Christ: Sermons by Saint Gregory Palamas. Veniamin, Christopher, ed. 2008. 150p. pap. 15.95 *(978-0-9774983-5-2(2))* Mount Thabor Publishing.
Samaniego, Eduardo & Keating, Helen. If You Preach It They Will Come. 2006. vi, 112p. *(978-0-89390-646-7(8))* Resource Pubns., Inc.
Smith, Argile Asa. Walking with God: And Other Cycle a Sermons for Proper 23 Through Thanksgiving: Based on the First Readings of the Revised Common Lectionary. 2010. ***(978-0-7880-2630-0(5))*** CSS Publishing Co.
Suskovic, Scott. Sermons on the Second Readings. 2008. 378p. pap. *(978-0-7880-2543-3(0))* CSS Publishing Co.
Talafous, Don. Homilies for Weekdays: Year 1. 2006. 219p. per. 16.95 *(978-0-8146-3031-0(6))* Liturgical Pr.
—Homilies for Weekdays Solemnities Feasts Memorials. 2009. 88p. pap. 16.95 *(978-0-8146-1871-4(5)*, Liturgical Pr. Bks.) Liturgical Pr.
Trần, Bình Trọng. Hàng Tuần Chúa Nói Vi Ta - Ta âp Tra Li Chúa: ê Cùng Chiêm Niem, Câu Nguyên, Diên Giang, T Dân àng Thiêng Liêng, Làm Giâu I Sông Tâm Linh Da Theo Li Hang Sông: Chúa Nhat, Lê Trong, Lê Kính, Lê Ac Biêt, Chu Ky Phuc Vu, Nam B. 2008. (Illus.). xvi, 329p. *(978-1-932708-23-3(5))* Tuoi Hoa Publishing.
Upchurch, Cackie & Yeary, Clifford, eds. A Year of Sundays: Gospel Reflections 2009. 2007. (Little Rock Scripture Study Ser.). 88p. per. 2.00 *(978-0-8146-3122-5(3)*, Liturgical Pr. Bks.) Liturgical Pr.
Wuchter, Michael D. Growing in Christ: Sermons for the Spring Season. 2007. *(978-0-7880-2508-2(2))*; 99p. per. 9.95 *(978-0-7880-2523-5(6))* CSS Publishing Co.
—Shining Through the Darkness: Sermons for the Winter Season. 2007. 95p. per. *(978-0-7880-2482-5(5))* CSS Publishing Co.
—Uplifting Christ Through Autumn: Sermons for the Fall Season. 2006. 82p. per. *(978-0-7880-2410-8(8))* CSS Publishing Co.

CHURCH YEAR SERMONS—OUTLINES, SYLLABI, ETC.

Mosser, David, ed. Abingdon Preaching Annual 2010. 2009. 448p. 24.00 *(978-0-687-65661-5(3))* Abingdon Pr.
Mosser, David Neil & Wellman, Ronda, eds. The Abingdon Preaching Annual. 2008. (Abingdon Preaching Annual Ser.). 439p. 24.00 incl. cd-rom *(978-0-687-65195-5(6))* Abingdon Pr.
Wood, Charles R. Sermon Outlines for Special Days & Occasions. 2007. (Wood Sermon Outlines Ser.). 64p. pap. 5.99 *(978-0-8254-4156-1(0))* Kregel Pubns.

CHURCHES

see Church Architecture; Church Buildings

CHURCHES—GARDENS

see Church Gardens

CHURCHES—LIBRARIES

see Church Libraries

CHURCHES—MANAGEMENT

see Church Management

CHURCHES—STATISTICAL METHODS

see Church Statistics

CHURCHES, AFRICAN AMERICAN

see African American Churches

CHURCHES, CITY

see City Churches

CHURCHES, RURAL

see Rural Churches

CHURCHES, SUBURBAN

see Suburban Churches

CHURCHES IN ART

see Church Buildings in Art

CHURCHES OF CHRIST

Here are entered works on a movement of autonomous local congregations stemming from the Restoration movement of Thomas and Alexander Campbell and Barton Stone, located primarily in the Southern and Southwestern United States and without national or regional headquarters.

Aubrecht, Michael. Historic Churches of Fredericksburg: Houses of the Holy. 2008. pap. 19.99 *(978-1-59629-393-9(4))* History Pr., The.
Barnhart, David. Living in the Times of the Signs. 2007. 492p. (ENG.). 35.99 *(978-1-60477-052-0(X))*; per. 23.99 *(978-1-60477-051-3(1))* Xulon Pr., Inc.
Bouwman, Hans. In Remembrance of These Things. 2007. 100p. per. *(978-1-897117-41-5(8))* Gospel Folio Pr.
Brumback, Robert H. History of the Church Through the Ages: From the Apostolic Age, Through the Apostasies, the Dark Ages, the Reformation, & the Restoration. 2007. 428p. pap. 47.00 *(978-1-55635-196-9(8)*, Wipf and Stock) Wipf & Stock Pubs.
Burwell, Robyn. I Was under a Heavy Burden: The Life of Annie C. Tuggle. 2011. 160p. pap. 15.99 ***(978-0-89112-548-8(5))*** Abilene Christian Univ. Pr.
Claiborne, Winford & Hardeman, Nicholas Brodie. The Tabernacle Sermons Today. 2007. (Illus.). 141p. *(978-0-929540-66-5(2))* Publishing Designs, Inc.
Cogdill, Roy E. Miraculous Divine Healing. 2011. 40p. 35.95 ***(978-1-258-02969-2(3))*** Literary Licensing, LLC.
Cogdill, Roy E. The New Testament: Book by Book. 2007. 204p. pap. 16.95 *(978-1-58427-218-2(X))* Guardian of Truth Foundation.
Comer, Robert Wickliffe & Allen, James A. Memoirs of Robert Wickliffe Comer. 2011. 98p. 38.95 ***(978-1-258-03428-3(X))*** Literary Licensing, LLC.
Crabtree, J. Russell. The Fly in the Ointment: Why Denominations Aren't Helping Their Congregations & How They Can. 2008. (Illus.). 192p. pap. 18.00 *(978-0-89869-606-6(2))* Church Publishing, Inc.
Edwards, Gene. The Organic Church vs the New Testament Church. 2007. per. 9.95 *(978-0-9778033-1-6(7))* Seedsowers, The.
Gatewood, Otis. Preaching in the Footsteps of Hitler. 2011. 276p. 47.95 ***(978-1-258-03498-6(0))*** Literary Licensing, LLC.
—Preaching in the Footsteps of Hitler. pap. 12.95 *(978-1-56794-214-9(8)*, C-2572) Star Bible & Tract Corp.
Guardian of Truth Foundation, ed. & compiled by. 2007-2008 Directory of Churches. 2007. 7.99 *(978-1-58427-204-5(X))* Guardian of Truth Foundation.
Hailey, Homer. Attitudes & Consequences in the Restoration Movement. 2011. 268p. pap. 19.95 ***(978-1-58427-334-9(8))*** Guardian of Truth Foundation.
Hawkins, Ralph K. A Heritage in Crisis: Where We've Been, Where We Are, & Where We're Going in the Churches of Christ. 2008. (ENG.). 160p. pap. 28.50 *(978-0-7618-4080-0(X))* Univ. Pr. of America, Inc.
Hodge, Charles B., Jr. The Agony & Glory of the Cross. 2007. (ENG.). 176p. pap. 5.95 *(978-0-9760327-7-9(5))* Resource Pubns.
—The Agony & Glory of the Cross: The Gift of God's Love. 2nd rev. ed. 2007. (ENG.). 160p. pap. 1.00 *(978-0-9760327-9-3(1))* Resource Pubns.
Houchen, Hoyt H. & Tatum, Ray. The Houchen-Tatum Debate, Four Subjects: Establishment of the Church, Baptism, Apostasy, Pre-Millennialism. 2011. 218p. 44.95 ***(978-1-258-04858-7(2))*** Literary Licensing, LLC.
Hughes, Richard T. Reviving the Ancient Faith: The Story of Churches of Christ in America. 2nd ed. 2008. xiii, 448p. pap. *(978-0-89112-525-9(6))* Abilene Christian Univ. Pr.
Keeble, Marshall & Robinson, Edward J. A Godsend to His People: The Essential Writings & Speeches of Marshall Keeble. 2008. (ENG., Illus.). 192p. 39.95 *(978-1-57233-619-3(X))* Univ. of Tennessee Pr.
Osburn, Carroll D., ed. Essays on Women in Earliest Christianity, Volume 1. 2007. 566p. pap. 48.00 *(978-1-55635-540-0(8))* Wipf & Stock Pubs.
Pittman, Samuel Parker & Buffaloe, W. Tom. Samuel Parker Pittman: A Biography. Cuff, Roger Penn, ed. 2011. 98p. 38.95 ***(978-1-258-08951-1(3))*** Literary Licensing, LLC.
Robinson, Edward J. The Fight Is on in Texas: A History of African American Churches of Christ in the Lone Star State, 1865-2000. 2009. 222p. 34.95 *(978-0-89112-532-7(9))* Abilene Christian Univ. Pr.
—The Fight Is on in Texas: A History of African American Churches of Christ in the Lone Star State1865-2000. 2008. 222p. pap. 19.95 *(978-0-89112-533-4(7))* Abilene Christian Univ. Pr.
—Show Us How You Do It: Marshall Keeble & the Rise of Black Churches of Christ in the United States, 1914-1968. 2nd ed. 2008. (Religion & American Culture Ser.). (ENG., Illus.). 256p. 39.95 *(978-0-8173-1612-9(4))* Univ. of Alabama Pr.
Robinson, Edward J., ed. To Lift up My Race: The Essential Writings of Samuel Robert Cassius. 2008. (ENG., Illus.). 215p. 46.95 *(978-1-57233-618-6(8))* Univ. of Tennessee Pr.
Stevenson, Jeffery S. All People, All Times: Rethinking Biblical Authority in Churches of Christ. 2009. 292p. pap. 16.99 *(978-1-60791-539-3(1))* Xulon Pr., Inc.
Taylor, Jerry. Courageous Compassion: A Prophetic Homiletic in Service to the Church. 2010. 208p. pap. 19.99 *(978-0-89112-545-7(0)*, ACU Pr.) Abilene Christian Univ. Pr.
Taylor, William. Partnership: Philippians: Concise, Portable Spiritual Food. 2007. (ENG.). 192p. per. 10.99 *(978-1-84550-231-7(0))* Christian Focus Pubns. GBR. Dist: STL Distribution North America.
Thomas, J. D. We Be Brethren: A Study in Biblical Interpretation. 2011. 276p. 47.95 ***(978-1-258-10042-1(8))*** Literary Licensing, LLC.
West, Earl Irvin. The Life & Times of David Lipscomb. 2011. 290p. 48.95 ***(978-1-258-05022-1(6))*** Literary Licensing, LLC.

CHURCHILL, CARYL, 1938-

Aston, Elaine & Diamond, Elin, eds. The Cambridge Companion to Caryl Churchill. 2009. (Cambridge Companions to Literature Ser.). (ENG.). 214p. (C). 78.00 *(978-0-521-49322-2(6))*; pap. 31.00 *(978-0-521-72894-2(0))* Cambridge Univ. Pr.
LUCKHURST. Caryl Churchill. 2009. (Routledge Modern & Contemporary Dramatists Ser.). 192p. pap. 29.95 *(978-0-415-34578-1(2))* Routledge.
Megson, Chris. Modern British Playwriting: The 70s: Voices, Documents, New Interpretations. 2012. (Illus.). 352p. (C). pap. 27.95 ***(978-1-4081-2938-8(8)***, 16714, Methuen Drama) A & C Black GBR. Dist: Bloomsbury Publishing Plc.
Tycer, Alicia. Caryl Churchill's Top Girls. 2008. (Modern Theatre Guides). (ENG.). 144p. 90.00 *(978-0-8264-9555-6(9))* Continuum International Publishing Group, Ltd. GBR. Dist: National Bk. Network.
Tycer, Alicia & Tycer. Caryl Churchill's Top Girls. 2008. (Modern Theatre Guides). (ENG.). 144p. 19.95 *(978-0-8264-9556-3(7))* Continuum International Publishing Group, Ltd. GBR. Dist: National Bk. Network.

CHURCHILL, CHARLES, 1731-1764

Brown, Wallace Cable & Churchill, Charles. Charles Churchill: Poet, Rake & Rebel. 2011. 254p. 46.95 ***(978-1-258-01589-3(7))*** Literary Licensing, LLC.

CHURCHILL, JENNIE JEROME, LADY RANDOLPH CHURCHILL, 1854-1921

see Churchill, Randolph Spencer, Lady, 1854-1921

CHURCHILL, RANDOLPH HENRY SPENCER, LORD, 1849-1895

Churchill, Winston S. Lord Randolph Churchill, 2. reprint ed. lib. bdg. 196.00 *(978-0-7426-2642-3(3))* Classic Bks.
Kraus, Rene. Young Lady Randolph: The Life & Times of Jennie Jerome, the American Mother of Winston Churchill. 2011. 398p. 54.95 ***(978-1-258-06215-6(1))*** Literary Licensing, LLC.
Lee, John & Lee, Celia. The Churchills: A Family Portrait. 2011. (ENG., Illus.). 288p. pap. 17.00 *(978-0-230-11220-9(X))* Palgrave Macmillan.
Mcnamara, Robert, ed. The Churchills in Ireland, 1660-1965: Connections & Controversies. 2012. 300p. 79.95 ***(978-0-7165-3084-8(8))*** Irish Academic Pr. IRL. Dist: International Specialized Bk. Services.

CHURCHILL, RANDOLPH SPENCER, LADY, 1854-1921

Cornwallis-West, George. The Reminiscences of Lady Randolph Churchill. 2007. (ENG.). 370p. 48.95 *(978-0-548-17395-4(8))*; 372p. per. 33.95 *(978-1-4304-7278-0(2))* Kessinger Publishing, LLC.
Higham, Charles. Dark Lady: Winston Churchill's Mother & Her World. 2006. (ENG., Illus.). 256p. 25.95 *(978-0-7867-1889-4(7))* Da Capo Pr., Inc.
Kelly, C. Brian & Smyer, Ingrid. The Life & Times of Winston Churchill. 2008. (ENG., Illus.). 430p. pap. 18.99 *(978-1-58182-634-0(6)*, Cumberland Hse.) Sourcebooks, Inc.
Martin, Ralph G. Jennie: The American Beauty Who Became the Toast — & Scandal — of Two Continents, Ruled an Age & Raised a Son - Winston Churchill - Who Shaped History. 2007. (ENG.). 768p. per. 17.95 *(978-1-4022-0972-7(X))* Sourcebooks, Inc.
McMenamin, Michael & Zoller, Curt. Becoming Winston Churchill: The Untold Story of Young Winston & His American Mentor. 2009. (ENG., Illus.). 300p. pap. 19.00 *(978-1-929631-87-2(1))* Enigma Bks.
McMenamin, Michael & Zoller, Curt J. Becoming Winston Churchill: The Untold Story of Young Winston & His American Mentor. 2007. (Illus.). 304p. 49.95 *(978-1-84645-005-1(5)*, GWP005) Greenwood Publishing Group, Inc.
Sebba, Anne. American Jennie: The Remarkable Life of Lady Randolph Churchill. 2007. (ENG., Illus.). 416p. 26.95 *(978-0-393-05772-0(0)*, 5772) Norton, W. W. & Co., Inc.

CHURCHILL, WINSTON, 1871-1947

Churchill, Winston. Churchill: the Power of Words. Gilbert, Martin, ed. 2012. (ENG., Illus.). 512p. 30.00 ***(978-0-306-82155-4(9))*** Da Capo Pr., Inc.
Churchill, Winston S. War, Now or Never. 2011. 12p. pap. 35.95 ***(978-1-258-06078-7(7))*** Literary Licensing, LLC.
Groth, Alexander J. Accomplices: Churchill, Roosevelt & the Holocaust. 2011. (C). 85.95 ***(978-1-4331-1463-2(1))*** Lang, Peter Publishing, Inc.
McCabe, Joseph. Winston Churchill: The Man & His Creed. Haldeman-Julius, E., ed. 2011. 98p. 38.95 ***(978-1-258-10257-9(9))*** Literary Licensing, LLC.

CHURCHILL, WINSTON, SIR, 1874-1965

Addison, Paul. Winston Churchill. 2007. (Very Interesting People Ser.). (ENG.). 152p. per. 9.99 *(978-0-19-921757-1(2))* Oxford Univ. Pr., Inc.
Alkon, Paul K. Winston Churchill's Imagination. 2006. (Illus.). 267p. 55.00 *(978-0-8387-5632-4(8))* Bucknell Univ. Pr.

C

Austin, Douglas. Churchill & Malta: A Special Relationship. 2006. (ENG., Illus.). 192p. 37.50 *(978-1-86227-356-6(1))* History Pr. Ltd.,The GBR. Dist: Independent Pubs. Group.

Austin, Douglas & Williams, Alfred. Churchill & Malta. 2011. (ENG., Illus.). 288p. 34.95 *(978-1-4456-0058-1(7))* Amberley Publishing GBR. Dist: Casemate Pubs. & Bk. Distributors, LLC.

Axelrod, Alan. Winston Churchill, CEO: 6 Principles to Guide & Inspire Modern Leaders. 2012. (CEO Ser.). (ENG., Illus.). 288p. pap. 14.95 ***(978-1-4027-9776-7(1))*** Sterling Publishing Co., Inc.

Batty, Peter. Hoodwinking Churchill: Tito's Great Confidence Trick. 2011. (ENG., Illus.). 384p. 42.95 ***(978-0-85683-282-6(0))*** Shepheard-Walwyn Pubs., Ltd. GBR. Dist: Independent Pubs. Group.

Baxendale, Alan S. Winston Leonard Spencer Churchill: Penal Reformer. 2010. 245p. pap. 56.95 *(978-3-03911-996-7(6))* Lang, Peter AG GBR. Dist: Lang, Peter.

Bennett, Gill. Churchill's Man of Mystery: Desmond Morton & the World of Intelligence. 2009. (Government Official History Ser.). (ENG.). 432p. pap. 39.95 *(978-0-415-48168-7(6))* Routledge.

—Churchill's Mystery Man: Desmond Morton & the World of Intelligence. 2006. (Whitehall Histories Ser.). (ENG., Illus.). 432p. 99.95 *(978-0-415-39430-7(9))* Routledge.

Berthon, Simon & Potts, Joanna. Warlords: An Extraordinary Re-Creation of World War II Through the Eyes & Minds of Hitler, Churchill, Roosevelt, & Stalin. 2007. (ENG., Illus.). 384p. per. 19.95 *(978-0-306-81538-6(9))* Da Capo Pr., Inc.

Black, Edgar. Sir Winston Churchill: The Compelling Life Story of One of the Towering Figures of the Twentieth Century. 2011. 304p. 48.95 ***(978-1-258-03782-6(3))*** Literary Licensing, LLC.

Buchanan, Patrick J. Churchill, Hitler, & the Unnecessary War: How Britain Lost Its Empire & the West Lost the World. 2009. (ENG., Illus.). 544p. pap. 20.00 *(978-0-307-40516-6(8))* Crown Publishing Group.

Buczacki, Stefan. Churchill & Chartwell: The Untold Story of Churchill's Houses & Gardens. 2007. (ENG., Illus.). 336p. 40.00 *(978-0-7112-2535-0(4))* Lincoln, Frances Ltd. GBR. Dist: Perseus-PGW.

Catherwood, Christopher. His Finest Hour: A Biography of Winston Churchill. 2010. (ENG., Illus.). 272p. 22.95 *(978-1-61608-094-5(9)*, 608094) Skyhorse Publishing Co., Inc.

—Winston Churchill: The Flawed Genius of WWII. 2010. (ENG.). 336p. (gr. 12-18). 16.00 *(978-0-425-23244-6(1)*, Berkley Trade) Penguin Group (USA) Inc.

Churchill, Winston. The Irrepressible Churchill: Winston's World, Wars & Wit. 2011. (ENG., Illus.). 352p. 14.95 *(978-1-84486-119-4(8)*, Conway Maritime Pr.) Anova Bks. GBR. Dist: Sterling Publishing Co., Inc.

—London to Ladysmith & Ian Hamilton's March. 2010. (Dover Military History, Weapons, Armor Ser.). (ENG.). 432p. pap. 16.95 *(978-0-486-47543-1(3))* Dover Pubns., Inc.

—The Story of the Malakand Field Force. 2010. (Dover Military History, Weapons, Armor Ser.). (ENG.). 304p. pap. 12.95 *(978-0-486-47474-8(7))* Dover Pubns., Inc.

Churchill, Winston. Winston Churchill Prime Minister. 2011. 58p. 36.95 ***(978-1-258-05603-2(8))*** Literary Licensing, LLC.

Churchill, Winston L. S. My African Journey. reprint ed. lib. bdg. 98.00 *(978-0-7426-2644-7(X))* Classic Bks.

—Prison & Prisoners: A Speech Delivered in the House of Commons 20th July, 1910. reprint ed. lib. bdg. 98.00 *(978-0-7426-2647-8(4))* Classic Bks.

—The Sinews of Peace: Post War Speeches. Churchill, Randolph S., ed. reprint ed. 30.00 *(978-0-404-20059-6(1))* AMS Pr., Inc.

Churchill, Winston S. The Churchill Documents, Volume 14: At the Admiralty, September 1939 - May 1940. Gilbert, Martin, ed. 2011. (ENG.). 1370p. 35.00 ***(978-0-916308-32-2(4))*** Hillsdale College Pr.

—The Churchill Documents, Volume 15: Never Surrender, May 1940 - December 1940. Gilbert, Martin, ed. 2011. (ENG.). 1359p. 35.00 ***(978-0-916308-33-9(2))*** Hillsdale College Pr.

—The Churchill Documents, Volume 16: The Ever-Widening War 1941. Gilbert, Martin, ed. 2011. (ENG.). 1821p. 35.00 ***(978-0-916308-34-6(0))*** Hillsdale College Pr.

—The Story of the Malakand Field Force. 2008. 280p. 25.99 *(978-0-554-32309-1(5))*; 28.99 *(978-0-554-23006-1(2))* BiblioBazaar.

—The Story of the Malakand Field Force. 2007. (ENG.). 180p. per. *(978-1-4068-4587-7(6))* Echo Library.

—The Story of the Malakand Field Force. 2007. (ENG.). 244p. pap. 12.45 *(978-1-60424-548-6(4)*, Book Jungle) Standard Pubns., Inc.

—Thoughts & Adventures: Churchill Reflects on Spies, Cartoons, Flying, & the Future. Muller, James W., ed. 2009. (ENG., Illus.). 350p. pap. 22.00 *(978-1-935191-46-9(2))* ISI Bks.

Churchill, Winston S. & Churchill, Winston. Blood, Toil, Tears & Sweat: The Great Speeches. Cannadine, David, ed. & intro. by. 2007. (ENG., Illus.). 416p. (gr. 12-18). 16.00 *(978-0-14-144206-8(9)*, Penguin Classics) Penguin Group (USA) Inc.

Churchill, Winston S. & Churchill, Winston Spencer. London to Ladysmith Via Pretori. 2011. 226p. ***(978-1-84902-471-6(5))*** Benediction Classics.

Clarke, Peter. The Last Thousand Days of the British Empire: Churchill, Roosevelt, & the Birth of the Pax Americana. 2009. (ENG., Illus.). 592p. pap. 20.00 *(978-1-59691-676-0(1))* Bloomsbury Publishing.

Clarke, Peter. Mr. Churchill's Profession: The Statesman as Author & the Book That Defined the 'Special Relationship' 2012. (ENG.). 368p. 30.00 ***(978-1-60819-372-1(1))*** Bloomsbury Publishing.

Clews, Graham T. Churchill's Dilemma: The Real Story Behind the Origins of the 1915 Dardanelles Campaign, 1 vol. 2010. (Illus.). 343p. 44.95 *(978-0-313-38474-5(6)*, A2929C); xx, 343p. E-Book *(978-0-313-38475-2(4))* Greenwood Publishing Group, Inc. (Praeger Pubs.).

Cohen, Michael J. Churchill & the Jews, 1900-1948. 2nd rev. ed. 2012. (ENG.). 388p. pap. 42.95 ***(978-0-415-62574-6(2))*** Routledge.

Corrigan, Gordon. Blood, Sweat & Arrogance: And the Myth of Churchill's War. 2007. (Phoenix Press Ser.). (Illus.). 495p. per. 14.95 *(978-0-304-36738-2(9)*, Phoenix) Orion Publishing Group, Ltd. GBR. Dist: Sterling Publishing Co., Inc.

Delaforce, Patrick. Churchills Secret Weapons. 2008. (Illus.). 224p. pap. 24.95 *(978-1-84415-464-7(5))* Pen & Sword Bks. Ltd. GBR. Dist: Casemate Pubs. & Bk. Distributors, LLC.

—Churchill's Secret Weapons: The Story of Hobart's Funnies. (Illus.). 256p. pap. 24.99 *(978-0-7090-6722-1(4))* Hale, Robert Ltd. GBR. Dist: Trafalgar Square Publishing.

D'Este, Carlo. Warlord: A Life of Winston Churchill at War, 1874-1945. (ENG.). 2009. 864p. pap. 17.99 *(978-0-06-057574-8(3)*, HarperPerennial) 2008. 784p. 39.95 *(978-0-06-057573-1(5))* HarperCollins Pubs.

Dixon, Jack. Dowding & Churchill: The Dark Side of the Battle of Britain. 2009. (Illus.). 320p. 50.00 *(978-1-84415-854-6(3))* Pen & Sword Bks. Ltd. GBR. Dist: Casemate Pubs. & Bk. Distributors, LLC.

Downing, Taylor. Churchill's War Lab: Code-Breakers, Scientists, & the the Mavericks Churchill Led to Victory. 2011. (ENG.). 416p. (gr. 12). 30.00 *(978-1-59020-565-5(0))* Overlook Pr., The.

El Glaoui, Hassan & Churchill, Winston. Meetings in Marrakech: The Paintings of Hassan el Glaoui & Winston Churchill. Glaoui, Touria El, ed. 2012. (ENG., Illus.). 96p. pap. 40.00 ***(978-88-572-1241-8(6))*** Skira Editore ITA. Dist: Random Hse., Inc.

Enright, Dominique. The Wicked Wit of Winston Churchill. 2011. (Wicked Wit of Ser.). (ENG., Illus.). 160p. 13.95 *(978-1-84317-565-0(7))* O'Mara, Michael Bks., Ltd. GBR. Dist: Independent Pubs. Group.

Fisher, David E. A Summer Bright & Terrible: Winston Churchill, Lord Dowding, Radar, & the Impossible Triumph of the Battle of Britain. 2006. (ENG., Illus.). 304p. per. 16.00 *(978-1-59376-116-5(3))* Counterpoint LLC.

Forster, Margaret Elizabeth. Churchill's Grandmama: A Life of Frances, 7th Duchess of Marlborough. 2010. (ENG., Illus.). 256p. 26.95 *(978-0-7524-5552-5(4))* History Pr. Ltd.,The GBR. Dist: Independent Pubs. Group.

Frankfurter, Alfred & Churchill, Winston. Catalogue of an Exhibition of Paintings by Winston Churchill: Winston Churchill the Painter. 2011. 48p. pap. 35.95 ***(978-1-258-06002-2(7))*** Literary Licensing, LLC.

Geroge, Robert Lloyd. David & Winston: How a Friendship Changed History. 2008. (ENG.). 336p. (gr. 12). 29.95 *(978-1-58567-930-0(5))* Overlook Pr., The.

Gilbert, Martin. Churchill & America. 2008. (ENG., Illus.). 528p. per. 30.99 *(978-0-7432-5993-4(9)*, Free Pr.) Free Pr.

—Churchill & the Jews: A Lifelong Friendship. 2008. (ENG., Illus.). 400p. pap. 18.00 *(978-0-8050-8864-9(4)*, Holt Paperback) Holt, Henry & Co.

—The Will of the People: Churchill & Parliamentary Democracy. 2006. (ENG., Illus.). 160p. pap. 13.50 *(978-0-679-31469-1(5)*, Vintage Canada) Random Hse. of Canada, Ltd. CAN. Dist: Random Hse., Inc.

—Winston S. Churchill, Volume 6: The Finest Hour, 1939-1941. 2011. (ENG.). 1150p. 45.00 *(978-0-916308-29-2(4))* Hillsdale College Pr.

Gilbert, Martin, et al. Churchill & the Great Republic. 2006. (ENG., Illus.). 96p. pap. 19.95 *(978-1-904832-00-3(8))* Giles, D. Ltd. GBR. Dist: Antique Collectors' Club.

Gilbert, Martine. Winston Churchill - the Wilderness Years: Speaking out Against Hitler in the Prelude to War. 2012. (ENG., Illus.). 240p. pap. 17.00 ***(978-1-84885-933-3(3)***, Tauris Parke Paperbacks) I. B. Tauris & Co., Ltd. GBR. Dist: Macmillan.

Hall, Douglas. The Book of Churchilliana. 2006. (ENG., Illus.). 192p. *(978-1-872727-44-8(1)*, New Cavendish Bks. Dist) Antique Collectors' Club.

Harmon, Christopher C. Are We Beasts? Churchill & the Moral Question of World War II Area Bombing. 2006. 35p. pap. 3.25 *(978-0-16-076995-5(7)*, Defense Dept.) United States Government Printing Office.

Hastings, Max. Winston's War: Churchill, 1940-1945. (Vintage Ser.). (Illus.). 2011. 608p. pap. 17.95 *(978-0-307-38871-1(9)*, Vintage) 2010. (ENG., 576p. 35.00 *(978-0-307-26839-6(X)*, Knopf) Knopf Doubleday Publishing Group.

Havardi, Jeremy. The Greatest Briton: Essays on Winston Churchill's Life & Political Philosophy. 2010. (ENG.). 400p. 49.95 *(978-0-85683-265-9(0))* Shepheard-Walwyn Pubs., Ltd. GBR. Dist: Independent Pubs. Group.

Hayward, Steven F. Greatness: Reagan, Churchill, & the Making of Extraordinary Leaders. 2006. (ENG.). 208p. per. 12.95 *(978-0-307-23719-4(2)*, Three Rivers Pr.) Crown Publishing Group.

Heiferman, Ronald Ian. The Cairo Conference of 1943: Roosevelt, Churchill, Chiang Kai-Shek & Madame Chiang. 2011. (ENG., Illus.). 207p. pap. 45.00 *(978-0-7864-4804-3(0))* McFarland & Co., Inc. Pubs.

Herman, Arthur. Gandhi & Churchill: The Epic Rivalry that Destroyed an Empire & Forged Our Age. 2009. (ENG., Illus.). 736p. pap. 20.00 *(978-0-553-38376-8(0))* Random House Publishing Group.

Herwig, Holger H. & Bercuson, David J. One Christmas in Washington: Roosevelt & Churchill Forge the Grand Alliance. 2006. (ENG., Illus.). 336p. (gr. 12). per. 15.95 *(978-1-58567-846-4(5))* Overlook Pr., The.

Hickman, Tom. Churchill's Bodyguard: The Authorised Biography of Walter H. Thompson. 2007. (ENG., Illus.). 320p. pap. 14.95 *(978-0-7553-1449-2(2))* Headline Bk. Publishing GBR. Dist: Independent Pubs. Group.

Higham, Charles. Dark Lady: Winston Churchill's Mother & Her World. 2006. (ENG., Illus.). 256p. 25.95 *(978-0-7867-1889-4(7))* Da Capo Pr., Inc.

Holmes, Richard. Churchill's Bunker: The Cabinet War Rooms & the Culture of Secrecy in Wartime London. (Illus.). 256p. 2011. pap. 18.00 *(978-0-300-17748-0(8))* 2010. 27.50 *(978-0-300-16040-6(2))* Yale Univ. Pr.

—In the Footsteps of Churchill: A Study in Character. 2006. (ENG., Illus.). 376p. per. 17.50 *(978-0-465-03083-5(1))* Basic Bks.

Irving, David. Churchill's War Vol. I: The Struggle for Power. 660p. 30.00 *(978-0-947117-56-6(3))* Focal Point Pubns. GBR. Dist: World War Two Bks. & Video.

Ive, Ruth. The Woman Who Censored Churchill. 2009. (ENG., Illus.). 160p. 29.95 *(978-0-7524-4716-2(5))* History Pr. Ltd.,The GBR. Dist: Independent Pubs. Group.

Johnson, Paul. Churchill. (ENG.). 192p. (gr. 12). 2010. 15.00 *(978-0-14-311799-5(8)*, Penguin (Non-Classics)) 2009. (Illus.). 24.95 *(978-0-670-02105-5(9)*, Viking Adult) Penguin Group (USA) Inc.

—Churchill. l.t. ed. 2010. (ENG.). 200p. 31.50 *(978-1-4104-2333-7(6))* Thorndike Pr.

Kajencki, Francis Casimir. American Betrayal: Franklin Roosevelt Casts Poland into Communist Captivity. 2007. (Illus.). 304p. 30.00 *(978-0-9627190-8-0(0))* Southwest Polonia Pr.

Kelly, C. Brian & Smyer, Ingrid. The Life & Times of Winston Churchill. 2008. (ENG., Illus.). 430p. pap. 18.99 *(978-1-58182-634-0(6)*, Cumberland Hse.) Sourcebooks, Inc.

Knight, Nigel. Churchill: The Greatest Briton Unmasked. 2008. (Illus.). 384p. 16.99 *(978-0-7153-2855-2(7))* David & Charles Pubs. GBR. Dist: F&W Media, Inc.

Langworth, Richard, ed. Churchill by Himself: The Definitive Collection of Quotations. 2011. (ENG., Illus.). 656p. pap. 21.99 *(978-1-58648-957-1(7))* PublicAffairs.

Lavery, Brian. Churchill Goes to War: Winston's Wartime Journeys. 2007. (Illus.). 392p. 34.95 *(978-1-59114-103-7(6))* Naval Institute Pr.

Leaming, Barbara. Churchill Defiant: Fighting On, 1945-1955. 2010. (ENG.). 400p. 26.99 *(978-0-06-133758-1(7))* HarperCollins Pubs.

—Churchill Defiant: Fighting On: 1945-1955. 2011. (ENG.). 368p. pap. 15.99 *(978-0-06-133760-4(9)*, HarperPerennial) HarperCollins Pubs.

Lee, John & Lee, Celia. The Churchills: A Family Portrait. 2011. (ENG., Illus.). 288p. pap. 17.00 *(978-0-230-11220-9(X))* Palgrave Macmillan.

Lovell, Mary S. The Churchills: In Love & War. 2011. (ENG., Illus.). 624p. 35.00 *(978-0-393-06230-4(9)*, 6230) Norton, W. W. & Co., Inc.

Lukacs, John. Churchill: Visionary, Statesman, Historian. 224p. pap. 23.00 *(978-0-908011-82-7(2))* Scribe Pubns. AUS. Dist: Independent Pubs. Group.

—Five Days in London, May 1940. 256p. pap. 25.00 *(978-0-908011-67-4(9))* Scribe Pubns. AUS. Dist: Independent Pubs. Group.

Lukacs, John R. Blood, Toil, Tears, & Sweat: The Dire Warning. 2009. (ENG.). 176p. pap. 14.00 *(978-0-465-01820-8(3))* Basic Bks.

Macrae, Stuart. Winston Churchill's Toyshop. 2011. (Illus.). 320p. pap. 24.95 ***(978-1-4456-0370-4(5))*** Amberley Publishing GBR. Dist: Casemate Pubs. & Bk. Distributors, LLC.

Makovsky, Michael. Churchill's Promised Land: Zionism & Statecraft. (New Republic Book Ser.). (ENG., Illus.). 368p. 2008. pap. 20.00 *(978-0-300-14324-9(9))* 2007. 35.00 *(978-0-300-11609-0(8))* Yale Univ. Pr.

Manchester, William & Reid, Paul. The Last Lion Box Set: Winston Spencer Churchill, 1874 - 1965. 2012. (ENG., Illus.). 125.00 ***(978-0-316-22778-0(1))*** Little Brown & Co.

McCullough, David. In the Dark Streets Shineth: A 1941 Christmas Eve Story. 2010. 56p. 19.99 *(978-1-60641-831-4(9)*, Shadow Mountain) Deseret Bk. Co.

McGinty, Stephen. Churchill's Cigar: A Lifelong Love Affair Through War & Peace. 2010. (ENG., Illus.). 214p. pap. 12.95 *(978-0-330-46121-4(4))* Macmillan Pubs., Ltd. GBR. Dist: Independent Pubs. Group.

McMenamin, Michael & Zoller, Curt. Becoming Winston Churchill: The Untold Story of Young Winston & His American Mentor. 2009. (ENG., Illus.). 300p. pap. 19.00 *(978-1-929631-87-2(1))* Enigma Bks.

McMenamin, Michael & Zoller, Curt J. Becoming Winston Churchill: The Untold Story of Young Winston & His American Mentor. 2007. (Illus.). 304p. 49.95 *(978-1-84645-005-1(5)*, GWP005) Greenwood Publishing Group, Inc.

Mcnamara, Robert, ed. The Churchills in Ireland, 1660-1965: Connections & Controversies. 2012. 300p. 79.95 ***(978-0-7165-3084-8(8))*** Irish Academic Pr. IRL. Dist: International Specialized Bk. Services.

Mitchell, John & Feast, Sean. Churchill's Navigator. 2010. (Illus.). 224p. 39.95 *(978-1-906502-74-4(9))* Grub Street GBR. Dist: Casemate Pubs. & Bk. Distributors, LLC.

Mukerjee, Madhusree. Churchill's Secret War: The British Empire & the Ravaging of India During World War II. (ENG., Illus.). 368p. (gr. 9). 2011. pap. 16.99 *(978-0-465-02481-0(5))* 2010. 28.95 *(978-0-465-00201-6(3))* Basic Bks.

Olson, Lynne. Citizens of London: The Americans Who Stood with Britain in Its Darkest, Finest Hour. (ENG., Illus.). 496p. 2011. pap. 17.00 *(978-0-8129-7935-0(4)*, Random Hse. Trade Paperbacks) 2010. 28.00 *(978-1-4000-6758-9(8)*, Random House) Random House Publishing Group.

—Troublesome Young Men: The Rebels Who Brought Churchill to Power & Helped Save England. 2008. (ENG., Illus.). 448p. pap. 17.00 *(978-0-374-53133-1(1))* Farrar, Straus & Giroux.

Parrish, Thomas. To Keep the British Isles Afloat: FDR's Men in Churchill's London 1941. 2009. (Illus.). 336p. 26.99 *(978-0-06-135793-0(6))* Smithsonian Institution Pr.

Pearce, Robert. Churchill. 2009. (Routledge Historical Biographies Ser.). pap. 25.95 *(978-0-415-18913-2(6))* Routledge.

Perry, John. Winston Churchill, 0 vols. 2010. (Christian Encounters Ser.). 192p. pap. 12.00 *(978-1-59555-306-5(1))* Nelson, Thomas Inc.

Plokhy, S. M. Yalta: The Price of Peace. 2011. (ENG., Illus.). 480p. (gr. 12). 18.00 *(978-0-14-311892-3(7)*, Penguin (Non-Classics)) Penguin Group (USA) Inc.

Powell, Charles. The Churchill Diaries. 2007. 305p. pap. 34.95 *(978-1-84799-881-1(X))* Lulu Enterprises Inc.

Press, Ammonite, ed. Churchill in Quotes: Wit & Wisdom from the Great Statesman. 2011. (ENG., Illus.). 192p. pap. 9.95 *(978-1-906672-61-4(X)*, Ammonite Pr.) AE Pubns. GBR. Dist: BookMasters Distribution Services (BDS).

Price, Bill. Winston Churchill: War Leader. 2010. (Pocket Essential Ser.). (ENG.). 160p. pap. 14.95 *(978-1-84243-322-5(9))* Pocket Essentials GBR. Dist: Independent Pubs. Group.

Rees, Laurence. World War II Behind Closed Doors: Stalin, the Nazis & the West. 2010. (Vintage Ser.). (ENG., Illus.). 464p. pap. 16.95 *(978-0-307-38962-6(6)*, Vintage) Knopf Doubleday Publishing Group.

Reid, Walter. Churchill 1940-1945: Under Friendly Fire. (Illus.). 416p. 2010. pap. 15.95 *(978-1-84341-050-8(8))* 2008. 51.50 *(978-1-84341-044-7(3))* Birlinn, Ltd. GBR. Dist: Casemate Pubs. & Bk. Distributors, LLC.

Reynolds, David. In Command of History: Churchill Fighting & Writing the Second World War. 2007. (ENG., Illus.). 672p. per. 19.95 *(978-0-465-00330-3(3))* Basic Bks.

Roberts, Andrew. Masters & Commanders: How Four Titans Won the War in the West, 1941-1945. 2010. 736p. pap. 18.99 *(978-0-06-122858-2(3)*, HarperPerennial) 2009. 720p. 35.00 *(978-0-06-122857-5(5))* HarperCollins Pubs.

Rose, Norman. Churchill: An Unruly Life. rev. ed. 2009. (ENG., Illus.). 456p. pap. 19.95 *(978-1-84511-863-1(4)*, Tauris Parke Paperbacks) I. B. Tauris & Co., Ltd. GBR. Dist: Macmillan.

Russell, Douglas. Winston Churchill: Soldier: The Military Life of a Gentleman at War. 2009. (ENG., Illus.). 496p. per. 17.95 *(978-1-84486-032-6(9))* Anova Bks. GBR. Dist: Sterling Publishing Co., Inc.

Sandys, Celia. Churchill: Wanted Dead or Alive. 2009. (ENG.). 304p. 9.99 *(978-0-7858-1701-7(8)*, 0785817018, Castle Bks., Inc.) Book Sales, Inc.

Singer, Barry. Churchill Style: The Art of Being Winston Churchill. 2012. (ENG., Illus.). 240p. 24.95 ***(978-0-8109-9643-4(X)***, Abrams Image) Abrams.

Smith, T O. Churchill, America & Vietnam, 1941-45. 2011. (ENG., Illus.). 200p. (C). 80.00 *(978-0-230-29820-0(6))*; pap. 28.95 *(978-0-230-29821-7(4))* Palgrave Macmillan.

Soames, Mary. A Daughter's Tale: The Memoir of Winston Churchill's Youngest Child. 2012. (ENG., Illus.). 368p. 28.00 ***(978-0-8129-9333-2(0)***, Random House) Random House Publishing Group.

Stewart, Graham. His Finest Hours: Great War Speeches of Winston Churchill. 2009. (ENG., Illus.). 208p. 12.99 *(978-1-84724-193-1(X)*, 184724193X) Quercus GBR. Dist: Book Sales, Inc.

Tenenbaum, Boris. Kasablanka. 2009.Tr. of Casablanca. (RUS., Illus.). 198p. pap. 14.00 *(978-1-934881-26-2(0)*, M-Graphics) M-Graphics Publishing.

Theakston, Kevin. Winston Churchill. 2012. (Shire Library). (ENG., Illus.). 56p. pap. 12.95 ***(978-0-7478-1045-2(1))*** Shire Pubns., Ltd. GBR. Dist: Random Hse., Inc.

Toye, Richard. Churchill's Empire: The World That Made Him & the World He Made. 2010. (ENG., Illus.). 448p. 32.00 *(978-0-8050-8795-6(8))* Holt, Henry & Co.

—Churchill's Empire: The World That Made Him & the World He Made. 2011. (ENG., Illus.). 464p. pap. 16.99 *(978-0-312-57713-1(3)*, St. Martin's Griffin) St. Martin's Pr.

Van der Vat, Dan. The Dardanelles Disaster: Winston Churchill's Greatest Failure. 2010. (ENG.). 240p. (gr. 12). pap. 15.95 *(978-1-59020-339-2(9))* Overlook Pr., The.

Weigold, Auriol. Churchill, Roosevelt & India: Propaganda During World War II. 2012. (Routledge Studies in Modern History Ser.). (ENG.). 224p. (C). pap. 42.95 ***(978-0-415-54107-7(7))*** Routledge.

Weigold, Auriol. Churchill, Roosevelt, & India: Propaganda During World War II. 2008. (Routledge Studies in Modern History Ser.). (ENG.). 224p. (C). 133.00 *(978-0-415-99002-8(5))* Routledge.

Weintraub, Stanley. Pearl Harbor Christmas: A World at War, December 1941. 2012. (ENG., Illus.). 224p. pap. 14.00 ***(978-0-306-82153-0(2))*** Da Capo Pr., Inc.

White, Philip. Our Supreme Task: How Winston Churchill's Iron Curtain Speech Defined the Cold War Alliance. 2012. ***(978-1-61039-060-6(1))***; (ENG., Illus.). 304p. 26.99 ***(978-1-61039-059-0(8))*** PublicAffairs.

Wigg, Richard. Churchill & Spain: The Survival of the Franco Regime, 1940-1945. 2008. (ENG.). 253p. (C). pap. 37.50 *(978-1-84519-283-9(4))* Sussex Academic Pr. GBR. Dist: International Specialized Bk. Services.

Williamson, Daniel C. Separate Agendas: Churchill, Eisenhower, & Anglo-American Relations, 1953-1955. 2006. (ENG.). 152p. pap. 19.99 *(978-0-7391-1895-5(1))* Lexington Bks.

Wrigley, Chris. Churchill. 2006. (British Prime Ministers of the 20th Century Ser.). (ENG., Illus.). 176p. pap. 16.95 *(978-1-904950-63-9(9))* Haus Publishing GBR. Dist: Consortium Bk. Sales & Distribution.

CHURCHILL, WINSTON, SIR, 1874-1965—BIBLIOGRAPHY

Cohen, Ronald I. Bibliography of Works of Sir Charles Winston Churchill. (Illus.). 896p. *(978-0-7201-2325-8(9)*, Burns & Oates) Continuum International Publishing Group, Ltd.

Langworth, Richard, ed. Churchill by Himself: The Definitive Collection of Quotations. 2008. (ENG., Illus.). 656p. 29.95 *(978-1-58648-638-9(1))* Perseus Bks. Group.

CHURCHILL, WINSTON, SIR, 1874-1965—PICTORIAL WORKS

Blundell, Nigel. Winston Churchill: Images of War. 2011. (Illus.). 112p. pap. 24.95 *(978-1-84884-168-0(X))* Pen & Sword Bks. Ltd. GBR. Dist: Casemate Pubs. & Bk. Distributors, LLC.

CHURCHILL FAMILY

Lovell, Mary S. The Churchills: In Love & War. (ENG., Illus.). 2012. 672p. pap. 18.95 ***(978-0-393-34225-3(5)***, 34225) 2011. 624p. 35.00 *(978-0-393-06230-4(9)*, 6230) Norton, W. W. & Co., Inc.

Mcnamara, Robert, ed. The Churchills in Ireland, 1660-1965: Connections & Controversies. 2012. 300p. 79.95 ***(978-0-7165-3084-8(8))*** Irish Academic Pr. IRL. Dist: International Specialized Bk. Services.

CHURCHWARDENS' ACCOUNTS

Middleton-Stewart, Judith, ed. Records of the Churchwardens of Mildenhall: Collections (1446-1454) & Accounts (1503-1553) 2011. (Suffolk Records Society Ser.: Volume 54). (Illus.). 318p. 60.00 *(978-0-85115-578-4(2)*, Boydell Press) Boydell & Brewer, Ltd. GBR. Dist: Boydell & Brewer, Inc.

Wright, Thomas, ed. Churchwardens' Accounts of the Town of Ludlow in Shropshire. (Camden Society, London, Publications, First Ser.: No. 102). reprint ed. 45.00 *(978-0-404-50202-7(4)*, A17-1267) AMS Pr., Inc.

CHURCHYARDS

see Cemeteries

CHUVASH LANGUAGE

Euro Talk. Talk Now! Chuvash. 2008. 29.99 *(978-1-84352-435-9(X))* TOPICS Entertainment.

—Vocabulary Builder Chuvash. 2008. 24.99 *(978-1-84352-835-7(5))* TOPICS Entertainment.

CHWEE LANGUAGE

see Twi Language

CHWI LANGUAGE

see Twi Language

C